BECKETT

THE #1 AUTHORITY ON COLLECTIBLES

BASEBALL CARD PRICE GUIDE

NUMBER 34

THE HOBBY'S MOST RELIABLE AND RELIED UPON SOURCE™

Edited By Brian Fleischer with the staff of

BECKETT BASEBALL

Founder & Advisor: Dr. James Beckett III

Manufactured in the United States of America
Published by Beckett Media LLC

Beckett Media LLC
4635 McEwen Dr.
Dallas, TX 75244

www.beckett.com

First Printing
ISBN 978-193668196-9

CONTENTS

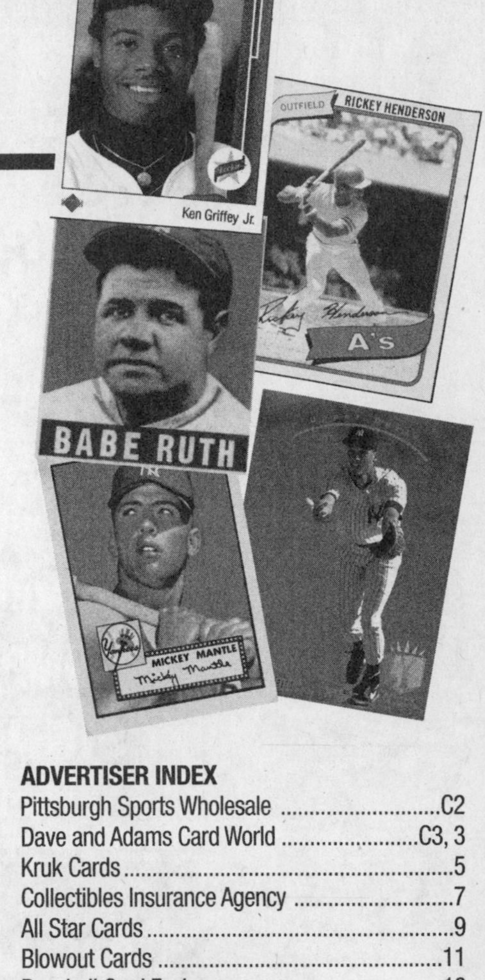

About the Author

Based in Dallas, Beckett Media LP is the leading publisher of sports and specialty market collectible products in the U.S. Beckett operates Beckett.com and is the premier publisher of monthly sports and entertainment collectibles magazines.

The growth of Beckett Media's sports magazines, *Beckett Baseball, Beckett Sports Card Monthly, Beckett Basketball, Beckett Football* and *Beckett Hockey,* is another indication of the unprecedented popularity of sports cards. Founded in 1984 by Dr. James Beckett, Beckett sports magazines contain the most extensive and accepted Price Guide, collectible superstar covers, colorful feature articles, the Hot List, tips for beginners, Readers write letters to and responses from the editors, information on errors and varieties, autograph collecting tips and profiles of the sport's hottest stars. Published 12 times a year, *Beckett Baseball* is the hobby's largest baseball periodical.

ebay
Power Seller
Dealernet B2B

HOW TO USE AND CONDITION GUIDE

Every year this book gets bigger and better with all the new sets coming out. But even more exciting is that every year there are more attractive choices and, subsequently, more interest in the cards we love so much. This edition has been enhanced and expanded from the previous edition. The cards you collect – who appears on them, what they look like, where they are from, and (most important to most of you) what their current values are – are enumerated within. Many of the features contained in the other Beckett Price Guides have been incorporated into this volume since condition grading, terminology, and many other aspects of collecting are common to the card hobby in general. We hope you find the book both interesting and useful in your collecting pursuits.

The *Beckett Baseball Card Price Guide* has been successful where other attempts have failed because it is complete, current, and valid. This Price Guide contains not just one, but two prices for all the baseball cards listed. These account for most of the baseball cards in existence. The prices were added to the card lists just prior to printing and reflect not the author's opinions or desires, but the going retail prices for each card based on the active market (sports memorabilia conventions and shows, sports card shops, mail-order catalogs, local club meetings, auction results, and other first-hand reports of actual realized prices).

What is the best price guide available on the market today? Of course card sellers will prefer the price guide with the highest prices, while card buyers will naturally prefer the one with the lowest prices. Accuracy, however, is the true test. Use the price guide used by more collectors and dealers than all the others combined because it's not the lowest and not the highest – but the most accurate guide, and is produced with integrity.

To facilitate your use of this book, read the complete introductory section on the following pages before going to the pricing pages. Every collectible field has its own terminology; we've tried to capture most of these terms and definitions in our glossary. Please read carefully the section on grading and the condition of your cards, as you will not be able to determine the value of your card without first knowing its condition.

HOW TO COLLECT

Each collection is personal and reflects the individuality of its owner. There are no set rules on how to collect cards. Since card collecting is a hobby or leisure pastime, what you collect, how much you collect, and how much time and money you spend collecting are entirely up to you. The funds you have available for collecting and your own personal taste should determine how you collect.

It is impossible to collect every card ever produced. Therefore, beginners as well as intermediate and advanced collectors usually specialize in some way. One of the reasons this hobby is popular is that individual collectors can define and tailor their collecting methods to match their own tastes.

Many collectors select complete sets from particular years, acquire only certain players, some collectors are only interested in the first cards or Rookie Cards of certain players, and others collect cards by team.

Remember, this is a hobby, so pick a style of collecting that appeals to you.

DETERMINING VALUE

Why are some cards more valuable than others? Obviously, the economic laws of supply and demand are applicable to card collecting just as they are to any other field where a commodity is bought, sold or traded in a free, unregulated market.

Supply (the number of cards available on the market) is less than the

GLOSSARY/LEGEND

Our glossary defines terms most frequently used in the card collecting hobby. Many of these terms are common to other types of sports memorabilia collecting. Some terms may have several meanings depending on the use and context.

AU – Certified autograph.

AS – All-Star card. A card portraying an All-Star Player that says "All-Star" on its face.

ATG – All-Time Great card.

Brick – A group of 50 or more cards having common characteristics that is intended to be bought, sold or traded as a unit.

Cabinet Card – Popular and highly valuable photographs on thick card stock produced in the 19th and early 20th century.

Checklist – A list of the cards contained in a particular set. The list is always in numerical order if the cards are numbered. Some unnumbered sets are artificially numbered in alphabetical order or by team.

CL – Checklist card. A card that lists, in order, the cards and players in the set or series.

CO – Coach.

Common Card – The typical card of any set. It has no premium value accruing from the subject matter, numerical scarcity, popular demand, or anomaly.

continued on page 8

total number of cards originally produced since attrition diminishes that original quantity. Each year a percentage of cards is typically thrown away, destroyed or otherwise lost to collectors. This percentage is much, much smaller today than it was in the past because more and more people have become increasingly aware of the value of their cards.

For those who collect only Mint condition cards, the supply of older cards can be quite small indeed. Until recently, collectors were not so conscious of the need to preserve the condition of their cards. For this reason, it is difficult to know exactly how many 1953 Topps are currently available, Mint or otherwise. It is generally accepted that there are fewer 1953 Topps available than 1963, 1973 or 1983 Topps cards. If demand were equal for each of these sets, the law of supply and demand would increase the price for the least available sets. Demand, however, is never equal for all sets, so price correlations can be complicated. The demand for a card is influenced by many factors. These include the age of the card, the number of cards printed, the player(s) portrayed on the card, the attractiveness and popularity of the set and the physical condition of the card.

In general, the older the card, the fewer the number of the cards printed, the more famous, popular and talented the player, the more attractive and popular the set, and the better the condition of the card, the higher the value of the card will be. There are exceptions to all but one of these factors: the condition of the card. Given two cards similar in all respects except condition, the one in the best condition will always be valued higher.

While those guidelines help to establish the value of a card, the countless exceptions and peculiarities make any simple, direct mathematical formula to determine card values impossible.

WHAT THE COLUMNS MEAN

The LO and HI columns reflect a range of current retail selling prices and are listed in U.S. dollars. The HI column represents the typical full retail selling price while the LO column represents the lowest price one could expect to find through extensive shopping. Both columns represent the same condition for the card listed. Keep in mind that market conditions can change quickly up and down based on extreme levels of demand. The published HI and LO column prices in this issue are a single snapshot in time and cannot be exact for every card listed.

PRICING PREMIUMS

Some cards can trade at premium price levels compared to values listed in this issue. Those include but are not limited to: cards of players who became hot since this book went to press, regional stars or fan favorites in high demand locally and memorabilia cards with unusually dramatic swatches or patches.

ONLY A REFERENCE

The data and pricing information contained within this publication is intended for reference only and is not to be used as an endorsement of any specific product(s) or as a recommendation to buy or sell any product(s). Beckett's goal is to provide the most accurate and verifiable information in the industry. However, Beckett cannot guarantee the accuracy of all data published. Typographical errors occasionally occur and unverifiable information may reach print from time to time. Buyers and sellers of sports collectibles should be aware of this and handle their personal transactions at their own risk. If you discover an error or misprint in this book, please notify us via email at baseballmag@beckett.com

GLOSSARY/LEGEND

Continued from page 6

Convention – A gathering of sealers and collectors at a single location of the purpose of buying, selling and trading sports memorabilia items. Conventions are open to the public and sometimes feature autograph guests, door prizes, contests, or seminars. They are frequently referred to as "shows."

COR – Corrected.

Dealer – A person who engages in the buying, selling and trading sports collectibles or supplies. A dealer may also be a collector, but as a dealer, his main goal it to earn a profit.

Die-cut – A card with part of its stock partial cut, allowing one or more parts to be folded or removed. After removal or appropriate folding, the remaining part of the card can frequently be made to stand up.

DK – Diamond King.

DP – Draft pick or double print. A double print is a card that was printed in double the quantity compared to other cards in the same series.

Dufex- A method of manufacturing technology patented by Pinnacle Brands, Inc. It involves refractive quality to a card with a foil coating.

ERR – Error card. A card with erroneous information, spelling or depiction on either side of the card. Most errors are not corrected by the manufacturer.

EXCH – Exchange.

High Number – The cards in the last series of a set in a year in which such high-numbered cards

continued on page 10

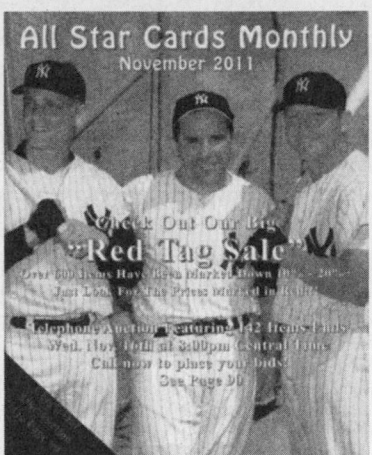

MULTIPLIERS

Some parallel sets and lightly traded insert sets are listed with multipliers to provide values of unlisted cards. Multiplier ranges (i.e. 10X to 20X HI) apply only to the HI column. Example: If basic-issue card A or the insert card in question lists for 20 to 50 cents, and the multiplier is "20X to 40X HI", then the parallel version of card A or the insert card in question is valued at $10 to $20. Please not that the term "basic card" used in the Price Guide refers to a player's standard regular-issue card. A "basic card" cannot be an insert or parallel card.

STATED ODDS AND PRINT RUNS

Odds of pulling insert cards are often listed as a ratio (1:12 – one in 12 packs). If the odds vary by pack type, they are generally listed separately. Stated print runs are also included in the set header lines or after the player's name for many serial numbered cards or for sets which the manufacturer has chosen to announce print runs. Stated odds and print runs are provided by the manufacturer based on the entire print run and should be considered very close estimates and not exact figures. The data provided in this book has been verified by Beckett to the best of our ability. Neither the stated odds nor print runs should be viewed as a guarantee by either Beckett or the manufacturer.

CONDITION GUIDE

The value of your card is dependent on the condition or "grade" of your card. Prices in this issue reflect the highest raw condition (i.e. not professionally graded by a third party) of the card most commonly found at shows, shops, on the internet and right out of the pack for brand new releases. This generally means Near Mint-Mint condition for modern era cards. Use the chart below as a guide to estimate the value of your cards in a variety of condition using the prices found in this Almanac. A complete condition guide follows.

The most widely used grades are defined on page 14. Obviously, many cards will not perfectly fit one of the definitions. Therefore, categories between the major grades known as in-between grades are used, such as Good to Very Good (G-Vg), Very Good to Excellent (VgEx), and Excellent-Mint to Near Mint (ExMt-NrMt). Such grades indicate a card with all qualities of the lower category but with at least a few qualities of the higher category.

Unopened packs, boxes and factory-collated sets are considered mint in their unknown (and presumed perfect) state. Once opened, however, each card can be graded (and valued) in its own right by taking into account any defects that may be present in spite of the fact that the card has never been handled.

CONDITION CHART

	Pre-1930	1930-47	1948-59	1960-80	1981-89	1990-Present
MT	N/A	300+%	300+%	250+%	100-150%	100-125%
NRMT-MT	300+%	150-300%	150-250%	125-200%	100%	100%
NRMT	150-300%	150%	100%	100%	30-50%	30-50%
EX-MT	100%	100%	50-75%	40-60%	25-40%	20-30%
EX	50-75%	50-75%	30-50%	20-40%	15-25%	10-20%
VG	30-50%	30-50%	15-30%	10-20%	5-15%	5-10%
G/F/P	10-30%	10-30%	5-15%	5-10%	5%	5%

GLOSSARY/LEGEND

Continued from page 8

were printed or distributed in significantly less amounts than the lower numbered cards. Not all years have high numbers in terms of this definition.

HOF – Hall of Fame or a card that pictures of Hall of Famer (HOFer).

HOR – Horizonal pose on a card as opposed to the standart vertical orientation found on most cards.

IA – In action.

Insert – A card or any other sports collectible contained and sold in the same package along with a card or cards from a major set. An insert card may or may not be numbered in the same sequence as the major set. Many times the inserts are randomly inserted in packs.

Issue – Synonymous with set, but usually used in conjunction with a manufacturer, e.g. a Topps issue.

JSY – Jersey.

Major Set – A set produced by a national manufacturer of cards.

Mini – A small card; for example a 1975 Topps card of identical desing but smaller dimensions than the regular 1975 Topps issue.

Multi-player Card – A single card depicting two or more players.

NNO – Unnumbered.

NNOF – No Name On Front.

Packs – A means by which cards are issued in terms of pack type (wx, cello, foil, rack, etc.) and channel of distribution (hobby, retail, etc.).

continued on page 12

HOW TO USE AND CONDITION GUIDE

GENERAL CARD FLAWS

CENTERING

Current centering terminology uses numbers representing the percentage of border on either side of the main design. Obviously, centering is diminished in importance for borderless cards.

Slightly Off-Center (60/40)
A slightly off-center card is one that upon close inspection is found to have one border bigger than the opposite border. This degree once was offensive to only purists, but now some hobbyists try to avoid cards that are anything other than perfectly centered.

Off-Center (70/30)
An off-center card has one border that is noticeably more than twice as wide as the opposite border.

Badly Off-Center (80/20 or worse)
A badly off-center card has virtually no border on one side of the card.

Miscut
A miscut card actually shows part of the adjacent card in its larger border and consequently a corresponding amount of its card is cut off.

CORNER WEAR

Corner wear is the most scrutinized grading criteria in the hobby.

Corner with a slight touch of wear
The corner still is sharp, but there is a slight touch of wear showing. On a dark-bordered card, this shows as a dot of white.

Fuzzy corner
The corner still comes to a point, but the point has just begun to fray. A slightly "dinged" corner is considered the same as a fuzzy corner.

Slightly rounded corner
The fraying of the corner has increased to where there is only a hint of a point. Mild layering may be evident. A "dinged" corner is considered the same as a slightly rounded corner.

Rounded corner
The point is completely gone. Some layering is noticeable.

Badly rounded corner
The corner is completely round and rough. Severe layering is evident.

CREASES

A third common defect is the crease. The degree of creasing in a card is difficult to show in a drawing or picture. On giving the specific condition of an expensive card for sale, the seller should note any creases additionally. Creases can be categorized as to severity according to the following scale.

Light Crease
A light crease is a crease that is barely noticeable upon close inspection. In fact, when cards are in plastic sheets or holders, a light crease may not be seen (until the card is taken out of the holder). A light crease on the front is much more serious than a light crease on the card back only.

Medium Crease
A medium crease is noticeable when held and studied at arm's length by the naked eye, but does not overly detract from the appearance of the card. It is an obvious crease, but not one that breaks the picture surface of the card.

Heavy Crease: A heavy crease is one that has torn or broken through the card's surface, e.g., puts a tear in the photo surface.

ALTERATIONS

Deceptive Trimming
This occurs when someone alters the card in order to shave off edge wear, to improve the sharpness of the corners, or to improve centering – obviously their objective is to falsely increase the perceived value of the card to an unsuspecting buyer. The shrinkage usually is evident only if the trimmed card is compared to an adjacent full-sized card or if the trimmed card is itself measured.

GLOSSARY/LEGEND

Continued from page 10

Parallel – A card that is similar in design to its counterpart from a basic set, but offers a distinguishing quality.

Premium – A card that is obtained in conjunction with, or redemption for, another card or product. The premium is not packaged in the same unit as the primary item.

(RC) – Rookie Logo Card. These cards feature the official MLBPA Rookie Logo. However, the player depicted on the card has already had a Rookie Card(s) issued in a previous year.

RC – Rookie Card.

Redemption – A program established by multiple card manufacturers that allows collectors to main in a special card (usually a random insert) in return for special cards, sets, or other prizes not available through conventional channels.

Refractor – A card that features a design element that enhances its color or appearance by deflecting light.

ROY – Rookie of the Year.

Series – The entire set of cards issued by a particular manufacturer in a particular year. Within a particular set, a series can refer to a group of consecutively numbered cards printed at the same time.

Set – One of each of the entire run of cards of the same type produced by a particular manufacturer during a single year.

Skip-numbered – A set that has many unissued

continued on page 14

Obvious Trimming
Trimming is noticeable. It is usually performed by non-collectors who give no thought to the present or future value of their cards.

Deceptively Retouched Borders
This occurs when the borders (especially on those cards with dark borders) are touched up on the edges and corners with magic marker or crayons of appropriate color in order to make the card appear to be Mint.

MISCELLANEOUS CARD FLAWS

The following are common minor flaws that, depending on severity, lower a card's condition by one to four grades and often render it no better than Excellent-Mint: bubbles (lumps in surface), gum and wax stains, diamond cutting (slanted borders), notching, off-centered backs, paper wrinkles, scratched-off cartoons or puzzles on back, rubber band marks, scratches, surface impressions and warping.

The following are common serious flaws that, depending on severity, lower a card's condition at least four grades and often render it no better than Good: chemical or sun fading, erasure marks, mildew, miscutting (severe off-centering), holes, bleached or retouched borders, tape marks, tears, trimming, water or coffee stains and writing.

GRADES

Mint (Mt)
A card with no flaws or wear. The card has four perfect corners, 55/45 or better centering from top to bottom and from left to right, original gloss, smooth edges and original color borders. A Mint card does not have print spots, color or focus imperfections.

Near Mint-Mint (NrMt-Mt)
A card with one minor flaw. Any one of the following would lower a Mint card to Near Mint-Mint: one corner with a slight touch of wear, barely noticeable print spots, color or focus imperfections. The card must have 60/40 or better centering in both directions, original gloss, smooth edges and original color border.

Near Mint (NrMt)
A card with one minor flaw. Any one of the following would lower a Mint card to Near Mint: one fuzzy corner or two to four corners with slight touches of wear, 70/30 to 60/40 centering, slightly rough edges, minor print spots, color or focus imperfections. The card must have original gloss and original color borders.

Excellent-Mint (ExMt)
A card with two or three fuzzy, but not rounded, corners and centering no worse than 80/20. The card may have no more than two of the following: slightly rough edges, slightly discolored borders, minor print spots, color or focus imperfections. The card must have original gloss.

Excellent (Ex)
A card with four fuzzy but definitely not rounded corners and centering no worse than 70/30. The card may have a small amount of original gloss lost, rough edges, slightly discolored borders and minor print spots, color or focus imperfections.

Very Good (Vg)
A card that has been handled but not abused: slightly rounded corners with slight layering, slight notching on edges, a significant amount of gloss lost from the surface but no scuffing and moderate discoloration of borders. The card may have a few light creases.

Good (G), Fair (F), Poor (P)
A well-worn, mishandled or abused card: badly rounded and layered corners, scuffing, most or all original gloss missing, seriously discolored borders, moderate or heavy creases, and one or more serious flaws. The grade of Good, Fair or Poor depends on the severity of wear and flaws. Good, Fair and Poor cards generally are used only as fillers.

GLOSSARY/LEGEND
Continued from page 12

card numbers between the lowest and highest number in the set. A major set in which only a few numbers were not printed is not considered to be skip-numbered.

SP – Single or Short Print. A short print is a card that was printed in less quantity compared to the other cards in the same series.

TC – Team card.

TP – Triple print. A card that was printed in triple the quantity compared to the other cards in the same series.

UER – Uncorrected error.

UNI – Uniform.

VAR – Variation card. One of two or more cards from the same series, with the same card number, that differ from one and other in some way. This sometimes occurs when the manufacture notices an error in one or more of the cards, corrects the mistake, and then resumes the printing process. In some cases, on of the variations may be relatively scarce.

XRC – Extended Rookie Card.

* – Used to denote multisport set or an announced print run of a particular card.

Note: Nearly all other abbreviations signify various subsets (i.e. B, G and S in 1996 Finest are short for Bronze, Gold and Silver. WS in the 1960s and 1970s Topps sets is short for World Series as examples).

CLASSIFIED ADVERTISING

MODERN MARKETPLACE

BY DAVID LEE AND JON GOLD

Collectors like choices, and when it comes to buying their favorite cards and products, today's hobby provides more buying options than ever.

Most collectors have experienced buying from hobby shops, retail stores and Internet auction sites and storefronts. Positive and negative experiences can be experienced from each. The important thing is to figure out what fits you best. Over the next few pages we will examine the pros and cons of buying from the hobby's three main avenues.

INTERNET

PROS +

GREAT PRICES +

Everyone loves a great deal, and if you're looking to score good prices on boxes and singles, your best bet is the Internet. With such a wide selection of product for sale from dealers and collectors across the country (and sometimes other countries), prices are generally going to be lower.

Internet auction sites like eBay can be a great place to upgrade your better cards.

"Ninety-eight and a half percent of my collection was obtained through the Internet," says collector Peter L. (a.k.a. jaderock on the Beckett.com Message Boards) from San Francisco.

Condition always plays a factor in price, and there is usually a broader spectrum of cards in various conditions to choose from. So, if your standards aren't too high, you can find low prices on great cards. A recent eBay search revealed various ungraded 1963 Topps Pete Rose Rookie Cards ($1,000 high book value) that sold for as low as $80 in poor condition to as high as $885 in near mint condition. Of course, there's the roadblock of not being able to inspect the card first-hand, which can also greatly affect price.

Many times, dealers and distributors will sell boxes of cards on sites like BeckettMarketplace.com and eBay. Depending on the popularity of the product and how long it's been on the market, you can find some great deals.

WIDER SELECTION +

"You basically can find whatever you want on the Internet," says Dayton Grissam of Lynchburg, Ohio. If you're looking for a particular card, it's just a matter of time before a copy pops up on the web. A recent search pulled up 13,877 Ken Griffey Jr. items for sale in eBay's sports cards category. More than 60,000 Griffey items were found on BeckettMarketplace.com at the same time.

With so many jersey cards produced these days, the Internet allows collectors to pick and choose which swatches they want for a lot of jersey cards. The two-color patch doesn't do enough for you? Just hold out for a sweet four-color patch, or better yet, a logo patch.

FAST AND EASY +

How many times have you jumped on the Internet and stumbled across cards from a new product that you didn't even know was out yet? It happens every month. That's how quickly the Internet market works.

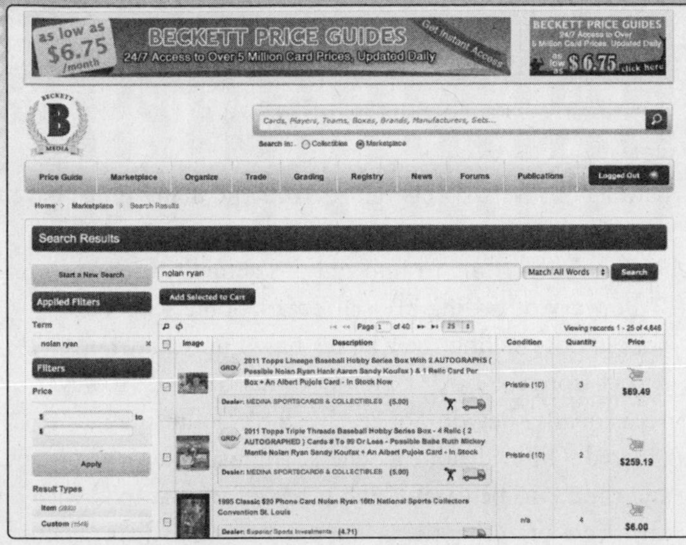

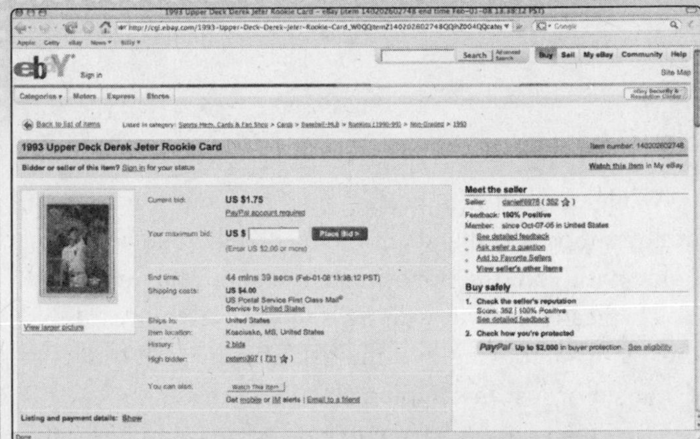

Online marketplaces like BeckettMarketplace.com and eBay have changed the hobby forever.

Cards you need can be yours with just a few clicks. Need those last few base cards to complete your set? Buy 'em all from one dealer on BeckettMarketplace.com. Don't want to mess with piecing together a Topps Chrome set? Buy one already completed. Third-party transaction services like PayPal make it easy to pay for your item.

ABILITY TO FIND RARE CARDS +

Let's face it: Card companies would never be able to make the rare cards that they do if collectors weren't able to buy and sell over the Internet. Cards numbered to 50 or 10 or 5 would probably never be seen if it weren't for the web. Say you pull a triple autograph of Alex Rodriguez, Albert Pujols and Ryan Howard. Would you be able to get the money you want for that card if there was no Internet?

COLLECTOR-TO-COLLECTOR +

"Auction sites allow collector-to-collector interaction. That normally means the lowest price," says Jay Z. of Pittsburgh, Pa. Collectors are free to buy, sell and trade via auction sites and collector communities. The Internet essentially turns every collector into a dealer. It's great to find fellow collectors who collect the same thing you do. The collector-to-collector interaction can mean bargain prices on some cards, but inflated prices on other cards that receive frenzied bidding.

CONS - OFF-SITE -

One of the main fundamental flaws with buying online is not being able to inspect the item in person. This creates a lot of problems, but most importantly, you run the risk of getting a damaged card. Sure, that Mickey Mantle Rookie Card looks fine on your screen, but when you get it, you find a 1-inch crease and a pen mark on the back. Some sellers will use a sample scan of a card instead of the actual card you receive. This usually happens with cheaper, higher-volume cards.

Be careful when buying ungraded vintage cards online. Scans sometimes don't accurately reflect the true condition of the card.

The fact is, scans can be deceiving, or worse yet, doctored to make the card look better. Older computer screens also can render an inaccurate image. A good way to keep this from happening to you is to stick to buying graded cards, especially vintage. Still, nothing beats being able to hold and inspect the card yourself.

SHIPPING –

While one of the appealing factors about buying from hobby shops is being able to immediately take your cards home with you, the opposite is true about buying online. You typically have to wait days to receive your card. Not only is this annoying, but the risk of your card being damaged or lost in shipping always looms.

How many times have you paid $5 for shipping only to receive your card in a top loader and a regular envelope? While auction sites like eBay have tried to crack down on sellers overcharging for shipping, you still need to check the shipping costs and methods before you buy.

BUYING COMPETITION –

Competition is usually a good thing. After all, that is how card values increase. But when you're on the buying end, competition is nothing more than a roadblock to getting your cards. Nearly every collector knows the feeling of losing the high bid on a card with 30 seconds left. This is especially annoying when the card you're trying to buy is rare and probably won't pop up again for months.

Buying competition is at its peak on the hottest cards, and the Internet is the prime way for collectors to jump on the hottest cards. This results in higher prices for you and the increased likelihood that you'll miss out on the card you want.

SELLER ANONYMITY –

One of the biggest complaints collectors have when buying online is not knowing who they are buying from. Buying from a faceless seller hundreds of miles away is always risky. You just never know when someone is trying to scam you.

"You have to do your research when buying online," says Scott Smith of Kissimmee, Fla. "When it comes to eBay, reading feedback is a must."

Pay attention to the title and description of the card or item you're buying. Some sellers will call any card picturing a rookie a Rookie Card, even when it's obviously a parallel or insert numbered to 10. How many times have you seen auctions for a "1968 Topps Nolan Ryan Rookie Card" only to find that it's actually a reprint?

Be wary of buying pre-sell boxes. Some sellers are honestly pre-selling their boxes based on what they expect from the card company or distributor. However, occasionally they do not receive the amount they ordered. Other deadbeat sellers will just take your money and run. Also be careful about buying autographs with a certificate of authenticity. Anyone can write a COA, but that doesn't make the autograph real. Look for COA's from legitimate authentication and autograph companies, such as PSA/DNA, Steiner, James Spence Authentication, UDA and Tri-Star.

Although fake patches have become less of a problem over the last few years, they still exist. Some sellers will replace ordinary jersey swatches with prime patch pieces. While there's no easy way to avoid this, stick with cards that you know were intended to have patches. Ask the seller for close-up scans of the card so that you can inspect the patch area for any signs of tampering.

HOBBY SHOPS/ SHOWS

PROS +
CUSTOMER SERVICE +

Nothing beats the hobby shop experience. One of the main reasons most people collect cards today is because they have (or had) a local hobby shop to go to. Whether you're looking for a particular product, picking up some supplies or just talking hobby, good customer service from your dealer and being able to interact with fellow collectors is invaluable.

"You get to talk to people with the same interests as yourself and brag about or show off your collections and hear about the big pulls out of the new products," says collector Alan Risa of Orangeburg, S.C.

Any good dealer will help you look for cards you need, even if this means searching the Internet and other shops for you. Many dealers keep boxes of duplicate cards from base sets and inserts for collectors to look through. This is helpful when completing base sets or looking for your favorite players.

"I have established a good relationship with several card shops in my area," says collector Michael Snyder of Charlestown, R.I. "They know the product and go out of their way to make sure you have a positive experience. They usually crack a few boxes of a product and can show you what comes in the box. One of my favorite card shops keeps an eye out for my favorite players and teams and cuts me a really good break on the price."

TRUSTWORTHY DEALERS +

The key here is to get to know your local dealers and develop a relationship with the ones you find you can trust. Those you can trust will always give you a fair price. You also don't have to worry about them selling you mixed-up packs from boxes that the big pulls have already been removed from. The risk of running into a dealer you don't know is greater at collectible shows.

IN-SHOP INCENTIVES/ PROMOTIONS +

Many hobby shops offer incentives and promotions, such as giveaways, contests and free products. One of the most frequently used is a weekly buying incentive in which shops hand out tickets to customers who spend a certain amount. At the end of the week, prizes and gift certificates are given away.

League promotions, like the NFL Player of Day, the MLB/Upper Deck Player of the Month, the NBA Hobby Shop Makeover, and card company promotions, like Topps Turn Back the Clock, have given collectors more reasons to visit their local hobby shops. Recently, Upper Deck began working with 200 hobby shops around the country to form its new redemption center program in which collectors submitted their redemption cards through the shops. More than three years ago, the major professional sports leagues, along with the card companies and other industry leaders, formed National Trading Card Day in which free cards were given away at shops around the country. The MLB still promotes the event, which takes place in the spring.

ABILITY TO INSPECT CARDS +

It's funny how the benefits of buying in-person from hobby shops are directly opposite of the disadvantages of buying from the Internet. A prime example is being able to inspect the cards first-hand at shops and shows. If you throw down $150 for that Alex Rodriguez Rookie Card, at least you were able to examine the card's condition to see if it meets your standards. You can feel comfortable with your decision. Card shows provide more opportunities to do this, since you can often find multiple copies of the card you're looking for.

Another great advantage is being able to buy boxes and packs from just about every current product on the market. Just ask your dealer when they are expecting a new product. Many dealers also keep boxes and packs of past products. Some great deals can be found with these.

CONS -
GENERALLY HIGHER PRICES -

Your dealer has to keep his shop running, and that means paying taxes and bills. Unfortunately, that usually translates into higher prices. While most dealers' prices may not be unfair, it's tough to shell out $40 on a card you can get for $25 online. But remember, they are called dealers. While some prices may be a little more than you're willing to pay, a lot of shop owners are willing to cut you a deal on multiple cards or trades.

SMALLER SELECTION -

With so many different products produced these days, and so many cards being produced in low quantities, it's tough for dealers to maintain an inventory of current cards that collectors are looking for. However, good dealers know their customers, and will try to keep an inventory tailored to their customers.

RETAIL

PROS +
CHEAPER PRODUCTS +

It's a fact: Most retail-only releases carry a lower SRP than their hobby-exclusive counterparts. Because retail outlets such as Target and Wal-Mart demand more impulse-purchase opportunities for their broader customer base, most retail products fall in the $1.99 to $2.99 pack range.

So, where as 2008 Topps Opening Day, for example, can be had for about a buck a pack at retail, the hobby version, 2008 Topps Series One, carries a $2 SRP in hobby shops.

By and large, most of the contents of those varied packs — with the possible exception of a few exclusive inserts on either side — are the same. But the odds of pulling those contents are typically much longer at retail.

"With retail, the biggest advantage is obviously the price," says collector Jeremy Lund. "But the biggest disadvantage is the long shot."

RETAIL EXCLUSIVES +

A relatively recent phenomenon, the inclusion of retail-exclusive inserts has served to liven up the retail-shopping experience and provide collectors the kind of bang for their buck — albeit on a smaller scale — that used to be the hobby's exclusive domain.

Most manufacturers have experimented with the idea; and most have experienced success. Bowman has produced two distinct exclusives for Target and Wal-Mart. Topps produced Target-exclusive Mickey Mantle Relic cards in 2006 and 2007.

It is a fact: Collectors are actively seeking these retail-exclusive cards—either in person at the store or online—just as they would any other short-printed cards.

2007 Bowman Signs of the Future autograph exclusives were retail-only.

READILY AVAILABLE LOCATIONS +

As the number of neighborhood hobby shops — once the bread and butter of any collector's existence — has continued to dwindle over the last decade, larger retail outlets continue to pop up all over the country on seemingly every street corner.

And most are equipped with a self-contained sports cards section full of variety.

Simply, finding a hobby shop in your zip code these days is a whole lot more difficult than it used to be. But locating a Target or a Wal-Mart or a Kmart or any other mass merchant can be as easy as opening your eyes.

What collectors lose in customer service and the sense of community afforded by hobby shops is often offset by the ease of use in finding a store that sells cards in the first place.

"[Chain stores] do an unbelievable amount of sales in hobby boxes," says Tim Franz of Excell Marketing, a major retail card distributor that handles Target, among other accounts. "There is a demand for product. For some, especially in rural areas, we are the hobby shop."

CONS -
PACK SEARCHING -

Pack searching stinks. Pack searchers stink. But it comes with the territory of buying sports cards at retail. When there's no one to mind the inventory (at least no one to strictly monitor every pack that's purchased like in a hobby shop) the buyer must beware. And most collectors are.

Obviously, not everyone is a pack searcher and not every pack has been searched. But the fact remains that the unsavory practice is a lot more apt to happen at retail than in your local hobby shop.

"I don't touch retail packs due to searching," says Beckett.com Message Board member panthergoergefan. "I have seen at least three offenders [in my area]. One guy had a scale on him and was weighing the packs at Target."

Adds Excell Marketing's Franz: "Obviously, a great concern that retailers have is shrinkage. We're concerned about stuff being stolen as things escalate in price."

TOUGHER ODDS -

As noted earlier, the trade-off for being able to readily find more affordable products at retail is that the goodies inside those products are usually a lot harder to come by. Take virtually any product you can think of that has a hobby/retail split and what you'll typically find are dramatically different odds. For example, most products that offer three or four "hits" per box at hobby will usually provide one such hit at retail.

As with just about any hobby, the bottom line is to be well informed. If you know what you're getting into before you get into it, you greatly reduce the potential for disappointment.

NO CUSTOMER SERVICE/CAMARADERIE -

One of the greatest joys of a local hobby shop isn't *just* the inventory. It's the sense of belonging and companionship you get with that inventory that keeps the people coming back. As the theme song from famed television series Cheers so eloquently pointed out: "Sometimes you want to go where everybody knows your name."

At your local hobby shop, it's likely that everyone does know your name. On the flipside, it's difficult to imagine the manager at Wal-Mart greeting you as you walk in the door and telling you that he set aside a few boxes of the new product for you.

There's an inherent warmth at most hobby shops—one based upon years of personal exchanges—that you just can't get at a store that sells razors and dog food along with your favorite baseball cards.

David Lee is the former editor of Beckett Football *and* Beckett Sports Card Monthly. *Jon Gold is a reporter for the* Los Angeles Daily News.

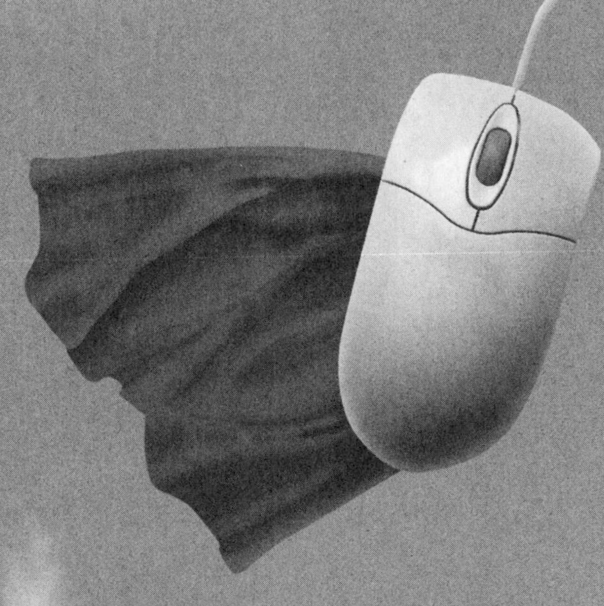

BECKETT
B
MEDIA

Online
PRICE
GUIDES

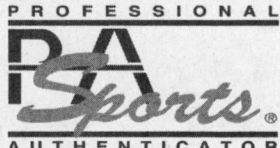

2001 Absolute Memorabilia

The 2001 Playoff Absolute Memorabilia set was issued in one series totally 200 cards. The set features color action player photos highlighted on metalized film board with the 50 rookie cards infused with a swatch of game-worn/used bat and jersey. The following cards were available via mail exchange cards (of which expired on June 1st, 2003): 151 - Bud Smith, 154 - Josh Beckett, 161 Ben Sheets, 164 - Carlos Garcia, 169 - Donaldo Mendez, 171 Jackson Melian, 173 Adrian Hernandez, 186 - C.C. Sabathia, 188 - Adam Pettyjohn, 193 - Alfonso Soriano, 196 - Billy Sylvester and 200 - Matt White.

COMP.SET w/o SP's (150)	15.00	40.00
COMMON CARD (1-150)	.30	.75
COMMON RPM (151-200)	3.00	8.00
1 Alex Rodriguez	1.25	3.00
2 Barry Bonds	2.00	5.00
3 Cal Ripken	2.50	6.00
4 Chipper Jones	.75	2.00
5 Derek Jeter	2.00	5.00
6 Troy Glaus	.30	.75
7 Frank Thomas	.75	2.00
8 Greg Maddux	1.25	3.00
9 Ivan Rodriguez	.50	1.25
10 Jeff Bagwell	.50	1.25
11 Ryan Dempster	.30	.75
12 Todd Helton	.50	1.25
13 Ken Griffey Jr.	1.25	3.00
14 Manny Ramirez Sox	.50	1.25
15 Mark McGwire	2.00	5.00
16 Mike Piazza	1.25	3.00
17 Nomar Garciaparra	1.25	3.00
18 Pedro Martinez	.50	1.25
19 Randy Johnson	.75	2.00
20 Rick Ankiel	.30	.75
21 Rickey Henderson	.75	2.00
22 Roger Clemens	1.50	4.00
23 Sammy Sosa	.75	2.00
24 Tony Gwynn	1.00	2.50
25 Vladimir Guerrero	.75	2.00
26 Kazuhiro Sasaki	.30	.75
27 Roberto Alomar	.50	1.25
28 Barry Zito	.50	1.25
29 Pat Burrell	.30	.75
30 Harold Baines	.30	.75
31 Carlos Delgado	.30	.75
32 J.D. Drew	.30	.75
33 Jim Edmonds	.30	.75
34 Darin Erstad	.30	.75
35 Jason Giambi	.30	.75
36 Tom Glavine	.50	1.25
37 Juan Gonzalez	.30	.75
38 Mark Grace	.50	1.25
39 Shawn Green	.30	.75
40 Tim Hudson	.30	.75
41 Andruw Jones	.50	1.25
42 David Justice	.30	.75
43 Jeff Kent	.30	.75
44 Barry Larkin	.50	1.25
45 Rafael Furcal	.30	.75
46 Mike Mussina	.50	1.25
47 Hideo Nomo	.75	2.00
48 Rafael Palmeiro	.50	1.25
49 Adam Piatt	.30	.75
50 Scott Rolen	.50	1.25
51 Gary Sheffield	.30	.75
52 Bernie Williams	.50	1.25
53 Bob Abreu	.30	.75
54 Edgardo Alfonzo	.30	.75
55 Edgar Renteria	.30	.75
56 Phil Nevin	.30	.75
57 Craig Biggio	.50	1.25
58 Andres Galarraga	.30	.75
59 Edgar Martinez	.50	1.25
60 Fred McGriff	.50	1.25
61 Magglio Ordonez	.30	.75
62 Jim Thome	.50	1.25
63 Matt Williams	.30	.75
64 Kerry Wood	.30	.75
65 Moises Alou	.30	.75
66 Brady Anderson	.30	.75
67 Garret Anderson	.30	.75
68 Russell Branyan	.30	.75
69 Tony Batista	.30	.75
70 Vernon Wells	.30	.75
71 Carlos Beltran	.30	.75
72 Adrian Beltre	.30	.75
73 Kris Benson	.30	.75
74 Lance Berkman	.30	.75
75 Kevin Brown	.30	.75
76 Dee Brown	.30	.75
77 Jeromy Burnitz	.30	.75
78 Timo Perez	.30	.75
79 Sean Casey	.30	.75
80 Luis Castillo	.30	.75
81 Eric Chavez	.30	.75
82 Jeff Cirillo	.30	.75
83 Bartolo Colon	.30	.75
84 David Cone	.30	.75
85 Freddy Garcia	.30	.75
86 Johnny Damon	.50	1.25
87 Ray Durham	.30	.75
88 Jermaine Dye	.30	.75
89 Juan Encarnacion	.30	.75
90 Terrence Long	.30	.75
91 Carl Everett	.30	.75
92 Steve Finley	.30	.75
93 Cliff Floyd	.30	.75
94 Brad Fullmer	.30	.75
95 Brian Giles	.30	.75
96 Luis Gonzalez	.30	.75
97 Rusty Greer	.30	.75
98 Jeffrey Hammonds	.30	.75
99 Mike Hampton	.30	.75
100 Orlando Hernandez	.30	.75
101 Richard Hidalgo	.30	.75
102 Geoff Jenkins	.30	.75
103 Jacque Jones	.30	.75
104 Brian Jordan	.30	.75
105 Gabe Kapler	.30	.75
106 Eric Karros	.30	.75
107 Jason Kendall	.30	.75
108 Adam Kennedy	.30	.75
109 Deion Sanders	.50	1.25
110 Ryan Klesko	.30	.75
111 Chuck Knoblauch	.30	.75
112 Paul Konerko	.30	.75
113 Carlos Lee	.30	.75
114 Kenny Lofton	.30	.75
115 Javy Lopez	.30	.75
116 Tino Martinez	.50	1.25
117 Ruben Mateo	.30	.75
118 Kevin Millwood	.30	.75
119 Jimmy Rollins	.30	.75
120 Raul Mondesi	.30	.75
121 Trot Nixon	.30	.75
122 John Olerud	.30	.75
123 Paul O' Neill	.50	1.25
124 Chan Ho Park	.30	.75
125 Andy Pettitte	.50	1.25
126 Jorge Posada	.50	1.25
127 Mark Quinn	.30	.75
128 Aramis Ramirez	.30	.75
129 Mariano Rivera	.75	2.00
130 Tim Salmon	.50	1.25
131 Curt Schilling	.30	.75
132 Richie Sexson	.30	.75
133 John Smoltz	.50	1.25
134 J.T. Snow	.30	.75
135 Jay Payton	.30	.75
136 Shannon Stewart	.30	.75
137 B.J. Surhoff	.30	.75
138 Mike Sweeney	.30	.75
139 Fernando Tatis	.30	.75
140 Miguel Tejada	.30	.75
141 Jason Varitek	.75	2.00
142 Greg Vaughn	.30	.75
143 Mo Vaughn	.30	.75
144 Robin Ventura	.30	.75
145 Jose Vidro	.30	.75
146 Omar Vizquel	.50	1.25
147 Larry Walker	.30	.75
148 David Wells	.30	.75
149 Rondell White	.30	.75
150 Preston Wilson	.30	.75
151 Bud Smith RPM RC	3.00	8.00
152 Cory Aldridge RPM RC	3.00	8.00
153 Wilmy Caceres RPM RC	3.00	8.00
154 Josh Beckett RPM	4.00	10.00
155 Wilson Betemit RPM RC	4.00	10.00
156 Jason Michaels RPM RC	3.00	8.00
157 Albert Pujols RPM RC	90.00	150.00
158 Andres Torres RPM RC	3.00	8.00
159 Jack Wilson RPM RC	4.00	10.00
160 Alex Escobar RPM	3.00	8.00
161 Ben Sheets RPM	4.00	10.00
162 Rafael Soriano RPM RC	3.00	8.00
163 Nate Frese RPM RC	3.00	8.00
164 Carlos Garcia RPM	3.00	8.00
165 Brandon Larson RPM RC	3.00	8.00
166 Alexis Gomez RPM RC	3.00	8.00
167 Jason Hart RPM	3.00	8.00
168 Nick Johnson RPM	3.00	8.00
169 Donaldo Mendez RPM	3.00	8.00
170 Christian Parker RPM RC	3.00	8.00
171 Jackson Melian RPM	3.00	8.00
172 Jack Cust RPM	3.00	8.00
173 Adrian Hernandez RPM	3.00	8.00
174 Joe Crede RPM	4.00	10.00
175 Jose Mieses RPM RC	3.00	8.00
176 Roy Oswalt RPM	4.00	10.00
177 Eric Munson RPM	3.00	8.00
178 Xavier Nady RPM	3.00	8.00
179 Horacio Ramirez RPM RC	4.00	10.00
180 Abraham Nunez RPM	3.00	8.00
181 Jose Ortiz RPM	3.00	8.00
182 Jeremy Owens RPM RC	3.00	8.00
183 Claudio Vargas RPM RC	3.00	8.00
184 Marcus Giles RPM	3.00	8.00
185 Aubrey Huff RPM	3.00	8.00
186 C.C. Sabathia RPM	3.00	8.00
187 Adam Dunn RPM	4.00	10.00
188 Adam Pettyjohn RPM	3.00	8.00
189 Elpidio Guzman RPM RC	3.00	8.00
190 Jay Gibbons RPM RC	4.00	10.00
191 Wilkin Ruan RPM RC	3.00	8.00
192 Tsuyoshi Shinjo RPM RC	4.00	10.00
193 Alfonso Soriano RPM	4.00	10.00
194 Corey Patterson RPM	3.00	8.00
195 Ichiro Suzuki RPM RC	40.00	80.00
196 Billy Sylvester RPM	3.00	8.00
197 Juan Uribe RPM RC	4.00	10.00
198 Johnny Estrada RPM RC	4.00	10.00
199 Carlos Valderrama RPM RC	3.00	8.00
200 Matt White RPM	3.00	8.00

2001 Absolute Memorabilia Ball Hoggs

Randomly inserted in packs, this 46 card set features color action player photos with swatches of game-used baseballs embedded in the cards. Each card was sequentially numbered and the print runs are listed after the players' names in the checklist below. The first 25 of each card are spotlighted with a holo-foil stamp and labeled "Boss Hoggs." Exchange cards were seeded into packs for the following players: Jeff Bagwell, Darin Erstad, Chipper Jones, Magglio Ordonez, Cal Ripken and Alex Rodriguez. The deadline to redeem the cards was June 1st, 2003.

BH1 Vladimir Guerrero/75	10.00	25.00
BH2 Troy Glaus/75	6.00	15.00
BH3 Tony Gwynn/75	10.00	25.00
BH4 Cal Ripken/175	20.00	50.00
BH5 Todd Helton/75	10.00	25.00
BH6 Jacque Jones/125	6.00	15.00
BH7 Shawn Green/100	6.00	15.00
BH8 Ichiro Suzuki/50	60.00	120.00
BH9 Scott Rolen/100	10.00	25.00
BH10 Roger Clemens/75	10.00	25.00
BH11 Ken Griffey Jr./25		
BH14 Sammy Sosa/75	10.00	25.00
BH15 J.D. Drew/50	6.00	15.00
BH16 Barry Bonds/75	15.00	40.00
BH17 Pat Burrell/75	6.00	15.00
BH18 Mark McGwire/75	12.50	30.00
BH19 Mike Piazza/50	10.00	25.00
BH20 Magglio Ordonez/125	6.00	15.00
BH21 Miguel Tejada/75	6.00	15.00
BH22 Albert Pujols/75	100.00	200.00
BH23 Derek Jeter/50	20.00	50.00
BH24 Johnny Damon/125	10.00	25.00
BH25 Mike Sweeney/75	6.00	15.00
BH26 Ben Grieve/125	6.00	15.00
BH27 Jeff Kent/75	6.00	15.00
BH28 Andres Galarraga/75	6.00	15.00
BH29 Richie Sexson/25		
BH30 J.Encarnacion/125	6.00	15.00
BH31 Ruben Mateo/75	6.00	15.00
BH33 Manny Ramirez Sox/75	10.00	25.00
BH35 Ivan Rodriguez/75	10.00	25.00
BH36 Darin Erstad/125	6.00	15.00
BH37 Carlos Delgado/100	6.00	15.00
BH38 Jeff Bagwell/125	10.00	25.00
BH39 Jermaine Dye/75	6.00	15.00
BH40 Jose Ortiz/50	6.00	15.00
BH41 Gary Sheffield/75	6.00	15.00
BH42 Eric Chavez/125	6.00	15.00
BH43 Mark Grace/75	10.00	25.00
BH44 Rafael Palmeiro/125	10.00	25.00
BH45 Tsuyoshi Shinjo/75	10.00	25.00
BH46 Terrence Long/75	6.00	15.00
BH47 Carlos Delgado/25		
BH48 Frank Thomas/75	10.00	25.00
BH49 Chipper Jones/25		
BH50 Jason Giambi/75	6.00	15.00

2001 Absolute Memorabilia Boss Hoggs

Randomly inserted in packs, this 50-card set is a parallel version of the regular insert set with a holo-foil stamp and labeled "Boss Hoggs." Each card features a patch of a game-used baseball. This set is the first 25 of each card printed in the regular insert set. The following cards are autographed: 1/2/3/5/10/22/32/34/41/49. Exchange cards (with a redemption deadline of June 1st, 2003) were issued in packs for Jeff Bagwell, Darin Erstad, Chipper Jones, Magglio Ordonez, Cal Ripken and Alex Rodriguez. The Chipper and A-Rod cards were intended to be redeemed for autograph cards, the others were all for non-autographed cards.

AU CL: 1-3/5/10/22/32/34/41/49

2001 Absolute Memorabilia Home Opener Souvenirs

Randomly inserted in packs at the rate of one per box, this 50-card set features color photos of top performers showcased on conventional board with foil featuring a swatch of an authentic game-used base embedded in the cards. Only 400 serially numbered sets were produced.

OD1 Barry Bonds	10.00	25.00
OD2 Cal Ripken	15.00	40.00
OD3 Pedro Martinez	4.00	10.00
OD4 Troy Glaus	3.00	8.00
OD5 Frank Thomas	4.00	10.00
OD6 Alex Rodriguez	6.00	15.00
OD7 Ivan Rodriguez	4.00	10.00
OD8 Jeff Bagwell	4.00	10.00
OD9 Mark McGwire	10.00	25.00
OD10 Todd Helton	4.00	10.00
OD11 Gary Sheffield	3.00	8.00
OD12 Manny Ramirez Sox	4.00	10.00
OD13 Mike Piazza	6.00	15.00
OD14 Sammy Sosa	4.00	10.00
OD15 Preston Wilson	3.00	8.00
OD16 Tony Gwynn	6.00	15.00
OD17 Vladimir Guerrero	4.00	10.00
OD18 Carlos Delgado	3.00	8.00
OD19 Roberto Alomar	4.00	10.00
OD20 Todd Helton	4.00	10.00
OD21 Albert Pujols UER	50.00	100.00
Base shows a DiamondBacks logo		
Dbacks did not play Cards opening day		
OD22 Jason Giambi	3.00	8.00
OD23 Sammy Sosa	4.00	10.00
OD24 Ken Griffey Jr.	6.00	15.00
OD25 Darin Erstad	3.00	8.00
OD26 Mark McGwire	15.00	40.00
OD27 Carlos Delgado	3.00	8.00
OD28 Juan Gonzalez	3.00	8.00
OD29 Mike Sweeney	3.00	8.00
OD30 Alex Rodriguez	6.00	15.00
OD31 Roger Clemens	6.00	15.00
OD32 Tsuyoshi Shinjo	4.00	10.00
OD33 Ben Grieve	3.00	8.00
OD34 Jeff Kent	3.00	8.00
OD35 Vladimir Guerrero	4.00	10.00
OD36 Shawn Green	3.00	8.00
OD37 Rafael Palmeiro	4.00	10.00
OD38 Tony Gwynn	6.00	15.00
OD39 Scott Rolen	4.00	10.00
OD40 Ken Griffey Jr.	6.00	15.00
OD41 Albert Pujols	30.00	60.00
OD42 Barry Bonds	10.00	25.00
OD43 Mark Grace	4.00	10.00
OD44 Bernie Williams	4.00	10.00
OD45 Frank Thomas	4.00	10.00
OD46 Jermaine Dye	3.00	8.00
OD47 Mike Piazza	6.00	15.00
OD48 Chipper Jones	4.00	10.00
OD49 Richie Sexson	3.00	8.00
OD50 Magglio Ordonez	3.00	8.00

2001 Absolute Memorabilia Home Opener Souvenirs Autographs

Randomly inserted in packs, this ten-card set features autographed action color photos of top players with a swatch of a game-used baseball and/or base embedded in the card. Only 25 serially numbered sets were produced but the cards are actually serial numbered out of 400 (whereby the first 25 of each card were signed by players participating in this program). No pricing is provided due to market scarcity. Exchange cards, with a redemption deadline of June 1st, 2003, were seeded into packs for Troy Glaus, Cal Ripken and Alex Rodriguez.

2001 Absolute Memorabilia Home Opener Souvenirs Double

Randomly inserted in packs, this 50-card set is parallel to the regular insert set with two swatches of game-used bases embedded in the card. Only 200 serially numbered sets were produced.

*DOUBLE: .6X TO 1.5X BASIC SOUV.

2001 Absolute Memorabilia Home Opener Souvenirs Triple

Randomly inserted in packs, this 50-card set is parallel to the regular insert set with three swatches of game-used bases embedded in the card. Only 75 serially numbered sets were produced.

*TRIPLE: 1.25X TO 3X BASIC SOUV.

2001 Absolute Memorabilia Signing Bonus Baseballs

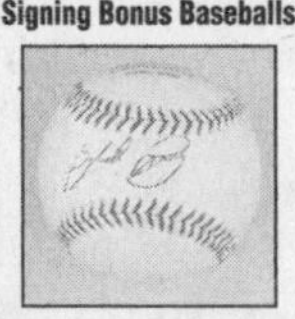

Randomly inserted one per box, this set features baseballs signed by a select group of stellar performers. The players' names are listed below in alphabetical order with the sequential numbering of the quantity signed following the names.

1 Al Oliver/500	10.00	25.00
2 Andre Dawson/550	10.00	25.00
3 Barry Bonds/25		
4 Bill Madlock/524	10.00	25.00
5 Bill Mazeroski/25		
6 Billy Williams/325	10.00	25.00
7 Bob Feller/550	10.00	25.00
8 Bob Gibson/25		
9 Bobby Doerr/300	10.00	25.00
10 Bobby Richardson/500	15.00	40.00
11 Boog Powell/500	10.00	25.00
12 Brian Jordan/25		
13 Bucky Dent/500	10.00	25.00
14 Charles Johnson/25		
15 Chipper Jones/25		
16 Clete Boyer/500	10.00	25.00
17 Dale Murphy/25		
18 Dave Concepcion/500	10.00	25.00
19 Dave Kingman/500	10.00	25.00
20 Don Larsen/200	10.00	25.00
21 Don Newcombe/500	10.00	25.00
22 Don Zimmer/500	10.00	25.00
23 Duke Snider/25		
24 Earl Weaver/300	10.00	25.00
25 Enos Slaughter/525	15.00	40.00
26 Fergie Jenkins/1000	10.00	25.00
27 Frank Howard/500	10.00	25.00
28 Frank Robinson/25		
29 Frank Thomas/25		
30 Gary Carter/200	10.00	25.00
31 Gaylord Perry/1000	10.00	25.00
32 George Foster/500	10.00	25.00
33 George Kell/300	15.00	40.00
34 Goose Gossage/500	10.00	25.00
35 Greg Maddux/25		
36 Hank Aaron/25		
37 Hank Bauer/500	10.00	25.00
38 Harmon Killebrew/200	30.00	60.00
39 Henry Rodriguez/400	10.00	25.00
40 Herb Score/500	10.00	25.00
41 Hoyt Wilhelm/500	15.00	40.00
42 J.D. Drew/25		
43 Javy Lopez/25		
44 Jim Edmonds/25		
45 Jim Palmer/500	10.00	25.00
46 Joe Pepitone/500	10.00	25.00
47 Johnny Bench/25		
48 Johnny Podres/500	10.00	25.00
49 Juan Marichal/485	10.00	25.00
50 Kirby Puckett/25		
51 Larry Doby/300	15.00	40.00
52 Lou Brock/25		
53 Luis Tiant/500	10.00	25.00
54 Magglio Ordonez/200	10.00	25.00
55 Manny Ramirez Sox/25		
56 Maury Wills/500	10.00	25.00
57 Mike Schmidt/25		
58 Minnie Minoso/1000	10.00	25.00
59 Monte Irvin/500	15.00	40.00
60 Moose Skowron/500	10.00	25.00
61 Nolan Ryan/25		
62 Ozzie Smith/25		
63 Phil Rizzuto/25		
64 Ralph Kiner/100	20.00	50.00
65 Randy Johnson/25		
66 Red Schoendienst/500	10.00	25.00
67 Reggie Jackson/25		
68 Rickey Henderson/25		
69 Robin Roberts/500	20.00	50.00
70 Roger Clemens/25		
71 Rollie Fingers/575	10.00	25.00
72 Ryne Sandberg/25		
73 Sean Casey/25		
74 Stan Musial/25		
75 Steve Carlton/25		
76 Steve Garvey/1000	10.00	25.00
77 Todd Helton/25		
78 Tom Glavine/25		
79 Tom Seaver/25		
80 Tommy John/1000	10.00	25.00
81 Tony Gwynn/25		
82 Tony Perez/400	10.00	25.00
83 Wade Boggs/25		
84 Warren Spahn/500	40.00	80.00
85 Whitey Ford/25		
86 Willie Mays/25		
87 Willie McCovey/25		
88 Willie Stargell/25		
89 Yogi Berra/25		

2001 Absolute Memorabilia Tools of the Trade

Randomly inserted in packs, this 50-card set features action color player images with game-worn/used jerseys, batting gloves, bats, and hats embedded in the cards. The cards with swatches of batting gloves were serially numbered to 50, with hats to 100, with bats to 100, and with jerseys to 300. Exchange cards with a redemption deadline of June 1st, 2003 were seeded into packs for the following cards: Roberto Alomar Bat, Roberto Alomar Glove, Jeff Bagwell Bat, Darin Erstad Bat, Troy Glaus Bat, Troy Glaus Hat, Troy Glaus Jsy, Tom Glavine Hat, Shawn Green Bat, Tony Gwynn Glove, David Justice Bat, Greg Maddux Hat, Kazuhiro Sasaki Jsy and Larry Walker Jsy.

TT1 Vladimir Guerrero Jsy	6.00	15.00
TT2 Troy Glaus Jsy	4.00	10.00
TT3 Tony Gwynn Jsy	10.00	25.00
TT4 Todd Helton Jsy	6.00	15.00
TT5 Scott Rolen Jsy	6.00	15.00
TT6 Roger Clemens Jsy	15.00	40.00
TT7 Pedro Martinez Jsy	6.00	15.00
TT8 Richie Sexson Jsy	4.00	10.00
TT9 Magglio Ordonez Jsy	4.00	10.00
TT10 Ben Grieve Jsy	4.00	10.00
TT11 Jeff Bagwell Jsy	6.00	15.00
TT12 Edgar Martinez Jsy	6.00	15.00
TT13 Greg Maddux Jsy	10.00	25.00
TT14 Larry Walker Jsy	4.00	10.00
TT15 Frank Thomas Jsy	6.00	15.00
TT16 Edgardo Alfonzo Jsy	4.00	10.00
TT17 Cal Ripken Jsy	20.00	50.00
TT18 Jose Vidro Jsy	4.00	10.00
TT19 Andruw Jones Jsy	6.00	15.00
TT20 Kaz Sasaki Jsy	4.00	10.00
TT21 Barry Bonds Bat	30.00	80.00
TT22 Juan Gonzalez Bat	10.00	25.00
TT23 Andruw Jones Bat	15.00	40.00
TT24 Cal Ripken Bat	40.00	100.00
TT25 Greg Maddux Bat	15.00	40.00
TT26 Manny Ramirez Sox Bat	15.00	40.00
TT27 Roberto Alomar Bat	15.00	40.00
TT28 Shawn Green Bat	10.00	25.00
TT29 Edgardo Alfonzo Bat	10.00	25.00
TT30 Rafael Palmeiro Bat	15.00	40.00
TT31 Hideo Nomo Bat	75.00	150.00
TT32 A. Galarraga Bat	10.00	25.00
TT33 Todd Helton Bat	15.00	40.00
TT34 Darin Erstad Bat	10.00	25.00
TT35 Ivan Rodriguez Bat	15.00	40.00
TT36 Sean Casey Bat	10.00	25.00
TT37 V. Guerrero Bat	15.00	40.00
TT38 David Justice Bat	10.00	25.00
TT39 Troy Glaus Bat	10.00	25.00
TT40 Jeff Bagwell Bat		
TT41 Barry Bonds Glove	75.00	150.00
TT42 Cal Ripken Glove	100.00	200.00
TT43 Rob Alomar Glove	15.00	40.00
TT44 Sean Casey Glove	10.00	25.00
TT45 Tony Gwynn Glove		
TT46 Bernie Williams Hat	15.00	40.00
TT47 Barry Zito Hat	15.00	40.00
TT48 Greg Maddux Hat		
TT49 Tom Glavine Hat	15.00	40.00
TT50 Troy Glaus Hat	10.00	25.00

2001 Absolute Memorabilia Tools of the Trade Autographs

Randomly inserted in packs, this 10-card set is an autographed partial parallel version of the regular insert set. Only 25 serially numbered sets were produced. Due to market scarcity, no pricing is provided. An exchange card with a redemption deadline of June 1st, 2003 was placed into packs for the Troy Glaus Bat card.

TT1 Vladimir Guerrero Jsy
TT3 Tony Gwynn Jsy
TT5 Scott Rolen Jsy
TT6 Roger Clemens Jsy
TT17 Cal Ripken Bat
TT22 Juan Gonzalez Bat
TT32 Andres Galarraga Bat
TT33 Todd Helton Bat
TT35 Ivan Rodriguez Bat
TT39 Troy Glaus Bat

2002 Absolute Memorabilia

This 200 card standard-size set was issued in August, 2002. The set was released in a big box which contained two nine pack mini-boxes as well as a "Signing Bonus" framed piece. The first 150 cards of this set featured veterans while the final cards feature rookies and prospects with a stated print run of 1000 serial numbered sets.

COMP.SET w/o SP's (150)	15.00	40.00
COMMON CARD (1-150)	.30	.75
COMMON CARD (151-200)	2.00	5.00
1 David Eckstein	.30	.75
2 Darin Erstad	.30	.75
3 Troy Glaus	.30	.75
4 Garret Anderson	.30	.75
5 Tim Salmon	.50	1.25
6 Curt Schilling	.30	.75
7 Randy Johnson	.75	2.00
8 Luis Gonzalez	.30	.75
9 Mark Grace	.50	1.25
10 Tom Glavine	.50	1.25
11 Greg Maddux	1.25	3.00
12 Chipper Jones	.75	2.00
13 Gary Sheffield	.30	.75
14 John Smoltz	.50	1.25
15 Andruw Jones	.50	1.25
16 Wilson Betemit	.30	.75
17 Tony Batista	.30	.75
18 Javier Vazquez	.30	.75
19 Scott Erickson	.30	.75
20 Josh Towers	.30	.75
21 Pedro Martinez	.50	1.25
22 Johnny Damon Sox	.50	1.25
23 Manny Ramirez	.50	1.25
24 Rickey Henderson	.75	2.00
25 Trot Nixon	.30	.75
26 Nomar Garciaparra	1.25	3.00
27 Juan Cruz	.30	.75
28 Kerry Wood	.30	.75
29 Fred McGriff	.50	1.25
30 Moises Alou	.30	.75
31 Sammy Sosa	.75	2.00
32 Corey Patterson	.30	.75
33 Mark Buehrle	.30	.75
34 Keith Foulke	.30	.75
35 Frank Thomas	.75	2.00
36 Kenny Lofton	.30	.75
37 Magglio Ordonez	.30	.75
38 Barry Larkin	.50	1.25
39 Ken Griffey Jr.	1.25	3.00
40 Adam Dunn	.30	.75
41 Juan Encarnacion	.30	.75
42 Sean Casey	.30	.75
43 Bartolo Colon	.30	.75
44 C.C. Sabathia	.30	.75
45 Travis Fryman	.30	.75
46 Jim Thome	.50	1.25
47 Omar Vizquel	.50	1.25
48 Ellis Burks	.30	.75
49 Russell Branyan	.30	.75
50 Mike Hampton	.30	.75
51 Todd Helton	.50	1.25
52 Jose Ortiz	.30	.75
53 Juan Uribe	.30	.75
54 Juan Pierre	.30	.75
55 Larry Walker	.30	.75
56 Mike Rivera	.30	.75
57 Robert Fick	.30	.75
58 Bobby Higginson	.30	.75
59 Josh Beckett	.30	.75
60 Richard Hidalgo	.30	.75
61 Cliff Floyd	.30	.75
62 Mike Lowell	.30	.75
63 Roy Oswalt	.30	.75
64 Morgan Ensberg	.30	.75
65 Jeff Bagwell	.50	1.25
66 Craig Biggio	.50	1.25
67 Lance Berkman	.30	.75
68 Carlos Beltran	.30	.75
69 Mike Sweeney	.30	.75
70 Neifi Perez	.30	.75
71 Kevin Brown	.30	.75
72 Hideo Nomo	.75	2.00
73 Paul Lo Duca	.30	.75
74 Adrian Beltre	.30	.75
75 Shawn Green	.30	.75
76 Eric Karros	.30	.75
77 Brad Radke	.30	.75
78 Corey Koskie	.30	.75
79 Doug Mientkiewicz	.30	.75
80 Torii Hunter	.30	.75
81 Jacque Jones	.30	.75
82 Ben Sheets	.30	.75
83 Richie Sexson	.30	.75
84 Geoff Jenkins	.30	.75
85 Tony Armas Jr.	.30	.75
86 Michael Barrett	.30	.75
87 Jose Vidro	.30	.75
88 Vladimir Guerrero	.75	2.00
89 Roger Clemens	1.50	4.00
90 Derek Jeter	2.00	5.00
91 Bernie Williams	.50	1.25
92 Jason Giambi	.30	.75
93 Jorge Posada	.50	1.25
94 Mike Mussina	.50	1.25
95 Andy Pettitte	.50	1.25
96 Nick Johnson	.30	.75
97 Alfonso Soriano	.30	.75
98 Shawn Estes	.30	.75
99 Al Leiter	.30	.75
100 Mike Piazza	1.25	3.00
101 Roberto Alomar	.50	1.25
102 Mo Vaughn	.30	.75
103 Jeromy Burnitz	.30	.75
104 Tim Hudson	.30	.75
105 Barry Zito	.30	.75
106 Mark Mulder	.30	.75
107 Eric Chavez	.30	.75
108 Miguel Tejada	.30	.75
109 Carlos Pena	.30	.75
110 Jermaine Dye	.30	.75
111 Mike Lieberthal	.30	.75
112 Scott Rolen	.50	1.25
113 Pat Burrell	.30	.75
114 Brandon Duckworth	.30	.75
115 Bobby Abreu	.30	.75
116 Jason Kendall	.30	.75
117 Aramis Ramirez	.30	.75
118 Brian Giles	.30	.75
119 Pokey Reese	.30	.75
120 Phil Nevin	.30	.75
121 Ryan Klesko	.30	.75
122 Jeremy Giambi	.30	.75
123 Trevor Hoffman	.30	.75
124 Barry Bonds	2.00	5.00
125 Rich Aurilia	.30	.75
126 Jeff Kent	.30	.75
127 Tsuyoshi Shinjo	.30	.75
128 Ichiro Suzuki	1.50	4.00
129 Edgar Martinez	.50	1.25
130 Freddy Garcia	.30	.75
131 Bret Boone	.30	.75
132 Matt Morris	.30	.75
133 Tino Martinez	.50	1.25
134 Albert Pujols	1.50	4.00
135 J.D. Drew	.30	.75
136 Jim Edmonds	.30	.75
137 Gabe Kapler	.30	.75
138 Paul Wilson	.30	.75
139 Ben Grieve	.30	.75
140 Wade Miller	.30	.75
141 Chan Ho Park	.30	.75
142 Alex Rodriguez	1.25	3.00
143 Rafael Palmeiro	.50	1.25
144 Juan Gonzalez	.30	.75
145 Ivan Rodriguez	.50	1.25
146 Carlos Delgado	.30	.75
147 Jose Cruz Jr.	.30	.75
148 Shannon Stewart	.30	.75
149 Raul Mondesi	.30	.75
150 Vernon Wells	.30	.75
151 So Taguchi RP RC	3.00	8.00
152 Kazuhisa Ishii RP RC	3.00	8.00
153 Hank Blalock RP	3.00	8.00
154 Sean Burroughs RP	2.00	5.00
155 Geronimo Gil RP	2.00	5.00
156 Jon Rauch RP	2.00	5.00
157 Fernando Rodney RP	2.00	5.00
158 Miguel Asencio RP RC	2.00	5.00
159 Franklyn German RP RC	2.00	5.00
160 Luis Ugueto RP RC	2.00	5.00
161 Jorge Sosa RP RC	3.00	8.00
162 Felix Escalona RP RC	2.00	5.00
163 Colby Lewis RP	2.00	5.00
164 Mark Teixeira RP	3.00	8.00
165 Mark Prior RP	3.00	8.00
166 Francis Beltran RP RC	2.00	5.00
167 Joe Thurston RP	2.00	5.00
168 Earl Snyder RP RC	2.00	5.00
169 Takahito Nomura RP RC	2.00	5.00
170 Bill Hall RP	2.00	5.00
171 Marlon Byrd RP	2.00	5.00
172 Dave Williams RP	2.00	5.00
173 Yorvit Torrealba RP	2.00	5.00
174 Brandon Backe RP RC	3.00	8.00
175 Jorge De La Rosa RP RC	2.00	5.00
176 Brian Mallette RP RC	2.00	5.00
177 Rodrigo Rosario RP RC	2.00	5.00
178 Anderson Machado RP RC	2.00	5.00
179 Jorge Padilla RP RC	2.00	5.00
180 Allan Simpson RP RC	2.00	5.00
181 Doug Devore RP RC	2.00	5.00
182 Steve Bechler RP RC	2.00	5.00
183 Raul Chavez RP RC	2.00	5.00
184 Tom Shearn RP RC	2.00	5.00
185 Ben Howard RP RC	2.00	5.00
186 Chris Baker RP RC	2.00	5.00
187 Travis Hughes RP RC	2.00	5.00

188 Kevin Mench RP 2.00 5.00
189 Drew Henson RP 2.00 5.00
190 Mike Moriarty RP RC 2.00 5.00
191 Corey Thurman RP RC 2.00 5.00
192 Bobby Hill RP 2.00 5.00
193 Steve Kent RP RC 2.00 5.00
194 Satoru Komiyama RP RC 2.00 5.00
195 Jason Lane RP 2.00 5.00
196 Angel Berroa RP 2.00 5.00
197 Brandon Puffer RP RC 2.00 5.00
198 Brian Fitzgerald RP RC 2.00 5.00
199 Rene Reyes RP RC 2.00 5.00
200 Hee Seop Choi RP 2.00 5.00
NNO Mark Prior Promo

2002 Absolute Memorabilia Spectrum

Randomly inserted into packs, this is a parallel to the basic set. The veteran cards (1-150) were issued to a stated print run of 100 serial numbered sets while the rookies and prospects were issued to a stated print run of 50 serial numbered sets.

*SPECTRUM 1-150: 2.5X TO 6X BASIC
72 Hideo Nomo 5.00 12.00
151 So Taguchi RP 4.00 10.00
152 Kazuhisa Ishii RP 4.00 10.00
153 Hank Blalock RP 4.00 10.00
154 Sean Burroughs RP 3.00 8.00
155 Geronimo Gil RP 3.00 8.00
156 Jon Rauch RP 3.00 8.00
157 Fernando Rodney RP 3.00 8.00
158 Miguel Asencio RP 3.00 8.00
159 Franklyn German RP 3.00 8.00
160 Luis Ugueto RP 3.00 8.00
161 Jorge Sosa RP 4.00 10.00
162 Felix Escalona RP 3.00 8.00
163 Colby Lewis RP 3.00 8.00
164 Mark Teixeira RP 6.00 15.00
165 Mark Prior RP 4.00 10.00
166 Francis Beltran RP 3.00 8.00
167 Joe Thurston RP 3.00 8.00
168 Earl Snyder RP 3.00 8.00
169 Takahito Nomura RP 6.00 15.00
170 Bill Hall RP 3.00 8.00
171 Marlon Byrd RP 3.00 8.00
172 Dave Williams RP 3.00 8.00
173 Yorvit Torrealba RP 3.00 8.00
174 Brandon Backe RP 4.00 10.00
175 Jorge De La Rosa RP 4.00 10.00
176 Brian Mallette RP 3.00 8.00
177 Rodrigo Rosario RP 3.00 8.00
178 Anderson Machado RP 3.00 8.00
179 Jorge Padilla RP 3.00 8.00
180 Allan Simpson RP 3.00 8.00
181 Doug Devore RP 3.00 8.00
182 Steve Bechler RP 3.00 8.00
183 Raul Chavez RP 3.00 8.00
184 Tom Shearn RP 3.00 8.00
185 Ben Howard RP 3.00 8.00
186 Chris Baker RP 3.00 8.00
187 Travis Hughes RP 3.00 8.00
188 Kevin Mench RP 3.00 8.00
189 Drew Henson RP 3.00 8.00
190 Mike Moriarty RP 3.00 8.00
191 Corey Thurman RP 3.00 8.00
192 Bobby Hill RP 3.00 8.00
193 Steve Kent RP 3.00 8.00
194 Satoru Komiyama RP 3.00 8.00
195 Jason Lane RP 3.00 8.00
196 Angel Berroa RP 3.00 8.00
197 Brandon Puffer RP 3.00 8.00
198 Brian Fitzgerald RP 3.00 8.00
199 Rene Reyes RP 3.00 8.00
200 Hee Seop Choi RP 3.00 8.00

2002 Absolute Memorabilia Absolutely Ink

Inserted into packs at stated odds of one in 22 hobby and one in 36 retail, these 59 cards feature a mix of active player and retired superstars who signed cards for this set. Many players were printed to shorter supply and we have notated that information next to their name in our checklist. Cards with a stated print run of 50 or fewer are not priced due to market scarcity.

GOLD PRINT RUN 25 SERIAL #'d SETS
NO GOLD PRICING DUE TO SCARCITY
1 Adrian Beltre 6.00 15.00
2 Alex Rodriguez SP/50 * 50.00 100.00
3 Ben Sheets 6.00 15.00
4 Bernie Williams SP/25 *
5 Bobby Doerr 6.00 15.00
6 Blaine Neal 4.00 10.00
7 Carlos Beltran 6.00 15.00
8 Carlos Pena 4.00 10.00
10 Corey Patterson SP/150 * 6.00 15.00
11 Curt Schilling SP/15 *
12 Dave Parker 6.00 15.00
13 David Justice SP/65 * 10.00 25.00
14 Don Mattingly SP/75 * 40.00 80.00
15 Duaner Sanchez 4.00 10.00
16 Eric Chavez SP/100 * 6.00 15.00
17 Freddy Garcia SP/200 * 6.00 15.00
18 Gary Carter SP/150 * 6.00 15.00
19 Gary Sheffield SP/25 *
20 George Brett SP/25 *
21 Greg Maddux SP/25 *
22 Ivan Rodriguez SP/50 * 20.00 50.00
23 J.D. Drew SP/100 * 6.00 15.00
24 Jack Cust 4.00 10.00
25 Jason Michaels 4.00 10.00
26 Jermaine Dye SP/125 * 6.00 15.00
27 Jim Palmer SP/150 * 6.00 15.00
28 Jose Vidro 4.00 10.00
29 Josh Towers 4.00 10.00
30 Kerry Wood SP/50 * 15.00 40.00
31 Kirby Puckett SP/50 * 50.00 100.00
32 Luis Gonzalez SP/75 * 10.00 25.00
33 Luis Rivera 4.00 10.00
34 Manny Ramirez SP/50 * 20.00 50.00
35 Marcus Giles 6.00 15.00
36 Mark Prior SP/100 * 10.00 25.00
37 Mark Teixeira SP/100 * 15.00 40.00
38 Marlon Byrd SP/250 * 6.00 15.00
39 Matt Ginter 4.00 10.00
40 Moises Alou SP/150 * 6.00 15.00
41 Nate Frese 4.00 10.00
42 Nick Johnson 6.00 15.00
43 Nomar Garciaparra SP/15 *
44 Pablo Ozuna 4.00 10.00
45 Paul Lo Duca SP/200 * 6.00 15.00
46 Richie Sexson 6.00 15.00
47 Roberto Alomar SP/100 * 10.00 25.00
48 Roy Oswalt SP/300 * 6.00 15.00
49 Ryan Klesko SP/75 * 10.00 25.00
50 Sean Casey SP/125 * 6.00 15.00
51 Shannon Stewart 6.00 15.00
52 So Taguchi 6.00 15.00
53 Terrence Long 4.00 10.00
54 Timo Perez 4.00 10.00
55 Todd Helton SP/25 *
56 Tony Gwynn SP/50 * 40.00 80.00
57 Troy Glaus SP/300 * 10.00 25.00
58 Vladimir Guerrero SP/225 * 15.00 40.00
59 Wade Miller 4.00 10.00
60 Wilson Betemit 4.00 10.00

2002 Absolute Memorabilia Absolutely Ink Numbers

This is a parallel to the Absolutely Ink insert set. Each card can be identified as they were issued to that player's print unifoirm number. If a player signed 25 or fewer or these cards, there is no pricing due to market scarcity.

1 Adrian Beltre/29 12.50 30.00
2 Alex Rodriguez/3
3 Ben Sheets/15
5 Bobby Doerr/1
7 Carlos Beltran/15
8 Carlos Pena/15
10 Corey Patterson/20
12 Dave Parker/39 10.00 25.00
13 David Justice/23
14 Don Mattingly/23
16 Eric Chavez/3
17 Freddy Garcia/34 12.50 30.00
18 Gary Carter/8
19 Gary Sheffield/10
20 George Brett/5
21 Greg Maddux/31 60.00 120.00
22 Ivan Rodriguez/7
23 J.D. Drew/7
24 Jack Cust/67 6.00 15.00
25 Jason Michaels/22
26 Jermaine Dye/24
27 Jim Palmer/22
28 Jose Vidro/3
29 Josh Towers/35 8.00 20.00
30 Kerry Wood/34 20.00 50.00
31 Kirby Puckett/34 60.00 120.00
32 Luis Gonzalez/20
33 Luis Rivera/60 6.00 15.00
34 Manny Ramirez/24
35 Marcus Giles/22
36 Mark Prior/22
40 Moises Alou/18
42 Nick Johnson/36 12.50 30.00
43 Nomar Garciaparra/5
44 Pablo Ozuna/3
45 Paul Lo Duca/16
46 Richie Sexson/11
47 Roberto Alomar/12
48 Roy Oswalt/44 10.00 25.00
49 Ryan Klesko/30 12.50 30.00
50 Sean Casey/21
51 Shannon Stewart/24
52 So Taguchi/99 10.00 25.00
53 Terrence Long/12
54 Timo Perez/6
56 Tony Gwynn/19
57 Troy Glaus/25
58 Vladimir Guerrero/27 30.00 60.00
59 Wade Miller/52 6.00 15.00
60 Wilson Betemit/24

2002 Absolute Memorabilia Signing Bonus

Inserted into "full" boxes at one per box and with a SRP of $40 per frame, these 313 items was highlighted by a signature of the featured player. These frame have all different stated print runs and we have notated that information in our checklist next to their names.

Frames with a print run of 25 or less are not priced due to market scarcity.

1 Bob Abreu Gray-N/53 15.00 40.00
2 Bob Abreu Stripe-N/53 15.00 40.00
3 Grover Alexander Gray/1
4 Rob Alomar Gray-N/12
5 Rob Alomar Gray-N/100 15.00 40.00
6 Rob Alomar Stripe-N/100 15.00 40.00
7 Moises Alou Blue-L/250 10.00 25.00
8 Moises Alou Blue-N/18
9 Moises Alou Gray-N/18
10 Moises Alou Stripe-L/250 10.00 25.00
11 Moises Alou Stripe-N/18
12 Jeff Bagwell Gray-N/5
13 Jeff Bagwell Red-N/5
14 Jeff Bagwell Stripe-N/5
15 Jeff Bagwell White-N/5
16 Carlos Beltran Black-N/15
17 Carlos Beltran Blue-N/50 15.00 40.00
18 Carlos Beltran Gray-N/50 15.00 40.00
19 Carlos Beltran White-N/15
20 Adrian Beltre Blue-N/150 10.00 25.00
21 Adrian Beltre Gray-N/150 10.00 25.00
22 Adrian Beltre White-N/29 20.00 50.00
23 Lance Berkman Gray-N/17
24 Lance Berkman Red-N/17
25 Lance Berkman Stripe-N/17
26 Lance Berkman White-N/17
27 Angel Berroa Black-N/100 8.00 20.00
28 Angel Berroa Blue-N/100 8.00 20.00
29 Angel Berroa Gray-N/50 10.00 25.00
30 Angel Berroa White-N/4
31 Wilson Betemit Gray-N/250 6.00 15.00
32 Wilson Betemit White-N/250 6.00 15.00
33 Craig Biggio Gray-N/7
34 Craig Biggio Red-N/7
35 Craig Biggio Stripe-N/7
36 Craig Biggio White-N/7
37 Hank Blalock Blue-N/12
38 Hank Blalock Gray-N/50 15.00 40.00
39 Hank Blalock White-N/100 12.50 30.00
40 George Brett Blue-N/5
41 George Brett Gray-N/5
42 George Brett White-N/5
43 Lou Brock Gray-N/100 15.00 40.00
44 Lou Brock White-N/200 12.50 30.00
45 Kevin Brown Blue-N/27 20.00 50.00
46 Kevin Brown Gray-N/150 10.00 25.00
47 Kevin Brown White-N/100 12.50 30.00
48 Mark Buehrle Black-N/200 15.00 40.00
49 Mark Buehrle Gray-N/200 15.00 40.00
50 Mark Buehrle Stripe-N/56 40.00 80.00
51 Sean Burroughs Blue-N/21
52 Sean Burroughs Gray-N/21
53 Sean Burroughs White-N/21
54 Marlon Byrd Gray-N/61 10.00 25.00
55 Marlon Byrd Stripe-N/61 10.00 25.00
56 Steve Carlton Gray-N/100 12.50 30.00
57 Steve Carlton Stripe-N/150 10.00 25.00
58 Sean Casey Gray-N/21
59 Sean Casey Stripe-L/100 12.50 30.00
60 Sean Casey Stripe-N/21
61 Eric Chavez Gray-N/25
62 Eric Chavez Green-N/3
63 Eric Chavez White-N/28 20.00 50.00
64 Roger Clemens Gray-N/10
65 Roger Clemens Stripe-N/10
66 Ty Cobb Gray/6
67 Eddie Collins Gray/1
68 Juan Cruz Blue-L/51 10.00 25.00
69 Juan Cruz Blue-N/51 10.00 25.00
70 Juan Cruz Gray-N/51 10.00 25.00
71 Juan Cruz Stripe-L/51 10.00 25.00
72 Juan Cruz Stripe-N/51 10.00 25.00
73 J.D. Drew Gray-N/100 12.50 30.00
74 J.D. Drew White-N/7
75 Bran Duckworth Gray-N/56 10.00 25.00
76 B.Duckworth Stripe-N/150 6.00 15.00
77 Adam Dunn Gray-N/10
78 Adam Dunn Stripe-L/10
79 Adam Dunn Stripe-N/44 30.00 60.00
80 Jermaine Dye Gray-N/250 10.00 25.00
81 Jermaine Dye Green-N/100 12.50 30.00
82 Jermaine Dye White-N/100 12.50 30.00
83 Morg Ensberg Gray-N/100 12.50 30.00
84 Morg Ensberg Red-N/100 12.50 30.00
85 Morg Ensberg Stripe-N/100 12.50 30.00
86 Morg Ensberg White-N/100 12.50 30.00
87 Darin Erstad Gray-N/5
88 Darin Erstad White-N/17
89 Cliff Floyd Gray-N/200 10.00 25.00
90 Cliff Floyd Stripe-N/200 10.00 25.00
91 Jimmie Foxx Gray/1
92 Freddy Garcia Blue-N/34 20.00 50.00
93 Freddy Garcia Gray-N/34 20.00 50.00
94 Freddy Garcia White-N/125 10.00 25.00
95 Nomar Garciaparra Gray-N/5
96 Nomar Garciaparra White-N/5
97 Troy Glaus Gray-N/50 30.00 60.00
98 Troy Glaus White-N/100 15.00 40.00
99 Tom Glavine Gray-N/25
100 Tom Glavine White-N/200 20.00 50.00
101 Luis Gonzalez Black-N/20
102 Luis Gonzalez Gray-N/125 10.00 25.00
103 Luis Gonzalez Purple-N/125 10.00 25.00
104 Luis Gonzalez Stripe-N/125 10.00 25.00
105 Hank Greenberg Gray/1
106 Vlad Guerrero Gray-N/27 60.00 120.00
107 V.Guerrero Stripe-N/150 40.00 80.00
108 Tony Gwynn Blue-N/19
109 Tony Gwynn Gray-N/19
110 Tony Gwynn White-N/19
111 Rich Hidalgo Gray-N/100 8.00 20.00
112 Rich Hidalgo Red-N/135 6.00 15.00
113 Rich Hidalgo Stripe-N/15
114 Rich Hidalgo White-N/150 6.00 15.00
115 Rogers Hornsby Gray/1
116 Tim Hudson Gray-N/50 30.00 60.00
117 Tim Hudson Green-N/100 15.00 40.00
118 Tim Hudson White-N/15
119 Kazuhisa Ishii Blue-N/17
120 Kazuhisa Ishii Gray-N/17
121 Kazuhisa Ishii White-N/17
122 Reg Jackson Gray-N/44 40.00 80.00
123 Reg Jackson Stripe-N/44 50.00 100.00
124 Nick Johnson Gray-N/200 10.00 25.00
125 Nick Johnson Stripe-N/200 10.00 25.00
126 Walter Johnson Gray/4
127 Andruw Jones Gray-N/75 30.00 60.00
128 Andruw Jones White-N/25
129 Chipper Jones Gray-N/10
130 Chipper Jones White-N/10
131 Al Kaline Gray-N/6
132 Al Kaline White-L/250 20.00 50.00
133 Al Kaline White-N/6
134 Gabe Kapler Blue-N/125 10.00 25.00
135 Gabe Kapler Gray-N/18
136 Gabe Kapler White-N/175 10.00 25.00
137 Ryan Klesko Blue-N/30 20.00 50.00
138 Ryan Klesko Gray-N/30 20.00 50.00
139 Ryan Klesko White-N/30 20.00 50.00
140 Nap Lajoie Gray/1
141 Jason Lane Gray-N/100 12.50 30.00
142 Jason Lane Red-N/100 12.50 30.00
143 Jason Lane Stripe-N/100 12.50 30.00
144 Jason Lane White-N/100 12.50 30.00
145 Barry Larkin Gray-N/50 30.00 60.00
146 Barry Larkin Stripe-L/100 15.00 40.00
147 Barry Larkin Stripe-N/11
148 Paul LoDuca Blue-N/16
149 Paul LoDuca Gray-N/16
150 Paul LoDuca White-N/50 15.00 40.00
151 Fred Lynn Gray-N/250 10.00 25.00
152 Fred Lynn White-N/150 10.00 25.00
153 Connie Mack Gray/2
154 Greg Maddux Gray-N/31 100.00 200.00
155 Greg Maddux White-N/31 100.00 200.00
156 Roger Maris Gray/3
157 Edgar Martinez Blue-N/150 20.00 50.00
158 Edgar Martinez Gray-N/150 20.00 50.00
159 Edgar Martinez White-N/11
160 Pedro Martinez Gray-N/5
161 P.Martinez White-N/45 60.00 120.00
162 Don Mattingly Gray-N/100 60.00 120.00
163 D.Mattingly Stripe-N/100 60.00 120.00
164 Will McCovey Gray-N/190 12.50 30.00
165 Will McCovey White-N/250 12.50 30.00
166 Wade Miller Gray-N/150 6.00 15.00
167 Wade Miller Stripe-N/250 6.00 15.00
168 Wade Miller Red-N/52 10.00 25.00
169 Wade Miller White-N/52 10.00 25.00
170 Paul Molitor Blue-N/75 15.00 40.00
171 Paul Molitor Gray-N/100 12.50 30.00
172 Paul Molitor White-N/125 10.00 25.00
173 Mark Mulder Gray-N/20
174 Mark Mulder Green-N/20
175 Mark Mulder White-N/40 15.00 40.00
176 Mike Mussina Gray-N/5
177 Mike Mussina Stripe-N/5
178 Jose Ortiz Gray-N/125 6.00 15.00
179 Jose Ortiz Purple-N/125 6.00 15.00
180 Jose Ortiz Stripe-L/125 6.00 15.00
181 Jose Ortiz Stripe-N/125 6.00 15.00
182 Roy Oswalt Gray-N/44 15.00 40.00
183 Roy Oswalt Red-N/44 15.00 40.00
184 Roy Oswalt Stripe-N/100 12.50 30.00
185 Roy Oswalt White-N/100 12.50 30.00
186 Mel Ott Gray/3
187 Rafael Palmeiro Blue-N/25
188 Rafael Palmeiro Gray-N/25
189 Rafael Palmeiro White-N/25
190 Jim Palmer Gray-N/250 10.00 25.00
191 Jim Palmer White-N/150 10.00 25.00
192 Dave Parker Black-N/150 12.50 30.00
193 Dave Parker White-N/150 12.50 30.00
194 Cor Patterson Blue-L/250 10.00 25.00
195 Cor Patterson Blue-N/20
196 Cor Patterson Gray-N/250 10.00 25.00
197 Cor Patterson Stripe-L/250 10.00 25.00
198 Cor Patterson Stripe-N/250 2.00 5.00
199 Carlos Pena Gray-N/19
200 Carlos Pena Green-N/250 6.00 15.00
201 Carlos Pena White-N/150 6.00 15.00
202 Tony Perez Gray-N/24
203 Tony Perez Stripe-L/250 10.00 25.00
204 Tony Perez Stripe-N/24
205 Juan Pierre Gray-N/75 15.00 40.00
206 Juan Pierre Purple-N/75 10.00 25.00
207 Juan Pierre White-L/75 10.00 25.00
208 Juan Pierre White-N/75 10.00 25.00
209 Mark Prior Blue-L/75 15.00 40.00
210 Mark Prior Blue-N/125 12.50 30.00
211 Mark Prior Gray-N/75 15.00 40.00
212 Mark Prior Stripe-L/50 15.00 40.00
213 Mark Prior Stripe-N/22
214 Kirby Puckett Blue-N/34 60.00 120.00
215 Kirby Puckett Gray-N/34
216 Kirby Puckett Stripe-N/34 60.00 120.00
217 Albert Pujols Gray-N/5
218 Albert Pujols White-N/100 150.00 250.00
219 Aram Ramirez Black-N/125 10.00 25.00
220 Aram Ramirez Gray-N/50 15.00 40.00
221 Aram Ramirez White-N/16
222 Manny Ramirez Gray-N/24
223 Manny Ramirez White-N/5
224 Phil Rizzuto Gray-N/250 40.00 80.00
225 Phil Rizzuto Stripe-N/10
226 B.Robinson Gray-N/250 12.50 30.00
227 B.Robinson White-N/150 40.00 80.00
227A Brooks Robinson ERR White-N/150
Card says in print it was signed by Jim Palmer
228 Jackie Robinson Gray/3
229 Alex Rodriguez Blue-N/3
230 Alex Rodriguez Gray-N/15
231 Alex Rodriguez White-N/15
232 Ivan Rodriguez Blue-N/7
233 Ivan Rodriguez Gray-N/7
234 Ivan Rodriguez White-N/7
235 Scott Rolen Gray-N/17
236 Scott Rolen Stripe-N/17
237 Babe Ruth Gray/8
238 N.Ryan Angel Gray-N/30 125.00 250.00
239 N.Ryan Angel White-N/30 125.00 250.00
240 N.Ryan Astro Gray-N/34 125.00 250.00
241 N.Ryan Astro White-N/34 125.00 250.00
242 N.Ryan Rgr Blue-N/34 125.00 250.00
243 N.Ryan Rgr Gray-N/34 125.00 250.00
244 N.Ryan Rgr White-N/34 125.00 250.00
245 C.C. Sabathia Blue-N/15
246 C.C. Sabathia Gray-N/10
247 C.C. Sabathia White-N/10
248 Ryne Sandberg Blue-L/50 75.00 150.00
249 Ryne Sandberg Blue-N/23
250 Ryne Sandberg Gray-N/23
251 R.Sandberg Stripe-L/50 75.00 150.00
252 Ryne Sandberg Stripe-N/23
253 Curt Schilling Black-N/10
254 Curt Schilling Gray-N/10
255 Curt Schilling Purple-N/10
256 Curt Schilling Stripe-N/5
257 Mike Schmidt Gray-N/100 60.00 120.00
258 M.Schmidt Stripe-N/100 60.00 120.00
259 Richie Sexson Blue-N/100 12.50 30.00
260 Richie Sexson Gray-N/100 12.50 30.00
261 Richie Sexson White-N/100 12.50 30.00
262 Ben Sheets Blue-N/150 10.00 25.00
263 Ben Sheets Gray-N/100 12.50 30.00
264 Ben Sheets White-N/100 12.50 30.00
265 Gary Sheffield Gray-N/11
266 Gary Sheffield White-N/11
267 George Sisler Gray/3
268 Alfonso Soriano Gray-N/12
269 A.Soriano Stripe-N/100 15.00 40.00
270 Tris Speaker Gray/1
271 Shan Stewart Blue-N/150 10.00 25.00
272 Shan Stewart Gray-N/100 8.00 20.00
273 Shan Stewart White-N/24
274 Mike Sweeney Black-N/100 12.50 30.00
275 Mike Sweeney Blue-N/100 12.50 30.00
276 Mike Sweeney Gray-N/100 12.50 30.00
277 Mike Sweeney White-N/100 12.50 30.00
278 So Taguchi Gray-N/99 20.00 50.00
279 So Taguchi White-N/99 20.00 50.00
280 Mark Teixeira Blue-N/100 20.00 50.00
281 Mark Teixeira Gray-N/23
282 Mark Teixeira White-N/100 20.00 50.00
283 Miguel Tejada Gray-N/50 30.00 60.00
284 Miguel Tejada Green-N/4
285 Miguel Tejada White-N/40 30.00 60.00
286 Frank Thomas Black-N/35 60.00 120.00
287 Frank Thomas Gray-N/10
288 Frank Thomas White-N/10
289 Juan Uribe Gray-N/25
290 Juan Uribe Purple-N/25
291 Juan Uribe White-L/4
292 Juan Uribe White-N/4
293 Jav Vazquez Gray-N/125 10.00 25.00
294 Jav Vazquez Stripe-N/125 10.00 25.00
295 Jose Vidro Gray-N/150 6.00 15.00
296 Jose Vidro Stripe-N/150 6.00 15.00
297 Honus Wagner Gray/11
298 Bernie Williams Gray-N/15
299 Bernie Williams Stripe-N/15
300 Ted Williams Gray/1
301 Hack Wilson Gray/1
302 Dave Winfield Gray-N/25
303 Dave Winfield Stripe-N/25
304 Kerry Wood Blue-L/34 40.00 80.00
305 Kerry Wood Blue-N/34 40.00 80.00
306 Kerry Wood Gray-N/34 40.00 80.00
307 Kerry Wood Stripe-L/34 40.00 80.00
308 Kerry Wood Stripe-N/34 40.00 80.00
309 Cy Young Gray/2
310 Barry Zito Gray-N/25
311 Barry Zito Green-N/25
312 Barry Zito White-N/50 30.00 60.00

2002 Absolute Memorabilia Signing Bonus Entry Cards

Issued one per pack, these 20 cards are "contest" cards which when sent in enabled collectors to win various items relating to the featured player.

2002 Absolute Memorabilia Team Quads

Inserted into hobby packs at a stated rate of one in 18, these cards feature four players from 20 of the 30 different major league teams.

*GOLD: .75X TO 2X BASIC QUADS
*SPECTRUM: .6X TO 1.5X BASIC QUADS
SPECTRUM ODDS 1:36 HOBBY
1 Troy Glaus 2.00 5.00
Darin Erstad
Garret Anderson
Troy Percival
2 Curt Schilling 2.00 5.00
Randy Johnson
Luis Gonzalez
Mark Grace
3 Chipper Jones 3.00 8.00
Andruw Jones
Greg Maddux
Tom Glavine
4 Nomar Garciaparra 3.00 8.00
Manny Ramirez
Trot Nixon
Pedro Martinez
5 Kerry Wood 2.00 5.00
Sammy Sosa
Fred McGriff
Moises Alou
6 Frank Thomas 2.00 5.00
Magglio Ordonez
Mark Buehrle
Kenny Lofton
7 Ken Griffey Jr. 3.00 8.00
Barry Larkin
Adam Dunn
Sean Casey
8 C.C Sabathia 2.00 5.00
Jim Thome
Bartolo Colon
Russell Branyan
9 Todd Helton 2.00 5.00
Larry Walker
Juan Pierre
Mike Hampton
10 Jeff Bagwell 2.00 5.00
Craig Biggio
Lance Berkman
Richard Hidalgo
11 Shawn Green 2.00 5.00
Adrian Beltre
Hideo Nomo
Paul Lo Duca
12 Mike Piazza 3.00 8.00
Roberto Alomar
Mo Vaughn
Roger Cedeno
13 Roger Clemens 5.00 12.00
Derek Jeter
Jason Giambi
Mike Mussina
14 Barry Zito 2.00 5.00
Tim Hudson
Eric Chavez
Miguel Tejada
15 Pat Burrell 2.00 5.00
Scott Rolen
Bobby Abreu
Marlon Byrd
16 Bernie Williams 2.00 5.00
Jorge Posada
Alfonso Soriano
Andy Pettitte
17 Barry Bonds 4.00 10.00
Rich Aurilia
Tsuyoshi Shinjo
Jeff Kent
18 Ichiro Suzuki 4.00 10.00
Kazuhiro Sasaki
Bret Boone
Edgar Martinez
19 Albert Pujols 4.00 10.00
J.D. Drew
Jim Edmonds
Tino Martinez
20 Alex Rodriguez 3.00 8.00
Ivan Rodriguez
Juan Gonzalez
Rafael Palmeiro

2002 Absolute Memorabilia Team Quads Materials

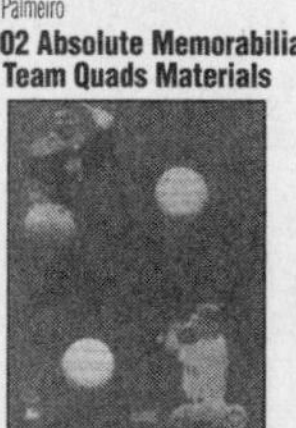

Randomly inserted into packs, these 19 cards parallel the Team Quads insert set. Each card be identified by both the four pieces of memorabilia on the card as well as having a stated print run of 100 serial numbered sets. Please note that card number 7 does not exist.

GOLD PRINT RUN 25 SERIAL #'d SETS
NO GOLD PRICING DUE TO SCARCITY
1 Troy Glaus Jsy 10.00 25.00
Darin Erstad Jsy
Garret Anderson Jsy
Troy Percival Jsy
2 Curt Schilling Jsy 15.00 40.00
Randy Johnson Jsy
Luis Gonzalez Jsy
Mark Grace Jsy
3 Chipper Jones Jsy 20.00 50.00
Andruw Jones Jsy
Greg Maddux Jsy
Tom Glavine Jsy
4 Nomar Garciaparra Jsy 20.00 50.00
Manny Ramirez Jsy
Pedro Martinez Jsy
Trot Nixon Bat
5 Kerry Wood Base 15.00 40.00
Sammy Sosa Base
Fred McGriff Base
Moises Alou Base
6 Frank Thomas Jsy 15.00 40.00
Magglio Ordonez Jsy
Mark Buehrle Jsy
Kenny Lofton Bat
8 C.C Sabathia Jsy 15.00 40.00
Jim Thome Jsy
Bartolo Colon Jsy
Russell Branyan Jsy
9 Todd Helton Jsy 15.00 40.00
Larry Walker Jsy
Juan Pierre Jsy
Mike Hampton Jsy
10 Jeff Bagwell Jsy 15.00 40.00
Craig Biggio Jsy
Lance Berkman Jsy
Richard Hidalgo Pants
11 Shawn Green Jsy 30.00 60.00
Adrian Beltre Jsy
Hideo Nomo Jsy
Paul Lo Duca Jsy
12 Mike Piazza Jsy 15.00 40.00
Roberto Alomar Shoe
Mo Vaughn Bat
Roger Cedeno Bat
13 Roger Clemens Base 40.00 80.00
Derek Jeter Ball
Jason Giambi Ball
Mike Mussina Ball
14 Barry Zito Jsy 10.00 25.00
Tim Hudson Jsy
Eric Chavez Bat
Miguel Tejada Jsy
15 Pat Burrell Jsy 15.00 40.00
Scott Rolen Jsy
Bobby Abreu Jsy
Marlon Byrd Jsy
16 Bernie Williams Jsy 15.00 40.00
Jorge Posada Jsy
Alfonso Soriano Bat
Andy Pettitte Jsy
17 Barry Bonds Ball 20.00 50.00
Rich Aurilia Base
Tsuyoshi Shinjo Base
Jeff Kent Base
18 Ichiro Deck Deck 40.00 80.00
Kazuhiro Sasaki Deck
Edgar Martinez Base
Bret Boone Base
19 Albert Pujols Ball 30.00 60.00
J.D. Drew Base
Jim Edmonds Base
Tino Martinez Base
20 Alex Rodriguez Jsy 15.00 40.00
Ivan Rodriguez Jsy
Juan Gonzalez Jsy
Rafael Palmeiro Jsy

2002 Absolute Memorabilia Team Tandems

Inserted into hobby packs at stated odds of one in 12 hobby and one in 36 retail packs, these 40 cards feature two stars who are also teammates.

*GOLD: .75X TO 2X BASIC TANDEMS
GOLD ODDS 1:72 HOBBY, 1:216 RETAIL
*SPECTRUM: .6X TO 1.5X BASIC TANDEMS
SPECTRUM ODDS 1:36 HOBBY
1 Troy Glaus 1.25 3.00
Darin Erstad
2 Curt Schilling 2.00 5.00
Randy Johnson
3 Chipper Jones 2.00 5.00
Andruw Jones
4 Greg Maddux 3.00 8.00
Tom Glavine
5 Nomar Garciaparra 3.00 8.00
Manny Ramirez
6 Pedro Martinez 1.25 3.00
Trot Nixon
7 Kerry Wood 2.00 5.00
Sammy Sosa
8 Frank Thomas 2.00 5.00
Magglio Ordonez
9 Ken Griffey Jr. 3.00 8.00
Barry Larkin
10 C.C Sabathia 1.25 3.00
Jim Thome
11 Todd Helton 1.25 3.00
Larry Walker
12 Bobby Higginson 1.25 3.00
Shane Halter
13 Cliff Floyd 1.25 3.00
Brad Penny
14 Jeff Bagwell 1.25 3.00
Craig Biggio
15 Shawn Green 1.25 3.00
Adrian Beltre
16 Ben Sheets 1.25 3.00
Richie Sexson
17 Vladimir Guerrero 2.00 5.00
Jose Vidro
18 Mike Piazza 3.00 8.00
Roberto Alomar
19 Roger Clemens 4.00 10.00
Mike Mussina
20 Derek Jeter 5.00 12.00
Jason Giambi
21 Barry Zito 1.25 3.00
Tim Hudson
22 Eric Chavez 1.25 3.00
Miguel Tejada
23 Pat Burrell 1.25 3.00
Scott Rolen
24 Brian Giles 1.25 3.00
Aramis Ramirez
25 Ryan Klesko 1.25 3.00
Phil Nevin
26 Barry Bonds 4.00 10.00
Rich Aurilia
27 Ichiro Suzuki 4.00 10.00
Kazuhiro Sasaki
28 Albert Pujols 4.00 10.00
J.D. Drew
29 Alex Rodriguez 3.00 8.00
Ivan Rodriguez
30 Carlos Delgado 1.25 3.00
Shannon Stewart
31 Mo Vaughn 1.25 3.00
Roger Cedeno
32 Carlos Beltran 1.25 3.00
Mike Sweeney
33 Edgar Martinez 1.25 3.00
Bret Boone
34 Juan Gonzalez 1.25 3.00
Rafael Palmeiro
35 Johnny Damon 2.00 5.00
Rickey Henderson
36 Sean Casey 1.25 3.00
Adam Dunn
37 Jeff Kent 1.25 3.00
Tsuyoshi Shinjo
38 Lance Berkman 1.25 3.00

Card	Low	High
Richard Hidalgo		
39 So Taguchi	1.25	3.00
Tino Martinez		
40 Hideo Nomo	1.25	3.00
Kazuhisa Ishii		

2002 Absolute Memorabilia Team Tandems Materials

Inserted into hobby packs at a stated rate of one in 33 hobby and one in 164 retail, these 40 cards form a complete parallel to the Team Tandem insert set. These cards feature two pieces of memorabilia on each card. According to the manufacturer a few cards were printed in shorter supply and we have notated the announced print runs next to the card in our checklist. It was believed shortly after release that card 27 was not produced. Copies of the card eventually did surface but it's generally accepted to be one of the shortest cards in the set with a rumored print run of 100 copies.

Card	Low	High
1 Troy Glaus Jsy	4.00	10.00
Darin Erstad Bat		
2 Curt Schilling Jsy	6.00	15.00
Randy Johnson Jsy		
3 Chipper Jones Bat	6.00	15.00
Andruw Jones Bat		
4 Greg Maddux Jsy	10.00	25.00
Tom Glavine Jsy		
5 Nomar Garciaparra Bat	10.00	25.00
Manny Ramirez Bat SP/200 *		
6 Pedro Martinez Jsy	8.00	20.00
Trot Nixon Bat SP/200 *		
7 Kerry Wood Base	8.00	20.00
Sammy Sosa Base SP/250 *		
8 Frank Thomas Bat	6.00	15.00
Magglio Ordonez Bat		
9 Ken Griffey Jr. Base	6.00	15.00
Barry Larkin Base		
10 C.C Sabathia Jsy	8.00	20.00
Jim Thome Bat SP/225 *		
11 Todd Helton Bat	6.00	15.00
Larry Walker Bat		
12 Bobby Higginson Bat	4.00	10.00
Shane Halter Bat		
13 Cliff Floyd Bat	4.00	10.00
Brad Penny Jsy		
14 Jeff Bagwell Bat	6.00	15.00
Craig Biggio Bat		
15 Shawn Green Bat	4.00	10.00
Adrian Beltre Bat		
16 Ben Sheets Jsy	4.00	10.00
Richie Sexson Bat		
17 Vladimir Guerrero Bat	6.00	15.00
Jose Vidro Bat		
18 Mike Piazza Bat	8.00	20.00
Roberto Alomar Bat SP/250 *		
19 Roger Clemens Fld Glv	50.00	100.00
Mike Mussina Fld Glv SP/50 *		
20 Derek Jeter Base	12.50	30.00
Jason Giambi Base SP/200 *		
21 Barry Zito Jsy	6.00	15.00
Tim Hudson Shoe SP/200 *		
22 Eric Chavez Bat	6.00	15.00
Miguel Tejada Bat SP/200 *		
23 Pat Burrell Bat	6.00	15.00
Scott Rolen Bat		
24 Brian Giles Bat	4.00	10.00
Aramis Ramirez Bat		
25 Ryan Klesko Bat	6.00	15.00
Phil Nevin Jsy SP/250 *		
26 Barry Bonds Base	8.00	20.00
Rich Aurilia Base		
27 Ichiro Suzuki Deck		
Kazuhiro Sasaki Deck SP		
28 Albert Pujols Base	8.00	20.00
J.D. Drew Base SP/150 *		
29 Alex Rodriguez Bat	8.00	20.00
Ivan Rodriguez Bat		
30 Carlos Delgado Bat	4.00	10.00
Shannon Stewart Bat		
31 Mo Vaughn Bat	4.00	10.00
Roger Cedeno Bat		
32 Carlos Beltran Bat	4.00	10.00
Mike Sweeney Bat		
33 Edgar Martinez Bat	6.00	15.00
Bret Boone Bat		
34 Juan Gonzalez Bat	6.00	15.00
Rafael Palmeiro Bat		
35 Johnny Damon Bat	6.00	15.00
Rickey Henderson Bat		
36 Sean Casey Bat	6.00	15.00
Adam Dunn Shoe SP/100 *		
37 Jeff Kent Bat	6.00	15.00
Tsuyoshi Shinjo Bat SP/250 *		
38 Lance Berkman Bat	4.00	10.00
Richard Hidalgo Bat		
39 So Taguchi Bat	8.00	20.00
Tino Martinez Bat SP/100 *		
40 Hideo Nomo Jsy	15.00	40.00
Kazuhisa Ishii Jsy SP/50 *		

2002 Absolute Memorabilia Team Tandems Materials Gold

Randomly inserted into packs, this is a parallel to the Team Tandem insert set. Each card has gold foil and was issued to a stated print run of 50 serial numbered sets.

Card	Low	High
1 Troy Glaus Jsy	10.00	25.00
Darin Erstad Jsy		
2 Curt Schilling Jsy	15.00	40.00
Randy Johnson Jsy		
3 Chipper Jones Jsy	15.00	40.00
Andruw Jones Jsy		
4 Greg Maddux Jsy	25.00	60.00
Tom Glavine Jsy		
5 Nomar Garciaparra Jsy	20.00	50.00
Manny Ramirez Jsy		
6 Pedro Martinez Jsy	15.00	40.00
Trot Nixon Bat		
7 Kerry Wood Base	15.00	40.00
Sammy Sosa Ball		
8 Frank Thomas Jsy	15.00	40.00
Magglio Ordonez Jsy		
9 Ken Griffey Jr. Base	15.00	40.00
Barry Larkin Base		
10 C.C Sabathia Jsy	15.00	40.00
Jim Thome Jsy		
11 Todd Helton Jsy	15.00	40.00
Larry Walker Jsy		
12 Bobby Higginson Bat	10.00	25.00
Shane Halter Bat		
13 Cliff Floyd Jsy	10.00	25.00
Brad Penny Jsy		
14 Jeff Bagwell Jsy	15.00	40.00
Craig Biggio Jsy		
15 Shawn Green Jsy	10.00	25.00
Adrian Beltre Jsy		
16 Ben Sheets Jsy	10.00	25.00
Richie Sexson Jsy		
17 Vladimir Guerrero Jsy	15.00	40.00
Jose Vidro Jsy		
18 Mike Piazza Jsy	15.00	40.00
Roberto Alomar Shoe		
19 Roger Clemens Jsy	50.00	120.00
Mike Mussina Shoe		
20 Derek Jeter Ball	25.00	60.00
Jason Giambi Ball		
21 Barry Zito Jsy	12.50	30.00
Tim Hudson Jsy		
22 Eric Chavez Bat	12.50	30.00
Miguel Tejada Jsy		
23 Pat Burrell Jsy	15.00	40.00
Scott Rolen Jsy		
24 Brian Giles Jsy	10.00	25.00
Aramis Ramirez Jsy		
25 Ryan Klesko Fld Glv	12.50	30.00
Phil Nevin Jsy		
26 Barry Bonds Ball	20.00	50.00
Rich Aurilia Base		
27 Ichiro Suzuki Ball	50.00	100.00
Kazuhiro Sasaki Deck		
28 Albert Pujols Ball	15.00	40.00
J.D. Drew Base		
29 Alex Rodriguez Jsy	20.00	50.00
Ivan Rodriguez Jsy		
30 Carlos Delgado Jsy	10.00	25.00
Shannon Stewart Jsy		
31 Mo Vaughn Bat	10.00	25.00
Roger Cedeno Bat		
32 Carlos Beltran Jsy	10.00	25.00
Mike Sweeney Jsy		
33 Edgar Martinez Jsy	15.00	40.00
Bret Boone Jsy		
34 Juan Gonzalez Jsy	15.00	40.00
Rafael Palmeiro Jsy		
35 Johnny Damon Bat	15.00	40.00
Rickey Henderson Bat		
36 Sean Casey Jsy	10.00	25.00
Adam Dunn Hat		
37 Jeff Kent Jsy	12.50	30.00
Tsuyoshi Shinjo Bat		
38 Lance Berkman Jsy	10.00	25.00
Richard Hidalgo Pants		
39 So Taguchi Jsy	12.50	30.00
Tino Martinez Bat		
40 Hideo Nomo Jsy		
Kazuhisa Ishii Jsy		

2002 Absolute Memorabilia Tools of the Trade

Issued in hobby packs at stated odds of one in nine hobby and one in 24 retail, these 95 cards feature many of the leading players in the game.

*GOLD: .75X TO 2X BASIC TOOLS
GOLD ODDS 1:45 HOBBY, 1:144 RETAIL

Card	Low	High
1 Mike Mussina	1.50	4.00
2 Rickey Henderson	2.50	6.00
3 Raul Mondesi	1.00	2.50
4 Nomar Garciaparra	4.00	10.00
5 Randy Johnson	2.50	6.00
6 Roger Clemens	5.00	12.00
7 Shawn Green	1.00	2.50
8 Todd Helton	1.50	4.00
9 Aramis Ramirez	1.00	2.50
10 Barry Larkin	1.50	4.00
11 Byung-Hyun Kim	1.00	2.50
12 C.C. Sabathia	1.00	2.50
13 Curt Schilling	1.00	2.50
14 Darin Erstad	1.00	2.50
15 Eric Karros	1.00	2.50
16 Freddy Garcia	1.00	2.50
17 Greg Maddux	4.00	10.00
18 Jason Kendall	1.00	2.50
19 Jim Thome	1.50	4.00
20 Juan Gonzalez	1.00	2.50
21 Kazuhiro Sasaki	1.00	2.50
22 Kerry Wood	1.00	2.50
23 Luis Gonzalez	1.00	2.50
24 Mark Mulder	1.00	2.50
25 Rich Aurilia	1.00	2.50
26 Ray Durham	1.00	2.50
27 Ben Grieve	1.00	2.50
28 Bret Boone	1.00	2.50
29 Edgar Martinez	1.50	4.00
30 Ivan Rodriguez	1.50	4.00
31 Jorge Posada	1.50	4.00
32 Mike Piazza	4.00	10.00
33 Pat Burrell	1.00	2.50
34 Robin Ventura	1.00	2.50
35 Trot Nixon	1.00	2.50
36 Adrian Beltre	1.00	2.50
37 Bernie Williams	1.50	4.00
38 Bobby Abreu	1.00	2.50
39 Carlos Delgado	1.00	2.50
40 Craig Biggio	1.50	4.00
41 Garret Anderson	1.00	2.50
42 Jermaine Dye	1.00	2.50
43 Johnny Damon Sox	1.50	4.00
44 Tim Salmon	1.50	4.00
45 Tino Martinez	1.50	4.00
46 Fred McGriff	1.50	4.00
47 Gary Sheffield	1.00	2.50
48 Adam Dunn	1.00	2.50
49 Joe Mays	1.00	2.50
50 Kenny Lofton	1.00	2.50
51 Josh Beckett	1.00	2.50
52 Bud Smith	1.00	2.50
53 Johnny Estrada	1.00	2.50
54 Charles Johnson	1.00	2.50
55 Craig Wilson	1.00	2.50
56 Terrence Long	1.00	2.50
57 Andy Pettitte	1.50	4.00
58 Brian Giles	1.00	2.50
59 Juan Pierre	1.00	2.50
60 Cliff Floyd	1.00	2.50
61 Ivan Rodriguez	1.50	4.00
62 Andruw Jones	1.50	4.00
63 Lance Berkman	1.00	2.50
64 Mark Buehrle	1.00	2.50
65 Miguel Tejada	1.00	2.50
66 Wade Miller	1.00	2.50
67 Johnny Estrada	1.00	2.50
68 Tsuyoshi Shinjo	1.00	2.50
69 Scott Rolen	1.50	4.00
70 Roberto Alomar	1.50	4.00
71 Mark Grace	1.50	4.00
72 Larry Walker	1.00	2.50
73 Jim Edmonds	1.00	2.50
74 Jeff Kent	1.00	2.50
75 Frank Thomas	2.50	6.00
76 Carlos Beltran	1.00	2.50
77 Barry Zito	1.00	2.50
78 Alex Rodriguez	4.00	10.00
79 Troy Glaus	1.00	2.50
80 Ryan Klesko	1.00	2.50
81 Tom Glavine	1.50	4.00
82 Ben Sheets	1.00	2.50
83 Manny Ramirez	1.50	4.00
84 Shannon Stewart	1.00	2.50
85 Vladimir Guerrero	2.50	6.00
86 Chipper Jones	2.50	6.00
87 Jeff Bagwell	1.50	4.00
88 Richie Sexson	1.00	2.50
89 Sean Casey	1.00	2.50
90 Tim Hudson	1.00	2.50
91 J.D. Drew	1.00	2.50
92 Ivan Rodriguez	1.50	4.00
93 Magglio Ordonez	1.00	2.50
94 John Buck	1.00	2.50
95 Paul Lo Duca	1.00	2.50

2002 Absolute Memorabilia Tools of the Trade Materials

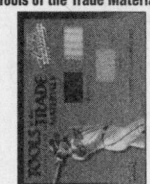

Randomly inserted into packs, this is a parallel to the Tools of the Trade insert set. Each card features a game worn piece(or pieces) of the featued player. Cards in this set were printed to all sorts of different print runs which we have notated.

1-32 PRINT RUN 300 SERIAL #'d SETS
33-47 PRINT RUN 250 SERIAL #'d SETS
48-55 PRINT RUN 150 SERIAL #'d SETS
56-61 PRINT RUN 125 SERIAL #'d SETS
62-66 PRINT RUN 50 SERIAL #'d SETS
67 PRINT RUN 100 SERIAL #'d CARDS
68-82 PRINT RUN 200 SERIAL #'d SETS
83-87 PRINT RUN 75 SERIAL #'d SETS
88-95 PRINT RUN 50 SERIAL #'d SETS

Card	Low	High
1 Mike Mussina Jsy	4.00	10.00
2 Rickey Henderson Jsy	4.00	10.00
3 Raul Mondesi Jsy	3.00	8.00
4 Nomar Garciaparra Jsy	6.00	15.00
5 Randy Johnson Jsy	4.00	10.00
6 Roger Clemens Jsy	6.00	15.00
7 Shawn Green Jsy	3.00	8.00
8 Todd Helton Jsy	4.00	10.00
9 Aramis Ramirez Jsy	3.00	8.00
10 Barry Larkin Jsy	4.00	10.00
11 Byung-Hyun Kim Jsy	4.00	10.00
12 C.C. Sabathia Jsy	3.00	8.00
13 Curt Schilling Jsy	3.00	8.00
14 Darin Erstad Jsy	3.00	8.00
15 Eric Karros Jsy	3.00	8.00
16 Freddy Garcia Jsy	3.00	8.00
17 Greg Maddux Jsy	6.00	15.00
18 Jason Kendall Jsy	3.00	8.00
19 Jim Thome Jsy	4.00	10.00
20 Juan Gonzalez Jsy	3.00	8.00
21 Kazuhiro Sasaki Jsy	3.00	8.00
22 Kerry Wood Jsy	3.00	8.00
23 Luis Gonzalez Jsy	3.00	8.00
24 Mark Mulder Jsy	3.00	8.00
25 Rich Aurilia Jsy	3.00	8.00
26 Ray Durham Jsy	3.00	8.00
27 Ben Grieve Jsy	3.00	8.00
28 Bret Boone Jsy	3.00	8.00
29 Edgar Martinez Jsy	4.00	10.00
30 Ivan Rodriguez Jsy	4.00	10.00
31 Jorge Posada Jsy	4.00	10.00
32 Mike Piazza Jsy	6.00	15.00
33 Pat Burrell Bat	3.00	8.00
34 Robin Ventura Bat	3.00	8.00
35 Trot Nixon Bat	3.00	8.00
36 Adrian Beltre Bat	3.00	8.00
37 Bernie Williams Bat	4.00	10.00
38 Bobby Abreu Bat	3.00	8.00
39 Carlos Delgado Bat	3.00	8.00
40 Craig Biggio Bat	4.00	10.00
41 Garret Anderson Bat	3.00	8.00
42 Jermaine Dye Bat	3.00	8.00
43 Johnny Damon Sox Bat	4.00	10.00
44 Tim Salmon Bat	4.00	10.00
45 Tino Martinez Bat	4.00	10.00
46 Fred McGriff Bat	4.00	10.00
47 Gary Sheffield Bat	3.00	8.00
48 Adam Dunn Shoe	4.00	10.00
49 Joe Mays Shoe	4.00	10.00
50 Kenny Lofton Shoe	6.00	15.00
51 Josh Beckett Shoe	4.00	10.00
52 Bud Smith Shoe	4.00	10.00
53 Johnny Estrada Shin	4.00	10.00
54 Charles Johnson Shin	4.00	10.00
55 Craig Wilson Shin	4.00	10.00
56 Terrence Long Fld Glv	4.00	10.00
57 Andy Pettitte Fld Glv	6.00	15.00
58 Brian Giles Fld Glv	4.00	10.00
59 Juan Pierre Fld Glv	4.00	10.00
60 Cliff Floyd Fld Glv	4.00	10.00
61 Ivan Rodriguez Fld Glv	10.00	25.00
62 Andruw Jones Hat	10.00	25.00
63 Lance Berkman Hat	6.00	15.00
64 Mark Buehrle Hat	6.00	15.00
65 Miguel Tejada Hat	6.00	15.00
66 Wade Miller Hat	6.00	15.00
67 Johnny Estrada Mask	4.00	10.00
68 Tsuyoshi Shinjo Bat-Shoe	6.00	15.00
69 Scott Rolen Jsy-Bat	8.00	20.00
70 Roberto Alomar Bat-Shoe	8.00	20.00
71 Mark Grace Jsy-Fld Glv	6.00	15.00
72 Larry Walker Jsy-Bat	6.00	15.00
73 Jim Edmonds Jsy-Bat	6.00	15.00
74 Jeff Kent Jsy-Bat	6.00	15.00
75 Frank Thomas Jsy-Bat	8.00	20.00
76 Carlos Beltran Jsy-Bat	6.00	15.00
77 Barry Zito Jsy-Shoe	6.00	15.00
78 Alex Rodriguez Jsy-Bat	10.00	25.00
79 Troy Glaus Jsy-Jsy	6.00	15.00
80 Ryan Klesko Bat-Fld Glv	6.00	15.00
81 Tom Glavine Jsy-Shoe	8.00	20.00
82 Ben Sheets Jsy-Bat	6.00	15.00
83 Manny Ramirez	15.00	40.00
Jsy-Fld Glv-Shoe		
84 Shannon Stewart	8.00	20.00
Jsy-Bat-Hat		
85 Vladimir Guerrero	20.00	50.00
Jsy-Bat-Fld Glv		
86 Chipper Jones	20.00	50.00
Jsy-Bat-Fld Glv		
87 Jeff Bagwell	15.00	40.00
Jsy-Bat-Hat		
88 Richie Sexson	15.00	40.00
Jsy-Bat-Shoe-Btg Glv		
89 Sean Casey	15.00	40.00
Jsy-Bat-Shoe-Hat		
90 Tim Hudson	15.00	40.00
Jsy-Hat-Shoe-Fld Glv		
91 J.D. Drew	15.00	40.00
Jsy-Bat-Hat-Shoe		
92 Ivan Rodriguez	15.00	40.00
Fld Glv-Chest-Jsy-Mask		
93 Magglio Ordonez	15.00	40.00
Jsy-Shoe-Hat-Btg Glv		
94 John Buck	10.00	25.00
Fld Glv-Chest-Shin-Mask		
95 Paul Lo Duca	15.00	40.00
Jsy-Chest-Shin-Mask		

2003 Absolute Memorabilia

This 208-card set was issued in two separate series. The primary Absolute Memorabilia product - containing cards 1-200 from the basic set - was released in July, 2003. The cards were issued in six card packs with an approximate SRP of $7.50 which came 18 packs to a box and 16 boxes to a case. The first 150 cards feature veterans while the final 50 cards feature a mix of rookies and veterans. Those cards were issued to a stated print run of 1500 serial numbered sets. Cards 201-208 were randomly seeded into packs of DLP Rookies and Traded issued in December, 2003. Each card was serial-numbered to 1000 copies.

Card	Low	High
COMP.LO SET w/o SP's (150)	15.00	40.00
COMMON CARD (1-150)	.30	.75
COMMON CARD (151-208)	1.50	4.00
1 Nomar Garciaparra	1.25	3.00
2 Barry Bonds	2.00	5.00
3 Greg Maddux	1.25	3.00
4 Roger Clemens	1.50	4.00
5 Derek Jeter	2.00	5.00
6 Alex Rodriguez	1.25	3.00
7 Chipper Jones	.75	2.00
8 Sammy Sosa	.75	2.00
9 Alfonso Soriano	.30	.75
10 Albert Pujols	1.50	4.00
11 Adam Dunn	.30	.75
12 Tom Glavine	.50	1.25
13 Pedro Martinez	.50	1.25
14 Jim Thome	.50	1.25
15 Hideo Nomo	.75	2.00
16 Roberto Alomar	.50	1.25
17 Barry Zito	.30	.75
18 Troy Glaus	.30	.75
19 Kerry Wood	.30	.75
20 Magglio Ordonez	.30	.75
21 Todd Helton	.50	1.25
22 Craig Biggio	.50	1.25
23 Roy Oswalt	.30	.75
24 Torii Hunter	.30	.75
25 Miquel Tejada	.30	.75
26 Tsuyoshi Shinjo	.30	.75
27 Scott Rolen	.50	1.25
28 Rafael Palmeiro	.50	1.25
29 Victor Martinez	.50	1.25
30 Hank Blalock	.30	.75
31 Jason Lane	.30	.75
32 Junior Spivey	.30	.75
33 Gary Sheffield	.30	.75
34 Corey Patterson	.30	.75
35 Corky Miller	.30	.75
36 Brian Tallet	.30	.75
37 Cliff Lee	.60	1.50
38 Jason Jennings	.30	.75
39 Kirk Saarloos	.30	.75
40 Wade Miller	.30	.75
41 Angel Berroa	.30	.75
42 Mike Sweeney	.30	.75
43 Paul Lo Duca	.30	.75
44 A.J. Pierzynski	.30	.75
45 Drew Henson	.30	.75
46 Eric Chavez	.30	.75
47 Tim Hudson	.30	.75
48 Aramis Ramirez	.30	.75
49 Jack Wilson	.30	.75
50 Ryan Klesko	.30	.75
51 Antonio Perez	.30	.75
52 Dewon Brazelton	.30	.75
53 Mark Teixeira	.50	1.25
54 Eric Hinske	.30	.75
55 Freddy Sanchez	.30	.75
56 Mike Rivera	.30	.75
57 Alfredo Amezaga	.30	.75
58 Cliff Floyd	.30	.75
59 Brandon Larson	.30	.75
60 Richard Hidalgo	.30	.75
61 Cesar Izturis	.30	.75
62 Richie Sexson	.30	.75
63 Michael Cuddyer	.30	.75
64 Javier Vazquez	.30	.75
65 Brandon Claussen	.30	.75
66 Carlos Rivera	.30	.75
67 Vernon Wells	.30	.75
68 Kenny Lofton	.30	.75
69 Aubrey Huff	.30	.75
70 Adam LaRoche	.30	.75
71 Jeff Baker	.30	.75
72 Jose Castillo	.30	.75
73 Joe Borchard	.30	.75
74 Walter Young	.30	.75
75 Jose Morban	.30	.75
76 Vinnie Chulk	.30	.75
77 Christian Parker	.30	.75
78 Mike Piazza	1.25	3.00
79 Ichiro Suzuki	1.50	4.00
80 Kazuhisa Ishii	.30	.75
81 Rickey Henderson	.75	2.00
82 Ken Griffey Jr.	1.25	3.00
83 Jason Giambi	.30	.75
84 Randy Johnson	.75	2.00
85 Curt Schilling	.30	.75
86 Manny Ramirez	.50	1.25
87 Barry Larkin	.50	1.25
88 Jeff Bagwell	.50	1.25
89 Vladimir Guerrero	.75	2.00
90 Mike Mussina	.50	1.25
91 Juan Gonzalez	.30	.75
92 Andruw Jones	.50	1.25
93 Frank Thomas	.75	2.00
94 Sean Casey	.30	.75
95 Josh Beckett	.30	.75
96 Lance Berkman	.30	.75
97 Shawn Green	.30	.75
98 Bernie Williams	.50	1.25
99 Pat Burrell	.30	.75
100 Edgar Martinez	.50	1.25
101 Ivan Rodriguez	.50	1.25
102 Jeremy Guthrie	.30	.75
103 Alexis Rios	.40	1.00
104 Nic Jackson	.30	.75
105 Jason Anderson	.30	.75
106 Travis Chapman	.30	.75
107 Mac Suzuki	.30	.75
108 Toby Hall	.30	.75
109 Mark Prior	.50	1.25
110 So Taguchi	.30	.75
111 Marlon Byrd	.30	.75
112 Garret Anderson	.30	.75
113 Luis Gonzalez	.30	.75
114 Jay Gibbons	.30	.75
115 Mark Buehrle	.30	.75
116 Wily Mo Pena	.30	.75
117 C.C. Sabathia	.30	.75
118 Ricardo Rodriguez	.30	.75
119 Robert Fick	.30	.75
120 Rodrigo Rosario	.30	.75
121 Alexis Gomez	.30	.75
122 Carlos Beltran	.30	.75
123 Joe Thurston	.30	.75
124 Ben Sheets	.30	.75
125 Jose Vidro	.30	.75
126 Nick Johnson	.30	.75
127 Mark Mulder	.30	.75
128 Bobby Abreu	.30	.75
129 Brian Giles	.30	.75
130 Brian Lawrence	.30	.75
131 Jeff Kent	.30	.75
132 Chris Snelling	.30	.75
133 Kevin Mench	.30	.75
134 Carlos Delgado	.30	.75
135 Orlando Hudson	.30	.75
136 Juan Cruz	.30	.75
137 Jim Edmonds	.30	.75
138 Geronimo Gil	.30	.75
139 Joe Crede	.30	.75
140 Wilson Valdez	.30	.75
141 Runelvys Hernandez	.30	.75
142 Nick Neugebauer	.30	.75
143 Takahito Nomura	.30	.75
144 Andres Galarraga	.30	.75
145 Mark Grace	.50	1.25
146 Brandon Duckworth	.30	.75
147 Oliver Perez	.30	.75
148 Xavier Nady	.30	.75
149 Rafael Soriano	.30	.75
150 Ben Kozlowski	.30	.75
151 Pr. Redman ROO RC	1.50	4.00
152 Craig Brazell ROO RC	1.50	4.00
153 Nook Logan ROO RC	2.00	5.00
154 Greg Aquino ROO RC	1.50	4.00
155 Matt Kata ROO RC	1.50	4.00
156 Ian Ferguson ROO RC	1.50	4.00
157 C.Wang ROO RC	4.00	10.00
158 Beau Kemp ROO RC	1.50	4.00
159 Alej. Machado ROO RC	1.50	4.00
160 Mi. Hessman ROO RC	1.50	4.00
161 Fran. Rosario ROO RC	1.50	4.00
162 Pedro Liriano ROO	1.50	4.00
163 Rich Fischer ROO RC	1.50	4.00
164 Franklin Perez ROO RC	1.50	4.00
165 Oscar Villarreal ROO RC	1.50	4.00
166 Arnie Munoz ROO RC	1.50	4.00
167 Tim Olson ROO RC	1.50	4.00
168 Jose Contreras ROO RC	2.00	5.00
169 Fran. Cruceta ROO RC	1.50	4.00
170 Jer. Bonderman ROO RC	3.00	8.00
171 Jeremy Griffiths ROO RC	1.50	4.00
172 John Webb ROO	1.50	4.00
173 Phil Seibel ROO RC	1.50	4.00
174 Aaron Looper ROO RC	1.50	4.00
175 Brian Stokes ROO RC	1.50	4.00
176 G.Quiroz ROO RC	1.50	4.00
177 Fern. Cabrera ROO RC	1.50	4.00
178 Josh Hall ROO RC	1.50	4.00
179 D. Markwell ROO RC	1.50	4.00
180 Andrew Brown ROO RC	2.00	5.00
181 Doug Waechter ROO RC	2.00	5.00
182 Felix Sanchez ROO RC	1.50	4.00
183 Gerardo Garcia ROO	1.50	4.00
184 Matt Bruback ROO RC	1.50	4.00
185 Mi. Hernandez ROO RC	1.50	4.00
186 Rett Johnson ROO RC	1.50	4.00
187 Ryan Cameron ROO RC	1.50	4.00
188 Rob Hammock ROO RC	1.50	4.00
189 Clint Barmes ROO RC	1.25	3.00
190 Brandon Webb ROO RC	3.00	8.00
191 Jon Leicester ROO RC	1.50	4.00
192 Shane Bazzell ROO RC	1.50	4.00
193 Joe Valentine ROO RC	1.50	4.00
194 Josh Stewart ROO RC	1.50	4.00
195 Pete LaForest ROO RC	1.50	4.00
196 Shane Victorino ROO RC	2.50	6.00
197 Terrmel Sledge ROO RC	1.50	4.00
198 Lew Ford ROO RC	2.00	5.00
199 T.Wellemeyer ROO RC	1.50	4.00
200 Hideki Matsui ROO RC	4.00	10.00
201 Adam Loewen ROO RC	2.00	5.00
202 Ramon Nivar ROO RC	1.50	4.00
203 Dan Haren ROO RC	2.50	6.00
204 Dontrelle Willis ROO	2.00	5.00
205 Chad Gaudin ROO RC	1.50	4.00
206 Rickie Weeks ROO RC	3.00	8.00
207 Ryan Wagner ROO RC	1.50	4.00
208 Delmon Young ROO RC	5.00	12.00

2003 Absolute Memorabilia Spectrum

*SPECTRUM 1-150: 2.5X TO 6X BASIC
*SPECTRUM 151-208: .6X TO 1.5X BASIC
STATED PRINT RUN 100 SERIAL #'d SETS

Card	Low	High
157 Chien-Ming Wang ROO	12.50	30.00
190 Brandon Webb ROO	5.00	12.00
200 Hideki Matsui ROO	6.00	15.00
201 Adam Loewen ROO	3.00	8.00
206 Rickie Weeks ROO	5.00	12.00
208 Delmon Young ROO	8.00	20.00

2003 Absolute Memorabilia Absolutely Ink

Inserted at a stated rate of one in 552, these 40 cards feature authentic autographs from a mix of established major leaguers and some of the best prospects. Due to market scarcity, no pricing is provided for these cards.

STATED ODDS 1:552
NO PRICING DUE TO SCARCITY

2003 Absolute Memorabilia Absolutely Ink Blue

PRINT RUNS B/WN 10-25 COPIES PER
NO PRICING DUE TO SCARCITY

2003 Absolute Memorabilia Glass Plaques

Inserted at the stated rate of one per sealed box, these 273 cards feature etched-glass collectibles with an autograph and/or a piece of game-used memorabilia. We have identified what comes with the card along with the stated print run in our checklist. Please note that for plaques with stated print runs of 25 or fewer no pricing is provided due to market scarcity.

Card	Low	High
1 Roberto Alomar AU/25		
2 Roberto Alomar AU-Jsy/25		
3 Roberto Alomar Bat-Jsy/100	15.00	40.00
4 Roberto Alomar Jsy/150	10.00	25.00
5 Jeff Bagwell AU/15		
6 Jeff Bagwell AU-Jsy/10		
7 Jeff Bagwell Bat-Jsy/100	15.00	40.00
8 Jeff Bagwell Jsy/150		
9 Ernie Banks AU/15		
10 Ernie Banks AU-Jsy/10		
11 Ernie Banks Bat-Jsy/25		
12 Ernie Banks Jsy/150	10.00	25.00
13 Lance Berkman AU/25		
14 Lance Berkman AU-Jsy/25		
15 Lance Berkman Bat-Jsy/100	10.00	25.00
16 Lance Berkman Jsy/150	6.00	15.00
17 Yogi Berra AU/25		
18 Yogi Berra AU-Jsy/25		
19 Yogi Berra Bat-Jsy/150		
20 Yogi Berra Jsy/150		
21 Barry Bonds Ball-Base/50	40.00	80.00
22 Barry Bonds Ball-Base/100	30.00	60.00
23 Barry Bonds Base/200	20.00	50.00
24 George Brett AU/15		
25 George Brett AU-Jsy/10		
26 George Brett Bat-Jsy/50	100.00	200.00
27 George Brett Jsy/200	40.00	80.00
28 Pat Burrell AU/25		
29 Pat Burrell AU-Jsy/25		
30 Pat Burrell Bat-Jsy/100	10.00	25.00
31 Pat Burrell Jsy/150	6.00	15.00
32 Steve Carlton AU/50	20.00	50.00
33 Steve Carlton AU-Jsy/25		
34 Steve Carlton Bat-Jsy/100		
35 Steve Carlton Jsy/150	6.00	15.00
36 R.Clemens Sox AU/15		
37 R.Clemens Sox AU-Jsy/25		
38 R.Clemens Sox Fld Glv-Jsy/50	40.00	80.00
39 R.Clemens Sox Jsy/150	40.00	80.00
40 R.Clemens Yanks AU/15		
41 R.Clemens Yanks AU-Jsy/10		
42 Clemens Yanks Glv-Jsy/50	100.00	200.00
43 R.Clemens Yanks Jsy/200	40.00	80.00
44 Roberto Clemente Bat-Jsy/50		
45 Roberto Clemente Bat-Jsy/150		
46 Roberto Clemente Jsy/200		
47 Jose Contreras AU/25		
48 Jose Contreras AU-Jsy/25		
49 Jose Contreras Jsy-Jsy/100	15.00	40.00
50 Jose Contreras Jsy/150		
51 Adam Dunn AU/25		
52 Adam Dunn AU-Jsy/25		
53 Adam Dunn Bat-Jsy/100	10.00	25.00
54 Adam Dunn Jsy/150	6.00	15.00
55 Bob Feller AU/50	15.00	40.00
56 Bob Feller AU-Jsy/25		
57 Bob Feller Jsy-Jsy/50	15.00	40.00
58 Bob Feller Jsy/100	6.00	15.00
59 N.Garciaparra Bat-Jsy/100	40.00	80.00
60 N.Garciaparra Jsy/200	30.00	60.00
61 Jason Giambi Bat-Jsy/100	10.00	25.00
62 Jason Giambi Jsy/150	6.00	15.00
63 Troy Glaus AU/25		
64 Troy Glaus AU-Jsy/25		
65 Troy Glaus Bat-Jsy/100		
66 Troy Glaus Jsy/150	6.00	15.00
67 Juan Gonzalez AU/15		
68 Juan Gonzalez AU-Jsy/10		
69 Juan Gonzalez Bat-Jsy/100		
70 Juan Gonzalez Jsy/150		
71 Luis Gonzalez AU/25		
72 Luis Gonzalez AU-Jsy/25		
73 Luis Gonzalez Bat-Jsy/100	10.00	25.00
74 Luis Gonzalez Jsy/150	6.00	15.00
75 Mark Grace AU/50	60.00	120.00
76 Mark Grace AU-Jsy/25		
77 Mark Grace Bat-Jsy/100		
78 Mark Grace Jsy/150	10.00	25.00
79 Shawn Green AU/15		
80 Shawn Green AU-Jsy/10		
81 Shawn Green Bat-Jsy/100	10.00	25.00
82 Shawn Green Jsy/150	6.00	15.00
83 Ken Griffey Jr. Ball-Base/50		
84 Ken Griffey Jr. Ball-Base/100		
85 Ken Griffey Jr. Base/200		
86 Vladimir Guerrero AU/25		
87 Vladimir Guerrero AU-Jsy/25		
88 Vladimir Guerrero Bat-Jsy/100	15.00	40.00
89 Vladimir Guerrero Jsy/150		
90 Tony Gwynn AU/15		
91 Tony Gwynn AU-Jsy/10		
92 Tony Gwynn Bat-Jsy/150		
93 Tony Gwynn Jsy/200		
94 Todd Helton AU/25		
95 Todd Helton AU-Jsy/25		
96 Todd Helton Bat-Jsy/100		
97 Todd Helton Jsy/150		
98 R.Henderson AU/15		
99 R.Henderson AU-Jsy/10		
100 R.Henderson Bat-Jsy/100	15.00	40.00
101 R.Henderson Jsy/200	10.00	25.00
102 Tim Hudson AU/50	30.00	60.00
103 Tim Hudson AU-Jsy/25		
104 Tim Hudson Hat-Jsy/100	10.00	25.00
105 Tim Hudson Jsy/150	6.00	15.00
106 Torii Hunter AU/50	20.00	50.00
107 Torii Hunter AU-Jsy/25		
108 Torii Hunter Hat-Jsy/100	10.00	25.00
109 Torii Hunter Jsy/150		
110 Kazuhisa Ishii AU/15		
111 Kazuhisa Ishii AU-Jsy/10		
112 Kazuhisa Ishii Bat-Jsy/100	10.00	25.00
113 Kazuhisa Ishii Jsy/200	6.00	15.00
114 Derek Jeter Ball-Base/50		
115 Derek Jeter Ball-Base/150		
116 Derek Jeter Base/200		
117 Randy Johnson AU/15		
118 Randy Johnson AU-Jsy/10		
119 Randy Johnson Bat -Jsy/100	15.00	40.00
120 Randy Johnson Jsy/150	10.00	25.00
121 Andruw Jones AU/25		
122 Andruw Jones AU-Jsy/25		
123 Andruw Jones Bat-Jsy/100		
124 Andruw Jones Jsy/150	10.00	25.00
125 Chipper Jones AU/15		
126 Chipper Jones AU-Jsy/10		
127 Chipper Jones Bat-Jsy/100	15.00	40.00
128 Chipper Jones Jsy/150	10.00	25.00
129 Al Kaline AU/50		
130 Al Kaline AU-Jsy/25		
131 Al Kaline Bat-Jsy/100	15.00	40.00
132 Al Kaline Jsy/150	10.00	25.00
133 Barry Larkin AU/50	30.00	60.00
134 Barry Larkin AU-Jsy/25		
135 Barry Larkin Bat-Jsy/100	15.00	40.00
136 Barry Larkin Jsy/150	10.00	25.00
137 Greg Maddux AU/15		
138 Greg Maddux AU-Jsy/10		
139 Greg Maddux Bat -Jsy/100	30.00	60.00
140 Greg Maddux Jsy/200	20.00	50.00
141 Pedro Martinez AU/10		
142 Pedro Martinez AU-Jsy/10		
143 Pedro Martinez Bat-Jsy/100	15.00	40.00
144 Pedro Martinez Jsy/150	10.00	25.00
145 H.Matsui Ball-Base/50	50.00	100.00
146 H.Matsui Ball-Base/150	30.00	60.00
147 H.Matsui Base/200	15.00	40.00
148 Don Mattingly AU/25		
149 Don Mattingly AU-Jsy/25		
150 Don Mattingly Bat-Jsy/100		
151 Don Mattingly Jsy/200		
152 Mark Mulder AU/50	20.00	50.00
153 Mark Mulder AU-Jsy/25		
154 Mark Mulder Jsy/150	6.00	15.00
155 Mark Mulder Jsy-Jsy/100	10.00	25.00
156 Stan Musial AU/15		
157 Stan Musial AU-Jsy/10		
158 Stan Musial Bat-Jsy/150		
159 Stan Musial Jsy/200		
160 Hideo Nomo AU/15		
161 Hideo Nomo AU-Jsy/10		
162 Hideo Nomo Bat-Jsy/50	60.00	120.00
163 Hideo Nomo Bat-Jsy/100	15.00	40.00
164 Hideo Nomo Jsy/200	10.00	25.00
165 Magglio Ordonez AU/50	20.00	50.00

166 Maggio Ordonez AU-Jsy/25
167 M.Ordonez Bat-Jsy/100 10.00 25.00
168 Maggio Ordonez Jsy/150 6.00 15.00
169 Roy Oswalt AU/50 20.00 50.00
170 Roy Oswalt AU-Jsy/25
171 Roy Oswalt Bat-Jsy/100 10.00 25.00
172 Roy Oswalt Jsy/150 6.00 15.00
173 Rafael Palmeiro AU/25
174 Rafael Palmeiro AU-Jsy/25
175 Rafael Palmeiro Bat-Jsy/100 15.00 40.00
176 Rafael Palmeiro Jsy/150 10.00 25.00
177 Mike Piazza AU/15
178 Mike Piazza AU-Jsy/10
179 Mike Piazza Bat-Jsy/50 50.00 100.00
180 Mike Piazza Bat-Jsy/100 30.00 60.00
181 Mike Piazza Jsy/200 20.00 50.00
182 Mark Prior AU/25
183 Mark Prior AU-Jsy/25
184 Mark Prior Bat-Jsy/100 15.00 40.00
185 Mark Prior Jsy/150 10.00 25.00
186 Albert Pujols AU/25
187 Albert Pujols AU-Jsy/25
188 Albert Pujols Bat-Jsy/150 50.00 100.00
189 Albert Pujols Jsy/150 40.00 80.00
190 Manny Ramirez AU/15
191 Manny Ramirez AU-Jsy/10
192 Manny Ramirez Bat-Jsy/100 15.00 40.00
193 Manny Ramirez Jsy/150 10.00 25.00
194 Cal Ripken AU/15
195 Cal Ripken AU-Jsy/10
196 Cal Ripken Bat-Jsy/150 60.00 120.00
197 Cal Ripken Jsy/200 50.00 100.00
198 Frank Robinson AU/50 30.00 60.00
199 Frank Robinson AU-Jsy/25
200 Frank Robinson Bat-Jsy/100 15.00 40.00
201 Frank Robinson Jsy/150 10.00 25.00
202 Alex Rodriguez AU/15
203 Alex Rodriguez AU-Jsy/25
204 Alex Rodriguez Bat-Jsy/100
205 Alex Rodriguez Jsy/200
206 N.Ryan Angels AU/15
207 N.Ryan Angels AU-Jsy/25
208 N.Ryan Angels Jacket-Jsy/150
209 N.Ryan Angels Jsy/200 50.00 100.00
210 N.Ryan Astros AU/15
211 N.Ryan Astros AU-Jsy/25
212 N.Ryan Astros Fld Glv-Jsy/25
213 N.Ryan Astros Jsy/200 50.00 100.00
214 N.Ryan Astros Jsy-Jsy/100 60.00 120.00
215 N.Ryan Rgr AU/15
216 N.Ryan Rgr AU-Jsy/10
217 N.Ryan Rgr Fld Glv-Jsy/25
218 N.Ryan Rgr Jsy/200 50.00 100.00
219 N.Ryan Rgr Jsy-Jsy/100 60.00 120.00
220 R.Sandberg AU/15
221 R.Sandberg AU-Jsy/10
222 R.Sandberg Bat-Jsy G/50 75.00 150.00
223 R.Sandberg Bat-Jsy S/50 75.00 150.00
224 R.Sandberg Jsy/200 40.00 80.00
225 Curt Schilling AU/25
226 Curt Schilling AU-Jsy/25
227 Curt Schilling Fld Glv-Jsy/50
228 Curt Schilling Jsy/150 6.00 15.00
229 Mike Schmidt AU/25
230 Mike Schmidt AU-Jsy/25
231 Mike Schmidt Bat-Jsy/100 50.00 100.00
232 Mike Schmidt Jsy/200 40.00 80.00
233 Ozzie Smith AU/15
234 Ozzie Smith AU-Jsy/10
235 Ozzie Smith Bat-Jsy/100 50.00 100.00
236 Ozzie Smith Jsy/150 40.00 80.00
237 A.Soriano AU/15
238 A.Soriano AU-Jsy/10
239 A.Soriano Bat-Jsy/150 10.00 25.00
240 A.Soriano Jsy/150 6.00 15.00
241 Sammy Sosa Bat-Jsy/150 15.00 40.00
242 Sammy Sosa Jsy/200 10.00 25.00
243 Junior Spivey AU/50
244 Junior Spivey AU-Jsy/25
245 Junior Spivey Bat-Jsy/100 10.00 25.00
246 Junior Spivey Jsy/150 6.00 15.00
247 I.Suzuki Ball-Base/50 60.00 120.00
248 I.Suzuki Ball-Base/150 50.00 100.00
249 I.Suzuki Base/200 30.00 60.00
250 Mark Teixeira AU/50
251 Mark Teixeira AU-Jsy/25
252 Mark Teixeira Bat-Jsy/100 15.00 40.00
253 Mark Teixeira Jsy/150 10.00 25.00
254 Miguel Tejada AU/50 30.00 60.00
255 Miguel Tejada AU-Jsy/25
256 Miguel Tejada Bat-Jsy/100 10.00 25.00
257 Miguel Tejada Jsy/150 6.00 15.00
258 Frank Thomas AU/25
259 Frank Thomas AU-Jsy/25
260 Frank Thomas Bat-Jsy/100 15.00 40.00
261 Frank Thomas Jsy/150 10.00 25.00
262 Bernie Williams AU/15
263 Bernie Williams AU-Jsy/10
264 Bernie Williams Bat-Jsy/100 15.00 40.00
265 Bernie Williams Jsy/150 10.00 25.00
266 Kerry Wood AU/50 30.00 60.00
267 Kerry Wood AU-Jsy/25
268 Kerry Wood Bat-Jsy/100 10.00 25.00
269 Kerry Wood Jsy/150 6.00 15.00
270 Barry Zito AU/50 20.00 50.00
271 Barry Zito AU-Jsy/25
272 Barry Zito Hat-Jsy/100 10.00 25.00
273 Barry Zito Jsy/150 6.00 15.00

2003 Absolute Memorabilia Player Collection

*PLAY.COLL: .75X TO 2X PRESTIGE PC
STATED PRINT RUN 75 SERIAL #'d SETS
SEE 2003 PRESTIGE PLAY.COLL FOR PRICING
SPECTRUM PRINT RUN 25 SERIAL #'d SETS
NO SPECTRUM PRICING DUE TO SCARCITY

2003 Absolute Memorabilia Portraits Promos

STATED ODDS ONE PER BOX
1 Vladimir Guerrero 1.00 2.50
2 Luis Gonzalez .40 1.00
3 Andruw Jones .60 1.50
4 Manny Ramirez .60 1.50
5 Derek Jeter 2.50 6.00
6 Eric Hinske .40 1.00
7 Curt Schilling .40 1.00
8 Adam Dunn .40 1.00
9 Jason Jennings .40 1.00
10 Mike Piazza 1.50 4.00
11 Jason Giambi .40 1.00
12 Jeff Bagwell .60 1.50
13 Rickey Henderson 1.00 2.50
14 Randy Johnson 1.00 2.50
15 Roger Clemens 2.00 5.00
16 Troy Glaus .40 1.00
17 Hideo Nomo 1.00 2.50
18 Joe Borchard .40 1.00
19 Torii Hunter .40 1.00
20 Lance Berkman .40 1.00
21 Todd Helton .60 1.50
22 Mike Mussina .40 1.00
23 Vernon Wells .40 1.00
24 Pat Burrell .40 1.00
25 Ichiro Suzuki 2.00 5.00
26 Shawn Green .40 1.00
27 Frank Thomas 1.00 2.50
28 Barry Zito .40 1.00
29 Barry Bonds 2.50 6.00
30 Ken Griffey Jr. 1.50 4.00
31 Albert Pujols 2.00 5.00
32 Roberto Alomar .60 1.50
33 Barry Larkin .60 1.50
34 Tony Gwynn 1.25 3.00
35 Chipper Jones 1.00 2.50
36 Pedro Martinez .60 1.50
37 Juan Gonzalez .40 1.00
38 Greg Maddux 1.50 4.00
39 Tim Hudson .40 1.00
40 Sammy Sosa 1.00 2.50
41 Victor Martinez .60 1.50
42 Mark Buehrle .40 1.00
43 Austin Kearns .40 1.00
44 Kerry Wood .40 1.00
45 Nomar Garciaparra 1.50 4.00
46 Alfonso Soriano .40 1.00
47 Mark Prior .60 1.50
48 Richie Sexson .40 1.00
49 Mark Teixeira .60 1.50
50 Craig Biggio .60 1.50
51 Rafael Palmeiro .60 1.50
52 Carlos Beltran .40 1.00
53 Bernie Williams .60 1.50
54 Eric Chavez .40 1.00
55 Paul Konerko .40 1.00
56 Nolan Ryan 2.50 6.00
57 Mark Mulder .40 1.00
58 Miguel Tejada .40 1.00
59 Roy Oswalt .40 1.00
60 Jim Edmonds .40 1.00
61 Ryan Klesko .40 1.00
62 Cal Ripken 3.00 8.00
63 Josh Beckett .40 1.00
64 Kazuhisa Ishii .40 1.00
65 Alex Rodriguez 1.50 4.00
66 Mike Sweeney .40 1.00
67 C.C. Sabathia .40 1.00
68 Jose Vidro .40 1.00
69 Magglio Ordonez .40 1.00
70 Carlos Delgado .40 1.00
71 Jorge Posada .60 1.50
72 Bobby Abreu .40 1.00

2003 Absolute Memorabilia Rookie Materials Jersey Number

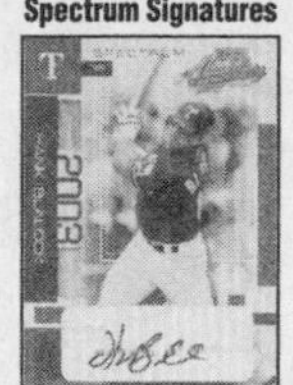

Randomly inserted into packs, these 15 cards feature not only game-worn jersey swatches but were printed to a stated print run which matched the player's jersey number. For cards with a print run of 25 or fewer, no pricing is provided due to market scarcity.

PRINT RUNS B/WN 5-51 COPIES PER
NO PRICING ON QTY OF 25 OR LESS
1 Stan Musial Jsy/6
2 Yogi Berra Jsy/35 20.00 50.00
3 Vladimir Guerrero Jsy/27 20.00 50.00
4 Randy Johnson Jsy/51 20.00 50.00
5 Andruw Jones Jsy/25
6 Jeff Kent Jsy/11
7 Nomar Garciaparra Jsy/5
8 Hideo Nomo Jsy/16
9 Ivan Rodriguez Jsy/7
10 Alfonso Soriano Jsy/33 20.00 50.00
11 Scott Rolen Jsy/17
12 Juan Gonzalez Jsy/19
13 Rafael Palmeiro Bat/25
14 Mike Schmidt Bat/20
15 Cal Ripken Bat/8

2003 Absolute Memorabilia Rookie Materials Season

Randomly inserted into packs, these 15 cards feature not only game-worn jersey swatches but were printed to a stated print run which matched the player's debut season.

PRINT RUNS B/WN 42-101 COPIES PER
1 Stan Musial Jsy/42 60.00 120.00
2 Yogi Berra Jsy/47 30.00 60.00
3 Vladimir Guerrero Jsy/97 10.00 25.00
4 Randy Johnson Jsy/89 10.00 25.00
5 Andruw Jones Jsy/96 10.00 25.00
6 Jeff Kent Jsy/92 6.00 15.00
8 Hideo Nomo Jsy/95 15.00 40.00
9 Ivan Rodriguez Jsy/91 10.00 25.00
10 Alfonso Soriano Jsy/101 6.00 15.00
11 Scott Rolen Jsy/96 10.00 25.00
12 Juan Gonzalez Jsy/89 6.00 15.00
13 Rafael Palmeiro Bat/86 10.00 25.00
14 Mike Schmidt Bat/73 30.00 60.00
15 Cal Ripken Bat/82 40.00 80.00

2003 Absolute Memorabilia Signing Bonus

Randomly inserted into packs, these 10 cards feature authentic autographs of baseball legends. Each of these cards were issued to a stated print run of 15 serial numbered sets and no pricing is provided due to market scarcity.

STATED PRINT RUN 15 SERIAL #'d SETS
BLUE PRINT RUN 10 SERIAL #'d SETS
GOLD PRINT RUN 5 SERIAL #'d SETS
NO PRICING DUE TO SCARCITY

2003 Absolute Memorabilia Spectrum Signatures

Randomly inserted into packs, these cards not only parallel the basic Playoff Absolute Memorabilia set but also were signed by the featured player. Cards 201-208 were randomly seeded into packs of DLP Rookies and Traded. Quantities of each card range from 5-304 copies per. Please note that we have put the stated print run next to the player's name in our checklist. If 25 or fewer of a card was signed, there is no pricing due to market scarcity.

3 Greg Maddux/10
4 Roger Clemens/15
6 Alex Rodriguez/15
7 Chipper Jones/10
9 Alfonso Soriano/15
10 Albert Pujols/10
11 Adam Dunn/15
12 Tom Glavine/25
13 Pedro Martinez/5
14 Jim Thome/10
15 Hideo Nomo/5
16 Roberto Alomar/15
17 Barry Zito/25
18 Troy Glaus/10
19 Kerry Wood/15
20 Magglio Ordonez/25
21 Todd Helton/10
22 Craig Biggio/10
23 Roy Oswalt/25
24 Torii Hunter/25
25 Miguel Tejada/25
27 Scott Rolen/10
28 Rafael Palmeiro/10
29 Victor Martinez/100 15.00 40.00
30 Hank Blalock/50 10.00 25.00
31 Jason Lane/50
32 Junior Spivey/50 6.00 15.00
33 Gary Sheffield/10
34 Corey Patterson/50 6.00 15.00
35 Corky Miller/100
36 Brian Tallet/100
37 Cliff Lee/100 10.00 25.00
38 Jason Jennings/100
39 Kirk Saarloos/100
40 Wade Miller/50 6.00 15.00
41 Angel Berroa/100 6.00 15.00
42 Mike Sweeney/50 10.00 25.00
43 Paul Lo Duca/50 10.00 25.00
44 A.J. Pierzynski/100 10.00 25.00
45 Drew Henson/50 6.00 15.00
46 Eric Chavez/10
47 Tim Hudson/50 15.00 40.00
48 Aramis Ramirez/10
49 Jack Wilson/25
50 Ryan Klesko/25
51 Antonio Perez/25
52 Dewon Brazelton/50 6.00 15.00
53 Mark Teixeira/50 15.00 40.00
54 Eric Hinske/100 6.00 15.00
55 Freddy Sanchez/100 6.00 15.00
56 Mike Rivera/25
57 Alfredo Amezaga/100 6.00 15.00
58 Cliff Floyd/25
59 Brandon Larson/100
60 Richard Hidalgo/100 6.00 15.00
61 Cesar Izturis/25
62 Richie Sexson/25
63 Michael Cuddyer/100 6.00 15.00
64 Javier Vazquez/25
65 Brandon Claussen/25
66 Carlos Rivera/100
67 Vernon Wells/25
68 Kenny Lofton/50 15.00 40.00
69 Aubrey Huff/100 10.00 25.00
70 Adam LaRoche/100 6.00 15.00
71 Jeff Baker/100 6.00 15.00
72 Jose Castillo/100 6.00 15.00
73 Joe Borchard/100 6.00 15.00
74 Walter Young/100 6.00 15.00
75 Jose Morban/100
76 Vinnie Chulk/100 6.00 15.00
77 Christian Parker/25
78 Mike Piazza/5
80 Kazuhisa Ishii/25
81 Rickey Henderson/5
85 Curt Schilling/10
86 Manny Ramirez/10
87 Barry Larkin/50 40.00 80.00
88 Jeff Bagwell/5
89 Vladimir Guerrero/50 10.00 25.00
90 Mike Mussina/10
91 Juan Gonzalez/5
92 Andruw Jones/25
94 Sean Casey/10
95 Josh Beckett/100 6.00 15.00
96 Lance Berkman/25
97 Shawn Green/25
98 Bernie Williams/10
99 Pat Burrell/10
100 Edgar Martinez/50 20.00 50.00
101 Ivan Rodriguez/5
102 Jeremy Guthrie/100 6.00 15.00
103 Alexis Rios/100 10.00 25.00
104 Nic Jackson/100 6.00 15.00
105 Jason Anderson/100
106 Travis Chapman/100 6.00 15.00
107 Mac Suzuki/304 10.00 25.00
108 Toby Hall/25
109 Mark Prior/50 12.50 30.00
110 So Taguchi/25
111 Marlon Byrd/100 6.00 15.00
112 Garret Anderson/10
113 Luis Gonzalez/10
114 Jay Gibbons/100 6.00 15.00
115 Mark Buehrle/25
116 Wily Mo Pena/25
117 C.C. Sabathia/25
118 Ricardo Rodriguez/100 6.00 15.00
119 Robert Fick/100 6.00 15.00
120 Rodrigo Rosario/25
121 Alexis Gomez/100 6.00 15.00
122 Carlos Beltran/25
123 Joe Thurston/100
124 Ben Sheets/50 10.00 25.00
125 Jose Vidro/25
126 Nick Johnson/50 10.00 25.00
127 Mark Mulder/50 10.00 25.00
128 Bobby Abreu/25
129 Brian Giles/10
130 Brian Lawrence/25
132 Chris Snelling/100 6.00 15.00
133 Kevin Mench/100 10.00 25.00
135 Orlando Hudson/50 6.00 15.00
136 Juan Cruz/100
138 Geronimo Gil/25
139 Joe Crede/100 6.00 15.00
140 Wilson Valdez/25
141 Runelvys Hernandez/100 6.00 15.00
142 Nick Neugebauer/25
143 Takahito Nomura/47 10.00 25.00
144 Andres Galarraga/25
145 Mark Grace/25
146 Brandon Duckworth/25
147 Oliver Perez/50 10.00 25.00
148 Xavier Nady/100 6.00 15.00
149 Rafael Soriano/25
150 Ben Kozlowski/100 6.00 15.00
151 Prentice Redman ROO/250 4.00 10.00
152 Craig Brazell ROO/250 4.00 10.00
153 Nook Logan ROO/250 6.00 15.00
154 Greg Aquino ROO/250 4.00 10.00
155 Matt Kata ROO/250 4.00 10.00
156 Ian Ferguson ROO/250 4.00 10.00
157 Chien Wang ROO/250 60.00 120.00
158 Beau Kemp ROO/250 4.00 10.00
159 Alej Machado ROO/250 4.00 10.00
160 Mike Hessman ROO/250 4.00 10.00
161 Franc Rosario ROO/250 4.00 10.00
162 Pedro Liriano ROO/250 4.00 10.00
163 Rich Fischer ROO/250 4.00 10.00
164 Franklin Perez ROO/250
165 Oscar Villarreal ROO/250 4.00 10.00
166 Arnie Munoz ROO/250 4.00 10.00
167 Tim Olson ROO/250 4.00 10.00
168 Jose Contreras ROO/250 8.00 20.00
169 Franc Cruceta ROO/250 4.00 10.00
170 J.Bonderman ROO/250 20.00 50.00
171 Jeremy Griffiths ROO/250 4.00 10.00
172 John Webb ROO/250
173 Phil Seibel ROO/250
174 Aaron Looper ROO/250 4.00 10.00
175 Brian Stokes ROO/250 4.00 10.00
176 Guillermo Quiroz ROO/250 4.00 10.00
177 Fernando Cabrera ROO/250 4.00 10.00
178 Josh Hall ROO/250 4.00 10.00
179 Diego Markwell ROO/250 4.00 10.00
180 Andrew Brown ROO/250 6.00 15.00
181 Doug Waechter ROO/250 6.00 15.00
182 Felix Sanchez ROO/250 4.00 10.00
183 Gerardo Garcia ROO/250
184 Matt Bruback ROO/250 4.00 10.00
185 Michel Hernandez ROO/250
186 Rett Johnson ROO/250 4.00 10.00
187 Ryan Cameron ROO/250 4.00 10.00
188 Rob Hammock ROO/250 4.00 10.00
189 Clint Barmes ROO/250 6.00 15.00
190 Brandon Webb ROO/250 12.50 30.00
191 Jon Leicester ROO/250 4.00 10.00
192 Shane Bazzell ROO/250 4.00 10.00
193 Joe Valentine ROO/250 4.00 10.00
194 Josh Stewart ROO/250
195 Pete LaForest ROO/250 4.00 10.00
196 Shane Victorino ROO/250 20.00 50.00
197 Termel Sledge ROO/250 4.00 10.00
198 Lew Ford ROO/250 6.00 15.00
199 Todd Wellemeyer ROO/250 4.00 10.00
201 Adam Loewen ROO/100 10.00 25.00
202 Ramon Nivar ROO/100 4.00 10.00
203 Dan Haren ROO/100 10.00 25.00
204 Dontrelle Willis ROO/25
205 Chad Gaudin ROO/50 6.00 15.00
206 Rickie Weeks ROO/25
207 Ryan Wagner ROO/100 4.00 10.00
208 Delmon Young ROO/25

2003 Absolute Memorabilia Team Tandems

STATED ODDS 1:48
*SPECTRUM: 1.25X TO 3X BASIC
SPECTRUM PRINT RUN 100 #'d SETS
1 Sammy Sosa / Mark Prior 2.00 5.00
2 Vladimir Guerrero / Jose Vidro 2.00 5.00
3 Bernie Williams / Alfonso Soriano 2.00 5.00
4 Mike Sweeney / Carlos Beltran 1.25 3.00
5 Magglio Ordonez / Paul Konerko 1.25 3.00
6 Adam Dunn / Austin Kearns 1.25 3.00
7 Randy Johnson / Curt Schilling 2.00 5.00
8 Hideo Nomo / Kazuhisa Ishii 2.00 5.00
9 Pat Burrell / Bobby Abreu 1.25 3.00
10 Todd Helton / Larry Walker 2.00 5.00

2003 Absolute Memorabilia Team Tandems Materials

1-7/10 PRINT RUN 100 SERIAL #'d SETS
8-9 PRINT RUN 40 SERIAL #'d SETS
SPECTRUM 1-7/10 PRINT RUN 25 #'d SETS
SPECTRUM 8-9 PRINT RUN 10 #'d SETS
NO SPECTRUM PRICING DUE TO SCARCITY
ALL FEATURE DUAL JERSEY SWATCHES
1 Sammy Sosa / Mark Prior 10.00 25.00
2 Vladimir Guerrero / Jose Vidro 10.00 25.00
3 Bernie Williams / Alfonso Soriano 10.00 25.00
4 Mike Sweeney / Carlos Beltran 6.00 15.00
5 Magglio Ordonez / Paul Konerko 6.00 15.00
6 Adam Dunn / Austin Kearns 6.00 15.00
7 Randy Johnson / Curt Schilling 10.00 25.00
8 Hideo Nomo / Kazuhisa Ishii/40 20.00 50.00
9 Pat Burrell / Bobby Abreu/40 10.00 25.00
10 Todd Helton / Larry Walker 10.00 25.00

2003 Absolute Memorabilia Team Trios

STATED ODDS 1:88
*SPECTRUM: 1X TO 2.5X BASIC
SPECTRUM PRINT RUN 50 SERIAL #'d SETS
1 Greg Maddux / Chipper Jones / Andruw Jones 6.00 15.00
2 Sammy Sosa / Mark Prior / Kerry Wood 4.00 10.00
3 Pedro Martinez / Nomar Garciaparra / Manny Ramirez 6.00 15.00
4 Jason Giambi / Alfonso Soriano / Roger Clemens 6.00 15.00
5 Alex Rodriguez / Rafael Palmeiro / Mark Teixeira 6.00 15.00
6 Mike Piazza / Roberto Alomar / Tsuyoshi Shinjo 6.00 15.00
7 Jeff Bagwell / Craig Biggio / Lance Berkman 4.00 10.00
8 Troy Glaus / Garret Anderson / Troy Percival 4.00 10.00
9 Miguel Tejada / Eric Chavez / Barry Zito 4.00 10.00
10 Luis Gonzalez / Randy Johnson / Curt Schilling 4.00 10.00

2003 Absolute Memorabilia Team Trios Materials

1-2/4-5/7/9-10 PRINT RUN 100 #'d SETS
3/6/8 PRINT RUNS B/WN 40-50 COPIES PER
SPECTRUM 1-2/4-5/7/9-10 PRINT 25 #'d SETS
SPECTRUM 3/6/8 PRINT RUN 10 #'d SETS
NO SPECTRUM PRICING DUE TO SCARCITY
ALL FEATURE THREE JERSEY SWATCHES
1 Greg Maddux / Chipper Jones / Andruw Jones 15.00 40.00
2 Sammy Sosa / Mark Prior / Kerry Wood 15.00 40.00
3 Pedro Martinez / Nomar Garciaparra / Manny Ramirez/50 40.00 80.00
4 Jason Giambi / Alfonso Soriano / Roger Clemens 20.00 50.00
5 Alex Rodriguez / Rafael Palmeiro / Mark Teixeira 15.00 40.00
6 Mike Piazza / Roberto Alomar / Tsuyoshi Shinjo/40 30.00 60.00
7 Jeff Bagwell / Craig Biggio / Lance Berkman 15.00 40.00
8 Troy Glaus / Garret Anderson / Troy Percival/40 15.00 40.00
9 Miguel Tejada / Eric Chavez / Barry Zito 15.00 40.00
10 Luis Gonzalez / Randy Johnson / Curt Schilling 15.00 40.00

2003 Absolute Memorabilia Tools of the Trade

STATED ODDS 1:5
*SPECTRUM: 1X TO 2.5X BASIC
SPECTRUM PRINT RUN 100 #'d SETS
1 Sammy Sosa 1.50 4.00
2 Nomar Garciaparra 2.50 6.00
3 Andruw Jones 1.00 2.50
4 Troy Glaus .60 1.50
5 Greg Maddux 2.50 6.00
6 Rickey Henderson 1.50 4.00
7 Alex Rodriguez 2.50 6.00
8 Manny Ramirez 1.00 2.50
9 Lance Berkman .60 1.50
10 Roger Clemens 3.00 8.00
11 Ivan Rodriguez 1.00 2.50
12 Kazuhisa Ishii .60 1.50
13 Alfonso Soriano .60 1.50
14 Austin Kearns .60 1.50
15 Mike Piazza 2.50 6.00
16 Curt Schilling .60 1.50
17 Jeff Bagwell 1.00 2.50
18 Todd Helton 1.00 2.50
19 Randy Johnson 1.50 4.00
20 Vladimir Guerrero 1.50 4.00
21 Kerry Wood .60 1.50
22 Rafael Palmeiro 1.00 2.50
23 Roy Oswalt .60 1.50
24 Chipper Jones 1.50 4.00
25 Pat Burrell .60 1.50
26 Jason Giambi .60 1.50
27 Pedro Martinez 1.00 2.50
28 Roberto Alomar 1.00 2.50
29 Shawn Green .60 1.50
30 Adam Dunn .60 1.50
31 Juan Gonzalez .60 1.50
32 Mark Prior 1.00 2.50
33 Hideo Nomo 1.50 4.00
34 Torii Hunter .60 1.50
35 Mark Teixeira 1.00 2.50
36 Craig Biggio 1.00 2.50
37 Rafael Palmeiro 1.00 2.50
38 Jeff Bagwell 1.00 2.50
39 Albert Pujols 3.00 8.00
40 Richie Sexson .60 1.50
41 Alex Rodriguez 2.50 6.00
42 Carlos Delgado .60 1.50
43 Frank Thomas 1.50 4.00
44 Sammy Sosa 1.50 4.00
45 Marlon Byrd .60 1.50
46 Mark Prior 1.00 2.50
47 Adrian Beltre .60 1.50
48 Tom Glavine 1.00 2.50
49 So Taguchi .60 1.50
50 Jeff Bagwell 1.00 2.50
51 Mike Sweeney .60 1.50
52 Luis Gonzalez .60 1.50
53 Chipper Jones 1.50 4.00
54 Jason Giambi .60 1.50
55 Miguel Tejada .60 1.50
56 Todd Helton 1.00 2.50
57 Andruw Jones 1.00 2.50
58 Mike Piazza 2.50 6.00
59 Manny Ramirez 1.00 2.50
60 Randy Johnson 1.50 4.00
61 Carlos Beltran .60 1.50
62 Victor Martinez 1.00 2.50
63 Orlando Hudson .60 1.50
64 Jeff Kent .60 1.50
65 Greg Maddux 2.50 6.00
66 Garret Anderson .60 1.50
67 Joe Thurston .60 1.50
68 Mark Teixeira 1.00 2.50
69 Kazuhisa Ishii .60 1.50
70 Austin Kearns .60 1.50
71 Pat Burrell .60 1.50
72 Joe Borchard .60 1.50
73 Josh Phelps .60 1.50
74 Travis Hafner .60 1.50
75 So Taguchi .60 1.50
76 Victor Martinez 1.00 2.50
77 Paul Lo Duca .60 1.50
78 Bernie Williams 1.00 2.50
79 Josh Phelps .60 1.50
80 Marlon Byrd .60 1.50
81 Manny Ramirez 1.00 2.50
82 Jason Giambi .60 1.50
83 Jeff Bagwell 1.00 2.50
84 Sammy Sosa 1.50 4.00
85 Josh Phelps .60 1.50
86 Tim Hudson .60 1.50
87 Randy Johnson 1.50 4.00
88 Troy Glaus .60 1.50
89 Joe Thurston .60 1.50
90 Miguel Tejada .60 1.50
91 Adam Dunn .60 1.50
92 Magglio Ordonez .60 1.50
93 Mike Sweeney .60 1.50
94 Andruw Jones 1.00 2.50
95 Carlos Beltran .60 1.50
96 Joe Borchard .60 1.50
97 Austin Kearns .60 1.50
98 Richie Sexson .60 1.50
99 Mark Prior 1.00 2.50
100 Mark Teixeira 1.00 2.50
101 Ryan Klesko .60 1.50
102 Jason Jennings .60 1.50
103 Travis Hafner .60 1.50
104 Mark Buehrle .60 1.50
105 Eric Hinske .60 1.50
106 Rafael Palmeiro 1.00 2.50
107 Roy Oswalt .60 1.50
108 Kerry Wood .60 1.50
109 Brian Giles .60 1.50
110 Ivan Rodriguez 1.00 2.50

2003 Absolute Memorabilia Tools of the Trade Materials

1-74 PRINT RUNS B/WN 40-250 COPIES PER
75-90 PRINT RUNS B/WN 50-125 COPIES PER
91-97 PRINT RUN 100 SERIAL #'d SETS
98-104 PRINT RUN 50 SERIAL #'d SETS
105-110 PRINT RUN 50 SERIAL #'d SETS
1 Sammy Sosa Jsy/250 4.00 10.00
2 Nomar Garciaparra Jsy/250 6.00 15.00
3 Andruw Jones Jsy/250 4.00 10.00
4 Troy Glaus Jsy/250 3.00 8.00
5 Greg Maddux Jsy/250 4.00 10.00
6 Rickey Henderson Jsy/40 10.00 25.00
7 Alex Rodriguez Jsy/250 6.00 15.00
8 Manny Ramirez Jsy/250 4.00 10.00
9 Lance Berkman Jsy/250 3.00 8.00
10 Roger Clemens Jsy/250 6.00 15.00
11 Ivan Rodriguez Jsy/250 4.00 10.00
12 Kazuhisa Ishii Jsy/40 6.00 15.00
13 Alfonso Soriano Jsy/250 3.00 8.00
14 Austin Kearns Jsy/250 3.00 8.00
15 Mike Piazza Jsy/250 4.00 10.00
16 Curt Schilling Jsy/250 3.00 8.00
17 Jeff Bagwell Jsy/250 4.00 10.00
18 Todd Helton Jsy/250 4.00 10.00
19 Randy Johnson Jsy/250 4.00 10.00
20 Vladimir Guerrero Jsy/250 4.00 10.00
21 Kerry Wood Jsy/250 3.00 8.00
22 Rafael Palmeiro Jsy/250 4.00 10.00
23 Roy Oswalt Jsy/250 3.00 8.00
24 Chipper Jones Jsy/250 4.00 10.00
25 Pat Burrell Jsy/40 6.00 15.00
26 Jason Giambi Jsy/250 3.00 8.00
27 Pedro Martinez Jsy/250 4.00 10.00
28 Roberto Alomar Jsy/40 10.00 25.00
29 Shawn Green Jsy/250 3.00 8.00
30 Adam Dunn Jsy/250 3.00 8.00
31 Juan Gonzalez Jsy/40 6.00 15.00
32 Mark Prior Jsy/250 4.00 10.00
33 Hideo Nomo Jsy/250 6.00 15.00
34 Torii Hunter Jsy/250 3.00 8.00
35 Mark Teixeira Jsy/250 4.00 10.00
36 Craig Biggio Pants/250 4.00 10.00

37 Rafael Palmeiro Pants/250 4.00 10.00
38 Jeff Bagwell Pants/250 4.00 10.00
39 Albert Pujols Jsy/200 6.00 15.00
40 Richie Sexson Pants/250 3.00 8.00
41 Alex Rodriguez Bat/250 6.00 15.00
42 Carlos Delgado Bat/250 3.00 8.00
43 Frank Thomas Bat/75 6.00 15.00
44 Sammy Sosa Bat/250 4.00 10.00
45 Marlon Byrd Bat/250 3.00 8.00
46 Mark Prior Bat/250 4.00 10.00
47 Adrian Beltre Bat/250 3.00 8.00
48 Tom Glavine Bat/250 4.00 10.00
49 So Taguchi Bat/250 3.00 8.00
50 Jeff Bagwell Bat/250 4.00 10.00
51 Mike Sweeney Bat/250 3.00 8.00
52 Luis Gonzalez Bat/250 3.00 8.00
53 Chipper Jones Bat/100 6.00 15.00
54 Jason Giambi Bat/250 3.00 8.00
55 Miguel Tejada Bat/250 3.00 8.00
56 Todd Helton Bat/250 4.00 10.00
57 Andruw Jones Bat/250 4.00 10.00
58 Mike Piazza Bat/250 4.00 10.00
59 Manny Ramirez Bat/250 4.00 10.00
60 Randy Johnson Bat/250 4.00 10.00
61 Carlos Beltran Bat/250 3.00 8.00
62 Victor Martinez Bat/250 4.00 10.00
63 Orlando Hudson Bat/250 3.00 8.00
64 Jeff Kent Bat/250 3.00 8.00
65 Greg Maddux Bat/250 4.00 10.00
66 Garret Anderson Bat/150 3.00 8.00
67 Joe Thurston Bat/250 3.00 8.00
68 Mark Teixeira Bat/250 4.00 10.00
69 Kazuhisa Ishii Bat/250 3.00 8.00
70 Austin Kearns Bat/250 3.00 8.00
71 Pat Burrell Bat/100 4.00 10.00
72 Joe Borchard Bat/250 3.00 8.00
73 Josh Phelps Bat/250 3.00 8.00
74 Travis Hafner Bat/250 3.00 8.00
75 So Taguchi Shoe/125 4.00 10.00
76 Victor Martinez Fld Glv/125 6.00 15.00
77 Paul Lo Duca Shoe/125 4.00 10.00
78 Bernie Williams Shoe/125 6.00 15.00
79 Josh Phelps Shoe/125 4.00 10.00
80 Marlon Byrd Fld Glv/125 4.00 10.00
81 Manny Ramirez Hat/100 6.00 15.00
82 Jason Giambi Hat/125 3.00 8.00
83 Jeff Bagwell Hat/50
84 Sammy Sosa Shoe/125 6.00 15.00
85 Josh Phelps Hat/125 4.00 10.00
86 Tim Hudson Hat/125 4.00 10.00
87 Randy Johnson Hat/125
88 Troy Glaus Btg Glv/125 4.00 10.00
89 Joe Thurston Fld Glv/125 4.00 10.00
90 Miguel Tejada Hat/125 4.00 10.00
91 Adam Dunn Btg Glv-Fld Glv/100 6.00 15.00
92 Magglio Ordonez Btg Glv-Hat/100 6.00 15.00
93 Mike Sweeney Btg Glv-Fld Glv/100 6.00 15.00
94 Andruw Jones Btg-Glv-Hat/100 10.00 25.00
95 Carlos Beltran Hat-Shoe/100 6.00 15.00
96 Joe Borchard Fld Glv-Shoe/100 6.00 15.00
97 Austin Kearns Hat-Shoe/100 6.00 15.00
98 Richie Sexson 10.00 25.00
Btg Glv-Fld Glv-Hat/50
99 Mark Prior 15.00 40.00
Fld Glv-Hat-Shoe/50
100 Mark Teixeira 15.00 40.00
Fld Glv-Hat-Shoe/50
101 Ryan Klesko 10.00 25.00
Btg Glv-Hat-Shoe/50
102 Jason Jennings
Btg Glv-Hat-Shoe/50
103 Travis Hafner 10.00 25.00
Btg Glv-Fld Glv-Shoe/50
104 Mark Buehrle 10.00 25.00
Btg Glv-Fld Glv-Hat/50
105 Eric Hinske 10.00 25.00
Btg Glv-Fld Glv-Hat-Shoe/50
106 Rafael Palmeiro 30.00 60.00
Btg Glv-Fld Glv-Hat-Shoe/50
107 Roy Oswalt 15.00 40.00
Btg Glv-Fld Glv-Hat-Shoe/50
108 Kerry Wood 15.00 40.00
Btg Glv-Fld Glv-Hat-Shoe/50
109 Brian Giles 15.00 40.00
Btg Glv-Fld Glv-Hat-Shoe/50
110 Ivan Rodriguez 30.00 60.00
Btg Glv-Fld Glv-Hat-Shoe/50

2003 Absolute Memorabilia Tools of the Trade Materials Spectrum

*SPECTRUM p/r 40-50: 1.25X TO 3X BASIC
PRINT RUNS B/WN 10-50 COPIES PER
NO PRICING ON QTY OF 25 OR LESS

2003 Absolute Memorabilia Total Bases

STATED ODDS 1:16
1 Albert Pujols 3.00 8.00
2 Nomar Garciaparra 2.50 6.00
3 Jason Giambi .60 1.50
4 Miguel Tejada .60 1.50
5 Rafael Palmeiro 1.00 2.50
6 Sammy Sosa 1.50 4.00
7 Pat Burrell .60 1.50
8 Lance Berkman .60 1.50
9 Bernie Williams 1.00 2.50
10 Jim Thome 1.00 2.50
11 Carlos Beltran .60 1.50
12 Eric Chavez .60 1.50
13 Alex Rodriguez 2.50 6.00
14 Magglio Ordonez .60 1.50
15 Brian Giles .60 1.50
16 Alfonso Soriano .60 1.50
17 Shawn Green .60 1.50
18 Vladimir Guerrero 1.50 4.00
19 Garret Anderson .60 1.50
20 Todd Helton 1.00 2.50
21 Barry Bonds 4.00 10.00
22 Jeff Kent .60 1.50
23 Torii Hunter .60 1.50
24 Ichiro Suzuki 3.00 8.00
25 Derek Jeter 4.00 10.00
26 Chipper Jones 1.50 4.00
27 Jeff Bagwell 1.00 2.50
28 Mike Piazza 2.50 6.00
29 Rickey Henderson 1.50 4.00
30 Ken Griffey Jr. 2.50 6.00

2003 Absolute Memorabilia Total Bases Materials 1B

PRINT RUNS B/WN 28-165 COPIES PER
1 Albert Pujols/109 8.00 20.00
2 Nomar Garciaparra/112 8.00 20.00
3 Jason Giambi/100 4.00 10.00
4 Miguel Tejada/140 4.00 10.00
5 Rafael Palmeiro/58 10.00 25.00
6 Sammy Sosa/90 6.00 15.00
7 Pat Burrell/87 4.00 10.00
8 Lance Berkman/90 4.00 10.00
9 Bernie Williams/146 4.00 10.00
10 Jim Thome/73 12.50 30.00
11 Carlos Beltran/94 4.00 10.00
12 Eric Chavez/93 4.00 10.00
13 Alex Rodriguez/101 8.00 20.00
14 Magglio Ordonez/103 4.00 10.00
15 Brian Giles/68 4.00 10.00
16 Alfonso Soriano/117 4.00 10.00
17 Shawn Green/92 4.00 10.00
18 Vladimir Guerrero/128 4.00 10.00
19 Garret Anderson/107 4.00 10.00
20 Todd Helton/109 6.00 15.00
21 Barry Bonds/70 12.50 30.00
22 Jeff Kent/114 4.00 10.00
23 Torii Hunter/92 4.00 10.00
24 Ichiro Suzuki/165 15.00 40.00
25 Derek Jeter/147 15.00 40.00
26 Chipper Jones/117 6.00 15.00
27 Jeff Bagwell/100 6.00 15.00
28 Mike Piazza/76
29 Rickey Henderson/28 15.00 40.00
30 Ken Griffey Jr./36

2003 Absolute Memorabilia Total Bases Materials 2B

PRINT RUNS B/WN 6-56 COPIES PER
NO PRICING ON QTY OF 25 OR LESS
1 Albert Pujols/40 20.00 50.00
2 Nomar Garciaparra/56 15.00 40.00
3 Jason Giambi/34
4 Miguel Tejada/30
5 Rafael Palmeiro/34
6 Sammy Sosa/19
7 Pat Burrell/39 6.00 15.00
8 Lance Berkman/35 10.00 25.00
9 Bernie Williams/37
10 Jim Thome/19
11 Carlos Beltran/44 6.00 15.00
12 Eric Chavez/31
13 Alex Rodriguez/27 30.00 80.00
14 Magglio Ordonez/47 6.00 15.00
15 Brian Giles/37
16 Alfonso Soriano/51 6.00 15.00
17 Shawn Green/31 10.00 25.00
18 Vladimir Guerrero/37 10.00 25.00
19 Garret Anderson/56 6.00 15.00
20 Todd Helton/39 10.00 25.00
21 Barry Bonds/31 25.00 60.00
22 Jeff Kent/42 6.00 15.00
23 Torii Hunter/37 6.00 15.00
24 Ichiro Suzuki/27
25 Derek Jeter/26 30.00 80.00
26 Chipper Jones/35 15.00 40.00
27 Jeff Bagwell/33 15.00 40.00
28 Mike Piazza/23
29 Rickey Henderson/6
30 Ken Griffey Jr./8

2003 Absolute Memorabilia Total Bases Materials 3B

PRINT RUNS B/WN 1-8 COPIES PER
NO PRICING DUE TO SCARCITY

2003 Absolute Memorabilia Total Bases Materials HR

PRINT RUNS B/WN 5-57 COPIES PER
NO PRICING ON QTY OF 25 OR LESS
1 Albert Pujols/34 25.00 60.00
2 Nomar Garciaparra/24
3 Jason Giambi/41 6.00 15.00
4 Miguel Tejada/34 10.00 25.00
5 Rafael Palmeiro/43 10.00 25.00
6 Sammy Sosa/49 10.00 25.00
7 Pat Burrell/37 6.00 15.00
8 Lance Berkman/42 6.00 15.00
9 Bernie Williams/19
10 Jim Thome/52 10.00 25.00
11 Carlos Beltran/29 10.00 25.00
12 Eric Chavez/34 10.00 25.00
13 Alex Rodriguez/57 15.00 40.00
14 Magglio Ordonez/38 6.00 15.00
15 Brian Giles/38 6.00 15.00
16 Alfonso Soriano/39 6.00 15.00
17 Shawn Green/42 6.00 15.00
18 Vladimir Guerrero/39 10.00 25.00
19 Garret Anderson/29 10.00 25.00
20 Todd Helton/30
21 Barry Bonds/46 20.00 50.00
22 Jeff Kent/37 6.00 15.00
23 Torii Hunter/29 10.00 25.00
24 Ichiro Suzuki/8
25 Derek Jeter/18
26 Chipper Jones/26 15.00 40.00
27 Jeff Bagwell/31 15.00 40.00
28 Mike Piazza/33 20.00 50.00
29 Rickey Henderson/5
30 Ken Griffey Jr./8

2004 Absolute Memorabilia

This 250-card set was released in June, 2004. The set was issued in four-card packs with an $35 SRP which came six packs to a box and 12 boxes to a case. The first 200 cards of the set feature veterans while the final 50 cards in the set feature Rookie Cards printed to various print runs. Cards numbered 1-200 were issued to a stated print run of 1349 serial numbered sets. The final 50 cards were randomly inserted into packs.

COMMON ACTIVE (1-200) .50 1.25
COMMON RETIRED (1-200) .75 2.00
1-200 PRINT RUN 1349 SERIAL #'d SETS
COMMON CARD (201-250) .75 2.00
COMMON AU (201-250) 3.00 8.00
201-250 RANDOM INSERTS IN PACKS
201-250 NON AU PRINT RUNS 1000 #'d PER
201-250 AU PRINTS B/WN 500-700 #'d PER
1 Troy Glaus .50 1.25
2 Garret Anderson .50 1.25
3 Tim Salmon .50 1.25
4 Bartolo Colon .50 1.25
5 Troy Percival .50 1.25
6 Nolan Ryan Angels 4.00 10.00
7 Vladimir Guerrero 1.25 3.00
8 Richie Sexson .50 1.25
9 Shea Hillenbrand .50 1.25
10 Luis Gonzalez .50 1.25
11 Brandon Webb .50 1.25
12 Randy Johnson 1.25 3.00
13 Robby Hammock .50 1.25
14 Edgar Gonzalez .50 1.25
15 Roberto Alomar .75 2.00
16 Andruw Jones .50 1.25
17 Chipper Jones 1.25 3.00
18 Dale Murphy .75 2.00
19 Rafael Furcal .50 1.25
20 J.D. Drew .50 1.25
21 Bubba Nelson .50 1.25
22 Julio Franco .50 1.25
23 Adam LaRoche .50 1.25
24 Michael Hessman .50 1.25
25 Warren Spahn .75 2.00
26 Jay Gibbons .50 1.25
27 Cal Ripken 5.00 12.00
28 Miguel Tejada .75 2.00
29 Adam Loewen .50 1.25
30 Rafael Palmeiro .75 2.00
31 Javy Lopez .50 1.25
32 Luis Matos .50 1.25
33 Jason Varitek 1.25 3.00
34 Carl Yastrzemski 1.25 3.00
35 Manny Ramirez 1.25 3.00
36 Trot Nixon .50 1.25
37 Curt Schilling .75 2.00
38 Pedro Martinez .75 2.00
39 Nomar Garciaparra 1.25 3.00
40 Luis Tiant .50 1.25
41 Kevin Youkilis .75 2.00
42 Michel Hernandez .50 1.25
43 Sammy Sosa 1.25 3.00
44 Greg Maddux 2.00 5.00
45 Kerry Wood .50 1.25
46 Mark Prior .75 2.00
47 Ernie Banks 1.25 3.00
48 Aramis Ramirez .50 1.25
49 Brendan Harris .50 1.25
50 Todd Wellemeyer .50 1.25
51 Frank Thomas 1.25 3.00
52 Magglio Ordonez .75 2.00
53 Carlos Lee .50 1.25
54 Joe Crede .50 1.25
55 Joe Borchard .50 1.25
56 Mark Buehrle .75 2.00
57 Sean Casey .50 1.25
58 Adam Dunn .75 2.00
59 Austin Kearns .50 1.25
60 Ken Griffey Jr. 2.00 5.00
61 Barry Larkin .75 2.00
62 Ryan Wagner .50 1.25
63 Jody Gerut .50 1.25
64 Jeremy Guthrie .50 1.25
65 Travis Hafner .50 1.25
66 Brian Tallet .50 1.25
67 Todd Helton .75 2.00
68 Preston Wilson .50 1.25
69 Jeff Baker .50 1.25
70 Clint Barmes .75 2.00
71 Joe Kennedy .50 1.25
72 Jack Morris .50 1.25
73 George Kell .50 1.25
74 Preston Larrison .50 1.25
75 Dmitri Young .50 1.25
76 Ivan Rodriguez .75 2.00
77 Dontrelle Willis .50 1.25
78 Josh Beckett .75 2.00
79 Miguel Cabrera 1.25 3.00
80 Mike Lowell .50 1.25
81 Luis Castillo .50 1.25
82 Juan Pierre .50 1.25
83 Jeff Bagwell .75 2.00
84 Jeff Kent .50 1.25
85 Craig Biggio .75 2.00
86 Lance Berkman .75 2.00
87 Andy Pettitte .75 2.00
88 Roy Oswalt .75 2.00
89 Chris Burke .50 1.25
90 Jason Lane .50 1.25
91 Roger Clemens 1.50 4.00
92 Mike Sweeney .50 1.25
93 Carlos Beltran .50 1.25
94 Angel Berroa .50 1.25
95 Juan Gonzalez .50 1.25
96 Ken Harvey .50 1.25
97 Byron Gettis .50 1.25
98 Alexis Gomez .50 1.25
99 Ian Ferguson .50 1.25
100 Duke Snider .75 2.00
101 Shawn Green .50 1.25
102 Hideo Nomo 1.25 3.00
103 Kazuhisa Ishii .50 1.25
104 Edwin Jackson .50 1.25
105 Fred McGriff .50 1.25
106 Hong-Chih Kou .50 1.25
107 Don Sutton .50 1.25
108 Rickey Henderson 1.25 3.00
109 Cesar Izturis .50 1.25
110 Robin Ventura .50 1.25
111 Paul Lo Duca .50 1.25
112 Rickie Weeks .50 1.25
113 Scott Podsednik .50 1.25
114 Junior Spivey .50 1.25
115 Lyle Overbay .50 1.25
116 Tony Oliva .50 1.25
117 Jacque Jones .50 1.25
118 Shannon Stewart .50 1.25
119 Torii Hunter .50 1.25
120 Johan Santana 1.25 3.00
121 J.D. Durbin .50 1.25
122 Jason Kubel .50 1.25
123 Michael Cuddyer .50 1.25
124 Nick Johnson .50 1.25
125 Jose Vidro .50 1.25
126 Orlando Cabrera .50 1.25
127 Zach Day .50 1.25
128 Mike Piazza 1.25 3.00
129 Tom Glavine .75 2.00
130 Jae Weong Seo .50 1.25
131 Gary Carter .50 1.25
132 Phil Seibel .50 1.25
133 Edwin Almonte .50 1.25
134 Aaron Boone .50 1.25
135 Kenny Lofton .50 1.25
136 Don Mattingly 2.50 6.00
137 Jason Giambi .50 1.25
138 Alex Rodriguez Yanks 2.00 5.00
139 Jorge Posada .75 2.00
140 Bernie Williams .75 2.00
141 Hideki Matsui 2.00 5.00
142 Mike Mussina .75 2.00
143 Mariano Rivera 1.25 3.00
144 Gary Sheffield .50 1.25
145 Derek Jeter 3.00 8.00
146 Chien-Ming Wang 2.50 6.00
147 Javier Vazquez .50 1.25
148 Jose Contreras .50 1.25
149 Whitey Ford .75 2.00
150 Kevin Brown .50 1.25
151 Eric Chavez .50 1.25
152 Barry Zito .50 1.25
153 Mark Mulder .50 1.25
154 Tim Hudson .75 2.00
155 Rich Harden .50 1.25
156 Eric Byrnes .50 1.25
157 Jim Thome .75 2.00
158 Bobby Abreu .50 1.25
159 Marlon Byrd .50 1.25
160 Lenny Dykstra .50 1.25
161 Steve Carlton .50 1.25
162 Ryan Howard 1.50 4.00
163 Bobby Hill .50 1.25
164 Jose Castillo .50 1.25
165 Jay Payton .50 1.25
166 Ryan Klesko .50 1.25
167 Brian Giles .50 1.25
168 Henri Stanley .50 1.25
169 Jason Schmidt .50 1.25
170 Jerome Williams .50 1.25
171 J.T. Snow .50 1.25
172 Bret Boone .50 1.25
173 Edgar Martinez .75 2.00
174 Ichiro Suzuki 2.00 5.00
175 Jamie Moyer .50 1.25
176 Rich Aurilia .50 1.25
177 Chris Snelling .50 1.25
178 Scott Rolen .75 2.00
179 Albert Pujols 3.00 8.00
180 Jim Edmonds .75 2.00
181 Stan Musial 2.00 5.00
182 Dan Haren .50 1.25
183 Red Schoendienst .50 1.25
184 Aubrey Huff .50 1.25
185 Delmon Young .75 2.00
186 Rocco Baldelli .50 1.25
187 Dewon Brazelton .50 1.25
188 Mark Teixeira 1.25 3.00
189 Hank Blalock .50 1.25
190 Nolan Ryan Rgr 4.00 10.00
191 Alfonso Soriano .50 1.25
192 Michael Young .50 1.25
193 Vernon Wells .50 1.25
194 Roy Halladay 1.25 3.00
195 Carlos Delgado .50 1.25
196 Dustin McGowan .50 1.25
197 Josh Phelps .50 1.25
198 Alexis Rios .75 2.00
199 Eric Hinske .50 1.25
200 Josh Towers .50 1.25
201 Kazuo Matsui/1000 RC 1.25 3.00
202 Fernando Nieve AU/500 RC 3.00 8.00
203 Mike Rouse/1000 RC .75 2.00
204 Dennis Sarfate AU/500 RC 3.00 8.00
205 Josh Labandeira AU/500 RC 3.00 8.00
206 Chris Oxspring AU/500 RC 3.00 8.00
207 Alfredo Simon/1000 RC .75 2.00
208 Cory Sullivan AU/500 RC 3.00 8.00
209 Ruddy Yan AU/500 3.00 8.00
210 Jason Bartlett AU/500 RC 4.00 10.00
211 Akinori Otsuka/1000 RC .75 2.00
212 Lincoln Holdzkom/1000 RC .75 2.00
213 Justin Leone/1000 RC .75 2.00
214 Jorge Sequea AU/500 RC 3.00 8.00
215 John Gall/1000 RC .75 2.00
216 Jerome Gamble/1000 RC .75 2.00
217 Tim Bittner AU/500 RC 3.00 8.00
218 Ronny Cedeno AU/500 RC 6.00 15.00
219 Justin Hampson/1000 RC .75 2.00
220 Ryan Wing AU/500 RC 3.00 8.00
221 Mariano Gomez AU/500 RC 3.00 8.00
222 Carlos Vasquez/1000 RC .75 2.00
223 Casey Daigle AU/500 RC 3.00 8.00
224 Renyel Pinto AU/500 RC 3.00 8.00
225 Chris Shelton AU/500 RC 10.00 25.00
226 Mike Gosling AU/700 RC 3.00 8.00
227 Aarom Baldiris AU/700 RC 3.00 8.00
228 Ramon Ramirez AU/700 RC 3.00 8.00
229 Roberto Novoa AU/500 RC 3.00 8.00
230 Sean Henn AU/500 RC 3.00 8.00
231 Jamie Brown AU/500 RC 3.00 8.00
232 Nick Regilio AU/500 RC 3.00 8.00
233 Dave Crouthers AU/700 RC 3.00 8.00
234 Greg Dobbs AU/500 RC 3.00 8.00
235 Angel Chavez AU/500 RC 3.00 8.00
236 Willy Taveras AU/500 RC 8.00 20.00
237 Justin Knoedler AU/500 RC 3.00 8.00
238 Ian Snell AU/700 RC 6.00 15.00
239 Jason Frasor AU/500 RC 3.00 8.00
240 Jerry Gil AU/500 RC 3.00 8.00
241 Carlos Hines AU/500 RC 3.00 8.00
242 Ivan Ochoa AU/500 RC 3.00 8.00
243 Jose Capellan AU/700 RC 3.00 8.00
244 Onil Joseph AU/700 RC 3.00 8.00
245 Hector Gimenez AU/700 RC 3.00 8.00
246 Shawn Hill AU/700 RC 3.00 8.00
247 Freddy Guzman AU/700 RC 3.00 8.00
248 Graham Koonce AU/500 3.00 8.00
249 Ronald Belisario AU/500 RC 3.00 8.00
250 Merkin Valdez AU/700 RC 4.00 10.00

2004 Absolute Memorabilia Retail

*RETAIL 1-200 : .1X TO .25X BASIC
1-200 ISSUED IN RETAIL PACKS
RETAIL CARDS ARE NOT SERIAL #'d

2004 Absolute Memorabilia Spectrum Gold

*GOLD 1-200: 1.5X TO 4X BASIC ACTIVE
*GOLD 1-200: 1.5X TO 4X BASIC RETIRED
*GOLD 201-250: .6X TO 1.5X BASIC
*GOLD 201-250: .3X TO .8X BASIC AU
STATED PRINT RUN 50 SERIAL #'d SETS

2004 Absolute Memorabilia Spectrum Platinum

STATED PRINT RUN 1 SERIAL #'d SET
NO PRICING DUE TO SCARCITY

2004 Absolute Memorabilia Spectrum Silver

*SILVER 1-200: 1X TO 2.5X BASIC ACTIVE
*SILVER 1-200: 1X TO 2.5X BASIC RETIRED
*SILVER 201-250: .4X TO 1X BASIC
*SILVER 201-250: .2X TO .5X BASIC AU
STATED PRINT RUN 100 SERIAL #'d SETS

2004 Absolute Memorabilia Signature Spectrum Gold

PRINT RUNS B/WN 1-100 COPIES PER
NO PRICING ON QTY OF 10 OR LESS
1 Troy Glaus/15 30.00 60.00
2 Garret Anderson/100 6.00 15.00
6 Nolan Ryan Angels/10
7 Vladimir Guerrero/25 30.00 60.00
8 Richie Sexson/15 15.00 40.00
9 Shea Hillenbrand/100 6.00 15.00
11 Brandon Webb/100 4.00 10.00
12 Randy Johnson/1
15 Roberto Alomar/25 20.00 50.00
16 Andruw Jones/5
17 Chipper Jones/5
18 Dale Murphy/100 10.00 25.00
19 Rafael Furcal/100 6.00 15.00
22 Julio Franco/25 12.50 30.00
23 Adam LaRoche/100 4.00 10.00
25 Warren Spahn/5
26 Jay Gibbons/100 4.00 10.00
27 Cal Ripken/1
29 Adam Loewen/100 4.00 10.00
30 Rafael Palmeiro/1
32 Luis Matos/50 5.00 12.00
33 Jason Varitek/25 30.00 60.00
34 Carl Yastrzemski/1
35 Manny Ramirez/1
36 Trot Nixon/100 6.00 15.00
37 Curt Schilling/1
40 Luis Tiant/50 8.00 20.00
41 Kevin Youkilis/25 8.00 20.00
43 Sammy Sosa/5
45 Kerry Wood/25 20.00 50.00
46 Mark Prior/100 10.00 25.00
47 Ernie Banks/100 20.00 50.00
48 Aramis Ramirez/5
51 Frank Thomas/5
52 Magglio Ordonez/100 6.00 15.00
53 Carlos Lee/100 6.00 15.00
54 Joe Crede/50 8.00 20.00
56 Mark Buehrle/10
57 Sean Casey/1
58 Adam Dunn/5
59 Austin Kearns/100 4.00 10.00
61 Barry Larkin/25 20.00 50.00
62 Ryan Wagner/50 5.00 12.00
63 Jody Gerut/100 4.00 10.00
64 Jeremy Guthrie/25 8.00 20.00
65 Travis Hafner/25 8.00 20.00
67 Todd Helton/5
68 Preston Wilson/100 6.00 15.00
69 Jeff Baker/25 8.00 20.00
72 Jack Morris/100
73 George Kell/100 10.00 25.00
77 Dontrelle Willis/10
78 Josh Beckett/5
79 Miguel Cabrera/100 10.00 25.00
80 Mike Lowell/1
81 Luis Castillo/25 8.00 20.00
83 Jeff Bagwell/25 40.00 80.00
85 Craig Biggio/5
86 Lance Berkman/5
87 Andy Pettitte/25 30.00 60.00
88 Roy Oswalt/10
93 Carlos Beltran/100 6.00 15.00
94 Angel Berroa/100 4.00 10.00
95 Juan Gonzalez/10
100 Duke Snider/100 10.00 25.00
101 Shawn Green/1
102 Hideo Nomo/1
103 Kazuhisa Ishii/5
104 Edwin Jackson/50 12.50 30.00
105 Fred McGriff/1
106 Hong-Chih Kou/25 40.00 80.00
107 Don Sutton/25 12.50 30.00
108 Rickey Henderson/5
110 Robin Ventura/10
111 Paul Lo Duca/5
112 Rickie Weeks/24 12.50 30.00
113 Scott Podsednik/100 10.00 25.00
114 Junior Spivey/10
115 Lyle Overbay/10
116 Tony Oliva/50 8.00 20.00
117 Jacque Jones/100 6.00 15.00
118 Shannon Stewart/5
119 Torii Hunter/100 6.00 15.00
120 Johan Santana/10
124 Nick Johnson/5
125 Jose Vidro/10
126 Orlando Cabrera/10
128 Mike Piazza/1
130 Jae Weong Seo/100 6.00 15.00
131 Gary Carter/100 6.00 15.00
136 Don Mattingly/100 30.00 60.00
138 Alex Rodriguez/1
139 Jorge Posada/25 20.00 50.00
140 Bernie Williams/5
142 Mike Mussina/1
143 Mariano Rivera/1
144 Gary Sheffield/25 20.00 50.00
146 Chien-Ming Wang/25 125.00 200.00
147 Javier Vazquez/5
148 Jose Contreras/5
149 Whitey Ford/5
151 Eric Chavez/1
152 Barry Zito/1
153 Mark Mulder/100 6.00 15.00
154 Tim Hudson/5
155 Rich Harden/50 8.00 20.00
158 Bobby Abreu/5
159 Marlon Byrd/100 4.00 10.00
160 Lenny Dykstra/100 6.00 15.00
161 Steve Carlton/50 8.00 20.00
164 Jose Castillo/50 5.00 12.00
165 Jay Payton/100 4.00 10.00
166 Ryan Klesko/5
170 Jerome Williams/50 5.00 12.00
171 J.T. Snow/10
173 Edgar Martinez/5
175 Jamie Moyer/5
176 Rich Aurilia/5
178 Scott Rolen/50 12.50 30.00
179 Albert Pujols/1
180 Jim Edmonds/10
181 Stan Musial/100 30.00 60.00
182 Dan Haren/25 8.00 20.00
183 Red Schoendienst/100 6.00 15.00
184 Aubrey Huff/100 6.00 15.00
185 Delmon Young/100 10.00 25.00
186 Rocco Baldelli/5
187 Dewon Brazelton/25 8.00 20.00
188 Mark Teixeira/50 12.50 30.00
189 Hank Blalock/25 12.50 30.00
190 Nolan Ryan Rgr/10
192 Michael Young/100 10.00 25.00
193 Vernon Wells/10
194 Roy Halladay/25 75.00 150.00
197 Josh Phelps/5
198 Alexis Rios/50 8.00 20.00
199 Eric Hinske/1
202 Fernando Nieve/100 6.00 15.00
205 Josh Labandeira/100 4.00 10.00
206 Chris Oxspring/100 4.00 10.00
208 Cory Sullivan/100 4.00 10.00
209 Ruddy Yan/100 4.00 10.00
210 Jason Bartlett/100 6.00 15.00
212 Lincoln Holdzkom/100 4.00 10.00
213 Justin Leone/100 6.00 15.00
214 Jorge Sequea/100 4.00 10.00
217 Tim Bittner/100 4.00 10.00
219 Justin Hampson/100 4.00 10.00
220 Ryan Wing/100 4.00 10.00
221 Mariano Gomez/100 4.00 10.00
222 Carlos Vasquez/100 6.00 15.00
224 Renyel Pinto/100 5.00 12.00
225 Chris Shelton/100 10.00 25.00
226 Mike Gosling/10
227 Aarom Baldiris/10
228 Ramon Ramirez/10
230 Sean Henn/100 4.00 10.00
232 Nick Regilio/100 4.00 10.00
233 Dave Crouthers/10
234 Greg Dobbs/50 6.00 15.00
235 Angel Chavez/100 4.00 10.00
238 Ian Snell/10
242 Ivan Ochoa/100 4.00 10.00
243 Jose Capellan/10
244 Onil Joseph/10
245 Hector Gimenez/10
246 Shawn Hill/10
247 Freddy Guzman/10
248 Graham Koonce/100 4.00 10.00
250 Merkin Valdez/10

2004 Absolute Memorabilia Signature Spectrum Platinum

STATED PRINT RUN 1 SERIAL #'d SET
NO PRICING DUE TO SCARCITY

2004 Absolute Memorabilia Signature Spectrum Silver

PRINT RUNS B/WN 1-250 COPIES PER
NO PRICING ON QTY OF 14 OR LESS
1 Troy Glaus/34 15.00 40.00
2 Garret Anderson/100 6.00 15.00
6 Nolan Ryan Angels/25 75.00 150.00
7 Vladimir Guerrero/100 12.50 30.00
8 Richie Sexson/34 10.00 25.00
9 Shea Hillenbrand/100 6.00 15.00
11 Brandon Webb/100 4.00 10.00
12 Randy Johnson/1
13 Robby Hammock/250 4.00 10.00
14 Edgar Gonzalez/104 4.00 10.00
15 Roberto Alomar/32 15.00 40.00
16 Andruw Jones/50 12.50 30.00
17 Chipper Jones/10
18 Dale Murphy/100 10.00 25.00
19 Rafael Furcal/100 6.00 15.00
21 Bubba Nelson/250 4.00 10.00
22 Julio Franco/100 6.00 15.00
23 Adam LaRoche/100 4.00 10.00
24 Michael Hessman/250 4.00 10.00
25 Warren Spahn/10
26 Jay Gibbons/100 4.00 10.00
27 Cal Ripken/5
29 Adam Loewen/100 4.00 10.00
30 Rafael Palmeiro/5
32 Luis Matos/100 4.00 10.00
33 Jason Varitek/50 15.00 40.00
34 Carl Yastrzemski/5
35 Manny Ramirez/5
36 Trot Nixon/100 6.00 15.00
37 Curt Schilling/5
40 Luis Tiant/100 6.00 15.00
41 Kevin Youkilis/25 6.00 15.00
42 Michael Hernandez/190 4.00 10.00
43 Sammy Sosa/21 50.00 100.00
45 Kerry Wood/50 12.50 30.00
46 Mark Prior/100 8.00 20.00
47 Ernie Banks/100 20.00 50.00
48 Aramis Ramirez/50 8.00 20.00
49 Brendan Harris/250 4.00 10.00
50 Todd Wellemeyer/250 4.00 10.00
51 Frank Thomas/50 15.00 40.00
52 Magglio Ordonez/100 6.00 15.00
53 Carlos Lee/100 6.00 15.00
54 Joe Crede/100 6.00 15.00
55 Joe Borchard/250 4.00 10.00
56 Mark Buehrle/10
57 Sean Casey/50 8.00 20.00
58 Adam Dunn/100 10.00 25.00
59 Austin Kearns/100 4.00 10.00
61 Barry Larkin/50 12.50 30.00
62 Ryan Wagner/100 4.00 10.00
63 Jody Gerut/100 4.00 10.00
64 Jeremy Guthrie/50 5.00 12.00
65 Travis Hafner/50 5.00 12.00
66 Brian Tallet/250 4.00 10.00
67 Todd Helton/10
68 Preston Wilson/100 6.00 15.00
69 Jeff Baker/50 5.00 12.00
70 Clint Barmes/250 6.00 15.00
71 Joe Kennedy/250 4.00 10.00
72 Jack Morris/96
73 George Kell/100 10.00 25.00
74 Preston Larrison/250 4.00 10.00
77 Dontrelle Willis/100 10.00 25.00
78 Josh Beckett/25 15.00 40.00
79 Miguel Cabrera/100 15.00 40.00
80 Mike Lowell/25 10.00 25.00
81 Luis Castillo/50 5.00 12.00
83 Jeff Bagwell/50 30.00 60.00
85 Craig Biggio/50 8.00 20.00
86 Lance Berkman/25 15.00 40.00
87 Andy Pettitte/25 20.00 50.00
88 Roy Oswalt/25 10.00 25.00
89 Chris Burke/250 6.00 15.00
90 Jason Lane/231 6.00 15.00
93 Carlos Beltran/100 6.00 15.00
94 Angel Berroa/100 4.00 10.00
95 Juan Gonzalez/25 10.00 25.00
96 Ken Harvey/200 4.00 10.00
97 Byron Gettis/250 4.00 10.00
98 Alexis Gomez/250 4.00 10.00
99 Ian Ferguson/104 4.00 10.00
100 Duke Snider/100 10.00 25.00
101 Shawn Green/1
102 Hideo Nomo/1
103 Kazuhisa Ishii/25 10.00 25.00
104 Edwin Jackson/100 10.00 25.00
105 Fred McGriff/50 30.00 60.00
106 Hong-Chih Kou/50 20.00 50.00
107 Don Sutton/100 6.00 15.00
108 Rickey Henderson/10
109 Cesar Izturis/101 4.00 10.00
110 Robin Ventura/25 10.00 25.00
111 Paul Lo Duca/50 8.00 20.00
112 Rickie Weeks/21 10.00 25.00
113 Scott Podsednik/100 10.00 25.00
114 Junior Spivey/89 4.00 10.00
115 Lyle Overbay/89 4.00 10.00
116 Tony Oliva/72 6.00 15.00
117 Jacque Jones/100 6.00 15.00
118 Shannon Stewart/100 6.00 15.00
119 Torii Hunter/100 6.00 15.00
120 Johan Santana/50 12.50 30.00
121 J.D. Durbin/250 4.00 10.00
122 Jason Kubel/250 4.00 10.00
123 Michael Cuddyer/225 4.00 10.00
124 Nick Johnson/25 10.00 25.00
125 Jose Vidro/25 6.00 15.00
126 Orlando Cabrera/25 10.00 25.00
127 Zach Day/100 4.00 10.00
128 Mike Piazza/5
130 Jae Weong Seo/100 6.00 15.00
131 Gary Carter/100 6.00 15.00
132 Phil Seibel/177 4.00 10.00
133 Edwin Almonte/250 4.00 10.00
136 Don Mattingly/100 30.00 60.00
138 Alex Rodriguez/1
139 Jorge Posada/50 12.50 30.00
140 Bernie Williams/10
142 Mike Mussina/1
143 Mariano Rivera/5
144 Gary Sheffield/100 10.00 25.00
146 Chien-Ming Wang/50 75.00 150.00
147 Javier Vazquez/25 10.00 25.00
148 Jose Contreras/25 10.00 25.00
149 Whitey Ford/50 12.50 30.00
151 Eric Chavez/50 8.00 20.00
152 Barry Zito/1
153 Mark Mulder/100 6.00 15.00
154 Tim Hudson/50 12.50 30.00
155 Rich Harden/100 6.00 15.00
156 Eric Byrnes/250 4.00 10.00
158 Bobby Abreu/10
159 Marlon Byrd/100 4.00 10.00
160 Lenny Dykstra/100 6.00 15.00
161 Steve Carlton/100 6.00 15.00
162 Ryan Howard/250 30.00 60.00
163 Bobby Hill/250 4.00 10.00
164 Jose Castillo/100 4.00 10.00
165 Jay Payton/100 4.00 10.00
168 Henri Stanley/112 4.00 10.00
170 Jerome Williams/100 4.00 10.00
171 J.T. Snow/89 6.00 15.00
173 Edgar Martinez/50 12.50 30.00
175 Jamie Moyer/19 15.00 40.00
176 Rich Aurilia/25 6.00 15.00
177 Chris Snelling/177 4.00 10.00
178 Scott Rolen/100 10.00 25.00
179 Albert Pujols/5
180 Jim Edmonds/50 12.50 30.00
181 Stan Musial/100 30.00 60.00
182 Dan Haren/200 4.00 10.00
183 Red Schoendienst/100 10.00 25.00

184 Aubrey Huff/100 6.00 15.00
185 Delmon Young/100 10.00 25.00
186 Rocco Baldelli/50 8.00 20.00
187 Dewon Brazelton/50 5.00 12.00
188 Mark Teixeira/100 10.00 25.00
189 Hank Blalock/50 8.00 20.00
190 Nolan Ryan Rgr/25 75.00 150.00
192 Michael Young/100 10.00 25.00
193 Vernon Wells/14
194 Roy Halladay/50 50.00 100.00
196 Dustin McGowan/250 4.00 10.00
197 Josh Phelps/25 6.00 15.00
198 Aaron Miles/100 6.00 15.00
199 Eric Hinske/5
200 Josh Towers/158 4.00 10.00
202 Fernando Nieve/250 5.00 12.00
203 Mike Rouse/100 4.00 10.00
204 Dennis Sarfate/100 4.00 10.00
205 Josh Labandeira/250 4.00 10.00
206 Chris Oxspring/250 4.00 10.00
207 Alfredo Simon/100 4.00 10.00
208 Cory Sullivan/250 4.00 10.00
209 Ruddy Yan/250 4.00 10.00
210 Jason Bartlett/250 6.00 15.00
211 Akinori Otsuka/100 12.50 30.00
212 Lincoln Holdzkom/250 4.00 10.00
213 Justin Leone/250 6.00 15.00
214 Jorge Sequea/250 4.00 10.00
215 John Gall/50 8.00 20.00
217 Tim Bittner/250 4.00 10.00
219 Justin Hampson/250 4.00 10.00
220 Ryan Wing/250 4.00 10.00
221 Mariano Gomez/250 4.00 10.00
222 Carlos Vasquez/250 6.00 15.00
223 Casey Daigle/150 4.00 10.00
224 Renyel Pinto/250 4.00 10.00
229 Roberto Novoa/225 5.00 12.00
230 Sean Henn/250 4.00 10.00
231 Jamie Brown/200 4.00 10.00
232 Nick Regilio/250 4.00 10.00
234 Greg Dobbs/250 4.00 10.00
235 Angel Chavez/250 4.00 10.00
237 Justin Knoedler/225 4.00 10.00
239 Jason Frasor/225 4.00 10.00
240 Jerry Gil/225 4.00 10.00
241 Carlos Hines/225 4.00 10.00
242 Ivan Ochoa/250 4.00 10.00
248 Graham Koonce/250 4.00 10.00
249 Ronald Belisario/225 4.00 10.00

2004 Absolute Memorabilia Absolutely Ink

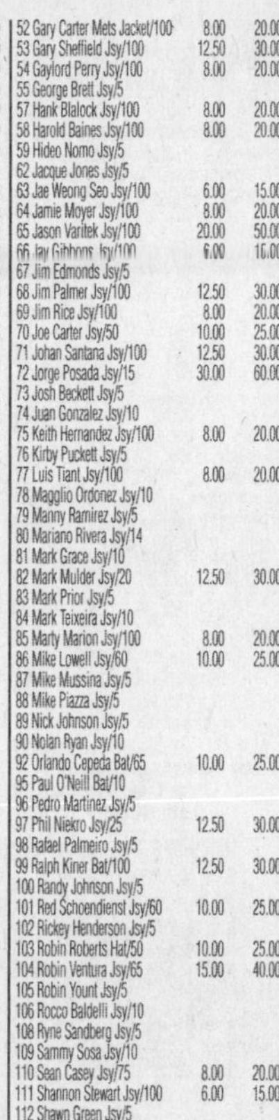

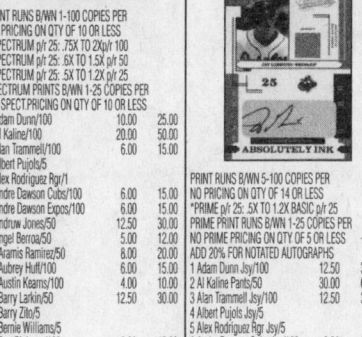

PRINT RUNS B/WN 1-100 COPIES PER
NO PRICING ON QTY OF 10 OR LESS
*SPECTRUM p/r 25: .75X TO 2X p/r 100
*SPECTRUM p/r 25: .6X TO 1.5X p/r 50
*SPECTRUM p/r 25: .5X TO 1.2X p/r 25
SPECTRUM PRINTS B/WN 1-25 COPIES PER
NO SPECT.PRICING ON QTY OF 10 OR LESS
1 Adam Dunn/100 10.00 25.00
2 Al Kaline/100 20.00 50.00
3 Alan Trammell/100 6.00 15.00
4 Albert Pujols/5
5 Alex Rodriguez Rgr/1
6 Andre Dawson Cubs/100 6.00 15.00
7 Andre Dawson Expos/100 6.00 15.00
8 Andruw Jones/50 12.50 30.00
9 Angel Berroa/50 5.00 12.00
10 Aramis Ramirez/50 8.00 20.00
11 Aubrey Huff/100 6.00 15.00
12 Austin Kearns/100 4.00 10.00
13 Barry Larkin/50 12.50 30.00
14 Barry Zito/5
15 Bernie Williams/5
16 Bert Blyleven/100 6.00 15.00
17 Billy Williams/100 6.00 15.00
18 Bo Jackson/5
19 Bob Feller/100 10.00 25.00
20 Bob Gibson/25 20.00 50.00
21 Bobby Doerr/100 6.00 15.00
22 Brandon Webb/100 10.00 25.00
23 Brett Myers/50 8.00 20.00
24 Brooks Robinson/100 10.00 25.00
25 Cal Ripken/5
26 Carl Yastrzemski/5
27 Carlos Beltran/100 6.00 15.00
28 Carlos Lee/100 6.00 15.00
29 Carlton Fisk/10
30 Chipper Jones/5
31 Craig Biggio/50 8.00 20.00
32 Curt Schilling/5
33 Dale Murphy/100 10.00 25.00
34 Darryl Strawberry/100 6.00 15.00
35 Dave Concepcion/50 8.00 20.00
36 Dave Parker/50 8.00 20.00
37 Deion Sanders/10
38 Don Mattingly/100 30.00 60.00
39 Dontrelle Willis/100 10.00 25.00
40 Duke Snider/100 10.00 25.00
41 Dwight Gooden/100 6.00 15.00
42 Edgar Martinez/50 12.50 30.00
43 Eric Chavez/50 8.00 20.00
44 Ernie Banks/100 20.00 50.00
45 Fergie Jenkins/100 6.00 15.00
46 Frank Robinson/100 10.00 25.00
47 Frank Thomas/25 30.00 60.00
48 Fred Lynn/50 5.00 12.00
49 Fred McGriff/25 40.00 80.00
50 Garret Anderson/100 6.00 15.00
51 Gary Carter Expos/100 6.00 15.00
52 Gary Carter Mets/100 6.00 15.00
53 Gary Sheffield/50 12.50 30.00
54 Gaylord Perry/100 6.00 15.00
55 George Brett/5
57 Hank Blalock/100 6.00 15.00
58 Harold Baines/50 8.00 20.00
59 Hideo Nomo/1
62 Jacque Jones/100 6.00 15.00
63 Jae Weong Seo/100 6.00 15.00
64 Jamie Moyer/25 12.50 30.00
65 Jason Varitek/50 20.00 50.00
66 Jay Gibbons/50 5.00 12.00
67 Jim Edmonds/25 20.00 50.00
68 Jim Palmer/100 10.00 25.00
69 Jim Rice/50 8.00 20.00
70 Joe Carter/5
71 Johan Santana/50 12.50 30.00
72 Jorge Posada/50 12.50 30.00
73 Josh Beckett/25 20.00 50.00
74 Juan Gonzalez/25 12.50 30.00
75 Keith Hernandez/100 6.00 15.00
76 Kirby Puckett/25 50.00 100.00
77 Luis Tiant/100 6.00 15.00
78 Magglio Ordonez/100 6.00 15.00
79 Manny Ramirez/1
80 Mariano Rivera/1
81 Mark Grace/25 30.00 60.00
82 Mark Mulder/100 6.00 15.00
83 Mark Prior/100 10.00 25.00
84 Mark Teixeira/100 10.00 25.00
85 Marty Marion/100 6.00 15.00
86 Mike Lowell/25 12.50 30.00
87 Mike Mussina/1
88 Mike Piazza/5
89 Nick Johnson/10
90 Nolan Ryan/25 75.00 150.00
91 Orel Hershiser/100 15.00 40.00
92 Orlando Cepeda/100 6.00 15.00
95 Paul O'Neill/5
96 Pedro Martinez/1
97 Phil Niekro/100 6.00 15.00
98 Rafael Palmeiro/5
99 Ralph Kiner/100 10.00 25.00
100 Randy Johnson/5
101 Red Schoendienst/100 6.00 15.00
102 Rickey Henderson/10
103 Robin Roberts/50 8.00 20.00
104 Robin Ventura/100 6.00 15.00
105 Robin Yount/5
106 Rocco Baldelli/25 12.50 30.00
108 Ryne Sandberg/10
109 Sammy Sosa/21 50.00 100.00
110 Sean Casey/23 12.50 30.00
111 Shannon Stewart/50 5.00 12.00
112 Shawn Green/10
113 Stan Musial/100 30.00 60.00
114 Steve Carlton/50 8.00 20.00
115 Steve Garvey/100 6.00 15.00
116 Todd Helton/10
117 Tommy John/100 6.00 15.00
118 Tony Gwynn/25 40.00 80.00
119 Tony Oliva/100 6.00 15.00
120 Torii Hunter/100 6.00 15.00
121 Trot Nixon/50 8.00 20.00
122 Troy Glaus/50 12.50 30.00
123 Vernon Wells/25 12.50 30.00
124 Vladimir Guerrero/100 15.00 40.00
125 Will Clark/100 10.00 25.00

2004 Absolute Memorabilia Absolutely Ink Material

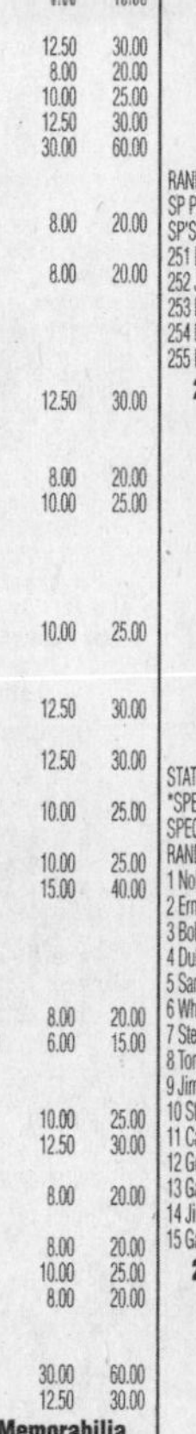

PRINT RUNS B/WN 5-100 COPIES PER
NO PRICING ON QTY OF 14 OR LESS
*PRIME p/r 25: .5X TO 1.2X BASIC p/r 25
PRIME PRINT RUNS B/WN 1-25 COPIES PER
NO PRIME PRICING ON QTY OF 5 OR LESS
ADD 20% FOR NOTATED AUTOGRAPHS
1 Adam Dunn Jsy/100 12.50 30.00
2 Al Kaline Pants/50 30.00 60.00
3 Alan Trammell Jsy/100 12.50 30.00
4 Albert Pujols Jsy/5
5 Alex Rodriguez Rgr Jsy/5
6 Andre Dawson Cubs Jsy/100 8.00 20.00
7 Andre Dawson Expos Jsy/100 8.00 20.00
8 Andruw Jones Jsy/10
9 Angel Berroa Jsy/100 6.00 15.00
11 Aubrey Huff Jsy/100 8.00 20.00
12 Austin Kearns Jsy/100 6.00 15.00
13 Barry Larkin Jsy/10
14 Barry Zito Jsy/5
15 Bernie Williams Jsy/5
16 Bert Blyleven Jsy/100 8.00 20.00
17 Billy Williams Jsy/100 12.50 30.00
18 Bo Jackson Jsy/10
19 Bob Feller Jsy/100 12.50 30.00
20 Bob Gibson Jsy/7
21 Bobby Doerr Jsy/100 8.00 20.00
22 Brandon Webb Jsy/50 15.00 40.00
23 Brett Myers Jsy/100 8.00 20.00
24 Brooks Robinson Jsy/100 12.50 30.00
25 Cal Ripken Jsy/5
26 Carl Yastrzemski Jsy/5
27 Carlos Beltran Jsy/100 8.00 20.00
28 Carlos Lee Jsy/100 8.00 20.00
29 Carlton Fisk Jsy/5
30 Chipper Jones Jsy/5
31 Craig Biggio Jsy/10
32 Curt Schilling Jsy/5
33 Dale Murphy Jsy/100 12.50 30.00
34 Darryl Strawberry Jsy/100 8.00 20.00
35 Dave Concepcion Jsy/50 15.00 40.00
36 Dave Parker Jsy/100 8.00 20.00
37 Deion Sanders Jsy/7
38 Don Mattingly Jsy/50 50.00 100.00
39 Dontrelle Willis Jsy/20 20.00 50.00
41 Dwight Gooden Jsy/60 10.00 25.00
42 Edgar Martinez Jsy/100 20.00 50.00
43 Eric Chavez Jsy/10
44 Ernie Banks Jsy/50 30.00 60.00
45 Fergie Jenkins Pants/100 8.00 20.00
46 Frank Robinson Jsy/50 15.00 40.00
47 Frank Thomas Jsy/5
48 Fred Lynn Jsy/100 6.00 15.00
49 Fred McGriff Jsy/20 40.00 80.00
50 Garret Anderson Jsy/100 8.00 20.00
51 Gary Carter Expos Jsy/100 8.00 20.00
52 Gary Carter Mets Jacket/100 8.00 20.00
53 Gary Sheffield Jsy/100 12.50 30.00
54 Gaylord Perry Jsy/100 8.00 20.00
55 George Brett Jsy/5
57 Hank Blalock Jsy/100 8.00 20.00
58 Harold Baines Jsy/100 8.00 20.00
59 Hideo Nomo Jsy/5
62 Jacque Jones Jsy/5
63 Jae Weong Seo Jsy/100 6.00 15.00
64 Jamie Moyer Jsy/100 8.00 20.00
65 Jason Varitek Jsy/100 20.00 50.00
66 Jay Gibbons Jsy/100 6.00 15.00
67 Jim Edmonds Jsy/5
68 Jim Palmer Jsy/100 12.50 30.00
69 Jim Rice Jsy/100 8.00 20.00
70 Joe Carter Jsy/50 10.00 25.00
71 Johan Santana Jsy/100 12.50 30.00
72 Jorge Posada Jsy/15 30.00 60.00
73 Josh Beckett Jsy/5
74 Juan Gonzalez Jsy/10
75 Keith Hernandez Jsy/100 8.00 20.00
76 Kirby Puckett Jsy/5
77 Luis Tiant Jsy/100 8.00 20.00
78 Magglio Ordonez Jsy/10
79 Manny Ramirez Jsy/5
80 Mariano Rivera Jsy/14
81 Mark Grace Jsy/10
82 Mark Mulder Jsy/20 12.50 30.00
83 Mark Prior Jsy/5
84 Mark Teixeira Jsy/10
85 Marty Marion Jsy/100 8.00 20.00
86 Mike Lowell Jsy/60 10.00 25.00
87 Mike Mussina Jsy/5
88 Mike Piazza Jsy/5
89 Nick Johnson Jsy/5
90 Nolan Ryan Jsy/10
92 Orlando Cepeda Bat/65 10.00 25.00
95 Paul O'Neill Bat/10
96 Pedro Martinez Jsy/5
97 Phil Niekro Jsy/25 12.50 30.00
98 Rafael Palmeiro Jsy/5
99 Ralph Kiner Bat/100 12.50 30.00
100 Randy Johnson Jsy/5
101 Red Schoendienst Jsy/60 10.00 25.00
102 Rickey Henderson Jsy/5
103 Robin Roberts Hat/50 10.00 25.00
104 Robin Ventura Jsy/65 15.00 40.00
105 Robin Yount Jsy/5
106 Rocco Baldelli Jsy/10
108 Ryne Sandberg Jsy/10
109 Sammy Sosa Jsy/10
110 Sean Casey Jsy/75 8.00 20.00
111 Shannon Stewart Jsy/100 6.00 15.00
112 Shawn Green Jsy/5
113 Stan Musial Jsy/5
114 Steve Carlton Jsy/50 10.00 25.00
115 Steve Garvey Bat/100 12.50 30.00
116 Todd Helton Jsy/5
117 Tommy John Jsy/100 8.00 20.00
118 Tony Gwynn Jsy/5
119 Tony Oliva Jsy/100 8.00 20.00
120 Torii Hunter Jsy/50 10.00 25.00
121 Trot Nixon Jsy/100 8.00 20.00
122 Troy Glaus Jsy/10
123 Vernon Wells Jsy/5
124 Vladimir Guerrero Jsy/55 30.00 60.00
125 Will Clark Jsy/100 12.50 30.00

2004 Absolute Memorabilia Absolutely Ink Combo Material

*COMBO p/r 100: .5X TO 1.2X p/r 100
*COMBO p/r 50-65: .6X TO 1.5X p/r 75-100
*COMBO p/r 50-65: .5X TO 1.2X p/r 50-65
*COMBO p/r 25: .75X TO 2X p/r 100
PRINT RUNS B/WN 1-100 COPIES PER
NO PRICING ON QTY OF 10 OR LESS
PRIME PRINT RUNS B/WN 1-5 COPIES PER
NO PRIME PRICING DUE TO SCARCITY
RANDOM INSERTS IN PACKS
43 E.Chavez Bat-Jsy/15 15.00 40.00
74 J.Gonzalez Bat-Jsy/15 15.00 40.00

2004 Absolute Memorabilia Absolutely Ink Triple Material

PRINT RUNS B/WN 1-10 COPIES PER
PRIME PRINT RUNS B/WN 1-5 COPIES PER
RANDOM INSERTS IN PACKS
NO PRICING DUE TO SCARCITY

2004 Absolute Memorabilia Fans of the Game

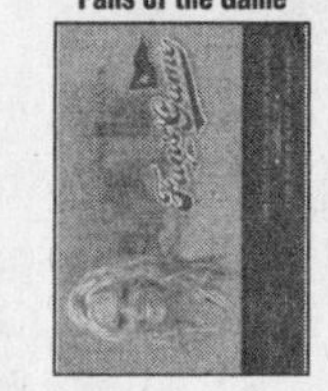

251 Landon Donovan 3.00 8.00
252 Jennie Finch 2.00 5.00
253 Bonnie Blair .75 2.00
254 Dan Jansen .75 2.00
255 Kerri Strug 1.25 3.00

2004 Absolute Memorabilia Fans of the Game Autographs

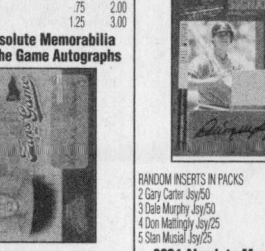

RANDOM INSERTS IN RETAIL PACKS
SP PRINT RUNS PROVIDED BY DONRUSS
SP'S ARE NOT SERIAL-NUMBERED
251 Landon Donovan 50.00 100.00
252 Jennie Finch 90.00 150.00
253 Bonnie Blair SP/250 15.00 40.00
254 Dan Jansen SP/250 10.00 25.00
255 Kerri Strug SP/250 20.00 50.00

2004 Absolute Memorabilia Marks of Fame

STATED PRINT RUN 100 SERIAL #'d SETS
*SPECTRUM: .75X TO 2X BASIC
SPECTRUM PRINT RUN 25 SERIAL #'d SETS
RANDOM INSERTS IN PACKS
1 Nolan Ryan 5.00 12.00
2 Ernie Banks 1.50 4.00
3 Bob Feller .60 1.50
4 Duke Snider 1.00 2.50
5 Sammy Sosa 1.50 4.00
6 Whitey Ford 1.00 2.50
7 Steve Carlton .60 1.50
8 Tony Gwynn 1.50 4.00
9 Jim Bunning .60 1.50
10 Stan Musial 2.50 6.00
11 Cal Ripken 6.00 15.00
12 George Brett 3.00 8.00
13 Gary Carter .60 1.50
14 Jim Palmer .60 1.50
15 Gaylord Perry .60 1.50

2004 Absolute Memorabilia Marks of Fame Signature

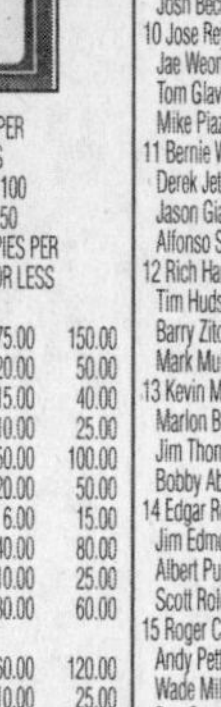

PRINT RUNS B/WN 10-100 COPIES PER
NO PRICING ON QTY OF 10 OR LESS
*SPECTRUM p/r 25: .6X TO 1.5X p/r 100
*SPECTRUM p/r 25: .5X TO 1.2X p/r 50
SPECTRUM PRINT RUNS B/WN 1-25 COPIES PER
NO SPECT.PRICING ON QTY OF 10 OR LESS
RANDOM INSERTS IN PACKS
1 Nolan Ryan/50 75.00 150.00
2 Ernie Banks/50 20.00 50.00
3 Bob Feller/100 15.00 40.00
4 Duke Snider/100 10.00 25.00
5 Sammy Sosa/21 50.00 100.00
6 Whitey Ford/25 20.00 50.00
7 Steve Carlton/100 6.00 15.00
8 Tony Gwynn/25 40.00 80.00
9 Jim Bunning/100 10.00 25.00
10 Stan Musial/50 30.00 60.00
11 Cal Ripken/10
12 George Brett/25 60.00 120.00
13 Gary Carter/100 10.00 25.00
14 Jim Palmer/50 8.00 20.00
15 Gaylord Perry/100 6.00 15.00

2004 Absolute Memorabilia Signature Club

PRINT RUNS B/WN 5-50 COPIES PER
NO PRICING ON QTY OF 5 OR LESS
1 Sammy Sosa Bat/5
2 Gary Sheffield Bat/50 15.00 40.00
3 Vladimir Guerrero Bat/5
4 Will Clark Bat/50 15.00 40.00
5 Ernie Banks Bat/50 30.00 60.00

2004 Absolute Memorabilia Signature Material

PRINT RUNS B/WN 25-50 COPIES PER
PRIME PRINT RUN 5 SERIAL #'d SETS
NO PRIME PRICING DUE TO SCARCITY
*COMBO: .5X TO 1.2X BASIC
COMBO PRINTS B/WN 25-50 COPIES PER
COMBO PRIME PRINT 5 SERIAL #'d SETS
NO COMBO PRIME PRICE DUE SCARCITY

RANDOM INSERTS IN PACKS
2 Gary Carter Jsy/50 10.00 25.00
3 Dale Murphy Jsy/50 15.00 40.00
4 Don Mattingly Jsy/25 60.00 120.00
5 Stan Musial Jsy/25 60.00 120.00

2004 Absolute Memorabilia Team Quad

STATED PRINT RUN 100 SERIAL #'d SETS
*SPECTRUM: 1X TO 2.5X BASIC
SPECTRUM PRINT RUN 25 SERIAL #'d SETS
RANDOM INSERTS IN PACKS
1 Craig Biggio 1.00 2.50
Lance Berkman
Jeff Kent
Jeff Bagwell
2 Nomar Garciaparra 1.50 4.00
Manny Ramirez
Pedro Martinez
Trot Nixon
3 Paul Konerko 1.00 2.50
Carlos Lee
Magglio Ordonez
Frank Thomas
4 John Smoltz 1.50 4.00
Chipper Jones
Andruw Jones
Rafael Furcal
5 Garret Anderson .60 1.50
Troy Percival
Troy Glaus
Darin Erstad
6 Steve Finley 1.50 4.00
Brandon Webb
Randy Johnson
Luis Gonzalez
7 Paul Lo Duca 1.50 4.00
Hideo Nomo
Shawn Green
Kazuhisa Ishii
8 Larry Walker 1.00 2.50
Todd Helton
Jason Jennings
Preston Wilson
9 A.J. Burnett .60 1.50
Dontrelle Willis
Brad Penny
Josh Beckett
10 Jose Reyes 1.50 4.00
Jae Weong Seo
Tom Glavine
Mike Piazza
11 Bernie Williams 4.00 10.00
Derek Jeter
Jason Giambi
Alfonso Soriano
12 Rich Harden 1.00 2.50
Tim Hudson
Barry Zito
Mark Mulder
13 Kevin Millwood 1.00 2.50
Marlon Byrd
Jim Thome
Bobby Abreu
14 Edgar Renteria 4.00 10.00
Jim Edmonds
Albert Pujols
Scott Rolen
15 Roger Clemens 1.00 2.50
Andy Pettitte
Wade Miller
Roy Oswalt

2004 Absolute Memorabilia Team Quad Material

STATED PRINT RUN 100 SERIAL #'d SETS
PRIME PRINT RUN 5 SERIAL #'d SETS
NO PRIME PRICING DUE TO SCARCITY
RANDOM INSERTS IN PACKS
ALL HAVE 4 JSY SWATCHES UNLESS NOTED
CARD 15 IS BAT-BAT-JSY-JSY
1 Jeff Kent 10.00 25.00
Lance Berkman
Craig Biggio
Jeff Bagwell
2 Nomar Garciaparra 15.00 40.00
Manny Ramirez
Pedro Martinez
Trot Nixon
3 Paul Konerko 10.00 25.00
Carlos Lee
Magglio Ordonez
Frank Thomas
4 John Smoltz 10.00 25.00
Chipper Jones
Andruw Jones
Rafael Furcal
5 Garret Anderson 6.00 15.00
Troy Percival
Troy Glaus
Darin Erstad
6 Steve Finley 10.00 25.00
Brandon Webb
Randy Johnson
Luis Gonzalez
7 Paul Lo Duca 10.00 25.00
Hideo Nomo
Shawn Green
Kazuhisa Ishii
8 Larry Walker 10.00 25.00
Todd Helton
Jason Jennings
Preston Wilson
9 A.J. Burnett 10.00 25.00
Dontrelle Willis
Brad Penny
Josh Beckett
10 Jose Reyes 10.00 25.00
Jae Weong Seo
Tom Glavine
Mike Piazza
11 Bernie Williams 15.00 40.00
Derek Jeter
Jason Giambi
Alfonso Soriano
12 Rich Harden 6.00 15.00
Tim Hudson
Barry Zito
Mark Mulder
13 Kevin Millwood 10.00 25.00
Marlon Byrd
Jim Thome
Bobby Abreu
14 Edgar Renteria 15.00 40.00
Jim Edmonds
Albert Pujols
Scott Rolen
15 Roger Clemens Bat 15.00 40.00
Andy Pettitte Bat
Wade Miller Jsy
Roy Oswalt Jsy

2004 Absolute Memorabilia Team Tandem

STATED PRINT RUN 250 SERIAL #'d SETS
*SPECTRUM: 2X TO 5X BASIC
SPECTRUM PRINT RUN 25 SERIAL #'d SETS
RANDOM INSERTS IN PACKS
1 Vladimir Guerrero 1.50 4.00
Reggie Jackson
2 Dale Murphy 1.00 2.50
Chipper Jones
3 Gary Carter 1.50 4.00
Mike Piazza
4 Miguel Tejada 1.00 2.50
Cal Ripken
5 Gary Sheffield 4.00 10.00
Derek Jeter
6 Curt Schilling 1.00 2.50
Pedro Martinez
7 Roger Clemens 2.00 5.00
Andy Pettitte
8 Mike Sweeney 3.00 8.00
George Brett
9 Kazuhisa Ishii 1.50 4.00
Hideo Nomo
10 Austin Kearns 1.00 2.50
Adam Dunn
11 Miguel Cabrera .60 1.50
Dontrelle Willis
12 Don Mattingly 4.00 10.00
Derek Jeter
13 Barry Zito .60 1.50
Eric Chavez
14 Jim Thome 2.50 6.00
Mike Schmidt
15 Albert Pujols 4.00 10.00
Stan Musial
16 Nolan Ryan 5.00 12.00
Alex Rodriguez
17 Kerry Wood 1.00 2.50
Mark Prior
18 Rafael Palmeiro 1.00 2.50
Jay Gibbons
19 Nomar Garciaparra 1.50 4.00
Manny Ramirez
20 Ivan Rodriguez 1.50 4.00
Mike Piazza

2004 Absolute Memorabilia Team Tandem Material

STATED PRINT RUN 250 SERIAL #'d SETS
PRIME PRINT RUN 5 SERIAL #'d SETS
NO PRIME PRICING DUE TO SCARCITY
RANDOM INSERTS IN PACKS
1 Reggie Jackson Bat 4.00 10.00
Vladimir Guerrero Bat
2 Chipper Jones Jsy 4.00 10.00
Dale Murphy Jsy
3 Gary Carter Jsy 4.00 10.00
Mike Piazza Jsy
4 Miguel Tejada Bat 10.00 25.00
Cal Ripken Bat
5 Derek Jeter Bat 10.00 25.00
Gary Sheffield Bat
6 Curt Schilling Bat 4.00 10.00
Pedro Martinez Bat
7 Roger Clemens Bat 6.00 15.00
Andy Pettitte Bat
8 Mike Sweeney Jsy 6.00 15.00
George Brett Jsy
9 Kazuhisa Ishii Jsy 4.00 10.00
Hideo Nomo Jsy
10 Austin Kearns Jsy 3.00 8.00
Adam Dunn Jsy
11 Dontrelle Willis Jsy 4.00 10.00
Miguel Cabrera Jsy
12 Don Mattingly Jsy 15.00 40.00
Derek Jeter Jsy
13 Barry Zito Jsy 3.00 8.00
Eric Chavez Jsy
14 Jim Thome Jsy 8.00 20.00
Mike Schmidt Jsy
15 Albert Pujols Jsy 15.00 40.00
Stan Musial Jsy
16 Nolan Ryan Jsy 12.50 30.00
Alex Rodriguez Jsy
17 Mark Prior Jsy 6.00 15.00
Kerry Wood Jsy
18 Rafael Palmeiro Jsy 4.00 10.00
Jay Gibbons Jsy
19 Nomar Garciaparra Jsy 6.00 15.00
Manny Ramirez Jsy
20 Ivan Rodriguez Jsy 4.00 10.00
Mike Piazza Jsy

2004 Absolute Memorabilia Team Trio

STATED PRINT RUN 100 SERIAL #'d SETS
*SPECTRUM: 1X TO 2.5X BASIC
SPECTRUM PRINT RUN 25 SERIAL #'d SETS
RANDOM INSERTS IN PACKS
1 Kerry Wood 1.50 4.00
Mark Prior
Sammy Sosa
2 Hank Blalock 2.50 6.00
Mark Teixeira
Alex Rodriguez
3 Vernon Wells 1.50 4.00
Roy Halladay
Carlos Delgado
4 Mike Mussina 1.50 4.00
Jorge Posada
Mariano Rivera
5 Shannon Stewart .60 1.50
Torii Hunter
Jacque Jones
6 Carlos Beltran .60 1.50
Mike Sweeney
Angel Berroa
7 Dontrelle Willis .60 1.50
Miguel Cabrera
Josh Beckett
8 Jeff Bagwell 1.00 2.50
Craig Biggio
Lance Berkman
9 Nomar Garciaparra 1.50 4.00
Pedro Martinez
Manny Ramirez
10 Shawn Green 1.50 4.00
Kazuhisa Ishii
Hideo Nomo
11 Mark Mulder 1.00 2.50
Barry Zito
Tim Hudson
12 Jim Edmonds 4.00 10.00
Scott Rolen
Albert Pujols
13 Cal Ripken 6.00 15.00
Jay Gibbons
Rafael Palmeiro
14 Sammy Sosa 1.00 2.50
Mark Grace
Ryne Sandberg
15 Nolan Ryan 5.00 12.00
Roger Clemens
Randy Johnson

2004 Absolute Memorabilia Team Trio Material

STATED PRINT RUN 100 SERIAL #'d SETS
CARD 15 PRINT RUN 25 SERIAL #'d CARDS
PRIME PRINT RUN 5 SERIAL #'d SETS
NO PRIME PRICING DUE TO SCARCITY
RANDOM INSERTS IN PACKS
ALL HAVE 3 JSY SWATCHES UNLESS NOTED
CARD 15 HAS FIELD GLOVE SWATCHES
1 Sammy Sosa 6.00 15.00
Mark Prior
Kerry Wood
2 Hank Blalock 6.00 15.00
Mark Teixeira
Alex Rodriguez
3 Vernon Wells 4.00 10.00
Roy Halladay

Carlos Delgado
4 Mike Mussina 12.50 30.00
Jorge Posada
Mariano Rivera
5 Shannon Stewart 4.00 10.00
Jacque Jones
Torii Hunter
6 Carlos Beltran 4.00 10.00
Mike Sweeney
Angel Berroa
7 Dontrelle Willis 6.00 15.00
Miguel Cabrera
Josh Beckett
8 Jeff Bagwell 6.00 15.00
Craig Biggio
Lance Berkman
9 Nomar Garciaparra 10.00 25.00
Pedro Martinez
Manny Ramirez
10 Shawn Green 6.00 15.00
Kazuhisa Ishii
Hideo Nomo
11 Mark Mulder 4.00 10.00
Barry Zito
Tim Hudson
12 Jim Edmonds 10.00 25.00
Scott Rolen
Albert Pujols
13 Cal Ripken 20.00 50.00
Jay Gibbons
Rafael Palmeiro
14 Sammy Sosa 15.00 40.00
Mark Grace
Ryne Sandberg
15 Roger Clemens Fld Glv 50.00 100.00
Nolan Ryan Fld Glv
Randy Johnson Fld Glv/25

2004 Absolute Memorabilia Tools of the Trade Blue

STATED PRINT RUN 250 SERIAL #'d SETS
BLACK PRINT RUN 1 SERIAL #'d SET
NO BLACK PRICING DUE TO SCARCITY
BLACK SPECTRUM PRINT RUN 1 #'d SET
NO BLACK SPEC.PRICING DUE TO SCARCITY
*BLUE SPEC: .75X TO 2X BASIC
BLUE SPECTRUM PRINT RUN 125 #'d SETS
*GREEN: .6X TO 1.5X BASIC
GREEN PRINT RUN 150 SERIAL #'d SETS
*GREEN SPEC: 1.5X TO 4X BASIC
GREEN SPECTRUM PRINT RUN 50 #'d SETS
*RED: .5X TO 1.2X BASIC
RED PRINT RUN 200 SERIAL #'d SETS
*RED SPECTRUM: 1X TO 2.5X BASIC
RED SPECTRUM PRINT RUN 100 #'d SETS
1 Adam Dunn H .75 2.00
2 Adam Dunn A .75 2.00
3 Alan Trammell .50 1.25
4 Albert Pujols H 3.00 8.00
5 Albert Pujols A 3.00 8.00
6 Alex Rodriguez M's 2.00 5.00
7 Alex Rodriguez Rgr H 2.00 5.00
8 Alex Rodriguez Rgr Alt 2.00 5.00
9 Alfonso Soriano .50 1.25
10 Andre Dawson .75 2.00
11 Andruw Jones H .50 1.25
12 Andruw Jones A .50 1.25
13 Andy Pettitte H .50 1.25
14 Andy Pettitte A .75 2.00
15 Angel Berroa .50 1.25
16 Aubrey Huff .50 1.25
17 Austin Kearns .50 1.25
18 Barry Zito Alt .50 1.25
19 Barry Zito H .50 1.25
20 Bernie Williams .75 2.00
21 Bobby Abreu .50 1.25
22 Brandon Webb .50 1.25
23 Cal Ripken H 5.00 12.00
24 Cal Ripken A 5.00 12.00
25 Cal Ripken Alt 5.00 12.00
26 Carlos Beltran .50 1.25
27 Carlos Delgado H .50 1.25
28 Carlos Delgado A .50 1.25
29 Carlos Lee .50 1.25
30 Chipper Jones H 1.25 3.00
31 Chipper Jones A 1.25 3.00
32 Craig Biggio H .75 2.00
33 Craig Biggio A .75 2.00
34 Curt Schilling D'backs .75 2.00
35 Curt Schilling Phils .75 2.00
36 Dale Murphy H .75 2.00
37 Dale Murphy A .75 2.00
38 Darryl Strawberry .50 1.25
39 Derek Jeter H 3.00 8.00
40 Derek Jeter A 3.00 8.00
41 Don Mattingly H 2.50 6.00
42 Don Mattingly A 2.50 6.00
43 Dontrelle Willis H .50 1.25
44 Dontrelle Willis A .50 1.25
45 Dwight Gooden .50 1.25
46 Edgar Martinez .75 2.00
47 Eric Chavez .50 1.25
48 Frank Thomas A 1.25 3.00
49 Frank Thomas Alt 1.25 3.00
50 Garret Anderson .50 1.25
51 Gary Carter .50 1.25
52 Gary Sheffield .50 1.25
53 George Brett H 2.50 6.00
54 George Brett A 2.50 6.00
55 Greg Maddux 2.00 5.00
56 Hank Blalock .50 1.25
57 Hideo Nomo 1.25 3.00
58 Ivan Rodriguez Marlins .75 2.00
59 Ivan Rodriguez Rgr .75 2.00
60 Jacque Jones .50 1.25
61 Jae Weong Seo .50 1.25
62 Jason Giambi Yanks .50 1.25
63 Jason Giambi A's .50 1.25
64 Javy Lopez .50 1.25
65 Jay Gibbons .50 1.25
66 Jeff Bagwell A .75 2.00
67 Jeff Bagwell Alt .75 2.00
68 Jeff Kent .50 1.25
69 Jim Edmonds .75 2.00
70 Jim Thome .75 2.00
71 Jorge Posada .75 2.00
72 Jose Canseco .75 2.00
73 Jose Reyes .75 2.00
74 Josh Beckett .75 2.00
75 Juan Gonzalez .50 1.25
76 Kazuhisa Ishii .50 1.25
77 Kerry Wood H .50 1.25
78 Kerry Wood Alt .50 1.25
79 Kirby Puckett 1.25 3.00
80 Lance Berkman .75 2.00
81 Lou Brock .75 2.00
82 Luis Castillo .50 1.25
83 Luis Gonzalez .50 1.25
84 Magglio Ordonez .75 2.00
85 Manny Ramirez Sox 1.25 3.00
86 Manny Ramirez Indians 1.25 3.00
87 Marcus Giles .50 1.25
88 Mark Grace .75 2.00
89 Mark Mulder .50 1.25
90 Mark Prior H .75 2.00
91 Mark Prior A .75 2.00
92 Mark Teixeira 1.25 3.00
93 Marlon Byrd .50 1.25
94 Miguel Cabrera 1.25 3.00
95 Miguel Tejada .75 2.00
96 Mike Lowell .50 1.25
97 Mike Mussina O's .75 2.00
98 Mike Mussina Yanks .75 2.00
99 Mike Piazza Marlins 1.25 3.00
100 Mike Piazza Dodgers 1.25 3.00
101 Mike Piazza Mets 1.25 3.00
102 Mike Schmidt H 2.00 5.00
103 Mike Schmidt A 2.00 5.00
104 Mike Sweeney .50 1.25
105 Nick Johnson .50 1.25
106 Nolan Ryan Angels 4.00 10.00
107 Nolan Ryan Astros 4.00 10.00
108 Nolan Ryan Rangers 4.00 10.00
109 Nomar Garciaparra H 1.25 3.00
110 Nomar Garciaparra A 1.25 3.00
111 Pat Burrell .50 1.25
112 Paul Lo Duca .50 1.25
113 Pedro Martinez Sox .75 2.00
114 Pedro Martinez Expos .75 2.00
115 Preston Wilson .50 1.25
116 Rafael Palmeiro O's .75 2.00
117 Rafael Palmeiro Rgr .75 2.00
118 Randy Johnson D'backs 1.25 3.00
119 Randy Johnson M's 1.25 3.00
120 Richie Sexson .50 1.25
121 Rickey Henderson A's 1.25 3.00
122 Rickey Henderson Padres 1.25 3.00
123 Rickey Henderson M's 1.25 3.00
124 Roberto Alomar .75 2.00
125 Rocco Baldelli .75 2.00
126 Rod Carew .75 2.00
127 Roger Clemens Sox 1.50 4.00
128 Roger Clemens Yanks 1.50 4.00
129 Roy Halladay .50 1.25
130 Roy Oswalt .75 2.00
131 Ryne Sandberg 2.50 6.00
132 Sammy Sosa H 1.25 3.00
133 Sammy Sosa A 1.25 3.00
134 Sammy Sosa Sox 1.25 3.00
135 Scott Rolen .75 2.00
136 Shawn Green .50 1.25
137 Steve Carlton .50 1.25
138 Tim Hudson .75 2.00
139 Todd Helton H .75 2.00
140 Todd Helton A .75 2.00
141 Tom Glavine Braves .75 2.00
142 Tom Glavine Mets .75 2.00
143 Tony Gwynn A 1.25 3.00
144 Tony Gwynn Alt 1.25 3.00
145 Torii Hunter .50 1.25
146 Trot Nixon .50 1.25
147 Troy Glaus .50 1.25
148 Vernon Wells .50 1.25
149 Vladimir Guerrero 1.25 3.00
150 Will Clark .75 2.00

2004 Absolute Memorabilia Tools of the Trade Signature Blue Spectrum

PRINT RUNS B/WN 1-100 COPIES PER
NO PRICING ON QTY OF 10 OR LESS
BLACK PRINT RUN 1 SERIAL #'d SET
NO BLACK PRICING DUE TO SCARCITY
GREEN PRINT RUN B/WN 1-10 COPIES PER
NO GREEN PRICING DUE TO SCARCITY
*RED p/r 50: .5X TO 1.2X BLUE p/r 100
*RED p/r 25: .6X TO 1.5X BLUE p/r 100
*RED p/r 23-25: .5X TO 1.2X BLUE p/r 50
*RED p/r 25: .4X TO 1X BLUE p/r 25
RED PRINT RUNS B/WN 1-50 COPIES PER
NO RED PRICING ON QTY OF 11 OR LESS
1 Adam Dunn H/10
2 Adam Dunn A/10
3 Alan Trammell/100 6.00 15.00
4 Albert Pujols H/1
5 Albert Pujols A/1
10 Andre Dawson/100 6.00 15.00
11 Andruw Jones H/1
12 Andruw Jones A/1
13 Andy Pettitte H/1
14 Andy Pettitte A/1
15 Angel Berroa/100 4.00 10.00
16 Aubrey Huff/100 6.00 15.00
17 Austin Kearns/100 4.00 10.00
18 Barry Zito Alt/1
19 Barry Zito A/1
20 Bernie Williams/1
22 Brandon Webb/100 4.00 10.00
23 Cal Ripken H/8
24 Cal Ripken A/8
25 Cal Ripken Alt/8
26 Carlos Beltran/100 6.00 15.00
29 Carlos Lee/100 6.00 15.00
30 Chipper Jones H/10
31 Chipper Jones A/10
32 Craig Biggio H/1
33 Craig Biggio A/1
34 Curt Schilling D'backs/1
35 Curt Schilling Phils/1
36 Dale Murphy H/50 15.00 40.00
37 Dale Murphy A/50 15.00 40.00
38 Darryl Strawberry/50 10.00 25.00
41 Don Mattingly H/50 40.00 80.00
42 Don Mattingly A/50 40.00 80.00
43 Dontrelle Willis H/25 20.00 50.00
44 Dontrelle Willis A/25 20.00 50.00
45 Dwight Gooden/50 10.00 25.00
46 Edgar Martinez/25 20.00 50.00
47 Eric Chavez/1
48 Frank Thomas A/25 30.00 60.00
49 Frank Thomas Alt/25 30.00 60.00
50 Garret Anderson/100 6.00 15.00
51 Gary Carter/100 6.00 15.00
52 Gary Sheffield/10
53 George Brett H/5
54 George Brett A/5
56 Hank Blalock/10
57 Hideo Nomo/1
60 Jacque Jones/50 10.00 25.00
61 Jae Weong Seo/25 12.50 30.00
65 Jay Gibbons/50 6.00 15.00
66 Jeff Bagwell A/5
67 Jeff Bagwell Alt/5
69 Jim Edmonds/25 20.00 50.00
71 Jorge Posada/25 20.00 50.00
73 Jose Reyes/25 12.50 30.00
74 Josh Beckett/5
75 Juan Gonzalez/20 12.50 30.00
76 Kazuhisa Ishii/5
77 Kerry Wood H/25 20.00 50.00
78 Kerry Wood Alt/25 20.00 50.00
79 Kirby Puckett/10
80 Lance Berkman/10
81 Lou Brock/100 10.00 25.00
82 Luis Castillo/10
84 Magglio Ordonez/50 10.00 25.00
85 Manny Ramirez Sox/1
86 Manny Ramirez Indians/1
87 Marcus Giles/50 10.00 25.00
88 Mark Grace/25 20.00 50.00
89 Mark Mulder/100 6.00 15.00
90 Mark Prior H/50 12.50 30.00
91 Mark Prior A/50 12.50 30.00
92 Mark Teixeira/50 15.00 40.00
93 Marlon Byrd/50 6.00 15.00
94 Miguel Cabrera/100 10.00 25.00
96 Mike Lowell/1
99 Mike Piazza Marlins/5
100 Mike Piazza Dodgers/5
101 Mike Piazza Mets/5
102 Mike Schmidt H/25 50.00 100.00
103 Mike Schmidt A/25 30.00 60.00
105 Nick Johnson/1
106 Nolan Ryan Angels/25 75.00 150.00
107 Nolan Ryan Astros/25 75.00 150.00
108 Nolan Ryan Rangers/25 75.00 150.00
112 Paul Lo Duca/50 10.00 25.00
115 Preston Wilson/100 6.00 15.00
116 Rafael Palmeiro O's/1
117 Rafael Palmeiro Rgr/1
118 Randy Johnson D'backs/1
119 Randy Johnson M's/1
121 Rickey Henderson A's/10
122 Rickey Henderson Padres/5
123 Rickey Henderson M's/5
124 Roberto Alomar/10
125 Rocco Baldelli/10
126 Rod Carew/10
129 Roy Halladay/25 12.50 30.00
130 Roy Oswalt/25 12.50 30.00
131 Ryne Sandberg/5
132 Sammy Sosa H/5
133 Sammy Sosa A/5
134 Sammy Sosa Sox/5
135 Scott Rolen/50 15.00 40.00
136 Shawn Green/1
137 Steve Carlton/50 10.00 25.00
138 Tim Hudson/10
139 Todd Helton H/1
140 Todd Helton A/1
141 Tom Glavine Braves/10
142 Tom Glavine Mets/10
143 Tony Gwynn A/25 40.00 80.00
144 Tony Gwynn Alt/25 40.00 80.00
145 Torii Hunter/50 10.00 25.00
146 Trot Nixon/25 12.50 30.00
147 Troy Glaus/1
148 Vernon Wells/10
149 Vladimir Guerrero/25 30.00 60.00
150 Will Clark/50 15.00 40.00

2004 Absolute Memorabilia Tools of the Trade Material Combo

PRINT RUNS B/WN 25-250 COPIES PER
SINGLE PRINT RUNS B/WN 1-5 COPIES PER
NO SINGLE PRICING DUE TO SCARCITY
SINGLE PS PRINT RUN 1 SERIAL #'d SET
NO SINGLE PS PRICING DUE TO SCARCITY
*COMBO PS p/r 25: 1.5X TO 4X COM.p/r 250
*COMBO PS p/r 25: 1X TO 2.5X COM.p/r 100
COMBO PS PRINT RUNS B/WN 1-25 PER
NO COMBO PS PRICING ON 10 OR LESS
*TRIO p/r 100: .6X TO 1.5X COMBO p/r 250
*TRIO p/r 100: .4X TO 1X COMBO p/r 100
*TRIO p/r 50: 1X TO 2.5X COMBO p/r 250
*TRIO p/r 50: .6X TO 1.5X COMBO p/r 100
*TRIO p/r 25: 1.5X TO 4X COMBO p/r 250
*TRIO p/r 25: .75X TO 2X COMBO p/r 100
TRIO PRINT RUNS B/WN 5-100 COPIES PER
NO TRIO PRICING ON QTY OF 10 OR LESS
TRIO PS PRINT RUNS B/WN 1-10 PER
NO TRIO PS PRICING DUE TO SCARCITY
*QUAD p/r 50: 1.5X TO 4X COMBO p/r 250
*QUAD p/r 50: 1.25X TO 3X COMBO p/r 100
*QUAD p/r 50: .6X TO 1.5X COMBO p/r 25
*QUAD p/r 25: 2X TO 5X COMBO p/r 250
*QUAD p/r 25: 1X TO 2.5X COMBO p/r 100
QUAD PRINT RUNS B/WN 1-50 COPIES PER
NO QUAD PRICING ON QTY OF 10 OR LESS
QUAD PS PRINT RUNS B/WN 1-10 PER
NO QUAD PS PRICING DUE TO SCARCITY
*FIVE p/r 25: 2.5X TO 6X COMBO p/r 250
*FIVE p/r 25: 2X TO 5X COMBO p/r 100
*FIVE p/r 25: .75X TO 2X COMBO p/r 25
FIVE PRINT RUNS B/WN 10-25 COPIES PER
NO FIVE PRICING ON QTY OF 10 OR LESS
FIVE PS PRINT RUNS B/WN 1-5 COPIES PER
NO FIVE PS PRICING DUE TO SCARCITY
*SIX p/r 25: 3X TO 8X COMBO p/r 250
*SIX p/r 25: 2.5X TO 6X COMBO p/r 100
SIX PRINT RUNS B/WN 5-25 COPIES PER
NO SIX PRICING ON QTY OF 5 OR LESS
SIX PS PRINT RUNS B/WN 1-5 COPIES PER
NO SIX PS PRICING DUE TO SCARCITY
1 A.Dunn H Bat-Jsy/250 2.50 6.00
2 A.Dunn A Bat-Jsy/250 2.50 6.00
3 A.Trammell Bat-Jsy/250 2.50 6.00
4 A.Pujols H Bat-Jsy/250 8.00 20.00
5 A.Pujols A Bat-Jsy/250 8.00 20.00
6 A.Rod M's Bat-Jsy/250 4.00 10.00
7 A.Rod Rgr H Bat-Jsy/250 4.00 10.00
8 A.Rod Rgr Alt Bat-Jsy/250 4.00 10.00
9 A.Soriano Bat-Jsy/100 3.00 8.00
10 A.Dawson Bat-Jsy/250 2.50 6.00
11 A.Jones H Bat-Jsy/100 4.00 10.00
12 A.Jones A Bat-Jsy/250 3.00 8.00
13 A.Pettitte H Bat-Jsy/100 4.00 10.00
14 A.Pettitte A Bat-Jsy/100 4.00 10.00
15 A.Berroa Bat-Jsy/250 2.00 5.00
16 A.Huff Bat-Jsy/250 2.00 5.00
17 A.Kearns Bat-Jsy/250 2.00 5.00
18 B.Zito Alt Bat-Jsy/250 2.50 6.00
19 B.Zito A Bat-Jsy/250 2.50 6.00
20 B.Williams Bat-Jsy/250 3.00 8.00
21 B.Abreu Bat-Jsy/250 2.50 6.00
22 B.Webb Bat-Jsy/250 2.00 5.00
23 C.Ripken H Bat-Jsy/250 12.50 30.00
24 C.Ripken A Bat-Jsy/250 12.50 30.00
25 C.Ripken Alt Bat-Jsy/250 12.50 30.00
26 C.Beltran Bat-Jsy/250 2.50 6.00
27 C.Delgado H Bat-Jsy/250 2.50 6.00
28 C.Delgado A Bat-Jsy/250 2.50 6.00
29 C.Lee Bat-Jsy/250 2.50 6.00
30 C.Jones H Bat-Jsy/250 4.00 10.00
31 C.Jones A Bat-Jsy/250 4.00 10.00
32 C.Biggio H Bat-Jsy/250 2.50 6.00
33 C.Biggio A Bat-Jsy/100 3.00 8.00
34 C.Schill D'backs Bat-Jsy/250 2.50 6.00
35 C.Schill Phils Bat-Jsy/250 2.50 6.00
36 D.Murphy H Bat-Jsy/250 3.00 8.00
37 D.Murphy A Bat-Jsy/100 4.00 10.00
38 D.Strawberry Bat-Jsy/250 2.50 6.00
39 D.Jeter H Bat-Jsy/100 15.00 40.00
40 D.Jeter A Bat-Jsy/100 15.00 40.00
41 D.Mattingly H Bat-Jsy/100 10.00 25.00
42 D.Mattingly A Bat-Jsy/100 10.00 25.00
43 D.Willis H Bat-Jsy/250 3.00 8.00
44 D.Willis A Bat-Jsy/250 3.00 8.00
45 D.Gooden Bat-Jsy/250 2.50 6.00
46 E.Martinez Bat-Jsy/250 3.00 8.00
47 E.Chavez Bat-Jsy/250 2.50 6.00
48 F.Thomas A Bat-Jsy/250 4.00 10.00
49 F.Thomas Alt Bat-Jsy/250 4.00 10.00
50 G.Anderson Bat-Jsy/250 2.50 6.00
51 G.Carter Bat-Jsy/250 2.50 6.00
52 G.Sheffield Bat-Jsy/250 2.50 6.00
53 G.Brett H Bat-Jsy/250 8.00 20.00
54 G.Brett A Bat-Jsy/250 8.00 20.00
55 G.Maddux Bat-Jsy/250 5.00 12.00
56 H.Blalock Bat-Jsy/250 2.50 6.00
57 H.Nomo Bat-Jsy/250 5.00 12.00
58 I.Rod Marlins Bat-Jsy/250 3.00 8.00
59 I.Rod Rgr Bat-Jsy/250 3.00 8.00
60 J.Jones Bat-Jsy/250 2.50 6.00
62 J.Giambi Yanks Bat-Jsy/250 2.50 6.00
63 J.Giambi A's Bat-Jsy/250 2.50 6.00
64 J.Lopez Bat-Jsy/250 2.50 6.00
65 J.Gibbons Bat-Jsy/250 2.00 5.00
66 J.Bagwell A Bat-Jsy/250 3.00 8.00
67 J.Bagwell Alt Bat-Jsy/250 3.00 8.00
68 J.Kent Bat-Jsy/250 2.50 6.00
69 J.Edmonds Bat-Jsy/250 2.50 6.00
70 J.Thome Bat-Jsy/250 3.00 8.00
71 J.Posada Bat-Jsy/250 3.00 8.00
72 J.Canseco Bat-Jsy/250 3.00 8.00
73 J.Reyes Bat-Jsy/250 2.50 6.00
74 J.Beckett Bat-Jsy/250 2.50 6.00
75 J.Gonzalez Bat-Jsy/250 2.50 6.00
76 K.Ishii Bat-Jsy/250 2.50 6.00
77 K.Wood H Bat-Jsy/250 2.50 6.00
78 K.Wood Alt Bat-Jsy/250 2.50 6.00
79 K.Puckett Bat-Jsy/250 6.00 15.00
80 L.Berkman Bat-Jsy/250 2.50 6.00
81 L.Brock Bat-Jsy/250 3.00 8.00
82 L.Castillo Bat-Jsy/250 2.00 5.00
83 L.Gonzalez Bat-Jsy/250 2.50 6.00
84 M.Ordonez Bat-Jsy/250 2.50 6.00
85 M.Ramirez Sox Bat-Jsy/250 3.00 8.00
86 M.Ram Indians Bat-Jsy/250 3.00 8.00
87 M.Giles Bat-Jsy/25 6.00 15.00
88 M.Grace Bat-Jsy/250 3.00 8.00
89 M.Mulder Bat-Jsy/250 2.50 6.00
90 M.Prior H Bat-Jsy/250 2.50 6.00
91 M.Prior A Bat-Jsy/250 3.00 8.00
92 M.Teixeira Bat-Jsy/250 3.00 8.00
93 M.Byrd Bat-Jsy/250 2.00 5.00
94 M.Cabrera Bat-Jsy/250 3.00 8.00
95 M.Tejada Bat-Jsy/250 2.50 6.00
96 M.Lowell Bat-Jsy/250 2.50 6.00
97 M.Muss O's Jsy-Pants/250 3.00 8.00
98 M.Muss Yanks Jsy-Jsy/250 3.00 8.00
99 M.Piazza Marlins Bat-Jsy/250 5.00 12.00
100 M.Piaz Dodgers Bat-Jsy/250 5.00 12.00
101 M.Piazza Mets Bat-Jsy/250 5.00 12.00
102 M.Schmidt H Bat-Jsy/100 10.00 25.00
103 M.Schmidt A Bat-Jsy/100 10.00 25.00
104 M.Sweeney Bat-Jsy/250 2.50 6.00
105 N.Johnson Bat-Jsy/250 2.50 6.00
106 N.Ryan Angels Jkt-Jsy/250 10.00 25.00
107 N.Ryan Astros Jkt-Jsy/250 10.00 25.00
108 N.Ryan Rgr Jsy-Pants/250 10.00 25.00
109 N.Garciaparra H Bat-Jsy/250 5.00 12.00
110 N.Garciaparra A Bat-Jsy/250 5.00 12.00
111 P.Burrell Bat-Jsy/250 2.50 6.00
112 P.Lo Duca Bat-Jsy/250 2.50 6.00
113 P.Martinez Sox Bat-Jsy/250 3.00 8.00
114 P.Mart Expos Bat-Jsy/250 3.00 8.00
115 P.Wilson Bat-Jsy/250 2.50 6.00
116 R.Palmeiro O's Bat-Jsy/250 3.00 8.00
117 R.Palmeiro Rgr Bat-Jsy/250 3.00 8.00
118 R.John D'backs Bat-Jsy/250 4.00 10.00
119 R.Johnson M's Bat-Jsy/250 4.00 10.00
120 R.Sexson Bat-Jsy/250 2.50 6.00
121 R.Hend A's Bat-Jsy/250 4.00 10.00
122 R.Hend Padres Bat-Jsy/250 4.00 10.00
123 R.Hend M's Bat-Jsy/250 4.00 10.00
124 R.Alomar Bat-Jsy/250 3.00 8.00
125 R.Baldelli Bat-Jsy/250 2.50 6.00
126 R.Carew Bat-Jsy/250 3.00 8.00
127 R.Clemens Sox Bat-Jsy/250 6.00 15.00
128 R.Clem Yanks Bat-Jsy/250 6.00 15.00
129 R.Halladay Jsy-Jsy/250 2.50 6.00
130 R.Oswalt Bat-Jsy/250 2.50 6.00
131 R.Sandberg Bat-Jsy/250 6.00 15.00
132 S.Sosa H Bat-Jsy/250 4.00 10.00
133 S.Sosa A Bat-Jsy/250 4.00 10.00
134 S.Sosa Sox Bat-Jsy/250 4.00 10.00
135 S.Rolen Bat-Jsy/250 3.00 8.00
136 S.Green Bat-Jsy/250 2.50 6.00
137 S.Carlton Bat-Jsy/250 2.50 6.00
138 T.Hudson Bat-Jsy/250 2.50 6.00
139 T.Helton H Bat-Jsy/250 3.00 8.00
140 T.Helton A Bat-Jsy/250 3.00 8.00
141 T.Glav Braves Bat-Jsy/250 3.00 8.00
142 T.Glav Mets Bat-Jsy/250 3.00 8.00
143 T.Gwynn A Bat-Jsy/250 6.00 15.00
144 T.Gwynn Alt Bat-Jsy/250 6.00 15.00
145 T.Hunter Bat-Jsy/250 2.50 6.00
146 T.Nixon Bat-Jsy/250 2.50 6.00
147 T.Glaus Bat-Jsy/250 2.50 6.00
148 V.Wells Bat-Jsy/250 2.50 6.00
149 V.Guerrero Bat-Jsy/250 4.00 10.00
150 W.Clark Bat-Jsy/250 3.00 8.00

2004 Absolute Memorabilia Tools of the Trade Material Signature Single

PRINT RUNS B/WN 1-50 COPIES PER
NO PRICING ON QTY OF 11 OR LESS
SINGLE PS PRINT RUNS B/WN 1-5 PER
NO SINGLE PS PRICING DUE TO SCARCITY
*COMBO p/r 25: .5X TO 1.2X SINGLE p/r 50
COMBO PRINT RUNS B/WN 1-25 PER
NO COMBO PRICES ON QTY OF 10 OR LESS
COMBO PS PRINT RUNS B/WN 1-5 PER
NO COMBO PS PRICING DUE TO SCARCITY
TRIO PRINT RUNS B/WN 1-10 COPIES PER
NO TRIO PRICING DUE TO SCARCITY
TRIO PS PRINT RUNS B/WN 1-5 PER
NO TRIO PS PRICING DUE TO SCARCITY
QUAD PRINT RUNS B/WN 1-10 COPIES PER
NO QUAD PRICING DUE TO SCARCITY
QUAD PS PRINT RUNS B/WN 1-5 PER
NO QUAD PS PRICING DUE TO SCARCITY
1 Adam Dunn H Jsy/25 20.00 50.00
2 Adam Dunn A Jsy/25 20.00 50.00
3 Alan Trammell Jsy/25 20.00 50.00
4 Albert Pujols H Jsy/5
5 Albert Pujols A Jsy/5
6 Alex Rodriguez M's Jsy/5
7 Alex Rodriguez Rgr H Jsy/5
8 Alex Rodriguez Rgr Alt Jsy/5
10 Andre Dawson Jsy/25 12.50 30.00
11 Andruw Jones H Jsy/5
12 Andruw Jones A Jsy/5
15 Angel Berroa Jsy/50 6.00 15.00
16 Aubrey Huff Jsy/1
17 Austin Kearns Jsy/28 10.00 25.00
18 Barry Zito Alt Jsy/1
19 Barry Zito A Jsy/1
20 Bernie Williams Jsy/5
21 Bobby Abreu Jsy/25 12.50 30.00
22 Brandon Webb Jsy/25 10.00 25.00
23 Cal Ripken H Jsy/8
24 Cal Ripken A Pants/8
25 Cal Ripken Alt Jsy/8
26 Carlos Beltran Jsy/15 15.00 40.00
29 Carlos Lee Jsy/25 12.50 30.00
30 Chipper Jones H Jsy/10
31 Chipper Jones A Jsy/10
32 Craig Biggio A Jsy/7
33 Craig Biggio A Jsy/7
34 Curt Schilling D'backs Jsy/1
35 Curt Schilling Phils Jsy/1
36 Dale Murphy H Jsy/25 20.00 50.00
37 Dale Murphy A Jsy/25 20.00 50.00
38 Darryl Strawberry Jsy/39 10.00 25.00
41 Don Mattingly H Jsy/5
42 Don Mattingly A Jsy/5
43 Dontrelle Willis H Jsy/25 20.00 50.00
44 Dontrelle Willis A Jsy/25 20.00 50.00
45 Dwight Gooden Jsy/16 15.00 40.00
46 Edgar Martinez Jsy/11
47 Eric Chavez Jsy/3
48 Frank Thomas A Jsy/5
49 Frank Thomas Alt Jsy/5
50 Garret Anderson Jsy/16 15.00 40.00
51 Gary Carter Jsy/8
52 Gary Sheffield Jsy/11
53 George Brett H Jsy/5
54 George Brett A Jsy/5
55 Greg Maddux Jsy/1
56 Hank Blalock Jsy/9
57 Hideo Nomo Jsy/1
60 Jacque Jones Jsy/1
61 Jae Weong Seo Jsy/25 10.00 25.00
65 Jay Gibbons Jsy/5
66 Jeff Bagwell A Jsy/5
67 Jeff Bagwell Alt Jsy/5
69 Jim Edmonds Jsy/5
71 Jorge Posada Jsy/20 20.00 50.00
72 Jose Canseco Jsy/5
74 Josh Beckett Jsy/21 20.00 50.00
75 Juan Gonzalez Jsy/5
76 Kazuhisa Ishii Jsy/5
79 Kirby Puckett Jsy/5
80 Lance Berkman Jsy/5
81 Lou Brock Jsy/5
82 Luis Castillo Jsy/25 10.00 25.00
84 Magglio Ordonez Jsy/5
85 Manny Ramirez Sox Jsy/5
86 Manny Ramirez Indians Jsy/5
88 Mark Grace Jsy/5
89 Mark Mulder Jsy/20 12.50 30.00
90 Mark Prior H Jsy/10
91 Mark Prior A Jsy/10
92 Mark Teixeira Jsy/10
93 Marlon Byrd Jsy/29 10.00 25.00
94 Miguel Cabrera Jsy/20 20.00 50.00
96 Mike Lowell Jsy/19 15.00 40.00
97 Mike Mussina O's Jsy/5
98 Mike Mussina Yanks Jsy/5
99 Mike Piazza Marlins Jsy/1
100 Mike Piazza Dodgers Jsy/1
101 Mike Piazza Mets Jsy/1
106 Nolan Ryan Angels Jsy/5
107 Nolan Ryan Astros Jsy/5
108 Nolan Ryan Rgr Jsy/5
112 Paul Lo Duca Jsy/50 10.00 25.00
113 Pedro Martinez Sox Jsy/1
114 Pedro Martinez Expos Jsy/1
115 Preston Wilson Jsy/44 10.00 25.00
116 Rafael Palmeiro O's Jsy/5
117 Rafael Palmeiro Rgr Jsy/5
118 Randy Johnson D'backs Jsy/1
119 Randy Johnson M's Jsy/1
120 Richie Sexson Jsy/11
125 Rocco Baldelli Jsy/25 12.50 30.00
126 Rod Carew Jsy/10
129 Roy Halladay Jsy/32 20.00 50.00
130 Roy Oswalt Jsy/10
131 Ryne Sandberg Jsy/5
132 Sammy Sosa H Jsy/1
133 Sammy Sosa A Jsy/1
134 Sammy Sosa Sox Jsy/1
137 Steve Carlton Jsy/25 12.50 30.00
138 Tim Hudson Jsy/5
139 Todd Helton H Jsy/5
140 Todd Helton A Jsy/5
141 Tom Glavine Braves Jsy/5
142 Tom Glavine Mets Jsy/5
143 Tony Gwynn A Jsy/10
144 Tony Gwynn Alt Jsy/10
145 Torii Hunter Jsy/25 12.50 30.00
146 Trot Nixon Jsy/25 12.50 30.00
147 Troy Glaus Jsy/5
148 Vernon Wells Jsy/10
149 Vladimir Guerrero Jsy/5
150 Will Clark Jsy/10

2005 Absolute Memorabilia

This 100-card set was released in June, 2005. The set was issued in four-pack boxes which came 18 to a case. Cards numbered 1 through 95 feature active veterans while cards numbered 96 through 100 feature Rookie Cards. An 100-card update set was released in December, 2005. That update set was the final product released by Donruss/Leaf/Playoff to fulfill their contract with MLB and MLBPA which began in 2001.

COMMON CARD (1-200) .25 .60
1 Andruw Jones .25 .60
2 B.J. Upton .40 1.00
3 Jim Edmonds .40 1.00
4 Johan Santana .60 1.50
5 Jeff Bagwell .40 1.00
6 Derek Jeter 1.50 4.00
7 Eric Chavez .25 .60
8 Albert Pujols 1.50 4.00
9 Craig Biggio .40 1.00
10 Hank Blalock .25 .60
11 Chipper Jones .60 1.50
12 Jacque Jones .25 .60
13 Alfonso Soriano .40 1.00
14 Carl Crawford .40 1.00
15 Ben Sheets .25 .60
16 Garret Anderson .25 .60
17 Luis Gonzalez .25 .60
18 Andy Pettitte .40 1.00
19 Miguel Tejada .40 1.00
20 Carlos Delgado .25 .60
21 Austin Kearns .25 .60
22 Adrian Beltre .25 .60
23 Rafael Palmeiro .40 1.00
24 Greg Maddux 1.00 2.50
25 Jason Bay .25 .60
26 Jason Varitek .60 1.50
27 David Ortiz .60 1.50
28 Dontrelle Willis .25 .60
29 Adam Dunn .40 1.00
30 Carlos Lee .25 .60
31 Manny Ramirez .60 1.50
32 Rocco Baldelli .25 .60
33 Jeff Kent .25 .60
34 Jake Peavy .25 .60
35 Vernon Wells .25 .60
36 Ichiro Suzuki 1.00 2.50
37 C.C. Sabathia .40 1.00
38 Hideki Matsui 1.00 2.50
39 Gary Sheffield .25 .60
40 Paul Lo Duca .25 .60
41 Vladimir Guerrero .60 1.50
42 Omar Vizquel .40 1.00
43 Lance Berkman .40 1.00
44 Shawn Green .25 .60
45 Josh Beckett .40 1.00
46 Barry Zito .25 .60
47 Roger Clemens .75 2.00
48 Sean Casey .25 .60
49 Edgar Renteria .25 .60
50 Mark Teixeira .60 1.50
51 Frank Thomas .60 1.50
52 Khalil Greene .25 .60
53 Bobby Abreu .25 .60
54 Rafael Furcal .25 .60
55 Jose Vidro .25 .60
56 Nomar Garciaparra .60 1.50
57 Melvin Mora .25 .60
58 Trot Nixon .25 .60
59 Magglio Ordonez .40 1.00
60 Michael Young .40 1.00
61 Richie Sexson .25 .60
62 Alex Rodriguez 1.00 2.50
63 Tim Hudson .40 1.00
64 Todd Helton .40 1.00
65 Mike Lowell .25 .60
66 Mark Mulder .25 .60
67 Sammy Sosa .60 1.50
68 Mark Prior .40 1.00
69 Shannon Stewart .25 .60
70 Miguel Cabrera .60 1.50
71 Troy Glaus .25 .60
72 Scott Rolen .40 1.00
73 Ken Griffey Jr. 1.00 2.50
74 Mike Piazza .60 1.50
75 Roy Halladay .60 1.50
76 Larry Walker .40 1.00
77 Kerry Wood .25 .60
78 Mike Mussina .40 1.00
79 Curt Schilling .40 1.00
80 Rich Harden .25 .60
81 Victor Martinez .40 1.00
82 Roy Oswalt .40 1.00
83 Pedro Martinez .40 1.00
84 Tom Glavine .40 1.00
85 Randy Johnson .60 1.50
86 Ivan Rodriguez .40 1.00
87 Carlos Beltran .25 .60
88 Torii Hunter .25 .60
89 Hideo Nomo .60 1.50
90 Jim Thome .40 1.00
91 Aramis Ramirez .25 .60
92 J.D. Drew .25 .60
93 Javy Lopez .25 .60
94 David Wright 1.00 2.50
95 Bobby Crosby .25 .60
96 Jeff Niemann RC .60 1.50
97 Yuniesky Betancourt RC 1.00 2.50
98 Tadahito Iguchi RC .40 1.00
99 Phil Humber RC .60 1.50
100 Justin Verlander RC 5.00 12.00
101 Al Kaline .60 1.50
102 Albert Pujols 1.50 4.00
103 Alex Rodriguez 1.00 2.50
104 Andrew Jones .25 .60
105 Aubrey Huff .25 .60
106 Barry Zito .25 .60
107 Ben Sheets .25 .60
108 Chipper Jones .60 1.50
109 Curt Schilling .25 .60
110 Dale Murphy .25 .60
111 David Dellucci .25 .60
112 David Ortiz .60 1.50
113 Dennis Eckersley .25 .60
114 Derek Jeter 1.50 4.00
115 Don Mattingly 1.25 3.00
116 Don Sutton .25 .60
117 Dontrelle Willis .25 .60
118 Duke Snider .40 1.00
119 Edgar Renteria .25 .60
120 Fergie Jenkins .25 .60
121 Frank Robinson .40 1.00
122 Frank Thomas .60 1.50
123 Garret Anderson .25 .60
124 Gary Sheffield .25 .60
125 Greg Maddux 1.00 2.50
126 Hideki Matsui 1.00 2.50
127 Hideo Nomo .60 1.50
128 Ichiro Suzuki 1.00 2.50
129 Jamie Moyer .25 .60
130 Jason Varitek .25 .60
131 Jeff Bagwell .40 1.00
132 Stephen Drew RC 1.25 3.00
133 Jeff Niemann .60 1.50
134 Jeremy Bonderman .25 .60
135 Jim Bunning .25 .60
136 Jim Leyritz .25 .60
137 Jim Thome .40 1.00
138 Johan Santana .60 1.50
139 John Kruk .25 .60
140 Johnny Podres .25 .60
141 Jose Guillen .25 .60
142 Justin Verlander 5.00 12.00
143 Keiichi Yabu RC .25 .60
144 Keith Foulke .25 .60
145 Keith Hernandez .25 .60
146 Ken Griffey Jr. 1.00 2.50
147 Kent Hrbek .25 .60
148 Anthony Lerew .25 .60
149 Larry Walker .40 1.00
150 Lew Ford .25 .60
151 Lou Brock .40 1.00
152 Luis Aparicio .25 .60
153 Luis Tiant .25 .60
154 Manny Ramirez .60 1.50
155 Mark Mulder .25 .60
156 Mark Prior .40 1.00
157 Mark Teixeira .60 1.50
158 Marty Marion .25 .60
159 Miguel Cabrera .60 1.50
160 Miguel Tejada .40 1.00
161 Mike Lieberthal .25 .60
162 Mike Piazza .60 1.50
163 Minnie Minoso .25 .60
164 Monte Irvin .25 .60
165 Morgan Ensberg .25 .60
166 Nolan Ryan 1.50 4.00
167 Octavio Dotel .25 .60
168 Omar Vizquel .40 1.00
169 Ozzie Smith 1.00 2.50
170 Pedro Martinez .40 1.00
171 Phil Humber .25 .60
172 Phil Rizzuto .40 1.00
173 Prince Fielder RC 1.25 3.00
174 Ralph Kiner .25 .60
175 Randy Johnson .60 1.50
176 Red Schoendienst .25 .60
177 Rich Gossage .25 .60
178 Rick Dempsey .25 .60
179 Rickie Weeks .40 1.00
180 Robin Roberts .25 .60
181 Rod Carew .40 1.00
182 Roger Clemens .75 2.00
183 Rollie Fingers .25 .60
184 Ron Guidry .25 .60

185 Ron Santo .40 1.00
186 Russ Ortiz .25 .60
187 Ryne Sandberg 1.25 3.00
188 Sammy Sosa .60 1.50
189 Scott Rolen .40 1.00
190 Stan Musial 1.00 2.50
191 Steve Carlton .25 .60
192 Steve Garvey .25 .60
193 Steve Stone .25 .60
194 Tim Salmon .25 .60
195 Todd Helton .40 1.00
196 Todd Walker .25 .60
197 Tom Gordon .25 .60
198 Trot Nixon .25 .60
199 Troy Percival .25 .60
200 Vladimir Guerrero .60 1.50

2005 Absolute Memorabilia Retail

*RETAIL: .12X TO .3X BASIC
ISSUED ONLY IN RETAIL PACKS
RETAIL CARDS LACK FOIL FRONTS

2005 Absolute Memorabilia Black

*BLACK 1-95: X TO X BASIC
*BLACK 96-100: X TO X BASIC
STATED ODDS 1:18 RETAIL

2005 Absolute Memorabilia Blue

*BLUE 1-95: X TO X BASIC
*BLUE 96-100: X TO X BASIC
STATED ODDS 1:3 RETAIL

2005 Absolute Memorabilia Red

*RED 1-95: X TO X BASIC
*RED 96-100: X TO X BASIC
STATED ODDS 1:8 RETAIL

2005 Absolute Memorabilia Spectrum Gold

*GOLD p/r 50: 1.25X TO 3X BASIC
*GOLD p/r 50: 1.25X TO 3X BASIC RC
*GOLD p/r 25: 1.5X TO 4X BASIC
RANDOM INSERTS IN PACKS
PRINT RUNS B/WN 10-50 COPIES PER
NO PRICING ON QTY OF 10
NO RC YR PRICING ON QTY OF 25

2005 Absolute Memorabilia Spectrum Platinum

RANDOM INSERTS IN PACKS
STATED PRINT RUN 1 SERIAL #'d SET
NO PRICING DUE TO SCARCITY

2005 Absolute Memorabilia Spectrum Silver

*SILVER p/r 100-150: 1X TO 2.5X BASIC
*SILVER p/r 100-150 : 1X TO 2.5X BASIC RC
RANDOM INSERTS IN PACKS
1-100 PRINT RUN 100 SERIAL #'d SETS
101-200 PRINT RUN 150 SERIAL #'d SETS

2005 Absolute Memorabilia Autograph Spectrum Gold

*GOLD p/r 41-50: .5X TO 1.2X SILV p/r 74-150
*GOLD p/r 41-50: .4X TO 1X SILV p/r 40-64
*GOLD p/r 21-34: .6X TO 1.5X SILV p/r 74-150
*GOLD p/r 21-34: .5X TO 1.2X SILV p/r 40-64
*GOLD p/r 21-34: .4X TO 1X SILV p/r 22-34
OVERALL AU-GU ODDS ONE PER PACK
PRINT RUNS B/WN 1-50 COPIES PER
NO PRICING ON QTY OF 14 OR LESS
120 Fergie Jenkins/50 8.00 20.00
122 Frank Thomas/25 20.00 50.00
131 Jeff Bagwell/27 20.00 50.00

2005 Absolute Memorabilia Autograph Spectrum Platinum

OVERALL AU-GU ODDS ONE PER PACK
STATED PRINT RUN 1 SERIAL #'d SET
NO PRICING DUE TO SCARCITY

2005 Absolute Memorabilia Autograph Spectrum Silver

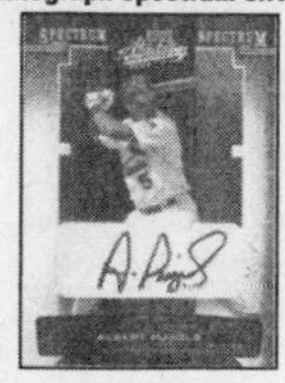

OVERALL AU-GU ODDS ONE PER PACK
PRINT RUNS B/WN 1-150 COPIES PER
NO PRICING ON QTY OF 13 OR LESS
101 Al Kaline/150 12.50 30.00
102 Albert Pujols/9
104 Andruw Jones/4
106 Barry Zito/74 6.00 15.00
107 Ben Sheets/93 6.00 15.00
109 Curt Schilling/5
110 Dale Murphy/10
111 David Dellucci/150 6.00 15.00
113 Dennis Eckersley/100 6.00 15.00
115 Don Mattingly/22 40.00 80.00
116 Don Sutton/137 6.00 15.00
117 Dontrelle Willis/4
118 Duke Snider/50 12.50 30.00
119 Edgar Renteria/148 6.00 15.00
120 Fergie Jenkins/10
121 Frank Robinson/150 10.00 25.00
122 Frank Thomas/13
123 Garret Anderson/64 8.00 20.00
124 Gary Sheffield/100 10.00 25.00
125 Greg Maddux/50 50.00 100.00
127 Hideo Nomo/5
129 Jamie Moyer/150 6.00 15.00
131 Jeff Bagwell/1
133 Jeff Niemann/150 6.00 15.00
134 Jeremy Bonderman/43 8.00 20.00
135 Jim Bunning/150 10.00 25.00
136 Jim Leyritz/99 4.00 10.00
138 Johan Santana/40 15.00 40.00
140 Johnny Podres/150 6.00 15.00
141 Jose Guillen/145 4.00 10.00
142 Justin Verlander/150 20.00 50.00
143 Keiichi Yabu/150 6.00 15.00
144 Keith Foulke/150 10.00 25.00
145 Keith Hernandez/149 6.00 15.00
147 Kent Hrbek/98 6.00 15.00
150 Lew Ford/150 4.00 10.00
151 Lou Brock/126 10.00 25.00
152 Luis Aparicio/110 6.00 15.00
153 Luis Tiant/147 6.00 15.00
154 Manny Ramirez/34 30.00 60.00
155 Mark Mulder/150 6.00 15.00
156 Mark Prior/10
157 Mark Teixeira/91 10.00 25.00
158 Marty Marion/150 6.00 15.00
159 Miguel Cabrera/146 10.00 25.00
161 Mike Lieberthal/150 6.00 15.00
162 Mike Piazza/3
163 Minnie Minoso/150 6.00 15.00
164 Monte Irvin/150 6.00 15.00
166 Nolan Ryan/50 40.00 80.00
167 Octavio Dotel/150 4.00 10.00
168 Omar Vizquel/150 10.00 25.00
169 Ozzie Smith/50 20.00 50.00
171 Phil Humber/108 6.00 15.00
172 Phil Rizzuto/109 10.00 25.00
173 Prince Fielder/45 50.00 100.00
174 Ralph Kiner/150 10.00 25.00
176 Red Schoendienst/150 6.00 15.00
177 Rich Gossage/150 6.00 15.00
178 Rick Dempsey/104 4.00 10.00
179 Rickie Weeks/148 6.00 15.00
180 Robin Roberts/148 15.00 40.00
181 Rod Carew/150 10.00 25.00
182 Roger Clemens/10
183 Rollie Fingers/120 6.00 15.00
184 Ron Guidry/150 10.00 25.00
185 Ron Santo/142 15.00 40.00
186 Russ Ortiz/150 4.00 10.00
187 Ryne Sandberg/150 20.00 50.00
188 Sammy Sosa/15 50.00 100.00
189 Scott Rolen/87 10.00 25.00
190 Stan Musial/150 30.00 60.00
191 Steve Carlton/100 6.00 15.00
192 Steve Garvey/144 6.00 15.00
193 Steve Stone/150 6.00 15.00
194 Tim Salmon/147 6.00 15.00
195 Todd Helton/5
196 Todd Walker/150 4.00 10.00
197 Tom Gordon/150 4.00 10.00
198 Trot Nixon/43 8.00 20.00
199 Troy Percival/144 6.00 15.00

2005 Absolute Memorabilia Absolutely Ink

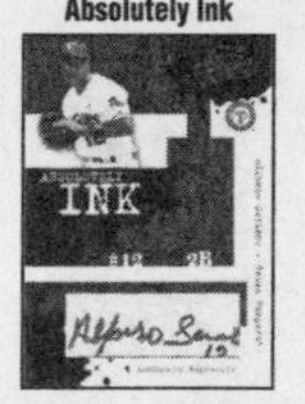

OVERALL AU-GU ODDS ONE PER PACK
PRINT RUNS B/WN 1-150 COPIES PER
NO PRICING ON QTY OF 14 OR LESS
101 Al Kaline/150 12.50 30.00
102 Alan Trammell/1
103 Alfonso Soriano/67 6.00 15.00
104 Barry Larkin/12
105 Ben Sheets/150 6.00 15.00
106 Bill Madlock/1
107 Bobby Doerr/1
109 Cal Ripken/25 75.00 150.00
110 Dale Murphy/8
111 Dennis Eckersley/150 6.00 15.00
112 Don Sutton/150 6.00 15.00
113 Duke Snider/150 10.00 25.00
114 Fergie Jenkins/100 6.00 15.00
115 Frank Thomas/50 20.00 50.00
116 Gary Sheffield/25 15.00 40.00
117 Gaylord Perry/100 6.00 15.00
118 Jacque Jones/100 6.00 15.00
119 Jae Weong Seo/100 6.00 15.00
120 Jeremy Bonderman/100 6.00 15.00
121 Jim Rice/14
122 Joe Torre/25 15.00 40.00
123 Johan Santana/1
124 Juan Gonzalez/10
125 Junior Spivey/75 4.00 10.00
126 Luis Aparicio/150 6.00 15.00
127 Magglio Ordonez/100 6.00 15.00
128 Mark Grace/1
129 Michael Young/75 6.00 15.00
130 Mike Schmidt/17 40.00 80.00
131 Morgan Ensberg/51 8.00 20.00
132 Orlando Cabrera/100 6.00 15.00
133 Paul Konerko/100 5.00 12.00
134 Rollie Fingers/100 6.00 15.00
135 Roy Oswalt/100 6.00 15.00
136 Scott Rolen/27 15.00 40.00
137 Sean Casey/63 8.00 20.00
138 Tom Seaver/12
139 Torii Hunter/100 6.00 15.00
140 Wade Boggs/50 12.50 30.00

2005 Absolute Memorabilia Absolutely Ink Spectrum

*SPEC p/r 74: .4X TO 1X INK p/r 67-150
*SPEC p/r 39-50: .5X TO 1.2X INK p/r 67-150
*SPEC p/r 25-34: .6X TO 1.5X INK p/r 67-150
*SPEC p/r 25-34: .5X TO 1.2X INK p/r 50-63
*SPEC p/r 16-19: .75X TO 2X INK p/r 67-150
OVERALL AU-GU ODDS ONE PER PACK
PRINT RUNS B/WN 1-74 COPIES PER
NO PRICING ON QTY OF 14 OR LESS
109 Cal Ripken/25 75.00 150.00

2005 Absolute Memorabilia Absolutely Ink Swatch Single

OVERALL AU-GU ODDS ONE PER PACK
PRINT RUNS B/WN 1-50 COPIES PER
NO PRICING ON QTY OF 10 OR LESS
1 Rafael Furcal Jsy/50 10.00 25.00
2 Shawn Green Jsy/5
3 Dale Murphy Jsy/50 15.00 40.00
4 Duke Snider Pants/25 20.00 50.00
5 Bill Madlock Bat/50 10.00 25.00
6 J.T. Snow Jsy/5
7 Bobby Crosby Jsy/50 10.00 25.00
8 Cal Ripken Jsy/25 75.00 150.00
9 Hank Blalock Jsy/25 12.50 30.00
10 Vernon Wells Jsy/50 10.00 25.00
11 Lyle Overbay Jsy/50 6.00 15.00
12 Melvin Mora Jsy/5
13 Omar Vizquel Jsy/50 15.00 40.00
14 Ernie Banks Jsy/10
15 Ben Sheets Jsy/25 12.50 30.00
16 Aramis Ramirez Jsy/25 12.50 30.00
17 Todd Helton Jsy/5
18 Travis Hafner Jsy/50 10.00 25.00
19 Mike Lowell Jsy/25 8.00 20.00
20 Frank Robinson Bat/50 15.00 40.00
21 Josh Beckett Jsy/10
22 Juan Gonzalez Jsy/50 10.00 25.00
24 Manny Ramirez Jsy/5
25 Jim Edmonds Jsy/10
26 Dave Concepcion Jsy/1
27 Darryl Strawberry Jsy/50 10.00 25.00
28 Alexis Rios Bat/50 10.00 25.00
30 Magglio Ordonez Jsy/50 10.00 25.00
31 Jay Gibbons Jsy/50 6.00 15.00
32 Steve Carlton Jsy/25 12.50 30.00
34 Kerry Wood Jsy/25 20.00 50.00
35 Dontrelle Willis Jsy/15 30.00 60.00
36 Eric Chavez Jsy/25 12.50 30.00
37 Keith Hernandez Jsy/50 10.00 25.00
38 Carlos Zambrano Jsy/50 10.00 25.00
39 Brett Myers Jsy/50 6.00 15.00
40 Rich Harden Jsy/50 10.00 25.00
41 Danny Kolb Jsy/50 6.00 15.00
42 Mark Prior Jsy/25 15.00 40.00
43 Joey Gathright Jsy/25 8.00 20.00
44 David Cone Jsy/50 10.00 25.00
45 Carlos Lee Jsy/50 10.00 25.00
46 Deion Sanders Jsy/5
47 Jack Morris Jsy/50 10.00 25.00
48 Torii Hunter Jsy/50 10.00 25.00
49 Garret Anderson Jsy/50 10.00 25.00
50 Craig Biggio Jsy/10
51 Dave Parker Bat/50 10.00 25.00
52 C.C. Sabathia Jsy/50 10.00 25.00
53 Dennis Eckersley A's Jsy/50 10.00 25.00
54 Barry Larkin Jsy/25 20.00 50.00
55 Brandon Webb Pants/50 12.50 30.00
56 Sean Casey Jsy/50 10.00 25.00
57 Johan Santana Jsy/50 20.00 50.00
58 Miguel Cabrera Jsy/50 15.00 40.00
59 Bert Blyleven Jsy/50 6.00 15.00
60 Casey Kotchman Jsy/50 10.00 25.00
61 Dwight Gooden Jsy/50 10.00 25.00
62 Milton Bradley Jsy/50 6.00 15.00
63 John Kruk Jsy/50 15.00 40.00
64 Michael Young Jsy/50 10.00 25.00
65 Mike Mussina Jsy/5
66 Robin Ventura Jsy/50 10.00 25.00
67 Tim Hudson Jsy/25 20.00 50.00
68 Will Clark Bat/50 15.00 40.00
69 Lew Ford Jsy/50 6.00 15.00
70 Jody Gerut Jsy/50 6.00 15.00
71 Don Sutton Jsy/50 6.00 15.00
72 B.J. Upton Bat/25 12.50 30.00
73 Austin Kearns Jsy/50 6.00 15.00
74 Rollie Fingers Jsy/5
75 Barry Zito Jsy/10
76 Lee Smith Jsy/5
77 Ryan Wagner Jsy/50 6.00 15.00
78 Jermaine Dye Jsy/50 10.00 25.00
79 Scott Rolen Jsy/10
80 Al Oliver Jsy/50 10.00 25.00
81 Angel Berroa Pants/50 6.00 15.00
82 Edgar Renteria Jsy/50 10.00 25.00
83 Dennis Eckersley Sox Jsy/25 12.50 30.00
84 Roy Oswalt Jsy/50 10.00 25.00
85 David Ortiz Jsy/5
86 Dave Righetti Jsy/50 10.00 25.00
87 Aubrey Huff Jsy/25 12.50 30.00
88 Chipper Jones Jsy/10
89 Jose Vidro Jsy/50 6.00 15.00
90 Harold Baines Jsy/50 10.00 25.00
92 Mark Mulder Jsy/10
93 Ken Harvey Jsy/50 6.00 15.00
94 Orel Hershiser Jsy/10
95 Jason Bay Jsy/50 10.00 25.00
96 Dwight Evans Jsy/50 15.00 40.00
97 Luis Tiant Pants/50 6.00 15.00
98 Ron Santo Bat/50 15.00 40.00
99 Brian Roberts Jsy/50 10.00 25.00
100 Marty Marion Jsy/50 10.00 25.00
101 Al Kaline Bat/50 15.00 40.00
102 Alan Trammell Jsy/63 10.00 25.00
103 Alfonso Soriano Bat/100 8.00 20.00
104 Barry Larkin Bat/150 12.50 30.00
105 Ben Sheets Jsy/40 10.00 25.00
106 Bill Madlock Bat/150 8.00 20.00
107 Bobby Doerr Pants/82 8.00 20.00
108 Brandon Webb Pants/46 12.50 30.00
109 Cal Ripken Jsy/50 60.00 120.00
110 Dale Murphy Jsy/50 15.00 40.00
111 Dennis Eckersley Jsy/150 8.00 20.00
112 Don Sutton Jsy/10
114 Fergie Jenkins Pants/55 10.00 25.00
115 Frank Thomas Bat/50 30.00 60.00
116 Gary Sheffield Fld Glv/150 12.50 30.00
117 Gaylord Perry Jsy/150 8.00 20.00
118 Jacque Jones Bat/45 10.00 25.00
119 Jae Weong Seo Jsy/1
120 Jeremy Bonderman Jsy/15 15.00 40.00
121 Jim Rice Jsy/95 8.00 20.00
122 Joe Torre Jsy/1
123 Johan Santana Jsy/118 15.00 40.00
124 Juan Gonzalez Jsy/75 8.00 20.00
125 Junior Spivey Jsy/75 5.00 12.00
126 Luis Aparicio Bat/10
127 Magglio Ordonez Bat/150 8.00 20.00
128 Mark Grace Fld Glv/150 8.00 20.00
129 Michael Young Jsy/10
130 Mike Schmidt Sock/75 30.00 60.00
132 Orlando Cabrera Jsy/45 10.00 25.00
133 Paul Konerko Bat/34 20.00 50.00
134 Rollie Fingers Jsy/1
135 Roy Oswalt Bat/44 10.00 25.00
136 Scott Rolen Jsy/150 12.50 30.00
137 Sean Casey Jsy/10
138 Tom Seaver Hat/150 15.00 40.00
139 Torii Hunter Jsy/1
140 Wade Boggs Bat/150 12.50 30.00

2005 Absolute Memorabilia Absolutely Ink Swatch Single Spectrum

*SPEC p/r 36-50: .5X TO 1.2X SNG p/r 75-150
*SPEC p/r 36-50: .4X TO 1X SNG p/r 40-63
*SPEC p/r 25: .6X TO 1.5X SNG p/r 75-150
*SPEC p/r 25: .5X TO 1.2X SNG p/r 40-63
*SPEC p/r 15-17: .75X TO 2X SNG p/r 75-150
*SPEC p/r 15-17: .6X TO 1.5X SNG p/r 40-63
*SPEC p/r 15-17: .5X TO 1.2X SNG p/r 25-34
OVERALL AU-GU ODDS ONE PER PACK
PRINT RUNS B/WN 1-50 COPIES PER
NO PRICING ON QTY OF 13 OR LESS
23 Mark Teixeira Jsy/25 20.00 50.00
92 Mark Mulder Jsy/25 12.50 30.00
109 Cal Ripken Jsy/25 75.00 150.00

2005 Absolute Memorabilia Absolutely Ink Swatch Single Spectrum Prime

*PRIMEp/r70-100: .5X TO 1.2X SNGp/r75-150
*PRIME p/r 70-100: .4X TO 1X SNG p/r 40-63
*PRIME p/r 20-35: .75X TO 2X SNG p/r 75-150
*PRIME p/r 20-35: .4X TO 1X SNG p/r 15
OVERALL AU-GU ODDS ONE PER PACK
PRINT RUNS B/WN 1-100 COPIES PER
NO PRICING ON QTY OF 10 OR LESS
112 Don Sutton Jsy/100 8.00 20.00
119 Jae Weong Seo Jsy/45 12.50 30.00
122 Joe Torre Jsy/70 12.50 30.00
126 Luis Aparicio Jsy/25 15.00 40.00
134 Rollie Fingers Jsy/25 15.00 40.00

2005 Absolute Memorabilia Absolutely Ink Swatch Double

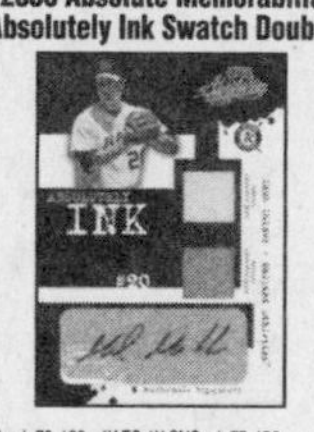

*DBL p/r 70-100: .4X TO 1X SNG p/r 75-150
*DBL p/r 50: .5X TO 1.2X SNG p/r 75-150
*DBL p/r 50: .4X TO 1X SNG p/r 40-63
*DBL p/r 20-30: .6X TO 1.5X SNG p/r 75-150
*DBL p/r 20-30: .5X TO 1.2X SNG p/r 40-63
*DBL p/r 20-30: .4X TO 1X SNG p/r 25-34
*DBL p/r 15-18: .75X TO 2X SNG p/r 75-150
*DBL p/r 15-18: .6X TO 1.5X SNG p/r 40-63
*DBL p/r 15-18: .5X TO 1.2X SNG p/r 25-34
OVERALL AU-GU ODDS ONE PER PACK
PRINT RUNS B/WN 1-100 COPIES PER
NO PRICING ON QTY OF 10 OR LESS
23 Mark Teixeira Fld Glv-Jsy/50 15.00 40.00
92 Mark Mulder Jsy-Jsy/20 12.50 30.00
122 Joe Torre B-J/70 12.50 30.00
129 Michael Young B-J/25 12.50 30.00
137 Sean Casey J-SH/100 8.00 20.00

2005 Absolute Memorabilia Absolutely Ink Swatch Double Spectrum

*SPEC p/r 40-50: .5X TO 1.2X SNG p/r 75-150
*SPEC p/r 40-50: .4X TO 1X SNG p/r 40-63
*SPEC p/r 20-30: .6X TO 1.5X SNG p/r 75-150
*SPEC p/r 20-30: .5X TO 1.2X SNG p/r 40-63
*SPEC p/r 15: .75X TO 2X SNG p/r 75-150
*SPEC p/r 15: .6X TO 1.5X SNG p/r 40-63
OVERALL AU-GU ODDS ONE PER PACK
PRINT RUNS B/WN 1-50 COPIES PER
NO PRICING ON QTY OF 10 OR LESS
122 Joe Torre B-J/15 30.00 60.00
129 Michael Young B-J/25 12.50 30.00
137 Sean Casey J-SH/50 10.00 25.00

2005 Absolute Memorabilia Absolutely Ink Swatch Double Spectrum Prime

*PRIME p/r 50: .6X TO 1.5X SNG p/r 75-150
*PRIME p/r 25: .75X TO 2X SNG p/r 75-150
*PRIME p/r 25: .6X TO 1.5X SNG p/r 40-63
*PRIME p/r 15: 1X TO 2.5X SNG p/r 75-150
OVERALL AU-GU ODDS ONE PER PACK
PRINT RUNS B/ON 1-50 COPIES PER
NO PRICING ON QTY OF 10 OR LESS
134 Rollie Fingers J-J/25 15.00 40.00

2005 Absolute Memorabilia Absolutely Ink Swatch Triple

*TRIP p/r 75: .4X TO 1X SNG p/r 40-63
*TRIP p/r 50: .6X TO 1.5X SNG p/r 75-150
*TRIP p/r 50: .5X TO 1.2X SNG p/r 40-63
*TRIP p/r 25: .75X TO 2X SNG p/r 75-150
*TRIP p/r 25: .6X TO 1.5X SNG p/r 40-63
*TRIP p/r 25: .5X TO 1.2X SNG p/r 25-34
*TRIP p/r 15: .75X TO 2X SNG p/r 40-63
OVERALL AU-GU ODDS ONE PER PACK
PRINT RUNS B/WN 1-75 COPIES PER
NO PRICING ON QTY OF 10 OR LESS
8 Cal Ripken Bat-Jsy-Pants/25 90.00 180.00
23 Mark Teixeira Bat-Hat-Jsy/75 15.00 40.00
126 Luis Aparicio B-J-P/15 20.00 50.00
129 Michael Young B-J-J/25 15.00 40.00

2005 Absolute Memorabilia Absolutely Ink Swatch Triple Spectrum

*SPEC p/r 25: .75X TO 2X SNG p/r 75-150
*SPEC p/r 25: .6X TO 1.5X SNG p/r 40-63
OVERALL AU-GU ODDS ONE PER PACK
PRINT RUNS B/WN 1-25 COPIES PER
NO PRICING ON QTY OF 10 OR LESS
23 Mark Teixeira Bat-Hat-Jsy/25 30.00 60.00
129 Michael Young B-J-J/25 15.00 40.00

2005 Absolute Memorabilia Absolutely Ink Swatch Triple Spectrum Prime

*PRIME p/r 25: 1X TO 2.5X SNG p/r 75-150
*PRIME p/r 15: 1X TO 2.5X SNG p/r 40-63
OVERALL AU-GU ODDS ONE PER PACK
PRINT RUNS B/WN 1-25 COPIES PER
NO PRICING ON QTY OF 10 OR LESS

2005 Absolute Memorabilia Heroes

STATED PRINT RUN 250 SERIAL #'d SETS
*SPEC 1-50: 1X TO 2.5X BASIC
*SPEC 51-70: .75X TO 2X BASIC
SPEC 1-50 PRINT RUN 50 #'d SETS
SPEC 51-70 PRINT RUN 100 #'d SETS
*REV.SPEC: 1.5X TO 4X BASIC
REVERSE SPEC.PRINT RUN 25 #'d SETS
RANDOM INSERTS IN PACKS
1 Billy Martin .75 2.00
2 Rickey Henderson .75 2.00
3 Alan Trammell .50 1.25
4 Lenny Dykstra .50 1.25
5 Jeff Bagwell .75 2.00
6 Steve Garvey .50 1.25
7 Catfish Hunter .50 1.25
8 Cal Ripken 5.00 12.00
9 Reggie Jackson 1.25 3.00
10 Gary Sheffield .50 1.25
11 Edgar Martinez .75 2.00
12 Roberto Alomar .75 2.00
13 Luis Tiant .50 1.25
14 Jim Rice .50 1.25
15 Carlos Beltran .50 1.25
16 Hideo Nomo 1.25 3.00
17 Mark Grace .75 2.00
18 Joe Cronin .50 1.25
19 Tony Gwynn 1.50 4.00
20 Bo Jackson 1.25 3.00
21 Roger Clemens Sox 1.50 4.00
22 Roger Clemens Yanks 1.50 4.00
23 Don Mattingly 2.50 6.00
24 Willie Mays 2.50 6.00
25 Andruw Jones .50 1.25
26 Andre Dawson .75 2.00
27 Carlton Fisk .75 2.00
28 Robin Yount 1.25 3.00
29 Joe Carter .50 1.25
30 Dale Murphy .50 1.25
31 Greg Maddux 2.00 5.00
32 Ichiro Suzuki 2.00 5.00
33 Jose Canseco .75 2.00
34 Nolan Ryan 3.00 8.00
35 Frank Thomas 1.25 3.00
36 Fred Lynn .50 1.25
37 Curt Schilling Phils .75 2.00
38 Curt Schilling Sox .75 2.00
39 Dave Parker .50 1.25
40 Randy Johnson M's 1.25 3.00
41 Randy Johnson Expos 1.25 3.00
42 Vladimir Guerrero 1.25 3.00
43 Bernie Williams .75 2.00
44 Wade Boggs .75 2.00
45 Pedro Martinez .75 2.00
46 Andy Pettitte .75 2.00
47 Fergie Jenkins .50 1.25
48 Darryl Strawberry .50 1.25
49 Rafael Palmeiro .75 2.00
50 Albert Pujols 3.00 8.00
51 Adrian Beltre .50 1.25
52 Albert Pujols 3.00 8.00
53 Andre Dawson .75 2.00
54 Carlos Beltran .50 1.25
55 Don Mattingly 2.50 6.00
56 Greg Maddux 2.00 5.00
57 Ivan Rodriguez .75 2.00
58 John Smoltz 1.25 3.00
59 Manny Ramirez 1.25 3.00
60 Mark Grace .75 2.00
61 Mark Teixeira 1.25 3.00
62 Mike Mussina .75 2.00
63 Paul Lo Duca .50 1.25
64 Pedro Martinez .75 2.00
65 Scott Rolen .75 2.00
66 Shawn Green .50 1.25
67 Tony Gwynn 1.50 4.00
68 Tony Oliva .50 1.25
69 Torii Hunter .50 1.25
70 Wade Boggs .75 2.00

2005 Absolute Memorabilia Heroes Button

PRINT RUNS B/WN 1-6 COPIES PER
SPECTRUM PRINT RUN 1 #'d SET
OVERALL AU-GU ODDS ONE PER PACK
NO PRICING DUE TO SCARCITY
54 Carlos Beltran/3
55 Don Mattingly/1
67 Tony Gwynn/6
70 Wade Boggs/3

2005 Absolute Memorabilia Heroes MLB Logo

PRINT RUNS B/WN 1-5 COPIES PER
SPECTRUM PRINT RUN 1 #'d SET
OVERALL AU-GU ODDS ONE PER PACK
NO PRICING DUE TO SCARCITY
56 Greg Maddux/5
57 Ivan Rodriguez/2
59 Manny Ramirez/1
64 Pedro Martinez/3

2005 Absolute Memorabilia Heroes Swatch Double

OVERALL AU-GU ODDS ONE PER PACK
PRINT RUNS B/WN 1-150 COPIES PER
NO PRICING ON QTY OF 1
1 Billy Martin Jsy-Pants/50 10.00 25.00
2 Rickey Henderson Bat-Jsy/50 5.00 12.00
3 Alan Trammell Bat-Jsy/50 4.00 10.00
4 Lenny Dykstra Bat-Jsy/50 4.00 10.00
5 Jeff Bagwell Bat-Jsy/50 4.00 10.00
6 Steve Garvey Bat-Jsy/50 4.00 10.00
7 Catfish Hunter Jsy-Jsy/25 6.00 15.00
8 Cal Ripken Jsy-Pants/50 15.00 40.00
9 Reggie Jackson Jkt-Jsy/50 5.00 12.00
10 Gary Sheffield Fld Glv-Jsy/50 3.00 8.00
11 Edgar Martinez Jsy-Jsy/50 4.00 10.00
12 Roberto Alomar Jsy-Jsy/50 4.00 10.00
13 Luis Tiant Hat-Jsy/25 5.00 12.00
14 Jim Rice Jsy-Pants/50 4.00 10.00
15 Carlos Beltran Bat-Jsy/50 3.00 8.00
16 Hideo Nomo Bat-Jsy/50 6.00 15.00
17 Mark Grace Fld Glv-Jsy/50 4.00 10.00
18 Joe Cronin Jsy-Pants/50 10.00 25.00
19 Tony Gwynn Bat-Jsy/50 8.00 20.00
20 Bo Jackson Bat-Jsy/50 6.00 15.00
21 Roger Clemens Sox Jsy-Jsy/50 8.00 20.00
22 R.Clemens Yanks Jsy-Jsy/50 8.00 20.00
23 Don Mattingly Bat-Jsy/50 10.00 25.00
24 Willie Mays Bat-Jsy/50 20.00 50.00
25 Andruw Jones Bat-Jsy/50 4.00 10.00
26 Andre Dawson Jsy-Pants/50 4.00 10.00
28 Robin Yount Hat-Jsy/50 6.00 15.00
29 Joe Carter Bat-Jsy/50 4.00 10.00
30 Dale Murphy Bat-Jsy/50 5.00 12.00
31 Greg Maddux Jsy-Jsy/50 8.00 20.00
33 Jose Canseco Hat-Jsy/50 6.00 15.00
34 Nolan Ryan Bat-Jsy/50 12.50 30.00
35 Frank Thomas Jsy-Pants/50 5.00 12.00
36 Fred Lynn Bat-Jsy/50 4.00 10.00
37 Curt Schilling Phils Jsy-Jsy/50 3.00 8.00
38 Curt Schilling Sox Jsy-Jsy/50 4.00 10.00
39 Dave Parker Bat-Jsy/50 4.00 10.00
40 Randy Johnson M's Jsy-Jsy/50 5.00 12.00
41 R.Johnson Expos Bat-Jsy/25 6.00 15.00
42 Vladimir Guerrero Jsy-Jsy/50 5.00 12.00
43 Bernie Williams Jsy-Jsy/50 4.00 10.00
44 Wade Boggs Bat-Jsy/50 5.00 12.00
45 Pedro Martinez Jsy-Jsy/50 4.00 10.00
46 Andy Pettitte Jsy-Jsy/50 4.00 10.00
47 Fergie Jenkins Hat-Jsy/50 4.00 10.00
48 Darryl Strawberry Jsy-Pants/50 4.00 10.00
49 Rafael Palmeiro Bat-Jsy/50 4.00 10.00
50 Albert Pujols Jsy-Jsy/50 12.50 30.00
51 Adrian Beltre H-S/120 2.50 6.00
52 Albert Pujols B-J/150 10.00 25.00
53 Andre Dawson J-P/35 5.00 12.00
54 Carlos Beltran J-J/45 3.00 8.00
55 Don Mattingly B-H/1
56 Greg Maddux J-J/150 6.00 15.00
57 Ivan Rodriguez B-J/150 3.00 8.00
58 John Smoltz J-J/150 3.00 8.00
59 Manny Ramirez B-J/1
60 Mark Grace FG-J/25 5.00 12.00
61 Mark Teixeira B-J/1
62 Mike Mussina J-S/50 4.00 10.00
63 P.Lo Duca Bat-Chest Prot/150 2.50 6.00
64 Pedro Martinez J-J/50 4.00 10.00
65 Scott Rolen J-J/50 4.00 10.00
66 Shawn Green B-J/150 2.50 6.00
67 Tony Gwynn J-P/150 6.00 15.00
68 Tony Oliva B-J/150 3.00 8.00
69 Torii Hunter B-J/71 2.50 6.00

2005 Absolute Memorabilia Heroes Swatch Double Spectrum Prime

*PRIME p/r 100: .5X TO 1.2X DBL p/r 71-150
*PRIME p/r 45: .6X TO 1.5X DBL p/r 71-150
*PRIME p/r 25: .6X TO 1.5X DBL p/r 45-50
*PRIME p/r 25: .5X TO 1.2X DBL p/r 25-35
*PRIME p/r 15: 1X TO 2.5X DBL p/r 71-150
OVERALL AU-GU ODDS ONE PER PACK
PRINT RUNS B/WN 1-100 COPIES PER
NO PRICING ON QTY OF 10 OR LESS
27 Carlton Fisk Bat-Jsy/25 8.00 20.00
59 Manny Ramirez B-J/25 8.00 20.00

2005 Absolute Memorabilia Heroes Swatch Triple

*TRIP p/r 70-150: .5X TO 1.2X DBL p/r 71-150
*TRIP p/r 70-150: .3X TO .8X DBL p/r 25-35
*TRIP p/r 36-50: .6X TO 1.5X DBL p/r 71-150
*TRIP p/r 36-50: .5X TO 1.2X DBL p/r 45-50
*TRIP p/r 20-30: .75X TO 2X DBL p/r 71-150
*TRIP p/r 20-30: .6X TO 1.5X DBL p/r 45-50
*TRIP p/r 15: .75X TO 2X DBL p/r 45-50
*TRIP p/r 15: .6X TO 1.5X DBL p/r 25-35
OVERALL AU-GU ODDS ONE PER PACK
PRINT RUNS B/WN 1-150 COPIES PER
NO PRICING ON QTY OF 1
24 Willie Mays Bat-Jsy-Pants/25 40.00 80.00
55 D.Mattingly B-BG-H/70 15.00 40.00
59 Manny Ramirez B-J-S/20 6.00 15.00
61 Mark Teixeira B-FG-S/40 5.00 12.00

2005 Absolute Memorabilia Heroes Swatch Triple Spectrum Prime

*PRIME p/r 15: 1.25X TO 3X DBL p/r 45-50
*PRIME p/r 15: 1X TO 2.5X DBL p/r 25-35
OVERALL AU-GU ODDS ONE PER PACK
PRINT RUNS B/WN 1-100 COPIES PER
NO PRICING ON QTY OF 10 OR LESS
27 Carlton Fisk Bat-Jsy-Jsy/15 15.00 40.00
53 Andre Dawson B-J-P/95 6.00 15.00
54 Carlos Beltran J-J-J/70 6.00 15.00
56 Greg Maddux J-J-J/30 20.00 50.00
58 John Smoltz J-J-J/100 8.00 20.00
59 Manny Ramirez B-J-J/25 12.50 30.00
64 Pedro Martinez H-J-J/25 12.50 30.00
66 Shawn Green B-J-J/100 6.00 15.00
68 Tony Oliva B-J-J/75 6.00 15.00
69 Torii Hunter B-H-J/50 8.00 20.00

2005 Absolute Memorabilia Heroes Autograph

OVERALL AU-GU ODDS ONE PER PACK
PRINT RUNS B/WN 1-79 COPIES PER
NO PRICING ON QTY OF 8 OR LESS
51 Adrian Beltre/8
55 Don Mattingly/50 30.00 60.00
56 Greg Maddux/5
60 Mark Grace/1
61 Mark Teixeira/79 10.00 25.00
65 Scott Rolen/27 15.00 40.00
67 Tony Gwynn/19 30.00 60.00
69 Torii Hunter/50 8.00 20.00
70 Wade Boggs/26 15.00 40.00

2005 Absolute Memorabilia Heroes Autograph Spectrum

*SPEC p/r 50: .5X TO 1.2X AUTO p/r 79
OVERALL AU-GU ODDS ONE PER PACK
PRINT RUNS B/WN 1-50 COPIES PER
NO PRICING ON QTY OF 5 OR LESS

2005 Absolute Memorabilia Heroes Autograph Swatch Double Spectrum Prime

PRINT RUNS B/WN 1-20 COPIES PER
NO PRICING ON QTY OF 8 OR LESS
TRIPLE PRINT RUN B/WN 1-5 COPIES PER
NO TRIPLE PRICING DUE TO SCARCITY
OVERALL AU-GU ODDS ONE PER PACK
2 Rickey Henderson Bat-Jsy/5
3 Alan Trammell Bat-Jsy/15 20.00 50.00
4 Lenny Dykstra Bat-Jsy/15 20.00 50.00
5 Jeff Bagwell Bat-Jsy/5
6 Steve Garvey Bat-Jsy/15 20.00 50.00
8 Cal Ripken Jsy-Pants/8
9 Reggie Jackson Jkt-Jsy/15 40.00 80.00
10 Gary Sheffield Fld Glv-Jsy/15 40.00 80.00
11 Edgar Martinez Jsy-Jsy/15 40.00 80.00
12 Roberto Alomar Jsy-Jsy/15 40.00 80.00
13 Luis Tiant Hat-Jsy/15 12.50 30.00
14 Jim Rice Jsy-Pants/15 20.00 50.00
15 Carlos Beltran Bat-Jsy/15 20.00 50.00
16 Hideo Nomo Bat-Jsy/5
17 Mark Grace Fld Glv-Jsy/15 20.00 50.00
19 Tony Gwynn Bat-Jsy/15 40.00 80.00
20 Bo Jackson Bat-Jsy/15 50.00 100.00
21 Roger Clemens Sox Jsy-Jsy/5
22 Roger Clemens Yanks Jsy-Jsy/5
23 Don Mattingly Bat-Jsy/15 50.00 100.00
24 Willie Mays Bat-Jsy/1
26 Andre Dawson Jsy-Pants/15 20.00 50.00
27 Carlton Fisk Bat-Jsy/15 40.00 80.00
28 Robin Yount Hat-Jsy/15 50.00 100.00
29 Joe Carter Bat-Jsy/5
30 Dale Murphy Bat-Jsy/15 40.00 80.00
31 Greg Maddux Jsy-Jsy/5
33 Jose Canseco Hat-Jsy/15 50.00 100.00
34 Nolan Ryan Bat-Jsy/15 125.00 200.00
35 Frank Thomas Jsy-Pants/15 50.00 100.00
36 Fred Lynn Bat-Jsy/15 20.00 50.00
37 Curt Schilling Phils Jsy-Jsy/5
38 Curt Schilling Sox Jsy-Jsy/5
39 Dave Parker Bat-Jsy/15 20.00 50.00
40 Randy Johnson M's Jsy-Jsy/5
41 Randy Johnson Expos Bat-Jsy/5
42 Vladimir Guerrero Jsy-Jsy/5
44 Wade Boggs Bat-Jsy/15 40.00 80.00
45 Pedro Martinez Jsy-Jsy/5
47 Fergie Jenkins Hat-Jsy/15 12.50 30.00
48 Darryl Strawberry Jsy-Pants/15 20.00 50.00
49 Rafael Palmeiro Bat-Jsy/5
50 Albert Pujols Jsy-Jsy/5
55 Don Mattingly B-J/1
56 Greg Maddux J-J/20 75.00 150.00
61 Mark Teixeira B-H/20 30.00 60.00
65 Scott Rolen J-J/1
67 Tony Gwynn J-P/1
69 Torii Hunter B-J/1
70 Wade Boggs B-J/1

2005 Absolute Memorabilia Marks of Fame

STATED PRINT RUN 150 SERIAL #'d SETS
*SPEC: 1.25X TO 3X BASIC

SPECTRUM PRINT RUN 25 #'d SETS
RANDOM INSERTS IN PACKS
1 Bobby Doerr .75 2.00
2 Reggie Jackson Yanks 2.00 5.00
3 Harmon Killebrew 2.00 5.00
4 Duke Snider 1.25 3.00
5 Brooks Robinson 1.25 3.00
6 Al Kaline 2.00 5.00
7 Carlton Fisk 1.25 3.00
8 Willie Stargell 1.25 3.00
9 Enos Slaughter .75 2.00
10 Nolan Ryan Rgr 5.00 12.00
11 Luis Aparicio R.Sox .75 2.00
12 Hoyt Wilhelm 1.25 3.00
13 Orlando Cepeda .75 2.00
14 Mike Schmidt 4.00 10.00
15 Frank Robinson 1.25 3.00
16 Whitey Ford 1.25 3.00
17 Don Sutton .75 2.00
18 Joe Morgan .75 2.00
19 Bob Feller .75 2.00
20 Lou Brock 1.25 3.00
21 Warren Spahn 1.25 3.00
22 Jim Palmer .75 2.00
23 Reggie Jackson Angels 2.00 5.00
24 Willie Mays 4.00 10.00
25 George Brett 4.00 10.00
26 Billy Williams .75 2.00
27 Juan Marichal .75 2.00
28 Early Wynn .75 2.00
29 Rod Carew 1.25 3.00
30 Maury Wills .75 2.00
31 Fergie Jenkins .75 2.00
32 Steve Carlton .75 2.00
33 Eddie Murray 2.00 5.00
34 Kirby Puckett 2.00 5.00
35 Johnny Bench 2.00 5.00
36 Gaylord Perry .75 2.00
37 Gary Carter .75 2.00
38 Tony Perez .75 2.00
39 Tony Oliva .75 2.00
40 Luis Aparicio W.Sox .75 2.00
41 Tom Seaver 1.25 3.00
42 Paul Molitor 2.00 5.00
43 Dennis Eckersley .75 2.00
44 Willie McCovey 1.25 3.00
45 Bob Gibson 1.25 3.00
46 Robin Roberts .75 2.00
47 Carl Yastrzemski 2.50 6.00
48 Ozzie Smith 3.00 8.00
49 Nolan Ryan Angels 5.00 12.00
50 Stan Musial 3.00 8.00
51 Bob Feller .75 2.00
52 Bob Gibson 1.25 3.00
53 Cal Ripken 8.00 20.00
54 Carl Yastrzemski 2.50 6.00
55 Carlton Fisk 1.25 3.00
56 Duke Snider Dgr 1.25 3.00
57 Duke Snider Mets 1.25 3.00
58 Gary Carter .75 2.00
59 George Brett 4.00 10.00
60 Johnny Bench 2.00 5.00
61 Juan Marichal .75 2.00
62 Kirby Puckett 2.00 5.00
63 Mike Schmidt 4.00 10.00
64 Nolan Ryan 5.00 12.00
65 Ozzie Smith 3.00 8.00
66 Paul Molitor 2.00 5.00
67 Phil Niekro .75 2.00
68 Ryne Sandberg 4.00 10.00
69 Wade Boggs 1.25 3.00
70 Willie McCovey 1.25 3.00

2005 Absolute Memorabilia Marks of Fame Button

PRINT RUNS B/WN 1-9 COPIES PER
SPECTRUM PRINT RUN 1 SERIAL #'d SET
OVERALL AU-GU ODDS ONE PER PACK
NO PRICING DUE TO SCARCITY
52 Bob Gibson/1
53 Cal Ripken/1
54 Carl Yastrzemski/8
55 Carlton Fisk/9
56 Duke Snider Dgr/5
57 Duke Snider Mets/4
58 Gary Carter/5
60 Johnny Bench/3
61 Juan Marichal/3
62 Kirby Puckett/5
64 Nolan Ryan/5
66 Paul Molitor/1
69 Wade Boggs/3

2005 Absolute Memorabilia Marks of Fame Swatch Double

OVERALL AU-GU ODDS ONE PER PACK
PRINT RUNS B/WN 1-50 COPIES PER
NO PRICING ON QTY OF 10 OR LESS
1 Bobby Doerr Bat-Pants/50 4.00 10.00
2 Reggie Jackson Yanks Bat-Pants/50 5.00 12.00
3 Harmon Killebrew Bat-Jsy/50 6.00 15.00
4 Duke Snider Jsy-Pants/25 6.00 15.00
5 Brooks Robinson Bat-Jsy/50 6.00 15.00
7 Carlton Fisk Bat-Jkt/50 5.00 12.00
8 Willie Stargell Bat-Jsy/50 5.00 12.00
9 Enos Slaughter Jsy-Jsy/50 4.00 10.00
10 Nolan Ryan Rgr Jsy Pants/50 12.50 30.00
11 Luis Aparicio Bat-Jsy/50 4.00 10.00
12 Hoyt Wilhelm Jsy-Jsy/50 4.00 10.00
13 Orlando Cepeda Bat-Pants/50 4.00 10.00
14 Mike Schmidt Bat-Jsy/50 10.00 25.00
15 Frank Robinson Bat-Shoes/50 4.00 10.00
16 Whitey Ford Jsy-Jsy/25 6.00 15.00
17 Don Sutton Jsy-Jsy/50 4.00 10.00
18 Joe Morgan Bat-Jsy/50 4.00 10.00
20 Lou Brock Bat-Jkt/50 5.00 12.00
21 Warren Spahn Jsy-Jsy/50 6.00 15.00
22 Jim Palmer Hat-Pants/50 4.00 10.00
23 Reggie Jackson Angels Bat-Jsy/50 5.00 12.00
24 Willie Mays Bat-Jsy/25 30.00 60.00
25 George Brett Hat-Jsy/10
26 Billy Williams Jsy-Jsy/50 4.00 10.00
27 Juan Marichal Jsy-Pants/50 4.00 10.00
28 Early Wynn Jsy-Jsy/25 6.00 15.00
29 Rod Carew Bat-Jsy/50 5.00 12.00
30 Maury Wills Jsy-Jsy/1
31 Fergie Jenkins Fld Glv-Pants/50 4.00 10.00
32 Steve Carlton Bat-Pants/50 4.00 10.00
33 Eddie Murray Bat-Jsy/50 8.00 20.00
34 Kirby Puckett Bat-Jsy/50 6.00 15.00
35 Johnny Bench Bat-Jsy/50 6.00 15.00
36 Gaylord Perry Jsy-Jsy/50 4.00 10.00
37 Gary Carter Bat-Jsy/50 4.00 10.00
38 Tony Perez Fld Glv-Jsy/10
39 Tony Oliva Bat-Jsy/50 4.00 10.00
40 Luis Aparicio Bat-Pants/5
41 Tom Seaver Jsy-Pants/50 5.00 12.00
42 Paul Molitor Bat-Jsy/50 4.00 10.00
43 Dennis Eckersley Jsy-Jsy/50 4.00 10.00
44 Willie McCovey Jsy-Pants/50 5.00 12.00
47 Carl Yastrzemski Bat-Jsy/50 10.00 25.00
48 Ozzie Smith Hat-Pants/50 8.00 20.00
49 Nolan Ryan Angels Jkt-Jsy/50 12.50 30.00
50 Stan Musial Bat-Pants/50 12.50 30.00
53 Cal Ripken JK-P/100 10.00 25.00
54 Carl Yastrzemski B-H/70 10.00 25.00
55 Carlton Fisk B-J/1
57 Duke Snider J-P/100 4.00 10.00
58 Gary Carter FG-J/100 3.00 8.00
60 Johnny Bench J-P/1
61 Juan Marichal J-P/1
62 Kirby Puckett FG-S/20 8.00 20.00
64 Nolan Ryan J-P/1
66 Paul Molitor B-J/100 3.00 8.00
67 Phil Niekro B-J/10
68 Ryne Sandberg FG-J/1

2005 Absolute Memorabilia Marks of Fame Swatch Double Spectrum Prime

*PRIME p/r 44-50: .6X TO 1.5X DBL p/r 70-100
*PRIME p/r 25: .6X TO 1.5X DBL p/r 50
*PRIME p/r 25: .5X TO 1.2X DBL p/r 20-25
*PRIME p/r 15: 1X TO 2.5X DBL p/r 70-100
OVERALL AU-GU ODDS ONE PER PACK
PRINT RUNS B/WN 1-75 COPIES PER
NO PRICING ON QTY OF 10 OR LESS
21 Warren Spahn Jsy-Pants/25 40.00 80.00
24 Willie Mays Bat-Jsy/25 50.00 100.00
30 Maury Wills Jsy-Jsy/25 6.00 15.00
52 Bob Gibson J-J/75 5.00 12.00
67 Phil Niekro B-J/50 5.00 12.00
70 Willie McCovey J-J/44 6.00 15.00

2005 Absolute Memorabilia Marks of Fame Swatch Triple

*TRIP p/r 50-55: .6X TO 1.5X DBL p/r 70-100
*TRIP p/r 50-55: .4X TO 1X DBL p/r 20-25
*TRIP p/r 25: .6X TO 1.5X DBL p/r 50
OVERALL AU-GU ODDS ONE PER PACK
PRINT RUNS B/WN 1-55 COPIES PER
NO PRICING ON QTY OF 10 OR LESS
21 Warren Spahn Jsy-Jsy-Pants/25 40.00 80.00
24 Willie Mays Bat-Jsy-Pants/25 40.00 80.00

2005 Absolute Memorabilia Marks of Fame Swatch Triple Spectrum Prime

*PRIME p/r 15: 1.25X TO 3X DBL p/r 50
OVERALL AU-GU ODDS ONE PER PACK
PRINT RUNS B/WN 1-50 COPIES PER
NO PRICING ON QTY OF 10 OR LESS
21 Warren Spahn Jsy-Jsy-Pants/15 60.00 120.00
67 Phil Niekro B-J-J/50 6.00 15.00
70 Willie McCovey J-J-J/15 12.50 30.00

2005 Absolute Memorabilia Marks of Fame Autograph

OVERALL AU-GU ODDS ONE PER PACK
PRINT RUNS B/WN 2-200 COPIES PER
NO PRICING ON QTY OF 11 OR LESS
51 Bob Feller/150 6.00 15.00
52 Bob Gibson/150 10.00 25.00
53 Cal Ripken/8
55 Carlton Fisk/77 10.00 25.00
56 Duke Snider Dgr/150 10.00 25.00
57 Duke Snider Mets/150 10.00 25.00
58 Gary Carter/25 10.00 25.00
59 George Brett/54 40.00 80.00
60 Johnny Bench/200 15.00 40.00
61 Juan Marichal/19 12.50 30.00
62 Kirby Puckett/5
63 Mike Schmidt/35 20.00 50.00
64 Nolan Ryan/100 40.00 80.00
65 Ozzie Smith/150 15.00 40.00
66 Paul Molitor/11
67 Phil Niekro/4
68 Ryne Sandberg/100 20.00 50.00
69 Wade Boggs/26 15.00 40.00
70 Willie McCovey/2

2005 Absolute Memorabilia Marks of Fame Autograph Spectrum

*SPEC p/r 133: .4X TO 1X AUTO p/r 77-200
*SPEC p/r 50: .5X TO 1.2X AUTO p/r 77-200
*SPEC p/r 20-23: .6X TO 1.5X AUTOp/r77-200
OVERALL AU-GU ODDS ONE PER PACK
PRINT RUNS B/WN 1-133 COPIES PER
NO PRICING ON QTY OF 10 OR LESS

2005 Absolute Memorabilia Marks of Fame Autograph Swatch Single

OVERALL AU-GU ODDS ONE PER PACK
PRINT RUNS B/WN 1-125 COPIES PER
NO PRICING ON QTY OF 10 OR LESS
1 Bobby Doerr Pants/125 5.00 12.00
2 Reggie Jackson Yanks Pants/10

3 Harmon Killebrew Jsy/50 30.00 60.00
4 Duke Snider Jsy/25 20.00 50.00
5 Brooks Robinson Jsy/125 12.50 30.00
6 Al Kaline Bat/125 15.00 40.00
7 Carlton Fisk Jkt/50 15.00 40.00
10 Nolan Ryan Rgr Pants/50 50.00 100.00
11 Luis Aparicio Bos Jsy/125 8.00 20.00
12 Hoyt Wilhelm Jsy/10
13 Orlando Cepeda Pants/50 10.00 25.00
14 Mike Schmidt Jsy/50 30.00 60.00
15 Frank Robinson Bat/125 12.50 30.00
16 Whitey Ford Jsy/50 20.00 50.00
17 Don Sutton Jsy/125 5.00 12.00
19 Bob Feller Pants/125 12.50 30.00
20 Lou Brock Jkt/125 12.50 30.00
22 Jim Palmer Pants/50 10.00 25.00
23 Reggie Jackson Angels Jsy/10
24 Willie Mays Pants/25
25 George Brett Jsy/10
26 Billy Williams Jsy/50 10.00 25.00
27 Juan Marichal Pants/125 8.00 20.00
29 Rod Carew Jsy/50 15.00 40.00
30 Maury Wills Jsy/10
31 Fergie Jenkins Pants/125 8.00 20.00
32 Steve Carlton Pants/125 8.00 20.00
34 Kirby Puckett Jsy/10
35 Johnny Bench Pants/50 20.00 50.00
36 Gaylord Perry Jsy/125 8.00 20.00
37 Gary Carter Pants/50 10.00 25.00
38 Tony Perez Jsy/50 10.00 25.00
39 Tony Oliva Jsy/125 8.00 20.00
40 Luis Aparicio Chi Bat/125 8.00 20.00
41 Tom Seaver Pants/50 20.00 50.00
42 Paul Molitor Pants/50 10.00 25.00
43 Dennis Eckersley Jsy/125 8.00 20.00
44 Willie McCovey Pants/50 15.00 40.00
45 Bob Gibson Hat/5
46 Robin Roberts Hat/50 10.00 25.00
47 Carl Yastrzemski Pants/10
48 Ozzie Smith Pants/50 20.00 50.00
49 Nolan Ryan Angels Jkt/50 50.00 100.00
50 Stan Musial Pants/50 40.00 80.00
51 Bob Feller Pants/15 30.00 60.00
52 Bob Gibson Jsy/113 12.50 30.00
53 Cal Ripken Jsy/25 75.00 150.00
55 Carlton Fisk Jsy/5
57 Duke Snider Mets Jsy/5
58 Gary Carter Jsy/100 8.00 20.00
59 George Brett Jsy/1
60 Johnny Bench Pants/9
61 Juan Marichal Pants/50 10.00 25.00
63 Mike Schmidt Sock/25 30.00 60.00
64 Nolan Ryan Jsy/50 50.00 100.00
66 Paul Molitor Jsy/48 10.00 25.00
70 Willie McCovey Jsy/44 15.00 40.00

2005 Absolute Memorabilia Marks of Fame Autograph Swatch Double

*DBL p/r 75-100: .4X TO 1X SNG p/r 100-125
*DBL p/r 75-100: .3X TO .8X SNG p/r 44-50
*DBL p/r 50: .5X TO 1.2X SNG p/r 100-125
*DBL p/r 50: .4X TO 1X SNG p/r 44-50
*DBL p/r 25-30: .6X TO 1.5X SNG p/r 100-125
*DBL p/r 25-30: .5X TO 1.2X SNG p/r 44-50
*DBL p/r 25-30: .4X TO 1X SNG p/r 25
OVERALL AU-GU ODDS ONE PER PACK
PRINT RUNS B/WN 1-100 COPIES PER
NO PRICING ON QTY OF 10 OR LESS
12 Hoyt Wilhelm Jsy-Jsy/25 20.00 50.00
53 Cal Ripken JK-P/25 75.00 150.00
55 Carlton Fisk B-J/30 20.00 50.00

2005 Absolute Memorabilia Marks of Fame Autograph Swatch Double Spectrum Prime

*PRIME p/r 20-25: .6X TO 1.5X SNG p/r 44-50
OVERALL AU-GU ODDS ONE PER PACK
PRINT RUNS B/WN 1-25 COPIES PER
NO PRICING ON QTY OF 10 OR LESS

2005 Absolute Memorabilia Marks of Fame Autograph Swatch Triple

PRINT RUNS B/WN 1-25 COPIES PER
NO PRICING ON QTY OF 10 OR LESS
PRIME PRINT RUNS B/WN 1-10 PER
NO PRIME PRICING DUE TO SCARCITY
OVERALL AU-GU ODDS ONE PER PACK
53 Cal Ripken JK-J-P/25 90.00 180.00
55 Carlton Fisk B-J-J/25 30.00 60.00

2005 Absolute Memorabilia Recollection Autographs

OVERALL AU-GU ODDS ONE PER PACK
NO PRICING ON QTY OF 18 OR LESS
PRINT RUNS B/WN 1-73 COPIES PER
DMU3 D.Murphy 87 Don DK/72 10.00 25.00
DMU6 D.Murphy 03 DK/73 10.00 25.00
DS1 Duke Snider 04 DK/20 15.00 40.00
DY1 Delmon Young 03 DK/46 20.00 50.00
HB1 Hank Blalock 02 DR/20 10.00 25.00
HB2 Hank Blalock 03 Don/20 10.00 25.00
KG2 Kirk Gibson 86 Don DK/20 10.00 25.00
MC2 Miguel Cabrera 04 DK/33 15.00 40.00
OS1 O.Smith 87 Don DK/30 20.00 50.00
OS8 O.Smith 03 DK/33 20.00 50.00

2005 Absolute Memorabilia Team Tandems

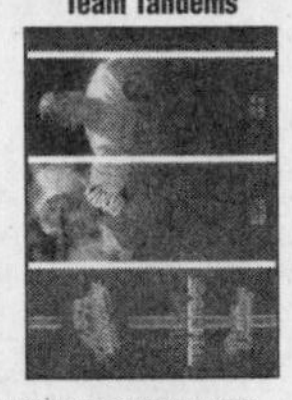

STATED PRINT RUN 250 SERIAL #'d SETS
*SPEC: .5X TO 1.2X BASIC
SPECTRUM PRINT RUN 150 #'d SETS
RANDOM INSERTS IN PACKS
1 Mark Prior .75 2.00
Kerry Wood
2 Barry Zito .75 2.00
Tim Hudson
3 Curt Schilling .75 2.00
Pedro Martinez
4 Will Clark .75 2.00
Matt Williams
5 Bernie Williams .75 2.00
Jason Giambi
6 Vernon Wells 1.25 3.00
Roy Halladay
7 Josh Beckett .75 2.00
A.J. Burnett
8 Dale Murphy .50 1.25
Phil Niekro
9 Mike Schmidt 2.50 6.00
Steve Carlton
10 Tony Oliva 1.25 3.00
Harmon Killebrew
11 Robin Yount 1.25 3.00
Paul Molitor
12 Francisco Rodriguez .75 2.00
Troy Percival
13 Ben Sheets .50 1.25
Danny Kolb
14 Andruw Jones .50 1.25
Rafael Furcal
15 Todd Helton .75 2.00
Preston Wilson
16 Wade Boggs .75 2.00
Fred McGriff
17 Manny Ramirez 1.25 3.00
David Ortiz
18 Miguel Cabrera 1.25 3.00
Dontrelle Willis
19 Edgar Renteria .75 2.00
Scott Rolen
20 Carlos Beltran .50 1.25
Jeff Kent
21 Eric Davis .75 2.00
Deion Sanders
22 Frank Thomas .75 2.00
Paul Konerko
23 Mike Piazza 1.25 3.00
Al Leiter
24 Sean Burroughs .50 1.25
Ryan Klesko
25 Ken Harvey .50 1.25
Mike Sweeney
26 Deion Sanders 2.00 5.00
Hideki Matsui
27 Steve Carlton .75 2.00
Mark Buehrle
28 Gaylord Perry 1.25 3.00
Randy Johnson
29 Joe Morgan .50 1.25
Steve Carlton
30 Vladimir Guerrero 1.25 3.00
Orlando Cabrera
31 Scott Rolen .75 2.00
John Kruk
32 Aaron Boone .50 1.25
Dmitri Young
33 Rickey Henderson 1.25 3.00
Vladimir Guerrero
34 Charles Johnson .50 1.25
Cliff Floyd
35 Cal Ripken 5.00 12.00
Rafael Palmeiro
36 Nolan Ryan .75 2.00
Francisco Rodriguez
37 Darin Erstad .75 2.00
Jim Edmonds
38 Troy Glaus .75 2.00
Rickey Henderson
39 Byung-Hyun Kim .50 1.25
Reggie Sanders
40 Andres Galarraga 1.25 3.00
David Justice
41 Brian Jordan .50 1.25
Ryan Klesko
42 Erik Bedard .50 1.25
Geronimo Gil
43 Brooks Robinson .75 2.00
Will Clark
44 Josh Towers .50 1.25
Erik Bedard
45 Nomar Garciaparra 1.25 3.00
Wade Boggs
46 Jason Varitek 1.25 3.00
Wade Boggs
47 Juan Cruz .50 1.25
Hee Seop Choi
48 Derrek Lee .50 1.25
Corey Patterson
49 Joe Borchard .50 1.25
Ray Durham
50 Eric Davis .50 1.25
Sean Casey
51 Dmitri Young .50 1.25
Wily Mo Pena
52 Early Wynn .75 2.00
Hal Newhouser
53 Sean Casey .50 1.25
Russell Branyan
54 Bert Blyleven .75 2.00
Jim Thome
55 Juan Uribe .50 1.25
Juan Pierre
56 Juan Encarnacion .50 1.25
Robert Fick
57 Dmitri Young .50 1.25
Juan Encarnacion
58 Magglio Ordonez .75 2.00
Bobby Higginson
59 Charles Johnson .50 1.25
Ryan Dempster
60 Cliff Floyd .50 1.25
Ryan Dempster
61 Mike Lowell .50 1.25
Cliff Floyd
62 Dontrelle Willis .50 1.25
Charles Johnson
63 Jose Cruz .50 1.25
Kirk Saarloos
64 Jeff Bagwell .75 2.00
Richard Hidalgo
65 Lance Berkman .75 2.00
Richard Hidalgo
66 Runelvys Hernandez .50 1.25
Mike Sweeney
67 Runelvys Hernandez .50 1.25
Willie Wilson
68 John Buck .50 1.25
Runelvys Hernandez
69 Angel Berroa .50 1.25
Jeremy Affeldt
70 Chan Ho Park .75 2.00
Kazuhisa Ishii
71 Shawn Green .50 1.25
Kazuhisa Ishii
72 Shawn Green .75 2.00
Rickey Henderson
73 Richie Sexson .50 1.25
Lyle Overbay
74 David Ortiz 1.25 3.00
J.C. Romero
75 David Ortiz 1.25 3.00
Kirby Puckett
76 Michael Barrett .50 1.25
Rondell White
77 Zach Day .50 1.25
Michael Barrett
78 Tony Armas Jr. .50 1.25
Zach Day
79 Rickey Henderson .75 2.00
Edgardo Alfonzo
80 Hideki Matsui 2.00 5.00
Bernie Williams
81 Don Mattingly 2.50 6.00
Hideki Matsui
82 Mark Ellis .50 1.25
Terrence Long
83 Ramon Hernandez .50 1.25
Erubiel Durazo
84 Brandon Duckworth .50 1.25
Anderson Machado
85 Craig Wilson .50 1.25
Freddy Sanchez
86 Brian Lawrence .50 1.25
Dennis Tankersley
87 Tony Gwynn .75 2.00
Trevor Hoffman
88 Andres Galarraga .50 1.25
Pedro Feliz
89 Jeff Kent .50 1.25
J.T. Snow
90 Freddy Garcia .50 1.25
John Olerud
91 Freddy Garcia .75 2.00
Edgar Martinez
92 So Taguchi .50 1.25
J.D. Drew
93 Ben Grieve .50 1.25
Brandon Backe
94 Dewon Brazelton .50 1.25
Joe Kennedy
95 Toby Hall .50 1.25
Pete LaForest
96 Frankie Francisco .50 1.25
Gabe Kapler
97 Travis Hafner .50 1.25
Doug Davis
98 Jeff Kent .50 1.25
Raul Mondesi
99 Shawn Green .50 1.25
Orlando Hudson
100 Marlon Byrd .50 1.25
Preston Wilson

2005 Absolute Memorabilia Team Tandems Swatch Single

OVERALL AU-GU ODDS ONE PER PACK
PRINT RUNS B/WN 5-150 COPIES PER
NO PRICING ON QTY OF 10 OR LESS
ALL ARE DUAL JERSEY UNLESS NOTED
1 Mark Prior Jsy 3.00 8.00
Kerry Wood Jsy/125
2 Barry Zito Jsy 2.50 6.00
Tim Hudson Jsy/125
3 Curt Schilling Jsy 3.00 8.00
Pedro Martinez Jsy/125
4 Will Clark Jsy 3.00 8.00
Matt Williams Jsy/125
5 Bernie Williams Jsy 3.00 8.00
Jason Giambi Jsy/125
6 Vernon Wells Jsy 2.50 6.00
Roy Halladay Jsy/125
7 Josh Beckett Jsy 2.50 6.00
A.J. Burnett Jsy/125
8 Dale Murphy Jsy 6.00 15.00
Phil Niekro Jsy/125
9 Mike Schmidt Jsy 6.00 15.00
Steve Carlton Jsy/125
10 Tony Oliva Jsy 10.00 25.00
Harmon Killebrew Jsy/50
11 Robin Yount Jsy 6.00 15.00
Paul Molitor Jsy/125
12 Francisco Rodriguez Jsy 4.00 10.00
Troy Percival Jsy/25
13 Ben Sheets Jsy 2.50 6.00
Danny Kolb Jsy/125
14 Andruw Jones Jsy 3.00 8.00
Rafael Furcal Jsy/125
15 Todd Helton Jsy 3.00 8.00
Preston Wilson Jsy/125
16 Wade Boggs Jsy 4.00 10.00
Fred McGriff Jsy/50
17 Manny Ramirez Jsy 5.00 12.00
David Ortiz Jsy/125
18 Miguel Cabrera Jsy 3.00 8.00
Dontrelle Willis Jsy/125
19 Edgar Renteria Jsy 3.00 8.00
Scott Rolen Jsy/125
20 Carlos Beltran Jsy 2.50 6.00
Jeff Kent Bat/125
21 Eric Davis Bat 3.00 8.00
Deion Sanders Jsy/125
22 Frank Thomas Jsy 5.00 12.00
Paul Konerko Jsy/50
23 Mike Piazza Jsy 4.00 10.00
Al Leiter Jsy/125
24 Sean Burroughs Jsy 2.50 6.00
Ryan Klesko Jsy/125
25 Ken Harvey Jsy 2.50 6.00
Mike Sweeney Jsy/125
26 Hideki Matsui Jsy 10.00 25.00
Deion Sanders Jsy/125
27 Steve Carlton Jsy 3.00 8.00
Mark Buehrle Jsy/50
28 Randy Johnson Jsy 4.00 10.00
Gaylord Perry Jsy/125
29 Joe Morgan Jsy 4.00 10.00
Steve Carlton Jsy/25
30 Vladimir Guerrero Jsy
Orlando Cabrera Jsy/10
31 Scott Rolen Jsy 3.00 8.00
John Kruk Jsy/125
32 Aaron Boone Jsy 2.50 6.00
Dmitri Young Jsy/125
33 Rickey Henderson Hat 6.00 15.00
Vladimir Guerrero Jsy/25
34 Cliff Floyd Jsy 2.50 6.00
Charles Johnson Jsy/125
35 Rafael Palmeiro Jsy 10.00 25.00
Cal Ripken Jsy/125
36 Nolan Ryan Jsy 10.00 25.00
Francisco Rodriguez Jsy/75
37 Darin Erstad Jsy 4.00 10.00
Jim Edmonds Bat/25
38 Troy Glaus Jsy 4.00 10.00
Rickey Henderson Bat/150
39 Byung-Hyun Kim Jsy 2.50 6.00
Reggie Sanders Jsy/150
40 Andres Galarraga Jsy 3.00 8.00
David Justice Jsy/150
41 Brian Jordan Jsy 2.50 6.00
Ryan Klesko Jsy/150
42 Erik Bedard Jsy
Geronimo Gil Jsy/5
43 Brooks Robinson Bat 3.00 8.00
Will Clark Bat/150
44 Josh Towers Pants 2.50 6.00
Erik Bedard Jsy/150
45 Nomar Garciaparra Bat 4.00 10.00
Wade Boggs Bat/150
46 Jason Varitek Bat 4.00 10.00
Wade Boggs Bat/150
47 Juan Cruz Hat 2.50 6.00
Hee Seop Choi Jsy/75
48 Derrek Lee Jsy 4.00 10.00
Corey Patterson Shoe/50
49 Joe Borchard Jsy 2.50 6.00
Ray Durham Jsy/75
50 Eric Davis Bat 2.50 6.00
Sean Casey Jsy/150
51 Dmitri Young Jsy 2.50 6.00
Wily Mo Pena Bat/150
52 Early Wynn Jsy 3.00 8.00
Hal Newhouser Jsy/150
53 Sean Casey Jsy 2.50 6.00
Russell Branyan Jsy/150
55 Juan Uribe Jsy 2.50 6.00
Juan Pierre Bat/150
56 Juan Encarnacion Jsy 2.50 6.00
Robert Fick Bat/150
57 Dmitri Young Jsy 2.50 6.00
Juan Encarnacion Jsy/150
58 Magglio Ordonez Bat 2.50 6.00
Bobby Higginson Bat/150
59 Charles Johnson Jsy 2.50 6.00
Ryan Dempster Jsy/150
60 Cliff Floyd Bat 2.50 6.00
Ryan Dempster Jsy/150
61 Mike Lowell Jsy 2.50 6.00
Cliff Floyd Bat/150
62 Dontrelle Willis Bat 2.50 6.00
Charles Johnson Jsy/150
63 Jose Cruz Jsy 2.50 6.00
Kirk Saarloos Jsy/150
64 Jeff Bagwell Pants 3.00 8.00
Richard Hidalgo Jsy/150
65 Lance Berkman Bat 2.50 6.00
Richard Hidalgo Pants/150
66 Runelvys Hernandez Jsy 3.00 8.00
Mike Sweeney Bat/50
67 Runelvys Hernandez Jsy 3.00 8.00
Willie Wilson Bat/50
68 John Buck Bat 3.00 8.00
Runelvys Hernandez Jsy/50
69 Angel Berroa Bat 2.50 6.00
Jeremy Affeldt Shoe/100
70 Chan Ho Park Jsy 2.50 6.00
Kazuhisa Ishii Jsy/150
71 Shawn Green Bat 2.50 6.00
Kazuhisa Ishii Jsy/150
72 Shawn Green Bat 4.00 10.00
Rickey Henderson Bat/150
73 Richie Sexson Jsy 2.50 6.00
Lyle Overbay Jsy/100
74 David Ortiz Jsy 4.00 10.00
J.C. Romero Jsy/150
75 David Ortiz Jsy 4.00 10.00
Kirby Puckett Bat/150
76 Michael Barrett Jsy 3.00 8.00
Rondell White Jsy/150
77 Zach Day Jsy 3.00 8.00
Michael Barrett Jsy/50
78 Tony Armas Jr. Jsy 2.50 6.00
Zach Day Jsy/150
79 Rickey Henderson Jkt 4.00 10.00
Edgardo Alfonzo Bat/150
80 Hideki Matsui Bat 10.00 25.00
Bernie Williams Bat/150
81 Don Mattingly Bat 10.00 25.00
Hideki Matsui Bat/150
82 Mark Ellis Jsy 2.50 6.00
Terrence Long Jsy/150
83 Ramon Hernandez Jsy 2.50 6.00
Erubiel Durazo Bat/150
84 Brandon Duckworth Jsy 2.50 6.00
Anderson Machado Jsy/150
85 Craig Wilson Bat 2.50 6.00
Freddy Sanchez Bat/150
86 Brian Lawrence Bat 2.50 6.00
Dennis Tankersley Bat/150
87 Tony Gwynn Pants 6.00 15.00
Trevor Hoffman Jsy/150
88 Andres Galarraga Bat 4.00 10.00
Pedro Feliz Shoe/50
89 Jeff Kent Jsy 2.50 6.00
J.T. Snow Jsy/150
90 Freddy Garcia Jsy 3.00 8.00
John Olerud Jsy/50
91 Freddy Garcia Jsy 3.00 8.00
Edgar Martinez Jsy/100
92 So Taguchi Jsy 2.50 6.00
J.D. Drew Bat/150
93 Ben Grieve Jsy 2.50 6.00
Brandon Backe Jsy/100
94 Dewon Brazelton Jsy 2.50 6.00
Joe Kennedy Bat/75
95 Toby Hall Jsy 2.50 6.00
Pete LaForest Bat/150
96 Frankie Francisco Jsy 2.50 6.00
Gabe Kapler Jsy/100
97 Travis Hafner Jsy 2.50 6.00
Doug Davis Jsy/100
98 Jeff Kent Jsy 2.50 6.00
Raul Mondesi Jsy/100
100 Marlon Byrd Bat 2.50 6.00
Preston Wilson Bat/150

2005 Absolute Memorabilia Team Tandems Swatch Single Spectrum

*SPEC: p/r 75: .4X TO 1X SNG p/r 75-150
*SPEC: p/r 25: .6X TO 1.5X SNG p/r 75-150
*SPEC: p/r 25: .5X TO 1.2X SNG p/r 50
*SPEC: p/r 15: .6X TO 1.5X SNG p/r 50
OVERALL AU-GU ODDS ONE PER PACK
PRINT RUNS B/WN 1-75 COPIES PER
NO PRICING ON QTY OF 10 OR LESS

2005 Absolute Memorabilia Team Tandems Swatch Single Spectrum Prime Black

*PRIMEp/r70-150: .5X TO 1.2X SNGp/r75-150
*PRIME p/r 70-150: .4X TO 1X SNG p/r 50
*PRIMEp/r40-65: .6X TO 1.5X SNGp/r75-150
*PRIME p/r 25: .75X TO 2X SNG p/r 75-150
*PRIME p/r 15: 1X TO 2.5X SNG p/r 75-150
*PRIME p/r 15: .75X TO 2X SNG p/r 50
*PRIME p/r 15: .6X TO 1.5X SNG p/r 25
OVERALL AU-GU ODDS ONE PER PACK
PRINT RUNS B/WN 1-150 COPIES PER
NO PRICING ON QTY OF 1
30 Vladimir Guerrero Jsy 10.00 25.00
Orlando Cabrera Jsy/15
42 Erik Bedard Jsy 4.00 10.00
Geronimo Gil Jsy/65
54 Bert Blyleven Jsy 4.00 10.00
Jim Thome Jsy/125

2005 Absolute Memorabilia Team Tandems Swatch Double

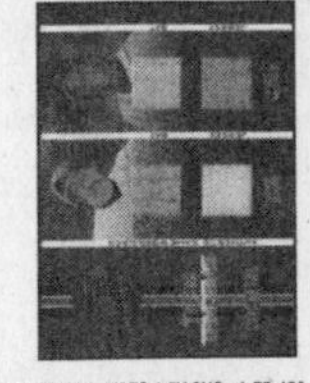

*DBL p/r 70-150: .6X TO 1.5X SNG p/r 75-150
*DBL p/r 70-150: .5X TO 1.2X SNG p/r 50
*DBL p/r 70-150: .4X TO 1X SNG p/r 25
*DBL p/r 50: .75X TO 2X SNG p/r 75-150
*DBL p/r 50: .6X TO 1.5X SNG p/r 50
*DBL p/r 50: .5X TO 1.2X SNG p/r 25
*DBL p/r 25: 1X TO 2.5X SNG p/r 75-150
*DBL p/r 25: .75X TO 2X SNG p/r 50
*DBL p/r 25: .6X TO 1.5X SNG p/r 25
OVERALL AU-GU ODDS ONE PER PACK
PRINT RUNS B/WN 1-150 COPIES PER
NO PRICING ON QTY OF 10 OR LESS
42 Geronimo Gil Bat-Jsy 4.00 10.00
Erik Bedard Bat-Jsy/150

2005 Absolute Memorabilia Team Tandems Swatch Double Spectrum

*SPECp/r70-100: .6X TO 1.5X SNGp/r75-150
*SPEC p/r 70-100: .5X TO 1.2X SNG p/r 50
*SPEC p/r 50-65: .75X TO 2X SNG p/r 75-150
*SPEC p/r 25: 1X TO 2.5X SNG p/r 75-150
*SPEC p/r 25: .6X TO 1.5X SNG p/r 50
OVERALL AU-GU ODDS ONE PER PACK
PRINT RUNS B/WN 1-100 COPIES PER
NO PRICING ON QTY OF 10 OR LESS
42 Erik Bedard Bat-Jsy 5.00 12.00
Geronimo Gil Bat-Jsy/65

2005 Absolute Memorabilia Team Tandems Swatch Double Spectrum Prime Black

*PRIME p/r 15: 1.5X TO 4X SNG p/r 125
*PRIME p/r 15: 1.25X TO 3X SNG p/r 50
*PRIME p/r 15: 1X TO 2.5X SNG p/r 25
OVERALL AU-GU ODDS ONE PER PACK
PRINT RUNS B/WN 1-15 COPIES PER
NO PRICING ON QTY OF 1
30 Vladimir Guerrero Jsy-Jsy 15.00 40.00
Orlando Cabrera Bat-Jsy/15

2005 Absolute Memorabilia Team Trios

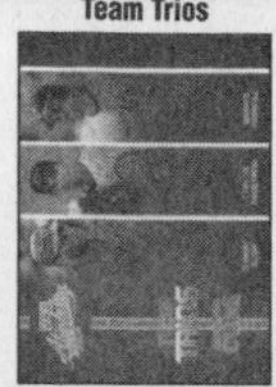

STATED PRINT RUN 200 SERIAL #'d SETS
*SPEC: .5X TO 1.2X BASIC
SPECTRUM PRINT RUN 125 #'d SETS
RANDOM INSERTS IN PACKS
1 Cal Ripken 6.00 15.00
Jim Palmer
Eddie Murray
2 Roger Clemens 2.00 5.00
Wade Boggs
Dwight Evans
3 Rafael Palmeiro 1.00 2.50
Miguel Tejada
Javy Lopez
4 Carl Crawford 1.00 2.50
Rocco Baldelli
B.J. Upton
5 Mark Buehrle 1.00 2.50
Magglio Ordonez
Carlos Lee
6 Victor Martinez 1.00 2.50
Travis Hafner
Jody Gerut
7 Bobby Abreu .60 1.50
Brett Myers
Kevin Millwood
8 Sammy Sosa 1.00 2.50
Aramis Ramirez
Carlos Zambrano
9 Bo Jackson 3.00 8.00
George Brett
Carlos Beltran
10 Hideo Nomo .60 1.50
Adrian Beltre
Shawn Green
11 Craig Wilson .60 1.50
Jack Wilson
Jason Bay
12 Tom Seaver 4.00 10.00
Nolan Ryan
Dwight Gooden
13 David Dellucci .60 1.50
Laynce Nix
Kevin Mench
14 Alan Trammell .60 1.50
Jack Morris
Kirk Gibson
15 Matt Williams 1.50 4.00
Mark Grace
Randy Johnson
16 Andre Dawson 1.00 2.50
Gary Carter
Tony Perez
17 Dale Murphy .60 1.50
John Kruk
Lenny Dykstra
18 Brian Roberts .60 1.50
Jay Gibbons
Larry Bigbie
19 Mike Lowell 1.00 2.50
Ivan Rodriguez
Brad Penny
20 Eddie Murray .60 1.50
Darryl Strawberry
Al Oliver
21 Gary Sheffield 1.00 2.50
Rickey Henderson
Darryl Strawberry
22 Roberto Alomar 1.00 2.50
Ray Durham
Joe Crede
23 Jason Kendall .60 1.50
Aramis Ramirez
Brian Giles
24 Delmon Young 1.50 4.00
Aubrey Huff
Tino Martinez
25 Jeff Bagwell 1.00 2.50
Joe Morgan
Jose Cruz
26 Jeff Kent .60 1.50
Rich Aurilia
J.T. Snow
27 Fergie Jenkins .60 1.50
Nolan Ryan
Francisco Cordero
28 Kenny Lofton 1.00 2.50
Roberto Alomar
Jim Thome
29 Jason Jennings 1.00 2.50
Garrett Atkins
Todd Helton
30 Pedro Martinez 1.50 4.00
Gary Carter
Randy Johnson
31 Francisco Rodriguez 1.00 2.50
Troy Glaus
Casey Kotchman
32 Byung-Hyun Kim .60 1.50
Matt Williams
Tony Womack
33 David Justice 1.50 4.00
Wilson Betemit
Horacio Ramirez
34 Brian Jordan .60 1.50
Rafael Furcal
Wes Helms
35 Brooks Robinson 1.00 2.50
Luis Matos
Rodrigo Lopez
36 Rickey Henderson 1.50 4.00
Nomar Garciaparra
Wade Boggs
37 Hee Seop Choi .60 1.50
Moises Alou
Kenny Lofton
38 Bo Jackson .60 1.50
Charles Johnson
Joe Borchard
39 Brandon Phillips .60 1.50
Russell Branyan
Josh Bard
40 Juan Pierre .60 1.50
Garrett Atkins
Jason Jennings
41 Craig Monroe 1.00 2.50
Magglio Ordonez
Mike Maroth
42 Juan Pierre .60 1.50
Cliff Floyd
Ryan Dempster
43 Jeff Bagwell 1.00 2.50
Moises Alou
Richard Hidalgo
44 Lance Berkman 1.00 2.50
Richard Hidalgo
Moises Alou
45 Runelvys Hernandez .60 1.50
Frank White
Willie Wilson
46 Al Oliver 1.00 2.50
Chan Ho Park
Kazuhisa Ishii
47 Paul Molitor 1.50 4.00
Keith Ginter
Richie Sexson
48 Paul Molitor 1.50 4.00
Geoff Jenkins
Lyle Overbay
49 David Ortiz 1.50 4.00
Doug Mientkiewicz
Michael Cuddyer
50 Cliff Floyd .60 1.50
Edgardo Alfonzo
Jay Payton
51 Edgardo Alfonzo .60 1.50
Roger Cedeno
Robin Ventura
52 Jason Giambi .60 1.50
Tommy John
Kenny Lofton
53 Brandon Duckworth .60 1.50
Kenny Lofton
Marlon Byrd
54 Kenny Lofton .60 1.50
Freddy Sanchez
Craig Wilson
55 Tony Gwynn 2.00 5.00
Joe Carter
Brian Lawrence
56 J.T. Snow .60 1.50
Edgardo Alfonzo
Deivi Cruz
57 Albert Pujols 4.00 10.00
Jim Edmonds
J.D. Drew
58 Carlos Delgado .60 1.50
David Wells
Raul Mondesi
59 Orlando Hudson 1.50 4.00
Eric Hinske
Roy Halladay
60 Marlon Byrd .60 1.50
Esteban Loaiza
Preston Wilson

2005 Absolute Memorabilia Team Trios Swatch Single

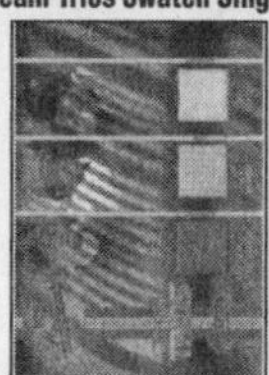

OVERALL AU-GU ODDS ONE PER PACK
PRINT RUNS B/WN 25-150 COPIES PER
1 Cal Ripken Jsy 20.00 50.00
Jim Palmer Jsy
Eddie Murray Jsy/50
2 Roger Clemens Jsy 12.50 30.00
Wade Boggs Jsy
Dwight Evans Jsy/50
3 Rafael Palmeiro Jsy 6.00 15.00
Miguel Tejada Jsy
Javy Lopez Jsy/50
4 Carl Crawford Jsy 5.00 12.00
Rocco Baldelli Jsy
B.J. Upton Bat/50
5 Mark Buehrle Jsy 5.00 12.00
Magglio Ordonez Jsy
Carlos Lee Jsy/50
6 Victor Martinez Jsy 5.00 12.00
Travis Hafner Jsy
Jody Gerut Jsy/50
7 Bobby Abreu Jsy 5.00 12.00
Brett Myers Jsy
Kevin Millwood Jsy/50
8 Sammy Sosa Jsy 8.00 20.00
Aramis Ramirez Jsy
Carlos Zambrano Jsy/50
9 Bo Jackson Jsy 12.50 30.00
George Brett Jsy
Carlos Beltran Jsy/50
10 Hideo Nomo Jsy 8.00 20.00
Adrian Beltre Jsy
Shawn Green Jsy/50
11 Craig Wilson Jsy 5.00 12.00
Jack Wilson Jsy
Jason Bay Jsy/50
12 Tom Seaver Bat 15.00 40.00
Nolan Ryan Jsy
Dwight Gooden Jsy/50
13 David Dellucci Jsy 5.00 12.00
Laynce Nix Jsy
Kevin Mench Jsy/50
14 Alan Trammell Jsy 5.00 12.00
Jack Morris Jsy
Kirk Gibson Jsy/50
15 Matt Williams Jsy 8.00 20.00
Mark Grace Bat
Randy Johnson Jsy/50
16 Andre Dawson Jsy 5.00 12.00
Gary Carter Jsy
Tony Perez Jsy/50
17 Dale Murphy Jsy 8.00 20.00
John Kruk Jsy
Lenny Dykstra Jsy/50
18 Brian Roberts Jsy 5.00 12.00
Jay Gibbons Jsy
Larry Bigbie Jsy/50
19 Mike Lowell Jsy 6.00 15.00
Ivan Rodriguez Jsy
Brad Penny Jsy/50
20 Eddie Murray Jsy 8.00 20.00
Darryl Strawberry Jsy
Al Oliver Jsy/50
21 Darryl Strawberry Jsy 6.00 15.00
Rickey Henderson Pants
Gary Sheffield Jsy/50
22 Roberto Alomar Jsy 6.00 15.00
Joe Crede Hat
Ray Durham Jsy/50
23 Jason Kendall Jsy 6.00 15.00
Brian Giles Jsy
Aramis Ramirez Jsy/25
24 Delmon Young Bat 6.00 15.00
Aubrey Huff Jsy
Tino Martinez Jsy/50
25 Jeff Bagwell Jsy 6.00 15.00
Jose Cruz Jsy
Joe Morgan Bat/50
26 J.T. Snow Jsy 5.00 12.00
Rich Aurilia Jsy
Jeff Kent Jsy/50
27 Fergie Jenkins Jsy 10.00 25.00
Nolan Ryan Jsy
Francisco Cordero Jsy/50
28 Kenny Lofton Fld Glv 6.00 15.00
Jim Thome Bat
Roberto Alomar Jsy/50
29 Garrett Atkins Jsy 6.00 15.00
Todd Helton Jsy
Jason Jennings Jsy/50
30 Gary Carter Jsy 8.00 20.00
Pedro Martinez Jsy
Randy Johnson Jsy/50
31 Francisco Rodriguez Jsy 4.00 10.00
Troy Glaus Bat
Casey Kotchman Bat/150
32 Byung-Hyun Kim Jsy 5.00 12.00
Matt Williams Bat
Tony Womack Jsy/150
33 David Justice Bat 5.00 12.00
Horacio Ramirez Fld Glv
Wilson Betemit Hat/50
34 Brian Jordan Jsy 4.00 10.00
Rafael Furcal Bat
Wes Helms Jsy/150
35 Brooks Robinson Bat 5.00 12.00
Luis Matos Jsy
Rodrigo Lopez Jsy/150
36 Rickey Henderson Bat 6.00 15.00
Nomar Garciaparra Bat
Wade Boggs Bat/150
37 Hee Seop Choi Jsy 4.00 10.00
Moises Alou Bat
Kenny Lofton Bat/150
38 Bo Jackson Bat 6.00 15.00
Charles Johnson Bat
Joe Borchard Bat/150
39 Brandon Phillips Bat 4.00 10.00
Russell Branyan Jsy
Josh Bard Jsy/150
40 Juan Pierre Bat 4.00 10.00
Jason Jennings Bat
Garrett Atkins Jsy/150
41 Craig Monroe Bat 4.00 10.00
Magglio Ordonez Bat
Mike Maroth Jsy/150
42 Juan Pierre Bat 4.00 10.00
Cliff Floyd Bat
Ryan Dempster Jsy/150
43 Jeff Bagwell Pants 5.00 12.00
Moises Alou Bat
Richard Hidalgo Pants/150
44 Lance Berkman Bat 4.00 10.00
Moises Alou Jsy
Richard Hidalgo Pants/150
45 Runelvys Hernandez Jsy 4.00 10.00
Frank White Bat
Willie Wilson Bat/150
46 Al Oliver Jsy 4.00 10.00
Chan Ho Park Jsy
Kazuhisa Ishii Jsy/150
47 Paul Molitor Bat 6.00 15.00
Richie Sexson Jsy
Keith Ginter Shoe/25
48 Paul Molitor Bat 4.00 10.00
Lyle Overbay Jsy
Geoff Jenkins Jsy/150
49 David Ortiz Jsy 5.00 12.00
Doug Mientkiewicz Bat
Michael Cuddyer Bat/150
50 Cliff Floyd Bat 4.00 10.00
Edgardo Alfonzo Bat
Jay Payton Jsy/150
51 Edgardo Alfonzo Bat 4.00 10.00
Robin Ventura Bat
Roger Cedeno Bat/150
52 Jason Giambi Jsy 4.00 10.00
Tommy John Bat
Kenny Lofton Bat/150
53 Brandon Duckworth Jsy 4.00 10.00
Kenny Lofton Bat
Marlon Byrd Bat/150
54 Kenny Lofton Bat 4.00 10.00
Craig Wilson Bat
Freddy Sanchez Bat/150
55 Tony Gwynn Pants 6.00 15.00
Joe Carter Bat
Brian Lawrence Jsy/150
56 J.T. Snow Jsy 4.00 10.00
Edgardo Alfonzo Bat
Deivi Cruz Bat/150
57 Albert Pujols Bat 10.00 25.00
Jim Edmonds Bat
J.D. Drew Bat/100
59 Orlando Hudson Bat 4.00 10.00
Eric Hinske Jsy
Roy Halladay Jsy/150
60 Marlon Byrd Bat 4.00 10.00
Preston Wilson Bat
Esteban Loaiza Bat/150

2005 Absolute Memorabilia Team Trios Swatch Single Spectrum

*SPEC p/r 50: .4X TO 1X SNG p/r 50
*SPEC p/r 25: .6X TO 1.5X SNG p/r 100-150
*SPEC p/r 25: .5X TO 1.2X SNG p/r 50
*SPEC p/r 25: .4X TO 1X SNG p/r 25
OVERALL AU-GU ODDS ONE PER PACK
PRINT RUNS B/WN 10-50 COPIES PER
NO PRICING ON QTY OF 10

2005 Absolute Memorabilia Team Trios Swatch Single Spectrum Prime Black

*PRIMEp/r40-50: .6X TO 1.5X SNGp/r100-150
*PRIMEp/r100-150:.5XTO1.2XSNGp/r100-150
OVERALL AU-GU ODDS ONE PER PACK
PRINT RUNS B/WN 10-150 COPIES PER
NO PRICING ON QTY OF 10

2005 Absolute Memorabilia Team Trios Swatch Double

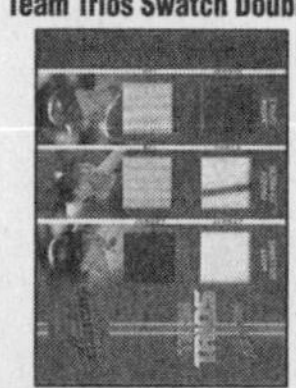

*DBL p/r 100: .6X TO 1.5X SNG p/r 50
*DBL p/r 50: .75X TO 2X SNG p/r 50
*DBL p/r 25: 1X TO 2.5X SNG p/r 50
OVERALL AU-GU ODDS ONE PER PACK
PRINT RUNS B/WN 25-100 COPIES PER

2005 Absolute Memorabilia Team Trios Swatch Double Spectrum

*SPEC p/r 35: .5X TO 1.2X SNG p/r 50
PRINT RUNS B/WN 5-35 COPIES PER
NO PRICING ON QTY OF 10 OR LESS
PRIME BLACK PRINT RUNS B/WN 5-10 PER
NO PRIME BLK PRICING DUE TO SCARCITY
OVERALL AU-GU ODDS ONE PER PACK

2005 Absolute Memorabilia Team Quads

STATED PRINT RUN 150 SERIAL #'d SETS
*SPEC: .5X TO 1.2X BASIC
SPECTRUM PRINT RUN 100 #'d SETS
RANDOM INSERTS IN PACKS
1 Albert Pujols 4.00 10.00
Larry Walker
Scott Rolen
Jim Edmonds
2 Lou Boudreau 1.00 2.50
Bob Feller
Early Wynn
Hal Newhouser
3 Don Sutton 1.50 4.00
Rod Carew
Reggie Jackson
Tommy John
4 Jim Rice 1.00 2.50
Fred Lynn
Luis Tiant
Carlton Fisk
5 Hideki Matsui 2.50 6.00
Gary Sheffield
Mike Mussina
Jorge Posada
6 Greg Maddux 2.50 6.00
Tom Glavine
Chipper Jones
David Justice
7 Johnny Damon 1.00 2.50
Jermaine Dye
Eric Chavez
Mark Ellis
8 Vladimir Guerrero 1.50 4.00
Garret Anderson
Troy Glaus
Darin Erstad
9 Michael Young 1.50 4.00
Alfonso Soriano
Hank Blalock
Mark Teixeira
10 Torii Hunter 1.50 4.00
Shannon Stewart
Johan Santana
Jacque Jones
11 Mike Piazza 1.50 4.00
Kazuo Matsui
Jose Reyes
Tom Glavine
12 Roger Clemens 4.00 10.00
Nolan Ryan
Don Sutton
Randy Johnson
13 Tony Gwynn 2.00 5.00
Rickey Henderson
Steve Garvey
Willie McCovey
14 Sean Casey 1.00 2.50
Adam Dunn
Austin Kearns
Ryan Wagner
15 Nolan Ryan 4.00 10.00
Ivan Rodriguez
Juan Gonzalez
Rafael Palmeiro
16 Roger Clemens 3.00 8.00
Phil Rizzuto
Whitey Ford
Don Mattingly
17 Dennis Eckersley 2.50 6.00
Ozzie Smith
Edgar Renteria
Keith Hernandez
18 Willie Stargell .60 1.50
Bill Madlock
Dave Parker
Jason Bay
19 Mark Prior 1.00 2.50
Mark Grace
Andre Dawson
Ron Santo
20 Paul Molitor 1.50 4.00
Rod Carew
Kirby Puckett
Torii Hunter
21 Troy Glaus 1.00 2.50
Casey Kotchman
Darin Erstad
Rickey Henderson
22 Curt Schilling 1.00 2.50
Tony Womack
Matt Kata
Tony Clark
23 Dale Murphy .60 1.50
Chipper Jones
Kenny Lofton
Ryan Klesko
24 Greg Maddux 1.50 4.00
Tom Glavine
John Smoltz
Phil Niekro
25 Andres Galarraga 1.00 2.50
Deion Sanders
Kenny Lofton
Ryan Klesko
26 Luis Matos 1.00 2.50
Rodrigo Lopez
Brooks Robinson
Erik Bedard
27 Manny Ramirez 1.50 4.00
Jason Varitek
Wade Boggs
Nomar Garciaparra
28 Roger Clemens 2.00 5.00
Wade Boggs
Carlton Fisk
Nomar Garciaparra
29 David Ortiz 1.50 4.00
Trot Nixon
Jason Varitek
Manny Ramirez
30 Andre Dawson 1.50 4.00
Sammy Sosa
Hee Seop Choi
Kenny Lofton
31 Roberto Alomar 1.50 4.00
Frank Thomas
Ray Durham
Carl Everett
32 Bo Jackson .60 1.50
Joe Borchard
Carlos Lee
Charles Johnson
33 Bo Jackson 1.00 2.50
Magglio Ordonez
Carlton Fisk
Robin Ventura
34 Dave Concepcion .60 1.50
Joe Morgan
George Foster
Eric Davis
35 Adam Dunn 1.00 2.50
Sean Casey
Wily Mo Pena
Dmitri Young
36 Joe Morgan 1.00 2.50
George Foster
Paul O'Neill
Adam Dunn
37 C.C. Sabathia 1.00 2.50
Joe Carter
Russell Branyan
Sean Casey
38 Larry Walker 1.00 2.50
Clint Barmes
Charles Johnson
Garrett Atkins
39 Garrett Atkins .60 1.50
Jeff Baker
Jason Jennings
Juan Pierre
40 Bobby Higginson .60 1.50
Craig Monroe
Mike Maroth
Franklyn German
41 A.J. Burnett 1.00 2.50
Dontrelle Willis
Juan Pierre
Paul Lo Duca
42 Paul Lo Duca .60 1.50
Mike Lowell
Juan Pierre
Cliff Floyd
43 Craig Biggio 1.00 2.50
Jeff Bagwell
Moises Alou
Jason Lane
44 Jose Cruz 1.00 2.50
Kirk Saarloos
Jeff Bagwell
Richard Hidalgo
45 Joe Morgan 1.00 2.50
Wade Miller
Lance Berkman
Richard Hidalgo
46 Frank White .60 1.50
Willie Wilson
Angel Berroa
John Buck
47 Rickey Henderson .60 1.50
Kazuhisa Ishii
Shawn Green
Al Oliver
48 Chan Ho Park 1.00 2.50
Kazuhisa Ishii
Shawn Green
Kevin Brown
49 Paul Molitor 1.50 4.00
Richie Sexson
Lyle Overbay
Geoff Jenkins
50 Kirby Puckett 1.50 4.00
Harmon Killebrew
Paul Molitor
Tony Oliva
51 Kirby Puckett 1.50 4.00
David Ortiz
Michael Cuddyer
Matt Lawton
52 Kirby Puckett 1.50 4.00
Paul Molitor
David Ortiz
Michael Cuddyer
53 Tony Armas Jr. .60 1.50
Zach Day
Cliff Floyd
Jose Vidro
54 Javier Vazquez .60 1.50
Cliff Floyd
Tony Armas Jr.
Zach Day
55 Willie Mays 3.00 8.00
Mike Piazza
Edgardo Alfonzo
Robin Ventura
56 Rickey Henderson 2.50 6.00
Robin Ventura
David Wright
Edgardo Alfonzo
57 Don Mattingly 3.00 8.00
Jason Giambi
Bernie Williams
Jorge Posada
58 Mariano Rivera 1.50 4.00
Tommy John
Phil Niekro
Paul O'Neill
59 Wade Boggs 1.00 2.50
Robin Ventura
Paul O'Neill
Kenny Lofton
60 Erubiel Durazo .60 1.50
Mark Ellis
Ramon Hernandez
Terrence Long
61 Bobby Abreu .60 1.50
Joe Morgan
Kenny Lofton
Marlon Byrd
62 Kenny Lofton .60 1.50
Kevin Millwood
Marlon Byrd
Matt Kata
63 Kenny Lofton .60 1.50
Craig Wilson
Freddy Sanchez
Jason Bay
64 Tony Gwynn 1.00 2.50
Joe Carter
Trevor Hoffman
Brian Lawrence
65 Willie McCovey 1.00 2.50
Andres Galarraga
Kenny Lofton
Jose Cruz Jr.
66 Andres Galarraga .60 1.50
J.T. Snow
Jose Cruz Jr.
Deivi Cruz
67 John Olerud .60 1.50
Freddy Garcia
Chris Snelling
Bret Boone
68 Albert Pujols 4.00 10.00
Scott Rolen
J.D. Drew
So Taguchi
69 Brandon Backe .60 1.50
Chad Gaudin
Dewon Brazelton
Toby Hall
70 Wade Boggs 1.50 4.00
Delmon Young
Toby Hall
Joey Gathright
71 Alfonso Soriano 1.50 4.00
Hank Blalock
Mark Teixeira
Michael Young
72 Ivan Rodriguez .60 1.50
Kevin Mench
Gabe Kapler
Richard Hidalgo
73 Mark Teixeira 1.50 4.00
Travis Hafner
Gabe Kapler
Frankie Francisco
74 Shawn Green .60 1.50
Orlando Hudson
Josh Phelps
Shannon Stewart
75 Carlos Delgado .60 1.50
Josh Phelps
Raul Mondesi
Orlando Hudson

2005 Absolute Memorabilia Team Quads Swatch Single

OVERALL AU-GU ODDS ONE PER PACK
PRINT RUNS B/WN 25-150 COPIES PER
1 Albert Pujols Jsy 10.00 25.00
Larry Walker Bat
Scott Rolen Jsy
Jim Edmonds Jsy/100
2 Lou Boudreau Jsy 15.00 40.00
Bob Feller Pants
Early Wynn Jsy
Hal Newhouser Jsy/100
3 Don Sutton Jsy 6.00 15.00
Rod Carew Jkt
Reggie Jackson Jsy
Tommy John Jsy/100
4 Jim Rice Jsy 6.00 15.00
Fred Lynn Jsy
Luis Tiant Hat
Carlton Fisk Bat/100
5 Hideki Matsui Jsy 10.00 25.00
Gary Sheffield Jsy
Mike Mussina Jsy
Jorge Posada Jsy/100
6 Greg Maddux Jsy 10.00 25.00
Tom Glavine Jsy
Chipper Jones Jsy
David Justice Jsy/100
7 Johnny Damon Hat 6.00 15.00
Jermaine Dye Jsy
Eric Chavez Jsy
Mark Ellis Jsy/100
8 Vladimir Guerrero Jsy 8.00 20.00
Garret Anderson Jsy
Troy Glaus Jsy
Darin Erstad Jsy/100
9 Michael Young Jsy 6.00 15.00
Alfonso Soriano Jsy
Hank Blalock Jsy
Mark Teixeira Jsy/100
10 Torii Hunter Jsy 10.00 25.00
Shannon Stewart Jsy
Johan Santana Jsy
Jacque Jones Jsy/25
11 Mike Piazza Jsy 8.00 20.00
Kazuo Matsui Jsy
Jose Reyes Jsy
Tom Glavine Jsy/100
12 Roger Clemens Jsy 15.00 40.00
Nolan Ryan Jsy
Don Sutton Jsy
Randy Johnson Jsy/100
13 Tony Gwynn Jsy 10.00 25.00
Rickey Henderson Jsy
Steve Garvey Jsy
Willie McCovey Jsy/100
14 Sean Casey Jsy 5.00 12.00
Adam Dunn Jsy
Austin Kearns Jsy
Ryan Wagner Jsy/100
15 Nolan Ryan Jsy 12.50 30.00
Ivan Rodriguez Jsy
Juan Gonzalez Jsy
Rafael Palmeiro Jsy/100
16 Whitey Ford Jsy 20.00 50.00
Don Mattingly Jsy
Phil Rizzuto Pants
Roger Clemens Jsy/100
17 Ozzie Smith Pants 15.00 40.00
Dennis Eckersley Jsy
Keith Hernandez Jsy
Edgar Renteria Jsy/25
18 Willie Stargell Jsy 6.00 15.00
Dave Parker Jsy
Jason Bay Jsy
Bill Madlock Bat/100
19 Ron Santo Bat 6.00 15.00
Andre Dawson Jsy
Mark Grace Jsy
Mark Prior Jsy/100
20 Paul Molitor Jsy 8.00 20.00
Rod Carew Jsy
Kirby Puckett Jsy
Torii Hunter Jsy/100
21 Troy Glaus Jsy 8.00 20.00
Rickey Henderson Bat
Casey Kotchman Bat
Darin Erstad Jsy/150
22 Curt Schilling Jsy 5.00 12.00
Tony Womack Jsy
Matt Kata Bat
Tony Clark Bat/150
23 Dale Murphy Bat 8.00 20.00
Chipper Jones Bat
Kenny Lofton Bat
Ryan Klesko Jsy/150
24 Greg Maddux Jsy 10.00 25.00
Phil Niekro Bat
Tom Glavine Jsy
John Smoltz Jsy/150
25 Andres Galarraga Bat 6.00 15.00
Deion Sanders Bat
Kenny Lofton Bat
Ryan Klesko Jsy/150
26 Luis Matos Jsy 6.00 15.00
Rodrigo Lopez Jsy
Brooks Robinson Bat
Erik Bedard Jsy/150
27 Manny Ramirez Bat 8.00 20.00
Jason Varitek Bat
Wade Boggs Bat
Nomar Garciaparra Bat/150
28 Roger Clemens Jsy 10.00 25.00
Wade Boggs Bat
Carlton Fisk Bat
Nomar Garciaparra Bat/150
29 David Ortiz Jsy 8.00 20.00
Trot Nixon Jsy
Jason Varitek Bat
Manny Ramirez Bat/150
30 Andre Dawson Bat 8.00 20.00
Sammy Sosa Bat
Hee Seop Choi Jsy
Kenny Lofton Bat/150
31 Roberto Alomar Jsy 8.00 20.00
Frank Thomas Bat
Ray Durham Jsy
Carl Everett Bat/150

32 Bo Jackson Bat 8.00 20.00
Joe Borchard Bat
Carlos Lee Bat
Charles Johnson Bat/150
33 Bo Jackson Bat 8.00 20.00
Carlton Fisk Bat
Robin Ventura Bat
Magglio Ordonez Bat/150
34 Dave Concepcion Bat 5.00 12.00
Joe Morgan Bat
George Foster Bat
Eric Davis Bat/100
35 Adam Dunn Bat 5.00 12.00
Sean Casey Jsy
Wily Mo Pena Bat
Dmitri Young Jsy/150
36 Joe Morgan Bat 5.00 12.00
George Foster Bat
Paul O'Neill Bat
Adam Dunn Bat/150
37 C.C. Sabathia Jsy 5.00 12.00
Joe Carter Bat
Russell Branyan Jsy
Sean Casey Jsy/150
38 Larry Walker Jsy 5.00 12.00
Clint Barmes Bat
Charles Johnson Bat
Garrett Atkins Jsy/150
39 Garrett Atkins Jsy 5.00 12.00
Jeff Baker Bat
Jason Jennings Bat
Juan Pierre Bat/150
40 Bobby Higginson Bat 5.00 12.00
Craig Monroe Bat
Mike Maroth Jsy
Franklyn German Bat/150
41 A.J. Burnett Bat 5.00 12.00
Dontrelle Willis Bat
Juan Pierre Bat
Paul Lo Duca Bat/150
42 Paul Lo Duca Bat 5.00 12.00
Mike Lowell Jsy
Juan Pierre Bat
Cliff Floyd Jsy/150
43 Craig Biggio Bat 6.00 15.00
Jeff Bagwell Pants
Moises Alou Bat
Jason Lane Bat/150
44 Jose Cruz Jsy 6.00 15.00
Kirk Saarloos Jsy
Jeff Bagwell Pants
Richard Hidalgo Pants/150
45 Joe Morgan Bat 5.00 12.00
Wade Miller Fld Glv
Lance Berkman Bat
Richard Hidalgo Bat/150
46 Frank White Bat 5.00 12.00
Willie Wilson Bat
Angel Berroa Bat
John Buck Bat/150
47 Rickey Henderson Bat 8.00 20.00
Kazuhisa Ishii Jsy
Shawn Green Bat
Al Oliver Bat/150
48 Chan Ho Park Jsy 5.00 12.00
Kazuhisa Ishii Jsy
Shawn Green Bat
Kevin Brown Jsy/150
49 Paul Molitor Bat 5.00 12.00
Richie Sexson Pants
Lyle Overbay Jsy
Geoff Jenkins Jsy/100
50 Kirby Puckett Bat 8.00 20.00
Harmon Killebrew Jsy
Paul Molitor Jsy
Tony Oliva Jsy/150
51 Kirby Puckett Bat 8.00 20.00
David Ortiz Jsy
Michael Cuddyer Bat
Matt Lawton Bat/150
52 Kirby Puckett Bat 8.00 20.00
Paul Molitor Jsy
David Ortiz Jsy
Michael Cuddyer Bat/150
53 Tony Armas Jr. Jsy 5.00 12.00
Zach Day Jsy
Cliff Floyd Bat
Jose Vidro Bat/150
54 Javier Vazquez Jsy 5.00 12.00
Cliff Floyd Bat
Tony Armas Jr. Jsy
Zach Day Pants/150
55 Willie Mays Jsy 15.00 40.00
Mike Piazza Pants
Edgardo Alfonzo Bat
Robin Ventura Bat/150
56 Rickey Henderson Jkt 8.00 20.00
Robin Ventura Bat
David Wright Bat
Edgardo Alfonzo Bat/150
57 Don Mattingly Bat 20.00 50.00
Jason Giambi Jsy
Bernie Williams Bat
Jorge Posada Jsy/150
58 Mariano Rivera Jsy 8.00 20.00
Tommy John Bat
Phil Niekro Bat
Paul O'Neill Bat/100
59 Wade Boggs Bat 6.00 15.00
Robin Ventura Bat
Paul O'Neill Bat
Kenny Lofton Bat/150
60 Erubiel Durazo Bat 5.00 12.00
Ramon Hernandez Jsy
Terrence Long Jsy
Mark Ellis Jsy/150
61 Bobby Abreu Jsy 5.00 12.00
Joe Morgan Bat
Kenny Lofton Bat
Marlon Byrd Bat/75
62 Kenny Lofton Bat 5.00 12.00
Kevin Millwood Jsy
Marlon Byrd Bat
Matt Kata Bat/150
63 Kenny Lofton Bat 5.00 12.00
Craig Wilson Jsy
Freddy Sanchez Bat
Jason Bay Bat/150
64 Tony Gwynn Pants 8.00 20.00
Joe Carter Bat
Trevor Hoffman Jsy
Brian Lawrence Bat/150
65 Willie McCovey Jsy 6.00 15.00
Andres Galarraga Jsy
Kenny Lofton Bat
Jose Cruz Jr. Bat/150
66 Andres Galarraga Bat 6.00 15.00
J.T. Snow Jsy
Jose Cruz Jr. Bat
Deivi Cruz Bat/150
67 John Olerud Bat 5.00 12.00
Freddy Garcia Jsy
Chris Snelling Bat
Bret Boone Jsy/150
68 Albert Pujols Bat 10.00 25.00
Scott Rolen Jsy
J.D. Drew Bat
So Taguchi Bat/135
69 Brandon Backe Jsy 5.00 12.00
Chad Gaudin Jsy
Dewon Brazelton Jsy
Toby Hall Jsy/150
71 Alfonso Soriano Bat 6.00 15.00
Hank Blalock Jsy
Mark Teixeira Bat
Michael Young Bat/150
72 Ivan Rodriguez Jsy 6.00 15.00
Kevin Mench Jsy
Gabe Kapler Jsy
Richard Hidalgo Bat/150
73 Mark Teixeira Bat 6.00 15.00
Gabe Kapler Jsy
Frankie Francisco Jsy
Travis Hafner Jsy/150
74 Shawn Green Bat 5.00 12.00
Orlando Hudson Bat
Josh Phelps Bat
Shannon Stewart Bat/150
75 Carlos Delgado Bat 5.00 12.00
Orlando Hudson Bat
Josh Phelps Bat
Raul Mondesi Bat/150

2005 Absolute Memorabilia Team Quads Swatch Single Spectrum

*SPEC p/r 75-100: .4X TO 1X SNG p/r 75-150
*SPEC p/r 45-50: .5X TO 1.2X SNG p/r 75-150
*SPEC p/r 25-35: .6X TO 1.5X SNG p/r 75-150
OVERALL AU-GU ODDS ONE PER PACK
PRINT RUNS B/WN 10-100 COPIES PER
NO PRICING ON QTY OF 10

2005 Absolute Memorabilia Team Quads Swatch Single Spectrum Prime Black

*PRIMEp/r100-150:.6XTO1.5XSNGp/r75-150
*PRIMEp/r50-60: .75X TO 2X SNGp/r75-150
OVERALL AU-GU ODDS ONE PER PACK
PRINT RUNS B/WN 10-150 COPIES PER
NO PRICING ON QTY OF 10

2005 Absolute Memorabilia Team Quads Swatch Double

*DBL p/r 75: .6X TO 1.5X SNG p/r 100
*DBL p/r 25: 1X TO 2.5X SNG p/r 100
*DBL p/r 25: .6X TO 1.5X SNG p/r 25
OVERALL AU-GU ODDS ONE PER PACK
PRINT RUNS B/WN 25-75 COPIES PER

2005 Absolute Memorabilia Team Quads Swatch Double Spectrum

*SPEC p/r 25: 1X TO 2.5X SNG p/r 100
PRINT RUNS B/WN 1-25 COPIES PER
NO PRICING ON QTY OF 10 OR LESS
PRIME BLK PRINT RUNS B/WN 1-5 PER
NO PRIME BLK PRICING DUE TO SCARCITY
OVERALL AU-GU ODDS ONE PER PACK

2005 Absolute Memorabilia Team Six

STATED PRINT RUN 100 SERIAL #'d SETS
*SPEC: .6X TO 1.5X BASIC
SPECTRUM PRINT RUN 50 #'d SETS
RANDOM INSERTS IN PACKS
1 Willie Mays 4.00 10.00
Willie McCovey
Juan Marichal
Gaylord Perry
Orlando Cepeda
Will Clark
2 Roger Clemens 2.50 6.00
Jeff Bagwell
Lance Berkman
Craig Biggio
Andy Pettitte
Roy Oswalt
3 Tom Seaver 2.00 5.00
Johnny Bench
Joe Morgan
Dave Concepcion
George Foster
Tony Perez
4 Marty Marion 1.25 3.00
Stan Musial
Bob Gibson
Lou Brock
Frankie Frisch
Red Schoendienst
5 Don Mattingly 2.00 5.00
Catfish Hunter
Dave Righetti
Tommy John
Phil Niekro
Reggie Jackson
6 Ernie Banks 3.00 8.00
Greg Maddux
Sammy Sosa
Fergie Jenkins
Nomar Garciaparra
Kerry Wood
7 Curt Schilling 1.25 3.00
Luis Gonzalez
Steve Finley
Junior Spivey
Brandon Webb
Lyle Overbay
8 Duke Snider 2.00 5.00
Rickey Henderson
Mike Piazza
Pedro Martinez
Don Sutton
Hideo Nomo
9 Vladimir Guerrero 1.25 3.00
Tim Salmon
Casey Kotchman
Francisco Rodriguez
Ramon Ortiz
Chone Figgins
10 Roger Clemens 2.50 6.00
Curt Schilling
Carl Yastrzemski
Bobby Doerr
Nomar Garciaparra
Wade Boggs
11 Edgar Martinez .75 2.00
Adrian Beltre
Rickey Henderson
Ichiro Suzuki
Bret Boone
Richie Sexson
12 Bo Jackson 1.25 3.00
Frank Thomas
Carlton Fisk
Sammy Sosa
Hoyt Wilhelm
Harold Baines
13 Mike Schmidt .75 2.00
Dale Murphy
Jim Thome
Curt Schilling
Bobby Abreu
Steve Carlton
14 Nolan Ryan 5.00 12.00
Gary Carter
Duke Snider
Mike Piazza
Rickey Henderson
Roberto Alomar
15 Dale Murphy .75 2.00
Deion Sanders
Gary Sheffield
J.D. Drew
David Justice
Chipper Jones
16 Rickey Henderson 1.25 3.00
Jim Edmonds
Troy Glaus
Casey Kotchman
Francisco Rodriguez
Darin Erstad
17 Curt Schilling .75 2.00
Matt Williams
Reggie Sanders
Byung-Hyun Kim
Travis Lee
Tony Womack
18 John Smoltz 2.00 5.00
Tom Glavine
Greg Maddux
Wes Helms
Kenny Lofton
Andruw Jones
19 Chipper Jones .75 2.00
Dale Murphy
Andruw Jones
Wes Helms
Rafael Furcal
Andres Galarraga
20 Brooks Robinson 1.25 3.00
Luis Matos
Rodrigo Lopez
Geronimo Gil
Josh Towers
Erik Bedard
21 Roger Clemens 2.50 6.00
Wade Boggs
Carlton Fisk
Rickey Henderson
Nomar Garciaparra
Bobby Doerr
22 David Ortiz 2.50 6.00
Roger Clemens
Nomar Garciaparra
Wade Boggs
Rickey Henderson
Jason Varitek
23 Andre Dawson .75 2.00
Aramis Ramirez
Derrek Lee
Kenny Lofton
Moises Alou
Hee Seop Choi
24 Sammy Sosa .75 2.00
Nomar Garciaparra
Derrek Lee
Hee Seop Choi
Kenny Lofton
Matt Lawton
25 Carlton Fisk 1.25 3.00
Frank Thomas
Magglio Ordonez
Carl Everett
Esteban Loaiza
Robin Ventura
26 Bo Jackson 1.25 3.00
Magglio Ordonez
Roberto Alomar
Robin Ventura
Kenny Lofton
Joe Borchard
27 Adam Dunn 1.25 3.00
Eric Davis
Joe Morgan
Paul O'Neill
Wily Mo Pena
Juan Encarnacion
28 Tony Perez 1.25 3.00
Dave Concepcion
George Foster
Dmitri Young
Adam Dunn
Eric Davis
29 Bert Blyleven 1.25 3.00
Early Wynn
Hal Newhouser
C.C. Sabathia
Joe Carter
Russell Branyan
30 Jim Thome 1.25 3.00
Victor Martinez
Sean Casey
Russell Branyan
Josh Bard
Kenny Lofton
31 Larry Walker 1.25 3.00
Clint Barmes
Garrett Atkins
Juan Pierre
Mike Hampton
Juan Uribe
32 Larry Walker 1.25 3.00
Jeff Baker
Juan Pierre
Garrett Atkins
Juan Uribe
Jason Jennings
33 Kirk Gibson 1.25 3.00
Magglio Ordonez
Brandon Inge
Bobby Higginson
Craig Monroe
Mike Maroth
34 Dontrelle Willis .75 2.00
Ryan Dempster
Juan Pierre
Mike Lowell
Cliff Floyd
Charles Johnson
35 Jeff Bagwell 1.25 3.00
Carlos Beltran
Lance Berkman
Richard Hidalgo
Jose Cruz
Jason Lane
36 Jeff Bagwell 1.25 3.00
Lance Berkman
Joe Morgan
Craig Biggio
Jason Lane
Jose Cruz
37 Roy Oswalt 1.25 3.00
Morgan Ensberg
Lance Berkman
Jeff Bagwell
Jason Lane
Craig Biggio
38 Frank White .75 2.00
Willie Wilson
Mike Sweeney
Angel Berroa
John Buck
Runelvys Hernandez
39 Hideo Nomo 1.25 3.00
Kazuhisa Ishii
Chan Ho Park
Rickey Henderson
Shawn Green
Al Oliver
40 Steve Garvey 1.25 3.00
Darryl Strawberry
Rickey Henderson
Kazuhisa Ishii
Paul Lo Duca
Kevin Brown
41 Johan Santana 2.00 5.00
Joe Mays
Justin Morneau
Torii Hunter
Shannon Stewart
Michael Cuddyer
42 Kirby Puckett 2.00 5.00
David Ortiz
Harmon Killebrew
Doug Mientkiewicz
Torii Hunter
Matt Lawton
43 Kirby Puckett 2.00 5.00
Shannon Stewart
David Ortiz
Doug Mientkiewicz
Torii Hunter
Michael Cuddyer
44 Tony Perez .75 2.00
Javier Vazquez
Rondell White
Cliff Floyd
Jose Vidro
Zach Day
45 Willie Mays 4.00 10.00
Roger Cedeno
Mike Piazza
Edgardo Alfonzo
Jay Payton
Robin Ventura
46 Mike Piazza .75 2.00
Robin Ventura
John Olerud
Roger Cedeno
Edgardo Alfonzo
Timo Perez
47 Roger Clemens 4.00 10.00
Don Mattingly
Wade Boggs
Jason Giambi
Jorge Posada
Hideki Matsui
48 Wade Boggs 1.25 3.00
Tommy John
Phil Niekro
Robin Ventura
Paul O'Neill
Kenny Lofton
49 Joe Morgan .75 2.00
Kenny Lofton
Kevin Millwood
Marlon Byrd
Matt Kata
Eric Valent
50 Bill Madlock .75 2.00
Kenny Lofton
Craig Wilson
Freddy Sanchez
Jason Bay
Jose Castillo
51 Tony Gwynn .75 2.00
Rickey Henderson
Joe Carter
Brian Lawrence
Robert Fick
Dennis Tankersley
52 Willie Mays 4.00 10.00
Willie McCovey
Joe Morgan
Matt Williams
J.T. Snow
Deivi Cruz
53 Stan Musial 5.00 12.00
Albert Pujols
Lou Brock
Enos Slaughter
Red Schoendienst
Will Clark
54 Bob Gibson 5.00 12.00
Albert Pujols
Jim Edmonds
J.D. Drew
Matt Morris
So Taguchi
55 Wade Boggs .75 2.00
Delmon Young
Rocco Baldelli
Joe Kennedy
Toby Hall
Pete LaForest
56 Alfonso Soriano 2.00 5.00
Mark Teixeira
Hank Blalock
Richard Hidalgo
Kevin Mench
Frankie Francisco
57 Nolan Ryan 5.00 12.00
Rafael Palmeiro
Ivan Rodriguez
Andres Galarraga
Doug Davis
Ricardo Rodriguez
58 Carlos Delgado 2.00 5.00
David Wells
Shawn Green
Roy Halladay
Josh Phelps
Orlando Hudson
59 Carlos Delgado .75 2.00
Joe Carter
Jeff Kent
John Olerud
Jose Cruz Jr.
Orlando Hudson
60 Shawn Green .75 2.00
Shannon Stewart
Joe Carter
Carlos Delgado
Orlando Hudson
Raul Mondesi

2005 Absolute Memorabilia Team Six Swatch Single

OVERALL AU-GU ODDS ONE PER PACK
PRINT RUNS B/WN 14-150 COPIES PER
NO PRICING ON QTY OF 14
1 Willie Mays Pants 50.00 100.00
Willie McCovey Jsy
Juan Marichal Jsy
Gaylord Perry Jsy
Orlando Cepeda Pants
Will Clark Jsy/50
2 Roger Clemens Jsy 15.00 40.00
Jeff Bagwell Jsy
Lance Berkman Jsy
Craig Biggio Jsy
Andy Pettitte Jsy
Roy Oswalt Jsy/50
3 Tom Seaver Jsy 20.00 50.00
Johnny Bench Jsy
Joe Morgan Bat
Dave Concepcion Jsy
George Foster Jsy
Tony Perez Fld Glv/15
4 Marty Marion Jsy 50.00 100.00
Stan Musial Pants
Bob Gibson Jsy
Lou Brock Jsy
Frankie Frisch Jkt
Red Schoendienst Jsy/15
5 Don Mattingly Jsy 30.00 60.00
Catfish Hunter Jsy
Dave Righetti Jsy
Tommy John Jsy
Phil Niekro Jsy
Reggie Jackson Jsy/50
6 Ernie Banks Jsy 15.00 40.00
Greg Maddux Jsy
Sammy Sosa Jsy
Fergie Jenkins Pants
Nomar Garciaparra Bat
Kerry Wood Jsy/50
7 Curt Schilling Jsy 8.00 20.00
Luis Gonzalez Jsy
Steve Finley Jsy
Junior Spivey Jsy
Brandon Webb Pants
Lyle Overbay Jsy/50
8 Duke Snider Pants 12.50 30.00
Rickey Henderson Jsy
Mike Piazza Jsy
Pedro Martinez Jsy
Don Sutton Jsy
Hideo Nomo Jsy/50
9 Vladimir Guerrero Jsy 12.50 30.00
Tim Salmon Jsy
Casey Kotchman Jsy
Francisco Rodriguez Jsy
Ramon Ortiz Jsy
Chone Figgins Jsy/50
10 Roger Clemens Jsy 20.00 50.00
Curt Schilling Jsy
Carl Yastrzemski Pants
Bobby Doerr Pants
Nomar Garciaparra Bat
Wade Boggs Jsy/50
12 Bo Jackson Jsy 12.50 30.00
Frank Thomas Jsy
Carlton Fisk Jkt
Sammy Sosa Jsy
Hoyt Wilhelm Jsy
Harold Baines Jsy/50
13 Mike Schmidt Jsy 15.00 40.00
Dale Murphy Jsy
Jim Thome Jsy
Curt Schilling Jsy
Bobby Abreu Jsy
Steve Carlton Jsy/50
14 Nolan Ryan Jsy 20.00 50.00
Gary Carter Pants
Duke Snider Pants
Mike Piazza Jsy
Rickey Henderson Jsy
Roberto Alomar Jsy/50
15 Dale Murphy Jsy 12.50 30.00
Deion Sanders Jsy
Gary Sheffield Jsy
J.D. Drew Bat
Chipper Jones Jsy
David Justice Jsy/50
16 Rickey Henderson Bat 10.00 25.00
Jim Edmonds Bat
Troy Glaus Jsy
Casey Kotchman Bat
Francisco Rodriguez Jsy
Darin Erstad Bat/150
17 Curt Schilling Jsy 8.00 20.00
Matt Williams Bat
Reggie Sanders Jsy
Byung-Hyun Kim Jsy
Travis Lee Jsy
Tony Womack Jsy/150
18 John Smoltz Jsy 15.00 40.00
Tom Glavine Jsy
Greg Maddux Jsy
Wes Helms Jsy
Kenny Lofton Bat
Andruw Jones Bat/150
19 Chipper Jones Bat 10.00 25.00
Dale Murphy Bat
Andruw Jones Bat
Wes Helms Jsy
Rafael Furcal Bat
Andres Galarraga Bat/150
20 Brooks Robinson Bat 8.00 20.00
Luis Matos Jsy
Rodrigo Lopez Jsy
Geronimo Gil Bat
Josh Towers Pants
Erik Bedard Bat/150
21 Roger Clemens Jsy 15.00 40.00
Wade Boggs Bat
Carlton Fisk Bat
Rickey Henderson Bat
Nomar Garciaparra Bat
Bobby Doerr Pants/150
22 David Ortiz Jsy 15.00 40.00
Roger Clemens Jsy
Nomar Garciaparra Bat
Wade Boggs Bat
Rickey Henderson Bat
Jason Varitek Bat/150
23 Andre Dawson Bat 8.00 20.00
Aramis Ramirez Jsy
Derrek Lee Jsy
Kenny Lofton Bat
Moises Alou Bat
Hee Seop Choi Jsy/150
24 Sammy Sosa Bat 10.00 25.00
Nomar Garciaparra Bat
Derrek Lee Bat
Hee Seop Choi Jsy
Kenny Lofton Bat
Matt Lawton Bat/150
25 Carlton Fisk Bat 10.00 25.00
Frank Thomas Bat
Magglio Ordonez Bat
Carl Everett Bat
Esteban Loaiza Bat
Robin Ventura Bat/150
26 Bo Jackson Jsy 10.00 25.00
Magglio Ordonez Bat
Roberto Alomar Jsy
Robin Ventura Bat
Kenny Lofton Bat
Joe Borchard Bat/150
27 Adam Dunn Bat 6.00 15.00
Eric Davis Bat
Joe Morgan Bat
Paul O'Neill Bat
Wily Mo Pena Bat
Juan Encarnacion Bat/150
28 Tony Perez Fld Glv 6.00 15.00
Dave Concepcion Jsy
George Foster Bat
Dmitri Young Jsy
Adam Dunn Bat
Eric Davis Bat/150
29 Bert Blyleven Jsy
Early Wynn Jsy
Hal Newhouser Jsy
C.C. Sabathia Jsy
Joe Carter Bat
Russell Branyan Jsy/14
30 Jim Thome Bat 8.00 20.00
Victor Martinez Jsy
Sean Casey Jsy
Russell Branyan Jsy
Josh Bard Jsy
Kenny Lofton Bat/150
31 Larry Walker Jsy 6.00 15.00
Clint Barmes Bat
Garrett Atkins Jsy
Juan Pierre Bat
Mike Hampton Jsy
Juan Uribe Jsy/150
32 Larry Walker Jsy 6.00 15.00
Jeff Baker Bat
Juan Pierre Bat
Garrett Atkins Jsy
Juan Uribe Jsy
Jason Jennings Bat/150
33 Kirk Gibson Bat 6.00 15.00
Magglio Ordonez Bat
Brandon Inge Jsy
Bobby Higginson Bat
Craig Monroe Bat
Mike Maroth Jsy/150
34 Dontrelle Willis Bat 6.00 15.00
Ryan Dempster Jsy
Juan Pierre Bat
Mike Lowell Bat
Cliff Floyd Bat
Charles Johnson Jsy/150
35 Jeff Bagwell Pants 8.00 20.00
Carlos Beltran Jsy
Lance Berkman Bat
Richard Hidalgo Bat
Jose Cruz Jsy
Jason Lane Bat/150
36 Jeff Bagwell Pants 8.00 20.00
Lance Berkman Bat
Joe Morgan Bat
Craig Biggio Bat
Jason Lane Bat
Jose Cruz Jsy/150
37 Roy Oswalt Bat 8.00 20.00
Morgan Ensberg Fld Glv
Lance Berkman Bat
Jeff Bagwell Pants
Jason Lane Bat
Craig Biggio Bat/150
38 Frank White Bat 6.00 15.00
Willie Wilson Bat
Mike Sweeney Bat
Angel Berroa Bat
John Buck Bat
Runelvys Hernandez Jsy/150
39 Hideo Nomo Pants 10.00 25.00
Kazuhisa Ishii Jsy
Chan Ho Park Jsy
Rickey Henderson Bat
Shawn Green Bat
Al Oliver Bat/75
40 Steve Garvey Bat 10.00 25.00
Darryl Strawberry Bat
Rickey Henderson Jsy
Kazuhisa Ishii Jsy
Paul Lo Duca Chest Prot
Kevin Brown Jsy/150
41 Johan Santana Jsy 8.00 20.00
Joe Mays Jsy
Justin Morneau Bat
Torii Hunter Bat
Shannon Stewart Bat
Michael Cuddyer Bat/150
42 Kirby Puckett Bat 10.00 25.00
David Ortiz Jsy
Harmon Killebrew Jsy
Doug Mientkiewicz Bat
Torii Hunter Bat
Matt Lawton Bat/150
43 Kirby Puckett Bat 10.00 25.00
Shannon Stewart Bat
David Ortiz Jsy
Doug Mientkiewicz Bat
Torii Hunter Bat
Michael Cuddyer Bat/150
44 Tony Perez Jsy 6.00 15.00
Javier Vazquez Jsy
Rondell White Jsy
Cliff Floyd Bat
Jose Vidro Bat
Zach Day Pants/150
45 Willie Mays Jsy 20.00 50.00
Roger Cedeno Bat
Mike Piazza Pants
Edgardo Alfonzo Bat
Jay Payton Jsy
Robin Ventura Bat/150
46 Mike Piazza Pants 10.00 25.00
Robin Ventura Bat
John Olerud Bat
Roger Cedeno Bat
Edgardo Alfonzo Bat
Timo Perez Bat/150
47 Roger Clemens Jsy 20.00 50.00
Don Mattingly Bat
Wade Boggs Bat
Jason Giambi Jsy
Jorge Posada Jsy
Hideki Matsui Bat/150
48 Wade Boggs Bat 8.00 20.00
Tommy John Pants
Phil Niekro Bat
Robin Ventura Bat
Paul O'Neill Bat
Kenny Lofton Bat/150
49 Joe Morgan Bat 6.00 15.00
Kenny Lofton Bat
Kevin Millwood Jsy
Marlon Byrd Bat
Matt Kata Bat
Eric Valent Shoe/150
50 Bill Madlock Bat 6.00 15.00
Kenny Lofton Bat
Craig Wilson Bat
Freddy Sanchez Bat
Jason Bay Bat
Jose Castillo Bat/150
51 Tony Gwynn Pants 10.00 25.00
Rickey Henderson Pants
Joe Carter Bat
Brian Lawrence Bat

Robert Fick Bat
Dennis Tankersley Bat/150
52 Willie Mays Bat 20.00 50.00
Willie McCovey Jsy
Joe Morgan Bat
Matt Williams Bat
J.T. Snow Jsy
Deivi Cruz Bat/150
54 Bob Gibson Jsy 15.00 40.00
Albert Pujols Bat
Jim Edmonds Bat
J.D. Drew Bat
Matt Morris Jsy
So Taguchi Bat/150
56 Alfonso Soriano Bat 8.00 20.00
Mark Teixeira Bat
Hank Blalock Bat
Richard Hidalgo Bat
Kevin Mench Jsy
Frankie Francisco Jsy/150
57 Nolan Ryan Jsy 15.00 40.00
Rafael Palmeiro Pants
Ivan Rodriguez Jsy
Andres Galarraga Bat
Doug Davis Jsy
Ricardo Rodriguez Bat/100
58 Carlos Delgado Jsy 6.00 15.00
David Wells Jsy
Shawn Green Bat
Roy Halladay Jsy
Josh Phelps Bat
Orlando Hudson Bat/150
59 Carlos Delgado Bat 6.00 15.00
Joe Carter Bat
Jeff Kent Jsy
John Olerud Bat
Jose Cruz Jr. Bat
Orlando Hudson Bat/150

2005 Absolute Memorabilia Team Six Swatch Single Spectrum

*SPEC p/r 75-100: .4X TO 1X SNG p/r 75-150
*SPEC p/r 50: .5X TO 1.2X SNG p/r 75-150
*SPEC p/r 25: .6X TO 1.5X SNG p/r 75-150
*SPEC p/r 25: .5X TO 1.2X SNG p/r 50
PRINT RUNS B/WN 1-100 COPIES PER
NO PRICING ON QTY OF 10 OR LESS
PRIME BLACK PRINT RUN 5 #'d SETS
NO PRIME BLK PRICING DUE TO SCARCITY
OVERALL AU-GU ODDS ONE PER PACK

2005 Absolute Memorabilia Tools of the Trade Red

STATED PRINT RUN 250 SERIAL #'d SETS
*BLACK: .6X TO 1.5X BASIC
BLACK PRINT RUN 100 SERIAL #'d SETS
*BLUE: .5X TO 1.2X BASIC
BLUE PRINT RUN 150 SERIAL #'d SETS
REV.SPEC.BLACK PRINT RUN 5 #'d SETS
NO REV.SPEC.BLACK PRICING AVAILABLE
REV.SPEC.BLUE PRINT RUN 10 #'d SETS
NO REV.SPEC.BLUE PRICING AVAILABLE
*REV.SPEC.RED: 1X TO 2.5X BASIC
REV.SPEC.RED PRINT RUN 50 #'d SETS
1 Ozzie Smith 2.00 5.00
2 Carlos Beltran Astros .50 1.25
3 Dale Murphy .50 1.25
4 Paul Molitor 1.25 3.00
5 George Brett 2.50 6.00
6 Stan Musial 2.00 5.00
7 Ivan Rodriguez Marlins .75 2.00
8 Carl Yastrzemski 1.50 4.00
9 Reggie Jackson A's 1.25 3.00
10 Hideo Nomo 1.25 3.00
11 Gary Sheffield .50 1.25
12 Roberto Alomar .75 2.00
13 Pedro Martinez .75 2.00
14 Ernie Banks 1.25 3.00
15 Tim Hudson .50 1.25
16 Dwight Gooden .50 1.25
17 Lance Berkman .75 2.00
18 Darryl Strawberry Mets .50 1.25
19 Larry Walker .75 2.00
20 Lou Brock .75 2.00
21 Roger Clemens 1.50 4.00
22 Paul Lo Duca .50 1.25
23 Don Mattingly 2.50 6.00
24 Willie Mays 2.50 6.00
25 Rafael Palmeiro .75 2.00
26 Roy Oswalt .75 2.00
27 Vladimir Guerrero .75 2.00
28 Austin Kearns .50 1.25
29 Rod Carew .75 2.00
30 Nolan Ryan Angels 3.00 8.00
31 Richie Sexson .50 1.25
32 Steve Carlton .50 1.25
33 Eddie Murray 1.25 3.00
34 Nolan Ryan Rgr 3.00 8.00
35 Mike Mussina O's .75 2.00
36 Sean Casey .50 1.25
37 Juan Gonzalez Rgr .50 1.25
38 Curt Schilling Sox .75 2.00
39 Darryl Strawberry Yanks .75 2.00
40 Alfonso Soriano .75 2.00
41 Tom Seaver .75 2.00
42 Mike Schmidt 2.50 6.00
43 Todd Helton .75 2.00
44 Reggie Jackson Yanks 1.25 3.00
45 Shawn Green .50 1.25
46 Mike Mussina Yanks .75 2.00
47 Tom Glavine .75 2.00
48 Torii Hunter .50 1.25
49 Kerry Wood .50 1.25
50 Carlos Delgado .50 1.25
51 Randy Johnson Astros 1.25 3.00
52 David Ortiz 1.25 3.00
53 Troy Glaus .50 1.25
54 Rickey Henderson Mets .75 2.00
55 Craig Biggio .75 2.00
56 Brad Penny .50 1.25
57 Gary Carter Mets .50 1.25
58 Andy Pettitte .75 2.00
59 Mark Prior .75 2.00
60 Kirby Puckett 1.25 3.00
61 Willie McCovey .75 2.00
62 Andre Dawson Expos .75 2.00
63 Greg Maddux 2.00 5.00
64 Adrian Beltre .50 1.25
65 Andruw Jones .50 1.25
66 Juan Gonzalez Indians .50 1.25
67 Frank Thomas 1.25 3.00
68 Victor Martinez .75 2.00
69 Randy Johnson D'backs 1.25 3.00
70 Andre Dawson Cubs .75 2.00
71 Adam Dunn .75 2.00
72 Carlton Fisk .75 2.00
73 Cal Ripken 5.00 12.00
74 Kenny Lofton .50 1.25
75 Barry Zito .50 1.25
76 Sammy Sosa 1.25 3.00
77 Deion Sanders .75 2.00
78 Tony Gwynn 1.50 4.00
79 Mike Piazza 1.25 3.00
80 Jeff Bagwell .75 2.00
81 Manny Ramirez 1.25 3.00
82 Carlos Beltran Royals .50 1.25
83 Mark Grace .75 2.00
84 Robin Yount 1.25 3.00
85 Albert Pujols 3.00 8.00
86 Dontrelle Willis .50 1.25
87 Jim Thome .75 2.00
88 Magglio Ordonez .75 2.00
89 Miguel Tejada .75 2.00
90 Mark Teixeira 1.25 3.00
91 Gary Carter Expos .50 1.25
92 Ivan Rodriguez Rgr .75 2.00
93 Jason Giambi .50 1.25
94 Rickey Henderson A's .75 2.00
95 Curt Schilling D'backs .75 2.00
96 Bobby Doerr .50 1.25
97 Chipper Jones 1.25 3.00
98 Eric Chavez .50 1.25
99 Johnny Bench 1.25 3.00
100 Harmon Killebrew 1.25 3.00
101 Andre Dawson .75 2.00
102 Babe Ruth 3.00 8.00
103 Bernie Williams .75 2.00
104 Billy Wagner .50 1.25
105 Billy Williams .50 1.25
106 Bo Jackson 1.25 3.00
107 Bob Gibson .75 2.00
108 Brad Penny .50 1.25
109 Burleigh Grimes .75 2.00
110 Cal Ripken 5.00 12.00
111 Casey Fossum .50 1.25
112 Curt Schilling .75 2.00
113 Dale Murphy .50 1.25
114 Darryl Strawberry .50 1.25
115 Dave Concepcion .50 1.25
116 Dave Winfield .50 1.25
117 David Cone .50 1.25
118 Fergie Jenkins .50 1.25
119 Gary Carter .50 1.25
120 Gary Sheffield .50 1.25
121 Gaylord Perry .50 1.25
122 Hank Aaron 2.50 6.00
123 Harmon Killebrew 1.25 3.00
124 Harold Baines .50 1.25
125 Hideki Matsui 2.00 5.00
126 Hideo Nomo 1.25 3.00
127 Hoyt Wilhelm .75 2.00
128 Jason Giambi Yanks .50 1.25
129 Jason Giambi A's .50 1.25
130 Jeff Bagwell .75 2.00
131 Jim Palmer .50 1.25
132 Jim Thorpe 2.00 5.00
133 Joe Mays .50 1.25
134 John Buck .50 1.25
135 John Kruk .50 1.25
136 Jorge Posada .75 2.00
137 Josh Beckett .75 2.00
138 Josh Phelps .50 1.25
139 Juan Pierre .50 1.25
140 Kazuhisa Ishii .50 1.25
141 Kenny Lofton .50 1.25
142 Kevin Brown .50 1.25
143 Kevin Millwood Braves .50 1.25
144 Kevin Millwood Phils .50 1.25
145 Lance Berkman .75 2.00
146 Lenny Dykstra .50 1.25
147 Lou Boudreau .50 1.25
148 Magglio Ordonez .75 2.00
149 Marcus Giles .50 1.25
150 Mark Grace .75 2.00
151 Mark Prior .75 2.00
152 Marlon Byrd .50 1.25
153 Miguel Tejada .75 2.00
154 Mike Lowell .75 2.00
155 Mike Piazza 1.25 3.00
156 Mike Sweeney .50 1.25
157 Morgan Ensberg .50 1.25
158 Nolan Ryan 3.00 8.00
159 Orel Hershiser .50 1.25
160 Ozzie Smith 2.00 5.00
161 Pedro Martinez .75 2.00
162 Phil Rizzuto .75 2.00
163 Rafael Furcal .75 2.00
164 Rafael Palmeiro .75 2.00
165 Randy Johnson D'backs 1.25 3.00
166 Randy Johnson Astros 1.25 3.00
167 Richie Sexson .50 1.25
168 Rickey Henderson Mets .75 2.00
169 Rickey Henderson A's .75 2.00
170 Rickey Henderson M's .75 2.00
171 Roberto Alomar .75 2.00
172 Roberto Clemente 3.00 8.00
173 Robin Yount 1.25 3.00
174 Rod Carew .75 2.00
175 Roger Clemens 1.50 4.00
176 Roger Maris A's 1.25 3.00
177 Roger Maris Yanks 1.25 3.00
178 Ron Cey .50 1.25
179 Ryan Klesko .50 1.25
180 Ryne Sandberg 2.50 6.00
181 Sammy Sosa 1.25 3.00
182 Shawn Green .50 1.25
183 Stan Musial 2.00 5.00
184 Steve Carlton .50 1.25
185 Ted Williams 2.50 6.00
186 Ted Williams 2.50 6.00
187 Tim Hudson .75 2.00
188 Todd Helton .75 2.00
189 Tom Glavine .75 2.00
190 Tom Seaver .75 2.00
191 Tommy John .50 1.25
192 Tony Gwynn 1.50 4.00
193 Vladimir Guerrero .75 2.00
194 Wade Boggs Sox .75 2.00
195 Wade Boggs Rays .75 2.00
196 Warren Spahn .75 2.00
197 Willie Mays 2.50 6.00
198 Willie McCovey .75 2.00
199 Willie Stargell .75 2.00
200 Yogi Berra 1.25 3.00

2005 Absolute Memorabilia Tools of the Trade Bat

OVERALL AU-GU ODDS ONE PER PACK
PRINT RUNS B/WN 1-250 COPIES PER
NO PRICING ON QTY OF 1
102 Babe Ruth/250 90.00 150.00
122 Hank Aaron/250 10.00 25.00
172 Roberto Clemente/250 15.00 40.00
176 Roger Maris A's/100 12.50 30.00
177 Roger Maris Yanks/61 15.00 40.00
185 Ted Williams/250 20.00 50.00
197 Willie Mays/50 15.00 40.00

2005 Absolute Memorabilia Tools of the Trade Bat Reverse

*REV p/r 100-150: .4X TO 1X BAT p/r 100-250
*REV p/r 50: .4X TO 1X BAT p/r 50-61
*REV p/r 24-35: .6X TO 1.5X BAT p/r 100-250
*REV p/r 24-35: .5X TO 1.2X BAT p/r 50-61
OVERALL AU-GU ODDS ONE PER BOX
PRINT RUNS B/WN 1-150 COPIES PER
NO PRICING ON QTY OF 1
102 Babe Ruth/150 90.00 150.00

2005 Absolute Memorabilia Tools of the Trade Bat Red

*RED p/r 50: .5X TO 1.2X BAT p/r 100-250
*RED p/r 21-25: .6X TO 1.5X BAT p/r 100-250
PRINT RUNS B/WN 1-50 COPIES PER
NO PRICING ON QTY OF 10 OR LESS
BLACK PRINT RUN 1 SERIAL #'d SET
NO BLACK PRICING DUE TO SCARCITY
OVERALL AU-GU ODDS ONE PER PACK
102 Babe Ruth/25 100.00 175.00

2005 Absolute Memorabilia Tools of the Trade Button Red

PRINT RUNS B/WN 1-21 COPIES PER
BLACK PRINT RUN 1 SERIAL #'d SET
OVERALL AU-GU ODDS ONE PER PACK
NO PRICING DUE TO SCARCITY

2005 Absolute Memorabilia Tools of the Trade Jersey

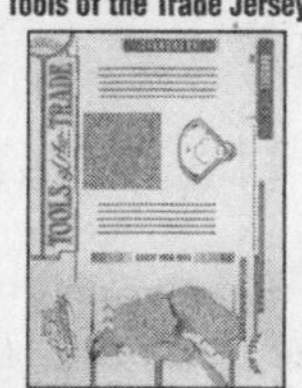

OVERALL AU-GU ODDS ONE PER PACK
PRINT RUNS B/WN 1-250 COPIES PER
NO PRICING ON QTY OF 14 OR LESS
102 Babe Ruth/100 175.00 300.00
122 Hank Aaron/250 10.00 25.00
132 Jim Thorpe/250 50.00 100.00
177 R.Maris Yanks Pants/100 15.00 40.00
186 Ted Williams/75 30.00 60.00
197 Willie Mays/24 15.00 40.00

2005 Absolute Memorabilia Tools of the Trade Jersey Reverse

*REV p/r 150: .4X TO 1X JSY p/r 75-250
*REV p/r 41-50: .5X TO 1.2X JSY p/r 75-250
OVERALL AU-GU ODDS ONE PER PACK
PRINT RUNS B/WN 1-150 COPIES PER
NO PRICING ON QTY OF 10 OR LESS
102 Babe Ruth/50 175.00 300.00
132 Jim Thorpe/150 50.00 100.00
199 Willie Stargell/25 5.00 12.00

2005 Absolute Memorabilia Tools of the Trade Jersey Red

*RED p/r 25: .6X TO 1.5X JSY p/r 75-250
PRINT RUNS B/WN 1-25 COPIES PER
NO PRICING ON QTY OF 10 OR LESS
BLACK PRINT RUN 1 SERIAL #'d SET
NO BLACK PRICING DUE TO SCARCITY
OVERALL AU-GU ODDS ONE PER PACK
102 Babe Ruth/25 250.00 400.00
132 Jim Thorpe/25 75.00 150.00

2005 Absolute Memorabilia Tools of the Trade Laundry Tag Prime Red

OVERALL AU-GU ODDS ONE PER PACK
STATED PRINT RUN 1 SERIAL #'d SET
NO PRICING DUE TO SCARCITY

2005 Absolute Memorabilia Tools of the Trade MLB Logo Red

PRINT RUNS B/WN 1-5 COPIES PER
BLACK PRINT RUN 1 SERIAL #'d SET
OVERALL AU-GU ODDS ONE PER PACK
NO PRICING DUE TO SCARCITY

2005 Absolute Memorabilia Tools of the Trade Swatch Single Jumbo

*SNG p/r 75-250: .6X TO 1.5X DBL p/r 70-200
*SNG p/r 75-250: .5X TO 1.2X DBL p/r 50-60
*SNG p/r 75-250: .4X TO 1X DBL p/r 20-29
*SNG p/r 45-62: .75X TO 2X DBL p/r 70-200
*SNG p/r 45-62: .6X TO 1.5X DBL p/r 50-60
*SNG p/r 45-62: .5X TO 1.2X DBL p/r 20-29
*SNG p/r 25: 1X TO 2.5X DBL p/r 70-200
*SNG p/r 25: .75X TO 2X DBL p/r 50-60
*SNG p/r 25: .6X TO 1.5X DBL p/r 20-29
OVERALL AU-GU ODDS ONE PER PACK
PRINT RUNS B/WN 1-250 COPIES PER
NO PRICING ON QTY OF 10 OR LESS
37 J.Gonzalez Rgr Jsy/25 6.00 15.00
70 A.Dawson Cubs Jsy/50 6.00 15.00
98 Eric Chavez Jsy/100 4.00 10.00
102 Babe Ruth Jsy/95 1500.00 2500.00
104 Billy Wagner Jsy/250 4.00 10.00
105 Billy Williams Jsy/85 5.00 12.00
106 Bo Jackson Jsy/250 8.00 20.00
107 Bob Gibson Jsy/50 10.00 25.00
109 B.Grimes Pants/83 75.00 150.00
111 Casey Fossum Jsy/250 3.00 8.00
114 D.Strawberry Jsy/100 5.00 12.00
118 Fergie Jenkins Jsy/95 5.00 12.00
127 Hoyt Wilhelm Jsy/225 8.00 20.00
132 Jim Thorpe Jsy/200 200.00 300.00
136 Jorge Posada Jsy/250 6.00 15.00
138 Josh Phelps Jsy/200 3.00 8.00
139 Juan Pierre Jsy/250 4.00 10.00
142 Kevin Brown Jsy/250 4.00 10.00
143 K.Millwood Braves Jsy/250 4.00 10.00
144 K.Millwood Phils Jsy/250 4.00 10.00
146 Lenny Dykstra Jsy/100 5.00 12.00
147 Lou Boudreau Jsy/75 15.00 40.00
152 Marlon Byrd Jsy/25 5.00 12.00
154 Mike Lowell Jsy/200 4.00 10.00
159 Orel Hershiser Jsy/100 5.00 12.00
161 Pedro Martinez Jsy/175 5.00 12.00
162 Phil Rizzuto Jsy/100 15.00 40.00
176 R.Maris A's Jsy/199 40.00 80.00
177 R.Maris Yanks Jsy/250 40.00 80.00
178 Ron Cey Jsy/250 5.00 12.00
179 Ryan Klesko Jsy/250 4.00 10.00
185 Ted Williams Jsy/50 90.00 150.00
186 Ted Williams Jkt/100 60.00 120.00
198 W.McCovey Pants/100 8.00 20.00

2005 Absolute Memorabilia Tools of the Trade Swatch Single Jumbo Reverse

*REV p/r 75-150: .6X TO 1.5X DBL p/r 70-200
*REV p/r 75-150: .5X TO 1.2X DBL p/r 50-60
*REV p/r 75-150: .4X TO 1X DBL p/r 20-29
*REV p/r 44-59: .75X TO 2X DBL p/r 70-200
*REV p/r 20-25: 1X TO 2.5X DBL p/r 70-200
*REV p/r 20-25: .75X TO 2X DBL p/r 50-60
*REV p/r 20-25: .6X TO 1.5X DBL p/r 20-29
*REV p/r 15-17: 1.25X TO 3X DBL p/r 70-200
OVERALL AU-GU ODDS ONE PER PACK
PRINT RUNS B/WN 1-50 COPIES PER
NO PRICING ON QTY OF 10 OR LESS
70 A.Dawson Cubs Jsy/25 8.00 20.00
98 Eric Chavez Jsy/50 5.00 12.00
102 Babe Ruth Jsy/24 1200.00 2000.00
104 Billy Wagner Jsy/100 4.00 10.00
105 Billy Williams Jsy/25 8.00 20.00
106 Bo Jackson Jsy/150 8.00 20.00
107 Bob Gibson Jsy/25 12.50 30.00
109 B.Grimes Pants/23 100.00 175.00
111 Casey Fossum Jsy/150 3.00 8.00
114 Darryl Strawberry Jsy/25 8.00 20.00
118 Fergie Jenkins Jsy/25 8.00 20.00
127 Hoyt Wilhelm Jsy/50 10.00 25.00
132 Jim Thorpe Jsy/50 250.00 350.00
135 John Kruk Jsy/20 8.00 20.00
136 Jorge Posada Jsy/150 6.00 15.00
138 Josh Phelps Jsy/50 4.00 10.00
139 Juan Pierre Jsy/150 4.00 10.00
142 Kevin Brown Jsy/150 4.00 10.00
143 K.Millwood Braves Jsy/100 4.00 10.00
144 K.Millwood Phils Jsy/150 4.00 10.00
146 Lenny Dykstra Jsy/50 6.00 15.00
147 Lou Boudreau Jsy/25 20.00 50.00
154 Mike Lowell Jsy/100 4.00 10.00
159 Orel Hershiser Jsy/25 8.00 20.00
161 Pedro Martinez Jsy/100 5.00 12.00
176 R.Maris A's Jsy/50 50.00 100.00
177 R.Maris Yanks Jsy/59 50.00 100.00
179 Ryan Klesko Jsy/100 4.00 10.00
186 Ted Williams Jkt/25 100.00 175.00
198 W.McCovey Pants/44 10.00 25.00
200 Yogi Berra Pants/100 20.00 50.00

2005 Absolute Memorabilia Tools of the Trade Swatch Single Jumbo Prime Black

*BLACK p/r 25: .6X TO 1.5X RED p/r 75
*BLACK p/r 25: .5X TO 1.2X RED p/r 40-50
OVERALL AU-GU ODDS ONE PER PACK
PRINT RUNS B/WN 1-25 COPIES PER
NO PRICING ON QTY OF 10 OR LESS

2005 Absolute Memorabilia Tools of the Trade Swatch Single Jumbo Prime Red

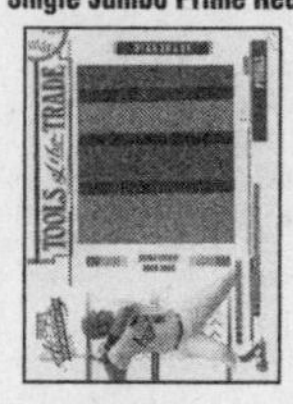

OVERALL AU-GU ODDS ONE PER PACK
PRINT RUNS B/WN 1-50 COPIES PER
NO PRICING ON QTY OF 10 OR LESS
*LISTED PRICES ARE FOR 3-COLOR PATCH
*ADD 20% FOR 4-COLOR+ PATCH
*REDUCE 20% FOR 2-COLOR PATCH
NO PRICING AVAIL.FOR LOGO PATCHES
LOGO PATCHES COMMAND BIG PREMIUMS
7 I.Rodriguez M's Jsy/25 40.00 80.00
10 Hideo Nomo Jsy/25 75.00 150.00
12 Roberto Alomar Jsy/25 40.00 80.00
15 Tim Hudson Jsy/50 20.00 50.00
17 Lance Berkman Jsy/25 20.00 50.00
19 Larry Walker Jsy/50 20.00 50.00
22 Paul Lo Duca Jsy/50 15.00 40.00
25 Rafael Palmeiro Jsy/25 40.00 80.00
27 Vladimir Guerrero Jsy/25 60.00 120.00
31 Richie Sexson Jsy/50 15.00 40.00
36 Sean Casey Jsy/50 15.00 40.00
43 Todd Helton Jsy/15 40.00 80.00
45 Shawn Green Jsy/50 15.00 40.00
47 Tom Glavine Jsy/50 40.00 80.00
50 Carlos Delgado Jsy/25 20.00 50.00
53 Troy Glaus Jsy/50 15.00 40.00
59 Mark Prior Jsy/25 40.00 80.00
63 Greg Maddux Jsy/25 125.00 200.00
64 Adrian Beltre Jsy/50 15.00 40.00
65 Andruw Jones Jsy/50 40.00 80.00
67 Frank Thomas Jsy/25 75.00 150.00
68 Victor Martinez Jsy/15 20.00 50.00
71 Adam Dunn Jsy/25 20.00 50.00
73 Cal Ripken Jsy/25 150.00 250.00
76 Sammy Sosa Jsy/50 50.00 100.00
78 Tony Gwynn Jsy/50 60.00 120.00
79 Mike Piazza Jsy/25 75.00 150.00
80 Jeff Bagwell Jsy/25 50.00 100.00
82 Carlos Beltran Royals Jsy/50 15.00 40.00
85 Albert Pujols Jsy/25 175.00 300.00
88 M.Ordonez Jsy/50 15.00 40.00
89 Miguel Tejada Jsy/50 20.00 50.00
90 Mark Teixeira Jsy/25 40.00 80.00
92 I.Rodriguez Rgr Jsy/25 40.00 80.00
98 Eric Chavez Jsy/15 20.00 50.00
112 Curt Schilling Jsy/25 40.00 80.00
115 D.Concepcion Jsy/50 40.00 80.00
117 David Cone Jsy/35 20.00 50.00
128 J.Giambi Yanks Jsy/15 40.00 80.00
138 Josh Phelps Jsy/45 10.00 25.00
142 Kevin Brown Jsy/30 20.00 50.00
143 K.Millwood Braves Jsy/40 15.00 40.00
144 K.Millwood Phils Jsy/75 10.00 25.00
152 Marlon Byrd Jsy/75 6.00 15.00
159 Orel Hershiser Jsy/25 50.00 100.00
161 P.Martinez Expos Jsy/25 50.00 100.00
168 R.Hend Mets Jkt/15 75.00 150.00
169 R.Hend A's Jsy/15 75.00 150.00
170 R.Hend M's Jsy/44 60.00 120.00
173 Robin Yount Jsy/50 60.00 120.00
181 Sammy Sosa Jsy/50 50.00 100.00
187 Tim Hudson Jsy/25 20.00 50.00
189 Tom Glavine Jsy/25 50.00 100.00
191 Tommy John Jsy/15 40.00 80.00
199 Willie Stargell Jsy/50 75.00 150.00

2005 Absolute Memorabilia Tools of the Trade Swatch Double

OVERALL AU-GU ODDS ONE PER PACK
PRINT RUNS B/WN 1-200 COPIES PER
NO PRICING ON QTY OF 10 OR LESS
B ='s Bat, BL ='s Belt, BG ='s Batting Glove
CP ='s Chest Protector, FG ='s Fielding Glove
H ='s Hat, HM ='s Helmet, JK ='s Jacket
J ='s Jersey, P ='s Pants, SG ='s Shin Guard
S ='s Shoes, SO ='s Socks, ST ='s Stirrups
SW ='s Sweatband
1 Ozzie Smith Bat-Pants/50 8.00 20.00
2 Carlos Beltran Astros Jsy-Shoes/50 3.00 8.00
3 Dale Murphy Jsy-Jsy/50 5.00 12.00
4 Paul Molitor Jsy-Pants/150 3.00 8.00
5 George Brett Bat-Hat/25 12.50 30.00
6 Stan Musial Bat-Pants/25 15.00 40.00
7 Ivan Rodriguez M's Jsy-Jsy/150 3.00 8.00
8 Carl Yastrzemski Bat-Jsy/25 12.50 30.00
9 Reggie Jackson A's Jsy-Jsy/50 5.00 12.00
10 Hideo Nomo Jsy-Pants/150 5.00 12.00
11 Gary Sheffield Hat-Jsy/25 4.00 10.00
12 Roberto Alomar Bat-Jsy/150 3.00 8.00
13 Pedro Martinez Jsy-Pants/150 3.00 8.00
15 Tim Hudson Hat-Jsy/100 2.50 6.00
17 Lance Berkman Bat-Jsy/150 2.50 6.00
19 Larry Walker Jsy-Jsy/150 3.00 8.00
20 Lou Brock Bat-Jkt/150 4.00 10.00
21 Roger Clemens Bat-Jsy/150 6.00 15.00
22 Paul Lo Duca Bat-Jsy/50 3.00 8.00
23 Don Mattingly Btg Glv-Pants/50 10.00 25.00
24 Willie Mays Bat-Pants/25 30.00 60.00
25 Rafael Palmeiro Bat-Jsy/150 3.00 8.00
27 Vladimir Guerrero Bat-Jsy/150 4.00 10.00
29 Rod Carew Jkt-Jkt/150 4.00 10.00
30 N.Ryan Angels Bat-Jkt/150 10.00 25.00
31 Richie Sexson Hat-Jsy/150 2.50 6.00
32 Steve Carlton Bat-Hat/150 4.00 10.00
33 Eddie Murray Bat-Jsy/150 6.00 15.00
34 Nolan Ryan Rgr Bat-Jsy/150 10.00 25.00
35 Mike Mussina O's Jsy-Pants/125 3.00 8.00
36 Sean Casey Jsy-Pants/150 2.50 6.00
37 Juan Gonzalez Rgr Jsy-Pants/10
38 Curt Schilling Sox Jsy-Jsy/150 3.00 8.00
39 Darryl Strawberry Yanks Bat-Jsy/150 3.00 8.00
40 Alfonso Soriano Jsy-Jsy/5
41 Tom Seaver Jsy-Pants/150 4.00 10.00
42 Mike Schmidt Bat-Jsy/150 8.00 20.00
43 Todd Helton Bat-Jsy/150 3.00 8.00
45 Shawn Green Bat-Jsy/150 2.50 6.00
46 Mike Mussina Yanks Jsy-Shoes/1
47 Tom Glavine Bat-Jsy/150 3.00 8.00
49 Kerry Wood Fld Glv-Jsy/150 2.50 6.00
50 Carlos Delgado Bat-Jsy/100 2.50 6.00
51 Randy Johnson Astros Jsy-Pants/150 4.00 10.00
52 David Ortiz Bat-Jsy/150 4.00 10.00
53 Troy Glaus Jsy-Jsy/150 2.50 6.00
54 Rickey Henderson Mets Bat-Jsy/150 4.00 10.00
55 Craig Biggio Bat-Jsy/150 4.00 10.00
56 Brad Penny Fld Glv-Jsy/150 2.00 5.00
57 Gary Carter Mets Jsy-Pants/150 3.00 8.00
58 Andy Pettitte Jsy-Jsy/150 3.00 8.00
59 Mark Prior Fld Glv-Jsy/150 3.00 8.00
60 Kirby Puckett Bat-Fld Glv/100 5.00 12.00
61 Willie McCovey Jsy-Pants/150 4.00 10.00
62 A.Dawson Expos Bat-Jsy/20 5.00 12.00
63 Greg Maddux Bat-Jsy/50 8.00 20.00
64 Adrian Beltre Bat-Jsy/150 2.50 6.00
65 Andruw Jones Bat-Jsy/150 2.50 6.00
66 Juan Gonzalez Indians Bat-Jsy/5
67 Frank Thomas Jsy-Jsy/150 4.00 10.00
68 Victor Martinez Chest Prot-Jsy/150 2.50 6.00
69 Randy Johnson D'backs Jsy-Pants/150 4.00 10.00
70 A.Dawson Cubs Jsy-Pants/5
71 Adam Dunn Bat-Jsy/95 2.50 6.00
72 Carlton Fisk Bat-Jsy/150 4.00 10.00
73 Cal Ripken Jsy-Pants/150 10.00 25.00
74 Kenny Lofton Bat-Hat/150 3.00 8.00
75 Barry Zito Jsy-Jsy/150 2.50 6.00
76 Sammy Sosa Bat-Jsy/150 4.00 10.00
77 Deion Sanders Jsy-Pants/150 6.00 15.00
78 Tony Gwynn Jsy-Pants/150 6.00 15.00
79 Mike Piazza Jsy-Pants/150 4.00 10.00
80 Jeff Bagwell Jsy-Pants/150 3.00 8.00
81 Manny Ramirez Bat-Jsy/150 3.00 8.00
82 Carlos Beltran Royals Hat-Jsy/10
83 Mark Grace Bat-Jsy/50 4.00 10.00
84 Robin Yount Bat-Jsy/150 5.00 12.00
85 Albert Pujols Bat-Jsy/150 10.00 25.00
86 Dontrelle Willis Bat-Jsy/150 2.50 6.00
88 Magglio Ordonez Bat-Shoes/150 2.50 6.00
89 Miguel Tejada Hat-Jsy/150 3.00 8.00
90 Mark Teixeira Fld Glv-Jsy/150 3.00 8.00
91 Gary Carter Expos Bat-Jsy/150 5.00 12.00
92 Ivan Rodriguez Rgr Chest Prot-Jsy/150 3.00 8.00
93 Jason Giambi Hat-Jsy/50 3.00 8.00
94 Rickey Henderson A's Bat-Pants/150 4.00 10.00
95 Curt Schilling D'backs Jsy-Jsy/150 2.50 6.00
96 Bobby Doerr Bat-Pants/150 3.00 8.00
97 Chipper Jones Bat-Jsy/150 4.00 10.00
98 Eric Chavez Bat-Jsy/1
99 Johnny Bench Bat-Pants/150 5.00 12.00
100 Harmon Killebrew Hat-Jsy/50 10.00 25.00
101 Andre Dawson B-J/50 4.00 10.00
102 Babe Ruth B-P/150 150.00 250.00
103 Bernie Williams B-J/85 3.00 8.00
106 Bo Jackson B-J/1
108 Brad Penny FG-S/70 2.00 5.00
110 Cal Ripken JK-P/100 10.00 25.00
111 Casey Fossum J-S/1
112 Curt Schilling FG-J/100 2.50 6.00
113 Dale Murphy B-J/1
114 Darryl Strawberry B-J/1
115 Dave Concepcion B-J/60 5.00 12.00
116 Dave Winfield FG-H/75 3.00 8.00
120 Gary Sheffield FG-H/1
122 Hank Aaron B-J/200 12.50 30.00
123 Harmon Killebrew B-J/1
124 Harold Baines J-Jsy/75 3.00 8.00
125 Hideki Matsui B-P/150 8.00 20.00
126 Hideo Nomo J-P/125 4.00 10.00
128 Jason Giambi Yanks J-Jsy/100 2.50 6.00
129 Jason Giambi A's J-Jsy/1
130 Jeff Bagwell P-Pants/150 3.00 8.00
133 Joe Mays FG-J/150 2.00 5.00
134 John Buck B-J/150 2.00 5.00
138 Josh Phelps B-J/1
139 Juan Pierre B-J/1
140 Kazuhisa Ishii J-Jsy/150 2.50 6.00
141 Kenny Lofton B-FG/125 3.00 8.00
142 Kevin Brown J-Jsy/1
144 Kevin Millwood Phils J-Jsy/1
145 Lance Berkman B-J/10
146 Lenny Dykstra B-J/1
148 M.Ordonez Bat-Btg Glv/1
149 Marcus Giles J-S/135 2.50 6.00
151 Mark Prior H-S/1
152 Marlon Byrd B-J/1
153 Miguel Tejada J-Jsy/75 2.50 6.00
154 Mike Lowell B-J/1
155 Mike Piazza B-P/150 4.00 10.00
156 M.Sweeney B-FG/55 3.00 8.00
157 M.Ensberg FG-H/55 3.00 8.00
161 Pedro Martinez J-Jsy/1
163 Rafael Furcal B-J/150 2.50 6.00
164 R.Palmeiro B-P/150 3.00 8.00
165 Randy Johnson D'backs J-Jsy/75 4.00 10.00
166 R.John Astros J-P/150 4.00 10.00
167 Richie Sexson J-P/150 2.50 6.00
168 R.Hend Mets B-JK/150 5.00 12.00
169 R.Hend A's J-P/100 5.00 12.00
170 R.Hend M's B-J/150 5.00 12.00
171 Roberto Alomar B-J/25 6.00 15.00
174 Rod Carew J-Jsy/29 6.00 15.00
175 Roger Clemens B-J/100 6.00 15.00
176 Roger Maris A's J-P/50 30.00 60.00
177 R.Maris Yanks J-P/25 20.00 50.00
181 Sammy Sosa B-J/150 4.00 10.00
182 Shawn Green B-J/150 2.50 6.00
184 Steve Carlton FG-P/150 3.00 8.00
185 Ted Williams JK-J/100 30.00 60.00
186 Ted Williams B-J/100 30.00 60.00
187 Tim Hudson H-J/150 2.50 6.00
188 Todd Helton B-J/150 3.00 8.00
189 Tom Glavine B-J/25 5.00 12.00
190 Tom Seaver J-P/150 4.00 10.00
191 Tommy John B-J/150 3.00 8.00
192 Tony Gwynn J-P/150 6.00 15.00
193 V.Guerrero B-J/100 4.00 10.00
196 Warren Spahn J-P/150 10.00 25.00
197 Willie Mays B-J/150 15.00 40.00
198 Willie McCovey J-P/10
199 Willie Stargell B-J/25 6.00 15.00
200 Yogi Berra J-P/25 12.50 30.00

2005 Absolute Memorabilia Tools of the Trade Swatch Double Prime Black

*PRIME p/r 100: .75X TO 2X DBL p/r 20-29
*PRIME p/r 45-50: .6X TO 1.5X DBL p/r 70-200
*PRIME p/r 45-50: .5X TO 1.2X DBL p/r 50-60
*PRIME p/r 45-50: .4X TO 1X DBL p/r 20-29
*PRIME p/r 20-35: .75X TO 2X DBL p/r 70-200
*PRIME p/r 20-35: .6X TO 1.5X DBL p/r 50-60
*PRIME p/r 20-35: .5X TO 1.2X DBL p/r 20-25
*PRIME p/r 15: 1X TO 2.5X DBL p/r 70-200
*PRIME p/r 15: .6X TO 1.5X DBL p/r 20-29
OVERALL AU-GU ODDS ONE PER PACK
PRINT RUNS B/WN 1-100 COPIES PER
NO PRICING ON QTY OF 10 OR LESS
16 Dwight Gooden Jsy-Shoes/20 6.00 15.00
18 Darryl Strawberry Mets Bat-Jsy/50 5.00 12.00
26 Roy Oswalt Jsy-Shoes/25 5.00 12.00
28 Austin Kearns Bat-Jsy/25 4.00 10.00
37 Juan Gonzalez Rgr Jsy-Pants/50 4.00 10.00
48 Torii Hunter Bat-Jsy/50 4.00 10.00
66 Juan Gonzalez Indians Bat-Jsy/50 4.00 10.00
82 Carlos Beltran Royals Hat-Jsy/25 5.00 12.00
104 Billy Wagner J-Jsy/25 5.00 12.00
105 Billy Williams J-Jsy/50 5.00 12.00
107 Bob Gibson J-Jsy/25 10.00 25.00
111 Casey Fossum J-Jsy/50 3.00 8.00
114 D.Strawberry B-J/35 6.00 15.00
116 Dave Winfield B-JK/30 6.00 15.00
136 Jorge Posada J-Jsy/45 6.00 15.00
143 K.Millw Braves J-Jsy/35 5.00 12.00
144 K.Millw Phils J-Jsy/50 4.00 10.00
159 Orel Hershiser J-Jsy/15 8.00 20.00
161 Pedro Martinez J-Jsy/15 8.00 20.00

2005 Absolute Memorabilia Tools of the Trade Swatch Double Prime Red

*PRIME p/r 75-150: .5X TO 1.2X DBL p/r 70-200
*PRIME p/r 75-150: .4X TO 1X DBL p/r 50-60
*PRIME p/r 75-150: .3X TO .8X DBL p/r 20-29
*PRIME p/r 40-55: .6X TO 1.5X DBL p/r 70-200
*PRIME p/r 40-55: .5X TO 1.2X DBL p/r 50-60
*PRIME p/r 40-55: .4X TO 1X DBL p/r 20-29
*PRIME p/r 20-35: .75X TO 2X DBL p/r 70-200
*PRIME p/r 20-35: .6X TO 1.5X DBL p/r 50-60
*PRIME p/r 20-35: .5X TO 1.2X DBL p/r 20-29
*PRIME p/r 15: 1X TO 2.5X DBL p/r 70-200
*PRIME p/r 15: .6X TO 1.5X DBL p/r 20-29
OVERALL AU-GU ODDS ONE PER PACK
PRINT RUNS B/WN 1-150 COPIES PER
NO PRICING ON QTY OF 12 OR LESS
14 Ernie Banks Bat-Jsy/25 30.00 60.00
16 Dwight Gooden Jsy-Shoes/50 5.00 12.00
18 Darryl Strawberry Mets Bat-Jsy/50 5.00 12.00
26 Roy Oswalt Jsy-Shoes/50 4.00 10.00
28 Austin Kearns Bat-Jsy/50 3.00 8.00
37 Juan Gonzalez Rgr Jsy-Pants/100 3.00 8.00
48 Torii Hunter Bat-Jsy/100 3.00 8.00
66 Juan Gonzalez Indians Bat-Jsy/100 3.00 8.00
70 Andre Dawson Cubs Jsy-Pants/15 8.00 20.00
82 Carlos Beltran Royals Hat-Jsy/50 4.00 10.00
87 Jim Thome Jsy-Jsy/25 6.00 15.00
98 Eric Chavez Bat-Jsy/25 5.00 12.00
104 Billy Wagner J-Jsy/90 3.00 8.00
105 Billy Williams J-Jsy/150 4.00 10.00
107 Bob Gibson J-Jsy/50 8.00 20.00
111 Casey Fossum J-Jsy/110 2.50 6.00
113 Dale Murphy B-J/15 10.00 25.00
114 Darryl Strawberry B-J/150 4.00 10.00
118 Fergie Jenkins J-Jsy/50 8.00 20.00
119 Gary Carter B-JK/50 5.00 12.00

121 Gaylord Perry J-Jsy/20 6.00 15.00
127 Hoyt Wilhelm J-Jsy/30 10.00 25.00
129 J.Giambi A's B-H/20 5.00 12.00
142 Kevin Brown J-Jsy/25 5.00 12.00
143 Kevin Millwood Braves J-Jsy/150 3.00 8.00
144 Kevin Millwood Phils J-Jsy/150 3.00 8.00
159 Orel Hershiser J-Jsy/55 5.00 12.00
161 Pedro Martinez J-Jsy/50 5.00 12.00

2005 Absolute Memorabilia Tools of the Trade Swatch Triple

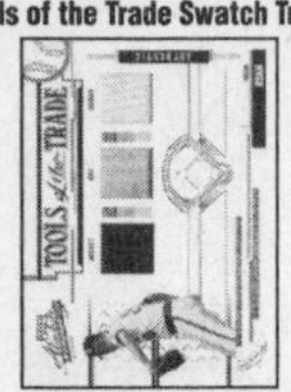

*TRIP p/r 70-175: .5X TO 1.2X DBL p/r 70-200
*TRIP p/r 70-175: .4X TO 1X DBL p/r 50-60
*TRIP p/r 50-55: .4X TO 1X DBL p/r 20-29
*TRIP p/r 20-25: .75X TO 2X DBL p/r 70-200
*TRIP p/r 20-25: .6X TO 1.5X DBL p/r 50-60
*TRIP p/r 20-25: .5X TO 1.2X DBL p/r 20-29
*TRIP p/r 15: 1X TO 2.5X DBL p/r 70-200
*TRIP p/r 15: .75X TO 2X DBL p/r 50-60
OVERALL AU-GU ODDS ONE PER PACK
PRINT RUNS B/WN 1-175 COPIES PER
NO PRICING ON QTY OF 10 OR LESS
14 Ernie Banks Bat-Hat-Jsy/15 20.00 50.00
18 Darryl Strawberry Mets 8.00 20.00
(Bat-Fld Glv-Shoes/15
37 Juan Gonzalez Rgr Bat-Jsy-Pants/25 5.00 12.00
70 A.Dawson Cubs Bat-Jsy-Pants/25 6.00 15.00
82 Carlos Beltran 6.00 15.00
Royals Bat-Jsy-Shoes/15
98 Eric Chavez Bat-Jsy-Jsy/25 5.00 12.00
102 Babe Ruth B-J-P/25 450.00 750.00
111 Casey Fossum FG-J-S/55 3.00 8.00
122 Hank Aaron B-H-J/175 15.00 40.00
138 Josh Phelps B-FG-J/115 2.50 6.00
139 Juan Pierre B-BG-J/180 3.00 8.00
142 Kevin Brown B-J-J/25 6.00 15.00
146 L.Dykstra B-FG-J/125 4.00 10.00
154 Mike Lowell B-J-J/175 3.00 8.00
176 R.Maris A's B-J-P/50 40.00 80.00
177 R.Maris Yanks B-J-P/100 30.00 60.00
179 Ryan Klesko FG-J-J/50 4.00 10.00
185 Ted Williams B-JK-J/50 90.00 150.00
186 Ted Williams B-JK-J/50 90.00 150.00
197 Willie Mays B-J-P/100 30.00 60.00
200 Yogi Berra J-J-P/25 20.00 50.00

2005 Absolute Memorabilia Tools of the Trade Swatch.Triple Prime Black

*PRIME p/r 40-50: 1X TO 2.5X DBL p/r 70-200
*PRIME p/r 40-50: .75X TO 2X DBL p/r 50-60
*PRIMEp/r25-30: 1.25X TO 3X DBL p/r70-200
*PRIME p/r 25-30: .75X TO 2X DBL p/r 20-29
*PRIME p/r 15: 1.5X TO 4X DBL p/r 70-200
OVERALL AU-GU ODDS ONE PER PACK
PRINT RUNS B/WN 1-50 COPIES PER
NO PRICING ON QTY OF 10 OR LESS
26 Roy Oswalt Btg Glv-Fld Glv-Jsy/15 10.00 25.00
37 J.Gonzalez Rgr Bat-Jsy-Pants/15 10.00 25.00
48 Torii Hunter Bat-Jsy-Jsy/15 10.00 25.00
66 Juan Gonzalez Indians Bat-Jsy-Jsy/15 10.00 25.00
111 Casey Fossum J-J-S/15 5.00 12.00
114 D.Strawberry B-J-J/50 8.00 20.00
119 Gary Carter BG-JK-S/30 10.00 25.00
127 Hoyt Wilhelm J-J-J/25 15.00 40.00
129 J.Giambi A's H-J-J/15 10.00 25.00
138 Josh Phelps FG-J-J/40 5.00 12.00
142 Kevin Brown B-J-J/50 6.00 15.00
144 K.Millw Phils J-J-J/50 6.00 15.00
151 Mark Prior B-H-H/25 10.00 25.00
152 Marlon Byrd B-J-J/50 5.00 12.00
161 Pedro Martinez B-J-J/25 10.00 25.00

2005 Absolute Memorabilia Tools of the Trade Swatch Triple Prime Red

*PRIME p/r 75-100: .75X TO 2X DBLp/r70-200
*PRIME p/r 75-100: .6X TO 1.5X DBLp/r 50-60
*PRIME p/r 40-65: 1X TO 2.5X DBL p/r 70-200
*PRIME p/r 40-65: .75X TO 2X DBL p/r 50-60
*PRIME p/r 40-65: .6X TO 1.5X DBL p/r 20-29
*PRIMEp/r24-35: 1.25X TO 3X DBLp/r70-200
*PRIMEp/r24-35: .75X TO 2X DBLp/r20-29
*PRIME p/r 15: 1.5X TO 4X DBL p/r 70-200
*PRIME p/r 15: 1.25X TO 3X DBL p/r 50-60
*PRIME p/r 15: 1X TO 2.5X DBL p/r 20-29
OVERALL AU-GU ODDS ONE PER PACK
PRINT RUNS B/WN 1-100 COPIES PER
NO PRICING ON QTY OF 10 OR LESS
26 Roy Oswalt Btg Glv-Fld Glv-Jsy/25 8.00 20.00
28 Austin Kearns Bat-Fld Glv-Jsy/15 8.00 20.00
37 Juan Gonzalez Rgr Bat-Jsy-Pants/25 8.00 20.00
40 Alfonso Soriano Bat-Jsy-Jsy/25 8.00 20.00
48 Torii Hunter Bat-Jsy-Jsy/25 8.00 20.00
66 Juan Gonzalez Indians Bat-Jsy-Jsy/25 8.00 20.00
70 Andre Dawson Cubs Bat-Jsy-Pants/15 12.50 30.00
87 Jim Thome Jsy-Jsy-Jsy/15 12.50 30.00
98 Eric Chavez Bat-Jsy-Jsy/15 10.00 25.00
111 Casey Fossum J-J-S/100 4.00 10.00
114 D.Strawberry B-J-J/100 6.00 15.00
119 Gary Carter BG-JK-S/50 8.00 20.00
122 Hank Aaron B-H-J/100 30.00 80.00
127 Hoyt Wilhelm J-J-J/75 10.00 25.00
129 J.Giambi A's H-J-J/35 8.00 20.00
138 Josh Phelps FG-J-J/75 4.00 10.00
142 Kevin Brown B-J-J/100 5.00 12.00
144 K.Millw Phils J-J-J/100 5.00 12.00
151 Mark Prior B-H-H/40 8.00 20.00
152 Marlon Byrd B-J-J/100 4.00 10.00
161 Pedro Martinez B-J-J/75 6.00 15.00
197 Willie Mays B-J-P/24 75.00 150.00

2005 Absolute Memorabilia Tools of the Trade Swatch Quad

*QUAD p/r 75-150: .75X TO 2X DBL p/r 70-200
*QUAD p/r 75-150: .6X TO 1.5X DBL p/r 50-60
*QUAD p/r 75-150: .5X TO 1.2X DBL p/r 20-29
*QUAD p/r 50-65: 1X TO 2.5X DBL p/r 70-200
*QUAD p/r 50-65: .75X TO 2X DBL p/r 50-60
*QUAD p/r 20-35: 1.25X TO 3X DBL p/r 70-200

*QUAD p/r 20-35: 1X TO 2.5X DBL p/r 50-60
*QUAD p/r 20-35: .75X TO 2X DBL p/r 20-29
*QUAD p/r 15: 1.5X TO 4X DBL p/r 70-200
*QUAD p/r 15: 1.25X TO 3X DBL p/r 50-60
OVERALL AU-GU ODDS ONE PER PACK
PRINT RUNS B/WN 1-150 COPIES PER
NO PRICING ON QTY OF 10 OR LESS
14 Ernie Banks Bat-Hat-Jsy-Jsy/25 30.00 60.00
24 Willie Mays Bat-Jsy-Jsy-Pants/25 75.00 150.00
26 Roy Oswalt 8.00 20.00
Btg Glv-Fld Glv-Jsy-Shoes/30
37 Juan Gonzalez 10.00 25.00
Rangers Bat-Hat-Jsy-Pants/15
46 Mike Mussina 10.00 25.00
Yanks Hat-Jsy-Jsy-Shoes/25
66 Juan Gonzalez Indians 8.00 20.00
Bat-Jsy-Jsy-Jsy/30
70 Andre Dawson 10.00 25.00
Cubs Bat-Jsy-Jsy-Pants/25
82 Carlos Beltran 8.00 20.00
Royals Bat-Hat-Jsy-Shoes/20
98 Eric Chavez Bat-Jsy-Jsy-Jsy/15 10.00 25.00
102 Babe Ruth B-J-J-P/20 700.00 1200.00
111 C.Fossum FG-H-J-S/150 4.00 10.00
113 Dale Murphy B-H-J-J/30 12.50 30.00
114 D.Straw B-FG-J-J/75 6.00 15.00
120 G.Sheffield B-FG-H-S/25 8.00 20.00
122 Hank Aaron B-H-J-J/150 30.00 60.00
129 J.Giam A's B-H-J-J/150 5.00 12.00
138 Josh Phelps B-FG-J-S/75 4.00 10.00
139 Juan Pierre B-H-J-S/112 5.00 12.00
151 Mark Prior B-H-J-S/50 8.00 20.00
152 Marlon Byrd B-J-J-S/35 6.00 15.00
161 P.Martinez B-J-P-J/150 6.00 15.00
173 Robin Yount H-HM-J-J/15 20.00 50.00
179 Ryan Klesko FG-H-J-J/25 8.00 20.00
186 T.Williams B-JK-J-J/50 125.00 200.00

2005 Absolute Memorabilia Tools of the Trade Swatch Quad Reverse

*REV p/r 100: .75X TO 2X DBL p/r 70-200
*REV p/r 40-65: 1X TO 2.5X DBL p/r 70-200
*REV p/r 20-35: 1.25X TO 3X DBL p/r 70-200
*REV p/r 20-35: .75X TO 2X DBL p/r 20-29
*REV p/r 15: 1.5X TO 4X DBL p/r 70-200
*REV p/r 15: 1.25X TO 3X DBL p/r 50-60
OVERALL AU-GU ODDS ONE PER PACK
PRINT RUNS B/WN 1-100 COPIES PER
NO PRICING ON QTY OF 10 OR LESS
111 C.Fossum FG-H-J-S/65 5.00 12.00
114 D.Straw B-FG-J-J/25 10.00 25.00
122 Hank Aaron B-H-J-J/100 30.00 60.00
129 J.Giambi A's B-H-J-J/50 6.00 15.00
138 Josh Phelps B-FG-J-S/25 6.00 15.00
139 Juan Pierre B-H-J-S/65 6.00 15.00
151 Mark Prior B-H-J-S/25 10.00 25.00
152 Marlon Byrd B-J-J-S/15 8.00 20.00
161 P.Martinez B-J-P-J/50 8.00 20.00

2005 Absolute Memorabilia Tools of the Trade Swatch Quad Prime Black

*PRIME p/r 25: 1.5X TO 4X DBL p/r 70-200
*PRIME p/r 25: 1.25X TO 3X DBL p/r 50-60
OVERALL AU-GU ODDS ONE PER PACK
PRINT RUNS B/WN 1-25 COPIES PER
NO PRICING ON QTY OF 5 OR LESS
119 G.Cart BG-CP-FG-JK/25 12.50 30.00
142 Kevin Brown B-J-J-J/25 10.00 25.00
148 M.Ordonez B-BG-J-S/25 10.00 25.00
154 Mike Lowell B-J-J-J/25 10.00 25.00

2005 Absolute Memorabilia Tools of the Trade Swatch Quad Prime Red

*PRIME p/r 50: 1.25X TO 3X DBL p/r 70-200
*PRIME p/r 50: 1X TO 2.5X DBL p/r 50-60
OVERALL AU-GU ODDS ONE PER PACK
PRINT RUNS B/WN 1-75 COPIES PER
NO PRICING ON QTY OF 12 OR LESS
119 G.Cart BG-CP-FG-JK/75 8.00 20.00
142 Kevin Brown B-J-J-J/50 8.00 20.00
148 M.Ordonez B-BG-J-S/50 8.00 20.00
154 Mike Lowell B-J-J-J/50 8.00 20.00
164 R.Palmeiro B-H-P-S/15 15.00 40.00
193 V.Guerrero B-FG-J-J/25 15.00 40.00

2005 Absolute Memorabilia Tools of the Trade Swatch Five

*FIVE p/r 75-150: 1X TO 2.5X DBL p/r 70-200
*FIVE p/r 75-150: .6X TO 1.5X DBL p/r 20-29
*FIVE p/r 40-50: 1.25X TO 3X DBL p/r 70-200
*FIVE p/r 40-50: 1X TO 2.5X DBL p/r 50-60
*FIVE p/r 20-35: 1.5X TO 4X DBL p/r 70-200
*FIVE p/r 20-35: 1.25X TO 3X DBL p/r 50-60
*FIVE p/r 20-35: 1X TO 2.5X DBL p/r 20-29
*FIVE p/r 15-17: 2X TO 5X DBL p/r 70-200
*FIVE p/r 15-17: 1.5X TO 4X DBL p/r 50-60
OVERALL AU-GU ODDS ONE PER PACK
PRINT RUNS B/WN 1-150 COPIES PER
NO PRICING ON QTY OF 10 OR LESS
26 Roy Oswalt 10.00 25.00
Bat-Btg Glv-Fld Glv-Jsy-Shoes/25
28 Austin Kearns 8.00 20.00
Bat-Hat-Jsy-Jsy-Shoes/25
82 Carlos Beltran Royals Bat-Hat-
Jsy-Jsy-Shoes/20 10.00 25.00
123 H.Kill B-H-J-J-S/25 20.00 50.00
129 J.Giam A's B-H-J-J-J/20 10.00 25.00
138 J.Phelps B-FG-H-J-S/15 10.00 25.00
145 L.Berk B-BG-FG-J-S/20 10.00 25.00
152 M.Byrd B-FG-H-J-S/25 8.00 20.00
179 R.Klesko BG-FG-H-J-J/25 10.00 25.00

2005 Absolute Memorabilia Tools of the Trade Swatch Five Reverse

*REV p/r 75-100: 1X TO 2.5X DBL p/r 70-200
*REV p/r 20-35: 1.5X TO 4X DBL p/r 70-200
*REV p/r 20-35: 1X TO 2.5X DBL p/r 20-29
*REV p/r 15: 2X TO 5X DBL p/r 70-200
*REV p/r 15: 1.5X TO 4X DBL p/r 50-60
*REV p/r 15: 1.25X TO 3X DBL p/r 20-29
OVERALL AU-GU ODDS ONE PER PACK
PRINT RUNS B/WN 1-15 COPIES PER
NO PRICING ON QTY OF 10 OR LESS
26 Roy Oswalt Bat-Btg Glv-Fld Glv-
Jsy-Shoes/15 12.50 30.00
28 Austin Kearns Bat-Hat-Jsy-
Jsy-Shoes/15 10.00 25.00
123 H.Kill B-H-J-J-S/15 30.00 60.00
152 M.Byrd B-FG-H-J-S/15 10.00 25.00

2005 Absolute Memorabilia Tools of the Trade Swatch Five Prime Red

*PRIME p/r 25: 2X TO 5X DBL p/r 70-200
*PRIME p/r 15: 1.5X TO 4X DBL p/r 20-29
PRINT RUNS B/WN 1-25 COPIES PER
NO PRICING ON QTY OF 10 OR LESS
PRIME BLACK PRINT B/WN 1-10 PER
NO PRIME BLACK PRICING DUE TO SCARCITY
OVERALL AU-GU ODDS ONE PER PACK

2005 Absolute Memorabilia Tools of the Trade Swatch Six

*SIX p/r 75-150: 1.5X TO 4X DBL p/r 70-200
*SIX p/r 50: 2X TO 5X DBL p/r 70-200
*SIX p/r 50: 1.5X TO 4X DBL p/r 50-60
*SIX p/r 25-30: 2.5X TO 6X DBL p/r 70-200
*SIX p/r 15: 3X TO 8X DBL p/r 70-200
*SIX p/r 15: 2.5X TO 6X DBL p/r 50-60
*SIX p/r 15: 2X TO 5X DBL p/r 20-29
OVERALL AU-GU ODDS ONE PER PACK
PRINT RUNS B/WN 1-150 COPIES PER
NO PRICING ON QTY OF 10 OR LESS
26 Roy Oswalt 20.00 50.00
Btg Glv-Fld Glv-Hat-Jsy-Jsy-Shoes/15
123 H.Kill B-H-J-J-P-S/30 30.00 80.00
138 J.Phelps B-FG-H-J-J-S/150 8.00 20.00
145 L.Berk B-BG-FG-H-J-S/25 15.00 40.00
152 M.Byrd B-BG-FG-H-J-S/150 8.00 20.00
179 R.Klesko BG-FG-H-J-J-S/100 10.00 25.00

2005 Absolute Memorabilia Tools of the Trade Swatch Six Reverse

*REV p/r 20-25: 2.5X TO 6X DBL p/r 70-200
OVERALL AU-GU ODDS ONE PER PACK
PRINT RUNS B/WN 1-50 COPIES PER
NO PRICING ON QTY OF 10 OR LESS
123 H.Kill B-H-J-J-P-S/15 50.00 100.00
138 J.Phelps B-FG-H-J-S/50 10.00 25.00
152 M.Byrd B-BG-FG-H-J-S/45 10.00 25.00
179 R.Klesko BG-FG-H-J-J-S/25 15.00 40.00

2005 Absolute Memorabilia Tools of the Trade Swatch Six Prime Black

*PRIME p/r 25: 3X TO 8X DBL p/r 70-200
OVERALL AU-GU ODDS ONE PER PACK
PRINT RUNS B/WN 1-25 COPIES PER
NO PRICING ON QTY OF 10 OR LESS

2005 Absolute Memorabilia Tools of the Trade Swatch Six Prime Red

*PRIME p/r 50: 2.5X TO 6X DBL p/r 70-200
*PRIME p/r 25: 3X TO 8X DBL p/r 70-200
OVERALL AU-GU ODDS ONE PER PACK
PRINT RUNS B/WN 1-50 COPIES PER
NO PRICING ON QTY OF 9 OR LESS

2005 Absolute Memorabilia Tools of the Trade Autograph

OVERALL AU-GU ODDS ONE PER PACK
PRINT RUNS B/WN 1-150 COPIES PER
NO PRICING ON QTY OF 11 OR LESS
105 Billy Williams/150 6.00 15.00
107 Bob Gibson/88 15.00 40.00
117 David Cone/75 6.00 15.00
118 Fergie Jenkins/100 6.00 15.00
119 Gary Carter/43 8.00 20.00
120 Gary Sheffield/36 12.50 30.00
121 Gaylord Perry/16 12.50 30.00
122 Hank Aaron/100 100.00 175.00
131 Jim Palmer/106 6.00 15.00
137 Josh Beckett/56 12.50 30.00
150 Mark Grace/50 12.50 30.00
158 Nolan Ryan/75 40.00 80.00
159 Orel Hershiser/21 10.00 25.00
160 Ozzie Smith/150 15.00 40.00
162 Phil Rizzuto/99 10.00 25.00
174 Rod Carew/150 10.00 25.00
178 Ron Cey/100 6.00 15.00
180 Ryne Sandberg/150 15.00 40.00
183 Stan Musial/150 30.00 60.00
184 Steve Carlton/150 6.00 15.00
188 Todd Helton/100 10.00 25.00
190 Tom Seaver/18 30.00 60.00
194 Wade Boggs Sox/70 10.00 25.00
195 Wade Boggs Rays/35 15.00 40.00

2005 Absolute Memorabilia Tools of the Trade Autograph Reverse

*REV p/r 75-100: .4X TO 1X AU p/r 70-150
*REV p/r 37-50: .5X TO 1.2X AU p/r 70-150
*REV p/r 37-50: .4X TO 1X AU p/r 36-56
*REV p/r 20-32: .6X TO 1.5X AU p/r 70-150
*REV p/r 20-32: .4X TO 1X AU p/r 21-35
*REV p/r 20-32: .3X TO .8X AU p/r 16-18
*REV p/r 15: .6X TO 1.5X AU p/r 36-56
OVERALL AU-GU ODDS ONE PER PACK
PRINT RUNS B/WN 1-100 COPIES PER
NO PRICING ON QTY OF 7 OR LESS
122 Hank Aaron/32 125.00 200.00
183 Stan Musial/100 30.00 60.00
192 Tony Gwynn/25 20.00 50.00

2005 Absolute Memorabilia Tools of the Trade Autograph Red

*RED p/r 25-30: .6X TO 1.5X AU p/r 70-150
*RED p/r 16-19: .75X TO 2X AU p/r 70-150
PRINT RUNS B/WN 1-30 COPIES PER
NO PRICING ON QTY OF 12 OR LESS
BLACK PRINT RUN 1 SERIAL #'d SET
BLACK CARD 175 PRINT RUN 4 #'d COPIES
NO BLACK PRICING DUE TO SCARCITY
OVERALL AU-GU ODDS ONE PER PACK
192 Tony Gwynn/19 20.00 50.00

2005 Absolute Memorabilia Tools of the Trade Autograph Bat

*BAT p/r 100: .3X TO .8X AU p/r 36-56
*BAT p/r 50: .5X TO 1.2X AU p/r 70-150
*BAT p/r 50: .3X TO .8X AU p/r 21-35
OVERALL AU-GU ODDS ONE PER PACK
PRINT RUNS B/WN 1-100 COPIES PER
NO PRICING ON QTY OF 7 OR LESS
113 Dale Murphy/100 10.00 25.00

2005 Absolute Memorabilia Tools of the Trade Autograph Bat Reverse

*BAT p/r 25: .6X TO 1.5X AU p/r 70-150
*BAT p/r 25: .5X TO 1.2X AU p/r 36-56
*BAT p/r 25: .4X TO 1X AU p/r 21-35
OVERALL AU-GU ODDS ONE PER PACK
PRINT RUNS B/WN 1-50 COPIES PER
NO PRICING ON QTY OF 3 OR LESS
113 Dale Murphy/50 12.50 30.00

2005 Absolute Memorabilia Tools of the Trade Autograph Bat Red

PRINT RUNS B/WN 1-10 COPIES PER
BLACK PRINT RUN 1 SERIAL #'d SET
OVERALL AU-GU ODDS ONE PER PACK
NO PRICING DUE TO SCARCITY

2005 Absolute Memorabilia Tools of the Trade Autograph Jersey

*JSY p/r 75-150: .4X TO 1X AU p/r 70-150
*JSY p/r 50: .5X TO 1.2X AU p/r 70-150
*JSY p/r 25-35: .6X TO 1.5X AU p/r 70-150
*JSY p/r 25-35: .5X TO 1.2X AU p/r 36-56
*JSY p/r 25-35: .3X TO .6X AU p/r 16-18
OVERALL AU-GU ODDS ONE PER PACK
PRINT RUNS B/WN 1-150 COPIES PER
NO PRICING ON QTY OF 10 OR LESS
113 Dale Murphy/50 12.50 30.00

122 Hank Aaron/50 125.00 200.00
135 John Kruk/150 6.00 15.00
192 Tony Gwynn/100 15.00 40.00

2005 Absolute Memorabilia Tools of the Trade Autograph Jersey Reverse

*JSY p/r 97-100: .4X TO 1X AU p/r 70-150
*JSY p/r 50: .5X TO 1.2X AU p/r 70-150
*JSY p/r 25: .6X TO 1.5X AU p/r 70-150
*JSY p/r 15: .6X TO 1.5X AU p/r 36-56
OVERALL AU-GU ODDS ONE PER PACK
PRINT RUNS B/WN 1-100 COPIES PER
NO PRICING ON QTY OF 10 OR LESS
113 Dale Murphy/25 15.00 40.00
122 Hank Aaron/25 125.00 200.00
123 Harmon Killebrew/15 40.00 80.00
135 John Kruk/100 6.00 15.00
192 Tony Gwynn/50 15.00 40.00

2005 Absolute Memorabilia Tools of the Trade Autograph Jersey Red

*RED p/r 25: .6X TO 1.5X AU p/r 70-150
OVERALL AU-GU ODDS ONE PER PACK
PRINT RUNS B/WN 1-25 COPIES PER
NO PRICING ON QTY OF 10 OR LESS
135 John Kruk/25 10.00 25.00
192 Tony Gwynn/25 20.00 50.00

2005 Absolute Memorabilia Tools of the Trade Autograph Swatch Single Jumbo

*SNG p/r 100: .5X TO 1.2X DBL p/r 75-100
*SNG p/r 44-50: .6X TO 1.5X DBL p/r 75-100
*SNG p/r 44-50: .5X TO 1.2X DBL p/r 40-65
OVERALL AU-GU ODDS ONE PER PACK
PRINT RUNS B/WN 1-100 COPIES PER
NO PRICING ON QTY OF 10 OR LESS
105 Billy Williams Jsy/25 12.50 30.00
118 Fergie Jenkins Jsy/25 12.50 30.00
135 John Kruk Jsy/25 12.50 30.00
159 Orel Hershiser Jsy/25 12.50 30.00
162 Phil Rizzuto Jsy/100 20.00 50.00
198 Willie McCovey Pants/44 15.00 40.00

2005 Absolute Memorabilia Tools of the Trade Autograph Swatch Single Jumbo Prime Red

PRINT RUNS B/WN 1-30 COPIES PER
NO PRICING ON QTY OF 10 OR LESS
PRIME BLACK PRINT RUNS B/WN 1-10 PER
NO PRIME BLK PRICING DUE TO SCARCITY
OVERALL AU-GU ODDS ONE PER PACK
121 Gaylord Perry Jsy/30 12.50 30.00

2005 Absolute Memorabilia Tools of the Trade Autograph Swatch Double

OVERALL AU-GU ODDS ONE PER PACK
PRINT RUNS B/WN 1-100 COPIES PER
NO PRICING ON QTY OF 10 OR LESS
1 Ozzie Smith Bat-Pants/25 30.00 60.00
2 Carlos Beltran Astros Jsy-Shoes/10
3 Dale Murphy Jsy-Jsy/50 15.00 40.00
4 Paul Molitor Jsy-Pants/25 12.50 30.00
5 George Brett Bat-Hat/5
6 Stan Musial Bat-Pants/10
10 Hideo Nomo Jsy-Pants/1
12 Roberto Alomar Bat-Jsy/10
13 Pedro Martinez Jsy-Pants/1
14 Ernie Banks Bat-Jsy/1
15 Tim Hudson Hat-Jsy/15 30.00 60.00
16 Dwight Gooden Jsy-Shoes/5
18 Darryl Strawberry Mets Bat-Jsy/1
20 Lou Brock Bat-Jkt/50 15.00 40.00
21 Roger Clemens Bat-Jsy/5
22 Paul Lo Duca Bat-Jsy/25 12.50 30.00
24 Willie Mays Bat-Pants/5
25 Rafael Palmeiro Bat-Jsy/1
26 Roy Oswalt Jsy-Shoes/1
30 Nolan Ryan Angels Bat-Jkt/15 75.00 150.00
34 Nolan Ryan Rgr Bat-Jsy/15 75.00 150.00
36 Sean Casey Jsy-Pants/50 10.00 25.00
37 Juan Gonzalez Rgr Jsy-Pants/25 12.50 30.00
38 Curt Schilling Sox Jsy-Jsy/5
39 Darryl Strawberry Yanks Bat-Jsy/50 10.00 25.00
40 Alfonso Soriano Jsy-Jsy/1
41 Tom Seaver Jsy-Pants/25 30.00 60.00
42 Mike Schmidt Bat-Jsy/15 50.00 100.00
45 Shawn Green Bat-Jsy/1
48 Torii Hunter Bat-Jsy/40 10.00 25.00
49 Kerry Wood Fld Glv-Jsy/5
54 Rickey Henderson Mets Bat-Jsy/5
56 Brad Penny Fld Glv-Jsy/75 5.00 12.00
57 Gary Carter Mets Jsy-Pants/25 12.50 30.00
59 Mark Prior Fld Glv-Jsy/10
60 Kirby Puckett Bat-Fld Glv/1
61 Willie McCovey Jsy-Pants/15 30.00 60.00
62 Andre Dawson Expos Bat-Jsy/50 10.00 25.00
64 Adrian Beltre Bat-Jsy/50 10.00 25.00
66 Juan Gonzalez Indians Bat-Jsy/25 12.50 30.00
67 Frank Thomas Jsy-Jsy/10
68 Victor Martinez Chest Prot-Jsy/10
70 Andre Dawson Cubs Jsy-Pants/50 10.00 25.00
71 Adam Dunn Bat-Jsy/5
72 Carlton Fisk Bat-Jsy/15 30.00 60.00
73 Cal Ripken Jsy-Pants/25 75.00 150.00
75 Barry Zito Jsy-Jsy/5
78 Tony Gwynn Jsy-Pants/15 30.00 60.00
80 Jeff Bagwell Jsy-Pants/5
81 Manny Ramirez Bat-Jsy/5
82 Carlos Beltran Royals Hat-Jsy/10
83 Mark Grace Bat-Jsy/10
84 Robin Yount Bat-Jsy/10
85 Albert Pujols Bat-Jsy/1
86 Dontrelle Willis Bat-Jsy/1
88 Magglio Ordonez Bat-Shoes/25 12.50 30.00
90 Mark Teixeira Fld Glv-Jsy/1
91 Gary Carter Expos Bat-Jsy/25 12.50 30.00
94 Rickey Henderson A's Bat-Jsy/5
95 Curt Schilling D'backs Jsy-Jsy/5
96 Bobby Doerr Bat-Pants/50 6.00 15.00
97 Chipper Jones Bat-Jsy/10
98 Eric Chavez Bat-Jsy/25 12.50 30.00
99 Johnny Bench Bat-Pants/15 40.00 80.00
100 Harmon Killebrew Hat-Jsy/25 40.00 80.00
107 Bob Gibson J-Jsy/10
110 Cal Ripken J-Jsy/25 75.00 150.00
112 Curt Schilling J-Jsy/1
113 Dale Murphy B-J/1
114 Darryl Strawberry B-J/1
118 Fergie Jenkins FG-J/1
120 Gary Sheffield FG-H/50 15.00 40.00
122 Hank Aaron B-J/25 150.00 250.00
123 Harmon Killebrew B-J/65 30.00 60.00
126 Hideo Nomo J-P/30 150.00 250.00
130 Jeff Bagwell P-Pants/25 30.00 60.00
131 Jim Palmer H-P/40 10.00 25.00
137 Josh Beckett B-FG/10
146 Lenny Dykstra B-J/75 8.00 20.00
148 Magglio Ordonez B-BG/1
151 Mark Prior H-S/25 12.50 30.00
152 Marlon Byrd B-J/100 5.00 12.00
163 Rafael Furcal B-J/10
165 Randy Johnson D'backs Jsy-Jsy/1
166 R.Johnson Astros J-P/1
174 Rod Carew J-Jsy/100 12.50 30.00
184 Steve Carlton FG-P/32 12.50 30.00
187 Tim Hudson H-J/15 30.00 60.00
188 Todd Helton B-J/17 30.00 60.00
190 Tom Seaver J-P/100 15.00 40.00
191 Tommy John B-J/5
192 Tony Gwynn J-P/50 15.00 40.00
198 Willie McCovey J-P/10

2005 Absolute Memorabilia Tools of the Trade Autograph Swatch Double Reverse

*REV p/r 75: .3X TO .8X DBL p/r 40-65
*REV p/r 41-50: .5X TO 1.2X DBL p/r 75-100
*REV p/r 41-50: .4X TO 1X DBL p/r 40-65
*REV p/r 25-29: .6X TO 1.5X DBL p/r 75-100
*REV p/r 25-29: .5X TO 1.2X DBL p/r 40-65
*REV p/r 25-29: .4X TO 1X DBL p/r 20-32
*REV p/r 15: .5X TO 1.2X DBL p/r 20-32
OVERALL AU-GU ODDS ONE PER PACK
PRINT RUNS B/WN 1-75 COPIES PER
NO PRICING ON QTY OF 10 OR LESS
113 Dale Murphy B-J/25 20.00 50.00
122 Hank Aaron B-J/15 150.00 250.00

2005 Absolute Memorabilia Tools of the Trade Autograph Swatch Double Prime Black

OVERALL AU-GU ODDS ONE PER PACK
PRINT RUNS B/WN 1-15 COPIES PER
NO PRICING ON QTY OF 10 OR LESS
159 Orel Hershiser J-Jsy/15 15.00 40.00

2005 Absolute Memorabilia Tools of the Trade Autograph Swatch Double Prime Red

*PRIME p/r 40-50: .6X TO 1.5X DBL p/r 75-100
*PRIME p/r 40-50: .5X TO 1.2X DBL p/r 40-65
*PRIME p/r 40-50: .4X TO 1X DBL p/r 20-32
*PRIME p/r 25: .75X TO 2X DBL p/r 75-100
*PRIME p/r 25: .5X TO 1.2X DBL p/r 20-32
*PRIME p/r 15: .75X TO 2X DBL p/r 40-65
*PRIME p/r 15: .6X TO 1.5X DBL p/r 20-32
OVERALL AU-GU ODDS ONE PER PACK
PRINT RUNS B/WN 1-50 COPIES PER
NO PRICING ON QTY OF 10 OR LESS
2 Carlos Beltran Astros Bat-Jsy/25 15.00 40.00
16 Dwight Gooden Jsy-Shoes/45 12.50 30.00
18 Darryl Strawberry Mets Bat-Jsy/50 12.50 30.00
82 Carlos Beltran Royals Hat-Jsy/25 15.00 40.00
146 Magglio Ordonez B-J/15 20.00 50.00
159 Orel Hershiser J-Jsy/25 15.00 40.00
163 Rafael Furcal B-J/15 20.00 50.00
198 Willie McCovey J-P/25 30.00 60.00

2005 Absolute Memorabilia Tools of the Trade Autograph Swatch Triple

*TRIP p/r 75-100: .5X TO 1.2X DBL p/r 75-100
*TRIP p/r 75-100: .4X TO 1X DBL p/r 40-65
*TRIP p/r 75-100: .3X TO .8X DBL p/r 20-32
*TRIP p/r 45-50: .6X TO 1.5X DBL p/r 75-100
*TRIP p/r 45-50: .5X TO 1.2X DBL p/r 40-65
*TRIP p/r 45-50: .4X TO 1X DBL p/r 20-32
*TRIP p/r 25-32: .75X TO 2X DBL p/r 75-100
*TRIP p/r 25-32: .6X TO 1.5X DBL p/r 40-65
*TRIP p/r 25-32: .5X TO 1.2X DBL p/r 25
*TRIP p/r 15: .6X TO 1.5X DBL p/r 20-32
OVERALL AU-GU ODDS ONE PER PACK
PRINT RUNS B/WN 1-100 COPIES PER
NO PRICING ON QTY OF 10 OR LESS
2 Carlos Beltran Astros Bat-Jsy-Jsy/25 15.00 40.00
18 Darryl Strawberry Mets 10.00 25.00
Bat-Fld Glv-Shoes/75
73 Cal Ripken Bat-Jsy-Pants/25 90.00 180.00
82 Carlos Beltran 15.00 40.00
Royals Bat-Jsy-Shoes/25
108 Brad Penny FG-J-S/30 10.00 25.00
110 Cal Ripken JK-J-P/25 90.00 180.00
113 Dale Murphy B-J-J/45 20.00 50.00
122 Hank Aaron B-H-J/25 175.00 300.00
126 Hideo Nomo J-J-P/25 175.00 300.00
163 Rafael Furcal B-J-J/25 15.00 40.00
165 R.John D'backs J-J-P/15 60.00 120.00
166 R.John Astros H-J-P/50 40.00 80.00

2005 Absolute Memorabilia Tools of the Trade Autograph Swatch Triple Reverse

*REV p/r 50: .6X TO 1.5X DBL p/r 75-100
*REV p/r 50: .5X TO 1.2X DBL p/r 40-65
*REV p/r 25: .75X TO 2X DBL p/r 75-100
*REV p/r 25: .6X TO 1.5X DBL p/r 40-65
*REV p/r 25: .5X TO 1.2X DBL p/r 20-32
*REV p/r 15: 1X TO 2.5X DBL p/r 75-100
*REV p/r 15: .75X TO 2X DBL p/r 40-65
*REV p/r 15: .6X TO 1.5X DBL p/r 20-32
OVERALL AU-GU ODDS ONE PER PACK
PRINT RUNS B/WN 1-50 COPIES PER
NO PRICING ON QTY OF 10 OR LESS
18 Darryl Strawberry Mets 12.50 30.00
Bat-Fld Glv-Shoes/50
110 Cal Ripken JK-J-P/25 90.00 180.00
113 Dale Murphy B-J-J/15 30.00 60.00
122 Hank Aaron B-J-J/15 175.00 300.00
126 Hideo Nomo J-J-P/15 175.00 300.00
166 R.John Astros H-J-P/25 50.00 100.00

2005 Absolute Memorabilia Tools of the Trade Autograph Swatch Triple Prime Red

*PRIME p/r 25: 1X TO 2.5X DBL p/r 75-100
*PRIME p/r 25: .75X TO 2X DBL p/r 40-65
PRINT RUNS B/WN 1-25 COPIES PER
NO PRICING ON QTY OF 13 OR LESS
PRIME BLACK PRINT RUNS B/WN 1-10 PER
NO PRIME BLK PRICING DUE TO SCARCITY
OVERALL AU-GU ODDS ONE PER PACK
16 Dwight Gooden Bat-Jsy-Jsy/15 30.00 60.00
28 Austin Kearns Bat-Fld Glv-Jsy/25 12.50 30.00

2005 Absolute Memorabilia Tools of the Trade Autograph Swatch Quad

*QUAD p/r 25: 1X TO 2.5X DBL p/r 75-100
*QUAD p/r 25: .75X TO 2X DBL p/r 40-65
*QUAD p/r 25: .6X TO 1.5X DBL p/r 20-32
*QUAD p/r 25: .5X TO 1.2X DBL p/r 15
*QUAD p/r 15: 1X TO 2.5X DBL p/r 40-65
*QUAD p/r 15: .6X TO 1.5X DBL p/r 15-17
OVERALL AU-GU ODDS ONE PER PACK
PRINT RUNS B/WN 1-25 COPIES PER
NO PRICING ON QTY OF 10 OR LESS
23 Don Mattingly Bat-Jkt-Jsy-Shoes/25 60.00 120.00

73 Cal Ripken Bat-Hat-Jkt-Jsy/25 125.00 200.00
83 Mark Grace Bat-Fld Glv-Jsy-Jsy/15 30.00 60.00
192 Tony Gwynn FG-J-P-S/25 60.00 120.00

2005 Absolute Memorabilia Tools of the Trade Autograph Swatch Quad Reverse

*REV p/r 15: 1.25X TO 3X DBL p/r 75-100
*REV p/r 15: 1X TO 2.5X DBL p/r 40-65
*REV p/r 15: .75X TO 2X DBL p/r 20-32
*REV p/r 15: .6X TO 1.5X DBL p/r 15-17
OVERALL AU-GU ODDS ONE PER PACK
PRINT RUNS B/WN 1-15 COPIES PER
NO PRICING ON QTY OF 10 OR LESS
23 Don Mattingly 75.00 150.00
Bat-Jkt-Jsy-Shoes/15
73 Cal Ripken Bat-Hat-Jkt-Jsy/15 150.00 250.00
77 Deion Sanders Bat-Jsy-Jsy-Pants/15 50.00 100.00

2005 Absolute Memorabilia Tools of the Trade Autograph Swatch Quad Prime Red

PRINT RUNS B/WN 1-10 COPIES PER
PRIME BLACK PRINT RUN 1 #'d SET
OVERALL AU-GU ODDS ONE PER PACK
NO PRICING DUE TO SCARCITY

2005 Artifacts

This product was released in April, 2005 but cards 201-285 were released within packs of '05 Upper Deck Update in February, 2006. The product was issued in four-card packs which came 10 packs to a box and 20 boxes to a case. The first 100 cards of the set feature active veterans while cards 101-150 feature leading prospects and cards 151-200 feature retired greats. Cards 101-150 were issued at a stated rate of one in five and were issued to a state print run of 1350 serial numbered sets while cards 151-200 were inserted at a stated rate of one in three and were issued to a stated print run of 1999 serial numbered sets. Cards 201-285 are serial #'d of 799.

COMP.SET w/o SP's (100) 15.00 40.00
COMMON CARD (1-100) .20 .50
COMMON CARD (101-150) .60 1.50
COMMON CARD (151-200) .60 1.50
COMMON CARD (201-285) .60 1.50
201-285 ISSUED IN 05 UD UPDATE PACKS
201-285: ONE #'d CARD OR AU PER PACK
201-285 PRINT RUN 799 SERIAL #'d SETS
1 Adam Dunn .30 .75
2 Adrian Beltre .20 .50
3 Albert Pujols 1.25 3.00
4 Alex Rodriguez .75 2.00
5 Alfonso Soriano .30 .75
6 Andruw Jones .20 .50
7 Andy Pettitte .30 .75
8 Aramis Ramirez .20 .50
9 Aubrey Huff .20 .50
10 Barry Larkin .30 .75
11 Ben Sheets .20 .50
12 Bernie Williams .30 .75
13 Bobby Abreu .20 .50
14 Brad Penny .20 .50
15 Bret Boone .20 .50
16 Brian Giles .20 .50
17 Carl Crawford .30 .75
18 Carl Pavano .20 .50
19 Carlos Beltran .20 .50
20 Carlos Delgado .20 .50
21 Carlos Guillen .20 .50
22 Carlos Lee .20 .50
23 Carlos Zambrano .30 .75
24 Chipper Jones .50 1.25
25 Craig Biggio .30 .75
26 Craig Wilson .20 .50
27 Curt Schilling .30 .75
28 David Ortiz .50 1.25
29 Derek Jeter 1.25 3.00
30 Eric Chavez .20 .50
31 Eric Gagne .20 .50
32 Frank Thomas .50 1.25
33 Garret Anderson .20 .50
34 Gary Sheffield .20 .50
35 Greg Maddux .75 2.00
36 Hank Blalock .20 .50
37 Hideki Matsui .75 2.00
38 Ichiro Suzuki .75 2.00
39 Ivan Rodriguez .30 .75
40 J.D. Drew .20 .50
41 Jake Peavy .20 .50
42 Jason Kendall .20 .50
43 Jason Schmidt .20 .50
44 Jeff Bagwell .30 .75
45 Jeff Kent .20 .50
46 Jim Edmonds .30 .75
47 Jim Thome .30 .75
48 Joe Mauer .50 1.25
49 Johan Santana .50 1.25
50 John Smoltz .50 1.25
51 Jose Reyes .30 .75
52 Jose Vidro .20 .50
53 Josh Beckett .30 .75
54 Ken Griffey Jr. .75 2.00
55 Kerry Wood .20 .50
56 Kevin Brown .20 .50
57 Lance Berkman .30 .75
58 Larry Walker .30 .75
59 Livan Hernandez .20 .50
60 Luis Gonzalez .20 .50
61 Lyle Overbay .20 .50
62 Magglio Ordonez .30 .75
63 Manny Ramirez .50 1.25
64 Mark Mulder .20 .50
65 Mark Prior .30 .75
66 Mark Teixeira .50 1.25
67 Melvin Mora .20 .50
68 Michael Young .30 .75
69 Miguel Cabrera .30 1.25
70 Miguel Tejada .30 .75
71 Mike Lowell .20 .50
72 Mike Mussina .30 .75
73 Mike Piazza .50 1.25
74 Mike Sweeney .20 .50
75 Nomar Garciaparra .50 1.25
76 Oliver Perez .20 .50
77 Paul Konerko .30 .75
78 Pedro Martinez .30 .75
79 Preston Wilson .20 .50
80 Rafael Furcal .20 .50
81 Rafael Palmeiro .30 .75
82 Randy Johnson .50 1.25
83 Richie Sexson .20 .50
84 Roger Clemens .60 1.50
85 Roy Halladay .50 1.25
86 Roy Oswalt .30 .75
87 Sammy Sosa .50 1.25
88 Scott Podsednik .20 .50
89 Scott Rolen .30 .75
90 Shawn Green .20 .50
91 Steve Finley .20 .50
92 Tim Hudson .30 .75
93 Todd Helton .30 .75
94 Tom Glavine .30 .75
95 Torii Hunter .20 .50
96 Travis Hafner .20 .50
97 Troy Glaus .20 .50
98 Vernon Wells .20 .50
99 Victor Martinez .30 .75
100 Vladimir Guerrero .50 1.25
101 Aaron Rowand FS .60 1.50
102 Adam LaRoche FS .60 1.50
103 Adrian Gonzalez FS 1.00 2.50
104 Alexis Rios FS 1.00 2.50
105 Angel Guzman FS .60 1.50
106 B.J. Upton FS 1.00 2.50
107 Bobby Crosby FS .60 1.50
108 Bobby Madritsch FS .60 1.50
109 Brandon Claussen FS .60 1.50
110 Bucky Jacobsen FS .60 1.50
111 Casey Kotchman FS .60 1.50
112 Chad Cordero FS .60 1.50
113 Chase Utley FS 1.00 2.50
114 Chris Burke FS .60 1.50
115 Dallas McPherson FS .60 1.50
116 Daniel Cabrera FS .60 1.50
117 David DeJesus FS .60 1.50
118 David Wright FS 2.50 6.00
119 Eddy Rodriguez FS .60 1.50
120 Edwin Jackson FS .60 1.50
121 Gabe Gross FS .60 1.50
122 Garrett Atkins FS .60 1.50
123 Gavin Floyd FS .60 1.50
124 Gerald Laird FS .60 1.50
125 Guillermo Quiroz FS .60 1.50
126 J.D. Closser FS .60 1.50
127 Jason Bay FS .60 1.50
128 Jason DuBois FS .60 1.50
129 Jason Lane FS .60 1.50
130 Jayson Werth FS 1.00 2.50
131 Jeff Francis FS .60 1.50
132 Jesse Crain FS .60 1.50
133 Joe Blanton FS .60 1.50
134 Joe Mauer FS 1.50 4.00
135 Jose Capellan FS .60 1.50
136 Kevin Youkilis FS .60 1.50
137 Khalil Greene FS .60 1.50
138 Laynce Nix FS .60 1.50
139 Nick Swisher FS 1.50 4.00
140 Oliver Perez FS .60 1.50
141 Rickie Weeks FS 1.00 2.50
142 Robb Quinlan FS .60 1.50
143 Roman Colon FS .60 1.50
144 Ryan Howard FS 3.00 8.00
145 Ryan Wagner FS .60 1.50
146 Scott Kazmir FS 1.50 4.00
147 Scott Proctor FS .60 1.50
148 Wily Mo Pena FS .60 1.50
149 Yhency Brazoban FS .60 1.50
150 Zack Greinke FS 1.00 2.50
151 Al Kaline LGD 1.50 4.00
152 Babe Ruth LGD 4.00 10.00
153 Billy Williams LGD .60 1.50
154 Bob Feller LGD .60 1.50
155 Bob Gibson LGD 1.00 2.50
156 Bob Lemon LGD .60 1.50
157 Bobby Doerr LGD .60 1.50
158 Brooks Robinson LGD 1.00 2.50
159 Cal Ripken LGD 6.00 15.00
160 Christy Mathewson LGD 1.50 4.00
161 Cy Young LGD 1.00 2.50
162 Dizzy Dean LGD 1.00 2.50
163 Don Drysdale LGD 1.00 2.50
164 Eddie Mathews LGD 1.00 2.50
165 Enos Slaughter LGD .60 1.50
166 Ernie Banks LGD 1.50 4.00
167 Fergie Jenkins LGD .60 1.50
168 George Sisler LGD .60 1.50
169 Harmon Killebrew LGD 1.50 4.00
170 Honus Wagner LGD 1.00 2.50
171 Jackie Robinson LGD 1.00 2.50
172 Jimmie Foxx LGD 1.00 2.50
173 Joe DiMaggio LGD 4.00 10.00
174 Joe Morgan LGD .60 1.50
175 Juan Marichal LGD .60 1.50
176 Lou Brock LGD 1.00 2.50
177 Lou Gehrig LGD 3.00 8.00
178 Luis Aparicio LGD .60 1.50
179 Mel Ott LGD 1.50 4.00
180 Mickey Cochrane LGD .60 1.50
181 Mickey Mantle LGD 5.00 12.00
182 Mike Schmidt LGD 3.00 8.00
183 Nolan Ryan LGD 4.00 10.00
184 Pee Wee Reese LGD 1.00 2.50
185 Phil Rizzuto LGD 1.00 2.50
186 Ralph Kiner LGD .60 1.50
187 Rogers Hornsby LGD .60 1.50
188 Roy Campanella LGD 1.00 2.50
189 Satchel Paige LGD 1.50 4.00
190 Stan Musial LGD 2.50 6.00
191 Rick Ferrell LGD .60 1.50
192 Thurman Munson LGD 1.00 2.50
193 Tom Seaver LGD 1.00 2.50
194 Ty Cobb LGD 2.50 6.00
195 Walter Johnson LGD 1.00 2.50
196 Warren Spahn LGD 1.00 2.50
197 Whitey Ford LGD 1.00 2.50
198 Willie McCovey LGD 1.00 2.50
199 Willie Stargell LGD 1.00 2.50
200 Yogi Berra LGD 1.50 4.00
201 Adam Shabala FS RC .60 1.50
202 Ambiorix Burgos FS RC .60 1.50
203 Ambiorix Concepcion FS RC .60 1.50
204 Anibal Sanchez FS RC 3.00 8.00
205 Bill McCarthy FS RC .60 1.50
206 Brandon McCarthy FS RC 1.00 2.50
207 Brian Burres FS RC .60 1.50
208 Carlos Ruiz FS RC .60 1.50
209 Casey Rogowski FS RC 1.00 2.50
210 Chad Orvella FS RC .60 1.50
211 Chris Resop FS RC .60 1.50
212 Chris Roberson FS RC .60 1.50
213 Chris Seddon FS RC .60 1.50
214 Colter Bean FS RC .60 1.50
215 Dae-Sung Koo FS RC .60 1.50
216 Dave Gassner FS RC .60 1.50
217 Brian Anderson FS RC 1.00 2.50
218 D.J. Houlton FS RC .60 1.50
219 Derek Wathan FS RC .60 1.50
220 Devon Lowery FS RC .60 1.50
221 Enrique Gonzalez FS RC .60 1.50
222 Eude Brito FS RC .60 1.50
223 Francisco Butto FS RC .60 1.50
224 Franquelis Osoria FS RC .60 1.50
225 Garrett Jones FS RC 1.00 2.50
226 Geovany Soto FS RC 3.00 8.00
227 Hayden Penn FS RC .60 1.50
228 Ismael Ramirez FS RC .60 1.50
229 Jared Gothreaux FS RC .60 1.50
230 Jason Hammel FS RC .60 1.50
231 Jeff Miller FS RC .60 1.50
232 Jeff Niemann FS RC 1.50 4.00
233 Joel Peralta FS RC .60 1.50
234 John Hattig FS RC .60 1.50
235 Jorge Campillo FS RC .60 1.50
236 Juan Morillo FS RC .60 1.50
237 Justin Verlander FS RC 12.00 30.00
238 Ryan Garko FS RC .60 1.50
239 Keiichi Yabu FS RC .60 1.50
240 Kendry Morales FS RC 1.50 4.00
241 Luis Hernandez FS RC .60 1.50
242 Luis Pena FS RC .60 1.50
243 Luis O.Rodriguez FS RC .60 1.50
244 Luke Scott FS RC 1.50 4.00
245 Marcos Carvajal FS RC .60 1.50
246 Mark Woodyard FS RC .60 1.50
247 Matt A.Smith FS RC .60 1.50
248 Matthew Lindstrom FS RC .60 1.50
249 Miguel Negron FS RC 1.00 2.50
250 Mike Morse FS RC 1.50 4.00
251 Nate McLouth FS RC 1.00 2.50
252 Nelson Cruz FS RC 2.50 6.00
253 Nick Masset FS RC .60 1.50
254 Oscar Robles FS RC .60 1.50
255 Paulino Reynoso FS RC .60 1.50
256 Pedro Lopez FS RC .60 1.50
257 Pete Orr FS RC 1.00 2.50
258 Philip Humber FS RC 1.50 4.00
259 Prince Fielder FS RC 3.00 8.00
260 Randy Messenger FS RC .60 1.50
261 Randy Williams FS RC .60 1.50
262 Raul Tablado FS RC .60 1.50
263 Ronny Paulino FS RC 1.00 2.50
264 Russ Rohlicek FS RC .60 1.50
265 Russell Martin FS RC 2.50 6.00
266 Scott Baker FS RC 1.00 2.50
267 Scott Munter FS RC .60 1.50
268 Sean Thompson FS RC .60 1.50
269 Sean Tracey FS RC .60 1.50
270 Shane Costa FS RC .60 1.50
271 Stephen Drew FS RC 3.00 8.00
272 Steve Schmoll FS RC .60 1.50
273 Tadahito Iguchi FS RC 1.00 2.50
274 Tony Giarratano FS RC .60 1.50
275 Tony Pena FS RC .60 1.50
276 Travis Bowyer FS RC .60 1.50
277 Ubaldo Jimenez FS RC 2.00 5.00
278 Wladimir Balentien FS RC 1.00 2.50
279 Yorman Bazardo FS RC .60 1.50
280 Yuniesky Betancourt FS RC 2.50 6.00
281 Ryan Zimmerman FS RC 5.00 12.00
282 Chris Denorfia FS RC .60 1.50
283 Dana Eveland FS RC .60 1.50
284 Jermaine Van Buren FS .60 1.50
285 Mark McLemore FS RC .60 1.50

2005 Artifacts Rainbow Blue

*BLUE 1-100: 2.5X TO 6X BASIC
*BLUE 101-150: .6X TO 1.5X BASIC
*BLUE POST-WAR 151-200: .75X TO 2X
*BLUE PRE-WAR 151-200: .6X TO 1.5X
1-200 OVERALL PARALLEL ODDS 1:10
*BLUE 201-285: .6X TO 1.5X BASIC
201-285 ISSUED IN '05 UD UPDATE PACKS
201-285 ONE #'d CARD OR AU PER PACK
STATED PRINT RUN 100 SERIAL #'d SETS

2005 Artifacts Rainbow Gold

*GOLD 1-100: 6X TO 15X BASIC
*GOLD 101-150: 1.5X TO 4X BASIC
*GOLD POST-WAR 151-200: 2X TO 5X
*GOLD PRE-WAR 151-200: 1.5X TO 4X
1-200 OVERALL PARALLEL ODDS 1:10
201-285 ISSUED IN '05 UD UPDATE PACKS
201-285 ONE #'d CARD OR AU PER PACK
STATED PRINT RUN 25 SERIAL #'d SETS
201-285 NO PRICING DUE TO SCARCITY

2005 Artifacts Rainbow Platinum

1-200 OVERALL PARALLEL ODDS 1:10
201-285 ISSUED IN '05 UD UPDATE PACKS
201-285 ONE #'d CARD OR AU PER PACK
STATED PRINT RUN 1 SERIAL #'d SET
NO PRICING DUE TO SCARCITY

2005 Artifacts Rainbow Red

*RED 1-100: 4X TO 10X BASIC
*RED 101-150: 1X TO 2.5X BASIC
*RED POST-WAR 151-200: 1.25X TO 3X
*RED PRE-WAR 151-200: 1X TO 2.5X
1-200 OVERALL PARALLEL ODDS 1:10
*RED 201-285: 1X TO 2.5X BASIC
201-285 ISSUED IN '05 UD UPDATE PACKS
201-285 ONE #'d CARD OR AU PER PACK
STATED PRINT RUN 50 SERIAL #'d SETS

2005 Artifacts AL/NL Artifacts

OVERALL GAME-USED ODDS 1:3
PRINT RUNS B/WN 100-325 COPIES PER
AB Adrian Beltre Jsy/325 3.00 8.00
AD Andre Dawson Jsy/325 3.00 8.00
AH Aubrey Huff Jsy/325 3.00 8.00
AK Al Kaline Jsy/325 5.00 12.00
AO Akinori Otsuka Jsy/325 3.00 8.00
AP Albert Pujols Jsy/325 6.00 15.00
BA Bobby Abreu Jsy/325 3.00 8.00
BB Bert Blyleven Jsy/325 3.00 8.00
BC Bobby Crosby Jsy/325 3.00 8.00
BD Bobby Doerr Bat/325 3.00 8.00
BE Johnny Bench Jsy/325 5.00 12.00
BF Bob Feller Pants/325 4.00 10.00
BG Bob Gibson Pants/325 4.00 10.00
BPA Boog Powell Jsy/325 3.00 8.00
BPN Brad Penny Jsy/325 3.00 8.00
BR Brooks Robinson Jsy/325 4.00 10.00
BS Ben Sheets Jsy/325 3.00 8.00
BU B.J. Upton Jsy/325 3.00 8.00
CA Steve Carlton Jsy/325 3.00 8.00
CB Carlos Beltran Jsy/325 3.00 8.00
CK Casey Kotchman Jsy/325 3.00 8.00
CP Corey Patterson Jsy/325 3.00 8.00
CR Cal Ripken Jsy/325 10.00 25.00
CY Carl Yastrzemski Jsy/325 6.00 15.00
CZ Carlos Zambrano Jsy/325 3.00 8.00
DG Dwight Gooden Pants/325 3.00 8.00
DJ Derek Jeter Jsy/325 8.00 20.00
DK Dave Kingman Bat/325 3.00 8.00
DL Derrek Lee Jsy/325 3.00 8.00
DMA Dallas McPherson Jsy/325 3.00 8.00
DMN Dale Murphy Jsy/150 4.00 10.00
DO David Ortiz Jsy/325 3.00 8.00
DW David Wright Jsy/325 6.00 15.00
EC Eric Chavez Jsy/325 3.00 8.00
EG Eric Gagne Jsy/325 3.00 8.00
FL Fred Lynn Bat/325 3.00 8.00
FR Frank Robinson Jsy/325 3.00 8.00
GB George Brett Jsy/325 6.00 15.00
GI Brian Giles Jsy/325 3.00 8.00
GK George Kell Bat/325 3.00 8.00
GM Greg Maddux Jsy/275 6.00 15.00
GN Graig Nettles Jsy/325 3.00 8.00
GR Ken Griffey Sr. Jsy/325 3.00 8.00
HB Hank Blalock Jsy/325 3.00 8.00
HK Harmon Killebrew Jsy/325 5.00 12.00
JB Jason Bay Jsy/325 3.00 8.00
JK Jim Kaat Jsy/325 3.00 8.00
JM Joe Mauer Jsy/325 3.00 8.00
JPA Jim Palmer Jsy/325 3.00 8.00
JPN Jake Peavy Jsy/325 3.00 8.00
JRA Jim Rice Jsy/325 3.00 8.00
JRN Jose Reyes Jsy/250 3.00 8.00
JSA Johan Santana Jsy/325 4.00 10.00
JSN Jason Schmidt Jsy/325 3.00 8.00
KG Ken Griffey Jr. Jsy/325 6.00 15.00
KHA Kent Hrbek Jsy/325 3.00 8.00
KHN Keith Hernandez Bat/325 3.00 8.00
KL Khalil Greene Jsy/325 3.00 8.00
KW Kerry Wood Jsy/325 3.00 8.00
LN Laynce Nix Jsy/325 3.00 8.00
MA Don Mattingly Jsy/325 6.00 15.00
MC Miguel Cabrera Jsy/325 3.00 8.00
MG Marcus Giles Jsy/325 3.00 8.00
MK Mark Grace Jsy/175 4.00 10.00
ML Mike Lowell Jsy/325 3.00 8.00
MM Mark Mulder Jsy/325 3.00 8.00
MP Mark Prior Jsy/325 3.00 8.00
MS Mike Schmidt Jsy/325 6.00 15.00
MT Mark Teixeira Jsy/325 3.00 8.00
MW Maury Wills Jsy/325 3.00 8.00
MY Michael Young Jsy/325 3.00 8.00
NR Nolan Ryan Jsy/325 8.00 20.00
OC Orlando Cepeda Jsy/185 3.00 8.00
PM Paul Molitor Jsy/325 3.00 8.00
PN Phil Niekro Jsy/325 3.00 8.00
RCA Rod Carew Jsy/325 4.00 10.00
RCN Roger Clemens Jsy/325 4.00 10.00
RH Rich Harden Jsy/325 3.00 8.00
RJ Randy Johnson Jsy/325 4.00 10.00
RK Ralph Kiner Bat/325 4.00 10.00
RO Roy Oswalt Jsy/325 3.00 8.00
RP Rico Petrocelli Pants/325 3.00 8.00
RW Rickie Weeks Jsy/325 3.00 8.00
RY Robin Yount Jsy/325 5.00 12.00
SC Sean Casey Jsy/325 3.00 8.00
SL Sparky Lyle Pants/325 3.00 8.00
SM John Smoltz Jsy/325 3.00 8.00
SP Scott Podsednik Jsy/325 3.00 8.00
SR Scott Rolen Jsy/325 3.00 8.00
ST Shingo Takatsu Jsy/325 3.00 8.00
SU Bruce Sutter Jsy/325 3.00 8.00
TG Tony Gwynn Jsy/325 5.00 12.00
TH Travis Hafner Jsy/325 3.00 8.00
TS Tom Seaver Jsy/325 4.00 10.00
VM Victor Martinez Jsy/325 3.00 8.00
WB Wade Boggs Jsy/325 4.00 10.00
WC Will Clark Jsy/100 5.00 12.00
WM Willie McCovey Jsy/325 4.00 10.00
YB Yogi Berra Pants/325 6.00 15.00

2005 Artifacts AL/NL Artifacts Rainbow

*RAINBOW p/r 99: .5X TO 1.2X p/r 150-325
*RAINBOW p/r 50: .5X TO 1.2X p/r 100
OVERALL GAME-USED ODDS 1:3
PRINT RUNS B/WN 50-99 COPIES PER

2005 Artifacts AL/NL Artifacts Signatures

STATED PRINT RUN 30 SERIAL #'d SETS
RARE PRINT RUN 1 SERIAL #'d SET
NO RARE PRICING DUE TO SCARCITY
OVERALL AUTO ODDS 1:10
EXCHANGE DEADLINE 04/11/08
AB Adrian Beltre Jsy 10.00 25.00
AD Andre Dawson Jsy 10.00 25.00
AH Aubrey Huff Jsy 10.00 25.00
AK Al Kaline Jsy 30.00 60.00
AO Akinori Otsuka Jsy 15.00 40.00
BB Bert Blyleven Jsy 10.00 25.00
BD Bobby Doerr Bat 10.00 25.00
BE Johnny Bench Jsy 30.00 60.00
BF Bob Feller Pants 15.00 40.00
BG Bob Gibson Pants 15.00 40.00
BPA Boog Powell Jsy 15.00 40.00
BPN Brad Penny Jsy 10.00 25.00
BR Brooks Robinson Jsy 30.00 60.00
BU B.J. Upton Jsy 10.00 25.00
CA Steve Carlton Jsy 10.00 25.00
CK Casey Kotchman Jsy 10.00 25.00
CR Cal Ripken Jsy 125.00 200.00
CY Carl Yastrzemski Jsy 40.00 80.00
CZ Carlos Zambrano Jsy 15.00 40.00
DG Dwight Gooden Pants 10.00 25.00
DJ Derek Jeter Jsy 125.00 200.00
DK Dave Kingman Bat 10.00 25.00
DL Derrek Lee Jsy 15.00 40.00
DMN Dale Murphy Jsy 15.00 40.00
DO David Ortiz Jsy 30.00 60.00
DW David Wright Jsy 40.00 80.00
EC Eric Chavez Jsy 10.00 25.00
FL Fred Lynn Bat 10.00 25.00
FR Frank Robinson Jsy 15.00 40.00
GB George Brett Jsy 50.00 100.00
GI Brian Giles Jsy 10.00 25.00
GK George Kell Bat 15.00 40.00
GN Graig Nettles Jsy 15.00 40.00
GR Ken Griffey Sr. Jsy 10.00 25.00
HB Hank Blalock Jsy 10.00 25.00
HK Harmon Killebrew Jsy 40.00 80.00
JB Jason Bay Jsy 10.00 25.00
JK Jim Kaat Jsy 10.00 25.00
JPA Jim Palmer Jsy 15.00 40.00
JPN Jake Peavy Jsy 15.00 40.00
JRA Jim Rice Jsy 10.00 25.00
JSN Jason Schmidt Jsy 10.00 25.00
KG Ken Griffey Jr. Jsy 75.00 150.00
KHA Kent Hrbek Jsy 30.00 60.00
KHN Keith Hernandez Bat 10.00 25.00
KL Khalil Greene Jsy 15.00 40.00
KW Kerry Wood Jsy 15.00 40.00
LN Laynce Nix Jsy 6.00 15.00
MA Don Mattingly Jsy 50.00 100.00
MC Miguel Cabrera Jsy 15.00 40.00
MG Marcus Giles Jsy 10.00 25.00
MK Mark Grace Jsy 15.00 40.00
ML Mike Lowell Jsy 10.00 25.00
MM Mark Mulder Jsy 10.00 25.00
MP Mark Prior Jsy 15.00 40.00
MS Mike Schmidt Jsy 40.00 80.00
MT Mark Teixeira Jsy 15.00 40.00
MW Maury Wills Jsy 10.00 25.00
NR Nolan Ryan Jsy 75.00 150.00
OC Orlando Cepeda Jsy 10.00 25.00
PM Paul Molitor Jsy 10.00 25.00
PN Phil Niekro Jsy 10.00 25.00
RCA Rod Carew Jsy 15.00 40.00
RH Rich Harden Jsy 10.00 25.00
RK Ralph Kiner Bat 15.00 40.00
RO Roy Oswalt Jsy 10.00 25.00
RP Rico Petrocelli Pants 10.00 25.00
RW Rickie Weeks Jsy 10.00 25.00
RY Robin Yount Jsy 30.00 60.00
SC Sean Casey Jsy 10.00 25.00
SL Sparky Lyle Pants 10.00 25.00
SP Scott Podsednik Jsy 15.00 40.00
ST Shingo Takatsu Jsy 10.00 25.00
SU Bruce Sutter Jsy 15.00 40.00
TG Tony Gwynn Jsy 40.00 80.00
TH Travis Hafner Jsy 10.00 25.00
TS Tom Seaver Jsy 30.00 60.00
VM Victor Martinez Jsy 10.00 25.00
WB Wade Boggs Jsy 15.00 40.00
WC Will Clark Jsy 30.00 60.00
WM Willie McCovey Jsy 30.00 60.00
YB Yogi Berra Pants 30.00 60.00

2005 Artifacts Autofacts

PRINT RUNS B/WN 15-699 COPIES PER
NO PRICING ON QTY OF 15
RAINBOW PRINT RUN 1 SERIAL #'d SET
NO RAINBOW PRICING DUE TO SCARCITY
OVERALL AUTO ODDS 1:10
EXCHANGE DEADLINE 04/11/08
AD Andre Dawson/25 10.00 25.00
AH Aubrey Huff/350 6.00 15.00
AK Al Kaline/15
AO Akinori Otsuka/599 10.00 25.00
BE Johnny Bench/15
BF Bob Feller/25 15.00 40.00
BH Burt Hooton/599 4.00 10.00
BM Bill Mazeroski/15
BP Brad Penny/599 4.00 10.00
BR Brooks Robinson/25 20.00 50.00
BU B.J. Upton/599 6.00 15.00
CA Rod Carew/15
CK Casey Kotchman/599 6.00 15.00
CR Cal Ripken/15
CY Carl Yastrzemski/15
DG1 Dwight Gooden Mets/350 6.00 15.00
DG2 Dwight Gooden Yanks/350 6.00 15.00
DJ Derek Jeter/350 75.00 150.00
DK Dave Kingman/75 6.00 15.00
DM Dale Murphy/75 10.00 25.00
DO David Ortiz/15
DW David Wright/599 30.00 60.00
EB Ernie Banks/15
EC Eric Chavez/25 10.00 25.00
EK Ed Kranepool/599 6.00 15.00
FL Fred Lynn/25 10.00 25.00
GB George Brett/15
GI Marcus Giles/350 6.00 15.00
GK George Kell/15
GN Graig Nettles/75 6.00 15.00
GR Khalil Greene/599 10.00 25.00
HB Hank Blalock/25 10.00 25.00
HK Harmon Killebrew/15
HO Ken Holtzman/599 4.00 10.00
HR Kent Hrbek/599 6.00 15.00
JA Jake Peavy/75 10.00 25.00
JB Jason Bay/599 6.00 15.00
JK1 Jim Kaat Cards/458 6.00 15.00
JK2 Jim Kaat Twins/458 6.00 15.00
JL Jim Lonborg/599 4.00 10.00
JP Jim Palmer/25 15.00 40.00
JR Ken Griffey Jr./699 30.00 60.00
KG1 Ken Griffey Sr. Reds/699 6.00 15.00
KG2 Ken Griffey Sr. Yanks/699 6.00 15.00
KH1 Keith Hernandez Mets/350 6.00 15.00
KH2 Keith Hernandez Cards/350 6.00 15.00
KW Kerry Wood/15
LD1 Lenny Dykstra Mets/599 6.00 15.00
LD2 Lenny Dykstra Phils/599 6.00 15.00
LN Laynce Nix/599 4.00 10.00
LT Luis Tiant/75 6.00 15.00
MA Don Mattingly/15
MG Mark Grace/25 15.00 40.00
MI Miguel Cabrera/25 15.00 40.00
ML Mike Lowell/75 6.00 15.00
MP Mark Prior/15
MS Mike Schmidt/15
MT Mark Teixeira/25 15.00 40.00
MW Maury Wills/15
NG Nomar Garciaparra/15
NR Nolan Ryan/15
OC Orlando Cepeda/25 15.00 40.00
OP Oliver Perez/350 4.00 10.00
PE Jim Perry/599 4.00 10.00
PM Paul Molitor/15
PN1 Phil Niekro Braves/75 6.00 15.00
PN2 Phil Niekro Yanks/75 6.00 15.00
PO Boog Powell/350 6.00 15.00
RC Rocky Colavito/75 40.00 80.00
RH Rich Harden/599 6.00 15.00
RI Jim Rice/25 10.00 25.00
RK Ralph Kiner/25 15.00 40.00
RO Roy Oswalt/350 6.00 15.00
RP Rico Petrocelli/599 6.00 15.00
RW Rickie Weeks/75 6.00 15.00
RY Robin Yount/15
SC Steve Carlton/15
SF Sid Fernandez/599 6.00 15.00
SL1 Sparky Lyle Sox/599 6.00 15.00
SL2 Sparky Lyle Yanks/599 6.00 15.00
SP Scott Podsednik/75 10.00 25.00
ST Shingo Takatsu/599 6.00 15.00
SU Bruce Sutter/350 10.00 25.00
TG Tony Gwynn/15
TH Travis Hafner/599 6.00 15.00
VM Victor Martinez/599 6.00 15.00
WB Wade Boggs/15
WC Will Clark/15
WM Willie McCovey/15
YB Yogi Berra/15

2005 Artifacts Dual Artifacts

OVERALL GAME-USED ODDS 1:3
STATED PRINT RUN 99 SERIAL #'d SETS
CLARK/MCCOVEY PRINT RUN 56 #'d CARDS
KILLEB/MCCOVEY PRINT RUN 44 #'d CARDS
AB Bobby Abreu Jsy 4.00 10.00
Carlos Beltran Jsy
AD Adrian Beltre Jsy 4.00 10.00
Dallas McPherson Jsy
AG Bobby Abreu Jsy 8.00 20.00
Ken Griffey Jr. Jsy
BB George Brett Jsy 10.00 25.00
Wade Boggs Jsy
BC Adrian Beltre Jsy 4.00 10.00
Eric Chavez Jsy
BD Bob Gibson Pants 8.00 20.00
Dwight Gooden Pants
BE Bobby Crosby Jsy 4.00 10.00
Eric Chavez Jsy
BJ Brooks Robinson Jsy 8.00 20.00
Jim Palmer Jsy
BK Jason Bay Jsy 8.00 20.00
Ralph Kiner Bat
BM Brian Giles Jsy 4.00 10.00
Marcus Giles Jsy
BN Hank Blalock Jsy 4.00 10.00
Laynce Nix Jsy
BP Carlos Beltran Jsy 4.00 10.00
Corey Patterson Jsy
BR Ernie Banks Pants 8.00 20.00
Frank Robinson Jsy
BS Ben Sheets Jsy 4.00 10.00
Scott Podsednik Jsy
BY Hank Blalock Jsy 4.00 10.00
Michael Young Jsy
CB Jason Bay Jsy 4.00 10.00
Bobby Crosby Jsy
CC Miguel Cabrera Jsy 6.00 15.00
Orlando Cepeda Jsy
CG Dwight Gooden Pants 6.00 15.00
Gary Carter Jsy
CH Sean Casey Jsy 4.00 10.00
Travis Hafner Jsy
CK Harmon Killebrew Jsy 8.00 20.00
Rod Carew Jsy
CL Miguel Cabrera Jsy 6.00 15.00
Mike Lowell Jsy
CM Will Clark Jsy 12.50 30.00
Willie McCovey Jsy/56
CN Eric Chavez Jsy 6.00 15.00
Graig Nettles Jsy
CO Roger Clemens Jsy 6.00 15.00
Roy Oswalt Jsy
CR Bobby Crosby Jsy 15.00 40.00
Cal Ripken Jsy
DC Andre Dawson Jsy 6.00 15.00
Orlando Cepeda Jsy
DK Bobby Doerr Bat 6.00 15.00
George Kell Bat
FB Carlton Fisk Jsy 8.00 20.00
Johnny Bench Jsy
FW Bob Feller Pants 8.00 20.00
Kerry Wood Jsy
GB Brian Giles Jsy 4.00 10.00
Jason Bay Jsy
GC Ken Griffey Jr. Jsy 8.00 20.00
Sean Casey Jsy
GG Ken Griffey Sr. Jsy 10.00 25.00
Ken Griffey Jr. Jsy
GK Ken Griffey Jr. Jsy 8.00 20.00
Ralph Kiner Bat
GL Eric Gagne Jsy 6.00 15.00
Sparky Lyle Pants
GS Dwight Gooden Pants 8.00 20.00
Tom Seaver Jsy
HC Bobby Crosby Jsy 4.00 10.00
Rich Harden Jsy
HG Keith Hernandez Bat 8.00 20.00
Mark Grace Jsy
HH Aubrey Huff Jsy 4.00 10.00
Travis Hafner Jsy
HM Travis Hafner Jsy 4.00 10.00
Victor Martinez Jsy
HU Aubrey Huff Jsy 4.00 10.00
B.J. Upton Jsy
HW Harmon Killebrew Jsy 12.50 30.00
Willie McCovey Jsy/44
JG Derek Jeter Jsy 12.50 30.00
Khalil Greene Jsy
JJ Joe Mauer Jsy 6.00 15.00
Johan Santana Jsy
JR Jim Rice Jsy 6.00 15.00
Rico Petrocelli Pants
JW Derek Jeter Jsy 12.50 30.00
Maury Wills Jsy
JY Johnny Bench Jsy 12.50 30.00
Yogi Berra Pants
KB Jim Kaat Jsy 6.00 15.00
Bert Blyleven Jsy
KC Jim Kaat Jsy 6.00 15.00
Steve Carlton Jsy
KD Keith Hernandez Bat 10.00 25.00
Don Mattingly Jsy
KK Al Kaline Jsy 8.00 20.00
Ralph Kiner Bat
KM Al Kaline Jsy 8.00 20.00
Dale Murphy Jsy
KN Jim Kaat Jsy 6.00 15.00
Phil Niekro Jsy
LC Derrek Lee Jsy 6.00 15.00
Sean Casey Jsy
LG Derrek Lee Jsy 8.00 20.00
Mark Grace Jsy
LP Fred Lynn Bat 6.00 15.00
Rico Petrocelli Pants
LR Fred Lynn Bat 6.00 15.00
Jim Rice Jsy
MC Don Mattingly Jsy 10.00 25.00
Will Clark Jsy
MD Bill Mazeroski Jsy 8.00 20.00
Bobby Doerr Bat
MH Mark Mulder Jsy 4.00 10.00
Rich Harden Jsy
MK Bill Mazeroski Jsy 8.00 20.00
Ralph Kiner Bat
MM Joe Mauer Jsy 4.00 10.00
Victor Martinez Jsy
MS Dale Murphy Jsy 12.50 30.00
Mike Schmidt Jsy
MW Paul Molitor Jsy 6.00 15.00
Rickie Weeks Jsy
NL Graig Nettles Jsy 6.00 15.00
Sparky Lyle Pants
NT Laynce Nix Jsy 8.00 20.00
Mark Teixeira Jsy
NY Laynce Nix Jsy 6.00 15.00
Michael Young Jsy
OF David Ortiz Jsy 8.00 20.00
Carlton Fisk Jsy
OG Akinori Otsuka Jsy 6.00 15.00
Khalil Greene Jsy
OP Akinori Otsuka Jsy 6.00 15.00
Jake Peavy Jsy
OT Akinori Otsuka Jsy 6.00 15.00
Shingo Takatsu Jsy
PD Andre Dawson Jsy 6.00 15.00
Corey Patterson Jsy
PG Brad Penny Jsy 4.00 10.00
Eric Gagne Jsy
PH Jake Peavy Jsy 4.00 10.00
Rich Harden Jsy
PP Boog Powell Jsy 6.00 15.00
Jim Palmer Jsy
PR Boog Powell Jsy 10.00 25.00
Brooks Robinson Jsy
PS Brad Penny Jsy 4.00 10.00
Jason Schmidt Jsy
RB Ernie Banks Pants 20.00 50.00
Cal Ripken Jsy
RC Nolan Ryan Jsy 12.50 30.00
Steve Carlton Jsy
RJ Jose Reyes Jsy 4.00 10.00
Rickie Weeks Jsy
RP Frank Robinson Jsy 6.00 15.00
Boog Powell Jsy
RR Frank Robinson Jsy 10.00 25.00

Brooks Robinson Jsy
RW David Wright Jsy 6.00 15.00
Scott Rolen Jsy
SB Bert Blyleven Jsy 8.00 20.00
Johan Santana Jsy
SC Johan Santana Jsy 8.00 20.00
Roger Clemens Jsy
SF Ben Sheets Jsy 8.00 20.00
Bob Feller Pants
SG Bruce Sutter Jsy 6.00 15.00
Eric Gagne Jsy
SM Jason Schmidt Jsy 4.00 10.00
Mark Mulder Jsy
SO Ben Sheets Jsy 4.00 10.00
Roy Oswalt Jsy
SP Ben Sheets Jsy 4.00 10.00
Brad Penny Jsy
TH Mark Teixeira Jsy 6.00 15.00
Travis Hafner Jsy
TL Shingo Takatsu Jsy 6.00 15.00
Sparky Lyle Pants
TY Mark Teixeira Jsy 6.00 15.00
Michael Young Jsy
UJ B.J. Upton Jsy 12.50 30.00
Derek Jeter Jsy
WL David Wright Jsy 6.00 15.00
Mike Lowell Jsy
WR David Wright Jsy 8.00 20.00
Jose Reyes Jsy
YM Robin Yount Jsy 12.50 30.00
Paul Molitor Jsy
YP Carl Yastrzemski Jsy 10.00 25.00
Rico Petrocelli Pants
ZM Carlos Zambrano Jsy 8.00 20.00
Greg Maddux Jsy
ZP Carlos Zambrano Jsy 6.00 15.00
Mark Prior Jsy
ZW Carlos Zambrano Jsy 4.00 10.00
Kerry Wood Jsy

2005 Artifacts Dual Artifacts Rainbow

*RAINBOW: .6X TO 1.5X p/r 99
*RAINBOW: .5X TO 1.2X p/r 44-56
OVERALL GAME-USED ODDS 1:3
STATED PRINT RUN 25 SERIAL #'d SETS

2005 Artifacts Dual Artifacts Signatures

OVERALL AUTO ODDS 1:10
STATED PRINT RUN 10 SERIAL #'d SETS
NO PRICING DUE TO SCARCITY
EXCHANGE DEADLINE 04/11/08

2005 Artifacts Dual Artifacts Bat

OVERALL GAME-USED ODDS 1:3
STATED PRINT RUN 25 SERIAL #'d SETS
BC Josh Beckett 10.00 25.00
Miguel Cabrera
BW Josh Beckett 6.00 15.00
Kerry Wood
DR Carlos Delgado 10.00 25.00
Manny Ramirez
GC Ken Griffey Jr. 15.00 40.00
Miguel Cabrera
GS Ken Griffey Jr. 60.00 120.00
Ichiro Suzuki
JP Derek Jeter 20.00 50.00
Mike Piazza
JR Derek Jeter 20.00 50.00
Manny Ramirez
RG Manny Ramirez 10.00 25.00
Vladimir Guerrero
RJ Cal Ripken 50.00 100.00
Derek Jeter
RT Cal Ripken 40.00 80.00
Miguel Tejada
SG Ichiro Suzuki
Vladimir Guerrero
WP Kerry Wood 10.00 25.00
Mark Prior

2005 Artifacts MLB Apparel

OVERALL GAME-USED ODDS 1:3
PRINT RUNS B/WN 100-325 COPIES PER
AB Adrian Beltre Jsy/325 3.00 8.00
AD Andre Dawson Jsy/325 3.00 8.00
AH Aubrey Huff Jsy/325 3.00 8.00
AK Al Kaline Jsy/325 5.00 12.00
AO Akinori Otsuka Jsy/325 3.00 8.00
BA Bobby Abreu Jsy/325 3.00 8.00
BB Bert Blyleven Jsy/150 3.00 8.00
BC Bobby Crosby Jsy/325 3.00 8.00
BE Johnny Bench Jsy/325 5.00 12.00
BF Bob Feller Pants/325 4.00 10.00
BG Bob Gibson Pants/325 4.00 10.00
BM Bill Mazeroski Jsy/100 5.00 12.00
BO Bret Boone Jsy/325 3.00 8.00
BP Boog Powell Jsy/325 3.00 8.00
BR Brooks Robinson Jsy/325 4.00 10.00
BS Ben Sheets Jsy/325 3.00 8.00
BU B.J. Upton Jsy/325 3.00 8.00
CA Steve Carlton Jsy/325 3.00 8.00
CB Carlos Beltran Jsy/325 3.00 8.00
CF Carlton Fisk R.Sox Jsy/175 4.00 10.00
CF1 Carlton Fisk W.Sox Jsy/175 4.00 10.00
CK Casey Kotchman Jsy/325 3.00 8.00
CL Roger Clemens Jsy/325 4.00 10.00
CP Corey Patterson Jsy/325 3.00 8.00
CR Cal Ripken Jsy/325 10.00 25.00
CY Carl Yastrzemski Jsy/325 6.00 15.00
CZ Carlos Zambrano Jsy/325 3.00 8.00
DG Dwight Gooden Pants/325 3.00 8.00
DJ Derek Jeter Jsy/325 8.00 20.00
DL Derrek Lee Jsy/325 3.00 8.00
DM Dale Murphy Jsy/150 4.00 10.00
DO David Ortiz Jsy/325 3.00 8.00
DW David Wright Jsy/325 6.00 15.00
EC Eric Chavez Jsy/325 3.00 8.00
EG Eric Gagne Jsy/325 3.00 8.00
FR Frank Robinson Jsy/325 3.00 8.00
GA Garret Anderson Jsy/325 3.00 8.00
GB George Brett Jsy/325 6.00 15.00
GC Gary Carter Jsy/325 3.00 8.00
GI Brian Giles Jsy/325 3.00 8.00
GN Graig Nettles Jsy/325 3.00 8.00
GR Ken Griffey Sr. Jsy/325 3.00 8.00
GS Marcus Giles Jsy/325 3.00 8.00
HB Hank Blalock Jsy/325 3.00 8.00
HK Harmon Killebrew Jsy/325 4.00 10.00
HU Tim Hudson Jsy/325 3.00 8.00
JB Jason Bay Jsy/325 3.00 8.00
JJ Jacque Jones Jsy/325 3.00 8.00
JK Jim Kaat Jsy/325 3.00 8.00
JM Joe Mauer Jsy/325 3.00 8.00
JP Jake Peavy Jsy/325 3.00 8.00
JR Jim Rice Jsy/325 3.00 8.00
JS Jason Schmidt Jsy/325 3.00 8.00
JV Jose Vidro Jsy/325 3.00 8.00
KG Ken Griffey Jr. Jsy/325 6.00 15.00
KH Kent Hrbek Jsy/325 3.00 8.00
KL Khalil Greene Jsy/325 3.00 8.00
KW Kerry Wood Jsy/325 3.00 8.00
LN Laynce Nix Jsy/325 3.00 8.00
MA Don Mattingly Jsy/325 6.00 15.00
MC Dallas McPherson Jsy/325 3.00 8.00
MI Miguel Cabrera Jsy/325 3.00 8.00
MK Mark Grace Jsy/175 4.00 10.00
ML Mike Lowell Jsy/325 3.00 8.00
MM Mark Mulder Jsy/325 3.00 8.00
MP Mark Prior Jsy/325 3.00 8.00
MS Mike Schmidt Jsy/325 6.00 15.00
MT Mark Teixeira Jsy/325 3.00 8.00
MW Maury Wills Jsy/325 3.00 8.00
MY Michael Young Jsy/325 3.00 8.00
NR Nolan Ryan Jsy/325 8.00 20.00
OC Orlando Cepeda Jsy/325 3.00 8.00
PA Jim Palmer Jsy/325 3.00 8.00
PE Brad Penny Jsy/325 3.00 8.00
PM Paul Molitor Jsy/325 3.00 8.00
PN Phil Niekro Jsy/325 3.00 8.00
RC Rod Carew Jsy/325 4.00 10.00
RE Jose Reyes Jsy/325 3.00 8.00
RH Rich Harden Jsy/325 3.00 8.00
RO Roy Oswalt Jsy/325 3.00 8.00
RP Rico Petrocelli Pants/325 3.00 8.00
RW Rickie Weeks Jsy/325 3.00 8.00
RY Robin Yount Jsy/325 5.00 12.00
SA Johan Santana Jsy/325 3.00 8.00
SC Sean Casey Jsy/325 3.00 8.00
SL Sparky Lyle Pants/325 3.00 8.00
SM John Smoltz Jsy/325 3.00 8.00
SP Scott Podsednik Jsy/325 3.00 8.00
SR Scott Rolen Jsy/325 3.00 8.00
ST Shingo Takatsu Jsy/325 3.00 8.00
SU Bruce Sutter Jsy/325 3.00 8.00
TG Tony Gwynn Jsy/325 5.00 12.00
TH Travis Hafner Jsy/325 3.00 8.00
TO Torii Hunter Jsy/325 3.00 8.00
TS Tom Seaver Jsy/300 4.00 10.00
VM Victor Martinez Jsy/325 3.00 8.00
WB Wade Boggs Jsy/325 4.00 10.00
WC Will Clark Jsy/100 4.00 10.00
WM Willie McCovey Jsy/325 4.00 10.00
YB Yogi Berra Pants/325 5.00 12.00

2005 Artifacts MLB Apparel Rainbow

*RAINBOW p/r 75-99: .5X TO 1.2X p/r 150-325
*RAINBOW p/r 75: .4X TO 1X p/r 100
*RAINBOW p/r 50: .5X TO 1.2X p/r 100
OVERALL GAME-USED ODDS 1:3
PRINT RUNS B/WN 50-99 COPIES PER

2005 Artifacts MLB Apparel Autographs

STATED PRINT RUN 30 SERIAL #'d SETS
RARE PRINT RUN 1 SERIAL #'d SET
NO RARE PRICING DUE TO SCARCITY
OVERALL AUTO ODDS 1:10
EXCHANGE DEADLINE 04/11/08
AB Adrian Beltre Jsy 10.00 25.00
AD Andre Dawson Jsy 10.00 25.00
AH Aubrey Huff Jsy 10.00 25.00
AK Al Kaline Jsy 30.00 60.00
AO Akinori Otsuka Jsy 15.00 40.00
BB Bert Blyleven Jsy 10.00 25.00
BE Johnny Bench Jsy 30.00 60.00
BF Bob Feller Pants 15.00 40.00
BG Bob Gibson Pants 15.00 40.00
BM Bill Mazeroski Jsy 15.00 40.00
BO Bret Boone Jsy 10.00 25.00
BP Boog Powell Jsy 15.00 40.00
BR Brooks Robinson Jsy 30.00 60.00
BU B.J. Upton Jsy 10.00 25.00
CA Steve Carlton Jsy 10.00 25.00
CF Carlton Fisk R.Sox Jsy 15.00 40.00
CF1 Carlton Fisk W.Sox Jsy 15.00 40.00
CK Casey Kotchman Jsy 10.00 25.00
CR Cal Ripken Jsy 125.00 200.00
CY Carl Yastrzemski Jsy 40.00 80.00
CZ Carlos Zambrano Jsy 15.00 40.00
DG Dwight Gooden Pants 10.00 25.00
DJ Derek Jeter Jsy 125.00 200.00
DL Derrek Lee Jsy 15.00 40.00
DM Dale Murphy Jsy 15.00 40.00
DO David Ortiz Jsy 30.00 60.00
DW David Wright Jsy 50.00 100.00
EG Eric Gagne Jsy 15.00 40.00
FR Frank Robinson Jsy 15.00 40.00
GA Garret Anderson Jsy 10.00 25.00
GB George Brett Jsy 50.00 100.00
GC Gary Carter Jsy 10.00 25.00
GI Brian Giles Jsy 10.00 25.00
GN Graig Nettles Jsy 15.00 40.00
GR Ken Griffey Sr. Jsy 10.00 25.00
GS Marcus Giles Jsy 10.00 25.00
HB Hank Blalock Jsy 10.00 25.00
HK Harmon Killebrew Jsy 40.00 80.00
HU Tim Hudson Jsy 15.00 40.00
JB Jason Bay Jsy 10.00 25.00
JJ Jacque Jones Jsy 10.00 25.00
JK Jim Kaat Jsy 10.00 25.00
JP Jake Peavy Jsy 15.00 40.00
JR Jim Rice Jsy 15.00 40.00
JS Jason Schmidt Jsy 10.00 25.00
JV Jose Vidro Jsy 10.00 25.00
KG Ken Griffey Jr. Jsy 75.00 150.00
KH Kent Hrbek Jsy 30.00 60.00
KL Khalil Greene Jsy 15.00 40.00
KW Kerry Wood Jsy 15.00 40.00
LN Laynce Nix Jsy 6.00 15.00
MA Don Mattingly Jsy 50.00 100.00
MI Miguel Cabrera Jsy 15.00 40.00
MK Mark Grace Jsy 15.00 40.00
ML Mike Lowell Jsy 10.00 25.00
MM Mark Mulder Jsy 10.00 25.00
MP Mark Prior Jsy 10.00 25.00
MS Mike Schmidt Jsy 40.00 80.00
MT Mark Teixeira Jsy 15.00 40.00
MW Maury Wills Jsy 10.00 25.00
NR Nolan Ryan Jsy 75.00 150.00
OC Orlando Cepeda Jsy 15.00 40.00
PA Jim Palmer Jsy 15.00 40.00
PE Brad Penny Jsy 10.00 25.00
PM Paul Molitor Jsy 10.00 25.00
PN Phil Niekro Jsy 10.00 25.00
RC Rod Carew Jsy 15.00 40.00
RH Rich Harden Jsy 10.00 25.00
RO Roy Oswalt Jsy 10.00 25.00
RP Rico Petrocelli Pants 10.00 25.00
RW Rickie Weeks Jsy 10.00 25.00
RY Robin Yount Jsy 30.00 60.00
SC Sean Casey Jsy 10.00 25.00
SL Sparky Lyle Pants 10.00 25.00
SP Scott Podsednik Jsy 15.00 40.00
ST Shingo Takatsu Jsy 10.00 25.00
SU Bruce Sutter Jsy 15.00 40.00
TG Tony Gwynn Jsy 40.00 80.00
TH Travis Hafner Jsy 10.00 25.00
TO Torii Hunter Jsy 10.00 25.00
TS Tom Seaver Jsy 30.00 60.00
VM Victor Martinez Jsy 10.00 25.00
WB Wade Boggs Jsy 15.00 40.00
WC Will Clark Jsy 30.00 60.00
WM Willie McCovey Jsy 30.00 60.00
YB Yogi Berra Pants 30.00 60.00

2005 Artifacts Patches

PRINT RUNS B/WN 3-50 COPIES PER
NO PRICING ON QTY OF 11 OR LESS
ACTIVE PRICES ARE 1 OR 2 COLOR PATCH
ADD 20% FOR ACTIVE 3-COLOR
ADD 50% OR MORE FOR ACTIVE 4-COLOR+
RETIRED PRICES ARE 1 COLOR PATCH
ADD 20% FOR RETIRED 2-COLOR+
ADD 50% OR MORE FOR RETIRED 3-COLOR+
SIG PATCH PRINT RUN B/WN 4-10 PER
NO SIG PATCH PRICING DUE TO SCARCITY
OVERALL GAME-USED ODDS 1:3
AB Adrian Beltre/50 6.00 15.00
AD Andre Dawson/50 6.00 15.00
AH Aubrey Huff/50 6.00 15.00
AO Akinori Otsuka/50 10.00 25.00
BA Bobby Abreu/50 6.00 15.00
BB Bert Blyleven/50 6.00 15.00
BC Bobby Crosby/50 6.00 15.00
BE Johnny Bench/50 10.00 25.00
BG Bob Gibson/10
BO Bret Boone/50 6.00 15.00
BP Boog Powell/50 10.00 25.00
BR Brooks Robinson/35 15.00 40.00
BS Ben Sheets/50 6.00 15.00
BU B.J. Upton/50 6.00 15.00
CA Steve Carlton/30 10.00 25.00
CB Carlos Beltran/50 6.00 15.00
CK Casey Kotchman/50 6.00 15.00
CL Roger Clemens/50 15.00 40.00
CP Corey Patterson/50 4.00 10.00
CR Cal Ripken/50 20.00 50.00
CY Carl Yastrzemski/50 15.00 40.00
CZ Carlos Zambrano/50 6.00 15.00
DG Dwight Gooden/50 6.00 15.00
DJ Derek Jeter/50 20.00 50.00
DL Derrek Lee/50 10.00 25.00
DM Dale Murphy/50 15.00 40.00
DO David Ortiz/50 10.00 25.00
DW David Wright/50 15.00 40.00
EC Eric Chavez/50 6.00 15.00
EG Eric Gagne/50 6.00 15.00
FR Frank Robinson/50 10.00 25.00
GA Garret Anderson/50 6.00 15.00
GB George Brett/50 15.00 40.00
GC Gary Carter/50 6.00 15.00
GI Brian Giles/50 6.00 15.00
GM Greg Maddux/50 15.00 40.00
GN Graig Nettles/50 10.00 25.00
GR Ken Griffey Sr./50 6.00 15.00
GS Marcus Giles/50 6.00 15.00
HB Hank Blalock/50 6.00 15.00
HK Harmon Killebrew/50 10.00 25.00
HU Tim Hudson/50 6.00 15.00
JB Jason Bay/50
JJ Jacque Jones/50 6.00 15.00
JK Jim Kaat/50 6.00 15.00
JM Joe Mauer/50 10.00 25.00
JP Jake Peavy/50 10.00 25.00
JR Jim Rice/3
JS Jason Schmidt/50 10.00 25.00
JV Jose Vidro/50 6.00 15.00
KG Ken Griffey Jr./50 10.00 25.00
KH Kent Hrbek/50 10.00 25.00
KL Khalil Greene/50 10.00 25.00
KW Kerry Wood/50 6.00 15.00
LN Laynce Nix/50 4.00 10.00
MA Don Mattingly/50 15.00 40.00
MC Dallas McPherson/50 4.00 10.00
MI Miguel Cabrera/50 10.00 25.00
MK Mark Grace/50 10.00 25.00
ML Mike Lowell/50 6.00 15.00
MM Mark Mulder/50 6.00 15.00
MP Mark Prior/50 10.00 25.00
MS Mike Schmidt/50 15.00 40.00
MT Mark Teixeira/50 10.00 25.00
MW Maury Wills/20 10.00 25.00
MY Michael Young/50 6.00 15.00
NR Nolan Ryan/50 20.00 50.00
OC Orlando Cepeda/3
PA Jim Palmer/50 6.00 15.00
PE Brad Penny/50 6.00 15.00
PM Paul Molitor/9
PN Phil Niekro/50 6.00 15.00
RC Rod Carew/50 10.00 25.00
RE Jose Reyes/50 6.00 15.00
RH Rich Harden/50 6.00 15.00
RJ Randy Johnson/50 10.00 25.00
RO Roy Oswalt/50 6.00 15.00
RW Rickie Weeks/50 6.00 15.00
RY Robin Yount/50 10.00 25.00
SA Johan Santana/50 10.00 25.00
SC Sean Casey/50 6.00 15.00
SM John Smoltz/50 10.00 25.00
SP Scott Podsednik/50 6.00 15.00
SR Scott Rolen/50 10.00 25.00
ST Shingo Takatsu/50 6.00 15.00
SU Bruce Sutter/50 6.00 15.00
TG Tony Gwynn/50 10.00 25.00
TH Travis Hafner/50 6.00 15.00
TO Torii Hunter/50 6.00 15.00
TS Tom Seaver/11
VM Victor Martinez/50 6.00 15.00
WB Wade Boggs/50 10.00 25.00
WC Will Clark/20 15.00 40.00
WM Willie McCovey/50 10.00 25.00

2006 Artifacts

This 100-card set was released in July, 2006. The set was issued in four card packs with an $9.99 SRP. The product was issued in 10 pack boxes which came 20 boxes to a case.

COMPLETE SET (100) 15.00 40.00
COMMON CARD (1-100) .20 .50
COMMON ROOKIE .30 .75
1 Luis Gonzalez .20 .50
2 Conor Jackson (RC) .50 1.25
3 Joey Devine RC .30 .75
4 Andruw Jones .20 .50
5 Chipper Jones .50 1.25
6 John Smoltz .50 1.25
7 Jeff Francoeur .50 1.25
8 Brian Roberts .20 .50
9 Miguel Tejada .30 .75
10 Nick Markakis (RC) .75 2.00
11 Curt Schilling .30 .75
12 David Ortiz .30 .75
13 Johnny Damon .30 .75
14 Manny Ramirez .50 1.25
15 Jonathan Papelbon (RC) 1.50 4.00
16 Aramis Ramirez .20 .50
17 Carlos Zambrano .20 .50
18 Derrek Lee .20 .50
19 Greg Maddux .75 2.00
20 Mark Prior .30 .75
21 Mark Buehrle .30 .75
22 Paul Konerko .30 .75
23 Adam Dunn .30 .75
24 Ken Griffey Jr. .75 2.00
25 Travis Hafner .20 .50
26 Victor Martinez .30 .75
27 Todd Helton .30 .75
28 Ivan Rodriguez .30 .75
29 Jeremy Bonderman .20 .50
30 Jeremy Hermida (RC) .30 .75
31 Carlos Delgado .20 .50
32 Dontrelle Willis .20 .50
33 Josh Beckett .30 .75
34 Miguel Cabrera .50 1.25
35 Craig Biggio .30 .75
36 Lance Berkman .30 .75
37 Roger Clemens .60 1.50
38 Roy Oswalt .30 .75
39 Josh Willingham (RC) .30 .75
40 Hanley Ramirez (RC) .75 2.00
41 Prince Fielder (RC) 1.25 3.00
42 Zack Greinke .30 .75
43 Francisco Rodriguez .30 .75
44 Vladimir Guerrero .50 1.25
45 Tim Hamulack (RC) .30 .75
46 Jeff Kent .20 .50
47 Ben Sheets .20 .50
48 Rickie Weeks .30 .75
49 Francisco Liriano (RC) .75 2.00
50 Joe Mauer .50 1.25
51 Johan Santana .50 1.25
52 Justin Morneau .50 1.25
53 Torii Hunter .20 .50
54 Carlos Beltran .20 .50
55 David Wright .75 2.00
56 Jose Reyes .30 .75
57 Mike Piazza .50 1.25
58 Pedro Martinez .30 .75
59 Alex Rodriguez .75 2.00
60 Derek Jeter 1.25 3.00
61 Hideki Matsui .50 1.25
62 Randy Johnson .50 1.25
63 Justin Verlander (RC) 2.50 6.00
64 Bobby Crosby .20 .50
65 Eric Chavez .20 .50
66 Brian Anderson (RC) .30 .75
67 Bobby Abreu .20 .50
68 Pat Burrell .20 .50
69 Jason Bay .20 .50
70 Oliver Perez .20 .50
71 Chuck James (RC) .30 .75
72 Brian Giles .20 .50
73 Jake Peavy .20 .50
74 Khalil Greene .20 .50
75 Jason Schmidt .20 .50
76 Kenji Johjima RC .75 2.00
77 Jeremy Accardo RC .30 .75
78 Adrian Beltre .20 .50
79 Ichiro Suzuki .75 2.00
80 Jeff Harris RC .30 .75
81 Felix Hernandez .50 1.25
82 Albert Pujols 1.25 3.00
83 Chris Carpenter .50 1.25
84 Jim Edmonds .30 .75
85 Scott Rolen .30 .75
86 Mike Jacobs (RC) .30 .75
87 Carl Crawford .30 .75
88 Anderson Hernandez (RC) .30 .75
89 Scott Kazmir .30 .75
90 Josh Rupe (RC) .30 .75
91 Scott Feldman RC .30 .75
92 Alfonso Soriano .30 .75
93 Hank Blalock .20 .50
94 Mark Teixeira .50 1.25
95 Michael Young .30 .75
96 Roy Halladay .50 1.25
97 Vernon Wells .20 .50
98 Jason Bergmann RC .30 .75
99 Ryan Zimmerman (RC) 1.50 4.00
100 Jose Vidro .20 .50

2006 Artifacts AL/NL Artifacts Blue

OVERALL GU ODDS 3:10
PRINT RUNS B/WN 200-325 COPIES PER
ADN Adam Dunn Jsy/250 5.00 12.00
AHN Aaron Harang Jsy/325 3.00 8.00
APN Albert Pujols Jsy/250 8.00 20.00
ASN Alfonso Soriano Jsy/325 5.00 12.00
BBA Ben Broussard Jsy/325 3.00 8.00
BHN Bill Hall Jsy/235 3.00 8.00
BLA Joe Blanton Jsy/325 3.00 8.00
BLN Brad Lidge Jsy/325 3.00 8.00
BMA Brandon McCarthy Jsy/325 3.00 8.00
BMN Brian McCann Jsy/325 4.00 10.00
CAN Chris Capuano Jsy/325 3.00 8.00
CBN Chris Burke Jsy/325 3.00 8.00
CCA Carl Crawford Jsy/325 5.00 12.00
CCN Chris Carpenter Jsy/325 4.00 10.00
CHN Chad Cordero Jsy/325 3.00 8.00
CJN Chipper Jones Jsy/325 4.00 10.00
CLA Cliff Lee Jsy/325 5.00 12.00
CLN Clint Barmes Jsy/325 3.00 8.00
COA Coco Crisp Jsy/325 3.00 8.00
CON Conor Jackson Jsy/325
CRA Joe Crede Jsy/325 3.00 8.00
CSA Chris Shelton Jsy/325 3.00 8.00
CUN Chase Utley Jsy/325 6.00 15.00
DAA Dan Johnson Jsy/325 3.00 8.00
DHA Dan Haren Jsy/325 3.00 8.00
DJA Derek Jeter Jsy/325 10.00 25.00
DLN Derrek Lee Jsy/325 3.00 8.00
DOA David Ortiz Jsy/325 4.00 10.00
DWN Dontrelle Willis Jsy/325 3.00 8.00
DYA Dmitri Young Jsy/325 3.00 8.00
ECA Eric Chavez Jsy/325 3.00 8.00
EGN Eric Gagne Jsy/325 3.00 8.00
ESA Ervin Santana Jsy/325 3.00 8.00
FHA Felix Hernandez Jsy/325 4.00 10.00
FLN Felipe Lopez Jsy/325 3.00 8.00
GAA Jon Garland Jsy/325 3.00 8.00
GAN Garrett Atkins Jsy/325 3.00 8.00
GCA Gustavo Chacin Jsy/325 3.00 8.00
GSA Grady Sizemore Jsy/325 4.00 10.00
HBA Hank Blalock Jsy/325 3.00 8.00
HSA Huston Street Jsy/325 3.00 8.00
IRA Ivan Rodriguez Jsy/325
JAN Jason Bay Jsy/325 3.00 8.00
JBA Jeremy Bonderman Jsy/325 3.00 8.00
JBN Jeff Bagwell Jsy/325
JCA Jorge Cantu Jsy/325 3.00 8.00
JEN Jim Edmonds Jsy/325
JFN Jeff Francoeur Jsy/325 6.00 15.00
JGA Jonny Gomes Jsy/325 3.00 8.00
JMA Joe Mauer Jsy/325 4.00 10.00
JNA Joe Nathan Jsy/325 3.00 8.00
JPA Joel Pineiro Jsy/325 3.00 8.00
JPN Jake Peavy Jsy/325 3.00 8.00
JRN Jose Reyes Jsy/325
JSN John Smoltz Jsy/250
JUA Justin Morneau Jsy/325 8.00 20.00
JVA Jason Varitek Jsy/325 4.00 10.00
JWA Jake Westbrook Jsy/325 3.00 8.00
JWN Jack Wilson Jsy/200 3.00 8.00
KGN Ken Griffey Jr. Jsy/325 6.00 15.00
LEN Carlos Lee Jsy/325 3.00 8.00
MAN Matt Cain Jsy/325
MBA Mark Buehrle Jsy/325 5.00 12.00
MCN Miguel Cabrera Jsy/325 4.00 10.00
MEN Morgan Ensberg Jsy/325 3.00 8.00
MGN Marcus Giles Jsy/325 3.00 8.00
MHN Matt Holliday Jsy/325 4.00 10.00
MLA Mark Loretta Jsy/325 3.00 8.00
MPN Mark Prior Jsy/325
MRA Manny Ramirez Jsy/325
MTA Miguel Tejada Jsy/325 5.00 12.00
MYA Michael Young Jsy/325 5.00 12.00
NJN Nick Johnson Jsy/325 3.00 8.00
NLN Noah Lowry Jsy/325 3.00 8.00
NSA Nick Swisher Jsy/325 8.00 20.00
PEA Jhonny Peralta Jsy/325 3.00 8.00
PFN Prince Fielder Jsy/325 4.00 10.00
PMN Pedro Martinez Jsy/325 4.00 10.00
RBA Rocco Baldelli Jsy/325 3.00 8.00
RCN Ryan Church Jsy/325 3.00 8.00
RHN Ramon Hernandez Jsy/325 3.00 8.00
RJA Randy Johnson Pants/235 4.00 10.00
RON Roy Oswalt Jsy/325 5.00 12.00
RWN Rickie Weeks Jsy/325 5.00 12.00
RYN Ryan Howard Jsy/325 10.00 25.00
RZN Ryan Zimmerman Jsy/325 6.00 15.00
SBA Scott Baker Jsy/325 3.00 8.00
SKA Scott Kazmir Jsy/325
SPA Scott Podsednik Jsy/325 3.00 8.00
THA Travis Hafner Jsy/325 3.00 8.00
THN Todd Helton Jsy/325
TIA Tadahito Iguchi Jsy/325 3.00 8.00
TRN Trevor Hoffman Jsy/325 5.00 12.00
VGA Vladimir Guerrero Jsy/325 4.00 10.00
VMA Victor Martinez Jsy/325 5.00 12.00
WRN David Wright Jsy/325 6.00 15.00
YMN Yadier Molina Jsy/325 4.00 10.00
ZDN Zach Duke Jsy/325 3.00 8.00

2006 Artifacts AL/NL Artifacts Green

*GREEN p/r 150: .5X TO 1.2X BLUE p/r 325
*GRN p/r 75-85: .5X TO 1.2X BLUEp/r200-250
*GRNp/r50-55: .6X TO 1.5X BLUEp/r200-250
OVERALL GU ODDS 3:10
PRINT RUNS B/WN 50-150 COPIES PER
FGA Freddy Garcia Jsy/75 5.00 12.00
JDA Jermaine Dye Jsy/150 4.00 10.00

2006 Artifacts AL/NL Artifacts Red

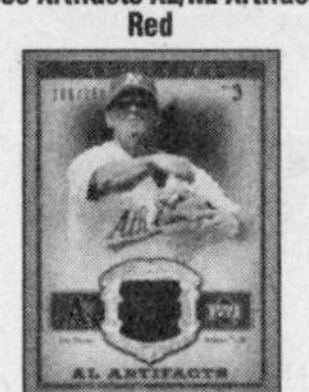

*RED p/r 150-250: .5X TO 1.2X BLUE p/r 325
*REDp/r150-250: .4X TO 1X BLUEp/r200-250
*REDp/r100-125: .5X TO 1.2XBLUEp/r200-250
OVERALL GU ODDS 3:10
PRINT RUNS B/WN 100-250 COPIES PER
FGA Freddy Garcia Jsy/175 4.00 10.00

2006 Artifacts Auto-Facts Signatures

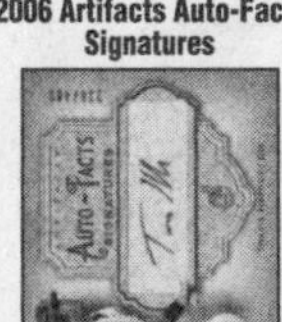

OVERALL AU ODDS 1:10
PRINT RUNS B/WN 5-800 COPIES PER
NO DUFFY PRICING DUE TO SCARCITY
AD Andre Dawson/300 6.00 15.00
AH Aaron Harang/800 4.00 10.00
AJ Andruw Jones/150 30.00 60.00
AM Aaron Miles/494 4.00 10.00
AR Aaron Rowand/520 6.00 15.00
AV Andy Van Slyke/800 6.00 15.00
BE Jason Bergmann/800 4.00 10.00
BI Bill Madlock/300 4.00 10.00
BL Barry Larkin/300 15.00 40.00
BO Bo Jackson/250 20.00 50.00
BR Brian Roberts/200 6.00 15.00
BY Clete Boyer/484 4.00 10.00
CA Chris Capuano/800 6.00 15.00
CB Clint Barmes/800 4.00 10.00
CC Chris Chambliss/400 4.00 10.00
CD Chris Demaria/800 4.00 10.00
CH Chris Carpenter/51 15.00 40.00
CJ Conor Jackson/800 6.00 15.00
CK Jack Clark/800 4.00 10.00
CL Cliff Lee/800 8.00 20.00
CO Coco Crisp/800 6.00 15.00
CP Jose Capellan/800 4.00 10.00
CR Cal Ripken/100 60.00 120.00
CS Chris Shelton/750 6.00 15.00
CU Chase Utley/200 30.00 60.00
CY Chris Young/700 10.00 25.00
CZ Carlos Zambrano/300 10.00 25.00
DA Chris Denorfia/659 4.00 10.00
DE Joey Devine/350 4.00 10.00
DH Dan Haren/800 4.00 10.00
DJ Derek Jeter/100 75.00 150.00
DL Derrek Lee/300 10.00 25.00
DU Chris Duffy/5
DW David Wright/300 15.00 40.00
DY Dmitri Young/300 4.00 10.00
ED Eric Davis/487 6.00 15.00
FH Felix Hernandez/300 10.00 25.00
GA Garrett Atkins/800 4.00 10.00
GB George Bell/715 6.00 15.00
GC Gustavo Chacin/800 4.00 10.00
GF George Foster/300 4.00 10.00
GG Goose Gossage/300 6.00 15.00
GN Graig Nettles/300 6.00 15.00
GO Jonny Gomes/700 4.00 10.00
HR Hanley Ramirez/800 8.00 20.00
HS Huston Street/500 6.00 15.00
IK Ian Kinsler/800 6.00 15.00
JA Jeremy Accardo/800 4.00 10.00
JB Jason Bay/200 6.00 15.00
JC Joe Carter/400 6.00 15.00
JD Jermaine Dye/652 6.00 15.00
JE Jeff Harris/800 4.00 10.00
JK Jason Kubel/400 4.00 10.00
JL Jason Lane/800 4.00 10.00
JM Joe Mauer/400 15.00 40.00
JN Joe Nathan/800 6.00 15.00
JP Jhonny Peralta/700 4.00 10.00
JR Jim Rice/200 6.00 15.00
JS Johan Santana/150 30.00 60.00
JV Justin Verlander/700 20.00 50.00
JW Jake Westbrook/650 4.00 10.00
KG Ken Griffey Jr./80 30.00 60.00
KH Kent Hrbek/239 6.00 15.00
LA Luis Aparicio/250 6.00 15.00
LD Lenny Dykstra/412 4.00 10.00
MA Matt Cain/700 6.00 15.00
MC Miguel Cabrera/250 8.00 20.00
MG Marcus Giles/350 6.00 15.00
MO Magglio Ordonez/437 15.00 40.00
MW Maury Wills/150 6.00 15.00
MY Michael Young/600 6.00 15.00
NS Nick Swisher/700 6.00 15.00
PF Prince Fielder/200 15.00 40.00
PM Pedro Martinez/100 30.00 60.00
RC Ryan Church/800 4.00 10.00
RE Chris Resop/800 4.00 10.00
RJ Reggie Jackson/200 20.00 50.00
RW Rickie Weeks/91 8.00 20.00
RZ Ryan Zimmerman/800 15.00 40.00
SF Scott Feldman/800 4.00 10.00
SG Steve Garvey/300 6.00 15.00
TH Travis Hafner/400 6.00 15.00
TI Tadahito Iguchi/700 15.00 40.00
TM Tim Hamulack/742 4.00 10.00
TO Tony Oliva/300 10.00 25.00
TP Tony Perez/251 10.00 25.00
WI Dontrelle Willis/50 10.00 25.00
WT Willy Taveras/500 4.00 10.00
YM Yadier Molina/800 12.50 30.00

2006 Artifacts Awesome Artifacts Jumbos

OVERALL GU ODDS 3:10
PRINT RUNS B/WN 21-45 COPIES PER
NO PRICING ON QTY OF 25 OR LESS
AD Adam Dunn Jsy/45 6.00 15.00
AH Aaron Harang Jsy/45 6.00 15.00
AP Albert Pujols Jsy/45 12.50 30.00
AR Aaron Rowand Jsy/45 6.00 15.00
AS Alfonso Soriano Jsy/45 6.00 15.00
AV Andy Van Slyke Jsy/45 10.00 25.00
BA Jeff Bagwell Jsy/45 10.00 25.00
BH Bill Hall Jsy/45 6.00 15.00
BL Joe Blanton Jsy/45 6.00 15.00
BM Brandon McCarthy Jsy/45 6.00 15.00
BO Bo Jackson Jsy/45 15.00 40.00
BR Brian McCann Jsy/45 10.00 25.00
BU Chris Burke Jsy/45 6.00 15.00
CA Matt Cain Jsy/45 6.00 15.00
CB Clint Barmes Jsy/45 6.00 15.00
CC Carl Crawford Jsy/45 6.00 15.00
CF Carlton Fisk Jsy/45 10.00 25.00
CH Chris Carpenter Jsy/45 6.00 15.00
CJ Chipper Jones Jsy/45 15.00 40.00
CL Cliff Lee Jsy/45 6.00 15.00
CO Conor Jackson Jsy/45 8.00 20.00
CR Cal Ripken Jsy/45 30.00 60.00
CS Chris Shelton Jsy/45 6.00 15.00
CU Chase Utley Jsy/45 15.00 40.00
CY Carl Yastrzemski Pants/25
DA Dan Johnson Jsy/45 6.00 15.00
DD Don Drysdale Pants/25
DE Derrek Lee Jsy/45 6.00 15.00
DH Dan Haren Jsy/45 6.00 15.00
DJ Derek Jeter Jsy/45 40.00 80.00
DL Don Larsen Pants/25
DO David Ortiz Jsy/45 10.00 25.00
DP Dave Parker Jsy/45 6.00 15.00
DW David Wells Jsy/45 6.00 15.00
EC Eric Chavez Jsy/45 6.00 15.00
EG Eric Gagne Jsy/45 6.00 15.00
EM Eddie Mathews Pants/45 30.00 60.00
ES Ervin Santana Jsy/45 6.00 15.00
FG Freddy Garcia Jsy/21
FH Felix Hernandez Jsy/45 10.00 25.00
FT Frank Thomas Jsy/45 10.00 25.00
GA Jon Garland Jsy/45 6.00 15.00
GC Gustavo Chacin Jsy/45 6.00 15.00
GF Gavin Floyd Jsy/45 6.00 15.00
GP Gaylord Perry Jsy/45 6.00 15.00
GS Grady Sizemore Jsy/45 10.00 25.00
HA Hank Blalock Jsy/45 6.00 15.00
HB Harold Baines Jsy/45 6.00 15.00
HS Huston Street Jsy/45 6.00 15.00
IR Ivan Rodriguez Jsy/45 10.00 25.00
JA Jason Schmidt Jsy/45 6.00 15.00

JB Jason Bay Jsy/45 6.00 15.00
JE Jim Edmonds Jsy/45 6.00 15.00
JF Jeff Francoeur Jsy/45 15.00 40.00
JG Jonny Gomes Jsy/45 6.00 15.00
JL Jason Lane Jsy/45 6.00 15.00
JM Johnny Mize Bat/25
JO Joel Pineiro Jsy/45 6.00 15.00
JP Jake Peavy Jsy/45 6.00 15.00
JS John Smoltz Jsy/45 15.00 40.00
JU Justin Morneau Jsy/45 6.00 15.00
JV Jason Varitek Jsy/45 10.00 25.00
JW Jack Wilson Jsy/45 6.00 15.00
KG Ken Griffey Jr. Jsy/45 15.00 40.00
LG Lou Gehrig Bat/25
MB Mark Buehrle Jsy/45 6.00 15.00
MC Miguel Cabrera Jsy/45 10.00 25.00
ME Morgan Ensberg Jsy/45 6.00 15.00
MI Miguel Tejada Jsy/45 6.00 15.00
MP Mark Prior Jsy/45 6.00 15.00
MR Manny Ramirez Jsy/45 10.00 25.00
NJ Nick Johnson Jsy/45 6.00 15.00
NL Noah Lowry Jsy/45 10.00 25.00
NS Nick Swisher Jsy/45 6.00 15.00
PE Jhonny Peralta Jsy/45 6.00 15.00
PF Prince Fielder Jsy/45 10.00 25.00
PM Pedro Martinez Jsy/45 10.00 25.00
RA Randy Johnson Pants/45 10.00 25.00
RB Rocco Baldelli Jsy/45 6.00 15.00
RH Rogers Hornsby Pants/25
RJ Reggie Jackson Jsy/25
RO Roy Oswalt Jsy/45 6.00 15.00
RS Ron Santo Jsy/45 10.00 25.00
RW Rickie Weeks Jsy/45 6.00 15.00
RY Ryan Howard Jsy/45 20.00 50.00
RZ Ryan Zimmerman Jsy/45 15.00 40.00
SB Scott Baker Jsy/45 6.00 15.00
SG Steve Garvey Pants/45 6.00 15.00
SP Satchel Paige Pants/45 75.00 150.00
TH Todd Helton Jsy/45 10.00 25.00
TM Thurman Munson Pants/25
TR Trevor Hoffman Jsy/45 6.00 15.00
VG Vladimir Guerrero Jsy/45 10.00 25.00
WC Will Clark Pants/45 10.00 25.00
WE Jake Westbrook Jsy/45 6.00 15.00
WI Dontrelle Willis Jsy/45 6.00 15.00
WR David Wright Jsy/45 15.00 40.00
YM Yadier Molina Jsy/45 10.00 25.00
ZD Zach Duke Jsy/45 6.00 15.00

2006 Artifacts MLB Game-Used Apparel

OVERALL GU ODDS 3:10
STATED PRINT RUN 325 SERIAL #'d SETS
M.SCHMIDT PRINT RUN 85 #'d CARDS
AH Aaron Harang Jsy/325 3.00 8.00
AR Aaron Rowand Jsy/325 3.00 8.00
AT Garrett Atkins Jsy/325 3.00 8.00
AV Andy Van Slyke Jsy/325 3.00 8.00
BA Clint Barmes Jsy/325 3.00 8.00
BB Ben Broussard Jsy/325 3.00 8.00
BC Brian McCann Jsy/325 4.00 10.00
BI Bill Madlock Jsy/325 3.00 8.00
BL Brad Lidge Jsy/325 3.00 8.00
BM Brandon McCarthy Jsy/325 3.00 8.00
BO Bo Jackson Jsy/325 4.00 10.00
BP Boog Powell Jsy/325 3.00 8.00
BR Brian Roberts Jsy/325 3.00 8.00
BY Jason Bay Jsy/325 3.00 8.00
CA Carl Crawford Jsy/325 3.00 8.00
CB Chris Burke Jsy/325 3.00 8.00
CD Chad Cordero Jsy/325 3.00 8.00
CF Carlton Fisk Jsy/325 4.00 10.00
CH Chris Carpenter Jsy/325 4.00 10.00
CJ Conor Jackson Jsy/325 4.00 10.00
CK Casey Kotchman Jsy/325 3.00 8.00
CL Cliff Lee Jsy/325 3.00 8.00
CO Coco Crisp Jsy/325 3.00 8.00
CR Cal Ripken Jsy/325 10.00 25.00
CS Chris Capuano Jsy/325 3.00 8.00
CU Chase Utley Jsy/325 6.00 15.00
CY Carl Yastrzemski Pants/325 6.00 15.00
DA Dan Johnson Jsy/325 3.00 8.00
DH Dan Haren Jsy/325 3.00 8.00
DJ Derek Jeter Jsy/325 10.00 25.00
DL Derrek Lee Jsy/325 3.00 8.00
DO Don Larsen Pants/325 4.00 10.00
DW Dontrelle Willis Jsy/325 3.00 8.00
DY Dmitri Young Jsy/325 3.00 8.00
ES Ervin Santana Jsy/325 3.00 8.00
FH Felix Hernandez Jsy/325 4.00 10.00
FL Felipe Lopez Jsy/325 3.00 8.00
FM Fred McGriff Jsy/325 4.00 10.00
GA Jon Garland Jsy/325 3.00 8.00
GC Gustavo Chacin Jsy/325 3.00 8.00
GF Gavin Floyd Jsy/325 3.00 8.00
GG Goose Gossage Jsy/325 3.00 8.00
GN Graig Nettles Jsy/325 3.00 8.00
GO Adrian Gonzalez Jsy/325 3.00 8.00
GP Gaylord Perry Jsy/325 3.00 8.00
GS Grady Sizemore Jsy/325 4.00 10.00
HB Harold Baines Jsy/325 3.00 8.00
HO Ryan Howard Jsy/325 10.00 25.00
HS Huston Street Jsy/325 3.00 8.00
JE Jeremy Bonderman Jsy/325 3.00 8.00
JG Jonny Gomes Jsy/325 3.00 8.00
JH Jeremy Hermida Jsy/325 4.00 10.00
JK John Kruk Jsy/325 3.00 8.00
JL Jason Lane Jsy/325 3.00 8.00
JM Joe Mauer Jsy/325 4.00 10.00
JN Joe Nathan Jsy/325 3.00 8.00
JO Joe Blanton Jsy/325 3.00 8.00
JP Jhonny Peralta Jsy/325 3.00 8.00
JR Jose Reyes Jsy/325 3.00 8.00
JU Jorge Cantu Jsy/325 3.00 8.00
JW Jake Westbrook Jsy/325 3.00 8.00
JY Jeremy Reed Jsy/325 3.00 8.00
KE Jason Kendall Jsy/325 3.00 8.00
KG Ken Griffey Jr. Jsy/325 6.00 15.00
LE Carlos Lee Jsy/325 3.00 8.00
MA Matt Cain Jsy/325 3.00 8.00
MC Miguel Cabrera Jsy/325 4.00 10.00
MG Marcus Giles Jsy/325 3.00 8.00
MH Matt Holliday Jsy/325 4.00 10.00
ML Mark Loretta Jsy/325 3.00 8.00
MO Justin Morneau Jsy/325 3.00 8.00
MS Mike Schmidt Jsy/85 10.00 25.00
MY Michael Young Jsy/325 3.00 8.00
NL Noah Lowry Jsy/325 3.00 8.00
NS Nick Swisher Jsy/325 3.00 8.00
OR Magglio Ordonez Jsy/325 3.00 8.00
PE Jake Peavy Jsy/325 3.00 8.00
PF Prince Fielder Jsy/325
PI Joel Pineiro Jsy/325 3.00 8.00
RB Rocco Baldelli Jsy/325 3.00 8.00
RC Ryan Church Jsy/325 3.00 8.00
RH Ramon Hernandez Jsy/325 3.00 8.00
RO Roy Oswalt Jsy/325 3.00 8.00
RS Ron Santo Jsy/325 6.00 15.00
RW Rickie Weeks Jsy/325 3.00 8.00
RZ Ryan Zimmerman Jsy/325 6.00 15.00
SB Scott Baker Jsy/325 3.00 8.00
SG Steve Garvey Pants/325 3.00 8.00
SH Chris Shelton Jsy/325 3.00 8.00
SK Scott Kazmir Jsy/325 3.00 8.00
SP Scott Podsednik Jsy/325 3.00 8.00
ST So Taguchi Jsy/325 3.00 8.00
TI Tadahito Iguchi Jsy/325 3.00 8.00
WC Will Clark Pants/325 4.00 10.00
WR David Wright Jsy/325 6.00 15.00
YB Yuniesky Betancourt Jsy/325 3.00 8.00
YM Yadier Molina Jsy/325 4.00 10.00

2006 Artifacts MLB Game-Used Apparel Gold Limited

*GOLD p/r 150: .5X TO 1.2X BASIC p/r 325
*GOLD p/r 30: .6X TO 1.5X BASIC p/r 85
OVERALL GU ODDS 3:10
STATED PRINT RUN 150 SERIAL #'d SETS
M.SCHMIDT PRINT RUN 30 #'d SETS
JD Jermaine Dye Jsy/150 4.00 10.00

2006 Artifacts MLB Game-Used Apparel Silver Limited

*SILVER p/r 250: .5X TO 1.2X BASIC p/r 325
*SILVER p/r 50: .5X TO 1.2X BASIC p/r 85
OVERALL GU ODDS 3:10
STATED PRINT RUN 250 SERIAL #'d SETS
M.SCHMIDT PRINT RUN 50 #'d SETS

2006 Artifacts MLB Game-Used Apparel Autographs

OVERALL AU ODDS 1:10
STATED PRINT RUN 30 SERIAL #'d SETS
R.SANTO PRINT RUN 28 SERIAL #'d CARDS
HOWARD PRINT RUN 23 SERIAL #'d CARDS
NO HOWARD PRICING DUE TO SCARCITY
AH Aaron Harang Jsy/30 6.00 15.00
AR Aaron Rowand Jsy/30 10.00 25.00
AT Garrett Atkins Jsy/30 6.00 15.00
AV Andy Van Slyke Jsy/30 10.00 25.00
BA Clint Barmes Jsy/30 6.00 15.00
BB Ben Broussard Jsy/30 6.00 15.00
BI Bill Madlock Jsy/30 6.00 15.00
BL Brad Lidge Jsy/30 10.00 25.00
BM Brandon McCarthy Jsy/30 6.00 15.00
BO Bo Jackson Jsy/30 60.00 120.00
BP Boog Powell Jsy/30 10.00 25.00
BY Jason Bay Jsy/30 10.00 25.00
CA Carl Crawford Jsy/30 10.00 25.00
CB Chris Burke Jsy/30 6.00 15.00
CD Chad Cordero Jsy/30 6.00 15.00
CF Carlton Fisk Jsy/30 15.00 40.00
CH Chris Carpenter Jsy/30 30.00 60.00
CJ Conor Jackson Jsy/30 15.00 40.00
CK Casey Kotchman Jsy/30 10.00 25.00
CL Cliff Lee Jsy/30 15.00 40.00
CO Coco Crisp Jsy/30 15.00 40.00
CR Cal Ripken Jsy/30 125.00 200.00
CS Chris Capuano Jsy/30 10.00 25.00
CU Chase Utley Jsy/30 40.00 80.00
CY Carl Yastrzemski Pants/30 40.00 80.00
DA Dan Johnson Jsy/30 6.00 15.00
DH Dan Haren Jsy/30 6.00 15.00
DJ Derek Jeter Jsy/30 125.00 200.00
DL Derrek Lee Jsy/30 15.00 40.00
DO Don Larsen Pants/30 10.00 25.00
DW Dontrelle Willis Jsy/30 15.00 40.00
DY Dmitri Young Jsy/30 6.00 15.00
FH Felix Hernandez Jsy/30 20.00 50.00
FL Felipe Lopez Jsy/30 6.00 15.00
GC Gustavo Chacin Jsy/30 6.00 15.00
GG Goose Gossage Jsy/30 10.00 25.00
GN Graig Nettles Jsy/30 15.00 40.00
GO Adrian Gonzalez Jsy/30 10.00 25.00
GP Gaylord Perry Jsy/30 10.00 25.00
HB Harold Baines Jsy/30 10.00 25.00
HO Ryan Howard Jsy/23
HS Huston Street Jsy/30 10.00 25.00
JD Jermaine Dye Jsy/30 10.00 25.00
JE Jeremy Bonderman Jsy/30 10.00 25.00
JG Jonny Gomes Jsy/30 6.00 15.00
JH Jeremy Hermida Jsy/30 15.00 40.00
JK John Kruk Jsy/30 10.00 25.00
JM Joe Mauer Jsy/30 50.00 100.00
JN Joe Nathan Jsy/30 10.00 25.00
JO Joe Blanton Jsy/30 6.00 15.00
JP Jhonny Peralta Jsy/30 6.00 15.00
JR Jose Reyes Jsy/30 15.00 40.00
JW Jake Westbrook Jsy/30 6.00 15.00
KG Ken Griffey Jr. Jsy/30 75.00 150.00
LE Carlos Lee Jsy/30 10.00 25.00
MA Matt Cain Jsy/30 15.00 40.00
MC Miguel Cabrera Jsy/30 15.00 40.00
MG Marcus Giles Jsy/30 10.00 25.00
MO Justin Morneau Jsy/30 10.00 25.00
MS Mike Schmidt Jsy/30 40.00 80.00
MY Michael Young Jsy/30 10.00 25.00
NL Noah Lowry Jsy/30 15.00 40.00
NS Nick Swisher Jsy/30 10.00 25.00
OR Magglio Ordonez Jsy/30 15.00 40.00
PE Jake Peavy Jsy/30 15.00 40.00
PF Prince Fielder Jsy/30 30.00 60.00
PI Joel Pineiro Jsy/30 6.00 15.00
RC Ryan Church Jsy/30 6.00 15.00
RH Ramon Hernandez Jsy/30 6.00 15.00
RO Roy Oswalt Jsy/30 10.00 25.00
RS Ron Santo Jsy/28 40.00 80.00
RW Rickie Weeks Jsy/30 10.00 25.00
RZ Ryan Zimmerman Jsy/30 40.00 80.00
SB Scott Baker Jsy/30 6.00 15.00
SG Steve Garvey Pants/30 15.00 40.00
SH Chris Shelton Jsy/30 4.00 10.00
SK Scott Kazmir Jsy/30 15.00 40.00
SP Scott Podsednik Jsy/30 15.00 40.00
TI Tadahito Iguchi Jsy/30 30.00 60.00
WC Will Clark Pants/30 20.00 50.00
WR David Wright Jsy/30 50.00 100.00
YB Yuniesky Betancourt Jsy/30 10.00 25.00
YM Yadier Molina Jsy/30 15.00 40.00

2006 Artifacts MLB Game-Used Patch Apparel Autographs

OVERALL AU ODDS 1:10
STATED PRINT RUN 10 SERIAL #'d SETS
NO PRICING DUE TO SCARCITY

2006 Artifacts MLB Rare Apparel Autographs

OVERALL AU ODDS 1:10
STATED PRINT RUN 1 SERIAL #'d SET
NO PRICING DUE TO SCARCITY

2007 Artifacts

This 100-card set was released in July, 2007. The set was issued through both hobby and retail channels. The hobby version was issued in four-card packs which came 10 packs to a box.Cards numbered 1-70 feature veterans which were sequenced in team alphabetical order while cards numbered 71-100 featured 2007 rookies.

COMPLETE SET (100) 15.00 40.00
COMMON CARD (1-70) .15 .40
COMMON ROOKIE (71-100) .30 .75
1 Miguel Tejada .25 .60
2 David Ortiz .25 .60
3 Manny Ramirez .40 1.00
4 Curt Schilling .25 .60
5 Jim Thome .25 .60
6 Paul Konerko .25 .60
7 Jermaine Dye .15 .40
8 Travis Hafner .15 .40
9 Victor Martinez .25 .60
10 Grady Sizemore .25 .60
11 Ivan Rodriguez .25 .60
12 Magglio Ordonez .25 .60
13 Justin Verlander .50 1.25
14 Mark Teahen .15 .40
15 Vladimir Guerrero .40 1.00
16 Jered Weaver .25 .60
17 Justin Morneau .40 1.00
18 Joe Mauer .40 1.00
19 Torii Hunter .15 .40
20 Johan Santana .40 1.00
21 Derek Jeter 1.00 2.50
22 Alex Rodriguez .60 1.50
23 Johnny Damon .25 .60
24 Huston Street .15 .40
25 Nick Swisher .40 1.00
26 Ichiro Suzuki .60 1.50
27 Richie Sexson .15 .40
28 Carl Crawford .25 .60
29 Scott Kazmir .25 .60
30 Michael Young .25 .60
31 Mark Teixeira .40 1.00
32 Vernon Wells .15 .40
33 Roy Halladay .40 1.00
34 Brandon Webb .25 .60
35 Stephen Drew .15 .40
36 Chipper Jones .40 1.00
37 Andruw Jones .15 .40
38 Derrek Lee .15 .40
39 Aramis Ramirez .15 .40
40 Ken Griffey Jr. .60 1.50
41 Adam Dunn .25 .60
42 Todd Helton .25 .60
43 Matt Holliday .40 1.00
44 Miguel Cabrera .40 1.00
45 Hanley Ramirez .40 1.00
46 Dontrelle Willis .15 .40
47 Lance Berkman .25 .60
48 Roy Oswalt .25 .60
49 Craig Biggio .25 .60
50 Nomar Garciaparra .40 1.00
51 Derek Lowe .15 .40
52 Prince Fielder .25 .60
53 Rickie Weeks .25 .60
54 Jose Reyes .25 .60
55 David Wright .60 1.50
56 Carlos Beltran .15 .40
57 Ryan Howard .60 1.50
58 Chase Utley .40 1.00
59 Jimmy Rollins .25 .60
60 Jason Bay .25 .60
61 Freddy Sanchez .15 .40
62 Trevor Hoffman .25 .60
63 Adrian Gonzalez .25 .60
64 Omar Vizquel .25 .60
65 Matt Cain .25 .60
66 Albert Pujols 1.00 2.50
67 Jim Edmonds .25 .60
68 Chris Carpenter .40 1.00
69 David Eckstein .15 .40
70 Ryan Zimmerman .25 .60
71 Alexi Casilla RC .50 1.25
72 Andrew Miller RC .75 2.00
73 Andy Cannizaro RC .30 .75
74 Brian Stokes (RC) .30 .75
75 Carlos Maldonado (RC) .30 .75
76 Cesar Jimenez RC .30 .75
77 Daisuke Matsuzaka RC 1.25 3.00
78 Delmon Young (RC) .50 1.25
79 Delwyn Young (RC) .30 .75
80 Fred Lewis (RC) .50 1.25
81 Glen Perkins (RC) .30 .75
82 Jeff Baker (RC) .30 .75
83 Jeff Fiorentino (RC) .30 .75
84 Jeff Salazar (RC) .30 .75
85 Jerry Owens (RC) .30 .75
86 Josh Fields (RC) .30 .75
87 Juan Perez RC .30 .75
88 Juan Salas (RC) .30 .75
89 Justin Hampson (RC) .30 .75
90 Kevin Kouzmanoff (RC) .30 .75
91 Michael Bourn (RC) .30 .75
92 Miguel Montero (RC) .30 .75
93 Mike Rabelo RC .30 .75
94 Oswaldo Navarro RC .30 .75
95 Philip Humber (RC) .30 .75
96 Ryan Braun RC .30 .75
97 Ryan Sweeney (RC) .30 .75
98 Sean Henn (RC) .30 .75
99 Jose Reyes RC .30 .75
100 Troy Tulowitzki (RC) 2.00 5.00

2007 Artifacts Antiquity Artifacts

RANDOM INSERTS IN PACKS
STATED PRINT RUN 199 SER.#'d SETS
AB Adrian Beltre 3.00 8.00
AJ Andruw Jones 3.00 8.00
AL Adam LaRoche 3.00 8.00
AP Albert Pujols 6.00 15.00
AR Aramis Ramirez 3.00 8.00
AT Garrett Atkins 3.00 8.00
BA Bobby Abreu 3.00 8.00
BC Bartolo Colon 3.00 8.00
BE Carlos Beltran 3.00 8.00
BG Brian Giles 3.00 8.00
BO Jeremy Bonderman 3.00 8.00
BR Brian Roberts 3.00 8.00
BU B.J. Upton 3.00 8.00
BW Billy Wagner 3.00 8.00
BZ Barry Zito 3.00 8.00
CA Miguel Cabrera 3.00 8.00
CB Craig Biggio 3.00 8.00
CC Carl Crawford 3.00 8.00
CF Chone Figgins 3.00 8.00
CH Chris Carpenter 3.00 8.00
CJ Chipper Jones 4.00 10.00
CL Carlos Lee 3.00 8.00
CR Cal Ripken Jr. 10.00 25.00
CS Curt Schilling 3.00 8.00
CU Chase Utley 4.00 10.00
DJ Derek Jeter 8.00 20.00
DO David Ortiz 4.00 10.00
DR J.D. Drew 3.00 8.00
DU Dan Uggla 3.00 8.00
DW Dontrelle Willis 3.00 8.00
EC Eric Chavez 3.00 8.00
ED Jim Edmonds 3.00 8.00
FG Freddy Garcia 3.00 8.00
FH Felix Hernandez 3.00 8.00
FL Francisco Liriano 3.00 8.00
FT Frank Thomas 4.00 10.00
GA Garret Anderson 3.00 8.00
GJ Geoff Jenkins 3.00 8.00
GM Greg Maddux 5.00 12.00
GR Ken Griffey Jr. 6.00 15.00
GS Grady Sizemore 3.00 8.00
HA Rich Harden 3.00 8.00
HB Hank Blalock 3.00 8.00
HO Trevor Hoffman 3.00 8.00
HR Hanley Ramirez 3.00 8.00
HS Huston Street 3.00 8.00
HU Torii Hunter 3.00 8.00
IR Ivan Rodriguez 3.00 8.00
JA Jason Bay 3.00 8.00
JC Jorge Cantu 3.00 8.00
JD Jermaine Dye 3.00 8.00
JE Johnny Estrada 3.00 8.00
JF Jeff Francoeur 4.00 10.00
JG Jason Giambi 3.00 8.00
JJ Josh Johnson 3.00 8.00
JK Jeff Kent 3.00 8.00
JM Joe Mauer 3.00 8.00
JP Jake Peavy 3.00 8.00
JR Jimmy Rollins 3.00 8.00
JS Jason Schmidt 3.00 8.00
JT Jim Thome 3.00 8.00
JV Justin Verlander 4.00 10.00
JZ Joel Zumaya 3.00 8.00
KG Khalil Greene 3.00 8.00
LB Lance Berkman 3.00 8.00
LG Luis Gonzalez 3.00 8.00
MO Justin Morneau 3.00 8.00
MR Manny Ramirez 3.00 8.00
MT Mark Teixeira 3.00 8.00
MY Michael Young 3.00 8.00
NS Nick Swisher 3.00 8.00
OR Magglio Ordonez 3.00 8.00
PA Jonathan Papelbon 4.00 10.00
PB Pat Burrell 3.00 8.00
PE Jhonny Peralta 3.00 8.00
PF Prince Fielder 4.00 10.00
PK Paul Konerko 3.00 8.00
PM Pedro Martinez 3.00 8.00
PO Jorge Posada 3.00 8.00
RC Roger Clemens 6.00 15.00
RE Jose Reyes 4.00 10.00
RH Roy Halladay 3.00 8.00
RJ Randy Johnson 4.00 10.00
RO Roy Oswalt 3.00 8.00
RW Rickie Weeks 3.00 8.00
RZ Ryan Zimmerman 4.00 10.00
SA Johan Santana 3.00 8.00
SK Scott Kazmir 3.00 8.00
SM John Smoltz 3.00 8.00
SR Scott Rolen 3.00 8.00
TE Miguel Tejada 3.00 8.00
TG Tom Glavine 3.00 8.00
TH Todd Helton 3.00 8.00
TI Tim Hudson 3.00 8.00
VA Jason Varitek 4.00 10.00
VG Vladimir Guerrero 4.00 10.00
VM Victor Martinez 3.00 8.00
VW Vernon Wells 3.00 8.00

2007 Artifacts Antiquity Artifacts Gold

*GOLD: .3X TO .75X BASIC
GOLD NOT SERIAL NUMBERED
RANDOM INSERTS IN RETAIL PACKS
TR Travis Hafner 2.50 6.00

2007 Artifacts Antiquity Artifacts Patch

*PATCH: .75X TO 2X BASIC
RANDOM INSERTS IN PACKS
STATED PRINT RUN 50 SER.#'d SETS
JB Josh Beckett 6.00 15.00
TR Travis Hafner 6.00 15.00
VA Jason Varitek 12.50 30.00

2007 Artifacts Autofacts

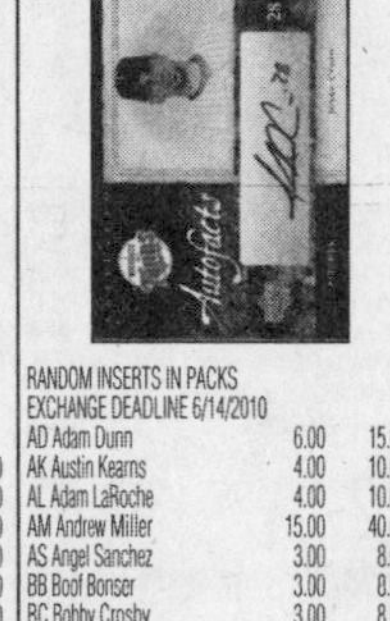

RANDOM INSERTS IN PACKS
EXCHANGE DEADLINE 6/14/2010
AD Adam Dunn 6.00 15.00
AK Austin Kearns 4.00 10.00
AL Adam LaRoche 4.00 10.00
AM Andrew Miller 15.00 40.00
AS Angel Sanchez 3.00 8.00
BB Boof Bonser 3.00 8.00
BC Bobby Crosby 3.00 8.00
BE Josh Beckett 15.00 40.00
BO Jeremy Bonderman 12.50 30.00
BR Brian Roberts
BT Jason Bartlett 3.00 8.00
BU Ambiorix Burgos 3.00 8.00
CH Cole Hamels 12.50 30.00
CJ Cesar Jimenez 3.00 8.00
CL Carlos Lee 6.00 15.00
CR Cal Ripken Jr.
CY Chris Young 6.00 15.00
CZ Carlos Zambrano 15.00 40.00
DJ Derek Jeter 100.00 175.00
DO David Ortiz 20.00 50.00
DW Dontrelle Willis 4.00 10.00
DY Delmon Young 6.00 15.00
EC Eric Chavez 4.00 10.00
FL Francisco Liriano
FT Frank Thomas
GA Garrett Atkins 4.00 10.00
HA Rich Harden 4.00 10.00
HG Hector Gimenez 3.00 8.00
HK Hong-Chih Kuo 10.00 25.00
HR Hanley Ramirez 10.00 25.00
IK Ian Kinsler 8.00 20.00
JA Joaquin Arias 3.00 8.00
JB Jason Bay 3.00 8.00
JC Jesse Crain 3.00 8.00
JE Johnny Estrada 4.00 10.00
JG Jonny Gomes 3.00 8.00
JJ Josh Johnson 5.00 12.00
JP Jake Peavy
JS John Smoltz 20.00 50.00
JT Jim Thome
JW Jered Weaver 4.00 10.00
JZ Joel Zumaya
KE Howie Kendrick 4.00 10.00
KG Ken Griffey Jr. 50.00 100.00
KM Kendry Morales 3.00 8.00
KN Jon Knott 3.00 8.00
KW Kerry Wood 10.00 25.00
MJ Mike Jacobs 6.00 15.00
MM Miguel Montero 3.00 8.00
MO Justin Morneau 10.00 25.00
PA Jonathan Papelbon 12.50 30.00
PE Jhonny Peralta 3.00 8.00
PH Philip Humber 3.00 8.00
PM Pedro Martinez 15.00 40.00
RA Chris Ray 3.00 8.00
RC Roger Clemens 75.00 125.00
RH Rich Hill 6.00 15.00
RW Rickie Weeks 4.00 10.00
SB Scott Baker 3.00 8.00
SD Stephen Drew 6.00 15.00
SK Scott Kazmir 5.00 12.00
SO Jeremy Sowers 3.00 8.00
SR Scott Rolen 10.00 25.00
TI Tadahito Iguchi 6.00 15.00
TT Troy Tulowitzki 10.00 25.00
UP B.J. Upton 5.00 12.00
VE Justin Verlander 12.50 30.00
VG Vladimir Guerrero 15.00 40.00
VM Victor Martinez 4.00 10.00
WI Josh Willingham 3.00 8.00
YB Yuniesky Betancourt 6.00 15.00
ZG Zack Greinke 10.00 25.00
ZS Zack Segovia 4.00 10.00

2007 Artifacts Awesome Artifacts

RANDOM INSERTS IN PACKS
PRINT RUNS B/WN 29-50 SER.#'d SETS
AD Adam Dunn 5.00 12.00
AG Adrian Gonzalez 5.00 12.00
AP Albert Pujols 15.00 40.00
AR Aramis Ramirez 5.00 12.00
AS Alfonso Soriano 5.00 12.00
BA Bobby Abreu 5.00 12.00
BC Bartolo Colon 5.00 12.00
BG Brian Giles 5.00 12.00
BI Craig Biggio 6.00 15.00
BR Brian Roberts 5.00 12.00
BW Billy Wagner 5.00 12.00
BZ Barry Zito 5.00 12.00
CA Carl Crawford 5.00 12.00
CB Carlos Beltran 5.00 12.00
CC Carl Crawford 5.00 12.00
CC Chris Carpenter 5.00 12.00
CD Carlos Delgado 5.00 12.00
CF Chone Figgins 5.00 12.00
CJ Chipper Jones 8.00 20.00
CL Carlos Lee 5.00 12.00
CR Cal Ripken Jr. 40.00 80.00
CS Curt Schilling 6.00 15.00
CU Chase Utley 8.00 20.00
DJ Derek Jeter 40.00 80.00
DO David Ortiz 8.00 20.00
DU Dan Uggla 6.00 15.00
DW Dontrelle Willis 5.00 12.00
EC Eric Chavez 5.00 12.00
FG Freddy Garcia 5.00 12.00
FH Felix Hernandez 6.00 15.00
FL Francisco Liriano 8.00 20.00
FT Frank Thomas 12.50 30.00
GA Garret Anderson 5.00 12.00
GM Greg Maddux 12.50 30.00
GR Khalil Greene 6.00 15.00
GS Grady Sizemore 6.00 15.00
HA Roy Halladay 5.00 12.00
HB Hank Blalock 5.00 12.00
HE Todd Helton 6.00 15.00
HR Hanley Ramirez 6.00 15.00
HS Huston Street 5.00 12.00
HU Torii Hunter 5.00 12.00
IK Ian Kinsler 5.00 12.00
IR Ivan Rodriguez 6.00 15.00
JA Jason Bay 5.00 12.00
JB Jeremy Bonderman 5.00 12.00
JC Jorge Cantu 5.00 12.00
JD Jermaine Dye 5.00 12.00
JE Jim Edmonds 6.00 15.00
JF Jeff Francoeur 12.50 30.00
JG Jason Giambi 5.00 12.00
JH Johnny Damon 6.00 15.00
JJ Josh Johnson 5.00 12.00
JK Jeff Kent 5.00 12.00
JM Joe Mauer 6.00 15.00
JO Josh Barfield 5.00 12.00
JP Jake Peavy 5.00 12.00
JR Jimmy Rollins 5.00 12.00
JS Jason Schmidt 5.00 12.00
JT Jim Thome 6.00 15.00
JV Justin Verlander 8.00 20.00
JW Jered Weaver 6.00 15.00
JZ Joel Zumaya 6.00 15.00
KG Ken Griffey Jr. 12.50 30.00
KM Kendry Morales 6.00 15.00
MC Miguel Cabrera 6.00 15.00
MO Justin Morneau 5.00 12.00
MR Manny Ramirez 6.00 15.00
MT Mark Teixeira 6.00 15.00
MY Michael Young 5.00 12.00
OR Magglio Ordonez 5.00 12.00
OS Roy Oswalt 5.00 12.00
PA Jonathan Papelbon 8.00 20.00
PB Pat Burrell 5.00 12.00
PE Jhonny Peralta 5.00 12.00
PF Prince Fielder 8.00 20.00
PO Jorge Posada 6.00 15.00
RC Robinson Cano 6.00 15.00
RE Jose Reyes 10.00 25.00
RF Rafael Furcal 5.00 12.00
RH Rich Harden 5.00 12.00
RJ Randy Johnson 8.00 20.00
RO Roger Clemens 15.00 40.00
RW Rickie Weeks 5.00 12.00
RZ Ryan Zimmerman 8.00 20.00
SK Scott Kazmir 6.00 15.00
SM John Smoltz 6.00 15.00
SR Scott Rolen 6.00 15.00
TG Tom Glavine 6.00 15.00
TH Trevor Hoffman 5.00 12.00
TI Tim Hudson 5.00 12.00
TR Travis Hafner 5.00 12.00
VA Jason Varitek 8.00 20.00
VG Vladimir Guerrero 8.00 20.00
VM Victor Martinez 5.00 12.00
VW Vernon Wells 5.00 12.00

2007 Artifacts Bat Knobs

RANDOM INSERTS IN PACKS
STATED PRINT RUN 1 SER.#'d SET
NO PRICING DUE TO SCARCITY

2007 Artifacts Divisional Artifacts

RANDOM INSERTS IN PACKS
PRINT RUNS B/WN 117-199 COPIES PER
AA Aaron Rowand 3.00 8.00
AD Adam Dunn 3.00 8.00
AJ Andruw Jones 4.00 10.00
AL Adam LaRoche 3.00 8.00
AR Aramis Ramirez 3.00 8.00
BA Bobby Abreu 3.00 8.00
BC Bartolo Colon 3.00 8.00
BE Carlos Beltran 3.00 8.00
BG Brian Giles 3.00 8.00
BO Jeremy Bonderman 3.00 8.00
BR Brian Roberts 3.00 8.00
BW Billy Wagner 3.00 8.00
BZ Barry Zito 3.00 8.00
CA Robinson Cano 4.00 10.00
CB Craig Biggio 3.00 8.00
CC Carl Crawford 3.00 8.00
CD Carlos Delgado 3.00 8.00
CH Chris Carpenter 3.00 8.00
CJ Chipper Jones 4.00 10.00
CL Carlos Lee 3.00 8.00
CR Cal Ripken Jr. 10.00 25.00
CS Curt Schilling 3.00 8.00
CU Chase Utley 4.00 10.00
DJ Derek Jeter 8.00 20.00
DL Derrek Lee 3.00 8.00
DO David Ortiz 4.00 10.00
DU Dan Uggla 3.00 8.00
DW Dontrelle Willis 3.00 8.00
EC Eric Chavez 3.00 8.00
FG Freddy Garcia 3.00 8.00
FH Felix Hernandez 3.00 8.00
FL Francisco Liriano 3.00 8.00
FT Frank Thomas 4.00 10.00
GA Garret Anderson 3.00 8.00
GM Greg Maddux 5.00 12.00
GR Ken Griffey Jr. 6.00 15.00
GS Grady Sizemore 3.00 8.00
HA Rich Harden 3.00 8.00
HB Hank Blalock 3.00 8.00
HO Trevor Hoffman 3.00 8.00
HR Hanley Ramirez 3.00 8.00
HU Torii Hunter 3.00 8.00
IK Ian Kinsler 3.00 8.00
IR Ivan Rodriguez 3.00 8.00
JA Jason Bay 3.00 8.00
JC Jorge Cantu 3.00 8.00
JD Jermaine Dye 3.00 8.00
JE Jim Edmonds 3.00 8.00
JF Jeff Francoeur 4.00 10.00
JG Jason Giambi 3.00 8.00
JJ Josh Johnson 3.00 8.00
JK Jeff Kent 3.00 8.00
JM Joe Mauer 3.00 8.00
JN Joe Nathan 3.00 8.00
JO Josh Barfield 3.00 8.00
JP Jake Peavy 3.00 8.00
JR Jimmy Rollins 3.00 8.00
JS Jason Schmidt 3.00 8.00
JT Jim Thome 3.00 8.00
JV Justin Verlander 4.00 10.00
JW Jered Weaver 3.00 8.00
JZ Joel Zumaya 3.00 8.00
KG Khalil Greene 3.00 8.00
KM Kendry Morales 3.00 8.00
LB Lance Berkman 3.00 8.00
MC Miguel Cabrera 4.00 10.00
ME Melky Cabrera 3.00 8.00
MO Justin Morneau 3.00 8.00
MR Manny Ramirez 3.00 8.00
MT Mark Teixeira 3.00 8.00
MY Michael Young 3.00 8.00
NS Nick Swisher 3.00 8.00
OR Magglio Ordonez 3.00 8.00
PA Jonathan Papelbon 4.00 10.00
PB Pat Burrell 3.00 8.00
PE Jhonny Peralta 3.00 8.00
PF Prince Fielder 4.00 10.00
PK Paul Konerko 3.00 8.00
PO Jorge Posada 3.00 8.00
RC Roger Clemens 6.00 15.00
RE Jose Reyes 4.00 10.00
RH Roy Halladay 3.00 8.00
RJ Randy Johnson 3.00 8.00
RO Roy Oswalt 3.00 8.00
RW Rickie Weeks 3.00 8.00
RZ Ryan Zimmerman 4.00 10.00
SK Scott Kazmir 3.00 8.00
SM John Smoltz 3.00 8.00
SR Scott Rolen 3.00 8.00
TG Tom Glavine 3.00 8.00
TH Todd Helton 3.00 8.00
TI Tim Hudson 3.00 8.00
TR Travis Hafner 3.00 8.00
VA Jason Varitek 4.00 10.00
VG Vladimir Guerrero 4.00 10.00

VM Victor Martinez 3.00 8.00
VW Vernon Wells 3.00 8.00

2007 Artifacts Divisional Artifacts Gold

*GOLD: .3X TO .75X BASIC
RANDOMLY INSERTED IN RETAIL PACKS
GOLD NOT SERIAL NUMBERED
AP Albert Pujols 5.00 12.00
PM Pedro Martinez 2.50 6.00
TE Miguel Tejada 2.50 6.00

2007 Artifacts Divisional Artifacts Limited

*LIMITED: .4X TO 1X BASIC
RANDOM INSERTS IN PACKS
STATED PRINT RUN 130 SER.#'d SETS
AP Albert Pujols 6.00 15.00
PM Pedro Martinez 3.00 8.00
TE Miguel Tejada 3.00 8.00

2007 Artifacts Divisional Artifacts Autographs

RANDOM INSERTS IN PACKS
STATED PRINT RUN 25 SER.#'d SETS
NO PRICING DUE TO SCARCITY

2007 Artifacts MLB Apparel

RANDOM INSERTS IN PACKS
PRINT RUNS B/WN 25-199 COPIES PER
AD Adam Dunn 3.00 8.00
AJ Andruw Jones 4.00 10.00
AL Adam LaRoche 3.00 8.00
AP Albert Pujols 6.00 15.00
AR Aramis Ramirez 3.00 8.00
AT Garrett Atkins 3.00 8.00
BA Bobby Abreu 3.00 8.00
BC Bartolo Colon 3.00 8.00
BG Brian Giles 3.00 8.00
BI Craig Biggio 3.00 8.00
BO Jeremy Bonderman 3.00 8.00
BR Brian Roberts 3.00 8.00
BU B.J. Upton 3.00 8.00
BW Billy Wagner 3.00 8.00
BZ Barry Zito 3.00 8.00
CB Carlos Beltran 3.00 8.00
CC Carl Crawford 3.00 8.00
CH Cole Hamels 3.00 8.00
CJ Chipper Jones 4.00 10.00
CL Carlos Lee 3.00 8.00
CR Cal Ripken Jr. 10.00 25.00
CS Curt Schilling 3.00 8.00
CU Chase Utley 4.00 10.00
DJ Derek Jeter 8.00 20.00
DO David Ortiz 4.00 10.00
DU Dan Uggla 3.00 8.00
DW Dontrelle Willis 3.00 8.00
DY Jermaine Dye 3.00 8.00
EC Eric Chavez 3.00 8.00
ES Johnny Estrada 3.00 8.00
FG Freddy Garcia 3.00 8.00
FH Felix Hernandez 3.00 8.00
FL Francisco Liriano 3.00 8.00
FT Frank Thomas 4.00 10.00
GA Garret Anderson 3.00 8.00
GJ Geoff Jenkins 3.00 8.00
GM Greg Maddux 5.00 12.00
GR Khalil Greene 3.00 8.00
GS Grady Sizemore 3.00 8.00
HA Roy Halladay 3.00 8.00
HB Hank Blalock 3.00 8.00
HE Todd Helton 3.00 8.00
HO Trevor Hoffman 3.00 8.00
HR Hanley Ramirez 3.00 8.00
HU Torii Hunter 3.00 8.00
IR Ivan Rodriguez 3.00 8.00
JB Jason Bay 3.00 8.00
JC Jorge Cantu 3.00 8.00
JD J.D. Drew 3.00 8.00
JE Jim Edmonds 3.00 8.00
JF Jeff Francoeur 4.00 10.00
JG Jason Giambi 3.00 8.00
JJ Josh Johnson 3.00 8.00
JK Jeff Kent 3.00 8.00
JM Joe Mauer 3.00 8.00
JN Joe Nathan 3.00 8.00
JO Johnny Damon 3.00 8.00
JP Jake Peavy 3.00 8.00
JR Jimmy Rollins 3.00 8.00
JS Jason Schmidt 3.00 8.00
JT Jim Thome 3.00 8.00
JV Justin Verlander 4.00 10.00
JZ Joel Zumaya 3.00 8.00
KG Ken Griffey Jr. 6.00 15.00
LB Lance Berkman 3.00 8.00
LG Luis Gonzalez 3.00 8.00
MC Miguel Cabrera 4.00 10.00
MO Justin Morneau 3.00 8.00
MR Manny Ramirez 3.00 8.00
MT Mark Teixeira 3.00 8.00
MY Michael Young 3.00 8.00
OR Magglio Ordonez 3.00 8.00
PA Jonathan Papelbon 4.00 10.00
PB Pat Burrell 3.00 8.00
PE Jhonny Peralta 3.00 8.00
PF Prince Fielder 4.00 10.00
PM Pedro Martinez 3.00 8.00
PO Jorge Posada 3.00 8.00
RC Roger Clemens 6.00 15.00
RE Jose Reyes 4.00 10.00
RH Rich Harden 3.00 8.00
RI Mariano Rivera 4.00 10.00
RJ Randy Johnson 3.00 8.00
RO Roy Oswalt 3.00 8.00
RW Rickie Weeks 3.00 8.00
RZ Ryan Zimmerman 4.00 10.00
SA Johan Santana 3.00 8.00
SK Scott Kazmir 4.00 10.00
SM John Smoltz 3.00 8.00
SR Scott Rolen 3.00 8.00
TG Tom Glavine 3.00 8.00
TH Tim Hudson 3.00 8.00
TR Travis Hafner 3.00 8.00
VA Jason Varitek 4.00 10.00
VG Vladimir Guerrero 4.00 10.00
VM Victor Martinez 3.00 8.00
VW Vernon Wells 3.00 8.00

2007 Artifacts MLB Apparel Gold

*GOLD: .3X TO .75X BASIC
RANDOM INSERTS IN RETAIL PACKS
GOLD NOT SERIAL NUMBERED
AB Adrian Beltre 2.50 6.00
BE Josh Beckett SP

2007 Artifacts MLB Apparel Limited

*LIMITED: .4X TO 1X BASIC
RANDOM INSERTS IN PACKS
PRINT RUNS B/WN 75-130 COPIES PER
AB Adrian Beltre 3.00 8.00
MT Miguel Tejada 3.00 8.00

2007 Artifacts MLB Apparel Rare Autographs

RANDOM INSERTS IN PACKS
STATED PRINT RUN 1 SER.#'d SET
NO PRICING DUE TO SCARCITY

2007 Artifacts MLB Apparel Autographs

RANDOM INSERTS IN PACKS
STATED PRINT RUN 25 SER.#'d SETS
NO PRICING DUE TO SCARCITY

1934-36 Batter-Up

The 1934-36 Batter-Up set, issued by National Chicle, contains 192 blank-backed die-cut cards. Numbers 1 to 80 are approximately 2 3/8" by 3 1/4" in size while 81 to 192 are 2 3/8" by 3". The latter are more difficult to find than the former. The pictures come in basic black and white or in tints of blue, brown, green, purple, red, or sepia. There are three combination cards (each featuring two players per card) in the high series (98, 111, and 115). Cards with the die-cut backing removed are graded fair at best.

COMPLETE SET (192) 10000.00 20000.00
COMMON CARD (1-80) 25.00 50.00
COMMON CARD (81-192) 50.00 100.00
WRAP.(1-CENT, CATCHER) 150.00 200.00
WRAP.(1-CENT, BAT) 500.00 600.00
1 Wally Berger 60.00 120.00
2 Ed Brandt 25.00 50.00
3 Al Lopez XRC 60.00 120.00
4 Dick Bartell 30.00 60.00
5 Carl Hubbell 75.00 150.00
6 Bill Terry 100.00 175.00
7 Pepper Martin 40.00 80.00
8 Jim Bottomley 60.00 120.00
9 Tommy Bridges 30.00 60.00
10 Rick Ferrell 60.00 120.00
11 Ray Benge 25.00 50.00
12 Wes Ferrell 30.00 60.00
13 Chalmer Cissell 25.00 50.00
14 Pie Traynor 75.00 150.00
15 Leroy Mahaffey 25.00 50.00
16 Chick Hafey XRC 60.00 120.00
17 Lloyd Waner 60.00 120.00
18 Jack Burns 25.00 50.00
19 Buddy Myer 30.00 60.00
20 Bob Johnson XRC 30.00 60.00
21 Arky Vaughan 60.00 120.00
22 Red Rolfe XRC 30.00 60.00
23 Lefty Gomez 100.00 175.00
24 Earl Averill 75.00 150.00
25 Mickey Cochrane 100.00 175.00
26 Van Lingle Mungo XRC 40.00 80.00
27 Mel Ott 150.00 250.00
28 Jimmie Foxx 200.00 300.00
29 Jimmy Dykes 30.00 60.00
30 Bill Dickey 150.00 250.00
31 Lefty Grove 150.00 250.00
32 Joe Cronin 100.00 175.00
33 Frankie Frisch 75.00 150.00
34 Al Simmons 75.00 150.00
35 Rogers Hornsby 200.00 300.00
36 Ted Lyons 60.00 120.00
37 Rabbit Maranville 60.00 120.00
38 Jimmy Wilson 30.00 60.00
39 Willie Kamm 25.00 50.00
40 Bill Hallahan 25.00 50.00
41 Gus Suhr 25.00 50.00
42 Charley Gehringer 75.00 150.00
43 Joe Heving XRC 25.00 50.00
44 Adam Comorosky 25.00 50.00
45 Tony Lazzeri 125.00 200.00
46 Sam Leslie XRC 25.00 50.00
47 Bob Smith 25.00 50.00
48 Willis Hudlin 25.00 50.00
49 Carl Reynolds 25.00 50.00
50 Fred Schulte 25.00 50.00
51 Cookie Lavagetto XRC 40.00 80.00
52 Hal Schumacher 30.00 60.00
53 Roger Cramer XRC 30.00 60.00
54 Sylvester Johnson XRC 25.00 50.00
55 Ollie Bejma XRC 25.00 50.00
56 Sam Byrd 25.00 50.00
57 Hank Greenberg XRC 200.00 300.00
58 Bill Knickerbocker XRC 25.00 50.00
59 Bill Urbanski 25.00 50.00
60 Eddie Morgan 25.00 50.00
61 Rabbit McNair XRC 25.00 50.00
62 Ben Chapman 30.00 60.00
63 Roy Johnson 25.00 50.00
64 Dizzy Dean 300.00 450.00
65 Zeke Bonura XRC 25.00 50.00
66 Fred Marberry 25.00 50.00
67 Gus Mancuso 25.00 50.00
68 Joe Vosmik XRC 25.00 50.00
69 Earl Grace RC 25.00 50.00
70 Tony Piet 25.00 50.00
71 Rollie Hemsley XRC 25.00 50.00
72 Fred Fitzsimmons 30.00 60.00
73 Hack Wilson 100.00 175.00
74 Chick Fullis XRC 25.00 50.00
75 Fred Frankhouse 25.00 50.00
76 Ethan Allen 25.00 50.00
77 Heinie Manush 60.00 120.00
78 Rip Collins XRC 25.00 50.00
79 Tony Cuccinello 25.00 50.00
80 Joe Kuhel 25.00 50.00
81 Tommy Bridges 60.00 120.00
82 Clint Brown XRC 50.00 100.00
83 Albert Blanche XRC 50.00 100.00
84 Boze Berger XRC 50.00 100.00
85 Goose Goslin 125.00 200.00
86 Lefty Gomez 150.00 250.00
87 Joe Glenn XRC 50.00 100.00
88 Cy Blanton XRC 50.00 100.00
89 Tom Carey XRC 50.00 100.00
90 Ralph Birkofer XRC 50.00 100.00
91 Fred Gabler XRC 50.00 100.00
92 Dick Coffman 50.00 100.00
93 Ollie Bejma XRC 50.00 100.00
94 Leroy Parmelee 50.00 100.00
95 Carl Reynolds 50.00 100.00
96 Ben Cantwell 50.00 100.00
97 Curtis Davis XRC 50.00 100.00
98 Earl Webb XRC 75.00 150.00
Wally Moses XRC
99 Ray Benge 50.00 100.00
100 Pie Traynor 150.00 250.00
101 Phil Cavarretta XRC 60.00 120.00
102 Pep Young XRC 50.00 100.00
103 Willis Hudlin 50.00 100.00
104 Mickey Haslin XRC 50.00 100.00
105 Ossie Bluege 60.00 120.00
106 Paul Andrews XRC 50.00 100.00
107 Ed Brandt 50.00 100.00
108 Don Taylor XRC 50.00 100.00
109 Thornton Lee XRC 60.00 120.00
110 Hal Schumacher 60.00 120.00
111 Frank Hayes XRC 75.00 150.00
Ted Lyons
112 Odell Hale XRC 50.00 100.00
113 Earl Averill 125.00 200.00
114 Italo Chelini XRC 50.00 100.00
115 Ivy Andrews 75.00 150.00
Jim Bottomley
116 Bill Walker 50.00 100.00
117 Bill Dickey 250.00 350.00
118 Gerald Walker XRC 50.00 100.00
119 Ted Lyons 125.00 200.00
120 Eldon Auker XRC 50.00 100.00
121 Bill Hallahan 60.00 120.00
122 Fred Lindstrom 125.00 200.00
123 Oral Hildebrand XRC 50.00 100.00
124 Luke Appling XRC 150.00 250.00
125 Pepper Martin 60.00 120.00
126 Rick Ferrell 125.00 200.00
127 Ival Goodman XRC 50.00 100.00
128 Joe Kuhel 50.00 100.00
129 Ernie Lombardi XRC 125.00 200.00
130 Charley Gehringer 150.00 250.00
131 Van Lingle Mungo XRC 60.00 120.00
132 Larry French XRC 50.00 100.00
133 Buddy Myer 60.00 120.00
134 Mel Harder XRC 60.00 120.00
135 Augie Galan XRC 50.00 100.00
136 Gabby Hartnett 125.00 200.00
137 Stan Hack XRC 60.00 120.00
138 Billy Herman 125.00 200.00
139 Bill Jurges 50.00 100.00
140 Bill Lee XRC 60.00 120.00
141 Zeke Bonura XRC 50.00 100.00
142 Tony Piet 50.00 100.00
143 Paul Dean XRC 60.00 120.00
144 Jimmie Foxx 300.00 450.00
145 Joe Medwick XRC 150.00 250.00
146 Rip Collins XRC 50.00 100.00
147 Mel Almada XRC 50.00 100.00
148 Allan Cooke XRC 50.00 100.00
149 Moe Berg 300.00 450.00
150 Dolph Camilli XRC 60.00 120.00
151 Oscar Melillo XRC 50.00 100.00
152 Bruce Campbell XRC 50.00 100.00
153 Lefty Grove 250.00 350.00
154 Johnny Murphy XRC 60.00 120.00
155 Luke Sewell 60.00 120.00
156 Leo Durocher 200.00 300.00
157 Lloyd Waner 125.00 200.00
158 Guy Bush 50.00 100.00
159 Jimmy Dykes 60.00 120.00
160 Steve O'Neill XRC 60.00 120.00
161 General Crowder 60.00 120.00
162 Joe Cascarella XRC 60.00 120.00
163 Daniel Haley XRC 60.00 120.00
164 Gilly Campbell XRC 50.00 100.00
165 Ray Hayworth XRC 50.00 100.00
166 Frank Demaree 50.00 100.00
167 John Babich XRC 50.00 100.00
168 Marvin Owen XRC 50.00 100.00
169 Ralph Kress 50.00 100.00
170 Mule Haas 50.00 100.00
171 Frank Higgins XRC 60.00 120.00
172 Wally Berger 60.00 120.00
173 Frankie Frisch 200.00 300.00
174 Wes Ferrell 60.00 120.00
175 Pete Fox XRC 50.00 100.00
176 John Vergez 50.00 100.00
177 Billy Rogell 50.00 100.00
178 Don Brennan XRC 50.00 100.00
179 Jim Bottomley 125.00 200.00
180 Travis Jackson 125.00 200.00
181 Red Rolfe XRC 60.00 120.00
182 Frank Crosetti 75.00 150.00
183 Joe Cronin 125.00 200.00
184 Schoolboy Rowe XRC 60.00 120.00
185 Chuck Klein 150.00 250.00
186 Lon Warneke 60.00 120.00
187 Gus Suhr 50.00 100.00
188 Ben Chapman 60.00 120.00
189 Clint Brown XRC 50.00 100.00
190 Paul Derringer XRC 60.00 120.00
191 John Burns XRC 50.00 100.00
192 John Broaca XRC 75.00 150.00

1959 Bazooka

The 23 full-color, unnumbered cards comprising the 1959 Bazooka set were cut from the bottom of the boxes of gum marketed nationally that year by Topps. Bazooka was the brand name which Topps had been using to sell its one cent bubblegum; this year Topps decided to distribute 25 dual pieces of Bazooka gum in a box. The cards themselves measure 2 13/16" by 4 15/16". Only nine cards were originally issued; 14 more were added to the set at a later date (these are marked with SP in the checklist). The latter are less plentiful and hence more valuable than the original nine. All the cards are blank backed and the catalog designation is R414-15. The prices below are for the cards cut from the box; complete boxes intact would be worth about 50 percent more. Hank Aaron's card can be found with his name in either white or yellow print. The Aaron variations are equally valued.

COMPLETE SET (23) 4000.00 8000.00
COMMON CARD (1-23) 25.00 50.00
COMMON CARD SP 100.00 200.00
1 Hank Aaron White Name 250.00 500.00
1 Hank Aaron Yellow Name 250.00 500.00
2 Richie Ashburn SP 200.00 400.00
3 Ernie Banks SP 300.00 600.00
4 Ken Boyer SP 150.00 300.00
5 Orlando Cepeda 100.00 200.00
6 Bob Cerv SP 100.00 200.00
7 Rocky Colavito SP 200.00 400.00
8 Del Crandall 25.00 50.00
9 Jim Davenport 25.00 50.00
10 Don Drysdale SP 250.00 500.00
11 Nellie Fox SP 200.00 400.00
12 Jackie Jensen SP 150.00 300.00
13 Harvey Kuenn SP 125.00 250.00
14 Mickey Mantle 800.00 1600.00
15 Willie Mays 300.00 600.00
16 Bill Mazeroski 100.00 200.00
17 Roy McMillan 25.00 50.00
18 Billy Pierce SP 125.00 250.00
19 Roy Sievers SP 100.00 200.00
20 Duke Snider SP 400.00 800.00
21 Gus Triandos SP 100.00 200.00
22 Bob Turley 50.00 100.00
23 Vic Wertz SP 100.00 200.00

1960 Bazooka

In 1960, Topps introduced a 36-card baseball player set in three card panels on the bottom of Bazooka gum boxes. The cards measure 1 13/16" by 2 3/4" and the panels measure 2 3/4" by 5 1/2". The cards carried full color pictures and were numbered at the bottom underneath the team position. The checklist below contains prices for individual cards. Complete panels of three would have a 50 percent more than the sum of the indiviudal cards (prices) on the panel and complete boxes would command a premium of another 50 percent above those prices.

COMPLETE INDIV.SET 600.00 1200.00
1 Ernie Banks 20.00 50.00
2 Bud Daley 8.00 20.00
3 Wally Moon 8.00 20.00
4 Hank Aaron 50.00 100.00
5 Milt Pappas 8.00 20.00
6 Dick Stuart 8.00 20.00
7 Roberto Clemente 125.00 250.00
8 Yogi Berra 40.00 80.00
9 Ken Boyer 8.00 20.00
10 Orlando Cepeda 12.50 30.00
11 Gus Triandos 8.00 20.00
12 Frank Malzone 8.00 20.00
13 Willie Mays 60.00 120.00
14 Camilo Pascual 8.00 20.00
15 Bob Cerv 8.00 20.00
16 Vic Power 8.00 20.00
17 Larry Sherry 8.00 20.00
18 Al Kaline 20.00 50.00
19 Warren Spahn 20.00 50.00
20 Harmon Killebrew 20.00 50.00
21 Jackie Jensen 8.00 20.00
22 Luis Aparicio 12.50 30.00
23 Gil Hodges 12.50 30.00
24 Richie Ashburn 15.00 40.00
25 Nellie Fox 15.00 40.00
26 Robin Roberts 15.00 40.00
27 Joe Cunningham 8.00 20.00
28 Early Wynn 12.50 30.00
29 Frank Robinson 20.00 50.00
30 Rocky Colavito 12.50 30.00
31 Mickey Mantle 175.00 350.00
32 Glen Hobbie 8.00 20.00
33 Roy McMillan 8.00 20.00
34 Harvey Kuenn 8.00 20.00
35 Johnny Antonelli 8.00 20.00
36 Del Crandall 8.00 20.00

1961 Bazooka

The 36 card set issued by Bazooka in 1961 follows the format established in 1960; three full color, numbered cards to each panel found on a Bazooka gum box. The individual cards measure 1 13/16" by 2 3/4" whereas the panels measure 2 3/4" by 5 1/2". The cards of 1960 and 1961 are similar in design but are easily distinguished from one another by their numbers. Complete panels of three would have a value of 40 percent more than the sum of the individual cards (prices) on the panel and complete boxes would command a premium of another 40 percent above those prices.

COMPLETE INDIV. SET 750.00 1500.00
1 Art Mahaffey 8.00 20.00
2 Mickey Mantle 300.00 600.00
3 Ron Santo 10.00 25.00
4 Bud Daley 8.00 20.00
5 Roger Maris 50.00 100.00
6 Eddie Yost 8.00 20.00
7 Minnie Minoso 10.00 25.00
8 Dick Groat 8.00 20.00
9 Frank Malzone 8.00 20.00
10 Dick Donovan 8.00 20.00
11 Eddie Mathews 40.00 80.00
12 Jim Lemon 8.00 20.00
13 Chuck Estrada 8.00 20.00
14 Ken Boyer 10.00 25.00
15 Harvey Kuenn 8.00 20.00
16 Ernie Broglio 8.00 20.00
17 Rocky Colavito 20.00 50.00
18 Ted Kluszewski 20.00 50.00
19 Ernie Banks 40.00 80.00
20 Al Kaline 40.00 80.00
21 Ed Bailey 8.00 20.00
22 Jim Perry 8.00 20.00
23 Willie Mays 75.00 150.00
24 Bill Mazeroski 20.00 50.00
25 Gus Triandos 8.00 20.00
26 Don Drysdale 30.00 60.00
27 Frank Herrera 8.00 20.00
28 Earl Battey 8.00 20.00
29 Warren Spahn 40.00 80.00
30 Gene Woodling 8.00 20.00
31 Frank Robinson 40.00 80.00
32 Pete Runnels 8.00 20.00
33 Woodie Held 8.00 20.00
34 Norm Larker 8.00 20.00
35 Luis Aparicio 20.00 50.00
36 Bill Tuttle 8.00 20.00

1962 Bazooka

The 1962 Bazooka set of 45 full color, blank backed, unnumbered cards was issued in panels of three on Bazooka bubble gum. The individual cards measure 1 13/16" by 2 3/4" whereas the panels measure 2 3/4" by 5 1/2". The cards below are numbered by panel alphabetically based on the last name of the player pictured on the far left card of the panel. The cards with SP in the checklist below are more difficult to obtain. Complete panels would have a value of 40 percent more than the sum of the individual cards (prices) on the panel and complete boxes would command a premium of another 40 percent above those prices.

COMPLETE INDIV. SET 1700.00 3400.00
COMMON CARD (1-45) 6.00 15.00
COMMON SP 100.00 200.00
1 Bob Allison SP 100.00 200.00
2 Eddie Mathews SP 250.00 500.00
3 Vada Pinson SP 125.00 250.00
4 Earl Battey 6.00 15.00
5 Warren Spahn 20.00 50.00
6 Lee Thomas 6.00 15.00
7 Orlando Cepeda 12.50 30.00
8 Woodie Held 6.00 15.00
9 Bob Aspromonte 6.00 15.00
10 Dick Howser 6.00 15.00
11 Roberto Clemente 125.00 250.00
12 Al Kaline 20.00 50.00
13 Joe Jay 6.00 15.00
14 Roger Maris 40.00 80.00
15 Frank Howard 8.00 20.00
16 Sandy Koufax 40.00 80.00
17 Jim Gentile 6.00 15.00
18 Johnny Callison 6.00 15.00
19 Jim Landis 6.00 15.00
20 Ken Boyer 8.00 20.00
21 Chuck Schilling 6.00 15.00
22 Art Mahaffey 6.00 15.00
23 Mickey Mantle 175.00 350.00
24 Dick Stuart 6.00 15.00
25 Ken McBride 6.00 15.00
26 Frank Robinson 20.00 50.00
27 Gil Hodges 15.00 40.00
28 Milt Pappas 6.00 15.00
29 Hank Aaron 50.00 100.00
30 Luis Aparicio 12.50 30.00
31 Johnny Romano SP 100.00 200.00
32 Ernie Banks SP 350.00 700.00
33 Norm Siebern SP 100.00 200.00
34 Ron Santo 10.00 25.00
35 Norm Cash 8.00 20.00
36 Jim Piersall 8.00 20.00
37 Don Schwall 6.00 15.00
38 Willie Mays 60.00 120.00
39 Norm Larker 6.00 15.00
40 Bill White 8.00 20.00
41 Whitey Ford 20.00 50.00
42 Rocky Colavito 12.50 30.00
43 Don Zimmer SP 50.00 100.00
44 Harmon Killebrew SP 350.00 700.00
45 Gene Woodling SP 100.00 200.00

1963 Bazooka

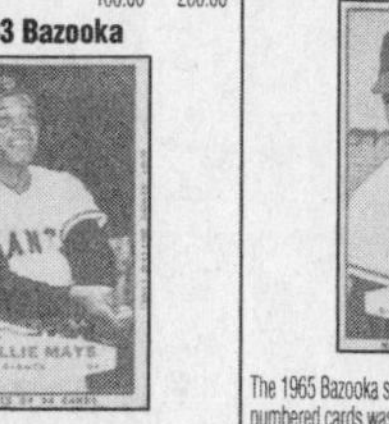

The 1963 Bazooka set of 36 full color, blank backed numbered cards was issued on Bazooka bubble gum boxes. This year marked a change in format from previous Bazooka issues with a smaller sized card being issued. The individual cards measure 1 9/16" by 2 1/2" whereas the panels measure 2 1/2" by 4 11/16". The card features a white strip with the player's name printed in black on the card. The number appears in the white border on the bottom of the card. Three cards were issued per panel. Complete panels of three would have a value of 15 percent more than the sum of the individual cards (prices) on the panel and complete boxes would command a premium of another 30 percent above those prices.

COMPLETE INDIV.SET 400.00 800.00
1 Mickey Mantle 125.00 250.00
2 Bob Rodgers 3.00 8.00
3 Ernie Banks 20.00 50.00
4 Norm Siebern 3.00 8.00
5 Warren Spahn 15.00 40.00
6 Bill Mazeroski 8.00 20.00
7 Harmon Killebrew 15.00 40.00
8 Dick Farrell 3.00 8.00
9 Hank Aaron 40.00 80.00
10 Dick Donovan 3.00 8.00
11 Jim Gentile 3.00 8.00
12 Willie Mays 40.00 80.00
13 Camilo Pascual 3.00 8.00
14 Roberto Clemente 50.00 100.00
15 Johnny Callison 3.00 8.00
16 Carl Yastrzemski 20.00 50.00
17 Don Drysdale 12.50 30.00
18 Johnny Romano 3.00 8.00
19 Al Jackson 3.00 8.00
20 Ralph Terry 3.00 8.00
21 Bill Monbouquette 3.00 8.00
22 Orlando Cepeda 8.00 20.00
23 Stan Musial 20.00 50.00
24 Floyd Robinson 3.00 8.00
25 Chuck Hinton 3.00 8.00
26 Bob Purkey 3.00 8.00
27 Ken Hubbs 4.00 10.00
28 Bill White 4.00 10.00
29 Ray Herbert 3.00 8.00
30 Brooks Robinson 20.00 50.00
31 Frank Robinson 20.00 50.00
32 Lee Thomas 3.00 8.00
33 Rocky Colavito 8.00 20.00
34 Al Kaline 20.00 50.00
35 Art Mahaffey 3.00 8.00
36 Tommy Davis 3.00 8.00

1964 Bazooka

The 1964 Bazooka set of 36 full color, blank backed, numbered cards were issued in panels of three on the backs of Bazooka bubble gum boxes. The individual cards measure 1 9/16" by 2 1/2" whereas the panels measure 2 1/2" by 4 11/16". Many players who were in the 1963 set have the same number in this set; however, the pictures are different. Complete panels of three would have a value of 15 percent more than the sum of the individual cards (prices) on the panel and complete boxes would command a premium of another 40 percent above those prices.

COMPLETE INDIV. SET 500.00 1000.00
1 Mickey Mantle 125.00 250.00
2 Dick Groat 3.00 8.00
3 Steve Barber 3.00 8.00
4 Ken McBride 3.00 8.00
5 Warren Spahn 15.00 40.00
6 Bob Friend 3.00 8.00
7 Harmon Killebrew 15.00 40.00
8 Dick Farrell 3.00 8.00
9 Hank Aaron 40.00 80.00
10 Rich Rollins 3.00 8.00
11 Jim Gentile 3.00 8.00
12 Willie Mays 40.00 80.00
13 Camilo Pascual 3.00 8.00
14 Roberto Clemente 60.00 120.00
15 Johnny Callison 3.00 8.00
16 Carl Yastrzemski 30.00 60.00
17 Billy Williams 8.00 20.00
18 Johnny Romano 3.00 8.00
19 Jim Maloney 3.00 8.00
20 Norm Cash 4.00 10.00
21 Willie McCovey 8.00 20.00
22 Jim Fregosi 3.00 8.00
23 George Altman 3.00 8.00
24 Floyd Robinson 3.00 8.00
25 Chuck Hinton 3.00 8.00
26 Ron Hunt 3.00 8.00
27 Gary Peters 3.00 8.00
28 Dick Ellsworth 3.00 8.00
29 Elston Howard 4.00 10.00
30 Brooks Robinson 20.00 50.00
31 Frank Robinson 20.00 50.00
32 Sandy Koufax 40.00 80.00
33 Rocky Colavito 8.00 20.00
34 Al Kaline 20.00 50.00
35 Ken Boyer 4.00 10.00
36 Tommy Davis 3.00 8.00

1965 Bazooka

The 1965 Bazooka set of 36 full color, blank backed, numbered cards was issued in panels of three on the backs of Bazooka bubble gum boxes. The individual cards measure 1 9/16" by 2 1/2" whereas the panels measure 2 1/2" by 4 11/16". As in the previous two years some of the players have the same numbers on their cards; however all pictures are different from the previous two years. Complete panels of three would have a value of 15 percent more than the sum of the individual cards (prices) on the panel and complete boxes would command a premium of another 40 percent above those prices.

COMPLETE INDIV. SET 400.00 800.00
1 Mickey Mantle 125.00 250.00
2 Larry Jackson 3.00 8.00
3 Chuck Hinton 3.00 8.00
4 Tony Oliva 6.00 15.00
5 Dean Chance 3.00 8.00
6 Jim O'Toole 3.00 8.00
7 Harmon Killebrew 12.50 30.00
8 Pete Ward 3.00 8.00
9 Hank Aaron 40.00 80.00
10 Dick Radatz 3.00 8.00
11 Boog Powell 4.00 10.00
12 Willie Mays 40.00 80.00
13 Bob Veale 3.00 8.00
14 Roberto Clemente 60.00 120.00
15 Johnny Callison 3.00 8.00
16 Joe Torre 6.00 15.00
17 Billy Williams 10.00 25.00
18 Bob Chance 3.00 8.00
19 Bob Aspromonte 3.00 8.00
20 Joe Christopher 3.00 8.00
21 Jim Bunning 8.00 20.00
22 Jim Fregosi 3.00 8.00
23 Bob Gibson 12.50 30.00
24 Juan Marichal 12.50 30.00
25 Dave Wickersham 3.00 8.00
26 Ron Hunt 3.00 8.00
27 Gary Peters 3.00 8.00
28 Ron Santo 6.00 15.00
29 Elston Howard 4.00 10.00
30 Brooks Robinson 15.00 40.00
31 Frank Robinson 15.00 40.00
32 Sandy Koufax 20.00 50.00
33 Rocky Colavito 8.00 20.00
34 Al Kaline 15.00 40.00
35 Ken Boyer 4.00 10.00
36 Tommy Davis 3.00 8.00

1966 Bazooka

The 1966 Bazooka set of 48 full color, blank backed, numbered cards was issued in panels of three on the backs of Bazooka bubble gum boxes. The individual cardsd measure 1 9/16" by 2 1/2" whereas the complete panels measure 2 1/2" by 4 11/16". The set is distinguishable from the previous years by mention of "48 card set" at the bottom of the card. Complete panels of three would have a value of 15 percent more than the sum of the individual cards (prices) on the panel and complete boxes would command a premium of another 40 percent above those prices.

COMPLETE INDIV. SET 500.00 1000.00
1 Sandy Koufax 20.00 50.00
2 Willie Horton 3.00 8.00
3 Frank Howard 4.00 10.00
4 Richie Allen 4.00 10.00
5 Mel Stottlemyre 4.00 10.00
6 Tony Conigliaro 5.00 12.00
7 Mickey Mantle 125.00 250.00
8 Leon Wagner 3.00 8.00
9 Ed Kranepool 3.00 8.00
10 Juan Marichal 10.00 25.00
11 Harmon Killebrew 10.00 25.00
12 Johnny Callison 3.00 8.00
13 Roy McMillan 3.00 8.00
14 Willie McCovey 10.00 25.00
15 Rocky Colavito 6.00 15.00
16 Willie Mays 40.00 80.00
17 Sam McDowell 3.00 8.00
18 Vern Law 3.00 8.00
19 Jim Fregosi 3.00 8.00
20 Ron Fairly 3.00 8.00
21 Bob Gibson 10.00 25.00

22 Carl Yastrzemski	15.00	40.00
23 Bill White	4.00	10.00
24 Bob Aspromonte	3.00	8.00
25 Dean Chance	3.00	8.00
26 Roberto Clemente	60.00	120.00
27 Tony Cloninger	3.00	8.00
28 Curt Blefary	3.00	8.00
29 Milt Pappas	3.00	8.00
30 Hank Aaron	40.00	80.00
31 Jim Bunning	6.00	15.00
32 Frank Robinson	12.50	30.00
33 Bill Skowron	4.00	10.00
34 Brooks Robinson	12.50	30.00
35 Jim Wynn	3.00	8.00
36 Joe Torre	5.00	12.00
37 Jim Grant	3.00	8.00
38 Pete Rose	30.00	60.00
39 Ron Santo	5.00	12.00
40 Tom Tresh	4.00	10.00
41 Tony Oliva	5.00	12.00
42 Don Drysdale	10.00	25.00
43 Pete Richert	3.00	8.00
44 Bert Campaneris	3.00	8.00
45 Jim Maloney	3.00	8.00
46 Al Kaline	12.50	30.00
47 Eddie Fisher	3.00	8.00
48 Billy Williams	8.00	20.00

1967 Bazooka

The 1967 Bazooka set of 48 full color, blank backed, numbered cards was issued in panels of three on the backs of Bazooka bubble gum boxes. The individual cards measure 1 9/16" by 2 1/2" whereas the complete panels measure 2 1/2" by 4 11/16". This set is virtually identical to the 1966 set with the exception of ten new cards as replacements for ten 1966 cards. The remaining 38 cards are identical in pose and number. The replacement cards are listed in the checklist below with an asterisk. Complete panels of three would have a value of 15 percent more than the sum of the individual cards (prices) on the panel and complete boxes would command a premium of another 40 percent above those prices.

COMPLETE INDIV. SET	500.00	1000.00
1 Rick Reichardt	3.00	8.00
2 Tommie Agee	3.00	8.00
3 Frank Howard	4.00	10.00
4 Richie Allen	4.00	10.00
5 Mel Stottlemyre	4.00	10.00
6 Tony Conigliaro	5.00	12.00
7 Mickey Mantle	125.00	250.00
8 Leon Wagner	3.00	8.00
9 Gary Peters	3.00	8.00
10 Juan Marichal	10.00	25.00
11 Harmon Killebrew	10.00	25.00
12 Johnny Callison	3.00	8.00
13 Denny McLain	5.00	12.00
14 Willie McCovey	10.00	25.00
15 Rocky Colavito	6.00	15.00
16 Willie Mays	40.00	80.00
17 Sam McDowell	3.00	8.00
18 Jim Kaat	5.00	12.00
19 Jim Fregosi	3.00	8.00
20 Ron Fairly	3.00	8.00
21 Bob Gibson	10.00	25.00
22 Carl Yastrzemski	15.00	40.00
23 Bill White	4.00	10.00
24 Bob Aspromonte	3.00	8.00
25 Dean Chance	3.00	8.00
26 Roberto Clemente	60.00	120.00
27 Tony Cloninger	3.00	8.00
28 Curt Blefary	3.00	8.00
29 Phil Regan	3.00	8.00
30 Hank Aaron	40.00	80.00
31 Jim Bunning	6.00	15.00
32 Frank Robinson	12.50	30.00
33 Ken Boyer	4.00	10.00
34 Brooks Robinson	12.50	30.00
35 Jim Wynn	3.00	8.00
36 Joe Torre	5.00	12.00
37 Tommy Davis	3.00	8.00
38 Pete Rose	30.00	60.00
39 Ron Santo	5.00	12.00
40 Tom Tresh	4.00	10.00
41 Tony Oliva	5.00	12.00
42 Don Drysdale	10.00	25.00
43 Pete Richert	3.00	8.00
44 Bert Campaneris	3.00	8.00
45 Jim Maloney	3.00	8.00
46 Al Kaline	12.50	30.00
47 Matty Alou	3.00	8.00
48 Billy Williams	8.00	20.00

2003 Bazooka

This 280 card set was released in March, 2003. The set was isssued in eight card packs that had an $2 SRP. These packs came 24 packs to a box and 10 boxes to a case. The Bazooka Joe card (number 7) was issued in a basic version as well as feauturing a logo of all the major league teams. In addition, 20 cards from the set featured a fascimile signature of the featured player as well as a colorized Bazooka logo. These regular and special logo cards of those player were printed to the same quantity.

COMP.SET w/LOGO's (330)	40.00	80.00
COMPLETE SET (310)	30.00	60.00
COMP.SET w/o JOE's (280)	25.00	50.00
COMMON CARD (1-280)	.15	.40
COMMON ROOKIE	.15	.40
COMMON LOGO	.15	.40
1 Luis Castillo	.15	.40
2 Randy Winn	.15	.40
3 Orlando Hudson	.15	.40
3A Orlando Hudson Logo	.15	.40
4 Fernando Vina	.15	.40
5 Pat Burrell	.15	.40
6 Brad Wilkerson	.15	.40
7 Bazooka Joe	.15	.40
7AN Bazooka Joe Angels	.15	.40
7AS Bazooka Joe A's	.15	.40
7AT Bazooka Joe Astros	.15	.40
7BL Bazooka Joe Blue Jays	.15	.40
7BR Bazooka Joe Braves	.15	.40
7BW Bazooka Joe Brewers	.15	.40
7CA Bazooka Joe Cardinals	.15	.40
7CU Bazooka Joe Cubs	.15	.40
7DE Bazooka Joe Devil Rays	.15	.40
7DI Bazooka Joe Diamondbacks	.15	.40
7DO Bazooka Joe Dodgers	.15	.40
7EX Bazooka Joe Expos	.15	.40
7GI Bazooka Joe Giants	.15	.40
7IN Bazooka Joe Indians	.15	.40
7MA Bazooka Joe Mariners	.15	.40
7ME Bazooka Joe Mets	.15	.40
7MR Bazooka Joe Marlins	.15	.40
7OR Bazooka Joe Orioles	.15	.40
7PA Bazooka Joe Padres	.15	.40
7PH Bazooka Joe Phillies	.15	.40
7PI Bazooka Joe Pirates	.15	.40
7RA Bazooka Joe Rangers	.15	.40
7RC Bazooka Joe Rockies	.15	.40
7RD Bazooka Joe Reds	.15	.40
7RS Bazooka Joe Red Sox	.15	.40
7RY Bazooka Joe Royals	.15	.40
7TI Bazooka Joe Tigers	.15	.40
7TW Bazooka Joe Twins	.15	.40
7WS Bazooka Joe White Sox	.15	.40
7YA Bazooka Joe Yankees	.15	.40
8 Javy Lopez	.15	.40
9 Juan Pierre	.15	.40
10 Hideo Nomo	.40	1.00
11 Barry Larkin	.25	.60
12 Alfonso Soriano	.15	.40
12A Alfonso Soriano Logo	.15	.40
13 Rodrigo Lopez	.15	.40
14 Mark Ellis	.15	.40
15 Tim Salmon	.25	.60
16 Garret Anderson	.15	.40
16A Garret Anderson Logo	.15	.40
17 Aaron Boone	.15	.40
18 Jason Kendall	.15	.40
19 Hee Seop Choi	.15	.40
20 Jorge Posada	.25	.60
21 Sammy Sosa	.40	1.00
22 Mark Prior	.25	.60
22A Mark Prior Logo	.25	.60
23 Mark Teixeira	.25	.60
24 Manny Ramirez	.25	.60
25 Jim Thome	.25	.60
26 A.J. Pierzynski	.15	.40
27 Scott Rolen	.25	.60
28 Austin Kearns	.15	.40
29 Bret Boone	.15	.40
30 Ken Griffey Jr.	.60	1.50
31 Greg Maddux	.60	1.50
32 Derek Lowe	.15	.40
33 David Wells	.15	.40
34 A.J. Burnett	.15	.40
35 Randall Simon	.15	.40
36 Nick Johnson	.15	.40
37 Junior Spivey	.15	.40
38 Eric Gagne	.15	.40
39 Darin Erstad	.15	.40
40 Marty Cordova	.15	.40
41 Brett Myers	.15	.40
42 Mo Vaughn	.15	.40
43 Randy Wolf	.15	.40
44 Vicente Padilla	.15	.40
45 Elmer Dessens	.15	.40
46 Jason Simontacchi	.15	.40
47 John Mabry	.15	.40
48 Torii Hunter	.15	.40
48A Torii Hunter Logo	.15	.40
49 Lyle Overbay	.15	.40
50 Kirk Saarloos	.15	.40
51 Bernie Williams	.25	.60
52 Wade Miller	.15	.40
53 Bobby Abreu	.15	.40
54 Wilson Betemit	.15	.40
55 Edwin Almonte	.15	.40
56 Jarrod Washburn	.15	.40
57 Drew Henson	.15	.40
58 Tony Batista	.15	.40
59 Juan Rivera	.15	.40
60 Larry Walker	.15	.40
61 Brandon Phillips	.15	.40
62 Franklyn German	.15	.40
63 Victor Martinez	.25	.60
63A Victor Martinez Logo	.25	.60
64 Moises Alou	.15	.40
65 Nomar Garciaparra	.60	1.50
66 Willie Harris	.15	.40
67 Sean Casey	.15	.40
68 Omar Vizquel	.25	.60
69 Robert Fick	.15	.40
70 Curt Schilling	.15	.40
70A Curt Schilling Logo	.15	.40
71 Adam Kennedy	.15	.40
72 Scott Hairston	.15	.40
73 Jimmy Journell	.15	.40
74 Rafael Furcal	.15	.40
75 Barry Zito	.15	.40
76 Ed Rogers	.15	.40
77 Cliff Floyd	.15	.40
78 Matt Clement	.15	.40
79 Mike Lowell	.15	.40
80 Randy Johnson	.40	1.00
81 Craig Biggio	.25	.60
82 Carlos Beltran	.15	.40
83 Paul Lo Duca	.15	.40
84 Jose Vidro	.15	.40
85 Gary Sheffield	.15	.40
86 Jacque Jones	.15	.40
87 Corey Hart	.15	.40
88 Roberto Alomar	.25	.60
89 Robin Ventura	.15	.40
90 Pedro Martinez	.25	.60
91 Scott Hatteberg	.15	.40
92 Marlon Byrd	.15	.40
93 Pokey Reese	.15	.40
94 Sean Burroughs	.15	.40
95 Magglio Ordonez	.15	.40
96 Mariano Rivera	.40	1.00
97 John Olerud	.15	.40
98 Edgar Renteria	.15	.40
99 Ben Grieve	.15	.40
100 Barry Bonds	1.00	2.50
100A Barry Bonds Logo	1.00	2.50
101 Ivan Rodriguez	.25	.60
102 Josh Phelps	.15	.40
103 Nobuaki Yoshida RC	.20	.50
103A Nobuaki Yoshida Logo	.20	.50
104 Roy Halladay	.15	.40
105 Mark Buehrle	.15	.40
106 Chan Ho Park	.15	.40
107 Joe Kennedy	.15	.40
108 Shin-Soo Choo	.15	.40
108A Shin-Soo Choo Logo	.15	.40
109 Ryan Jensen	.15	.40
110 Todd Helton	.25	.60
111 Chris Duncan RC	1.25	3.00
112 Taggert Bozied	.15	.40
113 Sean Burnett	.15	.40
114 Mike Lieberthal	.15	.40
115 Josh Beckett	.15	.40
116 Andy Pettitte	.25	.60
117 Jose Reyes	.15	.40
117A Jose Reyes Logo	.15	.40
118 Bartolo Colon	.15	.40
119 Justin Morneau	.15	.40
120 Lance Berkman	.15	.40
121 Mike Wodnicki RC	.20	.50
122 Craig Brazell RC	.20	.50
122A Craig Brazell Logo	.20	.50
123 Troy Glaus	.15	.40
124 John Smoltz	.25	.60
125 Mike Sweeney	.15	.40
126 Jay Gibbons	.15	.40
127 Kerry Wood	.15	.40
128 Ellis Burks	.15	.40
129 Carlos Pena	.15	.40
130 Shawn Green	.15	.40
131 Jason Stokes	.15	.40
131A Jason Stokes Logo	.15	.40
132 Raul Ibanez	.15	.40
133 Francisco Rodriguez	.15	.40
133A Francisco Rodriguez Logo	.15	.40
134 Adrian Beltre	.15	.40
135 Richie Sexson	.15	.40
136 Paul Byrd	.15	.40
137 Bobby Kielty	.15	.40
138 Dewon Brazelton	.15	.40
139 Jeremy Griffiths RC	.20	.50
140 Vladimir Guerrero	.40	1.00
140A Vladimir Guerrero Logo	.40	1.00
141 Jake Peavy	.15	.40
142 Bryan Bullington RC	.20	.50
143 Orlando Cabrera	.15	.40
144 Scott Erickson	.15	.40
145 Doug Mientkiewicz	.15	.40
146 Derrek Lee	.25	.60
147 Daryl Clark RC	.20	.50
148 Trevor Hoffman	.15	.40
149 Gabe Gross	.15	.40
150 Roger Clemens	.75	2.00
151 Khalil Greene	.40	1.00
151A Khalil Greene Logo	.40	1.00
152 Cory Doyne RC	.20	.50
153 Brandon Roberson RC	.20	.50
154 Josh Fogg	.15	.40
155 Eric Chavez	.15	.40
156 Kris Benson	.15	.40
157 Billy Koch	.15	.40
158 Jermaine Dye	.15	.40
159 Kip Bouknight RC	.30	.75
160 Brian Giles	.15	.40
161 Justin Huber	.15	.40
162 Mike Restovich	.15	.40
163 Brandon Webb RC	1.00	2.50
164 Odalis Perez	.15	.40
165 Phil Nevin	.15	.40
166 Dontrelle Willis	.40	1.00
167 Aaron Heilman	.15	.40
168 Dustin Moseley RC	.20	.50
169 Rylan Reed RC	.20	.50
170 Miguel Tejada	.15	.40
171 Nic Jackson	.15	.40
172 Anthony Webster RC	.30	.75
173 Jorge Julio	.15	.40
174 Kevin Millwood	.15	.40
175 Brian Jordan	.15	.40
176 Terry Tiffee RC	.20	.50
177 Dallas McPherson	.15	.40
178 Freddy Garcia	.15	.40
179 Jaime Moyer	.15	.40
180 Rafael Palmeiro	.25	.60
181 Mike O'Keefe RC	.20	.50
182 Kevin Youkilis RC	.60	1.50
183 Kip Wells	.15	.40
184 Joe Mauer	.40	1.00
185 Edgar Martinez	.25	.60
186 Jamie Bubela RC	.20	.50
187 Jose Hernandez	.15	.40
188 Josh Hamilton	.30	.75
189 Matt Diaz RC	.30	.75
190 Chipper Jones	.40	1.00
191 Kevin Mench	.15	.40
192 Joey Gomes RC	.20	.50
193 Shannon Stewart	.15	.40
194 David Eckstein	.15	.40
195 Mike Piazza	.60	1.50
196 Damian Moss	.15	.40
197 Mike Fontenot	.15	.40
198 Shea Hillenbrand	.15	.40
199 Evel Bastida-Martinez RC	.20	.50
200 Jason Giambi	.15	.40
201 Aron Weston RC	.20	.50
202 Frank Thomas	.40	1.00
203 Carlos Lee	.15	.40
204 C.C. Sabathia	.15	.40
205 Jim Edmonds	.15	.40
206 Jemel Spearman RC	.20	.50
207 Jason Jennings	.15	.40
208 Jeremy Bonderman RC	1.00	2.50
209 Preston Wilson	.15	.40
210 Eric Hinske	.15	.40
210A Eric Hinske Logo	.15	.40
211 Will Smith	.15	.40
212 Matthew Hagen RC	.20	.50
213 Joe Randa	.15	.40
214 James Loney	.20	.50
215 Carlos Delgado	.15	.40
216 Chris Kroski RC	.20	.50
217 Cristian Guzman	.15	.40
218 Tomo Ohka	.15	.40
219 Al Leiter	.15	.40
220 Adam Dunn	.15	.40
221 Raul Mondesi	.15	.40
222 Donald Hood RC	.30	.75
223 Mark Mulder	.15	.40
224 Mike Williams	.15	.40
225 Ryan Klesko	.15	.40
226 Rich Aurilia	.15	.40
227 Chris Snelling	.15	.40
228 Gary Schneidmiller RC	.20	.50
229 Ichiro Suzuki	.75	2.00
229A Ichiro Suzuki Logo	.75	2.00
230 Luis Gonzalez	.15	.40
231 Rocco Baldelli	.15	.40
232 Callix Crabbe RC	.30	.75
233 Adrian Gonzalez	.15	.40
234 Corey Koskie	.15	.40
235 Tom Glavine	.25	.60
236 Kevin Beavers RC	.20	.50
237 Frank Catalanotto	.15	.40
238 Kevin Cash	.15	.40
239 Nick Trzesniak RC	.20	.50
240 Paul Konerko	.15	.40
241 Jose Cruz Jr.	.15	.40
242 Hank Blalock	.15	.40
243 J.D. Drew	.15	.40
244 Kazuhiro Sasaki	.15	.40
245 Jeff Bagwell	.25	.60
246 Jason Schmidt	.15	.40
247 Xavier Nady	.15	.40
248 Aramis Ramirez	.15	.40
249 Jimmy Rollins	.15	.40
250 Alex Rodriguez	.60	1.50
250A Alex Rodriguez Logo	.60	1.50
251 Terrence Long	.15	.40
252 Derek Jeter	1.00	2.50
253 Edgardo Alfonzo	.15	.40
254 Toby Hall	.15	.40
255 Kazuhisa Ishii	.15	.40
256 Brad Nelson	.15	.40
257 Kevin Brown	.15	.40
258 Roy Oswalt	.15	.40
259 Mike Cameron	.15	.40
260 Juan Gonzalez	.15	.40
261 Dmitri Young	.15	.40
262 Jose Jimenez	.15	.40
263 Wily Mo Pena	.15	.40
264 Joe Borchard	.15	.40
265 Mike Mussina	.25	.60
266 Fred McGriff	.25	.60
267 Johnny Damon	.25	.60
268 Joel Pineiro	.15	.40
269 Andruw Jones	.25	.60
270 Tim Hudson	.15	.40
271 Chad Tracy	.15	.40
272 Brad Fullmer	.15	.40
273 Boof Bonser	.15	.40
274 Clint Nageotte	.15	.40
275 Jeff Kent	.15	.40
276 Tino Martinez	.25	.60
277 Matt Morris	.15	.40
278 Jonny Gomes	.25	.60
279 Benito Santiago	.15	.40
280 Albert Pujols	.75	2.00
280A Albert Pujols Logo	.75	2.00

2003 Bazooka Minis

Issued at a stated rate of one per pack, this is a complete parallel of the Bazooka set. All the cards were issued in this parallel set including all 31 Bazooka Joe cards as well as the 20 logo variation cards. These cards measure approximately 2 1/4" by 3 1/8"/

*MINIS: .75X TO 2X BASIC
*MINIS JOE'S: .75X TO 2X BASIC JOE'S
*MINIS LOGO'S: .75X TO 2X BASIC LOGO'S
*MINI'S RC'S: .75X TO 2X BASIC RC'S

2003 Bazooka Silver

Issued at a stated rate of almost one per pack, this is a complete parallel to the Bazooka set. These cards can be identified by their silver borders. Again, all the Bazooka Joe varieties as well as the logo cards were issued in a silver version.

*SILVER: .75X TO 2X BASIC
*SILVER JOE'S: .75X TO 2X BASIC JOE'S
*SILVER LOGO'S: .75X TO 2X BASIC LOGO'S
*SILVER RC'S: .75X TO 2X BASIC

2003 Bazooka 4 on 1 Sticker

Inserted at a stated rate of one in four hobby and one in 6 retail packs, these 55 sticker cards feature four players on the front

1 Mark Prior	.50	1.25
Roy Oswalt		
Jarrod Washburn		
Barry Zito		
2 Troy Glaus	.40	1.00
Shea Hillenbrand		
Eric Chavez		
Eric Hinske		
3 Orlando Hudson	.50	1.25
Alfonso Soriano		
Roberto Alomar		
Jose Vidro		
4 Nomar Garciaparra	2.00	5.00
Derek Jeter		
Miguel Tejada		
Alex Rodriguez		
5 Jason Giambi	.50	1.25
Jim Thome		
Todd Helton		
Rafael Palmeiro		
6 Mike Williams	.50	1.25
Trevor Hoffman		
Billy Koch		
John Smoltz		
7 Jorge Posada	1.25	3.00
Mike Piazza		
A.J. Pierzynski		
Ivan Rodriguez		
8 Vladimir Guerrero	.75	2.00
Jim Edmonds		
Manny Ramirez		
Brad Wilkerson		
9 Shawn Green	.75	2.00
Sammy Sosa		
Torri Hunter		
Larry Walker		
10 Bernie Williams	1.50	4.00
Ken Griffey Jr.		
Ichiro Suzuki		
Adam Dunn		
11 John Olerud	.40	1.00
Mike Lieberthal		
Terrence Long		
Drew Henson		
12 Edgar Martinez	.50	1.25
Bret Boone		
Mo Vaughn		
Robert Fick		
13 Randy Johnson	1.50	4.00
Roger Clemens		
Pedro Martinez		
Greg Maddux		
14 Curt Schilling	.75	2.00
Tim Hudson		
Tom Glavine		
Kerry Wood		
15 Paul Konerko	.50	1.25
Mike Sweeney		
Cristian Guzman		
Scott Rolen		
16 Josh Phelps	.40	1.00
Brandon Phillips		
Hee Seop Choi		
Hank Blalock		
17 Benito Santiago	.50	1.25
Barry Larkin		
Gary Sheffield		
Carlos Delgado		
18 Juan Rivera	.40	1.00
Jose Reyes		
Sean Burroughs		
Carlos Pena		
19 Tony Batista	.50	1.25
Tim Salmon		
Jeff Bagwell		
Raul Ibanez		
20 Edgardo Alfonzo	.40	1.00
Nic Jackson		
Luis Castillo		
David Eckstein		
21 David Wells	.40	1.00
Ryan Klesko		
Phil Nevin		
Jeff Kent		
22 Derek Lowe	.40	1.00
Vicente Padilla		
Kevin Millwood		
Joel Pineiro		
23 Fernando Vina	.40	1.00
Darin Erstad		
Jimmy Rollins		
Doug Mientkiewicz		
24 Joe Mauer	.75	2.00
Justin Huber		
Jason Stokes		
Chad Tracy		
25 Austin Kearns	.40	1.00
Junior Spivey		
Brett Myers		
Victor Martinez		
26 Khalil Greene	1.00	2.50
Gabe Gross		
Kevin Cash		
James Loney		
27 Albert Pujols	1.50	4.00
Mark Buehrle		
Chipper Jones		
Lance Berkman		
28 Adam Kennedy	.50	1.25
Craig Biggio		
Johnny Damon		
Randy Winn		
29 Brian Giles	.40	1.00
J.D. Drew		
Marlon Byrd		
Joe Borchard		
30 Al Leiter	.50	1.25
Mike Mussina		
Bartolo Colon		
Freddy Garcia		
31 Jason Kendall	.40	1.00
Richie Sexson		
Mike Lowell		
Paul LoDuca		
32 Pat Burrell	.50	1.25
Garret Anderson		
Cliff Floyd		
Andruw Jones		
33 Xavier Nady	.40	1.00
Bobby Abreu		
Taggert Bozied		
Adrian Beltre		
34 Rocco Baldelli	.75	2.00
Dontrelle Willis		
Chris Snelling		
Mark Teixeira		
35 Willie Harris	.40	1.00
Nick Johnson		
Jason Jennings		
Kazuhisa Ishii		
36 Mark Mulder	.40	1.00
Sean Burnett		
Paul Byrd		
Josh Beckett		
37 Corey Koskie	.50	1.25
Aramis Ramirez		
Tino Martinez		
Moises Alou		
38 Jose Cruz Jr.	.40	1.00
Roy Halladay		
Dewon Brazelton		
Jonny Gomes		
39 Odalis Perez	.40	1.00
Kevin Brown		
Matt Clement		
Randy Wolf		
40 Eric Gagne	.40	1.00
Jose Jimenez		
Franklyn German		
Edwin Almonte		
41 Luis Gonzalez	.40	1.00
Shannon Stewart		
Brian Jordan		
Juan Gonzalez		
42 Toby Hall	.40	1.00
Joe Kennedy		
Javier Lopez		
Damian Moss		
43 Maggio Ordonez	.40	1.00
Carlos Lee		
Randall Simon		
Dmitri Young		
44 Sean Casey	.40	1.00
Aaron Boone		
Jacque Jones		
Michael Restovich		
45 Adrian Gonzalez	.75	2.00
Corey Hart		
Fred McGriff		
Frank Thomas		
46 C.C. Sabathia	.50	1.25
Omar Vizquel		
Andy Pettitte		
Robin Ventura		
47 Jason Schmidt	.40	1.00
Ellis Burks		
Joe Randa		
Kris Benson		
48 Mike Cameron	.40	1.00
Pokey Reese		
Jermaine Dye		
Preston Wilson		
49 Chan Ho Park	.75	2.00
Kazuhiro Sasaki		
Tomo Ohka		
Hideo Nomo		
50 Jason Simontacchi	.40	1.00
Kip Wells		
Matt Morris		
Rodrigo Lopez		
51 Dallas McPherson	3.00	8.00
Josh Hamilton		
Jeremy Bonderman		
Aaron Heilman		
52 Nobuaki Yoshida	2.00	5.00
Chris Duncan		
Craig Brazell		
Bryan Bullington		
53 Daryl Clark	1.25	3.00
Brandon Webb		
Dustin Moseley		
Mike O'Keefe		
54 Kevin Youkilis	1.25	3.00
Jaime Bubela		
Matt Diaz		
Joey Gomes		
55 Chris Kroski	.40	1.00
Donald Hood		
Gary Schneidmiller		
Callix Crabbe		

2003 Bazooka Blasts Relics

Issued at different odds depending on what group the player belonged to, these 35 cards feature a game-used bat chip of the featured player.

GROUP A STATED ODDS 1:1666
GROUP B STATED ODDS 1:306
GROUP C STATED ODDS 1:197
GROUP D STATED ODDS 1:95
GROUP E STATED ODDS 1:52
GROUP F STATED ODDS 1:76
GROUP G STATED ODDS 1:326
GROUP H STATED ODDS 1:48
PARALLEL 25 ODDS 1:524
PARALLEL 25 PRINT RUN 25 #'d SETS
NO PARALLEL 25 PRICING DUE TO SCARCITY

AG Andres Galarraga C	3.00	8.00
ANR Aramis Ramirez E	3.00	8.00
AR Alex Rodriguez F	6.00	15.00
AS Alfonso Soriano D	3.00	8.00
BB Barry Bonds F	8.00	20.00
BW Bernie Williams D	4.00	10.00
CD Carlos Delgado D	3.00	8.00
CI Cesar Izturis B	4.00	10.00
CJ Chipper Jones E	4.00	10.00
DE Darin Erstad F	3.00	8.00
DH Drew Henson H	3.00	8.00
EM Edgar Martinez D	4.00	10.00
GS Gary Sheffield H	3.00	8.00
IR Ivan Rodriguez G	4.00	10.00
JD Johnny Damon H	4.00	10.00
JDD J.D. Drew D	4.00	10.00
JP Jorge Posada D	4.00	10.00
LB Lance Berkman E	3.00	8.00
LG Luis Gonzalez B	4.00	10.00
MP Mike Piazza H	6.00	15.00
MR Manny Ramirez F	4.00	10.00
MS Mike Sweeney C	3.00	8.00
NJ Nick Johnson B	4.00	10.00
PL Paul Lo Duca A	4.00	10.00
RA Roberto Alomar E	4.00	10.00
RH Rickey Henderson H	4.00	10.00
RK Ryan Klesko E	3.00	8.00
RM Raul Mondesi C	3.00	8.00
RP Rafael Palmeiro E	4.00	10.00
RV Robin Ventura F	3.00	8.00
SG Shawn Green D	3.00	8.00
TG Tony Gwynn H	6.00	15.00
TM Tino Martinez E	4.00	10.00
TS Tsuyoshi Shinjo E	3.00	8.00
WB Wilson Betemit E	3.00	8.00

2003 Bazooka Comics

Issued at a stated rate of one in four, these 24 comics, drawn in the style of the old Bazooka Joe comics, feature some of the leading players in the game.

COMPLETE SET (24)	10.00	25.00
1 Albert Pujols	1.00	2.50
2 Alex Rodriguez	.75	2.00
3 Alfonso Soriano	.40	1.00
4 Barry Zito	.40	1.00
5 Chipper Jones	.50	1.25
6 Derek Jeter	1.25	3.00
7 Greg Maddux	.75	2.00
8 Ichiro Suzuki	1.00	2.50
9 Jason Giambi	.40	1.00
10 Jim Thome	.40	1.00
11 John Smoltz	.40	1.00
12 Mike Piazza	.75	2.00
13 Randy Johnson	.50	1.25
14 Roger Clemens	1.00	2.50
15 Sammy Sosa	.50	1.25
16 Shawn Green	.40	1.00
17 Pedro Martinez	.40	1.00
18 Manny Ramirez	.40	1.00
19 Torii Hunter	.40	1.00
20 Ivan Rodriguez	.40	1.00
21 Miguel Tejada	.40	1.00
22 Troy Glaus	.40	1.00
23 Ken Griffey Jr.	.75	2.00
24 Nomar Garciaparra	.75	2.00

2003 Bazooka Piece of Americana Relics

These 30 cards, which feature game-work uniform swatches were issued at different odds depending on which group the card belonged to.

GROUP A STATED ODDS 1:1666
GROUP B STATED ODDS 1:611
GROUP C STATED ODDS 1:226
GROUP D STATED ODDS 1:118
GROUP E STATED ODDS 1:36
GROUP F STATED ODDS 1:73
GROUP G STATED ODDS 1:190
PARALLEL 25 ODDS 1:611
PARALLEL 25 PRINT RUN 25 #'d SETS
NO PARALLEL 25 PRICING DUE TO SCARCITY
ALL CARDS FEATURE JSERSEY SWATCHES

AD Adam Dunn G	3.00	8.00
AH Aubrey Huff F	3.00	8.00
AJ Andruw Jones E	4.00	10.00
AL Al Leiter D	3.00	8.00
BB Bret Boone E	3.00	8.00
CB Craig Biggio E	4.00	10.00
CD Carlos Delgado E	3.00	8.00
CG Cristian Guzman E	3.00	8.00
CJ Chipper Jones E	4.00	10.00
CS Curt Schilling D	3.00	8.00
DB Dewon Brazelton F	3.00	8.00
FT Frank Thomas F	4.00	10.00
IR Ivan Rodriguez D	4.00	10.00
JB Jeff Bagwell A	6.00	15.00
JE Jim Edmonds E	3.00	8.00
JK Jeff Kent D	3.00	8.00
LW Larry Walker D	3.00	8.00
MM Mike Mussina C	4.00	10.00
MO Magglio Ordonez E	3.00	8.00
MP Mike Piazza E	6.00	15.00
NG Nomar Garciaparra B	8.00	20.00
PA Albert Pujols E	6.00	15.00
PL Paul Lo Duca B	4.00	10.00
PW Preston Wilson C	3.00	8.00
RF Rafael Furcal C	3.00	8.00
RP Rafael Palmeiro E	4.00	10.00
SG Shawn Green E	3.00	8.00
TG Tony Gwynn G	6.00	15.00

TH Todd Helton E 4.00 10.00
THA Toby Hall F 3.00 8.00

2003 Bazooka Stand-Ups

Issued at a stated rate of one in eight hobby and one in 24 retail, this 25 card set features a design similar to the 1964 Topps Stand-Up set.

1 Albert Pujols 2.50 6.00
2 Alfonso Soriano .75 2.00
3 Ichiro Suzuki 2.50 6.00
4 Sammy Sosa 1.25 3.00
5 Randy Johnson 1.25 3.00
6 Barry Bonds 3.00 8.00
7 Vladimir Guerrero 1.25 3.00
8 Nomar Garciaparra 2.00 5.00
9 Alex Rodriguez 2.00 5.00
10 Troy Glaus .75 2.00
11 Barry Zito .75 2.00
12 Derek Jeter 3.00 8.00
13 Lance Berkman .75 2.00
14 Larry Walker .75 2.00
15 Adam Dunn .75 2.00
16 Shawn Green .75 2.00
17 Curt Schilling .75 2.00
18 Todd Helton .75 2.00
19 Pedro Martinez .75 2.00
20 Pat Burrell .75 2.00
21 Miguel Tejada .75 2.00
22 Manny Ramirez .75 2.00
23 Mike Piazza 2.00 5.00
24 Jim Thome .75 2.00
25 Jason Giambi .75 2.00

2003 Bazooka Stand-Ups Red

Issued as an unperforated card on top of each Bazooka box, these four cards feature some of the leading players. These cards can be differentiated from the regular stand-ups as they have a red border.

COMPLETE SET (4) 3.00 8.00
1 Barry Bonds 1.50 4.00
2 Albert Pujols 1.25 3.00
3 Jim Thome .60 1.50
4 Barry Zito .60 1.50

2004 Bazooka

This 300 card set was released in March, 2004. This was issued in eight-card hobby and retail packs with an $2 SRP which came 24 packs to a box and 10 boxes to a case. Cards numbered 1-270 feature veterans while cards 271-300 are all Rookie Cards. It is also important to note that there were 30 variation cards issued as part of this set; each of these variations were produced in the same quantity as their counterpart and thus there is no scarcity and a set is considered complete at 330 cards.

COMPLETE SET (330) 35.00 60.00
COMMON CARD (1-270) .15 .40
COMMON CARD (271-300) .15 .40
1 Bobby Abreu .15 .40
2 Jesse Foppert .15 .40
3 Shea Hillenbrand .15 .40
4 Jose Lima .15 .40
5 Manny Ramirez .40 1.00
6 Denny Neagle .15 .40
7 Frank Thomas .40 1.00
8 A.J. Burnett .25 .60
9 Carl Everett .15 .40
10A Scott Podsednik Blue Jsy .15 .40
10B Scott Podsednik White Jsy .15 .40
11 Travis Lee .15 .40
12 Mike Mussina .25 .60
13 Runelvys Hernandez .15 .40
14 Shannon Stewart .15 .40
15 Miguel Cabrera .40 1.00
16 Edgardo Alfonzo .15 .40
17 Victor Zambrano .15 .40
18 Rafael Furcal .15 .40
19 Eric Hinske .15 .40
20 Paul Lo Duca .15 .40
21 Phil Nevin .15 .40
22 Aramis Ramirez .15 .40
23 Jim Thome .25 .60
24 Jeromy Burnitz .15 .40
25A Mark Prior Glove Chest .25 .60
25B Mark Prior Glove Face .25 .60
26 Ramon Hernandez .15 .40
27 Cliff Lee .25 .60
28 Greg Myers .15 .40
29 Robert Fick .15 .40
30 Mike Sweeney .15 .40
31 Carlos Zambrano .25 .60
32 Roberto Alomar .25 .60
33 Orlando Cabrera .15 .40
34 Orlando Hudson .15 .40
35A Nomar Garciaparra Batting .40 1.00
35B Nomar Garciaparra Fielding .40 1.00
36 Esteban Loaiza .15 .40
37 Laynce Nix .15 .40
38 Joe Randa .15 .40
39 Juan Uribe .15 .40
40 Pat Burrell .15 .40
41 Steve Finley .15 .40
42 Livan Hernandez .15 .40
43 Al Leiter .15 .40
44 Brett Myers .15 .40
45 Jody Gerut .15 .40
46 Mark Teixeira .40 1.00
47 Barry Zito .15 .40
48 Moises Alou .15 .40
49 Mike Cameron .15 .40
50A Albert Pujols One Hand 1.00 2.50
50B Albert Pujols Two Hands 1.00 2.50
51 Tim Hudson .25 .60
52 Kenny Lofton .15 .40
53 Trot Nixon .15 .40
54 Tim Redding .15 .40
55 Marlon Byrd .15 .40
56 Javier Vazquez .15 .40
57 Sean Burroughs .15 .40
58 Cliff Floyd .15 .40
59 Juan Rivera .15 .40
60 Mike Lieberthal .15 .40
61 Xavier Nady .15 .40
62 Brad Radke .15 .40
63 Miguel Tejada .25 .60
64A Ichiro Suzuki Running .60 1.50
64B Ichiro Suzuki Throwing .60 1.50
65 Garret Anderson .15 .40
66 Sean Casey .15 .40
67A Jason Giambi Fielding .15 .40
67B Jason Giambi Hitting .15 .40
68 Aubrey Huff .15 .40
69 Javy Lopez .15 .40
70 Hideo Nomo .40 1.00
71 Mark Redman .15 .40
72 Jose Vidro .15 .40
73 Rich Aurilia .15 .40
74 Luis Castillo .15 .40
75 Jay Gibbons .15 .40
76 Torii Hunter .15 .40
77 Derek Lowe .15 .40
78 Wes Obermueller .15 .40
79 Edgar Renteria .15 .40
80 Jeff Bagwell .25 .60
81 Fernando Vina .15 .40
82 Frank Catalanotto .15 .40
83 Marcus Giles .15 .40
84 Raul Ibanez .15 .40
85 Mike Lowell .15 .40
86 Tomo Ohka .15 .40
87A Jose Reyes w/Bat .25 .60
87B Jose Reyes w/o Bat .25 .60
88 Omar Vizquel .25 .60
89 Shawn Chacon .15 .40
90 Rocco Baldelli .15 .40
91A Brian Giles w/Bat .15 .40
91B Brian Giles w/o Bat .15 .40
92 Kazuhisa Ishii .15 .40
93 Greg Maddux .60 1.50
94 John Olerud .15 .40
95 Eric Chavez .15 .40
96 Doug Waechter .15 .40
97 Tony Batista .15 .40
98 Jeriome Robertson .15 .40
99 Troy Glaus .15 .40
100A Eric Gagne Hand Out .15 .40
100B Eric Gagne Hand Up .15 .40
101A Pedro Martinez Leg Down .25 .60
101B Pedro Martinez Leg Up .25 .60
102 Magglio Ordonez .25 .60
103A Alex Rodriguez w/Bat .60 1.50
103B Alex Rodriguez w/o Bat .60 1.50
104 Jason Bay .25 .60
105 Larry Walker .25 .60
106 Matt Clement .15 .40
107 Tom Glavine .25 .60
108 Geoff Jenkins .15 .40
109 Victor Martinez .25 .60
110 David Ortiz .40 1.00
111 Ivan Rodriguez .25 .60
112 Jarrod Washburn .15 .40
113 Josh Beckett .25 .60
114 Bartolo Colon .15 .40
115 Juan Gonzalez .15 .40
116A Derek Jeter Fielding 1.00 2.50
116B Derek Jeter Hitting 1.00 2.50
117 Edgar Martinez .25 .60
118 Ramon Ortiz .15 .40
119 Scott Rolen .25 .60
120A Brandon Webb w/Ball .15 .40
120B Brandon Webb w/o Ball .15 .40
121 Carlos Beltran .15 .40
122 Jose Contreras .15 .40
123 Luis Gonzalez .15 .40
124 Jason Johnson .15 .40
125 Luis Matos .15 .40
126 Russ Ortiz .15 .40
127 Damian Rolls .15 .40
128 David Wells .15 .40
129 Adrian Beltre .15 .40
130 Shawn Green .15 .40
131 Nate Cornejo .15 .40
132 Nick Johnson .15 .40
133 Joe Mays .15 .40
134 Roy Oswalt .25 .60
135 C.C. Sabathia .25 .60
136A Vernon Wells Fielding .15 .40
136B Vernon Wells Hitting .15 .40
137 Kris Benson .15 .40
138 Carl Crawford .25 .60
139A Ken Griffey Jr. Fielding .60 1.50
139B Ken Griffey Jr. Hitting .60 1.50
140A Randy Johnson Black Jsy .40 1.00
140B Randy Johnson White Jsy .40 1.00
141 Fred McGriff .15 .40
142 Vicente Padilla .15 .40
143 Tim Salmon .15 .40
144 Kip Wells .15 .40
145 Lance Berkman .25 .60
146 Jose Cruz Jr. .15 .40
147 Marquis Grissom .15 .40
148 Jacque Jones .15 .40
149 Gil Meche .15 .40
150A Vladimir Guerrero Fielding .40 1.00
150B Vladimir Guerrero Hitting .40 1.00
151 Reggie Sanders .15 .40
152 Ty Wigginton .15 .40
153 Angel Berroa .15 .40
154 Johnny Damon .25 .60
155 Rafael Palmeiro .25 .60
156A Chipper Jones w/Bat .40 1.00
156B Chipper Jones w/o Bat .40 1.00
157 Kevin Millar .15 .40
158 Corey Patterson .15 .40
159A Johan Santana Both Feet .40 1.00
159B Johan Santana One Foot .40 1.00
160 Bernie Williams .25 .60
161 Craig Biggio .25 .60
162A Carlos Delgado Blue Jsy .15 .40
162B Carlos Delgado White Jsy .15 .40
163 Aaron Guiel .15 .40
164 Wade Miller .15 .40
165 Andruw Jones .15 .40
166 Jay Payton .15 .40
167 Benito Santiago .15 .40
168 Woody Williams .15 .40
169 Casey Blake .15 .40
170 Adam Dunn .25 .60
171 Jose Guillen .15 .40
172 Brian Jordan .15 .40
173 Kevin Millwood .15 .40
174 Carlos Pena .25 .60
175 Curt Schilling .25 .60
176 Jerome Williams .15 .40
177A Hank Blalock Grey Jsy .15 .40
177B Hank Blalock White Jsy .15 .40
178 Erubiel Durazo .15 .40
179 Cristian Guzman .15 .40
180 Austin Kearns .15 .40
181 Raul Mondesi .15 .40
182 Andy Pettitte .25 .60
183 Jason Schmidt .15 .40
184 Jeremy Bonderman .15 .40
185A Dontrelle Willis w/Ball .15 .40
185B Dontrelle Willis w/o Ball .15 .40
186 Ray Durham .15 .40
187 Jerry Hairston Jr. .15 .40
188 Jason Kendall .15 .40
189 Melvin Mora .15 .40
190 Jeff Kent .15 .40
191 Jae Weong Seo .15 .40
192 Jack Wilson .15 .40
193 Cesar Izturis .15 .40
194 Jermaine Dye .15 .40
195A Roy Halladay w/Ball .40 1.00
195B Roy Halladay w/o Ball .40 1.00
196 Jason Phillips .15 .40
197 Matt Morris .15 .40
198A Mike Piazza Fielding .40 1.00
198B Mike Piazza Running .40 1.00
199 Richie Sexson .15 .40
200 Alfonso Soriano .15 .40
201 Mark Mulder .15 .40
202 David Eckstein .15 .40
203 Mike Hampton .15 .40
204 Ryan Klesko .15 .40
205 Damian Moss .15 .40
206 Juan Pierre .15 .40
207 Ben Sheets .15 .40
208 Randy Winn .15 .40
209 Bret Boone .15 .40
210 Jim Edmonds .25 .60
211 Rich Harden .15 .40
212 Paul Konerko .25 .60
213 Jamie Moyer .15 .40
214 A.J. Pierzynski .15 .40
215 Gary Sheffield .15 .40
216 Randy Wolf .15 .40
217 Kevin Brown .15 .40
218 Morgan Ensberg .15 .40
219 Bo Hart .15 .40
220 Bill Mueller .15 .40
221 Corey Koskie .15 .40
222 Joel Pineiro .15 .40
223 Preston Wilson .15 .40
224 Aaron Boone .15 .40
225 Kerry Wood .15 .40
226 Darin Erstad .15 .40
227 Wes Helms .15 .40
228 Brian Lawrence .15 .40
229 Mark Buehrle .25 .60
230A Sammy Sosa w/Ball .40 1.00
230B Sammy Sosa w/Bat .40 1.00
231 Sidney Ponson .15 .40
232 Dmitri Young .15 .40
233 Ellis Burks .15 .40
234 Kelvim Escobar .15 .40
235 Todd Helton .25 .60
236 Matt Lawton .15 .40
237 Eric Munson .15 .40
238 Jorge Posada .25 .60
239 Mariano Rivera .40 1.00
240 Michael Young .15 .40
241 Ramon Nivar .15 .40
242 Edwin Jackson .15 .40
243 Felix Pie .15 .40
244 Joe Mauer .40 1.00
245 Grady Sizemore .25 .60
246 Bobby Jenks .15 .40
247 Chad Billingsley .15 .40
248 Casey Kotchman .15 .40
249 Bobby Crosby .15 .40
250 Khalil Greene .25 .60
251 Danny Garcia .15 .40
252 Nick Markakis .40 1.00
253 Bernie Castro .15 .40
254 Aaron Hill .15 .40
255 Josh Barfield .15 .40
256 Ryan Wagner .15 .40
257 Ryan Harvey .15 .40
258 Jimmy Gobble .15 .40
259 Ryan Madson .15 .40
260 Zack Greinke .25 .60
261 Rene Reyes .15 .40
262 Eric Duncan .15 .40
263 Chris Lubanski .15 .40
264 Jeff Mathis .15 .40
265 Rickie Weeks .15 .40
266 Justin Morneau .15 .40
267 Brian Snyder .15 .40
268 Neal Cotts .15 .40
269 Joe Borchard .15 .40
270 Larry Bigbie .15 .40
271 Marcus McBeth FY RC .15 .40
272 Tydus Meadows FY RC .15 .40
273 Zach Miner FY RC .25 .60
274A A.Lerew w/Ball FY RC .15 .40
274B A.Lerew w/o Ball FY RC .15 .40
275A Y.Molina w/Bat FY RC 1.00 2.50
275B Y.Molina w/o Bat FY RC 1.00 2.50
276A Jon Knott Bat Up FY RC .15 .40
276B Jon Knott Bat Down FY RC .15 .40
277 Matthew Moses FY RC .25 .60
278 Sung Jung FY RC .15 .40
279 Mike Gosling FY RC .15 .40
280 David Murphy FY RC .40 1.00
281 Tim Frend FY RC .15 .40
282 Casey Myers FY RC .15 .40
283 Brayan Pena FY RC .15 .40
284 Omar Falcon FY RC .15 .40
285 Blake Hawksworth FY RC .15 .40
286 Jesse Roman FY RC .15 .40
287 Kyle Davies FY RC .15 .40
288 Matt Creighton FY RC .15 .40
289 Rodney Choy Foo FY RC .15 .40
290 Kyle Sleeth FY RC .15 .40
291 Carlos Quentin FY RC .60 1.50
292 Khalid Ballouli FY RC .15 .40
293A Tim Stauffer w/Ball FY RC .25 .60
293B Tim Stauffer w/o Ball FY RC .25 .60
294 Craig Ansman FY RC .15 .40
295 Dioner Navarro FY RC .25 .60
296A Josh Labandeira w/Ball FY RC .15 .40
296B Josh Labandeira w/o Ball FY RC .15 .40
297 Jeffrey Allison FY RC .15 .40
298 Anthony Acevedo FY RC .15 .40
299 Brad Sullivan FY RC .15 .40
300 Conor Jackson FY RC 1.00 2.50

2004 Bazooka Red Chunks

*CHUNKS 1-270: .75X TO 2X BASIC
*CHUNKS 271-300: .75X TO 2X BASIC
ONE PER PACK

2004 Bazooka Minis

*MINIS 1-270: .75X TO 2X BASIC
*MINIS 271-300: .75X TO 2X BASIC
ONE PER PACK

2004 Bazooka 4 on 1 Sticker

STATED ODDS 1:4 H, 1:6 R
1 Rich Harden .40 1.00
Dontrelle Willis
Jerome Williams
Brandon Webb
2 Eric Duncan 2.50 6.00
Derek Jeter
Alfonso Soriano
Jason Giambi
3 Grady Sizemore .60 1.50
Rocco Baldelli
Ichiro Suzuki
Vladimir Guerrero
4 Roy Halladay 1.00 2.50
Pedro Martinez
Curt Schilling
Brett Myers
5 Alex Rodriguez 1.50 4.00
Angel Berroa
Jose Reyes
Khalil Greene
6 Kerry Wood .60 1.50
Adam Dunn
Jeff Kent
Scott Rolen
7 Miguel Cabrera 1.00 2.50
Scott Podsednik
Bo Hart
Mark Teixeira
8 Rickie Weeks .40 1.00
Josh Barfield
Albert Pujols
Vernon Wells
9 Torii Hunter 1.50 4.00
Garret Anderson
Bobby Abreu
Ken Griffey Jr.
10 Jay Gibbons 1.00 2.50
Chipper Jones
Mike Piazza
Mike Sweeney
11 David Ortiz 1.00 2.50
Nick Johnson
Carlos Delgado
Frank Thomas
12 Todd Helton .60 1.50
Jose Vidro
Mike Lowell
Miguel Tejada
13 Randy Wolf 1.00 2.50
Mark Mulder
Johan Santana
Randy Johnson
14 Bret Boone .40 1.00
Aubrey Huff
Eric Chavez
Javy Lopez
15 Jason Schmidt .60 1.50
Roy Oswalt
Joel Pineiro
Mark Prior
16 Kevin Millwood .60 1.50
Andy Pettitte
Matt Morris
Tim Hudson
17 Javier Vazquez .60 1.50
Esteban Loaiza
Orlando Cabrera
Roberto Alomar
18 Al Leiter .40 1.00
David Wells
Mike Hampton
Jarrod Washburn
19 Paul Lo Duca .40 1.00
Mike Lieberthal
Brian Giles
Andruw Jones
20 Magglio Ordonez .60 1.50
Corey Patterson
Aaron Boone
Jeff Bagwell
21 Troy Glaus 1.00 2.50
Edgar Martinez
Manny Ramirez
Raul Ibanez
22 Sammy Sosa 1.00 2.50
Barry Zito
Bartolo Colon
Austin Kearns
23 Jim Edmonds .60 1.50
Gary Sheffield
Preston Wilson
Shawn Green
24 Bernie Williams .60 1.50
Juan Pierre
Josh Beckett
Mike Mussina
25 Ramon Hernandez .40 1.00
Jason Kendall
Jason Phillips
A.J. Pierzynski
26 Pat Burrell .40 1.00
Laynce Nix
Mike Cameron
Cliff Floyd
27 Eric Gagne .60 1.50
Carl Crawford
Jose Guillen
Steve Finley
28 Ellis Burks .40 1.00
Livan Hernandez
Derek Lowe
Kazuhisa Ishii
29 Jorge Posada .60 1.50
Jeff Mathis
Victor Martinez
Ivan Rodriguez
30 Jim Thome 1.00 2.50
Marcus Giles
Nomar Garciaparra
Hank Blalock
31 Edgar Renteria .40 1.00
Bobby Crosby
Neal Cotts
Russ Ortiz
32 Zack Greinke .60 1.50
Cristian Guzman
Cesar Izturis
Kevin Brown
33 Bobby Jenks .40 1.00
Ramon Nivar
Richie Sexson
Ryan Klesko
34 Omar Vizquel .60 1.50
Carlos Pena
Rafael Furcal
Gil Meche
35 Kenny Lofton .60 1.50
Tim Salmon
Marquis Grissom
Craig Biggio
36 Kyle Davies .40 1.00
Anthony Lerew
Brayan Pena
Sung Jung
37 Rodney Choy Foo 1.00 2.50
Craig Ansman
David Murphy
Matthew Moses
38 Carlos Quentin 1.50 4.00
Dioner Navarro
Marcus McBeth
Josh Labandeira
39 Kyle Sleeth .40 1.00
Conor Jackson
Brad Sullivan
Jeffrey Allison
40 Yadier Molina 2.50 6.00
Jon Knott
Blake Hawksworth
Tim Stauffer

2004 Bazooka Adventures Relics

GROUP A ODDS 1:134 H, 1:187 R
GROUP B ODDS 1:207 H, 1:289 R
GROUP C ODDS 1:74 H, 1:104 R
GROUP D ODDS 1:57 H, 1:80 R
GROUP E ODDS 1:86 H, 1:119 R
OVERALL PARALLEL 25 ODDS 1:94
PARALLEL 25 PRINT RUN 25 #'d SETS
NO PARALLEL 25 PRICING DUE TO SCARCITY
AD1 Adam Dunn Stripe Jsy A 3.00 8.00
AD2 Adam Dunn Grey Jsy A 3.00 8.00
AJ Andruw Jones Jsy D 4.00 10.00
AP Albert Pujols Uni D 8.00 20.00
AR1 Alex Rodriguez Blue Jsy E 4.00 10.00
AR2 Alex Rodriguez White Jsy D 4.00 10.00
AS Alfonso Soriano Uni C 3.00 8.00
BG Ben Grieve Jsy A 3.00 8.00
BP Brad Penny Jsy A 3.00 8.00
BW Bernie Williams Jsy B 4.00 10.00
BZ Barry Zito Jsy B 3.00 8.00
CB Craig Biggio Uni A 4.00 10.00
CE Carl Everett Uni D 3.00 8.00
CF Cliff Floyd Jsy B 3.00 8.00
CG Cristian Guzman Jsy C 3.00 8.00
CJ Chipper Jones Jsy D 4.00 10.00
CS Curt Schilling Jsy A 4.00 10.00
DW Dontrelle Willis Uni D 4.00 10.00
EA Edgardo Alfonzo Uni D 3.00 8.00
EC Eric Chavez Uni A 3.00 8.00
GJ Geoff Jenkins Jsy E 3.00 8.00
GM Greg Maddux Jsy D 6.00 15.00
HN Hideo Nomo Jsy C 4.00 10.00
JB Jeff Bagwell Uni A 4.00 10.00
JDG Jeremy Giambi Jsy E 3.00 8.00
JG Jason Giambi Jsy D 3.00 8.00
JK Jason Kendall Jsy B 3.00 8.00
JO John Olerud Jsy E 3.00 8.00
JT Jim Thome Jsy C 4.00 10.00
JW Jarrod Washburn Uni C 3.00 8.00
KB Kevin Brown Jsy A 3.00 8.00
KM Kevin Millwood Jsy E 3.00 8.00
KW Kerry Wood Jsy A 3.00 8.00
LB Lance Berkman Jsy D 3.00 8.00
LC Luis Castillo Jsy D 3.00 8.00
LG Luis Gonzalez Uni A 3.00 8.00
LW Larry Walker Jsy A 3.00 8.00
MB Marlon Byrd Jsy C 3.00 8.00
MCM Mike Mussina Uni C 4.00 10.00
ML Mike Lowell Jsy D 3.00 8.00
MM Mark Mulder Uni A 3.00 8.00
MP1 M.Piazza 2nd Most Jsy C 6.00 15.00
MP2 M.Piazza 10 Straight Jsy D 6.00 15.00
MR Manny Ramirez Uni C 4.00 10.00
MT Miguel Tejada Uni E 3.00 8.00
MV Mo Vaughn Jsy A 3.00 8.00
NG Nomar Garciaparra Uni C 6.00 15.00
PB Pat Burrell Jsy E 3.00 8.00
PK Paul Konerko Jsy B 3.00 8.00
PL Paul Lo Duca Jsy C 3.00 8.00
PW Preston Wilson Jsy E 3.00 8.00
RJ Randy Johnson Jsy C 4.00 10.00
RP1 R.Palmeiro 500th HR Jsy D 4.00 10.00
RP2 R.Palmeiro 9 Straight Jsy D 4.00 10.00
SC Sean Casey Jsy D 3.00 8.00
SG Shawn Green Jsy C 3.00 8.00
TAH1 T.Hudson Most Wins Jsy B 3.00 8.00
TAH2 T.Hudson 3rd Best Uni D 3.00 8.00
TEG Troy Glaus Uni A 3.00 8.00
TG Tom Glavine Jsy A 4.00 10.00
TH Toby Hall Jsy A 3.00 8.00
TJS Tim Salmon Uni B 4.00 10.00
VG Vladimir Guerrero Jsy C 4.00 10.00

2004 Bazooka Blasts Bat Relics

GROUP A ODDS 1:62 H, 1:86 R
GROUP B ODDS 1:29 H, 1:40 R
OVERALL PARALLEL 25 ODDS 1:94
PARALLEL 25 PRINT RUN 25 #'d SETS
NO PARALLEL 25 PRICING DUE TO SCARCITY
AD Adam Dunn A 3.00 8.00
AG Adrian Gonzalez B 3.00 8.00
AH Aubrey Huff A 3.00 8.00
AJG Andres Galarraga A 3.00 8.00
ANR Aramis Ramirez B 3.00 8.00
AP Albert Pujols B 8.00 20.00
AR Alex Rodriguez B 4.00 10.00
AS Alfonso Soriano A 3.00 8.00
BB Bret Boone B 3.00 8.00
BF Brad Fullmer A 3.00 8.00
BW Bernie Williams A 4.00 10.00
CB Craig Biggio A 4.00 10.00
CC Carl Crawford A 3.00 8.00
CE Carl Everett B 3.00 8.00
CG Cristian Guzman A 3.00 8.00
CIB Carlos Beltran A 3.00 8.00
CJ Chipper Jones B 4.00 10.00
CL Carlos Lee A 3.00 8.00
CP Corey Patterson A 3.00 8.00
DM Doug Mientkiewicz A 3.00 8.00
EM Edgar Martinez B 4.00 10.00
FM Fred McGriff A 4.00 10.00
FT Frank Thomas B 4.00 10.00
GS Gary Sheffield B 3.00 8.00
HB Hank Blalock A 3.00 8.00
IR Ivan Rodriguez B 4.00 10.00
JAG Juan Gonzalez B 3.00 8.00
JB Jeff Bagwell A 4.00 10.00
JG Jason Giambi A 3.00 8.00
JNB Jeromy Burnitz A 3.00 8.00
JO John Olerud A 3.00 8.00
JP Jorge Posada A 4.00 10.00
JR Juan Rivera B 3.00 8.00
LB Lance Berkman B 3.00 8.00
LG Luis Gonzalez A 3.00 8.00
LW Larry Walker B 3.00 8.00
MA Moises Alou A 3.00 8.00
MAT Michael Tucker A 3.00 8.00
MCT Mark Teixeira A 4.00 10.00
MG Marquis Grissom B 3.00 8.00
ML Matt Lawton B 3.00 8.00
MO Magglio Ordonez B 3.00 8.00
MP Mike Piazza A 6.00 15.00
MR Manny Ramirez B 4.00 10.00
MT Miguel Tejada A 3.00 8.00
MV Mo Vaughn B 3.00 8.00
NG Nomar Garciaparra A 6.00 15.00
NH Nathan Haynes B 3.00 8.00
OV Omar Vizquel B 4.00 10.00
PK Paul Konerko A 3.00 8.00
PL Paul Lo Duca A 3.00 8.00
RA Roberto Alomar B 4.00 10.00
RB Rocco Baldelli A 3.00 8.00
RF Rafael Furcal B 3.00 8.00
RP Rafael Palmeiro B 4.00 10.00
RS Ruben Sierra B 3.00 8.00
RSA Rich Aurilia B 3.00 8.00
RW Rondell White B 3.00 8.00
SB Sean Burroughs B 3.00 8.00
SG Shawn Green B 3.00 8.00
SR Scott Rolen A 4.00 10.00
SS Shannon Stewart A 3.00 8.00
ST So Taguchi B 3.00 8.00
TB Tony Batista B 3.00 8.00
TG Troy Glaus A 3.00 8.00
TH Torii Hunter A 3.00 8.00
TJS Tim Salmon A 4.00 10.00
TKH Todd Helton B 4.00 10.00
TM Tino Martinez A 4.00 10.00
VG Vladimir Guerrero B 4.00 10.00
VW Vernon Wells A 3.00 8.00

2004 Bazooka Comics

COMPLETE SET (24) 10.00 25.00
STATED ODDS 1:4
BC1 Garret Anderson .40 1.00
BC2 Jeff Bagwell .60 1.50
BC3 Hank Blalock .40 1.00
BC4 Roy Halladay 1.00 2.50
BC5 Dontrelle Willis .40 1.00
BC6 Roger Clemens 1.25 3.00
BC7 Carlos Delgado .40 1.00
BC8 Rafael Furcal .40 1.00
BC9 Eric Gagne .40 1.00
BC10 Nomar Garciaparra 1.00 2.50
BC11 Derek Jeter 2.50 6.00
BC12 Esteban Loaiza .40 1.00
BC13 Kevin Millwood UER .40 1.00
Wrong date noted for his no-hitter
BC14 Bill Mueller .40 1.00
BC15 Rafael Palmeiro .60 1.50
BC16 Albert Pujols 2.50 6.00
BC17 Jose Reyes .60 1.50
BC18 Alex Rodriguez 1.50 4.00
BC19 Alfonso Soriano .40 1.00
BC20 Sammy Sosa 1.00 2.50
BC21 Ichiro Suzuki 1.50 4.00
BC22 Frank Thomas 1.00 2.50
BC23 Brad Wilkerson .40 1.00
BC24 Roy Oswalt .60 1.50
Pete Munro
Kirk Saarloos
Brad Lidge
Octavio Dotel
Billy Wagner

2004 Bazooka One-Liners Relics

GROUP A ODDS 1:62 H, 1:86 R
GROUP B ODDS 1:98 H, 1:136 R
OVERALL PARALLEL 25 ODDS 1:94
PARALLEL 25 PRINT RUN 25 #'d SETS
NO PARALLEL 25 PRICING DUE TO SCARCITY
AD Andre Dawson Bat A 4.00 10.00
BB Bert Blyleven Jsy A 4.00 10.00
BC Bert Campaneris Jsy A 4.00 10.00
BM Bill Madlock Bat A 4.00 10.00
BS Bret Saberhagen Jsy A 4.00 10.00
CS Chris Sabo Bat A 4.00 10.00
CY Carl Yastrzemski Uni A 12.50 30.00
DA Dick Allen Bat A 4.00 10.00
DE Dennis Eckersley Jsy A 4.00 10.00
DJ1 David Justice Bat A 4.00 10.00
DJ2 David Justice Uni A 4.00 10.00
DM Dale Murphy Bat A 6.00 15.00
DP Dave Parker Jsy A 4.00 10.00
DW Dwight Gooden Jsy A 4.00 10.00
EM Eddie Murray Uni A 10.00 25.00
FR Frank Robinson Uni A 4.00 10.00
GB George Brett Jsy B 8.00 20.00
GC Gary Carter Bat A 4.00 10.00
GP Gaylord Perry Uni A 4.00 10.00
HK Harmon Killebrew Jsy A 12.50 30.00
JB Johnny Bench Bat B 6.00 15.00
JC Jose Canseco Bat B 6.00 15.00
JCA Joe Carter Jsy A 4.00 10.00
JK Jerry Koosman Jsy A 4.00 10.00
JM Joe Morgan Jsy A 4.00 10.00
KG1 Kirk Gibson Bat A 4.00 10.00
KG2 Kirk Gibson Jsy A 4.00 10.00
KH Keith Hernandez Bat B 4.00 10.00
KP1 Kirby Puckett Bat B 6.00 15.00
KP2 Kirby Puckett Jsy B 6.00 15.00
MS Mike Schmidt Jsy B 8.00 20.00
NR Nolan Ryan Jsy A 30.00 60.00
OC Orlando Cepeda Bat A 4.00 10.00
PN Phil Niekro Uni A 4.00 10.00
RC Rod Carew Bat B 6.00 15.00
RD Ron Darling Jsy A 4.00 10.00

Card	Low	High
RJ Reggie Jackson Jsy A	6.00	15.00
RS Red Schoendienst Bat B	4.00	10.00
RSA Ron Santo Bat A	6.00	15.00
RY Robin Yount Bat A	6.00	15.00
TM Tug McGraw Jsy A	6.00	15.00
TS Tom Seaver Uni A	6.00	15.00
WB1 Wade Boggs Bat B	6.00	15.00
WB2 Wade Boggs Jsy B	6.00	15.00
WM Willie Mays Uni A	30.00	60.00
WMC Willie McGee Bat A	6.00	15.00
WS Willie Stargell Bat A	6.00	15.00

2004 Bazooka Stand Ups

STATED ODDS 1:8 H, 1:24 R

Card	Low	High
1 Jose Reyes	.60	1.50
2 Jim Thome	.60	1.50
3 Roy Halladay	1.00	2.50
4 Jason Giambi	.40	1.00
5 Dontrelle Willis	.40	1.00
6 Mike Piazza	1.00	2.50
7 Chipper Jones	1.00	2.50
8 Mark Prior	.60	1.50
9 Todd Helton	.60	1.50
10 Miguel Cabrera	1.00	2.50
11 Derek Jeter	2.50	6.00
12 Nomar Garciaparra	1.00	2.50
13 Alex Rodriguez	1.50	4.00
14 Miguel Tejada	.60	1.50
15 Carlos Delgado	.40	1.00
16 Pedro Martinez	.60	1.50
17 Sammy Sosa	1.00	2.50
18 Ichiro Suzuki	1.50	4.00
19 Vladimir Guerrero	1.00	2.50
20 Alfonso Soriano	.40	1.00
21 Eric Chavez	.40	1.00
22 Albert Pujols	2.50	6.00
23 Ivan Rodriguez	.60	1.50
24 Vernon Wells	.40	1.00
25 Eric Gagne	.40	1.00

2004 Bazooka Tattoos

STATED ODDS 1:4 H, 1:6 R

Card	Low	High
AD Adam Dunn	.60	1.50
AJ Andruw Jones	.40	1.00
AP Albert Pujols	2.50	6.00
AR Alex Rodriguez	1.50	4.00
AS Alfonso Soriano	.40	1.00
BAZ Bazooka Logo	.40	1.00
BP Brad Penny	.40	1.00
BW Bernie Williams	.60	1.50
BZ Barry Zito	.40	1.00
CB Craig Biggio	.60	1.50
CF Cliff Floyd	.40	1.00
CG Cristian Guzman	.40	1.00
CJ Chipper Jones	1.00	2.50
CS Curt Schilling	.60	1.50
DW Dontrelle Willis	.40	1.00
EC Eric Chavez	.40	1.00
GJ Geoff Jenkins	.40	1.00
GM Greg Maddux	1.50	4.00
HN Hideo Nomo	1.00	2.50
JB Jeff Bagwell	.60	1.50
JG Jason Giambi	.40	1.00
JK Jason Kendall	.40	1.00
JO John Olerud	.40	1.00
JT Jim Thome	.60	1.50
JW Jarrod Washburn	.40	1.00
KB Kevin Brown	.40	1.00
KM Kevin Millwood	.40	1.00
KW Kerry Wood	.40	1.00
LB Lance Berkman	.60	1.50
LC Luis Castillo	.40	1.00
LG Luis Gonzalez	.40	1.00
LW Larry Walker	.60	1.50
MB Marlon Byrd	.40	1.00
MCM Mike Mussina	.60	1.50
ML Mike Lowell	.40	1.00
MM Mark Mulder	.40	1.00
MP Mike Piazza	1.00	2.50
MR Manny Ramirez	1.00	2.50
MT Miguel Tejada	.60	1.50
NG Nomar Garciaparra	1.00	2.50
PB Pat Burrell	.40	1.00
PK Paul Konerko	.60	1.50
PL Paul Lo Duca	.40	1.00
PW Preston Wilson	.40	1.00
RJ Randy Johnson	1.00	2.50
RP Rafael Palmeiro	.60	1.50
SC Sean Casey	.40	1.00
SG Shawn Green	.40	1.00
TAH Tim Hudson	.60	1.50
TEG Troy Glaus	.40	1.00
TG Tom Glavine	.60	1.50
TH Toby Hall	.40	1.00
TJS Tim Salmon	.40	1.00
TOP Topps Logo	.40	1.00
VG Vladimir Guerrero	1.00	2.50

2005 Bazooka

This 220-card set was released in late January-early February, 2005. The set was issued in eight card hobby packs which came 24 packs to a box and 12 boxes to a case. Cards numbered 1-170 feature leading veterans while cards numbered 171-190 feature leading prospects and cards numbered 191-220 feature players in their 1st year on Topps company cards.

Card	Low	High
COMPLETE SET (220)	30.00	60.00
COMMON CARD (1-170)	.15	.40
COMMON CARD (171-190)	.20	.50
COMMON CARD (191-220)	.20	.50
1 Eric Gagne	.15	.40
2 Aramis Ramirez	.15	.40
3 Hank Blalock	.15	.40
4 Jason Kendall	.15	.40
5 Jeromy Burnitz	.15	.40
6 Jose Guillen	.15	.40
7 Tom Glavine	.25	.60
8 Adrian Beltre	.15	.40
9 Jason Bay	.15	.40
10 Mark Teixeira	.40	1.00
11 Moises Alou	.15	.40
12 Ronnie Belliard	.15	.40
13 Aaron Guiel	.15	.40
14 Vladimir Guerrero	.40	1.00
15 Scott Podsednik	.15	.40
16 Alfonso Soriano	.25	.60
17 Craig Wilson	.15	.40
18 Jose Reyes	.25	.60
19 Mark Prior	.25	.60
20 Preston Wilson	.15	.40
21 Shawn Green	.15	.40
22 Troy Glaus	.15	.40
23 Dmitri Young	.15	.40
24 Garret Anderson	.15	.40
25 Kazuo Matsui	.15	.40
26 Kerry Wood	.15	.40
27 Michael Young	.25	.60
28 Oliver Perez	.15	.40
29 Bartolo Colon	.15	.40
30 Richie Sexson	.15	.40
31 Brad Penny	.15	.40
32 Carlos Guillen	.15	.40
33 Carlos Zambrano	.25	.60
34 David Wright	.60	1.50
35 Al Leiter	.15	.40
36 Jack Wilson	.15	.40
37 Ryan Drese	.15	.40
38 Darin Erstad	.15	.40
39 Derrek Lee	.15	.40
40 Ivan Rodriguez	.25	.60
41 Kenny Rogers	.15	.40
42 Mike Piazza	.40	1.00
43 Phil Nevin	.15	.40
44 Geoff Jenkins	.15	.40
45 Jorge Posada	.25	.60
46 Khalil Greene	.15	.40
47 Randy Johnson	.40	1.00
48 Rondell White	.15	.40
49 Sammy Sosa	.40	1.00
50 Vernon Wells	.15	.40
51 Ben Sheets	.15	.40
52 Brian Giles	.15	.40
53 Carlos Delgado	.15	.40
54 Derek Jeter	1.00	2.50
55 Jeremy Bonderman	.15	.40
56 Magglio Ordonez	.25	.60
57 Chad Tracy	.15	.40
58 Kevin Brown	.15	.40
59 Luis Castillo	.15	.40
60 Lyle Overbay	.15	.40
61 Mark Buehrle	.25	.60
62 Mark Loretta	.15	.40
63 Orlando Hudson	.15	.40
64 Adam Dunn	.25	.60
65 Frank Thomas	.40	1.00
66 Jake Peavy	.15	.40
67 Jason Giambi	.15	.40
68 Joe Mauer	.40	1.00
69 Marcus Giles	.15	.40
70 Mike Lowell	.15	.40
71 Roy Halladay	.40	1.00
72 Aaron Rowand	.15	.40
73 Alex Rodriguez	.60	1.50
74 Brian Lawrence	.15	.40
75 Gabe Gross	.15	.40
76 Johnny Estrada	.15	.40
77 Justin Morneau	.40	1.00
78 Miguel Cabrera	.40	1.00
79 Alex Rios	.25	.60
80 Gary Sheffield	.15	.40
81 Jason Schmidt	.15	.40
82 Juan Pierre	.15	.40
83 Paul Konerko	.25	.60
84 Jermaine Dye	.15	.40
85 Rafael Furcal	.15	.40
86 Torii Hunter	.15	.40
87 A.J. Pierzynski	.15	.40
88 Carl Pavano	.15	.40
89 Carlos Lee	.15	.40
90 J.D. Drew	.15	.40
91 Javier Vazquez	.15	.40
92 Lew Ford	.15	.40
93 Ted Lilly	.15	.40
94 Austin Kearns	.15	.40
95 Chipper Jones	.40	1.00
96 Erubiel Durazo	.15	.40
97 Johan Santana	.40	1.00
98 Josh Beckett	.25	.60
99 Mariano Rivera	.40	1.00
100 Mark Mulder	.15	.40
101 Andruw Jones	.15	.40
102 Barry Zito	.15	.40
103 Bret Boone	.15	.40
104 Paul LoDuca	.15	.40
105 Shannon Stewart	.15	.40
106 Wily Mo Pena	.15	.40
107 Dontrelle Willis	.15	.40
108 Eric Chavez	.15	.40
109 Jamie Moyer	.15	.40
110 Joe Nathan	.15	.40
111 Sidney Ponson	.15	.40
112 John Smoltz	.40	1.00
113 Ichiro Suzuki	.60	1.50
114 Javy Lopez	.15	.40
115 Victor Martinez	.25	.60
116 Ken Griffey Jr.	.60	1.50
117 Lance Berkman	.25	.60
118 Scott Hatteberg	.15	.40
119 Jim Edmonds	.25	.60
120 Kazuhisa Ishii	.15	.40
121 Miguel Tejada	.25	.60
122 Roger Clemens	.50	1.25
123 Ryan Freel	.15	.40
124 Albert Pujols	1.00	2.50
125 Hideo Nomo	.40	1.00
126 Mark Kotsay	.15	.40
127 Melvin Mora	.15	.40
128 Roy Oswalt	.25	.60
129 Sean Casey	.15	.40
130 Casey Blake	.15	.40
131 Edgar Renteria	.15	.40
132 Jeff Kent	.15	.40
133 Rafael Palmeiro	.25	.60
134 Tim Hudson	.25	.60
135 Barry Bonds	.75	2.00
136 Andy Pettitte	.25	.60
137 Brian Roberts	.15	.40
138 Jose Vidro	.15	.40
139 Omar Vizquel	.25	.60
140 Rich Harden	.15	.40
141 Scott Rolen	.25	.60
142 Carlos Beltran	.15	.40
143 Chris Carpenter	.40	1.00
144 Manny Ramirez	.40	1.00
145 Nick Johnson	.15	.40
146 Pat Burrell	.15	.40
147 C.C. Sabathia	.25	.60
148 Johnny Damon	.25	.60
149 Juan Rivera	.15	.40
150 Ken Harvey	.15	.40
151 Kevin Millwood	.15	.40
152 Larry Walker	.25	.60
153 Aubrey Huff	.15	.40
154 Curt Schilling	.25	.60
155 Jake Westbrook	.15	.40
156 Randy Wolf	.15	.40
157 Zach Day	.15	.40
158 Zack Greinke	.25	.60
159 Brad Wilkerson	.15	.40
160 Carl Crawford	.25	.60
161 Jim Thome	.25	.60
162 Mike Sweeney	.15	.40
163 Pedro Martinez	.25	.60
164 Travis Hafner	.15	.40
165 Bobby Abreu	.15	.40
166 Cliff Floyd	.15	.40
167 David DeJesus	.15	.40
168 David Ortiz	.40	1.00
169 Rocco Baldelli	.15	.40
170 Todd Helton	.25	.60
171 Dallas McPherson PROS	.20	.50
172 Kevin Youkilis PROS	.20	.50
173 Val Majewski PROS	.20	.50
174 Grady Sizemore PROS	.30	.75
175 Joey Gathright PROS	.20	.50
176 Rickie Weeks PROS	.30	.75
177 Jason Kubel PROS	.20	.50
178 Robinson Cano PROS	.50	1.25
179 Nick Swisher PROS	.50	1.25
180 Ryan Howard PROS	1.00	2.50
181 Tim Stauffer PROS	.20	.50
182 Merkin Valdez PROS	.20	.50
183 B.J. Upton PROS	.30	.75
184 Scott Kazmir PROS	.50	1.25
185 Chris Burke PROS	.20	.50
186 Felix Hernandez PROS	.75	2.00
187 Freddy Guzman PROS	.20	.50
188 Josh Labandeira PROS	.20	.50
189 Willy Taveras PROS	.20	.50
190 Casey Kotchman PROS	.20	.50
191 Steve Doetsch FY RC	.20	.50
192 Melky Cabrera FY RC	.50	1.25
193 Luis Ramirez FY RC	.20	.50
194 Chris Seddon FY RC	.20	.50
195 Chad Orvella FY RC	.20	.50
196 Ian Kinsler FY RC	1.50	4.00
197 Brandon Moss FY RC	.75	2.00
198 Chadd Blasko FY RC	.30	.75
199 Jeremy West FY RC	.20	.50
200 Sean Marshall FY RC	.50	1.25
201 Matt DeSalvo FY RC	.20	.50
202 Ryan Sweeney FY RC	.30	.75
203 Matthew Lindstrom FY RC	.20	.50
204 Ryan Goleski FY RC	.20	.50
205 Brett Harper FY RC	.20	.50
206 Chris Roberson FY RC	.20	.50
207 Andre Ethier FY RC	1.50	4.00
208 Chris Denorfia FY RC	.20	.50
209 Darren Fenster FY RC	.20	.50
210 Elvys Quezada FY RC	.20	.50
211 Kevin West FY RC	.20	.50
212 Chaz Lytle FY RC	.30	.75
213 James Jurries FY RC	.20	.50
214 Matt Rogelstad FY RC	.20	.50
215 Wade Robinson FY RC	.20	.50
216 Ian Bladergroen FY RC	.20	.50
217 Jake Dittler FY	.20	.50
218 Nate McLouth FY RC	.30	.75
219 Kole Strayhorn FY RC	.20	.50
220 Jose Vaquedano FY RC	.20	.50

2005 Bazooka Gold Chunks

*GOLD 1-170: .75X TO 2X BASIC
*GOLD 171-190: .75X TO 2X BASIC
*GOLD 191-220: .75X TO 2X BASIC
ONE PER PACK

2005 Bazooka Minis

*MINIS 1-170: .75X TO 2X BASIC
*MINIS 171-190: .75X TO 2X BASIC
*MINIS 191-220: .75X TO 2X BASIC
ONE PER PACK

2005 Bazooka 4 on 1 Stickers

STATED ODDS 1:3 HOBBY, 1:6 RETAIL
ONE STICKER ALBUM PER HOBBY BOX

Card	Low	High
1 Alex Rodriguez	1.25	3.00
Hank Blalock		
Scott Rolen		
Mike Lowell		
2 Jorge Posada	.75	2.00
Ivan Rodriguez		
Joe Mauer		
Johnny Estrada		
3 Ichiro Suzuki	1.50	4.00
Carlos Beltran		
Jim Edmonds		
Brian Giles		
4 Jim Thome	.50	1.25
Mark Teixeira		
Paul Konerko		
Lyle Overbay		
5 Jose Reyes	.40	1.00
Mark Loretta		
Jose Vidro		
Luis Castillo		
6 Miguel Tejada	1.50	4.00
Derek Jeter		
Michael Young		
Edgar Renteria		
7 Roy Oswalt	.75	2.00
Rich Harden		
Johan Santana		
Mark Prior		
8 Mariano Rivera	.75	2.00
Eric Gagne		
Joe Nathan		
John Smoltz		
9 Larry Walker	.50	1.25
Carl Crawford		
Preston Wilson		
Garret Anderson		
10 Wily Mo Pena	.40	1.00
Mark Kotsay		
Alex Rios		
Geoff Jenkins		
11 Victor Martinez	1.25	3.00
David Wright		
Justin Morneau		
Jason Bay		
12 Carlos Lee	.50	1.25
Andruw Jones		
Ronnie Belliard		
Eric Chavez		
13 Vladimir Guerrero	.75	2.00
Vernon Wells		
Miguel Cabrera		
Adrian Beltre		
14 David Ortiz	.50	1.25
Marcus Giles		
Jeff Kent		
Bobby Abreu		
15 Juan Pierre	.40	1.00
Torii Hunter		
J.D. Drew		
Austin Kearns		
16 Bartolo Colon	1.25	3.00
Manny Ramirez		
Ken Griffey Jr.		
Dontrelle Willis		
17 Andy Pettitte	.75	2.00
Tim Hudson		
Curt Schilling		
Randy Johnson		
18 Jamie Moyer	.40	1.00
Zach Day		
Al Leiter		
Oliver Perez		
19 Kazuo Matsui	1.25	3.00
Roger Clemens		
Khalil Greene		
Javier Vazquez		
20 Pedro Martinez	.75	2.00
Rocco Baldelli		
Mike Piazza		
Melvin Mora		
21 Hideo Nomo	.75	2.00
Kazuhisa Ishii		
Ken Harvey		
Mike Sweeney		
22 Casey Blake	.40	1.00
Ryan Freel		
Bret Boone		
Javy Lopez		
23 Craig Wilson	.40	1.00
Shawn Green		
Aramis Ramirez		
Darin Erstad		
24 Troy Glaus	.40	1.00
Lance Berkman		
Scott Podsednik		
Adam Dunn		
25 Albert Pujols	1.50	4.00
Gary Sheffield		
Chipper Jones		
Magglio Ordonez		
26 Johnny Damon	.50	1.25
Carlos Zambrano		
Jason Schmidt		
Ted Lilly		
27 Sidney Ponson	.40	1.00
Chris Carpenter		
C.C. Sabathia		
Kevin Millwood		
28 Carl Pavano	.40	1.00
Mark Mulder		
Rafael Furcal		
Jack Wilson		
29 Jeremy Bonderman	.50	1.25
Jake Westbrook		
Zack Greinke		
Tom Glavine		
30 Omar Vizquel	.50	1.25
Carlos Guillen		
Roy Halladay		
Ben Sheets		
31 Kerry Wood	.40	1.00
Kevin Brown		
Moises Alou		
Travis Hafner		
32 Nick Johnson	.40	1.00
Erubiel Durazo		
Alfonso Soriano		
Jason Giambi		
33 Chad Tracy	.40	1.00
Richie Sexson		
Aubrey Huff		
Brian Roberts		
34 Todd Helton	.50	1.25
Dmitri Young		
Jeromy Burnitz		
Jose Guillen		
35 Juan Rivera	.75	2.00
Shannon Stewart		
Sammy Sosa		
Cliff Floyd		
36 Pat Burrell	.40	1.00
Gabe Gross		
Aaron Guiel		
Paul LoDuca		
37 A.J. Pierzynski	.40	1.00
Orlando Hudson		
David DeJesus		
Brian Lawrence		
38 Josh Beckett	.40	1.00
Barry Zito		
Mark Buehrle		
Randy Wolf		
39 Brad Penny	.40	1.00
Jake Peavy		
Rondell White		
Brad Wilkerson		
40 Ryan Drese	.40	1.00
Kenny Rogers		
Jermaine Dye		
Lew Ford		
41 Aaron Rowand	2.00	5.00
Jason Kendall		
Barry Bonds		
Derrek Lee		
42 Phil Nevin	.75	2.00
Sean Casey		
Rafael Palmeiro		
Frank Thomas		
43 Scott Hatteberg	.50	1.25
Josh Labandeira		
Jason Kubel		
Nick Swisher		
44 Freddy Guzman	1.50	4.00
Tim Stauffer		
Merkin Valdez		
Felix Hernandez		
45 Willy Taveras	.50	1.25
Grady Sizemore		
Joey Gathright		
Carlos Delgado		
46 Scott Kazmir	.40	1.00
Rickie Weeks		
Dallas McPherson		
Kevin Youkilis		
47 Val Majewski	.40	1.00
Casey Kotchman		
Ryan Howard		
Chris Burke		
48 Robinson Cano	.50	1.25
B.J. Upton		
Jake Dittler		
Ian Bladergroen		
49 Brett Harper	.50	1.25
James Jurries		
Jeremy West		
Matt Rogelstad		
50 Darren Fenster	1.00	2.50
Chad Orvella		
Brandon Moss		
Ryan Sweeney		
51 Chris Roberson	3.00	8.00
Steve Doetsch		
Andre Ethier		
Kevin West		
52 Melky Cabrera	1.50	4.00
Ryan Goleski		
Chris Denorfia		
Chaz Lytle		
53 Luis Ramirez	1.00	2.50
Matt DeSalvo		
Sean Marshall		
Jose Vaquedano		
54 Chris Seddon	.40	1.00
Chadd Blasko		
Elvys Quezada		
Wade Robinson		
55 Nate McLouth	2.00	5.00
Matthew Lindstrom		
Kole Strayhorn		
Ian Kinsler		
NNO Sticker Album	.75	2.00

2005 Bazooka Blasts Bat Relics

GROUP A ODDS 1:649 H, 1:1205 R
GROUP B ODDS 1:47 H, 1:65 R
GROUP C ODDS 1:29 H, 1:45 R
GROUP D ODDS 1:93 H, 1:140 R

GROUP E ODDS 1:104 H, 1:158 R
GROUP A PRINT RUN 100 SETS
GROUP A ARE NOT SERIAL-NUMBERED
GROUP A PRINT RUN PROVIDED BY TOPPS

Card	Low	High
AB Angel Berroa C	3.00	8.00
AD Adam Dunn B	3.00	8.00
AG Adrian Gonzalez B	3.00	8.00
AG1 Alex Gonzalez C	3.00	8.00
AR Aramis Ramirez B	3.00	8.00
AR1 Alex Rodriguez A/100 *	10.00	25.00
BU B.J. Upton A/100 *	6.00	15.00
CB Craig Biggio A/100 *	6.00	15.00
CE Carl Everett C	3.00	8.00
CF Chone Figgins B	3.00	8.00
CG Cristian Guzman B	3.00	8.00
CGU Carlos Guillen B	3.00	8.00
CS Curt Schilling B	4.00	10.00
DL Derrek Lee B	4.00	10.00
DO David Ortiz A/100 *	6.00	15.00
DW David Wright A/100 *	6.00	15.00
GS Gary Sheffield E	3.00	8.00
HB Hank Blalock A/100 *	4.00	10.00
JB Jeromy Burnitz B	3.00	8.00
JC Jeff Conine D	3.00	8.00
JF Julio Franco C	3.00	8.00
JK Jeff Kent B	3.00	8.00
JV Jose Valentin C	3.00	8.00
JV1 Jose Vidro C	3.00	8.00
JW Jayson Werth B	3.00	8.00
KM Kaz Matsui A/100 *	6.00	15.00
LG Luis Gonzalez B	3.00	8.00
LH Livan Hernandez C	3.00	8.00
LW Larry Walker E	4.00	10.00
MC Miguel Cabrera A/100 *	6.00	15.00
ML Mike Lowell A/100 *	4.00	10.00
MO Magglio Ordonez C	3.00	8.00
MR Manny Ramirez C	4.00	10.00
MT Miguel Tejada B	3.00	8.00
MY Michael Young B	3.00	8.00
NG Nomar Garciaparra B	4.00	10.00
PK Paul Konerko D	3.00	8.00
PM Pedro Martinez B	4.00	10.00
PW Preston Wilson B	3.00	8.00
RA Roberto Alomar C	4.00	10.00
RB Ron Belliard C	3.00	8.00
RH Richard Hidalgo C	3.00	8.00
RS Ruben Sierra C	3.00	8.00
TC Tony Clark B	3.00	8.00
TH Todd Helton C	4.00	10.00
TM Tino Martinez B	4.00	10.00
VC Vinny Castilla D	3.00	8.00
VG Vladimir Guerrero A/100 *	4.00	10.00
VM Victor Martinez A/100 *	3.00	8.00

2005 Bazooka Comics

Card	Low	High
COMPLETE SET (24)	10.00	25.00
STATED ODDS 1:4 H		
1 Randy Johnson	1.00	2.50
2 Gary Sheffield	.40	1.00
3 Ken Griffey Jr.	1.50	4.00
4 Alex Rodriguez	1.50	4.00
5 Vladimir Guerrero	1.00	2.50
6 David Bell	.40	1.00
7 Carlos Pena	.60	1.50
8 Eric Gagne	.40	1.00
9 Jim Thome	.60	1.50
10 Cleveland Indians	.40	1.00
11 Greg Maddux	1.50	4.00
12 Miguel Tejada	.60	1.50
13 Ichiro Suzuki	1.50	4.00
14 Mariano Rivera	1.00	2.50
15 Juan Pierre	.40	1.00
16 Carl Crawford	.60	1.50
17 Mike Mussina	.60	1.50
18 Vladimir Guerrero	1.00	2.50
19 Oliver Perez	.40	1.00
20 Ichiro Suzuki	1.50	4.00
21 Johan Santana	1.00	2.50
22 Kevin Brown	.40	1.00
23 Mike Piazza	1.00	2.50
24 Randy Johnson	1.00	2.50

2005 Bazooka Fun Facts Relics

GROUP A ODDS 1:3949 H, 1:6012 R
GROUP B ODDS 1:71 H, 1:108 R
GROUP C ODDS 1:330 H, 1:500 R
GROUP D ODDS 1:83 H, 1:126 R
GROUP E ODDS 1:278 H, 1:423 R
GROUP F ODDS 1:209 H, 1:316 R
GROUP A PRINT RUN 100 SETS
GROUP A ARE NOT SERIAL-NUMBERED
GROUP A PRINT RUN PROVIDED BY TOPPS

Card	Low	High
CF Cecil Fielder Bat D	6.00	15.00
CS Cory Snyder Bat B	3.00	8.00
DD Darren Daulton Bat D	3.00	8.00
DE Darrell Evans Bat E	3.00	8.00
DJ1 Dave Justice Jsy C	3.00	8.00
DJ2 Dave Justice Bat D	3.00	8.00
DP Dave Parker Bat B	3.00	8.00
DS Darryl Strawberry Bat B	3.00	8.00
GB George Brett Bat B	6.00	15.00
GC Gary Carter Bat B	3.00	8.00
HB Harold Baines Bat D	3.00	8.00
HR Harold Reynolds Bat D	3.00	8.00
JC Jose Canseco Jsy C	6.00	15.00
JL Jim Leyritz Bat B	3.00	8.00
MR Mickey Rivers Bat B	3.00	8.00
MS Mike Schmidt Bat B	6.00	15.00
OS Ozzie Smith Bat A/100 *	15.00	40.00
RC Rod Carew Bat A/100 *	10.00	25.00
RK Ron Kittle Bat B	3.00	8.00
WB Wade Boggs Bat B	4.00	10.00
WH Willie Horton Bat B	3.00	8.00
WJ Wally Joyner Bat F	3.00	8.00
WW Walt Weiss Bat B	3.00	8.00

2005 Bazooka Moments Relics

GROUP A ODDS 1:1132 H, 1:1718 R
GROUP B ODDS 1:110 H, 1:167 R
GROUP A PRINT RUN 100 SETS
GROUP A ARE NOT SERIAL-NUMBERED
GROUP A PRINT RUN PROVIDED BY TOPPS

Card	Low	High
AP Albert Pujols Cap A/100 *	15.00	40.00
AR Alex Rodriguez Uni A/100 *	10.00	25.00
AS Alfonso Soriano Uni A/100 *	4.00	10.00
FT Frank Thomas Uni B	4.00	10.00
IR Ivan Rodriguez Uni A/100 *	6.00	15.00
JP Jorge Posada Uni A/100 *	6.00	15.00
KR Kenny Rogers Uni B	3.00	8.00
MB Matt Bush Jsy B	3.00	8.00
MM Mark Mulder Uni A/100 *	4.00	10.00
MP Mike Piazza Uni A/100 *	6.00	15.00
MT Mark Teixeira Uni B	4.00	10.00
RH Ramon Hernandez Uni B	3.00	8.00
TL Terrence Long Uni B	3.00	8.00

2005 Bazooka Tattoos

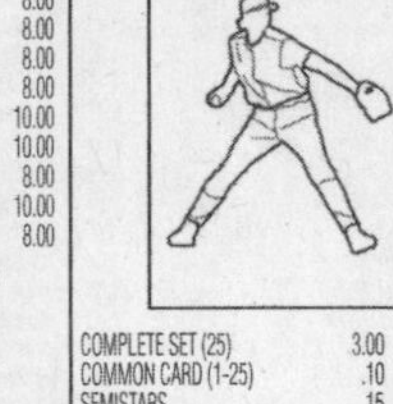

Card	Low	High
COMPLETE SET (25)	3.00	8.00
COMMON CARD (1-25)	.10	.25
SEMISTARS	.15	.40
UNLISTED STARS	.25	.60
STATED ODDS 1:4 HOBBY/RETAIL		
1 Alex Rodriguez	.40	1.00
2 Randy Johnson	.25	.60
3 Jim Thome	.15	.40
4 Pedro Martinez	.15	.40
5 Roger Clemens	.30	.75
6 Troy Glaus	.10	.25
7 Todd Helton	.15	.40
8 Albert Pujols	.60	1.50
9 Sammy Sosa	.25	.60
10 David Wright	.40	1.00
11 Mike Piazza	.25	.60
12 Gary Sheffield	.10	.25
13 David Ortiz	.25	.60
14 Hank Blalock	.10	.25
15 Miguel Tejada	.15	.40
16 Dontrelle Willis	.10	.25
17 Ivan Rodriguez	.15	.40
18 Nomar Garciaparra	.25	.60
19 Alfonso Soriano	.15	.40
20 Adrian Beltre	.10	.25
21 Torii Hunter	.10	.25
22 Brian Giles	.10	.25
23 Chipper Jones	.25	.60
24 Carlos Beltran	.10	.25
25 Manny Ramirez	.25	.60

2006 Bazooka

This 220-card set was released in March, 2006. The set was issued in eight-card hobby and retail packs with an $1.99 SRP. The first 200 card of the set are veterans while the final 20-cards in the set consist of players who qualified for the then-new RC designation which began in 2006.

Card	Low	High
COMPLETE SET (220)	15.00	40.00
COMMON CARD (1-200)	.15	.40
COMMON CARD (201-220)	.15	.40
1 Josh Gibson	.40	1.00
2 Scott Podsednik	.15	.40
3 Sammy Sosa	.40	1.00
4 Ivan Rodriguez	.25	.60
5 Derek Jeter	1.00	2.50
6 Manny Ramirez	.40	1.00
7 Nook Logan	.15	.40
8 Adam Dunn	.25	.60

9 Travis Hafner .15 .40
10 Felix Hernandez .40 1.00
11 Larry Bigbie .15 .40
12 Magglio Ordonez .25 .60
13 Josh Beckett .25 .60
14 Mike Sweeney .15 .40
15 Mickey Mantle 1.25 3.00
16 Grady Sizemore .25 .60
17 Brian Fuentes .15 .40
18 Willy Mo Pena .15 .40
19 Morgan Ensberg .15 .40
20 Tim Hudson .25 .60
21 Justin Verlander 1.25 3.00
22 Jermaine Dye .15 .40
23 Miguel Cabrera .40 1.00
24 Greg Maddux .60 1.50
25 Jason Giambi .15 .40
26 Ben Sheets .15 .40
27 Brad Radke .15 .40
28 Torii Hunter .15 .40
29 Mike Piazza .40 1.00
30 Jason Kendall .15 .40
31 Pat Burrell .15 .40
32 Khalil Greene .15 .40
33 Brian Roberts .15 .40
34 C.C. Sabathia .25 .60
35 Mike Mussina .25 .60
36 Bob Wickman .15 .40
37 Dmitri Young .15 .40
38 Dontrelle Willis .15 .40
39 David DeJesus .15 .40
40 J.D. Drew .15 .40
41 Chad Tracy .15 .40
42 Joe Mauer .40 1.00
43 Melvin Mora .15 .40
44 Carlos Zambrano .25 .60
45 Mariano Rivera .40 1.00
46 Coco Crisp .15 .40
47 Derrek Lee .15 .40
48 Cliff Floyd .15 .40
49 Willy Taveras .15 .40
50 Albert Pujols 1.00 2.50
51 Aaron Boone .15 .40
52 Mark Mulder .15 .40
53 Brad Wilkerson .15 .40
54 Hank Blalock .15 .40
55 Hideki Matsui .40 1.00
56 Victor Martinez .25 .60
57 Jeremy Bonderman .15 .40
58 Felipe Lopez .15 .40
59 Paul Lo Duca .15 .40
60 Derek Lowe .15 .40
61 Luis Gonzalez .15 .40
62 Paul Konerko .25 .60
63 Miguel Tejada .25 .60
64 Jeromy Burnitz .15 .40
65 Orlando Hernandez .15 .40
66 Curt Schilling .25 .60
67 Joe Nathan .15 .40
68 Jose Reyes .25 .60
69 David Wright .60 1.50
70 Eric Chavez .15 .40
71 Rich Harden .15 .40
72 A.J. Pierzynski .15 .40
73 Trevor Hoffman .25 .60
74 Adrian Beltre .15 .40
75 Alex Rodriguez .60 1.50
76 Jonathan Papelbon .75 2.00
77 Jorge Cantu .15 .40
78 Mark Teixeira .40 1.00
79 Chien-Ming Wang .25 .60
80 Jeff Francoeur .40 1.00
81 Ichiro Suzuki .60 1.50
82 Jhonny Peralta .15 .40
83 Todd Helton .25 .60
84 Brad Penny .15 .40
85 Shawn Chacon .15 .40
86 Billy Wagner .15 .40
87 Jason Schmidt .15 .40
88 Austin Kearns .15 .40
89 Chris Carpenter .40 1.00
90 Chipper Jones .40 1.00
91 Shawn Green .15 .40
92 A.J. Burnett .25 .60
93 Joe Crede UER .15 .40
Comic on back talks about Rafael Palmeiro
94 Mark Prior .25 .60
95 Andy Pettitte .25 .60
96 Edgar Renteria .15 .40
97 Roy Halladay .40 1.00
98 Eric Milton .15 .40
99 Craig Biggio .25 .60
100 Barry Bonds .75 2.00
101 Troy Glaus .15 .40
102 Aaron Rowand .15 .40
103 Aramis Ramirez .15 .40
104 Nomar Garciaparra .40 1.00
105 Randy Johnson .40 1.00
106 David Ortiz .25 .60
107 Vinny Castilla .15 .40
108 Carl Crawford .25 .60
109 Zach Duke .15 .40
110 Barry Zito .15 .40
111 Darin Erstad .15 .40
112 Chris Capuano .15 .40
113 Javy Lopez .15 .40
114 Lew Ford .15 .40
115 Robinson Cano .40 1.00
116 Ronnie Belliard .15 .40
117 Placido Polanco .15 .40
118 Rickie Weeks .25 .60
119 Brad Lidge .15 .40
120 Andruw Jones .15 .40
121 Nick Swisher .40 1.00
122 Bartolo Colon .15 .40
123 Juan Pierre .15 .40
124 Johan Santana .40 1.00
125 Jorge Posada .25 .60
126 Jeff Francis .15 .40
127 Matt Holliday .40 1.00
128 Carlos Delgado .15 .40
129 Zack Greinke .25 .60
130 Lyle Overbay .15 .40
131 Conor Jackson .25 .60
132 Mark Buehrle .25 .60
133 Chone Figgins .15 .40
134 Pedro Martinez .25 .60
135 Roger Clemens .50 1.25
136 Raul Ibanez .25 .60
137 Jim Edmonds .25 .60
138 Michael Young .25 .60
139 Preston Wilson .15 .40
140 Rafael Furcal .15 .40
141 Bobby Abreu .15 .40
142 Tadahito Iguchi .15 .40
143 B.J. Ryan .15 .40
144 Francisco Rodriguez UER .25 .60
Photo is Ervin Santana
145 J.T. Snow .15 .40
146 Aubrey Huff .15 .40
147 Mike Morse .15 .40
148 Jason Bay .15 .40
149 Roy Oswalt .25 .60
150 Carlos Beltran .15 .40
151 Carlos Lee .15 .40
152 Emil Brown .15 .40
153 Craig Monroe .15 .40
154 Kris Benson .15 .40
155 Gary Sheffield .15 .40
156 Jake Peavy .15 .40
157 David Eckstein .15 .40
158 Tom Glavine .25 .60
159 Jeff Kent .15 .40
160 Livan Hernandez .15 .40
161 Orlando Hudson .15 .40
162 Randy Winn .15 .40
163 Jimmy Rollins .25 .60
164 Luis Castillo .15 .40
165 Nick Johnson .15 .40
166 Johnny Damon .25 .60
167 Eric Gagne .15 .40
168 Geoff Jenkins .15 .40
169 Mike Cameron .15 .40
170 Marcus Giles .15 .40
171 Huston Street .15 .40
172 Moises Alou .15 .40
173 Scott Rolen .25 .60
174 Jose Vidro .15 .40
175 Alfonso Soriano .25 .60
176 Toby Hall .15 .40
177 Orlando Cabrera .15 .40
178 Brian Giles .15 .40
179 Erubiel Durazo .15 .40
180 Matt Morris .15 .40
181 Jack Wilson .15 .40
182 Brady Clark .15 .40
183 Shannon Stewart .15 .40
184 Kerry Wood .15 .40
185 Carl Pavano .15 .40
186 Chase Utley .40 1.00
187 Omar Vizquel .25 .60
188 Vladimir Guerrero .40 1.00
189 Richie Sexson .15 .40
190 John Smoltz .40 1.00
191 Garret Anderson UER .15 .40
Name spelled Garrett on front and back
192 Jon Garland .15 .40
193 Julio Lugo .15 .40
194 Rocco Baldelli .15 .40
195 Jaret Wright .15 .40
196 Matt Clement .15 .40
197 Vernon Wells .15 .40
198 Sean Casey .15 .40
199 Lance Berkman .25 .60
200 Justin Morneau .40 1.00
201 Shaun Marcum (RC) .15 .40
202 Chuck James (RC) .15 .40
203 Hong-Chih Kuo (RC) .40 1.00
204 Darrell Rasner (RC) .15 .40
205 Anthony Reyes (RC) .15 .40
206 Francisco Liriano (RC) .40 1.00
207 Joe Saunders (RC) .15 .40
208 Fausto Carmona (RC) .15 .40
209 Charlton Jimerson (RC) .15 .40
210 Bryan Bullington (RC) .15 .40
211 Tom Gorzelanny (RC) .15 .40
212 Anderson Hernandez (RC) .15 .40
213 Ryan Garko (RC) .15 .40
214 John Koronka (RC) .15 .40
215 Chris Denorfia (RC) .15 .40
216 Jeff Mathis (RC) .15 .40
217 Jose Bautista (RC) .40 1.00
218 Danny Sandoval RC .15 .40
219 Robert Andino RC .15 .40
220 Justin Huber (RC) .15 .40

2006 Bazooka Blue Fortune

*BLUE 1-200: .75X TO 2X BASIC
*BLUE 201-220: .75X TO 2X BASIC
ONE PER PACK

2006 Bazooka Gold Chunks

*GOLD 1-200: .75X TO 2X BASIC
*GOLD 201-220: .75X TO 2X BASIC
ONE CHUNK OR GU PER PACK

2006 Bazooka 4 on 1 Stickers

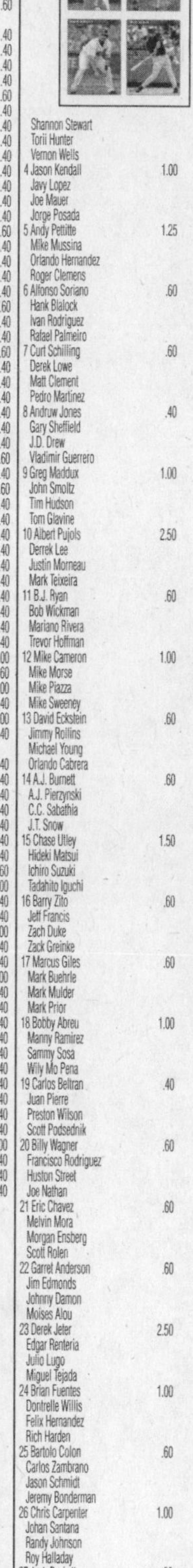

COMPLETE SET (55) 15.00 40.00
STATED ODDS 1:3 HOBBY, 1:6 RETAIL
1 Alex Rodriguez 3.00 8.00
Barry Bonds
Josh Gibson
Mickey Mantle
2 Carlos Delgado .60 1.50
David Ortiz
Jason Giambi
Chien-Ming Wang
3 Carl Crawford .60 1.50
Shannon Stewart
Torii Hunter
Vernon Wells
4 Jason Kendall 1.00 2.50
Javy Lopez
Joe Mauer
Jorge Posada
5 Andy Pettitte 1.25 3.00
Mike Mussina
Orlando Hernandez
Roger Clemens
6 Alfonso Soriano .60 1.50
Hank Blalock
Ivan Rodriguez
Rafael Palmeiro
7 Curt Schilling .60 1.50
Derek Lowe
Matt Clement
Pedro Martinez
8 Andruw Jones .40 1.00
Gary Sheffield
J.D. Drew
Vladimir Guerrero
9 Greg Maddux 1.00 2.50
John Smoltz
Tim Hudson
Tom Glavine
10 Albert Pujols 2.50 6.00
Derrek Lee
Justin Morneau
Mark Teixeira
11 B.J. Ryan .60 1.50
Bob Wickman
Mariano Rivera
Trevor Hoffman
12 Mike Cameron 1.00 2.50
Mike Morse
Mike Piazza
Mike Sweeney
13 David Eckstein .60 1.50
Jimmy Rollins
Michael Young
Orlando Cabrera
14 A.J. Burnett .60 1.50
A.J. Pierzynski
C.C. Sabathia
J.T. Snow
15 Chase Utley 1.50 4.00
Hideki Matsui
Ichiro Suzuki
Tadahito Iguchi
16 Barry Zito .60 1.50
Jeff Francis
Zach Duke
Zack Greinke
17 Marcus Giles .60 1.50
Mark Buehrle
Mark Mulder
Mark Prior
18 Bobby Abreu 1.00 2.50
Manny Ramirez
Sammy Sosa
Wily Mo Pena
19 Carlos Beltran .40 1.00
Juan Pierre
Preston Wilson
Scott Podsednik
20 Billy Wagner .60 1.50
Francisco Rodriguez
Huston Street
Joe Nathan
21 Eric Chavez .60 1.50
Melvin Mora
Morgan Ensberg
Scott Rolen
22 Garret Anderson .60 1.50
Jim Edmonds
Johnny Damon
Moises Alou
23 Derek Jeter 2.50 6.00
Edgar Renteria
Julio Lugo
Miguel Tejada
24 Brian Fuentes 1.00 2.50
Dontrelle Willis
Felix Hernandez
Rich Harden
25 Bartolo Colon .60 1.50
Carlos Zambrano
Jason Schmidt
Jeremy Bonderman
26 Chris Carpenter 1.00 2.50
Johan Santana
Randy Johnson
Roy Halladay
27 Josh Beckett .60 1.50
Kris Benson
Roy Oswalt
Shawn Chacon
28 Felipe Lopez .60 1.50
Jhonny Peralta
Jose Reyes
Rafael Furcal
29 Justin Verlander 3.00 8.00
Kerry Wood
Livan Hernandez
Matt Morris
30 Jack Wilson .40 1.00
Khalil Greene
Nomar Garciaparra
Omar Vizquel
31 Jason Bay .40 1.00
Pat Burrell
Rocco Baldelli
Shawn Green
32 Brad Lidge .40 1.00
Brad Penny
Brad Radke
Brian Roberts
33 Jeff Francoeur .60 1.50
Rickie Weeks
Robinson Cano
Willy Taveras
34 Geoff Jenkins .60 1.50
Lance Berkman
Larry Bigbie
Matt Holliday
35 Carlos Lee .60 1.50
Paul Lo
Toby Hall
Victor Martinez
36 Aramis Ramirez 1.50 4.00
Chipper Jones
David Wright
Troy Glaus
37 Aaron Rowand .40 1.00
Brad Wilkerson
Craig Monroe
Randy Winn
38 Aaron Boone .40 1.00
Adrian Beltre
Chone Figgins
Vinny Castilla
39 Adam Dunn .60 1.50
Cliff Floyd
Larry Walker
Luis Gonzalez
40 Jeff Kent .40 1.00
Jorge Cantu
Placido Polanco
Ronnie Belliard
41 Craig Biggio .60 1.50
Jose Vidro
Luis Castillo
Orlando Hudson
42 Brian Giles 1.00 2.50
Grady Sizemore
Lew Ford
Nick Swisher
43 Coco Crisp .40 1.00
David DeJesus
Emil Brown
Jeromy Burnitz
44 Eric Gagne .40 1.00
Eric Milton
Jake Peavy
Jaret Wright
45 Aubrey Huff .40 1.00
Austin Kearns
Brady Clark
Nook Logan
46 Ben Sheets .40 1.00
Carl Pavano
Chris Capuano
Jon Garland
47 Darin Erstad .40 1.00
Dmitri Young
Erubiel Durazo
Travis Hafner
48 Conor Jackson .60 1.50
Jermaine Dye
Magglio Ordonez
Miguel Cabrera
49 Chad Tracy .40 1.00
Lyle Overbay
Richie Sexson
Sean Casey
50 Nick Johnson .60 1.50
Paul Konerko
Raul Ibanez
Todd Helton
51 Chuck James 1.00 2.50
Darrell Rasner
Hong-Chih Kuo
Shaun Marcum
52 Anthony Reyes 1.00 2.50
Fausto Carmona
Francisco Liriano
Joe Saunders
53 Anderson Hernandez .40 1.00
Bryan Bullington
Charlton Jimerson
Tom Gorzelanny
54 Chris Denorfia .40 1.00
Jeff Mathis
John Koronka
Ryan Garko
55 Jose Bautista 1.00 2.50
Danny Sandoval
Robert Andino
Justin Huber

2006 Bazooka Basics Relics

GROUP A ODDS 1:285 H, 1:465 R
GROUP B ODDS 1:124 H, 1:204 R
GROUP C ODDS 1:95 H, 1:155 R
GROUP D ODDS 1:124 H, 1:204 R
AJ Andruw Jones Jsy B 4.00 10.00
AP Albert Pujols Jsy A 6.00 15.00
BA Bobby Abreu Jsy C 3.00 8.00
BR Brian Roberts Jsy C 3.00 8.00
BW Bernie Williams Uni C 4.00 10.00
CB Craig Biggio Jsy B 4.00 10.00
CD Carlos Delgado Jsy B 3.00 8.00
CJ Chipper Jones Jsy A 4.00 10.00
CS Curt Schilling Jsy B 4.00 10.00
DW Dontrelle Willis Jsy D 3.00 8.00
EG Eric Gagne Jsy A 3.00 8.00
HB Hank Blalock Jsy D 3.00 8.00
JD Johnny Damon Jsy B 4.00 10.00
JR Jose Reyes Jsy A 3.00 8.00
LB Lance Berkman Jsy C 3.00 8.00
MC Miguel Cabrera Uni C 4.00 10.00
MG Marcus Giles Jsy D 3.00 8.00
MH Matt Holliday Jsy A 4.00 10.00
ML Mike Lowell Uni C 3.00 8.00
MM Mark Mulder Uni B 3.00 8.00
MMU Mike Mussina Uni D 4.00 10.00
MR Manny Ramirez Jsy B 4.00 10.00
MT Mark Teixeira Jsy A 4.00 10.00
PM Pedro Martinez Uni B 4.00 10.00
SB Sean Burroughs Uni C 3.00 8.00
TH Tim Hudson Uni A 3.00 8.00

2006 Bazooka Blasts Bat Relics

GROUP A ODDS 1:4020 H, 1:6370 R
GROUP B ODDS 1:67 H, 1:108 R
GROUP C ODDS 1:29 H, 1:48 R
GROUP A PRINT RUN 100 SETS
GROUP A ARE NOT SERIAL-NUMBERED
GROUP A PRINT RUN PROVIDED BY TOPPS
AD Adam Dunn B 3.00 8.00
AJ Andruw Jones C 4.00 10.00
AR Alex Rodriguez B 4.00 10.00
ARA Aramis Ramirez C 3.00 8.00
BA Bobby Abreu C 3.00 8.00
BB Barry Bonds A/100 * 15.00 40.00
CB Carlos Beltran C 3.00 8.00
CC Coco Crisp B 3.00 8.00
CF Cliff Floyd C 3.00 8.00
CJ Chipper Jones C 4.00 10.00
CP Corey Patterson B 3.00 8.00
DL Derrek Lee C 4.00 10.00
DO David Ortiz B 4.00 10.00
DW David Wright C 4.00 10.00
GJ Geoff Jenkins B 3.00 8.00
GS Gary Sheffield C 3.00 8.00
HB Hank Blalock B 3.00 8.00
JB Jason Bay B 3.00 8.00
JD Johnny Damon C 4.00 10.00
JDD J.D. Drew B 3.00 8.00
JT Jim Thome B 4.00 10.00
MA Moises Alou C 3.00 8.00
ML Mark Loretta B 3.00 8.00
MM Mickey Mantle A/100 * 125.00 200.00
MP Mike Piazza B 4.00 10.00
MT Miguel Tejada B 3.00 8.00
PK Paul Konerko C 3.00 8.00
PL Paul LoDuca C 3.00 8.00
PW Preston Wilson C 3.00 8.00
SS Sammy Sosa B 4.00 10.00
TG Troy Glaus C 3.00 8.00
TN Trot Nixon B 3.00 8.00
VG Vladimir Guerrero C 4.00 10.00
VM Victor Martinez C 3.00 8.00

2006 Bazooka Comics

COMPLETE SET (24) 6.00 15.00
STATED ODDS 1:4 HOBBY
1 Greg Maddux 1.50 4.00
2 Alex Rodriguez 1.50 4.00
3 Trevor Hoffman .60 1.50
4 Rafael Palmeiro .60 1.50
5 Roy Oswalt .60 1.50
6 Bobby Abreu .40 1.00
7 Miguel Tejada .60 1.50
8 Vladimir Guerrero 1.00 2.50
9 Mark Teixeira 1.00 2.50
10 Zach Duke .40 1.00
11 Xavier Nady .40 1.00
12 Alex Rodriguez 1.50 4.00
13 Jeremy Hermida .40 1.00
14 Craig Biggio .60 1.50
15 Manny Ramirez 1.00 2.50
16 Texas Rangers .40 1.00
17 Oakland Athletics .40 1.00
18 Alex Rodriguez 1.50 4.00
19 Jason Giambi .40 1.00
20 Aaron Small .40 1.00
21 Jimmy Rollins .60 1.50
22 Roger Clemens 1.25 3.00
23 Chicago White Sox .40 1.00
Seattle Mariners
24 Andruw Jones .40 1.00

2006 Bazooka Mickey Mantle Jumbo Reprints

COMPLETE SET (16) 200.00 300.00
COMMON CARD (53-69) 10.00 25.00
ONE PER SEALED HOBBY BOX
1952 Mickey Mantle 1952 15.00 40.00
1953 Mickey Mantle 1953 6.00 15.00
1956 Mickey Mantle 1956 6.00 15.00
1957 Mickey Mantle 1957 6.00 15.00
1958 Mickey Mantle 1958 6.00 15.00
1959 Mickey Mantle 1959 6.00 15.00
1960 Mickey Mantle 1960 6.00 15.00
1961 Mickey Mantle 1961 6.00 15.00
1962 Mickey Mantle 1962 6.00 15.00
1963 Mickey Mantle 1963 6.00 15.00
1964 Mickey Mantle 1964 6.00 15.00
1965 Mickey Mantle 1965 6.00 15.00
1966 Mickey Mantle 1966 6.00 15.00
1967 Mickey Mantle 1967 6.00 15.00
1968 Mickey Mantle 1968 6.00 15.00
1969 Mickey Mantle 1969 6.00 15.00

2006 Bazooka Rewind Relics

GROUP A ODDS 1:2680 H, 1:4250 R
GROUP B ODDS 1:1066 H, 1:1700 R
GROUP C ODDS 1:400 H, 1:653 R
GROUP D ODDS 1:45 H, 1:74 R
GROUP E ODDS 1:56 H, 1:89 R
GROUP F ODDS 1:200 H, 1:324 R
GROUP G ODDS 1:251 H, 1:147 R
GROUP A PRINT RUN 100 SETS
GROUP A ARE NOT SERIAL-NUMBERED
GROUP A PRINT RUN PROVIDED BY TOPPS
NO GROUP A PRICING DUE TO SCARCITY
AJ Andruw Jones Uni C 4.00 10.00
AK Adam Kennedy Bat D 3.00 8.00
AML Adam LaRoche Jsy G 3.00 8.00
AP A.J. Pierzynski Bat D 3.00 8.00
AR Alex Rodriguez Bat D 6.00 15.00
ARO Aaron Rowand Bat E 3.00 8.00
BR Brian Roberts Bat C 3.00 8.00
BU B.J. Upton Jsy A/100 *
CB Clint Barmes Bat D 3.00 8.00
CBI Craig Biggio Jsy D 4.00 10.00
CC Carl Crawford Bat C 3.00 8.00
CE Carl Everett Uni C 3.00 8.00
CG Cristian Guzman Bat E 3.00 8.00
CJ Conor Jackson Jsy A/100 *
CL Carlos Lee Bat E 3.00 8.00
CU Chase Utley Bat D 4.00 10.00
DW Dontrelle Willis Jsy D 3.00 8.00
ER Edgar Renteria Bat E 3.00 8.00
FL Francisco Liriano Jsy B 6.00 15.00
FT Frank Thomas Bat D 4.00 10.00
HR Hanley Ramirez Jsy G 4.00 10.00
JB Jason Botts Bat D 3.00 8.00
JD Jermaine Dye Bat E 3.00 8.00
JDA Johnny Damon Bat E 4.00 10.00
JG Jon Garland Uni C 3.00 8.00
JGU Jose Guillen Bat D 3.00 8.00
JH Justin Huber Jsy F 3.00 8.00
JR Jimmy Rollins Bat D 3.00 8.00
JV Justin Verlander Jsy B 4.00 10.00
KT Kevin Thompson Jsy G 3.00 8.00
LB Lance Berkman Jsy D 3.00 8.00
MG Mark Grudzielanek Bat D 3.00 8.00
MJ Mike Jacobs Bat D 3.00 8.00
MR Manny Ramirez Uni E 4.00 10.00
NC Nelson Cruz Jsy G 3.00 8.00
NJ Nick Johnson Bat D 3.00 8.00
PB Pat Burrell Bat D 3.00 8.00
PK Paul Konerko Bat E 3.00 8.00
RC Robinson Cano Bat E 4.00 10.00
RG Ryan Garko Jsy B 3.00 8.00
RW Rickie Weeks Bat D 3.00 8.00
RWA Ryan Wagner Jsy D 3.00 8.00
SC Shin-Soo Choo Jsy F 3.00 8.00
SP Scott Podsednik Bat D 3.00 8.00
TS Termel Sledge Bat D 3.00 8.00
WB William Bergolla Jsy A/100 *
WB2 William Bergolla Jsy D 3.00 8.00
WT Willy Taveras Jsy D 3.00 8.00

2006 Bazooka Signature Line

GROUP A ODDS 1:21,250 H
GROUP B ODDS 1:3165 H
GROUP C ODDS 1:1261 H
GROUP D ODDS 1:314 H
GROUP A PRINT RUN 15 CARDS
GROUP B PRINT RUN 100 SETS
GROUP A-B ARE NOT SERIAL-NUMBERED
GROUP A-B PRINTS PROVIDED BY TOPPS
NO GROUP A PRICING DUE TO SCARCITY
AR Alex Rodriguez A/15 *
BM Brandon McCarthy D 6.00 15.00
KM Kevin Millar C 10.00 25.00
ML Victor Zambrano D 6.00 15.00
MM Mike Morse B/100 * 6.00 15.00

2006 Bazooka Stamps

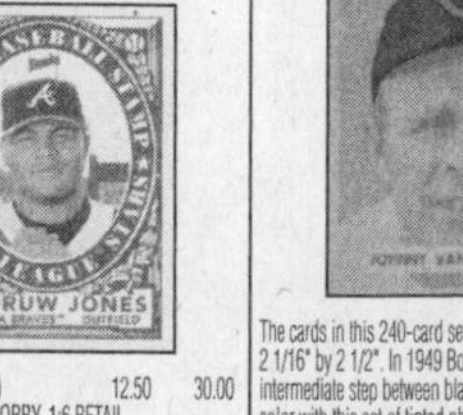

COMPLETE SET (30) 12.50 30.00
STATED ODDS 1:3 HOBBY, 1:6 RETAIL
1 Bobby Abreu .40 1.00
2 Lance Berkman .60 1.50
3 Hank Blalock .40 1.00
4 Barry Bonds 2.00 5.00
5 Mark Buehrle .60 1.50
6 Miguel Cabrera 1.00 2.50
7 Jim Edmonds .60 1.50
8 Morgan Ensberg .40 1.00
9 Jeff Francoeur 1.00 2.50
10 Roy Halladay 1.00 2.50
11 Tim Hudson .60 1.50
12 Derek Jeter 2.50 6.00
13 Andruw Jones .40 1.00
14 Chipper Jones 1.00 2.50
15 Derrek Lee .40 1.00
16 Mickey Mantle 3.00 8.00
17 Victor Martinez .60 1.50
18 Justin Morneau 1.00 2.50
19 Manny Ramirez 1.00 2.50
20 Brian Roberts .40 1.00
21 Alex Rodriguez 1.50 4.00
22 Ivan Rodriguez .60 1.50
23 Johan Santana 1.00 2.50
24 Alfonso Soriano .60 1.50
25 Huston Street .40 1.00
26 Ichiro Suzuki 1.50 4.00
27 Mark Teixeira 1.00 2.50
28 Miguel Tejada .60 1.50
29 Rickie Weeks .60 1.50
30 Dontrelle Willis .40 1.00

1948 Bowman

The 48-card Bowman set of 1948 was the first major set of the post-war period. Each 2 1/16" by 2 1/2" card had a black and white photo of a current player, with his biographical information printed in black ink on a gray back. Due to the printing process and the 36-card sheet size upon which Bowman was then printing, the 12 cards marked with an SP in the checklist are scarcer numerically, as they were removed from the printing sheet in order to make room for the 12 high numbers (37-48). Cards were issued in one-card penny packs. Many cards are found with over-printed, transposed, or blank backs. The set features the Rookie Cards of Hall of Famers Yogi Berra, Ralph Kiner, Stan Musial, Red Schoendienst, and Warren Spahn. Half of the cards in the set feature New York players (Yankees or Giants).

COMPLETE SET (48) 3000.00 5000.00
COMMON CARD (1-36) 10.00 20.00
COMMON CARD (37-48) 15.00 30.00
WRAPPER (5-CENT) 600.00 700.00
WRAPPER (1-CENT)
1 Bob Elliott RC 75.00 125.00
2 Ewell Blackwell RC 35.00 60.00
3 Ralph Kiner RC 150.00 250.00
4 Johnny Mize RC 75.00 125.00
5 Bob Feller RC 150.00 250.00
6 Yogi Berra RC 500.00 800.00
7 Pete Reiser SP RC 75.00 125.00
8 Phil Rizzuto SP RC 200.00 350.00
9 Walker Cooper RC 10.00 20.00
10 Buddy Rosar RC 10.00 20.00
11 Johnny Lindell RC 12.50 25.00
12 Johnny Sain RC 50.00 80.00
13 Willard Marshall SP RC 20.00 40.00
14 Allie Reynolds RC 35.00 60.00
15 Eddie Joost 10.00 20.00
16 Jack Lohrke SP RC 20.00 40.00
17 Enos Slaughter RC 60.00 100.00
18 Warren Spahn RC 175.00 300.00
19 Tommy Henrich 35.00 60.00
20 Buddy Kerr SP RC 20.00 40.00
21 Ferris Fain RC 20.00 40.00
22 Floyd Bevens SP RC 30.00 50.00
23 Larry Jansen RC 12.50 25.00
24 Dutch Leonard SP 20.00 40.00
25 Barney McCosky 10.00 20.00
26 Frank Shea SP RC 30.00 50.00
27 Sid Gordon RC 12.50 25.00
28 Emil Verban SP RC 20.00 40.00
29 Joe Page SP RC 50.00 80.00
30 Whitey Lockman SP RC 20.00 40.00
31 Bill McCahan RC 10.00 20.00
32 Bill Rigney RC 10.00 20.00
33 Bill Johnson RC 12.50 25.00
34 Sheldon Jones SP RC 20.00 40.00
35 Snuffy Stirnweiss RC 20.00 40.00
36 Stan Musial RC 500.00 800.00
37 Clint Hartung RC 15.00 30.00
38 Red Schoendienst RC 125.00 200.00
39 Augie Galan RC 15.00 30.00
40 Marty Marion RC 50.00 80.00
41 Rex Barney RC 35.00 60.00
42 Ray Poat RC 15.00 30.00
43 Bruce Edwards RC 20.00 40.00
44 Johnny Wyrostek RC 15.00 30.00
45 Hank Sauer RC 35.00 60.00
46 Herman Wehmeier RC 15.00 30.00
47 Bobby Thomson RC 60.00 100.00
48 Dave Koslo RC 50.00 80.00

1949 Bowman

The cards in this 240-card set measure approximately 2 1/16" by 2 1/2". In 1949 Bowman took an intermediate step between black and white and full color with this set of tinted photos on colored backgrounds. Collectors should note the series price variations, which reflect some inconsistencies in the printing process. There are four major varieties in name printing, which are noted in the checklist below: NOF: name on front; NNOF: no name on front; PR: printed name on back; and SCR: script name on back. Cards were issued in five card nickel packs which came 24 packs to a box. These variations resulted when Bowman used twelve of the lower numbers to fill out the last press sheet of 36 cards, adding to numbers 217-240. Cards 1-3 and 5-73 can be found with either gray or white backs. Certain cards have been seen with a "gray" or "slate" background on the front. These cards are a result of a color printing error and are rarely seen on the secondary market so no value is established for them. Not all numbers are known to exist in this fashion. However, within the numbers between 75 and 107, slightly more of these cards have appeared on the market. Within the high numbers series (145-240), these cards have been seen but the appearance of these cards are very rare. Other cards are known to be extant with double printed backs. The set features the Rookie Cards of Hall of Famers Roy Campanella, Bob Lemon, Robin Roberts, Duke Snider, and Early Wynn as well as Rookie Cards of Richie Ashburn and Gil Hodges.

COMP. MASTER SET (252)	10000.00	16000.00
COMPLETE SET (240)	10000.00	15000.00
COMMON CARD (1-144)	7.50	15.00
COMMON (145-240)	30.00	50.00
WRAPPER (1-CENT,Rd,Wh,Bl)		
WRAP.(5-CENT,GREEN)	200.00	250.00
WRAP.(5-CENT,BLUE)	150.00	200.00
1 Vern Bickford RC	75.00	125.00
2 Whitey Lockman	20.00	40.00
3 Bob Porterfield RC	7.50	15.00
4A Jerry Priddy NNOF RC	7.50	15.00
4B Jerry Priddy NOF	30.00	50.00
5 Hank Sauer	20.00	40.00
6 Phil Cavarretta RC	20.00	40.00
7 Joe Dobson RC	7.50	15.00
8 Murry Dickson RC	7.50	15.00
9 Ferris Fain	20.00	40.00
10 Ted Gray RC	7.50	15.00
11 Lou Boudreau MG RC	50.00	80.00
12 Cass Michaels RC	7.50	15.00
13 Bob Chesnes RC	7.50	15.00
14 Curt Simmons RC	20.00	40.00
15 Ned Garver RC	7.50	15.00
16 Al Kozar RC	7.50	15.00
17 Earl Torgeson RC	7.50	15.00
18 Bobby Thomson	20.00	40.00
19 Bobby Brown RC	35.00	60.00
20 Gene Hermanski RC	7.50	15.00
21 Frank Baumholtz RC	12.50	25.00
22 Peanuts Lowrey RC	7.50	15.00
23 Bobby Doerr	50.00	80.00
24 Stan Musial	350.00	600.00
25 Carl Scheib RC	7.50	15.00
26 George Kell RC	50.00	80.00
27 Bob Feller	200.00	300.00
28 Don Kolloway RC	7.50	15.00
29 Ralph Kiner	75.00	125.00
30 Andy Seminick	20.00	40.00
31 Dick Kokos RC	7.50	15.00
32 Eddie Yost RC	35.00	60.00
33 Warren Spahn	125.00	200.00
34 Dave Koslo	7.50	15.00
35 Vic Raschi RC	35.00	60.00
36 Pee Wee Reese	125.00	200.00
37 Johnny Wyrostek	7.50	15.00
38 Emil Verban	7.50	15.00
39 Billy Goodman RC	12.50	25.00
40 George Munger RC	7.50	15.00
41 Lou Brissie RC	7.50	15.00
42 Hoot Evers RC	7.50	15.00
43 Dale Mitchell RC	20.00	40.00
44 Dave Philley RC	7.50	15.00
45 Wally Westlake RC	7.50	15.00
46 Robin Roberts RC	150.00	250.00
47 Johnny Sain	35.00	60.00
48 Willard Marshall	7.50	15.00
49 Frank Shea	12.50	25.00
50 Jackie Robinson RC	900.00	1500.00
51 Herman Wehmeier	7.50	15.00
52 Johnny Schmitz RC	7.50	15.00
53 Jack Kramer RC	7.50	15.00
54 Marty Marion	35.00	60.00
55 Eddie Joost	7.50	15.00
56 Pat Mullin RC	7.50	15.00
57 Gene Bearden RC	20.00	40.00
58 Bob Elliott	20.00	40.00
59 Jack Lohrke	7.50	15.00
60 Yogi Berra	175.00	300.00
61 Rex Barney	20.00	40.00
62 Grady Hatton RC	7.50	15.00
63 Andy Pafko RC	20.00	40.00
64 Dom DiMaggio	35.00	60.00
65 Enos Slaughter	50.00	80.00
66 Elmer Valo RC	7.50	15.00
67 Alvin Dark RC	20.00	40.00
68 Sheldon Jones	7.50	15.00
69 Tommy Henrich	20.00	40.00
70 Carl Furillo RC	90.00	150.00
71 Vern Stephens RC	7.50	15.00
72 Tommy Holmes RC	20.00	40.00
73 Billy Cox RC	20.00	40.00
74 Tom McBride RC	7.50	15.00
75 Eddie Mayo RC	7.50	15.00
76 Bill Nicholson RC	12.50	25.00
77 Ernie Bonham RC	7.50	15.00
78A Sam Zoldak NNOF RC	7.50	15.00
78B Sam Zoldak NOF	30.00	50.00
79 Ron Northey RC	7.50	15.00
80 Bill McCahan	7.50	15.00
81 Virgil Stallcup RC	7.50	15.00
82 Joe Page	35.00	60.00
83A Bob Scheffing NNOF RC	7.50	15.00
83B Bob Scheffing NOF	30.00	50.00
84 Roy Campanella RC	500.00	800.00
85A Johnny Mize NNOF	60.00	100.00
85B Johnny Mize NOF	90.00	150.00
86 Johnny Pesky RC	35.00	60.00
87 Randy Gumpert RC	7.50	15.00
88A Bill Salkeld NNOF RC	7.50	15.00
88B Bill Salkeld NOF	30.00	50.00
89 Mizell Platt RC	7.50	15.00
90 Gil Coan RC	7.50	15.00
91 Dick Wakefield RC	7.50	15.00
92 Willie Jones RC	20.00	40.00
93 Ed Stevens RC	7.50	15.00
94 Mickey Vernon RC	20.00	40.00
95 Howie Pollet RC	7.50	15.00
96 Taft Wright	7.50	15.00
97 Danny Litwhiler RC	7.50	15.00
98A Phil Rizzuto NNOF	125.00	200.00
98B Phil Rizzuto NOF	150.00	250.00
99 Frank Gustine RC	7.50	15.00
100 Gil Hodges RC	150.00	250.00
101 Sid Gordon	7.50	15.00
102 Stan Spence RC	7.50	15.00
103 Joe Tipton RC	7.50	15.00
104 Eddie Stanky RC	20.00	40.00
105 Bill Kennedy RC	7.50	15.00
106 Jake Early RC	7.50	15.00
107 Eddie Lake RC	7.50	15.00
108 Ken Heintzelman RC	7.50	15.00
109A Ed Fitzgerald SCR RC	7.50	15.00
109B Ed Fitzgerald PR	35.00	60.00
110 Early Wynn RC	90.00	150.00
111 Red Schoendienst	60.00	100.00
112 Sam Chapman	20.00	40.00
113 Ray LaManno RC	7.50	15.00
114 Allie Reynolds	35.00	60.00
115 Dutch Leonard	7.50	15.00
116 Joe Hatten RC	7.50	15.00
117 Walker Cooper	7.50	15.00
118 Sam Mele RC	7.50	15.00
119 Floyd Baker RC	7.50	15.00
120 Cliff Fannin RC	7.50	15.00
121 Mark Christman RC	7.50	15.00
122 George Vico RC	7.50	15.00
123 Johnny Blatnik UER	7.50	15.00
Card spelled as Blatnick		
124A D.Murtaugh SCR RC	20.00	40.00
124B D.Murtaugh PR	35.00	60.00
125 Ken Keltner RC	12.50	25.00
126A Al Brazle SCR RC	7.50	15.00
126B Al Brazle PR	35.00	60.00
127A Hank Majeski SCR RC	7.50	15.00
127B Hank Majeski PR	35.00	60.00
128 Johnny VanderMeer	35.00	60.00
129 Bill Johnson	20.00	40.00
130 Harry Walker RC	7.50	15.00
131 Paul Lehner RC	7.50	15.00
132A Al Evans SCR RC	7.50	15.00
132B Al Evans PR	35.00	60.00
133 Aaron Robinson RC	7.50	15.00
134 Hank Borowy RC	7.50	15.00
135 Stan Rojek RC	7.50	15.00
136 Hank Edwards RC	7.50	15.00
137 Ted Wilks RC	7.50	15.00
138 Buddy Rosar	7.50	15.00
139 Hank Arft RC	7.50	15.00
140 Ray Scarborough RC	7.50	15.00
141 Tony Lupien RC	7.50	15.00
142 Eddie Waitkus RC	20.00	40.00
143A Bob Dillinger SCR RC	12.50	25.00
143B Bob Dillinger PR	35.00	60.00
144 Mickey Haefner RC	7.50	15.00
145 Sylvester Donnelly RC	30.00	50.00
146 Mike McCormick RC	30.00	50.00
147 Bert Singleton RC	30.00	50.00
148 Bob Swift RC	30.00	50.00
149 Roy Partee RC	30.00	50.00
150 Allie Clark RC	30.00	50.00
151 Mickey Harris RC	30.00	50.00
152 Clarence Maddern RC	30.00	50.00
153 Phil Masi RC	30.00	50.00
154 Clint Hartung	35.00	60.00
155 Mickey Guerra RC	30.00	50.00
156 Al Zarilla RC	30.00	50.00
157 Walt Masterson RC	30.00	50.00
158 Harry Brecheen RC	35.00	60.00
159 Glen Moulder RC	30.00	50.00
160 Jim Blackburn RC	30.00	50.00
161 Jocko Thompson RC	30.00	50.00
162 Preacher Roe RC	75.00	125.00
163 Clyde McCullough RC	30.00	50.00
164 Vic Wertz RC	50.00	80.00
165 Snuffy Stirnweiss	50.00	80.00
166 Mike Tresh RC	30.00	50.00
167 Babe Martin RC	30.00	50.00
168 Doyle Lade RC	30.00	50.00
169 Jeff Heath RC	35.00	60.00
170 Bill Rigney	35.00	60.00
171 Dick Fowler RC	30.00	50.00
172 Eddie Pellagrini RC	30.00	50.00
173 Eddie Stewart RC	30.00	50.00
174 Terry Moore RC	50.00	80.00
175 Luke Appling	90.00	150.00
176 Ken Raffensberger RC	30.00	50.00
177 Stan Lopata RC	35.00	60.00
178 Tom Brown RC	35.00	60.00
179 Hugh Casey	50.00	80.00
180 Connie Berry	30.00	50.00
181 Gus Niarhos RC	30.00	50.00
182 Hal Peck RC	30.00	50.00
183 Lou Stringer RC	30.00	50.00
184 Bob Chipman RC	30.00	50.00
185 Pete Reiser	50.00	80.00
186 Buddy Kerr	30.00	50.00
187 Phil Marchildon RC	30.00	50.00
188 Karl Drews RC	30.00	50.00
189 Earl Wooten RC	30.00	50.00
190 Jim Hearn RC	30.00	50.00
191 Joe Haynes RC	30.00	50.00
192 Harry Gumbert	30.00	50.00
193 Ken Trinkle RC	30.00	50.00
194 Ralph Branca RC	60.00	100.00
195 Eddie Bockman RC	30.00	50.00
196 Fred Hutchinson RC	35.00	60.00
197 Johnny Lindell	35.00	60.00
198 Steve Gromek RC	30.00	50.00
199 Tex Hughson RC	30.00	50.00
200 Jess Dobernic RC	30.00	50.00
201 Sibby Sisti RC	30.00	50.00
202 Larry Jansen	35.00	60.00
203 Barney McCosky	30.00	50.00
204 Bob Savage RC	30.00	50.00
205 Dick Sisler RC	35.00	60.00
206 Bruce Edwards	30.00	50.00
207 Johnny Hopp RC	30.00	50.00
208 Dizzy Trout	35.00	60.00
209 Charlie Keller	50.00	80.00
210 Joe Gordon RC	50.00	80.00
211 Boo Ferriss RC	30.00	50.00
212 Ralph Hamner RC	30.00	50.00
213 Red Barrett RC	30.00	50.00
214 Richie Ashburn RC	350.00	600.00
215 Kirby Higbe	30.00	50.00
216 Schoolboy Rowe	35.00	60.00
217 Marino Pieretti RC	30.00	50.00
218 Dick Kryhoski RC	30.00	50.00
219 Virgil Trucks RC	35.00	60.00
220 Johnny McCarthy	30.00	50.00
NY Giants Cap but listed as Sioux City MG		
221 Bob Muncrief RC	30.00	50.00
222 Alex Kellner RC	30.00	50.00
223 Bobby Hofman RC	30.00	50.00
224 Satchel Paige RC	1000.00	1500.00
225 Jerry Coleman RC	50.00	80.00
226 Duke Snider RC	600.00	1000.00
227 Fritz Ostermueller	30.00	50.00
228 Jackie Mayo RC	30.00	50.00
229 Ed Lopat RC	90.00	150.00
230 Augie Galan	35.00	60.00
231 Earl Johnson RC	30.00	50.00
232 George McQuinn	35.00	60.00
233 Larry Doby RC	175.00	300.00
234 Rip Sewell RC	30.00	50.00
235 Jim Russell RC	30.00	50.00
236 Fred Sanford RC	30.00	50.00
237 Monte Kennedy RC	30.00	50.00
238 Bob Lemon RC	125.00	200.00
239 Frank McCormick	30.00	50.00
240 Babe Young UER	60.00	100.00
(Photo actually Bobby Young)		

1950 Bowman

The cards in this 252-card set measure approximately 2 1/16" by 2 1/2". This set, marketed in 1950 by Bowman, represented a major improvement in terms of quality over their previous efforts. Each card was a beautifully colored line drawing developed from a simple photograph. The first 72 cards are the scarcest in the set, while the final 72 cards may be found with or without the copyright line. This was the only Bowman sports set to carry the famous "5-Star" logo. Cards were issued in five-card nickel packs. Key rookies in this set are Hank Bauer, Don Newcombe, and Al Rosen.

COMPLETE SET (252)	6000.00	8500.00
COMMON CARD (1-72)	30.00	50.00
COMMON CARD (73-252)	7.50	15.00
WRAPPER (1-CENT)	200.00	250.00
WRAPPER (5-CENT)	200.00	250.00
1 Mel Parnell RC	90.00	150.00
2 Vern Stephens	35.00	60.00
3 Dom DiMaggio	50.00	80.00
4 Gus Zernial RC	35.00	60.00
5 Bob Kuzava RC	30.00	50.00
6 Bob Feller	175.00	300.00
7 Jim Hegan	35.00	60.00
8 George Kell	50.00	80.00
9 Vic Wertz	35.00	60.00
10 Tommy Henrich	50.00	80.00
11 Phil Rizzuto	175.00	300.00
12 Joe Page	50.00	80.00
13 Ferris Fain	35.00	60.00
14 Alex Kellner	30.00	50.00
15 Al Kozar	30.00	50.00
16 Roy Sievers RC	50.00	80.00
17 Sid Hudson	30.00	50.00
18 Eddie Robinson RC	30.00	50.00
19 Warren Spahn	175.00	300.00
20 Bob Elliott	35.00	60.00
21 Pee Wee Reese	175.00	300.00
22 Jackie Robinson	700.00	1200.00
23 Don Newcombe RC	90.00	150.00
24 Johnny Schmitz	30.00	50.00
25 Hank Sauer	35.00	60.00
26 Grady Hatton	30.00	50.00
27 Herman Wehmeier	30.00	50.00
28 Bobby Thomson	50.00	80.00
29 Eddie Stanky	35.00	60.00
30 Eddie Waitkus	35.00	60.00
31 Del Ennis	50.00	80.00
32 Robin Roberts	90.00	150.00
33 Ralph Kiner	60.00	100.00
34 Murry Dickson	30.00	50.00
35 Enos Slaughter	60.00	100.00
36 Eddie Kazak RC	35.00	60.00
37 Luke Appling	50.00	80.00
38 Bill Wight RC	30.00	50.00
39 Larry Doby	60.00	100.00
40 Bob Lemon	50.00	80.00
41 Hoot Evers	30.00	50.00
42 Art Houtteman RC	30.00	50.00
43 Bobby Doerr	50.00	80.00
44 Joe Dobson	30.00	50.00
45 Al Zarilla	30.00	50.00
46 Yogi Berra	250.00	400.00
47 Jerry Coleman	50.00	80.00
48 Lou Brissie	30.00	50.00
49 Elmer Valo	30.00	50.00
50 Dick Kokos	30.00	50.00
51 Ned Garver	35.00	60.00
52 Sam Mele	30.00	50.00
53 Clyde Vollmer RC	30.00	50.00
54 Gil Coan	30.00	50.00
55 Buddy Kerr	30.00	50.00
56 Del Crandall RC	35.00	60.00
57 Vern Bickford	30.00	50.00
58 Carl Furillo	50.00	80.00
59 Ralph Branca	50.00	80.00
60 Andy Pafko	35.00	60.00
61 Bob Rush RC	30.00	50.00
62 Ted Kluszewski	75.00	125.00
63 Ewell Blackwell	35.00	60.00
64 Alvin Dark	35.00	60.00
65 Dave Koslo	30.00	50.00
66 Larry Jansen	35.00	60.00
67 Willie Jones	35.00	60.00
68 Curt Simmons	35.00	60.00
69 Wally Westlake	30.00	50.00
70 Bob Chesnes	30.00	50.00
71 Red Schoendienst	50.00	80.00
72 Howie Pollet	30.00	50.00
73 Willard Marshall	7.50	15.00
74 Johnny Antonelli RC	35.00	60.00
75 Roy Campanella	175.00	300.00
76 Rex Barney	20.00	40.00
77 Duke Snider	175.00	300.00
78 Mickey Owen	12.50	25.00
79 Johnny VanderMeer	20.00	40.00
80 Howard Fox RC	7.50	15.00
81 Ron Northey	7.50	15.00
82 Whitey Lockman	12.50	25.00
83 Sheldon Jones	7.50	15.00
84 Richie Ashburn	75.00	125.00
85 Ken Heintzelman	7.50	15.00
86 Stan Rojek	7.50	15.00
87 Bill Werle RC	7.50	15.00
88 Marty Marion	20.00	40.00
89 George Munger	7.50	15.00
90 Harry Brecheen	20.00	40.00
91 Cass Michaels	7.50	15.00
92 Hank Majeski	7.50	15.00
93 Gene Bearden	20.00	40.00
94 Lou Boudreau MG	35.00	60.00
95 Aaron Robinson	7.50	15.00
96 Virgil Trucks	12.50	25.00
97 Maurice McDermott RC	7.50	15.00
98 Ted Williams	600.00	1000.00
99 Billy Goodman	12.50	25.00
100 Vic Raschi	35.00	60.00
101 Bobby Brown	35.00	60.00
102 Billy Johnson	12.50	25.00
103 Eddie Joost	7.50	15.00
104 Sam Chapman	7.50	15.00
105 Bob Dillinger	7.50	15.00
106 Cliff Fannin	7.50	15.00
107 Sam Dente RC	7.50	15.00
108 Ray Scarborough	7.50	15.00
109 Sid Gordon	7.50	15.00
110 Tommy Holmes	12.50	25.00
111 Walker Cooper	7.50	15.00
112 Gil Hodges	75.00	125.00
113 Gene Hermanski	7.50	15.00
114 Wayne Terwilliger RC	7.50	15.00
115 Roy Smalley	7.50	15.00
116 Virgil Stallcup	7.50	15.00
117 Bill Rigney	7.50	15.00
118 Clint Hartung	7.50	15.00
119 Dick Sisler	12.50	25.00
120 John Thompson	7.50	15.00
121 Andy Seminick	12.50	25.00
122 Johnny Hopp	12.50	25.00
123 Dino Restelli RC	7.50	15.00
124 Clyde McCullough	7.50	15.00
125 Del Rice RC	7.50	15.00
126 Al Brazle	7.50	15.00
127 Dave Philley	7.50	15.00
128 Phil Masi	7.50	15.00
129 Joe Gordon	12.50	25.00
130 Dale Mitchell	12.50	25.00
131 Steve Gromek	7.50	15.00
132 Mickey Vernon	12.50	25.00
133 Don Kolloway	7.50	15.00
134 Paul Trout	7.50	15.00
135 Pat Mullin	7.50	15.00
136 Buddy Rosar	7.50	15.00
137 Johnny Pesky	12.50	25.00
138 Allie Reynolds	35.00	60.00
139 Johnny Mize	50.00	80.00
140 Pete Suder RC	7.50	15.00
141 Joe Coleman RC	12.50	25.00
142 Sherman Lollar RC	20.00	40.00
143 Eddie Stewart	7.50	15.00
144 Al Evans	7.50	15.00
145 Jack Graham RC	7.50	15.00
146 Floyd Baker	7.50	15.00
147 Mike Garcia RC	20.00	40.00
148 Early Wynn	50.00	80.00
149 Bob Swift	7.50	15.00
150 George Vico	7.50	15.00
151 Fred Hutchinson	12.50	25.00
152 Ellis Kinder RC	7.50	15.00
153 Walt Masterson	7.50	15.00
154 Gus Niarhos	7.50	15.00
155 Frank Shea	12.50	25.00
156 Fred Sanford	12.50	25.00
157 Mike Guerra	7.50	15.00
158 Paul Lehner	7.50	15.00
159 Joe Tipton	7.50	15.00
160 Mickey Harris	7.50	15.00
161 Sherry Robertson RC	7.50	15.00
162 Eddie Yost	12.50	25.00
163 Earl Torgeson	7.50	15.00
164 Sibby Sisti	7.50	15.00
165 Bruce Edwards	7.50	15.00
166 Joe Hatton	7.50	15.00
167 Preacher Roe	35.00	60.00
168 Bob Scheffing	7.50	15.00
169 Hank Edwards	7.50	15.00
170 Dutch Leonard	7.50	15.00
171 Harry Gumbert	7.50	15.00
172 Peanuts Lowrey	7.50	15.00
173 Lloyd Merriman RC	7.50	15.00
174 Hank Thompson RC	20.00	40.00
175 Monte Kennedy	7.50	15.00
176 Sylvester Donnelly	7.50	15.00
177 Hank Borowy	7.50	15.00
178 Ed Fitzgerald	7.50	15.00
179 Chuck Diering RC	7.50	15.00
180 Harry Walker	12.50	25.00
181 Marino Pieretti	7.50	15.00
182 Sam Zoldak	7.50	15.00
183 Mickey Haefner	7.50	15.00
184 Randy Gumpert	7.50	15.00
185 Howie Judson RC	7.50	15.00
186 Ken Keltner	12.50	25.00
187 Lou Stringer	7.50	15.00
188 Earl Johnson	7.50	15.00
189 Owen Friend RC	7.50	15.00
190 Ken Wood RC	7.50	15.00
191 Dick Starr RC	7.50	15.00
192 Bob Chipman	7.50	15.00
193 Pete Reiser	20.00	40.00
194 Billy Cox	35.00	60.00
195 Phil Cavarretta	20.00	40.00
196 Doyle Lade	7.50	15.00
197 Johnny Wyrostek	7.50	15.00
198 Danny Litwhiler	7.50	15.00
199 Jack Kramer	7.50	15.00
200 Kirby Higbe	12.50	25.00
201 Pete Castiglione RC	7.50	15.00
202 Cliff Chambers RC	7.50	15.00
203 Danny Murtaugh	12.50	25.00
204 Granny Hamner RC	20.00	40.00
205 Mike Goliat RC	7.50	15.00
206 Stan Lopata	12.50	25.00
207 Max Lanier RC	7.50	15.00
208 Jim Hearn	7.50	15.00
209 Johnny Lindell	7.50	15.00
210 Ted Gray	7.50	15.00
211 Charlie Keller	20.00	40.00
212 Jerry Priddy	7.50	15.00
213 Carl Scheib	7.50	15.00
214 Dick Fowler	7.50	15.00
215 Ed Lopat	35.00	60.00
216 Bob Porterfield	12.50	25.00
217 Casey Stengel MG	75.00	125.00
218 Cliff Mapes RC	12.50	25.00
219 Hank Bauer RC	60.00	100.00
220 Leo Durocher MG	35.00	60.00
221 Don Mueller RC	20.00	40.00
222 Bobby Morgan RC	7.50	15.00
223 Jim Russell	7.50	15.00
224 Jack Banta RC	7.50	15.00
225 Eddie Sawyer MG RC	12.50	25.00
226 Jim Konstanty RC	35.00	60.00
227 Bob Miller RC	12.50	25.00
228 Bill Nicholson	12.50	25.00
229 Frankie Frisch MG	35.00	60.00
230 Bill Serena RC	7.50	15.00
231 Preston Ward RC	7.50	15.00
232 Al Rosen RC	35.00	60.00
233 Allie Clark	7.50	15.00
234 Bobby Shantz RC	35.00	60.00
235 Harold Gilbert RC	7.50	15.00
236 Bob Cain RC	7.50	15.00
237 Bill Salkeld	7.50	15.00
238 Nippy Jones RC	7.50	15.00
239 Bill Howerton RC	7.50	15.00
240 Eddie Lake	7.50	15.00
241 Neil Berry RC	7.50	15.00
242 Dick Kryhoski	7.50	15.00
243 Johnny Groth RC	7.50	15.00
244 Dale Coogan RC	7.50	15.00
245 Al Papai RC	7.50	15.00
246 Walt Dropo RC	20.00	40.00
247 Irv Noren RC	12.50	25.00
248 Sam Jethroe RC	35.00	60.00
249 Snuffy Stirnweiss	12.50	25.00
250 Ray Coleman RC	7.50	15.00
251 Les Moss RC	7.50	15.00
252 Billy DeMars RC	35.00	60.00

1951 Bowman

The cards in this 324-card set measure approximately 2 1/16" by 3 1/8". Many of the obverses of the cards appearing in the 1951 Bowman set are enlargements of those appearing in the previous year. The high number series (253-324) is highly valued and contains the true "Rookie" cards of Mickey Mantle and Willie Mays. Card number 195 depicts Paul Richards in caricature. George Kell's card (number 46) incorrectly lists him as being in the "1941" Bowman series. Cards were issued either in one card penny packs which came 120 to a box or in six-card nickel packs which came 24 to a box. Player names are found printed in a panel on the front of the card. These cards were supposedly also sold in sheets in variety stores in the Philadelphia area.

COMPLETE SET (324)	15000.00	20000.00
COMMON CARD (1-252)	10.00	20.00
COMMON (253-324)	30.00	50.00
WRAPPER (1-CENT)	150.00	200.00
WRAPPER (5-CENT)	200.00	250.00
1 Whitey Ford RC	1500.00	2500.00
2 Yogi Berra	250.00	400.00
3 Robin Roberts	60.00	100.00
4 Del Ennis	12.50	25.00
5 Dale Mitchell	12.50	25.00
6 Don Newcombe	35.00	60.00
7 Gil Hodges	75.00	125.00
8 Paul Lehner	10.00	20.00
9 Sam Chapman	10.00	20.00
10 Red Schoendienst	35.00	60.00
11 George Munger	10.00	20.00
12 Hank Majeski	10.00	20.00
13 Eddie Stanky	12.50	25.00
14 Alvin Dark	20.00	40.00
15 Johnny Pesky	12.50	25.00
16 Maurice McDermott	10.00	20.00
17 Pete Castiglione	10.00	20.00
18 Gil Coan	10.00	20.00
19 Sid Gordon	10.00	20.00
20 Del Crandall UER	12.50	25.00
(Misspelled Crandell on card)		
21 Snuffy Stirnweiss	12.50	25.00
wearing St.L.Browns hat		
22 Hank Sauer	12.50	25.00
23 Hoot Evers	10.00	20.00
24 Ewell Blackwell	20.00	40.00
25 Vic Raschi	35.00	60.00
26 Phil Rizzuto	90.00	150.00
27 Jim Konstanty	12.50	25.00
28 Eddie Waitkus	10.00	20.00
29 Allie Clark	10.00	20.00
30 Bob Feller	75.00	125.00
31 Roy Campanella	175.00	300.00
32 Duke Snider	150.00	250.00
33 Bob Hooper RC	10.00	20.00
34 Marty Marion	20.00	40.00
35 Al Zarilla	10.00	20.00
36 Joe Dobson	10.00	20.00
37 Whitey Lockman	20.00	40.00
38 Al Evans	10.00	20.00
39 Ray Scarborough	10.00	20.00
40 Gus Bell RC	35.00	60.00
41 Eddie Yost	12.50	25.00
42 Vern Bickford	10.00	20.00
43 Billy DeMars	10.00	20.00
44 Roy Smalley	10.00	20.00
45 Art Houtteman	10.00	20.00
46 George Kell 1941 UER	35.00	60.00
47 Grady Hatton	10.00	20.00
48 Ken Raffensberger	10.00	20.00
49 Jerry Coleman	12.50	25.00
50 Johnny Mize	50.00	80.00
51 Andy Seminick	10.00	20.00
52 Dick Sisler	20.00	40.00
53 Bob Lemon	35.00	60.00
54 Ray Boone RC	20.00	40.00
55 Gene Hermanski	10.00	20.00
56 Ralph Branca	35.00	60.00
57 Alex Kellner	10.00	20.00
58 Enos Slaughter	35.00	60.00
59 Randy Gumpert	10.00	20.00
60 Chico Carrasquel RC	35.00	60.00
61 Jim Hearn	12.50	25.00
62 Lou Boudreau MG	35.00	60.00
63 Bob Dillinger	10.00	20.00
64 Bill Werle	10.00	20.00
65 Mickey Vernon	20.00	40.00
66 Bob Elliott	12.50	25.00
67 Roy Sievers	12.50	25.00
68 Dick Kokos	10.00	20.00
69 Johnny Schmitz	10.00	20.00
70 Ron Northey	10.00	20.00
71 Jerry Priddy	10.00	20.00
72 Lloyd Merriman	10.00	20.00
73 Tommy Byrne RC	10.00	20.00
74 Billy Johnson	12.50	25.00
75 Russ Meyer RC	12.50	25.00
76 Stan Lopata	12.50	25.00
77 Mike Goliat	10.00	20.00
78 Early Wynn	35.00	60.00
79 Jim Hegan	12.50	25.00
80 Pee Wee Reese	125.00	200.00
81 Carl Furillo	35.00	60.00
82 Joe Tipton	10.00	20.00
83 Carl Scheib	10.00	20.00
84 Barney McCosky	10.00	20.00
85 Eddie Kazak	10.00	20.00
86 Harry Brecheen	12.50	25.00
87 Floyd Baker	10.00	20.00
88 Eddie Robinson	10.00	20.00
89 Hank Thompson	12.50	25.00
90 Dave Koslo	10.00	20.00
91 Clyde Vollmer	10.00	20.00
92 Vern Stephens	12.50	25.00
93 Danny O'Connell RC	10.00	20.00
94 Clyde McCullough	10.00	20.00
95 Sherry Robertson	10.00	20.00
96 Sandy Consuegra RC	10.00	20.00
97 Bob Kuzava	10.00	20.00
98 Willard Marshall	10.00	20.00
99 Earl Torgeson	10.00	20.00
100 Sherm Lollar	12.50	25.00
101 Owen Friend	10.00	20.00
102 Dutch Leonard	10.00	20.00
103 Andy Pafko	20.00	40.00
104 Virgil Trucks	12.50	25.00
105 Don Kolloway	10.00	20.00
106 Pat Mullin	10.00	20.00
107 Johnny Wyrostek	10.00	20.00
108 Virgil Stallcup	10.00	20.00
109 Allie Reynolds	35.00	60.00
110 Bobby Brown	20.00	40.00
111 Curt Simmons	12.50	25.00
112 Willie Jones	10.00	20.00
113 Bill Nicholson	10.00	20.00
114 Sam Zoldak	10.00	20.00
Pictured in Indians uniform		
115 Steve Gromek	10.00	20.00
116 Bruce Edwards	10.00	20.00
117 Eddie Miksis RC	10.00	20.00
118 Preacher Roe	35.00	60.00
119 Eddie Joost	10.00	20.00
120 Joe Coleman	12.50	25.00
121 Gerry Staley RC	10.00	20.00
122 Joe Garagiola RC	60.00	100.00
123 Howie Judson	10.00	20.00
124 Gus Niarhos	10.00	20.00
125 Bill Rigney	12.50	25.00
126 Bobby Thomson	35.00	60.00
127 Sal Maglie RC	35.00	60.00
128 Ellis Kinder	10.00	20.00
129 Matt Batts	10.00	20.00
130 Tom Saffell RC	10.00	20.00
131 Cliff Chambers	10.00	20.00
132 Cass Michaels	10.00	20.00
133 Sam Dente	10.00	20.00
134 Warren Spahn	90.00	150.00
135 Walker Cooper	10.00	20.00
136 Ray Coleman	10.00	20.00
137 Dick Starr	10.00	20.00
138 Phil Cavarretta	12.50	25.00
139 Doyle Lade	10.00	20.00
140 Eddie Lake	10.00	20.00
141 Fred Hutchinson	12.50	25.00
142 Aaron Robinson	10.00	20.00
143 Ted Kluszewski	50.00	80.00
144 Herman Wehmeier	10.00	20.00
145 Fred Sanford	12.50	25.00
146 Johnny Hopp	12.50	25.00
147 Ken Heintzelman	10.00	20.00
148 Granny Hamner	10.00	20.00
149 Bubba Church RC	10.00	20.00
150 Mike Garcia	12.50	25.00
151 Larry Doby	35.00	60.00
152 Cal Abrams RC	10.00	20.00
153 Rex Barney	12.50	25.00
154 Pete Suder	10.00	20.00
155 Lou Brissie	10.00	20.00
156 Del Rice	10.00	20.00
157 Al Brazle	10.00	20.00
158 Chuck Diering	10.00	20.00
159 Eddie Stewart	10.00	20.00
160 Phil Masi	10.00	20.00
161 Wes Westrum RC	10.00	20.00
162 Larry Jansen	12.50	25.00
163 Monte Kennedy	10.00	20.00
164 Bill Wight	10.00	20.00
165 Ted Williams UER	500.00	800.00
Wrong birthdate		
166 Stan Rojek	10.00	20.00
Pictured in Pirates uniform		
167 Murry Dickson	10.00	20.00
168 Sam Mele	10.00	20.00
169 Sid Hudson	10.00	20.00
170 Sibby Sisti	10.00	20.00
171 Buddy Kerr	10.00	20.00
172 Ned Garver	10.00	20.00
173 Hank Arft	10.00	20.00
174 Mickey Owen	12.50	25.00
175 Wayne Terwilliger	10.00	20.00
176 Vic Wertz	20.00	40.00
177 Charlie Keller	12.50	25.00
178 Ted Gray	10.00	20.00
179 Danny Litwhiler	10.00	20.00
180 Howie Fox	10.00	20.00
181 Casey Stengel MG	50.00	80.00
182 Tom Ferrick RC	10.00	20.00
183 Hank Bauer	35.00	60.00
184 Eddie Sawyer MG	20.00	40.00
185 Jimmy Bloodworth	10.00	20.00
186 Richie Ashburn	60.00	100.00
187 Al Rosen	20.00	40.00
188 Bobby Avila RC	12.50	25.00
189 Erv Palica RC	10.00	20.00
190 Joe Hatten	10.00	20.00
191 Billy Hitchcock RC	10.00	20.00
192 Hank Wyse RC	10.00	20.00
193 Ted Wilks	10.00	20.00
194 Peanuts Lowrey	10.00	20.00
195 Paul Richards MG	12.50	25.00
(Caricature)		
196 Billy Pierce RC	35.00	60.00
197 Bob Cain	10.00	20.00
198 Monte Irvin RC	75.00	125.00
199 Sheldon Jones	10.00	20.00
200 Jack Kramer	10.00	20.00
Pictured in NY Giants uniform		
201 Steve O'Neill MG RC	10.00	20.00
202 Mike Guerra	10.00	20.00
203 Vernon Law RC	35.00	60.00
204 Vic Lombardi RC	10.00	20.00
205 Mickey Grasso RC	10.00	20.00
206 Conrado Marrero RC	10.00	20.00
207 Billy Southworth MG RC	10.00	20.00
208 Blix Donnelly	10.00	20.00
209 Ken Wood	10.00	20.00
210 Les Moss	10.00	20.00
Pictured in St.L.Browns uniform		
211 Hal Jeffcoat RC	10.00	20.00
212 Bob Rush	10.00	20.00
213 Neil Berry	10.00	20.00
214 Bob Swift	10.00	20.00
215 Ken Peterson	10.00	20.00
216 Connie Ryan RC	10.00	20.00
217 Joe Page	12.50	25.00
218 Ed Lopat	35.00	60.00
219 Gene Woodling RC	35.00	60.00
220 Bob Miller	10.00	20.00
221 Dick Whitman RC	10.00	20.00
222 Thurman Tucker RC	10.00	20.00
223 Johnny VanderMeer	20.00	40.00
224 Billy Cox	12.50	25.00
225 Dan Bankhead RC	20.00	40.00
226 Jimmy Dykes MG	10.00	20.00
227 Bobby Shantz UER	12.50	25.00
Sic, Schantz		
228 Cloyd Boyer RC	12.50	25.00
229 Bill Howerton	10.00	20.00
Pictured in St.L.Cardinals uniform		
230 Max Lanier	10.00	20.00
231 Luis Aloma RC	10.00	20.00
232 Nelson Fox RC	150.00	250.00
233 Leo Durocher MG	35.00	60.00
234 Clint Hartung	12.50	25.00
235 Jack Lohrke	10.00	20.00
236 Buddy Rosar	10.00	20.00
237 Billy Goodman	12.50	25.00
238 Pete Reiser	20.00	40.00
239 Bill MacDonald RC	10.00	20.00
240 Joe Haynes	10.00	20.00
241 Irv Noren	12.50	25.00
242 Sam Jethroe	12.50	25.00
243 Johnny Antonelli	12.50	25.00
244 Cliff Fannin	10.00	20.00
245 John Berardino RC	35.00	60.00
246 Bill Serena	10.00	20.00
247 Bob Ramazzotti RC	10.00	20.00
248 Johnny Klippstein RC	10.00	20.00
249 Johnny Groth	10.00	20.00
250 Hank Borowy	10.00	20.00
251 Willard Ramsdell RC	10.00	20.00
252 Dixie Howell RC	10.00	20.00
253 Mickey Mantle RC	5000.00	8000.00
254 Jackie Jensen RC	60.00	100.00
255 Milo Candini RC	30.00	50.00
256 Ken Silvestri RC	30.00	50.00
257 Birdie Tebbetts RC	35.00	60.00
258 Luke Easter RC	35.00	60.00
259 Chuck Dressen MG	35.00	60.00
260 Carl Erskine RC	60.00	100.00
261 Wally Moses	35.00	60.00
262 Gus Zernial	35.00	60.00
263 Howie Pollet	35.00	60.00
Pictured in Cardinals uniform		
264 Don Richmond RC	30.00	50.00
265 Steve Bilko RC	30.00	50.00
266 Harry Dorish RC	30.00	50.00
267 Ken Holcombe RC	30.00	50.00
268 Don Mueller	35.00	60.00
269 Ray Noble RC	30.00	50.00
270 Willard Nixon RC	30.00	50.00
271 Tommy Wright RC	30.00	50.00
272 Billy Meyer MG RC	30.00	50.00
273 Danny Murtaugh	35.00	60.00
274 George Metkovich RC	30.00	50.00
275 Bucky Harris MG	50.00	80.00
276 Frank Quinn RC	30.00	50.00
277 Roy Hartsfield RC	30.00	50.00
278 Norman Roy RC	30.00	50.00
279 Jim Delsing RC	30.00	50.00
280 Frank Overmire	30.00	50.00
Pictured in Browns uniform		
281 Al Widmar RC	30.00	50.00
282 Frank Frisch MG	60.00	100.00
283 Walt Dubiel RC	30.00	50.00
284 Gene Bearden	35.00	60.00
285 Johnny Lipon RC	30.00	50.00
286 Bob Usher RC	30.00	50.00
287 Jim Blackburn	30.00	50.00
288 Bobby Adams	30.00	50.00
289 Cliff Mapes	35.00	60.00
290 Bill Dickey CO	90.00	150.00
291 Tommy Henrich CO	50.00	80.00
292 Eddie Pellagrini	30.00	50.00
293 Ken Johnson RC	30.00	50.00
294 Jocko Thompson	30.00	50.00
295 Al Lopez MG RC	75.00	125.00
296 Bob Kennedy RC	35.00	60.00
297 Dave Philley	30.00	50.00
298 Joe Astroth RC	30.00	50.00
299 Clyde King RC	30.00	50.00
300 Hal Rice RC	30.00	50.00
301 Tommy Glaviano RC	30.00	50.00
302 Jim Busby RC	30.00	50.00
303 Marv Rotblatt RC	30.00	50.00
304 Al Gettell RC	30.00	50.00
305 Willie Mays RC	1800.00	2500.00
306 Jim Piersall RC	75.00	125.00

Card	Low	High
307 Walt Masterson	30.00	50.00
308 Ted Beard RC	30.00	50.00
309 Mel Queen RC	30.00	50.00
310 Erv Dusak RC	30.00	50.00
311 Mickey Harris	30.00	50.00
312 Gene Mauch RC	35.00	60.00
313 Ray Mueller RC	30.00	50.00
314 Johnny Sain	50.00	80.00
315 Zack Taylor MG	30.00	50.00
316 Duane Pillette RC	30.00	50.00
317 Smoky Burgess RC	50.00	80.00
318 Warren Hacker RC	30.00	50.00
319 Red Rolfe MG	35.00	60.00
320 Hal White RC	30.00	50.00
321 Earl Johnson	30.00	50.00
322 Luke Sewell MG	35.00	60.00
323 Joe Adcock RC	50.00	80.00
324 Johnny Pramesa RC	75.00	125.00

1952 Bowman

The cards in this 252-card set measure approximately 2 1/16" by 3 1/8". While the Bowman set of 1952 retained the card size introduced in 1951, it employed a modification of color tones from the two preceding years. The cards also appeared with a facsimile autograph on the front and, for the first time since 1949, premium advertising on the back. The 1952 set was apparently sold in sheets as well as in gum packs. Artwork for 15 cards that were never issued was discovered in the early 1980s. Cards were issued in one card penny packs or five card nickel packs. The five cent packs came 24 to a box. Notable Rookie Cards in this set are Lew Burdette, Gil McDougald, and Minnie Minoso.

Card	Low	High
COMPLETE SET (252)	5500.00	8500.00
COMMON CARD (1-216)	7.50	15.00
COMMON (217-252)	35.00	60.00
WRAPPER (1-CENT)	150.00	200.00
WRAPPER (5-CENT)	75.00	100.00
1 Yogi Berra	350.00	600.00
2 Bobby Thomson	20.00	40.00
3 Fred Hutchinson	12.50	25.00
4 Robin Roberts	50.00	80.00
5 Minnie Minoso RC	75.00	125.00
6 Virgil Stallcup	7.50	15.00
7 Mike Garcia	12.50	25.00
8 Pee Wee Reese	90.00	150.00
9 Vern Stephens	12.50	25.00
10 Bob Hooper	7.50	15.00
11 Ralph Kiner	35.00	60.00
12 Max Surkont RC	7.50	15.00
13 Cliff Mapes	7.50	15.00
14 Cliff Chambers	7.50	15.00
15 Sam Mele	7.50	15.00
16 Turk Lown RC	7.50	15.00
17 Ed Lopat	20.00	40.00
18 Don Mueller	12.50	25.00
19 Bob Cain	7.50	15.00
20 Willie Jones	7.50	15.00
21 Nellie Fox	60.00	100.00
22 Willard Ramsdell	7.50	15.00
23 Bob Lemon	35.00	60.00
24 Carl Furillo	20.00	40.00
25 Mickey McDermott	7.50	15.00
26 Eddie Joost	7.50	15.00
27 Joe Garagiola	20.00	40.00
28 Roy Hartsfield	7.50	15.00
29 Ned Garver	7.50	15.00
30 Red Schoendienst	35.00	60.00
31 Eddie Yost	12.50	25.00
32 Eddie Miksis	7.50	15.00
33 Gil McDougald RC	50.00	80.00
34 Alvin Dark	12.50	25.00
35 Granny Hamner	7.50	15.00
36 Cass Michaels	7.50	15.00
37 Vic Raschi	12.50	25.00
38 Whitey Lockman	12.50	25.00
39 Vic Wertz	12.50	25.00
40 Bubba Church	7.50	15.00
41 Chico Carrasquel	12.50	25.00
42 Johnny Wyrostek	7.50	15.00
43 Bob Feller	90.00	150.00
44 Roy Campanella	150.00	250.00
45 Johnny Pesky	12.50	25.00
46 Carl Scheib	7.50	15.00
47 Pete Castiglione	7.50	15.00
48 Vern Bickford	7.50	15.00
49 Jim Hearn	7.50	15.00
50 Gerry Staley	7.50	15.00
51 Gil Coan	7.50	15.00
52 Phil Rizzuto	90.00	150.00
53 Richie Ashburn	75.00	125.00
54 Billy Pierce	12.50	25.00
55 Ken Raffensberger	7.50	15.00
56 Clyde King	12.50	25.00
57 Clyde Vollmer	7.50	15.00
58 Hank Majeski	7.50	15.00
59 Murry Dickson	7.50	15.00
60 Sid Gordon	7.50	15.00
61 Tommy Byrne	7.50	15.00
62 Joe Presko RC	7.50	15.00
63 Irv Noren	7.50	15.00
64 Roy Smalley	7.50	15.00
65 Hank Bauer	20.00	40.00
66 Sal Maglie	12.50	25.00
67 Johnny Groth	7.50	15.00
68 Jim Busby	7.50	15.00
69 Joe Adcock	12.50	25.00
70 Carl Erskine	20.00	40.00
71 Vernon Law	12.50	25.00
72 Earl Torgeson	7.50	15.00
73 Jerry Coleman	12.50	25.00
74 Wes Westrum	12.50	25.00
75 George Kell	35.00	60.00
76 Del Ennis	12.50	25.00
77 Eddie Robinson	7.50	15.00
78 Lloyd Merriman	7.50	15.00
79 Lou Brissie	7.50	15.00
80 Gil Hodges	60.00	100.00
81 Billy Goodman	12.50	25.00
82 Gus Zernial	12.50	25.00
83 Howie Pollet	7.50	15.00
84 Sam Jethroe	12.50	25.00
85 Marty Marion CO	12.50	25.00
86 Cal Abrams	7.50	15.00
87 Mickey Vernon	12.50	25.00
88 Bruce Edwards	7.50	15.00
89 Billy Hitchcock	7.50	15.00
90 Larry Jansen	12.50	25.00
91 Don Kolloway	7.50	15.00
92 Eddie Waitkus	12.50	25.00
93 Paul Richards MG	12.50	25.00
94 Luke Sewell MG	12.50	25.00
95 Luke Easter	12.50	25.00
96 Ralph Branca	12.50	25.00
97 Willard Marshall	7.50	15.00
98 Jimmy Dykes MG	12.50	25.00
99 Clyde McCullough	7.50	15.00
100 Sibby Sisti	7.50	15.00
101 Mickey Mantle	1500.00	2500.00
102 Peanuts Lowrey	7.50	15.00
103 Joe Haynes	7.50	15.00
104 Hal Jeffcoat	7.50	15.00
105 Bobby Brown	12.50	25.00
106 Randy Gumpert	7.50	15.00
107 Del Rice	7.50	15.00
108 George Metkovich	7.50	15.00
109 Tom Morgan RC	7.50	15.00
110 Max Lanier	7.50	15.00
111 Hoot Evers	7.50	15.00
112 Smoky Burgess	12.50	25.00
113 Al Zarilla	7.50	15.00
114 Frank Hiller RC	7.50	15.00
115 Larry Doby	35.00	60.00
116 Duke Snider	125.00	200.00
117 Bill Wight	7.50	15.00
118 Ray Murray RC	7.50	15.00
119 Bill Howerton	7.50	15.00
120 Chet Nichols RC	7.50	15.00
121 Al Corwin RC	7.50	15.00
122 Billy Johnson	7.50	15.00
123 Sid Hudson	7.50	15.00
124 Birdie Tebbetts	7.50	15.00
125 Howie Fox	7.50	15.00
126 Phil Cavarretta	12.50	25.00
127 Dick Sisler	7.50	15.00
128 Don Newcombe	35.00	60.00
129 Gus Niarhos	7.50	15.00
130 Allie Clark	7.50	15.00
131 Bob Swift	7.50	15.00
132 Dave Cole RC	7.50	15.00
133 Dick Kryhoski	7.50	15.00
134 Al Brazle	7.50	15.00
135 Mickey Harris	7.50	15.00
136 Gene Hermanski	7.50	15.00
137 Stan Rojek	7.50	15.00
138 Ted Wilks	7.50	15.00
139 Jerry Priddy	7.50	15.00
140 Ray Scarborough	7.50	15.00
141 Hank Edwards	7.50	15.00
142 Early Wynn	35.00	60.00
143 Sandy Consuegra	7.50	15.00
144 Joe Hatton	7.50	15.00
145 Johnny Mize	35.00	60.00
146 Leo Durocher MG	35.00	60.00
147 Marlin Stuart RC	7.50	15.00
148 Ken Heintzelman	7.50	15.00
149 Howie Judson	7.50	15.00
150 Herman Wehmeier	7.50	15.00
151 Al Rosen	12.50	25.00
152 Billy Cox	7.50	15.00
153 Fred Hatfield RC	7.50	15.00
154 Ferris Fain	12.50	25.00
155 Billy Meyer MG	7.50	15.00
156 Warren Spahn	75.00	125.00
157 Jim Delsing	7.50	15.00
158 Bucky Harris MG	20.00	40.00
159 Dutch Leonard	7.50	15.00
160 Eddie Stanky	12.50	25.00
161 Jackie Jensen	20.00	40.00
162 Monte Irvin	35.00	60.00
163 Johnny Lipon	7.50	15.00
164 Connie Ryan	7.50	15.00
165 Saul Rogovin RC	7.50	15.00
166 Bobby Adams	7.50	15.00
167 Bobby Avila	12.50	25.00
168 Preacher Roe	12.50	25.00
169 Walt Dropo	12.50	25.00
170 Joe Astroth	7.50	15.00
171 Mel Queen	7.50	15.00
172 Ebba St.Claire RC	7.50	15.00
173 Gene Bearden	7.50	15.00
174 Mickey Grasso	7.50	15.00
175 Randy Jackson RC	7.50	15.00
176 Harry Brecheen	12.50	25.00
177 Gene Woodling	12.50	25.00
178 Dave Williams RC	12.50	25.00
179 Pete Suder	7.50	15.00
180 Ed Fitzgerald	7.50	15.00
181 Joe Collins RC	12.50	25.00
182 Dave Koslo	7.50	15.00
183 Pat Mullin	7.50	15.00
184 Curt Simmons	12.50	25.00
185 Eddie Stewart	7.50	15.00
186 Frank Smith RC	7.50	15.00
187 Jim Hegan	12.50	25.00
188 Chuck Dressen MG	12.50	25.00
189 Jimmy Piersall	12.50	25.00
190 Dick Fowler	7.50	15.00
191 Bob Friend RC	20.00	40.00
192 John Cusick RC	7.50	15.00
193 Bobby Young RC	7.50	15.00
194 Bob Porterfield	7.50	15.00
195 Frank Baumholtz	7.50	15.00
196 Stan Musial	300.00	500.00
197 Charlie Silvera RC	7.50	15.00
198 Chuck Diering	7.50	15.00
199 Ted Gray	7.50	15.00
200 Ken Silvestri	7.50	15.00
201 Ray Coleman	7.50	15.00
202 Harry Perkowski RC	7.50	15.00
203 Steve Gromek	7.50	15.00
204 Andy Pafko	12.50	25.00
205 Walt Masterson	7.50	15.00
206 Elmer Valo	7.50	15.00
207 George Strickland RC	7.50	15.00
208 Walker Cooper	7.50	15.00
209 Dick Littlefield RC	7.50	15.00
210 Archie Wilson RC	7.50	15.00
211 Paul Minner RC	7.50	15.00
212 Solly Hemus RC	7.50	15.00
213 Monte Kennedy	7.50	15.00
214 Ray Boone	7.50	15.00
215 Sheldon Jones	7.50	15.00
216 Matt Batts	7.50	15.00
217 Casey Stengel MG	90.00	150.00
218 Willie Mays	900.00	1500.00
219 Neil Berry	35.00	60.00
220 Russ Meyer	35.00	60.00
221 Lou Kretlow RC	35.00	60.00
222 Dixie Howell	35.00	60.00
223 Harry Simpson RC	35.00	60.00
224 Johnny Schmitz	35.00	60.00
225 Del Wilber RC	35.00	60.00
226 Alex Kellner	35.00	60.00
227 Clyde Sukeforth CO RC	35.00	60.00
228 Bob Chipman	35.00	60.00
229 Hank Arft	35.00	60.00
230 Frank Shea	35.00	60.00
231 Dee Fondy RC	35.00	60.00
232 Enos Slaughter	60.00	100.00
233 Bob Kuzava	35.00	60.00
234 Fred Fitzsimmons CO	35.00	60.00
235 Steve Souchock RC	35.00	60.00
236 Tommy Brown	35.00	60.00
237 Sherm Lollar	35.00	60.00
238 Roy McMillan RC	35.00	60.00
239 Dale Mitchell	35.00	60.00
240 Billy Loes RC	35.00	60.00
241 Mel Parnell	35.00	60.00
242 Everett Kell RC	35.00	60.00
243 George Munger	35.00	60.00
244 Lew Burdette RC	50.00	80.00
245 George Schmees RC	35.00	60.00
246 Jerry Snyder RC	35.00	60.00
247 Johnny Pramesa	35.00	60.00
248 Bill Werle	35.00	60.00
Full name in signature		
248A Bill Werle	35.00	60.00
Signature on front has no W		
249 Hank Thompson	35.00	60.00
250 Ike Delock RC	35.00	60.00
251 Jack Lohrke	35.00	60.00
252 Frank Crosetti CO	75.00	125.00

1953 Bowman Black and White

The cards in this 64-card set measure approximately 2 1/2" by 3 3/4". Some collectors believe that the high cost of producing the 1953 color series forced Bowman to issue this set in black and white, since the two sets are identical in design except for the element of color. This set was also produced in fewer numbers than its color counterpart, and is popular among collectors for the challenge involved in completing it and the lack of short prints. Cards were issued in one-card penny packs which came 120 to a box and five-card nickel packs. There are no key Rookie Cards in this set. Recently, a variation of the Hal Bevan card (number 43) was discovered, that card exists with him being born in either 1930 or 1950. The 1950 version is much more difficult.

Card	Low	High
COMPLETE SET (64)	2000.00	3000.00
WRAPPER (1-CENT)	300.00	350.00
1 Gus Bell	75.00	125.00
2 Willard Nixon	25.00	40.00
3 Bill Rigney	25.00	40.00
4 Pat Mullin	25.00	40.00
5 Dee Fondy	25.00	40.00
6 Ray Murray	25.00	40.00
7 Andy Seminick	25.00	40.00
8 Pete Suder	25.00	40.00
9 Walt Masterson	25.00	40.00
10 Dick Sisler	35.00	60.00
11 Dick Gernert	25.00	40.00
12 Randy Jackson	25.00	40.00
13 Joe Tipton	25.00	40.00
14 Bill Nicholson	35.00	60.00
15 Johnny Mize	75.00	125.00
16 Stu Miller RC	35.00	60.00
17 Virgil Trucks	35.00	60.00
18 Billy Hoeft	25.00	40.00
19 Paul LaPalme	25.00	40.00
20 Eddie Robinson	25.00	40.00
21 Clarence Podbielan	25.00	40.00
22 Matt Batts	25.00	40.00
23 Wilmer Mizell	35.00	60.00
24 Del Wilber	25.00	40.00
25 Johnny Sain	50.00	80.00
26 Preacher Roe	50.00	80.00
27 Bob Lemon	100.00	175.00
28 Hoyt Wilhelm	75.00	125.00
29 Sid Hudson	25.00	40.00
30 Walker Cooper	25.00	40.00
31 Gene Woodling	50.00	80.00
32 Rocky Bridges	25.00	40.00
33 Bob Kuzava	25.00	40.00
34 Ebba St.Claire	25.00	40.00
35 Johnny Wyrostek	25.00	40.00
36 Jimmy Piersall	50.00	80.00
37 Hal Jeffcoat	25.00	40.00
38 Dave Cole	25.00	40.00
39 Casey Stengel MG	200.00	350.00
40 Larry Jansen	35.00	60.00
41 Bob Ramazzotti	25.00	40.00
42 Howie Judson	25.00	40.00
43 Hal Bevan ERR RC	25.00	40.00
Born in 1950		
43A Hal Bevan COR	25.00	40.00
Born in 1930		
44 Jim Delsing	25.00	40.00
45 Irv Noren	35.00	60.00
46 Bucky Harris MG	50.00	80.00
47 Jack Lohrke	25.00	40.00
48 Steve Ridzik RC	25.00	40.00
49 Floyd Baker	25.00	40.00
50 Dutch Leonard	25.00	40.00
51 Lou Burdette	50.00	80.00
52 Ralph Branca	50.00	80.00
53 Morrie Martin	25.00	40.00
54 Bill Miller	25.00	40.00
55 Don Johnson	25.00	40.00
56 Roy Smalley	25.00	40.00
57 Andy Pafko	35.00	60.00
58 Jim Konstanty	35.00	60.00
59 Duane Pillette	25.00	40.00
60 Billy Cox	50.00	80.00
61 Tom Gorman RC	25.00	40.00
62 Keith Thomas RC	25.00	40.00
63 Steve Gromek	25.00	40.00
64 Andy Hansen	50.00	80.00

1953 Bowman Color

The cards in this 160-card set measure approximately 2 1/2" by 3 3/4". The 1953 Bowman Color set, considered by many to be the best looking set of the modern era, contains Kodachrome photographs with no names or facsimile autographs on the face. Cards were issued in five-card nickel packs in a 24 pack box with each pack having gum in it. The entire low number run were also printed in three card strips; it is believed that these three card strips in numerical order were box toppers to retailers. The box features an endorsement from Joe DiMaggio. Numbers 113 to 160 are somewhat more difficult to obtain, with numbers 113 to 128 being the most difficult. There are two cards of Al Corwin (126 and 149). There are no key Rookie Cards in this set.

Card	Low	High
COMPLETE SET (160)	9000.00	15000.00
COMMON CARD (1-112)	20.00	40.00
COMMON (113-128)	50.00	80.00
COMMON (129-160)	45.00	75.00
WRAPPER (1-CENT)	300.00	400.00
WRAPPER (5-CENT)	250.00	300.00
1 Dave Williams	100.00	175.00
2 Vic Wertz	30.00	50.00
3 Sam Jethroe	30.00	50.00
4 Art Houtteman	20.00	40.00
5 Sid Gordon	20.00	40.00
6 Joe Ginsberg	20.00	40.00
7 Harry Chiti RC	20.00	40.00
8 Al Rosen	30.00	50.00
9 Phil Rizzuto	150.00	225.00
10 Richie Ashburn	90.00	150.00
11 Bobby Shantz	30.00	50.00
12 Carl Erskine	35.00	60.00
13 Gus Zernial	30.00	50.00
14 Billy Loes	30.00	50.00
15 Jim Busby	20.00	40.00
16 Bob Friend	30.00	50.00
17 Gerry Staley	20.00	40.00
18 Nellie Fox	90.00	150.00
19 Alvin Dark	30.00	50.00
20 Don Lenhardt	20.00	40.00
21 Joe Garagiola	35.00	60.00
22 Bob Porterfield	20.00	40.00
23 Herman Wehmeier	20.00	40.00
24 Jackie Jensen	35.00	60.00
25 Hoot Evers	20.00	40.00
26 Roy McMillan	30.00	50.00
27 Vic Raschi	35.00	60.00
28 Smoky Burgess	30.00	50.00
29 Bobby Avila	30.00	50.00
30 Phil Cavarretta	30.00	50.00
31 Jimmy Dykes MG	30.00	50.00
32 Stan Musial	350.00	600.00
33 Pee Wee Reese	500.00	1000.00
34 Gil Coan	20.00	40.00
35 Maurice McDermott	20.00	40.00
36 Minnie Minoso	50.00	80.00
37 Jim Wilson	20.00	40.00
38 Harry Byrd RC	20.00	40.00
39 Paul Richards MG	30.00	50.00
40 Larry Doby	60.00	100.00
41 Sammy White	20.00	40.00
42 Tommy Brown	20.00	40.00
43 Mike Garcia	30.00	50.00
44 Yogi Berra	500.00	800.00
Hank Bauer		
Mickey Mantle		
45 Walt Dropo	30.00	50.00
46 Roy Campanella	200.00	350.00
47 Ned Garver	20.00	40.00
48 Hank Sauer	30.00	50.00
49 Eddie Stanky MG	30.00	50.00
50 Lou Kretlow	20.00	40.00
51 Monte Irvin	50.00	80.00
52 Marty Marion MG	30.00	50.00
53 Del Rice	20.00	40.00
54 Chico Carrasquel	20.00	40.00
55 Leo Durocher MG	50.00	80.00
56 Bob Cain	20.00	40.00
57 Lou Boudreau MG	50.00	80.00
58 Willard Marshall	20.00	40.00
59 Mickey Mantle	1200.00	2000.00
60 Granny Hamner	20.00	40.00
61 George Kell	50.00	80.00
62 Ted Kluszewski	60.00	100.00
63 Gil McDougald	50.00	80.00
64 Curt Simmons	30.00	50.00
65 Robin Roberts	75.00	125.00
66 Mel Parnell	30.00	50.00
67 Mel Clark RC	20.00	40.00
68 Allie Reynolds	35.00	60.00
69 Charlie Grimm MG	30.00	50.00
70 Clint Courtney RC	20.00	40.00
71 Paul Minner	20.00	40.00
72 Ted Gray	20.00	40.00
73 Billy Pierce	30.00	50.00
74 Don Mueller	30.00	50.00
75 Saul Rogovin	20.00	40.00
76 Jim Hearn	20.00	40.00
77 Mickey Grasso	20.00	40.00
78 Carl Furillo	35.00	60.00
79 Ray Boone	30.00	50.00
80 Ralph Kiner	60.00	100.00
81 Enos Slaughter	60.00	100.00
82 Joe Astroth	20.00	40.00
83 Jack Daniels RC	20.00	40.00
84 Hank Bauer	35.00	60.00
85 Solly Hemus	20.00	40.00
86 Harry Simpson	20.00	40.00
87 Harry Perkowski	20.00	40.00
88 Joe Dobson	20.00	40.00
89 Sandy Consuegra	20.00	40.00
90 Joe Nuxhall	30.00	50.00
91 Steve Souchock	20.00	40.00
92 Gil Hodges	175.00	300.00
93 Phil Rizzuto	175.00	300.00
Billy Martin		
94 Bob Addis	20.00	40.00
95 Wally Moses CO	30.00	50.00
96 Sal Maglie	30.00	50.00
97 Eddie Mathews	200.00	350.00
98 Hector Rodriguez RC	20.00	40.00
99 Warren Spahn	200.00	350.00
100 Bill Wight	20.00	40.00
101 Red Schoendienst	50.00	80.00
102 Jim Hegan	30.00	50.00
103 Del Ennis	30.00	50.00
104 Luke Easter	30.00	50.00
105 Eddie Joost	20.00	40.00
106 Ken Raffensberger	20.00	40.00
107 Alex Kellner	20.00	40.00
108 Bobby Adams	20.00	40.00
109 Ken Wood	20.00	40.00
110 Bob Rush	20.00	40.00
111 Jim Dyck RC	20.00	40.00
112 Toby Atwell	20.00	40.00
113 Karl Drews	50.00	80.00
114 Bob Feller	350.00	500.00
115 Cloyd Boyer	50.00	80.00
116 Eddie Yost	60.00	100.00
117 Duke Snider	350.00	600.00
118 Billy Martin	250.00	400.00
119 Dale Mitchell	60.00	100.00
120 Marlin Stuart	50.00	80.00
121 Yogi Berra	500.00	800.00
122 Bill Serena	50.00	80.00
123 Johnny Lipon	50.00	80.00
124 Charlie Dressen MG	60.00	100.00
125 Fred Hatfield	50.00	80.00
126 Al Corwin	50.00	80.00
127 Dick Kryhoski	50.00	80.00
128 Whitey Lockman	60.00	100.00
129 Russ Meyer	45.00	75.00
130 Cass Michaels	45.00	75.00
131 Connie Ryan	45.00	75.00
132 Fred Hutchinson	60.00	90.00
133 Willie Jones	45.00	75.00
134 Johnny Pesky	60.00	90.00
135 Bobby Morgan	45.00	75.00
136 Jim Brideweser RC	45.00	75.00
137 Sam Dente	45.00	75.00
138 Bubba Church	45.00	75.00
139 Pete Runnels	60.00	90.00
140 Al Brazle	45.00	75.00
141 Frank Shea	45.00	75.00
142 Larry Miggins RC	45.00	75.00
143 Al Lopez MG	70.00	110.00
144 Warren Hacker	45.00	75.00
145 George Shuba	60.00	90.00
146 Early Wynn	125.00	200.00
147 Clem Koshorek	45.00	75.00
148 Billy Goodman	60.00	90.00
149 Al Corwin	45.00	75.00
150 Carl Scheib	45.00	75.00
151 Joe Adcock	70.00	110.00
152 Clyde Vollmer	45.00	75.00
153 Whitey Ford	500.00	800.00
154 Turk Lown	45.00	75.00
155 Allie Clark	45.00	75.00
156 Max Surkont	45.00	75.00
157 Sherm Lollar	60.00	90.00
158 Howard Fox	45.00	75.00
159 Mickey Vernon UER	60.00	90.00
(Photo actually		
Floyd Baker)		
160 Cal Abrams	300.00	500.00

1954 Bowman

The cards in this 224-card set measure approximately 2 1/2" by 3 3/4". The set was distributed in two separate series: 1-128 in first series and 129-224 in second series. A contractual problem apparently resulted in the deletion of the number 66 Ted Williams card from this Bowman set, thereby creating a scarcity that is highly valued among collectors. The set price below does NOT include number 66 Williams but does include number 66 Jim Piersall, the apparent replacement for Williams in spite of the fact that Piersall was already number 210 to appear later in the set. Many errors in players' statistics exist (and some were corrected) while a few players' names were printed on the front, instead of appearing as a facsimile autograph. Most of these differences are so minor that there is no price differential for either card. The cards which changes were made on are numbers 12, 22,25,26,35,38,41,43,47,53,61,67,80,81,82,85,93,94, 99,103,105,124,138,139, 140,145,153,156,174,179,185,212,216 and 217. The set was issued in seven-card nickel packs and one-card penny packs. The penny packs were issued 120 to a box while the nickel packs were issued 24 to a box. The notable Rookie Cards in this set are Harvey Kuenn and Don Larsen.

Card	Low	High
COMPLETE SET (224)	2500.00	4000.00
WRAP.(1-CENT, DATED)	100.00	150.00
WRAP.(1-CENT, UNDATED)	150.00	200.00
WRAP.(5-CENT, DATED)	100.00	150.00
WRAP.(5-CENT, UNDATED)	50.00	60.00
1 Phil Rizzuto	100.00	175.00
2 Jackie Jensen	15.00	30.00
3 Marion Fricano	6.00	12.00
4 Bob Hooper	6.00	12.00
5 Billy Hunter	6.00	12.00
6 Nellie Fox	50.00	80.00
7 Walt Dropo	10.00	20.00
8 Jim Busby	6.00	12.00
9 Dave Williams	6.00	12.00
10 Carl Erskine	10.00	20.00
11 Sid Gordon	6.00	12.00
12A Roy McMillan	10.00	20.00
551/1290 At Bat		
12B Roy McMillan	10.00	20.00
557/1296 At Bat		
13 Paul Minner	6.00	12.00
14 Gerry Staley	6.00	12.00
15 Richie Ashburn	50.00	80.00
16 Jim Wilson	6.00	12.00
17 Tom Gorman	6.00	12.00
18 Hoot Evers	6.00	12.00
19 Bobby Shantz	10.00	20.00
20 Art Houtteman	6.00	12.00
21 Vic Wertz	10.00	20.00
22A Sam Mele	6.00	12.00
213/1661 Putouts		
22B Sam Mele	6.00	12.00
217/1665 Putouts		
23 Harvey Kuenn RC	15.00	30.00
24 Bob Porterfield	6.00	12.00
25A Wes Westrum	10.00	20.00
1.000/.987 Fielding Avg.		
25B Wes Westrum	10.00	20.00
.982/.986 Fielding Avg.		
26A Billy Cox	10.00	20.00
1.000/.960 Fielding Avg.		
26B Billy Cox	10.00	20.00
.972/.960 Fielding Avg.		
27 Dick Cole RC	6.00	12.00
28A Jim Greengrass	6.00	12.00
Birthplace Addison, NJ		
28B Jim Greengrass	6.00	12.00
Birthplace Addison, NY		
29 Johnny Klippstein	6.00	12.00
30 Del Rice	6.00	12.00
31 Smoky Burgess	10.00	20.00
32 Del Crandall	10.00	20.00
33A Vic Raschi	10.00	20.00
No Trade		
33B Vic Raschi	15.00	30.00
Traded to St.Louis		
34 Sammy White	6.00	12.00
35A Eddie Joost	6.00	12.00
Quiz Answer is 8		
35B Eddie Joost	6.00	12.00
Quiz Answer is 33		
36 George Strickland	6.00	12.00
37 Dick Kokos	6.00	12.00
38A Minnie Minoso	15.00	30.00
.895/.961 Fielding Avg.		
38B Minnie Minoso	15.00	30.00
.963/.963 Fielding Avg.		
39 Ned Garver	6.00	12.00
40 Gil Coan	6.00	12.00
41A Alvin Dark	10.00	20.00
.986/960 Fielding Avg.		
41B Alvin Dark	10.00	20.00
.968/.960 Fielding Avg.		
42 Billy Loes	10.00	20.00
43A Bob Friend	10.00	20.00
20 Shutouts in Quiz		
43B Bob Friend	10.00	20.00
16 Shutouts in Quiz		
44 Harry Perkowski	6.00	12.00
45 Ralph Kiner	25.00	50.00
46 Rip Repulski	6.00	12.00
47A Granny Hamner	6.00	12.00
.970/.953 Fielding Avg.		
47B Granny Hamner	6.00	12.00
.953/.951 Fielding Avg.		
48 Jack Dittmer	6.00	12.00
49 Harry Byrd	6.00	12.00
50 George Kell	25.00	50.00
51 Alex Kellner	6.00	12.00
52 Joe Ginsberg	6.00	12.00
53A Don Lenhardt	6.00	12.00
.969/.984 Fielding Avg.		
53B Don Lenhardt	6.00	12.00
.966/.983 Fielding Avg.		
54 Chico Carrasquel	6.00	12.00
55 Jim Delsing	6.00	12.00
56 Maurice McDermott	6.00	12.00
57 Hoyt Wilhelm	25.00	50.00
58 Pee Wee Reese	50.00	80.00
59 Bob Schultz	6.00	12.00
60 Fred Baczewski RC	6.00	12.00
61A Eddie Miksis	6.00	12.00
.954/.962 Fielding Avg.		
61B Eddie Miksis	6.00	12.00
.954/.961 Fielding Avg.		
62 Enos Slaughter	25.00	50.00
63 Earl Torgeson	6.00	12.00
64 Eddie Mathews	50.00	80.00
65 Mickey Mantle	900.00	1500.00
66A Ted Williams	1800.00	3000.00
66B Jimmy Piersall	50.00	80.00
67A Carl Scheib	6.00	12.00
.306 Pct. Two Lines under Bio		
67B Carl Scheib	6.00	12.00
.306 Pct. One Line under Bio		
67C Carl Scheib	6.00	12.00
.300 Pct.		
68 Bobby Avila	10.00	20.00
69 Clint Courtney	6.00	12.00
70 Willard Marshall	6.00	12.00
71 Ted Gray	6.00	12.00
72 Eddie Yost	10.00	20.00
73 Don Mueller	10.00	20.00
74 Jim Gilliam	15.00	30.00
75 Max Surkont	6.00	12.00
76 Joe Nuxhall	10.00	20.00
77 Bob Rush	6.00	12.00
78 Sal Yvars	6.00	12.00
79 Curt Simmons	10.00	20.00
80A Johnny Logan	6.00	12.00
106 Runs		
80B Johnny Logan	6.00	12.00
100 Runs		
81A Jerry Coleman	10.00	20.00
1.000/.975 Fielding Avg.		
81B Jerry Coleman	10.00	20.00
.952/.975 Fielding Avg.		
82A Bill Goodman	10.00	20.00
.965/.986 Fielding Avg.		
82B Bill Goodman	10.00	20.00
.972/.985 Fielding Avg.		
83 Ray Murray	6.00	12.00
84 Larry Doby	25.00	50.00
85A Jim Dyck	6.00	12.00
.926/.956 Fielding Avg.		
85B Jim Dyck	6.00	12.00
.947/.960 Fielding Avg.		
86 Harry Dorish	6.00	12.00
87 Don Lund	6.00	12.00
88 Tom Umphlett RC	6.00	12.00
89 Willie Mays	300.00	500.00
90 Roy Campanella	90.00	150.00
91 Cal Abrams	6.00	12.00
92 Ken Raffensberger	6.00	12.00
93A Bill Serena	6.00	12.00
.983/.966 Fielding Avg.		
93B Bill Serena	6.00	12.00
.977/.966 Fielding Avg.		
94A Solly Hemus	6.00	12.00
476/1343 Assists		
94B Solly Hemus	6.00	12.00
477/1343 Assists		
95 Robin Roberts	25.00	50.00
96 Joe Adcock	10.00	20.00
97 Gil McDougald	10.00	20.00
98 Ellis Kinder	6.00	12.00
99A Peter Suder	6.00	12.00
.985/.974 Fielding Avg.		
99B Peter Suder	6.00	12.00
.978/.974 Fielding Avg.		
100 Mike Garcia	10.00	20.00
101 Don Larsen RC	50.00	80.00
102 Billy Pierce	10.00	20.00
103A Stephen Souchock	6.00	12.00
144/1192 Putouts		
103B Stephen Souchock	6.00	12.00
147/1195 Putouts		
104 Frank Shea	6.00	12.00
105A Sal Maglie	10.00	20.00
Quiz Answer is 8		
105B Sal Maglie	10.00	20.00
Quiz Answer is 1904		
106 Clem Labine	10.00	20.00
107 Paul LaPalme	6.00	12.00
108 Bobby Adams	6.00	12.00
109 Roy Smalley	6.00	12.00
110 Red Schoendienst	25.00	50.00
111 Murry Dickson	6.00	12.00
112 Andy Pafko	10.00	20.00
113 Allie Reynolds	10.00	20.00
114 Willard Nixon	6.00	12.00
115 Don Bollweg	6.00	12.00
116 Luke Easter	10.00	20.00
117 Dick Kryhoski	6.00	12.00
118 Bob Boyd	6.00	12.00
119 Fred Hatfield	6.00	12.00
120 Mel Hoderlein RC	6.00	12.00
121 Ray Katt RC	6.00	12.00
122 Carl Furillo	15.00	30.00
123 Toby Atwell	6.00	12.00
124A Gus Bell	10.00	20.00
15/27 Errors		
124B Gus Bell	10.00	20.00
11/26 Errors		
125 Warren Hacker	6.00	12.00
126 Cliff Chambers	6.00	12.00
127 Del Ennis	10.00	20.00
128 Ebba St.Claire	6.00	12.00
129 Hank Bauer	15.00	30.00
130 Milt Bolling	6.00	12.00
131 Joe Astroth	6.00	12.00
132 Bob Feller	50.00	80.00
133 Duane Pillette	6.00	12.00
134 Luis Aloma	6.00	12.00
135 Johnny Pesky	10.00	20.00
136 Clyde Vollmer	6.00	12.00
137 Al Corwin	6.00	12.00
138A Gil Hodges	50.00	80.00
.993/.991 Fielding Avg.		
138B Gil Hodges	50.00	80.00
.992/.991 Fielding Avg.		
139A Preston Ward	6.00	12.00
.961/.992 Fielding Avg.		
139B Preston Ward	6.00	12.00
.990/.992 Fielding Avg.		
140A Saul Rogovin	6.00	12.00
7-12 W-L 2 Strikeouts		
140B Saul Rogovin	6.00	12.00
7-12 W-L 62 Strikeouts		
140C Saul Rogovin	6.00	12.00
8-12 W-L		
141 Joe Garagiola	15.00	30.00
142 Al Brazle	6.00	12.00
143 Willie Jones	6.00	12.00
144 Ernie Johnson RC	15.00	30.00
145A Billy Martin	50.00	80.00
.985/.983 Fielding Avg.		
145B Billy Martin	50.00	80.00
.983/.982 Fielding Avg.		
146 Dick Gernert	6.00	12.00
147 Joe DeMaestri	6.00	12.00
148 Dale Mitchell	10.00	20.00
149 Bob Young	6.00	12.00
150 Cass Michaels	6.00	12.00
151 Pat Mullin	6.00	12.00
152 Mickey Vernon	10.00	20.00
153A Whitey Lockman	10.00	20.00
100/331 Assists		
153B Whitey Lockman	10.00	20.00
102/333 Assists		
154 Don Newcombe	15.00	30.00
155 Frank Thomas RC	10.00	20.00
156A Rocky Bridges	6.00	12.00
320/467 Assists		
156B Rocky Bridges	6.00	12.00
328/475 Assists		
157 Turk Lown	6.00	12.00
158 Stu Miller	10.00	20.00
159 Johnny Lindell	6.00	12.00
160 Danny O'Connell	6.00	12.00
161 Yogi Berra	100.00	175.00
162 Ted Lepcio	6.00	12.00
163A Dave Philley	10.00	20.00
No Trade 152 Games		
163B Dave Philley	15.00	30.00
Traded to Cleveland 152 Games		
163C Dave Philley	15.00	30.00
Traded to Cleveland 157 Games		
164 Early Wynn	25.00	50.00
165 Johnny Groth	6.00	12.00

166 Sandy Consuegra 6.00 12.00
167 Billy Hoeft 6.00 12.00
168 Ed Fitzgerald 6.00 12.00
169 Larry Jansen 10.00 20.00
170 Duke Snider 150.00 250.00
171 Carlos Bernier 6.00 12.00
172 Andy Seminick 6.00 12.00
173 Dee Fondy 6.00 12.00
174A Pete Castiglione 6.00 12.00
.966/.959 Fielding Avg.
174B Pete Castiglione 6.00 12.00
.970/.959 Fielding Avg.
175 Mel Clark 6.00 12.00
176 Vern Bickford 6.00 12.00
177 Whitey Ford 60.00 100.00
178 Del Wilber 6.00 12.00
179A Morris Martin 6.00 12.00
44 ERA
179B Morris Martin 6.00 12.00
4.44 ERA
180 Joe Tipton 6.00 12.00
181 Les Moss 6.00 12.00
182 Sherm Lollar 10.00 20.00
183 Matt Batts 6.00 12.00
184 Mickey Grasso 6.00 12.00
185A Daryl Spencer 6.00 12.00
.941/.944 Fielding Avg. RC
185B Daryl Spencer 6.00 12.00
.933/.936 Fielding Avg.
186 Russ Meyer 6.00 12.00
187 Vern Law 10.00 20.00
188 Frank Smith 6.00 12.00
189 Randy Jackson 6.00 12.00
190 Joe Presko 6.00 12.00
191 Karl Drews 6.00 12.00
192 Lou Burdette 10.00 20.00
193 Eddie Robinson 6.00 12.00
194 Sid Hudson 6.00 12.00
195 Bob Cain 6.00 12.00
196 Bob Lemon 25.00 50.00
197 Lou Kretlow 6.00 12.00
198 Virgil Trucks 6.00 12.00
199 Steve Gromek 6.00 12.00
200 Conrado Marrero 6.00 12.00
201 Bobby Thomson 15.00 30.00
202 George Shuba 10.00 20.00
203 Vic Janowicz 10.00 20.00
204 Jack Collum RC 6.00 12.00
205 Hal Jeffcoat 6.00 12.00
206 Steve Bilko 6.00 12.00
207 Stan Lopata 6.00 12.00
208 Johnny Antonelli 10.00 20.00
209 Gene Woodling 6.00 12.00
UER Reversed Photo
210 Jimmy Piersall 15.00 30.00
211 Al Robertson RC 6.00 12.00
212A Owen Friend 6.00 12.00
.964/.957 Fielding Avg.
212B Owen Friend 6.00 12.00
.967/.958 Fielding Avg.
213 Dick Littlefield 6.00 12.00
214 Ferris Fain 10.00 20.00
215 Johnny Bucha 6.00 12.00
216A Jerry Snyder 6.00 12.00
.900/.900 Fielding Avg.
216B Jerry Snyder 6.00 12.00
.968/.968 Fielding Avg.
217A Henry Thompson 10.00 20.00
.956/.951 Fielding Avg.
217B Henry Thompson 10.00 20.00
.958/.952 Fielding Avg.
218 Preacher Roe 10.00 20.00
219 Hal Rice 6.00 12.00
220 Hobie Landrith RC 6.00 12.00
221 Frank Baumholtz 6.00 12.00
222 Memo Luna RC 6.00 12.00
223 Steve Ridzik 6.00 12.00
224 Bill Bruton 25.00 50.00

1955 Bowman

The cards in this 320-card set measure approximately 2 1/2" by 3 3/4". The Bowman set of 1955 is known as the "TV set" because each player photograph is cleverly shown within a television set design. The set contains umpire cards, some transposed pictures (e.g., Johnsons and Bollings), an incorrect spelling for Harvey Kuenn, and a traded line for Palica (all of which are noted in the checklist below). Some three-card advertising strips exist, the backs of these panels contain advertising for Bowman products. Print advertisments for these cards featured Willie Mays along with publicizing the great value in nine cards for a nickel. Advertising panels seen include Nellie Fox/Carl Furillo/Carl Erskine; Hank Aaron/Johnny Logan/Eddie Miksis; Bob Rush/Ray Katt/Willie Mays; Steve Gromek/Milt Bolling/Vern Stephens, Russ Kemmemer/ Hal Jeffcoat/Dee Fondy and a Bob Darnell/Early Wynn/Pee Wee Reese. Cards were issued either in nine-card nickel packs or one card penny packs. Cello packs containing approximately 20 cards have also been seen, albeit on a very limited basis. The notable Rookie Cards in this set are Elston Howard and Don Zimmer. Hall of Fame umpires pictured in the set are Al Barlick, Jocko Conlon and Cal Hubbard. Undated five cent wrappers are also known to exist for this set.

COMPLETE SET (320) 3500.00 6000.00
COMMON CARD (1-96) 6.00 12.00
COMMON CARD (97-224) 5.00 10.00
COMMON (225-320) 7.50 15.00
COMMON UMP. 225-320 18.00 30.00
WRAPPER (1-CENT) 50.00 60.00
WRAPPER (5-CENT) 50.00 60.00
1 Hoyt Wilhelm 60.00 100.00
2 Alvin Dark 7.50 15.00
3 Joe Coleman 7.50 15.00
4 Eddie Waitkus 7.50 15.00
5 Jim Robertson 6.00 12.00
6 Pete Suder 6.00 12.00
7 Gene Baker RC 6.00 12.00
8 Warren Hacker 6.00 12.00
9 Gil McDougald 10.00 20.00
10 Phil Rizzuto 75.00 125.00
11 Bill Bruton 7.50 15.00
12 Andy Pafko 7.50 15.00
13 Clyde Vollmer 6.00 12.00
14 Gus Keriazakos RC 6.00 12.00
15 Frank Sullivan RC 6.00 12.00
16 Jimmy Piersall 10.00 20.00
17 Del Ennis 7.50 15.00
18 Stan Lopata 6.00 12.00
19 Bobby Avila 7.50 15.00
20 Al Smith 7.50 15.00
21 Don Hoak 6.00 12.00
22 Roy Campanella 75.00 125.00
23 Al Kaline 90.00 150.00
24 Al Aber 6.00 12.00
25 Minnie Minoso 15.00 30.00
26 Virgil Trucks 7.50 15.00
27 Preston Ward 6.00 12.00
28 Dick Cole 6.00 12.00
29 Red Schoendienst 15.00 30.00
30 Bill Sami 6.00 12.00
31 Johnny Temple RC 7.50 15.00
32 Wally Post 7.50 15.00
33 Nellie Fox 30.00 50.00
34 Clint Courtney 6.00 12.00
35 Bill Tuttle RC 6.00 12.00
36 Wayne Belardi RC 6.00 12.00
37 Pee Wee Reese 60.00 100.00
38 Early Wynn 15.00 30.00
39 Bob Darnell RC 7.50 15.00
40 Vic Wertz 7.50 15.00
41 Mel Clark 6.00 12.00
42 Bob Greenwood RC 6.00 12.00
43 Bob Buhl 7.50 15.00
44 Danny O'Connell 6.00 12.00
45 Tom Umphlett 6.00 12.00
46 Mickey Vernon 7.50 15.00
47 Sammy White 6.00 12.00
48A Milt Bolling ERR 10.00 20.00
(Name on back is
Frank Bolling)
48B Milt Bolling COR 10.00 20.00
49 Jim Greengrass 6.00 12.00
50 Hobie Landrith 6.00 12.00
51 Elvin Tappe RC UER 6.00 12.00
Some information about Ted Tappe on the card
52 Hal Rice 6.00 12.00
53 Alex Kellner 6.00 12.00
54 Don Bollweg 6.00 12.00
55 Cal Abrams 6.00 12.00
56 Billy Cox 7.50 15.00
57 Bob Friend 7.50 15.00
58 Frank Thomas 7.50 15.00
59 Whitey Ford 60.00 100.00
60 Enos Slaughter 15.00 30.00
61 Paul LaPalme 6.00 12.00
62 Royce Lint RC 6.00 12.00
63 Irv Noren 7.50 15.00
64 Curt Simmons 7.50 15.00
65 Don Zimmer RC 10.00 20.00
66 George Shuba 10.00 20.00
67 Don Larsen 10.00 20.00
68 Elston Howard RC 50.00 80.00
69 Billy Hunter 6.00 12.00
70 Lou Burdette 10.00 20.00
71 Dave Jolly 6.00 12.00
72 Chet Nichols 6.00 12.00
73 Eddie Yost 7.50 15.00
74 Jerry Snyder 6.00 12.00
75 Brooks Lawrence RC 6.00 12.00
76 Tom Poholsky 6.00 12.00
77 Jim McDonald RC 6.00 12.00
78 Gil Coan 6.00 12.00
79 Willie Miranda 6.00 12.00
80 Lou Limmer 6.00 12.00
81 Bobby Morgan 6.00 12.00
82 Lee Walls RC 6.00 12.00
83 Max Surkont 6.00 12.00
84 George Freese RC 6.00 12.00
85 Cass Michaels 6.00 12.00
86 Ted Gray 6.00 12.00
87 Randy Jackson 6.00 12.00
88 Steve Bilko 6.00 12.00
89 Lou Boudreau MG 15.00 30.00
90 Art Ditmar RC 6.00 12.00
91 Dick Marlowe RC 6.00 12.00
92 George Zuverink 6.00 12.00
93 Andy Seminick 6.00 12.00
94 Hank Thompson 7.50 15.00
95 Sal Maglie 7.50 15.00
96 Ray Narleski RC 6.00 12.00
97 Johnny Podres 15.00 30.00
98 Jim Gilliam 10.00 20.00
99 Jerry Coleman 7.50 15.00
100 Tom Morgan 5.00 10.00
101A Don Johnson ERR 10.00 20.00
(Photo actually
Ernie Johnson)
101B Don Johnson COR 10.00 20.00
102 Bobby Thomson 7.50 15.00
103 Eddie Mathews 50.00 80.00
104 Bob Porterfield 5.00 10.00
105 Johnny Schmitz 5.00 10.00
106 Del Rice 5.00 10.00
107 Solly Hemus 5.00 10.00
108 Lou Kretlow 5.00 10.00
109 Vern Stephens 7.50 15.00
110 Bob Miller 5.00 10.00
111 Steve Ridzik 5.00 10.00
112 Granny Hamner 5.00 10.00
113 Bob Hall RC 5.00 10.00
114 Vic Janowicz 7.50 15.00
115 Roger Bowman RC 5.00 10.00
116 Sandy Consuegra 5.00 10.00
117 Johnny Groth 5.00 10.00
118 Bobby Adams 5.00 10.00
119 Joe Astroth 5.00 10.00
120 Ed Burtschy RC 5.00 10.00
121 Rufus Crawford RC 5.00 10.00
122 Al Corwin 5.00 10.00
123 Marv Grissom RC 5.00 10.00
124 Johnny Antonelli 7.50 15.00
125 Paul Giel RC 7.50 15.00
126 Billy Goodman 7.50 15.00
127 Hank Majeski 5.00 10.00
128 Mike Garcia 7.50 15.00
129 Hal Naragon RC 5.00 10.00
130 Richie Ashburn 30.00 50.00
131 Willard Marshall 5.00 10.00
132A Harvey Kueen ERR 30.00 50.00
(Sic& Kuenn)
132B Harvey Kuenn COR 15.00 30.00
133 Charles King RC 5.00 10.00
134 Bob Feller 50.00 80.00
135 Lloyd Merriman 5.00 10.00
136 Rocky Bridges 5.00 10.00
137 Bob Talbot 5.00 10.00
138 Davey Williams 7.50 15.00
139 Shantz Brothers 7.50 15.00
Wilmer Shantz
Bobby Shantz
140 Bobby Shantz 7.50 15.00
141 Wes Westrum 7.50 15.00
142 Rudy Regalado RC 5.00 10.00
143 Don Newcombe 15.00 30.00
144 Art Houtteman 5.00 10.00
145 Bob Nieman RC 5.00 10.00
146 Don Liddle 5.00 10.00
147 Sam Mele 5.00 10.00
148 Bob Chakales 5.00 10.00
149 Cloyd Boyer 5.00 10.00
150 Billy Klaus RC 5.00 10.00
151 Jim Brideweser 5.00 10.00
152 Johnny Klippstein 5.00 10.00
153 Eddie Robinson 5.00 10.00
154 Frank Lary RC 7.50 15.00
155 Gerry Staley 5.00 10.00
156 Jim Hughes 7.50 15.00
157A Ernie Johnson ERR 10.00 20.00
(Photo actually
Don Johnson)
157B Ernie Johnson COR 10.00 20.00
158 Gil Hodges 30.00 50.00
159 Harry Byrd 5.00 10.00
160 Bill Skowron 10.00 20.00
161 Matt Batts 5.00 10.00
162 Charlie Maxwell 5.00 10.00
163 Sid Gordon 7.50 15.00
164 Toby Atwell 5.00 10.00
165 Maurice McDermott 5.00 10.00
166 Jim Busby 5.00 10.00
167 Bob Grim RC 10.00 20.00
168 Yogi Berra 75.00 125.00
169 Carl Furillo 15.00 30.00
170 Carl Erskine 10.00 20.00
171 Robin Roberts 30.00 50.00
172 Willie Jones 5.00 10.00
173 Chico Carrasquel 5.00 10.00
174 Sherm Lollar 7.50 15.00
175 Wilmer Shantz RC 5.00 10.00
176 Joe DeMaestri 5.00 10.00
177 Willard Nixon 5.00 10.00
178 Tom Brewer RC 5.00 10.00
179 Hank Aaron 150.00 250.00
180 Johnny Logan 7.50 15.00
181 Eddie Miksis 5.00 10.00
182 Bob Rush 5.00 10.00
183 Ray Katt 5.00 10.00
184 Willie Mays 150.00 250.00
185 Vic Raschi 5.00 10.00
186 Alex Grammas 5.00 10.00
187 Fred Hatfield 5.00 10.00
188 Ned Garver 5.00 10.00
189 Jack Collum 5.00 10.00
190 Fred Baczewski 5.00 10.00
191 Bob Lemon 15.00 30.00
192 George Strickland 5.00 10.00
193 Howie Judson 5.00 10.00
194 Joe Nuxhall 7.50 15.00
195A Erv Palica 7.50 15.00
(Without trade)
195B Erv Palica 20.00 40.00
(With trade)
196 Russ Meyer 7.50 15.00
197 Ralph Kiner 15.00 30.00
198 Dave Pope RC 5.00 10.00
199 Vern Law 7.50 15.00
200 Dick Littlefield 5.00 10.00
201 Allie Reynolds 10.00 20.00
202 Mickey Mantle UER 500.00 800.00
Birthdate listed as 10/30/31
Should be 10/20/31
203 Steve Gromek 5.00 10.00
204A Frank Bolling ERR RC 10.00 20.00
(Name on back is
Milt Bolling)
204B Frank Bolling COR 10.00 20.00
205 Rip Repulski 5.00 10.00
206 Ralph Beard RC 5.00 10.00
207 Frank Shea 5.00 10.00
208 Ed Fitzgerald 5.00 10.00
209 Smoky Burgess 7.50 15.00
210 Earl Torgeson 5.00 10.00
211 Sonny Dixon RC 5.00 10.00
212 Jack Dittmer 5.00 10.00
213 George Kell 15.00 30.00
214 Billy Pierce 7.50 15.00
215 Bob Kuzava 5.00 10.00
216 Preacher Roe 10.00 20.00
217 Del Crandall 7.50 15.00
218 Joe Adcock 7.50 15.00
219 Whitey Lockman 7.50 15.00
220 Jim Hearn 5.00 10.00
221 Hector Brown 5.00 10.00
222 Russ Kemmerer RC 5.00 10.00
223 Hal Jeffcoat 5.00 10.00
224 Dee Fondy 5.00 10.00
225 Paul Richards MG 7.50 15.00
226 Bill McKinley UMP 18.00 30.00
227 Frank Baumholtz 7.50 15.00
228 John Phillips RC 7.50 15.00
229 Jim Brosnan RC 10.00 20.00
230 Al Brazle 7.50 15.00
231 Jim Konstanty 10.00 20.00
232 Birdie Tebbetts MG 10.00 20.00
233 Bill Serena 7.50 15.00
234 Dick Bartell CO 10.00 20.00
235 Joe Paparella UMP 18.00 30.00
236 Murry Dickson 7.50 15.00
237 Johnny Wyrostek 7.50 15.00
238 Eddie Stanky MG 10.00 20.00
239 Edwin Rommel UMP 20.00 40.00
240 Billy Loes 10.00 20.00
241 Johnny Pesky CO 10.00 20.00
242 Ernie Banks 200.00 350.00
243 Gus Bell 10.00 20.00
244 Duane Pillette 7.50 15.00
245 Bill Miller 7.50 15.00
246 Hank Bauer 15.00 30.00
247 Dutch Leonard CO 7.50 15.00
248 Harry Dorish 7.50 15.00
249 Billy Gardner RC 10.00 20.00
250 Larry Napp UMP 18.00 30.00
251 Stan Jok 7.50 15.00
252 Roy Smalley 7.50 15.00
253 Jim Wilson 7.50 15.00
254 Bennett Flowers RC 7.50 15.00
255 Pete Runnels 10.00 20.00
256 Owen Friend 7.50 15.00
257 Tom Alston RC 7.50 15.00
258 John Stevens UMP 18.00 30.00
259 Don Mossi RC 15.00 30.00
260 Edwin Hurley UMP 18.00 30.00
261 Walt Moryn RC 10.00 20.00
262 Jim Lemon 7.50 15.00
263 Eddie Joost 7.50 15.00
264 Bill Henry RC 7.50 15.00
265 Albert Barlick UMP 50.00 80.00
266 Mike Fornieles 7.50 15.00
267 Jim Honochick UMP 50.00 80.00
268 Roy Lee Hawes RC 7.50 15.00
269 Joe Amalfitano RC 10.00 20.00
270 Chico Fernandez RC 10.00 20.00
271 Bob Hooper 7.50 15.00
272 John Flaherty UMP 18.00 30.00
273 Bubba Church 7.50 15.00
274 Jim Delsing 7.50 15.00
275 William Grieve UMP 18.00 30.00
276 Ike Delock 7.50 15.00
277 Ed Runge UMP 18.00 30.00
278 Charlie Neal RC 20.00 40.00
279 Hank Soar UMP 20.00 40.00
280 Clyde McCullough 7.50 15.00
281 Charles Berry UMP 20.00 40.00
282 Phil Cavarretta 10.00 20.00
283 Nestor Chylak UMP 50.00 80.00
284 Bill Jackowski UMP 18.00 30.00
285 Walt Dropo 10.00 20.00
286 Frank Secory UMP 18.00 30.00
287 Ron Mrozinski RC 7.50 15.00
288 Dick Smith RC 7.50 15.00
289 Arthur Gore UMP 18.00 30.00
290 Hershell Freeman RC 7.50 15.00
291 Frank Dascoli UMP 18.00 30.00
292 Marv Blaylock RC 7.50 15.00
293 Thomas Gorman UMP 20.00 40.00
294 Wally Moses CO 7.50 15.00
295 Lee Ballanfant UMP 18.00 30.00
296 Bill Virdon RC 15.00 30.00
297 Dusty Boggess UMP 18.00 30.00
298 Charlie Grimm MG 10.00 20.00
299 Lon Warneke UMP 20.00 40.00
300 Tommy Byrne 10.00 20.00
301 William Engeln UMP 18.00 30.00
302 Frank Malzone RC 15.00 30.00
303 Jocko Conlan UMP 50.00 80.00
304 Harry Chiti 7.50 15.00
305 Frank Umont UMP 18.00 30.00
306 Bob Cerv 10.00 20.00
307 Babe Pinelli UMP 20.00 40.00
308 Al Lopez MG 30.00 50.00
309 Hal Dixon UMP 18.00 30.00
310 Ken Lehman RC 7.50 15.00
311 Lawrence Goetz UMP 18.00 30.00
312 Bill Wight 7.50 15.00
313 Augie Donatelli UMP 30.00 50.00
314 Dale Mitchell 10.00 20.00
315 Cal Hubbard UMP 50.00 80.00
316 Marion Fricano 7.50 15.00
317 W. Summers UMP 10.00 20.00
318 Sid Hudson 7.50 15.00
319 Al Schroll RC 7.50 15.00
320 George Susce RC 30.00 50.00

1989 Bowman

The 1989 Bowman set, produced by Topps, contains 484 slightly oversized cards (measuring 2 1/2" by 3 3/4"). The cards were released in midseason 1989 in wax, rack, cello and factory set formats. The fronts have white-bordered color photos with facsimile autographs and small Bowman logos. The backs feature charts detailing 1988 player performances vs. each team. The cards are ordered alphabetically according to teams in the AL and NL. Cards 258-261 form a father/son subset. Rookie Cards in this set include Sandy Alomar Jr., Steve Finley, Ken Griffey Jr., Tino Martinez, Gary Sheffield, John Smoltz and Robin Ventura.

COMPLETE SET (484) 10.00 25.00
COMP.FACT.SET (484) 10.00 25.00
1 Oswald Peraza .01 .05
2 Brian Holton .01 .05
3 Jose Bautista RC .02 .10
4 Pete Harnisch RC .08 .25
5 Dave Schmidt .01 .05
6 Gregg Olson RC .08 .25
7 Jeff Ballard .01 .05
8 Bob Melvin .01 .05
9 Cal Ripken .30 .75
10 Randy Milligan .01 .05
11 Juan Bell RC .02 .10
12 Billy Ripken .01 .05
13 Jim Traber .01 .05
14 Pete Stanicek .01 .05
15 Steve Finley RC .30 .75
16 Larry Sheets .01 .05
17 Phil Bradley .01 .05
18 Brady Anderson RC .15 .40
19 Lee Smith .02 .10
20 Tom Fischer .01 .05
21 Mike Boddicker .01 .05
22 Rob Murphy .01 .05
23 Wes Gardner .01 .05
24 John Dopson .01 .05
25 Bob Stanley .01 .05
26 Roger Clemens .40 1.00
27 Rich Gedman .01 .05
28 Marty Barrett .01 .05
29 Luis Rivera .01 .05
30 Jody Reed .01 .05
31 Nick Esasky .01 .05
32 Wade Boggs .05 .15
33 Jim Rice .02 .10
34 Mike Greenwell .01 .05
35 Dwight Evans .05 .15
36 Ellis Burks .02 .10
37 Chuck Finley .02 .10
38 Kirk McCaskill .01 .05
39 Jim Abbott RC * .40 1.00
40 Bryan Harvey RC * .08 .25
41 Bert Blyleven .02 .10
42 Mike Witt .01 .05
43 Bob McClure .01 .05
44 Bill Schroeder .01 .05
45 Lance Parrish .02 .10
46 Dick Schofield .01 .05
47 Wally Joyner .02 .10
48 Jack Howell .01 .05
49 Johnny Ray .01 .05
50 Chili Davis .02 .10
51 Tony Armas .02 .10
52 Claudell Washington .01 .05
53 Brian Downing .02 .10
54 Devon White .02 .10
55 Bobby Thigpen .01 .05
56 Bill Long .01 .05
57 Jerry Reuss .01 .05
58 Shawn Hillegas .01 .05
59 Melido Perez .01 .05
60 Jeff Bittiger .01 .05
61 Jack McDowell .02 .10
62 Carlton Fisk .05 .15
63 Steve Lyons .01 .05
64 Ozzie Guillen .02 .10
65 Robin Ventura RC .30 .75
66 Fred Manrique .01 .05
67 Dan Pasqua .01 .05
68 Ivan Calderon .01 .05
69 Ron Kittle .01 .05
70 Daryl Boston .01 .05
71 Dave Gallagher .01 .05
72 Harold Baines .02 .10
73 Charles Nagy RC .08 .25
74 John Farrell .01 .05
75 Kevin Wickander .01 .05
76 Greg Swindell .01 .05
77 Mike Walker .01 .05
78 Doug Jones .01 .05
79 Rich Yett .01 .05
80 Tom Candiotti .01 .05
81 Jesse Orosco .01 .05
82 Bud Black .01 .05
83 Andy Allanson .01 .05
84 Pete O'Brien .01 .05
85 Jerry Browne .01 .05
86 Brook Jacoby .01 .05
87 Mark Lewis RC .08 .25
88 Luis Aguayo .01 .05
89 Cory Snyder .01 .05
90 Oddibe McDowell .01 .05
91 Joe Carter .02 .10
92 Frank Tanana .02 .10
93 Jack Morris .02 .10
94 Doyle Alexander .01 .05
95 Steve Searcy .01 .05
96 Randy Bockus .01 .05
97 Jeff M. Robinson .01 .05
98 Mike Henneman .01 .05
99 Paul Gibson .01 .05
100 Frank Williams .01 .05
101 Matt Nokes .01 .05
102 Rico Brogna RC UER .15 .40
(Misspelled Ricco
on card back)
103 Lou Whitaker .02 .10
104 Al Pedrique .01 .05
105 Alan Trammell .02 .10
106 Chris Brown .01 .05
107 Pat Sheridan .01 .05
108 Chet Lemon .02 .10
109 Keith Moreland .01 .05
110 Mel Stottlemyre Jr. .01 .05
111 Bret Saberhagen .02 .10
112 Floyd Bannister .01 .05
113 Jeff Montgomery .01 .05
114 Steve Farr .01 .05
115 Tom Gordon UER RC .15 .40
(Front shows auto-
graph of Don Gordon)
116 Charlie Leibrandt .01 .05
117 Mark Gubicza .01 .05
118 Mike Macfarlane RC .08 .25
119 Bob Boone .02 .10
120 Kurt Stillwell .01 .05
121 George Brett .25 .60
122 Frank White .02 .10
123 Kevin Seitzer .01 .05
124 Willie Wilson .02 .10
125 Pat Tabler .01 .05
126 Bo Jackson .08 .25
127 Hugh Walker RC .02 .10
128 Danny Tartabull .01 .05
129 Teddy Higuera .01 .05
130 Don August .01 .05
131 Juan Nieves .01 .05
132 Mike Birkbeck .01 .05
133 Dan Plesac .01 .05
134 Chris Bosio .01 .05
135 Bill Wegman .01 .05
136 Chuck Crim .01 .05
137 B.J. Surhoff .02 .10
138 Joey Meyer .01 .05
139 Dale Sveum .01 .05
140 Paul Molitor .02 .10
141 Jim Gantner .01 .05
142 Gary Sheffield RC .60 1.50
143 Greg Brock .01 .05
144 Robin Yount .15 .40
145 Glenn Braggs .01 .05
146 Rob Deer .01 .05
147 Fred Toliver .01 .05
148 Jeff Reardon .02 .10
149 Allan Anderson .01 .05
150 Frank Viola .02 .10
151 Shane Rawley .01 .05
152 Juan Berenguer .01 .05
153 Johnny Ard .01 .05
154 Tim Laudner .01 .05
155 Brian Harper .01 .05
156 Al Newman .01 .05
157 Kent Hrbek .02 .10
158 Gary Gaetti .02 .10
159 Wally Backman .01 .05
160 Gene Larkin .01 .05
161 Greg Gagne .01 .05
162 Kirby Puckett .08 .25
163 Dan Gladden .01 .05
164 Randy Bush .01 .05
165 Dave LaPoint .01 .05
166 Andy Hawkins .01 .05
167 Dave Righetti .02 .10
168 Lance McCullers .01 .05
169 Jimmy Jones .01 .05
170 Al Leiter .08 .25
171 John Candelaria .01 .05
172 Don Slaught .01 .05
173 Jamie Quirk .01 .05
174 Rafael Santana .01 .05
175 Mike Pagliarulo .01 .05
176 Don Mattingly .25 .60
177 Ken Phelps .01 .05
178 Steve Sax .01 .05
179 Dave Winfield .02 .10
180 Stan Jefferson .01 .05
181 Rickey Henderson .08 .25
182 Bob Brower .01 .05
183 Roberto Kelly .01 .05
184 Curt Young .01 .05
185 Gene Nelson .01 .05
186 Bob Welch .02 .10
187 Rick Honeycutt .01 .05
188 Dave Stewart .02 .10
189 Mike Moore .01 .05
190 Dennis Eckersley .05 .15
191 Eric Plunk .01 .05
192 Storm Davis .01 .05
193 Terry Steinbach .02 .10
194 Ron Hassey .01 .05
195 Stan Royer RC .02 .10
196 Walt Weiss .01 .05
197 Mark McGwire .40 1.00
198 Carney Lansford .02 .10
199 Glenn Hubbard .01 .05
200 Dave Henderson .01 .05
201 Jose Canseco .08 .25
202 Dave Parker .02 .10
203 Scott Bankhead .01 .05
204 Tom Niedenfuer .01 .05
205 Mark Langston .01 .05
206 Erik Hanson RC .08 .25
207 Mike Jackson .01 .05
208 Dave Valle .01 .05
209 Scott Bradley .01 .05
210 Harold Reynolds .02 .10
211 Tino Martinez RC .75 2.00
212 Rich Renteria .01 .05
213 Rey Quinones .01 .05
214 Jim Presley .01 .05
215 Alvin Davis .01 .05
216 Edgar Martinez .08 .25
217 Darnell Coles .01 .05
218 Jeffrey Leonard .01 .05
219 Jay Buhner .02 .10
220 Ken Griffey Jr. RC 2.50 6.00
221 Drew Hall .01 .05
222 Bobby Witt .01 .05
223 Jamie Moyer .02 .10
224 Charlie Hough .02 .10
225 Nolan Ryan .40 1.00
226 Jeff Russell .01 .05
227 Jim Sundberg .02 .10
228 Julio Franco .02 .10
229 Buddy Bell .02 .10
230 Scott Fletcher .01 .05
231 Jeff Kunkel .01 .05
232 Steve Buechele .01 .05
233 Monty Fariss .01 .05
234 Rick Leach .01 .05
235 Ruben Sierra .02 .10
236 Cecil Espy .01 .05
237 Rafael Palmeiro .08 .25
238 Pete Incaviglia .01 .05
239 Dave Stieb .02 .10
240 Jeff Musselman .01 .05
241 Mike Flanagan .01 .05
242 Todd Stottlemyre .01 .05
243 Jimmy Key .02 .10
244 Tony Castillo RC .02 .10
245 Alex Sanchez RC .01 .05
246 Tom Henke .01 .05
247 John Cerutti .01 .05
248 Ernie Whitt .01 .05
249 Bob Brenly .01 .05
250 Rance Mulliniks .01 .05
251 Kelly Gruber .01 .05
252 Ed Sprague RC .08 .25
253 Fred McGriff .05 .15
254 Tony Fernandez .01 .05
255 Tom Lawless .01 .05
256 George Bell .02 .10
257 Jesse Barfield .02 .10
258 Roberto Alomar .05 .15
Sandy Alomar
259 Ken Griffey Jr. .40 1.00
Ken Griffey Sr.
260 Cal Ripken Jr. .08 .25
Cal Ripken Sr.
261 Mel Stottlemyre Jr. .01 .05
Mel Stottlemyre Sr.
262 Zane Smith .01 .05
263 Charlie Puleo .01 .05
264 Derek Lilliquist RC .02 .10
265 Paul Assenmacher .01 .05
266 John Smoltz RC .60 1.50
267 Tom Glavine .08 .25
268 Steve Avery RC .08 .25
269 Pete Smith .01 .05
270 Jody Davis .01 .05
271 Bruce Benedict .01 .05
272 Andres Thomas .01 .05
273 Gerald Perry .01 .05
274 Ron Gant .02 .10
275 Darrell Evans .02 .10
276 Dale Murphy .05 .15
277 Dion James .01 .05
278 Lonnie Smith .01 .05
279 Geronimo Berroa .01 .05
280 Steve Wilson RC .02 .10
281 Rick Sutcliffe .02 .10
282 Kevin Coffman .01 .05
283 Mitch Williams .01 .05
284 Greg Maddux .20 .50
285 Paul Kilgus .01 .05
286 Mike Harkey RC .02 .10
287 Lloyd McClendon .01 .05
288 Damon Berryhill .01 .05
289 Ty Griffin .01 .05
290 Ryne Sandberg .15 .40
291 Mark Grace .08 .25
292 Curt Wilkerson .01 .05
293 Vance Law .01 .05
294 Shawon Dunston .01 .05
295 Jerome Walton RC .08 .25
296 Mitch Webster .01 .05
297 Dwight Smith RC .08 .25
298 Andre Dawson .02 .10
299 Jeff Sellers .01 .05
300 Jose Rijo .02 .10
301 John Franco .02 .10
302 Rick Mahler .01 .05
303 Ron Robinson .01 .05
304 Danny Jackson .01 .05
305 Rob Dibble RC .15 .40
306 Tom Browning .01 .05
307 Bo Diaz .01 .05
308 Manny Trillo .01 .05
309 Chris Sabo RC * .15 .40
310 Ron Oester .01 .05
311 Barry Larkin .05 .15
312 Todd Benzinger .01 .05
313 Paul O'Neill .05 .15
314 Kal Daniels .01 .05
315 Joel Youngblood .01 .05
316 Eric Davis .02 .10
317 Dave Smith .01 .05
318 Mark Portugal .01 .05
319 Brian Meyer .01 .05
320 Jim Deshaies .01 .05
321 Juan Agosto .01 .05
322 Mike Scott .02 .10
323 Rick Rhoden .01 .05
324 Jim Clancy .01 .05
325 Larry Andersen .01 .05
326 Alex Trevino .01 .05
327 Alan Ashby .01 .05
328 Craig Reynolds .01 .05
329 Bill Doran .01 .05
330 Rafael Ramirez .01 .05
331 Glenn Davis .01 .05
332 Willie Ansley RC .02 .10
333 Gerald Young .01 .05
334 Cameron Drew .01 .05
335 Jay Howell .01 .05
336 Tim Belcher .01 .05
337 Fernando Valenzuela .02 .10
338 Ricky Horton .01 .05
339 Tim Leary .01 .05
340 Bill Bene .01 .05
341 Orel Hershiser .02 .10
342 Mike Scioscia .02 .10
343 Rick Dempsey .01 .05
344 Willie Randolph .02 .10
345 Alfredo Griffin .01 .05
346 Eddie Murray .08 .25
347 Mickey Hatcher .01 .05
348 Mike Sharperson .01 .05
349 John Shelby .01 .05
350 Mike Marshall .01 .05
351 Kirk Gibson .02 .10
352 Mike Davis .01 .05
353 Bryn Smith .01 .05
354 Pascual Perez .01 .05
355 Kevin Gross .01 .05
356 Andy McGaffigan .01 .05
357 Brian Holman RC * .02 .10
358 Dave Wainhouse RC .02 .10
359 Dennis Martinez .02 .10
360 Tim Burke .01 .05
361 Nelson Santovenia .01 .05
362 Tim Wallach .01 .05
363 Spike Owen .01 .05
364 Rex Hudler .01 .05
365 Andres Galarraga .02 .10
366 Otis Nixon .01 .05
367 Hubie Brooks .01 .05
368 Mike Aldrete .01 .05
369 Tim Raines .02 .10
370 Dave Martinez .01 .05
371 Bob Ojeda .01 .05
372 Ron Darling .02 .10
373 Wally Whitehurst RC .02 .10
374 Randy Myers .02 .10
375 David Cone .02 .10
376 Dwight Gooden .02 .10
377 Sid Fernandez .01 .05
378 Dave Proctor .01 .05
379 Gary Carter .02 .10
380 Keith Miller .01 .05
381 Gregg Jefferies .01 .05
382 Tim Teufel .01 .05
383 Kevin Elster .01 .05
384 Dave Magadan .01 .05
385 Keith Hernandez .02 .10
386 Mookie Wilson .02 .10
387 Darryl Strawberry .02 .10
388 Kevin McReynolds .01 .05
389 Mark Carreon .01 .05
390 Jeff Parrett .01 .05
391 Mike Maddux .01 .05
392 Don Carman .01 .05
393 Bruce Ruffin .01 .05
394 Ken Howell .01 .05
395 Steve Bedrosian .01 .05
396 Floyd Youmans .01 .05
397 Larry McWilliams .01 .05
398 Pat Combs RC * .02 .10
399 Steve Lake .01 .05
400 Dickie Thon .01 .05
401 Ricky Jordan RC * .08 .25
402 Mike Schmidt .20 .50
403 Tom Herr .01 .05
404 Chris James .01 .05
405 Juan Samuel .01 .05
406 Von Hayes .01 .05
407 Ron Jones .02 .10
408 Curt Ford .01 .05
409 Bob Walk .01 .05
410 Jeff D. Robinson .01 .05
411 Jim Gott .01 .05
412 Scott Medvin .01 .05

413 John Smiley .01 .05
414 Bob Kipper .01 .05
415 Brian Fisher .01 .05
416 Doug Drabek .01 .05
417 Mike LaValliere .01 .05
418 Ken Oberkfell .01 .05
419 Sid Bream .01 .05
420 Austin Manahan .01 .05
421 Jose Lind .01 .05
422 Bobby Bonilla .02 .10
423 Glenn Wilson .01 .05
424 Andy Van Slyke .05 .15
425 Gary Redus .01 .05
426 Barry Bonds .60 1.50
427 Don Heinkel .01 .05
428 Ken Dayley .01 .05
429 Todd Worrell .01 .05
430 Brad DuVall .01 .05
431 Jose DeLeon .01 .05
432 Joe Magrane .01 .05
433 John Ericks .01 .05
434 Frank DiPino .01 .05
435 Tony Pena .01 .05
436 Ozzie Smith .15 .40
437 Terry Pendleton .02 .10
438 Jose Oquendo .01 .05
439 Tim Jones .01 .05
440 Pedro Guerrero .02 .10
441 Milt Thompson .01 .05
442 Willie McGee .02 .10
443 Vince Coleman .01 .05
444 Tom Brunansky .01 .05
445 Walt Terrell .01 .05
446 Eric Show .01 .05
447 Mark Davis .01 .05
448 Andy Benes RC .15 .40
449 Ed Whitson .01 .05
450 Dennis Rasmussen .01 .05
451 Bruce Hurst .01 .05
452 Pat Clements .01 .05
453 Benito Santiago .02 .10
454 Sandy Alomar Jr. RC .15 .40
455 Garry Templeton .01 .05
456 Jack Clark .02 .10
457 Tim Flannery .01 .05
458 Roberto Alomar .08 .25
459 Carmelo Martinez .01 .05
460 John Kruk .02 .10
461 Tony Gwynn .10 .30
462 Jerald Clark RC .02 .10
463 Don Robinson .01 .05
464 Craig Lefferts .01 .05
465 Kelly Downs .01 .05
466 Rick Reuschel .02 .10
467 Scott Garrelts .01 .05
468 Wil Tejada .01 .05
469 Kirt Manwaring .01 .05
470 Terry Kennedy .01 .05
471 Jose Uribe .01 .05
472 Royce Clayton RC .15 .40
473 Robby Thompson .01 .05
474 Kevin Mitchell .02 .10
475 Ernie Riles .01 .05
476 Will Clark .05 .15
477 Donell Nixon .01 .05
478 Candy Maldonado .01 .05
479 Tracy Jones .01 .05
480 Brett Butler .02 .10
481 Checklist 1-121 .01 .05
482 Checklist 122-242 .01 .05
483 Checklist 243-363 .01 .05
484 Checklist 364-484 .01 .05

1989 Bowman Tiffany

This is a parallel to the regular 1989 Bowman set. This set was issued with a glossy front and white-stock backs, thus joining other sets known in the Topps family as "Tiffany" sets. The set measure 2 1/2" by 3 3/4" and was issued in factory set form only. In addition to the 484 regular cards, the 11 Reprint inserts were also included in the factory set. Reportedly, only 6,000 factory sets were printed.

COMP.FACT.SET (495) 125.00 200.00
*STARS: 6X TO 15X BASIC CARDS
*ROOKIES: 6X TO 15X BASIC CARDS
DISTRIBUTED ONLY IN FACTORY SET FORM
211 Tino Martinez 6.00 15.00
220 Ken Griffey Jr. 40.00 80.00

1989 Bowman Reprint Inserts

The 1989 Bowman Reprint Inserts set contains 11 cards measuring approximately 2 1/2" by 3 3/4". The fronts depict reproduced actual size "classic" Bowman cards, which are noted as reprints. The backs are devoted to a sweepstakes entry form. One of these reprint cards was included in each 1989 Bowman wax pack thus making these "reprints" quite easy to find. Since the cards are unnumbered, they are ordered below in alphabetical order by player's name and year within player.

COMPLETE SET (11) .75 2.00
ONE PER PACK
*TIFFANY: 10X TO 20X HI COLUMN
ONE TIFF.REP.SET PER TIFF.FACT.SET
1 Richie Ashburn 49 .15 .40
2 Yogi Berra 48 .08 .25
3 Whitey Ford 51 .15 .40
4 Gil Hodges 49 .20 .50
5 Mickey Mantle 51 .40 1.00
6 Mickey Mantle 53 .40 1.00
7 Willie Mays 51 .20 .50
8 Satchel Paige 49 .20 .50
9 Jackie Robinson 50 .20 .50
10 Duke Snider 49 .08 .25
11 Ted Williams 54 .20 .50

1990 Bowman

The 1990 Bowman set (produced by Topps) consists of 528 standard-size cards. The cards were issued in wax packs and factory sets. Each wax pack contained one of 11 different 1950's retro art cards. Unlike most sets, player selection focused primarily on rookies instead of proven major leaguers. The cards feature a white border with the player's photo inside and the Bowman logo on top. The card numbering is in team order with the teams themselves being ordered alphabetically within each league. Notable Rookie Cards include Moises Alou, Travis Fryman, Juan Gonzalez, Chuck Knoblauch, Ray Lankford, Sammy Sosa, Frank Thomas, Mo Vaughn, Larry Walker, and Bernie Williams.

COMPLETE SET (528) 10.00 25.00
COMP.FACT.SET (528) 10.00 25.00
1 Tommy Greene RC .02 .10
2 Tom Glavine .05 .15
3 Andy Nezelek .01 .05
4 Mike Stanton RC .08 .25
5 Rick Luecken RC .01 .05
6 Kent Mercker RC .08 .25
7 Derek Lilliquist .01 .05
8 Charlie Leibrandt .01 .05
9 Steve Avery .01 .05
10 John Smoltz .08 .25
11 Mark Lemke .01 .05
12 Lonnie Smith .01 .05
13 Oddibe McDowell .01 .05
14 Tyler Houston RC .08 .25
15 Jeff Blauser .01 .05
16 Ernie Whitt .01 .05
17 Alexis Infante .01 .05
18 Jim Presley .01 .05
19 Dale Murphy .05 .15
20 Nick Esasky .01 .05
21 Rick Sutcliffe .02 .10
22 Mike Bielecki .01 .05
23 Steve Wilson .01 .05
24 Kevin Blankenship .01 .05
25 Mitch Williams .01 .05
26 Dean Wilkins RC .01 .05
27 Greg Maddux .15 .40
28 Mike Harkey .01 .05
29 Mark Grace .05 .15
30 Ryne Sandberg .15 .40
31 Greg Smith RC .01 .05
32 Dwight Smith .01 .05
33 Damon Berryhill .01 .05
34 E.Cunningham UER RC .02 .10
(Errant * by the word in)
35 Jerome Walton .01 .05
36 Lloyd McClendon .01 .05
37 Ty Griffin .01 .05
38 Shawon Dunston .01 .05
39 Andre Dawson .02 .10
40 Luis Salazar .01 .05
41 Tim Layana RC .01 .05
42 Rob Dibble .02 .10
43 Tom Browning .01 .05
44 Danny Jackson .01 .05
45 Jose Rijo .01 .05
46 Scott Scudder .01 .05
47 Randy Myers UER .02 .10
(Career ERA .274, should be 2.74)
48 Brian Lane RC .02 .10
49 Paul O'Neill .05 .15
50 Barry Larkin .05 .15
51 Reggie Jefferson RC .08 .25
52 Jeff Branson RC .02 .10
53 Chris Sabo .01 .05
54 Joe Oliver .01 .05
55 Todd Benzinger .01 .05
56 Rolando Roomes .01 .05
57 Hal Morris .01 .05
58 Eric Davis .02 .10
59 Scott Bryant RC .01 .05
60 Ken Griffey Sr. .02 .10
61 Darryl Kile RC .20 .50
62 Dave Smith .01 .05
63 Mark Portugal .01 .05
64 Jeff Juden RC .02 .10
65 Bill Gullickson .01 .05
66 Danny Darwin .01 .05
67 Larry Andersen .01 .05
68 Jose Cano RC .01 .05
69 Dan Schatzeder .01 .05
70 Jim Deshaies .01 .05
71 Mike Scott .01 .05
72 Gerald Young .01 .05
73 Ken Caminiti .02 .10
74 Ken Oberkfell .01 .05
75 Dave Rohde RC .01 .05
76 Bill Doran .01 .05
77 Andujar Cedeno RC .02 .10
78 Craig Biggio .08 .25
79 Karl Rhodes RC .08 .25
80 Glenn Davis .01 .05
81 Eric Anthony RC .02 .10
82 John Wetteland .08 .25
83 Jay Howell .01 .05
84 Orel Hershiser .02 .10
85 Tim Belcher .01 .05
86 Kiki Jones RC .01 .05
87 Mike Hartley RC .01 .05
88 Ramon Martinez .01 .05
89 Mike Scioscia .01 .05
90 Willie Randolph .02 .10
91 Juan Samuel .01 .05
92 Jose Offerman RC .08 .25
93 Dave Hansen RC .08 .25
94 Jeff Hamilton .01 .05
95 Alfredo Griffin .01 .05
96 Tom Goodwin RC .08 .25
97 Kirk Gibson .02 .10
98 Jose Vizcaino RC .08 .25
99 Kal Daniels .01 .05
100 Hubie Brooks .01 .05
101 Eddie Murray .08 .25
102 Dennis Boyd .01 .05
103 Tim Burke .01 .05
104 Bill Sampen RC .01 .05
105 Brett Gideon .01 .05
106 Mark Gardner RC .02 .10
107 Howard Farmer RC .01 .05
108 Mel Rojas RC .02 .10
109 Kevin Gross .01 .05
110 Dave Schmidt .01 .05
111 Dennis Martinez .02 .10
112 Jerry Goff RC .01 .05
113 Andres Galarraga .02 .10
114 Tim Wallach .01 .05
115 Marquis Grissom RC .20 .50
116 Spike Owen .01 .05
117 Larry Walker RC .40 1.00
118 Tim Raines .02 .10
119 Delino DeShields RC .08 .25
120 Tom Foley .01 .05
121 Dave Martinez .01 .05
122 Frank Viola UER .01 .05
(Career ERA .384 should be 3.84)
123 Julio Valera RC .01 .05
124 Alejandro Pena .01 .05
125 David Cone .02 .10
126 Dwight Gooden .02 .10
127 Kevin D. Brown RC .01 .05
128 John Franco .02 .10
129 Terry Bross RC .01 .05
130 Blaine Beatty RC .01 .05
131 Sid Fernandez .01 .05
132 Mike Marshall .01 .05
133 Howard Johnson .01 .05
134 Jaime Roseboro RC .01 .05
135 Alan Zinter RC .02 .10
136 Keith Miller .01 .05
137 Kevin Elster .01 .05
138 Kevin McReynolds .01 .05
139 Barry Lyons .01 .05
140 Gregg Jefferies .01 .05
141 Darryl Strawberry .02 .10
142 Todd Hundley RC .08 .25
143 Scott Service .01 .05
144 Chuck Malone RC .01 .05
145 Steve Ontiveros .01 .05
146 Roger McDowell .01 .05
147 Ken Howell .01 .05
148 Pat Combs .01 .05
149 Jeff Parrett .01 .05
150 Chuck McElroy RC .02 .10
151 Jason Grimsley RC .02 .10
152 Len Dykstra .02 .10
153 Mickey Morandini RC .08 .25
154 John Kruk .02 .10
155 Dickie Thon .01 .05
156 Ricky Jordan .01 .05
157 Jeff Jackson RC .02 .10
158 Darren Daulton .02 .10
159 Tom Herr .01 .05
160 Von Hayes .01 .05
161 Dave Hollins RC .08 .25
162 Carmelo Martinez .01 .05
163 Bob Walk .01 .05
164 Doug Drabek .01 .05
165 Walt Terrell .01 .05
166 Bill Landrum .01 .05
167 Scott Ruskin RC .01 .05
168 Bob Patterson .01 .05
169 Bobby Bonilla .02 .10
170 Jose Lind .01 .05
171 Andy Van Slyke .05 .15
172 Mike LaValliere .01 .05
173 Willie Greene RC .02 .10
174 Jay Bell .02 .10
175 Sid Bream .01 .05
176 Tom Prince .01 .05
177 Wally Backman .01 .05
178 Moises Alou RC .30 .75
179 Steve Carter .01 .05
180 Gary Redus .01 .05
181 Barry Bonds .40 1.00
182 Don Slaught UER .01 .05
(Card back shows headings for a pitcher)
183 Joe Magrane .01 .05
184 Bryn Smith .01 .05
185 Todd Worrell .01 .05
186 Jose DeLeon .01 .05
187 Frank DiPino .01 .05
188 John Tudor .01 .05
189 Howard Hilton RC .01 .05
190 John Ericks .01 .05
191 Ken Dayley .01 .05
192 Ray Lankford RC .20 .50
193 Todd Zeile .02 .10
194 Willie McGee .02 .10
195 Ozzie Smith .15 .40
196 Milt Thompson .01 .05
197 Terry Pendleton .02 .10
198 Vince Coleman .01 .05
199 Paul Coleman RC .01 .05
200 Jose Oquendo .01 .05
201 Pedro Guerrero .02 .10
202 Tom Brunansky .01 .05
203 Roger Smithberg RC .01 .05
204 Eddie Whitson .01 .05
205 Dennis Rasmussen .01 .05
206 Craig Lefferts .01 .05
207 Andy Benes .02 .10
208 Bruce Hurst .01 .05
209 Eric Show .01 .05
210 Rafael Valdez RC .01 .05
211 Joey Cora .02 .10
212 Thomas Howard .01 .05
213 Rob Nelson .01 .05
214 Jack Clark .02 .10
215 Garry Templeton .01 .05
216 Fred Lynn .01 .05
217 Tony Gwynn .10 .30
218 Benito Santiago .02 .10
219 Mike Pagliarulo .01 .05
220 Joe Carter .02 .10
221 Roberto Alomar .05 .15
222 Bip Roberts .01 .05
223 Rick Reuschel .01 .05
224 Russ Swan RC .01 .05
225 Eric Gunderson RC .01 .05
226 Steve Bedrosian .01 .05
227 Mike Remlinger RC .01 .05
228 Scott Garrelts .01 .05
229 Ernie Camacho .01 .05
230 Andres Santana RC .02 .10
231 Will Clark .05 .15
232 Kevin Mitchell .01 .05
233 Robby Thompson .01 .05
234 Bill Bathe .01 .05
235 Tony Perezchica .01 .05
236 Gary Carter .02 .10
237 Brett Butler .02 .10
238 Matt Williams .02 .10
239 Ernie Riles .01 .05
240 Kevin Bass .01 .05
241 Terry Kennedy .01 .05
242 Steve Hosey RC .02 .10
243 Ben McDonald RC .08 .25
244 Jeff Ballard .01 .05
245 Joe Price .01 .05
246 Curt Schilling .40 1.00
247 Pete Harnisch .01 .05
248 Mark Williamson .01 .05
249 Gregg Olson .02 .10
250 Chris Myers RC .01 .05
251A David Segui ERR .20 .50
(Missing vital stats at top of card under name)
251B David Segui COR RC .20 .50
252 Joe Orsulak .01 .05
253 Craig Worthington .01 .05
254 Mickey Tettleton .01 .05
255 Cal Ripken .30 .75
256 Bill Ripken .01 .05
257 Randy Milligan .01 .05
258 Brady Anderson .02 .10
259 Chris Hoiles RC UER .08 .25
Baltimore is spelled Baltimore
260 Mike Devereaux .01 .05
261 Phil Bradley .01 .05
262 Leo Gomez RC .02 .10
263 Lee Smith .02 .10
264 Mike Rochford .01 .05
265 Jeff Reardon .02 .10
266 Wes Gardner .01 .05
267 Mike Boddicker .01 .05
268 Roger Clemens .40 1.00
269 Rob Murphy .01 .05
270 Mickey Pina RC .01 .05
271 Tony Pena .01 .05
272 Jody Reed .01 .05
273 Kevin Romine .01 .05
274 Mike Greenwell .01 .05
275 Mo Vaughn RC .40 1.00
276 Danny Heep .01 .05
277 Scott Cooper RC .02 .10
278 Greg Blosser RC .02 .10
279 Dwight Evans UER .05 .15
(* by 1990 Team Breakdown)
280 Ellis Burks .05 .15
281 Wade Boggs .05 .15
282 Marty Barrett .01 .05
283 Kirk McCaskill .01 .05
284 Mark Langston .01 .05
285 Bert Blyleven .02 .10
286 Mike Fetters RC .08 .25
287 Kyle Abbott RC .01 .05
288 Jim Abbott .05 .15
289 Chuck Finley .02 .10
290 Gary DiSarcina RC .08 .25
291 Dick Schofield .01 .05
292 Devon White .02 .10
293 Bobby Rose .01 .05
294 Brian Downing .01 .05
295 Lance Parrish .02 .10
296 Jack Howell .01 .05
297 Claudell Washington .01 .05
298 John Orton RC .01 .05
299 Wally Joyner .02 .10
300 Lee Stevens .01 .05
301 Chili Davis .02 .10
302 Johnny Ray .01 .05
303 Greg Hibbard RC .01 .05
304 Eric King .01 .05
305 Jack McDowell .01 .05
306 Bobby Thigpen .01 .05
307 Adam Peterson .01 .05
308 Scott Radinsky RC .08 .25
309 Wayne Edwards RC .01 .05
310 Melido Perez .01 .05
311 Robin Ventura .08 .25
312 Sammy Sosa RC 1.25 3.00
313 Dan Pasqua .01 .05
314 Carlton Fisk .05 .15
315 Ozzie Guillen .02 .10
316 Ivan Calderon .01 .05
317 Daryl Boston .01 .05
318 Craig Grebeck RC .08 .25
319 Scott Fletcher .01 .05
320 Frank Thomas RC .75 2.00
321 Steve Lyons .01 .05
322 Carlos Martinez .01 .05
323 Joe Skalski .01 .05
324 Tom Candiotti .01 .05
325 Greg Swindell .01 .05
326 Steve Olin RC .08 .25
327 Kevin Wickander .01 .05
328 Doug Jones .01 .05
329 Jeff Shaw .01 .05
330 Kevin Bearse RC .01 .05
331 Dion James .01 .05
332 Jerry Browne .01 .05
333 Joey Belle .08 .25
334 Felix Fermin .01 .05
335 Candy Maldonado .01 .05
336 Cory Snyder .01 .05
337 Sandy Alomar Jr. .02 .10
338 Mark Lewis .01 .05
339 Carlos Baerga RC .08 .25
340 Chris James .01 .05
341 Brook Jacoby .01 .05
342 Keith Hernandez .02 .10
343 Frank Tanana .01 .05
344 Scott Aldred RC .01 .05
345 Mike Henneman .01 .05
346 Steve Wapnick RC .01 .05
347 Greg Gohr RC .02 .10
348 Eric Stone RC .01 .05
349 Brian DuBois RC .01 .05
350 Kevin Ritz RC .01 .05
351 Rico Brogna .08 .25
352 Mike Heath .01 .05
353 Alan Trammell .02 .10
354 Chet Lemon .01 .05
355 Dave Bergman .01 .05
356 Lou Whitaker .02 .10
357 Cecil Fielder UER .02 .10
* by 1990 Team Breakdown
358 Milt Cuyler RC .02 .10
359 Tony Phillips .01 .05
360 Travis Fryman RC .20 .50
361 Ed Romero .01 .05
362 Lloyd Moseby .01 .05
363 Mark Gubicza .01 .05
364 Bret Saberhagen .02 .10
365 Tom Gordon .02 .10
366 Steve Farr .01 .05
367 Kevin Appier .02 .10
368 Storm Davis .01 .05
369 Mark Davis .01 .05
370 Jeff Montgomery .02 .10
371 Frank White .02 .10
372 Brent Mayne RC .08 .25
373 Bob Boone .02 .10
374 Jim Eisenreich .01 .05
375 Danny Tartabull .01 .05
376 Kurt Stillwell .01 .05
377 Bill Pecota .01 .05
378 Bo Jackson .08 .25
379 Bob Hamelin RC .08 .25
380 Kevin Seitzer .01 .05
381 Rey Palacios .01 .05
382 George Brett .25 .60
383 Gerald Perry .01 .05
384 Teddy Higuera .01 .05
385 Tom Filer .01 .05
386 Dan Plesac .01 .05
387 Cal Eldred RC .08 .25
388 Jaime Navarro .01 .05
389 Chris Bosio .01 .05
390 Randy Veres .01 .05
391 Gary Sheffield .08 .25
392 George Canale RC .01 .05
393 B.J. Surhoff .02 .10
394 Tim McIntosh RC .01 .05
395 Greg Brock .01 .05
396 Greg Vaughn .01 .05
397 Darryl Hamilton .01 .05
398 Dave Parker .02 .10
399 Paul Molitor .02 .10
400 Jim Gantner .01 .05
401 Rob Deer .01 .05
402 Billy Spiers .01 .05
403 Glenn Braggs .01 .05
404 Robin Yount .15 .40
405 Rick Aguilera .02 .10
406 Johnny Ard .01 .05
407 Kevin Tapani RC .08 .25
408 Park Pittman RC .01 .05
409 Allan Anderson .01 .05
410 Juan Berenguer .01 .05
411 Willie Banks RC .02 .10
412 Rich Yett .01 .05
413 Dave West .01 .05
414 Greg Gagne .01 .05
415 Chuck Knoblauch RC .20 .50
416 Randy Bush .01 .05
417 Gary Gaetti .02 .10
418 Kent Hrbek .02 .10
419 Al Newman .01 .05
420 Danny Gladden .01 .05
421 Paul Sorrento RC .08 .25
422 Derek Parks RC .02 .10
423 Scott Leius RC .01 .05
424 Kirby Puckett .08 .25
425 Willie Smith .01 .05
426 Dave Righetti .01 .05
427 Jeff D. Robinson .01 .05
428 Alan Mills RC .02 .10
429 Tim Leary .01 .05
430 Pascual Perez .01 .05
431 Alvaro Espinoza .01 .05
432 Dave Winfield .02 .10
433 Jesse Barfield .01 .05
434 Randy Velarde .01 .05
435 Rick Cerone .01 .05
436 Steve Balboni .01 .05
437 Mel Hall .01 .05
438 Bob Geren .01 .05
439 Bernie Williams RC .60 1.50
440 Kevin Maas RC .08 .25
441 Mike Blowers RC .02 .10
442 Steve Sax .01 .05
443 Don Mattingly .25 .60
444 Roberto Kelly .01 .05
445 Mike Moore .01 .05
446 Reggie Harris RC .02 .10
447 Scott Sanderson .01 .05
448 Dave Otto .01 .05
449 Dave Stewart .02 .10
450 Rick Honeycutt .01 .05
451 Dennis Eckersley .02 .10
452 Carney Lansford .02 .10
453 Scott Hemond RC .01 .05
454 Mark McGwire .40 1.00
455 Felix Jose .01 .05
456 Terry Steinbach .02 .10
457 Rickey Henderson .08 .25
458 Dave Henderson .01 .05
459 Mike Gallego .01 .05
460 Jose Canseco .05 .15
461 Walt Weiss .01 .05
462 Ken Phelps .01 .05
463 Darren Lewis RC .02 .10
464 Ron Hassey .01 .05
465 Roger Salkeld RC .02 .10
466 Scott Bankhead .01 .05
467 Keith Comstock .01 .05
468 Randy Johnson .20 .50
469 Erik Hanson .01 .05
470 Mike Schooler .01 .05
471 Gary Eave RC .01 .05
472 Jeffrey Leonard .01 .05
473 Dave Valle .01 .05
474 Omar Vizquel .08 .25
475 Pete O'Brien .01 .05
476 Henry Cotto .01 .05
477 Jay Buhner .02 .10
478 Harold Reynolds .02 .10
479 Alvin Davis .01 .05
480 Darnell Coles .01 .05
481 Ken Griffey Jr. .30 .75
482 Greg Briley .01 .05
483 Scott Bradley .01 .05
484 Tino Martinez .20 .50
485 Jeff Russell .01 .05
486 Nolan Ryan .40 1.00
487 Robb Nen RC .20 .50
488 Kevin Brown .02 .10
489 Brian Bohanon RC .02 .10
490 Ruben Sierra .02 .10
491 Pete Incaviglia .01 .05
492 Juan Gonzalez RC .40 1.00
493 Steve Buechele .01 .05
494 Scott Coolbaugh .01 .05
495 Geno Petralli .01 .05
496 Rafael Palmeiro .05 .15
497 Julio Franco .02 .10
498 Gary Pettis .01 .05
499 Donald Harris RC .01 .05
500 Monty Fariss .01 .05
501 Harold Baines .02 .10
502 Cecil Espy .01 .05
503 Jack Daugherty RC .01 .05
504 Willie Blair RC .02 .10
505 Dave Stieb .02 .10
506 Tom Henke .01 .05
507 John Cerutti .01 .05
508 Paul Kilgus .01 .05
509 Jimmy Key .02 .10
510 John Olerud RC .40 1.00
511 Ed Sprague .02 .10
512 Manuel Lee .01 .05
513 Fred McGriff .08 .25
514 Glenallen Hill .01 .05
515 George Bell .01 .05
516 Mookie Wilson .02 .10
517 Luis Sojo RC .08 .25
518 Nelson Liriano .01 .05
519 Kelly Gruber .01 .05
520 Greg Myers .01 .05
521 Pat Borders .01 .05
522 Junior Felix .01 .05
523 Eddie Zosky RC .02 .10
524 Tony Fernandez .01 .05
525 Checklist 1-132 UER .01 .05
(No copyright mark on the back)
526 Checklist 133-264 .01 .05
527 Checklist 265-396 .01 .05
528 Checklist 397-528 .01 .05

1990 Bowman Tiffany

These 528 standard-size cards were issued as a factory set by Topps. These cards parallel the regular Bowman issue except they have glossy fronts and a very easy to read white stock back. In addition to the 528 basic cards, the 11 insert art cards were also included in the factory set. According to published reports at the time, approximately 3,000 of these sets were produced.

COMP.FACT.SET (539) 100.00 200.00
*STARS: 6X TO 15X BASIC CARDS
*ROOKIES: 4X TO 10X BASIC CARDS

1990 Bowman Art Inserts

These standard-size cards were included as an insert in every 1990 Bowman pack. This set, which consists of 11 superstars, depicts drawings by Craig Pursley with the backs being descriptions of the 1990 Bowman sweepstakes. We have checklisted the set alphabetically by player. All the cards in this set can be found with either one asterisk or two on the back.

COMPLETE SET (11) .75 2.00
*TIFFANY: 8X TO 20X BASIC ART INSERT
ONE TIFF.REP.SET PER TIFF.FACT.SET
1 Will Clark .05 .15
2 Mark Davis .01 .05
3 Dwight Gooden .02 .10
4 Bo Jackson .08 .25
5 Don Mattingly .25 .60
6 Kevin Mitchell .01 .05
7 Gregg Olson .02 .10
8 Nolan Ryan .40 1.00
9 Bret Saberhagen .02 .10
10 Jerome Walton .01 .05
11 Robin Yount .15 .40

1991 Bowman

This single-series 704-card standard-size set marked the third straight year that Topps issued a set weighted towards prospects using the Bowman name. Cards were issued in wax packs and factory sets. The cards share a design very similar to the 1990 Bowman set with white borders enframing a color photo. The player

name, however, is more prominent than in the previous year set. The cards are arranged in team order by division as follows: AL East, AL West, NL East, and NL West. Subsets include Rod Carew Tribute (1-5), Minor League MVP's (180-185/693-698), AL Silver Sluggers (367-375), NL Silver Sluggers (376-384) and checklists (699-704). Rookie Cards in this set include Jeff Bagwell, Jeromy Burnitz, Carl Everett, Chipper Jones, Eric Karros, Ryan Klesko, Kenny Lofton, Javier Lopez, Raul Mondesi, Mike Mussina, Ivan "Pudge" Rodriguez, Tim Salmon, Jim Thome, and Rondell White. There are two instances of misnumbering in the set; Ken Griffey (should be 255) and Ken Griffey Jr. are both numbered 246 and Donovan Osborne (should be 406) and Thomson/Branca share number 410.

COMPLETE SET (704) 15.00 40.00
COMP.FACT.SET (704) 15.00 40.00
1 Rod Carew I .05 .15
2 Rod Carew II .05 .15
3 Rod Carew III .05 .15
4 Rod Carew IV .05 .15
5 Rod Carew V .05 .15
6 Willie Fraser .01 .05
7 John Olerud .02 .10
8 William Suero RC .01 .05
9 Roberto Alomar .05 .15
10 Todd Stottlemyre .01 .05
11 Joe Carter .02 .10
12 Steve Karsay RC .20 .50
13 Mark Whiten .01 .05
14 Pat Borders .01 .05
15 Mike Timlin RC .20 .50
16 Tom Henke .01 .05
17 Eddie Zosky .01 .05
18 Kelly Gruber .01 .05
19 Jimmy Key .02 .10
20 Jerry Schunk RC .01 .05
21 Manuel Lee .01 .05
22 Dave Stieb .01 .05
23 Pat Hentgen RC .20 .50
24 Glenallen Hill .01 .05
25 Rene Gonzales .01 .05
26 Ed Sprague .01 .05
27 Ken Dayley .01 .05
28 Pat Tabler .01 .05
29 Denis Boucher RC .05 .15
30 Devon White .02 .10
31 Dante Bichette .02 .10
32 Paul Molitor .02 .10
33 Greg Vaughn .01 .05
34 Dan Plesac .01 .05
35 Chris George RC .05 .15
36 Tim McIntosh .01 .05
37 Franklin Stubbs .01 .05
38 Bo Dodson RC .05 .15
39 Ron Robinson .01 .05
40 Ed Nunez .01 .05
41 Greg Brock .01 .05
42 Jaime Navarro .01 .05
43 Chris Bosio .01 .05
44 B.J. Surhoff .02 .10
45 Chris Johnson RC .01 .05
46 Willie Randolph .02 .10
47 Narciso Elvira RC .01 .05
48 Jim Gantner .01 .05
49 Kevin Brown .01 .05
50 Julio Machado .01 .05
51 Chuck Crim .01 .05
52 Gary Sheffield .02 .10
53 Angel Miranda RC .05 .15
54 Ted Higuera .01 .05
55 Robin Yount .15 .40
56 Cal Eldred .01 .05
57 Sandy Alomar Jr. .01 .05
58 Greg Swindell .01 .05
59 Brook Jacoby .01 .05
60 Efrain Valdez RC .01 .05
61 Ever Magallanes RC .01 .05
62 Tom Candiotti .01 .05
63 Eric King .01 .05
64 Alex Cole .01 .05
65 Charles Nagy .01 .05
66 Mitch Webster .01 .05
67 Chris James .01 .05
68 Jim Thome RC 2.00 5.00
69 Carlos Baerga .01 .05
70 Mark Lewis .01 .05
71 Jerry Browne .01 .05
72 Jesse Orosco .01 .05
73 Mike Huff .01 .05
74 Jose Escobar RC .01 .05
75 Jeff Manto .01 .05
76 Turner Ward RC .05 .15
77 Doug Jones .01 .05
78 Bruce Egloff RC .01 .05
79 Tim Costo RC .05 .15
80 Beau Allred .01 .05
81 Albert Belle .02 .10
82 John Farrell .01 .05
83 Glenn Davis .01 .05
84 Joe Orsulak .01 .05
85 Mark Williamson .01 .05
86 Ben McDonald .01 .05
87 Billy Ripken .01 .05
88 Leo Gomez UER .01 .05
Baltimore is spelled Baltimore
89 Bob Melvin .01 .05
90 Jeff M. Robinson .01 .05
91 Jose Mesa .01 .05
92 Gregg Olson .01 .05
93 Mike Devereaux .01 .05
94 Luis Mercedes RC .05 .15
95 Arthur Rhodes RC .20 .50
96 Juan Bell .01 .05
97 Mike Mussina RC 1.50 4.00
98 Jeff Ballard .01 .05
99 Chris Hoiles .01 .05

100 Brady Anderson .02 .10
101 Bob Milacki .01 .05
102 David Segui .01 .05
103 Dwight Evans .05 .15
104 Cal Ripken .30 .75
105 Mike Linskey RC .01 .05
106 Jeff Tackett RC .05 .15
107 Jeff Reardon .02 .10
108 Dana Kiecker .01 .05
109 Ellis Burks .02 .10
110 Dave Owen .01 .05
111 Danny Darwin .01 .05
112 Mo Vaughn .02 .10
113 Jeff McNeely RC .05 .15
114 Tom Bolton .01 .05
115 Greg Blosser .01 .05
116 Mike Greenwell .01 .05
117 Phil Plantier RC .05 .15
118 Roger Clemens .30 .75
119 John Marzano .01 .05
120 Jody Reed .01 .05
121 Scott Taylor RC .05 .15
122 Jack Clark .02 .10
123 Derek Livernois RC .01 .05
124 Tony Pena .01 .05
125 Tom Brunansky .01 .05
126 Carlos Quintana .01 .05
127 Tim Naehring .01 .05
128 Matt Young .01 .05
129 Wade Boggs .05 .15
130 Kevin Morton RC .01 .05
131 Pete Incaviglia .01 .05
132 Rob Deer .01 .05
133 Bill Gullickson .01 .05
134 Rico Brogna .01 .05
135 Lloyd Moseby .01 .05
136 Cecil Fielder .02 .10
137 Tony Phillips .01 .05
138 Mark Leiter RC .05 .15
139 John Cerutti .01 .05
140 Mickey Tettleton .01 .05
141 Milt Cuyler .01 .05
142 Greg Gohr .01 .05
143 Tony Bernazard .01 .05
144 Dan Gakeler RC .01 .05
145 Travis Fryman .02 .10
146 Dan Petry .01 .05
147 Scott Aldred .01 .05
148 John DeSilva RC .01 .05
149 Rusty Meacham RC .05 .15
150 Lou Whitaker .02 .10
151 Dave Haas RC .01 .05
152 Luis de los Santos .01 .05
153 Ivan Cruz RC .01 .05
154 Alan Trammell .02 .10
155 Pat Kelly RC .01 .05
156 Carl Everett RC .60 1.50
157 Greg Cadaret .01 .05
158 Kevin Maas .01 .05
159 Jeff Johnson RC .01 .05
160 Willie Smith .01 .05
161 Gerald Williams RC .20 .50
162 Mike Humphreys RC .05 .15
163 Alvaro Espinoza .01 .05
164 Matt Nokes .01 .05
165 Wade Taylor RC .01 .05
166 Roberto Kelly .01 .05
167 John Habyan .01 .05
168 Steve Farr .01 .05
169 Jesse Barfield .01 .05
170 Steve Sax .01 .05
171 Jim Leyritz .01 .05
172 Robert Eenhoorn RC .05 .15
173 Bernie Williams .08 .25
174 Scott Lusader .01 .05
175 Torey Lovullo .01 .05
176 Chuck Cary .01 .05
177 Scott Sanderson .01 .05
178 Don Mattingly .25 .60
179 Mel Hall .01 .05
180 Juan Gonzalez .08 .25
181 Hensley Meulens .01 .05
182 Jose Offerman .01 .05
183 Jeff Bagwell RC 1.25 3.00
184 Jeff Conine RC .40 1.00
185 Henry Rodriguez RC .20 .50
186 Jimmie Reese CO .02 .10
187 Kyle Abbott .01 .05
188 Lance Parrish .02 .10
189 Rafael Montalvo RC .01 .05
190 Floyd Bannister .01 .05
191 Dick Schofield .01 .05
192 Scott Lewis RC .01 .05
193 Jeff D. Robinson .01 .05
194 Kent Anderson .01 .05
195 Wally Joyner .02 .10
196 Chuck Finley .02 .10
197 Luis Sojo .01 .05
198 Jeff Richardson RC .01 .05
199 Dave Parker .02 .10
200 Jim Abbott .05 .15
201 Junior Felix .01 .05
202 Mark Langston .01 .05
203 Tim Salmon RC .60 1.50
204 Cliff Young .01 .05
205 Scott Bailes .01 .05
206 Bobby Rose .01 .05
207 Gary Gaetti .02 .10
208 Ruben Amaro RC .05 .15
209 Luis Polonia .01 .05
210 Dave Winfield .02 .10
211 Bryan Harvey .01 .05
212 Mike Moore .01 .05
213 Rickey Henderson .08 .25
214 Steve Chitren RC .01 .05
215 Bob Welch .01 .05
216 Terry Steinbach .01 .05
217 Earnest Riles .01 .05
218 Todd Van Poppel RC .20 .50
219 Mike Gallego .01 .05
220 Curt Young .01 .05
221 Todd Burns .01 .05
222 Vance Law .01 .05
223 Eric Show .01 .05
224 Don Peters RC .01 .05
225 Dave Stewart .02 .10
226 Dave Henderson .01 .05
227 Jose Canseco .05 .15
228 Walt Weiss .01 .05
229 Dann Howitt .01 .05
230 Willie Wilson .01 .05
231 Harold Baines .02 .10
232 Scott Hemond .01 .05
233 Joe Slusarski RC .01 .05
234 Mark McGwire .30 .75
235 K.Dressendorfer RC .05 .15
236 Craig Paquette RC .20 .50
237 Dennis Eckersley .02 .10
238 Dana Allison RC .01 .05
239 Scott Bradley .01 .05
240 Brian Holman .01 .05
241 Mike Schooler .01 .05
242 Rich DeLucia RC .01 .05
243 Edgar Martinez .05 .15
244 Henry Cotto .01 .05
245 Omar Vizquel .05 .15
246 Ken Griffey Jr. .20 .50
(See also 255)
247 Jay Buhner .02 .10
248 Bill Krueger .01 .05
249 Dave Fleming RC .05 .15
250 Patrick Lennon RC .01 .05
251 Dave Valle .01 .05
252 Harold Reynolds .02 .10
253 Randy Johnson .10 .30
254 Scott Bankhead .01 .05
255 Ken Griffey Sr. UER .01 .05
(Card number is 246)
256 Greg Briley .01 .05
257 Tino Martinez .08 .25
258 Alvin Davis .01 .05
259 Pete O'Brien .01 .05
260 Erik Hanson .01 .05
261 Bret Boone RC .60 1.50
262 Roger Salkeld .01 .05
263 Dave Burba RC .20 .50
264 Kerry Woodson RC .05 .15
265 Julio Franco .02 .10
266 Dan Peltier RC .05 .15
267 Jeff Russell .01 .05
268 Steve Buechele .01 .05
269 Donald Harris .01 .05
270 Robb Nen .05 .15
271 Rich Gossage .02 .10
272 Ivan Rodriguez RC 1.50 4.00
273 Jeff Huson .01 .05
274 Kevin Brown .02 .10
275 Dan Smith RC .05 .15
276 Gary Pettis .01 .05
277 Jack Daugherty .01 .05
278 Mike Jeffcoat .01 .05
279 Brad Arnsberg .01 .05
280 Nolan Ryan .40 1.00
281 Eric McCray RC .01 .05
282 Scott Chiamparino .01 .05
283 Ruben Sierra .02 .10
284 Geno Petralli .01 .05
285 Monty Fariss .01 .05
286 Rafael Palmeiro .05 .15
287 Bobby Witt .01 .05
288 Dean Palmer UER .02 .10
Photo is Dan Peltier
289 Tony Scruggs RC .01 .05
290 Kenny Rogers .02 .10
291 Bret Saberhagen .02 .10
292 Brian McRae RC .20 .50
293 Storm Davis .01 .05
294 Danny Tartabull .01 .05
295 David Howard RC .01 .05
296 Mike Boddicker .01 .05
297 Joel Johnston RC .05 .15
298 Tim Spehr RC .01 .05
299 Hector Wagner RC .01 .05
300 George Brett .25 .60
301 Mike Macfarlane .01 .05
302 Kirk Gibson .02 .10
303 Harvey Pulliam RC .05 .15
304 Jim Eisenreich .01 .05
305 Kevin Seitzer .01 .05
306 Mark Davis .01 .05
307 Kurt Stillwell .01 .05
308 Jeff Montgomery .01 .05
309 Kevin Appier .02 .10
310 Bob Hamelin .01 .05
311 Tom Gordon .01 .05
312 Kerwin Moore RC .05 .15
313 Hugh Walker .01 .05
314 Terry Shumpert .01 .05
315 Warren Cromartie .01 .05
316 Gary Thurman .01 .05
317 Steve Bedrosian .01 .05
318 Danny Gladden .01 .05
319 Jack Morris .02 .10
320 Kirby Puckett .08 .25
321 Kent Hrbek .02 .10
322 Kevin Tapani .01 .05
323 Denny Neagle RC .20 .50
324 Rich Garces RC .05 .15
325 Larry Casian RC .01 .05
326 Shane Mack .01 .05
327 Allan Anderson .01 .05
328 Junior Ortiz .01 .05
329 Paul Abbott RC .05 .15
330 Chuck Knoblauch .02 .10
331 Chili Davis .02 .10
332 Todd Ritchie RC .20 .50
333 Brian Harper .01 .05
334 Rick Aguilera .02 .10
335 Scott Erickson .01 .05
336 Pedro Munoz RC .05 .15
337 Scott Leius .01 .05
338 Greg Gagne .01 .05
339 Mike Pagliarulo .01 .05
340 Terry Leach .01 .05
341 Willie Banks .01 .05
342 Bobby Thigpen .01 .05
343 Roberto Hernandez RC .20 .50
344 Melido Perez .01 .05
345 Carlton Fisk .05 .15
346 Norberto Martin RC .01 .05
347 Johnny Ruffin RC .05 .15
348 Jeff Carter .01 .05
349 Lance Johnson .01 .05
350 Sammy Sosa .08 .25
351 Alex Fernandez .01 .05
352 Jack McDowell .01 .05
353 Bob Wickman RC .60 1.50
354 Wilson Alvarez .01 .05
355 Charlie Hough .02 .10
356 Ozzie Guillen .02 .10
357 Cory Snyder .01 .05
358 Robin Ventura .02 .10
359 Scott Fletcher .01 .05
360 Cesar Bernhardt RC .01 .05
361 Dan Pasqua .01 .05
362 Tim Raines .02 .10
363 Brian Drahman RC .01 .05
364 Wayne Edwards .01 .05
365 Scott Radinsky .01 .05
366 Frank Thomas .08 .25
367 Cecil Fielder SLUG .01 .05
368 Julio Franco SLUG .01 .05
369 Kelly Gruber SLUG .01 .05
370 Alan Trammell SLUG .02 .10
371 R.Henderson SLUG .05 .15
372 Jose Canseco SLUG .02 .10
373 Ellis Burks SLUG .01 .05
374 Lance Parrish SLUG .01 .05
375 Dave Parker SLUG .01 .05
376 Eddie Murray SLUG .05 .15
377 Ryne Sandberg SLUG .08 .25
378 Matt Williams SLUG .01 .05
379 Barry Larkin SLUG .02 .10
380 Barry Bonds SLUG .20 .50
381 Bobby Bonilla SLUG .01 .05
382 D.Strawberry SLUG .01 .05
383 Benny Santiago SLUG .01 .05
384 Don Robinson SLUG .01 .05
385 Paul Coleman .01 .05
386 Milt Thompson .01 .05
387 Lee Smith .02 .10
388 Ray Lankford .02 .10
389 Tom Pagnozzi .01 .05
390 Ken Hill .01 .05
391 Jamie Moyer .02 .10
392 Greg Carmona RC .01 .05
393 John Ericks .01 .05
394 Bob Tewksbury .01 .05
395 Jose Oquendo .01 .05
396 Rheal Cormier RC .05 .15
397 Mike Milchin RC .01 .05
398 Ozzie Smith .15 .40
399 Aaron Holbert RC .05 .15
400 Jose DeLeon .01 .05
401 Felix Jose .01 .05
402 Juan Agosto .01 .05
403 Pedro Guerrero .02 .10
404 Todd Zeile .01 .05
405 Gerald Perry .01 .05
406 D.Osborne UER RC .05 .15
Card number is 410)
407 Bryn Smith .01 .05
408 Bernard Gilkey .01 .05
409 Rex Hudler .01 .05
410 Bobby Thomson .08 .25
Ralph Branca
Shot Heard Round the World
See also 406
411 Lance Dickson RC .05 .15
412 Danny Jackson .01 .05
413 Jerome Walton .01 .05
414 Sean Cheetham RC .01 .05
415 Joe Girardi .01 .05
416 Ryne Sandberg .15 .40
417 Mike Harkey .01 .05
418 George Bell .01 .05
419 Rick Wilkins RC .05 .15
420 Earl Cunningham .01 .05
421 Heathcliff Slocumb RC .05 .15
422 Mike Bielecki .01 .05
423 Jessie Hollins RC .05 .15
424 Shawon Dunston .01 .05
425 Dave Smith .01 .05
426 Greg Maddux .15 .40
427 Jose Vizcaino .01 .05
428 Luis Salazar .01 .05
429 Andre Dawson .02 .10
430 Rick Sutcliffe .02 .10
431 Paul Assenmacher .01 .05
432 Erik Pappas RC .01 .05
433 Mark Grace .05 .15
434 Dennis Martinez .02 .10
435 Marquis Grissom .02 .10
436 Wil Cordero RC .20 .50
437 Tim Wallach .01 .05
438 Brian Barnes RC .01 .05
439 Barry Jones .01 .05
440 Ivan Calderon .01 .05
441 Stan Spencer RC .01 .05
442 Larry Walker .08 .25
443 Chris Haney RC .05 .15
444 Hector Rivera RC .01 .05
445 Delino DeShields .02 .10
446 Andres Galarraga .02 .10
447 Gilberto Reyes .01 .05
448 Willie Greene .01 .05
449 Greg Colbrunn RC .20 .50
450 Rondell White RC .40 1.00
451 Steve Frey .01 .05
452 Shane Andrews RC .05 .15
453 Mike Fitzgerald .01 .05
454 Spike Owen .01 .05
455 Dave Martinez .01 .05
456 Dennis Boyd .01 .05
457 Eric Bullock .01 .05
458 Reid Cornelius RC .05 .15
459 Chris Nabholz .01 .05
460 David Cone .02 .10
461 Hubie Brooks .01 .05
462 Sid Fernandez .01 .05
463 Doug Simons RC .01 .05
464 Howard Johnson .01 .05
465 Chris Donnels RC .01 .05
466 Anthony Young RC .05 .15
467 Todd Hundley .01 .05
468 Rick Cerone .01 .05
469 Kevin Elster .01 .05
470 Wally Whitehurst .01 .05
471 Vince Coleman .01 .05
472 Dwight Gooden .02 .10
473 Charlie O'Brien .01 .05
474 Jeromy Burnitz RC .40 1.00
475 John Franco .02 .10
476 Daryl Boston .01 .05
477 Frank Viola .02 .10
478 D.J. Dozier .01 .05
479 Kevin McReynolds .01 .05
480 Tom Herr .01 .05
481 Gregg Jefferies .02 .10
482 Pete Schourek RC .05 .15
483 Ron Darling .01 .05
484 Dave Magadan .01 .05
485 Andy Ashby RC .20 .50
486 Dale Murphy .05 .15
487 Von Hayes .01 .05
488 Kim Batiste RC .05 .15
489 Tony Longmire RC .05 .15
490 Wally Backman .01 .05
491 Jeff Jackson .01 .05
492 Mickey Morandini .01 .05
493 Darrel Akerfelds .01 .05
494 Ricky Jordan .01 .05
495 Randy Ready .01 .05
496 Darrin Fletcher .01 .05
497 Chuck Malone .01 .05
498 Pat Combs .01 .05
499 Dickie Thon .01 .05
500 Roger McDowell .01 .05
501 Len Dykstra .02 .10
502 Joe Boever .01 .05
503 John Kruk .02 .10
504 Terry Mulholland .01 .05
505 Wes Chamberlain RC .05 .15
506 Mike Lieberthal RC .40 1.00
507 Darren Daulton .02 .10
508 Charlie Hayes .01 .05
509 John Smiley .01 .05
510 Gary Varsho .01 .05
511 Curt Wilkerson .01 .05
512 Orlando Merced RC .05 .15
513 Barry Bonds .40 1.00
514 Mike LaValliere .01 .05
515 Doug Drabek .01 .05
516 Gary Redus .01 .05
517 W.Pennyfeather RC .05 .15
518 Randy Tomlin RC .01 .05
519 Mike Zimmerman RC .05 .15
520 Jeff King .01 .05
521 Kurt Miller RC .05 .15
522 Jay Bell .02 .10
523 Bill Landrum .01 .05
524 Zane Smith .01 .05
525 Bobby Bonilla .02 .10
526 Bob Walk .01 .05
527 Austin Manahan .01 .05
528 Joe Ausanio RC .01 .05
529 Andy Van Slyke .05 .15
530 Jose Lind .01 .05
531 Carlos Garcia RC .05 .15
532 Don Slaught .01 .05
533 Gen.Colin Powell .20 .50
534 Frank Bolick RC .05 .15
535 Gary Scott RC .01 .05
536 Nikco Riesgo RC .01 .05
537 Reggie Sanders RC .60 1.50
538 Tim Howard RC .05 .15
539 Ryan Bowen RC .05 .15
540 Eric Anthony .01 .05
541 Jim Deshaies .01 .05
542 Tom Nevers RC .05 .15
543 Ken Caminiti .02 .10
544 Karl Rhodes .01 .05
545 Xavier Hernandez .01 .05
546 Mike Scott .01 .05
547 Jeff Juden .01 .05
548 Darryl Kile .02 .10
549 Willie Ansley .01 .05
550 Luis Gonzalez RC .60 1.50
551 Mike Simms RC .01 .05
552 Mark Portugal .01 .05
553 Jimmy Jones .01 .05
554 Jim Clancy .01 .05
555 Pete Harnisch .01 .05
556 Craig Biggio .05 .15
557 Eric Yelding .01 .05
558 Dave Rohde .01 .05
559 Casey Candaele .01 .05
560 Curt Schilling .08 .25
561 Steve Finley .02 .10
562 Javier Ortiz .01 .05
563 Andujar Cedeno .01 .05
564 Rafael Ramirez .01 .05
565 Kenny Lofton RC .60 1.50
566 Steve Avery .01 .05
567 Lonnie Smith .01 .05
568 Kent Mercker .01 .05
569 Chipper Jones RC 2.50 6.00
570 Terry Pendleton .02 .10
571 Otis Nixon .01 .05
572 Juan Berenguer .01 .05
573 Charlie Leibrandt .01 .05
574 David Justice .02 .10
575 Keith Mitchell RC .05 .15
576 Tom Glavine .05 .15
577 Greg Olson .01 .05
578 Rafael Belliard .01 .05
579 Ben Rivera RC .05 .15
580 John Smoltz .05 .15
581 Tyler Houston .01 .05
582 Mark Wohlers RC .20 .50
583 Ron Gant .02 .10
584 Ramon Caraballo RC .05 .15
585 Sid Bream .01 .05
586 Jeff Treadway .01 .05
587 Javy Lopez RC 1.25 3.00
588 Deion Sanders .05 .15
589 Mike Heath .01 .05
590 Ryan Klesko RC .40 1.00
591 Bob Ojeda .01 .05
592 Alfredo Griffin .01 .05
593 Raul Mondesi RC .40 1.00
594 Greg Smith .01 .05
595 Orel Hershiser .02 .10
596 Juan Samuel .01 .05
597 Brett Butler .02 .10
598 Gary Carter .02 .10
599 Stan Javier .01 .05
600 Kal Daniels .01 .05
601 Jamie McAndrew RC .05 .15
602 Mike Sharperson .01 .05
603 Jay Howell .01 .05
604 Eric Karros RC .60 1.50
605 Tim Belcher .01 .05
606 Dan Opperman RC .01 .05
607 Lenny Harris .01 .05
608 Tom Goodwin .01 .05
609 Darryl Strawberry .02 .10
610 Ramon Martinez .01 .05
611 Kevin Gross .01 .05
612 Zakary Shinall RC .01 .05
613 Mike Scioscia .01 .05
614 Eddie Murray .08 .25
615 Ronnie Walden RC .01 .05
616 Will Clark .05 .15
617 Adam Hyzdu RC .20 .50
618 Matt Williams .02 .10
619 Don Robinson .01 .05
620 Jeff Brantley .01 .05
621 Greg Litton .01 .05
622 Steve Decker RC .01 .05
623 Robby Thompson .01 .05
624 Mark Leonard RC .01 .05
625 Kevin Bass .01 .05
626 Scott Garrelts .01 .05
627 Jose Uribe .01 .05
628 Eric Gunderson .01 .05
629 Steve Hosey .01 .05
630 Trevor Wilson .01 .05
631 Terry Kennedy .01 .05
632 Dave Righetti .02 .10
633 Kelly Downs .01 .05
634 Johnny Ard .01 .05
635 E.Christopherson RC .05 .15
636 Kevin Mitchell .01 .05
637 John Burkett .01 .05
638 Kevin Rogers RC .05 .15
639 Bud Black .01 .05
640 Willie McGee .02 .10
641 Royce Clayton .01 .05
642 Tony Fernandez .01 .05
643 Ricky Bones RC .05 .15
644 Thomas Howard .01 .05
645 Dave Staton RC .05 .15
646 Jim Presley .01 .05
647 Tony Gwynn .10 .30
648 Marty Barrett .01 .05
649 Scott Coolbaugh .01 .05
650 Craig Lefferts .01 .05
651 Eddie Whitson .01 .05
652 Oscar Azocar .01 .05
653 Wes Gardner .01 .05
654 Bip Roberts .01 .05
655 Robbie Beckett RC .05 .15
656 Benito Santiago .02 .10
657 Greg W.Harris .01 .05
658 Jerald Clark .01 .05
659 Fred McGriff .05 .15
660 Larry Andersen .01 .05
661 Bruce Hurst .01 .05
662 Steve Martin UER RC .05 .15
Card said he pitched at Waterloo
he's an outfielder)
663 Rafael Valdez .01 .05
664 Paul Faries RC .01 .05
665 Andy Benes .01 .05
666 Randy Myers .01 .05
667 Rob Dibble .02 .10
668 Glenn Sutko RC .01 .05
669 Glenn Braggs .01 .05
670 Billy Hatcher .01 .05
671 Joe Oliver .01 .05
672 Freddie Benavides RC .05 .15
673 Barry Larkin .05 .15
674 Chris Sabo .01 .05
675 Mariano Duncan .01 .05
676 Chris Jones RC .01 .05
677 Gino Minutelli RC .01 .05
678 Reggie Jefferson .01 .05
679 Jack Armstrong .01 .05
680 Chris Hammond .01 .05
681 Jose Rijo .01 .05
682 Bill Doran .01 .05
683 Terry Lee RC .01 .05
684 Tom Browning .01 .05
685 Paul O'Neill .05 .15
686 Eric Davis .02 .10
687 Dan Wilson RC .20 .50
688 Ted Power .01 .05
689 Tim Layana .01 .05
690 Norm Charlton .01 .05
691 Hal Morris .01 .05
692 Rickey Henderson .05 .15
693 Sam Militello RC .05 .15
694 Matt Mieske RC .05 .15
695 Paul Russo RC .05 .15
696 Domingo Mota MVP .01 .05
697 Todd Guggiana RC .05 .15
698 Marc Newfield RC .05 .15
699 Checklist 1-122 .01 .05
700 Checklist 123-244 .01 .05
701 Checklist 245-366 .01 .05
702 Checklist 367-471 .01 .05
703 Checklist 472-593 .01 .05
704 Checklist 594-704 .01 .05

1992 Bowman

This 705-card standard-size set was issued in one comprehensive series. Unlike the previous Bowman issues, the 1992 set was radically upgraded to slick stock with gold foil subset cards in an attempt to reposition the brand as a premium level product. It initially stumbled out of the gate, but its superior selection of prospects enabled it to eventually gain acceptance in the hobby and now stands as one of the more important issues of the 1990's. Cards were distributed in plastic wrap packs, retail jumbo packs and special 80-card retail carton packs. Card fronts feature posed and action color player photos on a UV-coated white card face. . Forty-five foil cards inserted at a stated rate of one per wax pack and two per jumbo (23 regular cards) pack. These foil cards feature past and present Team USA players and minor league POY Award winners. Each foil card has an extremely slight variation in that the photos are cropped differently. There is no additional value to either version. Some of the regular and special cards picture prospects in civilian clothing who were still in the farm system. Rookie Cards in this set include Garret Anderson, Carlos Delgado, Mike Hampton, Brian Jordan, Mike Piazza, Manny Ramirez and Mariano Rivera.

COMPLETE SET (705) 60.00 120.00
1 Ivan Rodriguez .50 1.25
2 Kirk McCaskill .20 .50
3 Scott Livingstone .20 .50
4 Salomon Torres RC .20 .50
5 Carlos Hernandez .20 .50
6 Dave Hollins .20 .50
7 Scott Fletcher .20 .50
8 Jorge Fabregas RC .20 .50
9 Andujar Cedeno .20 .50
10 Howard Johnson .20 .50
11 Trevor Hoffman RC 4.00 10.00
12 Roberto Kelly .20 .50
13 Gregg Jefferies .20 .50
14 Marquis Grissom .20 .50
15 Mike Ignasiak .20 .50
16 Jack Morris .20 .50
17 William Pennyfeather .20 .50
18 Todd Stottlemyre .20 .50
19 Chito Martinez .20 .50
20 Roberto Alomar .30 .75
21 Sam Militello .20 .50
22 Hector Fajardo RC .20 .50
23 Paul Quantrill RC .20 .50
24 Chuck Knoblauch .20 .50
25 Reggie Jefferson .20 .50
26 Jeremy McGarity RC .20 .50
27 Jerome Walton .20 .50
28 Chipper Jones 5.00 12.00
29 Brian Barber RC .20 .50
30 Ron Darling .20 .50
31 Roberto Petagine RC .20 .50
32 Chuck Finley .20 .50
33 Edgar Martinez .30 .75
34 Napoleon Robinson .20 .50
35 Andy Van Slyke .30 .75
36 Bobby Thigpen .20 .50
37 Travis Fryman .20 .50
38 Eric Christopherson .20 .50
39 Terry Mulholland .20 .50
40 Darryl Strawberry .20 .50
41 Manny Alexander RC .20 .50
42 Tracy Sanders RC .20 .50
43 Pete Incaviglia .20 .50
44 Kim Batiste .20 .50
45 Frank Rodriguez .20 .50
46 Greg Swindell .20 .50
47 Delino DeShields .20 .50
48 John Ericks .20 .50
49 Franklin Stubbs .20 .50
50 Tony Gwynn .60 1.50
51 Clifton Garrett RC .20 .50
52 Mike Gardella .20 .50
53 Scott Erickson .20 .50
54 Gary Caraballo RC .20 .50
55 Jose Oliva RC .20 .50
56 Brook Fordyce .20 .50
57 Mark Whiten .20 .50
58 Joe Slusarski .20 .50
59 J.R. Phillips RC .20 .50
60 Barry Bonds 1.50 4.00
61 Bob Milacki .20 .50
62 Keith Mitchell .20 .50
63 Angel Miranda .20 .50
64 Raul Mondesi .20 .50
65 Brian Koelling RC .20 .50
66 Brian McRae .20 .50
67 John Patterson RC .20 .50
68 John Wetteland .20 .50
69 Wilson Alvarez .20 .50
70 Wade Boggs .30 .75
71 Darryl Ratliff RC .20 .50
72 Jeff Jackson .20 .50
73 Jeremy Hernandez RC .20 .50
74 Darryl Hamilton .20 .50
75 Rafael Belliard .20 .50
76 Rick Trlicek RC .20 .50
77 Felipe Crespo RC .20 .50
78 Carney Lansford .20 .50
79 Ryan Long RC .20 .50
80 Kirby Puckett .50 1.25
81 Earl Cunningham .20 .50
82 Pedro Martinez 4.00 10.00
83 Scott Hatteberg RC .40 1.00
84 Juan Gonzalez UER .30 .75
(65 doubles vs. Tigers)
85 Robert Nutting RC .20 .50
86 Pokey Reese RC .40 1.00
87 Dave Silvestri .20 .50
88 Scott Ruffcorn RC .20 .50
89 Rick Aguilera .20 .50
90 Cecil Fielder .20 .50
91 Kirk Dressendorfer .20 .50
92 Jerry DiPoto RC .20 .50
93 Mike Felder .20 .50
94 Craig Paquette .20 .50
95 Elvin Paulino RC .20 .50
96 Donovan Osborne .20 .50
97 Hubie Brooks .20 .50
98 Derek Lowe RC 1.50 4.00
99 David Zancanaro .20 .50
100 Ken Griffey Jr. .75 2.00
101 Todd Hundley .20 .50
102 Mike Trombley RC .20 .50
103 Ricky Gutierrez RC .40 1.00
104 Braulio Castillo .20 .50
105 Craig Lefferts .20 .50
106 Rick Sutcliffe .20 .50
107 Dean Palmer .20 .50
108 Henry Rodriguez .20 .50
109 Mark Clark RC .40 1.00
110 Kenny Lofton .30 .75
111 Mark Carreon .20 .50
112 J.T. Bruett .20 .50
113 Gerald Williams .20 .50
114 Frank Thomas .50 1.25
115 Kevin Reimer .20 .50
116 Sammy Sosa .50 1.25
117 Mickey Tettleton .20 .50
118 Reggie Sanders .20 .50
119 Trevor Wilson .20 .50
120 Cliff Brantley .20 .50
121 Spike Owen .20 .50
122 Jeff Montgomery .20 .50
123 Alex Sutherland .20 .50
124 Brien Taylor RC .40 1.00
125 Brian Williams RC .20 .50
126 Kevin Seitzer .20 .50
127 Carlos Delgado RC 4.00 10.00
128 Gary Scott .20 .50
129 Scott Cooper .20 .50
130 Domingo Jean RC .20 .50
131 Pat Mahomes RC .40 1.00
132 Mike Boddicker .20 .50
133 Roberto Hernandez .20 .50
134 Dave Valle .20 .50
135 Kurt Stillwell .20 .50
136 Brad Pennington RC .20 .50
137 Jermaine Swinton RC .20 .50
138 Ryan Hawblitzel RC .20 .50
139 Tito Navarro RC .20 .50
140 Sandy Alomar Jr. .20 .50
141 Todd Benzinger .20 .50
142 Danny Jackson .20 .50
143 Melvin Nieves RC .20 .50
144 Jim Campanis .20 .50
145 Luis Gonzalez .20 .50
146 D.Dooneweerd RC .20 .50
147 Charlie Hayes .20 .50
148 Greg Maddux .75 2.00
149 Brian Harper .20 .50
150 Brent Miller RC .20 .50
151 Shawn Estes RC .40 1.00
152 Mike Williams RC .40 1.00
153 Charlie Hough .20 .50
154 Randy Myers .20 .50
155 Kevin Young RC .40 1.00
156 Rick Wilkins .20 .50
157 Terry Shumpert .20 .50
158 Steve Karsay .20 .50
159 Gary DiSarcina .20 .50
160 Deion Sanders .30 .75
161 Tom Browning .20 .50
162 Dickie Thon .20 .50
163 Luis Mercedes .20 .50
164 Riccardo Ingram .20 .50
165 Tavo Alvarez RC .20 .50
166 Rickey Henderson .50 1.25
167 Jaime Navarro .20 .50
168 Billy Ashley RC .20 .50
169 Phil Dauphin RC .20 .50
170 Ivan Cruz .20 .50
171 Harold Baines .20 .50
172 Bryan Harvey .20 .50
173 Alex Cole .20 .50
174 Curtis Shaw RC .20 .50
175 Matt Williams .20 .50
176 Felix Jose .20 .50
177 Sam Horn .20 .50
178 Randy Johnson .50 1.25
179 Ivan Calderon .20 .50
180 Steve Avery .20 .50
181 William Suero .20 .50
182 Bill Swift .20 .50
183 Howard Battle RC .20 .50
184 Ruben Amaro .20 .50
185 Jim Abbott .30 .75
186 Mike Fitzgerald .20 .50
187 Bruce Hurst .20 .50
188 Jeff Juden .20 .50
189 Jeromy Burnitz .20 .50
190 Dave Burba .20 .50
191 Kevin Brown .20 .50
192 Patrick Lennon .20 .50
193 Jeff McNeely .20 .50
194 Wil Cordero .20 .50
195 Chili Davis .20 .50
196 Milt Cuyler .20 .50
197 Von Hayes .20 .50
198 Todd Revenig RC .20 .50
199 Joel Johnston .20 .50
200 Jeff Bagwell .50 1.25
201 Alex Fernandez .20 .50
202 Todd Jones RC 1.00 2.50
203 Charles Nagy .20 .50
204 Tim Raines .20 .50
205 Kevin Maas .20 .50
206 Julio Franco .20 .50
207 Randy Velarde .20 .50
208 Lance Johnson .20 .50
209 Scott Leius .20 .50
210 Derek Lee .20 .50
211 Joe Sondrini RC .20 .50
212 Royce Clayton .20 .50
213 Chris George .20 .50
214 Gary Sheffield .20 .50
215 Mark Gubicza .20 .50
216 Mike Moore .20 .50
217 Rick Huisman RC .20 .50
218 Jeff Russell .20 .50
219 D.J. Dozier .20 .50
220 Dave Martinez .20 .50
221 Alan Newman RC .20 .50
222 Nolan Ryan 1.50 4.00
223 Teddy Higuera .20 .50
224 Damon Buford RC .20 .50
225 Ruben Sierra .20 .50
226 Tom Nevers .20 .50
227 Tommy Greene .20 .50
228 Nigel Wilson RC .20 .50
229 John DeSilva .20 .50
230 Bobby Witt .20 .50
231 Greg Cadaret .20 .50
232 John Vander Wal RC .40 1.00
233 Jack Clark .20 .50
234 Bill Doran .20 .50
235 Bobby Bonilla .20 .50
236 Steve Olin .20 .50
237 Derek Bell .20 .50
238 David Cone .20 .50
239 Victor Cole RC .20 .50
240 Rod Bolton RC .20 .50
241 Tom Pagnozzi .20 .50
242 Rob Dibble .20 .50
243 Michael Carter RC .20 .50
244 Don Peters .20 .50
245 Mike LaValliere .20 .50
246 Joe Perona RC .20 .50
247 Mitch Williams .20 .50
248 Jay Buhner .20 .50
249 Andy Benes .20 .50
250 Alex Ochoa RC .20 .50
251 Greg Blosser .20 .50
252 Jack Armstrong .20 .50
253 Juan Samuel .20 .50
254 Terry Pendleton .20 .50
255 Ramon Martinez .20 .50
256 Rico Brogna .20 .50
257 John Smiley .20 .50
258 Carl Everett .30 .75
259 Tim Salmon .30 .75
260 Will Clark .30 .75
261 Ugueth Urbina RC .40 1.00
262 Jason Wood RC .20 .50

263 Dave Magadan .20 .50
264 Dante Bichette .20 .50
265 Jose DeLeon .20 .50
266 Mike Neill RC .40 1.00
267 Paul O'Neill .30 .75
268 Anthony Young .20 .50
269 Greg W. Harris .20 .50
270 Todd Van Poppel .20 .50
271 Pedro Castellano RC .20 .50
272 Tony Phillips .20 .50
273 Mike Gallego .20 .50
274 Steve Cooke RC .20 .50
275 Robin Ventura .20 .50
276 Kevin Mitchell .20 .50
277 Doug Linton RC .20 .50
278 Robert Eenhoorn .20 .50
279 Gabe White RC .20 .50
280 Dave Stewart .20 .50
281 Mo Sanford .20 .50
282 Greg Perschke .20 .50
283 Kevin Flora RC .20 .50
284 Jeff Williams RC .40 1.00
285 Keith Miller .20 .50
286 Andy Ashby .20 .50
287 Doug Dascenzo .20 .50
288 Eric Karros .20 .50
289 Glenn Murray RC .20 .50
290 Troy Percival RC 1.25 3.00
291 Orlando Merced .20 .50
292 Peter Hoy .20 .50
293 Tony Fernandez .20 .50
294 Juan Guzman .20 .50
295 Jesse Barfield .20 .50
296 Sid Fernandez .20 .50
297 Scott Cepicky .20 .50
298 Garret Anderson RC 2.00 5.00
299 Cal Eldred .20 .50
300 Ryne Sandberg 1.00 2.50
301 Jim Gantner .20 .50
302 Mariano Rivera RC 20.00 50.00
303 Ron Lockett RC .20 .50
304 Jose Offerman .20 .50
305 Dennis Martinez .20 .50
306 Luis Ortiz RC .20 .50
307 David Howard .20 .50
308 Russ Springer RC .40 1.00
309 Chris Howard .20 .50
310 Kyle Abbott .20 .50
311 Aaron Sele RC .40 1.00
312 David Justice .20 .50
313 Pete O'Brien .20 .50
314 Greg Hansell RC .20 .50
315 Dave Winfield .20 .50
316 Lance Dickson .20 .50
317 Eric King .20 .50
318 Vaughn Eshelman RC .20 .50
319 Tim Belcher .20 .50
320 Andres Galarraga .20 .50
321 Scott Bullett RC .20 .50
322 Doug Strange .20 .50
323 Jerald Clark .20 .50
324 Dave Righetti .20 .50
325 Greg Hibbard .20 .50
326 Eric Hillman RC .20 .50
327 Shane Reynolds RC .40 1.00
328 Chris Hammond .20 .50
329 Albert Belle .20 .50
330 Rich Becker RC .20 .50
331 Eddie Williams .20 .50
332 Donald Harris .20 .50
333 Dave Smith .20 .50
334 Steve Fireovid .20 .50
335 Steve Buechele .20 .50
336 Mike Schooler .20 .50
337 Kevin McReynolds .20 .50
338 Hensley Meulens .20 .50
339 Benji Gil RC .40 1.00
340 Don Mattingly 1.25 3.00
341 Alvin Davis .20 .50
342 Alan Mills .20 .50
343 Kelly Downs .20 .50
344 Leo Gomez .20 .50
345 Tarrik Brock RC .20 .50
346 Ryan Turner RC .20 .50
347 John Smoltz .30 .75
348 Bill Sampen .20 .50
349 Paul Byrd RC 1.25 3.00
350 Mike Bordick .20 .50
351 Jose Lind .20 .50
352 David Wells .20 .50
353 Barry Larkin .30 .75
354 Bruce Ruffin .20 .50
355 Luis Rivera .20 .50
356 Sid Bream .20 .50
357 Julian Vasquez RC .20 .50
358 Jason Bere RC .40 1.00
359 Ben McDonald .20 .50
360 Scott Stahoviak RC .20 .50
361 Kirt Manwaring .20 .50
362 Jeff Johnson .20 .50
363 Rob Deer .20 .50
364 Tony Pena .20 .50
365 Melido Perez .20 .50
366 Clay Parker .20 .50
367 Dale Sveum .20 .50
368 Mike Scioscia .20 .50
369 Roger Salkeld .20 .50
370 Mike Stanley .20 .50
371 Jack McDowell .20 .50
372 Tim Wallach .20 .50
373 Billy Ripken .20 .50
374 Mike Christopher .20 .50
375 Paul Molitor .20 .50
376 Dave Stieb .20 .50
377 Pedro Guerrero .20 .50
378 Russ Swan .20 .50
379 Bob Ojeda .20 .50
380 Donn Pall .20 .50
381 Eddie Zosky .20 .50
382 Darnell Coles .20 .50
383 Tom Smith RC .20 .50
384 Mark McGwire 1.25 3.00
385 Gary Carter .20 .50
386 Rich Amaral RC .20 .50
387 Alan Embree RC .40 1.00
388 Jonathan Hurst RC .20 .50
389 Bobby Jones RC .40 1.00
390 Rico Rossy .20 .50
391 Dan Smith .20 .50
392 Terry Steinbach .20 .50
393 Jon Farrell RC .20 .50
394 Dave Anderson .20 .50
395 Benny Santiago .20 .50
396 Mark Wohlers .20 .50
397 Mo Vaughn .20 .50
398 Randy Kramer .20 .50
399 John Jaha RC .40 1.00
400 Cal Ripken 1.50 4.00
401 Ryan Bowen .20 .50
402 Tim McIntosh .20 .50
403 Bernard Gilkey .20 .50
404 Junior Felix .20 .50
405 Cris Colon RC .20 .50
406 Marc Newfield .20 .50
407 Bernie Williams .30 .75
408 Jay Howell .20 .50
409 Zane Smith .20 .50
410 Jeff Shaw .20 .50
411 Kerry Woodson .20 .50
412 Wes Chamberlain .20 .50
413 Dave Mlicki RC .40 1.00
414 Benny Distefano .20 .50
415 Kevin Rogers .20 .50
416 Tim Naehring .20 .50
417 Clemente Nunez RC .20 .50
418 Luis Sojo .20 .50
419 Kevin Ritz .20 .50
420 Omar Olivares .20 .50
421 Manuel Lee .20 .50
422 Julio Valera .20 .50
423 Omar Vizquel .30 .75
424 Darren Burton RC .20 .50
425 Mel Hall .20 .50
426 Dennis Powell .20 .50
427 Lee Stevens .20 .50
428 Glenn Davis .20 .50
429 Willie Greene .20 .50
430 Kevin Wickander .20 .50
431 Dennis Eckersley .20 .50
432 Joe Orsulak .20 .50
433 Eddie Murray .50 1.25
434 Matt Stairs RC .40 1.00
435 Wally Joyner .20 .50
436 Rondell White .20 .50
437 Rob Maurer .20 .50
438 Joe Redfield .20 .50
439 Mark Lewis .20 .50
440 Darren Daulton .20 .50
441 Mike Henneman .20 .50
442 John Cangelosi .20 .50
443 Vince Moore RC .20 .50
444 John Wehner .20 .50
445 Kent Hrbek .20 .50
446 Mark McLemore .20 .50
447 Bill Wegman .20 .50
448 Robby Thompson .20 .50
449 Mark Anthony RC .20 .50
450 Archi Cianfrocco RC .20 .50
451 Johnny Ruffin .20 .50
452 Javy Lopez .75 2.00
453 Greg Gohr .20 .50
454 Tim Scott .20 .50
455 Stan Belinda .20 .50
456 Darrin Jackson .20 .50
457 Chris Gardner .20 .50
458 Esteban Beltre .20 .50
459 Phil Plantier .20 .50
460 Jim Thome 3.00 8.00
461 Mike Piazza RC 8.00 20.00
462 Matt Sinatro .20 .50
463 Scott Servais .20 .50
464 Brian Jordan RC .75 2.00
465 Doug Drabek .20 .50
466 Carl Willis .20 .50
467 Bret Barberie .20 .50
468 Hal Morris .20 .50
469 Steve Sax .20 .50
470 Jerry Willard .20 .50
471 Dan Wilson .20 .50
472 Chris Hoiles .20 .50
473 Rheal Cormier .20 .50
474 John Morris .20 .50
475 Jeff Reardon .20 .50
476 Mark Leiter .20 .50
477 Tom Gordon .20 .50
478 Kent Bottenfield RC .40 1.00
479 Gene Larkin .20 .50
480 Dwight Gooden .20 .50
481 B.J. Surhoff .20 .50
482 Andy Stankiewicz .20 .50
483 Tino Martinez .30 .75
484 Craig Biggio .30 .75
485 Denny Neagle .20 .50
486 Rusty Meacham .20 .50
487 Kal Daniels .20 .50
488 Dave Henderson .20 .50
489 Tim Costo .20 .50
490 Doug Davis .20 .50
491 Frank Viola .20 .50
492 Cory Snyder .20 .50
493 Chris Martin .20 .50
494 Dion James .20 .50
495 Randy Tomlin .20 .50
496 Greg Vaughn .20 .50
497 Dennis Cook .20 .50
498 Rosario Rodriguez .20 .50
499 Dave Staton .20 .50
500 George Brett 1.25 3.00
501 Brian Barnes .20 .50
502 Butch Henry RC .20 .50
503 Harold Reynolds .20 .50
504 David Nied RC .20 .50
505 Lee Smith .20 .50
506 Steve Chitren .20 .50
507 Ken Hill .20 .50
508 Robbie Beckett .20 .50
509 Troy Afenir .20 .50
510 Kelly Gruber .20 .50
511 Bret Boone .30 .75
512 Jeff Branson .20 .50
513 Mike Jackson .20 .50
514 Pete Harnisch .20 .50
515 Chad Kreuter .20 .50
516 Joe Vitko RC .20 .50
517 Orel Hershiser .20 .50
518 John Doherty RC .20 .50
519 Jay Bell .20 .50
520 Mark Langston .20 .50
521 Dann Howitt .20 .50
522 Bobby Reed RC .20 .50
523 Bobby Munoz RC .20 .50
524 Todd Ritchie .20 .50
525 Bip Roberts .20 .50
526 Pat Listach RC .40 1.00
527 Scott Brosius RC .75 2.00
528 John Roper RC .20 .50
529 Phil Hiatt RC .20 .50
530 Denny Walling .20 .50
531 Carlos Baerga .20 .50
532 Manny Ramirez RC 3.00 8.00
533 Pat Clements UER .20 .50
(Mistakenly numbered 553)
534 Ron Gant .20 .50
535 Pat Kelly .20 .50
536 Bill Spiers .20 .50
537 Darren Reed .20 .50
538 Ken Caminiti .20 .50
539 Butch Huskey RC .20 .50
540 Matt Nokes .20 .50
541 John Kruk .20 .50
542 John Jaha FOIL .20 .50
543 Justin Thompson RC .20 .50
544 Steve Hosey .20 .50
545 Joe Kmak .20 .50
546 John Franco .20 .50
547 Devon White .20 .50
548 Elston Hansen FOIL SP RC .20 .50
549 Ryan Klesko .20 .50
550 Danny Tartabull .20 .50
551 Frank Thomas FOIL .50 1.25
552 Kevin Tapani .20 .50
553 Willie Banks .20 .50
(See also 533)
554 B.J.Wallace FOIL RC .20 .50
555 Orlando Miller RC .20 .50
556 Mark Smith RC .20 .50
557 Tim Wallach FOIL .20 .50
558 Bill Gullickson .20 .50
559 Derek Bell FOIL .20 .50
560 Joe Randa FOIL RC 1.25 3.00
561 Frank Seminara RC .20 .50
562 Mark Gardner .20 .50
563 Rick Greene FOIL RC .20 .50
564 Gary Gaetti .20 .50
565 Ozzie Guillen .20 .50
566 Charles Nagy FOIL .20 .50
567 Mike Milchin .20 .50
568 Ben Shelton RC .20 .50
569 Chris Roberts FOIL .20 .50
570 Ellis Burks .20 .50
571 Scott Scudder .20 .50
572 Jim Abbott FOIL .30 .75
573 Joe Carter .20 .50
574 Steve Finley .20 .50
575 Jim Olander FOIL .20 .50
576 Carlos Garcia .20 .50
577 Gregg Olson .20 .50
578 Greg Swindell FOIL .20 .50
579 Matt Williams FOIL .20 .50
580 Mark Grace .30 .75
581 Howard House FOIL RC .20 .50
582 Luis Polonia .20 .50
583 Erik Hanson .20 .50
584 Salomon Torres FOIL .20 .50
585 Carlton Fisk .30 .75
586 Bret Saberhagen .20 .50
587 Chad McConnell FOIL RC .20 .50
588 Jimmy Key .20 .50
589 Mike Macfarlane .20 .50
590 Barry Bonds FOIL 1.50 4.00
591 Jamie McAndrew .20 .50
592 Shane Mack .20 .50
593 Kerwin Moore .20 .50
594 Joe Oliver .20 .50
595 Chris Sabo .20 .50
596 Alex Gonzalez RC .40 1.00
597 Brett Butler .20 .50
598 Mark Hutton RC .20 .50
599 Andy Benes FOIL .20 .50
600 Jose Canseco .30 .75
601 Darryl Kile .20 .50
602 Matt Stairs FOIL .20 .50
603 Rob Butler FOIL RC .20 .50
604 Willie McGee .20 .50
605 Jack McDowell FOIL .20 .50
606 Tom Candiotti .20 .50
607 Ed Martel RC .20 .50
608 Matt Mieske FOIL .20 .50
609 Darrin Fletcher .20 .50
610 Rafael Palmeiro .30 .75
611 Bill Swift FOIL .20 .50
612 Mike Mussina .50 1.25
613 Vince Coleman .20 .50
614 Scott Cepicky COR .20 .50
614A S.Cepicky FOIL UER .20 .50
Bats: LEFLT
615 Mike Greenwell .20 .50
616 Kevin McGehee RC .20 .50
617 J.Hammonds FOIL .20 .50
618 Scott Taylor .20 .50
619 Dave Otto .20 .50
620 Mark McGwire FOIL 1.25 3.00
621 Kevin Tatar RC .20 .50
622 Steve Farr .20 .50
623 Ryan Klesko FOIL .20 .50
624 Dave Fleming .20 .50
625 Andre Dawson .20 .50
626 Tino Martinez FOIL .30 .75
627 Chad Curtis RC .40 1.00
628 Mickey Morandini .20 .50
629 Gregg Olson FOIL .20 .50
630 Lou Whitaker .20 .50
631 Arthur Rhodes .20 .50
632 Brandon Wilson RC .20 .50
633 Lance Jennings RC .20 .50
634 Allen Watson RC .20 .50
635 Len Dykstra .20 .50
636 Joe Girardi .20 .50
637 Kiki Hernandez FOIL RC .20 .50
638 Mike Hampton RC .75 2.00
639 Al Osuna .20 .50
640 Kevin Appier .20 .50
641 Rick Helling FOIL .20 .50
642 Jody Reed .20 .50
643 Ray Lankford .20 .50
644 John Olerud .20 .50
645 Paul Molitor FOIL .20 .50
646 Pat Borders .20 .50
647 Mike Morgan .20 .50
648 Larry Walker .30 .75
649 P.Castellano FOIL .20 .50
650 Fred McGriff .30 .75
651 Walt Weiss .20 .50
652 Calvin Murray FOIL RC .40 1.00
653 Dave Nilsson .20 .50
654 Greg Pirkl RC .20 .50
655 Robin Ventura FOIL .20 .50
656 Mark Portugal .20 .50
657 Roger McDowell .20 .50
658 Rick Hirtensteiner FOIL RC .20 .50
659 Glenallen Hill .20 .50
660 Greg Gagne .20 .50
661 Charles Johnson FOIL .20 .50
662 Brian Hunter .20 .50
663 Mark Lemke .20 .50
664 Tim Belcher FOIL .20 .50
665 Rich DeLucia .20 .50
666 Bob Walk .20 .50
667 Joe Carter FOIL .20 .50
668 Jose Guzman .20 .50
669 Otis Nixon .20 .50
670 Phil Nevin FOIL .20 .50
671 Eric Davis .20 .50
672 Damion Easley RC .40 1.00
673 Will Clark FOIL .30 .75
674 Mark Kiefer RC .20 .50
675 Ozzie Smith .75 2.00
676 Manny Ramirez FOIL 3.00 8.00
677 Gregg Olson .20 .50
678 Cliff Floyd RC 1.25 3.00
679 Duane Singleton RC .20 .50
680 Jose Rijo .20 .50
681 Willie Randolph .20 .50
682 Michael Tucker FOIL RC .40 1.00
683 Darren Lewis .20 .50
684 Dale Murphy .30 .75
685 Mike Pagliarulo .20 .50
686 Paul Miller RC .20 .50
687 Mike Robertson RC .20 .50
688 Mike Devereaux .20 .50
689 Pedro Astacio RC .40 1.00
690 Alan Trammell .20 .50
691 Roger Clemens 1.00 2.50
692 Bud Black .20 .50
693 Turk Wendell RC .40 1.00
694 Barry Larkin FOIL .30 .75
695 Todd Zeile .20 .50
696 Pat Hentgen .20 .50
697 Eddie Taubensee RC .40 1.00
698 Guillermo Velasquez RC .20 .50
699 Tom Glavine .30 .75
700 Robin Yount .75 2.00
701 Checklist 1-141 .20 .50
702 Checklist 142-282 .20 .50
703 Checklist 283-423 .20 .50
704 Checklist 424-564 .20 .50
705 Checklist 565-705 .20 .50

1993 Bowman

This 708-card standard-size set (produced by Topps) was issued in one series and features one of the more comprehensive selection of prospects and rookies available that year. Cards were distributed in 14-card plastic wrapped packs and jumbo packs. Each 14-card pack contained one silver foil bordered subset card. The basic issue card fronts feature white-bordered color action player photos. The 48 foil subset cards (339-374 and 693-704) feature sixteen 1992 MVPs of the Minor Leagues, top prospects and a few father/son combinations. Rookie Cards in this set include James Baldwin, Roger Cedeno, Derek Jeter, Jason Kendall, Andy Pettitte, Jose Vidro and Preston Wilson.

COMPLETE SET (708) 15.00 40.00
1 Glenn Davis .05 .15
2 Hector Roa RC .08 .25
3 Ken Ryan RC .08 .25
4 Derek Wallace RC .08 .25
5 Jorge Fabregas .05 .15
6 Joe Oliver .05 .15
7 Brandon Wilson .05 .15
8 Mark Thompson RC .08 .25
9 Tracy Sanders .05 .15
10 Rich Renteria .05 .15
11 Lou Whitaker .10 .30
12 Brian L. Hunter RC .20 .50
13 Joe Vitiello .05 .15
14 Eric Karros .10 .30
15 Joe Kmak .05 .15
16 Tavo Alvarez .05 .15
17 Steve Dunn RC .08 .25
18 Tony Fernandez .05 .15
19 Melido Perez .05 .15
20 Mike Lieberthal .10 .30
21 Terry Steinbach .05 .15
22 Stan Belinda .05 .15
23 Jay Buhner .10 .30
24 Allen Watson .05 .15
25 Daryl Henderson RC .08 .25
26 Ray McDavid RC .08 .25
27 Shawn Green .40 1.00
28 Bud Black .05 .15
29 Sherman Obando RC .08 .25
30 Mike Hostetler RC .08 .25
31 Nate Minchey RC .08 .25
32 Randy Myers .05 .15
33 Brian Grebeck .05 .15
34 John Roper .05 .15
35 Larry Thomas .05 .15
36 Alex Cole .05 .15
37 Tom Kramer RC .08 .25
38 Matt Whisenant RC .08 .25
39 Chris Gomez RC .20 .50
40 Luis Gonzalez .10 .30
41 Kevin Appier .10 .30
42 Omar Daal RC .08 .25
43 Duane Singleton .05 .15
44 Bill Risley .05 .15
45 Pat Meares RC .20 .50
46 Butch Huskey .05 .15
47 Bobby Munoz .05 .15
48 Juan Bell .05 .15
49 Scott Lydy RC .08 .25
50 Dennis Moeller .05 .15
51 Marc Newfield .05 .15
52 Tripp Cromer RC .08 .25
53 Kurt Miller .05 .15
54 Jim Pena .05 .15
55 Juan Guzman .05 .15
56 Matt Williams .10 .30
57 Harold Reynolds .10 .30
58 Donnie Elliott RC .08 .25
59 Jon Shave RC .08 .25
60 Kevin Roberson RC .08 .25
61 Hilly Hathaway RC .08 .25
62 Jose Rijo .05 .15
63 Kerry Taylor RC .05 .15
64 Ryan Hawblitzel .05 .15
65 Glenallen Hill .05 .15
66 Ramon Martinez RC .08 .25
67 Travis Fryman .10 .30
68 Tom Nevers .05 .15
69 Phil Hiatt .05 .15
70 Tim Wallach .05 .15
71 B.J. Surhoff .10 .30
72 Rondell White .10 .30
73 Denny Hocking RC .20 .50
74 Mike Oquist RC .08 .25
75 Paul O'Neill .20 .50
76 Willie Banks .05 .15
77 Bob Welch .05 .15
78 Jose Sandoval RC .08 .25
79 Bill Haselman .05 .15
80 Rheal Cormier .05 .15
81 Dean Palmer .10 .30
82 Pat Gomez RC .08 .25
83 Steve Karsay .05 .15
84 Carl Hanselman RC .08 .25
85 T.R. Lewis RC .08 .25
86 Chipper Jones .30 .75
87 Scott Hatteberg .05 .15
88 Greg Hibbard .05 .15
89 Lance Painter RC .08 .25
90 Chad Mottola RC .20 .50
91 Jason Bere .05 .15
92 Dante Bichette .10 .30
93 Sandy Alomar Jr. .05 .15
94 Carl Everett .10 .30
95 Danny Bautista RC .20 .50
96 Steve Finley .10 .30
97 David Cone .10 .30
98 Todd Hollandsworth .05 .15
99 Matt Mieske .05 .15
100 Larry Walker .10 .30
101 Shane Mack .05 .15
102 Aaron Ledesma RC .08 .25
103 Andy Pettitte RC 3.00 8.00
104 Kevin Stocker .05 .15
105 Mike Mohler RC .08 .25
106 Tony Menendez .05 .15
107 Derek Lowe .10 .30
108 Basil Shabazz .05 .15
109 Dan Smith .05 .15
110 Scott Sanders RC .20 .50
111 Todd Stottlemyre .05 .15
112 Benji Simonton RC .08 .25
113 Rick Sutcliffe .10 .30
114 Lee Heath RC .08 .25
115 Jeff Russell .05 .15
116 Dave Stevens RC .08 .25
117 Mark Holzemer RC .08 .25
118 Tim Belcher .05 .15
119 Bobby Thigpen .05 .15
120 Roger Bailey RC .08 .25
121 Tony Mitchell RC .08 .25
122 Junior Felix .05 .15
123 Rich Robertson RC .08 .25
124 Andy Cook RC .08 .25
125 Brian Bevil RC .08 .25
126 Darryl Strawberry .10 .30
127 Cal Eldred .05 .15
128 Cliff Floyd .10 .30
129 Alan Newman .05 .15
130 Howard Johnson .05 .15
131 Jim Abbott .20 .50
132 Chad McConnell .05 .15
133 Miguel Jimenez RC .08 .25
134 Brett Backlund RC .08 .25
135 John Cummings RC .08 .25
136 Brian Barber .05 .15
137 Rafael Palmeiro .20 .50
138 Tim Worrell RC .08 .25
139 Jose Pett RC .08 .25
140 Barry Bonds .75 2.00
141 Damon Buford .05 .15
142 Jeff Blauser .05 .15
143 Frankie Rodriguez .05 .15
144 Mike Morgan .05 .15
145 Gary DiSarcina .05 .15
146 Pokey Reese .05 .15
147 Johnny Ruffin .05 .15
148 David Nied .05 .15
149 Charles Nagy .05 .15
150 Mike Myers RC .08 .25
151 Kenny Carlyle RC .08 .25
152 Eric Anthony .05 .15
153 Jose Lind .05 .15
154 Pedro Martinez .60 1.50
155 Mark Kiefer .05 .15
156 Tim Laker RC .08 .25
157 Pat Mahomes .05 .15
158 Bobby Bonilla .10 .30
159 Domingo Jean .05 .15
160 Darren Daulton .10 .30
161 Mark McGwire .75 2.00
162 Jason Kendall RC .75 2.00
163 Desi Relaford .05 .15
164 Ozzie Canseco .05 .15
165 Rick Helling .05 .15
166 Steve Pegues RC .08 .25
167 Paul Molitor .10 .30
168 Larry Carter RC .05 .15
169 Arthur Rhodes .05 .15
170 Damon Hollins RC .20 .50
171 Frank Viola .10 .30
172 Steve Trachsel RC .40 1.00
173 J.T. Snow RC .40 1.00
174 Keith Gordon RC .08 .25
175 Carlton Fisk .20 .50
176 Jason Bates RC .08 .25
177 Mike Crosby RC .08 .25
178 Benny Santiago .10 .30
179 Mike Moore .05 .15
180 Jeff Juden .05 .15
181 Darren Burton .05 .15
182 Todd Williams RC .20 .50
183 John Jaha .05 .15
184 Mike Lansing RC .20 .50
185 Pedro Grifol RC .08 .25
186 Vince Coleman .05 .15
187 Pat Kelly .05 .15
188 Clemente Alvarez RC .08 .25
189 Ron Darling .05 .15
190 Orlando Merced .05 .15
191 Chris Bosio .05 .15
192 Steve Dixon RC .08 .25
193 Doug Dascenzo .05 .15
194 Ray Holbert RC .08 .25
195 Howard Battle .05 .15
196 Willie McGee .10 .30
197 John O'Donoghue RC .08 .25
198 Steve Avery .05 .15
199 Greg Blosser .05 .15
200 Ryne Sandberg .50 1.25
201 Joe Grahe .05 .15
202 Dan Wilson .10 .30
203 Domingo Martinez RC .08 .25
204 Andres Galarraga .10 .30
205 Jamie Taylor RC .08 .25
206 Darrell Whitmore RC .08 .25
207 Ben Blomdahl RC .08 .25
208 Doug Drabek .05 .15
209 Keith Miller .05 .15
210 Billy Ashley .05 .15
211 Mike Farrell RC .08 .25
212 John Wetteland .10 .30
213 Randy Tomlin .05 .15
214 Sid Fernandez .05 .15
215 Quilvio Veras RC .20 .50
216 Dave Hollins .05 .15
217 Mike Neill .05 .15
218 Andy Van Slyke .20 .50
219 Bret Boone .10 .30
220 Tom Pagnozzi .05 .15
221 Mike Welch RC .08 .25
222 Frank Seminara .05 .15
223 Ron Villone .05 .15
224 D.J. Thielen RC .08 .25
225 Cal Ripken 1.00 2.50
226 Pedro Borbon Jr. RC .08 .25
227 Carlos Quintana .05 .15
228 Tommy Shields .05 .15
229 Tim Salmon .20 .50
230 John Smiley .05 .15
231 Ellis Burks .10 .30
232 Pedro Castellano .05 .15
233 Paul Byrd .10 .30
234 Bryan Harvey .05 .15
235 Scott Livingstone .05 .15
236 James Mouton RC .08 .25
237 Joe Randa .10 .30
238 Pedro Astacio .05 .15
239 Darryl Hamilton .05 .15
240 Joey Eischen RC .08 .25
241 Edgar Herrera RC .08 .25
242 Dwight Gooden .10 .30
243 Sam Militello .05 .15
244 Ron Blazier RC .08 .25
245 Ruben Sierra .10 .30
246 Al Martin .05 .15
247 Mike Felder .05 .15
248 Bob Tewksbury .05 .15
249 Craig Lefferts .05 .15
250 Luis Lopez RC .08 .25
251 Devon White .10 .30
252 Will Clark .20 .50
253 Mark Smith .05 .15
254 Terry Pendleton .10 .30
255 Aaron Sele .05 .15
256 Jose Viera RC .08 .25
257 Damion Easley .05 .15
258 Rod Lofton RC .08 .25
259 Chris Snopek RC .08 .25
260 Q.McCracken RC .20 .50
261 Mike Matthews RC .08 .25
262 Hector Carrasco RC .08 .25
263 Rick Greene .05 .15
264 Chris Holt RC .20 .50
265 George Brett .75 2.00
266 Rick Gorecki RC .08 .25
267 Francisco Gamez RC .08 .25
268 Marquis Grissom .10 .30
269 Kevin Tapani UER .05 .15
(Misspelled Tapan
on card front)
270 Ryan Thompson .05 .15
271 Gerald Williams .05 .15
272 Paul Fletcher RC .08 .25
273 Lance Blankenship .05 .15
274 Marty Neff RC .08 .25
275 Shawn Estes .05 .15
276 Rene Arocha RC .20 .50
277 Scott Eyre RC .08 .25
278 Phil Plantier .05 .15
279 Paul Spoljaric RC .08 .25
280 Chris Gambs .05 .15
281 Harold Baines .10 .30
282 Jose Oliva .05 .15
283 Matt Whiteside RC .08 .25
284 Brant Brown RC .20 .50
285 Russ Springer .05 .15
286 Chris Sabo .05 .15
287 Ozzie Guillen .10 .30
288 Marcus Moore RC .08 .25
289 Chad Ogea .05 .15
290 Walt Weiss .05 .15
291 Brian Edmondson .05 .15
292 Jimmy Gonzalez .05 .15
293 Danny Miceli RC .20 .50
294 Jose Offerman .05 .15
295 Greg Vaughn .05 .15
296 Frank Bolick .05 .15
297 Mike Maksudian RC .08 .25
298 John Franco .10 .30
299 Danny Tartabull .05 .15
300 Len Dykstra .10 .30
301 Bobby Witt .05 .15
302 Trey Beamon RC .08 .25
303 Tino Martinez .20 .50
304 Aaron Holbert .05 .15
305 Juan Gonzalez .10 .30
306 Billy Hall RC .08 .25
307 Duane Ward .05 .15
308 Rod Beck .05 .15
309 Jose Mercedes RC .08 .25
310 Otis Nixon .05 .15
311 Gettys Glaze RC .08 .25
312 Candy Maldonado .05 .15
313 Chad Curtis .05 .15
314 Tim Costo .05 .15
315 Mike Robertson .05 .15
316 Nigel Wilson .05 .15
317 Greg McMichael RC .20 .50
318 Scott Pose RC .08 .25
319 Ivan Cruz .05 .15
320 Greg Swindell .05 .15
321 Kevin McReynolds .05 .15
322 Tom Candiotti .05 .15
323 Rob Wishnevski RC .08 .25
324 Ken Hill .05 .15
325 Kirby Puckett .30 .75
326 Tim Bogar RC .08 .25
327 Mariano Rivera 2.50 6.00
328 Mitch Williams .05 .15
329 Craig Paquette .05 .15
330 Jay Bell .10 .30
331 Jose Martinez RC .08 .25
332 Rob Deer .05 .15
333 Brook Fordyce .05 .15
334 Matt Nokes .05 .15
335 Derek Lee .05 .15
336 Paul Ellis RC .08 .25
337 Desi Wilson RC .08 .25
338 Roberto Alomar .20 .50
339 Jim Tatum FOIL RC .08 .25
340 J.T. Snow FOIL .40 1.00
341 Tim Salmon FOIL .20 .50
342 Russ Davis FOIL RC .20 .50
343 Javy Lopez FOIL .20 .50
344 Troy O'Leary FOIL RC .20 .50
345 M.Cordova FOIL RC .20 .50
346 Bubba Smith RC FOIL .08 .25
347 Chipper Jones FOIL .30 .75
348 Jessie Hollins FOIL .05 .15
349 Willie Greene FOIL .05 .15
350 Mark Thompson FOIL .05 .15
351 Nigel Wilson FOIL .05 .15
352 Todd Jones FOIL .10 .30
353 Raul Mondesi FOIL .10 .30
354 Cliff Floyd FOIL .10 .30
355 Bobby Jones FOIL .10 .30
356 Kevin Stocker FOIL .05 .15
357 M.Cummings FOIL .05 .15
358 Allen Watson FOIL .05 .15
359 Ray McDavid FOIL .05 .15
360 Steve Hosey FOIL .05 .15
361 B.Pennington FOIL .05 .15
362 F.Rodriguez FOIL .05 .15
363 Troy Percival FOIL .20 .50
364 Jason Bere FOIL .05 .15
365 Manny Ramirez FOIL .50 1.25
366 J.Thompson FOIL .05 .15
367 Joe Vitiello FOIL .05 .15
368 Tyrone Hill FOIL .05 .15
369 David McCarty FOIL .05 .15
370 Brien Taylor FOIL .05 .15
371 T.Van Poppel FOIL .05 .15
372 Marc Newfield FOIL .05 .15
373 T.Lowery RC FOIL .20 .50
374 Alex Gonzalez FOIL .05 .15
375 Ken Griffey Jr. .50 1.25
376 Donovan Osborne .05 .15
377 Ritchie Moody RC .08 .25
378 Shane Andrews .05 .15
379 Carlos Delgado .30 .75
380 Bill Swift .05 .15
381 Leo Gomez .05 .15
382 Ron Gant .10 .30
383 Scott Fletcher .05 .15
384 Matt Walbeck RC .20 .50
385 Chuck Finley .10 .30
386 Kevin Mitchell .05 .15
387 Wilson Alvarez UER .05 .15
(Misspelled Alverez
on card front)
388 John Burke RC .08 .25
389 Alan Embree .05 .15
390 Trevor Hoffman .30 .75
391 Alan Trammell .10 .30
392 Todd Jones .10 .30
393 Felix Jose .05 .15
394 Orel Hershiser .10 .30
395 Pat Listach .05 .15
396 Gabe White .05 .15
397 Dan Serafini RC .08 .25
398 Todd Hundley .05 .15
399 Wade Boggs .20 .50
400 Tyler Green .05 .15
401 Mike Bordick .05 .15
402 Scott Bullett .05 .15
403 LaGrande Russell RC .08 .25
404 Ray Lankford .10 .30
405 Nolan Ryan 1.25 3.00
406 Robbie Beckett .05 .15
407 Brent Bowers RC .08 .25
408 Adell Davenport RC .08 .25
409 Brady Anderson .10 .30
410 Tom Glavine .20 .50
411 Doug Hecker RC .08 .25
412 Jose Guzman .05 .15
413 Luis Polonia .05 .15
414 Brian Williams .05 .15
415 Bo Jackson .30 .75
416 Eric Young .05 .15
417 Kenny Lofton .10 .30
418 Orestes Destrade .05 .15
419 Tony Phillips .05 .15
420 Jeff Bagwell .20 .50
421 Mark Gardner .05 .15
422 Brett Butler .10 .30
423 Graeme Lloyd RC .20 .50
424 Delino DeShields .05 .15
425 Scott Erickson .05 .15
426 Jeff Kent .30 .75
427 Jimmy Key .10 .30
428 Mickey Morandini .05 .15
429 Marcos Armas RC .08 .25
430 Don Slaught .05 .15
431 Randy Johnson .30 .75
432 Omar Olivares .05 .15
433 Charlie Leibrandt .05 .15
434 Kurt Stillwell .05 .15
435 Scott Brow RC .08 .25
436 Robby Thompson .05 .15
437 Ben McDonald .05 .15

438 Deion Sanders .20 .50
439 Tony Pena .05 .15
440 Mark Grace .20 .50
441 Eduardo Perez .05 .15
442 Tim Pugh RC .08 .25
443 Scott Ruffcorn .05 .15
444 Jay Gainer RC .08 .25
445 Albert Belle .10 .30
446 Bret Barberie .05 .15
447 Justin Mashore .05 .15
448 Pete Harnisch .05 .15
449 Greg Gagne .05 .15
450 Eric Davis .10 .30
451 Dave Mlicki .05 .15
452 Moises Alou .10 .30
453 Rick Aguilera .05 .15
454 Eddie Murray .30 .75
455 Bob Wickman .05 .15
456 Wes Chamberlain .05 .15
457 Brent Gates .05 .15
458 Paul Wagner .05 .15
459 Mike Hampton .10 .30
460 Ozzie Smith .50 1.25
461 Tom Henke .05 .15
462 Ricky Gutierrez .05 .15
463 Jack Morris .10 .30
464 Joel Chimelis .05 .15
465 Gregg Olson .05 .15
466 Javy Lopez .20 .50
467 Scott Cooper .05 .15
468 Willie Wilson .05 .15
469 Mark Langston .05 .15
470 Barry Larkin .20 .50
471 Rod Bolton .05 .15
472 Freddie Benavides .05 .15
473 Ken Ramos RC .08 .25
474 Chuck Carr .05 .15
475 Cecil Fielder .10 .30
476 Eddie Taubensee .05 .15
477 Chris Eddy RC .08 .25
478 Greg Hansell .05 .15
479 Kevin Reimer .05 .15
480 Dennis Martinez .10 .30
481 Chuck Knoblauch .10 .30
482 Mike Draper .05 .15
483 Spike Owen .05 .15
484 Terry Mulholland .05 .15
485 Dennis Eckersley .10 .30
486 Blas Minor .05 .15
487 Dave Fleming .05 .15
488 Dan Cholowsky .05 .15
489 Ivan Rodriguez .20 .50
490 Gary Sheffield .10 .30
491 Ed Sprague .05 .15
492 Steve Hosey .05 .15
493 Jimmy Haynes RC .20 .50
494 John Smoltz .20 .50
495 Andre Dawson .10 .30
496 Rey Sanchez .05 .15
497 Ty Van Burkleo .05 .15
498 Bobby Ayala RC .08 .25
499 Tim Raines .10 .30
500 Charlie Hayes .05 .15
501 Paul Sorrento .05 .15
502 Richie Lewis RC .08 .25
503 Jason Pfaff RC .08 .25
504 Ken Caminiti .10 .30
505 Mike Macfarlane .05 .15
506 Jody Reed .05 .15
507 Bobby Hughes RC .08 .25
508 Wil Cordero .05 .15
509 George Tsamis RC .08 .25
510 Bret Saberhagen .10 .30
511 Derek Jeter RC 12.50 30.00
512 Gene Schall .05 .15
513 Curtis Shaw .05 .15
514 Steve Cooke .05 .15
515 Edgar Martinez .20 .50
516 Mike Milchin .05 .15
517 Billy Ripken .05 .15
518 Andy Benes .05 .15
519 Juan de la Rosa RC .08 .25
520 John Burkett .05 .15
521 Alex Ochoa .05 .15
522 Tony Tarasco RC .20 .50
523 Luis Ortiz .05 .15
524 Rick Wilkins .05 .15
525 Chris Turner RC .08 .25
526 Rob Dibble .10 .30
527 Jack McDowell .05 .15
528 Daryl Boston .05 .15
529 Bill Wertz RC .08 .25
530 Charlie Hough .10 .30
531 Sean Bergman .05 .15
532 Doug Jones .05 .15
533 Jeff Montgomery .05 .15
534 Roger Cedeno RC .20 .50
535 Robin Yount .50 1.25
536 Mo Vaughn .10 .30
537 Brian Harper .05 .15
538 Juan Castillo RC .05 .15
539 Steve Farr .05 .15
540 John Kruk .10 .30
541 Troy Neel .05 .15
542 Danny Clyburn RC .08 .25
543 Jim Converse RC .08 .25
544 Gregg Jefferies .05 .15
545 Jose Canseco .20 .50
546 Julio Bruno RC .08 .25
547 Rob Butler .05 .15
548 Royce Clayton .05 .15
549 Chris Hoiles .05 .15
550 Greg Maddux .50 1.25
551 Joe Ciccarella RC .08 .25
552 Ozzie Timmons .05 .15
553 Chili Davis .10 .30
554 Brian Koelling .05 .15
555 Frank Thomas .30 .75
556 Vinny Castilla .30 .75
557 Reggie Jefferson .05 .15
558 Rob Natal .05 .15
559 Mike Henneman .05 .15
560 Craig Biggio .20 .50
561 Billy Brewer .05 .15
562 Dan Melendez .05 .15
563 Kenny Felder RC .08 .25
564 Miguel Batista RC .40 1.00
565 Dave Winfield .10 .30
566 Al Shirley .05 .15
567 Robert Eenhoorn .05 .15
568 Mike Williams .05 .15
569 Tanyon Sturtze RC .20 .50
570 Tim Wakefield .30 .75
571 Greg Pirkl .05 .15
572 Sean Lowe RC .08 .25
573 Terry Burrows RC .08 .25
574 Kevin Higgins .05 .15
575 Joe Carter .10 .30
576 Kevin Rogers .05 .15
577 Manny Alexander .05 .15
578 David Justice .10 .30
579 Brian Conroy RC .08 .25
580 Jessie Hollins .05 .15
581 Ron Watson RC .08 .25
582 Bip Roberts .05 .15
583 Tom Urbani RC .08 .25
584 Jason Hutchins RC .08 .25
585 Carlos Baerga .05 .15
586 Jeff Mutis .05 .15
587 Justin Thompson .05 .15
588 Orlando Miller .05 .15
589 Brian McRae .05 .15
590 Ramon Martinez .05 .15
591 Dave Nilsson .05 .15
592 Jose Vidro RC .75 2.00
593 Rich Becker .05 .15
594 Preston Wilson RC .60 1.50
595 Don Mattingly .75 2.00
596 Tony Longmire .05 .15
597 Kevin Seitzer .05 .15
598 Midre Cummings RC .08 .25
599 Omar Vizquel .20 .50
600 Lee Smith .10 .30
601 David Hulse RC .08 .25
602 Darrell Sherman RC .08 .25
603 Alex Gonzalez .05 .15
604 Geronimo Pena .05 .15
605 Mike Devereaux .05 .15
606 S.Hitchcock RC .20 .50
607 Mike Greenwell .05 .15
608 Steve Buechele .05 .15
609 Troy Percival .20 .50
610 Roberto Kelly .05 .15
611 James Baldwin RC .20 .50
612 Jerald Clark .05 .15
613 Albie Lopez RC .08 .25
614 Dave Magadan .05 .15
615 Mickey Tettleton .05 .15
616 Sean Runyan RC .08 .25
617 Bob Hamelin .05 .15
618 Raul Mondesi .10 .30
619 Tyrone Hill .05 .15
620 Darrin Fletcher .05 .15
621 Mike Trombley .05 .15
622 Jeromy Burnitz .10 .30
623 Bernie Williams .20 .50
624 Mike Farmer RC .08 .25
625 Rickey Henderson .30 .75
626 Carlos Garcia .05 .15
627 Jeff Darwin RC .08 .25
628 Todd Zeile .05 .15
629 Benji Gil .05 .15
630 Tony Gwynn .40 1.00
631 Aaron Small RC .40 1.00
632 Joe Rosselli RC .08 .25
633 Mike Mussina .20 .50
634 Ryan Klesko .10 .30
635 Roger Clemens .60 1.50
636 Sammy Sosa .30 .75
637 Orlando Palmeiro RC .08 .25
638 Willie Greene .05 .15
639 George Bell .05 .15
640 Garvin Alston RC .08 .25
641 Pete Janicki RC .08 .25
642 Chris Sheff RC .08 .25
643 Felipe Lira RC .08 .25
644 Roberto Petagine .05 .15
645 Wally Joyner .10 .30
646 Mike Piazza 1.25 3.00
647 Jaime Navarro .05 .15
648 Jeff Hartsock .05 .15
649 David McCarty .05 .15
650 Bobby Jones .10 .30
651 Mark Hutton .05 .15
652 Kyle Abbott .05 .15
653 Steve Cox RC .08 .25
654 Jeff King .05 .15
655 Norm Charlton .05 .15
656 Mike Gulan RC .08 .25
657 Julio Franco .10 .30
658 C.Cairncross RC .08 .25
659 John Olerud .05 .15
660 Salomon Torres .05 .15
661 Brad Pennington .05 .15
662 Melvin Nieves .05 .15
663 Ivan Calderon .05 .15
664 Turk Wendell .05 .15
665 Chris Pritchett .05 .15
666 Reggie Sanders .10 .30
667 Robin Ventura .10 .30
668 Joe Girardi .05 .15
669 Manny Ramirez .50 1.25
670 Jeff Conine .10 .30
671 Greg Gohr .05 .15
672 Andujar Cedeno .05 .15
673 Les Norman RC .08 .25
674 Mike James RC .08 .25
675 Marshall Boze RC .08 .25
676 B.J. Wallace .05 .15
677 Kent Hrbek .10 .30
678 Jack Voigt RC .08 .25
679 Brien Taylor .05 .15
680 Curt Schilling .10 .30
681 Todd Van Poppel .05 .15
682 Kevin Young .10 .30
683 Tommy Adams .05 .15
684 Bernard Gilkey .05 .15
685 Kevin Brown .10 .30
686 Fred McGriff .20 .50
687 Pat Borders .05 .15
688 Kirt Manwaring .05 .15
689 Sid Bream .05 .15
690 John Valentin .05 .15
691 Steve Olsen RC .08 .25
692 Roberto Mejia RC .08 .25
693 Carlos Delgado FOIL .30 .75
694 S.Gibralter FOIL RC .08 .25
695 Gary Mota FOIL RC .08 .25
696 Jose Malave FOIL RC .08 .25
697 Larry Sutton FOIL RC .08 .25
698 Dan Frye FOIL RC .08 .25
699 Tim Clark FOIL RC .08 .25
700 Brian Rupp FOIL RC .08 .25
701 Felipe Alou FOIL .10 .30
Moises Alou
702 Barry Bonds FOIL .40 1.00
Bobby Bonds
703 Ken Griffey Sr. FOIL .30 .75
Ken Griffey Jr.
704 Brian McRae FOIL .05 .15
Hal McRae
705 Checklist 1 .05 .15
706 Checklist 2 .05 .15
707 Checklist 3 .05 .15
708 Checklist 4 .05 .15

1994 Bowman

The 1994 Bowman set consists of 682 standard-size, full-bleed cards primarily distributed in plastic wrap packs and jumbo packs. There are 52 Foil cards (337-388) that include a number of top young stars and prospects. These foil cards were issued one per foil pack and two per jumbo. Rookie Cards of note include Edgardo Alfonzo, Tony Clark, Jermaine Dye, Brad Fullmer, Richard Hidalgo, Derrek Lee, Chan Ho Park, Jorge Posada, Edgar Renteria and Billy Wagner.

COMPLETE SET (682) 30.00 60.00
1 Joe Carter .15 .40
2 Marcus Moore .08 .25
3 Doug Creek RC .15 .40
4 Pedro Martinez .40 1.00
5 Ken Griffey Jr. .60 1.50
6 Greg Swindell .08 .25
7 J.J. Johnson .08 .25
8 Homer Bush RC .15 .40
9 Arquimedez Pozo RC .15 .40
10 Bryan Harvey .08 .25
11 J.T. Snow .15 .40
12 Alan Benes RC .40 1.00
13 Chad Kreuter .08 .25
14 Eric Karros .15 .40
15 Frank Thomas .40 1.00
16 Bret Saberhagen .15 .40
17 Terrell Lowery .08 .25
18 Rod Bolton .08 .25
19 Harold Baines .15 .40
20 Matt Walbeck .08 .25
21 Tom Glavine .25 .60
22 Todd Jones .08 .25
23 Alberto Castillo RC .15 .40
24 Ruben Sierra .15 .40
25 Don Mattingly 1.00 2.50
26 Mike Morgan .08 .25
27 Jim Musselwhite RC .15 .40
28 Matt Brunson RC .15 .40
29 A.Meinershagen RC .15 .40
30 Joe Girardi .08 .25
31 Shane Halter .08 .25
32 Jose Paniagua RC .40 1.00
33 Paul Perkins RC .15 .40
34 John Hudek RC .15 .40
35 Frank Viola .15 .40
36 David Lamb RC .15 .40
37 Marshall Boze .08 .25
38 Jorge Posada RC 3.00 8.00
39 Brian Anderson RC .40 1.00
40 Mark Whiten .08 .25
41 Sean Bergman .08 .25
42 Jose Parra RC .15 .40
43 Mike Robertson .08 .25
44 Pete Walker RC .15 .40
45 Juan Gonzalez .15 .40
46 Cleveland Ladell RC .15 .40
47 Mark Smith .08 .25
48 Kevin Jarvis UER .15 .40
(team listed as Yankees on back)
49 Amaury Telemaco RC .15 .40
50 Andy Van Slyke .25 .60
51 Rikkert Faneyte RC .15 .40
52 Curtis Shaw .08 .25
53 Matt Drews RC .15 .40
54 Wilson Alvarez .08 .25
55 Manny Ramirez .40 1.00
56 Bobby Munoz .08 .25
57 Ed Sprague .08 .25
58 Jamey Wright RC .40 1.00
59 Jeff Montgomery .08 .25
60 Kirk Rueter .08 .25
61 Edgar Martinez .25 .60
62 Luis Gonzalez .15 .40
63 Tim Vanegmond RC .15 .40
64 Bip Roberts .08 .25
65 John Jaha .08 .25
66 Chuck Carr .08 .25
67 Chuck Finley .15 .40
68 Aaron Holbert .08 .25
69 Cecil Fielder .15 .40
70 Tom Engle RC .15 .40
71 Ron Karkovice .08 .25
72 Joe Orsulak .08 .25
73 Duff Brumley RC .15 .40
74 Craig Clayton RC .15 .40
75 Cal Ripken 1.25 3.00
76 Brad Fullmer RC .40 1.00
77 Tony Tarasco .08 .25
78 Terry Farrar RC .15 .40
79 Matt Williams .15 .40
80 Rickey Henderson .40 1.00
81 Terry Mulholland .08 .25
82 Sammy Sosa .40 1.00
83 Paul Sorrento .08 .25
84 Pete Incaviglia .08 .25
85 Darren Hall RC .15 .40
86 Scott Klingenbeck .08 .25
87 Dario Perez RC .15 .40
88 Ugueth Urbina .08 .25
89 Dave Vanhof RC .15 .40
90 Domingo Jean .08 .25
91 Otis Nixon .08 .25
92 Andres Berumen .08 .25
93 Jose Valentin .08 .25
94 Edgar Renteria RC 2.50 6.00
95 Chris Turner .08 .25
96 Ray Lankford .15 .40
97 Danny Bautista .08 .25
98 Chan Ho Park RC .60 1.50
99 Glenn DiSarcina RC .15 .40
100 Butch Huskey .08 .25
101 Ivan Rodriguez .25 .60
102 Johnny Ruffin .08 .25
103 Alex Ochoa .08 .25
104 Torii Hunter RC 2.00 5.00
105 Ryan Klesko .15 .40
106 Jay Bell .15 .40
107 Kurt Peltzer RC .15 .40
108 Miguel Jimenez .08 .25
109 Russ Davis .08 .25
110 Derek Wallace .08 .25
111 Keith Lockhart RC .40 1.00
112 Mike Lieberthal .15 .40
113 Dave Stewart .15 .40
114 Tom Schmidt .08 .25
115 Brian McRae .08 .25
116 Moises Alou .15 .40
117 Dave Fleming .08 .25
118 Jeff Bagwell .25 .60
119 Luis Ortiz .08 .25
120 Tony Gwynn .50 1.25
121 Jaime Navarro .08 .25
122 Benito Santiago .15 .40
123 Darrell Whitmore .08 .25
124 John Mabry RC .40 1.00
125 Mickey Tettleton .08 .25
126 Tom Candiotti .08 .25
127 Tim Raines .15 .40
128 Bobby Bonilla .15 .40
129 John Dettmer .08 .25
130 Hector Carrasco .08 .25
131 Chris Hoiles .08 .25
132 Rick Aguilera .08 .25
133 David Justice .15 .40
134 Esteban Loaiza RC .60 1.50
135 Barry Bonds 1.00 2.50
136 Bob Welch .08 .25
137 Mike Stanley .08 .25
138 Roberto Hernandez .08 .25
139 Sandy Alomar Jr. .08 .25
140 Darren Daulton .15 .40
141 Angel Martinez RC .15 .40
142 Howard Johnson .08 .25
143 Bob Hamelin UER .08 .25
(name and card number colors don't match)
144 J.J. Thobe RC .15 .40
145 Roger Salkeld .08 .25
146 Orlando Miller .08 .25
147 Dmitri Young .15 .40
148 Tim Hyers RC .15 .40
149 Mark Loretta RC 2.00 5.00
150 Chris Hammond .08 .25
151 Joel Moore RC .15 .40
152 Todd Zeile .08 .25
153 Wil Cordero .08 .25
154 Chris Smith .08 .25
155 James Baldwin .08 .25
156 Edgardo Alfonzo RC .40 1.00
157 Kym Ashworth RC .15 .40
158 Paul Bako RC .15 .40
159 Rick Krivda RC .15 .40
160 Pat Mahomes .08 .25
161 Damon Hollins .08 .25
162 Felix Martinez RC .15 .40
163 Jason Myers RC .15 .40
164 Izzy Molina RC .15 .40
165 Brien Taylor .08 .25
166 Kevin Orie RC .15 .40
167 Casey Whitten RC .15 .40
168 Tony Longmire .08 .25
169 John Olerud .08 .25
170 Mark Thompson .08 .25
171 Jorge Fabregas .08 .25
172 John Wetteland .15 .40
173 Dan Wilson .08 .25
174 Doug Drabek .08 .25
175 Jeff McNeely .08 .25
176 Melvin Nieves .08 .25
177 Doug Glanville RC .40 1.00
178 Javier De La Hoya RC .15 .40
179 Chad Curtis .08 .25
180 Brian Barber .08 .25
181 Mike Henneman .08 .25
182 Jose Offerman .08 .25
183 Robert Ellis RC .15 .40
184 John Franco .15 .40
185 Benji Gil .08 .25
186 Hal Morris .08 .25
187 Chris Sabo .08 .25
188 Blaise Ilsley RC .15 .40
189 Steve Avery .08 .25
190 Rick White RC .08 .25
191 Rod Beck .08 .25
192 Mark McGwire UER 1.00 2.50
(No card number on back)
193 Jim Abbott .25 .60
194 Randy Myers .08 .25
195 Kenny Lofton .15 .40
196 Mariano Duncan .08 .25
197 Lee Daniels RC .15 .40
198 Armando Reynoso .08 .25
199 Joe Randa .15 .40
200 Cliff Floyd .15 .40
201 Tim Harkrider RC .15 .40
202 Kevin Gallaher RC .15 .40
203 Scott Cooper .08 .25
204 Phil Stidham RC .15 .40
205 Jeff D'Amico RC .40 1.00
206 Matt Whisenant .08 .25
207 De Shawn Warren .08 .25
208 Rene Arocha .08 .25
209 Tony Clark RC .60 1.50
210 Jason Jacome RC .15 .40
211 Scott Christman RC .15 .40
212 Bill Pulsipher .15 .40
213 Dean Palmer .15 .40
214 Chad Mottola .08 .25
215 Manny Alexander .08 .25
216 Rich Becker .08 .25
217 Andre King RC .15 .40
218 Carlos Garcia .08 .25
219 Ron Pezzoni RC .15 .40
220 Steve Karsay .08 .25
221 Jose Musset RC .15 .40
222 Karl Rhodes .08 .25
223 Frank Cimorelli RC .15 .40
224 Kevin Jordan RC .15 .40
225 Duane Ward .08 .25
226 John Burke .08 .25
227 Mike Macfarlane .08 .25
228 Mike Lansing .08 .25
229 Chuck Knoblauch .15 .40
230 Ken Caminiti .15 .40
231 Gar Finnvold RC .15 .40
232 Derrek Lee RC 3.00 8.00
233 Brady Anderson .15 .40
234 Vic Darensbourg RC .15 .40
235 Mark Langston .08 .25
236 T.J. Mathews RC .15 .40
237 Lou Whitaker .15 .40
238 Roger Cedeno .08 .25
239 Alex Fernandez .08 .25
240 Ryan Thompson .08 .25
241 Kerry Lacy RC .15 .40
242 Reggie Sanders .15 .40
243 Brad Pennington .08 .25
244 Bryan Eversgerd RC .15 .40
245 Greg Maddux .60 1.50
246 Jason Kendall .15 .40
247 J.R. Phillips .08 .25
248 Bobby Witt .08 .25
249 Paul O'Neill .25 .60
250 Ryne Sandberg .60 1.50
251 Charles Nagy .08 .25
252 Kevin Stocker .08 .25
253 Shawn Green .40 1.00
254 Charlie Hayes .08 .25
255 Donnie Elliott .08 .25
256 Rob Fitzpatrick RC .15 .40
257 Tim Davis .08 .25
258 James Mouton .08 .25
259 Mike Greenwell .08 .25
260 Ray McDavid .08 .25
261 Mike Kelly .08 .25
262 Andy Larkin RC .15 .40
263 Marquis Riley UER .08 .25
(No card number on back)
264 Bob Tewksbury .08 .25
265 Brian Edmondson .08 .25
266 Eduardo Lantigua RC .15 .40
267 Brandon Wilson .08 .25
268 Mike Welch .08 .25
269 Tom Henke .08 .25
270 Pokey Reese .08 .25
271 Greg Zaun RC .40 1.00
272 Todd Ritchie .08 .25
273 Javier Lopez .15 .40
274 Kevin Young .08 .25
275 Kirt Manwaring .08 .25
276 Bill Taylor RC .15 .40
277 Robert Eenhoorn .08 .25
278 Jessie Hollins .08 .25
279 Julian Tavarez RC .40 1.00
280 Gene Schall .08 .25
281 Paul Molitor .15 .40
282 Neifi Perez RC .40 1.00
283 Greg Gagne .08 .25
284 Marquis Grissom .15 .40
285 Randy Johnson .40 1.00
286 Pete Harnisch .08 .25
287 Joel Bennett RC .15 .40
288 Derek Bell .08 .25
289 Darryl Hamilton .08 .25
290 Gary Sheffield .15 .40
291 Eduardo Perez .08 .25
292 Basil Shabazz .08 .25
293 Eric Davis .15 .40
294 Pedro Astacio .08 .25
295 Robin Ventura .15 .40
296 Jeff Kent .25 .60
297 Rick Helling .08 .25
298 Joe Oliver .08 .25
299 Lee Smith .15 .40
300 Dave Winfield .15 .40
301 Deion Sanders .25 .60
302 R.Manzanillo RC .15 .40
303 Mark Portugal .08 .25
304 Brent Gates .08 .25
305 Wade Boggs .25 .60
306 Rick Wilkins .08 .25
307 Carlos Baerga .08 .25
308 Curt Schilling .15 .40
309 Shannon Stewart .40 1.00
310 Darren Holmes .08 .25
311 Robert Toth RC .15 .40
312 Gabe White .08 .25
313 Mac Suzuki RC .40 1.00
314 Alvin Morman RC .15 .40
315 Mo Vaughn .15 .40
316 Bryce Florie RC .15 .40
317 Gabby Martinez RC .15 .40
318 Carl Everett .15 .40
319 Kerwin Moore .08 .25
320 Tom Pagnozzi .08 .25
321 Chris Gomez .08 .25
322 Todd Williams .08 .25
323 Pat Hentgen .08 .25
324 Kirk Presley RC .15 .40
325 Kevin Brown .15 .40
326 J.Isringhausen RC 1.25 3.00
327 Rick Forney RC .15 .40
328 Carlos Pulido RC .15 .40
329 Terrell Wade RC .15 .40
330 Al Martin .08 .25
331 Dan Carlson RC .15 .40
332 Mark Acre RC .15 .40
333 Sterling Hitchcock .08 .25
334 Jon Ratliff RC .15 .40
335 Alex Ramirez RC .15 .40
336 Phil Geisler RC .08 .25
337 E.Zambrano FOIL RC .15 .40
338 Jim Thome FOIL .25 .60
339 James Mouton FOIL .08 .25
340 Cliff Floyd FOIL .15 .40
341 Carlos Delgado FOIL .25 .60
342 R.Petagine FOIL .08 .25
343 Tim Clark FOIL .08 .25
344 Bubba Smith FOIL .08 .25
345 Randy Curtis FOIL RC .15 .40
346 Joe Biasucci FOIL RC .15 .40
347 D.J. Boston FOIL .08 .25
348 R.Rivera FOIL RC .15 .40
349 Bryan Link FOIL RC .15 .40
350 Mike Bell FOIL RC .15 .40
351 M.Watson FOIL RC .15 .40
352 Jason Myers FOIL .08 .25
353 Chipper Jones FOIL .40 1.00
354 B.Kieschnick FOIL .15 .40
355 Pokey Reese FOIL .08 .25
356 John Burke FOIL .08 .25
357 Kurt Miller FOIL .08 .25
358 Orlando Miller FOIL .08 .25
359 T.Hollandsworth FOIL .08 .25
360 Rondell White FOIL .15 .40
361 Bill Pulsipher FOIL .15 .40
362 Tyler Green FOIL .08 .25
363 M.Cummings FOIL .08 .25
364 Brian Barber FOIL .08 .25
365 Melvin Nieves FOIL .08 .25
366 Salomon Torres FOIL .08 .25
367 Alex Ochoa FOIL .08 .25
368 F.Rodriguez FOIL .08 .25
369 Brian Anderson FOIL .15 .40
370 James Baldwin FOIL .08 .25
371 Manny Ramirez FOIL .40 1.00
372 J.Thompson FOIL .08 .25
373 Johnny Damon FOIL .25 .60
374 Jeff D'Amico FOIL .15 .40
375 Rich Becker FOIL .08 .25
376 Derek Jeter FOIL 1.25 3.00
377 Steve Karsay FOIL .08 .25
378 Mac Suzuki FOIL .15 .40
379 Benji Gil FOIL .08 .25
380 Alex Gonzalez FOIL .08 .25
381 Jason Bere FOIL .08 .25
382 Brett Butler FOIL .15 .40
383 Jeff Conine FOIL .15 .40
384 Darren Daulton FOIL .15 .40
385 Jeff Kent FOIL .25 .60
386 Don Mattingly FOIL 1.00 2.50
387 Mike Piazza FOIL .75 2.00
388 Ryne Sandberg FOIL .60 1.50
389 Rich Amaral .08 .25
390 Craig Biggio .25 .60
391 Jeff Suppan RC .75 2.00
392 Andy Benes .08 .25
393 Cal Eldred .08 .25
394 Jeff Conine .15 .40
395 Tim Salmon .25 .60
396 Ray Suplee RC .15 .40
397 Tony Phillips .08 .25
398 Ramon Martinez .08 .25
399 Julio Franco .15 .40
400 Dwight Gooden .15 .40
401 Kevin Lomon RC .15 .40
402 Jose Rijo .08 .25
403 Mike Devereaux .08 .25
404 Mike Zolecki RC .15 .40
405 Fred McGriff .25 .60
406 Danny Clyburn .08 .25
407 Robby Thompson .08 .25
408 Terry Steinbach .08 .25
409 Luis Polonia .08 .25
410 Mark Grace .25 .60
411 Albert Belle .15 .40
412 John Kruk .15 .40
413 Scott Spiezio RC .40 1.00
414 Ellis Burks UER .15 .40
(Name spelled Elkis on front)
415 Joe Vitiello .08 .25
416 Tim Costo .08 .25
417 Marc Newfield .08 .25
418 Oscar Henriquez RC .15 .40
419 Matt Perisho RC .15 .40
420 Julio Bruno .08 .25
421 Kenny Felder .08 .25
422 Tyler Green .08 .25
423 Jim Edmonds .40 1.00
424 Ozzie Smith .60 1.50
425 Rick Greene .08 .25
426 Todd Hollandsworth .08 .25
427 Eddie Pearson RC .15 .40
428 Quilvio Veras .08 .25
429 Kenny Rogers .15 .40
430 Willie Greene .08 .25
431 Vaughn Eshelman .08 .25
432 Pat Meares .08 .25
433 Jermaine Dye RC 2.50 6.00
434 Steve Cooke .08 .25
435 Bill Swift .08 .25
436 Fausto Cruz RC .15 .40
437 Mark Hutton .08 .25
438 B.Kieschnick RC .15 .40
439 Yorkis Perez .08 .25
440 Len Dykstra .15 .40
441 Pat Borders .08 .25
442 Doug Walls RC .15 .40
443 Wally Joyner .15 .40
444 Ken Hill .08 .25
445 Eric Anthony .08 .25
446 Mitch Williams .08 .25
447 Cory Bailey RC .15 .40
448 Dave Staton .08 .25
449 Greg Vaughn .08 .25
450 Dave Magadan .08 .25
451 Chili Davis .15 .40
452 Gerald Santos RC .15 .40
453 Joe Perona .08 .25
454 Delino DeShields .08 .25
455 Jack McDowell .08 .25
456 Todd Hundley .08 .25
457 Ritchie Moody .08 .25
458 Bret Boone .15 .40
459 Ben McDonald .08 .25
460 Kirby Puckett .40 1.00
461 Gregg Olson .08 .25
462 Rich Aude RC .15 .40
463 John Burkett .08 .25
464 Troy Neel .08 .25
465 Jimmy Key .15 .40
466 Ozzie Timmons .08 .25
467 Eddie Murray .40 1.00
468 Mark Tranberg RC .15 .40
469 Alex Gonzalez .08 .25
470 David Nied .08 .25
471 Barry Larkin .25 .60
472 Brian Looney RC .15 .40
473 Shawn Estes .08 .25
474 A.J. Sager RC .15 .40
475 Roger Clemens .75 2.00
476 Vince Moore .08 .25
477 Scott Karl RC .15 .40
478 Kurt Miller .08 .25
479 Garret Anderson .40 1.00
480 Allen Watson .08 .25
481 Jose Lima RC .40 1.00
482 Rick Gorecki .08 .25
483 Jimmy Hurst RC .15 .40
484 Preston Wilson .15 .40
485 Will Clark .25 .60
486 Mike Ferry RC .15 .40
487 Curtis Goodwin RC .15 .40
488 Mike Myers .08 .25
489 Chipper Jones .40 1.00
490 Jeff King .08 .25
491 W.VanLandingham RC .15 .40
492 Carlos Reyes RC .15 .40
493 Andy Pettitte .40 1.00
494 Brant Brown .08 .25
495 Daron Kirkreit .08 .25
496 Ricky Bottalico RC .15 .40
497 Devon White .15 .40
498 Jason Johnson RC .40 1.00
499 Vince Coleman .08 .25
500 Larry Walker .15 .40
501 Bobby Ayala .08 .25
502 Steve Finley .15 .40
503 Scott Fletcher .08 .25
504 Brad Ausmus .25 .60
505 Scott Talanoa RC .15 .40
506 Orestes Destrade .08 .25
507 Gary DiSarcina .08 .25
508 Willie Smith RC .15 .40
509 Alan Trammell .15 .40
510 Mike Piazza .75 2.00
511 Ozzie Guillen .15 .40
512 Jeromy Burnitz .15 .40
513 Darren Oliver RC .40 1.00
514 Kevin Mitchell .08 .25
515 Rafael Palmeiro .25 .60
516 David McCarty .08 .25
517 Jeff Blauser .08 .25
518 Trey Beamon .08 .25
519 Royce Clayton .08 .25
520 Dennis Eckersley .15 .40
521 Bernie Williams .25 .60
522 Steve Buechele .08 .25
523 Dennis Martinez .15 .40
524 Dave Hollins .08 .25
525 Joey Hamilton .08 .25
526 Andres Galarraga .15 .40
527 Jeff Granger .08 .25
528 Joey Eischen .08 .25
529 Desi Relaford .08 .25
530 Roberto Petagine .08 .25
531 Andre Dawson .15 .40
532 Ray Holbert .08 .25
533 Duane Singleton .08 .25
534 Kurt Abbott RC .15 .40
535 Bo Jackson .40 1.00
536 Gregg Jefferies .08 .25
537 David Mysel .08 .25
538 Raul Mondesi .15 .40
539 Chris Snopek .08 .25
540 Brook Fordyce .08 .25
541 Ron Frazier RC .15 .40
542 Brian Koelling .08 .25
543 Jimmy Haynes .08 .25
544 Marty Cordova .15 .40
545 Jason Green RC .15 .40
546 Orlando Merced .08 .25
547 Lou Pote RC .15 .40
548 Todd Van Poppel .08 .25
549 Pat Kelly .08 .25
550 Turk Wendell .08 .25
551 Herbert Perry RC .15 .40
552 Ryan Karp RC .15 .40
553 Juan Guzman .08 .25
554 Bryan Rekar RC .15 .40
555 Kevin Appier .15 .40
556 Chris Schwab RC .15 .40
557 Jay Buhner .15 .40
558 Andujar Cedeno .08 .25
559 Ryan McGuire RC .15 .40
560 Ricky Gutierrez .08 .25
561 Keith Kimsey RC .15 .40
562 Tim Clark .08 .25
563 Damion Easley .08 .25
564 Clint Davis RC .15 .40
565 Mike Moore .08 .25
566 Orel Hershiser .15 .40
567 Jason Bere .08 .25
568 Kevin McReynolds .08 .25
569 Leland Macon RC .15 .40
570 John Courtright RC .15 .40
571 Sid Fernandez .08 .25
572 Chad Roper .08 .25
573 Terry Pendleton .15 .40
574 Danny Miceli .08 .25
575 Joe Rosselli .08 .25
576 Mike Bordick .08 .25
577 Danny Tartabull .08 .25
578 Jose Guzman .08 .25
579 Omar Vizquel .25 .60
580 Tommy Greene .08 .25
581 Paul Spoljaric .08 .25
582 Walt Weiss .08 .25
583 Oscar Jimenez RC .15 .40
584 Rod Henderson .08 .25
585 Derek Lowe .08 .25
586 Richard Hidalgo RC .40 1.00
587 Shayne Bennett RC .15 .40
588 Tim Belk RC .15 .40
589 Matt Mieske .08 .25
590 Nigel Wilson .08 .25
591 Jeff Knox RC .15 .40
592 Bernard Gilkey .08 .25
593 David Cone .15 .40
594 Paul LoDuca RC 2.00 5.00
595 Scott Ruffcorn .08 .25
596 Chris Roberts .08 .25
597 Oscar Munoz RC .15 .40
598 Scott Sullivan RC .15 .40
599 Matt Jarvis RC .08 .25
600 Jose Canseco .25 .60
601 Tony Graffanino RC .60 1.50
602 Don Slaught .08 .25
603 Brett King RC .15 .40
604 Jose Herrera RC .15 .40
605 Melido Perez .08 .25
606 Mike Hubbard RC .15 .40
607 Chad Ogea .08 .25
608 Wayne Gomes RC .40 1.00
609 Roberto Alomar .25 .60
610 Angel Echevarria RC .15 .40
611 Jose Lind .08 .25
612 Darrin Fletcher .08 .25

613 Chris Bosio	.08	.25
614 Darryl Kile	.15	.40
615 Frankie Rodriguez	.08	.25
616 Phil Plantier	.08	.25
617 Pat Listach	.08	.25
618 Charlie Hough	.15	.40
619 Ryan Hancock RC	.15	.40
620 Darrel Deak RC	.15	.40
621 Travis Fryman	.15	.40
622 Brett Butler	.15	.40
623 Lance Johnson	.08	.25
624 Pete Smith	.08	.25
625 James Hurst RC	.15	.40
626 Roberto Kelly	.08	.25
627 Mike Mussina	.25	.60
628 Kevin Tapani	.08	.25
629 John Smoltz	.25	.60
630 Midre Cummings	.08	.25
631 Salomon Torres	.08	.25
632 Willie Adams	.08	.25
633 Derek Jeter	1.25	3.00
634 Steve Trachsel	.08	.25
635 Albie Lopez	.08	.25
636 Jason Moler	.08	.25
637 Carlos Delgado	.25	.60
638 Roberto Mejia	.08	.25
639 Darren Burton	.08	.25
640 B.J. Wallace	.08	.25
641 Brad Clontz RC	.15	.40
642 Billy Wagner RC	1.50	4.00
643 Aaron Sele	.08	.25
644 Cameron Cairncross	.08	.25
645 Brian Harper	.08	.25
646 Marc Valdes UER	.08	.25
(No card number on back)		
647 Mark Ratekin	.08	.25
648 Terry Bradshaw RC	.15	.40
649 Justin Thompson	.08	.25
650 Mike Busch RC	.15	.40
651 Joe Hall RC	.15	.40
652 Bobby Jones	.08	.25
653 Kelly Stinnett RC	.40	1.00
654 Rod Steph RC	.15	.40
655 Jay Powell RC	.40	1.00
656 K.Garagozzo RC UER	.15	.40
No card number on back		
657 Todd Dunn	.08	.25
658 Charles Peterson RC	.15	.40
659 Darren Lewis	.08	.25
660 John Wasdin RC	.15	.40
661 Tate Seefried RC	.15	.40
662 Hector Trinidad RC	.15	.40
663 John Carter RC	.08	.25
664 Larry Mitchell	.08	.25
665 David Catlett RC	.15	.40
666 Dante Bichette	.15	.40
667 Felix Jose	.08	.25
668 Rondell White	.15	.40
669 Tino Martinez	.25	.60
670 Brian L. Hunter	.08	.25
671 Jose Malave	.08	.25
672 Archi Cianfrocco	.08	.25
673 Mike Matheny RC	.60	1.50
674 Bret Barberie	.08	.25
675 Andrew Lorraine RC	.15	.40
676 Brian Jordan	.15	.40
677 Tim Belcher	.08	.25
678 Antonio Osuna RC	.15	.40
679 Checklist	.08	.25
680 Checklist	.08	.25
681 Checklist	.08	.25
682 Checklist	.08	.25

1995 Bowman

Cards from this 439-card standard-size prospect-oriented set were primarily issued in plastic wrapped packs and jumbo packs. Card fronts feature white borders enframing full color photos. The left border is a reversed negative of the photo. The set includes 54 silver foil subset cards (221-274). The foil subset, largely comprising of minor league stars, have embossed borders and are found one per pack and two per jumbo pack. Rookie Cards of note include Bob Abreu, Bartolo Colon, Vladmir Guerrero, Andruw Jones, Hideo Nomo and Scott Rolen.

COMPLETE SET (439)	90.00	150.00
1 Billy Wagner	.30	.75
2 Chris Widger	.08	.25
3 Brent Bowers	.08	.25
4 Bob Abreu RC	3.00	8.00
5 Lou Collier RC	.40	1.00
6 Juan Acevedo RC	.20	.50
7 Jason Kelley RC	.20	.50
8 Brian Sackinsky	.08	.25
9 Scott Christman	.08	.25
10 Damon Hollins	.08	.25
11 Willis Otanez RC	.20	.50
12 Jason Ryan RC	.20	.50
13 Jason Giambi	.30	.75
14 Andy Taulbee RC	.20	.50
15 Mark Thompson	.08	.25
16 Hugo Pivaral RC	.20	.50
17 Brien Taylor	.08	.25
18 Antonio Osuna	.08	.25
19 Edgardo Alfonzo	.08	.25
20 Carl Everett	.20	.50
21 Matt Drews	.08	.25
22 Bartolo Colon RC	1.50	4.00
23 Andruw Jones RC	5.00	12.00
24 Robert Person RC	.40	1.00
25 Derrek Lee	.50	1.25
26 John Ambrose RC	.20	.50
27 Eric Knowles RC	.20	.50
28 Chris Roberts	.08	.25
29 Don Wengert	.08	.25
30 Marcus Jensen RC	.40	1.00
31 Brian Barber	.08	.25
32 Kevin Brown C	.20	.50
33 Benji Gil	.08	.25
34 Mike Hubbard	.08	.25
35 Bart Evans RC	.20	.50
36 Enrique Wilson RC	.20	.50
37 Brian Buchanan RC	.20	.50
38 Ken Ray RC	.20	.50
39 Micah Franklin RC	.20	.50
40 Ricky Otero RC	.20	.50
41 Jason Kendall	.20	.50
42 Jimmy Hurst	.08	.25
43 Jerry Wolak RC	.20	.50
44 Jayson Peterson RC	.20	.50
45 Allen Battle RC	.20	.50
46 Scott Stahoviak	.08	.25
47 Steve Schrenk RC	.20	.50
48 Travis Miller RC	.20	.50
49 Eddie Rios RC	.20	.50
50 Mike Hampton	.20	.50
51 Chad Frontera RC	.20	.50
52 Tom Evans	.08	.25
53 C.J. Nitkowski	.08	.25
54 Clay Caruthers RC	.20	.50
55 Shannon Stewart	.20	.50
56 Jorge Posada	.50	1.25
57 Aaron Holbert	.08	.25
58 Harry Berrios RC	.20	.50
59 Steve Rodriguez	.08	.25
60 Shane Andrews	.08	.25
61 Will Cunnane RC	.20	.50
62 Richard Hidalgo	.08	.25
63 Bill Selby RC	.20	.50
64 Jay Cranford RC	.20	.50
65 Jeff Suppan	.20	.50
66 Curtis Goodwin	.08	.25
67 John Thomson RC	.40	1.00
68 Justin Thompson	.08	.25
69 Troy Percival	.20	.50
70 Matt Wagner RC	.20	.50
71 Terry Bradshaw	.08	.25
72 Greg Hansell	.08	.25
73 John Burke	.08	.25
74 Jeff D'Amico	.08	.25
75 Ernie Young	.08	.25
76 Jason Bates	.08	.25
77 Chris Stynes	.08	.25
78 Cade Gaspar RC	.20	.50
79 Melvin Nieves	.08	.25
80 Rick Gorecki	.08	.25
81 Felix Rodriguez RC	.20	.50
82 Ryan Hancock	.08	.25
83 Chris Carpenter RC	3.00	8.00
84 Ray McDavid	.08	.25
85 Chris Wimmer	.08	.25
86 Doug Glanville	.08	.25
87 DeShawn Warren	.08	.25
88 Damian Moss RC	.20	.50
89 Rafael Orellano RC	.20	.50
90 Vladimir Guerrero RC	6.00	15.00
91 Raul Casanova RC	.20	.50
92 Karim Garcia RC	.20	.50
93 Bryce Florie	.08	.25
94 Kevin Orie	.08	.25
95 Ryan Nye RC	.20	.50
96 Matt Sachse RC	.20	.50
97 Ivan Arteaga RC	.20	.50
98 Glenn Murray	.08	.25
99 Stacy Hollins RC	.20	.50
100 Jim Pittsley	.08	.25
101 Craig Mattson RC	.20	.50
102 Neifi Perez	.08	.25
103 Keith Williams	.08	.25
104 Roger Cedeno	.08	.25
105 Tony Terry RC	.20	.50
106 Jose Malave	.08	.25
107 Joe Rosselli	.08	.25
108 Kevin Jordan	.08	.25
109 Sid Roberson RC	.20	.50
110 Alan Embree	.08	.25
111 Terrell Wade	.08	.25
112 Bob Wolcott	.08	.25
113 Carlos Perez RC	.40	1.00
114 Mike Bovee RC	.20	.50
115 Tommy Davis RC	.20	.50
116 Jeremey Kendall RC	.20	.50
117 Rich Aude	.08	.25
118 Rick Huisman	.08	.25
119 Tim Belk	.08	.25
120 Edgar Renteria	.20	.50
121 Calvin Maduro RC	.20	.50
122 Jerry Martin RC	.20	.50
123 Ramon Fermin RC	.20	.50
124 Kimera Bartee RC	.20	.50
125 Mark Farris	.08	.25
126 Frank Rodriguez	.08	.25
127 Bobby Higginson RC	.75	2.00
128 Bret Wagner	.08	.25
129 Edwin Diaz RC	.20	.50
130 Jimmy Haynes	.08	.25
131 Chris Weinke RC	.40	1.00
132 Damian Jackson RC	.20	.50
133 Felix Martinez	.08	.25
134 Edwin Hurtado RC	.20	.50
135 Matt Raleigh RC	.20	.50
136 Paul Wilson	.08	.25
137 Ron Villone	.08	.25
138 E.Stuckenschneider RC	.20	.50
139 Tate Seefried	.08	.25
140 Rey Ordonez RC	.75	2.00
141 Eddie Pearson	.08	.25
142 Kevin Gallaher	.08	.25
143 Torii Hunter	.30	.75
144 Daron Kirkreit	.08	.25
145 Craig Wilson	.08	.25
146 Ugueth Urbina	.08	.25
147 Chris Snopek	.08	.25
148 Kym Ashworth	.08	.25
149 Wayne Gomes	.08	.25
150 Mark Loretta	.20	.50
151 Ramon Morel RC	.20	.50
152 Trot Nixon	.20	.50
153 Desi Relaford	.08	.25
154 Scott Sullivan	.08	.25
155 Marc Barcelo	.08	.25
156 Willie Adams	.08	.25
157 Derrick Gibson RC	.20	.50
158 Brian Meadows RC	.20	.50
159 Julian Tavarez	.08	.25
160 Bryan Rekar	.08	.25
161 Steve Gibralter	.08	.25
162 Esteban Loaiza	.08	.25
163 John Wasdin	.08	.25
164 Kirk Presley	.08	.25
165 Mariano Rivera	1.25	3.00
166 Andy Larkin	.08	.25
167 Sean Whiteside RC	.20	.50
168 Matt Apana RC	.20	.50
169 Shawn Senior RC	.20	.50
170 Scott Gentile	.08	.25
171 Quilvio Veras	.08	.25
172 Eli Marrero RC	.60	1.50
173 Mendy Lopez RC	.20	.50
174 Homer Bush	.08	.25
175 Brian Stephenson RC	.20	.50
176 Jon Nunnally	.08	.25
177 Jose Herrera	.08	.25
178 Corey Avrard RC	.20	.50
179 David Bell	.08	.25
180 Jason Isringhausen	.20	.50
181 Jamey Wright	.08	.25
182 Lonell Roberts RC	.08	.25
183 Marty Cordova	.08	.25
184 Amaury Telemaco	.08	.25
185 John Mabry	.08	.25
186 Andrew Vessel RC	.20	.50
187 Jim Cole RC	.20	.50
188 Marquis Riley	.08	.25
189 Todd Dunn	.08	.25
190 John Carter	.08	.25
191 Donnie Sadler RC	.40	1.00
192 Mike Bell	.08	.25
193 Chris Cumberland RC	.20	.50
194 Jason Schmidt	.50	1.25
195 Matt Brunson	.08	.25
196 James Baldwin	.08	.25
197 Bill Simas RC	.20	.50
198 Gus Gandarillas	.08	.25
199 Mac Suzuki	.08	.25
200 Rick Holifield RC	.20	.50
201 Fernando Lunar RC	.20	.50
202 Kevin Jarvis	.08	.25
203 Everett Stull	.08	.25
204 Steve Wojciechowski	.08	.25
205 Shawn Estes	.08	.25
206 Jermaine Dye	.20	.50
207 Marc Kroon	.08	.25
208 Peter Munro RC	.40	1.00
209 Pat Watkins	.08	.25
210 Matt Smith	.08	.25
211 Joe Vitiello	.08	.25
212 Gerald Witasick Jr.	.08	.25
213 Freddy A. Garcia RC	.20	.50
214 Glenn Dishman RC	.20	.50
215 Jay Canizaro RC	.20	.50
216 Angel Martinez	.08	.25
217 Yamil Benitez RC	.20	.50
218 Fausto Macey RC	.20	.50
219 Eric Owens	.08	.25
220 Checklist	.08	.25
221 D.Hosey FOIL RC	.20	.50
222 B.Woodall FOIL RC	.20	.50
223 Billy Ashley FOIL	.08	.25
224 M.Grudzielanek FOIL RC	.75	2.00
225 M.Johnson FOIL RC	.40	1.00
226 Tim Unroe FOIL RC	.20	.50
227 Todd Greene FOIL	.08	.25
228 Larry Sutton FOIL	.08	.25
229 Derek Jeter FOIL	1.50	4.00
230 Sal Fasano FOIL RC	.20	.50
231 Ruben Rivera FOIL	.08	.25
232 Chris Truby FOIL RC	.20	.50
233 John Donati FOIL	.08	.25
234 D.Conner FOIL RC	.20	.50
235 Sergio Nunez FOIL RC	.20	.50
236 Ray Brown FOIL RC	.20	.50
237 Juan Melo FOIL RC	.20	.50
238 Hideo Nomo FOIL RC	2.00	5.00
239 Jamie Bluma RC FOIL	.20	.50
240 Jay Payton FOIL RC	.75	2.00
241 Paul Konerko FOIL	1.50	4.00
242 Scott Elarton FOIL RC	.40	1.00
243 Jeff Abbott FOIL RC	.40	1.00
244 Jim Brower FOIL RC	.20	.50
245 Geoff Blum FOIL RC	.75	2.00
246 Aaron Boone FOIL RC	.75	2.00
247 J.R. Phillips FOIL	.08	.25
248 Alex Ochoa FOIL	.08	.25
249 N.Garciaparra FOIL	1.50	4.00
250 Garret Anderson FOIL	.20	.50
251 Ray Durham FOIL	.20	.50
252 Paul Shuey FOIL	.08	.25
253 Tony Clark FOIL	.08	.25
254 Johnny Damon FOIL	.30	.75
255 Duane Singleton FOIL	.08	.25
256 LaTroy Hawkins FOIL	.08	.25
257 Andy Pettitte FOIL	.30	.75
258 Ben Grieve FOIL	.08	.25
259 Marc Newfield FOIL	.08	.25
260 Terrell Lowery FOIL	.08	.25
261 Shawn Green FOIL	.20	.50
262 Chipper Jones FOIL	.50	1.25
263 B.Kieschnick FOIL	.08	.25
264 Pokey Reese FOIL	.08	.25
265 Doug Million FOIL	.08	.25
266 Marc Valdes FOIL	.08	.25
267 Brian L.Hunter FOIL	.08	.25
268 T.Hollandsworth FOIL	.08	.25
269 Rod Henderson FOIL	.08	.25
270 Bill Pulsipher FOIL	.08	.25
271 Scott Rolen FOIL RC	5.00	12.00
272 Trey Beamon FOIL	.08	.25
273 Alan Benes FOIL	.08	.25
274 D.Hermanson FOIL	.08	.25
275 Ricky Bottalico	.08	.25
276 Albert Belle	.20	.50
277 Deion Sanders	.30	.75
278 Matt Williams	.20	.50
279 Jeff Bagwell	.30	.75
280 Kirby Puckett	.50	1.25
281 Dave Hollins	.08	.25
282 Don Mattingly	1.25	3.00
283 Joey Hamilton	.08	.25
284 Bobby Bonilla	.20	.50
285 Moises Alou	.20	.50
286 Tom Glavine	.30	.75
287 Brett Butler	.20	.50
288 Chris Hoiles	.08	.25
289 Kenny Rogers	.20	.50
290 Larry Walker	.20	.50
291 Tim Raines	.20	.50
292 Kevin Appier	.20	.50
293 Roger Clemens	1.00	2.50
294 Chuck Carr	.08	.25
295 Randy Myers	.08	.25
296 Dave Nilsson	.08	.25
297 Joe Carter	.20	.50
298 Chuck Finley	.20	.50
299 Ray Lankford	.20	.50
300 Roberto Kelly	.08	.25
301 Jon Lieber	.08	.25
302 Travis Fryman	.20	.50
303 Mark McGwire	1.25	3.00
304 Tony Gwynn	.60	1.50
305 Kenny Lofton	.20	.50
306 Mark Whiten	.08	.25
307 Doug Drabek	.08	.25
308 Terry Steinbach	.08	.25
309 Ryan Klesko	.20	.50
310 Mike Piazza	.75	2.00
311 Ben McDonald	.08	.25
312 Reggie Sanders	.20	.50
313 Alex Fernandez	.08	.25
314 Aaron Sele	.08	.25
315 Gregg Jefferies	.08	.25
316 Rickey Henderson	.50	1.25
317 Brian Anderson	.08	.25
318 Jose Valentin	.08	.25
319 Rod Beck	.08	.25
320 Marquis Grissom	.20	.50
321 Ken Griffey Jr.	.75	2.00
322 Bret Saberhagen	.20	.50
323 Juan Gonzalez	.20	.50
324 Paul Molitor	.20	.50
325 Gary Sheffield	.20	.50
326 Darren Daulton	.20	.50
327 Bill Swift	.08	.25
328 Brian McRae	.08	.25
329 Robin Ventura	.20	.50
330 Lee Smith	.20	.50
331 Fred McGriff	.30	.75
332 Delino DeShields	.08	.25
333 Edgar Martinez	.30	.75
334 Mike Mussina	.30	.75
335 Orlando Merced	.08	.25
336 Carlos Baerga	.08	.25
337 Wil Cordero	.08	.25
338 Tom Pagnozzi	.08	.25
339 Pat Hentgen	.08	.25
340 Chad Curtis	.08	.25
341 Darren Lewis	.08	.25
342 Jeff Kent	.20	.50
343 Bip Roberts	.08	.25
344 Ivan Rodriguez	.30	.75
345 Jeff Montgomery	.08	.25
346 Hal Morris	.08	.25
347 Danny Tartabull	.08	.25
348 Raul Mondesi	.20	.50
349 Ken Hill	.08	.25
350 Pedro Martinez	.30	.75
351 Frank Thomas	.50	1.25
352 Manny Ramirez	.30	.75
353 Tim Salmon	.30	.75
354 W. VanLandingham	.08	.25
355 Andres Galarraga	.20	.50
356 Paul O'Neill	.30	.75
357 Brady Anderson	.20	.50
358 Ramon Martinez	.08	.25
359 John Olerud	.20	.50
360 Ruben Sierra	.20	.50
361 Cal Eldred	.08	.25
362 Jay Buhner	.20	.50
363 Jay Bell	.20	.50
364 Wally Joyner	.20	.50
365 Chuck Knoblauch	.20	.50
366 Len Dykstra	.20	.50
367 John Wetteland	.20	.50
368 Roberto Alomar	.30	.75
369 Craig Biggio	.30	.75
370 Ozzie Smith	.75	2.00
371 Terry Pendleton	.20	.50
372 Sammy Sosa	.50	1.25
373 Carlos Garcia	.08	.25
374 Jose Rijo	.08	.25
375 Chris Gomez	.08	.25
376 Barry Bonds	1.25	3.00
377 Steve Avery	.08	.25
378 Rick Wilkins	.08	.25
379 Pete Harnisch	.08	.25
380 Dean Palmer	.20	.50
381 Bob Hamelin	.08	.25
382 Jason Bere	.08	.25
383 Jimmy Key	.20	.50
384 Dante Bichette	.20	.50
385 Rafael Palmeiro	.30	.75
386 David Justice	.20	.50
387 Chili Davis	.20	.50
388 Mike Greenwell	.08	.25
389 Todd Zeile	.08	.25
390 Jeff Conine	.20	.50
391 Rick Aguilera	.08	.25
392 Eddie Murray	.50	1.25
393 Mike Stanley	.08	.25
394 Cliff Floyd UER	.20	.50
(numbered 294)		
395 Randy Johnson	.50	1.25
396 David Nied	.08	.25
397 Devon White	.20	.50
398 Royce Clayton	.08	.25
399 Andy Benes	.08	.25
400 John Hudek	.08	.25
401 Bobby Jones	.08	.25
402 Eric Karros	.20	.50
403 Will Clark	.30	.75
404 Mark Langston	.08	.25
405 Kevin Brown	.20	.50
406 Greg Maddux	.75	2.00
407 David Cone	.20	.50
408 Wade Boggs	.30	.75
409 Steve Trachsel	.08	.25
410 Greg Vaughn	.08	.25
411 Mo Vaughn	.20	.50
412 Wilson Alvarez	.08	.25
413 Cal Ripken	1.50	4.00
414 Rico Brogna	.08	.25
415 Barry Larkin	.30	.75
416 Cecil Fielder	.20	.50
417 Jose Canseco	.30	.75
418 Jack McDowell	.08	.25
419 Mike Lieberthal	.20	.50
420 Andrew Lorraine	.08	.25
421 Rich Becker	.08	.25
422 Tony Phillips	.08	.25
423 Scott Ruffcorn	.08	.25
424 Jeff Granger	.08	.25
425 Greg Pirkl	.08	.25
426 Dennis Eckersley	.20	.50
427 Jose Lima	.08	.25
428 Russ Davis	.08	.25
429 Armando Benitez	.08	.25
430 Alex Gonzalez	.08	.25
431 Carlos Delgado	.20	.50
432 Chan Ho Park	.20	.50
433 Mickey Tettleton	.08	.25
434 Dave Winfield	.20	.50
435 John Burkett	.08	.25
436 Orlando Miller	.08	.25
437 Rondell White	.20	.50
438 Jose Oliva	.08	.25
439 Checklist	.08	.25

1995 Bowman Gold Foil

Numbered 221-274, this 54-card standard-size set is the gold insert parallel version of the silver foil subset found in the basic issue. The odds of finding a gold foil version are one in six packs.

COMPLETE SET (54)	75.00	150.00

*STARS: .6X TO 1.5X BASIC CARDS
*ROOKIES: .5X TO 1.2X BASIC
STATED ODDS 1:6

1996 Bowman

The 1996 Bowman set was issued in one series totalling 385 cards. The 11-card packs retailed for $2.50 each. The fronts feature color action player photos in a tan-checkered frame with the player's name printed in silver foil at the bottom. The backs carry another color player photo with player information, 1995 and career player statistics. Each pack contained 10 regular issue cards plus either one foil parallel or an insert card. In a special promotional program, Topps offered collector's a $100 guarantee on complete sets. To get the guarantee, collectors had to mail in a Guaranteed Value Certificate request form, found in packs, along with a $5 processing and registration fee before the December 31st, 1996 deadline. Collectors would then receive a $100 Guaranteed Value Certificate, of which they could mail back to Topps between August 31st, 1999 and December 31st, 1999, along with their complete set, to receive $100. A reprint version of the 1952 Bowman Mickey Mantle card was randomly inserted into packs. Rookie Cards in this set include Russell Branyan, Mike Cameron, Luis Castillo, Ryan Dempster, Livan Hernandez, Geoff Jenkins, Ben Petrick and Mike Sweeney

COMPLETE SET (385)	20.00	50.00
1 Cal Ripken	1.00	2.50
2 Ray Durham	.10	.30
3 Ivan Rodriguez	.20	.50
4 Fred McGriff	.20	.50
5 Hideo Nomo	.30	.75
6 Troy Percival	.10	.30
7 Moises Alou	.10	.30
8 Mike Stanley	.10	.30
9 Jay Buhner	.10	.30
10 Shawn Green	.10	.30
11 Ryan Klesko	.10	.30
12 Andres Galarraga	.10	.30
13 Dean Palmer	.10	.30
14 Jeff Conine	.10	.30
15 Brian L.Hunter	.10	.30
16 J.T. Snow	.10	.30
17 Larry Walker	.10	.30
18 Barry Larkin	.20	.50
19 Alex Gonzalez	.10	.30
20 Edgar Martinez	.20	.50
21 Mo Vaughn	.10	.30
22 Mark McGwire	.75	2.00
23 Jose Canseco	.20	.50
24 Jack McDowell	.10	.30
25 Dante Bichette	.10	.30
26 Wade Boggs	.20	.50
27 Mike Piazza	.50	1.25
28 Ray Lankford	.10	.30
29 Craig Biggio	.20	.50
30 Rafael Palmeiro	.20	.50
31 Ron Gant	.10	.30
32 Javy Lopez	.10	.30
33 Brian Jordan	.10	.30
34 Paul O'Neill	.20	.50
35 Mark Grace	.20	.50
36 Matt Williams	.10	.30
37 Pedro Martinez UER	.20	.50
Wrong birthdate		
38 Rickey Henderson	.30	.75
39 Bobby Bonilla	.10	.30
40 Todd Hollandsworth	.10	.30
41 Jim Thome	.20	.50
42 Gary Sheffield	.30	.75
43 Tim Salmon	.20	.50
44 Gregg Jefferies	.10	.30
45 Roberto Alomar	.20	.50
46 Carlos Baerga	.10	.30
47 Mark Grudzielanek	.10	.30
48 Randy Johnson	.30	.75
49 Tino Martinez	.20	.50
50 Robin Ventura	.10	.30
51 Ryne Sandberg	.50	1.25
52 Jay Bell	.10	.30
53 Jason Schmidt	.20	.50
54 Frank Thomas	.30	.75
55 Kenny Lofton	.10	.30
56 Ariel Prieto	.10	.30
57 David Cone	.10	.30
58 Reggie Sanders	.10	.30
59 Michael Tucker	.10	.30
60 Vinny Castilla	.10	.30
61 Len Dykstra	.10	.30
62 Todd Hundley	.10	.30
63 Brian McRae	.10	.30
64 Dennis Eckersley	.10	.30
65 Rondell White	.10	.30
66 Eric Karros	.10	.30
67 Greg Maddux	.50	1.25
68 Kevin Appier	.10	.30
69 Eddie Murray	.30	.75
70 John Olerud	.10	.30
71 Tony Gwynn	.40	1.00
72 David Justice	.10	.30
73 Ken Caminiti	.10	.30
74 Terry Steinbach	.10	.30
75 Alan Benes	.10	.30
76 Chipper Jones	.30	.75
77 Jeff Bagwell	.20	.50
78 Barry Bonds	.75	2.00
79 Ken Griffey Jr.	.60	1.50
80 Roger Cedeno	.10	.30
81 Joe Carter	.10	.30
82 Henry Rodriguez	.10	.30
83 Jason Isringhausen	.10	.30
84 Chuck Knoblauch	.10	.30
85 Manny Ramirez	.20	.50
86 Tom Glavine	.20	.50
87 Jeffrey Hammonds	.10	.30
88 Paul Molitor	.10	.30
89 Roger Clemens	.60	1.50
90 Greg Vaughn	.10	.30
91 Marty Cordova	.10	.30
92 Albert Belle	.10	.30
93 Mike Mussina	.20	.50
94 Garret Anderson	.10	.30
95 Juan Gonzalez	.10	.30
96 John Valentin	.10	.30
97 Jason Giambi	.10	.30
98 Kirby Puckett	.30	.75
99 Jim Edmonds	.10	.30
100 Cecil Fielder	.10	.30
101 Mike Aldrete	.10	.30
102 Marquis Grissom	.10	.30
103 Derek Bell	.10	.30
104 Raul Mondesi	.10	.30
105 Sammy Sosa	.30	.75
106 Travis Fryman	.10	.30
107 Rico Brogna	.10	.30
108 Will Clark	.20	.50
109 Bernie Williams	.20	.50
110 Brady Anderson	.10	.30
111 Torii Hunter	.10	.30
112 Derek Jeter	.75	2.00
113 Mike Kusiewicz RC	.20	.50
114 Scott Rolen	.30	.75
115 Ramon Castro	.10	.30
116 Jose Guillen RC	1.25	3.00
117 Wade Walker RC	.20	.50
118 Shawn Senior	.10	.30
119 Onan Masaoka RC	.40	1.00
120 Marlon Anderson RC	.40	1.00
121 Katsuhiro Maeda RC	.40	1.00
122 G.Stephenson RC	.20	.50
123 Butch Huskey	.10	.30
124 D'Angelo Jimenez RC	.40	1.00
125 Tony Mounce RC	.20	.50
126 Jay Canizaro	.10	.30
127 Juan Melo	.10	.30
128 Steve Gibralter	.10	.30
129 Freddy Garcia	.10	.30
130 Julio Santana UER	.10	.30
Card has him born in 1993		
131 Richard Hidalgo	.10	.30
132 Jermaine Dye	.10	.30
133 Willie Adams	.10	.30
134 Everett Stull	.10	.30
135 Ramon Morel	.10	.30
136 Chan Ho Park	.10	.30
137 Jamey Wright	.10	.30
138 Luis R.Garcia RC	.20	.50
139 Dan Serafini	.10	.30
140 Ryan Dempster RC	.75	2.00
141 Tate Seefried	.10	.30
142 Jimmy Hurst	.10	.30
143 Travis Miller	.10	.30
144 Curtis Goodwin	.10	.30
145 Rocky Coppinger RC	.20	.50
146 Enrique Wilson	.10	.30
147 Jaime Bluma	.10	.30
148 Andrew Vessel	.10	.30
149 Damian Moss	.10	.30
150 Shawn Gallagher RC	.20	.50
151 Pat Watkins	.10	.30
152 Jose Paniagua	.10	.30
153 Danny Graves	.10	.30
154 Bryon Gainey RC	.20	.50
155 Steve Soderstrom	.10	.30
156 Cliff Brumbaugh RC	.20	.50
157 Eugene Kingsale RC	.20	.50
158 Lou Collier	.10	.30
159 Todd Walker	.10	.30
160 Kris Detmers RC	.20	.50
161 Josh Booty RC	.20	.50
162 Greg Whiteman RC	.20	.50
163 Damian Jackson	.10	.30
164 Tony Clark	.10	.30
165 Jeff D'Amico	.10	.30
166 Johnny Damon	.20	.50
167 Rafael Orellano	.10	.30
168 Ruben Rivera	.10	.30
169 Alex Ochoa	.10	.30
170 Jay Powell	.10	.30
171 Tom Evans	.10	.30
172 Ron Villone	.10	.30
173 Shawn Estes	.10	.30
174 John Wasdin	.10	.30
175 Bill Simas	.10	.30
176 Kevin Brown	.10	.30
177 Shannon Stewart	.10	.30
178 Todd Greene	.10	.30
179 Bob Wolcott	.10	.30
180 Chris Snopek	.10	.30
181 Nomar Garciaparra	.60	1.50
182 Cameron Smith RC	.20	.50
183 Matt Drews	.10	.30
184 Jimmy Haynes	.10	.30
185 Chris Carpenter	.20	.50
186 Desi Relaford	.10	.30
187 Ben Grieve	.10	.30
188 Mike Bell	.10	.30
189 Luis Castillo RC	.60	1.50
190 Ugueth Urbina	.10	.30
191 Paul Wilson	.10	.30
192 Andruw Jones	.50	1.25
193 Wayne Gomes	.10	.30
194 Craig Counsell RC	.60	1.50
195 Jim Cole	.10	.30
196 Brooks Kieschnick	.10	.30
197 Trey Beamon	.10	.30
198 Marino Santana RC	.20	.50
199 Bob Abreu	.30	.75
200 Pokey Reese	.10	.30
201 Dante Powell	.10	.30
202 George Arias	.10	.30
203 Jorge Velandia RC	.20	.50
204 George Lombard RC	.20	.50
205 Byron Browne RC	.20	.50
206 John Frascatore	.10	.30
207 Terry Adams	.10	.30
208 Wilson Delgado RC	.20	.50
209 Billy McMillon	.10	.30
210 Jeff Abbott	.10	.30
211 Trot Nixon	.10	.30
212 Amaury Telemaco	.10	.30
213 Scott Sullivan	.10	.30
214 Justin Thompson	.10	.30
215 Decomba Conner	.10	.30
216 Ryan McGuire	.10	.30
217 Matt Luke	.10	.30
218 Doug Million	.10	.30
219 Jason Dickson RC	.20	.50
220 Ramon Hernandez RC	.75	2.00
221 Mark Bellhorn RC	.75	2.00
222 Eric Ludwick RC	.20	.50
223 Luke Wilcox RC	.20	.50
224 Marty Malloy RC	.20	.50
225 Gary Coffee RC	.20	.50
226 Wendell Magee RC	.20	.50
227 Brett Tomko RC	.40	1.00
228 Derek Lowe	.10	.30
229 Jose Rosado RC	.20	.50
230 Steve Bourgeois RC	.20	.50
231 Neil Weber RC	.20	.50
232 Jeff Ware	.10	.30
233 Edwin Diaz	.10	.30
234 Greg Norton	.10	.30
235 Aaron Boone	.10	.30
236 Jeff Suppan	.10	.30
237 Bret Wagner	.10	.30
238 Elieser Marrero	.10	.30
239 Will Cunnane	.10	.30
240 Brian Barkley RC	.20	.50
241 Jay Payton	.10	.30
242 Marcus Jensen	.10	.30
243 Ryan Nye	.10	.30
244 Chad Mottola	.10	.30
245 Scott McClain RC	.20	.50
246 Jessie Ibarra RC	.20	.50
247 Mike Darr RC	.20	.50
248 Bobby Estalella RC	.20	.50
249 Michael Barrett	.10	.30
250 Jamie Lopiccolo RC	.20	.50
251 Shane Spencer RC	.40	1.00
252 Ben Petrick RC	.20	.50
253 Jason Bell RC	.20	.50
254 Arnold Gooch RC	.20	.50
255 T.J. Mathews	.10	.30
256 Jason Ryan	.10	.30
257 Pat Cline RC	.20	.50
258 Rafael Carmona RC	.20	.50
259 Carl Pavano RC	.75	2.00
260 Ben Davis	.10	.30
261 Matt Lawton RC	.40	1.00
262 Kevin Sefcik RC	.20	.50
263 Chris Fussell RC	.20	.50
264 Mike Cameron RC	.60	1.50
265 Marty Janzen RC	.20	.50
266 Livan Hernandez RC	.75	2.00
267 Raul Ibanez RC	2.00	5.00
268 Juan Encarnacion	.10	.30
269 David Yocum RC	.20	.50
270 Jonathan Johnson RC	.20	.50
271 Reggie Taylor	.10	.30
272 Danny Buxbaum RC	.20	.50
273 Jacob Cruz	.10	.30
274 Bobby Morris RC	.20	.50
275 Andy Fox RC	.20	.50
276 Greg Keagle	.10	.30
277 Charles Peterson	.10	.30
278 Derrek Lee	.20	.50
279 Bryant Nelson RC	.20	.50
280 Antone Williamson	.10	.30
281 Scott Elarton	.10	.30
282 Shad Williams RC	.20	.50
283 Rich Hunter RC	.20	.50
284 Chris Sheff	.10	.30
285 Derrick Gibson	.10	.30
286 Felix Rodriguez	.10	.30
287 Brian Banks RC	.20	.50
288 Jason McDonald	.10	.30
289 Glendon Rusch RC	.40	1.00
290 Gary Rath	.10	.30
291 Peter Munro	.10	.30
292 Tom Fordham	.10	.30
293 Jason Kendall	.10	.30
294 Russ Johnson	.10	.30
295 Joe Long	.10	.30
296 Robert Smith RC	.20	.50
297 Jarrod Washburn RC	.60	1.50
298 Dave Coggin RC	.20	.50
299 Jeff Yoder RC	.20	.50
300 Jed Hansen RC	.20	.50
301 Matt Morris RC	1.00	2.50
302 Josh Bishop RC	.20	.50
303 Dustin Hermanson	.10	.30
304 Mike Gulan	.10	.30
305 Felipe Crespo	.10	.30
306 Quinton McCracken	.10	.30
307 Jim Bonnici RC	.20	.50
308 Sal Fasano	.10	.30
309 Gabe Alvarez RC	.20	.50
310 Heath Murray RC	.20	.50
311 Javier Valentin RC	.20	.50
312 Bartolo Colon	.30	.75
313 Olmedo Saenz	.10	.30
314 Norm Hutchins RC	.20	.50

315 Chris Holt .10 .30
316 David Doster RC .20 .50
317 Robert Person .10 .30
318 Donne Wall RC .20 .50
319 Adam Riggs RC .20 .50
320 Homer Bush .10 .30
321 Brad Rigby RC .20 .50
322 Lou Merloni RC .20 .50
323 Neifi Perez .10 .30
324 Chris Cumberland .10 .30
325 Alvie Shepherd RC .20 .50
326 Jarrod Patterson RC .20 .50
327 Ray Ricken RC .20 .50
328 Danny Klassen RC .20 .50
329 David Miller RC .20 .50
330 Chad Alexander RC .20 .50
331 Matt Beaumont .10 .30
332 Damon Hollins .10 .30
333 Todd Dunn .10 .30
334 Mike Sweeney RC .75 2.00
335 Richie Sexson .20 .50
336 Billy Wagner .10 .30
337 Ron Wright RC .20 .50
338 Paul Konerko .30 .75
339 Tommy Phelps RC .20 .50
340 Karim Garcia .10 .30
341 Mike Grace RC .20 .50
342 Russell Branyan RC .40 1.00
343 Randy Winn RC .60 1.50
344 A.J. Pierzynski RC 1.50 4.00
345 Mike Busby RC .20 .50
346 Matt Beech RC .20 .50
347 Jose Cepeda RC .20 .50
348 Brian Stephenson .10 .30
349 Rey Ordonez .10 .30
350 Rich Aurilia RC .40 1.00
351 Edgard Velazquez RC .20 .50
352 Raul Casanova .10 .30
353 Carlos Guillen RC .75 2.00
354 Bruce Aven RC .20 .50
355 Ryan Jones RC .20 .50
356 Derek Aucoin RC .20 .50
357 Brian Rose RC .20 .50
358 Richard Almanzar RC .20 .50
359 Fletcher Bates RC .20 .50
360 Russ Ortiz RC .60 1.50
361 Wilton Guerrero RC .20 .50
362 Geoff Jenkins RC .60 1.50
363 Pete Janicki .10 .30
364 Yamil Benitez .10 .30
365 Aaron Holbert .10 .30
366 Tim Belk .10 .30
367 Terrell Wade .10 .30
368 Terrence Long .10 .30
369 Brad Fullmer .10 .30
370 Matt Wagner .10 .30
371 Craig Wilson RC .20 .50
372 Mark Loretta .10 .30
373 Eric Owens .10 .30
374 Vladimir Guerrero .60 1.50
375 Tommy Davis .10 .30
376 Donnie Sadler .10 .30
377 Edgar Renteria .10 .30
378 Todd Helton .60 1.50
379 Ralph Milliard RC .20 .50
380 Darin Blood RC .20 .50
381 Shayne Bennett .10 .30
382 Mark Redman .10 .30
383 Felix Martinez .10 .30
384 Sean Watkins RC .20 .50
385 Oscar Henriquez .10 .30
M20 Mickey Mantle 2.00 5.00
1952 Bowman Reprint
NNO Checklists .10 .30

1996 Bowman Foil

These parallel foil cards were seeded at an approximate rate of one per pack. Packs that did not contain a Foil card had a Bowman's Best Preview or Minor League Player of the Year insert card instead. The striking silver foil card fronts differ them from the base 1996 Bowman cards.

COMPLETE SET (385) 150.00 300.00
*STARS: 1X TO 2.5X BASIC CARDS
*ROOKIES: 1.25X TO 2.5X BASIC CARDS
TWO FOILS PER RETAIL PACK
267 Raul Ibanez 4.00 10.00

1997 Bowman

The 1997 Bowman set was issued in two series (series one numbers 1-221, series two numbers 222-441) and was distributed in 10 card packs with a suggested retail price of $2.50. The 441-card set features color photos of 300 top prospects with silver and blue foil stamping and 140 veteran stars designated by silver and red foil stamping. An unannounced Hideki Irabu red bordered card (number 441) was also included in series two packs. Players that were featured for the first time on a Bowman card also carried a blue foil "1st Bowman Card" logo on the card front. Topps offered collectors a $125 guarantee on complete sets. To get the guarantee, collectors had to mail in the Guaranteed Certificate Request Form which was found in every three packs of either series along with a $5 registration and processing fee. To redeem the guarantee, collectors had to send a complete set of Bowman regular cards (441 cards in both series) along with the certificate to Topps between August 31 and December 31 in the year 2000. Rookie Cards in this set include Adrian Beltre, Kris Benson, Eric Chavez, Jose Cruz Jr, Travis Lee, Aramis Ramirez, Miguel Tejada and Kerry Wood. Please note that cards 155 and 158 don't exist. Calvin "Pokey" Reese and George Arias are both numbered 156 (Reese is an uncorrected error - should be numbered 155). Chris Carpenter and Eric Milton are both numbered 159 (Carpenter is an uncorrected error - should be numbered 158).

COMPLETE SET (441) 25.00 60.00
COMP. SERIES 1 (221) 12.50 30.00
COMP. SERIES 2 (220) 12.50 30.00
1 Derek Jeter .75 2.00
2 Edgar Renteria .10 .30
3 Chipper Jones .30 .75
4 Hideo Nomo .30 .75
5 Tim Salmon .20 .50
6 Jason Giambi .10 .30
7 Robin Ventura .10 .30
8 Tony Clark .10 .30
9 Barry Larkin .20 .50
10 Paul Molitor .10 .30
11 Bernard Gilkey .10 .30
12 Jack McDowell .10 .30
13 Andy Benes .10 .30
14 Ryan Klesko .10 .30
15 Mark McGwire .75 2.00
16 Ken Griffey Jr. .50 1.25
17 Robb Nen .10 .30
18 Cal Ripken 1.00 2.50
19 John Valentin .10 .30
20 Ricky Bottalico .10 .30
21 Mike Lansing .10 .30
22 Ryne Sandberg .50 1.25
23 Carlos Delgado .10 .30
24 Craig Biggio .20 .50
25 Eric Karros .10 .30
26 Kevin Appier .10 .30
27 Mariano Rivera .30 .75
28 Vinny Castilla .10 .30
29 Juan Gonzalez .10 .30
30 Al Martin .10 .30
31 Jeff Cirillo .10 .30
32 Eddie Murray .30 .75
33 Ray Lankford .10 .30
34 Manny Ramirez .20 .50
35 Roberto Alomar .20 .50
36 Will Clark .20 .50
37 Chuck Knoblauch .10 .30
38 Harold Baines .10 .30
39 Trevor Hoffman .10 .30
40 Edgar Martinez .20 .50
41 Geronimo Berroa .10 .30
42 Rey Ordonez .10 .30
43 Mike Stanley .10 .30
44 Mike Mussina .20 .50
45 Kevin Brown .10 .30
46 Dennis Eckersley .10 .30
47 Henry Rodriguez .10 .30
48 Tino Martinez .20 .50
49 Eric Young .10 .30
50 Bret Boone .10 .30
51 Raul Mondesi .10 .30
52 Sammy Sosa .30 .75
53 John Smoltz .20 .50
54 Billy Wagner .10 .30
55 Jeff D'Amico .10 .30
56 Ken Caminiti .10 .30
57 Jason Kendall .10 .30
58 Wade Boggs .20 .50
59 Andres Galarraga .10 .30
60 Jeff Brantley .10 .30
61 Mel Rojas .10 .30
62 Brian L. Hunter .10 .30
63 Bobby Bonilla .10 .30
64 Roger Clemens .60 1.50
65 Jeff Kent .10 .30
66 Matt Williams .10 .30
67 Albert Belle .10 .30
68 Jeff King .10 .30
69 John Wetteland .10 .30
70 Deion Sanders .20 .50
71 Bubba Trammell RC .25 .60
72 Felix Heredia RC .15 .40
73 Billy Koch RC .40 1.00
74 Sidney Ponson RC .40 1.00
75 Ricky Ledee RC .25 .60
76 Brett Tomko .10 .30
77 Braden Looper RC .15 .40
78 Damian Jackson .10 .30
79 Jason Dickson .10 .30
80 Chad Green RC .15 .40
81 R.A. Dickey RC .15 .40
82 Jeff Liefer .10 .30
83 Matt Wagner .10 .30
84 Richard Hidalgo .10 .30
85 Adam Riggs .10 .30
86 Robert Smith .10 .30
87 Chad Hermansen RC .15 .40
88 Felix Martinez .10 .30
89 J.J. Johnson .10 .30
90 Todd Dunwoody .10 .30
91 Katsuhiro Maeda .10 .30
92 Darin Erstad .10 .30
93 Elieser Marrero .10 .30
94 Bartolo Colon .10 .30
95 Chris Fussell .10 .30
96 Ugueth Urbina .10 .30
97 Josh Paul RC .15 .40
98 Jaime Bluma .10 .30
99 Seth Greisinger RC .15 .40
100 Jose Cruz Jr. RC .25 .60
101 Todd Dunn .10 .30
102 Joe Young RC .15 .40
103 Jonathan Johnson .10 .30
104 Justin Towle RC .15 .40
105 Brian Rose .10 .30
106 Jose Guillen .10 .30
107 Andruw Jones .20 .50
108 Mark Kotsay RC .60 1.50
109 Wilton Guerrero .10 .30
110 Jacob Cruz .10 .30
111 Mike Sweeney .10 .30
112 Julio Mosquera .10 .30
113 Matt Morris .10 .30
114 Wendell Magee .10 .30
115 John Thomson .10 .30
116 Javier Valentin .10 .30
117 Tom Fordham .10 .30
118 Ruben Rivera .10 .30
119 Mike Drumright RC .15 .40
120 Chris Holt .10 .30
121 Sean Maloney .10 .30
122 Michael Barrett .10 .30
123 Tony Saunders RC .15 .40
124 Kevin Brown C .10 .30
125 Richard Almanzar .10 .30
126 Mark Redman .10 .30
127 Anthony Sanders RC .15 .40
128 Jeff Abbott .10 .30
129 Eugene Kingsale .10 .30
130 Paul Konerko .20 .50
131 Randall Simon RC .25 .60
132 Andy Larkin .10 .30
133 Rafael Medina .10 .30
134 Mendy Lopez .10 .30
135 Freddy Adrian Garcia .10 .30
136 Karim Garcia .10 .30
137 Larry Rodriguez RC .15 .40
138 Carlos Guillen .10 .30
139 Aaron Boone .10 .30
140 Donnie Sadler .10 .30
141 Brooks Kieschnick .10 .30
142 Scott Spiezio .10 .30
143 Everett Stull .10 .30
144 Enrique Wilson .10 .30
145 Milton Bradley RC .75 2.00
146 Kevin Orie .10 .30
147 Derek Wallace .10 .30
148 Russ Johnson .10 .30
149 Joe Lagarde RC .15 .40
150 Luis Castillo .10 .30
151 Jay Payton .10 .30
152 Joe Long .10 .30
153 Livan Hernandez .10 .30
154 Vladimir Nunez RC .25 .60
155 Pokey Reese UER .10 .30
Card actually numbered 156
156 George Arias .10 .30
157 Homer Bush .10 .30
158 Chris Carpenter UER .10 .30
Card numbered 159
159 Eric Milton RC .25 .60
160 Richie Sexson .10 .30
161 Carl Pavano .10 .30
162 Chris Gissell RC .15 .40
163 Mac Suzuki .10 .30
164 Pat Cline .10 .30
165 Ron Wright .10 .30
166 Dante Powell .10 .30
167 Mark Bellhorn .10 .30
168 George Lombard .10 .30
169 Pee Wee Lopez RC .15 .40
170 Paul Wilder RC .15 .40
171 Brad Fullmer .10 .30
172 Willie Martinez RC .15 .40
173 Dario Veras RC .15 .40
174 Dave Coggin .10 .30
175 Kris Benson RC .40 1.00
176 Torii Hunter .10 .30
177 D.T. Cromer .10 .30
178 Nelson Figueroa RC .15 .40
179 Hiram Bocachica RC .15 .40
180 Shane Monahan .10 .30
181 Jimmy Anderson RC .15 .40
182 Juan Melo .10 .30
183 Pablo Ortega RC .15 .40
184 Calvin Pickering RC .15 .40
185 Reggie Taylor .10 .30
186 Jeff Farnsworth RC .15 .40
187 Terrence Long .10 .30
188 Geoff Jenkins .10 .30
189 Steve Rain RC .15 .40
190 Nerio Rodriguez RC .15 .40
191 Derrick Gibson .10 .30
192 Darin Blood .10 .30
193 Ben Davis .10 .30
194 Adrian Beltre RC 1.25 3.00
195 Damian Sapp RC UER .15 .40
196 Kerry Wood RC 2.00 5.00
197 Nate Rolison RC .15 .40
198 Fernando Tatis RC .15 .40
199 Brad Penny RC 1.25 3.00
200 Jake Westbrook RC .40 1.00
201 Edwin Diaz .10 .30
202 Joe Fontenot RC .25 .60
203 Matt Halloran RC .15 .40
204 Blake Stein RC .15 .40
205 Onan Masaoka .10 .30
206 Ben Petrick .10 .30
207 Matt Clement RC .40 1.00
208 Todd Greene .10 .30
209 Ray Ricken .10 .30
210 Eric Chavez RC 1.50 4.00
211 Edgard Velazquez .10 .30
212 Bruce Chen RC .40 1.00
213 Danny Patterson .10 .30
214 Jeff Yoder .10 .30
215 Luis Ordaz RC .15 .40
216 Chris Widger .10 .30
217 Jason Brester .10 .30
218 Carlton Loewer .10 .30
219 Chris Reitsma RC .25 .60
220 Neifi Perez .10 .30
221 Hideki Irabu RC .25 .60
222 Ellis Burks .10 .30
223 Pedro Martinez UER .20 .50
Wrong birthdate
224 Kenny Lofton .10 .30
225 Randy Johnson .30 .75
226 Terry Steinbach .10 .30
227 Bernie Williams .20 .50
228 Dean Palmer .10 .30
229 Alan Benes .10 .30
230 Marquis Grissom .10 .30
231 Gary Sheffield .10 .30
232 Curt Schilling .10 .30
233 Reggie Sanders .10 .30
234 Bobby Higginson .10 .30
235 Moises Alou .10 .30
236 Tom Glavine .20 .50
237 Mark Grace .20 .50
238 Ramon Martinez .10 .30
239 Rafael Palmeiro .20 .50
240 John Olerud .10 .30
241 Dante Bichette .10 .30
242 Greg Vaughn .10 .30
243 Jeff Bagwell .20 .50
244 Barry Bonds .75 2.00
245 Pat Hentgen .10 .30
246 Jim Thome .20 .50
247 J.Allensworth .10 .30
248 Andy Pettitte .20 .50
249 Jay Bell .10 .30
250 John Jaha .10 .30
251 Jim Edmonds .10 .30
252 Ron Gant .10 .30
253 David Cone .10 .30
254 Jose Canseco .20 .50
255 Jay Buhner .10 .30
256 Greg Maddux .50 1.25
257 Brian McRae .10 .30
258 Lance Johnson .10 .30
259 Travis Fryman .10 .30
260 Paul O'Neill .20 .50
261 Ivan Rodriguez .20 .50
262 Gregg Jefferies .10 .30
263 Fred McGriff .20 .50
264 Derek Bell .10 .30
265 Jeff Conine .10 .30
266 Mike Piazza .50 1.25
267 Mark Grudzielanek .10 .30
268 Brady Anderson .10 .30
269 Marty Cordova .10 .30
270 Ray Durham .10 .30
271 Joe Carter .10 .30
272 Brian Jordan .10 .30
273 David Justice .10 .30
274 Tony Gwynn .40 1.00
275 Larry Walker .10 .30
276 Cecil Fielder .10 .30
277 Mo Vaughn .10 .30
278 Alex Fernandez .10 .30
279 Michael Tucker .10 .30
280 Jose Valentin .10 .30
281 Sandy Alomar Jr. .10 .30
282 Todd Hollandsworth .10 .30
283 Rico Brogna .10 .30
284 Rusty Greer .10 .30
285 Roberto Hernandez .10 .30
286 Hal Morris .10 .30
287 Johnny Damon .20 .50
288 Todd Hundley .10 .30
289 Rondell White .10 .30
290 Frank Thomas .30 .75
291 Don Denbow RC .15 .40
292 Derrek Lee .20 .50
293 Todd Walker .10 .30
294 Scott Rolen .20 .50
295 Wes Helms .10 .30
296 Bob Abreu .20 .50
297 John Patterson RC .60 1.50
298 Alex Gonzalez RC .40 1.00
299 Grant Roberts RC .15 .40
300 Jeff Suppan .10 .30
301 Luke Wilcox .10 .30
302 Marion Anderson .10 .30
303 Ray Brown .10 .30
304 Mike Caruso RC .15 .40
305 Sam Marsonek RC .15 .40
306 Brady Raggio RC .15 .40
307 Kevin McGlinchy RC .25 .60
308 Roy Halladay RC 5.00 12.00
309 Jeremi Gonzalez RC .15 .40
310 Aramis Ramirez RC 1.50 4.00
311 Dee Brown RC .15 .40
312 Justin Thompson .10 .30
313 Jay Tessmer RC .15 .40
314 Mike Johnson RC .15 .40
315 Danny Clyburn .10 .30
316 Bruce Aven .10 .30
317 Keith Foulke RC .60 1.50
318 Jimmy Osting RC .25 .60
319 Val De Los Santos RC .15 .40
320 Shannon Stewart .10 .30
321 Willie Adams .10 .30
322 Larry Barnes RC .15 .40
323 Mark Johnson RC .15 .40
324 Chris Stowers RC .15 .40
325 Brandon Reed .10 .30
326 Randy Winn .10 .30
327 Steve Chavez RC .15 .40
328 Nomar Garciaparra .50 1.25
329 Jacque Jones RC .60 1.50
330 Chris Clemons .10 .30
331 Todd Helton .30 .75
332 Ryan Brannan RC .15 .40
333 Alex Sanchez RC .25 .60
334 Arnold Gooch .10 .30
335 Russell Branyan .10 .30
336 Daryle Ward .10 .30
337 John LeRoy RC .15 .40
338 Steve Cox .10 .30
339 Kevin Witt .10 .30
340 Norm Hutchins .10 .30
341 Gabby Martinez .10 .30
342 Kris Detmers .10 .30
343 Mike Villano RC .15 .40
344 Preston Wilson .10 .30
345 James Manias RC .15 .40
346 Deivi Cruz RC .25 .60
347 Donzell McDonald RC .15 .40
348 Rod Myers RC .15 .40
349 Shawn Chacon RC .40 1.00
350 Elvin Hernandez RC .25 .60
351 Orlando Cabrera RC .60 1.50
352 Brian Banks .10 .30
353 Robbie Bell .15 .40
354 Brad Rigby .10 .30
355 Scott Elarton .10 .30
356 Kevin Sweeney RC .15 .40
357 Steve Soderstrom .10 .30
358 Ryan Nye .10 .30
359 Marlon Allen RC .15 .40
360 Donny Leon RC .15 .40
361 Garrett Neubart RC .25 .60
362 Abraham Nunez RC .25 .60
363 Adam Eaton RC .40 1.00
364 Octavio Dotel RC .25 .60
365 Dean Crow RC .15 .40
366 Jason Baker RC .15 .40
367 Sean Casey .40 1.00
368 Joe Lawrence RC .15 .40
369 Adam Johnson RC .15 .40
370 S.Schoeneweis RC .25 .60
371 Gerald Witasick Jr. .10 .30
372 Ronnie Belliard RC .50 1.25
373 Russ Ortiz .10 .30
374 Robert Stratton RC .25 .60
375 Bobby Estalella .10 .30
376 Corey Lee RC .15 .40
377 Carlos Beltran .75 2.00
378 Mike Cameron .10 .30
379 Scott Randall RC .15 .40
380 Corey Erickson RC .15 .40
381 Jay Canizaro .10 .30
382 Kerry Robinson RC .15 .40
383 Todd Noel RC .15 .40
384 A.J. Zapp RC .15 .40
385 Jarrod Washburn .10 .30
386 Ben Grieve .10 .30
387 Javier Vazquez RC .60 1.50
388 Tony Graffanino .10 .30
389 Travis Lee RC .25 .60
390 DaRond Stovall .10 .30
391 Dennis Reyes RC .25 .60
392 Danny Buxbaum .10 .30
393 Marc Lewis RC .15 .40
394 Kelvim Escobar RC .40 1.00
395 Danny Klassen .10 .30
396 Ken Cloude RC .15 .40
397 Gabe Alvarez .10 .30
398 Jaret Wright RC .25 .60
399 Raul Casanova .10 .30
400 Clayton Bruner RC .15 .40
401 Jason Marquis RC .60 1.50
402 Marc Kroon .10 .30
403 Jamey Wright .10 .30
404 Matt Snyder RC .15 .40
405 Josh Garrett RC .15 .40
406 Juan Encarnacion .10 .30
407 Heath Murray .10 .30
408 Brett Herbison RC .25 .60
409 Brent Butler RC .15 .40
410 Danny Peoples RC .15 .40
411 Miguel Tejada RC 2.00 5.00
412 Damian Moss .10 .30
413 Jim Pittsley .10 .30
414 Dmitri Young .10 .30
415 Glendon Rusch .10 .30
416 Vladimir Guerrero .30 .75
417 Cole Liniak RC .25 .60
418 R.Hernandez UER .10 .30
Card back says 1st Bowman card is 1997, he had a 1996 Bowman
419 Cliff Politte RC .15 .40
420 Mel Rosario RC .15 .40
421 Jorge Carrion RC .15 .40
422 John Barnes RC .15 .40
423 Chris Stowe RC .15 .40
424 Vernon Wells RC 2.00 5.00
425 Brett Caradonna RC .15 .40
426 Scott Hodges RC .25 .60
427 Jon Garland RC 1.00 2.50
428 Nathan Haynes RC .15 .40
429 Geoff Goetz RC .15 .40
430 Adam Kennedy RC .40 1.00
431 T.J. Tucker RC .15 .40
432 Aaron Akin RC .15 .40
433 Jayson Werth RC 2.00 5.00
434 Glenn Davis RC .15 .40
435 Mark Mangum RC .15 .40
436 Troy Cameron RC .15 .40
437 J.J. Davis RC .15 .40
438 Lance Berkman RC 4.00 10.00
439 Jason Standridge RC .15 .40
440 Jason Dellaero RC .25 .60
441 Hideki Irabu .25 .60

1997 Bowman International

Inserted one in every pack, this 441-card set is parallel to the regular Bowman set. The difference is found in the flag in the background of each card that tells in what country the pictured player was born.

COMPLETE SET (441) 60.00 160.00
COMP.SERIES 1 (221) 30.00 80.00
COMP.SERIES 2 (220) 30.00 80.00
*STARS: 1X TO 2.5X BASIC CARDS
*ROOKIES: .5X TO 1.2X BASIC CARDS

1997 Bowman 1998 ROY Favorites

Randomly inserted in 1997 Bowman Series two packs at the rate of one in 12, this 15-card set features color photos of prospective 1998 Rookie of the Year candidates.

COMPLETE SET (15) 6.00 15.00
SER.2 STATED ODDS 1:12
ROY1 Jeff Abbott .40 1.00
ROY2 Karim Garcia .40 1.00
ROY3 Todd Helton 1.00 2.50
ROY4 Richard Hidalgo .40 1.00
ROY5 Geoff Jenkins .40 1.00
ROY6 Russ Johnson .40 1.00
ROY7 Paul Konerko .60 1.50
ROY8 Mark Kotsay .75 2.00
ROY9 Ricky Ledee .30 .75
ROY10 Travis Lee .30 .75
ROY11 Derrek Lee .60 1.50
ROY12 Elieser Marrero .40 1.00
ROY13 Juan Melo .40 1.00
ROY14 Brian Rose .40 1.00
ROY15 Fernando Tatis .20 .50

1997 Bowman Certified Blue Ink Autographs

Randomly inserted in first and second series packs at a rate of one in 96 and ANCO packs at one in 115, this 90-card set features color player photos of top prospects with blue ink autographs and printed on sturdy 16 pt. card stock with the Topps Certified Autograph Issue Stamp. The Derek Jeter blue ink and green ink versions are seeded in every 1,928 packs.

STATED ODDS 1:96, ANCO 1:115
*BLACK INK: .5X TO 1.2X BLUE INK
BLACK STATED ODDS 1:503, ANCO 1:600
*GOLD INK: 1X TO 2.5X BLUE INK
GOLD: STATED ODDS 1:1509, ANCO 1:1795
*GREEN JETER: SAME VALUE AS BLUE INK
D.JETER BLUE SER.1 ODDS 1:1928
D.JETER GREEN SER.2 ODDS 1:1928
CA1 Jeff Abbott 3.00 8.00
CA2 Bob Abreu 15.00 40.00
CA3 Willie Adams 3.00 8.00
CA4 Brian Banks 3.00 8.00
CA5 Kris Benson 5.00 12.00
CA6 Darin Blood 3.00 8.00
CA7 Jaime Bluma 3.00 8.00
CA8 Kevin L. Brown 3.00 8.00
CA9 Ray Brown 3.00 8.00
CA10 Homer Bush 3.00 8.00
CA11 Mike Cameron 5.00 12.00
CA12 Jay Canizaro 3.00 8.00
CA13 Luis Castillo 5.00 12.00
CA14 Dave Coggin 3.00 8.00
CA15 Bartolo Colon 5.00 12.00
CA16 Rocky Coppinger 3.00 8.00
CA17 Jacob Cruz 3.00 8.00
CA18 Jose Cruz Jr. 3.00 8.00
CA19 Jeff D'Amico 3.00 8.00
CA20 Ben Davis 3.00 8.00
CA21 Mike Drumright 3.00 8.00
CA22 Scott Elarton 3.00 8.00
CA23 Darin Erstad 5.00 12.00
CA24 Bobby Estalella 3.00 8.00
CA25 Joe Fontenot 3.00 8.00
CA26 Tom Fordham 3.00 8.00
CA27 Brad Fullmer 3.00 8.00
CA28 Chris Fussell 3.00 8.00
CA29 Karim Garcia 3.00 8.00
CA30 Kris Detmers 3.00 8.00
CA31 Todd Greene 3.00 8.00
CA32 Ben Grieve 3.00 8.00
CA33 Vladimir Guerrero 15.00 40.00
CA34 Jose Guillen 5.00 12.00
CA35 Roy Halladay 200.00 400.00
CA36 Wes Helms 3.00 8.00
CA37 Chad Hermansen 3.00 8.00
CA38 Richard Hidalgo 5.00 12.00
CA39 Todd Hollandsworth 3.00 8.00
CA40 Damian Jackson 3.00 8.00
CA41 Derek Jeter 75.00 150.00
CA42 Andruw Jones 10.00 25.00
CA43 Brooks Kieschnick 3.00 8.00
CA44 Eugene Kingsale 3.00 8.00
CA45 Paul Konerko 10.00 25.00
CA46 Marc Kroon 3.00 8.00
CA47 Derrek Lee 15.00 40.00
CA48 Travis Lee 3.00 8.00
CA49 Terrence Long 3.00 8.00
CA50 Curt Lyons 3.00 8.00
CA51 Eli Marrero 3.00 8.00
CA52 Rafael Medina 3.00 8.00
CA53 Juan Melo 3.00 8.00
CA54 Shane Monahan 3.00 8.00
CA55 Julio Mosquera 3.00 8.00
CA56 Heath Murray 3.00 8.00
CA57 Ryan Nye 3.00 8.00
CA58 Kevin Orie 3.00 8.00
CA59 Russ Ortiz 5.00 12.00
CA60 Carl Pavano 5.00 12.00
CA61 Jay Payton 3.00 8.00
CA62 Neifi Perez 3.00 8.00
CA63 Sidney Ponson 5.00 12.00
CA64 Pokey Reese 5.00 12.00
CA65 Ray Ricken 3.00 8.00
CA66 Brad Rigby 3.00 8.00
CA67 Adam Riggs 3.00 8.00
CA68 Ruben Rivera 3.00 8.00
CA69 J.J. Johnson 3.00 8.00
CA70 Scott Rolen 10.00 25.00
CA71 Tony Saunders 3.00 8.00
CA72 Donnie Sadler 3.00 8.00
CA73 Richie Sexson 5.00 12.00
CA74 Scott Spiezio 3.00 8.00
CA75 Everett Stull 3.00 8.00
CA76 Mike Sweeney 5.00 12.00
CA77 Fernando Tatis 5.00 12.00
CA78 Miguel Tejada 20.00 50.00
CA79 Justin Thompson 3.00 8.00
CA80 Justin Towle 3.00 8.00
CA81 Billy Wagner 5.00 12.00
CA82 Todd Walker 5.00 12.00
CA83 Luke Wilcox 3.00 8.00
CA84 Paul Wilder 3.00 8.00
CA85 Enrique Wilson 3.00 8.00
CA86 Kerry Wood 20.00 50.00
CA87 Jamey Wright 3.00 8.00
CA88 Ron Wright 4.00 10.00
CA89 Dmitri Young 5.00 12.00
CA90 Nelson Figueroa 3.00 8.00

1997 Bowman International Best

Randomly inserted in series two packs at the rate of one in 12, this 20-card set features color photos of both prospects and veterans from far and wide who have made an impact on the game.

COMPLETE SET (20) 20.00 50.00
SER.2 STATED ODDS 1:12
*ATOMIC: 1.5X TO 4X BASIC INT.BEST
ATOMIC SER.2 STATED ODDS 1:96
*REFRACTORS: .75X TO 2X BASIC INT.BEST
REFRACTOR SER.2 STATED ODDS 1:48
BBI1 Frank Thomas 1.25 3.00
BBI2 Ken Griffey Jr. 2.00 5.00
BBI3 Juan Gonzalez .50 1.25
BBI4 Bernie Williams .75 2.00
BBI5 Hideo Nomo 1.25 3.00
BBI6 Sammy Sosa 1.25 3.00
BBI7 Larry Walker .50 1.25
BBI8 Vinny Castilla .50 1.25
BBI9 Mariano Rivera 1.25 3.00
BBI10 Rafael Palmeiro .75 2.00
BBI11 Nomar Garciaparra 2.00 5.00
BBI12 Todd Walker .50 1.25
BBI13 Andruw Jones .75 2.00
BBI14 Vladimir Guerrero 1.25 3.00
BBI15 Ruben Rivera .50 1.25
BBI16 Bob Abreu .75 2.00
BBI17 Karim Garcia .50 1.25
BBI18 Katsuhiro Maeda .50 1.25
BBI19 Jose Cruz Jr. .50 1.25
BBI20 Damian Moss .50 1.25

1997 Bowman Scout's Honor Roll

Randomly inserted in first series packs at a rate of one in 12, this 15-card set features color photos of top prospects and rookies printed on double-etched foil cards.

COMPLETE SET (15) 12.50 25.00
SER.1 STATED ODDS 1:12
1 Dmitri Young .30 .75
2 Bob Abreu .50 1.25
3 Vladimir Guerrero .75 2.00
4 Paul Konerko .50 1.25
5 Kevin Orie .30 .75
6 Todd Walker .30 .75
7 Ben Grieve .30 .75
8 Darin Erstad .30 .75
9 Derrek Lee .50 1.25
10 Jose Cruz Jr. .30 .75
11 Scott Rolen .50 1.25
12 Travis Lee .30 .75
13 Andruw Jones .50 1.25
14 Wilton Guerrero .30 .75
15 Nomar Garciaparra 1.25 3.00

1998 Bowman Previews

Randomly inserted in Stadium Club first series hobby and retail packs at the rate of one in 12 and first series Home Team Advantage packs at a rate of one in four, this 10-card set is a sneak preview of the Bowman series and features color photos of top players. The cards are numbered with a BP prefix on the backs.

COMPLETE SET (10) 10.00 25.00
SER.1 STATED ODDS 1:12 H/R, 1:4 HTA
BP1 Nomar Garciaparra 1.50 4.00
BP2 Scott Rolen .60 1.50
BP3 Ken Griffey Jr. 1.50 4.00
BP4 Frank Thomas 1.00 2.50
BP5 Larry Walker .40 1.00
BP6 Mike Piazza 1.50 4.00
BP7 Chipper Jones 1.00 2.50
BP8 Tino Martinez .60 1.50
BP9 Mark McGwire 2.50 6.00
BP10 Barry Bonds 2.50 6.00

1998 Bowman Prospect Previews

Randomly seeded in Stadium Club second series hobby and retail packs at a rate of one in twelve and second series Home Team Advantage packs at a rate of one in four, this ten card set previewed the upcoming 1998 Bowman brand, featuring a selection of top youngsters expected to make an impact in 1998.

COMPLETE SET (10) 4.00 10.00
SER.2 STATED ODDS 1:12 H/R, 1:4 HTA
BP1 Ben Grieve .40 1.00

BP2 Brad Fullmer .40 1.00
BP3 Ryan Anderson .40 1.00
BP4 Mark Kotsay .50 1.25
BP5 Bobby Estalella .40 1.00
BP6 Juan Encarnacion .40 1.00
BP7 Todd Helton .60 1.50
BP8 Mike Lowell 2.00 5.00
BP9 A.J. Hinch .40 1.00
BP10 Richard Hidalgo .40 1.00

1998 Bowman

The complete 1998 Bowman set was distributed amongst two series with a total of 441 cards. The 10-card packs retailed for $2.50 each. Series one contains 221 cards while series two contains 220 cards. Each player's facsimile signature taken from the contract they signed with Topps is also on the left border. Players new to Bowman are marked with the new Bowman Rookie Card stamp. Notable Rookie Cards include Ryan Anderson, Jack Cust, Troy Glaus, Orlando Hernandez, Gabe Kapler, Ruben Mateo, Kevin Millwood and Magglio Ordonez. The 1991 BBM (Major Japanese Card set) cards of Shigetoshi Hasegawa, Hideki Irabu and Hideo Nomo (All of which are considered Japanese Rookie Cards) were randomly inserted into these packs.

COMPLETE SET (441) 20.00 50.00
COMP. SERIES 1 (221) 10.00 25.00
COMP. SERIES 2 (220) 10.00 25.00
1 Nomar Garciaparra .50 1.25
2 Scott Rolen .20 .50
3 Andy Pettitte .20 .50
4 Ivan Rodriguez .20 .50
5 Mark McGwire .75 2.00
6 Jason Dickson .10 .30
7 Jose Cruz Jr. .10 .30
8 Jeff Kent .10 .30
9 Mike Mussina .20 .50
10 Jason Kendall .10 .30
11 Brett Tomko .10 .30
12 Jeff King .10 .30
13 Brad Radke .10 .30
14 Robin Ventura .10 .30
15 Jeff Bagwell .20 .50
16 Greg Maddux .50 1.25
17 John Jaha .10 .30
18 Mike Piazza .50 1.25
19 Edgar Martinez .20 .50
20 David Justice .10 .30
21 Todd Hundley .10 .30
22 Tony Gwynn .40 1.00
23 Larry Walker .10 .30
24 Bernie Williams .20 .50
25 Edgar Renteria .10 .30
26 Rafael Palmeiro .20 .50
27 Tim Salmon .20 .50
28 Matt Morris .10 .30
29 Shawn Estes .10 .30
30 Vladimir Guerrero .30 .75
31 Fernando Tatis .10 .30
32 Justin Thompson .10 .30
33 Ken Griffey Jr. .50 1.25
34 Edgardo Alfonzo .10 .30
35 Mo Vaughn .10 .30
36 Marty Cordova .10 .30
37 Craig Biggio .20 .50
38 Roger Clemens .60 1.50
39 Mark Grace .20 .50
40 Ken Caminiti .10 .30
41 Tony Womack .10 .30
42 Albert Belle .10 .30
43 Tino Martinez .20 .50
44 Sandy Alomar Jr. .10 .30
45 Jeff Cirillo .10 .30
46 Jason Giambi .10 .30
47 Darin Erstad .10 .30
48 Livan Hernandez .10 .30
49 Mark Grudzielanek .10 .30
50 Sammy Sosa .30 .75
51 Curt Schilling .10 .30
52 Brian Hunter .10 .30
53 Neifi Perez .10 .30
54 Todd Walker .10 .30
55 Jose Guillen .10 .30
56 Jim Thome .20 .50
57 Tom Glavine .20 .50
58 Todd Greene .10 .30
59 Rondell White .10 .30
60 Roberto Alomar .20 .50
61 Tony Clark .10 .30
62 Vinny Castilla .10 .30
63 Barry Larkin .20 .50
64 Hideki Irabu .10 .30
65 Johnny Damon .20 .50
66 Juan Gonzalez .10 .30
67 John Olerud .10 .30
68 Gary Sheffield .10 .30
69 Raul Mondesi .10 .30
70 Chipper Jones .30 .75
71 David Ortiz 1.00 2.50
72 Warren Morris RC .15 .40
73 Alex Gonzalez .10 .30
74 Nick Bierbrodt .10 .30
75 Roy Halladay .60 1.50
76 Danny Buxbaum .10 .30
77 Adam Kennedy .10 .30
78 Jared Sandberg .10 .30
79 Michael Barrett .10 .30
80 Gil Meche .25 .60
81 Jayson Werth .10 .30
82 Abraham Nunez .10 .30
83 Ben Petrick .10 .30
84 Brett Caradonna .10 .30
85 Mike Lowell RC 1.25 3.00
86 Clayton Bruner .10 .30
87 John Curtice RC .25 .60
88 Bobby Estalella .10 .30
89 Juan Melo .10 .30
90 Arnold Gooch .10 .30
91 Kevin Millwood RC .60 1.50
92 Richie Sexson .10 .30
93 Orlando Cabrera .10 .30
94 Pat Cline .10 .30
95 Anthony Sanders .10 .30
96 Russ Johnson .10 .30
97 Ben Grieve .10 .30
98 Kevin McGlinchy .10 .30
99 Paul Wilder .10 .30
100 Russ Ortiz .10 .30
101 Ryan Jackson RC .15 .40
102 Heath Murray .10 .30
103 Brian Rose .10 .30
104 R.Radmanovich RC .15 .40
105 Ricky Ledee .10 .30
106 Jeff Wallace RC .15 .40
107 Ryan Minor RC .15 .40
108 Dennis Reyes .10 .30
109 James Manias .10 .30
110 Chris Carpenter .10 .30
111 Daryle Ward .10 .30
112 Vernon Wells .10 .30
113 Chad Green .10 .30
114 Mike Stoner RC .15 .40
115 Brad Fullmer .10 .30
116 Adam Eaton .10 .30
117 Jeff Liefer .10 .30
118 Corey Koskie RC .40 1.00
119 Todd Helton .20 .50
120 Jaime Jones RC .15 .40
121 Mel Rosario .10 .30
122 Geoff Goetz .10 .30
123 Adrian Beltre .10 .30
124 Jason Dellaero .10 .30
125 Gabe Kapler RC .40 1.00
126 Scott Schoeneweis .10 .30
127 Ryan Brannan .10 .30
128 Aaron Akin .10 .30
129 Ryan Anderson RC .15 .40
130 Brad Penny .10 .30
131 Bruce Chen .10 .30
132 Eli Marrero .10 .30
133 Eric Chavez .10 .30
134 Troy Glaus RC 1.50 4.00
135 Troy Cameron .10 .30
136 Brian Sikorski RC .15 .40
137 Mike Kinkade RC .15 .40
138 Braden Looper .10 .30
139 Mark Mangum .10 .30
140 Danny Peoples .10 .30
141 J.J. Davis .10 .30
142 Ben Davis .10 .30
143 Jacque Jones .10 .30
144 Derrick Gibson .10 .30
145 Bronson Arroyo .60 1.50
146 L.De Los Santos RC UER .15 .40
has hitting stat line instead of pitching
147 Jeff Abbott .10 .30
148 Mike Cuddyer RC .60 1.50
149 Jason Romano .10 .30
150 Shane Monahan .10 .30
151 Ntema Ndungidi RC .15 .40
152 Alex Sanchez .10 .30
153 Jack Cust RC .75 2.00
154 Brent Butler .10 .30
155 Ramon Hernandez .10 .30
156 Norm Hutchins .10 .30
157 Jason Marquis .10 .30
158 Jacob Cruz .10 .30
159 Rob Burger RC .15 .40
160 Dave Coggin .10 .30
161 Preston Wilson .10 .30
162 Jason Fitzgerald RC .15 .40
163 Dan Serafini .10 .30
164 Peter Munro .10 .30
165 Trot Nixon .10 .30
166 Homer Bush .10 .30
167 Dermal Brown .10 .30
168 Chad Hermansen .10 .30
169 Julio Moreno RC .15 .40
170 John Roskos RC .15 .40
171 Grant Roberts .10 .30
172 Ken Cloude .10 .30
173 Jason Brester .10 .30
174 Jason Conti .10 .30
175 Jon Garland .10 .30
176 Robbie Bell .10 .30
177 Nathan Haynes .10 .30
178 Ramon Ortiz RC .25 .60
179 Shannon Stewart .10 .30
180 Pablo Ortega .10 .30
181 Jimmy Rollins RC 2.00 5.00
182 Sean Casey .10 .30
183 Ted Lilly RC .40 1.00
184 Chris Enochs RC .15 .40
185 M.Ordonez UER RC 2.00 5.00
Front photo is Mario Valdez
186 Mike Drumright .10 .30
187 Aaron Boone .10 .30
188 Matt Clement .10 .30
189 Todd Dunwoody .10 .30
190 Larry Rodriguez .10 .30
191 Todd Noel .10 .30
192 Geoff Jenkins .10 .30
193 George Lombard .10 .30
194 Lance Berkman .10 .30
195 Marcus McCain .10 .30
196 Ryan McGuire .10 .30
197 Jhensy Sandoval .10 .30
198 Corey Lee .10 .30
199 Mario Valdez .10 .30
200 Robert Fick RC .25 .60
201 Donnie Sadler .10 .30
202 Marc Kroon .10 .30
203 David Miller .10 .30
204 Jarrod Washburn .10 .30
205 Miguel Tejada .30 .75
206 Raul Ibanez .10 .30
207 John Patterson .10 .30
208 Calvin Pickering .10 .30
209 Felix Martinez .10 .30
210 Mark Redman .10 .30
211 Scott Elarton .10 .30
212 Jose Amado RC .15 .40
213 Kerry Wood .10 .30
214 Dante Powell .10 .30
215 Aramis Ramirez .10 .30
216 A.J. Hinch .10 .30
217 Dustin Carr RC .15 .40
218 Mark Kotsay .10 .30
219 Jason Standridge .10 .30
220 Luis Ordaz .10 .30
221 O.Hernandez RC .75 2.00
222 Cal Ripken 1.00 2.50
223 Paul Molitor .10 .30
224 Derek Jeter .75 2.00
225 Barry Bonds .75 2.00
226 Jim Edmonds .10 .30
227 John Smoltz .20 .50
228 Eric Karros .10 .30
229 Ray Lankford .10 .30
230 Rey Ordonez .10 .30
231 Kenny Lofton .10 .30
232 Alex Rodriguez .50 1.25
233 Dante Bichette .10 .30
234 Pedro Martinez .20 .50
235 Carlos Delgado .10 .30
236 Rod Beck .10 .30
237 Matt Williams .10 .30
238 Charles Johnson .10 .30
239 Rico Brogna .10 .30
240 Frank Thomas .30 .75
241 Paul O'Neill .20 .50
242 Jaret Wright .10 .30
243 Brant Brown .10 .30
244 Ryan Klesko .10 .30
245 Chuck Finley .10 .30
246 Derek Bell .10 .30
247 Delino DeShields .10 .30
248 Chan Ho Park .10 .30
249 Wade Boggs .20 .50
250 Jay Buhner .10 .30
251 Butch Huskey .10 .30
252 Steve Finley .10 .30
253 Will Clark .20 .50
254 John Valentin .10 .30
255 Bobby Higginson .10 .30
256 Darryl Strawberry .10 .30
257 Randy Johnson .30 .75
258 Al Martin .10 .30
259 Travis Fryman .10 .30
260 Fred McGriff .20 .50
261 Jose Valentin .10 .30
262 Andruw Jones .20 .50
263 Kenny Rogers .10 .30
264 Moises Alou .10 .30
265 Denny Neagle .10 .30
266 Ugueth Urbina .10 .30
267 Derrek Lee .20 .50
268 Ellis Burks .10 .30
269 Mariano Rivera .30 .75
270 Dean Palmer .10 .30
271 Eddie Taubensee .10 .30
272 Brady Anderson .10 .30
273 Brian Giles .10 .30
274 Quinton McCracken .10 .30
275 Henry Rodriguez .10 .30
276 Andres Galarraga .10 .30
277 Jose Canseco .20 .50
278 David Segui .10 .30
279 Bret Saberhagen .10 .30
280 Kevin Brown .20 .50
281 Chuck Knoblauch .10 .30
282 Jeromy Burnitz .10 .30
283 Jay Bell .10 .30
284 Manny Ramirez .20 .50
285 Rick Helling .10 .30
286 Francisco Cordova .10 .30
287 Bob Abreu .10 .30
288 J.T. Snow .10 .30
289 Hideo Nomo .30 .75
290 Brian Jordan .10 .30
291 Javy Lopez .10 .30
292 Travis Lee .10 .30
293 Russell Branyan .10 .30
294 Paul Konerko .10 .30
295 Masato Yoshii RC .25 .60
296 Kris Benson .10 .30
297 Juan Encarnacion .10 .30
298 Eric Milton .10 .30
299 Mike Caruso .10 .30
300 R.Aramboles RC .15 .40
301 Bobby Smith .10 .30
302 Billy Koch .10 .30
303 Richard Hidalgo .10 .30
304 Justin Baughman RC .15 .40
305 Chris Gissell .10 .30
306 Donnie Bridges RC .15 .40
307 Nelson Lara RC .15 .40
308 Randy Wolf RC .25 .60
309 Jason LaRue RC .25 .60
310 Jason Gooding RC .15 .40
311 Edgard Clemente .10 .30
312 Andrew Vessel .10 .30
313 Chris Reitsma .10 .30
314 Jesus Sanchez RC .15 .40
315 Buddy Carlyle RC .15 .40
316 Randy Winn .10 .30
317 Luis Rivera RC .15 .40
318 Marcus Thames RC 1.00 2.50
319 A.J. Pierzynski .10 .30
320 Scott Randall .10 .30
321 Damian Sapp .10 .30
322 Ed Yarnall RC .15 .40
323 Luke Allen RC .15 .40
324 J.D. Smart .10 .30
325 Willie Martinez .10 .30
326 Alex Ramirez .10 .30
327 Eric DuBose RC .15 .40
328 Kevin Witt .10 .30
329 Dan McKinley RC .15 .40
330 Cliff Politte .10 .30
331 Vladimir Nunez .10 .30
332 John Halama RC .15 .40
333 Nerio Rodriguez .10 .30
334 Desi Relaford .10 .30
335 Robinson Checo .10 .30
336 John Nicholson .20 .50
337 Tom LaRosa RC .15 .40
338 Kevin Nicholson RC .15 .40
339 Javier Vazquez .10 .30
340 A.J. Zapp .10 .30
341 Tom Evans .10 .30
342 Kerry Robinson .10 .30
343 Gabe Gonzalez RC .15 .40
344 Ralph Milliard .10 .30
345 Enrique Wilson .10 .30
346 Elvin Hernandez .10 .30
347 Mike Lincoln RC .15 .40
348 Cesar King RC .15 .40
349 Cristian Guzman RC .25 .60
350 Donzell McDonald .10 .30
351 Jim Parque RC .15 .40
352 Mike Saipe RC .15 .40
353 Carlos Febles RC .25 .60
354 Dernell Stenson RC .15 .40
355 Mark Osborne RC .15 .40
356 Odalis Perez RC .60 1.50
357 Jason Dewey RC .15 .40
358 Joe Fontenot .10 .30
359 Jason Grilli RC .15 .40
360 Kevin Haverbusch RC .15 .40
361 Jay Yennaco RC .15 .40
362 Brian Buchanan .10 .30
363 John Barnes .10 .30
364 Chris Fussell .10 .30
365 Kevin Gibbs RC .15 .40
366 Joe Lawrence .10 .30
367 DaRond Stovall .10 .30
368 Brian Fuentes RC .15 .40
369 Jimmy Anderson .10 .30
370 Lariel Gonzalez RC .15 .40
371 Scott Williamson RC .15 .40
372 Milton Bradley .10 .30
373 Jason Halper RC .15 .40
374 Brent Billingsley RC .15 .40
375 Joe DePastino RC .15 .40
376 Jake Westbrook .10 .30
377 Octavio Dotel .10 .30
378 Jason Williams RC .15 .40
379 Julio Ramirez RC .15 .40
380 Seth Greisinger .10 .30
381 Mike Judd RC .15 .40
382 Ben Ford RC .15 .40
383 Tom Bennett RC .15 .40
384 Adam Butler RC .15 .40
385 Wade Miller RC .40 1.00
386 Kyle Peterson RC .15 .40
387 Tommy Peterman RC .15 .40
388 Onan Masaoka .10 .30
389 Jason Rakers RC .15 .40
390 Rafael Medina .10 .30
391 Luis Lopez RC .15 .40
392 Jeff Yoder .10 .30
393 Vance Wilson RC .15 .40
394 F.Seguignol RC .15 .40
395 Ron Wright .10 .30
396 Ruben Mateo RC .15 .40
397 Steve Lomasney RC .25 .60
398 Damian Jackson .10 .30
399 Mike Jerzembeck RC .15 .40
400 Luis Rivas RC .40 1.00
401 Kevin Burford RC .15 .40
402 Glenn Davis .10 .30
403 Robert Luce RC .15 .40
404 Cole Liniak .10 .30
405 Matt LeCroy RC .25 .60
406 Jeremy Giambi RC .25 .60
407 Shawn Chacon .10 .30
408 Dewayne Wise RC .15 .40
409 Steve Woodard .10 .30
410 F.Cordero RC .40 1.00
411 Damon Minor RC .15 .40
412 Lou Collier .10 .30
413 Justin Towle .10 .30
414 Juan LeBron .10 .30
415 Michael Coleman .10 .30
416 Felix Rodriguez .10 .30
417 Paul Ah Yat RC .15 .40
418 Kevin Barker RC .15 .40
419 Brian Meadows .10 .30
420 Darnell McDonald RC .15 .40
421 Matt Kinney RC .15 .40
422 Mike Vavrek RC .15 .40
423 Courtney Duncan RC .15 .40
424 Kevin Millar RC .60 1.50
425 Ruben Rivera .10 .30
426 Steve Shoemaker RC .15 .40
427 Dan Reichert RC .15 .40
428 Carlos Lee RC 1.25 3.00
429 Rod Barajas .40 1.00
430 Pablo Ozuna RC .25 .60
431 Todd Belitz RC .15 .40
432 Sidney Ponson .10 .30
433 Steve Carver RC .15 .40
434 Esteban Yan RC .25 .60
435 Cedrick Bowers .10 .30
436 Marlon Anderson .10 .30
437 Carl Pavano .10 .30
438 Jae Weong Seo RC .25 .60
439 Jose Taveras RC .15 .40
440 Matt Anderson RC .15 .40
441 Darron Ingram RC .15 .40
CL1 Series 1 CL 1 .10 .30
CL2 Series 1 CL 2 .10 .30
CL3 Series 2 CL 1 .10 .30
CL4 Series 2 CL 2 .10 .30
NNO S.Hasegawa '91 BBM 4.00 10.00
NNO H.Irabu '91 BBM 4.00 10.00
NNO H.Nomo '91 BBM 10.00 25.00

1998 Bowman Golden Anniversary

Randomly inserted in first series packs at a rate of one in 237 and second series packs at a rate of one in 194, this 441-card set is a parallel to the Bowman base set. The set celebrates Bowman's 50th birthday. Each card is highlighted by gold-stamped facsimile autographs (instead of silver foil on the basic cards) and are sequentially numbered to 50.

*STARS: 12.5X TO 30X BASIC CARDS
*ROOKIES: 10X TO 20X BASIC CARDS
SER.1 STATED ODDS 1:237
SER.2 STATED ODDS 1:194
424 Kevin Millar 15.00 30.00

1998 Bowman International

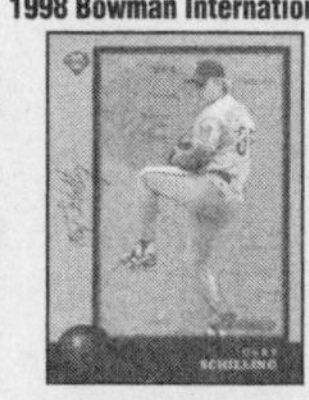

Inserted one per pack, this 441-card set is a parallel to the Bowman base set. The set allows collectors to see where their favorite players were born and learn the vitals on each of them as translated in the player's home language.

COMPLETE SET (441) 60.00 150.00
COMP. SERIES 1 (221) 30.00 75.00
COMP. SERIES 2 (220) 30.00 75.00
*STARS: 1.25X TO 3X BASIC CARDS
*ROOKIES: .6X TO 1.5X BASIC CARDS

1998 Bowman 1999 ROY Favorites

Randomly inserted in second series packs at a rate of one in 12, this 10-card insert features color action photography on borderless, double-etched foil cards. The players featured on these cards were among the leading early candidates for the 1999 ROY award.

COMPLETE SET (10) 8.00 20.00
SER.2 STATED ODDS 1:12
ROY1 Adrian Beltre .50 1.25
ROY2 Troy Glaus 1.50 4.00
ROY3 Chad Hermansen .50 1.25
ROY4 Matt Clement .50 1.25
ROY5 Eric Chavez .50 1.25
ROY6 Kris Benson .50 1.25
ROY7 Richie Sexson .50 1.25
ROY8 Randy Wolf 1.00 2.50
ROY9 Ryan Minor .60 1.50
ROY10 Alex Gonzalez .50 1.25

1998 Bowman Certified Blue Autographs

Randomly inserted in first series packs at a rate of one in 149 and second series packs at a rate of one in 122.

SER.1 STATED ODDS 1:149
SER.2 STATED ODDS 1:122
*GOLD FOIL: 1.5X TO 4X BLUE AU'S
SER.1 GOLD FOIL STATED ODDS 1:2976
SER.2 GOLD FOIL STATED ODDS 1:2445
*SILVER FOIL: .75X TO 2X BLUE AU'S
SER.1 SILVER FOIL STATED ODDS 1:992
SER.2 SILVER FOIL STATED ODDS 1:815
1 Adrian Beltre 15.00 40.00
2 Brad Fullmer 4.00 10.00
3 Ricky Ledee 4.00 10.00
4 David Ortiz 15.00 40.00
5 Fernando Tatis 4.00 10.00
6 Kerry Wood 10.00 25.00
7 Mel Rosario 4.00 10.00
8 Cole Liniak 4.00 10.00
9 A.J. Hinch 4.00 10.00
10 Jhensy Sandoval 4.00 10.00
11 Jose Cruz Jr. 4.00 10.00
12 Richard Hidalgo 4.00 10.00
13 Geoff Jenkins 6.00 15.00
14 Carl Pavano 8.00 20.00
15 Richie Sexson 6.00 15.00
16 Tony Womack 4.00 10.00
17 Scott Rolen 10.00 25.00
18 Ryan Minor 4.00 10.00
19 Eli Marrero 4.00 10.00
20 Jason Marquis 6.00 15.00
21 Mike Lowell 6.00 15.00
22 Todd Helton 10.00 25.00
23 Chad Green 4.00 10.00
24 Scott Elarton 4.00 10.00
25 Russell Branyan 4.00 10.00
26 Mike Drumright 4.00 10.00
27 Ben Grieve 4.00 10.00
28 Jacque Jones 6.00 15.00
29 Jared Sandberg 4.00 10.00
30 Grant Roberts 4.00 10.00
31 Mike Stoner 4.00 10.00
32 Brian Rose 4.00 10.00
33 Randy Winn 4.00 10.00
34 Justin Towle 4.00 10.00
35 Anthony Sanders 4.00 10.00
36 Rafael Medina 4.00 10.00
37 Corey Lee 4.00 10.00
38 Mike Kinkade 4.00 10.00
39 Norm Hutchins 4.00 10.00
40 Jason Brester 4.00 10.00
41 Ben Davis 4.00 10.00
42 Nomar Garciaparra 20.00 50.00
43 Jeff Liefer 4.00 10.00
44 Eric Milton 4.00 10.00
45 Preston Wilson 6.00 15.00
46 Miguel Tejada 15.00 40.00
47 Luis Ordaz 4.00 10.00
48 Travis Lee 4.00 10.00
49 Kris Benson 6.00 15.00
50 Jacob Cruz 4.00 10.00
51 Dermal Brown 4.00 10.00
52 Marc Kroon 4.00 10.00
53 Chad Hermansen 4.00 10.00
54 Roy Halladay 150.00 300.00
55 Eric Chavez 10.00 25.00
56 Jason Conti 4.00 10.00
57 Juan Encarnacion 6.00 15.00
58 Paul Wilder 4.00 10.00
59 Aramis Ramirez 10.00 25.00
60 Cliff Politte 4.00 10.00
61 Todd Dunwoody 4.00 10.00
62 Paul Konerko 10.00 25.00
63 Shane Monahan 4.00 10.00
64 Alex Sanchez 4.00 10.00
65 Jeff Abbott 4.00 10.00
66 John Patterson 6.00 15.00
67 Peter Munro 4.00 10.00
68 Jarrod Washburn 4.00 10.00
69 Derrek Lee 10.00 25.00
70 Ramon Hernandez 4.00 10.00

1998 Bowman Minor League MVP's

Randomly inserted in second series packs at a rate of one in 12, this 11-card insert features former Minor League MVP award winners in color action photography.

COMPLETE SET (11) 10.00 25.00
SER.2 STATED ODDS 1:12
MVP1 Jeff Bagwell .60 1.50
MVP2 Andres Galarraga .40 1.00
MVP3 Juan Gonzalez .40 1.00
MVP4 Tony Gwynn 1.25 3.00
MVP5 Vladimir Guerrero 1.00 2.50
MVP6 Derek Jeter 2.50 6.00
MVP7 Andruw Jones .60 1.50
MVP8 Tino Martinez .60 1.50
MVP9 Manny Ramirez .60 1.50
MVP10 Gary Sheffield .40 1.00
MVP11 Jim Thome .60 1.50

1998 Bowman Scout's Choice

Randomly inserted in first series packs at a rate of one in 12, this borderless 21-card set is an insert featuring leading minor league prospects.

COMPLETE SET (21) 10.00 25.00
SER.1 STATED ODDS 1:12
SC1 Paul Konerko .75 2.00
SC2 Richard Hidalgo .75 2.00
SC3 Mark Kotsay .75 2.00
SC4 Ben Grieve .75 2.00
SC5 Chad Hermansen .75 2.00
SC6 Matt Clement .75 2.00
SC7 Brad Fullmer .75 2.00
SC8 Eli Marrero .75 2.00
SC9 Kerry Wood 1.00 2.50
SC10 Adrian Beltre .75 2.00
SC11 Ricky Ledee .75 2.00
SC12 Travis Lee .75 2.00
SC13 Abraham Nunez .75 2.00
SC14 Brian Rose .75 2.00
SC15 Dermal Brown .75 2.00
SC16 Juan Encarnacion .75 2.00
SC17 Aramis Ramirez .75 2.00
SC18 Todd Helton 1.25 3.00
SC19 Kris Benson .75 2.00
SC20 Russell Branyan .75 2.00
SC21 Mike Stoner 1.00 2.50

1999 Bowman

The 1999 Bowman set was issued in two series and was distributed in 10 card packs with a suggested retail price of $3.00. The 440-card set featured the newest faces and potential talent that would carry Major League Baseball into the next millennium. This set features 300 top prospects and and 140 veterans. Prospect cards are designated with a silver and blue design while the veteran cards are shown with a silver and red design. Prospects making their debut on a Bowman card each featured a "Bowman Rookie Card" stamp on front. Notable Rookie Cards include Pat Burrell, Sean Burroughs, Carl Crawford, Adam Dunn, Rafael Furcal, Tim Hudson, Nick Johnson, Austin Kearns, Corey Patterson, Wily Mo Pena, Adam Piatt and Alfonso Soriano.

COMPLETE SET (440) 30.00 80.00
COMP. SERIES 1 (220) 12.50 30.00
COMP. SERIES 2 (220) 20.00 50.00
1 Ben Grieve .10 .30
2 Kerry Wood .10 .30
3 Ruben Rivera .10 .30
4 Sandy Alomar Jr. .10 .30
5 Cal Ripken 1.00 2.50
6 Mark McGwire .75 2.00
7 Vladimir Guerrero .30 .75
8 Moises Alou .10 .30
9 Jim Edmonds .10 .30
10 Greg Maddux .50 1.25
11 Gary Sheffield .10 .30
12 John Valentin .10 .30
13 Chuck Knoblauch .10 .30
14 Tony Clark .10 .30
15 Rusty Greer .10 .30
16 Al Leiter .10 .30
17 Travis Lee .10 .30
18 Jose Cruz Jr. .10 .30
19 Pedro Martinez .10 .50
20 Paul O'Neill .20 .50
21 Todd Walker .10 .30
22 Vinny Castilla .10 .30
23 Barry Larkin .20 .50
24 Curt Schilling .10 .30
25 Jason Kendall .10 .30
26 Scott Erickson .10 .30
27 Andres Galarraga .10 .30
28 Jeff Shaw .10 .30
29 John Olerud .10 .30
30 Orlando Hernandez .10 .30
31 Larry Walker .10 .30
32 Andruw Jones .20 .50
33 Jeff Cirillo .10 .30
34 Barry Bonds .75 2.00
35 Manny Ramirez .20 .50
36 Mark Kotsay .10 .30
37 Ivan Rodriguez .20 .50
38 Jeff King .10 .30
39 Brian Hunter .10 .30
40 Ray Durham .10 .30
41 Bernie Williams .20 .50
42 Darin Erstad .10 .30
43 Chipper Jones .30 .75
44 Pat Hentgen .10 .30
45 Eric Young .10 .30
46 Jaret Wright .10 .30
47 Juan Guzman .10 .30
48 Jorge Posada .20 .50
49 Bobby Higginson .10 .30
50 Jose Guillen .10 .30
51 Trevor Hoffman .10 .30
52 Ken Griffey Jr. .50 1.25
53 David Justice .10 .30
54 Matt Williams .10 .30
55 Eric Karros .10 .30
56 Derek Bell .10 .30
57 Ray Lankford .10 .30
58 Mariano Rivera .30 .75
59 Brett Tomko .10 .30
60 Mike Mussina .20 .50
61 Kenny Lofton .10 .30
62 Chuck Finley .10 .30
63 Alex Gonzalez .10 .30
64 Mark Grace .20 .50
65 Raul Mondesi .10 .30
66 David Cone .10 .30
67 Brad Fullmer .10 .30
68 Andy Benes .10 .30
69 John Smoltz .20 .50
70 Shane Reynolds .10 .30
71 Bruce Chen .10 .30
72 Adam Kennedy .10 .30
73 Jack Cust .10 .30
74 Matt Clement .10 .30
75 Derrick Gibson .10 .30
76 Darnell McDonald .10 .30
77 Adam Everett RC .40 1.00
78 Ricardo Aramboles .10 .30
79 Mark Quinn RC .15 .40
80 Jason Rakers .10 .30
81 Seth Etherton RC .15 .40
82 Jeff Urban RC .25 .60
83 Manny Aybar .10 .30
84 Mike Nannini RC .15 .40
85 Onan Masaoka .10 .30
86 Rod Barajas .10 .30
87 Mike Frank .10 .30
88 Scott Randall .10 .30
89 Justin Bowles RC .15 .40
90 Chris Haas .10 .30
91 Arturo McDowell RC .15 .40
92 Matt Belisle RC .15 .40
93 Scott Elarton .10 .30
94 Vernon Wells .10 .30
95 Pat Cline .10 .30
96 Ryan Anderson .10 .30
97 Kevin Barker .10 .30
98 Ruben Mateo .10 .30
99 Robert Fick .10 .30
100 Corey Koskie .10 .30
101 Ricky Ledee .10 .30
102 Rick Elder RC .15 .40
103 Jack Cressend RC .15 .40
104 Joe Lawrence .10 .30
105 Mike Lincoln .10 .30
106 Kit Pellow RC .15 .40
107 Matt Burch RC .25 .60
108 Cole Liniak .10 .30
109 Jason Dewey .10 .30
110 Cesar King .10 .30
111 Julio Ramirez .10 .30
112 Jake Westbrook .10 .30
113 Eric Valent RC .25 .60
114 Roosevelt Brown RC .15 .40
115 Choo Freeman RC .25 .60
116 Juan Melo .10 .30
117 Jason Grilli .10 .30
118 Jared Sandberg .10 .30
119 Glenn Davis .10 .30
120 David Riske RC .15 .40
121 Jacque Jones .10 .30
122 Corey Lee .10 .30
123 Michael Barrett .10 .30
124 Lariel Gonzalez .10 .30
125 Mitch Meluskey .10 .30
126 Freddy Adrian Garcia .10 .30
127 Tony Torcato RC .15 .40
128 Jeff Liefer .10 .30
129 Ntema Ndungidi .10 .30
130 Andy Brown RC .15 .40
131 Ryan Mills RC .15 .40
132 Andy Abad RC .15 .40

133 Carlos Febles .10 .30
134 Jason Tyner RC .15 .40
135 Mark Osborne .10 .30
136 Phil Norton RC .15 .40
137 Nathan Haynes .15 .40
138 Roy Halladay .30 .75
139 Juan Encarnacion .10 .30
140 Brad Penny .10 .30
141 Grant Roberts .10 .30
142 Aramis Ramirez .10 .30
143 Cristian Guzman .10 .30
144 Mamon Tucker RC .15 .40
145 Ryan Bradley .10 .30
146 Brian Simmons .10 .30
147 Dan Reichert .10 .30
148 Russ Branyan .10 .30
149 Victor Valencia RC .20 .50
150 Scott Schoeneweis .10 .30
151 Sean Spencer RC .15 .40
152 Odalis Perez .10 .30
153 Joe Fontenot .10 .30
154 Milton Bradley .10 .30
155 Josh McKinley RC .15 .40
156 Terrence Long .10 .30
157 Danny Klassen .10 .30
158 Paul Hoover RC .25 .60
159 Ron Belliard .10 .30
160 Armando Rios .10 .30
161 Ramon Hernandez .10 .30
162 Jason Conti .10 .30
163 Chad Hermansen .10 .30
164 Jason Standridge .10 .30
165 Jason Dellaero .10 .30
166 John Curtice .10 .30
167 Clayton Andrews RC .15 .40
168 Jeremy Giambi .10 .30
169 Alex Ramirez .10 .30
170 Gabe Molina RC .15 .40
171 M.Encarnacion RC .15 .40
172 Mike Zywica RC .15 .40
173 Chip Ambres RC .15 .40
174 Trot Nixon .10 .30
175 Pat Burrell RC 1.25 3.00
176 Jeff Yoder .10 .30
177 Chris Jones RC .15 .40
178 Kevin Witt .10 .30
179 Keith Luuloa RC .15 .40
180 Billy Koch .10 .30
181 Damaso Marte RC .15 .40
182 Ryan Glynn RC .15 .40
183 Calvin Pickering .10 .30
184 Michael Cuddyer .10 .30
185 Nick Johnson RC .75 2.00
186 D.Mientkiewicz RC .40 1.00
187 Nate Cornejo RC .15 .40
188 Octavio Dotel .10 .30
189 Wes Helms .10 .30
190 Nelson Lara .10 .30
191 Chuck Abbott RC .15 .40
192 Tony Armas Jr. .10 .30
193 Gil Meche .10 .30
194 Ben Petrick .10 .30
195 Chris George RC .15 .40
196 Scott Hunter RC .15 .40
197 Ryan Brannan .10 .30
198 Amaury Garcia RC .25 .60
199 Chris Gissell .10 .30
200 Austin Kearns RC 1.25 3.00
201 Alex Gonzalez .10 .30
202 Wade Miller .10 .30
203 Scott Williamson .10 .30
204 Chris Enochs .10 .30
205 Fernando Seguignol .10 .30
206 Marlon Anderson .10 .30
207 Todd Sears RC .15 .40
208 Nate Bump RC .15 .40
209 J.M. Gold RC .15 .40
210 Matt LeCroy .10 .30
211 Alex Hernandez .10 .30
212 Luis Rivera .10 .30
213 Troy Cameron .10 .30
214 Alex Escobar RC .25 .60
215 Jason LaRue .10 .30
216 Kyle Peterson .10 .30
217 Brent Butler .10 .30
218 Dernell Stenson .10 .30
219 Adrian Beltre .10 .30
220 Daryle Ward .10 .30
221 Jim Thome .20 .50
222 Cliff Floyd .10 .30
223 Rickey Henderson .30 .75
224 Garret Anderson .10 .30
225 Ken Caminiti .10 .30
226 Bret Boone .10 .30
227 Jeromy Burnitz .10 .30
228 Steve Finley .10 .30
229 Miguel Tejada .10 .30
230 Greg Vaughn .10 .30
231 Jose Offerman .10 .30
232 Andy Ashby .10 .30
233 Albert Belle .10 .30
234 Fernando Tatis .10 .30
235 Todd Helton .20 .50
236 Sean Casey .10 .30
237 Brian Giles .10 .30
238 Andy Pettitte .20 .50
239 Fred McGriff .20 .50
240 Roberto Alomar .20 .50
241 Edgar Martinez .20 .50
242 Lee Stevens .10 .30
243 Shawn Green .10 .30
244 Ryan Klesko .10 .30
245 Sammy Sosa .30 .75
246 Todd Hundley .10 .30
247 Shannon Stewart .10 .30
248 Randy Johnson .30 .75
249 Rondell White .10 .30
250 Mike Piazza .50 1.25
251 Craig Biggio .20 .50
252 David Wells .10 .30
253 Brian Jordan .10 .30
254 Edgar Renteria .10 .30
255 Bartolo Colon .10 .30
256 Frank Thomas .30 .75
257 Will Clark .20 .50
258 Dean Palmer .10 .30
259 Dmitri Young .10 .30
260 Scott Rolen .20 .50
261 Jeff Kent .10 .30
262 Dante Bichette .10 .30
263 Nomar Garciaparra .50 1.25
264 Tony Gwynn .40 1.00
265 Alex Rodriguez .50 1.25
266 Jose Canseco .20 .50
267 Jason Giambi .10 .30
268 Jeff Bagwell .20 .50
269 Carlos Delgado .10 .30
270 Tom Glavine .20 .50
271 Eric Davis .10 .30
272 Edgardo Alfonzo .10 .30
273 Tim Salmon .20 .50
274 Johnny Damon .20 .50
275 Rafael Palmeiro .20 .50
276 Denny Neagle .10 .30
277 Neifi Perez .10 .30
278 Roger Clemens .60 1.50
279 Brant Brown .10 .30
280 Kevin Brown .20 .50
281 Jay Bell .10 .30
282 Jay Buhner .10 .30
283 Matt Lawton .10 .30
284 Robin Ventura .10 .30
285 Juan Gonzalez .10 .30
286 Mo Vaughn .10 .30
287 Kevin Millwood .10 .30
288 Tino Martinez .20 .50
289 Justin Thompson .10 .30
290 Derek Jeter .75 2.00
291 Ben Davis .10 .30
292 Mike Lowell .10 .30
293 Calvin Murray .10 .30
294 Micah Bowie RC .15 .40
295 Lance Berkman .10 .30
296 Jason Marquis .10 .30
297 Chad Green .10 .30
298 Dee Brown .10 .30
299 Jerry Hairston Jr. .10 .30
300 Gabe Kapler .10 .30
301 Brent Stentz RC .25 .60
302 Scott Mullen RC .15 .40
303 Brandon Reed .10 .30
304 Shea Hillenbrand RC .60 1.50
305 J.D. Closser RC .25 .60
306 Gary Matthews Jr. .10 .30
307 Toby Hall RC .25 .60
308 Jason Phillips RC .15 .40
309 Jose Macias RC .15 .40
310 Jung Bong RC .15 .40
311 Ramon Soler RC .15 .40
312 Kelly Dransfeldt RC .15 .40
313 Carl. E. Hernandez RC .25 .60
314 Kevin Haverbusch .10 .30
315 Aaron Myette RC .15 .40
316 Chad Harville RC .15 .40
317 Kyle Farnsworth RC .25 .60
318 Gookie Dawkins RC .25 .60
319 Willie Martinez .10 .30
320 Carlos Lee .10 .30
321 Carlos Pena RC .30 .75
322 Peter Bergeron RC .15 .40
323 A.J. Burnett RC .60 1.50
324 Bucky Jacobsen RC .25 .60
325 Mo Bruce RC .15 .40
326 Reggie Taylor .10 .30
327 Jackie Rexrode .10 .30
328 Alvin Morrow RC .15 .40
329 Carlos Beltran .20 .50
330 Eric Chavez .10 .30
331 John Patterson .10 .30
332 Jayson Werth .10 .30
333 Richie Sexson .10 .30
334 Randy Wolf .10 .30
335 Eli Marrero .10 .30
336 Paul LoDuca .10 .30
337 J.D Smart .10 .30
338 Ryan Minor .10 .30
339 Kris Benson .10 .30
340 George Lombard .10 .30
341 Troy Glaus .20 .50
342 Eddie Yarnall .10 .30
343 Kip Wells RC .25 .60
344 C.C. Sabathia RC 1.25 3.00
345 Sean Burroughs RC .40 1.00
346 Felipe Lopez RC 1.00 2.50
347 Ryan Rupe RC .15 .40
348 Orber Moreno RC .15 .40
349 Rafael Roque RC .15 .40
350 Alfonso Soriano RC 2.50 6.00
351 Pablo Ozuna .10 .30
352 Corey Patterson RC .60 1.50
353 Braden Looper .10 .30
354 Robbie Bell .10 .30
355 Mark Mulder RC 1.00 2.50
356 Angel Pena .10 .30
357 Kevin McGlinchy .10 .30
358 M.Restovich RC .25 .60
359 Eric DuBose .10 .30
360 Geoff Jenkins .10 .30
361 Mark Harriger RC .15 .40
362 Junior Herndon RC .15 .40
363 Tim Raines Jr. RC .15 .40
364 Rafael Furcal RC 1.00 2.50
365 Marcus Giles RC .60 1.50
366 Ted Lilly .10 .30
367 Jorge Toca RC .25 .60
368 David Kelton RC .15 .40
369 Adam Dunn RC 2.00 5.00
370 Guillermo Mota RC .15 .40
371 Brett Laxton RC .15 .40
372 Travis Harper RC .25 .60
373 Tom Davey RC .15 .40
374 Darren Blakely RC .15 .40
375 Tim Hudson RC 1.50 4.00
376 Jason Romano .10 .30
377 Dan Reichert .10 .30
378 Julio Lugo RC .40 1.00
379 Jose Garcia RC .15 .40
380 Erubiel Durazo RC .25 .60
381 Jose Jimenez .10 .30
382 Chris Fussell .10 .30
383 Steve Lomasney .10 .30
384 Juan Pena RC .25 .60
385 Allen Levrault RC .15 .40
386 Juan Rivera RC .60 1.50
387 Steve Colyer RC .15 .40
388 Joe Nathan RC .75 2.00
389 Ron Walker RC .15 .40
390 Nick Bierbrodt .10 .30
391 Luke Prokopec RC .15 .40
392 Dave Roberts RC .40 1.00
393 Mike Darr .10 .30
394 Abraham Nunez RC .25 .60
395 G.Chiaramonte RC .15 .40
396 J.Van Buren RC .15 .40
397 Mike Kusiewicz .10 .30
398 Matt Wise RC .15 .40
399 Joe McEwing RC .25 .60
400 Matt Holliday RC 2.50 6.00
401 Willi Mo Pena RC 2.00 5.00
402 Ruben Quevedo RC .15 .40
403 Rob Ryan RC .15 .40
404 Freddy Garcia RC .60 1.50
405 Kevin Eberwein RC .15 .40
406 Jesus Colome RC .15 .40
407 Chris Singleton .10 .30
408 Bubba Crosby RC .40 1.00
409 Jesus Cordero RC .15 .40
410 Donny Leon .10 .30
411 G.Tomlinson RC .25 .60
412 Jeff Winchester RC .15 .40
413 Adam Piatt RC .15 .40
414 Robert Stratton .10 .30
415 T.J. Tucker .10 .30
416 Ryan Langerhans RC .40 1.00
417 A.Shumaker RC .15 .40
418 Matt Miller RC .15 .40
419 Doug Clark RC .15 .40
420 Kory DeHaan RC .15 .40
421 David Eckstein RC 1.25 3.00
422 Brian Cooper RC .15 .40
423 Brady Clark RC .60 1.50
424 Chris Magruder RC .25 .60
425 Bobby Seay RC .15 .40
426 Aubrey Huff RC .75 2.00
427 Mike Jerzembeck .10 .30
428 Matt Blank RC .25 .60
429 Benny Agbayani RC .25 .60
430 Kevin Beirne RC .15 .40
431 Josh Hamilton RC 4.00 10.00
432 Josh Girdley RC .15 .40
433 Kyle Snyder RC .15 .40
434 Mike Paradis RC .15 .40
435 Jason Jennings RC .40 1.00
436 David Walling RC .15 .40
437 Omar Ortiz RC .25 .60
438 Jay Gehrke RC .25 .60
439 Casey Burns RC .25 .60
440 Carl Crawford RC 2.00 5.00

1999 Bowman Gold

Randomly inserted in first series packs at a rate of one in 111 and second series packs at a rate of one in 59, this 440-card set is a parallel to the Bowman base set. The set features facsimile autographs printed in gold foil with gold border designs. Each card is serial numbered to 99 on the back.

*STARS: 10X TO 25X BASIC CARDS
*ROOKIES: 4X TO 10X BASIC CARDS
SER.1 STATED ODDS 1:111
SER.2 STATED ODDS 1:59
431 Josh Hamilton 40.00 80.00

1999 Bowman International

Inserted one per pack, this 440-card set is a parallel to the Bowman base set. Card fronts contain each player's nationality with a background photograph of a landmark native to his homeland. Card backs contain vital information which are translated into the player's home language giving the collector insight into the player's background. Card fronts are printed on a distinctive foil board.

COMPLETE SET (440) 100.00 200.00
COMP.SERIES 1 (220) 40.00 80.00
COMP.SERIES 2 (220) 60.00 120.00
*STARS: 1X TO 2.5X BASIC CARDS
*ROOKIES: .6X TO 1.5X BASIC CARDS

1999 Bowman Autographs

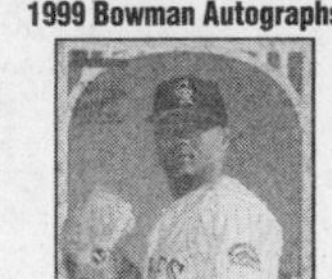

This set contains a selection of top young prospects, all of whom participated by signing their cards in blue ink. Card rarity is differentiated by either a blue, silver or gold foil Topps Certified Autograph Issue Stamp. The insert rates for Blue are at a rate of one in 162, Silver one in 485 and Gold one in 1,194.

BLUE FOIL SER.1 ODDS 1:162
BLUE FOIL SER.2 ODDS 1:85
SILVER FOIL SER.1 ODDS 1:485
SILVER FOIL SER.2 ODDS 1:256
GOLD FOIL SER.1 ODDS 1:1941
GOLD FOIL SER.2 ODDS 1:1024
BA1 Ruben Mateo B 4.00 10.00
BA2 Troy Glaus G 6.00 15.00
BA3 Ben Davis G 6.00 15.00
BA4 Jayson Werth B 12.50 30.00
BA5 Jerry Hairston Jr. S 4.00 10.00
BA6 Darnell McDonald B 4.00 10.00
BA7 Calvin Pickering S 6.00 15.00
BA8 Ryan Minor S 6.00 15.00
BA9 Alex Escobar B 4.00 10.00
BA10 Grant Roberts B 4.00 10.00
BA11 Carlos Guillen B 6.00 15.00
BA12 Ryan Anderson S 6.00 15.00
BA13 Gil Meche S 6.00 15.00
BA14 Russell Branyan S 6.00 15.00
BA15 Alex Ramirez S 6.00 15.00
BA16 Jason Rakers S 6.00 15.00
BA17 Eddie Yarnall B 4.00 10.00
BA18 Freddy Garcia B 4.00 10.00
BA19 Jason Conti B 4.00 10.00
BA20 Corey Koskie B 6.00 15.00
BA21 Roosevelt Brown B 4.00 10.00
BA22 Willie Martinez B 4.00 10.00
BA23 Mike Jerzembeck B 4.00 10.00
BA24 Lariel Gonzalez B 4.00 10.00
BA25 F.Seguignol B 6.00 15.00
BA26 Robert Fick S 6.00 15.00
BA27 J.D. Smart B 4.00 10.00
BA28 Ryan Mills B 4.00 10.00
BA29 Chad Hermansen G 6.00 15.00
BA30 Jason Grilli B 4.00 10.00
BA31 Michael Cuddyer B 8.00 20.00
BA32 Jacque Jones S 10.00 25.00
BA33 Reggie Taylor B 4.00 10.00
BA34 Richie Sexson G 10.00 25.00
BA35 Michael Barrett B 4.00 10.00
BA36 Paul LoDuca B 6.00 15.00
BA37 Adrian Beltre G 12.50 30.00
BA38 Peter Bergeron B 4.00 10.00
BA39 Joe Fontenot B 4.00 10.00
BA40 Randy Wolf B 6.00 15.00
BA41 Nick Johnson B 6.00 15.00
BA42 Ryan Bradley B 4.00 10.00
BA43 Mike Lowell S 4.00 10.00
BA44 Ricky Ledee G 4.00 10.00
BA45 Mike Lincoln S 6.00 15.00
BA46 Jeremy Giambi B 4.00 10.00
BA47 Dermal Brown S 6.00 15.00
BA48 Derrick Gibson B 4.00 10.00
BA49 Scott Randall B 4.00 10.00
BA50 Ben Petrick S 6.00 15.00
BA51 Jason LaRue B 6.00 15.00
BA52 Cole Liniak B 4.00 10.00
BA53 John Curtice B 4.00 10.00
BA54 Jackie Rexrode B 4.00 10.00
BA55 John Patterson B 6.00 15.00
BA56 Brad Penny S 10.00 25.00
BA57 Jared Sandberg B 6.00 15.00
BA58 Kerry Wood G 10.00 25.00
BA59 Eli Marrero S 6.00 15.00
BA60 Jason Marquis B 6.00 15.00
BA61 George Lombard S 6.00 15.00
BA62 Bruce Chen S 6.00 15.00
BA63 Kevin Witt S 6.00 15.00
BA64 Vernon Wells B 8.00 20.00
BA65 Billy Koch B 6.00 15.00
BA66 Roy Halladay G 60.00 120.00
BA67 Nathan Haynes B 4.00 10.00
BA68 Ben Grieve G 4.00 10.00
BA69 Eric Chavez G 4.00 10.00
BA70 Lance Berkman S 15.00 40.00

1999 Bowman 2000 ROY Favorites

Randomly inserted in second series packs at a rate of one in twelve, this 10-card insert set features borderless, double-etched foil cards and feature players that had serious potential to win the 2000 Rookie of the Year award.

COMPLETE SET (10) 5.00 10.00
SER.2 STATED ODDS 1:12
ROY1 Ryan Anderson .20 .50
ROY2 Pat Burrell .75 2.00
ROY3 A.J. Burnett .40 1.00
ROY4 Ruben Mateo .20 .50
ROY5 Alex Escobar .20 .50
ROY6 Pablo Ozuna .20 .50
ROY7 Mark Mulder .60 1.50
ROY8 Corey Patterson .40 1.00
ROY9 George Lombard .20 .50
ROY10 Nick Johnson .40 1.00

1999 Bowman Early Risers

Randomly inserted in second series packs at a rate of one in twelve, this 11-card insert set features current superstars who have already won a ROY award and who continue to prove their worth on the diamond.

COMPLETE SET (11) 10.00 25.00
SER.2 STATED ODDS 1:12
ER1 Mike Piazza 1.00 2.50
ER2 Cal Ripken 2.00 5.00
ER3 Jeff Bagwell .40 1.00
ER4 Ben Grieve .25 .60
ER5 Kerry Wood .25 .60
ER6 Mark McGwire 1.50 4.00
ER7 Nomar Garciaparra 1.00 2.50
ER8 Derek Jeter 1.50 4.00
ER9 Scott Rolen .40 1.00
ER10 Jose Canseco .40 1.00
ER11 Raul Mondesi .25 .60

1999 Bowman Late Bloomers

Randomly inserted in first series packs at a rate of one in twelve, this 10-card insert set features late round picks from previous drafts. Players featured include Mike Piazza and Jim Thome.

COMPLETE SET (10) 4.00 8.00
SER.1 STATED ODDS 1:12
LB1 Mike Piazza 1.00 2.50
LB2 Jim Thome .40 1.00
LB3 Larry Walker .25 .60
LB4 Vinny Castilla .25 .60
LB5 Andy Pettitte .40 1.00
LB6 Jim Edmonds .25 .60
LB7 Kenny Lofton .25 .60
LB8 John Smoltz .40 1.00
LB9 Mark Grace .40 1.00
LB10 Trevor Hoffman .25 .60

1999 Bowman Scout's Choice

Randomly inserted in first series packs at a rate of one in twelve, this 21-card insert set features a selection of gifted prospects.

COMPLETE SET (21) 10.00 20.00
SER.1 STATED ODDS 1:12
SC1 Ruben Mateo .40 1.00
SC2 Ryan Anderson .40 1.00
SC3 Pat Burrell 1.00 2.50
SC4 Troy Glaus .60 1.50
SC5 Eric Chavez .40 1.00
SC6 Adrian Beltre .40 1.00
SC7 Bruce Chen .40 1.00
SC8 Carlos Beltran .60 1.50
SC9 Alex Gonzalez .40 1.00
SC10 Carlos Lee .40 1.00
SC11 George Lombard .40 1.00
SC12 Matt Clement .40 1.00
SC13 Calvin Pickering .40 1.00
SC14 Marlon Anderson .40 1.00
SC15 Chad Hermansen .40 1.00
SC16 Russell Branyan .40 1.00
SC17 Jeremy Giambi .40 1.00
SC18 Ricky Ledee .40 1.00
SC19 John Patterson .40 1.00
SC20 Roy Halladay 1.00 2.50
SC21 Michael Barrett .40 1.00

2000 Bowman

The 2000 Bowman product was released in May, 2000 as a 440-card set. The set features 140 veteran players and 300 rookies and prospects. Each pack contained 10 cards and carried a suggested retail price of $3.00. Rookie Cards include Rick Asadoorian, Bobby Bradley, Kevin Mench, Nick Neugebauer, Ben Sheets and Barry Zito.

COMPLETE SET (440) 25.00 60.00
1 Vladimir Guerrero .30 .75
2 Chipper Jones .30 .75
3 Todd Walker .10 .30
4 Barry Larkin .20 .50
5 Bernie Williams .20 .50
6 Todd Helton .20 .50
7 Jermaine Dye .10 .30
8 Brian Giles .10 .30
9 Freddy Garcia .10 .30
10 Greg Vaughn .10 .30
11 Alex Gonzalez .10 .30
12 Luis Gonzalez .10 .30
13 Ron Belliard .10 .30
14 Ben Grieve .10 .30
15 Carlos Delgado .10 .30
16 Brian Jordan .10 .30
17 Fernando Tatis .10 .30
18 Ryan Rupe .10 .30
19 Miguel Tejada .10 .30
20 Mark Grace .20 .50
21 Kenny Lofton .10 .30
22 Eric Karros .10 .30
23 Cliff Floyd .10 .30
24 John Halama .10 .30
25 Cristian Guzman .10 .30
26 Scott Williamson .10 .30
27 Mike Lieberthal .10 .30
28 Tim Hudson .10 .30
29 Warren Morris .10 .30
30 Pedro Martinez .20 .50
31 John Smoltz .20 .50
32 Ray Durham .10 .30
33 Chad Allen .10 .30
34 Tony Clark .10 .30
35 Tino Martinez .20 .50
36 J.T. Snow .10 .30
37 Kevin Brown .10 .30
38 Bartolo Colon .10 .30
39 Rey Ordonez .10 .30
40 Jeff Bagwell .20 .50
41 Ivan Rodriguez .20 .50
42 Eric Chavez .10 .30
43 Eric Milton .10 .30
44 Jose Canseco .20 .50
45 Shawn Green .10 .30
46 Rich Aurilia .10 .30
47 Roberto Alomar .20 .50
48 Brian Daubach .10 .30
49 Magglio Ordonez .10 .30
50 Derek Jeter .75 2.00
51 Kris Benson .10 .30
52 Albert Belle .10 .30
53 Rondell White .10 .30
54 Justin Thompson .10 .30
55 Nomar Garciaparra .50 1.25
56 Chuck Finley .10 .30
57 Omar Vizquel .20 .50
58 Luis Castillo .10 .30
59 Richard Hidalgo .10 .30
60 Barry Bonds .75 2.00
61 Craig Biggio .20 .50
62 Doug Glanville .10 .30
63 Gabe Kapler .10 .30
64 Johnny Damon .20 .50
65 Pokey Reese .10 .30
66 Andy Pettitte .20 .50
67 B.J. Surhoff .10 .30
68 Richie Sexson .10 .30
69 Javy Lopez .10 .30
70 Raul Mondesi .10 .30
71 Darin Erstad .10 .30
72 Kevin Millwood .10 .30
73 Ricky Ledee .10 .30
74 John Olerud .10 .30
75 Sean Casey .10 .30
76 Carlos Febles .10 .30
77 Paul O'Neill .20 .50
78 Bob Abreu .10 .30
79 Neifi Perez .10 .30
80 Tony Gwynn .40 1.00
81 Russ Ortiz .10 .30
82 Matt Williams .10 .30
83 Chris Carpenter .10 .30
84 Roger Cedeno .10 .30
85 Tim Salmon .20 .50
86 Billy Koch .10 .30
87 Jeromy Burnitz .10 .30
88 Edgardo Alfonzo .10 .30
89 Jay Bell .10 .30
90 Manny Ramirez .20 .50
91 Frank Thomas .30 .75
92 Mike Mussina .20 .50
93 J.D. Drew .10 .30
94 Adrian Beltre .10 .30
95 Alex Rodriguez .50 1.25
96 Larry Walker .10 .30
97 Juan Encarnacion .10 .30
98 Mike Sweeney .10 .30
99 Rusty Greer .10 .30
100 Randy Johnson .30 .75
101 Jose Vidro .10 .30
102 Preston Wilson .10 .30
103 Greg Maddux .50 1.25
104 Jason Giambi .10 .30
105 Cal Ripken 1.00 2.50
106 Carlos Beltran .10 .30
107 Vinny Castilla .10 .30
108 Mariano Rivera .30 .75
109 Mo Vaughn .10 .30
110 Rafael Palmeiro .20 .50
111 Shannon Stewart .10 .30
112 Mike Hampton .10 .30
113 Joe Nathan .10 .30
114 Ben Davis .10 .30
115 Andruw Jones .20 .50
116 Robin Ventura .10 .30
117 Damion Easley .10 .30
118 Jeff Cirillo .10 .30
119 Kerry Wood .10 .30
120 Scott Rolen .20 .50
121 Sammy Sosa .30 .75
122 Ken Griffey Jr. .50 1.25
123 Shane Reynolds .10 .30
124 Troy Glaus .10 .30
125 Tom Glavine .20 .50
126 Michael Barrett .10 .30
127 Al Leiter .10 .30
128 Jason Kendall .10 .30
129 Roger Clemens .60 1.50
130 Juan Gonzalez .10 .30
131 Corey Koskie .10 .30
132 Curt Schilling .10 .30
133 Mike Piazza .50 1.25
134 Gary Sheffield .10 .30
135 Jim Thome .20 .50
136 Orlando Hernandez .10 .30
137 Ray Lankford .10 .30
138 Geoff Jenkins .10 .30
139 Jose Lima .10 .30
140 Mark McGwire .75 2.00
141 Adam Piatt .10 .30
142 Pat Manning RC .10 .30
143 Marcos Castillo RC .10 .30
144 Lesli Brea RC .10 .30
145 Humberto Cota RC .20 .50
146 Ben Petrick .10 .30
147 Kip Wells .10 .30
148 Willy Pena .10 .30
149 Chris Wakeland RC .10 .30
150 Brad Baker RC .10 .30
151 Robbie Morrison RC .10 .30
152 Reggie Taylor .10 .30
153 Matt Ginter RC .10 .30
154 Peter Bergeron .10 .30
155 Roosevelt Brown .10 .30
156 Matt Cepicky RC .10 .30
157 Ramon Castro .10 .30
158 Brad Baisley RC .10 .30
159 Jeff Goldbach RC .10 .30
160 Mitch Meluskey .10 .30
161 Chad Harville .10 .30
162 Brian Cooper .10 .30
163 Marcus Giles .10 .30
164 Jim Morris .30 .75
165 Geoff Goetz .10 .30
166 Bobby Bradley RC .10 .30
167 Rob Bell .10 .30
168 Joe Crede .60 1.50
169 Michael Restovich .10 .30
170 Quincy Foster RC .10 .30
171 Enrique Cruz RC .10 .30
172 Mark Quinn .10 .30
173 Nick Johnson .10 .30
174 Jeff Liefer .10 .30
175 Kevin Mench RC .75 2.00
176 Steve Lomasney .10 .30
177 Jayson Werth .10 .30
178 Tim Drew .10 .30
179 Chip Ambres .10 .30
180 Ryan Anderson .10 .30
181 Matt Blank .10 .30
182 G.Chiaramonte .10 .30
183 Corey Myers RC .10 .30
184 Jeff Yoder .10 .30
185 Craig Dingman RC .10 .30
186 Jon Hamilton RC .10 .30
187 Toby Hall .10 .30
188 Russell Branyan .10 .30
189 Brian Falkenborg RC .10 .30
190 Aaron Harang RC 1.00 2.50
191 Juan Pena .10 .30
192 Travis Thompson RC .10 .30
193 Alfonso Soriano .30 .75
194 Alejandro Diaz RC .10 .30
195 Carlos Pena .10 .30
196 Kevin Nicholson .10 .30
197 Mo Bruce .10 .30
198 C.C. Sabathia .10 .30
199 Carl Crawford .10 .30
200 Rafael Furcal .10 .30
201 Andrew Beinbrink RC .10 .30
202 Jimmy Osting .10 .30
203 Aaron McNeal RC .10 .30
204 Brett Laxton .10 .30
205 Chris George .10 .30
206 Felipe Lopez .10 .30
207 Ben Sheets RC 1.00 2.50
208 Mike Meyers RC .20 .50
209 Jason Conti .10 .30
210 Milton Bradley .10 .30
211 Chris Mears RC .10 .30
212 Carlos Hernandez RC .30 .75
213 Jason Romano .10 .30
214 Geofrey Tomlinson .10 .30
215 Jimmy Rollins .10 .30
216 Pablo Ozuna .10 .30
217 Steve Cox .10 .30
218 Terrence Long .10 .30
219 Jeff DaVanon RC .20 .50
220 Rick Ankiel .10 .30
221 Jason Standridge .10 .30
222 Tony Armas Jr. .10 .30
223 Jason Tyner .10 .30
224 Ramon Ortiz .10 .30
225 Daryle Ward .10 .30
226 Enger Veras RC .10 .30
227 Chris Jones .10 .30
228 Eric Cammack RC .10 .30
229 Ruben Mateo .10 .30
230 Ken Harvey RC .20 .50
231 Jake Westbrook .10 .30
232 Rob Purvis RC .10 .30
233 Choo Freeman .10 .30
234 Aramis Ramirez .10 .30
235 A.J. Burnett .10 .30
236 Kevin Barker .10 .30
237 Chance Caple RC .10 .30
238 Jarrod Washburn .10 .30
239 Lance Berkman .10 .30
240 Michael Wenner RC .10 .30
241 Alex Sanchez .10 .30
242 Pat Daneker .10 .30
243 Grant Roberts .10 .30
244 Mark Ellis RC .20 .50
245 Donny Leon .10 .30
246 David Eckstein .10 .30
247 Dicky Gonzalez RC .10 .30
248 John Patterson .10 .30
249 Chad Green .10 .30
250 Scot Shields RC .10 .30
251 Troy Cameron .10 .30
252 Jose Molina .10 .30
253 Rob Pugmire RC .10 .30
254 Rick Elder .10 .30
255 Sean Burroughs .10 .30
256 Josh Kalinowski RC .10 .30
257 Matt LeCroy .10 .30
258 Alex Graman RC .10 .30
259 Tomo Ohka RC .20 .50
260 Brady Clark .10 .30
261 Rico Washington RC .10 .30
262 Gary Matthews Jr. .10 .30
263 Matt Wise .10 .30
264 Keith Reed RC .10 .30
265 Santiago Ramirez RC .10 .30
266 Ben Broussard RC .50 1.25
267 Ryan Langerhans .10 .30
268 Juan Rivera .10 .30
269 Shawn Gallagher .10 .30
270 Jorge Toca .10 .30
271 Brad Lidge .20 .50
272 Leoncio Estrella RC .10 .30
273 Ruben Quevedo .10 .30
274 Jack Cust .10 .30
275 T.J. Tucker .10 .30
276 Mike Colangelo .10 .30
277 Brian Schneider .10 .30
278 Calvin Murray .10 .30
279 Josh Girdley .10 .30
280 Mike Paradis .10 .30
281 Chad Hermansen .10 .30
282 Ty Howington RC .10 .30
283 Aaron Myette .10 .30
284 D'Angelo Jimenez .10 .30
285 Dernell Stenson .10 .30
286 Jerry Hairston Jr. .10 .30
287 Gary Majewski RC .20 .50
288 Derrin Ebert .10 .30
289 Steve Fish RC .10 .30
290 Carlos E. Hernandez .10 .30
291 Allen Levrault .10 .30
292 Sean McNally RC .10 .30
293 Randey Dorame RC .10 .30
294 Wes Anderson RC .10 .30
295 B.J. Ryan .10 .30
296 Alan Webb RC .10 .30
297 Brandon Inge RC .75 2.00
298 David Walling .10 .30

299 Sun Woo Kim RC	.10	.30
300 Pat Burrell	.10	.30
301 Rick Guttormson RC	.10	.30
302 Gil Meche	.10	.30
303 Carlos Zambrano RC	2.00	5.00
304 Eric Byrnes UER RC	.20	.50
Bo Porter pictured		
305 Robb Quinlan RC	.20	.50
306 Jackie Rexrode	.10	.30
307 Nate Bump	.10	.30
308 Sean DePaula RC	.10	.30
309 Matt Riley	.10	.30
310 Ryan Minor	.10	.30
311 J.J. Davis	.10	.30
312 Randy Wolf	.10	.30
313 Jason Jennings	.10	.30
314 Scott Seabol RC	.10	.30
315 Doug Davis	.10	.30
316 Todd Moser RC	.10	.30
317 Rob Ryan	.10	.30
318 Bubba Crosby	.10	.30
319 Ryan Knox RC	.50	1.25
320 Mario Encarnacion	.10	.30
321 F.Rodriguez RC	1.25	3.00
322 Michael Cuddyer	.10	.30
323 Ed Yarnall	.10	.30
324 Cesar Saba RC	.10	.30
325 Gookie Dawkins	.10	.30
326 Alex Escobar	.10	.30
327 Julio Zuleta RC	.10	.30
328 Josh Hamilton	.40	1.00
329 Nick Neugebauer RC	.10	.30
330 Matt Belisle	.10	.30
331 Kurt Ainsworth RC	.10	.30
332 Tim Raines Jr.	.10	.30
333 Eric Munson	.10	.30
334 Donzell McDonald	.10	.30
335 Larry Bigbie RC	.30	.75
336 Matt Watson RC	.10	.30
337 Aubrey Huff	.10	.30
338 Julio Ramirez	.10	.30
339 Jason Grabowski RC	.10	.30
340 Jon Garland	.10	.30
341 Austin Kearns	.10	.30
342 Josh Pressley RC	.10	.30
343 Miguel Olivo RC	.30	.75
344 Julio Lugo	.10	.30
345 Roberto Vaz	.10	.30
346 Ramon Soler	.10	.30
347 Brandon Phillips RC	.60	1.50
348 Vince Faison RC	.10	.30
349 Mike Venafro	.10	.30
350 Rick Asadoorian RC	.20	.50
351 B.J. Garbe RC	.10	.30
352 Dan Reichert	.10	.30
353 Jason Stumm RC	.10	.30
354 Ruben Salazar RC	.10	.30
355 Francisco Cordero	.10	.30
356 Juan Guzman RC	.10	.30
357 Mike Bacsik RC	.10	.30
358 Jared Sandberg	.10	.30
359 Rod Barajas	.10	.30
360 Junior Brignac RC	.10	.30
361 J.M. Gold	.10	.30
362 Octavio Dotel	.10	.30
363 David Kelton	.10	.30
364 Scott Morgan	.10	.30
365 Wascar Serrano RC	.10	.30
366 Wilton Veras	.10	.30
367 Eugene Kingsale	.10	.30
368 Ted Lilly	.10	.30
369 George Lombard	.10	.30
370 Chris Haas	.10	.30
371 Wilton Pena RC	.10	.30
372 Vernon Wells	.10	.30
373 Jason Royer RC	.10	.30
374 Jeff Heaverlo RC	.10	.30
375 Calvin Pickering	.10	.30
376 Mike Lamb RC	.30	.75
377 Kyle Snyder	.10	.30
378 Javier Cardona RC	.10	.30
379 Aaron Rowand RC	.75	2.00
380 Dee Brown	.10	.30
381 Brett Myers RC	.60	1.50
382 Abraham Nunez	.10	.30
383 Eric Valent	.10	.30
384 Jody Gerut RC	.20	.50
385 Adam Dunn	.30	.75
386 Jay Gehrke	.10	.30
387 Omar Ortiz	.10	.30
388 Darnell McDonald	.10	.30
389 Tony Schrager RC	.10	.30
390 J.D. Closser	.10	.30
391 Ben Christensen RC	.10	.30
392 Adam Kennedy	.10	.30
393 Nick Green RC	.10	.30
394 Ramon Hernandez	.10	.30
395 Roy Oswalt RC	2.50	6.00
396 Andy Tracy RC	.10	.30
397 Eric Gagne	.30	.75
398 Michael Tejera RC	.10	.30
399 Adam Everett	.10	.30
400 Corey Patterson	.10	.30
401 Gary Knotts RC	.10	.30
402 Ryan Christianson RC	.10	.30
403 Eric Ireland RC	.10	.30
404 Andrew Good RC	.10	.30
405 Brad Penny	.10	.30
406 Jason LaRue	.10	.30
407 Kit Pellow	.10	.30
408 Kevin Beirne	.10	.30
409 Kelly Dransfeldt	.10	.30
410 Jason Grilli	.10	.30
411 Scott Downs RC	.10	.30
412 Jesus Colome	.10	.30
413 John Sneed RC	.10	.30
414 Tony McKnight	.10	.30
415 Luis Rivera	.10	.30
416 Adam Eaton	.10	.30
417 Mike MacDougal RC	.20	.50
418 Mike Nannini	.10	.30
419 Barry Zito RC	1.50	4.00
420 DeWayne Wise	.10	.30
421 Jason Dellaero	.10	.30
422 Chad Moeller	.10	.30
423 Jason Marquis	.10	.30
424 Tim Redding RC	.20	.50
425 Mark Mulder	.10	.30
426 Josh Paul	.10	.30
427 Chris Enochs	.10	.30
428 W.Rodriguez RC	.10	.30
429 Kevin Witt	.10	.30
430 Scott Sobkowiak RC	.10	.30
431 McKay Christensen	.10	.30
432 Jung Bong	.10	.30
433 Keith Evans RC	.10	.30
434 Garry Maddox Jr. RC	.10	.30
435 Ramon Santiago RC	.10	.30
436 Alex Cora	.10	.30
437 Carlos Lee	.10	.30
438 Jason Repko RC	.30	.75
439 Matt Burch	.10	.30
440 Shawn Sonnier RC	.10	.30

2000 Bowman Gold

Randomly inserted into hobby/retail packs at one in 64, this 440-card insert is a complete parallel of the Bowman base set. Each card features a gold facsimile autograph that runs down the right side of the card. Each card in the set is also individually serial numbered to 99.

*STARS: 10X TO 25X BASIC CARDS
*ROOKIES: 5X TO 12X BASIC CARDS

2000 Bowman Retro/Future

Randomly inserted into hobby/retail packs at one per pack, this 440-card insert is a complete parallel of the Bowman base set. Each card features a television border similar to that of the classic 1955 Bowman set.

COMPLETE SET (440)	75.00	200.00

*STARS: 1X TO 2.5X BASIC CARDS
*ROOKIES: .6X TO 1.5X BASIC CARDS

2000 Bowman Autographs

Randomly inserted into packs, this 40-card insert features autographed cards from young players like Corey Patterson, Ruben Mateo, and Alfonso Soriano. Please note that this is a three tiered autographed set. Cards that are marked with a "B" are part of the Blue Tier (1:144 HOB/RET, 1:69 HTC). Cards marked with an "S" are part of the Silver Tier (1:312 HOB/RET, 1:148 HTC), and cards marked with a "G" are part of the Gold Tier (1:1604 HOB/RET, 1:762 HTC).

AD Adam Dunn B	8.00	20.00
AH Aubrey Huff B	10.00	25.00
AK Austin Kearns B	4.00	10.00
AP Adam Piatt S	6.00	15.00
AS Alfonso Soriano S	10.00	25.00
BP Ben Petrick G	10.00	25.00
BS Ben Sheets B	12.50	30.00
BWP Brad Penny B	4.00	10.00
CA Chip Ambres B	4.00	10.00
CB Carlos Beltran G	10.00	25.00
CF Choo Freeman B	4.00	10.00
CP Corey Patterson S	6.00	15.00
DB Dee Brown S	6.00	15.00
DK David Kelton B	4.00	10.00
EV Eric Valent B	4.00	10.00
EY Ed Yarnall S	6.00	15.00
JC Jack Cust S	6.00	15.00
JDC J.D. Closser B	4.00	10.00
JDD J.D. Drew G	10.00	25.00
JJ Jason Jennings B	4.00	10.00
JR Jason Romano B	4.00	10.00
JV Jose Vidro S	6.00	15.00
JZ Julio Zuleta B	4.00	10.00
KJW Kevin Witt S	6.00	15.00
KLW Kerry Wood S	10.00	25.00
LB Lance Berkman S	10.00	25.00
MC Michael Cuddyer S	6.00	15.00
MJR Mike Restovich B	4.00	10.00
MM Mike Meyers B	4.00	10.00
MQ Mark Quinn S	6.00	15.00
MR Matt Riley S	6.00	15.00
NJ Nick Johnson S	8.00	20.00
RA Rick Ankiel G	20.00	50.00
RF Rafael Furcal S	10.00	25.00
RM Ruben Mateo G	10.00	25.00
SB Sean Burroughs S	6.00	15.00
SC Steve Cox B	4.00	10.00
SD Scott Downs S	6.00	15.00
SW Scott Williamson G	10.00	25.00
VW Vernon Wells G	10.00	25.00

2000 Bowman Early Indications

Randomly inserted into hobby/retail packs at one in 24, this 10-card insert features players that put up big numbers early on in their careers. Card backs carry an "E" prefix.

COMPLETE SET (10)	20.00	50.00
E1 Nomar Garciaparra	2.00	5.00
E2 Cal Ripken	4.00	10.00
E3 Derek Jeter	3.00	8.00
E4 Mark McGwire	3.00	8.00
E5 Alex Rodriguez	2.00	5.00
E6 Chipper Jones	1.25	3.00
E7 Todd Helton	.75	2.00
E8 Vladimir Guerrero	1.25	3.00
E9 Mike Piazza	2.00	5.00
E10 Jose Canseco	.75	2.00

2000 Bowman Major Power

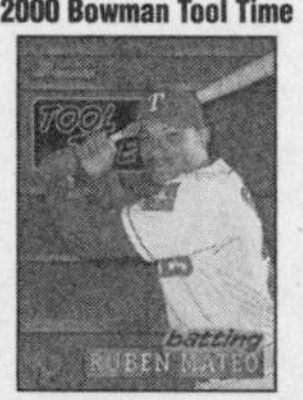

Randomly inserted into hobby/retail packs at one in 24, this 10-card insert features the major league's top sluggers. Card backs carry a "MP" prefix.

COMPLETE SET (10)	20.00	50.00
MP1 Mark McGwire	3.00	8.00
MP2 Chipper Jones	1.25	3.00
MP3 Alex Rodriguez	2.00	5.00
MP4 Sammy Sosa	1.25	3.00
MP5 Rafael Palmeiro	.75	2.00
MP6 Ken Griffey Jr.	2.00	5.00
MP7 Nomar Garciaparra	2.00	5.00
MP8 Barry Bonds	3.00	8.00
MP9 Derek Jeter	3.00	8.00
MP10 Jeff Bagwell	.75	2.00

2000 Bowman Tool Time

Randomly inserted into hobby/retail packs at one in eight, this 20-card insert grades the major league's top prospects on their batting, power, speed, arm strength, and defensive skills. Card backs carry a "TT" prefix.

COMPLETE SET (20)	8.00	20.00
TT1 Pat Burrell	.40	1.00
TT2 Aaron Rowand	.75	2.00
TT3 Chris Wakeland	.40	1.00
TT4 Ruben Mateo	.40	1.00
TT5 Pat Burrell	.40	1.00
TT6 Adam Piatt	.40	1.00
TT7 Nick Johnson	.40	1.00
TT8 Jack Cust	.40	1.00
TT9 Rafael Furcal	.40	1.00
TT10 Julio Ramirez	.40	1.00
TT11 Gookie Dawkins	.40	1.00
TT12 Corey Patterson	.40	1.00
TT13 Ruben Mateo	.40	1.00
TT14 Jason Dellaero	.40	1.00
TT15 Sean Burroughs	.40	1.00
TT16 Ryan Langerhans	.40	1.00
TT17 D'Angelo Jimenez	.40	1.00
TT18 Corey Patterson	.40	1.00
TT19 Troy Cameron	.40	1.00
TT20 Michael Cuddyer	.40	1.00

2000 Bowman Draft

The 2000 Bowman Draft Picks set was released in November, 2000 as a 110-card set. Each factory set was initially distributed in a tight, clear cello wrap and contained the 110-card set plus one of 60 different autographs. Topps announced that due to the unavailability of certain players previously scheduled to sign autographs, a small quantity (less than ten percent) of autographed cards from the 2000 Topps Baseball Rookies/Traded set were be included into its 2000 Bowman Baseball Draft Picks set. Rookie Cards include Chin-Feng Chen, Adrian Gonzalez, Kazuhiro Sasaki, Grady Sizemore and Chin-Hui Tsao.

COMP.FACT.SET (111)	20.00	40.00
COMPLETE SET (110)	10.00	25.00
1 Pat Burrell	.10	.30
2 Rafael Furcal	.10	.30
3 Grant Roberts	.10	.30
4 Barry Zito	.60	1.50
5 Julio Zuleta	.10	.30
6 Mark Mulder	.10	.30
7 Rob Bell	.10	.30
8 Adam Piatt	.10	.30
9 Mike Lamb	.25	.60
10 Pablo Ozuna	.10	.30
11 Jason Tyner	.10	.30
12 Jason Marquis	.10	.30
13 Eric Munson	.10	.30
14 Seth Etherton	.10	.30
15 Milton Bradley	.10	.30
16 Nick Green	.10	.30
17 Chin-Feng Chen RC	.25	.60
18 Matt Boone RC	.10	.30
19 Kevin Gregg RC	.10	.30
20 Eddy Garabito RC	.10	.30
21 Aaron Capista RC	.10	.30
22 Esteban German RC	.10	.30
23 Derek Thompson RC	.10	.30
24 Phil Merrell RC	.10	.30
25 Brian O'Connor RC	.10	.30
26 Yamid Haad	.10	.30
27 Hector Mercado RC	.10	.30
28 Jason Woolf RC	.10	.30
29 Eddy Furniss RC	.10	.30
30 Cha Sueng Baek RC	.10	.30
31 Colby Lewis RC	.25	.60
32 Pasqual Coco RC	.10	.30
33 Jorge Cantu RC	1.00	2.50
34 Erasmo Ramirez RC	.10	.30
35 Bobby Kielty RC	.15	.40
36 Joaquin Benoit RC	.10	.30
37 Brian Esposito RC	.10	.30
38 Michael Wenner	.10	.30
39 Juan Rincon RC	.10	.30
40 Yorvit Torrealba RC	1.25	3.00
41 Chad Durham RC	.10	.30
42 Jim Mann RC	.10	.30
43 Shane Loux RC	.10	.30
44 Luis Rivas	.10	.30
45 Ken Chenard RC	.10	.30
46 Mike Lockwood RC	.10	.30
47 Yovanny Lara RC	.10	.30
48 Bubba Carpenter RC	.10	.30
49 Ryan Dittfurth RC	.10	.30
50 John Stephens RC	.10	.30
51 Pedro Feliz RC	.40	1.00
52 Kenny Kelly RC	.10	.30
53 Neil Jenkins RC	.10	.30
54 Mike Glendenning RC	.10	.30
55 Bo Porter	.10	.30
56 Eric Byrnes	.10	.30
57 Tony Alvarez RC	.10	.30
58 Kazuhiro Sasaki RC	.25	.60
59 Chad Durbin RC	.10	.30
60 Mike Bynum RC	.10	.30
61 Travis Wilson RC	.10	.30
62 Jose Leon RC	.10	.30
63 Ryan Vogelsong RC	1.50	4.00
64 Geraldo Guzman RC	.10	.30
65 Craig Anderson RC	.10	.30
66 Carlos Silva RC	.15	.40
67 Brad Thomas RC	.10	.30
68 Chin-Hui Tsao RC	.75	2.00
69 Mark Buehrle RC	3.00	8.00
70 Juan Salas RC	.10	.30
71 Denny Abreu RC	.10	.30
72 Keith McDonald RC	.10	.30
73 Chris Richard RC	.10	.30
74 Tomas De la Rosa RC	.10	.30
75 Vicente Padilla RC	.15	.40
76 Justin Brunette RC	.10	.30
77 Scott Linebrink RC	.10	.30
78 Jeff Sparks RC	.10	.30
79 Tike Redman RC	.25	.60
80 John Lackey RC	1.00	2.50
81 Joe Strong RC	.10	.30
82 Brian Tollberg RC	.10	.30
83 Steve Sisco RC	.10	.30
84 Chris Clapinski RC	.10	.30
85 Augie Ojeda RC	.10	.30
86 Adrian Gonzalez RC	3.00	8.00
87 Mike Stodolka RC	.10	.30
88 Adam Johnson RC	.10	.30
89 Matt Wheatland RC	.10	.30
90 Corey Smith RC	.10	.30
91 Rocco Baldelli RC	.75	2.00
92 Keith Bucktrot RC	.10	.30
93 Adam Wainwright RC	.75	2.00
94 Blaine Boyer RC	.10	.30
95 Aaron Herr RC	.15	.40
96 Scott Thorman RC	.40	1.00
97 Bryan Digby RC	.10	.30
98 Josh Shortslef RC	.20	.50
99 Sean Smith RC	.10	.30
100 Alex Cruz RC	.10	.30
101 Marc Love RC	.10	.30
102 Kevin Lee RC	.10	.30
103 Victor Ramos RC	.10	.30
104 Jason Kaanoi RC	.10	.30
105 Luis Escobar RC	.10	.30
106 Tripper Johnson RC	.10	.30
107 Phil Dumatrait RC	.10	.30
108 Bryan Edwards RC	.10	.30
109 Grady Sizemore RC	4.00	10.00
110 Thomas Mitchell RC	.10	.30

2000 Bowman Draft Autographs

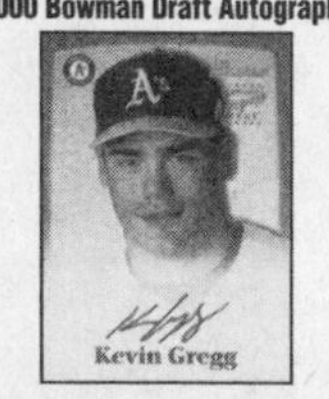

Inserted into 2000 Bowman Draft Pick sets at one per set, this 55-card insert features autographed cards of some of the hottest prospects in baseball. Card backs carry a "BDPA" prefix. Please note that cards BDPA16, BDPA32, BDPA34, BDPA45, BDPA56 do not exist.

BDPA1 Pat Burrell	6.00	15.00
BDPA2 Rafael Furcal	8.00	20.00
BDPA3 Grant Roberts	4.00	10.00
BDPA4 Barry Zito	15.00	40.00
BDPA5 Julio Zuleta	4.00	10.00
BDPA6 Mark Mulder	6.00	15.00
BDPA7 Rob Bell	4.00	10.00
BDPA8 Adam Piatt	4.00	10.00
BDPA9 Mike Lamb	6.00	15.00
BDPA10 Pablo Ozuna	4.00	10.00
BDPA11 Jason Tyner	4.00	10.00
BDPA12 Jason Marquis	6.00	15.00
BDPA13 Eric Munson	4.00	10.00
BDPA14 Seth Etherton	4.00	10.00
BDPA15 Milton Bradley	6.00	15.00
BDPA17 Michael Wenner	4.00	10.00
BDPA18 M.Glendenning	4.00	10.00
BDPA19 Tony Alvarez	4.00	10.00
BDPA20 Adrian Gonzalez	150.00	250.00
BDPA21 Corey Smith	4.00	10.00
BDPA22 Matt Wheatland	4.00	10.00
BDPA23 Adam Johnson	4.00	10.00
BDPA24 Mike Stodolka	4.00	10.00
BDPA25 Rocco Baldelli	60.00	100.00
BDPA26 Juan Rincon	4.00	10.00
BDPA27 Chad Durbin	4.00	10.00
BDPA28 Yorvit Torrealba	12.50	30.00
BDPA29 Nick Green	4.00	10.00
BDPA30 Derek Thompson	4.00	10.00
BDPA31 John Lackey	30.00	60.00
BDPA33 Kevin Gregg	4.00	10.00
BDPA35 Denny Abreu	4.00	10.00
BDPA36 Brian Tollberg	4.00	10.00
BDPA37 Yamid Haad	4.00	10.00
BDPA38 Grady Sizemore	50.00	100.00
BDPA39 Carlos Silva	4.00	10.00
BDPA40 Jorge Cantu	30.00	60.00
BDPA41 Bobby Kielty	4.00	10.00
BDPA42 Scott Thorman	30.00	80.00
BDPA43 Juan Salas	4.00	10.00
BDPA44 Phil Dumatrait	8.00	20.00
BDPA46 Mike Lockwood	4.00	10.00
BDPA47 Yovanny Lara	4.00	10.00
BDPA48 Tripper Johnson	4.00	10.00
BDPA49 Colby Lewis	8.00	20.00
BDPA50 Neil Jenkins	4.00	10.00
BDPA51 Keith Bucktrot	4.00	10.00
BDPA52 Eric Byrnes	4.00	10.00
BDPA53 Aaron Herr	4.00	10.00
BDPA54 Erasmo Ramirez	4.00	10.00
BDPA55 Chris Richard	4.00	10.00
BDPA57 Mike Bynum	4.00	10.00
BDPA58 Brian Esposito	4.00	10.00
BDPA59 Chris Clapinski	4.00	10.00
BDPA60 Augie Ojeda	4.00	10.00

2001 Bowman

Issued in one series, this 440 card set features a mix of 140 veteran cards along with 300 cards of young players. The cards were issued in either 10-card retail or hobby packs or 21-card hobby collector packs. The 10 card packs had an SRP of $3 while the jumbo packs had an SRP of $6. The 10 card packs were inserted 24 packs to a box and 12 boxes to a case. The 21 card packs were inserted 12 packs per box and eight boxes per case. An exchange card with a redemption deadline of May 31st, 2002, good for a signed Sean Burroughs baseball, was randomly seeded into packs at a miniscule rate of 1:30,432. Only eighty exchange cards were produced. In addition, a special card featuring game-used jersey swatches of A.L. and N.L. Rookie of the Year winners Kazuhiro Sasaki and Rafael Furcal was randomly seeded into packs at the following rates; hobby 1:2,202 and Home Team Advantage 1:1,045.

COMPLETE SET (440)	90.00	150.00
COMMON CARD (1-440)	.10	.30
COMMON RC	.15	.40
1 Jason Giambi	.10	.30
2 Rafael Furcal	.10	.30
3 Rick Ankiel	.10	.30
4 Freddy Garcia	.10	.30
5 Magglio Ordonez	.10	.30
6 Bernie Williams	.20	.50
7 Kenny Lofton	.10	.30
8 Al Leiter	.10	.30
9 Albert Belle	.10	.30
10 Craig Biggio	.20	.50
11 Mark Mulder	.10	.30
12 Carlos Delgado	.10	.30
13 Darin Erstad	.10	.30
14 Richie Sexson	.10	.30
15 Randy Johnson	.30	.75
16 Greg Maddux	.50	1.25
17 Cliff Floyd	.10	.30
18 Mark Buehrle	.20	.50
19 Chris Singleton	.10	.30
20 Orlando Hernandez	.10	.30
21 Javier Vazquez	.10	.30
22 Jeff Kent	.10	.30
23 Jim Thome	.20	.50
24 John Olerud	.10	.30
25 Jason Kendall	.10	.30
26 Scott Rolen	.20	.50
27 Tony Gwynn	.40	1.00
28 Edgardo Alfonzo	.10	.30
29 Pokey Reese	.10	.30
30 Todd Helton	.20	.50
31 Mark Quinn	.10	.30
32 Dan Tosca RC	.15	.40
33 Dean Palmer	.10	.30
34 Jacque Jones	.10	.30
35 Ray Durham	.10	.30
36 Rafael Palmeiro	.20	.50
37 Carl Everett	.10	.30
38 Ryan Dempster	.10	.30
39 Randy Wolf	.10	.30
40 Vladimir Guerrero	.30	.75
41 Livan Hernandez	.10	.30
42 Mo Vaughn	.10	.30
43 Shannon Stewart	.10	.30
44 Preston Wilson	.10	.30
45 Jose Vidro	.10	.30
46 Fred McGriff	.20	.50
47 Kevin Brown	.10	.30
48 Peter Bergeron	.10	.30
49 Miguel Tejada	.10	.30
50 Chipper Jones	.30	.75
51 Edgar Martinez	.20	.50
52 Tony Batista	.10	.30
53 Jorge Posada	.20	.50
54 Ricky Ledee	.10	.30
55 Sammy Sosa	.30	.75
56 Steve Cox	.10	.30
57 Tony Armas Jr.	.10	.30
58 Gary Sheffield	.10	.30
59 Bartolo Colon	.10	.30
60 Pat Burrell	.10	.30
61 Jay Payton	.10	.30
62 Sean Casey	.10	.30
63 Larry Walker	.10	.30
64 Mike Mussina	.20	.50
65 Nomar Garciaparra	.50	1.25
66 Darren Dreifort	.10	.30
67 Richard Hidalgo	.10	.30
68 Troy Glaus	.10	.30
69 Ben Grieve	.10	.30
70 Jim Edmonds	.10	.30
71 Raul Mondesi	.10	.30
72 Andruw Jones	.20	.50
73 Luis Castillo	.10	.30
74 Mike Sweeney	.10	.30
75 Derek Jeter	.75	2.00
76 Ruben Mateo	.10	.30
77 Carlos Lee	.10	.30
78 Cristian Guzman	.10	.30
79 Mike Hampton	.10	.30
80 J.D. Drew	.10	.30
81 Matt Lawton	.10	.30
82 Moises Alou	.10	.30
83 Terrence Long	.10	.30
84 Geoff Jenkins	.10	.30
85 Manny Ramirez Sox	.20	.50
86 Johnny Damon	.20	.50
87 Barry Larkin	.20	.50
88 Pedro Martinez	.20	.50
89 Juan Gonzalez	.10	.30
90 Roger Clemens	.60	1.50
91 Carlos Beltran	.10	.30
92 Brad Radke	.10	.30
93 Orlando Cabrera	.10	.30
94 Roberto Alomar	.20	.50
95 Barry Bonds	.75	2.00
96 Tim Hudson	.10	.30
97 Tom Glavine	.20	.50
98 Jeromy Burnitz	.10	.30
99 Adrian Beltre	.10	.30
100 Mike Piazza	.50	1.25
101 Kerry Wood	.10	.30
102 Steve Finley	.10	.30
103 Alex Cora	.10	.30
104 Bob Abreu	.10	.30
105 Neifi Perez	.10	.30
106 Mark Redman	.10	.30
107 Paul Konerko	.10	.30
108 Jermaine Dye	.10	.30
109 Brian Giles	.10	.30
110 Ivan Rodriguez	.20	.50
111 Vinny Castilla	.10	.30
112 Adam Kennedy	.10	.30
113 Eric Chavez	.10	.30
114 Billy Koch	.10	.30
115 Shawn Green	.10	.30
116 Matt Williams	.10	.30
117 Greg Vaughn	.10	.30
118 Gabe Kapler	.10	.30
119 Jeff Cirillo	.10	.30
120 Frank Thomas	.30	.75
121 David Justice	.10	.30
122 Cal Ripken	1.00	2.50
123 Rich Aurilia	.10	.30
124 Curt Schilling	.10	.30
125 Barry Zito	.20	.50
126 Brian Jordan	.10	.30
127 Chan Ho Park	.10	.30
128 J.T. Snow	.10	.30
129 Kazuhiro Sasaki	.10	.30
130 Alex Rodriguez	.50	1.25
131 Mariano Rivera	.30	.75
132 Eric Milton	.10	.30
133 Andy Pettitte	.20	.50
134 Scott Elarton	.10	.30
135 Ken Griffey Jr.	.50	1.25
136 Bengie Molina	.10	.30
137 Jeff Bagwell	.20	.50
138 Kevin Millwood	.10	.30
139 Tino Martinez	.20	.50
140 Mark McGwire	.75	2.00
141 Larry Barnes	.10	.30
142 John Buck RC	.40	1.00
143 Freddie Bynum RC	.15	.40
144 Abraham Nunez	.10	.30
145 Felix Diaz RC	.15	.40
146 Horacio Estrada	.10	.30
147 Ben Diggins	.10	.30
148 Tsuyoshi Shinjo RC	.40	1.00
149 Rocco Baldelli	.10	.30
150 Rod Barajas	.10	.30
151 Luis Terrero	.10	.30
152 Milton Bradley	.10	.30
153 Kurt Ainsworth	.10	.30
154 Russell Branyan	.10	.30
155 Ryan Anderson	.10	.30
156 Mitch Jones RC	.25	.60
157 Chip Ambres	.10	.30
158 Steve Bennett RC	.15	.40
159 Ivanon Coffie	.10	.30
160 Sean Burroughs	.10	.30
161 Keith Bucktrot	.10	.30
162 Tony Alvarez	.10	.30
163 Joaquin Benoit	.10	.30
164 Rick Asadoorian	.10	.30
165 Ben Broussard	.10	.30
166 Ryan Madson RC	.50	1.25
167 Dee Brown	.10	.30
168 Sergio Contreras RC	.25	.60
169 John Barnes	.10	.30
170 Ben Washburn RC	.15	.40
171 Erick Almonte RC	.15	.40
172 Shawn Fagan RC	.15	.40
173 Gary Johnson RC	.15	.40
174 Brady Clark	.10	.30
175 Grant Roberts	.10	.30
176 Tony Torcato	.10	.30
177 Ramon Castro	.10	.30
178 Esteban German	.10	.30
179 Joe Hamer RC	.25	.60
180 Nick Neugebauer	.10	.30
181 Dernell Stenson	.10	.30
182 Yhency Brazoban RC	.40	1.00
183 Aaron Myette	.10	.30
184 Juan Sosa	.10	.30
185 Brandon Inge	.10	.30
186 Domingo Guante RC	.15	.40
187 Adrian Brown	.10	.30
188 Deivi Mendez RC	.15	.40
189 Luis Matos	.10	.30
190 Pedro Liriano RC	.25	.60
191 Donnie Bridges	.10	.30
192 Alex Cintron	.10	.30
193 Jace Brewer	.10	.30
194 Ron Davenport RC	.25	.60
195 Jason Belcher RC	.15	.40
196 Adrian Hernandez RC	.15	.40
197 Bobby Kielty	.10	.30
198 Reggie Griggs RC	.25	.60
199 R. Abercrombie RC	.40	1.00
200 Troy Farnsworth RC	.25	.60
201 Matt Belisle	.10	.30
202 Miguel Villilo RC	.25	.60
203 Adam Everett	.10	.30
204 John Lackey	.10	.30
205 Pasqual Coco	.10	.30
206 Adam Wainwright	.25	.60
207 Matt White RC	.25	.60
208 Chin-Feng Chen	.10	.30
209 Jeff Andra RC	.15	.40
210 Willie Bloomquist	.10	.30
211 Wes Anderson	.10	.30
212 Enrique Cruz	.10	.30
213 Jerry Hairston Jr.	.10	.30
214 Mike Bynum	.10	.30
215 Brian Hitchcox RC	.15	.40
216 Ryan Christianson	.10	.30
217 J.J. Davis	.10	.30
218 Jovanny Cedeno	.10	.30
219 Elvin Nina	.10	.30
220 Alex Graman	.10	.30
221 Arturo McDowell	.10	.30
222 Deivis Santos RC	.15	.40
223 Jody Gerut	.10	.30
224 Sun Woo Kim	.10	.30
225 Jimmy Rollins	.10	.30
226 Ntema Ndungidi	.10	.30
227 Ruben Salazar	.10	.30
228 Josh Girdley	.10	.30
229 Carl Crawford	.10	.30
230 Luis Montanez RC	.30	.75
231 Ramon Carvajal RC	.25	.60
232 Matt Riley	.10	.30
233 Ben Davis	.10	.30
234 Jason Grabowski	.10	.30
235 Chris George	.10	.30
236 Hank Blalock RC	1.00	2.50
237 Roy Oswalt	.30	.75
238 Eric Reynolds RC	.15	.40
239 Brian Cole	.10	.30
240 Denny Bautista RC	.40	1.00
241 Hector Garcia RC	.15	.40
242 Joe Thurston RC	.25	.60
243 Brad Cresse	.10	.30
244 Corey Patterson	.10	.30
245 Brett Evert RC	.15	.40
246 Elpidio Guzman RC	.15	.40
247 Vernon Wells	.10	.30
248 Roberto Miniel RC	.25	.60
249 Brian Bass RC	.15	.40
250 Mark Burnett RC	.25	.60
251 Juan Silvestre	.10	.30
252 Pablo Ozuna	.10	.30
253 Jayson Werth	.10	.30
254 Russ Jacobson	.10	.30
255 Chad Hermansen	.10	.30
256 Travis Hafner RC	4.00	10.00
257 Brad Baker	.10	.30
258 Gookie Dawkins	.10	.30
259 Michael Cuddyer	.10	.30
260 Mark Buehrle	.20	.50
261 Ricardo Aramboles	.10	.30
262 Esix Snead RC	.15	.40
263 Wilson Betemit RC	1.25	3.00
264 Albert Pujols RC	30.00	60.00
265 Joe Lawrence	.10	.30
266 Ramon Ortiz	.10	.30
267 Ben Sheets	.20	.50
268 Luke Lockwood RC	.25	.60
269 Toby Hall	.10	.30
270 Jack Cust	.10	.30
271 Pedro Feliz UER	.10	.30
No facsimile signature on card		
272 Noel Devarez RC	.25	.60
273 Josh Beckett	.20	.50
274 Alex Escobar	.10	.30
275 Doug Gredvig RC	.15	.40
276 Marcus Giles	.10	.30
277 Jon Rauch	.10	.30
278 Brian Schmitt RC	.15	.40
279 Seung Song RC	.25	.60
280 Kevin Mench	.10	.30
281 Adam Eaton	.10	.30
282 Shawn Sonnier	.10	.30
283 Andy Van Hekken RC	.15	.40
284 Aaron Rowand	.10	.30
285 Tony Blanco RC	.25	.60
286 Ryan Kohlmeier	.10	.30
287 C.C. Sabathia	.10	.30
288 Bubba Crosby	.10	.30
289 Josh Hamilton	.25	.60
290 Dee Haynes RC	.15	.40
291 Jason Marquis	.10	.30
292 Julio Zuleta	.10	.30
293 Carlos Hernandez	.10	.30
294 Matt Lecroy	.10	.30
295 Andy Beal RC	.15	.40
296 Carlos Pena	.10	.30
297 Reggie Taylor	.10	.30
298 Bob Keppel RC	.15	.40
299 Miguel Cabrera UER	.60	1.50
Photo is Manuel Esquivia		
300 Ryan Franklin	.10	.30
301 Brandon Phillips	.10	.30
302 Victor Hall RC	.25	.60
303 Tony Pena Jr.	.10	.30
304 Jim Journell RC	.25	.60
305 Cristian Guerrero	.10	.30
306 Miguel Olivo	.10	.30
307 Jin Ho Cho	.10	.30
308 Choo Freeman	.10	.30
309 Danny Borrell RC	.15	.40
310 Doug Mientkiewicz	.10	.30

Card	Low	High
311 Aaron Herr	.10	.30
312 Keith Ginter	.10	.30
313 Felipe Lopez	.10	.30
314 Jeff Goldbach	.10	.30
315 Travis Harper	.10	.30
316 Paul LoDuca	.10	.30
317 Joe Torres	.10	.30
318 Eric Byrnes	.10	.30
319 George Lombard	.10	.30
320 Dave Krynzel	.10	.30
321 Ben Christensen	.10	.30
322 Aubrey Huff	.10	.30
323 Lyle Overbay	.10	.30
324 Sean McGowan	.10	.30
325 Jeff Heaverlo	.10	.30
326 Timo Perez	.10	.30
327 Octavio Martinez RC	.25	.60
328 Vince Faison	.10	.30
329 David Parrish RC	.15	.40
330 Bobby Bradley	.10	.30
331 Jason Miller RC	.15	.40
332 Corey Spencer RC	.15	.40
333 Craig House	.10	.30
334 Maxim St. Pierre RC	.25	.60
335 Adam Johnson	.10	.30
336 Joe Crede	.30	.75
337 Greg Nash RC	.15	.40
338 Chad Durbin	.10	.30
339 Pat Magness RC	.25	.60
340 Matt Wheatland	.10	.30
341 Julio Lugo	.10	.30
342 Grady Sizemore	.60	1.50
343 Adrian Gonzalez	.75	2.00
344 Tim Raines Jr.	.10	.30
345 Ranier Olmedo RC	.25	.60
346 Phil Dumatrait	.10	.30
347 Brandon Mims RC	.15	.40
348 Jason Jennings	.10	.30
349 Phil Wilson RC	.25	.60
350 Jason Hart	.10	.30
351 Cesar Izturis	.10	.30
352 Matt Butler RC	.25	.60
353 David Kelton	.10	.30
354 Luke Prokopec	.10	.30
355 Corey Smith	.10	.30
356 Joel Pineiro	.25	.60
357 Ken Chenard	.10	.30
358 Keith Reed	.10	.30
359 David Walling	.10	.30
360 Alexis Gomez RC	.15	.40
361 Justin Morneau RC	4.00	10.00
362 Josh Fogg RC	.25	.60
363 J.R. House	.10	.30
364 Andy Tracy	.10	.30
365 Kenny Kelly	.10	.30
366 Aaron McNeal	.10	.30
367 Nick Johnson	.10	.30
368 Brian Esposito	.10	.30
369 Charles Frazier RC	.15	.40
370 Scott Heard	.10	.30
371 Pat Strange	.10	.30
372 Mike Meyers	.10	.30
373 Ryan Ludwick RC	3.00	8.00
374 Brad Wilkerson	.10	.30
375 Allen Levrault	.10	.30
376 Seth McClung RC	.25	.60
377 Joe Nathan	.10	.30
378 Rafael Soriano RC	.25	.60
379 Chris Richard	.10	.30
380 Jared Sandberg	.10	.30
381 Tike Redman	.10	.30
382 Adam Dunn UER	.20	.50
Card lists him as a pitcher		
383 Jared Abruzzo RC	.15	.40
384 Jason Richardson RC	.15	.40
385 Matt Holliday	.15	.40
386 Darwin Cubillan RC	.15	.40
387 Mike Nannini	.10	.30
388 Blake Williams RC	.15	.40
389 V. Pascucci RC	.25	.60
390 Jon Garland	.10	.30
391 Josh Pressley	.10	.30
392 Jose Ortiz	.10	.30
393 Ryan Hannaman RC	.25	.60
394 Steve Smyth RC	.25	.60
395 John Patterson	.10	.30
396 Chad Petty RC	.15	.40
397 Jake Peavy RC	2.50	6.00
UER last name misspelled Peavey		
398 Onix Mercado RC	.25	.60
399 Jason Romano	.10	.30
400 Luis Torres RC	.25	.60
401 Casey Fossum RC	.15	.40
402 Eduardo Figueroa RC	.15	.40
403 Bryan Barnowski RC	.15	.40
404 Tim Redding	.10	.30
405 Jason Standridge	.10	.30
406 Marvin Seale RC	.25	.60
407 Todd Moser	.10	.30
408 Alex Gordon	.10	.30
409 Steve Smitherman RC	.25	.60
410 Ben Petrick	.10	.30
411 Eric Munson	.10	.30
412 Luis Rivas	.10	.30
413 Matt Ginter	.10	.30
414 Alfonso Soriano	.20	.50
415 Rafael Boitel RC	.15	.40
416 Dany Morban RC	.15	.40
417 Justin Woodrow RC	.25	.60
418 Wilfredo Rodriguez	.10	.30
419 Derrick Van Dusen RC	.15	.40
420 Josh Spoerl RC	.25	.60
421 Juan Pierre	.10	.30
422 J.C. Romero	.10	.30
423 Ed Rogers RC	.15	.40
424 Tomo Ohka	.10	.30
425 Ben Hendrickson RC	.15	.40
426 Carlos Zambrano	.20	.50
427 Brett Myers	.10	.30
428 Scott Seabol	.10	.30
429 Thomas Mitchell	.10	.30
430 Jose Reyes RC	5.00	12.00
431 Kip Wells	.10	.30
432 Donzell McDonald	.10	.30
433 Adam Pettyjohn RC	.15	.40
434 Austin Kearns	.10	.30
435 Rico Washington	.10	.30
436 Doug Nickle RC	.15	.40
437 Steve Lomasney	.10	.30
438 Jason Jones RC	.15	.40
439 Bobby Seay	.10	.30
440 Justin Wayne RC	.25	.60
ROYR Kazuhiro Sasaki	6.00	15.00
Rafael Furcal ROY Jsy		
NNO Sean Burroughs Ball/80	6.00	15.00

2001 Bowman Gold

Inserted one per pack, these 440 cards are a parallel to the basic Bowman set.

*STARS: 1.25X TO 3X BASIC CARDS
*ROOKIES: .6X TO 1.5X BASIC

Card	Low	High
264 Albert Pujols	60.00	120.00
430 Jose Reyes	6.00	15.00

2001 Bowman Autographs

Inserted at a rate of one in 74 hobby packs and one in 35 HTA packs, these 40 cards feature autographs from some of the leading prospects in the Bowman set. Dustin McGowan did not return his cards in time for inclusion in the product and exchange cards with a redemption deadline of April 30th, 2003 were seeded into packs in their place.

Card	Low	High
BAAE Alex Escobar	4.00	10.00
BAAG Adrian Gonzalez	20.00	50.00
BAAJ Adam Johnson	4.00	10.00
BAAP Albert Pujols	500.00	800.00
BAADP Adam Piatt	4.00	10.00
BAAJG Alex Graman	4.00	10.00
BAAKG Alex Gordon	4.00	10.00
BABB Brian Barnowski	4.00	10.00
BABD Ben Diggins	4.00	10.00
BABS Ben Sheets	10.00	25.00
BABW Brad Wilkerson	6.00	15.00
BABZ Barry Zito	10.00	25.00
BACG Cristian Guerrero	4.00	10.00
BADK Dave Krynzel	4.00	10.00
BADM D. McGowan EXCH	6.00	15.00
BADWK David Kelton	4.00	10.00
BAFB Freddie Bynum	4.00	10.00
BAJB Jason Botts	6.00	15.00
BAJD Jose Diaz	6.00	15.00
BAJH Josh Hamilton	20.00	50.00
BAJM Justin Morneau	60.00	120.00
BAJP Josh Pressley	4.00	10.00
BAJRH J.R. House	4.00	10.00
BAJWH Jason Hart	4.00	10.00
BAKM Kevin Mench	6.00	15.00
BALM Luis Montanez	15.00	40.00
BALO Lyle Overbay	6.00	15.00
BAMV Miguel Villilo	4.00	10.00
BAND Noel Devarez	4.00	10.00
BAPL Pedro Liriano	4.00	10.00
BARF Rafael Furcal	4.00	10.00
BARJ Russ Jacobson	4.00	10.00
BASB Sean Burroughs	4.00	10.00
BASM S. McGowan EXCH	4.00	10.00
BASS Shawn Sonnier	4.00	10.00
BASU Sixto Urena	4.00	10.00
BASDS Steve Smyth	4.00	10.00
BATH Travis Hafner	6.00	15.00
BATJ Tripper Johnson	4.00	10.00
BAWB Wilson Betemit	10.00	25.00

2001 Bowman AutoProofs

Inserted at a rate of 1 in 18,239 hobby packs and 1 in 8,306 HTA packs; these 10 cards feature players signing their actual Bowman Rookie Cards. Each player signed 25 cards for this promotion. Hank Bauer, Pat Burrell, Carlos Delgado, Chipper Jones, Ralph Kiner, Gil McDougald, and Ivan Rodriguez did not return their cards in time for inclusion in this product and exchange cards with a redemption deadline of April 30th, 2003 were seeded in to packs in their place.

2001 Bowman Futures Game Relics

Inserted at overall odds of one in 82 hobby packs and one in 39 HTA packs, these 34 cards feature relics used by the featured players in the futures game. These cards were inserted at different ratios and our checklist provides that information as to what group each insert belongs to.

GROUP A ODDS 1:293 HOB, 1:139 HTA
GROUP B ODDS 1:365 HOB, 1:174 HTA
GROUP C ODDS 1:418 HOB, 1:199 HTA
GROUP D ODDS 1:274 HOB, 1:130 HTA

Card	Low	High
FGRAE Alex Escobar A	4.00	10.00
FGRAM Aaron Myette B	4.00	10.00
FGRBB Bobby Bradley B	4.00	10.00
FGRBP Ben Petrick C	4.00	10.00
FGRBS Ben Sheets B	6.00	15.00
FGRBW Brad Wilkerson C	4.00	10.00
FGRBZ Barry Zito B	6.00	15.00
FGRCA Craig Anderson B	4.00	10.00
FGRCC Chin-Feng Chen A	15.00	40.00
FGRCG Chris George D	4.00	10.00
FGRCH C. Hernandez D	4.00	10.00
FGRCP Corey Patterson A	4.00	10.00
FGRCP Carlos Pena A	4.00	10.00
FGRCT Chin-Hui Tsao D	10.00	25.00
FGREM Eric Munson A	4.00	10.00
FGRFL Felipe Lopez A	4.00	10.00
FGRGR Grant Roberts D	4.00	10.00
FGRJC Jack Cust A	4.00	10.00
FGRJH Josh Hamilton A	8.00	20.00
FGRJR Jason Romano C	4.00	10.00
FGRJZ Julio Zuleta A	4.00	10.00
FGRKA Kurt Ainsworth B	4.00	10.00
FGRMB Mike Bynum D	4.00	10.00
FGRMG Marcus Giles A	4.00	10.00
FGRNN N. Ndungidi A	4.00	10.00
FGRRA Ryan Anderson B	4.00	10.00
FGRRC Ramon Castro C	4.00	10.00
FGRRD R. Dorame D	4.00	10.00
FGRRO Ramon Ortiz D	4.00	10.00
FGRSK Sun Woo Kim D	4.00	10.00
FGRTD Travis Dawkins C	4.00	10.00
FGRTO Tomokazu Ohka B	4.00	10.00
FGRTW Travis Wilson A	4.00	10.00
FGRVW Vernon Wells C	4.00	10.00

2001 Bowman Multiple Game Relics

Issued at overall odds of one in 1,476 hobby packs and one in 701 HTA packs, these cards have three different pieces of memorabilia on them. These cards feature a piece of a jersey, helmet and a base fragment.

GROUP A ODDS 1:1883 HOB, 1:895 HTA
GROUP B ODDS 1:6842 HOB, 1:3230 HTA

Card	Low	High
MGRAE Alex Escobar B	10.00	25.00
MGRBP Ben Petrick A	10.00	25.00
MGRBW B. Wilkerson B	10.00	25.00
MGRCC C. Chen A	90.00	150.00
MGRCP Carlos Pena A	10.00	25.00
MGREM Eric Munson B	10.00	25.00
MGRFL Felipe Lopez A	12.50	30.00
MGRJC Jack Cust A	10.00	25.00
MGRJH Josh Hamilton B	20.00	50.00
MGRJR Jason Romano A	10.00	25.00
MGRJZ Julio Zuleta A	10.00	25.00
MGRMG Marcus Giles A	12.50	30.00
MGRNN N. Ndungidi A	10.00	25.00
MGRRC Ramon Castro A	10.00	25.00
MGRTD Travis Dawkins A	10.00	25.00
MGRTW Travis Wilson A	10.00	25.00
MGRVW Vernon Wells A	12.50	30.00
MGRDCP C. Patterson B	10.00	25.00

2001 Bowman Rookie Reprints

Inserted at a rate of one in 12, these 25 cards feature reprint cards of various stars who made their debut between 1948 and 1955.

Card	Low	High
COMPLETE SET (25)	25.00	60.00
1 Yogi Berra	2.00	5.00
2 Ralph Kiner	1.25	3.00
3 Stan Musial	4.00	10.00
4 Warren Spahn	1.25	3.00
5 Roy Campanella	2.00	5.00
6 Bob Lemon	1.25	3.00
7 Robin Roberts	1.25	3.00
8 Duke Snider	1.25	3.00
9 Early Wynn	1.25	3.00
10 Richie Ashburn	1.25	3.00
11 Gil Hodges	2.00	5.00
12 Hank Bauer	1.25	3.00
13 Don Newcombe	1.25	3.00
14 Al Rosen	1.25	3.00
15 Willie Mays	5.00	12.00
16 Joe Garagiola	1.25	3.00
17 Whitey Ford	1.25	3.00
18 Lew Burdette	1.25	3.00
19 Gil McDougald	1.25	3.00
20 Minnie Minoso	1.25	3.00
21 Eddie Mathews	2.00	5.00
22 Harvey Kuenn	1.25	3.00
23 Don Larsen	1.25	3.00
24 Elston Howard	1.25	3.00
25 Don Zimmer	1.25	3.00

2001 Bowman Rookie Reprints Autographs

Inserted at a rate of one in 2,467 hobby packs and one in 1,162 HTA packs, these 10 cards feature the players signing their rookie reprint cards. Duke Snider did not return his card in time for inclusion in packs. His card was redeemable until April 30, 2003. Please note that card number 7 does not exist. Though the cards lack serial-numbering, Topps did announce that only 100 sets were produced. Card number 7 does not exist.

Card	Low	High
1 Yogi Berra	40.00	80.00
2 Willie Mays	150.00	250.00
3 Stan Musial	75.00	150.00
4 Duke Snider	30.00	60.00
5 Warren Spahn	30.00	60.00
6 Ralph Kiner	10.00	25.00
8 Don Larsen	10.00	25.00
9 Don Zimmer	10.00	25.00
10 Minnie Minoso	10.00	25.00

2001 Bowman Rookie Reprints Relic Bat

Issued at a rate of one in 1,954 hobby packs and one in 928 HTA packs, these five cards feature not only the rookie reprint of these players but also a piece of a bat they used during their career.

Card	Low	High
1 Willie Mays	40.00	80.00
2 Duke Snider	10.00	25.00
3 Minnie Minoso	6.00	15.00
4 Hank Bauer	6.00	15.00
5 Gil McDougald	6.00	15.00

2001 Bowman Rookie Reprints Relic Bat Autographs

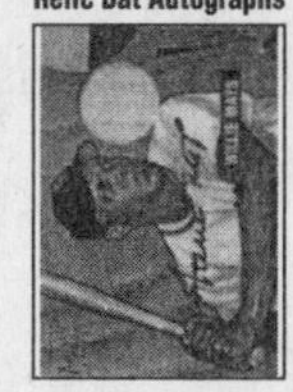

Issued at a rate of one in 18,259 hobby packs and one in 8,306 HTA packs, these five cards feature not only the rookie reprint of these players but also a piece of a bat they used during their career as well as an authentic autograph.

2001 Bowman Draft

Issued as a 112-card factory set with a SRP of $45.99, these sets feature 100 cards of young players along with an autograph and relic card in each box. Twelve sets were included in each case. Cards BDP51 and BDP71 featuring Alex Herrera and Brad Thomas are uncorrected errors in that the card backs were switched for each player.

Card	Low	High
COMP.FACT.SET (112)	30.00	60.00
COMPLETE SET (110)	20.00	50.00
BDP1 Alfredo Amezaga RC	.10	.30
BDP2 Andrew Good	.10	.30
BDP3 Kelly Johnson RC	1.25	3.00
BDP4 Larry Bigbie	.10	.30
BDP5 Matt Thompson RC	.15	.40
BDP6 Wilton Chavez RC	.15	.40
BDP7 Joe Borchard RC	.15	.40
BDP8 David Espinosa	.10	.30
BDP9 Zach Day RC	.15	.40
BDP10 Brad Hawpe RC	1.00	2.50
BDP11 Nate Cornejo	.10	.30
BDP12 Matt Cooper RC	.15	.40
BDP13 Brad Lidge	.10	.30
BDP14 Angel Berroa RC	.25	.60
BDP15 L. Matthews RC	.15	.40
BDP16 Jose Garcia	.10	.30
BDP17 Grant Balfour RC	.10	.30
BDP18 Ron Chiavacci RC	.10	.30
BDP19 Jae Seo	.10	.30
BDP20 Juan Rivera	.10	.30
BDP21 D'Angelo Jimenez	.10	.30
BDP22 Juan A.Pena RC	.15	.40
BDP23 Marlon Byrd RC	.15	.40
BDP24 Sean Burnett	.10	.30
BDP25 Josh Pearce RC	.15	.40
BDP26 B. Duckworth RC	.10	.30
BDP27 Jack Taschner RC	.10	.30
BDP28 Marcus Thames	.10	.30
BDP29 Brent Abernathy	.10	.30
BDP30 David Elder RC	.10	.30
BDP31 Scott Cassidy RC	.15	.40
BDP32 D. Tankersley RC	.10	.30
BDP33 Denny Stark	.10	.30
BDP34 Dave Williams RC	.10	.30
BDP35 Boof Bonser RC	.10	.30
BDP36 Kris Foster RC	.10	.30
BDP37 Luis Garcia RC	.15	.40
BDP38 Shawn Chacon	.10	.30
BDP39 Mike Rivera RC	.15	.40
BDP40 Will Smith RC	.15	.40
BDP41 M. Ensberg RC	.75	2.00
BDP42 Ken Harvey	.10	.30
BDP43 R. Rodriguez RC	.15	.40
BDP44 Jose Mieses RC	.15	.40
BDP45 Luis Maza RC	.10	.30
BDP46 Julio Perez RC	.15	.40
BDP47 Dustan Mohr RC	.15	.40
BDP48 Randy Flores RC	.10	.30
BDP49 Covelli Crisp RC	2.00	5.00
BDP50 Kevin Reese RC	.15	.40
BDP51 Brad Thomas UER	.10	.30
Card back is BDP71 Alex Herrera		
BDP52 Xavier Nady	.10	.30
BDP53 Ryan Vogelsong	.10	.30
BDP54 Carlos Silva	.10	.30
BDP55 Dan Wright	.10	.30
BDP56 Brent Butler	.10	.30
BDP57 Brandon Knight RC	.10	.30
BDP58 Brian Reith RC	.10	.30
BDP59 M. Valenzuela RC	.15	.40
BDP60 Bobby Hill RC	.15	.40
BDP61 Rich Rundles RC	.15	.40
BDP62 Rick Elder	.10	.30
BDP63 J.D. Closser	.10	.30
BDP64 Scot Shields	.10	.30
BDP65 Miguel Olivo	.10	.30
BDP66 Stubby Clapp RC	.10	.30
BDP67 J. Williams RC	.25	.60
BDP68 Jason Lane RC	.25	.60
BDP69 Chase Utley RC	8.00	20.00
BDP70 Erik Bedard RC	2.00	5.00
BDP71 A. Herrera UER RC	.10	.30
Card back is BDP51 Brad Thomas		
BDP72 Juan Cruz RC	.15	.40
BDP73 Billy Martin RC	.10	.30
BDP74 Ronnie Merrill RC	.15	.40
BDP75 Jason Kinchen RC	.10	.30
BDP76 Wilkin Ruan RC	.15	.40
BDP77 Cody Ransom RC	.10	.30
BDP78 Bud Smith RC	.10	.30
BDP79 Wily Mo Pena	.10	.30
BDP80 Jeff Nettles RC	.15	.40
BDP81 Jamal Strong RC	.10	.30
BDP82 Bill Ortega RC	.10	.30
BDP83 Mike Bell	.10	.30
BDP84 Ichiro Suzuki RC	4.00	10.00
BDP85 F. Rodney RC	.10	.30
BDP86 Chris Smith RC	.10	.30
BDP87 J.VanBenschoten RC	.15	.40
BDP88 Bobby Crosby RC	1.50	4.00
BDP89 Kenny Baugh RC	.10	.30
BDP90 Jake Gautreau RC	.10	.30
BDP91 Gabe Gross RC	.25	.60
BDP92 Kris Honel RC	.15	.40
BDP93 Dan Denham RC	.10	.30
BDP94 Aaron Heilman RC	.15	.40
BDP95 Irvin Guzman RC	1.50	4.00
BDP96 Mike Jones RC	.25	.60
BDP97 J. Griffin RC	.15	.40
BDP98 Macay McBride RC	.40	1.00
BDP99 J. Rheinecker RC	.40	1.00
BDP100 B. Sardinha RC	.10	.30
BDP101 J. Weintraub RC	.10	.30
BDP102 J.D. Martin RC	.10	.30
BDP103 Jayson Nix RC	.15	.40
BDP104 Noah Lowry RC	1.00	2.50
BDP105 Richard Lewis RC	.15	.40
BDP106 B. Hennessey RC	.25	.60
BDP107 Jeff Mathis RC	.25	.60
BDP108 Jon Skaggs RC	.15	.40
BDP109 Justin Pope RC	.15	.40
BDP110 Josh Burrus RC	.15	.40

2001 Bowman Draft Autographs

Inserted one per Bowman draft pick factory set, these 37 cards feature autographs of some of the leading players from the Bowman Draft Pick set.

Card	Low	High
BDPAAA A. Amezaga	4.00	10.00
BDPAAC Alex Cintron	4.00	10.00
BDPAAE Adam Everett	4.00	10.00
BDPAAF Alex Fernandez	4.00	10.00
BDPAAG Alexis Gomez	4.00	10.00
BDPAAH Aaron Herr	4.00	10.00
BDPAAK Austin Kearns	6.00	15.00
BDPABB Bobby Bradley	4.00	10.00
BDPABH Beau Hale	4.00	10.00
BDPABP Brandon Phillips	8.00	20.00
BDPABS Bud Smith	4.00	10.00
BDPACG C. Guerrero	4.00	10.00
BDPACI Cesar Izturis	4.00	10.00
BDPACP Christian Parra	4.00	10.00
BDPAER Ed Rogers	4.00	10.00
BDPAFL Felipe Lopez	6.00	15.00
BDPAGA Garrett Atkins	30.00	60.00
BDPAGJ Gary Johnson	4.00	10.00
BDPAJA Jared Abruzzo	4.00	10.00
BDPAJK Joe Kennedy	6.00	15.00
BDPAJL John Lackey	6.00	15.00
BDPAJP Joel Pineiro	6.00	15.00
BDPAJT Joe Torres	4.00	10.00
BDPANJ Nick Johnson	6.00	15.00
BDPANR Nick Regilio	4.00	10.00
BDPARC Ryan Church	6.00	15.00
BDPARD Ryan Dittfurth	4.00	10.00
BDPARL Ryan Ludwick	10.00	25.00
BDPARO Roy Oswalt	10.00	25.00
BDPASH Scott Heard	4.00	10.00
BDPASS Scott Seabol	4.00	10.00
BDPATO Tomo Ohka	6.00	15.00
BDPAANC A. Cameron	4.00	10.00
BDPABJS Brian Specht	4.00	10.00
BDPAJMW Justin Wayne	4.00	10.00
BDPARMM Ryan Madson	10.00	25.00
BDPAROC R. Carvajal	4.00	10.00

2001 Bowman Draft Futures Game Relics

Inserted one per factory set, these 26 cards feature relics from the futures game.

Card	Low	High
FGRAA Alfredo Amezaga	2.00	5.00
FGRAD Adam Dunn	3.00	8.00
FGRAG Adrian Gonzalez	4.00	10.00
FGRAH Alex Herrera	2.00	5.00
FGRBM Brett Myers	2.00	5.00
FGRCD Cody Ransom	2.00	5.00
FGRCG Chris George	2.00	5.00
FGRCH Carlos Hernandez	2.00	5.00
FGRCU Chase Utley	30.00	60.00
FGREB Erik Bedard	4.00	10.00
FGRGB Grant Balfour	2.00	5.00
FGRHB Hank Blalock	4.00	10.00
FGRJB Joe Borchard	2.00	5.00
FGRJC Juan Cruz	2.00	5.00
FGRJP Josh Pearce	2.00	5.00
FGRJR Juan Rivera	2.00	5.00
FGRJAP Juan A.Pena	2.00	5.00
FGRLG Luis Garcia	2.00	5.00
FGRMC Miguel Cabrera	6.00	15.00
FGRMR Mike Rivera	2.00	5.00
FGRRR R. Rodriguez	2.00	5.00
FGRSC Scott Chiasson	2.00	5.00
FGRSS Seung Song	2.00	5.00
FGRTB Toby Hall	2.00	5.00
FGRWB Wilson Betemit	4.00	10.00
FGRWP Wily Mo Pena	2.00	5.00

2001 Bowman Draft Relics

Inserted one per factory set, these six cards feature relics from some of the most popular prospects in the Bowman Draft Pick set.

Card	Low	High
BDPRCI Cesar Izturis	4.00	10.00
BDPRGJ Gary Johnson	4.00	10.00
BDPRNR Nick Regilio	4.00	10.00
BDPRRC Ryan Church	6.00	15.00
BDPRBJS Brian Specht	4.00	10.00
BDPRJRH J.R. House	4.00	10.00

2002 Bowman

This 440 card set was issued in May, 2002. It was issued in 10 card packs which were packed 24 packs to a box and 12 boxes per case. These packs had an SRP of $3 per pack. The first 110 cards of this set featured veterans while the rest of the set featured rookies and prospects.

Card	Low	High
COMPLETE SET (440)	40.00	80.00
COMMON CARD (1-110)	.10	.30
COMMON CARD (111-440)	.10	.30
1 Adam Dunn	.10	.30
2 Derek Jeter	.75	2.00
3 Alex Rodriguez	.50	1.25
4 Miguel Tejada	.10	.30
5 Nomar Garciaparra	.50	1.25
6 Toby Hall	.10	.30
7 Brandon Duckworth	.10	.30
8 Paul LoDuca	.10	.30
9 Brian Giles	.10	.30
10 C.C. Sabathia	.10	.30
11 Curt Schilling	.10	.30
12 Tsuyoshi Shinjo	.10	.30
13 Ramon Hernandez	.10	.30
14 Jose Cruz Jr.	.10	.30
15 Albert Pujols	.60	1.50
16 Joe Mays	.10	.30
17 Javy Lopez	.10	.30
18 J.T. Snow	.10	.30
19 David Segui	.10	.30
20 Jorge Posada	.20	.50
21 Doug Mientkiewicz	.10	.30
22 Jerry Hairston Jr.	.10	.30
23 Bernie Williams	.20	.50
24 Mike Sweeney	.10	.30
25 Jason Giambi	.10	.30
26 Ryan Dempster	.10	.30
27 Ryan Klesko	.10	.30
28 Mark Quinn	.10	.30
29 Jeff Kent	.10	.30
30 Eric Chavez	.10	.30
31 Adrian Beltre	.10	.30
32 Andruw Jones	.20	.50
33 Alfonso Soriano	.10	.30
34 Aramis Ramirez	.10	.30
35 Greg Maddux	.50	1.25
36 Andy Pettitte	.20	.50
37 Bartolo Colon	.10	.30
38 Ben Sheets	.10	.30
39 Bobby Higginson	.10	.30
40 Ivan Rodriguez	.20	.50
41 Brad Penny	.10	.30
42 Carlos Lee	.10	.30
43 Damion Easley	.10	.30
44 Preston Wilson	.10	.30
45 Jeff Bagwell	.20	.50
46 Eric Milton	.10	.30
47 Rafael Palmeiro	.20	.50
48 Gary Sheffield	.10	.30
49 J.D. Drew	.10	.30
50 Jim Thome	.20	.50
51 Ichiro Suzuki	.60	1.50
52 Bud Smith	.10	.30
53 Chan Ho Park	.10	.30
54 D'Angelo Jimenez	.10	.30
55 Ken Griffey Jr.	.50	1.25
56 Wade Miller	.10	.30
57 Vladimir Guerrero	.30	.75
58 Troy Glaus	.10	.30
59 Shawn Green	.10	.30
60 Kerry Wood	.10	.30
61 Jack Wilson	.10	.30
62 Kevin Brown	.10	.30
63 Marcus Giles	.10	.30
64 Pat Burrell	.10	.30
65 Larry Walker	.10	.30
66 Sammy Sosa	.30	.75
67 Raul Mondesi	.10	.30
68 Tim Hudson	.10	.30
69 Lance Berkman	.10	.30
70 Mike Mussina	.20	.50
71 Barry Zito	.10	.30
72 Jimmy Rollins	.10	.30
73 Barry Bonds	.75	2.00
74 Craig Biggio	.20	.50
75 Todd Helton	.20	.50
76 Roger Clemens	.60	1.50
77 Frank Catalanotto	.10	.30
78 Josh Towers	.10	.30
79 Roy Oswalt	.10	.30
80 Chipper Jones	.30	.75
81 Cristian Guzman	.10	.30
82 Darin Erstad	.10	.30
83 Freddy Garcia	.10	.30
84 Jason Tyner	.10	.30
85 Carlos Delgado	.10	.30
86 Jon Lieber	.10	.30
87 Juan Pierre	.10	.30
88 Matt Morris	.10	.30
89 Phil Nevin	.10	.30
90 Jim Edmonds	.10	.30
91 Magglio Ordonez	.10	.30
92 Mike Hampton	.10	.30
93 Rafael Furcal	.10	.30
94 Richie Sexson	.10	.30
95 Luis Gonzalez	.10	.30
96 Scott Rolen	.20	.50
97 Tim Redding	.10	.30
98 Moises Alou	.10	.30
99 Jose Vidro	.10	.30
100 Mike Piazza	.50	1.25
101 Pedro Martinez UER	.20	.50
Career strikeout total incorrect		
102 Geoff Jenkins	.10	.30
103 Johnny Damon Sox	.20	.50
104 Mike Cameron	.10	.30
105 Randy Johnson	.30	.75
106 David Eckstein	.10	.30
107 Javier Vazquez	.10	.30
108 Mark Mulder	.10	.30
109 Robert Fick	.10	.30
110 Roberto Alomar	.20	.50
111 Wilson Betemit	.10	.30
112 Chris Tritle RC	.10	.30
113 Ed Rogers	.10	.30
114 Juan Pena	.10	.30
115 Josh Beckett	.15	.40
116 Juan Cruz	.10	.30
117 Noochie Varner RC	.15	.40
118 Taylor Buchholz RC	.25	.60
119 Mike Rivera	.10	.30
120 Hank Blalock	.25	.60
121 Hansel Izquierdo RC	.15	.40
122 Orlando Hudson	.10	.30
123 Bill Hall	.15	.40
124 Jose Reyes	.25	.60
125 Juan Rivera	.10	.30
126 Eric Valent	.10	.30
127 Scotty Layfield RC	.15	.40
128 Austin Kearns	.10	.30
129 Nic Jackson RC	.15	.40
130 Chris Baker RC	.15	.40
131 Chad Qualls RC	.20	.50
132 Marcus Thames	.10	.30
133 Nathan Haynes	.10	.30
134 Brett Evert	.10	.30
135 Joe Borchard	.10	.30
136 Ryan Christianson	.10	.30
137 Josh Hamilton	.25	.60
138 Corey Patterson	.10	.30
139 Travis Wilson	.10	.30
140 Alex Escobar	.10	.30
141 Alexis Gomez	.10	.30
142 Nick Johnson	.15	.40
143 Kenny Kelly	.10	.30
144 Marlon Byrd	.10	.30
145 Kory DeHaan	.10	.30
146 Matt Belisle	.10	.30
147 Carlos Hernandez	.10	.30
148 Sean Burroughs	.10	.30
149 Angel Berroa	.10	.30
150 Aubrey Huff	.15	.40
151 Travis Hafner	.15	.40
152 Brandon Berger	.10	.30
153 David Krynzel	.10	.30
154 Ruben Salazar	.10	.30
155 J.R. House	.10	.30
156 Juan Silvestre	.10	.30

157 Dewon Brazelton	.10	.30
158 Jayson Werth	.10	.30
159 Larry Barnes	.10	.30
160 Elvis Pena	.10	.30
161 Ruben Gotay RC	.20	.50
162 Tommy Marx RC	.15	.40
163 John Suomi RC	.15	.40
164 Javier Colina	.10	.30
165 Greg Sain RC	.15	.40
166 Robert Cosby RC	.15	.40
167 Angel Pagan RC	.20	.50
168 Ralph Santana RC	.15	.40
169 Joe Orloski RC	.15	.40
170 Shayne Wright RC	.15	.40
171 Jay Caligiuri RC	.15	.40
172 Greg Montalbano RC	.15	.40
173 Rich Harden RC	1.25	3.00
174 Rich Thompson RC	.15	.40
175 Fred Bastardo RC	.15	.40
176 Alejandro Giron RC	.15	.40
177 Jesus Medrano RC	.15	.40
178 Kevin Deaton RC	.15	.40
179 Mike Rosamond RC	.15	.40
180 Jon Guzman RC	.15	.40
181 Gerard Oakes RC	.15	.40
182 Francisco Liriano RC	1.50	4.00
183 Matt Allegra RC	.15	.40
184 Mike Snyder RC	.15	.40
185 James Shanks RC	.15	.40
186 Anderson Hernandez RC	.15	.40
187 Dan Trumble RC	.15	.40
188 Luis DePaula RC	.15	.40
189 Randall Shelley RC	.15	.40
190 Richard Lane RC	.15	.40
191 Antwon Rollins RC	.15	.40
192 Ryan Bukvich RC	.15	.40
193 Derrick Lewis	.10	.30
194 Eric Miller RC	.15	.40
195 Justin Schuda RC	.15	.40
196 Brian West RC	.15	.40
197 Adam Roller RC	.15	.40
198 Neal Frendling RC	.15	.40
199 Jeremy Hill RC	.15	.40
200 James Barrett RC	.15	.40
201 Brett Kay RC	.15	.40
202 Ryan Mottl RC	.15	.40
203 Brad Nelson RC	.15	.40
204 Juan M. Gonzalez RC	.15	.40
205 Curtis Legendre RC	.15	.40
206 Ronald Acuna RC	.15	.40
207 Chris Flinn RC	.15	.40
208 Nick Alvarez RC	.15	.40
209 Jason Ellison RC	.30	.75
210 Blake McGinley RC	.15	.40
211 Dan Phillips RC	.15	.40
212 Demetrius Heath RC	.15	.40
213 Eric Bruntlett RC	.15	.40
214 Joe Jiannetti RC	.15	.40
215 Mike Hill RC	.15	.40
216 Ricardo Cordova RC	.15	.40
217 Mark Hamilton RC	.15	.40
218 David Mattox RC	.15	.40
219 Jose Morban RC	.15	.40
220 Scott Wiggins RC	.10	.30
221 Steve Green	.10	.30
222 Brian Rogers	.10	.30
223 Chin-Hui Tsao	.15	.40
224 Kenny Baugh	.10	.30
225 Nate Teut	.10	.30
226 Josh Wilson RC	.15	.40
227 Christian Parker	.10	.30
228 Tim Raines Jr.	.10	.30
229 Anastacio Martinez RC	.15	.40
230 Richard Lewis	.10	.30
231 Tim Kalita RC	.15	.40
232 Edwin Almonte RC	.15	.40
233 Hee-Seop Choi	.10	.30
234 Ty Howington	.10	.30
235 Victor Alvarez RC	.15	.40
236 Morgan Ensberg	.15	.40
237 Jeff Austin RC	.15	.40
238 Luis Terrero	.10	.30
239 Adam Wainwright	.20	.50
240 Clint Weibl RC	.10	.30
241 Eric Cyr	.10	.30
242 Marlyn Tisdale RC	.15	.40
243 John VanBenschoten	.10	.30
244 Ryan Raburn RC	.15	.40
245 Miguel Cabrera	.60	1.50
246 Jung Bong	.10	.30
247 Raul Chavez RC	.10	.30
248 Erik Bedard	.15	.40
249 Chris Snelling RC	.25	.60
250 Joe Rogers RC	.15	.40
251 Nate Field RC	.15	.40
252 Matt Herges RC	.10	.30
253 Matt Childers RC	.15	.40
254 Erick Almonte	.10	.30
255 Nick Neugebauer	.10	.30
256 Ron Calloway RC	.15	.40
257 Seung Song	.10	.30
258 Brandon Phillips	.10	.30
259 Cole Barthel RC	.10	.30
260 Jason Lane	.15	.40
261 Jae Seo	.10	.30
262 Randy Flores	.10	.30
263 Scott Chiasson	.10	.30
264 Chase Utley	1.00	2.50
265 Tony Alvarez	.10	.30
266 Ben Howard RC	.15	.40
267 Nelson Castro RC	.15	.40
268 Mark Lukasiewicz RC	.10	.30
269 Eric Glaser RC	.15	.40
270 Rob Henkel RC	.15	.40
271 Jose Valverde RC	.15	.40
272 Ricardo Rodriguez	.10	.30
273 Chris Smith	.10	.30
274 Mark Prior	.25	.60
275 Miguel Olivo	.10	.30
276 Ben Broussard	.10	.30
277 Zach Sorensen	.10	.30
278 Brian Mallette RC	.10	.30
279 Brad Wilkerson	.10	.30
280 Carl Crawford	.15	.40
281 Chone Figgins RC	.60	1.50
282 Jimmy Alvarez RC	.15	.40
283 Gavin Floyd RC	.40	1.00
284 Josh Bonifay RC	.15	.40
285 Garrett Guzman RC	.15	.40
286 Blake Williams	.10	.30
287 Matt Holliday	.10	.30
288 Ryan Madson	.10	.30
289 Luis Torres	.10	.30
290 Jeff Verplancke RC	.15	.40
291 Nate Espy RC	.15	.40
292 Jeff Lincoln RC	.15	.40
293 Ryan Snare RC	.15	.40
294 Jose Ortiz	.10	.30
295 Eric Munson	.10	.30
296 Denny Bautista	.10	.30
297 Willy Aybar	.15	.40
298 Kelly Johnson	.25	.60
299 Justin Morneau	.15	.40
300 Derrick Van Dusen	.10	.30
301 Chad Petty	.10	.30
302 Mike Restovich	.10	.30
303 Shawn Fagan	.10	.30
304 Yurendell DeCaster RC	.15	.40
305 Justin Wayne	.10	.30
306 Mike Peeples RC	.10	.30
307 Joel Guzman	.40	1.00
308 Ryan Vogelsong	.10	.30
309 Jorge Padilla RC	.15	.40
310 Grady Sizemore	.40	1.00
311 Joe Jester RC	.15	.40
312 Jim Journell	.10	.30
313 Bobby Seay	.10	.30
314 Ryan Church RC	.40	1.00
315 Grant Balfour	.10	.30
316 Mitch Jones	.10	.30
317 Travis Foley RC	.15	.40
318 Bobby Crosby	.40	1.00
319 Adrian Gonzalez	.10	.30
320 Ronnie Merrill	.10	.30
321 Joel Pineiro	.10	.30
322 John-Ford Griffin	.10	.30
323 Brian Forystek RC	.15	.40
324 Sean Douglass	.10	.30
325 Manny Delcarmen RC	.20	.50
326 Donnie Bridges	.10	.30
327 Jim Kavourias RC	.15	.40
328 Gabe Gross	.10	.30
329 Jon Rauch	.10	.30
330 Bill Ortega	.10	.30
331 Joey Hammond RC	.15	.40
332 Ramon Moreta RC	.15	.40
333 Ron Davenport	.10	.30
334 Brett Myers	.15	.40
335 Carlos Pena	.10	.30
336 Ezequiel Astacio RC	.15	.40
337 Edwin Yan RC	.15	.40
338 Josh Girdley	.10	.30
339 Shaun Boyd	.10	.30
340 Juan Rincon	.10	.30
341 Chris Duffy RC	.20	.50
342 Jason Kinchen	.10	.30
343 Brad Thomas	.10	.30
344 David Kelton	.10	.30
345 Rafael Soriano	.10	.30
346 Colin Young RC	.15	.40
347 Eric Byrnes	.10	.30
348 Chris Narveson RC	.20	.50
349 John Rheinecker	.10	.30
350 Mike Wilson RC	.15	.40
351 Justin Sherrod RC	.15	.40
352 Deivi Mendez	.10	.30
353 Wily Mo Pena	.15	.40
354 Brett Roneberg RC	.15	.40
355 Trey Lunsford RC	.15	.40
356 Jimmy Gobble RC	.15	.40
357 Brent Butler	.10	.30
358 Aaron Heilman	.10	.30
359 Wilkin Ruan	.10	.30
360 Brian Wolfe RC	.15	.40
361 Cody Ransom	.10	.30
362 Koyie Hill	.10	.30
363 Scott Cassidy	.10	.30
364 Tony Fontana RC	.15	.40
365 Mark Teixeira	.60	1.50
366 Doug Sessions RC	.15	.40
367 Victor Hall	.10	.30
368 Josh Cisneros RC	.15	.40
369 Kevin Mench	.10	.30
370 Tike Redman	.10	.30
371 Jeff Heaverlo	.10	.30
372 Carlos Brackley RC	.15	.40
373 Brad Hawpe	.10	.30
374 Jesus Colome	.10	.30
375 David Espinosa	.10	.30
376 Jesse Foppert RC	.20	.50
377 Ross Peeples RC	.15	.40
378 Alex Requena RC	.15	.40
379 Joe Mauer RC	8.00	20.00
380 Carlos Silva	.10	.30
381 David Wright RC	5.00	12.00
382 Craig Kuzmic RC	.15	.40
383 Pete Zamora RC	.15	.40
384 Matt Parker RC	.15	.40
385 Keith Ginter	.10	.30
386 Gary Cates Jr.	.15	.40
387 Justin Reid RC	.15	.40
388 Jake Mauer RC	.15	.40
389 Dennis Tankersley	.10	.30
390 Josh Barfield RC	1.00	2.50
391 Luis Maza	.10	.30
392 Henry Pichardo RC	.15	.40
393 Michael Floyd RC	.15	.40
394 Clint Nageotte RC	.20	.50
395 Raymond Cabrera RC	.15	.40
396 Mauricio Lara RC	.15	.40
397 Alejandro Cadena RC	.15	.40
398 Jonny Gomes RC	1.00	2.50
399 Jason Bulger RC	.15	.40
400 Bobby Jenks RC	.60	1.50
401 David Gil RC	.15	.40
402 Joel Crump RC	.15	.40
403 Kazuhisa Ishii RC	.30	.75
404 So Taguchi RC	.30	.75
405 Ryan Doumit RC	.25	.60
406 Macay McBride	.15	.40
407 Brandon Claussen	.10	.30
408 Chin-Feng Chen	.15	.40
409 Josh Phelps	.10	.30
410 Freddie Money RC	.20	.50
411 Cliff Bartosh RC	.15	.40
412 Josh Pearce	.10	.30
413 Lyle Overbay	.10	.30
414 Ryan Anderson	.10	.30
415 Terrance Hill RC	.15	.40
416 John Rodriguez RC	.20	.50
417 Richard Stahl	.10	.30
418 Brian Specht	.10	.30
419 Chris Latham RC	.10	.30
420 Carlos Cabrera RC	.15	.40
421 Jose Bautista RC	4.00	10.00
422 Kevin Frederick RC	.15	.40
423 Jerome Williams	.10	.30
424 Napoleon Calzado RC	.15	.40
425 Benito Baez	.10	.30
426 Xavier Nady	.10	.30
427 Jason Botts RC	.25	.60
428 Steve Bechler RC	.15	.40
429 Reed Johnson RC	.40	1.00
430 Mark Outlaw RC	.15	.40
431 Billy Sylvester	.10	.30
432 Luke Lockwood	.10	.30
433 Jake Peavy	.25	.60
434 Alfredo Amezaga	.10	.30
435 Aaron Cook RC	.15	.40
436 Josh Shaffer RC	.15	.40
437 Dan Wright	.10	.30
438 Ryan Gripp RC	.15	.40
439 Alex Herrera	.10	.30
440 Jason Bay RC	2.00	5.00

2002 Bowman Gold

Inserted one per pack, this is a parallel to the 2002 Bowman set. These cards can be differentiated by the Bowman logo and the facsimile signature in gold foil stamping.

COMPLETE SET (440)	75.00	200.00
*RED 1-110: 1.25X TO 3X BASIC		
*BLUE 111-440: .75X TO 2X BASIC		
*BLUE ROOKIES 111-440: .75X TO 2X BASIC		
182 Francisco Liriano	2.50	6.00
379 Joe Mauer	10.00	25.00
381 David Wright	6.00	15.00

2002 Bowman Autographs

Inserted in packs at overall odds of one in 40 hobby packs, one in 24 HTA packs and one in 53 retail packs, this 45 card set featued autographs of leading rookies and prospects.

GROUP A 1:67 H, 1:39 HTA, 1:89 R
GROUP B 1:129 H, 1:74 HTA, 1:170 R
GROUP C 1:881 H, 1:507 HTA, 1:1165 R
GROUP D 1:1558 H, 1:896 HTA, 1:2060 R
GROUP E 1:1685 H, 1:968 HTA, 1:2238 R
OVERALL ODDS 1:40 H, 1:24 HTA, 1:53 R
ONE ADD'L AUTO PER SEALED HTA BOX

BAAA Alfredo Amezaga A	4.00	10.00
BAAH Aubrey Huff A	4.00	10.00
BABA Brandon Claussen A	4.00	10.00
BABC Ben Christensen A	4.00	10.00
BABD Brian Cardwell A	4.00	10.00
BABBC Boof Bonser A	4.00	10.00
BABJC Brian Specht C	4.00	10.00
BABSS Bud Smith B	4.00	10.00
BACK Charles Kegley A	4.00	10.00
BACR Cody Ransom B	4.00	10.00
BACS Chris Smith B	4.00	10.00
BACT Chris Tritle B	4.00	10.00
BACU Chase Utley A	40.00	80.00
BADV Domingo Valdez A	4.00	10.00
BADW Dan Wright B	4.00	10.00
BAGA Garrett Atkins A	8.00	20.00
BAGJ Gary Johnson C	4.00	10.00
BAHB Hank Blalock B	6.00	15.00
BAJB Josh Beckett B	10.00	25.00
BAJD Jeff Davanon A	4.00	10.00
BAJL Jason Lane A	6.00	15.00
BAJP Juan Pena A	4.00	10.00
BAJS Juan Silvestre A	4.00	10.00
BAJAB Jason Botts B	6.00	15.00
BAJLW Jerome Williams A	4.00	10.00
BAKG Keith Ginter B	4.00	10.00
BALB Larry Bigbie A	6.00	15.00
BAMB Marlon Byrd B	4.00	10.00
BAMC Matt Cooper A	4.00	10.00
BAMD Manny Delcarmen A	4.00	10.00
BAME Morgan Ensberg A	6.00	15.00
BAMP Mark Prior B	6.00	15.00
BANJ Nick Johnson B	6.00	15.00
BANN Nick Neugebauer E	4.00	10.00
BANV Noochie Varner B	4.00	10.00
BARF Randy Flores D	4.00	10.00
BARF Ryan Franklin B	4.00	10.00
BARH Ryan Hannaman A	4.00	10.00
BARO Roy Oswalt B	12.50	30.00
BARV Ryan Vogelsong B	30.00	60.00
BATB Tony Blanco A	4.00	10.00
BATH Toby Hall B	4.00	10.00
BATS Termel Sledge B	4.00	10.00
BAWB Wilson Betemit B	4.00	10.00
BAWS Will Smith A	4.00	10.00

2002 Bowman Futures Game Autograph Relics

Inserted at overall odds of one in 196 hobby packs, one in 113 HTA packs and one in 259 retail packs for jersey cards and one in 126 HTA packs for base cards, these cards feature pieces of memorabilia and the player's autograph from the 2001 Futures Game.

GROUP A JSY 1:2193 H, 1:1262 HTA, 1:2898 R
GROUP B JSY 1:1599 H, 1:923 HTA, 1:2125 R
GROUP C JSY 1:522 H, 1:301 HTA, 1:688 R
GROUP D JSY 1:1533 H, 1:882 HTA, 1:2028 R

GROUP E JSY 1:1425 H, 1:822 HTA, 1:1882 R
GROUP F JSY 1:1316 H, 1:759 HTA, 1:1738 R
OVERALL JSY 1:196 H, 1:113 HTA, 1:259 R
BASE ODDS 1:126 HTA

CH Carlos Hernandez Jsy B	10.00	25.00
CP Carlos Pena Jsy D	10.00	25.00
DT Dennis Tankersley Jsy E	10.00	25.00
JRH J.R. House Jsy C	10.00	25.00
JW Jerome Williams Jsy F	10.00	25.00
NJ Nick Johnson Jsy C	10.00	25.00
RL Ryan Ludwick Jsy C	12.50	30.00
TH Toby Hall Base	10.00	25.00
WB Wilson Betemit Jsy A	10.00	25.00

2002 Bowman Game Used Relics

Inserted at an overall stated odd of one in 74 hobby packs, one in 43 HTA packs and one in 99 retail packs, these 26 cards features some of the leading prospects from the set along a piece of game-used memorabilia.

GROUP A BAT 1:3236 H, 1:1866 HTA, 1:4331 R
GROUP B BAT 1:1472 H, 1:849 HTA, 1:1949 R
GROUP C BAT 1:1647 H, 1:948 HTA, 1:2180 R
GROUP D BAT 1:894 H, 1:515 HTA, 1:1180 R
GROUP E BAT 1:375 H, 1:216 HTA, 1:496 R
GROUP F BAT 1:1042 H, 1:601 HTA, 1:1381 R
GROUP G BAT 1:939 H, 1:541 HTA, 1:1237 R
OVERALL BAT 1:135 H, 1:78 HTA, 1:179 R
GROUP A JSY 1:2085 H,1:1202 HTA,1:2762 R
GROUP B JSY 1:1916 H, 1:528 HTA, 1:1213 R
GROUP C JSY 1:223 H, 1:129 HTA, 1:295 R
OVERALL JSY 1:165 H, 1:95 HTA, 1:219 R
OVERALL RELIC 1:74 H, 1:43 HTA, 1: R

BRAB Angel Berroa Bat B	4.00	10.00
BRAC Antoine Cameron Bat C	4.00	10.00
BRAE Adam Everett Bat E	3.00	8.00
BRAF Alex Fernandez Bat B	4.00	10.00
BRAF Alex Fernandez Jsy C	3.00	8.00
BRAG Alexis Gomez Bat A	4.00	10.00
BRAK Austin Kearns Bat E	3.00	8.00
BRALC Alex Cintron Bat E	3.00	8.00
BRCG Cristian Guerrero Bat E	3.00	8.00
BRCI Cesar Izturis Bat D	3.00	8.00
BRCP Corey Patterson Bat B	4.00	10.00
BRCY Colin Young Jsy C	3.00	8.00
BRDJ D'Angelo Jimenez Bat C	4.00	10.00
BRFJ Forrest Johnson Bat G	3.00	8.00
BRGA Garrett Atkins Bat F	4.00	10.00
BRJA Jared Abruzzo Bat D	3.00	8.00
BRJA Jared Abruzzo Jsy C	3.00	8.00
BRJL Jason Lane Jsy B	3.00	8.00
BRJS Jamal Strong Jsy A	3.00	8.00
BRNC Nate Cornejo Jsy C	3.00	8.00
BRNN Nick Neugebauer Jsy C	3.00	8.00
BRRC Ryan Church Bat D	3.00	8.00
BRRD Ryan Dittfurth Jsy C	3.00	8.00
BRRM Ryan Madson Bat E	3.00	8.00
BRRS Ruben Salazar Bat A	4.00	10.00
BRRST Richard Stahl Jsy B	3.00	8.00

2002 Bowman Draft

This 165 card set was issued in December, 2002. These cards were issued in seven card packs which came 24 packs to a box and 10 boxes to a case. Each pack contained four regular Bowman Draft Pick Cards, two Bowman Chrome Draft cards and one Bowman gold card.

COMPLETE SET (165)	25.00	50.00
BDP1 Clint Everts RC	.20	.50
BDP2 Fred Lewis RC	.15	.40
BDP3 Jon Broxton RC	.40	1.00
BDP4 Jason Anderson RC	.15	.40
BDP5 Mike Eusebio RC	.15	.40
BDP6 Zack Greinke RC	2.00	5.00
BDP7 Joe Blanton RC	.75	2.00
BDP8 Sergio Santos RC	.20	.50
BDP9 Jason Cooper RC	.15	.40
BDP10 Delwyn Young RC	.40	1.00
BDP11 Jeremy Hermida RC	1.00	2.50
BDP12 Dan Ortmeier RC	.20	.50
BDP13 Kevin Jepsen RC	.20	.50
BDP14 Russ Adams RC	.20	.50
BDP15 Mike Nixon RC	.15	.40
BDP16 Nick Swisher RC	2.00	5.00
BDP17 Cole Hamels RC	3.00	8.00
BDP18 Brian Dopirak RC	.40	1.00
BDP19 James Loney RC	2.50	6.00
BDP20 Denard Span RC	.75	2.00
BDP21 Billy Petrick RC	.15	.40
BDP22 Jared Doyle RC	.15	.40
BDP23 Jeff Francoeur RC	2.50	6.00
BDP24 Nick Bourgeois RC	.15	.40
BDP25 Matt Cain RC	1.50	4.00
BDP26 John McCurdy RC	.15	.40
BDP27 Mark Kiger RC	.15	.40
BDP28 Bill Murphy RC	.15	.40
BDP29 Matt Craig RC	.20	.50
BDP30 Mike Megrew RC	.15	.40
BDP31 Ben Crockett RC	.15	.40
BDP32 Luke Hagerty RC	.15	.40
BDP33 Matt Whitney RC	.15	.40
BDP34 Dan Meyer RC	.20	.50
BDP35 Jeremy Brown RC	.15	.40
BDP36 Doug Johnson RC	.15	.40
BDP37 Steve Obenchain RC	.15	.40
BDP38 Matt Clanton RC	.15	.40
BDP39 Mark Teahen RC	.40	1.00
BDP40 Tom Carrow RC	.15	.40
BDP41 Micah Schilling RC	.15	.40
BDP42 Blair Johnson RC	.15	.40
BDP43 Jason Pridie RC	.15	.40
BDP44 Joey Votto RC	5.00	12.00
BDP45 Taber Lee RC	.15	.40
BDP46 Adam Peterson RC	.15	.40
BDP47 Adam Donachie RC	.15	.40
BDP48 Josh Murray RC	.15	.40
BDP49 Brent Clevlen RC	.75	2.00
BDP50 Chad Pleiness RC	.15	.40
BDP51 Zach Hammes RC	.15	.40
BDP52 Chris Snyder RC	.20	.50
BDP53 Chris Smith RC	.15	.40
BDP54 Justin Maureau RC	.15	.40
BDP55 David Bush RC	.40	1.00
BDP56 Tim Gilhooly RC	.15	.40
BDP57 Blair Barbier RC	.15	.40
BDP58 Zach Segovia RC	.15	.40
BDP59 Jeremy Reed RC	.40	1.00
BDP60 Matt Pender RC	.15	.40
BDP61 Eric Thomas RC	.15	.40
BDP62 Justin Jones RC	.20	.50
BDP63 Brian Slocum RC	.15	.40
BDP64 Larry Broadway RC	.15	.40
BDP65 Bo Flowers RC	.15	.40
BDP66 Scott White RC	.15	.40
BDP67 Steve Stanley RC	.15	.40
BDP68 Alex Merricks RC	.15	.40
BDP69 Josh Womack RC	.15	.40
BDP70 Dave Jensen RC	.15	.40
BDP71 Curtis Granderson RC	3.00	8.00
BDP72 Pat Osborn RC	.15	.40
BDP73 Nic Carter RC	.15	.40
BDP74 Mitch Talbot RC	.15	.40
BDP75 Don Murphy RC	.15	.40
BDP76 Val Majewski RC	.15	.40
BDP77 Javy Rodriguez RC	.15	.40
BDP78 Fernando Pacheco RC	.15	.40
BDP79 Steve Russell RC	.15	.40
BDP80 Jon Slack RC	.15	.40
BDP81 John Baker RC	.15	.40
BDP82 Aaron Coonrod RC	.15	.40
BDP83 Josh Johnson RC	2.00	5.00
BDP84 Jake Blalock RC	2.00	5.00
BDP85 Alex Hart RC	.15	.40
BDP86 Wes Bankston RC	.75	2.00
BDP87 Josh Rupe RC	.15	.40
BDP88 Dan Cevette RC	.15	.40
BDP89 Kiel Fisher RC	.20	.50
BDP90 Alan Rick RC	.15	.40
BDP91 Charlie Morton RC	.15	.40
BDP92 Chad Spann RC	.15	.40
BDP93 Kyle Boyer RC	.15	.40
BDP94 Bob Malek RC	.15	.40
BDP95 Ryan Rodriguez RC	.15	.40
BDP96 Jordan Renz RC	.15	.40
BDP97 Randy Frye RC	.15	.40
BDP98 Rich Hill RC	2.00	5.00
BDP99 B.J. Upton RC	2.00	5.00
BDP100 Dan Christensen RC	.15	.40
BDP101 Casey Kotchman RC	.40	1.00
BDP102 Eric Good RC	.10	.30
BDP103 Mike Fontenot RC	.15	.40
BDP104 John Webb RC	.15	.40
BDP105 Jason Dubois RC	.20	.50
BDP106 Ryan Kibler RC	.15	.40
BDP107 Jhonny Peralta RC	1.00	2.50
BDP108 Kirk Saarloos RC	.15	.40
BDP109 Rhett Parrott RC	.15	.40
BDP110 Jason Grove RC	.15	.40
BDP111 Colt Griffin RC	.15	.40
BDP112 Dallas McPherson RC	.40	1.00
BDP113 Oliver Perez RC	.40	1.00
BDP114 Mar. McDougall RC	.15	.40
BDP115 Mike Wood RC	.15	.40
BDP116 Scott Hairston RC	.20	.50
BDP117 Jason Simontacchi RC	.15	.40
BDP118 Taggert Bozied RC	.20	.50
BDP119 Shelley Duncan RC	1.25	3.00
BDP120 Dontrelle Willis RC	1.00	2.50
BDP121 Sean Burnett	.10	.30
BDP122 Aaron Cook	.10	.30
BDP123 Brett Evert	.10	.30
BDP124 Jimmy Journell	.10	.30
BDP125 Brett Myers	.10	.30
BDP126 Brad Baker	.10	.30
BDP127 Billy Traber RC	.15	.40
BDP128 Adam Wainwright	.20	.50
BDP129 Jason Young RC	.10	.30
BDP130 John Buck	.10	.30
BDP131 Kevin Cash RC	.15	.40
BDP132 Jason Stokes RC	.20	.50
BDP133 Drew Henson	.10	.30
BDP134 Chad Tracy RC	.40	1.00
BDP135 Orlando Hudson	.10	.30
BDP136 Brandon Phillips	.10	.30
BDP137 Joe Borchard	.10	.30
BDP138 Marlon Byrd	.10	.30
BDP139 Carl Crawford	.10	.30
BDP140 Michael Restovich	.10	.30
BDP141 Corey Hart RC	.60	1.50
BDP142 Edwin Almonte	.10	.30
BDP143 Francis Beltran RC	.15	.40
BDP144 Jorge De La Rosa RC	.15	.40
BDP145 Gerardo Garcia RC	.15	.40
BDP146 Franklyn German RC	.15	.40
BDP147 Francisco Liriano	1.25	3.00
BDP148 Francisco Rodriguez	.10	.30
BDP149 Ricardo Rodriguez	.10	.30
BDP150 Seung Song	.10	.30
BDP151 John Stephens	.10	.30
BDP152 Justin Huber RC	.30	.75
BDP153 Victor Martinez	.30	.75
BDP154 Hee Seop Choi	.10	.30
BDP155 Justin Morneau	.10	.30
BDP156 Miguel Cabrera	.50	1.25
BDP157 Victor Diaz RC	.30	.75
BDP158 Jose Reyes	.20	.50
BDP159 Omar Infante	.10	.30
BDP160 Angel Berroa	.10	.30
BDP161 Tony Alvarez	.10	.30
BDP162 Shin Soo Choo RC	.75	2.00
BDP163 Wily Mo Pena	.10	.30
BDP164 Andres Torres	.10	.30
BDP165 Jose Lopez RC	.75	2.00

2002 Bowman Draft Gold

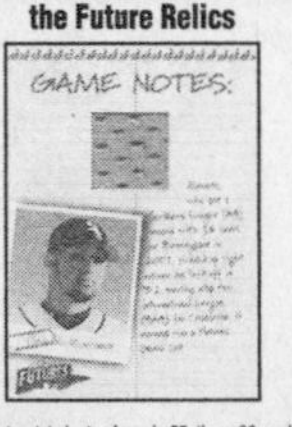

Issued one per pack, this is a parallel to the Bowman Draft Set. These cards have the player's fascimile autograph set off in gold foil.

COMPLETE SET (165)	30.00	80.00
*GOLD: 1.25X TO 3X BASIC		
*GOLD RC'S: .6X TO 1.5X BASIC		
BDP17 Cole Hamels	6.00	15.00
BDP147 Francisco Liriano	2.50	6.00

2002 Bowman Draft Fabric of the Future Relics

Inserted at a stated rate of one in 55, these 28 cards feature prospects from the 2002 All-Star Futures Game who are very close to be major leaguers. All of these cards have a game-worn jersey relic piece on them.

STATED ODDS 1:55
ALL CARDS FEATURE JERSEY SWATCHES

AB Angel Berroa	3.00	8.00
AT Andres Torres	3.00	8.00
AW Adam Wainwright	5.00	12.00
BM Brett Myers	3.00	8.00
BT Billy Traber	2.00	5.00
CC Carl Crawford	4.00	10.00
CH Corey Hart	4.00	10.00
CT Chad Tracy	3.00	8.00
DH Drew Henson	3.00	8.00
EA Edwin Almonte	2.00	5.00
FB Francis Beltran	2.00	5.00
FG Franklyn German	2.00	5.00
FL Francisco Liriano	4.00	10.00
GG Gerardo Garcia	2.00	5.00
HC Hee Seop Choi	4.00	10.00
JH Justin Huber	3.00	8.00
JK Josh Karp	2.00	5.00
JL Jose Lopez	3.00	8.00
JR Jorge De La Rosa	2.00	5.00
JS1 Jason Stokes	2.00	5.00
JS2 John Stephens	3.00	8.00
KC Kevin Cash	2.00	5.00
MR Michael Restovich	3.00	8.00
SB Sean Burnett	3.00	8.00
SC Shin Soo Choo	6.00	15.00
TA Tony Alvarez	3.00	8.00
VD Victor Diaz	3.00	8.00
WP Wily Mo Pena	4.00	10.00

2002 Bowman Draft Freshman Fiber

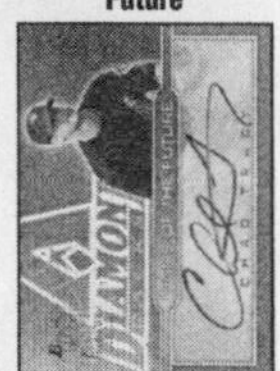

Issued at a stated rate of one in 605 for the bat cards and one in 45 for the jersey cards, these 13 cards feature some of the leading young players in the game along with a game-worn piece.

AH Aubrey Huff Jsy	2.00	5.00
AK Austin Kearns Bat	3.00	8.00
BA Brent Abernathy Jsy	2.00	5.00
DB Dewon Brazelton Jsy	2.00	5.00
JH Josh Hamilton Jsy	6.00	15.00
JK Joe Kennedy Jsy	2.00	5.00
JS Jared Sandberg Jsy	2.00	5.00
JV John VanBenschoten Jsy	2.00	5.00
JWS Jason Standridge Jsy	2.00	5.00
MB Marlon Byrd Bat	3.00	8.00
MT Mark Teixeira Bat	6.00	15.00
NB Nick Bierbrodt Jsy	2.00	5.00
TH Toby Hall Jsy	2.00	5.00

2002 Bowman Draft Signs of the Future

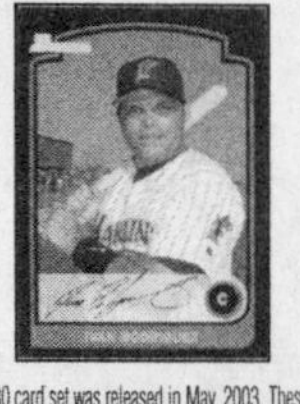

Inserted at different odds depending on what group the player belonged to, these 21 cards feature authentic autographs of the featured player.

GROUP A ODDS 1:100
GROUP B ODDS 1:110
GROUP C ODDS 1:1028
GROUP D ODDS 1:1103
GROUP E ODDS 1:386
GROUP F ODDS 1:2807

BI Brandon Inge E	5.00	12.00
BK Bob Keppel C	4.00	10.00
BP Brandon Phillips B	8.00	20.00
BS Bud Smith E	4.00	10.00
CP Christian Parra D	4.00	10.00
CT Chad Tracy A	6.00	15.00
DD Dan Denham A	4.00	10.00
EB Erik Bedard A	6.00	15.00
JEM Justin Morneau B	10.00	25.00
JM Jake Mauer B	4.00	10.00
JR Juan Rivera B	4.00	10.00
JW Jerome Williams F	4.00	10.00
KH Kris Honel A	4.00	10.00
LB Larry Bigbie E	4.00	10.00
LN Lance Niekro A	6.00	15.00
ME Morgan Ensberg E	4.00	10.00
MF Mike Fontenot A	4.00	10.00
MJ Mitch Jones A	4.00	10.00
NJ Nic Jackson B	4.00	10.00
TB Taylor Buchholz B	4.00	10.00
TL Todd Linden B	6.00	15.00

2003 Bowman

This 330 card set was released in May, 2003. These cards were mixed between veteran cards with red borders on the bottom (1-155) and rookie/prospect cards with blue on the bottom (156-330). This set was issued in 10 card packs which came 24 packs to a box and 12 boxes to a case with an $3 SRP per pack. A special card was inserted featured game-used relics of the two 2002 Major League Rookie of the Years.

COMPLETE SET (330)	25.00	60.00
COMMON CARD (1-155)	.10	.30
COMMON CARD (156-330)	.10	.30
1 Garret Anderson	.10	.30
2 Derek Jeter	.75	2.00
3 Gary Sheffield	.10	.30
4 Matt Morris	.10	.30
5 Derek Lowe	.10	.30
6 Andy Van Hekken	.10	.30
7 Sammy Sosa	.30	.75
8 Ken Griffey Jr.	.50	1.25
9 Omar Vizquel	.20	.50
10 Jorge Posada	.20	.50
11 Lance Berkman	.10	.30
12 Mike Sweeney	.10	.30
13 Adrian Beltre	.10	.30
14 Richie Sexson	.10	.30
15 A.J. Pierzynski	.10	.30
16 Bartolo Colon	.10	.30
17 Mike Mussina	.20	.50
18 Paul Byrd	.10	.30
19 Bobby Abreu	.10	.30
20 Miguel Tejada	.10	.30
21 Aramis Ramirez	.10	.30
22 Edgardo Alfonzo	.10	.30
23 Edgar Martinez	.20	.50
24 Albert Pujols	.60	1.50
25 Carl Crawford	.10	.30
26 Eric Hinske	.10	.30
27 Tim Salmon	.20	.50
28 Luis Gonzalez	.10	.30
29 Jay Gibbons	.10	.30
30 John Smoltz	.20	.50
31 Tim Wakefield	.10	.30
32 Mark Prior	.20	.50
33 Magglio Ordonez	.10	.30
34 Adam Dunn	.10	.30
35 Larry Walker	.10	.30
36 Luis Castillo	.10	.30
37 Wade Miller	.10	.30
38 Carlos Beltran	.10	.30
39 Odalis Perez	.10	.30
40 Alex Sanchez	.10	.30
41 Torii Hunter	.10	.30
42 Cliff Floyd	.10	.30
43 Andy Pettitte	.20	.50
44 Francisco Rodriguez	.10	.30
45 Eric Chavez	.10	.30
46 Kevin Millwood	.10	.30
47 Dennis Tankersley	.10	.30
48 Hideo Nomo	.30	.75
49 Freddy Garcia	.10	.30
50 Randy Johnson	.30	.75
51 Aubrey Huff	.10	.30
52 Carlos Delgado	.10	.30
53 Troy Glaus	.10	.30
54 Junior Spivey	.10	.30
55 Mike Hampton	.10	.30
56 Sidney Ponson	.10	.30
57 Aaron Boone	.10	.30
58 Kerry Wood	.10	.30
59 Runelvys Hernandez	.10	.30
60 Nomar Garciaparra	.50	1.25
61 Todd Helton	.20	.50
62 Mike Lowell	.10	.30
63 Roy Oswalt	.10	.30
64 Raul Ibanez	.10	.30
65 Brian Jordan	.10	.30
66 Geoff Jenkins	.10	.30
67 Jermaine Dye	.10	.30
68 Tom Glavine	.20	.50
69 Bernie Williams	.20	.50
70 Vladimir Guerrero	.30	.75
71 Mark Mulder	.10	.30
72 Jimmy Rollins	.10	.30
73 Oliver Perez	.10	.30
74 Rich Aurilia	.10	.30

75 Joel Pineiro .10 .30
76 J.D. Drew .10 .30
77 Ivan Rodriguez .20 .50
78 Josh Phelps .10 .30
79 Darin Erstad .10 .30
80 Curt Schilling .10 .30
81 Paul Lo Duca .10 .30
82 Marty Cordova .10 .30
83 Manny Ramirez .20 .50
84 Bobby Hill .10 .30
85 Paul Konerko .10 .30
86 Austin Kearns .10 .30
87 Jason Jennings .10 .30
88 Brad Penny .10 .30
89 Jeff Bagwell .20 .50
90 Shawn Green .10 .30
91 Jason Schmidt .10 .30
92 Doug Mientkiewicz .10 .30
93 Jose Vidro .10 .30
94 Bret Boone .10 .30
95 Jason Giambi .10 .30
96 Barry Zito .10 .30
97 Roy Halladay .10 .30
98 Pat Burrell .10 .30
99 Sean Burroughs .10 .30
100 Barry Bonds .75 2.00
101 Kazuhiro Sasaki .10 .30
102 Fernando Vina .10 .30
103 Chan Ho Park .10 .30
104 Andruw Jones .20 .50
105 Adam Kennedy .10 .30
106 Shea Hillenbrand .10 .30
107 Greg Maddux .50 1.25
108 Jim Edmonds .10 .30
109 Pedro Martinez .20 .50
110 Moises Alou .10 .30
111 Jeff Weaver .10 .30
112 C.C. Sabathia .10 .30
113 Robert Fick .10 .30
114 A.J. Burnett .10 .30
115 Jeff Kent .10 .30
116 Kevin Brown .10 .30
117 Rafael Furcal .10 .30
118 Cristian Guzman .10 .30
119 Brad Wilkerson .10 .30
120 Mike Piazza .50 1.25
121 Alfonso Soriano .10 .30
122 Mark Ellis .10 .30
123 Vicente Padilla .10 .30
124 Eric Gagne .10 .30
125 Ryan Klesko .10 .30
126 Ichiro Suzuki .60 1.50
127 Tony Batista .10 .30
128 Roberto Alomar .20 .50
129 Alex Rodriguez .50 1.25
130 Jim Thome .20 .50
131 Jarrod Washburn .10 .30
132 Orlando Hudson .10 .30
133 Chipper Jones .30 .75
134 Rodrigo Lopez .10 .30
135 Johnny Damon .20 .50
136 Matt Clement .10 .30
137 Frank Thomas .30 .75
138 Ellis Burks .10 .30
139 Carlos Pena .10 .30
140 Josh Beckett .10 .30
141 Joe Randa .10 .30
142 Brian Giles .10 .30
143 Kazuhisa Ishii .10 .30
144 Corey Koskie .10 .30
145 Orlando Cabrera .10 .30
146 Mark Buehrle .10 .30
147 Roger Clemens .60 1.50
148 Tim Hudson .10 .30
149 Randy Wolf UER .10 .30
resume says AL leaders; he pitches in NL
150 Josh Fogg .10 .30
151 Phil Nevin .10 .30
152 John Olerud .10 .30
153 Scott Rolen .20 .50
154 Joe Kennedy .10 .30
155 Rafael Palmeiro .20 .50
156 Chad Hutchinson .10 .30
157 Quincy Carter XRC .15 .40
158 Hee Seop Choi .10 .30
159 Joe Borchard .10 .30
160 Brandon Phillips .10 .30
161 Wily Mo Pena .10 .30
162 Victor Martinez .20 .50
163 Jason Stokes .10 .30
164 Ken Harvey .10 .30
165 Juan Rivera .10 .30
166 Jose Contreras RC .60 1.50
167 Dan Haren RC .60 1.50
168 Michel Hernandez RC .15 .40
169 Eider Torres RC .15 .40
170 Chris De La Cruz RC .15 .40
171 Ramon Nivar-Martinez RC .15 .40
172 Mike Adams RC .15 .40
173 Justin Arneson RC .15 .40
174 Jamie Athas RC .15 .40
175 Dwaine Bacon RC .15 .40
176 Clint Barmes RC .40 1.00
177 B.J. Barns RC .15 .40
178 Tyler Johnson RC .15 .40
179 Bobby Basham RC .15 .40
180 T.J. Bohn RC .15 .40
181 J.D. Durbin RC .15 .40
182 Brandon Bowe RC .15 .40
183 Craig Brazell RC .15 .40
184 Dusty Brown RC .15 .40
185 Brian Bruney RC .20 .50
186 Greg Bruso RC .15 .40
187 Jaime Bubela RC .15 .40
188 Bryan Bullington RC .15 .40
189 Brian Burgamy RC .15 .40
190 Eny Cabreja RC .50 1.25
191 Daniel Cabrera RC .30 .75
192 Ryan Cameron RC .15 .40
193 Lance Caraccioli RC .15 .40
194 David Cash RC .15 .40
195 Bernie Castro RC .15 .40
196 Ismael Castro RC .20 .50
197 Daryl Clark RC .15 .40
198 Jeff Clark RC .15 .40
199 Chris Colton RC .15 .40
200 Dexter Cooper RC .15 .40
201 Callix Crabbe RC .20 .50
202 Chien-Ming Wang RC 1.25 3.00
203 Eric Crozier RC .20 .50
204 Nook Logan RC .20 .50
205 David DeJesus RC .30 .75
206 Matt DeMarco RC .15 .40
207 Chris Duncan RC 1.50 4.00
208 Eric Eckenstahler .10 .30
209 Willie Eyre RC .15 .40
210 Evel Bastida-Martinez RC .15 .40
211 Chris Fallon RC .15 .40
212 Mike Flannery RC .15 .40
213 Mike O'Keefe RC .15 .40
214 Ben Francisco RC .15 .40
215 Kason Gabbard RC .15 .40
216 Mike Gallo RC .15 .40
217 Jairo Garcia RC .20 .50
218 Angel Garcia RC .20 .50
219 Michael Garciaparra RC .10 .30
220 Joey Gomes RC .15 .40
221 Dusty Gomon RC .20 .50
222 Bryan Grace RC .15 .40
223 Tyson Graham RC .15 .40
224 Henry Guerrero RC .15 .40
225 Franklin Gutierrez RC .40 1.00
226 Carlos Guzman RC .20 .50
227 Matthew Hagen RC .15 .40
228 Josh Hall RC .15 .40
229 Rob Hammock RC .15 .40
230 Brendan Harris RC .20 .50
231 Gary Harris RC .15 .40
232 Clay Hensley RC .15 .40
233 Michael Hinckley RC .20 .50
234 Luis Hodge RC .15 .40
235 Donnie Hood RC .20 .50
236 Travis Ishikawa RC .40 1.00
237 Edwin Jackson RC .20 .50
238 Ardley Jansen RC .20 .50
239 Ferenc Jongejan RC .15 .40
240 Matt Kata RC .15 .40
241 Kazuhiro Takeoka RC .15 .40
242 Beau Kemp RC .15 .40
243 Il Kim RC .15 .40
244 Brennan King RC .15 .40
245 Chris Kroski RC .15 .40
246 Jason Kubel RC .75 2.00
247 Pete LaForest RC .15 .40
248 Wil Ledezma RC .15 .40
249 Jeremy Bonderman RC 1.25 3.00
250 Gonzalo Lopez RC .15 .40
251 Brian Luderer RC .15 .40
252 Ruddy Lugo RC .15 .40
253 Wayne Lydon RC .15 .40
254 Mark Malaska RC .15 .40
255 Andy Marte RC 1.25 3.00
256 Tyler Martin RC .15 .40
257 Branden Florence RC .15 .40
258 Aneudis Mateo RC .15 .40
259 Derell McCall RC .15 .40
260 Brian McCann RC 3.00 8.00
261 Mike McNutt RC .15 .40
262 Jacobo Meque RC .15 .40
263 Derek Michaelis RC .15 .40
264 Aaron Miles RC .20 .50
265 Jose Morales RC .15 .40
266 Dustin Moseley RC .15 .40
267 Adrian Myers RC .15 .40
268 Dan Neil RC .15 .40
269 Jon Nelson RC .20 .50
270 Mike Neu RC .15 .40
271 Leigh Neuage RC .15 .40
272 Wes O'Brien RC .15 .40
273 Trent Oeltjen RC .20 .50
274 Tim Olson RC .15 .40
275 David Pahucki RC .15 .40
276 Nathan Panther RC .15 .40
277 Arnie Munoz RC .15 .40
278 Dave Pember RC .15 .40
279 Jason Perry RC .20 .50
280 Matthew Peterson RC .15 .40
281 Ryan Shealy RC 1.00 2.50
282 Jorge Piedra RC .20 .50
283 Simon Pond RC .15 .40
284 Aaron Rakers RC .15 .40
285 Hanley Ramirez RC 2.50 6.00
286 Manuel Ramirez RC .20 .50
287 Kevin Randel RC .15 .40
288 Darrell Rasner RC .15 .40
289 Prentice Redman RC .15 .40
290 Eric Reed RC .15 .40
291 Wilton Reynolds RC .15 .40
292 Eric Riggs RC .20 .50
293 Carlos Rijo RC .15 .40
294 Rajai Davis RC .15 .40
295 Aron Weston RC .15 .40
296 Arturo Rivas RC .15 .40
297 Kyle Roat RC .15 .40
298 Bubba Nelson RC .20 .50
299 Levi Robinson RC .15 .40
300 Ray Sadler RC .15 .40
301 Gary Schneidmiller RC .15 .40
302 Jon Schuerholz RC .15 .40
303 Corey Shafer RC .15 .40
304 Brian Shackelford RC .15 .40
305 Bill Simon RC .15 .40
306 Haj Turay RC .10 .30
307 Sean Smith RC .15 .40
308 Ryan Spataro RC .15 .40
309 Jemel Spearman RC .15 .40
310 Keith Stamler RC .15 .40
311 Luke Steidlmayer RC .15 .40
312 Adam Stern RC .10 .30
313 Jay Sitzman RC .15 .40
314 Thomari Story-Harden RC .20 .50
315 Terry Tiffee RC .15 .40
316 Nick Trzesniak RC .15 .40
317 Denny Tussen RC .15 .40
318 Scott Tyler RC .20 .50
319 Shane Victorino RC .40 1.00
320 Doug Waechter RC .20 .50
321 Brandon Watson RC .15 .40
322 Todd Wellemeyer RC .15 .40
323 Eli Whiteside RC .15 .40
324 Josh Willingham RC .40 1.00
325 Travis Wong RC .20 .50
326 Brian Wright RC .15 .40
327 Kevin Youkilis RC 1.25 3.00
328 Andy Sisco RC .20 .50
329 Dustin Yount RC .20 .50
330 Andrew Dominique RC .15 .40

NNO Eric Hinske Bat 6.00 15.00
Jason Jennings Jsy
ROY Relic

2003 Bowman Gold

COMPLETE SET (330) 75.00 150.00
*RED 1-155: 1.25X TO 3X BASIC
*BLUE 156-330: 1.25X TO 3X BASIC
*BLUE ROOKIES: .75X TO 2X BASIC
ONE PER PACK

2003 Bowman Uncirculated Metallic Gold

These cards were originally issued as exchange cards in the silver packs which were inserted one per hobby box. In addition, these exchange cards were seeded into retail packs at a stated rate of one in 49. These cards could be mailed into the Pit.Com for redemption for a hermetically sealed card. Please note that the original stated print run for these cards are 230 sets. These cards could be redeemed until April 30th, 2004.

NNO Exchange Card

2003 Bowman Uncirculated Silver

These cards were issued at a stated rate of one per silver pack, which were inserted one per sealed hobby box. This is a parallel set to the basic Bowman set and each card was issued in already sealed holder. Please note that each card was issued to a stated print run of 250 serial numbered sets. In addition, a few cards were issued as redemption cards for the entire Uncirculated Silver set. These cards could be redeemed until April 30th, 2004.

*UNC.SILVER 1-155: 5X TO 12X BASIC
*UNC.SILVER 156-330: 5X TO 12X BASIC
*UNC.SILVER ROOKIES: 2.5X TO 6X BASIC
202 Chien-Ming Wang 8.00 20.00

2003 Bowman Future Fiber Bats

GROUP A ODDS 1:96 H, 1:34 HTA, 1:196 R
GROUP B ODDS 1:933 H, 1:140 HTA, 1:803 R
AG Adrian Gonzalez A 3.00 8.00
AH Aubrey Huff A 3.00 8.00
AK Austin Kearns A 3.00 8.00
BS Bud Smith B 3.00 8.00
CD Chris Duffy B 3.00 8.00
CK Casey Kotchman A 3.00 8.00
DH Drew Henson A 3.00 8.00
DW David Wright A 6.00 15.00
ES Esix Snead A 3.00 8.00
EY Edwin Yan B 3.00 8.00
FS Freddy Sanchez A 3.00 8.00
HB Hank Blalock A 3.00 8.00
JB Jason Botts A 2.00 5.00
JDM Jake Mauer A 3.00 8.00
JG Jason Grove A 3.00 8.00
JH Josh Hamilton A 6.00 15.00
JM Joe Mauer A 6.00 15.00
JW Justin Wayne B 3.00 8.00
KC Kevin Cash B 3.00 8.00
KD Kory DeHaan A 3.00 8.00
MR Michael Restovich A 3.00 8.00
NH Nathan Haynes A 3.00 8.00
PF Pedro Feliz A 3.00 8.00
RB Rocco Baldelli B 3.00 8.00
RJ Reed Johnson A 3.00 8.00
RK Ryan Langerhans A 3.00 8.00
RS Randall Shelley A 3.00 8.00
SB Sean Burroughs A 3.00 8.00
ST So Taguchi A 3.00 8.00
TW Travis Wilson A 3.00 8.00
WB Wilson Betemit A 3.00 8.00
WR Wilkin Ruan B 3.00 8.00
XN Xavier Nady A 3.00 8.00

2003 Bowman Futures Game Base Autograph

STATED ODDS 1:141 HTA
JR Jose Reyes 12.50 30.00

2003 Bowman Futures Game Gear Jersey Relics

STATED ODDS 1:26 H, 1:9 HTA, 1:52 R
AC Aaron Cook 3.00 8.00
AW Adam Wainwright 3.00 8.00
BB Brad Baker 3.00 8.00
BE Brett Evert 3.00 8.00
BH Bill Hall 3.00 8.00
BM Brett Myers 3.00 8.00
BP Brandon Phillips 3.00 8.00
BT Billy Traber 3.00 8.00
CC Carl Crawford 3.00 8.00
CH Corey Hart 3.00 8.00
CT Chad Tracy 3.00 8.00
DH Drew Henson 3.00 8.00
EA Edwin Almonte 3.00 8.00
FB Francis Beltran 3.00 8.00
FL Francisco Liriano 6.00 15.00
FR Francisco Rodriguez 3.00 8.00
GG Gerardo Garcia 3.00 8.00
HC Hee Seop Choi 3.00 8.00
JB John Buck 3.00 8.00
JDR Jorge De La Rosa 3.00 8.00
JEB Joe Borchard 3.00 8.00
JH Justin Huber 3.00 8.00
JJ Jimmy Journell 3.00 8.00
JK Josh Karp 3.00 8.00
JL Jose Lopez 4.00 10.00
JM Justin Morneau 3.00 8.00
JMS John Stephens 3.00 8.00
JR Jose Reyes 3.00 8.00
JS Jason Stokes 3.00 8.00
JY Jason Young 3.00 8.00
KC Kevin Cash 3.00 8.00
LO Lyle Overbay 3.00 8.00
MB Marlon Byrd 3.00 8.00
MC Miguel Cabrera 4.00 10.00
MR Michael Restovich 3.00 8.00
OH Orlando Hudson 3.00 8.00
OI Omar Infante 3.00 8.00
RD Ryan Dittfurth 3.00 8.00
RR Ricardo Rodriguez 3.00 8.00
SB Sean Burnett 3.00 8.00
SC Shin Soo Choo 3.00 8.00
SS Seung Song 3.00 8.00
TA Tony Alvarez 3.00 8.00
VD Victor Diaz 3.00 8.00
VM Victor Martinez 4.00 10.00
WP Wily Mo Pena 3.00 8.00

2003 Bowman Signs of the Future

GROUP A ODDS 1:39 H, 1:13 HTA, 1:79 R
GROUP B ODDS 1:183 H, 1:65 HTA, 1:374 R
GROUP C ODDS 1:2288 H, 1:816 HTA, 1:4720 R
*RED INK: 1.25X TO 3X GROUP A
*RED INK: 1.25X TO 3X GROUP B
*RED INK: .75X TO 2X GROUP C
RED INK ODDS 1:687 H, 1:245 HTA, 1:1402 R
AV Andy Van Hekken A 4.00 10.00
BB Bryan Bullington A 4.00 10.00
BJ Bobby Jenks B 6.00 15.00
BK Ben Kozlowski A 4.00 10.00
BL Brandon League B 4.00 10.00
BS Brian Slocum A 4.00 10.00
CH Cole Hamels A 30.00 60.00
CJH Corey Hart A 10.00 25.00
CMH Chad Hutchinson C 4.00 10.00
CP Chris Piersoll B 4.00 10.00
DG Doug Gredvig A 4.00 10.00
DHM Dustin McGowan A 4.00 10.00
DL Donald Levinski A 3.00 8.00
DS Doug Sessions B 3.00 8.00
FL Fred Lewis A 4.00 10.00
FS Freddy Sanchez B 6.00 15.00
HR Hanley Ramirez A 40.00 80.00
JA Jason Arnold B 4.00 10.00
JB John Buck A 4.00 10.00
JC Jesus Cota B 4.00 10.00
JG Jason Grove B 4.00 10.00
JGU Jeremy Guthrie A 4.00 10.00
JL James Loney A 10.00 25.00
JOG Jonny Gomes B 6.00 15.00
JR Jose Reyes A 12.50 30.00
JRH Joel Hanrahan A 4.00 10.00
JSC Jason St. Clair B 4.00 10.00
KG Khalil Greene A 12.50 30.00
KH Koyie Hill B 4.00 10.00
MT Mitch Talbot A 6.00 15.00
NC Nelson Castro B 4.00 10.00
OV Oscar Villareal A 3.00 8.00
PR Prentice Redman A 3.00 8.00
QC Quincy Carter C 6.00 15.00
RC Ryan Church B 6.00 15.00
RS Ryan Snare B 4.00 10.00
TL Todd Linden B 4.00 10.00
VM Val Majewski A 4.00 10.00
ZG Zack Greinke A 15.00 40.00
ZS Zach Segovia A 4.00 10.00

2003 Bowman Signs of the Future Dual

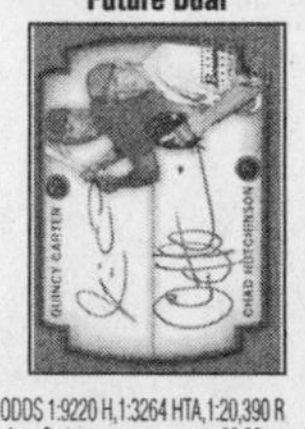

STAT.ODDS 1:9220 H, 1:3264 HTA, 1:20,390 R
CH Quincy Carter 20.00 50.00
Chad Hutchinson

2003 Bowman Draft

This 165-card standard-size set was released in December, 2003. The set was issued in 10 card packs with a $2.99 SRP which came 24 packs to a box and 10 boxes to a case. Please note that each Draft pack included 2 Chrome cards.

COMPLETE SET (165) 20.00 50.00
1 Dontrelle Willis .30 .75
2 Freddy Sanchez .10 .30
3 Miguel Cabrera .30 .75
4 Ryan Ludwick .10 .30
5 Ty Wigginton .10 .30
6 Mark Teixeira .20 .50
7 Trey Hodges .10 .30
8 Laynce Nix .10 .30
9 Antonio Perez .10 .30
10 Jody Gerut .10 .30
11 Jae Weong Seo .10 .30
12 Erick Almonte .10 .30
13 Lyle Overbay .10 .30
14 Billy Traber .10 .30
15 Andres Torres .10 .30
16 Jose Valverde .10 .30
17 Aaron Heilman .10 .30
18 Brandon Larson .10 .30
19 Jung Bong .10 .30
20 Jesse Foppert .10 .30
21 Angel Berroa .10 .30
22 Jeff DaVanon .10 .30
23 Kurt Ainsworth .10 .30
24 Brandon Claussen .10 .30
25 Xavier Nady .10 .30
26 Travis Hafner .10 .30
27 Jerome Williams .10 .30
28 Jose Reyes .10 .30
29 Sergio Mitre RC .20 .50
30 Bo Hart RC .15 .40
31 Adam Miller RC 1.00 2.50
32 Brian Finch RC .15 .40
33 Taylor Mattingly RC .20 .50
34 Daric Barton RC 1.00 2.50
35 Chris Ray RC .40 1.00
36 Jarrod Saltalamacchia RC 3.00 8.00
37 Dennis Dove RC .20 .50
38 James Houser RC .20 .50
39 Clint King RC .20 .50
40 Lou Palmisano RC .20 .50
41 Dan Moore RC .15 .40
42 Craig Stansberry RC .20 .50
43 Jo Jo Reyes RC .50 1.25
44 Jake Stevens RC .20 .50
45 Tom Gorzelanny RC .50 1.25
46 Brian Marshall RC .15 .40
47 Scott Beerer RC .15 .40
48 Javi Herrera RC .20 .50
49 Steve LeRud RC .20 .50
50 Josh Banks RC .30 .75
51 Jon Papelbon RC 5.00 12.00
52 Juan Valdes RC .20 .50
53 Beau Vaughan RC .20 .50
54 Matt Chico RC .20 .50
55 Todd Jennings RC .20 .50
56 Anthony Gwynn RC .50 1.25
57 Matt Harrison RC .30 .75
58 Aaron Marsden RC .20 .50
59 Casey Abrams RC .15 .40
60 Cory Stuart RC .15 .40
61 Mike Wagner RC .15 .40
62 Jordan Pratt RC .20 .50
63 Andre Randolph RC .20 .50
64 Blake Balkcom RC .20 .50
65 Josh Muecke RC .15 .40
66 Jamie D'Antona RC .30 .75
67 Cole Seifrig RC .20 .50
68 Josh Anderson RC .20 .50
69 Matt Lorenzo RC .20 .50
70 Nate Spears RC .20 .50
71 Chris Goodman RC .15 .40
72 Brian McFall RC .15 .40
73 Billy Hogan RC .20 .50
74 Jamie Romak RC .20 .50
75 Jeff Cook RC .20 .50
76 Brooks McNiven RC .15 .40
77 Xavier Paul RC .20 .50
78 Bob Zimmerman RC UER .15 .40
Name is spelled Zimmermann
79 Mickey Hall RC .20 .50
80 Shaun Marcum RC .20 .50
81 Matt Nachreiner RC .20 .50
82 Chris Kinsey RC .15 .40
83 Jonathan Fulton RC .20 .50
84 Edgardo Baez RC .20 .50
85 Robert Valido RC .20 .50
86 Kenny Lewis RC .20 .50
87 Trent Peterson RC .15 .40
88 Johnny Woodard RC .20 .50
89 Wes Littleton RC .20 .50
90 Sean Rodriguez RC .60 1.50
91 Kyle Pearson RC .15 .40
92 Josh Rainwater RC .20 .50
93 Travis Schlichting RC .20 .50
94 Tim Battle RC .30 .75
95 Aaron Hill RC .60 1.50
96 Bob McCrory RC .15 .40
97 Rick Guarno RC .20 .50
98 Brandon Yarbrough RC .15 .40
99 Peter Stonard RC .15 .40
100 Darin Downs RC .20 .50
101 Matt Bruback RC .10 .30
102 Danny Garcia RC .15 .40
103 Cory Stewart RC .15 .40
104 Ferdin Tejeda RC .15 .40
105 Kade Johnson RC .15 .40
106 Andrew Brown RC .20 .50
107 Aquilino Lopez RC .15 .40
108 Stephen Randolph RC .15 .40
109 Dave Matranga RC .15 .40
110 Dustin McGowan RC .20 .50
111 Juan Camacho RC .15 .40
112 Cliff Lee .75 2.00
113 Jeff Duncan RC .15 .40
114 C.J. Wilson .50 1.25
115 Brandon Roberson RC .15 .40
116 David Corrente RC .15 .40
117 Kevin Beavers RC .15 .40
118 Anthony Webster RC .20 .50
119 Oscar Villarreal RC .15 .40
120 Hong-Chih Kuo RC 1.00 2.50
121 Josh Barfield .10 .30
122 Denny Bautista .10 .30
123 Chris Burke RC .50 1.25
124 Robinson Cano RC 4.00 10.00
125 Jose Castillo .10 .30
126 Neal Cotts .10 .30
127 Jorge De La Rosa .10 .30
128 J.D. Durbin .15 .40
129 Edwin Encarnacion .40 1.00
130 Gavin Floyd .10 .30
131 Alexis Gomez .10 .30
132 Edgar Gonzalez RC .15 .40
133 Khalil Greene .30 .75
134 Zack Greinke .10 .30
135 Franklin Gutierrez .20 .50
136 Rich Harden .20 .50
137 J.J. Hardy RC 2.00 5.00
138 Ryan Howard RC 5.00 12.00
139 Justin Huber .10 .30
140 David Kelton .10 .30
141 Dave Krynzel .10 .30
142 Pete LaForest .15 .40
143 Adam LaRoche .10 .30
144 Preston Larrison RC .20 .50
145 John Maine RC 2.00 5.00
146 Andy Marte .50 1.25
147 Jeff Mathis .10 .30
148 Joe Mauer UER .30 .75
Card has playing for New Haven
149 Clint Nageotte .10 .30
150 Chris Narveson .10 .30
151 Ramon Nivar .15 .40
152 Felix Pie RC 2.00 5.00
153 Guillermo Quiroz RC .15 .40
154 Rene Reyes .10 .30
155 Royce Ring .10 .30
156 Alexis Rios .40 1.00
157 Grady Sizemore .30 .75
158 Stephen Smitherman .10 .30
159 Seung Song .10 .30
160 Scott Thorman .10 .30
161 Chad Tracy .10 .30
162 Chin-Hui Tsao .10 .30
163 John VanBenschoten .10 .30
164 Kevin Youkilis 1.50 4.00
165 Chien-Ming Wang 1.00 2.50

2003 Bowman Draft Gold

COMPLETE SET (165) 50.00 100.00
*GOLD: 1.25X TO 3X BASIC
*GOLD RC'S: .6X TO 1.5X BASIC
*GOLD RC YR: .6X TO 1.5X BASIC
ONE PER PACK
51 Jon Papelbon 6.00 15.00
138 Ryan Howard 5.00 12.00
165 Chien-Ming Wang 1.25 3.00

2003 Bowman Draft Fabric of the Future Jersey Relics

GROUP A ODDS 1:721 H, 1:720 R
GROUP B ODDS 1:315 H/R
GROUP C ODDS 1:98 H/R
GROUP D ODDS 1:81 H, 1:82 R
GROUP E ODDS 1:263 H/R
GROUP F ODDS 1:241 H, 1:240 R
AL Adam LaRoche D 2.00 5.00
AM Andy Marte D 4.00 10.00
CN Chris Narveson C 2.00 5.00
EG Edgar Gonzalez D 2.00 5.00
FG Franklin Gutierrez C 3.00 8.00
FP Felix Pie A 4.00 10.00
GF Gavin Floyd E 2.00 5.00
GS Grady Sizemore D 4.00 10.00
JB Josh Barfield B 3.00 8.00
JD J.D. Durbin D 2.00 5.00
JH Justin Huber D 2.00 5.00
JM Joe Mauer C 8.00 20.00
JSM Jeff Mathis B 2.00 5.00
KG Khalil Greene D 4.00 10.00
RC Robinson Cano C 6.00 15.00
RH Rich Harden C 4.00 10.00
RJH Ryan Howard F 8.00 20.00
RR Rene Reyes E 2.00 5.00
RRR Royce Ring F 2.00 5.00
ZG Zack Greinke C 8.00 20.00

2003 Bowman Draft Prospect Premiums Relics

GROUP A ODDS 1:216 H/R
GROUP B ODDS 1:470 H, 1:469 R
AK Austin Kearns Jsy B 2.00 5.00
BH Brendan Harris Bat A 3.00 8.00
BM Brett Myers Jsy B 2.00 5.00
CC Carl Crawford Bat A 3.00 8.00
CS Chris Snelling Bat A 3.00 8.00
CU Chase Utley Bat A 8.00 20.00
HB Hank Blalock Bat A 3.00 8.00
JM Justin Morneau Bat A 3.00 8.00
JT Joe Thurston Bat A 3.00 8.00
NH Nathan Haynes Bat A 3.00 8.00
RB Rocco Baldelli Bat A 3.00 8.00
TH Travis Hafner Bat A 3.00 8.00

2003 Bowman Draft Signs of the Future

GROUP A ODDS 1:385 H, 1:720 R
GROUP B ODDS 1:491 H, 1:491 R
GROUP C ODDS 1:2160 H, 1:12,185 R
AT Andres Torres A 4.00 10.00
CS Cory Stewart B 4.00 10.00
DT Dennis Tankersley A 4.00 10.00
JA Jason Arnold B 4.00 10.00
ZG Zack Greinke C 15.00 40.00

2004 Bowman

This 330-card set was released in May, 2004. The set was issued in hobby, retail and HTA versions. The hobby version was 10 card packs with an $3 SRP which came 24 packs to a box and 12 boxes to a case. The HTA version had 21 card packs with an $6 SRP which came 12 packs to a box and eight boxes to a case. Meanwhile the Retail version consisted of seven card packs with an $3 SRP which came 24 packs to a box and 12 boxes to a case. Cards numbered 1 through 144 feature veterans while cards cards 145 through 165 feature prospects and cards numbered 166 through 330 feature Rookie Cards. Please note that there is a special card featuring memorabilia pieces from 2003 ROY's Dontrelle Willis and Angel Berroa which we have notated at the end of our checklist.

COMPLETE SET (330) 40.00 80.00
COMMON CARD (1-165) .10 .30
COMMON CARD (166-330) .10 .30
ROY ODDS 1:829 H, 1:284 HTA, 1:1632 R
1 Garret Anderson .12 .30
2 Larry Walker .20 .50
3 Derek Jeter .75 2.00
4 Curt Schilling .20 .50
5 Carlos Zambrano .20 .50
6 Shawn Green .12 .30
7 Manny Ramirez .30 .75
8 Randy Johnson .30 .75
9 Jeremy Bonderman .12 .30
10 Alfonso Soriano .12 .30
11 Scott Rolen .20 .50
12 Kerry Wood .12 .30
13 Eric Gagne .12 .30
14 Ryan Klesko .12 .30
15 Kevin Millar .12 .30
16 Ty Wigginton .12 .30
17 David Ortiz .30 .75
18 Luis Castillo .12 .30
19 Bernie Williams .20 .50
20 Edgar Renteria .12 .30
21 Matt Kata .12 .30
22 Bartolo Colon .12 .30
23 Derrek Lee .12 .30
24 Gary Sheffield .12 .30

2004 Bowman

25 Nomar Garciaparra .30 .75
26 Kevin Millwood .12 .30
27 Corey Patterson .12 .30
28 Carlos Beltran .12 .30
29 Mike Lieberthal .12 .30
30 Troy Glaus .12 .30
31 Preston Wilson .12 .30
32 Jorge Posada .20 .50
33 Bo Hart .12 .30
34 Mark Prior .20 .50
35 Hideo Nomo .30 .75
36 Jason Kendall .12 .30
37 Roger Clemens .40 1.00
38 Dmitri Young .12 .30
39 Jason Giambi .12 .30
40 Jim Edmonds .20 .50
41 Ryan Ludwick .12 .30
42 Brandon Webb .12 .30
43 Todd Helton .20 .50
44 Jacque Jones .12 .30
45 Jamie Moyer .12 .30
46 Tim Salmon .12 .30
47 Kelvim Escobar .12 .30
48 Tony Batista .12 .30
49 Nick Johnson .12 .30
50 Jim Thome .20 .50
51 Casey Blake .12 .30
52 Trot Nixon .12 .30
53 Luis Gonzalez .12 .30
54 Dontrelle Willis .12 .30
55 Mike Mussina .20 .50
56 Carl Crawford .20 .50
57 Mark Buehrle .20 .50
58 Scott Podsednik .12 .30
59 Brian Giles .12 .30
60 Rafael Furcal .12 .30
61 Miguel Cabrera .30 .75
62 Rich Harden .12 .30
63 Mark Teixeira .30 .75
64 Frank Thomas .30 .75
65 Johan Santana .30 .75
66 Jason Schmidt .12 .30
67 Aramis Ramirez .12 .30
68 Jose Reyes .20 .50
69 Magglio Ordonez .20 .50
70 Mike Sweeney .12 .30
71 Eric Chavez .12 .30
72 Rocco Baldelli .12 .30
73 Sammy Sosa .30 .75
74 Javy Lopez .12 .30
75 Roy Oswalt .20 .50
76 Raul Ibanez .12 .30
77 Ivan Rodriguez .20 .50
78 Jerome Williams .12 .30
79 Carlos Lee .12 .30
80 Geoff Jenkins .12 .30
81 Sean Burroughs .12 .30
82 Marcus Giles .12 .30
83 Mike Lowell .12 .30
84 Barry Zito .12 .30
85 Aubrey Huff .12 .30
86 Esteban Loaiza .12 .30
87 Torii Hunter .12 .30
88 Phil Nevin .12 .30
89 Andruw Jones .12 .30
90 Josh Beckett .20 .50
91 Mark Mulder .12 .30
92 Hank Blalock .12 .30
93 Jason Phillips .12 .30
94 Russ Ortiz .12 .30
95 Juan Pierre .12 .30
96 Tom Glavine .20 .50
97 Gil Meche .12 .30
98 Ramon Ortiz .12 .30
99 Richie Sexson .12 .30
100 Albert Pujols .75 2.00
101 Javier Vazquez .12 .30
102 Johnny Damon .20 .50
103 Alex Rodriguez Yanks .50 1.25
104 Omar Vizquel .20 .50
105 Chipper Jones .30 .75
106 Lance Berkman .20 .50
107 Tim Hudson .20 .50
108 Carlos Delgado .12 .30
109 Austin Kearns .12 .30
110 Orlando Cabrera .12 .30
111 Edgar Martinez .20 .50
112 Melvin Mora .12 .30
113 Jeff Bagwell .20 .50
114 Marlon Byrd .12 .30
115 Vernon Wells .12 .30
116 C.C. Sabathia .20 .50
117 Cliff Floyd .12 .30
118 Ichiro Suzuki .50 1.25
119 Miguel Olivo .12 .30
120 Mike Piazza .30 .75
121 Adam Dunn .20 .50
122 Paul Lo Duca .12 .30
123 Brett Myers .12 .30
124 Michael Young .12 .30
125 Sidney Ponson .12 .30
126 Greg Maddux .50 1.25
127 Vladimir Guerrero .30 .75
128 Miguel Tejada .20 .50
129 Andy Pettitte .20 .50
130 Rafael Palmeiro .20 .50
131 Ken Griffey Jr. .50 1.25
132 Shannon Stewart .12 .30
133 Joel Pineiro .12 .30
134 Luis Matos .12 .30
135 Jeff Kent .12 .30
136 Randy Wolf .12 .30
137 Chris Woodward .12 .30
138 Jody Gerut .12 .30
139 Jose Vidro .12 .30
140 Bret Boone .12 .30
141 Bill Mueller .12 .30
142 Angel Berroa .12 .30
143 Bobby Abreu .12 .30
144 Roy Halladay .30 .75
145 Delmon Young .20 .50
146 Jonny Gomes .12 .30
147 Rickie Weeks .12 .30
148 Edwin Jackson .12 .30
149 Neal Cotts .12 .30
150 Jason Bay .20 .50
151 Khalil Greene .20 .50
152 Joe Mauer .30 .75
153 Bobby Jenks .12 .30
154 Chin-Feng Chen .12 .30
155 Chien-Ming Wang .60 1.50
156 Mickey Hall .12 .30
157 James Houser .12 .30
158 Jay Sborz .12 .30
159 Jonathan Fulton .12 .30
160 Steven Lerud .12 .30
161 Grady Sizemore .20 .50
162 Felix Pie .12 .30
163 Dustin McGowan .12 .30
164 Chris Lubanski .12 .30
165 Tom Gorzelanny .12 .30
166 Rudy Guillen FY RC .12 .30
167 Bobby Brownlie FY RC .12 .30
168 Conor Jackson FY RC .75 2.00
169 Matt Moses FY RC .20 .50
170 Ervin Santana FY RC .30 .75
171 Merkin Valdez FY RC .12 .30
172 Erick Aybar FY RC .20 .50
173 Brad Sullivan FY RC .12 .30
174 David Aardsma FY RC .12 .30
175 Brad Snyder FY RC .12 .30
176 Alberto Callaspo FY RC .30 .75
177 Brandon Medders FY RC .12 .30
178 Zach Miner FY RC .20 .50
179 Charlie Zink FY RC .12 .30
180 Adam Greenberg FY RC .12 .30
181 Kevin Howard FY RC .12 .30
182 Wanell Severino FY RC .12 .30
183 Kevin Kouzmanoff FY RC .75 2.00
184 Joel Zumaya FY RC .75 2.00
185 Skip Schumaker FY RC .20 .50
186 Nic Ungs FY RC .12 .30
187 Todd Self FY RC .12 .30
188 Brian Steffek FY RC .12 .30
189 Brock Peterson FY RC .12 .30
190 Greg Thissen FY RC .12 .30
191 Frank Brooks FY RC .12 .30
192 Estee Harris FY RC .12 .30
193 Chris Mabeus FY RC .12 .30
194 Dan Giese FY RC .12 .30
195 Jared Wells FY RC .12 .30
196 Carlos Sosa FY RC .12 .30
197 Bobby Madritsch FY .12 .30
198 Calvin Hayes FY RC .12 .30
199 Omar Quintanilla FY RC .12 .30
200 Chris O'Riordan FY RC .12 .30
201 Tim Hutting FY RC .12 .30
202 Carlos Quentin FY RC .50 1.25
203 Brayan Pena FY RC .12 .30
204 Jeff Salazar FY RC .12 .30
205 David Murphy FY RC .30 .75
206 Alberto Garcia FY RC .12 .30
207 Ramon Ramirez FY RC .12 .30
208 Luis Bolivar FY RC .12 .30
209 Rodney Choy Foo FY RC .12 .30
210 Kyle Sleeth FY RC .12 .30
211 Anthony Acevedo FY RC .12 .30
212 Chad Santos FY RC .12 .30
213 Jason Frasor FY RC .12 .30
214 Jesse Roman FY RC .12 .30
215 James Tomlin FY RC .12 .30
216 Josh Labandeira FY RC .12 .30
217 Joaquin Arias FY RC .30 .75
218 Don Sutton FY UER RC .12 .30
Nick Swisher pictured
219 Danny Gonzalez FY RC .12 .30
220 Javier Guzman FY RC .12 .30
221 Anthony Lerew FY RC .12 .30
222 Jon Knott FY RC .12 .30
223 Jesse English FY RC .12 .30
224 Felix Hernandez FY RC 2.50 6.00
225 Travis Hanson FY RC .12 .30
226 Jesse Floyd FY RC .12 .30
227 Nick Gorneault FY RC .12 .30
228 Craig Ansman FY RC .12 .30
229 Wardell Starling FY RC .12 .30
230 Carl Loadenthal FY RC .12 .30
231 Dave Crouthers FY RC .12 .30
232 Harvey Garcia FY RC .12 .30
233 Casey Kopitzke FY RC .12 .30
234 Ricky Nolasco FY RC .20 .50
235 Miguel Perez FY RC .12 .30
236 Ryan Mulhern FY RC .12 .30
237 Chris Aguila FY RC .12 .30
238 Brooks Conrad FY RC .12 .30
239 Damaso Espino FY RC .12 .30
240 Jereme Milons FY RC .12 .30
241 Luke Hughes FY RC .12 .30
242 Kory Casto FY RC .12 .30
243 Jose Valdez FY RC .12 .30
244 J.T. Stotts FY RC .12 .30
245 Lee Gwaltney FY RC .12 .30
246 Yoann Torrealba FY RC .12 .30
247 Omar Falcon FY RC .12 .30
248 Jon Coutlangus FY RC .12 .30
249 George Sherrill FY RC .12 .30
250 John Santor FY RC .12 .30
251 Tony Richie FY RC .12 .30
252 Kevin Richardson FY RC .12 .30
253 Tim Bittner FY RC .12 .30
254 Dustin Nippert FY RC .12 .30
255 Jose Capellan FY RC .12 .30
256 Donald Levinski FY RC .12 .30
257 Jerome Gamble FY RC .12 .30
258 Jeff Keppinger FY RC .20 .50
259 Jason Szuminski FY RC .12 .30
260 Akinori Otsuka FY RC .12 .30
261 Ryan Budde FY RC .12 .30
262 Shingo Takatsu FY RC .12 .30
263 Jeff Allison FY RC .12 .30
264 Hector Gimenez FY RC .12 .30
265 Tim Frend FY RC .12 .30
266 Tom Farmer FY RC .12 .30
267 Shawn Hill FY RC .12 .30
268 Lastings Milledge FY RC .75 2.00
269 Scott Proctor FY RC .12 .30
270 Jorge Mejia FY RC .12 .30
271 Terry Jones FY RC .12 .30
272 Zach Duke FY RC .20 .50
273 Tim Stauffer FY RC .20 .50
274 Luke Anderson FY RC .12 .30
275 Hunter Brown FY RC .12 .30
276 Matt Lemanczyk FY RC .12 .30
277 Fernando Cortez FY RC .12 .30
278 Vince Perkins FY RC .12 .30
279 Tommy Murphy FY RC .12 .30
280 Mike Gosling FY RC .12 .30
281 Paul Bacot FY RC .12 .30
282 Matt Capps FY RC .12 .30
283 Juan Gutierrez FY RC .12 .30
284 Teodoro Encarnacion FY RC .12 .30
285 Juan Cedeno FY RC .12 .30
286 Matt Creighton FY RC .12 .30
287 Ryan Hankins FY RC .12 .30
288 Leo Nunez FY RC .12 .30
289 Dave Wallace FY RC .12 .30
290 Rob Tejeda FY RC .12 .30
291 Lincoln Holdzkom FY RC .12 .30
292 Jason Hirsh FY RC .12 .30
293 Tydus Meadows FY RC .12 .30
294 Khalid Ballouli FY RC .12 .30
295 Benji DeQuin FY RC .12 .30
296 Tyler Davidson FY RC .12 .30
297 Brant Colamarino FY RC .12 .30
298 Marcus McBeth FY RC .12 .30
299 Brad Eldred FY RC .12 .30
300 David Pauley FY RC .20 .50
301 Yadier Molina FY RC .75 2.00
302 Chris Shelton FY RC .12 .30
303 Travis Blackley FY RC .12 .30
304 Jon DeVries FY RC .12 .30
305 Sheldon Fulse FY RC .12 .30
306 Vito Chiaravalloti FY RC .12 .30
307 Warner Madrigal FY RC .12 .30
308 Reid Gorecki FY RC .12 .30
309 Sung Jung FY RC .12 .30
310 Pete Shier FY RC .12 .30
311 Michael Mooney FY RC .12 .30
312 Kenny Perez FY RC .12 .30
313 Michael Mallory FY RC .12 .30
314 Ben Himes FY RC .12 .30
315 Ivan Ochoa FY RC .12 .30
316 Donald Kelly FY RC .20 .50
317 Logan Kensing FY RC .12 .30
318 Kevin Davidson FY RC .12 .30
319 Brian Pilkington FY RC .12 .30
320 Alex Romero FY RC .12 .30
321 Chad Chop FY RC .12 .30
322 Dioner Navarro FY RC .20 .50
323 Casey Myers FY RC .12 .30
324 Mike Rouse FY RC .12 .30
325 Sergio Silva FY RC .12 .30
326 J.J. Furmaniak FY RC .12 .30
327 Brad Vericker FY RC .12 .30
328 Blake Hawksworth FY RC .12 .30
329 Brock Jacobsen FY RC .12 .30
330 Alec Zumwalt FY RC .12 .30
BW Angel Berroa Bat 6.00 15.00
Dontrelle Willis Jsy ROY

2004 Bowman 1st Edition

*1ST EDITION 1-165: .75X TO 2X BASIC
*1ST EDITION 166-330: .75X TO 2X BASIC
ISSUED IN FIRST EDITION PACKS

2004 Bowman Gold

COMPLETE SET (330) 60.00 150.00
*GOLD 1-165: 1.25X TO 3X BASIC
*GOLD 166-330: 1X TO 2.5X BASIC
ONE PER HOBBY PACK
ONE PER HTA PACK
ONE PER RETAIL PACK

2004 Bowman Uncirculated Gold

ONE EXCH.CARD PER SILVER PACK
ONE SILVER PACK PER SEALED HOBBY BOX
ONE SILVER PACK PER SEALED HTA BOX
STATED ODDS 1:44 RETAIL
STATED PRINT RUN 210 SETS
SEE WWW.THEPIT.COM FOR PRICING
NNO Exchange Card 2.00 5.00

2004 Bowman Uncirculated Silver

*UNC.SILVER 1-165: 5X TO 12X BASIC
*UNC.SILVER 166-330: 3X TO 8X BASIC
ONE PER SILVER PACK
ONE SILVER PACK PER SEALED HOBBY BOX
ONE SILVER PACK PER SEALED HTA BOX
SET EXCH.CARD ODDS 1:9159 H, 1:3718 HTA
STATED PRINT RUN 245 SERIAL #'d SETS
1ST 100 SETS PRINTED HELD FOR EXCH.
LAST 145 SETS PRINTED DIST.IN BOXES
EXCHANGE DEADLINE 05/31/06

2004 Bowman Autographs

STATED ODDS 1:72 H, 1:24 HTA, 1:139 R
RED INK ODDS 1:1466 H,1:501 HTA,1:2901 R
RED INK PRINT RUN 25 SETS
RED INK ARE NOT SERIAL-NUMBERED
RED INK PRINT RUN PROVIDED BY TOPPS
NO RED INK PRICING DUE TO SCARCITY
161 Grady Sizemore 6.00 15.00
162 Felix Pie 6.00 15.00
163 Dustin McGowan 3.00 8.00
164 Chris Lubanski 4.00 10.00
165 Tom Gorzelanny 3.00 8.00
166 Rudy Guillen 4.00 10.00
167 Bobby Brownlie 4.00 10.00
168 Conor Jackson 10.00 25.00
169 Matt Moses 6.00 15.00
170 Ervin Santana 6.00 15.00
171 Merkin Valdez 4.00 10.00
172 Erick Aybar 8.00 20.00
173 Brad Sullivan 4.00 10.00
174 David Aardsma 4.00 10.00
175 Brad Snyder 4.00 10.00

2004 Bowman Relics

GROUP A 1:346 H, 1:118 HTA, 1:1685 R
GROUP B 1:133 H, 1:44 HTA, 1:269 R
HS JSY MEANS HIGH SCHOOL JERSEY
154 Chin-Feng Chen Jsy B 6.00 15.00
155 Chien-Ming Wang Uni B 6.00 15.00
156 Mickey Hall HS Jsy B 3.00 8.00
157 James Houser HS Jsy A 3.00 8.00
158 Jay Sborz HS Jsy B 3.00 8.00
159 Jonathan Fulton HS Jsy B 3.00 8.00
160 Steve Lerud HS Jsy A 3.00 8.00
164 Chris Lubanski HS Jsy B 3.00 8.00
192 Estee Harris HS Jsy A 3.00 8.00
221 Anthony Lerew Jsy B 3.00 8.00

2004 Bowman Base of the Future Autograph

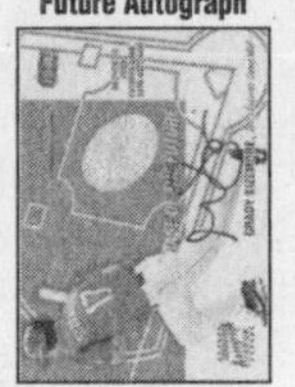

STATED ODDS 1:110 HTA
RED INK ODDS 1:5112 HTA
RED INK PRINT RUN 25 SERIAL #'d CARDS
NO RED INK PRICING DUE TO SCARCITY
GS Grady Sizemore 20.00 50.00

2004 Bowman Futures Game Gear Jersey Relics

GROUP A 1:167 H, 1:58 HTA, 1:333 R
GROUP B 1:71 H, 1:23 HTA, 1:148 R
GROUP C 1:181 H, 1:63 HTA, 1:362 R
GROUP D 1:173 H, 1:59 HTA, 1:341 R
GROUP E 1:145 H, 1:70 HTA, 1:318 R
AR Alexis Rios A 3.00 8.00
CB Chris Burke B 3.00 8.00
CN Clint Nageotte B 3.00 8.00
CT Chad Tracy B 3.00 8.00
CW Chien-Ming Wang C 15.00 40.00
DB Denny Bautista D 3.00 8.00
DBK Dave Krynzel B 3.00 8.00
DK David Kelton E 3.00 8.00
EE Edwin Encarnacion A 3.00 8.00
EJ Edwin Jackson C 3.00 8.00
ES Ervin Santana D 4.00 10.00
GQ Guillermo Quiroz A 3.00 8.00
JC Jose Castillo E 3.00 8.00
JD Jorge De La Rosa C 3.00 8.00
JH J.J. Hardy A 3.00 8.00
JM John Maine B 4.00 10.00
JV John VanBenschoten B 3.00 8.00
KY Kevin Youkilis E 3.00 8.00
MV Merkin Valdez F 3.00 8.00
NC Neal Cotts D 3.00 8.00
PL Pete LaForest B 3.00 8.00
PWL Preston Larrison B 3.00 8.00
RN Ramon Nivar A 3.00 8.00
SH Shawn Hill D 3.00 8.00
SJS Seung Song B 3.00 8.00
SS Stephen Smitherman B 3.00 8.00
ST Scott Thorman C 3.00 8.00
TB Travis Blackley B 3.00 8.00

2004 Bowman Signs of the Future

GROUP A 1:75 H, 1:25 HTA, 1:147 R
GROUP B 1:847 H, 1:289 HTA, 1:1675 R
GROUP C 1:582 H, 1:198 HTA, 1:1148 R
GROUP D 1:315 H, 1:105 HTA, 1:605 R
RED INK ODDS 1:1466 H,1:501 HTA,1:2901 R
RED INK PRINT RUN 25 SETS
RED INK CARDS ARE NOT SERIAL #'d
RED INK PRINT RUN PROVIDED BY TOPPS
NO RED INK PRICING DUE TO SCARCITY
AH Aaron Hill A 10.00 25.00
BC Brent Clevlen A 8.00 20.00
BF Brian Finch D 4.00 10.00
BM Brandon Medders A 3.00 8.00
BS Brian Snyder D 4.00 10.00
BW Brandon Wood B 8.00 20.00
CS Corey Shafer A 3.00 8.00
DS Denard Span A 3.00 8.00
ED Eric Duncan D 6.00 15.00
GS Grady Sizemore D 12.50 30.00
IC Ismael Castro A 3.00 8.00
JB Justin Backsmeyer D 4.00 10.00
JH James Houser A 3.00 8.00
JV Joey Votto A 50.00 100.00
MM Matt Murton D 6.00 15.00
NM Nick Markakis C 8.00 20.00
RH Ryan Harvey C 4.00 10.00
TJ Tyler Johnson A 3.00 8.00
TL Todd Linden A 3.00 8.00

2004 Bowman Draft

This 165-card set was released in November-December, 2004. The set was issued in seven-card hobby and retail packs, both with an $3 SRP which were issued 24 packs to a box and 10 boxes to a case. The hobby and retial packs can be differentiated by the insert odds.

COMPLETE SET (165) 15.00 40.00
COMMON CARD (1-165) .12 .30
COMMON RC (1-165) .12 .30
COMMON RC YR .12 .30
PLATES ODDS 1:559 HOBBY
PLATES PRINT RUN 1 SERIAL #'d SET
BLACK-CYAN-MAGENTA-YELLOW EXIST
NO PLATES PRICING DUE TO SCARCITY
1 Lyle Overbay .12 .30
2 David Newhan .12 .30
3 J.R. House .12 .30
4 Chad Tracy .12 .30
5 Humberto Quintero .12 .30
6 Dave Bush .12 .30
7 Scott Hairston .12 .30
8 Mike Wood .12 .30
9 Alexis Rios .20 .50
10 Sean Burnett .12 .30
11 Wilson Valdez .12 .30
12 Lew Ford .12 .30
13 Freddy Thon RC .12 .30
14 Zack Greinke .20 .50
15 Bucky Jacobsen .12 .30
16 Kevin Youkilis .20 .50
17 Grady Sizemore .20 .50
18 Denny Bautista .12 .30
19 David DeJesus .12 .30
20 Casey Kotchman .12 .30
21 David Kelton .12 .30
22 Charles Thomas RC .12 .30
23 Kazuhito Tadano RC .12 .30
24 Justin Leone RC .12 .30
25 Eduardo Villacis RC .12 .30
26 Brian Dallimore RC .12 .30
27 Nick Green .12 .30
28 Sam McConnell RC .12 .30
29 Brad Halsey RC .12 .30
30 Roman Colon RC UER .12 .30
Letter T missing in how acquired -- Free Agen
31 Josh Fields RC .20 .50
32 Cody Bunkelman RC .12 .30
33 Jay Rainville RC .12 .30
34 Richie Robnett RC .12 .30
35 Jon Poterson RC .12 .30
36 Huston Street RC .30 .75
37 Erick San Pedro RC .12 .30
38 Cory Dunlap RC .12 .30
39 Kurt Suzuki RC .40 1.00
40 Anthony Swarzak RC .20 .50
41 Ian Desmond RC .30 .75
42 Chris Covington RC .12 .30
43 Christian Garcia RC .20 .50
44 Gaby Hernandez RC .30 .75
45 Steven Register RC .12 .30
46 Eduardo Morlan RC .20 .50
47 Collin Balester RC .12 .30
48 Nathan Phillips RC .12 .30
49 Dan Schwartzbauer RC .12 .30
50 Rafael Gonzalez RC .12 .30
51 K.C. Herren RC .12 .30
52 William Susdorf RC .12 .30
53 Rob Johnson RC .12 .30
54 Louis Marson RC .20 .50
55 Joe Koshansky RC .12 .30
56 Jamar Walton RC .12 .30
57 Mark Lowe RC .20 .50
58 Matt Macri RC .20 .50
59 Donny Lucy RC .12 .30
60 Mike Ferris RC .12 .30
61 Mike Nickeas RC .12 .30
62 Eric Hurley RC .12 .30
63 Scott Elbert RC .12 .30
64 Blake DeWitt RC .50 1.25
65 Danny Putnam RC .12 .30
66 J.P. Howell RC .12 .30
67 John Wiggins RC .12 .30
68 Justin Orenduff RC .20 .50
69 Ray Liotta RC .12 .30
70 Billy Buckner RC .12 .30
71 Eric Campbell RC .12 .30
72 Olin Wick RC .12 .30
73 Sean Gamble RC .12 .30
74 Seth Smith RC .30 .75
75 Wade Davis RC .40 1.00
76 Joe Jacobitz RC .12 .30
77 J.A. Happ RC .30 .75
78 Eric Ridener RC .12 .30
79 Matt Tuiasosopo RC .30 .75
80 Brad Bergesen RC .12 .30
81 Javy Guerra RC .12 .30
82 Buck Shaw RC .12 .30
83 Paul Janish RC .20 .50
84 Sean Kazmar RC .12 .30
85 Josh Johnson RC .12 .30
86 Angel Salome RC .12 .30
87 Jordan Parraz RC .20 .50
88 Kelvin Vazquez RC .12 .30
89 Grant Hansen RC .12 .30
90 Matt Fox RC .12 .30
91 Trevor Plouffe RC .30 .75
92 Wes Whisler RC .12 .30
93 Curtis Thigpen RC .12 .30
94 Donnie Smith RC .12 .30
95 Luis Rivera RC .12 .30
96 Jesse Hoover RC .12 .30
97 Jason Vargas RC .30 .75
98 Clary Carlsen RC .12 .30
99 Mark Robinson RC .12 .30
100 J.C. Holt RC .12 .30
101 Chad Blackwell RC .12 .30
102 Daryl Jones RC .12 .30
103 Jonathan Tierce RC .12 .30
104 Patrick Bryant RC .12 .30
105 Eddie Prasch RC .12 .30
106 Mitch Einertson RC .12 .30
107 Kyle Waldrop RC .12 .30
108 Jeff Marquez RC .12 .30
109 Zach Jackson RC .12 .30
110 Josh Wahpepah RC .12 .30
111 Adam Lind RC .40 1.00
112 Kyle Bloom RC .12 .30
113 Ben Harrison RC .12 .30
114 Taylor Tankersley RC .12 .30
115 Steven Jackson RC .12 .30
116 David Purcey RC .20 .50
117 Jacob McGee RC .30 .75
118 Lucas Harrell RC .12 .30
119 Brandon Allen RC .50 1.25
120 Van Pope RC .12 .30
121 Jeff Francis .12 .30
122 Joe Blanton .12 .30
123 Wil Ledezma .12 .30
124 Bryan Bullington .12 .30
125 Jairo Garcia .12 .30
126 Matt Cain .12 .30
127 Arnie Munoz .12 .30
128 Clint Everts .12 .30
129 Jesus Cota .12 .30
130 Gavin Floyd .12 .30
131 Edwin Encarnacion .20 .50
132 Koyie Hill .12 .30
133 Ruben Gotay .12 .30
134 Jeff Mathis .12 .30
135 Andy Marte .12 .30
136 Dallas McPherson .12 .30
137 Justin Morneau .12 .30
138 Rickie Weeks .12 .30
139 Joel Guzman .12 .30
140 Shin Soo Choo .20 .50
141 Yusmeiro Petit RC .20 .50
142 Jorge Cortes RC .12 .30
143 Val Majewski .12 .30
144 Felix Pie .12 .30
145 Aaron Hill .12 .30
146 Jose Capellan .12 .30
147 Dioner Navarro .20 .50
148 Fausto Carmona RC .20 .50
149 Robinzon Diaz RC .12 .30
150 Felix Hernandez 2.50 6.00
151 Andres Blanco RC .12 .30
152 Jason Kubel .12 .30
153 Willy Taveras RC .30 .75
154 Merkin Valdez .12 .30
155 Robinson Cano .30 .75
156 Bill Murphy .12 .30
157 Chris Burke .12 .30
158 Kyle Sleeth .12 .30
159 B.J. Upton .20 .50
160 Tim Stauffer .20 .50
161 David Wright .50 1.25
162 Conor Jackson .75 2.00
163 Brad Thompson RC .20 .50
164 Delmon Young .20 .50
165 Jeremy Reed .12 .30

2004 Bowman Draft Gold

COMPLETE SET (165) 25.00 60.00
*GOLD RC's: .6X TO 1.5X BASIC
*GOLD RC YR: .6X TO 1.5X BASIC
ONE PER PACK

2004 Bowman Draft Red

STATED ODDS 1:4471 HOBBY
STATED PRINT RUN 1 SERIAL #'d SET
NO PRICING DUE TO SCARCITY

2004 Bowman Draft AFLAC Promos

Little is known about how many of these six cards have appeared on the secondary market. A few of these cards surfaced in the AFLAC redemption packs issued to dealers. These cards were issued instead of some of the standard 12 cards in those packs. If you know of other cards issued this way or can provide extra information, that would be very appreciated.

DISTRIBUTED TO DEALERS
11 Cameron Maybin
15 Ryan DeLaughter
17 Jeremy Hellickson
18 Austin Jackson
19 Ryan Mitchell
30 Ralphie Henriquez
38 Kent Matthes

2004 Bowman Draft AFLAC

COMP.FACT.SET (12) 3.00 8.00
ONE SET VIA MAIL PER AFLAC EXCH.CARD
ONE EXCH.PER '04 BOW.DRAFT HOBBY BOX
EXCH.CARD DEADLINE WAS 11/30/05
SETS ACTUALLY SENT OUT JANUARY, 2006
1 C.J. Henry .20 .50
2 John Drennen .20 .50
3 Beau Jones .20 .50
4 Jeff Lyman .20 .50
5 Andrew McCutchen 2.00 5.00
6 Chris Volstad .30 .75
7 Jonathan Egan .20 .50
8 P.J. Phillips .20 .50
9 Steve Johnson .20 .50
10 Ryan Tucker .20 .50
11 Cameron Maybin .60 1.50
12 Shane Funk .20 .50

2004 Bowman Draft Futures Game Jersey Relics

STATED ODDS 1:31 HOBBY, 1:30 RETAIL
146 Jose Capellan 3.00 8.00
147 Dioner Navarro 3.00 8.00
148 Fausto Carmona 2.00 5.00
149 Robinzon Diaz 2.00 5.00
150 Felix Hernandez 10.00 25.00
151 Andres Blanco 2.00 5.00
152 Jason Kubel 2.00 5.00
153 Willy Taveras 3.00 8.00
154 Merkin Valdez 3.00 8.00
155 Robinson Cano 6.00 15.00
156 Bill Murphy 2.00 5.00
157 Chris Burke 2.00 5.00
158 Kyle Sleeth 3.00 8.00
159 B.J. Upton 3.00 8.00
160 Tim Stauffer 3.00 8.00
161 David Wright 12.50 30.00
162 Conor Jackson 3.00 8.00
163 Brad Thompson 3.00 8.00
164 Delmon Young 3.00 8.00
165 Jeremy Reed 2.00 5.00

2004 Bowman Draft Prospect Premiums Relics

GROUP A ODDS 1:145 H, 1:153 R
GROUP B ODDS 1:387 H, 1:411 R
AB Angel Berroa Bat A 2.00 5.00
BU B.J. Upton Bat B 3.00 8.00
CJ Conor Jackson Bat B 3.00 8.00
CQ Carlos Quentin Bat B 3.00 8.00
DN Dioner Navarro Bat A 2.00 5.00
DY Delmon Young Bat A 3.00 8.00
EJ Edwin Jackson Jsy A 2.00 5.00
JR Jeremy Reed Bat A 2.00 5.00
KC Kevin Cash Bat B 2.00 5.00
LM Lastings Milledge Bat A 4.00 10.00

NS Nick Swisher Bat B 2.00 5.00
RH Ryan Harvey Bat A 2.00 5.00

2004 Bowman Draft Signs of the Future

GROUP A ODDS 1:127 H, 1:127 R
GROUP B ODDS 1:509 H, 1:511 R
EXCHANGE DEADLINE 11/30/05
AL Adam Loewen A 6.00 15.00
CC Chad Cordero B 6.00 15.00
JH James Houser B 4.00 10.00
PM Paul Maholm A 4.00 10.00
TP Tyler Pelland A 4.00 10.00
TT Terry Tiffee A 4.00 10.00

2005 Bowman

This 330-card set was released in May, 2005. The set was issued in 10-card hobby and retail packs which had an $3 SRP and which came 24 packs to a box and 12 boxes to a case. These cards were also issued in "HTA" or jumbo packs with an $6 SRP which had 21 cards per pack and came 12 packs to a box and eight boxes to a case. The first 140 cards in this set feature active veterans while cards number 141 through 165 feature leading prospects and cards 166 through 330 feature Rookie Cards. There was also a card randomly inserted into packs featuring game-used relics of the 2004 Rookies of the Year.

COMPLETE SET (330) 40.00 80.00
COMMON CARD (1-140) .10 .30
COMMON CARD (141-165) .15 .40
COMMON CARD (166-330) .15 .40
PLATE ODDS 1:695 HOBBY, 1:177 HTA
PLATE PRINT RUN 1 SET PER COLOR
BLACK-CYAN-MAGENTA-YELLOW ISSUED
NO PLATE PRICING DUE TO SCARCITY
ROY ODDS 1:668 H, 1:248 HTA, 1:1535 R
1 Gavin Floyd .12 .30
2 Eric Chavez .12 .30
3 Miguel Tejada .20 .50
4 Dmitri Young .12 .30
5 Hank Blalock .12 .30
6 Kerry Wood .12 .30
7 Andy Pettitte .20 .50
8 Pat Burrell .12 .30
9 Johnny Estrada .12 .30
10 Frank Thomas .30 .75
11 Juan Pierre .12 .30
12 Tom Glavine .20 .50
13 Lyle Overbay .12 .30
14 Jim Edmonds .20 .50
15 Steve Finley .12 .30
16 Jermaine Dye .12 .30
17 Omar Vizquel .20 .50
18 Nick Johnson .12 .30
19 Brian Giles .12 .30
20 Justin Morneau .30 .75
21 Preston Wilson .12 .30
22 Wily Mo Pena .12 .30
23 Rafael Palmeiro .20 .50
24 Scott Kazmir .30 .75
25 Derek Jeter .75 2.00
26 Barry Zito .12 .30
27 Mike Lowell .12 .30
28 Jason Bay .12 .30
29 Ken Harvey .12 .30
30 Nomar Garciaparra .30 .75
31 Roy Halladay .30 .75
32 Todd Helton .20 .50
33 Mark Kotsay .12 .30
34 Jake Peavy .12 .30
35 David Wright .50 1.25
36 Dontrelle Willis .12 .30
37 Marcus Giles .12 .30
38 Chone Figgins .12 .30
39 Sidney Ponson .12 .30
40 Randy Johnson .30 .75
41 John Smoltz .30 .75
42 Kevin Millar .12 .30
43 Mark Teixeira .30 .75
44 Alex Rios .20 .50
45 Mike Piazza .30 .75
46 Victor Martinez .20 .50
47 Jeff Bagwell .20 .50
48 Shawn Green .12 .30
49 Ivan Rodriguez .20 .50
50 Alex Rodriguez .50 1.25
51 Kazuo Matsui .12 .30
52 Mark Mulder .12 .30
53 Michael Young .20 .50
54 Javy Lopez .12 .30
55 Johnny Damon .20 .50
56 Jeff Francis .12 .30
57 Rich Harden .12 .30
58 Bobby Abreu .12 .30
59 Mark Loretta .12 .30
60 Gary Sheffield .12 .30
61 Jamie Moyer .12 .30
62 Garret Anderson .12 .30
63 Vernon Wells .12 .30
64 Orlando Cabrera .12 .30
65 Magglio Ordonez .20 .50
66 Ronnie Belliard .12 .30
67 Carlos Lee .12 .30
68 Carl Pavano .12 .30
69 Jon Lieber .12 .30
70 Aubrey Huff .12 .30
71 Rocco Baldelli .12 .30
72 Jason Schmidt .12 .30
73 Bernie Williams .20 .50
74 Hideki Matsui .50 1.25
75 Ken Griffey Jr. .50 1.25
76 Josh Beckett .20 .50
77 Mark Buehrle .20 .50
78 David Ortiz .30 .75
79 Luis Gonzalez .12 .30
80 Scott Rolen .30 .60
81 Joe Mauer .30 .75
82 Jose Reyes .20 .50
83 Adam Dunn .20 .50
84 Greg Maddux .50 1.25
85 Bartolo Colon .12 .30
86 Bret Boone .12 .30
87 Mike Mussina .20 .50
88 Ben Sheets .12 .30
89 Lance Berkman .20 .50
90 Miguel Cabrera .30 .75
91 C.C. Sabathia .20 .50
92 Mike Maroth .12 .30
93 Andruw Jones .12 .30
94 Jack Wilson .12 .30
95 Ichiro Suzuki .50 1.25
96 Geoff Jenkins .12 .30
97 Zack Greinke .20 .50
98 Jorge Posada .20 .50
99 Travis Hafner .12 .30
100 Barry Bonds .60 1.50
101 Aaron Rowand .12 .30
102 Aramis Ramirez .12 .30
103 Curt Schilling .20 .50
104 Melvin Mora .12 .30
105 Albert Pujols .75 2.00
106 Austin Kearns .12 .30
107 Shannon Stewart .12 .30
108 Carl Crawford .20 .50
109 Carlos Zambrano .20 .50
110 Roger Clemens .40 1.00
111 Javier Vazquez .12 .30
112 Randy Wolf .12 .30
113 Chipper Jones .30 .75
114 Larry Walker .20 .50
115 Alfonso Soriano .20 .50
116 Brad Wilkerson .12 .30
117 Bobby Crosby .12 .30
118 Jim Thome .20 .50
119 Oliver Perez .12 .30
120 Vladimir Guerrero .30 .75
121 Roy Oswalt .20 .50
122 Torii Hunter .12 .30
123 Rafael Furcal .12 .30
124 Luis Castillo .12 .30
125 Carlos Beltran .12 .30
126 Mike Sweeney .12 .30
127 Johan Santana .30 .75
128 Tim Hudson .20 .50
129 Troy Glaus .12 .30
130 Manny Ramirez .30 .75
131 Jeff Kent .12 .30
132 Jose Vidro .12 .30
133 Edgar Renteria .12 .30
134 Russ Ortiz .12 .30
135 Sammy Sosa .30 .75
136 Carlos Delgado .12 .30
137 Richie Sexson .12 .30
138 Pedro Martinez .20 .50
139 Adrian Beltre .12 .30
140 Mark Prior .20 .50
141 Omar Quintanilla .15 .40
142 Carlos Quentin .25 .60
143 Dan Johnson .15 .40
144 Jake Stevens .15 .40
145 Nate Schierholtz .15 .40
146 Neil Walker .15 .40
147 Bill Bray .15 .40
148 Taylor Tankersley .15 .40
149 Trevor Plouffe .15 .40
150 Felix Hernandez .60 1.50
151 Philip Hughes .25 .60
152 James Houser UER .15 .40
Facsimile Signature is J.R. House
153 David Murphy .25 .60
154 Ervin Santana UER .15 .40
Card has Johan Santana's facsimile autograph
155 Anthony Whittington .15 .40
156 Chris Lambert .15 .40
157 Jeremy Sowers .15 .40
158 Giovanny Gonzalez .25 .60
159 Blake DeWitt .25 .60
160 Thomas Diamond .15 .40
161 Greg Golson .15 .40
162 David Aardsma .15 .40
163 Paul Maholm .15 .40
164 Mark Rogers .15 .40
165 Homer Bailey .15 .40
166 Chip Cannon FY RC .15 .40
167 Tony Giarratano FY RC .15 .40
168 Darren Fenster FY RC .15 .40
169 Elvys Quezada FY RC .15 .40
170 Glen Perkins FY RC .15 .40
171 Ian Kinsler FY RC 1.25 3.00
172 Mike Bourn FY RC .40 1.00
173 Jeremy West FY RC .15 .40
174 Justin Verlander FY RC 3.00 8.00
175 Kevin West FY RC .15 .40
176 Luis Hernandez FY RC .15 .40
177 Matt Campbell FY RC .15 .40
178 Nate McLouth FY RC .25 .60
179 Ryan Goleski FY RC .15 .40
180 Matthew Lindstrom FY RC .15 .40
181 Matt DeSalvo FY RC .15 .40
182 Kole Strayhorn FY RC .15 .40
183 Jose Vaquedano FY RC .15 .40
184 James Jurries FY RC .15 .40
185 Ian Bladergroen FY RC .15 .40
186 Eric Nielsen FY RC .15 .40
187 Chris Vines FY RC .15 .40
188 Chris Denorfia FY RC .15 .40
189 Kevin Melillo FY RC .15 .40
190 Melky Cabrera FY RC .40 1.00
191 Ryan Sweeney FY RC .25 .60
192 Sean Marshall FY RC .40 1.00
193 Andy LaRoche FY RC .75 2.00
194 Tyler Pelland FY RC .15 .40
195 Mike Morse FY RC .40 1.00
196 Wes Swackhamer FY RC .15 .40
197 Wade Robinson FY RC .15 .40
198 Dan Santin FY RC .15 .40
199 Steve Doetsch FY RC .15 .40
200 Shane Costa FY RC .15 .40
201 Scott Mathieson FY RC .60 1.50
202 Ben Jones FY RC .15 .40
203 Michael Rogers FY RC .15 .40
204 Matt Rogelstad FY RC .15 .40
205 Luis Ramirez FY RC .15 .40
206 Landon Powell FY RC .15 .40
207 Erik Cordier FY RC .15 .40
208 Chris Seddon FY RC .15 .40
209 Chris Roberson FY RC .15 .40
210 Thomas Oldham FY RC .15 .40
211 Dana Eveland FY RC .15 .40
212 Cody Haerther FY RC .15 .40
213 Danny Core FY RC .15 .40
214 Craig Tatum FY RC .15 .40
215 Elliot Johnson FY RC .15 .40
216 Ender Chavez FY RC .15 .40
217 Errol Simonitsch FY RC .15 .40
218 Matt Van Der Bosch FY RC .15 .40
219 Eulogio de la Cruz FY RC .15 .40
220 C.J. Smith FY RC .15 .40
221 Adam Boeve FY RC .15 .40
222 Adam Harben FY RC .15 .40
223 Baltazar Lopez FY RC .15 .40
224 Russ Martin FY RC .60 1.50
225 Brian Bannister FY RC .25 .60
226 Brian Miller FY RC .15 .40
227 Casey McGehee FY RC .50 1.25
228 Humberto Sanchez FY RC .25 .60
229 Javon Moran FY RC .15 .40
230 Brandon McCarthy FY RC .25 .60
231 Danny Zell FY RC .15 .40
232 Jake Postlewait FY RC .15 .40
233 Juan Tejeda FY RC .15 .40
234 Keith Ramsey FY RC .15 .40
235 Lorenzo Scott FY RC .15 .40
236 Wladimir Balentien FY RC .25 .60
237 Martin Prado FY RC 1.00 2.50
238 Matt Albers FY RC .15 .40
239 Brian Schweiger FY RC .15 .40
240 Brian Stavisky FY RC .15 .40
241 Pat Misch FY RC .15 .40
242 Pat Osborn FY .15 .40
243 Ryan Feierabend FY RC .15 .40
244 Shaun Marcum FY .40 1.00
245 Kevin Collins FY RC .15 .40
246 Stuart Pomeranz FY RC .15 .40
247 Tetsu Yofu FY RC .15 .40
248 Hernan Iribarren FY RC .15 .40
249 Mike Spidale FY RC .15 .40
250 Tony Arnerich FY RC .15 .40
251 Manny Parra FY RC .40 1.00
252 Drew Anderson FY RC .15 .40
253 T.J. Beam FY RC .15 .40
254 Pedro Lopez FY RC .15 .40
255 Andy Sides FY RC .15 .40
256 Bear Bay FY RC .15 .40
257 Bill McCarthy FY RC .15 .40
258 Daniel Haigwood FY RC .15 .40
259 Brian Sprout FY RC .15 .40
260 Bryan Triplett FY RC .15 .40
261 Steven Bondurant FY RC .15 .40
262 Darwinson Salazar FY RC .15 .40
263 David Shepard FY RC .15 .40
264 Johan Silva FY RC .15 .40
265 J.B. Thurmond FY RC .15 .40
266 Brandon Moorhead FY RC .15 .40
267 Kyle Nichols FY RC .15 .40
268 Jonathan Sanchez FY RC .60 1.50
269 Mike Esposito FY RC .15 .40
270 Erik Schindewolf FY RC .15 .40
271 Peeter Ramos FY RC .15 .40
272 Juan Senreiso FY RC .15 .40
273 Matthew Kemp FY RC 2.00 5.00
274 Vinny Rottino FY RC .15 .40
275 Micah Furtado FY RC .15 .40
276 George Kottaras FY RC .25 .60
277 Billy Butler FY RC .75 2.00
278 Buck Coats FY RC .15 .40
279 Kenny Durost FY RC .15 .40
280 Nick Touchstone FY RC .15 .40
281 Jerry Owens FY RC .15 .40
282 Stefan Bailie FY RC .15 .40
283 Jesse Gutierrez FY RC .15 .40
284 Chuck Tiffany FY RC .40 1.00
285 Brendan Ryan FY RC .15 .40
286 Hayden Penn FY RC .15 .40
287 Shawn Bowman FY RC .15 .40
288 Alexander Smit FY RC .15 .40
289 Micah Schnurstein FY RC .15 .40
290 Jared Gothreaux FY RC .15 .40
291 Jair Jurrjens FY RC .75 2.00
292 Bobby Livingston FY RC .15 .40
293 Ryan Speier FY RC .15 .40
294 Zach Parker FY RC .15 .40
295 Christian Colonel FY RC .15 .40
296 Scott Mitchinson FY RC .15 .40
297 Neil Wilson FY RC .15 .40
298 Chuck James FY RC .40 1.00
299 Heath Totten FY RC .15 .40
300 Sean Tracey FY RC .15 .40
301 Ismael Ramirez FY RC .15 .40
302 Matt Brown FY RC .15 .40
303 Franklin Morales FY RC .25 .60
304 Brandon Sing FY RC .15 .40
305 D.J. Houlton FY RC .15 .40
306 Jayce Tingler FY RC .15 .40
307 Mitchell Arnold FY RC .15 .40
308 Jim Burt FY RC .15 .40
309 Jason Motte FY RC .25 .60
310 David Gassner FY RC .15 .40
311 Andy Santana FY RC UER .15 .40
Spelled Santan
312 Kelvin Pichardo FY RC .15 .40
313 Carlos Carrasco FY RC .40 1.00
314 Willy Mota FY RC .15 .40
315 Frank Mata FY RC .15 .40
316 Carlos Gonzalez FY RC 1.50 4.00
317 Jeff Niemann FY RC .40 1.00
318 Chris B.Young FY RC .60 1.50
319 Billy Sadler FY RC .15 .40
320 Ricky Barrett FY RC .15 .40
321 Ben Harrison FY .15 .40
322 Steve Nelson FY RC .15 .40
323 Daryl Thompson FY RC .15 .40
324 Philip Humber FY RC .40 1.00
325 Jeremy Harts FY RC .15 .40
326 Nick Massel FY RC .15 .40
327 Mike Rodriguez FY RC .15 .40
328 Mike Garber FY RC .15 .40
329 Kennard Bibbs FY RC .15 .40
330 Ryan Garko FY RC .15 .40
BC Jason Bay Bat 6.00 15.00
Bobby Crosby Bat ROY

2005 Bowman 1st Edition

This parallel set was issued in 1st Edition boxes - of which were produced exclusively for hobby shops. Each sealed case contained two boxes. Each box contained 20 packs and each pack contained 10 cards. Each pack carried suggested retail price of $2.99. No insert cards were made available in these packs.

*1ST EDITION 1-165: .75X TO 2X BASIC
*1ST EDITION 166-330: .75X TO 2X BASIC
ISSUED IN 1ST EDITION PACKS

2005 Bowman Gold

COMPLETE SET (330) 75.00 150.00
*GOLD 1-165: 1.25X TO 3X BASIC
*GOLD 166-330: .75X TO 2X BASIC
ONE PER HOBBY PACK
ONE PER HTA PACK
ONE PER RETAIL PACK

2005 Bowman Red

STATED ODDS 1:2768 H, 1:708 HTA
STATED PRINT RUN 1 SERIAL #'d SET
NO PRICING DUE TO SCARCITY

2005 Bowman White

*WHITE 1-165: 4X TO 10X BASIC
*WHITE 166-330: 3X TO 8X BASIC
STATED ODDS 1:23 HOBBY, 1:6 HTA
STATED PRINT RUN 240 SERIAL #'d SETS
UNCIRCULATED EXCH.ODDS 1:94 H, 1:23 R
FOUR PIT.COM CARDS PER UNCIRC.EXCH
UNCIRCULATED EXCH DEADLINE 12/31/05
50% OF PRINT SEEDED INTO PACKS
50% OF PRINT AVAIL VIA PIT.COM EXCH

2005 Bowman Autographs

GROUP A ODDS 1:74 H, 1:26 HTA, 1:118 R
GROUP B ODDS 1:95 H, 1:33 HTA, 1:212 R
RED INK ODDS 1:1599 H, 1:599 HTA, 1:3672 R
RED INK PRINT RUN 25 SETS
RED INK ARE NOT SERIAL-NUMBERED
RED INK PRINT RUN PROVIDED BY TOPPS
NO RED INK PRICING DUE TO SCARCITY
GROUP A IS CARDS 141-151
GROUP B IS CARDS 152-165
EXCHANGE DEADLINE 05/31/07
141 Omar Quintanilla A 4.00 10.00
142 Carlos Quentin A 6.00 15.00
143 Dan Johnson A 4.00 10.00
144 Jake Stevens A 4.00 10.00
145 Nate Schierholtz A 4.00 10.00
146 Neil Walker A 4.00 10.00
147 Bill Bray A 4.00 10.00
148 Taylor Tankersley A 4.00 10.00
149 Trevor Plouffe A 4.00 10.00
150 Felix Hernandez A 15.00 40.00
151 Philip Hughes A 12.50 30.00
152 James Houser B 4.00 10.00
153 David Murphy B 4.00 10.00
154 Ervin Santana B 4.00 10.00
155 Anthony Whittington B 4.00 10.00
156 Chris Lambert B 4.00 10.00
157 Jeremy Sowers B 6.00 15.00
158 Giovanny Gonzalez B 4.00 10.00
159 Blake DeWitt B 10.00 25.00
160 Thomas Diamond B 6.00 15.00
161 Greg Golson B 4.00 10.00
163 Paul Maholm B 4.00 10.00
164 Mark Rogers B 6.00 15.00
165 Homer Bailey B 10.00 25.00

2005 Bowman Relics

STATED ODDS 1:50 H, 1:19 HTA, 1:114 R
2 Eric Chavez Jsy 3.00 8.00
5 Hank Blalock Bat 3.00 8.00
23 Rafael Palmeiro Bat 4.00 10.00
43 Mark Teixeira Bat 4.00 10.00
49 Ivan Rodriguez Bat 4.00 10.00
50 Alex Rodriguez Bat 6.00 15.00
60 Gary Sheffield Bat 3.00 8.00
65 Magglio Ordonez Bat 3.00 8.00
78 David Ortiz Bat 4.00 10.00
83 Adam Dunn Jsy 3.00 8.00
90 Miguel Cabrera Bat 4.00 10.00
93 Andruw Jones Bat 4.00 10.00
100 Barry Bonds Jsy 10.00 25.00
104 Melvin Mora Jsy 3.00 8.00
105 Albert Pujols Bat 6.00 15.00
115 Alfonso Soriano Bat 3.00 8.00
120 Vladimir Guerrero Bat 4.00 10.00
125 Carlos Beltran Bat 3.00 8.00
130 Manny Ramirez Bat 4.00 10.00
135 Sammy Sosa Bat 4.00 10.00

2005 Bowman A-Rod Throwback

COMPLETE SET (4) 3.00 8.00
STATED ODDS 1:12 HOBBY
94 Alex Rodriguez 1994 .75 2.00
95 Alex Rodriguez 1995 .75 2.00
96 Alex Rodriguez 1996 .75 2.00
97 Alex Rodriguez 1997 .75 2.00

2005 Bowman A-Rod Throwback Autographs

1994 BOW ODDS 1:108,288 HTA
1995 BOW ODDS 1:27,684 H, 1:13,536 HTA
1996 BOW ODDS 1:9039 H, 1:4922 HTA
1996 BOW.DRAFT ODDS 1:44,837 H
1997 BOW ODDS 1:6815 H, 1:3734 HTA
1997 BOW.DRAFT ODDS 1:8664 H
1994 PRINT RUN 1 SERIAL #'d CARD
1995 PRINT RUN 25 SERIAL #'d CARDS
1996 PRINT RUN 75 SERIAL #'d CARDS
1997 PRINT RUN 225 SERIAL #'d CARDS
NO PRICING ON QTY OF 25 OR LESS
75 OF 99 1996 CARDS ARE IN BOWMAN
25 OF 99 1996 CARDS ARE IN BOW.DRAFT
100 OF 225 1997 CARDS ARE IN BOWMAN
125 OF 225 1997 CARDS ARE IN BOW.DRAFT
94A Alex Rodriguez 1994/1
95A Alex Rodriguez 1995/25
96A Alex Rodriguez 1996/99 100.00 175.00
97A Alex Rodriguez 1997/225 50.00 100.00

2005 Bowman A-Rod Throwback Jersey Relics

1994 ODDS 1:108,288 HTA
1995 ODDS 1:27,684 H, 1:13,536 HTA
1996 ODDS 1:6815 H, 1:3734 HTA
1997 ODDS 1:849 H, 1:461 HTA
1994 PRINT RUN 1 SERIAL #'d CARD
1995 PRINT RUN 25 SERIAL #'d CARDS
1996 PRINT RUN 99 SERIAL #'d CARDS
1997 PRINT RUN 800 SERIAL #'d CARDS
NO PRICING ON QTY OF 25 OR LESS
94R Alex Rodriguez 1994/1
95R Alex Rodriguez 1995/25
96R Alex Rodriguez 1996/99 15.00 40.00
97R Alex Rodriguez 1997/800 6.00 15.00

2005 Bowman A-Rod Throwback Posters

ONE PER SEALED HOBBY BOX
05 POSTER ISSUED IN BECKETT MONTHLY
1994 Alex Rodriguez 1994 .40 1.00
1995 Alex Rodriguez 1995 .40 1.00
1996 Alex Rodriguez 1996 .40 1.00
1997 Alex Rodriguez 1997 .40 1.00
2005 Alex Rodriguez 2005 .40 1.00

2005 Bowman Base of the Future Autograph Relic

STATED ODDS 1:106 HTA
RED INK ODDS 1:4708 HTA
RED INK PRINT RUN 25 CARDS
RED INK IS NOT SERIAL-NUMBERED
RED INK PRINT RUN PROVIDED BY TOPPS
NO RED INK PRICING DUE TO SCARCITY
AH Aaron Hill 6.00 15.00

2005 Bowman Futures Game Gear Jersey Relics

STATED ODDS 1:36 H, 1:14 HTA, 1:83 R
AH Aaron Hill 2.00 5.00
AM Arnie Munoz 2.00 5.00
AMA Andy Marte 3.00 8.00
BB Bryan Bullington 2.00 5.00
CE Clint Everts 2.00 5.00
DM Dallas McPherson 2.00 5.00
EE Edwin Encarnacion 3.00 8.00
FP Felix Pie 3.00 8.00
GF Gavin Floyd 2.00 5.00
JB Joe Blanton 2.00 5.00
JC Jesus Cota 2.00 5.00
JCO Jorge Cortes 2.00 5.00
JF Jeff Francis 2.00 5.00
JG Jairo Garcia 2.00 5.00
JGU Joel Guzman 3.00 8.00
JM Jeff Mathis 2.00 5.00
JMO Justin Morneau 3.00 8.00
KH Koyie Hill 2.00 5.00
MC Matt Cain 4.00 10.00
RG Ruben Gotay 2.00 5.00
RW Rickie Weeks 3.00 8.00
SC Shin Soo Choo 2.00 5.00
VM Val Majewski 2.00 5.00
WL Wilfredo Ledezma 2.00 5.00
YP Yusmeiro Petit 3.00 8.00

2005 Bowman Signs of the Future

GROUP A ODDS 1:252 H, 1:93 HTA, 1:571 R
GROUP B ODDS 1:219 H, 1:82 HTA, 1:502 R
GROUP C ODDS 1:167 H, 1:63 HTA,1:382 R
GROUP D ODDS 1:636 H, 1:239 HTA, 1:1448 R
D.WRIGHT PRINT RUN 100 CARDS
D.WRIGHT IS NOT SERIAL-NUMBERED
D.WRIGHT PRINT RUN GIVEN BY TOPPS
EXCHANGE DEADLINE 05/31/07
AL Adam Loewen C 4.00 10.00
AW Anthony Whittington B 4.00 10.00
BB Brian Bixler B 4.00 10.00
BC Bobby Crosby B 6.00 15.00
BD Blake DeWitt C 6.00 15.00
BS Brad Sullivan C 4.00 10.00
CC Chad Cordero D 4.00 10.00
CG Christian Garcia C 4.00 10.00
DM Dallas McPherson B 4.00 10.00
DP Dan Putnam B 4.00 10.00
DW David Wright D/100 * 30.00 60.00
ES Ervin Santana D 4.00 10.00
HS Huston Street C 8.00 20.00
JR Jay Rainville C 4.00 10.00
JS Jay Sborz C 4.00 10.00
KW Kyle Waldrop B 4.00 10.00
MC Melky Cabrera C 6.00 15.00
PH Philip Hughes C 10.00 25.00
PM Paul Maholm C 4.00 10.00
RC Robinson Cano D 15.00 40.00
RR Richie Robnett A 4.00 10.00
RW Ryan Wagner C 4.00 10.00
SK Scott Kazmir D 8.00 20.00
SO Scott Olson D 4.00 10.00
TG Tom Gorzelanny C 4.00 10.00
TH Tim Hutting A 3.00 8.00
TP Trevor Plouffe D 6.00 15.00
TT Taylor Tankersley D 4.00 10.00

2005 Bowman Two of a Kind Autographs

STATED ODDS 1:55,368 H, 1:21,658 HTA
STATED PRINT RUN 13 SERIAL #'d CARDS
NO PRICING DUE TO SCARCITY
ARHA Alex Rodriguez
Hank Aaron

2005 Bowman Draft

This 165-card set was released in November, 2005. The set was issued in seven-card packs (which included two Bowman Chrome Draft Cards) with an $2 SRP which came 24 packs to a box and 10 boxes to a case.

COMPLETE SET (165) 15.00 40.00
COMMON CARD (1-165) .10 .30
COMMON RC .10 .30
COMMON RC YR .10 .30
OVERALL PLATE ODDS 1:826 HOBBY
PLATE PRINT RUN 1 SET PER COLOR
BLACK-CYAN-MAGENTA-YELLOW ISSUED
NO PLATE PRICING DUE TO SCARCITY
1 Rickie Weeks .20 .50
2 Kyle Davies .12 .30
3 Garrett Atkins .12 .30
4 Chien-Ming Wang .50 1.25
5 Dallas McPherson .12 .30
6 Dan Johnson .12 .30
7 Andy Sisco .12 .30
8 Ryan Doumit .12 .30
9 J.P. Howell .12 .30
10 Tim Stauffer .12 .30
11 Willy Taveras
12 Aaron Hill .20 .50
13 Victor Diaz .12 .30
14 Wilson Betemit .12 .30
15 Ervin Santana UER .12 .30
Facsimile Signature is Johan Santana
16 Mike Morse .30 .75
17 Yadier Molina .20 .50
18 Kelly Johnson .12 .30
19 Clint Barmes .12 .30
20 Robinson Cano .30 .75
21 Brad Thompson .12 .30
22 Jorge Cantu .12 .30
23 Brad Halsey .12 .30
24 Lance Niekro .12 .30
25 D.J. Houlton .12 .30
26 Ryan Church .12 .30
27 Hayden Penn .12 .30
28 Chris Young .20 .50
29 Chad Orvella RC .12 .30
30 Mark Teahen .12 .30
31 Mark McCormick FY RC .12 .30
32 Jay Bruce FY RC UER 1.00 2.50
Card has drafted by the wrong team
33 Beau Jones FY RC .30 .75
34 Tyler Greene FY RC .12 .30
35 Zach Ward FY RC .12 .30
36 Josh Bell FY RC .40 1.00
37 Josh Wall FY RC .20 .50
38 Nick Webber FY RC .12 .30
39 Travis Buck FY RC .12 .30
40 Kyle Winters FY RC .12 .30
41 Mitch Boggs FY RC .12 .30
42 Tommy Mendoza FY RC .12 .30
43 Brad Corley FY RC .12 .30
44 Drew Butera FY RC .12 .30
45 Ryan Mount FY RC .12 .30
46 Tyler Herron FY RC .12 .30
47 Nick Weglarz FY RC .12 .30
48 Brandon Erbe FY RC .40 1.00
49 Cody Allen FY RC .12 .30
50 Eric Fowler FY RC .12 .30
51 James Boone FY RC .12 .30
52 Josh Flores FY RC .12 .30
53 Brandon Monk FY RC .12 .30
54 Kieron Pope FY RC .12 .30
55 Kyle Cofield FY RC .12 .30
56 Brent Lillibridge FY RC .12 .30
57 Daryl Jones FY RC .12 .30
58 Eli Iorg FY RC .12 .30
59 Brett Hayes FY RC .12 .30
60 Mike Durant FY RC .12 .30
61 Michael Bowden FY RC .20 .50
62 Paul Kelly FY RC .12 .30
63 Andrew McCutchen FY RC 1.00 2.50
64 Travis Wood FY RC .30 .75
65 Cesar Ramos FY RC .12 .30
66 Chaz Roe FY RC .12 .30
67 Matt Torra FY RC .12 .30
68 Kevin Slowey FY RC .60 1.50
69 Trayvon Robinson FY RC .30 .75
70 Reid Engel FY RC .12 .30
71 Kris Harvey FY RC .12 .30
72 Craig Italiano FY RC .12 .30
73 Matt Maloney FY RC .12 .30
74 Sean West FY RC .20 .50
75 Henry Sanchez FY RC .20 .50
76 Scott Blue FY RC .12 .30
77 Jordan Schafer FY RC .60 1.50
78 Chris Robinson FY RC .12 .30
79 Chris Hobdy FY RC .12 .30
80 Brandon Durden FY RC .12 .30
81 Clay Buchholz FY RC .60 1.50
82 Josh Geer FY RC .12 .30
83 Sam LeCure FY RC .12 .30
84 Justin Thomas FY RC .12 .30
85 Brett Gardner FY RC .40 1.00
86 Tommy Manzella FY RC .12 .30

87 Matt Green FY RC .12 .30
88 Yunel Escobar FY RC .50 1.25
89 Mike Costanzo FY RC .12 .30
90 Nick Hundley FY RC .12 .30
91 Zach Simons FY RC .12 .30
92 Jacob Marceaux FY RC .12 .30
93 Jed Lowrie FY RC .60 1.50
94 Brandon Snyder FY RC .30 .75
95 Matt Goyen FY RC .12 .30
96 Jon Egan FY RC .12 .30
97 Drew Thompson FY RC .12 .30
98 Bryan Anderson FY RC .12 .30
99 Clayton Richard FY RC .12 .30
100 Jimmy Shull FY RC .12 .30
101 Mark Pawelek FY RC .12 .30
102 P.J. Phillips FY RC .12 .30
103 John Drennen FY RC .12 .30
104 Nolan Reimold FY RC .50 1.25
105 Troy Tulowitzki FY RC 1.50 4.00
106 Kevin Whelan FY RC .12 .30
107 Wade Townsend FY RC .12 .30
108 Micah Owings FY RC .12 .30
109 Ryan Tucker FY RC .12 .30
110 Jeff Clement FY RC .40 1.00
111 Josh Sullivan FY RC .12 .30
112 Jeff Lyman FY RC .12 .30
113 Brian Bogusevic FY RC .12 .30
114 Trevor Bell FY RC .12 .30
115 Brent Cox FY RC .12 .30
116 Michael Billek FY RC .12 .30
117 Garrett Olson FY RC .12 .30
118 Steven Johnson FY RC .12 .30
119 Chase Headley FY RC .50 1.25
120 Daniel Carte FY RC .12 .30
121 Francisco Liriano PROS .20 .50
122 Fausto Carmona PROS .12 .30
123 Zach Jackson PROS .12 .30
124 Adam Loewen PROS .12 .30
125 Chris Lambert PROS .12 .30
126 Scott Mathieson FY .50 1.25
127 Paul Maholm PROS .12 .30
128 Fernando Nieve PROS .12 .30
129 Justin Verlander FY 2.50 6.00
130 Yusmeiro Petit PROS .12 .30
131 Joel Zumaya PROS .20 .50
132 Merkin Valdez PROS .12 .30
133 Ryan Garko FY .12 .30
134 Edison Volquez FY RC .60 1.50
135 Russ Martin FY .50 1.25
136 Conor Jackson PROS .12 .30
137 Miguel Montero FY RC .75 2.00
138 Josh Barfield PROS .20 .50
139 Delmon Young PROS .30 .75
140 Andy LaRoche FY .60 1.50
141 William Bergolla PROS .12 .30
142 B.J. Upton PROS .20 .50
143 Hernan Iribarren FY .12 .30
144 Brandon Wood PROS .20 .50
145 Jose Bautista PROS 1.50 4.00
146 Edwin Encarnacion PROS .20 .50
147 Javier Herrera FY RC .12 .30
148 Jeremy Hermida PROS .20 .50
149 Frank Diaz PROS RC .12 .30
150 Chris B.Young FY .50 1.25
151 Shin-Soo Choo PROS .20 .50
152 Kevin Thompson PROS RC .12 .30
153 Hanley Ramirez PROS .20 .50
154 Lastings Milledge PROS .12 .30
155 Luis Montanez PROS .12 .30
156 Justin Huber PROS .12 .30
157 Zach Duke PROS .12 .30
158 Jeff Francoeur PROS .30 .75
159 Melky Cabrera FY .30 .75
160 Bobby Jenks PROS .12 .30
161 Ian Snell PROS .12 .30
162 Fernando Cabrera PROS .12 .30
163 Troy Patton PROS .12 .30
164 Anthony Lerew PROS .12 .30
165 Nelson Cruz FY RC .50 1.25

2005 Bowman Draft Gold

COMPLETE SET (165) 25.00 60.00
*GOLD: 1.25X TO 3X BASIC
*GOLD: .6X TO 1.5X BASIC RC
*GOLD: .6X TO 1.5X BASIC RC YR
ONE PER PACK

2005 Bowman Draft Red

STATED ODDS 1:6609 HOBBY
STATED PRINT RUN 1 SERIAL #'d SET
NO PRICING DUE TO SCARCITY

2005 Bowman Draft White

*WHITE: 4X TO 10X BASIC
*WHITE: 3X TO 8X BASIC RC
*WHITE: 2.5X TO 6X BASIC RC YR
STATED ODDS 1:35 HOBBY, 1:72 RETAIL
STATED PRINT RUN 225 SERIAL #'d SETS

2005 Bowman Draft Futures Game Jersey Relics

STATED ODDS 1:24 HOBBY
121 Francisco Liriano 6.00 15.00
122 Fausto Carmona 4.00 10.00
123 Zach Jackson 3.00 8.00
124 Adam Loewen 3.00 8.00
125 Chris Lambert 3.00 8.00
126 Scott Mathieson 3.00 8.00
127 Paul Maholm 3.00 8.00
128 Fernando Nieve 3.00 8.00
129 Justin Verlander 6.00 15.00
130 Yusmeiro Petit 3.00 8.00
131 Joel Zumaya 3.00 8.00
132 Merkin Valdez 3.00 8.00
133 Ryan Garko 3.00 8.00
134 Edison Volquez 6.00 15.00
135 Russ Martin 4.00 10.00
136 Conor Jackson 3.00 8.00
137 Miguel Montero 4.00 10.00
138 Josh Barfield 3.00 8.00
139 Delmon Young 3.00 8.00
140 Andy LaRoche 4.00 10.00
141 William Bergolla 3.00 8.00
142 B.J. Upton 3.00 8.00
143 Hernan Iribarren 3.00 8.00
144 Brandon Wood 6.00 15.00
145 Jose Bautista 6.00 15.00
146 Edwin Encarnacion 3.00 8.00
147 Javier Herrera 3.00 8.00
148 Jeremy Hermida 3.00 8.00
149 Frank Diaz 3.00 8.00
150 Chris B.Young 6.00 15.00

2005 Bowman Draft A-Rod Throwback Autograph

SEE 2005 BOWMAN A-ROD AU'S FOR INFO

2005 Bowman Draft Signs of the Future

GROUP A ODDS 1:232 H, 1:232 R
GROUP B ODDS 1:823 H, 1:819 R
GROUP C ODDS 1:232 H, 1:232 R
GROUP D ODDS 1:1157 H, 1:1166 R
GROUP E ODDS 1:348 H, 1:349 R
GROUP F ODDS 1:1746 H, 1:1749 R
AG Angel Guzman E 3.00 8.00
BB Bill Bray E 3.00 8.00
DL Donald Lucey F 3.00 8.00
DM David Murphy E 5.00 12.00
DP David Purcey C 3.00 8.00
GG Greg Golson C 3.00 8.00
HB Homer Bailey D 6.00 15.00
JF Jeff Frazier C 3.00 8.00
JH Justin Hoyman A 3.00 8.00
JJ Justin Jones B 3.00 8.00
JP Jonathan Poterson C 3.00 8.00
JS Jeremy Sowers E 4.00 10.00
RR Richie Robnett A 3.00 8.00
TL Tyler Lumsden A 3.00 8.00

2005 Bowman Draft AFLAC Exchange Cards

STATED ODDS 1:32 HOBBY
PLATES PRINT RUN 1 SET PER COLOR
NO PLATES PRICING DUE TO SCARCITY
EXCHANGE DEADLINE 12/25/06
1 Basic Set 3.00 8.00
2 Printing Plates Set/4

2005 Bowman Draft AFLAC

COMP.FACT.SET (14) 4.00 10.00
STATED ODDS 1:32 '05 BOW.DRAFT HOB.
EXCHANGE DEADLINE 12/26/06
ONE SET VIA MAIL PER AFLAC EXCH.CARD
SETS ACTUALLY SENT OUT JANUARY, 2007
PLATE PRINT RUN 1 SET PER COLOR
BLACK-CYAN-MAGENTA-YELLOW ISSUED
NO PLATE PRICING DUE TO SCARCITY
1 Billy Rowell .75 2.00
2 Kasey Kiker .50 1.25
3 Chris Marrero 1.00 2.50
4 Jeremy Jeffress .30 .75
5 Kyle Drabek 1.00 2.50
6 Chris Parmelee .50 1.25
7 Colton Willems .30 .75
8 Cody Johnson .30 .75
9 Hank Conger .50 1.25
10 Cory Rasmus .30 .75
11 David Christensen .30 .75
12 Chris Tillman .75 2.00
13 Torre Langley .30 .75
14 Robby Alcombrack .30 .75

2006 Bowman

This 231-card set was released in May, 2006. The first 200 cards in the set consist of veterans while the last 31 cards in the set are players who were Rookie Cards under the then-new rules used in 2006. Cards number 219 and 220 come either signed or unsigned. The cards were issued in 10-card hobby packs with an $3 SRP which came 24 packs to a box and 12 boxes to a case. In addition, these cards were issued in 21-card HTA packs with an $6 SRP which were produced in 12-pack boxes which came eight boxes to a case and also in 10-card retail packs with an $3 SRP which came 24 packs to a box and 12 boxes to a case.

COMP.SET w/o AU's (220) 15.00 40.00
COMP.SET w/PROS (330) 40.00 80.00
COMMON CARD (1-200) .10 .30
COMMON ROOKIE (201-220) .15 .40
219-220 AU ODDS 1:1150 HOBBY, 1:699 HTA
COMMON AUTO (221-231) 4.00 10.00
221-231 AU ODDS 1:82 HOBBY, 1:40 HTA
1-220 PLATE ODDS 1:588 HOBBY, 1:575 HTA
221-231 AU PLATES 1:15,700 H, 1:4100 HTA
PLATE PRINT RUN 1 SET PER COLOR
BLACK-CYAN-MAGENTA-YELLOW ISSUED
NO PLATE PRICING DUE TO SCARCITY
1 Nick Swisher .30 .75
2 Ted Lilly .12 .30
3 John Smoltz .30 .75
4 Lyle Overbay .12 .30
5 Alfonso Soriano .20 .50
6 Javier Vazquez .12 .30
7 Ronnie Belliard .12 .30
8 Jose Reyes .20 .50
9 Brian Roberts .12 .30
10 Curt Schilling .20 .50
11 Adam Dunn .20 .50
12 Zack Greinke .20 .50
13 Carlos Guillen .12 .30
14 Jon Garland .12 .30
15 Robinson Cano .30 .75
16 Chris Burke .12 .30
17 Barry Zito .12 .30
18 Russ Adams .12 .30
19 Chris Capuano .12 .30
20 Scott Rolen .20 .50
21 Kerry Wood .12 .30
22 Scott Kazmir .20 .50
23 Brandon Webb .20 .50
24 Jeff Kent .12 .30
25 Albert Pujols .75 2.00
26 C.C. Sabathia .20 .50
27 Adrian Beltre .12 .30
28 Brad Wilkerson .12 .30
29 Randy Wolf .12 .30
30 Jason Bay .12 .30
31 Austin Kearns .12 .30
32 Clint Barmes .12 .30
33 Mike Sweeney .12 .30
34 Justin Verlander 1.00 2.50
35 Justin Morneau .30 .75
36 Scott Podsednik .12 .30
37 Jason Giambi .12 .30
38 Steve Finley .12 .30
39 Morgan Ensberg .12 .30
40 Eric Chavez .12 .30
41 Roy Halladay .30 .75
42 Horacio Ramirez .12 .30
43 Ben Sheets .12 .30
44 Chris Carpenter .30 .75
45 Andruw Jones .12 .30
46 Carlos Zambrano .20 .50
47 Jonny Gomes .12 .30
48 Shawn Green .12 .30
49 Moises Alou .12 .30
50 Ichiro Suzuki .50 1.25
51 Juan Pierre .12 .30
52 Grady Sizemore .20 .50
53 Kazuo Matsui .12 .30
54 Jose Vidro .12 .30
55 Jake Peavy .12 .30
56 Dallas Mcpherson .12 .30
57 Ryan Howard .50 1.25
58 Zach Duke .12 .30
59 Michael Young .20 .50
60 Todd Helton .20 .50
61 David Dejesus .20 .50
62 Ivan Rodriguez .20 .50
63 Johan Santana .30 .75
64 Danny Haren .12 .30
65 Derek Jeter .75 2.00
66 Greg Maddux .50 1.25
67 Jorge Cantu .12 .30
68 Conor Jackson .20 .50
69 Victor Martinez .20 .50
70 David Wright .50 1.25
71 Ryan Church .12 .30
72 Khalil Greene .12 .30
73 Jimmy Rollins .20 .50
74 Hank Blalock .12 .30
75 Pedro Martinez .20 .50
76 Jon Papelbon .75 2.00
77 Felipe Lopez .12 .30
78 Jeff Francis .12 .30
79 Andy Sisco .12 .30
80 Hideki Matsui .30 .75
81 Ken Griffey Jr. .50 1.25
82 Nomar Garciaparra .30 .75
83 Kevin Millwood .12 .30
84 Paul Konerko .20 .50
85 A.J. Burnett .20 .50
86 Mike Piazza .30 .75
87 Brian Giles .12 .30
88 Johnny Damon .20 .50
89 Jim Thome .20 .50
90 Roger Clemens .40 1.00
91 Aaron Rowand .12 .30
92 Rafael Furcal .12 .30
93 Gary Sheffield .12 .30
94 Mike Cameron .12 .30
95 Carlos Delgado .12 .30
96 Jorge Posada .20 .50
97 Denny Bautista .12 .30
98 Mike Maroth .12 .30
99 Brad Radke .12 .30
100 Alex Rodriguez .50 1.25
101 Freddy Garcia .12 .30
102 Oliver Perez .12 .30
103 Jon Lieber .12 .30
104 Melvin Mora .12 .30
105 Travis Hafner .12 .30
106 Matt Cain .30 .75
107 Derek Lowe .12 .30
108 Luis Castillo .12 .30
109 Livan Hernandez .12 .30
110 Tadahito Iguchi .12 .30
111 Shawn Chacon .12 .30
112 Frank Thomas .30 .75
113 Josh Beckett .20 .50
114 Aubrey Huff .12 .30
115 Derrek Lee .12 .30
116 Chien-Ming Wang .20 .50
117 Joe Crede .12 .30
118 Torii Hunter .12 .30
119 J.D. Drew .12 .30
120 Troy Glaus .12 .30
121 Sean Casey .12 .30
122 Edgar Renteria .12 .30
123 Craig Wilson .12 .30
124 Adam Eaton .12 .30
125 Jeff Francoeur .30 .75
126 Bruce Chen .12 .30
127 Cliff Floyd .12 .30
128 Jeremy Reed .12 .30
129 Jake Westbrook .12 .30
130 Wily Mo Pena .12 .30
131 Toby Hall .12 .30
132 David Ortiz .20 .50
133 David Eckstein .12 .30
134 Brady Clark .12 .30
135 Marcus Giles .12 .30
136 Aaron Hill .12 .30
137 Mark Kotsay .12 .30
138 Carlos Lee .12 .30
139 Roy Oswalt .20 .50
140 Chone Figgins .12 .30
141 Mike Mussina .20 .50
142 Orlando Hernandez .12 .30
143 Magglio Ordonez .12 .30
144 Jim Edmonds .20 .50
145 Bobby Abreu .12 .30
146 Nick Johnson .12 .30
147 Carlos Beltran .12 .30
148 Jhonny Peralta .12 .30
149 Pedro Feliz .12 .30
150 Miguel Tejada .20 .50
151 Luis Gonzalez .12 .30
152 Carl Crawford .20 .50
153 Yadier Molina .20 .50
154 Rich Harden .12 .30
155 Tim Wakefield .12 .30
156 Rickie Weeks .20 .50
157 Johnny Estrada .12 .30
158 Gustavo Chacin .12 .30
159 Dan Johnson .12 .30
160 Willy Taveras .12 .30
161 Garret Anderson .12 .30
162 Randy Johnson .30 .75
163 Jermaine Dye .12 .30
164 Joe Mauer .30 .75
165 Ervin Santana .12 .30
166 Jeremy Bonderman .12 .30
167 Garrett Atkins .12 .30
168 Manny Ramirez .30 .75
169 Brad Eldred .12 .30
170 Chase Utley .30 .75
171 Mark Loretta .12 .30
172 John Patterson .12 .30
173 Tom Glavine .20 .50
174 Dontrelle Willis .12 .30
175 Mark Teixeira .30 .75
176 Felix Hernandez .30 .75
177 Cliff Lee .20 .50
178 Jason Schmidt .12 .30
179 Chad Tracy .12 .30
180 Rocco Baldelli .12 .30
181 Aramis Ramirez .12 .30
182 Andy Pettitte .20 .50
183 Mark Mulder .12 .30
184 Geoff Jenkins .12 .30
185 Chipper Jones .30 .75
186 Vernon Wells .12 .30
187 Bobby Crosby .12 .30
188 Lance Berkman .20 .50
189 Vladimir Guerrero .30 .75
190 Jose Capellan .12 .30
191 Brad Penny .12 .30
192 Jose Guillen .12 .30
193 Brett Myers .12 .30
194 Miguel Cabrera .30 .75
195 Bartolo Colon .12 .30
196 Craig Biggio .20 .50
197 Tim Hudson .20 .50
198 Mark Prior .20 .50
199 Mark Buehrle .20 .50
200 Barry Bonds .60 1.50
201 Anderson Hernandez (RC) .15 .40
202 Charlton Jimerson (RC) .15 .40
203 Jeremy Accardo RC .15 .40
204 Hanley Ramirez (RC) .40 1.00
205 Matt Capps (RC) .15 .40
206 John-Ford Griffin (RC) .15 .40
207 Chuck James (RC) .15 .40
208 Jaime Bubela (RC) .15 .40
209 Mark Woodyard (RC) .15 .40
210 Jason Botts (RC) .15 .40
211 Chris Demaria RC .15 .40
212 Miguel Perez (RC) .15 .40
213 Tom Gorzelanny (RC) .15 .40
214 Adam Wainwright (RC) .40 1.00
215 Ryan Garko (RC) .15 .40
216 Jason Bergmann RC .15 .40
217 J.J. Furmaniak (RC) .15 .40
218 Francisco Liriano (RC) .40 1.00
219 Kenji Johjima RC .40 1.00
219a Kenji Johjima AU 30.00 60.00
220 Craig Hansen RC .40 1.00
220a Craig Hansen AU 20.00 50.00
221 Ryan Zimmerman AU (RC) 20.00 50.00
222 Joey Devine AU RC 4.00 10.00
223 Scott Olsen AU (RC) 4.00 10.00
224 Darrel Rasner AU (RC) 4.00 10.00
225 Craig Breslow AU RC 4.00 10.00
226 Reggie Abercrombie AU (RC) 4.00 10.00
227 Dan Uggla AU (RC) 6.00 15.00
228 Willie Eyre AU (RC) 4.00 10.00
229 Joel Zumaya AU (RC) 12.50 30.00
230 Ricky Nolasco AU (RC) 4.00 10.00
231 Ian Kinsler AU (RC) 8.00 20.00

2006 Bowman Blue

*BLUE 1-200: 2X TO 5X BASIC
*BLUE 76/201-220: 2X TO 5X BASIC
*BLUE 221-231: .4X TO 1X BASIC AU
1-220 ODDS 1:8 HOBBY, 1:4 HTA
221-231 AU ODDS 1:225 HOBBY, 1:115 HTA
STATED PRINT RUN 500 SERIAL #'d SETS
227 Dan Uggla AU 10.00 25.00

2006 Bowman Gold

*GOLD 1-200: 1.25X TO 3X BASIC
*GOLD 201-220: 1X TO 2.5X BASIC
ONE PER HOBBY PACK
ONE PER HTA PACK

2006 Bowman Red

STATED ODDS 1:3750 HOBBY, 1:1754 HTA
221-231 AU ODDS 1:114,583 H, 1:58,464 HTA
STATED PRINT RUN 1 SERIAL #'d SET
NO PRICING DUE TO SCARCITY

2006 Bowman White

*WHITE 1-200: 3X TO 8X BASIC
*WHITE 76/201-220: 3X TO 8X BASIC
*WHITE 221-231: .6X TO 1.5X BASIC AU
1-220 ODDS 1:32 HOBBY, 1:15 HTA
221-231 AU ODDS 1:1020 HOBBY, 1:500 HTA
STATED PRINT RUN 120 SERIAL #'d SETS
227 Dan Uggla AU 30.00 80.00
231 Ian Kinsler AU 30.00 60.00

2006 Bowman Prospects

For the first time, the non-major league prospects in Bowman had their own seperate set. These cards were inserted at a stated rate of two cards for every Bowman hobby pack and four cards for every HTA pack. The final 14 cards in this insert set were signed and were inserted at a stated rate of one in 62 hobby and one in 35 HTA.

COMP.SET w/o AU's (110) 25.00 50.00
COMMON CARD (B1-B110) .15 .40
B1-B110 STATED ODDS 2:1 HOBBY, 4:1 HTA
B111-B124 AU ODDS 1:62 HOBBY, 1:35 HTA
B1-B110 PLATE ODDS 1:588 H, 1:575 HTA
B111-B124 AU PLATE 1:15,700 H, 1:4100 HTA
PLATE PRINT RUN 1 PER COLOR
BLACK-CYAN-MAGENTA-YELLOW ISSUED
NO PLATE PRICING DUE TO SCARCITY
B1 Alex Gordon .50 1.25
B2 Jonathan George .15 .40
B3 Scott Walter .15 .40
B4 Brian Holliday .15 .40
B5 Ben Copeland .15 .40
B6 Bobby Wilson .15 .40
B7 Mayker Sandoval .15 .40
B8 Alejandro de Aza .15 .40
B9 David Munoz .15 .40
B10 Josh LeBlanc .15 .40
B11 Philippe Valiquette .15 .40
B12 Edwin Bellorin .15 .40
B13 Jason Quarles .15 .40
B14 Mark Trumbo .60 1.50
B15 Steve Kelly .15 .40
B16 Jamie Hoffman .15 .40
B17 Joe Bauserman .15 .40
B18 Nick Adenhart .15 .40
B19 Mike Butia .15 .40
B20 Jon Weber .15 .40
B21 Luis Valdez .15 .40
B22 Rafael Rodriguez .15 .40
B23 Wyatt Toregas .15 .40
B24 John Vanden Berg .15 .40
B25 Mike Connolly .15 .40
B26 Mike O'Connor .15 .40
B27 Garrett Mock .15 .40
B28 Bill Layman .15 .40
B29 Luis Pena .15 .40
B30 Billy Killian .15 .40
B31 Ross Ohlendorf .15 .40
B32 Marc Keiser .15 .40
B33 Ryan Costello .15 .40
B34 Dale Thayer .15 .40
B35 Steve Garrabrants .15 .40
B36 Samuel Deduno .15 .40
B37 Juan Portes .15 .40
B38 Javier Martinez .15 .40
B39 Clint Sammons .15 .40
B40 Andrew Kown .15 .40
B41 Matt Tolbert .15 .40
B42 Michael Ekstrom .15 .40
B43 Shawn Norris .15 .40
B44 Diory Hernandez .15 .40
B45 Chris Maples .15 .40
B46 Aaron Hathaway .15 .40
B47 Steven Baker .15 .40
B48 Greg Creek .15 .40
B49 Collin Mahoney .15 .40
B50 Corey Ragsdale .15 .40
B51 Ariel Nunez .15 .40
B52 Max Ramirez .25 .60
B53 Eric Rodland .15 .40
B54 Dante Brinkley .15 .40
B55 Casey Craig .15 .40
B56 Ryan Spilborghs .15 .40
B57 Fredy Deza .15 .40
B58 Jeff Frazier .15 .40
B59 Vince Cordova .15 .40
B60 Oswaldo Navarro .15 .40
B61 Jarod Rine .15 .40
B62 Jordan Tata .15 .40
B63 Ben Julianel .15 .40
B64 Yung-Chi Chen .25 .60
B65 Carlos Torres .15 .40
B66 Juan Francia .15 .40
B67 Brett Smith .15 .40
B68 Francisco Leandro .15 .40
B69 Chris Turner .15 .40
B70 Matt Joyce .75 2.00
B71 Jason Jones .15 .40
B72 Jose Diaz .15 .40
B73 Kevin Ool .15 .40
B74 Nate Bumstead .15 .40
B75 Omir Santos .15 .40
B76 Shawn Riggans .15 .40
B77 Willy Castro .15 .40
B78 Mike Rozier .15 .40
B79 Wilkin Ramirez .25 .60
B80 Yobal Duenas .15 .40
B81 Adam Bourassa .15 .40
B82 Tony Granadillo .15 .40
B83 Brad McCann .15 .40
B84 Dustin Majewski .15 .40
B85 Kelvin Jimenez .15 .40
B86 Mark Reed .15 .40
B87 Asdrubal Cabrera .75 2.00
B88 James Barthmaier .15 .40
B89 Brandon Boggs .15 .40
B90 Raul Valdez .15 .40
B91 Jose Campusano .15 .40
B92 Henry Owens .15 .40
B93 Tug Hulett .15 .40
B94 Nate Gold .15 .40
B95 Lee Mitchell .15 .40
B96 John Hardy .15 .40
B97 Aaron Wideman .15 .40
B98 Brandon Roberts .15 .40
B99 Lou Santangelo .15 .40
B100 Kyle Kendrick .40 1.00
B101 Michael Collins .15 .40
B102 Camilo Vazquez .15 .40
B103 Mark McLemore .15 .40
B104 Alexander Peralta .15 .40
B105 Josh Whitesell .15 .40
B106 Carlos Guevara .15 .40
B107 Michael Aubrey .25 .60
B108 Brandon Chaves .15 .40
B109 Leonard Davis .15 .40
B110 Kendry Morales .40 1.00
B111 Koby Clemens AU 10.00 25.00
B112 Lance Broadway AU 6.00 15.00
B113 Cameron Maybin AU 10.00 25.00
B114 Mike Aviles AU 4.00 10.00
B115 Kyle Blanks AU 10.00 25.00
B116 Chris Dickerson AU 6.00 15.00
B117 Sean Gallagher AU 10.00 25.00
B118 Jamar Hill AU 4.00 10.00
B119 Garrett Mock AU 4.00 10.00
B120 Kendry Morales AU 6.00 15.00
B121 Russ Rohlicek AU 4.00 10.00
B122 Clete Thomas AU 4.00 10.00
B123 Josh Kinney AU 4.00 10.00
B124 Justin Huber AU 4.00 10.00

2006 Bowman Prospects Blue

*BLUE B1-B110: 1.5X TO 4X BASIC
*BLUE B111-B124: .4X TO 1X BASIC
B1-B110 ODDS 1:8 HOBBY, 1:4 HTA
B111-B124 AU ODDS 1:170 H, 1:100 HTA
STATED PRINT RUN 500 SERIAL #'d SETS
B113 Cameron Maybin AU 15.00 40.00

2006 Bowman Prospects Gold

*GOLD B1-B110: .75X TO 2X BASIC
ONE PER HOBBY PACK
ONE PER HTA PACK

2006 Bowman Prospects Red

B1-B110 ODDS 1:3750 HOBBY, 1:1754 HTA
B111-B124 AU ODDS 1:80,208 H, 1:56,464 HTA
STATED PRINT RUN 1 SERIAL #'d SET
NO PRICING DUE TO SCARCITY

2006 Bowman Prospects White

*WHITE B1-B110: 2.5X TO 6X BASIC
*WHITE B111-B124: .6X TO 1.5X BASIC
B1-B110 ODDS 1:32 HOBBY, 1:15 HTA
B111-B124 AU ODDS 1:750 H, 1:450 HTA
STATED PRINT RUN 120 SERIAL #'d SETS
B113 Cameron Maybin AU 40.00 80.00

2006 Bowman Base of the Future

STATED ODDS 1:173 HTA
RED INK ODDS 1:7800 HTA
NO RED INK PRICING DUE TO SCARCITY
JH Justin Huber 4.00 10.00

2006 Bowman Signs of the Future

ONE PER SEALED HTA BOX
GROUP A ODDS 1:5 HTA BOXES, 1:150 RETAIL
GROUP B ODDS 1:4 HTA BOXES, 1:105 RETAIL
GROUP C-D ODDS 1:6 HTA BOXES, 1:200 R
GROUP E ODDS 1:19 HTA BOXES, 1:1050 R
AT Aaron Thompson D 4.00 10.00
BB Brian Bogusevic A 4.00 10.00
BC Ben Copeland C 4.00 10.00
CR Cesar Ramos E 4.00 10.00
DS Denard Span B 6.00 15.00
GO Garrett Olson C 4.00 10.00
HS Henry Sanchez D 4.00 10.00
JC Jeff Clement B 10.00 25.00
JD John Drennen C 4.00 10.00
JE Jacoby Ellsbury D UER 30.00 60.00

The words the signing run together instead of being seperated

Card	Low	High
JM John Mayberry Jr. E	4.00	10.00
MB Michael Bowden B	6.00	15.00
MC Mike Costanzo D	4.00	10.00
RB Ryan Braun E	20.00	50.00
RR Ricky Romero B	5.00	12.00
RT Ryan Tucker C	4.00	10.00
SW Sean West D	4.00	10.00
TB Travis Buck D	6.00	15.00
TC Trevor Crowe B	4.00	10.00
TT Troy Tulowitzki A	10.00	25.00
YE Yunel Escobar A	10.00	25.00

2006 Bowman Draft

Card	Low	High
COMPLETE SET (55)	6.00	15.00
COMMON RC (1-55)	.15	.40

APPX. TWO PER HOBBY/RETAL PACK
ODDS INFO PROVIDED BY BECKETT
OVERALL PLATE ODDS 1:990 HOBBY
PLATE PRINT RUN 1 SET PER COLOR
BLACK-CYAN-MAGENTA-YELLOW ISSUED
NO PLATE PRICING DUE TO SCARCITY

Card	Low	High
1 Matt Kemp (RC)	.75	2.00
2 Taylor Tankersley (RC)	.15	.40
3 Mike Napoli RC	.50	1.25
4 Brian Bannister (RC)	.15	.40
5 Melky Cabrera (RC)	.25	.60
6 Bill Bray (RC)	.15	.40
7 Brian Anderson (RC)	.15	.40
8 Jered Weaver (RC)	.40	1.00
9 Chris Duncan (RC)	.25	.60
10 Boof Bonser (RC)	.25	.60
11 Mike Rouse (RC)	.15	.40
12 David Pauley (RC)	.15	.40
13 Russ Martin (RC)	.25	.60
14 Jeremy Sowers (RC)	.15	.40
15 Kevin Reese (RC)	.15	.40
16 John Rheinecker (RC)	.15	.40
17 Tommy Murphy (RC)	.15	.40
18 Sean Marshall (RC)	.25	.60
19 Jason Kubel (RC)	.15	.40
20 Chad Billingsley (RC)	.25	.60
21 Kendry Morales (RC)	.40	1.00
22 Jon Lester RC	.60	1.50
23 Brandon Fahey RC	.15	.40
24 Josh Johnson (RC)	.40	1.00
25 Kevin Frandsen (RC)	.15	.40
26 Casey Janssen RC	.15	.40
27 Scott Thorman (RC)	.15	.40
28 Scott Mathieson (RC)	.15	.40
29 Jeremy Hermida (RC)	.15	.40
30 Dustin Nippert (RC)	.15	.40
31 Kevin Thompson (RC)	.15	.40
32 Bobby Livingston (RC)	.15	.40
33 Travis Ishikawa (RC)	.15	.40
34 Jeff Mathis (RC)	.15	.40
35 Charlie Haeger RC	.25	.60
36 Josh Willingham (RC)	.15	.40
37 Taylor Buchholz (RC)	.15	.40
38 Joel Guzman (RC)	.15	.40
39 Zach Jackson (RC)	.15	.40
40 Howie Kendrick (RC)	.40	1.00
41 T.J. Beam (RC)	.15	.40
42 Ty Taubenheim RC	.25	.60
43 Erick Aybar (RC)	.15	.40
44 Anibal Sanchez (RC)	.15	.40
45 Michael Pelfrey RC	.40	1.00
46 Shawn Hill (RC)	.15	.40
47 Chris Roberson (RC)	.15	.40
48 Carlos Villanueva RC	.15	.40
49 Andre Ethier (RC)	.60	1.50
50 Anthony Reyes (RC)	.15	.40
51 Franklin Gutierrez (RC)	.15	.40
52 Angel Guzman (RC)	.15	.40
53 Michael O'Connor RC	.15	.40
54 James Shields RC	.50	1.25
55 Nate McLouth (RC)	.15	.40

2006 Bowman Draft Gold

Card	Low	High
COMPLETE SET (55)	8.00	20.00

*GOLD: .75X TO 2X BASIC
APPX. ODDS 1:3 HOBBY, 1:3 RETAIL
ODDS INFO PROVIDED BY BECKETT

2006 Bowman Draft Red

STATED ODDS 1:7934 HOBBY
STATED PRINT RUN 1 SERIAL #'d SET
NO PRICING DUE TO SCARCITY

2006 Bowman Draft White

*WHITE: 2.5X TO 6X BASIC
STATED ODDS 1:43 H,1:93 R
STATED PRINT RUN 225 SER.#'d SETS

2006 Bowman Draft Draft Picks

Card	Low	High
COMPLETE SET (65)	8.00	20.00

APPX. ODDS 1:1 HOBBY, 1:1 RETAIL
ODDS INFO PROVIDED BY BECKETT
OVERALL PLATE ODDS 1:990 HOBBY
PLATE PRINT RUN 1 SET PER COLOR
BLACK-CYAN-MAGENTA-YELLOW ISSUED
NO PLATE PRICING DUE TO SCARCITY

Card	Low	High
1 Tyler Colvin	.40	1.00
2 Chris Marrero	.60	1.50
3 Hank Conger	.25	.60
4 Chris Parmelee	.25	.60
5 Jason Place	.15	.40
6 Billy Rowell	.40	1.00
7 Travis Snider	.50	1.25
8 Colton Willems	.15	.40
9 Chase Fontaine	.15	.40
10 Jon Jay	.40	1.00
11 Wade Leblanc	.15	.40
12 Justin Masterson	.50	1.25
13 Gary Daley	.15	.40
14 Justin Edwards	.15	.40
15 Charlie Yarbrough	.15	.40
16 Cyle Hankerd	.15	.40
17 Zach McAllister	.15	.40
18 Tyler Robertson	.15	.40
19 Joe Smith	.15	.40
20 Nate Culp	.15	.40
21 John Holdzkom	.15	.40
22 Patrick Bresnehan	.15	.40
23 Chad Lee	.15	.40
24 Ryan Morris	.15	.40
25 D'Arby Myers	.15	.40
26 Garrett Olson	.15	.40
27 Jon Still	.15	.40
28 Brandon Rice	.15	.40
29 Chris Davis	1.00	2.50
30 Zack Daeges	.15	.40
31 Bobby Henson	.15	.40
32 George Kontos	.15	.40
33 Jermaine Mitchell	.15	.40
34 Adam Coe	.15	.40
35 Dustin Richardson	.15	.40
36 Allen Craig	.40	1.00
37 Austin McClune	.15	.40
38 Doug Fister	.50	1.25
39 Corey Madden	.15	.40
40 Justin Jacobs	.15	.40
41 Jim Negrych	.15	.40
42 Tyler Norrick	.15	.40
43 Adam Davis	.15	.40
44 Brett Logan	.15	.40
45 Brian Omogrosso	.15	.40
46 Kyle Drabek	.50	1.25
47 Jamie Ortiz	.15	.40
48 Alex Presley	.15	.40
49 Terrance Warren	.15	.40
50 David Christensen	.15	.40
51 Helder Velazquez	.15	.40
52 Matt McBride	.15	.40
53 Quintin Berry	.15	.40
54 Michael Eisenberg	.15	.40
55 Dan Garcia	.15	.40
56 Scott Cousins	.15	.40
57 Sean Land	.15	.40
58 Kristopher Medlen	.40	1.00
59 Tyler Reves	.15	.40
60 John Shelby	.15	.40
61 Jordan Newton	.15	.40
62 Ricky Orta	.15	.40
63 Jason Donald	.15	.40
64 David Huff	.15	.40
65 Brett Sinkbeil	.15	.40

2006 Bowman Draft Draft Picks Gold

*GOLD: .75X TO 2X BASIC
APPX. ODDS 1:2 HOBBY, 1:2 RETAIL
ODDS INFO PROVIDED BY BECKETT

2006 Bowman Draft Draft Picks Red

STATED ODDS 1:7934 HOBBY
STATED PRINT RUN 1 SERIAL #'d SET
NO PRICING DUE TO SCARCITY

2006 Bowman Draft Draft Picks White

*WHITE: 2.5X TO 6X BASIC
STATED ODDS 1:43 H,1:93 R
STATED PRINT RUN 225 SER.#'d SETS

2006 Bowman Draft Future's Game Prospects

Card	Low	High
COMPLETE SET (45)	6.00	15.00

APPX. ODDS 1:1 HOBBY, 1:1 RETAIL
ODDS INFO PROVIDED BY BECKETT
OVERALL PLATE ODDS 1:990 HOBBY
PLATE PRINT RUN 1 SET PER COLOR
BLACK-CYAN-MAGENTA-YELLOW ISSUED
NO PLATE PRICING DUE TO SCARCITY

Card	Low	High
1 Nick Adenhart	.15	.40
2 Joel Guzman	.15	.40
3 Ryan Braun	.75	2.00
4 Carlos Carrasco	.25	.60
5 Neil Walker	.15	.40
6 Pablo Sandoval	1.50	4.00
7 Gio Gonzalez	.15	.40
8 Joey Votto	1.00	2.50
9 Luis Cruz	.15	.40
10 Nolan Reimold	.25	.60
11 Juan Salas	.15	.40
12 Josh Fields	.15	.40
13 Yovani Gallardo	.50	1.25
14 Radhames Liz	.15	.40
15 Eric Patterson	.15	.40
16 Cameron Maybin	.50	1.25
17 Edgar Martinez	.15	.40
18 Hunter Pence	.75	2.00
19 Philip Hughes	.40	1.00
20 Trent Oeltjen	.15	.40
21 Nick Pereira	.15	.40
22 Wladimir Balentien	.15	.40
23 Stephen Drew	.40	1.00
24 Davis Romero	.15	.40
25 Joe Koshansky	.15	.40
26 Chin Lung Hu	.50	1.25
27 Jason Hirsh	.15	.40
28 Jose Tabata	1.00	2.50
29 Eric Hurley	.15	.40
30 Yung Chi Chen	.25	.60
31 Howie Kendrick	.40	1.00
32 Humberto Sanchez	.15	.40
33 Alex Gordon	.50	1.25
34 Yunel Escobar	.15	.40
35 Travis Buck	.15	.40
36 Billy Butler	.40	1.00
37 Homer Bailey	.40	1.00
38 George Kottaras	.15	.40
39 Kurt Suzuki	.15	.40
40 Joaquin Arias	.15	.40
41 Matt Lindstrom	.15	.40
42 Sean Smith	.15	.40
43 Carlos Gonzalez	.40	1.00
44 Jaime Garcia	.75	2.00
45 Jose Garcia	.15	.40

2006 Bowman Draft Future's Game Prospects Gold

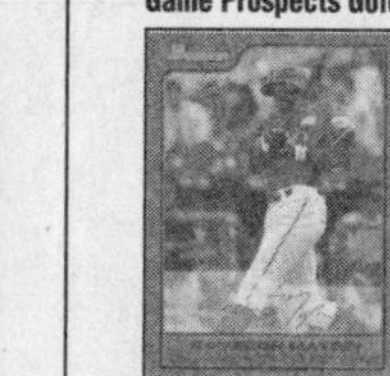

*GOLD: 1X TO 2.5X BASIC
APPX. ODDS 1:6 HOBBY, 1:6 RETAIL
ODDS INFO PROVIDED BY BECKETT

2006 Bowman Draft Future's Game Prospects Red

STATED ODDS 1:7934 HOBBY
STATED PRINT RUN 1 SERIAL #'d SET
NO PRICING DUE TO SCARCITY

2006 Bowman Draft Future's Game Prospects White

*WHITE: 2.5X TO 6X BASIC
STATED ODDS 1:43 H,1:93 R
STATED PRINT RUN 225 SER.#'d SETS

2006 Bowman Draft Future's Game Prospects Relics

GROUP A ODDS 1:285 H,1:285 R
GROUP B ODDS 1:26 H,1:25 R
PRICES LISTED FOR JSY SWATCHES
NO PATCH PRICING DUE TO SCARCITY

Card	Low	High
1 Nick Adenhart Jsy B	4.00	10.00
2 Joel Guzman Jsy B	2.50	6.00
3 Ryan Braun Jsy B	5.00	12.00
4 Carlos Carrasco Jsy B	2.50	6.00
6 Pablo Sandoval Jsy B	6.00	15.00
7 Gio Gonzalez Jsy B	2.50	6.00
8 Joey Votto Jsy B	4.00	10.00
9 Luis Cruz Jsy B	2.50	6.00
10 Nolan Reimold Jsy B	3.00	8.00
11 Juan Salas Jsy B	2.50	6.00
12 Josh Fields Jsy B	2.50	6.00
13 Yovani Gallardo Jsy B	6.00	15.00
14 Radhames Liz Jsy B	2.50	6.00
15 Eric Patterson Jsy A	2.50	6.00
16 Cameron Maybin Jsy B	3.00	8.00
17 Edgar Martinez Jsy B	2.50	6.00
18 Hunter Pence Jsy B	6.00	15.00
19 Philip Hughes Jsy B	4.00	10.00
20 Trent Oeltjen Jsy B	2.50	6.00
21 Nick Pereira Jsy B	2.50	6.00
22 Wladimir Balentien Jsy B	2.50	6.00
23 Stephen Drew Jsy B	3.00	8.00
24 Davis Romero Jsy A	2.50	6.00
25 Joe Koshansky Jsy B	2.50	6.00
26 Chin-Lung Hu Jsy Black B	10.00	25.00
26b Chin-Lung Hu Jsy Red	60.00	120.00
26c Chin-Lung Hu Jsy Yellow	50.00	100.00
27 Jason Hirsh Jsy B	2.50	6.00
28 Jose Tabata Jsy B	3.00	8.00
29 Eric Hurley Jsy B	2.50	6.00
30 Yung-Chi Chen Jsy Black B	10.00	25.00
30b Yung-Chi Chen Jsy Red	60.00	120.00
30c Yung-Chi Chen Jsy Yellow	50.00	100.00
31 Howie Kendrick Jsy A	3.00	8.00
32 Humberto Sanchez Jsy B	2.50	6.00
33 Alex Gordon Jsy B	6.00	15.00
34 Yunel Escobar Jsy A	6.00	15.00
35 Travis Buck Jsy B	6.00	15.00
36 Billy Butler Jsy B	4.00	10.00
37 Homer Bailey Jsy B	4.00	10.00
38 George Kottaras Jsy B	2.50	6.00
39 Kurt Suzuki Jsy B	2.50	6.00
40 Joaquin Arias Jsy B	2.50	6.00
43 Carlos Gonzalez Jsy B	4.00	10.00
44 Jaime Garcia Jsy B	3.00	8.00
45 Jose Garcia Jsy B	2.50	6.00

2006 Bowman Draft Head of the Class Dual Autograph

STATED ODDS 1:7640 HOBBY
STATED PRINT RUN 174 SER.#'d SETS
GOLD REF. ODDS 1:56,000 HOBBY
GOLD REF. PRINT RUN 25 SER.#'d SETS
NO GOLD PRICING DUE TO SCARCITY
SUPERFRAC. ODDS 1:261,680 HOBBY
SUPERFRAC. PRINT RUN 1 SER.#'d SET
NO SUPERFRAC.PRICING DUE TO SCARCITY

Card	Low	High
RU Alex Rodriguez / Justin Upton	100.00	200.00

2006 Bowman Draft Head of the Class Dual Autograph Refractor

STATED ODDS 1:27,000 HOBBY
STATED PRINT RUN 50 SERIAL #'d SETS

Card	Low	High
RU Alex Rodriguez / Justin Upton	125.00	250.00

2006 Bowman Draft Signs of the Future

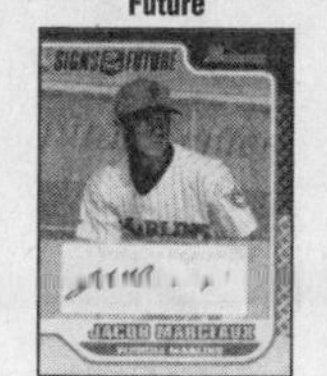

GROUP A ODDS 1:973 H, 1:973 R
GROUP B ODDS 1:324 H, 1:323 R
GROUP C ODDS 1:430 H, 1:431 R
GROUP D ODDS 1:1140 H, 1:1140 R
GROUP E ODDS 1:322 H, 1:323 R
GROUP F ODDS 1:387 H, 1:388 R

Card	Low	High
AG Alex Gordon A	6.00	15.00
BJ Beau Jones B	3.00	8.00
BS Brandon Snyder A	4.00	10.00
CDR Chaz Roe C	3.00	8.00
CI Chris Iannetta A	4.00	10.00
CR Clayton Richard B	3.00	8.00
CRA Cesar Ramos F	3.00	8.00
CTI Craig Italiano C	3.00	8.00
DJ Daryl Jones B	6.00	15.00
HS Henry Sanchez E	3.00	8.00
JB Jay Bruce D	10.00	25.00
JC Jeff Clement B	6.00	15.00
JM Jacob Marceaux C	3.00	8.00
KC Koby Clemens A	8.00	20.00
MC Mike Costanzo F	3.00	8.00
MM Mark McCormick E	3.00	8.00
MO Micah Owings B	6.00	15.00
TB Travis Buck B	4.00	10.00
WT Wade Townsend E	3.00	8.00

2007 Bowman

This 237-card set was released in June, 2007. This set was issued through both hobby and retail channels. The hobby version came in 10-card packs with an $3 SRP which came 24 packs to a box and 12 boxes to a case. In addition, hobby HTA packs were also produced and those packs contained 32 cards with an $10 SRP. Those packs were issued 12 to a box and eight boxes to a case. Card #219, Hideki Okajima comes in three versions; a standard version, an signed version in English and a signed Japanese version. In addition, card number 234 was never issued. Cards number 1-200 feature veterans, cards numbered 201-219 feature 2007 rookies and the aforementioned Okajima signed versions and cards numbered 221-236 are signed. Those cards were inserted into packs at a stated rate of one in 98 hobby and one in 25 HTA packs.

Card	Low	High
COMP.SET w/o AU's (221)	20.00	50.00
COMMON CARD (1-200)	.12	.30
COMMON ROOKIE (201-220)	.15	.40
COMMON AUTO (221-236)	4.00	10.00

219/221-236 AU ODDS 1:98 HOBBY, 1:25 HTA
BONDS ODDS 1:51 HTA, 1:610 RETAIL
1-220 PLATE ODDS 1:1468 H, 1:212 HTA
221-231 AU PLATES 1:8200 H, 1:1150 HTA
BONDS PLATE ODDS 1:106,000 HTA
PLATE PRINT RUN 1 SET PER COLOR
BLACK-CYAN-MAGENTA-YELLOW ISSUED
NO PLATE PRICING DUE TO SCARCITY

Card	Low	High
1 Hanley Ramirez	.30	.75
2 Justin Verlander	.40	1.00
3 Ryan Zimmerman	.20	.50
4 Jered Weaver	.20	.50
5 Stephen Drew	.12	.30
6 Jonathan Papelbon	.30	.75
7 Melky Cabrera	.12	.30
8 Francisco Liriano	.30	.75
9 Prince Fielder	.20	.50
10 Dan Uggla	.20	.50
11 Jeremy Sowers	.12	.30
12 Carlos Quentin	.12	.30
13 Chuck James	.12	.30
14 Andre Ethier	.20	.50
15 Cole Hamels UER (Utley pictured on back)	.30	.75
16 Kenji Johjima	.30	.75
17 Chad Billingsley	.12	.30
18 Ian Kinsler	.20	.50
19 Jason Hirsh	.12	.30
20 Nick Markakis	.30	.75
21 Jeremy Hermida	.12	.30
22 Ryan Shealy	.12	.30
23 Scott Olsen	.12	.30
24 Russell Martin	.12	.30
25 Conor Jackson	.12	.30
26 Erik Bedard	.12	.30
27 Brian McCann	.12	.30
28 Michael Barrett	.12	.30
29 Brandon Phillips	.12	.30
30 Garrett Atkins	.12	.30
31 Freddy Garcia	.12	.30
32 Mark Loretta	.12	.30
33 Craig Biggio	.20	.50
34 Jeremy Bonderman	.12	.30
35 Johan Santana	.30	.75
36 Jorge Posada	.20	.50
37 Brian Bannister	.12	.30
38 Carlos Delgado	.12	.30
39 Gary Matthews Jr.	.12	.30
40 Mike Cameron	.12	.30
41 Adrian Beltre	.12	.30
42 Freddy Sanchez	.12	.30
43 Austin Kearns	.12	.30
44 Mark Buehrle	.20	.50
45 Miguel Cabrera	.30	.75
46 Josh Beckett	.20	.50
47 Chone Figgins	.12	.30
48 Edgar Renteria	.12	.30
49 Derek Lowe	.12	.30
50 Ryan Howard	.50	1.25
51 Shawn Green	.12	.30
52 Jason Giambi	.12	.30
53 Ervin Santana	.12	.30
54 Jack Wilson	.12	.30
55 Roy Oswalt	.20	.50
56 Dan Haren	.12	.30
57 Jose Vidro	.12	.30
58 Kevin Millwood	.12	.30
59 Jim Edmonds	.20	.50
60 Carl Crawford	.20	.50
61 Randy Wolf	.12	.30
62 Paul LoDuca	.12	.30
63 Johnny Estrada	.12	.30
64 Brian Roberts	.12	.30
65 Manny Ramirez	.30	.75
66 Jose Contreras	.12	.30
67 Josh Barfield	.12	.30
68 Juan Pierre	.12	.30
69 David DeJesus	.12	.30
70 Gary Sheffield	.12	.30
71 Jon Lieber	.12	.30
72 Randy Johnson	.30	.75
73 Rickie Weeks	.20	.50
74 Brian Giles	.12	.30
75 Ichiro Suzuki	.50	1.25
76 Nick Swisher	.30	.75
77 Justin Morneau	.30	.75
78 Scott Kazmir	.20	.50
79 Lyle Overbay	.12	.30
80 Alfonso Soriano	.20	.50
81 Brandon Webb	.20	.50
82 Joe Crede	.12	.30
83 Corey Patterson	.12	.30
84 Kenny Rogers	.12	.30
85 Ken Griffey Jr	.50	1.25
86 Cliff Lee	.20	.50
87 Mike Lowell	.12	.30
88 Marcus Giles	.12	.30
89 Orlando Cabrera	.12	.30
90 Derek Jeter	.75	2.00
91 Josh Johnson	.30	.75
92 Carlos Guillen	.12	.30
93 Bill Hall	.12	.30
94 Michael Cuddyer	.12	.30
95 Miguel Tejada	.20	.50
96 Todd Helton	.20	.50
97 C.C. Sabathia	.20	.50
98 Tadahito Iguchi	.12	.30
99 Jose Reyes	.20	.50
100 David Wright	.50	1.25
101 Barry Zito	.12	.30
102 Jake Peavy	.12	.30
103 Richie Sexson	.12	.30
104 A.J. Burnett	.20	.50
105 Eric Chavez	.12	.30
106 Jorge Cantu	.12	.30
107 Grady Sizemore	.20	.50
108 Bronson Arroyo	.12	.30
109 Mike Mussina	.20	.50
110 Maggio Ordonez	.20	.50
111 Anibal Sanchez	.12	.30
112 Jeff Francoeur	.30	.75
113 Kevin Youkilis	.12	.30
114 Aubrey Huff	.12	.30
115 Carlos Zambrano	.20	.50
116 Mark Teahen	.12	.30
117 Carlos Silva	.12	.30
118 Pedro Martinez	.20	.50
119 Hideki Matsui	.30	.75
120 Mike Piazza	.30	.75
121 Jason Schmidt	.12	.30
122 Greg Maddux	.50	1.25
123 Joe Blanton	.12	.30
124 Chris Carpenter	.30	.75
125 David Ortiz	.20	.50
126 Alex Rios	.20	.50
127 Nick Johnson	.12	.30
128 Carlos Lee	.12	.30
129 Pat Burrell	.12	.30
130 Ben Sheets	.12	.30
131 Kazuo Matsui	.12	.30
132 Adam Dunn	.20	.50
133 Jermaine Dye	.12	.30
134 Curt Schilling	.20	.50
135 Chad Tracy	.12	.30
136 Vladimir Guerrero	.30	.75
137 Melvin Mora	.12	.30
138 John Smoltz	.30	.75
139 Craig Monroe	.12	.30
140 Dontrelle Willis	.12	.30
141 Jeff Francis	.12	.30
142 Chipper Jones	.30	.75
143 Frank Thomas	.30	.75
144 Brett Myers	.12	.30
145 Xavier Nady	.12	.30
146 Robinson Cano	.30	.75
147 Jeff Kent	.12	.30
148 Scott Rolen	.20	.50
149 Roy Halladay	.30	.75
150 Joe Mauer	.30	.75
151 Bobby Abreu	.12	.30
152 Matt Cain	.20	.50
153 Hank Blalock	.12	.30
154 Chris Capuano	.12	.30
155 Jake Westbrook	.12	.30
156 Javier Vazquez	.12	.30
157 Garret Anderson	.12	.30
158 Aramis Ramirez	.12	.30
159 Mark Kotsay	.12	.30
160 Matt Kemp	.20	.50
161 Adrian Gonzalez	.20	.50
162 Felix Hernandez	.30	.75
163 David Eckstein	.12	.30
164 Curtis Granderson	.20	.50
165 Paul Konerko	.20	.50
166 Orlando Hudson	.12	.30
167 Tim Hudson	.20	.50
168 J.D. Drew	.12	.30
169 Chien-Ming Wang	.20	.50
170 Jimmy Rollins	.20	.50
171 Matt Morris	.12	.30
172 Raul Ibanez	.20	.50
173 Mark Teixeira	.30	.75
174 Ted Lilly	.12	.30
175 Albert Pujols	.75	2.00
176 Carlos Beltran	.12	.30
177 Lance Berkman	.20	.50
178 Ivan Rodriguez	.20	.50
179 Torii Hunter	.12	.30
180 Johnny Damon	.20	.50
181 Chase Utley	.30	.75
182 Jason Bay	.20	.50
183 Jeff Weaver	.12	.30
184 Troy Glaus	.12	.30
185 Rocco Baldelli	.12	.30
186 Rafael Furcal	.12	.30
187 Jim Thome	.20	.50
188 Travis Hafner	.12	.30
189 Matt Holliday	.30	.75
190 Andruw Jones	.12	.30
191 Ramon Hernandez	.12	.30
192 Victor Martinez	.20	.50
193 Aaron Hill	.12	.30
194 Michael Young	.20	.50
195 Vernon Wells	.12	.30
196 Mark Mulder	.12	.30
197 Derrek Lee	.12	.30
198 Tom Glavine	.20	.50
199 Chris Young	.12	.30
200 Alex Rodriguez	.50	1.25
201 Delmon Young (RC)	.25	.60
202 Alexi Casilla RC	.25	.60
203 Shawn Riggans (RC)	.15	.40
204 Jeff Baker (RC)	.15	.40
205 Hector Gimenez (RC)	.15	.40
206 Ubaldo Jimenez (RC)	1.00	2.50
207 Adam Lind (RC)	.15	.40
208 Joaquin Arias (RC)	.15	.40
209 David Murphy (RC)	.15	.40
210 Daisuke Matsuzaka RC	2.00	5.00
211 Jerry Owens (RC)	.15	.40
212 Ryan Sweeney (RC)	.15	.40
213 Kei Igawa RC	.60	1.50
214 Fred Lewis (RC)	.25	.60
215 Philip Humber (RC)	.15	.40
216 Kevin Hooper (RC)	.15	.40
217 Jeff Fiorentino (RC)	.15	.40
218 Michael Bourn (RC)	.15	.40
219 Hideki Okajima RC	.75	2.00
219b Hideki Okajima English AU	4.00	10.00
219c Hideki Okajima Japanese AU	20.00	50.00
220 Josh Fields (RC)	.15	.40
221 Andrew Miller AU RC	4.00	10.00
222 Troy Tulowitzki AU (RC)	12.50	30.00
223 Ryan Braun AU RC	4.00	10.00
224 Oswaldo Navarro AU RC	4.00	10.00
225 Philip Humber AU (RC)	4.00	10.00
226 Mitch Maier AU RC	4.00	10.00
227 Jerry Owens AU (RC)	4.00	10.00
228 Mike Rabelo AU RC	4.00	10.00
229 Delwyn Young AU (RC)	4.00	10.00
230 Miguel Montero AU (RC)	4.00	10.00
231 Akinori Iwamura AU RC	8.00	20.00
232 Matt Lindstrom AU (RC)	4.00	10.00
233 Josh Hamilton AU (RC)	12.50	30.00
235 Elijah Dukes AU RC	6.00	15.00
236 Sean Henn AU (RC)	4.00	10.00
237 Barry Bonds	.60	1.50

2007 Bowman Blue

*BLUE 1-200: 2X TO 5X BASIC
*BLUE 201-220: 2X TO 5X BASIC
*BLUE 219 AU/221-236: .4X TO 1X BASIC AU
1-220 ODDS 1:17 HOB; 1:3 HTA, 1:30 RET
221-236 AU ODDS 1:241 HOBBY, 1:60 HTA
BONDS ODDS 1:1261 HTA, 1:15,500 RETAIL
STATED PRINT RUN 500 SERIAL #'d SETS

2007 Bowman Gold

*GOLD 1-200: 1.2X TO 3X BASIC
*GOLD 201-220: 1.2X TO 3X BASIC
OVERALL GOLD ODDS 1 PER PACK

2007 Bowman Orange

*ORANGE 1-200: 3X TO 8X BASIC
*ORANGE 201-220: 3X TO 8X BASIC
*ORANGE 219 AU/221-236: .5X TO 1.2X BASIC AU
1-220 ODDS 1:33 HOB, 1:6 HTA, 1:65 RET
221-236 AU ODDS 1:486 HOBBY, 1:119 HTA
BONDS ODDS 1:2521 HTA, 1:30,000 RETAIL
STATED PRINT RUN 250 SERIAL #'d SETS

Card	Low	High
219b Hideki Okajima English AU	15.00	40.00
219c Hideki Okajima Japanese AU	40.00	80.00
221 Andrew Miller AU	5.00	12.00
222 Troy Tulowitzki AU	40.00	80.00
233 Josh Hamilton AU	20.00	50.00

2007 Bowman Red

1-220 ODDS 1:6036 HOBBY, 1:1400 HTA
221-236 AU ODDS 1:222,220 H, 1:27,000 HTA
BONDS ODDS 1:211,776 HTA
STATED PRINT RUN 1 SER.#'d SET
NO PRICING DUE TO SCARCITY

2007 Bowman Prospects

COMP.SET w/o AU's (110) 20.00 50.00
111-135 AU ODDS 1:64 HOBBY, 1:16 HTA
1-110 PLATE ODDS 1:1468 H, 1:212 HTA
111-135 AU PLATES 1:8200 H, 1:1150 HTA
PLATE PRINT RUN 1 SET PER COLOR
BLACK-CYAN-MAGENTA-YELLOW ISSUED
NO PLATE PRICING DUE TO SCARCITY
BP1 Cooper Brannon .20 .50
BP2 Jason Taylor .30 .75
BP3 Shawn O'Malley .20 .50
BP4 Robert Alcombrack .20 .50
BP5 Dellin Betances .50 1.25
BP6 Jeremy Papelbon .20 .50
BP7 Adam Carr .20 .50
BP8 Matthew Clarkson .20 .50
BP9 Darin McDonald .20 .50
BP10 Brandon Rice .20 .50
BP11 Matthew Sweeney .60 1.50
BP12 Scott Deal .20 .50
BP13 Brennan Boesch .60 1.50
BP14 Scott Taylor .20 .50
BP15 Michael Brantley .50 1.25
BP16 Yahmed Yema .20 .50
BP17 Brandon Morrow 1.00 2.50
BP18 Cole Garner .20 .50
BP19 Erik Lis .30 .75
BP20 Lucas French .20 .50
BP21 Aaron Cunningham .30 .75
BP22 Ryan Schreppel .20 .50
BP23 Kevin Russo .20 .50
BP24 Yohan Pino .30 .75
BP25 Michael Sullivan .20 .50
BP26 Trey Shields .20 .50
BP27 Daniel Matienzo .20 .50
BP28 Chuck Lofgren .50 1.25
BP29 Gerrit Simpson .20 .50
BP30 David Haehnel .20 .50
BP31 Marvin Lowrance .20 .50
BP32 Kevin Ardoin .20 .50
BP33 Edwin Maysonet .20 .50
BP34 Derek Griffith .20 .50
BP35 Sam Fuld .60 1.50
BP36 Chase Wright .50 1.25
BP37 Brandon Roberts .20 .50
BP38 Kyle Aselton .20 .50
BP39 Steven Sollmann .20 .50
BP40 Mike Devaney .20 .50
BP41 Charlie Fermaint .20 .50
BP42 Jesse Litsch .30 .75
BP43 Bryan Hansen .20 .50
BP44 Ramon Garcia .20 .50
BP45 John Otness .20 .50
BP46 Trey Hearne .20 .50
BP47 Habelito Hernandez .20 .50
BP48 Edgar Garcia .20 .50
BP49 Seth Fortenberry .20 .50
BP50 Reid Brignac .30 .75
BP51 Derek Rodriguez .20 .50
BP52 Ervin Alcantara .20 .50
BP53 Thomas Hottovy .20 .50
BP54 Jesus Flores .20 .50
BP55 Matt Palmer .20 .50
BP56 Brian Henderson .20 .50
BP57 John Gragg .20 .50
BP58 Jay Garthwaite .20 .50
BP59 Esmerling Vasquez .20 .50
BP60 Gilberto Mejia .20 .50
BP61 Aaron Jensen .20 .50
BP62 Cedric Brooks .20 .50
BP63 Brandon Mann .20 .50
BP64 Myron Leslie .20 .50
BP65 Ray Aguilar .20 .50
BP66 Jesus Guzman .30 .75
BP67 Sean Thompson .20 .50
BP68 Jarrett Hoffpauir .20 .50
BP69 Matt Goodson .20 .50
BP70 Neal Musser .20 .50
BP71 Tony Abreu .50 1.25
BP72 Tony Peguero .20 .50
BP73 Michael Bertram .20 .50
BP74 Randy Wells .50 1.25
BP75 Bradley Davis .20 .50
BP76 Jay Sawatski .20 .50
BP77 Vic Buttler .20 .50
BP78 Jose Oyervidez .20 .50
BP79 Doug Deeds .20 .50
BP80 Dan Dement .20 .50
BP81 Spike Lundberg .20 .50
BP82 Ricardo Nanita .20 .50
BP83 Brad Knox .20 .50
BP84 Will Venable .30 .75
BP85 Greg Smith .30 .75
BP86 Pedro Powell .20 .50
BP87 Gabriel Medina .20 .50
BP88 Duke Sardinha .20 .50
BP89 Mike Madsen .20 .50
BP90 Rayner Bautista .20 .50
BP91 T.J. Nall .20 .50
BP92 Neil Sellers .20 .50
BP93 Andrew Dobies .20 .50
BP94 Leo Daigle .20 .50
BP95 Brian Duensing .20 .50
BP96 Vincent Blue .20 .50
BP97 Fernando Rodriguez .20 .50
BP98 Derin McMains .20 .50
BP99 Adam Bass .20 .50
BP100 Justin Ruggiano .20 .50
BP101 Jared Burton .20 .50
BP102 Mike Parisi .20 .50
BP103 Aaron Peel .20 .50
BP104 Evan Englebrook .20 .50
BP105 Sendy Vasquez .20 .50
BP106 Desmond Jennings .60 1.50
BP107 Clay Harris .20 .50
BP108 Cody Strait .20 .50
BP109 Ryan Mullins .20 .50
BP110 Ryan Webb .20 .50
BP111 Kyle Drabek AU 4.00 10.00
BP112 Evan Longoria AU 30.00 60.00
BP113 Tyler Colvin AU 6.00 15.00
BP114 Matt Long AU 4.00 10.00
BP115 Jeremy Jeffress AU 3.00 8.00
BP116 Kasey Kiker AU 4.00 10.00
BP117 Hank Conger AU 5.00 12.00
BP118 Cody Johnson AU 4.00 10.00
BP119 David Huff AU 4.00 10.00
BP120 Tommy Hickman AU 4.00 10.00
BP121 Chris Parmelee AU 6.00 15.00
BP122 Dustin Evans AU 4.00 10.00
BP123 Brett Sinkbeil AU 4.00 10.00
BP124 Andrew Carpenter AU 4.00 10.00
BP125 Colten Willems AU 4.00 10.00
BP126 Matt Antonelli AU 4.00 10.00
BP127 Marcus Sanders AU 4.00 10.00
BP128 Joshua Rodriguez AU 4.00 10.00
BP129 Keith Weiser AU 4.00 10.00
BP130 Chad Tracy AU 4.00 10.00
BP131 Matthew Sulentic AU 6.00 15.00
BP132 Adam Ottavino AU 4.00 10.00
BP133 Jarrod Saltalamacchia AU 8.00 20.00
BP134 Kyle Blanks AU 5.00 12.00
BP135 Brad Eldred AU 4.00 10.00

2007 Bowman Prospects Blue

*BLUE 1-110: 2X TO 5X BASIC
*BLUE 111-135: .4X TO 1X BASIC AU
1-110 ODDS 1:17 HOB, 1:3 HTA, 1:30 RET
111-135 AU ODDS 1:156 HOBBY, 1:38 HTA
STATED PRINT RUN 500 SERIAL #'d SETS
BP111 Kyle Drabek AU 6.00 15.00
BP112 Evan Longoria AU 40.00 80.00

2007 Bowman Prospects Gold

*GOLD 1-110: .75X TO 2X BASIC
OVERALL GOLD ODDS 1 PER PACK

2007 Bowman Prospects Orange

*ORANGE 1-110: 2.5X TO 6X BASIC
*ORANGE 111-135: .5X TO 1.2X BASIC AU
1-110 ODDS 1:33 HOB, 1:6 HTA, 1:65 RET
111-135 AU ODDS 1:311 HOBBY, 1:77 HTA
STATED PRINT RUN 250 SERIAL #'d SETS
BP111 Kyle Drabek AU 10.00 25.00
BP112 Evan Longoria AU 40.00 80.00
BP113 Tyler Colvin AU 15.00 40.00
BP115 Jeremy Jeffress AU 5.00 12.00
BP121 Chris Parmelee AU 10.00 25.00
BP131 Matthew Sulentic AU 10.00 25.00

2007 Bowman Prospects Red

1-110 ODDS 1:6036 HOBBY, 1:1400 HTA
111 135 AU ODDS 80,000 H, 1:19,252 HTA
STATED PRINT RUN 1 SER.#'d SET
NO PRICING DUE TO SCARCITY

2007 Bowman Signs of the Future

GROUP A ODDS 1:2725 RETAIL
GROUP B ODDS 1:385 RETAIL

GROUP C ODDS 1:268 RETAIL
GROUP D ODDS 1:82 RETAIL
GROUP E ODDS 1:63 RETAIL
GROUP F ODDS 1:89 RETAIL
PRINTING PLATE ODDS 1:8200 H, 1:1150 HTA
PLATE PRINT RUN 1 SET PER COLOR
BLACK-CYAN-MAGENTA-YELLOW ISSUED
NO PLATE PRICING DUE TO SCARCITY
AM Andrew McCutchen 10.00 25.00
AR Adam Russell 3.00 8.00
BB Brian Bixler 3.00 8.00
BM Brandon Moss 4.00 10.00
CG Chris Getz 3.00 8.00
CJS Chris Seddon 3.00 8.00
CL Chris Lubanski 4.00 10.00
CM Chris McConnell 3.00 8.00
JW Jared Wells 3.00 8.00
CS Chad Santos 3.00 8.00
DB Dellin Betances 15.00 40.00
DS Denard Span 4.00 10.00
EH Estee Harris 6.00 15.00
ER Eric Reed 6.00 15.00
FP Felix Pie 8.00 20.00
JB John Baker 3.00 8.00
CR Chris Robinson 3.00 8.00
JBC J. Brent Cox 6.00 15.00
JC Jesus Cota 3.00 8.00
JCB Jordan Brown 3.00 8.00
JD John Drennen 6.00 15.00
JBB John Bowker 3.00 8.00
JJ Jair Jurrjens 20.00 50.00
MM Matt Merricks 3.00 8.00
BF Ben Fritz 3.00 8.00
KC Koby Clemens 6.00 15.00
KD Kyle Drabek 6.00 15.00
KS Kurt Suzuki 4.00 10.00
MA Mike Aviles 3.00 8.00
ME Mike Edwards 3.00 8.00
JDA Jaime D'Antona 3.00 8.00
MN Mike Neu 3.00 8.00
MR Michael Rogers 3.00 8.00
RB Reid Brignac 6.00 15.00
RG Richie Gardner 4.00 10.00
RO Ross Ohlendorf 6.00 15.00
SG Sean Gallagher 4.00 10.00
SK Shane Komine 4.00 10.00
TT Taylor Teagarden 10.00 25.00

2007 Bowman Draft

This 54-card set, featuring 2007 rookies, was released in December, 2007. The set was issued in seven-card packs, which included two Bowman Chrome Draft cards, which came 24 packs to a box and 10 boxes per case.

COMMON RC (1-54) .15 .40
SEE 07 BOWMAN FOR BONDS PRICING
OVERALL PLATE ODDS 1:1294 HOBBY
PLATE PRINT RUN 1 SET PER COLOR
BLACK-CYAN-MAGENTA-YELLOW ISSUED
NO PLATE PRICING DUE TO SCARCITY
BDP1 Travis Buck (RC) .15 .40
BDP2 Matt Chico (RC) .15 .40
BDP3 Justin Upton RC 1.25 3.00
BDP4 Chase Wright RC .40 1.00
BDP5 Kevin Kouzmanoff (RC) .15 .40
BDP6 John Danks RC .25 .60
BDP7 Alejandro De Aza RC .25 .60
BDP8 Jamie Vermilyea RC .15 .40
BDP9 Jesus Flores RC .15 .40
BDP10 Glen Perkins (RC) .15 .40
BDP11 Tim Lincecum RC 2.50 6.00
BDP12 Cameron Maybin RC .25 .60
BDP13 Brandon Morrow RC .75 2.00
BDP14 Mike Rabelo RC .15 .40
BDP15 Alex Gordon RC .50 1.25
BDP16 Zack Segovia (RC) .15 .40
BDP17 Jon Knott (RC) .15 .40
BDP18 Joba Chamberlain RC .75 2.00
BDP19 Danny Putnam (RC) .15 .40
BDP20 Matt DeSalvo (RC) .15 .40
BDP21 Fred Lewis (RC) .25 .60
BDP22 Sean Gallagher (RC) .15 .40
BDP23 Brandon Wood (RC) .15 .40
BDP24 Dennis Dove (RC) .15 .40
BDP25 Hunter Pence (RC) .75 2.00
BDP26 Jarrod Saltalamacchia (RC) .25 .60
BDP27 Ben Francisco (RC) .15 .40
BDP28 Doug Slaten RC .15 .40
BDP29 Tony Abreu RC .40 1.00
BDP30 Billy Butler (RC) .25 .60
BDP31 Jesse Litsch RC .25 .60
BDP32 Nate Schierholtz (RC) .15 .40
BDP33 Jared Burton RC .15 .40
BDP34 Matt Brown RC .15 .40
BDP35 Dallas Braden RC 1.00 2.50
BDP36 Carlos Gomez RC .25 .60
BDP37 Brian Stokes (RC) .15 .40
BDP38 Kory Casto (RC) .15 .40
BDP39 Mark McLemore (RC) .15 .40
BDP40 Andy LaRoche (RC) .15 .40
BDP41 Tyler Clippard (RC) .25 .60
BDP42 Curtis Thigpen (RC) .15 .40
BDP43 Yunel Escobar (RC) .15 .40
BDP44 Andy Sonnanstine RC .15 .40
BDP45 Felix Pie (RC) .15 .40
BDP46 Homer Bailey (RC) .25 .60
BDP47 Kyle Kendrick RC .40 1.00
BDP48 Angel Sanchez RC .15 .40
BDP49 Phil Hughes (RC) .75 2.00
BDP50 Ryan Braun (RC) .75 2.00
BDP51 Kevin Slowey (RC) .40 1.00
BDP52 Brendan Ryan (RC) .15 .40
BDP53 Yovani Gallardo (RC) .40 1.00
BDP54 Mark Reynolds RC 1.25 3.00

2007 Bowman Draft Blue

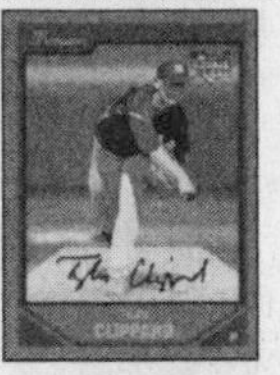

*BLUE: 1.2X TO 3X BASIC
STATED ODDS 1:29 HOBBY,1:84 RETAIL
STATED PRINT RUN 399 SER.#'d SETS

2007 Bowman Draft Gold

*GOLD: .6X TO 1.5X BASIC
APPX.GOLD ODDS ONE PER PACK

2007 Bowman Draft Red

STATED ODDS 1:10,377 HOBBY
STATED PRINT RUN ONE SER.#'d SET
NO PRICING DUE TO SCARCITY

2007 Bowman Draft Draft Picks

OVERALL PLATE ODDS 1:1294 HOBBY
PLATE PRINT RUN 1 SET PER COLOR
BLACK-CYAN-MAGENTA-YELLOW ISSUED
NO PLATE PRICING DUE TO SCARCITY
BDPP1 Cody Crowell .15 .40
BDPP2 Karl Bolt .25 .60
BDPP3 Corey Brown .25 .60
BDPP4 Tyler Mach .25 .60
BDPP5 Trevor Pippin .25 .60
BDPP6 Ed Easley .15 .40
BDPP7 Cory Luebke .15 .40
BDPP8 Darin Mastroianni .15 .40
BDPP9 Ryan Zink .25 .60
BDPP10 Brandon Hamilton .15 .40
BDPP11 Kyle Lotzkar .25 .60
BDPP12 Freddie Freeman 1.00 2.50
BDPP13 Nicholas Barnese .25 .60
BDPP14 Travis d'Arnaud .25 .60
BDPP15 Eric Eiland .15 .40
BDPP16 John Ely .15 .40
BDPP17 Oliver Marmol .15 .40
BDPP18 Eric Sogard .15 .40
BDPP19 Lars Davis .15 .40
BDPP20 Sam Runion .15 .40
BDPP21 Austin Gallagher .25 .60
BDPP22 Matt West .25 .60
BDPP23 Derek Norris .40 1.00
BDPP24 Taylor Holiday .25 .60
BDPP25 Dustin Biell .15 .40
BDPP26 Julio Borbon .50 1.25
BDPP27 Brant Rustich .25 .60
BDPP28 Andrew Lambo .50 1.25
BDPP29 Cory Kluber .15 .40
BDPP30 Justin Jackson .25 .60
BDPP31 Scott Carroll .15 .40
BDPP32 Danny Rams .15 .40
BDPP33 Thomas Eager .15 .40
BDPP34 Matt Dominguez .40 1.00
BDPP35 Steven Souza .15 .40
BDPP36 Craig Heyer .15 .40
BDPP37 Michael Taylor .60 1.50
BDPP38 Drew Bowman .15 .40
BDPP39 Frank Gailey .15 .40
BDPP40 Jeremy Hefner .15 .40
BDPP41 Reynaldo Navarro .25 .60
BDPP42 Daniel Descalso .25 .60
BDPP43 Leroy Hunt .15 .40
BDPP44 Jason Kiley .15 .40
BDPP45 Ryan Pope .40 1.00
BDPP46 Josh Horton .15 .40
BDPP47 Jason Monti .15 .40
BDPP48 Richard Lucas .15 .40
BDPP49 Jonathan Lucroy .40 1.00
BDPP50 Sean Doolittle .40 1.00
BDPP51 Mike McDade .25 .60
BDPP52 Charlie Culberson .25 .60
BDPP53 Michael Moustakas .60 1.50
BDPP54 Jason Heyward 1.25 3.00
BDPP55 David Price 1.00 2.50
BDPP56 Brad Mills .15 .40
BDPP57 John Tolisano .50 1.25
BDPP58 Jarrod Parker .40 1.00
BDPP59 Wendell Fairley .25 .60
BDPP60 Gary Gattis .15 .40
BDPP61 Madison Bumgarner 1.00 2.50
BDPP62 Danny Payne .15 .40
BDPP63 Jake Smolinski .50 1.25
BDPP64 Matt LaPorta .60 1.50
BDPP65 Jackson Williams .15 .40

2007 Bowman Draft Draft Picks Blue

*BLUE: 2X TO 5X BASIC
STATED ODDS 1:29 HOBBY,1:84 RETAIL
STATED PRINT RUN 399 SER.#'d SETS

2007 Bowman Draft Draft Picks Gold

*GOLD: .75X TO 2X BASIC
APPX.GOLD ODDS ONE PER PACK

2007 Bowman Draft Draft Picks Red

STATED ODDS 1:10,377 HOBBY
STATED PRINT RUN ONE SER.#'d SET
NO PRICING DUE TO SCARCITY

2007 Bowman Draft Future's Game Prospects

COMPLETE SET (45) 8.00 20.00
OVERALL PLATE ODDS 1:1294 HOBBY
PLATE PRINT RUN 1 SET PER COLOR
BLACK-CYAN-MAGENTA-YELLOW ISSUED
NO PLATE PRICING DUE TO SCARCITY
BDPP66 Pedro Beato .12 .30
BDPP67 Collin Balester .12 .30
BDPP68 Carlos Carrasco .12 .30
BDPP69 Clay Buchholz .75 2.00
BDPP70 Emiliano Fruto .12 .30
BDPP71 Joba Chamberlain .60 1.50
BDPP72 Deolis Guerra .30 .75
BDPP73 Kevin Mulvey .30 .75
BDPP74 Franklin Morales .20 .50
BDPP75 Luke Hochevar .40 1.00
BDPP76 Henry Sosa .20 .50
BDPP77 Clayton Kershaw 1.00 2.50
BDPP78 Rich Thompson .12 .30
BDPP79 Chuck Lofgren .30 .75
BDPP80 Rick VandenHurk .12 .30
BDPP81 Michael Madsen .12 .30
BDPP82 Robinzon Diaz .12 .30
BDPP83 Jeff Niemann .20 .50
BDPP84 Max Ramirez .20 .50
BDPP85 Geovany Soto .50 1.25
BDPP86 Elvis Andrus .30 .75
BDPP87 Bryan Anderson .12 .30
BDPP88 German Duran .50 1.25
BDPP89 J.R. Towles .40 1.00
BDPP90 Alcides Escobar .20 .50
BDPP91 Brian Bocock .12 .30
BDPP92 Chin-Lung Hu .50 1.25
BDPP93 Adrian Cardenas .20 .50
BDPP94 Freddy Sandoval .12 .30
BDPP95 Chris Coghlan .40 1.00
BDPP96 Craig Stansberry .12 .30
BDPP97 Brent Lillibridge .12 .30
BDPP98 Joey Votto .75 2.00
BDPP99 Evan Longoria 1.25 3.00
BDPP100 Wladimir Balentien .12 .30
BDPP101 Johnny Whittleman .12 .30
BDPP102 Gorkys Hernandez .30 .75
BDPP103 Jay Bruce .75 2.00
BDPP104 Matt Tolbert .12 .30
BDPP105 Jacoby Ellsbury 1.00 2.50
BDPP106 Michael Saunders .40 1.00
BDPP107 Cameron Maybin .20 .50
BDPP108 Carlos Gonzalez .30 .75
BDPP109 Colby Rasmus .75 2.00
BDPP110 Justin Upton 1.00 2.50

2007 Bowman Draft Future's Game Prospects Blue

*BLUE: 1.2X TO 3X BASIC
STATED ODDS 1:29 HOBBY,1:84 RETAIL
STATED PRINT RUN 399 SER.#'d SETS

2007 Bowman Draft Future's Game Prospects Gold

*GOLD: .6X TO 1.5X BASIC
APPX.GOLD ODDS ONE PER PACK

2007 Bowman Draft Future's Game Prospects Red

STATED ODDS 1:10,377 HOBBY
STATED PRINT RUN ONE SER.#'d SET
NO PRICING DUE TO SCARCITY

2007 Bowman Draft Future's Game Prospects Jerseys

STATED ODDS 1:24 RETAIL
BDPP68 Carlos Carrasco 3.00 8.00
BDPP69 Clay Buchholz 5.00 12.00
BDPP71 Joba Chamberlain 10.00 25.00
BDPP73 Kevin Mulvey 3.00 8.00
BDPP74 Franklin Morales 3.00 8.00
BDPP75 Luke Hochevar 3.00 8.00
BDPP78 Rich Thompson 3.00 8.00
BDPP83 Jeff Niemann 3.00 8.00
BDPP84 Max Ramirez 3.00 8.00
BDPP89 J.R. Towles 3.00 8.00
BDPP95 Chris Coghlan 3.00 8.00
BDPP96 Craig Stansberry 3.00 8.00
BDPP97 Brent Lillibridge 3.00 8.00
BDPP98 Joey Votto 5.00 12.00
BDPP102 Gorkys Hernandez 3.00 8.00
BDPP105 Jacoby Ellsbury 8.00 20.00
BDPP106 Michael Saunders 3.00 8.00
BDPP107 Cameron Maybin 5.00 12.00
BDPP108 Carlos Gonzalez 4.00 10.00
BDPP110 Justin Upton 6.00 15.00

2007 Bowman Draft Future's Game Prospects Patches

STATED ODDS 1:384 HOBBY
STATED PRINT RUN 99 SER.#'d SETS
BDPP66 Pedro Beato 10.00 25.00
BDPP67 Collin Balester 10.00 25.00
BDPP68 Carlos Carrasco 12.50 30.00
BDPP69 Clay Buchholz 15.00 40.00
BDPP70 Emiliano Fruto 4.00 10.00
BDPP71 Joba Chamberlain 20.00 50.00
BDPP72 Deolis Guerra 12.50 30.00
BDPP73 Kevin Mulvey 6.00 15.00
BDPP74 Franklin Morales 6.00 15.00
BDPP75 Luke Hochevar 10.00 25.00
BDPP76 Henry Sosa 6.00 15.00
BDPP77 Clayton Kershaw 10.00 25.00
BDPP78 Rich Thompson 6.00 15.00
BDPP79 Chuck Lofgren 6.00 15.00
BDPP80 Rick VandenHurk 6.00 15.00
BDPP81 Michael Madsen 4.00 10.00
BDPP82 Robinzon Diaz 4.00 10.00
BDPP83 Jeff Niemann 6.00 15.00
BDPP84 Max Ramirez 10.00 25.00
BDPP85 Geovany Soto 15.00 40.00
BDPP86 Elvis Andrus 10.00 25.00
BDPP87 Bryan Anderson 10.00 25.00
BDPP88 German Duran 6.00 15.00
BDPP89 J.R. Towles 6.00 15.00
BDPP90 Alcides Escobar 6.00 15.00
BDPP91 Brian Bocock 6.00 15.00
BDPP92 Chin-Lung Hu 20.00 50.00
BDPP93 Adrian Cardenas 15.00 40.00
BDPP94 Freddy Sandoval 6.00 15.00
BDPP95 Chris Coghlan 6.00 15.00
BDPP96 Craig Stansberry 4.00 10.00
BDPP97 Brent Lillibridge 6.00 15.00
BDPP98 Joey Votto 10.00 25.00
BDPP99 Evan Longoria 15.00 40.00
BDPP100 Wladimir Balentien 6.00 15.00
BDPP101 Johnny Whittleman 6.00 15.00
BDPP102 Gorkys Hernandez 10.00 25.00
BDPP103 Jay Bruce 15.00 40.00
BDPP104 Matt Tolbert 15.00 40.00
BDPP105 Jacoby Ellsbury 15.00 40.00
BDPP106 Michael Saunders 10.00 25.00
BDPP107 Cameron Maybin 12.50 30.00
BDPP108 Carlos Gonzalez 10.00 25.00
BDPP109 Colby Rasmus 10.00 25.00
BDPP110 Justin Upton 15.00 40.00

2007 Bowman Draft Head of the Class Dual Autograph

STATED ODDS 1:4965 HOBBY
STATED PRINT RUN 174 SER.#'d SETS
EXCHANGE DEADLINE 12/31/2009
GH Jonathan Gilmore 60.00 120.00
Jason Heyward

2007 Bowman Draft Head of the Class Dual Autograph Refractors

*REF: .6X TO 1.5X BASIC
STATED ODDS 1:18,000 HOBBY
STATED PRINT RUN 50 SER.#'d SETS
EXCHANGE DEADLINE 12/31/2009
GH Jonathan Gilmore 150.00 300.00
Jason Heyward

2007 Bowman Draft Head of the Class Dual Autograph Gold Refractors

STATED ODDS 1:34,500 HOBBY
STATED PRINT RUN 25 SER.#'d SETS
NO PRICING DUE TO SCARCITY
EXCHANGE DEADLINE 12/31/2009

2007 Bowman Draft Head of the Class Dual Autograph SuperFractors

STATED ODDS 1:809,400 HOBBY
STATED PRINT RUN ONE SER.#'d SET
NO PRICING DUE TO SCARCITY

2007 Bowman Draft Signs of the Future

GROUP A ODDS 1:233 RETAIL
GROUP B ODDS 1:30 RETAIL
GROUP C ODDS 1:194 RETAIL
GROUP D ODDS 1:146 RETAIL
GROUP E ODDS 1:2945 RETAIL
AL Anthony Lerew 6.00 15.00
AM Adam Miller 5.00 12.00
BA Brandon Allen 4.00 10.00
CD Chris Dickerson 3.00 8.00
CM Casey McGehee 8.00 20.00
CMC Chris McConnell 4.00 10.00
CMM Carlos Marmol 6.00 15.00
CV Carlos Villanueva 3.00 8.00
FM Fernando Martinez 6.00 15.00
JGA Jamie Garcia 10.00 25.00
JK John Koronka 3.00 8.00
JR John Rheinecker 3.00 8.00
JV Jonathan Van Every 3.00 8.00
PH Philip Humber 4.00 10.00
RD Ryan Delaughter 3.00 8.00

SM Sergio Mitre 3.00 8.00
TC Trevor Crowe 3.00 8.00

2008 Bowman

COMP.SET w/o AU's (220) 10.00 25.00
COMMON CARD (1-200) .12 .30
COMMON ROOKIE (201-220) .15 .40
COMMON AUTO (221-230) 4.00 10.00
AU RC ODDS 1:233 HOBBY
1-220 PLATE ODDS 1:732 HOBBY
221-231 AU PLATES 1:4700 HOBBY
PLATE PRINT RUN 1 SET PER COLOR
BLACK-CYAN-MAGENTA-YELLOW ISSUED
NO PLATE PRICING DUE TO SCARCITY
1 Ryan Braun .40 1.00
2 David DeJesus .12 .30
3 Brandon Phillips .12 .30
4 Mark Teixeira .30 .75
5 Daisuke Matsuzaka .30 .75
6 Justin Upton .20 .50
7 Jered Weaver .12 .30
8 Todd Helton .20 .50
9 Cameron Maybin .12 .30
10 Erik Bedard .12 .30
11 Jason Bay .20 .50
12 Cole Hamels .30 .75
13 Bobby Abreu .12 .30
14 Carlos Zambrano .20 .50
15 Vladimir Guerrero .30 .75
16 Joe Blanton .12 .30
17 Bengie Molina .12 .30
18 Paul Maholm .12 .30
19 Adrian Gonzalez .20 .50
20 Brandon Webb .20 .50
21 Carl Crawford .20 .50
22 A.J. Burnett .20 .50
23 Dmitri Young .12 .30
24 Jeremy Hermida .12 .30
25 C.C. Sabathia .20 .50
26 Adam Dunn .20 .50
27 Matt Garza .12 .30
28 Adrian Beltre .12 .30
29 Kevin Millwood .12 .30
30 Manny Ramirez .30 .75
31 Javier Vazquez .12 .30
32 Carlos Delgado .12 .30
33 Jason Schmidt .12 .30
34 Torii Hunter .12 .30
35 Ivan Rodriguez .20 .50
36 Nick Markakis .30 .75
37 Gil Meche .12 .30
38 Garrett Atkins .12 .30
39 Fausto Carmona .12 .30
40 Joe Mauer .30 .75
41 Tom Glavine .20 .50
42 Hideki Matsui .30 .75
43 Scott Rolen .20 .50
44 Tim Lincecum .50 1.25
45 Prince Fielder .20 .50
46 Ted Lilly .12 .30
47 Frank Thomas .30 .75
48 Tom Gorzelanny .12 .30
49 Lance Berkman .20 .50
50 David Ortiz .20 .50
51 Dontrelle Willis .12 .30
52 Travis Hafner .12 .30
53 Aaron Harang .12 .30
54 Chris Young .12 .30
55 Vernon Wells .12 .30
56 Francisco Liriano .20 .50
57 Eric Chavez .12 .30
58 Phil Hughes .30 .75
59 Melvin Mora .12 .30
60 Johan Santana .30 .75
61 Brian McCann .20 .50
62 Pat Burrell .12 .30
63 Chris Carpenter .30 .75
64 Brian Giles .12 .30
65 Jose Reyes .20 .50
66 Hanley Ramirez .30 .75
67 Ubaldo Jimenez .20 .50
68 Felix Pie .12 .30
69 Jeremy Bonderman .12 .30
70 Jimmy Rollins .20 .50
71 Miguel Tejada .20 .50
72 Derek Lowe .12 .30
73 Alex Gordon .20 .50
74 John Maine .12 .30
75 Alfonso Soriano .20 .50
76 Richie Sexson .12 .30
77 Ben Sheets .12 .30
78 Hunter Pence .30 .75
79 Magglio Ordonez .20 .50
80 Josh Beckett .20 .50
81 Victor Martinez .20 .50
82 Mark Buehrle .20 .50
83 Jason Varitek .30 .75
84 Chien-Ming Wang .20 .50
85 Ken Griffey Jr. .50 1.25
86 Billy Butler .12 .30
87 Brad Penny .12 .30
88 Carlos Beltran .12 .30
89 Curt Schilling .20 .50
90 Jorge Posada .20 .50
91 Andruw Jones .12 .30
92 Bobby Crosby .12 .30
93 Freddy Sanchez .12 .30
94 Barry Zito .12 .30
95 Miguel Cabrera .30 .75
96 B.J. Upton .20 .50
97 Matt Cain .12 .30
98 Lyle Overbay .12 .30
99 Austin Kearns .12 .30
100 Alex Rodriguez .50 1.25
101 Rich Harden .12 .30
102 Justin Morneau .30 .75
103 Oliver Perez .12 .30
104 Gary Matthews .12 .30
105 Matt Holliday .30 .75
106 Justin Verlander .40 1.00
107 Orlando Cabrera .12 .30
108 Rich Hill .12 .30
109 Tim Hudson .20 .50
110 Ryan Zimmerman .20 .50
111 Roy Oswalt .20 .50
112 Nick Swisher .30 .75
113 Raul Ibanez .20 .50
114 Kelly Johnson .12 .30
115 Alex Rios .20 .50
116 John Lackey .12 .30
117 Robinson Cano .30 .75
118 Michael Young .20 .50
119 Jeff Francis .12 .30
120 Grady Sizemore .20 .50
121 Mike Lowell .12 .30
122 Aramis Ramirez .12 .30
123 Stephen Drew .12 .30
124 Yovani Gallardo .12 .30
125 Chase Utley .30 .75
126 Dan Haren .12 .30
127 Jose Vidro .12 .30
128 Ronnie Belliard .12 .30
129 Yunel Escobar .12 .30
130 Greg Maddux .40 1.00
131 Garret Anderson .12 .30
132 Aubrey Huff .12 .30
133 Paul Konerko .20 .50
134 Dan Uggla .20 .50
135 Roy Halladay .30 .75
136 Andre Ethier .20 .50
137 Orlando Hernandez .12 .30
138 Troy Tulowitzki .30 .75
139 Carlos Guillen .12 .30
140 Scott Kazmir .20 .50
141 Aaron Rowand .12 .30
142 Jim Edmonds .20 .50
143 Jermaine Dye .12 .30
144 Orlando Hudson .12 .30
145 Derrek Lee .12 .30
146 Travis Buck .12 .30
147 Zack Greinke .20 .50
148 Jeff Kent .12 .30
149 John Smoltz .30 .75
150 David Wright .40 1.00
151 Joba Chamberlain .20 .50
152 Adam LaRoche .12 .30
153 Kevin Youkilis .20 .50
154 Troy Glaus .20 .50
155 Nick Johnson .12 .30
156 J.J. Hardy .12 .30
157 Felix Hernandez .30 .75
158 Khalil Greene .12 .30
159 Gary Sheffield .12 .30
160 Albert Pujols .75 2.00
161 Chuck James .12 .30
162 Rocco Baldelli .12 .30
163 Eric Byrnes .12 .30
164 Brad Hawpe .12 .30
165 Delmon Young .20 .50
166 Chris Young .12 .30
167 Brian Roberts .12 .30
168 Russell Martin .12 .30
169 Hank Blalock .12 .30
170 Yadier Molina .20 .50
171 Jeremy Guthrie .12 .30
172 Chipper Jones .30 .75
173 Johnny Damon .20 .50
174 Ryan Garko .12 .30
175 Jake Peavy .12 .30
176 Chone Figgins .12 .30
177 Edgar Renteria .12 .30
178 Jim Thome .20 .50
179 Carlos Pena .20 .50
180 Corey Patterson .12 .30
181 Dustin Pedroia .40 1.00
182 Brett Myers .12 .30
183 Josh Hamilton .30 .75
184 Randy Johnson .30 .75
185 Ichiro Suzuki .50 1.25
186 Aaron Hill .12 .30
187 Jarrod Saltalamacchia .12 .30
188 Michael Cuddyer .12 .30
189 Jeff Francoeur .20 .50
190 Derek Jeter .75 2.00
191 Curtis Granderson .20 .50
192 James Loney .20 .50
193 Brian Bannister .12 .30
194 Carlos Lee .12 .30
195 Pedro Martinez .20 .50
196 Asdrubal Cabrera .20 .50
197 Kenji johjima .12 .30
198 Bartolo Colon .12 .30
199 Jacoby Ellsbury .50 1.25
200 Ryan Howard .40 1.00
201 Radhames Liz RC .25 .60
202 Justin Ruggiano RC .25 .60
203 Lance Broadway (RC) .15 .40
204 Joey Votto (RC) .60 1.50
205 Billy Buckner (RC) .15 .40
206 Joe Koshansky (RC) .15 .40
207 Ross Detwiler RC .40 1.00
208 Chin-Lung Hu (RC) .25 .60
209 Luke Hochevar RC .25 .60
210 Jeff Clement (RC) .25 .60
211 Troy Patton (RC) .15 .40
212 Hiroki Kuroda RC .25 .60
213 Emilio Bonifacio RC .40 1.00
214 Armando Galarraga RC .25 .60
215 Josh Anderson (RC) .15 .40
216 Nick Blackburn RC .25 .60
217 Seth Smith (RC) .15 .40
218 Jonathan Meloan RC .25 .60
219 Alberto Gonzalez RC .25 .60
220 Josh Banks (RC) .15 .40
221 Clay Buchholz AU (RC) 8.00 20.00
222 Nyjer Morgan AU (RC) 4.00 10.00
223 Brandon Jones AU RC 4.00 10.00
224 Sam Fuld AU RC 8.00 20.00
225 Daric Barton AU (RC) 4.00 10.00
226 Chris Seddon AU (RC) 4.00 10.00
227 J.R. Towles AU RC 4.00 10.00
228 Steve Pearce AU RC 4.00 10.00
229 Ross Ohlendorf AU RC 4.00 10.00
230 Clint Sammons AU (RC) 4.00 10.00

2008 Bowman Blue

*BLUE 1-200: 2X TO 5X BASIC
*BLUE 201-220: 2X TO 5X BASIC
*BLUE AU 221-230: .4X TO 1X BASIC AU
1-220 ODDS 1:14 HOBBY,1:32 RETAIL
221-230 AU ODDS 1:620 HOBBY
STATED PRINT RUN 500 SERIAL #'d SETS
221 Clay Buchholz AU 10.00 25.00

2008 Bowman Gold

*GOLD 1-200: 1.2X TO 3X BASIC
*GOLD 201-220: 1.2X TO 3X BASIC
OVERALL GOLD ODDS 1 PER PACK

2008 Bowman Orange

*ORANGE 1-200: 2.5X TO 6X BASIC
*ORANGE 201-220: 2.5X TO 6X BASIC
*ORANGE AU 221-230: .5X TO 1.2X BASIC AU
1-220 ODDS 1:26 HOBBY,1:65 RETAIL
221-230 AU ODDS 1:1160 HOBBY
STATED PRINT RUN 250 SERIAL #'d SETS
221 Clay Buchholz AU 12.50 30.00

2008 Bowman Red

1-220 ODDS 1:4512 HOBBY
221-230 AU ODDS 1:243,648 HOBBY
STATED PRINT RUN 1 SER.#'d SET
NO PRICING DUE TO SCARCITY

2008 Bowman Prospects

COMPLETE SET (110) 12.50 30.00
PRINTING PLATE ODDS 1:732 HOBBY
PLATE PRINT RUN 1 SET PER COLOR
BLACK-CYAN-MAGENTA-YELLOW ISSUED
NO PLATE PRICING DUE TO SCARCITY
BP1 Max Sapp .25 .60
BP2 Jamie Richmond .15 .40
BP3 Darren Ford .15 .40
BP4 Sergio Romo .15 .40
BP5 Jacob Butler .15 .40
BP6 Glenn Gibson .15 .40
BP7 Tom Hagan .15 .40
BP8 Michael McCormick .15 .40
BP9 Gregorio Petit .25 .60
BP10 Bobby Parnell .15 .40
BP11 Jeff Kindel .25 .60
BP12 Anthony Claggett .25 .60
BP13 Christopher Frey .15 .40
BP14 Jonah Nickerson .25 .60
BP15 Anthony Martinez .15 .40
BP16 Rusty Ryal .25 .60
BP17 Justin Berg .25 .60
BP18 Gerardo Parra .15 .40
BP19 Wesley Wright .15 .40
BP20 Stephen Chapman .15 .40
BP21 Chance Chapman .15 .40
BP22 Brett Pill 1.00 2.50
BP23 Zachary Phillips .25 .60
BP24 John Raynor .40 1.00
BP25 Danny Duffy .50 1.25
BP26 Brian Finegan .15 .40
BP27 Jonathan Venters .15 .40
BP28 Steve Tolleson .15 .40
BP29 Ben Jukich .25 .60
BP30 Matthew Weston .15 .40
BP31 Kyle Mura .15 .40
BP32 Luke Hetherington .15 .40
BP33 Michael Daniel .25 .60
BP34 Jake Renshaw .15 .40
BP35 Greg Halman .25 .60
BP36 Ryan Khoury .15 .40
BP37 Ryan Ouellette .15 .40
BP38 Mike Brantley .15 .40
BP39 Eric Brown .15 .40
BP40 Jose Duarte .15 .40
BP41 Eli Tintor .15 .40
BP42 Kent Sakamoto .15 .40
BP43 Luke Montz .25 .60
BP44 Alex Cobb .15 .40
BP45 Michael McKenry .15 .40
BP46 Javier Castillo .15 .40
BP47 Jeffrey Stevens .15 .40
BP48 Greg Burns .15 .40
BP49 Blake Johnson .15 .40
BP50 Austin Jackson .75 2.00
BP51 Anthony Recker .15 .40
BP52 Luis Durango .75 2.00
BP53 Engel Beltre .50 1.25
BP54 Seth Bynum .15 .40
BP55 Ryan Strieby .25 .60
BP56 Iggy Suarez .15 .40
BP57 Ryan Morris .25 .60
BP58 Scott Van Slyke .15 .40
BP59 Tyler Kolodny .50 1.25
BP60 Joseph Martinez .15 .40
BP61 Aaron Mathews .15 .40
BP62 Phillip Cuadrado .15 .40
BP63 Alex Liddi .50 1.25
BP64 Alex Burnett .25 .60
BP65 Brian Barton .25 .60
BP66 David Welch .15 .40
BP67 Kyle Reynolds .15 .40
BP68 Francisco Hernandez .15 .40
BP69 Logan Morrison 1.25 3.00
BP70 Ronald Ramirez .15 .40
BP71 Brad Miller .15 .40
BP72 Braedyn Pruitt .25 .60
BP73 Jason Fernandez .25 .60
BP74 Joseph Mahoney .15 .40
BP75 Quentin Davis .25 .60
BP76 P.J. Walters .40 1.00
BP77 Jordan Czarniecki .15 .40
BP78 Jonathan Mota .15 .40
BP79 Michael Hernandez .15 .40
BP80 James Guerrero .15 .40
BP81 Chris Johnson .15 .40
BP82 Daniel Cortes .40 1.00
BP83 Sal Sanchez .25 .60
BP84 Sean Henry .15 .40
BP85 Caleb Gindl .15 .40
BP86 Tommy Everidge .15 .40
BP87 Matt Rizzotti .15 .40
BP88 Luis Munoz .15 .40
BP89 Matthew Klimas .15 .40
BP90 Angel Reyes .15 .40
BP91 Sean Danielson .15 .40
BP92 Omar Poveda .25 .60
BP93 Mario Lisson .15 .40
BP94 Brian Mathews .15 .40
BP95 Matthew Buschmann .15 .40
BP96 Greg Thomson .15 .40
BP97 Matt Inouye .15 .40
BP98 Aneury Rodriguez .25 .60
BP99 Brad Harman .25 .60
BP100 Aaron Bates .40 1.00
BP101 Graham Taylor .15 .40
BP102 Ken Holmberg .15 .40
BP103 Greg Dowling .15 .40
BP104 Ronnie Ray .15 .40
BP105 Michael Wlodarczyk .15 .40
BP106 Jose Martinez .50 1.25
BP107 Jason Stephens .25 .60
BP108 Will Rhymes .15 .40
BP109 Joey Side .15 .40
BP110 Brandon Waring .50 1.25

2008 Bowman Prospects Blue

*BLUE 1-110: 1.2X TO 3X BASIC
1-110 ODDS 1:14 HOBBY,1:32 RETAIL
STATED PRINT RUN 500 SER.#'d SETS

2008 Bowman Prospects Gold

*GOLD 1-110: .75X TO 2X BASIC
OVERALL GOLD ODDS 1 PER PACK

2008 Bowman Prospects Orange

*ORANGE 1-110: 2X TO 5X BASIC
1-110 ODDS 1:26 HOBBY,1:65 RETAIL
STATED PRINT RUN 250 SER.#'d SETS

2008 Bowman Prospects Red

STATED ODDS 1:4512 HOBBY
STATED PRINT RUN 1 SER.#'d SET
NO PRICING DUE TO SCARCITY

2008 Bowman Scouts Autographs

GROUP A ODDS 1:176 HOB,1:410 RET
GROUP B ODDS 1:390 HOB,1:910 RET
EXCHANGE DEADLINE 5/31/2010
AS Alex Smith B 3.00 8.00
BB Bill Buck B 3.00 8.00
BE Bob Engle B 3.00 8.00
BF Bob Fontaine Jr. A 3.00 8.00
BS Bowman Scout A 3.00 8.00
CB Chris Bourjos A 3.00 8.00
DJ Dave Jennings B 3.00 8.00
DL Don Lyle B 3.00 8.00
DO Dan Ontiveros B 3.00 8.00
JC Jerome Cochran B EXCH 3.00 8.00
JD Jon Deeble A EXCH 3.00 8.00
JH Josue Herrera B 3.00 8.00
JL Jerry Lafferty A 3.00 8.00
JM Joe Mason B 3.00 8.00
LW Leon Wurth A 3.00 8.00
MR Mike Rizzo A 3.00 8.00
RA Ralph Avila A 3.00 8.00
TC Ty Coslow A 3.00 8.00
TCU Tom Couston A 3.00 8.00
TD Tony DeMacio A 3.00 8.00
TK Tim Kelly B 3.00 8.00

2008 Bowman Signs of the Future

GROUP A ODDS 1:26 RETAIL
GROUP B ODDS 1:305 RETAIL
EXCHANGE DEADLINE 5/31/2010
PLATE PRINT RUN 1 SET PER COLOR
BLACK-CYAN-MAGENTA-YELLOW ISSUED
NO PLATE PRICING DUE TO SCARCITY
AC Adam Carr 3.00 8.00
BK Brad Knox 3.00 8.00
BO Brian Omogrosso 3.00 8.00
BW Brian Wilson 50.00 100.00
CN Chris Nowak 4.00 10.00
CR Colby Rasmus 12.50 30.00
CT Clayton Tanner 3.00 8.00
CTI Chris Tillman 4.00 10.00
DS David Shafer 3.00 8.00
EJ Elliot Johnson 3.00 8.00
GM Garrett Mock 3.00 8.00
GP Gerardo Parra 4.00 10.00
GS Greg Smith 4.00 10.00
JE Jack Egbert 3.00 8.00
JG Jaime Garcia 6.00 15.00
JH Joel Hanrahan 3.00 8.00
JHI Jamar Hill 3.00 8.00
JHU Jon Huber 3.00 8.00
JJ Jason Jaramillo 3.00 8.00
JK Josh Kroeger 3.00 8.00
JL Jeff Locke 4.00 10.00
JM Jose Mijares EXCH 3.00 8.00
JV Jonathan Van Every 3.00 8.00
KB Kyle Bloom 3.00 8.00
LM Lou Marson 3.00 8.00
MC Mike Costanzo 3.00 8.00
ME Mitch Einertson 4.00 10.00
MP Matt Peterson 3.00 8.00
RK Ryan Kalish 8.00 20.00
RS Ryan Speier 3.00 8.00
SR Steven Register 3.00 8.00
TC Tyler Colvin 8.00 20.00
TM Tommy Manzella 3.00 8.00
TO Tim Olson 3.00 8.00
WI Will Inman 4.00 10.00

2009 Bowman

COMP.SET w/o AU's (220) 12.50 30.00
COMMON CARD (1-190) .12 .30
COMMON ROOKE (66/191-220) .25 .60
COMMON AU RC (221-230) 4.00 10.00
PLATE PRINT RUN 1 SET PER COLOR
BLACK-CYAN-MAGENTA-YELLOW ISSUED
NO PLATE PRICING DUE TO SCARCITY
1 David Wright .40 1.00
2 Albert Pujols .75 2.00
3 Alex Rodriguez .50 1.25
4 Chase Utley .30 .75
5 Chien-Ming Wang .20 .50
6 Jimmy Rollins .20 .50
7 Ken Griffey Jr. .50 1.25
8 Manny Ramirez .30 .75
9 Chipper Jones .30 .75
10 Ichiro Suzuki .50 1.25
11 Justin Morneau .30 .75
12 Hanley Ramirez .30 .75
13 Cliff Lee .20 .50
14 Ryan Howard .40 1.00
15 Ian Kinsler .20 .50
16 Jose Reyes .20 .50
17 Ted Lilly .12 .30
18 Miguel Cabrera .30 .75
19 Nate McLouth .12 .30
20 Josh Beckett .20 .50
21 John Lackey .12 .30
22 David Ortiz .20 .50
23 Carlos Lee .12 .30
24 Adam Dunn .20 .50
25 B.J. Upton .20 .50
26 Curtis Granderson .20 .50
27 David DeJesus .12 .30
28 CC Sabathia .20 .50
29 Russell Martin .12 .30
30 Torii Hunter .12 .30
31 Rich Harden .12 .30
32 Johnny Damon .20 .50
33 Cristian Guzman .12 .30
34 Grady Sizemore .20 .50
35 Jorge Posada .20 .50
36 Placido Polanco .12 .30
37 Ryan Ludwick .20 .50
38 Dustin Pedroia .40 1.00
39 Matt Garza .12 .30
40 Prince Fielder .20 .50
41 Rick Ankiel .12 .30
42 Jonathan Sanchez .12 .30
43 Erik Bedard .12 .30
44 Ryan Braun .40 1.00
45 Ervin Santana .12 .30
46 Brian Roberts .12 .30
47 Mike Jacobs .12 .30
48 Phil Hughes .20 .50
49 Justin Masterson .12 .30
50 Felix Hernandez .30 .75
51 Stephen Drew .12 .30
52 Bobby Abreu .12 .30
53 Jay Bruce .20 .50
54 Josh Hamilton .30 .75
55 Garrett Atkins .12 .30
56 Jacoby Ellsbury .30 .75
57 Johan Santana .30 .75
58 James Shields .12 .30
59 Armando Galarraga .12 .30
60 Carlos Pena .20 .50
61 Matt Kemp .20 .50
62 Joey Votto .30 .75
63 Raul Ibanez .20 .50
64 Casey Kotchman .12 .30
65 Hunter Pence .20 .50
66 Daniel Murphy RC .60 1.50
67 Carlos Beltran .12 .30
68 Evan Longoria .40 1.00
69 Daisuke Matsuzaka .30 .75
70 Cole Hamels .30 .75
71 Robinson Cano .30 .75
72 Clayton Kershaw .30 .75
73 Kenji Johjima .20 .50
74 Kazuo Matsui .12 .30
75 Jayson Werth .20 .50
76 Brian McCann .20 .50
77 Barry Zito .12 .30
78 Glen Perkins .12 .30
79 Jeff Francoeur .20 .50
80 Derek Jeter .75 2.00
81 Ryan Doumit .12 .30
82 Dan Haren .12 .30
83 Justin Duchscherer .12 .30
84 Marlon Byrd .12 .30
85 Derek Lowe .12 .30
86 Pat Burrell .12 .30
87 Jair Jurrjens .12 .30
88 Zack Greinke .20 .50
89 Jon Lester .30 .75
90 Justin Verlander .40 1.00
91 Jorge Cantu .12 .30
92 John Maine .12 .30
93 Brad Hawpe .12 .30
94 Mike Aviles .12 .30
95 Victor Martinez .20 .50
96 Ryan Dempster .12 .30
97 Miguel Tejada .20 .50
98 Joe Mauer .30 .75
99 Scott Olsen .12 .30
100 Tim Lincecum .50 1.25
101 Francisco Liriano .12 .30
102 Chris Iannetta .12 .30
103 Jamie Moyer .12 .30
104 Milton Bradley .12 .30
105 John Lannan .12 .30
106 Yovani Gallardo .12 .30
107 Xavier Nady .12 .30
108 Jermaine Dye .12 .30
109 Dioner Navarro .12 .30
110 Joba Chamberlain .20 .50
111 Nelson Cruz .20 .50
112 Johnny Cueto .12 .30
113 Adam LaRoche .12 .30
114 Aaron Rowand .12 .30
115 Jason Bay .20 .50
116 Aaron Cook .12 .30
117 Mark Teixeira .30 .75
118 Gavin Floyd .12 .30
119 Magglio Ordonez .20 .50
120 Rafael Furcal .12 .30
121 Mark Buehrle .20 .50
122 Alexi Casilla .12 .30
123 Scott Kazmir .12 .30
124 Nick Swisher .30 .75
125 Carlos Gomez .12 .30
126 Javier Vazquez .12 .30
127 Paul Konerko .20 .50
128 Ronnie Belliard .12 .30
129 Pat Neshek .20 .50
130 Josh Johnson .20 .50
131 Carlos Zambrano .20 .50
132 Chris Davis .12 .30
133 Bobby Crosby .12 .30
134 Alex Gordon .20 .50
135 Chris Young .12 .30
136 Carlos Delgado .12 .30
137 Adam Wainwright .20 .50
138 Justin Upton .20 .50
139 Tim Hudson .20 .50
140 J.D. Drew .12 .30
141 Adam Lind .12 .30
142 Mike Lowell .12 .30
143 Lance Berkman .20 .50
144 J.J. Hardy .12 .30
145 A.J. Burnett .20 .50
146 Jake Peavy .12 .30
147 Blake DeWitt .12 .30
148 Matt Holliday .30 .75
149 Carl Crawford .20 .50
150 Andre Ethier .20 .50
151 Howie Kendrick .12 .30
152 Ryan Zimmerman .20 .50
153 Troy Tulowitzki .30 .75
154 Brett Myers .12 .30
155 Chris Young .12 .30
156 Jered Weaver .12 .30
157 Jeff Clement .12 .30
158 Alex Rios .20 .50
159 Shane Victorino .12 .30
160 Jeremy Hermida .12 .30
161 James Loney .20 .50
162 Michael Young .20 .50
163 Aramis Ramirez .12 .30
164 Geovany Soto .20 .50
165 Aubrey Huff .12 .30
166 Delmon Young .20 .50
167 Vernon Wells .12 .30
168 Chone Figgins .12 .30
169 Carlos Quentin .20 .50
170 Chad Billingsley .12 .30
171 Matt Cain .12 .30
172 Derrek Lee .12 .30
173 A.J. Pierzynski .12 .30
174 Collin Balester .12 .30
175 Greg Smith .12 .30
176 Alfonso Soriano .20 .50
177 Adrian Gonzalez .20 .50
178 George Sherrill .12 .30
179 Nick Markakis .30 .75
180 Brandon Webb .20 .50
181 Vladimir Guerrero .30 .75
182 Roy Oswalt .20 .50
183 Adam Jones .20 .50
184 Edinson Volquez .12 .30
185 Yunel Escobar .12 .30
186 Joe Saunders .12 .30
187 Yadier Molina .20 .50
188 Kevin Youkilis .20 .50
189 Dan Uggla .20 .50
190 Kosuke Fukudome .30 .75
191 Matt Antonelli RC .40 1.00
192 Jeff Baisley RC .25 .60
193 Jason Bourgeois (RC) .25 .60
194 Michael Bowden (RC) .25 .60
195 Andrew Carpenter RC .40 1.00
196 Phil Coke RC .40 1.00
197 Aaron Cunningham RC .25 .60
198 Alcides Escobar RC .60 1.50
199 Dexter Fowler (RC) .40 1.00
200 Mat Gamel RC .60 1.50
201 Josh Geer (RC) .25 .60
202 Greg Golson (RC) .25 .60
203 John Jaso RC .25 .60
204 Kila Ka'aihue (RC) .40 1.00
205 George Kottaras (RC) .25 .60
206 Lou Marson (RC) .25 .60
207 Shairon Martis RC .40 1.00
208 Juan Miranda RC .40 1.00
209 Luke Montz RC .25 .60
210 Jonathon Niese RC .40 1.00
211 Bobby Parnell RC .40 1.00
212 Fernando Perez (RC) .25 .60
213 David Price RC .60 1.50
214 Angel Salome (RC) .25 .60
215 Gaby Sanchez RC .40 1.00
216 Freddy Sandoval (RC) .25 .60
217 Travis Snider RC .40 1.00
218 Will Venable RC .25 .60
219 Edwin Maysonet RC .25 .60
220 Josh Outman RC .40 1.00
221 Luke Montz AU 4.00 10.00
222 Kila Ka'aihue AU 4.00 10.00
223 Conor Gillaspie AU RC 5.00 12.00
224 Aaron Cunningham AU 4.00 10.00
225 Mat Gamel AU 5.00 12.00
226 Matt Antonelli AU 4.00 10.00
227 Bobby Parnell AU 4.00 10.00
228 Jose Mijares AU RC 4.00 10.00
229 Josh Geer AU 4.00 10.00
230 Shairon Martis AU 6.00 15.00

2009 Bowman Blue

*BLUE 1-190: 2X TO 5X BASIC
*BLUE 66/191-220: 1.5X TO 4X BASIC
*BLUE AU 221-230: .4X TO 1X BASIC AU
1-220 ODDS 1:12 HOBBY
STATED PRINT RUN 500 SER.#'d SETS

2009 Bowman Gold

*GOLD 1-190: 1.2X TO 3X BASIC
*GOLD 66/191-220: 1X TO 2.5X BASIC
OVERALL GOLD ODDS 1 PER PACK

2009 Bowman Orange

*ORANGE 1-190: 2.5X TO 6X BASIC
*ORANGE 66/191-220: 2X TO 5X BASIC
*ORANGE AU 221-230: .5X TO 1.2X BASIC AU
1-220 ODDS 1:24 HOBBY
STATED PRINT RUN 250 SER.#'d SETS

2009 Bowman Red

1-220 STATED ODDS 1:2720 HOBBY
STATED PRINT RUN 1 SER.#'d SETS
NO PRICING DUE TO SCARCITY

2009 Bowman Checklists

RANDOM INSERTS IN PACKS
1 Checklist 1 .12 .30
2 Checklist 2 .12 .30
3 Checklist 3 .12 .30

2009 Bowman Major League Scout Autographs

SCBB Billy Blitzer 3.00 8.00
SCCJ Clarence Johns 3.00 8.00
SCDC Darrell Conner 3.00 8.00
SCFR Fred Repke 3.00 8.00
SCLP Larry Pardo 3.00 8.00
SCMW Mark Wilson 3.00 8.00
SCPC Paul Cogan 3.00 8.00
SCPD Pat Daugherty 3.00 8.00

2009 Bowman Prospects

COMPLETE SET (90) 15.00 40.00
PLATE PRINT RUN 1 SET PER COLOR
BLACK-CYAN-MAGENTA-YELLOW ISSUED
NO PLATE PRICING DUE TO SCARCITY
BP1 Neftali Feliz .50 1.25
BP2 Oscar Tejeda .50 1.25
BP3 Greg Veloz .15 .40
BP4 Julio Teheran 1.25 3.00
BP5 Michael Almanzar .40 1.00
BP6 Stolmy Pimentel .25 .60
BP7 Matthew Moore 2.50 6.00
BP8 Jericho Jones .15 .40
BP9 Kelvin de la Cruz .40 1.00
BP10 Jose Ceda .15 .40
BP11 Jesse Darcy .15 .40
BP12 Kenneth Gilbert .15 .40
BP13 Will Smith .25 .60
BP14 Samuel Freeman .15 .40
BP15 Adam Reifer .15 .40
BP16 Ehire Adrianza .40 1.00
BP17 Michael Pineda 2.50 6.00
BP18 Jordan Walden .25 .60
BP19 Angel Morales .25 .60
BP20 Neil Ramirez .25 .60
BP21 Kyeong Kang .25 .60
BP22 Luis Jimenez .25 .60
BP23 Tyler Flowers .40 1.00
BP24 Petey Paramore .25 .60
BP25 Jeremy Hamilton .15 .40
BP26 Tyler Yockey .25 .60
BP27 Sawyer Carroll .25 .60
BP28 Jeremy Farrell .15 .40
BP29 Tyson Brummett .15 .40
BP30 Alex Buchholz .25 .60
BP31 Luis Sumoza .25 .60
BP32 Jonathan Waltenbury .25 .60
BP33 Edgar Osuna .15 .40
BP34 Curt Smith .15 .40
BP35 Evan Bigley .25 .60
BP36 Miguel Fermin .15 .40
BP37 Ben Lasater .15 .40
BP38 David Freese 1.25 3.00
BP39 Jon Kibler .25 .60
BP40 Cristian Beltre .25 .60
BP41 Alfredo Figaro .15 .40
BP42 Marc Rzepczynski .25 .60
BP43 Joshua Collmenter .25 .60
BP44 Adam Mills .15 .40
BP45 Wilson Ramos .50 1.25
BP46 Esmil Rogers .15 .40
BP47 Jon Mark Owings .15 .40
BP48 Chris Johnson .60 1.50
BP49 Abraham Almonte .15 .40
BP50 Patrick Ryan .15 .40
BP51 Yefri Carvajal .40 1.00
BP52 Ruben Tejada .15 .40
BP53 Edilio Colina .25 .60
BP54 Wilber Bucardo .25 .60
BP55 Nelson Perez .25 .60
BP56 Andrew Rundle .25 .60
BP57 Anthony Ortega .15 .40
BP58 Wilin Rosario .25 .60
BP59 Parker Frazier .15 .40
BP60 Kyle Farrell .15 .40
BP61 Erik Komatsu .25 .60
BP62 Michael Stutes .15 .40
BP63 David Genao .25 .60
BP64 Jack Cawley .15 .40
BP65 Jacob Goldberg .15 .40
BP66 Jarred Bogany .15 .40
BP67 Jason McEachern .15 .40
BP68 Matt Rigoli .15 .40
BP69 Jose Duran .25 .60
BP70 Justin Greene .25 .60
BP71 Nino Leyja .25 .60
BP72 Michael Swinson .25 .60
BP73 Miguel Flores .25 .60
BP74 Nick Buss .15 .40
BP75 Brett Oberholtzer .25 .60
BP76 Pat McAnaney .25 .60
BP77 Sean Conner .15 .40
BP78 Ryan Verdugo .25 .60
BP79 Will Atwood .15 .40
BP80 Tommy Johnson .40 1.00
BP81 Rene Garcia .25 .60
BP82 Robert Brooks .25 .60
BP83 Seth Garrison .15 .40
BP84 Steven Upchurch .15 .40
BP85 Zach Moore .15 .40
BP86 Derrick Phillips .15 .40
BP87 Dominic De La Osa .40 1.00
BP88 Jose Barajas .15 .40
BP89 Bryan Petersen .15 .40
BP90 Michael Cisco .25 .60

2009 Bowman Prospects Blue

*BLUE: 1.2X TO 3X BASIC
STATED ODDS 1:12 HOBBY
STATED PRINT RUN 500 SER.#'d SETS

2009 Bowman Prospects Gold

*GOLD: 1X TO 2.5X BASIC
OVERALL GOLD ODDS 1 PER PACK

2009 Bowman Prospects Orange

*ORANGE: 2X TO 5X BASIC
STATED ODDS 1:24 HOBBY
STATED PRINT RUN 250 SER.#'d SETS

2009 Bowman Prospects Red

STATED ODDS 1:2720 HOBBY
STATED PRINT RUN 1 SER.#'d SETS
NO PRICING DUE TO SCARCITY

2009 Bowman Prospects Autographs

BPAAH Anthony Hewitt 5.00 12.00
BPABH Brad Hand 5.00 12.00
BPADG Deolis Guerra 5.00 12.00
BPAGB Gordon Beckham 10.00 25.00
BPAGK George Kontos 5.00 12.00
BPAJK Jason Knapp 5.00 12.00
BPANG Nick Gorneault 5.00 12.00
BPAPB Buster Posey 30.00 60.00
BPARK Ryan Kalish 6.00 15.00
BPATD Travis D'Arnaud 5.00 12.00

2009 Bowman WBC Prospects

COMPLETE SET (20) 6.00 15.00
PLATE PRINT RUN 1 SET PER COLOR
BLACK-CYAN-MAGENTA-YELLOW ISSUED
NO PLATE PRICING DUE TO SCARCITY
BW1 Yu Darvish 4.00 10.00
BW2 Phillippe Aumont 1.00 2.50
BW3 Concepcion Rodriguez .40 1.00
BW4 Michel Enriquez .40 1.00
BW5 Yulieski Gurriel .60 1.50
BW6 Shinnosuke Abe .60 1.50
BW7 Gift Ngoepe .40 1.00
BW8 Dylan Lindsay .60 1.50
BW9 Nick Weglarz .40 1.00
BW10 Mitch Dening .40 1.00
BW11 Justin Erasmus .40 1.00
BW12 Aroldis Chapman 1.50 4.00
BW13 Alex Liddi 1.25 3.00
BW14 Alexander Smit .40 1.00
BW15 Juan Carlos Sulbaran .40 1.00
BW16 Cheng-Min Peng .60 1.50
BW17 Chenhao Li .40 1.00
BW18 Tao Bu .40 1.00
BW19 Gregory Halman .60 1.50
BW20 Fu-Te Ni .60 1.50

2009 Bowman WBC Prospects Blue

*BLUE: 1.2X TO 3X BASIC
STATED ODDS 1:12 HOBBY

2009 Bowman WBC Prospects Gold

*GOLD: .75X TO 2X BASIC
OVERALL GOLD ODDS ONE PER PACK

2009 Bowman WBC Prospects Orange

*ORANGE: 1.5X TO 4X BASIC
STATED ODDS 1:24 HOBBY

2009 Bowman WBC Prospects Red

STATED ODDS 1:2720 HOBBY
STATED PRINT RUN 1 SER.#'d SETS
NO PRICING DUE TO SCARCITY

2010 Bowman

COMPLETE SET (220) 12.50 30.00
COMMON CARD (1-190) .12 .30
COMMON RC (191-220) .40 1.00
PLATE PRINT RUN 1 SET PER COLOR
BLACK-CYAN-MAGENTA-YELLOW ISSUED
NO PLATE PRICING DUE TO SCARCITY
1 Ryan Braun .40 1.00
2 Kevin Youkilis .20 .50
3 Jay Bruce .20 .50
4 Will Venable .12 .30
5 Zack Greinke .20 .50
6 Adrian Gonzalez .20 .50
7 Carl Crawford .20 .50
8 Scott Baker .12 .30
9 Matt Kemp .20 .50
10 Stephen Drew .12 .30
11 Jair Jurrjens .12 .30
12 Jose Reyes .20 .50
13 Josh Hamilton .30 .75
14 Carlos Pena .20 .50
15 Ubaldo Jimenez .20 .50
16 Jason Kubel .12 .30
17 Josh Beckett .20 .50
18 Martin Prado .12 .30
19 Jake Peavy .12 .30
20 Shin-Soo Choo .20 .50
21 Luke Hochever .12 .30
22 Alcides Escobar .20 .50
23 Brandon Webb .20 .50
24 Raul Ibanez .20 .50
25 Ryan Zimmerman .20 .50
26 Jeff Niemann .12 .30
27 Adam Dunn .20 .50
28 Matt Cain .20 .50
29 Robinson Cano .30 .75
30 Andre Ethier .20 .50
31 Jhoulys Chacin .12 .30
32 Mark Buehrle .20 .50
33 Magglio Ordonez .20 .50
34 Michael Cuddyer .12 .30
35 Andrew Bailey .12 .30
36 Akinori Iwamura .12 .30
37 Brian Roberts .12 .30
38 Howie Kendrick .12 .30
39 Derek Holland .12 .30
40 Ken Griffey Jr. .50 1.25
41 A.J. Burnett .20 .50
42 Scott Rolen .20 .50
43 Kenshin Kawakami .20 .50
44 Carlos Lee .12 .30
45 Chris Carpenter .30 .75
46 Adam Lind .20 .50
47 Jered Weaver .12 .30
48 Chris Coghlan .12 .30
49 Clayton Kershaw .30 .75
50 Prince Fielder .20 .50
51 Freddy Sanchez .12 .30
52 CC Sabathia .20 .50
53 Jayson Werth .20 .50
54 David Price .30 .75
55 Matt Holliday .30 .75
56 Brett Anderson .20 .50
57 Alexei Ramirez .12 .30
58 Johnny Cueto .12 .30
59 Bobby Abreu .12 .30
60 Ian Kinsler .20 .50
61 Ricky Romero .12 .30
62 Cristian Guzman .12 .30
63 Ryan Doumit .12 .30
64 Mat Latos .12 .30
65 Andrew McCutchen .30 .75
66 John Maine .12 .30
67 Kurt Suzuki .12 .30
68 Carlos Beltran .12 .30
69 Chad Billingsley .12 .30
70 Nick Markakis .30 .75
71 Yovani Gallardo .12 .30
72 Dexter Fowler .12 .30
73 David Ortiz .20 .50
74 Kosuke Fukudome .30 .75
75 Daisuke Matsuzaka .30 .75
76 Michael Young .20 .50
77 Rajai Davis .12 .30
78 Yadier Molina .20 .50
79 Francisco Liriano .12 .30
80 Evan Longoria .40 1.00
81 Trevor Cahill .12 .30
82 Aramis Ramirez .12 .30
83 Jimmy Rollins .20 .50
84 Russell Martin .12 .30
85 Dan Haren .12 .30
86 Billy Butler .12 .30
87 James Shields .12 .30
88 Dan Uggla .20 .50
89 Wandy Rodriguez .12 .30
90 Chase Utley .30 .75
91 Ryan Dempster .12 .30
92 Ben Zobrist .12 .30
93 Jeff Francoeur .20 .50
94 Koji Uehara .20 .50
95 Victor Martinez .20 .50
96 Tim Hudson .20 .50
97 Carlos Gonzalez .20 .50
98 David DeJesus .12 .30
99 Brad Hawpe .12 .30
100 Justin Upton .20 .50
101 Jorge Posada .20 .50
102 Cole Hamels .30 .75
103 Elvis Andrus .20 .50
104 Adam Wainwright .20 .50
105 Alfonso Soriano .20 .50
106 James Loney .20 .50
107 Vernon Wells .12 .30
108 Lance Berkman .20 .50
109 Matt Garza .12 .30
110 Gordon Beckham .20 .50
111 Torii Hunter .12 .30
112 Brandon Phillips .12 .30
113 Nelson Cruz .20 .50
114 Chris Tillman .12 .30
115 Miguel Cabrera .30 .75
116 Kevin Slowey .12 .30
117 Shane Victorino .20 .50
118 Paul Maholm .12 .30
119 Kyle Blanks .12 .30
120 Johan Santana .30 .75
121 Nate McLouth .12 .30
122 Kazuo Matsui .12 .30
123 Troy Tulowitzki .30 .75
124 Jon Lester .30 .75
125 Chipper Jones .30 .75
126 Clay Buchholz .20 .50
127 Todd Helton .20 .50
128 Alex Gordon .20 .50
129 Derrek Lee .12 .30
130 Justin Morneau .30 .75
131 Michael Bourn .12 .30
132 B.J. Upton .20 .50
133 Jose Lopez .12 .30
134 Justin Verlander .40 1.00
135 Hunter Pence .20 .50
136 Daniel Murphy .12 .30
137 Delmon Young .20 .50
138 Carlos Quentin .20 .50
139 Edinson Volquez .12 .30
140 Dustin Pedroia .40 1.00
141 Justin Masterson .12 .30
142 Josh Willingham .12 .30
143 Miguel Montero .12 .30
144 Alex Rios .20 .50
145 David Wright .40 1.00
146 Curtis Granderson .20 .50
147 Rich Harden .12 .30
148 Hideki Matsui .30 .75
149 Edwin Jackson .12 .30
150 Miguel Tejada .20 .50
151 John Lackey .12 .30
152 Vladimir Guerrero .30 .75
153 Max Scherzer .12 .30
154 Jason Bay .20 .50
155 Javier Vasquez .12 .30
156 Johnny Damon .20 .50
157 Cliff Lee .20 .50
158 Chone Figgins .12 .30
159 Kevin Millwood .12 .30
160 Roy Halladay .30 .75
161 Alex Rodriguez .50 1.25
162 Pablo Sandoval .20 .50
163 Ryan Howard .40 1.00
164 Rick Porcello .12 .30
165 Hanley Ramirez .30 .75
166 Brian McCann .20 .50
167 Kendry Morales .12 .30
168 Josh Johnson .20 .50
169 Joe Mauer .30 .75
170 Grady Sizemore .20 .50
171 J.A. Happ .20 .50
172 Ichiro Suzuki .50 1.25
173 Aaron Hill .12 .30
174 Mark Teixeira .30 .75
175 Tim Lincecum .50 1.25
176 Denard Span .12 .30
177 Roy Oswalt .20 .50
178 Manny Ramirez .30 .75
179 Jorge De La Rosa .12 .30
180 Joey Votto .30 .75
181 Neftali Feliz .12 .30
182 Yunel Escobar .12 .30
183 Carlos Zambrano .20 .50
184 Erick Aybar .12 .30
185 Albert Pujols .75 2.00
186 Felix Hernandez .30 .75
187 Adam Jones .20 .50
188 Jacoby Ellsbury .30 .75
189 Mark Reynolds .12 .30
190 Derek Jeter .75 2.00
191 John Raynor RC .40 1.00
192 Carlos Monasterios RC .60 1.50
193 Kanekoa Texeira RC .40 1.00
194 David Herndon RC .40 1.00
195 Ruben Tejada RC .60 1.50
196 Mike Leake RC 1.25 3.00
197 Jenrry Mejia RC .60 1.50
198 Austin Jackson RC .60 1.50
199 Scott Sizemore RC .60 1.50
200 Jason Heyward RC 2.50 6.00
201 Neil Walker (RC) .60 1.50
202 Tommy Manzella (RC) .40 1.00
203 Wade Davis (RC) .40 1.00
204 Eric Young Jr. (RC) .40 1.00
205 Luis Durango RC .40 1.00
206 Madison Bumgarner RC 1.00 2.50
207 Brent Dlugach (RC) .40 1.00
208 Buster Posey RC 4.00 10.00
209 Henry Rodriguez RC .40 1.00
210 Tyler Flowers RC .60 1.50
211 Michael Dunn RC .40 1.00
212 Drew Stubbs RC 1.00 2.50
213 Brandon Allen (RC) .40 1.00
214 Daniel McCutchen RC .60 1.50
215 Juan Francisco RC .60 1.50
216 Eric Hacker RC .60 1.50
217 Michael Brantley RC .40 1.00
218 Dustin Richardson RC .40 1.00
219 Josh Thole RC .60 1.50
220 Daniel Hudson RC .60 1.50

2010 Bowman Blue

*BLUE 1-190: 1.5X TO 4X BASIC
*BLUE: 191-220: .75X TO 2X BASIC
STATED ODDS 1:17 HOBBY
STATED PRINT RUN 520 SER.#'d SETS
200 Jason Heyward 8.00 20.00
208 Buster Posey 10.00 25.00

2010 Bowman Gold

COMPLETE SET (220) 20.00 50.00
*GOLD 1-190: .75X TO 2X BASIC
*GOLD: 191-220: .6X TO 1.5X BASIC

2010 Bowman Orange

*ORANGE 1-190: 2.5X TO 6X BASIC
*ORAGE: 191-220: 1.2X TO 3X BASIC
STATED ODDS 1:35 HOBBY
STATED PRINT RUN 250 SER.#'d SETS
208 Buster Posey 20.00 50.00

2010 Bowman Red

STATED ODDS 1:3400 HOBBY
STATED PRINT RUN 1 SER.#'d SET
NO PRICING DUE TO SCARCITY

2010 Bowman 1992 Bowman Throwbacks

COMPLETE SET (110) 15.00 40.00
STATED ODDS 1:2 HOBBY
BT1 Jimmy Rollins .50 1.25
BT2 Ryan Zimmerman .50 1.25
BT3 Alex Rodriguez 1.25 3.00
BT4 Andrew McCutchen .75 2.00
BT5 Mark Reynolds .30 .75
BT6 Jason Bay .50 1.25
BT7 Hideki Matsui .75 2.00
BT8 Carlos Beltran .30 .75
BT9 Justin Morneau .75 2.00
BT10 Matt Cain .50 1.25
BT11 Russell Martin .30 .75
BT12 Alfonso Soriano .50 1.25
BT13 Joe Mauer .75 2.00
BT14 Troy Tulowitzki .75 2.00
BT15 Miguel Tejada .50 1.25
BT16 Adrian Gonzalez .50 1.25
BT17 Carlos Zambrano .50 1.25
BT18 Hunter Pence .50 1.25
BT19 Torii Hunter .30 .75
BT20 Michael Young .50 1.25
BT21 Pablo Sandoval .50 1.25
BT22 Manny Ramirez .75 2.00
BT23 Jose Reyes .50 1.25
BT24 Carl Crawford .50 1.25
BT25 CC Sabathia .50 1.25
BT26 Josh Beckett .50 1.25
BT27 Dan Uggla .50 1.25
BT28 Josh Johnson .50 1.25
BT29 Raul Ibanez .50 1.25
BT30 Grady Sizemore .50 1.25
BT31 Nate McLouth .30 .75
BT32 Robinson Cano .75 2.00
BT33 Carlos Lee .30 .75
BT34 Jorge Posada .50 1.25
BT35 B.J. Upton .50 1.25
BT36 Ubaldo Jimenez .50 1.25
BT37 Ryan Braun 1.00 2.50
BT38 Aaron Hill .30 .75
BT39 Rick Porcello .30 .75
BT40 Nick Markakis .75 2.00
BT41 Felix Hernandez .75 2.00
BT42 Matt Holliday .75 2.00
BT43 Prince Fielder .50 1.25
BT44 Yadier Molina .50 1.25
BT45 Justin Upton .50 1.25
BT46 Carlos Pena .50 1.25
BT47 Miguel Cabrera .75 2.00
BT48 Dan Haren .30 .75
BT49 Cliff Lee .50 1.25
BT50 Victor Martinez .50 1.25
BT51 Josh Hamilton .75 2.00
BT52 Evan Longoria 1.00 2.50
BT53 Johan Santana .75 2.00
BT54 Ryan Howard 1.00 2.50
BT55 Jon Lester .75 2.00
BT56 Mark Buehrle .50 1.25
BT57 Lance Berkman .50 1.25
BT58 Roy Oswalt .50 1.25
BT59 Dustin Pedroia 1.00 2.50
BT60 Daisuke Matsuzaka .75 2.00
BT61 Joey Votto .75 2.00
BT62 Ken Griffey Jr. 1.25 3.00
BT63 Jacoby Ellsbury .75 2.00
BT64 David Wright 1.00 2.50
BT65 Derek Jeter 2.00 5.00
BT66 Chase Utley .75 2.00
BT67 Mark Teixeira .75 2.00
BT68 Justin Verlander 1.00 2.50
BT69 Kendry Morales .30 .75
BT70 Adam Jones .50 1.25
BT71 Vladimir Guerrero .75 2.00
BT72 Albert Pujols 2.00 5.00
BT73 Roy Halladay .75 2.00
BT74 Matt Kemp .50 1.25
BT75 Kevin Youkilis .50 1.25
BT76 Jake Peavy .30 .75
BT77 Hanley Ramirez .75 2.00
BT78 Ian Kinsler .50 1.25
BT79 Ichiro Suzuki 1.25 3.00
BT80 Curtis Granderson .50 1.25
BT81 Gordon Beckham .50 1.25
BT82 Jayson Werth .50 1.25
BT83 Brandon Webb .50 1.25
BT84 Adam Dunn .50 1.25
BT85 David Ortiz .50 1.25
BT86 Cole Hamels .75 2.00
BT87 Brian McCann .50 1.25
BT88 Zack Greinke .50 1.25
BT89 Tim Lincecum 1.25 3.00
BT90 Andre Ethier .50 1.25
BT91 Matt Garza .30 .75
BT92 Billy Butler .30 .75
BT93 Yovani Gallardo .30 .75
BT94 Chone Figgins .30 .75
BT95 Yunel Escobar .30 .75
BT96 Alexei Ramirez .30 .75
BT97 Clayton Kershaw .75 2.00
BT98 Chris Coghlan .30 .75
BT99 Denard Span .30 .75
BT100 A.J. Burnett .50 1.25
BT101 Ivan Rodriguez .50 1.25
BT102 Chipper Jones .75 2.00
BT103 Carlos Delgado .30 .75
BT104 Gary Sheffield .30 .75
BT105 Garret Anderson .30 .75
BT106 Mariano Rivera .75 2.00
BT107 John Smoltz .75 2.00
BT108 Omar Vizquel .50 1.25
BT109 Jim Thome .50 1.25
BT110 Manny Ramirez .75 2.00

2010 Bowman Expectations

COMPLETE SET (50) 15.00 40.00
STATED ODDS 1:3 HOBBY
BE1 Jorge Posada 2.50 6.00
Jesus Montero
BE2 Ryan Howard 1.50 4.00
Domonic Brown
BE3 Hanley Ramirez 1.50 4.00
Mike Stanton
BE4 Chipper Jones 1.50 4.00
Freddie Freeman
BE5 Tim Lincecum 3.00 8.00
Stephen Strasburg
BE6 Jose Reyes 1.00 2.50
Wilmer Flores
BE7 David Wright 1.25 3.00
Ike Davis
BE8 Alfonso Soriano 1.50 4.00
Starlin Castro
BE9 Jay Bruce .60 1.50
Todd Frazier
BE10 Ryan Braun 1.25 3.00
Mat Gamel
BE11 Jon Lester 1.00 2.50
Madison Bumgarner
BE12 Ubaldo Jimenez 1.00 2.50
Tyler Matzek
BE13 Joe Mauer 4.00 10.00
Buster Posey
BE14 Carl Crawford .60 1.50
Desmond Jennings
BE15 Evan Longoria 1.25 3.00
Alex Liddi
BE16 Andrew McCutchen 1.00 2.50
Jose Tabata
BE17 Chipper Jones 2.50 6.00
Jason Heyward
BE18 Aramis Ramirez .40 1.00
Josh Vitters
BE19 Ryan Zimmerman .60 1.50
Ian Desmond
BE20 Alex Gordon 1.25 3.00
Mike Moustakas
BE21 Adam Dunn .60 1.50
Chris Marrero
BE22 Mike Napoli .60 1.50
Hank Conger
BE23 Pablo Sandoval .60 1.50
Thomas Neal
BE24 Carlos Quentin .60 1.50
Tyler Flowers
BE25 Victor Martinez 1.25 3.00
Carlos Santana
BE26 Carlos Zambrano .60 1.50
Andrew Cashner
BE27 Jose Lopez 1.50 4.00
Dustin Ackley
BE28 Rich Harden .40 1.00
Neftali Feliz
BE29 Johnny Damon 1.25 3.00
Slade Heathcott
BE30 Kevin Youkilis 1.00 2.50
Lars Anderson
BE31 Dan Haren 1.00 2.50
Jarrod Parker
BE32 Matt Kemp .60 1.50
Jared Mitchell
BE33 Will Venable 1.00 2.50
Donavan Tate
BE34 Andre Ethier .60 1.50
Andrew Lambo
BE35 Brian McCann 1.00 2.50
Tony Sanchez
BE36 Josh Beckett .60 1.50
Chris Withrow
BE37 Matt Cain .60 1.50
Zack Wheeler
BE38 Johnny Cueto .60 1.50
Jenrry Mejia
BE39 David Price 1.00 2.50
Jake McGee
BE40 Matt Garza 1.50 4.00
Jeremy Hellickson
BE41 Nick Markakis 1.00 2.50
Josh Bell
BE42 Ivan Rodriguez .60 1.50
Derek Norris
BE43 Elvis Andrus .60 1.50
Jiovanni Mier
BE44 Mark Reynolds .60 1.50
Bobby Borchering
BE45 Prince Fielder .60 1.50
Chris Carter
BE46 Grady Sizemore .60 1.50
Jordan Brown
BE47 Stephen Drew .40 1.00
Pedro Ciriaco
BE48 Chad Billingsley .40 1.00
John Ely
BE49 Justin Morneau 1.00 2.50
Christopher Parmelee
BE50 Roy Halladay .60 1.50
Kyle Drabek

2010 Bowman Futures Game Triple Relic

STATED ODDS 1:402 HOBBY
STATED PRINT RUN 99 SER.#'d SETS
AE Alcides Escobar 5.00 12.00
AL Alex Liddi 4.00 10.00
BC Barbaro Canizares 4.00 10.00
BL Brad Lincoln 4.00 10.00
CC Chris Carter 6.00 15.00
CH Chris Heisey 10.00 25.00
CS Carlos Santana 10.00 25.00
CT Chris Tillman 4.00 10.00
DD Danny Duffy 10.00 25.00
DJ Daryl Jones 4.00 10.00
DV Dayan Viciedo 4.00 10.00
EY Eric Young Jr. 4.00 10.00
FS Francisco Samuel 4.00 10.00
JC Jhoulys Chacin 4.00 10.00
JH Jason Heyward 30.00 60.00
JM Jesus Montero 10.00 25.00
JP Jarrod Parker 8.00 20.00
JV Josh Vitters 8.00 20.00
KD Kyle Drabek 5.00 12.00
KK Kyeong Kang 4.00 10.00
LD Luis Durango 5.00 12.00
LS Leyson Septimo 4.00 10.00
MB Madison Bumgarner 4.00 10.00
ML Mat Latos 5.00 12.00
MS Mike Stanton 10.00 25.00
NF Neftali Feliz 5.00 12.00
NW Nick Weglarz 8.00 20.00
PB Pedro Baez 4.00 10.00
RT Rene Tosoni 5.00 12.00
SC Starlin Castro 12.50 30.00
SS Scott Sizemore 5.00 12.00
TF Tyler Flowers 4.00 10.00
TG Tyson Gillies 5.00 12.00
TR Trevor Reckling 5.00 12.00
WF Wilmer Flores 5.00 12.00
YF Yohan Flande 4.00 10.00
DJE Desmond Jennings 8.00 20.00

2010 Bowman Prospects

COMP.SET w/o AU (110) 15.00 40.00
STRASBURG AU ODDS 1:2013 HOBBY
PLATE PRINT RUN 1 SET PER COLOR
BLACK-CYAN-MAGENTA-YELLOW ISSUED
NO PLATE PRICING DUE TO SCARCITY
BP1a Stephen Strasburg 6.00 15.00
BP1b Stephen Strasburg AU 250.00 500.00
BP2 Melky Mesa .30 .75
BP3 Cole McCurry .20 .50
BP4 Tyler Henley .20 .50
BP5 Andrew Cashner .20 .50
BP6 Konrad Schmidt .20 .50
BP7 Jean Segura .50 1.25
BP8 Jon Gaston .30 .75
BP9 Nick Santomauro .20 .50
BP10 Aroldis Chapman .75 2.00
BP11 Logan Watkins .20 .50
BP12 Bo Bowman .20 .50
BP13 Jeff Antigua .20 .50
BP14 Matt Adams .30 .75
BP15 Joseph Cruz .30 .75
BP16 Sebastian Valle .30 .75
BP17 Stefan Gartrell .20 .50
BP18 Pedro Ciriaco .20 .50
BP19 Tyson Gillies .50 1.25
BP20 Casey Crosby .60 1.50
BP21 Luis Exposito .20 .50
BP22 Welington Dotel .20 .50
BP23 Alexander Torres .20 .50
BP24 Byron Wiley .20 .50
BP25 Pedro Florimon .20 .50
BP26 Cody Satterwhite .30 .75
BP27 Craig Clark .75 2.00
BP28 Jason Christian .20 .50
BP29 Tommy Mendonca .20 .50
BP30 Ryan Dent .20 .50
BP31 Jhan Marinez .20 .50
BP32 Eric Niesen .20 .50
BP33 Gustavo Nunez .20 .50
BP34 Scott Shaw .20 .50
BP35 Welinton Ramirez .20 .50
BP36 Trevor May .75 2.00
BP37 Mitch Moreland .30 .75
BP38 Nick Czyz .20 .50
BP39 Edinson Rincon .20 .50
BP40 Domingo Santana 1.00 2.50
BP41 Carson Blair .20 .50
BP42 Rashun Dixon .20 .50
BP43 Alexander Colome .50 1.25
BP44 Allan Dykstra .20 .50
BP45 J.J. Hoover .20 .50
BP46 Abner Abreu .30 .75
BP47 Daniel Nava .30 .75
BP48 Simon Castro .30 .75
BP49 Brian Baisley .20 .50
BP50 Tony Delmonico .20 .50
BP51 Chase D'Arnaud .20 .50
BP52 Sheng-An Kuo .20 .50
BP53 Leandro Castro .20 .50
BP54 Charlie Leesman .20 .50
BP55 Caleb Joseph .20 .50
BP56 Rolando Gomez .20 .50
BP57 John Lamb .50 1.25
BP58 Adam Wilk .30 .75
BP59 Randall Delgado 1.00 2.50
BP60 Neil Medchill .30 .75
BP61 Josh Donaldson .20 .50
BP62 Zach Gentile .20 .50
BP63 Kiel Roling .20 .50
BP64 Wes Freeman .20 .50
BP65 Brian Pellegrini .30 .75
BP66 Kyle Jensen .20 .50
BP67 Evan Anundsen .20 .50
BP68 Hak-Ju Lee .75 2.00
BP69 C.J. Retherford .20 .50
BP70 Dillon Gee .50 1.25
BP71 Bo Greenwell .20 .50
BP72 Matt Tucker .30 .75
BP73 Joe Serafin .20 .50
BP74 Matt Brown .20 .50
BP75 Alexis Oliveras .20 .50
BP76 James Beresford .20 .50
BP77 Steve Lombardozzi .20 .50
BP78 Curtis Petersen .20 .50
BP79 Eric Farris .20 .50
BP80 Yen-Wen Kuo .20 .50
BP81 Caleb Brewer .20 .50
BP82 Jacob Elmore .30 .75
BP83 Jared Clark .30 .75
BP84 Yowill Espinal .30 .75
BP85 Jae-Hoon Ha .20 .50
BP86 Michael Wing .20 .50
BP87 Wilmer Font .20 .50
BP88 Jake Kahaulelio .20 .50
BP89 Dustin Ackley 1.25 3.00
BP90 Donavan Tate .50 1.25
BP91 Nolan Arenado .60 1.50
BP92 Rex Brothers .20 .50
BP93 Brett Jackson .60 1.50
BP94 Chad Jenkins .20 .50
BP95 Slade Heathcott .60 1.50
BP96 J.R. Murphy .30 .75
BP97 Patrick Schuster .20 .50
BP98 Alexia Amarista .20 .50
BP99 Thomas Neal .30 .75
BP100 Starlin Castro .75 2.00
BP101 Anthony Rizzo .60 1.50
BP102 Felix Doubront .20 .50
BP103 Nick Franklin .50 1.25
BP104 Anthony Gose .30 .75
BP105 Julio Teheran .50 1.25
BP106 Grant Green .30 .75
BP107 David Lough .20 .50
BP108 Jose Iglesias .75 2.00
BP109 Jaff Decker .50 1.25
BP110 D.J. LeMahieu .20 .50

2010 Bowman Prospects Black

COMPLETE SET (110) 20.00 50.00
*BLACK: .75X TO 2X BASIC
ISSUED VIA WRAPPER REDEMPTION PROGRAM
BP1 Stephen Strasburg 8.00 20.00

2010 Bowman Prospects Blue

*BLUE: 1.2X TO 3X BASIC
STATED ODDS 1:17 HOBBY
STATED PRINT RUN 520 SER.#'d SETS
STRASBURG AU ODDS 1:5700 HOBBY
STRASBURG PRINT RUN 250 SER.#'d SETS
BP1a Stephen Strasburg 20.00 50.00
BP1b Stephen Strasburg AU 300.00 600.00

2010 Bowman Prospects Orange

*ORANGE: 2X TO 5X BASIC
STATED ODDS 1:35 HOBBY
STATED PRINT RUN 250 SER.#'d SETS
STRASBURG AU ODDS 1:56,500 HOBBY
STRASBURG PRINT RUN 25 SER.#'d SETS
NO STRASBURG PRICING AVAILABLE
BP1a Stephen Strasburg 40.00 80.00

2010 Bowman Prospects Red

STATED ODDS 1:3400 HOBBY
STATED PRINT RUN 1 SER.#'d SET
NO PRICING DUE TO SCARCITY

2010 Bowman Prospect Autographs

BM Brent Morel 5.00 12.00
CV Cesar Valdez 3.00 8.00
DC Dusty Coleman 3.00 8.00
DH Darin Holcomb 3.00 8.00
DT Donavan Tate 6.00 15.00
EB Eric Berger 3.00 8.00
JB Justin Bristow 3.00 8.00
JF Jeremy Farrell 3.00 8.00
LF Logan Forsythe 3.00 8.00
MH Matt Hobgood 3.00 8.00
TS Tony Sanchez 3.00 8.00
ZS Zach Simons 3.00 8.00

2010 Bowman Topps 100 Prospects

COMPLETE SET (100) 30.00 60.00
STATED ODDS 1:3 HOBBY
TP1 Stephen Strasburg 5.00 12.00
TP2 Aroldis Chapman 1.50 4.00
TP3 Jason Heyward 2.50 6.00
TP4 Jesus Montero 2.50 6.00
TP5 Mike Stanton 1.50 4.00
TP6 Mike Moustakas 1.25 3.00
TP7 Kyle Drabek .60 1.50
TP8 Tyler Matzek 1.00 2.50
TP9 Austin Jackson .60 1.50
TP10 Starlin Castro 1.50 4.00
TP11 Todd Frazier .40 1.00
TP12 Carlos Santana 1.25 3.00
TP13 Josh Vitters .40 1.00
TP14 Neftali Feliz .40 1.00
TP15 Tyler Flowers .60 1.50
TP16 Alcides Escobar .60 1.50
TP17 Ike Davis 1.00 2.50
TP18 Domonic Brown 1.50 4.00
TP19 Donavan Tate 1.00 2.50
TP20 Buster Posey 4.00 10.00
TP21 Dustin Ackley 2.50 6.00
TP22 Desmond Jennings .60 1.50
TP23 Brandon Allen .40 1.00
TP24 Freddie Freeman 1.50 4.00
TP25 Jake Arrieta .60 1.50
TP26 Bobby Borchering .60 1.50
TP27 Logan Morrison .60 1.50
TP28 Christian Friederich .60 1.50
TP29 Wilmer Flores 1.00 2.50
TP30 Austin Romine .60 1.50
TP31 Tony Sanchez 1.00 2.50
TP32 Madison Bumgarner 1.00 2.50
TP33 Mike Montgomery .60 1.50
TP34 Andrew Lambo .40 1.00
TP35 Derek Norris .60 1.50
TP36 Chris Withrow .40 1.00
TP37 Thomas Neal .60 1.50
TP38 Trevor Reckling .40 1.00
TP39 Andrew Cashner .40 1.00
TP40 Daniel Hudson .60 1.50
TP41 Jiovanni Mier .60 1.50
TP42 Grant Green .60 1.50
TP43 Jeremy Hellickson 1.50 4.00
TP44 Felix Doubront .40 1.00
TP45 Martin Perez .60 1.50
TP46 Jenrry Mejia .60 1.50
TP47 Adrian Cardenas .40 1.00
TP48 Ivan DeJesus Jr. .40 1.00
TP49 Nolan Arenado 1.25 3.00
TP50 Slade Heathcott 1.25 3.00
TP51 Ian Desmond .60 1.50
TP52 Michael Taylor .60 1.50
TP53 Jaime Garcia .60 1.50
TP54 Jose Tabata 1.00 2.50
TP55 Josh Bell .40 1.00
TP56 Jarrod Parker 1.00 2.50
TP57 Matt Dominguez .40 1.00
TP58 Koby Clemens .60 1.50
TP59 Angel Morales .40 1.00
TP60 Juan Francisco .60 1.50
TP61 John Ely .40 1.00
TP62 Brett Jackson 1.25 3.00
TP63 Chad Jenkins .40 1.00
TP64 Jose Iglesias 1.50 4.00
TP65 Logan Forsythe .40 1.00
TP66 Alex Liddi .60 1.50
TP67 Eric Arnett .40 1.00
TP68 Wilkin Ramirez .40 1.00
TP69 Lars Anderson 1.00 2.50
TP70 Jared Mitchell .60 1.50
TP71 Mike Leake 1.25 3.00
TP72 D.J. LeMahieu .40 1.00
TP73 Chris Marrero .40 1.00
TP74 Matt Moore 5.00 12.00
TP75 Jordan Brown .40 1.00
TP76 Christopher Parmelee .40 1.00
TP77 Ryan Kalish .60 1.50
TP78 A.J. Pollock .60 1.50
TP79 Alex White .60 1.50
TP80 Scott Sizemore .60 1.50
TP81 Jay Austin .40 1.00
TP82 Zach McAllister .60 1.50
TP83 Max Stassi .60 1.50
TP84 Robert Stock .40 1.00
TP85 Jake McGee .40 1.00
TP86 Zack Wheeler .60 1.50
TP87 Chase D'Arnaud .40 1.00
TP88 Danny Duffy .60 1.50
TP89 Josh Lindblom .40 1.00
TP90 Anthony Gose .60 1.50
TP91 Simon Castro .60 1.50
TP92 Chris Carter .40 1.00
TP93 Matt Hobgood 1.00 2.50
TP94 Ben Revere .40 1.00
TP95 Mat Gamel .40 1.00
TP96 Anthony Hewitt .40 1.00
TP97 Julio Teheran 1.00 2.50
TP98 Josh Reddick .40 1.00
TP99 Hank Conger .40 1.00
TP100 Jordan Walden .40 1.00

2011 Bowman

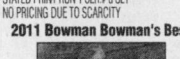

COMPLETE SET (220) 12.50 30.00
COMMON CARD (1-190) .12 .30
COMMON RC (191-220) .40 1.00
PLATE PRINT RUN 1 SET PER COLOR
BLACK-CYAN-MAGENTA-YELLOW ISSUED
NO PLATE PRICING DUE TO SCARCITY
1 Buster Posey .40 1.00
2 Alex Avila .12 .30
3 Edwin Jackson .12 .30
4 Miguel Montero .12 .30
5 Ryan Dempster .12 .30
6 Albert Pujols .75 2.00
7 Carlos Santana .30 .75
8 Ted Lilly .12 .30
9 Marlon Byrd .12 .30
10 Hanley Ramirez .30 .75
11 Josh Hamilton .30 .75
12 Orlando Hudson .12 .30
13 Matt Kemp .20 .50
14 Shane Victorino .20 .50
15 Domonic Brown .30 .75
16 Jeff Niemann .12 .30
17 Chipper Jones .30 .75
18 Joey Votto .30 .75
19 Brandon Phillips .12 .30
20 Michael Bourn .12 .30
21 Jason Heyward .40 1.00
22 Curtis Granderson .20 .50
23 Brian McCann .20 .50
24 Mike Pelfrey .12 .30
25 Grady Sizemore .20 .50
26 Dustin Pedroia .40 1.00
27 Chris Johnson .12 .30
28 Brian Matusz .30 .75
29 Jason Bay .20 .50
30 Mark Teixeira .30 .75
31 Carlos Quentin .20 .50
32 Miguel Tejada .20 .50
33 Ryan Howard .40 1.00
34 Adrian Beltre .12 .30
35 Joe Mauer .30 .75
36 Johan Santana .30 .75
37 Logan Morrison .12 .30
38 C.J. Wilson .12 .30
39 Carlos Lee .12 .30
40 Ian Kinsler .20 .50
41 Shin-Soo Choo .20 .50
42 Adam Wainwright .20 .50
43 Derek Lowe .12 .30
44 Carlos Gonzalez .20 .50
45 Lance Berkman .20 .50
46 Jon Lester .30 .75
47 Miguel Cabrera .30 .75
48 Justin Verlander .40 1.00
49 Tyler Colvin .20 .50
50 Matt Cain .20 .50
51 Brett Anderson .20 .50
52 Gordon Beckham .20 .50
53 David DeJesus .12 .30
54 Jonathan Sanchez .12 .30
55 Jorge Posada .20 .50
56 Neil Walker .12 .30
57 Jorge De La Rosa .12 .30
58 Torii Hunter .12 .30
59 Andrew McCutchen .30 .75
60 Mat Latos .12 .30
61 CC Sabathia .20 .50
62 Brett Myers .12 .30
63 Ryan Zimmerman .20 .50
64 Trevor Cahill .12 .30
65 Clayton Kershaw .30 .75
66 Andre Ethier .20 .50
67 Kosuke Fukudome .30 .75
68 Justin Upton .20 .50
69 B.J. Upton .20 .50
70 J.P. Arencibia .20 .50
71 Phil Hughes .12 .30
72 Tim Hudson .20 .50
73 Francisco Liriano .12 .30
74 Ike Davis .20 .50
75 Delmon Young .20 .50
76 Paul Konerko .20 .50
77 Carlos Beltran .12 .30
78 Mike Stanton .20 .50
79 Adam Jones .20 .50
80 Jimmy Rollins .20 .50
81 Alex Rios .20 .50
82 Chad Billingsley .12 .30
83 Tommy Hanson .20 .50
84 Travis Wood .12 .30
85 Magglio Ordonez .20 .50
86 Jake Peavy .12 .30
87 Adrian Gonzalez .20 .50
88 Aaron Hill .12 .30
89 Kendry Morales .12 .30
90 Manny Ramirez .30 .75
91 Hunter Pence .20 .50
92 Josh Beckett .20 .50
93 Mark Reynolds .12 .30
94 Drew Stubbs .12 .30
95 Dan Haren .12 .30
96 Chris Carpenter .30 .75
97 Mitch Moreland .12 .30
98 Starlin Castro .30 .75
99 Roy Halladay .30 .75
100 Stephen Drew .12 .30
101 Aramis Ramirez .12 .30
102 Daniel Hudson .12 .30
103 Alexei Ramirez .12 .30
104 Rickie Weeks .20 .50
105 Will Venable .12 .30
106 David Price .30 .75
107 Dan Uggla .20 .50
108 Austin Jackson .12 .30
109 Evan Longoria .40 1.00
110 Ryan Ludwick .12 .30
111 Chase Utley .30 .75
112 Johnny Cueto .12 .30
113 Billy Butler .12 .30
114 David Wright .40 1.00
115 Jose Reyes .20 .50
116 Robinson Cano .30 .75
117 Josh Johnson .20 .50
118 Chris Coghlan .12 .30
119 David Ortiz .20 .50
120 Jay Bruce .20 .50
121 Jayson Werth .20 .50
122 Matt Holliday .30 .75
123 John Danks .12 .30
124 Franklin Gutierrez .12 .30
125 Zack Greinke .20 .50
126 Jacoby Ellsbury .30 .75
127 Madison Bumgarner .12 .30
128 Mike Leake .20 .50
129 Carl Crawford .20 .50
130 Clay Buchholz .20 .50
131 Gavin Floyd .12 .30
132 Mike Minor .12 .30
133 Jose Tabata .20 .50
134 Jason Castro .12 .30
135 Chris Young .12 .30
136 Jose Bautista .20 .50
137 Felix Hernandez .30 .75
138 Koji Uehara .12 .30
139 Dexter Fowler .12 .30
140 J.A. Happ .20 .50
141 Tim Lincecum .30 .75
142 Todd Helton .20 .50
143 Ubaldo Jimenez .20 .50
144 Yovani Gallardo .12 .30
145 Derek Jeter .75 2.00
146 Wade Davis .12 .30
147 Hiroki Kuroda .12 .30
148 Nelson Cruz .20 .50
149 Martin Prado .12 .30
150 Michael Cuddyer .12 .30
151 Mark Buehrle .20 .50
152 Danny Valencia .20 .50
153 Ichiro Suzuki .50 1.25
154 Brett Wallace .12 .30
155 Troy Tulowitzki .30 .75
156 Pedro Alvarez RC .60 1.50
157 Brandon Morrow .12 .30
158 Jered Weaver .12 .30
159 Michael Young .20 .50
160 Wandy Rodriguez .12 .30
161 Alfonso Soriano .20 .50
162 Kelly Johnson .12 .30
163 Roy Oswalt .20 .50
164 Brian Roberts .12 .30
165 Jaime Garcia .20 .50
166 Edinson Volquez .12 .30
167 Vladimir Guerrero .30 .75
168 Cliff Lee .30 .75
169 Johnny Damon .20 .50
170 Alex Rodriguez .50 1.25
171 Nick Markakis .30 .75
172 Cole Hamels .30 .75
173 Prince Fielder .20 .50
174 Kurt Suzuki .12 .30
175 Ryan Braun .40 1.00
176 Justin Morneau .30 .75
177 Denard Span .12 .30
178 Elvis Andrus .20 .50
179 Stephen Strasburg .60 1.50
180 Adam Lind .20 .50
181 Corey Hart .12 .30
182 Adam Dunn .20 .50
183 Bobby Abreu .12 .30
184 Gaby Sanchez .12 .30
185 Ian Kennedy .20 .50
186 Kevin Youkilis .20 .50
187 Vernon Wells .12 .30
188 Matt Garza .12 .30
189 Victor Martinez .20 .50
190 Casey McGehee .12 .30
191 Jake McGee (RC) .40 1.00
192 Lars Anderson RC .60 1.50
193 Mark Trumbo (RC) .60 1.50
194 Konrad Schmidt RC .40 1.00
195 Jeremy Jeffress RC .40 1.00
196 Brent Morel RC .40 1.00
197 Aroldis Chapman RC 1.25 3.00
198 Greg Halman RC .60 1.50
199 Jeremy Hellickson RC 1.25 3.00
200 Yunesky Maya RC .40 1.00
201 Kyle Drabek RC .60 1.50
202 Ben Revere RC .60 1.50
203 Desmond Jennings RC 1.00 2.50
204 Brandon Beachy RC 1.00 2.50
205 Freddie Freeman RC 1.50 4.00
206 Andrew Romine RC .40 1.00
207 John Lindsey RC .40 1.00
208 Mark Rogers (RC) .40 1.00
209 Brian Bogusevic (RC) .40 1.00
210 Yonder Alonso RC .60 1.50
211 Gregory Infante RC .40 1.00
212 Dillon Gee RC .60 1.50
213 Ozzie Martinez RC .40 1.00
214 Brandon Snyder (RC) .40 1.00
215 Daniel Descalso RC .40 1.00
216 Brett Sinkbeil RC .40 1.00
217 Lucas Duda RC .60 1.50
218 Cory Luebke RC .40 1.00
219 Hank Conger RC .60 1.50
220 Chris Sale RC .60 1.50

2011 Bowman Blue

*BLUE 1-190: 1.5X TO 4X BASIC
*BLUE: 191-220: .75X TO 2X BASIC
STATED PRINT RUN 500 SER.#'d SETS

2011 Bowman Gold

COMPLETE SET (220) 40.00 80.00
*GOLD 1-190: .75X TO 2X BASIC
*GOLD: 191-220: .5X TO 1.2X BASIC

2011 Bowman Green

*GREEN 1-190: 2X TO 5X BASIC
*GREEN: 191-220: .75X TO 2X BASIC
STATED PRINT RUN 450 SER.#'d SETS

2011 Bowman International

*INTER 1-190: 1.2X TO 3X BASIC
*INTER 191-220: .6X TO 1.5X BASIC
INT.PLATE PRINT RUN 1 SET PER COLOR
BLACK-CYAN-MAGENTA-YELLOW ISSUED
NO PLATE PRICING DUE TO SCARCITY

2011 Bowman Orange

*ORANGE 1-190: 2.5X TO 6X BASIC
*ORANGE 191-220: .75X TO 2X BASIC
STATED PRINT RUN 250 SER.#'d SETS

2011 Bowman Red

STATED PRINT RUN 1 SER.#'d SET
NO PRICING DUE TO SCARCITY

2011 Bowman Bowman's Best

COMPLETE SET (25) 10.00 25.00
*REF: 3X TO 8X BASIC
REF PRINT RUN 99 SER.#'d SETS
ATOMIC PRINT RUN 1 SER.#'d SET
NO ATOMIC PRICING AVAILABLE
XF PRINT RUN 25 SER.#'d SETS
NO XF PRICING DUE TO SCARCITY
BB1 Buster Posey 1.00 2.50
BB2 Roy Halladay .75 2.00
BB3 Miguel Cabrera .75 2.00
BB4 Mark Teixeira .75 2.00
BB5 Robinson Cano .75 2.00
BB6 Chase Utley .75 2.00
BB7 Ichiro Suzuki 1.25 3.00
BB8 Ryan Braun 1.00 2.50
BB9 Josh Hamilton .75 2.00
BB10 Mike Stanton .50 1.25
BB11 Derek Jeter 2.00 5.00
BB12 Joey Votto .75 2.00
BB13 Alex Rodriguez 1.25 3.00
BB14 Albert Pujols 2.00 5.00
BB15 Jason Heyward 1.00 2.50
BB16 Adrian Gonzalez .50 1.25
BB17 Troy Tulowitzki .75 2.00
BB18 Stephen Strasburg 1.50 4.00
BB19 Tim Lincecum .75 2.00
BB20 Felix Hernandez .75 2.00
BB21 Kevin Youkilis .50 1.25
BB22 Joe Mauer .75 2.00
BB23 Ubaldo Jimenez .50 1.25
BB24 Ryan Howard 1.00 2.50
BB25 Carl Crawford .50 1.25

2011 Bowman Bowman's Best Prospects

COMPLETE SET (50) 30.00 80.00
51-75 ODDS 1:8 HOBBY
51-75 REF.ODDS 1:256 HOBBY
51-75 ATOMIC ODDS 1:25,343 HOBBY
ATOMIC PRINT RUN 1 SER.#'d SET
NO ATOMIC PRICING AVAILABLE
51-75 XF ODDS 1:1013 HOBBY
XF PRINT RUN 25 SER.#'d SETS
NO XF PRICING DUE TO SCARCITY
BBP1 Bryce Harper 5.00 12.00
BBP2 Grant Green .30 .75
BBP3 Nick Franklin .50 1.25
BBP4 Simon Castro .50 1.25
BBP5 Manny Machado 1.00 2.50
BBP6 Dustin Ackley 1.25 3.00
BBP7 Mike Moustakas .75 2.00
BBP8 Michael Pineda 1.25 3.00
BBP9 Mike Trout 2.00 5.00
BBP10 Jerry Sands 1.25 3.00
BBP11 Brett Jackson .50 1.25
BBP12 Jesus Montero 1.25 3.00
BBP13 Jameson Taillon 1.00 2.50
BBP14 Julio Teheran 1.00 2.50
BBP15 Dee Gordon .75 2.00
BBP16 Shelby Miller .75 2.00
BBP17 Jacob Turner 1.25 3.00
BBP18 Brandon Belt 1.25 3.00
BBP19 Gary Sanchez .75 2.00
BBP20 Miguel Sano .75 2.00
BBP21 Devin Mesoraco .50 1.25
BBP22 Zach Britton .75 2.00
BBP23 Tyler Matzek .50 1.25
BBP24 Matt Dominguez .50 1.25
BBP25 Wil Myers .50 1.25
BBP51 Bryce Harper 5.00 12.00
BBP52 Shelby Miller .75 2.00
BBP53 Arodys Vizcaino .30 .75
BBP54 Jonathan Singleton .50 1.25
BBP55 Manny Machado 1.00 2.50
BBP56 Matt Moore 1.50 4.00
BBP57 Devin Mesoraco .50 1.25
BBP58 Christian Colon .30 .75
BBP59 Chris Archer .30 .75
BBP60 Martin Perez .30 .75
BBP61 Aaron Hicks .75 2.00
BBP62 Jean Segura .30 .75
BBP63 Delino DeShields Jr. .30 .75
BBP64 Wil Myers .50 1.25
BBP65 Jacob Turner 1.25 3.00
BBP66 Josh Sale .50 1.25
BBP67 Miguel Sano .75 2.00
BBP68 Jason Kipnis 1.00 2.50
BBP69 Luis Heredia .30 .75
BBP70 Anthony Ranaudo .75 2.00
BBP71 Stetson Allie .50 1.25
BBP72 Joe Benson .30 .75
BBP73 Nick Castellanos .50 1.25
BBP74 Billy Hamilton .75 2.00
BBP75 Manny Banuelos 1.00 2.50

2011 Bowman Bowman's Best Prospects Refractors

*REF: 3X TO 8X BASIC
51-75 STATED ODDS 1:256 HOBBY
STATED PRINT RUN 99 SER.#'d SETS
BBP1 Bryce Harper 60.00 120.00
BBP51 Bryce Harper 75.00 150.00

2011 Bowman Bowman's Brightest

COMPLETE SET (25) 15.00 40.00
BBR1 Bryce Harper 5.00 12.00
BBR2 Mike Moustakas .75 2.00
BBR3 Mark Trumbo .50 1.25
BBR4 Paul Goldschmidt 1.50 4.00
BBR5 Rich Poythress .30 .75
BBR6 Mike Trout 2.00 5.00
BBR7 Dee Gordon .75 2.00
BBR8 Tyson Auer .30 .75
BBR9 Jay Austin .30 .75
BBR10 Eury Perez .30 .75
BBR11 Slade Heathcott .75 2.00
BBR12 Michael Taylor .30 .75
BBR13 Johermyn Chavez .30 .75
BBR14 Engel Beltre .30 .75
BBR15 Wilin Rosario .30 .75
BBR16 Freddie Freeman 1.25 3.00
BBR17 Wilmer Flores .50 1.25
BBR18 Domonic Brown .75 2.00
BBR19 Manny Machado 1.00 2.50
BBR20 Lonnie Chisenhall .50 1.25
BBR21 Jose Iglesias .50 1.25
BBR22 Desmond Jennings .75 2.00
BBR23 Jurickson Profar 1.00 2.50
BBR24 Tony Sanchez .50 1.25
BBR25 Jedd Gyorko .75 2.00

2011 Bowman Buyback Cut Signatures

STATED PRINT RUN 1 SER.#'d SET
NO PRICING DUE TO SCARCITY

2011 Bowman Checklists

COMPLETE SET (5) .40 1.00
RED: 4X TO 10X BASIC
RED PRINT RUN 500 SER.#'d SETS

2011 Bowman Finest Futures

COMPLETE SET (25) 8.00 20.00
FF1 Jason Heyward .75 2.00
FF2 Buster Posey .75 2.00
FF3 Gordon Beckham .40 1.00
FF4 Brian Matusz .60 1.50
FF5 Mike Stanton .40 1.00
FF6 Starlin Castro .60 1.50
FF7 Carlos Santana .60 1.50
FF8 Aroldis Chapman .75 2.00
FF9 Pedro Alvarez .40 1.00
FF10 Freddie Freeman 1.00 2.50
FF11 Troy Tulowitzki .60 1.50
FF12 Domonic Brown .60 1.50
FF13 Chris Carter .25 .60
FF14 Ubaldo Jimenez .40 1.00
FF15 Ike Davis .40 1.00
FF16 Austin Jackson .25 .60
FF17 J.P. Arencibia .40 1.00
FF18 Ryan Braun .75 2.00
FF19 Justin Upton .40 1.00
FF20 Mat Latos .25 .60
FF21 Clayton Kershaw .60 1.50
FF22 Carlos Gonzalez .60 1.50
FF23 Stephen Strasburg 1.25 3.00
FF24 Andrew McCutchen .60 1.50
FF25 Madison Bumgarner .25 .60

2011 Bowman Future's Game Triple Relics

STATED PRINT RUN 99 SER.#'d SETS
AL Alex Liddi 5.00 12.00
AR Austin Romine 5.00 12.00
AS Anthony Slama 4.00 10.00
AT Alex Torres 5.00 12.00
BJ Brett Jackson 10.00 25.00
BM Bryan Morris 5.00 12.00
BR Ben Revere 5.00 12.00
CC Chun-Hsiu Chen 10.00 25.00
CF Christian Friedrich 4.00 10.00
CP Carlos Peguero 4.00 10.00
DB Domonic Brown 12.50 30.00
DE Danny Espinosa 5.00 12.00
DG Dee Gordon 6.00 15.00
DJ Desmond Jennings 5.00 12.00
EP Eury Perez 4.00 10.00
ES Eduardo Sanchez 8.00 20.00
FP Francisco Peguero 4.00 10.00
GG Grant Green 5.00 12.00
GH Gorkys Hernandez 4.00 10.00
HA Henderson Alvarez 4.00 10.00
HC Hank Conger 5.00 12.00
HL Hak-Ju Lee 8.00 20.00
HN Hector Noesi 5.00 12.00
JF Jeurys Familia 4.00 10.00
JH Jeremy Hellickson 6.00 15.00
JT Julio Teheran 6.00 15.00
LC Lonnie Chisenhall 6.00 15.00
LJ Luis Jimenez 8.00 20.00
LM Logan Morrison 4.00 10.00
MM Mike Minor 6.00 15.00
MMO Mike Moustakas 10.00 25.00
MT Mike Trout 15.00 40.00
OM Ozzie Martinez 4.00 10.00
PB Pedro Baez 4.00 10.00
PC Pedro Ciriaco 5.00 12.00
PV Philippe Valiquette 8.00 20.00
SC Simon Castro 4.00 10.00
SM Shelby Miller 12.50 30.00
SP Stolmy Pimentel 4.00 10.00
TM Trystan Magnuson 4.00 10.00
WR Wilin Rosario 5.00 12.00
WRA Wilkin Ramirez 4.00 10.00
ZB Zach Britton 5.00 12.00
ZW Zack Wheeler 6.00 15.00

2011 Bowman Prospect Autographs

EXCHANGE DEADLINE 4/30/2014
BB Bryce Brentz 4.00 10.00
BBR Brett Brach 4.00 10.00
BC Brandon Crawford 5.00 12.00
CC Chevez Clarke 4.00 10.00
DD Daniel Descalso 4.00 10.00
DS Domingo Santana 4.00 10.00
JD Justin De Fratus 5.00 12.00
JG Joe Gardner 4.00 10.00
JO Justin O'Conner 4.00 10.00
JS Josh Sale 4.00 10.00
KC Kaleb Cowart 4.00 10.00
KV Kolbrin Vitek 4.00 10.00
MC Michael Choice 6.00 15.00
MM Manny Machado EXCH 12.50 30.00
MP Michael Pineda 20.00 50.00
TB Tim Beckham 4.00 10.00
YR Yorman Rodriguez 4.00 10.00
ZC Zack Cox 5.00 12.00
ZW Zack Wheeler 6.00 15.00

2011 Bowman Prospects

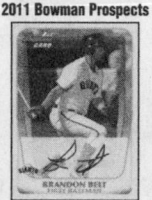

COMP.SET w/o AU (110) 20.00 50.00
PLATE PRINT RUN 1 SET PER COLOR
BLACK-CYAN-MAGENTA-YELLOW ISSUED
NO PLATE PRICING DUE TO SCARCITY
EXCHANGE DEADLINE 4/30/2014
BP1A Bryce Harper 5.00 12.00
BP1B Bryce Harper AU 150.00 300.00
BP2 Chris Dennis .15 .40
BP3 Jeremy Barfield .15 .40
BP4 Nate Freiman .15 .40
BP5 Tyler Moore .25 .60
BP6 Anthony Carter .15 .40
BP7 Ryan Cavan .15 .40
BP8 Stephen Vogt .15 .40
BP9 Carlo Testa .15 .40
BP10 Erik Davis .15 .40
BP11 Jack Shuck .40 1.00
BP12 Charles Brewer .15 .40
BP13 Alex Castellanos .25 .60
BP14 Anthony Vasquez .15 .40
BP15 Michael Brenly .15 .40
BP16 Kody Hinze .25 .60
BP17 Hector Noesi .25 .60
BP18 Tyler Bortnick .15 .40
BP19 Thomas Layne .15 .40
BP20 Everett Teaford .15 .40
BP21 Jose Pirela .15 .40
BP22 Joel Carreno .15 .40
BP23 Vinnie Catricala .60 1.50
BP24 Tom Koehler .15 .40
BP25 Jonathan Schoop .40 1.00
BP26 Chun-Hsiu Chen .40 1.00
BP27 Amaury Rivas .15 .40
BP28 Oswaldo Arcia .15 .40
BP29 Johermyn Chavez .15 .40
BP30 Michael Spina .15 .40
BP31 Kyle McPherson .25 .60
BP32 Albert Cartwright .15 .40
BP33 Joseph Wieland .40 1.00
BP34 Ben Paulsen .15 .40
BP35 Jason Hagerty .15 .40
BP36 Marcell Ozuna .25 .60
BP37 Dave Sappelt .50 1.25
BP38 Eduardo Escobar .15 .40
BP39 Aaron Baker .15 .40
BP40 Deryk Hooker .15 .40
BP41 Ty Morrison .15 .40
BP42 Keon Broxton .15 .40
BP43 Corey Jones .15 .40
BP44 Manny Banuelos .50 1.25
BP45 Brandon Guyer .25 .60
BP46 Juan Nicasio .15 .40
BP47 Sean Ochinko .15 .40
BP48 Adam Warren .25 .60
BP49 Phillip Cerreto .15 .40
BP50 Mychal Givens .15 .40
BP51 James Fuller .15 .40
BP52 Ronnie Welty .15 .40
BP53 Dan Straily .15 .40
BP54 Gabriel Jacobo .15 .40
BP55 David Rubinstein .15 .40
BP56 Kevin Mailloux .15 .40
BP57 Angel Castillo .15 .40
BP58 Adrian Salcedo .25 .60
BP59 Ronald Bermudez .15 .40
BP60 Jarek Cunningham .25 .60
BP61 Matt Magill .25 .60
BP62 Willie Cabrera .15 .40
BP63 Austin Hyatt .25 .60
BP64 Cody Puckett .25 .60
BP65 Jacob Goebbert .25 .60
BP66 Matt Carpenter .25 .60
BP67 Dan Klein .25 .60
BP68 Sean Ratliff .15 .40
BP69 Elih Villanueva .15 .40
BP70 Wade Gaynor .15 .40
BP71 Evan Crawford .15 .40
BP72 Avisail Garcia .30 .75
BP73 Kevin Rivers .15 .40
BP74 Jim Gallagher .15 .40
BP75 Brian Broderick .15 .40
BP76 Tyson Auer .15 .40
BP77 Matt Klinker .15 .40
BP78 Cole Figueroa .15 .40
BP79 Rafael Ynoa .15 .40
BP80 Dee Gordon .40 1.00
BP81 Blake Forsythe .15 .40
BP82 Jurickson Profar .50 1.25
BP83 Jedd Gyorko .40 1.00
BP84 Matt Hague .15 .40
BP85 Mason Williams .40 1.00
BP86 Stetson Allie .25 .60
BP87 Jarred Cosart .25 .60
BP88 Wagner Mateo .40 1.00
BP89 Allen Webster .25 .60
BP90 Adron Chambers .15 .40
BP91 Blake Smith .15 .40
BP92 J.D. Martinez .25 .60
BP93 Brandon Belt .60 1.50
BP94 Drake Britton .15 .40
BP95 Addison Reed .15 .40
BP96 Adonis Cardona .25 .60
BP97 Yordy Cabrera .15 .40
BP98 Tony Wolters .15 .40
BP99 Paul Goldschmidt .75 2.00
BP100 Sean Coyle .40 1.00
BP101 Rymer Liriano .25 .60
BP102 Eric Thames .15 .40
BP103 Brian Fletcher .15 .40
BP104 Ben Gamel .25 .60
BP105 Kyle Russell .25 .60
BP106 Sammy Solis .15 .40
BP107 Garin Cecchini .40 1.00
BP108 Carlos Perez .15 .40
BP109 Darin Mastroianni .15 .40
BP110 Jonathan Villar .15 .40

2011 Bowman Prospects Blue

*BLUE: 1.5X TO 4X BASIC
STATED PRINT RUN 500 SER.#'d SETS
HARPER AU PRINT RUN 250 SER.#'d SETS
EXCHANGE DEADLINE 4/30/2014
BP1A Bryce Harper 20.00 50.00
BP1B Bryce Harper AU 300.00 500.00

2011 Bowman Prospects Green

*GREEN: 1.5X TO 4X BASIC
STATED PRINT RUN 450 SER.#'d SETS
BP1 Bryce Harper 20.00 50.00

2011 Bowman Prospects International

*INTERNATIONAL : 1.5X TO 4X BASIC
BP1 Bryce Harper 20.00 50.00

2011 Bowman Prospects Orange

*ORANGE: 3X TO 8X BASIC
STATED PRINT RUN 250 SER.#'d SETS
HARPER AU PRINT RUN 25 SER.#'d SETS
NO HARPER AU PRICING DUE TO SCARCITY
EXCHANGE DEADLINE 4/30/2014
BP1A Bryce Harper 20.00 50.00

2011 Bowman Prospects Purple

*PURPLE: 1.5X TO 4X BASIC
HARPER AU PRINT RUN 55 SER.#'d SETS
EXCHANGE DEADLINE 4/30/2014
BP1A Bryce Harper 12.50 30.00
BP1B Bryce Harper AU 1000.00 1400.00

2011 Bowman Prospects Red

STATED PRINT RUN 1 SER.#'d SET
NO PRICING DUE TO SCARCITY

2011 Bowman Topps 100

COMPLETE SET (100) 40.00 80.00
TP1 Bryce Harper 3.00 8.00
TP2 Jonathan Singleton .50 1.25
TP3 Tony Sanchez .50 1.25
TP4 Ryan Lavarnway .75 2.00
TP5 Rex Brothers .30 .75
TP6 Brandon Belt 1.25 3.00
TP7 Christian Colon .30 .75
TP8 Reymond Fuentes .30 .75
TP9 Alex Liddi .30 .75
TP10 Zack Cox .50 1.25
TP11 Derek Norris .30 .75
TP12 Hayden Simpson .30 .75
TP13 Alex Colome .30 .75
TP14 Lonnie Chisenhall .50 1.25
TP15 Mike Montgomery .50 1.25
TP16 Gary Sanchez .75 2.00
TP17 Shelby Miller .75 2.00
TP18 Matt Moore 1.50 4.00
TP19 Austin Romine .30 .75
TP20 Delino DeShields .30 .75
TP21 Drew Pomeranz .75 2.00
TP22 Michael Pineda 1.00 2.50
TP23 Thomas Neal .30 .75
TP24 Chun-Hsiu Chen .75 2.00
TP25 Arodys Vizcaino .30 .75
TP26 Grant Green .30 .75
TP27 Eric Thames .30 .75
TP28 Matt Davidson 1.00 2.50
TP29 Deck McGuire .30 .75
TP30 Adeiny Hechavarria .30 .75
TP31 Jean Segura .30 .75
TP32 Paul Goldschmidt 1.50 4.00
TP33 Simon Castro .50 1.25
TP34 Garin Cecchini .75 2.00
TP35 Julio Teheran 1.00 2.50
TP36 Hak-Ju Lee .50 1.25
TP37 Randall Delgado .50 1.25
TP38 Sammy Solis .30 .75
TP39 Wil Myers .50 1.25
TP40 Miguel Sano .75 2.00
TP41 Michael Taylor .30 .75
TP42 Nolan Arenado 1.00 2.50
TP43 John Lamb .30 .75
TP44 Jurickson Profar 1.00 2.50
TP45 Jacob Turner 1.25 3.00
TP46 Anthony Rizzo .50 1.25
TP47 Slade Heathcott .75 2.00
TP48 Brody Colvin .30 .75
TP49 Yasmani Grandal .50 1.25
TP50 Dellin Betances .75 2.00
TP51 Charles Brewer .30 .75
TP52 Jared Mitchell .50 1.25
TP53 Nick Franklin .50 1.25
TP54 Manny Machado 1.00 2.50
TP55 Manny Banuelos 1.00 2.50
TP56 Allen Webster .50 1.25
TP57 Kolbrin Vitek .50 1.25
TP58 Jesus Montero 1.25 3.00
TP59 Wilmer Flores .50 1.25
TP60 Jarrod Parker 1.25 3.00
TP61 Zach Lee .50 1.25
TP62 Alex Torres .30 .75
TP63 Adron Chambers .30 .75
TP64 Tyler Skaggs .75 2.00
TP65 Kyle Seager .50 1.25
TP66 Josh Vitters .50 1.25
TP67 Matt Harvey .50 1.25
TP68 Rudy Owens .30 .75
TP69 Donavan Tate .75 2.00
TP70 Jose Iglesias .50 1.25
TP71 Alex White .30 .75
TP72 Robbie Erlin .50 1.25
TP73 Johermyn Chavez .30 .75
TP74 Mauricio Robles .30 .75
TP75 Matt Dominguez .50 1.25
TP76 Jason Kipnis 1.00 2.50
TP77 Aaron Sanchez .30 .75
TP78 Tyler Matzek .50 1.25
TP79 Chance Ruffin .30 .75
TP80 Jarred Cosart .50 1.25
TP81 Chris Withrow .30 .75
TP82 Drake Britton .30 .75
TP83 Michael Choice .50 1.25
TP84 Freddie Freeman 1.25 3.00
TP85 Jameson Taillon 1.00 2.50
TP86 Devin Mesoraco .50 1.25
TP87 Brandon Laird .50 1.25
TP88 Keon Broxton .30 .75
TP89 Mike Moustakas .75 2.00
TP90 Mike Trout 2.00 5.00
TP91 Danny Duffy .50 1.25
TP92 Brett Jackson .50 1.25
TP93 Dustin Ackley 1.25 3.00
TP94 Jerry Sands 1.25 3.00
TP95 Jake Skole .30 .75
TP96 Kyle Gibson .50 1.25
TP97 Martin Perez .30 .75
TP98 Zach Britton .75 2.00
TP99 Xavier Avery .30 .75
TP100 Dee Gordon .75 2.00

2011 Bowman Topps of the Class

COMPLETE SET (25) 10.00 25.00
TC1 Jerry Sands 1.25 3.00
TC2 Mike Olt .50 1.25
TC3 Jared Clark .30 .75
TC4 Nick Franklin .50 1.25
TC5 Paul Goldschmidt 1.50 4.00
TC6 Mike Moustakas .75 2.00
TC7 Greg Halman .50 1.25
TC8 Chris Carter .30 .75
TC9 Rich Poythress .30 .75
TC10 Mark Trumbo .50 1.25
TC11 Johermyn Chavez .30 .75
TC12 Brandon Allen .30 .75
TC13 Brandon Laird .50 1.25
TC14 J.P. Arencibia .50 1.25
TC15 Marcell Ozuna .30 .75
TC16 Kevin Mailloux .30 .75
TC17 Clint Robinson .30 .75
TC18 Tyler Moore .50 1.25
TC19 Joe Benson .30 .75
TC20 Anthony Rizzo .50 1.25
TC21 Jesus Montero 1.25 3.00
TC22 Tim Pahuta .30 .75
TC23 Grant Green .30 .75
TC24 Lucas Duda .50 1.25
TC25 Michael Spina .30 .75

2011 Bowman USA Baseball Logo Patch

STATED PRINT RUN 25 SER.#'d SETS
NO PRICING DUE TO SCARCITY

2011 Bowman USA Baseball Retro Patch

STATED PRINT RUN 25 SER.#'d SETS
NO PRICING DUE TO SCARCITY

2008 Bowman Draft

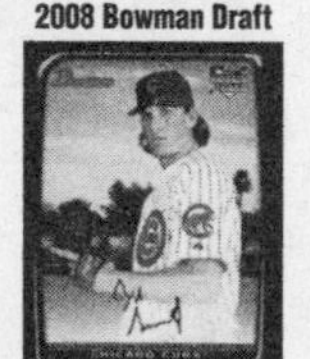

This set was released on November 28, 2008. The base set consists of 55 cards.

COMPLETE SET (55) 10.00 25.00
COMMON CARD (1-55) .20 .50
OVERALL PLATE ODDS 1:750 HOBBY
PLATE PRINT RUN 1 SET PER COLOR
BLACK-CYAN-MAGENTA-YELLOW ISSUED
NO PLATE PRICING DUE TO SCARCITY
BDP1 Nick Adenhart (RC) .20 .50
BDP2 Michael Aubrey RC .30 .75
BDP3 Mike Aviles RC .30 .75
BDP4 Burke Badenhop RC .30 .75
BDP5 Wladimir Balentien (RC) .20 .50
BDP6 Collin Balester (RC) .20 .50
BDP7 Josh Banks (RC) .20 .50
BDP8 Wes Bankston (RC) .20 .50
BDP9 Joey Votto (RC) .75 2.00
BDP10 Mitch Boggs (RC) .20 .50
BDP11 Jay Bruce (RC) .75 2.00
BDP12 Chris Carter (RC) .30 .75
BDP13 Justin Christian RC .30 .75
BDP14 Chris Davis RC .50 1.25
BDP15 Blake DeWitt (RC) .50 1.25

BDP16 Nick Evans RC .20 .50
BDP17 Jaime Garcia RC .75 2.00
BDP18 Brett Gardner (RC) .50 1.25
BDP19 Carlos Gonzalez (RC) .50 1.25
BDP20 Matt Harrison (RC) .20 .50
BDP21 Micah Hoffpauir RC .60 1.50
BDP22 Nick Hundley (RC) .20 .50
BDP23 Eric Hurley (RC) .20 .50
BDP24 Elliot Johnson (RC) .20 .50
BDP25 Matt Joyce RC .50 1.25
BDP26 Clayton Kershaw RC 1.00 2.50
BDP27 Evan Longoria RC 1.00 2.50
BDP28 Matt Macri (RC) .20 .50
BDP29 Chris Perez RC .30 .75
BDP30 Max Ramirez RC .20 .50
BDP31 Greg Reynolds RC .30 .75
BDP32 Brooks Conrad (RC) .20 .50
BDP33 Max Scherzer RC .60 1.50
BDP34 Daryl Thompson (RC) .20 .50
BDP35 Taylor Teagarden RC .30 .75
BDP36 Rich Thompson RC .30 .75
BDP37 Ryan Tucker (RC) .20 .50
BDP38 Jonathan Van Every RC .20 .50
BDP39 Chris Volstad (RC) .20 .50
BDP40 Michael Hollimon RC .20 .50
BDP41 Brad Ziegler RC 1.00 2.50
BDP42 Jamie D'Antona (RC) .20 .50
BDP43 Clayton Richard (RC) .20 .50
BDP44 Edgar Gonzalez (RC) .20 .50
BDP45 Bryan LaHair RC .20 .50
BDP46 Warner Madrigal (RC) .20 .50
BDP47 Reid Brignac (RC) .30 .75
BDP48 David Robertson RC .50 1.25
BDP49 Nick Stavinoha RC .30 .75
BDP50 Jai Miller (RC) .20 .50
BDP51 Charlie Morton (RC) .20 .50
BDP52 Brandon Boggs (RC) .30 .75
BDP53 Joe Mather RC .30 .75
BDP54 Gregorio Petit RC .30 .75
BDP55 Jeff Samardzija RC .60 1.50

2008 Bowman Draft Blue

*BLUE: 1X TO 2.5X BASIC
STATED ODDS 1:19 HOBBY
STATED PRINT RUN 399 SER.#'d SETS

2008 Bowman Draft Gold

*GOLD: .6X TO 1.5X BASIC
APPX.GOLD ODDS ONE PER PACK

2008 Bowman Draft Red

STATED ODDS 1:6025 HOBBY
STATED PRINT RUN 1 SER.#'d SET
NO PRICING DUE TO SCARCITY

2008 Bowman Draft AFLAC Autographs

STATED ODDS 1:215 HOBBY
AF Anthony Ferrara 6.00 15.00
AN Adrian Nieto 4.00 10.00
BB Blake Beavan 6.00 15.00
DB Drake Britton 15.00 40.00
DR Danny Rams 8.00 20.00
FF Freddie Freeman 75.00 150.00
IG Isaac Galloway 10.00 25.00
JG Jon Gilmore 8.00 20.00
JH Jason Heyward 150.00 300.00
JS Josh Smoker 4.00 10.00
JT John Tolisano 8.00 20.00
JV Josh Vitters 10.00 25.00
MB Madison Bumgarner 30.00 60.00
MM Michael Main 12.50 30.00
NN Nick Noonan 8.00 20.00
PD Paul Demny 4.00 10.00
QM Quinton Miller 6.00 15.00
RP Rick Porcello 40.00 80.00
TA Tim Alderson 10.00 25.00
XA Xavier Avery 4.00 10.00

2008 Bowman Draft Prospects

COMPLETE SET (110) 12.50 30.00
COMMON CARD (1-65) .20 .50
OVERALL PLATE ODDS 1:750 HOBBY
PLATE PRINT RUN 1 SET PER COLOR
BLACK-CYAN-MAGENTA-YELLOW ISSUED
NO PLATE PRICING DUE TO SCARCITY
BDPP1 Rick Porcello DP 1.00 2.50
BDPP2 Braeden Schlehuber DP .20 .50
BDPP3 Kenny Wilson DP .20 .50
BDPP4 Jeff Lanning DP .20 .50
BDPP5 Kevin Dubler DP .20 .50
BDPP6 Eric Campbell DP .30 .75
BDPP7 Tyler Chatwood DP .30 .75
BDPP8 Tyreace House DP .20 .50
BDPP9 Adrian Nieto DP .20 .50
BDPP10 Robbie Grossman DP .30 .75
BDPP11 Jordan Danks DP .50 1.25
BDPP12 Jay Austin DP .20 .50
BDPP13 Ryan Perry DP .30 .75
BDPP14 Ryan Chaffee DP .30 .75
BDPP15 Niko Vasquez DP .50 1.25
BDPP16 Shane Dyer DP .20 .50
BDPP17 Benji Gonzalez DP .20 .50
BDPP18 Miles Reagan DP .20 .50
BDPP19 Anthony Ferrara DP .20 .50
BDPP20 Markus Brisker DP .20 .50
BDPP21 Justin Bristow DP .20 .50
BDPP22 Richard Bleier DP .30 .75
BDPP23 Jeremy Beckham DP .30 .75
BDPP24 Xavier Avery DP .50 1.25
BDPP25 Christian Vazquez DP .30 .75
BDPP26 Nick Romero DP .20 .50
BDPP27 Trey Watten DP .20 .50
BDPP28 Brett Jacobson DP .20 .50
BDPP29 Tyler Sample DP .20 .50
BDPP30 T.J. Steele DP .30 .75
BDPP31 Christian Friedrich DP .60 1.50
BDPP32 Graham Hicks DP .30 .75
BDPP33 Shane Peterson DP .30 .75
BDPP34 Brett Hunter DP .20 .50
BDPP35 Tim Federowicz DP .30 .75
BDPP36 Isaac Galloway DP .30 .75
BDPP37 Logan Schafer DP .20 .50
BDPP38 Paul Demny DP .20 .50
BDPP39 Clayton Shunick DP .20 .50
BDPP40 Andrew Liebel DP .20 .50
BDPP41 Brandon Crawford DP .30 .75
BDPP42 Blake Tekotte DP .30 .75
BDPP43 Jason Corder DP .20 .50
BDPP44 Bryan Shaw DP .20 .50
BDPP45 Edgar Olmos DP .20 .50
BDPP46 Dusty Coleman DP .20 .50
BDPP47 Johnny Giavotella DP .60 1.50
BDPP48 Tyson Ross DP .30 .75
BDPP49 Brent Morel DP .30 .75
BDPP50 Dennis Raben DP .30 .75
BDPP51 Jake Odorizzi DP .60 1.50
BDPP52 Ryne White DP .30 .75
BDPP53 Devaris Strange-Gordon DP .20 .50
BDPP54 Tim Murphy DP .20 .50
BDPP55 Jake Jefferies DP .20 .50
BDPP56 Anthony Capra DP .20 .50
BDPP57 Kyle Weiland DP .50 1.25
BDPP58 Anthony Bass DP .30 .75
BDPP59 Scott Green DP .20 .50
BDPP60 Zeke Spruill DP .50 1.25
BDPP61 L.J. Hoes DP .50 1.25
BDPP62 Tyler Cline DP .20 .50
BDPP63 Matt Cerda DP .20 .50
BDPP64 Bobby Lanigan DP .20 .50
BDPP65 Mike Sheridan DP .20 .50
BDPP66 Carlos Carrasco FG .20 .50
BDPP67 Nate Schierholtz FG .20 .50
BDPP68 Jesus Delgado FG .20 .50
BDPP69 Andrew McCutchen FG .60 1.50
BDPP70 Shairon Martis FG .30 .75
BDPP71 Matt LaPorta FG .50 1.25
BDPP72 Eddie Morlan FG .20 .50
BDPP73 Greg Golson FG .20 .50
BDPP74 Julio Pimentel FG .20 .50
BDPP75 Dexter Fowler FG .20 .50
BDPP76 Henry Rodriguez FG .20 .50
BDPP77 Cliff Pennington FG .20 .50
BDPP78 Hector Rondon FG .20 .50
BDPP79 Wes Hodges FG .20 .50
BDPP80 Polin Trinidad FG .20 .50
BDPP81 Chris Getz FG .20 .50
BDPP82 Welington Castillo FG .20 .50
BDPP83 Mat Gamel FG .50 1.25
BDPP84 Pablo Sandoval FG 1.25 3.00
BDPP85 Jason Donald FG .20 .50
BDPP86 Jesus Montero FG 1.50 4.00
BDPP87 Jamie D'Antona FG .20 .50
BDPP88 Will Inman FG .20 .50
BDPP89 Elvis Andrus FG .30 .75
BDPP90 Taylor Teagarden FG .30 .75
BDPP91 Scott Campbell FG .20 .50
BDPP92 Jake Arrieta FG .20 .50
BDPP93 Juan Francisco FG .50 1.25
BDPP94 Lou Marson FG .20 .50
BDPP95 Luke Hughes FG .20 .50
BDPP96 Bryan Anderson FG .20 .50
BDPP97 Ramiro Pena FG .20 .50
BDPP98 Jesse Todd FG .20 .50
BDPP99 Gorkys Hernandez FG .20 .50
BDPP100 Casey Weathers FG .20 .50
BDPP101 Fernando Martinez FG .30 .75
BDPP102 Clayton Richard FG .20 .50
BDPP103 Gerardo Parra FG .20 .50
BDPP104 Kevin Pucetas FG .30 .75
BDPP105 Wilkin Ramirez FG .20 .50
BDPP106 Ryan Mattheus FG .20 .50
BDPP107 Angel Villalona FG .50 1.25
BDPP108 Brett Anderson FG .30 .75
BDPP109 Chris Valaika FG .20 .50
BDPP110 Trevor Cahill FG .50 1.25

2008 Bowman Draft Prospects Blue

*BLUE: 1.5X TO 4X BASIC
STATED ODDS 1:19 HOBBY
STATED PRINT RUN 399 SER.#'d SETS

2008 Bowman Draft Prospects Gold

*GOLD: .75X TO 2X BASIC
APPX.GOLD ODDS ONE PER PACK

2008 Bowman Draft Prospects Red

STATED ODDS 1:6025 HOBBY
STATED PRINT RUN 1 SER.#'d SET
NO PRICING DUE TO SCARCITY

2008 Bowman Draft Prospects Jerseys

RANDOM INSERTS IN RETAIL PACKS
NO PRICING DUE TO LACK OF MARKET INFO
BDPP68 Jesus Delgado FG
BDPP69 Andrew McCutchen FG
BDPP70 Shairon Martis FG
BDPP71 Matt LaPorta FG 3.00 8.00
BDPP72 Eddie Morlan FG
BDPP74 Julio Pimentel FG
BDPP75 Dexter Fowler FG 3.00 8.00
BDPP77 Cliff Pennington FG
BDPP80 Polin Trinidad FG
BDPP82 Welington Castillo FG
BDPP87 Jamie D'Antona FG
BDPP88 Will Inman FG
BDPP93 Juan Francisco FG
BDPP94 Lou Marson FG
BDPP96 Bryan Anderson FG
BDPP97 Ramiro Pena FG
BDPP98 Jesse Todd FG
BDPP102 Clayton Richard FG
BDPP103 Gerardo Parra FG
BDPP105 Wilkin Ramirez FG

2008 Bowman Draft Signs of the Future

RANDOM INSERTS IN RETAIL PACKS
AC Adrain Cardenas 4.00 10.00
BP Billy Petrick 3.00 8.00
BS Brad Salmon 3.00 8.00
CW Corey Wimberly 6.00 15.00
DM Daniel Murphy 15.00 40.00
DS David Shafer 3.00 8.00
EM Evan MaClane 3.00 8.00
FG Freddy Galvis 8.00 20.00
GK George Kontos 3.00 8.00
JW Johnny Whittleman 3.00 8.00
KD Kyle Drabek 6.00 15.00
OP Omar Poveda 3.00 8.00
OS Oswaldo Sosa 3.00 8.00
TD Travis D'Arnaud 3.00 8.00
TS Travis Snider 5.00 12.00

2009 Bowman Draft

COMPLETE SET (55) 6.00 15.00
COMMON CARD (1-55) .20 .50
OVERALL PLATE ODDS 1:1531 HOBBY
PLATE PRINT RUN 1 SET PER COLOR
BLACK-CYAN-MAGENTA-YELLOW ISSUED
NO PLATE PRICING DUE TO SCARCITY
BDP1 Tommy Hanson RC .60 1.50
BDP2 Jeff Manship RC .20 .50
BDP3 Trevor Bell (RC) .20 .50
BDP4 Trevor Cahill RC .50 1.25
BDP5 Trent Oeltjen (RC) .20 .50
BDP6 Wyatt Toregas RC .20 .50
BDP7 Kevin Mulvey RC .20 .50
BDP8 Rusty Ryal RC .20 .50
BDP9 Mike Carp (RC) .30 .75
BDP10 Jorge Padilla (RC) .20 .50
BDP11 J.D. Martin (RC) .20 .50
BDP12 Dusty Ryan RC .20 .50
BDP13 Alex Avila RC .30 .75
BDP14 Brandon Allen (RC) .20 .50
BDP15 Tommy Everidge (RC) .30 .75
BDP16 Bud Norris RC .20 .50
BDP17 Neftali Feliz RC .60 1.50
BDP18 Mat Latos RC .60 1.50
BDP19 Ryan Perry RC .50 1.25
BDP20 Craig Tatum (RC) .20 .50
BDP21 Chris Tillman RC .30 .75
BDP22 Jhoulys Chacin RC .30 .75
BDP23 Michael Saunders RC .30 .75
BDP24 Jeff Stevens RC .20 .50
BDP25 Luis Valdez RC .20 .50
BDP26 Robert Manuel RC .20 .50
BDP27 Ryan Webb (RC) .20 .50
BDP28 Marc Rzepczynski RC .30 .75
BDP29 Travis Schlichting (RC) .30 .75
BDP30 Barbaro Canizares RC .20 .50
BDP31 Brad Mills RC .20 .50
BDP32 Dusty Brown (RC) .20 .50
BDP33 Tim Wood RC .20 .50
BDP34 Drew Sutton RC .30 .75
BDP35 Jarrett Hoffpauir (RC) .20 .50
BDP36 Jose Lobaton RC .20 .50
BDP37 Aaron Bates RC .20 .50
BDP38 Clayton Mortensen RC .20 .50
BDP39 Ryan Sadowski RC .20 .50
BDP40 Fu-Te Ni RC .30 .75
BDP41 Casey McGehee (RC) .20 .50
BDP42 Omir Santos RC .20 .50
BDP43 Brent Leach RC .30 .75
BDP44 Diory Hernandez RC .20 .50
BDP45 Wilkin Castillo RC .20 .50
BDP46 Trevor Crowe RC .20 .50
BDP47 Sean West (RC) .30 .75
BDP48 Clayton Richard (RC) .20 .50
BDP49 Julio Borbon RC .30 .75
BDP50 Kyle Blanks RC .30 .75
BDP51 Jeff Gray RC .20 .50
BDP52 Gio Gonzalez (RC) .20 .50
BDP53 Vin Mazzaro RC .20 .50
BDP54 Josh Reddick RC .30 .75
BDP55 Fernando Martinez RC .50 1.25

2009 Bowman Draft Blue

*BLUE: 1.5X TO 4X BASIC
STATED ODDS 1:12 HOBBY
STATED PRINT RUN 399 SER.#'d SETS

2009 Bowman Draft Gold

*GOLD: .75X TO 2X BASIC
APPX.GOLD ODDS ONE PER PACK

2009 Bowman Draft Red

STATED ODDS 1:4266 HOBBY
STATED PRINT RUN 1 SER.#'d SET
NO PRICING DUE TO SCARCITY

2009 Bowman Draft AFLAC Autographs

STATED ODDS 1:238 HOBBY
PRINT RUNS B/WN 142-248 COPIES PER
1 Brooks Pounders/240 10.00 25.00
2 Jiovanni Mier/245 15.00 40.00
3 Max Stassi/174 20.00 50.00
4 Zack Wheeler/244 30.00 60.00
5 Neil Ramirez/240 12.50 30.00
6 Robert Stock/236 15.00 40.00
7 Sequoyah Stonecipher/248 12.50 30.00
8 Donovan Tate/244 40.00 80.00
9 Tyler Matzek/244 30.00 60.00
10 D.J. Lemahieu/142 15.00 40.00
11 David Nick/243 15.00 40.00
12 Matthew Davidson/206 15.00 40.00
13 Wesley Freeman/231 8.00 20.00

2009 Bowman Draft Prospect Autographs

RANDOM INSERTS IN RETAIL PACKS
AH Anthony Hewitt 5.00 12.00
AM Adam Moore
BH Brad Hand 3.00 8.00
BP Buster Posey 30.00 60.00
JK Jason Knapp 6.00 15.00
LC Lonnie Chisenhall 4.00 10.00
LM Logan Morrison 12.50 30.00
MI Michael Inoa 3.00 8.00
MM Michael Moustakas 10.00 25.00
ZC Zach Collier 5.00 12.00

2009 Bowman Draft Prospects

COMPLETE SET (75) 8.00 20.00
OVERALL PLATE ODDS 1:1531 HOBBY
PLATE PRINT RUN 1 SET PER COLOR
BLACK-CYAN-MAGENTA-YELLOW ISSUED
NO PLATE PRICING DUE TO SCARCITY
BDPP1 Tanner Bushue .30 .75
BDPP2 Billy Hamilton 1.25 3.00
BDPP3 Enrique Hernandez .20 .50
BDPP4 Virgil Hill .20 .50
BDPP5 Josh Hodges .30 .75
BDPP6 Christopher Lovett .20 .50
BDPP7 Michael Belfiore .20 .50
BDPP8 Jobduan Morales .20 .50
BDPP9 Anthony Morris .20 .50
BDPP10 Telvin Nash .30 .75
BDPP11 Brooks Pounders .30 .75
BDPP12 Kyle Rose .20 .50
BDPP13 Seth Schwindenhammer .30 .75
BDPP14 Patrick Lehman .30 .75
BDPP15 Mathew Weaver .30 .75
BDPP16 Brian Dozier .20 .50
BDPP17 Sequoyah Stonecipher .30 .75
BDPP18 Shannon Wilkerson .20 .50
BDPP19 Jerry Sullivan .20 .50
BDPP20 Jamie Johnson .20 .50
BDPP21 Kent Matthes .20 .50
BDPP22 Ben Paulsen .20 .50
BDPP23 Matthew Davidson .30 .75
BDPP24 Benjamin Carlson .20 .50
BDPP25 Brock Holt .20 .50
BDPP26 Ben Orloff .20 .50
BDPP27 D.J. LeMahieu .30 .75
BDPP28 Erik Castro .30 .75
BDPP29 James Jones .20 .50
BDPP30 Cory Burns .20 .50
BDPP31 Chris Wade .20 .50
BDPP32 Jaff Decker .30 .75
BDPP33 Naoya Washiya .20 .50
BDPP34 Brandt Walker .20 .50
BDPP35 Jordan Henry .30 .75
BDPP36 Austin Adams .20 .50
BDPP37 Andrew Bellatti .30 .75
BDPP38 Paul Applebee .30 .75
BDPP39 Robert Stock .30 .75
BDPP40 Michael Flacco .20 .50
BDPP41 Jonathan Meyer .20 .50
BDPP42 Cody Rogers .30 .75
BDPP43 Matt Heidenreich .20 .50
BDPP44 David Holmberg .50 1.25
BDPP45 Mycal Jones .20 .50
BDPP46 David Hale .20 .50
BDPP47 Dusty Odenbach .20 .50
BDPP48 Robert Hefflinger .20 .50
BDPP49 Buddy Baumann .20 .50
BDPP50 Thomas Berryhill .20 .50
BDPP51 Darrell Ceciliani .20 .50
BDPP52 Derek McCallum .20 .50
BDPP53 Taylor Freeman .20 .50
BDPP54 Tyler Townsend .30 .75
BDPP55 Tobias Streich .30 .75
BDPP56 Ryan Jackson .20 .50
BDPP57 Chris Herrmann .30 .75
BDPP58 Robert Shields .20 .50
BDPP59 Devin Fuller .20 .50
BDPP60 Brad Stillings .20 .50
BDPP61 Ryan Goins .20 .50
BDPP62 Chase Austin .20 .50
BDPP63 Brett Nommensen .20 .50
BDPP64 Egan Smith .20 .50
BDPP65 Daniel Mahoney .20 .50
BDPP66 Darin Gorski .20 .50
BDPP67 Dustin Dickerson .30 .75
BDPP68 Victor Black .30 .75
BDPP69 Dallas Keuchel .30 .75
BDPP70 Nate Baker .20 .50
BDPP71 David Nick .30 .75
BDPP72 Brian Moran .20 .50
BDPP73 Mark Fleury .20 .50
BDPP74 Brett Wallach .30 .75
BDPP75 Adam Buschini .20 .50

2009 Bowman Draft Prospects Blue

*BLUE: 1.5X TO 4X BASIC
STATED ODDS 1:12 HOBBY
STATED PRINT RUN 399 SER.#'d SETS

2009 Bowman Draft Prospects Gold

*GOLD: .75X TO 2X BASIC
APPX.GOLD ODDS ONE PER PACK

2009 Bowman Draft Prospects Red

STATED ODDS 1:4266 HOBBY
STATED PRINT RUN 1 SER.#'d SET
NO PRICING DUE TO SCARCITY

2009 Bowman Draft WBC Prospects

COMPLETE SET (35) 6.00 15.00
OVERALL PLATE ODDS 1:1531 HOBBY
PLATE PRINT RUN 1 SET PER COLOR
BLACK-CYAN-MAGENTA-YELLOW ISSUED
NO PLATE PRICING DUE TO SCARCITY
BDPW1 Ichiro Suzuki .75 2.00
BDPW2 Yu Darvish 2.00 5.00
BDPW3 Phillippe Aumont .50 1.25
BDPW4 Derek Jeter 1.25 3.00
BDPW5 Dustin Pedroia .60 1.50
BDPW6 Earl Agnoly .20 .50
BDPW7 Jose Reyes .30 .75
BDPW8 Michel Enriquez .20 .50
BDPW9 David Ortiz .30 .75
BDPW10 Chunhua Dong .30 .75
BDPW11 Munenori Kawasaki .50 1.25
BDPW12 Arquimedes Nieto .20 .50
BDPW13 Bernie Williams .30 .75
BDPW14 Pedro Lazo .20 .50
BDPW15 Jing-Chao Wang .30 .75
BDPW16 Chris Barnwell .20 .50
BDPW17 Elmer Dessens .20 .50
BDPW18 Russell Martin .20 .50
BDPW19 Luca Panerati .20 .50
BDPW20 Adam Dunn .30 .75
BDPW21 Andy Gonzalez .20 .50
BDPW22 Daisuke Matsuzaka .50 1.25
BDPW23 Daniel Berg .20 .50
BDPW24 Aroldis Chapman .75 2.00
BDPW25 Justin Morneau .50 1.25
BDPW26 Miguel Cabrera .50 1.25
BDPW27 Magglio Ordonez .30 .75
BDPW28 Shawn Bowman .20 .50
BDPW29 Robbie Cordemans .20 .50
BDPW30 Paolo Espino .20 .50
BDPW31 Chipper Jones .50 1.25
BDPW32 Frederich Cepeda .30 .75
BDPW33 Ubaldo Jimenez .30 .75
BDPW34 Seiichi Uchikawa .30 .75
BDPW35 Norichika Aoki .30 .75

2009 Bowman Draft WBC Prospects Blue

*BLUE: 1.5X TO 4X BASIC
STATED ODDS 1:12 HOBBY
STATED PRINT RUN 399 SER.#'d SETS

2009 Bowman Draft WBC Prospects Gold

*GOLD: .75X TO 2X BASIC
APPX.GOLD ODDS ONE PER PACK

2009 Bowman Draft WBC Prospects Red

STATED ODDS 1:4266 HOBBY
STATED PRINT RUN 1 SER.#'d SET
NO PRICING DUE TO SCARCITY

2009 Bowman AFLAC

DISTRIBUTED AT 2009 AFLAC GAME
AC Andrew Cole 4.00 10.00
AS Aaron Sanchez 3.00 8.00
AV A.J. Vanegas 2.00 5.00
AW Austin Wilson 4.00 10.00
BH Bryce Harper 75.00 150.00
BR Brian Ragira 2.00 5.00
BS Brandon Stephens 2.00 5.00
CB Cameron Bedrosian 5.00 12.00
CC Chevez Clarke 3.00 8.00
CG Conrad Gregor 2.00 5.00
CN Connor Narron 2.00 5.00
DC Dylan Covey 4.00 10.00
DS DeAndre Smelter 4.00 10.00
JJ Jacoby Jones 2.00 5.00
JL Jared Lakind 2.00 5.00
JO Justin O'Conner 5.00 12.00
JS Josh Sale 4.00 10.00
JT Jameson Taillon 12.50 30.00
KB1 Krey Bratsen 4.00 10.00
KB2 Kris Bryant 4.00 10.00
KC Kaleb Cowart 4.00 10.00
KG Kevin Gausman 2.00 5.00
KS Kellen Sweeney 2.00 5.00
KW Karsten Whitson 4.00 10.00
MA Michael Arencibia 2.00 5.00
ML1 Matt Lipka 2.00 5.00
ML2 Marcus Littlewood 4.00 10.00
ML3 Michael Lorenzen 2.00 5.00
PT Peter Tago 4.00 10.00
RA Robert Aviles 2.00 5.00
RG Reggie Golden 4.00 10.00
SA Stetson Allie 4.00 10.00
SR Shane Rowland 2.00 5.00
SS Stefan Sabol 4.00 10.00
TA Tyler Austin 2.00 5.00
TG Trey Griffin 4.00 10.00
TS Tyler Shreve 2.00 5.00
TW Tony Wolters 3.00 8.00
YC Yordy Cabrera 5.00 12.00
ZA Zach Alvord 2.00 5.00

2010 Bowman Draft

COMPLETE SET (110) 8.00 20.00
COMMON CARD (1-110) .20 .50
PLATE PRINT RUN 1 SET PER COLOR
BLACK-CYAN-MAGENTA-YELLOW ISSUED
NO PLATE PRICING DUE TO SCARCITY
BDP1 Stephen Strasburg RC 1.25 3.00
BDP2 Josh Bell (RC) .20 .50
BDP3 Ivan Nova RC 1.00 2.50
BDP4 Starlin Castro RC .75 2.00
BDP5 John Axford RC .20 .50
BDP6 Colin Curtis RC .20 .50
BDP7 Brennan Boesch RC .50 1.25
BDP8 Ike Davis RC .50 1.25
BDP9 Madison Bumgarner RC .50 1.25
BDP10 Austin Jackson RC .30 .75
BDP11 Andrew Cashner RC .20 .50
BDP12 Jose Tabata RC .50 1.25
BDP13 Wade Davis (RC) .20 .50
BDP14 Ian Desmond (RC) .30 .75
BDP15 Felix Doubront RC .20 .50
BDP16 Danny Worth RC .20 .50
BDP17 John Ely RC .20 .50
BDP18 Jon Jay RC .30 .75
BDP19 Mike Leake RC .60 1.50
BDP20 Daniel Nava RC .30 .75
BDP21 Brad Lincoln RC .30 .75
BDP22 Jonathan Lucroy RC .20 .50
BDP23 Brian Matusz RC .50 1.25
BDP24 Chris Nelson (RC) .30 .75
BDP25 Andy Oliver RC .20 .50
BDP26 Adam Ottavino RC .20 .50
BDP27 Trevor Plouffe (RC) .20 .50
BDP28 Vance Worley RC .75 2.00
BDP29 Daniel McCutchen RC .30 .75
BDP30 Mike Stanton RC .75 2.00
BDP31 Drew Storen RC .30 .75
BDP32 Tyler Colvin RC .30 .75
BDP33 Travis Wood (RC) .30 .75
BDP34 Eric Young Jr. (RC) .20 .50
BDP35 Sam Demel RC .20 .50
BDP36 Welington Castillo RC .20 .50
BDP37 Sam LeCure (RC) .20 .50
BDP38 Danny Valencia RC 1.25 3.00
BDP39 Fernando Salas RC .20 .50
BDP40 Jason Heyward RC 1.25 3.00
BDP41 Jake Arrieta RC .30 .75
BDP42 Kevin Russo RC .20 .50
BDP43 Josh Donaldson RC .20 .50
BDP44 Luis Atilano RC .20 .50
BDP45 Jason Donald RC .20 .50
BDP46 Jonny Venters RC .20 .50
BDP47 Bryan Anderson (RC) .20 .50
BDP48 Jay Sborz (RC) .20 .50
BDP49 Chris Heisey RC .30 .75
BDP50 Daniel Hudson RC .30 .75
BDP51 Ruben Tejada RC .30 .75
BDP52 Jeffrey Marquez RC .30 .75
BDP53 Brandon Hicks RC .30 .75
BDP54 Jeanmar Gomez RC .30 .75
BDP55 Erik Kratz RC .30 .75
BDP56 Lorenzo Cain RC .30 .75
BDP57 Jhan Marinez RC .20 .50
BDP58 Omar Beltre (RC) .20 .50
BDP59 Drew Stubbs RC .50 1.25
BDP60 Alex Sanabia RC .20 .50
BDP61 Buster Posey RC 2.00 5.00
BDP62 Anthony Slama RC .20 .50
BDP63 Brad Davis RC .20 .50
BDP64 Logan Morrison RC .30 .75
BDP65 Luke Hughes (RC) .20 .50
BDP66 Thomas Diamond (RC) .20 .50
BDP67 Tommy Manzella (RC) .20 .50
BDP68 Jordan Smith RC .20 .50
BDP69 Carlos Santana RC .60 1.50
BDP70 Domonic Brown RC .75 2.00
BDP71 Scott Sizemore RC .30 .75
BDP72 Jordan Brown RC .20 .50
BDP73 Josh Thole RC .30 .75
BDP74 Jordan Norberto RC .20 .50
BDP75 Dayan Viciedo RC .30 .75
BDP76 Josh Tomlin RC .50 1.25
BDP77 Adam Moore RC .20 .50
BDP78 Kenley Jansen RC .75 2.00
BDP79 Juan Francisco RC .30 .75
BDP80 Blake Wood RC .20 .50
BDP81 John Hester RC .20 .50
BDP82 Lucas Harrell (RC) .20 .50
BDP83 Neil Walker (RC) .30 .75
BDP84 Cesar Valdez RC .20 .50
BDP85 Lance Zawadzki RC .20 .50
BDP86 Rommie Lewis RC .20 .50
BDP87 Steve Tolleson RC .20 .50
BDP88 Jeff Frazier (RC) .20 .50
BDP89 Drew Butera (RC) .20 .50
BDP90 Michael Brantley RC .20 .50
BDP91 Mitch Moreland RC .30 .75
BDP92 Alex Burnett RC .20 .50
BDP93 Allen Craig RC .50 1.25
BDP94 Sergio Santos (RC) .20 .50
BDP95 Matt Carson (RC) .20 .50
BDP96 Jenrry Mejia RC .30 .75
BDP97 Rhyne Hughes RC .20 .50
BDP98 Tyson Ross RC .20 .50
BDP99 Argenis Diaz RC .30 .75
BDP100 Hisanori Takahashi RC .30 .75
BDP101 Cole Gillespie RC .20 .50
BDP102 Ryan Kalish RC .30 .75
BDP103 J.P. Arencibia RC .30 .75
BDP104 Peter Bourjos RC .30 .75
BDP105 Justin Turner RC .20 .50
BDP106 Michael Dunn RC .20 .50
BDP107 Mike McCoy RC .20 .50
BDP108 Will Rhymes RC .20 .50
BDP109 Wilson Ramos RC .50 1.25
BDP110 Josh Butler RC .20 .50

2010 Bowman Draft Blue

*BLUE: 1.5X TO 4X BASIC
STATED PRINT RUN 399 SER.#'d SETS

2010 Bowman Draft Gold

*GOLD: 1X TO 2.5X BASIC

2010 Bowman Draft Red

STATED PRINT RUN 1 SER.#'d SET
NO PRICING DUE TO SCARCITY

2010 Bowman Draft AFLAC Autographs

PRINT RUNS B/WN 22-230 COPIES PER
NO TURNER PRICING AVAILABLE
1 Luke Bailey/230 10.00 25.00
2 Tim Beckham/127 60.00 120.00
3 Chevez Clarke/35 75.00 150.00
4 Christian Colon/49 150.00 250.00
5 Kaleb Cowart/230 30.00 60.00
6 Scooter Gennett/230 8.00 20.00
7 Mychal Givens/230 8.00 20.00
8 Yasmani Grandal/230 30.00 60.00
9 Bryce Harper/230 800.00 1000.00
10 Matt Harvey/230 40.00 80.00
11 Slade Heathcott/81 40.00 80.00
12 BJ Hermsen/127 8.00 20.00
13 Ian Krol/127 12.50 30.00
14 Matt Lipka/37 60.00 120.00
15 Justin O'Conner/230 20.00 50.00
16 Cameron Rupp/43 30.00 60.00
17 Josh Sale/230 60.00 120.00
18 Keyvius Sampson/127 20.00 50.00
19 Aaron Sanchez/38 40.00 80.00
20 Jonathan Singleton/127 125.00 250.00
21 Peter Tago/230 20.00 50.00
22 Jameson Taillon/230 75.00 150.00
23 Jacob Turner/22
24 Daniel Tuttle/106 8.00 20.00
25 Everett Williams/127 20.00 50.00

2010 Bowman Draft Prospect Autographs

AL Andrew Liebel 3.00 8.00
AR Anthony Rizzo 8.00 20.00
BS Bryan Shaw 3.00 8.00
CG Conor Graham 3.00 8.00
DT Donavan Tate 6.00 15.00
EK Eddie Kunz 3.00 8.00
GH Graham Hicks 3.00 8.00
JJ Jake Jefferies 6.00 15.00
JM Jiovanni Mier 3.00 8.00
JP Jason Place 4.00 10.00
MH Matt Hobgood 3.00 8.00
MM Mike Montgomery 4.00 10.00
MY Michael Ynoa 3.00 8.00
NC Nick Carr 3.00 8.00
RC Ryan Chaffee 3.00 8.00
RG Randal Grichuk 3.00 8.00
RM Ryan Mattheus 3.00 8.00
SG Steve Garrison 3.00 8.00
SH Slade Heathcott 5.00 12.00
SP Shane Peterson 3.00 8.00
ZM Zach McAllister 3.00 8.00
JPI Julio Pimentel 3.00 8.00

2010 Bowman Draft Prospect Autographs Blue

*BLUE: .75X TO 2X BASIC
STATED PRINT RUN 199 SER.#'d SETS

2010 Bowman Draft Prospect Autographs Red

*RED: 1.2X TO 3X BASIC
STATED PRINT RUN 50 SER.#'d SETS

2010 Bowman Draft Prospects

PLATE PRINT RUN 1 SET PER COLOR
BLACK-CYAN-MAGENTA-YELLOW ISSUED
NO PLATE PRICING DUE TO SCARCITY
BDPP1 Sam Tuivailala .25 .60
BDPP2 Alex Burgos .25 .60
BDPP3 Henry Ramos .40 1.00
BDPP4 Pat Dean .40 1.00
BDPP5 Ryan Brett .25 .60
BDPP6 Jesse Biddle .60 1.50
BDPP7 Leon Landry .40 1.00
BDPP8 Ryan LaMarre .25 .60
BDPP9 Josh Rutledge .15 .40
BDPP10 Tyler Thornburg .25 .60
BDPP11 Carter Jurica .15 .40
BDPP12 J.R. Bradley .15 .40
BDPP13 Devin Lohman .15 .40
BDPP14 Addison Reed .15 .40
BDPP15 Micah Gibbs .25 .60
BDPP16 Derek Dietrich .50 1.25
BDPP18 Stephen Pryor .15 .40
BDPP19 Eddie Rosario .25 .60
BDPP20 Blake Forsythe .15 .40
BDPP21 Rangel Ravelo .15 .40
BDPP22 Nick Longmire .25 .60
BDPP23 Andrelton Simmons .25 .60
BDPP24 Chad Bettis .15 .40
BDPP25 Peter Tago .25 .60
BDPP26 Tyrell Jenkins .40 1.00
BDPP27 Marcus Knecht .15 .40
BDPP28 Seth Blair .25 .60
BDPP29 Brodie Greene .15 .40
BDPP30 Jason Martinson .15 .40
BDPP31 Bryan Morgado .25 .60
BDPP32 Eric Cantrell .15 .40
BDPP33 Niko Goodrum .25 .60
BDPP34 Bobby Doran .15 .40
BDPP35 Cody Wheeler .15 .40
BDPP36 Cole Leonida .15 .40
BDPP37 Nate Roberts .15 .40
BDPP38 Dave Filak .15 .40
BDPP39 Taijuan Walker .50 1.25
BDPP40 Hayden Simpson .25 .60
BDPP41 Cameron Rupp .25 .60
BDPP42 Ben Heath .15 .40
BDPP43 Tyler Waldron .15 .40
BDPP44 Greg Garcia .15 .40
BDPP45 Vincent Velasquez .25 .60
BDPP46 Jake Lemmerman .50 1.25
BDPP47 Russell Wilson .75 2.00
BDPP48 Cody Stanley .15 .40
BDPP49 Matt Suschak .15 .40
BDPP50 Logan Darnell .15 .40
BDPP51 Kevin Keyes .15 .40
BDPP52 Thomas Royse .15 .40
BDPP53 Scott Alexander .15 .40
BDPP54 Tony Thompson .15 .40
BDPP55 Seth Rosin .25 .60
BDPP56 Mickey Wiswall .15 .40
BDPP57 Albert Almora .25 .60
BDPP58 Cole Billingsley .25 .60
BDPP58 Cody Hawn .25 .60
BDPP59 Drew Vettleson .25 .60
BDPP60 Matt Lipka .60 1.50
BDPP61 Michael Choice .25 .60
BDPP62 Zack Cox .50 1.25
BDPP63 Bryce Brentz .40 1.00
BDPP64 Chance Ruffin .15 .40
BDPP65 Mike Olt .40 1.00
BDPP66 Kellin Deglan .15 .40
BDPP67 Yasmani Grandal .40 1.00
BDPP68 Kolbrin Vitek .40 1.00
BDPP69 Justin O'Conner .15 .40
BDPP70 Gary Brown .40 1.00
BDPP71 Mike Foltynewicz .25 .60
BDPP72 Chevez Clarke .25 .60
BDPP73 Cito Culver .25 .60
BDPP74 Aaron Sanchez .25 .60
BDPP75 Noah Syndergaard .25 .60
BDPP76 Taylor Lindsey .25 .60
BDPP77 Josh Sale .50 1.25
BDPP78 Christian Yelich .25 .60
BDPP79 Jameson Taillon .60 1.50
BDPP80 Manny Machado 1.25 3.00
BDPP81 Christian Colon .25 .60
BDPP82 Drew Pomeranz .50 1.25
BDPP83 Delino DeShields .25 .60
BDPP84 Matt Harvey .60 1.50
BDPP85 Ryan Bolden .15 .40
BDPP86 Deck McGuire .25 .60
BDPP87 Zach Lee .40 1.00
BDPP88 Alex Wimmers .25 .60
BDPP89 Kaleb Cowart .25 .60

BDPP90 Mike Kvansnicka	.15	.40
BDPP91 Jake Skole	.25	.60
BDPP92 Chris Sale	.40	1.00
BDPP93 Sean Brady	.15	.40
BDPP94 Marc Brakeman	.15	.40
BDPP95 Alex Bregman	.25	.60
BDPP96 Ryan Burr	.25	.60
BDPP97 Chris Chinea	.25	.60
BDPP98 Troy Conyers	.15	.40
BDPP99 Zach Green	.15	.40
BDPP100 Carson Kelly	.15	.40
BDPP101 Timmy Lopes	.15	.40
BDPP102 Adrian Marin	.25	.60
BDPP103 Chris Okey	.15	.40
BDPP104 Matt Olson	.15	.40
BDPP105 Ivan Pelaez	.15	.40
BDPP106 Felipe Perez	.15	.40
BDPP107 Nelson Rodriguez	.15	.40
BDPP108 Corey Seager	.25	.60
BDPP109 Lucas Sims	.15	.40
BDPP110 Nick Travieso	.25	.60

2010 Bowman Draft Prospects Blue

*BLUE: 2X TO 5X BASIC
STATED PRINT RUN 399 SER.#'d SETS

2010 Bowman Draft Prospects Gold

*GOLD: 1X TO 2.5X BASIC

2010 Bowman Draft Prospects Red

STATED PRINT RUN 1 SER.#'d SET
NO PRICING DUE TO SCARCITY

2010 Bowman Draft USA Baseball Jerseys

STATED PRINT RUN 949 SER.#'d SETS

USAR1 Albert Almora	3.00	8.00
USAR2 Cole Billingsley	3.00	8.00
USAR3 Sean Brady	4.00	10.00
USAR4 Marc Brakeman	3.00	8.00
USAR5 Alex Bregman	4.00	10.00
USAR6 Ryan Burr	3.00	8.00
USAR7 Chris Chinea	4.00	10.00
USAR8 Troy Conyers	3.00	8.00
USAR9 Zach Green	3.00	8.00
USAR10 Carson Kelly	3.00	8.00
USAR11 Timmy Lopes	3.00	8.00
USAR12 Adrian Marin	3.00	8.00
USAR13 Chris Okey	3.00	8.00
USAR14 Matt Olson	3.00	8.00
USAR15 Ivan Pelaez	3.00	8.00
USAR16 Felipe Perez	3.00	8.00
USAR17 Nelson Rodriguez	3.00	8.00
USAR18 Corey Seager	3.00	8.00
USAR19 Lucas Sims	3.00	8.00
USAR20 Sheldon Neuse	3.00	8.00

2010 Bowman Draft USA Baseball Jerseys Blue

*BLUE: .5X TO 1.2X BASIC
STATED PRINT RUN 199 SER.#'d SETS

2010 Bowman Draft USA Baseball Jerseys Red

*RED: .6X TO 1.5X BASIC
STATED PRINT RUN 50 SER.#'d SETS

2011 Bowman Draft

COMPLETE SET (110)	8.00	20.00
COMMON CARD (1-110)	.20	.50
STATED PLATE ODDS 1:928 HOBBY		
PLATE PRINT RUN 1 SET PER COLOR		
BLACK-CYAN-MAGENTA-YELLOW ISSUED		
NO PLATE PRICING DUE TO SCARCITY		
1 Mike Moustakas RC	.50	1.25
2 Ryan Adams RC	.20	.50
3 Alexi Amarista RC	.20	.50
4 Anthony Bass RC	.20	.50
5 Pedro Beato RC	.20	.50
6 Bruce Billings RC	.20	.50
7 Charlie Blackmon RC	.20	.50
8 Brian Broderick RC	.20	.50
9 Rex Brothers RC	.20	.50
10 Tyler Chatwood RC	.20	.50
11 Jose Altuve RC	.30	.75
12 Salvador Perez RC	.30	.75
13 Mark Hamburger RC	.20	.50
14 Matt Carpenter RC	.30	.75
15 Ezequiel Carrera RC	.20	.50
16 Jose Ceda RC	.20	.50
17 Andrew Brown RC	.30	.75
18 Maikel Cleto RC	.20	.50
19 Steve Cishek RC	.20	.50
20 Lonnie Chisenhall RC	.30	.75
21 Henry Sosa RC	.20	.50
22 Tim Collins RC	.20	.50
23 Josh Collmenter RC	.20	.50
24 David Cooper RC	.20	.50
25 Brandon Crawford RC	.20	.50
26 Brandon Laird RC	.30	.75
27 Tony Cruz RC	.50	1.25
28 Chase d'Arnaud RC	.30	.75
29 Fautino De Los Santos RC	.20	.50
30 Rubby De La Rosa RC	.50	1.25
31 Andy Dirks RC	.20	.50
32 Jarrod Dyson RC	.20	.50
33 Cody Eppley RC	.20	.50
34 Logan Forsythe RC	.20	.50
35 Todd Frazier RC	.30	.75
36 Eric Fryer RC	.30	.75
37 Charlie Furbush RC	.20	.50
38 Cory Gearrin RC	.20	.50
39 Graham Godfrey RC	.20	.50
40 Dee Gordon RC	.50	1.25
41 Brandon Gomes RC	.20	.50
42 Bryan Shaw RC	.20	.50
43 Brandon Guyer RC	.30	.75
44 Mark Hamilton RC	.30	.75
45 Brad Hand RC	.20	.50
46 Anthony Recker RC	.20	.50
47 Jeremy Horst RC	.30	.75
48 Tommy Hottovy (RC)	.30	.75
49 Jose Iglesias RC	.30	.75
50 Craig Kimbrel RC	.50	1.25
51 Josh Judy RC	.20	.50
52 Cole Kimball RC	.20	.50
53 Alan Johnson RC	.20	.50
54 Brandon Kintzler RC	.20	.50
55 Pete Kozma RC	.50	1.25
56 D.J. LeMahieu RC	.20	.50
57 Duane Below RC	.30	.75
58 Josh Lindblom RC	.30	.75
59 Zack Cozart RC	.50	1.25
60 Al Alburquerque RC	.20	.50
61 Trystan Magnuson RC	.20	.50
62 Michael Martinez RC	.30	.75
63 Michael McKenry RC	.30	.75
64 Daniel Moskos RC	.20	.50
65 Lance Lynn RC	.20	.50
66 Juan Nicasio RC	.20	.50
67 Joe Paterson RC	.30	.75
68 Lance Pendleton RC	.20	.50
69 Luis Perez RC	.20	.50
70 Anthony Rizzo RC	.30	.75
71 Joel Carreno RC	.20	.50
72 Alex Presley RC	.50	1.25
73 Vinnie Pestano RC	.20	.50
74 Aneury Rodriguez RC	.20	.50
75 Josh Rodriguez RC	.20	.50
76 Eduardo Sanchez RC	.30	.75
77 Matt Young RC	.20	.50
78 Amauri Sanit RC	.20	.50
79 Nathan Eovaldi RC	.20	.50
80 Javy Guerra (RC)	.30	.75
81 Eric Sogard RC	.20	.50
82 Henderson Alvarez RC	.20	.50
83 Ryan Lavarnway RC	.50	1.25
84 Michael Stutes RC	.30	.75
85 Everett Teaford RC	.20	.50
86 Blake Tekotte RC	.20	.50
87 Eric Thames RC	.20	.50
88 Arodys Vizcaino RC	.20	.50
89 Rene Tosoni RC	.20	.50
90 Alex White RC	.20	.50
91 Brayan Villarreal RC	.20	.50
92 Tony Watson RC	.20	.50
93 Johnny Giavotella RC	.20	.50
94 Kevin Whelan (RC)	.20	.50
95 Mike Nickeas (RC)	.20	.50
96 Elih Villanueva RC	.20	.50
97 Tom Wilhelmsen RC	.20	.50
98 Adam Wilk RC	.30	.75
99 Mike Wilson (RC)	.20	.50
100 Jerry Sands RC	.75	2.00
101 Mike Trout RC	1.25	3.00
102 Kyle Weiland RC	.20	.50
103 Kyle Seager RC	.30	.75
104 Jason Kipnis RC	.60	1.50
105 Chance Ruffin RC	.20	.50
106 J.B. Shuck RC	.50	1.25
107 Jacob Turner RC	.75	2.00
108 Paul Goldschmidt RC	1.00	2.50
109 Justin Sellers RC	.30	.75
110 Trayvon Robinson (RC)	.30	.75

2011 Bowman Draft Blue

*BLUE: 1.5X TO 4X BASIC
STATED ODDS 1:17 HOBBY
STATED PRINT RUN 499 SER.#'d SETS

2011 Bowman Draft Gold

*GOLD: 1X TO 2.5X BASIC

2011 Bowman Draft Red

STATED ODDS 1:7410 HOBBY
STATED PRINT RUN 1 SER.#'d SET
NO PRICING DUE TO SCARCITY

2011 Bowman Draft AFLAC Autographs

STATED ODDS 1:1036 HOBBY

AB Archie Bradley	40.00	80.00
BS Blake Swihart	20.00	50.00
DB Dylan Bundy	60.00	120.00
FL Francisco Lindor	30.00	60.00
LG Larry Greene	20.00	50.00
RS Robert Stephenson	20.00	50.00
TH Travis Harrison	20.00	50.00

2011 Bowman Draft Bryce Harper Green Border Autograph

STATED ODDS 1:6500 HOBBY
EXCHANGE DEADLINE 11/30/2014

BH Bryce Harper EXCH	175.00	350.00

2011 Bowman Draft Bryce Harper Relic Autographs

STATED BASE ODDS 1:23,660 HOBBY
STATED BLUE ODDS 1:32,500 HOBBY
STATED GOLD ODDS 1:65,000 HOBBY
STATED GREEN ODDS 1:312,000 HOBBY
STATED RED ODDS 1:1,560,000 HOBBY
BASE PRINT RUN 69 SER.#'d SETS
BLUE PRINT RUN 50 SER.#'d SETS
GOLD PRINT RUN 25 SER.#'d SETS
GREEN PRINT RUN 5 SER.#'d SETS
RED PRINT RUN 1 SER.#'d SET
NO PRICING ON QTY 25 OR LESS

BHAR1A Bryce Harper/69	150.00	300.00
BHAR1B Bryce Harper Blue/50	200.00	400.00
BHAR1C Bryce Harper Gold/25		
BHAR1D Bryce Harper Green/5		
BHAR1E Bryce Harper Red/1		

2011 Bowman Draft Future's Game Relic Jumbo Patch

STATED ODDS 1:7,700 HOBBY
STATED PRINT RUN 5 SER.#'d SETS
NO PRICING DUE TO SCARCITY

2011 Bowman Draft Future's Game Relic MLB Logo

STATED ODDS 1:38,000 HOBBY
STATED PRINT RUN 1 SER.#'d SET
NO PRICING DUE TO SCARCITY

2011 Bowman Draft Future's Game Relic Patch

STATED ODDS 1:38,000 HOBBY
STATED PRINT RUN 1 SER.#'d SET
NO PRICING DUE TO SCARCITY

2011 Bowman Draft Future's Game Relics

AL Alex Liddi	3.00	8.00
AR Austin Romine	3.00	8.00
AS Alfredo Silverio	4.00	10.00
AV Arodys Vizcaino	3.00	8.00
BH Bryce Harper	40.00	80.00
BP Brad Peacock	4.00	10.00
DM Devin Mesoraco	10.00	25.00
DP Drew Pomeranz	6.00	15.00
DV Dayan Viciedo	4.00	10.00
GB Gary Brown	5.00	12.00
GG Grant Green	3.00	8.00
GI Gregory Infante	4.00	10.00
HA Henderson Alvarez	5.00	12.00
HL Hak-Ju Lee	6.00	15.00
JA Jose Altuve	5.00	12.00
JC Jarred Cosart	3.00	8.00
JD James Darnell	3.00	8.00
JK Jason Kipnis	6.00	15.00
JM Jhan Marinez	3.00	8.00
JS Jonathan Schoop	5.00	12.00
KG Kyle Gibson	5.00	12.00
KH Kelvin Herrera	4.00	10.00
LH Liam Hendriks	4.00	10.00
MH Matt Harvey	5.00	12.00
MM Manny Machado	10.00	25.00
MP Martin Perez	3.00	8.00
NA Nolan Arenado	6.00	15.00
PG Paul Goldschmidt	8.00	20.00
RF Reymond Fuentes	3.00	8.00
SM Starling Marte	6.00	15.00
SV Sebastian Valle	3.00	8.00
TS Tyler Skaggs	4.00	10.00
TT Tyler Thornburg	8.00	20.00
WM Wil Myers	5.00	12.00
WR Wilin Rosario	3.00	8.00
YA Yonder Alonso	5.00	12.00
JMA Jefry Marte	3.00	8.00
JPR Jurickson Profar	4.00	10.00
JTU Jacob Turner	8.00	20.00
MMO Matt Moore	8.00	20.00
SMI Shelby Miller	6.00	15.00
WMI Will Middlebrooks	5.00	12.00

2011 Bowman Draft Future's Game Relics Blue

*BLUE: .4X TO 1X BASIC
STATED PRINT RUN 199 SER.#'d SETS
NO PRICING DUE TO SCARCITY

2011 Bowman Draft Future's Game Relics Gold

*GOLD: .5X TO 1.2X BASIC
STATED PRINT RUN 50 SER.#'d SETS
NO PRICING DUE TO SCARCITY

BH Bryce Harper	125.00	250.00

2011 Bowman Draft Future's Game Relics Green

STATED PRINT RUN 25 SER.#'d SETS
NO PRICING DUE TO SCARCITY

2011 Bowman Draft Prospects

COMPLETE SET (110)	12.50	30.00
STATED PLATE ODDS 1:928 HOBBY		
PLATE PRINT RUN 1 SET PER COLOR		
BLACK-CYAN-MAGENTA-YELLOW ISSUED		
NO PLATE PRICING DUE TO SCARCITY		
BDPP1 John Hicks UER	.25	.60
Drafted by Mariners; pictured as Diamondback Front incorrectly lists as pitcher		
BDPP2 Cody Asche	.25	.60
BDPP3 Tyler Anderson	.15	.40
BDPP4 Jack Armstrong	.25	.60
BDPP5 Pratt Maynard	.60	1.50
BDPP6 Javier Baez	.40	1.00
BDPP7 Kenneth Peoples-Walls	.15	.40
BDPP8 Matt Barnes	.25	.60
BDPP9 Trevor Bauer	.60	1.50
BDPP10 Daniel Vogelbach	.25	.60
BDPP11 Mike Wright UER	.15	.40
Drafted by Orioles; pictured as National		
BDPP12 Dante Bichette	.60	1.50
BDPP13 Hudson Boyd	.15	.40
BDPP14 Archie Bradley	.50	1.25
BDPP15 Matthew Skole	.25	.60
BDPP16 Jed Bradley	.15	.40
BDPP17 Tyler Pill	.15	.40
BDPP18 Dylan Bundy	.75	2.00
BDPP19 Harold Martinez	.25	.60
BDPP20 Will Lamb	.15	.40
BDPP21 Harold Riggins	.15	.40
BDPP22 Zach Cone	.25	.60
BDPP23 Kyle Gaedele	.15	.40
BDPP24 Kyle Crick	.15	.40
BDPP25 C.J. Cron	.40	1.00
BDPP26 Nicholas Delmonico	.25	.60
BDPP27 Alex Dickerson	.25	.60
BDPP28 Tony Cingrani	.25	.60
BDPP29 Jose Fernandez	.15	.40
BDPP30 Michael Fulmer	.15	.40
BDPP31 Carl Thomore	.15	.40
BDPP32 Sean Gilmartin	.25	.60
BDPP33 Tyler Goeddel	.15	.40
BDPP34 Drew Gagnon	.15	.40
BDPP35 Sonny Gray	.25	.60
BDPP36 Larry Greene	.40	1.00
BDPP37 Nick Martini	.15	.40
BDPP38 Taylor Guerrieri	.25	.60
BDPP39 Jake Hager	.15	.40
BDPP40 James Harris	.15	.40
BDPP41 Travis Harrison	.15	.40
BDPP42 Nick DeSantiago	.25	.60
BDPP43 Chase Larsson	.15	.40
BDPP44 Logan Moore	.15	.40
BDPP45 Mason Hope	.15	.40
BDPP46 Adrian Houser	.25	.60
BDPP47 Sean Buckley	.15	.40
BDPP48 Rick Anton	.15	.40
BDPP49 Scott Woodward	.25	.60
BDPP50 David Goforth	.15	.40
BDPP51 Taylor Jungmann	.25	.60
BDPP52 Blake Snell	.15	.40
BDPP53 Francisco Lindor	.40	1.00
BDPP54 Mikie Mahtook	.40	1.00
BDPP55 Brandon Martin	.25	.60
BDPP56 Kevin Quackenbush	.25	.60
BDPP57 Kevin Matthews	.15	.40
BDPP58 C.J. McElroy	.15	.40
BDPP59 Anthony Meo	.15	.40
BDPP60 Justin James	.25	.60
BDPP61 Levi Michael UER	.25	.60
Drafted by Twins; pictured as Ranger		
BDPP62 Joseph Musgrove	.25	.60
BDPP63 Brandon Nimmo	.40	1.00
BDPP64 Brandon Culbreth	.15	.40
BDPP65 Javaris Reynolds	.15	.40
BDPP66 Adam Ehrlich	.15	.40
BDPP67 Henry Owens	.25	.60
BDPP68 Joe Panik	.50	1.25
BDPP69 Jace Peterson	.15	.40
BDPP70 Lance Jeffries	.15	.40
BDPP71 Matthew Budgell	.15	.40
BDPP72 Dan Gamache	.15	.40
BDPP73 Christopher Lee	.15	.40
BDPP74 Kyle Kubitza	.15	.40
BDPP75 Nick Ahmed	.15	.40
BDPP76 Josh Parr	.15	.40
BDPP77 Dwight Smith	.25	.60
BDPP78 Steven Gruver	.15	.40
BDPP79 Jeffrey Soptic	.15	.40
BDPP80 Cory Spangenberg	.25	.60
BDPP81 George Springer	.25	.60
BDPP82 Bubba Starling	.75	2.00
BDPP83 Robert Stephenson	.25	.60
BDPP84 Trevor Story	.15	.40
BDPP85 Madison Boer	.15	.40
BDPP86 Blake Swihart	.25	.60
BDPP87 [illegible]	.15	.40
BDPP88 Joe Tuschak	.15	.40
BDPP89 Keenyn Walker	.15	.40
BDPP91A William Abreu	.15	.40
BDPP91B Kolten Wong	.40	1.00
BDPP92 Tyler Alamo	.15	.40
BDPP93 Bryson Brigman	.15	.40
BDPP94 Nick Ciuffo	.15	.40
BDPP95 Trevor Clifton	.15	.40
BDPP96 Zach Collins	.15	.40
BDPP97 Joe DeMers	.15	.40
BDPP98 Steven Farinaro	.15	.40
BDPP99 Jake Jarvis	.15	.40
BDPP100 Austin Meadows	.25	.60
BDPP101 Hunter Mercado-Hood	.15	.40
BDPP102 Dom Nunez	.15	.40
BDPP103 Arden Pabst	.15	.40
BDPP104 Christian Pelaez	.15	.40
BDPP105 Carson Sands	.25	.60
BDPP106 Jordan Sheffield	.15	.40
BDPP107 Keegan Thompson	.15	.40
BDPP108 Dany Toussaint	.15	.40
BDPP109 Riley Unroe	.15	.40
BDPP110 Matt Vogel	.15	.40

2011 Bowman Draft Prospects Blue

*BLUE: 1.5X TO 4X BASIC
STATED ODDS 1:17 HOBBY
STATED PRINT RUN 499 SER.#'d SETS

2011 Bowman Draft Prospects Gold

*GOLD: 1.2X TO 3X BASIC

2011 Bowman Draft Prospects Red

STATED ODDS 1:7410 HOBBY
STATED PRINT RUN 1 SER.#'d SET
NO PRICING DUE TO SCARCITY

2011 Bowman Draft Prospect Autographs

FOUND IN RETAIL PACKS
PLATE PRINT RUN 1 SET PER COLOR
BLACK-CYAN-MAGENTA-YELLOW ISSUED
NO PLATE PRICING DUE TO SCARCITY

AK Aaron Kurcz	5.00	12.00
AT Alex Torres	3.00	8.00
AW Alex Wimmers	3.00	8.00
CS Cody Scarpetta	3.00	8.00
EG Erik Goeddel	3.00	8.00
HA Henderson Alvarez	4.00	10.00
JC Jarek Cunningham	3.00	8.00
JK Joe Kelly	3.00	8.00
JW Joe Wieland	5.00	12.00
ML Matt Lollis	5.00	12.00
RP Rich Poythress	3.00	8.00
SV Sebastian Valle	6.00	15.00
TT Tyler Thornburg	12.50	30.00
BHO Bryan Holaday	4.00	10.00
CBM Chris Balcolm-Miller	3.00	8.00

2011 Bowman Draft Prospect Autographs Blue

*GOLD: X TO X BASIC
FOUND IN RETAIL PACKS
STATED PRINT RUN 50 SER.#'d SETS

2011 Bowman Draft Prospect Autographs Gold

*GOLD: 1.2X TO 3X BASIC
FOUND IN RETAIL PACKS
STATED PRINT RUN 50 SER.#'d SETS

2011 Bowman Draft Prospect Autographs Red

FOUND IN RETAIL PACKS
STATED PRINT RUN 25 SER.#'d SETS
NO PRICING DUE TO SCARCITY

1997 Bowman Chrome

The 1997 Bowman Chrome set was issued in one series totalling 300 cards and was distributed in four-card packs with a suggested retail price of $3.00. The cards parallel the 1997 Bowman brand and the 300 card set represents a selection of top cards taken from the 441-card 1997 Bowman set. The product was released in the Winter, after the end of the 1997 season. The fronts feature color action player photos printed on dazzling chromium stock. The backs carry player information. Rookie Cards in this set include Adrian Beltre, Kris Benson, Lance Berkman, Kris Benson, Eric Chavez, Jose Cruz Jr., Travis Lee, Aramis Ramirez, Miguel Tejada, Vernon Wells and Kerry Wood.

COMPLETE SET (300)	75.00	150.00
1 Derek Jeter	1.25	3.00
2 Chipper Jones	.50	1.25
3 Hideo Nomo	.50	1.25
4 Tim Salmon	.30	.75
5 Robin Ventura	.20	.50
6 Tony Clark	.20	.50
7 Barry Larkin	.30	.75
8 Paul Molitor	.20	.50
9 Andy Benes	.20	.50
10 Ryan Klesko	.20	.50
11 Mark McGwire	1.25	3.00
12 Ken Griffey Jr.	.75	2.00
13 Robb Nen	.20	.50
14 Cal Ripken	1.50	4.00
15 John Valentin	.20	.50
16 Ricky Bottalico	.20	.50
17 Mike Lansing	.20	.50
18 Ryne Sandberg	.75	2.00
19 Carlos Delgado	.20	.50
20 Craig Biggio	.30	.75
21 Eric Karros	.20	.50
22 Kevin Appier	.20	.50
23 Mariano Rivera	.50	1.25
24 Vinny Castilla	.20	.50
25 Juan Gonzalez	.20	.50
26 Al Martin	.20	.50
27 Jeff Cirillo	.20	.50
28 Ray Lankford	.20	.50
29 Manny Ramirez	.30	.75
30 Roberto Alomar	.30	.75
31 Will Clark	.30	.75
32 Chuck Knoblauch	.20	.50
33 Harold Baines	.20	.50
34 Edgar Martinez	.30	.75
35 Mike Mussina	.30	.75
36 Kevin Brown	.20	.50
37 Dennis Eckersley	.20	.50
38 Tino Martinez	.30	.75
39 Raul Mondesi	.20	.50
40 Sammy Sosa	.50	1.25
41 John Smoltz	.30	.75
42 Billy Wagner	.20	.50
43 Ken Caminiti	.20	.50
44 Wade Boggs	.30	.75
45 Andres Galarraga	.20	.50
46 Roger Clemens	1.00	2.50
47 Matt Williams	.20	.50
48 Albert Belle	.20	.50
49 Jeff King	.20	.50
50 John Wetteland	.20	.50
51 Deion Sanders	.30	.75
52 Ellis Burks	.20	.50
53 Pedro Martinez	.30	.75
54 Kenny Lofton	.20	.50
55 Randy Johnson	.50	1.25
56 Bernie Williams	.30	.75
57 Marquis Grissom	.20	.50
58 Gary Sheffield	.20	.50
59 Curt Schilling	.20	.50
60 Reggie Sanders	.20	.50
61 Bobby Higginson	.20	.50
62 Moises Alou	.20	.50
63 Tom Glavine	.30	.75
64 Mark Grace	.30	.75
65 Rafael Palmeiro	.30	.75
66 John Olerud	.20	.50
67 Dante Bichette	.20	.50
68 Jeff Bagwell	.30	.75
69 Barry Bonds	1.25	3.00
70 Pat Hentgen	.20	.50
71 Jim Thome	.30	.75
72 Andy Pettitte	.30	.75
73 Jay Bell	.20	.50
74 Jim Edmonds	.20	.50
75 Ron Gant	.20	.50
76 David Cone	.20	.50
77 Jose Canseco	.30	.75
78 Jay Buhner	.20	.50
79 Greg Maddux	.75	2.00
80 Lance Johnson	.20	.50
81 Travis Fryman	.20	.50
82 Paul O'Neill	.30	.75
83 Ivan Rodriguez	.30	.75
84 Fred McGriff	.30	.75
85 Mike Piazza	.75	2.00
86 Brady Anderson	.20	.50
87 Marty Cordova	.20	.50
88 Joe Carter	.20	.50
89 Brian Jordan	.20	.50
90 David Justice	.20	.50
91 Tony Gwynn	.60	1.50
92 Larry Walker	.20	.50
93 Mo Vaughn	.20	.50
94 Sandy Alomar Jr.	.20	.50
95 Rusty Greer	.20	.50
96 Roberto Hernandez	.20	.50
97 Hal Morris	.20	.50
98 Todd Hundley	.20	.50
99 Rondell White	.20	.50
100 Frank Thomas	.50	1.25
101 Bubba Trammell RC	.60	1.50
102 Sidney Ponson RC	1.00	2.50
103 Ricky Ledee RC	.60	1.50
104 Brett Tomko	.20	.50
105 Braden Looper RC	.40	1.00
106 Jason Dickson	.20	.50
107 Chad Green RC	.40	1.00
108 R.A. Dickey RC	.40	1.00
109 Jeff Liefer	.20	.50
110 Richard Hidalgo	.20	.50
111 Chad Hermansen RC	.40	1.00
112 Felix Martinez	.20	.50
113 J.J. Johnson	.20	.50
114 Todd Dunwoody	.20	.50
115 Katsuhiro Maeda	.20	.50
116 Darin Erstad	.20	.50
117 Elieser Marrero	.20	.50
118 Bartolo Colon	.20	.50
119 Ugueth Urbina	.20	.50
120 Jaime Bluma	.20	.50
121 Seth Greisinger RC	.40	1.00
122 Jose Cruz Jr. RC	.60	1.50
123 Todd Dunn	.20	.50
124 Justin Towle RC	.40	1.00
125 Brian Rose	.20	.50
126 Jose Guillen	.20	.50
127 Andruw Jones	.30	.75
128 Mark Kotsay RC	1.50	4.00
129 Wilton Guerrero	.20	.50
130 Jacob Cruz	.20	.50
131 Mike Sweeney	.20	.50
132 Matt Morris	.20	.50
133 John Thomson	.20	.50
134 Javier Valentin	.20	.50
135 Mike Drumright RC	.40	1.00
136 Michael Barrett	.20	.50
137 Tony Saunders RC	.40	1.00
138 Kevin Brown	.20	.50
139 Anthony Sanders RC	.40	1.00
140 Jeff Abbott	.20	.50
141 Eugene Kingsale	.20	.50
142 Paul Konerko	.30	.75
143 Randall Simon RC	.60	1.50
144 Freddy Adrian Garcia	.20	.50
145 Karim Garcia	.20	.50
146 Carlos Guillen	.20	.50
147 Aaron Boone	.20	.50
148 Donnie Sadler	.20	.50
149 Brooks Kieschnick	.20	.50
150 Scott Spiezio	.20	.50
151 Kevin Orie	.20	.50
152 Russ Johnson	.20	.50
153 Livan Hernandez	.20	.50
154 Vladimir Nunez RC	.40	1.00
155 Pokey Reese	.20	.50
156 Chris Carpenter	.20	.50
157 Eric Milton RC	.60	1.50
158 Richie Sexson	.20	.50
159 Carl Pavano	.20	.50
160 Pat Cline	.20	.50
161 Ron Wright	.20	.50
162 Dante Powell	.20	.50
163 Mark Bellhorn	.20	.50
164 George Lombard	.20	.50
165 Paul Wilder RC	.40	1.00
166 Brad Fullmer	.20	.50
167 Kris Benson RC	1.00	2.50
168 Torii Hunter	.20	.50
169 D.T. Cromer RC	.40	1.00
170 Nelson Figueroa RC	.40	1.00
171 Hiram Bocachica RC	.40	1.00
172 Shane Monahan	.20	.50
173 Juan Melo	.20	.50
174 Calvin Pickering RC	.40	1.00
175 Reggie Taylor	.20	.50
176 Geoff Jenkins	.20	.50
177 Steve Rain RC	.40	1.00
178 Nerio Rodriguez RC	.40	1.00
179 Derrick Gibson	.20	.50
180 Darin Blood	.20	.50
181 Ben Davis	.20	.50
182 Adrian Beltre RC	3.00	8.00
183 Kerry Wood RC	5.00	12.00
184 Nate Rolison RC	.40	1.00
185 Fernando Tatis RC	.40	1.00
186 Jake Westbrook RC	1.00	2.50
187 Edwin Diaz	.20	.50
188 Joe Fontenot RC	.40	1.00
189 Matt Halloran RC	.40	1.00
190 Matt Clement RC	1.00	2.50
191 Todd Greene	.20	.50
192 Eric Chavez RC	4.00	10.00
193 Edgard Velazquez	.20	.50
194 Bruce Chen RC	1.00	2.50
195 Jason Brester	.20	.50
196 Chris Reitsma RC	.60	1.50
197 Neifi Perez	.20	.50
198 Hideki Irabu RC	.60	1.50
199 Don Denbow RC	.40	1.00
200 Derrek Lee	.30	.75
201 Todd Walker	.20	.50
202 Scott Rolen	.30	.75
203 Wes Helms	.20	.50
204 Bob Abreu	.30	.75
205 John Patterson RC	1.50	4.00
206 Alex Gonzalez RC	1.00	2.50
207 Grant Roberts RC	.40	1.00
208 Jeff Suppan	.20	.50
209 Luke Wilcox	.20	.50
210 Marlon Anderson	.20	.50
211 Mike Caruso RC	.40	1.00
212 Roy Halladay RC	15.00	40.00
213 Jeremi Gonzalez RC	.40	1.00
214 Aramis Ramirez RC	4.00	10.00
215 Dee Brown RC	.40	1.00
216 Justin Thompson	.20	.50
217 Danny Clyburn	.20	.50
218 Bruce Aven	.20	.50
219 Keith Foulke RC	1.50	4.00
220 Shannon Stewart	.20	.50
221 Larry Barnes RC	.40	1.00
222 Mark Johnson RC	.40	1.00
223 Randy Winn	.20	.50
224 Nomar Garciaparra	.75	2.00
225 Jacque Jones RC	1.50	4.00
226 Chris Clemons	.20	.50
227 Todd Helton	.50	1.25
228 Ryan Brannan RC	.40	1.00
229 Alex Sanchez RC	.60	1.50
230 Russell Branyan	.20	.50
231 Daryle Ward	.40	1.00
232 Kevin Witt	.20	.50
233 Gabby Martinez	.20	.50
234 Preston Wilson	.20	.50
235 Donzell McDonald RC	.40	1.00
236 Orlando Cabrera RC	1.50	4.00
237 Brian Banks	.20	.50
238 Robbie Bell	.40	1.00
239 Brad Rigby	.20	.50
240 Scott Elarton	.20	.50
241 Donny Leon RC	.40	1.00
242 Abraham Nunez RC	.40	1.00
243 Adam Eaton RC	1.00	2.50
244 Octavio Dotel RC	.60	1.50
245 Sean Casey	1.00	2.50
246 Joe Lawrence RC	.40	1.00
247 Adam Johnson RC	.40	1.00
248 Ronnie Belliard RC	1.25	3.00
249 Bobby Estalella	.20	.50
250 Corey Lee RC	.40	1.00
251 Mike Cameron	.20	.50
252 Kerry Robinson RC	.40	1.00
253 A.J. Zapp RC	.40	1.00
254 Jarrod Washburn	.20	.50
255 Ben Grieve	.20	.50
256 Javier Vazquez RC	1.50	4.00
257 Travis Lee RC	.60	1.50
258 Dennis Reyes RC	.40	1.00
259 Danny Buxbaum	.20	.50
260 Kelvim Escobar RC	1.00	2.50
261 Danny Klassen	.20	.50
262 Ken Cloude RC	.40	1.00
263 Gabe Alvarez	.20	.50
264 Clayton Bruner RC	.40	1.00
265 Jason Marquis RC	1.50	4.00
266 Jamey Wright	.20	.50
267 Matt Snyder RC	.40	1.00
268 Josh Garrett RC	.40	1.00
269 Juan Encarnacion	.20	.50
270 Heath Murray	.20	.50
271 Brent Butler RC	.40	1.00
272 Danny Peoples RC	.40	1.00
273 Miguel Tejada RC	5.00	12.00
274 Jim Pittsley	.20	.50
275 Dmitri Young	.20	.50
276 Vladimir Guerrero	.50	1.25
277 Cole Liniak RC	.40	1.00
278 Ramon Hernandez	.20	.50
279 Cliff Politte RC	.40	1.00
280 Mel Rosario RC	.40	1.00
281 Jorge Carrion RC	.40	1.00
282 John Barnes RC	.40	1.00
283 Chris Stowe RC	.40	1.00
284 Vernon Wells RC	3.00	8.00
285 Brett Caradonna RC	.40	1.00
286 Scott Hodges RC	.40	1.00
287 Jon Garland RC	[illegible]	[illegible]
288 Nathan Haynes RC	.40	1.00
289 Geoff Goetz RC	.40	1.00
290 Adam Kennedy RC	1.00	2.50
291 T.J. Tucker RC	.40	1.00
292 Aaron Akin RC	.40	1.00
293 Jayson Werth RC	3.00	8.00
294 Glenn Davis RC	.40	1.00
295 Mark Mangum RC	.40	1.00
296 Troy Cameron RC	.40	1.00
297 J.J. Davis RC	.40	1.00
298 Lance Berkman RC	6.00	15.00
299 Jason Standridge RC	.40	1.00
300 Jason Dellaero RC	.40	1.00

1997 Bowman Chrome International

Randomly inserted in packs at the rate of one in four, this 300-card set is parallel to the base set and is distinguished by the flag on the background of each card front identifying the country where that player was born.

*STARS: 1.25X TO 3X BASIC CARDS
*ROOKIES: .4X TO 1X BASIC CARDS
STATED ODDS 1:4

212 Roy Halladay	40.00	80.00
298 Lance Berkman	12.50	30.00

1997 Bowman Chrome International Refractors

Randomly inserted in packs at the rate of one in 24, this 300-card set is a parallel version of the Bowman Chrome International set and is similar in design. The difference is found in the refractive quality of the card front.

*STARS: 6X TO 15X BASIC CARDS
*ROOKIES: 2X TO 5X BASIC CARDS
STATED ODDS 1:24

183 Kerry Wood	30.00	60.00
212 Roy Halladay	100.00	200.00
273 Miguel Tejada	30.00	60.00
284 Vernon Wells	15.00	40.00
293 Jayson Werth	30.00	60.00
298 Lance Berkman	50.00	100.00

1997 Bowman Chrome Refractors

Randomly inserted in packs at the rate of one in 12, this 300-card set is parallel to the base set and is similar in design. The difference can be found in the refractive quality of the cards fronts.

*STARS: 3X TO 8X BASIC CARDS
*ROOKIES: 1.5X TO 4X BASIC CARDS
STATED ODDS 1:12
INT'L REF.STATED ODDS 1:24

183 Kerry Wood	20.00	50.00
212 Roy Halladay	100.00	200.00
273 Miguel Tejada	20.00	50.00
284 Vernon Wells	12.50	30.00
298 Lance Berkman	20.00	50.00

1997 Bowman Chrome 1998 ROY Favorites

Randomly inserted in packs at the rate of one in 24, cards from this 15-card set features color action photos of 1998 Rookie of the Year prospective candidtates printed on chromium cards.

COMPLETE SET (15)	12.50	25.00
STATED ODDS 1:24		

*REFRACTORS: .75X TO 2X BASIC ROY
REFRACTOR STATED ODDS 1:72
ROY1 Jeff Abbott .60 1.50
ROY2 Karim Garcia .60 1.50
ROY3 Todd Helton 1.50 4.00
ROY4 Richard Hidalgo .60 1.50
ROY5 Geoff Jenkins .60 1.50
ROY6 Russ Johnson .60 1.50
ROY7 Paul Konerko 1.00 2.50
ROY8 Mark Kotsay 1.00 2.50
ROY9 Ricky Ledee .40 1.00
ROY10 Travis Lee .40 1.00
ROY11 Derrek Lee 1.00 2.50
ROY12 Elieser Marrero .60 1.50
ROY13 Juan Melo .60 1.50
ROY14 Brian Rose .60 1.50
ROY15 Fernando Tatis .25 .60

1997 Bowman Chrome Scout's Honor Roll

Randomly inserted in packs at a rate of one in 12, this 15-card set features color photos of top prospects and rookies printed on chromium cards. The backs carry player information.

COMPLETE SET (15) 15.00 30.00
STATED ODDS 1:12
*REF: .75X TO 2X BASIC CHR.HONOR
REFRACTOR STATED ODDS 1:36
SHR1 Dmitri Young .50 1.25
SHR2 Bob Abreu .75 2.00
SHR3 Vladimir Guerrero 1.25 3.00
SHR4 Paul Konerko .75 2.00
SHR5 Kevin Orie .50 1.25
SHR6 Todd Walker .50 1.25
SHR7 Ben Grieve .50 1.25
SHR8 Darin Erstad .50 1.25
SHR9 Derrek Lee .75 2.00
SHR10 Jose Cruz Jr. .50 1.25
SHR11 Scott Rolen .75 2.00
SHR12 Travis Lee .50 1.25
SHR13 Andruw Jones .75 2.00
SHR14 Wilton Guerrero .50 1.25
SHR15 Nomar Garciaparra 2.00 5.00

1998 Bowman Chrome

The 1998 Bowman Chrome set was issued in two separate series with a total of 441 cards. The four-card packs retailed for $3.00 each. These cards are parallel to the regular Bowman set but with a premium Chrome finish. Unlike the 1997 brand, the 1998 issue parallels the entire Bowman brand. Rookie Cards include Ryan Anderson, Jack Cust, Troy Glaus, Orlando Hernandez, Gabe Kapler, Carlos Lee, Ted Lilly, Ruben Mateo, Kevin Millwood, Magglio Ordonez and Jimmy Rollins.

COMPLETE SET (441) 60.00 160.00
COMP. SERIES 1 (221) 30.00 80.00
COMP. SERIES 2 (220) 30.00 80.00
1 Nomar Garciaparra .75 2.00
2 Scott Rolen .30 .75
3 Andy Pettitte .30 .75
4 Ivan Rodriguez .30 .75
5 Mark McGwire 1.25 3.00
6 Jason Dickson .20 .50
7 Jose Cruz Jr. .20 .50
8 Jeff Kent .20 .50
9 Mike Mussina .30 .75
10 Jason Kendall .20 .50
11 Brett Tomko .20 .50
12 Jeff King .20 .50
13 Brad Radke .20 .50
14 Robin Ventura .20 .50
15 Jeff Bagwell .30 .75
16 Greg Maddux .75 2.00
17 John Jaha .20 .50
18 Mike Piazza .75 2.00
19 Edgar Martinez .30 .75
20 David Justice .20 .50
21 Todd Hundley .20 .50
22 Tony Gwynn .60 1.50
23 Larry Walker .20 .50
24 Bernie Williams .30 .75
25 Edgar Renteria .20 .50
26 Rafael Palmeiro .30 .75
27 Tim Salmon .30 .75
28 Matt Morris .20 .50
29 Shawn Estes .20 .50
30 Vladimir Guerrero .50 1.25
31 Fernando Tatis .20 .50
32 Justin Thompson .20 .50
33 Ken Griffey Jr. .75 2.00
34 Edgardo Alfonzo .20 .50
35 Mo Vaughn .20 .50
36 Marty Cordova .20 .50
37 Craig Biggio .30 .75
38 Roger Clemens 1.00 2.50
39 Mark Grace .30 .75
40 Ken Caminiti .20 .50
41 Tony Womack .20 .50
42 Albert Belle .20 .50
43 Tino Martinez .30 .75
44 Sandy Alomar Jr. .20 .50
45 Jeff Cirillo .20 .50
46 Jason Giambi .20 .50
47 Darin Erstad .20 .50
48 Livan Hernandez .20 .50
49 Mark Grudzielanek .20 .50
50 Sammy Sosa .50 1.25
51 Curt Schilling .20 .50
52 Brian Hunter .20 .50
53 Neifi Perez .20 .50
54 Todd Walker .20 .50
55 Jose Guillen .20 .50
56 Jim Thome .30 .75
57 Tom Glavine .30 .75
58 Todd Greene .20 .50
59 Rondell White .20 .50
60 Roberto Alomar .30 .75
61 Tony Clark .20 .50
62 Vinny Castilla .20 .50
63 Barry Larkin .30 .75
64 Hideki Irabu .20 .50
65 Johnny Damon .30 .75
66 Juan Gonzalez .20 .50
67 John Olerud .20 .50
68 Gary Sheffield .20 .50
69 Raul Mondesi .20 .50
70 Chipper Jones .50 1.25
71 David Ortiz 2.50 6.00
72 Warren Morris RC .40 1.00
73 Alex Gonzalez .20 .50
74 Nick Bierbrodt .20 .50
75 Roy Halladay 1.00 2.50
76 Danny Buxbaum .20 .50
77 Adam Kennedy .20 .50
78 Jared Sandberg .20 .50
79 Michael Barrett .20 .50
80 Gil Meche .60 1.50
81 Jayson Werth .20 .50
82 Abraham Nunez .20 .50
83 Ben Petrick .20 .50
84 Brett Caradonna .20 .50
85 Mike Lowell RC 2.50 6.00
86 Clay Bruner .20 .50
87 John Curtice RC .60 1.50
88 Bobby Estalella .20 .50
89 Juan Melo .20 .50
90 Arnold Gooch .20 .50
91 Kevin Millwood RC 1.50 4.00
92 Richie Sexson .20 .50
93 Orlando Cabrera .20 .50
94 Pat Cline .20 .50
95 Anthony Sanders .20 .50
96 Russ Johnson .20 .50
97 Ben Grieve .20 .50
98 Kevin McGlinchy .20 .50
99 Paul Wilder .20 .50
100 Russ Ortiz .20 .50
101 Ryan Jackson RC .40 1.00
102 Heath Murray .20 .50
103 Brian Rose .20 .50
104 R.Radmanovich RC .40 1.00
105 Ricky Ledee .20 .50
106 Jeff Wallace RC .40 1.00
107 Ryan Minor RC .40 1.00
108 Dennis Reyes .20 .50
109 James Manias .20 .50
110 Chris Carpenter .20 .50
111 Daryle Ward .20 .50
112 Vernon Wells .20 .50
113 Chad Green .20 .50
114 Mike Stoner RC .40 1.00
115 Brad Fullmer .20 .50
116 Adam Eaton .20 .50
117 Jeff Liefer .20 .50
118 Corey Koskie RC 1.00 2.50
119 Todd Helton .30 .75
120 Jaime Jones RC .40 1.00
121 Mel Rosario .20 .50
122 Geoff Goetz .20 .50
123 Adrian Beltre .20 .50
124 Jason Dellaero .20 .50
125 Gabe Kapler RC 1.00 2.50
126 Scott Schoeneweis .20 .50
127 Ryan Brannan .20 .50
128 Aaron Akin .20 .50
129 Ryan Anderson RC .40 1.00
130 Brad Penny .20 .50
131 Bruce Chen .20 .50
132 Eli Marrero .20 .50
133 Eric Chavez .20 .50
134 Troy Glaus RC 3.00 8.00
135 Troy Cameron .20 .50
136 Brian Sikorski RC .40 1.00
137 Mike Kinkade RC .40 1.00
138 Braden Looper .20 .50
139 Mark Mangum .20 .50
140 Danny Peoples .20 .50
141 J.J. Davis .20 .50
142 Ben Davis .20 .50
143 Jacque Jones .20 .50
144 Derrick Gibson .20 .50
145 Bronson Arroyo 1.50 4.00
146 L.De Los Santos RC .40 1.00
147 Jeff Abbott .20 .50
148 Mike Cuddyer RC 1.50 4.00
149 Jason Romano .20 .50
150 Shane Monahan .20 .50
151 Ntema Ndungidi RC .40 1.00
152 Alex Sanchez .20 .50
153 Jack Cust RC 3.00 8.00
154 Brent Butler .20 .50
155 Ramon Hernandez .20 .50
156 Norm Hutchins .20 .50
157 Jason Marquis .20 .50
158 Jacob Cruz .20 .50
159 Rob Burger RC .40 1.00
160 Dave Coggin .20 .50
161 Preston Wilson .20 .50
162 Jason Fitzgerald RC .40 1.00
163 Dan Serafini .20 .50
164 Pete Munro .20 .50
165 Trot Nixon .20 .50
166 Homer Bush .20 .50
167 Dermal Brown .20 .50
168 Chad Hermansen .20 .50
169 Julio Moreno RC .40 1.00
170 John Roskos RC .40 1.00
171 Grant Roberts .20 .50
172 Ken Cloude .20 .50
173 Jason Brester .20 .50
174 Jason Conti .20 .50
175 Jon Garland .20 .50
176 Robbie Bell .20 .50
177 Nathan Haynes .20 .50
178 Ramon Ortiz RC .60 1.50
179 Shannon Stewart .20 .50
180 Pablo Ortega .20 .50
181 Jimmy Rollins RC 3.00 8.00
182 Sean Casey .20 .50
183 Ted Lilly RC 1.00 2.50
184 Chris Enochs RC .40 1.00
185 Magglio Ordonez UER RC 4.00 10.00
Front picture is Mario Valdez
186 Mike Drumright .20 .50
187 Aaron Boone .20 .50
188 Matt Clement .20 .50
189 Todd Dunwoody .20 .50
190 Larry Rodriguez .20 .50
191 Todd Noel .20 .50
192 Geoff Jenkins .20 .50
193 George Lombard .20 .50
194 Lance Berkman .20 .50
195 Marcus McCain .20 .50
196 Ryan McGuire .20 .50
197 Jhensy Sandoval .20 .50
198 Corey Lee .20 .50
199 Mario Valdez .20 .50
200 Robert Fick RC .60 1.50
201 Donnie Sadler .20 .50
202 Marc Kroon .20 .50
203 David Miller .20 .50
204 Jarrod Washburn .20 .50
205 Miguel Tejada .50 1.25
206 Raul Ibanez .20 .50
207 John Patterson .20 .50
208 Calvin Pickering .20 .50
209 Felix Martinez .20 .50
210 Mark Redman .20 .50
211 Scott Elarton .20 .50
212 Jose Amado RC .40 1.00
213 Kerry Wood .20 .50
214 Dante Powell .20 .50
215 Aramis Ramirez .20 .50
216 A.J. Hinch .20 .50
217 Dustin Carr RC .40 1.00
218 Mark Kotsay .20 .50
219 Jason Standridge .20 .50
220 Luis Ordaz .20 .50
221 O.Hernandez RC 2.00 5.00
222 Cal Ripken 1.50 4.00
223 Paul Molitor .20 .50
224 Derek Jeter 1.25 3.00
225 Barry Bonds 1.25 3.00
226 Jim Edmonds .20 .50
227 John Smoltz .30 .75
228 Eric Karros .20 .50
229 Ray Lankford .20 .50
230 Rey Ordonez .20 .50
231 Kenny Lofton .20 .50
232 Alex Rodriguez .75 2.00
233 Dante Bichette .20 .50
234 Pedro Martinez .30 .75
235 Carlos Delgado .20 .50
236 Rod Beck .20 .50
237 Matt Williams .20 .50
238 Charles Johnson .20 .50
239 Rico Brogna .20 .50
240 Frank Thomas .50 1.25
241 Paul O'Neill .30 .75
242 Jaret Wright .20 .50
243 Brant Brown .20 .50
244 Ryan Klesko .20 .50
245 Chuck Finley .20 .50
246 Derek Bell .20 .50
247 Delino DeShields .20 .50
248 Chan Ho Park .20 .50
249 Wade Boggs .30 .75
250 Jay Buhner .20 .50
251 Butch Huskey .20 .50
252 Steve Finley .20 .50
253 Will Clark .30 .75
254 John Valentin .20 .50
255 Bobby Higginson .20 .50
256 Darryl Strawberry .20 .50
257 Randy Johnson .50 1.25
258 Al Martin .20 .50
259 Travis Fryman .20 .50
260 Fred McGriff .30 .75
261 Jose Valentin .20 .50
262 Andruw Jones .30 .75
263 Kenny Rogers .20 .50
264 Moises Alou .20 .50
265 Denny Neagle .20 .50
266 Ugueth Urbina .20 .50
267 Derrek Lee .30 .75
268 Ellis Burks .20 .50
269 Mariano Rivera .50 1.25
270 Dean Palmer .20 .50
271 Eddie Taubensee .20 .50
272 Brady Anderson .20 .50
273 Brian Giles .20 .50
274 Quinton McCracken .20 .50
275 Henry Rodriguez .20 .50
276 Andres Galarraga .20 .50
277 Jose Canseco .30 .75
278 David Segui .20 .50
279 Bret Saberhagen .20 .50
280 Kevin Brown .30 .75
281 Chuck Knoblauch .20 .50
282 Jeromy Burnitz .20 .50
283 Jay Bell .20 .50
284 Manny Ramirez .30 .75
285 Rick Helling .20 .50
286 Francisco Cordova .20 .50
287 Bob Abreu .20 .50
288 J.T. Snow .20 .50
289 Hideo Nomo .50 1.25
290 Brian Jordan .20 .50
291 Javy Lopez .20 .50
292 Travis Lee .20 .50
293 Russell Branyan .20 .50
294 Paul Konerko .20 .50
295 Masato Yoshii RC .60 1.50
296 Kris Benson .20 .50
297 Juan Encarnacion .20 .50
298 Eric Milton .20 .50
299 Mike Caruso .20 .50
300 R. Aramboles RC .40 1.00
301 Bobby Smith .20 .50
302 Billy Koch .20 .50
303 Richard Hidalgo .20 .50
304 Justin Baughman RC .40 1.00
305 Chris Gissell .20 .50
306 Donnie Bridges RC .40 1.00
307 Nelson Lara RC .40 1.00
308 Randy Wolf RC .60 1.50
309 Jason LaRue RC .60 1.50
310 Jason Gooding RC .40 1.00
311 Edgard Clemente .20 .50
312 Andrew Vessel .20 .50
313 Chris Reitsma .20 .50
314 Jesus Sanchez RC .40 1.00
315 Buddy Carlyle RC .40 1.00
316 Randy Winn .20 .50
317 Luis Rivera RC .40 1.00
318 Marcus Thames RC 2.50 6.00
319 A.J. Pierzynski .20 .50
320 Scott Randall .20 .50
321 Damian Sapp .20 .50
322 Ed Yarnall RC .40 1.00
323 Luke Allen RC .40 1.00
324 J.D. Smart .20 .50
325 Willie Martinez .20 .50
326 Alex Ramirez .20 .50
327 Eric DuBose RC .40 1.00
328 Kevin Witt .20 .50
329 Dan McKinley RC .40 1.00
330 Cliff Politte .20 .50
331 Vladimir Nunez .20 .50
332 John Halama RC .40 1.00
333 Nerio Rodriguez .20 .50
334 Desi Relaford .20 .50
335 Robinson Checo .20 .50
336 John Nicholson .30 .75
337 Tom LaRosa RC .40 1.00
338 Kevin Nicholson RC .40 1.00
339 Javier Vazquez .20 .50
340 A.J. Zapp .20 .50
341 Tom Evans .20 .50
342 Kerry Robinson .20 .50
343 Gabe Gonzalez RC .40 1.00
344 Ralph Milliard .20 .50
345 Enrique Wilson .20 .50
346 Elvin Hernandez .20 .50
347 Mike Lincoln RC .40 1.00
348 Cesar King RC .40 1.00
349 Cristian Guzman RC .60 1.50
350 Donzell McDonald .20 .50
351 Jim Parque RC .40 1.00
352 Mike Saipe RC .40 1.00
353 Carlos Febles RC .60 1.50
354 Dernell Stenson RC .40 1.00
355 Mark Osborne RC .40 1.00
356 Odalis Perez RC 1.50 4.00
357 Jason Dewey RC .40 1.00
358 Joe Fontenot .20 .50
359 Jason Grilli RC .40 1.00
360 Kevin Haverbusch RC .40 1.00
361 Jay Yennaco RC .40 1.00
362 Brian Buchanan .20 .50
363 John Barnes .20 .50
364 Chris Fussell .20 .50
365 Kevin Gibbs RC .40 1.00
366 Joe Lawrence .20 .50
367 DaRond Stovall .20 .50
368 Brian Fuentes RC .40 1.00
369 Jimmy Anderson .20 .50
370 Lariel Gonzalez RC .40 1.00
371 Scott Williamson RC .40 1.00
372 Milton Bradley .20 .50
373 Jason Halper RC .40 1.00
374 Brent Billingsley RC .40 1.00
375 Joe DePastino RC .40 1.00
376 Jake Westbrook .20 .50
377 Octavio Dotel .20 .50
378 Jason Williams RC .40 1.00
379 Julio Ramirez RC .40 1.00
380 Seth Greisinger .20 .50
381 Mike Judd RC .40 1.00
382 Ben Ford RC .40 1.00
383 Tom Bennett RC .40 1.00
384 Adam Butler RC .40 1.00
385 Wade Miller RC 1.00 2.50
386 Kyle Peterson RC .40 1.00
387 Tommy Peterman RC .40 1.00
388 Onan Masaoka .20 .50
389 Jason Rakers RC .40 1.00
390 Rafael Medina .20 .50
391 Luis Lopez RC .40 1.00
392 Jeff Yoder .20 .50
393 Vance Wilson RC .40 1.00
394 F. Seguignol RC .40 1.00
395 Ron Wright .20 .50
396 Ruben Mateo RC .40 1.00
397 Steve Lomasney RC .60 1.50
398 Damian Jackson .20 .50
399 Mike Jerzembeck RC .40 1.00
400 Luis Rivas RC 1.00 2.50
401 Kevin Burford RC .40 1.00
402 Glenn Davis .20 .50
403 Robert Luce RC .40 1.00
404 Cole Liniak .20 .50
405 Matt LeCroy RC .60 1.50
406 Jeremy Giambi RC .60 1.50
407 Shawn Chacon .20 .50
408 Dewayne Wise RC .40 1.00
409 Steve Woodard .20 .50
410 F.Cordero RC 1.00 2.50
411 Damon Minor RC .40 1.00
412 Lou Collier .20 .50
413 Justin Towle .20 .50
414 Juan LeBron .20 .50
415 Michael Coleman .20 .50
416 Felix Rodriguez .20 .50
417 Paul Ah Yat RC .40 1.00
418 Kevin Barker RC .40 1.00
419 Brian Meadows .20 .50
420 Darnell McDonald RC .40 1.00
421 Matt Kinney RC .40 1.00
422 Mike Vavrek RC .40 1.00
423 Courtney Duncan RC .40 1.00
424 Kevin Millar RC 1.50 4.00
425 Ruben Rivera .20 .50
426 Steve Shoemaker RC .40 1.00
427 Dan Reichert RC .40 1.00
428 Carlos Lee RC 2.50 6.00
429 Rod Barajas 1.00 2.50
430 Pablo Ozuna RC .60 1.50
431 Todd Belitz RC .40 1.00
432 Sidney Ponson .20 .50
433 Steve Carver RC .40 1.00
434 Esteban Yan RC .60 1.50
435 Cedrick Bowers .20 .50
436 Marlon Anderson .20 .50
437 Carl Pavano .20 .50
438 Jae Weong Seo RC .60 1.50
439 Jose Taveras RC .40 1.00
440 Matt Anderson RC .40 1.00
441 Darron Ingram RC .40 1.00

1998 Bowman Chrome Golden Anniversary

Randomly inserted in first series packs at a rate of one in 164 and second series packs at a rate of one in 133, this 441-card set is a parallel to the Bowman Chrome base set. The set is sequentially numbered to 50 and is highlighted by gold facsimile signatures.

*STARS: 6X TO 15X BASIC CARDS
*ROOKIES: 3X TO 8X BASIC CARDS
SER.1 STATED ODDS 1:164
SER.2 STATED ODDS 1:133

1998 Bowman Chrome Golden Anniversary Refractors

Randomly inserted in first series hobby packs at a rate of one in 1279 and second series packs at one in 1022, this 441-card insert is a parallel to the Bowman Chrome base set. The set is sequentially numbered to five and is also highlighted by gold facsimile signatures. These cards are not priced due to scarcity.

SER.1 STATED ODDS 1:1279
SER.2 STATED ODDS 1:1022

1998 Bowman Chrome International

Randomly inserted in packs at a rate of one in four, this 441-card set is a parallel to the Bowman Chrome base set. These cards are differentiated by maps of the player's hometown area in the background of each card front.

COMPLETE SET (441) 350.00 700.00
COMP. SERIES 1 (221) 200.00 400.00
COMP. SERIES 2 (220) 150.00 300.00
*STARS: 1.5X TO 4X BASIC CARDS
*ROOKIES: .4X TO 1X BASIC CARDS
STATED ODDS 1:4

1998 Bowman Chrome International Refractors

Randomly inserted in packs at a rate of one in 24, this 441-card set is a parallel to the Bowman Chrome base set. These cards are differentiated by maps of the player's hometown area in the background of each card front.

*STARS: 5X TO 12X BASIC CARDS
*ROOKIES: 2X TO 5X BASIC CARDS
STATED ODDS 1:24

1998 Bowman Chrome Refractors

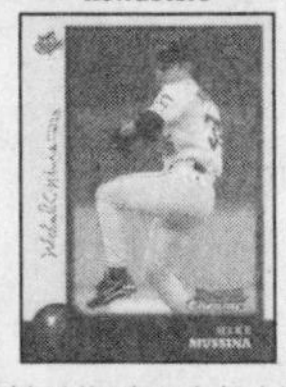

Randomly inserted in packs at a rate of one in 12, this 441-card set is a parallel of the Bowman Chrome base set. The refractive quality of the card fronts differentiate themselves from basic issue cards.

*STARS: 3X TO 8X BASIC CARDS
*ROOKIES: 1.5X TO 4X BASIC CARDS
STATED ODDS 1:12

1998 Bowman Chrome Reprints

Randomly inserted in first and second packs at a rate of one in 12, these cards are replicas of classic Bowman Rookie Cards from 1948-1955 and 1989-present. Odd numbered cards (1, 3, 5 etc) were distributed in first

series packs and even numbered cards in second series packs. The upgraded Chrome silver-colored stock gives them a striking appearance and makes them easy to differentiate from the originals.

COMPLETE SET (50) 60.00 160.00
COMPLETE SERIES 1 (25) 30.00 80.00
COMPLETE SERIES 2 (25) 30.00 80.00
STATED ODDS 1:12
*REFRACTORS: 1X TO 2.5X BASIC REPRINTS
REFRACTOR STATED ODDS 1:36
1 Yogi Berra 1.50 4.00
2 Jackie Robinson 1.50 4.00
3 Don Newcombe .60 1.50
4 Satchell Paige 1.50 4.00
5 Willie Mays 4.00 10.00
6 Gil McDougald .60 1.50
7 Don Larsen .60 1.50
8 Elston Howard 1.00 2.50
9 Robin Ventura .60 1.50
10 Brady Anderson .60 1.50
11 Gary Sheffield .60 1.50
12 Tino Martinez 1.00 2.50
13 Ken Griffey Jr. 2.50 6.00
14 John Smoltz 1.00 2.50
15 Sandy Alomar Jr. .40 1.00
16 Larry Walker .60 1.50
17 Todd Hundley .40 1.00
18 Mo Vaughn .60 1.50
19 Sammy Sosa 1.50 4.00
20 Frank Thomas 1.50 4.00
21 Chuck Knoblauch .60 1.50
22 Bernie Williams 1.00 2.50
23 Juan Gonzalez .60 1.50
24 Mike Mussina 1.00 2.50
25 Jeff Bagwell 1.00 2.50
26 Tim Salmon 1.00 2.50
27 Ivan Rodriguez 1.00 2.50
28 Kenny Lofton .60 1.50
29 Chipper Jones 1.50 4.00
30 Javy Lopez .60 1.50
31 Ryan Klesko .60 1.50
32 Raul Mondesi .60 1.50
33 Jim Thome 1.00 2.50
34 Carlos Delgado .60 1.50
35 Mike Piazza 2.50 6.00
36 Manny Ramirez 1.00 2.50
37 Andy Pettitte 1.00 2.50
38 Derek Jeter 4.00 10.00
39 Brad Fullmer .40 1.00
40 Richard Hidalgo .40 1.00
41 Tony Clark .40 1.00
42 Andruw Jones 1.00 2.50
43 Vladimir Guerrero 1.50 4.00
44 Nomar Garciaparra 2.50 6.00
45 Paul Konerko .60 1.50
46 Ben Grieve .40 1.00
47 Hideo Nomo 1.50 4.00
48 Scott Rolen 1.00 2.50
49 Jose Guillen .60 1.50
50 Livan Hernandez .60 1.50

1999 Bowman Chrome

The 1999 Bowman Chrome set was issued in two distinct series and were distributed in four card packs with a suggested retail price of $3.00. The set contains 440 regular cards printed on brilliant chromium 18-pt. Stock. Within the set are 300 top prospects that are designated with silver and blue foil. Each player's facsimile rookie signature are featured on these cards. There are also 140 vereran stars designated with a red and silver foil stamp. The backs contain information on each player's rookie and most recent season, career statistics and a scouting report from early league days Rookie Cards include Pat Burrell, Carl Crawford, Adam Dunn, Rafael Furcal, Freddy Garcia, Tim Hudson, Nick Johnson, Austin Kearns, Willy Mo Pena, Adam Piatt, Corey Patterson and Alfonso Soriano.

COMPLETE SET (440) 100.00 200.00
COMP. SERIES 1 (220) 40.00 80.00
COMP. SERIES 2 (220) 60.00 120.00
1 Ben Grieve .20 .50
2 Kerry Wood .20 .50
3 Ruben Rivera .20 .50
4 Sandy Alomar Jr. .20 .50
5 Cal Ripken 1.50 4.00
6 Mark McGwire 1.25 3.00
7 Vladimir Guerrero .50 1.25
8 Moises Alou .20 .50
9 Jim Edmonds .20 .50
10 Greg Maddux .75 2.00
11 Gary Sheffield .20 .50
12 John Valentin .20 .50
13 Chuck Knoblauch .20 .50
14 Tony Clark .20 .50
15 Rusty Greer .20 .50
16 Al Leiter .20 .50
17 Travis Lee .20 .50
18 Jose Cruz Jr. .20 .50
19 Pedro Martinez .30 .75
20 Paul O'Neill .30 .75
21 Todd Walker .20 .50
22 Vinny Castilla .20 .50
23 Barry Larkin .30 .75
24 Curt Schilling .20 .50
25 Jason Kendall .20 .50
26 Scott Erickson .20 .50
27 Andres Galarraga .20 .50
28 Jeff Shaw .20 .50
29 John Olerud .20 .50
30 Orlando Hernandez .20 .50
31 Larry Walker .20 .50
32 Andruw Jones .30 .75
33 Jeff Cirillo .20 .50
34 Barry Bonds 1.25 3.00
35 Manny Ramirez .30 .75
36 Mark Kotsay .20 .50
37 Ivan Rodriguez .30 .75
38 Jeff King .20 .50
39 Brian Hunter .20 .50
40 Ray Durham .20 .50
41 Bernie Williams .30 .75
42 Darin Erstad .20 .50
43 Chipper Jones .50 1.25
44 Pat Hentgen .20 .50
45 Eric Young .20 .50
46 Jaret Wright .20 .50
47 Juan Guzman .20 .50
48 Jorge Posada .30 .75
49 Bobby Higginson .20 .50
50 Jose Guillen .20 .50
51 Trevor Hoffman .20 .50
52 Ken Griffey Jr. .75 2.00
53 David Justice .20 .50
54 Matt Williams .20 .50
55 Eric Karros .20 .50
56 Derek Bell .20 .50
57 Ray Lankford .20 .50
58 Mariano Rivera .50 1.25
59 Brett Tomko .20 .50
60 Mike Mussina .30 .75
61 Kenny Lofton .20 .50
62 Chuck Finley .20 .50
63 Alex Gonzalez .20 .50
64 Mark Grace .30 .75
65 Raul Mondesi .20 .50
66 David Cone .20 .50
67 Brad Fullmer .20 .50
68 Andy Benes .20 .50
69 John Smoltz .30 .75
70 Shane Reynolds .20 .50
71 Bruce Chen .20 .50
72 Adam Kennedy .20 .50
73 Jack Cust .20 .50
74 Matt Clement .20 .50
75 Derrick Gibson .20 .50
76 Darnell McDonald .20 .50
77 Adam Everett RC 1.00 2.50
78 Ricardo Aramboles .20 .50
79 Mark Quinn RC .40 1.00
80 Jason Rakers .20 .50
81 Seth Etherton RC .40 1.00
82 Jeff Urban RC .40 1.00
83 Manny Aybar .20 .50
84 Mike Nannini RC .40 1.00
85 Onan Masaoka .20 .50
86 Rod Barajas .20 .50
87 Mike Frank .20 .50
88 Scott Randall .20 .50
89 Justin Bowles RC .40 1.00
90 Chris Haas .20 .50
91 Arturo McDowell RC .40 1.00
92 Matt Belisle RC .40 1.00
93 Scott Elarton .20 .50
94 Vernon Wells .20 .50
95 Pat Cline .20 .50
96 Ryan Anderson .20 .50
97 Kevin Barker .20 .50
98 Ruben Mateo .20 .50
99 Robert Fick .20 .50
100 Corey Koskie .20 .50
101 Ricky Ledee .20 .50
102 Rick Elder RC .40 1.00
103 Jack Cressend RC .40 1.00
104 Joe Lawrence .20 .50
105 Mike Lincoln .20 .50
106 Kit Pellow RC .40 1.00
107 Matt Burch RC .40 1.00
108 Cole Liniak .20 .50
109 Jason Dewey .20 .50
110 Cesar King .20 .50
111 Julio Ramirez .20 .50
112 Jake Westbrook .20 .50
113 Eric Valent RC .60 1.50
114 Roosevelt Brown RC .40 1.00
115 Choo Freeman RC .60 1.50
116 Juan Melo .20 .50
117 Jason Grilli .20 .50
118 Jared Sandberg .20 .50
119 Glenn Davis .20 .50
120 David Riske RC .40 1.00
121 Jacque Jones .20 .50
122 Corey Lee .20 .50
123 Michael Barrett .20 .50
124 Lariel Gonzalez .20 .50
125 Mitch Meluskey .20 .50
126 Freddy Adrian Garcia .20 .50
127 Tony Torcato RC .40 1.00
128 Jeff Liefer .20 .50
129 Ntema Ndungidi .20 .50
130 Andy Brown RC .40 1.00
131 Ryan Mills RC .40 1.00
132 Andy Abad RC .40 1.00
133 Carlos Febles .20 .50
134 Jason Tyner RC .40 1.00
135 Mark Osborne .20 .50
136 Phil Norton RC .40 1.00
137 Nathan Haynes .20 .50
138 Roy Halladay .50 1.25
139 Juan Encarnacion .20 .50
140 Brad Penny .20 .50
141 Grant Roberts .20 .50
142 Aramis Ramirez .20 .50
143 Cristian Guzman .20 .50
144 Mamon Tucker RC .40 1.00
145 Ryan Bradley .20 .50
146 Brian Simmons .20 .50
147 Dan Reichert .20 .50
148 Russell Branyan .20 .50
149 Victor Valencia RC .40 1.00
150 Scott Schoeneweis .20 .50
151 Sean Spencer RC .40 1.00
152 Odalis Perez .20 .50
153 Joe Fontenot .20 .50
154 Milton Bradley .20 .50
155 Josh McKinley RC .40 1.00

156 Terrence Long .20 .50
157 Danny Klassen .20 .50
158 Paul Hoover RC .40 1.00
159 Ron Belliard .20 .50
160 Armando Rios .20 .50
161 Ramon Hernandez .20 .50
162 Jason Conti .20 .50
163 Chad Hermansen .20 .50
164 Jason Standridge .20 .50
165 Jason Dellaero .20 .50
166 John Curtice .20 .50
167 Clayton Andrews RC .40 1.00
168 Jeremy Giambi .20 .50
169 Alex Ramirez .20 .50
170 Gabe Molina RC .40 1.00
171 M.Encarnacion RC .40 1.00
172 Mike Zywica RC .40 1.00
173 Chip Ambres RC .40 1.00
174 Trot Nixon .20 .50
175 Pat Burrell RC 3.00 8.00
176 Jeff Yoder .20 .50
177 Chris Jones RC .40 1.00
178 Kevin Witt .20 .50
179 Keith Luuloa RC .40 1.00
180 Billy Koch .20 .50
181 Damaso Marte RC .40 1.00
182 Ryan Glynn RC .40 1.00
183 Calvin Pickering .20 .50
184 Michael Cuddyer .20 .50
185 Nick Johnson RC 2.00 5.00
186 D.Mientkiewicz RC 1.00 2.50
187 Nate Cornejo RC .40 1.00
188 Octavio Dotel .20 .50
189 Wes Helms .20 .50
190 Nelson Lara .20 .50
191 Chuck Abbott RC .40 1.00
192 Tony Armas Jr. .20 .50
193 Gil Meche .20 .50
194 Ben Petrick .20 .50
195 Chris George RC .40 1.00
196 Scott Hunter RC .40 1.00
197 Ryan Brannan .20 .50
198 Amaury Garcia RC .40 1.00
199 Chris Gissell .20 .50
200 Austin Kearns RC 3.00 8.00
201 Alex Gonzalez .20 .50
202 Wade Miller .20 .50
203 Scott Williamson .20 .50
204 Chris Enochs .20 .50
205 Fernando Seguignol .20 .50
206 Marlon Anderson .20 .50
207 Todd Sears RC .40 1.00
208 Nate Bump RC .40 1.00
209 J.M. Gold RC .40 1.00
210 Matt LeCroy .20 .50
211 Alex Hernandez .20 .50
212 Luis Rivera .20 .50
213 Troy Cameron .20 .50
214 Alex Escobar RC .60 1.50
215 Jason LaRue .20 .50
216 Kyle Peterson .20 .50
217 Brent Butler .20 .50
218 Dernell Stenson .20 .50
219 Adrian Beltre .20 .50
220 Daryle Ward .20 .50
221 Jim Thome .30 .75
222 Cliff Floyd .20 .50
223 Rickey Henderson .50 1.25
224 Garret Anderson .20 .50
225 Ken Caminiti .20 .50
226 Bret Boone .20 .50
227 Jeromy Burnitz .20 .50
228 Steve Finley .20 .50
229 Miguel Tejada .20 .50
230 Greg Vaughn .20 .50
231 Jose Offerman .20 .50
232 Andy Ashby .20 .50
233 Albert Belle .20 .50
234 Fernando Tatis .20 .50
235 Todd Helton .30 .75
236 Sean Casey .20 .50
237 Brian Giles .20 .50
238 Andy Pettitte .30 .75
239 Fred McGriff .30 .75
240 Roberto Alomar .30 .75
241 Edgar Martinez .30 .75
242 Lee Stevens .20 .50
243 Shawn Green .20 .50
244 Ryan Klesko .20 .50
245 Sammy Sosa .50 1.25
246 Todd Hundley .20 .50
247 Shannon Stewart .20 .50
248 Randy Johnson .50 1.25
249 Rondell White .20 .50
250 Mike Piazza .75 2.00
251 Craig Biggio .30 .75
252 David Wells .20 .50
253 Brian Jordan .20 .50
254 Edgar Renteria .20 .50
255 Bartolo Colon .20 .50
256 Frank Thomas .50 1.25
257 Will Clark .30 .75
258 Dean Palmer .20 .50
259 Dmitri Young .20 .50
260 Scott Rolen .30 .75
261 Jeff Kent .20 .50
262 Dante Bichette .20 .50
263 Nomar Garciaparra .75 2.00
264 Tony Gwynn .60 1.50
265 Alex Rodriguez .75 2.00
266 Jose Canseco .30 .75
267 Jason Giambi .20 .50
268 Jeff Bagwell .30 .75
269 Carlos Delgado .20 .50
270 Tom Glavine .30 .75
271 Eric Davis .20 .50
272 Edgardo Alfonzo .20 .50
273 Tim Salmon .30 .75
274 Johnny Damon .30 .75
275 Rafael Palmeiro .30 .75
276 Denny Neagle .20 .50
277 Neifi Perez .20 .50
278 Roger Clemens 1.00 2.50
279 Brant Brown .20 .50
280 Kevin Brown .30 .75
281 Jay Bell .20 .50
282 Jay Buhner .20 .50
283 Matt Lawton .20 .50
284 Robin Ventura .20 .50
285 Juan Gonzalez .20 .50
286 Mo Vaughn .20 .50
287 Kevin Millwood .20 .50
288 Tino Martinez .30 .75
289 Justin Thompson .20 .50
290 Derek Jeter 1.25 3.00
291 Ben Davis .20 .50
292 Mike Lowell .20 .50
293 Calvin Murray .20 .50
294 Micah Bowie RC .40 1.00
295 Lance Berkman .20 .50
296 Jason Marquis .20 .50
297 Chad Green .20 .50
298 Dee Brown .20 .50
299 Jerry Hairston Jr. .20 .50
300 Gabe Kapler .20 .50
301 Brent Stentz RC .40 1.00
302 Scott Mullen RC .40 1.00
303 Brandon Reed .20 .50
304 Shea Hillenbrand RC 1.50 4.00
305 J.D. Closser RC .60 1.50
306 Gary Matthews Jr. .20 .50
307 Toby Hall RC .60 1.50
308 Jason Phillips RC .40 1.00
309 Jose Macias RC .40 1.00
310 Jung Bong RC .40 1.00
311 Ramon Soler RC .40 1.00
312 Kelly Dransfeldt RC .40 1.00
313 Carlos E. Hernandez RC .60 1.50
314 Kevin Haverbusch .20 .50
315 Aaron Myette RC .40 1.00
316 Chad Harville RC .40 1.00
317 Kyle Farnsworth RC .60 1.50
318 Gookie Dawkins RC .60 1.50
319 Willie Martinez .20 .50
320 Carlos Lee .20 .50
321 Carlos Pena RC 1.25 3.00
322 Peter Bergeron RC .40 1.00
323 A.J. Burnett RC 1.50 4.00
324 Bucky Jacobsen RC .60 1.50
325 Mo Bruce RC .40 1.00
326 Reggie Taylor .20 .50
327 Jackie Rexrode .20 .50
328 Alvin Morrow RC .40 1.00
329 Carlos Beltran .30 .75
330 Eric Chavez .20 .50
331 John Patterson .20 .50
332 Jayson Werth .20 .50
333 Richie Sexson .20 .50
334 Randy Wolf .20 .50
335 Eli Marrero .20 .50
336 Paul LoDuca .20 .50
337 J.D Smart .20 .50
338 Ryan Minor .20 .50
339 Kris Benson .20 .50
340 George Lombard .20 .50
341 Troy Glaus .30 .75
342 Eddie Yarnall .20 .50
343 Kip Wells RC .60 1.50
344 C.C. Sabathia RC 6.00 15.00
345 Sean Burroughs RC 1.00 2.50
346 Felipe Lopez RC 2.50 6.00
347 Ryan Rupe RC .40 1.00
348 Orber Moreno RC .40 1.00
349 Rafael Roque RC .40 1.00
350 Alfonso Soriano RC 5.00 12.00
351 Pablo Ozuna .20 .50
352 Cdrey Patterson RC 1.50 4.00
353 Braden Looper .20 .50
354 Robbie Bell .20 .50
355 Mark Mulder RC 2.50 6.00
356 Angel Pena .20 .50
357 Kevin McGlinchy .20 .50
358 M.Restovich RC .60 1.50
359 Eric DuBose .20 .50
360 Geoff Jenkins .20 .50
361 Mark Harriger RC .40 1.00
362 Junior Herndon RC .40 1.00
363 Tim Raines Jr. RC .40 1.00
364 Rafael Furcal RC 2.50 6.00
365 Marcus Giles RC 1.50 4.00
366 Ted Lilly .20 .50
367 Jorge Toca RC .60 1.50
368 David Kelton RC .40 1.00
369 Adam Dunn RC 5.00 12.00
370 Guillermo Mota RC .40 1.00
371 Brett Laxton RC .40 1.00
372 Travis Harper RC .40 1.00
373 Tom Davey RC .40 1.00
374 Darren Blakely RC .40 1.00
375 Tim Hudson RC 3.00 8.00
376 Jason Romano .20 .50
377 Dan Reichert .20 .50
378 Julio Lugo RC 1.00 2.50
379 Jose Garcia RC .40 1.00
380 Erubiel Durazo RC .60 1.50
381 Jose Jimenez .20 .50
382 Chris Fussell .20 .50
383 Steve Lomasney .20 .50
384 Juan Pena RC .40 1.00
385 Allen Levrault RC .40 1.00
386 Juan Rivera RC 1.50 4.00
387 Steve Colyer RC .40 1.00
388 Joe Nathan RC 2.00 5.00
389 Ron Walker RC .40 1.00
390 Nick Bierbrodt .20 .50
391 Luke Prokopec RC .40 1.00
392 Dave Roberts RC 1.00 2.50
393 Mike Darr .20 .50
394 Abraham Nunez RC .60 1.50
395 G.Chiaramonte RC .40 1.00
396 J.Van Buren RC .40 1.00
397 Mike Kusiewicz .20 .50
398 Matt Wise RC .40 1.00
399 Joe McEwing RC .60 1.50
400 Matt Holliday RC 5.00 12.00
401 Willi Mo Pena RC 5.00 12.00
402 Ruben Quevedo RC .40 1.00
403 Rob Ryan RC .40 1.00
404 Freddy Garcia RC 1.50 4.00
405 Kevin Eberwein RC .40 1.00
406 Jesus Colome RC .40 1.00
407 Chris Singleton .20 .50
408 Bubba Crosby RC 1.00 2.50
409 Jesus Cordero RC .40 1.00
410 Donny Leon .20 .50
411 G.Tomlinson RC .40 1.00
412 Jeff Winchester RC .40 1.00
413 Adam Piatt RC .40 1.00
414 Robert Stratton .20 .50
415 T.J. Tucker .20 .50
416 Ryan Langerhans RC 1.00 2.50
417 A.Shumaker RC .40 1.00
418 Matt Miller RC .40 1.00
419 Doug Clark RC .40 1.00
420 Kory DeHaan RC .40 1.00
421 David Eckstein RC 3.00 8.00
422 Brian Cooper RC .40 1.00
423 Brady Clark RC 1.50 4.00
424 Chris Magruder RC .40 1.00
425 Bobby Seay RC .40 1.00
426 Aubrey Huff RC 2.00 5.00
427 Mike Jerzembeck .20 .50
428 Matt Blank RC .40 1.00
429 Benny Agbayani RC .60 1.50
430 Kevin Beirne RC .40 1.00
431 Josh Hamilton RC 6.00 15.00
432 Josh Girdley RC .40 1.00
433 Kyle Snyder RC .40 1.00
434 Mike Paradis RC .40 1.00
435 Jason Jennings RC 1.00 2.50
436 David Walling RC .40 1.00
437 Omar Ortiz RC .40 1.00
438 Jay Gehrke RC .60 1.50
439 Casey Burns RC .40 1.00
440 Carl Crawford RC 4.00 10.00

1999 Bowman Chrome Gold

Randomly inserted in first series packs a rate of one in twelve , and second series packs at one in 24, this 440-card set is highlighted by gold facsimile signatures and borders and is a parallel to the 1999 Bowman Chrome base set.

*SER.1 STARS: 2.5X TO 6X BASIC CARDS
*SER.1 ROOKIES: .75X TO 2X BASIC
SER.1 STATED ODDS 1:12
*SER.2 STARS: 3X TO 8X BASIC CARDS
*SER.2 ROOKIES: 1X TO 2.5X BASIC
SER.2 STATED ODDS 1:24
369 Adam Dunn 12.50 30.00
400 Matt Holliday 20.00 50.00

1999 Bowman Chrome Gold Refractors

Randomly inserted in first series packs at a rate of one in 305 and second series packs at a rate of one in 200, this 440-card set is a parallel insert to the Bowman Chrome base set. Gold foil fascimile signatures and refractive chrome fronts highlight the design. In addition, only 25 serial numbered sets were printed.

*STARS: 20X TO 50X BASIC CARDS
SER.1 STATED ODDS 1:305
SER.2 STATED ODDS 1:200

1999 Bowman Chrome International

Randomly inserted in first series packs at a rate of one in four, and second series packs at a rate of one in 12, this 440-card set is a parallel insert to the Bowman Chrome Base set. Metallic foil fronts and backgrounds taken from notable scenes of the featured players hometown highlight the design.

COMPLETE SET (440) 450.00 900.00
COMP. SERIES 1 (220) 150.00 300.00
COMP. SERIES 2 (220) 300.00 600.00
*SER.1 STARS: 1.25X TO 3X BASIC CARDS
*SER.1 ROOKIES: .4X TO 1X BASIC
SER.1 STATED ODDS 1:4
*SER.2 STARS: 2X TO 5X BASIC CARDS
*SER.2 ROOKIES: .5X TO 1.2X BASIC
SER.2 STATED ODDS 1:12
369 Adam Dunn 6.00 15.00

1999 Bowman Chrome International Refractors

Randomly inserted in first series packs at a rate of one in 76 and second series packs at a rate of one in 50, this 440-card set is a refractive parallel insert to the Bowman Chrome International set. Only 100 serial numbered sets were printed.

*STARS: 6X TO 15X BASIC CARDS
*ROOKIES: 4X TO 8X BASIC
SER.1 STATED ODDS 1:76
SER.2 STATED ODDS 1:50
321 Carlos Pena 40.00 80.00
369 Adam Dunn 50.00 100.00
400 Matt Holliday 60.00 120.00
431 Josh Hamilton 100.00 200.00
440 Carl Crawford 40.00 100.00

1999 Bowman Chrome Refractors

Randomly inserted at a rate of one in twelve, this 440-card set is a refractive parallel insert to the Bowman Chrome base set. The refractive sheen of each card highlights the design.

*STARS: 4X TO 10X BASIC CARDS
*ROOKIES: 1.5X TO 4X BASIC
SER.1 AND SER.2 STATED ODDS 1:12
431 Josh Hamilton 60.00 120.00

1999 Bowman Chrome 2000 ROY Favorites

Randomly inserted in second series packs at a rate of one in 20, this 10-card insert set features borderless, double-etched foil cards and feature players that had potential to win Rookie of the Year honors for the 2000 seasons.

COMPLETE SET (10) 8.00 20.00
SER.2 STATED ODDS 1:20
*REF: .75X TO 2X BASIC CHR.2000 ROY
REFRACTOR SER.2 STATED ODDS 1:100
ROY1 Ryan Anderson .40 1.00
ROY2 Pat Burrell 1.25 3.00
ROY3 A.J. Burnett .60 1.50
ROY4 Ruben Mateo .40 1.00
ROY5 Alex Escobar .40 1.00
ROY6 Pablo Ozuna .40 1.00
ROY7 Mark Mulder 1.00 2.50
ROY8 Corey Patterson .60 1.50
ROY9 George Lombard .40 1.00
ROY10 Nick Johnson .60 1.50

1999 Bowman Chrome Diamond Aces

Randomly inserted in first series packs at the rate of one in 21, this 18-card set features nine emerging stars such as Pat Burrell and Troy Glaus as well as nine proven veterans including Derek Jeter and Ken Griffey Jr.

COMPLETE SET (18) 30.00 80.00
SER.1 STATED ODDS 1:21
*REF: .75X TO 2X BASIC CHR.ACES
REFRACTOR SER.1 ODDS 1:84
DA1 Troy Glaus 1.00 2.50
DA2 Eric Chavez .60 1.50
DA3 Fernando Seguignol .60 1.50
DA4 Ryan Anderson .60 1.50
DA5 Ruben Mateo .60 1.50
DA6 Carlos Beltran 1.00 2.50
DA7 Adrian Beltre .60 1.50
DA8 Bruce Chen .60 1.50
DA9 Pat Burrell 2.00 5.00
DA10 Mike Piazza 2.50 6.00
DA11 Ken Griffey Jr. 2.50 6.00
DA12 Chipper Jones 1.50 4.00
DA13 Derek Jeter 4.00 10.00
DA14 Mark McGwire 4.00 10.00
DA15 Nomar Garciaparra 2.50 6.00
DA16 Sammy Sosa 1.50 4.00
DA17 Juan Gonzalez .60 1.50
DA18 Alex Rodriguez 2.50 6.00

1999 Bowman Chrome Impact

Randomly inserted in second series packs at the rate of one in 15, this 15-card insert set features 20 players separated into three distinct categories; Early Impact, Initial Impact and Lasting Impact.

COMPLETE SET (20) 30.00 80.00
SER.2 STATED ODDS 1:15
*REF 1-10: .75X TO 2X BASIC IMPACT
*REF 11-20: .75X TO 2X BASIC IMPACT
REFRACTOR SER.2 STATED ODDS 1:75
I1 Alfonso Soriano 2.00 5.00
I2 Pat Burrell 1.25 3.00
I3 Ruben Mateo .50 1.25
I4 A.J. Burnett .50 1.25
I5 Corey Patterson .75 2.00
I6 Daryle Ward .50 1.25
I7 Eric Chavez .50 1.25
I8 Troy Glaus .75 2.00
I9 Sean Casey .50 1.25
I10 Joe McEwing .20 .50
I11 Gabe Kapler .50 1.25
I12 Michael Barrett .50 1.25
I13 Sammy Sosa 1.25 3.00
I14 Alex Rodriguez 2.00 5.00
I15 Mark McGwire 3.00 8.00
I16 Derek Jeter 3.00 8.00
I17 Nomar Garciaparra 2.00 5.00
I18 Mike Piazza 2.00 5.00
I19 Chipper Jones 1.25 3.00
I20 Ken Griffey Jr. 2.00 5.00

1999 Bowman Chrome Scout's Choice

Randomly inserted in first series packs at the rate of one in twelve, this 21-card insert set features borderless, double-etched foil cards showcase a selection of the game's top young prospects.

COMPLETE SET (21) 10.00 25.00
SER.1 STATED ODDS 1:12
*REFRACTORS: .75X TO 2X BASIC SCOUT'S
REFRACTOR SER.1 ODDS 1:48
SC1 Ruben Mateo .60 1.50
SC2 Ryan Anderson .60 1.50
SC3 Pat Burrell 1.25 3.00
SC4 Troy Glaus 1.00 2.50
SC5 Eric Chavez .60 1.50
SC6 Adrian Beltre .60 1.50
SC7 Bruce Chen .60 1.50
SC8 Carlos Beltran 1.00 2.50
SC9 Alex Gonzalez .60 1.50
SC10 Carlos Lee .60 1.50
SC11 George Lombard .60 1.50
SC12 Matt Clement .60 1.50
SC13 Calvin Pickering .60 1.50
SC14 Marlon Anderson .60 1.50
SC15 Chad Hermansen .60 1.50
SC16 Russell Branyan .60 1.50
SC17 Jeremy Giambi .60 1.50
SC18 Ricky Ledee .60 1.50
SC19 John Patterson .60 1.50
SC20 Roy Halladay 1.50 4.00
SC21 Michael Barrett .60 1.50

2000 Bowman Chrome

The 2000 Bowman Chrome product was released in late July, 2000 as a 440-card set that featured 140 veteran players (1-140), and 300 rookies and prospects (141-440). Each pack contained four cards, and carried a suggested retail price of $3.00. Rookie Cards include Rick Asadoorian, Bobby Bradley, Kevin Mench, Ben Sheets and Barry Zito. In addition, Topps designated five prospects as Bowman Chrome "exclusives" whereby their only appearance in a Topps brand for the year 2000 would be in this set. Jason Hart and Chin-Hui Tsao highlight this selection of Bowman Chrome exclusive Rookie Cards.

COMPLETE SET (440) 60.00 120.00
1 Vladimir Guerrero .50 1.25
2 Chipper Jones .50 1.25
3 Todd Walker .20 .50
4 Barry Larkin .30 .75
5 Bernie Williams .30 .75
6 Todd Helton .30 .75
7 Jermaine Dye .20 .50
8 Brian Giles .20 .50
9 Freddy Garcia .20 .50
10 Greg Vaughn .20 .50
11 Alex Gonzalez .20 .50
12 Luis Gonzalez .20 .50
13 Ron Belliard .20 .50
14 Ben Grieve .20 .50
15 Carlos Delgado .20 .50
16 Brian Jordan .20 .50
17 Fernando Tatis .20 .50
18 Ryan Rupe .20 .50
19 Miguel Tejada .20 .50
20 Mark Grace .30 .75
21 Kenny Lofton .20 .50
22 Eric Karros .20 .50
23 Cliff Floyd .20 .50
24 John Halama .20 .50
25 Cristian Guzman .20 .50
26 Scott Williamson .20 .50
27 Mike Lieberthal .20 .50
28 Tim Hudson .20 .50
29 Warren Morris .20 .50
30 Pedro Martinez .30 .75
31 John Smoltz .30 .75
32 Ray Durham .20 .50
33 Chad Allen .20 .50
34 Tony Clark .20 .50
35 Tino Martinez .30 .75
36 J.T. Snow .20 .50
37 Kevin Brown .30 .75
38 Bartolo Colon .20 .50
39 Rey Ordonez .20 .50
40 Jeff Bagwell .30 .75
41 Ivan Rodriguez .30 .75
42 Eric Chavez .20 .50
43 Eric Milton .20 .50
44 Jose Canseco .30 .75
45 Shawn Green .20 .50
46 Rich Aurilia .20 .50
47 Roberto Alomar .30 .75
48 Brian Daubach .20 .50
49 Maggiio Ordonez .20 .50
50 Derek Jeter 1.25 3.00
51 Kris Benson .20 .50
52 Albert Belle .20 .50
53 Rondell White .20 .50
54 Justin Thompson .20 .50
55 Nomar Garciaparra .75 2.00
56 Chuck Finley .20 .50
57 Omar Vizquel .30 .75
58 Luis Castillo .20 .50
59 Richard Hidalgo .20 .50
60 Barry Bonds 1.25 3.00
61 Craig Biggio .30 .75
62 Doug Glanville .20 .50
63 Gabe Kapler .20 .50
64 Johnny Damon .30 .75
65 Pokey Reese .20 .50
66 Andy Pettitte .30 .75
67 B.J. Surhoff .20 .50
68 Richie Sexson .20 .50
69 Javy Lopez .20 .50
70 Raul Mondesi .20 .50
71 Darin Erstad .20 .50
72 Kevin Millwood .20 .50
73 Ricky Ledee .20 .50
74 John Olerud .20 .50
75 Sean Casey .20 .50
76 Carlos Febles .20 .50
77 Paul O'Neill .30 .75
78 Bob Abreu .20 .50
79 Neifi Perez .20 .50
80 Tony Gwynn .60 1.50
81 Russ Ortiz .20 .50
82 Matt Williams .20 .50
83 Chris Carpenter .20 .50
84 Roger Cedeno .20 .50
85 Tim Salmon .30 .75
86 Billy Koch .20 .50
87 Jeromy Burnitz .20 .50
88 Edgardo Alfonzo .20 .50
89 Jay Bell .20 .50
90 Manny Ramirez .30 .75
91 Frank Thomas .50 1.25
92 Mike Mussina .30 .75
93 J.D. Drew .20 .50
94 Adrian Beltre .20 .50
95 Alex Rodriguez .75 2.00
96 Larry Walker .20 .50
97 Juan Encarnacion .20 .50
98 Mike Sweeney .20 .50
99 Rusty Greer .20 .50
100 Randy Johnson .50 1.25
101 Jose Vidro .20 .50
102 Preston Wilson .20 .50
103 Greg Maddux .75 2.00
104 Jason Giambi .20 .50
105 Cal Ripken 1.50 4.00
106 Carlos Beltran .20 .50
107 Vinny Castilla .20 .50
108 Mariano Rivera .50 1.25
109 Mo Vaughn .20 .50
110 Rafael Palmeiro .30 .75
111 Shannon Stewart .20 .50
112 Mike Hampton .20 .50
113 Joe Nathan .20 .50
114 Ben Davis .20 .50
115 Andruw Jones .30 .75
116 Robin Ventura .20 .50
117 Damion Easley .20 .50
118 Jeff Cirillo .20 .50
119 Kerry Wood .20 .50
120 Scott Rolen .30 .75
121 Sammy Sosa .50 1.25
122 Ken Griffey Jr. .75 2.00
123 Shane Reynolds .20 .50
124 Troy Glaus .20 .50
125 Tom Glavine .30 .75
126 Michael Barrett .20 .50
127 Al Leiter .20 .50
128 Jason Kendall .20 .50
129 Roger Clemens 1.00 2.50
130 Juan Gonzalez .20 .50
131 Corey Koskie .20 .50
132 Curt Schilling .20 .50
133 Mike Piazza .75 2.00
134 Gary Sheffield .20 .50
135 Jim Thome .30 .75
136 Orlando Hernandez .20 .50
137 Ray Lankford .20 .50
138 Geoff Jenkins .20 .50
139 Jose Lima .20 .50
140 Mark McGwire 1.25 3.00
141 Adam Piatt .20 .50
142 Pat Manning RC .30 .75
143 Marcos Castillo RC .30 .75
144 Lesli Brea RC .30 .75
145 Humberto Cota RC .50 1.25
146 Ben Petrick .20 .50
147 Kip Wells .20 .50
148 Wily Pena .20 .50
149 Chris Wakeland RC .30 .75
150 Brad Baker RC .30 .75
151 Robbie Morrison RC .30 .75
152 Reggie Taylor .20 .50
153 Matt Ginter RC .30 .75
154 Peter Bergeron .20 .50
155 Roosevelt Brown .20 .50
156 Matt Cepicky RC .30 .75
157 Ramon Castro .20 .50
158 Brad Baisley RC .30 .75
159 Jason Hart RC .30 .75
160 Mitch Meluskey .20 .50
161 Chad Harville .20 .50
162 Brian Cooper .20 .50
163 Marcus Giles .20 .50
164 Jim Morris .50 1.25
165 Geoff Goetz .20 .50
166 Bobby Bradley RC .30 .75
167 Rob Bell .20 .50
168 Joe Crede 1.00 2.50
169 Michael Restovich .20 .50
170 Quincy Foster RC .30 .75
171 Enrique Cruz RC .30 .75
172 Mark Quinn .20 .50
173 Nick Johnson .20 .50
174 Jeff Liefer .20 .50
175 Kevin Mench RC 2.00 5.00
176 Steve Lomasney .20 .50
177 Jayson Werth .20 .50
178 Tim Drew .20 .50
179 Chip Ambres .20 .50
180 Ryan Anderson .20 .50
181 Matt Blank .20 .50
182 G. Chiaramonte .20 .50
183 Corey Myers RC .30 .75
184 Jeff Yoder .20 .50
185 Craig Dingman RC .30 .75
186 Jon Hamilton RC .30 .75
187 Toby Hall .20 .50
188 Russell Branyan .20 .50
189 Brian Falkenborg RC .30 .75
190 Aaron Harang RC 2.00 5.00
191 Juan Pena .20 .50
192 Chin-Hui Tsao RC 2.00 5.00
193 Alfonso Soriano .50 1.25
194 Alejandro Diaz RC .30 .75
195 Carlos Pena .20 .50
196 Kevin Nicholson .20 .50
197 Mo Bruce .20 .50
198 C.C. Sabathia .20 .50
199 Carl Crawford .20 .50
200 Rafael Furcal .20 .50
201 Andrew Beinbrink RC .30 .75
202 Jimmy Osting .20 .50
203 Aaron McNeal RC .30 .75
204 Brett Laxton .20 .50
205 Chris George .20 .50
206 Felipe Lopez .20 .50
207 Ben Sheets RC 2.50 6.00
208 Mike Meyers RC .50 1.25
209 Jason Conti .20 .50
210 Milton Bradley .20 .50
211 Chris Mears RC .30 .75
212 Carlos Hernandez RC .50 1.25
213 Jason Romano .20 .50
214 Geofrey Tomlinson .20 .50
215 Jimmy Rollins .20 .50
216 Pablo Ozuna .20 .50
217 Steve Cox .20 .50
218 Terrence Long .20 .50
219 Jeff DaVanon RC .50 1.25
220 Rick Ankiel .20 .50
221 Jason Standridge .20 .50
222 Tony Armas Jr. .20 .50
223 Jason Tyner .20 .50
224 Ramon Ortiz .20 .50
225 Daryle Ward .20 .50
226 Enger Veras RC .30 .75
227 Chris Jones .20 .50
228 Eric Cammack RC .30 .75
229 Ruben Mateo .20 .50
230 Ken Harvey RC .50 1.25
231 Jake Westbrook .20 .50
232 Rob Purvis RC .30 .75
233 Choo Freeman .20 .50
234 Aramis Ramirez .20 .50
235 A.J. Burnett .20 .50
236 Kevin Barker .20 .50
237 Chance Caple RC .30 .75
238 Jarrod Washburn .20 .50
239 Lance Berkman .20 .50
240 Michael Wenner RC .30 .75
241 Alex Sanchez .20 .50
242 Pat Daneker .20 .50
243 Grant Roberts .20 .50
244 Mark Ellis RC .50 1.25
245 Donny Leon .20 .50
246 David Eckstein .20 .50
247 Dicky Gonzalez RC .30 .75
248 John Patterson .20 .50
249 Chad Green .20 .50
250 Scot Shields RC .30 .75
251 Troy Cameron .20 .50
252 Jose Molina .20 .50
253 Rob Pugmire RC .30 .75
254 Rick Elder .20 .50
255 Sean Burroughs .20 .50
256 Josh Kalinowski RC .30 .75
257 Matt LeCroy .20 .50
258 Alex Graman RC .30 .75
259 Juan Silvestre RC .30 .75
260 Brady Clark .20 .50
261 Rico Washington RC .30 .75
262 Gary Matthews Jr. .20 .50
263 Matt Wise .20 .50
264 Keith Reed RC .30 .75
265 Santiago Ramirez RC .30 .75
266 Ben Broussard RC 1.25 3.00
267 Ryan Langerhans .20 .50
268 Juan Rivera .20 .50
269 Shawn Gallagher .20 .50
270 Jorge Toca .20 .50
271 Brad Lidge .30 .75
272 Leoncio Estrella RC .30 .75
273 Ruben Quevedo .20 .50
274 Jack Cust .20 .50
275 T.J. Tucker .20 .50
276 Mike Colangelo .20 .50
277 Brian Schneider .20 .50
278 Calvin Murray .20 .50
279 Josh Girdley .20 .50
280 Mike Paradis .20 .50
281 Chad Hermansen .20 .50
282 Ty Howington RC .30 .75
283 Aaron Myette .20 .50
284 D'Angelo Jimenez .20 .50
285 Dernell Stenson .20 .50
286 Jerry Hairston Jr. .20 .50
287 Gary Majewski RC .50 1.25
288 Derrin Ebert .20 .50
289 Steve Fish RC .30 .75
290 Carlos E. Hernandez .20 .50
291 Allen Levrault .20 .50
292 Sean McNally RC .30 .75
293 Randey Dorame RC .30 .75
294 Wes Anderson RC .30 .75
295 B.J. Ryan .20 .50
296 Alan Webb RC .30 .75
297 Brandon Inge RC 2.00 5.00
298 David Walling .20 .50

299 Sun Woo Kim RC .30 .75
300 Pat Burrell .20 .50
301 Rick Guttormson RC .30 .75
302 Gil Meche .20 .50
303 Carlos Zambrano RC 2.00 5.00
304 Eric Byrnes UER RC .40 1.00
Bo Porter pictured
305 Robb Quinlan RC .50 1.25
306 Jackie Rexrode .20 .50
307 Nate Bump .20 .50
308 Sean DePaula RC .30 .75
309 Matt Riley .20 .50
310 Ryan Minor .20 .50
311 J.J. Davis .20 .50
312 Randy Wolf .20 .50
313 Jason Jennings .20 .50
314 Scott Seabol RC .30 .75
315 Doug Davis .20 .50
316 Todd Moser RC .30 .75
317 Rob Ryan .20 .50
318 Bubba Crosby .20 .50
319 Lyle Overbay RC 1.25 3.00
320 Mario Encarnacion .20 .50
321 F.Rodriguez RC 2.50 6.00
322 Michael Cuddyer .20 .50
323 Ed Yarnall .20 .50
324 Cesar Saba RC .30 .75
325 Gookie Dawkins .20 .50
326 Alex Escobar .20 .50
327 Julio Zuleta RC .30 .75
328 Josh Hamilton .60 1.50
329 Carlos Urquiola RC .30 .75
330 Matt Belisle .20 .50
331 Kurt Ainsworth RC .30 .75
332 Tim Raines Jr. .20 .50
333 Eric Munson .20 .50
334 Donzell McDonald .20 .50
335 Larry Bigbie RC .75 2.00
336 Matt Watson RC .30 .75
337 Aubrey Huff .20 .50
338 Julio Ramirez .20 .50
339 Jason Grabowski RC .30 .75
340 Jon Garland .20 .50
341 Austin Kearns .20 .50
342 Josh Pressley RC .30 .75
343 Miguel Olivo RC .75 2.00
344 Julio Lugo .20 .50
345 Roberto Vaz .20 .50
346 Ramon Soler .20 .50
347 Brandon Phillips RC 1.50 4.00
348 Vince Faison RC .30 .75
349 Mike Venafro .20 .50
350 Rick Asadoorian RC .50 1.25
351 B.J. Garbe RC .30 .75
352 Dan Reichert .20 .50
353 Jason Stumm RC .30 .75
354 Ruben Salazar RC .30 .75
355 Francisco Cordero .20 .50
356 Juan Guzman RC .30 .75
357 Mike Bacsik RC .30 .75
358 Jared Sandberg .20 .50
359 Rod Barajas .20 .50
360 Junior Brignac RC .30 .75
361 J.M. Gold .20 .50
362 Octavio Dotel .20 .50
363 David Kelton .20 .50
364 Scott Morgan .20 .50
365 Wascar Serrano RC .30 .75
366 Wilton Veras .20 .50
367 Eugene Kingsale .20 .50
368 Ted Lilly .20 .50
369 George Lombard .20 .50
370 Chris Haas .20 .50
371 Wilton Pena RC .30 .75
372 Vernon Wells .20 .50
373 Keith Ginter RC .30 .75
374 Jeff Heaverlo RC .30 .75
375 Calvin Pickering .20 .50
376 Mike Lamb RC .75 2.00
377 Kyle Snyder .20 .50
378 Javier Cardona RC .30 .75
379 Aaron Rowand RC 2.00 5.00
380 Dee Brown .20 .50
381 Brett Myers RC 1.50 4.00
382 Abraham Nunez .20 .50
383 Eric Valent .20 .50
384 Jody Gerut RC .50 1.25
385 Adam Dunn .50 1.25
386 Jay Gehrke .20 .50
387 Omar Ortiz .20 .50
388 Darnell McDonald .20 .50
389 Tony Schrager RC .30 .75
390 J.D. Closser .20 .50
391 Ben Christensen RC .30 .75
392 Adam Kennedy .20 .50
393 Nick Green RC .30 .75
394 Ramon Hernandez .20 .50
395 Roy Oswalt RC 5.00 12.00
396 Andy Tracy RC .30 .75
397 Eric Gagne .50 1.25
398 Michael Tejera RC .30 .75
399 Adam Everett .20 .50
400 Corey Patterson .20 .50
401 Gary Knotts RC .30 .75
402 Ryan Christianson RC .30 .75
403 Eric Ireland RC .30 .75
404 Andrew Good RC .30 .75
405 Brad Penny .20 .50
406 Jason LaRue .20 .50
407 Kit Pellow .20 .50
408 Kevin Beirne .20 .50
409 Kelly Dransfeldt .20 .50
410 Jason Grilli .20 .50
411 Scott Downs RC .30 .75
412 Jesus Colome .20 .50
413 John Sneed RC .30 .75
414 Tony McKnight .20 .50
415 Luis Rivera .20 .50
416 Adam Eaton .20 .50
417 Mike MacDougal RC .50 1.25
418 Mike Nannini .20 .50
419 Barry Zito RC 4.00 10.00
420 DeWayne Wise .20 .50
421 Jason Dellaero .20 .50
422 Chad Moeller .20 .50
423 Jason Marquis .20 .50
424 Tim Redding RC .50 1.25
425 Mark Mulder .20 .50
426 Josh Paul .20 .50
427 Chris Enochs .20 .50
428 W.Rodriguez RC .30 .75
429 Kevin Witt .20 .50
430 Scott Sobkowiak RC .30 .75
431 McKay Christensen .20 .50
432 Jung Bong .20 .50
433 Keith Evans RC .30 .75
434 Garry Maddox Jr. RC .30 .75
435 Ramon Santiago RC .30 .75
436 Alex Cora .20 .50
437 Carlos Lee .20 .50
438 Jason Repko RC .75 2.00
439 Matt Burch .20 .50
440 Shawn Sonnier RC .30 .75

2000 Bowman Chrome Oversize

Inserted into hobby boxes as a chip-topper at one per box, this eight-card oversized set features some of the Major Leagues most promising young players.

COMPLETE SET (8) 6.00 15.00
1 Pat Burrell .50 1.25
2 Josh Hamilton 1.25 3.00
3 Rafael Furcal .20 .50
4 Corey Patterson .30 .75
5 A.J. Burnett .30 .75
6 Eric Munson .30 .75
7 Nick Johnson .20 .50
8 Alfonso Soriano .20 .50

2000 Bowman Chrome Refractors

Randomly inserted into packs at one in 12, this 440-card insert is a complete parallel of the Bowman Chrome base set. This parallel was produced using Topps' refractor technology.

*STARS: 3X TO 8X BASIC CARDS
*ROOKIES: 2X TO 5X BASIC CARDS

2000 Bowman Chrome Retro/Future

Randomly inserted into hobby/retail packs at one in six, this 440-card insert is a complete parallel of the Bowman Chrome base set. Each card features a television border similar to that of the 1955 Bowman set.

*STARS: 1.5X TO 4X BASIC CARDS
*ROOKIES: .5X TO 1.2X BASIC CARDS

2000 Bowman Chrome Retro/Future Refractors

Randomly inserted into hobby/retail packs at one in 60, this 440-card insert is a complete parallel of the Bowman Chrome base set. Each card features a television border similar to that of the 1955 Bowman set. These cards were produced using Topps' refractor technology.

*STARS: 6X TO 15X BASIC CARDS
*ROOKIES: 4X TO 10X BASIC CARDS

2000 Bowman Chrome Bidding for the Call

Randomly inserted into packs at one in 16, this 15-card insert features players that are looking to break into the Major Leagues during the 2000 season. Card backs carry a "BC" prefix. It's worth noting that top prospect Chin-Feng Chen's very first MLB-licensed card was included in this set.

COMPLETE SET (15) 12.50 30.00
*REFFRACTORS: 1.25X TO 3X BASIC BID
REFRACTOR STATED ODDS 1:160
BC1 Adam Piatt .40 1.00
BC2 Pat Burrell .40 1.00
BC3 Mark Mulder .40 1.00
BC4 Nick Johnson .40 1.00
BC5 Alfonso Soriano .75 2.00
BC6 Chin-Feng Chen .40 1.00
BC7 Scott Sobkowiak .40 1.00
BC8 Corey Patterson .40 1.00
BC9 Jack Cust .40 1.00
BC10 Sean Burroughs .40 1.00
BC11 Josh Hamilton 1.50 4.00
BC12 Corey Myers .40 1.00
BC13 Eric Munson .40 1.00
BC14 Wes Anderson .40 1.00
BC15 Lyle Overbay .75 2.00

2000 Bowman Chrome Meteoric Rise

Randomly inserted into packs at one in 24, this 10-card insert features players that have risen to the occasion during their careers. Card backs carry a "MR" prefix.

COMPLETE SET (10) 20.00 50.00
*REF: 1.25X TO 3X BASIC METEORIC
REFRACTOR STATED ODDS 1:240
MR1 Nomar Garciaparra 2.00 5.00
MR2 Mark McGwire 3.00 8.00
MR3 Ken Griffey Jr. 2.00 5.00
MR4 Chipper Jones 1.25 3.00
MR5 Manny Ramirez .75 2.00
MR6 Mike Piazza 2.00 5.00
MR7 Cal Ripken 4.00 10.00
MR8 Ivan Rodriguez .75 2.00
MR9 Greg Maddux 2.00 5.00
MR10 Randy Johnson 1.25 3.00

2000 Bowman Chrome Rookie Class 2000

Randomly inserted into packs at one in 24, this 10-card insert features players that made their Major League debuts in 2000. Card backs carry a "RC" prefix.

COMPLETE SET (10) 8.00 20.00
*REF: 1.25X TO 3X BASIC ROOKIE CLASS
REFRACTOR STATED ODDS 1:240
RC1 Pat Burrell .60 1.50
RC2 Rick Ankiel .60 1.50
RC3 Ruben Mateo .60 1.50
RC4 Vernon Wells .60 1.50
RC5 Mark Mulder .60 1.50
RC6 A.J. Burnett .60 1.50
RC7 Chad Hermansen .60 1.50
RC8 Corey Patterson .60 1.50
RC9 Rafael Furcal .60 1.50
RC10 Mike Lamb 1.00 2.50

2000 Bowman Chrome Teen Idols

Randomly inserted into packs at one in 16, this 15-card insert set features Major League players that either made it to the majors as teenagers or are top current prospects who are still in their teens in 2000. Card backs carry a "TI" prefix.

COMPLETE SET (15) 20.00 50.00
*SINGLES: 1X TO 2.5X BASIC CARDS
*REFRACTORS: 1.25X TO 3X BASIC TEEN
REFRACTOR STATED ODDS 1:160
TI1 Alex Rodriguez 2.50 6.00
TI2 Andruw Jones 1.00 2.50
TI3 Juan Gonzalez .60 1.50
TI4 Ivan Rodriguez 1.00 2.50
TI5 Ken Griffey Jr. 2.50 6.00
TI6 Bobby Bradley .60 1.50
TI7 Brett Myers 1.00 2.50
TI8 C.C. Sabathia .60 1.50
TI9 Ty Howington .60 1.50
TI10 Brandon Phillips 1.50 4.00
TI11 Rick Asadoorian .60 1.50
TI12 Wily Mo Pena .60 1.50
TI13 Sean Burroughs .60 1.50
TI14 Josh Hamilton 1.50 4.00
TI15 Rafael Furcal .60 1.50

2000 Bowman Chrome Draft

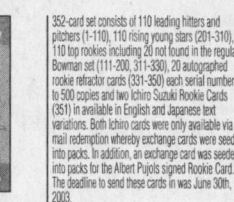

The 2000 Bowman Chrome Draft Picks and Prospects set was released in December, 2000 as a 110-card parallel of the 2000 Bowman Draft Picks set. This product was distributed only in factory set form. Each set features Topps' Chrome technology. A limited selection of prospects were switched out from the Bowman checklist and are featured exclusively in this Bowman Chrome set. The most notable of these players include Timo Perez and Jon Rauch. Other notable Rookie Cards include Chin-Feng Chen and Adrian Gonzalez.

COMP.FACT.SET (110) 20.00 50.00
1 Pat Burrell .20 .50
2 Rafael Furcal .20 .50
3 Grant Roberts .20 .50
4 Barry Zito 1.50 4.00
5 Julio Zuleta .20 .50
6 Mark Mulder .20 .50
7 Rob Bell .20 .50
8 Adam Piatt .20 .50
9 Mike Lamb .30 .75
10 Pablo Ozuna .20 .50
11 Jason Tyner .20 .50
12 Jason Marquis .20 .50
13 Eric Munson .20 .50
14 Seth Etherton .20 .50
15 Milton Bradley .20 .50
16 Nick Green .20 .50
17 Chin-Feng Chen RC .60 1.50
18 Matt Boone RC .20 .50
19 Kevin Gregg RC .20 .50
20 Eddy Garabito RC .20 .50
21 Aaron Capista RC .20 .50
22 Esteban German RC .20 .50
23 Derek Thompson RC .20 .50
24 Phil Merrell RC .20 .50
25 Brian O'Connor RC .20 .50
26 Yamid Haad .20 .50
27 Hector Mercado RC .20 .50
28 Jason Woolf RC .20 .50
29 Eddy Furniss RC .20 .50
30 Cha Sueng Baek RC .20 .50
31 Colby Lewis RC .40 1.00
32 Pasqual Coco RC .20 .50
33 Jorge Cantu RC 2.00 5.00
34 Erasmo Ramirez RC .20 .50
35 Bobby Kielty RC .40 1.00
36 Joaquin Benoit RC .20 .50
37 Brian Esposito RC .20 .50
38 Michael Wenner .20 .50
39 Juan Rincon RC .20 .50
40 Yorvit Torrealba RC 1.25 3.00
41 Chad Durham RC .20 .50
42 Jim Mann RC .20 .50
43 Shane Loux RC .20 .50
44 Luis Rivas .20 .50
45 Ken Chenard RC .20 .50
46 Mike Lockwood RC .20 .50
47 Yovanny Lara RC .20 .50
48 Bubba Carpenter RC .20 .50
49 Ryan Dittfurth RC .20 .50
50 John Stephens RC .20 .50
51 Pedro Feliz RC 1.00 2.50
52 Kenny Kelly RC .20 .50
53 Neil Jenkins RC .20 .50
54 Mike Glendenning RC .20 .50
55 Bo Porter .20 .50
56 Eric Byrnes .20 .50
57 Tony Alvarez RC .20 .50
58 Kazuhiro Sasaki RC .60 1.50
59 Chad Durbin RC .20 .50
60 Mike Bynum RC .20 .50
61 Travis Wilson RC .20 .50
62 Jose Leon RC .20 .50
63 Ryan Vogelsong RC 2.50 6.00
64 Geraldo Guzman RC .20 .50
65 Craig Anderson RC .20 .50
66 Carlos Silva RC .40 1.00
67 Brad Thomas RC .20 .50
68 Chin-Hui Tsao .60 1.50
69 Mark Buehrle RC 4.00 10.00
70 Juan Salas RC .20 .50
71 Denny Abreu RC .20 .50
72 Keith McDonald RC .20 .50
73 Chris Richard RC .20 .50
74 Tomas De la Rosa RC .20 .50
75 Vicente Padilla RC .40 1.00
76 Justin Brunette RC .20 .50
77 Scott Linebrink RC .20 .50
78 Jeff Sparks RC .20 .50
79 Tike Redman RC .60 1.50
80 John Lackey RC 2.00 5.00
81 Joe Strong RC .20 .50
82 Brian Tollberg RC .20 .50
83 Steve Sisco RC .20 .50
84 Chris Clapinski RC .20 .50
85 Augie Ojeda RC .20 .50
86 Adrian Gonzalez RC 10.00 25.00
87 Mike Stodolka RC .20 .50
88 Adam Johnson RC .20 .50
89 Matt Wheatland RC .20 .50
90 Corey Smith RC .20 .50
91 Rocco Baldelli RC 2.00 5.00
92 Keith Bucktrot RC .20 .50
93 Adam Wainwright RC 1.50 4.00
94 Blaine Boyer RC .20 .50
95 Aaron Herr RC .40 1.00
96 Scott Thorman RC 1.00 2.50
97 Bryan Digby RC .20 .50
98 Josh Shortslef RC .20 .50
99 Sean Smith RC .20 .50
100 Alex Cruz RC .20 .50
101 Marc Love RC .20 .50
102 Kevin Lee RC .20 .50
103 Timo Perez RC .40 1.00
104 Alex Cabrera RC .40 1.00
105 Shane Heams RC .20 .50
106 Tripper Johnson RC .20 .50
107 Brent Abernathy RC .20 .50
108 John Cotton RC .20 .50
109 Brad Wilkerson RC 1.00 2.50
110 Jon Rauch RC .20 .50

2001 Bowman Chrome

The 2001 Bowman Chrome set was distributed in four-card packs with a suggested retail price of $3.99. This 352-card set consists of 110 leading hitters and pitchers (1-110), 110 rising young stars (201-310), 110 top rookies including 20 not found in the regular Bowman set (111-200, 311-330), 20 autographed rookie refractor cards (331-350) each serial numbered to 500 copies and two Ichiro Suzuki Rookie Cards (351) in available in English and Japanese text variations. Both Ichiro cards were only available via mail redemption whereby exchange cards were seeded into packs. In addition, an exchange card was seeded into packs for the Albert Pujols signed Rookie Card. The deadline to send these cards in was June 30th, 2003.

COMP.SET w/o SP's (220) 20.00 50.00
COMMON (1-110/201-310) .20 .50
COMMON (111-200/311-330) 2.00 5.00
COMMON (331-350) 6.00 15.00
1 Jason Giambi .20 .50
2 Rafael Furcal .20 .50
3 Bernie Williams .30 .75
4 Kenny Lofton .20 .50
5 Al Leiter .20 .50
6 Albert Belle .20 .50
7 Craig Biggio .30 .75
8 Mark Mulder .20 .50
9 Carlos Delgado .20 .50
10 Darin Erstad .20 .50
11 Richie Sexson .20 .50
12 Randy Johnson .50 1.25
13 Greg Maddux .75 2.00
14 Orlando Hernandez .20 .50
15 Javier Vazquez .20 .50
16 Jeff Kent .20 .50
17 Jim Thome .30 .75
18 John Olerud .20 .50
19 Jason Kendall .20 .50
20 Scott Rolen .30 .75
21 Tony Gwynn .60 1.50
22 Edgardo Alfonzo .20 .50
23 Pokey Reese .20 .50
24 Todd Helton .30 .75
25 Mark Quinn .20 .50
26 Dean Palmer .20 .50
27 Ray Durham .20 .50
28 Rafael Palmeiro .30 .75
29 Carl Everett .20 .50
30 Vladimir Guerrero .50 1.25
31 Livan Hernandez .20 .50
32 Preston Wilson .20 .50
33 Jose Vidro .20 .50
34 Fred McGriff .30 .75
35 Kevin Brown .20 .50
36 Miguel Tejada .20 .50
37 Chipper Jones .50 1.25
38 Edgar Martinez .30 .75
39 Tony Batista .20 .50
40 Jorge Posada .30 .75
41 Sammy Sosa .50 1.25
42 Gary Sheffield .20 .50
43 Bartolo Colon .20 .50
44 Pat Burrell .20 .50
45 Jay Payton .20 .50
46 Mike Mussina .30 .75
47 Nomar Garciaparra .75 2.00
48 Darren Dreifort .20 .50
49 Richard Hidalgo .20 .50
50 Troy Glaus .20 .50
51 Ben Grieve .20 .50
52 Jim Edmonds .20 .50
53 Raul Mondesi .20 .50
54 Andruw Jones .30 .75
55 Mike Sweeney .20 .50
56 Derek Jeter 1.25 3.00
57 Ruben Mateo .20 .50
58 Cristian Guzman .20 .50
59 Mike Hampton .20 .50
60 J.D. Drew .20 .50
61 Matt Lawton .20 .50
62 Moises Alou .20 .50
63 Terrence Long .20 .50
64 Geoff Jenkins .20 .50
65 Manny Ramirez Sox .30 .75
66 Johnny Damon .30 .75
67 Pedro Martinez .30 .75
68 Juan Gonzalez .20 .50
69 Roger Clemens 1.00 2.50
70 Carlos Beltran .20 .50
71 Roberto Alomar .30 .75
72 Barry Bonds 1.25 3.00
73 Tim Hudson .20 .50
74 Tom Glavine .30 .75
75 Jeromy Burnitz .20 .50
76 Adrian Beltre .20 .50
77 Mike Piazza .75 2.00
78 Kerry Wood .20 .50
79 Steve Finley .20 .50
80 Bob Abreu .20 .50
81 Neifi Perez .20 .50
82 Mark Redman .20 .50
83 Paul Konerko .20 .50
84 Jermaine Dye .20 .50
85 Brian Giles .20 .50
86 Ivan Rodriguez .30 .75
87 Adam Kennedy .20 .50
88 Eric Chavez .20 .50
89 Billy Koch .20 .50
90 Shawn Green .20 .50
91 Matt Williams .20 .50
92 Greg Vaughn .20 .50
93 Jeff Cirillo .20 .50
94 Frank Thomas .50 1.25
95 David Justice .20 .50
96 Cal Ripken 1.50 4.00
97 Curt Schilling .20 .50
98 Barry Zito .30 .75
99 Brian Jordan .20 .50
100 Chan Ho Park .20 .50
101 J.T. Snow .20 .50
102 Kazuhiro Sasaki .20 .50
103 Alex Rodriguez .75 2.00
104 Mariano Rivera .50 1.25
105 Eric Milton .20 .50
106 Andy Pettitte .30 .75
107 Ken Griffey Jr. .75 2.00
108 Bengie Molina .20 .50
109 Jeff Bagwell .30 .75
110 Mark McGwire 1.25 3.00
111 Dan Tosca RC 2.00 5.00
112 Sergio Contreras RC 3.00 8.00
113 Mitch Jones RC 3.00 8.00
114 Ramon Carvajal RC 3.00 8.00
115 Ryan Madson RC 4.00 10.00
116 Hank Blalock RC 6.00 15.00
117 Ben Washburn RC 2.00 5.00
118 Erick Almonte RC 2.00 5.00
119 Shawn Fagan RC 3.00 8.00
120 Gary Johnson RC 2.00 5.00
121 Brett Evert RC 2.00 5.00
122 Joe Hamer RC 3.00 8.00
123 Yhency Brazoban RC 4.00 10.00
124 Domingo Guante RC 2.00 5.00
125 Deivi Mendez RC 2.00 5.00
126 Adrian Hernandez RC 2.00 5.00
127 R. Abercrombie RC 4.00 10.00
128 Steve Bennett RC 2.00 5.00
129 Matt White RC 3.00 8.00
130 Brian Hitchcox RC 2.00 5.00
131 Deivis Santos RC 2.00 5.00
132 Luis Montanez RC 4.00 10.00
133 Eric Reynolds RC 2.00 5.00
134 Denny Bautista RC 4.00 10.00
135 Hector Garcia RC 2.00 5.00
136 Joe Thurston RC 3.00 8.00
137 Tsuyoshi Shinjo RC 4.00 10.00
138 Elpidio Guzman RC 2.00 5.00
139 Brian Bass RC 2.00 5.00
140 Mark Burnett RC 3.00 8.00
141 Russ Jacobson UER 2.00 5.00
Last name misspelled Jacobsen on front
142 Travis Hafner RC 5.00 12.00
143 Wilson Betemit RC 6.00 15.00
144 Luke Lockwood RC 3.00 8.00
145 Noel Devarez RC 3.00 8.00
146 Doug Gredvig RC 2.00 5.00
147 Seung Song RC 3.00 8.00
148 Andy Van Hekken RC 2.00 5.00
149 Ryan Kohlmeier 2.00 5.00
150 Dee Haynes RC 2.00 5.00
151 Jim Journell RC 3.00 8.00
152 Chad Petty RC 2.00 5.00
153 Danny Borrell RC 2.00 5.00
154 Dave Krynzel 2.00 5.00
155 Octavio Martinez RC 3.00 8.00
156 David Parrish RC 2.00 5.00
157 Jason Miller RC 2.00 5.00
158 Corey Spencer RC 2.00 5.00
159 Maxim St. Pierre RC 3.00 8.00
160 Pat Magness RC 3.00 8.00
161 Ranier Olmedo RC 3.00 8.00
162 Brandon Mims RC 2.00 5.00
163 Phil Wilson RC 3.00 8.00
164 Jose Reyes RC 30.00 60.00
165 Matt Butler RC 3.00 8.00
166 Joel Pineiro 3.00 8.00
167 Ken Chenard 2.00 5.00
168 Alexis Gomez RC 2.00 5.00
169 Justin Morneau RC 20.00 50.00
170 Josh Fogg RC 3.00 8.00
171 Charles Frazier RC 2.00 5.00
172 Ryan Ludwick RC 10.00 25.00
173 Seth McClung RC 3.00 8.00
174 Justin Wayne RC 3.00 8.00
175 Rafael Soriano RC 4.00 10.00
176 Jared Abruzzo RC 2.00 5.00
177 Jason Richardson RC 2.00 5.00
178 Darwin Cubillan RC 2.00 5.00
179 Blake Williams RC 2.00 5.00
180 V. Pascucci RC 3.00 8.00
181 Ryan Hannaman RC 3.00 8.00
182 Steve Smyth RC 3.00 8.00
183 Jake Peavy RC 15.00 40.00
184 Onix Mercado RC 3.00 8.00
185 Luis Torres RC 3.00 8.00
186 Casey Fossum RC 2.00 5.00
187 Eduardo Figueroa RC 2.00 5.00
188 Bryan Barnowski RC 2.00 5.00
189 Jason Standridge 2.00 5.00
190 Marvin Seale RC 3.00 8.00
191 Steve Smitherman RC 3.00 8.00
192 Rafael Boitel RC 2.00 5.00
193 Dany Morban RC 2.00 5.00
194 Justin Woodrow RC 3.00 8.00
195 Ed Rogers RC 2.00 5.00
196 Ben Hendrickson RC 2.00 5.00
197 Thomas Mitchell 2.00 5.00
198 Adam Pettyjohn RC 2.00 5.00
199 Doug Nickle RC 2.00 5.00
200 Jason Jones RC 2.00 5.00
201 Larry Barnes .20 .50
202 Ben Diggins .20 .50
203 Dee Brown .20 .50
204 Rocco Baldelli .20 .50
205 Luis Terrero .20 .50
206 Milton Bradley .20 .50
207 Kurt Ainsworth .20 .50
208 Sean Burroughs .20 .50
209 Rick Asadoorian .20 .50
210 Ramon Castro .20 .50
211 Nick Neugebauer .20 .50
212 Aaron Myette .20 .50
213 Luis Matos .20 .50
214 Donnie Bridges .20 .50
215 Alex Cintron .20 .50
216 Bobby Kielty .20 .50
217 Matt Belisle .20 .50
218 Adam Everett .20 .50
219 John Lackey .20 .50
220 Adam Wainwright .75 2.00
221 Jerry Hairston Jr. .20 .50
222 Mike Bynum .20 .50
223 Ryan Christianson .20 .50
224 J.J. Davis .20 .50
225 Alex Graman .20 .50
226 Abraham Nunez .20 .50
227 Sun Woo Kim .20 .50
228 Jimmy Rollins .20 .50
229 Ruben Salazar .20 .50
230 Josh Girdley .20 .50
231 Carl Crawford .20 .50
232 Ben Davis .20 .50
233 Jason Grabowski .20 .50
234 Chris George .20 .50
235 Roy Oswalt .50 1.25
236 Brian Cole .20 .50
237 Corey Patterson .20 .50
238 Vernon Wells .20 .50
239 Brad Baker .20 .50
240 Gookie Dawkins .20 .50
241 Michael Cuddyer .20 .50
242 Ricardo Aramboles .20 .50
243 Ben Sheets .30 .75
244 Toby Hall .20 .50
245 Jack Cust .20 .50
246 Pedro Feliz .20 .50
247 Josh Beckett .30 .75
248 Alex Escobar .20 .50
249 Marcus Giles .20 .50
250 Jon Rauch .20 .50
251 Kevin Mench .20 .50
252 Shawn Sonnier .20 .50
253 Aaron Rowand .20 .50
254 C.C. Sabathia .20 .50
255 Bubba Crosby .20 .50
256 Josh Hamilton .40 1.00
257 Carlos Hernandez .20 .50
258 Carlos Pena .20 .50
259 Miguel Cabrera 1.50 4.00
260 Brandon Phillips .20 .50
261 Tony Pena Jr. .20 .50
262 Cristian Guerrero .20 .50
263 Jin Ho Cho .20 .50
264 Aaron Herr .20 .50
265 Keith Ginter .20 .50
266 Felipe Lopez .20 .50
267 Travis Harper .20 .50
268 Joe Torres .20 .50
269 Eric Byrnes .20 .50
270 Ben Christensen .20 .50
271 Aubrey Huff .20 .50
272 Lyle Overbay .20 .50
273 Vince Faison .20 .50
274 Bobby Bradley .20 .50
275 Joe Crede .50 1.25
276 Matt Wheatland .20 .50
277 Grady Sizemore .75 2.00
278 Adrian Gonzalez 1.25 3.00
279 Tim Raines Jr. .20 .50
280 Phil Dumatrait .20 .50
281 Jason Hart .20 .50
282 David Kelton .20 .50
283 David Walling .20 .50
284 J.R. House .20 .50
285 Kenny Kelly .20 .50
286 Aaron McNeal .20 .50
287 Nick Johnson .20 .50
288 Scott Heard .20 .50
289 Brad Wilkerson .20 .50
290 Allen Levrault .20 .50
291 Chris Richard .20 .50
292 Jared Sandberg .20 .50
293 Tike Redman .20 .60
294 Adam Dunn .30 .75
295 Josh Pressley .20 .50
296 Jose Ortiz .20 .50
297 Jason Romano .20 .50
298 Tim Redding .20 .50
299 Alex Gordon .20 .50
300 Ben Petrick .20 .50
301 Eric Munson .20 .50
302 Luis Rivas .20 .50
303 Matt Ginter .20 .50
304 Alfonso Soriano .30 .75
305 Wilfredo Rodriguez .20 .50
306 Brett Myers .20 .50
307 Scott Seabol .20 .50
308 Tony Alvarez .20 .50
309 Donzell McDonald .20 .50
310 Austin Kearns .20 .50
311 Will Ohman RC 3.00 8.00
312 Ryan Soules RC 2.00 5.00
313 Cody Ross RC 6.00 15.00
314 Bill Whitecotton RC 2.00 5.00
315 Mike Burns RC 3.00 8.00
316 Manuel Acosta RC 2.00 5.00
317 Lance Niekro RC 4.00 10.00
318 Travis Thompson RC 3.00 8.00
319 Zach Sorensen RC 3.00 8.00
320 Austin Evans RC 2.00 5.00
321 Brad Stiles RC 2.00 5.00
322 Joe Kennedy RC 4.00 10.00
323 Luke Martin RC 3.00 8.00
324 Juan Diaz RC 3.00 8.00
325 Pat Hallmark RC 2.00 5.00
326 Christian Parker RC 2.00 5.00
327 Ronny Corona RC 3.00 8.00
328 Jermaine Clark RC 2.00 5.00
329 Scott Dunn RC 3.00 8.00
330 Scott Chiasson RC 3.00 8.00
331 Greg Nash AU RC 6.00 15.00
332 Brad Cresse AU 6.00 15.00
333 John Buck AU RC 12.50 30.00
334 Freddie Bynum AU RC 6.00 15.00
335 Felix Diaz AU RC 6.00 15.00
336 Jason Belcher AU RC 6.00 15.00
337 T.Farnsworth AU RC 6.00 15.00
338 Roberto Miniel AU RC 6.00 15.00
339 Esix Snead AU RC 6.00 15.00
340 Albert Pujols AU RC 3000.00 4000.00
341 Jeff Andra AU RC 6.00 15.00
342 Victor Hall AU RC 6.00 15.00
343 Pedro Liriano AU RC 6.00 15.00
344 Andy Beal AU RC 6.00 15.00
345 Bob Keppel AU RC 6.00 15.00
346 Brian Schmitt AU RC 6.00 15.00
347 Ron Davenport AU RC 90.00 150.00
348 Tony Blanco AU RC 6.00 15.00
349 Reggie Griggs AU RC 6.00 15.00
350 D. Van Dusen AU RC 6.00 15.00
351A I. Suzuki English RC 75.00 150.00
351B I. Suzuki Japan RC 75.00 150.00

2001 Bowman Chrome Gold Refractors

Randomly inserted in packs at the rate of one in 47, this 330-card set is a parallel version of the base set with a distinctive gold refractive quality. Only 99 serially numbered sets were produced. Exchange cards with a redemption deadline of June 30th, 2003 for two separate Ichiro Suzuki issues were seeded into packs.

One of the features English text on the card back with 50 copies produced and the other features Japanese text on the card back with 49 copies produced. Both cards were serial-numbered together resulting in an intermingled print run of 99 copies with English cards featuring odd serial-numbering (i.e. 1/99, 3/99, 5/99 etc.) and Japanese cards featuring even serial-numbering (i.e. 2/99, 4/99, 6/99 etc.).

*STARS: 8X TO 20X BASIC CARDS
*ROOKIES: 1.5X TO 4X BASIC CARDS
ICHIRO JAPAN PRINT RUN 49 #'d CARDS
ICHIRO ENGLISH ARE EVEN SERIAL #'d
ICHIRO ENGLISH ARE ODD SERIAL #'d

Card	Low	High
NNOA Ichiro Suzuki English/50 EXCH	400.00	800.00
NNOB Ichiro Suzuki Japan/49 EXCH	400.00	800.00

2001 Bowman Chrome X-Fractors

Randomly inserted in packs at the rate of one in 23, this 330-card set is a parallel version of the base set highlighted by a distinct background pattern. Exchange cards with a redemption deadline of June 30th, 2003 for two separate Ichiro Suzuki issues (English text and Japanese text) were randomly seeded into packs.

*STARS: 4X TO 10X BASIC CARDS
*ROOKIES: .75X TO 2X BASIC CARDS

2001 Bowman Chrome Futures Game Relics

Randomly inserted in packs at the rate of one in 460, this 30-card set features color photos of players who participated in the 2000 Futures Game in Atlanta with pieces of game-worn uniform numbers and letters embedded in the cards.

Card	Low	High
FGRAE Alex Escobar	3.00	8.00
FGRAM Aaron Myette	3.00	8.00
FGRBB Bobby Bradley	3.00	8.00
FGRBP Ben Petrick	3.00	8.00
FGRBS Ben Sheets	6.00	15.00
FGRBW Brad Wilkerson	3.00	8.00
FGRBZ Barry Zito	6.00	15.00
FGRCA Craig Anderson	3.00	8.00
FGRCC Chin-Feng Chen	30.00	60.00
FGRCG Chris George	3.00	8.00
FGRCH Carlos Hernandez	4.00	10.00
FGRCP Carlos Pena	10.00	25.00
FGRCT Chin-Hui Tsao	40.00	80.00
FGREM Eric Munson	3.00	8.00
FGRFL Felipe Lopez	4.00	10.00
FGRJC Jack Cust	3.00	8.00
FGRJH Josh Hamilton	6.00	15.00
FGRJR Jason Romano	3.00	8.00
FGRJZ Julio Zuleta	3.00	8.00
FGRKA Kurt Ainsworth	3.00	8.00
FGRMB Mike Bynum	3.00	8.00
FGRMG Marcus Giles	4.00	10.00
FGRNN Ntema Ndungidi	3.00	8.00
FGRRA Ryan Anderson	3.00	8.00
FGRRC Ramon Castro	3.00	8.00
FGRRD Randey Dorame	3.00	8.00
FGRSK Sun Woo Kim	3.00	8.00
FGRTO Tomo Ohka	3.00	8.00
FGRTW Travis Wilson	3.00	8.00
FGRDCP Corey Patterson	3.00	8.00

2001 Bowman Chrome Rookie Reprints

Randomly inserted in packs at the rate of one in 12, this 25-card set features reprints of classic 1948-1955 Bowman rookies printed on polished Chrome finishes.

Card	Low	High
COMPLETE SET (25)	20.00	50.00
*REFRACTORS: .75X TO 2X BASIC REPRINT		
REFRACTOR STATED ODDS 1:203		
REF.PRINT RUN 299 SERIAL #'d SETS		
1 Yogi Berra	3.00	8.00
2 Ralph Kiner	1.50	4.00
3 Stan Musial	5.00	12.00
4 Warren Spahn	1.50	4.00
5 Roy Campanella	3.00	8.00
6 Bob Lemon	1.50	4.00
7 Robin Roberts	1.50	4.00
8 Duke Snider	1.50	4.00
9 Early Wynn	1.50	4.00
10 Richie Ashburn	1.50	4.00
11 Gil Hodges	2.50	6.00
12 Hank Bauer	1.50	4.00
13 Don Newcombe	1.50	4.00
14 Al Rosen	1.50	4.00
15 Willie Mays	6.00	15.00
16 Joe Garagiola	1.50	4.00
17 Whitey Ford	1.50	4.00
18 Lew Burdette	1.50	4.00
19 Gil McDougald	1.50	4.00
20 Minnie Minoso	1.50	4.00
21 Eddie Mathews	2.50	6.00
22 Harvey Kuenn	1.50	4.00
23 Don Larsen	1.50	4.00
24 Elston Howard	1.50	4.00
25 Don Zimmer	1.50	4.00

2001 Bowman Chrome Rookie Reprints Relics

This six-card insert set features color player photos with pieces of their Rookie Season game-worn jerseys or game-used bats embedded in the cards. The insertion rate for the Mike Piazza Bat card is one in 3674 and one in 244 for the jersey cards. Three cards are Bowman Rookie card reprints and three cards are re-created "cards that never were."

Card	Low	High
1 David Justice Jsy	4.00	10.00
2 Richie Sexson Jsy	4.00	10.00
3 Sean Casey Jsy	4.00	10.00
4 Mike Piazza Bat	15.00	40.00
5 Carlos Delgado Jsy	4.00	10.00
6 Chipper Jones Jsy	6.00	15.00

2002 Bowman Chrome

This 405 card set was issued in July, 2002. It was issued in four card packs with an SRP of $4 which were packed 18 packs to a box and 12 boxes to a case. The first 110 card of the set featured veteran players. The next grouping of cards (111-383) featured a mix of rookies and prospect cards. The then final grouping (384-405) featured signed rookie cards. Both So Taguchi and Kazuhisa Ishii were also printed without autographs on their cards. An exchange was inserted into packs for Jake Mauer's autographed RC. The exchange card was intended to be card number 388 in the checklist but the actual Mauer autograph mailed out to collectors was card number 324. Thus, this set actually has two cards numbered 324 (the Jake Mauer autograph and a basic-issue Ben Broussard card) and no number 388.

Card	Low	High
COMP.RED SET (110)	15.00	40.00
COMP.BLUE w/o SP's (110)	15.00	40.00
COMMON RED (1-110)	.20	.50
COMMON BLUE (111-383)	.30	.75
COMMON AU (324B/384-405)	4.00	10.00
324B/384-405 GROUP A AUTO ODDS 1:28		
403-404 GROUP B AUTO ODDS 1:1290		
324B/384-405 OVERALL AUTO ODDS 1:27		
1 Adam Dunn	.20	.50
2 Derek Jeter	1.25	3.00
3 Alex Rodriguez	.75	2.00
4 Miguel Tejada	.20	.50
5 Nomar Garciaparra	.75	2.00
6 Toby Hall	.20	.50
7 Brandon Duckworth	.20	.50
8 Paul LoDuca	.20	.50
9 Brian Giles	.20	.50
10 C.C. Sabathia	.20	.50
11 Curt Schilling	.20	.50
12 Tsuyoshi Shinjo	.20	.50
13 Ramon Hernandez	.20	.50
14 Jose Cruz Jr.	.20	.50
15 Albert Pujols	1.00	2.50
16 Joe Mays	.20	.50
17 Javy Lopez	.20	.50
18 J.T. Snow	.20	.50
19 David Segui	.20	.50
20 Jorge Posada	.30	.75
21 Doug Mientkiewicz	.20	.50
22 Jerry Hairston Jr.	.20	.50
23 Bernie Williams	.30	.75
24 Mike Sweeney	.20	.50
25 Jason Giambi	.20	.50
26 Ryan Dempster	.20	.50
27 Ryan Klesko	.20	.50
28 Mark Quinn	.20	.50
29 Jeff Kent	.20	.50
30 Eric Chavez	.20	.50
31 Adrian Beltre	.20	.50
32 Andruw Jones	.30	.75
33 Alfonso Soriano	.20	.50
34 Aramis Ramirez	.20	.50
35 Greg Maddux	.75	2.00
36 Andy Pettitte	.30	.75
37 Bartolo Colon	.20	.50
38 Ben Sheets	.20	.50
39 Bobby Higginson	.20	.50
40 Ivan Rodriguez	.30	.75
41 Brad Penny	.20	.50
42 Carlos Lee	.20	.50
43 Damion Easley	.20	.50
44 Preston Wilson	.20	.50
45 Jeff Bagwell	.30	.75
46 Eric Milton	.20	.50
47 Rafael Palmeiro	.30	.75
48 Gary Sheffield	.20	.50
49 J.D. Drew	.20	.50
50 Jim Thome	.30	.75
51 Ichiro Suzuki	1.00	2.50
52 Bud Smith	.20	.50
53 Chan Ho Park	.20	.50
54 D'Angelo Jimenez	.20	.50
55 Ken Griffey Jr.	.75	2.00
56 Wade Miller	.20	.50
57 Vladimir Guerrero	.50	1.25
58 Troy Glaus	.20	.50
59 Shawn Green	.20	.50
60 Kerry Wood	.20	.50
61 Jack Wilson	.20	.50
62 Kevin Brown	.20	.50
63 Marcus Giles	.20	.50
64 Pat Burrell	.20	.50
65 Larry Walker	.20	.50
66 Sammy Sosa	.50	1.25
67 Raul Mondesi	.20	.50
68 Tim Hudson	.20	.50
69 Lance Berkman	.20	.50
70 Mike Mussina	.30	.75
71 Barry Zito	.20	.50
72 Jimmy Rollins	.20	.50
73 Barry Bonds	1.25	3.00
74 Craig Biggio	.30	.75
75 Todd Helton	.30	.75
76 Roger Clemens	1.00	2.50
77 Frank Catalanotto	.20	.50
78 Josh Towers	.20	.50
79 Roy Oswalt	.20	.50
80 Chipper Jones	.50	1.25
81 Cristian Guzman	.20	.50
82 Darin Erstad	.20	.50
83 Freddy Garcia	.20	.50
84 Jason Tyner	.20	.50
85 Carlos Delgado	.20	.50
86 Jon Lieber	.20	.50
87 Juan Pierre	.20	.50
88 Matt Morris	.20	.50
89 Phil Nevin	.20	.50
90 Jim Edmonds	.20	.50
91 Magglio Ordonez	.20	.50
92 Mike Hampton	.20	.50
93 Rafael Furcal	.20	.50
94 Richie Sexson	.20	.50
95 Luis Gonzalez	.20	.50
96 Scott Rolen	.30	.75
97 Tim Redding	.20	.50
98 Moises Alou	.20	.50
99 Jose Vidro	.20	.50
100 Mike Piazza	.75	2.00
101 Pedro Martinez	.30	.75
102 Geoff Jenkins	.20	.50
103 Johnny Damon Sox	.30	.75
104 Mike Cameron UER	.20	.50
Card has fascimile autograph of Troy Cameron		
105 Randy Johnson	.50	1.25
106 David Eckstein	.20	.50
107 Javier Vazquez	.20	.50
108 Mark Mulder	.20	.50
109 Robert Fick	.20	.50
110 Roberto Alomar	.30	.75
111 Wilson Betemit	.30	.75
112 Chris Tritle SP RC	2.00	5.00
113 Ed Rogers	.30	.75
114 Juan Pena	.30	.75
115 Josh Beckett	.50	1.25
116 Juan Cruz	.30	.75
117 Noochie Varner SP RC	2.00	5.00
118 Blake Williams	.30	.75
119 Mike Rivera	.30	.75
120 Hank Blalock	.75	2.00
121 Hansel Izquierdo SP RC	2.00	5.00
122 Orlando Hudson	.30	.75
123 Bill Hall SP	2.00	5.00
124 Jose Reyes	.75	2.00
125 Juan Rivera	.30	.75
126 Eric Valent	.30	.75
127 Scotty Layfield SP RC	2.00	5.00
128 Austin Kearns	.30	.75
129 Nic Jackson SP RC	2.00	5.00
130 Scott Chiasson	.30	.75
131 Chad Qualls SP RC	3.00	8.00
132 Marcus Thames	.30	.75
133 Nathan Haynes	.30	.75
134 Joe Borchard	.30	.75
135 Josh Hamilton	.60	1.50
136 Corey Patterson	.30	.75
137 Travis Wilson	.30	.75
138 Alex Escobar	.30	.75
139 Alexis Gomez	.30	.75
140 Nick Johnson	.50	1.25
141 Marlon Byrd	.30	.75
142 Kory DeHaan	.30	.75
143 Carlos Hernandez	.30	.75
144 Sean Burroughs	.30	.75
145 Angel Berroa	.30	.75
146 Aubrey Huff	.50	1.25
147 Travis Hafner	.50	1.25
148 Brandon Berger	.30	.75
149 J.R. House	.30	.75
150 Dewon Brazelton	.30	.75
151 Jayson Werth	.30	.75
152 Larry Barnes	.30	.75
153 Ruben Gotay SP RC	3.00	8.00
154 Tommy Marx SP RC	2.00	5.00
155 John Suomi SP RC	2.00	5.00
156 Javier Colina SP	2.00	5.00
157 Greg Sain SP RC	2.00	5.00
158 Robert Cosby SP RC	2.00	5.00
159 Angel Pagan SP RC	3.00	8.00
160 Ralph Santana RC	.50	1.25
161 Joe Orloski RC	.50	1.25
162 Shayne Wright SP RC	2.00	5.00
163 Jay Caligiuri SP RC	2.00	5.00
164 Greg Montalbano SP RC	2.00	5.00
165 Rich Harden SP RC	4.00	10.00
166 Rich Thompson SP RC	2.00	5.00
167 Fred Bastardo SP RC	2.00	5.00
168 Alejandro Giron SP RC	2.00	5.00
169 Jesus Medrano SP RC	2.00	5.00
170 Kevin Deaton SP RC	2.00	5.00
171 Mike Rosamond RC	.50	1.25
172 Jon Guzman SP RC	2.00	5.00
173 Gerard Oakes SP RC	2.00	5.00
174 Francisco Liriano SP RC	8.00	20.00
175 Matt Allegra SP RC	2.00	5.00
176 Mike Snyder SP RC	2.00	5.00
177 James Shanks SP RC	2.00	5.00
178 And. Hernandez SP RC	2.00	5.00
179 Dan Trumble SP RC	2.00	5.00
180 Luis DePaula SP RC	2.00	5.00
181 Randall Shelley SP RC	2.00	5.00
182 Richard Lane SP RC	2.00	5.00
183 Antwon Rollins SP RC	2.00	5.00
184 Ryan Bukvich SP RC	2.00	5.00
185 Derrick Lewis SP	2.00	5.00
186 Eric Miller SP RC	2.00	5.00
187 Justin Schuda SP RC	2.00	5.00
188 Brian West SP RC	2.00	5.00
189 Brad Wilkerson	.30	.75
190 Neal Frendling SP RC	2.00	5.00
191 Jeremy Hill SP RC	2.00	5.00
192 James Barrett SP RC	2.00	5.00
193 Brett Kay SP RC	2.00	5.00
194 Ryan Mottl SP RC	2.00	5.00
195 Brad Nelson SP RC	2.00	5.00
196 Juan M. Gonzalez SP RC	2.00	5.00
197 Curtis Legendre SP RC	2.00	5.00
198 Ronald Acuna SP RC	2.00	5.00
199 Chris Flinn SP RC	2.00	5.00
200 Nick Alvarez SP RC	2.00	5.00
201 Jason Ellison SP RC	4.00	10.00
202 Blake McGinley SP RC	2.00	5.00
203 Dan Phillips SP RC	2.00	5.00
204 Demetrius Heath SP RC	2.00	5.00
205 Eric Bruntlett SP RC	2.00	5.00
206 Joe Jiannetti SP RC	2.00	5.00
207 Mike Hill SP RC	2.00	5.00
208 Ricardo Cordova SP RC	2.00	5.00
209 Mark Hamilton SP RC	2.00	5.00
210 David Mattox SP RC	2.00	5.00
211 Jose Morban SP RC	2.00	5.00
212 Scott Wiggins SP RC	2.00	5.00
213 Steve Green	.30	.75
214 Brian Rogers SP	2.00	5.00
215 Kenny Baugh	.30	.75
216 Anastacio Martinez SP RC	2.00	5.00
217 Richard Lewis	.30	.75
218 Tim Kalita SP RC	2.00	5.00
219 Edwin Almonte SP RC	2.00	5.00
220 Hee Seop Choi	.30	.75
221 Ty Howington	.30	.75
222 Victor Alvarez SP RC	2.00	5.00
223 Morgan Ensberg	.50	1.25
224 Jeff Austin SP RC	2.00	5.00
225 Clint Weibl SP RC	2.00	5.00
226 Eric Cyr	.30	.75
227 Marlyn Tisdale SP RC	2.00	5.00
228 John VanBenschoten	.30	.75
229 David Krynzel	.30	.75
230 Raul Chavez SP RC	2.00	5.00
231 Brett Evert	.30	.75
232 Joe Rogers SP RC	2.00	5.00
233 Adam Wainwright	.50	1.25
234 Matt Herges RC	.30	.75
235 Matt Childers SP RC	2.00	5.00
236 Nick Neugebauer	.30	.75
237 Carl Crawford	.50	1.25
238 Seung Song	.30	.75
239 Randy Flores	.30	.75
240 Jason Lane	.50	1.25
241 Chase Utley	4.00	10.00
242 Ben Howard SP RC	2.00	5.00
243 Eric Glaser SP RC	2.00	5.00
244 Josh Wilson RC	.50	1.25
245 Jose Valverde SP RC	2.00	5.00
246 Chris Smith	.30	.75
247 Mark Prior	.75	2.00
248 Brian Mallette SP RC	2.00	5.00
249 Chone Figgins SP RC	3.00	8.00
250 Jimmy Alvarez SP RC	2.00	5.00
251 Luis Terrero	.30	.75
252 Josh Bonifay SP RC	2.00	5.00
253 Garrett Guzman SP RC	2.00	5.00
254 Jeff Verplancke SP RC	2.00	5.00
255 Nate Espy SP RC	2.00	5.00
256 Jeff Lincoln SP RC	2.00	5.00
257 Ryan Snare SP RC	2.00	5.00
258 Jose Ortiz	.30	.75
259 Denny Bautista	.30	.75
260 Willy Aybar	.30	.75
261 Kelly Johnson	1.25	3.00
262 Shawn Fagan	.30	.75
263 Yurendell DeCaster SP RC	2.00	5.00
264 Mike Peeples SP RC	2.00	5.00
265 Joel Guzman	1.25	3.00
266 Ryan Vogelsong	.30	.75
267 Jorge Padilla SP RC	2.00	5.00
268 Joe Jester SP RC	2.00	5.00
269 Ryan Church SP RC	4.00	10.00
270 Mitch Jones	.30	.75
271 Travis Foley SP RC	2.00	5.00
272 Bobby Crosby	1.25	3.00
273 Adrian Gonzalez	.30	.75
274 Ronnie Merrill	.30	.75
275 Joel Pineiro	.30	.75
276 John-Ford Griffin	.30	.75
277 Brian Forystek SP RC	2.00	5.00
278 Sean Douglass	.30	.75
279 Manny Delcarmen SP RC	3.00	8.00
280 Jim Kavourias SP RC	2.00	5.00
281 Gabe Gross	.30	.75
282 Bill Ortega	.30	.75
283 Joey Hammond SP RC	2.00	5.00
284 Brett Myers	.50	1.25
285 Carlos Pena	.30	.75
286 Ezequiel Astacio SP RC	2.00	5.00
287 Edwin Yan SP RC	2.00	5.00
288 Chris Duffy SP RC	3.00	8.00
289 Jason Kinchen	.30	.75
290 Rafael Soriano	.30	.75
291 Colin Young RC	2.00	5.00
292 Eric Byrnes	.30	.75
293 Chris Narveson SP RC	3.00	8.00
294 John Rheinecker	.30	.75
295 Mike Wilson SP RC	2.00	5.00
296 Justin Sherrod SP RC	2.00	5.00
297 Deivi Mendez	.30	.75
298 Wily Mo Pena	.50	1.25
299 Brett Roneberg SP RC	2.00	5.00
300 Trey Lunsford SP RC	2.00	5.00
301 Christian Parker	.30	.75
302 Brent Butler	.30	.75
303 Aaron Heilman	.30	.75
304 Wilkin Ruan	.30	.75
305 Kenny Kelly	.30	.75
306 Cody Ransom	.30	.75
307 Koyie Hill SP	2.00	5.00
308 Tony Fontana SP RC	2.00	5.00
309 Mark Teixeira	2.00	5.00
310 Doug Sessions SP RC	2.00	5.00
311 Josh Cisneros SP RC	2.00	5.00
312 Carlos Brackley SP RC	2.00	5.00
313 Tim Raines Jr.	.30	.75
314 Ross Peeples SP RC	2.00	5.00
315 Alex Requena SP RC	2.00	5.00
316 Chin-Hui Tsao	.50	1.25
317 Tony Alvarez	.30	.75
318 Craig Kuzmic SP RC	2.00	5.00
319 Pete Zamora SP RC	2.00	5.00
320 Matt Parker SP RC	2.00	5.00
321 Keith Ginter	.30	.75
322 Gary Cates Jr. SP RC	2.00	5.00
323 Matt Belisle	.30	.75
324A Ben Broussard	.30	.75
324B Ja.Mauer AU A RC EXCH UER	4.00	10.00
Card was mistakenly numbered as 324		
325 Dennis Tankersley	.30	.75
326 Juan Silvestre	.30	.75
327 Henry Pichardo SP RC	2.00	5.00
328 Michael Floyd SP RC	2.00	5.00
329 Clint Nageotte SP RC	3.00	8.00
330 Raymond Cabrera SP RC	2.00	5.00
331 Mauricio Lara SP RC	2.00	5.00
332 Alejandro Cadena SP RC	2.00	5.00
333 Jonny Gomes SP RC	6.00	15.00
334 Jason Bulger SP RC	2.00	5.00
335 Nate Teut	.30	.75
336 David Gil SP RC	2.00	5.00
337 Joel Crump SP RC	2.00	5.00
338 Brandon Phillips	.30	.75
339 Macay McBride	.50	1.25
340 Brandon Claussen	.30	.75
341 Josh Phelps	.30	.75
342 Freddie Money SP RC	2.00	5.00
343 Cliff Bartosh SP RC	2.00	5.00
344 Terrance Hill SP RC	2.00	5.00
345 John Rodriguez SP RC	3.00	8.00
346 Chris Latham SP RC	2.00	5.00
347 Carlos Cabrera SP RC	2.00	5.00
348 Jose Bautista SP RC	15.00	40.00
349 Kevin Frederick SP RC	2.00	5.00
350 Jerome Williams	.30	.75
351 Napoleon Calzado SP RC	2.00	5.00
352 Benito Baez SP	2.00	5.00
353 Xavier Nady	.30	.75
354 Jason Botts SP RC	3.00	8.00
355 Steve Bechler SP RC	2.00	5.00
356 Reed Johnson SP RC	4.00	10.00
357 Mark Outlaw SP RC	2.00	5.00
358 Jake Peavy	.75	2.00
359 Josh Shaffer SP RC	2.00	5.00
360 Dan Wright SP	2.00	5.00
361 Ryan Gripp SP RC	2.00	5.00
362 Nelson Castro SP RC	2.00	5.00
363 Jason Bay SP RC	6.00	15.00
364 Franklyn German SP RC	2.00	5.00
365 Corwin Malone SP RC	2.00	5.00
366 Kelly Ramos SP RC	2.00	5.00
367 John Ennis SP RC	2.00	5.00
368 George Perez SP	2.00	5.00
369 Rene Reyes SP RC	2.00	5.00
370 Rolando Viera SP RC	2.00	5.00
371 Earl Snyder SP RC	2.00	5.00
372 Kyle Kane SP RC	2.00	5.00
373 Mario Ramos SP RC	2.00	5.00
374 Tyler Yates SP RC	2.00	5.00
375 Jason Young SP RC	2.00	5.00
376 Chris Bootcheck SP RC	2.00	5.00
377 Jesus Cota SP RC	2.00	5.00
378 Corky Miller SP	2.00	5.00
379 Matt Erickson SP RC	2.00	5.00
380 Justin Huber SP RC	4.00	10.00
381 Felix Escalona SP RC	2.00	5.00
382 Kevin Cash SP RC	2.00	5.00
383 J.J. Putz SP RC	3.00	8.00
384 Chris Snelling AU A RC	8.00	20.00
385 David Wright AU A RC	75.00	150.00
386 Brian Wolfe AU A RC	4.00	10.00
387 Justin Reid AU A RC	4.00	10.00
389 Ryan Raburn AU A RC	4.00	10.00
390 Josh Barfield AU A RC	25.00	50.00
391 Joe Mauer AU A RC	150.00	250.00
392 Bobby Jenks AU A RC	4.00	10.00
393 Rob Henkel AU A RC	4.00	10.00
394 Jimmy Gobble AU A RC	4.00	10.00
395 Jesse Foppert AU A RC	4.00	10.00
396 Gavin Floyd AU A RC	6.00	15.00
397 Nate Field AU A RC	4.00	10.00
398 Ryan Doumit AU A RC	6.00	15.00
399 Ron Calloway AU A RC	4.00	10.00
400 Taylor Buchholz AU A RC	4.00	10.00
401 Adam Roller AU A RC	4.00	10.00
402 Cole Barthel AU A RC	4.00	10.00
403 Kazuhisa Ishii SP RC	3.00	8.00
403A Kazuhisa Ishii AU B	30.00	50.00
404 So Taguchi SP RC	3.00	8.00
404A So Taguchi AU B	30.00	50.00
405 Chris Baker AU A RC	4.00	10.00

2002 Bowman Chrome Facsimile Autograph Variations

This 20 card partial parallel to the Bowman Chrome set were issued in this special version with a facsimile autograph as part of the card. These cards were not originally expected to be issued and caused some confusion in the secondary market upon the product's release. It's estimated that as few as 50 copies of each card were produced.

118 Taylor Buchholz
130 Chris Baker
189 Adam Roller
229 Ryan Raburn
231 Chris Snelling
233 Nate Field
237 Ron Calloway
239 Cole Barthel
244 Rob Henkel
251 Gavin Floyd
301 Jimmy Gobble
305 Brian Wolfe
313 Jesse Foppert
316 Joe Mauer
317 David Wright
323 Justin Reid
324 Jake Mauer
326 Josh Barfield
335 Bobby Jenks
338 Ryan Doumit

2002 Bowman Chrome Refractors

This is a complete parallel set to the Bowman Chrome set. These cards were issued in several different tiers but it is important to note that most of these cards have a stated print run of 500 sets. The Ishii and Taguchi autograph cards have a stated print run of 100 sets.

Card	Low	High
*REF RED: 1.5X TO 4X BASIC		
*REF BLUE: 1X TO 2.5X BASIC		
*REF BLUE SP: .6X TO 1.5X BASIC		
*REF AU: .5X TO 1.2X BASIC AU'S		
324B/384-405 GROUP A AUTO ODDS 1:88		
403-404 GROUP B AUTO ODDS 1:4392		
324B/384-405 OVERALL AUTO ODDS 1:86		
1-383/403-404 PRINT 500 SERIAL #'d SETS		
324B/384-405 GROUP A PRINT RUN 500 SETS		
403-404 GROUP B PRINT RUN 100 SETS		
159 Angel Pagan	8.00	20.00
165 Rich Harden	30.00	60.00
348 Jose Bautista	40.00	80.00
363 Jason Bay	12.50	30.00
391 Joe Mauer AU A	200.00	400.00
392 Bobby Jenks AU A	5.00	12.00
403 Kazuhisa Ishii AU B	40.00	80.00
404 So Taguchi AU B	30.00	60.00

2002 Bowman Chrome Gold Refractors

This is a complete parallel set to the Bowman Chrome set. These cards were issued in several different tiers but it is important to note that most of these cards have a stated print run of 50 sets. The Ishii and Taguchi autograph cards have a stated print run of 10 sets.

Card	Low	High
*GOLD REF RED: 5X TO 12X BASIC		
*GOLD REF BLUE: 4X TO 10X BASIC		
*GOLD REF BLUE SP: 2X TO 5X BASIC		
*GOLD REF AU: 1.5X TO 4X BASIC		
384-405 GROUP A AUTO ODDS 1:879		
403-404 GROUP B AUTO ODDS 1:59,616		
324B/384-405 OVERALL AUTO ODDS 1:866		
1-383/403-404 PRINT 50 SERIAL #'d SETS		
324B/384-405 GROUP A AU PRINT 50 SETS		
403-404 GROUP B AU PRINT RUN 10 SETS		
159 Angel Pagan	20.00	50.00
165 Rich Harden	100.00	200.00
241 Chase Utley	75.00	150.00
348 Jose Bautista	150.00	300.00
363 Jason Bay	100.00	200.00
385 David Wright AU A	1000.00	1500.00
391 Joe Mauer AU A	2500.00	3000.00
392 Bobby Jenks AU A	15.00	40.00

2002 Bowman Chrome X-Fractors

This is a complete parallel set to the Bowman Chrome set. These cards were issued in several different tiers but it is important to note that most of these cards have a stated print run of 250 sets. The Ishii and Taguchi autograph cards have a stated print run of 50 sets.

Card	Low	High
*XFRACT RED: 3X TO 8X BASIC		
*XFRACT BLUE: 1.5X TO 4X BASIC		
*XFRACT BLUE SP: .75X TO 2X BASIC		
*XFRACT AU: .75X TO 2X BASIC		
324B/384-405 GROUP A AUTO ODDS 1:176		
403-404 GROUP B AUTO ODDS 1:9072		
324B/384-405 OVERALL AUTO ODDS 1:173		
1-383/403-404 PRINT 250 SERIAL #'d SETS		
324B/384-405 GROUP A PRINT RUN 250 SETS		
403-404 GROUP B PRINT RUN 50 SETS		
159 Angel Pagan	10.00	25.00
165 Rich Harden	50.00	100.00
348 Jose Bautista	60.00	120.00
363 Jason Bay	15.00	40.00
391 Joe Mauer AU A	400.00	600.00
392 Bobby Jenks AU A	8.00	20.00
403 Kazuhisa Ishii AU B	60.00	100.00
404 So Taguchi AU B	60.00	100.00

2002 Bowman Chrome Reprints

Isssued at stated odds of one in six, these 20 cards feature reprint cards of players who have made their debut since Bowman was reintroduced as a major brand in 1989.

Card	Low	High
COMPLETE SET (20)	10.00	25.00
*BLACK REF: .6X TO 1.5X BASIC REPRINTS		
BLACK REFRACTOR ODDS 1:18		
BCRAJ Andruw Jones 95	.75	2.00
BCRBC Bartolo Colon 95	.75	2.00
BCRBW Bernie Williams 90	.75	2.00
BCRCD Carlos Delgado 92	.75	2.00
BCRCJ Chipper Jones 91	1.00	2.50
BCRDJ Derek Jeter 93	3.00	8.00
BCRFT Frank Thomas 90	1.00	2.50
BCRGS Gary Sheffield 89	.75	2.00
BCRIR Ivan Rodriguez 91	.75	2.00
BCRJB Jeff Bagwell 91	.75	2.00
BCRJG Juan Gonzalez 90	.75	2.00
BCRJK Jason Kendall 93	.75	2.00
BCRJP Jorge Posada 94	.75	2.00
BCRKG Ken Griffey Jr. 89	2.00	5.00
BCRLG Luis Gonzalez 91	.75	2.00
BCRLW Larry Walker 90	.75	2.00
BCRMP Mike Piazza 92	2.00	5.00
BCRMS Mike Sweeney 96	.75	2.00
BCRSR Scott Rolen 95	.75	2.00
BCRVG Vladimir Guerrero 95	1.00	2.50

2002 Bowman Chrome Draft

Inserted two per Bowman Draft pack, this is a parallel to the Bowman Draft Pick set. Each of these cards uses the Topps "Chrome" technology and these cards were inserted two per bowman draft pack. Cards numbered 166 through 175 are not parallels to the regular Bowman cards and they feature autographs of the players. Those ten cards were issued at a stated rate of one in 45 Bowman Draft packs.

Card	Low	High
COMPLETE SET (175)	200.00	350.00
COMP.SET w/o AU's (165)	135.00	200.00
COMMON CARD (1-165)	.15	.40
COMMON CARD (166-175)	4.00	10.00
1 Clint Everts RC	.60	1.50
2 Fred Lewis RC	.40	1.00
3 Jon Broxton RC	1.25	3.00
4 Jason Anderson RC	.40	1.00
5 Mike Eusebio RC	.40	1.00
6 Zack Greinke RC	3.00	8.00
7 Joe Blanton RC	2.00	5.00
8 Sergio Santos RC	.60	1.50
9 Jason Cooper RC	.40	1.00
10 Delwyn Young RC	1.25	3.00
11 Jeremy Hermida RC	2.00	5.00
12 Dan Ortmeier RC	.60	1.50
13 Kevin Jepsen RC	.60	1.50
14 Russ Adams RC	.60	1.50
15 Mike Nixon RC	.40	1.00
16 Nick Swisher RC	3.00	8.00
17 Cole Hamels RC	6.00	15.00
18 Brian Dopirak RC	1.25	3.00
19 James Loney RC	5.00	12.00
20 Denard Span RC	1.50	4.00
21 Billy Petrick RC	.40	1.00
22 Jared Doyle RC	.40	1.00
23 Jeff Francoeur RC	4.00	10.00
24 Nick Bourgeois RC	.40	1.00
25 Matt Cain RC	4.00	10.00
26 John McCurdy RC	.40	1.00
27 Mark Kiger RC	.40	1.00
28 Bill Murphy RC	.40	1.00
29 Matt Craig RC	.60	1.50
30 Mike Megrew RC	.40	1.00
31 Ben Crockett RC	.40	1.00
32 Luke Hagerty RC	.40	1.00
33 Matt Whitney RC	.40	1.00
34 Dan Meyer RC	.60	1.50
35 Jeremy Brown RC	.40	1.00
36 Doug Johnson RC	.40	1.00
37 Steve Obenchain RC	.40	1.00
38 Matt Clanton RC	.40	1.00
39 Mark Teahen RC	1.25	3.00
40 Tom Carrow RC	.40	1.00
41 Micah Schilling RC	.40	1.00
42 Blair Johnson RC	.40	1.00
43 Jason Pridie RC	.40	1.00
44 Joey Votto RC	12.50	30.00
45 Taber Lee RC	.40	1.00
46 Adam Peterson RC	.40	1.00
47 Adam Donachie RC	.40	1.00
48 Josh Murray RC	.40	1.00
49 Brent Clevlen RC	2.50	6.00
50 Chad Pleiness RC	.40	1.00
51 Zach Hammes RC	.40	1.00
52 Chris Snyder RC	.60	1.50
53 Chris Smith RC	.40	1.00
54 Justin Maureau RC	.40	1.00
55 David Bush RC	1.25	3.00
56 Tim Gilhooly RC	.40	1.00
57 Blair Barbier RC	.40	1.00
58 Zach Segovia RC	.40	1.00
59 Jeremy Reed RC	1.25	3.00
60 Matt Pender RC	.40	1.00
61 Eric Thomas RC	.40	1.00
62 Justin Jones RC	.60	1.50
63 Brian Slocum RC	.40	1.00
64 Larry Broadway RC	.40	1.00
65 Bo Flowers RC	.40	1.00
66 Scott White RC	.40	1.00
67 Steve Stanley RC	.40	1.00
68 Alex Merricks RC	.40	1.00
69 Josh Womack RC	.40	1.00
70 Dave Jensen RC	.40	1.00

71 Curtis Granderson RC 10.00 25.00
72 Pat Osborn RC .40 1.00
73 Nic Carter RC .40 1.00
74 Mitch Talbot RC .25 .60
75 Don Murphy RC .40 1.00
76 Val Majewski RC .40 1.00
77 Javy Rodriguez RC .40 1.00
78 Fernando Pacheco RC .40 1.00
79 Steve Russell RC .40 1.00
80 Jon Slack RC .40 1.00
81 John Baker RC .40 1.00
82 Aaron Coonrod RC .40 1.00
83 Josh Johnson RC 5.00 12.00
84 Jake Blalock RC .60 1.50
85 Alex Hart RC .40 1.00
86 Wes Bankston RC 2.50 6.00
87 Josh Rupe RC .40 1.00
88 Dan Cevette RC .40 1.00
89 Kiel Fisher RC .60 1.50
90 Alan Rick RC .40 1.00
91 Charlie Morton RC .40 1.00
92 Chad Spann RC .40 1.00
93 Kyle Boyer RC .40 1.00
94 Bob Malek RC .40 1.00
95 Ryan Rodriguez RC .40 1.00
96 Jordan Renz RC .40 1.00
97 Randy Frye RC .40 1.00
98 Rich Hill RC 5.00 12.00
99 B.J. Upton RC 5.00 12.00
100 Dan Christensen RC .40 1.00
101 Casey Kotchman RC 2.50 6.00
102 Eric Good RC .40 1.00
103 Mike Fontenot RC .40 1.00
104 John Webb RC .40 1.00
105 Jason Dubois RC .60 1.50
106 Ryan Kibler RC .40 1.00
107 Jhonny Peralta RC 3.00 8.00
108 Kirk Saarloos RC .40 1.00
109 Rhett Parrott RC .40 1.00
110 Jason Grove RC .40 1.00
111 Colt Griffin RC .40 1.00
112 Dallas McPherson RC UER 1.25 3.00
Reversed Negative
113 Oliver Perez RC 1.25 3.00
114 Marshall McDougall RC .40 1.00
115 Mike Wood RC .40 1.00
116 Scott Hairston RC .60 1.50
117 Jason Simontacchi RC .40 1.00
118 Taggert Bozied RC .60 1.50
119 Shelley Duncan RC 4.00 10.00
120 Dontrelle Willis RC 2.00 5.00
121 Sean Burnett .15 .40
122 Aaron Cook .25 .60
123 Brett Evert .15 .40
124 Jimmy Journell .15 .40
125 Brett Myers .25 .60
126 Brad Baker .15 .40
127 Billy Traber RC .40 1.00
128 Adam Wainwright .25 .60
129 Jason Young .40 1.00
130 John Buck .15 .40
131 Kevin Cash .40 1.00
132 Jason Stokes RC .60 1.50
133 Drew Henson .15 .40
134 Chad Tracy RC 2.00 5.00
135 Orlando Hudson .15 .40
136 Brandon Phillips .15 .40
137 Joe Borchard .15 .40
138 Marlon Byrd .15 .40
139 Carl Crawford .25 .60
140 Michael Restovich .15 .40
141 Corey Hart RC 2.00 5.00
142 Edwin Almonte .25 .60
143 Francis Beltran RC .40 1.00
144 Jorge De La Rosa RC .40 1.00
145 Gerardo Garcia RC .40 1.00
146 Franklyn German RC .40 1.00
147 Francisco Liriano 2.50 6.00
148 Francisco Rodriguez .25 .60
149 Ricardo Rodriguez .15 .40
150 Seung Song .15 .40
151 John Stephens .15 .40
152 Justin Huber RC 1.00 2.50
153 Victor Martinez .60 1.50
154 Hee Seop Choi .15 .40
155 Justin Morneau .25 .60
156 Miguel Cabrera 1.00 2.50
157 Victor Diaz RC 1.00 2.50
158 Jose Reyes .40 1.00
159 Omar Infante .15 .40
160 Angel Berroa .15 .40
161 Tony Alvarez .15 .40
162 Shin Soo Choo RC 3.00 8.00
163 Wily Mo Pena .25 .60
164 Andres Torres .15 .40
165 Jose Lopez RC 2.50 6.00
166 Scott Moore AU RC 4.00 10.00
167 Chris Gruler AU RC 4.00 10.00
168 Joe Saunders AU RC 5.00 12.00
169 Jeff Francis AU RC 4.00 10.00
170 Royce Ring AU RC 4.00 10.00
171 Greg Miller AU RC 6.00 15.00
172 Brandon Weeden AU RC 8.00 20.00
173 Drew Meyer AU RC 4.00 10.00
174 Khalil Greene AU RC 4.00 10.00
175 Mark Schramek AU RC 4.00 10.00

2002 Bowman Chrome Draft Refractors

Issued at a stated rate of one in 11 Bowman Draft packs, these cards are refractor parallels of the Bowman Chrome Draft set. Cards 1-165 have a stated print run of 300 serial numbered sets. Cards numbered 166 through 175, which are autographed, but lack serial-numbering, were issued at a stated rate of one in 154 Bowman Draft packs.

*REFRACTOR 1-165: 2.5X TO 6X BASIC
*REFRACTOR RC 1-165: 2X TO 5X BASIC
*REFRACTOR 166-175: .5X TO 1.2X BASIC
17 Cole Hamels 15.00 40.00
19 James Loney 20.00 50.00
25 Matt Cain 30.00 60.00
83 Josh Johnson 50.00 100.00
99 B.J. Upton 20.00 50.00
113 Oliver Perez 8.00 20.00
119 Shelley Duncan 15.00 40.00
168 Joe Saunders AU 10.00 25.00

2002 Bowman Chrome Draft Gold Refractors

Issued at a stated rate of one in 67 Bowman Draft packs, these cards are gold refractors of the Bowman Chrome Draft set. Cards 1-165 have a stated print run of 50 serial numbered sets. Cards numbered 166 through 175, which are autographed but lack serial-numbering, were issued at a stated rate of one in 1546 Bowman Draft cards and there is no pricing provided on these cards due to market scarcity. Though never confirmed by the manufacturer, based upon research conducted by the Price Guide staff at Beckett Baseball, it's estimated that as few as 35 copies of AU subset card were produced.

*GOLD REF 1-165: 8X TO 20X BASIC
*GOLD REF RC 1-165: 10X TO 20X BASIC
1-165 ODDS 1:67 BOWMAN DRAFT
166-175 AU ODDS 1:1546 BOWMAN DRAFT
1-165 PRINT RUN 50 SERIAL #'d SETS
166-175 ARE NOT SERIAL-NUMBERED
166-175 NO PRICING DUE TO SCARCITY
3 Jon Broxton 40.00 80.00
17 Cole Hamels 100.00 200.00
19 James Loney 250.00 350.00
25 Matt Cain 100.00 200.00
39 Mark Teahen 40.00 80.00
44 Joey Votto 400.00 800.00
71 Curtis Granderson 300.00 600.00
83 Josh Johnson 175.00 350.00
86 Wes Bankston 40.00 80.00
98 Rich Hill 125.00 300.00
99 B.J. Upton 100.00 200.00
113 Oliver Perez 40.00 80.00
119 Shelley Duncan 100.00 200.00

2002 Bowman Chrome Draft X-Fractors

Issued at a stated rate of one in 22 Bowman Draft packs, these cards are x-fractor parallels of the Bowman Chrome Draft set. Cards 1-165 have a stated print run of 150 serial numbered sets. Cards numbered 166 through 175, which are autographed but lack serial-numbering, were issued at a stated rate of one in 309 Bowman Draft packs.

*X-FRACTOR 1-165: 3X TO 8X BASIC
*X-FRACTOR RC 1-165: 3X TO 6X BASIC
*X-FRACTOR 166-175: .75X TO 1.5X BASIC
17 Cole Hamels 20.00 50.00
19 James Loney 60.00 120.00
25 Matt Cain 40.00 80.00
39 Mark Teahen 12.50 30.00
83 Josh Johnson 75.00 150.00
99 B.J. Upton 30.00 60.00
113 Oliver Perez 12.50 30.00
119 Shelley Duncan 30.00 60.00
168 Joe Saunders AU 12.50 30.00

2003 Bowman Chrome

This 351 card set was released in July, 2003. The set was issued in four-card packs with an $4 SRP which came 18 to a box and 12 boxes to a case. Cards numbered 1 through 165 feature veteran players while cards 166 through 330 feature rookie players. Cards numbered 331 through 350 feature autograph cards of Rookie Cards. Each of those cards, with the exception of Jose Contreras (number 332) was issued to a stated print run of 1700 sets and were seeded at a stated rate of one in 26. The Contreras card was issued to a stated print run of 340 cards and was issued at a stated rate of one in 3,3351 packs. The final card of the set features baseball legend Willie Mays. That card was issued as a box-loader and an authentic autograph on that card was also randomly inserted into packs. The autograph card was inserted at a stated rate of one in 384 box loader packs and was issued to a stated print run of 150 sets. Bryan Bullington did not return his cards in time for pack out and those cards could be redeemed until July 31st, 2005.

COMPLETE SET (351) 300.00 500.00
COMP.SET w/o AU's (331) 75.00 150.00
COMMON CARD (1-165) .20 .50
COMMON CARD (166-330) .20 .50
COMMON RC (156-330) .40 1.00
COMP.SET w/o AU'S INCLUDES 351 MAYS
MAYS AU IS NOT PART OF 351-CARD SET
1 Garret Anderson .20 .50
2 Derek Jeter 1.25 3.00
3 Gary Sheffield .20 .50
4 Matt Morris .20 .50
5 Derek Lowe .20 .50
6 Andy Van Hekken .20 .50
7 Sammy Sosa .50 1.25
8 Ken Griffey Jr. .75 2.00
9 Omar Vizquel .30 .75
10 Jorge Posada .30 .75
11 Lance Berkman .30 .75
12 Mike Sweeney .20 .50
13 Adrian Beltre .20 .50
14 Richie Sexson .20 .50
15 A.J. Pierzynski .20 .50
16 Bartolo Colon .20 .50
17 Mike Mussina .30 .75
18 Paul Byrd .20 .50
19 Bobby Abreu .20 .50
20 Miguel Tejada .30 .75
21 Aramis Ramirez .20 .50
22 Edgardo Alfonzo .20 .50
23 Edgar Martinez .30 .75
24 Albert Pujols 1.25 3.00
25 Carl Crawford .30 .75
26 Eric Hinske .20 .50
27 Tim Salmon .20 .50
28 Luis Gonzalez .20 .50
29 Jay Gibbons .20 .50
30 John Smoltz .50 1.25
31 Tim Wakefield .20 .50
32 Mark Prior .30 .75
33 Magglio Ordonez .30 .75
34 Adam Dunn .30 .75
35 Larry Walker .30 .75
36 Luis Castillo .20 .50
37 Wade Miller .20 .50
38 Carlos Beltran .30 .75
39 Odalis Perez .20 .50
40 Alex Sanchez .20 .50
41 Torii Hunter .20 .50
42 Cliff Floyd .20 .50
43 Andy Pettitte .30 .75
44 Francisco Rodriguez .30 .75
45 Eric Chavez .20 .50
46 Kevin Millwood .20 .50
47 Dennis Tankersley .20 .50
48 Hideo Nomo .50 1.25
49 Freddy Garcia .20 .50
50 Randy Johnson .50 1.25
51 Aubrey Huff .20 .50
52 Carlos Delgado .20 .50
53 Troy Glaus .20 .50
54 Junior Spivey .20 .50
55 Mike Hampton .20 .50
56 Sidney Ponson .20 .50
57 Aaron Boone .20 .50
58 Kerry Wood .20 .50
59 Willie Harris .20 .50
60 Nomar Garciaparra .50 1.25
61 Todd Helton .30 .75
62 Mike Lowell .20 .50
63 Roy Oswalt .30 .75
64 Raul Ibanez .30 .75
65 Brian Jordan .20 .50
66 Geoff Jenkins .20 .50
67 Jermaine Dye .20 .50
68 Tom Glavine .30 .75
69 Bernie Williams .30 .75
70 Vladimir Guerrero .50 1.25
71 Mark Mulder .20 .50
72 Jimmy Rollins .30 .75
73 Oliver Perez .20 .50
74 Rich Aurilia .20 .50
75 Joel Pineiro .20 .50
76 J.D. Drew .20 .50
77 Ivan Rodriguez .30 .75
78 Josh Phelps .20 .50
79 Darin Erstad .20 .50
80 Curt Schilling .30 .75
81 Paul Lo Duca .20 .50
82 Marty Cordova .20 .50
83 Manny Ramirez .50 1.25
84 Bobby Hill .20 .50
85 Paul Konerko .30 .75
86 Austin Kearns .20 .50
87 Jason Jennings .20 .50
88 Brad Penny .20 .50
89 Jeff Bagwell .30 .75
90 Shawn Green .20 .50
91 Jason Schmidt .20 .50
92 Doug Mientkiewicz .20 .50
93 Jose Vidro .20 .50
94 Bret Boone .20 .50
95 Jason Giambi .20 .50
96 Barry Zito .20 .50
97 Roy Halladay .50 1.25
98 Pat Burrell .20 .50
99 Sean Burroughs .20 .50
100 Barry Bonds 1.00 2.50
101 Kazuhiro Sasaki .20 .50
102 Fernando Vina .20 .50
103 Chan Ho Park .30 .75
104 Andruw Jones .20 .50
105 Adam Kennedy .20 .50
106 Shea Hillenbrand .20 .50
107 Greg Maddux .75 2.00
108 Jim Edmonds .30 .75
109 Pedro Martinez .30 .75
110 Moises Alou .30 .75
111 Jeff Weaver .20 .50
112 C.C. Sabathia .30 .75
113 Robert Fick .20 .50
114 A.J. Burnett .30 .75
115 Jeff Kent .20 .50
116 Kevin Brown .20 .50
117 Rafael Furcal .20 .50
118 Cristian Guzman .20 .50
119 Brad Wilkerson .20 .50
120 Mike Piazza .50 1.25
121 Alfonso Soriano .50 1.25
122 Mark Ellis .20 .50
123 Vicente Padilla .20 .50
124 Eric Gagne .20 .50
125 Ryan Klesko .20 .50
126 Ichiro Suzuki .75 2.00
127 Tony Batista .20 .50
128 Roberto Alomar .30 .75
129 Alex Rodriguez .75 2.00
130 Jim Thome .30 .75
131 Jarrod Washburn .20 .50
132 Orlando Hudson .20 .50
133 Chipper Jones .50 1.25
134 Rodrigo Lopez .20 .50
135 Johnny Damon .30 .75
136 Matt Clement .20 .50
137 Frank Thomas .50 1.25
138 Ellis Burks .20 .50
139 Carlos Pena .30 .75
140 Josh Beckett .30 .75
141 Joe Randa .20 .50
142 Brian Giles .20 .50
143 Kazuhisa Ishii .20 .50
144 Corey Koskie .20 .50
145 Orlando Cabrera .20 .50
146 Mark Buehrle .30 .75
147 Roger Clemens .60 1.50
148 Tim Hudson .30 .75
149 Randy Wolf .20 .50
150 Josh Fogg .20 .50
151 Phil Nevin .20 .50
152 John Olerud .20 .50
153 Scott Rolen .30 .75
154 Joe Kennedy .20 .50
155 Rafael Palmeiro .30 .75
156 Chad Hutchinson .20 .50
157 Quincy Carter XRC .40 1.00
158 Hee Seop Choi .20 .50
159 Joe Borchard .20 .50
160 Brandon Phillips .20 .50
161 Wily Mo Pena .20 .50
162 Victor Martinez .30 .75
163 Jason Stokes .20 .50
164 Ken Harvey .20 .50
165 Juan Rivera .20 .50
166 Joe Valentine RC .40 1.00
167 Dan Haren RC 2.00 5.00
168 Michel Hernandez RC .40 1.00
169 Eider Torres RC .40 1.00
170 Chris De La Cruz RC .40 1.00
171 Ramon Nivar-Martinez RC .40 1.00
172 Mike Adams RC .60 1.50
173 Justin Arneson RC .40 1.00
174 Jamie Athas RC .40 1.00
175 Dwaine Bacon RC .40 1.00
176 Clint Barmes RC 1.00 2.50
177 B.J. Barns RC .40 1.00
178 Tyler Johnson RC .40 1.00
179 Brandon Webb RC 1.25 3.00
180 T.J. Bohn RC .40 1.00
181 Ozzie Chavez RC .40 1.00
182 Brandon Bowe RC .40 1.00
183 Craig Brazell RC .40 1.00
184 Dusty Brown RC .40 1.00
185 Brian Bruney RC .40 1.00
186 Greg Bruso RC .40 1.00
187 Jaime Bubela RC .40 1.00
188 Matt Diaz RC .60 1.50
189 Brian Burgamy RC .40 1.00
190 Eny Cabreja RC 1.50 4.00
191 Daniel Cabrera RC .60 1.50
192 Ryan Cameron RC .40 1.00
193 Lance Caraccioli RC .40 1.00
194 David Cash RC .40 1.00
195 Bernie Castro RC .40 1.00
196 Ismael Castro RC .40 1.00
197 Cory Doyne RC .40 1.00
198 Jeff Clark RC .40 1.00
199 Chris Colton RC .40 1.00
200 Dexter Cooper RC .40 1.00
201 Callix Crabbe RC .40 1.00
202 Chien-Ming Wang RC 1.50 4.00
203 Eric Crozier RC .40 1.00
204 Nook Logan RC .40 1.00
205 David DeJesus RC 1.00 2.50
206 Matt DeMarco RC .40 1.00
207 Chris Duncan RC 1.25 3.00
208 Eric Eckenstahler .20 .50
209 Willie Eyre RC .40 1.00
210 Evel Bastida-Martinez RC .40 1.00
211 Chris Fallon RC .40 1.00
212 Mike Flannery RC .40 1.00
213 Mike O'Keefe RC .40 1.00
214 Lew Ford RC .40 1.00
215 Kason Gabbard RC .40 1.00
216 Mike Gallo RC .40 1.00
217 Jairo Garcia RC .40 1.00
218 Angel Garcia RC .40 1.00
219 Michael Garciaparra RC .40 1.00
220 Jeremy Griffiths RC .40 1.00
221 Dusty Gomon RC .40 1.00
222 Bryan Grace RC .40 1.00
223 Tyson Graham RC .40 1.00
224 Henry Guerrero RC .40 1.00
225 Franklin Gutierrez RC 1.00 2.50
226 Carlos Guzman RC .40 1.00
227 Matthew Hagen RC .40 1.00
228 Josh Hall RC .40 1.00
229 Rob Hammock RC .40 1.00
230 Brendan Harris RC .40 1.00
231 Gary Harris RC .40 1.00
232 Clay Hensley RC .40 1.00
233 Michael Hinckley RC .40 1.00
234 Luis Hodge RC .40 1.00
235 Donnie Hood RC .40 1.00
236 Matt Hensley RC .40 1.00
237 Edwin Jackson RC .60 1.50
238 Ardley Jansen RC .40 1.00
239 Ferenc Jongejan RC .40 1.00
240 Matt Kata RC .40 1.00
241 Kazuhiro Takeoka RC .40 1.00
242 Charlie Manning RC .40 1.00
243 Il Kim RC .40 1.00
244 Brennan King RC .40 1.00
245 Chris Kroski RC .40 1.00
246 David Martinez RC .40 1.00
247 Pete LaForest RC .40 1.00
248 Wil Ledezma RC .40 1.00
249 Jeremy Bonderman RC 3.00 8.00
250 Gonzalo Lopez RC .40 1.00
251 Brian Luderer RC .40 1.00
252 Ruddy Lugo RC .40 1.00
253 Wayne Lydon RC .40 1.00
254 Mark Malaska RC .40 1.00
255 Andy Marte RC 1.00 2.50
256 Tyler Martin RC .40 1.00
257 Branden Florence RC .40 1.00
258 Aneudis Mateo RC .40 1.00
259 Derell McCall RC .40 1.00
260 Elizardo Ramirez RC .40 1.00
261 Mike McNutt RC .40 1.00
262 Jacobo Meque RC .40 1.00
263 Derek Michaelis RC .40 1.00
264 Aaron Miles RC .40 1.00
265 Jose Morales RC .40 1.00
266 Dustin Moseley RC .40 1.00
267 Adrian Myers RC .40 1.00
268 Dan Neil RC .40 1.00
269 Jon Nelson RC .40 1.00
270 Mike Neu RC .40 1.00
271 Leigh Neuage RC .40 1.00
272 Wes O'Brien RC .40 1.00
273 Trent Oeltjen RC .40 1.00
274 Tim Olson RC .40 1.00
275 David Pahucki RC .40 1.00
276 Nathan Panther RC .40 1.00
277 Arnie Munoz RC .40 1.00
278 Dave Pember RC .40 1.00
279 Jason Perry RC .40 1.00
280 Matthew Peterson RC .40 1.00
281 Greg Aquino RC .40 1.00
282 Jorge Piedra RC .40 1.00
283 Simon Pond RC .40 1.00
284 Aaron Rakers RC .40 1.00
285 Felix Sanchez RC .40 1.00
286 Manuel Ramirez RC .40 1.00
287 Kevin Randel RC .40 1.00
288 Kelly Shoppach RC .60 1.50
289 Prentice Redman RC .40 1.00
290 Eric Reed RC .40 1.00
291 Wilton Reynolds RC .40 1.00
292 Eric Riggs RC .40 1.00
293 Carlos Rijo RC .40 1.00
294 Tyler Adamczyk RC .40 1.00
295 Jon-Mark Sprowl RC .40 1.00
296 Arturo Rivas RC .40 1.00
297 Kyle Roat RC .40 1.00
298 Bubba Nelson RC .40 1.00
299 Levi Robinson RC .40 1.00
300 Ray Sadler RC .40 1.00
301 Rylan Reed RC .40 1.00
302 Jon Schuerholz RC .40 1.00
303 Nobuaki Yoshida RC .40 1.00
304 Brian Shackelford RC .40 1.00
305 Bill Simon RC .40 1.00
306 Haj Turay RC .40 1.00
307 Sean Smith RC .40 1.00
308 Ryan Spataro RC .40 1.00
309 Jemel Spearman RC .40 1.00
310 Keith Stamler RC .40 1.00
311 Luke Steidlmayer RC .40 1.00
312 Adam Stern RC .40 1.00
313 Jay Sitzman RC .40 1.00
314 Mike Wodnicki RC .40 1.00
315 Terry Tiffee RC .40 1.00
316 Nick Trzesniak RC .40 1.00
317 Denny Tussen RC .40 1.00
318 Scott Tyler RC .40 1.00
319 Shane Victorino RC 2.00 5.00
320 Doug Waechter RC .40 1.00
321 Brandon Watson RC .40 1.00
322 Todd Wellemeyer RC .40 1.00
323 Eli Whiteside RC .40 1.00
324 Josh Willingham RC 1.50 4.00
325 Travis Wong RC .40 1.00
326 Brian Wright RC .40 1.00
327 Felix Pie RC 2.00 5.00
328 Andy Sisco RC .40 1.00
329 Dustin Yount RC .40 1.00
330 Andrew Dominique RC .40 1.00
331 Brian McCann AU A RC 20.00 50.00
332 Jose Contreras AU B RC 30.00 60.00
333 Corey Shafer AU A RC 4.00 10.00
334 Hanley Ramirez AU A RC 60.00 120.00
335 Ryan Shealy AU A RC 4.00 10.00
336 Kevin Youkilis AU A RC 30.00 60.00
337 Jason Kubel AU A RC 5.00 12.00
338 Aron Weston AU A RC 4.00 10.00
338B Rajai Davis AU A ERR
339 J.D. Durbin AU A RC 4.00 10.00
340 G. Schneidmiller AU A RC 4.00 10.00
341 Travis Ishikawa AU A RC 4.00 10.00
342 Ben Francisco AU A RC 4.00 10.00
343 Bobby Basham AU A RC 4.00 10.00
344 Joey Gomes AU A RC 4.00 10.00
345 Beau Kemp AU A RC 4.00 10.00
346 T.Story-Harden AU A RC 4.00 10.00
347 Daryl Clark AU A RC 4.00 10.00
348 Bryan Bullington AU A RC 4.00 10.00
349 Rajai Davis AU A RC 4.00 10.00
350 Darrell Rasner AU A RC 4.00 10.00
351 Willie Mays 1.00 2.50
351AU Willie Mays AU 150.00 250.00

2003 Bowman Chrome Refractors

This is a complete parallel to the regular Bowman Chrome set. Cards numbered 1-330 were issued at a stated rate of one in four hobby packs. Cards numbers 331-350 (with the exception of number 332) were issued at a stated rate of one in 92 packs. Those cards were issued to a stated print run of 500 sets. Card number 332 was issued at a stated rate of one in 11,479 packs and was issued to a stated print run of 100 sets. Card number 351 featuring Willie Mays was issued at a stated rate of one in 12 box loader packs.

*REF 1-155: 1.5X TO 4X BASIC
*REF 156-330: 2X TO 5X BASIC
*REF 156-330 RC'S: 1X TO 2.5X BASIC
*REF AU A 331/333-350: .5X TO 1.2X BASIC
*REF.MAYS: 2X TO 5X BASIC
167 Dan Haren 5.00 12.00
202 Chien-Ming Wang 10.00 25.00
207 Chris Duncan 12.50 30.00
237 Edwin Jackson 4.00 10.00
319 Shane Victorino 4.00 10.00
327 Felix Pie 12.50 30.00
332 Jose Contreras AU B 30.00 60.00

2003 Bowman Chrome Blue Refractors

These cards were issued at a stated rate of one per box loader pack. Each of those packs contained an exchange card for an uncirculated card of which had to be redeemed from ThePit.Com by November 30th, 2005.

*BLUE: 1.5X TO 4X BASIC

2003 Bowman Chrome Gold Refractors

This is a full parallel to the 2003 Bowman Chrome set. Cards 1-330 were issued at a stated rate of one per box loader pack. The cards 331-350 were inserted at much tougher odds. Cards 331-350 (except for number 332) were issued at a stated rate of one in 1202 hobby packs and were issued to a stated print run of 50 sets. Card number 332 was issued at a stated rate of one in 177,606 hobby packs and was issued to a stated rate of 10 sets. The Willie Mays card (number 351) was issued at a stated rate of one in 116 box loader packs. There were also cards inserted for a complete set of these randomly inserted in packs at a stated rate of one in 78,936 packs. That exchange card was issued to a stated print run on 10 sets and those cards could be redeemed until November 30th, 2005.

*GOLD REF 1-155: 3X TO 8X BASIC
*GOLD REF 156-330: 3X TO 8X BASIC
*GOLD REF RC'S 156-330: 3X TO 8X BASIC
1-330 ODDS ONE PER BOX LOADER PACK
1-330 PRINT RUN 170 SERIAL #'d SETS
202 Chien-Ming Wang 100.00 200.00
207 Chris Duncan 60.00 120.00
237 Edwin Jackson 20.00 50.00
255 Andy Marte 90.00 150.00
319 Shane Victorino 12.50 30.00
327 Felix Pie 75.00 150.00
331 Brian McCann AU A 125.00 250.00
333 Corey Shafer AU A 30.00 60.00
334 Hanley Ramirez AU A 350.00 700.00
335 Ryan Shealy AU A 30.00 60.00
336 Kevin Youkilis AU A 125.00 250.00
337 Jason Kubel AU A 40.00 80.00
338 Aron Weston AU A 30.00 60.00
339 J.D. Durbin AU A 30.00 60.00
340 Gary Schneidmiller AU A 30.00 60.00
341 Travis Ishikawa AU A 30.00 60.00
342 Ben Francisco AU A 30.00 60.00
343 Bobby Basham AU A 30.00 60.00
344 Joey Gomes AU A 30.00 60.00
345 Beau Kemp AU A 30.00 60.00
346 Thomari Story-Harden AU A 30.00 60.00
347 Daryl Clark AU A 30.00 60.00
348 Bryan Bullington AU A 30.00 60.00
349 Rajai Davis AU A 30.00 60.00
350 Darrell Rasner AU A 30.00 60.00

2003 Bowman Chrome X-Fractors

This is a complete parallel to the basic Bowman Chrome set. Cards numbered 1-330 were issued at a stated rate of one in nine hobby packs. Cards numbered 331-350 (with the exception of number 332) were issued at a stated rate of one in 199 hobby packs and were issued to a stated print run of 250 sets. The Jose Contreras Card (number 332) was issued at a stated rate of one in 22,959 sets and was issued to a stated print run of 50 sets. The Willie Mays card (number 351) was issued at a stated rate of one in 58 box loader packs.

*X-FR 1-155: 2.5X TO 6X BASIC
*X-FR 156-330: 2.5X TO 6X BASIC
*X-FR RC'S 156-330: 1.25X TO 3X BASIC
*X-FR AU A 331/333-350: .6X TO 1.5X BASIC
*X-FR MAYS: 4X TO 10X BASIC
167 Dan Haren 10.00 25.00
202 Chien-Ming Wang 15.00 40.00
207 Chris Duncan 30.00 60.00
237 Edwin Jackson 10.00 25.00
249 Jeremy Bonderman 20.00 50.00
319 Shane Victorino 5.00 12.00
327 Felix Pie 30.00 60.00
331 Brian McCann AU A 60.00 120.00
332 Jose Contreras AU B 40.00 80.00

2003 Bowman Chrome Draft

This 176-card set was inserted as part of the 2003 Bowman Draft Pack. Each pack contained 2 Bowman Chrome Cards numbered between 1-165. In addition, cards numbered 166 through 176 were inserted at a stated rate of one in 41 packs. Each of those cards can be easily identified as they were autographed. Please note that these cards were issued as a mix of live and exchange cards with a deadline for redeeming the exchange cards of November 30, 2005.

COMPLETE SET (176) 400.00 550.00
COMP.SET w/o AU's (165) 50.00 100.00
COMMON CARD (1-165) .20 .50
COMMON RC .40 1.00
COMMON RC YR .20 .50
1-165 TWO PER BOWMAN DRAFT PACK
COMMON CARD (166-176) 4.00 10.00
166-176 STATED ODDS 1:41 H/R
LUBANSKI IS AN SP BY 1000 COPIES
1 Dontrelle Willis .20 .50
2 Freddy Sanchez .20 .50
3 Miguel Cabrera .50 1.25
4 Ryan Ludwick .20 .50
5 Ty Wigginton .20 .50
6 Mark Teixeira .50 1.25
7 Trey Hodges .20 .50
8 Laynce Nix .20 .50
9 Antonio Perez .20 .50
10 Jody Gerut .20 .50
11 Jae Weong Seo .20 .50
12 Erick Almonte .20 .50
13 Lyle Overbay .20 .50
14 Billy Traber .20 .50
15 Andres Torres .20 .50
16 Jose Valverde .20 .50
17 Aaron Heilman .20 .50
18 Brandon Larson .20 .50
19 Jung Bong .20 .50
20 Jesse Foppert .20 .50
21 Angel Berroa .20 .50
22 Jeff DaVanon .20 .50
23 Kurt Ainsworth .20 .50
24 Brandon Claussen .20 .50
25 Xavier Nady .20 .50
26 Travis Hafner .20 .50
27 Jerome Williams .20 .50
28 Jose Reyes .50 1.25
29 Sergio Mitre RC .40 1.00
30 Bo Hart RC .40 1.00
31 Adam Miller RC 4.00 10.00
32 Brian Finch RC .40 1.00
33 Taylor Mattingly RC .40 1.00
34 Daric Barton RC 2.50 6.00
35 Chris Ray RC 1.25 3.00
36 Jarrod Saltalamacchia RC 6.00 15.00
37 Dennis Dove RC .40 1.00
38 James Houser RC .40 1.00
39 Clint King RC .40 1.00
40 Lou Palmisano RC .40 1.00
41 Dan Moore RC .40 1.00
42 Craig Stansberry RC .40 1.00
43 Jo Jo Reyes RC 1.25 3.00
44 Jake Stevens RC .40 1.00
45 Tom Gorzelanny RC 2.00 5.00
46 Brian Marshall RC .40 1.00
47 Scott Beerer RC .40 1.00
48 Javi Herrera RC .40 1.00
49 Steve LeRud RC .40 1.00
50 Josh Banks RC .40 1.00
51 Jon Papelbon RC 5.00 12.00
52 Juan Valdes RC .40 1.00
53 Beau Vaughan RC .40 1.00
54 Matt Chico RC .40 1.00
55 Todd Jennings RC .40 1.00
56 Anthony Gwynn RC 1.50 4.00
57 Matt Harrison RC 1.00 2.50
58 Aaron Marsden RC .40 1.00
59 Casey Abrams RC .40 1.00
60 Cory Stuart RC .40 1.00
61 Mike Wagner RC .40 1.00
62 Jordan Pratt RC .40 1.00
63 Andre Randolph RC .40 1.00
64 Blake Balkcom RC .40 1.00
65 Josh Muecke RC .40 1.00
66 Jamie D'Antona RC .40 1.00
67 Cole Seifrig RC .40 1.00
68 Josh Anderson RC .40 1.00
69 Matt Lorenzo RC .40 1.00
70 Nate Spears RC .40 1.00
71 Chris Goodman RC .40 1.00
72 Brian McFall RC .40 1.00
73 Billy Hogan RC .40 1.00
74 Jamie Romak RC .40 1.00
75 Jeff Cook RC .40 1.00
76 Brooks McNiven RC .40 1.00
77 Xavier Paul RC .40 1.00
78 Bob Zimmerman RC UER .40 1.00
Name is really Zimmermann
79 Mickey Hall RC .40 1.00
80 Shaun Marcum RC .40 1.00
81 Matt Nachreiner RC .40 1.00
82 Chris Kinsey RC .40 1.00
83 Jonathan Fulton RC .40 1.00
84 Edgardo Baez RC .40 1.00
85 Robert Valido RC .40 1.00
86 Kenny Lewis RC .40 1.00
87 Trent Peterson RC .40 1.00
88 Johnny Woodard RC .40 1.00
89 Wes Littleton RC .40 1.00
90 Sean Rodriguez RC 2.00 5.00
91 Kyle Pearson RC .40 1.00
92 Josh Rainwater RC .40 1.00
93 Travis Schlichting RC .40 1.00
94 Tim Battle RC .40 1.00
95 Aaron Hill RC 2.00 5.00
96 Bob McCrory RC .40 1.00
97 Rick Guarno RC .40 1.00
98 Brandon Yarbrough RC .40 1.00
99 Peter Stonard RC .40 1.00
100 Darin Downs RC .40 1.00
101 Matt Bruback RC .40 1.00

102 Danny Garcia RC .40 1.00
103 Cory Stewart RC .40 1.00
104 Ferdin Tejeda RC .40 1.00
105 Kade Johnson RC .40 1.00
106 Andrew Brown RC .40 1.00
107 Aquilino Lopez RC .40 1.00
108 Stephen Randolph RC .40 1.00
109 Dave Matranga RC .40 1.00
110 Dustin McGowan RC .40 1.00
111 Juan Camacho RC .40 1.00
112 Cliff Lee 3.00 8.00
113 Jeff Duncan RC .40 1.00
114 C.J. Wilson 1.25 3.00
115 Brandon Roberson RC .40 1.00
116 David Corrente RC .40 1.00
117 Kevin Beavers RC .40 1.00
118 Anthony Webster RC .40 1.00
119 Oscar Villarreal RC .40 1.00
120 Hong-Chih Kuo RC 3.00 8.00
121 Josh Barfield .20 .50
122 Denny Bautista .20 .50
123 Chris Burke RC 1.50 4.00
124 Robinson Cano RC 12.50 30.00
125 Jose Castillo .20 .50
126 Neal Cotts .20 .50
127 Jorge De La Rosa .20 .50
128 J.D. Durbin .20 .50
129 Edwin Encarnacion .50 1.25
130 Gavin Floyd .20 .50
131 Alexis Gomez .20 .50
132 Edgar Gonzalez RC .40 1.00
133 Khalil Greene .30 .75
134 Zack Greinke .30 .75
135 Franklin Gutierrez .50 1.25
136 Rich Harden .30 .75
137 J.J. Hardy RC 4.00 10.00
138 Ryan Howard RC 10.00 25.00
139 Justin Huber .20 .50
140 David Kelton .20 .50
141 Dave Krynzel .20 .50
142 Pete LaForest .20 .50
143 Adam LaRoche .20 .50
144 Preston Larrison RC .40 1.00
145 John Maine RC 5.00 12.00
146 Andy Marte 1.50 4.00
147 Jeff Mathis .20 .50
148 Joe Mauer .50 1.25
149 Clint Nageotte .20 .50
150 Chris Narveson .20 .50
151 Ramon Nivar .20 .50
152 Felix Pie 2.00 5.00
153 Guillermo Quiroz RC .40 1.00
154 Rene Reyes .20 .50
155 Royce Ring .20 .50
156 Alexis Rios 1.25 3.00
157 Grady Sizemore .30 .75
158 Stephen Smitherman .20 .50
159 Seung Song .20 .50
160 Scott Thorman .20 .50
161 Chad Tracy .20 .50
162 Chin-Hui Tsao .20 .50
163 John VanBenschoten .20 .50
164 Kevin Youkilis 2.00 5.00
165 Chien-Ming Wang 1.25 3.00
166 Chris Lubanski AU SP RC 10.00 25.00
167 Ryan Harvey AU RC 4.00 10.00
168 Matt Murton AU RC 4.00 10.00
169 Jay Sborz AU RC 4.00 10.00
170 Brandon Wood AU RC 6.00 15.00
171 Nick Markakis AU RC 40.00 80.00
172 Rickie Weeks AU RC 12.50 30.00
173 Eric Duncan AU RC 6.00 15.00
174 Chad Billingsley AU RC 12.50 30.00
175 Ryan Wagner AU RC 4.00 10.00
176 Delmon Young AU RC 12.50 30.00

2003 Bowman Chrome Draft Refractors

*REFRACTOR 1-165: 1.5X TO 4X BASIC
*REFRACTOR RC 1-165: 1.25X TO 3X BASIC
*REFRACTOR RC YR 1-165: 1.5X TO 4X BASIC
*REFRACTOR AU 166-176: .6X TO 1.5X BASIC
1-165 ODDS 1:11 BOWMAN DRAFT H/R
166-176 AU ODDS 1:196 BOW.DRAFT HOBBY
166-176 AU ODDS 1:197 BOW.DRAFT RETAIL
166-176 AU PRINT RUN 500 SETS
166-176 AU PRINT RUN PROVIDED BY TOPPS
166-176 AU'S ARE NOT SERIAL-NUMBERED
31 Adam Miller 15.00 40.00
36 Jarrod Saltalamacchia 15.00 40.00
56 Anthony Gwynn 6.00 15.00
112 Cliff Lee 10.00 25.00
120 Hong-Chih Kuo 12.50 30.00
124 Robinson Cano 100.00 200.00
137 J.J. Hardy 15.00 40.00
138 Ryan Howard 20.00 50.00
145 John Maine 20.00 50.00
152 Felix Pie 8.00 20.00
165 Chien-Ming Wang 6.00 15.00
171 Nick Markakis AU 60.00 120.00

2003 Bowman Chrome Draft Gold Refractors

*GOLD REF 1-165: 8X TO 20X BASIC
*GOLD REF RC 1-165: 10X TO 20X BASIC
*GOLD REF RC YR 1-165: 7.5X TO 15X BASIC
1-165 ODDS 1:98 BOWMAN DRAFT HOBBY
166-176 AU ODDS 1:1479 BOW.DRAFT HOBBY
1-165 PRINT RUN 50 SERIAL #'d SETS
166-176 AU PRINT RUN 50 SETS
166-176 AU PRINT RUN PROVIDED BY TOPPS
166-176 AU'S ARE NOT SERIAL-NUMBERED
GOLD.REF ARE HOBBY-ONLY DISTRIBUTION
31 Adam Miller 150.00 250.00
36 Jarrod Saltalamacchia 150.00 250.00
112 Cliff Lee 60.00 120.00
120 Hong-Chih Kuo 100.00 200.00
123 Chris Burke 100.00 200.00
124 Robinson Cano 400.00 600.00
137 J.J. Hardy 200.00 300.00
138 Ryan Howard 300.00 600.00
145 John Maine 200.00 275.00
152 Felix Pie 50.00 100.00
165 Chien-Ming Wang 50.00 100.00
166 Chris Lubanski AU 30.00 60.00
167 Ryan Harvey AU 30.00 60.00
168 Matt Murton AU 30.00 60.00
169 Jay Sborz AU 30.00 60.00
171 Nick Markakis AU 350.00 550.00
172 Rickie Weeks AU 150.00 300.00
173 Eric Duncan AU 40.00 80.00
174 Chad Billingsley AU 175.00 350.00
175 Ryan Wagner AU 30.00 60.00
176 Delmon Young AU 200.00 400.00

2003 Bowman Chrome Draft X-Fractors

*X-FRACTOR 1-165: 3X TO 8X BASIC
*X-FRACTOR RC 1-165: 2.5X TO 6X BASIC
*X-FRACTOR RC YR 1-165: 2.5X TO 6X BASIC
*X-FRACTOR AU 166-176: .75X TO 2X BASIC
1-165 ODDS 1:50 BOWMAN DRAFT HOBBY
1-165 ODDS 1:52 BOWMAN DRAFT RETAIL
166-176 AU ODDS 1:393 BOW.DRAFT HOBBY
166-176 AU ODDS 1:394 BOW.DRAFT RETAIL
1-165 PRINT RUN 130 SERIAL #'d SETS
166-176 AU PRINT RUN 250 SETS
166-176 AU PRINT RUN PROVIDED BY TOPPS
166-176 AU'S ARE NOT SERIAL-NUMBERED
31 Adam Miller 30.00 60.00
45 Tom Gorzelanny 15.00 40.00
90 Sean Rodriguez 20.00 50.00
95 Aaron Hill 20.00 50.00
112 Cliff Lee 20.00 50.00
120 Hong-Chih Kuo 20.00 50.00
124 Robinson Cano 60.00 120.00
137 J.J. Hardy 30.00 60.00
138 Ryan Howard 60.00 120.00
145 John Maine 40.00 80.00
165 Chien-Ming Wang 10.00 25.00
171 Nick Markakis AU 75.00 150.00

2004 Bowman Chrome

This 350-card set was released in August, 2004. The set was issued in four card packs with an $4 SRP which came 18 packs and 12 boxes to a case. The first 144 cards feature veterans while cards numbered 145 through 165 feature leading prospects. Cards numbered 166 through 350 are all Rookie Cards with the last 20 cards of the set being autographed. The Autographed cards (331-350) were inserted at a stated rate of one in 25 with a stated print run of 2000 sets. The Bobby Brownlie cards were issued as exchange cards with a stated expiry date of August 31, 2006.

COMPLETE SET (350) 250.00 400.00
COMP.SET w/o AU's (330) 60.00 120.00
COMMON CARD (1-150) .20 .50
COMMON CARD (151-165) .20 .50
COMMON CARD (166-330) .40 1.00
COMMON AUTO (331-350) 4.00 10.00
331-350 AU STATED ODDS 1:25
331-350 AU PRINT RUN 2000 SETS
331-350 AU'S ARE NOT SERIAL-NUMBERED
331-350 PRINT RUN PROVIDED BY TOPPS
EXCHANGE DEADLINE 08/31/06
1 Garret Anderson .20 .50
2 Larry Walker .30 .75
3 Derek Jeter 1.25 3.00
4 Curt Schilling .30 .75
5 Carlos Zambrano .30 .75
6 Shawn Green .20 .50
7 Manny Ramirez .50 1.25
8 Randy Johnson .50 1.25
9 Jeremy Bonderman .20 .50
10 Alfonso Soriano .20 .50
11 Scott Rolen .30 .75
12 Kerry Wood .20 .50
13 Eric Gagne .20 .50
14 Ryan Klesko .20 .50
15 Kevin Millar .20 .50
16 Ty Wigginton .20 .50
17 David Ortiz .50 1.25
18 Luis Castillo .20 .50
19 Bernie Williams .30 .75
20 Edgar Renteria .20 .50
21 Matt Kata .20 .50
22 Bartolo Colon .20 .50
23 Derrek Lee .20 .50
24 Gary Sheffield .20 .50
25 Nomar Garciaparra .50 1.25
26 Kevin Millwood .20 .50
27 Corey Patterson .20 .50
28 Carlos Beltran .20 .50
29 Mike Lieberthal .20 .50
30 Troy Glaus .20 .50
31 Preston Wilson .20 .50
32 Jorge Posada .30 .75
33 Bo Hart .20 .50
34 Mark Prior .30 .75
35 Hideo Nomo .50 1.25
36 Jason Kendall .20 .50
37 Roger Clemens .60 1.50
38 Dmitri Young .20 .50
39 Jason Giambi .20 .50
40 Jim Edmonds .30 .75
41 Ryan Ludwick .20 .50
42 Brandon Webb .20 .50
43 Todd Helton .30 .75
44 Jacque Jones .20 .50
45 Jamie Moyer .20 .50
46 Tim Salmon .20 .50
47 Kelvim Escobar .20 .50
48 Tony Batista .20 .50
49 Nick Johnson .20 .50
50 Jim Thome .30 .75
51 Casey Blake .20 .50
52 Trot Nixon .20 .50
53 Luis Gonzalez .20 .50
54 Dontrelle Willis .20 .50
55 Mike Mussina .30 .75
56 Carl Crawford .30 .75
57 Mark Buehrle .30 .75
58 Scott Podsednik .20 .50
59 Brian Giles .20 .50
60 Rafael Furcal .20 .50
61 Miguel Cabrera .50 1.25
62 Rich Harden .20 .50
63 Mark Teixeira .50 1.25
64 Frank Thomas .50 1.25
65 Johan Santana .50 1.25
66 Jason Schmidt .20 .50
67 Aramis Ramirez .20 .50
68 Jose Reyes .30 .75
69 Magglio Ordonez .30 .75
70 Mike Sweeney .20 .50
71 Eric Chavez .20 .50
72 Rocco Baldelli .20 .50
73 Sammy Sosa .50 1.25
74 Javy Lopez .20 .50
75 Roy Oswalt .30 .75
76 Raul Ibanez .20 .50
77 Ivan Rodriguez .30 .75
78 Jerome Williams .20 .50
79 Carlos Lee .20 .50
80 Geoff Jenkins .20 .50
81 Sean Burroughs .20 .50
82 Marcus Giles .20 .50
83 Mike Lowell .20 .50
84 Barry Zito .20 .50
85 Aubrey Huff .20 .50
86 Esteban Loaiza .20 .50
87 Torii Hunter .20 .50
88 Phil Nevin .20 .50
89 Andruw Jones .20 .50
90 Josh Beckett .30 .75
91 Mark Mulder .20 .50
92 Hank Blalock .20 .50
93 Jason Phillips .20 .50
94 Russ Ortiz .20 .50
95 Juan Pierre .20 .50
96 Tom Glavine .30 .75
97 Gil Meche .20 .50
98 Ramon Ortiz .20 .50
99 Richie Sexson .20 .50
100 Albert Pujols 1.25 3.00
101 Javier Vazquez .20 .50
102 Johnny Damon .30 .75
103 Alex Rodriguez .75 2.00
104 Omar Vizquel .30 .75
105 Chipper Jones .50 1.25
106 Lance Berkman .30 .75
107 Tim Hudson .30 .75
108 Carlos Delgado .20 .50
109 Austin Kearns .20 .50
110 Orlando Cabrera .20 .50
111 Edgar Martinez .30 .75
112 Melvin Mora .20 .50
113 Jeff Bagwell .30 .75
114 Marlon Byrd .20 .50
115 Vernon Wells .20 .50
116 C.C. Sabathia .30 .75
117 Cliff Floyd .20 .50
118 Ichiro Suzuki .75 2.00
119 Miguel Olivo .20 .50
120 Mike Piazza .50 1.25
121 Adam Dunn .30 .75
122 Paul Lo Duca .20 .50
123 Brett Myers .20 .50
124 Michael Young .20 .50
125 Sidney Ponson .20 .50
126 Greg Maddux .75 2.00
127 Vladimir Guerrero .50 1.25
128 Miguel Tejada .30 .75
129 Andy Pettitte .30 .75
130 Rafael Palmeiro .30 .75
131 Ken Griffey Jr. .75 2.00
132 Shannon Stewart .20 .50
133 Joel Pineiro .20 .50
134 Luis Matos .20 .50
135 Jeff Kent .20 .50
136 Randy Wolf .20 .50
137 Chris Woodward .20 .50
138 Jody Gerut .20 .50
139 Jose Vidro .20 .50
140 Bret Boone .20 .50
141 Bill Mueller .20 .50
142 Angel Berroa .20 .50
143 Bobby Abreu .20 .50
144 Roy Halladay .50 1.25
145 Delmon Young .30 .75
146 Jonny Gomes .20 .50
147 Rickie Weeks .20 .50
148 Edwin Jackson .20 .50
149 Neal Cotts .20 .50
150 Jason Bay .30 .75
151 Khalil Greene .30 .75
152 Joe Mauer .50 1.25
153 Bobby Jenks .20 .50
154 Chin-Feng Chen .20 .50
155 Chien-Ming Wang 1.00 2.50
156 Mickey Hall .20 .50
157 James Houser .20 .50
158 Jay Sborz .20 .50
159 Jonathan Fulton .20 .50
160 Steven Lerud .20 .50
161 Grady Sizemore .30 .75
162 Felix Pie .20 .50
163 Dustin McGowan .20 .50
164 Chris Lubanski .20 .50
165 Tom Gorzelanny .20 .50
166 Rudy Guillen RC .40 1.00
167 Aarom Baldiris RC .40 1.00
168 Conor Jackson RC 2.50 6.00
169 Matt Moses RC .60 1.50
170 Ervin Santana RC 1.00 2.50
171 Merkin Valdez RC .40 1.00
172 Erick Aybar RC .60 1.50
173 Brad Sullivan RC .40 1.00
174 Joey Gathright RC .40 1.00
175 Brad Snyder RC .40 1.00
176 Alberto Callaspo RC 1.00 2.50
177 Brandon Medders RC .40 1.00
178 Zach Miner RC .60 1.50
179 Charlie Zink RC .40 1.00
180 Adam Greenberg RC .40 1.00
181 Kevin Howard RC .40 1.00
182 Wanell Severino RC .40 1.00
183 Chin-Lung Hu RC .40 1.00
184 Joel Zumaya RC 2.50 6.00
185 Skip Schumaker RC .60 1.50
186 Nic Ungs RC .40 1.00
187 Todd Self RC .40 1.00
188 Brian Steffek RC .40 1.00
189 Brock Peterson RC .40 1.00
190 Greg Thissen RC .40 1.00
191 Frank Brooks RC .40 1.00
192 Scott Olsen RC .40 1.00
193 Chris Mabeus RC .40 1.00
194 Dan Giese RC .40 1.00
195 Jared Wells RC .40 1.00
196 Carlos Sosa RC .40 1.00
197 Bobby Madritsch .40 1.00
198 Calvin Hayes RC .40 1.00
199 Omar Quintanilla RC .40 1.00
200 Chris O'Riordan RC .40 1.00
201 Tim Hutting RC .40 1.00
202 Carlos Quentin RC 1.50 4.00
203 Brayan Pena RC .40 1.00
204 Jeff Salazar RC .40 1.00
205 David Murphy RC 1.00 2.50
206 Alberto Garcia RC .40 1.00
207 Ramon Ramirez RC .40 1.00
208 Luis Bolivar RC .40 1.00
209 Rodney Choy Foo RC .40 1.00
210 Fausto Carmona RC .60 1.50
211 Anthony Acevedo RC .40 1.00
212 Chad Santos RC .40 1.00
213 Jason Frasor RC .40 1.00
214 Jesse Roman RC .40 1.00
215 James Tomlin RC .40 1.00
216 Josh Labandeira RC .40 1.00
217 Ryan Meaux RC .40 1.00
218 Don Sutton RC .40 1.00
219 Danny Gonzalez RC .40 1.00
220 Javier Guzman RC .40 1.00
221 Anthony Lerew RC .40 1.00
222 Jon Connolly RC .40 1.00
223 Jesse English RC .40 1.00
224 Hector Made RC .40 1.00
225 Travis Hanson RC .40 1.00
226 Jesse Floyd RC .40 1.00
227 Nick Gorneault RC .40 1.00
228 Craig Ansman RC .40 1.00
229 Paul McAnulty RC .40 1.00
230 Carl Loadenthal RC .40 1.00
231 Dave Crouthers RC .40 1.00
232 Harvey Garcia RC .40 1.00
233 Casey Kopitzke RC .40 1.00
234 Ricky Nolasco RC .60 1.50
235 Miguel Perez RC .40 1.00
236 Ryan Mulhern RC .40 1.00
237 Chris Aguila RC .40 1.00
238 Brooks Conrad RC .40 1.00
239 Damaso Espino RC .40 1.00
240 Jereme Milons RC .40 1.00
241 Luke Hughes RC .40 1.00
242 Kory Casto RC .40 1.00
243 Jose Valdez RC .40 1.00
244 J.T. Stotts RC .40 1.00
245 Lee Gwaltney RC .40 1.00
246 Yoann Torrealba RC .40 1.00
247 Omar Falcon RC .40 1.00
248 Jon Coutlangus RC .40 1.00
249 George Sherrill RC .40 1.00
250 John Santor RC .40 1.00
251 Tony Richie RC .40 1.00
252 Kevin Richardson RC .40 1.00
253 Tim Bittner RC .40 1.00
254 Chris Saenz RC .40 1.00
255 Jose Capellan RC .40 1.00
256 Donald Levinski RC .40 1.00
257 Jerome Gamble RC .40 1.00
258 Jeff Keppinger RC .60 1.50
259 Jason Szuminski RC .40 1.00
260 Akinori Otsuka RC .40 1.00
261 Ryan Budde RC .40 1.00
262 Marland Williams RC .40 1.00
263 Jeff Allison RC .40 1.00
264 Hector Gimenez RC .40 1.00
265 Tim Frend RC .40 1.00
266 Tom Farmer RC .40 1.00
267 Shawn Hill RC .40 1.00
268 Mike Huggins RC .40 1.00
269 Scott Proctor RC .40 1.00
270 Jorge Mejia RC .40 1.00
271 Terry Jones RC .40 1.00
272 Zach Duke RC .60 1.50
273 Jesse Crain RC .40 1.00
274 Luke Anderson RC .40 1.00
275 Hunter Brown RC .40 1.00
276 Matt Lemanczyk RC .40 1.00
277 Fernando Cortez RC .40 1.00
278 Vince Perkins RC .40 1.00
279 Tommy Murphy RC .40 1.00
280 Mike Gosling RC .40 1.00
281 Paul Bacot RC .40 1.00
282 Matt Capps RC .40 1.00
283 Juan Gutierrez RC .40 1.00
284 Teodoro Encarnacion RC .40 1.00
285 Chad Bentz RC .40 1.00
286 Kazuo Matsui RC .60 1.50
287 Ryan Hankins RC .40 1.00
288 Leo Nunez RC .40 1.00
289 Dave Wallace RC .40 1.00
290 Rob Tejeda RC .40 1.00
291 Paul Maholm RC .60 1.50
292 Casey Daigle RC .40 1.00
293 Tydus Meadows RC .40 1.00
294 Khalid Ballouli RC .40 1.00
295 Benji DeQuin RC .40 1.00
296 Tyler Davidson RC .40 1.00
297 Brant Colamarino RC .40 1.00
298 Marcus McBeth RC .40 1.00
299 Brad Eldred RC .40 1.00
300 David Pauley RC .60 1.50
301 Yadier Molina RC 2.50 6.00
302 Chris Shelton RC .40 1.00
303 Nyjer Morgan RC .40 1.00
304 Jon DeVries RC .40 1.00
305 Sheldon Fulse RC .40 1.00
306 Vito Chiaravalloti RC .40 1.00
307 Warner Madrigal RC .40 1.00
308 Reid Gorecki RC .40 1.00
309 Sung Jung RC .40 1.00
310 Pete Shier RC .40 1.00
311 Michael Mooney RC .40 1.00
312 Kenny Perez RC .40 1.00
313 Michael Mallory RC .40 1.00
314 Ben Himes RC .40 1.00
315 Ivan Ochoa RC .40 1.00
316 Donald Kelly RC .60 1.50
317 Tom Mastny RC .40 1.00
318 Kevin Davidson RC .40 1.00
319 Brian Pilkington RC .40 1.00
320 Alex Romero RC .40 1.00
321 Chad Chop RC .40 1.00
322 Kody Kirkland RC .40 1.00
323 Casey Myers RC .40 1.00
324 Mike Rouse RC .40 1.00
325 Sergio Silva RC .40 1.00
326 J.J. Furmaniak RC .40 1.00
327 Brad Vericker RC .40 1.00
328 Blake Hawksworth RC .40 1.00
329 Brock Jacobsen RC .40 1.00
330 Alec Zumwalt RC .40 1.00
331 Wardell Starling AU RC 4.00 10.00
332 Estee Harris AU RC 4.00 10.00
333 Kyle Sleeth AU RC 4.00 10.00
334 Dioner Navarro AU RC 6.00 15.00
335 Logan Kensing AU RC 4.00 10.00
336 Travis Blackley AU RC 4.00 10.00
337 Lincoln Holdzkom AU RC 4.00 10.00
338 Jason Hirsh AU RC 10.00 25.00
339 Juan Cedeno AU RC 4.00 10.00
340 Matt Creighton AU RC 4.00 10.00
341 Tim Stauffer AU RC 6.00 15.00
342 Shingo Takatsu AU RC 6.00 15.00
343 Lastings Milledge AU RC 20.00 50.00
344 Dustin Nippert AU RC 4.00 10.00
345 Felix Hernandez AU RC 75.00 150.00
346 Joaquin Arias AU RC 6.00 15.00
347 Kevin Kouzmanoff AU RC 10.00 25.00
348 B.Brownlie AU RC 4.00 10.00
349 David Aardsma AU RC 4.00 10.00
350 Jon Knott AU RC 6.00 15.00

2004 Bowman Chrome Refractors

*REF 1-150: 1.5X TO 4X BASIC
*REF 151-165: 2X TO 5X BASIC
*REF 166-330: 1X TO 2.5X BASIC
1-330 STATED ODDS 1:4 HOBBY
*REF AU 331-350: .5X TO 1.2X BASIC
331-350 AU ODDS 1:100 HOBBY
331-350 AU PRINT RUN 500 SETS
331-350 AU'S ARE NOT SERIAL-NUMBERED
331-350 PRINT RUN PROVIDED BY TOPPS
EXCHANGE DEADLINE 08/31/06
334 Dioner Navarro AU 8.00 20.00
342 Shingo Takatsu AU 8.00 20.00
343 Lastings Milledge AU 30.00 60.00
345 Felix Hernandez AU 100.00 200.00
347 Kevin Kouzmanoff AU 15.00 40.00

2004 Bowman Chrome Blue Refractors

*BLUE REF 166-330: 1.25X TO 3X BASIC
EXCH.CARDS AVAIL VIA PIT.COM WEBSITE
ONE EXCH.CARD PER BOX-LOADER PACK
ONE BOX-LOADER PACK PER HOBBY BOX
STATED PRINT RUN 290 SETS
NNO Exchange Card

2004 Bowman Chrome Gold Refractors

*GOLD REF 1-150: 5X TO 12X BASIC
*GOLD REF 151-165: 8X TO 20X BASIC
*GOLD REF 166-330: 6X TO 15X BASIC
1-330 STATED ODDS 1:60 HOBBY
1-330 PRINT RUN 50 SERIAL #'d SETS
*GOLD REF 331-350: 2X TO 4X BASIC
331-350 AU ODDS 1:1003 HOBBY
331-350 AU STATED PRINT RUN 50 SETS
331-350 AU'S ARE NOT SERIAL-NUMBERED
331-350 PRINT RUN PROVIDED BY TOPPS
EXCHANGE DEADLINE 08/31/06
333 Kyle Sleeth AU 30.00 60.00
334 Dioner Navarro AU 30.00 60.00
336 Travis Blackley AU 20.00 50.00
341 Tim Stauffer AU 30.00 60.00
342 Shingo Takatsu AU 30.00 60.00
343 Lastings Milledge AU 200.00 400.00
344 Dustin Nippert AU 50.00 100.00
345 Felix Hernandez AU 600.00 800.00
346 Joaquin Arias AU 30.00 60.00
347 Kevin Kouzmanoff AU 100.00 200.00
349 David Aardsma AU 20.00 50.00

2004 Bowman Chrome X-Fractors

*X-FR 1-150: 3X TO 8X BASIC
*X-FR 151-165: 4X TO 10X BASIC
*X-FR 166-330: 2X TO 5X BASIC
1-330 ODDS ONE PER BOX LOADER PACK
ONE BOX LOADER PACK PER HOBY BOX
INSTANT WIN 1-330 ODDS 1:103,968 H
1-330 PRINT RUN 172 SERIAL #'d SETS
SETS 1-10 AVAIL.VIA INSTANT WIN CARD
SETS 11-172 ISSUED IN BOX-LOADER PACKS
*X-FR AU 331-350: .6X TO 1.5X BASIC
331-350 AU ODDS 1:200 HOBBY
331-350 AU STATED PRINT RUN 250 SETS
331-350 AU'S ARE NOT SERIAL-NUMBERED
331-350 PRINT RUNS PROVIDED BY TOPPS
EXCHANGE DEADLINE 08/31/06
334 Dioner Navarro AU 10.00 25.00
342 Shingo Takatsu AU 10.00 25.00
343 Lastings Milledge AU 60.00 120.00
345 Felix Hernandez AU 150.00 250.00
347 Kevin Kouzmanoff AU 30.00 60.00
NNO Complete 1-330 Instant Win/10

2004 Bowman Chrome Stars of the Future

STATED ODDS 1:600 HOBBY
STATED PRINT RUN 500 SETS
CARDS ARE NOT SERIAL-NUMBERED
PRINT RUN INFO PROVIDED BY TOPPS
REFRACTORS RANDOM INSERTS IN PACKS
NO REFRACTOR PRICING DUE TO SCARCITY
EXCHANGE DEADLINE 08/31/06
LHC Chris Lubanski 15.00 40.00
Ryan Harvey
Chad Cordero
MHD Nick Markakis 20.00 50.00
Aaron Hill
Eric Duncan
YSS Delmon Young 20.00 50.00
Kyle Sleeth
Tim Stauffer

2004 Bowman Chrome Draft

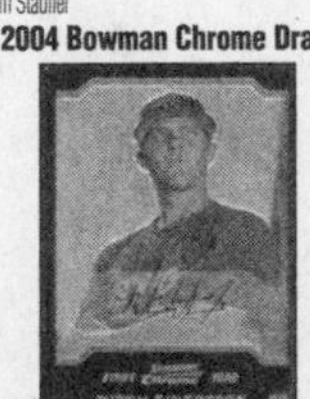

This 175-card set was issued as part of the Bowman Draft release. The first 165 cards were issued at a stated rate of two per Bowman Draft pack while the final 10 cards, all of which were autographed, were issued at a stated rate of one in 60 hobby and retail packs and were issued to a stated print run of 1695 sets.

COMPLETE SET (175) 175.00 300.00
COMP.SET w/o SP's (165) 50.00 100.00
COMMON CARD (1-165) .15 .40
COMMON RC .40 1.00
COMMON RC YR .15 .40
1-165 TWO PER BOWMAN DRAFT PACK
COMMON CARD (166-175) 4.00 10.00
166-175 ODDS 1:60 BOWMAN DRAFT HOBBY
166-175 ODDS 1:60 BOWMAN DRAFT RETAIL
166-175 STATED PRINT RUN 1695 SETS
166-175 ARE NOT SERIAL-NUMBERED
166-175 PRINT RUN PROVIDED BY TOPPS
PLATES 1-165 ODDS 1:559 HOBBY
PLATES 166-175 ODDS 1:18,354 HOBBY
PLATES PRINT RUN 1 SERIAL #'d SET
BLACK-CYAN-MAGENTA-YELLOW EXIST
NO PLATES PRICING DUE TO SCARCITY
1 Lyle Overbay .15 .40
2 David Newhan .15 .40
3 J.R. House .15 .40
4 Chad Tracy .15 .40
5 Humberto Quintero .15 .40
6 Dave Bush .15 .40
7 Scott Hairston .15 .40
8 Mike Wood .15 .40
9 Alexis Rios .25 .60
10 Sean Burnett .15 .40
11 Wilson Valdez .15 .40
12 Lew Ford .15 .40
13 Freddy Thon RC .40 1.00
14 Zack Greinke .25 .60
15 Bucky Jacobsen .15 .40
16 Kevin Youkilis .25 .60
17 Grady Sizemore .25 .60
18 Denny Bautista .15 .40
19 David DeJesus .15 .40
20 Casey Kotchman .15 .40
21 David Kelton .15 .40
22 Charles Thomas RC .40 1.00
23 Kazuhito Tadano RC .40 1.00
24 Justin Leone RC .40 1.00
25 Eduardo Villacis RC .40 1.00
26 Brian Dallimore RC .40 1.00
27 Nick Green .15 .40
28 Sam McConnell RC .40 1.00
29 Brad Halsey RC .40 1.00
30 Roman Colon RC .40 1.00
31 Josh Fields RC .60 1.50
32 Cody Bunkelman RC .40 1.00
33 Jay Rainville RC .40 1.00
34 Richie Robnett RC .40 1.00
35 Jon Poterson RC .40 1.00
36 Huston Street RC 1.00 2.50
37 Erick San Pedro RC .40 1.00
38 Cory Dunlap RC .40 1.00
39 Kurt Suzuki RC 1.25 3.00
40 Anthony Swarzak RC .60 1.50
41 Ian Desmond RC 1.00 2.50
42 Chris Covington RC .40 1.00
43 Christian Garcia RC .60 1.50
44 Gaby Hernandez RC 1.00 2.50
45 Steven Register RC .40 1.00
46 Eduardo Morlan RC .60 1.50
47 Collin Balester RC .40 1.00
48 Nathan Phillips RC .40 1.00
49 Dan Schwartzbauer RC .40 1.00
50 Rafael Gonzalez RC .40 1.00
51 K.C. Herren RC .40 1.00
52 William Susdorf RC .40 1.00
53 Rob Johnson RC .40 1.00
54 Louis Marson RC .60 1.50
55 Joe Koshansky RC .40 1.00
56 Jamar Walton RC .40 1.00
57 Mark Lowe RC .60 1.50
58 Matt Macri RC .60 1.50
59 Donny Lucy RC .40 1.00
60 Mike Ferris RC .40 1.00
61 Mike Nickeas RC .40 1.00
62 Eric Hurley RC .40 1.00
63 Scott Elbert RC .40 1.00
64 Blake DeWitt RC 1.50 4.00
65 Danny Putnam RC .40 1.00
66 J.P. Howell RC .40 1.00
67 John Wiggins RC .40 1.00
68 Justin Orenduff RC .60 1.50
69 Ray Liotta RC .40 1.00
70 Billy Buckner RC .40 1.00
71 Eric Campbell RC .40 1.00
72 Olin Wick RC .40 1.00
73 Sean Gamble RC .40 1.00
74 Seth Smith RC 1.00 2.50
75 Wade Davis RC 1.25 3.00
76 Joe Jacobitz RC .40 1.00
77 J.A. Happ RC 1.00 2.50
78 Eric Ridener RC .40 1.00
79 Matt Tuiasosopo RC 1.00 2.50
80 Brad Bergesen RC .40 1.00
81 Javy Guerra RC .40 1.00
82 Buck Shaw RC .40 1.00
83 Paul Janish RC .60 1.50
84 Sean Kazmar RC .40 1.00
85 Josh Johnson RC .40 1.00
86 Angel Salome RC .40 1.00
87 Jordan Parraz RC .60 1.50
88 Kelvin Vazquez RC .40 1.00
89 Grant Hansen RC .40 1.00
90 Matt Fox RC .40 1.00
91 Trevor Plouffe RC 1.00 2.50
92 Wes Whisler RC .40 1.00
93 Curtis Thigpen RC .40 1.00
94 Donnie Smith RC .40 1.00
95 Luis Rivera RC .40 1.00
96 Jesse Hoover RC .40 1.00
97 Jason Vargas RC 1.00 2.50
98 Clary Carlsen RC .40 1.00
99 Mark Robinson RC .40 1.00
100 J.C. Holt RC .40 1.00
101 Chad Blackwell RC .40 1.00
102 Daryl Jones RC .40 1.00
103 Jonathan Tierce RC .40 1.00
104 Patrick Bryant RC .40 1.00
105 Eddie Prasch RC .40 1.00
106 Mitch Einertson RC .40 1.00
107 Kyle Waldrop RC .40 1.00
108 Jeff Marquez RC .40 1.00
109 Zach Jackson RC .40 1.00
110 Josh Wahpepah RC .40 1.00
111 Adam Lind RC 1.25 3.00
112 Kyle Bloom RC .40 1.00
113 Ben Harrison RC .40 1.00
114 Taylor Tankersley RC .40 1.00
115 Steven Jackson RC .40 1.00
116 David Purcey RC .60 1.50
117 Jacob McGee RC 1.00 2.50
118 Lucas Harrell RC .40 1.00
119 Brandon Allen RC 1.50 4.00
120 Van Pope RC .40 1.00
121 Jeff Francis .15 .40
122 Joe Blanton .15 .40
123 Wil Ledezma .15 .40
124 Bryan Bullington .15 .40
125 Jairo Garcia .15 .40
126 Matt Cain .15 .40
127 Arnie Munoz .15 .40
128 Clint Everts .15 .40
129 Jesus Cota .15 .40
130 Gavin Floyd .15 .40
131 Edwin Encarnacion .25 .60
132 Koyie Hill .15 .40
133 Ruben Gotay .15 .40
134 Jeff Mathis .15 .40

Card	Low	High
135 Andy Marte	.15	.40
136 Dallas McPherson	.15	.40
137 Justin Morneau	.15	.40
138 Rickie Weeks	.15	.40
139 Joel Guzman	.15	.40
140 Shin Soo Choo	.25	.60
141 Yusmeiro Petit RC	.60	1.50
142 Jorge Cortes RC	.40	1.00
143 Val Majewski	.15	.40
144 Felix Pie	.15	.40
145 Aaron Hill	.15	.40
146 Jose Capellan	.15	.40
147 Dioner Navarro	.25	.60
148 Fausto Carmona	.25	.60
149 Robinzon Diaz RC	.40	1.00
150 Felix Hernandez	3.00	8.00
151 Andres Blanco RC	.40	1.00
152 Jason Kubel	.15	.40
153 Willy Taveras RC	1.00	2.50
154 Merkin Valdez	.15	.40
155 Robinson Cano	.40	1.00
156 Bill Murphy	.15	.40
157 Chris Burke	.15	.40
158 Kyle Sleeth	.15	.40
159 B.J. Upton	.25	.60
160 Tim Stauffer	.25	.60
161 David Wright	.60	1.50
162 Conor Jackson	1.00	2.50
163 Brad Thompson RC	.60	1.50
164 Delmon Young	.25	.60
165 Jeremy Reed	.15	.40
166 Matt Bush AU RC	10.00	25.00
167 Mark Rogers AU RC	8.00	20.00
168 Thomas Diamond AU RC UER	6.00	15.00
Many errors in informational blurb		
169 Greg Golson AU RC	8.00	20.00
170 Homer Bailey AU RC	6.00	15.00
171 Chris Lambert AU RC	4.00	10.00
172 Neil Walker AU RC	12.50	30.00
173 Bill Bray AU RC	4.00	10.00
174 Philip Hughes AU RC	20.00	50.00
175 Gio Gonzalez AU RC	12.50	30.00

2004 Bowman Chrome Draft Refractors

*REF 1-165: 8X TO 20X BASIC
*REF RC 1-165: 1.25X TO 3X BASIC
*REF RC YR 1-165: 1.5X TO 4X BASIC
1-165 ODDS 1:11 BOWMAN DRAFT HOBBY
1-165 ODDS 1:11 BOWMAN DRAFT RETAIL
*REF AU 166-175: .6X TO 1.5X BASIC
166-175 AU ODDS BOW.DRAFT 1:204 HOB
166-175 AU ODDS BOW.DRAFT 1:204 RET
166-175 STATED PRINT RUN 500 SETS
166-175 ARE NOT SERIAL-NUMBERED
166-175 PRINT RUN PROVIDED BY TOPPS

Card	Low	High
166 Matt Bush AU	15.00	40.00
172 Neil Walker AU	20.00	50.00

2004 Bowman Chrome Draft Gold Refractors

*GOLD REF 1-165: 8X TO 20X BASIC
*GOLD REF RC 1-165: 8X TO 20X BASIC
*GOLD REF RC YR 1-165: 6X TO 15X BASIC
1-165 ODDS 1:119 BOWMAN DRAFT HOBBY
1-165 ODDS 1:205 BOWMAN DRAFT RETAIL
1-165 PRINT RUN 50 SERIAL #'d SETS
*GOLD REF 166-175: 4X TO 8X BASIC
166-175 AU ODDS 1:2045 BOW.DRAFT HOB
166-175 AU ODDS 1:2055 BOW.DRAFT RET
166-175 STATED PRINT RUN 50 SETS
166-175 ARE NOT SERIAL-NUMBERED
166-175 PRINT RUN PROVIDED BY TOPPS

Card	Low	High
166 Matt Bush AU	125.00	200.00
167 Mark Rogers AU	90.00	150.00
168 Thomas Diamond AU	60.00	120.00
169 Greg Golson AU	75.00	150.00
172 Neil Walker AU	125.00	200.00

2004 Bowman Chrome Draft Red Refractors

STATED ODDS 1:4471 BOW.DRAFT HOBBY
STATED PRINT RUN 1 SERIAL #'d SET
NO PRICING DUE TO SCARCITY

2004 Bowman Chrome Draft X-Fractors

*XF 1-165: 3X TO 8X BASIC
*XF RC 1-165: 2.5X TO 6X BASIC
*XF RC YR 1-165: 2.5X TO 6X BASIC
1-165 ODDS 1:48 BOWMAN DRAFT HOBBY
1-165 ODDS 1:80 BOWMAN DRAFT RETAIL
1-165 PRINT RUN 125 SERIAL #'d SETS
*XF AU 166-175: .75X TO 2X BASIC

166-175 AU ODDS 1:407 BOW.DRAFT HOB
166-175 AU ODDS 1:407 BOW.DRAFT RET
166-175 STATED PRINT RUN 250 SETS
166-175 ARE NOT SERIAL-NUMBERED
166-175 PRINT RUN PROVIDED BY TOPPS

Card	Low	High
166 Matt Bush AU	20.00	50.00
172 Neil Walker AU	30.00	60.00
175 Gio Gonzalez AU	30.00	60.00

2004 Bowman Chrome Draft AFLAC

Card	Low	High
COMP.FACT.SET (12)	10.00	25.00

ONE SET VIA MAIL PER AFLAC EXCH.CARD
ONE EXCH.PER '04 BOW.DRAFT HOBBY BOX
EXCH.CARD DEADLINE WAS 11/30/05
SETS ACTUALLY SENT OUT JANUARY, 2006

Card	Low	High
1 C.J. Henry	.60	1.50
2 John Drennen	.60	1.50
3 Beau Jones	.60	1.50
4 Jeff Lyman	.60	1.50
5 Andrew McCutchen	6.00	15.00
6 Chris Volstad	1.00	2.50
7 Jonathan Egan	.60	1.50
8 P.J. Phillips	.60	1.50
9 Steve Johnson	.60	1.50
10 Ryan Tucker	.60	1.50
11 Cameron Maybin	2.00	5.00
12 Shane Funk	.60	1.50

2004 Bowman Chrome Draft AFLAC Refractors

Card	Low	High
COMP.FACT.SET (12)	60.00	120.00

*REF: 1.5X TO 4X BASIC
ONE SET VIA MAIL PER AFLAC EXCH.CARD
ONE EXCH.PER '04 BOW.DRAFT HOBBY BOX
STATED PRINT RUN 550 SERIAL #'d SETS
EXCH.CARD DEADLINE WAS 11/30/05
SETS ACTUALLY SENT OUT JANUARY, 2006

2004 Bowman Chrome Draft AFLAC Gold Refractors

*GOLD REF: X TO X BASIC
ONE SET VIA MAIL PER AFLAC EXCH.CARD
ONE EXCH.PER '04 BOW.DRAFT HOBBY BOX
STATED PRINT RUN 50 SERIAL #'d SETS
EXCH.CARD DEADLINE WAS 11/30/05
SETS ACTUALLY SENT OUT JANUARY, 2006

2004 Bowman Chrome Draft AFLAC X-Fractors

Card	Low	High
COMP.FACT.SET (12)	175.00	300.00

*X-FRAC: 4X TO 10X BASIC
ONE SET VIA MAIL PER AFLAC EXCH.CARD
ONE EXCH.PER '04 BOW.DRAFT HOBBY BOX
STATED PRINT RUN 125 SERIAL #'d SETS
EXCH.CARD DEADLINE WAS 11/30/05
SETS ACTUALLY SENT OUT JANUARY, 2006

2004 Bowman Chrome Draft AFLAC Autograph Refractors

ONE SET VIA MAIL PER GOLD EXCH.CARD
STATED PRINT RUN 125 SERIAL #'d SETS
SETS ACTUALLY SENT OUT JUNE, 2006

Card	Low	High
AM Andrew McCutchen	300.00	400.00
CH C.J. Henry	75.00	125.00
CM Cameron Maybin	200.00	400.00
JU Justin Upton	800.00	1000.00

2005 Bowman Chrome

This 353-card set was released in August, 2005. The set was issued in four card packs with an $4 SRP which came 18 packs to a box and 12 boxes to a case. Cards 1-140 feature active veterans while cards 141-165 feature leading prospects and cards 166-330 feature Rookies. Cards 331-353 are signed Rookie Cards which were inserted into boxes at a stated rate of one in 28 packs.

Card	Low	High
COMP.SET w/o AU's (330)	60.00	120.00
COMMON CARD (1-140)	.20	.50
COMMON CARD (141-165)	.20	.50
COMMON CARD (166-330)	.40	1.00
COMMON AUTO (331-353)	4.00	10.00

1-330 PLATE ODDS 1:779 HOBBY
331-353 AU PLATE ODDS 1:10,996 HOBBY
PLATE PRINT RUN 1 SET PER COLOR
BLACK-CYAN-MAGENTA-YELLOW ISSUED
NO PLATE PRICING DUE TO SCARCITY

Card	Low	High
1 Gavin Floyd	.20	.50
2 Eric Chavez	.20	.50
3 Miguel Tejada	.30	.75
4 Dmitri Young	.20	.50
5 Hank Blalock	.20	.50
6 Kerry Wood	.20	.50
7 Andy Pettitte	.30	.75
8 Pat Burrell	.20	.50
9 Johnny Estrada	.20	.50
10 Frank Thomas	.50	1.25
11 Juan Pierre	.20	.50
12 Tom Glavine	.30	.75
13 Lyle Overbay	.20	.50
14 Jim Edmonds	.30	.75
15 Steve Finley	.20	.50
16 Jermaine Dye	.20	.50
17 Omar Vizquel	.30	.75
18 Nick Johnson	.20	.50
19 Brian Giles	.20	.50
20 Justin Morneau	.50	1.25
21 Preston Wilson	.20	.50
22 Wily Mo Pena	.20	.50
23 Rafael Palmeiro	.30	.75
24 Scott Kazmir	.50	1.25
25 Derek Jeter	1.25	3.00
26 Barry Zito	.20	.50
27 Mike Lowell	.20	.50
28 Jason Bay	.20	.50
29 Ken Harvey	.20	.50
30 Nomar Garciaparra	.50	1.25
31 Roy Halladay	.50	1.25
32 Todd Helton	.30	.75
33 Mark Kotsay	.20	.50
34 Jake Peavy	.20	.50
35 David Wright	.75	2.00
36 Dontrelle Willis	.20	.50
37 Marcus Giles	.20	.50
38 Chone Figgins	.20	.50
39 Sidney Ponson	.20	.50
40 Randy Johnson	.50	1.25
41 John Smoltz	.50	1.25
42 Kevin Millar	.20	.50
43 Mark Teixeira	.50	1.25
44 Alex Rios	.30	.75
45 Mike Piazza	.50	1.25
46 Victor Martinez	.30	.75
47 Jeff Bagwell	.30	.75
48 Shawn Green	.20	.50
49 Ivan Rodriguez	.30	.75
50 Alex Rodriguez	.75	2.00
51 Kazuo Matsui	.20	.50
52 Mark Mulder	.20	.50
53 Michael Young	.30	.75
54 Javy Lopez	.20	.50
55 Johnny Damon	.30	.75
56 Jeff Francis	.20	.50
57 Rich Harden	.20	.50
58 Bobby Abreu	.20	.50
59 Mark Loretta	.20	.50
60 Gary Sheffield	.20	.50
61 Jamie Moyer	.20	.50
62 Garret Anderson	.20	.50
63 Vernon Wells	.20	.50
64 Orlando Cabrera	.20	.50
65 Magglio Ordonez	.30	.75
66 Ronnie Belliard	.20	.50
67 Carlos Lee	.20	.50
68 Carl Pavano	.20	.50
69 Jon Lieber	.20	.50
70 Aubrey Huff	.20	.50
71 Rocco Baldelli	.20	.50
72 Jason Schmidt	.20	.50
73 Bernie Williams	.30	.75
74 Hideki Matsui	.75	2.00
75 Ken Griffey Jr.	.75	2.00
76 Josh Beckett	.30	.75
77 Mark Buehrle	.30	.75
78 David Ortiz	.50	1.25
79 Luis Gonzalez	.20	.50
80 Scott Rolen	.30	.75
81 Joe Mauer	.50	1.25
82 Jose Reyes	.30	.75
83 Adam Dunn	.30	.75
84 Greg Maddux	.75	2.00
85 Bartolo Colon	.20	.50
86 Bret Boone	.20	.50
87 Mike Mussina	.30	.75
88 Ben Sheets	.20	.50
89 Lance Berkman	.30	.75
90 Miguel Cabrera	.50	1.25
91 C.C. Sabathia	.30	.75
92 Mike Maroth	.20	.50
93 Andruw Jones	.20	.50
94 Jack Wilson	.20	.50
95 Ichiro Suzuki	.75	2.00
96 Geoff Jenkins	.20	.50
97 Zack Greinke	.30	.75
98 Jorge Posada	.30	.75
99 Travis Hafner	.20	.50
100 Barry Bonds	1.00	2.50
101 Aaron Rowand	.20	.50
102 Aramis Ramirez	.20	.50
103 Curt Schilling	.30	.75
104 Melvin Mora	.20	.50
105 Albert Pujols	1.25	3.00
106 Austin Kearns	.20	.50
107 Shannon Stewart	.20	.50
108 Carl Crawford	.30	.75
109 Carlos Zambrano	.30	.75
110 Roger Clemens	.60	1.50
111 Javier Vazquez	.20	.50
112 Randy Wolf	.20	.50
113 Chipper Jones	.50	1.25
114 Larry Walker	.30	.75
115 Alfonso Soriano	.30	.75
116 Brad Wilkerson	.20	.50
117 Bobby Crosby	.20	.50
118 Jim Thome	.30	.75
119 Oliver Perez	.20	.50
120 Vladimir Guerrero	.50	1.25
121 Roy Oswalt	.30	.75
122 Torii Hunter	.20	.50
123 Rafael Furcal	.20	.50
124 Luis Castillo	.20	.50
125 Carlos Beltran	.20	.50
126 Mike Sweeney	.20	.50
127 Johan Santana	.50	1.25
128 Tim Hudson	.30	.75
129 Troy Glaus	.20	.50
130 Manny Ramirez	.50	1.25
131 Jeff Kent	.20	.50
132 Jose Vidro	.20	.50
133 Edgar Renteria	.20	.50
134 Russ Ortiz	.20	.50
135 Sammy Sosa	.50	1.25
136 Carlos Delgado	.20	.50
137 Richie Sexson	.20	.50
138 Pedro Martinez	.30	.75
139 Adrian Beltre	.20	.50
140 Mark Prior	.30	.75
141 Omar Quintanilla	.20	.50
142 Carlos Quentin	.30	.75
143 Dan Johnson	.20	.50
144 Jake Stevens	.20	.50
145 Nate Schierholtz	.20	.50
146 Neil Walker	.20	.50
147 Bill Bray	.20	.50
148 Taylor Tankersley	.20	.50
149 Trevor Plouffe	.20	.50
150 Felix Hernandez	.75	2.00
151 Philip Hughes	.30	.75
152 James Houser	.20	.50
153 David Murphy	.30	.75
154 Ervin Santana UER	.20	.50
Facsimile signature is Johan Santana		
155 Anthony Whittington	.20	.50
156 Chris Lambert	.20	.50
157 Jeremy Sowers	.20	.50
158 Giovanny Gonzalez	.30	.75
159 Blake DeWitt	.30	.75
160 Thomas Diamond	.20	.50
161 Greg Golson	.20	.50
162 David Aardsma	.20	.50
163 Paul Maholm	.20	.50
164 Mark Rogers	.20	.50
165 Homer Bailey	.20	.50
166 Elvin Puello RC	.40	1.00
167 Tony Giarratano RC	.40	1.00
168 Darren Fenster RC	.40	1.00
169 Elvys Quezada RC	.40	1.00
170 Glen Perkins RC	.40	1.00
171 Ian Kinsler RC	3.00	8.00
172 Adam Bostick RC	.40	1.00
173 Jeremy West RC	.40	1.00
174 Brett Harper RC	.40	1.00
175 Kevin West RC	.40	1.00
176 Luis Hernandez RC	.40	1.00
177 Matt Campbell RC	.40	1.00
178 Nate McLouth RC	.60	1.50
179 Ryan Goleski RC	.40	1.00
180 Matthew Lindstrom RC	.40	1.00
181 Matt DeSalvo RC	.40	1.00
182 Kole Strayhorn RC	.40	1.00
183 Jose Vaquedano RC	.40	1.00
184 James Jurries RC	.40	1.00
185 Ian Bladergroen RC	.40	1.00
186 Kila Kaaihue RC	1.00	2.50
187 Luke Scott RC	1.00	2.50
188 Chris Denorfia RC	.40	1.00
189 Jai Miller RC	.40	1.00
190 Melky Cabrera RC	1.00	2.50
191 Ryan Sweeney RC	.60	1.50
192 Sean Marshall RC	1.00	2.50
193 Erick Abreu RC	.40	1.00
194 Tyler Pelland RC	.40	1.00
195 Cole Armstrong RC	.40	1.00
196 John Hudgins RC	.40	1.00
197 Wade Robinson RC	.40	1.00
198 Dan Santin RC	.40	1.00
199 Steve Doetsch RC	.40	1.00
200 Shane Costa RC	.40	1.00
201 Scott Mathieson RC	1.50	4.00
202 Ben Jones RC	.40	1.00
203 Michael Rogers RC	.40	1.00
204 Matt Rogelstad RC	.40	1.00
205 Luis Ramirez RC	.40	1.00
206 Landon Powell RC	.40	1.00
207 Erik Cordier RC	.40	1.00
208 Chris Seddon RC	.40	1.00
209 Chris Roberson RC	.40	1.00
210 Thomas Oldham RC	.40	1.00
211 Dana Eveland RC	.40	1.00
212 Cody Haerther RC	.40	1.00
213 Danny Core RC	.40	1.00
214 Craig Tatum RC	.40	1.00
215 Elliot Johnson RC	.40	1.00
216 Ender Chavez RC	.40	1.00
217 Errol Simonitsch RC	.40	1.00
218 Matt Van Der Bosch RC	.40	1.00
219 Eulogio de la Cruz RC	.40	1.00
220 Drew Toussaint RC	.40	1.00
221 Adam Boeve RC	.40	1.00
222 Adam Harben RC	.40	1.00
223 Baltazar Lopez RC	.40	1.00
224 Russ Martin RC	1.50	4.00
225 Brian Bannister RC	.60	1.50
226 Chris Walker RC	.40	1.00
227 Casey McGehee RC	1.25	3.00
228 Humberto Sanchez RC	.60	1.50
229 Javon Moran RC	.40	1.00
230 Brandon McCarthy RC	.60	1.50
231 Danny Zell RC	.40	1.00
232 Kevin Barry RC	.40	1.00
233 Juan Tejeda RC	.40	1.00
234 Keith Ramsey RC	.40	1.00
235 Lorenzo Scott RC	.40	1.00
236 Jon Barratt RC	.40	1.00
237 Martin Prado RC	2.50	6.00
238 Matt Albers RC	.40	1.00
239 Brian Schweiger RC	.40	1.00
240 Raul Tablado RC	.40	1.00
241 Pat Misch RC	.40	1.00
242 Pat Osborn	.40	1.00
243 Ryan Feierabend RC	.40	1.00
244 Shaun Marcum	1.00	2.50
245 Kevin Collins RC	.40	1.00
246 Stuart Pomeranz RC	.40	1.00
247 Tetsu Yofu RC	.40	1.00
248 Hernan Iribarren RC	.40	1.00
249 Mike Spidale RC	.40	1.00
250 Tony Americh RC	.40	1.00
251 Manny Parra RC	1.00	2.50
252 Drew Anderson RC	.40	1.00
253 T.J. Beam RC	.40	1.00
254 Claudio Arias RC	.40	1.00
255 Andy Sides RC	.40	1.00
256 Bear Bay RC	.40	1.00
257 Bill McCarthy RC	.40	1.00
258 Daniel Haigwood RC	.40	1.00
259 Brian Sprout RC	.40	1.00
260 Bryan Triplett RC	.40	1.00
261 Steven Bondurant RC	.40	1.00
262 Darwinson Salazar RC	.40	1.00
263 David Shepard RC	.40	1.00
264 Johan Silva RC	.40	1.00
265 J.B. Thurmond RC	.40	1.00
266 Brandon Moorhead RC	.40	1.00
267 Kyle Nichols RC	.40	1.00
268 Jonathan Sanchez RC	1.50	4.00
269 Mike Esposito RC	.40	1.00
270 Erik Schindewolf RC	.40	1.00
271 Peeter Ramos RC	.40	1.00
272 Juan Senreiso RC	.40	1.00
273 Travis Chick RC	.40	1.00
274 Vinny Rottino RC	.40	1.00
275 Micah Furtado RC	.40	1.00
276 George Kottaras RC	.60	1.50
277 Abel Gomez RC	.40	1.00
278 Buck Coats RC	.40	1.00
279 Kenny Durost RC	.40	1.00
280 Nick Touchstone RC	.40	1.00
281 Jerry Owens RC	.40	1.00
282 Stefan Bailie RC	.40	1.00
283 Jesse Gutierrez RC	.40	1.00
284 Chuck Tiffany RC	1.00	2.50
285 Brendan Ryan RC	.40	1.00
286 Julio Pimentel RC	.40	1.00
287 Shawn Bowman RC	.40	1.00
288 Alexander Smit RC	.40	1.00
289 Micah Schnurstein RC	.40	1.00
290 Jared Gothreaux RC	.40	1.00
291 Jair Jurrjens RC	2.00	5.00
292 Bobby Livingston RC	.40	1.00
293 Ryan Speier RC	.40	1.00
294 Zach Parker RC	.40	1.00
295 Christian Colonel RC	.40	1.00
296 Scott Mitchinson RC	.40	1.00
297 Neil Wilson RC	.40	1.00
298 Chuck James RC	1.00	2.50
299 Heath Totten RC	.40	1.00
300 Sean Tracey RC	.40	1.00
301 Tadahito Iguchi RC	.60	1.50
302 Matt Brown RC	.40	1.00
303 Franklin Morales RC	.60	1.50
304 Brandon Sing RC	.40	1.00
305 D.J. Houlton RC	.40	1.00
306 Jayce Tingler RC	.40	1.00
307 Mitchell Arnold RC	.40	1.00
308 Jim Burt RC	.40	1.00
309 Jason Motte RC	.60	1.50
310 David Gassner RC	.40	1.00
311 Andy Santana RC	.40	1.00
312 Kelvin Pichardo RC	.40	1.00
313 Carlos Carrasco RC	1.00	2.50
314 Willy Mota RC	.40	1.00
315 Frank Mata RC	.40	1.00
316 Carlos Gonzalez RC	4.00	10.00
317 Jesse Floyd	.40	1.00
318 Chris B.Young RC	1.50	4.00
319 Billy Sadler RC	.40	1.00
320 Ricky Barrett RC	.40	1.00
321 Ben Harrison	.40	1.00
322 Steve Nelson RC	.40	1.00
323 Daryl Thompson RC	.40	1.00
324 Davis Romero RC	.40	1.00
325 Jeremy Harts RC	.40	1.00
326 Nick Masset RC	.40	1.00
327 Thomas Pauly RC	.40	1.00
328 Mike Garber RC	.40	1.00
329 Kennard Bibbs RC	.40	1.00
330 Colter Bean RC	.40	1.00
331 Justin Verlander AU RC	75.00	150.00
332 Chip Cannon AU RC	10.00	25.00
333 Kevin Melillo AU RC	6.00	15.00
334 Jake Postlewait AU RC	4.00	10.00
335 Wes Swackhamer AU RC	4.00	10.00
336 Mike Rodriguez AU RC	4.00	10.00
337 Philip Humber AU RC	10.00	25.00
338 Jeff Niemann AU RC	6.00	15.00
339 Brian Miller AU RC	4.00	10.00
340 Chris Vines AU RC	4.00	10.00
341 Andy LaRoche AU RC	10.00	25.00
342 Mike Bourn AU RC	10.00	25.00
343 Eric Nielsen AU RC	4.00	10.00
344 Wladimir Balentien AU RC	20.00	50.00
345 Ismael Ramirez AU RC	4.00	10.00
346 Pedro Lopez AU RC	4.00	10.00
347 Shawn Bowman AU	6.00	15.00
348 Hayden Penn AU RC	10.00	25.00
349 Matthew Kemp AU RC	50.00	100.00
350 Brian Stavisky AU RC	4.00	10.00
351 C.J. Smith AU RC	4.00	10.00
352 Mike Morse AU RC	8.00	20.00
353 Billy Butler AU RC	20.00	50.00

2005 Bowman Chrome Refractors

*REF 1-140: 1.5X TO 4X BASIC
*REF 141-165: 1.25X TO 3X BASIC
*REF 166-330: 1X TO 2.5X BASIC
1-330 ODDS 1:4 HOBBY, 1: 6 RETAIL
*REF AU 331-353: .5X TO 1.2X BASIC AU
331-353 AU ODDS 1:88 HOB, 1:259 RET
331-353 PRINT RUN 500 SERIAL #'d SETS

Card	Low	High
331 Justin Verlander AU	100.00	200.00
341 Andy LaRoche AU	30.00	60.00
349 Matthew Kemp AU	60.00	120.00

2005 Bowman Chrome Blue Refractors

*BLUE REF 1-140: 3X TO 8X BASIC
*BLUE REF 141-165: 2.5X TO 6X BASIC
*BLUE REF 166-330: 2X TO 5X BASIC
1-330 ODDS 1:20 HOBBY, 1:69 RETAIL
*BLUE REF AU 331-353: 1.25X TO 2.5X BASIC
331-353 AU ODDS 1:294 HOB, 1:866 RET

STATED PRINT RUN 150 SERIAL #'d SETS

Card	Low	High
331 Justin Verlander AU	175.00	350.00
332 Chip Cannon AU	15.00	40.00
341 Andy LaRoche AU	125.00	200.00
342 Mike Bourn AU	50.00	100.00
344 Wladimir Balentien AU	90.00	150.00
349 Matthew Kemp AU	100.00	200.00
352 Mike Morse AU	40.00	80.00

2005 Bowman Chrome Gold Refractors

*GOLD REF 1-140: 8X TO 20X BASIC
*GOLD REF 141-165: 6X TO 15X BASIC
*GOLD REF 166-330: 10X TO 25X BASIC
1-330 ODDS 1:61 HOBBY, 1:206 RETAIL
*GOLD REF AU 331-353: 3X TO 6X BASIC
331-353 AU ODDS 1:880 HOB, 1:2612 RET
STATED PRINT RUN 50 SERIAL #'d SETS

Card	Low	High
316 Carlos Gonzalez	250.00	500.00
331 Justin Verlander AU	700.00	1000.00
332 Chip Cannon AU	60.00	120.00
333 Kevin Melillo AU	30.00	60.00
334 Jake Postlewait AU	30.00	60.00
335 Wes Swackhamer AU	30.00	60.00
336 Mike Rodriguez AU	30.00	60.00
337 Philip Humber AU	150.00	250.00
338 Jeff Niemann AU	50.00	100.00
339 Brian Miller AU	30.00	60.00
340 Chris Vines AU	30.00	60.00
341 Andy LaRoche AU	300.00	500.00
342 Mike Bourn AU	100.00	200.00
343 Eric Nielsen AU	30.00	60.00
344 Wladimir Balentien AU	200.00	300.00
345 Ismael Ramirez AU	30.00	60.00
346 Pedro Lopez AU	30.00	60.00
347 Shawn Bowman AU	50.00	100.00
348 Hayden Penn AU	75.00	150.00
349 Matthew Kemp AU	250.00	500.00
350 Brian Stavisky AU	30.00	60.00
351 C.J. Smith AU	30.00	60.00

2005 Bowman Chrome Green Refractors

*GREEN: 1.5X TO 4X BASIC
ISSUED VIA THE PIT.COM
STATED PRINT RUN 225 SERIAL #'d SETS

2005 Bowman Chrome Red Refractors

1-330 ODDS 1:606 H, 1:2112 R
331-353 AU ODDS 1:8773 H, 1:32,160 R
STATED PRINT RUN 5 SERIAL #'d SETS
NO PRICING DUE TO SCARCITY

2005 Bowman Chrome Super-Fractors

1-330 STATED ODDS 1:3117 H
331-353 AU STATED ODDS 1:47,238 H
STATED PRINT RUN 1 SERIAL #'d SET
NO PRICING DUE TO SCARCITY

2005 Bowman Chrome X-Fractors

*X-FRACTOR 1-140: 2X TO 5X BASIC
*X-FRACTOR 141-165: 1.5X TO 4X BASIC
*X-FRACTOR 166-330: 2X TO 5X BASIC
1-330 ODDS 1:13 HOBBY, 1:61 RETAIL
*X-FRACT AU 331-353: 1X TO 2X BASIC AU
331-353 AU ODDS 1:196 HOB, 1:573 RET

STATED PRINT RUN 225 SERIAL #'d SETS

Card	Low	High
331 Justin Verlander AU	125.00	250.00
338 Jeff Niemann AU	10.00	25.00
341 Andy LaRoche AU	50.00	100.00
344 Wladimir Balentien AU	60.00	120.00
349 Matthew Kemp AU	75.00	150.00
352 Mike Morse AU	20.00	50.00

2005 Bowman Chrome A-Rod Throwback

Card	Low	High
COMPLETE SET (4)	4.00	10.00
COMMON CARD (94-97)	1.25	3.00

STATED ODDS 1:9 HOBBY, 1:12 RETAIL
*REF: 1X TO 2.5X BASIC
REFRACTOR ODDS 1:445 HOBBY
REFRACTOR PRINT RUN 499 #'d SETS
SUPER-FRACTOR ODDS 1:226,044 HOBBY
SUPER-FRACTOR PRINT RUN 1 #'d SET
NO SUPER-FRACTOR PRICING AVAILABLE
*X-FRACTOR: 1.5X TO 4X BASIC
X-FRACTOR ODDS 1:2241 HOBBY
X-FRACTOR PRINT RUN 99 #'d SETS

Card	Low	High
94AR Alex Rodriguez 1994	1.25	3.00
95AR Alex Rodriguez 1995	1.25	3.00
96AR Alex Rodriguez 1996	1.25	3.00
97AR Alex Rodriguez 1997	1.25	3.00

2005 Bowman Chrome A-Rod Throwback Autographs

1994 CARD STATED ODDS 1:614,088 H
1995 CARD STATED ODDS 1:36,122 H
1996 CARD STATED ODDS 1:18,061 H
1997 CARD STATED ODDS 1:9042 H
1994 CARD PRINT RUN 1 #'d CARD
1995 CARD PRINT RUN 25 #'d CARDS
1996 CARD PRINT RUN 50 #'d CARDS
1997 CARD PRINT RUN 99 #'d CARDS
NO PRICING ON 1994 CARD AVAILABLE

Card	Low	High
94AR A.Rodriguez 1994 SF/1		
95AR A.Rodriguez 1995 XF/25		
96AR A.Rodriguez 1996 RF/50	100.00	175.00
97AR A.Rodriguez 1997 CH/99	60.00	120.00

2005 Bowman Chrome Two of a Kind Autographs

STATED ODDS 1:76,761 HOBBY
STATED PRINT RUN 13 SERIAL #'d CARDS
NO PRICING DUE TO SCARCITY
ARCR Alex Rodriguez
Cal Ripken/13

2005 Bowman Chrome Draft

These cards were issued two per Bowman Draft Pack. Cards numbered 166 through 180, which were not issued as regular Bowman cards feature signed cards of some leading prospects. Those cards were issued at different odds depending on the player who signed the cards.

Card	Low	High
COMP.SET w/o SP's (165)	50.00	100.00
COMMON CARD (1-165)	.15	.40
COMMON RC	.40	1.00
COMMON RC YR	.15	.40

1-165 TWO PER BOWMAN DRAFT PACK
166-180 GROUP A ODDS 1:671 H, 1:643 R
166-180 GROUP B ODDS 1:69 H, 1:69 R
1-165 PLATE ODDS 1:826 HOBBY
166-180 AU PLATE ODDS 1:18,411 HOBBY
PLATE PRINT RUN 1 SET PER COLOR

BLACK-CYAN-MAGENTA-YELLOW ISSUED
NO PLATE PRICING DUE TO SCARCITY
1 Rickie Weeks .25 .60
2 Kyle Davies .15 .40
3 Garrett Atkins .15 .40
4 Chien-Ming Wang .60 1.50
5 Dallas McPherson .15 .40
6 Dan Johnson .15 .40
7 Andy Sisco .15 .40
8 Ryan Doumit .15 .40
9 J.P. Howell .15 .40
10 Tim Stauffer .15 .40
11 Willy Taveras .15 .40
12 Aaron Hill .25 .60
13 Victor Diaz .15 .40
14 Wilson Betemit .15 .40
15 Ervin Santana .15 .40
16 Mike Morse .40 1.00
17 Yadier Molina .25 .60
18 Kelly Johnson .15 .40
19 Clint Barmes .15 .40
20 Robinson Cano .40 1.00
21 Brad Thompson .15 .40
22 Jorge Cantu .15 .40
23 Brad Halsey .15 .40
24 Lance Niekro .15 .40
25 D.J. Houlton .15 .40
26 Ryan Church .15 .40
27 Hayden Penn .15 .40
28 Chris Young .25 .60
29 Chad Orvella RC .40 1.00
30 Mark Teahen .15 .40
31 Mark McCormick FY RC .40 1.00
32 Jay Bruce FY RC 3.00 0.00
33 Beau Jones FY RC 1.00 2.50
34 Tyler Greene FY RC .40 1.00
35 Zach Ward FY RC .40 1.00
36 Josh Bell FY RC 1.25 3.00
37 Josh Wall FY RC .60 1.50
38 Nick Webber FY RC .40 1.00
39 Travis Buck FY RC .40 1.00
40 Kyle Winters FY RC .40 1.00
41 Mitch Boggs FY RC .40 1.00
42 Tommy Mendoza FY RC .40 1.00
43 Brad Corley FY RC .40 1.00
44 Drew Butera FY RC .40 1.00
45 Ryan Mount FY RC .40 1.00
46 Tyler Herron FY RC .40 1.00
47 Nick Weglarz FY RC .40 1.00
48 Brandon Erbe FY RC 1.25 3.00
49 Cody Allen FY RC .40 1.00
50 Eric Fowler FY RC .40 1.00
51 James Boone FY RC .40 1.00
52 Josh Flores FY RC .40 1.00
53 Brandon Monk FY RC .40 1.00
54 Kieron Pope FY RC .40 1.00
55 Kyle Cofield FY RC .40 1.00
56 Brent Lillibridge FY RC .40 1.00
57 Daryl Jones FY RC .40 1.00
58 Eli Iorg FY RC .40 1.00
59 Brett Hayes FY RC .40 1.00
60 Mike Durant FY RC .40 1.00
61 Michael Bowden FY RC .60 1.50
62 Paul Kelly FY RC .40 1.00
63 Andrew McCutchen FY RC 3.00 8.00
64 Travis Wood FY RC 1.00 2.50
65 Cesar Ramos FY RC .40 1.00
66 Chaz Roe FY RC .40 1.00
67 Matt Torra FY RC .40 1.00
68 Kevin Slowey FY RC 2.00 5.00
69 Trayvon Robinson FY RC 1.00 2.50
70 Reid Engel FY RC .40 1.00
71 Kris Harvey FY RC .40 1.00
72 Craig Italiano FY RC .40 1.00
73 Matt Maloney FY RC .40 1.00
74 Sean West FY RC .60 1.50
75 Henry Sanchez FY RC .60 1.50
76 Scott Blue FY RC .40 1.00
77 Jordan Schafer FY RC 2.00 5.00
78 Chris Robinson FY RC .40 1.00
79 Chris Hobdy FY RC .40 1.00
80 Brandon Durden FY RC .40 1.00
81 Clay Buchholz FY RC 2.00 5.00
82 Josh Geer FY RC .40 1.00
83 Sam LeCure FY RC .40 1.00
84 Justin Thomas FY RC .40 1.00
85 Brett Gardner FY RC 1.25 3.00
86 Tommy Manzella FY RC .40 1.00
87 Matt Green FY RC .40 1.00
88 Yunel Escobar FY RC 1.50 4.00
89 Mike Costanzo FY RC .40 1.00
90 Nick Hundley FY RC .40 1.00
91 Zach Simons FY RC .40 1.00
92 Jacob Marceaux FY RC .40 1.00
93 Jed Lowrie FY RC 2.00 5.00
94 Brandon Snyder FY RC 1.00 2.50
95 Matt Goyen FY RC .40 1.00
96 Jon Egan FY RC .40 1.00
97 Drew Thompson FY RC .40 1.00
98 Bryan Anderson FY RC .40 1.00
99 Clayton Richard FY RC .40 1.00
100 Jimmy Shull FY RC .40 1.00
101 Mark Pawelek FY RC .40 1.00
102 P.J. Phillips FY RC .40 1.00
103 John Drennen FY RC .40 1.00
104 Nolan Reimold FY RC 1.50 4.00
105 Troy Tulowitzki FY RC 5.00 12.00
106 Kevin Whelan FY RC .40 1.00
107 Wade Townsend FY RC .40 1.00
108 Micah Owings FY RC .40 1.00
109 Ryan Tucker FY RC .40 1.00
110 Jeff Clement FY RC 1.25 3.00
111 Josh Sullivan FY RC .40 1.00
112 Jeff Lyman FY RC .40 1.00
113 Brian Bogusevic FY RC .40 1.00
114 Trevor Bell FY RC .40 1.00
115 Brent Cox FY RC .40 1.00
116 Michael Billek FY RC .40 1.00
117 Garrett Olson FY RC .40 1.00
118 Steven Johnson FY RC .40 1.00
119 Chase Headley FY RC 1.50 4.00
120 Daniel Carte FY RC .40 1.00
121 Francisco Liriano PROS .25 .60
122 Fausto Carmona PROS .15 .40
123 Zach Jackson PROS .15 .40
124 Adam Loewen PROS .15 .40
125 Chris Lambert PROS .15 .40
126 Scott Mathieson FY .60 1.50
127 Paul Maholm PROS .15 .40
128 Fernando Nieve PROS .15 .40
129 Justin Verlander FY 3.00 8.00
130 Yusmeiro Petit PROS .15 .40
131 Joel Zumaya PROS .25 .60
132 Merkin Valdez PROS .15 .40
133 Ryan Garko FY RC .40 1.00
134 Edison Volquez FY RC 2.00 5.00
135 Russ Martin FY .60 1.50
136 Conor Jackson PROS .25 .60
137 Miguel Montero FY RC 2.50 6.00
138 Josh Barfield PROS .25 .60
139 Delmon Young PROS .40 1.00
140 Andy LaRoche FY .75 2.00
141 William Bergolla PROS .15 .40
142 B.J. Upton PROS .25 .60
143 Hernan Iribarren FY .15 .40
144 Brandon Wood PROS .25 .60
145 Jose Bautista PROS 2.00 5.00
146 Edwin Encarnacion PROS .25 .60
147 Javier Herrera FY RC .40 1.00
148 Jeremy Hermida PROS .25 .60
149 Frank Diaz PROS RC .40 1.00
150 Chris B.Young FY .60 1.50
151 Shin-Soo Choo PROS .25 .60
152 Kevin Thompson PROS RC .40 1.00
153 Hanley Ramirez PROS .25 .60
154 Lastings Milledge PROS .15 .40
155 Luis Montanez PROS .15 .40
156 Justin Huber PROS .15 .40
157 Zach Duke PROS .15 .40
158 Jeff Francoeur PROS .40 1.00
159 Melky Cabrera FY .40 1.00
160 Bobby Jenks PROS .15 .40
161 Ian Snell PROS .15 .40
162 Fernando Cabrera PROS .15 .40
163 Troy Patton PROS .15 .40
164 Anthony Lerew PROS .15 .40
165 Nelson Cruz FY RC 1.50 4.00
166 Stephen Drew AU A RC 20.00 50.00
167 Jered Weaver AU A RC 30.00 60.00
168 Ryan Braun AU B RC 100.00 200.00
169 John Mayberry Jr. AU B RC 6.00 15.00
170 Aaron Thompson AU B RC 6.00 15.00
171 Cesar Carrillo AU B RC 10.00 25.00
172 Jacoby Ellsbury AU B RC 50.00 100.00
173 Matt Garza AU B RC 8.00 20.00
174 Cliff Pennington AU B RC 4.00 10.00
175 Colby Rasmus AU B RC 8.00 20.00
176 Chris Volstad AU B RC 12.50 30.00
177 Ricky Romero AU B RC 10.00 25.00
178 Ryan Zimmerman AU B RC 40.00 80.00
179 C.J. Henry AU B RC 10.00 25.00
180 Eddy Martinez AU B RC 6.00 15.00

2005 Bowman Chrome Draft Refractors

*REF 1-165: 8X TO 20X BASIC
*REF 1-165: 1.25X TO 3X BASIC RC
*REF 1-165: 1.25X TO 3X BASIC RC YR
1-165 ODDS 1:11 BOWMAN DRAFT HOBBY
1-165 ODDS 1:11 BOWMAN DRAFT RETAIL
*REF AU 166-180: .6X TO 1.5X BASIC
166-180 AU ODDS BOW.DRAFT 1:204 HOB
166-180 AU ODDS 1:186 BOW.DRAFT RET
166-180 PRINT RUN 500 SERIAL #'d SETS
166 Stephen Drew AU 60.00 120.00
167 Jered Weaver AU 40.00 80.00
168 Ryan Braun AU 150.00 300.00
172 Jacoby Ellsbury AU 60.00 120.00
178 Ryan Zimmerman AU 50.00 100.00

2005 Bowman Chrome Draft Blue Refractors

*BLUE 1-165: 4X TO 10X BASIC
*BLUE 1-165: 1X TO 2.5X BASIC RC
*BLUE 1-165: 3X TO 8X BASIC RC YR
1-165 ODDS 1:52 BOWMAN DRAFT HOBBY
1-165 ODDS 1:107 BOWMAN DRAFT RETAIL
*BLUE AU 166-180: 1.25X TO 2.5X BASIC
166-180 AU ODDS 1:619 BOW.DRAFT HOB
166-180 AU ODDS 1:619 BOW.DRAFT RET
STATED PRINT RUN 150 SERIAL #'d SETS
105 Troy Tulowitzki FY 100.00 200.00
166 Stephen Drew AU 150.00 250.00
167 Jered Weaver AU 100.00 200.00
168 Ryan Braun AU 300.00 500.00
172 Jacoby Ellsbury AU 175.00 300.00
178 Ryan Zimmerman AU 125.00 250.00

2005 Bowman Chrome Draft Gold Refractors

*GOLD REF 1-165: 10X TO 25X BASIC
*GOLD REF 1-165: 12.5X TO 25X BASIC RC
*GOLD REF 1-165: 12.5X TO 30X BASIC RC YR
1-165 ODDS 1:155 BOWMAN DRAFT HOBBY
1-165 ODDS 1:323 BOWMAN DRAFT HOBBY
*GOLD REF AU 166-180: 4X TO 8X BASIC
166-180 AU ODDS 1:1857 BOW.DRAFT HOB
166-180 AU ODDS 1:1856 BOW.DRAFT RET
STATED PRINT RUN 50 SERIAL #'d SETS
129 Justin Verlander FY 175.00 350.00
166 Stephen Drew AU 375.00 500.00
167 Jered Weaver AU 300.00 600.00
168 Ryan Braun AU 1000.00 1400.00
172 Jacoby Ellsbury AU 500.00 700.00
178 Ryan Zimmerman AU 700.00 900.00

2005 Bowman Chrome Draft Red Refractors

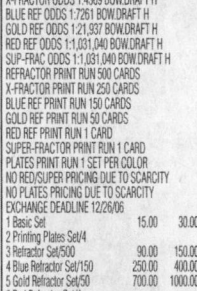

1-165 ODDS 1:6609 HOBBY
166-180 AU ODDS 1:73,645 HOBBY
STATED PRINT RUN 1 SERIAL #'d SET
NO PRICING DUE TO SCARCITY

2005 Bowman Chrome Draft SuperFractors

1-165 ODDS 1:6609 HOBBY
166-180 AU ODDS 1:73,645 HOBBY
STATED PRINT RUN 1 SERIAL #'d SET
NO PRICING DUE TO SCARCITY

2005 Bowman Chrome Draft X-Fractors

*XF 1-165: 2X TO 5X BASIC
*XF 1-165: 2.5X TO 6X BASIC RC
*XF 1-165: 2X TO 5X BASIC RC YR
1-165 ODDS 1:31 BOWMAN DRAFT HOBBY
1-165 ODDS 1:64 BOWMAN DRAFT RETAIL
*XF AU 166-180: 1X TO 2X BASIC
166-180 AU ODDS 1:372 BOW.DRAFT HOB
166-180 AU ODDS 1:371 BOW.DRAFT RET
STATED PRINT RUN 250 SERIAL #'d SETS
166 Stephen Drew AU 75.00 150.00
167 Jered Weaver AU 75.00 150.00
168 Ryan Braun AU 300.00 400.00
172 Jacoby Ellsbury AU 100.00 200.00
178 Ryan Zimmerman AU 60.00 120.00

2005 Bowman Chrome Draft AFLAC Exchange Cards

BASIC ODDS 1:109 BOW.DRAFT H
REFRACTOR ODDS 1:2184 BOW.DRAFT H
X-FRACTOR ODDS 1:4369 BOW.DRAFT H
BLUE REF ODDS 1:7261 BOW.DRAFT H
GOLD REF ODDS 1:21,937 BOW.DRAFT H
RED REF ODDS 1:1,031,040 BOW.DRAFT H
SUP-FRAC ODDS 1:1,031,040 BOW.DRAFT H
REFRACTOR PRINT RUN 500 CARDS
X-FRACTOR PRINT RUN 250 CARDS
BLUE REF PRINT RUN 150 CARDS
GOLD REF PRINT RUN 50 CARDS
RED REF PRINT RUN 1 CARD
SUPER-FRACTOR PRINT RUN 1 CARD
PLATES PRINT RUN 1 SET PER COLOR
NO RED/SUPER PRICING DUE TO SCARCITY
NO PLATES PRICING DUE TO SCARCITY
EXCHANGE DEADLINE 12/26/06
1 Basic Set 15.00 30.00
2 Printing Plates Set/4
3 Refractor Set/500 90.00 150.00
4 Blue Refractor Set/150 250.00 400.00
5 Gold Refractor Set/50 700.00 1000.00
6 Red Refractor Set/1
7 Super-Fractor Set/1
8 X-Fractor Set/250 175.00 300.00

2005 Bowman Chrome Draft AFLAC

COMP.FACT.SET (14) 8.00 20.00
ONE SET VIA MAIL PER AFLAC EXCH.CARD
BASIC ODDS 1:109 '05 BOW.DRAFT HOB.
SETS ACTUALLY SENT OUT JANUARY, 2007
EXCHANGE DEADLINE 12/26/06
PLATE PRINT RUN 1 SET PER COLOR
BLACK-CYAN-MAGENTA-YELLOW ISSUED
NO PLATE PRICING DUE TO SCARCITY
1 Billy Rowell 1.50 4.00
2 Kasey Kiker 1.00 2.50
3 Chris Marrero 2.00 5.00
4 Jeremy Jeffress .60 1.50
5 Kyle Drabek 2.00 5.00
6 Chris Parmelee 1.00 2.50
7 Colton Willems .60 1.50
8 Cody Johnson .60 1.50
9 Hank Conger 1.00 2.50
10 Cory Rasmus .60 1.50
11 David Christensen .60 1.50
12 Chris Tillman 1.50 4.00
13 Torre Langley .60 1.50
14 Robby Alcombrack .60 1.50

2005 Bowman Chrome Draft AFLAC Refractors

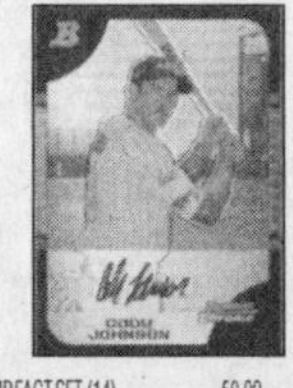

COMP.FACT.SET (14) 50.00 100.00
*REF: 1.2X TO 3X BASIC
ONE SET VIA MAIL PER EXCH.CARD
STATED ODDS 1:2184 BOW.DRAFT H
STATED PRINT RUN 500 SER.#'d SETS
EXCHANGE DEADLINE 12/26/06
SETS ACTUALLY SENT OUT JANUARY, 2007

2005 Bowman Chrome Draft AFLAC Blue Refractors

COMP.FACT.SET (14) 150.00 300.00
*BLUE REF: 4X TO 10X BASIC
ONE SET VIA MAIL PER EXCH.CARD
STATED ODDS 1:7261 BOW.DRAFT H
STATED PRINT RUN 150 SER.#'d SETS
EXCHANGE DEADLINE 12/26/06
SETS ACTUALLY SENT OUT JANUARY, 2007

2005 Bowman Chrome Draft AFLAC Gold Refractors

*GOLD REF: 12X TO 30X BASIC
ONE SET VIA MAIL PER EXCH.CARD
STATED ODDS 1:21,937 BOW.DRAFT H
STATED PRINT RUN 50 SER.#'d SETS
EXCHANGE DEADLINE 12/26/06
SETS ACTUALLY SENT OUT JANUARY, 2007

2005 Bowman Chrome Draft AFLAC Red Refractors

STATED ODDS 1:1,031,040 BOW.DRAFT H
STATED PRINT RUN 1 SER.#'d SET
ONE SET VIA MAIL PER EXCH.CARD
NO PRICING DUE TO SCARCITY
EXCHANGE DEADLINE 12/26/06
SETS ACTUALLY SENT OUT JANUARY, 2007

2005 Bowman Chrome Draft AFLAC SuperFractors

STATED ODDS 1:1,031,040 BOW.DRAFT H
STATED PRINT RUN 1 SER.#'d SET
NO PRICING DUE TO SCARCITY
ONE SET VIA MAIL PER EXCH.CARD
EXCHANGE DEADLINE 12/26/06
SETS ACTUALLY SENT OUT JANUARY, 2007

2005 Bowman Chrome Draft AFLAC X-Fractors

COMP.FACT.SET (14) 100.00 200.00
*X-FRAC: 2.5X TO 6X BASIC
STATED ODDS 1:4369 BOW.DRAFT H
ONE SET VIA MAIL PER EXCH.CARD
STATED PRINT RUN 250 SER.#'d SETS
EXCHANGE DEADLINE 12/26/06
SETS ACTUALLY SENT OUT JANUARY, 2007

2006 Bowman Chrome

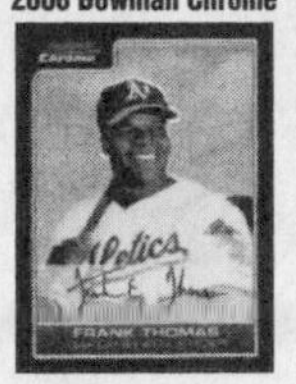

This 224-card set was released in August, 2006. The set was issued in four card hobby packs with an $3 SRP which came 18 packs to a box and 12 boxes to a case. Card number 219, Kenji Johjima was available in both a regular and an autographed version. Cards numbered 221 through 224 were only available in a signed form. The first 200-cards of this set feature veterans while the rest of this set features players who qualified for the Rookie Card designation under the new Rookie Card rules which began in 2006.

COMP.SET w/o AU's (220) 30.00 60.00
COMMON CARD (1-200) .20 .50
COMMON ROOKIE (201-220) .25 .60
219 AU ODDS 1:2734 HOBBY, 1:6617 RETAIL
221-224 AU ODDS 1:27 HOBBY, 1:65 RETAIL
1-220 PLATE ODDS 1:836 HOBBY
219 AU PLATE ODDS 1:292,536 HOBBY
221-224 AU PLATES ODDS 1:9,000 HOBBY
PLATE PRINT RUN 1 SET PER COLOR
BLACK-CYAN-MAGENTA-YELLOW ISSUED
NO PLATE PRICING DUE TO SCARCITY
1 Nick Swisher .50 1.25
2 Ted Lilly .20 .50
3 John Smoltz .50 1.25
4 Lyle Overbay .20 .50
5 Alfonso Soriano .30 .75
6 Javier Vazquez .20 .50
7 Ronnie Belliard .20 .50
8 Jose Reyes .30 .75
9 Brian Roberts .20 .50
10 Curt Schilling .30 .75
11 Adam Dunn .30 .75
12 Zack Greinke .30 .75
13 Carlos Guillen .20 .50
14 Jon Garland .20 .50
15 Robinson Cano .50 1.25
16 Chris Burke .20 .50
17 Barry Zito .20 .50
18 Russ Adams .20 .50
19 Chris Capuano .20 .50
20 Scott Rolen .30 .75
21 Kerry Wood .20 .50
22 Scott Kazmir .30 .75
23 Brandon Webb .30 .75
24 Jeff Kent .20 .50
25 Albert Pujols 1.25 3.00
26 C.C. Sabathia .30 .75
27 Adrian Beltre .20 .50
28 Brad Wilkerson .20 .50
29 Randy Wolf .20 .50
30 Jason Bay .20 .50
31 Austin Kearns .20 .50
32 Clint Barmes .20 .50
33 Mike Sweeney .20 .50
34 Kevin Youkilis .20 .50
35 Justin Morneau .50 1.25
36 Scott Podsednik .20 .50
37 Jason Giambi .20 .50
38 Steve Finley .20 .50
39 Morgan Ensberg .20 .50
40 Eric Chavez .20 .50
41 Roy Halladay .50 1.25
42 Horacio Ramirez .20 .50
43 Ben Sheets .20 .50
44 Chris Carpenter .50 1.25
45 Andruw Jones .20 .50
46 Carlos Zambrano .30 .75
47 Jonny Gomes .20 .50
48 Shawn Green .20 .50
49 Moises Alou .20 .50
50 Ichiro Suzuki .75 2.00
51 Juan Pierre .20 .50
52 Grady Sizemore .30 .75
53 Kazuo Matsui .20 .50
54 Jose Vidro .20 .50
55 Jake Peavy .20 .50
56 Dallas McPherson .20 .50
57 Ryan Howard .75 2.00
58 Zach Duke .20 .50
59 Michael Young .30 .75
60 Todd Helton .30 .75
61 David DeJesus .20 .50
62 Ivan Rodriguez .30 .75
63 Johan Santana .50 1.25
64 Danny Haren .20 .50
65 Derek Jeter 1.25 3.00
66 Greg Maddux .75 2.00
67 Jorge Cantu .20 .50
68 J.J. Hardy .20 .50
69 Victor Martinez .30 .75
70 David Wright .75 2.00
71 Ryan Church .20 .50
72 Khalil Greene .20 .50
73 Jimmy Rollins .30 .75
74 Hank Blalock .20 .50
75 Pedro Martinez .30 .75
76 Chris Shelton .20 .50
77 Felipe Lopez .20 .50
78 Jeff Francis .20 .50
79 Andy Sisco .20 .50
80 Hideki Matsui .50 1.25
81 Ken Griffey Jr. .75 2.00
82 Nomar Garciaparra .50 1.25
83 Kevin Millwood .20 .50
84 Paul Konerko .30 .75
85 A.J. Burnett .30 .75
86 Mike Piazza .50 1.25
87 Brian Giles .20 .50
88 Johnny Damon .30 .75
89 Jim Thome .30 .75
90 Roger Clemens .60 1.50
91 Aaron Rowand .20 .50
92 Rafael Furcal .20 .50
93 Gary Sheffield .20 .50
94 Mike Cameron .20 .50
95 Carlos Delgado .20 .50
96 Jorge Posada .30 .75
97 Denny Bautista .20 .50
98 Mike Maroth .20 .50
99 Brad Radke .20 .50
100 Alex Rodriguez .75 2.00
101 Freddy Garcia .20 .50
102 Oliver Perez .20 .50
103 Jon Lieber .20 .50
104 Melvin Mora .20 .50
105 Travis Hafner .20 .50
106 Alex Rios .30 .75
107 Derek Lowe .20 .50
108 Luis Castillo .20 .50
109 Livan Hernandez .20 .50
110 Tadahito Iguchi .20 .50
111 Shawn Chacon .20 .50
112 Frank Thomas .50 1.25
113 Josh Beckett .30 .75
114 Aubrey Huff .20 .50
115 Derrek Lee .20 .50
116 Chien-Ming Wang .30 .75
117 Joe Crede .20 .50
118 Torii Hunter .20 .50
119 J.D. Drew .20 .50
120 Troy Glaus .20 .50
121 Sean Casey .20 .50
122 Edgar Renteria .20 .50
123 Craig Wilson .20 .50
124 Adam Eaton .20 .50
125 Jeff Francoeur .50 1.25
126 Bruce Chen .20 .50
127 Cliff Floyd .20 .50
128 Jeremy Reed .20 .50
129 Jake Westbrook .20 .50
130 Wily Mo Pena .20 .50
131 Toby Hall .20 .50
132 David Ortiz .30 .75
133 David Eckstein .20 .50
134 Brady Clark .20 .50
135 Marcus Giles .20 .50
136 Aaron Hill .20 .50
137 Mark Kotsay .20 .50
138 Carlos Lee .20 .50
139 Roy Oswalt .30 .75
140 Chone Figgins .20 .50
141 Mike Mussina .30 .75
142 Orlando Hernandez .20 .50
143 Magglio Ordonez .30 .75
144 Jim Edmonds .30 .75
145 Bobby Abreu .20 .50
146 Nick Johnson .20 .50
147 Carlos Beltran .20 .50
148 Jhonny Peralta .20 .50
149 Pedro Feliz .20 .50
150 Miguel Tejada .30 .75
151 Luis Gonzalez .20 .50
152 Carl Crawford .30 .75
153 Yadier Molina .30 .75
154 Rich Harden .20 .50
155 Tim Wakefield .20 .50
156 Rickie Weeks .30 .75
157 Johnny Estrada .20 .50
158 Gustavo Chacin .20 .50
159 Dan Johnson .20 .50
160 Willy Taveras .20 .50
161 Garret Anderson .20 .50
162 Randy Johnson .50 1.25
163 Jermaine Dye .20 .50
164 Joe Mauer .50 1.25
165 Ervin Santana .20 .50
166 Jeremy Bonderman .20 .50
167 Garrett Atkins .20 .50
168 Manny Ramirez .50 1.25
169 Brad Eldred .20 .50
170 Chase Utley .50 1.25
171 Mark Loretta .20 .50
172 John Patterson .20 .50
173 Tom Glavine .30 .75
174 Dontrelle Willis .20 .50
175 Mark Teixeira .50 1.25
176 Felix Hernandez .50 1.25
177 Cliff Lee .30 .75
178 Jason Schmidt .20 .50
179 Chad Tracy .20 .50
180 Rocco Baldelli .20 .50
181 Aramis Ramirez .20 .50
182 Andy Pettitte .30 .75
183 Mark Mulder .20 .50
184 Geoff Jenkins .20 .50
185 Chipper Jones .50 1.25
186 Vernon Wells .20 .50
187 Bobby Crosby .20 .50
188 Lance Berkman .30 .75
189 Vladimir Guerrero .50 1.25
190 Coco Crisp .20 .50
191 Brad Penny .20 .50
192 Jose Guillen .20 .50
193 Brett Myers .20 .50
194 Miguel Cabrera .50 1.25
195 Bartolo Colon .20 .50
196 Craig Biggio .30 .75
197 Tim Hudson .30 .75
198 Mark Prior .30 .75
199 Mark Buehrle .30 .75
200 Barry Bonds 1.00 2.50
201 Anderson Hernandez (RC) .25 .60
202 Jose Capellan (RC) .25 .60
203 Jeremy Accardo RC .25 .60
204 Hanley Ramirez (RC) .60 1.50
205 Matt Capps (RC) .25 .60
206 Jonathan Papelbon (RC) 1.25 3.00
207 Chuck James (RC) .25 .60
208 Matt Cain (RC) .60 1.50
209 Cole Hamels (RC) 1.00 2.50
210 Jason Botts (RC) .25 .60
211 Lastings Milledge (RC) .25 .60
212 Conor Jackson (RC) .40 1.00
213 Yusmeiro Petit (RC) .25 .60
214 Alay Soler RC .25 .60
215 Willy Aybar (RC) .25 .60
216 Adam Loewen (RC) .25 .60
217 Justin Verlander (RC) 2.00 5.00
218 Francisco Liriano (RC) .60 1.50
219 Kenji Johjima RC .60 1.50
219a Kenji Johjima AU 10.00 25.00
220 Craig Hansen RC .60 1.50
221 Prince Fielder AU (RC) 30.00 60.00
222 Josh Barfield AU (RC) 6.00 15.00
223 Fausto Carmona AU (RC) 6.00 15.00
224 James Loney AU (RC) 6.00 15.00

2006 Bowman Chrome Refractors

*REF 1-200: 1.5X TO 4X BASIC
*REF 201-220: 1X TO 2.5X BASIC
1-220 ODDS 1:4 HOB, 1:6 RET
219 AU ODDS 1:5100 HOB, 1:12,432 RET
219 AU PRINT RUN 250 SERIAL #'d CARDS
*REF AU 221-224: .5X TO 1.2X BASIC
221-224 AU ODDS 1:82 HOB, 1:200 RET
221-224 AU PRINT RUN 500 SER.#'d SETS
221 Prince Fielder AU 40.00 80.00
223 Fausto Carmona AU 8.00 20.00
219a Kenji Johjima AU/250 15.00 40.00

2006 Bowman Chrome Blue Refractors

*BLUE REF 1-200: 4X TO 10X BASIC
*BLUE REF 201-220: 4X TO 10X BASIC
1-220 ODDS 1:25 HOB, 1:73 RET
219 AU ODDS 1:16,877 HOB, 1:61,760 RET
219 AU PRINT RUN 75 SERIAL #'d CARDS
*BLUE REF AU 221-224: .75X TO 2X BASIC
221-224 AU ODDS 1:266 HOB, 1:890 RET
STATED PRINT RUN 150 SERIAL #'d SETS
219a Kenji Johjima AU/75 30.00 60.00

2006 Bowman Chrome Gold Refractors

*GOLD REF 1-200: 8X TO 20X BASIC
*GOLD REF 201-220: 6X TO 15X BASIC
1-220 ODDS 1:74 HOB, 1:247 RET
219 AU ODDS 1:26,000 HOB, 1:52,937 RET
*GOLD REF AU 221-224: 2X TO 5X BASIC
221-224 AU ODDS 1:820 HOB, 1:1910 RET
STATED PRINT RUN 50 SERIAL #'d SETS
221 Prince Fielder AU 250.00 400.00
223 Fausto Carmona AU 40.00 80.00
224 James Loney AU 50.00 100.00
219a Kenji Johjima AU 40.00 80.00

2006 Bowman Chrome Orange Refractors

*ORANGE REF 1-200: 15X TO 40X BASIC
1-220 ODDS 1:181 HOB, 1:182 RET
219 AU ODDS 1:62,666 HOB, 1:62,607 RET
221-224 AU ODDS 1:1640 HOB, 1:3820 RET
STATED PRINT RUN 25 SERIAL #'d SETS
NO RC/AU PRICING DUE TO SCARCITY

2006 Bowman Chrome Red Refractors

1-220 ODDS 1:906 HOB, 1:908 RET
219 AU ODDS 1:438,929 HOBBY
221-224 AU ODDS 1:6250 H,1:19,500 R
STATED PRINT RUN 5 SERIAL #'d SETS
NO PRICING DUE TO SCARCITY

2006 Bowman Chrome SuperFractors

1-220 ODDS 1:3350 HOBBY
219 AU ODDS 1:877,608 HOBBY
221-224 AU ODDS 1:35,592 HOBBY
STATED PRINT RUN 1 SERIAL #'d SET
NO PRICING DUE TO SCARCITY

2006 Bowman Chrome X-Fractors

*X-FRACTOR 1-200: 3X TO 8X BASIC
*X-FRACTOR 201-220: 2.5X TO 6X BASIC
1-220 ODDS 1:15 HOB, 1:44 RET
1-220 PRINT RUN 250 SERIAL #'d SETS
219 AU ODDS 1:10,205 HOB 1:28,500 RET
219 AU PRINT RUN 125 SERIAL #'d CARDS
*X-FRAC AU 221-224: .6X TO 1.5X BASIC
221-224 AU ODDS 1:182 HOB, 1:478 RET
221-224 AU PRINT RUN 225 SERIAL #'d SETS
221 Prince Fielder AU 60.00 120.00
223 Fausto Carmona AU 10.00 25.00
219a Kenji Johjima AU/125 20.00 50.00

2006 Bowman Chrome Prospects

COMP.SET w/o AU's (220) 75.00 150.00
COMP.SERIES 1 SET (110) 30.00 60.00
COMP.SERIES 2 SET (110) 40.00 80.00
1-110 TWO PER HOBBY PACK
1-110 FOUR PER HTA PACK
111-220 TWO PER HOB/RET PACKS
221-247 AU ODDS 1:27 HOB, 1:65 RET
1-110 PLATE ODDS 1:588 HOB,1:575 HTA
111-220 PLATE ODDS 1:836 HOBBY
221-247 AU PLATES 1: 9000 HOBBY
PLATE PRINT RUN 1 PER COLOR
BLACK-CYAN-MAGENTA-YELLOW ISSUED
NO PLATE PRICING DUE TO SCARCITY
1-110 ISSUED IN BOWMAN PACKS
111-247 ISSUED IN BOW.CHROME PACKS
EXCHANGE DEADLINE 8/31/08
BC1 Alex Gordon 1.25 3.00
BC2 Jonathan George .40 1.00
BC3 Scott Walter .40 1.00
BC4 Brian Holliday .40 1.00
BC5 Ben Copeland .40 1.00
BC6 Bobby Wilson .40 1.00
BC7 Mayker Sandoval .40 1.00
BC8 Alejandro de Aza .40 1.00
BC9 David Munoz .40 1.00
BC10 Josh LeBlanc .40 1.00
BC11 Philippe Valiquette .40 1.00
BC12 Edwin Bellorin .40 1.00
BC13 Jason Quarles .40 1.00
BC14 Mark Trumbo 1.50 4.00
BC15 Steve Kelly .40 1.00
BC16 Jamie Hoffman .40 1.00
BC17 Joe Bauserman .40 1.00
BC18 Nick Adenhart .40 1.00
BC19 Mike Butia .40 1.00
BC20 Jon Weber .40 1.00
BC21 Luis Valdez .40 1.00
BC22 Rafael Rodriguez .40 1.00
BC23 Wyatt Toregas .40 1.00
BC24 John Vanden Berg .40 1.00
BC25 Mike Connolly .40 1.00
BC26 Mike O'Connor .40 1.00
BC27 Garrett Mock .40 1.00
BC28 Bill Layman .40 1.00
BC29 Luis Pena .40 1.00
BC30 Billy Killian .40 1.00
BC31 Ross Ohlendorf .40 1.00
BC32 Marc Kaiser .40 1.00
BC33 Ryan Costello .40 1.00
BC34 Dale Thayer .40 1.00
BC35 Steve Garrabrants .40 1.00
BC36 Samuel Deduno .40 1.00
BC37 Juan Portes .40 1.00
BC38 Javier Martinez .40 1.00
BC39 Clint Sammons .40 1.00
BC40 Andrew Kown .40 1.00
BC41 Matt Tolbert .40 1.00
BC42 Michael Ekstrom .40 1.00
BC43 Shawn Norris .40 1.00
BC44 Diory Hernandez .40 1.00
BC45 Chris Maples .40 1.00
BC46 Aaron Hathaway .40 1.00
BC47 Steven Baker .40 1.00
BC48 Greg Creek .40 1.00
BC49 Collin Mahoney .40 1.00
BC50 Corey Ragsdale .40 1.00
BC51 Ariel Nunez .40 1.00
BC52 Max Ramirez .60 1.50
BC53 Eric Rodland .40 1.00
BC54 Dante Brinkley .40 1.00
BC55 Casey Craig .40 1.00
BC56 Ryan Spilborghs .40 1.00
BC57 Fredy Deza .40 1.00
BC58 Jeff Frazier .40 1.00
BC59 Vince Cordova .40 1.00
BC60 Oswaldo Navarro .40 1.00
BC61 Jarod Rine .40 1.00
BC62 Jordan Tata .40 1.00
BC63 Ben Julianel .40 1.00
BC64 Yung-Chi Chen .60 1.50
BC65 Carlos Torres .40 1.00
BC66 Juan Francia .40 1.00
BC67 Brett Smith .40 1.00
BC68 Francisco Leandro .40 1.00
BC69 Chris Turner .40 1.00
BC70 Matt Joyce 2.00 5.00
BC71 Jason Jones .40 1.00
BC72 Jose Diaz .40 1.00
BC73 Kevin Ool .40 1.00
BC74 Nate Bumstead .40 1.00
BC75 Omir Santos .40 1.00
BC76 Shawn Riggans .40 1.00
BC77 Otilio Castro .40 1.00
BC78 Mike Rozier .40 1.00
BC79 Wilkin Ramirez .60 1.50
BC80 Yobal Duenas .40 1.00
BC81 Adam Bourassa .40 1.00
BC82 Tony Granadillo .40 1.00
BC83 Brad McCann .40 1.00
BC84 Dustin Majewski .40 1.00
BC85 Kelvin Jimenez .40 1.00
BC86 Mark Reed .40 1.00
BC87 Asdrubal Cabrera 2.00 5.00
BC88 James Barthmaier .40 1.00
BC89 Brandon Boggs .40 1.00
BC90 Raul Valdez .40 1.00
BC91 Jose Campusano .40 1.00
BC92 Henry Owens .40 1.00
BC93 Tug Hulett .40 1.00
BC94 Nate Gold .40 1.00
BC95 Lee Mitchell .40 1.00
BC96 John Hardy .40 1.00
BC97 Aaron Wideman .40 1.00
BC98 Brandon Roberts .40 1.00
BC99 Lou Santangelo .40 1.00
BC100 Kyle Kendrick 1.00 2.50
BC101 Michael Collins .40 1.00
BC102 Camilo Vazquez .40 1.00
BC103 Mark McLemore .40 1.00
BC104 Alexander Peralta .40 1.00
BC105 Josh Whitesell .40 1.00
BC106 Carlos Guevara .40 1.00
BC107 Michael Aubrey .60 1.50
BC108 Brandon Chaves .40 1.00
BC109 Leonard Davis .40 1.00
BC110 Kendry Morales 1.00 2.50
BC111 Koby Clemens .60 1.50
BC112 Lance Broadway .40 1.00
BC113 Cameron Maybin 1.25 3.00
BC114 Mike Aviles .40 1.00
BC115 Kyle Blanks 1.50 4.00
BC116 Chris Dickerson .60 1.50
BC117 Sean Gallagher .40 1.00
BC118 Jamar Hill .40 1.00
BC119 Garrett Mock .40 1.00
BC120 Russ Rohlicek .40 1.00
BC121 Clete Thomas .40 1.00
BC122 Elvis Andrus 2.00 5.00
BC123 Brandon Moss .40 1.00
BC124 Mark Holliman .40 1.00
BC125 Jose Tabata 2.50 6.00
BC126 Corey Wimberly .40 1.00
BC127 Bobby Wilson .40 1.00
BC128 Edward Mujica .40 1.00
BC129 Hunter Pence 2.00 5.00
BC130 Adam Heether .40 1.00
BC131 Andy Wilson .40 1.00
BC132 Radhames Liz .40 1.00
BC133 Garrett Patterson .40 1.00
BC134 Carlos Gomez 2.00 5.00
BC135 Jared Lansford .40 1.00
BC136 Jose Arredondo .40 1.00
BC137 Renee Cortez .40 1.00
BC138 Francisco Rosario .40 1.00
BC139 Brian Stokes .40 1.00
BC140 Will Thompson .40 1.00
BC141 Ernesto Frieri .40 1.00
BC142 Jose Mijares .40 1.00
BC143 Jeremy Slayden .40 1.00
BC144 Brandon Fahey .40 1.00
BC145 Jason Windsor .40 1.00
BC146 Shawn Nottingham .40 1.00
BC147 Dallas Trahern .40 1.00
BC148 Jon Niese 1.00 2.50
BC149 A.J. Shappi .40 1.00
BC150 Jordan Pals .40 1.00
BC151 Tim Moss .40 1.00
BC152 Stephen Marek .40 1.00
BC153 Mat Gamel 1.50 4.00
BC154 Sean Henn .40 1.00
BC155 Matt Guillory .40 1.00
BC156 Brandon Jones .40 1.00
BC157 Gary Galvez .40 1.00
BC158 Shane Lindsay 1.00 2.50
BC159 Jesus Reina .40 1.00
BC160 Lorenzo Cain 1.00 2.50
BC161 Chris Britton .40 1.00
BC162 Yovani Gallardo 1.25 3.00
BC163 Matt Walker .40 1.00
BC164 Shaun Cumberland .40 1.00
BC165 Ryan Patterson .40 1.00
BC166 Michael Hollimon .40 1.00
BC167 Eude Brito .40 1.00
BC168 John Bowker .40 1.00
BC169 James Avery .40 1.00
BC170 John Bannister .40 1.00
BC171 Juan Ciriaco .40 1.00
BC172 Manuel Corpas .40 1.00
BC173 Leo Rosales .40 1.00
BC174 Tim Kennelly .40 1.00
BC175 Adam Russell .40 1.00
BC176 Jeremy Hellickson 3.00 8.00
BC177 Ryan Klosterman .40 1.00
BC178 Evan Meek .40 1.00
BC179 Steve Murphy .40 1.00
BC180 Scott Feldman .40 1.00
BC181 Pablo Sandoval 4.00 10.00
BC182 Dexter Fowler 1.25 3.00
BC183 Jairo Cuevas .40 1.00
BC184 Andrew Pinckney .40 1.00
BC185 Marino Salas .40 1.00
BC186 Justin Christian .40 1.00
BC187 Ching-Lung Lo .40 1.00
BC188 Randy Roth .40 1.00
BC189 Andy Sonnanstine .40 1.00
BC190 Josh Outman .40 1.00
BC191 Yuber Rodriguez .40 1.00
BC192 Hainley Statia .40 1.00
BC193 Kevin Estrada .40 1.00
BC194 Jeff Karstens .40 1.00
BC195 Corey Coles .40 1.00
BC196 Gustavo Espinoza .40 1.00
BC197 Brian Horwitz .40 1.00
BC198 Landon Jacobsen .40 1.00
BC199 Ben Krosschell .40 1.00
BC200 Jason Jaramillo .40 1.00
BC201 Josh Wilson .40 1.00
BC202 Jason Ray .40 1.00
BC203 Brent Dlugach .40 1.00
BC204 Cesar Jimenez .40 1.00
BC205 Eric Haberer .40 1.00
BC206 Felipe Paulino .40 1.00
BC207 Alcides Escobar 2.50 6.00
BC208 Jose Ascanio .40 1.00
BC209 Yoel Hernandez .40 1.00
BC210 Geoff Vandel .40 1.00
BC211 Travis Denker .40 1.00
BC212 Ramon Alvarado .40 1.00
BC213 Welinson Baez .40 1.00
BC214 Chris Kolkhorst .40 1.00
BC215 Emiliano Fruto .40 1.00
BC216 Luis Cota .40 1.00
BC217 Mark Worrell .40 1.00
BC218 Cla Meredith .40 1.00
BC219 Emmanuel Garcia .40 1.00
BC220 B.J. Szymanski .40 1.00
BC221 Alex Gordon AU 20.00 50.00
BC223 Justin Upton AU 50.00 100.00
BC224 Sean West AU 6.00 15.00
BC225 Tyler Greene AU 6.00 15.00
BC226 Josh Kinney AU 6.00 15.00
BC227 Pedro Lopez AU 6.00 15.00
BC228 Troy Patton AU 8.00 20.00
BC229 Chris Iannetta AU 12.50 30.00
BC230 Jared Wells AU 6.00 15.00
BC231 Brandon Wood AU 6.00 15.00
BC232 Josh Geer AU 6.00 15.00
BC233 Cesar Carrillo AU 6.00 15.00
BC234 Franklin Gutierrez AU 6.00 15.00
BC235 Matt Garza AU 10.00 25.00
BC236 Eli Iorg AU 6.00 15.00
BC237 Trevor Bell AU 6.00 15.00
BC238 Jeff Lyman AU 6.00 15.00
BC239 Jon Lester AU 20.00 50.00
BC240 Kendry Morales AU 10.00 25.00
BC241 J. Brent Cox AU 6.00 15.00
BC242 Jose Bautista AU 30.00 60.00
BC243 Josh Sullivan AU 6.00 15.00
BC244 Brandon Snyder AU 6.00 15.00
BC245 Elvin Puello AU 6.00 15.00
BC247 Jacob Marceaux AU 6.00 15.00

2006 Bowman Chrome Prospects Refractors

*REF 1-110: 1.25X TO 3X BASIC
*REF 111-220: 1.25X TO 3X BASIC
1-110 ODDS 1:36 HOBBY, 1:12 HTA
111-220 ODDS 1:22 HOBBY, 1:81 RETAIL
*REF AU 221-247: .5X TO 1.2X BASIC
221-247 AU ODDS 1:82 HOB, 1:200 RET
STATED PRINT RUN 500 SERIAL #'d SETS
1-110 ISSUED IN BOWMAN PACKS
111-247 ISSUED IN BOW.CHROME PACKS
EXCHANGE DEADLINE 8/31/08
BC223 Justin Upton AU 75.00 150.00
BC239 Jon Lester AU 40.00 80.00
BC242 Jose Bautista AU 60.00 120.00

2006 Bowman Chrome Prospects Blue Refractors

*BLUE REF 1-220: 2.5X TO 6X BASIC
1-110 ODDS 1:118 HOBBY, 1:39 HTA
111-220 ODDS 1:25 HOBBY
*BLUE AU 221-247: .75X TO 2X BASIC
221-247 AU ODDS 1:266 HOB, 1:890 RET
STATED PRINT RUN 150 SERIAL #'d SETS
1-110 ISSUED IN BOWMAN PACKS
111-247 ISSUED IN BOW.CHROME PACKS
EXCHANGE DEADLINE 8/31/08
BC176 Jeremy Hellickson 75.00 150.00
BC223 Justin Upton AU 125.00 250.00
BC228 Troy Patton AU 20.00 50.00
BC229 Chris Iannetta AU 40.00 80.00
BC239 Jon Lester AU 60.00 120.00
BC242 Jose Bautista AU 75.00 150.00

2006 Bowman Chrome Prospects Gold Refractors

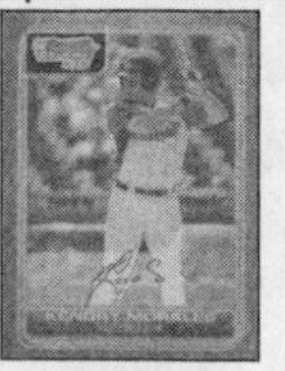

*GOLD REF 1-110: 10X TO 25X BASIC
*GOLD REF 111-220: 8X TO 20X BASIC
1-110 ODDS 1:355 HOBBY, 1:116 HTA
111-220 ODDS: 1:74 HOBBY
COMMON AUTO (221-247) 30.00 60.00
221-247 AU ODDS 1:820 HOB, 1:1910 RET
STATED PRINT RUN 50 SERIAL #'d SETS
1-110 ISSUED IN BOWMAN PACKS
111-247 ISSUED IN BOW.CHROME PACKS
EXCHANGE DEADLINE 8/31/08
BC221 Alex Gordon AU 150.00 300.00
BC223 Justin Upton AU 400.00 600.00
BC226 Josh Kinney AU 20.00 50.00
BC228 Troy Patton AU 40.00 80.00
BC229 Chris Iannetta AU 75.00 150.00
BC235 Matt Garza AU 60.00 120.00
BC239 Jon Lester AU 100.00 200.00
BC240 Kendry Morales AU 75.00 150.00
BC242 Jose Bautista AU 175.00 350.00

2006 Bowman Chrome Prospects Orange Refractors

1-110 ODDS 1:710 HOBBY, 1:233 HTA
111-220 ODDS 1:181 HOBBY
221-247 AU ODDS 1:1640 HOB, 1:3820 RET
STATED PRINT RUN 25 SERIAL #'d SETS
1-110 ISSUED IN BOWMAN PACKS
111-247 ISSUED IN BOW.CHROME PACKS
NO PRICING DUE TO SCARCITY
EXCHANGE DEADLINE 8/31/08

2006 Bowman Chrome Prospects Red Refractors

1-110 ODDS 1:3000 HOBBY, 1:690 HTA
111-220 ODDS 1:906 HOBBY
221-247 AU ODDS 1:8250 H, 1:19,500 R
STATED PRINT RUN 5 SERIAL #'d SETS
NO PRICING DUE TO SCARCITY
1-110 ISSUED IN BOWMAN PACKS
111-247 ISSUED IN BOW.CHROME PACKS
EXCHANGE DEADLINE 8/31/08

2006 Bowman Chrome Prospects SuperFractors

1-110 ODDS 1:15,425 HOBBY, 1:3373 HTA
111-220 ODDS 1:3350 HOBBY
221-247 AU ODDS 1:35,592 HOBBY
STATED PRINT RUN 1 SERIAL #'d SET
NO PRICING DUE TO SCARCITY
1-110 ISSUED IN BOWMAN PACKS
111-247 ISSUED IN BOW.CHROME PACKS
EXCHANGE DEADLINE 8/31/08

2006 Bowman Chrome Prospects X-Fractors

*X-F 1-220: 1.5X TO 4X BASIC
1-110 ODDS 1:72 HOBBY, 1:23 HTA
111-220 ODDS 1:15 HOBBY
1-220 PRINT RUN 250 SERIAL #'d SETS
*X-F AU 221-247: .6X TO 1.5X BASIC
221-247 AU ODDS 1:182 HOB, 1:478 RET
221-247 AU PRINT RUN 225 SERIAL #'d SETS
1-110 ISSUED IN BOWMAN PACKS
111-247 ISSUED IN BOW.CHROME PACKS
EXCHANGE DEADLINE 8/31/08
BC223 Justin Upton AU 100.00 200.00
BC239 Jon Lester AU 50.00 100.00
BC242 Jose Bautista AU 100.00 200.00

2006 Bowman Chrome Draft

This 55-card set was issued at a stated rate of one card in every other pack of Bowman Draft Picks. All fifty-five cards in this set feature players who made their major league debut in 2006.

COMPLETE SET (55) 15.00 40.00
COMMON RC (1-55) .40 1.00
APPX. ODDS 1:2 HOBBY, 1:2 RETAIL
ODDS INFO PROVIDED BY BECKETT
OVERALL PLATE ODDS 1:990 HOBBY
PLATE PRINT RUN 1 SET PER COLOR
BLACK-CYAN-MAGENTA-YELLOW ISSUED
NO PLATE PRICING DUE TO SCARCITY
1 Matt Kemp (RC) 2.00 5.00
2 Taylor Tankersley (RC) .40 1.00
3 Mike Napoli RC 1.25 3.00
4 Brian Bannister (RC) .40 1.00
5 Melky Cabrera (RC) .60 1.50
6 Bill Bray (RC) .40 1.00
7 Brian Anderson (RC) .40 1.00
8 Jered Weaver (RC) 1.00 2.50
9 Chris Duncan (RC) .60 1.50
10 Boof Bonser (RC) .60 1.50
11 Mike Rouse (RC) .40 1.00
12 David Pauley (RC) .40 1.00
13 Russ Martin (RC) .60 1.50
14 Jeremy Sowers (RC) .40 1.00
15 Kevin Reese (RC) .40 1.00
16 John Rheinecker (RC) .40 1.00
17 Tommy Murphy (RC) .40 1.00
18 Sean Marshall (RC) .60 1.50
19 Jason Kubel (RC) .40 1.00
20 Chad Billingsley (RC) .60 1.50
21 Kendry Morales (RC) 1.00 2.50
22 Jon Lester RC 1.50 4.00
23 Brandon Fahey RC .40 1.00
24 Josh Johnson (RC) 1.00 2.50
25 Kevin Frandsen (RC) .40 1.00
26 Casey Janssen RC .40 1.00
27 Scott Thorman (RC) .40 1.00
28 Scott Mathieson (RC) .40 1.00
29 Jeremy Hermida (RC) .40 1.00
30 Dustin Nippert (RC) .40 1.00
31 Kevin Thompson (RC) .40 1.00
32 Bobby Livingston (RC) .40 1.00
33 Travis Ishikawa (RC) .40 1.00
34 Jeff Mathis (RC) .40 1.00
35 Charlie Haeger RC .60 1.50
36 Josh Willingham (RC) .40 1.00
37 Taylor Buchholz (RC) .40 1.00
38 Joel Guzman (RC) .40 1.00
39 Zach Jackson (RC) .40 1.00
40 Howie Kendrick (RC) 1.00 2.50
41 T.J. Beam (RC) .40 1.00
42 Ty Taubenheim RC .60 1.50
43 Erick Aybar (RC) .40 1.00
44 Anibal Sanchez (RC) .40 1.00
45 Michael Pelfrey RC 1.00 2.50
46 Shawn Hill (RC) .40 1.00
47 Chris Roberson (RC) .40 1.00
48 Carlos Villanueva RC .40 1.00
49 Andre Ethier (RC) 1.50 4.00
50 Anthony Reyes (RC) .40 1.00
51 Franklin Gutierrez (RC) .40 1.00
52 Angel Guzman (RC) .40 1.00
53 Michael O'Connor RC .40 1.00
54 James Shields RC 1.25 3.00
55 Nate McLouth (RC) .40 1.00

2006 Bowman Chrome Draft Refractors

*REF: 1.25X TO 3X BASIC
STATED ODDS 1:11 HOBBY, 1:11 RETAIL

2006 Bowman Chrome Draft Blue Refractors

*BLUE REF: 3X TO 8X BASIC
STATED ODDS 1:50 HOBBY, 1:94 RETAIL
STATED PRINT RUN 199 SER.#'d SETS

2006 Bowman Chrome Draft Gold Refractors

*GOLD REF: 5X TO 12X BASIC
STATED ODDS 1:197 H, 1:388 R
STATED PRINT RUN 50 SER.#'d SETS

2006 Bowman Chrome Draft Orange Refractors

STATED ODDS 1:395 HOBBY, 1:770 RETAIL
STATED PRINT RUN 25 SERIAL #'d SETS
NO PRICING DUE TO SCARCITY

2006 Bowman Chrome Draft Red Refractors

STATED ODDS 1:1585 HOBBY
STATED PRINT RUN 5 SERIAL #'d SETS
NO PRICING DUE TO SCARCITY

2006 Bowman Chrome Draft SuperFractors

STATED ODDS 1:7934 HOBBY
STATED PRINT RUN 1 SERIAL #'d SET
NO PRICING DUE TO SCARCITY

2006 Bowman Chrome Draft X-Fractors

*X-F: 2X TO 5X BASIC
STATED ODDS 1:32 H, 1:74 R
STATED PRINT RUN 299 SER.#'d SETS

2006 Bowman Chrome Draft Draft Picks

APPX. ODDS 1:1 HOBBY, 1:1 RETAIL
ODDS INFO PROVIDED BY BECKETT
66-90 AU ODDS 1:50 HOB.,1:51 RET.
1-65 PLATE ODDS 1:990 HOBBY
66-90 AU PLATE ODDS 1:13,200 HOBBY
PLATE PRINT RUN 1 SET PER COLOR
BLACK-CYAN-MAGENTA-YELLOW ISSUED
NO PLATE PRICING DUE TO SCARCITY
1 Tyler Colvin 1.00 2.50
2 Chris Marrero 1.50 4.00
3 Hank Conger .60 1.50
4 Chris Parmelee .60 1.50
5 Jason Place .40 1.00
6 Billy Rowell 1.00 2.50
7 Travis Snider 1.25 3.00
8 Colton Willems .40 1.00
9 Chase Fontaine .40 1.00
10 Jon Jay 1.00 2.50
11 Wade Leblanc .40 1.00
12 Justin Masterson 1.25 3.00
13 Gary Daley .40 1.00
14 Justin Edwards .40 1.00
15 Charlie Yarbrough .40 1.00
16 Cyle Hankerd .40 1.00
17 Zach McAllister .40 1.00
18 Tyler Robertson .40 1.00
19 Joe Smith .40 1.00
20 Nate Culp .40 1.00
21 John Holdzkom .40 1.00
22 Patrick Bresnehan .40 1.00
23 Chad Lee .40 1.00
24 Ryan Morris .40 1.00
25 D'Arby Myers .40 1.00
26 Garrett Olson .40 1.00
27 Jon Still .40 1.00
28 Brandon Rice .40 1.00
29 Chris Davis 2.50 6.00
30 Zack Daeges .40 1.00
31 Bobby Henson .40 1.00
32 George Kontos .40 1.00
33 Jermaine Mitchell .40 1.00
34 Adam Coe .40 1.00
35 Dustin Richardson .40 1.00
36 Allen Craig 1.00 2.50
37 Austin McClune .40 1.00
38 Doug Fister 1.25 3.00
39 Corey Madden .40 1.00
40 Justin Jacobs .40 1.00
41 Jim Negrych .40 1.00
42 Tyler Norrick .40 1.00
43 Adam Davis .40 1.00
44 Brett Logan .40 1.00
45 Brian Omogrosso .40 1.00
46 Kyle Drabek 1.25 3.00
47 Jamie Ortiz .40 1.00
48 Alex Presley .40 1.00
49 Terrance Warren .40 1.00
50 David Christensen .40 1.00
51 Helder Velazquez .40 1.00
52 Matt McBride .40 1.00
53 Quintin Berry .40 1.00
54 Michael Eisenberg .40 1.00
55 Dan Garcia .40 1.00
56 Scott Cousins .40 1.00
57 Sean Land .40 1.00
58 Kristopher Medlen 1.00 2.50
59 Tyler Reves .40 1.00
60 John Shelby .40 1.00
61 Jordan Newton .40 1.00
62 Ricky Orta .40 1.00
63 Jason Donald .40 1.00
64 David Huff .40 1.00
65 Brett Sinkbeil .40 1.00
66 Evan Longoria AU 100.00 200.00
67 Cody Johnson AU 12.50 30.00
68 Kris Johnson AU 6.00 15.00
69 Kasey Kiker AU 4.00 10.00
70 Ronnie Bourquin AU 6.00 15.00
71 Adrian Cardenas AU 5.00 12.00
72 Matt Antonelli AU 4.00 10.00
73 Brooks Brown AU 4.00 10.00
74 Steven Evarts AU 6.00 15.00
75 Joshua Butler AU 4.00 10.00
76 Chad Huffman AU 4.00 10.00
77 Steven Wright AU 4.00 10.00
78 Cory Rasmus AU 6.00 15.00
79 Brad Furnish AU 4.00 10.00
80 Andrew Carpenter AU 5.00 12.00
81 Dustin Evans AU 4.00 10.00
82 Tommy Hickman AU 8.00 20.00
83 Matt Long AU 4.00 10.00
84 Clayton Kershaw AU 60.00 120.00
85 Kyle McCulloch AU 6.00 15.00
86 Pedro Beato AU 4.00 10.00
87 Kyler Burke AU 8.00 20.00
88 Stephen Englund AU 8.00 20.00
89 Michael Felix AU 4.00 10.00
90 Sean Watson AU 4.00 10.00

2006 Bowman Chrome Draft Draft Picks Refractors

*REF 1-65: 1.25X TO 3X BASIC
1-65 ODDS 1:11 HOBBY, 1:11 RETAIL
*REF AU 66-90: .5X TO 1.2X BASIC AU
AU 66-90 ODDS 1:156 HOB, 1:157 RET
66-90 AU PRINT RUN 500 SER.#'d SETS
66 Evan Longoria AU 150.00 300.00
68 Kris Johnson AU 10.00 25.00
84 Clayton Kershaw AU 60.00 120.00

2006 Bowman Chrome Draft Draft Picks Blue Refractors

*BLUE REF 1-65: 5X TO 12X BASIC
1-65 STATED ODDS 1:50 H, 1:94 R
1-65 PRINT RUN 199 SER.#'d SETS
*BLUE AU 66-90: 1.25X TO 3X BASIC AU
66-90 STATED ODDS 1:535 H, 1:535 R
66-90 PRINT RUN 150 SER.#'d SETS
66 Evan Longoria AU 250.00 500.00
82 Tommy Hickman AU 40.00 80.00
84 Clayton Kershaw AU 150.00 300.00

2006 Bowman Chrome Draft Draft Picks Gold Refractors

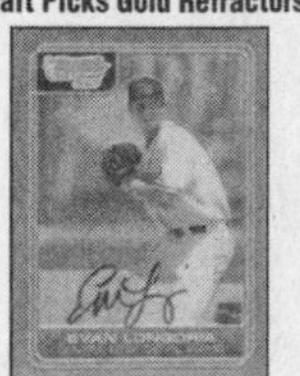

*GOLD REF 1-65: 10X TO 25X BASIC
1-65 STATED ODDS 1:197 H, 1:388 R
66-90 AU ODDS 1:1575 H, 1:1600 R
STATED PRINT RUN 50 SER.#'d SETS
66 Evan Longoria AU 800.00 1200.00
67 Cody Johnson AU 75.00 150.00
68 Kris Johnson AU 60.00 120.00
70 Ronnie Bourquin AU 60.00 120.00
73 Brooks Brown AU 40.00 80.00
74 Steven Evarts AU 60.00 120.00
75 Joshua Butler AU 40.00 80.00
77 Steven Wright AU 40.00 80.00
78 Cory Rasmus AU 75.00 150.00
79 Brad Furnish AU 30.00 60.00
80 Andrew Carpenter AU 40.00 80.00
81 Dustin Evans AU 30.00 60.00
82 Tommy Hickman AU 100.00 200.00
83 Matt Long AU 30.00 60.00
84 Clayton Kershaw AU 350.00 700.00
85 Kyle McCulloch AU 60.00 120.00
86 Pedro Beato AU 30.00 60.00
87 Kyler Burke AU 60.00 120.00
88 Stephen Englund AU 75.00 150.00
89 Michael Felix AU 50.00 100.00
90 Sean Watson AU 30.00 60.00

2006 Bowman Chrome Draft Draft Picks Orange Refractors

1-65 STATD ODDS 1:395 HOB.,1:770 RET.
66-90 AU ODDS 1:3232 HOB.,1:3232 RET.
STATED PRINT RUN 25 SERIAL #'d SETS
NO PRICING DUE TO SCARCITY

2006 Bowman Chrome Draft Draft Picks Red Refractors

1-65 ODDS 1:1585 HOBBY
66-90 AU ODDS 1:13,166 HOBBY
STATED PRINT RUN 5 SERIAL #'d SETS
NO PRICING DUE TO SCARCITY

2006 Bowman Chrome Draft Draft Picks SuperFractors

1-65 STATED ODDS 1:7934 HOBBY
66-90 AU STATED ODDS 53,812 HOBBY
STATED PRINT RUN 1 SERIAL #'d SET
NO PRICING DUE TO SCARCITY

2006 Bowman Chrome Draft Draft Picks X-Fractors

*X-F 1-65: 2X TO 5X BASIC
1-65 STATED ODDS 1:32 H, 1:74 R
1-65 PRINT RUN 299 SER.#'d SETS
*X-F AU 66-90: .75X TO 2X BASIC
66-90 AU STATED ODDS 1:351 H, 1:353 R
66-90 AU PRINT RUN 225 SER.#'d SETS
66 Evan Longoria AU 200.00 400.00
67 Cody Johnson AU 15.00 40.00
68 Kris Johnson AU 15.00 40.00
82 Tommy Hickman AU 20.00 50.00
84 Clayton Kershaw AU 100.00 175.00

2006 Bowman Chrome Draft Future's Game Prospects

COMPLETE SET (45) 10.00 25.00
APPX. ODDS 1:2 HOBBY, 1:2 RETAIL
ODDS INFO PROVIDED BY BECKETT
OVERALL PLATE ODDS 1:990 HOBBY
PLATE PRINT RUN 1 SET PER COLOR
BLACK-CYAN-MAGENTA-YELLOW ISSUED
NO PLATE PRICING DUE TO SCARCITY
1 Nick Adenhart .40 1.00
2 Joel Guzman .40 1.00
3 Ryan Braun 2.00 5.00
4 Carlos Carrasco .60 1.50
5 Neil Walker .40 1.00
6 Pablo Sandoval 4.00 10.00
7 Gio Gonzalez .40 1.00
8 Joey Votto 2.50 6.00
9 Luis Cruz .40 1.00
10 Nolan Reimold .60 1.50
11 Juan Salas .40 1.00
12 Josh Fields .40 1.00
13 Yovani Gallardo 1.25 3.00
14 Radhames Liz .40 1.00
15 Eric Patterson .40 1.00
16 Cameron Maybin 1.25 3.00
17 Edgar Martinez .40 1.00
18 Hunter Pence 2.00 5.00
19 Philip Hughes 1.00 2.50
20 Trent Oeltjen .40 1.00
21 Nick Pereira .40 1.00
22 Wladimir Balentien .40 1.00
23 Stephen Drew 1.00 2.50
24 Davis Romero .40 1.00
25 Joe Koshansky .40 1.00
26 Chin Lung Hu 1.25 3.00
27 Jason Hirsh .40 1.00
28 Jose Tabata 2.50 6.00
29 Eric Hurley .40 1.00
30 Yung Chi Chen .60 1.50
31 Howie Kendrick 1.00 2.50
32 Humberto Sanchez .40 1.00
33 Alex Gordon 1.25 3.00
34 Yunel Escobar .40 1.00
35 Travis Buck .40 1.00
36 Billy Butler 1.00 2.50
37 Homer Bailey 1.00 2.50
38 George Kottaras .40 1.00
39 Kurt Suzuki .40 1.00
40 Joaquin Arias .40 1.00
41 Matt Lindstrom .40 1.00
42 Sean Smith .40 1.00
43 Carlos Gonzalez 1.00 2.50
44 Jaime Garcia 2.00 5.00
45 Jose Garcia .40 1.00

2006 Bowman Chrome Draft Future's Game Prospects Refractors

*REF: .75X TO 2X BASIC
STATED ODDS 1:11 HOBBY, 1:11 RETAIL

2006 Bowman Chrome Draft Future's Game Prospects Blue Refractors

*BLUE REF: 1.5X TO 4X BASIC
STATED ODDS 1:50 HOBBY, 1:94 RETAIL
STATED PRINT RUN 199 SER.#'d SETS

2006 Bowman Chrome Draft Future's Game Prospects Gold Refractors

*GOLD REF: 4X TO 10X BASIC
STATED ODDS 1:197 H, 1:388 R
STATED PRINT RUN 50 SER.#'d SETS

2006 Bowman Chrome Draft Future's Game Prospects Orange Refractors

STATED ODDS 1:395 HOBBY, 1:770 RETAIL
STATED PRINT RUN 25 SERIAL #'d SETS
NO PRICING DUE TO SCARCITY

2006 Bowman Chrome Draft Future's Game Prospects Red Refractors

STATED ODDS 1:1585 HOBBY
STATED PRINT RUN 5 SERIAL #'d SETS
NO PRICING DUE TO SCARCITY

2006 Bowman Chrome Draft Future's Game Prospects SuperFractors

STATED ODDS 1:7934 HOBBY
STATED PRINT RUN 1 SERIAL #'d SET
NO PRICING DUE TO SCARCITY

2006 Bowman Chrome Draft Future's Game Prospects X-Fractors

*X-F: 1.25X TO 3X BASIC
STATED ODDS 1:32 H, 1:74 R
STATED PRINT RUN 299 SER.#'d SETS

2007 Bowman Chrome

This 220-card set was released in August, 2007. The set was issued through both hobby and retail channels. The hobby version was issued on in standard (no HTA) packs and those four-card packs with an $4 SRP were issued 18 packs per box and 12 boxes per case. Cards numbered 1-190 feature veterans while cards 191-220 honored 2007 rookies.

COMPLETE SET (220) 30.00 60.00
COMMON CARD (1-190) .20 .50
COMMON ROOKIE (191-220) .30 .75
1-220 PLATE ODDS 1:1054 HOBBY
PLATE PRINT RUN 1 SET PER COLOR
BLACK-CYAN-MAGENTA-YELLOW ISSUED
NO PLATE PRICING DUE TO SCARCITY
1 Hanley Ramirez .50 1.25
2 Justin Verlander .60 1.50
3 Ryan Zimmerman .30 .75
4 Jered Weaver .30 .75
5 Stephen Drew .20 .50
6 Jonathan Papelbon .50 1.25
7 Melky Cabrera .20 .50
8 Francisco Liriano .50 1.25
9 Prince Fielder .30 .75
10 Dan Uggla .30 .75
11 Jeremy Sowers .20 .50
12 Carlos Quentin .20 .50
13 Chuck James .20 .50
14 Andre Ethier .30 .75
15 Cole Hamels .50 1.25
16 Kenji Johjima .50 1.25
17 Chad Billingsley .20 .50
18 Ian Kinsler .30 .75
19 Jason Hirsh .20 .50
20 Nick Markakis .50 1.25
21 Jeremy Hermida .20 .50
22 Ryan Shealy .20 .50
23 Scott Olsen .20 .50
24 Russell Martin .20 .50
25 Conor Jackson .20 .50
26 Erik Bedard .20 .50
27 Brian McCann .20 .50
28 Michael Barrett .20 .50
29 Brandon Phillips .20 .50
30 Garrett Atkins .20 .50
31 Freddy Garcia .20 .50
32 Mark Loretta .20 .50
33 Craig Biggio .30 .75
34 Jeremy Bonderman .20 .50
35 Johan Santana .50 1.25
36 Jorge Posada .30 .75
37 Victor Martinez .30 .75
38 Carlos Delgado .20 .50
39 Gary Matthews Jr. .20 .50
40 Mike Cameron .20 .50
41 Adrian Beltre .20 .50
42 Freddy Sanchez .20 .50
43 Austin Kearns .20 .50
44 Mark Buehrle .30 .75
45 Miguel Cabrera .50 1.25
46 Josh Beckett .30 .75
47 Chone Figgins .20 .50
48 Edgar Renteria .20 .50
49 Derek Lowe .20 .50
50 Ryan Howard .75 2.00
51 Shawn Green .20 .50
52 Jason Giambi .20 .50
53 Ervin Santana .20 .50
54 Aaron Hill .20 .50
55 Roy Oswalt .30 .75
56 Dan Haren .20 .50
57 Jose Vidro .20 .50
58 Kevin Millwood .20 .50
59 Jim Edmonds .30 .75
60 Carl Crawford .30 .75
61 Randy Wolf .20 .50
62 Paul LoDuca .20 .50
63 Johnny Estrada .20 .50
64 Brian Roberts .20 .50
65 Manny Ramirez .50 1.25
66 Jose Contreras .20 .50
67 Josh Barfield .20 .50
68 Juan Pierre .20 .50
69 David DeJesus .20 .50
70 Gary Sheffield .20 .50
71 Michael Young .30 .75
72 Randy Johnson .50 1.25
73 Rickie Weeks .30 .75
74 Brian Giles .20 .50
75 Ichiro Suzuki .75 2.00
76 Nick Swisher .50 1.25
77 Justin Morneau .50 1.25
78 Scott Kazmir .30 .75
79 Lyle Overbay .20 .50
80 Alfonso Soriano .30 .75
81 Brandon Webb .30 .75
82 Joe Crede .20 .50
83 Corey Patterson .20 .50
84 Kenny Rogers .20 .50
85 Ken Griffey Jr. .75 2.00
86 Cliff Lee .30 .75
87 Mike Lowell .20 .50
88 Marcus Giles .20 .50
89 Orlando Cabrera .20 .50
90 Derek Jeter 1.25 3.00
91 Ramon Hernandez .20 .50
92 Carlos Guillen .20 .50
93 Bill Hall .20 .50
94 Michael Cuddyer .20 .50
95 Miguel Tejada .30 .75
96 Todd Helton .30 .75
97 C.C. Sabathia .30 .75
98 Tadahito Iguchi .20 .50
99 Jose Reyes .30 .75
100 David Wright .75 2.00
101 Barry Zito .20 .50
102 Jake Peavy .20 .50
103 Richie Sexson .20 .50
104 A.J. Burnett .30 .75
105 Eric Chavez .20 .50
106 Vernon Wells .20 .50
107 Grady Sizemore .30 .75
108 Bronson Arroyo .20 .50
109 Mike Mussina .30 .75
110 Magglio Ordonez .30 .75
111 Anibal Sanchez .20 .50
112 Jeff Francoeur .50 1.25
113 Kevin Youkilis .20 .50
114 Aubrey Huff .20 .50
115 Carlos Zambrano .30 .75
116 Mark Teahen .20 .50
117 Mark Mulder .20 .50
118 Pedro Martinez .30 .75
119 Hideki Matsui .50 1.25
120 Mike Piazza .50 1.25
121 Jason Schmidt .20 .50
122 Greg Maddux .75 2.00
123 Joe Blanton .20 .50
124 Chris Carpenter .50 1.25
125 David Ortiz .30 .75
126 Alex Rios .30 .75
127 Nick Johnson .20 .50
128 Carlos Lee .20 .50
129 Pat Burrell .20 .50
130 Ben Sheets .20 .50
131 Derrek Lee .20 .50
132 Adam Dunn .30 .75
133 Jermaine Dye .20 .50
134 Curt Schilling .30 .75
135 Chad Tracy .20 .50
136 Vladimir Guerrero .50 1.25
137 Melvin Mora .20 .50
138 John Smoltz .50 1.25
139 Craig Monroe .20 .50
140 Dontrelle Willis .20 .50
141 Jeff Francis .20 .50
142 Chipper Jones .50 1.25
143 Frank Thomas .50 1.25
144 Brett Myers .20 .50
145 Tom Glavine .30 .75
146 Robinson Cano .50 1.25
147 Jeff Kent .20 .50
148 Scott Rolen .30 .75
149 Roy Halladay .50 1.25
150 Joe Mauer .50 1.25
151 Bobby Abreu .20 .50
152 Matt Cain .30 .75
153 Hank Blalock .20 .50
154 Chris Young .20 .50
155 Jake Westbrook .20 .50
156 Javier Vazquez .20 .50
157 Garret Anderson .20 .50
158 Aramis Ramirez .20 .50
159 Mark Kotsay .20 .50
160 Matt Kemp .30 .75
161 Adrian Gonzalez .30 .75
162 Felix Hernandez .50 1.25
163 David Eckstein .20 .50
164 Curtis Granderson .30 .75
165 Paul Konerko .30 .75
166 Alex Rodriguez .75 2.00
167 Tim Hudson .30 .75
168 J.D. Drew .20 .50
169 Chien-Ming Wang .30 .75
170 Jimmy Rollins .30 .75
171 Matt Morris .20 .50
172 Raul Ibanez .30 .75
173 Mark Teixeira .50 1.25
174 Ted Lilly .20 .50
175 Albert Pujols 1.25 3.00
176 Carlos Beltran .20 .50
177 Lance Berkman .30 .75
178 Ivan Rodriguez .30 .75
179 Torii Hunter .20 .50
180 Johnny Damon .30 .75
181 Chase Utley .50 1.25
182 Jason Bay .30 .75
183 Jeff Weaver .20 .50
184 Troy Glaus .20 .50
185 Rocco Baldelli .20 .50
186 Rafael Furcal .20 .50
187 Jim Thome .30 .75
188 Travis Hafner .20 .50
189 Matt Holliday .50 1.25
190 Andruw Jones .20 .50
191 Andrew Miller RC .75 2.00
192 Ryan Braun RC .30 .75
193 Oswaldo Navarro RC .30 .75
194 Mike Rabelo RC .30 .75
195 Delwyn Young (RC) .30 .75
196 Miguel Montero (RC) .30 .75
197 Matt Lindstrom (RC) .30 .75
198 Josh Hamilton (RC) 1.25 3.00
199 Elijah Dukes RC .50 1.25
200 Sean Henn (RC) .30 .75
201 Delmon Young (RC) .50 1.25
202 Alexi Casilla RC .50 1.25
203 Hunter Pence (RC) 1.50 4.00
204 Jeff Baker (RC) .30 .75
205 Hector Gimenez (RC) .30 .75
206 Ubaldo Jimenez (RC) 2.00 5.00
207 Adam Lind (RC) .30 .75
208 Joaquin Arias (RC) .30 .75
209 David Murphy (RC) .30 .75
210 Daisuke Matsuzaka RC 1.25 3.00
211 Jerry Owens (RC) .30 .75
212 Ryan Sweeney (RC) .30 .75
213 Kei Igawa RC .75 2.00
214 Mitch Maier RC .30 .75
215 Philip Humber (RC) .30 .75
216 Troy Tulowitzki (RC) 2.00 5.00
217 Tim Lincecum RC 5.00 12.00
218 Michael Bourn (RC) .30 .75
219 Hideki Okajima RC 1.50 4.00
220 Josh Fields (RC) .30 .75

2007 Bowman Chrome Refractors

*REF 1-190: 1.25X TO 3X BASIC
*REF 191-220: .75X TO 2X BASIC
1-220 ODDS 1:4 HOBBY, 1:6 RETAIL

2007 Bowman Chrome Blue Refractors

*BLUE REF 1-190: 3X TO 8X BASIC
*BLUE REF 191-220: 2X TO 5X BASIC
1-220 ODDS 1:30 HOBBY, 1:205 RETAIL
STATED PRINT RUN 150 SERIAL #'d SETS

2007 Bowman Chrome Gold Refractors

*GOLD REF 1-190: 8X TO 20X BASIC
*GOLD REF 191-220: 5X TO 12X BASIC
1-220 ODDS 1:88 HOBBY, 1:615 RETAIL
STATED PRINT RUN 50 SERIAL #'d SETS

2007 Bowman Chrome Orange Refractors

*ORANGE REF 1-190: 10X TO 25X BASIC
1-220 ODDS 1:176 HOBBY, 1:1220 RETAIL
STATED PRINT RUN 25 SERIAL #'d SETS
NO RC 191-220 PRICING DUE TO SCARCITY
75 Ichiro Suzuki 40.00 80.00
85 Ken Griffey Jr. 40.00 80.00
169 Chien-Ming Wang 60.00 120.00

2007 Bowman Chrome Red Refractors

1-220 ODDS 1:882 HOBBY, 1:6000 RETAIL
STATED PRINT RUN 5 SERIAL #'d SETS
NO PRICING DUE TO SCARCITY

2007 Bowman Chrome SuperFractors

1-220 ODDS 1:4218 HOBBY
STATED PRINT RUN 1 SERIAL #'d SET
NO PRICING DUE TO SCARCITY

2007 Bowman Chrome X-Fractors

*X-FRACTOR 1-190: 2.5X TO 6X BASIC
*X-FRACTOR 191-220: 1.5X TO 4X BASIC
1-220 ODDS 1:18 HOBBY, 1:123 RETAIL
STATED PRINT RUN 250 SER.#'d SETS

2007 Bowman Chrome Prospects

COMP.SET w/o AU's (220) 40.00 100.00
COMP.SERIES 1 SET (110) 20.00 50.00
COMP.SERIES 2 SET (110) 20.00 50.00
COMMON AUTO (221-256) 3.00 8.00
AU MINORS 4.00 10.00
221-256 AU ODDS 1:29 HOB, 1:59 RET
1-110 PLATE ODDS 1:1468 H, 1:212 HTA
111-220 PLATE ODDS 1:1054 HOBBY
221-256 AU PLATE ODDS 1:9668 HOBBY
PLATE PRINT RUN 1 SET PER COLOR
BLACK-CYAN-MAGENTA-YELLOW ISSUED
NO PLATE PRICING DUE TO SCARCITY
1-110 ISSUED IN BOWMAN PACKS
111-256 ISSUED IN BOW.CHROME PACKS
EXCHANGE DEADLINE 8/31/2009
BC1 Cooper Brannon .30 .75
BC2 Jason Taylor .50 1.25
BC3 Shawn O'Malley .30 .75
BC4 Robert Alcombrack .30 .75
BC5 Dellin Betances .75 2.00
BC6 Jeremy Papelbon .30 .75
BC7 Adam Carr .30 .75
BC8 Matthew Clarkson .30 .75
BC9 Darin McDonald .30 .75
BC10 Brandon Rice .30 .75
BC11 Matthew Sweeney 1.00 2.50
BC12 Scott Deal .30 .75
BC13 Brennan Boesch 1.00 2.50
BC14 Scott Taylor .30 .75
BC15 Michael Brantley .75 2.00
BC16 Yahmed Yema .30 .75
BC17 Brandon Morrow 1.50 4.00
BC18 Cole Garner .30 .75
BC19 Erik Lis .50 1.25
BC20 Lucas French .30 .75
BC21 Aaron Cunningham .50 1.25
BC22 Ryan Schreppel .30 .75
BC23 Kevin Russo .30 .75
BC24 Yohan Pino .50 1.25
BC25 Michael Sullivan .30 .75
BC26 Trey Shields .30 .75
BC27 Daniel Matienzo .30 .75
BC28 Chuck Lofgren .75 2.00
BC29 Gerrit Simpson .30 .75
BC30 David Haehnel .30 .75
BC31 Marvin Lowrance .30 .75
BC32 Kevin Ardoin .30 .75
BC33 Edwin Maysonet .30 .75
BC34 Derek Griffith .30 .75
BC35 Sam Fuld 1.00 2.50
BC36 Chase Wright .75 2.00
BC37 Brandon Roberts .30 .75
BC38 Kyle Aselton .30 .75
BC39 Steven Sollmann .30 .75
BC40 Mike Devaney .30 .75
BC41 Charlie Fermaint .30 .75
BC42 Jesse Litsch .50 1.25
BC43 Bryan Hansen .30 .75
BC44 Ramon Garcia .30 .75
BC45 John Otness .30 .75
BC46 Trey Hearne .30 .75
BC47 Habelito Hernandez .30 .75
BC48 Edgar Garcia .30 .75
BC49 Seth Fortenberry .30 .75
BC50 Reid Brignac .50 1.25
BC51 Derek Rodriguez .30 .75
BC52 Ervin Alcantara .30 .75
BC53 Thomas Hottovy .30 .75
BC54 Jesus Flores .30 .75
BC55 Matt Palmer .30 .75
BC56 Brian Henderson .30 .75
BC57 John Gragg .30 .75
BC58 Jay Garthwaite .30 .75
BC59 Esmerling Vasquez .30 .75
BC60 Gilberto Mejia .30 .75
BC61 Aaron Jensen .30 .75
BC62 Cedric Brooks .30 .75
BC63 Brandon Mann .30 .75
BC64 Myron Leslie .30 .75
BC65 Ray Aguilar .30 .75
BC66 Jesus Guzman .50 1.25
BC67 Sean Thompson .30 .75
BC68 Jarrett Hoffpauir .30 .75
BC69 Matt Goodson .30 .75
BC70 Neal Musser .30 .75
BC71 Tony Abreu .75 2.00
BC72 Tony Peguero .30 .75
BC73 Michael Bertram .30 .75
BC74 Randy Wells .75 2.00
BC75 Bradley Davis .30 .75
BC76 Jay Sawatski .30 .75
BC77 Vic Buttler .30 .75
BC78 Jose Oyervidez .30 .75
BC79 Doug Deeds .30 .75
BC80 Dan Dement .30 .75
BC81 Spike Lundberg .30 .75
BC82 Ricardo Nanita .30 .75
BC83 Brad Knox .30 .75
BC84 Will Venable .50 1.25
BC85 Greg Smith .50 1.25
BC86 Pedro Powell .30 .75
BC87 Gabriel Medina .30 .75
BC88 Duke Sardinha .30 .75
BC89 Mike Madsen .30 .75
BC90 Rayner Bautista .30 .75
BC91 T.J. Nall .30 .75
BC92 Neil Sellers .30 .75
BC93 Andrew Dobies .30 .75
BC94 Leo Daigle .30 .75
BC95 Brian Duensing .30 .75
BC96 Vincent Blue .30 .75
BC97 Fernando Rodriguez .30 .75
BC98 Derin McMains .30 .75
BC99 Adam Bass .30 .75
BC100 Justin Ruggiano .30 .75
BC101 Jared Burton .30 .75
BC102 Mike Parisi .30 .75
BC103 Aaron Peel .30 .75
BC104 Evan Englebrook .30 .75
BC105 Sendy Vasquez .30 .75
BC106 Desmond Jennings 1.00 2.50
BC107 Clay Harris .30 .75
BC108 Cody Strait .30 .75
BC109 Ryan Mullins .30 .75
BC110 Ryan Webb .30 .75
BC111 Mike Carp 1.00 2.50
BC112 Gregory Porter .30 .75
BC113 Joe Ness .30 .75
BC114 Matt Camp .30 .75
BC115 Carlos Fisher .30 .75
BC116 Bryan Bass .30 .75
BC117 Jeff Baisley .50 1.25
BC118 Burke Badenhop .50 1.25
BC119 Grant Psomas .30 .75
BC120 Eric Young Jr. .50 1.25
BC121 Henry Rodriguez .30 .75
BC122 Carlos Fernandez-Oliva .50 1.25
BC123 Chris Errecart .50 1.25
BC124 Brandon Hynick .75 2.00
BC125 Jose Constanza .30 .75
BC126 Steve Delabar .30 .75
BC127 Raul Barron .30 .75
BC128 Nick DeBarr .30 .75
BC129 Reegie Corona .50 1.25
BC130 Thomas Fairchild .30 .75
BC131 Bryan Byrne .30 .75
BC132 Kurt Mertins .30 .75
BC133 Erik Averill .30 .75
BC134 Matt Young .30 .75
BC135 Ryan Rogowski .30 .75
BC136 Andrew Bailey 1.25 3.00
BC137 Jonathan Van Every .30 .75
BC138 Scott Shoemaker .30 .75
BC139 Steve Singleton .30 .75
BC140 Mitch Atkins .30 .75
BC141 Robert Rohrbaugh .50 1.25
BC142 Ole Sheldon .30 .75
BC143 Adam Ricks .30 .75
BC144 Daniel Mayora .75 2.00
BC145 Johnny Cueto 1.00 2.50
BC146 Jim Fasano .30 .75
BC147 Jared Goedert .75 2.00
BC148 Jonathan Ash .30 .75
BC149 Derek Miller .50 1.25
BC150 Juan Miranda .50 1.25
BC151 J.R. Mathes .30 .75
BC152 Craig Cooper .50 1.25
BC153 Drew Locke .30 .75
BC154 Michael MacDonald .30 .75
BC155 Ryan Norwood .30 .75
BC156 Tony Butler .75 2.00
BC157 Pat Dobson .30 .75
BC158 Cody Ehlers .30 .75
BC159 Dan Fournier .30 .75
BC160 Joe Gaetti .30 .75
BC161 Mark Wagner .50 1.25
BC162 Tommy Hanson 1.25 3.00
BC163 Sharlon Schoop .30 .75
BC164 Woods Fines .30 .75
BC165 Chad Boyd .30 .75
BC166 Kala Kaaihue .50 1.25
BC167 Chris Salamida .30 .75
BC168 Brendan Katin .30 .75
BC169 Terrance Blunt .30 .75
BC170 Tobi Stoner .30 .75
BC171 Phil Coke .75 2.00
BC172 O.D. Gonzalez .30 .75
BC173 Christopher Cody .30 .75
BC174 Cedric Hunter .75 2.00
BC175 Whit Robbins .30 .75
BC176 Chris Begg .30 .75
BC177 Nathan Southard .30 .75
BC178 Dan Brauer .30 .75
BC179 Jared Keel .30 .75
BC180 Chance Douglass .30 .75
BC181 Daniel Murphy .50 1.25
BC182 Anthony Hatch .30 .75
BC183 Justin Byler .30 .75
BC184 Scott Lewis .75 2.00
BC185 Andrew Fie .30 .75
BC186 Chorye Spoone .50 1.25
BC187 Cole Bruce .30 .75
BC188 Adam Cowart .75 2.00
BC189 Chris Nowak .30 .75
BC190 Gorkys Hernandez .75 2.00
BC191 Devin Ivany .30 .75
BC192 Jordan Smith .30 .75
BC193 Philip Britton .30 .75
BC194 Cole Gillespie .50 1.25
BC195 Brett Anderson 1.00 2.50
BC196 Joe Mather .30 .75
BC197 Eddie Degerman .30 .75
BC198 Ronald Prettyman .30 .75
BC199 Patrick Reilly .30 .75
BC200 Tyler Clippard .50 1.25
BC201 Nick Van Stratten .30 .75
BC202 Todd Redmond .30 .75
BC203 Michael Martinez .30 .75
BC204 Alberto Bastardo .30 .75
BC205 Vasili Spanos .30 .75
BC206 Shane Benson .30 .75
BC207 Brent Johnson .30 .75
BC208 Brett Campbell .30 .75
BC209 Dustin Martin .30 .75
BC210 Chris Carter 2.00 5.00
BC211 Alfred Joseph .30 .75
BC212 Carlos Leon .30 .75
BC213 Gabriel Sanchez .50 1.25
BC214 Carlos Corporan .30 .75
BC215 Emerson Frostad .30 .75
BC216 Karl Gelinas .30 .75
BC217 Ryan Finan .30 .75
BC218 Noe Rodriguez .30 .75
BC219 Archie Gilbert .30 .75
BC220 Jeff Locke .75 2.00
BC221 Fernando Martinez AU 10.00 25.00
BC222 Jeremy Papelbon AU 3.00 8.00
BC223 Ryan Adams AU 3.00 8.00
BC224 Chris Perez AU 5.00 12.00
BC225 J.R. Towles AU 5.00 12.00
BC226 Tommy Mendoza AU 3.00 8.00
BC227 Jeff Samardzija AU 10.00 25.00
BC228 Sergio Perez AU 3.00 8.00
BC229 Justin Reed AU 3.00 8.00
BC230 Luke Hochevar AU 5.00 12.00
BC231 Ivan De Jesus Jr. AU 6.00 15.00
BC232 Kevin Mulvey AU 5.00 12.00
BC233 Chris Coghlan AU 10.00 25.00
BC234 Trevor Cahill AU 8.00 20.00
BC235 Peter Bourjos AU 6.00 15.00
BC236 Joba Chamberlain AU 30.00 60.00
BC237 Josh Rodriguez AU 3.00 8.00
BC238 Tim Lincecum AU 100.00 200.00
BC239 Josh Papelbon AU 4.00 10.00

BC240 Greg Reynolds AU 3.00 8.00
BC241 Wes Hodges AU 8.00 20.00
BC242 Chad Reineke AU 4.00 10.00
BC243 Emmanuel Burriss AU 4.00 10.00
BC244 Henry Sosa AU 5.00 12.00
BC245 Cesar Nicolas AU 3.00 8.00
BC246 Young Il Jung AU 3.00 8.00
BC247 Eric Patterson AU 3.00 8.00
BC248 Hunter Pence AU 12.50 30.00
BC249 Dellin Betances AU 12.50 30.00
BC250 Will Venable AU 4.00 10.00
BC251 Zach McAllister AU 4.00 10.00
BC252 Mark Hamilton AU 3.00 8.00
BC253 Paul Estrada AU 3.00 8.00
BC254 Brad Lincoln AU 4.00 10.00
BC255 Cedric Hunter AU 6.00 15.00
BC256 Chad Rodgers AU 3.00 8.00

2007 Bowman Chrome Prospects Refractors

*REF 1-110: 2X TO 5X BASIC CHROME
*REF 111-220: 2X TO 5X BASIC CHROME
1-110 ODDS 1:48 H, 1:8 HTA, 1:142 R
111-220 ODDS 1:27 HOB, 1:186 RET
*REF AU 221-256: .5X TO 1.2X BASIC
221-256 AU ODDS 1:89 HOB, 1:197 RET
STATED PRINT RUN 500 SERIAL #'d SETS
1-110 ISSUED IN BOWMAN PACKS
111-256 ISSUED IN BOW.CHROME PACKS
EXCHANGE DEADLINE 8/31/2009
BC233 Chris Coghlan AU 20.00 50.00
BC235 Peter Bourjos AU 10.00 25.00
BC238 Tim Lincecum AU 150.00 300.00
BC249 Dellin Betances AU 30.00 60.00

2007 Bowman Chrome Prospects Blue Refractors

*BLUE 1-110: 4X TO 10X BASIC CHROME
*BLUE 111-220: 4X TO 10X BASIC CHROME
1-110 ODDS 1:481 H, 1:80 HTA, 1:1375 R
111-220 ODDS 1:30 H, 1:205 R
*BLUE AU 221-256: 1X TO 2.5X BASIC
221-256 AU ODDS 1:296 HOB, 1:825 RET
STATED PRINT RUN 150 SER.#'d SETS
1-110 ISSUED IN BOWMAN PACKS
111-256 ISSUED IN BOW.CHROME PACKS
EXCHANGE DEADLINE 8/31/2009
BC233 Chris Coghlan AU 60.00 120.00
BC238 Tim Lincecum AU 300.00 500.00
BC244 Henry Sosa AU 12.50 30.00
BC249 Dellin Betances AU 50.00 100.00

2007 Bowman Chrome Prospects Gold Refractors

*GOLD 1-110: 12X TO 30X BASIC CHROME
*GOLD 111-220: 12X TO 30X BASIC CHROME
1-110 ODDS 1:481 H, 1:80 HTA, 1:1375 R
111-220 ODDS 1:88 HOB, 1:615 RET
221-256 AU ODDS 1:889 HOB, 1:8500 RET
STATED PRINT RUN 50 SER.#'d SETS
1-110 ISSUED IN BOWMAN PACKS
111-256 ISSUED IN BOW.CHROME PACKS
EXCHANGE DEADLINE 8/31/2009
BC221 Fernando Martinez AU 75.00 150.00
BC222 Jeremy Papelbon AU 30.00 60.00
BC223 Ryan Adams AU 30.00 60.00
BC224 Chris Perez AU 40.00 80.00
BC225 J.R. Towles AU 50.00 100.00
BC226 Tommy Mendoza AU 30.00 60.00
BC227 Jeff Samardzija AU 100.00 200.00
BC228 Sergio Perez AU 30.00 60.00
BC229 Justin Reed AU 30.00 60.00
BC230 Luke Hochevar AU 40.00 80.00
BC231 Ivan De Jesus Jr. AU 40.00 80.00
BC232 Kevin Mulvey AU 30.00 60.00
BC233 Chris Coghlan AU 75.00 150.00
BC234 Trevor Cahill AU 100.00 200.00
BC235 Peter Bourjos AU 50.00 100.00
BC236 Joba Chamberlain AU 300.00 600.00
BC237 Josh Rodriguez AU 30.00 60.00
BC238 Tim Lincecum AU 1200.00 1600.00
BC239 Josh Papelbon AU 30.00 60.00
BC240 Greg Reynolds AU 30.00 60.00
BC242 Chad Reineke AU 30.00 60.00
BC243 Emmanuel Burriss AU 20.00 50.00
BC244 Henry Sosa AU 50.00 100.00
BC245 Cesar Nicolas AU 30.00 60.00
BC246 Young Il Jung AU 30.00 60.00
BC247 Eric Patterson AU 30.00 60.00
BC248 Hunter Pence AU 75.00 510.00
BC249 Dellin Betances AU 100.00 200.00
BC250 Will Venable AU 40.00 80.00
BC251 Zach McAllister AU 20.00 50.00
BC252 Mark Hamilton AU 30.00 60.00
BC253 Paul Estrada AU 30.00 60.00
BC254 Brad Lincoln AU 30.00 60.00
BC255 Cedric Hunter AU 60.00 120.00
BC256 Chad Rodgers AU 30.00 60.00

2007 Bowman Chrome Prospects Orange Refractors

1-110 ODDS 1:961 H, 1:160 HTA, 1:2800 R
111-220 ODDS 1:176 HOB, 1:1220 RET
221-256 AU ODDS 1:1780 HOB, 1:3650 RET
STATED PRINT RUN 25 SER.#'d SETS
1-110 ISSUED IN BOWMAN PACKS
111-220 ISSUED IN BOW.CHROME PACKS
NO PRICING DUE TO SCARCITY
EXCHANGE DEADLINE 8/31/2009

2009 Bowman Chrome WBC Prospects Orange Refractors

1-20 STATED ODDS 1:542 HOBBY
21-60 STATED ODDS 1:100 HOBBY
STATED PRINT RUN 25 SER.#'d SETS
NO PRICING DUE TO SCARCITY

2007 Bowman Chrome Prospects Red Refractors

1-110 ODDS 1:4817 H, 1:799 HTA, 1:14,000 R
111-220 ODDS 1:882 H, 1:6000 R
221-256 AU ODDS 1:8914 H, 1:18,000 R
STATED PRINT RUN 5 SER.#'d SETS
1-110 ISSUED IN BOWMAN PACKS
111-220 ISSUED IN BOW.CHROME PACKS
NO PRICING DUE TO SCARCITY
EXCHANGE DEADLINE 8/31/2009

2007 Bowman Chrome Prospects SuperFractors

1-110 ODDS 1:16,803 H, 1:4073 HTA
111-220 ODDS 1:4218 HOBBY
221-256 AU ODDS 1:39,392 HOB
STATED PRINT RUN 1 SER.#'d SET
1-110 ISSUED IN BOWMAN PACKS
111-220 ISSUED IN BOW.CHROME PACKS
NO PRICING DUE TO SCARCITY
EXCHANGE DEADLINE 8/31/2009

2007 Bowman Chrome Prospects X-Fractors

*X-F 1-110: 2.5X TO 6X BASIC CHROME
*X-F 111-220: 2.5X TO 6X BASIC CHROME
1-110 ODDS 1:87 H, 1:15 HTA, 1:260 R
111-220 ODDS 1:18 H, 1:123 R
1-110 PRINT RUN 275 SER.#'d SETS
111-220 PRINT RUN 250 SER.#'d SETS
*X-F AU 221-256: .6X TO 1.5X BASIC
221-256 AU ODDS 1:198 HOB, 1:480 RET
221-256 PRINT RUN 225 SERIAL #'d SETS
1-110 ISSUED IN BOWMAN PACKS
111-256 ISSUED IN BOW.CHROME PACKS
EXCHANGE DEADLINE 8/31/2009
BC233 Chris Coghlan AU 30.00 60.00
BC235 Peter Bourjos AU 12.50 30.00
BC238 Tim Lincecum AU 150.00 300.00
BC241 Wes Hodges AU 15.00 40.00
BC249 Dellin Betances AU 40.00 80.00

2007 Bowman Chrome Draft

This 55-card set, was inserted at a stated rate of two per Bowman Draft pack. This set was also released in December, 2007. In addition to the same 54 players from the basic Bowman Draft set, card #237 featuring Barry Bonds was also included in this set.

COMPLETE SET (55) 15.00 40.00
COMMON RC (1-55) .25 .60
OVERALL PLATE ODDS 1:1294 HOBBY
PLATE PRINT RUN 1 SET PER COLOR
BLACK-CYAN-MAGENTA-YELLOW ISSUED
NO PLATE PRICING DUE TO SCARCITY
BDP1 Travis Buck (RC) .25 .60
BDP2 Matt Chico (RC) .25 .60
BDP3 Justin Upton RC 2.00 5.00
BDP4 Chase Wright RC .60 1.50
BDP5 Kevin Kouzmanoff (RC) .25 .60
BDP6 John Danks RC .40 1.00
BDP7 Alejandro De Aza RC .40 1.00
BDP8 Jamie Vermilyea RC .25 .60
BDP9 Jesus Flores RC .25 .60
BDP10 Glen Perkins (RC) .25 .60
BDP11 Tim Lincecum RC 4.00 10.00
BDP12 Cameron Maybin RC .40 1.00
BDP13 Brandon Morrow RC UER 1.25 3.00
Stats header lines are for batting; Morrow is a pitcher
BDP14 Mike Rabelo RC .25 .60
BDP15 Alex Gordon RC .75 2.00
BDP16 Zack Segovia (RC) .25 .60
BDP17 Jon Knott (RC) .25 .60
BDP18 Joba Chamberlain RC 1.25 3.00
BDP19 Danny Putnam (RC) .25 .60
BDP20 Matt DeSalvo (RC) .25 .60
BDP21 Fred Lewis (RC) .40 1.00
BDP22 Sean Gallagher (RC) .25 .60
BDP23 Brandon Wood (RC) .25 .60
BDP24 Dennis Dove (RC) .25 .60
BDP25 Hunter Pence (RC) 1.25 3.00
BDP26 Jarrod Saltalamacchia (RC) .40 1.00
BDP27 Ben Francisco (RC) .25 .60
BDP28 Doug Slaten RC .25 .60
BDP29 Tony Abreu RC .60 1.50
BDP30 Billy Butler (RC) .40 1.00
BDP31 Jesse Litsch RC .40 1.00
BDP32 Nate Schierholtz (RC) .25 .60
BDP33 Jared Burton RC .25 .60
BDP34 Matt Brown RC .25 .60
BDP35 Dallas Braden RC 1.50 4.00
BDP36 Carlos Gomez RC .40 1.00
BDP37 Brian Stokes (RC) .25 .60
BDP38 Kory Casto (RC) .25 .60
BDP39 Mark McLemore (RC) .25 .60
BDP40 Andy LaRoche (RC) .25 .60
BDP41 Tyler Clippard (RC) .40 1.00
BDP42 Curtis Thigpen (RC) .25 .60
BDP43 Yunel Escobar (RC) .25 .60
BDP44 Andy Sonnanstine RC .25 .60
BDP45 Felix Pie (RC) .25 .60
BDP46 Homer Bailey (RC) .40 1.00
BDP47 Kyle Kendrick RC .60 1.50
BDP48 Angel Sanchez RC .25 .60
BDP49 Phil Hughes (RC) 1.25 3.00
BDP50 Ryan Braun (RC) 1.25 3.00
BDP51 Kevin Slowey (RC) .60 1.50
BDP52 Brendan Ryan (RC) .25 .60
BDP53 Yovani Gallardo (RC) .60 1.50
BDP54 Mark Reynolds RC 2.00 5.00
237 Barry Bonds 1.25 3.00

2007 Bowman Chrome Draft Refractors

*REF: 1X TO 2.5X BASIC
STATED ODDS 1:11 HOBBY,1:11 RETAIL

2007 Bowman Chrome Draft Blue Refractors

*BLUE REF: 2X TO 5X BASIC
STATED ODDS 1:58 HOBBY,1:171 RETAIL
STATED PRINT RUN 199 SER.#'d SETS

2007 Bowman Chrome Draft Gold Refractors

*GOLD REF: 5X TO 12X BASIC
STATED ODDS 1:232 H, 1:659 R
STATED PRINT RUN 50 SER.#'d SETS

2007 Bowman Chrome Draft Orange Refractors

STATED ODDS 1:463 H, 1:1349 R
STATED PRINT RUN 25 SER.#'d SETS
NO PRICING DUE TO SCARCITY

2007 Bowman Chrome Draft Red Refractors

STATED ODDS 1:2300 H, 1:7080 R
STATED PRINT RUN 5 SER.#'d SETS
NO PRICING DUE TO SCARCITY

2007 Bowman Chrome Draft SuperFractors

STATED ODDS 1:10,377 HOBBY
STATED PRINT RUN 1 SER.#'d SETS
NO PRICING DUE TO SCARCITY

2007 Bowman Chrome Draft X-Fractors

*X-F: 1.5X TO 4X BASIC
STATED ODDS 1:39 HOBBY,1:106 RETAIL
STATED PRINT RUN 299 SER.#'d SETS

2007 Bowman Chrome Draft Draft Picks

66-95 AU ODDS 1:38 HOBBY,1:575 RETAIL
1-65 PLATE ODDS 1:1294 HOBBY
66-95 AU PLATE ODDS 1:14,255 HOBBY
PLATE PRINT RUN 1 SET PER COLOR
BLACK-CYAN-MAGENTA-YELLOW ISSUED
NO PLATE PRICING DUE TO SCARCITY
BDPP1 Cody Crowell .30 .75
BDPP2 Karl Bolt .50 1.25
BDPP3 Corey Brown .50 1.25
BDPP4 Tyler Mach .50 1.25
BDPP5 Trevor Pippin .50 1.25
BDPP6 Ed Easley .30 .75
BDPP7 Cory Luebke .30 .75
BDPP8 Darin Mastroianni .30 .75
BDPP9 Ryan Zink .50 1.25
BDPP10 Brandon Hamilton .30 .75
BDPP11 Kyle Lotzkar .50 1.25
BDPP12 Freddie Freeman 2.00 5.00
BDPP13 Nicholas Barnese .50 1.25
BDPP14 Travis d'Arnaud .50 1.25
BDPP15 Eric Eiland .30 .75
BDPP16 John Ely .30 .75
BDPP17 Oliver Marmol .30 .75
BDPP18 Eric Sogard .30 .75
BDPP19 Lars Davis .30 .75
BDPP20 Sam Runion .30 .75
BDPP21 Austin Gallagher .50 1.25
BDPP22 Matt West .50 1.25
BDPP23 Derek Norris .75 2.00
BDPP24 Taylor Holiday .50 1.25
BDPP25 Dustin Biell .30 .75
BDPP26 Julio Borbon 1.00 2.50
BDPP27 Brant Rustich .50 1.25
BDPP28 Andrew Lambo 1.00 2.50
BDPP29 Cory Kluber .30 .75
BDPP30 Justin Jackson .50 1.25
BDPP31 Scott Carroll .30 .75
BDPP32 Danny Rams .30 .75
BDPP33 Thomas Eager .30 .75
BDPP34 Matt Dominguez .75 2.00
BDPP35 Steven Souza .30 .75
BDPP36 Craig Heyer .30 .75
BDPP37 Michael Taylor 1.25 3.00
BDPP38 Drew Bowman .30 .75
BDPP39 Frank Gailey .30 .75
BDPP40 Jeremy Hefner .30 .75
BDPP41 Reynaldo Navarro .50 1.25
BDPP42 Daniel Descalso .50 1.25
BDPP43 Leroy Hunt .30 .75
BDPP44 Jason Kiley .30 .75
BDPP45 Ryan Pope .75 2.00
BDPP46 Josh Horton .30 .75
BDPP47 Jason Monti .30 .75
BDPP48 Richard Lucas .30 .75
BDPP49 Jonathan Lucroy .75 2.00
BDPP50 Sean Doolittle .75 2.00
BDPP51 Mike McDade .50 1.25
BDPP52 Charlie Culberson .50 1.25
BDPP53 Michael Moustakas 1.25 3.00
BDPP54 Jason Heyward 2.50 6.00
BDPP55 David Price 2.00 5.00
BDPP56 Brad Mills .30 .75
BDPP57 John Tolisano 1.00 2.50
BDPP58 Jarrod Parker .75 2.00
BDPP59 Wendell Fairley .50 1.25
BDPP60 Gary Gattis .30 .75
BDPP61 Madison Bumgarner 2.00 5.00
BDPP62 Danny Payne .30 .75
BDPP63 Jake Smolinski 1.00 2.50
BDPP64 Matt LaPorta 1.25 3.00
BDPP65 Jackson Williams .30 .75
BDPP111 Daniel Moskos AU 4.00 10.00
BDPP112 Ross Detwiler AU 5.00 12.00
BDPP113 Tim Alderson AU 12.50 30.00
BDPP114 Beau Mills AU 12.50 30.00
BDPP115 Devin Mesoraco AU 8.00 20.00
BDPP116 Kyle Lotzkar AU 4.00 10.00
BDPP117 Blake Beavan AU 5.00 12.00
BDPP118 Peter Kozma AU 5.00 12.00
BDPP119 Chris Withrow AU 6.00 15.00
BDPP120 Cory Luebke AU 3.00 8.00
BDPP121 Nick Schmidt AU 3.00 8.00
BDPP122 Michael Main AU 6.00 15.00
BDPP123 Aaron Poreda AU 5.00 12.00
BDPP124 James Simmons AU 5.00 12.00
BDPP125 Ben Revere AU 8.00 20.00
BDPP126 Joe Savery AU 5.00 12.00
BDPP127 Jonathan Gilmore AU 3.00 8.00
BDPP128 Todd Frazier AU 8.00 20.00
BDPP129 Matt Mangini AU 3.00 8.00
BDPP130 Casey Weathers AU 3.00 8.00
BDPP131 Nick Noonan AU 8.00 20.00
BDPP132 Kellen Kulbacki AU 6.00 15.00
BDPP133 Michael Burgess AU 4.00 10.00
BDPP134 Nick Hagadone AU 6.00 15.00
BDPP135 Clayton Mortensen AU 4.00 10.00
BDPP136 Justin Jackson AU 4.00 10.00
BDPP137 Ed Easley AU 3.00 8.00
BDPP138 Corey Brown AU 3.00 8.00
BDPP139 Danny Payne AU 3.00 8.00
BDPP140 Travis d'Arnaud AU 6.00 15.00

2007 Bowman Chrome Draft Draft Picks Refractors

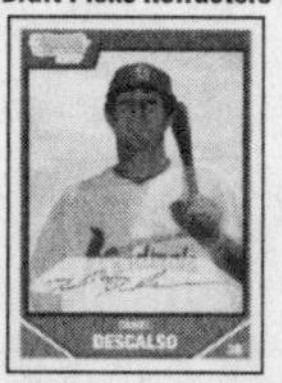

*REF 1-65: 1.5X TO 4X BASIC
1-65 ODDS 1:11 HOBBY,1:11 RETAIL
*REF AU 66-95: .5X TO 1.2X BASIC AU
AU 66-95 ODDS 1:118 H, 1:1700 R
66-95 AU PRINT RUN 500 SER.#'d SETS

2007 Bowman Chrome Draft Draft Picks Blue Refractors

*BLUE REF 1-65: 4X TO 10X BASIC
1-65 ODDS 1:58 HOBBY, 1:171 HOBBY
1-65 PRINT RUN 199 SER.#'d SETS
*BLUE REF AU 66-95: 1X TO 2.5X BASIC AU
AU 66-95 ODDS 1:400 H, 1:12,000 R
66-95 AU PRINT RUN 150 SER.#'d SETS
BDPP122 Michael Main AU 30.00 60.00

2007 Bowman Chrome Draft Draft Picks Gold Refractors

*GOLD REF 1-65: 10X TO 25X BASIC
1-65 ODDS 1:232 H, 1:659 R
1-65 PRINT RUN 50 SER.#'d SETS
COMMON AUTO (66-95) 40.00 80.00
AU 66-95 ODDS 1:1270 H, 1:9440 R
66-95 AU PRINT RUN 50 SER.#'d SETS
BDPP111 Daniel Moskos AU 30.00 60.00
BDPP112 Ross Detwiler AU 50.00 100.00
BDPP113 Tim Alderson AU 150.00 250.00
BDPP114 Beau Mills AU 150.00 250.00
BDPP115 Devin Mesoraco AU 75.00 150.00
BDPP116 Kyle Lotzkar AU 40.00 80.00
BDPP117 Blake Beavan AU 50.00 100.00
BDPP118 Peter Kozma AU 30.00 60.00
BDPP119 Chris Withrow AU 40.00 80.00
BDPP120 Cory Luebke AU 30.00 60.00
BDPP121 Nick Schmidt AU 30.00 60.00
BDPP122 Michael Main AU 60.00 120.00
BDPP123 Aaron Poreda AU 50.00 100.00
BDPP124 James Simmons AU 30.00 60.00
BDPP125 Ben Revere AU 60.00 120.00
BDPP126 Joe Savery AU 30.00 60.00
BDPP127 Jonathan Gilmore AU 40.00 80.00
BDPP128 Todd Frazier AU 50.00 100.00
BDPP129 Matt Mangini AU 30.00 60.00
BDPP130 Casey Weathers AU 30.00 60.00
BDPP131 Nick Noonan AU 75.00 150.00
BDPP132 Kellen Kulbacki AU 40.00 80.00
BDPP133 Michael Burgess AU 25.00 60.00
BDPP134 Nick Hagadone AU 60.00 120.00
BDPP135 Clayton Mortensen AU 30.00 60.00
BDPP136 Justin Jackson AU 50.00 100.00
BDPP137 Ed Easley AU 30.00 60.00
BDPP138 Corey Brown AU 30.00 60.00
BDPP139 Danny Payne AU 30.00 60.00
BDPP140 Travis d'Arnaud AU 50.00 100.00

2007 Bowman Chrome Draft Draft Picks Orange Refractors

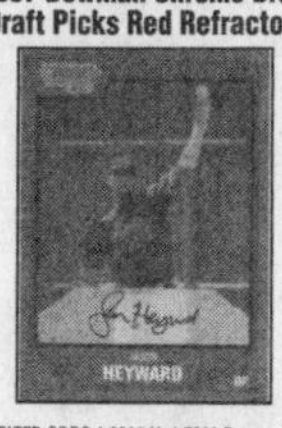

1-65 STATED ODDS 1:463 H,1:1349 R
66-95 AU ODDS 1:2345 H, 1:28,320 R
STATED PRINT RUN 25 SERIAL #'d SETS
NO PRICING DUE TO SCARCITY

2007 Bowman Chrome Draft Draft Picks Red Refractors

1-65 STATED ODDS 1:2300 H, 1:7080 R
66-95 AU ODDS 1:11,400 HOBBY
STATED PRINT RUN 5 SERIAL #'d SETS
NO PRICING DUE TO SCARCITY

2007 Bowman Chrome Draft Draft Picks SuperFractors

1-65 STATED ODDS 1:10,377 HOBBY
66-95 AU ODDS 1:57,814 HOBBY
STATED PRINT RUN 1 SERIAL #'d SET
NO PRICING DUE TO SCARCITY

2007 Bowman Chrome Draft Draft Picks X-Fractors

*X-F 1-65: 2.5X TO 6X BASIC
1-65 STATED ODDS 1:39 H, 1:106 R
1-65 PRINT RUN 299 SER.#'d SETS
*X-F AU 66-95: .6X TO 1.5X BASIC
66-95 AU STATED ODDS 1:262 H,1:14,000 R
66-95 AU PRINT RUN 225 SER.#'d SETS

2007 Bowman Chrome Draft Future's Game Prospects

COMPLETE SET (45) 12.50 30.00
OVERALL PLATE ODDS 1:1294 HOBBY
PLATE PRINT RUN 1 SET PER COLOR
BLACK-CYAN-MAGENTA-YELLOW ISSUED
NO PLATE PRICING DUE TO SCARCITY
BDPP66 Pedro Beato .20 .50
BDPP67 Collin Balester .20 .50
BDPP68 Carlos Carrasco .20 .50
BDPP69 Clay Buchholz 1.25 3.00
BDPP70 Emiliano Fruto .20 .50
BDPP71 Joba Chamberlain 1.00 2.50
BDPP72 Deolis Guerra .50 1.25
BDPP73 Kevin Mulvey .50 1.25
BDPP74 Franklin Morales .20 .50
BDPP75 Luke Hochevar .60 1.50
BDPP76 Henry Sosa .30 .75
BDPP77 Clayton Kershaw 1.50 4.00
BDPP78 Rich Thompson .20 .50
BDPP79 Chuck Lofgren .50 1.25
BDPP80 Rick VandenHurk .20 .50
BDPP81 Michael Madsen .20 .50
BDPP82 Robinzon Diaz .20 .50
BDPP83 Jeff Niemann .30 .75
BDPP84 Max Ramirez .20 .50
BDPP85 Geovany Soto .75 2.00
BDPP86 Elvis Andrus .50 1.25
BDPP87 Bryan Anderson .20 .50
BDPP88 German Duran .75 2.00
BDPP89 J.R. Towles .60 1.50
BDPP90 Alcides Escobar .30 .75
BDPP91 Brian Bocock .20 .50
BDPP92 Chin-Lung Hu .75 2.00
BDPP93 Adrian Cardenas .30 .75
BDPP94 Freddy Sandoval .20 .50
BDPP95 Chris Coghlan .60 1.50
BDPP96 Craig Stansberry .20 .50
BDPP97 Brent Lillibridge .20 .50
BDPP98 Joey Votto 1.25 3.00
BDPP99 Evan Longoria 2.00 5.00
BDPP100 Wladimir Balentien .20 .50
BDPP101 Johnny Whittleman .20 .50
BDPP102 Gorkys Hernandez .50 1.25
BDPP103 Jay Bruce 1.25 3.00
BDPP104 Matt Tolbert .20 .50
BDPP105 Jacoby Ellsbury 1.50 4.00
BDPP106 Michael Saunders .60 1.50
BDPP107 Cameron Maybin .30 .75
BDPP108 Carlos Gonzalez .50 1.25
BDPP109 Colby Rasmus 1.25 3.00
BDPP110 Justin Upton 1.50 4.00

2007 Bowman Chrome Draft Future's Game Prospects Refractors

*REF: 1X TO 2.5X BASIC
STATED ODDS 1:11 HOBBY,1:11 RETAIL

2007 Bowman Chrome Draft Future's Game Prospects Blue Refractors

*BLUE REF: 2X TO 5X BASIC
STATED ODDS 1:58 HOBBY,1:171 RETAIL
STATED PRINT RUN 199 SER.#'d SETS

2007 Bowman Chrome Draft Future's Game Prospects Gold Refractors

*GOLD REF: 5X TO 12X BASIC
STATED ODDS 1:232 H, 1:659 R
STATED PRINT RUN 50 SER.#'d SETS

2007 Bowman Chrome Draft Future's Game Prospects Orange Refractors

STATED ODDS 1:463 H, 1:1349 R
STATED PRINT RUN 25 SER.#'d SETS
NO PRICING DUE TO SCARCITY

2007 Bowman Chrome Draft Future's Game Prospects Red Refractors

STATED ODDS 1:2300 H, 1:7080 R
STATED PRINT RUN 5 SER.#'d SETS
NO PRICING DUE TO SCARCITY

2007 Bowman Chrome Draft Future's Game Prospects SuperFractors

STATED ODDS 1:10,377 HOBBY
STATED PRINT RUN 1 SER.#'d SETS
NO PRICING DUE TO SCARCITY

2007 Bowman Chrome Draft Future's Game Prospects X-Fractors

*X-F: 1.5X TO 4X BASIC
STATED ODDS 1:39 HOBBY,1:106 RETAIL
STATED PRINT RUN 299 SER.#'d SETS

2007 Bowman Chrome Draft Future's Game Prospects Bases

STATED ODDS 1:633 HOBBY
STATED PRINT RUN 135 SER.#'d SETS
BDPP86 Elvis Andrus 4.00 10.00
BDPP87 Bryan Anderson 3.00 8.00
BDPP88 German Duran 3.00 8.00
BDPP89 J.R. Towles 3.00 8.00
BDPP91 Brian Bocock 3.00 8.00
BDPP92 Chin-Lung Hu 10.00 25.00
BDPP93 Adrian Cardenas 3.00 8.00
BDPP94 Freddy Sandoval 3.00 8.00
BDPP95 Chris Coghlan 3.00 8.00
BDPP97 Brent Lillibridge 4.00 10.00
BDPP98 Joey Votto 5.00 12.00
BDPP99 Evan Longoria 12.50 30.00
BDPP101 Johnny Whittleman 3.00 8.00
BDPP102 Gorkys Hernandez 4.00 10.00
BDPP103 Jay Bruce 6.00 15.00
BDPP105 Jacoby Ellsbury 6.00 15.00
BDPP106 Michael Saunders 4.00 10.00
BDPP108 Carlos Gonzalez 4.00 10.00
BDPP109 Colby Rasmus 6.00 15.00
BDPP110 Justin Upton 10.00 25.00

2008 Bowman Chrome

COMPLETE SET (220) 15.00 40.00
COMMON CARD (1-190) .20 .50
COMMON ROOKIE (1-220) .60 1.50
1-220 PLATE ODDS 1:1382 HOBBY
PLATE PRINT RUN 1 SET PER COLOR
BLACK-CYAN-MAGENTA-YELLOW ISSUED
NO PLATE PRICING DUE TO SCARCITY
1 Ryan Braun .60 1.50
2 David DeJesus .20 .50
3 Brandon Phillips .20 .50
4 Mark Teixeira .50 1.25
5 Daisuke Matsuzaka .50 1.25
6 Justin Upton .30 .75
7 Jered Weaver .20 .50
8 Todd Helton .30 .75
9 Adam Jones .30 .75
10 Erik Bedard .20 .50
11 Jason Bay .30 .75
12 Cole Hamels .50 1.25
13 Bobby Abreu .20 .50
14 Carlos Zambrano .30 .75
15 Vladimir Guerrero .50 1.25
16 Joe Blanton .20 .50
17 Paul Maholm .20 .50
18 Adrian Gonzalez .30 .75
19 Brandon Webb .30 .75
20 Carl Crawford .30 .75
21 A.J. Burnett .30 .75
22 Dmitri Young .20 .50
23 Jeremy Hermida .20 .50
24 C.C. Sabathia .30 .75
25 Adam Dunn .30 .75
26 Matt Garza .20 .50
27 Adrian Beltre .20 .50
28 Kevin Milwood .20 .50
29 Manny Ramirez .50 1.25
30 Javier Vazquez .20 .50
31 Carlos Delgado .20 .50
32 Torii Hunter .20 .50
33 Ivan Rodriguez .30 .75
34 Nick Markakis .50 1.25
35 Gil Meche .20 .50
36 Garrett Atkins .20 .50
37 Fausto Carmona .20 .50
38 Joe Mauer .50 1.25
39 Tom Glavine .30 .75
40 Hideki Matsui .50 1.25
41 Scott Rolen .30 .75
42 Tim Lincecum .75 2.00
43 Prince Fielder .30 .75
44 Kazuo Matsui .20 .50
45 Tom Gorzelanny .20 .50
46 Lance Berkman .30 .75
47 David Ortiz .30 .75
48 Dontrelle Willis .20 .50
49 Travis Hafner .20 .50
50 Aaron Harang .20 .50
51 Chris Young .20 .50
52 Vernon Wells .20 .50
53 Francisco Liriano .30 .75
54 Eric Chavez .20 .50
55 Phil Hughes .50 1.25
56 Melvin Mora .20 .50
57 Johan Santana .50 1.25
58 Brian McCann .30 .75
59 Pat Burrell .20 .50
60 Chris Carpenter .50 1.25
61 Brian Giles .20 .50
62 Jose Reyes .30 .75
63 Hanley Ramirez .50 1.25
64 Ubaldo Jimenez .30 .75
65 Felix Pie .20 .50
66 Jeremy Bonderman .20 .50
67 Jimmy Rollins .30 .75
68 Miguel Tejada .30 .75
69 Derek Lowe .20 .50
70 Alex Gordon .30 .75
71 John Maine .20 .50
72 Alfonso Soriano .30 .75
73 Ben Sheets .20 .50
74 Hunter Pence .50 1.25
75 Maglio Ordonez .30 .75
76 Josh Beckett .30 .75
77 Victor Martinez .30 .75
78 Mark Buehrle .30 .75
79 Jason Varitek .50 1.25
80 Chien-Ming Wang .30 .75
81 Ken Griffey Jr. .75 2.00
82 Billy Butler .20 .50
83 Brad Penny .20 .50
84 Carlos Beltran .20 .50
85 Curt Schilling .30 .75
86 Jorge Posada .30 .75
87 Andruw Jones .20 .50
88 Bobby Crosby .20 .50
89 Freddy Sanchez .20 .50
90 Barry Zito .20 .50
91 Miguel Cabrera .50 1.25
92 B.J. Upton .30 .75
93 Matt Cain .20 .50
94 Lyle Overbay .20 .50
95 Austin Kearns .20 .50
96 Alex Rodriguez .75 2.00
97 Rich Harden .20 .50
98 Justin Morneau .50 1.25
99 Oliver Perez .20 .50
100 Gary Matthews .20 .50
101 Matt Holliday .50 1.25
102 Justin Verlander .60 1.50
103 Orlando Cabrera .20 .50
104 Rich Hill .20 .50
105 Tim Hudson .30 .75
106 Ryan Zimmerman .30 .75
107 Roy Oswalt .30 .75
108 Nick Swisher .50 1.25
109 Raul Ibanez .30 .75
110 Kelly Johnson .20 .50
111 Alex Rios .30 .75
112 John Lackey .20 .50
113 Robinson Cano .50 1.25
114 Michael Young .30 .75
115 Jeff Francis .20 .50
116 Grady Sizemore .30 .75
117 Mike Lowell .20 .50
118 Aramis Ramirez .20 .50
119 Stephen Drew .20 .50
120 Yovani Gallardo .20 .50
121 Chase Utley .50 1.25
122 Dan Haren .20 .50
123 Yunel Escobar .20 .50
124 Greg Maddux .60 1.50
125 Garret Anderson .20 .50
126 Aubrey Huff .20 .50
127 Paul Konerko .30 .75
128 Dan Uggla .30 .75
129 Roy Halladay .50 1.25
130 Andre Ethier .30 .75
131 Orlando Hernandez .20 .50
132 Troy Tulowitzki .50 1.25
133 Carlos Guillen .20 .50
134 Scott Kazmir .30 .75
135 Aaron Rowand .20 .50
136 Jim Edmonds .30 .75
137 Jermaine Dye .20 .50
138 Orlando Hudson .20 .50
139 Derrek Lee .20 .50
140 Travis Buck .20 .50
141 Zack Greinke .30 .75
142 Jeff Kent .20 .50
143 John Smoltz .50 1.25
144 David Wright .60 1.50
145 Joba Chamberlain .30 .75
146 Adam LaRoche .20 .50
147 Kevin Youkilis .30 .75
148 Troy Glaus .30 .75
149 Nick Johnson .20 .50
150 J.J. Hardy .20 .50
151 Felix Hernandez .50 1.25
152 Gary Sheffield .20 .50
153 Albert Pujols 1.25 3.00
154 Chuck James .20 .50
155 Kosuke Fukudome RC 4.00 10.00
155b Kosuke Fukudome Japan 4.00 10.00
155c Kosuke Fukudome 10.00 25.00
No Signature/1600 *
156 Eric Byrnes .20 .50
157 Brad Hawpe .20 .50
158 Delmon Young .30 .75
159 Brian Roberts .20 .50
160 Russ Martin .30 .75
161 Hank Blalock .20 .50
162 Yadier Molina .30 .75
163 Jeremy Guthrie .20 .50
164 Chipper Jones .50 1.25
165 Johnny Damon .30 .75
166 Ryan Garko .20 .50
167 Jake Peavy .20 .50
168 Chone Figgins .20 .50
169 Edgar Renteria .20 .50
170 Jim Thome .30 .75
171 Carlos Pena .30 .75
172 Dustin Pedroia .60 1.50
173 Brett Myers .20 .50
174 Josh Hamilton .50 1.25
175 Randy Johnson .50 1.25
176 Ichiro Suzuki .75 2.00
177 Aaron Hill .20 .50
178 Corey Hart .20 .50
179 Jarrod Saltalamacchia .20 .50
180 Jeff Francoeur .30 .75
181 Derek Jeter 1.25 3.00
182 Curtis Granderson .30 .75
183 James Loney .30 .75
184 Brian Bannister .20 .50
185 Carlos Lee .20 .50
186 Pedro Martinez .30 .75
187 Asdrubal Cabrera .30 .75
188 Kenji Johjima .20 .50
189 Jacoby Ellsbury .75 2.00
190 Ryan Howard .60 1.50
191 Sean Rodriguez (RC) .60 1.50
192 Justin Ruggiano RC 1.00 2.50
193 Jed Lowrie (RC) 1.50 4.00
194 Joey Votto (RC) 2.50 6.00
195 Denard Span (RC) 1.00 2.50
196 Brad Harman RC 1.00 2.50
197 Jeff Niemann (RC) .60 1.50
198 Chin-Lung Hu (RC) 1.00 2.50
199 Luke Hochevar RC 1.00 2.50
200 German Duran RC 1.00 2.50
201 Troy Patton (RC) .60 1.50
202 Hiroki Kuroda RC 1.00 2.50
203 David Purcey (RC) .60 1.50
204 Armando Galarraga RC 1.00 2.50
205 John Bowker (RC) .60 1.50
206 Nick Blackburn RC 1.00 2.50
207 Hernan Iribarren (RC) 1.00 2.50
208 Greg Smith RC .60 1.50
209 Alberto Gonzalez RC 1.00 2.50
210 Justin Masterson RC 1.50 4.00
211 Brian Barton RC 1.00 2.50
212 Robinzon Diaz (RC) .60 1.50
213 Clete Thomas RC 1.00 2.50
214 Kazuo Fukumori RC 1.00 2.50
215 Jayson Nix (RC) .60 1.50
216 Evan Longoria RC 3.00 8.00
217 Johnny Cueto RC 1.00 2.50
218 Matt Tolbert RC 1.00 2.50
219 Masahide Kobayashi RC 1.00 2.50
220 Callix Crabbe (RC) .60 1.50

2008 Bowman Chrome Refractors

*REF 1-190: 1X TO 2.5X BASIC
*REF 1-221: .6X TO 1.5X BASIC
1-221 ODDS

2008 Bowman Chrome Blue Refractors

*BLUE REF 1-190: 2.5X TO 6X BASIC
*BLUE REF 1-221: 1.2X TO 3X BASIC
1-221 ODDS 1:66 HOBBY
STATED PRINT RUN 150 SERIAL #'d SETS
198 Chin-Lung Hu 10.00 25.00
204 Armando Galarraga 10.00 25.00

2008 Bowman Chrome Gold Refractors

*GOLD REF 1-190: 4X TO 10X BASIC
*GOLD REF 1-221: 2X TO 5X BASIC
1-221 ODDS 1:197 HOBBY
STATED PRINT RUN 50 SERIAL #'d SETS
42 Tim Lincecum 15.00 40.00
80 Chien-Ming Wang 60.00 120.00
96 Alex Rodriguez 20.00 50.00
176 Ichiro Suzuki 20.00 50.00
181 Derek Jeter 30.00 60.00
189 Jacoby Ellsbury 15.00 40.00
198 Chin-Lung Hu 30.00 60.00
204 Armando Galarraga 30.00 60.00
210 Justin Masterson 20.00 50.00
216 Evan Longoria 60.00 120.00

2008 Bowman Chrome Orange Refractors

STATED ODDS 1:393 HOBBY
STATED PRINT RUN 25 SER.#'d SETS
NO PRICING DUE TO SCARCITY

2008 Bowman Chrome Red Refractors

STATED ODDS 1:1972 HOBBY
STATED PRINT RUN 5 SER.#'d SETS
NO PRICING DUE TO SCARCITY

2008 Bowman Chrome SuperFractors

STATED ODDS 1:8308 HOBBY
STATED PRINT RUN 1 SER.#'d SET
NO PRICING DUE TO SCARCITY

2008 Bowman Chrome X-Fractors

*X-FRACTOR 1-190: 2X TO 5X BASIC
*X-FRACTOR 1-221: 1X TO 2.5X BASIC
1-221 ODDS 1:40 HOBBY
STATED PRINT RUN 250 SER.#'d SETS
155 Kosuke Fukudome 10.00 25.00
155b Kosuke Fukudome Japan 10.00 25.00
198 Chin-Lung Hu 5.00 12.00
204 Armando Galarraga 8.00 20.00
216 Evan Longoria 20.00 50.00

2008 Bowman Chrome Head of the Class Dual Autograph

STATED ODDS 1:1773 HOBBY
STATED PRINT RUN 350 SER.#'d SETS
CH Joba Chamberlain 20.00 50.00
Phil Hughes
FL Prince Fielder 20.00 50.00
Matt LaPorta
LP Evan Logoria 60.00 120.00
David Price

2008 Bowman Chrome Head of the Class Dual Autograph X-Fractors

*X-F: .6X TO 1.5X BASIC
STATED ODDS 1:12,823 HOBBY
STATED PRINT RUN 50 SER.#'d SETS
LP Evan Logoria 125.00 250.00
David Price

2008 Bowman Chrome Head of the Class Dual Autograph Refractors

*REF: .5X TO 1.2X BASIC
STATED ODDS 1:6298 HOBBY
STATED PRINT RUN 99 SER.#'d SETS
LP Evan Logoria 75.00 150.00
David Price

2008 Bowman Chrome Head of the Class Dual Autograph SuperFractors

STATED ODDS 1:589,824 HOBBY
STATED PRINT RUN 1 SER.#'d SET
NO PRICING DUE TO SCARCITY

2008 Bowman Chrome Prospects

COMP.SET w/o AU's (220) 40.00 100.00
COMP.SET w/o AU's (1-110) 20.00 50.00
COMP.SET w/o AU's (131-240) 20.00 50.00
111-130 AU ODDS 1:37 HOBBY
241-285 AU ODDS 1:31 HOBBY
1-110 PLATE ODDS 1:732 HOBBY
111-130 AU PLATE ODDS 1:4700 HOBBY
131-240 PLATE ODDS 1:1132 HOBBY
241-285 AU PLATES 1:10,471 HOBBY
PLATE PRINT RUN 1 SET PER COLOR
BLACK-CYAN-MAGENTA-YELLOW ISSUED
NO PLATE PRICING DUE TO SCARCITY
BCP1 Max Sapp .30 .75
BCP2 Jamie Richmond .20 .50
BCP3 Darren Ford .20 .50
BCP4 Sergio Romo .20 .50
BCP5 Jacob Butler .20 .50
BCP6 Glenn Gibson .20 .50
BCP7 Tom Hagan .20 .50
BCP8 Michael McCormick .20 .50
BCP9 Gregorio Petit .30 .75
BCP10 Bobby Parnell .20 .50
BCP11 Jeff Kindel .30 .75
BCP12 Anthony Claggett .30 .75
BCP13 Christopher Frey .20 .50
BCP14 Jonah Nickerson .30 .75
BCP15 Anthony Martinez .20 .50
BCP16 Rusty Ryal .30 .75
BCP17 Justin Berg .30 .75
BCP18 Gerardo Parra .20 .50
BCP19 Wesley Wright .20 .50
BCP20 Stephen Chapman .20 .50
BCP21 Chance Chapman .20 .50
BCP22 Brett Pill 1.25 3.00
BCP23 Zachary Phillips .30 .75
BCP24 John Raynor .50 1.25
BCP25 Danny Duffy .60 1.50
BCP26 Brian Finegan .20 .50
BCP27 Jonathan Venters .20 .50
BCP28 Steve Tolleson .20 .50
BCP29 Ben Jukich .30 .75
BCP30 Matthew Weston .20 .50
BCP31 Kyle Mura .20 .50
BCP32 Luke Hetherington .20 .50
BCP33 Michael Daniel .30 .75
BCP34 Jake Renshaw .20 .50
BCP35 Greg Halman .30 .75
BCP36 Ryan Khoury .20 .50
BCP37 Ryan Ouellette .20 .50
BCP38 Mike Brantley .20 .50
BCP39 Eric Brown .20 .50
BCP40 Jose Duarte .20 .50
BCP41 Eli Tintor .20 .50
BCP42 Kent Sakamoto .20 .50
BCP43 Luke Montz .30 .75
BCP44 Alex Cobb .20 .50
BCP45 Michael McKenry .20 .50
BCP46 Javier Castillo .20 .50
BCP47 Jeffrey Stevens .20 .50
BCP48 Greg Burns .20 .50
BCP49 Blake Johnson .20 .50
BCP50 Austin Jackson 1.00 2.50
BCP51 Anthony Recker .20 .50
BCP52 Luis Durango 1.00 2.50
BCP53 Engel Beltre .60 1.50
BCP54 Seth Bynum .20 .50
BCP55 Ryan Strieby .30 .75
BCP56 Iggy Suarez .20 .50
BCP57 Ryan Morris .30 .75
BCP58 Scott Van Slyke .20 .50
BCP59 Tyler Kolodny .60 1.50
BCP60 Joseph Martinez .20 .50
BCP61 Aaron Mathews .20 .50
BCP62 Phillip Cuadrado .20 .50
BCP63 Alex Liddi .60 1.50
BCP64 Alex Burnett .30 .75
BCP65 Brian Barton .30 .75
BCP66 David Welch .20 .50
BCP67 Kyle Reynolds .20 .50
BCP68 Francisco Hernandez .20 .50
BCP69 Logan Morrison 1.50 4.00
BCP70 Ronald Ramirez .20 .50
BCP71 Brad Miller .20 .50
BCP72 Braedyn Pruitt .30 .75
BCP73 Jason Fernandez .30 .75
BCP74 Joseph Mahoney .20 .50
BCP75 Quentin Davis .30 .75
BCP76 P.J. Walters .50 1.25
BCP77 Jordan Czarniecki .20 .50
BCP78 Jonathan Mota .20 .50
BCP79 Michael Hernandez .20 .50
BCP80 James Guerrero .20 .50
BCP81 Chris Johnson .75 2.00
BCP82 Daniel Cortes .50 1.25
BCP83 Sal Sanchez .30 .75
BCP84 Sean Henry .20 .50
BCP85 Caleb Gindl .20 .50
BCP86 Tommy Everidge .20 .50
BCP87 Matt Rizzotti .20 .50
BCP88 Luis Munoz .20 .50
BCP89 Matthew Klimas .20 .50
BCP90 Angel Reyes .20 .50
BCP91 Sean Danielson .20 .50
BCP92 Omar Poveda .30 .75
BCP93 Mario Lisson .20 .50
BCP94 Brian Mathews .20 .50
BCP95 Matthew Buschmann .20 .50
BCP96 Greg Thomson .20 .50
BCP97 Matt Inouye .20 .50
BCP98 Aneury Rodriguez .30 .75
BCP99 Brad Harman .30 .75
BCP100 Aaron Bates .50 1.25
BCP101 Graham Taylor .20 .50
BCP102 Ken Holmberg .20 .50
BCP103 Greg Dowling .20 .50
BCP104 Ronnie Ray .20 .50
BCP105 Michael Wlodarczyk .20 .50
BCP106 Jose Martinez .60 1.50
BCP107 Jason Stephens .30 .75
BCP108 Will Rhymes .20 .50
BCP109 Joey Side .20 .50
BCP110 Brandon Waring .60 1.50
BCP111 David Price AU 30.00 60.00
BCP112 Michael Moustakas AU 40.00 80.00
BCP113 Matt LaPorta AU 12.50 30.00
BCP114 Wendell Fairley AU 4.00 10.00
BCP115 Josh Vitters AU 12.50 30.00
BCP116 Jonathan Bachanov AU 4.00 10.00
BCP117 Edward Kunz AU 4.00 10.00
BCP118 Matt Dominguez AU 6.00 15.00
BCP119 Kyle Lotzkar AU 4.00 10.00
BCP120 Madison Bumgarner AU 20.00 50.00
BCP121 Jason Heyward AU 50.00 100.00
BCP122 Julio Borbon AU 4.00 10.00
BCP123 Josh Smoker AU 4.00 10.00
BCP124 Jarrod Parker AU 12.50 30.00
BCP125 Kevin Ahrens AU 4.00 10.00
BCP126 J.P. Arencibia AU 10.00 25.00
BCP127 Josh Bell AU 8.00 20.00
BCP128 Scott Cousins AU 4.00 10.00
BCP129 Brandon Hynick AU 4.00 10.00
BCP130 Alan Johnson AU 4.00 10.00
BCP131 Zhenwang Zhang .30 .75
BCP132 Chris Nash .20 .50
BCP133 Sergio Morales .20 .50
BCP134 Carlos Santana 1.50 4.00
BCP135 Carlos Monasterios .20 .50
BCP136 Quincy Latimore .20 .50
BCP137 Yamaico Navarro .60 1.50
BCP138 Ryan Mullins .20 .50
BCP139 Collin DeLome .30 .75
BCP140 Hector Correa .20 .50
BCP141 Mitch Canham .20 .50
BCP142 Robert Fish .20 .50
BCP143 Ryan Royster .20 .50
BCP144 Eric Barrett .20 .50
BCP145 Deibinson Romero .30 .75
BCP146 Jeff Gerbe .20 .50
BCP147 Lucas Duda .30 .75
BCP148 Bryan Morris .30 .75
BCP149 Andrew Romine .20 .50
BCP150 Glenn Gibson .20 .50
BCP151 Danny Brezeale .20 .50
BCP152 Shairon Martis .30 .75
BCP153 Helder Velazquez .20 .50
BCP154 Alan Farina .20 .50
BCP155 Brandon Barnes .20 .50
BCP156 Waldis Joaquin .20 .50
BCP157 Luis De La Cruz .20 .50
BCP158 Yunesky Sanchez .20 .50
BCP159 Mitch Hilligross .20 .50
BCP160 Vin Mazzaro .60 1.50
BCP161 Marcus Davis .20 .50
BCP162 Tony Barnette .20 .50
BCP163 Joe Benson .50 1.25
BCP164 Jake Arrieta .20 .50
BCP165 Alfredo Silverio .50 1.25
BCP166 Duane Below .20 .50
BCP167 Kai Liu .30 .75
BCP168 Zach Britton .60 1.50
BCP169 Jamie Pedroza .30 .75
BCP170 Frank Herrmann .20 .50
BCP171 Justin Turner .30 .75
BCP172 Jeff Manship .20 .50
BCP173 Paul Winterling .20 .50
BCP174 Nathan Vineyard .30 .75
BCP175 Jason Delaney .20 .50
BCP176 Ivan Nova 1.50 4.00
BCP177 Esmailyn Gonzalez .60 1.50
BCP178 Brett Cecil .60 1.50
BCP179 Jose Martinez .20 .50
BCP180 Brad Peacock .75 2.00
BCP181 Justin Snyder .30 .75
BCP182 Steve Garrison .20 .50
BCP183 Joe Mahoney .20 .50
BCP184 Graham Godfrey .20 .50
BCP185 Larry Wiliams .20 .50
BCP186 Jeremy Haynes .20 .50
BCP187 Brent Brewer .50 1.25
BCP188 Jhoulys Chacin .75 2.00
BCP189 Nevin Ashley .30 .75
BCP190 Justin Cassel .20 .50
BCP191 Jon Jay .30 .75
BCP192 Chris Huseby .20 .50
BCP193 D.J. Jones .30 .75
BCP194 David Bromberg .30 .75
BCP195 Juan Francisco .50 1.25
BCP196 Zach Jevne .20 .50
BCP197 Darwin Barney 1.00 2.50
BCP198 Jose Ortegano .30 .75
BCP199 Dominic Brown 3.00 8.00
BCP200 Kyle Ginley .20 .50
BCP201 David Wood .20 .50
BCP202 Jhonny Nunez .20 .50
BCP203 Carlos Rivero .50 1.25
BCP204 Anthony Varvaro .20 .50
BCP205 Christian Lopez .20 .50
BCP206 Travis Banwart .20 .50
BCP207 Rhyne Hughes .20 .50
BCP208 Heath Rollins .30 .75
BCP209 Zack Cozart .30 .75
BCP210 Mike Dunn .20 .50
BCP211 Chris Pettit .20 .50
BCP212 Dan Berlind .20 .50
BCP213 Ernesto Mejia .30 .75
BCP214 Hector Rondon .20 .50
BCP215 Jose Vallejo .30 .75
BCP216 Kyle Schmidt .20 .50
BCP217 Bubba Bell .50 1.25
BCP218 Charlie Furbush .20 .50
BCP219 Pedro Baez .50 1.25
BCP220 Brandon MaGee .20 .50
BCP221 Clint Robinson .20 .50
BCP222 Fabio Castillo .30 .75
BCP223 Brad Emaus .30 .75
BCP224 Mike DeJesus .20 .50
BCP225 Brandon Laird .50 1.25
BCP226 R.J. Seidel .20 .50
BCP227 Agustin Murillo .20 .50
BCP228 Trevor Reckling .60 1.50
BCP229 Hector Gomez .50 1.25
BCP230 Jordan Norberto .20 .50
BCP231 Steve Hill .20 .50
BCP232 Hassan Pena .20 .50
BCP233 Justin Henry .30 .75
BCP234 Chase Lirette .20 .50
BCP235 Christian Marrero .30 .75
BCP236 Will Kline .20 .50
BCP237 Johan Limonta .20 .50
BCP238 Duke Welker .20 .50
BCP239 Jeudy Valdez .30 .75
BCP240 Elvin Ramirez .20 .50
BCP241 Josh Kreuzer AU 4.00 10.00
BCP242 Ryan Zink AU 5.00 12.00
BCP243 Matt Harrison AU 4.00 10.00
BCP244 Dustin Richardson AU 5.00 12.00
BCP245 Fautino De Los Santos AU 6.00 15.00
BCP246 Austin Jackson AU 20.00 50.00
BCP247 Jordan Schafer AU 20.00 50.00
BCP248 Daryl Thompson AU 5.00 12.00
BCP249 Lars Anderson AU 20.00 50.00
BCP250 Tim Bascom AU 6.00 15.00
BCP251 Brandon Hicks AU 6.00 15.00
BCP252 David Kopp AU 5.00 12.00
BCP253 Danny Lehmann AU 4.00 10.00
BCP254 Jordan Zimmerman AU UER 8.00 20.00
Last name misspelled
BCP255 Cale Iorg AU 4.00 10.00
BCP256 Austin Romine AU 10.00 25.00
BCP257 Chaz Roe AU 6.00 15.00
BCP258 Danny Rams AU 6.00 15.00
BCP259 Daniel Bard AU 10.00 25.00
BCP260 Engel Beltre AU 10.00 25.00
BCP261 Michael Watt AU 4.00 10.00
BCP262 Brennan Boesch AU 12.50 30.00
BCP263 Matt Latos AU 12.50 30.00
BCP264 John Jaso AU 5.00 12.00
BCP265 Adrian Alaniz AU 4.00 10.00
BCP266 Matt Green AU 4.00 10.00
BCP267 Andrew Lambo AU 6.00 15.00
BCP268 Michael McCardell AU 6.00 15.00
BCP269 Chris Valaika AU 8.00 20.00
BCP270 Cole Rohrbough AU 8.00 20.00
BCP271 Andrew Brackman AU 5.00 12.00
BCP272 Bud Norris AU 5.00 12.00
BCP273 Ryan Kalish AU 10.00 25.00
BCP274 Jake McGee AU 5.00 12.00
BCP275 Aaron Cunningham AU 6.00 15.00
BCP276 Mitch Boggs AU 4.00 10.00
BCP277 Bradley Suttle AU 4.00 10.00
BCP278 Henry Rodriguez AU 6.00 15.00
BCP279 Mario Lisson AU 4.00 10.00
BCP280 Ludovicus Van Mil AU 5.00 12.00
BCP281 Angel Villalona AU 5.00 12.00
BCP282 Mark Melancon AU 6.00 15.00
BCP283 Brian Dinkelman AU 4.00 10.00
BCP284 Daniel McCutchen AU 4.00 10.00
BCP285 Rene Tosoni AU 5.00 12.00

2008 Bowman Chrome Prospects Refractors

*REF 1-110: 2.5X TO 6X BASIC
*REF 131-240: 2.5X TO 6X BASIC
1-110 ODDS 1:34 HOBBY,1:88 RETAIL
131-240 ODDS 1:40 HOBBY
1-110 PRINT RUN 599 SER.#'d SETS
131-240 PRINT RUN 500 SER.#'d SETS
*REF AU 111-130: .5X TO 1.2X BASIC
*REF AU 241-285: .5X TO 1.2X BASIC
111-130 AU ODDS 1:113 HOBBY
241-285 AU ODDS 1:88 HOBBY
111-130 AU PRINT RUN 500 SER.#'d SETS
241-285 AU PRINT RUN 500 SER.#'d SETS
BCP120 Madison Bumgarner AU 40.00 80.00
BCP273 Ryan Kalish AU 12.50 30.00
BCP275 Aaron Cunningham AU 10.00 25.00
BCP282 Mark Melancon AU 10.00 25.00

2008 Bowman Chrome Prospects Blue Refractors

*BLUE 1-110: 5X TO 12X BASIC
*BLUE 131-240: 5X TO 12X BASIC
1-110 ODDS 1:126 HOBBY,1:350 RETAIL
131-240 ODDS 1:131 HOBBY
1-110 PRINT RUN 150 SER.#'d SETS
131-240 PRINT RUN 150 SER.#'d SETS
*BLUE AU 111-130: 1.2X TO 3X BASIC
*BLUE AU 241-285: 1.2X TO 3X BASIC
111-130 AU ODDS 1:372 HOBBY
241-285 AU ODDS 1:295 HOBBY
111-130 AU PRINT RUN 150 SER.#'d SETS
241-285 AU PRINT RUN 150 SER.#'d SETS
BCP18 Gerardo Parra 20.00 50.00
BCP53 Engel Beltre 20.00 50.00
BCP55 Ryan Strieby 15.00 40.00
BCP110 Brandon Waring 40.00 80.00
BCP121 Jason Heyward AU 150.00 300.00
BCP137 Yamaico Navarro 30.00 60.00
BCP141 Mitch Canham 6.00 15.00
BCP143 Ryan Royster 10.00 25.00
BCP169 Jamie Pedroza 6.00 15.00
BCP177 Esmailyn Gonzalez 15.00 40.00
BCP178 Brett Cecil 10.00 25.00
BCP179 Jose Martinez 20.00 50.00
BCP194 David Bromberg 10.00 25.00
BCP225 Brandon Laird 10.00 25.00
BCP228 Trevor Reckling 20.00 50.00
BCP229 Hector Gomez 12.50 30.00
BCP249 Lars Anderson AU 75.00 150.00
BCP260 Engel Beltre AU 30.00 60.00
BCP273 Ryan Kalish AU 30.00 60.00

2008 Bowman Chrome Prospects Gold Refractors

*GOLD 1-110: 12X TO 30X BASIC
*GOLD 131-240: 12X TO 30X BASIC
1-110 ODDS 1:380 HOB, 1:1040 RET
131-240 ODDS 1:393 HOBBY
1-110 PRINT RUN 50 SER.#'d SETS
131-240 PRINT RUN 50 SER.#'d SETS
111-130 AU ODDS 1:1155 HOBBY
241-285 AU ODDS 1:953 HOBBY
111-130 AU PRINT RUN 50 SER.#'d SETS
241-285 AU PRINT RUN 50 SER.#'d SETS
BCP2 Jamie Richmond 15.00 40.00
BCP11 Jeff Kindel 30.00 60.00
BCP18 Gerardo Parra 40.00 80.00
BCP43 Luke Montz 20.00 50.00
BCP50 Austin Jackson 60.00 120.00
BCP53 Engel Beltre 40.00 80.00
BCP55 Ryan Strieby 20.00 50.00
BCP58 Scott Van Slyke 20.00 50.00
BCP92 Omar Poveda 30.00 60.00
BCP110 Brandon Waring 90.00 150.00
BCP111 David Price AU 200.00 400.00
BCP112 Michael Moustakas AU 175.00 350.00
BCP114 Wendell Fairley AU 30.00 60.00
BCP115 Josh Vitters AU 75.00 150.00
BCP116 Jonathan Bachanov AU 30.00 60.00
BCP118 Matt Dominguez AU 60.00 120.00
BCP120 Madison Bumgarner AU 175.00 350.00
BCP121 Jason Heyward AU 400.00 800.00
BCP123 Josh Smoker AU 30.00 60.00
BCP124 Jarrod Parker AU 100.00 200.00
BCP125 Kevin Ahrens AU 30.00 60.00
BCP126 J.P. Arencibia AU 75.00 150.00
BCP143 Ryan Royster 12.50 30.00
BCP164 Jake Arrieta 60.00 120.00
BCP193 D.J. Jones 20.00 50.00
BCP194 David Bromberg 20.00 50.00
BCP195 Juan Francisco 60.00 120.00
BCP203 Carlos Rivero 30.00 60.00
BCP229 Hector Gomez 20.00 50.00
BCP245 Fautino De Los Santos AU 60.00 120.00
BCP247 Jordan Schafer AU 100.00 200.00
BCP249 Lars Anderson AU 125.00 250.00
BCP254 Jordan Zimmerman AU UER 75.00 150.00
Last name misspelled
BCP256 Austin Romine AU 60.00 120.00
BCP260 Engel Beltre AU 75.00 150.00
BCP263 Matt Latos AU 100.00 200.00
BCP267 Andrew Lambo AU 100.00 200.00
BCP270 Cole Rohrbough AU 60.00 120.00
BCP271 Andrew Brackman AU 40.00 80.00
BCP273 Ryan Kalish AU 75.00 150.00
BCP274 Jake McGee AU 30.00 60.00
BCP275 Aaron Cunningham AU 50.00 100.00
BCP282 Mark Melancon AU 30.00 60.00

2008 Bowman Chrome Prospects Orange Refractors

1-110 ODDS 1:750 HOB, 1:2075 RET
111-130 AU ODDS 1:2495 HOBBY
131-240 ODDS 1:785 HOBBY
241-285 AU ODDS 1:1784 HOBBY
STATED PRINT RUN 25 SER.#'d SETS
NO PRICING DUE TO SCARCITY

2008 Bowman Chrome Prospects Red Refractors

1-110 ODDS 1:3600 HOBBY
111-130 AU ODDS 1:11,075 HOBBY
131-240 ODDS 1:3924 HOBBY
241-285 AU ODDS 1:8549 HOBBY
STATED PRINT RUN 5 SER.#'d SETS
NO PRICING DUE TO SCARCITY

2008 Bowman Chrome Prospects SuperFractors

1-110 ODDS 1:18,274 HOBBY
111-130 AU ODDS 1:55,000 HOBBY
131-240 ODDS 1:16,694 HOBBY
241-285 AU ODDS 1:40,216 HOBBY
STATED PRINT RUN 1 SER.#'d SET
NO PRICING DUE TO SCARCITY

2008 Bowman Chrome Prospects X-Fractors

*X-F 1-110: 3X TO 8X BASIC
*X-F 131-240: 3X TO 8X BASIC
1-110 ODDS 1:65 HOBBY,1:188 RETAIL
131-240 ODDS 1:79 HOBBY
1-110 PRINT RUN 275 SER.#'d SETS
131-240 PRINT RUN 250 SER.#'d SETS
*X-F AU 111-130: .6X TO 1.5X BASIC
*X-F AU 241-285: .6X TO 1.5X BASIC
111-130 X-F AU ODDS 1:226 HOBBY
241-285 X-F AU ODDS 1:175 HOBBY
111-130 AU PRINT RUN 275 SER.#'d SETS
241-285 AU PRINT RUN 250 SER.#'d SETS
BCP120 Madison Bumgarner AU 50.00 100.00
BCP254 Jordan Zimmerman AU UER 15.00 40.00
Last name misspelled
BCP267 Andrew Lambo AU 20.00 50.00
BCP273 Ryan Kalish AU 20.00 50.00
BCP275 Aaron Cunningham AU 12.50 30.00
BCP282 Mark Melancon AU 12.50 30.00

2008 Bowman Chrome Draft

This set was released on Nobember 28, 2008. The base set consists of 60 cards.

COMP.SET w/o AU's (55) 12.50 30.00
COMMON CARD (1-60) .25 .60
COMMON AUTO 4.00 10.00
AU ODDS 1:627 HOBBY
OVERALL PLATE ODDS 1:750 HOBBY
AUTO PLATE ODDS 1:49,870 HOBBY
PLATE PRINT RUN 1 SET PER COLOR
BLACK-CYAN-MAGENTA-YELLOW ISSUED
NO PLATE PRICING DUE TO SCARCITY
BDP1 Nick Adenhart (RC) .25 .60
BDP2 Michael Aubrey RC .40 1.00
BDP3 Mike Aviles RC .40 1.00
BDP4 Burke Badenhop RC .40 1.00
BDP5 Wladimir Balentien (RC) .25 .60
BDP6a Collin Balester (RC) .25 .60
BDP6b Collin Balester AU 4.00 10.00
BDP7 Josh Banks (RC) .25 .60
BDP8 Wes Bankston (RC) .25 .60
BDP9 Joey Votto (RC) 1.00 2.50
BDP10 Mitch Boggs (RC) .25 .60
BDP11 Jay Bruce (RC) 1.00 2.50
BDP12 Chris Carter (RC) .40 1.00
BDP13 Justin Christian RC .40 1.00
BDP14 Chris Davis RC .60 1.50
BDP15a Blake DeWitt (RC) .60 1.50
BDP15b Blake DeWitt AU 8.00 20.00
BDP16 Nick Evans RC .25 .60
BDP17 Jaime Garcia RC 1.00 2.50
BDP18 Brett Gardner (RC) .60 1.50

BDP19 Carlos Gonzalez (RC) .60 1.50
BDP20 Matt Harrison (RC) .25 .60
BDP21 Micah Hoffpauir RC .75 2.00
BDP22 Nick Hundley (RC) .25 .60
BDP23 Eric Hurley (RC) .25 .60
BDP24 Elliot Johnson (RC) .25 .60
BDP25 Matt Joyce RC .60 1.50
BDP26a Clayton Kershaw RC 1.25 3.00
BDP26b Clayton Kershaw AU 15.00 40.00
BDP27a Evan Longoria RC 1.25 3.00
BDP27b Evan Longoria AU 40.00 80.00
BDP28 Matt Macri (RC) .25 .60
BDP29 Chris Perez RC .40 1.00
BDP30 Max Ramirez RC .25 .60
BDP31 Greg Reynolds RC .40 1.00
BDP32 Brooks Conrad (RC) .25 .60
BDP33 Max Scherzer RC .75 2.00
BDP34 Daryl Thompson (RC) .25 .60
BDP35 Taylor Teagarden RC .40 1.00
BDP36 Rich Thompson RC .40 1.00
BDP37 Ryan Tucker (RC) .25 .60
BDP38 Jonathan Van Every RC .25 .60
BDP39a Chris Volstad (RC) .25 .60
BDP39b Chris Volstad AU 4.00 10.00
BDP40 Michael Hollimon RC .25 .60
BDP41 Brad Ziegler RC 1.25 3.00
BDP42 Jamie D'Antona (RC) .25 .60
BDP43 Clayton Richard (RC) .25 .60
BDP44 Edgar Gonzalez (RC) .25 .60
BDP45 Bryan LaHair RC .25 .60
BDP46 Warner Madrigal (RC) .25 .60
BDP47 Reid Brignac (RC) .40 1.00
BDP48 David Robertson RC .60 1.50
BDP49 Nick Stavinoha RC .40 1.00
BDP50 Jai Miller (RC) .25 .60
BDP51 Charlie Morton (RC) .25 .60
BDP52 Brandon Boggs (RC) .40 1.00
BDP53 Joe Mather RC .40 1.00
BDP54 Gregorio Petit RC .40 1.00
BDP55 Jeff Samardzija RC UER .75 2.00
Name spelled incorrectly

2008 Bowman Chrome Draft Refractors

*REF: 1X TO 2.5X BASIC
RANDOM INSERTS IN PACKS
*REF AU: .5X TO 1.2X BASIC AU
REF AUTO ODDS 1:2,000 PACKS
REF AUTO PRINT RUN 99 SER.#'d SETS

2008 Bowman Chrome Draft Blue Refractors

*BLUE REF: 2.5X TO 6X BASIC
STATED ODDS 1:76 HOBBY
STATED PRINT RUN 99 SER.#'d SETS
BDP27 Evan Longoria 15.00 40.00

2008 Bowman Chrome Draft Gold Refractors

*GOLD REF: 5X TO 12X BASIC
STATED ODDS 1:150 HOBBY
STATED PRINT RUN 50 SER.#'d SETS
*GODL REF AU: 1.2X TO 3X BASIC AU
GLD.REF AUTO ODDS 1:3965 PACKS
GLD.REF AU PRINT RUN 50 SER.#'d SETS

2008 Bowman Chrome Draft Orange Refractors

STATED ODDS 1:301 HOBBY
AUTO ODDS 1:7962 HOBBY
STATED PRINT RUN 25 SER.#'d SETS
NO PRICING DUE TO SCARCITY

2008 Bowman Chrome Draft Red Refractors

STATED ODDS 1:1518 HOBBY
AUTO ODDS 1:39,500 HOBBY
STATED PRINT RUN 5 SER.#'d SETS
NO PRICING DUE TO SCARCITY

2008 Bowman Chrome Draft SuperFractors

STATED ODDS 1:6025 HOBBY
AUTO ODDS 1:189,500 HOBBY
STATED PRINT RUN 1 SER.#'d SET
NO PRICING DUE TO SCARCITY

2008 Bowman Chrome Draft X-Fractors

*X-F: 1.2X TO 3X BASIC
STATED ODDS 1:38 HOBBY
STATED PRINT RUN 199 SER.#'d SETS
BDP27 Evan Longoria 8.00 20.00

2008 Bowman Chrome Draft Prospects

COMP.SET w/o AU's (110) 20.00 50.00
STATED AUTO ODDS 1:38 HOBBY
OVERALL PLATE ODDS 1:750 HOBBY
AUTO PLATE ODDS 1:13,732 HOBBY
PLATE PRINT RUN 1 SET PER COLOR
BLACK-CYAN-MAGENTA-YELLOW ISSUED
NO PLATE PRICING DUE TO SCARCITY
EXCHANGE DEADLINE 11/30/2010
BDPP1 Rick Porcello DP 1.50 4.00
BDPP2 Braeden Schlehuber DP .30 .75
BDPP3 Kenny Wilson DP .30 .75
BDPP4 Jeff Lanning DP .30 .75
BDPP5 Kevin Dubler DP .30 .75
BDPP6 Eric Campbell DP .50 1.25
BDPP7 Tyler Chatwood DP .50 1.25
BDPP8 Tyreace House DP .30 .75
BDPP9 Adrian Nieto DP .30 .75
BDPP10 Robbie Grossman DP .50 1.25
BDPP11 Jordan Danks DP .75 2.00
BDPP12 Jay Austin DP .30 .75
BDPP13 Ryan Perry DP .50 1.25
BDPP14 Ryan Chaffee DP .50 1.25
BDPP15 Niko Vasquez DP .75 2.00
BDPP16 Shane Dyer DP .30 .75
BDPP17 Benji Gonzalez DP .30 .75
BDPP18 Miles Reagan DP .30 .75
BDPP19 Anthony Ferrara DP .30 .75
BDPP20 Markus Brisker DP .30 .75
BDPP21 Justin Bristow DP .30 .75
BDPP22 Richard Bleier DP .50 1.25
BDPP23 Jeremy Beckham DP .50 1.25
BDPP24 Xavier Avery DP .75 2.00
BDPP25 Christian Vazquez DP .50 1.25
BDPP26 Nick Romero DP .30 .75
BDPP27 Trey Watten DP .30 .75
BDPP28 Brett Jacobson DP .30 .75
BDPP29 Tyler Sample DP .30 .75
BDPP30 T.J. Steele DP .50 1.25
BDPP31 Christian Friedrich DP 1.00 2.50
BDPP32 Graham Hicks DP .50 1.25
BDPP33 Shane Peterson DP .50 1.25
BDPP34 Brett Hunter DP .30 .75
BDPP35 Tim Federowicz DP .50 1.25
BDPP36 Isaac Galloway DP .50 1.25
BDPP37 Logan Schafer DP .30 .75
BDPP38 Paul Demny DP .30 .75
BDPP39 Clayton Shunick DP .30 .75
BDPP40 Andrew Liebel DP .30 .75
BDPP41 Brandon Crawford DP .50 1.25
BDPP42 Blake Tekotte DP .50 1.25
BDPP43 Jason Corder DP .30 .75
BDPP44 Bryan Shaw DP .30 .75
BDPP45 Edgar Olmos DP .30 .75
BDPP46 Dusty Coleman DP .30 .75
BDPP47 Johnny Giavotella DP 1.00 2.50
BDPP48 Tyson Ross DP .50 1.25
BDPP49 Brent Morel DP .50 1.25
BDPP50 Dennis Raben DP .50 1.25
BDPP51 Jake Odorizzi DP 1.00 2.50
BDPP52 Ryne White DP .50 1.25
BDPP53 Devaris Strange-Gordon DP .30 .75
BDPP54 Tim Murphy DP .30 .75
BDPP55 Jake Jefferies DP .30 .75
BDPP56 Anthony Capra DP .30 .75
BDPP57 Kyle Weiland DP .75 2.00
BDPP58 Anthony Bass DP .50 1.25
BDPP59 Scott Green DP .30 .75
BDPP60 Zeke Spruill DP .75 2.00
BDPP61 L.J. Hoes DP .75 2.00
BDPP62 Tyler Cline DP .30 .75
BDPP63 Matt Cerda DP .30 .75
BDPP64 Bobby Lanigan DP .30 .75
BDPP65 Mike Sheridan DP .30 .75
BDPP66 Carlos Carrasco FG .30 .75
BDPP67 Nate Schierholtz FG .30 .75
BDPP68 Jesus Delgado FG .30 .75
BDPP69 Andrew McCutchen FG 1.00 2.50
BDPP70 Shairon Martis FG .50 1.25
BDPP71 Matt LaPorta FG .75 2.00
BDPP72 Eddie Morlan FG .30 .75
BDPP73 Greg Golson FG .30 .75
BDPP74 Julio Pimentel FG .30 .75
BDPP75 Dexter Fowler FG .30 .75
BDPP76 Henry Rodriguez FG .30 .75
BDPP77 Cliff Pennington FG .30 .75
BDPP78 Hector Rondon FG .30 .75
BDPP79 Wes Hodges FG .30 .75
BDPP80 Polin Trinidad FG .30 .75
BDPP81 Chris Getz FG .30 .75
BDPP82 Welington Castillo FG .30 .75
BDPP83 Mat Gamel FG .75 2.00
BDPP84 Pablo Sandoval FG 2.00 5.00
BDPP85 Jason Donald FG .30 .75
BDPP86 Jesus Montero FG 2.50 6.00
BDPP87 Jamie D'Antona FG .30 .75
BDPP88 Will Inman FG .30 .75
BDPP89 Elvis Andrus FG .50 1.25
BDPP90 Taylor Teagarden FG .50 1.25
BDPP91 Scott Campbell FG .30 .75
BDPP92 Jake Arrieta FG .30 .75
BDPP93 Juan Francisco FG .75 2.00
BDPP94 Lou Marson FG .30 .75
BDPP95 Luke Hughes FG .30 .75
BDPP96 Bryan Anderson FG .30 .75
BDPP97 Ramiro Pena FG .30 .75
BDPP98 Jesse Todd FG .30 .75
BDPP99 Gorkys Hernandez FG .30 .75
BDPP100 Casey Weathers FG .30 .75
BDPP101 Fernando Martinez FG .50 1.25
BDPP102 Clayton Richard FG .30 .75
BDPP103 Gerardo Parra FG .30 .75
BDPP104 Kevin Pucetas FG .50 1.25
BDPP105 Wilkin Ramirez FG .30 .75
BDPP106 Ryan Mattheus FG .30 .75
BDPP107 Angel Villalona FG .75 2.00
BDPP108 Brett Anderson FG .50 1.25
BDPP109 Chris Valaika FG .30 .75
BDPP110 Trevor Cahill FG .75 2.00
BDPP111 Wilmer Flores AU 20.00 50.00
BDPP112 Lonnie Chisenhall AU 10.00 25.00
BDPP113 Carlos Gutierrez AU 4.00 10.00
BDPP114 Derek Holland AU 10.00 25.00
BDPP115 Michael Stanton AU 60.00 120.00
BDPP116 Ike Davis AU 15.00 40.00
BDPP117 Anthony Hewitt AU 4.00 10.00
BDPP118 Gordon Beckham AU 10.00 25.00
BDPP119 Daniel Schlereth AU 4.00 10.00
BDPP120 Zach Collier AU 8.00 20.00
BDPP121 Evan Frederickson AU 4.00 10.00
BDPP122 Mike Montgomery AU 10.00 25.00
BDPP123 Cody Adams AU 4.00 10.00
BDPP124 Brad Hand AU 5.00 12.00
BDPP125 Josh Reddick AU 10.00 25.00
BDPP127 Jesus Montero AU 60.00 120.00
BDPP128 Buster Posey AU 90.00 150.00
BDPP142 Michael Inoa AU 10.00 25.00

2008 Bowman Chrome Draft Prospects Refractors

*REF: 1.5X TO 4X BASIC
RANDOM INSERTS IN PACKS
*REF AU: .5X TO 1.2X BASIC
REF.AU ODDS 1:118 HOBBY
REF.AU PRINT RUN 500 SER.#'d SETS
EXCHANGE DEADLINE 11/30/2010
BDPP115 Michael Stanton AU 75.00 150.00
BDPP125 Josh Reddick AU 15.00 40.00
BDPP127 Jesus Montero AU 100.00 200.00
BDPP128 Buster Posey AU 125.00 250.00

2008 Bowman Chrome Draft Prospects Blue Refractors

*BLUE REF: 4X TO 10X BASIC
STATED ODDS 1:76 HOBBY
STATED PRINT RUN 99 SER.#'d SETS
*BLUE REF AU: 1X TO 2.5X BASIC
BLUE REF.AU ODDS 1:396 HOBBY
BLUE REF.AU PRINT RUN 150 SER.#'d SETS
EXCHANGE DEADLINE 11/30/2010
BDPP1 Rick Porcello DP 30.00 60.00
BDPP36 Isaac Galloway DP 15.00 40.00
BDPP111 Wilmer Flores AU 100.00 175.00
BDPP115 Michael Stanton AU 200.00 400.00
BDPP125 Josh Reddick AU 40.00 80.00
BDPP127 Jesus Montero AU 150.00 300.00
BDPP128 Buster Posey AU 200.00 400.00

2008 Bowman Chrome Draft Prospects Gold Refractors

*GOLD REF: 12.5X TO 30X BASIC
STATED ODDS 1:150 HOBBY
STATED PRINT RUN 50 SER.#'d SETS
*GOLD REF AU: 2.5X TO 6X BASIC
GOLD REF.AU ODDS 1:1258 HOBBY
GOLD AU PRINT RUN 50 SER.#'d SETS
EXCHANGE DEADLINE 11/30/2010
BDPP1 Rick Porcello DP 75.00 150.00
BDPP9 Adrian Nieto DP 20.00 50.00
BDPP36 Isaac Galloway DP 30.00 60.00
BDPP51 Jake Odorizzi DP 30.00 60.00
BDPP57 Kyle Weiland DP 30.00 60.00
BDPP112 Lonnie Chisenhall AU 100.00 200.00
BDPP115 Michael Stanton AU 400.00 800.00
BDPP125 Josh Reddick AU 75.00 150.00
BDPP127 Jesus Montero AU 400.00 600.00
BDPP128 Buster Posey AU 400.00 800.00

2008 Bowman Chrome Draft Prospects Orange Refractors

STATED ODDS 1:301 HOBBY
AUTO ODDS 1:2700 HOBBY
STATED PRINT RUN 25 SER.#'d SETS
NO PRICING DUE TO SCARCITY

2008 Bowman Chrome Draft Prospects Red Refractors

STATED ODDS 1:518 HOBBY
AUTO ODDS 1:11,017 HOBBY
STATED PRINT RUN 5 SER.#'d SETS
NO PRICING DUE TO SCARCITY

2008 Bowman Chrome Draft Prospects SuperFractors

STATED ODDS 1:6025 HOBBY
AUTO ODDS 1:55,736 HOBBY
STATED PRINT RUN 1 SER.#'d SET
NO PRICING DUE TO SCARCITY

2008 Bowman Chrome Draft Prospects X-Fractors

*X-F: 2.5X TO 6X BASIC
STATED ODDS 1:38 HOBBY
STATED PRINT RUN 199 SER.#'d SETS
*X-F AU: .6X TO 1.5X BASIC
X-F.AU ODDS 1:270 HOBBY
X-F.AU PRINT RUN 225 SER.#'d SETS
EXCHANGE DEADLINE 11/30/2010
BDPP111 Wilmer Flores AU 50.00 100.00
BDPP115 Michael Stanton AU 100.00 200.00
BDPP125 Josh Reddick AU 20.00 50.00
BDPP127 Jesus Montero AU 125.00 250.00
BDPP128 Buster Posey AU 150.00 300.00

2009 Bowman Chrome

COMPLETE SET (220) 75.00 150.00
COMMON CARD (1-190) .20 .50
COMMON ROOKIE .60 1.50
PRINTING PLATE ODDS 1:538 HOBBY
PLATE PRINT RUN 1 SET PER COLOR
BLACK-CYAN-MAGENTA-YELLOW ISSUED
NO PLATE PRICING DUE TO SCARCITY
1 David Wright .60 1.50
2 Albert Pujols 1.25 3.00
3 Alex Rodriguez .75 2.00
4 Chase Utley .50 1.25
5 Chien-Ming Wang .30 .75
6 Jimmy Rollins .30 .75
7 Ken Griffey Jr. .75 2.00
8 Manny Ramirez .50 1.25
9 Chipper Jones .50 1.25
10 Ichiro Suzuki .75 2.00
11 Justin Morneau .50 1.25
12 Hanley Ramirez .50 1.25
13 Cliff Lee .30 .75
14 Ryan Howard .60 1.50
15 Ian Kinsler .30 .75
16 Jose Reyes .30 .75
17 Ted Lilly .20 .50
18 Miguel Cabrera .50 1.25
19 Nate McLouth .20 .50
20 Josh Beckett .30 .75
21 John Lackey .20 .50
22 David Ortiz .30 .75
23 Carlos Lee .20 .50
24 Adam Dunn .30 .75
25 B.J. Upton .30 .75
26 Curtis Granderson .30 .75
27 David DeJesus .20 .50
28 CC Sabathia .30 .75
29 Russell Martin .20 .50
30 Torii Hunter .20 .50
31 Rich Harden .20 .50
32 Johnny Damon .30 .75
33 Cristian Guzman .20 .50
34 Grady Sizemore .30 .75
35 Jorge Posada .30 .75
36 Placido Polanco .20 .50
37 Ryan Ludwick .30 .75
38 Dustin Pedroia .60 1.50
39 Matt Garza .20 .50
40 Prince Fielder .30 .75
41 Rick Ankiel .20 .50
42 David Huff RC .60 1.50
43 Erik Bedard .20 .50
44 Ryan Braun .60 1.50
45 Ervin Santana .20 .50
46 Brian Roberts .20 .50
47 Mike Jacobs .20 .50
48 Phil Hughes .30 .75
49 Justin Masterson .20 .50
50 Felix Hernandez .50 1.25
51 Stephen Drew .20 .50
52 Bobby Abreu .20 .50
53 Jay Bruce .30 .75
54 Josh Hamilton .50 1.25
55 Garrett Atkins .20 .50
56 Jacoby Ellsbury .50 1.25
57 Johan Santana .50 1.25
58 James Shields .20 .50
59 Sergio Escalona RC 1.00 2.50
60 Carlos Pena .30 .75
61 Matt Kemp .30 .75
62 Joey Votto .50 1.25
63 Raul Ibanez .30 .75
64 Casey Kotchman .20 .50
65 Hunter Pence .30 .75
66 Daniel Murphy RC 1.50 4.00
67 Carlos Beltran .20 .50
68 Evan Longoria .60 1.50
69 Daisuke Matsuzaka .50 1.25
70 Cole Hamels .50 1.25
71 Robinson Cano .50 1.25
72 Clayton Kershaw .50 1.25
73 Kenji Johjima .30 .75
74 Kazuo Matsui .20 .50
75 Jayson Werth .30 .75
76 Brian McCann .30 .75
77 Barry Zito .20 .50
78 Glen Perkins .20 .50
79 Jeff Francoeur .30 .75
80 Derek Jeter 1.25 3.00
81 Ryan Doumit .20 .50
82 Dan Haren .20 .50
83 Justin Duchscherer .20 .50
84 Marlon Byrd .20 .50
85 Derek Lowe .20 .50
86 Pat Burrell .20 .50
87 Jair Jurrjens .20 .50
88 Zack Greinke .30 .75
89 Jon Lester .50 1.25
90 Justin Verlander .60 1.50
91 Jorge Cantu .20 .50
92 John Maine .20 .50
93 Brad Hawpe .20 .50
94 Mike Aviles .20 .50
95 Victor Martinez .30 .75
96 Ryan Dempster .20 .50
97 Miguel Tejada .30 .75
98 Joe Mauer .50 1.25
99 Scott Olsen .20 .50
100 Tim Lincecum .75 2.00
101 Francisco Liriano .20 .50
102 Chris Iannetta .20 .50
103 Greg Burke RC 1.00 2.50
104 Milton Bradley .20 .50
105 John Lannan .20 .50
106 Yovani Gallardo .20 .50
107 Luke French (RC) .60 1.50
108 Jermaine Dye .20 .50
109 Dioner Navarro .20 .50
110 Joba Chamberlain .30 .75
111 Nelson Cruz .30 .75
112 Johnny Cueto .20 .50
113 Adam LaRoche .20 .50
114 Aaron Rowand .20 .50
115 Jason Bay .30 .75
116 Roy Halladay .50 1.25
117 Mark Teixeira .50 1.25
118 Gavin Floyd .20 .50
119 Magglio Ordonez .30 .75
120 Rafael Furcal .20 .50
121 Mark Buehrle .30 .75
122 Alexi Casilla .20 .50
123 Scott Kazmir .20 .50
124 Nick Swisher .50 1.25
125 Carlos Gomez .20 .50
126 Javier Vazquez .20 .50
127 Paul Konerko .30 .75
128 Nolan Reimold (RC) .60 1.50
129 Gerardo Parra RC 1.00 2.50
130 Josh Johnson .30 .75
131 Carlos Zambrano .30 .75
132 Chris Davis .20 .50
133 Bobby Crosby .20 .50
134 Alex Gordon .30 .75
135 Chris Young .20 .50
136 Carlos Delgado .20 .50
137 Adam Wainwright .30 .75
138 Justin Upton .30 .75
139 Chris Coghlan RC 1.50 4.00
140 J.D. Drew .20 .50
141 Adam Lind .20 .50
142 Mike Lowell .20 .50
143 Lance Berkman .30 .75
144 J.J. Hardy .20 .50
145 A.J. Burnett .30 .75
146 Jake Peavy .20 .50
147 Xavier Paul (RC) .60 1.50
148 Matt Holliday .50 1.25
149 Carl Crawford .30 .75
150 Andre Ethier .30 .75
151 Howie Kendrick .20 .50
152 Ryan Zimmerman .30 .75
153 Troy Tulowitzki .50 1.25
154 Brett Myers .20 .50
155 Chris Young .20 .50
156 Jered Weaver .20 .50
157 Jeff Clement .20 .50
158 Alex Rios .30 .75
159 Shane Victorino .20 .50
160 Jeremy Hermida .20 .50
161 James Loney .30 .75
162 Michael Young .30 .75
163 Aramis Ramirez .20 .50
164 Geovany Soto .30 .75
165 Aubrey Huff .20 .50
166 Rick Porcello RC 2.00 5.00
167 Vernon Wells .20 .50
168 Chone Figgins .20 .50
169 Carlos Quentin .30 .75
170 Chad Billingsley .20 .50
171 Matt Cain .20 .50
172 Derrek Lee .20 .50
173 A.J. Pierzynski .20 .50
174 Daniel Bard RC .60 1.50
175 Bobby Scales RC 1.00 2.50
176 Alfonso Soriano .30 .75
177 Adrian Gonzalez .30 .75
178 Andrew McCutchen (RC) 2.50 6.00
179 Nick Markakis .50 1.25
180 Brandon Webb .30 .75
181 Vladimir Guerrero .50 1.25
182 Roy Oswalt .30 .75
183 Adam Jones .30 .75
184 Edinson Volquez .20 .50
185 Gordon Beckham RC 5.00 12.00
186 Joe Saunders .20 .50
187 Yadier Molina .30 .75
188 Kevin Youkilis .30 .75
189 Dan Uggla .30 .75
190 Kosuke Fukudome .50 1.25
191 Matt LaPorta RC 1.50 4.00
192 Trevor Cahill RC 1.50 4.00
193 Derek Holland RC 1.00 2.50
194 Michael Bowden (RC) .60 1.50
195 Andrew Carpenter RC 1.00 2.50
196 Phil Coke RC 1.00 2.50
197 Graham Taylor RC 1.00 2.50
198 Alcides Escobar RC 1.50 4.00
199 Dexter Fowler (RC) 1.00 2.50
200 Mat Gamel RC 1.50 4.00
201 Jordan Zimmermann RC .60 1.50
202 Greg Golson (RC) .60 1.50
203 Andrew Bailey RC 1.50 4.00
204 David Hernandez RC .60 1.50
205 George Kottaras (RC) .60 1.50
206 Lou Marson (RC) .60 1.50
207 Shairon Martis RC 1.00 2.50
208 Juan Miranda RC 1.00 2.50
209 Tyler Greene (RC) .60 1.50
210 Jonathon Niese RC 1.00 2.50
211 Bobby Parnell RC 1.00 2.50
212 Colby Rasmus (RC) 1.50 4.00
213 David Price RC 1.50 4.00
214 Angel Salome (RC) .60 1.50
215 Gaby Sanchez RC 1.00 2.50
216 Freddy Sandoval (RC) .60 1.50
217 Travis Snider RC 1.00 2.50
218 Will Venable RC .60 1.50
219 Brett Anderson RC 1.00 2.50
220 Josh Outman RC 1.00 2.50

2009 Bowman Chrome Refractors

*REF VET: 1X TO 2.5X BASIC
*REF RC: .6X TO 1.5X BASIC RC
STATED ODDS 1:4 HOBBY

2009 Bowman Chrome Blue Refractors

*BLUE VET: 2X TO 6X BASIC
*BLUE RC: 1.2X TO 3X BASIC RC
STATED ODDS 1:17 HOBBY
STATED PRINT RUN 150 SER.#'d SETS

2009 Bowman Chrome Gold Refractors

*GOLD VET: 5X TO 12X BASIC
*GOLD RC: 2X TO 5X BASIC RC
STATED ODDS 1:50 HOBBY
STATED PRINT RUN 50 SER.#'d SETS

2009 Bowman Chrome Orange Refractors

STATED ODDS 1:100 HOBBY
STATED PRINT RUN 25 SER.#'d SETS
NO PRICING DUE TO SCARCITY

2009 Bowman Chrome Red Refractors

STATED ODDS 1:496 HOBBY
STATED PRINT RUN 5 SER.#'d SETS
NO PRICING DUE TO SCARCITY

2009 Bowman Chrome SuperFractors

STATED ODDS 1:2150 HOBBY
STATED PRINT RUN 1 SER.#'d SET
NO PRICING DUE TO SCARCITY

2009 Bowman Chrome X-Fractors

*XF VET: 1.5X TO 4X BASIC
*XF RC: 1X TO 2.5X BASIC RC
STATED ODDS 1:10 HOBBY
STATED PRINT RUN 250 SER.#'d SETS

2009 Bowman Chrome Prospects

COMP.SET w/o AU's (160) 30.00 60.00
BOWMAN AU ODDS 1:47 HOBBY
BOW.CHR AU ODDS 1:34 HOBBY
PRINTING PLATE ODDS 1:538 HOBBY
AU PRINT.PLATE ODDS 1:7400 HOBBY
PLATE PRINT RUN 1 SET PER COLOR
BLACK-CYAN-MAGENTA-YELLOW ISSUED
NO PLATE PRICING DUE TO SCARCITY
BCP1 Neftali Feliz .60 1.50
BCP2 Oscar Tejada .60 1.50
BCP3 Greg Veloz .20 .50
BCP4 Julio Teheran 1.50 4.00
BCP5 Michael Almanzar .50 1.25
BCP6 Stolmy Pimentel .30 .75
BCP7 Matthew Moore 3.00 8.00
BCP8 Jericho Jones .20 .50
BCP9 Kelvin de la Cruz .50 1.25
BCP10 Jose Ceda .20 .50
BCP11 Jesse Darcy .20 .50
BCP12 Kenneth Gilbert .20 .50
BCP13 Will Smith .30 .75
BCP14 Samuel Freeman .20 .50
BCP15 Adam Reifer .20 .50
BCP16 Ehire Adrianza .50 1.25
BCP17 Michael Pineda 3.00 8.00
BCP18 Jordan Walden .30 .75
BCP19 Angel Morales .30 .75
BCP20 Neil Ramirez .30 .75
BCP21 Kyeong Kang .30 .75
BCP22 Luis Jimenez .30 .75
BCP23 Tyler Flowers .50 1.25
BCP24 Peley Paramore .30 .75
BCP25 Jeremy Hamilton .20 .50
BCP26 Tyler Yockey .30 .75
BCP27 Sawyer Carroll .30 .75
BCP28 Jeremy Farrell .20 .50
BCP29 Tyson Brummett .20 .50
BCP30 Alex Buchholz .30 .75
BCP31 Luis Sumoza .30 .75
BCP32 Jonathan Waltenbury .30 .75
BCP33 Edgar Osuna .20 .50
BCP34 Curt Smith .20 .50
BCP35 Evan Bigley .30 .75
BCP36 Miguel Fermin .20 .50
BCP37 Ben Lasater .20 .50
BCP38 David Freese 1.50 4.00
BCP39 Jon Kibler .30 .75
BCP40 Cristian Beltre .30 .75
BCP41 Alfredo Figaro .20 .50
BCP42 Marc Rzepczynski .30 .75
BCP43 Joshua Collmenter .30 .75
BCP44 Adam Mills .20 .50
BCP45 Wilson Ramos .60 1.50
BCP46 Esmil Rogers .20 .50
BCP47 Jon Mark Owings .20 .50
BCP48 Chris Johnson .75 2.00
BCP49 Abraham Almonte .20 .50
BCP50 Patrick Ryan .20 .50
BCP51 Yetri Carvajal .50 1.25
BCP52 Ruben Tejada .20 .50
BCP53 Edilio Colina .30 .75
BCP54 Wilber Bucardo .30 .75
BCP55 Nelson Perez .30 .75
BCP56 Andrew Rundle .30 .75
BCP57 Anthony Ortega .20 .50
BCP58 Wilin Rosario .30 .75
BCP59 Parker Frazier .20 .50
BCP60 Kyle Farrell .20 .50
BCP61 Erik Komatsu .30 .75
BCP62 Michael Stutes .20 .50
BCP63 David Genao .30 .75
BCP64 Jack Cawley .20 .50
BCP65 Jacob Goldberg .20 .50
BCP66 Jarred Bogany .20 .50
BCP67 Jason McEachern .20 .50
BCP68 Matt Rigoli .20 .50
BCP69 Jose Duran .30 .75
BCP70 Justin Greene .30 .75
BCP71 Nino Leyja .30 .75
BCP72 Michael Swinson .30 .75
BCP73 Miguel Flores .30 .75
BCP74 Nick Buss .20 .50
BCP75 Brett Oberholtzer .30 .75
BCP76 Pat McAnaney .30 .75
BCP77 Sean Conner .20 .50
BCP78 Ryan Verdugo .30 .75
BCP79 Will Atwood .20 .50
BCP80 Tommy Johnson .50 1.25
BCP81 Rene Garcia .30 .75
BCP82 Robert Brooks .30 .75
BCP83 Seth Garrison .20 .50
BCP84 Steven Upchurch .20 .50
BCP85 Zach Moore .20 .50
BCP86 Derrick Phillips .20 .50
BCP87 Dominic De La Osa .50 1.25
BCP88 Jose Barajas .20 .50
BCP89 Bryan Petersen .20 .50
BCP90 Michael Cisco .30 .75
BCP91 Rinku Singh AU 4.00 10.00
BCP92 Dinesh Kumar Patel AU 6.00 15.00
BCP93 Matt Miller AU 4.00 10.00
BCP94 Pat Venditte AU 10.00 25.00
BCP95 Zach Putnam AU 5.00 12.00
BCP96 Robbie Grossman AU 4.00 10.00
BCP97 Tommy Hanson AU 20.00 50.00
BCP98 Graham Hicks AU 4.00 10.00
BCP99 Matt Mitchell AU 4.00 10.00
BCP100 Christopher Marrero AU 8.00 20.00
BCP101 Freddie Freeman AU 50.00 100.00
BCP102 Chris Johnson AU 10.00 25.00
BCP103 Edgar Olmos AU 4.00 10.00
BCP104 Argenis Diaz AU 4.00 10.00
BCP105 Brett Anderson AU 10.00 25.00
BCP106 Juancarlos Sulbaran AU 6.00 15.00
BCP107 Cody Scarpetta AU 8.00 20.00
BCP108 Carlos Santana AU 15.00 40.00
BCP109 Brad Emaus AU 4.00 10.00
BCP110 Dayan Viciedo AU 12.50 30.00
BCP111b Tim Federowicz AU 8.00 20.00
BCP111a Beamer Weems AU 4.00 10.00
BCP112a Logan Morrison AU 12.50 30.00
BCP112b Allen Craig AU 10.00 25.00
BCP113b Kyle Weiland AU 6.00 15.00
BCP113a Greg Halman AU 6.00 15.00
BCP114a Logan Forsythe AU 5.00 12.00
BCP114b Connor Graham AU 5.00 12.00
BCP115 Lance Lynn AU 6.00 15.00
BCP116 Javier Rodriguez AU 4.00 10.00
BCP117 Josh Lindblom AU 4.00 10.00
BCP118 Blake Tekotte AU 4.00 10.00
BCP119 Johnny Giavotella AU 8.00 20.00
BCP120 Jason Knapp AU 4.00 10.00
BCP121 Charlie Blackmon AU 6.00 15.00
BCP122 David Hernandez AU 4.00 10.00
BCP123 Adam Moore AU 4.00 10.00
BCP124 Bobby Lanigan AU 4.00 10.00
BCP125 Jay Austin AU 4.00 10.00
BCP126 Quinton Miller AU 4.00 10.00
BCP127 Eric Sogard AU 4.00 10.00
BCP128 Efrain Nieves .30 .75
BCP129 Kam Mickolio .20 .50
BCP130 Terrell Alliman .20 .50
BCP131 J.R. Higley .30 .75
BCP132 Rashun Dixon .50 1.25
BCP133 Brian Baisley .20 .50
BCP134 Tim Collins .30 .75
BCP135 Kyle Greenwalt .50 1.25
BCP136 C.J. Lee .20 .50
BCP137 Hector Correa .20 .50
BCP138 Wily Peralta .30 .75
BCP139 Bryan Price .20 .50
BCP140 Jarrod Holloway .20 .50
BCP141 Alfredo Silverio .20 .50
BCP142 Brad Dydalewicz .30 .75
BCP143 Alexander Torres .30 .75
BCP144 Chris Hicks .20 .50
BCP145 Andy Parrino .20 .50
BCP146 Christopher Schwinden .20 .50
BCP147 Matt Mitchell .20 .50
BCP148 Mathew Kennelly .20 .50
BCP149 Freddy Galvis .30 .75
BCP150 Mauricio Robles .50 1.25
BCP151 Kevin Eichhorn .20 .50
BCP152 Dan Hudson .60 1.50
BCP153 Carlos Martinez .30 .75
BCP154 Danny Carroll .20 .50
BCP155 Maikel Cleto .20 .50
BCP156 Michael Affronti .20 .50
BCP157 Mike Pontius .30 .75
BCP158 Richard Castillo .20 .50
BCP159 Jon Redding .20 .50
BCP160 Aaron King .20 .50
BCP161 Mark Hallberg .20 .50
BCP162 Chris Luck .50 1.25
BCP163 Wilmer Font .50 1.25
BCP164 Chad Lundahl .20 .50
BCP165 Isaias Asencio .20 .50
BCP166 Denny Almonte .30 .75
BCP167 Carmen Angelini .20 .50
BCP168 Paul Clemens .20 .50
BCP169 Federico Hernandez .30 .75
BCP170 Mario Martinez .30 .75
BCP171 Bryan Shaw .20 .50
BCP172 Bryan Augenstein .20 .50
BCP173 Santos Rodriguez .30 .75
BCP174 Delvi Cid .30 .75
BCP175 Todd Doolittle .20 .50
BCP176 Rossmel Perez .20 .50
BCP177 Philippe-Alexandre Valiquette .20 .50
BCP178 Julian Sampson .30 .75
BCP179 Eric Farris .20 .50
BCP180 Taylor Harbin .20 .50
BCP181 Clayton Cook .30 .75
BCP182 Jovan Rosa .20 .50
BCP183 Starlin Castro 5.00 12.00
BCP184 Brock Huntzinger .20 .50
BCP185 Jack McGeary .20 .50
BCP186 Moises Sierra .30 .75
BCP187 Luis Exposito .50 1.25
BCP188 Danny Farquhar .20 .50
BCP189 Layton Hiller .20 .50
BCP190 Michael Harrington .20 .50
BCP191 Nate Tenbrink .20 .50
BCP192 Jason Rook .20 .50
BCP193 Ryan Kulik .20 .50
BCP194 Kennil Gomez .20 .50
BCP195 Brad James .20 .50
BCP196 John Anderson .20 .50
BCP197 Perneil Halliman .20 .50

2009 Bowman Chrome Prospects Refractors

*REF 1-197: 2.5X TO 6X BASIC
1-90 ODDS 1:22 HOBBY
128-197 ODDS 1:15 HOBBY
NON-AU PRINT RUN 599 SER.#'d SETS
*REF AU: .5X TO 1.2X BASIC
BOW.REF.AU ODDS 1:95 HOBBY
BOW.CHR. AU ODDS 1:70 HOBBY
AUTO PRINT RUN 500 SER.#'d SETS

2009 Bowman Chrome Prospects Blue Refractors

COMPLETE SET (201)
*BLUE REF: 5X TO 12X BASIC
BLUE 1-90 ODDS 1:90 HOBBY
BLUE 128-197 ODDS 1:17 HOBBY
BLUE NON-AU PRT RUN 150 SER.#'d SETS
*BLUE REF AU: .75X TO 2X BASIC
BOW.BLU.REF AU ODDS 1:314 HOBBY
BOW.CHR.BLU.REF ODDS 1:246 HOBBY
BLUE REF AU PRINT RUN 150 SER.#'d SETS
BCP101 Freddie Freeman AU 100.00 200.00

2009 Bowman Chrome Prospects Gold Refractors

COMPLETE SET (201)
*GOLD REF: 12X TO 30X BASIC
GOLD 1-90 ODDS 1:271 HOBBY
GOLD 128-197 ODDS 1:50 HOBBY
GOLD PRINT RUN 50 SER.#'d SETS
*GOLD REF AU: 2X TO 5X BASIC
BOW.GLD.REF AU ODDS 1:943 HOBBY
BOW.CHR.GLD.REF AU ODDS 1:715 HOBBY
GOLD REF AU PRINT RUN 50 SER.#'d SETS

2009 Bowman Chrome Prospects Orange Refractors

1-90 STATED ODDS 1:542 HOBBY
91-110 STATED ODDS 1:1500 HOBBY
111-127 STATED ODDS 1:1882 HOBBY
128-197 STATED ODDS 1:100 HOBBY
STATED PRINT RUN 25 SER.#'d SETS
NO PRICING DUE TO SCARCITY

2009 Bowman Chrome Prospects Red Refractors

1-90 STATED ODDS 1:2190 HOBBY
91-110 STATED ODDS 1:6830 HOBBY
111-127 STATED ODDS 1:9450 HOBBY
128-197 STATED ODDS 1:496 HOBBY
STATED PRINT RUN 5 SER.#'d SETS
NO PRICING DUE TO SCARCITY

2009 Bowman Chrome Prospects SuperFractors

1-90 STATED ODDS 1:11,100 HOBBY
91-110 STATED ODDS 1:29,605 HOBBY
111-127 STATED ODDS 1:49,000 HOBBY
128-197 STATED ODDS 1:2150 HOBBY
STATED PRINT RUN 1 SER.#'d SET
NO PRICING DUE TO SCARCITY

2009 Bowman Chrome Prospects X-Fractors

*X-FRAC: 4X TO 10X BASIC
X-FRAC 1-90 ODDS 1:45 HOBBY
1-90 X-F PRINT RUN 299 SER.#'d SETS
128-197 X-F PRINT RUN 250 SER.#'d SETS
*X-F AU: .6X TO 1.5X BASIC
BOW.X-F AU ODDS 1:198 HOBBY
BOW.CHR.X-F AU ODDS 1:144 HOBBY
X-F AU PRINT RUN 250 SER.#'d SETS

2009 Bowman Chrome WBC Prospects

21-60 PRINTING PLATE ODDS 1:538 HOBBY
PLATE PRINT RUN 1 SET PER COLOR
BLACK-CYAN-MAGENTA-YELLOW ISSUED
NO PLATE PRICING DUE TO SCARCITY
BCW1 Yu Darvish 6.00 15.00
BCW2 Phillippe Aumont 1.50 4.00
BCW3 Concepcion Rodriguez .60 1.50
BCW4 Michel Enriquez .60 1.50
BCW5 Yulieski Gurriel 1.00 2.50
BCW6 Shinnosuke Abe 1.00 2.50
BCW7 Gift Ngoepe .60 1.50
BCW8 Dylan Lindsay 1.00 2.50
BCW9 Nick Weglarz .60 1.50
BCW10 Mitch Dening .60 1.50
BCW11 Justin Erasmus .60 1.50
BCW12 Aroldis Chapman 2.50 6.00
BCW13 Alex Liddi 2.00 5.00
BCW14 Alexander Smit .60 1.50
BCW15 Juan Carlos Sulbaran .60 1.50
BCW16 Cheng-Min Peng 1.00 2.50
BCW17 Chenhao Li .60 1.50
BCW18 Tao Bu .60 1.50
BCW19 Gregory Halman 1.00 2.50
BCW20 Fu-Te Ni 1.00 2.50
BCW21 Norichika Aoki 1.00 2.50
BCW22 Hasashi Iwakuma 1.00 2.50
BCW23 Tae Kyun Kim .60 1.50
BCW24 Dae Ho Lee .60 1.50
BCW25 Wang Chao .60 1.50
BCW26 Yi-Chuan Lin 1.00 2.50
BCW27 James Beresford .60 1.50
BCW28 Shuichi Murata 1.00 2.50
BCW29 Hung-Wen Chen .60 1.50
BCW30 Masahiro Tanaka 1.50 4.00
BCW31 Kao Kuo-Ching .60 1.50
BCW32 Po Yu Lin .60 1.50
BCW33 Yolexis Ulacia .60 1.50
BCW34 Kwang-Hyun Kim 1.00 2.50
BCW35 Kenley Jansen 1.50 4.00

BCW36 Luis Durango .60 1.50
BCW37 Ray Chang .60 1.50
BCW38 Hein Robb .60 1.50
BCW39 Kyuji Fujikawa 1.00 2.50
BCW40 Ruben Tejada .60 1.50
BCW41 Hector Olivera .60 1.50
BCW42 Bryan Engelhardt .60 1.50
BCW43 Dennis Neuman .60 1.50
BCW44 Vladimir Garcia .60 1.50
BCW45 Michihiro Ogasawara 1.00 2.50
BCW46 Yen-Wen Kuo .60 1.50
BCW47 Takahiro Mahara .60 1.50
BCW48 Hiroyuki Nakajima 1.00 2.50
BCW49 Yoennis Cespedes 5.00 12.00
BCW50 Alfredo Despaigne .60 1.50
BCW51 Suk Min-Yoon .60 1.50
BCW52 Chih-Hsien Chiang 1.50 4.00
BCW53 Hyun-Soo Kim .60 1.50
BCW54 Chih-Kang Kao .60 1.50
BCW55 Frederich Cepeda 1.00 2.50
BCW56 Yi-Feng Kuo .60 1.50
BCW57 Toshiya Sugiuchi .60 1.50
BCW58 Shunsuke Watanabe 1.00 2.50
BCW59 Max Ramirez .60 1.50
BCW60 Brad Harman .60 1.50

2009 Bowman Chrome WBC Prospects Refractors

*REF: 1.2X TO 3X BASIC
1-20 ODDS 1:22 HOBBY
21-60 ODDS 1:15 HOBBY
1-20 PRINT RUN 599 SER.#'d SETS
21-60 PRINT RUN 500 SER.#'d SETS

2009 Bowman Chrome WBC Prospects Blue Refractors

*BLUE REF: 2X TO 5X BASIC
1-20 ODDS 1:90 HOBBY
21-60 ODDS 1:50 HOBBY
STATED PRINT RUN 150 SER.#'d SETS

2009 Bowman Chrome WBC Prospects Gold Refractors

*GOLD REF: 4X TO 10X BASIC
1-20 ODDS 1:271 HOBBY
21-60 ODDS 1:150 HOBBY
STATED PRINT RUN 50 SER.#'d SETS
BCW1 Yu Darvish 125.00 250.00
BCW6 Shinnosuke Abe 25.00 60.00
BCW7 Gift Ngoepe 15.00 40.00
BCW13 Alex Liddi 50.00 120.00

2009 Bowman Chrome WBC Prospects Red Refractors

1-20 STATED ODDS 1:2190 HOBBY
21-60 STATED ODDS 1:496 HOBBY
STATED PRINT RUN 5 SER.#'D SETS
NO PRICING DUE TO SCARCITY

2009 Bowman Chrome WBC Prospects SuperFractors

1-20 STATED ODDS 1:11,100 HOBBY
21-60 STATED ODDS 1:2151 HOBBY
STATED PRINT RUN 1 SER.#'d SET
NO PRICING DUE TO SCARCITY

2009 Bowman Chrome WBC Prospects X-Fractors

*X-F: 1.5X TO 4X BASIC
1-20 ODDS 1:45 HOBBY
21-60 ODDS 1:10 HOBBY
1-20 PRINT RUN 275 SER.#'d SETS
21-60 PRINT RUN 250 SER.#'d SETS
BCW1 Yu Darvish 30.00 80.00

2009 Bowman Chrome Draft

COMPLETE SET (55) 10.00 25.00
COMMON CARD (1-55) .30 .75
OVERALL PLATE ODDS 1:1531 HOBBY
PLATE PRINT RUN 1 SET PER COLOR
BLACK-CYAN-MAGENTA-YELLOW ISSUED
NO PLATE PRICING DUE TO SCARCITY
BDP1 Tommy Hanson RC 1.00 2.50
BDP2 Jeff Manship RC .30 .75
BDP3 Trevor Bell (RC) .30 .75
BDP4 Trevor Cahill RC .75 2.00
BDP5 Trent Oeltjen (RC) .30 .75
BDP6 Wyatt Toregas RC .30 .75
BDP7 Kevin Mulvey RC .30 .75
BDP8 Rusty Ryal RC .30 .75
BDP9 Mike Carp (RC) .50 1.25
BDP10 Jorge Padilla (RC) .30 .75
BDP11 J.D. Martin (RC) .30 .75
BDP12 Dusty Ryan RC .30 .75
BDP13 Alex Avila RC .50 1.25
BDP14 Brandon Allen (RC) .30 .75
BDP15 Tommy Everidge (RC) .50 1.25
BDP16 Bud Norris RC .30 .75
BDP17 Neftali Feliz RC 1.00 2.50
BDP18 Mat Latos RC 1.00 2.50
BDP19 Ryan Perry RC .75 2.00
BDP20 Craig Tatum (RC) .30 .75
BDP21 Chris Tillman RC .50 1.25
BDP22 Jhoulys Chacin RC .50 1.25
BDP23 Michael Saunders RC .50 1.25
BDP24 Jeff Stevens RC .30 .75
BDP25 Luis Valdez RC .30 .75
BDP26 Robert Manuel RC .30 .75
BDP27 Ryan Webb (RC) .30 .75
BDP28 Marc Rzepczynski RC .50 1.25
BDP29 Travis Schlichting (RC) .50 1.25
BDP30 Barbaro Canizares RC .30 .75
BDP31 Brad Mills RC .30 .75
BDP32 Dusty Brown (RC) .30 .75
BDP33 Tim Wood RC .30 .75
BDP34 Drew Sutton RC .50 1.25
BDP35 Jarrett Hoffpauir (RC) .30 .75
BDP36 Jose Lobaton RC .30 .75
BDP37 Aaron Bates RC .30 .75
BDP38 Clayton Mortensen RC .30 .75
BDP39 Ryan Sadowski RC .30 .75
BDP40 Fu-Te Ni RC .50 1.25
BDP41 Casey McGehee (RC) .30 .75
BDP42 Omir Santos RC .30 .75
BDP43 Brent Leach RC .50 1.25
BDP44 Diory Hernandez RC .30 .75
BDP45 Wilkin Castillo RC .30 .75
BDP46 Trevor Crowe RC .30 .75
BDP47 Sean West (RC) .50 1.25
BDP48 Clayton Richard (RC) .30 .75
BDP49 Julio Borbon RC .50 1.25
BDP50 Kyle Blanks RC .50 1.25
BDP51 Jeff Gray RC .30 .75
BDP52 Gio Gonzalez (RC) .30 .75
BDP53 Vin Mazzaro RC .30 .75
BDP54 Josh Reddick RC .50 1.25
BDP55 Fernando Martinez RC .75 2.00

2009 Bowman Chrome Draft Refractors

*REF: 1X TO 2.5X BASIC
STATED ODDS 1:11 HOBBY

2009 Bowman Chrome Draft Blue Refractors

*BLUE REF: 2.5X TO 6X BASIC
STATED ODDS 1:49 HOBBY
STATED PRINT RUN 99 SER.#'d SETS
BDP13 Alex Avila 8.00 20.00
BDP40 Fu-Te Ni 15.00 40.00

2009 Bowman Chrome Draft Gold Refractors

*GOLD: 4X TO 10X BASIC
STATED ODDS 1:96 HOBBY
STATED PRINT RUN 50 SER.#'d SETS
BDP13 Alex Avila 12.00 30.00
BDP40 Fu-Te Ni 30.00 80.00

2009 Bowman Chrome Draft Orange Refractors

STATED ODDS 1:192 HOBBY
STATED PRINT RUN 25 SER.#'d SETS
NO PRICING DUE TO SCARCITY

2009 Bowman Chrome Draft Purple Refractors

*PURPLE: 2X TO 5X BASIC
RANDOM INSERTS IN RETAIL PACKS

2009 Bowman Chrome Draft Red Refractors

STATED ODDS 1:955 HOBBY
STATED PRINT RUN 5 SER.#'d SETS
NO PRICING DUE TO SCARCITY

2009 Bowman Chrome Draft SuperFractors

STATED ODDS 1:4266 HOBBY
STATED PRINT RUN 1 SER.#'d SET
NO PRICING DUE TO SCARCITY

2009 Bowman Chrome Draft X-Fractors

*X-F: 1.5X TO 4X BASIC
STATED ODDS 1:24 HOBBY
STATED PRINT RUN 199 SER.#'d SETS
BDP40 Fu-Te Ni 6.00 15.00

2009 Bowman Chrome Draft Prospects

COMP.SET w/o AU's (75) 12.50 30.00
STATED AU ODDS 1:24 HOBBY
OVERALL PLATE ODDS 1:1531 HOBBY
OVERALL AUTO PLATE ODDS 1:7973 HOBBY
PLATE PRINT RUN 1 SET PER COLOR
BLACK-CYAN-MAGENTA-YELLOW ISSUED
NO PLATE PRICING DUE TO SCARCITY
BDPP1 Tanner Bushue .50 1.25
BDPP2 Billy Hamilton 2.00 5.00
BDPP3 Enrique Hernandez .30 .75
BDPP4 Virgil Hill .30 .75
BDPP5 Josh Hodges .50 1.25
BDPP6 Christopher Lovett .30 .75
BDPP7 Michael Belfiore .30 .75
BDPP8 Jobduan Morales .30 .75
BDPP9 Anthony Morris .30 .75
BDPP10 Telvin Nash .50 1.25
BDPP11 Brooks Pounders .50 1.25
BDPP12 Kyle Rose .30 .75
BDPP13 Seth Schwindenhammer .50 1.25
BDPP14 Patrick Lehman .50 1.25
BDPP15 Mathew Weaver .50 1.25
BDPP16 Brian Dozier .30 .75
BDPP17 Sequoyah Stonecipher .50 1.25
BDPP18 Shannon Wilkerson .30 .75
BDPP19 Jerry Sullivan .30 .75
BDPP20 Jamie Johnson .30 .75
BDPP21 Kent Matthes .30 .75
BDPP22 Ben Paulsen .30 .75
BDPP23 Matthew Davidson .50 1.25
BDPP24 Benjamin Carlson .30 .75
BDPP25 Brock Holt .30 .75
BDPP26 Ben Orloff .30 .75
BDPP27 D.J. LeMahieu .50 1.25
BDPP28 Erik Castro .50 1.25
BDPP29 James Jones .30 .75
BDPP30 Cory Burns .30 .75
BDPP31 Chris Wade .30 .75
BDPP32 Jaff Decker .50 1.25
BDPP33 Naoya Washiya .30 .75
BDPP34 Brandt Walker .30 .75
BDPP35 Jordan Henry .50 1.25
BDPP36 Austin Adams .30 .75
BDPP37 Andrew Bellatti .50 1.25
BDPP38 Paul Applebee .50 1.25
BDPP39 Robert Stock .50 1.25
BDPP40 Michael Flacco .30 .75
BDPP41 Jonathan Meyer .30 .75
BDPP42 Cody Rogers .50 1.25
BDPP43 Matt Heidenreich .30 .75
BDPP44 David Holmberg .75 2.00
BDPP45 Mycal Jones .30 .75
BDPP46 David Hale .30 .75
BDPP47 Dusty Odenbach .30 .75
BDPP48 Robert Hefflinger .30 .75
BDPP49 Buddy Baumann .30 .75
BDPP50 Thomas Berryhill .30 .75
BDPP51 Darrell Ceciliani .30 .75
BDPP52 Derek McCallum .30 .75
BDPP53 Taylor Freeman .30 .75
BDPP54 Tyler Townsend .50 1.25
BDPP55 Tobias Streich .50 1.25
BDPP56 Ryan Jackson .30 .75
BDPP57 Chris Herrmann .50 1.25
BDPP58 Robert Shields .30 .75
BDPP59 Devin Fuller .30 .75
BDPP60 Brad Stillings .30 .75
BDPP61 Ryan Goins .30 .75
BDPP62 Chase Austin .30 .75
BDPP63 Brett Nommensen .30 .75
BDPP64 Egan Smith .30 .75
BDPP65 Daniel Mahoney .30 .75
BDPP66 Darin Gorski .30 .75
BDPP67 Dustin Dickerson .50 1.25
BDPP68 Victor Black .50 1.25
BDPP69 Dallas Keuchel .50 1.25
BDPP70 Nate Baker .30 .75
BDPP71 David Nick .50 1.25
BDPP72 Brian Moran .30 .75
BDPP73 Mark Fleury .30 .75
BDPP74 Brett Wallach .50 1.25
BDPP75 Adam Buschini .30 .75
BDPP76 Tony Sanchez AU 10.00 25.00
BDPP77 Eric Arnett AU 5.00 12.00
BDPP78 Tim Wheeler AU 10.00 25.00
BDPP79 Matt Hobgood AU 10.00 25.00
BDPP80 Matt Bashore AU 5.00 12.00
BDPP81 Randal Grichuk AU 10.00 25.00
BDPP82 A.J. Pollock AU 8.00 20.00
BDPP83 Reymond Fuentes AU 6.00 15.00
BDPP84 Jiovanni Mier AU 6.00 15.00
BDPP85 Steve Matz AU 8.00 20.00
BDPP86 Zack Wheeler AU 12.50 30.00
BDPP87 Mike Minor AU 6.00 15.00
BDPP88 Jared Mitchell AU 5.00 12.00
BDPP89 Mike Trout AU 50.00 100.00
BDPP90 Alex White AU 8.00 20.00
BDPP91 Bobby Borchering AU 12.50 30.00
BDPP92 Chad James AU 5.00 12.00
BDPP93 Tyler Matzek AU 6.00 15.00
BDPP94 Max Stassi AU 5.00 12.00
BDPP95 Drew Storen AU 8.00 20.00
BDPP96 Brad Boxberger AU 5.00 12.00
BDPP97 Mike Leake AU 8.00 20.00

2009 Bowman Chrome Draft Prospects Refractors

*REF: 1.5X TO 4X BASIC
STATED ODDS 1:11 HOBBY
*REF AU: .5X TO 1.2X BASIC AU
STATED AUTO ODDS 1:71 HOBBY
AUTO PRINT RUN 500 SER.#'d SETS
BDPP89 Mike Trout AU 75.00 150.00

2009 Bowman Chrome Draft Prospects Blue Refractors

*BLUE REF: 4X TO 10X BASIC
STATED ODDS 1:49 HOBBY
STATED PRINT RUN 99 SER.#'d SETS
*BLUE REF AU: 1X TO 2.5X BASIC AU
STATED AUTO ODDS 1:241 HOBBY
AUTO PRINT RUN 150 SER.#'d SETS
BDPP23 Matthew Davidson 10.00 25.00
BDPP89 Mike Trout AU 200.00 400.00

2009 Bowman Chrome Draft Prospects Gold Refractors

*GOLD REF: 8X TO 20X BASIC
STATED ODDS 1:96 HOBBY
STATED PRINT RUN 50 SER.#'d SETS
*GOLD REF AU: 2X TO 5X BASIC AU
STATED AUTO ODDS 1:736 HOBBY
AUTO PRINT RUN 50 SER.#'d SETS
BDPP23 Matthew Davidson 25.00 60.00
BDPP39 Robert Stock 20.00 50.00
BDPP83 Reymond Fuentes AU 75.00 150.00
BDPP89 Mike Trout AU 500.00 700.00

2009 Bowman Chrome Draft Prospects Orange Refractors

STATED ODDS 1:192 HOBBY
STATED AUTO ODDS 1:1545 HOBBY
STATED PRINT RUN 25 SER.#'d SETS
NO PRICING DUE TO SCARCITY

2009 Bowman Chrome Draft Prospects Purple Refractors

*PURPLE: 2X TO 5X BASIC
RANDOM INSERTS IN RETAIL PACKS

2009 Bowman Chrome Draft Prospects Red Refractors

STATED ODDS 1:955 HOBBY
STATED PRINT RUN 5 SER.#'d SETS
STATED AUTO ODDS 1:6378 HOBBY
NO PRICING DUE TO SCARCITY

2009 Bowman Chrome Draft Prospects SuperFractors

STATED ODDS 1:4266 HOBBY
STATED AUTO ODDS 1:31,900 HOBBY
STATED PRINT RUN 1 SER.#'d SET
NO PRICING DUE TO SCARCITY

2009 Bowman Chrome Draft Prospects X-Fractors

*X-F: 2.5X TO 6X BASIC
STATED ODDS 1:24 HOBBY
STATED PRINT RUN 199 SER.#'d SETS
*X-F AU: .6X TO 1.5X BASIC AU
STATED AUTO ODDS 1:159 HOBBY
AUTO PRINT RUN 225 SER.#'d SETS
BDPP89 Mike Trout AU 100.00 200.00

2009 Bowman Chrome Draft WBC Prospects

COMPLETE SET (35) 8.00 20.00
OVERALL PLATE ODDS 1:1531 HOBBY
PLATE PRINT RUN 1 SET PER COLOR
BLACK-CYAN-MAGENTA-YELLOW ISSUED
NO PLATE PRICING DUE TO SCARCITY
BDPW1 Ichiro Suzuki 1.25 3.00
BDPW2 Yu Darvish 3.00 8.00
BDPW3 Phillippe Aumont .75 2.00
BDPW4 Derek Jeter 2.00 5.00
BDPW5 Dustin Pedroia 1.00 2.50
BDPW6 Earl Agnoly .30 .75
BDPW7 Jose Reyes .50 1.25
BDPW8 Michel Enriquez .30 .75
BDPW9 David Ortiz .50 1.25
BDPW10 Chunhua Dong .50 1.25
BDPW11 Munenori Kawasaki .75 2.00
BDPW12 Arquimedes Nieto .30 .75
BDPW13 Bernie Williams .50 1.25
BDPW14 Pedro Lazo .30 .75
BDPW15 Jing-Chao Wang .50 1.25
BDPW16 Chris Barnwell .30 .75
BDPW17 Elmer Dessens .30 .75
BDPW18 Russell Martin .30 .75
BDPW19 Luca Panerati .30 .75
BDPW20 Adam Dunn .50 1.25
BDPW21 Andy Gonzalez .30 .75
BDPW22 Daisuke Matsuzaka .75 2.00
BDPW23 Daniel Berg .30 .75
BDPW24 Aroldis Chapman 1.25 3.00
BDPW25 Justin Morneau .75 2.00
BDPW26 Miguel Cabrera .75 2.00
BDPW27 Magglio Ordonez .50 1.25
BDPW28 Shawn Bowman .30 .75
BDPW29 Robbie Cordemans .30 .75
BDPW30 Paolo Espino .30 .75
BDPW31 Chipper Jones .75 2.00
BDPW32 Frederich Cepeda .50 1.25
BDPW33 Ubaldo Jimenez .50 1.25
BDPW34 Seiichi Uchikawa .50 1.25
BDPW35 Norichika Aoki .50 1.25

2009 Bowman Chrome Draft WBC Prospects Refractors

*REF: 1X TO 2.5X BASIC
STATED ODDS 1:11 HOBBY

2009 Bowman Chrome Draft WBC Prospects Blue Refractors

*BLUE REF: 2.5X TO 6X BASIC
STATED ODDS 1:49 HOBBY
STATED PRINT RUN 99 SER.#'d SETS
BDPW2 Yu Darvish 40.00 80.00

2009 Bowman Chrome Draft WBC Prospects Gold Refractors

*GOLD: 4X TO 10X BASIC
STATED ODDS 1:96 HOBBY
STATED PRINT RUN 50 SER.#'d SETS
BDPW2 Yu Darvish 125.00 250.00

2009 Bowman Chrome Draft WBC Prospects Orange Refractors

STATED ODDS 1:192 HOBBY
STATED PRINT RUN 25 SER.#'d SETS
NO PRICING DUE TO SCARCITY

2009 Bowman Chrome Draft WBC Prospects Red Refractors

STATED ODDS 1:955 HOBBY
STATED PRINT RUN 5 SER.#'d SETS
NO PRICING DUE TO SCARCITY

2009 Bowman Chrome Draft WBC Prospects SuperFractors

STATED ODDS 1:4266 HOBBY
STATED PRINT RUN 1 SER.#'d SET
NO PRICING DUE TO SCARCITY

2009 Bowman Chrome Draft WBC Prospects X-Fractors

*X-F: 1.5X TO 4X BASIC
STATED ODDS 1:24 HOBBY
STATED PRINT RUN 199 SER.#'d SETS

2010 Bowman Chrome

COMP.SET w/o AU's (220) 40.00 80.00
COMMON CARD (1-180) .20 .50
COMMON RC (181-220) .60 1.50
COMMON AU 3.00 8.00
BOW.STATED AU ODDS 1:113 HOBBY
STRASBURG AU ODDS 1:3810 HOBBY
BOW.CHR.PLATE ODDS 1:1405 HOBBY
STRASBURG AU PLATE ODDS 1:12,000 HOBBY
PLATE PRINT RUN 1 SET PER COLOR
BLACK-CYAN-MAGENTA-YELLOW ISSUED
NO PLATE PRICING DUE TO SCARCITY
EXCHANGE DEADLINE 9/30/2013
1 Ryan Braun .60 1.50
2 Will Venable .20 .50
3 Zack Greinke .30 .75
4 Matt Kemp .30 .75
5 Jair Jurrjens .20 .50
6 Josh Hamilton .50 1.25
7 Josh Beckett .30 .75
8 Jake Peavy .20 .50
9 Luke Hochevar .20 .50
10 Ryan Zimmerman .30 .75
11 Robinson Cano .50 1.25
12 Magglio Ordonez .30 .75
13 Brian Roberts .20 .50
14 A.J. Burnett .30 .75
15 Chris Carpenter .50 1.25
16 Clayton Kershaw .50 1.25
17 Jayson Werth .30 .75
18 Alexei Ramirez .20 .50
19 Ricky Romero .20 .50
20 Andrew McCutchen .50 1.25
21 Chad Billingsley .20 .50
22 David Ortiz .30 .75
23 Rajai Davis .20 .50
24 Trevor Cahill .20 .50
25 Dan Haren .20 .50
26 Dan Uggla .30 .75
27 Ryan Dempster .20 .50
28 Koji Uehara .30 .75
29 Carlos Gonzalez .30 .75
30 Justin Upton .30 .75
31 Elvis Andrus .30 .75
32 James Loney .30 .75
33 Matt Garza .20 .50
34 Brandon Phillips .20 .50
35 Miguel Cabrera .50 1.25
36 Shane Victorino .30 .75
37 Kyle Blanks .20 .50
38 Troy Tulowitzki .50 1.25
39 Chipper Jones .50 1.25
40 Todd Helton .30 .75
41 Derrek Lee .20 .50
42 Michael Bourn .20 .50
43 Jose Lopez .20 .50
44 Hunter Pence .30 .75
45 Edinson Volquez .20 .50
46 Miguel Montero .20 .50
47 Kevin Youkilis .30 .75
48 Adrian Gonzalez .30 .75
49 Carl Crawford .30 .75
50 Stephen Drew .20 .50
51 Carlos Pena .30 .75
52 Ubaldo Jimenez .30 .75
53 Martin Prado .20 .50
54 Alcides Escobar .30 .75
55 Jeff Niemann .20 .50
56 Andre Ethier .30 .75
57 Michael Cuddyer .20 .50
58 Howard Kendrick .20 .50
59 Scott Rolen .30 .75
60 Adam Lind .30 .75
61 Prince Fielder .30 .75
62 David Price .50 1.25
63 Johnny Cueto .20 .50
64 John Maine .20 .50
65 Nick Markakis .50 1.25
66 Kosuke Fukudome .50 1.25
67 Yadier Molina .30 .75
68 Aramis Ramirez .20 .50
69 Billy Butler .20 .50
70 Wandy Rodriguez .20 .50
71 Ben Zobrist .20 .50
72 Victor Martinez .30 .75
73 Jorge Posada .30 .75
74 Adam Wainwright .30 .75
75 Vernon Wells .20 .50
76 Gordon Beckham .30 .75
77 Nelson Cruz .30 .75
78 Kevin Slowey .20 .50
79 Paul Maholm .20 .50
80 Johan Santana .50 1.25
81 Kazuo Matsui .20 .50
82 Jon Lester .50 1.25
83 Clay Buchholz .30 .75
84 Alex Gordon .30 .75
85 Justin Morneau .50 1.25
86 B.J. Upton .30 .75
87 Justin Verlander .60 1.50
88 Carlos Quentin .30 .75
89 Dustin Pedroia .60 1.50
90 Josh Willingham .20 .50
91 Alex Rios .30 .75
92 David Wright .60 1.50
93 Adam Dunn .30 .75
94 Jhoulys Chacin .20 .50
95 Andrew Bailey .20 .50
96 Derek Holland .20 .50
97 Kenshin Kawakami .30 .75
98 Jered Weaver .20 .50
99 Freddy Sanchez .20 .50
100 Matt Holliday .50 1.25
101 Bobby Abreu .20 .50
102 Ryan Doumit .20 .50
103 Kurt Suzuki .20 .50
104 Yovani Gallardo .20 .50
105 Daisuke Matsuzaka .50 1.25
106 Francisco Liriano .20 .50
107 Jimmy Rollins .30 .75
108 James Shields .20 .50
109 Chase Utley .50 1.25
110 Jeff Francoeur .30 .75
111 Tim Hudson .30 .75
112 Brad Hawpe .20 .50
113 Cole Hamels .50 1.25
114 Alfonso Soriano .30 .75
115 Lance Berkman .30 .75
116 Torii Hunter .20 .50
117 Chris Tillman .20 .50
118 Alex Rodriguez .75 2.00
119 Pablo Sandoval .30 .75
120 Ryan Howard .60 1.50
121 Rick Porcello .20 .50
122 Hanley Ramirez .50 1.25
123 Brian McCann .30 .75
124 Kendry Morales .20 .50
125 Josh Johnson .30 .75
126 Joe Mauer .50 1.25
127 Grady Sizemore .30 .75
128 J.A. Happ .30 .75
129 Ichiro .75 2.00
130 Aaron Hill .20 .50
131 Mark Teixeira .50 1.25
132 Tim Lincecum .75 2.00
133 Denard Span .20 .50
134 Roy Oswalt .30 .75
135 Manny Ramirez .50 1.25
136 Jorge De La Rosa .20 .50
137 Joey Votto .50 1.25
138 Neftali Feliz .20 .50
139 Yunel Escobar .20 .50
140 Carlos Zambrano .30 .75
141 Erick Aybar .20 .50
142 Albert Pujols 1.25 3.00
143 Felix Hernandez .50 1.25
144 Adam Jones .30 .75
145 Jacoby Ellsbury .50 1.25
146 Mark Reynolds .20 .50
147 Derek Jeter 1.25 3.00
148 Scott Baker .20 .50
149 Jose Reyes .30 .75
150 Jason Kubel .20 .50
151 Shin-Soo Choo .30 .75
152 Raul Ibanez .30 .75
153 Matt Cain .30 .75
154 Mark Buehrle .30 .75
155 Ken Griffey Jr. .75 2.00
156 Carlos Lee .20 .50
157 Chris Coghlan .20 .50
158 CC Sabathia .30 .75
159 Brett Anderson .30 .75
160 Ian Kinsler .30 .75
161 Mat Latos .20 .50
162 Carlos Beltran .20 .50
163 Dexter Fowler .20 .50
164 Michael Young .30 .75
165 Evan Longoria .60 1.50
166 Curtis Granderson .30 .75
167 Rich Harden .20 .50
168 Hideki Matsui .50 1.25
169 Edwin Jackson .20 .50
170 Miguel Tejada .30 .75
171 John Lackey .20 .50
172 Vladimir Guerrero .50 1.25
173 Max Scherzer .20 .50
174 Jason Bay .30 .75
175 Javier Vazquez .20 .50
176 Johnny Damon .30 .75
177 Cliff Lee .30 .75
178 Chone Figgins .20 .50
179 Kevin Millwood .20 .50
180 Roy Halladay .50 1.25
181 Drew Butera (RC) .60 1.50
182 Matt Carson (RC) .60 1.50
183 Ian Desmond (RC) 1.00 2.50
184 Kila Ka'aihue (RC) 1.00 2.50
185 Brian Matusz RC 1.50 4.00
186 Mike Leake RC 2.00 5.00
187 Jenrry Mejia RC 1.00 2.50
188 Austin Jackson RC 1.00 2.50
189 Scott Sizemore RC 1.00 2.50
190 Jason Heyward RC 4.00 10.00
191 Travis Wood (RC) 1.00 2.50
192 Josh Donaldson RC .60 1.50
193 John Ely RC .60 1.50
194 Eric Young Jr. (RC) .60 1.50
195 Jason Donald RC .60 1.50
196 Andrew Cashner RC .60 1.50
197 Kevin Russo RC .60 1.50
198A Austin Jackson AU 12.50 30.00
198B Mike Stanton RC 2.50 6.00
199A Scott Sizemore AU 5.00 12.00
199B Drew Storen RC 1.00 2.50
200A Jason Heyward AU 15.00 40.00
200B Jonathan Lucroy RC .60 1.50
201 Wade Davis (RC) .60 1.50
202 Jon Jay RC 1.00 2.50
203 Ike Davis RC 1.50 4.00
204 Michael Brantley RC .60 1.50
205A Stephen Strasburg RC 4.00 10.00
205B Stephen Strasburg AU 125.00 250.00
206 Drew Stubbs RC 1.50 4.00
207 Daniel McCutchen RC 1.00 2.50
208 Brennan Boesch RC 1.50 4.00
209A Henry Rodriguez AU 3.00 8.00
209B Wilson Ramos RC 1.50 4.00
210 Chris Heisey RC 1.00 2.50
211A Michael Dunn AU 3.00 8.00
211B Starlin Castro RC 2.50 6.00
212A Drew Stubbs AU 6.00 15.00
212B Trevor Plouffe (RC) .60 1.50
213A Brandon Allen AU 3.00 8.00
213B Luis Atilano RC .60 1.50
214A Daniel McCutchen AU 3.00 8.00
214B Carlos Santana RC 2.00 5.00
215A Juan Francisco AU 5.00 12.00
215B Allen Craig RC 1.50 4.00
216A Eric Hacker AU 3.00 8.00
216B Ruben Tejada RC 1.00 2.50
217A Michael Brantley AU 5.00 12.00
217B Andy Oliver RC .60 1.50
218A Dustin Richardson AU 3.00 8.00
218B Tyler Colvin RC 1.00 2.50
219A Josh Thole AU 5.00 12.00
219B Cesar Valdez RC .60 1.50
220A Daniel Hudson AU 5.00 12.00
220B Lance Zawadzki RC .60 1.50

2010 Bowman Chrome Refractors

*REF VET: 1X TO 2.5X BASIC
*REF RC: .6X TO 1.5X BASIC RC
REF ODDS 1:4 HOBBY
REF PRINT RUN 500 SER.#'d SETS
*REF AU: .6X TO 1.5X BASIC
REF AU ODDS 1:277 HOBBY
STRASBURG AU ODDS 1:105 HOBBY
REF AU PRINT RUN 500 SER.#'d SETS
EXCHANGE DEADLINE 9/30/2013
205B Stephen Strasburg AU 150.00 300.00
220A Daniel Hudson AU 8.00 20.00

2010 Bowman Chrome Blue Refractors

*BLUE VET: 2.5X TO 6X BASIC
*BLUE RC: 1.2X TO 3X BASIC
BLUE REF ODDS 1:48 HOBBY
STATED PRINT RUN 150 SER.#'d SETS
*BLUE AU: .75X TO 2X BASIC
BLUE AU ODDS 1:545 HOBBY
BLUE STRASBURG AU ODDS 1:352 HOBBY
BLUE AU PRINT RUN 250 SER.#'d SETS
EXCHANGE DEADLINE 9/30/2013
190 Jason Heyward 15.00 40.00
205B Stephen Strasburg AU 250.00 400.00
212A Drew Stubbs AU 20.00 50.00
220A Daniel Hudson AU 15.00 40.00

2010 Bowman Chrome Gold Refractors

*GOLD VET: 5X TO 12X BASIC
*GOLD RC: 2X TO 5X BASIC
GOLD REF ODDS 1:142 HOBBY
STATED PRINT RUN 50 SER.#'d SETS
*GOLD AU: 1.2X TO 3X BASIC
GOLD AU ODDS 1:2733 HOBBY
GOLD STRASBURG AU ODDS 1:1073 HOBBY
GOLD AU PRINT RUN 50 SER.#'d SETS
EXCHANGE DEADLINE 9/30/2013
190 Jason Heyward 50.00 100.00
200A Jason Heyward AU 150.00 300.00
205A Stephen Strasburg 75.00 150.00
205B Stephen Strasburg AU 500.00 1000.00
212A Drew Stubbs AU 60.00 120.00
213A Brandon Allen AU 20.00 50.00
215A Juan Francisco AU 30.00 60.00
217A Michael Brantley AU 30.00 60.00
219A Josh Thole AU 40.00 80.00
220A Daniel Hudson AU 50.00 100.00

2010 Bowman Chrome Red Refractors

STATED ODDS 1:1420 HOBBY
STRASBURG AU ODDS 1:10,600 HOBBY
STATED PRINT RUN 5 SER.#'d SETS
NO PRICING DUE TO SCARCITY
EXCHANGE DEADLINE 9/30/2013

2010 Bowman Chrome SuperFractors

STATED PRINT RUN 1 SER.#'d SET
NO PRICING DUE TO SCARCITY
BOW.STATED AU ODDS 1:141,400 HOBBY
STATED ODDS 1:5625 HOBBY
STRASBURG AU ODDS 1:48,000 HOBBY
EXCHANGE DEADLINE 9/30/2013

2010 Bowman Chrome 18U USA Baseball

COMPLETE SET (20) 15.00 40.00
STATED ODDS 1:4 HOBBY
PLATE PRINT RUN 1 SET PER COLOR
BLACK-CYAN-MAGENTA-YELLOW ISSUED
NO PLATE PRICING DUE TO SCARCITY
18BC1 Cody Buckel .60 1.50
18BC2 Nick Castellanos 2.00 5.00
18BC3 Garin Cecchini 2.00 5.00
18BC4 Sean Coyle .60 1.50
18BC5 Nicky Delmonico .60 1.50
18BC6 Kevin Gausman .60 1.50
18BC7 Cory Hahn .60 1.50
18BC8 Bryce Harper 40.00 80.00
18BC9 Kavin Keyes .60 1.50
18BC10 Manny Machado 5.00 12.00
18BC11 Connor Mason .60 1.50
18BC12 Ladson Montgomery .60 1.50
18BC13 Phillip Pfeifer .60 1.50
18BC14 Brian Ragira .60 1.50
18BC15 Robbie Ray .60 1.50
18BC16 Kyle Ryan .60 1.50
18BC17 Jameson Taillon 2.50 6.00
18BC18 A.J. Vanegas 1.00 2.50
18BC19 Karsten Whitson 2.00 5.00
18BC20 Tony Wolters 1.00 2.50

2010 Bowman Chrome 18U USA Baseball Refractors

*REF: .75X TO 2X BASIC
STATED ODDS 1:16 HOBBY
STATED PRINT RUN 777 SER.#'d SETS
18BC8 Bryce Harper 100.00 200.00

2010 Bowman Chrome 18U USA Baseball Blue Refractors

*BLUE REF: 2X TO 5X BASIC
STATED ODDS 1:46 HOBBY
STATED PRINT RUN 250 SER.#'d SETS
18BC8 Bryce Harper 175.00 350.00

2010 Bowman Chrome 18U USA Baseball Gold Refractors

*GOLD REF: 6X TO 15X BASIC
STATED ODDS 1:228 HOBBY
STATED PRINT RUN 50 SER.#'d SETS
18BC8 Bryce Harper 600.00 1200.00

2010 Bowman Chrome 18U USA Baseball Orange Refractors

STATED ODDS 1:463 HOBBY
STATED PRINT RUN 25 SER.#'d SETS
NO PRICING DUE TO SCARCITY

2010 Bowman Chrome 18U USA Baseball Red Refractors

STATED ODDS 1:2828 HOBBY
STATED PRINT RUN 5 SER.#'d SETS
NO PRICING DUE TO SCARCITY

2010 Bowman Chrome 18U USA Baseball SuperFractors

STATED ODDS 1:11,000 HOBBY
STATED PRINT RUN 1 SER.#'d SET
NO PRICING DUE TO SCARCITY

2010 Bowman Chrome 18U USA Baseball Autographs

STATED ODDS 1:207 HOBBY
PRINTING PLATE ODDS 1:24,605 HOBBY
PLATE PRINT RUN 1 SET PER COLOR
BLACK-CYAN-MAGENTA-YELLOW ISSUED
NO PLATE PRICING DUE TO SCARCITY
AA Albert Almora 6.00 15.00
AV A.J. Vanegas 6.00 15.00
BR Brian Ragira 5.00 12.00
BS Bubba Starling 40.00 80.00
CL Christian Lopes 8.00 20.00
CM Christian Montgomery 5.00 12.00
DC Daniel Camarena 5.00 12.00
DM Dillon Maples 6.00 15.00
ES Elvin Soto 6.00 15.00
FL Francisco Lindor 12.50 30.00
HO Henry Owens 8.00 20.00
JH John Hochstatter 5.00 12.00
JS John Simms 5.00 12.00
LM Lance McCullers 10.00 25.00
ML Marcus Littlewood 6.00 15.00
ND Nicky Delmonico 8.00 20.00
PP Phillip Pfeifer III 6.00 15.00
TW Tony Wolters 5.00 12.00
BSW Blake Swihart 10.00 25.00
MIL Michael Lorenzen 5.00 12.00

2010 Bowman Chrome 18U USA Baseball Autographs Refractors

*REF: .6X TO 1.5X BASIC
STATED ODDS 1:646 HOBBY
STATED PRINT RUN 199 SER.#'d SETS

2010 Bowman Chrome 18U USA Baseball Autographs Blue Refractors

*BLUE REF: 1X TO 2.5X BASIC
STATED ODDS 1:1310 HOBBY
STATED PRINT RUN 99 SER.#'d SETS

2010 Bowman Chrome 18U USA Baseball Autographs Gold Refractors

*GOLD REF: 2X TO 5X BASIC
STATED ODDS 1:2630 HOBBY
STATED PRINT RUN 50 SER.#'d SETS

HO Henry Owens 75.00 150.00
BSW Blake Swihart 100.00 175.00

2010 Bowman Chrome 18U USA Baseball Autographs Orange Refractors

STATED ODDS 1:5410 HOBBY
STATED PRINT RUN 25 SER.#'d SETS
NO PRICING DUE TO SCARCITY

2010 Bowman Chrome 18U USA Baseball Autographs Red Refractors

STATED ODDS 1:25,500 HOBBY
STATED PRINT RUN 5 SER.#'d SETS
NO PRICING DUE TO SCARCITY

2010 Bowman Chrome 18U USA Baseball Autographs SuperFractors

STATED ODDS 1:98,420 HOBBY
STATED PRINT RUN 1 SER.#'d SET
NO PRICING DUE TO SCARCITY

2010 Bowman Chrome Prospects

COMP.SET w/o AU's (220) 60.00 120.00
BOW.STATED AU ODDS 1:38 HOBBY
BOW.CHR.STATED AU ODDS 1:24 HOBBY
PLATE ODDS 1:1405 HOBBY
PLATE AU ODDS 1:12,000 HOBBY
PLATE PRINT RUN 1 SET PER COLOR
BLACK-CYAN-MAGENTA-YELLOW ISSUED
NO PLATE PRICING DUE TO SCARCITY
BCP1 Stephen Strasburg 8.00 20.00
BCP2 Melky Mesa .50 1.25
BCP3 Cole McCurry .30 .75
BCP4 Tyler Henley .30 .75
BCP5 Andrew Cashner .30 .75
BCP6 Konrad Schmidt .30 .75
BCP7 Jean Segura .75 2.00
BCP8 Jon Gaston .50 1.25
BCP9 Nick Santomauro .30 .75
BCP10 Aroldis Chapman 1.25 3.00
BCP11 Logan Watkins .30 .75
BCP12 Bo Bowman .30 .75
BCP13 Jeff Antigua .30 .75
BCP14 Matt Adams .50 1.25
BCP15 Joseph Cruz .50 1.25
BCP16 Sebastian Valle .50 1.25
BCP17 Stefan Gartrell .30 .75
BCP18 Pedro Ciriaco .30 .75
BCP19 Tyson Gillies .75 2.00
BCP20 Casey Crosby 1.00 2.50
BCP21 Luis Exposito .30 .75
BCP22 Welington Dotel .30 .75
BCP23 Alexander Torres .30 .75
BCP24 Byron Wiley .30 .75
BCP25 Pedro Florimon .30 .75
BCP26 Cody Satterwhite .50 1.25
BCP27 Craig Clark 1.25 3.00
BCP28 Jason Christian .30 .75
BCP29 Tommy Mendonca .30 .75
BCP30 Ryan Dent .30 .75
BCP31 Jhan Marinez .30 .75
BCP32 Eric Niesen .30 .75
BCP33 Gustavo Nunez .30 .75
BCP34 Scott Shaw .30 .75
BCP35 Welinton Ramirez .30 .75
BCP36 Trevor May 1.25 3.00
BCP37 Mitch Moreland .50 1.25
BCP38 Nick Czyz .30 .75
BCP39 Edinson Rincon .30 .75
BCP40 Domingo Santana 1.50 4.00
BCP41 Carson Blair .30 .75
BCP42 Rashun Dixon .30 .75
BCP43 Alexander Colome .75 2.00
BCP44 Allan Dykstra .30 .75
BCP45 J.J. Hoover .30 .75
BCP46 Abner Abreu .50 1.25
BCP47 Daniel Nava .50 1.25
BCP48 Simon Castro .50 1.25
BCP49 Brian Baisley .30 .75
BCP50 Tony Delmonico .30 .75
BCP51 Chase D'Arnaud .30 .75
BCP52 Sheng-An Kuo .30 .75
BCP53 Leandro Castro .30 .75
BCP54 Charlie Leesman .30 .75
BCP55 Caleb Joseph .30 .75
BCP56 Rolando Gomez .30 .75
BCP57 John Lamb .75 2.00
BCP58 Adam Wilk .50 1.25
BCP59 Randall Delgado 1.50 4.00
BCP60 Neil Medchill .50 1.25
BCP61 Josh Donaldson .30 .75
BCP62 Zach Gentile .30 .75
BCP63 Kiel Roling .30 .75
BCP64 Wes Freeman .30 .75
BCP65 Brian Pellegrini .50 1.25
BCP66 Kyle Jensen .30 .75
BCP67 Evan Anundsen .30 .75
BCP68 Hak-Ju Lee 1.25 3.00
BCP69 C.J. Retherford .30 .75
BCP70 Dillon Gee .75 2.00
BCP71 Bo Greenwell .30 .75
BCP72 Matt Tucker .50 1.25
BCP73 Joe Serafin .30 .75
BCP74 Matt Brown .30 .75
BCP75 Alexis Oliveras .30 .75
BCP76 James Beresford .30 .75
BCP77 Steve Lombardozzi .30 .75
BCP78 Curtis Petersen .30 .75
BCP79 Eric Farris .30 .75
BCP80 Yen-Wen Kuo .30 .75
BCP81 Caleb Brewer .30 .75
BCP82 Jacob Elmore .50 1.25
BCP83 Jared Clark .50 1.25
BCP84 Yowill Espinal .50 1.25
BCP85 Jae-Hoon Ha .30 .75
BCP86 Michael Wing .30 .75
BCP87 Wilmer Font .30 .75
BCP88 Jake Kahaulelio .30 .75
BCP89A Dustin Ackley 2.00 5.00
BCP89B Dustin Ackley AU 30.00 60.00
BCP90A Donavan Tate .75 2.00
BCP90B Donavan Tate AU 10.00 25.00
BCP91A Nolan Arenado 1.00 2.50
BCP91B Nolan Arenado AU 15.00 40.00
BCP92A Rex Brothers .30 .75
BCP92B Rex Brothers AU 3.00 8.00
BCP93A Brett Jackson 1.00 2.50
BCP93B Brett Jackson AU 12.50 30.00
BCP94A Chad Jenkins .30 .75
BCP94B Chad Jenkins AU 4.00 10.00
BCP95A Slade Heathcott 1.00 2.50
BCP95B Slade Heathcott AU 8.00 20.00
BCP96A J.R. Murphy .50 1.25
BCP96B J.R. Murphy AU 4.00 10.00
BCP97A Patrick Schuster .30 .75
BCP97B Patrick Schuster AU 3.00 8.00
BCP98A Alexia Amarista .30 .75
BCP98B Alexia Amarista AU 5.00 12.00
BCP99A Thomas Neal .50 1.25
BCP99B Thomas Neal AU 6.00 15.00
BCP100A Starlin Castro 1.25 3.00
BCP100B Starlin Castro AU 50.00 100.00
BCP101A Anthony Rizzo 1.00 2.50
BCP101B Anthony Rizzo AU 12.50 30.00
BCP102A Felix Doubront .30 .75
BCP102B Felix Doubront AU 6.00 15.00
BCP103A Nick Franklin .75 2.00
BCP103B Nick Franklin AU 10.00 25.00
BCP104A Anthony Gose .50 1.25
BCP104B Anthony Gose AU 4.00 10.00
BCP105A Julio Teheran .75 2.00
BCP105B Julio Teheran AU 30.00 60.00
BCP106A Grant Green .50 1.25
BCP106B Grant Green AU 12.50 30.00
BCP107A David Lough .30 .75
BCP107B David Lough AU 3.00 8.00
BCP108A Jose Iglesias 1.25 3.00
BCP108B Jose Iglesias AU 15.00 40.00
BCP109A Jaff Decker .75 2.00
BCP109B Jaff Decker AU 12.50 30.00
BCP110A D.J. LeMahieu .30 .75
BCP110B D.J. LeMahieu AU 4.00 10.00
BCP111A Craig Clark 1.25 3.00
BCP111B Craig Clark AU 3.00 8.00
BCP112A Jefry Marte .30 .75
BCP112B Jefry Marte AU 6.00 15.00
BCP113A Josh Donaldson .30 .75
BCP113B Josh Donaldson AU 3.00 8.00
BCP114A Steven Hensley .30 .75
BCP114B Steven Hensley AU 4.00 10.00
BCP115A James Darnell .50 1.25
BCP115B James Darnell AU 6.00 15.00
BCP116A Kirk Nieuwenhuis .30 .75
BCP116B Kirk Nieuwenhuis AU 6.00 15.00
BCP117A Wil Myers 1.50 4.00
BCP117B Wil Myers AU 30.00 60.00
BCP118A Bryan Mitchell .30 .75
BCP118B Bryan Mitchell AU 5.00 12.00
BCP119A Martin Perez .50 1.25
BCP119B Martin Perez AU 10.00 25.00
BCP120 Taylor Sinclair .30 .75
BCP121 Max Walla .30 .75
BCP122 Darin Ruf .50 1.25
BCP123 Nicholas Hernandez .75 2.00
BCP124 Salvador Perez .30 .75
BCP125 Yan Gomes .30 .75
BCP126 Riaan Spanjer-Furstenburg .30 .75
BCP127 Andrei Lobanov .30 .75
BCP128 Eliezer Mesa .30 .75
BCP129 Scott Barnes .30 .75
BCP130 Jerry Sands .75 2.00
BCP131 Chris Masters .30 .75
BCP132 Brandon Short .30 .75
BCP133 Rafael Dolis .30 .75
BCP134 Kevin Coddington .30 .75
BCP135 Jordan Pacheco .75 2.00
BCP136 Mike Zuanich .30 .75
BCP137 Jose Altuve 2.50 6.00
BCP138 Jimmy Paredes .30 .75
BCP139 Yohan Flande .30 .75
BCP140 Drew Cumberland .30 .75
BCP141 Jose Yepez .30 .75
BCP142 Joe Gardner .30 .75
BCP143 Michael Kirkman .30 .75
BCP144 Thomas Di Benedetto .30 .75
BCP145 Blake Lalli .30 .75
BCP146 Avery Barnes .30 .75
BCP147 Brayan Villareal .30 .75
BCP148 Zoilo Almonte .50 1.25
BCP149 Tommy Pham .30 .75
BCP150 Vince Belnome .30 .75
BCP151 Carlos Pimentel .30 .75
BCP152 Jeremy Barnes .30 .75
BCP153 Josh Stinson .30 .75
BCP154 Brady Shoemaker .30 .75
BCP155 Rudy Owens .75 2.00
BCP156 Kevin Mahoney .30 .75
BCP157 Luke Putkonen .30 .75
BCP158 Taylor Green .30 .75
BCP159 Anderson Hidalgo .30 .75
BCP160 Jonathan Villar .50 1.25
BCP161 Justin Bour .30 .75
BCP162 Evan Bronson .30 .75
BCP163 Rossmel Perez .30 .75
BCP164 Jacob Cowan .30 .75
BCP165 J.D. Martinez 1.25 3.00
BCP166 Chris Schwinden .30 .75
BCP167 Rawley Bishop .30 .75
BCP168 Tim Pahuta .30 .75
BCP169 Buck Afenir .30 .75
BCP170 Eduardo Nunez .50 1.25
BCP171 Ethan Hollingsworth .30 .75
BCP172 Brad Correll .30 .75
BCP173 Armando Rodriguez .30 .75
BCP174 Ryan Wiegand .30 .75
BCP175 Terry Doyle .30 .75
BCP176 Grant Hogue .50 1.25
BCP177 Stephen Parker .30 .75
BCP178 Nathan Adcock .50 1.25
BCP179 Will Middlebrooks .50 1.25
BCP180 Chris Archer 1.50 4.00
BCP181A T.J. McFarland .30 .75
BCP181B T.J. McFarland AU 4.00 10.00
BCP182A Alex Liddi .50 1.25
BCP182B Alex Liddi AU 8.00 20.00
BCP183A Liam Hendriks .30 .75
BCP183B Liam Hendriks AU 5.00 12.00
BCP184A Ozzie Martinez .30 .75
BCP184B Ozzie Martinez AU 4.00 10.00
BCP185A Eury Perez .30 .75
BCP185B Eury Perez AU 4.00 10.00
BCP186A Jhan Marinez .30 .75
BCP186B Jhan Marinez AU 4.00 10.00
BCP187A Carlos Peguero .50 1.25
BCP187B Carlos Peguero AU 5.00 12.00
BCP188A Tyler Chatwood .30 .75
BCP188B Tyler Chatwood AU 4.00 10.00
BCP189A Francisco Peguero .30 .75
BCP189B Francisco Peguero AU 5.00 12.00
BCP190A Pedro Baez .30 .75
BCP190B Pedro Baez AU 4.00 10.00
BCP191A Wilkin Ramirez .30 .75
BCP191B Wilkin Ramirez AU 4.00 10.00
BCP192A Wilin Rosario .30 .75
BCP192B Wilin Rosario AU 6.00 15.00
BCP193A Dan Tuttle .30 .75
BCP193B Dan Tuttle AU 3.00 8.00
BCP194A Trevor Reckling .30 .75
BCP194B Trevor Reckling AU 4.00 10.00
BCP195A Kyle Seager .30 .75
BCP195B Kyle Seager AU 4.00 10.00
BCP196A Jason Kipnis .50 1.25
BCP196B Jason Kipnis AU 10.00 25.00
BCP197A Jeurys Familia .50 1.25
BCP197B Jeurys Familia AU 6.00 15.00
BCP198A Adeinis Hechavarria .30 .75
BCP198B Adeinis Hechavarria AU 4.00 10.00
BCP199A Aroldis Chapman 1.25 3.00
BCP199B Aroldis Chapman AU 10.00 25.00
BCP200A Everett Williams .30 .75
BCP200B Everett Williams AU 3.00 8.00
BCP201A Ehire Adrianza .30 .75
BCP201B Ehire Adrianza AU 3.00 8.00
BCP202A Kyle Gibson 1.25 3.00
BCP202B Kyle Gibson AU 12.50 30.00
BCP203A Max Kepler .50 1.25
BCP203B Max Kepler AU 8.00 20.00
BCP204A Shelby Miller 1.25 3.00
BCP204B Shelby Miller AU 15.00 40.00
BCP205A Miguel Sano 1.50 4.00
BCP205B Miguel Sano AU 20.00 50.00
BCP206A Scooter Gennett .30 .75
BCP206B Scooter Gennett AU 4.00 10.00
BCP207A Gary Sanchez 1.00 2.50
BCP207B Gary Sanchez AU 15.00 40.00
BCP208A Graham Stoneburner .50 1.25
BCP208B Graham Stoneburner AU 5.00 12.00
BCP209 Josh Satin .50 1.25
BCP210A Matt Davidson .50 1.25
BCP210B Matt Davidson AU 8.00 20.00
BCP211A Arodys Vizcaino .50 1.25
BCP211B Arodys Vizcaino AU 8.00 20.00
BCP212A Anthony Bass .30 .75
BCP212B Anthony Bass AU 3.00 8.00
BCP213A Robinson Chirinos .30 .75
BCP213B Robinson Chirinos AU 3.00 8.00
BCP214A Trayce Thompson .50 1.25
BCP214B Trayce Thompson AU 5.00 12.00
BCP215A Simon Castro .50 1.25
BCP215B Simon Castro AU 4.00 10.00
BCP216A Corban Joseph .30 .75
BCP216B Corban Joseph AU 4.00 10.00
BCP217 Noel Arguelles .50 1.25
BCP218A Daniel Fields .30 .75
BCP218B Daniel Fields AU 5.00 12.00
BCP219A Robbie Erlin .75 2.00
BCP219B Robbie Erlin AU 8.00 20.00
BCP220A Juan Urbina .50 1.25
BCP220B Juan Urbina AU 4.00 10.00
BCP221 Marc Krauss AU 5.00 12.00
BCP222 Ryan Wheeler AU 3.00 8.00

2010 Bowman Chrome Prospects Refractors

*1-110 REF: 1.5X TO 4X BASIC
*111-220 REF: 1.5X TO 4X BASIC
BOW.ODDS 1:16 HOBBY
BOW.CHR.ODDS 1:39 HOBBY
1-110 PRINT RUN 777 SER.#'d SETS
111-220 PRINT RUN 500 SER.#'d SETS
*REF AU: .5X TO 1.2X BASIC
BOW.REF AU ODDS 1:96 HOBBY
BOW.CHR.REF AU ODDS 1:105 HOBBY
REF AU PRINT RUN 500 SER.#'d SETS
BCP1 Stephen Strasburg 50.00 100.00
BCP89B Dustin Ackley AU 50.00 100.00
BCP91B Nolan Arenado AU 30.00 60.00
BCP204B Shelby Miller AU 40.00 80.00
BCP205B Miguel Sano AU 40.00 80.00

2010 Bowman Chrome Prospects Blue Refractors

*BLUE REF: 3X TO 8X BASIC
BOW.ODDS 1:46 HOBBY
BOW.CHR.ODDS 1:48 HOBBY
1-110 PRINT RUN 250 SER.#'d SETS
111-220 PRINT RUN 150 SER.#'d SETS
*BLUE REF AU: 1.2X TO 3X BASIC
BOW.BLUE AU ODDS 1:139 HOBBY
BOW.CHR.BLUE AU ODDS 1:352 HOBBY
REF AU PRINT RUN 150 SER.#'d SETS
BCP1 Stephen Strasburg 75.00 150.00
BCP91B Nolan Arenado AU 75.00 150.00
BCP100B Starlin Castro AU 175.00 350.00
BCP199B Aroldis Chapman AU 30.00 60.00
BCP204B Shelby Miller AU 75.00 150.00
BCP207B Gary Sanchez AU 60.00 120.00

2010 Bowman Chrome Prospects Gold Refractors

*GOLD REF: 8X TO 20X BASIC
BOW.ODDS 1:228 HOBBY
BOW.CHR.ODDS 1:142 HOBBY
STATED PRINT RUN 50 SER.#'d SETS
*GOLD REF AU: 2.5X TO 6X BASIC
BOW.GOLD AU ODDS 1:957 HOBBY
BOW.CHR.GOLD AU ODDS 1:1073 HOBBY
GOLD AU PRINT RUN 50 SER.#'d SETS
BCP1 Stephen Strasburg 350.00 700.00
BCP89A Dustin Ackley 75.00 150.00
BCP89B Dustin Ackley AU 250.00 400.00
BCP91B Nolan Arenado AU 175.00 350.00
BCP93A Brett Jackson 30.00 60.00
BCP93B Brett Jackson AU 75.00 150.00
BCP95B Slade Heathcott AU 75.00 150.00
BCP98B Alexia Amarista AU 60.00 120.00
BCP99B Thomas Neal AU 60.00 120.00
BCP100A Starlin Castro 40.00 80.00
BCP100B Starlin Castro AU 400.00 600.00
BCP102B Felix Doubront AU 60.00 120.00
BCP103B Nick Franklin AU 125.00 250.00
BCP105B Julio Teheran AU 200.00 400.00
BCP108B Jose Iglesias AU 125.00 250.00
BCP109B Jaff Decker AU 125.00 250.00
BCP114B Steven Hensley AU 50.00 100.00
BCP115B James Darnell AU 60.00 120.00
BCP119B Martin Perez AU 75.00 150.00
BCP205B Miguel Sano AU 200.00 400.00
BCP207B Gary Sanchez AU 125.00 300.00

2010 Bowman Chrome Prospects Green X-Fractors

*X-F: 1.2X TO 3X BASIC
RANDOM INSERTS IN RETAIL PACKS

2010 Bowman Chrome Prospects Orange Refractors

BOW.STATED ODDS 1:463 HOBBY
BOW.STATED AU ODDS 1:1917 HOBBY
BOW.CHR.ODDS 1:284 HOBBY
BOW.CHR.AU ODDS 1:2200 HOBBY
STATED PRINT RUN 25 SER.#'d SETS
NO PRICING DUE TO SCARCITY

2010 Bowman Chrome Prospects Purple Refractors

*REF: 1X TO 2.5X BASIC
1-110 PRINT RUN 999 SER.#'d SETS
111-220 PRINT RUN 899 SER.#'d SETS
BCP1 Stephen Strasburg 20.00 50.00

2010 Bowman Chrome Prospects Red Refractors

BOW.STATED ODDS 1:2828 HOBBY
BOW.STATED AU ODDS 1:9587 HOBBY
BOW.CHR.ODDS 1:1420 HOBBY
BOW.CHR.AU ODDS 1:10,600 HOBBY
STATED PRINT RUN 5 SER.#'d SETS
NO PRICING DUE TO SCARCITY

2010 Bowman Chrome Prospects SuperFractors

BOW.STATED ODDS 1:11,000 HOBBY
BOW.STATED AU ODDS 1:47,000 HOBBY
BOW.CHR.ODDS 1:5625 HOBBY
BOW.CHR.AU ODDS 1:48,000 HOBBY
STATED PRINT RUN 1 SER.#'d SET
NO PRICING DUE TO SCARCITY

2010 Bowman Chrome Topps 100 Prospects

STATED ODDS 1:28 HOBBY
STATED PRINT RUN 999 SER.#'d SETS
*REF: .5X TO 1.2X BASIC
REFRACTOR ODDS 1:55 HOBBY
REFRACTOR PRINT RUN 499 SER.#'d SETS
*GOLD REF: 2X TO 5X BASIC
GOLD REF ODDS 1:610 HOBBY
GOLD REF PRINT RUN 50 SER.#'d SETS
SUPERFRACTOR ODDS 1:19,684 HOBBY
SUPERFRACTOR PRINT RUN 1 SER.#'d SET
NO SUPERFRACTOR PRICING AVAILABLE
TPC1 Stephen Strasburg 3.00 8.00
TPC2 Aroldis Chapman 2.00 5.00
TPC3 Jason Heyward 3.00 8.00
TPC4 Jesus Montero 3.00 8.00
TPC5 Mike Stanton 2.00 5.00
TPC6 Mike Moustakas 1.50 4.00
TPC7 Kyle Drabek .75 2.00
TPC8 Tyler Matzek 1.25 3.00
TPC9 Austin Jackson .75 2.00
TPC10 Starlin Castro 2.00 5.00
TPC11 Todd Frazier .50 1.25
TPC12 Carlos Santana 1.50 4.00
TPC13 Josh Vitters .50 1.25
TPC14 Neftali Feliz .50 1.25
TPC15 Tyler Flowers .75 2.00
TPC16 Alcides Escobar .75 2.00
TPC17 Ike Davis 1.25 3.00
TPC18 Domonic Brown 2.00 5.00
TPC19 Donavan Tate 1.25 3.00
TPC20 Buster Posey 5.00 12.00
TPC21 Dustin Ackley 3.00 8.00
TPC22 Desmond Jennings .75 2.00
TPC23 Brandon Allen .50 1.25
TPC24 Freddie Freeman 2.00 5.00
TPC25 Jake Arrieta .75 2.00
TPC26 Bobby Borchering .75 2.00
TPC27 Logan Morrison .75 2.00
TPC28 Christian Friederich .75 2.00
TPC29 Wilmer Flores 1.25 3.00
TPC30 Austin Romine .75 2.00
TPC31 Tony Sanchez 1.25 3.00
TPC32 Madison Bumgarner 1.25 3.00
TPC33 Mike Montgomery .75 2.00
TPC34 Andrew Lambo .50 1.25
TPC35 Derek Norris .75 2.00
TPC36 Chris Withrow .50 1.25
TPC37 Thomas Neal .75 2.00
TPC38 Trevor Reckling .50 1.25
TPC39 Andrew Cashner .50 1.25
TPC40 Daniel Hudson .75 2.00
TPC41 Jiovanni Mier .75 2.00
TPC42 Grant Green .75 2.00
TPC43 Jeremy Hellickson 2.00 5.00
TPC44 Felix Doubront .50 1.25
TPC45 Martin Perez .75 2.00
TPC46 Jenrry Mejia .75 2.00
TPC47 Adrian Cardenas .50 1.25
TPC48 Ivan DeJesus Jr. .50 1.25
TPC49 Nolan Arenado 1.50 4.00
TPC50 Slade Heathcott 1.50 4.00
TPC51 Ian Desmond .75 2.00
TPC52 Michael Taylor .75 2.00
TPC53 Jaime Garcia .75 2.00
TPC54 Jose Tabata 1.25 3.00
TPC55 Josh Bell .50 1.25
TPC56 Jarrod Parker 1.25 3.00
TPC57 Matt Dominguez .50 1.25
TPC58 Koby Clemens .75 2.00
TPC59 Angel Morales .50 1.25
TPC60 Juan Francisco .75 2.00
TPC61 John Ely .50 1.25
TPC62 Brett Jackson 1.50 4.00
TPC63 Chad Jenkins .50 1.25
TPC64 Jose Iglesias 2.00 5.00
TPC65 Logan Forsythe .50 1.25
TPC66 Alex Liddi .75 2.00
TPC67 Eric Arnett .50 1.25
TPC68 Wilkin Ramirez .50 1.25
TPC69 Lars Anderson 1.25 3.00
TPC70 Jared Mitchell .75 2.00
TPC71 Mike Leake 1.50 4.00
TPC72 D.J. LeMahieu .50 1.25
TPC73 Chris Marrero .50 1.25
TPC74 Matt Moore 6.00 15.00
TPC75 Jordan Brown .50 1.25
TPC76 Christopher Parmelee .50 1.25
TPC77 Ryan Kalish .75 2.00
TPC78 A.J. Pollock .75 2.00
TPC79 Alex White .75 2.00
TPC80 Scott Sizemore .75 2.00
TPC81 Jay Austin .50 1.25
TPC82 Zach McAllister .75 2.00
TPC83 Max Stassi .75 2.00
TPC84 Robert Stock .50 1.25
TPC85 Jake McGee .50 1.25
TPC86 Zack Wheeler .75 2.00
TPC87 Chase D'Arnaud .50 1.25
TPC88 Danny Duffy .75 2.00
TPC89 Josh Lindblom .50 1.25
TPC90 Anthony Gose .75 2.00
TPC91 Simon Castro .75 2.00
TPC92 Chris Carter .75 2.00
TPC93 Matt Hobgood 1.25 3.00
TPC94 Ben Revere .50 1.25
TPC95 Mat Gamel .50 1.25
TPC96 Anthony Hewitt .50 1.25
TPC97 Julio Teheran 1.25 3.00
TPC98 Josh Reddick .50 1.25
TPC99 Hank Conger .50 1.25
TPC100 Jordan Walden .50 1.25

2010 Bowman Chrome USA Baseball

COMPLETE SET (22) 10.00 25.00
STATED ODDS 1:4 HOBBY
PLATE PRINT RUN 1 SET PER COLOR
BLACK-CYAN-MAGENTA-YELLOW ISSUED
NO PLATE PRICING DUE TO SCARCITY
BC1 Trevor Bauer 3.00 8.00
BC2 Chad Bettis .60 1.50
BC3 Bryce Brentz 1.50 4.00
BC4 Michael Choice 1.00 2.50
BC5 Gerrit Cole 3.00 8.00
BC6 Christian Colon 1.00 2.50
BC7 Blake Forsythe .60 1.50
BC8 Yasmani Grandal 1.50 4.00
BC9 Sonny Gray 1.00 2.50
BC10 Rick Hague .60 1.50
BC11 Tyler Holt .60 1.50
BC12 Casey McGrew .60 1.50
BC13 Brad Miller .60 1.50
BC14 Matt Newman .60 1.50
BC15 Nick Pepitone .60 1.50
BC16 Drew Pomeranz 2.00 5.00
BC17 T.J. Walz .60 1.50
BC18 Cody Wheeler .60 1.50
BC19 Andy Wilkins .60 1.50
BC20 Asher Wojciechowski 1.50 4.00
BC21 Kolten Wong 1.00 2.50
BC22 Tony Zych .60 1.50

2010 Bowman Chrome USA Baseball Refractors

*REF: .75X TO 2X BASIC
STATED ODDS 1:16 HOBBY
STATED PRINT RUN 777 SER.#'d SETS

2010 Bowman Chrome USA Baseball Blue Refractors

*BLUE REF: 2X TO 5X BASIC
STATED ODDS 1:46 HOBBY
STATED PRINT RUN 250 SER.#'d SETS

2010 Bowman Chrome USA Baseball Gold Refractors

*GOLD REF: 6X TO 15X BASIC
STATED ODDS 1:228 HOBBY
STATED PRINT RUN 50 SER.#'d SETS

2010 Bowman Chrome USA Baseball Orange Refractors

STATED ODDS 1:463 HOBBY
STATED PRINT RUN 25 SER.#'d SETS
NO PRICING DUE TO SCARCITY

2010 Bowman Chrome USA Baseball Red Refractors

STATED ODDS 1:2828 HOBBY
STATED PRINT RUN 5 SER.#'d SETS
NO PRICING DUE TO SCARCITY

2010 Bowman Chrome USA Baseball SuperFractors

STATED ODDS 1:11,000 HOBBY
STATED PRINT RUN 1 SER.#'d SET
NO PRICING DUE TO SCARCITY

2010 Bowman Chrome USA Baseball Dual Autographs

STATED ODDS 1:1393 HOBBY
STATED PRINT RUN 500 SER.#'d SETS
USAD1 Bubba Starling / Lance McCullers 15.00 40.00
USAD2 Elvin Soto / Blake Swihart 6.00 15.00
USAD3 Nicky Delmonico / Tony Wolters 6.00 15.00
USAD4 Henry Owens / Phillip Pfeifer III 6.00 15.00
USAD5 Christian Montgomery / John Simms 6.00 15.00
USAD6 Albert Almora / Brian Ragira 6.00 15.00
USAD7 Marcus Littlewood / Christian Lopes 6.00 15.00
USAD8 Dillon Maples / A.J. Vanegas 6.00 15.00
USAD9 Daniel Camarena / John Hochstatter 6.00 15.00
USAD10 Francisco Lindor / Michael Lorenzen 8.00 20.00

2010 Bowman Chrome USA Baseball Buyback Autographs

ISSUED VIA WRAPPER REDEMPTION PROGRAM
STATED PRINT RUN 100 SER.#'d SETS
BC3 Bryce Brentz 50.00 100.00
BC4 Michael Choice 60.00 120.00
BC6 Christian Colon 60.00 120.00
BC8 Yasmani Grandal 50.00 100.00
BC16 Drew Pomeranz 50.00 100.00
18BC8 Bryce Harper 1400.00 1800.00
18BC10 Manny Machado 150.00 300.00
18BC17 Jameson Taillon 100.00 200.00

2010 Bowman Chrome USA Baseball Wrapper Redemption Autographs

ISSUED VIA WRAPPER REDEMPTION PROGRAM
STATED PRINT RUN 99 SER.#'d SETS
WR3 Kyle Winkler 10.00 25.00
WR6 AJ Vanegas 8.00 20.00
WR7 Albert Almora 15.00 40.00
WR8 Blake Swihart 30.00 60.00
WR10 Bubba Starling 60.00 120.00
WR11 Christian Lopes 12.50 30.00
WR13 Dillon Maples 12.50 30.00
WR14 Elvin Soto 10.00 25.00
WR15 Francisco Lindor 50.00 100.00
WR16 Henry Owens 15.00 40.00
WR17 John Simms 8.00 20.00
WR18 Lance McCullers 20.00 50.00
WR19 Marcus Littlewood 10.00 25.00
WR20 Michael Lorenzen 12.50 30.00
WR21 Phillip Pfeifer 10.00 25.00
WR23 Andrew Maggi 10.00 25.00
WR24 Brad Miller 15.00 40.00
WR25 Brett Mooneyham 10.00 25.00
WR26 Brian Johnson
WR27 George Springer 100.00 200.00
WR28 Gerrit Cole 175.00 350.00
WR29 Jackie Bradley Jr. 100.00 175.00
WR30 Jason Esposito 30.00 60.00
WR32 Matt Barnes 50.00 100.00
WR33 Mikie Mahtook 40.00 80.00
WR34 Nick Ramirez 15.00 40.00
WR35 Noe Ramirez 15.00 40.00
WR36 Nolan Fontana 10.00 25.00
WR37 Peter O'Brien 20.00 50.00
WR38 Ryan Wright 8.00 20.00
WR39 Scott McGough 8.00 20.00
WR40 Sean Gilmartin 15.00 40.00
WR41 Steve Rodriguez 8.00 20.00

2010 Bowman Chrome USA Baseball Wrapper Redemption Autographs Black

ISSUED VIA WRAPPER REDMPTION PROGRAM
STATED PRINT RUN 25 SER.#'d SETS
NO PRICING DUE TO SCARCITY

2010 Bowman Chrome USA Stars

COMPLETE SET (20) 6.00 15.00
USA1 Albert Almora 1.00 2.50
USA2 Daniel Camarena .60 1.50
USA3 Nicky Delmonico .60 1.50
USA4 John Hochstatter .60 1.50
USA5 Francisco Lindor 1.50 4.00
USA6 Marcus Littlewood 1.00 2.50
USA7 Christian Lopes 1.00 2.50
USA8 Michael Lorenzen .60 1.50
USA9 Dillon Maples .60 1.50
USA10 Lance McCullers 1.00 2.50
USA11 Christian Montgomery .60 1.50
USA12 Henry Owens 1.00 2.50
USA13 Phillip Pfeifer III .60 1.50
USA14 Brian Ragira .60 1.50
USA15 John Simms .60 1.50
USA16 Elvin Soto .60 1.50
USA17 Bubba Starling 3.00 8.00
USA18 Blake Swihart 1.00 2.50
USA19 A.J. Vanegas 1.00 2.50
USA20 Tony Wolters 1.00 2.50

2010 Bowman Chrome USA Stars Refractors

*REF: 1X TO 2.5X BASIC
STATED ODDS 1:39 HOBBY
STATED PRINT RUN 500 SER.#'d SETS

2010 Bowman Chrome USA Stars Blue Refractors

*BLUE REF: 2X TO 5X BASIC
STATED ODDS 1:48 HOBBY
STATED PRINT RUN 150 SER.#'d SETS

2010 Bowman Chrome USA Stars Gold Refractors

*GOLD REF: 5X TO 12X BASIC
STATED ODDS 1:142 HOBBY
STATED PRINT RUN 50 SER.#'d SETS

2010 Bowman Chrome USA Stars Orange Refractors

STATED ODDS 1:284 HOBBY
STATED PRINT RUN 25 SER.#'d SETS
NO PRICING DUE TO SCARCITY

2010 Bowman Chrome USA Stars Red Refractors

STATED ODDS 1:1420 HOBBY
STATED PRINT RUN 5 SER.#'d SETS
NO PRICING DUE TO SCARCITY

2010 Bowman Chrome USA Stars Superfractors

STATED ODDS 1:1562 HOBBY
STATED PRINT RUN 1 SER.#'d SET
NO PRICING DUE TO SCARCITY

2010 Bowman Chrome Wrapper Redemption Autographs

ISSUED VIA WRAPPER REDEMPTION PROGRAM
STATED PRINT RUN 100 SER.#'d SETS
WR1 Buster Posey 200.00 300.00
WR2 Mike Stanton 75.00 150.00
WR3 Mike Moustakas 60.00 120.00
WR4 Miguel Sano 100.00 200.00
WR5 Dustin Ackley 75.00 150.00

2011 Bowman Chrome

COMP.SET w/o AU's (220) 20.00 50.00
COMMON RC (171-220) .40 1.00
STATED PLATE ODDS 1:960 HOBBY
PLATE PRINT RUN 1 SET PER COLOR
BLACK-CYAN-MAGENTA-YELLOW ISSUED
NO PLATE PRICING DUE TO SCARCITY
EXCHANGE DEADLINE 9/30/2014
1 Buster Posey .60 1.50
2 Alex Avila .20 .50
3 Edwin Jackson .20 .50
4 Miguel Montero .20 .50
5 Albert Pujols 1.25 3.00
6 Carlos Santana .50 1.25
7 Marlon Byrd .20 .50
8 Hanley Ramirez .50 1.25
9 Josh Hamilton .50 1.25
10 Matt Kemp .30 .75
11 Shane Victorino .30 .75
12 Domonic Brown .50 1.25
13 Chipper Jones .50 1.25
14 Joey Votto .50 1.25
15 Brandon Phillips .20 .50
16 Jason Heyward .60 1.50
17 Curtis Granderson .30 .75
18 Brian McCann .30 .75
19 Dustin Pedroia .60 1.50
20 Chris Johnson .20 .50
21 Brian Matusz .50 1.25
22 Mark Teixeira .50 1.25
23 Miguel Tejada .30 .75
24 Ryan Howard .60 1.50
25 Adrian Beltre .20 .50
26 Joe Mauer .50 1.25
27 Logan Morrison .20 .50
28 Brian Wilson .50 1.25
29 Carlos Lee .20 .50
30 Ian Kinsler .30 .75
31 Shin-Soo Choo .30 .75
32 Adam Wainwright .30 .75
33 Carlos Gonzalez .30 .75
34 Lance Berkman .30 .75
35 Jon Lester .50 1.25
36 Miguel Cabrera .50 1.25
37 Justin Verlander .60 1.50
38 Tyler Colvin .30 .75
39 Matt Cain .30 .75
40 Brett Anderson .30 .75
41 Gordon Beckham .30 .75
42 David DeJesus .20 .50
43 Jonathan Sanchez .20 .50
44 Jorge De La Rosa .20 .50
45 Torii Hunter .20 .50
46 Andrew McCutchen .50 1.25
47 Mat Latos .20 .50
48 CC Sabathia .30 .75
49 Brett Myers .20 .50
50 Ryan Zimmerman .30 .75
51 Trevor Cahill .20 .50
52 Clayton Kershaw .50 1.25
53 Andre Ethier .30 .75
54 Justin Upton .30 .75
55 B.J. Upton .30 .75
56 J.P. Arencibia .30 .75
57 Phil Hughes .20 .50
58 Tim Hudson .30 .75
59 Francisco Liriano .20 .50
60 Ike Davis .30 .75
61 Delmon Young .30 .75
62 Paul Konerko .30 .75
63 Carlos Beltran .20 .50
64 Mike Stanton .30 .75
65 Adam Jones .30 .75
66 Jimmy Rollins .30 .75
67 Alex Rios .30 .75
68 Chad Billingsley .20 .50
69 Tommy Hanson .30 .75
70 Travis Wood .20 .50
71 Magglio Ordonez .30 .75
72 Jake Peavy .20 .50
73 Adrian Gonzalez .30 .75
74 Aaron Hill .20 .50
75 Kendrys Morales .20 .50
76 Ryan Dempster .20 .50
77 Hunter Pence .30 .75
78 Josh Beckett .30 .75
79 Mark Reynolds .20 .50
80 Drew Stubbs .30 .75
81 Dan Haren .20 .50
82 Chris Carpenter .50 1.25
83 Mitch Moreland .20 .50
84 Starlin Castro .50 1.25
85 Roy Halladay .50 1.25
86 Stephen Drew .20 .50
87 Aramis Ramirez .20 .50
88 Daniel Hudson .20 .50
89 Alexei Ramirez .20 .50
90 Rickie Weeks .30 .75
91 Will Venable .20 .50
92 David Price .50 1.25
93 Dan Uggla .30 .75
94 Austin Jackson .20 .50
95 Evan Longoria .60 1.50
96 Ryan Ludwick .20 .50
97 Chase Utley .50 1.25
98 Johnny Cueto .20 .50
99 Billy Butler .20 .50
100 David Wright .60 1.50
101 Jose Reyes .30 .75
102 Robinson Cano .50 1.25
103 Josh Johnson .30 .75
104 Chris Coghlan .20 .50
105 David Ortiz .30 .75
106 Jay Bruce .30 .75
107 Jayson Werth .30 .75
108 Matt Holliday .50 1.25
109 John Danks .20 .50
110 Franklin Gutierrez .20 .50
111 Zack Greinke .30 .75
112 Jacoby Ellsbury .50 1.25
113 Madison Bumgarner .20 .50
114 Mike Leake .30 .75
115 Carl Crawford .30 .75

116 Clay Buchholz .30 .75
117 Gavin Floyd .20 .50
118 Mike Minor .20 .50
119 Jose Tabata .30 .75
120 Jason Castro .20 .50
121 Chris Young .20 .50
122 Jose Bautista .30 .75
123 Felix Hernandez .50 1.25
124 Dexter Fowler .20 .50
125 Tim Lincecum .50 1.25
126 Todd Helton .30 .75
127 Ubaldo Jimenez .30 .75
128 Yovani Gallardo .20 .50
129 Derek Jeter 1.25 3.00
130 Wade Davis .20 .50
131 Nelson Cruz .30 .75
132 Michael Cuddyer .20 .50
133 Mark Buehrle .30 .75
134 Danny Valencia .30 .75
135 Ichiro Suzuki .75 2.00
136 Brett Wallace .20 .50
137 Troy Tulowitzki .50 1.25
138 Pedro Alvarez .30 .75
139 Brandon Morrow .20 .50
140 Jered Weaver .20 .50
141 Michael Young .30 .75
142 Wandy Rodriguez .20 .50
143 Alfonso Soriano .30 .75
144 Roy Oswalt .30 .75
145 Brian Roberts .20 .50
146 Jaime Garcia .30 .75
147 Edinson Volquez .20 .50
148 Vladimir Guerrero .50 1.25
149 Cliff Lee .50 1.25
150 Johnny Damon .30 .75
151 Alex Rodriguez .75 2.00
152 Nick Markakis .50 1.25
153 Cole Hamels .50 1.25
154 Prince Fielder .30 .75
155 Kurt Suzuki .20 .50
156 Ryan Braun .60 1.50
157 Justin Morneau .50 1.25
158 Elvis Andrus .30 .75
159 Stephen Strasburg 1.00 2.50
160 Adam Lind .30 .75
161 Corey Hart .20 .50
162 Adam Dunn .30 .75
163 Bobby Abreu .20 .50
164 Gaby Sanchez .20 .50
165 Ian Kennedy .30 .75
166 Kevin Youkilis .30 .75
167 Vernon Wells .20 .50
168 Matt Garza .20 .50
169 Victor Martinez .30 .75
170 Casey McGehee .20 .50
171 Jake McGee (RC) .40 1.00
172 Lars Anderson RC .60 1.50
173 Mark Trumbo (RC) .60 1.50
174 Konrad Schmidt RC .40 1.00
175 Mike Trout RC 2.50 6.00
176 Brent Morel RC .40 1.00
177 Aroldis Chapman RC 1.25 3.00
178 Greg Halman RC .60 1.50
179 Jeremy Hellickson RC 1.25 3.00
180 Yunesky Maya RC .40 1.00
181 Kyle Drabek RC .60 1.50
182 Ben Revere RC .60 1.50
183 Desmond Jennings RC 1.00 2.50
184 Brandon Beachy RC
185 Freddie Freeman RC 1.50 4.00
186 Randall Delgado RC .60 1.50
187 John Lindsey RC .40 1.00
188 Mark Rogers (RC) .40 1.00
189 Brian Bogusevic (RC) .40 1.00
190 Yonder Alonso RC .60 1.50
191 Gregory Infante RC .40 1.00
192 Dillon Gee RC .60 1.50
193 Ozzie Martinez RC .40 1.00
194 Brandon Snyder (RC) .40 1.00
195 Daniel Descalso RC .40 1.00
196A Eric Hosmer RC 3.00 8.00
196B Eric Hosmer AU EXCH 100.00 200.00
197 Lucas Duda RC .60 1.50
198 Cory Luebke RC .40 1.00
199 Hank Conger RC .60 1.50
200 Chris Sale RC .60 1.50
201 Julio Teheran RC 1.25 3.00
202 Danny Duffy RC .60 1.50
203 Brandon Belt RC 1.50 4.00
204 Ivan Nova (RC) .60 1.50
205 Danny Espinosa RC .40 1.00
206 Alexi Ogando RC 1.00 2.50
207 Darwin Barney RC 1.25 3.00
208 Jordan Walden RC .40 1.00
209 Tsuyoshi Nishioka RC 1.25 3.00
210 Zach Britton RC 1.00 2.50
211 Andrew Cashner (RC) .40 1.00
212A Dustin Ackley RC 1.50 4.00
212B Dustin Ackley AU 50.00 100.00
213 Carlos Peguero RC .60 1.50
214 Hector Noesi RC .60 1.50
215 Eduardo Nunez RC .40 1.00
216 Michael Pineda RC 1.25 3.00
217 Alex Cobb RC .40 1.00
218 Ivan DeJesus Jr. RC .40 1.00
219 Scott Cousins RC .40 1.00
220 Aaron Crow RC .60 1.50

2011 Bowman Chrome Refractors

*REF: 1X TO 2.5X BASIC
*REF RC: .5X TO 1.2X BASIC RC
STATED ODDS 1:4 HOBBY

2011 Bowman Chrome Blue Refractors

*BLUE REF: 2X TO 5X BASIC
*BLUE REF RC: 2X TO 5X BASIC RC
STATED ODDS 1:31 HOBBY
STATED PRINT RUN 150 SER.#'d SETS

2011 Bowman Chrome Gold Canary Diamond

STATED ODDS 1:3840 HOBBY
STATED PRINT RUN 1 SER.#'d SET
NO PRICING DUE TO SCARCITY

2011 Bowman Chrome Gold Refractors

*GOLD REF: 6X TO 15X BASIC
*GOLD REF RC: 3X TO 8X BASIC RC
STATED ODDS 1:94 HOBBY
STATED PRINT RUN 50 SER.#'d SETS
EXCHANGE DEADLINE 9/30/2014
196B Eric Hosmer AU EXCH 400.00 600.00
212B Dustin Ackley AU 125.00 250.00

2011 Bowman Chrome Orange

STATED ODDS 1:198 HOBBY
STATED PRINT RUN 25 SER.#'d SETS
NO PRICING DUE TO SCARCITY
EXCHANGE DEADLINE 9/30/2014

2011 Bowman Chrome Red Refractors

STATED ODDS 1:900 HOBBY
STATED PRINT RUN 5 SER.#'d SETS
NO PRICING DUE TO SCARCITY

2011 Bowman Chrome Superfractors

STATED ODDS 1:3840 HOBBY
STATED PRINT RUN 1 SER.#'d SET
NO PRICING DUE TO SCARCITY

2011 Bowman Chrome 18U USA National Team Refractors

STATED ODDS 1:2063 HOBBY
STATED PLATE ODDS 1:365,000 HOBBY
PLATE PRINT RUN 1 SET PER COLOR
BLACK-CYAN-MAGENTA-YELLOW ISSUED
NO PLATE PRICING DUE TO SCARCITY
EXCHANGE DEADLINE 10/26/2012
NNO EXCH Card 20.00 50.00

2011 Bowman Chrome 18U USA National Team Blue Refractors

STATED ODDS 1:13,205 HOBBY
STATED PRINT RUN 99 SER.#'d SETS
EXCHANGE DEADLINE 10/26/2012
NNO EXCH Card 60.00 120.00

2011 Bowman Chrome 18U USA National Team Gold Refractors

STATED ODDS 1:27,000 HOBBY
STATED PRINT RUN 50 SER.#'d SETS
EXCHANGE DEADLINE 10/26/2012
NNO EXCH Card 100.00 200.00

2011 Bowman Chrome 18U USA National Team Orange Refractors

STATED ODDS 1:50,685 HOBBY
STATED PRINT RUN 25 SER.#'d SETS
NO PRICING DUE TO SCARCITY
EXCHANGE DEADLINE 10/26/2012

2011 Bowman Chrome 18U USA National Team Red Refractors

STATED ODDS 1:253,424 HOBBY
STATED PRINT RUN 5 SER.#'d SETS
NO PRICING DUE TO SCARCITY
EXCHANGE DEADLINE 10/26/2012

2011 Bowman Chrome 18U USA National Team Superfractors

STATED ODDS 1:267,122 HOBBY
STATED PRINT RUN 1 SER.#'d SET
NO PRICING DUE TO SCARCITY
EXCHANGE DEADLINE 10/26/2012

2011 Bowman Chrome 18U USA National Team X-Fractors

STATED ODDS 1:4281 HOBBY
STATED PRINT RUN 299 SER.#'d SETS
EXCHANGE DEADLINE 10/26/2012
NNO EXCH Card 40.00 80.00

2011 Bowman Chrome 18U USA National Team Autographs Refractors

STATED ODDS 1:192 HOBBY
STATED PRINT RUN 417 SER.#'d SETS
STATED PLATE ODDS 1:15,839 HOBBY
PLATE PRINT RUN 1 SET PER COLOR
BLACK-CYAN-MAGENTA-YELLOW ISSUED
NO PLATE PRICING DUE TO SCARCITY
18U1 Albert Almora 6.00 15.00
18U2 Alex Bregman 5.00 12.00
18U3 Gavin Cecchini 10.00 25.00
18U4 Troy Conyers 5.00 12.00
18U6 Chase DeJong 5.00 12.00
18U8 Carson Fulmer 5.00 12.00
18U13 Cole Irvin 5.00 12.00
18U15 Jeremy Martinez 5.00 12.00
18U15 Clate Schmidt 5.00 12.00
18U17 Chris Okey 5.00 12.00
18U18 Cody Poteet 5.00 12.00
18U19 Nelson Rodriguez 8.00 20.00
18U21 Addison Russell 8.00 20.00
18U24 Hunter Virant 5.00 12.00
18U25 Walker Weickel 5.00 12.00
18U26 Mikey White 5.00 12.00
18U28 Jesse Winker 5.00 12.00

2011 Bowman Chrome 18U USA National Team Autographs Blue Refractors

*BLUE REF: .75X TO 2X BASIC
STATED ODDS 1:829 HOBBY
STATED PRINT RUN 99 SER.#'d SETS
18U3 Gavin Cecchini 25.00 60.00

2011 Bowman Chrome 18U USA National Team Autographs Gold Refractors

*GOLD REF: 1.5X TO 4X BASIC
STATED ODDS 1:1695 HOBBY
STATED PRINT RUN 50 SER.#'d SETS

2011 Bowman Chrome 18U USA National Team Autographs Orange Refractors

STATED ODDS 1:3625 HOBBY
STATED PRINT RUN 25 SER.#'d SETS
NO PRICING DUE TO SCARCITY

2011 Bowman Chrome 18U USA National Team Autographs Red Refractors

STATED ODDS 1:15,919 HOBBY
STATED PRINT RUN 5 SER.#'d SETS
NO PRICING DUE TO SCARCITY

2011 Bowman Chrome 18U USA National Team Autographs Supefractors

STATED ODDS 1:63,356 HOBBY
STATED PRINT RUN 1 SER.#'d SET
NO PRICING DUE TO SCARCITY

2011 Bowman Chrome 18U USA National Team Autographs X-Fractors

*X-FRACTOR: .5X TO 1.2X BASIC
STATED ODDS 1:268 HOBBY
STATED PRINT RUN 299 SER.#'d SETS

2011 Bowman Chrome Bryce Harper Retail Exclusive

INSERTED IN RETAIL VALUE BOXES
BCE1G Bryce Harper Gold 12.50 30.00
BCE1R Bryce Harper Red 4.00 10.00
BCE1S Bryce Harper Silver 8.00 20.00

2011 Bowman Chrome Futures

COMPLETE SET (25) 12.50 30.00
STATED ODDS 1:9 HOBBY
MICRO-FRAC. ODDS 1:2035 HOBBY
MICRO-FRAC. PRINT RUN 25 SER.#'d SETS
NO MICRO-FRAC.PRICING AVAILABLE
1 Bryce Harper 4.00 10.00
2 Manny Machado 1.25 3.00
3 Jameson Taillon 1.25 3.00
4 Delino DeShields Jr. .40 1.00
5 Grant Green .40 1.00
6 Devin Mesoraco .60 1.50
7 Anthony Ranaudo 1.00 2.50
8 Stetson Allie .60 1.50
9 Shelby Miller 1.00 2.50
10 Arodys Vizcaino .40 1.00
11 Manny Banuelos 1.25 3.00
12 Jonathan Singleton .60 1.50
13 Tyler Matzek .60 1.50
14 Gary Sanchez 1.00 2.50
15 Jean Segura .40 1.00
16 Peter Tago .40 1.00
17 Matt Dominguez .60 1.50
18 Miguel Sano 1.00 2.50
19 Jesus Montero 1.50 4.00
20 Josh Sale .60 1.50
21 Brett Jackson .60 1.50
22 Mike Montgomery .60 1.50
23 Chris Archer .40 1.00
24 Jacob Turner 1.50 4.00
25 Wil Myers .60 1.50

2011 Bowman Chrome Futures Refractors

*REF: .5X TO 1.2X BASIC

2011 Bowman Chrome Futures Fusion-Fractors 99

*FUSION: 2X TO 5X BASIC
STATED ODDS 1:512 HOBBY
STATED PRINT RUN 99 SER.#'d SETS
1 Bryce Harper 60.00 120.00

2011 Bowman Chrome Futures Future-Fractors

*FUTURE: .6X TO 1.5X BASIC

2011 Bowman Chrome Prospect Autographs

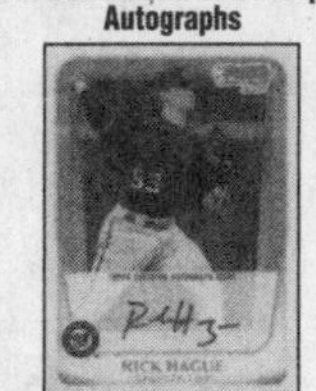

111-220 PLATE ODDS 1:9051 HOBBY
PLATE PRINT RUN 1 SET PER COLOR
BLACK-CYAN-MAGENTA-YELLOW ISSUED
NO PLATE PRICING DUE TO SCARCITY
EXCHANGE DEADLINE 4/30/2014
BCP80 Dee Gordon 8.00 20.00
BCP81 Blake Forsythe 3.00 8.00
BCP82 Jurickson Profar 20.00 50.00
BCP83 Jedd Gyorko 8.00 20.00
BCP84 Matt Hague 3.00 8.00
BCP85 Mason Williams 12.50 30.00
BCP86 Stetson Allie 4.00 10.00
BCP87 Jarred Cosart 5.00 12.00
BCP88 Wagner Mateo 4.00 10.00
BCP89 Allen Webster 4.00 10.00
BCP90 Adron Chambers 4.00 10.00
BCP91 Blake Smith 3.00 8.00
BCP92 J.D. Martinez 6.00 15.00
BCP93 Brandon Belt 15.00 40.00
BCP94 Drake Britton 3.00 8.00
BCP95 Addison Reed 3.00 8.00
BCP96 Adonis Cardona 4.00 10.00
BCP97 Yordy Cabrera 4.00 10.00
BCP98 Tony Wolters 4.00 10.00
BCP99 Paul Goldschmidt 20.00 50.00
BCP100 Sean Coyle 4.00 10.00
BCP101 Rymer Liriano 5.00 12.00
BCP102 Eric Thames 4.00 10.00
BCP103 Brian Fletcher 3.00 8.00
BCP104 Ben Gamel 3.00 8.00
BCP105 Kyle Russell 3.00 8.00
BCP106 Sammy Solis 3.00 8.00
BCP107 Garin Cecchini 8.00 20.00
BCP108 Carlos Perez 3.00 8.00
BCP110 Jonathan Villar 4.00 10.00
BCP111A Adam Warren 5.00 12.00
BCP111B Bryce Harper 150.00 300.00
BCP112 Rick Hague 3.00 8.00
BCP113 Carlos Perez 3.00 8.00
BCP130 Hunter Morris 4.00 10.00
BCP131 Jean Segura 5.00 12.00
BCP132 Melky Mesa 4.00 10.00
BCP133 Manny Banuelos 20.00 50.00
BCP134 Chris Archer 5.00 12.00
BCP157 Danny Brewer 4.00 10.00
BCP158 David Bromberg 3.00 8.00
BCP160 A.J. Cole 5.00 12.00
BCP161 Alex Colome 4.00 10.00
BCP162 Brody Colvin 5.00 12.00
BCP163 Khris Davis 4.00 10.00
BCP164 Cutter Dykstra 3.00 8.00
BCP165 Nathan Eovaldi 5.00 12.00
BCP167 Garrett Gould 4.00 10.00
BCP168 Brandon Guyer 3.00 8.00
BCP169 Shaeffer Hall 3.00 8.00
BCP170 Reese Havens 5.00 12.00
BCP171 Luis Heredia 6.00 15.00
BCP172 Aaron Hicks 10.00 25.00
BCP173 Bryan Holaday 3.00 8.00
BCP174 Brad Holt 3.00 8.00
BCP175 Brett Lawrie EXCH 75.00 150.00
BCP176 Matt Lollis 5.00 12.00
BCP178 Starling Marte 10.00 25.00
BCP179 Ethan Martin 4.00 10.00
BCP180 Trey McNutt 4.00 10.00
BCP182 Keyvius Sampson 6.00 15.00
BCP183 Jordan Swagerty 4.00 10.00
BCP184 Dickie Joe Thon 3.00 8.00
BCP185 Jacob Turner EXCH 30.00 80.00
BCP186 Christopher Wallace 3.00 8.00
BCP189 Kendrick Perkins 3.00 8.00
BCP192 Enny Romero 5.00 12.00
BCP212 Brock Holt 3.00 8.00
BCP214 Brandon Laird 4.00 10.00
BCP220 Matt Moore 20.00 50.00

2011 Bowman Chrome Prospect Autographs Refractors

*REF: .6X TO 1.5X BASIC
111-220 STATED ODDS 1:88 HOBBY
STATED PRINT RUN 500 SER.#'d SETS
EXCHANGE DEADLINE 4/30/2014
BCP111B Bryce Harper 200.00 400.00
BCP175 Brett Lawrie EXCH
BCP185 Jacob Turner EXCH

2011 Bowman Chrome Prospect Autographs Blue Refractors

*BLUE REF: 1.2X TO 3X BASIC
111-220 STATED ODDS 1:295 HOBBY
STATED PRINT RUN 150 SER.#'d SETS
EXCHANGE DEADLINE 4/30/2014
BCP82 Jurickson Profar 150.00 250.00
BCP93 Brandon Belt 75.00 150.00
BCP111B Bryce Harper 500.00 700.00
BCP171 Luis Heredia 30.00 60.00
BCP172 Aaron Hicks 50.00 100.00
BCP175 Brett Lawrie EXCH 200.00 300.00
BCP185 Jacob Turner EXCH 60.00 120.00
BCP220 Matt Moore 150.00 250.00

2011 Bowman Chrome Prospect Autographs Gold Refractors

*GOLD REF: 2.5X TO 6X BASIC
111-220 STATED ODDS 1:916 HOBBY
STATED PRINT RUN 50 SER.#'d SETS
EXCHANGE DEADLINE 4/30/2014
BCP82 Jurickson Profar 300.00 400.00
BCP93 Brandon Belt 175.00 350.00
BCP96 Adonis Cardona 60.00 120.00
BCP110 Jonathan Villar 50.00 100.00
BCP111B Bryce Harper 1000.00 1500.00
BCP131 Jean Segura 50.00 100.00
BCP134 Chris Archer 75.00 150.00
BCP165 Nathan Eovaldi 50.00 100.00
BCP167 Garrett Gould 40.00 80.00
BCP171 Luis Heredia 75.00 150.00
BCP175 Brett Lawrie EXCH 400.00 600.00
BCP185 Jacob Turner EXCH 100.00 200.00
BCP220 Matt Moore 350.00 450.00

2011 Bowman Chrome Prospect Autographs Orange Refractors

111-220 STATED ODDS 1:1936 HOBBY
STATED PRINT RUN 25 SER.#'d SETS
NO PRICING DUE TO SCARCITY
EXCHANGE DEADLINE 4/30/2014

2011 Bowman Chrome Prospect Autographs Red Refractors

111-220 STATED ODDS 1:8675 HOBBY
STATED PRINT RUN 5 SER.#'d SETS
NO PRICING DUE TO SCARCITY
EXCHANGE DEADLINE 4/30/2014

2011 Bowman Chrome Prospect Autographs Superfractors

111-220 STATED ODDS 1:36,203 HOBBY
STATED PRINT RUN 1 SER.#'d SET
NO PRICING DUE TO SCARCITY
EXCHANGE DEADLINE 4/30/2014

2011 Bowman Chrome Prospects

COMPLETE SET (221) 40.00 80.00
1-110 ISSUED IN BOWMAN
111-220 ISSUED IN BOWMAN CHROME
STATED PLATE ODDS 1:960 HOBBY
PLATE PRINT RUN 1 SET PER COLOR
BLACK-CYAN-MAGENTA-YELLOW ISSUED
NO PLATE PRICING DUE TO SCARCITY
BCP1 Bryce Harper 5.00 12.00
BCP2 Chris Dennis .25 .60
BCP3 Jeremy Barfield .25 .60
BCP4 Nate Freiman .25 .60
BCP5 Tyler Moore .40 1.00
BCP6 Anthony Carter .25 .60
BCP7 Ryan Cavan .25 .60
BCP8 Stephen Vogt .25 .60
BCP9 Carlo Testa .25 .60
BCP10 Erik Davis .25 .60
BCP11 Jack Shuck .60 1.50
BCP12 Charles Brewer .25 .60
BCP13 Alex Castellanos .40 1.00
BCP14 Anthony Vasquez .25 .60
BCP15 Michael Brenly .25 .60
BCP16 Kody Hinze .40 1.00
BCP17 Hector Noesi .40 1.00
BCP18 Tyler Bortnick .25 .60
BCP19 Thomas Layne .25 .60
BCP20 Everett Teaford .25 .60
BCP21 Jose Pirela .25 .60
BCP22 Joel Carreno .25 .60
BCP23 Vinnie Catricala 1.00 2.50
BCP24 Tom Koehler .25 .60
BCP25 Jonathan Schoop .60 1.50
BCP26 Chun-Hsiu Chen .60 1.50
BCP27 Amaury Rivas .25 .60
BCP28 Oswaldo Arcia .25 .60
BCP29 Johermyn Chavez .25 .60
BCP30 Michael Spina .25 .60
BCP31 Kyle McPherson .40 1.00
BCP32 Albert Cartwright .25 .60
BCP33 Joseph Wieland .60 1.50
BCP34 Ben Paulsen .25 .60
BCP35 Jason Hagerty .25 .60
BCP36 Marcell Ozuna .40 1.00
BCP37 Dave Sappelt .75 2.00
BCP38 Eduardo Escobar .25 .60
BCP39 Aaron Baker .25 .60
BCP40 Deryk Hooker .25 .60
BCP41 Ty Morrison .25 .60
BCP42 Keon Broxton .25 .60
BCP43 Corey Jones .25 .60
BCP44 Manny Banuelos .75 2.00
BCP45 Brandon Guyer .40 1.00
BCP46 Juan Nicasio .25 .60
BCP47 Sean Ochinko .25 .60
BCP48 Adam Warren .40 1.00
BCP49 Phillip Cerreto .25 .60
BCP50 Mychal Givens .25 .60
BCP51 James Fuller .25 .60
BCP52 Ronnie Welty .25 .60
BCP53 Dan Straily .25 .60
BCP54 Gabriel Jacobo .25 .60
BCP55 David Rubinstein .25 .60
BCP56 Kevin Mailloux .25 .60
BCP57 Angel Castillo .25 .60
BCP58 Adrian Salcedo .40 1.00
BCP59 Ronald Bermudez .25 .60
BCP60 Jarek Cunningham .40 1.00
BCP61 Matt Magill .40 1.00
BCP62 Willie Cabrera .25 .60
BCP63 Austin Hyatt .40 1.00
BCP64 Cody Puckett .40 1.00
BCP65 Jacob Goebbert .40 1.00
BCP66 Matt Carpenter .40 1.00
BCP67 Dan Klein .40 1.00
BCP68 Sean Ratliff .25 .60
BCP69 Elih Villanueva .25 .60
BCP70 Wade Gaynor .25 .60
BCP71 Evan Crawford .25 .60
BCP72 Avisail Garcia .40 1.00
BCP73 Kevin Rivers .25 .60
BCP74 Jim Gallagher .25 .60
BCP75 Brian Broderick .25 .60
BCP76 Tyson Auer .25 .60
BCP77 Matt Klinker .25 .60
BCP78 Cole Figueroa .25 .60
BCP79 Rafael Ynoa .25 .60
BCP80 Dee Gordon .60 1.50
BCP81 Blake Forsythe .25 .60
BCP82 Jurickson Profar .75 2.00
BCP83 Jedd Gyorko .60 1.50
BCP84 Matt Hague .25 .60
BCP85 Mason Williams .60 1.50
BCP86 Stetson Allie .40 1.00
BCP87 Jarred Cosart .40 1.00
BCP88 Wagner Mateo .60 1.50
BCP89 Allen Webster .40 1.00
BCP90 Adron Chambers .25 .60
BCP91 Blake Smith .25 .60
BCP92 J.D. Martinez .40 1.00
BCP93 Brandon Belt 1.00 2.50
BCP94 Drake Britton .25 .60
BCP95 Addison Reed .25 .60
BCP96 Adonis Cardona .40 1.00
BCP97 Yordy Cabrera .25 .60
BCP98 Tony Wolters .25 .60
BCP99 Paul Goldschmidt 1.25 3.00
BCP100 Sean Coyle .60 1.50
BCP101 Rymer Liriano .40 1.00
BCP102 Eric Thames .25 .60
BCP103 Brian Fletcher .25 .60
BCP104 Ben Gamel .40 1.00
BCP105 Kyle Russell .40 1.00
BCP106 Sammy Solis .25 .60
BCP107 Garin Cecchini .60 1.50
BCP108 Carlos Perez .25 .60
BCP109 Darin Mastroianni .25 .60
BCP110 Jonathan Villar .25 .60
BCP111 Bryce Harper 5.00 12.00
BCP112 Aaron Altherr .25 .60
BCP113 Oswaldo Arcia .25 .60
BCP114 Kyle Blair .25 .60
BCP115 Nick Bucci .25 .60
BCP116 Jose Casilla .25 .60
BCP117 Zach Cates .25 .60
BCP118 Dimaster Delgado .25 .60
BCP119 Jose DePaula .25 .60
BCP120 Zack Dodson .25 .60
BCP121 John Gast .25 .60
BCP122 Cesar Hernandez .40 1.00
BCP123 Kyle Higashioka .25 .60
BCP124 Luke Jackson .40 1.00
BCP125 Jiwan James .25 .60
BCP126 Jonathan Joseph .25 .60
BCP127A Gustavo Pierre .25 .60
BCP127B Ryan Tatusko .40 1.00
BCP128 Jeff Kobernus .25 .60
BCP129 Tom Koehler .25 .60
BCP130 Hunter Morris .25 .60
BCP131 Jean Segura .25 .60
BCP132 Melky Mesa .25 .60
BCP133 Manny Banuelos .75 2.00
BCP134 Chris Archer .25 .60
BCP135 Ian Krol .25 .60
BCP136 Trystan Magnuson .25 .60
BCP137 Roman Mendez .25 .60
BCP138 Tyler Moore .40 1.00
BCP139 Ramon Morla .25 .60
BCP140 Ty Morrison .25 .60
BCP141 Tyler Pastornicky .40 1.00
BCP142 Jon Pettibone .25 .60
BCP143 Zach Quate .25 .60
BCP144 J.C. Ramirez .25 .60
BCP145 Elmer Reyes .25 .60
BCP146 Aderlin Rodriguez .25 .60
BCP147 Conner Crumbliss .40 1.00
BCP148 David Rohm .25 .60
BCP149 Adrian Sanchez .25 .60
BCP150 Tommy Shirley .25 .60
BCP151 Matt Packer .25 .60
BCP152 Jake Thompson .25 .60
BCP153 Miguel Velazquez .25 .60
BCP154 Dakota Watts .25 .60
BCP155 Chase Whitley .40 1.00
BCP156 Cameron Bedrosian .25 .60
BCP157 Daniel Brewer .25 .60
BCP158 Dave Bromberg .25 .60
BCP159 Jorge Polanco .25 .60
BCP160 A.J. Cole .25 .60
BCP161 Alex Colome .25 .60
BCP162 Brody Colvin .25 .60
BCP163 Khris Davis .25 .60
BCP164 Cutter Dykstra .25 .60
BCP165 Nathan Eovaldi .25 .60
BCP166 Ramon Flores .60 1.50
BCP167 Garrett Gould .25 .60
BCP168 Brandon Guyer .40 1.00
BCP169 Shaeffer Hall .40 1.00
BCP170 Reese Havens .25 .60
BCP171 Luis Heredia .25 .60
BCP172 Aaron Hicks .60 1.50
BCP173 Bryan Holaday .25 .60
BCP174 Brad Holt .25 .60
BCP175 Brett Lawrie 2.00 5.00
BCP176 Matt Lollis .40 1.00
BCP177 Cesar Puello .40 1.00
BCP178 Starling Marte .60 1.50
BCP179 Ethan Martin .25 .60
BCP180 Trey McNutt .25 .60
BCP181 Anthony Ranaudo .60 1.50
BCP182 Keyvius Sampson .25 .60
BCP183 Jordan Swagerty .40 1.00
BCP184 Dickie Joe Thon .40 1.00
BCP185 Jacob Turner 1.00 2.50
BCP186 Rob Brantly .60 1.50
BCP187 Arquimedes Caminero .25 .60
BCP188 Miles Head .60 1.50
BCP189 Erasmo Ramirez .25 .60
BCP190 Ryan Pressly .25 .60
BCP191 Colton Cain .25 .60
BCP192 Enny Romero .25 .60
BCP193 Zack Von Rosenberg .25 .60
BCP194 Tyler Skaggs .60 1.50
BCP195 Michael Blanke .25 .60
BCP196 Juan Duran .40 1.00
BCP197 Kyle Parker .60 1.50
BCP198 Jake Marisnick .60 1.50
BCP199 Manuel Soliman .25 .60
BCP200 Jordany Valdespin .25 .60
BCP201 Brock Holt .25 .60
BCP202 Chris Owings .25 .60
BCP203 Cameron Garfield .25 .60
BCP204 Rob Scahill .25 .60
BCP205 Ronnie Welty .25 .60
BCP206 Scott Maine .25 .60
BCP207 Kyle Smit .25 .60
BCP208 Spencer Arroyo .25 .60
BCP209 Mariekson Gregorious .25 .60
BCP210 Neftali Soto .40 1.00
BCP211 Wade Gaynor .25 .60
BCP212 Chris Carpenter .25 .60
BCP213 Josh Judy .25 .60
BCP214 Brandon Laird .40 1.00
BCP215 Peter Tago .25 .60
BCP216 Andy Dirks .25 .60
BCP217 Steve Cishek ERR NNO .25 .60
BCP218 Cory Riordan .25 .60
BCP219 Fernando Abad .25 .60
BCP220 Matt Moore 1.25 3.00

2011 Bowman Chrome Prospects Refractors

*REF: 2.5X TO 6X BASIC
111-220 STATED ODDS 1:28 HOBBY
1-110 PRINT RUN 799 SER.#'d SETS
111-220 PRINT RUN 500 SER.#'d SETS
BCP1 Bryce Harper 20.00 50.00
BCP111 Bryce Harper 20.00 50.00

2011 Bowman Chrome Prospects Blue Refractors

*BLUE REF: 4X TO 10X BASIC
111-220 STATED ODDS 1:31 HOBBY
1-110 PRINT RUN 250 SER.#'d SETS
111-220 PRINT RUN 150 SER.#'d SETS
BCP1 Bryce Harper 75.00 150.00
BCP111 Bryce Harper 75.00 150.00

2011 Bowman Chrome Prospects Gold Canary Diamond

STATED ODDS 1:3840 HOBBY
STATED PRINT RUN 1 SER.#'d SET
NO PRICING DUE TO SCARCITY

2011 Bowman Chrome Prospects Gold Refractors

*GOLD REF: 10X TO 25X BASIC
111-220 STATED ODDS 1:94 HOBBY
STATED PRINT RUN 50 SER.#'d SETS
BCP1 Bryce Harper 400.00 800.00
BCP111 Bryce Harper 400.00 800.00

2011 Bowman Chrome Prospects Green X-Fractors

*GREEN XF: 1.5X TO 4X BASIC
RETAIL ONLY PARALLEL
BCP111 Bryce Harper 12.50 30.00

2011 Bowman Chrome Prospects Orange Refractors

111-220 STATED ODDS 1:198 HOBBY
STATED PRINT RUN 25 SER.#'d SETS
NO PRICING DUE TO SCARCITY

2011 Bowman Chrome Prospects Purple Refractors

*PURPLE REF: 2.5X TO 6X BASIC
1-110 PRINT RUN 700 SER.#'d SETS
111-220 PRINT RUN 799 SER.#'d SETS
BCP1 Bryce Harper 20.00 50.00
BCP111 Bryce Harper 20.00 50.00

2011 Bowman Chrome Prospects Red Refractors

111-220 STATED ODDS 1:900 HOBBY
STATED PRINT RUN 5 SER.#'d SETS
NO PRICING DUE TO SCARCITY

2011 Bowman Chrome Prospects Superfractors

111-220 STATED ODDS 1:3840 HOBBY
STATED PRINT RUN 1 SER.#'d SET
NO PRICING DUE TO SCARCITY

2011 Bowman Chrome Rookie Autographs

PLATE PRINT RUN 1 SET PER COLOR
BLACK-CYAN-MAGENTA-YELLOW ISSUED
NO PLATE PRICING DUE TO SCARCITY
EXCHANGE DEADLINE 4/30/2014
191 Jake McGee AU 4.00 10.00
192 Lars Anderson AU 4.00 10.00
195 Jeremy Jeffress AU 4.00 10.00
196 Brent Morel AU 4.00 10.00
197 Aroldis Chapman AU 10.00 25.00
198 Greg Halman AU 5.00 12.00
199 Jeremy Hellickson AU 10.00 25.00
200 Yunesky Maya AU 4.00 10.00
201 Kyle Drabek AU 4.00 10.00
203 Desmond Jennings AU 8.00 20.00
205 Freddie Freeman AU 10.00 25.00
209 Brian Bogusevic AU 4.00 10.00
210 Yonder Alonso AU 6.00 15.00
212 Dillon Gee AU 4.00 10.00
220 Chris Sale AU 4.00 10.00

2011 Bowman Chrome Rookie Autographs Refractors

*REF: .5X TO 1.2X BASIC
STATED PRINT RUN 500 SER.#'d SETS
EXCHANGE DEADLINE 4/30/2014

2011 Bowman Chrome Rookie Autographs Blue Refractors

*BLUE REF: .6X TO 1.5X BASIC
STATED PRINT RUN 250 SER.#'d SETS
EXCHANGE DEADLINE 4/30/2014
199 Jeremy Hellickson AU 25.00 60.00
203 Desmond Jennings AU 25.00 60.00
210 Yonder Alonso AU 20.00 50.00

2011 Bowman Chrome Rookie Autographs Gold Refractors

*GOLD REF: 1.5X TO 4X BASIC
STATED PRINT RUN 50 SER.#'d SETS
EXCHANGE DEADLINE 4/30/2014
199 Jeremy Hellickson AU 125.00 250.00
203 Desmond Jennings AU 100.00 200.00
205 Freddie Freeman AU 75.00 150.00
210 Yonder Alonso AU 50.00 120.00

2011 Bowman Chrome Throwbacks

COMPLETE SET (25) 10.00 25.00
STATED ODDS 1:8 HOBBY
ATOMIC ODDS 1:25,353 HOBBY
ATOMIC PRINT RUN 1 SER.#'d SET
NO ATOMIC PRICING DUE TO SCARCITY
X-FRACTOR ODDS 1:1013 HOBBY
X-FRACTOR PRINT RUN 25 SER.#'d SETS
NO X-FRACTOR PRICING AVAILABLE
37 Chipper Jones 1.00 2.50
103 Alex Rodriguez 1.50 4.00
340 Albert Pujols 2.50 6.00
351A Ichiro Suzuki English 1.50 4.00
351B Ichiro Suzuki Japanese 1.50 4.00
BCT1 Tony Sanchez .60 1.50
BCT2 Dee Gordon 1.00 2.50
BCT3 Anthony Rizzo .60 1.50
BCT4 Nick Franklin .60 1.50
BCT5 Jameson Taillon 1.25 3.00
BCT6 Wil Myers .60 1.50
BCT7 Grant Green .40 1.00
BCT8 Jacob Turner 1.50 4.00
BCT9 Tyler Matzek .60 1.50
BCT10 Bryce Harper 5.00 12.00
BCT11 Manny Banuelos 1.25 3.00
BCT12 Brett Lawrie 3.00 8.00
BCT13 Devin Mesoraco .60 1.50
BCT14 Shelby Miller 1.00 2.50
BCT15 Delino DeShields Jr. .40 1.00
BCT16 Dustin Ackley 1.50 4.00
BCT17 Manny Machado 1.25 3.00
BCT18 Lonnie Chisenhall .60 1.50
BCT19 Arodys Vizcaino .40 1.00
BCT20 Stetson Allie .60 1.50

2011 Bowman Chrome Throwbacks Refractors

*REF: 2.5X TO 6X BASIC
STATED ODDS 1:256 HOBBY
STATED PRINT RUN 99 SER.#'d SETS
340 Albert Pujols 50.00 100.00
BCT10 Bryce Harper 50.00 100.00

2011 Bowman Chrome Rookie Autographs Superfractors

STATED PRINT RUN 1 SER.#'d SET
NO PRICING DUE TO SCARCITY
EXCHANGE DEADLINE 4/30/2014

2010 Bowman Chrome Draft

COMP.SET w/o AU (110) 15.00 40.00
PLATE PRINT RUN 1 SET PER COLOR
BLACK-CYAN-MAGENTA-YELLOW ISSUED
NO PLATE PRICING DUE TO SCARCITY
BDP1A Stephen Strasburg RC 2.00 5.00
BDP1B Stephen Strasburg AU 125.00 250.00
BDP2 Josh Bell (RC) .30 .75
BDP3 Ivan Nova RC 1.50 4.00
BDP4 Starlin Castro RC 1.25 3.00
BDP5 John Axford RC .30 .75
BDP6 Colin Curtis RC .30 .75
BDP7 Brennan Boesch RC .75 2.00
BDP8 Ike Davis RC .75 2.00
BDP9 Madison Bumgarner RC .75 2.00
BDP10 Austin Jackson RC .50 1.25
BDP11 Andrew Cashner RC .30 .75
BDP12 Jose Tabata RC .75 2.00
BDP13 Wade Davis (RC) .30 .75
BDP14 Ian Desmond (RC) .50 1.25
BDP15 Felix Doubront RC .30 .75
BDP16 Danny Worth RC .30 .75
BDP17 John Ely RC .30 .75
BDP18 Jon Jay RC .50 1.25
BDP19 Mike Leake RC 1.00 2.50
BDP20 Daniel Nava RC .50 1.25
BDP21 Brad Lincoln RC .50 1.25
BDP22 Jonathan Lucroy RC .30 .75
BDP23 Brian Matusz RC .75 2.00
BDP24 Chris Nelson (RC) .50 1.25
BDP25 Andy Oliver RC .30 .75
BDP26 Adam Ottavino RC .30 .75

BDP27 Trevor Plouffe (RC) .30 .75
BDP28 Vance Worley RC 1.25 3.00
BDP29 Daniel McCutchen RC .50 1.25
BDP30 Mike Stanton RC 1.25 3.00
BDP31 Drew Storen RC .50 1.25
BDP32 Tyler Colvin RC .50 1.25
BDP33 Travis Wood (RC) .50 1.25
BDP34 Eric Young Jr. (RC) .30 .75
BDP35 Sam Demel RC .30 .75
BDP36 Welington Castillo RC .30 .75
BDP37 Sam LeCure (RC) .30 .75
BDP38 Danny Valencia RC 2.00 5.00
BDP39 Fernando Salas RC .30 .75
BDP40 Jason Heyward RC 2.00 5.00
BDP41 Jake Arrieta RC .50 1.25
BDP42 Kevin Russo RC .30 .75
BDP43 Josh Donaldson RC .30 .75
BDP44 Luis Atilano RC .30 .75
BDP45 Jason Donald RC .30 .75
BDP46 Jonny Venters RC .30 .75
BDP47 Bryan Anderson (RC) .30 .75
BDP48 Jay Sborz (RC) .30 .75
BDP49 Chris Heisey RC .50 1.25
BDP50 Daniel Hudson RC .50 1.25
BDP51 Ruben Tejada RC .50 1.25
BDP52 Jeffrey Marquez RC .50 1.25
BDP53 Brandon Hicks RC .50 1.25
BDP54 Jeanmar Gomez RC .50 1.25
BDP55 Erik Kratz RC .50 1.25
BDP56 Lorenzo Cain RC .50 1.25
BDP57 Jhan Marinez RC .30 .75
BDP58 Omar Beltre (RC) .30 .75
BDP59 Drew Stubbs RC .75 2.00
BDP60 Alex Sanabia RC .30 .75
BDP61 Buster Posey RC 3.00 8.00
BDP62 Anthony Slama RC .30 .75
BDP63 Brad Davis RC .30 .75
BDP64 Logan Morrison RC .50 1.25
BDP65 Luke Hughes (RC) .30 .75
BDP66 Thomas Diamond (RC) .30 .75
BDP67 Tommy Manzella (RC) .30 .75
BDP68 Jordan Smith RC .30 .75
BDP69 Carlos Santana RC 1.00 2.50
BDP70 Domonic Brown RC 1.25 3.00
BDP71 Scott Sizemore RC .50 1.25
BDP72 Jordan Brown RC .30 .75
BDP73 Josh Thole RC .50 1.25
BDP74 Jordan Norberto RC .30 .75
BDP75 Dayan Viciedo RC .50 1.25
BDP76 Josh Tomlin RC .75 2.00
BDP77 Adam Moore RC .30 .75
BDP78 Kenley Jansen RC 1.25 3.00
BDP79 Juan Francisco RC .50 1.25
BDP80 Blake Wood RC .30 .75
BDP81 John Hester RC .30 .75
BDP82 Lucas Harrell (RC) .30 .75
BDP83 Neil Walker (RC) .50 1.25
BDP84 Cesar Valdez RC .30 .75
BDP85 Lance Zawadzki RC .30 .75
BDP86 Rommie Lewis RC .30 .75
BDP87 Steve Tolleson RC .30 .75
BDP88 Jeff Frazier (RC) .30 .75
BDP89 Drew Butera (RC) .30 .75
BDP90 Michael Brantley RC .30 .75
BDP91 Mitch Moreland RC .50 1.25
BDP92 Alex Burnett RC .30 .75
BDP93 Allen Craig RC .75 2.00
BDP94 Sergio Santos (RC) .30 .75
BDP95 Matt Carson (RC) .30 .75
BDP96 Jenrry Mejia RC .50 1.25
BDP97 Rhyne Hughes RC .30 .75
BDP98 Tyson Ross RC .30 .75
BDP99 Argenis Diaz RC .50 1.25
BDP100 Hisanori Takahashi RC .50 1.25
BDP101 Cole Gillespie RC .30 .75
BDP102 Ryan Kalish RC .50 1.25
BDP103 J.P. Arencibia RC .50 1.25
BDP104 Peter Bourjos RC .50 1.25
BDP105 Justin Turner RC .30 .75
BDP106 Michael Dunn RC .30 .75
BDP107 Mike McCoy RC .30 .75
BDP108 Will Rhymes RC .30 .75
BDP109 Wilson Ramos RC .75 2.00
BDP110 Josh Butler RC .30 .75

2010 Bowman Chrome Draft Refractors

*REF: .75X TO 2X BASIC

2010 Bowman Chrome Draft Blue Refractors

*BLUE REF: 2X TO 5X BASIC
STATED PRINT RUN 199 SER.#'d SETS

2010 Bowman Chrome Draft Gold Refractors

*GOLD REF: 3X TO 8X BASIC
STATED PRINT RUN 50 SER.#'d SETS
BDP1 Stephen Strasburg 50.00 100.00
BDP30 Mike Stanton 20.00 50.00
BDP61 Buster Posey- 50.00 100.00

2010 Bowman Chrome Draft Orange Refractors

STATED PRINT RUN 25 SER.#'d SETS
NO PRICING DUE TO SCARCITY

2010 Bowman Chrome Draft Purple Refractors

*PURPLE REF: .75X TO 2X BASIC

2010 Bowman Chrome Draft Red Refractors

STATED PRINT RUN 5 SER.#'d SETS
NO PRICING DUE TO SCARCITY

2010 Bowman Chrome Draft Superfractors

STATED PRINT RUN 1 SER.#'d SET
NO PRICING DUE TO SCARCITY

2010 Bowman Chrome Draft Prospect Autographs

PLATE PRINT RUN 1 SET PER COLOR
BLACK-CYAN-MAGENTA-YELLOW ISSUED
NO PLATE PRICING DUE TO SCARCITY
BDPP61 Michael Choice 10.00 25.00
BDPP62 Zack Cox 10.00 25.00
BDPP63 Bryce Brentz 12.50 30.00
BDPP64 Chance Ruffin 4.00 10.00
BDPP65 Mike Olt 12.50 30.00
BDPP66 Kellin Deglan 4.00 10.00
BDPP67 Yasmani Grandal 10.00 25.00
BDPP68 Kolbrin Vitek 8.00 20.00
BDPP69 Justin O'Conner 5.00 12.00
BDPP70 Gary Brown 10.00 25.00
BDPP71 Mike Foltynewicz 5.00 12.00
BDPP72 Chevez Clarke 5.00 12.00
BDPP73 Cito Culver 8.00 20.00
BDPP74 Aaron Sanchez 5.00 12.00
BDPP75 Noah Syndergaard 5.00 12.00
BDPP76 Taylor Lindsey 4.00 10.00
BDPP77 Josh Sale 15.00 40.00
BDPP78 Christian Yelich 10.00 25.00
BDPP79 Jameson Taillon 20.00 50.00
BDPP80 Manny Machado 50.00 100.00
BDPP81 Christian Colon 10.00 25.00
BDPP82 Drew Pomeranz 12.50 30.00
BDPP83 Delino DeShields 8.00 20.00
BDPP84 Matt Harvey 12.50 30.00
BDPP85 Ryan Bolden 4.00 10.00
BDPP86 Deck McGuire 5.00 12.00
BDPP87 Zach Lee 12.50 30.00
BDPP88 Alex Wimmers 6.00 15.00
BDPP89 Kaleb Cowart 10.00 25.00
BDPP90 Mike Kvasnicka 4.00 10.00
BDPP91 Jake Skole 8.00 20.00
BDPP92 Chris Sale 6.00 15.00

2010 Bowman Chrome Draft Prospect Autographs Refractors

*REF: .5X TO 1.2X BASIC
STATED PRINT RUN 500 SER.#'d SETS
BDPP63 Bryce Brentz 30.00 60.00

2010 Bowman Chrome Draft Prospect Autographs Blue Refractors

*BLUE REF: 1.2X TO 3X BASIC
STATED PRINT RUN 150 SER.#'d SETS
BDPP63 Bryce Brentz 60.00 120.00

2010 Bowman Chrome Draft Prospect Autographs Gold Refractors

*GOLD REF: 2.5X TO 6X BASIC
STATED PRINT RUN 50 SER.#'d SETS
BDPP62 Zack Cox 125.00 250.00
BDPP63 Bryce Brentz 125.00 250.00
BDPP79 Jameson Taillon 150.00 250.00
BDPP81 Christian Colon 100.00 200.00
BDPP89 Kaleb Cowart 100.00 200.00
BDPP91 Jake Skole 75.00 150.00

2010 Bowman Chrome Draft Prospect Autographs Orange Refractors

STATED PRINT RUN 25 SER.#'d SETS
NO PRICING DUE TO SCARCITY

2010 Bowman Chrome Draft Prospect Autographs Red Refractors

STATED PRINT RUN 5 SER.#'d SETS
NO PRICING DUE TO SCARCITY

2010 Bowman Chrome Draft Prospect Autographs Superfractors

STATED PRINT RUN 1 SER.#'d SET
NO PRICING DUE TO SCARCITY

2010 Bowman Chrome Draft Prospects

PLATE PRINT RUN 1 SET PER COLOR
BLACK-CYAN-MAGENTA-YELLOW ISSUED
NO PLATE PRICING DUE TO SCARCITY
BDPP1 Sam Tuivailala .30 .75
BDPP2 Alex Burgos .30 .75
BDPP3 Henry Ramos .50 1.25
BDPP4 Pat Dean .50 1.25
BDPP5 Ryan Brett .30 .75
BDPP6 Jesse Biddle .75 2.00
BDPP7 Leon Landry .50 1.25
BDPP8 Ryan LaMarre .30 .75
BDPP9 Josh Rutledge .20 .50
BDPP10 Tyler Thornburg .30 .75
BDPP11 Carter Jurica .20 .50
BDPP12 J.R. Bradley .20 .50
BDPP13 Devin Lohman .20 .50
BDPP14 Addison Reed .20 .50
BDPP15 Micah Gibbs .30 .75
BDPP16 Derek Dietrich .60 1.50
BDPP18 Stephen Pryor .20 .50
BDPP19 Eddie Rosario .30 .75
BDPP20 Blake Forsythe .20 .50
BDPP21 Rangel Ravelo .20 .50
BDPP22 Nick Longmire .30 .75
BDPP23 Andrelton Simmons .30 .75
BDPP24 Chad Bettis .20 .50
BDPP25 Peter Tago .30 .75
BDPP26 Tyrell Jenkins .50 1.25
BDPP27 Marcus Knecht .20 .50
BDPP28 Seth Blair .30 .75
BDPP29 Brodie Greene .20 .50
BDPP30 Jason Martinson .20 .50
BDPP31 Bryan Morgado .30 .75
BDPP32 Eric Cantrell .20 .50
BDPP33 Niko Goodrum .30 .75
BDPP34 Bobby Doran .20 .50
BDPP35 Cody Wheeler .20 .50
BDPP36 Cole Leonida .20 .50
BDPP37 Nate Roberts .20 .50
BDPP38 Dave Filak .20 .50
BDPP39 Taijuan Walker .60 1.50
BDPP40 Hayden Simpson .30 .75
BDPP41 Cameron Rupp .30 .75
BDPP42 Ben Heath .20 .50
BDPP43 Tyler Waldron .20 .50
BDPP44 Greg Garcia .20 .50
BDPP45 Vincent Velasquez .30 .75
BDPP46 Jake Lemmerman .60 1.50
BDPP47 Russell Wilson 1.00 2.50
BDPP48 Cody Stanley .20 .50
BDPP49 Matt Suschak .20 .50
BDPP50 Logan Darnell .20 .50
BDPP51 Kevin Keyes .20 .50
BDPP52 Thomas Royse .20 .50
BDPP53 Scott Alexander .20 .50
BDPP54 Tony Thompson .20 .50
BDPP55 Seth Rosin .30 .75
BDPP56 Mickey Wiswall .20 .50
BDPP57 Albert Almora .30 .75
BDPP58 Cole Billingsley .30 .75
BDPP58 Cody Hawn .30 .75
BDPP59 Drew Vettleson .30 .75
BDPP60 Matt Lipka .75 2.00
BDPP61 Michael Choice .30 .75
BDPP62 Zack Cox .60 1.50
BDPP63 Bryce Brentz .50 1.25
BDPP64 Chance Ruffin .20 .50
BDPP65 Mike Olt .50 1.25
BDPP66 Kellin Deglan .20 .50
BDPP67 Yasmani Grandal .50 1.25
BDPP68 Kolbrin Vitek .50 1.25
BDPP69 Justin O'Conner .20 .50
BDPP70 Gary Brown .50 1.25
BDPP71 Mike Foltynewicz .30 .75
BDPP72 Chevez Clarke .30 .75
BDPP73 Cito Culver .30 .75
BDPP74 Aaron Sanchez .30 .75
BDPP75 Noah Syndergaard .30 .75
BDPP76 Taylor Lindsey .30 .75
BDPP77 Josh Sale .60 1.50
BDPP78 Christian Yelich .30 .75
BDPP79 Jameson Taillon .75 2.00
BDPP80 Manny Machado 1.50 4.00
BDPP81 Christian Colon .30 .75
BDPP82 Drew Pomeranz .60 1.50
BDPP83 Delino DeShields .30 .75
BDPP84 Matt Harvey .75 2.00
BDPP85 Ryan Bolden .20 .50
BDPP86 Deck McGuire .30 .75
BDPP87 Zach Lee .50 1.25
BDPP88 Alex Wimmers .30 .75
BDPP89 Kaleb Cowart .30 .75
BDPP90 Mike Kvansnicka .20 .50
BDPP91 Jake Skole .30 .75
BDPP92 Chris Sale .50 1.25
BDPP93 Sean Brady .20 .50
BDPP94 Marc Brakeman .20 .50
BDPP95 Alex Bregman .30 .75
BDPP96 Ryan Burr .30 .75
BDPP97 Chris Chinea .30 .75
BDPP98 Troy Conyers .20 .50
BDPP99 Zach Green .20 .50
BDPP100 Carson Kelly .20 .50
BDPP101 Timmy Lopes .20 .50
BDPP102 Adrian Marin .30 .75
BDPP103 Chris Okey .20 .50
BDPP104 Matt Olson .20 .50
BDPP105 Ivan Pelaez .20 .50
BDPP106 Felipe Perez .20 .50
BDPP107 Nelson Rodriguez .20 .50
BDPP108 Corey Seager .30 .75
BDPP109 Lucas Sims .20 .50
BDPP110 Nick Travieso .30 .75

2010 Bowman Chrome Draft Prospects Refractors

*REF: 2X TO 5X BASIC

2010 Bowman Chrome Draft Prospects Blue Refractors

*BLUE REF: 4X TO 10X BASIC
STATED PRINT RUN 199 SER.#'d SETS

2010 Bowman Chrome Draft Prospects Gold Refractors

*GOLD REF: 8X TO 20X BASIC
STATED PRINT RUN 50 SER.#'d SETS
BDPP79 Jameson Taillon 50.00 100.00
BDPP80 Manny Machado 75.00 150.00

2010 Bowman Chrome Draft Prospects Orange Refractors

STATED PRINT RUN 25 SER.#'d SETS
NO PRICING DUE TO SCARCITY

2010 Bowman Chrome Draft Prospects Purple Refractors

*PURPLE REF: 1.2X TO 3X BASIC

2010 Bowman Chrome Draft Prospects Red Refractors

STATED PRINT RUN 5 SER.#'d SETS
NO PRICING DUE TO SCARCITY

2010 Bowman Chrome Draft Prospects Superfractors

STATED PRINT RUN 1 SER.#'d SET
NO PRICING DUE TO SCARCITY

2010 Bowman Chrome Draft USA Baseball Autographs

USAA1 Albert Almora 6.00 15.00
USAA2 Cole Billingsley 4.00 10.00
USAA3 Sean Brady 4.00 10.00
USAA4 Marc Brakeman 4.00 10.00
USAA5 Alex Bregman 8.00 20.00
USAA6 Ryan Burr 5.00 12.00
USAA7 Chris Chinea 4.00 10.00
USAA8 Troy Conyers 4.00 10.00
USAA9 Zach Green 5.00 12.00
USAA10 Carson Kelly 5.00 12.00
USAA11 Timmy Lopes 4.00 10.00
USAA12 Adrian Marin 4.00 10.00
USAA13 Chris Okey 4.00 10.00
USAA14 Matt Olson 5.00 12.00
USAA15 Ivan Pelaez 4.00 10.00
USAA16 Felipe Perez 4.00 10.00
USAA17 Nelson Rodriguez 4.00 10.00
USAA18 Corey Seager 5.00 12.00
USAA19 Lucas Sims 4.00 10.00
USAA20 Sheldon Neuse 4.00 10.00

2010 Bowman Chrome Draft USA Baseball Autographs Refractors

*REF: .5X TO 1.2X BASIC
STATED PRINT RUN 199 SER.#'d SETS

2010 Bowman Chrome Draft USA Baseball Autographs Blue Refractors

*BLUE REF: 1.2X TO 3X BASIC
STATED PRINT RUN 99 SER.#'d SETS

2010 Bowman Chrome Draft USA Baseball Autographs Gold Refractors

*GOLD REF: 2X TO 5X BASIC
STATED PRINT RUN 50 SER.#'d SETS

2010 Bowman Chrome Draft USA Baseball Autographs Orange Refractors

STATED PRINT RUN 25 SER.#'d SETS
NO PRICING DUE TO SCARCITY

2010 Bowman Chrome Draft USA Baseball Autographs Red Refractors

STATED PRINT RUN 5 SER.#'d SETS
NO PRICING DUE TO SCARCITY

2010 Bowman Chrome Draft USA Baseball Autographs Superfractors

STATED PRINT RUN 1 SER.#'d SET
NO PRICING DUE TO SCARCITY

2011 Bowman Chrome Draft

COMPLETE SET (110) 12.50 30.00
COMMON CARD (1-110) .30 .75
STATED PLATE ODDS 1:928 HOBBY
PLATE PRINT RUN 1 SET PER COLOR
BLACK-CYAN-MAGENTA-YELLOW ISSUED
NO PLATE PRICING DUE TO SCARCITY
1 Mike Moustakas RC .75 2.00
2 Ryan Adams RC .30 .75
3 Alexi Amarista RC .30 .75
4 Anthony Bass RC .30 .75
5 Pedro Beato RC .30 .75
6 Bruce Billings RC .30 .75
7 Charlie Blackmon RC .30 .75
8 Brian Broderick RC .30 .75
9 Rex Brothers RC .30 .75
10 Tyler Chatwood RC .30 .75
11 Jose Altuve RC .50 1.25
12 Salvador Perez RC .50 1.25
13 Mark Hamburger RC .30 .75
14 Matt Carpenter RC .50 1.25
15 Ezequiel Carrera RC .30 .75
16 Jose Ceda RC .30 .75
17 Andrew Brown RC .50 1.25
18 Maikel Cleto RC .30 .75
19 Steve Cishek RC .30 .75
20 Lonnie Chisenhall RC .50 1.25
21 Henry Sosa RC .30 .75
22 Tim Collins RC .30 .75
23 Josh Collmenter RC .30 .75
24 David Cooper RC .30 .75
25 Brandon Crawford RC .30 .75
26 Brandon Laird RC .50 1.25
27 Tony Cruz RC .75 2.00
28 Chase d'Arnaud RC .50 1.25
29 Faulino De Los Santos RC .30 .75
30 Rubby De La Rosa RC .75 2.00
31 Andy Dirks RC .30 .75
32 Jarrod Dyson RC .30 .75
33 Cody Eppley RC .30 .75
34 Logan Forsythe RC .30 .75
35 Todd Frazier RC .50 1.25
36 Eric Fryer RC .50 1.25
37 Charlie Furbush RC .30 .75
38 Cory Gearrin RC .30 .75
39 Graham Godfrey RC .30 .75
40 Dee Gordon RC .75 2.00
41 Brandon Gomes RC .30 .75
42 Bryan Shaw RC .30 .75
43 Brandon Guyer RC .50 1.25
44 Mark Hamilton RC .50 1.25
45 Brad Hand RC .30 .75
46 Anthony Recker RC .30 .75
47 Jeremy Horst RC .50 1.25
48 Tommy Hottovy (RC) .50 1.25
49 Jose Iglesias RC .50 1.25
50 Craig Kimbrel RC .75 2.00
51 Josh Judy RC .30 .75
52 Cole Kimball RC .30 .75
53 Alan Johnson RC .30 .75
54 Brandon Kintzler RC .30 .75
55 Pete Kozma RC .75 2.00
56 D.J. LeMahieu RC .30 .75
57 Duane Below RC .50 1.25
58 Josh Lindblom RC .50 1.25
59 Zack Cozart RC .75 2.00
60 Al Alburquerque RC .30 .75
61 Trystan Magnuson RC .30 .75
62 Michael Martinez RC .50 1.25
63 Michael McKenry RC .50 1.25
64 Daniel Moskos RC .30 .75
65 Lance Lynn RC .30 .75
66 Juan Nicasio RC .30 .75
67 Joe Paterson RC .50 1.25
68 Lance Pendleton RC .30 .75
69 Luis Perez RC .30 .75
70 Anthony Rizzo RC .50 1.25
71 Joel Carreno RC .30 .75
72 Alex Presley RC .75 2.00
73 Vinnie Pestano RC .30 .75
74 Aneury Rodriguez RC .30 .75
75 Josh Rodriguez RC .30 .75
76 Eduardo Sanchez RC .50 1.25
77 Matt Young RC .30 .75
78 Amauri Sanit RC .30 .75
79 Nathan Eovaldi RC .30 .75
80 Javy Guerra (RC) .50 1.25
81 Eric Sogard RC .30 .75
82 Henderson Alvarez RC .30 .75
83 Ryan Lavarnway RC .75 2.00
84 Michael Stutes RC .50 1.25
85 Everett Teaford RC .30 .75
86 Blake Tekotte RC .30 .75
87 Eric Thames RC .30 .75
88 Arodys Vizcaino RC .30 .75
89 Rene Tosoni RC .30 .75
90 Alex White RC .30 .75
91 Brayan Villarreal RC .30 .75
92 Tony Watson RC .30 .75
93 Johnny Giavotella RC .30 .75
94 Kevin Whelan (RC) .30 .75
95 Mike Nickeas (RC) .30 .75
96 Elih Villanueva RC .30 .75
97 Tom Wilhelmsen RC .30 .75
98 Adam Wilk RC .50 1.25
99 Mike Wilson (RC) .30 .75
100 Jerry Sands RC 1.25 3.00
101 Mike Trout RC 2.00 5.00
102 Kyle Weiland RC .30 .75
103 Kyle Seager RC .50 1.25
104 Jason Kipnis RC 1.00 2.50
105 Chance Ruffin RC .30 .75
106 J.B. Shuck RC .75 2.00
107 Jacob Turner RC 1.25 3.00
108 Paul Goldschmidt RC 1.50 4.00
109 Justin Sellers RC .50 1.25
110 Trayvon Robinson (RC) .50 1.25

2011 Bowman Chrome Draft Refractors

*REF: .75X TO 2X BASIC
STATED ODDS 1:4 HOBBY

2011 Bowman Chrome Draft Blue Refractors

*BLUE REF: 2X TO 5X BASIC
STATED ODDS 1:41 HOBBY
STATED PRINT RUN 199 SER.#'d SETS

2011 Bowman Chrome Draft Gold Canary Diamond

STATED ODDS 1:7410 HOBBY
STATED PRINT RUN 1 SER.#'d SET
NO PRICING DUE TO SCARCITY

2011 Bowman Chrome Draft Gold Refractors

*GOLD REF: 3X TO 8X BASIC
STATED ODDS 1:162 HOBBY
STATED PRINT RUN 50 SER.#'d SETS

2011 Bowman Chrome Draft Orange Refractors

STATED ODDS 1:324 HOBBY
STATED PRINT RUN 25 SER.#'d SETS
NO PRICING DUE TO SCARCITY

2011 Bowman Chrome Draft Purple Refractors

*PURPLE REF: .75X TO 2X BASIC

2011 Bowman Chrome Draft Red Refractors

STATED ODDS 1:1620 HOBBY
STATED PRINT RUN 5 SER.#'d SETS
NO PRICING DUE TO SCARCITY

2011 Bowman Chrome Draft Superfractors

STATED ODDS 1:7410 HOBBY
STATED PRINT RUN 1 SER.#'d SET
NO PRICING DUE TO SCARCITY

2011 Bowman Chrome Draft 16U USA National Team Autographs

STATED ODDS 1:763 HOBBY
STATED PLATE ODDS 1:20,280 HOBBY
PLATE PRINT RUN 1 SET PER COLOR
BLACK-CYAN-MAGENTA-YELLOW ISSUED
NO PLATE PRICING DUE TO SCARCITY
AM Austin Meadows 12.50 30.00
AP Arden Pabst 4.00 10.00
BB Bryson Brigman 5.00 12.00
CP Christian Pelaez 4.00 10.00
CS Carson Sands 5.00 12.00
DN Dom Nunez 4.00 10.00
DT Dany Toussaint 4.00 10.00
HM Hunter Mercado-Hood 4.00 10.00
JD Joe DeMers 5.00 12.00
JJ Jake Jarvis 4.00 10.00
JS Jordan Sheffield 4.00 10.00
KT Keegan Thompson 5.00 12.00
MV Matt Vogel 5.00 12.00
NC Nick Ciuffo 4.00 10.00
RU Riley Unroe 4.00 10.00
SF Steven Farinaro 4.00 10.00
TA Tyler Alamo 5.00 12.00
TC Trevor Clifton 4.00 10.00
WA William Abreu 4.00 10.00
ZC Zach Collins 6.00 15.00

2011 Bowman Chrome Draft 16U USA National Team Autographs Refractors

*REF: .6X TO 1.5X BASIC
STATED ODDS 1:410 HOBBY
STATED PRINT RUN 199 SER.#'d SETS

2011 Bowman Chrome Draft 16U USA National Team Autographs Blue Refractors

*BLUE REF: 1X TO 2.5X BASIC
STATED ODDS 1:825 HOBBY
STATED PRINT RUN 99 SER.#'d SETS

2011 Bowman Chrome Draft 16U USA National Team Autographs Gold Refractors

*GOLD REF: 2X TO 5X BASIC
STATED ODDS 1:1635 HOBBY
STATED PRINT RUN 50 SER.#'d SETS

2011 Bowman Chrome Draft 16U USA National Team Autographs Orange Refractors

STATED ODDS 1:3273 HOBBY
STATED PRINT RUN 25 SER.#'d SETS
NO PRICING DUE TO SCARCITY

2011 Bowman Chrome Draft 16U USA National Team Autographs Purple Refractors

STATED ODDS 1:8176 HOBBY
STATED PRINT RUN 10 SER.#'d SETS
NO PRICING DUE TO SCARCITY

2011 Bowman Chrome Draft 16U USA National Team Autographs Red Refractors

STATED ODDS 1:16,348 HOBBY
STATED PRINT RUN 5 SER.#'d SETS
NO PRICING DUE TO SCARCITY

2011 Bowman Chrome Draft 16U USA National Team Autographs Superfractors

STATED ODDS 1:82,191 HOBBY
STATED PRINT RUN 1 SER.#'d SET
NO PRICING DUE TO SCARCITY

2011 Bowman Chrome Draft Prospects

COMPLETE SET (110) 20.00 50.00
STATED PLATE ODDS 1:928 HOBBY
PLATE PRINT RUN 1 SET PER COLOR
BLACK-CYAN-MAGENTA-YELLOW ISSUED
NO PLATE PRICING DUE TO SCARCITY
BDPP1 John Hicks UER .40 1.00
Drafted by Mariners; pictured as Diamondback
Front incorrectly lists as pitcher
BDPP2 Cody Asche .40 1.00
BDPP3 Tyler Anderson .25 .60
BDPP4 Jack Armstrong .40 1.00
BDPP5 Pratt Maynard 1.00 2.50
BDPP6 Javier Baez .60 1.50
BDPP7 Kenneth Peoples-Walls .25 .60
BDPP8 Matt Barnes .40 1.00
BDPP9 Trevor Bauer 1.00 2.50
BDPP10 Daniel Vogelbach .40 1.00
BDPP11 Mike Wright UER .25 .60
Drafted by Orioles; pictured as National
BDPP12 Dante Bichette 1.00 2.50
BDPP13 Hudson Boyd .25 .60
BDPP14 Archie Bradley .75 2.00
BDPP15 Matthew Skole .40 1.00
BDPP16 Jed Bradley .25 .60
BDPP17 Tyler Pill .25 .60
BDPP18 Dylan Bundy 1.25 3.00
BDPP19 Harold Martinez .40 1.00
BDPP20 Will Lamb .25 .60
BDPP21 Harold Riggins .25 .60
BDPP22 Zach Cone .40 1.00
BDPP23 Kyle Gaedele .25 .60
BDPP24 Kyle Crick .25 .60
BDPP25 C.J. Cron .60 1.50
BDPP26 Nicholas Delmonico .40 1.00
BDPP27 Alex Dickerson .40 1.00
BDPP28 Tony Cingrani .40 1.00
BDPP29 Jose Fernandez .25 .60
BDPP30 Michael Fulmer .25 .60
BDPP31 Carl Thomore .25 .60
BDPP32 Sean Gilmartin .40 1.00
BDPP33 Tyler Goeddel .25 .60
BDPP34 Drew Gagnon .25 .60
BDPP35 Sonny Gray .40 1.00
BDPP36 Larry Greene .60 1.50
BDPP37 Nick Martini .25 .60
BDPP38 Taylor Guerrieri .40 1.00
BDPP39 Jake Hager .25 .60
BDPP40 James Harris .25 .60
BDPP41 Travis Harrison .25 .60
BDPP42 Nick DeSantiago .40 1.00
BDPP43 Chase Larsson .25 .60
BDPP44 Logan Moore .25 .60
BDPP45 Mason Hope .25 .60
BDPP46 Adrian Houser .40 1.00
BDPP47 Sean Buckley .25 .60
BDPP48 Rick Anton .25 .60
BDPP49 Scott Woodward .40 1.00
BDPP50 David Goforth .25 .60
BDPP51 Taylor Jungmann .40 1.00
BDPP52 Blake Snell .25 .60
BDPP53 Francisco Lindor .60 1.50
BDPP54 Mikie Mahtook .60 1.50
BDPP55 Brandon Martin .40 1.00
BDPP56 Kevin Quackenbush .40 1.00
BDPP57 Kevin Matthews .25 .60
BDPP58 C.J. McElroy .25 .60
BDPP59 Anthony Meo .25 .60
BDPP60 Justin James .40 1.00
BDPP61 Levi Michael UER .40 1.00
Drafted by Twins; pictured as Ranger
BDPP62 Joseph Musgrove .40 1.00
BDPP63 Brandon Nimmo .60 1.50
BDPP64 Brandon Culbreth .25 .60
BDPP65 Javaris Reynolds .25 .60
BDPP66 Adam Ehrlich .25 .60
BDPP67 Henry Owens .40 1.00
BDPP68 Joe Panik .75 2.00
BDPP69 Jace Peterson .25 .60
BDPP70 Lance Jeffries .25 .60
BDPP71 Matthew Budgell .25 .60
BDPP72 Dan Gamache .25 .60
BDPP73 Christopher Lee .25 .60
BDPP74 Kyle Kubitza .25 .60
BDPP75 Nick Ahmed .25 .60
BDPP76 Josh Parr .25 .60
BDPP77 Dwight Smith .40 1.00
BDPP78 Steven Gruver .25 .60
BDPP79 Jeffrey Soptic .25 .60
BDPP80 Cory Spangenberg .40 1.00
BDPP81 George Springer .40 1.00
BDPP82 Bubba Starling 1.25 3.00
BDPP83 Robert Stephenson .40 1.00
BDPP84 Trevor Story .25 .60
BDPP85 Madison Boer .25 .60
BDPP86 Blake Swihart .40 1.00
BDPP87 Kellen Moen .25 .60
BDPP88 Joe Tuschak .25 .60
BDPP89 Keenyn Walker .25 .60
BDPP90 Kolten Wong .60 1.50
BDPP91 William Abreu .25 .60
BDPP92 Tyler Alamo .25 .60
BDPP93 Bryson Brigman .25 .60
BDPP94 Nick Ciuffo .25 .60
BDPP95 Trevor Clifton .25 .60
BDPP96 Zach Collins .25 .60
BDPP97 Joe DeMers .25 .60
BDPP98 Steven Farinaro .25 .60
BDPP99 Jake Jarvis .25 .60
BDPP100 Austin Meadows .40 1.00
BDPP101 Hunter Mercado-Hood .25 .60
BDPP102 Dom Nunez .25 .60
BDPP103 Arden Pabst .25 .60
BDPP104 Christian Pelaez .25 .60
BDPP105 Carson Sands .40 1.00
BDPP106 Jordan Sheffield .25 .60
BDPP107 Keegan Thompson .25 .60
BDPP108 Dany Toussaint .25 .60
BDPP109 Riley Unroe .25 .60
BDPP110 Matt Vogel .25 .60

2011 Bowman Chrome Draft Prospects Refractors

*REF: 1.5X TO 4X BASIC
STATED ODDS 1:4 HOBBY

2011 Bowman Chrome Draft Prospects Blue Refractors

*BLUE REF: 4X TO 10X BASIC
STAED ODDS 1:41 HOBBY
STATED PRINT RUN 199 SER.#'d SETS

2011 Bowman Chrome Draft Prospects Gold Canary Diamond

STATED ODDS 1:7410 HOBBY
STATED PRINT RUN 1 SER.#'d SET
NO PRICING DUE TO SCARCITY

2011 Bowman Chrome Draft Prospects Gold Refractors

*GOLD REF: 10X TO 25X BASIC
STAED ODDS 1:162 HOBBY
STATED PRINT RUN 50 SER.#'d SETS

2011 Bowman Chrome Draft Prospects Orange Refractors

STATED ODDS 1:324 HOBBY
STATED PRINT RUN 25 SER.#'d SETS
NO PRICING DUE TO SCARCITY

2011 Bowman Chrome Draft Prospects Purple Refractors

*PURPLE REF: 1.5X TO 4X BASIC

2011 Bowman Chrome Draft Prospects Red Refractors

STATED ODDS 1:1620 HOBBY
STATED PRINT RUN 5 SER.#'d SETS
NO PRICING DUE TO SCARCITY

2011 Bowman Chrome Draft Prospects Superfractors

STATED ODDS 1:7410 HOBBY
STATED PRINT RUN 1 SER.#'d SET
NO PRICING DUE TO SCARCITY

2011 Bowman Chrome Draft Prospect Autographs

STATED ODDS 1:37 HOBBY
STATED PLATE ODDS 1:120,000 HOBBY
PLATE PRINT RUN 1 SET PER COLOR
BLACK-CYAN-MAGENTA-YELLOW ISSUED
NO PLATE PRICING DUE TO SCARCITY
EXCHANGE DEADLINE 11/30/2014
AB Archie Bradley 12.50 30.00
BM Brandon Martin 4.00 10.00
BN Brandon Nimmo 12.50 30.00
BS Bubba Starling EXCH 30.00 60.00
CC C.J. Cron 12.50 30.00
CS Cory Spangenberg 6.00 15.00
DB Dylan Bundy 20.00 50.00
DV Daniel Vogelbach 5.00 12.00
FL Francisco Lindor 10.00 25.00
GS George Springer 8.00 20.00
JB Jed Bradley 5.00 12.00
JF Jose Fernandez EXCH 4.00 10.00
JH James Harris 4.00 10.00
JP Joe Panik 12.50 30.00
KM Kevin Matthews 4.00 10.00
KW Kolten Wong 8.00 20.00
LG Larry Greene 10.00 25.00
MB Matt Barnes 6.00 15.00
MF Michael Fulmer 4.00 10.00
RS Robert Stephenson 5.00 12.00
TA Tyler Anderson 4.00 10.00
TB Trevor Bauer 20.00 50.00
TG Tyler Goeddel 4.00 10.00
TH Travis Harrison 5.00 12.00
TJ Taylor Jungmann 8.00 20.00
TS Trevor Story 5.00 12.00
BSN Blake Snell 4.00 10.00
BSW Blake Swihart 8.00 20.00
JBA Javier Baez 10.00 25.00
JHA Jake Hager 4.00 10.00
KCR Kyle Crick 5.00 12.00
KWA Keenyn Walker 4.00 10.00
SGR Sonny Gray 8.00 20.00
TGU Taylor Guerrieri 5.00 12.00

2011 Bowman Chrome Draft Prospect Autographs Refractors

*REF: .6X TO 1.5X BASIC
STATED ODDS 1:101 HOBBY
STATED PRINT RUN 500 SER.#'d SETS
EXCHANGE DEADLINE 11/30/2014

2011 Bowman Chrome Draft Prospect Autographs Blue Refractors

*BLUE REF: 1.5X TO 4X BASIC
STATED ODDS 1:337 HOBBY
STATED PRINT RUN 150 SER.#'d SETS
EXCHANGE DEADLINE 11/30/2014

2011 Bowman Chrome Draft Prospect Autographs Gold Refractors

*GOLD REF: 2.5X TO 6X BASIC
STATED ODDS 1:1004 HOBBY
STATED PRINT RUN 50 SER.#'d SETS
EXCHANGE DEADLINE 11/30/2014
AB Archie Bradley 150.00 250.00
BN Brandon Nimmo 150.00 250.00
BS Bubba Starling EXCH 300.00 500.00
DB Dylan Bundy 250.00 400.00
FL Francisco Lindor 125.00 250.00
GS George Springer 75.00 150.00
JF Jose Fernandez EXCH 40.00 80.00
JP Joe Panik 150.00 250.00
KW Kolten Wong 75.00 150.00
MB Matt Barnes 75.00 150.00
RS Robert Stephenson 60.00 120.00
TB Trevor Bauer 200.00 300.00
TJ Taylor Jungmann 125.00 250.00
BSW Blake Swihart 75.00 150.00
JBA Javier Baez 125.00 250.00
KCR Kyle Crick 40.00 100.00
SGR Sonny Gray 75.00 150.00

2011 Bowman Chrome Draft Prospect Autographs Orange Refractors

STATED ODDS 1:2008 HOBBY
STATED PRINT RUN 25 SER.#'d SETS
NO PRICING DUE TO SCARCITY
EXCHANGE DEADLINE 11/30/2014

2011 Bowman Chrome Draft Prospect Autographs Purple Refractors

STATED ODDS 1:5050 HOBBY
STATED PRINT RUN 10 SER.#'d SETS
NO PRICING DUE TO SCARCITY
EXCHANGE DEADLINE 11/30/2014

2011 Bowman Chrome Draft Prospect Autographs Red Refractors

STATED ODDS 1:10,150 HOBBY
STATED PRINT RUN 5 SER.#'d SETS
NO PRICING DUE TO SCARCITY
EXCHANGE DEADLINE 11/30/2014

2011 Bowman Chrome Draft Prospect Autographs Superfractors

STATED ODDS 1:47,200 HOBBY
STATED PRINT RUN 1 SER.#'d SET

NO PRICING DUE TO SCARCITY
EXCHANGE DEADLINE 11/30/2014

2001 Bowman Heritage

This 440-card product was issued in 10 card packs, along with a slab of gum, with an SRP of $3 per pack. The packs were issued 16 to a box with 24 boxes to a case. Cards numbered 331-440 were inserted at a rate of one every two packs.

COMPLETE SET (440) 125.00 200.00
COMP.SET w/o SP's (330) 20.00 50.00
COMMON CARD (1-330) .15 .40
COMMON RC (1-330) .15 .40
COMMON (331-440) .75 2.00
1 Chipper Jones .40 1.00
2 Pete Harnisch .15 .40
3 Brian Giles .15 .40
4 J.T. Snow .15 .40
5 Bartolo Colon .15 .40
6 Jorge Posada .25 .60
7 Shawn Green .15 .40
8 Derek Jeter 1.00 2.50
9 Benito Santiago .15 .40
10 Ramon Hernandez .15 .40
11 Bernie Williams .25 .60
12 Greg Maddux .60 1.50
13 Barry Bonds 1.00 2.50
14 Roger Clemens .75 2.00
15 Miguel Tejada .15 .40
16 Pedro Feliz .15 .40
17 Jim Edmonds .15 .40
18 Tom Glavine .25 .60
19 David Justice .15 .40
20 Rich Aurilia .15 .40
21 Jason Giambi .15 .40
22 Orlando Hernandez .15 .40
23 Shawn Estes .15 .40
24 Nelson Figueroa .15 .40
25 Terrence Long .15 .40
26 Mike Mussina .25 .60
27 Eric Davis .15 .40
28 Jimmy Rollins .15 .40
29 Andy Pettitte .25 .60
30 Shawon Dunston .15 .40
31 Tim Hudson .15 .40
32 Jeff Kent .15 .40
33 Scott Brosius .15 .40
34 Livan Hernandez .15 .40
35 Alfonso Soriano .25 .60
36 Mark McGwire 1.00 2.50
37 Russ Ortiz .15 .40
38 Fernando Vina .15 .40
39 Ken Griffey Jr. .60 1.50
40 Edgar Renteria .15 .40
41 Kevin Brown .15 .40
42 Robb Nen .15 .40
43 Paul LoDuca .15 .40
44 Bobby Abreu .15 .40
45 Adam Dunn .25 .60
46 Osvaldo Fernandez .15 .40
47 Marvin Benard .15 .40
48 Mark Gardner .15 .40
49 Alex Rodriguez .60 1.50
50 Preston Wilson .15 .40
51 Roberto Alomar .25 .60
52 Ben Davis .15 .40
53 Derek Bell .15 .40
54 Ken Caminiti .15 .40
55 Barry Zito .25 .60
56 Scott Rolen .25 .60
57 Geoff Jenkins .15 .40
58 Mike Cameron .15 .40
59 Ben Grieve .15 .40
60 Chuck Knoblauch .15 .40
61 Matt Lawton .15 .40
62 Chan Ho Park .15 .40
63 Lance Berkman .15 .40
64 Carlos Beltran .15 .40
65 Dean Palmer .15 .40
66 Alex Gonzalez .15 .40
67 Larry Walker .15 .40
68 Magglio Ordonez .15 .40
69 Ellis Burks .15 .40
70 Mark Mulder .15 .40
71 Randy Johnson .40 1.00
72 John Smoltz .25 .60
73 Jerry Hairston Jr. .15 .40
74 Pedro Martinez .25 .60
75 Fred McGriff .25 .60
76 Sean Casey .15 .40
77 C.C. Sabathia .15 .40
78 Todd Helton .25 .60
79 Brad Penny .15 .40
80 Mike Sweeney .15 .40
81 Billy Wagner .15 .40
82 Mark Buehrle .25 .60
83 Cristian Guzman .15 .40
84 Jose Vidro .15 .40
85 Pat Burrell .15 .40
86 Jermaine Dye .15 .40
87 Brandon Inge .15 .40
88 David Wells .15 .40
89 Mike Piazza .60 1.50
90 Jose Cabrera .15 .40
91 Cliff Floyd .15 .40
92 Matt Morris .15 .40
93 Raul Mondesi .15 .40
94 Joe Kennedy RC .25 .60
95 Jack Wilson RC .25 .60
96 Andruw Jones .25 .60
97 Mariano Rivera .40 1.00
98 Mike Hampton .15 .40
99 Roger Cedeno .15 .40
100 Jose Cruz .15 .40
101 Mike Lowell .15 .40
102 Pedro Astacio .15 .40
103 Joe Mays .15 .40
104 John Franco .15 .40
105 Tim Redding .15 .40
106 Sandy Alomar Jr. .15 .40
107 Bret Boone .15 .40
108 Josh Towers RC .25 .60
109 Matt Stairs .15 .40
110 Chris Truby .15 .40
111 Jeff Suppan .15 .40
112 J.C. Romero .15 .40
113 Felipe Lopez .15 .40
114 Ben Sheets .25 .60
115 Frank Thomas .40 1.00
116 A.J. Burnett .15 .40
117 Tony Clark .15 .40
118 Mac Suzuki .15 .40
119 Brad Radke .15 .40
120 Jeff Shaw .15 .40
121 Nick Neugebauer .15 .40
122 Kenny Lofton .15 .40
123 Jacque Jones .15 .40
124 Brent Mayne .15 .40
125 Carlos Hernandez .15 .40
126 Shane Spencer .15 .40
127 John Lackey .15 .40
128 Sterling Hitchcock .15 .40
129 Darren Dreifort .15 .40
130 Rusty Greer .15 .40
131 Michael Cuddyer .15 .40
132 Tyler Houston .15 .40
133 Chin-Feng Chen .15 .40
134 Ken Harvey .15 .40
135 Marquis Grissom .15 .40
136 Russell Branyan .15 .40
137 Eric Karros .15 .40
138 Josh Beckett .25 .60
139 Todd Zeile .15 .40
140 Corey Koskie .15 .40
141 Steve Sparks .15 .40
142 Bobby Seay .15 .40
143 Tim Raines Jr. .15 .40
144 Julio Zuleta .15 .40
145 Jose Lima .15 .40
146 Dante Bichette .15 .40
147 Randy Keisler .15 .40
148 Brent Butler .15 .40
149 Antonio Alfonseca .15 .40
150 Bryan Rekar .15 .40
151 Jeffrey Hammonds .15 .40
152 Larry Bigbie .15 .40
153 Blake Stein .15 .40
154 Robin Ventura .15 .40
155 Rondell White .15 .40
156 Juan Silvestre .15 .40
157 Marcus Thames .15 .40
158 Sidney Ponson .15 .40
159 Juan A. Pena RC .15 .40
160 C.J. Nitkowski .15 .40
161 Adam Everett .15 .40
162 Eric Munson .15 .40
163 Jason Isringhausen .15 .40
164 Brad Fullmer .15 .40
165 Miguel Olivo .15 .40
166 Fernando Tatis .15 .40
167 Freddy Garcia .15 .40
168 Tom Goodwin .15 .40
169 Armando Benitez .15 .40
170 Paul Konerko .15 .40
171 Jeff Cirillo .15 .40
172 Shane Reynolds .15 .40
173 Kevin Tapani .15 .40
174 Joe Crede .40 1.00
175 Omar Infante RC .15 .40
176 Jake Peavy RC 2.00 5.00
177 Corey Patterson .15 .40
178 Mike Penney RC .15 .40
179 Jeromy Burnitz .15 .40
180 David Segui .15 .40
181 Marcus Giles .15 .40
182 Paul O'Neill .25 .60
183 John Olerud .15 .40
184 Andy Benes .15 .40
185 Brad Cresse .15 .40
186 Ricky Ledee .15 .40
187 Allen Levrault UER .15 .40
Last name misspelled Leverault
188 Royce Clayton .15 .40
189 Kelly Johnson RC 1.25 3.00
190 Quilvio Veras .15 .40
191 Mike Williams .15 .40
192 Jason Lane RC .25 .60
193 Rick Helling .15 .40
194 Tim Wakefield .15 .40
195 James Baldwin .15 .40
196 Cody Ransom RC .15 .40
197 Bobby Kielty .15 .40
198 Bobby Jones .15 .40
199 Steve Cox .15 .40
200 Jamal Strong RC .15 .40
201 Steve Lomasney .15 .40
202 Brian Cardwell RC .15 .40
203 Mike Matheny .15 .40
204 Jeff Randazzo RC .15 .40
205 Aubrey Huff .15 .40
206 Chuck Finley .15 .40
207 Denny Bautista RC .25 .60
208 Terry Mulholland .15 .40
209 Rey Ordonez .15 .40
210 Keith Surkont RC .15 .40
211 Orlando Cabrera .15 .40
212 Juan Encarnacion .15 .40
213 Dustin Hermanson .15 .40
214 Luis Rivas .15 .40
215 Mark Quinn .15 .40
216 Randy Velarde .15 .40
217 Billy Koch .15 .40
218 Ryan Rupe .15 .40
219 Keith Ginter .15 .40
220 Woody Williams .15 .40
221 Ryan Franklin .15 .40
222 Aaron Myette .15 .40
223 Joe Borchard RC .15 .40
224 Nate Cornejo .15 .40
225 Julian Tavarez .15 .40
226 Kevin Millwood .15 .40
227 Travis Hafner RC 2.00 5.00
228 Charles Nagy .15 .40
229 Mike Lieberthal .15 .40
230 Jeff Nelson .15 .40
231 Ryan Dempster .15 .40
232 Andres Galarraga .15 .40
233 Chad Durbin .15 .40
234 Timo Perez .15 .40
235 Troy O'Leary .15 .40
236 Kevin Young .15 .40
237 Gabe Kapler .15 .40
238 Juan Cruz RC .15 .40
239 Masato Yoshii .15 .40
240 Aramis Ramirez .15 .40
241 Matt Cooper RC .15 .40
242 Randy Flores RC .15 .40
243 Rafael Furcal .15 .40
244 David Eckstein .15 .40
245 Matt Clement .15 .40
246 Craig Biggio .25 .60
247 Rick Reed .15 .40
248 Jose Macias .15 .40
249 Alex Escobar .15 .40
250 Roberto Hernandez .15 .40
251 Andy Ashby .15 .40
252 Tony Armas Jr. .15 .40
253 Jamie Moyer .15 .40
254 Jason Tyner .15 .40
255 Charles Kegley RC .15 .40
256 Jeff Conine .15 .40
257 Francisco Cordova .15 .40
258 Ted Lilly .15 .40
259 Joe Randa .15 .40
260 Jeff D'Amico .15 .40
261 Albie Lopez .15 .40
262 Kevin Appier .15 .40
263 Richard Hidalgo .15 .40
264 Omar Daal .15 .40
265 Ricky Gutierrez .15 .40
266 John Rocker .15 .40
267 Ray Lankford .15 .40
268 Beau Hale RC .15 .40
269 Tony Blanco RC .15 .40
270 Derrek Lee UER .25 .60
First name misspelled Derrick
271 Jamey Wright .15 .40
272 Alex Gordon .15 .40
273 Jeff Weaver .15 .40
274 Jaret Wright .15 .40
275 Jose Hernandez .15 .40
276 Bruce Chen .15 .40
277 Todd Hollandsworth .15 .40
278 Wade Miller .15 .40
279 Luke Prokopec .15 .40
280 Rafael Soriano RC .15 .40
281 Damion Easley .15 .40
282 Darren Oliver .15 .40
283 B. Duckworth RC .15 .40
284 Aaron Herr .15 .40
285 Ray Durham .15 .40
286 Wilmy Caceres RC .15 .40
287 Ugueth Urbina .15 .40
288 Scott Seabol .15 .40
289 Lance Niekro RC .25 .60
290 Trot Nixon .15 .40
291 Adam Kennedy .15 .40
292 Brian Schmitt RC .15 .40
293 Grant Roberts .15 .40
294 Benny Agbayani .15 .40
295 Travis Lee .15 .40
296 Erick Almonte RC .15 .40
297 Jim Thome .25 .60
298 Eric Young .15 .40
299 Dan Denham RC .15 .40
300 Boof Bonser RC .15 .40
301 Denny Neagle .15 .40
302 Kenny Rogers .15 .40
303 J.D. Closser .15 .40
304 Chase Utley RC 5.00 12.00
305 Rey Sanchez .15 .40
306 Sean McGowan .15 .40
307 Justin Pope RC .15 .40
308 Torii Hunter .15 .40
309 B.J. Surhoff .15 .40
310 Aaron Heilman RC .20 .50
311 Gabe Gross RC .25 .60
312 Lee Stevens .15 .40
313 Todd Hundley .15 .40
314 Macay McBride RC .40 1.00
315 Edgar Martinez .25 .60
316 Omar Vizquel .25 .60
317 Reggie Sanders .15 .40
318 John-Ford Griffin RC .15 .40
319 Tim Salmon UER .15 .40
Photo is Troy Glaus
320 Pokey Reese .15 .40
321 Jay Payton .15 .40
322 Doug Glanville .15 .40
323 Greg Vaughn .15 .40
324 Ruben Sierra .15 .40
325 Kip Wells .15 .40
326 Carl Everett .15 .40
327 Garret Anderson .15 .40
328 Jay Bell .15 .40
329 Barry Larkin .25 .60
330 Jeff Mathis RC .25 .60
331 Adrian Gonzalez SP 5.00 12.00
332 Juan Rivera SP .75 2.00
333 Tony Alvarez SP .75 2.00
334 Xavier Nady SP .75 2.00
335 Josh Hamilton SP 1.50 4.00
336 Will Smith SP RC .75 2.00
337 Israel Alcantara SP .75 2.00
338 Chris George SP .75 2.00
339 Sean Burroughs SP .75 2.00
340 Jack Cust SP .75 2.00
341 Henry Mateo SP RC .75 2.00
342 Carlos Pena SP .75 2.00
343 J.R. House SP .75 2.00
344 Carlos Silva SP .75 2.00
345 Mike Rivera SP RC .75 2.00
346 Adam Johnson SP .75 2.00
347 Scott Heard SP .75 2.00
348 Alex Cintron SP .75 2.00
349 Miguel Cabrera SP 3.00 8.00
350 Nick Johnson SP .75 2.00
351 Albert Pujols SP RC 40.00 80.00
352 Ichiro Suzuki SP RC 10.00 25.00
353 Carlos Delgado SP .75 2.00
354 Troy Glaus SP .75 2.00
355 Sammy Sosa SP 1.25 3.00
356 Ivan Rodriguez SP 1.25 3.00
357 Vladimir Guerrero SP 1.25 3.00
358 Manny Ramirez Sox SP 1.25 3.00
359 Luis Gonzalez SP .75 2.00
360 Roy Oswalt SP 1.25 3.00
361 Moises Alou SP .75 2.00
362 Juan Gonzalez SP .75 2.00
363 Tony Gwynn SP 1.50 4.00
364 Hideo Nomo SP 1.25 3.00
365 T. Shinjo SP RC 1.25 3.00
366 Kazuhiro Sasaki SP .75 2.00
367 Cal Ripken SP 4.00 10.00
368 Rafael Palmeiro SP 1.25 3.00
369 J.D. Drew SP .75 2.00
370 Doug Mientkiewicz SP .75 2.00
371 Jeff Bagwell SP 1.25 3.00
372 Darin Erstad SP .75 2.00
373 Tom Gordon SP .75 2.00
374 Ben Petrick SP .75 2.00
375 Eric Milton SP .75 2.00
376 N. Garciaparra SP 2.00 5.00
377 Julio Lugo SP .75 2.00
378 Tino Martinez SP 1.25 3.00
379 Javier Vazquez SP .75 2.00
380 Jeremy Giambi SP .75 2.00
381 Marty Cordova SP .75 2.00
382 Adrian Beltre SP .75 2.00
383 John Burkett SP .75 2.00
384 Aaron Boone SP .75 2.00
385 Eric Chavez SP .75 2.00
386 Curt Schilling SP .75 2.00
387 Cory Lidle UER .75 2.00
First name misspelled Corey
388 Jason Schmidt SP .75 2.00
389 Johnny Damon SP 1.25 3.00
390 Steve Finley SP .75 2.00
391 Edgardo Alfonzo SP .75 2.00
392 Jose Valentin SP .75 2.00
393 Jose Canseco SP 1.25 3.00
394 Ryan Klesko SP .75 2.00
395 David Cone SP .75 2.00
396 Jason Kendall UER .75 2.00
Last name misspelled Kendell
397 Placido Polanco SP .75 2.00
398 Glendon Rusch SP .75 2.00
399 Aaron Sele SP .75 2.00
400 D'Angelo Jimenez SP .75 2.00
401 Mark Grace SP 1.25 3.00
402 Al Leiter SP .75 2.00
403 Brian Jordan SP .75 2.00
404 Phil Nevin SP .75 2.00
405 Brent Abernathy SP .75 2.00
406 Kerry Wood SP .75 2.00
407 Alex Gonzalez SP .75 2.00
408 Robert Fick SP .75 2.00
409 Dmitri Young UER .75 2.00
First name misspelled Dimitri
410 Wes Helms SP .75 2.00
411 Trevor Hoffman SP .75 2.00
412 Rickey Henderson SP 1.25 3.00
413 Bobby Higginson SP .75 2.00
414 Gary Sheffield SP .75 2.00
415 Darryl Kile SP .75 2.00
416 Richie Sexson SP .75 2.00
417 F. Menechino SP RC .75 2.00
418 Javy Lopez SP .75 2.00
419 Carlos Lee SP .75 2.00
420 Jon Lieber SP .75 2.00
421 Hank Blalock SP RC 1.25 3.00
422 Marlon Byrd SP RC 1.25 3.00
423 Jason Kinchen SP RC .75 2.00
424 M. Ensberg SP RC UER 2.00 5.00
Front photo is Adam Everett
425 Greg Nash SP RC .75 2.00
426 D. Tankersley SP RC .75 2.00
427 Nate Murphy SP RC .75 2.00
428 Chris Smith SP RC .75 2.00
429 Jake Gautreau SP RC .75 2.00
430 J. VanBenschoten SP RC .75 2.00
431 T.Thompson SP RC .75 2.00
432 O.Hudson SP RC 1.25 3.00
433 J.Williams SP RC 1.25 3.00
434 Kevin Reese SP RC .75 2.00
435 Ed Rogers SP RC .75 2.00
436 Ryan Jamison SP RC .75 2.00
437 A. Pettyjohn SP RC .75 2.00
438 Hee Seop Choi SP RC 1.25 3.00
439 J. Morneau SP RC 5.00 12.00
440 Mitch Jones SP RC .75 2.00

2001 Bowman Heritage Chrome

Inserted at a rate of one in 12 packs, the first 110 cards of this set are featured in this partial parallel set. Please see the multipliers to assess the values for the individual cards.

*CHROME STARS: 4X TO 10X BASIC CARDS
*CHROME RC'S: 2.5X TO 6X BASIC CARDS

2001 Bowman Heritage 1948 Reprints

Issued one per two packs, these 13 cards feature reprints of the featured players 1948 Bowman card.

COMPLETE SET (13) 4.00 10.00
1 Ralph Kiner .40 1.00
2 Johnny Mize .40 1.00
3 Bobby Thomson .40 1.00
4 Yogi Berra .60 1.50
5 Phil Rizzuto .50 1.25
6 Bob Feller .40 1.00
7 Enos Slaughter .40 1.00
8 Stan Musial .75 2.00
9 Hank Sauer .40 1.00
10 Ferris Fain .40 1.00
11 Red Schoendienst .40 1.00
12 Allie Reynolds UER .40 1.00
Original Card number is incorrect
13 Johnny Sain .40 1.00

2001 Bowman Heritage 1948 Reprints Autographs

Inserted at an overall rate of one in 1,523 these two cards have autographs from the feature players on their 1948 reprint cards.

GROUP 1 ODDS 1:3,018
GROUP 2 ODDS 1:3,074
1 Warren Spahn 1 30.00 60.00
2 Bob Feller 2 20.00 50.00

2001 Bowman Heritage 1948 Reprints Relics

Issued at an overall odds of one in 53, these 12 cards feature relic cards from the featured players. The cards featuring pieces of actual seats were inserted at a rate of one in 291 while the odds for bats were one in 2,113 and the odds for jerseys were one in 2,905.

SEAT GROUP A ODDS 1:97
SEAT GROUP B ODDS 1:194
SEAT GROUP C ODDS 1:291
BHMBF Bob Feller Seat A 6.00 15.00
BHMBT Bobby Thomson Seat C 6.00 15.00
BHMES Enos Slaughter Seat C 6.00 15.00
BHMFF Ferris Fain Seat A 6.00 15.00
BHMHS Hank Sauer Seat A 6.00 15.00
BHMJM Johnny Mize Seat C 8.00 20.00
BHMPR Phil Rizzuto Seat B 8.00 20.00
BHMRK Ralph Kiner Seat B 6.00 15.00
BHMRS R.Schoendienst Bat 6.00 15.00
BHMSM1 Stan Musial Seat C 12.50 30.00
BHMYB1 Yogi Berra Seat B 10.00 25.00
BHMYB2 Yogi Berra Jsy 15.00 40.00

2001 Bowman Heritage Autographs

Inserted at overall odds of one in 358, these three cards feature active players who signed cards for the Bowman Heritage set.

GROUP A ODDS 1:775
GROUP B ODDS 1:664
HAAR Alex Rodriguez B 50.00 100.00
HABB Barry Bonds A 100.00 175.00
HARC Roger Clemens A 30.00 60.00

2002 Bowman Heritage

This 440 card standard-size, designed in the style of the 1954 Bowman set, was released in August, 2002. The 10-card packs had an SRP of $3 per pack and were issued 24 packs to a box and 16 boxes to a case. 110 cards were issued in shorter supply than the rest of the set and we have notated that information next to the player's name in our checklist. There were two versions of card number 66 which paid tribute to the Ted Williams/Jim Piersall numbering issue in the original 1954 Bowman set.

COMP.SET w/o SP's (324) 25.00 50.00
COMMON CARD (1-439) .15 .40
COMMON SP .75 2.00
1 Brent Abernathy .15 .40
2 Jermaine Dye .15 .40
3 James Shanks RC .15 .40
4 Chris Flinn RC .15 .40
5 Mike Peeples SP RC .75 2.00
6 Gary Sheffield .15 .40
7 Livan Hernandez SP .75 2.00
8 Jeff Austin RC .15 .40
9 Jeremy Giambi .15 .40
10 Adam Roller RC .15 .40
11 Sandy Alomar Jr. SP .75 2.00
12 Matt Williams SP .75 2.00
13 Hee Seop Choi .15 .40
14 Jose Offerman .15 .40
15 Robin Ventura .15 .40
16 Craig Biggio .25 .60
17 David Wells .15 .40
18 Rob Henkel RC .15 .40
19 Edgar Martinez .25 .60
20 Matt Morris SP .75 2.00
21 Jose Valentin .15 .40
22 Barry Bonds 1.00 2.50
23 Justin Schuda RC .15 .40
24 Josh Phelps .15 .40
25 John Rodriguez RC .20 .50
26 Angel Pagan RC 1.25 3.00
27 Aramis Ramirez .15 .40
28 Jack Wilson .15 .40
29 Roger Clemens .75 2.00
30 Kazuhisa Ishii RC .20 .50
31 Carlos Beltran .15 .40
32 Drew Henson SP .75 2.00
33 Kevin Young SP .75 2.00
34 Juan Cruz SP .75 2.00
35 Curtis Legendre RC .15 .40
36 Jose Morban RC .15 .40
37 Ricardo Cordova SP RC .75 2.00
38 Adam Everett .15 .40
39 Mark Prior .25 .60
40 Jose Bautista RC 3.00 8.00
41 Travis Foley RC .15 .40
42 Kerry Wood .15 .40
43 B.J. Surhoff .15 .40
44 Moises Alou .15 .40
45 Joey Hammond .15 .40
46 Eric Bruntlett RC .15 .40
47 Carlos Guillen .15 .40
48 Joe Crede .15 .40
49 Dan Phillips RC .15 .40
50 Jason LaRue .15 .40
51 Javy Lopez .15 .40
52 Larry Bigbie SP .75 2.00
53 Chris Baker RC .15 .40
54 Marty Cordova .15 .40
55 C.C. Sabathia .15 .40
56 Mike Piazza .60 1.50
57 Brian Giles .15 .40
58 Mike Bordick SP .75 2.00
59 Tyler Houston SP .75 2.00
60 Gabe Kapler .15 .40
61 Ben Broussard .15 .40
62 Steve Finley SP .75 2.00
63 Koyie Hill .15 .40
64 Jeff D'Amico .15 .40
65 Edwin Almonte RC .15 .40
66 Pedro Martinez .25 .60
66B Nomar Garciaparra 66 .60 1.50
67 Travis Fryman SP .75 2.00
68 Brady Clark SP .75 2.00
69 Reed Johnson SP RC 1.50 4.00
70 Mark Grace SP 1.25 3.00
71 Tony Batista SP .75 2.00
72 Roy Oswalt .15 .40
73 Pat Burrell SP .75 2.00
74 Dennis Tankersley .15 .40
75 Ramon Ortiz .15 .40
76 Neal Frendling SP RC .75 2.00
77 Omar Vizquel SP 1.25 3.00
78 Hideo Nomo .40 1.00
79 Orlando Hernandez SP .75 2.00
80 Andy Pettitte .25 .60
81 Cole Barthel RC .15 .40
82 Bret Boone .15 .40
83 Alfonso Soriano .15 .40
84 Brandon Duckworth .15 .40
85 Ben Grieve .15 .40
86 Mike Rosamond SP RC .75 2.00
87 Luke Prokopec .15 .40
88 Chone Figgins RC .60 1.50
89 Rick Ankiel SP .75 2.00
90 David Eckstein .15 .40
91 Corey Koskie .15 .40
92 David Justice .15 .40
93 Jimmy Alvarez RC .15 .40
94 Jason Schmidt .15 .40
95 Reggie Sanders .15 .40
96 Victor Alvarez RC .15 .40
97 Brett Roneberg RC .15 .40
98 D'Angelo Jimenez .15 .40
99 Hank Blalock .25 .60
100 Juan Rivera .15 .40
101 Mark Buehrle SP .75 2.00
102 Juan Uribe .15 .40
103 Royce Clayton SP .75 2.00
104 Brett Kay RC .15 .40
105 John Olerud .15 .40
106 Richie Sexson .15 .40
107 Chipper Jones .40 1.00
108 Adam Dunn .15 .40
109 Tim Salmon SP 1.25 3.00
110 Eric Karros .15 .40
111 Jose Vidro .15 .40
112 Jerry Hairston Jr. .15 .40
113 Anastacio Martinez RC .15 .40
114 Robert Fick SP .75 2.00
115 Randy Johnson .40 1.00
116 Trot Nixon SP .75 2.00
117 Nick Bierbrodt SP .75 2.00
118 Jim Edmonds .15 .40
119 Rafael Palmeiro .25 .60
120 Jose Macias .15 .40
121 Josh Beckett .15 .40
122 Sean Douglass .15 .40
123 Jeff Kent .15 .40
124 Tim Redding .15 .40
125 Xavier Nady .15 .40
126 Carl Everett .15 .40
127 Joe Randa .15 .40
128 Luke Hudson SP .75 2.00
129 Eric Miller RC .15 .40
130 Melvin Mora .15 .40
131 Adrian Gonzalez .15 .40
132 Larry Walker SP .75 2.00
133 Nic Jackson SP RC .75 2.00
134 Mike Lowell SP .75 2.00
135 Jim Thome .25 .60
136 Eric Milton .15 .40
137 Rich Thompson SP RC .75 2.00
138 Placido Polanco SP .75 2.00
139 Juan Pierre .15 .40
140 David Segui .15 .40
141 Chuck Finley .15 .40
142 Felipe Lopez .15 .40
143 Toby Hall .15 .40
144 Fred Bastardo RC .15 .40
145 Troy Glaus .15 .40
146 Todd Helton .25 .60
147 Ruben Golay SP RC 1.25 3.00
148 Darin Erstad .15 .40
149 Ryan Gripp SP RC .75 2.00
150 Orlando Cabrera .15 .40
151 Jason Young RC .15 .40
152 Sterling Hitchcock SP .75 2.00
153 Miguel Tejada .15 .40
154 Al Leiter .15 .40
155 Taylor Buchholz RC .20 .50
156 Juan M. Gonzalez RC .15 .40
157 Damion Easley .15 .40
158 Jimmy Gobble RC .15 .40
159 Dennis Ulacia SP RC .75 2.00
160 Shane Reynolds SP .75 2.00
161 Javier Colina .15 .40
162 Frank Thomas .40 1.00
163 Chuck Knoblauch .15 .40
164 Sean Burroughs .15 .40
165 Greg Maddux .60 1.50
166 Jason Ellison RC .30 .75
167 Tony Womack .15 .40
168 Randall Shelley SP RC .75 2.00
169 Jason Marquis .15 .40
170 Brian Jordan .15 .40
171 Vicente Padilla .15 .40
172 Barry Zito .15 .40
173 Matt Allegra SP RC .75 2.00
174 Ralph Santana SP RC .75 2.00
175 Carlos Lee .15 .40
176 Richard Hidalgo SP .75 2.00
177 Kevin Deaton RC .15 .40
178 Juan Encarnacion .15 .40
179 Mark Quinn .15 .40
180 Rafael Furcal .15 .40
181 Garret Anderson UER .15 .40
Photo is Chone Figgins
182 David Wright RC 6.00 15.00
183 Jose Reyes .25 .60
184 Mario Ramos SP RC .75 2.00
185 J.D. Drew .15 .40
186 Juan Gonzalez .15 .40
187 Nick Neugebauer .15 .40
188 Alejandro Giron RC .15 .40
189 John Burkett .15 .40
190 Ben Sheets .15 .40
191 Vinny Castilla SP .75 2.00
192 Cory Lidle .15 .40
193 Fernando Vina .15 .40
194 Russell Branyan SP .75 2.00
195 Ben Davis .15 .40
196 Angel Berroa .15 .40
197 Alex Gonzalez .15 .40
198 Jared Sandberg .15 .40
199 Travis Lee SP .75 2.00
200 Luis DePaula SP .75 2.00
201 Ramon Hernandez SP .75 2.00
202 Brandon Inge .15 .40
203 Aubrey Huff .15 .40
204 Mike Rivera .15 .40
205 Brad Nelson RC .15 .40
206 Colt Griffin SP RC .75 2.00
207 Joel Pineiro .15 .40
208 Adam Pettyjohn .15 .40
209 Mark Redman .15 .40
210 Roberto Alomar SP 1.25 3.00
211 Denny Neagle .15 .40
212 Adam Kennedy .15 .40
213 Jason Arnold SP RC .75 2.00
214 Jamie Moyer .15 .40
215 Aaron Boone .15 .40
216 Doug Glanville .15 .40
217 Nick Johnson SP .75 2.00
218 Mike Cameron SP .75 2.00
219 Tim Wakefield SP .75 2.00
220 Todd Stottlemyre SP .75 2.00
221 Mo Vaughn SP .75 2.00
222 Vladimir Guerrero .40 1.00
223 Bill Ortega .15 .40
224 Kevin Brown .15 .40
225 Peter Bergeron SP .75 2.00
226 Shannon Stewart SP .75 2.00
227 Eric Chavez .15 .40
228 Clint Weibl RC .15 .40
229 Todd Hollandsworth SP .75 2.00
230 Jeff Bagwell .25 .60
231 Chad Qualls RC .20 .50
232 Ben Howard RC .15 .40
233 Rondell White SP .75 2.00
234 Fred McGriff .25 .60
235 Steve Cox SP .75 2.00
236 Chris Tritle RC .15 .40
237 Eric Valent .15 .40
238 Joe Mauer RC 4.00 10.00
239 Shawn Green .15 .40
240 Jimmy Rollins .15 .40
241 Edgar Renteria .15 .40
242 Edwin Yan RC .15 .40
243 Noochie Varner RC .15 .40
244 Kris Benson SP .75 2.00
245 Mike Hampton .15 .40
246 So Taguchi RC .25 .60
247 Sammy Sosa .40 1.00
248 Terrence Long .15 .40
249 Jason Bay RC 2.00 5.00
250 Kevin Millar SP .75 2.00
251 Albert Pujols .75 2.00
252 Chris Latham RC .15 .40
253 Eric Byrnes .15 .40
254 Napoleon Calzado SP RC .75 2.00
255 Bobby Higginson .15 .40
256 Ben Molina .15 .40
257 Torii Hunter SP .75 2.00
258 Jason Giambi .15 .40
259 Bartolo Colon .15 .40
260 Benito Baez .15 .40
261 Ichiro Suzuki .75 2.00
262 Mike Sweeney .15 .40
263 Brian West RC .15 .40
264 Brad Penny .15 .40
265 Kevin Millwood SP .75 2.00
266 Orlando Hudson .15 .40
267 Doug Mientkiewicz .15 .40
268 Luis Gonzalez SP .75 2.00
269 Jay Caligiuri RC .15 .40
270 Nate Cornejo SP .75 2.00
271 Lee Stevens .15 .40

272 Eric Hinske .15 .40
273 Antwon Rollins RC .15 .40
274 Bobby Jenks RC .60 1.50
275 Joe Mays .15 .40
276 Josh Shaffer RC .15 .40
277 Jonny Gomes RC 1.00 2.50
278 Bernie Williams .25 .60
279 Ed Rogers .15 .40
280 Carlos Delgado .15 .40
281 Raul Mondesi SP .75 2.00
282 Jose Ortiz .15 .40
283 Cesar Izturis .15 .40
284 Ryan Dempster SP .75 2.00
285 Brian Daubach .15 .40
286 Hansel Izquierdo RC .15 .40
287 Mike Lieberthal SP .75 2.00
288 Marcus Thames .15 .40
289 Nomar Garciaparra .60 1.50
290 Brad Fullmer .15 .40
291 Tino Martinez .25 .60
292 James Barrett RC .15 .40
293 Jacque Jones .15 .40
294 Nick Alvarez SP RC .75 2.00
295 Jason Grove SP RC .75 2.00
296 Mike Wilson SP RC .75 2.00
297 J.T. Snow .15 .40
298 Cliff Floyd .15 .40
299 Todd Hundley SP .75 2.00
300 Tony Clark SP .75 2.00
301 Demetrius Heath RC .15 .40
302 Morgan Ensberg .15 .40
303 Cristian Guzman .15 .40
304 Frank Catalanotto .15 .40
305 Jeff Weaver .15 .40
306 Tim Hudson .15 .40
307 Scott Wiggins SP RC .75 2.00
308 Shea Hillenbrand SP .75 2.00
309 Todd Walker SP .75 2.00
310 Tsuyoshi Shinjo .15 .40
311 Adrian Beltre .15 .40
312 Craig Kuzmic RC .15 .40
313 Paul Konerko .15 .40
314 Scott Hairston RC .20 .50
315 Chan Ho Park .15 .40
316 Jorge Posada .25 .60
317 Chris Snelling RC .30 .75
318 Keith Foulke .15 .40
319 John Smoltz .25 .60
320 Ryan Church SP RC 1.50 4.00
321 Mike Mussina .25 .60
322 Tony Armas Jr. SP .75 2.00
323 Craig Counsell .15 .40
324 Marcus Giles .15 .40
325 Greg Vaughn .15 .40
326 Curt Schilling .15 .40
327 Jeromy Burnitz .15 .40
328 Eric Byrnes .15 .40
329 Johnny Damon Sox .25 .60
330 Michael Floyd SP RC .75 2.00
331 Edgardo Alfonzo .15 .40
332 Jeremy Hill RC .15 .40
333 Josh Bonifay RC .15 .40
334 Byung-Hyun Kim .15 .40
335 Keith Ginter .15 .40
336 Ronald Acuna SP RC .75 2.00
337 Mike Hill SP RC .75 2.00
338 Sean Casey .15 .40
339 Matt Anderson SP .75 2.00
340 Dan Wright .15 .40
341 Ben Petrick .15 .40
342 Mike Sirotka SP .75 2.00
343 Alex Rodriguez .60 1.50
344 Einar Diaz .15 .40
345 Derek Jeter 1.00 2.50
346 Jeff Conine .15 .40
347 Ray Durham SP .75 2.00
348 Wilson Betemit SP .75 2.00
349 Jeffrey Hammonds .15 .40
350 Dan Trumble RC .15 .40
351 Phil Nevin SP .75 2.00
352 A.J. Burnett .15 .40
353 Bill Mueller .15 .40
354 Charles Nagy .15 .40
355 Rusty Greer SP .75 2.00
356 Jason Botts RC .20 .50
357 Magglio Ordonez .15 .40
358 Kevin Appier .15 .40
359 Brad Radke .15 .40
360 Chris George .15 .40
361 Chris Piersoll RC .15 .40
362 Ivan Rodriguez .25 .60
363 Jim Kavourias RC .15 .40
364 Rick Helling SP .75 2.00
365 Dean Palmer .15 .40
366 Rich Aurilia SP .75 2.00
367 Ryan Vogelsong .15 .40
368 Matt Lawton .15 .40
369 Wade Miller .15 .40
370 Dustin Hermanson .15 .40
371 Craig Wilson .15 .40
372 Todd Zeile SP .75 2.00
373 Jon Guzman RC .15 .40
374 Ellis Burks .15 .40
375 Robert Cosby SP RC .75 2.00
376 Jason Kendall .15 .40
377 Scott Rolen SP 1.25 3.00
378 Andruw Jones .25 .60
379 Greg Sain RC .15 .40
380 Paul LoDuca .15 .40
381 Scotty Layfield RC .15 .40
382 Tomo Ohka .15 .40
383 Garrett Guzman RC .15 .40
384 Jack Cust SP .75 2.00
385 Shayne Wright RC .15 .40
386 Derrek Lee .25 .60
387 Jesus Medrano RC .15 .40
388 Javier Vazquez .15 .40
389 Preston Wilson SP .75 2.00
390 Gavin Floyd RC .40 1.00
391 Sidney Ponson SP .75 2.00
392 Jose Hernandez .15 .40
393 Scott Erickson SP .75 2.00
394 Jose Valverde RC .15 .40
395 Mark Hamilton SP RC .75 2.00
396 Brad Cresse .15 .40
397 Danny Bautista .15 .40
398 Ray Lankford SP .75 2.00
399 Miguel Batista SP .75 2.00
400 Brent Butler .15 .40
401 Manny Delcarmen SP RC 1.25 3.00
402 Kyle Farnsworth SP .75 2.00
403 Freddy Garcia .15 .40
404 Joe Jiannetti RC .15 .40
405 Josh Barfield RC 1.00 2.50
406 Corey Patterson .15 .40
407 Josh Towers .15 .40
408 Carlos Pena .15 .40
409 Jeff Cirillo .15 .40
410 Jon Lieber .15 .40
411 Woody Williams SP .75 2.00
412 Richard Lane SP RC .75 2.00
413 Alex Gonzalez .15 .40
414 Wilkin Ruan .15 .40
415 Geoff Jenkins .15 .40
416 Carlos Hernandez .15 .40
417 Matt Clement SP .75 2.00
418 Jose Cruz Jr. .15 .40
419 Jake Mauer RC .15 .40
420 Matt Childers RC .15 .40
421 Tom Glavine SP 1.25 3.00
422 Ken Griffey Jr. .60 1.50
423 Anderson Hernandez RC .15 .40
424 John Suomi RC .15 .40
425 Doug Sessions RC .15 .40
426 Jaret Wright .15 .40
427 Rolando Viera SP RC .75 2.00
428 Aaron Sele .15 .40
429 Dmitri Young .15 .40
430 Ryan Klesko .15 .40
431 Kevin Tapani SP .75 2.00
432 Joe Kennedy .15 .40
433 Austin Kearns .15 .40
434 Roger Cedeno SP .75 2.00
435 Lance Berkman .15 .40
436 Frank Menechino .15 .40
437 Brett Myers .15 .40
438 Bob Abreu .15 .40
439 Shawn Estes SP .75 2.00

2002 Bowman Heritage Black Box

Issued at stated odds of one in two packs, these 55 cards form a partial parallel of the Bowman Heritage set. These cards can be notated by the players "signature" being placed in a black box.

13 Hee Seop Choi .30 .75
22 Barry Bonds 2.00 5.00
23 Justin Schuda .25 .60
27 Aramis Ramirez .30 .75
30 Kazuhisa Ishii .30 .75
39 Mark Prior .50 1.25
41 Travis Foley .25 .60
56 Mike Piazza 1.25 3.00
66 Nomar Garciaparra .50 1.25
72 Roy Oswalt .30 .75
96 Victor Alvarez .25 .60
99 Hank Blalock .50 1.25
107 Chipper Jones .75 2.00
108 Adam Dunn .30 .75
120 Jose Macias .30 .75
121 Josh Beckett .30 .75
139 Juan Pierre .30 .75
143 Toby Hall .30 .75
145 Troy Glaus .30 .75
146 Todd Helton .50 1.25
153 Miguel Tejada .30 .75
167 Tony Womack .30 .75
180 Rafael Furcal .30 .75
182 David Wright 6.00 15.00
185 J.D. Drew .30 .75
222 Vladimir Guerrero .75 2.00
227 Eric Chavez .30 .75
238 Joe Mauer 4.00 10.00
240 Jimmy Rollins .30 .75
246 So Taguchi .30 .75
247 Sammy Sosa .75 2.00
251 Albert Pujols 1.50 4.00
258 Jason Giambi .30 .75
261 Ichiro Suzuki 1.50 4.00
266 Orlando Hudson .30 .75
269 Jay Caligiuri .25 .60
274 Bobby Jenks 1.00 2.50
275 Joe Mays .30 .75
277 Jonny Gomes 1.50 4.00
310 Tsuyoshi Shinjo .30 .75
314 Scott Hairston .30 .75
316 Jorge Posada .50 1.25
317 Chris Snelling .50 1.25
335 Keith Ginter .30 .75
343 Alex Rodriguez 1.25 3.00
345 Derek Jeter 2.00 5.00
362 Ivan Rodriguez .50 1.25
390 Gavin Floyd .60 1.50
396 Brad Cresse .30 .75
405 Josh Barfield 1.50 4.00
414 Wilkin Ruan .30 .75
416 Carlos Hernandez .30 .75
418 Jose Cruz Jr. .30 .75
422 Ken Griffey Jr. 1.25 3.00
433 Austin Kearns .30 .75

2002 Bowman Heritage Chrome Refractors

Issued at stated odds of one in 16, these 110 cards partially parallel the regular Bowman Heritage set. Please note that although the numbering is different, the cards are the same as the regular cards except for the Chrome technology used. These cards were issued to a stated print run of 350 serial numbered sets.

*CHROME: 4X TO 10X BASIC CARDS
*CHROME SP's: .75X TO 2X BASIC SP'S
*CHROME RC's: 3X TO 8X BASIC RC'S

2002 Bowman Heritage Gold Chrome Refractors

Issued at stated odds of one in 32, these 110 cards partially parallel the regular Bowman Heritage set. Please note that although the numbering is different, the cards are the same as the regular cards except for the Chrome technology used. Each card was issued to a stated print run of 175 serial numbered sets.

*GOLD: 6X TO 15X BASIC CARDS
*GOLD SP'S: 1.25X TO 3X BASIC SP'S
*GOLD RC'S: 5X TO 12X BASIC RC'S

2002 Bowman Heritage 1954 Reprints

Issued at stated odds of one in 12, these 20 cards feature reprinted versions of the featured player 1954 Bowman card.

COMPLETE SET (20) 20.00 50.00
BHRAR Allie Reynolds .75 2.00
BHRBF Bob Feller .75 2.00
BHRCL Clem Labine .75 2.00
BHRDC Del Crandall .75 2.00
BHRDL Don Larsen .75 2.00
BHRDM Don Mueller .75 2.00
BHRDS Duke Snider 2.00 5.00
BHRDW Dave Williams .75 2.00
BHRES Enos Slaughter .75 2.00
BHRGM Gil McDougald .75 2.00
BHRHW Hoyt Wilhelm .75 2.00
BHRJL Johnny Logan .75 2.00
BHRJP Jim Piersall .75 2.00
BHRNF Nellie Fox 1.25 3.00
BHRPR Phil Rizzuto 1.25 3.00
BHRRA Richie Ashburn 1.25 3.00
BHRWF Whitey Ford 1.25 3.00
BHRWM Willie Mays 4.00 10.00
BHRWW Wes Westrum .75 2.00
BHRYB Yogi Berra 2.00 5.00

2002 Bowman Heritage 1954 Reprints Autographs

Inserted at stated odds of one in 126, these six cards have autographs of the featured player on their 1954 Reprint card.

*SPEC.ED: .75X TO 2X BASIC AUTOS
SPEC.ED STATED ODDS 1:1910
SPEC.ED. PRINT RUN 54 SERIAL #'d SETS
BHRACL Clem Labine 10.00 25.00
BHRADC Del Crandall 15.00 40.00
BHRADM Don Mueller 10.00 25.00
BHRADW Dave Williams 10.00 25.00
BHRAJL Johnny Logan 15.00 40.00
BHRAYB Yogi Berra 40.00 80.00

2002 Bowman Heritage Autographs

Issued at overall stated odds of one in 45, these 13 cards feature players signing copies of their Bowman Heritage card. Please note that these cards were issued in three different groups with differing odds and we have noted which players belong to which group in our checklist.

GROUP A STATED ODDS 1:620
GROUP B STATED ODDS 1:89
GROUP C STATED ODDS 1:103
OVERALL STATED ODDS 1:45
BHAAP Albert Pujols A 200.00 350.00
BHACI Cesar Izturis B 4.00 10.00
BHADH Drew Henson B 4.00 10.00
BHAHB Hank Blalock C 6.00 15.00
BHAJM Joe Mauer C 60.00 120.00
BHAJR Juan Rivera C 6.00 15.00
BHAKG Keith Ginter B 4.00 10.00
BHAKI Kazuhisa Ishii A 12.50 30.00
BHALB Lance Berkman B 8.00 20.00
BHAMP Mark Prior B 6.00 15.00
BHAPL Paul LoDuca C 6.00 15.00
BHARO Roy Oswalt B 6.00 15.00
BHATH Toby Hall B 4.00 10.00

2002 Bowman Heritage Relics

Inserted in packs at overall stated odds of one in 47 for Jersey cards and one in 75 for Uniform cards, these 26 cards feature game-worn swatches on them. Many cards belong to different groups and we have noted that information next to their name in our checklist.

GROUP A JSY ODDS 1:1910
GROUP B JSY ODDS 1:1551
GROUP C JSY ODDS 1:138
GROUP D JSY ODDS 1:207
GROUP E JSY ODDS 1:165
GROUP F JSY ODDS 1:2072
GROUP G JSY ODDS 1:653
GROUP A UNI ODDS 1:1551
GROUP B UNI ODDS 1:855
GROUP C UNI ODDS 1:124
GROUP D UNI ODDS 1:284
BHAP Albert Pujols Uni C 10.00 25.00
BHBB Barry Bonds Uni D 10.00 25.00
BHCD Carlos Delgado Jsy G 4.00 10.00
BHCJ Chipper Jones Jsy C 6.00 15.00
BHDE Darin Erstad Uni C 4.00 10.00
BHEA Edgardo Alfonzo Jsy C 4.00 10.00
BHEC Eric Chavez Jsy C 4.00 10.00
BHEM Edgar Martinez Jsy C 6.00 15.00
BHFT Frank Thomas Jsy F 6.00 15.00
BHGM Greg Maddux Jsy C 6.00 15.00
BHIR Ivan Rodriguez Uni B 6.00 15.00
BHJB Josh Beckett Jsy E 4.00 10.00
BHJE Jim Edmonds Jsy D 4.00 10.00
BHJS John Smoltz Jsy C 6.00 15.00
BHJT Jim Thome Jsy E 6.00 15.00
BHKS Kazuhiro Sasaki Jsy C 4.00 10.00
BHLW Larry Walker Jsy C 4.00 10.00
BHMP Mike Piazza Uni A 6.00 15.00
BHMR Mariano Rivera Uni C 6.00 15.00
BHNG Nomar Garciaparra Jsy A 8.00 20.00
BHPK Paul Konerko Jsy E 4.00 10.00
BHPW Preston Wilson Jsy B 4.00 10.00
BHSR Scott Rolen Jsy C 6.00 15.00
BHTG Tony Gwynn Jsy D 6.00 15.00
BHTH Todd Helton Jsy D 6.00 15.00
BHTS Tim Salmon Uni C 6.00 15.00

2003 Bowman Heritage

This 300-card standard-size set was released in December, 2003. The set was issued in four-card packs with an $3 SRP which came 24 packs to a box and 10 boxes to a case. This set was designed in the style of what the 1956 Bowman set would have been if that set had been issued. Cards numbered 161 through 170 feature players who debuted in the 2003 season and each of those players have a double image. Cards numbered 171-180 featured retired greats and those cards were issued in three styles: Regular design, Double Image and Knothole Design, Cards number 180 through 300 are all Rookie Cards and all those cards are issued in the knothole design.

COMPLETE SET (300) 60.00 120.00
1 Jorge Posada .25 .60
2 Todd Helton .25 .60
3 Marcus Giles .15 .40
4 Eric Chavez .15 .40
5 Edgar Martinez .25 .60
6 Luis Gonzalez .15 .40
7 Corey Patterson .15 .40
8 Preston Wilson .15 .40
9 Ryan Klesko .15 .40
10 Randy Johnson .40 1.00
11 Jose Guillen .15 .40
12 Carlos Lee .15 .40
13 Steve Finley .15 .40
14 A.J. Pierzynski .15 .40
15 Troy Glaus .15 .40
16 Darin Erstad .15 .40
17 Moises Alou .15 .40
18 Torii Hunter .15 .40
19 Marlon Byrd .15 .40
20 Mark Prior .25 .60
21 Shannon Stewart .15 .40
22 Craig Biggio .25 .60
23 Johnny Damon .25 .60
24 Robert Fick .15 .40
25 Jason Giambi .15 .40
26 Fernando Vina .15 .40
27 Aubrey Huff .15 .40
28 Benito Santiago .15 .40
29 Jay Gibbons .15 .40
30 Ken Griffey Jr. .60 1.50
31 Rocco Baldelli .15 .40
32 Pat Burrell .15 .40
33 A.J. Burnett .15 .40
34 Omar Vizquel .25 .60
35 Greg Maddux .60 1.50
36 Cliff Floyd .15 .40
37 C.C. Sabathia .15 .40
38 Geoff Jenkins .15 .40
39 Ty Wigginton .15 .40
40 Jeff Kent .15 .40
41 Orlando Hudson .15 .40
42 Edgardo Alfonzo .15 .40
43 Greg Myers .15 .40
44 Melvin Mora .15 .40
45 Sammy Sosa .40 1.00
46 Russ Ortiz .15 .40
47 Josh Beckett .15 .40
48 David Wells .15 .40
49 Woody Williams .15 .40
50 Alex Rodriguez .60 1.50
51 Randy Wolf .15 .40
52 Carlos Beltran .15 .40
53 Austin Kearns .15 .40
54 Trot Nixon .15 .40
55 Ivan Rodriguez .25 .60
56 Shea Hillenbrand .15 .40
57 Roberto Alomar .25 .60
58 John Olerud .15 .40
59 Michael Young .25 .60
60 Garret Anderson .15 .40
61 Mike Lieberthal .15 .40
62 Adam Dunn .15 .40
63 Raul Ibanez .15 .40
64 Kenny Lofton .15 .40
65 Ichiro Suzuki .75 2.00
66 Jarrod Washburn .15 .40
67 Shawn Chacon .15 .40
68 Alex Gonzalez .15 .40
69 Roy Halladay .15 .40
70 Vladimir Guerrero .40 1.00
71 Hee Seop Choi .15 .40
72 Jody Gerut .15 .40
73 Ray Durham .15 .40
74 Mark Teixeira .25 .60
75 Hank Blalock .15 .40
76 Jerry Hairston Jr. .15 .40
77 Erubiel Durazo .15 .40
78 Frank Catalanotto .15 .40
79 Jacque Jones .15 .40
80 Bobby Abreu .15 .40
81 Mike Hampton .15 .40
82 Zach Day .15 .40
83 Jimmy Rollins .15 .40
84 Joel Pineiro .15 .40
85 Brett Myers .15 .40
86 Frank Thomas .40 1.00
87 Aramis Ramirez .15 .40
88 Paul Lo Duca .15 .40
89 Dmitri Young .15 .40
90 Brian Giles .15 .40
91 Jose Cruz Jr. .15 .40
92 Derek Lowe .15 .40
93 Mark Buehrle .15 .40
94 Wade Miller .15 .40
95 Derek Jeter 1.00 2.50
96 Bret Boone .15 .40
97 Tony Batista .15 .40
98 Sean Casey .15 .40
99 Eric Hinske .15 .40
100 Albert Pujols .75 2.00
101 Runelvys Hernandez .15 .40
102 Vernon Wells .15 .40
103 Kerry Wood .15 .40
104 Lance Berkman .15 .40
105 Alfonso Soriano .15 .40
106 Bill Mueller .15 .40
107 Bartolo Colon .15 .40
108 Andy Pettitte .25 .60
109 Rafael Furcal .15 .40
110 Dontrelle Willis .40 1.00
111 Carl Crawford .15 .40
112 Scott Rolen .25 .60
113 Chipper Jones .40 1.00
114 Magglio Ordonez .15 .40
115 Bernie Williams .25 .60
116 Roy Oswalt .15 .40
117 Kevin Brown .15 .40
118 Cristian Guzman .15 .40
119 Kazuhisa Ishii .15 .40
120 Larry Walker .15 .40
121 Miguel Tejada .15 .40
122 Manny Ramirez .25 .60
123 Mike Mussina .25 .60
124 Mike Lowell .15 .40
125 Scott Podsednik .15 .40
126 Aaron Boone .15 .40
127 Carlos Delgado .15 .40
128 Jose Vidro .15 .40
129 Brad Radke .15 .40
130 Rafael Palmeiro .25 .60
131 Mark Mulder .15 .40
132 Jason Schmidt .15 .40
133 Gary Sheffield .15 .40
134 Richie Sexson .15 .40
135 Barry Zito .15 .40
136 Tom Glavine .25 .60
137 Jim Edmonds .15 .40
138 Andruw Jones .25 .60
139 Pedro Martinez .25 .60
140 Curt Schilling .15 .40
141 Phil Nevin .15 .40
142 Nomar Garciaparra .60 1.50
143 Vicente Padilla .15 .40
144 Kevin Millwood .15 .40
145 Shawn Green .15 .40
146 Jeff Bagwell .25 .60
147 Hideo Nomo .40 1.00
148 Fred McGriff .25 .60
149 Matt Morris .15 .40
150 Roger Clemens .75 2.00
151 Jerome Williams .15 .40
152 Orlando Cabrera .15 .40
153 Tim Hudson .15 .40
154 Mike Sweeney .15 .40
155 Jim Thome .25 .60
156 Rich Aurilia .15 .40
157 Mike Piazza .60 1.50
158 Edgar Renteria .15 .40
159 Javy Lopez .15 .40
160 Jamie Moyer .15 .40
161 Miguel Cabrera DI .40 1.00
162 Adam Loewen DI RC .40 1.00
163 Jose Reyes DI .15 .40
164 Zack Greinke DI .15 .40
165 Gavin Floyd DI .15 .40
166 Jeremy Guthrie DI .15 .40
167 Victor Martinez DI .25 .60
168 Rich Harden DI .25 .60
169 Joe Mauer DI .40 1.00
170 Khalil Greene DI .40 1.00
171A Willie Mays .75 2.00
171B Willie Mays DI .75 2.00
171C Willie Mays KN .75 2.00
172A Phil Rizzuto .25 .60
172B Phil Rizzuto DI .25 .60
172C Phil Rizzuto KN .25 .60
173A Al Kaline .40 1.00
173B Al Kaline DI .40 1.00
173C Al Kaline KN .40 1.00
174A Warren Spahn .25 .60
174B Warren Spahn DI .25 .60
174C Warren Spahn KN .25 .60
175A Jimmy Piersall .15 .40
175B Jimmy Piersall DI .15 .40
175C Jimmy Piersall KN .15 .40
176A Luis Aparicio .15 .40
176B Luis Aparicio DI .15 .40
176C Luis Aparicio KN .15 .40
177A Whitey Ford .25 .60
177B Whitey Ford DI .25 .60
177C Whitey Ford KN .25 .60
178A Harmon Killebrew .40 1.00
178B Harmon Killebrew DI .40 1.00
178C Harmon Killebrew KN .40 1.00
179A Duke Snider .25 .60
179B Duke Snider DI .25 .60
179C Duke Snider KN .25 .60
180A Roberto Clemente 1.00 2.50
180B Roberto Clemente DI 1.00 2.50
180C Roberto Clemente KN 1.00 2.50
181 David Martinez KN RC .15 .40
182 Felix Pie KN RC 1.50 4.00
183 Kevin Correia KN RC .15 .40
184 Brandon Webb KN RC 1.00 2.50
185 Matt Diaz KN RC .30 .75
186 Lew Ford KN RC .20 .50
187 Jeremy Griffiths KN RC .15 .40
188 Matt Hensley KN RC .15 .40
189 Danny Garcia KN RC .15 .40
190 Elizardo Ramirez KN RC .20 .50
191 Greg Aquino KN RC .15 .40
192 Felix Sanchez KN RC .15 .40
193 Kelly Shoppach KN RC .30 .75
194 Bubba Nelson KN RC .20 .50
195 Mike O'Keefe KN RC .15 .40
196 Hanley Ramirez KN RC 1.50 4.00
197 Todd Wellemeyer KN RC .15 .40
198 Dustin Moseley KN RC .15 .40
199 Eric Crozier KN RC .20 .50
200 Ryan Shealy KN RC 1.00 2.50
201 Jeremy Bonderman KN RC 1.00 2.50
202 Bo Hart KN RC .15 .40
203 Dusty Brown KN RC .15 .40
204 Rob Hammock KN RC .15 .40
205 Jorge Piedra KN RC .20 .50
206 Jason Kubel KN RC .60 1.50
207 Stephen Randolph KN RC .15 .40
208 Andy Sisco KN RC .15 .40
209 Matt Kata KN RC .15 .40
210 Robinson Cano KN RC 4.00 10.00
211 Ben Francisco KN RC .15 .40
212 Arnie Munoz KN RC .15 .40
213 Ozzie Chavez KN RC .15 .40
214 Beau Kemp KN RC .15 .40
215 Travis Wong KN RC .20 .50
216 Brian McCann KN RC 2.50 6.00
217 Aquilino Lopez KN RC .15 .40
218 Bobby Basham KN RC .15 .40
219 Tim Olson KN RC .15 .40
220 Nathan Panther KN RC .15 .40
221 Wil Ledezma KN RC .15 .40
222 Josh Willingham KN RC .40 1.00
223 David Cash KN RC .15 .40
224 Oscar Villarreal KN RC .15 .40
225 Jeff Duncan KN RC .15 .40
226 Dan Haren KN RC .40 1.00
227 Michel Hernandez KN RC .15 .40
228 Matt Murton KN RC .75 2.00
229 Clay Hensley KN RC .15 .40
230 Tyler Johnson KN RC .15 .40
231 Tyler Martin KN RC .15 .40
232 J.D. Durbin KN RC .15 .40
233 Shane Victorino KN RC .40 1.00
234 Rajai Davis KN RC .15 .40
235 Chien-Ming Wang KN RC 1.00 2.50
236 Travis Ishikawa KN RC .30 .75
237 Eric Eckenstahler KN .15 .40
238 Dustin McGowan KN RC .20 .50
239 Prentice Redman KN RC .15 .40
240 Haj Turay KN RC .15 .40
241 Matt DeMarco KN RC .15 .40
242 Lou Palmisano KN RC .20 .50
243 Eric Reed KN RC .15 .40
244 Willie Eyre KN RC .15 .40
245 Ferdin Tejeda KN RC .15 .40
246 Michael Garciaparra KN RC .15 .40
247 Michael Hinckley KN RC .20 .50
248 Branden Florence KN RC .15 .40
249 Trent Oeltjen KN RC .20 .50
250 Mike Neu KN RC .15 .40
251 Chris Lubanski KN RC .40 1.00
252 Brandon Wood KN RC 4.00 10.00
253 Delmon Young KN RC 2.00 5.00
254 Matt Harrison KN RC .30 .75
255 Chad Billingsley KN RC 1.25 3.00
256 Josh Anderson KN RC .20 .50
257 Brian McFall KN RC .15 .40
258 Ryan Wagner KN RC .15 .40
259 Billy Hogan KN RC .20 .50
260 Nate Spears KN RC .20 .50
261 Ryan Harvey KN RC .75 2.00
262 Wes Littleton KN RC .20 .50
263 Xavier Paul KN RC .20 .50
264 Sean Rodriguez KN RC .75 2.00
265 Brian Finch KN RC .15 .40
266 Josh Rainwater KN RC .20 .50
267 Brian Snyder KN RC .20 .50
268 Eric Duncan KN RC .75 2.00
269 Rickie Weeks KN RC 1.25 3.00
270 Tim Battle KN RC .30 .75
271 Scott Beerer KN RC .15 .40
272 Aaron Hill KN RC .30 .75
273 Casey Abrams KN RC .15 .40
274 Jonathan Fulton KN RC .20 .50
275 Todd Jennings KN RC .20 .50
276 Jordan Pratt KN RC .20 .50
277 Tom Gorzelanny KN RC .50 1.25
278 Matt Lorenzo KN RC .20 .50
279 Jarrod Saltalamacchia KN RC 2.00 5.00
280 Mike Wagner KN RC .15 .40

2003 Bowman Heritage Autographs

This one-card set (featuring top prospect Delmon Young) was issued in packs at a rate of 1:1014 as an exchange card. The deadline to redeem the card was December 31st, 2005.

STATED ODDS 1:1014
253 Delmon Young KN 10.00 25.00

2003 Bowman Heritage Box Toppers

COMPLETE SET (8) 10.00 25.00
*BOX TOPPER: .4X TO 1X BASIC
ONE PER SEALED BOX

2003 Bowman Heritage Facsimile Signature

*FACSIMILE 161-170: 1X TO 2.5X BASIC
*FACSIMILE 171A-180C: 1X TO 2.5X BASIC
*FACSIMILE 181-280: .6X TO 1.5X BASIC
ONE PER PACK

2003 Bowman Heritage Gold Rainbow

STATED ODDS 1:4178
STATED PRINT RUN 1 SERIAL #'d SET
NO PRICING DUE TO SCARCITY

2003 Bowman Heritage Rainbow

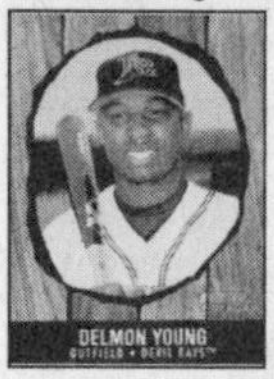

COMPLETE SET (100) 30.00 80.00
*RAINBOW: .5X TO 1.2X BASIC
ONE PER PACK

2003 Bowman Heritage Diamond Cuts Relics

BAT ODDS 1:133
JSY GROUP A ODDS 1:28
JSY GROUP B ODDS 1:936
JSY GROUP C ODDS 1:626
UNI ODDS 1:35
GOLD STATED ODDS 1:8193
GOLD PRINT RUN 1 SERIAL #'d SET
NO GOLD PRICING DUE TO SCARCITY
*RED BAT: .6X TO 1.5X BASIC BAT
*RED JSY: 1X TO 2.5X BASIC JSY
*RED UNI: 1X TO 2.5X BASIC UNI
RED STATED ODDS 1:143
RED PRINT RUN 56 SERIAL #'d SETS
AJ Andruw Jones Jsy A 4.00 10.00
AK Austin Kearns Jsy A 3.00 8.00
AP Albert Pujols Bat 10.00 25.00
AR1 Alex Rodriguez Bat 6.00 15.00
AR2 Alex Rodriguez Jsy A 4.00 10.00

AS Alfonso Soriano Bat 4.00 10.00
BB Bret Boone Jsy A 3.00 8.00
BM Brett Myers Jsy A 3.00 8.00
BW Bernie Williams Uni 4.00 10.00
BZ Barry Zito Uni 3.00 8.00
CB Craig Biggio Uni 4.00 10.00
CF Cliff Floyd Uni 3.00 8.00
CG Cristian Guzman Jsy A 3.00 8.00
CJ1 Chipper Jones Bat 6.00 15.00
CJ2 Chipper Jones Jsy A 4.00 10.00
EC Eric Chavez Uni 3.00 8.00
GS Gary Sheffield Uni 3.00 8.00
HB Hank Blalock Bat 4.00 10.00
HN Hideo Nomo Jsy A 4.00 10.00
JA Jeremy Affeldt Uni 3.00 8.00
JB Jeff Bagwell Jsy A 4.00 10.00
JE Jim Edmonds Uni 3.00 8.00
JG Jason Giambi Uni 3.00 8.00
JJ Jason Jennings Jsy A 3.00 8.00
JL Javy Lopez Jsy A 3.00 8.00
JLP Josh Phelps Jsy C 3.00 8.00
JR Jose Reyes Jsy A 3.00 8.00
JV Javier Vazquez Jsy A 3.00 8.00
JW Jarrod Washburn Uni 3.00 8.00
KI Kazuhiro Sasaki Jsy A 3.00 8.00
KM Kevin Millwood Jsy A 3.00 8.00
KW Kerry Wood Uni 3.00 8.00
MA Moises Alou Jsy C 3.00 8.00
MG Mark Grace Jsy B 4.00 10.00
ML Mike Lowell Jsy A 3.00 8.00
MM Mark Mulder Uni 3.00 8.00
MS Mike Sweeney Jsy A 3.00 8.00
MT Miguel Tejada Uni 3.00 8.00
PL Paul Lo Duca Jsy A 3.00 8.00
PM Pedro Martinez Jsy A 4.00 10.00
RC Roberto Clemente Bat 40.00 80.00
RH Rickey Henderson Bat 6.00 15.00
RP1 Rafael Palmeiro Bat 6.00 15.00
RP2 Rafael Palmeiro Uni 4.00 10.00
SR1 Scott Rolen Bat 6.00 15.00
SR2 Scott Rolen Uni 4.00 10.00
SS1 Sammy Sosa Bat 6.00 15.00
SS2 Sammy Sosa Jsy A 4.00 10.00
TA Tony Armas Jr. Jsy A 3.00 8.00
TG Troy Glaus Uni 3.00 8.00
TH Todd Helton Jsy A 4.00 10.00
THA Tim Hudson Uni 3.00 8.00
TW Ty Wigginton Uni 3.00 8.00
VG Vladimir Guerrero Bat 6.00 15.00
VW Vernon Wells Jsy A 3.00 8.00

2003 Bowman Heritage Olbermann Autograph

STATED ODDS 1:1421
KOA Keith Olbermann 30.00 60.00

2003 Bowman Heritage Signs of Greatness

STATED ODDS 1:30
RED INK STATED ODDS 1:32,141
RED INK PRINT RUN 1 SERIAL #'d SET
NO RED INK PRICING DUE TO SCARCITY
BF Brian Finch 3.00 8.00
BS Brian Snyder 3.00 8.00
CB Chad Billingsley 6.00 15.00
DW Dontrelle Willis 5.00 12.00
FP Felix Pie 15.00 40.00
JD Jeff Duncan 3.00 8.00
KY Kevin Youkilis 15.00 40.00
MM Matt Murton 6.00 15.00
RC Robinson Cano 100.00 200.00
RH Rich Harden 4.00 10.00
RW Rickie Weeks 10.00 25.00
TG Tom Gorzelanny 10.00 25.00

2004 Bowman Heritage

This 352-card set was released in December, 2004. The set was issued in eight-card packs with an $3 SRP which came 24 packs to a box and 10 boxes to a case. This set was issued in the style of 1955 Bowman and featured several twists similar to the original set - including some cards in which the biographies did not match the player pictured and a card number #140 featuring a pair of brothers. (as the original 55 set had pictures of the Shantz brothers at #140). There were also short prints scattered throughout the set as well as the first major manufacturer cards of many current umpires.

COMPLETE SET (351) 175.00 300.00
COMP.SET w/o SP's (300) 25.00 50.00
COMMON ACTIVE .15 .40
COMMON RETIRED .15 .40
COMMON UMPIRE .15 .40
COMMON RC .15 .40
COMMON DP RC .30 .75
COMMON SP 1.25 3.00
COMMON SP RC 1.25 3.00
SP STATED ODDS 1:3 HOBBY, 1:3 RETAIL
SP's: 2/9/13/21/25/40B/46/48B/50/55/61
SP's: 77/80/87/89/95/100/104/109/127/130
SP's: 132/141/183A/189/204/206/208/210
SP's: 213/216/220/224/228/234/240/243
SP's: 246/249/259/268/270-271/282/291
SP's: 304/318/327/334/342/348
PLATES STATED ODDS 1:240 HOBBY
PLATES PRINT RUN 1 #'d SET PER COLOR
PLATES: BLACK, CYAN, MAGENTA & YELLOW
NO PLATES PRICING DUE TO SCARCITY
ROOP BINDER ODDS 1:240 HOBBY
ROOP BINDER EXCH.DEADLINE 12/31/05
1 Tom Glavine .25 .60
2 Mike Piazza SP 3.00 8.00
3 Sidney Ponson .15 .40
4 Jerry Hairston Jr. .15 .40
5 Jermaine Dye .15 .40
6 Bobby Crosby .15 .40
7 Carlos Zambrano .25 .60
8 Moises Alou .15 .40
9 Alex Rodriguez SP 5.00 12.00
10 Derek Jeter 1.00 2.50
11 Rafael Furcal .15 .40
12 J.D. Drew .15 .40
13 Joe Mauer SP 3.00 8.00
14 Brad Radke .15 .40
15 Johnny Damon .25 .60
16 Derek Lowe .15 .40
17 Pat Burrell .15 .40
18 Mike Lieberthal .15 .40
19 Cliff Lee .25 .60
20 Ronnie Belliard .15 .40
21 Eric Gagne SP 1.25 3.00
22 Brad Penny .15 .40
23 Al Kaline RET .40 1.00
24 Mike Maroth .15 .40
25 Magglio Ordonez SP 2.00 5.00
26 Mark Buehrle .25 .60
27 Jack Wilson .15 .40
28 Oliver Perez .15 .40
29 Red Schoendienst RET .15 .40
30 Yadier Molina FY RC 1.00 2.50
31 Ryan Freel .15 .40
32 Adam Dunn .25 .60
33 Paul Konerko .25 .60
34 Esteban Loaiza .15 .40
35 Ivan Rodriguez .25 .60
36 Carlos Guillen .15 .40
37 Adrian Beltre .15 .40
38 C.C. Sabathia .25 .60
39 Hideo Nomo .40 1.00
40A Victor Martinez .25 .60
40B V.Martinez Pedro Stats SP 2.00 5.00
41 Bobby Abreu .15 .40
42 Randy Wolf .15 .40
43 Johnny Estrada .15 .40
44 Russ Ortiz .15 .40
45 Kenny Rogers .15 .40
46 Hank Blalock SP 1.25 3.00
47 David Ortiz .40 1.00
48A Pedro Martinez .25 .60
48B P.Martinez Victor Stats SP 2.00 5.00
49 Austin Kearns .15 .40
50 Ken Griffey Jr. SP 5.00 12.00
51 Mark Prior .25 .60
52 Kerry Wood .15 .40
53 Eric Chavez .15 .40
54 Tim Hudson .25 .60
55 Rafael Palmeiro SP 2.00 5.00
56 Javy Lopez .15 .40
57 Jason Bay .25 .60
58 Craig Wilson .15 .40
59 Whitey Ford RET .25 .60
60 Jason Giambi .15 .40
61 Scott Rolen SP 2.00 5.00
62 Matt Morris .15 .40
63 Javier Vazquez .15 .40
64 Jim Thome .25 .60
65 Don Zimmer RET .15 .40
66 Shawn Green .15 .40
67 Don Larsen RET .15 .40
68 Gary Sheffield .15 .40
69 Jorge Posada .25 .60
70 Bernie Williams .25 .60
71 Chipper Jones .40 1.00
72 Andruw Jones .15 .40
73 John Thomson .15 .40
74 Jim Edmonds .25 .60
75 Albert Pujols 1.00 2.50
76 Chris Carpenter .40 1.00
77 Aubrey Huff SP 1.25 3.00
78 Carl Crawford .25 .60
79 Victor Zambrano .15 .40
80 Alfonso Soriano SP 1.25 3.00
81 Lance Berkman .25 .60
82 Mike Sweeney .15 .40
83 Ken Harvey .15 .40
84 Angel Berroa .15 .40
85 A.J. Burnett .25 .60
86 Mike Lowell .15 .40
87 Miguel Cabrera SP 3.00 8.00
88 Preston Wilson .15 .40
89 Todd Helton SP 2.00 5.00
90 Larry Walker Cards .25 .60
91 Vladimir Guerrero .40 1.00
92 Garret Anderson .15 .40
93 Bartolo Colon .15 .40
94 Scott Hairston .15 .40
95 Richie Sexson SP 1.25 3.00
96 Sean Casey .15 .40
97 John Podres RET .15 .40
98 Andy Pettitte .25 .60
99 Roy Oswalt .25 .60
100 Roger Clemens SP 4.00 10.00
101 Scott Podsednik .15 .40
102 Ben Sheets .15 .40
103 Lyle Overbay .15 .40
104 Nick Johnson SP 1.25 3.00
105 Zach Day .15 .40
106 Jose Reyes .25 .60
107 Khalil Greene .25 .60
108 Sean Burroughs .15 .40
109 David Wells SP 1.25 3.00
110 Jason Schmidt .15 .40
111 Neifi Perez .15 .40
112 Edgar Renteria .15 .40
113 Rich Aurilia .15 .40
114 Edgar Martinez .25 .60
115 Joel Pineiro .15 .40
116 Mark Teixeira .40 1.00
117 Michael Young .15 .40
118 Ricardo Rodriguez .15 .40
119 Carlos Delgado .15 .40
120 Roy Halladay .40 1.00
121 Jose Guillen .15 .40
122 Troy Glaus .15 .40
123 Shea Hillenbrand .15 .40
124 Luis Gonzalez .15 .40
125 Horacio Ramirez .15 .40
126 Melvin Mora .15 .40
127 Miguel Tejada SP 2.00 5.00
128 Manny Ramirez .40 1.00
129 Tim Wakefield .15 .40
130 Curt Schilling SP 2.00 5.00
131 Aramis Ramirez .15 .40
132 Sammy Sosa SP 3.00 8.00
133 Matt Clement .15 .40
134 Juan Uribe .15 .40
135 Dontrelle Willis .15 .40
136 Paul Lo Duca .15 .40
137 Juan Pierre .15 .40
138 Kevin Brown .15 .40
139 Brian Giles .15 .40
Marcus Giles
140 Brian Giles .15 .40
141 Nomar Garciaparra SP 3.00 8.00
142 Cesar Izturis .15 .40
143 Don Newcombe RET .15 .40
144 Craig Biggio .25 .60
145 Carlos Beltran .15 .40
146 Torii Hunter .15 .40
147 Livan Hernandez .15 .40
148 Cliff Floyd .15 .40
149 Barry Zito .15 .40
150 Mark Mulder .15 .40
151 Rocco Baldelli .15 .40
152 Bret Boone .15 .40
153 Jamie Moyer .15 .40
154 Ichiro Suzuki .60 1.50
155 Brett Myers .15 .40
156 Carl Pavano .15 .40
157 Josh Beckett .25 .60
158 Randy Johnson .40 1.00
159 Trot Nixon .15 .40
160 Dmitri Young .15 .40
161 Jacque Jones .15 .40
162 Lew Ford .15 .40
163 Jose Vidro .15 .40
164 Mark Kotsay .15 .40
165 A.J. Pierzynski .15 .40
166 Dewon Brazelton .15 .40
167 Jeromy Burnitz .15 .40
168 Johan Santana .40 1.00
169 Greg Maddux .60 1.50
170 Carl Erskine RET .15 .40
171 Robin Roberts RET .15 .40
172 Freddy Garcia .15 .40
173 Carlos Lee .15 .40
174 Jeff Bagwell .25 .60
175 Jeff Kent .15 .40
176 Kazuhisa Ishii .15 .40
177 Orlando Cabrera .15 .40
178 Shannon Stewart .15 .40
179 Mike Cameron .15 .40
180 Mike Mussina .25 .60
181 Frank Thomas .40 1.00
182 Jaret Wright .15 .40
183A Alex Gonzalez Marlins SP 1.25 3.00
183B Alex Gonzalez Padres .15 .40
184 Matt Lawton .15 .40
185 Derrek Lee .15 .40
186 Omar Vizquel .25 .60
187 Jeremy Bonderman .15 .40
188 Jake Westbrook .15 .40
189 Zack Greinke SP 2.00 5.00
190 Chad Tracy .15 .40
191 Rondell White .15 .40
192 Alex Gonzalez .15 .40
193 Geoff Jenkins .15 .40
194 Ralph Kiner RET .25 .60
195 Al Leiter .15 .40
196 Kevin Millwood .15 .40
197 Jason Kendall .15 .40
198 Kris Benson .15 .40
199 Ryan Klesko .15 .40
200 Mark Loretta .15 .40
201 Richard Hidalgo .15 .40
202 Reed Johnson .15 .40
203 Luis Castillo .15 .40
204 Jon Zeringue DP SP RC 1.25 3.00
205 Matt Bush DP RC .50 1.25
206 Kurt Suzuki DP SP RC 4.00 10.00
207 Mark Rogers DP RC .50 1.25
208 Jason Vargas DP SP RC 3.00 8.00
209 Homer Bailey DP RC .50 1.25
210 Ray Liotta DP SP RC 1.25 3.00
211 Eric Campbell DP RC .30 .75
212 Thomas Diamond DP RC .30 .75
213 Gaby Hernandez DP SP RC 3.00 8.00
214 Neil Walker DP RC 1.50 4.00
215 Bill Bray DP RC .30 .75
216 Wade Davis DP SP RC 4.00 10.00
217 David Purcey DP RC .50 1.25
218 Scott Elbert DP RC .30 .75
219 Josh Fields DP RC .50 1.25
220 Josh Johnson DP SP RC 1.25 3.00
221 Chris Lambert DP RC .30 .75
222 Trevor Plouffe DP RC .75 2.00
223 Bruce Froemming UMP .15 .40
224 Matt Macri DP SP RC 2.00 5.00
225 Greg Golson DP RC .30 .75
226 Philip Hughes DP RC 2.50 6.00
227 Kyle Waldrop DP RC .30 .75
228 Matt Tuiasosopo DP SP RC 3.00 8.00
229 Richie Robnett DP RC .30 .75
230 Taylor Tankersley DP RC .30 .75
231 Blake DeWitt DP RC 1.25 3.00
232 Charlie Reliford UMP .15 .40
233 Eric Hurley DP RC .30 .75
234 Jordan Parraz DP SP RC 2.00 5.00
235 J.P. Howell DP RC .30 .75
236 Dana DeMuth UMP .15 .40
237 Zach Jackson DP RC .30 .75
238 Justin Orenduff DP RC .50 1.25
239 Brad Thompson FY RC .25 .60
240 J.C. Holt DP SP RC 1.25 3.00
241 Matt Fox DP RC .30 .75
242 Danny Putnam DP RC .30 .75
243 Daryl Jones DP SP RC 1.25 3.00
244 Jon Poterson DP RC .30 .75
245 Gio Gonzalez DP RC .75 2.00
246 Lucas Harrell DP SP RC 1.25 3.00
247 Jerry Crawford UMP .15 .40
248 Jay Rainville DP RC .30 .75
249 Donnie Smith DP SP RC 1.25 3.00
250 Huston Street DP RC .75 2.00
251 Jeff Marquez DP RC .30 .75
252 Reid Brignac DP RC .75 2.00
253 Yusmeiro Petit FY RC .25 .60
254 K.C. Herren DP RC .30 .75
255 Dale Scott UMP .15 .40
256 Erick San Pedro DP RC .30 .75
257 Ed Montague UMP .15 .40
258 Billy Buckner DP RC .30 .75
259 Mitch Einertson DP SP RC 1.25 3.00
260 Aaron Baldiris FY RC .15 .40
261 Conor Jackson FY RC 1.00 2.50
262 Rick Reed UMP .15 .40
263 Ervin Santana FY RC UER .40 1.00
Facsimile Signature is Johan Santana
264 Gerry Davis UMP .15 .40
265 Merkin Valdez FY RC .15 .40
266 Joey Gathright FY RC .15 .40
267 Alberto Callaspo FY RC .40 1.00
268 Carlos Quentin FY SP RC 5.00 12.00
269 Gary Darling UMP .15 .40
270 Jeff Salazar FY SP RC 1.25 3.00
271 Akinori Otsuka FY SP RC 1.25 3.00
272 Joe Brinkman UMP .15 .40
273 Omar Quintanilla FY RC .15 .40
274 Brian Runge UMP .15 .40
275 Tom Mastny FY RC .15 .40
276 John Hirschbeck UMP .15 .40
277 Warner Madrigal FY RC .15 .40
278 Joe West UMP .15 .40
279 Paul Maholm FY RC .25 .60
280 Larry Young UMP .15 .40
281 Mike Reilly UMP .15 .40
282 Kazuo Matsui FY SP RC 2.00 5.00
283 Randy Marsh UMP .15 .40
284 Frank Francisco FY RC .15 .40
285 Zach Duke FY RC .25 .60
286 Tim McClelland UMP .15 .40
287 Jesse Crain FY RC .15 .40
288 Hector Gimenez FY RC .15 .40
289 Marland Williams FY RC .15 .40
290 Brian Gorman UMP .15 .40
291 Jose Capellan FY SP RC 1.25 3.00
292 Tim Welke UMP .15 .40
293 Javier Guzman FY RC .15 .40
294 Paul McAnulty FY RC .15 .40
295 Hector Made FY RC .15 .40
296 Jon Connolly FY RC .15 .40
297 Don Sutton FY RC .15 .40
298 Fausto Carmona FY RC .25 .60
299 Ramon Ramirez FY RC .15 .40
300 Brad Snyder FY RC .15 .40
301 Chin-Lung Hu FY RC .15 .40
302 Rudy Guillen FY RC .15 .40
303 Matt Moses FY RC .25 .60
304 Brad Halsey FY SP RC 1.25 3.00
305 Erick Aybar FY RC .25 .60
306 Brad Sullivan FY RC .15 .40
307 Nick Gorneault FY RC .15 .40
308 Craig Ansman FY RC .15 .40
309 Ricky Nolasco FY RC .25 .60
310 Luke Hughes FY RC .15 .40
311 Danny Gonzalez FY RC .15 .40
312 Josh Labandeira FY RC .15 .40
313 Donald Levinski FY RC .15 .40
314 Vince Perkins FY RC .15 .40
315 Tommy Murphy FY RC .15 .40
316 Chad Bentz FY RC .15 .40
317 Chris Shelton FY RC .15 .40
318 Nyjer Morgan FY SP RC 1.25 3.00
319 Kody Kirkland FY RC .15 .40
320 Blake Hawksworth FY RC .15 .40
321 Alex Romero FY RC .15 .40
322 Mike Gosling FY RC .15 .40
323 Ryan Budde FY RC .15 .40
324 Kevin Howard FY RC .15 .40
325 Wanell Macia FY RC .15 .40
326 Travis Blackley FY RC .15 .40
327 Kazuhito Tadano FY SP RC 1.25 3.00
328 Shingo Takatsu FY RC .15 .40
329 Joaquin Arias FY RC .40 1.00
330 Juan Cedeno FY RC .15 .40
331 Bobby Brownlie FY RC .15 .40
332 Lastings Milledge FY RC 1.00 2.50
333 Estee Harris FY RC .15 .40
334 Tim Stauffer FY SP RC 2.00 5.00
335 Jon Knott FY RC .15 .40
336 David Aardsma FY RC .15 .40
337 Wardell Starling FY RC .15 .40
338 Dioner Navarro FY RC .25 .60
339 Logan Kensing FY RC .15 .40
340 Jason Hirsh FY RC .15 .40
341 Matt Creighton FY RC .15 .40
342 Felix Hernandez FY SP RC 6.00 15.00
343 Kyle Sleeth FY RC .15 .40
344 Dustin Nippert FY RC .15 .40
345 Anthony Lerew FY RC .15 .40
346 Chris Saenz FY RC .15 .40
347 Steve Palermo SUP .15 .40
348 Barry Bonds SP 6.00 15.00

2004 Bowman Heritage Black and White

COMPLETE SET (351) 225.00 325.00
*B/W: 1X TO 2.5X BASIC
*B/W: .6X TO 1.5X BASIC RC
*B/W: .5X TO 1.2X BASIC DP RC
*B/W: .12X TO .3X BASIC SP
*B/W: .06X TO .15X BASIC SP RC
*B/W: .1X TO .25X BASIC DP SP RC
ONE PER PACK

2004 Bowman Heritage Mahogany

STATED ODDS 1:39 HOBBY
STATED PRINT RUN 25 SERIAL #'d SETS
NO RC YR PRICING DUE TO SCARCITY

2004 Bowman Heritage Commissioner's Cut

STATED ODDS 1:320,720 HOBBY
STATED PRINT RUN 1 SERIAL #'d SET
NO PRICING DUE TO SCARCITY
FF Ford Frick

2004 Bowman Heritage Signs of Authority

STATED ODDS 1:49 HOBBY, 1:107 RETAIL
*RED: 1X TO 2.5X BASIC
RED STATED ODDS 1:499 HOB, 1:1019 RET
RED PRINT RUN 55 SERIAL #'d SETS
BF Bruce Froemming 6.00 15.00
BG Brian Gorman 6.00 15.00
BR Brian Runge 6.00 15.00
CM Charlie Reliford 6.00 15.00
DD Dana DeMuth 6.00 15.00
DS Dale Scott 6.00 15.00
EM Ed Montague 6.00 15.00
ER Rick Reed 6.00 15.00
GD Gerry Davis 6.00 15.00
GDA Gary Darling 6.00 15.00
JB Joe Brinkman 6.00 15.00
JC Jerry Crawford 6.00 15.00
JH John Hirschbeck 6.00 15.00
JW Joe West 6.00 15.00
LY Larry Young 6.00 15.00
MR Mike Reilly 6.00 15.00
RM Randy Marsh 6.00 15.00
SP Steve Palermo 6.00 15.00
TM Tim McClelland 6.00 15.00
TW Tim Welke 6.00 15.00

2004 Bowman Heritage Signs of Glory

STATED ODDS 1:246 HOBBY, 1:503 RETAIL
*RED: 1.25X TO 3X BASIC
RED ODDS 1:2019 HOBBY, 1:3961 RETAIL
RED PRINT RUN 55 SERIAL #'d SETS
BK Bob Kuzava 10.00 25.00
BS Bobby Shantz 10.00 25.00
GK George Kell 10.00 25.00
MS Bill Skowron 10.00 25.00
PR Preacher Roe 10.00 25.00

2004 Bowman Heritage Signs of Greatness

STATED ODDS 1:57 HOBBY, 1:122 RETAIL
*RED: 1.5X TO 4X BASIC
RED ODDS 1:999 HOBBY, 1:2038 RETAIL
RED PRINT RUN 55 SERIAL #'d SETS
CL Chris Lambert 3.00 8.00
GG Greg Golson 5.00 12.00
JM Jeff Marquez 3.00 8.00
JR Jay Rainville 5.00 12.00
MB Matt Bush 6.00 15.00
MR Mark Rogers 5.00 12.00
NW Neil Walker 8.00 20.00
PH Philip Hughes 15.00 40.00
TD Thomas Diamond 6.00 15.00
TP Trevor Plouffe 5.00 12.00

2004 Bowman Heritage Threads of Greatness

GROUP A ODDS 1:339 H, 1:799 R
GROUP B ODDS 1:229 H, 1:534 R
GROUP C ODDS 1:128 H, 1:279 R
GROUP D ODDS 1:48 H, 1:109 R
GROUP E ODDS 1:261 H, 1:621 R
GROUP F ODDS 1:26 H, 1:49 R
*RED: 1X TO 2.5X BASIC C-F
*RED: .75X TO 2X BASIC B

*RED: .6X TO 1.5X BASIC A
RED ODDS 1:115 HOBBY, 1:264 RETAIL
RED PRINT RUN 55 SERIAL #'d SETS
AB Adrian Beltre Bat C 2.00 5.00
AEP Andy Pettitte Uni F 3.00 8.00
AGB Armando Benitez Jsy F 2.00 5.00
AJ Andruw Jones Bat A 6.00 15.00
AMB Angel Berroa Bat B 3.00 8.00
AP Albert Pujols Jsy B 8.00 20.00
AP2 Albert Pujols Bat F 6.00 15.00
AR Alex Rodriguez Bat A 10.00 25.00
AS Alfonso Soriano Bat D 2.00 5.00
BB Bret Boone Bat C 2.00 5.00
BB2 Bret Boone Jsy F 2.00 5.00
BC Bobby Cox Uni F 3.00 8.00
BW Bernie Williams Bat C 3.00 8.00
BZ Barry Zito Uni F 2.00 5.00
CE Carl Everett Uni F 2.00 5.00
CS C.C. Sabathia Jsy F 2.00 5.00
DJ Dave Justice Uni F 3.00 8.00
DW Dontrelle Willis Jsy D 3.00 8.00
EC Eric Chavez Bat D 2.00 5.00
EC2 Eric Chavez Uni D 2.00 5.00
FT Frank Thomas Jsy F 3.00 8.00
GS Gary Sheffield Bat D 2.00 5.00
HB Hank Blalock Bat A 4.00 10.00
HB2 Hank Blalock Jsy F 2.00 5.00
HN Hideo Nomo Jsy E 3.00 8.00
JAG Juan Gonzalez Jsy B 3.00 8.00
JB Jeff Bagwell Bat C 3.00 8.00
JB2 Jeff Bagwell Jsy F 3.00 8.00
JD Johnny Damon Uni D 3.00 8.00
JDS Jason Schmidt Jsy C 2.00 5.00
JG Jason Giambi Uni F 2.00 5.00
JG2 Jason Giambi Jsy D 2.00 5.00
JL Javy Lopez Jsy B 3.00 8.00
JM Joe Mauer Bat B 4.00 10.00
JO John Olerud Bat E 3.00 8.00
JO2 John Olerud Jsy E 3.00 8.00
JPB Josh Beckett Jsy A 4.00 10.00
JPB2 Josh Beckett Bat D 3.00 8.00
JR Jose Reyes Jsy A 4.00 10.00
JS John Smoltz Jsy B 4.00 10.00
JS2 John Smoltz Jsy F 3.00 8.00
JT Jim Thome Jsy D 3.00 8.00
JT2 Jim Thome Bat E 3.00 8.00
JW Jarrod Washburn Uni F 2.00 5.00
KM Kevin Millwood Jsy F 2.00 5.00
KW Kerry Wood Jsy B 3.00 8.00
KW2 Kerry Wood Bat D 2.00 5.00
LB Lance Berkman Bat D 2.00 5.00
LB2 Lance Berkman Jsy D 2.00 5.00
MA Moises Alou Jsy A 4.00 10.00
MC Miguel Cabrera Bat D 3.00 8.00
MCD Mike McDougal Jsy F 2.00 5.00
MCT Mark Teixeira Jsy D 3.00 8.00
ML Mike Lowell Jsy F 2.00 5.00
MM Mark Mulder White Uni F 2.00 5.00
MM2 Mark Mulder White Uni F 2.00 5.00
MP Mike Piazza Bat D 4.00 10.00
MP2 Mike Piazza Jsy A 6.00 15.00
MR Manny Ramirez Uni B 4.00 10.00
MR2 Manny Ramirez Bat D 3.00 8.00
MS Mike Sweeney Bat F 2.00 5.00
MT Miguel Tejada Bat A 4.00 10.00
MT2 Miguel Tejada White Uni F 2.00 5.00
MT3 Miguel Tejada Gray Uni F 2.00 5.00
MY Michael Young Jsy A 4.00 10.00
NG Nomar Garciaparra Bat F 4.00 10.00
OV Omar Vizquel Bat C 3.00 8.00
PB Pat Burrell Bat D 2.00 5.00
PL Paul LoDuca Bat C 2.00 5.00
RB Rocco Baldelli Bat B 3.00 8.00
RC Roger Clemens Uni F 4.00 10.00
RH Roy Halladay Jsy F 2.00 5.00
RS Ruben Sierra Bat C 2.00 5.00
SS Sammy Sosa Blue Jsy A 6.00 15.00
SS2 Sammy Sosa Bat C 3.00 8.00
SS3 Sammy Sosa White Jsy F 3.00 8.00
TB Tony Batista Jsy D 2.00 5.00
TH Todd Helton Jsy D 3.00 8.00
VW Vernon Wells Jsy D 2.00 5.00
WB Wade Boggs Jsy A 6.00 15.00

2005 Bowman Heritage

This 350-card set was released in December, 2005. The set was issued in eight-card hobby and retail packs packs with an $3 SRP which came 24 packs to a box and 10 boxes to a case. Cards numbered 2 through 201 feature leading current major league players. Cards numbered 1 and 202 through 300 feature leading prospects. Cards numbered 301 through 350 were printed in shorter quantities than other cards in this set. Those cards which feature veteran players from 301 through 324 and leading prospects from 325-350 were issued at stated rates of one in three hobby or retail packs. Please note that card #350, originally issued as a "Mystery Redemption", turned out to be Mickey Mantle.

COMPLETE SET (350) 175.00 300.00
COMP.SET w/o SP's (300) 25.00 50.00
COMMON CARD (1-300) .15 .40
COMMON RC (1-300) .15 .40
COMMON SP (301-350) 1.00 2.50
COM.SP RC (301-350) .30 .75
301-350 SP ODDS 1:3 H, 1:3 R
PLATES STATED ODDS 1:343 HOBBY
PLATES PRINT RUN 1 #'d SET PER COLOR
PLATES: BLACK, CYAN, MAGENTA & YELLOW
NO PLATES PRICING DUE TO SCARCITY
ROOP BINDER EXCH ODDS 1:240 H
ROOP BINDER EXCH.DEADLINE 12/31/07
1 Steven White FY RC .15 .40
2 Jorge Posada .25 .60
3 Brett Myers .15 .40
4 Pat Burrell .15 .40
5 Grady Sizemore .25 .60
6 Jeff Weaver .15 .40
7 Jeff Kent .15 .40
8 Mark Kotsay .15 .40
9 Nick Swisher .40 1.00
10 Scott Rolen .25 .60
11 Matt Morris .15 .40
12 Luis Castillo .15 .40
13 Pedro Feliz .15 .40
14 Omar Vizquel .25 .60
15 Edgar Renteria .15 .40
16 David Wells .15 .40
17 Chad Cordero .15 .40
18 Brad Wilkerson .15 .40
19 Kelly Johnson .15 .40
20 Johnny Estrada .15 .40
21 Brian Roberts .15 .40
22 Jeromy Burnitz .15 .40
23 Magglio Ordonez .25 .60
24 Adam Dunn .25 .60
25 Randy Johnson .40 1.00
26 Derek Jeter 1.00 2.50
27 Jon Lieber .15 .40
28 Jim Thome .25 .60
29 Ronnie Belliard .15 .40
30 Jake Westbrook .15 .40
31 Bengie Molina .15 .40
32 J.D. Drew .15 .40
33 Rich Harden .15 .40
34 David Eckstein .15 .40
35 Scott Podsednik .15 .40
36 Mark Buehrle .25 .60
37 Barry Bonds .75 2.00
38 Brian Schneider .15 .40
39 Tim Wakefield .15 .40
40 Craig Wilson .15 .40
41 Jose Vidro .15 .40
42 Jacque Jones .15 .40
43 Felix Hernandez .60 1.50
44 Nomar Garciaparra .40 1.00
45 Neifi Perez .15 .40
46 Brandon Inge .15 .40
47 Felipe Lopez .15 .40
48 Ken Griffey Jr. .60 1.50
49 Robinson Cano .40 1.00
50 Jason Giambi .15 .40
51 Mike Lieberthal .15 .40
52 Bobby Abreu .15 .40
53 C.C. Sabathia .25 .60
54 Aaron Boone .15 .40
55 Milton Bradley .15 .40
56 Derek Lowe .15 .40
57 Barry Zito .15 .40
58 Jim Edmonds .25 .60
59 Jon Garland .15 .40
60 Tadahito Iguchi RC .25 .60
61 Jason Schmidt .15 .40
62 David Ortiz .40 1.00
63 Matt Lawton .15 .40
64 Zach Duke .15 .40
65 Gary Sheffield .15 .40
66 Chipper Jones .40 1.00
67 Sammy Sosa .40 1.00
68 Rafael Palmeiro .25 .60
69 Carlos Zambrano .25 .60
70 Aramis Ramirez .15 .40
71 Chris Shelton .15 .40
72 Wily Mo Pena .15 .40
73 Mike Mussina .25 .60
74 Chien-Ming Wang .60 1.50
75 Randy Wolf .15 .40
76 Jimmy Rollins .25 .60
77 Chase Utley .25 .60
78 Kevin Millwood .15 .40
79 Victor Martinez .15 .40
80 Morgan Ensberg .15 .40
81 Bartolo Colon .15 .40
82 Bobby Crosby .15 .40
83 Dan Johnson .15 .40
84 Dan Haren .15 .40
85 Yadier Molina .25 .60
86 Mark Mulder .15 .40
87 Russell Branyan .15 .40
88 Lyle Overbay .15 .40
89 Edgardo Alfonzo .15 .40
90 Mike Matheny .15 .40
91 J.T. Snow .15 .40
92 Curt Schilling .25 .60
93 Oliver Perez .15 .40
94 Mark Redman .15 .40
95 Esteban Loaiza .15 .40
96 Livan Hernandez .15 .40
97 Ryan Church .15 .40
98 Kyle Davies .15 .40
99 Mike Hampton .15 .40
100 Jeff Francoeur .40 1.00
101 Javy Lopez .15 .40
102 Mark Prior .25 .60
103 Kerry Wood .15 .40
104 Carlos Guillen .15 .40
105 Dmitri Young .15 .40
106 David Wright .60 1.50
107 Cliff Floyd .15 .40
108 Carlos Beltran .25 .60
109 Melky Cabrera RC .40 1.00
110 Carl Pavano .15 .40
111 Jamie Moyer .15 .40
112 Joel Pineiro .15 .40
113 Adrian Beltre .15 .40
114 Jhonny Peralta .15 .40
115 Travis Hafner .15 .40
116 Cesar Izturis .15 .40
117 Brad Penny .15 .40
118 Garret Anderson .15 .40
119 Scott Kazmir .40 1.00
120 Aubrey Huff .15 .40
121 Larry Walker .25 .60
122 Albert Pujols 1.00 2.50
123 Paul Konerko .25 .60
124 Frank Thomas .40 1.00

125 Phil Nevin .15 .40
126 Brian Giles .15 .40
127 Ramon Hernandez .15 .40
128 Johnny Damon .25 .60
129 Trot Nixon .15 .40
130 Rocco Baldelli .15 .40
131 Carl Crawford .25 .60
132 Alfonso Soriano .25 .60
133 Mark Teixeira .40 1.00
134 Gustavo Chacin .15 .40
135 Vernon Wells .15 .40
136 Erik Bedard .15 .40
137 Daniel Cabrera .15 .40
138 Michael Barrett .15 .40
139 Greg Maddux .60 1.50
140 Javier Vazquez .15 .40
141 Chad Tracy .15 .40
142 Michael Young .25 .60
143 Kenny Rogers .15 .40
144 Mike Piazza .40 1.00
145 Jose Reyes .25 .60
146 Geoff Jenkins .15 .40
147 Carlos Lee .15 .40
148 Brady Clark .15 .40
149 Torii Hunter .15 .40
150 Johan Santana .40 1.00
151 Steve Finley .15 .40
152 Darin Erstad .15 .40
153 Jake Peavy .15 .40
154 Xavier Nady .15 .40
155 Ryan Klesko .15 .40
156 Ichiro Suzuki .60 1.50
157 Richie Sexson .15 .40
158 Raul Ibanez .15 .40
159 Freddy Garcia .15 .40
160 Brad Hawpe .15 .40
161 Jeff Francis .15 .40
162 Todd Helton .25 .60
163 Clint Barmes .15 .40
164 Rodrigo Lopez .15 .40
165 Melvin Mora .15 .40
166 Brandon Webb .25 .60
167 Shawn Green .15 .40
168 Moises Alou .15 .40
169 Matt Clement .15 .40
170 John Smoltz .40 1.00
171 Rafael Furcal .15 .40
172 Jeff Bagwell .25 .60
173 Roger Clemens .50 1.25
174 Dontrelle Willis .15 .40
175 Paul Lo Duca .15 .40
176 Zack Greinke .25 .60
177 David DeJesus .15 .40
178 Mike Sweeney .15 .40
179 Ben Sheets .15 .40
180 Doug Davis .15 .40
181 Mike Cameron .15 .40
182 Lance Berkman .25 .60
183 Craig Biggio .25 .60
184 Shannon Stewart .15 .40
185 Joe Mauer .40 1.00
186 Justin Morneau .40 1.00
187 Mike Maroth .15 .40
188 Ivan Rodriguez .25 .60
189 Luis Gonzalez .15 .40
190 Troy Glaus .15 .40
191 Adam Eaton .15 .40
192 Khalil Greene .15 .40
193 Mike Lowell .15 .40
194 Miguel Cabrera .40 1.00
195 Roy Halladay .40 1.00
196 Ted Lilly .15 .40
197 Alex Rios .25 .60
198 Josh Beckett .25 .60
199 A.J. Burnett .25 .60
200 Juan Pierre .15 .40
201 Marcus Giles .15 .40
202 Craig Tatum FY RC .15 .40
203 Hayden Penn FY RC .15 .40
204 C.J. Smith FY RC .15 .40
205 Matt Albers FY RC .15 .40
206 Jared Gothreaux FY RC .15 .40
207 Mike Rodriguez FY RC .15 .40
208 Hernan Iribarren FY RC .15 .40
209 Manny Parra FY RC .40 1.00
210 Kevin Collins FY RC .15 .40
211 Buck Coats FY RC .15 .40
212 Jeremy West FY RC .15 .40
213 Ian Bladergroen FY RC .15 .40
214 Chuck Tiffany FY RC .40 1.00
215 Andy LaRoche FY RC .75 2.00
216 Frank Diaz FY RC .15 .40
217 Jai Miller FY RC .15 .40
218 Tony Giarratano FY RC .15 .40
219 Danny Zell FY RC .15 .40
220 Justin Verlander FY RC 3.00 8.00
221 Ryan Sweeney FY RC .25 .60
222 Brandon McCarthy FY RC .25 .60
223 Jerry Owens FY RC .15 .40
224 Glen Perkins FY RC .15 .40
225 Kevin West FY RC .15 .40
226 Billy Butler FY RC .75 2.00
227 Shane Costa FY RC .15 .40
228 Erik Schindewolf FY RC .15 .40
229 Miguel Montero FY RC 1.00 2.50
230 Stephen Drew FY RC .75 2.00
231 Matt DeSalvo FY RC .15 .40
232 Ben Jones FY RC .15 .40
233 Bill McCarthy FY RC .15 .40
234 Chuck James FY RC .40 1.00
235 Brandon Sing FY RC .15 .40
236 Andy Santana FY RC .15 .40
237 Brendan Ryan FY RC .15 .40
238 Wes Swackhamer FY RC .15 .40
239 Jeff Niemann FY RC .40 1.00
240 Ian Kinsler FY RC 1.25 3.00
241 Micah Furtado FY RC .15 .40
242 Ryan Mount FY RC .15 .40
243 P.J. Phillips FY RC .15 .40
244 Trevor Bell FY RC .15 .40
245 Jered Weaver FY RC .60 1.50
246 Eddy Martinez FY RC .15 .40
247 Brian Bannister FY RC .25 .60
248 Philip Humber FY RC .40 1.00
249 Michael Rogers FY RC .15 .40
250 Landon Powell FY RC .15 .40
251 Kennard Bibbs FY RC .15 .40
252 Nelson Cruz FY RC .60 1.50
253 Paul Kelly FY RC .15 .40
254 Kevin Slowey FY RC .75 2.00
255 Brandon Snyder FY RC .40 1.00
256 Nolan Reimold FY RC .60 1.50
257 Brian Stavisky FY RC .15 .40
258 Javier Herrera FY RC .15 .40
259 Russ Martin FY RC .60 1.50
260 Matthew Kemp FY RC 2.00 5.00
261 Wade Townsend FY RC .15 .40
262 Nick Touchstone FY RC .15 .40
263 Ryan Feierabend FY RC .15 .40
264 Bobby Livingston FY RC .15 .40
265 Wladimir Balentien FY RC .25 .60
266 Keiichi Yabu FY RC .15 .40
267 Craig Italiano FY RC .15 .40
268 Ryan Goleski FY RC .15 .40
269 Ryan Garko FY RC .15 .40
270 Mike Bourn FY RC .40 1.00
271 Scott Mathieson FY RC .60 1.50
272 Scott Mitchinson FY RC .15 .40
273 Tyler Greene FY RC .15 .40
274 Mark McCormick FY RC .15 .40
275 Daryl Jones FY RC .15 .40
276 Travis Chick FY RC .15 .40
277 Luis Hernandez FY RC .15 .40
278 Steve Doetsch FY RC .15 .40
279 Chris Vines FY RC .15 .40
280 Mike Costanzo FY RC .15 .40
281 Matt Maloney FY RC .15 .40
282 Matt Goyen FY RC .15 .40
283 Jacob Marceaux FY RC .15 .40
284 David Gassner FY RC .15 .40
285 Ricky Barrett FY RC .15 .40
286 Jon Egan FY RC .15 .40
287 Scott Blue FY RC .15 .40
288 Steven Bondurant FY RC .15 .40
289 Kevin Melillo FY RC .15 .40
290 Brad Corley FY RC .15 .40
291 Brent Lillibridge FY RC .15 .40
292 Mike Morse FY RC .40 1.00
293 Justin Thomas FY RC .15 .40
294 Nick Webber FY RC .15 .40
295 Mitch Boggs FY RC .15 .40
296 Jeff Lyman FY RC .15 .40
297 Jordan Schafer FY RC .75 2.00
298 Ismael Ramirez FY RC .15 .40
299 Chris B.Young FY RC .60 1.50
300 Brian Miller FY RC .15 .40
301 Jason Bay SP 1.00 2.50
302 Tim Hudson SP 1.50 4.00
303 Miguel Tejada SP 1.50 4.00
304 Jeremy Bonderman SP 1.00 2.50
305 Alex Rodriguez SP 4.00 10.00
306 Rickie Weeks SP 1.50 4.00
307 Manny Ramirez SP 2.50 6.00
308 Nick Johnson SP 1.00 2.50
309 Andruw Jones SP 1.00 2.50
310 Hideki Matsui SP 4.00 10.00
311 Jeremy Reed SP 1.00 2.50
312 Dallas McPherson SP 1.00 2.50
313 Vladimir Guerrero SP 2.50 6.00
314 Eric Chavez SP 1.00 2.50
315 Chris Carpenter SP 2.50 6.00
316 Aaron Hill SP 1.50 4.00
317 Derrek Lee SP 1.00 2.50
318 Mark Loretta SP 1.00 2.50
319 Garrett Atkins SP 1.00 2.50
320 Hank Blalock SP 1.00 2.50
321 Chris Young SP 1.50 4.00
322 Roy Oswalt SP 1.50 4.00
323 Carlos Delgado SP 1.00 2.50
324 Pedro Martinez SP 1.50 4.00
325 Jeff Clement FY SP RC 1.00 2.50
326 Jimmy Shull FY SP RC .30 .75
327 Daniel Carte FY SP RC .30 .75
328 Travis Buck FY SP RC .30 .75
329 Chris Volstad FY SP RC .75 2.00
330 A.McCutchen FY SP RC 2.50 6.00
331 Cliff Pennington FY SP RC .30 .75
332 John Mayberry Jr. FY SP RC .75 2.00
333 C.J. Henry FY SP RC .50 1.25
334 Ricky Romero FY SP RC .50 1.25
335 Aaron Thompson FY SP RC .50 1.25
336 Cesar Carrillo FY SP RC .50 1.25
337 Jacoby Ellsbury FY SP RC 2.00 5.00
338 Matt Garza FY SP RC .50 1.25
339 Colby Rasmus FY SP RC 1.50 4.00
340 Ryan Zimmerman FY SP RC 2.50 6.00
341 Ryan Braun FY SP RC 3.00 8.00
342 Brent Lillibridge FY SP .30 .75
343 Jay Bruce FY SP RC 2.50 6.00
344 Matt Green FY SP RC .30 .75
345 Brent Cox FY SP RC .30 .75
346 Jed Lowrie FY SP RC 1.50 4.00
347 Beau Jones FY SP RC .75 2.00
348 Eli Iorg FY SP RC .30 .75
349 Chaz Roe FY SP RC .30 .75
350 Mickey Mantle 15.00 40.00
NNO Roop Binder Redemption 6.00 15.00

2005 Bowman Heritage Draft Pick Variation

COMPLETE SET (25) 30.00 60.00
*DP VAR: .4X TO 1X BASIC
ONE 5-CARD DPV PACK PER HOBBY BOX

2005 Bowman Heritage Mahogany

COMPLETE SET (350) 225.00 325.00
*MAH 1-300: 1X TO 2.5X BASIC
*MAH 1-300: .6X TO 1.5X BASIC RC
ONE MAHOGANY OR RELIC PER PACK
ON AVG. 22 MAHOG'S PER 24 CT. BOX
150 Johan Santana 1.00 2.50
185 Joe Mauer 1.00 2.50
301 Jason Bay .40 1.00
302 Tim Hudson .60 1.50
303 Miguel Tejada .60 1.50
304 Jeremy Bonderman .40 1.00
305 Alex Rodriguez 1.50 4.00
306 Rickie Weeks .60 1.50
307 Manny Ramirez 1.00 2.50
308 Nick Johnson .40 1.00
309 Andruw Jones .40 1.00
310 Hideki Matsui 1.50 4.00
311 Jeremy Reed .40 1.00
312 Dallas McPherson .40 1.00
313 Vladimir Guerrero 1.00 2.50
314 Eric Chavez .40 1.00
315 Chris Carpenter 1.00 2.50
316 Aaron Hill .60 1.50
317 Derrek Lee .40 1.00
318 Mark Loretta .40 1.00
319 Garrett Atkins .40 1.00
320 Hank Blalock .40 1.00
321 Chris Young .60 1.50
322 Roy Oswalt .60 1.50
323 Carlos Delgado .40 1.00
324 Pedro Martinez .60 1.50
325 Jeff Clement 1.25 3.00
326 Jimmy Shull .40 1.00
327 Daniel Carte .40 1.00
328 Travis Buck .40 1.00
329 Chris Volstad 1.00 2.50
330 Andrew McCutchen 3.00 8.00
331 Cliff Pennington .40 1.00
332 John Mayberry Jr. 1.00 2.50
333 C.J. Henry .60 1.50
334 Ricky Romero .60 1.50
335 Aaron Thompson .60 1.50
336 Cesar Carrillo .60 1.50
337 Jacoby Ellsbury 2.50 6.00
338 Matt Garza .60 1.50
339 Colby Rasmus 2.00 5.00
340 Ryan Zimmerman 3.00 8.00
341 Ryan Braun 4.00 10.00
342 Brent Lillibridge .40 1.00
343 Jay Bruce 3.00 8.00
344 Matt Green .40 1.00
345 Brent Cox .40 1.00
346 Jed Lowrie 2.00 5.00
347 Beau Jones 1.00 2.50
348 Eli Iorg .40 1.00
349 Chaz Roe .40 1.00
350 Mystery Redemption 10.00 25.00

2005 Bowman Heritage Mini

COMPLETE SET (350) 225.00 325.00
*MINI 1-300: 1X TO 2.5X BASIC
*MINI 1-300: .6X TO 1.5X BASIC RC
ONE MINI OR BLUE/RED BACK PER PACK
ON AVG. 20 MINI'S PER 24 CT. BOX
150 Johan Santana 1.00 2.50
185 Joe Mauer 1.00 2.50
301 Jason Bay .40 1.00
302 Tim Hudson .60 1.50
303 Miguel Tejada .60 1.50
304 Jeremy Bonderman .40 1.00
305 Alex Rodriguez 1.50 4.00
306 Rickie Weeks .60 1.50
307 Manny Ramirez 1.00 2.50
308 Nick Johnson .40 1.00
309 Andruw Jones .40 1.00
310 Hideki Matsui 1.50 4.00
311 Jeremy Reed .40 1.00
312 Dallas McPherson .40 1.00
313 Vladimir Guerrero 1.00 2.50
314 Eric Chavez .40 1.00
315 Chris Carpenter 1.00 2.50
316 Aaron Hill .60 1.50
317 Derrek Lee .40 1.00
318 Mark Loretta .40 1.00
319 Garrett Atkins .40 1.00
320 Hank Blalock .40 1.00
321 Chris Young .60 1.50
322 Roy Oswalt .60 1.50
323 Carlos Delgado .40 1.00
324 Pedro Martinez .60 1.50
325 Jeff Clement 1.25 3.00
326 Jimmy Shull .40 1.00
327 Daniel Carte .40 1.00
328 Travis Buck .40 1.00
329 Chris Volstad 1.00 2.50
330 Andrew McCutchen 3.00 8.00
331 Cliff Pennington .40 1.00
332 John Mayberry Jr. 1.00 2.50
333 C.J. Henry .60 1.50
334 Ricky Romero .60 1.50
335 Aaron Thompson .60 1.50
336 Cesar Carrillo .60 1.50
337 Jacoby Ellsbury 2.50 6.00
338 Matt Garza .60 1.50
339 Colby Rasmus 2.00 5.00
340 Ryan Zimmerman 3.00 8.00
341 Ryan Braun 4.00 10.00
342 Brent Lillibridge .40 1.00
343 Jay Bruce 3.00 8.00
344 Matt Green .40 1.00
345 Brent Cox .40 1.00
346 Jed Lowrie 2.00 5.00
347 Beau Jones 1.00 2.50
348 Eli Iorg .40 1.00
349 Chaz Roe .40 1.00
350 Mystery Redemption 10.00 25.00

2005 Bowman Heritage Red

STATED ODDS 1:1374 HOBBY
STATED PRINT RUN 1 SERIAL #'d SET
NO PRICING DUE TO SCARCITY

2005 Bowman Heritage 51 Topps Heritage Blue Backs

OVERALL 51 HERITAGE ODDS 1:6 H/R
1 Adam Dunn 1.25 3.00
2 Zach Duke .75 2.00
3 Alex Rodriguez 3.00 8.00
4 Vladimir Guerrero 2.00 5.00
5 Andruw Jones .75 2.00
6 Travis Chick .75 2.00
7 Alfonso Soriano 1.25 3.00
8 Scott Rolen 1.25 3.00
9 Brian Bannister 1.25 3.00
10 Randy Johnson 2.00 5.00
11 Barry Bonds 4.00 10.00
12 Pat Burrell .75 2.00
13 Barry Zito .75 2.00
14 Nomar Garciaparra 2.00 5.00
15 C.C. Sabathia 1.25 3.00
16 Miguel Tejada 1.25 3.00
17 Hideki Matsui 3.00 8.00
18 John Smoltz 2.00 5.00
19 Ken Griffey Jr. 3.00 8.00
20 Chris Carpenter 2.00 5.00
21 Ian Kinsler 6.00 15.00
22 Chuck Tiffany 2.00 5.00
23 Gary Sheffield .75 2.00
24 Mark Mulder .75 2.00
25 Ichiro Suzuki 3.00 8.00
26 Kerry Wood .75 2.00
27 Jose Reyes 1.25 3.00
28 Derrek Lee .75 2.00
29 Justin Verlander 15.00 40.00
30 Johnny Damon 1.25 3.00
31 Chris Volstad 2.00 5.00
32 Jeremy Bonderman .75 2.00
33 David Ortiz 2.00 5.00
34 Morgan Ensberg .75 2.00
35 Mark Buehrle 1.25 3.00
36 Chuck James 2.00 5.00
37 Miguel Cabrera 2.00 5.00
38 Magglio Ordonez 1.25 3.00
39 Michael Young 1.25 3.00
40 Carlos Beltran .75 2.00
41 Nick Johnson .75 2.00
42 Billy Butler 4.00 10.00
43 Brian Giles .75 2.00
44 Paul Konerko 1.25 3.00
45 Roy Oswalt 1.25 3.00
46 Bobby Abreu .75 2.00
47 Sammy Sosa 2.00 5.00
48 Aramis Ramirez UER .75 2.00
Bio refers to Anthony Reyes
49 Torii Hunter .75 2.00
50 Aubrey Huff .75 2.00
51 Vernon Wells .75 2.00
52 Joe Mauer 2.00 5.00

2005 Bowman Heritage 51 Topps Heritage Red Backs

OVERALL 51 HERITAGE ODDS 1:6 H/R
1 Andy LaRoche 4.00 10.00
2 Mike Piazza 2.00 5.00
3 Pedro Martinez 1.25 3.00
4 Wladimir Balentien 1.25 3.00
5 Tim Hudson 1.25 3.00
6 Richie Sexson .75 2.00
7 Carlos Delgado .75 2.00
8 Derek Jeter 5.00 12.00
9 Ryan Zimmerman 6.00 15.00
10 Mark Teixeira 2.00 5.00
11 David Wright 3.00 8.00
12 Jake Peavy .75 2.00
13 Jose Vidro .75 2.00
14 Jim Thome 1.25 3.00
15 Carlos Zambrano 1.25 3.00
16 Hank Blalock .75 2.00
17 Johan Santana 2.00 5.00
18 Cliff Pennington .75 2.00
19 Rafael Palmeiro 1.25 3.00
20 Curt Schilling 1.25 3.00
21 Brandon McCarthy 1.25 3.00
22 Stephen Drew 4.00 10.00
23 Jeff Niemann 2.00 5.00
24 Eric Chavez .75 2.00
25 Hernan Iribarren .75 2.00
26 Jered Weaver 3.00 8.00
27 Edgar Renteria .75 2.00
28 Travis Hafner .75 2.00
29 Frank Thomas 2.00 5.00
30 Brian Roberts .75 2.00
31 Anthony Reyes 1.25 3.00
32 Scott Kazmir 2.00 5.00
33 Carlos Lee .75 2.00
34 Jimmy Rollins 1.25 3.00
35 Garret Anderson .75 2.00
36 Jason Schmidt .75 2.00
37 Jon Garland .75 2.00
38 Dontrelle Willis .75 2.00
39 C.J. Henry 1.25 3.00
40 Greg Maddux 3.00 8.00
41 Todd Helton 1.25 3.00
42 Ivan Rodriguez 1.25 3.00
43 Chipper Jones 2.00 5.00
44 Rich Harden .75 2.00
45 Mark Prior 1.25 3.00
46 Roy Halladay 2.00 5.00
47 Albert Pujols 5.00 12.00
48 Roger Clemens 2.50 6.00
49 Andrew McCutchen 6.00 15.00
50 Scott Podsednik .75 2.00
51 Manny Ramirez 2.00 5.00
52 Carl Crawford 1.25 3.00
53 Jim Edmonds 1.25 3.00
54 Wily Mo Pena .75 2.00

2005 Bowman Heritage Future Greatness Jersey Relics

GROUP A ODDS 1:1004 H, 1:3350 R
GROUP B ODDS 1:270 H, 1:1237 R
GROUP C ODDS 1:205 H, 1:875 R
GROUP D ODDS 1:61 H, 1:210 R
GROUP E ODDS 1:141 H, 1:500 R
*RAINBOW: .75X TO 2X GRP C-E
*RAINBOW: .75X TO 2X GRP B
*RAINBOW: .5X TO 1.2X GRP A
OVERALL RAINBOW ODDS 1:183 H, 1:735 R
RAINBOW PRINT RUN 51 SERIAL #'d SETS
OVERALL RAINBOW RED ODDS 1:7841 H
RAINBOW RED PRINT RUN 1 #'d SET
NO R'BOW RED PRICING DUE TO SCARCITY
AH Aaron Hill D 2.00 5.00
AM Arnie Munoz D 2.00 5.00
AMA Andy Marte D 3.00 8.00
BB Bryan Bullington D 2.00 5.00
BT Brad Thompson A 3.00 8.00
CE Clint Everts B 2.00 5.00
DM Dallas McPherson C 2.00 5.00
DY Delmon Young A 6.00 15.00
EE Edwin Encarnacion C 3.00 8.00
FC Fausto Carmona A 3.00 8.00
FP Felix Pie C 3.00 8.00
GF Gavin Floyd D 2.00 5.00
JB Joe Blanton D 3.00 8.00
JC Jorge Cortes B 2.00 5.00
JCO Jesus Cota D 2.00 5.00
JF Jeff Francis D 3.00 8.00
JG Joel Guzman E 3.00 8.00
JGA Jairo Garcia B 2.00 5.00
JK Jason Kubel A 3.00 8.00
JM Justin Morneau D 3.00 8.00
JMA Jeff Mathis B 3.00 8.00
JP Juan Perez E 2.00 5.00
KH Koyie Hill B 2.00 5.00
MC Matt Cain D 4.00 10.00
RG Ruben Gotay B 2.00 5.00
RW Rickie Weeks D 3.00 8.00
SC Shin Soo Choo C 3.00 8.00
TB Tony Bianco E 2.00 5.00
VM Val Majewski D 2.00 5.00
WL Wil Ledezma E 2.00 5.00
YP Yusmeiro Petit D 3.00 8.00

2005 Bowman Heritage Pieces of Greatness Relics

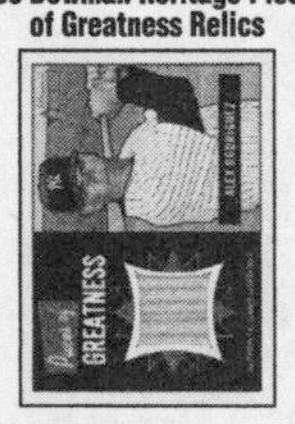

GROUP A ODDS 1:167 H, 1:555 R
GROUP B ODDS 1:47 H, 1:155 R
GROUP C ODDS 1:55 H, 1:188 R
AD Adam Dunn Bat A 3.00 8.00
AP Albert Pujols Jsy B 6.00 15.00
AR Alex Rodriguez Bat A 6.00 15.00
BB Barry Bonds Uni A 8.00 20.00
BC Bobby Crosby Uni C 3.00 8.00
BM Brett Myers Jsy A 3.00 8.00
BR Brian Roberts Bat B 3.00 8.00
BZ Barry Zito Uni C 3.00 8.00
CB Carlos Beltran Bat B 3.00 8.00
CD Carlos Delgado Bat B 3.00 8.00
DW Dontrelle Willis Jsy C 3.00 8.00
DWR David Wright Bat B 4.00 10.00
EC Eric Chavez Uni C 3.00 8.00
IS Ichiro Suzuki Jsy C 6.00 15.00
JB Josh Beckett Uni B 3.00 8.00
JD Johnny Damon Bat B 3.00 8.00
JG Josh Gibson Seat C 6.00 15.00
JK Jeff Kent Bat A 3.00 8.00
JS John Smoltz Jsy B 3.00 8.00
JT Jim Thome Bat B 3.00 8.00
MC Miguel Cabrera Bat A 3.00 8.00
MM Mark Mulder Uni B 3.00 8.00
MMO Melvin Mora Bat B 3.00 8.00
MR Manny Ramirez Bat B 3.00 8.00
MT Miguel Tejada Bat C 3.00 8.00
PK Paul Konerko Bat B 3.00 8.00
PM Pedro Martinez Bat B 3.00 8.00
RC Roger Clemens Jsy A 6.00 15.00
RH Rich Harden Jsy A 3.00 8.00
TG Troy Glaus Bat B 3.00 8.00
TH Todd Helton Jsy B 3.00 8.00

2005 Bowman Heritage Pieces of Greatness Rainbow Relics

*RAINBOW: .75X TO 2X GRP B-C
*RAINBOW: .75X TO 2X GRP A
OVERALL RAINBOW ODDS 1:183 H, 1:735 R
STATED PRINT RUN 51 SERIAL #'d SETS
RED STATED ODDS 1:7841 HOBBY
RED PRINT RUN 1 SERIAL #'d SET
NO RED PRICING DUE TO SCARCITY
BB Barry Bonds Uni 30.00 60.00
IS Ichiro Suzuki Jsy 30.00 60.00
JG Josh Gibson Seat 30.00 60.00

2005 Bowman Heritage Signs of Greatness

GROUP A ODDS 1:153 H, 1:154 R
GROUP B ODDS 1:40 H, 1:40 R
GROUP C ODDS 1:74 H, 1:75 R
*RED INK: 1.25X TO 3X BASIC
RED INK ODDS 1:634 H, 1:635 R
RED INK PRINT RUN 51 SERIAL #'d SETS
NO RC YR RED INK PRICING AVAILABLE
AG Angel Guzman C 3.00 8.00
AM Andrew McCutchen B 12.50 30.00
BL Brent Lillibridge B 3.00 8.00
CT Curtis Thigpen A 3.00 8.00
DJ Dan Johnson A 4.00 10.00
DL Donny Lucey A 3.00 8.00
DP David Purcey C 5.00 12.00
EM Eddy Martinez B 5.00 12.00
HS Huston Street C 6.00 15.00
JB Jay Bruce B 20.00 50.00
JH J.P. Howell C 3.00 8.00
JJ Jason Jaramillo B 3.00 8.00
JM John Mayberry Jr. B 4.00 10.00
JP Jon Papelbon C 12.50 30.00
JZ Jon Zeringue B 3.00 8.00
MB Matt Bush A 4.00 10.00
MG Matt Green B 3.00 8.00
PB Patrick Bryant A 3.00 8.00
PH Philip Humber B 6.00 15.00
RB Ryan Braun B 40.00 80.00
RR Ricky Romero B 5.00 12.00
RZ Ryan Zimmerman B 10.00 25.00
SE Scott Elbert C 3.00 8.00
TC Travis Chick B 3.00 8.00
TD Thomas Diamond B 3.00 8.00
WW Wesley Whisler B 3.00 8.00
ZJ Zach Jackson A 3.00 8.00

2006 Bowman Heritage

This 300-card set was released in December, 2006. The set was issued in eight-card hobby packs with an $3 SRP which came packaged 24 packs to a box and 12 boxes to a case. The first 200 cards in the set are veterans while their are two rookie subsets (201-250, 276-300). Interestingly, the even numbered cards between 200 and 300 were all short printed.

COMPLETE SET (300) 75.00 150.00
COMP.SET w/o SP's (250) 15.00 40.00
COMMON CARD (1-300) .15 .40
COMMON RC (1-300) .15 .40
COMMON SP (202-300) 2.00 5.00
COM.SP RC (202-300) 2.00 5.00
202-300 SP ODDS 1:3 H, 1:3 R
SP CL: EVEN #s B/WN 202-300
OVERALL PLATE ODDS 1:497 HOBBY
PLATE PRINT RUN 1 SET PER COLOR
BLACK-CYAN-MAGENTA-YELLOW ISSUED
NO PLATE PRICING DUE TO SCARCITY
1 David Wright .60 1.50
2 Andruw Jones .15 .40
3 Ryan Howard .60 1.50
4 Jason Bay .15 .40
5 Paul Konerko .25 .60
6 Jake Peavy .15 .40
7 Todd Jones .15 .40
8 Troy Glaus .15 .40
9 Rocco Baldelli .15 .40
10 Rafael Furcal .15 .40
11 Freddy Sanchez .15 .40
12 Jermaine Dye .15 .40
13 A.J. Burnett .25 .60
14 Michael Cuddyer .15 .40
15 Barry Zito .15 .40
16 Chipper Jones .40 1.00
17 Paul LoDuca .15 .40
18 Mark Mulder .15 .40
19 Raul Ibanez .25 .60
20 Carlos Delgado .15 .40
21 Marcus Giles .15 .40
22 Dan Haren .15 .40
23 Justin Morneau .40 1.00
24 Livan Hernandez .15 .40
25 Ken Griffey Jr. .60 1.50
26 Aaron Hill .15 .40
27 Tadahito Iguchi .15 .40
28 Nate Robertson .15 .40
29 Kevin Millwood .15 .40
30 Jim Thome .25 .60
31 Aubrey Huff .15 .40
32 Dontrelle Willis .15 .40
33 Khalil Greene .15 .40
34 Doug Davis .15 .40
35 Ivan Rodriguez .25 .60
36 Rickie Weeks .25 .60
37 Jhonny Peralta .15 .40
38 Yadier Molina .25 .60
39 Eric Chavez .15 .40
40 Alfonso Soriano .25 .60
41 Pat Burrell .15 .40
42 B.J. Ryan .15 .40
43 Carl Crawford .25 .60
44 Preston Wilson .15 .40
45 Jorge Posada .25 .60
46 Carlos Zambrano .25 .60
47 Mark Teahen .15 .40
48 Nick Johnson .15 .40
49 Mark Kotsay .15 .40
50 Derek Jeter 1.00 2.50
51 Moises Alou .15 .40
52 Ryan Freel .15 .40
53 Shannon Stewart .15 .40
54 Casey Blake .15 .40
55 Edgar Renteria .15 .40
56 Frank Thomas .40 1.00
57 Ty Wigginton .15 .40
58 Jeff Kent .15 .40
59 Chien-Ming Wang .25 .60
60 Josh Beckett .25 .60
61 Chase Utley .40 1.00
62 Gary Matthews .15 .40
63 Torii Hunter .15 .40
64 Bobby Jenks .15 .40
65 Wilson Betemit .15 .40
66 Jeremy Bonderman .15 .40
67 Scott Rolen .25 .60
68 Brad Penny .15 .40
69 Jacque Jones .15 .40
70 Jose Reyes .25 .60
71 Brian Roberts .15 .40
72 John Smoltz .40 1.00
73 Johnny Estrada .15 .40
74 Ronnie Belliard .15 .40
75 Vladimir Guerrero .40 1.00
76 A.J. Pierzynski .15 .40
77 Garrett Atkins .15 .40
78 Adam LaRoche .15 .40
79 Mark Loretta .15 .40
80 Todd Helton .25 .60
81 Jose Vidro .15 .40
82 Carlos Guillen .15 .40
83 Michael Barrett .15 .40
84 Lyle Overbay .15 .40
85 Travis Hafner .15 .40
86 Shea Hillenbrand .15 .40
87 Julio Lugo .15 .40
88 Tim Hudson .25 .60
89 Scott Podsednik .15 .40
90 Roy Halladay .40 1.00
91 Bartolo Colon .15 .40
92 Ryan Langerhans .15 .40
93 Tom Glavine .25 .60
94 Kenny Rogers .15 .40
95 Robinson Cano .40 1.00
96 Mark Prior .25 .60
97 Jason Schmidt .15 .40
98 Bengie Molina .15 .40
99 Jon Lieber .15 .40
100 Alex Rodriguez .60 1.50
101 Scott Kazmir .25 .60
102 Jeff Francoeur .40 1.00
103 Chris Carpenter .40 1.00
104 Juan Uribe .15 .40
105 Mariano Rivera .40 1.00
106 Rich Harden .15 .40
107 Jack Wilson .15 .40
108 Austin Kearns .15 .40
109 Marcus Thames .15 .40
110 Miguel Tejada .25 .60
111 Chone Figgins .15 .40
112 Bronson Arroyo .15 .40
113 Chad Cordero .15 .40
114 Bill Hall .15 .40
115 Curt Schilling .25 .60
116 David Eckstein .15 .40
117 Ramon Hernandez .15 .40
118 Eric Byrnes .15 .40
119 Clint Barmes .15 .40
120 Bobby Abreu .15 .40
121 Joe Crede .15 .40
122 Derek Lowe .15 .40
123 Jason Marquis .15 .40
124 Erik Bedard .15 .40
125 Derrek Lee .15 .40
126 Brian McCann .15 .40
127 Magglio Ordonez .25 .60
128 Ben Sheets .15 .40
129 Brandon Inge .15 .40
130 Miguel Cabrera .40 1.00
131 Jim Edmonds .25 .60
132 John Lackey .15 .40
133 Kevin Mench .15 .40
134 Adrian Beltre .15 .40
135 Curtis Granderson .25 .60
136 Shawn Green .15 .40
137 Jose Contreras .15 .40
138 Joe Nathan .15 .40
139 Bobby Crosby .15 .40
140 Johnny Damon .25 .60
141 Brad Hawpe .15 .40
142 Brandon Phillips .15 .40
143 Victor Martinez .25 .60
144 Jimmy Rollins .25 .60
145 Corey Patterson .15 .40
146 Grady Sizemore .25 .60
147 Placido Polanco .15 .40
148 Mike Lowell .15 .40
149 Francisco Rodriguez .25 .60
150 Ichiro Suzuki .60 1.50

151 Kris Benson .15 .40
152 Scott Hatteberg .15 .40
153 Akinori Otsuka .15 .40
154 Cesar Izturis .15 .40
155 Roger Clemens .50 1.25
156 Kerry Wood .15 .40
157 Tom Gordon .15 .40
158 Sean Casey .15 .40
159 Jose Lopez .15 .40
160 Orlando Hernandez .15 .40
161 Aramis Ramirez .15 .40
162 J.D. Drew .15 .40
163 David DeJesus .15 .40
164 Craig Biggio .25 .60
165 Brett Myers .15 .40
166 C.C. Sabathia .25 .60
167 Zach Duke .15 .40
168 Luis Castillo .15 .40
169 Hideki Matsui .40 1.00
170 Brian Giles .15 .40
171 Coco Crisp .15 .40
172 Richie Sexson .15 .40
173 Nomar Garciaparra .40 1.00
174 Roy Oswalt .25 .60
175 David Ortiz .25 .60
176 Matt Morris .15 .40
177 Felipe Lopez .15 .40
178 Garret Anderson .15 .40
179 Kevin Youkilis .15 .40
180 Alex Rios .25 .60
181 Jon Garland .15 .40
182 Luis Gonzalez .15 .40
183 Cliff Floyd .15 .40
184 Juan Encarnacion .15 .40
185 Nick Swisher .40 1.00
186 Mike Cameron .15 .40
187 Jose Castillo .15 .40
188 Ray Durham .15 .40
189 Jorge Cantu .15 .40
190 Andy Pettitte .25 .60
191 Chad Tracy .15 .40
192 Adrian Gonzalez .25 .60
193 Jose Valentin .15 .40
194 Mark Buehrle .25 .60
195 Huston Street .15 .40
196 Chris Capuano .15 .40
197 Aaron Rowand .15 .40
198 Billy Wagner .15 .40
199 Orlando Cabrera .15 .40
200 Albert Pujols 1.00 2.50
201 Dan Uggla (RC) .40 1.00
202 Alay Soler SP RC 2.00 5.00
203 Matt Kemp (RC) .75 2.00
204 Mike Napoli SP RC 2.50 6.00
205 Joel Zumaya (RC) .40 1.00
206 Mike Pelfrey SP RC 2.00 5.00
207 Ian Kinsler (RC) .50 1.25
208 Josh Willingham SP (RC) 2.00 5.00
209 Erick Aybar (RC) .15 .40
210 Willie Eyre SP (RC) 2.00 5.00
211 Kendry Morales (RC) .40 1.00
212 Luis Thorman SP (RC) 2.00 5.00
213 Hanley Ramirez (RC) .40 1.00
214 Boof Bonser SP (RC) 2.00 5.00
215 Anthony Reyes (RC) .15 .40
216 Justin Huber SP (RC) 2.00 5.00
217 Yusmeiro Petit (RC) .15 .40
218 Jason Bartlett SP (RC) 2.00 5.00
219 Shin-Soo Choo (RC) .25 .60
220 Francisco Liriano SP (RC) 2.00 5.00
221 Craig Hansen RC .40 1.00
222 Ricky Nolasco SP (RC) 2.00 5.00
223 Adam Loewen (RC) .15 .40
224 Scott Olsen SP (RC) 2.00 5.00
225 Cole Hamels (RC) .60 1.50
226 Martin Prado SP (RC) 3.00 8.00
227 James Loney (RC) .25 .60
228 Kevin Thompson SP (RC) 2.00 5.00
229 Adam Jones RC .60 1.50
230 Josh Johnson SP (RC) 3.00 8.00
231 Anderson Hernandez (RC) .15 .40
232 Tony Gwynn Jr. SP (RC) 2.00 5.00
233 Casey Janssen RC .15 .40
234 Taylor Tankersley SP (RC) 2.00 5.00
235 Mike Thompson RC .15 .40
236 Jeremy Sowers SP (RC) 2.00 5.00
237 Anibal Sanchez (RC) .15 .40
238 Adam Wainwright SP (RC) 3.00 8.00
239 Rich Hill (RC) .15 .40
240 Russ Martin SP (RC) 2.00 5.00
241 Joe Inglett RC .15 .40
242 Tony Pena SP (RC) 2.00 5.00
243 Josh Sharpless RC .15 .40
244 Darrell Rasner SP (RC) 2.00 5.00
245 Joe Saunders (RC) .15 .40
246 Jon Lester SP RC 2.00 5.00
247 Jeremy Hermida (RC) .15 .40
248 Chad Billingsley SP (RC) 2.00 5.00
249 Bobby Livingston (RC) .15 .40
250 Justin Verlander SP (RC) 6.00 15.00
251 Mickey Mantle 1.25 3.00
252 Hank Blalock SP 2.00 5.00
253 Manny Ramirez .40 1.00
254 Mike Mussina SP 2.00 5.00
255 Greg Maddux .60 1.50
Wearing a Cubs Cap; Back Notates Trade to Dodgers
256 Jason Giambi SP 2.00 5.00
257 Mark Teixeira .40 1.00
258 Carlos Beltran SP 2.00 5.00
259 Matt Holliday .40 1.00
260 Pedro Martinez SP 2.00 5.00
261 Joe Mauer .40 1.00
262 Melvin Mora SP 2.00 5.00
263 Mike Piazza .40 1.00
264 B.J. Upton SP 2.00 5.00
265 Vernon Wells .15 .40
266 Gary Sheffield SP 2.00 5.00
267 Randy Johnson .40 1.00
268 Ryan Zimmerman SP 2.00 5.00
269 Lance Berkman .25 .60
270 Johan Santana SP 3.00 8.00
271 Carlos Lee .15 .40
272 Brandon Webb SP 3.00 8.00
273 Adam Dunn .25 .60
274 Michael Young SP 3.00 8.00
275 Barry Bonds .75 2.00
276 Jonathan Papelbon SP (RC) 2.00 5.00
277 Howie Kendrick (RC) .40 1.00
278 Melky Cabrera SP (RC) 2.00 5.00
279 Jered Weaver (RC) .40 1.00
280 Josh Barfield SP (RC) 2.00 5.00
281 Chuck James (RC) .15 .40
282 Lastings Milledge SP (RC) 1.25 3.00
283 Nick Markakis (RC) .40 1.00
284 Jose Capellan SP (RC) 2.00 5.00
285 Prince Fielder (RC) .60 1.50
286 Jason Botts SP (RC) 2.00 5.00
287 Eliezer Alfonzo RC .15 .40
288 Sean Marshall SP (RC) 3.00 8.00
289 Ryan Garko (RC) .15 .40
290 Stephen Drew SP (RC) 2.00 5.00
291 Joel Guzman (RC) .15 .40
292 Hong-Chih Kuo SP (RC) 2.00 5.00
293 Zach Miner (RC) .15 .40
294 Angel Guzman SP (RC) 2.00 5.00
295 Andre Ethier (RC) .60 1.50
296 Fausto Carmona SP (RC) 2.00 5.00
297 Ronny Paulino (RC) .15 .40
298 Matt Cain SP (RC) 3.00 8.00
299 Carlos Quentin (RC) .25 .60
300 Kenji Johjima SP RC 1.00 2.50

2006 Bowman Heritage Black

STATED ODDS 1:1990 HOBBY
STATED PRINT RUN 1 SERIAL #'d SET
NO PRICING DUE TO SCARCITY

2006 Bowman Heritage Mini

COMPLETE SET (300) 100.00 200.00
*MINI 1-300: 1X TO 2.5X BASIC
*MINI 1-300: 1X TO 2.5X BASIC RC
COMMON BASIC SP (202-300) .40 1.00
BASIC SP SEMIS 202-300 .60 1.50
BASIC SP UNLISTED 202-300 1.00 2.50
OVERALL ODDS ONE PER PACK
NO SHORT PRINTS IN MINI SET

2006 Bowman Heritage Chrome

*CHROME 1-300: 1X TO 2.5X BASIC
*CHROME 1-300: 1X TO 2.5X BASIC RC
COMMON BASIC SP (202-300) .40 1.00
BASIC SP SEMIS 202-300 .60 1.50
BASIC SP UNLISTED 202-300 1.00 2.50
APPX. ODDS ONE PER PACK
ON AVG. 22 CHROME PER 24 CT.BOX
NO SHORT PRINTS IN CHROME SET

2006 Bowman Heritage White

*WHITE 1-300: .4X TO 1X BASIC
*WHITE 1-300: .4X TO 1X BASIC RC
COMMON BASIC SP (202-300) .40 1.00
BASIC SP SEMIS 202-300 .60 1.50
BASIC SP UNLISTED 202-300 1.00 2.50
STATED ODDS 1:6 HOBBY, 1:6 RETAIL
NO SHORT PRINTS IN WHITE SET

2006 Bowman Heritage Mini Draft Pick Variations

*DP VAR: 1X TO 2.5X BASIC
ONE 5-CARD DPV PACK PER HOBBY BOX
76 Evan Longoria 5.00 12.00
77 Adrian Cardenas 1.25 3.00
82 Matthew Sulentic .75 2.00
85 Clayton Kershaw 1.25 3.00
87 Chris Parmelee 1.25 3.00
88 Billy Rowell 1.50 4.00
90 Chris Marrero .75 2.00
95 Chad Huffman .75 2.00

2006 Bowman Heritage Pieces of Greatness

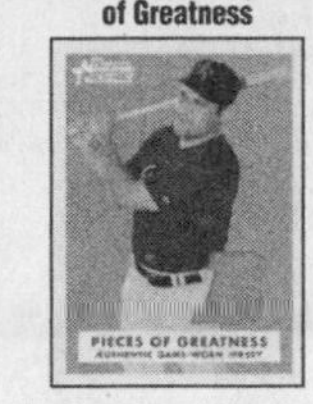

GROUP A ODDS 1:98 H, 1:99 R
GROUP B ODDS 1:62 H, 1:62 R
GROUP C ODDS 1:28 H, 1:28 R
GROUP D ODDS 1:43 H, 1:43 R
AD Adam Dunn Bat A 3.00 8.00
AJ Andruw Jones Jsy D 3.00 8.00
AJ2 Andruw Jones Bat C 3.00 8.00
AJP A.J. Pierzynski Bat A 3.00 8.00
AL Adam LaRoche Jsy B 3.00 8.00
AP Albert Pujols Bat C 8.00 20.00
AP2 Albert Pujols Jsy D 6.00 15.00
AR Alex Rodriguez Bat A 6.00 15.00
ARA Aramis Ramirez Bat A 3.00 8.00
BB Barry Bonds Jsy A 6.00 15.00
BR Brian Roberts Bat B 3.00 8.00
BW Brad Wilkerson Bat A 3.00 8.00
BZ Barry Zito Jsy C 3.00 8.00
CB Craig Biggio Jsy C 3.00 8.00
CF Cliff Floyd Bat B 3.00 8.00
CJ Chipper Jones Bat C 4.00 10.00
CJ2 Chipper Jones Jsy D 4.00 10.00
CS Curt Schilling Jsy C 3.00 8.00
CU Chase Utley Bat A 4.00 10.00
DE David Eckstein Bat A 3.00 8.00
DL Derrek Lee Bat B 3.00 8.00
DO David Ortiz Bat C 4.00 10.00
DW Dontrelle Willis Jsy D 3.00 8.00
EE Edwin Encarnacion Jsy C 3.00 8.00
GM Greg Maddux Bat B 4.00 10.00
GS Gary Sheffield Bat D 3.00 8.00
HB Hank Blalock Bat A 3.00 8.00
JD Jermaine Dye Bat C 3.00 8.00
JF Jeff Francoeur Bat A 4.00 10.00
JK Jeff Kent Jsy C 3.00 8.00
JL Javy Lopez Jsy C 3.00 8.00
JT Jim Thome Bat C 3.00 8.00
LB Lance Berkman Jsy C 3.00 8.00
MB Milton Bradley Bat A 3.00 8.00
ME Morgan Ensberg Jsy C 3.00 8.00
ML Mike Lowell Bat A 3.00 8.00
MO Magglio Ordonez Bat C 3.00 8.00
MR Manny Ramirez Bat D 3.00 8.00
MY Michael Young Jsy C 3.00 8.00
NJ Nick Johnson Bat B 3.00 8.00
NS Nick Swisher Bat C 3.00 8.00
RC Robinson Cano Bat C 4.00 10.00
RF Rafael Furcal Bat C 3.00 8.00
RH Ryan Howard Jsy C 6.00 15.00
SP Scott Podsednik Bat B 3.00 8.00
TH Torii Hunter Bat B 3.00 8.00
THE Todd Helton Jsy D 3.00 8.00
VG Vladimir Guerrero Bat B 4.00 10.00
VM Victor Martinez Bat B 3.00 8.00
XN Xavier Nady Bat C 3.00 8.00

2006 Bowman Heritage Pieces of Greatness White

*WHITE: .5X TO 1.2X GRP C-D
*WHITE: .5X TO 1.2X GRP A-B
OVERALL WHITE ODDS 1:387 H,1:387 R
STATED PRINT RUN 49 SERIAL #'d SETS
BLACK STATED ODDS 1:12,016 HOBBY
BLACK PRINT RUN 1 SERIAL #'d SET
NO BLACK PRICING DUE TO SCARCITY
AP Albert Pujols Bat 20.00 50.00
AP2 Albert Pujols Jsy 20.00 50.00
AR Alex Rodriguez Bat 12.50 30.00
BB Barry Bonds Jsy 20.00 50.00
GM Greg Maddux Bat 10.00 25.00
RC Robinson Cano Bat 8.00 20.00
RH Ryan Howard Jsy 12.50 30.00

2006 Bowman Heritage Prospects

COMPLETE SET (100) 15.00 40.00
COMMON CARD (1-100) .15 .40
OVERALL PLATE ODDS 1:1494 HOBBY
PLATE PRINT RUN 1 SET PER COLOR
BLACK-CYAN-MAGENTA-YELLOW ISSUED
NO PLATE PRICING DUE TO SCARCITY
1 Justin Upton 2.50 6.00
2 Koby Clemens .25 .60
3 Lance Broadway .15 .40
4 Cameron Maybin .50 1.25
5 Garrett Mock .15 .40
6 Alex Gordon .50 1.25
7 Ben Copeland .15 .40
8 Nick Adenhart .15 .40
9 Yung-Chi Chen .25 .60
10 Tim Moss .15 .40
11 Francisco Leandro .15 .40
12 Brad McCann .15 .40
13 Dallas Trahern .15 .40
14 Dustin Majewski .15 .40
15 James Barthmaier .15 .40
16 Nate Gold .15 .40
17 John Hardy .15 .40
18 Mark McLemore .15 .40
19 Michael Aubrey .25 .60
20A Mark Holliman .15 .40
20B Mark Holliman UER .15 .40
Michael Holliman,Tigers,pictured
21 Dallas Wilson .15 .40
22 Radhames Liz .15 .40
23 Jose Tabata 1.00 2.50
24 Jared Lansford .15 .40
25 Brent Dlugach .15 .40
26 Steve Garrabrants .15 .40
27 Eric Haberer .15 .40
28 Chris Dickerson .25 .60
29 Welinson Baez .15 .40
30 Chris Kolkhorst .15 .40
31 Brandon Moss .15 .40
32 Corey Wimberly .15 .40
33 Ryan Patterson .15 .40
35 John Bannister .15 .40
36 Pablo Sandoval 1.50 4.00
37 Dexter Fowler .50 1.25
38 Elvis Andrus .75 2.00
39 Jason Windsor .15 .40
40 B.J. Szymanski .15 .40
41 Yovani Gallardo .50 1.25
42 John Bowker .15 .40
43 Justin Christian .15 .40
44 Andy Sonnanstine .15 .40
45 Jeremy Slayden .15 .40
46 Brandon Jones .15 .40
47 Travis Denker .15 .40
48 Emmanuel Garcia .15 .40
49 Landon Jacobsen .15 .40
50 Kevin Estrada .15 .40
51 Ross Ohlendorf .15 .40
52 Wyatt Toregas .15 .40
53 Andrew Kown .15 .40
54 Steve Kelly .15 .40
55 Mike Butia .15 .40
56 Mike Connolly .15 .40
57 Brian Horwitz .15 .40
58 Dale Thayer .15 .40
59 Diory Hernandez .15 .40
60 Samuel Deduno .15 .40
61 Jamie Hoffman .15 .40
62 Matt Tolbert .15 .40
63 Michael Ekstrom .15 .40
64 Chris Maples .15 .40
65 Adam Coe .15 .40
66 Max Ramirez .25 .60
67 Evan MacLane .15 .40
68 Jose Campusano .15 .40
69 Lou Santangelo .15 .40
70 Shawn Riggans .15 .40
71 Kyle Kendrick .40 1.00
72 Oswaldo Navarro .15 .40
73 Eric Rodland .15 .40
74 Omir Santos .15 .40
75 Kyle McCulloch .40 1.00
76 Evan Longoria 4.00 10.00
77 Adrian Cardenas .25 .60
78 Steven Wright .15 .40
79 Andrew Carpenter .15 .40
80 Dustin Evans .15 .40
81 Chad Tracy .15 .40
82 Matthew Sulentic .40 1.00
83 Adam Ottavino .15 .40
84 Matt Long .15 .40
85 Clayton Kershaw 1.00 2.50
86 Matt Antonelli .15 .40
87 Chris Parmelee .25 .60
88 Billy Rowell .40 1.00
89 Chase Fontaine .15 .40
90 Chris Marrero .60 1.50
91 Jamie Ortiz .15 .40
92 Sean Watson .15 .40
93 Brooks Brown .15 .40
94 Brad Furnish .15 .40
95 Chad Huffman .40 1.00
96 Pedro Beato .15 .40
97 Kyler Burke .15 .40
98 Stephen Englund .15 .40
99 Tyler Norrick .15 .40
100 Brett Sinkbeil .15 .40

2006 Bowman Heritage Prospects Black

STATED ODDS 1:6008 HOBBY
STATED PRINT RUN 1 SERIAL #'d SET
NO PRICING DUE TO SCARCITY

2006 Bowman Heritage Prospects White

*WHITE: .4X TO 1X BASIC
STATED ODDS 1:6 HOBBY, 1:6 RETAIL

2006 Bowman Heritage Signs of Greatness

The John Drennan card was never produced.

GROUP A ODDS 1:719 H, 1:719 R
GROUP B ODDS 1:42 H, 1:42 R
GROUP C ODDS 1:61 H, 1:63 R
GROUP D ODDS 1:2172 H, 1:2175 R
RED INK ODDS 1:9737 HOBBY
RED INK PRINT RUN 5 SERIAL #'d SETS
NO RED INK PRICING DUE TO SCARCITY
SILVER INK ODDS 28,238 H,1:9500 R
SILVER INK PRINT RUN 1 SER.#'d SET
NO SILVER PRICING DUE TO SCARCITY
EXCHANGE DEADLINE 12/31/08
AG Alex Gordon B 8.00 20.00
BB Brian Bogusevic B 3.00 8.00
BS Brandon Snyder B 3.00 8.00
BW Brandon Wood A 6.00 15.00
CI Craig Italiano B 3.00 8.00
CM Cameron Maybin B 8.00 20.00
JC Jesus Cota B 3.00 8.00
JS Jarrod Saltalamacchia C 6.00 15.00
JU Justin Upton D 15.00 40.00
KW Kevin Whelan B 3.00 8.00
LB Lance Broadway B 4.00 10.00
MM Matt Maloney B 6.00 15.00
RT Ryan Tucker C 3.00 8.00
SG Sean Gallagher B 5.00 12.00
SL Sam LeCure C 3.00 8.00
ST Steve Tolleson B 3.00 8.00
WT Wade Townsend C 3.00 8.00

2007 Bowman Heritage

This 296-card set was released in November, 2007. The set was issued through hobby and retail channels. The hobby packs consisted of eight cards which came 24 packs to a box and 12 boxes to a case. Cards numbered 1-200 were veterans while cards numbered 201-251 were 2007 rookies. In addition, cards numbered 181-200 and 226-250 were issued both with facsimile signatures and without signatures. The cards without signatures were printed in shorter quantity and were inserted at a stated rate of one in three hobby packs. Our complete set price also includes the five Mickey Mantle cards listed as a seperate set.

COMP.SET w/o SPs (251) 15.00 40.00
COMMON CARD (1-200) .15 .40
COMMON ROOKIE (201-251) .20 .50
COMMON SP (181-200) 1.25 3.00
COMMON SP RC (226-250) 1.50 4.00
SP ODDS 1:3 HOBBY
NO SIG CARDS ARE SHORT PRINTS
COMP.SET INCLUDES ALL MANTLE VAR.
OVERALL PLATE ODDS 1:463 HOBBY
PLATE PRINT RUN 1 SET PER COLOR
BLACK-CYAN-MAGENTA-YELLOW ISSUED
NO PLATE PRICING DUE TO SCARCITY
1 Jeff Francoeur .40 1.00
2 Jered Weaver .25 .60
3 Derrek Lee .15 .40
4 Todd Helton .25 .60
5 Shawn Hill .15 .40
6 Ivan Rodriguez .25 .60
7 Mickey Mantle 1.25 3.00
8 Ramon Hernandez .15 .40
9 Randy Johnson .40 1.00
10 Jermaine Dye .15 .40
11 Brian Roberts .15 .40
12 Hank Blalock .15 .40
13 Chien-Ming Wang .25 .60
14 Mike Lowell .15 .40
15 Brandon Webb .25 .60
16 Kelly Johnson .15 .40
17 Nick Johnson .15 .40
18 Zach Duke .15 .40
19 Aaron Hill .15 .40
20 Miguel Tejada .25 .60
21 Mark Buehrle .25 .60
22 Michael Young .25 .60
23 Carlos Delgado .25 .60
24 Anibal Sanchez .15 .40
25 Vladimir Guerrero .40 1.00
26 Russell Martin .15 .40
27 Lance Berkman .25 .60
28 Bobby Crosby .15 .40
29 Javier Vazquez .15 .40
30 Manny Ramirez .40 1.00
31 Rich Hill .15 .40
32 Mike Sweeney .15 .40
33 Jeff Kent .15 .40
34 Noah Lowry .15 .40
35 Alfonso Soriano .25 .60
36 Paul Lo Duca .15 .40
37 J.D. Drew .15 .40
38 C.C Sabathia .25 .60
39 Craig Biggio .25 .60
40 Adam Dunn .25 .60
41 Josh Beckett .25 .60
42 Carlos Guillen .15 .40
43 Jeff Francis .15 .40
44 Orlando Hudson .15 .40
45 Grady Sizmore .25 .60
46 Jason Jennings .15 .40
47 Mark Teixeira .40 1.00
48 Freddy Garcia .15 .40
49 Adrian Gonzalez .25 .60
50 Albert Pujols 1.00 2.50
51 Tom Glavine .25 .60
52 J.J. Hardy .15 .40
53 Bobby Abreu .15 .40
54 Bartolo Colon .15 .40
55 Garrett Atkins .15 .40
56 Moises Alou .15 .40
57 Cliff Lee .25 .60
58 Michael Cuddyer .15 .40
59 Brandon Phillips .15 .40
60 Jeremy Bonderman .15 .40
61 Rickie Weeks .15 .40
62 Chris Carpenter .40 1.00
63 Frank Thomas .40 1.00
64 Victor Martinez .25 .60
65 Dontrelle Willis .15 .40
66 Jim Thome .25 .60
67 Aaron Rowand .15 .40
68 Andy Pettitte .25 .60
69 Brian McCann .15 .40
70 Roger Clemens .50 1.25
71 Gary Matthews .15 .40
72 Bronson Arroyo .15 .40
73 Jeremy Hermida .15 .40
74 Eric Chavez .15 .40
75 David Ortiz .25 .60
76 Stephen Drew .15 .40
77 Ronnie Belliard .15 .40
78 James Shields .15 .40
79 Richie Sexson .15 .40
80 Johan Santana .40 1.00
81 Orlando Cabrera .15 .40
82 Aramis Ramirez .15 .40
83 Greg Maddux .60 1.50
84 Reggie Sanders .15 .40
85 Carlos Zambrano .25 .60
86 Bengie Molina .15 .40
87 David DeJesus .15 .40
88 Adam Wainwright .25 .60
89 Conor Jackson .15 .40
90 David Wright .60 1.50
91 Ryan Garko .15 .40
92 Bill Hall .15 .40
93 Marcus Giles .15 .40
94 Kenny Rogers .15 .40
95 Joe Mauer .40 1.00
96 Hanley Ramirez .40 1.00
97 Brian Giles .15 .40
98 Dan Haren .15 .40
99 Robinson Cano .40 1.00
100 Ryan Howard .60 1.50
101 Andruw Jones .15 .40
102 Aaron Harang .15 .40
103 Hideki Matsui .40 1.00
104 Nick Swisher .40 1.00
105 Pedro Martinez .25 .60
106 Felipe Lopez .15 .40
107 Erik Bedard .15 .40
108 Rafael Furcal .15 .40
109 Curt Schilling .25 .60
110 Jose Reyes .25 .60
111 Adam LaRoche .15 .40
112 Mike Mussina .25 .60
113 Melvin Mora .15 .40
114 Zack Greinke .25 .60
115 Justin Morneau .40 1.00
116 Ervin Santana .15 .40
117 Ken Griffey Jr. .60 1.50
118 David Eckstein .15 .40
119 Jamie Moyer .15 .40
120 Jorge Posada .25 .60
121 Justin Verlander .50 1.25
122 Sammy Sosa .40 1.00
123 Jason Schmidt .15 .40
124 Josh Willingham .15 .40
125 Roy Oswalt .25 .60
126 Travis Hafner .15 .40
127 John Maine .15 .40
128 Willy Taveras .15 .40
129 Magglio Ordonez .25 .60
130 Barry Zito .25 .60
131 Prince Fielder .25 .60
132 Michael Barrett .15 .40
133 Livan Hernandez .15 .40
134 Troy Glaus .15 .40
135 Rocco Baldelli .15 .40
136 Jason Giambi .15 .40
137 Austin Kearns .15 .40
138 Dan Uggla .25 .60
139 Pat Burrell .15 .40
140 Carlos Beltran .25 .60
141 Carlos Quentin .15 .40
142 Johnny Estrada .15 .40
143 Torii Hunter .15 .40
144 Carlos Lee .15 .40
145 Mike Piazza .40 1.00
146 Mark Teahen .15 .40
147 Juan Pierre .15 .40
148 Paul Konerko .25 .60
149 Freddy Sanchez .15 .40
150 Derek Jeter 1.00 2.50
151 Orlando Hernandez .15 .40
152 Raul Ibanez .25 .60
153 John Smoltz .40 1.00
154 Scott Rolen .25 .60
155 Jimmy Rollins .25 .60
156 A.J. Burnett .15 .40
157 Jason Varitek .40 1.00
158 Ben Sheets .15 .40
159 Matt Cain .25 .60
160 Carl Crawford .25 .60
161 Jeff Suppan .15 .40
162 Tadahito Iguchi .15 .40
163 Kevin Millwood .15 .40
164 Chris Duncan .15 .40
165 Rich Harden .15 .40
166 Joe Crede .15 .40
167 Chipper Jones .40 1.00
168 Gary Sheffield .15 .40
169 Cole Hamels .40 1.00
170 Jason Bay .25 .60
171 Jhonny Peralta .15 .40
172 Aubrey Huff .15 .40
173 Xavier Nady .15 .40
174 Kazuo Matsui .15 .40
175 Vernon Wells .15 .40
176 Johnny Damon .25 .60
177 Jim Edmonds .25 .60
178 Jose Vidro .15 .40
179 Garret Anderson .15 .40
180 Alex Rios .25 .60
181a Ichiro Suzuki .60 1.50
181b Ichiro Suzuki SP 3.00 8.00
182a Jake Peavy .15 .40
182b Jake Peavy SP 1.25 4.00
183a Ian Kinsler .25 .60
183b Ian Kinsler SP 1.25 4.00
184a Tom Gorzelanny .15 .40
184b Tom Gorzelanny SP 1.25 4.00
185a Miguel Cabrera .40 1.00
185b Miguel Cabrera SP 2.00 5.00
186a Scott Kazmir .25 .60
186b Scott Kazmir SP 2.00 5.00
187a Matt Holliday .40 1.00
187b Matt Holliday SP 2.00 5.00
188a Roy Halladay .40 1.00
188b Roy Halladay SP 1.25 4.00
189a Ryan Zimmerman .25 .60
189b Ryan Zimmerman SP 2.00 5.00
190a Alex Rodriguez .60 1.50
190b Alex Rodriguez SP 3.00 8.00
191a Kenji Johjima .40 1.00
191b Kenji Johjima SP 2.00 5.00
192a Gil Meche .15 .40
192b Gil Meche SP 1.25 4.00
193a Chase Utley .40 1.00
193b Chase Utley SP 2.00 5.00
194a Jeremy Sowers .15 .40
194b Jeremy Sowers SP 1.25 3.00
195a John Lackey .15 .40
195b John Lackey SP 1.25 3.00
196a Nick Markakis .40 1.00
196b Nick Markakis SP 2.00 5.00
197a Tim Hudson .25 .60
197b Tim Hudson SP 1.25 3.00
198a B.J. Upton .15 .40
198b B.J. Upton SP 1.25 3.00
199a Felix Hernandez .40 1.00
199b Felix Hernandez SP 2.00 5.00
200a Barry Bonds .75 2.00
200b Barry Bonds SP 4.00 10.00
201 Jarrod Saltalamacchia (RC) .30 .75
202 Tim Lincecum RC 3.00 8.00
203 Kory Casto (RC) .20 .50
204 Sean Henn (RC) .20 .50
205 Hector Gimenez (RC) .20 .50
206 Homer Bailey (RC) .30 .75
207 Yunel Escobar (RC) .20 .50
208 Matt Lindstrom (RC) .20 .50
209 Tyler Clippard (RC) .30 .75
210 Joe Smith RC .20 .50
211 Tony Abreu RC .50 1.25
212 Billy Butler (RC) .30 .75
213 Gustavo Molina RC .20 .50
214 Brian Stokes (RC) .20 .50
215 Kevin Slowey (RC) .50 1.25
216 Curtis Thigpen (RC) .20 .50
217 Carlos Gomez RC .30 .75
218 Rick Vanden Hurk RC .20 .50
219 Michael Bourn (RC) .20 .50
220 Jeff Baker (RC) .20 .50
221 Andy LaRoche (RC) .20 .50
222 Andy Sonnanstine RC .20 .50
223 Chase Wright RC .50 1.25
224 Mark Reynolds RC 1.50 4.00
225 Matt Chico (RC) .20 .50
226a Hunter Pence (RC) 1.00 2.50
226b Hunter Pence SP 3.00 8.00
227a John Danks RC .30 .75
227b John Danks SP 1.50 4.00
228a Elijah Dukes RC .30 .75
228b Elijah Dukes SP 2.50 6.00
229a Kei Igawa RC .50 1.25
229b Kei Igawa SP 2.50 6.00
230a Felix Pie (RC) .20 .50
230b Felix Pie SP 1.50 4.00
231a Jesus Flores RC .20 .50
231b Jesus Flores SP 1.50 4.00
232a Dallas Braden RC 1.25 3.00
232b Dallas Braden SP 2.50 6.00
233a Akinori Iwamura RC .50 1.25
233b Akinori Iwamura SP 2.50 6.00
234a Ryan Braun (RC) 1.00 2.50
234b Ryan Braun SP 3.00 8.00
235a Alex Gordon RC .60 1.50
235b Alex Gordon SP 2.50 6.00
236a Micah Owings (RC) .20 .50
236b Micah Owings SP 1.50 4.00
237a Kevin Kouzmanoff (RC) .20 .50
237b Kevin Kouzmanoff SP 1.50 4.00
238a Glen Perkins (RC) .20 .50
238b Glen Perkins SP 1.50 4.00
239a Danny Putnam (RC) .20 .50
239b Danny Putnam SP 1.50 4.00
240a Philip Hughes (RC) 1.00 2.50
240b Philip Hughes SP 3.00 8.00
241a Ryan Sweeney (RC) .20 .50
241b Ryan Sweeney SP 1.50 4.00
242a Josh Hamilton (RC) .75 2.00
242b Josh Hamilton SP 5.00 12.00
243a Hideki Okajima RC 1.00 2.50
243b Hideki Okajima SP 3.00 8.00
244a Adam Lind (RC) .20 .50
244b Adam Lind SP 1.50 4.00
245a Travis Buck (RC) .20 .50
245b Travis Buck SP 1.50 4.00
246a Miguel Montero (RC) .20 .50
246b Miguel Montero SP 1.50 4.00
247a Brandon Morrow RC .75 2.00
247b Brandon Morrow SP 2.50 6.00
248a Troy Tulowitzki (RC) 1.25 3.00
248b Troy Tulowitzki SP 2.50 6.00
249a Delmon Young (RC) .30 .75
249b Delmon Young SP 2.50 6.00
250a Daisuke Matsuzaka RC .75 2.00
250b Daisuke Matsuzaka SP 4.00 10.00
251 Joba Chamberlain RC 1.00 2.50

2007 Bowman Heritage Black

*BLACK 1-200: 8X TO 20X BASIC
*BLACK 201-251: 6X TO 15X BASIC RC
COMMON BASIC SP (180-250) 3.00 8.00

BASIC SP SEMIS 5.00 12.00
BASIC SP UNLISTED 8.00 20.00
STATED ODDS 1:52 HOBBY, 1:97 RETAIL
NO SHORT PRINTS IN BLACK SET
181b Ichiro Suzuki No Sig 12.00 30.00
190b Alex Rodriguez No Sig 12.00 30.00
200b Barry Bonds No Sig 15.00 40.00
226b Hunter Pence No Sig 15.00 40.00
234b Ryan Braun No Sig 15.00 40.00
240b Philip Hughes No Sig 15.00 40.00
243b Hideki Okajima No Sig 15.00 40.00
250b Daisuke Matsuzaka No Sig 12.00 30.00

2007 Bowman Heritage Rainbow Foil

COMPLETE SET (299) 75.00 150.00
*CHROME 1-200: 1X TO 2.5X BASIC
*CHROME 201-250: .75X TO 2X BASIC RC
COMMON BASIC SP (180-250) .40 1.00
BASIC SP SEMIS .60 1.50
BASIC SP UNLISTED 1.00 2.50
APPX.ODDS 1:1 HOBBY
NO SHORT PRINTS IN CHROME SET
COMP.SET INCLUDES ALL MANTLE VAR.
181b Ichiro Suzuki No Sig 1.50 4.00
190b Alex Rodriguez No Sig 1.50 4.00
200b Barry Bonds No Sig 2.00 5.00
226b Hunter Pence No Sig 2.00 5.00
234b Ryan Braun No Sig 2.00 5.00
235b Alex Gordon No Sig 1.25 3.00
240b Philip Hughes No Sig 2.00 5.00
243b Hideki Okajima No Sig 2.00 5.00
250b Daisuke Matsuzaka No Sig 1.50 4.00

2007 Bowman Heritage Red

STATED ODDS 1:1569 HOBBY
STATED PRINT RUN 1 SER.#'d SET
NO PRICING DUE TO SCARCITY

2007 Bowman Heritage Mantle Short Prints

COMPLETE SET (5) 12.50 30.00
COMMON CARD 2.50 6.00
OVERALL SP ODDS 1:3 HOBBY
OVERALL PLATE ODDS 1:463 HOBBY
PLATE PRINT RUN 1 SET PER COLOR
BLACK-CYAN-MAGENTA-YELLOW ISSUED
NO PLATE PRICING DUE TO SCARCITY

2007 Bowman Heritage Mantle Short Prints Black

COMMON CARD 40.00 80.00
OVERALL BLACK ODDS 1:52 HOB,1:97 RET
STATED PRINT RUN 52 SER.#'d SETS

2007 Bowman Heritage Mantle Short Prints Rainbow Foil

COMPLETE SET (5) 15.00 40.00
COMMON CARD 3.00 8.00
OVERALL FOIL ODDS ONE PER PACK

2007 Bowman Heritage Mantle Short Prints Red

OVERALL RED ODDS 1:1569 HOBBY
STATED PRINT RUN 1 SER.#'d SET
NO PRICING DUE TO SCARCITY

2007 Bowman Heritage Pieces of Greatness

GROUP A ODDS 1:83 HOBBY,1:166 RETAIL
GROUP B ODDS 1:22 HOBBY,1:46 RETAIL
GROUP C ODDS 1:119 HOBBY,1:238 RETAIL
GROUP D ODDS 1:325 HOBBY,1:660 RETAIL
GROUP E ODDS 1:104 HOBBY,1:211 RETAIL
GROUP F ODDS 1:687 HOBBY,1:687 RETAIL
GROUP G ODDS 1:452 HOBBY,1:953 RETAIL
AD Adam Dunn Jsy C 3.00 8.00
AE Andre Ethier Jsy B 3.00 8.00
AG Alex Gonzalez Bat B 3.00 8.00
AJ Andruw Jones Bat C 3.00 8.00
AL Adam LaRoche Jsy B 3.00 8.00
AR Aramis Ramirez Bat A 3.00 8.00
ARO Alex Rodriguez Bat C 6.00 15.00
BB Barry Bonds Jsy A 6.00 15.00
BC Bobby Crosby Bat B 3.00 8.00
BG Brian Giles Bat A 3.00 8.00
BL Brad Lidge Jsy E 3.00 8.00
BZ Barry Zito Pants C 3.00 8.00
CB Craig Biggio Jsy B 3.00 8.00
CBE Carlos Beltran Bat B 3.00 8.00
CH Cole Hamels Jsy A 4.00 10.00
CK Cory Koskie Bat B 3.00 8.00
CP Corey Patterson Bat B 3.00 8.00
CS Curt Schilling Jsy C 3.00 8.00
CT Chad Tracy Bat B 3.00 8.00
CU Chase Utley Bat A 4.00 10.00
DE Darin Erstad Bat B 3.00 8.00
DO David Ortiz Bat B 3.00 8.00
DO2 David Ortiz Jsy A 3.00 8.00
DW Dontrelle Willis Jsy E 3.00 8.00
DWR David Wright Pants A 5.00 12.00
EC Eric Chavez Pants B 3.00 8.00
FT Frank Thomas Bat A 4.00 10.00
GM Greg Maddux Bat A 4.00 10.00
GS Gary Sheffield Bat B 3.00 8.00
GSI Grady Sizmore Jsy B 3.00 8.00
HM Hideki Matsui Bat A 4.00 10.00
IR Ivan Rodriguez Jsy E 3.00 8.00
JB Jeremy Bonderman Jsy B 3.00 8.00
JD Johnny Damon Bat A 3.00 8.00
JDD J.D. Drew Jsy B 3.00 8.00
JE Juan Encarnacion Bat B 3.00 8.00
JF Jeff Franceour Bat B 3.00 8.00
JFR Jeff Francis Jsy B 3.00 8.00
JK Jeff Kent Jsy A 3.00 8.00
JM Joe Mauer Bat B 3.00 8.00
JR Jose Reyes Jsy B 4.00 10.00
LB Lance Berkman Jsy A 3.00 8.00
LG Luis Gonzalez Bat B 3.00 8.00
MC Miguel Cabrera Jsy B 3.00 8.00
ML Mike Lowell Pants A 3.00 8.00
MM Mark Mulder Pants E 3.00 8.00
MO Magglio Ordonez Bat D 3.00 8.00
MP Mike Piazza Bat E 4.00 10.00
MR Manny Ramirez Jsy C 3.00 8.00
MR2 Manny Ramirez Bat G 3.00 8.00
MT Mark Teixeira Bat A 3.00 8.00
MTE Miguel Tejada Pants B 3.00 8.00
NS Nick Swisher Bat A 3.00 8.00
PK Paul Konerko Pants B 3.00 8.00
PK2 Paul Konerko Jsy B 3.00 8.00
RB Rocco Baldelli Jsy F 3.00 8.00
RC Robinson Cano Bat B 4.00 10.00
RC2 Robinson Cano Jsy B 4.00 10.00
RF Rafael Furcal Bat B 3.00 8.00
RH Rich Harden Jsy B 3.00 8.00
SG Shawn Green Bat B 3.00 8.00
TH Todd Helton Jsy B 3.00 8.00
TH2 Todd Helton Bat B 3.00 8.00
THU Tim Hudson Pants A 3.00 8.00
TI Tadahito Iguchi Bat A 3.00 8.00
TN Trot Nixon Bat A 3.00 8.00
TW Tim Wakefield Pants B 3.00 8.00
VG Vladimir Guerrero Bat B 3.00 8.00
YM Yadier Molina Jsy D 3.00 8.00

2007 Bowman Heritage Pieces of Greatness Black

*BLACK: .75X TO 2X BASIC
STATED ODDS 1:221 HOBBY,1:429 RETAIL
STATED PRINT RUN 52 SER.#'d SETS

2007 Bowman Heritage Pieces of Greatness Red

STATED ODDS 1:6854 HOBBY
STATED PRINT RUN 1 SER.#'d SET
NO PRICING DUE TO SCARCITY

2007 Bowman Heritage Prospects

COMPLETE SET (100) 15.00 40.00
STATED ODDS TWO PER PACK
OVERALL PLATE ODDS 1:1175 HOBBY
PLATE PRINT RUN 1 SET PER COLOR
BLACK-CYAN-MAGENTA-YELLOW ISSUED
NO PLATE PRICING DUE TO SCARCITY
BHP1 Thomas Fairchild .20 .50
BHP2 Peter Bourjos .30 .75
BHP3 Brett Campbell .20 .50
BHP4 Cesar Nicolas .20 .50
BHP5 Kala Kaaihue .30 .75
BHP6 Zach McAllister .30 .75
BHP7 Chad Reineke .20 .50
BHP8 Anthony Hatch .20 .50
BHP9 Cedric Hunter .50 1.25
BHP10 Chris Carter 1.25 3.00
BHP11 Tommy Hanson .75 2.00
BHP12 Dellin Betances .50 1.25
BHP13 John Otness .20 .50
BHP14 Derin McMains .20 .50
BHP15 Greg Reynolds .60 1.50
BHP16 Jonathan Van Every .20 .50
BHP17 Eddie Degerman .20 .50
BHP18 Cody Strait .20 .50
BHP19 Noe Rodriguez .20 .50
BHP20 Young-Il Jung .50 1.25
BHP21 Reegie Corona .30 .75
BHP22 Carlos Corporan .20 .50
BHP23 Chance Douglass .20 .50
BHP24 Leo Daigle .20 .50
BHP25 Jeff Samardzija .75 2.00
BHP26 Mark Wagner .30 .75
BHP27 Chuck Lofgren .50 1.25
BHP28 Bryan Byrne .20 .50
BHP29 Daniel Mayora .50 1.25
BHP30 Gorkys Hernandez .50 1.25
BHP31 Joshua Rodriguez .30 .75
BHP32 Brad Knox .20 .50
BHP33 Scott Lewis .50 1.25
BHP34 Joe Gaetti .20 .50
BHP35 Michael Saunders .60 1.50
BHP36 Brendan Katin .20 .50
BHP37 Brennan Boesch 3.00 8.00
BHP38 Jay Garthwaite .20 .50
BHP39 Mike Devaney .20 .50
BHP40 J.R. Towles .60 1.50
BHP41 Joe Ness .20 .50
BHP42 Michael Martinez .20 .50
BHP43 Justin Byler .20 .50
BHP44 Chris Coghlan .60 1.50
BHP45 Eric Young Jr. .30 .75
BHP46 J.R. Mathes .20 .50
BHP47 Ivan De Jesus Jr. .30 .75
BHP48 Woods Fines .20 .50
BHP49 Andrew Fie .20 .50
BHP50 Luke Hochevar .60 1.50
BHP51 Will Venable .30 .75
BHP52 Todd Redmond .20 .50
BHP53 Matthew Sweeney .60 1.50
BHP54 Trevor Cahill .50 1.25
BHP55 Mike Carp .60 1.50
BHP56 Henry Sosa .30 .75
BHP57 Emerson Frostad .20 .50
BHP58 Jeremy Jeffress .20 .50
BHP59 Whit Robbins .20 .50
BHP60 Joba Chamberlain 1.00 2.50
BHP61 Raul Barron .20 .50
BHP62 Aaron Cunningham .30 .75
BHP63 Greg Smith .30 .75
BHP64 Jeff Baisley .30 .75
BHP65 Vic Buttler .20 .50
BHP66 Steve Singleton .20 .50
BHP67 Josh Papelbon .20 .50
BHP68 Ryan Finan .20 .50
BHP69 Deolis Guerra .50 1.25
BHP70 Vasili Spanos .20 .50
BHP71 Patrick Reilly .20 .50
BHP72 Thomas Hottovy .20 .50
BHP73 Daniel Murphy .30 .75
BHP74 Matt Young .20 .50
BHP75 Brian Bocock .20 .50
BHP76 Chris Salamida .20 .50
BHP77 Nathan Southard .20 .50
BHP78 Brandon Hynick .50 1.25
BHP79 Chris Nowak .20 .50
BHP80 Reid Brignac .30 .75
BHP81 Cole Garner .20 .50
BHP82 Nick Van Stratten .20 .50
BHP83 Jeremy Papelbon .20 .50
BHP84 Jarrett Hoffpauir .20 .50
BHP85 Kevin Mulvey .50 1.25
BHP86 Matt Miller .20 .50
BHP87 Devin Ivany .20 .50
BHP88 Marcus Sanders .20 .50
BHP89 Michael MacDonald .20 .50
BHP90 Gabriel Sanchez .30 .75
BHP91 Ryan Norwood .20 .50
BHP92 Jim Fasano .20 .50
BHP93 Ryan Adams .30 .75
BHP94 Evan Englebrook .20 .50
BHP95 Juan Miranda .30 .75
BHP96 Gregory Porter .20 .50
BHP97 Shane Benson .20 .50
BHP98 Sam Fuld .60 1.50
BHP99 Cooper Brannan .20 .50
BHP100 Fernando Martinez .75 2.00

2007 Bowman Heritage Prospects Black

*BLACK: 4X TO 10X BASIC
STATED ODDS 1:153 HOBBY,1:295 RETAIL
STATED PRINT RUN 52 SER.#'d SETS
BHP37 Brennan Boesch 6.00 15.00

2007 Bowman Heritage Prospects Red

STATED ODDS 1:4740 HOBBY
STATED PRINT RUN 1 SER.#'d SET
NO PRICING DUE TO SCARCITY

2007 Bowman Heritage Red Man Box Topper

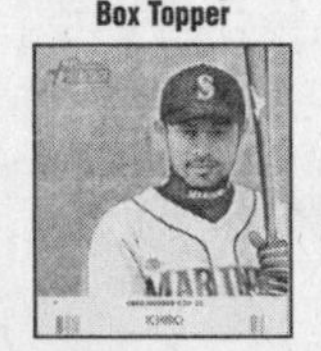

ONE PER HOBBY BOX TOPPER
AG Alex Gordon 2.50 6.00
AK Akinori Iwamura 2.00 5.00
AP Albert Pujols 5.00 12.00
AR Alex Rodriguez 3.00 8.00
AS Alfonso Soriano 1.25 3.00
BB Barry Bonds 4.00 10.00
DM Daisuke Matsuzaka 3.00 8.00
DO David Ortiz 1.25 3.00
DW David Wright 3.00 8.00
DY Delmon Young 1.25 3.00
FH Matt Holliday 2.00 5.00
FP Felix Pie .75 2.00
HM Hideki Matsui 2.00 5.00
HP Hunter Pence 4.00 10.00
IS Ichiro Suzuki 3.00 8.00
JH Josh Hamilton 3.00 8.00
JR Jose Reyes 1.25 3.00
KI Kei Igawa 2.00 5.00
MC Miguel Cabrera 2.00 5.00
MM Mickey Mantle 6.00 15.00
MR Manny Ramirez 2.00 5.00
PH Phil Hughes 4.00 10.00
RH Ryank Howard 3.00 8.00
TT Troy Tulowitzki 5.00 12.00
VG Vladimir Guerrero 2.00 5.00

2007 Bowman Heritage Signs of Greatness

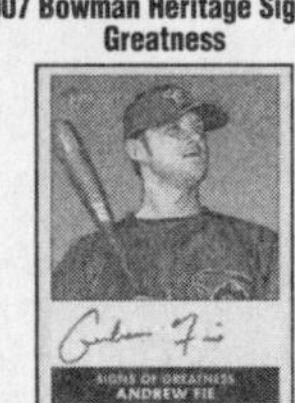

GROUP A ODDS 1:339 HOBBY,1:405 RETAIL
GROUP B ODDS 1:47 HOBBY, 1:53 RETAIL
GROUP C ODDS 1:58 HOBBY, 1:68 RETAIL
GROUP D ODDS 1:350 HOBBY,1:410 RETAIL
GROUP E ODDS 1:238 HOBBY,1:232 RETAIL
GROUP F ODDS 1:389 HOBBY,1:445 RETAIL
GROUP G ODDS 1:4450 HOBBY,1:4800 RETAIL
GROUP H ODDS 1:8100 HOBBY,1:7850 RETAIL
EXCH DEADLINE 10/31/2009
AF Andrew Fie G 3.00 8.00
AO Adam Ottavino D 3.00 8.00
BJ Blake Johnson C 3.00 8.00
BL Brad Lincoln E 3.00 8.00
CA Carlos Arroyo D 3.00 8.00
CC Carl Crawford C 8.00 20.00
CH Cole Hamels C 12.50 30.00
CJ Chipper Jones B 30.00 60.00
CS Chorye Spoone G 3.00 8.00
DW David Wright A 40.00 80.00
EJ Elliot Johnson F 3.00 8.00
GG Glenn Gibson F 3.00 8.00
GM Garrett Mock D 3.00 8.00
JB John Buck D 3.00 8.00
JC Jorge Cantu D 3.00 8.00
JCB Jordan Brown F 6.00 15.00
JH J.P. Howell C 3.00 8.00
JL Jeff Locke G 8.00 20.00
JM Jeff Manship F 6.00 15.00
JP Jorge Posada C 30.00 60.00
JT J.R. Towles G 6.00 15.00
JW Johnny Whittleman H 3.00 8.00
MM Matt Maloney E 3.00 8.00
MT Mike Thompson F 3.00 8.00
NR Nolan Reimold C 12.50 30.00
RD Rajai Davis E 3.00 8.00
SE Stephen Englund G 3.00 8.00
SJ Seth Johnston G 3.00 8.00
SK Sean Kazmar G 3.00 8.00
SP Steve Pearce G 10.00 25.00
SS Scott Sizemore F 4.00 10.00
TG Tony Giarratano F 3.00 8.00
WCS Cody Strait G 3.00 8.00
WJB Joe Benson F 6.00 15.00

2007 Bowman Heritage Signs of Greatness Black

*BLACK: .75X TO 2X BASIC
STATED ODDS 1:590 HOBBY,1:695 RETAIL
STATED PRINT RUN 52 SER.#'d SETS
EXCH DEADLINE 10/31/2009
CJ Chipper Jones 75.00 150.00
DW David Wright 60.00 120.00
JL Jeff Locke 40.00 80.00
NR Nolan Reimold 50.00 100.00
SP Steve Pearce 60.00 120.00

2007 Bowman Heritage Signs of Greatness Red

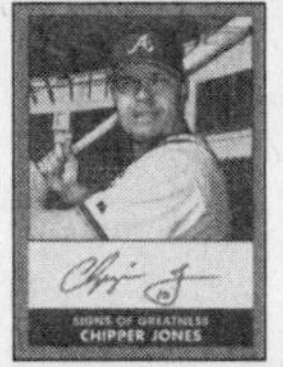

STATED ODDS 1:14,500 HOBBY
STATED PRINT RUN 1 SER.#'d SET
NO PRICING DUE TO SCARCITY

2006 Bowman Originals

This fifty-five card set was released in December, 2006. The set was issued in seven-card packs (five base cards plus 2 encased buy-back cards) which had an $75 SRP. The packs came six per box and there were also eight boxes per case.

COMMON CARD (1-35) .40 1.00
COMMON ROOKIE (36-55) .50 1.25
OVERALL PRINTING PLATE ODDS 1:66
PLATE PRINT RUN 1 SET PER COLOR
BLACK-CYAN-MAGENTA-YELLOW ISSUED
NO PLATE PRICING DUE TO SCARCITY
1 David Wright 1.50 4.00
2 Derek Jeter 2.50 6.00
3 Eric Chavez .40 1.00
4 Ken Griffey Jr. 1.50 4.00
5 Albert Pujols 2.50 6.00
6 Ryan Howard 1.50 4.00
7 Joe Mauer 1.00 2.50
8 Andruw Jones .40 1.00
9 Nomar Garciaparra 1.00 2.50
10 Michael Young .60 1.50
11 Miguel Tejada .60 1.50
12 Alfonso Soriano .60 1.50
13 Alex Rodriguez 1.50 4.00
14 Paul Konerko .60 1.50
15 Carl Crawford .60 1.50
16 Nick Johnson .40 1.00
17 Jim Thome .60 1.50
18 Ivan Rodriguez .60 1.50
19 Chipper Jones 1.00 2.50
20 Pedro Martinez .60 1.50
21 Carlos Delgado .40 1.00
22 Roger Clemens 1.25 3.00
23 Mark Teixeira 1.00 2.50
24 Manny Ramirez 1.00 2.50
25 Barry Bonds 2.00 5.00
26 Vernon Wells .40 1.00
27 Vladimir Guerrero 1.00 2.50
28 Miguel Cabrera 1.00 2.50
29 Victor Martinez .60 1.50
30 Derrek Lee .40 1.00
31 Carlos Lee .40 1.00
32 Ichiro Suzuki 1.50 4.00
33 Johan Santana 1.00 2.50
34 David Ortiz .60 1.50
35 Jason Bay .40 1.00
36 Kendry Morales (RC) 1.25 3.00
37 Nick Markakis (RC) 1.25 3.00
38 Conor Jackson (RC) .75 2.00
39 Justin Verlander (RC) 4.00 10.00
40 Ryan Zimmerman (RC) 2.50 6.00
41 Jeremy Hermida (RC) .50 1.25
42 Dan Uggla (RC) 1.25 3.00
43 Matt Kemp (RC) 2.50 6.00
44 Lastings Milledge (RC) .50 1.25
45 Kenji Johjima RC 1.25 3.00
46 Ian Kinsler (RC) 1.50 4.00
47 Hanley Ramirez (RC) 1.25 3.00
48 Melky Cabrera (RC) .75 2.00
49 Willy Aybar (RC) .50 1.25
50 Jonathan Papelbon (RC) 2.50 6.00
51 Prince Fielder (RC) 2.00 5.00
52 Cole Hamels (RC) 2.00 5.00
53 Josh Barfield (RC) .50 1.25
54 Alay Soler RC .50 1.25
55 Russ Martin (RC) .75 2.00

2006 Bowman Originals Black

*BLACK: 1X TO 2.5X BASIC
*BLACK RC: .75X TO 2X BASIC RC
STATED ODDS 1:4
STATED PRINT RUN 99 SERIAL #'d SETS

2006 Bowman Originals Blue

*BLUE: .6X TO 1.5X BASIC
*BLUE RC: .5X TO 1.2X BASIC RC
STATED ODDS 1:2
STATED PRINT RUN 249 SERIAL #'d SETS

2006 Bowman Originals Red

STATED ODDS 1:347
STATED PRINT RUN 1 SERIAL #'d SET
NO PRICING DUE TO SCARCITY

2006 Bowman Originals Buyback Autographs

GROUP A ODDS 1:3600
GROUP B ODDS 1:768
GROUP C ODDS 1:38
GROUP D ODDS 1:3
GROUP E ODDS 1:26
GROUP F ODDS 1:1
GROUP G ODDS 1:31
GROUP A PRINT RUN B/WN 10-20 PER
GROUP B PRINT RUN 50 CARDS
GROUP C PRINT RUN B/WN 1-61 PER
GROUP D PRINT RUN B/WN 1-466 PER
GROUP E PRINT RUN B/WN 1-472 PER
GROUP F PRINT RUN B/WN 1-1000 PER
GROUP G PRINT RUN B/WN 1-544 PER
NO PRICING ON QTY OF 25 OR LESS
2 Adam Loewen 05 BCDP/198 F 5.00 12.00
11 Adam Loewen 05 BDP/719 F 4.00 10.00
12 Adam Loewen 05 BDPGLD/68 F 5.00 12.00
15 Adrian Gonzalez 00 B/976 F 40.00 80.00
18 Albert Pujols 02 B/50 C 75.00 150.00
24 Albert Pujols 05 B/44 C 60.00 120.00
25 Alex Gordon 06 BCPROS/32 C 50.00 100.00
26 Alex Gordon 06 BPROS/49 C 50.00 100.00
47 Andrew McCutchen 04 BAFLAC/391 F 20.00 50.00
50 Andrew McCutchen 05 BDP/561 F 12.50 30.00
51 Andrew McCutchen 06 BDPGLD/33 F 12.50 30.00
55 Andruw Jones 04 B/48 C 30.00 60.00
56 Andruw Jones 04 BH/28 C 30.00 60.00
57 Andruw Jones 04 BH/34 C 30.00 60.00
58 Andy LaRoche 05 B/66 F 12.50 30.00
63 Andy LaRoche 05 BDP/734 F 6.00 15.00
64 Andy LaRoche 05 BDPGLD/60 F 12.50 30.00
75 B.J. Upton 04 BDP/120 F 12.50 30.00
77 B.J. Upton 05 BCDP/136 F 12.50 30.00
85 B.J. Upton 05 BDP/667 F 8.00 20.00
89 Beau Jones 05 BAFLAC/329 F 4.00 10.00
90 Beau Jones 05 BAFLAC/33 F 8.00 20.00
92 Beau Jones 05 BCDP/63 F 6.00 15.00
95 Beau Jones 05 BDP/576 F 4.00 10.00
98 Billy Buckner 04 BC/182 E 6.00 15.00
100 Billy Buckner 04 BDP/432 E 4.00 10.00
101 Billy Buckner 04 BDPGLD/33 E 8.00 20.00
102 Billy Buckner 04 BH/99 E 6.00 15.00
104 Billy Wagner 01 BH/99 D 8.00 20.00
108 Billy Wagner 94 BB/37 D 10.00 25.00
109 Billy Wagner 95 B/56 D 8.00 20.00
110 Billy Wagner 96 B/47 D 10.00 25.00
111 Billy Wagner 96 BB/64 D 8.00 20.00
116 Billy Wagner 97 B/90 D 8.00 20.00
117 Billy Wagner 97 BC/38 D 10.00 25.00
123 Brandon Phillips 01 B/26 F 6.00 15.00
124 Brandon Phillips 01 BC/46 F 6.00 15.00
126 Brandon Phillips 02 B/335 F 6.00 15.00
127 Brandon Phillips 02 BC/67 F 5.00 12.00
128 Brandon Phillips 02 BCDP/28 F 6.00 15.00
131 Brandon Phillips 02 BDP/140 F 5.00 12.00
133 Brandon Phillips 02 BDPGLD/32 F 6.00 15.00
135 Brandon Phillips 03 B/257 F 4.00 10.00
136 Brandon Phillips 03 BC/35 F 6.00 15.00
141 Brandon Snyder 05 BDP/461 D 4.00 10.00
145 Brandon Wood 05 BCDP/239 F 6.00 15.00
150 Brandon Wood 05 BDP/627 F 6.00 15.00
153 Brandon Wood 05 BDPGLD/100 F 6.00 15.00
155 Brent Cox 05 BCDP/240 F 5.00 12.00
159 Brent Cox 05 BDP/688 F 4.00 10.00
161 Brent Cox 05 BDPGLD/66 F 5.00 12.00
165 Carl Crawford 00 B/40 F 10.00 25.00
167 Carl Crawford 00 BC/37 F 10.00 25.00
171 Carl Crawford 02 B/279 F 8.00 20.00
178 Carl Crawford 04 B/30 F 10.00 25.00
181 Carl Crawford 05 B/71 F 10.00 25.00
184 Carl Crawford 05 BH/71 F 10.00 25.00
186 Carl Crawford 06 B/334 F 8.00 20.00
188 Carlos Silva 00 B/996 F 4.00 10.00
190 Cesar Ramos 05 BCDP/161 F 5.00 12.00
196 Cesar Ramos 05 BDP/732 F 4.00 10.00
197 Cesar Ramos 05 BDPGLD/76 F 5.00 12.00
200 Chase Utley 02 B/303 D 30.00 60.00
203 Chase Utley 06 B/150 D 20.00 50.00
204 Chaz Roe 05 BCDP/132 F 5.00 12.00
210 Chaz Roe 05 BDP/774 F 4.00 10.00
212 Chaz Roe 05 BDPGLD/73 F 5.00 12.00
224 Chris B. Young 05 B/81 F 15.00 40.00
228 Chris B. Young 05 BDP/558 F 8.00 20.00
229 Chris B. Young 05 BDPGLD/88 F 20.00 50.00
232 Chris B. Young 05 BH/44 F 20.00 50.00
235 Chris R. Young 05 BCDP/146 F 12.50 30.00
242 Chris R. Young 05 BDP/772 F 10.00 25.00
243 Chris R. Young 05 BDPGLD/70 F 12.50 30.00
245 Clint Barmes 03 B/61 F 5.00 12.00
246 Clint Barmes 05 BCDP/113 F 5.00 12.00
249 Clint Barmes 05 BDP/430 F 4.00 10.00
251 Clint Barmes 06 B/375 F 4.00 10.00
252 Conor Jackson 04 B/78 F 8.00 20.00
258 Conor Jackson 05 BDP/457 F 5.00 12.00
261 Conor Jackson 06 B/360 F 5.00 12.00
265 Craig Italiano 05 BCDP/163 F 5.00 12.00
268 Craig Italiano 05 BDP/658 F 4.00 10.00
269 Craig Italiano 05 BDPGLD/160 F 5.00 12.00
276 Dan Johnson 05 BCDP/101 F 5.00 12.00
281 Dan Johnson 05 BDP/575 F 4.00 10.00
283 Dan Johnson 05 BH/29 F 6.00 15.00
284 Dan Johnson 06 B/276 F 4.00 10.00
287 David Wright 02 B/264 F 50.00 100.00
290 David Wright 04 BDP/45 F 40.00 80.00
292 David Wright 05 B/64 F 40.00 80.00
294 David Wright 05 BH/62 F 40.00 80.00
295 David Wright 06 B/543 F 12.50 30.00
297 Derrek Lee 04 B/61 C 5.00 12.00
307 Dontrelle Willis 04 B/78 F 8.00 20.00
310 Dontrelle Willis 04 BH/79 F 8.00 20.00
311 Dontrelle Willis 05 B/147 F 8.00 20.00
313 Dontrelle Willis 05 BC/36 F 10.00 25.00
315 Dontrelle Willis 05 BH/55 F 8.00 20.00
319 Dontrelle Willis 06 B/525 F 5.00 12.00
327 Eli Iorg 05 BDP/672 F 4.00 10.00
328 Eli Iorg 05 BDPGLD/151 F 5.00 12.00
332 Eric Chavez 02 B/301 D 4.00 10.00
335 Eric Chavez 05 B/70 D 5.00 12.00
336 Eric Chavez 05 BH/62 D 5.00 12.00
338 Eric Chavez 06 B/34 D 6.00 15.00
339 Ervin Santana 04 B/76 F 6.00 15.00
340 Ervin Santana 04 BH/62 F 15.00 40.00
341 Ervin Santana 05 B/67 F 5.00 12.00
343 Ervin Santana 05 BCDP/109 F 5.00 12.00
348 Ervin Santana 05 BDP/51 F 5.00 12.00
349 Ervin Santana 05 BDP/544 F 4.00 10.00
351 Ervin Santana 06 B/369 F 4.00 10.00
354 Fausto Carmona 04 BDP/56 D 15.00 40.00
357 Fausto Carmona 05 BDP/263 D 15.00 40.00
359 Francisco Cordero 00 B/140 D 5.00 12.00
360 Francisco Cordero 00 BC/64 D 5.00 12.00
364 Francisco Cordero 98 B/138 D 5.00 12.00
365 Francisco Cordero 98 BB/87 D 5.00 12.00
367 Francisco Cordero 98 BC/49 D 6.00 15.00
370 Francisco Liriano 02 B/212 F 6.00 15.00
371 Francisco Liriano 02 BDP/63 F 6.00 15.00
373 Francisco Liriano 05 BCDP/142 F 6.00 15.00
375 Francisco Liriano 05 BDP/350 F 6.00 15.00
378 Francisco Liriano 06 B/222 F 6.00 15.00
383 Garrett Atkins 05 BDP/581 F 4.00 10.00
385 Garrett Atkins 05 BDPGLD/27 F 6.00 15.00
386 Garrett Atkins 06 B/209 F 5.00 12.00
390 Garrett Atkins 06 BGLD/38 F 6.00 15.00
391 Gustavo Chacin 05 BH/30 D 6.00 15.00
393 Gustavo Chacin 06 B/468 D 4.00 10.00
396 Hanley Ramirez 05 BCDP/98 F 12.50 30.00
399 Hanley Ramirez 05 BDP/435 F 8.00 20.00
400 Hanley Ramirez 06 B/466 F 8.00 20.00
402 Huston Street 05 BDP/54 5.00 12.00
404 Jason Bay 02 B/298 D 12.50 30.00
406 Jason Bay 04 BH/58 D 6.00 15.00
407 Jason Bay 05 B/70 D 6.00 15.00
408 Jason Bay 06 B/50 D 6.00 15.00
409 Jason Botts 02 B/269 F 4.00 10.00
412 Jason Botts 02 BH/46 F 6.00 15.00
413 Jason Botts 06 B/29 F 6.00 15.00
414 Jason Botts 06 B/577 F 4.00 10.00
418 Jason Botts 06 BGLD/31 F 6.00 15.00
419 Jason Kubel 03 B/77 D 5.00 12.00
424 Jason Kubel 04 BCDP/127 D 5.00 12.00
428 Jason Kubel 04 BDP/232 D 5.00 12.00
433 Jason Marquis 00 B/944 F 4.00 10.00
436 Jason Marquis 98 B/26 F 6.00 15.00
438 Jay Bruce 05 BDP/434 D 20.00 50.00
439 Jay Bruce 05 BDPGLD/66 D 50.00 100.00
442 Jed Lowrie 05 BDP/716 F 10.00 25.00
443 Jed Lowrie 05 BDPGLD/141 F 10.00 25.00
447 Jeff Mathis 01 BDP/71 D 5.00 12.00
451 Jeff Mathis 03 BDP/127 D 5.00 12.00
453 Jeff Mathis 04 BCDP/97 D 5.00 12.00
454 Jeff Mathis 04 BDP/185 D 5.00 12.00
457 Jerome Williams 02 B/292 D 4.00 10.00
459 Jerome Williams 03 BCDP/45 D 6.00 15.00
460 Jerome Williams 03 BDP/48 D 6.00 15.00
461 Jerome Williams 04 B/97 D 5.00 12.00
462 Joel Guzman 02 B/274 D 4.00 10.00
465 Joel Guzman 02 BDP/90 D 10.00 25.00
466 Joel Guzman 04 BC/54 D 5.00 12.00
467 Joel Guzman 04 BDP/53 D 5.00 12.00
469 Joel Zumaya 04 B/96 F 20.00 50.00
472 Joel Zumaya 05 BCDP/233 F 12.50 30.00
478 Joel Zumaya 05 BDP/582 F 10.00 25.00
479 Joel Zumaya 05 BDPGLD/57 F 20.00 50.00
483 John Drennen 05 BAFLAC/78 D 8.00 20.00
486 John Drennen 06 BDP/387 D 4.00 10.00
489 John Van Benschoten 01 BDP/51 D 5.00 12.00
490 John Van Benschoten 02 B/272 D 4.00 10.00
492 John Van Benschoten 03 BCDP/26 D 6.00 15.00
493 John Van Benschoten 03 BDP/130 D 5.00 12.00
495 Jonny Gomes 02 B/341 F 4.00 10.00
496 Jonny Gomes 02 BC/27 F 6.00 15.00

499 Jonny Gomes 04 B/175 F 5.00 12.00
506 Jonny Gomes 06 B/363 F 4.00 10.00
511 Josh Barfield 02 B/178 F 8.00 20.00
524 Josh Barfield 05 BDP/557 F 4.00 10.00
526 Josh Barfield 05 BDPGLD/31 F 6.00 15.00
529 Josh Geer 05 BCDP/138 D 5.00 12.00
531 Josh Geer 05 BDP/343 D 4.00 10.00
534 Justin Huber 02 BDP/26 F 12.50 30.00
536 Justin Huber 03 BCDP/37 F 12.50 30.00
539 Justin Huber 03 BDP/99 F 5.00 12.00
545 Justin Huber 05 BDP/572 F 4.00 10.00
547 Justin Huber 05 BDPGLD/32 F 6.00 15.00
550 Justin Upton [illegible]
551 Kevin Gregg 00 B/988 F 4.00 10.00
554 Lastings Milledge 04 B/158 F 12.50 30.00
558 Lastings Milledge 05 BCDP/166 F 12.50 30.00
560 Lastings Milledge 05 BDP/632 F 10.00 25.00
561 Lastings Milledge 05 BDPGLD/27 F 15.00 40.00
563 Mark Loretta 05 B/110 D 5.00 12.00
565 Mark Loretta 05 BH/73 D 5.00 12.00
566 Mark Loretta 06 B/289 D 4.00 10.00
582 Matt Cain 04 BDP/36 D 15.00 40.00
586 Matt Cain 06 B/389 D 10.00 25.00
590 Matt Maloney 05 B/350 D 6.00 15.00
595 Matt Maloney 05 BH/50 D 30.00 60.00
601 Matt Torra 06 BDP/456 D 4.00 10.00
603 Melky Cabrera 05 B/95 F 20.00 50.00
606 Melky Cabrera 05 BCDP/191 F 20.00 50.00
612 Melky Cabrera 05 BDP/606 F 10.00 25.00
613 Melky Cabrera 05 BDPGLD/60 F 20.00 50.00
616 Merkin Valdez 04 B/70 D 5.00 12.00
619 Merkin Valdez 04 BH/66 D 5.00 12.00
621 Merkin Valdez 05 BDP/325 D 4.00 10.00
622 Merkin Valdez 05 BDP/41 D 6.00 15.00
627 Micah Owings 06 BDP/648 F 6.00 15.00
628 Micah Owings 06 BDPGLD/138 F 12.50 30.00
631 Michael Bowden 05 BDP/449 D 8.00 20.00
632 Michael Bowden 05 BDPGLD/27 D 15.00 40.00
633 Miguel Cabrera 02 B/130 D 10.00 25.00
634 Miguel Cabrera 03 B/70 D 10.00 25.00
635 Miguel Cabrera 04 B/70 D 10.00 25.00
637 Miguel Cabrera 05 B/69 D 10.00 25.00
639 Miguel Cabrera 05 BH/63 D 12.50 30.00
641 Miguel Cabrera 06 B/98 D 10.00 25.00
645 Mike Costanzo 06 BDP/466 D 5.00 12.00
648 Mike Lamb 00 B/993 F 4.00 10.00
649 Morgan Ensberg 01 BDP/74 D 5.00 12.00
650 Morgan Ensberg 02 B/334 D 4.00 10.00
655 Morgan Ensberg 06 B/64 D 5.00 12.00
661 Nick Swisher 05 BH/73 D 5.00 12.00
663 Nick Swisher 06 B/342 D 4.00 10.00
668 Nick Swisher 06 BGLD/31 D 6.00 15.00
670 Nolan Reimold 05 BCDP/30 D 40.00 80.00
671 Nolan Reimold 05 BDP/419 D 12.50 30.00
674 Nolan Reimold 05 BH/41 D 40.00 80.00
677 Rich Harden 02 B/263 D 10.00 25.00
678 Rich Harden 03 B/70 D 5.00 12.00
679 Rich Harden 03 BDP/68 D 6.00 15.00
681 Rich Harden 04 B/87 D 5.00 12.00
682 Rich Harden 05 B/82 D 5.00 12.00
686 Ricky Nolasco 04 B/256 D 4.00 10.00
687 Ricky Nolasco 04 BC/148 D 5.00 12.00
693 Ricky Nolasco 04 BH/52 D 5.00 12.00
698 Robinson Cano 04 BDP/72 D 30.00 60.00
701 Robinson Cano 05 BCDP/90 D 20.00 50.00
702 Robinson Cano 05 BDP/222 D 15.00 40.00
705 Robinson Cano 06 B/101 D 8.00 20.00
706 Roy Oswalt 02 B/199 D 4.00 10.00
709 Roy Oswalt 04 B/61 D 5.00 12.00
710 Roy Oswalt 04 BH/63 D 10.00 25.00
711 Roy Oswalt 05 B/96 D 5.00 12.00
712 Roy Oswalt 06 B/42 D 6.00 15.00
713 Russ Martin 05 B/96 F 20.00 50.00
715 Russ Martin 05 BCDP/252 F 15.00 40.00
718 Russ Martin 05 BDP/577 F 10.00 25.00
719 Russ Martin 05 BDPGLD/33 F 20.00 50.00
724 Ryan Garko 05 BDP/394 F 4.00 10.00
726 Ryan Garko 06 B/580 F 4.00 10.00
728 Ryan Howard 03 BDP/50 B 150.00 250.00
729 Scott Elbert 04 BCDP/60 D 10.00 25.00
731 Scott Elbert 04 BDP/330 D 8.00 20.00
733 Scott Elbert 04 BH/79 D 15.00 40.00
734 Scott Kazmir 05 B/155 F 8.00 20.00
736 Scott Kazmir 05 BH/99 F 10.00 25.00
738 Scott Kazmir 06 B/661 F 8.00 20.00
742 Scott Kazmir 06 BGLD/26 F 10.00 25.00
744 Scott Mathieson 05 B/72 E 5.00 12.00
754 Scott Mathieson 05 BDP/472 E 4.00 10.00
759 Scott Thorman 00 B/980 F 4.00 10.00
761 Sean West 05 BCDP/70 D 12.50 30.00
764 Sean West 05 BDP/394 D 4.00 10.00
765 Sean West 05 BDPGLD/35 D 10.00 25.00
766 Shaun Marcum 03 BCDP/153 D 5.00 12.00
767 Shaun Marcum 03 BDP/138 D 5.00 12.00
768 Shaun Marcum 03 BDPGLD/33 D 6.00 15.00
769 Shaun Marcum 05 B/133 D 5.00 12.00
770 Shaun Marcum 05 BC/26 D 6.00 15.00
775 Travis Buck 05 BCDP/134 F 8.00 20.00
777 Travis Buck 05 BDP/747 F 5.00 12.00
778 Travis Buck 05 BDPGLD/60 F 20.00 50.00
782 Travis Buck 05 BS/44 F 20.00 50.00
784 Travis Hafner 02 B/280 F 6.00 15.00
787 Travis Hafner 03 BCDP/45 F 10.00 25.00
790 Travis Hafner 03 BDP/114 F 6.00 15.00
792 Travis Hafner 05 B/96 F 6.00 15.00
794 Travis Hafner 06 B/386 F 6.00 15.00
804 Trevor Bell 05 BDP/689 F 4.00 10.00
806 Trevor Bell 05 BDPGLD/134 F 5.00 12.00
807 Trevor Bell 05 BH/28 F 6.00 15.00
809 Troy Patton 05 BCDP/211 F 8.00 20.00
813 Troy Patton 05 BDP/736 F 4.00 10.00
814 Troy Patton 05 BDPGLD/50 F 5.00 12.00
817 Vernon Wells 00 B/56 F 15.00 40.00
820 Vernon Wells 01 B/29 F 15.00 40.00
823 Vernon Wells 04 B/96 F 10.00 25.00
826 Vernon Wells 05 B/100 F 10.00 25.00
828 Vernon Wells 05 BH/52 F 10.00 25.00
831 Vernon Wells 06 B/426 F 6.00 15.00
838 Vernon Wells 98 B/40 F 20.00 50.00
842 Vernon Wells 99 B/68 F 10.00 25.00
849 Vladimir Guerrero 05 B/45 C 20.00 50.00
851 Wade Townsend 05 BCDP/53 D 5.00 12.00
853 Wade Townsend 05 BDP/423 D 4.00 10.00
856 Wily Mo Pena 00 B/79 D 5.00 12.00
857 Wily Mo Pena 00 BB/27 D 6.00 15.00
860 Wily Mo Pena 02 B/134 D 5.00 12.00
863 Wily Mo Pena 02 BDP/70 D 5.00 12.00
865 Wily Mo Pena 03 B/62 D 5.00 12.00
866 Wily Mo Pena 05 B/69 D 5.00 12.00
868 Xavier Nady 01 BDP/192 F 5.00 12.00
869 Xavier Nady 02 B/294 F 4.00 10.00
870 Xavier Nady 02 BC/41 F 6.00 15.00
875 Xavier Nady 03 BCDP/72 F 5.00 12.00
877 Xavier Nady 03 BDP/213 F 5.00 12.00
878 Xavier Nady 03 BDPGLD/33 F 6.00 15.00
879 Xavier Nady 05 BH/105 F 5.00 12.00
884 Yunel Escobar 06 BCDP/28 D 15.00 40.00
885 Yunel Escobar 06 BDP/395 D 15.00 40.00
886 Yunel Escobar 06 BDPGLD/69 D 30.00 60.00
888 Yusmeiro Petit 04 BDP/102 F 5.00 12.00
891 Yusmeiro Petit 04 BH/68 F 5.00 12.00
893 Yusmeiro Petit 05 BCDP/160 F 5.00 12.00
897 Yusmeiro Petit 05 BDP/630 F 4.00 10.00

2006 Bowman Originals Prospects

COMMON CARD (1-55) .40 1.00
OVERALL PRINTING PLATE ODDS 1:86
PLATE PRINT RUN 1 SET PER COLOR
BLACK-CYAN-MAGENTA-YELLOW ISSUED
NO PLATE PRICING DUE TO SCARCITY
1 Cameron Maybin 1.25 3.00
2 Koby Clemens .60 1.50
3 Lance Broadway .40 1.00
4 Chris Dickerson .60 1.50
5 Garrett Mock .40 1.00
6 Ben Copeland .40 1.00
7 Nick Adenhart .40 1.00
8 Brad McCann .40 1.00
9 Dustin Majewski .40 1.00
10 Jimmy Barthmaier .40 1.00
11 Michael Aubrey .60 1.50
12 Evan Longoria 5.00 12.00
13 Clayton Kershaw 2.50 6.00
14 Juan Francia .40 1.00
15 Elvis Andrus 2.00 5.00
16 Mark Trumbo 1.50 4.00
17 Shawn Riggans .40 1.00
18 Asdrubal Cabrera 2.00 5.00
19 Mark McLemore .40 1.00
20 Radhames Liz .40 1.00
21 Mat Gamel 1.50 4.00
22 Wilkin Ramirez .60 1.50
23 Jared Lansford .40 1.00
24 Hunter Pence 2.00 5.00
25 Justin Upton 3.00 8.00
26 Brent Dlugach .40 1.00
27 B.J. Szymanski .40 1.00
28 Stephen Marek .40 1.00
29 Shaun Cumberland .40 1.00
30 Yovani Gallardo 1.25 3.00
31 Will Venable .40 1.00
32 A.J. Shappi .40 1.00
33 Dallas Trahern .40 1.00
34 Jason Jaramillo .40 1.00
35 Jose Tabata 2.50 6.00
36 Jose Campusano .40 1.00
37 Ryan Patterson .40 1.00
38 Andrew Pinckney .40 1.00
39 Dexter Fowler 1.25 3.00
40 Cody Johnson .40 1.00
41 Steve Murphy .40 1.00
42 Mark Reed .40 1.00
43 Chris Iannetta .40 1.00
44 Michael Hollimon UER .40 1.00
Mark Holliman is pictured on this card
45 Omir Santos .40 1.00
46 Diory Hernandez .40 1.00
47 Matt Tolbert .40 1.00
48 Jeff Frazier .40 1.00
49 Max Ramirez .60 1.50
50 Alex Gordon 1.25 3.00
51 Steve Garrabrants .40 1.00
52 Steven Baker .40 1.00
53 Ryan Klosterman .40 1.00
54 Michael Collins .40 1.00
55 Corey Wimberly .40 1.00

2006 Bowman Originals Prospects Black

*BLACK: .75X TO 2X BASIC
STATED ODDS 1:4
STATED PRINT RUN 99 SERIAL #'d SETS

2006 Bowman Originals Prospects Blue

*BLUE: .6X TO 1.5X BASIC
STATED ODDS 1:2
STATED PRINT RUN 249 SERIAL #'d SETS

2006 Bowman Originals Prospects Red

STATED ODDS 1:347
STATED PRINT RUN 1 SERIAL #'d SET
NO PRICING DUE TO SCARCITY

2010 Bowman Platinum

COMMON CARD (1-100) .15 .40
COMMON RC (1-100) .40 1.00
1 Stephen Strasburg RC 2.50 6.00
2 Derek Jeter 1.00 2.50
3 Felix Doubront RC .40 1.00
4 Miguel Cabrera .40 1.00
5 Albert Pujols 1.00 2.50
6 Domonic Brown RC 1.50 4.00
7 Ryan Braun .50 1.25
8 Justin Upton .25 .60
9 Dustin Pedroia .50 1.25
10 Shin-Soo Choo .25 .60
11 Jake Arrieta RC .60 1.50
12 Hanley Ramirez .40 1.00
13 Matt Kemp .25 .60
14 Joe Mauer .40 1.00
15 Joey Votto .40 1.00
16 Andrew Cashner RC .40 1.00
17 Josh Hamilton .40 1.00
18 Buster Posey RC 4.00 10.00
19 Ubaldo Jimenez .25 .60
20 Peter Bourjos RC .60 1.50
21 CC Sabathia .25 .60
22 Alfonso Soriano .25 .60
23 Carlos Santana RC 1.25 3.00
24 Kevin Youkilis .25 .60
25 Brian McCann .25 .60
26 Troy Tulowitzki .40 1.00
27 Hunter Pence .25 .60
28 Jay Sborz (RC) .40 1.00
29 Andre Ethier .25 .60
30 Kendry Morales .15 .40
31 Brian Matusz RC 1.00 2.50
32 Vladimir Guerrero .40 1.00
33 Prince Fielder .25 .60
34 J.P. Arencibia RC .60 1.50
35 Roy Halladay .40 1.00
36 Mark Teixeira .40 1.00
37 Ryan Kalish RC .60 1.50
38 Tim Lincecum .60 1.50
39 Andrew McCutchen .40 1.00
40 Johan Santana .40 1.00
41 Josh Bell (RC) .40 1.00
42 Daniel Nava RC .60 1.50
43 Manny Ramirez .40 1.00
44 Ichiro Suzuki .60 1.50
45 Pablo Sandoval .25 .60
46 Chris Coghlan .15 .40
47 Mike Leake RC 1.25 3.00
48 Adrian Gonzalez .25 .60
49 Torii Hunter .15 .40
50 Brennan Boesch RC 1.00 2.50
51 Justin Verlander .50 1.25
52 Matt Holliday .40 1.00
53 Evan Longoria .50 1.25
54 Adam Jones .25 .60
55 Wade Davis (RC) .40 1.00
56 Jose Reyes .25 .60
57 Martin Prado .15 .40
58 Brad Lincoln RC .60 1.50
59 Billy Butler .15 .40
60 Mat Latos .15 .40
61 Logan Morrison RC .60 1.50
62 Ryan Howard .50 1.25
63 Cliff Lee .25 .60
64 Adam Dunn .25 .60
65 David Ortiz .25 .60
66 Ike Davis RC 1.00 2.50
67 Victor Martinez .25 .60
68 Josh Johnson .25 .60
69 Dayan Viciedo RC .60 1.50
70 Jimmy Rollins .25 .60
71 Jered Weaver .15 .40
72 Robinson Cano .40 1.00
73 Madison Bumgarner RC 1.00 2.50
74 Clayton Kershaw .40 1.00
75 Tommy Hanson .25 .60
76 Carl Crawford .25 .60
77 Trevor Plouffe (RC) .40 1.00
78 Roy Oswalt .25 .60
79 Austin Jackson RC .60 1.50
80 Dan Haren .15 .40
81 Gordon Beckham .25 .60
82 Zack Greinke .25 .60
83 Neil Walker (RC) .60 1.50
84 Vernon Wells .15 .40
85 Lance Berkman .25 .60
86 Mike Stanton RC 1.50 4.00
87 Ryan Zimmerman .25 .60
88 Nick Markakis .40 1.00
89 Jose Tabata RC 1.00 2.50
90 Chipper Jones .40 1.00
91 Jason Heyward RC 2.50 6.00
92 Alex Rodriguez .60 1.50
93 Matt Cain .25 .60
94 Justin Morneau .40 1.00
95 Jon Lester .40 1.00
96 Starlin Castro RC 1.50 4.00
97 Chase Utley .40 1.00
98 Felix Hernandez .40 1.00
99 Wilson Ramos RC 1.00 2.50
100 David Wright .50 1.25

2010 Bowman Platinum Refractors

*REF VET: 2X TO 5X BASIC
*REF RC: .6X TO 1.5X BASIC
STATED PRINT RUN 999 SER.#'d SETS

2010 Bowman Platinum Gold Refractors

*GOLD VET: 4X TO 10X BASIC
*GOLD RC: 1.5X TO 4X RC
STATED PRINT RUN 539 SER.#'d SETS
1 Stephen Strasburg 15.00 40.00

2010 Bowman Platinum Dual Relic Autographs Refractors

STATED PRINT RUN 99 SER.#'d SETS
AJ Tyler Anderson 20.00 50.00
Brian Johnson
BM Matt Barnes 8.00 20.00
Scott McGough
BS Jackie Bradley Jr. 30.00 60.00
George Springer
DM Alex Dickerson 6.00 15.00
Andrew Maggi
ER Jason Esposito
Steve Rodriguez
FM Nolan Fontana
Mikie Mahtook
GC Sonny Gray 30.00 60.00
Gerrit Cole
GM Sean Gilmartin
Brett Mooneyham
MW Brad Miller 8.00 20.00
Ryan Wright
OR Peter O'Brien
Nick Ramirez
RW Noe Ramirez 6.00 15.00
Kyle Winkler
SH Stephen Strasburg
Jason Heyward

2010 Bowman Platinum Dual Relic Autographs Red

STATED PRINT RUN 10 SER.#'d SETS
NO PRICING DUE TO SCARCITY

2010 Bowman Platinum Dual Relic Autographs Superfractors

STATED PRINT RUN 1 SER.#'d SET
NO PRICING DUE TO SCARCITY

2010 Bowman Platinum Prospect Autographs Refractors

PLATE PRINT RUN 1 SET PER COLOR
BLACK-CYAN-MAGENTA-YELLOW ISSUED
NO PLATE PRICING DUE TO SCARCITY
AC Alexander Colome 4.00 10.00
AH Adeiny Hechavarria 5.00 12.00
AW Alex Wilson 4.00 10.00
CA Chris Archer 5.00 12.00
CD Chase D'Arnaud 4.00 10.00
CO Chris Owings 4.00 10.00
DM Dan Merklinger 3.00 8.00
ET Eric Thames 5.00 12.00
FF Freddie Freeman 15.00 40.00
FM Fabio Martinez 4.00 10.00
IK Ian Krol 4.00 10.00
JH Jordan Henry 4.00 10.00
JJ Jake Jefferies 4.00 10.00
JK Joe Kelly 4.00 10.00
JM Jesus Montero 15.00 40.00
JS Jerry Sands 8.00 20.00
JS Jonathan Singleton 12.50 30.00
LC Lonnie Chisenhall
LS Logan Schafer 3.00 8.00
MR Matt Rizzotti 5.00 12.00
MS Miguel Sano 20.00 50.00
MT Mike Trout 20.00 50.00
NB Nick Barnese 4.00 10.00
NN Nick Noonan 5.00 12.00
NT Nate Tenbrink 5.00 12.00
PC Pat Corbin 5.00 12.00
PG Paul Goldschmidt 15.00 40.00
RC Ryan Chaffee 3.00 8.00
RP Rich Poythress 6.00 15.00
RU Rudy Owens 6.00 15.00
SG Steve Garrison 4.00 10.00
SH Steven Hensley 4.00 10.00
TS Tony Sanchez 5.00 12.00
ACH Aroldis Chapman 15.00 40.00
AWE Allen Webster 4.00 10.00
JDM J.D. Martinez 8.00 20.00
JMA Justin Marks 4.00 10.00
JMC Jake McGee 3.00 8.00
JMI Jiovanni Mier 4.00 10.00
KSA Keyvius Sampson 8.00 20.00
MRO Mauricio Robles 3.00 8.00

2010 Bowman Platinum Prospect Autographs Blue Refractors

*BLUE: .75X TO 2X BASIC
STATED PRINT RUN 99 SER.#'d SETS

2010 Bowman Platinum Prospect Autographs Green Refractors

*GREEN: .6X TO 1.5X BASIC
STATED PRINT RUN 199 SER.#'d SETS

2010 Bowman Platinum Prospect Autographs Red Refractors

STATED PRINT RUN 10 SER.#'d SETS
NO PRICING DUE TO SCARCITY

2010 Bowman Platinum Prospect Autographs Superfractors

STATED PRINT RUN 1 SER.#'d SET
NO PRICING DUE TO SCARCITY

2010 Bowman Platinum Prospect Dual Autographs Refractors

STATED PRINT RUN 99 SER.#'d SETS
BD Jackie Bradley Jr. 20.00 50.00
Alex Dickerson
CB Gerrit Cole 50.00 100.00
Matt Barnes
GE Sonny Gray 8.00 20.00
Jason Esposito
GW Sean Gilmartin 8.00 20.00
Kyle Winkler
JM Brett Jackson
Jared Mitchell
JM Brian Johnson
Brett Mooneyham
MA Scott McGough
Tyler Anderson
MF Mikie Mahtook 8.00 20.00
Nolan Fontana
MS Brad Miller 20.00 50.00
George Springer
OR Peter O'Brien 8.00 20.00
Steve Rodriguez
RR Nick Ramirez 8.00 20.00
Noe Ramirez
WM Ryan Wright 8.00 20.00
Andrew Maggi

2010 Bowman Platinum Prospects

PLATE PRINT RUN 1 SET PER COLOR
BLACK-CYAN-MAGENTA-YELLOW ISSUED
NO PLATE PRICING DUE TO SCARCITY
PP1 Jerry Sands 1.00 2.50
PP2 Desmond Jennings .60 1.50
PP3 Jeremy Hellickson 1.50 4.00
PP4 Jesus Montero 2.50 6.00
PP5 Mike Trout 3.00 8.00
PP6 Dustin Ackley 2.50 6.00
PP7 Zach Britton 1.50 4.00
PP8 Adeiny Hechavarria .40 1.00
PP9 Mike Moustakas 1.25 3.00
PP10 Aroldis Chapman 1.50 4.00
PP11 Lonnie Chisenhall .60 1.50
PP12 Mike Montgomery .60 1.50
PP13 Freddie Freeman 1.50 4.00
PP14 Kyle Drabek .60 1.50
PP15 Grant Green .60 1.50
PP16 Brett Jackson 1.25 3.00
PP17 Slade Heathcott 1.25 3.00
PP18 Mike Minor .60 1.50
PP19 Austin Romine .60 1.50
PP20 Kyle Gibson 1.50 4.00
PP21 Chris Withrow .40 1.00
PP22 John Lamb 1.00 2.50
PP23 J.D. Martinez 1.50 4.00
PP24 Donavan Tate 1.00 2.50
PP25 Shelby Miller 1.50 4.00
PP26 Jose Iglesias 1.50 4.00
PP27 Hak-Ju Lee 1.50 4.00
PP28 Miguel Sano 2.00 5.00
PP29 Tyler Anderson .60 1.50
PP30 Matt Barnes 1.00 2.50
PP31 Jackie Bradley Jr. 1.25 3.00
PP32 Gerrit Cole 2.00 5.00
PP33 Alex Dickerson .40 1.00
PP34 Jason Esposito 1.00 2.50
PP35 Nolan Fontana 1.00 2.50
PP36 Sean Gilmartin .60 1.50
PP37 Sonny Gray .60 1.50
PP38 Brian Johnson .40 1.00
PP39 Andrew Maggi .40 1.00
PP40 Mikie Mahtook 1.00 2.50
PP41 Scott McGough 1.00 2.50
PP42 Brad Miller .40 1.00
PP43 Brett Mooneyham 1.00 2.50
PP44 Peter O'Brien .60 1.50
PP45 Nick Ramirez .60 1.50
PP46 Noe Ramirez .60 1.50
PP47 Steve Rodriguez .60 1.50
PP48 George Springer 1.00 2.50
PP49 Kyle Winkler 1.00 2.50
PP50 Ryan Wright .40 1.00

2010 Bowman Platinum Prospects Refractors Thick Stock

*REF: .75X TO 2X BASIC
STATED PRINT RUN 999 SER.#'d SETS

2010 Bowman Platinum Prospects Refractors Thin Stock

*REF: .75X TO 2X BASIC
STATED PRINT RUN 999 SER.#'d SETS

2010 Bowman Platinum Prospects Blue Refractors

*BLUE REF: 1.5X TO 4X BASIC
STATED PRINT RUN 99 SER.#'d SETS

2010 Bowman Platinum Prospects Gold Refractors Thick Stock

*GOLD REF: 1X TO 2.5X BASIC
STATED PRINT RUN 539 SER.#'d SETS

2010 Bowman Platinum Prospects Gold Refractors Thin Stock

*GOLD REF: 1X TO 2.5X BASIC
STATED PRINT RUN 539 SER.#'d SETS

2010 Bowman Platinum Prospects Green Refractors

*GREEN REF: 1X TO 2.5X BASIC
STATED PRINT RUN 499 SER.#'d SETS

2010 Bowman Platinum Prospects Purple Refractors

*PURPLE REF: .6X TO 1.5X BASIC

2010 Bowman Platinum Prospects Red Refractors

STATED PRINT RUN 25 SER.#'d SETS
NO PRICING DUE TO SCARCITY

2010 Bowman Platinum Prospects Superfractors

STATED PRINT RUN 1 SER.#'d SET
NO PRICING DUE TO SCARCITY

2010 Bowman Platinum Relic Autographs Refractors

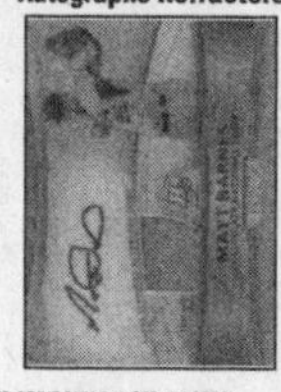

STATED PRINT RUN 740 SER.#'d SETS
STRASBURG PRINT RUN 240 SER.#'d SETS
AC Andrew Cashner 8.00 20.00
AD Alex Dickerson 5.00 12.00
AM Andrew Maggi 6.00 15.00
BC Brett Cecil 5.00 12.00
BJ Brian Johnson 5.00 12.00
BL Brad Lincoln 5.00 12.00
BM Brad Miller 5.00 12.00
CJ Chris Johnson EXCH 15.00 40.00
CP Carlos Pena 5.00 12.00
GC Gerrit Cole 30.00 60.00
GS George Springer 20.00 25.00
JD Jackie Bradley Jr. 10.00 25.00
JE Jason Esposito 10.00 25.00
JH Jason Heyward 60.00 120.00
JJ Josh Johnson 8.00 20.00
JT Jose Tabata 12.50 30.00
KW Kyle Winkler 5.00 12.00
MB Matt Barnes 8.00 20.00
MM Mikie Mahtook 10.00 25.00
NC Nelson Cruz 8.00 20.00
NF Nolan Fontana 5.00 12.00
NR Nick Ramirez 5.00 12.00
PF Prince Fielder 12.50 30.00
PO Peter O'Brien 8.00 20.00
PS Pablo Sandoval 10.00 25.00
RC Robinson Cano 15.00 40.00
RH Ryan Howard 20.00 50.00
RW Ryan Wright 5.00 12.00
SC Starlin Castro 30.00 60.00
SG Sean Gilmartin 5.00 12.00
SM Scott McGough 10.00 25.00
SR Steve Rodriguez 5.00 12.00
SS Stephen Strasburg/240 100.00 200.00
TA Tyler Anderson 5.00 12.00
AMC Andrew McCutchen 12.50 30.00
BMO Brett Mooneyham 6.00 15.00
JBA Jose Bautista 15.00 40.00
NRA Noe Ramirez 5.00 12.00
SGR Sonny Gray 8.00 20.00

2010 Bowman Platinum Relic Autographs Blue Refractors

*BLUE: .75X TO 2X BASIC
STATED PRINT RUN 50 SER.#'d SETS
GC Gerrit Cole 125.00 250.00

2010 Bowman Platinum Relic Autographs Green Refractors

*GREEN: .6X TO 1.5X BASIC
STATED PRINT RUN 199 SER.#'d SETS
GC Gerrit Cole 50.00 100.00

2010 Bowman Platinum Relic Autographs Red Refractors

STATED PRINT RUN 10 SER.#'d SETS
NO PRICING DUE TO SCARCITY

2010 Bowman Platinum Relic Autographs Superfractors

STATED PRINT RUN 1 SER.#'d SET
NO PRICING DUE TO SCARCITY

2010 Bowman Platinum Triple Autographs

STATED PRINT RUN 89 SER.#'d SETS
AJM Tyler Anderson
Brian Johnson
Brett Mooneyham
CBG Gerrit Cole 20.00 50.00
Matt Barnes
Sonny Gray
CVM David Wright 20.00 50.00
Josh Vitters
Michael Moustakas
MMF Andrew Maggi
Mikie Mahtook
Nolan Fontana
MOW Brad Miller
Peter O'Brien
Ryan Wright
REG Nick Ramirez 8.00 20.00
Jason Esposito
Sean Gilmartin
RWM Noe Ramirez
Kyle Winkler
Scott McGough
SBD George Springer
Jackie Bradley Jr.
Alex Dickerson
SPM Carlos Santana 75.00 150.00
Buster Posey
Jesus Montero
TRU Chris Tillman
Nolan Reimold
Koji Uehara

2011 Bowman Platinum

COMPLETE SET (100) 10.00 25.00
COMMON CARD (1-100) .12 .30
COMMON RC (1-100) .30 .75
1 Ryan Howard .40 1.00
2 Josh Rodriguez RC .30 .75
3 Adam Jones .20 .50
4 Jon Lester .30 .75
5 Brad Emaus RC .30 .75
6 Miguel Cabrera .30 .75
7 Hank Conger RC .50 1.25
8 Hanley Ramirez .30 .75
9 Derek Jeter .75 2.00
10 Austin Jackson .12 .30
11 Justin Upton .20 .50
12 Jimmy Rollins .20 .50
13 Carlos Santana .30 .75
14 Jeremy Hellickson RC 1.00 2.50
15 Roy Oswalt .20 .50
16 Carl Crawford .20 .50
17 Ryan Braun .40 1.00
18 Adam Dunn .20 .50
19 Carlos Gonzalez .20 .50
20 Pedro Alvarez RC .50 1.25
21 Mark Trumbo (RC) .50 1.25
22 Daniel Descalso RC .30 .75
23 Mike Stanton .20 .50
24 Andre Ethier .20 .50
25 Brandon Beachy RC .75 2.00
26 Robinson Cano .30 .75
27 Jake McGee (RC) .30 .75
28 Buster Posey .40 1.00
29 Brent Morel RC .30 .75
30 Felix Hernandez .30 .75
31 Adrian Gonzalez .20 .50
32 Jason Heyward .40 1.00
33 Madison Bumgarner .12 .30
34 Nick Markakis .30 .75
35 Chris Sale RC .50 1.25
36 Johan Santana .30 .75
37 Josh Johnson .20 .50
38 Manny Ramirez .30 .75
39 Brian McCann .20 .50
40 Clay Buchholz .20 .50
41 Gordon Beckham .20 .50
42 Ubaldo Jimenez .20 .50
43 Joey Votto .30 .75
44 Jeremy Jeffress RC .30 .75
45 Torii Hunter .12 .30
46 Kendry Morales .12 .30
47 Cory Luebke RC .30 .75
48 Mark Teixeira .30 .75
49 Joe Mauer .30 .75
50 Mat Latos .12 .30
51 Jose Bautista .20 .50
52 Brandon Belt RC 1.25 3.00
53 David Ortiz .20 .50
54 Matt Cain .20 .50
55 Michael Pineda RC 1.00 2.50
56 Jered Weaver .12 .30
57 Freddie Freeman RC 1.25 3.00
58 Clayton Kershaw .30 .75
59 Justin Morneau .30 .75
60 CC Sabathia .20 .50
61 Jayson Werth .20 .50
62 David Wright .40 1.00
63 Prince Fielder .20 .50
64 Hunter Pence .20 .50
65 Albert Pujols .75 2.00
66 Dustin Pedroia .40 1.00
67 Victor Martinez .20 .50
68 Stephen Strasburg .60 1.50
69 Jose Reyes .20 .50
70 Zack Greinke .20 .50
71 Dan Haren .12 .30
72 Tim Lincecum .30 .75
73 Ryan Zimmerman .20 .50
74 Starlin Castro .30 .75
75 Josh Hamilton .30 .75
76 Yonder Alonso RC .50 1.25
77 Dan Uggla .20 .50
78 Jonathan Sanchez .12 .30
79 Andrew McCutchen .30 .75
80 Billy Butler .12 .30
81 Carlos Pena .20 .50
82 Justin Verlander .40 1.00
83 Cole Hamels .30 .75
84 Ike Davis .20 .50
85 Jacoby Ellsbury .30 .75
86 Chipper Jones .30 .75
87 Cliff Lee .30 .75
88 Vernon Wells .12 .30
89 Shin-Soo Choo .20 .50
90 Alex Rodriguez .50 1.25
91 Troy Tulowitzki .30 .75
92 Kevin Youkilis .20 .50
93 Aroldis Chapman RC 1.00 2.50
94 Chase Utley .30 .75
95 Kyle Drabek RC .50 1.25
96 Matt Kemp .20 .50
97 Evan Longoria .40 1.00
98 Matt Holliday
99 Roy Halladay .30 .75
100 Ichiro Suzuki .50 1.25

2011 Bowman Platinum Emerald

*EMERALD: 2X TO 5X BASIC
*EMERALD RC: .75X TO 2X BASIC RC

2011 Bowman Platinum Gold

*GOLD: 1.5X TO 4X BASIC
*GOLD RC: .6X TO 1.5X BASIC RC

2011 Bowman Platinum Ruby

*RUBY: 3X TO 8X BASIC
*RUBY RC: 1.2X TO 3X BASIC RC

2011 Bowman Platinum Dual Autographs

STATED PRINT RUN 89 SER.#'d SETS
RED PRINT RUN 10 SER.#'d SETS
NO RED PRICING DUE TO SCARCITY
SUPERFRACTOR PRINT RUN 1 SER.#'d SET
NO SUPERFRACTOR PRICING AVAILABLE
EXCHANGE DEADLINE 7/31/2014
CM Lonnie Chisenhall 15.00 40.00
Mike Moustakas
DT Jaff Decker 10.00 25.00
Donavan Tate
GC Grant Green 15.00 40.00
Michael Choice
GL Dee Gordon 10.00 25.00
Leon Landry
HT Bryce Harper 175.00 350.00
Jameson Taillon
MC Manny Machado 20.00 50.00
Christian Colon
MM Mike Montgomery 15.00 40.00
Mike Moustakas
NW Hector Noesi 10.00 25.00
Adam Warren
SD Jake Skole 10.00 25.00
Kellin Deglan EXCH
SM Gary Sanchez 30.00 60.00
Jesus Montero

2011 Bowman Platinum Dual Autographs Red Refractors

STATED PRINT RUN 10 SER.#'d SETS
NO PRICING DUE TO SCARCITY
EXCHANGE DEADLINE 7/31/2014

2011 Bowman Platinum Dual Autographs Superfractors

STATED PRINT RUN 1 SER.#'d SET
NO PRICING DUE TO SCARCITY
EXCHANGE DEADLINE 7/31/2014

2011 Bowman Platinum Dual Relic Autographs

STATED PRINT RUN 89 SER.#'d SETS
RED PRINT RUN 10 SER.#'d SETS
NO RED PRICING DUE TO SCARCITY
SUPERFRACTOR PRINT RUN 1 SER.#'d SET
NO SUPERFRACTOR PRICING AVAILABLE
EXCHANGE DEADLINE 7/31/2014
CB Starlin Castro 12.50 30.00
Marlon Byrd
CP Joba Chamberlain 10.00 25.00
Ryan Perry
DP Ike Davis 12.50 30.00
Angel Pagan EXCH

GC Adrian Gonzalez 50.00 100.00
Carl Crawford
HK Dan Haren 10.00 25.00
Scott Kazmir
IV Raul Ibanez 15.00 40.00
Shane Victorino
JS Josh Johnson 30.00 60.00
Mike Stanton
JU Adam Jones 15.00 40.00
Justin Upton
JW Chris Johnson 10.00 25.00
Brett Wallace EXCH
KB Ian Kinsler 10.00 25.00
Gordon Beckham
SB Denard Span 15.00 40.00
Brennan Boesch
SM Pablo Sandoval 10.00 25.00
Casey McGehee

2011 Bowman Platinum Dual Relic Autographs Red Refractors
STATED PRINT RUN 10 SER.#'d SETS
NO PRICING DUE TO SCARCITY
EXCHANGE DEADLINE 7/31/2014

2011 Bowman Platinum Dual Relic Autographs Superfractors
STATED PRINT RUN 1 SER.#'d SET
NO PRICING DUE TO SCARCITY
EXCHANGE DEADLINE 7/31/2014

2011 Bowman Platinum Hexagraph Patches
STATED PRINT RUN 10 SER.#'d SETS
NO PRICING DUE TO SCARCITY

2011 Bowman Platinum Hexagraphs
STATED PRINT RUN 10 SER.#'d SETS
NO PRICING DUE TO SCARCITY

2011 Bowman Platinum Prospect Autograph Refractors
PLATE PRINT RUN 1 SET PER COLOR
BLACK-CYAN-MAGENTA-YELLOW ISSUED
NO PLATE PRICING DUE TO SCARCITY
EXCHANGE DEADLINE 7/31/2014
AF Anderson Feliz 3.00 8.00
AW Alex Wimmers 3.00 8.00
BE Brett Eibner 4.00 10.00
BG Brandon Guyer 3.00 8.00
BH Bryce Harper 75.00 150.00
CD Cutter Dykstra 3.00 8.00
CR Clint Robinson 3.00 8.00
CS Cody Scarpetta 3.00 8.00
DD Delino DeShields 4.00 10.00
DJ Dickie Joe Thon 3.00 8.00
DM Deck McGuire 3.00 8.00
DS Domingo Santana 5.00 12.00
GR Garrett Richards 3.00 8.00
HN Hector Noesi 5.00 12.00
HS Hayden Simpson 3.00 8.00
JB Joe Benson 3.00 8.00
JJ Jiwan James 4.00 10.00
JP Jimmy Paredes 3.00 8.00
JT Jameson Taillon 6.00 15.00
KP Kyle Parker 6.00 15.00
KS Kyle Seager 4.00 10.00
LL Leon Landry 3.00 8.00
MC Michael Choice 6.00 15.00
MD Miguel De Los Santos 3.00 8.00
MF Mike Foltynewicz 3.00 8.00
MH Matt Harvey EXCH 6.00 15.00
MM Manny Machado EXCH 10.00 25.00
RD Rashun Dixon 3.00 8.00
SH Shaeffer Hall 3.00 8.00
SM Shelby Miller 10.00 25.00
TS Tyler Skaggs 6.00 15.00
AWA Adam Warren 6.00 15.00
BHO Brad Holt 3.00 8.00
JPA Jordan Pacheco 4.00 10.00
JSE Jean Segura 3.00 8.00
JSW Jordan Swagerty 4.00 10.00
RDE Randall Delgado 6.00 15.00
NNO Mystery EXCH 10.00 25.00

2011 Bowman Platinum Prospect Autograph Blue Refractors
*BLUE: .75X TO 2X BASIC
STATED PRINT RUN 99 SER.#'d SETS
EXCHANGE DEADLINE 7/31/2014
BH Bryce Harper 300.00 500.00

2011 Bowman Platinum Prospect Autograph Gold Refractors
*GOLD : 1.2X TO 3X BASIC
STATED PRINT RUN 50 SER.#'d SETS
EXCHANGE DEADLINE 7/31/2014
BH Bryce Harper 600.00 1000.00
DM Deck McGuire 15.00 40.00

2011 Bowman Platinum Prospect Autograph Green Refractors
*GREEN : .5X TO 1.2X BASIC
STATED PRINT RUN 399 SER.#'d SETS
EXCHANGE DEADLINE 7/31/2014
BH Bryce Harper 125.00 250.00

2011 Bowman Platinum Prospect Autograph Red Refractors
STATED PRINT RUN 10 SER.#'d SETS
NO PRICING DUE TO SCARCITY
EXCHANGE DEADLINE 7/31/2014

2011 Bowman Platinum Prospect Autograph Superfractors
STATED PRINT RUN 1 SER.#'d SET
NO PRICING DUE TO SCARCITY
EXCHANGE DEADLINE 7/31/2014

2011 Bowman Platinum Prospects
COMPLETE SET (100) 40.00 80.00
PLATE PRINT RUN 1 SET PER COLOR
BLACK-CYAN-MAGENTA-YELLOW ISSUED
NO PLATE PRICING DUE TO SCARCITY
BPP1 Bryce Harper 4.00 10.00
BPP2 Dee Gordon 1.00 2.50
BPP3 Jesus Montero 1.50 4.00
BPP4 Daniel Fields .40 1.00
BPP5 Deck McGuire .40 1.00
BPP6 Zach Lee .60 1.50
BPP7 Travis D'Arnaud .40 1.00
BPP8 Anderson Feliz .40 1.00
BPP9 Blake Smith .40 1.00
BPP10 Jonathan Singleton .60 1.50
BPP11 Kyle Seager .60 1.50
BPP12 Avisail Garcia .60 1.50
BPP13 Miguel De Los Santos .40 1.00
BPP14 Ronnie Welty .40 1.00
BPP15 Ryan Lavarnway 1.00 2.50
BPP16 Yasmani Grandal .60 1.50
BPP17 Kolbrin Vitek .60 1.50
BPP18 Zack Cox .60 1.50
BPP19 Jimmy Paredes .40 1.00
BPP20 Joe Benson .40 1.00
BPP21 Austin Hyatt .60 1.50
BPP22 Corban Joseph .40 1.00
BPP23 Josh Zeid .40 1.00
BPP24 Oswaldo Arcia .40 1.00
BPP25 Jacob Turner 1.50 4.00
BPP26 Jose Iglesias .60 1.50
BPP27 Jarred Cosart .60 1.50
BPP28 Shaeffer Hall .60 1.50
BPP29 Manny Banuelos 1.25 3.00
BPP30 Tyler Skaggs 1.00 2.50
BPP31 Domingo Santana .40 1.00
BPP32 Dustin Ackley 1.50 4.00
BPP33 Dickie Joe Thon .60 1.50
BPP34 Jurickson Profar 1.25 3.00
BPP35 Tony Wolters .40 1.00
BPP36 Aderlin Rodriguez .40 1.00
BPP37 Cito Culver 1.50 4.00
BPP38 Billy Hamilton 1.00 2.50
BPP39 Yorman Rodriguez .60 1.50
BPP40 Matt Dominguez .60 1.50
BPP41 Delino DeShields .60 1.50
BPP42 Brandon Short .60 1.50
BPP43 Michael Choice .60 1.50
BPP44 Wilmer Flores .60 1.50
BPP45 Jake Marisnick 1.00 2.50
BPP46 Leon Landry .60 1.50
BPP47 Derek Norris .40 1.00
BPP48 Mike Foltynewicz .40 1.00
BPP49 Rashun Dixon .40 1.00
BPP50 Drew Pomeranz 1.00 2.50
BPP51 Alex Wimmers .40 1.00
BPP52 Cody Scarpetta .40 1.00
BPP53 Eduardo Escobar .40 1.00
BPP54 Jake Skole .40 1.00
BPP55 David Cooper .40 1.00
BPP56 Jarrod Parker 1.50 4.00
BPP57 Jacob Goebbert .60 1.50
BPP58 Carlos Perez .40 1.00
BPP59 Kevin Mailloux .40 1.00
BPP60 Drew Vettleson .40 1.00
BPP61 Hayden Simpson .40 1.00
BPP62 Hector Noesi .60 1.50
BPP63 Jonathan Schoop 1.00 2.50
BPP64 Nick Franklin .60 1.50
BPP65 Jameson Taillon 1.25 3.00
BPP66 Matt Harvey .60 1.50
BPP67 Keon Broxton .40 1.00
BPP68 Allen Webster .60 1.50
BPP69 Kyle Parker 1.00 2.50
BPP70 Brad Brach .40 1.00
BPP71 Johermyn Chavez .40 1.00
BPP72 Shelby Miller 1.00 2.50
BPP73 Julio Teheran 1.25 3.00
BPP74 Jordan Swagerty .60 1.50
BPP75 Sean Coyle 1.00 2.50
BPP76 Kyle Russell .60 1.50
BPP77 Cutter Dykstra .60 1.50
BPP78 Brad Holt .40 1.00
BPP79 Chun-Hsiu Chen 1.00 2.50
BPP80 Brandon Guyer .60 1.50
BPP81 Cesar Puello .60 1.50
BPP82 Garrett Richards .40 1.00
BPP83 Manny Machado 1.25 3.00
BPP84 Jared Mitchell .60 1.50
BPP85 Brody Colvin .40 1.00
BPP86 Tim Beckham .40 1.00
BPP87 Adron Chambers .40 1.00
BPP88 Marcell Ozuna .60 1.50
BPP89 Sammy Solis .40 1.00
BPP90 Gary Brown 1.00 2.50
BPP91 Kaleb Cowart .60 1.50
BPP92 Trey McNutt .40 1.00
BPP93 Jordan Pacheco .40 1.00
BPP94 Adam Warren .60 1.50
BPP95 Matt Lipka .60 1.50
BPP96 Christian Colon .40 1.00
BPP97 Carlos Perez .40 1.00
BPP98 Matt Moore 2.00 5.00
BPP99 Chris Archer .40 1.00
BPP100 Jeff Decker .40 1.00

2011 Bowman Platinum Prospects Refractors
*REF: .5X TO 1.2X BASIC
BPP1 Bryce Harper 6.00 15.00

2011 Bowman Platinum Prospects Blue Refractors
*BLUE: 1.2X TO 3X BASIC
STATED PRINT RUN 199 SER.#'d SETS
BPP1 Bryce Harper 40.00 80.00

2011 Bowman Platinum Prospects Gold Refractors
*GOLD: 3X TO 8X BASIC
STATED PRINT RUN 50 SER.#'d SETS
BPP1 Bryce Harper 100.00 200.00

2011 Bowman Platinum Prospects Green Refractors
*GREEN: .75X TO 2X BASIC
STATED PRINT RUN 599 SER.#'d SETS
BPP1 Bryce Harper 15.00 40.00

2011 Bowman Platinum Prospects Purple Refractors
*PURPLE: .6X TO 1.5X BASIC
BPP1 Bryce Harper 8.00 20.00

2011 Bowman Platinum Prospects Red Refractors
STATED PRINT RUN 25 SER.#'d SETS
NO PRICING DUE TO SCARCITY

2011 Bowman Platinum Prospects Superfractors
STATED PRINT RUN 1 SER.#'d SET
NO PRICING DUE TO SCARCITY

2011 Bowman Platinum Prospects X-Fractors
*X-FRACTOR: .6X TO 1.5X BASIC
BPP1 Bryce Harper 15.00 40.00

2011 Bowman Platinum Relic Autograph Refractors
PRINT RUN B/WN 115-1166 COPIES PER
COMPLETE SET (35)
AJ Austin Jackson/115 10.00 25.00
AR Adam Rosales/1166 4.00 10.00
BC Brett Cecil EXCH 4.00 10.00
CB Clay Buchholz
CC Carl Crawford
CG Carlos Gonzalez
CM Cristhian Martinez/1166 4.00 10.00
EB Emilio Bonifacio/1166 4.00 10.00
EE Edwin Encarnacion/1166 4.00 10.00
EL Evan Longoria
EM Evan Meek/1166 4.00 10.00
FF Freddie Freeman/115 40.00 80.00
FM Franklin Morales/1166 4.00 10.00
JA J.P. Arencibia/666 6.00 15.00
JC Jesse Crain/1166 4.00 10.00
JF Juan Francisco/1166 4.00 10.00
JH Josh Hamilton
JM Jake McGee/1166 4.00 10.00
JM Jhan Marinez/1166 4.00 10.00
JM John McDonald/1166 4.00 10.00
JM Juan Miranda/1166 4.00 10.00
LN Leo Nunez/1166 4.00 10.00
MR Max Ramirez/1166 4.00 10.00
MS Mike Stanton
NM Nick Markakis
OM Ozzie Martinez/1166 4.00 10.00
PH Phil Hughes
RT Robinson Tejeda/1166 4.00 10.00
SC Starlin Castro/666 12.50 30.00
TB Trevor Bell EXCH 4.00 10.00
VW Vance Worley
YN Yamaico Navarro/1166 4.00 10.00
ZG Zack Greinke
JHE Jason Heyward
JHL Jeremy Hellickson/1166 10.00 25.00

2011 Bowman Platinum Relic Autograph Blue Refractors
*BLUE: .6X TO 1.5X BASIC pr/666-1166
*BLUE: .4X TO 1X BASIC pr/115
STATED PRINT RUN 99 SER.#'d SETS
EXCHANGE DEADLINE 7/31/2014

2011 Bowman Platinum Relic Autograph Gold Refractors
STATED PRINT RUN 25 SER.#'d SETS
NO PRICING DUE TO SCARCITY
EXCHANGE DEADLINE 7/31/2014

2011 Bowman Platinum Relic Autograph Green Refractors
*GREEN: .5X TO 1.2X BASIC
STATED PRINT RUN 199 SER.#'d SETS
EXCHANGE DEADLINE 7/31/2014

2011 Bowman Platinum Relic Autograph Red Refractors
STATED PRINT RUN 10 SER.#'d SETS
NO PRICING DUE TO SCARCITY
EXCHANGE DEADLINE 7/31/2014

2011 Bowman Platinum Relic Autograph Superfractors
STATED PRINT RUN 1 SER.#'d SET
NO PRICING DUE TO SCARCITY
EXCHANGE DEADLINE 7/31/2014

2011 Bowman Platinum Team USA National Team Autographs
EXCHANGE DEADLINE 12/31/2012
NNO Mystery EXCH 10.00 25.00

2011 Bowman Platinum Triple Autographs Red Refractors
STATED PRINT RUN 10 SER.#'d SETS
NO PRICING DUE TO SCARCITY
EXCHANGE DEADLINE 7/31/2014

2011 Bowman Platinum Triple Autographs Superfractors
STATED PRINT RUN 1 SER.#'d SET
NO PRICING DUE TO SCARCITY
EXCHANGE DEADLINE 7/31/2014

2011 Bowman Platinum Triple Autographs
STATED PRINT RUN 89 SER.#'d SETS
RED PRINT RUN 10 SER.#'d SETS
NO RED PRICING DUE TO SCARCITY
SUPERFRACTOR PRINT RUN 1 SER.#'d SET
NO SUPERFRACTOR PRICING AVAILABLE
EXCHANGE DEADLINE 7/31/2014
CWJ Jason Castro 12.50 30.00
Brett Wallace
Chris Johnson EXCH
FHD Freddie Freeman 30.00 60.00
Ryan Howard
Ike Davis
HKW Dan Haren 12.50 30.00
Scott Kazmir
Jordan Walden
HSB Jason Heyward 75.00 150.00
Mike Stanton
Domonic Brown EXCH
MAC Jesus Montero 50.00 100.00
Dustin Ackley
Lonnie Chisenhall EXCH
PMM Buster Posey 75.00 150.00
Joe Mauer
Jesus Montero EXCH
SPG Geovany Soto 40.00 80.00
Carlos Pena
Matt Garza

2004 Bowman Sterling
This 138-card set was released in December, 2004. The set was issued in five-card packs with a $50 SRP and they came six packs to a box and four boxes to a case. Just about every basic card is a "hit" as the cards are either memorabilia cards of veterans, or rookie cards with the possibility of them being either autographed or with a jersey swatch on it. Despite the high price point for the packs, this product did extremely well in the secondary market.

COMMON FY .75 2.00
FY ODDS APPX.TWO PER HOBBY PACK

COMMON FY AU 3.00 8.00
FY AU ODDS APPX.ONE PER HOBBY PACK
COMMON AU-GU 4.00 10.00
AU-GU ODDS APPX.ONE PER HOBBY PACK
AU-GU 1:2 WRAPPER ODDS IS AN ERROR
COMMON AU-GU RC 4.00 10.00
COMMON GU 2.00 5.00
GU ODDS APPX. 1:5 PER HOBBY PACK
GU 1:2 WRAPPER ODDS IS AN ERROR
AB Angel Berroa Bat 2.00 5.00
ABA Aaron Baldiris FY RC .40 1.00
AC Alberto Callaspo FY AU RC 8.00 20.00
AD Adam Dunn Bat 2.00 5.00
AER Alex Rodriguez Bat 6.00 15.00
AJ Andruw Jones Jsy 3.00 8.00
AK Austin Kearns Jsy 2.00 5.00
ANR Aramis Ramirez Bat 2.00 5.00
AP Albert Pujols Jsy 8.00 20.00
AR Alex Romero FY AU RC 3.00 8.00
AW Adam Wainwright AU Jsy 8.00 20.00
AWH A.Whittington FY RC .40 1.00
AZ Alec Zumwalt FY AU RC 3.00 8.00
BB Brian Bixler AU Jsy RC 4.00 10.00
BBR Bill Bray FY RC .40 1.00
BBU Billy Buckner FY RC .40 1.00
BC2 Bobby Crosby Jsy 2.00 5.00
BD Blake DeWitt AU Jsy RC 6.00 15.00
BE Brad Eldred FY RC .40 1.00
BH B.Hawksworth FY AU RC 4.00 10.00
BT Brad Thompson FY RC .60 1.50
BU B.J. Upton AU Bat 8.00 20.00
BW Bernie Williams Jsy 3.00 8.00
CA Chris Aguila FY AU RC 3.00 8.00
CB Craig Biggio Jsy 3.00 8.00
CC Chad Cordero AU Jsy 6.00 15.00
CG Christian Garcia AU Jsy RC 6.00 15.00
CH Chin-Lung Hu FY RC .40 1.00
CIB Carlos Beltran Bat 2.00 5.00
CJ Conor Jackson FY RC 2.50 6.00
CL Chris Lubanski AU Bat 4.00 10.00
CLA Chris Lambert FY RC .40 1.00
CN Chris Nelson FY RC .40 1.00
CQ Carlos Quentin FY AU RC 8.00 20.00
CT Curtis Thigpen FY RC .40 1.00
DD David DeJesus AU Jsy 6.00 15.00
DP Danny Putnam AU Jsy RC 4.00 10.00
DPU David Purcey FY RC .60 1.50
DW David Wright AU Jsy 30.00 50.00
DWW Dontrelle Willis Jsy 3.00 8.00
DY Delmon Young AU Bat 5.00 12.00
EG Eric Gagne Jsy 2.00 5.00
EH Eric Hurley FY RC .40 1.00
ESP Erick San Pedro FY RC .40 1.00
FC Fausto Carmona FY RC .40 1.00
FG Freddy Guzman FY RC .60 1.50
FH Felix Hernandez FY RC 8.00 20.00
FP Felix Pie AU Jsy 10.00 25.00
FT Frank Thomas Bat 3.00 8.00
GG Greg Golson FY RC .40 1.00
GH Gaby Hernandez FY RC 1.00 2.50
GIG Gio Gonzalez FY RC 1.00 2.50
GS Gary Sheffield Bat 2.00 5.00
HB Homer Bailey AU Jsy RC 4.00 10.00
HC Hee Seop Choi Bat 2.00 5.00
HG Hector Gimenez FY AU RC 3.00 8.00
HJB Hank Blalock Bat 2.00 5.00
HM Hector Made FY RC .40 1.00
HS Huston Street AU Jsy RC 10.00 25.00
IR Ivan Rodriguez Bat 3.00 8.00
JB Jeff Bagwell Jsy 3.00 8.00
JC Jose Capellan FY RC .40 1.00
JCR Jesse Crain FY RC .40 1.00
JD Johnny Damon Bat 3.00 8.00
JE Johnny Estrada Bat 2.00 5.00
JFI Josh Fields FY RC .60 1.50
JG Joey Gathright FY RC .40 1.00
JH Jesse Hoover FY RC .40 1.00
JK Jason Kendall Bat 2.00 5.00
JM Jeff Marquez AU Jsy RC 6.00 15.00
JO Justin Orenduff FY RC .60 1.50
JP Juan Pierre Bat 2.00 5.00
JPH J.P. Howell FY RC .40 1.00
JR Jay Rainville FY AU RC 5.00 12.00
JS Jeremy Sowers FY AU RC 15.00 30.00
JZ Jon Zeringue FY RC .40 1.00
KCH K.C. Herren FY RC .40 1.00
KS Kurt Suzuki FY RC 1.25 3.00
KT Kazuhito Tadano FY RC .40 1.00
KW Kerry Wood Jsy 2.00 5.00
KWA Kyle Waldrop AU Jsy RC 6.00 15.00
LB Lance Berkman Jsy 2.00 5.00
LC Luis Castillo Jsy 2.00 5.00
LH Linc Holdzkom FY AU RC 3.00 8.00
LN Laynce Nix Bat 2.00 5.00
MA Moises Alou Bat 2.00 5.00
MAM Mark Mulder Jsy 2.00 5.00
MAR Manny Ramirez Bat 3.00 8.00
MB Matt Bush AU Jsy RC 10.00 25.00
MC Miguel Cabrera Bat 3.00 8.00
MCT Mark Teixeira Bat 3.00 8.00
ME Mitch Einertson FY RC .40 1.00
MF Mike Ferris FY RC .40 1.00
MFO Matt Fox FY RC .40 1.00
MJP Mike Piazza Bat 3.00 8.00
MM Matt Moses FY AU RC 6.00 15.00
MMC Matt Macri FY RC .60 1.50
MP Mark Prior Jsy 3.00 8.00
MR Mike Rouse FY AU RC 3.00 8.00
MRO Mark Rogers FY RC .60 1.50
MT M.Tuiasosopo AU Bat RC 12.50 30.00
MT1 Miguel Tejada Bat 2.00 5.00
MT2 Miguel Tejada Jsy 2.00 5.00
MW Marland Williams FY RC .40 1.00
MY Michael Young Bat 2.00 5.00
NJ Nick Johnson Bat 2.00 5.00
NM Nyjer Morgan FY RC .40 1.00
NS Nate Schierholtz FY RC .40 1.00
NW Neil Walker FY RC 2.00 5.00
OQ Omar Quintanilla FY RC .40 1.00
PGM Paul Maholm FY RC .60 1.50
PH Philip Hughes FY RC 3.00 8.00
PL Paul LoDuca Bat 2.00 5.00
PR Pokey Reese Bat 2.00 5.00
RB Rocco Baldelli Bat 2.00 5.00
RBR Reid Brignac FY RC 1.00 2.50
RC Robinson Cano AU Jsy 30.00 60.00
RH Ryan Harvey AU Bat 6.00 15.00
RJH Richard Hidalgo Bat 2.00 5.00
RM Ryan Meaux FY AU RC 3.00 8.00
RO Russ Ortiz Jsy 2.00 5.00
RP Rafael Palmeiro Bat 3.00 8.00
SK Scott Kazmir AU Jsy RC 6.00 15.00
SO Scott Olsen AU Jsy RC 15.00 30.00
SS Sammy Sosa Jsy 3.00 8.00
SSM Seth Smith FY RC 1.00 2.50
TD Thomas Diamond FY RC .40 1.00
TG Troy Glaus Bat 2.00 5.00
TLH Todd Helton Bat 3.00 8.00
TM Tino Martinez Bat 3.00 8.00
TMG Tom Glavine Jsy 3.00 8.00
TP Trevor Plouffe AU Jsy RC 6.00 15.00
TT T.Tankersley AU Jsy RC 4.00 10.00
VG Vladimir Guerrero Bat 3.00 8.00
VP Vince Perkins FY AU RC 4.00 10.00
YP Yusmeiro Petit FY RC .60 1.50
ZD Zach Duke FY RC .60 1.50
ZJ Zach Jackson FY RC .40 1.00

2004 Bowman Sterling Refractors

*REF.FY: 1.25X TO 3X BASIC
FY ODDS 1:4 HOBBY
*REF.FY AU: 1X TO 2.5X BASIC FY AU
FY AU ODDS 1:8 HOBBY
*REF.AU-GU: .6X TO 1.5X BASIC AU-GU
AU-GU ODDS 1:9 HOBBY
*REF.GU: .6X TO 1.5X BASIC GU
GU ODDS 1:5 HOBBY
STATED PRINT RUN 199 SERIAL #'d SETS
BD Blake DeWitt AU Jsy 8.00 20.00
CQ Carlos Quentin FY AU 25.00 60.00
DW David Wright AU Jsy 30.00 60.00
FP Felix Pie AU Jsy 12.50 30.00
JS Jeremy Sowers FY AU 30.00 60.00
MB Matt Bush AU Jsy 20.00 50.00
SK Scott Kazmir AU Jsy 20.00 50.00

2004 Bowman Sterling Black Refractors

FY ODDS 1:28 HOBBY
FY PRINT RUN 16 SERIAL #'d SETS
FY AU ODDS 1:64 HOBBY
FY AU PRINT RUN 25 SERIAL #'d SETS
AU-GU ODDS 1:37 HOBBY
AU-GU PRINT RUN 25 SERIAL #'d SETS
GU ODDS 1:28 HOBBY
GU PRINT RUN 16 SERIAL #'d SETS
ISSUED IN HOBBY BOX LOADER PACKS
NO PRICING DUE TO SCARCITY

2004 Bowman Sterling Red Refractors

FY ODDS 1:449 HOBBY
FY AU ODDS 1:1507 HOBBY
AU-GU ODDS 1:917 HOBBY
GU ODDS 1:449 HOBBY
STATED PRINT RUN 1 SERIAL #'d SET
NO PRICING DUE TO SCARCITY
ISSUED IN HOBBY BOX LOADER PACKS

2004 Bowman Sterling Original Autographs

GROUP A ODDS 1:221 HOBBY
GROUP B ODDS 1:25 HOBBY
GROUP A = A.ROD/BONDS
GROUP B = CHAVEZ/REYES/SORIANO
PRINT RUNS B/WN 1-106 COPIES PER
NO PRICING ON QTY OF 25 OR LESS
ISSUED IN HOBBY BOX LOADER PACKS
AR1 Alex Rodriguez 98B
AR2 Alex Rodriguez 99B/8
AR3 Alex Rodriguez 99BC
AR4 Alex Rodriguez 00B/16
AR5 Alex Rodriguez 00BC/6
AR6 Alex Rodriguez 01B
AR7 Alex Rodriguez 01BC/7
AR8 Alex Rodriguez 02B/3
AR9 Alex Rodriguez 02BC
AR10 Alex Rodriguez 03B/19
AR11 Alex Rodriguez 03BC/28 60.00 120.00
AS1 Alfonso Soriano 99B
AS2 Alfonso Soriano 99BC/1
AS3 Alfonso Soriano 00B
AS4 Alfonso Soriano 00BC/8
AS5 Alfonso Soriano 01B/7
AS6 Alfonso Soriano 01BC/13
AS7 Alfonso Soriano 02B/54 8.00 20.00
AS8 Alfonso Soriano 02BC/33 10.00 25.00
AS9 Alfonso Soriano 03B/102 8.00 20.00
AS10 Alfonso Soriano 03BC/49 8.00 20.00
AS11 Alfonso Soriano 04B/26 10.00 25.00
AS12 Alfonso Soriano 04BC
BB1 Barry Bonds 98BC/6
BB2 Barry Bonds 01BC/3
BB3 Barry Bonds 03BC/1
EC1 Eric Chavez 97B/8
EC2 Eric Chavez 98B/14
EC3 Eric Chavez 98BC/10
EC4 Eric Chavez 99B
EC5 Eric Chavez 99BC
EC6 Eric Chavez 00B/10
EC7 Eric Chavez 00BC/9
EC8 Eric Chavez 01B
EC9 Eric Chavez 01BC/16
EC10 Eric Chavez 02B/68 10.00 25.00
EC11 Eric Chavez 02BC/21 12.50 30.00
EC12 Eric Chavez 03B/106 10.00 25.00
EC13 Eric Chavez 03BC/22 12.50 30.00
JR1 Jose Reyes 02B/52 10.00 25.00
JR2 Jose Reyes 02BD/22 20.00 50.00
JR3 Jose Reyes 02BD/34 20.00 50.00
JR4 Jose Reyes 03BD/31 20.00 50.00
JR5 Jose Reyes 03BCD/41 10.00 25.00
JR6 Jose Reyes 03BD/92 10.00 25.00
JR7 Jose Reyes 03BCD

2005 Bowman Sterling
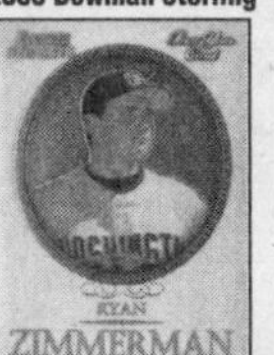

COMMON CARD .60 1.50
BASIC CARDS APPX.TWO PER HOBBY PACK
BASIC CARDS APPX.TWO PER RETAIL PACK
AU GROUP A ODDS 1:2 HOBBY
AU GROUP B ODDS 1:3 HOBBY
AU-GU GROUP A ODDS 1:2 H, 1:2 R
AU-GU GROUP B ODDS 1:37 H, 1:37 R
AU-GU GROUP C ODDS 1:11 H, 1:11 R
AU-GU GROUP D ODDS 1:10 H, 1:10 R
AU-GU GROUP E ODDS 1:27 H, 1:27 R
AU-GU GROUP F ODDS 1:13 H, 1:13 R
GU GROUP A ODDS 1:3 H, 1:3 R
GU GROUP B ODDS 1:5 H, 1:5 R
GU GROUP C ODDS 1:6 H, 1:6 R
ACL Andy LaRoche RC 3.00 8.00
AL Adam Lind AU Bat B 10.00 25.00
AM A.McCutchen AU Jsy D RC 30.00 60.00
AP Albert Pujols Jsy B 6.00 15.00
AR Alex Rodriguez Jsy UER 6.00 15.00
Card states Game-Used Bat
ARA Aramis Ramirez Bat A 2.00 5.00
AS Alfonso Soriano Bat A 2.00 5.00
AT Aaron Thompson AU A RC 4.00 10.00
BA Brian Anderson RC 1.00 2.50
BB Billy Buckner AU Jsy A 4.00 10.00
BBU Billy Butler RC 3.00 8.00
BC Brent Cox AU Jsy D RC 6.00 15.00
BCR Brad Corley RC .60 1.50
BE Brad Eldred AU Jsy C 4.00 10.00
BH Brett Hayes RC .60 1.50
BJ Beau Jones AU Jsy A RC 8.00 20.00
BL B.Livingston AU Jsy A RC 4.00 10.00
BLB Barry Bonds Jsy C 6.00 15.00
BM B.McCarthy AU Jsy A RC 10.00 25.00
BMU Bill Mueller Jsy C 2.00 5.00
BRB Brian Bogusevic RC .60 1.50
BS Brandon Sing AU A RC 4.00 10.00
BSN Brandon Snyder RC 1.50 4.00
BZ Barry Zito Uni A 2.00 5.00
CB Carlos Beltran Bat A 2.00 5.00
CBU Clay Buchholz RC 3.00 8.00
CC Cesar Carrillo RC 1.00 2.50
CD Carlos Delgado Jsy A 2.00 5.00
CH C.J. Henry AU B RC 5.00 12.00
CHE Chase Headley RC 2.50 6.00
CI Craig Italiano RC .60 1.50
CJ Chuck James RC 1.50 4.00
CLT Chuck Tiffany RC 1.50 4.00
CN Chris Nelson AU Jsy A 4.00 10.00
CP Cliff Pennington AU B RC 4.00 10.00
CPP C.Pignatiello AU Jsy A RC 4.00 10.00
CR Colby Rasmus AU Jsy A RC 20.00 50.00
CRA Cesar Ramos RC .60 1.50
CRO Chaz Roe AU Jsy A RC 6.00 15.00
CS C.J. Smith AU Jsy A RC 4.00 10.00
CSU Curt Schilling Jsy C 3.00 8.00
CT Curtis Thigpen AU Jsy A 4.00 10.00
CV Chris Volstad AU B RC 4.00 10.00
DC Dan Carte RC .60 1.50
DL Derrek Lee Bat A 3.00 8.00
DO David Ortiz Bat A 3.00 8.00
DP Dustin Pedroia AU Jsy A 40.00 80.00
DT Drew Thompson RC .60 1.50
DW Dontrelle Willis Jsy C 2.00 5.00
EC Eric Chavez Uni B 2.00 5.00
EI Eli Iorg AU Jsy C RC 6.00 15.00
EM Eddy Martinez AU A RC 4.00 10.00
GK George Kottaras AU A RC 4.00 10.00
GM Greg Maddux Jsy C 4.00 10.00
GO Garrett Olson AU A RC 6.00 15.00
GS Gary Sheffield Bat A 2.00 5.00
HAS Henry Sanchez RC 1.00 2.50
HB Hank Blalock Bat A 2.00 5.00
HI Hernan Iribarren RC .60 1.50
HM Hideki Matsui AS Jsy C 6.00 15.00
HS Hum Sanchez AU A RC 8.00 20.00
IR Ivan Rodriguez Bat A 3.00 8.00
JB Jay Bruce AU Jsy D RC 20.00 50.00
JBE Josh Beckett Uni A 2.00 5.00
JC Jeff Clement RC 2.00 5.00
JCN John Nelson AU Uni A RC 4.00 10.00
JD Johnny Damon Bat A 3.00 8.00
JDR John Drennen RC .60 1.50
JE J.Ellsbury AU Jsy E RC 40.00 80.00
JEG Jon Egan RC .60 1.50
JF Josh Fields AU Jsy A 5.00 12.00
JG Josh Geer AU Jsy A RC 4.00 10.00
JGI Josh Gibson Seat C 6.00 15.00
JL Jed Lowrie AU Jsy F RC 15.00 40.00
JLY Jeff Lyman RC .60 1.50
JM John Mayberry Jr. AU A RC 6.00 15.00
JMA Jacob Marceaux RC .60 1.50
JN Jeff Niemann AU Jsy A RC 6.00 15.00
JO Justin Olson AU Jsy A RC 4.00 10.00
JP Jorge Posada Bat A 3.00 8.00
JPE Jim Edmonds Jsy B 2.00 5.00
JS John Smoltz Jsy A 3.00 8.00
JV J.Verlander AU Jsy A RC 50.00 100.00
JW Josh Wall RC 1.00 2.50
JWE Jered Weaver RC 2.50 6.00
KG Khalil Greene Jsy B 3.00 8.00
KM Kevin Millar Bat A 2.00 5.00
KS Kevin Slowey RC 3.00 8.00
KW Kevin Whelan RC .60 1.50
LWJ Chipper Jones Bat A 3.00 8.00
MA Matt Albers AU A RC 4.00 10.00
MAM Matt Maloney RC .60 1.50
MB M.Bowden AU Jsy A RC 4.00 10.00
MC Mike Conroy AU Jsy A RC 4.00 10.00
MCA Miguel Cabrera Jsy A 3.00 8.00
MCO Mike Costanzo RC .60 1.50
MG Matt Green AU A RC 3.00 8.00
MGA Matt Garza RC 1.00 2.50
MGI Marcus Giles AS Jsy B 2.00 5.00
MM Mark Mulder Uni B 2.00 5.00
MMC Mark McCormick RC .60 1.50
MP Mike Piazza Bat A 3.00 8.00
MPR Mark Prior Jsy B 3.00 8.00
MR Manny Ramirez Bat A 3.00 8.00
MT Miguel Tejada Uni A 2.00 5.00
MTE Mark Teixeira Bat A 3.00 8.00
MTO Matt Torra RC .60 1.50
MY Michael Young Bat A 2.00 5.00
NH Nick Hundley RC .60 1.50
NR Nolan Reimold RC 2.50 6.00
NW Nick Webber RC .60 1.50
PH Philip Humber AU Jsy A RC 10.00 25.00
PK Paul Kelly RC .60 1.50
PL Paul Lo Duca Bat A 2.00 5.00
PM Pedro Martinez Jsy A 3.00 8.00
PP P.J. Phillips RC .60 1.50
RB Ryan Braun AU Jsy A RC 20.00 50.00
RBE Ronnie Belliard Bat A 2.00 5.00
RF Rafael Furcal Jsy A 2.00 5.00
RM Russ Martin AU Jsy F RC 10.00 25.00
RMO Ryan Mount RC .60 1.50
RR Ricky Romero RC 1.00 2.50
RT Raul Tablado AU Jsy A RC 4.00 10.00
RZ Ryan Zimmerman RC 5.00 12.00
SD Stephen Drew RC 3.00 8.00
SE Scott Elbert AU Jsy A 4.00 10.00
SM Steve Marek AU Jsy A RC 4.00 10.00
SR Scott Rolen Jsy B 3.00 8.00
SS Sammy Sosa Bat A 3.00 8.00
SW Steven White AU B RC 3.00 8.00
TB Trevor Bell AU Jsy C RC 6.00 15.00
TBU Travis Buck RC .60 1.50
TC Travis Chick AU A RC 3.00 8.00
TG Tyler Greene RC .60 1.50
TH Torii Hunter Bat A 2.00 5.00
THE Tyler Herron RC .60 1.50
THU Tim Hudson Uni A 2.00 5.00
TI Tadahito Iguchi RC 1.00 2.50
TLH Todd Helton Jsy B 3.00 8.00
TM Tyler Minges AU Jsy A RC 4.00 10.00
TM Tino Martinez Bat A 3.00 8.00
TN Trot Nixon Bat A 3.00 8.00
TT Troy Tulowitzki RC 8.00 20.00
TW Travis Wood RC 1.50 4.00
VG Vladimir Guerrero Bat A 3.00 8.00
VM Victor Martinez Bat A 2.00 5.00
WT Wade Townsend RC .60 1.50
YE Yunel Escobar RC 2.50 6.00
ZS Zach Simons RC .60 1.50

2005 Bowman Sterling Refractors
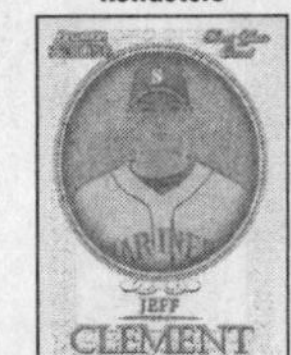

*REF: 1.25X TO 3X BASIC
BASIC ODDS 1:6 H, 1:6 R
*REF AU: 1X TO 2.5X BASIC AU
AU ODDS 1:13 HOBBY
*REF AU-GU: .6X TO 1.5X BASIC AU-GU
AU-GU ODDS 1:9 H, 1:9 R
*REF GU: .6X TO 1.5X BASIC GU
GU ODDS 1:6 H, 1: R
STATED PRINT RUN 199 SERIAL #'d SETS
AL Adam Lind AU Bat 20.00 50.00
AM A.McCutchen AU Jsy 40.00 80.00
BE Brad Eldred AU Jsy 12.50 30.00
CH C.J. Henry AU 15.00 40.00
CR Colby Rasmus AU Jsy 75.00 150.00
CV Chris Volstad AU 10.00 25.00
JB Jay Bruce AU Jsy 100.00 200.00
JL Jed Lowrie AU Jsy 40.00 80.00
MB Michael Bowden AU Jsy 5.00 12.00
RB Ryan Braun AU 125.00 250.00
RM Russ Martin AU Jsy 12.50 30.00

2005 Bowman Sterling Black Refractors

BASIC ODDS 1:5 BOX-LOADER
NO BASIC PRICING DUE TO SCARCITY
AU ODDS 1:17 BOX-LOADER
NO AU PRICING DUE TO SCARCITY
AU-GU ODDS 1:8 BOX-LOADER
NO AU-GU PRICING DUE TO SCARCITY
*BLACK GU: 2X TO 5X BASIC GU
GU ODDS 1:5 BOX-LOADER
ONE BOX-LOADER PACK PER HOBBY BOX
STATED PRINT RUN 25 SERIAL #'d SETS
BLB Barry Bonds Jsy 60.00 120.00

2005 Bowman Sterling Red Refractors

BASIC ODDS 1:128 BOX-LOADER
AU ODDS 1:428 BOX-LOADER
AU-GU ODDS 1:182 BOX-LOADER
GU ODDS 1:128 BOX-LOADER
ONE BOX-LOADER PACK PER HOBBY BOX
STATED PRINT RUN 1 SERIAL #'d SET
NO PRICING DUE TO SCARCITY

2005 Bowman Sterling MLB Logo Patch Autograph

STATED ODDS 1:665 BOX-LOADER
ONE BOX-LOADER PACK PER HOBBY BOX
STATED PRINT RUN 1 SERIAL #'d SET
NO PRICING DUE TO SCARCITY

2005 Bowman Sterling Original Autographs

GROUP A ODDS 1:665 BOX-LOADER
GROUP B ODDS 1:250 BOX-LOADER
GROUP C ODDS 1:63 BOX-LOADER
GROUP D ODDS 1:50 BOX-LOADER
GROUP E ODDS 1:42 BOX-LOADER
GROUP F ODDS 1:28 BOX-LOADER
GROUP G ODDS 1:25 BOX-LOADER
GROUP H ODDS 1:21 BOX-LOADER
GROUP I ODDS 1:6 BOX-LOADER
ONE BOX-LOADER PACK PER HOBBY BOX
PRINT RUNS B/WN 1-160 COPIES PER
NO PRICING ON QTY OF 13 OR LESS
AJ1 Andruw Jones 98 B/18 20.00 50.00
AJ2 Andruw Jones 99 B/18 20.00 50.00
AJ3 Andruw Jones 99 BC/4
AJ4 Andruw Jones 00 BC/8
AJ5 Andruw Jones 01 BC/5
AJ6 Andruw Jones 02 B/122 10.00 25.00
AJ7 Andruw Jones 02 BC/13
AJ8 Andruw Jones 03 B/112 10.00 25.00
AJ9 Andruw Jones 03 BC/18 20.00 50.00
AJ10 Andruw Jones 04 B/71 10.00 25.00
AP1 Albert Pujols 03 B/7
AP2 Albert Pujols 03 BC/11
AP3 Albert Pujols 04 B/7
AP4 Albert Pujols 04 BC/1
BB1 Barry Bonds 97 BC Int/1
BB2 Barry Bonds 99 BC/2
DL1 Derrek Lee 95 B/27 10.00 25.00
DL2 Derrek Lee 96 B/29 10.00 25.00
DL3 Derrek Lee 96 BB/15 12.50 30.00
DL4 Derrek Lee 97 BC/16 12.50 30.00
DL5 Derrek Lee 98 B/22 10.00 25.00
DL6 Derrek Lee 04 B/92 6.00 15.00
DL7 Derrek Lee 04 BC/26
DW1 David Wright 04 BD/98 30.00 60.00
DW2 David Wright 04 BCD/15
DW3 David Wright 05 B/139 30.00 60.00
GA1 Garret Anderson 96 B/3
GA2 Garret Anderson 99 B/8
GA3 Garret Anderson 03 B/33 6.00 15.00
GA4 Garret Anderson 04 B/33 6.00 15.00
GA5 Garret Anderson 04 BC/36 6.00 15.00
GA6 Garret Anderson 05 B/48 5.00 12.00
JR1 Jeremy Reed 04 BD/82 4.00 10.00
JR2 Jeremy Reed 04 BCD/48 5.00 12.00
MC1 M.Cabrera 02 B/7
MC2 M.Cabrera 02 BD/26 20.00 50.00
MC3 M.Cabrera 02 BCD/2
MC4 M.Cabrera 03 BD/27 20.00 50.00
MC5 M.Cabrera 03 BCD/25 20.00 50.00
MC6 M.Cabrera 04 B/127 12.50 30.00
MC7 M.Cabrera 04 BC/25 20.00 50.00
MC8 M.Cabrera 05 B/154 12.50 30.00
MC9 M.Cabrera 05 BC/25 20.00 50.00
MK1 Mark Kotsay 97 B/18 20.00 50.00
MK2 Mark Kotsay 97 BC/5
MK3 Mark Kotsay 98 B/56 8.00 20.00
MK4 Mark Kotsay 98 BC/23 10.00 25.00
MK5 Mark Kotsay 99 B/75 6.00 15.00
MK6 Mark Kotsay 99 BC/23 10.00 25.00
MK7 Mark Kotsay 05 B/160 6.00 15.00
MK8 Mark Kotsay 05 BC/46 8.00 20.00
MY1 Michael Young 04 B/148 6.00 15.00
MY2 Michael Young 04 BC/64 8.00 20.00
MY3 Michael Young 05 B/92 6.00 15.00

2006 Bowman Sterling

This 117-card set was released in January, 2007. This set was issued in five-card packs with an $50 SRP which came six packs per box and eight boxes per case. The set is a mix of game-used relics from veteran playerfs and players who were rookies in 2006. Some of the rookies either signed some of the cards or signed some of the cards and had a game-used relic included as well as their signature.

COMMON ROOKIE .75 2.00
COMMON AUTO RC 3.00 8.00
AU RC AUTO ODDS 1:4 HOBBY
COMMON AU-GU RC 4.00 10.00
AU-GU RC ODDS 1:4 HOBBY
COMMON GU VET 2.50 6.00
GU VET ODDS 1:4 HOBBY
OVERALL PLATE ODDS 1:23 BOXES
PLATE PRINT RUN 1 SET PER COLOR
BLACK-CYAN-MAGENTA-YELLOW ISSUED
NO PLATE PRICING DUE TO SCARCITY
EXCHANGE DEADLINE 12/31/08
AD Adam Dunn Jsy 2.50 6.00
AE Andre Ethier AU (RC) 10.00 25.00
AER Alex Rodriguez Bat 10.00 25.00
AJ Andruw Jones Jsy 3.00 8.00
ALS Alay Soler RC .75 2.00
AP Albert Pujols Jsy 8.00 20.00
AP2 Albert Pujols Bat 8.00 20.00
APS Alfonso Soriano Bat 4.00 10.00
AR Aramis Ramirez Bat UER 3.00 8.00
Front of card denotes game used jersey
AS Anibal Sanchez (RC) .75 2.00
BA Brian Anderson (RC) .75 2.00
BB Brian Bannister (RC) .75 2.00
BL Bobby Livingston Jsy AU (RC) 4.00 10.00
BLB Barry Bonds Bat 6.00 15.00
BON Boof Bonser (RC) 1.25 3.00
BR Brian Roberts Jsy 2.50 6.00
BZ Ben Zobrist (RC) 2.00 5.00
CB Carlos Beltran Jsy 2.50 6.00
CB2 Carlos Beltran Bat 2.50 6.00
CC Chris Carpenter Jsy 4.00 10.00
CH Cole Hamels Jsy AU (RC) 12.50 30.00
CHJ Chuck James (RC) .75 2.00
CI Chris Iannetta Jsy AU RC 8.00 20.00
CJ Conor Jackson (RC) 1.25 3.00
CJJ Casey Janssen RC .75 2.00
CQ Carlos Quentin (RC) 1.25 3.00
CRB Chad Billingsley (RC) 1.25 3.00
CRH Craig Hansen RC 2.00 5.00
CS Curt Schilling Jsy 3.00 8.00
DG David Gassner (RC) .75 2.00
DO David Ortiz Bat 4.00 10.00
DP David Pauley (RC) .75 2.00
DU Dan Uggla (RC) 2.00 5.00
DW David Wright Jsy 6.00 15.00
DWW Dontrelle Willis Jsy 2.50 6.00
EC Eric Chavez Pants 2.50 6.00
EG Enrique Gonzalez (RC) .75 2.00
FG Franklin Gutierrez (RC) .75 2.00
FL Francisco Liriano (RC) 2.00 5.00
GS Grady Sizemore Jsy 4.00 10.00
HB Hank Blalock Jsy 2.50 6.00
HK1 Howie Kendrick (RC) 2.00 5.00
HK2 Howie Kendrick Jsy AU 4.00 10.00
HM Hideki Matsui Bat 6.00 15.00
HP Hayden Penn (RC) .75 2.00
HR Hanley Ramirez (RC) 2.00 5.00
IK Ian Kinsler AU (RC) 8.00 20.00
IR Ivan Rodriguez Jsy 3.00 8.00
IS Ichiro Suzuki Jsy 10.00 25.00
JAS Johan Santana Jsy 4.00 10.00
JBS Jeremy Sowers (RC) .75 2.00
JCB Jason Botts AU (RC) 3.00 8.00
JD Joey Devine RC .75 2.00
JDD Johnny Damon Bat 4.00 10.00
JHT Jim Thome Bat 4.00 10.00
JI Joe Inglett AU RC 5.00 12.00
JJ Josh Johnson (RC) 2.00 5.00
JK Jeff Karstens RC .75 2.00
JL James Loney (RC) 1.25 3.00
JLB Josh Barfield AU (RC) 3.00 8.00
JM Jeff Mathis (RC) .75 2.00
JP Jonathan Papelbon (RC) 4.00 10.00
JRH Rich Harden Jsy 2.50 6.00
JS James Shields RC 2.50 6.00
JT Jack Taschner Jsy AU (RC) 4.00 10.00
JTA Jordan Tata RC .75 2.00
JTL Jon Lester Jsy AU RC 20.00 50.00
JV Justin Verlander (RC) 6.00 15.00
JW Jered Weaver (RC) 2.00 5.00
JZ Joel Zumaya (RC) 2.00 5.00
KF Kevin Frandsen (RC) .75 2.00
KJ Kenji Johjima RC 2.00 5.00
KM Kendry Morales (RC) 2.00 5.00
LB Lance Berkman Jsy 3.00 8.00
LM Lastings Milledge AU (RC) 8.00 20.00
LWJ Chipper Jones Jsy 4.00 10.00
MC Miguel Cabrera Jsy 3.00 8.00
MC2 Miguel Cabrera Bat 3.00 8.00
MCC Melky Cabrera (RC) 1.25 3.00
MCM Mickey Mantle Bat 30.00 60.00
MCT Mark Teixeira Bat 3.00 8.00
ME Morgan Ensberg Jsy 2.50 6.00
MJP Mike Piazza Bat 4.00 10.00
MK Matt Kemp (RC) 4.00 10.00
MM Mark Mulder Pants 2.50 6.00
MN Mike Napoli Jsy AU RC 10.00 25.00
MP Martin Prado Jsy AU (RC) 8.00 20.00
MPP Mike Pelfrey RC 2.00 5.00
MR Manny Ramirez Jsy 4.00 10.00
MR2 Manny Ramirez Bat 4.00 10.00
MS Matt Smith (RC) 1.25 3.00
MT Miguel Tejada Pants 2.50 6.00
NM Nick Markakis (RC) 2.00 5.00
PF Prince Fielder Jsy AU (RC) 20.00 50.00
PK Paul Konerko Bat 3.00 8.00
PM Pedro Martinez Pants 3.00 8.00
RC Robinson Cano Bat 5.00 12.00
RH Ryan Howard Jsy 8.00 20.00
RK Ryan Garko (RC) .75 2.00
RM Russ Martin (RC) 1.25 3.00
RN Ricky Nolasco AU (RC) 3.00 8.00
RP Ronny Paulino Jsy AU (RC) 6.00 15.00
RZ Ryan Zimmerman (RC) 4.00 10.00
SD Stephen Drew (RC) 2.00 5.00
SM Scott Mathieson (RC) .75 2.00
SO Scott Olsen (RC) .75 2.00
SR Scott Rolen Pants 3.00 8.00
TGJ Tony Gwynn Jr (RC) .75 2.00
TH Todd Helton Jsy 3.00 8.00
TT Taylor Tankersley (RC) .75 2.00
VG Vladimir Guerrero Jsy 3.00 8.00
WA Willy Aybar (RC) .75 2.00
YP Yusmeiro Petit Jsy AU (RC) 4.00 10.00
ZM Zach Miner AU (RC) 3.00 8.00

2006 Bowman Sterling Refractors

*REF RC: .6X TO 1.5X BASIC
RC ODDS 1:6 HOBBY
*REF AU RC: .6X TO 1.5X BASIC AU
AU RC ODDS 1:5 HOBBY
*REF AU-GU RC: .5X TO 1.2X BASIC AU-GU
AU-GU RC ODDS 1:20 HOBBY
*REF GU VET: .5X TO 1.2X BASIC GU
GU VET ODDS 1:7 HOBBY
STATED PRINT RUN 199 SERIAL #'d SETS
EXCHANGE DEADLINE 12/31/08
BLB Barry Bonds Bat 12.50 30.00
CI Chris Iannetta Jsy AU 12.50 30.00
HK2 Howie Kendrick Jsy AU 6.00 15.00
HM Hideki Matsui Bat 12.50 30.00
MCM Mickey Mantle Bat 40.00 80.00
PF Prince Fielder Jsy AU 30.00 60.00

2006 Bowman Sterling Black Refractors

STATED BLK RC ODDS 1:8 BOXES
STATED BLK AU-GU RC 1:26 BOXES
STATED BLK VET GU ODDS 1:8 BOXES
STATED PRINT RUN 25 SERIAL #'d SETS
NO PRICING DUE TO SCARCITY
EXCHANGE DEADLINE 12/31/08

2006 Bowman Sterling Gold Refractors

STATED GOLD RC ODDS 1:18 BOXES
STATED PRINT RUN 10 SERIAL #'d SETS
NO PRICING DUE TO SCARCITY

2006 Bowman Sterling Red Refractors

STATED RED RC ODDS 1:182 BOXES
STATED RED AU-GU RC 1:610 BOXES
STATED RED VET GU ODDS 1:199 BOXES
STATED PRINT RUN 1 SERIAL #'d SET
NO PRICING DUE TO SCARCITY
EXCHANGE DEADLINE 12/31/08

2006 Bowman Sterling Original Autographs

GROUP A ODDS 1:356 BOXES
GROUP B ODDS 1:90 BOXES
GROUP C ODDS 1:45 BOXES
GROUP D ODDS 1:8 BOXES
PRINT RUNS B/WN 1-233 COPIES PER
NO PRICING ON QTY OF 25 OR LESS
EXCHANGE DEADLINE 12/31/08
JD5 Johnny Damon 02 B/47 C 6.00 15.00
JM1 Justin Morneau 02 B/199 D 10.00 25.00
JM2 Justin Morneau 06 B/48 D 12.50 30.00
JP1 Jonathan Papelbon 03 BD/71 D 30.00 60.00
JP2 Jonathan Papelbon 06 B/225 D 15.00 40.00
JV1 Justin Verlander 05 BD/233 D 20.00 50.00
JV3 Justin Verlander 06 B/59 D 30.00 60.00

2006 Bowman Sterling Prospects

COMMON CARD .60 1.50
GROUP A AUTO ODDS 1:2 HOBBY
GROUP B AUTO ODDS 1:2 HOBBY
OVERALL PLATE ODDS 1:23 BOXES
PLATE PRINT RUN 1 SET PER COLOR
BLACK-CYAN-MAGENTA-YELLOW ISSUED
NO PLATE PRICING DUE TO SCARCITY
EXCHANGE DEADLINE 12/31/08
AC Adrian Cardenas AU A 4.00 10.00
ADC Adam Coe .60 1.50
AG Alex Gordon AU B 10.00 25.00
AJC Asdrubal Cabrera 3.00 8.00
AO Adam Ottovino AU A 5.00 12.00
AP Andrew Pinckney .50 1.25
AS A.J. Shappi .60 1.50
BA Brandon Allen AU B 4.00 10.00
BB Brooks Brown AU A 3.00 8.00
BC Ben Copeland .60 1.50
BD Brent Dlugach .60 1.50
BF Brad Furnish AU A 3.00 8.00
BH Brett Hayes AU B 3.00 8.00
BJ Brandon Jones .60 1.50
BJS B.J. Szymanski .60 1.50
BM Brandon Moss AU A 3.00 8.00
BS Brandon Snyder AU B 3.00 8.00
BSI Brett Sinkbeil AU B 6.00 15.00
BW Brandon Wood AU B 6.00 15.00
BWM Brad McCann .60 1.50
CD Chris Dickerson AU A 10.00 25.00
CD Chris Dickerson 1.00 2.50
CH Chase Headley AU B 10.00 25.00
CHH Chad Huffman AU B 10.00 25.00
CJ Cody Johnson AU B 5.00 12.00
CK Clayton Kershaw AU A 30.00 60.00
CM Cameron Maybin AU A 6.00 15.00
CMT Matt Tolbert .60 1.50
CP Chris Parmelee AU B 12.50 30.00
CR Cory Rasmus AU A 5.00 12.00
CT Chad Tracy AU A 3.00 8.00
CW Colton Willems AU B 10.00 25.00
CW Corey Wimberly .60 1.50
DE Dustin Evans AU A 3.00 8.00
DF Dexter Fowler 2.00 5.00
DH Daniel Haigwood AU B 3.00 8.00
DHU David Huff AU B 3.00 8.00
DIH Diory Hernandez .60 1.50
DM Dustin Majewski .60 1.50
DT Dallas Trahern .60 1.50
EA Elvis Andrus 3.00 8.00
EL Evan Longoria AU B 40.00 80.00
EM Evan MacLane .60 1.50
EP Elvin Puello AU A 3.00 8.00
GLM Garrett Mock .60 1.50
GM Garrett Mock AU B 3.00 8.00
HC Hank Conger AU B 5.00 12.00
HP Hunter Pence 3.00 8.00
JAC Jose Campusano .60 1.50
JBU Joshua Butler AU A 3.00 8.00
JC Jeff Clement AU B 6.00 15.00
JF Juan Francia .60 1.50
JJ Jeremy Jeffress AU B 4.00 10.00
JJ Jason Jaramillo .60 1.50
JKF Jeff Frazier .60 1.50
JN Jason Neighborgall AU B 3.00 8.00
JR Joshua Rodriguez AU A 3.00 8.00
JRB Jimmy Barthmaier .60 1.50
JS Jarrod Saltalamacchia AU A 8.00 20.00
JT Jose Tabata 4.00 10.00
JTL Jared Lansford .60 1.50
JU Justin Upton AU B 30.00 60.00
JW Johnny Whittleman AU B 8.00 20.00
KB Kyler Burke AU A 3.00 8.00
KC Koby Clemens AU A 10.00 25.00
KD Kyle Drabek AU B 5.00 12.00
KJ Kris Johnson AU A 5.00 12.00
KK Kasey Kiker AU B 3.00 8.00
KM Kyle McCulloch AU B 3.00 8.00
LH Luke Hochevar AU A 5.00 12.00
MA Mike Aviles AU B 3.00 8.00
MAA Matt Antonelli AU B 4.00 10.00
MC Michael Collins .60 1.50
MF Michael Felix AU A 3.00 8.00
MG Mat Gamel 2.50 6.00
MH Michael Hollimon .60 1.50
MM Mark McCormick AU B 3.00 8.00
MO Micah Owings AU B 6.00 15.00
MR Mark Reed .60 1.50
MRA Michael Aubrey 1.00 2.50
MRR Max Ramirez 1.00 2.50
MSM Mark McLemore .60 1.50
MT Mark Trumbo 2.50 6.00
NA Nick Adenhart .60 1.50
ON Oswaldo Navarro .60 1.50
OS Omir Santos .60 1.50
PB Pedro Beato AU A 3.00 8.00
PL Pedro Lopez AU A 3.00 8.00
RB Ronny Bourquin AU B 3.00 8.00
RK Ryan Klosterman .60 1.50
RL Radhames Liz .60 1.50
RP Ryan Patterson .60 1.50
SC Shaun Cumberland .60 1.50
SE Steven Evarts AU A 3.00 8.00
SGG Steve Garrabrants .60 1.50
SM Stephen Marek .60 1.50
SMM Steve Murphy .60 1.50
SR Shawn Riggans .60 1.50
SW Steven Wright AU A 3.00 8.00
SWA Sean Watson AU B 3.00 8.00
TB Travis Buck AU B 6.00 15.00
TC Trevor Crowe AU A 3.00 8.00
TC Tyler Colvin AU B 4.00 10.00
TP Troy Patton AU A 3.00 8.00
WR Wilkin Ramirez 1.00 2.50
WT Wade Townsend AU B 3.00 8.00
WV Will Venable .60 1.50
YC Yung-Chi Chen 1.00 2.50
YG Yovani Gallardo 2.00 5.00

2006 Bowman Sterling Prospects Refractors

*REF: .75X TO 2X BASIC
REF ODDS 1:6 HOBBY
*REF AU: .75X TO 2X BASIC AU
AU ODDS 1:5 HOBBY
STATED PRINT RUN 199 SERIAL #'d SETS
EXCHANGE DEADLINE 12/31/08
CK Clayton Kershaw AU 75.00 150.00
CM Cameron Maybin AU 50.00 100.00
EL Evan Longoria AU 50.00 100.00
HC Hank Conger AU 10.00 25.00
JU Justin Upton AU 90.00 150.00
JW Johnny Whittleman AU 15.00 40.00
KB Kyler Burke AU 10.00 25.00
LH Luke Hochevar AU 20.00 50.00
MO Micah Owings AU 12.50 30.00
TB Travis Buck AU 10.00 25.00

2006 Bowman Sterling Prospects Black Refractors

STATED BLACK ODDS 1:8 BOXES
STATED BLACK AU ODDS 1:6 BOXES
STATED PRINT RUN 25 SERIAL #'d SETS
NO PRICING DUE TO SCARCITY

2006 Bowman Sterling Prospects Gold Refractors

STATED GOLD ODDS 1:18 BOXES
STATED PRINT RUN 10 SERIAL #'d SETS
NO PRICING DUE TO SCARCITY

2006 Bowman Sterling Prospects Red Refractors

STATED RED ODDS 1:182 BOXES
STATED RED AU ODDS 1:133 BOXES
STATED PRINT RUN 1 SERIAL #'d SET
NO PRICING DUE TO SCARCITY
EXCHANGE DEADLINE 12/31/08

2007 Bowman Sterling

This 117-card set was released in January, 2008. The set was issued in five-card mini-boxes, with an $50 SRP, which came six mini-boxes per display box, four display boxes per carton and two cartons per case.

COMMON ROOKIE .40 1.00
COMMON AUTO RC 3.00 8.00
AU RC AUTO ODDS 1:2 PACKS
COMMON GU VET 2.50 6.00

GU VET GROUP A ODDS 1:5 PACKS
GU VET GROUP B ODDS 1:3 PACKS
GU VET GROUP C ODDS 1:253 PACKS
PRINTING PLATE ODDS 1:29 BOXES
PRINTING PLATE AU ODDS 1:41 BOXES
PLATE PRINT RUN 1 SET PER COLOR
BLACK-CYAN-MAGENTA-YELLOW ISSUED
NO PLATE PRICING DUE TO SCARCITY
AAL Adam Lind (RC) .40 1.00
AER Alex Rodriguez Bat A 6.00 15.00
AG Alex Gordon RC 1.25 3.00
AI Akinori Iwamura RC 1.00 2.50
AJ Andruw Jones Bat B 2.50 6.00
AL Andy LaRoche (RC) .40 1.00
AM Andrew Miller RC 1.00 2.50
AP Albert Pujols Jsy A 5.00 12.00
AR Alex Rios Jsy B 2.50 6.00
AS Alfonso Soriano Bat B 2.50 6.00
AS Andy Sonnanstine RC .40 1.00
BB Billy Butler (RC) .60 1.50
BF Ben Francisco (RC) .40 1.00
BLB Barry Bonds Pants A 4.00 10.00
BP Brad Penny Jsy B 2.50 6.00
BR Brian Roberts Jsy A 2.50 6.00
BS Brian Stokes (RC) .40 1.00
BU B.J. Upton Bat B 2.50 6.00
BW Brandon Webb Jsy B 2.50 6.00
BW Brandon Wood (RC) .40 1.00
CAB Craig Biggio Jsy B 3.00 8.00
CAG Carlos Guillen Jsy B 2.50 6.00
CG Carlos Gomez RC .60 1.50
CH Cole Hamels Jsy A 5.00 12.00
CH Chase Headley AU (RC) 5.00 12.00
CL Carlos Lee Jsy B 2.50 6.00
CM Cameron Maybin AU RC 6.00 15.00
CMS Curt Schilling Jsy B 2.50 6.00
CT Curtis Thigpen (RC) .40 1.00
DDY Dmitri Young Jsy B 2.50 6.00
DM Daisuke Matsuzaka RC 1.50 4.00
DMM David Murphy (RC) .40 1.00
DO David Ortiz Bat B 3.00 8.00
DP Danny Putnam (RC) .40 1.00
DW David Wright Bat B 4.00 10.00
DWW Dontrelle Willis Jsy B 2.50 6.00
DY Delmon Young (RC) .60 1.50
EC Eric Chavez Pants B 2.50 6.00
FL Fred Lewis (RC) .60 1.50
FP Felix Pie AU (RC) 3.00 8.00
GO Garrett Olson (RC) .40 1.00
GP Glen Perkins AU (RC) 4.00 10.00
HB Homer Bailey AU (RC) 4.00 10.00
HG Hector Gimenez (RC) .40 1.00
HO Hideki Okajima RC 2.00 5.00
HP Hunter Pence (RC) 2.00 5.00
IS Ichiro Suzuki Bat B 5.00 12.00
JAV Jason Varitek Jsy B 3.00 8.00
JB Jeff Baker (RC) .40 1.00
JBR Jose Reyes Jsy A 3.00 8.00
JC1 Joba Chamberlain RC 2.00 5.00
JC2 Joba Chamberlain AU 12.50 30.00
JD John Danks AU RC 5.00 12.00
JDF Josh Fields (RC) .40 1.00
JE Jim Edmonds Jsy B 3.00 8.00
JE Jacoby Ellsbury (RC) 3.00 8.00
JF Jesus Flores RC .40 1.00
JH Josh Hamilton AU (RC) 15.00 40.00
JL Jesse Litsch AU RC 3.00 8.00
JQF Jake Fox RC .40 1.00
JR Jo-Jo Reyes (RC) .40 1.00
JS Johan Santana Jsy A 3.00 8.00
JS Jarrod Saltalamacchia AU (RC) 4.00 10.00
JU Justin Upton RC 3.00 8.00
JV Justin Verlander Jsy B 3.00 8.00
KI Kei Igawa RC 1.00 2.50
KK Kevin Kouzmanoff (RC) .40 1.00
KKS Kurt Suzuki AU (RC) 3.00 8.00
KRK Kyle Kendrick AU RC 3.00 8.00
KS Kevin Slowey AU (RC) 6.00 15.00
LB Lance Berkman Jsy B 2.50 6.00
MAR Manny Ramirez Bat B 2.50 6.00
MB Michael Bourn (RC) .40 1.00
MC Melky Cabrera Bat B 2.50 6.00
MC Matt Chico AU (RC) 3.00 8.00
MCT Mark Teixeira Bat A 2.50 6.00
MF Mike Fontenot (RC) .40 1.00
MH Matt Holliday Jsy B 3.00 8.00
MJO Magglio Ordonez Bat B 2.50 6.00
MK Masumi Kuwata RC .40 1.00
MM Mickey Mantle Jsy C 40.00 80.00
MM Miguel Montero (RC) .40 1.00
MO Micah Owings (RC) .40 1.00
MP Manny Parra (RC) .40 1.00
MR Mark Reynolds RC 3.00 8.00
MSM Mark McLemore (RC) .40 1.00
MT Miguel Tejada Pants B 2.50 6.00
MY Michael Young Jsy B 2.50 6.00
NG Nick Gorneault AU (RC) 3.00 8.00
NS Nate Schierholtz AU (RC) 5.00 12.00
OC Orlando Cabrera Jsy 2.50 6.00
PF Prince Fielder Jsy A 3.00 8.00
PH Phil Hughes (RC) 2.00 5.00
PH Phil Hughes AU (RC) 10.00 25.00
RB Rocco Baldelli Jsy B 2.50 6.00
RB Ryan Braun AU (RC) 30.00 60.00
RC Roger Clemens Jsy B 4.00 10.00
RJC Robinson Cano Bat B 3.00 8.00
RJH Ryan Howard Bat A 4.00 10.00
RS Ryan Sweeney (RC) .40 1.00
RV Rick Vanden Hurk RC .40 1.00
RZ Ryan Zimmerman Bat B 3.00 8.00
SD Shelley Duncan (RC) 1.00 2.50
SG Sean Gallagher (RC) .60 1.50
SK Scott Kazmir Jsy B 2.50 6.00
TA Tony Abreu RC 1.50 4.00
TB Travis Buck (RC) .60 1.50
TC Tyler Clippard (RC) 1.00 2.50
TH Tim Hudson Jsy B 2.50 6.00
TL Tim Lincecum AU RC 75.00 150.00
TLH Todd Helton Bat A 2.50 6.00
TM Travis Metcalf RC 1.00 2.50
TW Tim Wakefield Jsy B 2.50 6.00
UJ Ubaldo Jimenez (RC) 2.50 6.00
VG Vladimir Guerrero Jsy A 2.50 6.00
YE Yunel Escobar (RC) .60 1.50
YG Yovani Gallardo AU (RC) 8.00 20.00

2007 Bowman Sterling Refractors

*REF RC: 1X TO 2.5X BASIC
RC ODDS 1:7 PACKS
*REF AU RC: .5X TO 1.2X BASIC AU
AU RC ODDS 1:5 PACKS
*REF GU VET: .5X TO 1.2X BASIC GU
GU VET ODDS 1:8 PACKS
STATED PRINT RUN 199 SERIAL #'d SETS
JC2 Joba Chamberlain AU 20.00 50.00
KS Kevin Slowey AU 10.00 25.00
PH Phil Hughes AU 15.00 40.00
TL Tim Lincecum AU 75.00 150.00

2007 Bowman Sterling Black Refractors

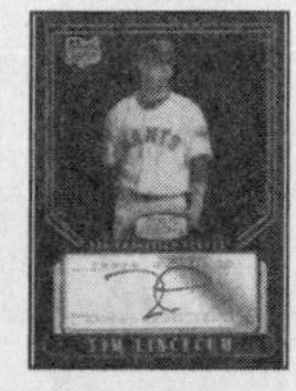

STATED BLK RC ODDS 1:11 BOXES
STATED BLK RELIC ODDS 1:10 BOXES
STATED BLK AU RC ODDS 1:7 BOXES
STATED PRINT RUN 25 SER.#'d SETS
NO PRICING DUE TO SCARCITY

2007 Bowman Sterling Red Refractors

STATED RED RC ODDS 1:230 BOXES
STATED RED RELIC ODDS 1:246 BOXES
STATED RED AU RC ODDS 1:164 BOXES
STATED PRINT RUN 1 SER.#'d SET
NO PRICING DUE TO SCARCITY

2007 Bowman Sterling Dual Autographs

STATED ODDS 1:5 BOXES
STATED PRINT RUN 275 SER.#'d SETS
BV Jay Bruce 40.00 80.00
Joey Votto
CH Shin Soo Choo 8.00 20.00
Chin-Lung Hu
GM Deolis Guerra 5.00 12.00
Fernando Martinez
HC Phil Hughes 40.00 80.00
Joba Chamberlain
HP Luke Hochevar 10.00 25.00
David Price
LC Evan Longoria 40.00 80.00
Carl Crawford
MM John Maine 4.00 10.00
Lastings Milledge
PB Hunter Pence 20.00 50.00
Ryan Braun
PP Jeremy Papelbon 4.00 10.00
Josh Papelbon
PS Felix Pie 30.00 60.00
Jeff Samardzija

2007 Bowman Sterling Dual Autographs Refractors

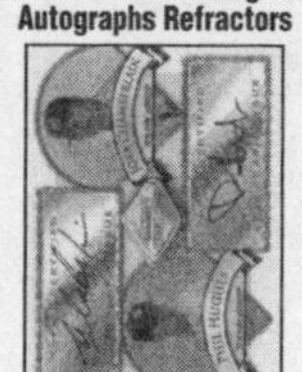

*REF: .4X TO 1X BASIC
STATED ODDS 1:6 BOXES
STATED PRINT RUN 199 SER.#'d SETS

2007 Bowman Sterling Dual Autographs Black Refractors

STATED ODDS 1:46 BOXES
STATED PRINT RUN 25 SER.#'d SETS
NO PRICING DUE TO SCARCITY

2007 Bowman Sterling Dual Autographs Red Refractors

STATED ODDS 1:1080 BOXES
STATED PRINT RUN 1 SER.#'d SET
NO PRICING DUE TO SCARCITY

2007 Bowman Sterling Prospects

COMMON CARD .50 1.25
COMMON AUTO 3.00 8.00
STATED AU ODDS 1:1 PACKS
COMMON AU-GU 3.00 8.00
AU-GU ODDS 1:5 PACKS
PRINTING PLATE ODDS 1:29 BOXES
PRINTING PLATE AU ODDS 1:41 BOXES
PLATE PRINT RUN 1 SET PER COLOR
BLACK-CYAN-MAGENTA-YELLOW ISSUED
NO PLATE PRICING DUE TO SCARCITY
AC Adrian Cardenas Jsy AU 4.00 10.00
AF Andrew Fie .50 1.25
ALC Aaron Cunningham .75 2.00
AP Aaron Poreda AU 4.00 10.00
BB Brian Bocock Jsy AU 3.00 8.00
BB Blake Beavan AU 5.00 12.00
BEL Brad Lincoln .50 1.25
BH Brandon Hamilton .50 1.25
BHB Burke Badenhop .75 2.00
BL Bryan LaHair AU 3.00 8.00
BM Brandon MaGee AU 3.00 8.00
BMI Beau Mills AU 6.00 15.00
BR Ben Revere AU 5.00 12.00
BWH Brandon Hynick 1.25 3.00
CB Collin Balester Jsy AU 3.00 8.00
CC Chris Carter 3.00 8.00
CD Chance Douglass .50 1.25
CG Cole Gillespie AU 3.00 8.00
CH Chin-Lung Hu Jsy AU 10.00 25.00
CH Cedric Hunter 1.25 3.00
CK Clayton Kershaw Jsy AU 15.00 40.00
CL Chuck Lofgren Jsy AU 4.00 10.00
CM Clayton Mortensen AU 3.00 8.00
CN Chris Nowak .50 1.25
CR Colby Rasmus Jsy AU 12.50 30.00
CS Cody Strait .50 1.25
CW Chris Withrow AU 4.00 10.00
CWW Casey Weathers AU 3.00 8.00
DB Daniel Bard AU 12.50 30.00
DBE Dellin Betances 1.25 3.00
DG Deolis Guerra Jsy AU 4.00 10.00
DI Devin Ivany .50 1.25
DJ Desmond Jennings 1.50 4.00
DL Drew Locke .50 1.25
DM Daniel Moskos AU 3.00 8.00
DME Devin Mesoraco AU 8.00 20.00
DMM Derek Miller .75 2.00
DPP David Price AU 20.00 50.00
DS James Simmons AU 3.00 8.00
EE Ed Easley .50 1.25
EL Evan Longoria Jsy AU 20.00 50.00
EL Erik Lis AU 3.00 8.00
EM Emerson Frostad .50 1.25
EY Eric Young Jr. .75 2.00
FF Freddie Freeman 3.00 8.00
GD German Duran Jsy AU 3.00 8.00
GH Gorkys Hernandez 1.25 3.00
GP Gregory Porter .50 1.25
GR Greg Reynolds 1.50 4.00
GS Greg Smith .75 2.00
HS Henry Sosa Jsy AU 4.00 10.00
ID Ivan De Jesus Jr. .75 2.00
IS Ian Stewart Jsy AU 5.00 12.00
JA J.P. Arencibia AU 8.00 20.00
JAA James Avery AU 3.00 8.00
JB Jay Bruce Jsy AU 15.00 40.00
JB Joe Benson AU 4.00 10.00
JBO Julio Borbon AU 6.00 15.00
JG Jonathan Gilmore AU 3.00 8.00
JGA Joe Gaetti .75 2.00
JGO Jared Goedert 2.00 5.00
JH Jason Heyward AU 40.00 80.00
JJ Justin Jackson 1.25 3.00
JL Jeff Locke 2.00 5.00
JM Joe Mather .75 2.00
JO Josh Outman AU 3.00 8.00
JP Jason Place 1.25 3.00
JPA Jeremy Papelbon .75 2.00
JPP Josh Papelbon .75 2.00
JS Joe Savery AU 3.00 8.00
JS Jeff Samardzija 3.00 8.00
JSM Jake Smolinski 2.50 6.00
JT J.R. Towles 2.50 6.00
JV Joey Votto Jsy AU 20.00 50.00
JV Josh Vitters AU 8.00 20.00
JVE Jonathan Van Every .75 2.00
JW Johnny Whittleman Jsy AU 3.00 8.00
KA Kevin Ahrens AU 3.00 8.00
KK Kellen Kulbacki AU 3.00 8.00
KK Kala Kaaihue .75 2.00
MB Michael Burgess AU 3.00 8.00
MBB Madison Bumgarner AU 20.00 50.00
MC Mike Carp 1.50 4.00
MCA Mitch Canham AU 3.00 8.00
MD Mike Daniel AU 3.00 8.00
MDE Mike Devaney .75 2.00
MDO Matt Dominguez AU 6.00 15.00
MH Mark Hamilton .75 2.00
MIM Michael Main AU 3.00 8.00
MLP Matt LaPorta AU 20.00 50.00
MM Michael Madsen Jsy AU 3.00 8.00
MM Matt McBride AU 3.00 8.00
MMG Matt Mangini AU 3.00 8.00
MP Mike Parisi AU 3.00 8.00
MS Michael Saunders 2.50 6.00
MY Matt Young .50 1.25
NH Nick Hagadone AU 4.00 10.00
NN Nick Noonan AU 5.00 12.00
NS Nick Schmidt AU 3.00 8.00
OS Ole Sheldon .75 2.00
PB Pedro Beato Jsy AU 3.00 8.00
PK Peter Kozma AU 3.00 8.00
RD Ross Detwiler AU 3.00 8.00
RM Ryan Mount AU 3.00 8.00
RT Rich Thompson .75 2.00
SF Sam Fuld 1.50 4.00
SP Steve Pearce Jsy AU 6.00 15.00
TA Tim Alderson AU 8.00 20.00
TF Todd Frazier AU 5.00 12.00
TF Thomas Fairchild .75 2.00
TM Thomas Manzella AU 3.00 8.00
TS Travis Snider AU 12.50 30.00
TW Ty Weeden AU 3.00 8.00
VB Vic Buttler .75 2.00
VS Vasili Spanos .75 2.00
WF Wendell Fairley AU 4.00 10.00
WT Wade Townsend AU 3.00 8.00
ZM Zach McAllister 1.25 3.00

2007 Bowman Sterling Prospects Refractors

*REF: 1.2X TO 3X BASIC
REF ODDS 1:7 PACKS
*REF AU: .75X TO 2X BASIC AU
REF AU ODDS 1:5 PACKS
*REF AU-GU RC: .5X TO 1.2X BASIC AU-GU
REF AU-GU ODDS 1:20 PACKS
STATED PRINT RUN 199 SERIAL #'d SETS
DB Daniel Bard AU 20.00 50.00
IS Ian Stewart Jsy AU 10.00 25.00
JA J.P. Arencibia AU 15.00 40.00
JB Jay Bruce Jsy AU 15.00 40.00
JBO Julio Borbon AU 15.00 40.00
JH Jason Heyward AU 100.00 200.00
MBB Madison Bumgarner AU 50.00 100.00
MDO Matt Dominguez AU 30.00 60.00
MLP Matt LaPorta AU 75.00 150.00
SP Steve Pearce Jsy AU 12.50 30.00
TA Tim Alderson AU 30.00 60.00
TF Todd Frazier AU 15.00 40.00

2007 Bowman Sterling Prospects Black Refractors

STATED BLK PROS ODDS 1:11 BOXES
STATED BLK RELIC ODDS 1:10 BOXES
STATED BLK AU PROS ODDS 1:7 BOXES
STATED BLK AU RELIC ODDS 1:26 BOXES
STATED PRINT RUN 25 SER.#'d SETS
NO PRICING DUE TO SCARCITY

2007 Bowman Sterling Prospects Red Refractors

STATED RED PROS ODDS 1:230 BOXES
STATED RED RELIC ODDS 1:246 BOXES
STATED RED AU PROS ODDS 1:164 BOXES
STATED RED AU RELIC ODDS 1:675 BOXES
STATED PRINT RUN 1 SER.#'d SET
NO PRICING DUE TO SCARCITY

2008 Bowman Sterling

This set was released on December 29, 2008.

COMMON GU VET 2.50 6.00
EXCHANGE DEADLINE 11/30/2010
COMMON RC 1.00 2.50
COMMON RC VAR 1.25 3.00
RC VAR ODDS 1:2 BOXES
RC VAR PRINT RUN 399 SER.#'d SETS
COMMON AU RC 3.00 8.00
AU RC ODDS 1:3 PACKS
PRINTING PLATE ODDS 1:93 PACKS
PRINTING PLATE AU ODDS 1:238 PACKS
PLATE PRINT RUN 1 SET PER COLOR
BLACK-CYAN-MAGENTA-YELLOW ISSUED
NO PLATE PRICING DUE TO SCARCITY
AAG Armando Galarraga AU RC 4.00 10.00
AP Albert Pujols Jsy 5.00 12.00
AR Alex Rodriguez Jsy 5.00 12.00
ARA Aramis Ramirez Mem 2.50 6.00
ARU Adam Russell AU (RC) 3.00 8.00
BG Brett Gardner (RC) 2.50 6.00
BH Brian Horwitz RC 1.00 2.50
BJ Brandon Jones RC 2.50 6.00
BJB Brian Bixler AU (RC) 3.00 8.00
BM Brian McCann Bat 2.50 6.00
BZ Brad Ziegler RC 5.00 12.00
CC Carl Crawford Jsy 2.50 6.00
CD Chris Davis RC 2.50 6.00
CDB Clay Buchholz (RC) 2.50 6.00
CEGa Carlos Gonzalez (RC) 2.50 6.00
CEGb Carlos Gonzalez VAR SP 3.00 8.00
CG Chris Getz AU RC 3.00 8.00
CG Curtis Granderson Mem 3.00 8.00
CH Cole Hamels Jsy 3.00 8.00
CJ Chipper Jones Jsy 3.00 8.00
CKa Clayton Kershaw RC 5.00 12.00
CKb Clayton Kershaw VAR SP 6.00 15.00
CLH Chin-Lung Hu (RC) 1.50 4.00
CM Charlie Morton (RC) 1.00 2.50
CMT Matt Tolbert RC 1.50 4.00
CP Chris Perez AU RC 3.00 8.00
CR Clayton Richard (RC) 1.00 2.50
CRPa Cliff Pennington (RC) 1.00 2.50
CRPb Cliff Pennington VAR SP 1.25 3.00
CU Chase Utley Jsy 4.00 10.00
CW Chien-Ming Wang Jsy 4.00 10.00
DB Daric Barton (RC) 1.00 2.50
DM Daisuke Matsuzaka Jsy 4.00 10.00
DO David Ortiz Jsy 3.00 8.00
DP David Purcey (RC) 1.00 2.50
DW David Wright Bat 4.00 10.00
DY Delmon Young Jsy 2.50 6.00
EH Eric Hurley (RC) 1.00 2.50
EL Evan Longoria AU RC 20.00 50.00
EV Edinson Volquez Jsy 2.50 6.00
FC Fausto Carmona Mem 3.00 8.00
GB Gregor Blanco (RC) 1.00 2.50
GD German Duran RC 1.50 4.00
GR Greg Reynolds RC 1.50 4.00
GS Geovany Soto Jsy 3.00 8.00
GTS Greg Smith AU RC 3.00 8.00
HI Hernan Iribarren (RC) 1.50 4.00
HKa Hiroki Kuroda RC 1.50 4.00
HKb Hiroki Kuroda VAR SP 2.00 5.00
HP Hunter Pence Jsy 3.00 8.00
HR Hanley Ramirez Jsy 2.50 6.00
IS Ichiro Suzuki Jsy 6.00 15.00
JABa Jay Bruce (RC) 4.00 10.00
JABb Jay Bruce VAR SP 5.00 12.00
JB Josh Banks (RC) 1.00 2.50
JBC Jeff Clement (RC) 1.50 4.00
JBR Jose Reyes Jsy 3.00 8.00
JC Joba Chamberlain Jsy 5.00 12.00
JCH Justin Christian RC 1.50 4.00
JCO Johnny Cueto RC 1.50 4.00
JE Jacoby Ellsbury Jsy 4.00 10.00
JH Josh Hamilton Jsy 5.00 12.00
JLa Jed Lowrie (RC) 2.50 6.00
JLb Jed Lowrie VAR SP 3.00 8.00
JMR Justin Ruggiano AU RC 3.00 8.00
JN Jeff Niemann (RC) 1.00 2.50
JR Jimmy Rollins Jsy 3.00 8.00
JSa Jeff Samardzija RC 3.00 8.00
JSb Jeff Samardzija VAR SP 4.00 10.00
JT J.R. Towles RC 1.50 4.00
JU Justin Upton Bat 2.50 6.00
JVa Joey Votto (RC) 4.00 10.00
JVb Joey Votto VAR SP 5.00 12.00
KFa Kosuke Fukudome RC 3.00 8.00
KFb Kosuke Fukudome VAR SP 4.00 10.00
LHb Luke Hochevar RC 1.50 4.00
MA Michael Aubrey RC 1.50 4.00
MC Miguel Cabrera Bat 3.00 8.00
MH Matt Holliday Bat 2.50 6.00
MJ Matt Joyce RC 2.50 6.00
MK Masahide Kobayashi RC 1.50 4.00
MM Mickey Mantle Jsy 30.00 60.00
MR Manny Ramirez Jsy 4.00 10.00
MRRa Max Ramirez RC 1.00 2.50
MRRb Max Ramirez VAR SP 1.25 3.00
MT Mark Teixeira Bat 3.00 8.00
MTA Miguel Tejada Mem 2.50 6.00
MTH Michael Holliman RC 1.00 2.50
NA Nick Adenhart (RC) 1.00 2.50
NB Nick Blackburn RC 1.50 4.00
NE Nick Evans RC 1.00 2.50
NH Nick Hundley (RC) 1.00 2.50
NLS Nick Stavinoha RC 1.50 4.00
NM Nick Markakis Jsy 4.00 10.00
PF Prince Fielder Jsy 3.00 8.00
RB Ryan Braun Jsy 4.00 10.00
RB Reid Brignac (RC) 1.50 4.00
RH Ryan Howard Jsy 4.00 10.00
RJM Jai Miller (RC) 1.00 2.50
RL Radhames Liz RC 1.50 4.00
RM Russ Martin Bat 3.00 8.00
RT Ryan Tucker (RC) 1.00 2.50
SR Sean Rodriguez (RC) 1.00 2.50
SS Seth Smith AU (RC) 3.00 8.00
TL Tim Lincecum Jsy 6.00 15.00
TT Taylor Teagarden AU RC 5.00 12.00
VG Vladimir Guerrero Jsy 2.50 6.00
VM Victor Martinez Jsy 2.50 6.00
WB Wladimir Balentien (RC) 1.00 2.50
WCC Chris Carter (RC) 1.50 4.00

2008 Bowman Sterling Refractors

*GU VET REF: .5X TO 1.2X BASIC
GU VET REF ODDS 1:5 PACKS
GU VET REF PRINT RUN 199 SER.#'d SETS
*RC REF: .5X TO 1.2X BASIC
RC REF ODDS 1:4 PACKS
RC REF PRINT RUN 199 SER.#'d SETS
*RC VAR REF: .4X TO 1X BASIC
RC VAR REF ODDS 1:5 BOXES
RC VAR REF PRINT RUN 149 SER.#'d SETS
*RC AU REF: .5X TO 1.2X BASIC
RC AU REF ODDS 1:5 PACKS
RC AU REF PRINT RUN 199 SER.#'d SETS
EL Evan Longoria AU 40.00 80.00

2008 Bowman Sterling Black Refractors

BLK VET GU ODDS 1:37 PACKS
BLK RC ODDS 1:30 PACKS
BLK AU RC ODDS 1:42 PACKS
BLK RC VAR ODDS 1:25 BOXES
STATED PRINT RUN 25 SER.#'d SETS
NO PRICING DUE TO SCARCITY

2008 Bowman Sterling Gold Refractors

*GU VET GLD: .75X TO 2X BASIC
GU VET GLD ODDS 1:19 PACKS
GU VET GLD PRINT RUN 50 SER.#'d SETS
*RC GLD: 1X TO 2.5X BASIC
RC GLD ODDS 1:15 PACKS
RC GLD PRINT RUN 50 SER.#'d SETS
*RC VAR GLD: .75X TO 2X BASIC
RC VAR GLD ODDS 1:13 BOXES
RC VAR GLD PRINT RUN 50 SER.#'d SETS
*RC AU GLD: .75X TO 2X BASIC
RC AU GLD ODDS 1:21 PACKS
RC AU GLD PRINT RUN 50 SER.#'d SETS
AAG Armando Galarraga AU 12.50 30.00
AP Albert Pujols Jsy 12.50 30.00
AR Alex Rodriguez Jsy 12.50 30.00
BZ Brad Ziegler 25.00 60.00
CD Chris Davis 12.00 30.00
CLH Chin-Lung Hu 6.00 15.00
CW Chien-Ming Wang Jsy 20.00 50.00
DM Daisuke Matsuzaka Jsy 10.00 25.00
EL Evan Longoria AU 75.00 150.00
HKa Hiroki Kuroda 8.00 20.00
HKb Hiroki Kuroda VAR 8.00 20.00
IS Ichiro Suzuki Jsy 15.00 40.00
JE Jacoby Ellsbury Jsy 15.00 40.00
TT Taylor Teagarden AU 20.00 50.00

2008 Bowman Sterling Red Refractors

RED VET GU ODDS 1:908 PACKS
RED RC ODDS 1:737 PACKS
RED AU RC ODDS 1:983 PACKS
RED RC VAR ODDS 1:590 BOXES
STATED PRINT RUN 1 SER.#'d SET
NO PRICING DUE TO SCARCITY

2008 Bowman Sterling Dual Autographs

STATED ODDS 1:29 PACKS
STATED PRINT RUN 325 SER.#'d SETS
LS Evan Longoria 15.00 40.00
Geovany Soto
MM Jesus Montero 15.00 40.00
Mark Melancon
PB Buster Posey 50.00 100.00
Gordon Beckham
RS Alex Rios 10.00 25.00
Travis Snider

2008 Bowman Sterling Dual Autographs Refractors

*REF: .5X TO 1.2X BASIC
STATED ODDS 1:93 PACKS
STATED PRINT RUN 99 SER.#'d SETS

2008 Bowman Sterling Dual Autographs Black Refractors

STATED ODDS 1:372 PACKS
STATED PRINT RUN 25 SER.#'d SETS
NO PRICING DUE TO SCARCITY

2008 Bowman Sterling Dual Autographs Gold Refractors

*GLD REF: .X TO X BASIC
STATED ODDS 1:185 PACKS
STATED PRINT RUN 50 SER.#'d SETS
LS Evan Longoria 30.00 60.00
Geovany Soto
MM Jesus Montero 50.00 100.00
Mark Melancon
PB Buster Posey 125.00 250.00
Gordon Beckham
RS Alex Rios 20.00 50.00
Travis Snider

2008 Bowman Sterling Dual Autographs Red Refractors

STATED ODDS 1:8850 PACKS
STATED PRINT RUN 1 SER.#'d SET
NO PRICING DUE TO SCARCITY

2008 Bowman Sterling Prospects

COMMON CARD .40 1.00
COMMON AU 3.00 8.00
STATED AUTO ODDS 1:3 PACKS
COMMON JSY AU 5.00 12.00
STATED JSY AU ODDS 1:4 PACKS
PRINTING PLATE ODDS 1:93 PACKS
PRINTING PLATE AU ODDS 1:238 PACKS
PLATE PRINT RUN 1 SET PER COLOR
BLACK-CYAN-MAGENTA-YELLOW ISSUED
NO PLATE PRICING DUE TO SCARCITY
AA Adrian Alaniz .40 1.00
AB Andrew Brackman 1.25 3.00
AC Alex Cobb .40 1.00
AC Andrew Cashner AU 6.00 15.00
AH Anthony Hewitt AU 4.00 10.00
AJ Austin Jackson 2.00 5.00
AM Aaron Mathews .40 1.00
AMO Adam Moore AU 3.00 8.00
AR Aneury Rodriguez .60 1.50
BB Bubba Bell 1.00 2.50
BC Brett Cecil 1.25 3.00
BH Brandon Hicks .40 1.00
BHA Brad Hand AU 3.00 8.00
BP Buster Posey AU 50.00 100.00
BS Braeden Schlehuber .40 1.00
BW Brandon Waring 1.25 3.00
CB Charlie Blackmon AU 3.00 8.00
CC Carlos Carrasco Jsy AU 5.00 12.00
CGU Carlos Gutierrez AU 3.00 8.00
CI Cale Iorg .40 1.00
CJ Chris Johnson 1.50 4.00
CSA Carlos Santana AU 15.00 40.00
CT Chris Tillman AU 3.00 8.00
CV Chris Valaika .40 1.00
DC Daniel Cortes 1.00 2.50
DD Danny Duffy 1.25 3.00
DH David Hernandez AU 4.00 10.00
DS Daniel Schlereth AU 3.00 8.00
EA Elvis Andrus Jsy AU 8.00 20.00
EB Engel Beltre 1.25 3.00
EH Eric Hacker AU 3.00 8.00
EK Edward Kunz .60 1.50
FM Fernando Martinez Jsy AU 6.00 15.00
FS Fautino de los Santos .40 1.00
GB Gordon Beckham AU 6.00 15.00
GGH Gorkys Hernandez Jsy AU 5.00 12.00
GH Greg Halman AU 6.00 15.00
GP Gerardo Parra .40 1.00
GT Graham Taylor .40 1.00
IDA Ike Davis AU 15.00 40.00
JA Jake Arrieta Jsy AU 6.00 15.00
JB Jonathan Bachanov .40 1.00
JC Jhoulys Chacin 1.50 4.00
JD Jason Donald Jsy AU 5.00 12.00
JJ Jon Jay .60 1.50
JK Jason Knapp AU 5.00 12.00
JL Jeff Locke AU 4.00 10.00
JLC Jordan Czarniecki .40 1.00
JLI Josh Lindblom AU 3.00 8.00
JM Jake McGee .40 1.00
JM Jesus Montero Jsy AU 30.00 60.00
JR Javier Rodriguez AU 3.00 8.00
JS Justin Snyder .60 1.50
JSM Josh Smoker .40 1.00
JZ Jordan Zimmermann .40 1.00
KK Kala Kaaihue AU 3.00 8.00
KW Kenny Wilson .40 1.00
LA Lars Anderson AU 10.00 25.00
LC Lonnie Chisenhall AU 6.00 15.00
LL Lance Lynn AU 6.00 15.00
LM Logan Morrison 3.00 8.00
MB Mike Brantley .40 1.00
MC Mitch Canham .40 1.00
MD Michael Daniel .60 1.50
MI Matt Inouye .40 1.00
MM Mark Melancon AU 4.00 10.00
MR Matt Rizzotti .40 1.00
MW Michael Watt .40 1.00
NR Nick Romero .40 1.00
NV Niko Vasquez 1.00 2.50
PT Polin Trinidad AU 3.00 8.00
QM Quinton Miller AU 3.00 8.00
RK Ryan Kalish 1.00 2.50
RM Ryan Morris .60 1.50
RP Rick Porcello 2.00 5.00
RR Rusty Ryal .60 1.50
RT Rene Tosoni .40 1.00
SM Shairon Martis .60 1.50
ST Steve Tolleson .40 1.00
TF Tim Fedroff AU 3.00 8.00
TH Tom Hagan .40 1.00
VM Vin Mazzaro AU 3.00 8.00
XA Xavier Avery 1.00 2.50
YS Yunesky Sanchez .40 1.00
ZB Zach Britton 1.25 3.00

2008 Bowman Sterling Prospects Refractors

*PROS REF: 1X TO 2.5X BASIC
PROS REF ODDS 1:4 PACKS
*PROS AU REF: .75X TO 2X BASIC
PROS AU REF ODDS 1:5 PACKS
*PROS JSY AU REF: .75X TO 2X BASIC
PROS JSY AU REF ODDS 1:28 PACKS
REFRACTOR PRINT RUN 199 SER.#'d SETS
BP Buster Posey AU 75.00 150.00
JM Jesus Montero Jsy AU 50.00 100.00
RP Rick Porcello 15.00 40.00

2008 Bowman Sterling Prospects Black Refractors

BLK PROSPECT ODDS 1:30 PACKS
BLK PROSPECT AU ODDS 1:42 PACKS
BLK PROSPECT GU AU ODDS 1:231 PACKS
STATED PRINT RUN 25 SER.#'d SETS
NO PRICING DUE TO SCARCITY

2008 Bowman Sterling Prospects Gold Refractors

*PROS GLD: 3X TO 8X BASIC
RC GLD ODDS 1:15 PACKS
*PROS AU GLD: 2X TO 5X BASIC
PROS AU GLD ODDS 1:21 PACKS
*PROS JSY AU GLD: 1.5X TO 4X BASIC
PROS JSY AU GLD ODDS 1:113 PACKS
GOLD REF PRINT RUN 50 SER.#'d SETS
BP Buster Posey AU 125.00 250.00
EA Elvis Andrus Jsy AU 30.00 60.00
JA Jake Arrieta Jsy AU 40.00 80.00
JM Jesus Montero Jsy AU 75.00 150.00

2008 Bowman Sterling Prospects Red Refractors

RED PROSPECT ODDS 1:737 PACKS
RED PROSPECT AU ODDS 1:983 PACKS
RED PROSPECT GU AU ODDS 1:5057 PACKS
STATED PRINT RUN 1 SER.#'d SET
NO PRICING DUE TO SCARCITY

2008 Bowman Sterling WBC Patch

STATED ODDS 1:24 PACKS
EXCHANGE DEADLIN 12/31/2009
2 Ichiro Suzuki 60.00 120.00
4 Yulieski Gourriel
6 Michel Enriquez
8 Chenhao Li 6.00 15.00
9 Xiaotian Zhang 20.00 50.00
10 Po Hsuan Keng 6.00 15.00
12 Yoennis Cespedes 10.00 25.00
16 Masahiro Tanaka
17 Gift Ngoepe• 6.00 15.00
18 Juan Carlos Sulbaran 6.00 15.00
21 Nick Weglarz
22 Alexander Mayeta 6.00 15.00
NNO EXCH Card 50.00 100.00

2009 Bowman Sterling

COMMON CARD 1.00 2.50
COMMON AU 4.00 10.00
OVERALL AUTO ODDS TWO PER PACK
PRINTING PLATE ODDS 1:91 HOBBY
AU PRINTING PLATE ODDS 1:245 HOBBY
PLATE PRINT RUN 1 SET PER COLOR
BLACK-CYAN-MAGENTA-YELLOW ISSUED
NO PLATE PRICING DUE TO SCARCITY
AA Alex Avila RC 1.50 4.00
AB Antonio Bastardo AU RC 4.00 10.00
AB Andrew Bailey RC 2.50 6.00
AC Andrew Carpenter RC 1.50 4.00
AM Andrew McCutchen (RC) 4.00 10.00
BD Brian Duensing RC 1.50 4.00
BN Brad Nelson (RC) 1.00 2.50
BS Bobby Scales RC 1.50 4.00
CC Chris Coghlan RC 2.50 6.00
CM Casey McGehee AU (RC) 8.00 20.00
CR Colby Rasmus (RC) 2.50 6.00
CT Chris Tillman AU RC 4.00 10.00
DB Daniel Bard RC 1.00 2.50
DF Dexter Fowler (RC) 1.50 4.00
DH David Hernandez RC 1.00 2.50
DP David Price RC 2.50 6.00
DS Daniel Schlereth AU RC 4.00 10.00
EC Everth Cabrera RC 1.50 4.00
EY Eric Young Jr. RC 1.00 2.50
FC Francisco Cervelli RC 2.50 6.00
FM Fernando Martinez RC 2.50 6.00
FN Fu-Te Ni RC 1.50 4.00
GB Gordon Beckham AU RC 12.50 30.00
GG Greg Golson (RC) 1.00 2.50
GK George Kottaras (RC) 1.00 2.50
GP Gerardo Parra RC 1.50 4.00
JB Julio Borbon RC 1.50 4.00
JC Jhoulys Chacin RC 1.50 4.00
JH Jarrett Hoffpauir (RC) 1.00 2.50
JM Justin Masterson AU (RC) 6.00 15.00
JM Juan Miranda RC 1.50 4.00
JS Jordan Schafer (RC) 1.50 4.00
JZ Jordan Zimmermann RC 1.00 2.50
KB Kyle Blanks RC 1.50 4.00
KK Kenshin Kawakimi RC 1.50 4.00
KU Koji Uehara RC 1.50 4.00
MG Mat Gamel RC 2.50 6.00
ML Mat Latos RC 3.00 8.00
MM Mark Melancon RC 1.00 2.50
MS Michael Saunders RC 1.50 4.00
MT Matt Tuiasosopo (RC) 1.00 2.50
NR Nolan Reimold AU 6.00 15.00
NR Nolan Reimold (RC) 1.00 2.50
RP Ryan Perry AU RC 4.00 10.00
RP Rick Porcello RC 3.00 8.00
SR Shane Robinson RC 1.00 2.50
TC Trevor Crowe RC 1.00 2.50
TG Tyler Greene (RC) 1.00 2.50
TH Tommy Hanson AU RC 10.00 25.00
TS Travis Snider RC 1.50 4.00
WR Wilkin Ramirez RC 1.00 2.50
WV Will Venable RC 1.00 2.50
ABB Aaron Bates RC 1.00 2.50
CTT Carlos Torres RC 1.00 2.50
DFR David Freese RC 8.00 20.00
DHE Diory Hernandez RC 1.00 2.50
DHO Derek Holland RC 1.50 4.00
JHO Jamie Hoffmann RC 1.00 2.50
JMA John Mayberry Jr. (RC) 1.00 2.50

2009 Bowman Sterling Refractors

*REF: .5X TO 1.2X BASIC
REF ODDS 1:4 HOBBY
*REF AUTO: .5X TO 1.2X BASIC AUTO
REF AUTO ODDS 1:5 HOBBY
STATED PRINT RUN 199 SER.#'d SETS

2009 Bowman Sterling Black Refractors

STATED ODDS 1:25 HOBBY
STATED AU ODDS 1:45 HOBBY
STATED PRINT RUN 25 SER.#'d SETS
NO PRICING DUE TO SCARCITY

2009 Bowman Sterling Gold Refractors

*GOLD REF: 1X TO 2.5X BASIC
GOLD REF ODDS 1:15 HOBBY
*GOLD REF AU: .75X TO 2X BASIC AU
GOLD REF AU ODDS 1:21 HOBBY
STATED PRINT RUN 50 SER.#'d SETS

2009 Bowman Sterling Red Refractors

STATED ODDS 1:724 HOBBY
STATED AU ODDS 1:1022 HOBBY
STATED PRINT RUN 1 SER.#'d SET
NO PRICING DUE TO SCARCITY

2009 Bowman Sterling Dual Autographs

STATED ODDS 1:8 HOBBY
*REF: .5X TO 1.2 BASIC
REF.ODDS 1:27 HOBBY
REF. PRINT RUN 199 SER.#'d SETS
BLK REF ODDS 1:238 HOBBY
BLK REF PRINT RUN 25 SER.#'d SETS
NO BLACK PRICING DUE TO SCARCITY
*GLD REF: .75X TO 2X BASIC
GLD REF ODDS 1:111 HOBBY
GLD REF PRINT RUN 50 SER.#'d SETS
RED REF ODDS 1:4968 HOBBY
RED REF PRINT RUN 1 SER.#'d SETS
NO RED PRICING DUE TO SCARCITY
BPFC Buster Posey 30.00 60.00
Francisco Cervelli
BPGB Buster Posey 30.00 60.00
Gordon Beckham
CTDH Chris Tillman 5.00 12.00
David Hernandez
JKZC Jason Knapp 5.00 12.00
Zach Collier
JMFD Jenny Mejia 6.00 15.00
Felix Doubront
NRJR Nolan Reimold 6.00 15.00
Josh Reddick
RPCI Ryan Perry 5.00 12.00
Cale Iorg

2009 Bowman Sterling Prospects

OVERALL AUTO ODDS TWO PER PACK
PRINTING PLATE ODDS 1:91 HOBBY
AU PRINTING PLATE ODDS 1:245 HOBBY
PLATE PRINT RUN 1 SET PER COLOR
BLACK-CYAN-MAGENTA-YELLOW ISSUED
NO PLATE PRICING DUE TO SCARCITY
AA Abraham Almonte .75 2.00
AB Alex Buchholz 1.25 3.00
AF Alfredo Figaro .75 2.00
AM Adam Mills .75 2.00
AO Anthony Ortega .75 2.00
AP A.J. Pollock AU 5.00 12.00
AR Andrew Rundle 1.25 3.00
AS Alfredo Silverio .75 2.00
AW Alex White AU 5.00 12.00
BB Bobby Borchering AU 10.00 25.00
BB Brian Baisley .75 2.00
BO Brett Oberholtzer 1.25 3.00
BP Bryan Pelersen .75 2.00
CA Carmen Angelini .75 2.00
CH Chris Heisey AU 8.00 20.00
CJ Chad Jenkins AU 4.00 10.00
CL C.J. Lee .75 2.00
CM Carlos Martinez 1.25 3.00
DA Denny Almonte 1.25 3.00
DH Daniel Hudson AU 6.00 15.00
DP Dinesh Patel AU 3.00 8.00
DS Drew Storen AU 5.00 12.00
DV Dayan Viciedo AU 10.00 25.00
EA Eric Arnett AU 3.00 8.00
EA Ehire Adrianza 2.00 5.00
EC Edilio Colina 1.25 3.00
EK Erik Komatsu 1.25 3.00
FG Freddy Galvis 1.25 3.00
GV Greg Veloz .75 2.00
JC Jose Ceda .75 2.00
JG Justin Greene 1.25 3.00
JM Jared Mitchell AU 4.00 10.00
JR Jovan Rosa .75 2.00
JT Julio Teheran 6.00 15.00
JW Jordan Walden 1.25 3.00
KK Kyeong Kang 1.25 3.00
LE Luis Exposito 2.00 5.00
LJ Luis Jimenez 1.25 3.00
LS Luis Sumoza 1.25 3.00
MA Michael Almanzar 2.00 5.00
MC Michael Cisco 1.25 3.00
MH Matt Hobgood AU 8.00 20.00
ML Mike Leake AU 8.00 20.00
MM Matthew Moore 12.00 30.00
MM Mike Minor AU 6.00 15.00
MP Michael Pineda 12.00 30.00
MS Michael Swinson 1.25 3.00
MT Mike Trout AU 40.00 80.00
NB Nick Buss .75 2.00
NP Nelson Perez 1.25 3.00
NR Neil Ramirez 1.25 3.00
OT Oscar Tejeda 2.50 6.00
PP Petey Paramore 1.25 3.00
PV Pat Venditte AU 6.00 15.00
RD Rashun Dixon 2.00 5.00
RF Reymond Fuentes AU 4.00 10.00
RG Robbie Grossman AU 3.00 8.00
RS Rinku Singh AU 3.00 8.00
RT Ruben Tejada .75 2.00
SC Scott Campbell AU 3.00 8.00
SP Stolmy Pimentel 1.25 3.00
SW Christopher Schwinden .75 2.00
TF Tyler Flowers 2.00 5.00
TM Tyler Matzek AU 5.00 12.00
TS Tony Sanchez AU 8.00 20.00
TW Tim Wheeler AU 6.00 15.00
TY Tyler Yockey 1.25 3.00
WF Wilmer Font 2.00 5.00
WR Wilin Rosario 1.25 3.00
WS Will Smith 1.25 3.00
ZW Zack Wheeler AU 6.00 15.00
CJA Chad James AU 4.00 10.00
CLU Chad Lundahl .75 2.00
JMM Jiovanni Mier AU 5.00 12.00
JMO Jon Mark Owings .75 2.00
MAF Michael Affronti .75 2.00
RGR Randal Grichuk AU 6.00 15.00
TME Tommy Mendonca AU 5.00 12.00

2009 Bowman Sterling Prospects Refractors

*REF: .5X TO 1.2X BASIC
REF ODDS 1:4 HOBBY
*REF AUTO: .5X TO 1.2X BASIC AUTO
REF AUTO ODDS 1:5 HOBBY
STATED PRINT RUN 199 SER.#'d SETS
MT Mike Trout AU 60.00 120.00

2009 Bowman Sterling Prospects Black Refractors

STATED ODDS 1:29 HOBBY
STATED AU ODDS 1:45 HOBBY
STATED PRINT RUN 25 SER.#'d SETS
NO PRICING DUE TO SCARCITY

2009 Bowman Sterling Prospects Gold Refractors

*GOLD REF: 1.5X TO 4X BASIC
GOLD REF ODDS 1:15 HOBBY
*GOLD REF AU: .75X TO 2X BASIC AU
GOLD REF AU ODDS 1:21 HOBBY
STATED PRINT RUN 50 SER.#'d SETS
MT Mike Trout AU 150.00 300.00

2009 Bowman Sterling Prospects Red Refractors

STATED ODDS 1:724 HOBBY
STATED AU ODDS 1:1022 HOBBY
STATED PRINT RUN 1 SER.#'d SET
NO PRICING DUE TO SCARCITY

2009 Bowman Sterling WBC Relics

STATED ODDS ONE PER PACK
AC Aroldis Chapman 6.00 15.00
AM Alexander Mayeta 3.00 8.00
AO Adam Ottavino 3.00 8.00
AS Alexander Smit 3.00 8.00
BW Bernie Williams 3.00 8.00
CL Chenhao Li 3.00 8.00
CR Concepcion Rodriguez 3.00 8.00
DL Dae Ho Lee 4.00 10.00
DN Drew Naylor 3.00 8.00
EG Edgar Gonzalez 3.00 8.00
FC Frederich Cepeda 3.00 8.00
FF Fei Feng 3.00 8.00
FN Fu-Te Ni 5.00 12.00
GH Greg Halman 3.00 8.00
HC Hung-Wen Chen 3.00 8.00
HO Hein Robb 3.00 8.00
HR Hanley Ramirez 3.00 8.00
IS Ichiro Suzuki 15.00 40.00
JC Johnny Cueto 3.00 8.00
JE Justin Erasmus 3.00 8.00
JL Jae Woo Lee 3.00 8.00
JS Juancarlos Sulbaran 3.00 8.00
KF Kosuke Fukudome 5.00 12.00
KK Kwang-Hyun Kim 4.00 10.00
KL Kai Liu 3.00 8.00
LH Luke Hughes 3.00 8.00
LR Luis Rodriguez 3.00 8.00
MC Miguel Cabrera 3.00 8.00
MD Mitchell Dening 3.00 8.00
ME Michel Enriquez 3.00 8.00
MT Miguel Tejada 3.00 8.00
NA Norichika Aoki 6.00 15.00
NP Nick Punto 3.00 8.00
NW Nick Weglarz 3.00 8.00
PA Phillippe Aumont 4.00 10.00
PK Po-Hsuan Keng 3.00 8.00
PM Pedro Martinez 3.00 8.00
RM Russell Martin 3.00 8.00
SA Shinnosuke Abe 5.00 12.00
SC Shin-Soo Choo 5.00 12.00
TK Tae Kyun Kim 4.00 10.00
XZ Xiaotian Zhang 3.00 8.00
YC Yoennis Cespedes 10.00 25.00
YD Yu Darvish 20.00 50.00
YG Yulieski Gourriel 3.00 8.00
HRR Hyun-Jin Ryu 4.00 10.00
JCC Jorge Cantu 3.00 8.00
JLL Jin Young Lee 4.00 10.00
LHH Liam Hendriks 3.00 8.00

2009 Bowman Sterling WBC Relics Refractors

*REF: .5X TO 1.2X BASIC
REF ODDS 1:5 HOBBY
REF PRINT RUN 199 SER.#'d SETS
YC Yoennis Cespedes 20.00 50.00

2009 Bowman Sterling WBC Relics Black Refractors

STATED ODDS 1:33 HOBBY
STATED PRINT RUN 25 SER.#'d SETS
NO PRICING DUE TO SCARCITY

2009 Bowman Sterling WBC Relics Blue Refractors

*BLUE REF: .5X TO 1.2X BASIC
BLUE REF ODDS ONE PER BOX LOADER
BLUE PRINT RUN 125 SER.#'d SETS
FN Fu-Te Ni 12.50 30.00
YC Yoennis Cespedes 20.00 50.00
YD Yu Darvish 50.00 100.00
HRR Hyun-Jin Ryu 10.00 25.00

2009 Bowman Sterling WBC Relics Gold Refractors

*GOLD REF: .75X TO 2X BASIC
GOLD REF ODDS 1:21 HOBBY

GOLD REF PRINT RUN 50 SER.#'d SETS
FN Fu-Te Ni 30.00 60.00
YC Yoennis Cespedes 50.00 100.00
YD Yu Darvish 100.00 200.00
HRR Hyun-Jin Ryu 20.00 50.00

2009 Bowman Sterling WBC Relics Red Refractors

STATED ODDS 1:724 HOBBY
STATED PRINT RUN 1 SER.#'d SET
NO PRICING DUE TO SCARCITY

2010 Bowman Sterling

COMMON CARD .75 2.00
PRINTING PLATE ODDS 1:105 HOBBY
PLATE PRINT RUN 1 SET PER COLOR
BLACK-CYAN-MAGENTA-YELLOW ISSUED
NO PLATE PRICING DUE TO SCARCITY
1 Stephen Strasburg RC 5.00 12.00
2 Josh Bell (RC) .75 2.00
3 Starlin Castro RC 3.00 8.00
4 J.P. Arencibia RC 1.25 3.00
5 Brennan Boesch RC 2.00 5.00
6 Ike Davis RC 2.00 5.00
7 Madison Bumgarner RC 2.00 5.00
8 Austin Jackson RC 1.25 3.00
9 Andrew Cashner RC .75 2.00
10 Jose Tabata RC 2.00 5.00
11 Wade Davis (RC) .75 2.00
12 Felix Doubront RC .75 2.00
13 Mike Leake RC 2.50 6.00
14 Logan Morrison RC 1.25 3.00
15 Brian Matusz RC 2.00 5.00
16 Trevor Plouffe (RC) .75 2.00
17 Mike Stanton RC 3.00 8.00
18 Drew Storen RC 1.25 3.00
19 Tyler Colvin RC 1.25 3.00
20 Jason Heyward RC 5.00 12.00
21 Jake Arrieta RC 1.25 3.00
22 Daniel Hudson RC 1.25 3.00
23 Buster Posey RC 8.00 20.00
24 Neil Walker (RC) 1.25 3.00
25 Carlos Santana RC 2.50 6.00
26 Josh Thole RC 1.25 3.00
27 Dayan Viciedo RC 1.25 3.00
28 Wilson Ramos RC 2.00 5.00
29 Ian Desmond (RC) 1.25 3.00
30 John Ely RC .75 2.00
31 Daniel Nava RC 1.25 3.00
32 Chris Nelson (RC) 1.25 3.00
33 Andy Oliver RC .75 2.00
34 Danny Valencia RC 5.00 12.00
35 Brad Lincoln RC 1.25 3.00
36 Domonic Brown RC 3.00 8.00
37 Jay Sborz (RC) .75 2.00
38 Daniel McCutchen RC 1.25 3.00
39 Eric Young Jr. (RC) .75 2.00
40 Peter Bourjos RC 1.25 3.00
41 Drew Stubbs RC 2.00 5.00
42 Chris Heisey RC 1.25 3.00
43 Jason Castro RC 2.00 5.00
44 Jason Donald RC .75 2.00
45 Ruben Tejada RC 1.25 3.00
46 Jon Jay RC 1.25 3.00
47 Travis Wood (RC) 1.25 3.00
48 Ryan Kalish RC 1.25 3.00
49 Mike Minor RC 1.25 3.00
50 Brett Wallace RC 2.00 5.00

2010 Bowman Sterling Refractors

*REF: .75X TO 2X BASIC
STATED ODDS 1:5 HOBBY
STATED PRINT RUN 199 SER.#'d SETS
1 Stephen Strasburg 20.00 50.00

2010 Bowman Sterling Black Refractors

STATED ODDS 1:34 HOBBY
STATED PRINT RUN 25 SER.#'d SETS
NO PRICING DUE TO SCARCITY

2010 Bowman Sterling Gold Refractors

*GOLD REF: 1.5X TO 4X BASIC
STATED ODDS 1:17 HOBBY
STATED PRINT RUN 50 SER.#'d SETS
1 Stephen Strasburg 75.00 150.00

2010 Bowman Sterling Purple Refractors

STATED ODDS 1:86 HOBBY
STATED PRINT RUN 10 SER.#'d SETS
NO PRICING DUE TO SCARCITY

2010 Bowman Sterling Red Refractors

STATED ODDS 1:834 HOBBY
STATED PRINT RUN 1 SER.#'d SET
NO PRICING DUE TO SCARCITY

2010 Bowman Sterling Dual Relics

ONE PER BOX TOPPER
STATED PRINT RUN 199 SER.#'d SETS
BL1 Albert Pujols 8.00 20.00
Miguel Cabrera
BL2 Derek Jeter 8.00 20.00
Hanley Ramirez
BL3 Joe Mauer 4.00 10.00
Brian McCann
BL4 Alex Rodriguez 8.00 20.00
Evan Longoria
BL5 Ryan Braun 5.00 12.00
Justin Upton
BL6 Prince Fielder 4.00 10.00
Pablo Sandoval
BL7 Roy Halladay 8.00 20.00
Cliff Lee
BL8 Josh Hamilton 4.00 10.00
Nelson Cruz
BL9 Jason Heyward 10.00 25.00
Mike Stanton
BL10 Ichiro Suzuki 15.00 40.00
Albert Pujols
BL11 Adrian Gonzalez 4.00 10.00
Justin Morneau
BL12 Dustin Pedroia 5.00 12.00
Kevin Youkilis
BL13 Mark Teixeira 4.00 10.00
Chipper Jones
BL14 Chase Utley 5.00 12.00
Robinson Cano
BL15 David Wright 5.00 12.00
Ryan Zimmerman
BL16 Jimmy Rollins 4.00 10.00
Ryan Howard
BL17 Stephen Strasburg 12.50 30.00
Jason Heyward
BL18 Troy Tulowitzki 5.00 12.00
Carlos Gonzalez
BL19 Derek Jeter 15.00 40.00
Alex Rodriguez

2010 Bowman Sterling Dual Relics Refractors

*REF: .5X TO 1.2X BASIC
STATED ODDS 1:4 BOXES
STATED PRINT RUN 99 SER.#'d SETS

2010 Bowman Sterling Dual Relics Black Refractors

STATED ODDS 1:16 BOXES
STATED PRINT RUN 25 SER.#'d SETS
NO PRICING DUE TO SCARCITY

2010 Bowman Sterling Dual Relics Gold Refractors

*GOLD REF: .6X TO 1.5X BASIC
STATED ODDS 1:8 BOXES
STATED PRINT RUN 50 SER.#'d SETS

2010 Bowman Sterling Dual Relics Red Refractors

STATED ODDS 1:371 BOXES
STATED PRINT RUN 1 SER.#'d SET
NO PRICING DUE TO SCARCITY

2010 Bowman Sterling Prospect Autographs

RANDOM INSERTS IN PACKS
PRINTING PLATE ODDS 1:250 HOBBY
PLATE PRINT RUN 1 SET PER COLOR
BLACK-CYAN-MAGENTA-YELLOW ISSUED
NO PLATE PRICING DUE TO SCARCITY
AC Aroldis Chapman 12.50 30.00
AM Aaron Miller 4.00 10.00
AW Alex Wimmers 4.00 10.00
CB Chad Bettis 3.00 8.00
CR Chance Ruffin 3.00 8.00
CS Chris Sale 3.00 8.00
CY Christian Yelich 6.00 15.00
DD Delino DeShields 4.00 10.00
DM Deck McGuire 3.00 8.00
DP Drew Pomeranz 6.00 15.00
GB Gary Brown 8.00 20.00
HS Hayden Simpson 4.00 10.00
JB Jesse Biddle 5.00 12.00
JS John Singleton 12.50 30.00
JS Jake Skole 4.00 10.00
JT Jameson Taillon 12.50 30.00
JW Justin Wilson 3.00 8.00
KD Kellin Deglan 3.00 8.00
MF Mike Foltynewicz 3.00 8.00
ML Matt Lipka 6.00 15.00
MO Mike Olt 6.00 15.00
PT Peter Tago 3.00 8.00
RL Ryan Lavarnway 10.00 25.00
SB Seth Blair 3.00 8.00
TB Tim Beckham 6.00 15.00
TJ Tyrell Jenkins 4.00 10.00
TL Taylor Lindsey 3.00 8.00
YG Yasmani Grandal 5.00 12.00
ZL Zach Lee 6.00 15.00
CCO Christian Colon 5.00 12.00
CPU Cesar Puello 5.00 12.00
RBO Ryan Bolden 3.00 8.00
TWA Taijuan Walker 8.00 20.00

2010 Bowman Sterling Prospect Autographs Refractors

*REF: .75X TO 2X BASIC
STATED ODDS 1:6 HOBBY
STATED PRINT RUN 199 SER.#'d SETS

2010 Bowman Sterling Prospect Autographs Black Refractors

STATED ODDS 1:42 HOBBY
STATED PRINT RUN 25 SER.#'d SETS
NO PRICING DUE TO SCARCITY

2010 Bowman Sterling Prospect Autographs Gold Refractors

*GOLD REF: 2.5X TO 6X BASIC
STATED ODDS 1:21 HOBBY
STATED PRINT RUN 50 SER.#'d SETS
AC Aroldis Chapman 50.00 100.00

2010 Bowman Sterling Prospect Autographs Red Refractors

STATED ODDS 1:1027 HOBBY
STATED PRINT RUN 1 SER.#'d SET
NO PRICING DUE TO SCARCITY

2010 Bowman Sterling Prospects

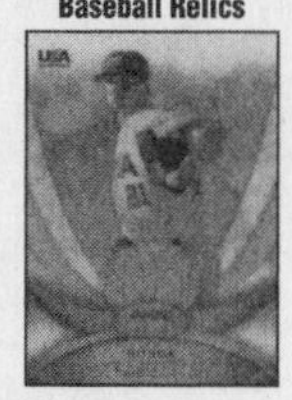

PRINTING PLATE ODDS 1:105 HOBBY
PLATE PRINT RUN 1 SET PER COLOR
BLACK-CYAN-MAGENTA-YELLOW ISSUED
NO PLATE PRICING DUE TO SCARCITY
AA Alexia Amarista .50 1.25
AC Aroldis Chapman 2.00 5.00
AD Allan Dykstra .50 1.25
AH Adeinis Hechavarria .50 1.25
AR Anthony Rizzo 1.50 4.00
AV Arodys Vizcaino .75 2.00
BJ Brett Jackson 1.50 4.00
BM Bryan Mitchell .50 1.25
BO Brett Oberholtzer .50 1.25
BS Brandon Short .50 1.25
CA Chris Archer 2.50 6.00
CJ Corban Joseph .50 1.25
CM Chris Masters .50 1.25
CP Carlos Peguero .75 2.00
DA Dustin Ackley 3.00 8.00
DC Drew Cumberland .50 1.25
DF Daniel Fields .50 1.25
DT Donavan Tate 1.25 3.00
GG Grant Green .75 2.00
GS Gary Sanchez 1.50 4.00
HL Hak-Ju Lee 2.00 5.00
JH J.J. Hoover .50 1.25
JI Jose Iglesias 2.00 5.00
JL John Lamb 1.25 3.00
JM J.D. Martinez 2.00 5.00
JS John Singleton 2.50 6.00
KG Kyle Gibson 2.00 5.00
KS Konrad Schmidt .50 1.25
MD Matt Davidson .75 2.00
MP Marlin Perez .75 2.00
MS Miguel Sano 2.50 6.00
NA Nolan Arenado 1.50 4.00
RB Rex Brothers .50 1.25
RE Robbie Erlin 1.25 3.00
SH Steven Hensley .50 1.25
SM Shelby Miller 2.00 5.00
SV Sebastian Valle .75 2.00
TB Tim Beckham 1.25 3.00
TC Tyler Chatwood .50 1.25
TN Thomas Neal .75 2.00
WM Wil Myers 2.50 6.00
YA Yonder Alonso 1.25 3.00
CPU Cesar Puello .50 1.25
FPE Francisco Peguero .50 1.25
JOS Josh Satin .75 2.00
JRM J.R. Murphy .75 2.00
JSA Jerry Sands 1.25 3.00
JSE Jean Segura 1.25 3.00
MKE Max Kepler .75 2.00
WMI Will Middlebrooks .75 2.00

2010 Bowman Sterling Prospects Refractors

*REF: 1X TO 2.5X BASIC
STATED ODDS 1:5 HOBBY
STATED PRINT RUN 199 SER.#'d SETS
SM Shelby Miller 10.00 25.00

2010 Bowman Sterling Prospects Black Refractors

STATED ODDS 1:34 HOBBY
STATED PRINT RUN 25 SER.#'d SETS
NO PRICING DUE TO SCARCITY

2010 Bowman Sterling Prospects Gold Refractors

*GOLD REF: 1.5X TO 4X BASIC
STATED ODDS 1:17 HOBBY
STATED PRINT RUN 50 SER.#'d SETS
DA Dustin Ackley 40.00 80.00
SM Shelby Miller 15.00 40.00

2010 Bowman Sterling Prospects Purple Refractors

STATED ODDS 1:86 HOBBY
STATED PRINT RUN 10 SER.#'d SETS
NO PRICING DUE TO SCARCITY

2010 Bowman Sterling Prospects Red Refractors

STATED ODDS 1:834 HOBBY
STATED PRINT RUN 1 SER.#'d SET
NO PRICING DUE TO SCARCITY

2010 Bowman Sterling Rookie Autographs

STATED ODDS 1:
STRASBURG ODDS 1:25 HOBBY
EXCHANGE DEADLINE 12/31/2013
PRINTING PLATE ODDS 1:250 HOBBY
STRASBURG PLATE ODDS 1:10,014 HOBBY
PLATE PRINT RUN 1 SET PER COLOR
BLACK-CYAN-MAGENTA-YELLOW ISSUED
NO PLATE PRICING DUE TO SCARCITY
1 Stephen Strasburg 60.00 120.00
10 Jose Tabata 8.00 20.00
20 Jason Heyward 30.00 60.00
22 Daniel Hudson 5.00 12.00
25 Carlos Santana 8.00 20.00
34 Danny Valencia 15.00 40.00
36 Domonic Brown 12.50 30.00
43 Josh Tomlin 5.00 12.00
46 Jon Jay 4.00 10.00
47 Travis Wood 6.00 15.00

2010 Bowman Sterling Rookie Autographs Refractors

*REF: .5X TO 1.2X BASIC
STATED ODDS 1:6 HOBBY
STRASBURG ODDS 1:212 HOBBY
STATED PRINT RUN 199 SER.#'d SETS
EXCHANGE DEADLINE 12/31/2013
1 Stephen Strasburg 75.00 150.00
36 Domonic Brown 30.00 60.00

2010 Bowman Sterling Rookie Autographs Black Refractors

STATED ODDS 1:42 HOBBY
STRASBURG ODDS 1:1741 HOBBY
STATED PRINT RUN 25 SER.#'d SETS
NO PRICING DUE TO SCARCITY
EXCHANGE DEADLINE 12/31/2013

2010 Bowman Sterling Rookie Autographs Gold Refractors

*GOLD: 1.2X TO 3X BASIC
STATED ODDS 1:21 HOBBY
STRASBURG ODDS 1:852 HOBBY
STATED PRINT RUN 50 SER.#'d SETS
EXCHANGE DEADLINE 12/31/2013
1 Stephen Strasburg 200.00 300.00
36 Domonic Brown 75.00 150.00

2010 Bowman Sterling Rookie Autographs Red Refractors

STATED ODDS 1:1027 HOBBY
STRASBURG ODDS 1:40,056 HOBBY
STATED PRINT RUN 1 SER.#'d SET
NO PRICING DUE TO SCARCITY
EXCHANGE DEADLINE 12/31/2013

2010 Bowman Sterling USA Baseball Autograph Relics

STATED ODDS 1:48 HOBBY
STATED PRINT RUN 25 SER.#'d SETS
NO PRICING DUE TO SCARCITY

2010 Bowman Sterling USA Baseball Autograph Relics Red

STATED ODDS 1:976 HOBBY
STATED PRINT RUN 1 SER.#'d SET
NO PRICING DUE TO SCARCITY

2010 Bowman Sterling USA Baseball Dual Autographs

NATIONAL TEAM ODDS 1:27 HOBBY
18U TEAM ODDS 1:18 HOBBY
PRINTING PLATE ODDS 1:494 HOBBY
PLATE PRINT RUN 1 SET PER COLOR
BLACK-CYAN-MAGENTA-YELLOW ISSUED
NO PLATE PRICING DUE TO SCARCITY
BSDA1 Tony Wolters 4.00 10.00
Nicky Delmonico
BSDA2 Phillip Pfeifer III 8.00 20.00
Henry Owens
BSDA3 Christian Lopes 5.00 12.00
Francisco Lindor
BSDA4 Bubba Starling 12.50 30.00
Lance McCullers
BSDA5 Blake Swihart 5.00 12.00
Daniel Camarena
BSDA6 Dillon Maples 4.00 10.00
A.J. Vanegas
BSDA7 Michael Lorenzen 4.00 10.00
Christian Montgomery
BSDA8 Albert Almora 5.00 12.00
Marcus Littlewood
BSDA9 John Hochstatter 4.00 10.00
Brian Ragira
BSDA10 John Simms 4.00 10.00
Elvin Soto
BSDA11 Matt Barnes 5.00 12.00
Brad Miller
BSDA12 Gerrit Cole 20.00 50.00
Jackie Bradley Jr.
BSDA13 Sonny Gray 12.50 30.00
George Springer
BSDA14 Ryan Wright 4.00 10.00
Nolan Fontana
BSDA15 Andrew Maggi 4.00 10.00
Kyle Winkler
BSDA16 Peter O'Brien 4.00 10.00
Alex Dickerson
BSDA17 Jason Esposito 4.00 10.00
Sean Gilmartin
BSDA18 Nick Ramirez 4.00 10.00
Steve Rodriguez
BSDA19 Tyler Anderson 8.00 20.00
Scott McGough
BSDA20 Noe Ramirez 4.00 10.00
Brett Mooneyham
BSDA21 Mikie Mahtook 5.00 12.00
Brian Johnson

2010 Bowman Sterling USA Baseball Dual Autographs Refractors

*REF: .5X TO 1.2X BASIC
STATED ODDS 1:21 HOBBY
STATED PRINT RUN 99 SER.#'d SETS

2010 Bowman Sterling USA Baseball Dual Autographs Black Refractors

STATED ODDS 1:87 HOBBY
STATED PRINT RUN 25 SER.#'d SETS
NO PRICING DUE TO SCARCITY

2010 Bowman Sterling USA Baseball Dual Autographs Gold Refractors

*GOLD REF: .75X TO 2X BASIC
STATED ODDS 1:42 HOBBY
STATED PRINT RUN 50 SER.#'d SETS

2010 Bowman Sterling USA Baseball Relics

RANDOM INSERTS IN PACKS
USAR1 Albert Almora 2.50 6.00
USAR2 Daniel Camarena 2.50 6.00
USAR3 Nicky Delmonico 2.50 6.00
USAR4 John Hochstatter 2.50 6.00
USAR5 Francisco Lindor 2.50 6.00
USAR6 Marcus Littlewood 2.50 6.00
USAR7 Christian Lopes 2.50 6.00
USAR8 Michael Lorenzen 2.50 6.00
USAR9 Dillon Maples 2.50 6.00
USAR10 Lance McCullers 2.50 6.00
USAR11 Ricardo Jacquez 2.50 6.00
USAR12 Henry Owens 2.50 6.00
USAR13 Phillip Pfeifer 2.50 6.00
USAR14 Brian Ragira 2.50 6.00
USAR15 John Simms 2.50 6.00
USAR16 Elvin Soto 2.50 6.00
USAR17 Bubba Starling 6.00 15.00
USAR18 Blake Swihart 2.50 6.00
USAR19 A.J. Vanegas 2.50 6.00
USAR20 Tony Wolters 2.50 6.00
USAR21 Tyler Anderson 2.50 6.00
USAR22 Matt Barnes 3.00 8.00
USAR23 Jackie Bradley Jr. 3.00 8.00
USAR24 Gerrit Cole 4.00 10.00
USAR25 Alex Dickerson 2.50 6.00
USAR26 Jason Esposito 2.50 6.00
USAR27 Nolan Fontana 2.50 6.00
USAR28 Sean Gilmartin 2.50 6.00
USAR29 Sonny Gray 2.50 6.00
USAR30 Brian Johnson 2.50 6.00
USAR31 Andrew Maggi 2.50 6.00
USAR32 Mikie Mahtook 2.50 6.00
USAR33 Scott McGough 2.50 6.00
USAR34 Brad Miller 2.50 6.00
USAR35 Brett Mooneyham 2.50 6.00
USAR36 Peter O'Brien 2.50 6.00
USAR37 Nick Ramirez 2.50 6.00
USAR38 Noe Ramirez 2.50 6.00
USAR39 Steve Rodriguez 2.50 6.00
USAR40 George Springer 3.00 8.00
USAR41 Kyle Winkler 2.50 6.00
USAR42 Ryan Wright 2.50 6.00

2010 Bowman Sterling USA Baseball Relics Refractors

*REF: .5X TO 1.2X BASIC
STATED ODDS 1:6 HOBBY
STATED PRINT RUN 99 SER.#'d SETS

2010 Bowman Sterling USA Baseball Relics Gold Refractors

*GOLD REF: .6X TO 1.5X BASIC
STATED ODDS 1:22 HOBBY
STATED PRINT RUN 50 SER.#'d SETS

1994 Bowman's Best

This 200-card standard-size set (produced by Topps) consists of 90 veteran stars, 90 rookies and prospects and 20 Mirror Image cards. The veteran cards have red fronts and are designated 1R-90R. The rookies and prospects cards have blue fronts and are designated 1B-90B. The Mirror Image cards feature a veteran star and a prospect matched by position in a horizontal design. These cards are numbered 91-110. Subsets featured are Super Vet (1R-6R), Super Rookie (82R-90R), and Blue Chip (1B-11B). Rookie Cards include Edgardo Alfonzo, Tony Clark, Brad Fullmer, Chan Ho Park, Jorge Posada and Edgar Renteria.

COMPLETE SET (200) 15.00 40.00
B1 Chipper Jones .50 1.25
B2 Derek Jeter 1.50 4.00
B3 Bill Pulsipher .20 .50
B4 James Baldwin .08 .25
B5 Brooks Kieschnick RC .20 .50
B6 Justin Thompson .08 .25
B7 Midre Cummings .08 .25
B8 Joey Hamilton .08 .25
B9 Pokey Reese .08 .25
B10 Brian Barber .08 .25
B11 John Burke .08 .25
B12 DeShawn Warren .08 .25
B13 Edgardo Alfonzo RC .40 1.00
B14 Eddie Pearson RC .20 .50
B15 Jimmy Haynes .08 .25
B16 Danny Bautista .08 .25
B17 Roger Cedeno .08 .25
B18 Jon Lieber .20 .50
B19 Billy Wagner RC 2.00 5.00
B20 Tate Seefried RC .20 .50
B21 Chad Mottola .08 .25
B22 Jose Malave .08 .25
B23 Terrell Wade RC .20 .50
B24 Shane Andrews .08 .25
B25 Chan Ho Park RC .60 1.50
B26 Kirk Presley RC .20 .50
B27 Robbie Beckett .08 .25
B28 Orlando Miller .08 .25
B29 Jorge Posada RC 4.00 10.00
B30 Frankie Rodriguez .08 .25
B31 Brian L. Hunter .08 .25
B32 Billy Ashley .08 .25
B33 Rondell White .20 .50
B34 John Roper .08 .25
B35 Marc Valdes .08 .25
B36 Scott Ruffcorn .08 .25
B37 Rod Henderson .08 .25
B38 Curtis Goodwin RC .20 .50
B39 Russ Davis .08 .25
B40 Rick Gorecki .08 .25
B41 Johnny Damon .50 1.25
B42 Roberto Petagine .08 .25
B43 Chris Snopek .08 .25
B44 Mark Acre RC .20 .50
B45 Todd Hollandsworth .08 .25
B46 Shawn Green .50 1.25
B47 John Carter RC .20 .50
B48 Jim Pittsley RC .20 .50
B49 John Wasdin RC .20 .50
B50 D.J. Boston RC .20 .50
B51 Tim Clark .08 .25
B52 Alex Ochoa .08 .25
B53 Chad Roper .08 .25
B54 Mike Kelly .08 .25
B55 Brad Fullmer RC .40 1.00
B56 Carl Everett .20 .50
B57 Tim Belk RC .20 .50
B58 Jimmy Hurst RC .20 .50
B59 Mac Suzuki RC .40 1.00
B60 Mike Moore .08 .25
B61 Alan Benes RC .20 .50
B62 Tony Clark RC .60 1.50
B63 Edgar Renteria RC 2.50 6.00
B64 Trey Beamon .08 .25
B65 LaTroy Hawkins RC .40 1.00
B66 Wayne Gomes RC .40 1.00
B67 Ray McDavid .08 .25
B68 John Dettmer .08 .25
B69 Willie Greene .08 .25
B70 Dave Stevens .08 .25
B71 Kevin Orie RC .20 .50
B72 Chad Ogea .08 .25
B73 Ben Van Ryn RC .20 .50
B74 Kym Ashworth RC .20 .50
B75 Dmitri Young .20 .50
B76 Herbert Perry RC .20 .50
B77 Joey Eischen .08 .25
B78 Arquimedez Pozo RC .20 .50
B79 Ugueth Urbina .08 .25
B80 Keith Williams RC .20 .50
B81 John Frascatore RC .20 .50
B82 Garey Ingram RC .20 .50
B83 Aaron Small .08 .25
B84 Olmedo Saenz RC .20 .50
B85 Jesus Tavarez RC .20 .50
B86 Jose Silva RC .40 1.00
B87 Jay Witasick RC .20 .50
B88 Jay Maldonado RC .20 .50
B89 Keith Heberling RC .20 .50
B90 Rusty Greer RC .60 1.50
R1 Paul Molitor .20 .50
R2 Eddie Murray .50 1.25
R3 Ozzie Smith .75 2.00
R4 Rickey Henderson .50 1.25
R5 Lee Smith .20 .50
R6 Dave Winfield .20 .50
R7 Roberto Alomar .30 .75
R8 Matt Williams .20 .50
R9 Mark Grace .30 .75
R10 Lance Johnson .08 .25
R11 Darren Daulton .20 .50
R12 Tom Glavine .30 .75
R13 Gary Sheffield .20 .50
R14 Rod Beck .08 .25
R15 Fred McGriff .30 .75
R16 Joe Carter .20 .50
R17 Dante Bichette .20 .50
R18 Danny Tartabull .08 .25
R19 Juan Gonzalez .20 .50
R20 Steve Avery .08 .25
R21 John Wetteland .20 .50
R22 Ben McDonald .08 .25
R23 Jack McDowell .08 .25
R24 Jose Canseco .30 .75
R25 Tim Salmon .30 .75
R26 Wilson Alvarez .08 .25
R27 Gregg Jefferies .08 .25
R28 John Burkett .08 .25
R29 Greg Vaughn .08 .25
R30 Robin Ventura .20 .50
R31 Paul O'Neill .30 .75
R32 Cecil Fielder .20 .50
R33 Kevin Mitchell .08 .25
R34 Jeff Conine .20 .50
R35 Carlos Baerga .08 .25
R36 Greg Maddux .75 2.00
R37 Roger Clemens 1.00 2.50
R38 Deion Sanders .30 .75
R39 Delino DeShields .08 .25
R40 Ken Griffey Jr. .75 2.00
R41 Albert Belle .20 .50
R42 Wade Boggs .30 .75
R43 Andres Galarraga .20 .50
R44 Aaron Sele .08 .25
R45 Don Mattingly 1.25 3.00
R46 David Cone .20 .50
R47 Len Dykstra .20 .50
R48 Brett Butler .20 .50
R49 Bill Swift .08 .25
R50 Bobby Bonilla .20 .50
R51 Rafael Palmeiro .30 .75
R52 Moises Alou .20 .50
R53 Jeff Bagwell .30 .75
R54 Mike Mussina .30 .75
R55 Frank Thomas .50 1.25
R56 Jose Rijo .08 .25
R57 Ruben Sierra .20 .50
R58 Randy Myers .08 .25
R59 Barry Bonds 1.25 3.00
R60 Jimmy Key .20 .50
R61 Travis Fryman .20 .50
R62 John Olerud .20 .50
R63 David Justice .20 .50
R64 Ray Lankford .20 .50
R65 Bob Tewksbury .08 .25
R66 Chuck Carr .08 .25
R67 Jay Buhner .20 .50
R68 Kenny Lofton .20 .50
R69 Marquis Grissom .20 .50
R70 Sammy Sosa .50 1.25
R71 Cal Ripken 1.50 4.00
R72 Ellis Burks .20 .50
R73 Jeff Montgomery .08 .25
R74 Julio Franco .20 .50
R75 Kirby Puckett .50 1.25
R76 Larry Walker .20 .50
R77 Andy Van Slyke .30 .75
R78 Tony Gwynn .60 1.50
R79 Will Clark .30 .75
R80 Mo Vaughn .20 .50
R81 Mike Piazza 1.00 2.50
R82 James Mouton .08 .25
R83 Carlos Delgado .30 .75
R84 Ryan Klesko .20 .50
R85 Javier Lopez .20 .50
R86 Raul Mondesi .20 .50
R87 Cliff Floyd .20 .50
R88 Manny Ramirez .50 1.25
R89 Hector Carrasco .08 .25
R90 Jeff Granger .08 .25
X91 Frank Thomas .30 .75
Dmitri Young
X92 Fred McGriff .20 .50
Brooks Kieschnick
X93 Matt Williams .08 .25
Shane Andrews
X94 Cal Ripken .75 2.00
Kevin Orie
X95 Barry Larkin .75 2.00
Derek Jeter
X96 Ken Griffey Jr. .40 1.00
Johnny Damon
X97 Barry Bonds .60 1.50
Rondell White
X98 Albert Belle .20 .50
Jimmy Hurst
X99 Raul Mondesi .20 .50
Ruben Rivera RC
X100 Roger Clemens .50 1.25
Scott Ruffcorn
X101 Greg Maddux .50 1.25
John Wasdin
X102 Tim Salmon .30 .75
Chad Mottola
X103 Carlos Baerga .08 .25
Arquimedez Pozo
X104 Mike Piazza .50 1.25
Bobby Hughes
X105 Carlos Delgado .30 .75
Melvin Nieves
X106 Javier Lopez 1.00 2.50
Jorge Posada
X107 Manny Ramirez .50 1.25
Jose Malave
X108 Travis Fryman .30 .75
Chipper Jones
X109 Steve Avery .08 .25
Bill Pulsipher
X110 John Olerud .50 1.25
Shawn Green

1994 Bowman's Best Refractors

This 200-card standard-size set is a parallel to the basic Bowman's Best issue. The cards were randomly inserted in packs at a rate of one in nine packs. The only difference is the refractive coating on front that allows for a brighter, shinier appearance.

*RED STARS: 4X TO 10X BASIC CARDS
*BLUE STARS: 4X TO 10X BASIC CARDS
*BLUE ROOKIES: 1.5X TO 4X BASIC
*MIRROR IMAGE STARS: 2X TO 5X BASIC
STATED ODDS 1:9
B2 Derek Jeter 30.00 60.00
B63 Edgar Renteria 10.00 25.00

1995 Bowman's Best

This 195 card standard-size set (produced by Topps) consists of 90 veteran stars, 90 rookies and prospects and 15 dual player Mirror Image cards. The packs contain seven cards and the suggested retail price was $5. The veteran cards have red fronts and are designated R1-R90. Cards of rookies and prospects have blue fronts and are designated B1-B90. The Mirror Image cards feature a veteran star and a prospect matched by position in a horizontal design. These cards are numbered X1-X15. Rookie Cards include Bob Abreu, Bartolo Colon, Scott Elarton, Juan Encarnacion, Vladimir Guerrero, Andruw Jones, Hideo Nomo, Rey Ordonez, Scott Rolen and Richie Sexson.

COMPLETE SET (195) 125.00 250.00

COMMON CARD (B1-R90)	.20	.50
COMMON CARD (X1-X15)	.20	.50
B1 Derek Jeter	1.25	3.00
B2 Vladimir Guerrero RC	10.00	25.00
B3 Bob Abreu RC	3.00	8.00
B4 Chan Ho Park	.20	.50
B5 Paul Wilson	.20	.50
B6 Chad Ogea	.20	.50
B7 Andruw Jones RC	6.00	15.00
B8 Brian Barber	.20	.50
B9 Andy Larkin	.20	.50
B10 Richie Sexson RC	4.00	10.00
B11 Everett Stull	.20	.50
B12 Brooks Kieschnick	.20	.50
B13 Matt Murray	.20	.50
B14 John Wasdin	.20	.50
B15 Shannon Stewart	.20	.50
B16 Luis Ortiz	.20	.50
B17 Marc Kroon	.20	.50
B18 Todd Greene	.20	.50
B19 Juan Acevedo RC	.40	1.00
B20 Tony Clark	.20	.50
B21 Jermaine Dye	.20	.50
B22 Derrek Lee	.50	1.25
B23 Pat Watkins	.20	.50
B24 Pokey Reese	.20	.50
B25 Ben Grieve	.20	.50
B26 Julio Santana RC	.20	.50
B27 Felix Rodriguez RC	.40	1.00
B28 Paul Konerko	3.00	8.00
B29 Nomar Garciaparra	2.00	5.00
B30 Pat Ahearne RC	.20	.50
B31 Jason Schmidt	.50	1.25
B32 Billy Wagner	.30	.75
B33 Rey Ordonez RC	1.25	3.00
B34 Curtis Goodwin	.20	.50
B35 Sergio Nunez RC	.40	1.00
B36 Tim Belk	.20	.50
B37 Scott Elarton RC	.75	2.00
B38 Jason Isringhausen	.20	.50
B39 Trot Nixon	.20	.50
B40 Sid Roberson RC	.40	1.00
B41 Ron Villone	.20	.50
B42 Ruben Rivera	.20	.50
B43 Rick Huisman	.20	.50
B44 Todd Hollandsworth	.20	.50
B45 Johnny Damon	.30	.75
B46 Garret Anderson	.20	.50
B47 Jeff D'Amico	.20	.50
B48 Dustin Hermanson	.20	.50
B49 Juan Encarnacion RC	1.25	3.00
B50 Andy Pettitte	.30	.75
B51 Chris Stynes	.20	.50
B52 Troy Percival	.20	.50
B53 LaTroy Hawkins	.20	.50
B54 Roger Cedeno	.20	.50
B55 Alan Benes	.20	.50
B56 Karim Garcia RC	.40	1.00
B57 Andrew Lorraine	.20	.50
B58 Gary Rath RC	.40	1.00
B59 Bret Wagner	.20	.50
B60 Jeff Suppan	.20	.50
B61 Bill Pulsipher	.20	.50
B62 Jay Payton RC	1.25	3.00
B63 Alex Ochoa	.20	.50
B64 Ugueth Urbina	.20	.50
B65 Armando Benitez	.20	.50
B66 George Arias	.20	.50
B67 Raul Casanova RC	.40	1.00
B68 Matt Drews	.20	.50
B69 Jimmy Haynes	.20	.50
B70 Jimmy Hurst	.20	.50
B71 C.J. Nitkowski	.20	.50
B72 Tommy Davis RC	.40	1.00
B73 Bartolo Colon RC	3.00	8.00
B74 Chris Carpenter RC	5.00	12.00
B75 Trey Beamon	.20	.50
B76 Bryan Rekar	.20	.50
B77 James Baldwin	.20	.50
B78 Marc Valdes	.20	.50
B79 Tom Fordham RC	.40	1.00
B80 Marc Newfield	.20	.50
B81 Angel Martinez	.20	.50
B82 Brian L. Hunter	.20	.50
B83 Jose Herrera	.20	.50
B84 Glenn Dishman RC	.40	1.00
B85 Jacob Cruz RC	.75	2.00
B86 Paul Shuey	.20	.50
B87 Scott Rolen RC	8.00	20.00
B88 Doug Million	.20	.50
B89 Desi Relaford	.20	.50
B90 Michael Tucker	.20	.50
R1 Randy Johnson	.50	1.25
R2 Joe Carter	.20	.50
R3 Chili Davis	.20	.50
R4 Moises Alou	.20	.50
R5 Gary Sheffield	.20	.50
R6 Kevin Appier	.20	.50
R7 Denny Neagle	.20	.50
R8 Ruben Sierra	.20	.50
R9 Darren Daulton	.20	.50
R10 Cal Ripken	1.50	4.00
R11 Bobby Bonilla	.20	.50
R12 Manny Ramirez	.30	.75
R13 Barry Bonds	1.25	3.00
R14 Eric Karros	.20	.50
R15 Greg Maddux	.75	2.00
R16 Jeff Bagwell	.30	.75
R17 Paul Molitor	.20	.50
R18 Ray Lankford	.20	.50
R19 Mark Grace	.30	.75
R20 Kenny Lofton	.20	.50
R21 Tony Gwynn	.60	1.50
R22 Will Clark	.30	.75
R23 Roger Clemens	1.00	2.50
R24 Dante Bichette	.20	.50
R25 Barry Larkin	.30	.75
R26 Wade Boggs	.30	.75
R27 Kirby Puckett	.50	1.25
R28 Cecil Fielder	.20	.50
R29 Jose Canseco	.30	.75
R30 Juan Gonzalez	.20	.50
R31 David Cone	.20	.50
R32 Craig Biggio	.30	.75
R33 Tim Salmon	.30	.75
R34 David Justice	.20	.50
R35 Sammy Sosa	.50	1.25
R36 Mike Piazza	.75	2.00
R37 Carlos Baerga	.20	.50
R38 Jeff Conine	.20	.50
R39 Rafael Palmeiro	.30	.75
R40 Bret Saberhagen	.20	.50
R41 Len Dykstra	.20	.50
R42 Mo Vaughn	.20	.50
R43 Wally Joyner	.20	.50
R44 Chuck Knoblauch	.20	.50
R45 Robin Ventura	.20	.50
R46 Don Mattingly	1.25	3.00
R47 Dave Hollins	.20	.50
R48 Andy Benes	.20	.50
R49 Ken Griffey Jr.	.75	2.00
R50 Albert Belle	.20	.50
R51 Matt Williams	.20	.50
R52 Rondell White	.20	.50
R53 Raul Mondesi	.20	.50
R54 Brian Jordan	.20	.50
R55 Greg Vaughn	.20	.50
R56 Fred McGriff	.30	.75
R57 Roberto Alomar	.30	.75
R58 Dennis Eckersley	.20	.50
R59 Lee Smith	.20	.50
R60 Eddie Murray	.50	1.25
R61 Kenny Rogers	.20	.50
R62 Ron Gant	.20	.50
R63 Larry Walker	.20	.50
R64 Chad Curtis	.20	.50
R65 Frank Thomas	.50	1.25
R66 Paul O'Neill	.30	.75
R67 Kevin Seitzer	.20	.50
R68 Marquis Grissom	.20	.50
R69 Mark McGwire	1.50	4.00
R70 Travis Fryman	.20	.50
R71 Andres Galarraga	.20	.50
R72 Carlos Perez RC	.75	2.00
R73 Tyler Green	.20	.50
R74 Marty Cordova	.20	.50
R75 Shawn Green	.20	.50
R76 Vaughn Eshelman	.20	.50
R77 John Mabry	.20	.50
R78 Jason Bates	.20	.50
R79 Jon Nunnally	.20	.50
R80 Ray Durham	.20	.50
R81 Edgardo Alfonzo	.20	.50
R82 Esteban Loaiza	.20	.50
R83 Hideo Nomo RC	3.00	8.00
R84 Orlando Miller	.20	.50
R85 Alex Gonzalez	.20	.50
R86 M.Grudzielanek RC	1.25	3.00
R87 Julian Tavarez	.20	.50
R88 Benji Gil	.20	.50
R89 Quilvio Veras	.20	.50
R90 Ricky Bottalico	.20	.50
X1 Ben Davis RC	.60	1.50
Ivan Rodriguez		
X2 Mark Redman RC	.60	1.50
Manny Ramirez		
X3 Reggie Taylor RC	.60	1.50
Deion Sanders		
X4 Ryan Jaroncyk RC	.20	.50
Shawn Green		
X5 Juan LeBron RC	3.00	8.00
Juan Gonzalez UER		
Card pictures Carlos Beltran instead of Juan LeBron.		
X6 Tony McKnight RC	.20	.50
Craig Biggio		
X7 Michael Barrett RC	.60	1.50
Travis Fryman		
X8 Corey Jenkins RC	.20	.50
Mo Vaughn		
X9 Ruben Rivera	.50	1.25
Frank Thomas		
X10 Curtis Goodwin	.20	.50
Kenny Lofton		
X11 Brian L. Hunter	.30	.75
Tony Gwynn		
X12 Todd Greene	.50	1.25
Ken Griffey Jr.		
X13 Karim Garcia	.20	.50
Matt Williams		
X14 Billy Wagner	.30	.75
Randy Johnson		
X15 Pat Watkins	.30	.75
Jeff Bagwell		

1995 Bowman's Best Refractors

Randomly inserted at a rate of one in six packs, this set is a parallel to the basic Bowman's Best issue. As far as the refractive qualities, the final 15 Mirror Image cards (X1-X15) are considered diffractors which reflects light in a different manner than the typical refractor. Unlike the 180 red and blue Refractors, the Mirror Image Diffractors are seeded into packs at a rate of 1:12. The veteran red refractor cards have been seen with or without the word refractor on the back. These cards without the refractor markings are valued at the same price as the regular refractors.

*STARS: 4X TO 10X BASIC CARDS
*RCs: 1.5X TO 4X BASIC CARDS
*MIRROR IMAGE: 1.25X TO 3X BASIC CARDS
RED/BLUE REF.STATED ODDS 1:6
MIRROR IMAGE REF.STATED ODDS 1:12

B1 Derek Jeter	75.00	150.00
B2 Vladimir Guerrero	75.00	150.00
B3 Bob Abreu	20.00	50.00
B7 Andruw Jones	40.00	80.00
B10 Richie Sexson	20.00	50.00
B73 Bartolo Colon	15.00	40.00
B74 Chris Carpenter	30.00	60.00
B87 Scott Rolen	60.00	120.00
X5 Juan LeBron	10.00	25.00
Juan Gonzalez UER		
Card pictures Carlos Beltran instead of Juan LeBron.		

1995 Bowman's Best Jumbo Refractors

This ten-card set was produced for various retail outlets. One card was inserted into each specially marked retail Topps box. According to Treat, Inc. there are no more than 9,000 of each card issued. Each over-sized card measures approximately 4" by 6". The most available of these cards are Albert Belle and Greg Maddux since they were distributed nationally. The other eight players were issued on a more regional basis. The cards are an exact parallel of the standard-size Refractor inserts except for their larger size.

COMPLETE SET (10)	50.00	125.00
COMMON CARD (1-10)	2.00	5.00
COMMON DP	1.50	4.00
1 Albert Belle DP	1.50	4.00
2 Ken Griffey Jr	6.00	15.00
3 Tony Gwynn	6.00	15.00
4 Greg Maddux DP	3.00	8.00
5 Hideo Nomo	6.00	15.00
6 Mike Piazza	6.00	15.00
7 Cal Ripken	12.50	30.00
8 Sammy Sosa	5.00	12.00
9 Frank Thomas	4.00	10.00
10 Cal Ripken	12.50	30.00

1996 Bowman's Best

This 180-card set was (produced by Topps) issued in packs of six cards at the cost of $4.99 per pack. The fronts feature a color action player cutout of 90 outstanding veteran players on a chromium gold background design and 90 up and coming prospects and rookies on a silver design. The backs carry a color player portrait, player information and statistics. Card number 33 was never actually issued. Instead, both Roger Clemens and Rafael Palmeiro are erroneously numbered 32. A chrome reprint of the 1952 Bowman Mickey Mantle was inserted at the rate of one in 24 packs. A Refractor version of the Mantle was seeded at 1:96 packs and an Atomic Refractor version was seeded at 1:192. Notable Rookie Cards include Geoff Jenkins and Mike Sweeney.

COMPLETE SET (180)	15.00	40.00
1 Hideo Nomo	.40	1.00
2 Edgar Martinez	.25	.60
3 Cal Ripken	1.25	3.00
4 Wade Boggs	.25	.60
5 Cecil Fielder	.15	.40
6 Albert Belle	.15	.40
7 Chipper Jones	.40	1.00
8 Ryne Sandberg	.60	1.50
9 Tim Salmon	.25	.60
10 Barry Bonds	1.00	2.50
11 Ken Caminiti	.15	.40
12 Ron Gant	.15	.40
13 Frank Thomas	.40	1.00
14 Dante Bichette	.15	.40
15 Jason Kendall	.15	.40
16 Mo Vaughn	.15	.40
17 Rey Ordonez	.15	.40
18 Henry Rodriguez	.15	.40
19 Ryan Klesko	.15	.40
20 Jeff Bagwell	.25	.60
21 Randy Johnson	.40	1.00
22 Jim Edmonds	.15	.40
23 Kenny Lofton	.15	.40
24 Andy Pettitte	.25	.60
25 Brady Anderson	.15	.40
26 Mike Piazza	.60	1.50
27 Greg Vaughn	.15	.40
28 Joe Carter	.15	.40
29 Jason Giambi	.15	.40
30 Ivan Rodriguez	.25	.60
31 Jeff Conine	.15	.40
32 Rafael Palmeiro	.25	.60
33 Roger Clemens UER	.75	2.00
Actually card #32		
34 Chuck Knoblauch	.15	.40
35 Reggie Sanders	.15	.40
36 Andres Galarraga	.15	.40
37 Paul O'Neill	.25	.60
38 Tony Gwynn	.50	1.25
39 Paul Wilson	.15	.40
40 Garret Anderson	.15	.40
41 David Justice	.15	.40
42 Eddie Murray	.40	1.00
43 Mike Grace RC	.20	.50
44 Marty Cordova	.15	.40
45 Kevin Appier	.15	.40
46 Raul Mondesi	.15	.40
47 Jim Thome	.25	.60
48 Sammy Sosa	.40	1.00
49 Craig Biggio	.25	.60
50 Marquis Grissom	.15	.40
51 Alan Benes	.15	.40
52 Manny Ramirez	.25	.60
53 Gary Sheffield	.15	.40
54 Mike Mussina	.25	.60
55 Robin Ventura	.15	.40
56 Johnny Damon	.25	.60
57 Jose Canseco	.25	.60
58 Juan Gonzalez	.15	.40
59 Tino Martinez	.25	.60
60 Brian Hunter	.15	.40
61 Fred McGriff	.25	.60
62 Jay Buhner	.15	.40
63 Carlos Delgado	.15	.40
64 Moises Alou	.15	.40
65 Roberto Alomar	.25	.60
66 Barry Larkin	.25	.60
67 Vinny Castilla	.15	.40
68 Ray Durham	.15	.40
69 Travis Fryman	.15	.40
70 Jason Isringhausen	.15	.40
71 Ken Griffey Jr.	.60	1.50
72 John Smoltz	.25	.60
73 Matt Williams	.15	.40
74 Chan Ho Park	.15	.40
75 Mark McGwire	1.25	3.00
76 Jeffrey Hammonds	.15	.40
77 Will Clark	.25	.60
78 Kirby Puckett	.40	1.00
79 Derek Jeter	1.25	3.00
80 Derek Bell	.15	.40
81 Eric Karros	.15	.40
82 Len Dykstra	.15	.40
83 Larry Walker	.15	.40
84 Mark Grudzielanek	.15	.40
85 Greg Maddux	.60	1.50
86 Carlos Baerga	.15	.40
87 Paul Molitor	.15	.40
88 John Valentin	.15	.40
89 Mark Grace	.25	.60
90 Ray Lankford	.15	.40
91 Andruw Jones	.60	1.50
92 Nomar Garciaparra	.75	2.00
93 Alex Ochoa	.15	.40
94 Derrick Gibson	.15	.40
95 Jeff D'Amico	.15	.40
96 Ruben Rivera	.15	.40
97 Vladimir Guerrero	.75	2.00
98 Pokey Reese	.15	.40
99 Richard Hidalgo	.15	.40
100 Bartolo Colon	.40	1.00
101 Karim Garcia	.15	.40
102 Ben Davis	.15	.40
103 Jay Powell	.15	.40
104 Chris Snopek	.15	.40
105 Glendon Rusch RC	.40	1.00
106 Enrique Wilson	.15	.40
107 A.Alfonseca RC	.40	1.00
108 Wilton Guerrero RC	.20	.50
109 Jose Guillen RC	1.50	4.00
110 Miguel Mejia RC	.20	.50
111 Jay Payton	.15	.40
112 Scott Elarton	.15	.40
113 Brooks Kieschnick	.15	.40
114 Dustin Hermanson	.15	.40
115 Roger Cedeno	.15	.40
116 Matt Wagner	.15	.40
117 Lee Daniels	.15	.40
118 Ben Grieve	.15	.40
119 Ugueth Urbina	.15	.40
120 Danny Graves	.15	.40
121 Dan Donato RC	.20	.50
122 Matt Ruebel RC	.20	.50
123 Mark Sievert RC	.20	.50
124 Chris Stynes	.15	.40
125 Jeff Abbott	.15	.40
126 Rocky Coppinger RC	.20	.50
127 Jermaine Dye	.15	.40
128 Todd Greene	.15	.40
129 Chris Carpenter	.25	.60
130 Edgar Renteria	.15	.40
131 Matt Drews	.15	.40
132 Edgard Velazquez RC	.20	.50
133 Casey Whitten	.15	.40
134 Ryan Jones RC	.20	.50
135 Todd Walker	.15	.40
136 Geoff Jenkins RC	.75	2.00
137 Matt Morris RC	1.50	4.00
138 Richie Sexson	.25	.60
139 Todd Dunwoody RC	.20	.50
140 Gabe Alvarez RC	.20	.50
141 J.J. Johnson	.15	.40
142 Shannon Stewart	.15	.40
143 Brad Fullmer	.15	.40
144 Julio Santana	.15	.40
145 Scott Rolen	.40	1.00
146 Amaury Telemaco	.15	.40
147 Trey Beamon	.15	.40
148 Billy Wagner	.15	.40
149 Todd Hollandsworth	.15	.40
150 Doug Million	.15	.40
151 Javier Valentin RC	.20	.50
152 Wes Helms RC	.40	1.00
153 Jeff Suppan	.15	.40
154 Luis Castillo RC	.60	1.50
155 Bob Abreu	.40	1.00
156 Paul Konerko	.40	1.00
157 Jamey Wright	.15	.40
158 Eddie Pearson	.15	.40
159 Jimmy Haynes	.15	.40
160 Derrek Lee	.25	.60
161 Damian Moss	.15	.40
162 Carlos Guillen RC	1.00	2.50
163 Chris Fussell RC	.20	.50
164 Mike Sweeney RC	1.00	2.50
165 Donnie Sadler	.15	.40
166 Desi Relaford	.15	.40
167 Steve Gibralter	.15	.40
168 Neifi Perez	.15	.40
169 Antone Williamson	.15	.40
170 Marty Janzen RC	.20	.50
171 Todd Helton	.75	2.00
172 Raul Ibanez RC	1.50	4.00
173 Bill Selby	.15	.40
174 Shane Monahan RC	.20	.50
175 Robin Jennings	.15	.40
176 Bobby Chouinard	.15	.40
177 Einar Diaz	.15	.40
178 Jason Thompson RC	.15	.40
179 Rafael Medina RC	.20	.50
180 Kevin Orie	.15	.40
NNO Mickey Mantle	4.00	10.00
1952 Bowman Atomic Ref.		
NNO Mickey Mantle	2.00	5.00
1952 Bowman Refractor		
NNO Mickey Mantle	1.00	2.50
1952 Bowman Chrome		

1996 Bowman's Best Atomic Refractors

Inserted one in every 48 hobby packs and one in every 80 retail packs, this 180-card set is parallel to the 1996 Bowman's Best set. It is similar in design to the regular set but was printed with sparkling refractor technology.

*GOLD STARS: 6X TO 15X BASIC CARDS
*SILVER STARS: 6X TO 15X BASIC CARDS
*ROOKIES: 4X TO 10X BASIC CARDS
STATED ODDS 1:48 HOB, 1:80 RET

1996 Bowman's Best Refractors

This 180-card set is parallel to the regular 1996 Bowman Best set and is similar in design. The difference is in the refractive quality of the cards. The cards were inserted at the rate of one in every 12 hobby packs and one in every 20 retail packs.

*GOLD STARS: 3X TO 8X BASIC CARDS
*SILVER STARS: 3X TO 8X BASIC CARDS
*ROOKIES: 2X TO 5X BASIC CARDS
STATED ODDS 1:12 HOB, 1:20 RET

1996 Bowman's Best Cuts

Randomly inserted in hobby packs at a rate of one in 24 and retail packs at a rate on one in 40, this chromium card die-cut set features 15 top hobby stars.

COMPLETE SET (15) 30.00 80.00
STATED ODDS 1:24 HOB, 1:40 RET
*REFRACTORS: .6X TO 1.5X BASIC CUTS
REF.STATED ODDS 1:48 HOB, 1:80 RET
*ATOMIC: 1X TO 2.5X BASIC CUTS
ATOMIC STATED ODDS 1:96 HOB, 1:160 RET

1 Ken Griffey Jr.	2.50	6.00
2 Jason Isringhausen	.60	1.50
3 Derek Jeter	5.00	12.00
4 Andruw Jones	2.50	6.00
5 Chipper Jones	1.50	4.00
6 Ryan Klesko	.60	1.50
7 Raul Mondesi	.60	1.50
8 Hideo Nomo	1.50	4.00
9 Mike Piazza	2.50	6.00
10 Manny Ramirez	1.00	2.50
11 Cal Ripken	5.00	12.00
12 Ruben Rivera	.60	1.50
13 Tim Salmon	1.00	2.50
14 Frank Thomas	1.50	4.00
15 Jim Thome	1.00	2.50

1996 Bowman's Best Mirror Image

Randomly inserted in hobby packs at a rate of one in 48 and retail packs at a rate of one in 80, this 10-card set features four top players on a single card at one of ten different positions. The fronts display a color photo of an AL veteran with a semicircle containing a color portrait of a prospect who plays the same position. The backs carry a color photo of an NL veteran with a semicircle color portrait of a prospect.

COMPLETE SET (10) 30.00 80.00
STATED ODDS 1:48 HOB, 1:80 RET
*REFRACTORS: .6X TO 1.5X BASIC CARDS
REFRACTOR ODDS 1:96 HOB, 1:160 RET
*ATOMIC REFRACTORS: 1.25X TO 3X BASIC CARDS
ATOMIC ODDS 1:192 HOB, 1:320 RET

1 Jeff Bagwell	1.50	4.00
Todd Helton		
Frank Thomas		
Richie Sexson		
2 Craig Biggio	1.50	4.00
Luis Castillo		
Roberto Alomar		
Desi Relaford		
3 Chipper Jones	1.50	4.00
Scott Rolen		
Wade Boggs		
George Arias		
4 Barry Larkin	6.00	15.00
Neifi Perez		
Cal Ripken		
Mark Bellhorn		
5 Larry Walker	1.50	4.00
Karim Garcia		
Albert Belle		
Ruben Rivera		
6 Barry Bonds	6.00	15.00
Andruw Jones		
Kenny Lofton		
Donnie Sadler		
7 Tony Gwynn	4.00	10.00
Vladimir Guerrero		
Ken Griffey		
Ben Grieve		
8 Mike Piazza	4.00	10.00
Ben Davis		
Ivan Rodriguez		
Javier Valentin		
9 Greg Maddux	5.00	12.00
Jamey Wright		
Mike Mussina		
Bartolo Colon		
10 Tom Glavine	1.50	4.00
Billy Wagner		
Randy Johnson		
Jarrod Washburn		

1997 Bowman's Best Preview

Randomly inserted in 1997 Bowman Series 1 packs at a rate of one in 12, this 20-card set features color photos of 10 rookies and 10 veterans that would be appearing in the 1997 Bowman's Best set. The background of each card features a flag of the featured player's homeland.

COMPLETE SET (20) 40.00 80.00
STATED ODDS 1:12
*REF: .75X TO 2X BASIC PREVIEWS
REFRACTOR STATED ODDS 1:48
*ATOMIC REF: 1.5X TO 4X BASIC PREVIEWS
ATOMIC STATED ODDS 1:96

1 Frank Thomas	1.50	4.00
2 Ken Griffey Jr.	2.50	6.00
3 Barry Bonds	4.00	10.00
4 Derek Jeter	4.00	10.00
5 Chipper Jones	1.50	4.00
6 Mark McGwire	5.00	12.00
7 Cal Ripken	5.00	12.00
8 Kenny Lofton	.60	1.50
9 Gary Sheffield	.60	1.50
10 Jeff Bagwell	1.00	2.50
11 Wilton Guerrero	.60	1.50
12 Scott Rolen	1.00	2.50
13 Todd Walker	.60	1.50
14 Ruben Rivera	.60	1.50
15 Andruw Jones	1.00	2.50
16 Nomar Garciaparra	2.50	6.00
17 Vladimir Guerrero	1.50	4.00
18 Miguel Tejada	1.50	4.00
19 Bartolo Colon	.60	1.50
20 Katsuhiro Maeda	.60	1.50

1997 Bowman's Best

The 1997 Bowman's Best set (produced by Topps) was issued in one series totalling 200 cards and was distributed in six-card packs (SRP $4.99). The fronts feature borderless color player photos printed on chromium card stock. The cards of the 100 current veteran stars display a classic gold design while the cards of the 100 top prospects carry a sleek silver design. Rookie Cards include Adrian Beltre, Kris Benson, Jose Cruz Jr., Travis Lee, Fernando Tatis, Miguel Tejada and Kerry Wood.

COMPLETE SET (200)	15.00	40.00
1 Ken Griffey Jr.	.60	1.50
2 Cecil Fielder	.15	.40
3 Albert Belle	.15	.40
4 Todd Hundley	.15	.40
5 Mike Piazza	.60	1.50
6 Matt Williams	.15	.40
7 Mo Vaughn	.15	.40
8 Ryne Sandberg	.60	1.50
9 Chipper Jones	.40	1.00
10 Edgar Martinez	.25	.60
11 Kenny Lofton	.15	.40
12 Ron Gant	.15	.40
13 Moises Alou	.15	.40
14 Pat Hentgen	.15	.40
15 Steve Finley	.15	.40
16 Mark Grace	.25	.60
17 Jay Buhner	.15	.40
18 Jeff Conine	.15	.40
19 Jim Edmonds	.15	.40
20 Todd Hollandsworth	.15	.40
21 Andy Pettitte	.25	.60
22 Jim Thome	.25	.60
23 Eric Young	.15	.40
24 Ray Lankford	.15	.40
25 Marquis Grissom	.15	.40
26 Tony Clark	.15	.40
27 Jermaine Allensworth	.15	.40
28 Ellis Burks	.15	.40
29 Tony Gwynn	.50	1.25
30 Barry Larkin	.25	.60
31 John Olerud	.15	.40
32 Mariano Rivera	.40	1.00
33 Paul Molitor	.15	.40
34 Ken Caminiti	.15	.40
35 Gary Sheffield	.15	.40
36 Al Martin	.15	.40
37 John Valentin	.15	.40
38 Frank Thomas	.40	1.00
39 John Jaha	.15	.40
40 Greg Maddux	.60	1.50
41 Alex Fernandez	.15	.40
42 Dean Palmer	.15	.40
43 Bernie Williams	.25	.60
44 Deion Sanders	.25	.60
45 Mark McGwire	1.25	3.00
46 Brian Jordan	.15	.40
47 Bernard Gilkey	.15	.40
48 Will Clark	.25	.60
49 Kevin Appier	.15	.40
50 Tom Glavine	.25	.60
51 Chuck Knoblauch	.15	.40
52 Rondell White	.15	.40
53 Greg Vaughn	.15	.40
54 Mike Mussina	.25	.60
55 Brian McRae	.15	.40
56 Chili Davis	.15	.40
57 Wade Boggs	.25	.60
58 Jeff Bagwell	.25	.60
59 Roberto Alomar	.25	.60
60 Dennis Eckersley	.15	.40
61 Ryan Klesko	.15	.40
62 Manny Ramirez	.25	.60
63 John Wetteland	.15	.40
64 Cal Ripken	1.25	3.00
65 Edgar Renteria	.15	.40
66 Tino Martinez	.25	.60
67 Larry Walker	.15	.40
68 Gregg Jefferies	.15	.40
69 Lance Johnson	.15	.40
70 Carlos Delgado	.15	.40
71 Craig Biggio	.25	.60
72 Jose Canseco	.25	.60
73 Barry Bonds	1.00	2.50
74 Juan Gonzalez	.15	.40
75 Eric Karros	.15	.40
76 Reggie Sanders	.15	.40
77 Robin Ventura	.15	.40
78 Hideo Nomo	.40	1.00
79 David Justice	.15	.40
80 Vinny Castilla	.15	.40
81 Travis Fryman	.15	.40
82 Derek Jeter	1.00	2.50
83 Sammy Sosa	.40	1.00
84 Ivan Rodriguez	.25	.60
85 Rafael Palmeiro	.25	.60
86 Roger Clemens	.75	2.00
87 Jason Giambi	.15	.40
88 Andres Galarraga	.15	.40
89 Jermaine Dye	.15	.40
90 Joe Carter	.15	.40
91 Brady Anderson	.15	.40
92 Derek Bell	.15	.40
93 Randy Johnson	.40	1.00
94 Fred McGriff	.25	.60
95 John Smoltz	.25	.60
96 Harold Baines	.15	.40
97 Raul Mondesi	.15	.40
98 Tim Salmon	.25	.60
99 Carlos Baerga	.15	.40
100 Dante Bichette	.15	.40
101 Vladimir Guerrero	.40	1.00
102 Richard Hidalgo	.15	.40
103 Paul Konerko	.25	.60
104 Alex Gonzalez RC	.40	1.00
105 Jason Dickson	.15	.40
106 Jose Rosado	.15	.40
107 Todd Walker	.15	.40
108 Seth Greisinger RC	.15	.40
109 Todd Helton	.40	1.00
110 Ben Davis	.15	.40
111 Bartolo Colon	.15	.40
112 Elieser Marrero	.15	.40
113 Jeff D'Amico	.15	.40
114 Miguel Tejada RC	1.50	4.00
115 Darin Erstad	.15	.40
116 Kris Benson RC	.40	1.00
117 Adrian Beltre RC	1.50	4.00
118 Neifi Perez	.15	.40
119 Pokey Reese	.15	.40
120 Carl Pavano	.15	.40
121 Juan Melo	.15	.40
122 Kevin McGlinchy RC	.15	.40
123 Pat Cline	.15	.40
124 Felix Heredia RC	.15	.40
125 Aaron Boone	.15	.40
126 Glendon Rusch	.15	.40
127 Mike Cameron	.15	.40
128 Justin Thompson	.15	.40
129 Chad Hermansen RC	.15	.40
130 Sidney Ponson RC	.40	1.00
131 Willie Martinez RC	.15	.40
132 Paul Wilder RC	.15	.40
133 Geoff Jenkins	.15	.40
134 Roy Halladay RC	5.00	12.00
135 Carlos Guillen	.15	.40
136 Tony Batista	.15	.40
137 Todd Greene	.15	.40
138 Luis Castillo	.15	.40
139 Jimmy Anderson RC	.15	.40
140 Edgard Velazquez	.15	.40
141 Chris Snopek	.15	.40
142 Ruben Rivera	.15	.40
143 Javier Valentin	.15	.40
144 Brian Rose	.15	.40
145 Fernando Tatis RC	.15	.40
146 Dean Crow RC	.15	.40
147 Karim Garcia	.15	.40
148 Dante Powell	.15	.40
149 Hideki Irabu RC	.25	.60
150 Matt Morris	.15	.40
151 Wes Helms	.15	.40
152 Russ Johnson	.15	.40
153 Jarrod Washburn	.15	.40
154 Kerry Wood RC	1.50	4.00
155 Joe Fontenot RC	.15	.40
156 Eugene Kingsale	.15	.40
157 Terrence Long	.15	.40
158 Calvin Maduro	.15	.40
159 Jeff Suppan	.15	.40
160 DaRond Stovall	.15	.40
161 Mark Redman	.15	.40
162 Ken Cloude RC	.15	.40
163 Bobby Estalella	.15	.40
164 Abraham Nunez RC	.15	.40
165 Derrick Gibson	.15	.40
166 Mike Drumright RC	.15	.40
167 Katsuhiro Maeda	.15	.40
168 Jeff Liefer	.15	.40
169 Ben Grieve	.15	.40
170 Bob Abreu	.25	.60
171 Shannon Stewart	.15	.40
172 Braden Looper RC	.30	.75
173 Brant Brown	.15	.40
174 Marlon Anderson	.15	.40
175 Brad Fullmer	.15	.40
176 Carlos Beltran	.75	2.00
177 Nomar Garciaparra	.60	1.50
178 Derrek Lee	.25	.60
179 Val.De Los Santos RC	.15	.40
180 Dmitri Young	.15	.40
181 Jamey Wright	.15	.40
182 Hiram Bocachica RC	.15	.40
183 Wilton Guerrero	.15	.40
184 Chris Carpenter	.15	.40
185 Scott Spiezio	.15	.40
186 Andruw Jones	.25	.60
187 Travis Lee RC	.25	.60

188 Jose Cruz Jr. RC .25 .60
189 Jose Guillen .15 .40
190 Jeff Abbott .15 .40
191 Ricky Ledee RC .25 .60
192 Mike Sweeney .15 .40
193 Donnie Sadler .15 .40
194 Scott Rolen .25 .60
195 Kevin Orie .15 .40
196 Jason Conti RC .15 .40
197 Mark Kotsay RC .60 1.50
198 Eric Milton RC .25 .60
199 Russell Branyan .15 .40
200 Alex Sanchez RC .25 .60

1997 Bowman's Best Atomic Refractors

Randomly inserted in packs at a rate of one in 24, cards from this 200 card set parallel the regular Bowman's Best set and were printed with sparkling cross-weave refractor technology.

*STARS: 5X TO 12X BASIC CARDS
*ROOKIES: 3X TO 8X BASIC CARDS
STATED ODDS 1:24
134 Roy Halladay 75.00 150.00

1997 Bowman's Best Refractors

Randomly inserted in packs at a rate of one in 12, this 200 card set is parallel to the regular set and is similar in design. The difference is found in the refractive quality of the cards.

*STARS: 2.5X TO 6X BASIC CARDS
*ROOKIES: 1.5X TO 4X BASIC CARDS
STATED ODDS 1:12
134 Roy Halladay 50.00 100.00

1997 Bowman's Best Autographs

Randomly inserted in packs at a rate of 1:170, this 10-card set features five silver rookie cards and five gold veteran cards with authentic autographs and a "Certified Autograph Issue" stamp.

COMPLETE SET (10) 125.00 250.00
STATED ODDS 1:170
*REF.STARS: .75X TO 2X BASIC CARDS
REFRACTOR STATED ODDS 1:2036
*ATOMIC STARS: 1.5X TO 4X BASIC CARDS
ATOMIC STATED ODDS 1:6107
SKIP-NUMBERED 10-CARD SET
29 Tony Gwynn 12.50 30.00
33 Paul Molitor 10.00 25.00
82 Derek Jeter 125.00 250.00
91 Brady Anderson 6.00 15.00
98 Tim Salmon 10.00 25.00
107 Todd Walker 6.00 15.00
183 Wilton Guerrero 2.00 5.00
185 Scott Spiezio 2.00 5.00
188 Jose Cruz Jr. 6.00 15.00
194 Scott Rolen 10.00 25.00

1997 Bowman's Best Best Cuts

Randomly inserted in packs at a rate of one in 24, this 20-card set features color player photos printed on intricate, Laser Cut Chromium card stock.

COMPLETE SET (20) 75.00 150.00
STATED ODDS 1:24
*REFRACTOR: .6X TO 1.5X BASIC CUTS
REFRACTOR STATED ODDS 1:48
*ATOMIC: 1X TO 2.5X BASIC CUTS
ATOMIC STATED ODDS 1:96
BC1 Derek Jeter 6.00 15.00
BC2 Chipper Jones 2.50 6.00
BC3 Frank Thomas 2.50 6.00
BC4 Cal Ripken 8.00 20.00
BC5 Mark McGwire 8.00 20.00
BC6 Ken Griffey Jr. 4.00 10.00
BC7 Jeff Bagwell 1.50 4.00
BC8 Mike Piazza 4.00 10.00
BC9 Ken Caminiti 1.00 2.50
BC10 Albert Belle 1.00 2.50

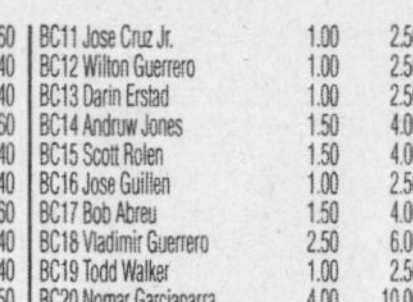

BC11 Jose Cruz Jr. 1.00 2.50
BC12 Wilton Guerrero 1.00 2.50
BC13 Darin Erstad 1.00 2.50
BC14 Andruw Jones 1.50 4.00
BC15 Scott Rolen 1.50 4.00
BC16 Jose Guillen 1.00 2.50
BC17 Bob Abreu 1.50 4.00
BC18 Vladimir Guerrero 2.50 6.00
BC19 Todd Walker 1.00 2.50
BC20 Nomar Garciaparra 4.00 10.00

1997 Bowman's Best Mirror Image

Randomly inserted in packs at a rate of one in 48, this 10-card set features color photos of four of the best players in the same position printed on double-sided chromium card stock. Two veterans and two rookies appear on each card. The veteran players are displayed in the larger photos with the rookies appearing in smaller corner photos.

COMPLETE SET (10) 40.00 80.00
STATED ODDS 1:48
*REFRACTORS: .6X TO 1.5X BASIC CARDS
REFRACTOR STATED ODDS 1:96
*ATOMIC REF: 1.25X TO 3X BASIC MI
ATOMIC STATED ODDS 1:192
*INVERTED: 2X VALUE OF NON-INVERTED
INVERTED: RANDOM INSERTS IN PACKS
INVERTED HAVE LARGER ROOKIE PHOTOS
MI1 Nomar Garciaparra 5.00 12.00
Derek Jeter
Hiram Bocachica
Barry Larkin
MI2 Travis Lee 2.00 5.00
Frank Thomas
Derrick Lee
Jeff Bagwell
MI3 Kerry Wood 2.00 5.00
Greg Maddux
Kris Benson
John Smoltz
MI4 Kevin Brown 3.00 8.00
Ivan Rodriguez
Eli Marrero
Mike Piazza
MI5 Jose Cruz Jr. 5.00 12.00
Ken Griffey Jr.
Andruw Jones
Barry Bonds
MI6 Jose Guillen 1.25 3.00
Juan Gonzalez
Richard Hidalgo
Gary Sheffield
MI7 Paul Konerko 5.00 12.00
Mark McGwire
Todd Helton
Rafael Palmeiro
MI8 Wilton Guerrero 1.25 3.00
Craig Biggio
Donnie Sadler
Chuck Knoblauch
MI9 Russell Branyan 1.50 4.00
Matt Williams
Adrian Beltre
Chipper Jones
MI10 Bob Abreu 2.00 5.00
Kenny Lofton
Vladimir Guerrero
Albert Belle

1997 Bowman's Best Jumbo

This 16-card set features selected cards from the 1997 regular Bowman's Best set in a 4" by 6" jumbo version available to Stadium Club members only by mail. Only 675 of each of the 16 cards were produced for this jumbo version. The cards are checklisted according to their number in the regular size set.

*REFRACTORS: 4X BASIC JUMBOS
*ATOMIC REFRACTORS: 8X BASIC JUMBOS
1 Ken Griffey Jr. 3.00 8.00
5 Mike Piazza 3.00 8.00
9 Chipper Jones 3.00 8.00
11 Kenny Lofton .75 2.00
29 Tony Gwynn 3.00 8.00
33 Paul Molitor 1.50 4.00
38 Frank Thomas 1.25 3.00
45 Mark McGwire 3.00 8.00
64 Cal Ripken Jr. 6.00 15.00
73 Barry Bonds 3.00 8.00
74 Juan Gonzalez .75 2.00
82 Derek Jeter 6.00 15.00
101 Vladimir Guerrero 1.50 4.00
177 Nomar Garciaparra 3.00 8.00
186 Andruw Jones 2.00 5.00
188 Jose Cruz Jr. .75 2.00

1998 Bowman's Best

The 1998 Bowman's Best set (produced by Topps) consists of 200 standard size cards and was released in August, 1998. The six-card packs retailed for a suggested price of $5 each. The card fronts feature 100 action photos with a gold background showcasing today's veteran players and 100 photos (combining posed shots with action shots) with a silver background showcasing rookies. The Bowman's Best

logo sits in the upper right corner and the featured player's name sits in the lower left corner. Rookie Cards include Ryan Anderson, Troy Glaus, Orlando Hernandez, Carlos Lee, Ruben Mateo and Magglio Ordonez.

COMPLETE SET (200) 15.00 40.00
1 Mark McGwire 1.00 2.50
2 Jeromy Burnitz .15 .40
3 Barry Bonds 1.00 2.50
4 Dante Bichette .15 .40
5 Chipper Jones .40 1.00
6 Frank Thomas .40 1.00
7 Kevin Brown .25 .60
8 Juan Gonzalez .15 .40
9 Jay Buhner .15 .40
10 Chuck Knoblauch .15 .40
11 Cal Ripken 1.25 3.00
12 Matt Williams .15 .40
13 Jim Edmonds .15 .40
14 Manny Ramirez .25 .60
15 Tony Clark .15 .40
16 Mo Vaughn .15 .40
17 Bernie Williams .25 .60
18 Scott Rolen .25 .60
19 Gary Sheffield .15 .40
20 Albert Belle .15 .40
21 Mike Piazza .60 1.50
22 John Olerud .15 .40
23 Tony Gwynn .50 1.25
24 Jay Bell .15 .40
25 Jose Cruz Jr. .15 .40
26 Justin Thompson .15 .40
27 Ken Griffey Jr. .60 1.50
28 Sandy Alomar Jr. .15 .40
29 Mark Grudzielanek .15 .40
30 Mark Grace .25 .60
31 Ron Gant .15 .40
32 Javy Lopez .15 .40
33 Jeff Bagwell .25 .60
34 Fred McGriff .25 .60
35 Rafael Palmeiro .25 .60
36 Vinny Castilla .15 .40
37 Andy Benes .15 .40
38 Pedro Martinez .25 .60
39 Andy Pettitte .25 .60
40 Marty Cordova .15 .40
41 Rusty Greer .15 .40
42 Kevin Orie .15 .40
43 Chan Ho Park .15 .40
44 Ryan Klesko .15 .40
45 Alex Rodriguez .60 1.50
46 Travis Fryman .15 .40
47 Jeff King .15 .40
48 Roger Clemens .75 2.00
49 Darin Erstad .15 .40
50 Brady Anderson .15 .40
51 Jason Kendall .15 .40
52 John Valentin .15 .40
53 Ellis Burks .15 .40
54 Brian Hunter .15 .40
55 Paul O'Neill .25 .60
56 Ken Caminiti .15 .40
57 David Justice .15 .40
58 Eric Karros .15 .40
59 Pat Hentgen .15 .40
60 Greg Maddux .60 1.50
61 Craig Biggio .25 .60
62 Edgar Martinez .25 .60
63 Mike Mussina .25 .60
64 Larry Walker .15 .40
65 Tino Martinez .25 .60
66 Jim Thome .25 .60
67 Tom Glavine .25 .60
68 Raul Mondesi .15 .40
69 Marquis Grissom .15 .40
70 Randy Johnson .40 1.00
71 Steve Finley .15 .40
72 Jose Guillen .15 .40
73 Nomar Garciaparra .60 1.50
74 Wade Boggs .25 .60
75 Bobby Higginson .15 .40
76 Robin Ventura .15 .40
77 Derek Jeter 1.00 2.50
78 Andruw Jones .25 .60
79 Ray Lankford .15 .40
80 Vladimir Guerrero .40 1.00
81 Kenny Lofton .15 .40
82 Ivan Rodriguez .25 .60
83 Neifi Perez .15 .40
84 John Smoltz .25 .60
85 Tim Salmon .25 .60
86 Carlos Delgado .15 .40
87 Sammy Sosa .40 1.00
88 Jaret Wright .15 .40
89 Roberto Alomar .25 .60
90 Paul Molitor .15 .40
91 Dean Palmer .15 .40
92 Barry Larkin .25 .60
93 Jason Giambi .15 .40
94 Curt Schilling .15 .40
95 Eric Young .15 .40
96 Denny Neagle .15 .40
97 Moises Alou .15 .40
98 Livan Hernandez .15 .40
99 Todd Hundley .15 .40
100 Andres Galarraga .15 .40
101 Travis Lee .15 .40
102 Lance Berkman .15 .40
103 Orlando Cabrera .15 .40
104 Mike Lowell RC 1.25 3.00
105 Ben Grieve .15 .40
106 Jae Weong Seo RC .25 .60
107 Richie Sexson .15 .40
108 Eli Marrero .15 .40
109 Aramis Ramirez .15 .40
110 Paul Konerko .15 .40
111 Carl Pavano .15 .40
112 Brad Fullmer .15 .40
113 Matt Clement .15 .40
114 Donzell McDonald .15 .40
115 Todd Helton .25 .60
116 Mike Caruso .15 .40
117 Donnie Sadler .15 .40
118 Bruce Chen .15 .40
119 Jarrod Washburn .15 .40
120 Adrian Beltre .15 .40
121 Ryan Jackson RC .15 .40
122 Kevin Millar RC .60 1.50
123 Corey Koskie RC .40 1.00
124 Dermal Brown .15 .40
125 Kerry Wood .15 .40
126 Juan Melo .15 .40
127 Ramon Hernandez .15 .40
128 Roy Halladay .75 2.00
129 Ron Wright .15 .40
130 Darnell McDonald RC .25 .60
131 Odalis Perez RC .60 1.50
132 Alex Cora RC .25 .60
133 Justin Towle .15 .40
134 Juan Encarnacion .15 .40
135 Brian Rose .15 .40
136 Russell Branyan .15 .40
137 Cesar King RC .15 .40
138 Ruben Rivera .15 .40
139 Ricky Ledee .15 .40
140 Vernon Wells .15 .40
141 Luis Rivas RC .40 1.00
142 Brent Butler .15 .40
143 Karim Garcia .15 .40
144 George Lombard .15 .40
145 Masato Yoshii RC .25 .60
146 Braden Looper .15 .40
147 Alex Sanchez .15 .40
148 Kris Benson .15 .40
149 Mark Kotsay .15 .40
150 Richard Hidalgo .15 .40
151 Scott Elarton .15 .40
152 Ryan Minor RC .15 .40
153 Troy Glaus RC 1.50 4.00
154 Carlos Lee RC 1.25 3.00
155 Michael Coleman .15 .40
156 Jason Grilli RC .15 .40
157 Julio Ramirez RC .15 .40
158 Randy Wolf RC .25 .60
159 Ryan Brannan .15 .40
160 Edgard Clemente .15 .40
161 Miguel Tejada .40 1.00
162 Chad Hermansen .15 .40
163 Ryan Anderson RC .15 .40
164 Ben Petrick .15 .40
165 Alex Gonzalez .15 .40
166 Ben Davis .15 .40
167 John Patterson .15 .40
168 Cliff Politte .15 .40
169 Randall Simon .15 .40
170 Javier Vazquez .15 .40
171 Kevin Witt .15 .40
172 Geoff Jenkins .15 .40
173 David Ortiz 1.50 4.00
174 Derrick Gibson .15 .40
175 Abraham Nunez .15 .40
176 A.J. Hinch .15 .40
177 Ruben Mateo RC .15 .40
178 Magglio Ordonez RC 2.00 5.00
179 Todd Dunwoody .15 .40
180 Daryle Ward .15 .40
181 Mike Kinkade RC .15 .40
182 Willie Martinez .15 .40
183 O.Hernandez RC .75 2.00
184 Eric Milton .15 .40
185 Eric Chavez .15 .40
186 Damian Jackson .15 .40
187 Jim Parque RC .25 .60
188 Dan Reichert RC .25 .60
189 Mike Drumright .15 .40
190 Todd Helton .25 .60
191 Shane Monahan .15 .40
192 Derrek Lee .25 .60
193 Jeremy Giambi RC .25 .60
194 Dan McKinley RC .15 .40
195 Tony Armas Jr. RC .25 .60
196 Matt Anderson RC .15 .40
197 Jim Chamblee RC .15 .40
198 F.Cordero RC .40 1.00
199 Calvin Pickering .15 .40
200 Reggie Taylor .15 .40

1998 Bowman's Best Atomic Refractors

The 1998 Bowman's Best Atomic Refractor set consists of 200 cards and is a parallel to the 1998 Bowman's Best base set. The cards are randomly inserted in packs at a rate of one in 82. The entire set is sequentially numbered to 100. Each card front featured a kaleidescopic refractive background.

*STARS: 8X TO 20X BASIC CARDS
*ROOKIES: 5X TO 12X BASIC CARDS
STATED ODDS 1:82
122 Kevin Millar 8.00 20.00

1998 Bowman's Best Refractors

The 1998 Bowman's Best Refractor set consists of 200 cards and is a parallel to the 1998 Bowman's Best base set. The cards are randomly inserted in packs at a rate of one in 20. The entire set is sequentially numbered to 400.

*STARS: 5X TO 12X BASIC CARDS
*ROOKIES: 2.5X TO 6X BASIC CARDS
STATED ODDS 1:20
122 Kevin Millar 4.00 10.00

1998 Bowman's Best Autographs

Randomly inserted in packs at a rate of one in 180, this 10-card set is an insert to the 1998 Bowman's Best brand. The fronts feature five gold veteran and five silver prospect cards sporting a Topps "Certified Autograph Issue" logo for authentication. The cards are designed in an identical manner to the basic issue 1998 Bowman's Best set except, of course, for the autograph and the certification logo.

COMPLETE SET (10) 200.00 400.00
STATED ODDS 1:180
*REFRACTORS: .75X TO 2X BASIC AU'S
REFRACTOR STATED ODDS 1:2158
*ATOMICS: 2X TO 4X BASIC AU'S
ATOMIC STATED ODDS 1:6437
SKIP-NUMBERED 10-CARD SET
5 Chipper Jones 20.00 50.00
10 Chuck Knoblauch 6.00 15.00
15 Tony Clark 4.00 10.00
20 Albert Belle 6.00 15.00
25 Jose Cruz Jr. 4.00 10.00
105 Ben Grieve 4.00 10.00
110 Paul Konerko 10.00 25.00
115 Todd Helton 10.00 25.00
120 Adrian Beltre 15.00 40.00
125 Kerry Wood 10.00 25.00

1998 Bowman's Best Mirror Image Fusion

Randomly inserted in packs at a rate of one in 12, this 20-card set is an insert to the 1998 Bowman's Best brand. The fronts feature a Major League veteran player with his positional protégé on the flip side. The player's name runs along the bottom of the card.

COMPLETE SET (20) 60.00 150.00
STATED ODDS 1:12
*REFRACTORS: 1.25X TO 3X BASIC MIRROR
REFRACTOR STATED ODDS 1:809
REF.PRINT RUN 100 SERIAL #'d SETS
ATOMIC STATED ODDS 1:3237
ATOMIC PRINT RUN 25 SERIAL #'d SETS
NO ATOMIC PRICING DUE TO SCARCITY
MI1 Frank Thomas 2.50 6.00
David Ortiz
MI2 Chuck Knoblauch 1.00 2.50
Enrique Wilson
MI3 Nomar Garciaparra 4.00 10.00
Miguel Tejada
MI4 Alex Rodriguez 4.00 10.00
Mike Caruso
MI5 Cal Ripken 8.00 20.00
Ryan Minor
MI6 Ken Griffey Jr. 4.00 10.00
Ben Grieve
MI7 Juan Gonzalez 1.00 2.50
Juan Encarnacion
MI8 Jose Cruz Jr. 1.00 2.50
Ruben Mateo
MI9 Randy Johnson 2.00 5.00
Ryan Anderson
MI10 Ivan Rodriguez 1.50 4.00
A.J. Hinch
MI11 Jeff Bagwell 1.50 4.00
Paul Konerko
MI12 Mark McGwire 6.00 15.00
Travis Lee
MI13 Craig Biggio 1.50 4.00
Chad Hermansen
MI14 Mark Grudzielanek 1.00 2.50
Alex Gonzalez
MI15 Chipper Jones 2.00 5.00
Adrian Beltre
MI16 Larry Walker 1.00 2.50
Mark Kotsay
MI17 Tony Gwynn 3.00 8.00
George Lombard
MI18 Barry Bonds 6.00 15.00
Richard Hidalgo
MI19 Greg Maddux 3.00 8.00
Kerry Wood
MI20 Mike Piazza 4.00 10.00
Ben Petrick

1998 Bowman's Best Performers

Randomly inserted in packs at a rate of one in six, this 10-card set is an insert to the 1998 Bowman's Best brand. The card fronts feature full color game-action photos of ten players with the best Minor League stats of 1997. The featured player's name is found below the photo with both Bowman's Best logo and the team logo above the photo.

COMPLETE SET (10) 6.00 15.00
STATED ODDS 1:6

*REFRACTORS: 5X TO 12X BASIC PERF.
REFRACTOR STATED ODDS 1:809
REF.PRINT RUN 200 SERIAL #'d SETS
*ATOMIC: 12.5X TO 30X BASIC PERF.
ATOMIC STATED ODDS 1:3237
ATOMIC PRINT RUN 50 SERIAL #'d SETS
BP1 Ben Grieve .60 1.50
BP2 Travis Lee .60 1.50
BP3 Ryan Minor .60 1.50
BP4 Todd Helton 1.00 2.50
BP5 Brad Fullmer .60 1.50
BP6 Paul Konerko .60 1.50
BP7 Adrian Beltre .60 1.50
BP8 Richie Sexson .60 1.50
BP9 Aramis Ramirez .60 1.50
BP10 Russell Branyan .60 1.50

1999 Bowman's Best

The 1999 Bowman's Best set (produced by Topps) consists of 200 standard size cards. The six-card packs, released in August, 1999, retailed for a suggested price of $5 each. The cards are printed on 27-pt. Serillusion stock and feature 85 veteran stars in a striking gold series, 15 Best Performers bonus subset captured in a bronze series, 50 rookies highlighted in a brilliant blue series and 50 prospects shown in a captivating silver series. The fifty rookies and prospects (cards 151-200) were seeded at a rate of one per pack. Notable Rookie Cards included Pat Burrell, Sean Burroughs, Nick Johnson, Austin Kearns, Corey Patterson and Alfonso Soriano.

COMPLETE SET (200) 15.00 40.00
COMP.SET w/o SP's (150) 10.00 25.00
COMMON CARD (1-150) .15 .40
COMMON (151-200) .20 .50
1 Chipper Jones .40 1.00
2 Brian Jordan .15 .40
3 David Justice .15 .40
4 Jason Kendall .15 .40
5 Mo Vaughn .15 .40
6 Jim Edmonds .15 .40
7 Wade Boggs .25 .60
8 Jeromy Burnitz .15 .40
9 Todd Hundley .15 .40
10 Rondell White .15 .40
11 Cliff Floyd .15 .40
12 Sean Casey .15 .40
13 Bernie Williams .25 .60
14 Dante Bichette .15 .40
15 Greg Vaughn .15 .40
16 Andres Galarraga .15 .40
17 Ray Durham .15 .40
18 Jim Thome .25 .60
19 Gary Sheffield .15 .40
20 Frank Thomas .40 1.00
21 Orlando Hernandez .15 .40
22 Ivan Rodriguez .25 .60
23 Jose Cruz Jr. .15 .40
24 Jason Giambi .15 .40
25 Craig Biggio .25 .60
26 Kerry Wood .15 .40
27 Manny Ramirez .25 .60
28 Curt Schilling .15 .40
29 Mike Mussina .25 .60
30 Tim Salmon .25 .60
31 Mike Piazza .60 1.50
32 Roberto Alomar .25 .60
33 Larry Walker .15 .40
34 Barry Larkin .25 .60
35 Nomar Garciaparra .60 1.50
36 Paul O'Neill .25 .60
37 Todd Walker .15 .40
38 Eric Karros .15 .40
39 Brad Fullmer .15 .40
40 John Olerud .15 .40
41 Todd Helton .25 .60
42 Raul Mondesi .15 .40
43 Jose Canseco .25 .60
44 Matt Williams .15 .40
45 Ray Lankford .15 .40
46 Carlos Delgado .15 .40
47 Darin Erstad .15 .40
48 Vladimir Guerrero .40 1.00
49 Robin Ventura .15 .40
50 Alex Rodriguez .60 1.50
51 Vinny Castilla .15 .40
52 Tony Clark .15 .40
53 Pedro Martinez .25 .60
54 Rafael Palmeiro .25 .60
55 Scott Rolen .25 .60
56 Tino Martinez .25 .60
57 Tony Gwynn .50 1.25
58 Barry Bonds 1.00 2.50
59 Kenny Lofton .15 .40
60 Javy Lopez .15 .40
61 Mark Grace .25 .60
62 Travis Lee .15 .40
63 Kevin Brown .25 .60
64 Al Leiter .15 .40
65 Albert Belle .15 .40
66 Sammy Sosa .40 1.00
67 Greg Maddux .60 1.50
68 Mark Kotsay .15 .40
69 Dmitri Young .15 .40
70 Mark McGwire 1.00 2.50
71 Juan Gonzalez .15 .40
72 Andruw Jones .25 .60
73 Derek Jeter 1.00 2.50
74 Randy Johnson .40 1.00
75 Cal Ripken 1.25 3.00
76 Shawn Green .15 .40
77 Moises Alou .15 .40
78 Tom Glavine .25 .60
79 Sandy Alomar Jr. .15 .40
80 Ken Griffey Jr. .60 1.50
81 Ryan Klesko .15 .40
82 Jeff Bagwell .25 .60
83 Ben Grieve .15 .40
84 John Smoltz .25 .60
85 Roger Clemens .75 2.00
86 Ken Griffey Jr. BP .40 1.00
87 Roger Clemens BP .40 1.00
88 Derek Jeter BP .50 1.25
89 Nomar Garciaparra BP .30 .75
90 Mark McGwire BP .50 1.25
91 Sammy Sosa BP .25 .60
92 Alex Rodriguez BP .30 .75
93 Greg Maddux BP .30 .75
94 Vladimir Guerrero BP .25 .60
95 Chipper Jones BP .25 .60
96 Kerry Wood BP .15 .40
97 Ben Grieve BP .15 .40
98 Tony Gwynn BP .25 .60
99 Juan Gonzalez BP .15 .40
100 Mike Piazza BP .30 .75
101 Eric Chavez .15 .40
102 Billy Koch .15 .40
103 Dernell Stenson .15 .40
104 Marlon Anderson .15 .40
105 Ron Belliard .15 .40
106 Bruce Chen .15 .40
107 Carlos Beltran .25 .60
108 Chad Hermansen .15 .40
109 Ryan Anderson .15 .40
110 Michael Barrett .15 .40
111 Matt Clement .15 .40
112 Ben Davis .15 .40
113 Calvin Pickering .15 .40
114 Brad Penny .15 .40
115 Paul Konerko .15 .40
116 Alex Gonzalez .15 .40
117 George Lombard .15 .40
118 John Patterson .15 .40
119 Rob Bell .15 .40
120 Ruben Mateo .15 .40
121 Troy Glaus .25 .60
122 Ryan Bradley .15 .40
123 Carlos Lee .15 .40
124 Gabe Kapler .15 .40
125 Ramon Hernandez .15 .40
126 Carlos Febles .15 .40
127 Mitch Meluskey .15 .40
128 Michael Cuddyer .15 .40
129 Pablo Ozuna .15 .40
130 Jayson Werth .15 .40
131 Ricky Ledee .15 .40
132 Jeremy Giambi .15 .40
133 Danny Klassen .15 .40
134 Mark DeRosa .15 .40
135 Randy Wolf .15 .40
136 Roy Halladay .40 1.00
137 Derrick Gibson .15 .40
138 Ben Petrick .15 .40
139 Warren Morris .15 .40
140 Lance Berkman .15 .40
141 Russell Branyan .15 .40
142 Adrian Beltre .15 .40
143 Juan Encarnacion .15 .40
144 Fernando Seguignol .15 .40
145 Corey Koskie .15 .40
146 Preston Wilson .15 .40
147 Homer Bush .15 .40
148 Daryle Ward .15 .40
149 Joe McEwing RC .25 .60
150 Peter Bergeron RC .20 .50
151 Pat Burrell RC 1.25 3.00
152 Choo Freeman RC .25 .60
153 Matt Belisle RC .20 .50
154 Carlos Pena RC .30 .75
155 A.J. Burnett RC .60 1.50
156 D.Mientkiewicz RC .40 1.00
157 Sean Burroughs RC .40 1.00
158 Mike Zywica RC .20 .50
159 Corey Patterson RC .60 1.50
160 Austin Kearns RC 1.25 3.00
161 Chip Ambres RC .20 .50
162 Kelly Dransfeldt RC .20 .50
163 Mike Nannini RC .20 .50
164 Mark Mulder RC 1.00 2.50
165 Jason Tyner RC .20 .50
166 Bobby Seay RC .20 .50
167 Alex Escobar RC .25 .60
168 Nick Johnson RC .60 1.50
169 Alfonso Soriano RC 3.00 8.00
170 Clayton Andrews RC .20 .50
171 C.C. Sabathia RC 1.50 4.00
172 Matt Holliday RC 3.00 8.00
173 Brad Lidge RC 1.50 4.00
174 Kit Pellow RC .20 .50
175 J.M. Gold RC .20 .50
176 Roosevelt Brown RC .20 .50
177 Eric Valent RC .25 .60
178 Adam Everett RC .40 1.00
179 Jorge Toca RC .25 .60
180 Matt Roney RC .20 .50
181 Andy Brown RC .20 .50
182 Phil Norton RC .20 .50
183 Mickey Lopez RC .20 .50
184 Chris George RC .20 .50
185 Arturo McDowell RC .20 .50
186 Jose Fernandez RC .20 .50
187 Seth Etherton RC .20 .50
188 Josh McKinley RC .20 .50
189 Nate Cornejo RC .20 .50
190 G.Chiaramonte RC .20 .50
191 Mamon Tucker RC .20 .50
192 Ryan Mills RC .20 .50
193 Chad Moeller RC .20 .50
194 Tony Torcato RC .20 .50
195 Jeff Winchester RC .20 .50
196 Rick Elder RC .20 .50
197 Matt Burch RC .20 .50
198 Jeff Urban RC .25 .60
199 Chris Jones RC .25 .60
200 Masao Kida RC .25 .60

1999 Bowman's Best Atomic Refractors

Randomly inserted at a rate of one in 62, this 200-card set is a parallel of the Bowman's Best Base set. Each card in this set is sequentially numbered to 100 and feature a refractive kaleidescope treatment on front.

*STARS: 10X TO 25X BASIC CARDS
*ROOKIES: 7.5X TO 15X BASIC CARDS
STATED ODDS 1:62

1999 Bowman's Best Refractors

Randomly inserted at a rate of one in 15, this 200-card set is a parallel of the Bowman's Best Base set and features iridescent select metallization technology. Each card in this set is sequentially numbered to 400.

*STARS: 5X TO 12X BASIC CARDS
*ROOKIES: 4X TO 8X BASIC CARDS
STATED ODDS 1:15

1999 Bowman's Best Franchise Best Mach I

Randomly inserted in packs at the rate of one in 41, this 10-card set features color photos of some of the Major's top stars printed on die-cut Serillusion stock and sequentially numbered to 3,000.

COMPLETE SET (10)	30.00	60.00
STATED ODDS 1:41		
*MACH II: .75X TO 2X MACH I		
MACH II STATED ODDS 1:124		
MACH II PRINT RUN 1000 SERIAL #'d SETS		
*MACH III: 1.25X TO 3X MACH I		
MACH III STATED ODDS 1:248		
MACH III PRINT RUN 500 SERIAL #'d SETS		
FB1 Mark McGwire	4.00	10.00
FB2 Ken Griffey Jr.	2.50	6.00
FB3 Sammy Sosa	1.50	4.00
FB4 Nomar Garciaparra	2.50	6.00
FB5 Alex Rodriguez	2.50	6.00
FB6 Derek Jeter	4.00	10.00
FB7 Mike Piazza	2.50	6.00
FB8 Frank Thomas	1.50	4.00
FB9 Chipper Jones	1.50	4.00
FB10 Juan Gonzalez	.60	1.50

1999 Bowman's Best Franchise Favorites

Randomly inserted in packs at the rate of one in 40, this six-card set features color photos of retired legends and current stars in three versions. Version A pictures the current star; Version B, a retired great; and Version C pairs the current star with the retired legend.

COMPLETE SET (6)	40.00	80.00
STATED ODDS 1:40		
FR1A Derek Jeter	8.00	20.00
FR1B Don Mattingly	8.00	20.00
FR1C Derek Jeter Don Mattingly	10.00	25.00
FR2A Scott Rolen	3.00	8.00
FR2B Mike Schmidt	5.00	12.00
FR2C Scott Rolen Mike Schmidt	8.00	20.00

1999 Bowman's Best Franchise Favorites Autographs

This six-card set is an autographed parallel version of the regular insert set with the "Topps Certified Autograph Issue" stamp. The insertion rate for these cards are: Versions A and B, 1:1550 packs; and Version C, 1:6174. Version C cards feature autographs from both players.

FR1A/FR2A STATED ODDS 1:1550		
FR1B/FR2B STATED ODDS 1:1550		
FR1C/FR2C STATED ODDS 1:6174		
FR1A Derek Jeter	60.00	120.00
FR1B Don Mattingly	30.00	60.00
FR1C Derek Jeter Don Mattingly	175.00	300.00
FR2A Scott Rolen	10.00	25.00
FR2B Mike Schmidt	12.50	30.00
FR2C Scott Rolen Mike Schmidt	60.00	120.00

1999 Bowman's Best Future Foundations Mach I

Randomly inserted into packs at the rate of one in 41, this 10-card set features color photos of some of the top young stars printed on die-cut Serillusion stock and sequentially numbered to 3,000.

COMPLETE SET (10)	15.00	30.00
STATED ODDS 1:41		
*MACH II: .75X TO 2X MACH I		
MACH II STATED ODDS 1:124		
MACH II PRINT RUN 1000 SERIAL #'d SETS		
*MACH III: 1.25X TO 3X MACH I		
MACH III STATED ODDS 1:248		
MACH III PRINT RUN 500 SERIAL #'d SETS		
FF1 Ruben Mateo	.40	1.00
FF2 Troy Glaus	1.00	2.50
FF3 Eric Chavez	.60	1.50
FF4 Pat Burrell	1.50	4.00
FF5 Adrian Beltre	.60	1.50
FF6 Ryan Anderson	.40	1.00
FF7 Alfonso Soriano	2.00	5.00
FF8 Brad Penny	.40	1.00
FF9 Derrick Gibson	.40	1.00
FF10 Bruce Chen	.40	1.00

1999 Bowman's Best Mirror Image

Randomly inserted into packs at the rate of one in 24, this 10-card double-sided set features color photos of a veteran ballplayer on one side and a hot prospect on the other.

COMPLETE SET (10)	30.00	60.00
STATED ODDS 1:24		
*REFRACTORS: .75X TO 2X BASIC MIR.IMAGE		
REFRACTOR STATED ODDS 1:96		
*ATOMIC: 1.25X TO 3X BASIC MIR.IMAGE		
ATOMIC STATED ODDS 1:192		
M1 Alex Rodriguez Alex Gonzalez	2.00	5.00
M2 Ken Griffey Jr. Ruben Mateo	2.00	5.00
M3 Derek Jeter Alfonso Soriano	4.00	10.00
M4 Sammy Sosa Corey Patterson	1.25	3.00
M5 Greg Maddux Bruce Chen	2.00	5.00
M6 Chipper Jones Eric Chavez	1.00	2.50
M7 Vladimir Guerrero Carlos Beltran	1.00	2.50
M8 Frank Thomas Nick Johnson	1.00	2.50
M9 Nomar Garciaparra Pablo Ozuna	2.00	5.00
M10 Mark McGwire Pat Burrell	3.00	8.00

1999 Bowman's Best Rookie Locker Room Autographs

Randomly inserted into packs at the rate of one in 248, this five-card set features autographed color photos of top prospects with the "Topps Certified Autograph Issue" logo stamp.

STATED ODDS 1:248		
RA1 Pat Burrell	8.00	20.00
RA2 Michael Barrett	4.00	10.00
RA3 Troy Glaus	6.00	15.00
RA4 Gabe Kapler	4.00	10.00
RA5 Eric Chavez	4.00	10.00

1999 Bowman's Best Rookie Locker Room Game Used Bats

Randomly inserted into packs at the rate of one in 517, this six-card set features color photos of top players with pieces of game-used bats embedded into the cards.

STATED ODDS 1:517		
RB1 Pat Burrell	6.00	15.00
RB2 Michael Barrett	3.00	8.00
RB3 Troy Glaus	4.00	10.00
RB4 Gabe Kapler	3.00	8.00
RB5 Eric Chavez	3.00	8.00
RB6 Richie Sexson	3.00	8.00

1999 Bowman's Best Rookie Locker Room Game Worn Jerseys

Randomly inserted into packs at the rate of one in 538, this four-card set features color photos of some of the hottest young stars with pieces of their game-used jerseys embedded in the cards.

STATED ODDS 1:538		
RJ1 Richie Sexson	4.00	10.00
RJ2 Michael Barrett	4.00	10.00
RJ3 Troy Glaus	6.00	15.00
RJ4 Eric Chavez	4.00	10.00

1999 Bowman's Best Rookie of the Year

Randomly inserted into packs at the rate of one in 95, this two-card set features color photos of the 1998 American and National League Rookies of the Year printed on Serillusion card stock. An autographed version of Ben Grieve's card with the "Topps Certified Autograph Issue" stamp was inserted at the rate of 1:1239 packs.

STATED ODDS 1:95		
GRIEVE AU STATED ODDS 1:1239		
ROY1 Ben Grieve	1.00	2.50
ROY2 Kerry Wood	1.00	2.50
ROY1A Ben Grieve AU	6.00	15.00

2000 Bowman's Best Previews

Randomly inserted into Bowman hobby/retail packs at one in 18, this 10-card insert set features preview cards from the 2000 Bowman's Best product. Card backs carry a "BB" prefix.

COMPLETE SET (10)	15.00	40.00
BB1 Derek Jeter	2.50	6.00
BB2 Ken Griffey Jr.	1.50	4.00
BB3 Nomar Garciaparra	1.50	4.00
BB4 Mike Piazza	1.50	4.00
BB5 Alex Rodriguez	1.50	4.00
BB6 Sammy Sosa	1.00	2.50
BB7 Mark McGwire	2.50	6.00
BB8 Pat Burrell	.40	1.00
BB9 Josh Hamilton	1.50	4.00
BB10 Adam Piatt	.40	1.00

2000 Bowman's Best

The 2000 Bowman's Best set (produced by Topps) was released in early August, 2000 and features a 200-card base set broken into tiers as follows: Base Veterans/Prospects (1-150) and Rookies (151-200) which were serial numbered to 2999. Each pack contained four cards, and carried a suggested retail of $5.00. Rookie Cards include Rick Asadoorian, Willie Bloomquist, Bobby Bradley, Ben Broussard, Chin-Feng Chen and Barry Zito. The added element of serial-numbered Rookie Cards was extremely popular with collectors and a much-need jolt of life for the Bowman's Best brand (which had been badly overshadowed for two years by the Bowman Chrome Brand).

COMP.SET w/o RC's (150)	15.00	40.00
COMMON CARD (1-150)	.15	.40
COMMON (151-200)	2.00	5.00
1 Nomar Garciaparra	.60	1.50
2 Chipper Jones	.40	1.00
3 Tony Clark	.15	.40
4 Bernie Williams	.25	.60
5 Barry Bonds	1.00	2.50
6 Jermaine Dye	.15	.40
7 John Olerud	.15	.40
8 Mike Hampton	.15	.40
9 Cal Ripken	1.25	3.00
10 Jeff Bagwell	.25	.60
11 Troy Glaus	.15	.40
12 J.D. Drew	.15	.40
13 Jeromy Burnitz	.15	.40
14 Carlos Delgado	.15	.40
15 Shawn Green	.15	.40
16 Kevin Millwood	.15	.40
17 Rondell White	.15	.40
18 Scott Rolen	.25	.60
19 Jeff Cirillo	.15	.40
20 Barry Larkin	.25	.60
21 Brian Giles	.15	.40
22 Roger Clemens	.75	2.00
23 Manny Ramirez	.25	.60
24 Alex Gonzalez	.15	.40
25 Mark Grace	.25	.60
26 Fernando Tatis	.15	.40
27 Randy Johnson	.40	1.00
28 Roger Cedeno	.15	.40
29 Brian Jordan	.15	.40
30 Kevin Brown	.15	.40
31 Greg Vaughn	.15	.40
32 Roberto Alomar	.25	.60
33 Larry Walker	.15	.40
34 Rafael Palmeiro	.25	.60
35 Curt Schilling	.15	.40
36 Orlando Hernandez	.15	.40
37 Todd Walker	.15	.40
38 Juan Gonzalez	.15	.40
39 Sean Casey	.15	.40
40 Tony Gwynn	.50	1.25
41 Albert Belle	.15	.40
42 Gary Sheffield	.15	.40
43 Michael Barrett	.15	.40
44 Preston Wilson	.15	.40
45 Jim Thome	.25	.60
46 Shannon Stewart	.15	.40
47 Mo Vaughn	.15	.40
48 Ben Grieve	.15	.40
49 Adrian Beltre	.15	.40
50 Sammy Sosa	.40	1.00
51 Bob Abreu	.15	.40
52 Edgardo Alfonzo	.15	.40
53 Carlos Febles	.15	.40
54 Frank Thomas	.40	1.00
55 Alex Rodriguez	.60	1.50
56 Cliff Floyd	.15	.40
57 Jose Canseco	.25	.60
58 Erubiel Durazo	.15	.40
59 Tim Hudson	.15	.40
60 Craig Biggio	.25	.60
61 Eric Karros	.15	.40
62 Mike Mussina	.25	.60
63 Robin Ventura	.15	.40
64 Carlos Beltran	.15	.40
65 Pedro Martinez	.25	.60
66 Gabe Kapler	.15	.40
67 Jason Kendall	.15	.40
68 Derek Jeter	1.00	2.50
69 Magglio Ordonez	.15	.40
70 Mike Piazza	.60	1.50
71 Mike Lieberthal	.15	.40
72 Andres Galarraga	.15	.40
73 Raul Mondesi	.15	.40
74 Eric Chavez	.15	.40
75 Greg Maddux	.60	1.50
76 Matt Williams	.15	.40
77 Kris Benson	.15	.40
78 Ivan Rodriguez	.25	.60
79 Pokey Reese	.15	.40
80 Vladimir Guerrero	.40	1.00
81 Mark McGwire	1.00	2.50
82 Vinny Castilla	.15	.40
83 Todd Helton	.25	.60
84 Andruw Jones	.25	.60
85 Ken Griffey Jr.	.60	1.50
86 Mark McGwire BP	.50	1.25
87 Derek Jeter BP	.50	1.25
88 Chipper Jones BP	.25	.60
89 Nomar Garciaparra BP	.40	1.00
90 Sammy Sosa BP	.25	.60
91 Cal Ripken BP	.60	1.50
92 Juan Gonzalez BP	.15	.40
93 Alex Rodriguez BP	.40	1.00
94 Barry Bonds BP	.50	1.25
95 Sean Casey BP	.15	.40
96 Vladimir Guerrero BP	.25	.60
97 Mike Piazza BP	.40	1.00
98 Shawn Green BP	.15	.40
99 Jeff Bagwell BP	.15	.40
100 Ken Griffey Jr. BP	.40	1.00
101 Rick Ankiel	.15	.40
102 John Patterson	.15	.40
103 David Walling	.15	.40
104 Michael Restovich	.15	.40
105 A.J. Burnett	.15	.40
106 Pablo Ozuna	.15	.40
107 Chad Hermansen	.15	.40
108 Choo Freeman	.15	.40
109 Mark Quinn	.15	.40
110 Corey Patterson	.15	.40
111 Ramon Ortiz	.15	.40
112 Vernon Wells	.15	.40
113 Milton Bradley	.15	.40
114 Gookie Dawkins	.15	.40
115 Sean Burroughs	.15	.40
116 Wily Mo Pena	.15	.40
117 Dee Brown	.15	.40
118 C.C. Sabathia	.15	.40
119 Adam Kennedy	.15	.40
120 Octavio Dotel	.15	.40
121 Kip Wells	.15	.40
122 Ben Petrick	.15	.40
123 Mark Mulder	.15	.40
124 Jason Standridge	.15	.40
125 Adam Piatt	.15	.40
126 Steve Lomasney	.15	.40
127 Jayson Werth	.15	.40
128 Alex Escobar	.15	.40
129 Ryan Anderson	.15	.40
130 Adam Dunn	.40	1.00
131 Ted Lilly	.15	.40
132 Brad Penny	.15	.40
133 Daryle Ward	.15	.40
134 Eric Munson	.15	.40
135 Nick Johnson	.15	.40
136 Jason Jennings	.15	.40
137 Tim Raines Jr.	.15	.40
138 Ruben Mateo	.15	.40
139 Jack Cust	.15	.40
140 Rafael Furcal	.15	.40
141 Eric Gagne	.40	1.00
142 Tony Armas Jr.	.15	.40
143 Mike Paradis	.15	.40
144 Peter Bergeron	.15	.40
145 Alfonso Soriano	.40	1.00
146 Josh Hamilton	.60	1.50
147 Michael Cuddyer	.15	.40
148 Jay Gehrke	.15	.40
149 Josh Girdley	.15	.40
150 Pat Burrell	.15	.40
151 Brett Myers RC	5.00	12.00
152 Scott Seabol RC	2.00	5.00
153 Keith Reed RC	2.00	5.00
154 F.Rodriguez RC	5.00	12.00
155 Barry Zito RC	6.00	15.00
156 Pat Manning RC	2.00	5.00
157 Ben Christensen RC	2.00	5.00
158 Corey Myers RC	2.00	5.00
159 Wascar Serrano RC	2.00	5.00
160 Wes Anderson RC	2.00	5.00
161 Andy Tracy RC	2.00	5.00
162 Cesar Saba RC	2.00	5.00
163 Mike Lamb RC	3.00	8.00
164 Bobby Bradley RC	2.00	5.00
165 Vince Faison RC	2.00	5.00
166 Ty Howington RC	2.00	5.00
167 Ken Harvey RC UER Card has pitching stats on the back	2.00	5.00
168 Josh Kalinowski RC	2.00	5.00
169 Ruben Salazar RC	2.00	5.00
170 Aaron Rowand RC	4.00	10.00
171 Ramon Santiago RC	2.00	5.00
172 Scott Sobkowiak RC	2.00	5.00
173 Lyle Overbay RC	3.00	8.00
174 Rico Washington RC	2.00	5.00
175 Rick Asadoorian RC	2.00	5.00
176 Matt Ginter RC	2.00	5.00
177 Jason Stumm RC	2.00	5.00
178 B.J. Garbe RC	2.00	5.00
179 Mike MacDougal RC	2.00	5.00
180 Ryan Christianson RC	2.00	5.00
181 Kurt Ainsworth RC	2.00	5.00
182 Brad Baisley RC	2.00	5.00
183 Ben Broussard RC	5.00	12.00
184 Aaron McNeal RC	2.00	5.00
185 John Sneed RC	2.00	5.00
186 Junior Brignac RC	2.00	5.00
187 Chance Caple RC	2.00	5.00
188 Scott Downs RC	2.00	5.00
189 Matt Cepicky RC	2.00	5.00
190 Chin-Feng Chen RC	15.00	30.00
191 Johan Santana RC	12.50	30.00
192 Brad Baker RC	2.00	5.00
193 Jason Repko RC	3.00	8.00
194 Craig Dingman RC	2.00	5.00
195 Chris Wakeland RC	2.00	5.00
196 Rogelio Arias RC	2.00	5.00
197 Luis Matos RC	2.00	5.00
198 Rob Ramsay	2.00	5.00
199 Willie Bloomquist RC	15.00	30.00
200 Tony Pena Jr. RC	2.00	5.00

2000 Bowman's Best Autographed Baseball Redemptions

Randomly inserted into packs at one in 688, this five-card insert features exchange cards for actual autographed baseballs from some of the Major League's hottest prospects. Please note the deadline to return these cards to Topps was June 30th, 2001.

1 Josh Hamilton	8.00	20.00
2 Rick Ankiel	15.00	40.00
3 Alfonso Soriano	30.00	60.00
4 Nick Johnson	15.00	40.00
5 Corey Patterson	15.00	40.00

2000 Bowman's Best Bets

Randomly inserted into packs at one in 15, this 10-card insert features prospects that are sure bets to excel at the Major League level. Card backs carry a "BBB" prefix.

COMPLETE SET (10)	10.00	25.00
BBB1 Pat Burrell	.60	1.50
BBB2 Alfonso Soriano	1.50	4.00
BBB3 Corey Patterson	.60	1.50
BBB4 Eric Munson	.60	1.50
BBB5 Sean Burroughs	.60	1.50
BBB6 Rafael Furcal	.60	1.50
BBB7 Rick Ankiel	.60	1.50
BBB8 Nick Johnson	.60	1.50
BBB9 Ruben Mateo	.60	1.50
BBB10 Josh Hamilton	1.50	4.00

2000 Bowman's Best Franchise 2000

Randomly inserted into packs at one in 18, this 25-card set features players that teams build around. Card backs carry an "F" prefix.

COMPLETE SET (25)	60.00	150.00
F1 Cal Ripken	8.00	20.00
F2 Nomar Garciaparra	4.00	10.00
F3 Frank Thomas	2.50	6.00
F4 Manny Ramirez	1.50	4.00
F5 Juan Gonzalez	1.00	2.50
F6 Carlos Beltran	1.00	2.50
F7 Derek Jeter	6.00	15.00
F8 Alex Rodriguez	4.00	10.00
F9 Ben Grieve	1.00	2.50
F10 Jose Canseco	1.50	4.00
F11 Ivan Rodriguez	1.50	4.00
F12 Mo Vaughn	1.00	2.50
F13 Randy Johnson	2.50	6.00
F14 Chipper Jones	2.50	6.00
F15 Sammy Sosa	2.50	6.00
F16 Ken Griffey Jr.	4.00	10.00
F17 Larry Walker	1.00	2.50
F18 Preston Wilson	1.00	2.50
F19 Jeff Bagwell	1.50	4.00
F20 Shawn Green	1.00	2.50
F21 Vladimir Guerrero	2.50	6.00
F22 Mike Piazza	4.00	10.00
F23 Scott Rolen	1.50	4.00
F24 Tony Gwynn	3.00	8.00
F25 Barry Bonds	6.00	15.00

2000 Bowman's Best Franchise Favorites

Randomly inserted into packs at one in 17, this six-card insert features players (past and present) that are franchise favorites. Card backs carry a "FR" prefix.

COMPLETE SET (6)	12.50	30.00
FR1A Sean Casey	1.00	2.50
FR1B Johnny Bench	1.50	4.00
FR1C Sean Casey Johnny Bench	1.50	4.00
FR2A Cal Ripken	4.00	10.00
FR2B Brooks Robinson	1.00	2.50
FR2C Cal Ripken Brooks Robinson	4.00	10.00

2000 Bowman's Best Franchise Favorites Autographs

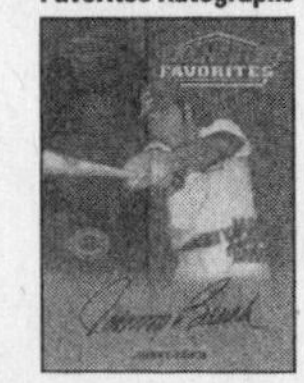

Randomly inserted into packs, this six-card insert is a complete parallel of the Franchise Favorites insert. Each of these cards were autographed by the players, and the set was broken into tiers as folllows: Group A (Sean Casey and Cal Ripken) were inserted at one in 1291, Group B (Johnny Bench and Brooks Robinson) were inserted at one in 1291, and Group C (Casey/Bench, and Ripken/Robinson) were inserted into packs at one in 1,513. The overall odds of getting an autograph cards were one in 574. Card backs carry a "FR" prefix.

GROUP A STATED ODDS 1:1291		
GROUP B STATED ODDS 1:1291		
GROUP C STATED ODDS 1:5153		
FR1A Sean Casey A	10.00	25.00
FR1B Johnny Bench B	30.00	60.00
FR1C Sean Casey Johnny Bench	60.00	120.00
FR2A Cal Ripken A	60.00	120.00
FR2B Brooks Robinson B	15.00	40.00
FR2C Cal Ripken Brooks Robinson	150.00	250.00

2000 Bowman's Best Locker Room Collection Autographs

Randomly inserted into packs, this 19-card insert features autographed cards of top Major League prospects. Card backs carry an "LRCA" prefix. Please note that these cards were broken into two groups. Group A cards were inserted at one in 1033 packs, and Group B cards were inserted at one in 61.

GROUP A STATED ODDS 1:1033		
GROUP B STATED ODDS 1:61		
LRCA1 Carlos Beltran B	6.00	15.00
LRCA2 Rick Ankiel A	10.00	25.00
LRCA3 Vernon Wells A	6.00	15.00
LRCA4 Ruben Mateo A	4.00	10.00
LRCA5 Ben Petrick A	4.00	10.00
LRCA6 Adam Piatt A	4.00	10.00
LRCA7 Eric Munson A	4.00	10.00
LRCA8 Alfonso Soriano A	15.00	40.00
LRCA9 Kerry Wood B	10.00	25.00
LRCA10 Jack Cust A	4.00	10.00
LRCA11 Rafael Furcal A	4.00	10.00
LRCA12 Josh Hamilton A	15.00	40.00
LRCA13 Brad Penny A	6.00	15.00
LRCA14 Dee Brown A	4.00	10.00
LRCA15 Milton Bradley A	6.00	15.00
LRCA16 Ryan Anderson A	4.00	10.00
LRCA17 John Patterson A	6.00	15.00
LRCA18 Nick Johnson A	6.00	15.00
LRCA19 Peter Bergeron A	4.00	10.00

2000 Bowman's Best Locker Room Collection Bats

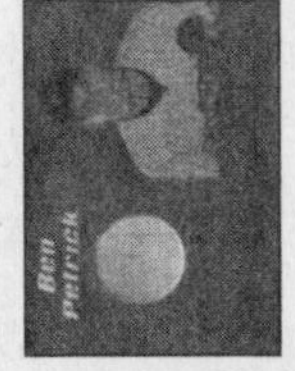

Randomly inserted into packs at one in 376, this 11-card insert features game-used bat cards of some of the hottest prospects in baseball. Card backs carry a "LRCL" prefix.

LRCLAP Adam Piatt	3.00	8.00
LRCLBP Ben Petrick	3.00	8.00
LRCLBP Brad Penny	4.00	10.00
LRCLCB Carlos Beltran	4.00	10.00
LRCLDB Dee Brown	3.00	8.00
LRCLEM Eric Munson	3.00	8.00
LRCLJD J.D. Drew	4.00	10.00
LRCLPB Pat Burrell	4.00	10.00
LRCLRA Rick Ankiel	6.00	15.00
LRCLRF Rafael Furcal	4.00	10.00
LRCLVW Vernon Wells	4.00	10.00

2000 Bowman's Best Locker Room Collection Jerseys

Randomly inserted into packs at one in 206, this five-card insert features swatches from actual game-used jerseys. Card backs carry a "LRCJ" prefix.

LRCJ1 Carlos Beltran	4.00	10.00
LRCJ2 Rick Ankiel	6.00	15.00
LRCJ3 Mark Quinn	3.00	8.00
LRCJ4 Ben Petrick	3.00	8.00
LRCJ5 Adam Piatt	3.00	8.00

2000 Bowman's Best Selections

Randomly inserted into packs at one in 30, this 15-card insert features players that turned out to be outstanding draft selections. Card backs carry a "BBS" prefix.

COMPLETE SET (15)	50.00	120.00
BBS1 Alex Rodriguez	4.00	10.00
BBS2 Ken Griffey Jr.	4.00	10.00
BBS3 Pat Burrell	1.00	2.50
BBS4 Mark McGwire	6.00	15.00
BBS5 Derek Jeter	6.00	15.00
BBS6 Nomar Garciaparra	4.00	10.00
BBS7 Mike Piazza	4.00	10.00
BBS8 Josh Hamilton	2.50	6.00
BBS9 Cal Ripken	8.00	20.00
BBS10 Jeff Bagwell	1.50	4.00
BBS11 Chipper Jones	2.50	6.00
BBS12 Jose Canseco	1.50	4.00
BBS13 Carlos Beltran	1.00	2.50

BBS14 Kerry Wood 1.00 2.50
BBS15 Ben Grieve 1.00 2.50

2000 Bowman's Best Year by Year

Randomly inserted into packs at one in 23, this 10-card insert features duos that made their Major League debuts in the same year. Card backs carry a "YY" prefix.

COMPLETE SET (10) 30.00 80.00
YY1 Sammy Sosa 3.00 8.00
Ken Griffey Jr.
YY2 Nomar Garciaparra 3.00 8.00
Vladimir Guerrero
YY3 Alex Rodriguez 3.00 8.00
Jeff Cirillo
YY4 Mike Piazza 3.00 8.00
Pedro Martinez
YY5 Derek Jeter 5.00 12.00
Edgardo Alfonzo
YY6 Alfonso Soriano .75 2.00
Rick Ankiel
YY7 Mark McGwire 5.00 12.00
Barry Bonds
YY8 Juan Gonzalez .75 2.00
Larry Walker
YY9 Ivan Rodriguez 1.25 3.00
Jeff Bagwell
YY10 Shawn Green 1.25 3.00
Manny Ramirez

2001 Bowman's Best

This 200-card set features color action player photos printed in an all new design and leading technology. The set was distributed in five-card packs with a suggested retail price of $5 and includes 35 Rookie and 15 Exclusive Rookie cards sequentially numbered to 2,999.

COMP.SET w/o SP's (150) 20.00 50.00
COMMON CARD (1-150) .15 .40
COMMON (151-200) 2.00 5.00
1 Vladimir Guerrero .40 1.00
2 Miguel Tejada .15 .40
3 Geoff Jenkins .15 .40
4 Jeff Bagwell .25 .60
5 Todd Helton .25 .60
6 Ken Griffey Jr. .60 1.50
7 Nomar Garciaparra .60 1.50
8 Chipper Jones .40 1.00
9 Darin Erstad .15 .40
10 Frank Thomas .40 1.00
11 Jim Thome .25 .60
12 Preston Wilson .15 .40
13 Kevin Brown .15 .40
14 Derek Jeter 1.00 2.50
15 Scott Rolen .25 .60
16 Ryan Klesko .15 .40
17 Jeff Kent .15 .40
18 Raul Mondesi .15 .40
19 Greg Vaughn .15 .40
20 Bernie Williams .25 .60
21 Mike Piazza .60 1.50
22 Richard Hidalgo .15 .40
23 Dean Palmer .15 .40
24 Roberto Alomar .25 .60
25 Sammy Sosa .40 1.00
26 Randy Johnson .40 1.00
27 Manny Ramirez Sox .25 .60
28 Roger Clemens .75 2.00
29 Terrence Long .15 .40
30 Jason Kendall .15 .40
31 Richie Sexson .15 .40
32 David Wells .15 .40
33 Andruw Jones .25 .60
34 Pokey Reese .15 .40
35 Juan Gonzalez .15 .40
36 Carlos Beltran .15 .40
37 Shawn Green .15 .40
38 Mariano Rivera .40 1.00
39 John Olerud .15 .40
40 Jim Edmonds .15 .40
41 Andres Galarraga .15 .40
42 Carlos Delgado .15 .40
43 Kris Benson .15 .40
44 Andy Pettitte .25 .60
45 Jeff Cirillo .15 .40
46 Magglio Ordonez .15 .40
47 Tom Glavine .25 .60
48 Garret Anderson .15 .40
49 Cal Ripken 1.25 3.00
50 Pedro Martinez .25 .60
51 Barry Bonds 1.00 2.50
52 Alex Rodriguez .60 1.50
53 Ben Grieve .15 .40
54 Edgar Martinez .25 .60
55 Jason Giambi .15 .40
56 Jeromy Burnitz .15 .40
57 Mike Mussina .25 .60
58 Moises Alou .15 .40
59 Sean Casey .15 .40
60 Greg Maddux .60 1.50
61 Tim Hudson .15 .40
62 Mark McGwire 1.00 2.50
63 Rafael Palmeiro .25 .60
64 Tony Batista .15 .40
65 Kazuhiro Sasaki .15 .40
66 Jorge Posada .25 .60
67 Johnny Damon .25 .60
68 Brian Giles .15 .40
69 Jose Vidro .15 .40
70 Jermaine Dye .15 .40
71 Craig Biggio .25 .60
72 Larry Walker .15 .40
73 Eric Chavez .15 .40
74 David Segui .15 .40
75 Tim Salmon .25 .60
76 Javy Lopez .15 .40
77 Paul Konerko .15 .40
78 Barry Larkin .25 .60
79 Mike Hampton .15 .40
80 Bobby Higginson .15 .40
81 Mark Mulder .15 .40
82 Pat Burrell .15 .40
83 Kerry Wood .15 .40
84 J.T. Snow .15 .40
85 Ivan Rodriguez .25 .60
86 Edgardo Alfonzo .15 .40
87 Orlando Hernandez .15 .40
88 Gary Sheffield .15 .40
89 Mike Sweeney .15 .40
90 Carlos Lee .15 .40
91 Rafael Furcal .15 .40
92 Troy Glaus .15 .40
93 Bartolo Colon .15 .40
94 Cliff Floyd .15 .40
95 Barry Zito .25 .60
96 J.D. Drew .15 .40
97 Eric Karros .15 .40
98 Jose Valentin .15 .40
99 Ellis Burks .15 .40
100 David Justice .15 .40
101 Larry Barnes .15 .40
102 Rod Barajas .15 .40
103 Tony Pena Jr. .15 .40
104 Jerry Hairston Jr. .15 .40
105 Keith Ginter .15 .40
106 Corey Patterson .15 .40
107 Aaron Rowand .15 .40
108 Miguel Olivo .15 .40
109 Gookie Dawkins .15 .40
110 C.C. Sabathia .15 .40
111 Ben Petrick .15 .40
112 Eric Munson .15 .40
113 Ramon Castro .15 .40
114 Alex Escobar .15 .40
115 Josh Hamilton .30 .75
116 Jason Marquis .15 .40
117 Ben Davis .15 .40
118 Alex Cintron .15 .40
119 Julio Zuleta .15 .40
120 Ben Broussard .15 .40
121 Adam Everett .15 .40
122 Ramon Carvajal RC .15 .40
123 Felipe Lopez .15 .40
124 Alfonso Soriano .25 .60
125 Jayson Werth .15 .40
126 Donzell McDonald .15 .40
127 Jason Hart .15 .40
128 Joe Crede .40 1.00
129 Sean Burroughs .15 .40
130 Jack Cust .15 .40
131 Corey Smith .15 .40
132 Adrian Gonzalez 1.00 2.50
133 J.R. House .15 .40
134 Steve Lomasney .15 .40
135 Tim Raines Jr. .15 .40
136 Tony Alvarez .15 .40
137 Doug Mientkiewicz .15 .40
138 Rocco Baldelli .15 .40
139 Jason Romano .15 .40
140 Vernon Wells .15 .40
141 Mike Bynum .15 .40
142 Xavier Nady .15 .40
143 Brad Wilkerson .15 .40
144 Ben Diggins .15 .40
145 Aubrey Huff .15 .40
146 Eric Byrnes .15 .40
147 Alex Gordon .15 .40
148 Roy Oswalt .40 1.00
149 Brian Esposito .15 .40
150 Scott Seabol .15 .40
151 Erick Almonte RC 2.00 5.00
152 Gary Johnson RC 2.00 5.00
153 Pedro Liriano RC 2.00 5.00
154 Matt White RC 2.00 5.00
155 Luis Montanez RC 2.50 6.00
156 Brad Cresse 2.00 5.00
157 Wilson Betemit RC 3.00 8.00
158 Octavio Martinez RC 2.00 5.00
159 Adam Pettyjohn RC 2.00 5.00
160 Corey Spencer RC 2.00 5.00
161 Mark Burnett RC 2.00 5.00
162 Ichiro Suzuki RC 25.00 50.00
163 Alexis Gomez RC 2.00 5.00
164 Greg Nash RC 2.00 5.00
165 Roberto Miniel RC 2.00 5.00
166 Justin Morneau RC 10.00 25.00
167 Ben Washburn RC 2.00 5.00
168 Bob Keppel RC 2.00 5.00
169 Deivi Mendez RC 2.00 5.00
170 Tsuyoshi Shinjo RC 3.00 8.00
171 Jared Abruzzo RC 2.00 5.00
172 Derrick Van Dusen RC 2.00 5.00
173 Hee Seop Choi RC 3.00 8.00
174 Albert Pujols RC 125.00 250.00
175 Travis Hafner RC 15.00 30.00
176 Ron Davenport RC 2.00 5.00
177 Luis Torres RC 2.00 5.00
178 Jake Peavy RC 10.00 25.00
179 Elvis Corporan RC 2.00 5.00
180 Dave Krynzel 2.00 5.00
181 Tony Blanco RC 2.00 5.00
182 Elpidio Guzman RC 2.00 5.00
183 Matt Butler RC 2.00 5.00
184 Joe Thurston RC 2.00 5.00
185 Andy Beal RC 2.00 5.00
186 Kevin Nulton RC 2.00 5.00
187 Sneidder Santos RC 2.00 5.00
188 Joe Dillon RC 2.00 5.00
189 Jeremy Blevins RC 2.00 5.00
190 Chris Amador RC 2.00 5.00
191 Mark Hendrickson RC 2.00 5.00
192 Willy Aybar RC 2.00 5.00
193 Antoine Cameron RC 2.00 5.00
194 J.J. Johnson RC 2.00 5.00
195 Ryan Ketchner RC 2.00 5.00
196 Bjorn Ivy RC 2.00 5.00
197 Josh Kroeger RC 2.00 5.00
198 Ty Wigginton RC 3.00 8.00
199 Stubby Clapp RC 2.00 5.00
200 Jerrod Riggan RC 2.00 5.00

2001 Bowman's Best Autographs

Randomly inserted in packs at the rate of one in 95, this seven-card set features autographed photos of top players.

BBAAG Adrian Gonzalez 30.00 60.00
BBABC Brad Cresse 4.00 10.00
BBAJH Josh Hamilton 20.00 50.00
BBAJR Jon Rauch 4.00 10.00
BBAJRH J.R. House 4.00 10.00
BBASB Sean Burroughs 4.00 10.00
BBATL Terrence Long 4.00 10.00

2001 Bowman's Best Exclusive Autographs

Randomly inserted in packs at the rate of one in 50, this nine-card set features autographed player photos. Stubby Clapp was an exchange card.

BBEABI Bjorn Ivy 3.00 8.00
BBEAJB Jeremy Blevins 3.00 8.00
BBEAJJ J.J. Johnson 3.00 8.00
BBEAJR Jerrod Riggan 3.00 8.00
BBEAMH M. Hendrickson 3.00 8.00
BBEASC Stubby Clapp 3.00 8.00
BBEASS Sneideer Santos 3.00 8.00
BBEATW Ty Wigginton 8.00 20.00
BBEAWA Willy Aybar 3.00 8.00

2001 Bowman's Best Franchise Favorites

Randomly inserted in packs at the rate of one in 16, this nine-card set features color photos of past and present players that are franchise favorites.

COMPLETE SET (9) 20.00 50.00
FFAR Alex Rodriguez 3.00 8.00
FFDE Darin Erstad 1.50 4.00
FFDM Don Mattingly 5.00 12.00
FFDW Dave Winfield 1.50 4.00
FFEJ Darin Erstad 1.50 4.00
Reggie Jackson
FFMW Don Mattingly 5.00 12.00
Dave Winfield
FFNR Nolan Ryan 5.00 12.00
FFRJ Reggie Jackson 1.50 4.00
FFRR Nolan Ryan 5.00 12.00
Alex Rodriguez

2001 Bowman's Best Franchise Favorites Autographs

Randomly inserted in packs, this nine-card set is an autographed parallel version of the regular insert set.

FFAAR Alex Rodriguez 50.00 100.00
FFADE Darin Erstad 6.00 15.00
FFADM Don Mattingly 30.00 60.00
FFADW Dave Winfield 10.00 25.00
FFAEJ Darin Erstad 40.00 80.00
Reggie Jackson
FFAMW Don Mattingly 125.00 200.00
Dave Winfield
FFANR Nolan Ryan 50.00 100.00
FFARJ Reggie Jackson 15.00 40.00
FFARR Nolan Ryan 175.00 350.00
Alex Rodriguez

2001 Bowman's Best Franchise Favorites Relics

Randomly inserted in packs at the rate of one in 58, this 12-card set features color player photos of franchise favorites along with memorabilia pieces.

FFRAR Alex Rodriguez 10.00 25.00
Jsy
FFRBB Craig Biggio Uni 15.00 40.00
Jeff Bagwell Uni
FFRCB Craig Biggio 6.00 15.00

Uni
FFRDE Darin Erstad Jsy 4.00 10.00
FFRDM Don Mattingly 15.00 40.00
Jsy
FFRDW Dave Winfield Jsy 4.00 10.00
FFREJ Darin Erstad Jsy 15.00 40.00
Reggie Jackson Jsy
FFRJB Jeff Bagwell 6.00 15.00
Uni
FFRMW Don Mattingly Jsy 50.00 100.00
Dave Winfield Jsy
FFRNR Nolan Ryan Jsy 20.00 50.00
FFRRJ Reggie Jackson 6.00 15.00
Jsy
FFRRR Nolan Ryan Jsy 40.00 80.00
Alex Rodriguez Jsy

2001 Bowman's Best Franchise Futures

Randomly inserted into packs at the rate of one in 24, this 12-card set displays color photos of top young players.

COMPLETE SET (12) 12.50 30.00
FF1 Josh Hamilton 1.50 4.00
FF2 Wes Helms .75 2.00
FF3 Alfonso Soriano .75 2.00
FF4 Nick Johnson .75 2.00
FF5 Jose Ortiz .75 2.00
FF6 Ben Sheets .75 2.00
FF7 Sean Burroughs .75 2.00
FF8 Ben Petrick .75 2.00
FF9 Corey Patterson .75 2.00
FF10 J.R. House .75 2.00
FF11 Alex Escobar .75 2.00
FF12 Travis Hafner 2.50 6.00

2001 Bowman's Best Impact Players

Randomly inserted in packs at the rate of one in seven, this 20-card set features color action photos of top players who have made their mark on the game.

COMPLETE SET (20) 12.50 30.00
IP1 Mark McGwire 2.00 5.00
IP2 Sammy Sosa .75 2.00
IP3 Manny Ramirez .50 1.25
IP4 Troy Glaus .40 1.00
IP5 Ken Griffey Jr. 1.25 3.00
IP6 Gary Sheffield .40 1.00
IP7 Vladimir Guerrero .75 2.00
IP8 Carlos Delgado .40 1.00
IP9 Jason Giambi .40 1.00
IP10 Frank Thomas .75 2.00
IP11 Vernon Wells .40 1.00
IP12 Carlos Pena .40 1.00
IP13 Joe Crede .75 2.00
IP14 Keith Ginter .40 1.00
IP15 Aubrey Huff .40 1.00
IP16 Brad Cresse .40 1.00
IP17 Austin Kearns .40 1.00
IP18 Nick Johnson .40 1.00
IP19 Josh Hamilton .75 2.00
IP20 Corey Patterson .40 1.00

2001 Bowman's Best Locker Room Collection Jerseys

Randomly inserted in packs at the rate of one in 133, this five-card set features color player photos with swatches of jerseys embedded in the cards and carry the "LRCL" prefix.

LRCJEC Eric Chavez 4.00 10.00
LRCJJP Jay Payton 3.00 8.00
LRCJMM Mark Mulder 4.00 10.00
LRCJPR Pokey Reese 3.00 8.00
LRCJPW Preston Wilson 4.00 10.00

2001 Bowman's Best Locker Room Collection Lumber

Randomly inserted in packs at the rate of one in 267, this five-card set features color player photos with

pieces of actual bats embedded in the cards and carry the "LRCL" prefix.

LRCLAG Adrian Gonzalez 3.00 8.00
LRCLCP Corey Patterson 3.00 8.00
LRCLEM Eric Munson 3.00 8.00
LRCLPB Pat Burrell 4.00 10.00
LRCLSB Sean Burroughs 3.00 8.00

2001 Bowman's Best Rookie Fever

Randomly inserted in packs at the rate of one in 10, this 10-card set features color photos of top players during their rookie year. Card backs display the "RF" prefix.

COMPLETE SET (10) 6.00 15.00
RF1 Chipper Jones .60 1.50
RF2 Preston Wilson .40 1.00
RF3 Todd Helton .40 1.00
RF4 Jay Payton .40 1.00
RF5 Ivan Rodriguez .40 1.00
RF6 Manny Ramirez .40 1.00
RF7 Derek Jeter 1.50 4.00
RF8 Orlando Hernandez .40 1.00
RF9 Mark Quinn .40 1.00
RF10 Terrence Long .40 1.00

2002 Bowman's Best

This 181 card set was released in August, 2002. The set was issued in five card packs which were issued 10 packs to a box and 10 boxes to a case with an SRP of $15. The first 90 cards of the set featured veteran players while cards 91 through 181 featured prospects or rookies along with either an autograph or a game-used bat piece of the featured player. The higher numbered cards were issued in different seeding ratios and we have notated the group the player belongs to next to their name in our checklist. Card number 181 features Kaz Ishii and was issued as an exchange card which could be redeemed until December 31, 2002.

COMP.SET w/o SP's (90) 40.00 100.00
COMMON CARD (1-90) .30 .75
COMMON AUTO A (91-180) 3.00 8.00
AUTO GROUP A ODDS 1:3
COMMON AUTO B (91-180) 4.00 10.00
AUTO GROUP B ODDS 1:19
COMMON BAT (91-180) 2.00 5.00
91-180 BAT STATED ODDS 1:5
181 ISHII BAT EXCHANGE ODDS 1:131
1 Josh Beckett .30 .75
2 Derek Jeter 2.00 5.00
3 Alex Rodriguez 1.25 3.00
4 Miguel Tejada .30 .75
5 Nomar Garciaparra 1.25 3.00
6 Aramis Ramirez .30 .75
7 Jeremy Giambi .30 .75
8 Bernie Williams .50 1.25
9 Juan Pierre .30 .75
10 Chipper Jones .75 2.00
11 Jimmy Rollins .30 .75
12 Alfonso Soriano .30 .75
13 Mark Prior .50 1.25
14 Paul Konerko .30 .75
15 Tim Hudson .30 .75
16 Doug Mientkiewicz .30 .75
17 Todd Helton .50 1.25
18 Moises Alou .30 .75
19 Juan Gonzalez .30 .75
20 Jorge Posada .50 1.25
21 Jeff Kent .30 .75
22 Roger Clemens 1.50 4.00
23 Phil Nevin .30 .75
24 Brian Giles .30 .75
25 Carlos Delgado .30 .75
26 Jason Giambi .30 .75
27 Vladimir Guerrero .75 2.00
28 Cliff Floyd .30 .75
29 Shea Hillenbrand .30 .75
30 Ken Griffey Jr. 1.25 3.00
31 Mike Piazza 1.25 3.00
32 Carlos Pena .30 .75
33 Larry Walker .30 .75
34 Magglio Ordonez .30 .75
35 Mike Mussina .50 1.25
36 Andruw Jones .50 1.25
37 Nick Johnson .30 .75
38 Curt Schilling .30 .75
39 Eric Chavez .30 .75
40 Bartolo Colon .30 .75
41 Eric Hinske .30 .75
42 Sean Burroughs .30 .75
43 Randy Johnson .75 2.00
44 Adam Dunn .30 .75
45 Pedro Martinez .50 1.25
46 Garret Anderson .30 .75
47 Jim Thome .50 1.25
48 Gary Sheffield .30 .75
49 Tsuyoshi Shinjo .30 .75
50 Albert Pujols 1.50 4.00
51 Ichiro Suzuki 1.50 4.00
52 C.C. Sabathia .30 .75
53 Bobby Abreu .30 .75
54 Ivan Rodriguez .50 1.25
55 J.D. Drew .30 .75
56 Jacque Jones .30 .75
57 Jason Kendall .30 .75
58 Javier Vazquez .30 .75
59 Jeff Bagwell .50 1.25
60 Greg Maddux 1.25 3.00
61 Jim Edmonds .30 .75
62 Hank Blalock .50 1.25
63 Jose Vidro .30 .75
64 Kevin Brown .30 .75
65 Mark Teixeira .75 2.00
66 Sammy Sosa .75 2.00
67 Lance Berkman .30 .75
68 Mark Mulder .30 .75
69 Marty Cordova .30 .75
70 Frank Thomas .75 2.00
71 Mike Cameron .30 .75
72 Mike Sweeney .30 .75
73 Barry Bonds 2.00 5.00
74 Troy Glaus .30 .75
75 Barry Zito .30 .75
76 Pat Burrell .30 .75
77 Paul LoDuca .30 .75
78 Rafael Palmeiro .50 1.25
79 Austin Kearns .30 .75
80 Darin Erstad .30 .75
81 Richie Sexson .30 .75
82 Roberto Alomar .50 1.25
83 Roy Oswalt .30 .75
84 Ryan Klesko .30 .75
85 Luis Gonzalez .30 .75
86 Scott Rolen .50 1.25
87 Shannon Stewart .30 .75
88 Shawn Green .30 .75
89 Toby Hall .30 .75
90 Bret Boone .30 .75
91 Casey Kotchman Bat RC 3.00 8.00
92 Jose Valverde AU A RC 5.00 12.00
93 Cole Barthel Bat RC 2.00 5.00
94 Brad Nelson AU A RC 3.00 8.00
95 Mauricio Lara AU A RC 3.00 8.00
96 Ryan Gripp Bat RC 2.00 5.00
97 Brian West AU A RC 3.00 8.00
98 Chris Piersoll AU B RC 4.00 10.00
99 Ryan Church AU B RC 6.00 15.00
100 Javier Colina AU A 3.00 8.00
101 Juan M. Gonzalez AU A RC 3.00 8.00
102 Benito Baez AU A 3.00 8.00
103 Mike Hill Bat RC 2.00 5.00
104 Jason Grove AU B RC 4.00 10.00
105 Koyie Hill AU B 4.00 10.00
106 Mark Outlaw AU A RC 3.00 8.00
107 Jason Bay Bat RC 6.00 15.00
108 Jorge Padilla AU A RC 3.00 8.00
109 Pete Zamora AU A RC 3.00 8.00
110 Joe Mauer AU A RC 75.00 150.00
111 Franklyn German AU A RC 3.00 8.00
112 Chris Flinn AU A RC 3.00 8.00
113 David Wright Bat RC 20.00 50.00
114 An. Martinez AU A RC 3.00 8.00
115 Nic Jackson Bat RC 2.00 5.00
116 Rene Reyes AU A RC 3.00 8.00
117 Colin Young AU A RC 3.00 8.00
118 Joe Orloski AU A RC 3.00 8.00
119 Mike Wilson AU A RC 3.00 8.00
120 Rich Thompson AU A RC 3.00 8.00
121 Jake Mauer AU B RC 4.00 10.00
122 Mario Ramos AU A RC 3.00 8.00
123 Doug Sessions AU B RC 4.00 10.00
124 Doug Devore Bat RC 2.00 5.00
125 Travis Foley AU A RC 3.00 8.00
126 Chris Baker AU A RC 3.00 8.00
127 Michael Floyd AU A RC 3.00 8.00
128 Josh Barfield Bat RC 4.00 10.00
129 Jose Bautista Bat RC 15.00 40.00
130 Gavin Floyd AU A RC 6.00 15.00
131 Jason Botts Bat RC 2.00 5.00
132 Clint Nageotte AU A RC 4.00 10.00
133 Jesus Cota AU B RC 4.00 10.00
134 Ron Calloway Bat RC 2.00 5.00
135 Kevin Cash Bat RC 2.00 5.00
136 Jonny Gomes AU B RC 8.00 20.00
137 Dennis Ulacia AU A RC 3.00 8.00
138 Ryan Snare AU A RC 3.00 8.00
139 Kevin Deaton AU A RC 3.00 8.00
140 Bobby Jenks AU B RC 6.00 15.00
141 Casey Kotchman AU A RC 6.00 15.00
142 Adam Walker AU A RC 3.00 8.00
143 Mike Gonzalez AU A RC 3.00 8.00
144 Ruben Gotay Bat RC 3.00 8.00
145 Jason Grove Bat RC 2.00 5.00
146 Freddy Sanchez AU B RC 12.50 30.00
147 Jason Arnold AU B RC 4.00 10.00
148 Scott Hairston AU A RC 4.00 10.00
149 Jason St. Clair AU B RC 4.00 10.00
150 Chris Tritle Bat RC 2.00 5.00
151 Edwin Yan Bat RC 2.00 5.00
152 Freddy Sanchez Bat RC 5.00 12.00
153 Greg Sain Bat RC 2.00 5.00
154 Yurendell De Caster Bat RC 2.00 5.00
155 Noochie Varner Bat RC 2.00 5.00
156 Nelson Castro AU B RC 4.00 10.00
157 Randall Shelley Bat RC 2.00 5.00
158 Reed Johnson Bat RC 3.00 8.00
159 Ryan Raburn AU A RC 3.00 8.00
160 Jose Morban Bat RC 2.00 5.00
161 Justin Schuda AU A RC 3.00 8.00
162 Henry Pichardo AU A RC 3.00 8.00
163 Josh Bard AU A RC 3.00 8.00
164 Josh Bonifay AU A RC 3.00 8.00
165 Brandon League AU B RC 4.00 10.00
166 Jorge-Julio DePaula AU A RC 3.00 8.00
167 Todd Linden AU B RC 6.00 15.00
168 Francisco Liriano AU A RC 20.00 50.00
169 Chris Snelling AU A RC 5.00 12.00
170 Blake McGinley AU A RC 3.00 8.00
171 Cody McKay AU A RC 3.00 8.00
172 Jason Stanford AU A RC 3.00 8.00
173 Lenny Dinardo AU A RC 3.00 8.00
174 Greg Montalbano AU A RC 3.00 8.00
175 Earl Snyder AU A RC 3.00 8.00
176 Justin Huber AU A RC 6.00 15.00
177 Chris Narveson AU A RC 3.00 8.00
178 Jon Switzer AU A RC 3.00 8.00
179 Ronald Acuna AU A RC 3.00 8.00
180 Chris Duffy Bat RC 3.00 8.00
181 Kazuhisa Ishii Bat RC 3.00 8.00

2002 Bowman's Best Blue

This 181 card set is a parallel of the regular Bowman's Best set. These cards were seeded into packs at different rates which we have notated. These card can be differentiated by their "blue" coloring. Cards numbered from 1 through 90 were issued to a stated print run of 300 serial numbered sets. Card number 181 features Kaz Ishii and was issued as an exchange card which could be redeemed until December 31, 2002.

*BLUE 1-90: 1X TO 2.5X BASIC
1-90 STATED ODDS 1:6
1-90 PRINT RUN 300 SERIAL #'d SETS
*BLUE AUTO: .4X TO 1X BASIC AU A
*BLUE AUTO: .3X TO .8X BASIC AU B
AUTO STATED ODDS 1:6
*BLUE BAT: .4X TO 1X BASIC BAT
BAT STATED ODDS 1:14
ISHII BAT EXCHANGE ODDS 1:335
ISHII BAT EXCHANGE DEADLINE 12/31/02
BLUE BATS FEATURE TEAM LOGOS!
140 Bobby Jenks AU 6.00 15.00
181 Kazuhisa Ishii Bat 3.00 8.00

2002 Bowman's Best Gold

This 181 card set is a parallel of the regular Bowman's Best set. These cards were seeded into packs at different rates which we have notated. These card can be differentiated by their "gold" coloring. Cards numbered from 1 through 90 were limited to a stated print run of 50 serial numbered sets. Card number 181 features Kaz Ishii and was issued as an exchange card which could be redeemed until December 31, 2002.

*GOLD 1-90: 3X TO 8X BASIC
1-90 STATED ODDS 1:31
1-90 PRINT RUN 50 SERIAL #'d SETS
*GOLD AUTO: 1X TO 2.5X BASIC AU A
*GOLD AUTO: .75X TO 2X BASIC AU B
GOLD AUTO STATED ODDS 1:51
*GOLD BAT: 1X TO 2.5X BASIC BAT
GOLD BAT STATED ODDS 1:115
ISHII BAT EXCHANGE ODDS 1:3444
ISHII BAT EXCHANGE DEADLINE 12/31/02
GOLD BATS FEATURE FACSIMILE AUTOS!
181 Kazuhisa Ishii Bat 8.00 20.00

2002 Bowman's Best Red

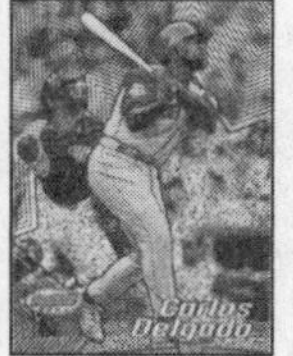

This 181 card set is a parallel of the regular Bowman's Best set. These cards were seeded into packs at different rates which we have notated. These card can be differentiated by their "red" coloring. Cards numbered from 1 through 90 were issued to a stated print run of 200 serial numbered sets. Card number 181 features Kaz Ishii and was issued as an exchange card which could be redeemed until December 31, 2002.

*RED 1-90: 1.25X TO 3X BASIC
1-90 PRINT RUN 200 SERIAL #'d SETS
*RED AUTO: .6X TO 1.5X BASIC AU A
*RED AUTO: .5X TO 1.2X BASIC AU B
AUTO STATED ODDS 1:17
*RED BATS: .6X TO 1.5X BASIC BATS
BAT STATED ODDS 1:39
ISHII BAT EXCHANGE ODDS 1:1117
ISHII BAT EXCHANGE DEADLINE 12/31/02
RED BATS FEATURE STATISTICS!
181 Kazuhisa Ishii Bat 5.00 12.00

2002 Bowman's Best Uncirculated

Ninety-one different scratch-off redemption cards were inserted into packs at overall odds of one in 92. Once the cards were scratched, a code number was revealed whereby collectors could enter the code at the Topps website to reveal which specific player they had won the rights to. The actual "Uncirculated" cards were straight parallels of the basic Bowman's Best autographed rookie cards - except these were sealed inside a hard plastic case of which was affixed with a tamper-proof Topps holographic logo. These cards were printed to a stated print run of 20 sets and there is no pricing provided due to scarcity. The deadline to redeem the cards was December 31st, 2002.

COMMON EXCH
AU STATED ODDS 1:129
BAT STATED ODDS 1:322
OVERALL STATED ODDS 1:92

2003 Bowman's Best

This 130 card set was released in September, 2003. This set was issued in five card packs which contained an autograph card. Each of these packs had an SRP of $15 and these packs were issued 10 to a box and 10 boxes to a case. This set was designed to be checklisted alphabetically as no numbering was used for this set. The first year cards which are autographed have the lettering FY AU RC after their name in the checklist. A few first year players had some cards issued with an bat piece included. Those bat cards were issued one per box-loader pack. In addition, high draft pick Bryan Bullington signed some of the actual boxes and those boxes were issued at a stated rate of one in 106.

COMP.SET w/o SP's (50) 15.00 40.00
COMMON CARD .40 1.00
COMMON AUTO 3.00 8.00
COMMON BAT 1.50 4.00
AB Andrew Brown FY AU RC 4.00 10.00
AK Austin Kearns .40 1.00
AM Aneudis Mateo FY AU RC 3.00 8.00
AP Albert Pujols 1.25 3.00
AR Alex Rodriguez 1.00 2.50
AS Alfonso Soriano .40 1.00
AW Aron Weston FY AU RC 3.00 8.00
BB Bryan Bullington FY AU RC 3.00 8.00
BC Bernie Castro FY RC .40 1.00
BFL Br. Florence FY AU RC 3.00 8.00
BFR Ben Francisco FY AU RC 3.00 8.00
BH Brendan Harris FY AU RC 4.00 10.00
BJH Bo Hart FY RC .40 1.00
BK Beau Kemp FY AU RC 3.00 8.00
BLB Barry Bonds 1.50 4.00
BM Brian McCann FY AU RC 20.00 50.00
BSG Brian Giles .40 1.00
BWB Bobby Basham FY AU RC 3.00 8.00
BZ Barry Zito .40 1.00
CAD Carlos Duran FY AU RC 3.00 8.00
CDC C. De La Cruz FY AU RC 3.00 8.00
CJ Chipper Jones .60 1.50
CJW C.J. Wilson FY AU 12.50 30.00
CM Charlie Manning FY AU RC 3.00 8.00
CMS Curt Schilling .40 1.00
CS Cory Stewart FY AU RC 3.00 8.00
CSS Corey Shafer FY AU RC 3.00 8.00
CW Chien-Ming Wang FY RC 2.50 6.00
CWA Chien-Ming Wang FY AU 60.00 120.00
DAM D. Moseley FY AU RC 3.00 8.00
DC David Cash FY AU RC 3.00 8.00
DH Dan Haren FY AU RC 8.00 20.00
DJ Derek Jeter 1.50 4.00
DM David Martinez FY AU RC 3.00 8.00
DMM D. McGowan FY AU RC 4.00 10.00
DR Darrell Rasner FY AU RC 3.00 8.00
DW Doug Waechter FY AU RC 4.00 10.00
DY Dustin Yount FY RC .60 1.50
ERA El. Ramirez FY AU RC 4.00 10.00
ERI Eric Riggs FY AU RC 4.00 10.00
ET Eider Torres FY AU RC 3.00 8.00
FP Felix Pie FY AU RC 12.50 30.00
FS Felix Sanchez FY AU RC 3.00 8.00
FT Ferdin Tejeda FY AU RC 3.00 8.00
GA Greg Aquino FY AU RC 3.00 8.00
GB Gregor Blanco FY AU RC 3.00 8.00
GJA Garret Anderson .40 1.00
GM Greg Maddux 1.00 2.50
GS G. Schneidmiller FY AU RC 3.00 8.00
HR Hanley Ramirez FY AU RC 50.00 100.00
HRB Hanley Ramirez FY Bat 10.00 25.00
HT Haj Turay FY RC .40 1.00
IS Ichiro Suzuki 1.25 3.00
JB Jeremy Bonderman FY RC 1.50 4.00
JC Jose Contreras FY RC .60 1.50
JDD J.D. Durbin FY AU RC 3.00 8.00
JFK Jeff Kent .40 1.00
JG Joey Gomes FY AU RC 3.00 8.00
JGB Joey Gomes FY Bat 1.50 4.00
JGG Jason Giambi .40 1.00
JK Jason Kubel FY AU RC 10.00 25.00
JKB Jason Kubel FY Bat 2.50 6.00
JLB Jaime Bubela FY AU RC 3.00 8.00
JM Jose Morales FY AU RC 3.00 8.00
JMS Jon-Mark Sprowl FY RC .40 1.00
JRG Jeremy Griffiths FY AU RC 3.00 8.00
JT Jim Thome .40 1.00
JV Joe Valentine FY AU RC 3.00 8.00
JW Josh Willingham FY AU RC 8.00 20.00
KBS Kelly Shoppach FY Bat 2.00 5.00
KG Ken Griffey Jr. 1.00 2.50
KJ Kade Johnson FY AU RC 3.00 8.00
KS Kelly Shoppach FY AU RC 4.00 10.00
KY Kevin Youkilis FY AU RC 15.00 40.00
KYE Kevin Youkilis FY Bat 6.00 15.00
LB Lance Berkman .40 1.00
LF Lew Ford FY AU RC 4.00 10.00
LFJ Lew Ford FY Bat 2.00 5.00
LW Larry Walker .40 1.00
MB Matt Bruback FY RC .40 1.00
MD Matt Diaz FY RC .75 2.00
MDA Matt Diaz FY AU 6.00 15.00
MDH Matt Hensley FY AU RC 3.00 8.00
MDM Mark Malaska FY AU RC 3.00 8.00
MH Mi. Hernandez FY AU RC 3.00 8.00
MHI Mi. Hinckley FY AU RC 4.00 10.00
MJP Mike Piazza 1.00 2.50
MK Matt Kata FY AU RC 3.00 8.00
MNH Matt Hagen FY AU RC 3.00 8.00
MO Mike O'Keefe FY RC .40 1.00
MOR Magglio Ordonez .40 1.00
MP Mark Prior .40 1.00
MR Manny Ramirez .40 1.00
MS Mike Sweeney .40 1.00
MT Miguel Tejada .40 1.00
NG Nomar Garciaparra 1.00 2.50
NL Nook Logan FY AU RC 4.00 10.00
OC Ozzie Chavez FY AU RC 3.00 8.00
PB Pat Burrell .40 1.00
PL Pete LaForest FY AU RC 3.00 8.00
PM Pedro Martinez .40 1.00
PR Prentice Redman FY AU RC 3.00 8.00
RC Ryan Cameron FY AU RC 3.00 8.00
RD Rajai Davis FY AU RC 3.00 8.00
RH Ryan Howard FY AU RC 75.00 150.00
RHJ Ryan Howard FY Bat 10.00 25.00
RJ Randy Johnson .60 1.50
RLD Rajai Davis FY Bat 1.50 4.00
RM R. Nivar-Martinez FY RC .40 1.00
RS Ryan Shealy FY AU RC 12.50 30.00
RSB Ryan Shealy FY Bat 5.00 12.00
RWH Rob. Hammock FY AU RC 3.00 8.00
SG Shawn Green .40 1.00
SS Sammy Sosa .60 1.50
ST Scott Tyler FY AU RC 4.00 10.00
SV Shane Victorino FY RC 1.50 4.00
TA Tyler Adamczyk FY AU RC 3.00 8.00
TH Todd Helton .40 1.00
TI Travis Ishikawa FY AU RC 4.00 10.00
TJ Tyler Johnson FY AU RC 3.00 8.00
TJB T.J. Bohn FY RC .40 1.00
TKH Torii Hunter .40 1.00
TO Tim Olson FY AU RC 3.00 8.00
TS T.Story-Harden FY AU RC 3.00 8.00
TSB T.Story-Harden FY Bat 1.50 4.00
TT Terry Tiffee FY RC .40 1.00
VG Vladimir Guerrero .60 1.50
WE Willie Eyre FY AU RC 3.00 8.00
WL Wil Ledezma FY AU RC 3.00 8.00
WRC Roger Clemens 1.25 3.00
NNO Bryan Bullington 10.00 25.00
Opened Box AU
NNO Bryan Bullington
Sealed Box AU

2003 Bowman's Best Blue

*BLUE: 1.5X TO 4X BASIC
*BLUE FY: 3X TO 8X BASIC FY
BLUE STATED ODDS 1:28
BLUE PRINT RUN 100 SERIAL #'d SETS
*BLUE AUTO: 1X TO 2.5X BASIC AUTO
BLUE AUTO ODDS 1:32
BLUE AUTO PRINT RUN 50 SETS
BLUE AUTO'S NOT SERIAL-NUMBERED
BLUE AU PRINT RUNS PROVIDED BY TOPPS
*BLUE BAT: 1X TO 2.5X BASIC FY BAT
BLUE BAT ODDS 1:22 BOXLOADER PACKS
BLUE BAT PRINT RUN 50 SETS
BLUE BATS NOT SERIAL-NUMBERED
BLUE BAT PRINTS PROVIDED BY TOPPS
BM Brian McCann FY AU 50.00 100.00
CW Chien-Ming Wang FY 15.00 40.00
CWA Chien-Ming Wang FY AU 125.00 250.00
DH Dan Haren FY AU 20.00 50.00
FP Felix Pie FY AU 100.00 200.00
HR Hanley Ramirez FY AU 100.00 200.00
KY Kevin Youkilis FY AU 40.00 80.00
RH Ryan Howard FY AU 200.00 500.00
RHJ Ryan Howard FY Bat 75.00 150.00

2003 Bowman's Best Red

*RED: 3X TO 8X BASIC RED
*RED FY: 4X TO 10X BASIC FY
RED STATED ODDS 1:55
RED STATED PRINT RUN 50 SERIAL #'d SETS
RED AUTO ODDS 1:63
RED AUTO PRINT RUN 25 SETS
RED AU PRINT RUNS PROVIDED BY TOPPS
RED AUTOS NOT SERIAL-NUMBERED
NO RED AUTO PRICING DUE TO SCARCITY
RED BAT ODDS 1:44 BOXLOADER PACKS
RED BAT PRINT RUN 25 SETS
RED BAT PRINT RUNS PROVIDED BY TOPPS
RED BATS NOT SERIAL-NUMBERED
NO RED BAT PRICING DUE TO SCARCITY
BWB Bobby Basham FY AU
CW Chien-Ming Wang FY 40.00 80.00

2003 Bowman's Best Double Play Autographs

STATED ODDS 1:55
EB Elizardo Ramirez 10.00 25.00
Bryan Bullington
GK Joey Gomes 15.00 40.00
Jason Kubel
HV Dan Haren 6.00 15.00
Joe Valentine
LL Nook Logan 6.00 15.00
Wil Ledezma

RS Prentice Redman 6.00 15.00
Gary Schneidmiller
SB Corey Shafer 6.00 15.00
Gregor Blanco
SR Felix Sanchez 6.00 15.00
Darrell Rasner
YS Kevin Youkilis 15.00 40.00
Kelly Shoppach

2003 Bowman's Best Triple Play Autographs

STATED ODDS 1:219
BCS Andrew Brown 10.00 25.00
David Cash
Cory Stewart
DRS Rajai Davis 15.00 40.00
Hanley Ramirez
Ryan Shealy

2004 Bowman's Best

This 108-card set was released in September, 2004. The set was issued in five-card packs with an $15 SRP which came 10 packs to a box and 10 boxes to a case. In an interesting twist, the cards are numbered using the initials of the players instead of using a numbering system. Fifty cards in this set feature veteran players and the rest of the set features either rookie cards some of whom signed cardd for this product.

COMP.SET w/o SP'S (50) 10.00 25.00
COMMON CARD .30 .75
COMMON RC .40 1.00
COMMON AUTO 3.00 8.00
ONE AUTO PER HOBBY PACK
COMMON RELIC 2.00 5.00
ONE RELIC PER BOX-LOADER PACK
ONE BOX-LOADER PACK PER HOBBY BOX
COMMON AU BOX 6.00 15.00
STAUFFER BOX RANDOM IN HOBBY CASES
OVERALL AU PLATE ODDS 1:391 HOBBY
AU PLATE PRINT RUN 1 SET PER COLOR
BLACK-CYAN-MAGENTA-YELLOW ISSUED
NO AU PLATE PRICING DUE TO SCARCITY
AER Alex Rodriguez 1.25 3.00
AG Adam Greenberg FY AU RC 4.00 10.00
AL Anthony Lerew FY RC .40 1.00
AO Akinori Otsuka FY RC .40 1.00
AP Albert Pujols 2.00 5.00
AS Alfonso Soriano .30 .75
BB Bobby Brownlie FY AU RC 4.00 10.00
BEM Brandon Medders FY AU RC 3.00 8.00
BG Brian Giles .30 .75
BMS Brad Snyder FY AU RC 4.00 10.00
BP Brayan Pena FY AU RC 3.00 8.00
BS Brad Sullivan FY AU RC 4.00 10.00
CB Carlos Beltran .30 .75
CD Carlos Delgado .30 .75
CJ Conor Jackson FY AU RC 10.00 25.00
CLH Chin-Lung Hu FY RC .40 1.00
CMA Craig Ansman FY AU RC 3.00 8.00
CMS Curt Schilling .50 1.25
CZ Charlie Zink FY AU RC 3.00 8.00
DA David Aardsma FY AU RC 4.00 10.00
DC Dave Crouthers FY AU RC 3.00 8.00
DDN Dustin Nippert FY AU RC 4.00 10.00
DG Danny Gonzalez FY RC .40 1.00
DK Donald Kelly FY AU RC 3.00 8.00
DL Donald Levinski FY AU RC 3.00 8.00
DM David Murphy FY AU RC 6.00 15.00
DN Dioner Navarro FY AU RC 3.00 8.00
DS Don Sutton FY RC .40 1.00
EA Erick Aybar FY AU RC 6.00 15.00
EC Eric Chavez .30 .75
EH Estee Harris FY AU RC 4.00 10.00
ES Ervin Santana FY AU RC 5.00 12.00
FH Felix Hernandez FY AU RC 30.00 60.00
GA Garret Anderson .30 .75
HB Hank Blalock .30 .75
HM Hector Made FY RC .40 1.00
IR Ivan Rodriguez .50 1.25
IS Ichiro Suzuki 1.25 3.00
JA Joaquin Arias FY AU RC 6.00 10.00
JAV Jose Vidro .30 .75
JC Juan Cedeno FY AU RC 3.00 8.00
JDS Jason Schmidt .30 .75
JE Jesse English FY AU RC 3.00 8.00
JGG Jason Giambi .30 .75
JH Jason Hirsh FY AU RC 10.00 25.00
JJC Jon Connolly FY RC .40 1.00
JK Jon Knott FY AU RC 3.00 8.00
JL Josh Labandeira FY AU RC 3.00 8.00
JLO Javy Lopez .30 .75
JP Jorge Posada .50 1.25
JRG Joey Gathright FY RC .40 1.00
JS Jeff Salazar FY AU RC 4.00 10.00
JSZ Jason Szuminski FY AU RC 3.00 8.00
JT Jim Thome .50 1.25
KC Kory Casto FY AU RC 6.00 15.00
KK Kevin Kouzmanoff FY AU RC 15.00 40.00
KM Kazuo Matsui FY Uni RC 2.00 5.00
KRK Kody Kirkland FY Bat RC 2.00 5.00
KS Kyle Sleeth FY RC .40 1.00
KT Kazuhito Tadano FY Jsy RC 3.00 8.00
LK Logan Kensing FY AU RC 3.00 8.00
LM Lastings Milledge FY AU RC 12.50 30.00
LO Lyle Overbay .30 .75
LTH Luke Hughes FY AU RC 10.00 25.00
LWJ Chipper Jones .75 2.00
MAR Manny Ramirez .75 2.00
MDC Matt Creighton FY AU RC 3.00 8.00
MG Mike Gosling FY RC .40 1.00
MJP Mike Piazza .75 2.00
MO Magglio Ordonez .50 1.25
MT Miguel Tejada .50 1.25
MTC Miguel Cabrera .75 2.00
MV Merkin Valdez FY AU RC 3.00 8.00
MWP Mark Prior .50 1.25
MY Michael Young .30 .75
NAG Nomar Garciaparra .75 2.00
NG Nick Gorneault FY RC .40 1.00
NU Nic Ungs FY AU RC 3.00 8.00
OQ Omar Quintanilla FY AU RC 4.00 10.00
PM Paul Maholm FY AU RC 4.00 10.00
PMM Paul McAnulty FY RC .40 1.00
RB Ryan Budde FY AU RC 3.00 8.00
RC Roger Clemens 1.00 2.50
RG Rudy Guillen FY AU RC 4.00 10.00
RJ Randy Johnson .75 2.00
RN Ricky Nolasco FY AU RC 8.00 20.00
RR Ramon Ramirez FY AU RC 3.00 8.00
RS Richie Sexson .30 .75
RT Rob Tejeda FY AU RC 6.00 15.00
SH Shawn Hill FY AU RC 3.00 8.00
SR Scott Rolen .50 1.25
SS Sammy Sosa .75 2.00
ST Shingo Takatsu FY Jsy RC 3.00 8.00
TB Travis Blackley FY Jsy RC 2.00 5.00
TD Tyler Davidson FY AU RC 4.00 10.00
TJ Terry Jones FY RC .40 1.00
TJS Tim Stauffer FY AU RC 4.00 10.00
TLH Todd Helton .50 1.25
TOH Travis Hanson FY AU RC 4.00 10.00
TRM Tom Mastny FY AU RC 3.00 8.00
TS Todd Self FY RC .40 1.00
VC Vito Chiaravalloti FY AU RC 3.00 8.00
VG Vladimir Guerrero .75 2.00
WM Warner Madrigal FY RC .60 1.50
WS Wardell Starling FY AU RC 3.00 8.00
YM Yadier Molina FY AU RC 12.50 30.00
ZD Zach Duke FY AU RC 20.00 40.00
NNO Tim Stauffer AU Box/100 10.00 25.00

2004 Bowman's Best Green

*GREEN: 1.5X TO 4X BASIC
*GREEN RC'S: 3X TO 8X BASIC RC'S
GREEN ODDS 1:18
GREEN PRINT RUN 100 SERIAL #'d SETS
*GREEN AU'S: 1X TO 2.5X BASIC AU'S
GREEN AU ODDS 1:32 HOBBY
GREEN AU PRINT RUN 50 SETS
GREEN AUTOS NOT SERIAL-NUMBERED
AUTO PRINT RUNS PROVIDED BY TOPPS
*GREEN RELICS: .75X TO 2X BASIC RELICS
GREEN RELIC ODDS 1:31 HOBBY BOXES
GREEN RELIC PRINT RUN 50 SETS
GREEN RELICS NOT SERIAL-NUMBERED
RELIC PRINT RUNS PROVIDED BY TOPPS
CJ Conor Jackson FY AU 50.00 100.00
FH Felix Hernandez FY AU 150.00 300.00
KK Kevin Kouzmanoff FY AU 50.00 100.00
LM Lastings Milledge FY AU 90.00 150.00
ZD Zach Duke FY AU 50.00 100.00

2004 Bowman's Best Red

*RED: 5X TO 12X BASIC
RED ODDS 1:90 HOBBY
RED PRINT RUN 20 SERIAL #'d SETS
NO RED RC PRICING DUE TO SCARCITY
RED AUTO ODDS 1:156 HOBBY
RED AU PRINT RUN 10 SETS
RED AU'S ARE NOT SERIAL-NUMBERED
PRINT RUN INFO PROVIDED BY TOPPS
NO RED AU PRICING DUE TO SCARCITY
RED RELIC ODDS 1:154 HOBBY BOXES
RED RELIC PRINT RUN 10 SETS
RED RELICS ARE NOT SERIAL-NUMBERED
PRINT RUN INFO PROVIDED BY TOPPS
NO RED RELIC PRICING DUE TO SCARCITY

2004 Bowman's Best Double Play Autographs

STATED ODDS 1:33 HOBBY
STATED PRINT RUN 236 SETS
CARDS ARE NOT SERIAL NUMBERED
PRINT RUN INFO PROVIDED BY TOPPS
CC Matt Creighton 8.00 20.00
Dave Crouthers
EN Jesse English 10.00 25.00
Ricky Nolasco
HJ Travis Hanson 10.00 25.00
Conor Jackson

MH Lastings Milledge 20.00 50.00
Estee Harris
MN Brandon Medders 6.00 15.00
Dustin Nippert
QS Omar Quintanilla 6.00 15.00
Brad Snyder
SC Tim Stauffer 6.00 15.00
Vito Chiaravalloti
SK Jeff Salazar 6.00 15.00
Jon Knott
SV Ervin Santana 6.00 15.00
Merkin Valdez
UK Nic Ungs 12.50 30.00
Kevin Kouzmanoff

2004 Bowman's Best Triple Play Autographs

STATED ODDS 1:109 HOBBY
STATED PRINT RUN 236 SETS
CARDS ARE NOT SERIAL NUMBERED
PRINT RUN INFO PROVIDED BY TOPPS
ALS David Aardsma 10.00 25.00
Donald Levinski
Brad Sullivan
CBA Juan Cedeno 10.00 25.00
Bobby Brownlie
Joaquin Arias
SSV Tim Stauffer 15.00 40.00
Ervin Santana
Merkin Valdez

2005 Bowman's Best

This 143-card set was released in September, 2005. The set was issued in five-card packs with an $10 SRP which came 10 packs to a box and 10 boxes to a case. The first 30 cards in the set feature active veterans while cards 31 through 143 feature Rookie Cards. Cards 101 through 143 are all autographed, and while most of them are Rookie Cards, a few of the cards are not Rookie Cards as the players had cards in the 31-100 grouping. Cards number 101 through 143 were issued at a stated rate of one in five hobby packs and those cards were issued to a stated print run of 974 serial numbered sets.

COMP.SET w/o SP's (100) 25.00 50.00
COMMON CARD (1-30) .20 .50
COMMON CARD (31-100) .40 1.00
COMMON AU (101-143) 3.00 8.00
OVERALL 1-100 PLATE ODDS 1:345 H
OVERALL 101-143 AU PLATE ODDS 1:805 H
PLATE PRINT RUN 1 SET PER COLOR
BLACK-CYAN-MAGENTA-YELLOW ISSUED
NO PLATE PRICING DUE TO SCARCITY
1 Jose Vidro .20 .50
2 Adam Dunn .30 .75
3 Manny Ramirez .50 1.25
4 Miguel Tejada .30 .75
5 Ken Griffey Jr. .75 2.00
6 Pedro Martinez .30 .75
7 Alex Rodriguez .75 2.00
8 Ichiro Suzuki .75 2.00
9 Alfonso Soriano .30 .75
10 Brian Giles .20 .50
11 Roger Clemens .60 1.50
12 Todd Helton .30 .75
13 Ivan Rodriguez .30 .75
14 David Ortiz .50 1.25
15 Sammy Sosa .50 1.25
16 Chipper Jones .50 1.25
17 Mark Buehrle .30 .75
18 Miguel Cabrera .50 1.25
19 Johan Santana .50 1.25
20 Randy Johnson .50 1.25
21 Jim Thome .30 .75
22 Vladimir Guerrero .50 1.25
23 Dontrelle Willis .20 .50
24 Nomar Garciaparra .50 1.25
25 Barry Bonds 1.00 2.50
26 Curt Schilling .30 .75
27 Carlos Beltran .20 .50
28 Albert Pujols 1.25 3.00
29 Mark Prior .30 .75
30 Derek Jeter 1.25 3.00
31 Ryan Garko FY RC .40 1.00
32 Eulogio De La Cruz FY RC .40 1.00
33 Luke Scott FY RC 1.00 2.50
34 Shane Costa FY RC .40 1.00
35 Casey McGehee FY RC 1.25 3.00
36 Jered Weaver FY RC 1.50 4.00
37 Bill McCarthy FY RC .40 1.00
38 D.J. Houlton FY RC .40 1.00
39 Brandon Moorhead FY RC .40 1.00
40 Jerry Owens FY RC .40 1.00
41 Elliot Johnson FY RC .40 1.00
42 Kevin West FY RC .40 1.00
43 Hernan Iribarren FY RC .40 1.00
44 Miguel Montero FY RC 2.50 6.00
45 Craig Tatum FY RC .40 1.00
46 Ryan Sweeney FY RC .60 1.50
47 Micah Furtado FY RC .40 1.00
48 Cody Haerther FY RC .40 1.00
49 Erick Abreu FY RC .40 1.00
50 Chuck Tiffany FY RC 1.00 2.50
51 Tadahito Iguchi FY RC .60 1.50
52 Frank Diaz FY RC .40 1.00
53 Errol Simonitsch FY RC .40 1.00
54 Wade Robinson FY RC .40 1.00
55 Adam Boeve FY RC .40 1.00
56 Steven Bondurant FY RC .40 1.00
57 Jason Motte FY RC .60 1.50
58 Juan Senreiso FY RC .40 1.00
59 Vinny Rottino FY RC .40 1.00
60 Jai Miller FY RC .40 1.00
61 Thomas Pauly FY RC .40 1.00
62 Tony Giarratano FY RC .40 1.00
63 Alexander Smit FY RC .40 1.00
64 Keiichi Yabu FY RC .40 1.00
65 Brian Bannister FY RC .60 1.50
66 Kennard Bibbs FY RC .40 1.00
67 Anthony Reyes FY RC .60 1.50
68 Thomas Oldham FY RC .40 1.00
69 Ben Harrison FY .40 1.00
70 Daryl Thompson FY RC .40 1.00
71 Kevin Collins FY RC .40 1.00
72 Wes Swackhamer FY RC .40 1.00
73 Landon Powell FY RC .40 1.00
74 Matt Brown FY RC .40 1.00
75 Russ Martin FY RC 1.50 4.00
76 Nick Touchstone FY RC .40 1.00
77 Steven White FY RC .40 1.00
78 Ian Bladergroen FY RC .40 1.00
79 Sean Marshall FY RC 1.00 2.50
80 Nick Masset FY RC .40 1.00
81 Ryan Goleski FY RC .40 1.00
82 Matt Campbell FY RC .40 1.00
83 Manny Parra FY RC 1.00 2.50
84 Melky Cabrera FY RC 1.00 2.50
85 Ryan Feierabend FY RC .40 1.00
86 Nate McLouth FY RC .60 1.50
87 Glen Perkins FY RC .40 1.00
88 Kila Kaaihue FY RC 1.00 2.50
89 Dana Eveland FY RC .40 1.00
90 Tyler Pelland FY RC .40 1.00
91 Matt Van Der Bosch FY RC .40 1.00
92 Andy Santana FY RC .40 1.00
93 Eric Nielsen FY RC .40 1.00
94 Brendan Ryan FY RC .40 1.00
95 Ian Kinsler FY RC 3.00 8.00
96 Matthew Kemp FY RC 5.00 12.00
97 Stephen Drew FY RC 2.00 5.00
98 Peeter Ramos FY RC .40 1.00
99 Chris Seddon FY RC .40 1.00
100 Chuck James FY RC 1.00 2.50
101 Travis Chick FY AU RC 4.00 10.00
102 Justin Verlander FY AU RC 20.00 50.00
103 Billy Butler FY AU RC 20.00 50.00
104 Chris B.Young FY AU RC 35.00 60.00
105 Jake Postlewait FY AU RC 3.00 8.00
106 C.J. Smith FY AU RC 3.00 8.00
107 Mike Rodriguez FY AU RC 3.00 8.00
108 Philip Humber FY AU RC 10.00 25.00
109 Jeff Niemann FY AU RC 4.00 10.00
110 Brian Miller FY AU RC 3.00 8.00
111 Chris Vines FY AU RC 3.00 8.00
112 Andy LaRoche FY AU RC 12.50 30.00
113 Mike Bourn FY AU RC 4.00 10.00
114 Wlad Balentein FY AU RC 12.50 30.00
115 Ismael Ramirez FY AU RC 3.00 8.00
116 Hayden Penn FY AU RC 4.00 10.00
117 Pedro Lopez FY AU RC 3.00 8.00
118 Shawn Bowman FY AU RC 4.00 10.00
119 Chad Orvella FY AU RC 3.00 8.00
120 Sean Tracey FY AU RC 3.00 8.00
121 Bobby Livingston FY AU RC 3.00 8.00
122 Michael Rogers FY AU RC 3.00 8.00
123 Willy Mota FY AU RC 3.00 8.00
124 Bran McCarthy FY AU RC 10.00 25.00
125 Mike Morse FY AU RC 4.00 10.00
126 Matt Lindstrom FY AU RC 3.00 8.00
127 Brian Stavisky FY AU RC 3.00 8.00
128 Richie Gardner FY AU RC 3.00 8.00
129 Scott Mitchinson FY AU RC 3.00 8.00
130 Billy McCarthy FY AU RC 3.00 8.00
131 Brandon Sing FY AU RC 4.00 10.00
132 Matt Albers FY AU RC 4.00 10.00
133 George Kottaras FY AU RC 4.00 10.00
134 Luis Hernandez FY AU RC 3.00 8.00
135 Hum Sanchez FY AU RC 12.50 30.00
136 Buck Coats FY AU RC 3.00 8.00
137 Jon Barratt FY AU RC 3.00 8.00
138 Raul Tablado FY AU RC 3.00 8.00
139 Jake Mullinax FY AU RC 3.00 8.00
140 Edgar Varela FY AU RC 3.00 8.00
141 Ryan Garko FY AU 6.00 15.00
142 Nate McLouth FY AU 10.00 25.00
143 Shane Costa FY AU 3.00 8.00

2005 Bowman's Best Black

STATED ODDS 1:1386 HOBBY
STATED PRINT RUN 1 SERIAL #'d SET
NO PRICING DUE TO SCARCITY

2005 Bowman's Best Blue

*BLUE 1-30: 1.25X TO 3X BASIC
*BLUE 31-100: .6X TO 1.5X BASIC
1-100 ODDS 1:4 HOBBY
1-100 PRINT RUN 499 #'d SETS
*BLUE AU 101-143: .5X TO 1.2X BASIC
AU 101-143 PRINT RUN 299 #'d SETS
AU 101-143 ODDS 1:14 HOBBY

2005 Bowman's Best Gold

*GOLD 1-30: 6X TO 15X BASIC
1-100 ODDS 1:69 HOBBY
1-100 PRINT RUN 25 #'d SETS
31-100 NO PRICING DUE TO SCARCITY
AU 101-143 ODDS 1:159 HOBBY
AU 101-143 PRINT RUN 25 #'d SETS
AU 101-143 NO PRICING DUE TO SCARCITY

2005 Bowman's Best Green

*GREEN 1-30: 1X TO 2.5X BASIC
*GREEN 31-100: .5X TO 1.2X BASIC
1-100 ODDS 1:2 HOBBY
1-100 PRINT RUN 899 #'d SETS
*GREEN AU 101-143: .5X TO 1.2X BASIC
AU 101-143 ODDS 1:10 HOBBY
AU 101-143 PRINT RUN 399 #'d SETS

2005 Bowman's Best Red

*RED 1-30: 1.5X TO 4X BASIC
*RED 31-100: 1X TO 2.5X BASIC
1-100 ODDS 1:9 HOBBY
1-100 PRINT RUN 199 #'d SETS
*RED AU 101-143: .6X TO 1.5X BASIC
AU 101-143 ODDS 1:20 HOBBY
AU 101-143 PRINT RUN 199 #'d SETS

2005 Bowman's Best Silver

*SILVER 1-30: 2.5X TO 6X BASIC
*SILVER 31-100: 1.25X TO 3X BASIC
1-100 ODDS 1:18 HOBBY
1-100 PRINT RUN 99 #'d SETS
*SILVER AU 101-143: .75X TO 2X BASIC
AU 101-143 ODDS 1:41 HOBBY
AU 101-143 PRINT RUN 99 #'d SETS

2005 Bowman's Best A-Rod Throwback Autograph

STATED ODDS 1:1402 HOBBY
STATED PRINT RUN 100 SERIAL #'d CARDS
AR Alex Rodriguez 1994 60.00 120.00

2005 Bowman's Best Mirror Image Spokesmen Dual Autograph

STATED ODDS 1:16,300 HOBBY
STATED PRINT RUN 10 SERIAL #'d CARDS
NO PRICING DUE TO SCARCITY
BR Barry Bonds
Alex Rodriguez

2005 Bowman's Best Mirror Image Throwback Dual Autograph

STATED ODDS 1:2835 HOBBY
STATED PRINT RUN 50 SERIAL #'d CARDS
RR Alex Rodriguez 175.00 350.00
Cal Ripken

2005 Bowman's Best Shortstops Triple Autograph

STATED ODDS 1:5927 HOBBY
STATED PRINT RUN 25 SERIAL #'d CARDS
NO PRICING DUE TO SCARCITY
RRB Alex Rodriguez
Cal Ripken
Matt Bush

2007 Bowman's Best

This 117-card set was released in January, 2008. The set consists of 33 base veteran cards, the last 11 of those cards also come in an autographed form. In addition, cards numbered 34-51 feature signed veterans. Cards numbered 52-81 are 2007 rookies which were inserted at a stated rate of one in two packs and those cards were issued to a stated print run of 799 serial numbered sets. The last 10 numbers in those rookies also come in a signed version which were inserted at a stated rate of one in 11. The set concludes with 18 signed 2007 rookie cards and those cards were also inserted at a stated rate of one in two. This set was issued in five-card packs with an $20 SRP which came five packs to a mini-box, three mini-boxes per full box and eight full boxes per case.

COMP.SET w/o AU (33) 6.00 15.00
COMMON CARD (1-33) .20 .50
COMMON AU VET VAR (23-33) 6.00 15.00
AU VET VAR GROUP A 1:15 PACKS
AU VET VAR GROUP B 1:122 PACKS
AU VET VAR GROUP C 1:381 PACKS
AU VET VAR GROUP D 1:113 PACKS
COMMON AU VET (34-51) 3.00 8.00
AU VET ODDS 1:2 PACKS
COMMON RC (52-81) .40 1.00
RC ODDS 1:2 PACKS
RC PRINT RUN 799 SER.#'D SETS
GU-RC ODDS 1:35 PACKS
COMMON AU VAR RC (71-81) 3.00 8.00
AU VAR RC ODDS 1:11 PACKS
COMMON AU RC (82-99) 3.00 8.00
AU RC ODDS 1:2 PACKS
PRINTING PLATE ODDS 1:88 PACKS
PRINTING PLATE AU ODDS 1:173 PACKS
PRINTING PLATE GU ODDS 1:8945 PACKS
PLATE PRINT RUN 1 SET PER COLOR
BLACK-CYAN-MAGENTA-YELLOW ISSUED
NO PLATE PRICING DUE TO SCARCITY
1 Jose Reyes .30 .75
2 Derek Jeter 1.25 3.00
3 Vladimir Guerrero .50 1.25
4 Ichiro Suzuki .75 2.00
5 Jason Bay .30 .75
6 Joe Mauer .50 1.25
7 Alfonso Soriano .30 .75
8 David Ortiz .30 .75
9 Andruw Jones .20 .50
10 Roger Clemens .60 1.50
11 Grady Sizemore .30 .75
12 Magglio Ordonez .30 .75
13 Carl Crawford .30 .75
14 Chase Utley .50 1.25
15 Mark Teixeira .50 1.25
16 Ryan Zimmerman .30 .75
17 Ken Griffey Jr. .75 2.00
18 Derrek Lee .20 .50
19 Barry Bonds 1.00 2.50
20 Chipper Jones .50 1.25
21 Vernon Wells .20 .50
22 Manny Ramirez .50 1.25
23a Alex Rodriguez .75 2.00
23b Alex Rodriguez AU A 60.00 120.00
24a Ryan Howard .75 2.00
24b Ryan Howard AU B 20.00 50.00
25a Tom Glavine .30 .75
25b Tom Glavine AU D 15.00 40.00
26a Gary Sheffield .20 .50
26b Gary Sheffield AU A 8.00 20.00
27a Miguel Cabrera .50 1.25
27b Miguel Cabrera AU A 8.00 20.00
28a Robinson Cano .50 1.25
28b Robinson Cano AU A 10.00 25.00
29a David Wright .75 2.00
29b David Wright AU A 20.00 50.00
30a Jim Thome .30 .75
30b Jim Thome AU A 10.00 25.00
31a Albert Pujols 1.25 3.00
31b Albert Pujols AU C 75.00 150.00
32 Jorge Posada .30 .75
33a Brian McCann .20 .50
33b Brian McCann AU A 6.00 15.00
34 Josh Barfield AU 3.00 8.00
35 Melky Cabrera AU 6.00 15.00
36 Bill Hall AU 3.00 8.00
37 Cole Hamels AU 10.00 [illegible]
38 Adam LaRoche AU 3.00 8.00
39 Matt Holliday AU 6.00 15.00
40 Jeremy Hermida AU 3.00 8.00
41 Jonathan Papelbon AU 8.00 20.00
42 Hanley Ramirez AU 6.00 15.00
43 Justin Verlander AU 20.00 50.00
44 Andre Ethier AU 10.00 25.00
46 Erik Bedard AU 5.00 12.00
47 Freddy Sanchez AU 3.00 8.00
48 Adrian Gonzalez AU 10.00 25.00
49 Russell Martin AU 5.00 12.00
50 B.J. Upton AU 4.00 10.00
51 Prince Fielder AU 10.00 25.00
52 Tony Abreu RC 1.00 2.50
53 Ben Francisco (RC) .40 1.00
54 Billy Butler (RC) .60 1.50
55 Philip Hughes (RC) 2.00 5.00
56 Josh Fields (RC) .40 1.00
57 Carlos Gomez RC .60 1.50
58 Akinori Iwamura RC 1.00 2.50
59 Matt Brown RC .40 1.00
60 Jesus Flores RC .40 1.00
61 Mike Fontenot (RC) .40 1.00
62 Ryan Feierabend (RC) .40 1.00
63 Miguel Montero (RC) .40 1.00
64a Daisuke Matsuzaka RC 1.50 4.00
64b Daisuke Matsuzaka Jsy 5.00 12.00
65 Kei Igawa RC 1.00 2.50
66 Shawn Riggans (RC) .40 1.00
67 Masumi Kuwata RC .40 1.00
68 Kevin Slowey (RC) 1.00 2.50
69 Josh Hamilton (RC) 1.50 4.00
70 Curtis Thigpen (RC) .40 1.00
71a Justin Upton RC 3.00 8.00
71b Justin Upton AU 20.00 50.00
72a Delmon Young (RC) .60 1.50
72b Delmon Young AU 8.00 20.00
73a Brandon Wood (RC) .40 1.00
73b Brandon Wood AU 6.00 15.00
74a Felix Pie (RC) .50 1.25
74b Felix Pie AU 4.00 10.00
75a Alex Gordon RC 1.25 3.00
75b Alex Gordon AU 8.00 20.00
76a Mark Reynolds RC 3.00 8.00
76b Mark Reynolds AU 12.50 30.00
77a Tyler Clippard (RC) .60 1.50
77b Tyler Clippard AU 4.00 10.00
78a Adam Lind (RC) .40 1.00
78b Adam Lind AU 3.00 8.00
79a Hunter Pence (RC) 2.00 5.00
79b Hunter Pence AU 20.00 50.00
80 Micah Owings (RC) .40 1.00
81a Jarrod Saltalamacchia (RC) .60 1.50
81b Jarrod Saltalamacchia AU 6.00 15.00
82 Kevin Kouzmanoff AU (RC) 3.00 8.00
83 Glen Perkins AU (RC) 3.00 8.00
84 Michael Bourn AU (RC) 3.00 8.00
85 Andrew Miller AU RC 4.00 10.00
86 Fred Lewis AU (RC) 3.00 8.00
88 Joba Chamberlain AU RC 12.50 30.00
89 Hideki Okajima AU RC 10.00 25.00
90 Troy Tulowitzki AU (RC) 12.50 30.00
91 Ryan Sweeney AU (RC) 3.00 8.00
92 Matt Lindstrom AU (RC) 3.00 8.00
93 Tim Lincecum AU RC UER 50.00 100.00
94 Homer Bailey AU (RC) 4.00 10.00
95 Matt DeSalvo AU (RC) 3.00 8.00
96 Alejandro De Aza AU RC 3.00 8.00
97 Ryan Braun AU (RC) 15.00 40.00
99 Andy LaRoche AU (RC) 6.00 15.00

2007 Bowman's Best Blue

*VET BLUE: 3X TO 8X BASIC VET
VET ODDS 1:11 PACKS
*AU VET BLUE: .5X TO 1.2X BASIC AU VET
AU VET ODDS 1:14 PACKS
*RC BLUE: 1X TO 2.5X BASIC RC
RC ODDS 1:12 PACKS
*AU RC BLUE: .5X TO 1.2X BASIC AU RC
AU RC ODDS 1:15 PACKS
*GU-RC BLUE: .75X TO 2X BASIC GU-RC
GU-RC ODDS 1:361 PACKS
STATED PRINT RUN 99 SER.#'d SETS
93 Tim Lincecum AU UER 75.00 150.00
Incorrect height and weight

2007 Bowman's Best Gold

*VET GOLD: 4X TO 10X BASIC VET
VET ODDS 1:22 PACKS
*AU VET GOLD: .6X TO 1.5X BASIC AU VET
AU VET ODDS 1:28 PACKS
*RC GOLD: 1.5X TO 4X BASIC RC
RC ODDS 1:24 PACKS
*AU RC GOLD: .6X TO 1.5X BASIC AU RC
AU RC ODDS 1:29 PACKS
*GU-RC GOLD: 1X TO 2.5X BASIC GU-RC
GU-RC ODDS 1:715 PACKS
STATED PRINT RUN 50 SER.#'d SETS
31b Albert Pujols AU 175.00 350.00
93 Tim Lincecum AU UER 125.00 250.00
Incorrect height and weight

2007 Bowman's Best Green

*VET GREEN: 1.5X TO 4X BASIC VET
VET ODDS 1:5 PACKS
*RC GREEN: .75X TO 2X BASIC RC
RC ODDS 1:5 PACKS
STATED PRINT RUN 249 SER.#'d SETS

2007 Bowman's Best Red

VET ODDS 1:1073 PACKS
AU VET ODDS 1:1325 PACKS
RC ODDS 1:1221 PACKS
AU RC ODDS 1:1376 PACKS
GU-RC ODDS 1:27,456 PACKS
STATED PRINT RUN 1 SER.#'d SET
NO PRICING DUE TO SCARCITY

2007 Bowman's Best Alex Rodriguez 500

COMPLETE SET (1) 1.50 4.00
COMMON CARD 1.50 4.00
STATED ODDS 1:
COMMON BLUE 8.00 20.00
BLUE ODDS 1:1107 PACKS
BLUE PRINT RUN 33 SER.#'d SETS
GOLD ODDS 1:2532 PACKS
GOLD PRINT RUN 15 SER.#'d SETS
NO GOLD PRICING DUE TO SCARCITY
COMMON GREEN 5.00 12.00
GREEN ODDS 1:361 PACKS
GREEN PRINT RUN 99 SER.#'d SETS
AR Alex Rodriguez 1.50 4.00

2007 Bowman's Best Barry Bonds 756

COMPLETE SET (1) 1.25 3.00
STATED ODDS 1:20 PACKS
PRINTING PLATE ODDS 1:8945 PACKS
PLATE PRINT RUN 1 SET PER COLOR
BLACK-CYAN-MAGENTA-YELLOW ISSUED
NO PLATE PRICING DUE TO SCARCITY
BB Barry Bonds 1.25 3.00

2007 Bowman's Best Prospects

COMMON PROSPECT (1-40) .25 .60
PROSPECT STATED ODDS 1:2 PACKS
PROSPECT PRINT RUN 499 SER.#'d SETS
COMMON PROS.AU VAR (37-40) 3.00 8.00
PROS AU VAR ODDS 1:25 PACKS
COMMON PROS.AUTO (41-60) 3.00 8.00
PROS.AUTO ODDS 1:26 PACKS
PRINTING PLATE ODDS 1:68 PACKS
PRINTING PLATE AU ODDS 1:173 PACKS
PLATE PRINT RUN 1 SET PER COLOR
BLACK-CYAN-MAGENTA-YELLOW ISSUED
NO PLATE PRICING DUE TO SCARCITY
BBP1 Greg Smith .40 1.00
BBP2 J.R. Towles .75 2.00
BBP3 Jeff Locke .60 1.50
BBP4 Henry Sosa .40 1.00
BBP5 Ivan De Jesus Jr. .40 1.00
BBP6 Brad Lincoln .25 .60
BBP7 Josh Papelbon .25 .60
BBP8 Mark Hamilton .25 .60
BBP9 Sam Fuld .75 2.00
BBP10 Thomas Fairchild .25 .60
BBP11 Chris Carter 1.50 4.00
BBP12 Chuck Lofgren .60 1.50
BBP13 Joe Gaetti .25 .60
BBP14 Zach McAllister .40 1.00
BBP15 Cole Gillespie .40 1.00
BBP16 Jeremy Papelbon .25 .60
BBP17 Mike Carp .75 2.00
BBP18 Cody Strait .25 .60
BBP19 Gorkys Hernandez .60 1.50
BBP20 Andrew Fie .25 .60
BBP21 Erik Lis .40 1.00
BBP22 Chance Douglass .25 .60
BBP23 Vasili Spanos .25 .60
BBP24 Desmond Jennings .75 2.00
BBP25 Vic Buttler .25 .60
BBP26 Cedric Hunter .60 1.50
BBP27 Emerson Frostad .25 .60
BBP28 Mike Devaney .25 .60
BBP29 Eric Young Jr. .40 1.00
BBP30 Evan Englebrook .25 .60
BBP31 Aaron Cunningham .40 1.00
BBP32 Dellin Betances .60 1.50
BBP33 Michael Saunders .75 2.00
BBP34 Deolis Guerra .60 1.50
BBP35 Brian Bocock .25 .60
BBP36 Rich Thompson .25 .60
BBP37a Greg Reynolds .75 2.00
BBP37b Greg Reynolds AU 5.00 12.00
BBP38a Jeff Samardzija 1.00 2.50
BBP38b Jeff Samardzija AU 12.50 30.00
BBP39a Evan Longoria 3.00 8.00
BBP39b Evan Longoria AU 15.00 40.00
BBP40a Luke Hochevar .75 2.00
BBP40b Luke Hochevar AU 15.00 40.00
BBP41 James Avery AU 3.00 8.00
BBP42 Joe Mather AU 6.00 15.00
BBP43 Hank Conger AU 4.00 10.00
BBP44 Adam Miller AU 4.00 10.00
BBP45 Clayton Kershaw AU 15.00 40.00
BBP46 Adam Ottavino AU 3.00 8.00
BBP47 Jason Place AU 5.00 12.00
BBP48 Billy Rowell AU 5.00 12.00
BBP49 Brett Sinkbeil AU 3.00 8.00
BBP50 Colton Willems AU 3.00 8.00
BBP51 Cameron Maybin AU 5.00 12.00
BBP52 Jeremy Jeffress AU 3.00 8.00
BBP53 Fernando Martinez AU 10.00 25.00
BBP54 Chris Marrero AU 20.00 50.00
BBP55 Kyle McCulloch AU 3.00 8.00
BBP56 Chris Parmelee AU 4.00 10.00
BBP57 Emmanuel Burris AU 4.00 10.00
BBP58 Chris Coghlan AU 8.00 20.00
BBP59 Chris Perez AU 4.00 10.00
BBP60 David Huff AU 4.00 10.00

2007 Bowman's Best Prospects Blue

*PROS BLUE: .6X TO 1.5X BASIC PROS
PROS ODDS 1:9 PACKS
*PROS AU BLUE: .6X TO 1.5X BASIC PROS AU
PROS AU ODDS 1:16 PACKS
STATED PRINT RUN 99 SER.#'d SETS
BBP45 Clayton Kershaw AU 40.00 80.00
BBP53 Fernando Martinez AU 40.00 80.00

2007 Bowman's Best Prospects Gold

*PROS GOLD: .75X TO 2X BASIC PROS
PROS ODDS 1:18 PACKS
*PROS AU GOLD: .75X TO 2X BASIC PROS AU
PROS AU ODDS 1:31 PACKS
STATED PRINT RUN 50 SER.#'d SETS
BBP38b Jeff Samardzija AU 40.00 80.00
BBP45 Clayton Kershaw AU 50.00 100.00
BBP48 Billy Rowell AU 20.00 50.00
BBP53 Fernando Martinez AU 50.00 100.00
BBP54 Chris Marrero AU 60.00 120.00

2007 Bowman's Best Prospects Green

PROS GREEN: .5X TO 1.2X BASIC PROS
STATED ODDS 1:4 PACKS
STATED PRINT RUN 249 SER.#'d SETS

2007 Bowman's Best Prospects Red

PROS. ODDS 1:908 PACKS
PROS. AU ODDS 1:1453 PACKS
STATED PRINT RUN 1 SER.#'d SET
NO PRICING DUE TO SCARCITY

2004 Classic Clippings

This 110-card set was released in May, 2004. This set was issued in five card packs which came 18 packs to a box and four boxes to a case. Cards number 1 through 75 featured veterans while cards 76 through 100 featured rookies and prospects while cards 101 through 110 featured players making their major league debut at the start of the 2004 season. Cards numbered 76 through 100 were inserted at a rate of one in 18 hobby and one in 108 retail packs and cards numbered 101-110 were random inserts in packs. All cards numbered 76 through 110 were printed to a stated print run of 500 serial numbered sets.

COMP.SET w/o SP's (75) 6.00 15.00
COMMON CARD (1-75) .12 .30
COMMON CARD (76-110) .75 2.00
COMMON RC (76-110) .75 2.00
76-100 ODDS 1:18 HOBBY, 1:108 RETAIL
101-110 RANDOM INSERTS IN PACKS
76-110 PRINT RUN 500 SERIAL #'d SETS
PROOFS RANDOM INSERTS IN PACKS
OVERALL PARALLEL ODDS 1:18 H, 1:120 R
PROOFS PRINT RUN 1 SET PER COLOR
BLACK-CYAN-MAGENTA-YELLOW ISSUED
NO PROOFS PRICING DUE TO SCARCITY
1 Juan Pierre .12 .30
2 Derek Jeter .75 2.00
3 Jose Reyes .20 .50
4 Eric Chavez .12 .30
5 Alex Rodriguez Yanks .50 1.25
6 Mark Prior .20 .50
7 Carlos Beltran .12 .30
8 Ichiro Suzuki .50 1.25
9 Shawn Green .12 .30
10 Richie Sexson .12 .30
11 Andruw Jones .12 .30
12 Geoff Jenkins .12 .30
13 Luis Gonzalez .12 .30
14 Garret Anderson .12 .30
15 Adam Dunn .20 .50
16 Nomar Garciaparra .30 .75
17 Albert Pujols .75 2.00
18 Jeff Bagwell .12 .30
19 Rocco Baldelli .12 .30
20 Preston Wilson .12 .30
21 Gary Sheffield .12 .30
22 Magglio Ordonez .20 .50
23 Kerry Wood .12 .30
24 Manny Ramirez .30 .75
25 Randy Johnson .30 .75
26 Ken Griffey Jr. .50 1.25
27 Rafael Palmeiro .20 .50
28 Vernon Wells .12 .30
29 Mike Piazza .30 .75
30 Hank Blalock .12 .30
31 Miguel Cabrera .30 .75
32 Jason Giambi .12 .30
33 Troy Glaus .12 .30
34 Angel Berroa .12 .30
35 Greg Maddux .50 1.25
36 Lance Berkman .20 .50
37 Austin Kearns .12 .30
38 Hideo Nomo .30 .75
39 Sammy Sosa .30 .75
40 Jose Vidro .12 .30
41 Curt Schilling .20 .50
42 Melvin Mora .12 .30
43 Scott Podsednik .12 .30
44 Dontrelle Willis .12 .30
45 Roy Halladay .30 .75
46 Hideki Matsui .50 1.25
47 Tom Glavine .20 .50
48 Torii Hunter .12 .30
49 Chipper Jones .30 .75
50 Barry Zito .12 .30
51 Vladimir Guerrero .30 .75
52 Jim Thome .20 .50
53 Shannon Stewart .12 .30
54 Miguel Tejada .20 .50
55 Roy Oswalt .20 .50
56 Jason Kendall .12 .30
57 Brian Giles .12 .30
58 Jason Schmidt .12 .30
59 Pedro Martinez .20 .50
60 Bret Boone .12 .30
61 Josh Beckett .20 .50
62 Scott Rolen .20 .50
63 Aubrey Huff .12 .30
64 Pat Burrell .12 .30
65 Mark Teixeira .30 .75
66 Alfonso Soriano .12 .30
67 Carlos Delgado .12 .30
68 Ivan Rodriguez .20 .50
69 Brandon Webb .12 .30
70 Eric Gagne .12 .30
71 Frank Thomas .30 .75
72 Jody Gerut .12 .30
73 Todd Helton .20 .50
74 Andy Pettitte .20 .50
75 Roger Clemens .40 1.00
76 Rickie Weeks ROO .75 2.00
77 Chien-Ming Wang ROO 4.00 10.00
78 Edwin Jackson ROO .75 2.00
79 Dallas McPherson ROO .75 2.00
80 John Gall ROO RC .75 2.00
81 Ryan Wagner ROO .75 2.00
82 Clint Barmes ROO 1.25 3.00
83 Khalil Greene ROO 1.25 3.00
84 Chin-Hui Tsao ROO .75 2.00
85 Alexis Rios ROO 1.25 3.00
86 Merkin Valdez ROO RC .75 2.00
87 Aarom Baldiris ROO RC .75 2.00
88 Onil Joseph ROO RC .75 2.00
89 Ruddy Yan ROO .75 2.00
90 Chad Bentz ROO RC .75 2.00
91 Shawn Hill ROO RC .75 2.00
92 Delmon Young ROO 1.25 3.00
93 Hector Gimenez ROO RC .75 2.00
94 William Bergolla ROO RC .75 2.00
95 Ronny Cedeno ROO RC .75 2.00
96 Angel Chavez ROO RC .75 2.00
97 Justin Leone ROO RC .75 2.00
98 Ivan Ochoa ROO RC .75 2.00
99 Ian Snell ROO RC .75 2.00
100 Rich Harden ROO .75 2.00
101 Joe Mauer DEB 2.00 5.00
102 Akinori Otsuka DEB RC .75 2.00
103 Bobby Crosby DEB .75 2.00
104 Garrett Atkins DEB .75 2.00
105 Dan Haren DEB .75 2.00
106 Koyie Hill DEB .75 2.00
107 Kaz Matsui DEB RC 1.25 3.00
108 Adam LaRoche DEB .75 2.00
109 Termel Sledge DEB .75 2.00
110 Shingo Takatsu DEB RC .75 2.00

2004 Classic Clippings First Edition

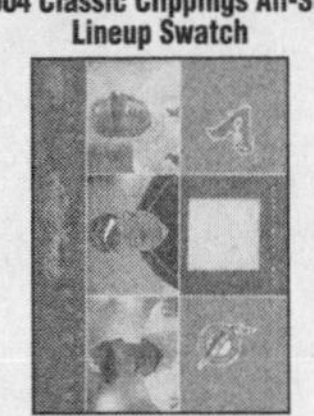

*1ST ED 1-75: 3X TO 8X BASIC
*1ST ED 76-110: .4X TO 1X BASIC
*1ST ED 76-110: .4X TO 1X BASIC RC
OVERALL PARALLEL ODDS 1:18 H, 1:120 R
STATED PRINT RUN 150 SERIAL #'d SETS

2004 Classic Clippings All-Star Lineup Swatch

STATED ODDS 1:28 RETAIL
AJ Gary Sheffield 3.00 8.00
Andruw Jones Jsy
Javy Lopez
AP Gary Sheffield 4.00 10.00
Albert Pujols Jsy
Preston Wilson
AR Nomar Garciaparra 4.00 10.00
Alex Rodriguez Jsy
Jason Giambi
AS Carlos Delgado 2.00 5.00
Alfonso Soriano Jsy
Troy Glaus
BZ Roger Clemens 2.00 5.00
Barry Zito Jsy
Roy Halladay
CD Vernon Wells 2.00 5.00
Carlos Delgado Jsy
Roy Halladay
DW Luis Castillo 3.00 8.00
Dontrelle Willis Jsy
Mike Lowell
HB Magglio Ordonez 2.00 5.00
Hank Blalock Jsy
Troy Glaus
HM Ichiro Suzuki 4.00 10.00
Hideki Matsui Base
Garret Anderson
MP Kerry Wood 3.00 8.00
Mark Prior Jsy
Dontrelle Willis
NG Alex Rodriguez 4.00 10.00
Nomar Garciaparra Jsy
Manny Ramirez
RC Alfonso Soriano 4.00 10.00
Roger Clemens Jsy
Jason Giambi
RS Todd Helton 2.00 5.00
Richie Sexson Jsy
Albert Pujols
SR Edgar Renteria 3.00 8.00
Scott Rolen Jsy
Albert Pujols
TH Luis Castillo 3.00 8.00
Todd Helton Jsy
Scott Rolen

2004 Classic Clippings All-Star Lineup Triple Swatch

STATED PRINT RUN 75 SERIAL #'d SETS
AST PATCH PRINT RUN 25 SERIAL #'d SETS
AST PATCH NO PRICES DUE TO SCARCITY
OVERALL GU ODDS 1:18 H, AU-GU 1:24 R
CARD SMA FEATURES GU BASE SWATCHES
ALL OTHERS ARE JERSEY SWATCHES
CHR Luis Castillo 6.00 15.00
Todd Helton
Scott Rolen
CWL Luis Castillo 6.00 15.00
Dontrelle Willis
Mike Lowell
CZH Roger Clemens 8.00 20.00
Barry Zito
Roy Halladay
DSG Carlos Delgado 4.00 10.00
Alfonso Soriano
Troy Glaus
GRG Nomar Garciaparra 12.50 30.00
Alex Rodriguez
Jason Giambi
HSP Todd Helton 8.00 20.00
Richie Sexson
Albert Pujols
OBG Magglio Ordonez 4.00 10.00
Hank Blalock
Troy Glaus
RGR Alex Rodriguez 10.00 25.00
Nomar Garciaparra
Manny Ramirez
RRP Edgar Renteria 15.00 40.00
Scott Rolen
Albert Pujols
SCG Alfonso Soriano 12.50 30.00
Roger Clemens
Jason Giambi
SJL Gary Sheffield 6.00 15.00
Andruw Jones
Javy Lopez
SMA Ichiro Suzuki Base [illegible] [illegible]
Hideki Matsui Base
Garret Anderson Base
SPW Gary Sheffield 8.00 20.00
Albert Pujols
Preston Wilson
WDH Vernon Wells 4.00 10.00
Carlos Delgado
Roy Halladay
WPW Kerry Wood 6.00 15.00
Mark Prior
Dontrelle Willis

2004 Classic Clippings Bat Rack Autograph Bronze

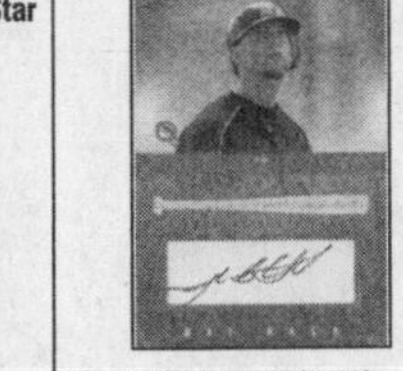

OVERALL AU ODDS 1:18 H, AU-GU 1:24 R
STATED PRINT RUN 75 SERIAL #'d SETS
AH Aubrey Huff 6.00 15.00
EM Edgar Martinez 10.00 25.00
GS Gary Sheffield 10.00 25.00
HB Hank Blalock 6.00 15.00
JB Josh Beckett 10.00 25.00
JE Jim Edmonds 10.00 25.00
JR Jose Reyes 6.00 15.00
MC Miguel Cabrera 10.00 25.00
MT Mark Teixeira 10.00 25.00
RA Roberto Alomar 10.00 25.00

2004 Classic Clippings Bat Rack Quad Green

STATED PRINT RUN 75 SERIAL #'d SETS
GOLD PRINT RUN 10 SERIAL #'d SETS
NO GOLD PRICING DUE TO SCARCITY
*RED: .5X TO 1.2X BASIC
RED PRINT RUN 25 SERIAL #'d SETS
OVERALL GU ODDS 1:18 H, AU-GU 1:24 R
BJPR Rocco Baldelli 8.00 20.00
Chipper Jones
Juan Pierre
Manny Ramirez
BLHD Jeff Bagwell 8.00 20.00
Derrek Lee
Aubrey Huff
Carlos Delgado
GTGP Vladimir Guerrero 12.50 30.00
Miguel Tejada
Jason Giambi
Mike Piazza
HRMR Todd Helton 15.00 40.00
Jose Reyes
Kaz Matsui
Scott Rolen
JRMG Derek Jeter 20.00 50.00
Alex Rodriguez
Kaz Matsui
Nomar Garciaparra
JRSG Derek Jeter 20.00 50.00
Alex Rodriguez
Gary Sheffield
Jason Giambi
PPRS Albert Pujols 15.00 40.00
Mark Prior
Alex Rodriguez
Curt Schilling
PRPR Mike Piazza 15.00 40.00
Jose Reyes
Albert Pujols
Scott Rolen
PSCB Juan Pierre 8.00 20.00
Gary Sheffield
Miguel Cabrera
Rocco Baldelli
SABG Alfonso Soriano 8.00 20.00
Roberto Alomar
Hank Blalock
Troy Glaus
SGEJ Sammy Sosa 8.00 20.00
Vladimir Guerrero
Jim Edmonds
Chipper Jones
SGWS Curt Schilling 10.00 25.00
Nomar Garciaparra
Brandon Webb
Richie Sexson
SPCB Sammy Sosa 8.00 20.00
Mark Prior
Miguel Cabrera
Josh Beckett
TBHL Jim Thome 8.00 20.00
Jeff Bagwell
Todd Helton
Derrek Lee
TBTD Jim Thome 8.00 20.00
Jeff Bagwell
Mark Teixeira
Carlos Delgado

2004 Classic Clippings Bat Rack Triple Green

STATED PRINT RUN 175 SERIAL #'d SETS
*GOLD: .6X TO 1.5X BASIC
GOLD PRINT RUN 25 SERIAL #'d SETS
*RED: .5X TO 1.2X BASIC
RED PRINT RUN 50 SERIAL #'d SETS
OVERALL GU ODDS 1:18 H, AU-GU 1:24 R
ARS Roberto Alomar 6.00 15.00
Jose Reyes
Alfonso Soriano
BHD Rocco Baldelli 4.00 10.00
Aubrey Huff
Carlos Delgado
BTH Jeff Bagwell 6.00 15.00
Jim Thome
Todd Helton
CPB Miguel Cabrera 6.00 15.00
Juan Pierre
Josh Beckett
DHG Carlos Delgado 4.00 10.00
Aubrey Huff
Jason Giambi
GPJ Vladimir Guerrero 6.00 15.00
Juan Pierre
Chipper Jones
GPS Vladimir Guerrero 10.00 25.00
Albert Pujols
Sammy Sosa
GRB Troy Glaus 6.00 15.00
Scott Rolen
Hank Blalock
GRS Nomar Garciaparra 8.00 20.00
Manny Ramirez
Curt Schilling
GTH Jason Giambi 6.00 15.00
Jim Thome
Todd Helton
JMG Derek Jeter 15.00 40.00
Kaz Matsui
Nomar Garciaparra
JRS Derek Jeter 15.00 40.00
Alex Rodriguez
Gary Sheffield
PBS Mark Prior 6.00 15.00
Josh Beckett
Curt Schilling
PRE Albert Pujols 15.00 40.00
Scott Rolen
Jim Edmonds
PRM Mike Piazza 10.00 25.00
Jose Reyes
Kaz Matsui
RTC Alex Rodriguez 6.00 15.00
Miguel Tejada
Miguel Cabrera
SBT Alfonso Soriano 6.00 15.00
Hank Blalock
Mark Teixeira
SLP Sammy Sosa 6.00 15.00
Derrek Lee
Mark Prior
SRB Gary Sheffield 6.00 15.00
Manny Ramirez
Rocco Baldelli
SWA Richie Sexson 6.00 15.00
Brandon Webb
Roberto Alomar

2004 Classic Clippings Inserts

1-20 PRINT RUN 750 SERIAL #'d SETS
21-25 PRINT RUN 100 SERIAL #'d SETS
STATED ODDS 1:18 HOBBY, 1:150 RETAIL
1 Nolan Ryan 4.00 10.00
2 Mike Schmidt 2.00 5.00
3 Cal Ripken 5.00 12.00
4 Don Mattingly 2.50 6.00
5 Roger Clemens 1.50 4.00
6 Randy Johnson 1.25 3.00
7 Mark Prior .75 2.00
8 Jim Thome .75 2.00
9 Sammy Sosa 1.25 3.00
10 Pedro Martinez .75 2.00
11 Chipper Jones 1.25 3.00
12 Vladimir Guerrero 1.25 3.00
13 Albert Pujols 3.00 8.00
14 Ichiro Suzuki 2.00 5.00
15 Derek Jeter 3.00 8.00
16 Alex Rodriguez 2.00 5.00
17 Greg Maddux 2.00 5.00
18 Nomar Garciaparra 1.25 3.00
19 Mike Piazza 1.25 3.00
20 Ken Griffey Jr. 2.00 5.00
21 Pie Traynor 1.25 3.00
22 Bill Dickey 1.25 3.00
23 George Sisler 1.25 3.00
24 Ted Williams 8.00 20.00
25 Enos Slaughter 1.25 3.00

2004 Classic Clippings Jersey Rack Autograph Bronze

OVERALL AU ODDS 1:18 H, AU-GU 1:24 R
STATED PRINT RUN 149 SERIAL #'d SETS
AB Angel Berroa 4.00 10.00
AP1 Andy Pettitte 15.00 40.00
AP2 Albert Pujols 150.00 250.00
BL Barry Larkin 10.00 25.00
BW Brandon Webb 4.00 10.00
CD Carlos Delgado 10.00 25.00
DH Dan Haren 4.00 10.00
DW Dontrelle Willis 10.00 25.00
EJ Edwin Jackson 4.00 10.00
GA1 Garret Anderson 10.00 25.00
GA2 Garrett Atkins 4.00 10.00
IR Ivan Rodriguez 15.00 40.00
JG Jody Gerut 4.00 10.00
KW Kerry Wood 10.00 25.00
MB Marlon Byrd 4.00 10.00
MC Miguel Cabrera 10.00 25.00
MM1 Mark Mulder 6.00 15.00
MM2 Mike Mussina 10.00 25.00
RB Rocco Baldelli 6.00 15.00
RH Roy Halladay 15.00 40.00
RW Ryan Wagner 4.00 10.00
SR Scott Rolen 10.00 25.00
TH Torii Hunter 6.00 15.00

2004 Classic Clippings Jersey Rack Autograph Gold Patch

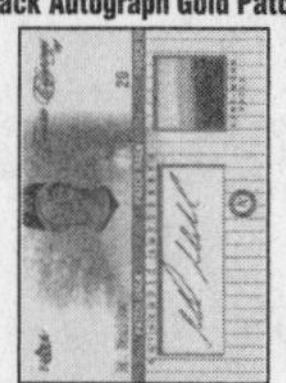

*GOLD PATCH p/r 36-55: 1X TO 2.5X BRZ
*GOLD PATCH p/r 21-35: 1X TO 2.5X BRZ
*GOLD PATCH p/r 16-20: 1.25X TO 3X BRZ
OVERALL AU ODDS 1:18 H, AU-GU 1:24 R
PRINT RUNS B/WN 4-55 COPIES PER
NO PRICING ON QTY OF 11 OR LESS
JB Josh Beckett/21 15.00 40.00

2004 Classic Clippings Jersey Rack Autograph Silver

*SILVER: .5X TO 1.2X BRONZE
OVERALL AU ODDS 1:18 H, AU-GU 1:24 R
STATED PRINT RUN 50 SERIAL #'d SETS
JB Josh Beckett 12.50 30.00

2004 Classic Clippings Jersey Rack Triple Blue

STATED PRINT RUN 225 SERIAL #'d SETS
*BRONZE: .4X TO 1X BASIC
BRONZE PRINT RUN 99 SERIAL #'d SETS
GOLD PATCH PRINT RUN 25 SER.#'d SETS
GOLD PATCH NO PRICE DUE TO SCARCITY
*SILVER p/r 64-117: .4X TO 1X BASIC
*SILVER p/r 40-56: .5X TO 1.2X BASIC
*SILVER p/r 20-34: .6X TO 1.5X BASIC
SILVER PRINT B/WN 20-117 COPIES PER
OVERALL GU ODDS 1:18 H, AU-GU 1:24 R
BCP Rocco Baldelli 8.00 20.00
Miguel Cabrera
Albert Pujols
CPB Roger Clemens 10.00 25.00
Mark Prior
Josh Beckett
CPO Roger Clemens 8.00 20.00
Andy Pettitte
Roy Oswalt
CWB Miguel Cabrera 6.00 15.00
Dontrelle Willis
Josh Beckett
DTS Carlos Delgado 4.00 10.00
Miguel Tejada
Alfonso Soriano
GMS Nomar Garciaparra 8.00 20.00
Pedro Martinez
Curt Schilling
JRG Derek Jeter 15.00 40.00
Alex Rodriguez
Jason Giambi
JSW Randy Johnson 6.00 15.00
Richie Sexson
Brandon Webb
PRL Mike Piazza 6.00 15.00
Ivan Rodriguez
Javy Lopez
PSR Albert Pujols 10.00 25.00
Sammy Sosa
Manny Ramirez
RJG Alex Rodriguez 20.00 50.00
Derek Jeter
Nomar Garciaparra
SWP Sammy Sosa 6.00 15.00
Kerry Wood
Mark Prior
WWB Dontrelle Willis 6.00 15.00
Brandon Webb
Angel Berroa
WWS Dontrelle Willis 6.00 15.00
Kerry Wood
Curt Schilling
ZHM Barry Zito 4.00 10.00
Tim Hudson
Mark Mulder

2004 Classic Clippings Phenom Lineup Autograph Red

STATED PRINT RUN 150 SERIAL #'d SETS
*GOLD: .6X TO 1.5X BASIC
GOLD PRINT RUN 50 SERIAL #'d SETS
*SILVER: .5X TO 1.2X BASIC
SILVER PRINT RUN 99 SERIAL #'d SETS
OVERALL AU ODDS 1:18 H, AU-GU 1:24 R
AB Nomar Garciaparra 4.00 10.00
Angel Berroa AU
Alex Rodriguez
AL Albert Pujols 4.00 10.00
Adam LaRoche AU
Jim Thome
AR Carlos Delgado 6.00 15.00
Alexis Rios AU
Vernon Wells
BC Nomar Garciaparra 6.00 15.00
Bobby Crosby AU
Alex Rodriguez
CW Hideki Matsui 75.00 150.00
Chien-Ming Wang AU
Jason Giambi
DM Troy Glaus 6.00 15.00
Dallas McPherson AU
Garret Anderson
DW Mark Prior 10.00 25.00
Dontrelle Willis AU
Kerry Wood
DY Ichiro Suzuki 10.00 25.00
(Delmon Young AU
Hideki Matsui
EJ Mark Prior 4.00 10.00
Edwin Jackson AU
Kerry Wood
GS Manny Ramirez 12.50 30.00
Grady Sizemore AU
Garret Anderson
HB Troy Glaus 6.00 15.00
Hank Blalock AU
Alex Rodriguez
JG Albert Pujols 4.00 10.00
John Gall AU
Scott Rolen
JR Kaz Matsui 6.00 15.00
Jose Reyes AU
Rickie Weeks
KG Edgar Renteria 10.00 25.00
Khalil Greene AU
Mike Lowell
LN Alex Rodriguez 4.00 10.00
Laynce Nix AU
Garret Anderson
MC Luis Castillo 10.00 25.00
Miguel Cabrera AU
Mike Lowell
MV Edwin Jackson 4.00 10.00
Merkin Valdez AU
Dontrelle Willis
RH1 Roy Halladay
Rich Harden AU
Barry Zito
RH2 Jim Thome 30.00 60.00
Ryan Howard AU
Todd Helton
RW1 Dontrelle Willis 4.00 10.00
Ryan Wagner AU
Mark Prior
RW2 Luis Castillo 10.00 25.00
Rickie Weeks AU
Jose Reyes
SP Albert Pujols 10.00 25.00
Scott Podsednik AU
Andruw Jones

2004 Classic Clippings Press Clippings

STATED ODDS 1:6 HOBBY/RETAIL
1 Josh Beckett .60 1.50
2 Albert Pujols 2.50 6.00
3 Derek Jeter 2.50 6.00
4 Alex Rodriguez 1.50 4.00
5 Jim Thome .60 1.50
6 Angel Berroa .40 1.00
7 Dontrelle Willis .40 1.00
8 Roy Halladay 1.00 2.50
9 Kerry Wood .40 1.00
10 Mark Prior .60 1.50
11 Roger Clemens 1.25 3.00
12 Hideki Matsui 1.50 4.00
13 Ichiro Suzuki 1.50 4.00
14 Eric Gagne .40 1.00
15 Miguel Cabrera 1.00 2.50
16 Nomar Garciaparra 1.00 2.50
17 Hank Blalock .40 1.00
18 Chipper Jones 1.00 2.50
19 Sammy Sosa 1.00 2.50
20 Alfonso Soriano .40 1.00

2004 Classic Clippings Signature Edition

STATED PRINT RUN 50 SERIAL #'d SETS
PURPLE PRINT RUN 1 SERIAL #'d SET
NO PURPLE PRICING DUE TO SCARCITY
OVERALL AU ODDS 1:18 H, AU-GU 1:24 R
AP Albert Pujols 150.00 250.00
CR Cal Ripken 100.00 200.00
DM Don Mattingly 40.00 80.00
EJ Edwin Jackson 5.00 12.00
KG Khalil Greene 12.50 30.00
MP Mark Prior 12.50 30.00
MS Mike Schmidt 40.00 80.00
NR Nolan Ryan 60.00 120.00
RH Rich Harden
RJ Randy Johnson 40.00 80.00
RW Rickie Weeks 8.00 20.00
VG Vladimir Guerrero 20.00 50.00

2005 Classic Clippings

This 125-card set was released in March, 2005. The set was issued in five-card hobby packs with an $7 SRP which came 18 packs to a box and 12 boxes to a case. In addition, these cards were also issued in retail packs with a $5 SRP which came 24 packs to a box and 20 boxes to a case. Cards number 1-75 feature active veterans while cards 76-105 feature retired greats and cards 106-125 feature leading prospects. The retired greats were issued to a stated print run of 999 serial numbered sets while the prospects were issued at a stated rate of one in six hobby packs and one in 12 retail packs.

COMP.SET w/o SP's (75) 6.00 15.00
COMMON CARD (1-75) .10 .30
COMMON CARD (76-105) .60 1.50
76-105 ODDS 1:9 H, 1:500 R
76-105 PRINT RUN 999 SERIAL #'d SETS
COMMON CARD (106-125) .30 .75
1 Frank Thomas .30 .75
2 Vladimir Guerrero .30 .75
3 Ken Griffey Jr. .50 1.25
4 Derek Jeter .75 2.00
5 Rafael Palmeiro .20 .50
6 Adrian Beltre .12 .30
7 Khalil Greene .12 .30
8 Richie Sexson .12 .30
9 Roger Clemens .40 1.00
10 Mike Piazza .30 .75
11 Chipper Jones .30 .75
12 Juan Pierre .12 .30
13 Todd Helton .20 .50
14 Ben Sheets .12 .30
15 John Smoltz .30 .75
16 Steve Finley .12 .30
17 Jim Thome .20 .50
18 Vernon Wells .12 .30
19 Melvin Mora .12 .30
20 Dontrelle Willis .12 .30
21 Eric Gagne .12 .30
22 Craig Wilson .12 .30
23 Curt Schilling .20 .50
24 Justin Morneau .30 .75
25 Jason Schmidt .12 .30
26 Kerry Wood .12 .30
27 Ivan Rodriguez .20 .50
28 Rocco Baldelli .12 .30
29 Mark Prior .20 .50
30 Josh Beckett .20 .50
31 Scott Rolen .20 .50
32 Nomar Garciaparra .30 .75
33 Carl Crawford .20 .50
34 Paul Konerko .20 .50
35 Miguel Cabrera .30 .75
36 Hank Blalock .12 .30
37 Sammy Sosa .30 .75
38 Jim Edmonds .20 .50
39 David Ortiz .30 .75
40 Lance Berkman .20 .50
41 Ichiro Suzuki .50 1.25
42 Adam Dunn .20 .50
43 Carlos Guillen .12 .30
44 Alfonso Soriano .20 .50
45 Victor Martinez .20 .50
46 Torii Hunter .12 .30
47 Kaz Matsui .12 .30
48 Andruw Jones .12 .30
49 Matt Holliday .30 .75
50 Eric Chavez .12 .30
51 Randy Johnson .30 .75
52 Lew Ford .12 .30
53 Hideki Matsui .50 1.25
54 Manny Ramirez .30 .75
55 Mark Teixeira .30 .75
56 Jose Vidro .12 .30
57 Mike Sweeney .12 .30
58 Jack Wilson .12 .30
59 Greg Maddux .50 1.25
60 Tony Batista .12 .30
61 Albert Pujols .75 2.00
62 Miguel Tejada .20 .50
63 Carlos Beltran .12 .30
64 Bobby Abreu .12 .30
65 Carlos Delgado .12 .30
66 Travis Hafner .12 .30
67 Scott Podsednik .12 .30
68 Gary Sheffield .12 .30
69 Johan Santana .30 .75
70 Barry Zito .12 .30
71 Pedro Martinez .20 .50
72 Brian Giles .12 .30
73 Garret Anderson .12 .30
74 Jeff Bagwell .20 .50
75 Alex Rodriguez .50 1.25
76 Johnny Bench LGD 1.50 4.00
77 Yogi Berra LGD 1.50 4.00
78 Lou Brock LGD 1.00 2.50
79 Rod Carew LGD 1.00 2.50
80 Orlando Cepeda LGD .60 1.50
81 Carlton Fisk LGD 1.00 2.50
82 Bob Gibson LGD 1.00 2.50
83 Reggie Jackson LGD 1.50 4.00
84 Al Kaline LGD 1.50 4.00
85 Harmon Killebrew LGD 1.50 4.00
86 Ralph Kiner LGD .60 1.50
87 Willie McCovey LGD 1.00 2.50
88 Eddie Murray LGD 1.50 4.00
89 Phil Rizzuto LGD 1.00 2.50
90 Brooks Robinson LGD 1.00 2.50
91 Nolan Ryan LGD 4.00 10.00
92 Mike Schmidt LGD 3.00 8.00
93 Tom Seaver LGD 1.00 2.50
94 Willie Stargell LGD 1.00 2.50
95 Rollie Fingers LGD .60 1.50
96 Dennis Eckersley LGD .60 1.50
97 Enos Slaughter LGD .60 1.50
98 Jim Palmer LGD .60 1.50
99 Warren Spahn LGD 1.00 2.50
100 Joe Morgan LGD .60 1.50
101 Richie Ashburn LGD 1.00 2.50
102 Robin Yount LGD 1.50 4.00
103 Bob Feller LGD .60 1.50
104 Pee Wee Reese LGD 1.00 2.50
105 Eddie Mathews LGD 1.00 2.50
106 David Wright ROO 1.25 3.00
107 David Aardsma ROO .30 .75
108 B.J. Upton ROO .50 1.25
109 Scott Kazmir ROO .75 2.00
110 Gavin Floyd ROO .30 .75
111 Jeff Francis ROO .30 .75
112 Dioner Navarro ROO .30 .75
113 Zack Greinke ROO .50 1.25
114 Nick Swisher ROO .75 2.00
115 Josh Kroeger ROO .30 .75
116 Ryan Raburn ROO .30 .75
117 Victor Diaz ROO .30 .75
118 Casey Kotchman ROO .30 .75
119 Joey Gathright ROO .30 .75
120 Jon Knott ROO .30 .75
121 J.D. Durbin ROO .30 .75
122 Andres Blanco ROO .30 .75
123 Charlton Jimerson ROO .30 .75
124 Russ Adams ROO .30 .75
125 Justin Verlander ROO RC 6.00 15.00

2005 Classic Clippings Final Edition

OVERALL PARALLEL ODDS 1:18 H, 1:100 R
STATED PRINT RUN 1 SERIAL #'d SET
NO PRICING DUE TO SCARCITY

2005 Classic Clippings First Edition

*1ST ED 1-75: 3X TO 8X BASIC
*1ST ED 76-105: .6X TO 1.5X BASIC
*1ST ED 106-125: 1X TO 2.5X BASIC
OVERALL PARALLEL ODDS 1:18 H, 1:100 R
STATED PRINT RUN 150 SERIAL #'d SETS

2005 Classic Clippings Bat Rack Quad Blue

STATED ODDS 1:118 HOBBY
STATED PRINT RUN 115 SETS
SP PRINT RUNS PROVIDED BY FLEER
CARDS ARE NOT SERIAL-NUMBERED
NO SP PRICING DUE TO SCARCITY
PURPLE PRINT RUN 1 SERIAL #'d SET
NO PURPLE PRICING DUE TO SCARCITY
SILVER PRINT RUN 10 SERIAL #'d SETS
NO SILVER PRICING DUE TO SCARCITY
OVERALL ODDS GU 1:9 H, AU-GU 1:24 R
ADBM Bobby Abreu 15.00 40.00
Adam Dunn
Rocco Baldelli
Hideki Matsui
BJMW Yogi Berra
Reggie Jackson
Don Mattingly
Bernie Williams SP/8
BRDY Wade Boggs 15.00 40.00
Manny Ramirez
Bobby Doerr
Carl Yastrzemski
CMMS Roberto Clemente 60.00 120.00
Bill Madlock
Bill Mazeroski
Willie Stargell
CRMP Gary Carter 10.00 25.00
Jose Reyes
Kaz Matsui
Mike Piazza
GHCK Tony Gwynn 30.00 60.00
Frank Howard
Rocky Colavito
Al Kaline
GPTD Jason Giambi 10.00 25.00
Rafael Palmeiro
Mark Teixeira
Carlos Delgado
GRSS Vladimir Guerrero 10.00 25.00
Manny Ramirez
Sammy Sosa
Gary Sheffield
HJKP Torii Hunter 15.00 40.00
Jacque Jones
Harmon Killebrew
Kirby Puckett
MMSW Joe Morgan
Bill Mazeroski
Alfonso Soriano
Rickie Weeks SP/13
RTGB Ivan Rodriguez 10.00 25.00
Miguel Tejada
Troy Glaus
Hank Blalock
THBP Jim Thome 15.00 40.00
Todd Helton
Jeff Bagwell
Albert Pujols
WJSC Brandon Webb 15.00 40.00
Randy Johnson
Curt Schilling
Roger Clemens

2005 Classic Clippings Cut of History Single Autograph Blue

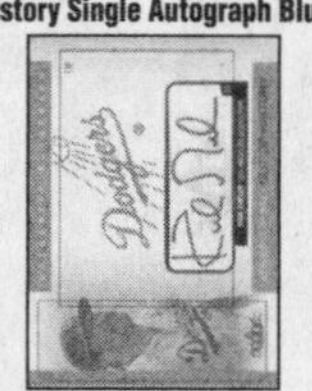

STATED ODDS 1:161 HOBBY
SP PRINT RUNS PROVIDED BY FLEER
SP'S ARE NOT SERIAL-NUMBERED
PURPLE PRINT RUN 1 SERIAL #'d SET
NO PURPLE PRICING DUE TO SCARCITY
SILVER PRINT RUN 25 SERIAL #'d SETS
NO SILVER PRICING AVAILABLE
OVERALL ODDS AU 1:18 H, AU-GU 1:24 R
BB Bill Buckner SP/48 10.00 25.00
BF Bob Feller SP/34 10.00 25.00
BR Brooks Robinson SP/49 15.00 40.00
DG Dwight Gooden SP/50 10.00 25.00
DL Don Larsen SP/49 10.00 25.00
DM Don Mattingly SP/39 30.00 60.00
DS Darryl Strawberry SP/51 10.00 25.00
JB Johnny Bench SP/38 30.00 60.00
JP Jim Palmer SP/50 10.00 25.00
KG Kirk Gibson 4.00 10.00
MW Mookie Wilson SP/49 10.00 25.00

2005 Classic Clippings Cut of History Single Jersey Blue

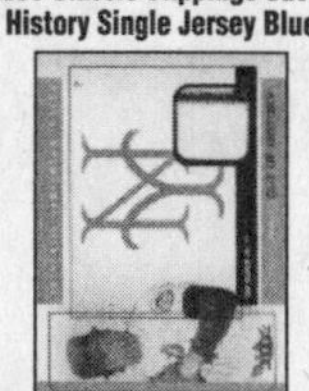

STATED ODDS 1:21 HOBBY, 1:28 RETAIL
SP PRINT RUNS PROVIDED BY FLEER
SP'S ARE NOT SERIAL-NUMBERED
PURPLE PATCH PRINT RUN 1 #'d SET
NO PURPLE PATCH PRICING AVAILABLE
SILVER PATCH PRINT RUN 25 #'d SETS
NO SILVER PATCH PRICING AVAILABLE
OVERALL ODDS GU 1:9 H, AU-GU 1:24 R
BG Bob Gibson 6.00 15.00
BR Brooks Robinson 6.00 15.00
CF Carlton Fisk 6.00 15.00
CR Cal Ripken 12.50 30.00
CY Carl Yastrzemski 8.00 20.00
DG Dwight Gooden 4.00 10.00
DM Don Mattingly 8.00 20.00
DS Darryl Strawberry 4.00 10.00
EM Eddie Murray 6.00 15.00
JB Johnny Bench 6.00 15.00
JM Joe Morgan SP/82 6.00 15.00
MS Mike Schmidt 8.00 20.00
NR Nolan Ryan 10.00 25.00
OC Orlando Cepeda 4.00 10.00
OS Ozzie Smith 6.00 15.00
RJ Reggie Jackson 6.00 15.00
SA Sparky Anderson 4.00 10.00
TS Tom Seaver 6.00 15.00
WM Willie McCovey 6.00 15.00
WS Willie Stargell 6.00 15.00

2005 Classic Clippings Cut of History Dual Autograph Blue

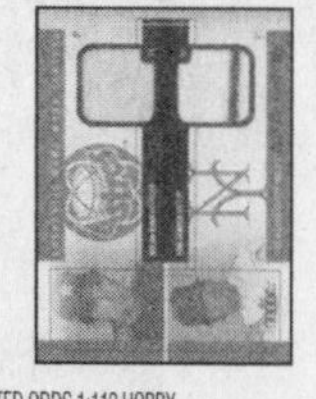

STATED PRINT RUN 49 SETS
PRINT RUN INFO PROVIDED BY FLEER
CARDS ARE NOT SERIAL-NUMBERED
PURPLE PRINT RUN 1 SERIAL #'d SET
NO PURPLE PRICING DUE TO SCARCITY
SILVER PRINT RUN 22 SERIAL #'d SETS
NO SILVER PRICING AVAILABLE
OVERALL ODDS AU 1:18 H, AU-GU 1:24 R
GE Kirk Gibson 15.00 40.00
Dennis Eckersley
GS Dwight Gooden 15.00 40.00
Darryl Strawberry
WB Mookie Wilson 15.00 40.00
Bill Buckner

2005 Classic Clippings Cut of History Dual Jersey Blue

STATED ODDS 1:112 HOBBY
PURPLE PATCH PRINT RUN 1 #'d SET
NO PURPLE PATCH PRICING AVAILABLE
SILVER PATCH PRINT RUN 15 #'d SETS
NO SILVER PATCH PRICING AVAILABLE
OVERALL ODDS GU 1:9 H, AU-GU 1:24 R
BF Johnny Bench 8.00 20.00
Carlton Fisk
BS Lou Brock 12.50 30.00
Mike Schmidt
CM Orlando Cepeda 8.00 20.00
Willie McCovey
GS Dwight Gooden 6.00 15.00
Darryl Strawberry
JY Reggie Jackson 10.00 25.00
Carl Yastrzemski
RS Cal Ripken 20.00 50.00
Ozzie Smith
RS Nolan Ryan 15.00 40.00
Tom Seaver
SJ Willie Stargell 8.00 20.00
Reggie Jackson

2005 Classic Clippings Cut of History Triple Autograph Blue

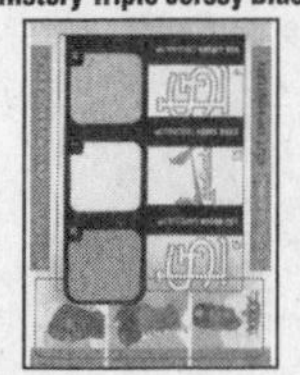

STATED PRINT RUN 15 SETS
PRINT RUN INFO PROVIDED BY FLEER
CARDS ARE NOT SERIAL-NUMBERED
PURPLE PRINT RUN 1 SERIAL #'d SET
SILVER PRINT RUN 5 SERIAL #'d SETS
OVERALL ODDS AU 1:18 H, AU-GU 1:24 R
NO PRICING DUE TO SCARCITY

2005 Classic Clippings Cut of History Triple Jersey Blue

STATED ODDS 1:67 HOBBY
PURPLE PATCH PRINT RUN 1 #'d SET
NO PURPLE PATCH PRICING AVAILABLE
SILVER PATCH PRINT RUN 25 #'d SETS
NO SILVER PATCH PRICING AVAILABLE
OVERALL ODDS GU 1:9 H, AU-GU 1:24 R
ACW Hank Aaron 100.00 175.00
Roberto Clemente

Ted Williams
BSG Lou Brock 20.00 50.00
Ozzie Smith
Bob Gibson
JKM Reggie Jackson 15.00 40.00
Harmon Killebrew
Willie McCovey
MMC Eddie Murray 15.00 40.00
Willie McCovey
Orlando Cepeda
MRS Don Mattingly 40.00 80.00
Cal Ripken
Mike Schmidt
OJM Paul O'Neill 20.00 50.00
Reggie Jackson
Don Mattingly
RCJ Nolan Ryan 20.00 50.00
Roger Clemens
Randy Johnson

2005 Classic Clippings Diamond Signings Single Blue

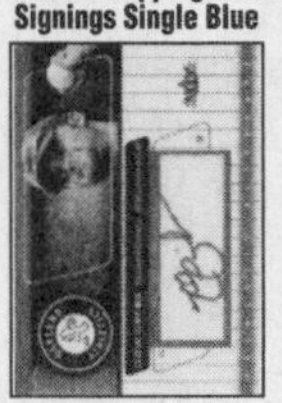

STATED ODDS 1:29 HOBBY
SP PRINT RUNS PROVIDED BY FLEER
SP's ARE NOT SERIAL-NUMBERED
NO PRICING ON SP/18-19 AVAILABLE
PURPLE PRINT RUN 1 SERIAL #'d SET
NO PURPLE PRICING DUE TO SCARCITY
SILVER PRINT RUN 25 SERIAL #'d SETS
NO SILVER PRICING AVAILABLE
OVERALL ODDS AU 1:18 H, AU-GU 1:24 R
AB Andres Blanco SP/98 6.00 15.00
BL Brad Lidge SP/97 15.00 40.00
BU B.J. Upton 6.00 15.00
CF Chone Figgins SP/150 6.00 15.00
CJ Charlton Jimerson SP/150 6.00 15.00
CK Casey Kotchman 4.00 10.00
DN Dioner Navarro 4.00 10.00
DO David Ortiz SP/19
DW David Wright SP/97 20.00 50.00
GF Gavin Floyd SP/150 6.00 15.00
JB Jason Bay SP/96 6.00 15.00
JM Justin Morneau SP/98 6.00 15.00
JP Jake Peavy 6.00 15.00
JV Justin Verlander SP/150 20.00 50.00
KG Khalil Greene SP/150 10.00 25.00
MR Manny Ramirez SP/18
NS Nick Swisher 6.00 15.00
SK Scott Kazmir SP/200 8.00 20.00
TH Travis Hafner 4.00 10.00
ZG Zack Greinke SP/96 10.00 25.00

2005 Classic Clippings Diamond Signings Dual Blue

STATED PRINT RUN 49 SERIAL #'d SETS
PURPLE PRINT RUN 1 SERIAL #'d SET
NO PURPLE PRICING DUE TO SCARCITY
SILVER PRINT RUN 22 SERIAL #'d SETS
NO SILVER PRICING DUE AVAILABLE
OVERALL ODDS AU 1:18 H, AU-GU 1:24 R
EXCHANGE DEADLINE 03/16/08
FU Gavin Floyd 20.00 50.00
Chase Utley
KM Casey Kotchman 15.00 40.00
Justin Morneau

2005 Classic Clippings Diamond Signings Triple Blue

PRINT RUNS BETWEEN 8-99 COPIES PER
NO PRICING ON QTY OF 8
PURPLE PRINT RUN 1 SERIAL #'d SET
NO PURPLE PRICING DUE TO SCARCITY
SILVER PRINT RUN 5 SERIAL #'d SETS
NO SILVER PRICING DUE TO SCARCITY
OVERALL ODDS AU 1:18 H, AU-GU 1:24 R
EXCHANGE DEADLINE 03/16/08
FKV Gavin Floyd 40.00 80.00
Scott Kazmir
Justin Verlander/99
FSJ Chone Figgins 12.50 30.00
Nick Swisher
Charlton Jimerson/99
KMB Casey Kotchman 12.50 30.00
Justin Morneau
Jason Bay/86
PRE Albert Pujols
Scott Rolen
Jim Edmonds/8
ROM Manny Ramirez
David Ortiz
Pedro Martinez/8

2005 Classic Clippings Jersey Rack Dual Blue

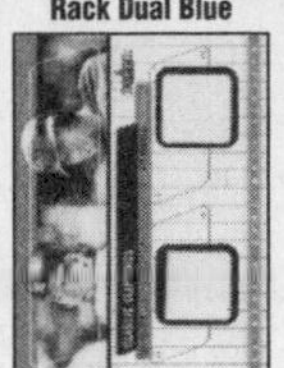

STATED ODDS 1:100 HOBBY
STATED PRINT RUN 75 SETS
PRINT RUN INFO PROVIDED BY FLEER
CARDS ARE NOT SERIAL NUMBERED
PURPLE PRINT RUN 1 SERIAL #'d SET
NO PURPLE PRICING DUE TO SCARCITY
SILVER PRINT RUN 25 SERIAL #'d SETS
NO SILVER PRICING DUE TO SCARCITY
OVERALL ODDS GU 1:9 H, AU-GU 1:24 R
BW Josh Beckett 4.00 10.00
Kerry Wood
CJ Miguel Cabrera 6.00 15.00
Andruw Jones
DB Adam Dunn 4.00 10.00
Lance Berkman
GS Vladimir Guerrero 6.00 15.00
Sammy Sosa
GT Khalil Greene 6.00 15.00
Miguel Tejada
HB Todd Helton 6.00 15.00
Jeff Bagwell
HE Torii Hunter 4.00 10.00
Jim Edmonds
JC Randy Johnson 10.00 25.00
Roger Clemens
JW Chipper Jones 6.00 15.00
David Wright
MM Hideki Matsui 15.00 40.00
Kaz Matsui
OG David Ortiz 6.00 15.00
Jason Giambi
RB Scott Rolen 6.00 15.00
Adrian Beltre
RS Manny Ramirez 6.00 15.00
Gary Sheffield
SG John Smoltz 6.00 15.00
Eric Gagne
SM Jason Schmidt 6.00 15.00
Pedro Martinez
SM1 Alfonso Soriano 4.00 10.00
Kaz Matsui
SP Curt Schilling 6.00 15.00
Mark Prior
TP Jim Thome 6.00 15.00
Mike Piazza
WS Dontrelle Willis 6.00 15.00
Johan Santana

2005 Classic Clippings Jersey Rack Triple Blue

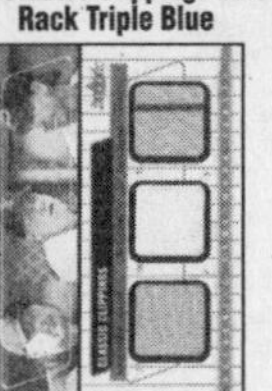

STATED ODDS 1:54 HOBBY
PURPLE PRINT RUN 1 SERIAL #'d SET
NO PURPLE PRICING DUE TO SCARCITY
SILVER PRINT RUN 25 SERIAL #'d SETS
NO SILVER PRICING AVAILABLE
OVERALL ODDS GU 1:9 H, AU-GU 1:24 R
BSG Carlos Beltran
Gary Sheffield
Vladimir Guerrero
CJS Roger Clemens 10.00 25.00
Randy Johnson
Jason Schmidt
CSJ Roger Clemens 10.00 25.00
Curt Schilling
Randy Johnson
EHJ Jim Edmonds 6.00 15.00
Torii Hunter
Andruw Jones
GRS Vladimir Guerrero 6.00 15.00
Manny Ramirez
Gary Sheffield
GSR Eric Gagne 6.00 15.00
John Smoltz
Mariano Rivera
HSB Todd Helton 4.00 10.00
Alfonso Soriano
Adrian Beltre
MGT Kaz Matsui 6.00 15.00
Khalil Greene
Miguel Tejada
MRG Hideki Matsui 12.50 30.00
Mariano Rivera
Jason Giambi
ORM David Ortiz 8.00 20.00
Manny Ramirez
Pedro Martinez
PRE Albert Pujols 12.50 30.00
Scott Rolen
Jim Edmonds
PTB Albert Pujols 10.00 25.00
Jim Thome
Jeff Bagwell
RBJ Scott Rolen 6.00 15.00
Adrian Beltre
Chipper Jones
SDC Sammy Sosa 6.00 15.00
Adam Dunn
Miguel Cabrera
SJJ John Smoltz 10.00 25.00
Chipper Jones
Andruw Jones
SPB Jason Schmidt 6.00 15.00
Mark Prior
Josh Beckett
STB Sammy Sosa 6.00 15.00
Miguel Tejada
Adrian Beltre
WPM David Wright 10.00 25.00
Mike Piazza
Kaz Matsui
WSW Dontrelle Willis 6.00 15.00
Johan Santana
Kerry Wood

2005 Classic Clippings MLB Game Worn Jersey Collection

*1 COLOR PATCH: ADD 20%
*2-COLOR+ PATCH: ADD 50%
*3-COLOR+ PATCH: ADD 100%
STATED ODDS 1:8 EXCEL RETAIL
19 David Ortiz 3.00 8.00
20 Mike Piazza 3.00 8.00
21 Adrian Beltre 2.00 5.00
22 Garret Anderson 2.00 5.00
23 Michael Young 2.00 5.00
24 Frank Thomas 3.00 8.00
25 Brian Giles 2.00 5.00
26 Luis Gonzalez 2.00 5.00
27 Eric Chavez 2.00 5.00
28 Jeremy Bonderman 2.00 5.00
29 Bret Boone 2.00 5.00
30 Vernon Wells 2.00 5.00
31 Omar Vizquel 3.00 8.00
32 Mike Lowell 2.00 5.00
33 Marcus Giles 2.00 5.00
34 Junior Spivey 2.00 5.00
35 A.J. Pierzynski 2.00 5.00
36 Jason Kendall 2.00 5.00

2005 Classic Clippings Official Box Score

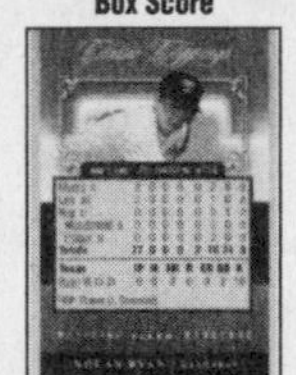

PRINT RUNS B/WN 1951-1995 COPIES PER
*GOLD: 1.5X TO 4X BASIC
GOLD PRINT RUN B/WN 51-95 COPIES PER
OVERALL INSERT ODDS 1:5 HOB, 1:17 RET
1 Nolan Ryan/1991 3.00 8.00
2 Cal Ripken/1995 5.00 12.00
3 Joe Carter/1993 .50 1.25
4 Bucky Dent/1978 .50 1.25
5 Kirk Gibson/1988 .50 1.25
6 Reggie Jackson/1977 1.25 3.00
7 Carlton Fisk/1975 .75 2.00
8 Bobby Thomson/1951 .75 2.00
9 Bill Mazeroski/1960 .75 2.00
10 Don Larsen/1956 .50 1.25

2005 Classic Clippings Press Clippings

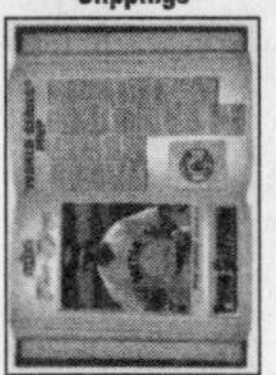

STATED ODDS 1:6 HOBBY, 1:24 RETAIL
GOLD PRINT RUN 4 SERIAL #'d SETS
NO GOLD PRICING DUE TO SCARCITY
1 Ichiro Suzuki 1.50 4.00
2 Manny Ramirez 1.00 2.50
3 Albert Pujols 2.50 6.00
4 David Ortiz 1.00 2.50
5 Greg Maddux 1.50 4.00
6 Ken Griffey Jr. 1.50 4.00
7 Vladimir Guerrero 1.00 2.50
8 Randy Johnson 1.00 2.50
9 Johan Santana 1.00 2.50
10 Roger Clemens 1.25 3.00
11 Bobby Crosby .40 1.00
12 Jason Bay .40 1.00

1994 Collector's Choice

Produced by Upper Deck, this 670 standard-size card set was distributed in two series of 320 and 350. Cards were issued in foil-wrapped 12-card packs and factory sets (of which contained five Gold Signature cards for a total of 675 cards). Basic card fronts feature color player action photos with white borders that are highlighted by vertical gray pinstripes. Subsets include Rookie Class (1-20), First Draft Picks (21-30), Top Performers (306-315), Up Close (631-640) and Future Foundation (641-650). Rookie Cards include Michael Jordan and Alex Rodriguez. A legitimate variation on the Alex Rodriguez card (#647) was verified several years after release. The standard card features the "A" from Alex on the card back text in grey/silver whereas the variation features his name in white. It's believed that the A-Rod "White A" variation is a significantly tougher card but exact estimates of it's scarcity are not known. In subsequent years other cards (such as Johnny Damon) were also verified to have this White Letter variation - thus it's generally believed that the entire Future Foundations subset was produced with white (and standard grey) letter variations.

COMPLETE SET (670) 20.00 50.00
COMP.FACT.SET (675) 20.00 50.00
COMP. SERIES 1 (320) 4.00 10.00
COMP. SERIES 2 (350) 6.00 15.00
1 Rich Becker .02 .10
2 Greg Blosser .02 .10
3 Midre Cummings .02 .10
4 Carlos Delgado .10 .30
5 Steve Dreyer RC .02 .10
6 Carl Everett .07 .20
7 Cliff Floyd .07 .20
8 Alex Gonzalez .02 .10
9 Shawn Green .20 .50
10 Butch Huskey .02 .10
11 Mark Hutton .02 .10
12 Miguel Jimenez .02 .10
13 Steve Karsay .02 .10
14 Marc Newfield .02 .10
15 Luis Ortiz .02 .10
16 Manny Ramirez .20 .50
17 Johnny Ruffin .02 .10
18 Scott Stahoviak .02 .10
19 Salomon Torres .02 .10
20 Gabe White .02 .10
21 Brian Anderson RC .08 .25
22 Wayne Gomes RC .02 .10
23 Jeff Granger .02 .10
24 Steve Soderstrom RC .02 .10
25 Trot Nixon RC .60 1.50
26 Kirk Presley RC .02 .10
27 Matt Brunson RC .02 .10
28 Brooks Kieschnick RC .02 .10
29 Billy Wagner RC .50 1.25
30 Matt Drews RC .02 .10
31 Kurt Abbott RC .02 .10
32 Luis Alicea .02 .10
33 Roberto Alomar .10 .30
34 Sandy Alomar Jr. .02 .10
35 Moises Alou .07 .20
36 Wilson Alvarez .02 .10
37 Rich Amaral .02 .10
38 Eric Anthony .02 .10
39 Luis Aquino .02 .10
40 Jack Armstrong .02 .10
41 Rene Arocha .02 .10
42 Rich Aude RC .02 .10
43 Brad Ausmus .10 .30
44 Steve Avery .02 .10
45 Bob Ayrault .02 .10
46 Willie Banks .02 .10
47 Bret Barberie .02 .10
48 Kim Batiste .02 .10
49 Rod Beck .02 .10
50 Jason Bere .02 .10
51 Sean Berry .02 .10
52 Dante Bichette .07 .20
53 Jeff Blauser .02 .10
54 Mike Blowers .02 .10
55 Tim Bogar .02 .10
56 Tom Bolton .02 .10
57 Ricky Bones .02 .10
58 Bobby Bonilla .07 .20
59 Bret Boone .07 .20
60 Pat Borders .02 .10
61 Mike Bordick .02 .10
62 Daryl Boston .02 .10
63 Ryan Bowen .02 .10
64 Jeff Branson .02 .10
65 George Brett .50 1.25
66 Steve Buechele .02 .10
67 Dave Burba .02 .10
68 John Burkett .02 .10
69 Jeromy Burnitz .07 .20
70 Brett Butler .07 .20
71 Rob Butler .02 .10
72 Ken Caminiti .07 .20
73 Cris Carpenter .02 .10
74 Vinny Castilla .07 .20
75 Andujar Cedeno .02 .10
76 Wes Chamberlain .02 .10
77 Archi Cianfrocco .02 .10
78 Dave Clark .02 .10
79 Jerald Clark .02 .10
80 Royce Clayton .02 .10
81 David Cone .07 .20
82 Jeff Conine .07 .20
83 Steve Cooke .02 .10
84 Scott Cooper .02 .10
85 Joey Cora .02 .10
86 Tim Costo .02 .10
87 Chad Curtis .02 .10
88 Ron Darling .02 .10
89 Danny Darwin .02 .10
90 Rob Deer .02 .10
91 Jim Deshaies .02 .10
92 Delino DeShields .02 .10
93 Rob Dibble .07 .20
94 Gary DiSarcina .02 .10
95 Doug Drabek .02 .10
96 Scott Erickson .02 .10
97 Rikkert Faneyte RC .02 .10
98 Jeff Fassero .02 .10
99 Alex Fernandez .02 .10
100 Cecil Fielder .07 .20
101 Dave Fleming .02 .10
102 Darrin Fletcher .02 .10
103 Scott Fletcher .02 .10
104 Mike Gallego .02 .10
105 Carlos Garcia .02 .10
106 Jeff Gardner .02 .10
107 Brent Gates .02 .10
108 Benji Gil .02 .10
109 Bernard Gilkey .02 .10
110 Chris Gomez .02 .10
111 Luis Gonzalez .07 .20
112 Tom Gordon .02 .10
113 Jim Gott .02 .10
114 Mark Grace .10 .30
115 Tommy Greene .02 .10
116 Willie Greene .02 .10
117 Ken Griffey Jr. .30 .75
118 Bill Gullickson .02 .10
119 Ricky Gutierrez .02 .10
120 Juan Guzman .02 .10
121 Chris Gwynn .02 .10
122 Tony Gwynn .25 .60
123 Jeffrey Hammonds .02 .10
124 Erik Hanson .02 .10
125 Gene Harris .02 .10
126 Greg W. Harris .02 .10
127 Bryan Harvey .02 .10
128 Billy Hatcher .02 .10
129 Hilly Hathaway .02 .10
130 Charlie Hayes .02 .10
131 Rickey Henderson .20 .50
132 Mike Henneman .02 .10
133 Pat Hentgen .02 .10
134 Roberto Hernandez .02 .10
135 Orel Hershiser .07 .20
136 Phil Hiatt .02 .10
137 Glenallen Hill .02 .10
138 Ken Hill .02 .10
139 Eric Hillman .02 .10
140 Chris Hoiles .02 .10
141 Dave Hollins .02 .10
142 David Hulse .02 .10
143 Todd Hundley .02 .10
144 Pete Incaviglia .02 .10
145 Danny Jackson .02 .10
146 John Jaha .02 .10
147 Domingo Jean .02 .10
148 Gregg Jefferies .02 .10
149 Reggie Jefferson .02 .10
150 Lance Johnson .02 .10
151 Bobby Jones .02 .10
152 Chipper Jones .20 .50
153 Todd Jones .02 .10
154 Brian Jordan .07 .20
155 Wally Joyner .07 .20
156 David Justice .07 .20
157 Ron Karkovice .02 .10
158 Eric Karros .07 .20
159 Jeff Kent .10 .30
160 Jimmy Key .07 .20
161 Mark Kiefer .02 .10
162 Darryl Kile .07 .20
163 Jeff King .02 .10
164 Wayne Kirby .02 .10
165 Ryan Klesko .07 .20
166 Chuck Knoblauch .07 .20
167 Chad Kreuter .02 .10
168 John Kruk .07 .20
169 Mark Langston .02 .10
170 Mike Lansing .02 .10
171 Barry Larkin .10 .30
172 Manuel Lee .02 .10
173 Phil Leftwich RC .02 .10
174 Darren Lewis .02 .10
175 Derek Lilliquist .02 .10
176 Jose Lind .02 .10
177 Albie Lopez .02 .10
178 Javier Lopez .07 .20
179 Torey Lovullo .02 .10
180 Scott Lydy .02 .10
181 Mike Macfarlane .02 .10
182 Shane Mack .02 .10
183 Greg Maddux .30 .75
184 Dave Magadan .02 .10
185 Joe Magrane .02 .10
186 Kirk Manwaring .02 .10
187 Al Martin .02 .10
188 Pedro A. Martinez RC .02 .10
189 Pedro Martinez .20 .50
190 Ramon Martinez .02 .10
191 Tino Martinez .10 .30
192 Don Mattingly .50 1.25
193 Derrick May .02 .10
194 David McCarty .02 .10
195 Ben McDonald .02 .10
196 Roger McDowell .02 .10
197 Fred McGriff UER .10 .30
(Stats on back have 73 stolen bases for 1989; should be 7)
198 Mark McLemore .02 .10
199 Greg McMichael .02 .10
200 Jeff McNeely .02 .10
201 Brian McRae .02 .10
202 Pat Meares .02 .10
203 Roberto Mejia .02 .10
204 Orlando Merced .02 .10
205 Jose Mesa .02 .10
206 Blas Minor .02 .10
207 Angel Miranda .02 .10
208 Paul Molitor .07 .20
209 Raul Mondesi .07 .20
210 Jeff Montgomery .02 .10
211 Mickey Morandini .02 .10
212 Mike Morgan .02 .10
213 Jamie Moyer .07 .20
214 Bobby Munoz .02 .10
215 Troy Neel .02 .10
216 Dave Nilsson .02 .10
217 John O'Donoghue .02 .10
218 Paul O'Neill .10 .30
219 Jose Offerman .02 .10
220 Joe Oliver .02 .10
221 Greg Olson .02 .10
222 Donovan Osborne .02 .10
223 Jayhawk Owens .02 .10
224 Mike Pagliarulo .02 .10
225 Craig Paquette .02 .10
226 Roger Pavlik .02 .10
227 Brad Pennington .02 .10
228 Eduardo Perez .02 .10
229 Mike Perez .02 .10
230 Tony Phillips .02 .10
231 Hipolito Pichardo .02 .10
232 Phil Plantier .02 .10
233 Curtis Pride RC .08 .25
234 Tim Pugh .02 .10
235 Scott Radinsky .02 .10
236 Pat Rapp .02 .10
237 Kevin Reimer .02 .10
238 Armando Reynoso .02 .10
239 Jose Rijo .02 .10
240 Cal Ripken .60 1.50
241 Kevin Roberson .02 .10
242 Kenny Rogers .07 .20
243 Kevin Rogers .02 .10
244 Mel Rojas .02 .10
245 John Roper .02 .10
246 Kirk Rueter .02 .10
247 Scott Ruffcorn .02 .10
248 Ken Ryan .02 .10
249 Nolan Ryan .75 2.00
250 Bret Saberhagen .07 .20
251 Tim Salmon .10 .30
252 Reggie Sanders .07 .20
253 Curt Schilling .07 .20
254 David Segui .02 .10
255 Aaron Sele .02 .10
256 Scott Servais .02 .10
257 Gary Sheffield .07 .20
258 Ruben Sierra .07 .20
259 Don Slaught .02 .10
260 Lee Smith .07 .20
261 Cory Snyder .02 .10
262 Paul Sorrento .02 .10
263 Sammy Sosa .20 .50
264 Bill Spiers .02 .10
265 Mike Stanley .02 .10
266 Dave Staton .02 .10
267 Terry Steinbach .02 .10
268 Kevin Stocker .02 .10
269 Todd Stottlemyre .02 .10
270 Doug Strange .02 .10
271 Bill Swift .02 .10
272 Kevin Tapani .02 .10
273 Tony Tarasco .02 .10
274 Julian Tavarez RC .02 .10
275 Mickey Tettleton .02 .10
276 Ryan Thompson .02 .10
277 Chris Turner .02 .10
278 John Valentin .02 .10
279 Todd Van Poppel .02 .10
280 Andy Van Slyke .10 .30
281 Mo Vaughn .07 .20
282 Robin Ventura .07 .20
283 Frank Viola .07 .20
284 Jose Vizcaino .02 .10
285 Omar Vizquel .10 .30
286 Larry Walker .07 .20
287 Duane Ward .02 .10
288 Allen Watson .02 .10
289 Bill Wegman .02 .10
290 Turk Wendell .02 .10
291 Lou Whitaker .07 .20
292 Devon White .07 .20
293 Rondell White .07 .20
294 Mark Whiten .02 .10
295 Darrel Whitmore .02 .10
296 Bob Wickman .02 .10
297 Rick Wilkins .02 .10
298 Bernie Williams .10 .30
299 Matt Williams .07 .20
300 Woody Williams .07 .20
301 Nigel Wilson .02 .10
302 Dave Winfield .07 .20
303 Anthony Young .02 .10
304 Eric Young .02 .10
305 Todd Zeile .02 .10
306 Jack McDowell TP .07 .20
John Burkett
Tom Glavine
307 Randy Johnson TP .10 .30
308 Randy Myers TP .02 .10
309 Jack McDowell TP .02 .10
310 Mike Piazza TP .20 .50
311 Barry Bonds TP .30 .75
312 Andres Galarraga TP .02 .10
313 Juan Gonzalez TP .30 .75
Barry Bonds
314 Albert Belle TP .07 .20
315 Kenny Lofton TP .02 .10
316 Barry Bonds CL .30 .75
317 Ken Griffey Jr. CL .20 .50
318 Mike Piazza CL .20 .50
319 Kirby Puckett CL .10 .30
320 Nolan Ryan CL .20 .50
321 Roberto Alomar CL .07 .20
322 Roger Clemens CL .20 .50
323 Juan Gonzalez CL .02 .10
324 Ken Griffey Jr. CL .20 .50
325 David Justice CL .02 .10
326 John Kruk CL .02 .10
327 Frank Thomas CL .07 .20
328 Tim Salmon TC .07 .20
329 Jeff Bagwell TC .07 .20
330 Mark McGwire TC .25 .60
331 Roberto Alomar TC .07 .20
332 David Justice TC .02 .10
333 Pat Listach TC .02 .10
334 Ozzie Smith TC .20 .50
335 Ryne Sandberg TC .20 .50
336 Mike Piazza TC .20 .50
337 Cliff Floyd TC .02 .10
338 Barry Bonds TC .30 .75
339 Albert Belle TC .07 .20
340 Ken Griffey Jr. TC .20 .50
341 Gary Sheffield TC .02 .10
342 Dwight Gooden TC .02 .10
343 Cal Ripken TC .30 .75
344 Tony Gwynn TC .10 .30
345 Lenny Dykstra TC .02 .10
346 Andy Van Slyke TC .07 .20
347 Juan Gonzalez TC .02 .10
348 Roger Clemens TC .20 .50
349 Barry Larkin TC .07 .20
350 Andres Galarraga TC .02 .10
351 Kevin Appier TC .02 .10
352 Cecil Fielder TC .02 .10
353 Kirby Puckett TC .10 .30
354 Frank Thomas TC .10 .30
355 Don Mattingly TC .25 .60
356 Bo Jackson .20 .50
357 Randy Johnson .20 .50
358 Darren Daulton .07 .20
359 Charlie Hough .07 .20
360 Andres Galarraga .07 .20
361 Mike Felder .02 .10
362 Chris Hammond .02 .10
363 Shawon Dunston .02 .10
364 Junior Felix .02 .10
365 Ray Lankford .07 .20
366 Darryl Strawberry .07 .20
367 Dave Magadan .02 .10
368 Gregg Olson .02 .10
369 Lenny Dykstra .07 .20
370 Darrin Jacks
371 Dave Stewar
372 Terry Pendle
373 Arthur Rhode
374 Benito Santia
375 Travis Fryma
376 Scott Brosius
377 Stan Belinda
378 Derek Parks
379 Kevin Seitzer .02 .10
380 Wade Boggs .10 .30
381 Wally Whitehurst .02 .10
382 Scott Leius .02 .10
383 Danny Tartabull .02 .10
384 Harold Reynolds .07 .20
385 Tim Raines .07 .20
386 Darryl Hamilton .02 .10
387 Felix Fermin .02 .10
388 Jim Eisenreich .02 .10
389 Kurt Abbott .02 .10
390 Kevin Appier .07 .20
391 Chris Bosio .02 .10
392 Randy Tomlin .02 .10
393 Bob Hamelin .02 .10
394 Kevin Gross .02 .10
395 Wil Cordero .02 .10
396 Joe Girardi .02 .10
397 Orestes Destrade .02 .10
398 Chris Haney .02 .10
399 Xavier Hernandez .02 .10
400 Mike Piazza .40 1.00
401 Alex Arias .02 .10
402 Tom Candiotti .02 .10
403 Kirk Gibson .07 .20
404 Chuck Carr .02 .10
405 Brady Anderson .07 .20
406 Greg Gagne .02 .10
407 Bruce Ruffin .02 .10
408 Scott Hemond .02 .10
409 Keith Miller .02 .10
410 John Wetteland .07 .20
411 Eric Anthony .02 .10
412 Andre Dawson .07 .20
413 Doug Henry .02 .10
414 John Franco .07 .20
415 Julio Franco .07 .20
416 Dave Hansen .02 .10
417 Mike Harkey .02 .10
418 Jack Armstrong .02 .10
419 Joe Orsulak .02 .10
420 John Smoltz .10 .30
421 Scott Livingstone .02 .10
422 Darren Holmes .02 .10
423 Ed Sprague .02 .10
424 Jay Buhner .07 .20
425 Kirby Puckett .20 .50
426 Phil Clark .02 .10
427 Anthony Young .02 .10
428 Reggie Jefferson .02 .10
429 Mariano Duncan .02 .10
430 Tom Glavine .10 .30
431 Dave Henderson .02 .10
432 Melido Perez .02 .10
433 Paul Wagner .02 .10
434 Tim Worrell .02 .10
435 Ozzie Guillen .07 .20
436 Mike Butcher .02 .10
437 Jim Deshaies .02 .10
438 Kevin Young .02 .10
439 Tom Browning .02 .10
440 Mike Greenwell .02 .10
441 Mike Stanton .02 .10
442 John Doherty .02 .10
443 John Dopson .02 .10
444 Carlos Baerga .02 .10
445 Jack McDowell .02 .10
446 Kent Mercker .02 .10
447 Ricky Jordan .02 .10
448 Jerry Browne .02 .10
449 Fernando Vina .02 .10
450 Jim Abbott .10 .30
451 Teddy Higuera .02 .10
452 Tim Naehring .02 .10
453 Jim Leyritz .02 .10
454 Frank Castillo .02 .10
455 Joe Carter .07 .20
456 Craig Biggio .10 .30
457 Geronimo Pena .02 .10
458 Alejandro Pena .02 .10
459 Mike Moore .02 .10
460 Randy Myers .02 .10
461 Greg Myers .02 .10
462 Greg Hibbard .02 .10
463 Jose Guzman .02 .10
464 Tom Pagnozzi .02 .10
465 Marquis Grissom .07 .20
466 Tim Wallach .02 .10
467 Joe Grahe .02 .10
468 Bob Tewksbury .02 .10
469 B.J. Surhoff .07 .20
470 Kevin Mitchell .02 .10
471 Bobby Witt .02 .10
472 Milt Thompson .02 .10
473 John Smiley .02 .10
474 Alan Trammell .07 .20
475 Mike Mussina .10 .30
476 Rick Aguilera .02 .10
477 Jose Valentin .02 .10
478 Harold Baines .07 .20
479 Bip Roberts .02 .10
480 Edgar Martinez .10 .30
481 Rheal Cormier .02 .10
482 Hal Morris .02 .10
483 Pat Kelly .02 .10
484 Roberto Kelly .02 .10
485 Chris Sabo .02 .10
486 Kent Hrbek .07 .20
487 Scott Kamieniecki .02 .10
488 Walt Weiss .02 .10
489 Karl Rhodes .02 .10
490 Derek Bell .02 .10
491 Chili Davis .07 .20
492 Brian Harper .02 .10
493 Felix Jose .02 .10
494 Trevor Hoffman .10 .30
495 Dennis Eckersley .07 .20
496 Pedro Astacio .02 .10
497 Jay Bell .07 .20
498 Randy Velarde .02 .10
499 David Wells .07 .20
500 Frank Thomas .20 .50

.02 .10
...ereaux .02 .10
...x McElroy .02 .10
...uis Polonia .02 .10
...5 Damion Easley .02 .10
506 Greg A. Harris .02 .10
507 Chris James .02 .10
508 Terry Mulholland .02 .10
509 Pete Smith .02 .10
510 Rickey Henderson .20 .50
511 Sid Fernandez .02 .10
512 Al Leiter .07 .20
513 Doug Jones .02 .10
514 Steve Farr .02 .10
515 Chuck Finley .07 .20
516 Bobby Thigpen .02 .10
517 Jim Edmonds .20 .50
518 Graeme Lloyd .02 .10
519 Dwight Gooden .07 .20
520 Pat Listach .02 .10
521 Kevin Bass .02 .10
522 Willie Banks .02 .10
523 Steve Finley .07 .20
524 Delino DeShields .02 .10
525 Mark McGwire .50 1.25
526 Greg Swindell .02 .10
527 Chris Nabholz .02 .10
528 Scott Sanders .02 .10
529 David Segui .02 .10
530 Howard Johnson .02 .10
531 Jaime Navarro .02 .10
532 Jose Vizcaino .02 .10
533 Mark Lewis .02 .10
534 Pete Harnisch .02 .10
535 Robby Thompson .02 .10
536 Marcus Moore .02 .10
537 Kevin Brown .07 .20
538 Mark Clark .02 .10
539 Sterling Hitchcock .02 .10
540 Will Clark .10 .30
541 Denis Boucher .02 .10
542 Jack Morris .07 .20
543 Pedro Munoz .02 .10
544 Bret Boone .07 .20
545 Ozzie Smith .30 .75
546 Dennis Martinez .07 .20
547 Dan Wilson .02 .10
548 Rick Sutcliffe .07 .20
549 Kevin McReynolds .02 .10
550 Roger Clemens .40 1.00
551 Todd Benzinger .02 .10
552 Bill Haselman .02 .10
553 Bobby Munoz .02 .10
554 Ellis Burks .07 .20
555 Ryne Sandberg .30 .75
556 Lee Smith .07 .20
557 Danny Bautista .02 .10
558 Rey Sanchez .02 .10
559 Norm Charlton .02 .10
560 Jose Canseco .10 .30
561 Tim Belcher .02 .10
562 Denny Neagle .07 .20
563 Eric Davis .07 .20
564 Jody Reed .02 .10
565 Kenny Lofton .07 .20
566 Gary Gaetti .07 .20
567 Todd Worrell .02 .10
568 Mark Portugal .02 .10
569 Dick Schofield .02 .10
570 Andy Benes .02 .10
571 Zane Smith .02 .10
572 Bobby Ayala .02 .10
573 Chip Hale .02 .10
574 Bob Welch .02 .10
575 Deion Sanders .10 .30
576 David Nied .02 .10
577 Pat Mahomes .02 .10
578 Charles Nagy .02 .10
579 Otis Nixon .02 .10
580 Dean Palmer .07 .20
581 Roberto Petagine .02 .10
582 Dwight Smith .02 .10
583 Jeff Russell .02 .10
584 Mark Dewey .02 .10
585 Greg Vaughn .02 .10
586 Brian Hunter .02 .10
587 Willie McGee .07 .20
588 Pedro Martinez .20 .50
589 Roger Salkeld .02 .10
590 Jeff Bagwell .10 .30
591 Spike Owen .02 .10
592 Jeff Reardon .07 .20
593 Erik Pappas .02 .10
594 Brian Williams .02 .10
595 Eddie Murray .20 .50
596 Henry Rodriguez .02 .10
597 Erik Hanson .02 .10
598 Stan Javier .02 .10
599 Mitch Williams .02 .10
600 John Olerud .07 .20
601 Vince Coleman .02 .10
602 Damon Berryhill .02 .10
603 Tom Brunansky .02 .10
604 Robb Nen .07 .20
605 Rafael Palmeiro .10 .30
606 Cal Eldred .02 .10
607 Jeff Brantley .02 .10
608 Alan Mills .02 .10
609 Jeff Nelson .02 .10
610 Barry Bonds .60 1.50
611 Carlos Pulido RC .02 .10
612 Tim Hyers RC .02 .10
613 Steve Howe .02 .10
614 Brian Turang RC .02 .10
615 Leo Gomez .02 .10
616 Jesse Orosco .02 .10
617 Dan Pasqua .02 .10
618 Marvin Freeman .02 .10
619 Tony Fernandez .02 .10
620 Albert Belle .07 .20
621 Eddie Taubensee .02 .10
622 Mike Jackson .02 .10
623 Jose Bautista .02 .10
624 Jim Thome .10 .30
625 Ivan Rodriguez .10 .30
626 Ben Rivera .02 .10
627 Dave Valle .02 .10
628 Tom Henke .02 .10
629 Omar Vizquel .10 .30
630 Juan Gonzalez .07 .20
631 Roberto Alomar UP .07 .20
632 Barry Bonds UP .30 .75
633 Juan Gonzalez UP .02 .10
634 Ken Griffey Jr. UP .20 .50
635 Michael Jordan UP 1.00 2.50
636 David Justice UP .02 .10
637 Mike Piazza UP .20 .50
638 Kirby Puckett UP .10 .30
639 Tim Salmon UP .07 .20
640 Frank Thomas UP .10 .30
641 Alan Benes FF RC .02 .10
642 Johnny Damon FF .20 .50
643 Brad Fullmer FF RC .08 .25
644 Derek Jeter FF .60 1.50
645 Derrek Lee FF RC UER .60 1.50
Biographical Information is incorrect
646 Alex Ochoa .02 .10
647 Alex Rodriguez FF RC 4.00 10.00
648 Jose Silva FF RC .02 .10
649 Terrell Wade FF RC .02 .10
650 Preston Wilson FF .07 .20
651 Shane Andrews .02 .10
652 James Baldwin .02 .10
653 Ricky Bottalico RC .02 .10
654 Tavo Alvarez .02 .10
655 Donnie Elliott .02 .10
656 Joey Eischen .02 .10
657 Jason Giambi .20 .50
658 Todd Hollandsworth .02 .10
659 Brian L. Hunter .02 .10
660 Charles Johnson .07 .20
661 Michael Jordan RC 2.00 5.00
662 Jeff Juden .02 .10
663 Mike Kelly .02 .10
664 James Mouton .02 .10
665 Ray Holbert .02 .10
666 Pokey Reese .02 .10
667 Ruben Santana RC .02 .10
668 Paul Spoljaric .02 .10
669 Luis Lopez .02 .10
670 Matt Walbeck .02 .10
P50 Ken Griffey Jr. Promo .40 1.00

1994 Collector's Choice White Letter Variation

A legitimate variation on the Alex Rodriguez card (#647) was verified several years after release. The standard card features the "A" from Alex on the card back text in grey/silver whereas the variation features his name in white. It's believed that the A-Rod "White A" variation is a significantly tougher card but exact estimates of it's scarcity are not known. In subsequent years other cards (such as Johnny Damon) were also verified to have this White Letter variation - thus it's generally believed that the entire Future Foundations subset was produced with white (and standard grey) letter variations.

RANDOM PRINTING ERRORS IN PACKS
PRICING AVAIL ONLY ON A-ROD FOR NOW
647 Alex Rodriguez 12.50 30.00

1994 Collector's Choice Gold Signature

This 670-card Gold Signature set is a parallel to the basic Collector's Choice issue. These cards were randomly inserted into first and second series hobby and retail packs at a rate of one in 36 and jumbo packs at a rate of one in 20. Gold cards were also issued five per factory set. These cards are identical to the basic issue except for gold foil fronts and a facsimile gold foil player's signature. Some subset cards feature borderless designs (unlike the basic player cards), thus their corresponding borderless Gold Foil Signature cards differ only by the gold foil replica autograph. The Jeffrey Hammonds card has the signature of Orioles General Manager Roland Hemond.

*STARS: 6X TO 15X BASIC CARDS
*ROOKIES: 6X TO 15X BASIC CARDS
RANDOM PRINTING ERRORS IN PACKS
FIVE PER FACTORY SET
635 Michael Jordan UP 8.00 20.00
644 Derek Jeter FF 100.00 200.00
647 Alex Rodriguez 50.00 100.00

1994 Collector's Choice Gold Signature White Letter Variation

RANDOM PRINTING ERRORS IN PACKS
NO PRICING DUE TO SCARCITY

1994 Collector's Choice Silver Signature

This 670-card set is a parallel to the basic Collector's Choice set. One card was inserted into every first and second series pack. Silver cards were also inserted at different rates in other pack forms. Each Silver Foil Signature card is identical in design to its corresponding regular issue card except for the silver borders and silver replica autograph. As with the gold set, the Jeffrey Hammonds card has the signature of Orioles General Manager Roland Hemond. A legitimate variation on the Alex Rodriguez card (#647) was verified several years after release. The standard card features the "A" from Alex on the card back text in grey/silver whereas the variation features his name in white. It's believed that the A-Rod "White A" variation is a significantly tougher card but exact estimates of it's scarcity are not known.

COMPLETE SET (670) 60.00 150.00
COMP. SERIES 1 (320) 20.00 50.00
COMP. SERIES 2 (350) 40.00 100.00
*STARS: 1.5X TO 4X BASIC CARDS
*ROOKIES: 1X TO 2.5X BASIC CARDS
647 Alex Rodriguez FF Grey A 6.00 15.00

1994 Collector's Choice Silver Signature White Letter Variation

A legitimate variation on the Alex Rodriguez card (#647) was verified several years after release. The standard card features the "A" from Alex on the card back text in grey/silver whereas the variation features his name in white. It's believed that the A-Rod "White A" variation is a significantly tougher card but exact estimates of it's scarcity are not known.

RANDOM VARIATIONS IN PACKS
NO PRICING DUE TO SCARCITY

1994 Collector's Choice Home Run All-Stars

This eight-card standard-size set served as the eighth place prize in the Crash the Game contest, which was a promotion in both series of Collector's Choice. The series one expiration was May 18, 1994; series two was Oct. 31, 1994. The cards are numbered with an "HA" prefix.

COMPLETE SET (8) 1.50 4.00
HA1 Juan Gonzalez .10 .30
HA2 Ken Griffey Jr. .50 1.25
HA3 Barry Bonds 1.00 2.50
HA4 Bobby Bonilla .10 .30
HA5 Cecil Fielder UER .10 .30
(Card number is HA4)
HA6 Albert Belle .10 .30
HA7 David Justice .10 .30
HA8 Mike Piazza .60 1.50

1994 Collector's Choice Team vs. Team

Issued one per second series pack, these 15 foldout, scratch-off game cards feature one team's lineup against the other. Various prizes were available through these game cards. The most plentiful was the eighth place Home Run All-Stars hologram set. Prizes were redeemable through October 31, 1994. Scratch-off rules and two small player photos are on the front with complete rules and provisions on the back. The cards fold out to expose the game portion. Cards that are scratched are half the values below.

COMPLETE SET (15) 2.00 5.00
1 Roberto Alomar .08 .25
Frank Thomas
2 Barry Bonds .15 .40
Ken Griffey Jr.
3 Roger Clemens .25 .60
Don Mattingly
4 Lenny Dykstra .02 .10
David Justice
5 Andres Galarraga .10 .30
Tony Gwynn
6 Dwight Gooden .02 .10
Gary Sheffield
7 Ken Griffey Jr. .15 .40
Juan Gonzalez
8 Barry Larkin .05 .15
Jeff Bagwell
9 Pat Listach .02 .10
Albert Belle
10 Mark McGwire .25 .60
Tim Salmon
11 Mike Piazza .20 .50
Barry Bonds
12 Kirby Puckett .08 .25
Brian McRae
13 Cal Ripken .30 .75
Cecil Fielder
14 Ryne Sandberg .15 .40
Ozzie Smith
15 Andy Van Slyke .02 .10
Cliff Floyd

1995 Collector's Choice

Produced by Upper Deck, this set contains 530 standard-size cards issued in 12-card foil hobby and retail packs of which carried a suggested price of 99 cents. The fronts have a color photo with a white border and the player's last name at the bottom in his team's color. The backs have an action photo at the top with statistics and information at the bottom with a silver Upper Deck hologram below that. Subsets featured are Rookie Class (1-27), Future Foundation (28-45), Best of the '90s (51-65) and What's the Call? (86-90). The key Rookie Card in this set is Hideo Nomo. The 55-card Trade set represents the cards a collector received when the five randomly inserted trade cards were redeemed. They are numbered in continuation of the regular Collector's Choice cards but have a "T" suffix. The cards numbered 542-552 were also issued as a bonus to dealers who ordered collector's choice factory sets. The trade cards offer expired on February 1, 1996.

COMPLETE SET (530) 8.00 20.00
COMP.FACT.SET (545) 15.00 30.00
COMMON CARD (1-530) .02 .10
COMP.TRADE SET (55) 4.00 10.00
COMMON TR. (531-585) .08 .25
1 Charles Johnson .07 .20
2 Scott Ruffcorn .02 .10
3 Ray Durham .07 .20
4 Armando Benitez .02 .10
5 Alex Rodriguez .50 1.25
6 Julian Tavarez .02 .10
7 Chad Ogea .02 .10
8 Quilvio Veras .02 .10
9 Phil Nevin .07 .20
10 Michael Tucker .02 .10
11 Mark Thompson .02 .10
12 Rod Henderson .02 .10
13 Andrew Lorraine .02 .10
14 Joe Randa .07 .20
15 Derek Jeter .50 1.25
16 Tony Clark .02 .10
17 Juan Castillo .02 .10
18 Mark Acre .02 .10
19 Orlando Miller .02 .10
20 Paul Wilson .02 .10
21 John Mabry .02 .10
22 Garey Ingram .02 .10
23 Garret Anderson .07 .20
24 Dave Stevens .02 .10
25 Dustin Hermanson .02 .10
26 Paul Shuey .02 .10
27 J.R. Phillips .02 .10
28 Ruben Rivera FF .02 .10
29 Nomar Garciaparra FF .50 1.25
30 John Wasdin FF .02 .10
31 Jim Pittsley FF .02 .10
32 Scott Elarton FF RC .08 .25
33 Raul Casanova FF RC .02 .10
34 Todd Greene FF .02 .10
35 Bill Pulsipher FF .02 .10
36 Trey Beamon FF .02 .10
37 Curtis Goodwin FF .02 .10
38 Doug Million FF .02 .10
39 Karim Garcia FF RC .02 .10
40 Ben Grieve FF .02 .10
41 Mark Farris FF .02 .10
42 Juan Acevedo FF RC .02 .10
43 C.J. Nitkowski FF .02 .10
44 Travis Miller FF RC .02 .10
45 Reid Ryan FF .07 .20
46 Nolan Ryan .75 2.00
47 Robin Yount .30 .75
48 Ryne Sandberg .30 .75
49 George Brett .50 1.25
50 Mike Schmidt .30 .75
51 Cecil Fielder B90 .02 .10
52 Nolan Ryan B90 .40 1.00
53 Rickey Henderson B90 .10 .30
54 George Brett B90 .20 .50
Robin Yount
Dave Winfield
55 Sid Bream B90 .02 .10
56 Carlos Baerga B90 .02 .10
57 Lee Smith B90 .02 .10
58 Mark Whiten B90 .02 .10
59 Joe Carter B90 .02 .10
60 Barry Bonds B90 .30 .75
61 Tony Gwynn B90 .10 .30
62 Ken Griffey Jr. B90 .20 .50
63 Greg Maddux B90 .20 .50
64 Frank Thomas B90 .20 .50
65 Dennis Martinez B90 .02 .10
Kenny Rogers
66 David Cone .07 .20
67 Greg Maddux .30 .75
68 Jimmy Key .07 .20
69 Fred McGriff .10 .30
70 Ken Griffey Jr. .30 .75
71 Matt Williams .07 .20
72 Paul O'Neill .10 .30
73 Tony Gwynn .25 .60
74 Randy Johnson .20 .50
75 Frank Thomas .20 .50
76 Jeff Bagwell .10 .30
77 Kirby Puckett .20 .50
78 Bob Hamelin .02 .10
79 Raul Mondesi .07 .20
80 Mike Piazza .30 .75
81 Kenny Lofton .07 .20
82 Barry Bonds .60 1.50
83 Albert Belle .07 .20
84 Juan Gonzalez .07 .20
85 Cal Ripken Jr. .60 1.50
86 Barry Bonds WC .30 .75
87 Mike Piazza WC .20 .50
88 Ken Griffey Jr. WC .20 .50
89 Frank Thomas WC .10 .30
90 Juan Gonzalez WC .02 .10
91 Jorge Fabregas .02 .10
92 J.T. Snow .07 .20
93 Spike Owen .02 .10
94 Eduardo Perez .02 .10
95 Bo Jackson .20 .50
96 Damion Easley .02 .10
97 Gary DiSarcina .02 .10
98 Jim Edmonds .10 .30
99 Chad Curtis .02 .10
100 Tim Salmon .10 .30
101 Chili Davis .07 .20
102 Chuck Finley .07 .20
103 Mark Langston .02 .10
104 Brian Anderson .02 .10
105 Lee Smith .07 .20
106 Phil Leftwich .02 .10
107 Chris Donnels .02 .10
108 John Hudek .02 .10
109 Craig Biggio .10 .30
110 Luis Gonzalez .07 .20
111 Brian L. Hunter .02 .10
112 James Mouton .02 .10
113 Scott Servais .02 .10
114 Tony Eusebio .02 .10
115 Derek Bell .02 .10
116 Doug Drabek .02 .10
117 Shane Reynolds .02 .10
118 Darryl Kile .07 .20
119 Greg Swindell .02 .10
120 Phil Plantier .02 .10
121 Todd Jones .02 .10
122 Steve Ontiveros .02 .10
123 Bobby Witt .02 .10
124 Brent Gates .02 .10
125 Rickey Henderson .20 .50
126 Scott Brosius .07 .20
127 Mike Bordick .02 .10
128 Fausto Cruz .02 .10
129 Stan Javier .02 .10
130 Mark McGwire .50 1.25
131 Geronimo Berroa .02 .10
132 Terry Steinbach .02 .10
133 Steve Karsay .02 .10
134 Dennis Eckersley .07 .20
135 Ruben Sierra .07 .20
136 Ron Darling .02 .10
137 Todd Van Poppel .02 .10
138 Alex Gonzalez .02 .10
139 John Olerud .07 .20
140 Roberto Alomar .10 .30
141 Darren Hall .02 .10
142 Ed Sprague .02 .10
143 Devon White .07 .20
144 Shawn Green .07 .20
145 Paul Molitor .07 .20
146 Pat Borders .02 .10
147 Carlos Delgado .07 .20
148 Juan Guzman .02 .10
149 Pat Hentgen .02 .10
150 Joe Carter .07 .20
151 Dave Stewart .07 .20
152 Todd Stottlemyre .02 .10
153 Dick Schofield .02 .10
154 Chipper Jones .20 .50
155 Ryan Klesko .07 .20
156 David Justice .07 .20
157 Mike Kelly .02 .10
158 Roberto Kelly .02 .10
159 Tony Tarasco .02 .10
160 Javier Lopez .07 .20
161 Steve Avery .02 .10
162 Greg McMichael .02 .10
163 Kent Mercker .02 .10
164 Mark Lemke .02 .10
165 Tom Glavine .10 .30
166 Jose Oliva .02 .10
167 John Smoltz .10 .30
168 Jeff Blauser .02 .10
169 Troy O'Leary .02 .10
170 Greg Vaughn .02 .10
171 Jody Reed .02 .10
172 Kevin Seitzer .02 .10
173 Jeff Cirillo .02 .10
174 B.J. Surhoff .07 .20
175 Cal Eldred .02 .10
176 Jose Valentin .02 .10
177 Turner Ward .02 .10
178 Darryl Hamilton .02 .10
179 Pat Listach .02 .10
180 Matt Mieske .02 .10
181 Brian Harper .02 .10
182 Dave Nilsson .02 .10
183 Mike Fetters .02 .10
184 John Jaha .02 .10
185 Ricky Bones .02 .10
186 Geronimo Pena .02 .10
187 Bob Tewksbury .02 .10
188 Todd Zeile .02 .10
189 Danny Jackson .02 .10
190 Ray Lankford .07 .20
191 Bernard Gilkey .02 .10
192 Brian Jordan .07 .20
193 Tom Pagnozzi .02 .10
194 Rick Sutcliffe .07 .20
195 Mark Whiten .02 .10
196 Tom Henke .02 .10
197 Rene Arocha .02 .10
198 Allen Watson .02 .10
199 Mike Perez .02 .10
200 Ozzie Smith .30 .75
201 Anthony Young .02 .10
202 Rey Sanchez .02 .10
203 Steve Buechele .02 .10
204 Shawon Dunston .02 .10
205 Mark Grace .10 .30
206 Glenallen Hill .02 .10
207 Eddie Zambrano .02 .10
208 Rick Wilkins .02 .10
209 Derrick May .02 .10
210 Sammy Sosa .20 .50
211 Kevin Roberson .02 .10
212 Steve Trachsel .02 .10
213 Willie Banks .02 .10
214 Kevin Foster .02 .10
215 Randy Myers .02 .10
216 Mike Morgan .02 .10
217 Rafael Bournigal .02 .10
218 Delino DeShields .02 .10
219 Tim Wallach .02 .10
220 Eric Karros .07 .20
221 Jose Offerman .02 .10
222 Tom Candiotti .02 .10
223 Ismael Valdes .02 .10
224 Henry Rodriguez .02 .10
225 Billy Ashley .02 .10
226 Darren Dreifort .02 .10
227 Ramon Martinez .02 .10
228 Pedro Astacio .02 .10
229 Orel Hershiser .07 .20
230 Brett Butler .07 .20
231 Todd Hollandsworth .02 .10
232 Chan Ho Park .07 .20
233 Mike Lansing .02 .10
234 Sean Berry .02 .10
235 Rondell White .07 .20
236 Ken Hill .02 .10
237 Marquis Grissom .07 .20
238 Larry Walker .07 .20
239 John Wetteland .07 .20
240 Cliff Floyd .07 .20
241 Joey Eischen .02 .10
242 Lou Frazier .02 .10
243 Darrin Fletcher .02 .10
244 Pedro Martinez .10 .30
245 Wil Cordero .02 .10
246 Jeff Fassero .02 .10
247 Butch Henry .02 .10
248 Mel Rojas .02 .10
249 Kirk Rueter .02 .10
250 Moises Alou .07 .20
251 Rod Beck .02 .10
252 John Patterson .02 .10
253 Robby Thompson .02 .10
254 Royce Clayton .02 .10
255 Wm. VanLandingham .02 .10
256 Darren Lewis .02 .10
257 Kirt Manwaring .02 .10
258 Mark Portugal .02 .10
259 Bill Swift .02 .10
260 Rikkert Faneyte .02 .10
261 Mike Jackson .02 .10
262 Todd Benzinger .02 .10
263 Bud Black .02 .10
264 Salomon Torres .02 .10
265 Eddie Murray .20 .50
266 Mark Clark .02 .10
267 Paul Sorrento .02 .10
268 Jim Thome .10 .30
269 Omar Vizquel .10 .30
270 Carlos Baerga .02 .10
271 Jeff Russell .02 .10
272 Herbert Perry .02 .10
273 Sandy Alomar Jr. .02 .10
274 Dennis Martinez .07 .20
275 Manny Ramirez .10 .30
276 Wayne Kirby .02 .10
277 Charles Nagy .02 .10
278 Albie Lopez .02 .10
279 Jeromy Burnitz .07 .20
280 Dave Winfield .07 .20
281 Tim Davis .02 .10
282 Marc Newfield .02 .10
283 Tino Martinez .10 .30
284 Mike Blowers .02 .10
285 Goose Gossage .07 .20
286 Luis Sojo .02 .10
287 Edgar Martinez .10 .30
288 Rich Amaral .02 .10
289 Felix Fermin .02 .10
290 Jay Buhner .07 .20
291 Dan Wilson .02 .10
292 Bobby Ayala .02 .10
293 Dave Fleming .02 .10
294 Greg Pirkl .02 .10
295 Reggie Jefferson .02 .10
296 Greg Hibbard .02 .10
297 Yorkis Perez .02 .10
298 Kurt Miller .02 .10
299 Chuck Carr .02 .10
300 Gary Sheffield .07 .20
301 Jerry Browne .02 .10
302 Dave Magadan .02 .10
303 Kurt Abbott .02 .10
304 Pat Rapp .02 .10
305 Jeff Conine .07 .20
306 Benito Santiago .07 .20
307 Dave Weathers .02 .10
308 Robb Nen .07 .20
309 Chris Hammond .02 .10
310 Bryan Harvey .02 .10
311 Charlie Hough .07 .20
312 Greg Colbrunn .02 .10
313 David Segui .02 .10
314 Rico Brogna .02 .10
315 Jeff Kent .07 .20
316 Jose Vizcaino .02 .10
317 Jim Lindeman .02 .10
318 Carl Everett .07 .20
319 Ryan Thompson .02 .10
320 Bobby Bonilla .07 .20
321 Joe Orsulak .02 .10
322 Pete Harnisch .02 .10
323 Doug Linton .02 .10
324 Todd Hundley .02 .10
325 Bret Saberhagen .07 .20
326 Kelly Stinnett .02 .10
327 Jason Jacome .02 .10
328 Bobby Jones .02 .10
329 John Franco .07 .20
330 Rafael Palmeiro .10 .30
331 Chris Hoiles .02 .10
332 Leo Gomez .02 .10
333 Chris Sabo .02 .10
334 Brady Anderson .07 .20
335 Jeffrey Hammonds .02 .10
336 Dwight Smith .02 .10
337 Jack Voigt .02 .10
338 Harold Baines .07 .20
339 Ben McDonald .02 .10
340 Mike Mussina .10 .30
341 Bret Barberie .02 .10
342 Jamie Moyer .07 .20
343 Mike Oquist .02 .10
344 Sid Fernandez .02 .10
345 Eddie Williams .02 .10
346 Joey Hamilton .02 .10
347 Brian Williams .02 .10
348 Luis Lopez .02 .10
349 Steve Finley .07 .20
350 Andy Benes .02 .10
351 Andujar Cedeno .02 .10
352 Bip Roberts .02 .10
353 Ray McDavid .02 .10
354 Ken Caminiti .07 .20
355 Trevor Hoffman .07 .20
356 Mel Nieves .02 .10
357 Brad Ausmus .07 .20
358 Andy Ashby .02 .10
359 Scott Sanders .02 .10
360 Gregg Jefferies .02 .10
361 Mariano Duncan .02 .10
362 Dave Hollins .02 .10
363 Kevin Stocker .02 .10
364 Fernando Valenzuela .07 .20
365 Lenny Dykstra .07 .20
366 Jim Eisenreich .02 .10
367 Ricky Bottalico .02 .10
368 Doug Jones .02 .10
369 Ricky Jordan .02 .10
370 Darren Daulton .07 .20
371 Mike Lieberthal .07 .20
372 Bobby Munoz .02 .10
373 John Kruk .07 .20
374 Curt Schilling .02 .10
375 Orlando Merced .02 .10
376 Carlos Garcia .02 .10
377 Lance Parrish .07 .20
378 Steve Cooke .02 .10
379 Jeff King .02 .10
380 Jay Bell .07 .20
381 Al Martin .02 .10
382 Paul Wagner .02 .10
383 Rick White .02 .10
384 Midre Cummings .02 .10
385 Jon Lieber .02 .10
386 Dave Clark .02 .10
387 Don Slaught .02 .10
388 Denny Neagle .07 .20
389 Zane Smith .02 .10
390 Andy Van Slyke .10 .30
391 Ivan Rodriguez .10 .30
392 David Hulse .02 .10
393 John Burkett .02 .10
394 Kevin Brown .07 .20
395 Dean Palmer .07 .20
396 Otis Nixon .02 .10
397 Rick Helling .02 .10
398 Kenny Rogers .07 .20
399 Darren Oliver .02 .10
400 Will Clark .10 .30
401 Jeff Frye .02 .10
402 Kevin Gross .02 .10
403 John Dettmer .02 .10
404 Manny Lee .02 .10
405 Rusty Greer .07 .20
406 Aaron Sele .02 .10
407 Carlos Rodriguez .02 .10
408 Scott Cooper .02 .10
409 John Valentin .02 .10
410 Roger Clemens .40 1.00
411 Mike Greenwell .02 .10
412 Tim Vanegmond .02 .10
413 Tom Brunansky .02 .10
414 Steve Farr .02 .10
415 Jose Canseco .10 .30
416 Joe Hesketh .02 .10
417 Ken Ryan .02 .10
418 Tim Naehring .02 .10
419 Frank Viola .07 .20
420 Andre Dawson .07 .20
421 Mo Vaughn .07 .20
422 Jeff Brantley .02 .10
423 Pete Schourek .02 .10
424 Hal Morris .02 .10
425 Deion Sanders .10 .30
426 Brian R. Hunter .02 .10
427 Bret Boone .07 .20
428 Willie Greene .02 .10
429 Ron Gant .07 .20
430 Barry Larkin .10 .30
431 Reggie Sanders .07 .20
432 Eddie Taubensee .02 .10
433 Jack Morris .07 .20
434 Jose Rijo .02 .10
435 Johnny Ruffin .02 .10
436 John Smiley .02 .10
437 John Roper .02 .10
438 Dave Nied .02 .10
439 Roberto Mejia .02 .10
440 Andres Galarraga .07 .20
441 Mike Kingery .02 .10
442 Curt Leskanic .02 .10
443 Walt Weiss .02 .10
444 Marvin Freeman .02 .10
445 Charlie Hayes .02 .10
446 Eric Young .02 .10
447 Ellis Burks .07 .20
448 Joe Girardi .02 .10
449 Lance Painter .02 .10
450 Dante Bichette .07 .20
451 Bruce Ruffin .02 .10
452 Jeff Granger .02 .10
453 Wally Joyner .07 .20
454 Jose Lind .02 .10
455 Jeff Montgomery .02 .10
456 Gary Gaetti .07 .20
457 Greg Gagne .02 .10
458 Vince Coleman .02 .10
459 Mike Macfarlane .02 .10
460 Brian McRae .02 .10
461 Tom Gordon .02 .10
462 Kevin Appier .07 .20
463 Billy Brewer .02 .10
464 Mark Gubicza .02 .10
465 Travis Fryman .07 .20
466 Danny Bautista .02 .10
467 Sean Bergman .02 .10
468 Mike Henneman .02 .10
469 Mike Moore .02 .10
470 Cecil Fielder .07 .20
471 Alan Trammell .07 .20
472 Kirk Gibson .07 .20
473 Tony Phillips .02 .10
474 Mickey Tettleton .02 .10
475 Lou Whitaker .07 .20
476 Chris Gomez .02 .10
477 John Doherty .02 .10
478 Greg Gohr .02 .10
479 Bill Gullickson .02 .10
480 Rick Aguilera .02 .10
481 Matt Walbeck .02 .10
482 Kevin Tapani .02 .10
483 Scott Erickson .02 .10
484 Steve Dunn .02 .10
485 David McCarty .02 .10
486 Scott Leius .02 .10
487 Pat Meares .02 .10
488 Jeff Reboulet .02 .10
489 Pedro Munoz .02 .10
490 Chuck Knoblauch .07 .20
491 Rich Becker .02 .10
492 Alex Cole .02 .10
493 Pat Mahomes .02 .10
494 Ozzie Guillen .07 .20
495 Tim Raines .07 .20
496 Kirk McCaskill .02 .10
497 Olmedo Saenz .02 .10
498 Scott Sanderson .02 .10
499 Lance Johnson .02 .10
500 Michael Jordan .60 1.50
501 Warren Newson .02 .10
502 Ron Karkovice .02 .10
503 Wilson Alvarez .02 .10
504 Jason Bere .02 .10
505 Robin Ventura .07 .20
506 Alex Fernandez .02 .10

507 Roberto Hernandez .02 .10
508 Norberto Martin .02 .10
509 Bob Wickman .02 .10
510 Don Mattingly .50 1.25
511 Melido Perez .02 .10
512 Pat Kelly .02 .10
513 Randy Velarde .02 .10
514 Tony Fernandez .02 .10
515 Jack McDowell .02 .10
516 Luis Polonia .02 .10
517 Bernie Williams .10 .30
518 Danny Tartabull .02 .10
519 Mike Stanley .02 .10
520 Wade Boggs .10 .30
521 Jim Leyritz .02 .10
522 Steve Howe .02 .10
523 Scott Kamieniecki .02 .10
524 Russ Davis .02 .10
525 Jim Abbott .10 .30
526 Eddie Murray CL .10 .30
527 Alex Rodriguez CL .20 .50
528 Jeff Bagwell CL .07 .20
529 Joe Carter CL .02 .10
530 Fred McGriff CL .07 .20
531T Tony Phillips TRADE .08 .25
532T D.Magadan TRADE .08 .25
533T Mike Gallego TRADE .08 .25
534T Dave Stewart TRADE .20 .50
535T T.Stottlemyre TRADE .08 .25
536T David Cone TRADE .20 .50
537T M. Grissom TRADE .20 .50
538T Derrick May TRADE .08 .25
539T Joe Oliver TRADE .08 .25
540T Scott Cooper TRADE .08 .25
541T Ken Hill TRADE .08 .25
542T H.Johnson TRADE DP .08 .25
543T B. McRae TRADE DP .08 .25
544T J.Navarro TRADE DP .08 .25
545T O.Timmons TRADE DP .08 .25
546T R. Kelly TRADE DP .08 .25
547T H.Nomo TRADE DP 1.50 4.00
548T S.Andrews TRADE DP .08 .25
549T M.Grudzi TRADE DP .40 1.00
550T C. Perez TRADE DP .20 .50
551T Henry Rodriguez TRADE DP .08 .25
552T T.Tarasco TRADE DP .08 .25
553T Glenallen Hill TRADE .08 .25
554T T.Mulholland TRADE .08 .25
555T O.Hershiser TRADE .20 .50
556T Darren Bragg TRADE .08 .25
557T John Burkett TRADE .08 .25
558T Bobby Witt TRADE .08 .25
559T T.Pendleton TRADE .20 .50
560T A.Dawson TRADE .20 .50
561T Brett Butler TRADE .20 .50
562T Kevin Brown TRADE .20 .50
563T Doug Jones TRADE .08 .25
564T A.Van Slyke TRADE .40 1.00
565T Jody Reed TRADE .08 .25
566T F. Valenzuela TRADE .20 .50
567T C.Hayes TRADE .08 .25
568T Benji Gil TRADE .08 .25
569T M.McLemore TRADE .08 .25
570T M.Tettleton TRADE .08 .25
571T B.Tewksbury TRADE .08 .25
572T R.Cormier TRADE .08 .25
573T V. Eshelman TRADE .08 .25
574T Mike Macfarlane TRADE .08 .25
575T Mark Whiten TRADE .08 .25
576T Benito Santiago TRADE .20 .50
577T Jason Bates TRADE .08 .25
578T Bill Swift TRADE .08 .25
579T Larry Walker TRADE .20 .50
580T Chad Curtis TRADE .08 .25
581T B.Higginson TRADE .40 1.00
582T M.Cordova TRADE .08 .25
583T M.Devereaux TRADE .08 .25
584T John Kruk TRADE .20 .50
585T J.Wetteland TRADE .20 .50
P172 K.Griffey Jr. Promo .40 1.00

1995 Collector's Choice Gold Signature

This set is a parallel of the 530 regular cards from the Collector's Choice set. Gold cards were inserted into one in every 35 packs, 12 per gold super pack and 15 per factory set. Unlike regular issue cards, each Gold Signature card features a gold border (except for a selection of borderless subset cards) and gold facsimile signature on front.

*STARS: 6X TO 15X BASIC CARDS
*ROOKIES: 5X TO 12X BASIC
STATED ODDS 1:35
12 PER GOLD SUPER PACK/15 PER FACT.SET
15 Derek Jeter 12.50 30.00

1995 Collector's Choice Silver Signature

This set is a parallel of the 530 regular cards from the Collector's Choice set. Silver Signature cards were inserted at a rate of one per pack, two per mini jumbo and 12 per silver super pack. Unlike regular issue cards, Silver Signature cards feature silver borders and a silver facsimile signature on front.

COMPLETE SET (530) 30.00 60.00
*STARS: 1.5X TO 4X BASIC CARDS
*ROOKIES: 1.25X TO 3X BASIC
TWELVE PER SUPER PACK

1995 Collector's Choice Crash the All-Star Game

This eight card standard-size set measures the standard size. The cards carry the names of players who participated in the 1995 All-Star game on July 11. The fronts feature color action player photos with a tri-colored border. The player's name and team name are printed in the bottom border. The backs contain the player's name, date of game, and the directions of how to claim a prize if the player hit a home run during the All-Star game. Winner cards could be mailed in, along with 2.00, and redeemed for a gold foil enhanced set. These enhanced cards are valued at the same value as the regular cards. The two winning cards were Mike Piazza and Frank Thomas. The cards are unnumbered and checklisted below in alphabetical order.

COMPLETE SET (8) 6.00 15.00
*REDEMPTION WINNERS: 3X VALUE
1 Albert Belle .30 .75
2 Barry Bonds 1.50 4.00
3 Fred McGriff .40 1.00
4 Mark McGwire 1.50 4.00
5 Raul Mondesi .20 .50
6 Mike Piazza 1.50 4.00
7 Manny Ramirez .75 2.00
8 Frank Thomas .60 1.50

1995 Collector's Choice Crash the Game

Cards from this 60-card standard-size set were randomly inserted in packs at a rate of one in five. The set was an interactive set in which all 20 players have three cards with a date on it. If the player hit a home run on that date, the collector could redeem the card for a complete enhanced set of all 20 players. The fronts have a color-action photo with the game background in yellow and a large date stamped in silver foil. The expiration date for redeeming these cards was February 1, 1996. Winning cards eligible for redemption at that time have been highlighted with a "W" in our listings below.

COMPLETE SET (60) 15.00 30.00
STATED ODDS 1:15
*GOLD: 2X TO 5X SILVER CRASH
GOLD: RANDOM INSERTS IN PACKS
THREE DATES PER PLAYER
*EXCHANGE: .2X TO .5X SILVER CRASH
*GOLD EXCH: 1.5X TO 4X SILVER CRASH
ONE EXCH.SET VIA MAIL PER WINNER
CG1 Jeff Bagwell 7/30 .10 .30
CG1B Jeff Bagwell 8/13 .10 .30
CG1C Jeff Bagwell 9/28 .10 .30
CG2 Albert Belle 6/18 .07 .20
CG2B Albert Belle 8/26 .07 .20
CG2C Albert Belle 9/20 .07 .20
CG3 Barry Bonds 6/28 .60 1.50
CG3B Barry Bonds 7/9 .60 1.50
CG3C Barry Bonds 9/6 .60 1.50
CG4 Jose Canseco 6/30 W .10 .30
CG4B J.Canseco 7/30 W .10 .30
CG4C Jose Canseco 9/3 .10 .30
CG5 Joe Carter 7/14 .07 .20
CG5B Joe Carter 8/9 .07 .20
CG5C Joe Carter 9/23 .07 .20
CG6 Cecil Fielder 7/4 .07 .20
CG6B Cecil Fielder 8/2 .07 .20
CG6C Cecil Fielder 10/1 .07 .20
CG7 Juan Gonzalez 6/29 .07 .20
CG7B Juan Gonzalez 8/13 .07 .20
CG7C J.Gonzalez 9/3 W .07 .20
CG8 Ken Griffey Jr. 7/2 .30 .75
CG8B K.Griffey Jr. 8/24 W .30 .75
CG8C Ken Griffey Jr. 9/15 .30 .75
CG9 Bob Hamelin 7/23 .02 .10
CG9B Bob Hamelin 8/1 .02 .10
CG9C Bob Hamelin 9/29 .02 .10
CG10 David Justice 6/24 .07 .20
CG10B David Justice 7/25 .07 .20
CG10C David Justice 9/17 .07 .20
CG11 Ryan Klesko 7/13 .07 .20
CG11B Ryan Klesko 8/20 .07 .20
CG11C Ryan Klesko 9/10 .07 .20
CG12 Fred McGriff 8/25 .10 .30
CG12B Fred McGriff 9/8 .10 .30
CG12C Fred McGriff 9/24 .10 .30
CG13 Mark McGwire 7/23 .50 1.25
CG13B M.McGwire 8/3 W .50 1.25
CG13C M.McGwire 9/27 .50 1.25
CG14 R.Mondesi 7/27 W .07 .20
CG14B Raul Mondesi 8/13 .07 .20
CG14C R.Mondesi 9/15 W .07 .20
CG15 Mike Piazza 7/23 W .30 .75
CG15B Mike Piazza 8/27 .30 .75
CG15C Mike Piazza 9/19 .30 .75
CG16 M.Ramirez 6/21 .10 .30
CG16B M.Ramirez 8/13 .10 .30
CG16C M.Ramirez 9/26 .10 .30
CG17 Alex Rodriguez 9/10 .50 1.25
CG17B A.Rodriguez 9/18 .50 1.25
CG17C A.Rodriguez 9/24 .50 1.25
CG18 Gary Sheffield .07 .20
CG18B Gary Sheffield 8/13 .07 .20
CG18C G.Sheffield 9/4 W .07 .20
CG19 Frank Thomas 7/26 .20 .50
CG19B F.Thomas 8/17 .20 .50
CG19C F.Thomas 9/23 .20 .50
CG20 Matt Williams 7/29 .07 .20
CG20B Matt Williams 8/12 .07 .20
CG20C Matt Williams 9/19 .07 .20

1995 Collector's Choice Trade Cards

To obtain the 55 "Traded and Update" cards for the base 1995 Collector's Choice set (cards 531-585) collectors had to find five different exchange Trade Cards randomly seeded into packs. The Trade exchange cards offer expired on February 1, 1996. Each different Trade exchange card was redeemable for an 11-card run (aka Trade exchange card TC1 could be redeemed for "Trade and Update" cards 531-542).

COMPLETE SET (5) 2.00 4.00
TC1 Larry Walker .50 1.25
TC2 David Cone .50 1.25
TC3 Marquis Grissom .50 1.25
TC4 Terry Pendleton .50 1.25
TC5 F.Valenzuela .50 1.25

1996 Collector's Choice

This 790-card standard-size set (produced by Upper Deck) was issued in 12-card packs with 36 packs per box and 20 boxes per case. Suggested retail price on these packs was 99 cents. The fronts of the regular set feature a player photo, his name and team logo. The backs feature another photo, vital stats and a baseball quiz. The set includes the following subsets: 1995 Stat Leaders (2-9), Rookie Class (10-39), Traditional Threads (100-108), Fantasy Team (268-279), International Flavor (325-342), Series 1 Checklists (358-365), Team Checklists (396-423), First HOF Class (500-504), Arizona Fall League (650-666), Award Winners (704-711) and Series 2 Checklists (753-760). Postseason Trade cards were inserted one every 11 packs. These cards had an ordering deadline of May 13 and were each redeemable for 10 cards depicting highlights from the playoffs and World Series, resulting in a 30-card redemption set. Finally, a 30-card Update set was included in each factory set and was also available through a Series 2 wrapper offer. The Cal Ripken Collection cards inserted into these packs, are priced in the Upper Deck area as Upper Deck Ripken Collection. Please check that section for pricing on this set. Notable Rookie Cards include Mike Sweeney.

COMPLETE SET (730) 12.00 24.00
COMP.FACT.SET (790) 10.00 30.00
COMP. SERIES 1 (365) 5.00 12.00
COMP. SERIES 2 (365) 5.00 12.00
COMMON (1-365/396-760) .07 .20
COMP.TRADE SET (30) 6.00 15.00
COMMON (366T-395T) .15 .40
COMP. UPDATE SET (30) 2.00 4.00
COMMON UPD. (761-790) .15 .40
1 Cal Ripken .60 1.50
2 Edgar Martinez SL .07 .20
Tony Gwynn
3 Albert Belle SL .07 .20
Dante Bichette
4 Albert Belle SL .07 .20
Mo Vaughn
Dante Bichette
5 Kenny Lofton SL .07 .20
Quilvio Veras
6 Mike Mussina SL .20 .50
Greg Maddux
7 Randy Johnson SL .20 .50
Hideo Nomo
8 Randy Johnson SL .20 .50
Greg Maddux
9 Jose Mesa SL .07 .20
Randy Myers
10 Johnny Damon .10 .30
11 Rick Krivda .07 .20
12 Roger Cedeno .07 .20
13 Angel Martinez .07 .20
14 Ariel Prieto .07 .20
15 John Wasdin .07 .20
16 Edwin Hurtado .07 .20
17 Lyle Mouton .07 .20
18 Chris Snopek .07 .20
19 Mariano Rivera .40 1.00
20 Ruben Rivera .07 .20
21 Juan Castro RC .07 .20
22 Jimmy Haynes .07 .20
23 Bob Wolcott .07 .20
24 Brian Barber .07 .20
25 Frank Rodriguez .07 .20
26 Jesus Tavarez .07 .20
27 Glenn Dishman .07 .20
28 Jose Herrera .07 .20
29 Chan Ho Park .07 .20
30 Jason Isringhausen .07 .20
31 Doug Johns .07 .20
32 Gene Schall .07 .20
33 Kevin Jordan .07 .20
34 Matt Lawton RC .08 .25
35 Karim Garcia .07 .20
36 George Williams .07 .20
37 Orlando Palmeiro .07 .20
38 Jamie Brewington RC .07 .20
39 Robert Person .07 .20
40 Greg Maddux .30 .75
41 Marquis Grissom .07 .20
42 Chipper Jones .20 .50
43 David Justice .07 .20
44 Mark Lemke .07 .20
45 Fred McGriff .10 .30
46 Javier Lopez .07 .20
47 Mark Wohlers .07 .20
48 Jason Schmidt .10 .30
49 John Smoltz .10 .30
50 Curtis Goodwin .07 .20
51 Greg Zaun .07 .20
52 Armando Benitez .07 .20
53 Manny Alexander .07 .20
54 Chris Hoiles .07 .20
55 Harold Baines .07 .20
56 Ben McDonald .07 .20
57 Scott Erickson .07 .20
58 Jeff Manto .07 .20
59 Luis Alicea .07 .20
60 Roger Clemens .40 1.00
61 Rheal Cormier .07 .20
62 Vaughn Eshelman .07 .20
63 Zane Smith .07 .20
64 Mike Macfarlane .07 .20
65 Erik Hanson .07 .20
66 Tim Naehring .07 .20
67 Lee Tinsley .07 .20
68 Troy O'Leary .07 .20
69 Garret Anderson .07 .20
70 Chili Davis .07 .20
71 Jim Edmonds .07 .20
72 Troy Percival .07 .20
73 Mark Langston .07 .20
74 Spike Owen .07 .20
75 Tim Salmon .10 .30
76 Brian Anderson .07 .20
77 Lee Smith .07 .20
78 Jim Abbott .10 .30
79 Jim Bullinger .07 .20
80 Mark Grace .10 .30
81 Todd Zeile .07 .20
82 Kevin Foster .07 .20
83 Howard Johnson .07 .20
84 Brian McRae .07 .20
85 Randy Myers .07 .20
86 Jaime Navarro .07 .20
87 Luis Gonzalez .07 .20
88 Ozzie Timmons .07 .20
89 Wilson Alvarez .07 .20
90 Frank Thomas .20 .50
91 James Baldwin .07 .20
92 Ray Durham .07 .20
93 Alex Fernandez .07 .20
94 Ozzie Guillen .07 .20
95 Tim Raines .07 .20
96 Roberto Hernandez .07 .20
97 Lance Johnson .07 .20
98 John Kruk .07 .20
99 Mark Portugal .07 .20
100 Don Mattingly TT .25 .60
101 Roger Clemens TT .20 .50
102 Raul Mondesi TT .07 .20
103 Cecil Fielder TT .07 .20
104 Ozzie Smith TT .20 .50
105 Frank Thomas TT .10 .30
106 Sammy Sosa TT .10 .30
107 Fred McGriff TT .07 .20
108 Barry Bonds TT .30 .75
109 Thomas Howard .07 .20
110 Ron Gant .07 .20
111 Eddie Taubensee .07 .20
112 Hal Morris .07 .20
113 Jose Rijo .07 .20
114 Pete Schourek .07 .20
115 Reggie Sanders .07 .20
116 Benito Santiago .07 .20
117 Jeff Brantley .07 .20
118 Julian Tavarez .07 .20
119 Carlos Baerga .07 .20
120 Jim Thome .10 .30
121 Jose Mesa .07 .20
122 Dennis Martinez .07 .20
123 Dave Winfield .07 .20
124 Eddie Murray .20 .50
125 Manny Ramirez .10 .30
126 Paul Sorrento .07 .20
127 Kenny Lofton .07 .20
128 Eric Young .07 .20
129 Jason Bates .07 .20
130 Bret Saberhagen .07 .20
131 Andres Galarraga .07 .20
132 Joe Girardi .07 .20
133 John Vander Wal .07 .20
134 David Nied .07 .20
135 Dante Bichette .07 .20
136 Vinny Castilla .07 .20
137 Kevin Ritz .07 .20
138 Felipe Lira .07 .20
139 Joe Boever .07 .20
140 Cecil Fielder .07 .20
141 John Flaherty .07 .20
142 Kirk Gibson .07 .20
143 Brian Maxcy .07 .20
144 Lou Whitaker .07 .20
145 Alan Trammell .07 .20
146 Bobby Higginson .07 .20
147 Chad Curtis .07 .20
148 Quilvio Veras .07 .20
149 Jerry Browne .07 .20
150 Andre Dawson .07 .20
151 Robb Nen .07 .20
152 Greg Colbrunn .07 .20
153 Chris Hammond .07 .20
154 Kurt Abbott .07 .20
155 Charles Johnson .07 .20
156 Terry Pendleton .07 .20
157 Dave Weathers .07 .20
158 Mike Hampton .07 .20
159 Craig Biggio .10 .30
160 Jeff Bagwell .10 .30
161 Brian L.Hunter .07 .20
162 Mike Henneman .07 .20
163 Dave Magadan .07 .20
164 Shane Reynolds .07 .20
165 Derek Bell .07 .20
166 Orlando Miller .07 .20
167 James Mouton .07 .20
168 Melvin Bunch .07 .20
169 Tom Gordon .07 .20
170 Kevin Appier .07 .20
171 Tom Goodwin .07 .20
172 Greg Gagne .07 .20
173 Gary Gaetti .07 .20
174 Jeff Montgomery .07 .20
175 Jon Nunnally .07 .20
176 Michael Tucker .07 .20
177 Joe Vitiello .07 .20
178 Billy Ashley .07 .20
179 Tom Candiotti .07 .20
180 Hideo Nomo .20 .50
181 Chad Fonville .07 .20
182 Todd Hollandsworth .07 .20
183 Eric Karros .07 .20
184 Roberto Kelly .07 .20
185 Mike Piazza .30 .75
186 Ramon Martinez .07 .20
187 Tim Wallach .07 .20
188 Jeff Cirillo .07 .20
189 Sid Roberson .07 .20
190 Kevin Seitzer .07 .20
191 Mike Fetters .07 .20
192 Steve Sparks .07 .20
193 Matt Mieske .07 .20
194 Joe Oliver .07 .20
195 B.J. Surhoff .07 .20
196 Alberto Reyes .07 .20
197 Fernando Vina .07 .20
198 LaTroy Hawkins .07 .20
199 Marty Cordova .07 .20
200 Kirby Puckett .20 .50
201 Brad Radke .07 .20
202 Pedro Munoz .07 .20
203 Scott Klingenbeck .07 .20
204 Pat Meares .07 .20
205 Chuck Knoblauch .07 .20
206 Scott Stahoviak .07 .20
207 Dave Stevens .07 .20
208 Shane Andrews .07 .20
209 Moises Alou .07 .20
210 David Segui .07 .20
211 Cliff Floyd .07 .20
212 Carlos Perez .07 .20
213 Mark Grudzielanek .07 .20
214 Butch Henry .07 .20
215 Rondell White .07 .20
216 Mel Rojas .07 .20
217 Ugueth Urbina .07 .20
218 Edgardo Alfonzo .07 .20
219 Carl Everett .07 .20
220 John Franco .07 .20
221 Todd Hundley .07 .20
222 Bobby Jones .07 .20
223 Bill Pulsipher .07 .20
224 Rico Brogna .07 .20
225 Jeff Kent .07 .20
226 Chris Jones .07 .20
227 Butch Huskey .07 .20
228 Robert Eenhoorn .07 .20
229 Sterling Hitchcock .07 .20
230 Wade Boggs .10 .30
231 Derek Jeter .50 1.25
232 Tony Fernandez .07 .20
233 Jack McDowell .07 .20
234 Andy Pettitte .10 .30
235 David Cone .07 .20
236 Mike Stanley .07 .20
237 Don Mattingly .50 1.25
238 Geronimo Berroa .07 .20
239 Scott Brosius .07 .20
240 Rickey Henderson .20 .50
241 Terry Steinbach .07 .20
242 Mike Gallego .07 .20
243 Jason Giambi .07 .20
244 Steve Ontiveros .07 .20
245 Dennis Eckersley .07 .20
246 Dave Stewart .07 .20
247 Don Wengert .07 .20
248 Paul Quantrill .07 .20
249 Ricky Bottalico .07 .20
250 Kevin Stocker .07 .20
251 Lenny Dykstra .07 .20
252 Tony Longmire .07 .20
253 Tyler Green .07 .20
254 Mike Mimbs .07 .20
255 Charlie Hayes .07 .20
256 Mickey Morandini .07 .20
257 Heathcliff Slocumb .07 .20
258 Jeff King .07 .20
259 Midre Cummings .07 .20
260 Mark Johnson .07 .20
261 Freddy Adrian Garcia .07 .20
262 Jon Lieber .07 .20
263 Esteban Loaiza .07 .20
264 Dan Miceli .07 .20
265 Orlando Merced .07 .20
266 Denny Neagle .07 .20
267 Steve Parris .07 .20
268 Greg Maddux FT .20 .50
269 Randy Johnson FT .10 .30
270 Hideo Nomo FT .10 .30
271 Jose Mesa FT .07 .20
272 Mike Piazza FT .20 .50
273 Mo Vaughn FT .07 .20
274 Craig Biggio FT .07 .20
275 Edgar Martinez FT .07 .20
276 Barry Larkin FT .07 .20
277 Sammy Sosa FT .10 .30
278 Dante Bichette FT .07 .20
279 Albert Belle FT .07 .20
280 Ozzie Smith .30 .75
281 Mark Sweeney .07 .20
282 Terry Bradshaw .07 .20
283 Allen Battle .07 .20
284 Danny Jackson .07 .20
285 Tom Henke .07 .20
286 Scott Cooper .07 .20
287 Tripp Cromer .07 .20
288 Bernard Gilkey .07 .20
289 Brian Jordan .07 .20
290 Tony Gwynn .25 .60
291 Brad Ausmus .07 .20
292 Bryce Florie .07 .20
293 Andres Berumen .07 .20
294 Ken Caminiti .07 .20
295 Bip Roberts .07 .20
296 Trevor Hoffman .07 .20
297 Roberto Petagine .07 .20
298 Jody Reed .07 .20
299 Fernando Valenzuela .07 .20
300 Barry Bonds .60 1.50
301 Mark Leiter .07 .20
302 Mark Carreon .07 .20
303 Royce Clayton .07 .20
304 Kirt Manwaring .07 .20
305 Glenallen Hill .07 .20
306 Deion Sanders .10 .30
307 Joe Rosselli .07 .20
308 Robby Thompson .07 .20
309 W. VanLandingham .07 .20
310 Ken Griffey Jr. .30 .75
311 Bobby Ayala .07 .20
312 Joey Cora .07 .20
313 Mike Blowers .07 .20
314 Darren Bragg .07 .20
315 Randy Johnson .20 .50
316 Alex Rodriguez .40 1.00
317 Andy Benes .15 .40
318 Tino Martinez .10 .30
319 Dan Wilson .07 .20
320 Will Clark .10 .30
321 Jeff Frye .07 .20
322 Benji Gil .07 .20
323 Rick Helling .07 .20
324 Mark McLemore .07 .20
325 Dave Nilsson IF .07 .20
326 Larry Walker IF .07 .20
327 Jose Canseco IF .07 .20
328 Raul Mondesi IF .07 .20
329 Manny Ramirez IF .07 .20
330 Robert Eenhoorn IF .07 .20
331 Chili Davis IF .07 .20
332 Hideo Nomo IF .10 .30
333 Benji Gil IF .07 .20
334 F.Valenzuela IF .07 .20
335 Dennis Martinez IF .07 .20
336 Roberto Kelly IF .07 .20
337 Carlos Baerga IF .07 .20
338 Juan Gonzalez IF .07 .20
339 Roberto Alomar IF .07 .20
340 Chan Ho Park IF .07 .20
341 Andres Galarraga IF .07 .20
342 Midre Cummings IF .07 .20
343 Otis Nixon .07 .20
344 Jeff Russell .07 .20
345 Ivan Rodriguez .10 .30
346 Mickey Tettleton .07 .20
347 Bob Tewksbury .07 .20
348 Domingo Cedeno .07 .20
349 Lance Parrish .07 .20
350 Joe Carter .07 .20
351 Devon White .07 .20
352 Carlos Delgado .07 .20
353 Alex Gonzalez .07 .20
354 Darren Hall .07 .20
355 Paul Molitor .07 .20
356 Al Leiter .07 .20
357 Randy Knorr .07 .20
358 Ken Caminiti CL .07 .20
Steve Finley
Brian Williams
Roberto Petagine
Andujar Cedeno
Phil Plantier
Derek Bell
Pedro A. Martinez
Doug Brocail
Craig Shipley
Ricky Gutierrez
359 Hideo Nomo CL .10 .30
360 Ramon J. Martinez CL .07 .20
Pedro Martinez
361 Robin Ventura CL .07 .20
362 Cal Ripken CL .30 .75
363 Ken Caminiti CL .07 .20
364 Albert Belle CL .10 .30
Eddie Murray
365 Randy Johnson CL .10 .30
366T Tony Pena TRADE .15 .40
367T Jim Thome TRADE .25 .60
368T D.Mattingly TRADE 1.00 2.50
369T Jim Leyritz TRADE .15 .40
370T K.Griffey Jr. TRADE .60 1.50
371T E.Martinez TRADE .25 .60
372T P.Schourek TRADE .15 .40
373T Mark Lewis TRADE .15 .40
374T C.Jones TRADE .40 1.00
375T Fred McGriff TRADE .25 .60
376T Javy Lopez TRADE .15 .40
377T Fred McGriff TRADE .25 .60
378T C.O'Brien TRADE .15 .40
379T M.Devereaux TRADE .15 .40
380T M.Wohlers TRADE .15 .40
381T Bob Wolcott TRADE .15 .40
382T M.Ramirez TRADE .25 .60
383T Jay Buhner TRADE .15 .40
384T O.Hershiser TRADE .15 .40
385T Kenny Lofton TRADE .15 .40
386T G.Maddux TRADE .60 1.50
387T Javier Lopez TRADE .15 .40
388T Kenny Lofton TRADE .15 .40
389T Eddie Murray TRADE .40 1.00
390T Luis Polonia TRADE .15 .40
391T P.Borbon TRADE .15 .40
392T Jim Thome TRADE .25 .60
393T O.Hershiser TRADE .15 .40
394T David Justice TRADE .15 .40
395T Tom Glavine TRADE .25 .60
396 Greg Maddux TC .20 .50
397 Rico Brogna TC .07 .20
398 Darren Daulton TC .07 .20
399 Gary Sheffield TC .07 .20
400 Moises Alou TC .07 .20
401 Barry Larkin TC .07 .20
402 Jeff Bagwell TC .07 .20
403 Sammy Sosa TC .10 .30
404 Ozzie Smith TC .20 .50
405 Jay Bell TC .07 .20
406 Mike Piazza TC .20 .50
407 Dante Bichette TC .07 .20
408 Tony Gwynn TC .10 .30
409 Barry Bonds TC .30 .75
410 Kenny Lofton TC .07 .20
411 Johnny Damon TC .07 .20
412 Frank Thomas TC .10 .30
413 Greg Vaughn TC .07 .20
414 Paul Molitor TC .07 .20
415 Ken Griffey Jr. TC .20 .50
416 Tim Salmon TC .07 .20
417 Juan Gonzalez TC .07 .20
418 Mark McGwire TC .25 .60
419 Roger Clemens TC .20 .50
420 Wade Boggs TC .07 .20
421 Cal Ripken TC .30 .75
422 Cecil Fielder TC .07 .20
423 Joe Carter TC .07 .20
424 O.Fernandez RC .07 .20
425 Billy Wagner .07 .20
426 George Arias .07 .20
427 Mendy Lopez .07 .20
428 Jeff Suppan .07 .20
429 Rey Ordonez .07 .20
430 Brooks Kieschnick .07 .20
431 Raul Ibanez RC .75 2.00
432 Livan Hernandez RC .30 .75
433 Shannon Stewart .07 .20
434 Steve Cox .07 .20
435 Trey Beamon .07 .20
436 Sergio Nunez .07 .20
437 Jermaine Dye .07 .20
438 Mike Sweeney RC .30 .75
439 Richard Hidalgo .07 .20
440 Todd Greene .07 .20
441 Robert Smith RC .07 .20
442 Rafael Orellano .07 .20
443 Wilton Guerrero RC .07 .20
444 David Doster .07 .20
445 Jason Kendall .07 .20
446 Edgar Renteria .07 .20
447 Scott Spiezio .07 .20
448 Jay Canizaro .07 .20
449 Enrique Wilson .07 .20
450 Bob Abreu .20 .50
451 Dwight Smith .07 .20
452 Jeff Blauser .07 .20
453 Steve Avery .07 .20
454 Brad Clontz .07 .20
455 Tom Glavine .10 .30
456 Mike Mordecai .07 .20
457 Rafael Belliard .07 .20
458 Greg McMichael .07 .20
459 Pedro Borbon .07 .20
460 Ryan Klesko .07 .20
461 Terrell Wade .07 .20
462 Brady Anderson .07 .20
463 Roberto Alomar .10 .30
464 Bobby Bonilla .07 .20
465 Mike Mussina .10 .30
466 Cesar Devarez .07 .20
467 Jeffrey Hammonds .07 .20
468 Mike Devereaux .07 .20
469 B.J. Surhoff .07 .20
470 Rafael Palmeiro .10 .30
471 John Valentin .07 .20
472 Mike Greenwell .07 .20
473 Dwayne Hosey .07 .20
474 Tim Wakefield .07 .20
475 Jose Canseco .10 .30
476 Aaron Sele .07 .20
477 Stan Belinda .07 .20
478 Mike Stanley .07 .20
479 Jamie Moyer .07 .20
480 Mo Vaughn .07 .20
481 Randy Velarde .07 .20
482 Gary DiSarcina .07 .20
483 Jorge Fabregas .07 .20
484 Rex Hudler .07 .20
485 Chuck Finley .07 .20
486 Tim Wallach .07 .20
487 Eduardo Perez .07 .20
488 Scott Sanderson .07 .20
489 J.T. Snow .07 .20
490 Sammy Sosa .20 .50
491 Terry Adams .07 .20
492 Matt Franco .07 .20
493 Scott Servais .07 .20
494 Frank Castillo .07 .20
495 Ryne Sandberg .30 .75
496 Rey Sanchez .07 .20
497 Steve Trachsel .07 .20
498 Jose Hernandez .07 .20
499 Dave Martinez .07 .20
500 Babe Ruth FC .40 1.00
501 Ty Cobb FC .20 .50
502 Walter Johnson FC .20 .50
503 C.Mathewson FC .20 .50
504 Honus Wagner FC .20 .50
505 Robin Ventura .07 .20
506 Jason Bere .07 .20
507 Mike Cameron RC .20 .50
508 Ron Karkovice .07 .20
509 Matt Karchner .07 .20
510 Harold Baines .07 .20
511 Kirk McCaskill .07 .20
512 Larry Thomas .07 .20
513 Danny Tartabull .07 .20
514 Steve Gibralter .07 .20
515 Bret Boone .07 .20
516 Jeff Branson .07 .20
517 Kevin Jarvis .07 .20
518 Xavier Hernandez .07 .20
519 Eric Owens .07 .20
520 Barry Larkin .10 .30
521 Dave Burba .07 .20
522 John Smiley .07 .20
523 Paul Assenmacher .07 .20
524 Chad Ogea .07 .20
525 Orel Hershiser .07 .20
526 Alan Embree .07 .20
527 Tony Pena .07 .20
528 Omar Vizquel .10 .30
529 Mark Clark .07 .20
530 Albert Belle .07 .20
531 Charles Nagy .07 .20
532 Herbert Perry .07 .20
533 Darren Holmes .07 .20
534 Ellis Burks .07 .20
535 Billy Swift .07 .20
536 Armando Reynoso .07 .20
537 Curtis Leskanic .07 .20
538 Quinton McCracken .07 .20
539 Steve Reed .07 .20
540 Larry Walker .07 .20
541 Walt Weiss .07 .20
542 Bryan Rekar .07 .20
543 Tony Clark .07 .20
544 Steve Rodriguez .07 .20

545 C.J. Nitkowski .07 .20
546 Todd Steverson .07 .20
547 Jose Lima .07 .20
548 Phil Nevin .07 .20
549 Chris Gomez .07 .20
550 Travis Fryman .07 .20
551 Mark Lewis .07 .20
552 Alex Arias .07 .20
553 Marc Valdes .07 .20
554 Kevin Brown .07 .20
555 Jeff Conine .07 .20
556 John Burkett .07 .20
557 Devon White .07 .20
558 Pat Rapp .07 .20
559 Jay Powell .07 .20
560 Gary Sheffield .07 .20
561 Jim Dougherty .07 .20
562 Todd Jones .07 .20
563 Tony Eusebio .07 .20
564 Darryl Kile .07 .20
565 Doug Drabek .07 .20
566 Mike Simms .07 .20
567 Derrick May .07 .20
568 Donne Wall .07 .20
569 Greg Swindell .07 .20
570 Jim Pittsley .07 .20
571 Bob Hamelin .07 .20
572 Mark Gubicza .07 .20
573 Chris Haney .07 .20
574 Keith Lockhart .07 .20
575 Mike Macfarlane .07 .20
576 Les Norman .07 .20
577 Joe Randa .07 .20
578 Chris Stynes .07 .20
579 Greg Gagne .07 .20
580 Raul Mondesi .07 .20
581 Delino DeShields .07 .20
582 Pedro Astacio .07 .20
583 Antonio Osuna .07 .20
584 Brett Butler .07 .20
585 Todd Worrell .07 .20
586 Mike Blowers .07 .20
587 Felix Rodriguez .07 .20
588 Ismael Valdes .07 .20
589 Ricky Bones .07 .20
590 Greg Vaughn .07 .20
591 Mark Loretta .07 .20
592 Cal Eldred .07 .20
593 Chuck Carr .07 .20
594 Dave Nilsson .07 .20
595 John Jaha .07 .20
596 Scott Karl .07 .20
597 Pat Listach .07 .20
598 Jose Valentin .07 .20
599 Mike Trombley .07 .20
600 Paul Molitor .07 .20
601 Dave Hollins .07 .20
602 Ron Coomer .07 .20
603 Matt Walbeck .07 .20
604 Roberto Kelly .07 .20
605 Rick Aguilera .07 .20
606 Pat Mahomes .07 .20
607 Jeff Reboulet .07 .20
608 Rich Becker .07 .20
609 Tim Scott .07 .20
610 Pedro Martinez .10 .30
611 Kirk Rueter .07 .20
612 Tavo Alvarez .07 .20
613 Yamil Benitez .07 .20
614 Darrin Fletcher .07 .20
615 Mike Lansing .07 .20
616 Henry Rodriguez .07 .20
617 Tony Tarasco .07 .20
618 Alex Ochoa .07 .20
619 Tim Bogar .07 .20
620 Bernard Gilkey .07 .20
621 Dave Mlicki .07 .20
622 Brent Mayne .07 .20
623 Ryan Thompson .07 .20
624 Pete Harnisch .07 .20
625 Lance Johnson .07 .20
626 Jose Vizcaino .07 .20
627 Doug Henry .07 .20
628 Scott Kamieniecki .07 .20
629 Jim Leyritz .07 .20
630 Ruben Sierra .07 .20
631 Pat Kelly .07 .20
632 Joe Girardi .07 .20
633 John Wetteland .07 .20
634 Melido Perez .07 .20
635 Paul O'Neill .10 .30
636 Jorge Posada .10 .30
637 Bernie Williams .10 .30
638 Mark Acre .07 .20
639 Mike Bordick .07 .20
640 Mark McGwire .50 1.25
641 Fausto Cruz .07 .20
642 Ernie Young .07 .20
643 Todd Van Poppel .07 .20
644 Craig Paquette .07 .20
645 Brent Gates .07 .20
646 Pedro Munoz .07 .20
647 Andrew Lorraine .07 .20
648 Sid Fernandez .07 .20
649 Jim Eisenreich .07 .20
650 Johnny Damon AFL .07 .20
651 D.Hermanson AFL .07 .20
652 Joe Randa AFL .07 .20
653 Michael Tucker AFL .07 .20
654 Alan Benes AFL .07 .20
655 Chad Fonville AFL .07 .20
656 David Bell AFL .07 .20
657 Jon Nunnally AFL .07 .20
658 Chan Ho Park AFL .07 .20
659 LaTroy Hawkins AFL .07 .20
660 J.Brewington AFL .07 .20
661 Q.McCracken AFL .07 .20
662 Tim Unroe AFL .07 .20
663 Jeff Ware AFL .07 .20
664 Todd Greene AFL .07 .20
665 Andrew Lorraine AFL .07 .20
666 Ernie Young AFL .07 .20
667 Toby Borland .07 .20
668 Lenny Webster .07 .20
669 Benito Santiago .07 .20
670 Gregg Jefferies .07 .20
671 Darren Daulton .07 .20
672 Curt Schilling .07 .20
673 Mark Whiten .07 .20
674 Todd Zeile .07 .20
675 Jay Bell .07 .20
676 Paul Wagner .07 .20
677 Dave Clark .07 .20
678 Nelson Liriano .07 .20
679 Ramon Morel .07 .20
680 Charlie Hayes .07 .20
681 Angelo Encarnacion .07 .20
682 Al Martin .07 .20
683 Jacob Brumfield .07 .20
684 Mike Kingery .07 .20
685 Carlos Garcia .07 .20
686 Tom Pagnozzi .07 .20
687 David Bell .07 .20
688 Todd Stottlemyre .07 .20
689 Jose Oliva .07 .20
690 Ray Lankford .07 .20
691 Mike Morgan .07 .20
692 John Frascatore .07 .20
693 John Mabry .07 .20
694 Mark Petkovsek .07 .20
695 Alan Benes .07 .20
696 Steve Finley .07 .20
697 Marc Newfield .07 .20
698 Andy Ashby .07 .20
699 Marc Kroon .07 .20
700 Wally Joyner .07 .20
701 Joey Hamilton .07 .20
702 Dustin Hermanson .07 .20
703 Scott Sanders .07 .20
704 Marty Cordova ROY .07 .20
705 Hideo Nomo ROY .10 .30
706 Mo Vaughn MVP .07 .20
707 Barry Larkin MVP .07 .20
708 Randy Johnson CY .10 .30
709 Greg Maddux CY .20 .50
710 Mark McGwire CB .25 .60
711 Ron Gant CB .07 .20
712 Andujar Cedeno .07 .20
713 Brian Johnson .07 .20
714 J.R. Phillips .07 .20
715 Rod Beck .07 .20
716 Sergio Valdez .07 .20
717 Marvin Benard RC .08 .25
718 Steve Scarsone .07 .20
719 Rich Aurilia RC .08 .25
720 Matt Williams .07 .20
721 John Patterson .07 .20
722 Shawn Estes .07 .20
723 Russ Davis .07 .20
724 Rich Amaral .07 .20
725 Edgar Martinez .10 .30
726 Norm Charlton .07 .20
727 Paul Sorrento .07 .20
728 Luis Sojo .07 .20
729 Arquimedez Pozo .07 .20
730 Jay Buhner .07 .20
731 Chris Bosio .07 .20
732 Chris Widger .07 .20
733 Kevin Gross .07 .20
734 Darren Oliver .07 .20
735 Dean Palmer .07 .20
736 Matt Whiteside .07 .20
737 Luis Ortiz .07 .20
738 Roger Pavlik .07 .20
739 Damon Buford .07 .20
740 Juan Gonzalez .07 .20
741 Rusty Greer .07 .20
742 Lou Frazier .07 .20
743 Pat Hentgen .07 .20
744 Tomas Perez .07 .20
745 Juan Guzman .07 .20
746 Otis Nixon .07 .20
747 Robert Perez .07 .20
748 Ed Sprague .07 .20
749 Tony Castillo .07 .20
750 John Olerud .07 .20
751 Shawn Green .07 .20
752 Jeff Ware .07 .20
753 Dante Bichette CL .07 .20
Vinny Castilla
Andres Galarraga
Larry Walker
754 Greg Maddux CL .20 .50
755 Marty Cordova CL .07 .20
756 Ozzie Smith CL .20 .50
757 John Vander Wal CL .07 .20
758 Andres Galarraga CL .07 .20
759 Frank Thomas CL .10 .30
760 Tony Gwynn CL .10 .30
761 Randy Myers UPD .15 .40
762 Kent Mercker UPD .15 .40
763 David Wells UPD .15 .40
764 Tom Gordon UPD .15 .40
765 Wil Cordero UPD .15 .40
766 Dave Magadan UPD .15 .40
767 Doug Jones UPD .15 .40
768 Kevin Tapani UPD .15 .40
769 Curtis Goodwin UPD .15 .40
770 Julio Franco UPD .15 .40
771 Jack McDowell UPD .15 .40
772 Al Leiter UPD .15 .40
773 Sean Berry UPD .15 .40
774 Bip Roberts UPD .15 .40
775 Jose Offerman UPD .15 .40
776 Ben McDonald UPD .15 .40
777 Dan Serafini UPD .15 .40
778 Ryan McGuire UPD .15 .40
779 Tim Raines UPD .15 .40
780 Tino Martinez UPD .25 .60
781 Kenny Rogers UPD .15 .40
782 Bob Tewksbury UPD .15 .40
783 R.Henderson UPD .40 1.00
784 Ron Gant UPD .15 .40
785 Gary Gaetti UPD .15 .40
786 Andy Benes UPD .15 .40
787 Royce Clayton UPD .15 .40
788 Darryl Hamilton UPD .15 .40
789 Ken Hill UPD .15 .40
790 Erik Hanson UPD .15 .40
P100 K.Griffey Jr. Promo .40 1.00

1996 Collector's Choice Gold Signature

This 730-card set parallels the basic Collector's Choice issue. These cards were inserted approximately one every 35 packs. Cards 1-365 were issued in first series and 396-730 in second series. The cards are similar to the regular issue except they have gold borders and a gold facsimile player's signature on front. Cards 366-395 do not exist.

*STARS: 10X TO 25X BASIC CARDS

*ROOKIES: 6X TO 15X BASIC CARDS
STATED ODDS 1:35

1996 Collector's Choice Silver Signature

This 730-card set parallels the regular Collector's Choice set. These cards were inserted one per pack in both first and second series packs. The cards are similar to the regular issue except for silver borders and a silver foil facsimile player's signature on the card front. Cards 366-395 do not exist.

COMPLETE SET (730) 65.00 110.00
COMP. SERIES 1 (365) 35.00 60.00
COMP. SERIES 2 (365) 30.00 50.00
*STARS: 1X TO 2.5X BASIC CARDS
*ROOKIES: .75X TO 2X BASIC CARDS

1996 Collector's Choice Crash the Game

Randomly inserted into one in every five series two packs, silver Crash the Game interactive cards feature a selection of thirty of baseball's top stars. If the featured player hit a home run during the series specified on the card, it was then eligible to be redeemed for a super premium Cell Card of the same player. Winning cards have been highlighted with a "W" in the listings below. The postmark expiration date for exchanging winning cards was November 18th, 1996.

COMPLETE SET (90) 20.00 50.00
SER.2 STATED ODDS 1:5
*GOLD: 2X TO 5X BASIC CRASH
GOLD SER.2 STATED ODDS 1:48
*EXCH: 2X TO 5X BASIC CRASH
ONE EXCH.CARD VIA MAIL PER WINNER
*GOLD EXCH: 6X TO 15X BASIC CRASH
ONE EXCH.VIA MAIL PER GOLD WINNER
CG1 C.Jones 7/11 W .30 .75
CG1B C.Jones 8/27 W .30 .75
CG1C Chipper Jones 9/19 .30 .75
CG2 Fred McGriff 7/1 .20 .50
CG2B Fred McGriff 8/30 .20 .50
CG2C Fred McGriff 9/10 W .20 .50
CG3 R.Palmeiro 7/4 W .20 .50
CG3B R.Palmeiro 8/29 .20 .50
CG3C R.Palmeiro 9/26 .20 .50
CG4 Cal Ripken 6/27 1.00 2.50
CG4B Cal Ripken 7/25 W 1.00 2.50
CG4C Cal Ripken 9/2 1.00 2.50
CG5 Jose Canseco 6/27 .20 .50
CG5B J.Canseco 7/11 W .20 .50
CG5C Jose Canseco 8/23 .20 .50
CG6 Mo Vaughn 6/21 W .10 .30
CG6B Mo Vaughn 7/18 W .10 .30
CG6C Mo Vaughn 9/20 .10 .30
CG7 Jim Edmonds 7/18 W .10 .30
CG7B J.Edmonds 8/16 W .10 .30
CG7C Jim Edmonds 9/20 .10 .30
CG8 Tim Salmon 6/20 .20 .50
CG8B Tim Salmon 7/30 .20 .50
CG8C Tim Salmon 9/9 .20 .50
CG9 Sammy Sosa 7/4 W .30 .75
CG9B Sammy Sosa 8/1 W .30 .75
CG9C Sammy Sosa 9/2 .30 .75
CG10 Frank Thomas 6/27 .30 .75
CG10B Frank Thomas 7/4 .30 .75
CG10C F.Thomas 9/2 W .30 .75
CG11 Albert Belle 6/25 .10 .30
CG11B Albert Belle 8/2 W .10 .30
CG11C Albert Belle 9/6 .10 .30
CG12 M.Ramirez 7/18 W .20 .50
CG12B M.Ramirez 8/26 .20 .50
CG12C M.Ramirez 9/9 W .20 .50
CG13 Jim Thome 6/27 .20 .50
CG13B Jim Thome 7/4 W .20 .50
CG13C Jim Thome 9/23 .20 .50
CG14 D.Bichette 7/11 W .10 .30
CG14B Dante Bichette 8/9 .10 .30
CG14C Dante Bichette 9/9 .10 .30
CG15 Vinny Castilla 7/1 .10 .30
CG15B V.Castilla 8/23 W .10 .30
CG15C V.Castilla 9/13 W .10 .30
CG16 Larry Walker 6/24 .10 .30
CG16B Larry Walker 7/18 .10 .30
CG16C Larry Walker 9/27 .10 .30
CG17 Cecil Fielder 6/27 .10 .30
CG17B C.Fielder 7/30 W .10 .30
CG17C C.Fielder 9/17 W .10 .30
CG18 Gary Sheffield 7/4 .10 .30
CG18B Gary Sheffield 8/2 .10 .30
CG18C G.Sheffield 9/5 W .10 .30
CG19 Jeff Bagwell 7/4 W .20 .50
CG19B Jeff Bagwell 8/16 .20 .50
CG19C Jeff Bagwell 9/13 .20 .50
CG20 Eric Karros 7/4 W .10 .30
CG20B Eric Karros 8/13 W .10 .30
CG20C Eric Karros 9/16 .10 .30
CG21 Mike Piazza 6/27 W .50 1.25
CG21B Mike Piazza 7/26 .50 1.25
CG21C M.Piazza 9/12 W .50 1.25
CG22 Ken Caminiti 7/11 W .10 .30
CG22B K.Caminiti 8/16 W .10 .30
CG22C K.Caminiti 9/19 W .10 .30
CG23 Barry Bonds 6/27 W 1.00 2.50
CG23B Barry Bonds 7/22 1.00 2.50
CG23C Barry Bonds 9/24 1.00 2.50
CG24 M.Williams 7/11 W .10 .30
CG24B Matt Williams 8/19 .10 .30
CG24C Matt Williams 9/27 .10 .30
CG25 Jay Buhner 6/20 .10 .30
CG25B Jay Buhner 7/25 .10 .30
CG25C Jay Buhner 8/29 W .10 .30
CG26 K.Griffey Jr. 7/18 W .50 1.25
CG26B Ken Griffey Jr. 8/16 W .50 1.25
CG26C Ken Griffey Jr. 9/20 W .50 1.25
CG27 Ron Gant 6/24 W .10 .30
CG27B Ron Gant 7/11 W .10 .30
CG27C Ron Gant 9/27 W .10 .30
CG28 J.Gonzalez 6/28 W .10 .30
CG28B J. Gonzalez 7/15 W .10 .30
CG28C Juan Gonzalez 8/6 .10 .30
CG29 M.Tettleton 7/4 W .10 .30
CG29B M.Tettleton 8/6 .10 .30
CG29C M. Tettleton 9/6 W .10 .30
CG30 Joe Carter 6/25 .10 .30
CG30B Joe Carter 8/5 .10 .30
CG30C Joe Carter 9/23 .10 .30

1996 Collector's Choice Griffey A Cut Above

These ten cards focus on Seattle Mariners superstar Ken Griffey Jr. The cards were inserted at a rate of one per pack in special six-card retail packs (five basic CC cards plus one Griffey ACA insert). The packs were sold at Wal-Mart's nationwide and carried a suggested retail price of $0.97.

COMPLETE SET (10) 2.50 6.00
COMMON CARD (CA1-CA10) .30 .75

1996 Collector's Choice Nomo Scrapbook

This five-card set was randomly inserted one in every 12 second series packs and features season highlights from Rookie of the Year, Hideo Nomo's first year in the Majors. The fronts display color action player cut-outs with yellow and red shadows on a metallic background. The backs carry a career fact about Nomo.

COMPLETE SET (5) 1.25 3.00
COMMON (1-5) .40 1.00
SER.2 STATED ODDS 1:12

1996 Collector's Choice You Make the Play

Cards from this 90-card set were inserted one per first series pack. Forty-five players are featured and each player is given two outcomes. The cards measure just about the standard-size but have rounded corners. In addition to being inserted into packs, dealers also were offered extra You Make the Play cards depending on how many cases ordered. A dealer who ordered one case received two 12-card packs of these cards for a total of 24 cards. Meanwhile, a dealer who ordered two cases received six 12-card packs for a total of 72 packs. Customers could also receive 12 of these cards by sending 10 wrappers and $2 to an a mail-in order. This offer expired on May 15, 1996.

COMPLETE SET (90) 5.00 12.00
*GOLD: 6X TO 15X BASIC PLAY
GOLD SER.1 STATED ODDS 1:35
1 Kevin Appier .07 .20
2 Carlos Baerga .07 .20
3 Jeff Bagwell .10 .30
4 Jay Bell .07 .20
5 Albert Belle .07 .20
6 Craig Biggio .10 .30
7 Wade Boggs .10 .30
8 Barry Bonds .60 1.50
9 Bobby Bonilla .07 .20
10 Jose Canseco .10 .30
11 Joe Carter .07 .20
12 Darren Daulton .07 .20
13 Cecil Fielder .07 .20
14 Ron Gant .07 .20
15 Juan Gonzalez .07 .20
16 Ken Griffey Jr. .30 .75
17 Tony Gwynn .25 .60
18 Randy Johnson .20 .50
19 Chipper Jones .20 .50
20 Barry Larkin .10 .30
21 Kenny Lofton .07 .20
22 Greg Maddux .30 .75
23 Don Mattingly .50 1.25
24 Fred McGriff .10 .30
25 Mark McGwire .50 1.25
26 Paul Molitor .07 .20
27 Raul Mondesi .07 .20
28 Eddie Murray .20 .50
29 Hideo Nomo .20 .50
30 Jon Nunnally .07 .20
31 Mike Piazza .30 .75
32 Kirby Puckett .20 .50
33 Cal Ripken .60 1.50
34 Alex Rodriguez .40 1.00
35 Tim Salmon .10 .30
36 Gary Sheffield .07 .20
37 Lee Smith .07 .20
38 Ozzie Smith .30 .75
39 Sammy Sosa .20 .50
40 Frank Thomas .20 .50
41 Greg Vaughn .07 .20
42 Mo Vaughn .07 .20
43 Larry Walker .07 .20
44 Rondell White .07 .20
45 Matt Williams .07 .20

1997 Collector's Choice

This 506-card set (produced by Upper Deck) was distributed in 12-card first series packs with a suggested retail price of $.99 and 14-card second series with a suggested retail price of $1.29. The fronts feature color action player photos while the backs carry player statistics. The first series set contains the following subsets: Rookie Class (1-27), League Leaders (56-63), Postseason (218-224) which recaps action from the 1996 playoffs and World Series Games and Ken Griffey Jr. Checklist (244-249) which also carry collecting tips. The second-series set contains the following: 199 regular player cards, 10 Ken Griffey Jr.'s Hot List (325-334), 18 Rookie Class, 3 Collecting 101 Set checklists, and 30 full-bleed All-Star cards. Notable Rookie Cards include Brian Giles.

COMPLETE SET (506) 10.00 25.00
COMP.FACT.SET (516) 10.00 25.00
COMP. SERIES 1 (246) 6.00 15.00
COMP. SERIES 2 (260) 6.00 15.00
1 Andruw Jones .10 .30
2 Rocky Coppinger .07 .20
3 Jeff D'Amico .07 .20
4 Dmitri Young .07 .20
5 Darin Erstad .07 .20
6 Jermaine Allensworth .07 .20
7 Damian Jackson .07 .20
8 Bill Mueller RC .30 .75
9 Jacob Cruz .07 .20
10 Vladimir Guerrero .20 .50
11 Marty Janzen .07 .20
12 Kevin L. Brown .07 .20
13 Willie Adams .07 .20
14 Wendell Magee .07 .20
15 Scott Rolen .10 .30
16 Matt Beech .07 .20
17 Neifi Perez .07 .20
18 Jamey Wright .07 .20
19 Jose Paniagua .07 .20
20 Todd Walker .07 .20
21 Justin Thompson .07 .20
22 Robin Jennings .07 .20
23 Dario Veras RC .07 .20
24 Brian Lesher RC .07 .20
25 Nomar Garciaparra .30 .75
26 Luis Castillo .07 .20
27 Brian Giles RC .40 1.00
28 Jermaine Dye .07 .20
29 Terrell Wade .07 .20
30 Fred McGriff .10 .30
31 Marquis Grissom .07 .20
32 Ryan Klesko .07 .20
33 Javier Lopez .07 .20
34 Mark Wohlers .07 .20
35 Tom Glavine .10 .30
36 Denny Neagle .07 .20
37 Scott Erickson .07 .20
38 Chris Hoiles .07 .20
39 Roberto Alomar .10 .30
40 Eddie Murray .20 .50
41 Cal Ripken .60 1.50
42 Randy Myers .07 .20
43 B.J. Surhoff .07 .20
44 Rick Krivda .07 .20
45 Jose Canseco .10 .30
46 Heathcliff Slocumb .07 .20
47 Jeff Suppan .07 .20
48 Tom Gordon .07 .20
49 Aaron Sele .07 .20
50 Mo Vaughn .07 .20
51 Darren Bragg .07 .20
52 Wil Cordero .07 .20
53 Scott Bullett .07 .20
54 Terry Adams .07 .20
55 Jackie Robinson .20 .50
56 Tony Gwynn LL .20 .50
Alex Rodriguez
57 Andres Galarraga LL .25 .60
Mark McGwire
58 Andres Galarraga LL .07 .20
Albert Belle
59 Eric Young LL .07 .20
Kenny Lofton
60 John Smoltz LL .07 .20
Andy Pettitte
61 John Smoltz LL .20 .50
Roger Clemens
62 Kevin Brown LL .07 .20
Juan Guzman
63 John Wetteland LL .07 .20
Todd Worrell
Jeff Brantley
64 Scott Servais .07 .20
65 Sammy Sosa .20 .50
66 Ryne Sandberg .30 .75
67 Frank Castillo .07 .20
68 Rey Sanchez .07 .20
69 Steve Trachsel .07 .20
70 Robin Ventura .07 .20
71 Wilson Alvarez .07 .20
72 Tony Phillips .07 .20
73 Lyle Mouton .07 .20
74 Mike Cameron .07 .20
75 Harold Baines .07 .20
76 Albert Belle .07 .20
77 Chris Snopek .07 .20
78 Reggie Sanders .07 .20
79 Jeff Brantley .07 .20
80 Barry Larkin .10 .30
81 Kevin Jarvis .07 .20
82 John Smiley .07 .20
83 Pete Schourek .07 .20
84 Thomas Howard .07 .20
85 Lee Smith .07 .20
86 Omar Vizquel .10 .30
87 Julio Franco .07 .20
88 Orel Hershiser .07 .20
89 Charles Nagy .07 .20
90 Matt Williams .07 .20
91 Dennis Martinez .07 .20
92 Jose Mesa .07 .20
93 Sandy Alomar Jr. .07 .20
94 Jim Thome .10 .30
95 Vinny Castilla .07 .20
96 Armando Reynoso .07 .20
97 Kevin Ritz .07 .20
98 Larry Walker .07 .20
99 Eric Young .07 .20
100 Dante Bichette .07 .20
101 Quinton McCracken .07 .20
102 John Vander Wal .07 .20
103 Phil Nevin .07 .20
104 Tony Clark .07 .20
105 Alan Trammell .07 .20
106 Felipe Lira .07 .20
107 Curtis Pride .07 .20
108 Bobby Higginson .07 .20
109 Mark Lewis .07 .20
110 Travis Fryman .07 .20
111 Al Leiter .07 .20
112 Devon White .07 .20
113 Jeff Conine .07 .20
114 Charles Johnson .07 .20
115 Andre Dawson .07 .20
116 Edgar Renteria .07 .20
117 Robb Nen .07 .20
118 Kevin Brown .07 .20
119 Derek Bell .07 .20
120 Bob Abreu .10 .30
121 Mike Hampton .07 .20
122 Todd Jones .07 .20
123 Billy Wagner .07 .20
124 Shane Reynolds .07 .20
125 Jeff Bagwell .10 .30
126 Brian L. Hunter .07 .20
127 Jeff Montgomery .07 .20
128 Rod Myers RC .07 .20
129 Tim Belcher .07 .20
130 Kevin Appier .07 .20
131 Mike Sweeney .07 .20
132 Craig Paquette .07 .20
133 Joe Randa .07 .20
134 Michael Tucker .07 .20
135 Raul Mondesi .07 .20
136 Tim Wallach .07 .20
137 Brett Butler .07 .20
138 Karim Garcia .07 .20
139 Todd Hollandsworth .07 .20
140 Eric Karros .07 .20
141 Hideo Nomo .20 .50
142 Ismael Valdes .07 .20
143 Cal Eldred .07 .20
144 Scott Karl .07 .20
145 Matt Mieske .07 .20
146 Mike Fetters .07 .20
147 Mark Loretta .07 .20
148 Fernando Vina .07 .20
149 Jeff Cirillo .07 .20
150 Dave Nilsson .07 .20
151 Kirby Puckett .20 .50
152 Rich Becker .07 .20
153 Chuck Knoblauch .07 .20
154 Marty Cordova .07 .20
155 Paul Molitor .07 .20
156 Rick Aguilera .07 .20
157 Pat Meares .07 .20
158 Frank Rodriguez .07 .20
159 David Segui .07 .20
160 Henry Rodriguez .07 .20
161 Shane Andrews .07 .20
162 Pedro Martinez .10 .30
163 Mark Grudzielanek .07 .20
164 Mike Lansing .07 .20
165 Rondell White .07 .20
166 Ugueth Urbina .07 .20
167 Rey Ordonez .07 .20
168 Robert Person .07 .20
169 Carlos Baerga .07 .20
170 Bernard Gilkey .07 .20
171 John Franco .07 .20
172 Pete Harnisch .07 .20
173 Butch Huskey .07 .20
174 Paul Wilson .07 .20
175 Dwight Gooden ERR .07 .20
incorrectly numbered 175
175 Bernie Williams .10 .30
177 Wade Boggs .10 .30
178 Ruben Rivera .07 .20
179 Jim Leyritz .07 .20
180 Derek Jeter .50 1.25
181 Tino Martinez .10 .30
182 Tim Raines .07 .20
183 Scott Brosius .07 .20
184 Jason Giambi .07 .20
185 Geronimo Berroa .07 .20
186 Ariel Prieto .07 .20
187 Scott Spiezio .07 .20
188 John Wasdin .07 .20
189 Ernie Young .07 .20
190 Mark McGwire .50 1.25
191 Jim Eisenreich .07 .20
192 Ricky Bottalico .07 .20
193 Darren Daulton .07 .20
194 David Doster .07 .20
195 Gregg Jefferies .07 .20
196 Lenny Dykstra .07 .20
197 Curt Schilling .07 .20
198 Todd Stottlemyre .07 .20
199 Willie McGee .07 .20
200 Ozzie Smith .30 .75
201 Dennis Eckersley .07 .20
202 Ray Lankford .07 .20
203 John Mabry .07 .20
204 Alan Benes .07 .20
205 Ron Gant .07 .20
206 Archi Cianfrocco .07 .20
207 Fernando Valenzuela .07 .20
208 Greg Vaughn .07 .20
209 Steve Finley .07 .20
210 Tony Gwynn .25 .60
211 Rickey Henderson .20 .50
212 Trevor Hoffman .07 .20
213 Jason Thompson .07 .20
214 Osvaldo Fernandez .07 .20
215 Glenallen Hill .07 .20
216 W. VanLandingham .07 .20
217 Marvin Benard .07 .20
218 Juan Gonzalez POST .07 .20
219 Roberto Alomar POST .07 .20
220 Brian Jordan POST .07 .20
221 John Smoltz POST .07 .20
222 Javy Lopez POST .07 .20
223 Bernie Williams POST .10 .30
224 Jim Leyritz POST .07 .20
John Wetteland
225 Barry Bonds .60 1.50
226 Rich Aurilia .07 .20
227 Jay Canizaro .07 .20
228 Dan Wilson .07 .20
229 Bob Wolcott .07 .20
230 Ken Griffey Jr. .30 .75
231 Sterling Hitchcock .07 .20
232 Edgar Martinez .10 .30
233 Joey Cora .07 .20
234 Norm Charlton .07 .20
235 Alex Rodriguez .30 .75
236 Bobby Witt .07 .20
237 Darren Oliver .07 .20
238 Kevin Elster .07 .20
239 Rusty Greer .07 .20
240 Juan Gonzalez .07 .20
241 Will Clark .10 .30
242 Dean Palmer .07 .20
243 Ivan Rodriguez .10 .30
244 Ken Griffey Jr. CL .08 .25
245 Ken Griffey Jr. CL .08 .25
246 Ken Griffey Jr. CL .08 .25
247 Ken Griffey Jr. CL .08 .25
248 Ken Griffey Jr. CL .08 .25
249 Ken Griffey Jr. CL .08 .25
250 Eddie Murray .20 .50
251 Troy Percival .07 .20
252 Garret Anderson .07 .20
253 Allen Watson .07 .20
254 Jason Dickson .07 .20
255 Jim Edmonds .07 .20
256 Chuck Finley .07 .20
257 Randy Velarde .07 .20
258 S. Hasegawa RC .15 .40
259 Todd Greene .07 .20
260 Tim Salmon .10 .30
261 Mark Langston .07 .20
262 Dave Hollins .07 .20
263 Gary DiSarcina .07 .20
264 Kenny Lofton .07 .20
265 John Smoltz .10 .30
266 Greg Maddux .30 .75
267 Jeff Blauser .07 .20
268 Alan Embree .07 .20
269 Mark Lemke .07 .20
270 Chipper Jones .20 .50
271 Mike Mussina .10 .30
272 Rafael Palmeiro .10 .30
273 Jimmy Key .07 .20
274 Mike Bordick .07 .20
275 Brady Anderson .07 .20
276 Eric Davis .07 .20
277 Jeffrey Hammonds .07 .20
278 Reggie Jefferson .07 .20
279 Tim Naehring .07 .20
280 John Valentin .07 .20
281 Troy O'Leary .07 .20
282 Shane Mack .07 .20
283 Mike Stanley .07 .20
284 Tim Wakefield .07 .20
285 Brian McRae .07 .20
286 Brooks Kieschnick .07 .20
287 Shawon Dunston .07 .20
288 Kevin Foster .07 .20
289 Mel Rojas .07 .20
290 Mark Grace .10 .30
291 Brant Brown .07 .20
292 Amaury Telemaco .07 .20
293 Dave Martinez .07 .20
294 Jaime Navarro .07 .20
295 Ray Durham .07 .20
296 Ozzie Guillen .07 .20
297 Roberto Hernandez .07 .20
298 Ron Karkovice .07 .20
299 James Baldwin .07 .20
300 Frank Thomas .20 .50
301 Eddie Taubensee .07 .20
302 Bret Boone .07 .20
303 Willie Greene .07 .20
304 Dave Burba .07 .20
305 Deion Sanders .10 .30
306 Reggie Sanders .07 .20
307 Hal Morris .07 .20
308 Pokey Reese .07 .20
309 Tony Fernandez .07 .20
310 Manny Ramirez .10 .30
311 Chad Ogea .07 .20
312 Jack McDowell .07 .20
313 Kevin Mitchell .07 .20
314 Chad Curtis .07 .20
315 Steve Kline .07 .20
316 Kevin Seitzer .07 .20
317 Kirt Manwaring .07 .20

318 Billy Swift .07 .20
319 Ellis Burks .07 .20
320 Andres Galarraga .07 .20
321 Bruce Ruffin .07 .20
322 Mark Thompson .07 .20
323 Walt Weiss .07 .20
324 Todd Jones .07 .20
325 Andruw Jones GHL .07 .20
326 Chipper Jones GHL .10 .30
327 Mo Vaughn GHL .07 .20
328 Frank Thomas GHL .10 .30
329 Albert Belle GHL .07 .20
330 Mark McGwire GHL .25 .60
331 Derek Jeter GHL .25 .60
332 Alex Rodriguez GHL .20 .50
333 Jay Buhner GHL with Ken Griffey Jr. .07 .20
334 Ken Griffey Jr. GHL .20 .50
335 Brian L. Hunter .07 .20
336 Brian Johnson .07 .20
337 Omar Olivares .07 .20
338 Deivi Cruz RC .10 .30
339 Damion Easley .07 .20
340 Melvin Nieves .07 .20
341 Moises Alou .07 .20
342 Jim Eisenreich .07 .20
343 Mark Hutton .07 .20
344 Alex Fernandez .07 .20
345 Gary Sheffield .07 .20
346 Pat Rapp .07 .20
347 Brad Ausmus .07 .20
348 Sean Berry .07 .20
349 Darryl Kile .07 .20
350 Craig Biggio .10 .30
351 Chris Holt .07 .20
352 Luis Gonzalez .07 .20
353 Pat Listach .07 .20
354 Jose Rosado .07 .20
355 Mike Macfarlane .07 .20
356 Tom Goodwin .07 .20
357 Chris Haney .07 .20
358 Chili Davis .07 .20
359 Jose Offerman .07 .20
360 Johnny Damon .10 .30
361 Bip Roberts .07 .20
362 Ramon Martinez .07 .20
363 Pedro Astacio .07 .20
364 Todd Zeile .07 .20
365 Mike Piazza .30 .75
366 Greg Gagne .07 .20
367 Chan Ho Park .07 .20
368 Wilton Guerrero .07 .20
369 Todd Worrell .07 .20
370 John Jaha .07 .20
371 Steve Sparks .07 .20
372 Mike Matheny .07 .20
373 Marc Newfield .07 .20
374 Jeromy Burnitz .07 .20
375 Jose Valentin .07 .20
376 Ben McDonald .07 .20
377 Roberto Kelly .07 .20
378 Bob Tewksbury .07 .20
379 Ron Coomer .07 .20
380 Brad Radke .07 .20
381 Matt Lawton .07 .20
382 Dan Naulty .07 .20
383 Scott Stahoviak .07 .20
384 Matt Wagner .07 .20
385 Jim Bullinger .07 .20
386 Carlos Perez .07 .20
387 Darrin Fletcher .07 .20
388 Chris Widger .07 .20
389 F.P. Santangelo .07 .20
390 Lee Smith .07 .20
391 Bobby Jones .07 .20
392 John Olerud .07 .20
393 Mark Clark .07 .20
394 Jason Isringhausen .07 .20
395 Todd Hundley .07 .20
396 Lance Johnson .07 .20
397 Edgardo Alfonzo .07 .20
398 Alex Ochoa .07 .20
399 Darryl Strawberry .07 .20
400 David Cone .07 .20
401 Paul O'Neill .10 .30
402 Joe Girardi .07 .20
403 Charlie Hayes .07 .20
404 Andy Pettitte .10 .30
405 Mariano Rivera .20 .50
406 Mariano Duncan .07 .20
407 Kenny Rogers .07 .20
408 Cecil Fielder .07 .20
409 George Williams .07 .20
410 Jose Canseco .10 .30
411 Tony Batista .07 .20
412 Steve Karsay .07 .20
413 Dave Telgheder .07 .20
414 Billy Taylor .07 .20
415 Mickey Morandini .07 .20
416 Calvin Maduro .07 .20
417 Mark Leiter .07 .20
418 Kevin Stocker .07 .20
419 Mike Lieberthal .07 .20
420 Rico Brogna .07 .20
421 Mark Portugal .07 .20
422 Rex Hudler .07 .20
423 Mark Johnson .07 .20
424 Esteban Loaiza .07 .20
425 Lou Collier .07 .20
426 Kevin Elster .07 .20
427 Francisco Cordova .07 .20
428 Marc Wilkins .07 .20
429 Joe Randa .07 .20
430 Jason Kendall .07 .20
431 Jon Lieber .07 .20
432 Steve Cooke .07 .20
433 Emil Brown RC .07 .20
434 Tony Womack RC .10 .30
435 Al Martin .07 .20
436 Jason Schmidt .07 .20
437 Andy Benes .07 .20
438 Delino DeShields .07 .20
439 Royce Clayton .07 .20
440 Brian Jordan .07 .20
441 Donovan Osborne .07 .20
442 Gary Gaetti .07 .20
443 Tom Pagnozzi .07 .20
444 Joey Hamilton .07 .20
445 Wally Joyner .07 .20
446 John Flaherty .07 .20
447 Chris Gomez .07 .20
448 Sterling Hitchcock .07 .20
449 Andy Ashby .07 .20
450 Ken Caminiti .07 .20
451 Tim Worrell .07 .20
452 Jose Vizcaino .07 .20
453 Rod Beck .07 .20
454 Wilson Delgado .07 .20
455 Darryl Hamilton .07 .20
456 Mark Lewis .07 .20
457 Mark Gardner .07 .20
458 Rick Wilkins .07 .20
459 Scott Sanders .07 .20
460 Kevin Orie .07 .20
461 Glendon Rusch .07 .20
462 Juan Melo .07 .20
463 Richie Sexson .07 .20
464 Bartolo Colon .07 .20
465 Jose Guillen .07 .20
466 Heath Murray .07 .20
467 Aaron Boone .07 .20
468 Bubba Trammell RC .10 .30
469 Jeff Abbott .07 .20
470 Derrick Gibson .07 .20
471 Matt Morris .07 .20
472 Ryan Jones .07 .20
473 Pat Cline .07 .20
474 Adam Riggs .07 .20
475 Jay Payton .07 .20
476 Derrek Lee .10 .30
477 Eli Marrero .07 .20
478 Lee Tinsley .07 .20
479 Jamie Moyer .07 .20
480 Jay Buhner .07 .20
481 Bob Wells .07 .20
482 Jeff Fassero .07 .20
483 Paul Sorrento .07 .20
484 Russ Davis .07 .20
485 Randy Johnson .20 .50
486 Roger Pavlik .07 .20
487 Damon Buford .07 .20
488 Julio Santana .07 .20
489 Mark McLemore .07 .20
490 Mickey Tettleton .07 .20
491 Ken Hill .07 .20
492 Benji Gil .07 .20
493 Ed Sprague .07 .20
494 Mike Timlin .07 .20
495 Pat Hentgen .07 .20
496 Orlando Merced .07 .20
497 Carlos Garcia .07 .20
498 Carlos Delgado .07 .20
499 Juan Guzman .07 .20
500 Roger Clemens .40 1.00
501 Erik Hanson .07 .20
502 Otis Nixon .07 .20
503 Shawn Green .07 .20
504 Charlie O'Brien .07 .20
505 Joe Carter .07 .20
506 Alex Gonzalez .07 .20

1997 Collector's Choice All-Star Connection

Inserted one in every series two packs, this 45-card set celebrates the unique history of Baseball's All Star Game and highlights the League's top All-Star caliber players. The fronts feature color player cut-outs on a big star background.

COMPLETE SET (45) 6.00 12.00
SER.2 ODDS 1:1 HOBBY, 2:1 RETAIL
1 Mark McGwire .50 1.25
2 Chuck Knoblauch .07 .20
3 Jim Thome .10 .30
4 Alex Rodriguez .30 .75
5 Ken Griffey Jr. .30 .75
6 Brady Anderson .07 .20
7 Albert Belle .07 .20
8 Ivan Rodriguez .10 .30
9 Pat Hentgen .07 .20
10 Frank Thomas .20 .50
11 Roberto Alomar .10 .30
12 Robin Ventura .07 .20
13 Cal Ripken .60 1.50
14 Juan Gonzalez .07 .20
15 Manny Ramirez .10 .30
16 Bernie Williams .10 .30
17 Terry Steinbach .07 .20
18 Andy Pettitte .10 .30
19 Jeff Bagwell .10 .30
20 Craig Biggio .10 .30
21 Ken Caminiti .07 .20
22 Barry Larkin .10 .30
23 Tony Gwynn .25 .60
24 Barry Bonds .60 1.50
25 Kenny Lofton .07 .20
26 Mike Piazza .30 .75
27 John Smoltz .10 .30
28 Andres Galarraga .07 .20
29 Ryne Sandberg .30 .75
30 Chipper Jones .20 .50
31 Mark Grudzielanek .07 .20
32 Sammy Sosa .20 .50
33 Steve Finley .07 .20
34 Gary Sheffield .07 .20
35 Todd Hundley .07 .20
36 Greg Maddux .30 .75
37 Mo Vaughn .07 .20
38 Eric Young .07 .20
39 Vinny Castilla .07 .20
40 Derek Jeter .50 1.25
41 Lance Johnson .07 .20
42 Ellis Burks .07 .20
43 Dante Bichette .07 .20
44 Javy Lopez .07 .20
45 Hideo Nomo .20 .50

1997 Collector's Choice Big Shots

Randomly inserted in series two packs at the rate of one in 12, this 19-card set features unique and exciting photos depicting some of the game's most recognized players.

COMPLETE SET (19) 35.00 60.00
SER.2 STATED ODDS 1:12
*GOLD: 1.5X TO 4X BASIC BIG SHOT
SER.2 STATED ODDS 1:144
1 Ken Griffey Jr. 1.50 4.00
2 Nomar Garciaparra 1.50 4.00
3 Brian Jordan .40 1.00
4 Scott Rolen .60 1.50
5 Alex Rodriguez 1.50 4.00
6 Larry Walker .40 1.00
7 Mariano Rivera 1.00 2.50
8 Cal Ripken 3.00 8.00
9 Deion Sanders .60 1.50
10 Frank Thomas 1.00 2.50
11 Dean Palmer .40 1.00
12 Ken Caminiti .40 1.00
13 Derek Jeter 2.50 6.00
14 Barry Bonds 3.00 8.00
15 Chipper Jones 1.00 2.50
16 Mo Vaughn .40 1.00
17 Jay Buhner .40 1.00
18 Mike Piazza 1.50 4.00
19 Tony Gwynn 1.25 3.00

1997 Collector's Choice The Big Show

Inserted one in every first series pack, cards from this 45-card set feature color photos of some of the hottest players in baseball. The backs carry comments about the pictured player by ESPN SportsCenter television sportscasters, Keith Olbermann and Dan Patrick.

COMPLETE SET (45) 5.00 10.00
SER.1 STATED ODDS 1:1
*WORLD HQ: 15X TO 40X BASIC BIG SHOW
WHQ SER.1 STATED ODDS 1:35
1 Greg Maddux .30 .75
2 Chipper Jones .20 .50
3 Andruw Jones .10 .30
4 John Smoltz .10 .30
5 Cal Ripken .60 1.50
6 Roberto Alomar .10 .30
7 Rafael Palmeiro .10 .30
8 Eddie Murray .20 .50
9 Jose Canseco .10 .30
10 Roger Clemens .40 1.00
11 Mo Vaughn .07 .20
12 Jim Edmonds .07 .20
13 Tim Salmon .10 .30
14 Sammy Sosa .20 .50
15 Albert Belle .07 .20
16 Frank Thomas .20 .50
17 Barry Larkin .10 .30
18 Kenny Lofton .07 .20
19 Manny Ramirez .10 .30
20 Matt Williams .07 .20
21 Dante Bichette .07 .20
22 Gary Sheffield .07 .20
23 Craig Biggio .10 .30
24 Jeff Bagwell .10 .30
25 Todd Hollandsworth .07 .20
26 Raul Mondesi .07 .20
27 Hideo Nomo .20 .50
28 Mike Piazza .30 .75
29 Paul Molitor .07 .20
30 Kirby Puckett .20 .50
31 Rondell White .07 .20
32 Rey Ordonez .07 .20
33 Paul Wilson .07 .20
34 Derek Jeter .50 1.25
35 Andy Pettitte .10 .30
36 Mark McGwire .50 1.25
37 Jason Kendall .07 .20
38 Ozzie Smith .30 .75
39 Tony Gwynn .25 .60
40 Barry Bonds .60 1.50
41 Alex Rodriguez .30 .75
42 Jay Buhner .07 .20
43 Ken Griffey Jr. .30 .75
44 Randy Johnson .20 .50
45 Juan Gonzalez .07 .20

1997 Collector's Choice Crash the Game

Inserted in series two packs at the rate of one in five, cards from this interactive game set features three separate cards each of 30 top home run hitters. If the featured player hit a home run during the series specified on the card, the card could than have been redeemed for a special card of the same player. The postmark expiration date for exchanging winning cards was December 1, 1997.

COMPLETE SET (90) 30.00 60.00
SER.2 STATED ODDS 1:5
*INSTANT WIN: 10X TO 20X BASIC CRASH
INSTANT WIN SER.2 STATED ODDS 1:721
1A Ryan Klesko July 20-30 L .15 .40
1B Ryan Klesko Aug 8-11 L .15 .40
1C Ryan Klesko Sept 19-21 L .15 .40
2A Chipper Jones Aug 15-17 L .40 1.00
2B Chipper Jones Aug 29-31 L .40 1.00
2C Chipper Jones Sept 12-14 L .40 1.00
3A Andruw Jones Aug 22-24 W .25 .60
3B Andruw Jones Sept 1-3 L .25 .60
3C Andruw Jones Sept 19-22 L .25 .60
4A Brady Anderson July 31-Aug 3 W .15 .40
4B Brady Anderson Sept 4-7 L .15 .40
4C Brady Anderson Sept 19-22 L .15 .40
5A Rafael Palmeiro July 29-30 L .25 .60
5B Rafael Palmeiro Aug 29-31 L .25 .60
5C Rafael Palmeiro Sept 26-28 L .25 .60
6A Cal Ripken Aug 8-10 1.25 3.00
6B Cal Ripken Sept 1-3 W 1.25 3.00
6C Cal Ripken Sept 11-14 L 1.25 3.00
7A Mo Vaughn Aug 14-17 L .15 .40
7B Mo Vaughn Aug 29-31 W .15 .40
7C Mo Vaughn Sept 23-25 W .15 .40
8A Sammy Sosa Aug 1-3 W .40 1.00
8B Sammy Sosa Aug 29-31 L .40 1.00
8C Sammy Sosa Sept 19-21 W .40 1.00
9A Albert Belle Aug 7-10 L .15 .40
9B Albert Belle Sept 11-14 L .15 .40
9C Albert Belle Sept 19-21 W .15 .40
10A Frank Thomas Aug 29-31 L .40 1.00
10B Frank Thomas Sept 1-3 L .40 1.00
10C Frank Thomas Sept 23-25 W .40 1.00
11A Manny Ramirez Aug 12-14 W .25 .60
11B Manny Ramirez Aug 29-31 L .25 .60
11C Manny Ramirez Sept 11-14 W .25 .60
12A Jim Thome July 28-30 L .25 .60
12B Jim Thome Aug 15-18 W .25 .60
12C Jim Thome Sept 19-22 L .25 .60
13A Matt Williams Aug 4-5 L .15 .40
13B Matt Williams Sept 1-3 W .15 .40
13C Matt Williams Sept 23-25 L .15 .40
14A Dante Bichette July 24-27 W .15 .40
14B Dante Bichette Aug 28-29 L .15 .40
14C Dante Bichette Sept 26-28 W .15 .40
15A Vinny Castilla Aug 12-13 L .15 .40
15B Vinny Castilla Sept 4-7 W .15 .40
15C Vinny Castilla Sept 19-21 L .15 .40
16A Andres Galarraga Aug 8-10 W .15 .40
16B Andres Galarraga Aug 30-31 L .15 .40
16C Andres Galarraga Sept 12-14 W .15 .40
17A Gary Sheffield Aug 1-3 W .15 .40
17B Gary Sheffield Sept 1-3 W .15 .40
17C Gary Sheffield Sept 12-14 W .15 .40
18A Jeff Bagwell Sept 9-10 L .25 .60
18B Jeff Bagwell Sept 19-22 W .25 .60
18C Jeff Bagwell Sept 23-25 W .25 .60
19A Eric Karros Aug 1-3 L .15 .40
19B Eric Karros Aug 15-17 L .15 .40
19C Eric Karros Sept 25-28 W .15 .40
20A Mike Piazza Aug 11-12 L .60 1.50
20B Mike Piazza Sept 5-8 W .60 1.50
20C Mike Piazza Sept 19-21 W .60 1.50
21A Vladimir Guerrero Aug 22-24 L .40 1.00
21B Vladimir Guerrero Aug 29-31 L .40 1.00
21C Vladimir Guerrero Sept 19-22 L .40 1.00
22A Cecil Fielder Aug 29-31 L .15 .40
22B Cecil Fielder Sept 4-7 L .15 .40
22C Cecil Fielder Sept 26-28 L .15 .40
23A Jose Canseco Sept 12-14 L .25 .60
23B Jose Canseco Sept 22-24 W .25 .60
23C Jose Canseco Sept 26-28 L .25 .60
24A Mark McGwire July 31-Aug 3 L 1.00 2.50
24B Mark McGwire Aug 30-31 L 1.00 2.50
24C Mark McGwire Sept 19-22 W 1.00 2.50
25A Ken Caminiti Aug 8-10 L .15 .40
25B Ken Caminiti Sept 4-7 W .15 .40
25C Ken Caminiti Sept 17-18 W .15 .40
26A Barry Bonds Aug 5-7 L 1.25 3.00
26B Barry Bonds Sept 4-7 L 1.25 3.00
26C Barry Bonds Sept 23-24 W 1.25 3.00
27A Jay Buhner Aug 7-10 L .15 .40
27B Jay Buhner Aug 28-29 L .15 .40
27C Jay Buhner Sept 1-3 L .15 .40
28A Ken Griffey Jr. Aug 22-24 W .60 1.50
28B Ken Griffey Jr. Aug 28-29 L .60 1.50
28C Ken Griffey Jr. Sept 19-22 W .60 1.50
29A Alex Rodriguez July 29-31 L .60 1.50
29B Alex Rodriguez Aug 30-31 L .60 1.50
29C Alex Rodriguez Sept 12-15 L .60 1.50
30A Juan Gonzalez Aug 11-13 W .15 .40
30B Juan Gonzalez Aug 30-31 L .15 .40
30C Juan Gonzalez Sept 19-21 W .15 .40

1997 Collector's Choice Griffey Clearly Dominant

Randomly inserted in first series packs at a rate of one in 144, this five-card set highlights superstar Ken Griffey Jr. with different color photos and information on each card.

COMPLETE SET (5) 15.00 40.00
COMMON (CD1-CD5) 4.00 10.00
SER.1 STATED ODDS 1:144

1997 Collector's Choice New Frontier

Randomly inserted one in every 69 series two packs, this 40-card set showcases the most anticipated InterLeague match-ups. Each card features a color player cut-out of a great player from either the American or National League on half of a baseball diamond background and is designed to fit with another card displaying a great player match-up from the opposite league to complete the diamond.

SER.2 STATED ODDS 1:69
NF1 Alex Rodriguez 8.00 20.00
NF2 Tony Gwynn 6.00 15.00
NF3 Jose Canseco 3.00 8.00
NF4 Hideo Nomo 5.00 12.00
NF5 Mark McGwire 12.50 30.00
NF6 Barry Bonds 15.00 40.00
NF7 Juan Gonzalez 2.00 5.00
NF8 Ken Caminiti 2.00 5.00
NF9 Tim Salmon 3.00 8.00
NF10 Mike Piazza 8.00 20.00
NF11 Ken Griffey Jr. 8.00 20.00
NF12 Andres Galarraga 2.00 5.00
NF13 Jay Buhner 2.00 5.00
NF14 Dante Bichette 2.00 5.00
NF15 Frank Thomas 5.00 12.00
NF16 Ryne Sandberg 8.00 20.00
NF17 Roger Clemens 10.00 25.00
NF18 Andruw Jones 3.00 8.00
NF19 Jim Thome 3.00 8.00
NF20 Sammy Sosa 5.00 12.00
NF21 Dave Justice 2.00 5.00
NF22 Deion Sanders 3.00 8.00
NF23 Todd Walker 2.00 5.00
NF24 Kevin Orie 2.00 5.00
NF25 Albert Belle 2.00 5.00
NF26 Jeff Bagwell 3.00 8.00
NF27 Manny Ramirez 3.00 8.00
NF28 Brian Jordan 2.00 5.00
NF29 Derek Jeter 12.50 30.00
NF30 Chipper Jones 5.00 12.00
NF31 Mo Vaughn 2.00 5.00
NF32 Gary Sheffield 2.00 5.00
NF33 Carlos Delgado 2.00 5.00
NF34 Vladimir Guerrero 5.00 12.00
NF35 Cal Ripken 15.00 40.00
NF36 Greg Maddux 8.00 20.00
NF37 Cecil Fielder 2.00 5.00
NF38 Todd Hundley 2.00 5.00
NF39 Mike Mussina 3.00 8.00
NF40 Scott Rolen 3.00 8.00

1997 Collector's Choice Premier Power

Randomly inserted in first series packs at a rate of one in 15, this silver version 20-card set features borderless color action player photos and information about the 20 top Major League Home Run hitters.

COMPLETE SET (20) 25.00 40.00
SER.1 STATED ODDS 1:15
*GOLD: 1.25X TO 3X BASIC PREM.POWER
GOLD SER.1 STATED ODDS 1:69
*JUMBOS: .25X BASIC PREMIER POWER
TEN JUMBO POWERS PER FACTORY SET
PP1 Mark McGwire 2.50 6.00
PP2 Brady Anderson .40 1.00
PP3 Ken Griffey Jr. 1.50 4.00
PP4 Albert Belle .40 1.00
PP5 Juan Gonzalez .40 1.00
PP6 Andres Galarraga .40 1.00
PP7 Jay Buhner .40 1.00
PP8 Mo Vaughn .40 1.00
PP9 Barry Bonds 3.00 8.00
PP10 Gary Sheffield .40 1.00
PP11 Todd Hundley .40 1.00
PP12 Frank Thomas 1.00 2.50
PP13 Sammy Sosa 1.00 2.50
PP14 Ken Caminiti .40 1.00
PP15 Vinny Castilla .40 1.00
PP16 Ellis Burks .40 1.00
PP17 Rafael Palmeiro .60 1.50
PP18 Alex Rodriguez 1.50 4.00
PP19 Mike Piazza 1.50 4.00
PP20 Eddie Murray 1.00 2.50

1997 Collector's Choice Stick'Ums

Randomly inserted in first series packs at a rate of one in three, cards from this 30-card set features color sticker images of star players. These interactive reusable stickers could be used to create mini baseball scenes.

COMPLETE SET (30) 7.50 15.00
SER.1 STATED ODDS 1:3
1 Ozzie Smith .50 1.25
2 Andruw Jones .20 .50
3 Alex Rodriguez .50 1.25
4 Paul Molitor .10 .30
5 Jeff Bagwell .20 .50
6 Manny Ramirez .20 .50
7 Kenny Lofton .10 .30
8 Albert Belle .10 .30
9 Jay Buhner .10 .30
10 Chipper Jones .30 .75
11 Barry Larkin .20 .50
12 Dante Bichette .10 .30
13 Mike Piazza .50 1.25
14 Andres Galarraga .10 .30
15 Barry Bonds 1.00 2.50
16 Brady Anderson .10 .30
17 Gary Sheffield .10 .30
18 Jim Thome .20 .50
19 Tony Gwynn .40 1.00
20 Cal Ripken 1.00 2.50
21 Sammy Sosa .30 .75
22 Juan Gonzalez .10 .30
23 Greg Maddux .50 1.25
24 Ken Griffey Jr. .50 1.25
25 Mark McGwire .75 2.00
26 Kirby Puckett .30 .75
27 Mo Vaughn .10 .30
28 Vladimir Guerrero .30 .75
29 Ken Caminiti .10 .30
30 Frank Thomas .30 .75

1997 Collector's Choice Stick'Ums Retail

This 28-card set features color sticker images of star players. These interactive reusable stickers could be used to create mini baseball scenes. The back of each sticker displays the checklist for the set. The set was distributed in packs of 15 stickers plus three regular Collector's Choice cards. The stickers are unnumbered and checklisted below in alphabetical order.

COMPLETE SET (28) 4.00 10.00
1 Brady Anderson .08 .25
2 Jeff Bagwell .30 .75
3 Albert Belle .07 .20
4 Dante Bichette .08 .25
5 Barry Bonds .60 1.50
6 Jay Buhner .08 .25
7 Ken Caminiti .08 .25
8 Andres Galarraga .07 .20
9 Juan Gonzalez .30 .75
10 Ken Griffey Jr. .60 1.50
11 Vladimir Guerrero .40 1.00
12 Tony Gwynn .60 1.50
13 Andruw Jones .50 1.25
14 Chipper Jones .60 1.50
15 Barry Larkin .30 .75
16 Kenny Lofton .08 .25
17 Greg Maddux .75 2.00
18 Mark McGwire .60 1.50
19 Paul Molitor .30 .75
20 Mike Piazza .75 2.00
21 Manny Ramirez .40 1.00
22 Cal Ripken Jr. 1.25 3.00
23 Alex Rodriguez .60 1.50
24 Gary Sheffield .40 1.00
25 Sammy Sosa .50 1.25
26 Frank Thomas .08 .25
27 Jim Thome .30 .75
28 Mo Vaughn .02 .10

1997 Collector's Choice Toast of the Town

Randomly inserted in series two packs at the rate of one in 35, this 30-card set features color photos of some of the best Major League players printed on premium, foil enhanced card stock.

COMPLETE SET (30) 100.00 200.00
SER.2 STATED ODDS 1:35
T1 Andruw Jones 1.50 4.00
T2 Chipper Jones 2.50 6.00
T3 Greg Maddux 4.00 10.00
T4 John Smoltz 1.50 4.00
T5 Kenny Lofton 1.00 2.50
T6 Brady Anderson 1.00 2.50
T7 Cal Ripken 8.00 20.00
T8 Mo Vaughn 1.00 2.50
T9 Sammy Sosa 2.50 6.00
T10 Albert Belle 1.00 2.50
T11 Frank Thomas 2.50 6.00
T12 Barry Larkin 1.50 4.00
T13 Manny Ramirez 1.50 4.00
T14 Jeff Bagwell 1.50 4.00
T15 Mike Piazza 4.00 10.00
T16 Paul Molitor 1.00 2.50
T17 Vladimir Guerrero 2.50 6.00
T18 Todd Hundley 1.00 2.50
T19 Derek Jeter 6.00 15.00
T20 Andy Pettitte 1.50 4.00
T21 Bernie Williams 1.50 4.00
T22 Mark McGwire 6.00 15.00
T23 Scott Rolen 1.50 4.00
T24 Ken Caminiti 1.00 2.50
T25 Tony Gwynn 3.00 8.00
T26 Barry Bonds 8.00 20.00
T27 Ken Griffey Jr. 4.00 10.00
T28 Alex Rodriguez 4.00 10.00
T29 Juan Gonzalez 1.00 2.50
T30 Roger Clemens 5.00 12.00

1997 Collector's Choice Update

This 30-card Update set was made available to collectors who mailed in 10 series two wrappers (plus a check or money order for $3 to cover postage and handling) prior to the December 1st, 1997 deadline. The cards share the same design as the basic issue 1997 Collector's Choice set and content focuses on traded veterans pictured in their new uniforms and a handful of prospects called up during the season (including Jose Cruz Jr. and Hideki Irabu).

COMPLETE SET (30) 2.50 5.00
U1 Jim Leyritz .07 .20
U2 Matt Perisho .07 .20
U3 Michael Tucker .07 .20
U4 Mike Johnson .07 .20
U5 Jaime Navarro .07 .20
U6 Doug Drabek .07 .20
U7 Terry Mulholland .07 .20
U8 Brett Tomko .07 .20
U9 Marquis Grissom .07 .20
U10 David Justice .07 .20
U11 Brian Moehler RC .10 .30
U12 Bobby Bonilla .07 .20
U13 Todd Dunwoody .07 .20
U14 Tony Saunders .07 .20
U15 Jay Bell .07 .20
U16 Jeff King .07 .20
U17 Terry Steinbach .07 .20

Card	Low	High
U18 Steve Bieser	.07	.20
U19 Takashi Kashiwada	.07	.20
U20 Hideki Irabu	.10	.30
U21 Damon Mashore	.07	.20
U22 Quilvio Veras	.07	.20
U23 Will Cunnane	.07	.20
U24 Jeff Kent	.07	.20
U25 J.T. Snow	.07	.20
U26 Dante Powell	.07	.20
U27 Jose Cruz Jr.	.10	.30
U28 John Burkett	.07	.20
U29 John Wetteland	.07	.20
U30 Benito Santiago	.07	.20

1997 Collector's Choice Teams

This set features color action and posed player photos either borderless or in white borders of 13 players each of selected major league baseball teams. The backs carry player information and career statistics. Each set was distributed in a special package along with a foil enhanced die cut 3 1/2" by 5" Home Team Heroes card displaying two star players of that team. The cards are checklisted below by teams with the Home Team Heroes cards, which was also issued seperately, priced as a Upper Deck set.

Card	Low	High
COMPLETE SET	30.00	80.00
AB Atl. Braves Logo CL	.08	.25
AB1 Andruw Jones	.75	2.00
AB2 Kenny Lofton	.20	.50
AB3 Fred McGriff	.30	.75
AB4 Michael Tucker	.08	.25
AB5 Ryan Klesko	.20	.50
AB6 Javier Lopez	.30	.75
AB7 Mark Wohlers	.08	.25
AB8 Tom Glavine	.40	1.00
AB9 Denny Neagle	.08	.25
AB10 Chipper Jones	1.00	2.50
AB11 Jeff Blauser	.08	.25
AB12 Greg Maddux	1.25	3.00
AB13 John Smoltz	.30	.75
BO Balt. Orioles Logo CL	.08	.25
BO1 Rocky Coppinger	.08	.25
BO2 Scott Erickson	.08	.25
BO3 Chris Hoiles	.08	.25
BO4 Roberto Alomar	.40	1.00
BO5 Cal Ripken Jr.	2.00	5.00
BO6 Randy Myers	.20	.50
BO7 B.J. Surhoff	.20	.50
BO8 Mike Mussina	.40	1.00
BO9 Rafael Palmeiro	.40	1.00
BO10 Jimmy Key	.20	.50
BO11 Mike Bordick	.08	.25
BO12 Brady Anderson	.20	.50
BO13 Eric Davis	.20	.50
CI Cleve. Indians Logo CL	.08	.25
CI1 Brian Giles	1.50	4.00
CI2 Omar Vizquel	.30	.75
CI3 Julio Franco	.20	.50
CI4 Orel Hershiser	.20	.50
CI5 Charles Nagy	.08	.25
CI6 Matt Williams	.30	.75
CI7 Jose Mesa	.20	.50
CI8 Sandy Alomar Jr.	.20	.50
CI9 Jim Thome	.50	1.25
CI10 David Justice	.40	1.00
CI11 Marquis Grissom	.20	.50
CI12 Chad Ogea	.08	.25
CI13 Manny Ramirez	.50	1.25
CR Colo. Rockies Logo CL	.08	.25
CR1 Dante Bichette	.20	.50
CR2 Vinny Castilla	.20	.50
CR3 Kevin Ritz	.08	.25
CR4 Larry Walker	.40	1.00
CR5 Eric Young	.20	.50
CR6 Quinton McCracken	.08	.25
CR7 John Vander Wal	.08	.25
CR8 Jamey Wright	.08	.25
CR9 Mark Thompson	.08	.25
CR10 Andres Galarraga	.40	1.00
CR11 Ellis Burks	.20	.50
CR12 Kirt Manwaring	.08	.25
CR13 Walt Weiss	.08	.25
CW Chi. White Sox Logo CL	.08	.25
CW1 Robin Ventura	.40	1.00
CW2 Wilson Alvarez	.20	.50
CW3 Tony Phillips	.08	.25
CW4 Lyle Mouton	.08	.25
CW5 James Baldwin	.08	.25
CW6 Harold Baines	.08	.25
CW7 Albert Belle	.20	.50
CW8 Chris Snopek	.08	.25
CW9 Ray Durham	.20	.50
CW10 Frank Thomas	.50	1.25
CW11 Ozzie Guillen	.20	.50
CW12 Roberto Hernandez	.20	.50
CW13 Jaime Navarro	.08	.25
FM Fla. Marlins Logo CL	.08	.25
FM1 Luis Castillo	.30	.75
FM2 Al Leiter	.20	.50
FM3 Devon White	.08	.25
FM4 Jeff Conine	.08	.25
FM5 Charles Johnson	.08	.25
FM6 Edgar Renteria	.40	1.00
FM7 Robb Nen	.08	.25
FM8 Kevin Brown	.20	.50
FM9 Gary Sheffield	.50	1.25
FM10 Alex Fernandez	.08	.25
FM11 Pat Rapp	.08	.25
FM12 Moises Alou	.20	.50
FM13 Bobby Bonilla	.20	.50
LA L.A. Dodgers Logo CL	.08	.25
LA1 Raul Mondesi	.20	.50
LA2 Brett Butler	.20	.50
LA3 Todd Hollandsworth	.08	.25
LA4 Eric Karros	.20	.50
LA5 Hideo Nomo	.60	1.50
LA6 Ismael Valdes	.08	.25
LA7 Wilton Guerrero	.08	.25
LA8 Ramon Martinez	.08	.25
LA9 Greg Gagne	.08	.25
LA10 Mike Piazza	1.25	3.00
LA11 Chan Ho Park	.20	.50
LA12 Todd Worrell	.08	.25
LA13 Todd Zeile	.20	.50
NY N.Y. Yankees Logo CL	.08	.25
NY1 Bernie Williams	.40	1.00
NY2 Dwight Gooden	.20	.50
NY3 Wade Boggs	.50	1.25
NY4 Ruben Rivera	.08	.25
NY5 Derek Jeter	2.00	5.00
NY6 Tino Martinez	.30	.75
NY7 Tim Raines	.20	.50
NY8 Joe Girardi	.08	.25
NY9 Charlie Hayes	.08	.25
NY10 Andy Pettitte	.30	.75
NY11 Cecil Fielder	.20	.50
NY12 Paul O'Neill	.20	.50
NY13 David Cone	.30	.75
SM Sea. Mariners Logo CL	.08	.25
SM1 Dan Wilson	.08	.25
SM2 Ken Griffey Jr.	1.00	2.50
SM3 Edgar Martinez	.30	.75
SM4 Joey Cora	.08	.25
SM5 Norm Charlton	.08	.25
SM6 Alex Rodriguez	1.50	4.00
SM7 Randy Johnson	.75	2.00
SM8 Paul Sorrento	.08	.25
SM9 Jamie Moyer	.20	.50
SM10 Jay Buhner	.20	.50
SM11 Russ Davis	.08	.25
SM12 Jeff Fassero	.08	.25
SM13 Bob Wells	.08	.25
TR Tex. Rangers Logo CL	.08	.25
TR1 Bobby Witt	.08	.25
TR2 Darren Oliver	.08	.25
TR3 Rusty Greer	.20	.50
TR4 Juan Gonzalez	.20	.50
TR5 Will Clark	.40	1.00
TR6 Dean Palmer	.20	.50
TR7 Ivan Rodriguez	.50	1.25
TR8 John Wetteland	.20	.50
TR9 Mark McLemore	.08	.25
TR10 John Burkett	.08	.25
TR11 Benji Gil	.08	.25
TR12 Ken Hill	.08	.25
TR13 Mickey Tettleton	.20	.50

1998 Collector's Choice

The 1998 Collector's Choice set (produced by Upper Deck) was issued in two separate series, each containing 265 cards. Packs for both first and second series contained 14 cards and carried a suggested retail price of $1.29. First series packs went live around March, 1998 and second series packs followed suit in June, 1998. Card fronts feature color glossy action player photos framed by a clean white or gray border. The backs carry statistical information and another color image. The set contains the topical subsets: Checklists (266-270), Cover Glory (1-18), Golden Jubilee (271-279), Rookie Class (100-126/415-432), Masked Marauders (181-189), and Top of the Charts (253-261). Key Rookie Cards in this set include Kevin Millwood and Maggio Ordonez. Card number 202A featuring Kerry Wood was issued in factory sets to replace Tony Barron

Card	Low	High
COMPLETE SET (530)	15.00	40.00
COMP. SERIES 1 (265)	8.00	20.00
COMP. SERIES 2 (265)	8.00	20.00
COMP.FACT.SET (530)	20.00	50.00
1 Nomar Garciaparra CG	.20	.50
2 Roger Clemens CG	.20	.50
3 Larry Walker CG	.07	.20
4 Mike Piazza CG	.20	.50
5 Mark McGwire CG	.25	.60
6 Tony Gwynn CG	.10	.30
7 Jose Cruz Jr. CG	.07	.20
8 Frank Thomas CG	.10	.30
9 Tino Martinez CG	.07	.20
10 Ken Griffey Jr. CG	.20	.50
11 Barry Bonds CG	.30	.75
12 Scott Rolen CG	.07	.20
13 Randy Johnson CG	.10	.30
14 Ryne Sandberg CG	.20	.50
15 Eddie Murray CG	.10	.30
16 Kevin Brown CG	.07	.20
17 Mike Mussina CG	.07	.20
18 Sandy Alomar Jr. CG	.07	.20
19 Ken Griffey Jr. CL	.10	.30
Adam Riggs		
20 Nomar Garciaparra CL	.10	.30
Charlie O'Brien		
21 Ben Grieve CL	.07	.20
Frank Thomas		
Tony Gwynn		
22 Mark McGwire CL	.10	.30
Cal Ripken		
23 Tino Martinez CL	.07	.20
24 Jason Dickson	.07	.20
25 Darin Erstad	.07	.20
26 Todd Greene	.07	.20
27 Chuck Finley	.07	.20
28 Garret Anderson	.07	.20
29 Dave Hollins	.07	.20
30 Rickey Henderson	.20	.50
31 John Smoltz	.10	.30
32 Michael Tucker	.07	.20
33 Jeff Blauser	.07	.20
34 Javier Lopez	.07	.20
35 Andruw Jones	.10	.30
36 Denny Neagle	.07	.20
37 Randall Simon	.07	.20
38 Mark Wohlers	.07	.20
39 Harold Baines	.07	.20
40 Cal Ripken	.60	1.50
41 Mike Bordick	.07	.20
42 Jimmy Key	.07	.20
43 Armando Benitez	.07	.20
44 Scott Erickson	.07	.20
45 Eric Davis	.07	.20
46 Bret Saberhagen	.07	.20
47 Darren Bragg	.07	.20
48 Steve Avery	.07	.20
49 Jeff Frye	.07	.20
50 Aaron Sele	.07	.20
51 Scott Hatteberg	.07	.20
52 Tom Gordon	.07	.20
53 Kevin Orie	.07	.20
54 Kevin Foster	.07	.20
55 Ryne Sandberg	.30	.75
56 Doug Glanville	.07	.20
57 Tyler Houston	.07	.20
58 Steve Trachsel	.07	.20
59 Mark Grace	.10	.30
60 Frank Thomas	.20	.50
61 Scott Eyre	.07	.20
62 Jeff Abbott	.07	.20
63 Chris Clemons	.07	.20
64 Jorge Fabregas	.07	.20
65 Robin Ventura	.07	.20
66 Matt Karchner	.07	.20
67 Jon Nunnally	.07	.20
68 Aaron Boone	.07	.20
69 Pokey Reese	.07	.20
70 Deion Sanders	.10	.30
71 Jeff Shaw	.07	.20
72 Eduardo Perez	.07	.20
73 Brett Tomko	.07	.20
74 Bartolo Colon	.07	.20
75 Manny Ramirez	.10	.30
76 Jose Mesa	.07	.20
77 Brian Giles	.07	.20
78 Richie Sexson	.07	.20
79 Orel Hershiser	.07	.20
80 Matt Williams	.07	.20
81 Walt Weiss	.07	.20
82 Jerry DiPoto	.07	.20
83 Quinton McCracken	.07	.20
84 Neifi Perez	.07	.20
85 Vinny Castilla	.07	.20
86 Ellis Burks	.07	.20
87 John Thomson	.07	.20
88 Willie Blair	.07	.20
89 Bob Hamelin	.07	.20
90 Tony Clark	.07	.20
91 Todd Jones	.07	.20
92 Deivi Cruz	.07	.20
93 Frank Catalanotto RC	.15	.40
94 Justin Thompson	.07	.20
95 Gary Sheffield	.07	.20
96 Kevin Brown	.10	.30
97 Charles Johnson	.07	.20
98 Bobby Bonilla	.07	.20
99 Livan Hernandez	.07	.20
100 Paul Konerko	.07	.20
101 Craig Counsell	.07	.20
102 Maggio Ordonez RC	.60	1.50
103 Garrett Stephenson	.07	.20
104 Ken Cloude	.07	.20
105 Miguel Tejada	.20	.50
106 Juan Encarnacion	.07	.20
107 Dennis Reyes	.07	.20
108 Orlando Cabrera	.07	.20
109 Kelvim Escobar	.07	.20
110 Ben Grieve	.07	.20
111 Brian Rose	.07	.20
112 Fernando Tatis	.07	.20
113 Tom Evans	.07	.20
114 Tom Fordham	.07	.20
115 Mark Kotsay	.07	.20
116 Mario Valdez	.07	.20
117 Jeremi Gonzalez	.07	.20
118 Todd Dunwoody	.07	.20
119 Javier Valentin	.07	.20
120 Todd Helton	.10	.30
121 Jason Varitek	.20	.50
122 Chris Carpenter	.07	.20
123 Kevin Millwood RC	.25	.60
124 Brad Fullmer	.07	.20
125 Jaret Wright	.07	.20
126 Brad Rigby	.07	.20
127 Edgar Renteria	.07	.20
128 Robb Nen	.07	.20
129 Tony Pena	.07	.20
130 Craig Biggio	.10	.30
131 Brad Ausmus	.07	.20
132 Shane Reynolds	.07	.20
133 Mike Hampton	.07	.20
134 Billy Wagner	.07	.20
135 Richard Hidalgo	.07	.20
136 Jose Rosado	.07	.20
137 Yamil Benitez	.07	.20
138 Felix Martinez	.07	.20
139 Jeff King	.07	.20
140 Jose Offerman	.07	.20
141 Joe Vitiello	.07	.20
142 Tim Belcher	.07	.20
143 Brett Butler	.07	.20
144 Greg Gagne	.07	.20
145 Mike Piazza	.30	.75
146 Ramon Martinez	.07	.20
147 Raul Mondesi	.07	.20
148 Adam Riggs	.07	.20
149 Eddie Murray	.20	.50
150 Jeff Cirillo	.07	.20
151 Scott Karl	.07	.20
152 Mike Fetters	.07	.20
153 Dave Nilsson	.07	.20
154 Antone Williamson	.07	.20
155 Jeff D'Amico	.07	.20
156 Jose Valentin	.07	.20
157 Brad Radke	.07	.20
158 Torii Hunter	.07	.20
159 Chuck Knoblauch	.07	.20
160 Paul Molitor	.07	.20
161 Travis Miller	.07	.20
162 Rich Robertson	.07	.20
163 Ron Coomer	.07	.20
164 Mark Grudzielanek	.07	.20
165 Lee Smith	.07	.20
166 Vladimir Guerrero	.20	.50
167 Dustin Hermanson	.07	.20
168 Ugueth Urbina	.07	.20
169 F.P. Santangelo	.07	.20
170 Rondell White	.07	.20
171 Bobby Jones	.07	.20
172 Edgardo Alfonzo	.07	.20
173 John Franco	.07	.20
174 Carlos Baerga	.07	.20
175 Butch Huskey	.07	.20
176 Rey Ordonez	.07	.20
177 Matt Franco	.07	.20
178 Dwight Gooden	.07	.20
179 Chad Curtis	.07	.20
180 Tino Martinez	.10	.30
181 Charlie O'Brien MM	.07	.20
182 Sandy Alomar Jr. MM	.07	.20
183 Raul Casanova MM	.07	.20
184 Javier Lopez MM	.07	.20
185 Mike Piazza MM	.20	.50
186 Ivan Rodriguez MM	.07	.20
187 Charles Johnson MM	.07	.20
188 Brad Ausmus MM	.07	.20
189 Brian Johnson MM	.07	.20
190 Wade Boggs	.10	.30
191 David Wells	.07	.20
192 Tim Raines	.07	.20
193 Ramiro Mendoza	.07	.20
194 Willie Adams	.07	.20
195 Matt Stairs	.07	.20
196 Jason McDonald	.07	.20
197 Dave Magadan	.07	.20
198 Mark Bellhorn	.07	.20
199 Ariel Prieto	.07	.20
200 Jose Canseco	.10	.30
201 Bobby Estalella	.07	.20
202 Tony Barron RC	.07	.20
202A Kerry Wood		
203 Midre Cummings	.07	.20
204 Ricky Bottalico	.07	.20
205 Mike Grace	.07	.20
206 Rico Brogna	.07	.20
207 Mickey Morandini	.07	.20
208 Lou Collier	.07	.20
209 Kevin Polcovich	.07	.20
210 Kevin Young	.07	.20
211 Jose Guillen	.07	.20
212 Esteban Loaiza	.07	.20
213 Marc Wilkins	.07	.20
214 Jason Schmidt	.07	.20
215 Gary Gaetti	.07	.20
216 Fernando Valenzuela	.07	.20
217 Willie McGee	.07	.20
218 Alan Benes	.07	.20
219 Eli Marrero	.07	.20
220 Mark McGwire	.50	1.25
221 Matt Morris	.07	.20
222 Trevor Hoffman	.07	.20
223 Will Cunnane	.07	.20
224 Joey Hamilton	.07	.20
225 Ken Caminiti	.07	.20
226 Derrek Lee	.10	.30
227 Mark Sweeney	.07	.20
228 Carlos Hernandez	.07	.20
229 Brian Johnson	.07	.20
230 Jeff Kent	.07	.20
231 Kirk Rueter	.07	.20
232 Bill Mueller	.07	.20
233 Dante Powell	.07	.20
234 J.T. Snow	.07	.20
235 Shawn Estes	.07	.20
236 Dennis Martinez	.07	.20
237 Jamie Moyer	.07	.20
238 Dan Wilson	.07	.20
239 Joey Cora	.07	.20
240 Ken Griffey Jr.	.30	.75
241 Paul Sorrento	.07	.20
242 Jay Buhner	.07	.20
243 Hanley Frias RC	.07	.20
244 John Burkett	.07	.20
245 Juan Gonzalez	.07	.20
246 Rick Helling	.07	.20
247 Darren Oliver	.07	.20
248 Mickey Tettleton	.07	.20
249 Ivan Rodriguez	.10	.30
250 Joe Carter	.07	.20
251 Pat Hentgen	.07	.20
252 Marty Janzen	.07	.20
253 Frank Thomas TOP	.07	.20
Tony Gwynn		
254 Mark McGwire TOP	.20	.50
Ken Griffey Jr.		
Larry Walker		
255 Ken Griffey Jr. TOP	.10	.30
Andres Galarraga		
256 Brian L.Hunter TOP	.07	.20
Tony Womack		
257 Roger Clemens TOP	.10	.30
Denny Neagle		
258 Roger Clemens TOP	.20	.50
Curt Schilling		
259 Roger Clemens TOP	.20	.50
Pedro Martinez		
260 Randy Myers TOP	.07	.20
Jeff Shaw		
261 N. Garciaparra TOP	.10	.30
Scott Rolen		
262 Charlie O'Brien	.07	.20
263 Shannon Stewart	.07	.20
264 Robert Person	.07	.20
265 Carlos Delgado	.07	.20
266 Matt Williams CL	.07	.20
Travis Lee		
267 Nomar Garciaparra CL	.10	.30
Cal Ripken		
268 Mark McGwire CL	.20	.50
Mike Piazza		
269 Tony Gwynn CL	.10	.30
Ken Griffey Jr.		
270 Fred McGriff CL	.07	.20
Jose Cruz Jr.		
271 Andruw Jones GJ	.07	.20
272 Alex Rodriguez GJ	.20	.50
273 Juan Gonzalez GJ	.07	.20
274 Nomar Garciaparra GJ	.20	.50
275 Ken Griffey Jr. GJ	.20	.50
276 Tino Martinez GJ	.07	.20
277 Roger Clemens GJ	.20	.50
278 Barry Bonds GJ	.30	.75
279 Mike Piazza GJ	.20	.50
280 Tim Salmon	.10	.30
281 Gary DiSarcina	.07	.20
282 Cecil Fielder	.07	.20
283 Ken Hill	.07	.20
284 Troy Percival	.07	.20
285 Jim Edmonds	.07	.20
286 Allen Watson	.07	.20
287 Brian Anderson	.07	.20
288 Jay Bell	.07	.20
289 Jorge Fabregas	.07	.20
290 Devon White	.07	.20
291 Yamil Benitez	.07	.20
292 Jeff Suppan	.07	.20
293 Tony Batista	.07	.20
294 Brent Brede	.07	.20
295 Andy Benes	.07	.20
296 Felix Rodriguez	.07	.20
297 Karim Garcia	.07	.20
298 Omar Daal	.07	.20
299 Andy Stankiewicz	.07	.20
300 Matt Williams	.07	.20
301 Willie Blair	.07	.20
302 Ryan Klesko	.07	.20
303 Tom Glavine	.10	.30
304 Walt Weiss	.07	.20
305 Greg Maddux	.30	.75
306 Chipper Jones	.20	.50
307 Keith Lockhart	.07	.20
308 Andres Galarraga	.07	.20
309 Chris Hoiles	.07	.20
310 Roberto Alomar	.10	.30
311 Joe Carter	.07	.20
312 Doug Drabek	.07	.20
313 Jeffrey Hammonds	.07	.20
314 Rafael Palmeiro	.10	.30
315 Mike Mussina	.10	.30
316 Brady Anderson	.07	.20
317 B.J. Surhoff	.07	.20
318 Dennis Eckersley	.07	.20
319 Jim Leyritz	.07	.20
320 Mo Vaughn	.07	.20
321 Nomar Garciaparra	.30	.75
322 Reggie Jefferson	.07	.20
323 Tim Naehring	.07	.20
324 Troy O'Leary	.07	.20
325 Pedro Martinez	.10	.30
326 John Valentin	.07	.20
327 Mark Clark	.07	.20
328 Rod Beck	.07	.20
329 Mickey Morandini	.07	.20
330 Sammy Sosa	.20	.50
331 Jeff Blauser	.07	.20
332 Lance Johnson	.07	.20
333 Scott Servais	.07	.20
334 Kevin Tapani	.07	.20
335 Henry Rodriguez	.07	.20
336 Jaime Navarro	.07	.20
337 Benji Gil	.07	.20
338 James Baldwin	.07	.20
339 Mike Cameron	.07	.20
340 Ray Durham	.07	.20
341 Chris Snopek	.07	.20
342 Eddie Taubensee	.07	.20
343 Bret Boone	.07	.20
344 Willie Greene	.07	.20
345 Barry Larkin	.10	.30
346 Chris Stynes	.07	.20
347 Pete Harnisch	.07	.20
348 Dave Burba	.07	.20
349 Sandy Alomar Jr.	.07	.20
350 Kenny Lofton	.07	.20
351 Geronimo Berroa	.07	.20
352 Omar Vizquel	.10	.30
353 Travis Fryman	.07	.20
354 Dwight Gooden	.07	.20
355 Jim Thome	.10	.30
356 David Justice	.07	.20
357 Charles Nagy	.07	.20
358 Chad Ogea	.07	.20
359 Pedro Astacio	.07	.20
360 Larry Walker	.07	.20
361 Mike Lansing	.07	.20
362 Kirt Manwaring	.07	.20
363 Dante Bichette	.07	.20
364 Jamey Wright	.07	.20
365 Darryl Kile	.07	.20
366 Luis Gonzalez	.07	.20
367 Joe Randa	.07	.20
368 Raul Casanova	.07	.20
369 Damion Easley	.07	.20
370 Brian Hunter	.07	.20
371 Bobby Higginson	.07	.20
372 Brian Moehler	.07	.20
373 Scott Sanders	.07	.20
374 Jim Eisenreich	.07	.20
375 Derrek Lee	.10	.30
376 Jay Powell	.07	.20
377 Cliff Floyd	.07	.20
378 Alex Fernandez	.07	.20
379 Felix Heredia	.07	.20
380 Jeff Bagwell	.10	.30
381 Bill Spiers	.07	.20
382 Chris Holt	.07	.20
383 Carl Everett	.07	.20
384 Derek Bell	.07	.20
385 Moises Alou	.07	.20
386 Ramon Garcia	.07	.20
387 Mike Sweeney	.07	.20
388 Glendon Rusch	.07	.20
389 Kevin Appier	.07	.20
390 Dean Palmer	.07	.20
391 Jeff Conine	.07	.20
392 Johnny Damon	.10	.30
393 Jose Vizcaino	.07	.20
394 Todd Hollandsworth	.07	.20
395 Eric Karros	.07	.20
396 Todd Zeile	.07	.20
397 Chan Ho Park	.07	.20
398 Ismael Valdes	.07	.20
399 Eric Young	.07	.20
400 Hideo Nomo	.20	.50
401 Mark Loretta	.07	.20
402 Doug Jones	.07	.20
403 Jeromy Burnitz	.07	.20
404 John Jaha	.07	.20
405 Marquis Grissom	.07	.20
406 Mike Matheny	.07	.20
407 Todd Walker	.07	.20
408 Marty Cordova	.07	.20
409 Matt Lawton	.07	.20
410 Terry Steinbach	.07	.20
411 Pat Meares	.07	.20
412 Rick Aguilera	.07	.20
413 Otis Nixon	.07	.20
414 Derrick May	.07	.20
415 Carl Pavano	.07	.20
416 A.J. Hinch	.07	.20
417 Dave Dellucci RC	.15	.40
418 Bruce Chen	.07	.20
419 Darron Ingram RC	.07	.20
420 Sean Casey	.07	.20
421 Mark L. Johnson	.07	.20
422 Gabe Alvarez	.07	.20
423 Alex Gonzalez	.07	.20
424 Daryle Ward	.07	.20
425 Russell Branyan	.07	.20
426 Mike Caruso	.07	.20
427 Mike Kinkade RC	.07	.20
428 Ramon Hernandez	.07	.20
429 Matt Clement	.07	.20
430 Travis Lee	.07	.20
431 Shane Monahan	.07	.20
432 Rich Butler RC	.07	.20
433 Chris Widger	.07	.20
434 Jose Vidro	.07	.20
435 Carlos Perez	.07	.20
436 Ryan McGuire	.07	.20
437 Brian McRae	.07	.20
438 Al Leiter	.07	.20
439 Rich Becker	.07	.20
440 Todd Hundley	.07	.20
441 Dave Mlicki	.07	.20
442 Bernard Gilkey	.07	.20
443 John Olerud	.07	.20
444 Paul O'Neill	.10	.30
445 Andy Pettitte	.10	.30
446 David Cone	.07	.20
447 Chili Davis	.07	.20
448 Bernie Williams	.10	.30
449 Joe Girardi	.07	.20
450 Derek Jeter	.50	1.25
451 Mariano Rivera	.20	.50
452 George Williams	.07	.20
453 Kenny Rogers	.07	.20
454 Tom Candiotti	.07	.20
455 Rickey Henderson	.20	.50
456 Jason Giambi	.07	.20
457 Scott Spiezio	.07	.20
458 Doug Glanville	.07	.20
459 Desi Relaford	.07	.20
460 Curt Schilling	.07	.20
461 Bob Abreu	.07	.20
462 Gregg Jefferies	.07	.20
463 Scott Rolen	.10	.30
464 Mike Lieberthal	.07	.20
465 Tony Womack	.07	.20
466 Jermaine Allensworth	.07	.20
467 Francisco Cordova	.07	.20
468 Jon Lieber	.07	.20
469 Al Martin	.07	.20
470 Jason Kendall	.07	.20
471 Todd Stottlemyre	.07	.20
472 Royce Clayton	.07	.20
473 Brian Jordan	.07	.20
474 John Mabry	.07	.20
475 Ray Lankford	.07	.20
476 Delino DeShields	.07	.20
477 Ron Gant	.07	.20
478 Mark Langston	.07	.20
479 Steve Finley	.07	.20
480 Tony Gwynn	.25	.60
481 Andy Ashby	.07	.20
482 Wally Joyner	.07	.20
483 Greg Vaughn	.07	.20
484 Sterling Hitchcock	.07	.20
485 Kevin Brown	.10	.30
486 Orel Hershiser	.07	.20
487 Charlie Hayes	.07	.20
488 Darryl Hamilton	.07	.20
489 Mark Gardner	.07	.20
490 Barry Bonds	.60	1.50
491 Robb Nen	.07	.20
492 Kirk Rueter	.07	.20
493 Randy Johnson	.20	.50
494 Jeff Fassero	.07	.20
495 Alex Rodriguez	.30	.75
496 David Segui	.07	.20
497 Rich Amaral	.07	.20
498 Russ Davis	.07	.20
499 Bubba Trammell	.07	.20
500 Wade Boggs	.10	.30
501 Roberto Hernandez	.07	.20
502 Dave Martinez	.07	.20
503 Dennis Springer	.07	.20
504 Paul Sorrento	.07	.20
505 Wilson Alvarez	.07	.20
506 Mike Kelly	.07	.20
507 Albie Lopez	.07	.20
508 Tony Saunders	.07	.20
509 John Flaherty	.07	.20
510 Fred McGriff	.10	.30
511 Quinton McCracken	.07	.20
512 Terrell Wade	.07	.20
513 Kevin Stocker	.07	.20
514 Kevin Elster	.07	.20
515 Will Clark	.10	.30
516 Bobby Witt	.07	.20
517 Tom Goodwin	.07	.20
518 Aaron Sele	.07	.20
519 Lee Stevens	.07	.20
520 Rusty Greer	.07	.20
521 John Wetteland	.07	.20
522 Darrin Fletcher	.07	.20
523 Jose Canseco	.10	.30
524 Randy Myers	.07	.20
525 Jose Cruz Jr.	.07	.20
526 Shawn Green	.07	.20
527 Tony Fernandez	.07	.20
528 Alex Gonzalez	.07	.20
529 Ed Sprague	.07	.20
530 Roger Clemens	.40	1.00

1998 Collector's Choice Prime Choice Reserve

This special parallel version of the 18-card Rookie Class subset (numbers 415-432) was added to the product at the last minute. Each card is serial numbered to 500 on back.

Card	Low	High
COMPLETE SET (18)	40.00	80.00
*STARS: 15X TO 40X BASIC CARDS		
*ROOKIES: 8X TO 20X BASIC CARDS		

1998 Collector's Choice Crash the Game

These 90 different game cards were randomly seed at a rate of 1:5 exclusively into second series packs. Thirty different sluggers were each featured on three different parallel cards. The only difference in each card was one of three different game dates printed on front. If the featured player hit a home run during the series specified on the card front, the collector could mail the card in prior to the December 1st, 1998 deadline for a special upgraded Crash the Game Exchange card. Winners and losers are specified below with a "W" or "L" after each card description.

Card	Low	High
COMPLETE SET (90)	30.00	80.00
SER.2 STATED ODDS 1:5		
*INSTANT WIN: .75X TO 2X BASIC CRASH		
INSTANT WIN SER.2 STATED ODDS 1:721		
CG1A Ken Griffey Jr.	.60	1.50
June 26-28 W		
CG1B Ken Griffey Jr.	.60	1.50
July 7 L		
CG1C Ken Griffey Jr.	.60	1.50
Sept 21-24 W		
CG2A Travis Lee	.15	.40
July 27-30 L		
CG2B Travis Lee	.15	.40
Aug 27-30 L		
CG2C Travis Lee	.15	.40
Sept 17-20 L		
CG3A Larry Walker	.15	.40
July 17-19 L		
CG3B Larry Walker	.15	.40
Aug 27-30 W		
CG3C Larry Walker	.15	.40
Sept 25-27 W		
CG4A Tony Clark	.15	.40
July 9-12 W		
CG4B Tony Clark	.15	.40
June 30-July 2 L		
CG4C Tony Clark	.15	.40
Sept 4-6 L		
CG5A Cal Ripken	1.25	3.00
June 22-25 W		
CG5B Cal Ripken	1.25	3.00
July 7 L		
CG5C Cal Ripken	1.25	3.00
Sept 4-6 W		
CG6A Tim Salmon	.25	.60
June 22-25 L		
CG6B Tim Salmon	.25	.60
Aug 28-30 L		
CG6C Tim Salmon	.25	.60
Sept 14-15 L		
CG7A Vinny Castilla	.15	.40
June30-July2 W		
CG7B Vinny Castilla	.15	.40
Aug 27-30 W		
CG7C Vinny Castilla	.15	.40
Sept 7-10 W		
CG8A Fred McGriff	.25	.60
June 22-25 L		
CG8B Fred McGriff	.25	.60
July 3-5 L		
CG8C Fred McGriff	.25	.60
Sept 18-20 W		
CG9A Matt Williams	.15	.40
July 17-19 L		
CG9B Matt Williams	.15	.40
Sept 14-16 W		
CG9C Matt Williams	.15	.40
Sept 18-20 L		
CG10A Mark McGwire	1.00	2.50
July 7 L		
CG10B Mark McGwire	1.00	2.50
July 24-26 W		
CG10C Mark McGwire	1.00	2.50
Aug 18-19 W		
CG11A Albert Belle	.25	.60
July 3-5 L		
CG11B Albert Belle	.25	.60
Aug 21-23 W		
CG11C Albert Belle	.25	.60
Sept 11-13 L		
CG12A Jay Buhner	.15	.40
July 9-12 W		
CG12B Jay Buhner	.15	.40
Aug 6-9 L		
CG12C Jay Buhner	.15	.40
Sept 24-27 L		
CG13A Vladimir Guerrero	.40	1.00
June 22-25 L		
CG13B Vladimir Guerrero	.40	1.00
Aug 10-12 W		
CG13C Vladimir Guerrero	.40	1.00
Sept 14-16 W		
CG14A Andruw Jones	.25	.60
July 16-19 W		
CG14B Andruw Jones	.25	.60
Aug 27-30 W		
CG14C Andruw Jones	.25	.60
Sept 17-20 L		
CG15A Nomar Garciaparra	.60	1.50
July 9-12 L		
CG15B Nomar Garciaparra	.60	1.50
Aug 13-16 W		
CG15C Nomar Garciaparra	.60	1.50
Sept 24-27 W		
CG16A Ken Caminiti	.15	.40
June 26-28 W		
CG16B Ken Caminiti	.15	.40
July 13-15 W		
CG16C Ken Caminiti	.15	.40
Sept 10-13 L		
CG17A Sammy Sosa	.40	1.00

July 9-12 W
CG17B Sammy Sosa .40 1.00
Aug 27-30 W
CG17C Sammy Sosa .40 1.00
Sept 18-20 L
CG18A Ben Grieve .15 .40
June 30-July 2 W
CG18B Ben Grieve .15 .40
Aug 14-16 L
CG18C Ben Grieve .15 .40
Sept 24-27 L
CG19A Mo Vaughn .10 .10
July 7 L
CG19B Mo Vaughn .15 .40
Sept 7-9 L
CG19C Mo Vaughn .15 .40
Sept 24-27 W
CG20A Frank Thomas .40 1.00
July 7 L
CG20B Frank Thomas .40 1.00
July 17-19 W
CG20C Frank Thomas .40 1.00
Sept 4-6 L
CG21A Manny Ramirez .25 .60
July 9-12 L
CG21B Manny Ramirez .25 .60
Aug 13-16 W
CG21C Manny Ramirez .25 .60
Sept 18-20 W
CG22A Jeff Bagwell .25 .60
July 7 L
CG22B Jeff Bagwell .25 .60
Aug 28-30 W
CG22C Jeff Bagwell .25 .60
Sept 4-6 W
CG23A Jose Cruz Jr. .15 .40
July 9-12 L
CG23B Jose Cruz Jr. .15 .40
Aug 13-16 L
CG23C Jose Cruz Jr. .15 .40
Sept 18-20 L
CG24A Alex Rodriguez .60 1.50
July 7 W
CG24B Alex Rodriguez .60 1.50
Aug 6-9 W
CG24C Alex Rodriguez .60 1.50
Sept 21-23 W
CG25A Mike Piazza .60 1.50
June 22-25 W
CG25B Mike Piazza .60 1.50
July 7 L
CG25C Mike Piazza .60 1.50
Sept 10-13 W
CG26A Tino Martinez .25 .60
June 26-28 W
CG26B Tino Martinez .25 .60
July 9-12 L
CG26C Tino Martinez .25 .60
Aug 13-16 L
CG27A Chipper Jones .40 1.00
July 3-5 L
CG27B Chipper Jones .40 1.00
Aug 23-30 L
CG27C Chipper Jones .40 1.00
Sept 17-20 L
CG28A Juan Gonzalez .15 .40
July 7 L
CG28B Juan Gonzalez .15 .40
Aug 6-9 W
CG28C Juan Gonzalez .15 .40
Sept 11-13 W
CG29A Jim Thome .25 .60
June 22-23 L
CG29B Jim Thome .25 .60
July 23-26 W
CG29C Jim Thome .25 .60
Sept 24-27 L
CG30A Barry Bonds 1.25 3.00
July 7 W
CG30B Barry Bonds 1.25 3.00
Sept 4-6 L
CG30C Barry Bonds 1.25 3.00
Sept 18-20 W

1998 Collector's Choice Evolution Revolution

Randomly inserted in series one packs at the rate of one in 13, this 28-card set features a color photo of one player from each of the Major League's 28 teams of 1997 printed on a baseball jersey shaped card which folded out to display the players accomplishments.

COMPLETE SET (28) 25.00 60.00
SER.1 STATED ODDS 1:13
ER1 Tim Salmon .60 1.50
ER2 Greg Maddux 1.50 4.00
ER3 Cal Ripken 3.00 8.00
ER4 Mo Vaughn .40 1.00
ER5 Sammy Sosa 1.00 2.50
ER6 Frank Thomas 1.00 2.50
ER7 Barry Larkin .60 1.50
ER8 Jim Thome .60 1.50
ER9 Larry Walker .40 1.00
ER10 Travis Fryman .40 1.00
ER11 Gary Sheffield .40 1.00
ER12 Jeff Bagwell .60 1.50
ER13 Johnny Damon .60 1.50
ER14 Mike Piazza 1.50 4.00
ER15 Jeff Cirillo .40 1.00
ER16 Paul Molitor .40 1.00
ER17 Vladimir Guerrero 1.00 2.50
ER18 Todd Hundley .40 1.00
ER19 Tino Martinez .60 1.50
ER20 Jose Canseco .60 1.50
ER21 Scott Rolen .60 1.50
ER22 Al Martin .40 1.00
ER23 Mark McGwire 2.50 6.00
ER24 Tony Gwynn 1.25 3.00
ER25 Barry Bonds 3.00 8.00
ER26 Ken Griffey Jr. 1.50 4.00
ER27 Juan Gonzalez .40 1.00
ER28 Roger Clemens 2.00 5.00

1998 Collector's Choice Mini Bobbing Heads

Randomly inserted in packs at a rate of one in three, this 30-card insert set features specially enhanced miniatures that fold into a stand-up figure with a removable bobbing head.

COMPLETE SET (30) 8.00 20.00
SER.2 STATED ODDS 1:3
1 Tim Salmon .20 .50
2 Travis Lee .10 .30
3 Matt Williams .10 .30
4 Chipper Jones .30 .75
5 Greg Maddux UER .50 1.25
Card is numbered as 6
6 Cal Ripken 1.00 2.50
7 Nomar Garciaparra .50 1.25
8 Mo Vaughn .10 .30
9 Sammy Sosa .30 .75
10 Frank Thomas .30 .75
11 Kenny Lofton .10 .30
12 Jaret Wright .10 .30
13 Larry Walker .10 .30
14 Tony Clark .10 .30
15 Edgar Renteria .10 .30
16 Jeff Bagwell .20 .50
17 Mike Piazza .50 1.25
18 Vladimir Guerrero .30 .75
19 Derek Jeter .75 2.00
20 Ben Grieve .10 .30
21 Scott Rolen .20 .50
22 Mark McGwire .75 2.00
23 Tony Gwynn .40 1.00
24 Barry Bonds 1.00 2.50
25 Ken Griffey Jr. .50 1.25
26 Alex Rodriguez .50 1.25
27 Fred McGriff .20 .50
28 Juan Gonzalez .10 .30
29 Roger Clemens .60 1.50
30 Jose Cruz Jr. .10 .30

1998 Collector's Choice StarQuest

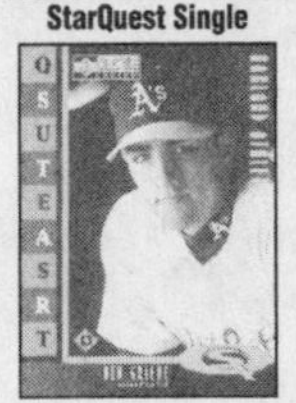

The 1998 Series one Collector's Choice 90-card tiered insert set, StarQuest, features color action player photos with a different number of stars printed below the player's name. The more stars on the card, the more collectible the card. The set contains the following subsets: Special Delivery (SQ1-SQ45), inserted one per pack; Students of the Game (SQ46-SQ65), randomly seeded at a rate of 1:21 packs; Super Powers (SQ66-SQ80), randomly seeded at a rate of 1:71 packs; and Superstar Domain (SQ81-SQ90), randomly seeded at a rate of 1:145 packs.

COMP.DELIV.SET (45) 8.00 20.00
COMMON DELIV (1-45) 2.50 6.00
COMP.STUDENT SET (20) 6.00 15.00
COMMON (46-65) 6.00 15.00
STUDENTS SER.1 STATED ODDS 1:21
COMP.POWERS SET (15) 6.00 15.00
COMM.POWERS (66-80) 6.00 15.00
POWERS SER.1 STATED ODDS 1:71
COMP.SUPERSTAR (10) 6.00 15.00
COM.SUPERSTAR (81-90) 6.00 15.00
SUPERSTAR SER.1 STATED ODDS 1:145
SQ1 N.Garciaparra SD .40 1.00
SQ2 Scott Rolen SD .15 .40
SQ3 Jason Dickson SD .08 .25
SQ4 Jaret Wright SD .08 .25
SQ5 Kevin Orie SD .08 .25
SQ6 Jose Guillen SD .08 .25
SQ7 Matt Morris SD .08 .25
SQ8 Mike Cameron SD .08 .25
SQ9 Kevin Polcovich SD .08 .25
SQ10 Jose Cruz Jr. SD .08 .25
SQ11 Miguel Tejada SD .25 .60
SQ12 Fernando Tatis SD .08 .25
SQ13 Todd Helton SD .15 .40
SQ14 Ken Cloude SD .08 .25
SQ15 Ben Grieve SD .08 .25
SQ16 Dante Powell SD .08 .25
SQ17 Bubba Trammell SD .08 .25
SQ18 J.Encarnacion SD .08 .25
SQ19 Derrek Lee SD .15 .40
SQ20 Paul Konerko SD .08 .25
SQ21 Richard Hidalgo SD .08 .25
SQ22 Denny Neagle SD .08 .25
SQ23 David Justice SD .08 .25
SQ24 Pedro Martinez SD .15 .40
SQ25 Greg Maddux SD .40 1.00
SQ26 Edgar Martinez SD .08 .25
SQ27 Cal Ripken SD .75 2.00
SQ28 Tim Salmon SD .15 .40
SQ29 Shawn Estes SD .08 .25
SQ30 Ken Griffey Jr. SD .40 1.00
SQ31 Brad Radke SD .08 .25
SQ32 Andy Pettitte SD .15 .40
SQ33 Curt Schilling SD .08 .25
SQ34 Raul Mondesi SD .08 .25
SQ35 Alex Rodriguez SD .40 1.00
SQ36 Jeff Kent SD .08 .25
SQ37 Jeff Bagwell SD .15 .40
SQ38 Juan Gonzalez SD .08 .25
SQ39 Barry Bonds SD .75 2.00
SQ40 Mark McGwire SD .60 1.50
SQ41 Frank Thomas SD .25 .60
SQ42 Ray Lankford SD .08 .25
SQ43 Tony Gwynn SD .30 .75
SQ44 Mike Piazza SD .40 1.00
SQ45 Tino Martinez SD .15 .40
SQ46 N.Garciaparra SG 2.50 6.00
SQ47 Paul Molitor SG .60 1.50
SQ48 C.Knoblauch SG .60 1.50
SQ49 Rusty Greer SG .60 1.50
SQ50 Cal Ripken SG 5.00 12.00
SQ51 Roberto Alomar SG 1.00 2.50
SQ52 Scott Rolen SG 1.00 2.50
SQ53 Derek Jeter SG 4.00 10.00
SQ54 Mark Grace SG 1.00 2.50
SQ55 Randy Johnson SG 1.50 4.00
SQ56 Craig Biggio SG 1.00 2.50
SQ57 Kenny Lofton SG .60 1.50
SQ58 Eddie Murray SG 1.50 4.00
SQ59 Ryne Sandberg SG 2.50 6.00
SQ60 R.Henderson SG 1.50 4.00
SQ61 Darin Erstad SG .60 1.50
SQ62 Jim Edmonds SG .60 1.50
SQ63 Ken Caminiti SG .60 1.50
SQ64 Ivan Rodriguez SG 1.00 2.50
SQ65 Tony Gwynn SG 2.00 5.00
SQ66 Tony Clark SP 1.50 4.00
SQ67 A.Galarraga SP 1.50 4.00
SQ68 Rafael Palmeiro SP 2.50 6.00
SQ69 Manny Ramirez SP 2.50 6.00
SQ70 Albert Belle SP 2.50 6.00
SQ71 Jay Buhner SP 1.50 4.00
SQ72 Mo Vaughn SP 1.50 4.00
SQ73 Barry Bonds SP 12.50 30.00
SQ74 Chipper Jones SP 4.00 10.00
SQ75 Jeff Bagwell SP 2.50 6.00
SQ76 Jim Thome SP 2.50 6.00
SQ77 Sammy Sosa SP 4.00 10.00
SQ78 Todd Hundley SP 1.50 4.00
SQ79 Matt Williams SP 1.50 4.00
SQ80 Vinny Castilla SP 1.50 4.00
SQ81 Jose Cruz Jr. SS 2.50 6.00
SQ82 Frank Thomas SS 6.00 15.00
SQ83 Juan Gonzalez SS 2.50 6.00
SQ84 Mike Piazza SS 10.00 25.00
SQ85 Alex Rodriguez SS 10.00 25.00
SQ86 Larry Walker SS 2.50 6.00
SQ87 Tino Martinez SS 4.00 10.00
SQ88 Greg Maddux SS 10.00 25.00
SQ89 Mark McGwire SS 15.00 40.00
SQ90 Ken Griffey Jr. SS 10.00 25.00

1998 Collector's Choice StarQuest Single

These cards, issued one per second series pack, feature 30 of the leading players in baseball. The fronts of the card have a player photo with the words "Star Quest" spelled down the left side. The player's name and position in on the bottom of the card. In addition, the bottom right corner mentions whether this is a singles, double, triple or home run.

COMPLETE SET (30) 4.00 10.00
*DOUBLE: 4X TO 10X STARQUEST SINGLE
DOUBLES SER.2 STATED ODDS 1:21
*TRIPLES: 12.5X TO 30X SQ SINGLE
TRIPLES SER.2 STATED ODDS 1:71
*HR'S: 30X TO 80X SQ SINGLE
HOME RUN: RANDOM INS.IN SER.2 PACKS
HOME RUN PRINT RUN 100 SERIAL #'d SETS
1 Ken Griffey Jr. .30 .75
2 Jose Cruz Jr. .07 .20
3 Cal Ripken .60 1.50
4 Roger Clemens .40 1.00
5 Frank Thomas .20 .50
6 Derek Jeter .50 1.25
7 Alex Rodriguez .30 .75
8 Andruw Jones .10 .30
9 Vladimir Guerrero .20 .50
10 Mark McGwire .50 1.25
11 Kenny Lofton .07 .20
12 Pedro Martinez .10 .30
13 Greg Maddux .30 .75
14 Larry Walker .07 .20
15 Barry Bonds .60 1.50
16 Chipper Jones .20 .50
17 Jeff Bagwell .10 .30
18 Juan Gonzalez .07 .20
19 Tony Gwynn .25 .60
20 Mike Piazza .30 .75
21 Tino Martinez .10 .30
22 Mo Vaughn .07 .20
23 Ben Grieve .07 .20
24 Scott Rolen .10 .30
25 Nomar Garciaparra .30 .75
26 Paul Konerko .07 .20
27 Jaret Wright .07 .20
28 Gary Sheffield .07 .20
29 Todd Helton .10 .30
30 Travis Lee .07 .20

1998 Collector's Choice Stick 'Ums

Randomly inserted at the rate of one in three first series packs, this 30-card set features color player photos printed on stickers that can be peeled off and restuck anywhere.

COMPLETE SET (30) 8.00 20.00
SER.1 STATED ODDS 1:3
1 Andruw Jones .20 .50
2 Chipper Jones .30 .75
3 Cal Ripken 1.00 2.50
4 Nomar Garciaparra .50 1.25
5 Mo Vaughn .10 .30
6 Ryne Sandberg .50 1.25
7 Sammy Sosa .30 .75
8 Frank Thomas .30 .75
9 Albert Belle .20 .50
10 Jim Thome .20 .50
11 Manny Ramirez .20 .50
12 Larry Walker .10 .30
13 Gary Sheffield .10 .30
14 Jeff Bagwell .20 .50
15 Mike Piazza .50 1.25
16 Paul Molitor .10 .30
17 Pedro Martinez .20 .50
18 Todd Hundley .10 .30
19 Derek Jeter .75 2.00
20 Tino Martinez .20 .50
21 Curt Schilling .10 .30
22 Mark McGwire .75 2.00
23 Tony Gwynn .40 1.00
24 Barry Bonds 1.00 2.50
25 Ken Griffey Jr. .50 1.25
26 Alex Rodriguez .50 1.25
27 Juan Gonzalez .10 .30
28 Ivan Rodriguez .20 .50
29 Roger Clemens .60 1.50
30 Jose Cruz Jr. .10 .30

1998 Collector's Choice Blowups 5x7

These 10 cards measure approximately 5" by 7". These cards were inserted one per second series retail box and feature oversize parallels of a selection of stars from the basic 1998 Collectors Choice set.

COMPLETE SET (10) 4.80 12.00
306 Chipper Jones .60 1.50
321 Nomar Garciaparra .50 1.25
360 Larry Walker .30 .75
450 Derek Jeter 1.25 3.00
463 Scott Rolen .30 .75
480 Tony Gwynn .60 1.50
490 Barry Bonds .60 1.50
495 Alex Rodriguez .75 2.00
525 Jose Cruz Jr. .20 .50
530 Roger Clemens .60 1.50

1998 Collector's Choice Cover Glory 5x7

This 10-card set measures approximately 5" by 7" and features action color player images on a red-and-black background. The backs carry player information with a "headline" and paragraph about the player.

COMPLETE SET (10) 5.00 12.00
1 Nomar Garciaparra .50 1.25
2 Roger Clemens .60 1.50
3 Larry Walker .20 .50
4 Mike Piazza .75 2.00
5 Mark McGwire 1.00 2.50
6 Tony Gwynn .60 1.50
7 Jose Cruz Jr. .20 .50
8 Frank Thomas .30 .75
9 Tino Martinez .20 .50
10 Ken Griffey Jr. 1.00 2.50

1998 Collector's Choice Golden Jubilee 5x7

These nine oversize cards measure approximately 5" by 7" and feature parallel cards of the golden jubilee subset in second series Collector's Choice.

COMPLETE SET (9) 4.80 12.00
271 Andruw Jones .40 1.00
272 Alex Rodriguez .60 1.50
273 Juan Gonzalez .20 .50
274 Nomar Garciaparra .60 1.50
275 Ken Griffey Jr. .75 2.00
276 Tino Martinez .20 .50
277 Roger Clemens .60 1.50
278 Barry Bonds .60 1.50
279 Mike Piazza .75 2.00

1998 Collector's Choice Retail Jumbos

These cards were available as a mail-away from Upper Deck. If a collector mailed in 10 wrappers and an amount for postage and handling they received this skip-numbered set from Upper Deck's redemption center.

COMPLETE SET (33) 12.00 30.00
1 Nomar Garciaparra .50 1.25
2 Roger Clemens .60 1.50
3 Larry Walker .25 .60
4 Mike Piazza .75 2.00
5 Mark McGwire .60 1.50
6 Tony Gwynn .60 1.50
7 Jose Cruz Jr. .08 .25
8 Frank Thomas .25 .60
35 Andruw Jones .30 .75
40 Cal Ripken 1.25 3.00
55 Ryne Sandberg .30 .75
60 Frank Thomas .25 .60
95 Gary Sheffield .30 .75
97 Charles Johnson .08 .25
145 Mike Piazza .75 2.00
160 Paul Molitor .30 .75
180 Tino Martinez .08 .25
220 Mark McGwire .60 1.50
225 Ken Caminiti .15 .40
240 Ken Griffey Jr. .60 1.50
242 Jay Buhner .08 .25
245 Juan Gonzalez .25 .60
249 Ivan Rodriguez .30 .75
SQ67 Andres Galarraga .15 .40
SQ68 Rafael Palmeiro .15 .40
SQ69 Manny Ramirez .30 .75
SQ70 Albert Belle .08 .25
SQ71 Jay Buhner .08 .25
SQ72 Mo Vaughn .08 .25
SQ73 Barry Bonds .60 1.50
SQ74 Chipper Jones .60 1.50
SQ75 Jeff Bagwell .30 .75
SQ76 Jim Thome .30 .75

1995 Collector's Choice SE

The 1995 Collector's Choice SE set (produced by Upper Deck) consists of 265 standard-size cards issued in foil packs. The fronts feature color action player photos with blue borders. The player's name, position and the team name are printed on the bottom of the photo. The SE logo in blue-foil appears in a top corner. On a white background, the backs carry another color player photo with a short player biography, career stats and 1994 highlights. Subsets featured include Rookie Class (1-25), Record Pace (26-30), Stat Leaders (137-144), Fantasy Team (249-260). There are no Rookie Cards in this set.

COMPLETE SET (265) 10.00 20.00
1 Alex Rodriguez .75 2.00
2 Derek Jeter .75 2.00
3 Dustin Hermanson .05 .15
4 Bill Pulsipher .05 .15
5 Terrell Wade .05 .15
6 Darren Dreifort .05 .15
7 LaTroy Hawkins .05 .15
8 Alex Ochoa .05 .15
9 Paul Wilson .05 .15
10 Ernie Young .05 .15
11 Alan Benes .05 .15
12 Garret Anderson .10 .30
13 Armando Benitez .05 .15
14 Robert Perez .05 .15
15 Herbert Perry .05 .15
16 Jose Silva .05 .15
17 Orlando Miller .05 .15
18 Russ Davis .05 .15
19 Jason Isringhausen .10 .30
20 Ray McDavid .05 .15
21 Duane Singleton .05 .15
22 Paul Shuey .05 .15
23 Steve Dunn .05 .15
24 Mike Lieberthal .10 .30
25 Chan Ho Park .10 .30
26 Ken Griffey Jr. RP .30 .75
27 Tony Gwynn RP .20 .50
28 Chuck Knoblauch RP .05 .15
29 Frank Thomas RP .20 .50
30 Matt Williams RP .05 .15
31 Chili Davis .10 .30
32 Chad Curtis .05 .15
33 Brian Anderson .05 .15
34 Chuck Finley .10 .30
35 Tim Salmon .20 .50
36 Bo Jackson .30 .75
37 Doug Drabek .05 .15
38 Craig Biggio .20 .50
39 Ken Caminiti .10 .30
40 Jeff Bagwell .20 .50
41 Darryl Kile .10 .30
42 John Hudek .05 .15
43 Brian L. Hunter .05 .15
44 Dennis Eckersley .10 .30
45 Mark McGwire .75 2.00
46 Brent Gates .05 .15
47 Steve Karsay .05 .15
48 Rickey Henderson .30 .75
49 Terry Steinbach .05 .15
50 Ruben Sierra .10 .30
51 Roberto Alomar .20 .50
52 Carlos Delgado .10 .30
53 Alex Gonzalez .05 .15
54 Joe Carter .10 .30
55 Paul Molitor .10 .30
56 Juan Guzman .05 .15
57 John Olerud .10 .30
58 Shawn Green .10 .30
59 Tom Glavine .20 .50
60 Greg Maddux .50 1.25
61 Roberto Kelly .05 .15
62 Ryan Klesko .10 .30
63 Javier Lopez .10 .30
64 Jose Oliva .05 .15
65 Fred McGriff .20 .50
66 Steve Avery .05 .15
67 David Justice .10 .30
68 Ricky Bones .05 .15
69 Cal Eldred .05 .15
70 Greg Vaughn .05 .15
71 Dave Nilsson .05 .15
72 Jose Valentin .05 .15
73 Matt Mieske .05 .15
74 Todd Zeile .05 .15
75 Ozzie Smith .50 1.25
76 Bernard Gilkey .05 .15
77 Ray Lankford .10 .30
78 Bob Tewksbury .05 .15
79 Mark Whiten .05 .15
80 Gregg Jefferies .05 .15
81 Randy Myers .05 .15
82 Shawon Dunston .05 .15
83 Mark Grace .20 .50
84 Derrick May .05 .15
85 Sammy Sosa .30 .75
86 Steve Trachsel .05 .15
87 Brett Butler .10 .30
88 Delino DeShields .05 .15
89 Orel Hershiser .10 .30
90 Mike Piazza .50 1.25
91 Todd Hollandsworth .05 .15
92 Eric Karros .10 .30
93 Ramon Martinez .05 .15
94 Tim Wallach .05 .15
95 Raul Mondesi .10 .30
96 Larry Walker .10 .30
97 Wil Cordero .05 .15
98 Marquis Grissom .10 .30
99 Ken Hill .05 .15
100 Cliff Floyd .10 .30
101 Pedro Martinez .20 .50
102 John Wetteland .10 .30
103 Rondell White .10 .30
104 Moises Alou .10 .30
105 Barry Bonds .75 2.00
106 Darren Lewis .05 .15
107 Mark Portugal .05 .15
108 Matt Williams .10 .30
109 W.VanLandingham .05 .15
110 Bill Swift .05 .15
111 Robby Thompson .05 .15
112 Rod Beck .05 .15
113 Darryl Strawberry .10 .30
114 Jim Thome .20 .50
115 Dave Winfield .10 .30
116 Eddie Murray .30 .75
117 Manny Ramirez .20 .50
118 Carlos Baerga .05 .15
119 Kenny Lofton .10 .30
120 Albert Belle .10 .30
121 Mark Clark .05 .15
122 Dennis Martinez .10 .30
123 Randy Johnson .30 .75
124 Jay Buhner .10 .30
125 Ken Griffey Jr. .50 1.25
126 Goose Gossage .10 .30
127 Tino Martinez .20 .50
128 Reggie Jefferson .05 .15
129 Edgar Martinez .20 .50
130 Gary Sheffield .10 .30
131 Pat Rapp .05 .15
132 Bret Barberie .05 .15
133 Chuck Carr .05 .15
134 Jeff Conine .10 .30
135 Charles Johnson .10 .30
136 Benito Santiago .10 .30
137 Matt Williams STL .05 .15
138 Jeff Bagwell STL .10 .30
139 Kenny Lofton STL .05 .15
140 Tony Gwynn STL .20 .50
141 Jimmy Key STL .05 .15
142 Greg Maddux STL .30 .75
143 Randy Johnson STL .20 .50
144 Lee Smith STL .05 .15
145 Bobby Bonilla .10 .30
146 Jason Jacome .05 .15
147 Jeff Kent .10 .30
148 Ryan Thompson .05 .15
149 Bobby Jones .05 .15
150 Bret Saberhagen .10 .30
151 John Franco .10 .30
152 Lee Smith .10 .30
153 Rafael Palmeiro .20 .50
154 Brady Anderson .10 .30
155 Cal Ripken Jr. 1.00 2.50
156 Jeffrey Hammonds .05 .15
157 Mike Mussina .20 .50
158 Chris Hoiles .05 .15
159 Ben McDonald .05 .15
160 Tony Gwynn .40 1.00
161 Joey Hamilton .05 .15
162 Andy Benes .05 .15
163 Trevor Hoffman .10 .30
164 Phil Plantier .05 .15
165 Derek Bell .05 .15
166 Bip Roberts .05 .15
167 Eddie Williams .05 .15
168 Fernando Valenzuela .10 .30
169 Mariano Duncan .05 .15
170 Lenny Dykstra .10 .30
171 Darren Daulton .10 .30
172 Danny Jackson .05 .15
173 Bobby Munoz .05 .15
174 Doug Jones .05 .15
175 Jay Bell .10 .30
176 Zane Smith .05 .15
177 Jon Lieber .05 .15
178 Carlos Garcia .05 .15
179 Orlando Merced .05 .15
180 Andy Van Slyke .20 .50
181 Rick Helling .05 .15
182 Rusty Greer .10 .30
183 Kenny Rogers UER .10 .30
(shows 110 wins in 1990)
184 Will Clark .20 .50
185 Jose Canseco .20 .50
186 Juan Gonzalez .10 .30
187 Dean Palmer .10 .30
188 Ivan Rodriguez .20 .50
189 John Valentin .05 .15
190 Roger Clemens .60 1.50
191 Aaron Sele .05 .15
192 Scott Cooper .05 .15
193 Mike Greenwell .05 .15
194 Mo Vaughn .10 .30
195 Andre Dawson .10 .30
196 Ron Gant .10 .30
197 Jose Rijo .05 .15
198 Bret Boone .10 .30
199 Deion Sanders .20 .50
200 Barry Larkin .20 .50
201 Hal Morris .05 .15
202 Reggie Sanders .10 .30
203 Kevin Mitchell .05 .15
204 Marvin Freeman .05 .15
205 Andres Galarraga .10 .30
206 Walt Weiss .05 .15
207 Charlie Hayes .05 .15
208 Dave Nied .05 .15
209 Dante Bichette .10 .30
210 David Cone .10 .30
211 Jeff Montgomery .05 .15
212 Felix Jose .05 .15
213 Mike Macfarlane .05 .15
214 Wally Joyner .10 .30
215 Bob Hamelin .05 .15
216 Brian McRae .05 .15
217 Kirk Gibson .10 .30
218 Lou Whitaker .10 .30
219 Chris Gomez .05 .15
220 Cecil Fielder .10 .30
221 Mickey Tettleton .05 .15
222 Travis Fryman .10 .30
223 Tony Phillips .05 .15
224 Rick Aguilera .05 .15
225 Scott Erickson .05 .15
226 Chuck Knoblauch .10 .30
227 Kent Hrbek .10 .30
228 Shane Mack .05 .15
229 Kevin Tapani .05 .15
230 Kirby Puckett .30 .75
231 Julio Franco .10 .30
232 Jack McDowell .05 .15
233 Jason Bere .05 .15
234 Alex Fernandez .05 .15
235 Frank Thomas .30 .75
236 Ozzie Guillen .10 .30
237 Robin Ventura .10 .30
238 Michael Jordan 1.00 2.50
239 Wilson Alvarez .05 .15
240 Don Mattingly .75 2.00
241 Jim Abbott .20 .50
242 Jim Leyritz .05 .15
243 Paul O'Neill .20 .50
244 Melido Perez .05 .15
245 Wade Boggs .20 .50
246 Mike Stanley .05 .15
247 Danny Tartabull .05 .15
248 Jimmy Key .10 .30
249 Greg Maddux FT .30 .75
250 Randy Johnson FT .20 .50
251 Bret Saberhagen FT .05 .15
252 John Wetteland FT .05 .15
253 Mike Piazza FT .30 .75
254 Jeff Bagwell FT .10 .30
255 Craig Biggio FT .10 .30
256 Matt Williams FT .05 .15
257 Wil Cordero FT .05 .15
258 Kenny Lofton FT .05 .15
259 Barry Bonds FT .40 1.00
260 Dante Bichette FT .05 .15
261 Ken Griffey Jr. CL .30 .75
262 Goose Gossage CL .05 .15
263 Cal Ripken CL .50 1.25
264 Kenny Rogers CL .05 .15
265 John Valentin CL .05 .15
P125 K.Griffey Jr. Promo .40 1.00

1995 Collector's Choice SE Gold Signature

A parallel to the basic 265-card Collector's Choice SE set, each card features a gold-foil replica signature on it. Inserted one in 35 packs, the fronts feature color action player photos with blue borders. Super packs inserted 1:720 contained 12 gold signature cards.

*STARS: 10X TO 25X BASIC CARDS
*ROOKIES: 8X TO 20X BASIC
STATED ODDS 1:35
TWELVE GOLD PER GOLD SUPER PACK

1995 Collector's Choice SE Silver Signature

A parallel to the basic 265-card Collector's Choice issue, each card has a silver-foil replica signature on the front. These cards were inserted one in every pack, two per mini jumbo and 12 per super pack (inserted 1:216).

COMPLETE SET (265) 30.00 60.00
*STARS: 1.25X TO 3X BASIC CARDS
*ROOKIES: 1X TO 2.5X BASIC
12 PER SILVER SUPER PACK

1914 Cracker Jack

The cards in this 144-card set measure approximately 2 1/4" by 3". This "Series of colored pictures of Famous Ball Players and Managers" was issued in packages of Cracker Jack in 1914. The cards have tinted photos set against red backgrounds and many are found with caramel stains. The set also contains Federal League players. The company claims to have printed 15 million cards. The 1914 series can be distinguished from the 1915 issue by the advertising found on the back of the cards. Team names are included for some players to show differences between the 1914 and 1915 issue.

Card	Low	High
COMPLETE SET (144)	70000.00	140000.00
1 Otto Knabe	300.00	600.00
2 Frank Baker	750.00	1500.00
3 Joe Tinker	1000.00	2000.00
4 Larry Doyle	200.00	400.00
5 Ward Miller	200.00	400.00
6 Eddie Plank	750.00	1500.00
Phila. AL		
7 Eddie Collins	750.00	1500.00
Phila. AL		
8 Rube Oldring	200.00	400.00
9 Artie Hoffman	200.00	400.00
10 John McInnis	200.00	400.00
11 George Stovall	200.00	400.00
12 Connie Mack MG	750.00	1500.00
13 Art Wilson	200.00	400.00
14 Sam Crawford	750.00	1500.00
15 Reb Russell	200.00	400.00
16 Howie Camnitz	200.00	400.00
17 Roger Bresnahan	750.00	1500.00
17B Roger Bresnahan NNO	2000.00	4000.00
18 Johnny Evers	750.00	1500.00
19 Chief Bender	750.00	1500.00
Phila. AL		
20 Cy Falkenberg	200.00	400.00
21 Heinie Zimmerman	200.00	400.00
22 Joe Wood	1250.00	2500.00
23 Chas.Comiskey OWN	750.00	1500.00
24 George Mullen	200.00	400.00
25 Michael Simon	200.00	400.00
26 James Scott	200.00	400.00
27 Bill Carrigan	200.00	400.00
28 Jack Barry	200.00	400.00
29 Vean Gregg	200.00	400.00
Cleveland		
30 Ty Cobb	5000.00	10000.00
31 Heinie Wagner	200.00	400.00
32 Mordecai Brown	750.00	1500.00
33 Amos Strunk	200.00	400.00
34 Ira Thomas	300.00	600.00
35 Harry Hooper	750.00	1500.00
36 Ed Walsh	750.00	1500.00
37 Grover C. Alexander	2000.00	4000.00
38 Red Dooin	200.00	400.00
Phila. NL		
39 Chick Gandil	750.00	1500.00
40 Jimmy Austin	200.00	400.00
St.L. AL		
41 Tommy Leach	200.00	400.00
42 Al Bridwell	200.00	400.00
43 Rube Marquard	750.00	1500.00
NY NL		
44 Charles Tesreau	200.00	400.00
45 Fred Luderus	200.00	400.00
46 Bob Groom	200.00	400.00
47 Josh Devore	200.00	400.00
Phila. NL		
48 Harry Lord	300.00	600.00
49 John Miller	200.00	400.00
50 John Hummell	200.00	400.00
51 Nap Rucker	200.00	400.00
52 Zach Wheat	750.00	1500.00
53 Otto Miller	200.00	400.00
54 Marty O'Toole	200.00	400.00
55 Dick Hoblitzel	200.00	400.00
Cinc.		
56 Clyde Milan	200.00	400.00
57 Walter Johnson	2000.00	4000.00
58 Wally Schang	200.00	400.00
59 Harry Gessler	200.00	400.00
60 Rollie Zeider	300.00	600.00
61 Ray Schalk	1000.00	2000.00
62 Jay Cashion	300.00	600.00
63 Babe Adams	200.00	400.00
64 Jimmy Archer	200.00	400.00
65 Tris Speaker	750.00	1500.00
66 Napoleon Lajoie	1250.00	2500.00
Cleve.		
67 Otis Crandall	200.00	400.00
68 Honus Wagner	4000.00	8000.00
69 John McGraw MG	750.00	1500.00
70 Fred Clarke	600.00	1200.00
71 Chief Meyers	200.00	400.00
72 John Boehling	200.00	400.00
73 Max Carey	750.00	1500.00
74 Frank Owens	200.00	400.00
75 Miller Huggins	600.00	1200.00
76 Claude Hendrix	200.00	400.00
77 Hughie Jennings MG	750.00	1500.00
78 Fred Merkle	200.00	400.00
79 Ping Bodie	200.00	400.00
80 Ed Ruelbach	200.00	400.00
81 Jim C. Delehanty	200.00	400.00
82 Gavvy Cravath	200.00	400.00
83 Russ Ford	200.00	400.00
84 Elmer E. Knetzer	200.00	400.00
85 Buck Herzog	200.00	400.00
86 Burt Shotton	200.00	400.00
87 Forrest Cady	200.00	400.00
88 Christy Mathewson	20000.00	50000.00
Pitching		
89 Lawrence Cheney	200.00	400.00
90 Frank Smith	200.00	400.00
91 Roger Peckinpaugh	200.00	400.00
92 Al Demaree N.Y. NL	200.00	400.00
93 Del Pratt	200.00	400.00
Throwing		
94 Eddie Cicotte	750.00	1500.00
95 Ray Keating	200.00	400.00
96 Beals Becker	200.00	400.00
97 John(Rube) Benton	200.00	400.00
98 Frank LaPorte	200.00	400.00
99 Frank Chance	2000.00	4000.00
100 Thomas Seaton	200.00	400.00
101 Frank Schulte	200.00	400.00
102 Ray Fisher	200.00	400.00
103 Joe Jackson	10000.00	20000.00
104 Vic Saier	200.00	400.00
105 James Lavender	200.00	400.00
106 Joe Birmingham	200.00	400.00
107 Tom Downey	200.00	400.00
108 Sherry Magee	200.00	400.00
Phila. NL		
109 Fred Blanding	200.00	400.00
110 Bob Bescher	200.00	400.00
111 Jim Callahan	200.00	400.00
112 Ed Sweeney	200.00	400.00
113 George Suggs	200.00	400.00
114 Geo.J. Moriarty	200.00	400.00
115 Addison Brennan	200.00	400.00
116 Rollie Zeider	200.00	400.00
117 Ted Easterly	200.00	400.00
118 Ed Konetchy	200.00	400.00
Pittsburgh		
119 George Perring	200.00	400.00
120 Mike Doolan	200.00	400.00
121 Hub Perdue	200.00	400.00
Boston NL		
122 Owen Bush	200.00	400.00
123 Slim Sallee	200.00	400.00
124 Earl Moore	200.00	400.00
125 Bert Niehoff	200.00	400.00
126 Walter Blair	200.00	400.00
127 Butch Schmidt	200.00	400.00
128 Steve Evans	200.00	400.00
129 Ray Caldwell	200.00	400.00
130 Ivy Wingo	200.00	400.00
131 George Baumgardner	200.00	400.00
132 Les Nunamaker	200.00	400.00
133 Branch Rickey MG	1000.00	2000.00
134 Armando Marsans	200.00	400.00
Cincinnati		
135 Bill Killefer	200.00	400.00
136 Rabbit Maranville	750.00	1500.00
137 William Rariden	200.00	400.00
138 Hank Gowdy	200.00	400.00
139 Rebel Oakes	200.00	400.00
140 Danny Murphy	200.00	400.00
141 Cy Barger	200.00	400.00
142 Eugene Packard	200.00	400.00
143 Jake Daubert	200.00	400.00
144 James C. Walsh	400.00	800.00

1915 Cracker Jack

The cards in this 176-card set measure approximately 2 1/4" by 3". When flipped over, a 1915 "series of 176" Cracker Jack card shows the back printing upside-down. Cards were available in boxes of Cracker Jack or from the company for "100 Cracker Jack coupons, or one coupon and 25 cents." An album was available for "50 coupons or one coupon and 10 cents." Because of this send-in offer, the 1915 Cracker Jack cards are noticeably easier to find than the 1914 Cracker Jack cards, although obviously neither set is plentiful. The set essentially duplicates E145-1 (1914 Cracker Jack) except for some additional cards and new poses. Players in the Federal League are indicated by FED in the checklist below.

Card	Low	High
COMPLETE SET (176)	35000.00	70000.00
COMMON CARD (1-144)	100.00	200.00
COMM. CARD (145-176)	125.00	250.00
1 Otto Knabe	300.00	600.00
2 Frank Baker	500.00	1000.00
3 Joe Tinker	400.00	800.00
4 Larry Doyle	125.00	250.00
5 Ward Miller	100.00	200.00
6 Eddie Plank	750.00	1500.00
St.L. FED		
7 Eddie Collins	400.00	800.00
Chicago AL		
8 Rube Oldring	100.00	200.00
9 Artie Hoffman	100.00	200.00
10 John McInnis	100.00	200.00
11 George Stovall	100.00	200.00
12 Connie Mack MG	400.00	800.00
13 Art Wilson	100.00	200.00
14 Sam Crawford	400.00	800.00
15 Reb Russell	100.00	200.00
16 Howie Camnitz	100.00	200.00
17 Roger Bresnahan	300.00	600.00
18 Johnny Evers	400.00	800.00
19 Chief Bender	400.00	800.00
Baltimore FED		
20 Cy Falkenberg	100.00	200.00
21 Heinie Zimmerman	100.00	200.00
22 Joe Wood	500.00	1000.00
23 C. Comiskey OWN	500.00	1000.00
24 George Mullen	100.00	200.00
25 Michael Simon	100.00	200.00
26 James Scott	100.00	200.00
27 Bill Carrigan	100.00	200.00
28 Jack Barry	125.00	250.00
29 Vean Gregg	100.00	200.00
Boston AL		
30 Ty Cobb	3000.00	6000.00
31 Heinie Wagner	100.00	200.00
32 Mordecai Brown	500.00	1000.00
33 Amos Strunk	100.00	200.00
34 Ira Thomas	100.00	200.00
35 Harry Hooper	300.00	600.00
36 Ed Walsh	400.00	800.00
37 Grover C. Alexander	1000.00	2000.00
38 Red Dooin	100.00	200.00
Cincinnati		
39 Chick Gandil	400.00	800.00
40 Jimmy Austin	125.00	250.00
Pitts. FED UER		
Biographical Information is wrong		
41 Tommy Leach	100.00	200.00
42 Al Bridwell	100.00	200.00
43 Rube Marquard	300.00	600.00
Brooklyn FED		
Although card says Federals, Marquard was in fact a Dodger in 1915		
44 Charles(Jeff) Tesreau	100.00	200.00
45 Fred Luderus	100.00	200.00
46 Bob Groom	100.00	200.00
47 Josh Devore	100.00	200.00
Boston NL		
48 Steve O'Neill	100.00	200.00
49 John Miller	100.00	200.00
50 John Hummell	100.00	200.00
51 Nap Rucker	100.00	200.00
52 Zach Wheat	300.00	600.00
53 Otto Miller	100.00	200.00
54 Marty O'Toole	100.00	200.00
55 Dick Hoblitzel	100.00	200.00
Boston AL		
56 Clyde Milan	100.00	200.00
57 Walter Johnson	1500.00	3000.00
58 Wally Schang	100.00	200.00
59 Harry Gessler	100.00	200.00
60 Oscar Dugey	100.00	200.00
61 Ray Schalk	400.00	800.00
62 Willie Mitchell	100.00	200.00
63 Babe Adams	100.00	200.00
64 Jimmy Archer	100.00	200.00
65 Tris Speaker	750.00	1500.00
66 Napoleon Lajoie	600.00	1200.00
Phila. AL		
67 Otis Crandall	100.00	200.00
68 Honus Wagner	3000.00	6000.00
69 John McGraw MG	400.00	800.00
70 Fred Clarke	300.00	600.00
71 Chief Meyers	125.00	250.00
72 John Boehling	100.00	200.00
73 Max Carey	400.00	800.00
74 Frank Owens	100.00	200.00
75 Miller Huggins	300.00	600.00
76 Claude Hendrix	100.00	200.00
77 Hughie Jennings MG	300.00	600.00
78 Fred Merkle	100.00	200.00
79 Ping Bodie	100.00	200.00
80 Ed Ruelbach	100.00	200.00
81 Jim C. Delehanty	100.00	200.00
82 Gavvy Cravath	100.00	200.00
83 Russ Ford	100.00	200.00
84 Elmer E. Knetzer	100.00	200.00
85 Buck Herzog	100.00	200.00
86 Burt Shotton	100.00	200.00
87 Forrest Cady	100.00	200.00
88 Christy Mathewson	1750.00	3500.00
Portrait		
89 Lawrence Cheney	100.00	200.00
90 Frank Smith	100.00	200.00
91 Roger Peckinpaugh	100.00	200.00
92 Al Demaree	100.00	200.00
Phila. NL		
93 Del Pratt	125.00	250.00
Portrait		
94 Eddie Cicotte	450.00	900.00
95 Ray Keating	100.00	200.00
96 Beals Becker	125.00	250.00
97 John(Rube) Benton	100.00	200.00
98 Frank LaPorte	100.00	200.00
99 Hal Chase	250.00	500.00
100 Thomas Seaton	100.00	200.00
101 Frank Schulte	100.00	200.00
102 Ray Fisher	100.00	200.00
103 Joe Jackson	7500.00	15000.00
104 Vic Saier	100.00	200.00
105 James Lavender	100.00	200.00
106 Joe Birmingham MG	100.00	200.00
107 Thomas Downey	100.00	200.00
108 Sherry Magee	100.00	200.00
Boston NL		
109 Fred Blanding	100.00	200.00
110 Bob Bescher	100.00	200.00
111 Herbie Moran	100.00	200.00
112 Ed Sweeney	100.00	200.00
113 George Suggs	100.00	200.00
114 Geo.J. Moriarty	100.00	200.00
115 Addison Brennan	100.00	200.00
116 Rollie Zeider	100.00	200.00
117 Ted Easterly	100.00	200.00
118 Ed Konetchy	100.00	200.00
Pitts. FED		
119 George Perring	100.00	200.00
120 Mike Doolan	100.00	200.00
121 Hub Perdue	100.00	200.00
St. Louis NL		
122 Owen Bush	100.00	200.00
123 Slim Sallee	100.00	200.00
124 Earl Moore	100.00	200.00
125 Bert Niehoff	100.00	200.00
Phila. NL		
126 Walter Blair	100.00	200.00
127 Butch Schmidt	100.00	200.00
128 Steve Evans	100.00	200.00
129 Ray Caldwell	100.00	200.00
130 Ivy Wingo	100.00	200.00
131 Geo. Baumgardner	100.00	200.00
132 Les Nunamaker	100.00	200.00
133 Branch Rickey MG	600.00	1200.00
134 Armando Marsans	125.00	250.00
St.L. FED		
135 William Killefer	100.00	200.00
136 Rabbit Maranville	300.00	600.00
137 William Rariden	100.00	200.00
138 Hank Gowdy	100.00	200.00
139 Rebel Oakes	100.00	200.00
140 Danny Murphy	100.00	200.00
141 Cy Barger	100.00	200.00
142 Eugene Packard	100.00	200.00
143 Jake Daubert	100.00	200.00
144 James C. Walsh	100.00	200.00
145 Ted Cather	125.00	250.00
146 George Tyler	125.00	250.00
147 Lee Magee	125.00	250.00
148 Owen Wilson	125.00	250.00
149 Hal Janvrin	125.00	250.00
150 Doc Johnston	125.00	250.00
151 George Whitted	125.00	250.00
152 George McQuillen	125.00	250.00
153 Bill James	125.00	250.00
154 Dick Rudolph	125.00	250.00
155 Joe Connolly	125.00	250.00
156 Jean Dubuc	125.00	250.00
157 George Kaiserling	125.00	250.00
158 Fritz Maisel	125.00	250.00
159 Heinie Groh	125.00	250.00
160 Benny Kauff	125.00	250.00
161 Edd Roush	500.00	1000.00
162 George Stallings MG	125.00	250.00
163 Bert Whaling	125.00	250.00
164 Bob Shawkey	125.00	250.00
165 Eddie Murphy	125.00	250.00
166 Joe Bush	125.00	250.00
167 Clark Griffith	300.00	600.00
168 Vin Campbell	125.00	250.00
169 Raymond Collins	125.00	250.00
170 Hans Lobert	125.00	250.00
171 Earl Hamilton	125.00	250.00
172 Erskine Mayer	125.00	250.00
173 Tilly Walker	125.00	250.00
174 Robert Veach	125.00	250.00
175 Joseph Benz	125.00	250.00
176 Hippo Vaughn	300.00	600.00

2002 Diamond Kings

This 160 card set was issued in two separate series. The first 150 cards were issued within the Diamond Kings brand of which was distributed in May, 2002. These cards were issued in four card packs with an SRP of $3.99 which came 24 packs to a box and 20 boxes to a case. Cards numbered 101 through 150 were printed in shorter supply than the other cards. Cards numbered 101 through 121 feature prospect while cards numbered 122 through 150 featured retired veterans. These cards were all issued at a stated rate of one in three packs. Cards 151-160 were issued within packs of 2002 Donruss the Rookies in mid-December, 2002 at the following ratios: hobby 1:10, retail 1:12. This set was noteworthy as Donruss/Playoff created a full set based on the tradition began in 1982 when the first Diamond King cards were created.

Card	Low	High
COMP.LOW SET (150)	100.00	200.00
COMP.LOW w/o SP's (100)	20.00	50.00
COMP.UPDATE SET (10)	15.00	40.00
COMMON CARD (1-100)	.20	.50
COMMON PROSPECT (101-150)	1.50	4.00
COMMON RETIRED (101-150)	1.50	4.00
COMMON CARD (151-160)	1.50	4.00
1 Vladimir Guerrero	.50	1.25
2 Adam Dunn	.20	.50
3 Tsuyoshi Shinjo	.20	.50
4 Adrian Beltre	.20	.50
5 Troy Glaus	.20	.50
6 Albert Pujols	1.00	2.50
7 Trot Nixon	.20	.50
8 Alex Rodriguez	.75	2.00
9 Tom Glavine	.30	.75
10 Alfonso Soriano	.20	.50
11 Todd Helton	.30	.75
12 Joe Torre	.30	.75
13 Tim Hudson	.20	.50
14 Andruw Jones	.30	.75
15 Shawn Green	.20	.50
16 Aramis Ramirez	.20	.50
17 Shannon Stewart	.20	.50
18 Barry Bonds	1.25	3.00
19 Sean Casey	.20	.50
20 Barry Larkin	.30	.75
21 Scott Rolen	.30	.75
22 Barry Zito	.20	.50
23 Sammy Sosa	.50	1.25
24 Bartolo Colon	.20	.50
25 Ryan Klesko	.20	.50
26 Ben Grieve	.20	.50
27 Roy Oswalt	.20	.50
28 Kazuhiro Sasaki	.20	.50
29 Roger Clemens	1.00	2.50
30 Bernie Williams	.30	.75
31 Roberto Alomar	.30	.75
32 Bobby Abreu	.20	.50
33 Robert Fick	.20	.50
34 Bret Boone	.20	.50
35 Rickey Henderson	.50	1.25
36 Brian Giles	.20	.50
37 Richie Sexson	.20	.50
38 Bud Smith	.20	.50
39 Richard Hidalgo	.20	.50
40 C. C. Sabathia	.20	.50
41 Rich Aurilia	.20	.50
42 Carlos Beltran	.20	.50
43 Raul Mondesi	.20	.50
44 Carlos Delgado	.20	.50
45 Randy Johnson	.50	1.25
46 Chan Ho Park	.20	.50
47 Rafael Palmeiro	.30	.75
48 Chipper Jones	.50	1.25
49 Phil Nevin	.20	.50
50 Cliff Floyd	.20	.50
51 Pedro Martinez	.30	.75
52 Craig Biggio	.30	.75
53 Paul LoDuca	.20	.50
54 Cristian Guzman	.20	.50
55 Pat Burrell	.20	.50
56 Curt Schilling	.20	.50
57 Orlando Cabrera	.20	.50
58 Darin Erstad	.20	.50
59 Omar Vizquel	.30	.75
60 Derek Jeter	1.25	3.00
61 Nomar Garciaparra	.75	2.00
62 Edgar Martinez	.30	.75
63 Moises Alou	.20	.50
64 Eric Chavez	.20	.50
65 Mike Sweeney	.20	.50
66 Frank Thomas	.50	1.25
67 Mike Piazza	.75	2.00
68 Gary Sheffield	.20	.50
69 Mike Mussina	.30	.75
70 Greg Maddux	.75	2.00
71 Juan Gonzalez	.20	.50
72 Hideo Nomo	.50	1.25
73 Miguel Tejada	.20	.50
74 Ichiro Suzuki	1.00	2.50
75 Matt Morris	.20	.50
76 Ivan Rodriguez	.30	.75
77 Mark Mulder	.20	.50
78 J.D. Drew	.20	.50
79 Mark Grace	.30	.75
80 Jason Giambi	.20	.50
81 Mark Buehrle	.20	.50
82 Jose Vidro	.20	.50
83 Manny Ramirez	.30	.75
84 Jeff Bagwell	.30	.75
85 Magglio Ordonez	.20	.50
86 Ken Griffey Jr.	.75	2.00
87 Luis Gonzalez	.20	.50
88 Jim Edmonds	.20	.50
89 Larry Walker	.20	.50
90 Jim Thome	.30	.75
91 Lance Berkman	.20	.50
92 Jorge Posada	.30	.75
93 Kevin Brown	.20	.50
94 Joe Mays	.20	.50
95 Kerry Wood	.20	.50
96 Mark Ellis	.20	.50
97 Austin Kearns	.20	.50
98 Jorge De La Rosa RC	.20	.50
99 Brandon Berger	.20	.50
100 Ryan Ludwick	.20	.50
101 Marlon Byrd SP	1.50	4.00
102 Brandon Backe SP RC	1.50	4.00
103 Juan Cruz SP	1.50	4.00
104 Anderson Machado SP RC	1.50	4.00
105 So Taguchi SP RC	1.50	4.00
106 Dewon Brazelton SP	1.50	4.00
107 Josh Beckett SP	1.50	4.00
108 John Buck SP	1.50	4.00
109 Jorge Padilla SP RC	1.50	4.00
110 Hee Seop Choi SP	1.50	4.00
111 Angel Berroa SP	1.50	4.00
112 Mark Teixeira SP	2.00	5.00
113 Victor Martinez SP	2.00	5.00
114 Kazuhisa Ishii SP RC	1.50	4.00
115 Dennis Tankersley SP	1.50	4.00
116 Wilson Valdez SP RC	1.50	4.00
117 Antonio Perez SP	1.50	4.00
118 Ed Rogers SP	1.50	4.00
119 Wilson Betemit SP	1.50	4.00
120 Mike Rivera SP	1.50	4.00
121 Mark Prior SP	1.25	3.00
122 Roberto Clemente SP	3.00	8.00
123 Roberto Clemente SP	3.00	8.00
124 Roberto Clemente SP	3.00	8.00
125 Roberto Clemente SP	3.00	8.00
126 Roberto Clemente SP	3.00	8.00
127 Babe Ruth SP	4.00	10.00
128 Ted Williams SP	3.00	8.00
129 Andre Dawson SP	1.50	4.00
130 Eddie Murray SP	2.00	5.00
131 Juan Marichal SP	1.50	4.00
132 Kirby Puckett SP	2.00	5.00
133 Alan Trammell SP	1.50	4.00
134 Bobby Doerr SP	1.50	4.00
135 Carlton Fisk SP	1.50	4.00
136 Eddie Mathews SP	2.00	5.00
137 Mike Schmidt SP	4.00	10.00
138 Catfish Hunter SP	1.50	4.00
139 Nolan Ryan SP UER	5.00	12.00
Wrong year notated for no-hitter		
140 George Brett SP	4.00	10.00
141 Gary Carter SP	1.50	4.00
142 Paul Molitor SP	1.50	4.00
143 Lou Gehrig SP	2.50	6.00
144 Ryne Sandberg SP	4.00	10.00
145 Tony Gwynn SP	2.50	6.00
146 Ron Santo SP	1.50	4.00
147 Cal Ripken SP	6.00	15.00
148 Al Kaline SP	2.00	5.00
149 Bo Jackson SP	2.00	5.00
150 Don Mattingly SP	4.00	10.00
151 Chris Snelling RC	1.50	4.00
152 Satoru Komiyama RC	1.50	4.00
153 Oliver Perez RC	1.50	4.00
154 Kirk Saarloos RC	1.50	4.00
155 Rene Reyes RC	1.50	4.00
156 Runelvys Hernandez RC	1.50	4.00
157 Rodrigo Rosario RC	1.50	4.00
158 Jason Simontacchi RC	1.50	4.00
159 Miguel Asencio RC	1.50	4.00
160 Aaron Cook RC	1.50	4.00

2002 Diamond Kings Bronze Foil

Inserted at a stated rate of one in six packs, this is a parallel to the Diamond King sets. These cards have white frames with bronze highlights.

*BRONZE 1-100: 1.5X TO 4X BASIC
*BRONZE 101-121: .4X TO 1X BASIC
*BRONZE 122-150: .4X TO 1X BASIC
*BRONZE 151-160: 1X TO 2.5X BASIC

2002 Diamond Kings Gold Foil

Randomly inserted in packs, this is a parallel to the Diamond Kings set. These cards can be differentiated by their having black frames with gold accents. 100 serial-numbered sets were printed.

*GOLD 1-100: 6X TO 15X BASIC
*GOLD 101-121: 1.5X TO 4X BASIC
*GOLD 122-150: 2.5X TO 6X BASIC
*GOLD 151-160: 1.5X TO 4X BASIC

2002 Diamond Kings Silver Foil

Randomly inserted in packs, this is a parallel to the Diamond Kings set. These cards can be differentiated by the grey frames and with silver accents. cards 1-150 are serial-numbered to 400 and 151-160 to 250.

*SILVER 1-100: 3X TO 8X BASIC
*SILVER 101-121: .75X TO 2X BASIC
*SILVER 122-150: 1.25X TO 3X BASIC
*SILVER 151-160: 1.25X TO 3X BASIC
151-160 PRINT RUN 250 SERIAL #'d SETS

2002 Diamond Kings Diamond Cut Collection

These 100 cards were inserted at an approximate rate of one per hobby box and as random inserts in retail packs. These cards feature a mix of autograph and memorabilia cards. The bat cards of Tony Gwynn and Kazuhisa Ishii were not ready by the time this product packed out. Thus, exchange cards with a deadline of November 1st, 2003 were seeded into packs. Serial-numbered print runs range between 100-500 copies per card.

Card	Low	High
DC1 Vladimir Guerrero AU/400	10.00	25.00
DC2 Mark Prior AU/400	10.00	25.00
DC3 Victor Martinez AU/500	8.00	20.00
DC4 Marlon Byrd AU/500	4.00	10.00
DC5 Bud Smith AU/400	4.00	10.00
DC6 Joe Mays AU/500	4.00	10.00
DC7 Troy Glaus AU/500	6.00	15.00
DC8 Ron Santo AU/500	12.50	30.00
DC9 Roy Oswalt AU/500	6.00	15.00
DC10 Angel Berroa AU/500	4.00	10.00
DC11 Mark Buehrle AU/500	12.50	30.00
DC12 John Buck AU/500	4.00	10.00
DC13 Barry Larkin AU/250	20.00	50.00
DC14 Gary Carter AU/250	10.00	25.00
DC15 Mark Teixeira AU/300	15.00	40.00
DC16 Alan Trammell AU/500	6.00	15.00
DC17 Kazuhisa Ishii AU/100	15.00	40.00
DC18 Rafael Palmeiro AU/125	30.00	60.00
DC19 Austin Kearns AU/500	4.00	10.00
DC20 Joe Torre AU/125	30.00	60.00
DC21 J.D. Drew AU/400	6.00	15.00
DC22 So Taguchi AU/400	12.50	30.00
DC23 Juan Marichal AU/500	6.00	15.00
DC24 Bobby Doerr AU/500	10.00	25.00
DC25 Carlos Beltran AU/500	6.00	15.00
DC26 Robert Fick AU/500	4.00	10.00
DC27 Albert Pujols AU/200	150.00	250.00
DC28 Shannon Stewart AU/500	6.00	15.00
DC29 Antonio Perez AU/500	4.00	10.00
DC30 Wilson Betemit AU/500	4.00	10.00
DC31 Alex Rodriguez Jsy/500	6.00	15.00
DC32 Curt Schilling Jsy/500	3.00	8.00
DC33 George Brett Jsy/300	10.00	25.00
DC34 Hideo Nomo Jsy/100	6.00	15.00
DC35 Ivan Rodriguez Jsy/500	4.00	10.00
DC36 Don Mattingly Jsy/200	10.00	25.00
DC37 Joe Mays Jsy/500	3.00	8.00
DC38 Lance Berkman Jsy/400	3.00	8.00
DC39 Tony Gwynn Jsy/500	6.00	15.00
DC40 Darin Erstad Jsy/400	3.00	8.00
DC41 Adrian Beltre Jsy/400	3.00	8.00
DC42 Frank Thomas Jsy/500	4.00	10.00
DC43 Cal Ripken Jsy/300	15.00	40.00
DC44 Jose Vidro Jsy/500	3.00	8.00
DC45 Randy Johnson Jsy/300	4.00	10.00
DC46 Carlos Delgado Jsy/500	3.00	8.00
DC47 Roger Clemens Jsy/400	6.00	15.00
DC48 Luis Gonzalez Jsy/500	3.00	8.00
DC49 Marlon Byrd Jsy/500	3.00	8.00
DC50 Carlton Fisk Jsy/500	4.00	10.00
DC51 Manny Ramirez Jsy/500	4.00	10.00
DC52 Vladimir Guerrero Jsy/500	4.00	10.00
DC53 Barry Larkin Jsy/500	4.00	10.00
DC54 Aramis Ramirez Jsy/500	3.00	8.00
DC55 Todd Helton Jsy/300	4.00	10.00
DC56 Carlos Beltran Jsy/250	3.00	8.00
DC57 Jeff Bagwell Jsy/250	4.00	10.00
DC58 Larry Walker Jsy/500	3.00	8.00
DC59 Al Kaline Jsy/200	4.00	10.00
DC60 Chipper Jones Jsy/500	4.00	10.00
DC61 Bernie Williams Jsy/500	4.00	10.00
DC62 Bud Smith Jsy/500	3.00	8.00
DC63 Edgar Martinez Jsy/500	4.00	10.00
DC64 Pedro Martinez Jsy/500	4.00	10.00
DC65 Andre Dawson Jsy/200	3.00	8.00
DC66 Mike Piazza Jsy/100	10.00	25.00
DC67 Barry Zito Jsy/500	3.00	8.00
DC68 Bo Jackson Jsy/300	4.00	10.00
DC69 Nolan Ryan Jsy/400	15.00	40.00
DC70 Troy Glaus Jsy/500	3.00	8.00
DC71 Jorge Posada Jsy/500	4.00	10.00
DC72 Ted Williams Jsy/100	50.00	100.00
DC73 N.Garciaparra Jsy/500	6.00	15.00
DC74 Catfish Hunter Jsy/100	6.00	15.00
DC75 Gary Carter Jsy/500	3.00	8.00
DC76 Craig Biggio Jsy/500	4.00	10.00
DC77 Andruw Jones Jsy/500	4.00	10.00
DC78 R.Henderson Jsy/300	4.00	10.00
DC79 Greg Maddux Jsy/400	6.00	15.00
DC80 Kerry Wood Jsy/500	3.00	8.00
DC81 Alex Rodriguez Bat/500	6.00	15.00
DC82 Don Mattingly Bat/425	10.00	25.00
DC83 Craig Biggio Bat/500	6.00	15.00
DC84 Kazuhisa Ishii Bat/375	4.00	10.00
DC85 Eddie Murray Bat/500	6.00	15.00
DC86 Carlton Fisk Bat/500	6.00	15.00
DC87 Tsuyoshi Shinjo Bat/500	4.00	10.00
DC88 Bo Jackson Bat/500	6.00	15.00
DC89 Eddie Mathews Bat/100	10.00	25.00
DC90 Chipper Jones Bat/500	6.00	15.00
DC91 Adam Dunn Bat/375	4.00	10.00
DC92 Tony Gwynn Bat/200	6.00	15.00
DC93 Kirby Puckett Bat/500	12.50	30.00
DC94 Andre Dawson Bat/500	4.00	10.00
DC95 Bernie Williams Bat/500	6.00	15.00
DC96 Rob. Clemente Bat/300	40.00	80.00
DC97 Babe Ruth Bat/100	150.00	250.00
DC98 Roberto Alomar Bat/500	6.00	15.00
DC99 Frank Thomas Bat/500	6.00	15.00
DC100 So Taguchi Bat/500	4.00	10.00

2002 Diamond Kings DK Originals

Randomly inserted in packs, these 15 cards are printed to a stated print run of 1000 serial numbered sets. These cards are printed on canvas board with a vintage Diamond King look to them.

Card	Low	High
COMPLETE SET (15)	75.00	150.00
DK1 Alex Rodriguez	5.00	12.00
DK2 Kazuhisa Ishii	3.00	8.00
DK3 Pedro Martinez	3.00	8.00
DK4 Nomar Garciaparra	5.00	12.00
DK5 Albert Pujols	6.00	15.00
DK6 Chipper Jones	3.00	8.00
DK7 So Taguchi	3.00	8.00
DK8 Jeff Bagwell	3.00	8.00
DK9 Vladimir Guerrero	3.00	8.00
DK10 Derek Jeter	8.00	20.00
DK11 Sammy Sosa	3.00	8.00
DK12 Ichiro Suzuki	6.00	15.00
DK13 Barry Bonds	8.00	20.00
DK14 Jason Giambi	3.00	8.00
DK15 Mike Piazza	5.00	12.00

2002 Diamond Kings Heritage Collection

Inserted in packs to a stated rate of one in 23 hobby and one in 46 retail packs, these 25 cards feature many of baseball's all-time greats highlighted on canvas board stock.

Card	Low	High
COMPLETE SET (25)	100.00	200.00
HC1 Lou Gehrig	4.00	10.00
HC2 Nolan Ryan	6.00	15.00
HC3 Ryne Sandberg	4.00	10.00
HC4 Ted Williams	5.00	12.00
HC5 Roberto Clemente	6.00	15.00
HC6 Mike Schmidt	5.00	12.00
HC7 Roger Clemens	5.00	12.00
HC8 Kirby Puckett	2.00	5.00
HC9 Andre Dawson	1.50	4.00
HC10 Carlton Fisk	1.50	4.00
HC11 Don Mattingly	5.00	12.00
HC12 Juan Marichal	1.50	4.00
HC13 George Brett	5.00	12.00
HC14 Bo Jackson	2.00	5.00
HC15 Eddie Mathews	2.00	5.00
HC16 Randy Johnson	2.00	5.00
HC17 Alan Trammell	1.50	4.00
HC18 Tony Gwynn	3.00	8.00
HC19 Paul Molitor	1.50	4.00
HC20 Barry Bonds	6.00	15.00
HC21 Eddie Murray	2.00	5.00
HC22 Catfish Hunter	1.50	4.00
HC23 Rickey Henderson	2.00	5.00
HC24 Cal Ripken	8.00	20.00
HC25 Babe Ruth	6.00	15.00

2002 Diamond Kings Recollection Autographs

Randomly inserted in packs, these cards are original Diamond Kings which Donruss/Playoff bought back and had the feature player sign. These cards are all numbered to differing amounts and we have notated that information in our checklist. No pricing is provided on quantities of 25 or less.

Card	Low	High
47 Alan Trammell 88 DK/110	15.00	40.00

2002 Diamond Kings T204

Randomly inserted in packs, these 25 cards are printed to a stated print run of 1000 serial numbered sets. These cards are designed just like the Ramly T204 set which was issued early in the 20th century.

Card	Low	High
COMPLETE SET (25)	125.00	250.00
RC1 Vladimir Guerrero	3.00	8.00
RC2 Jeff Bagwell	2.00	5.00

RC3 Barry Bonds 8.00 20.00
RC4 Rickey Henderson 3.00 8.00
RC5 Mike Piazza 5.00 12.00
RC6 Derek Jeter 8.00 20.00
RC7 Kazuhisa Ishii 2.00 5.00
RC8 Ichiro Suzuki 6.00 15.00
RC9 Chipper Jones 3.00 8.00
RC10 Sammy Sosa 3.00 8.00
RC11 Don Mattingly 6.00 15.00
RC12 Shawn Green 2.00 5.00
RC13 Nomar Garciaparra 5.00 12.00
RC14 Luis Gonzalez 2.00 5.00
RC15 Albert Pujols 6.00 15.00
RC16 Cal Ripken 10.00 25.00
RC17 Todd Helton 2.00 5.00
RC18 Hideo Nomo 3.00 8.00
RC19 Alex Rodriguez 5.00 12.00
RC20 So Taguchi 2.00 5.00
RC21 Lance Berkman 2.00 5.00
RC22 Tony Gwynn 4.00 10.00
RC23 Roger Clemens 6.00 15.00
RC24 Jason Giambi 2.00 5.00
RC25 Ken Griffey Jr. 5.00 12.00

2002 Diamond Kings Timeline

Issued at a stated rate of one in 60 hobby and one in 120 retail packs, these 10 cards feature two players who have something in common.

COMPLETE SET (10) 60.00 120.00
TL1 Lou Gehrig / Don Mattingly 6.00 15.00
TL2 Hideo Nomo / Ichiro Suzuki 4.00 10.00
TL3 Cal Ripken / Alex Rodriguez 8.00 20.00
TL4 Mike Schmidt / Scott Rolen 5.00 12.00
TL5 Ichiro Suzuki / Albert Pujols 5.00 12.00
TL6 Curt Schilling / Randy Johnson 4.00 10.00
TL7 Chipper Jones / Eddie Mathews 4.00 10.00
TL8 Lou Gehrig / Cal Ripken 8.00 20.00
TL9 Derek Jeter / Roger Clemens 6.00 15.00
TL10 Kazuhisa Ishii / So Taguchi 4.00 10.00

2002 Diamond Kings Hawaii

These cards were distributed in six-card cello-wrapped packets at the eBay booth of the Hawaii Trade Conference "Meet the Industry" event in late February, 2002. Each attendee received one packet at the presentation. The cards parallel the basic issue 2002 Donruss Diamond Kings distributed later that year, but can be readily distinguished by the "2002 Hawaii Trade Conference" gold foil logo stamped on the front.

*PARALLEL 20'S RANDOMLY INSERTED INTO PACKS
*PARALLEL: NO PRICING DUE TO SCARCITY
*BLUE PORT: RANDOMLY INSERTED INTO PACKS
*BLUE PORT: SERIAL #'D TO 1 OR 5
*BLUE PORT: NO PRICING DUE TO SCARCITY

2003 Diamond Kings Samples

Issued one per Beckett Baseball Card Magazine, these cards were issued to preview the 2003 Donruss Diamond Kings set. These cards parallel the regular set except the word "sample" is stamped in silver on the back.

*SAMPLES: 1.5X TO 4X BASIC CARDS

2003 Diamond Kings Samples Gold

Randomly inserted in Beckett Baseball Card Magazine, these cards feature the word "sample" on the back printed in gold. Usually the gold samples comprise 10 percent of all the samples produced.

*GOLD SAMPLES: 4X TO 10X BASIC CARDS

2003 Diamond Kings

This 200-card set was released in two separate series. The primary Diamond Kings product - containing cards 1-176 from the basic set - was issued in March, 2003. These cards were issued in five card packs with an $4 SRP. These packs came 24 packs to a box and 20 boxes to a case. Cards numbered 151 through 158 feature some of the leading rookie prospects and those cards were issued at a stated rate of one in six. Cards numbered 159 through 175 feature retired greats and those cards were also issued at a stated rate of one in six. Card number 176 features Cuban refugee Jose Contreras who was signed to a free agent contract before the 2003 season began. The Contreras card was not on the original checklist and is believed to be considerably scarcer than other RC's from the first series set. Cards 177-189/191-201 were distributed at a rate of 1:24 packs of DLP Rookies and Traded in December, 2003. Please note, card 190 does not exist.

COMP.LO SET (176) 60.00 150.00
COMP.LO SET w/o SP's (150) 20.00 50.00
COMMON CARD (1-150) .20 .50
COMMON CARD (151-158) .75 2.00
COMMON CARD (159-175) 1.50 4.00
COMMON CARD (177-201) 1.50 4.00
1 Darin Erstad .20 .50
2 Garret Anderson .20 .50
3 Troy Glaus .20 .50
4 David Eckstein .20 .50
5 Jarrod Washburn .20 .50
6 Adam Kennedy .20 .50
7 Jay Gibbons .20 .50
8 Tony Batista .20 .50
9 Melvin Mora .20 .50
10 Rodrigo Lopez .20 .50
11 Manny Ramirez .30 .75
12 Pedro Martinez .30 .75
13 Nomar Garciaparra .75 2.00
14 Rickey Henderson .50 1.25
15 Johnny Damon .30 .75
16 Derek Lowe .20 .50
17 Cliff Floyd .20 .50
18 Frank Thomas .50 1.25
19 Magglio Ordonez .20 .50
20 Paul Konerko .20 .50
21 Mark Buehrle .20 .50
22 C.C. Sabathia .20 .50
23 Omar Vizquel .30 .75
24 Jim Thome .30 .75
25 Ellis Burks .20 .50
26 Robert Fick .20 .50
27 Bobby Higginson .20 .50
28 Randall Simon .20 .50
29 Carlos Pena .20 .50
30 Carlos Beltran .20 .50
31 Paul Byrd .20 .50
32 Raul Ibanez .20 .50
33 Mike Sweeney .20 .50
34 Torii Hunter .20 .50
35 Corey Koskie .20 .50
36 A.J. Pierzynski .20 .50
37 Cristian Guzman .20 .50
38 Jacque Jones .20 .50
39 Derek Jeter 1.25 3.00
40 Bernie Williams .30 .75
41 Roger Clemens 1.00 2.50
42 Mike Mussina .30 .75
43 Jorge Posada .30 .75
44 Alfonso Soriano .30 .75
45 Jason Giambi .20 .50
46 Robin Ventura .20 .50
47 David Wells .20 .50
48 Tim Hudson .20 .50
49 Barry Zito .20 .50
50 Mark Mulder .20 .50
51 Miguel Tejada .20 .50
52 Eric Chavez .20 .50
53 Jermaine Dye .20 .50
54 Ichiro Suzuki 1.00 2.50
55 Edgar Martinez .30 .75
56 John Olerud .20 .50
57 Dan Wilson .20 .50
58 Joel Pineiro .20 .50
59 Kazuhiro Sasaki .20 .50
60 Freddy Garcia .20 .50
61 Aubrey Huff .20 .50
62 Steve Cox .20 .50
63 Randy Winn .20 .50
64 Alex Rodriguez .75 2.00
65 Juan Gonzalez .20 .50
66 Rafael Palmeiro .30 .75
67 Ivan Rodriguez .30 .75
68 Kenny Rogers .20 .50
69 Carlos Delgado .20 .50
70 Eric Hinske .20 .50
71 Roy Halladay .20 .50
72 Vernon Wells .20 .50
73 Shannon Stewart .20 .50
74 Curt Schilling .20 .50
75 Randy Johnson .50 1.25
76 Luis Gonzalez .20 .50
77 Mark Grace .30 .75
78 Junior Spivey .20 .50
79 Greg Maddux .75 2.00
80 Tom Glavine .30 .75
81 John Smoltz .30 .75
82 Chipper Jones .50 1.25
83 Gary Sheffield .20 .50
84 Andruw Jones .30 .75
85 Kerry Wood .20 .50
86 Fred McGriff .30 .75
87 Sammy Sosa .50 1.25
88 Mark Prior .30 .75
89 Ken Griffey Jr. .75 2.00
90 Barry Larkin .30 .75
91 Adam Dunn .20 .50
92 Sean Casey .20 .50
93 Austin Kearns .20 .50
94 Aaron Boone .20 .50
95 Larry Walker .20 .50
96 Todd Helton .30 .75
97 Jason Jennings .20 .50
98 Jay Payton .20 .50
99 Josh Beckett .20 .50
100 Mike Lowell .20 .50
101 A.J. Burnett .20 .50
102 Jeff Bagwell .30 .75
103 Craig Biggio .30 .75
104 Lance Berkman .20 .50
105 Roy Oswalt .20 .50
106 Wade Miller .20 .50
107 Shawn Green .20 .50
108 Adrian Beltre .20 .50
109 Hideo Nomo .50 1.25
110 Kazuhisa Ishii .20 .50
111 Odalis Perez .20 .50
112 Paul Lo Duca .20 .50
113 Ben Sheets .20 .50
114 Richie Sexson .20 .50
115 Jose Hernandez .20 .50
116 Vladimir Guerrero .50 1.25
117 Jose Vidro .20 .50
118 Tomo Ohka .20 .50
119 Andres Galarraga .20 .50
120 Bartolo Colon .20 .50
121 Mike Piazza .75 2.00
122 Roberto Alomar .30 .75
123 Mo Vaughn .20 .50
124 Al Leiter .20 .50
125 Edgardo Alfonzo .20 .50
126 Pat Burrell .20 .50
127 Bobby Abreu .20 .50
128 Mike Lieberthal .20 .50
129 Vicente Padilla .20 .50
130 Marlon Byrd .20 .50
131 Jason Kendall .20 .50
132 Brian Giles .20 .50
133 Aramis Ramirez .20 .50
134 Kip Wells .20 .50
135 Ryan Klesko .20 .50
136 Phil Nevin .20 .50
137 Brian Lawrence .20 .50
138 Sean Burroughs .20 .50
139 Mark Kotsay .20 .50
140 Barry Bonds 1.25 3.00
141 Jeff Kent .20 .50
142 Benito Santiago .20 .50
143 Kirk Rueter .20 .50
144 Jason Schmidt .20 .50
145 Jim Edmonds .20 .50
146 J.D. Drew .20 .50
147 Albert Pujols 1.00 2.50
148 Tino Martinez .30 .75
149 Matt Morris .20 .50
150 Scott Rolen .30 .75
151 Joe Borchard ROO .75 2.00
152 Cliff Lee ROO .75 2.00
153 Brian Tallet ROO .75 2.00
154 Freddy Sanchez ROO .75 2.00
155 Chone Figgins ROO .75 2.00
156 Kevin Cash ROO .75 2.00
157 Justin Wayne ROO .75 2.00
158 Ben Kozlowski ROO .75 2.00
159 Babe Ruth RET 4.00 10.00
160 Jackie Robinson RET 2.00 5.00
161 Ozzie Smith RET 3.00 8.00
162 Lou Gehrig RET 2.50 6.00
163 Stan Musial RET 2.50 6.00
164 Mike Schmidt RET 4.00 10.00
165 Carlton Fisk RET 2.00 5.00
166 George Brett RET 4.00 10.00
167 Dale Murphy RET 3.00 8.00
168 Cal Ripken RET 5.00 12.00
169 Tony Gwynn RET 2.00 5.00
170 Don Mattingly RET 4.00 10.00
171 Jack Morris RET 1.50 4.00
172 Ty Cobb RET 2.00 5.00
173 Nolan Ryan RET 4.00 10.00
174 Ryne Sandberg RET 3.00 8.00
175 Thurman Munson RET 2.00 5.00
176 Jose Contreras ROO RC 2.00 5.00
177 Hideki Matsui ROO RC 4.00 10.00
178 Jeremy Bonderman ROO RC 4.00 10.00
179 Brandon Webb ROO RC 3.00 8.00
180 Adam Loewen ROO RC 2.00 5.00
181 Chien-Ming Wang ROO RC 2.50 6.00
182 Hong-Chih Kuo ROO RC 3.00 8.00
183 Clint Barmes ROO RC 1.25 3.00
184 Guillermo Quiroz ROO RC 1.50 4.00
185 Edgar Gonzalez ROO RC 1.50 4.00
186 Todd Wellemeyer ROO RC 1.50 4.00
187 Dan Haren ROO RC 2.00 5.00
188 Dustin McGowan ROO RC 2.00 5.00
189 Preston Larrison ROO RC 2.00 5.00
191 Kevin Youkilis ROO RC 2.50 6.00
192 Bubba Nelson ROO RC 2.00 5.00
193 Chris Burke ROO RC 2.00 5.00
194 J.D. Durbin ROO RC 1.50 4.00
195 Ryan Howard ROO RC 8.00 20.00
196 Jason Kubel ROO RC 2.00 5.00
197 Brendan Harris ROO RC 2.00 5.00
198 Brian Bruney ROO RC 2.00 5.00
199 Ramon Nivar ROO RC 1.50 4.00
200 Rickie Weeks ROO RC 3.00 8.00
201 Delmon Young ROO RC 4.00 10.00

2003 Diamond Kings Bronze Foil

Randomly inserted in packs, this is a parallel to the Diamond Kings set. Cards 177-201 were randomly seeded into packs of DLP Rookies and Traded and unlike the first 176 cards are serial numbered to 200 copies per. The bronze cards can be identified by the white frames and the bronze foil used for the cards.

*BRONZE 1-150: 1.5X TO 4X BASIC
*BRONZE 151-158: .6X TO 1.5X BASIC
*BRONZE 159-175: .6X TO 1.5X BASIC
*BRONZE 176: .4X TO 1X BASIC
*BRZ 177-189/191-201: .5X TO 1.2X BASIC
181 Chien-Ming Wang ROO 10.00 25.00
182 Hong-Chih Kuo ROO 12.50 30.00
195 Ryan Howard ROO 12.50 30.00

2003 Diamond Kings Gold Foil

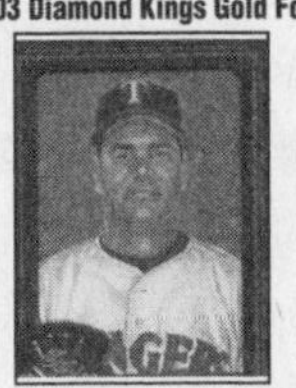

Randomly inserted into packs, this is a parallel to the Diamond Kings insert set. Cards 177-201 were randomly seeded into packs of DLP Rookies and Traded. These cards feature black frames which surround the gold foil usage. Cards 1-176 were issued to a stated print run of 100 serial numbered sets and 177-201 to a stated print run of 50 serial numbered copies per.

*GOLD 1-150: 6X TO 15X BASIC
*GOLD 151-158: 2X TO 5X BASIC
*GOLD 176: 1X TO 2.5X BASIC
*GOLD 177-201: 1.25X TO 3X BASIC
159 Babe Ruth RET 20.00 50.00
160 Jackie Robinson RET 10.00 25.00
161 Ozzie Smith RET 15.00 40.00
162 Lou Gehrig RET 12.50 30.00
163 Stan Musial RET 15.00 40.00
164 Mike Schmidt RET 20.00 50.00
165 Carlton Fisk RET 10.00 25.00
166 George Brett RET 20.00 50.00
167 Dale Murphy RET 25.00 60.00
168 Cal Ripken RET 30.00 80.00
169 Tony Gwynn RET 12.50 30.00
170 Don Mattingly RET 20.00 50.00
171 Jack Morris RET 8.00 20.00
172 Ty Cobb RET 15.00 40.00
173 Nolan Ryan RET 25.00 60.00
174 Ryne Sandberg RET 25.00 60.00
175 Thurman Munson RET 15.00 40.00
181 Chien-Ming Wang ROO 20.00 50.00
182 Hong-Chih Kuo ROO 30.00 60.00
195 Ryan Howard ROO 50.00 100.00
200 Rickie Weeks ROO 12.50 30.00
201 Delmon Young ROO 15.00 40.00

2003 Diamond Kings Silver Foil

Randomly inserted into packs, this is a parallel to the Diamond Kings set. Cards 177-201 were randomly seeded into packs of DLP Rookies and Traded. These cards can be identified by the grey frames surrounding the silver foil. Cards 1-176 were serial numbered to 400 and 177-201 were serial numbered to 100.

*SILVER 1-150: 3X TO 8X BASIC
*SILVER 151-158: 1X TO 2.5X BASIC
*SILVER 159-175: 1X TO 2.5X BASIC
*SILVER 176: .5X TO 1.2X BASIC
*SILVER 177-201: .6X TO 1.5X BASIC
181 Chien-Ming Wang ROO 12.50 30.00
182 Hong-Chih Kuo ROO 15.00 40.00
195 Ryan Howard ROO 20.00 50.00

2003 Diamond Kings Diamond Cut Collection

Randomly inserted into packs, this 110 card set features either an autograph or a game-used memorabilia piece. Since these cards are issued to a varying amount of cards, we have notated that information next to the player's name in our checklist.

1 Barry Zito AU/75 30.00 60.00
2 Edgar Martinez AU/125 30.00 60.00
3 Jay Gibbons AU/150 10.00 25.00
4 Joe Borchard AU/150 10.00 25.00
5 Marlon Byrd AU/150 10.00 25.00
6 Adam Dunn AU/150 20.00 50.00
7 Torii Hunter AU/150 12.50 30.00
8 Vladimir Guerrero AU/25
9 Wade Miller AU/150 10.00 25.00
10 Alfonso Soriano AU/100 20.00 50.00
11 Brian Lawrence AU/150 10.00 25.00
12 Cliff Floyd AU/100 12.50 30.00
13 Dale Murphy AU/75 30.00 60.00
14 Jack Morris AU/150 12.50 30.00
15 Eric Hinske AU/150 10.00 25.00
16 Jason Jennings AU/150 10.00 25.00
17 Mark Buehrle AU/150 30.00 60.00
18 Mark Prior AU/150 10.00 25.00
19 Mark Mulder AU/150 12.50 30.00
20 Mike Sweeney AU/150 12.50 30.00
21 Nolan Ryan AU/50 150.00 250.00
22 Don Mattingly AU/75 75.00 150.00
23 Andruw Jones AU/75 30.00 60.00
24 Aubrey Huff AU/150 12.50 30.00
25 Rickey Henderson AU/25
26 Nolan Ryan Jsy/250 20.00 50.00
27 Ozzie Smith Jsy/400 6.00 15.00
28 Rickey Henderson Jsy/300 4.00 10.00
29 Jack Morris Jsy/500 3.00 8.00
30 George Brett Jsy/350 8.00 20.00
31 Cal Ripken Jsy/300 15.00 40.00
32 Ryne Sandberg Jsy/450 8.00 20.00
33 Don Mattingly Jsy/400 8.00 20.00
34 Tony Gwynn Jsy/400 6.00 15.00
35 Dale Murphy Jsy/350 4.00 10.00
36 Carlton Fisk Jsy/400 4.00 10.00
37 Stan Musial Jsy/50
38 Lou Gehrig Jsy/50 150.00 250.00
39 Garret Anderson Jsy/450 3.00 8.00
40 Pedro Martinez Jsy/500 4.00 10.00
41 Nomar Garciaparra Jsy/350 6.00 15.00
42 Magglio Ordonez Jsy/450 3.00 8.00
43 C.C. Sabathia Jsy/500 3.00 8.00
44 Omar Vizquel Jsy/250 6.00 15.00
45 Jim Thome Jsy/500 4.00 10.00
46 Torii Hunter Jsy/500 3.00 8.00
47 Roger Clemens Jsy/500 6.00 15.00
48 Alfonso Soriano Jsy/400 3.00 8.00
49 Tim Hudson Jsy/500 3.00 8.00
50 Barry Zito Jsy/350 3.00 8.00
51 Mark Mulder Jsy/500 3.00 8.00
52 Miguel Tejada Jsy/400 3.00 8.00
53 John Olerud Jsy/350 3.00 8.00
54 Alex Rodriguez Jsy/500 6.00 15.00
55 Rafael Palmeiro Jsy/500 4.00 10.00
56 Curt Schilling Jsy/500 3.00 8.00
57 Randy Johnson Jsy/400 4.00 10.00
58 Greg Maddux Jsy/350 6.00 15.00
59 John Smoltz Jsy/400 4.00 10.00
60 Chipper Jones Jsy/450 4.00 10.00
61 Andruw Jones Jsy/500 4.00 10.00
62 Kerry Wood Jsy/500 3.00 8.00
63 Mark Prior Jsy/500 4.00 10.00
64 Adam Dunn Jsy/350 3.00 8.00
65 Larry Walker Jsy/500 3.00 8.00
66 Todd Helton Jsy/500 4.00 10.00
67 Jeff Bagwell Jsy/500 4.00 10.00
68 Roy Oswalt Jsy/500 3.00 8.00
69 Hideo Nomo Jsy/150 6.00 15.00
70 Kazuhisa Ishii Jsy/250 4.00 10.00
71 Vladimir Guerrero Jsy/500 4.00 10.00
72 Mike Piazza Jsy/500 6.00 15.00
73 Joe Borchard Jsy/500 3.00 8.00
74 Ryan Klesko Jsy/500 3.00 8.00
75 Shawn Green Jsy/500 3.00 8.00
76 George Brett Bat/350 8.00 20.00
77 Ozzie Smith Bat/450 6.00 15.00
78 Cal Ripken Bat/150 20.00 50.00
79 Don Mattingly Bat/400 8.00 20.00
80 Babe Ruth Bat/50 150.00 250.00
81 Dale Murphy Bat/350 4.00 10.00
82 Rickey Henderson Bat/500 4.00 10.00
83 Ivan Rodriguez Bat/500 4.00 10.00
84 Marlon Byrd Bat/500 3.00 8.00
85 Eric Chavez Bat/500 3.00 8.00
86 Nomar Garciaparra Bat/500 6.00 15.00
87 Alex Rodriguez Bat/500 6.00 15.00
88 Vladimir Guerrero Bat/500 4.00 10.00
89 Paul Lo Duca Bat/500 3.00 8.00
90 Richie Sexson Bat/500 3.00 8.00
91 Mike Piazza Bat/350 6.00 15.00
92 J.D. Drew Bat/500 3.00 8.00
93 Juan Gonzalez Bat/500 3.00 8.00
94 Pat Burrell Bat/500 3.00 8.00
95 Adam Dunn Bat/250 4.00 10.00
96 Mike Schmidt Bat/500 8.00 20.00
97 Ryne Sandberg Bat/500 8.00 20.00
98 Edgardo Alfonzo Bat/500 3.00 8.00
99 Andruw Jones Bat/500 4.00 10.00
100 Carlos Beltran Bat/500 3.00 8.00
101 Jeff Bagwell Bat/500 4.00 10.00
102 Lance Berkman Bat/500 3.00 8.00
103 Luis Gonzalez Bat/500 3.00 8.00
104 Carlos Delgado Bat/500 3.00 8.00
105 Jim Edmonds Bat/250 4.00 10.00
106 Alf Soriano Hat-Jsy/75 10.00 25.00
107 Greg Maddux Jsy-AU/50 100.00 200.00
108 Ty Cobb Pants-Bat/25
109 Adam Dunn Bat-AU/50 40.00 80.00
110 R.Henderson Jsy-Bat/50 10.00 25.00

2003 Diamond Kings DK Evolution

Issued at a stated rate of one in 18 hobby and one in 36 retail, this 25 card set features both the original photo as well as the artwork.

1 Cal Ripken 8.00 20.00
2 Ichiro Suzuki 5.00 12.00
3 Randy Johnson 2.50 6.00
4 Pedro Martinez 2.00 5.00
5 Nolan Ryan 6.00 15.00
6 Derek Jeter 6.00 15.00
7 Kerry Wood 2.00 5.00
8 Alex Rodriguez 4.00 10.00
9 Magglio Ordonez 2.00 5.00
10 Greg Maddux 4.00 10.00
11 Todd Helton 2.00 5.00
12 Sammy Sosa 2.50 6.00
13 Lou Gehrig 5.00 12.00
14 Lance Berkman 2.00 5.00
15 Barry Zito 2.00 5.00
16 Barry Bonds 6.00 15.00
17 Tom Glavine 2.00 5.00
18 Shawn Green 2.00 5.00
19 Roger Clemens 5.00 12.00
20 Nomar Garciaparra 4.00 10.00
21 Tony Gwynn 3.00 8.00
22 Vladimir Guerrero 2.50 6.00
23 Albert Pujols 5.00 12.00
24 Chipper Jones 2.50 6.00
25 Alfonso Soriano 2.00 5.00

2003 Diamond Kings Heritage Collection

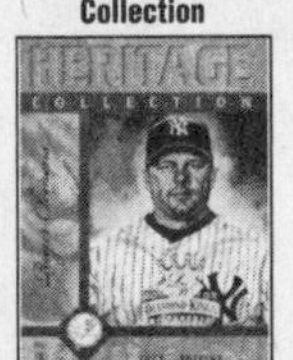

Issued at a stated rate of one in 23, this 25 card set features a mix of past and present superstars spotlighted with silver holo-foil on canvas board.

1 Ozzie Smith 4.00 10.00
2 Lou Gehrig 5.00 12.00
3 Stan Musial 4.00 10.00
4 Mike Schmidt 5.00 12.00
5 Carlton Fisk 2.00 5.00
6 George Brett 5.00 12.00
7 Dale Murphy 2.00 5.00
8 Cal Ripken 8.00 20.00
9 Tony Gwynn 3.00 8.00
10 Don Mattingly 5.00 12.00
11 Jack Morris 2.00 5.00
12 Ty Cobb 4.00 10.00
13 Nolan Ryan 6.00 15.00
14 Ryne Sandberg 5.00 12.00
15 Thurman Munson 2.50 6.00
16 Ichiro Suzuki 5.00 12.00
17 Derek Jeter 6.00 15.00
18 Greg Maddux 4.00 10.00
19 Sammy Sosa 2.50 6.00
20 Pedro Martinez 2.00 5.00
21 Alex Rodriguez 4.00 10.00
22 Roger Clemens 5.00 12.00
23 Barry Bonds 6.00 15.00
24 Lance Berkman 2.00 5.00
25 Vladimir Guerrero 2.50 6.00

2003 Diamond Kings HOF Heroes Reprints

Issued in the style of the 1983 Donruss Hall of Fame Heroes set, this set was issued at a stated rate of one in 43 hobby and one in 67 retail.

1 Bob Feller 3.00 8.00
2 Al Kaline 3.00 8.00
3 Lou Boudreau 3.00 8.00
4 Duke Snider 3.00 8.00
5 Jackie Robinson 3.00 8.00
6 Early Wynn 3.00 8.00
7 Yogi Berra 3.00 8.00
8 Stan Musial 4.00 10.00
9 Ty Cobb 4.00 10.00
10 Ted Williams 5.00 12.00

2003 Diamond Kings Recollection Autographs

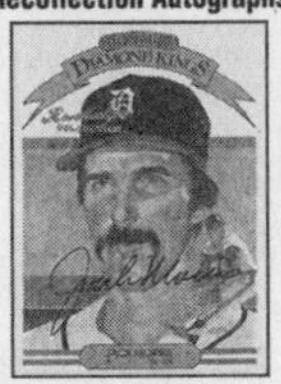

Randomly inserted in packs, these cards feature not only repurchased Donruss Diamond King cards but also an authentic autograph of the featured player. These cards were issued to a varying print run amount and we have notated that information next to the player's name in our checklist. Please note that for cards with a print run of 40 of fewer, no pricing is provided due to market scarcity.

SEE BECKETT.COM FOR PRINT RUNS
NO PRICING ON QTY OF 40 OR LESS
2 Brandon Berger 02 DK/99 6.00 15.00
9 Mark Buehrle 02 DK/73 15.00 40.00

2003 Diamond Kings Team Timeline

Randomly inserted into packs, these 10 cards feature both an active and retired player from the same team. Each of these cards are printed on canvas board and were issued to a stated print run of 1000 sets.

1 Nolan Ryan / Roy Oswalt 6.00 15.00
2 Dale Murphy / Chipper Jones 3.00 8.00
3 Stan Musial / Jim Edmonds 4.00 10.00
4 George Brett / Mike Sweeney 6.00 15.00
5 Tony Gwynn / Ryan Klesko 3.00 8.00
6 Carlton Fisk / Magglio Ordonez 3.00 8.00
7 Mike Schmidt / Pat Burrell 6.00 15.00
8 Don Mattingly / Bernie Williams 6.00 15.00
9 Ryne Sandberg / Kerry Wood 6.00 15.00
10 Lou Gehrig / Alfonso Soriano 5.00 12.00

2003 Diamond Kings Team Timeline Jerseys

Randomly inserted into packs, this is a parallel to the Team Timeline insert set. Each of these cards feature two game-worn jersey swatches and were issued to a stated print run of 100 serial numbered sets.

1 Nolan Ryan / Roy Oswalt 30.00 60.00
2 Dale Murphy / Chipper Jones 15.00 40.00
3 Stan Musial / Jim Edmonds 20.00 50.00
4 George Brett / Mike Sweeney 40.00 80.00
5 Tony Gwynn / Ryan Klesko 20.00 50.00
6 Carlton Fisk / Magglio Ordonez 15.00 40.00
7 Mike Schmidt / Pat Burrell 40.00 80.00
8 Don Mattingly / Bernie Williams 40.00 80.00
9 Ryne Sandberg / Kerry Wood 40.00 80.00
10 Lou Gehrig / Alfonso Soriano/50 150.00 250.00

2003 Diamond Kings Atlantic City National

Collectors who opened enough packs of Donruss product at the Donruss corporate booth at the 2003 National held in Atlantic City received copies of these Diamond King cards. The fronts of the card had special Atlantic City embossing while the backs were serial numbered to a stated print of five serial numbered copies. Due to market scarcity, no pricing is provided for these cards.

PRINT RUN 5 SERIAL #'d SETS

2003 Diamond Kings Chicago Collection

These cards were issued at the March, 2003 Chicago Sun-Times show. These cards parallel the Donruss Diamond King set and were available to collectors who opened three packs at the Donruss booth. For each three packs collectors opened, they received a specially stamped Diamond Kings cards stamped as "March Chicago Collection" and also with a stamped serial number. Each of these cards were issued to a stated print run of five serial numbered sets and no pricing is available due to market scarcity.

DIST.AT MARCH 03 SUN TIMES SHOW
STATED PRINT RUN 5 SERIAL #'d SETS
NO PRICING DUE TO SCARCITY

2003 Diamond Kings Heritage Collection Hawaii

These cards, which parallel the Diamond Kings Heritage Collection set were distributed at the Hawaii Trade Show conference. These cards were issued to a stated print run of 20 serial numbered sets and no pricing is available due to market scarcity.

DISTRIBUTED AT 2003 HAWAII CONFERENCE
STATED PRINT RUN 20 SERIAL #'d SETS
NO PRICING DUE TO SCARCITY

2003 Diamond Kings Team Timeline Hawaii

This set parallels the Team Timeline insert set. Each of these cards were specially distributed at the Hawaii Conference and were issued to a stated print run of 50 serial numbered sets.

*HAWAII: 2X TO 5X BASIC TIMELINE
DISTRIBUTED AT 2003 HAWAII CONFERENCE
STATED PRINT RUN 50 SERIAL #'d SETS

2003 Diamond Kings HOF Heroes Reprints Hawaii

These cards, which parallel the HOF Heroes Reprint set was distributed at the 2003 Hawaii Conference. These cards were issued to a stated print run of 50 serial numbered sets.

*HAWAII: 1X TO 2.5X BASIC HOF REPRINTS
DISTRIBUTED AT 2003 HAWAII CONFERENCE
STATED PRINT RUN 50 SERIAL #'d SETS

2004 Diamond Kings

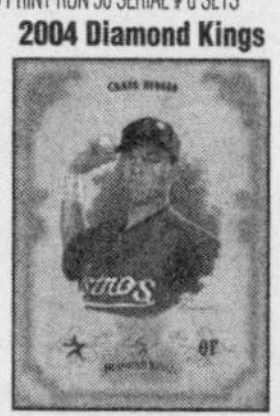

This 175-card set was released in February, 2004. This set was issued in five-card packs with an $6 SRP which came 12 packs to a box and 16 boxes to a case. This product has a dizzying amount of parallels and insert cards which included DK Materials which had two memorabilia pieces on each card and DK Combos which had not only those two memorabilia pieces but also had an authentic autograph from the player. In addition, many other insert sets were issued including a 134-card recollection autograph insert set as well as many other insert sets. This product; despite the seeming never-ending array of parallel and insert sets which made identifying cards difficult actually became one of the hobby hits of the first part of 2004. Cards numbered 1 through 150 feature current major leaguers while cards 151 through 158 are a flashback featuring some of today's players in an then and now format and cards numbered 159 through 175 is a legends subset. Cards numbered 151 through 175 were randomly inserted into packs.

COMPLETE SET w/Sepia (200)	75.00	200.00
COMPLETE SET (175)	40.00	100.00
COMP.SET w/o SP's (150)	15.00	40.00
COMMON CARD (1-150)	.20	.50
COMMON CARD (151-175)	.40	1.00
151-175 RANDOM INSERTS IN PACKS		
1 Alex Rodriguez	.75	2.00
2 Andruw Jones	.20	.50
3 Nomar Garciaparra	.50	1.25
4 Kerry Wood	.20	.50
5 Magglio Ordonez	.30	.75
6 Victor Martinez	.30	.75
7 Jeremy Bonderman	.20	.50
8 Josh Beckett	.30	.75
9 Jeff Kent	.20	.50
10 Carlos Beltran	.20	.50
11 Hideo Nomo	.50	1.25
12 Richie Sexson	.20	.50
13 Jose Vidro	.20	.50
14 Jae Weong Seo	.20	.50
15 Alfonso Soriano	.20	.50
16 Barry Zito	.20	.50
17 Brett Myers	.20	.50
18 Brian Giles	.20	.50
19 Edgar Martinez	.30	.75
20 Jim Edmonds	.30	.75
21 Rocco Baldelli	.20	.50
22 Mark Teixeira	.50	1.25
23 Carlos Delgado	.20	.50
24 Julius Matos	.20	.50
25 Jose Reyes	.30	.75
26 Marlon Byrd	.20	.50
27 Albert Pujols	1.25	3.00
28 Vernon Wells	.20	.50
29 Garret Anderson	.20	.50
30 Jerome Williams	.20	.50
31 Chipper Jones	.50	1.25
32 Rich Harden	.20	.50
33 Manny Ramirez	.50	1.25
34 Derek Jeter	1.25	3.00
35 Brandon Webb	.20	.50
36 Mark Prior	.30	.75
37 Roy Halladay	.50	1.25
38 Frank Thomas	.50	1.25
39 Rafael Palmeiro	.30	.75
40 Adam Dunn	.30	.75
41 Aubrey Huff	.20	.50
42 Todd Helton	.30	.75
43 Matt Morris	.20	.50
44 Dontrelle Willis	.20	.50
45 Lance Berkman	.30	.75
46 Mike Sweeney	.20	.50
47 Kazuhisa Ishii	.20	.50
48 Torii Hunter	.20	.50
49 Vladimir Guerrero	.50	1.25
50 Mike Piazza	.50	1.25
51 Alexis Rios	.30	.75
52 Shannon Stewart	.20	.50
53 Eric Hinske	.20	.50
54 Jason Jennings	.20	.50
55 Jason Giambi	.20	.50
56 Brandon Claussen	.20	.50
57 Joe Thurston	.20	.50
58 Ramon Nivar	.20	.50
59 Jay Gibbons	.20	.50
60 Eric Chavez	.20	.50
61 Jimmy Gobble	.20	.50
62 Walter Young	.20	.50
63 Mark Grace	.30	.75
64 Austin Kearns	.20	.50
65 Bob Abreu	.20	.50
66 Hee Seop Choi	.20	.50
67 Brandon Phillips	.20	.50
68 Rickie Weeks	.20	.50
69 Luis Gonzalez	.20	.50
70 Mariano Rivera	.50	1.25
71 Jason Lane	.20	.50
72 Xavier Nady	.20	.50
73 Runelvys Hernandez	.20	.50
74 Aramis Ramirez	.20	.50
75 Ichiro Suzuki	.75	2.00
76 Cliff Lee	.30	.75
77 Chris Snelling	.20	.50
78 Ryan Wagner	.20	.50
79 Miguel Tejada	.30	.75
80 Juan Gonzalez	.20	.50
81 Joe Borchard	.20	.50
82 Gary Sheffield	.20	.50
83 Wade Miller	.20	.50
84 Jeff Bagwell	.30	.75
85 Ryan Church	.20	.50
86 Adrian Beltre	.20	.50
87 Jeff Baker	.20	.50
88 Adam Loewen	.20	.50
89 Bernie Williams	.30	.75
90 Pedro Martinez	.30	.75
91 Carlos Rivera	.20	.50
92 Junior Spivey	.20	.50
93 Tim Hudson	.30	.75
94 Troy Glaus	.20	.50
95 Ken Griffey Jr.	.75	2.00
96 Alexis Gomez	.20	.50
97 Antonio Perez	.20	.50
98 Dan Haren	.20	.50
99 Ivan Rodriguez	.30	.75
100 Randy Johnson	.50	1.25
101 Lyle Overbay	.20	.50
102 Oliver Perez	.20	.50
103 Miguel Cabrera	.50	1.25
104 Scott Rolen	.30	.75
105 Roger Clemens	.60	1.50
106 Brian Tallet	.20	.50
107 Nic Jackson	.20	.50
108 Angel Berroa	.20	.50
109 Hank Blalock	.20	.50
110 Ryan Klesko	.20	.50
111 Jose Castillo	.20	.50
112 Paul Konerko	.30	.75
113 Greg Maddux	.75	2.00
114 Mark Mulder	.20	.50
115 Pat Burrell	.20	.50
116 Garrett Atkins	.20	.50
117 Jeremy Guthrie	.20	.50
118 Orlando Cabrera	.20	.50
119 Nick Johnson	.20	.50
120 Tom Glavine	.30	.75
121 Morgan Ensberg	.20	.50
122 Sean Casey	.20	.50
123 Orlando Hudson	.20	.50
124 Hideki Matsui	.75	2.00
125 Craig Biggio	.30	.75
126 Adam LaRoche	.20	.50
127 Hong-Chih Kuo	.20	.50
128 Paul Lo Duca	.20	.50
129 Shawn Green	.20	.50
130 Luis Castillo	.20	.50
131 Joe Crede	.20	.50
132 Ken Harvey	.20	.50
133 Freddy Sanchez	.20	.50
134 Roy Oswalt	.30	.75
135 Curt Schilling	.30	.75
136 Alfredo Amezaga	.20	.50
137 Chien-Ming Wang	1.00	2.50
138 Barry Larkin	.30	.75
139 Trot Nixon	.20	.50
140 Jim Thome	.30	.75
141 Bret Boone	.20	.50
142 Jacque Jones	.20	.50
143 Travis Hafner	.20	.50
144 Sammy Sosa	.50	1.25
145 Mike Mussina	.30	.75
146 Vinny Chulk	.20	.50
147 Chad Gaudin	.20	.50
148 Delmon Young	.30	.75
149 Mike Lowell	.20	.50
150 Rickey Henderson	.50	1.25
151 Roger Clemens FB	1.25	3.00
152 Mark Grace FB	.60	1.50
153 Rickey Henderson FB	1.00	2.50
154 Alex Rodriguez FB	1.50	4.00
155 Rafael Palmeiro FB	.60	1.50
156 Greg Maddux FB	1.50	4.00
157 Mike Piazza FB	1.00	2.50
158 Mike Mussina FB	.60	1.50
159 Dale Murphy LGD	.60	1.50
160 Cal Ripken LGD	4.00	10.00
161 Carl Yastrzemski LGD	1.00	2.50
162 Marty Marion LGD	.40	1.00
163 Don Mattingly LGD	2.00	5.00
164 Robin Yount LGD	1.00	2.50
165 Andre Dawson LGD	.60	1.50
166 Jim Palmer LGD	.40	1.00
167 George Brett LGD	2.00	5.00
168 Whitey Ford LGD	.60	1.50
169 Roy Campanella LGD	1.00	2.50
170 Roger Maris LGD	1.00	2.50
171 Duke Snider LGD	.60	1.50
172 Steve Carlton LGD	.40	1.00
173 Stan Musial LGD	1.50	4.00
174 Nolan Ryan LGD	3.00	8.00
175 Deion Sanders LGD	.60	1.50

2004 Diamond Kings Sepia

*SEPIA: .75X TO 2X BASIC

2004 Diamond Kings Bronze

*BRONZE 1-150: 3X TO 8X BASIC
*BRONZE 151-175: 1.25X TO 3X BASIC
STATED PRINT RUN 100 SERIAL #'d SETS

2004 Diamond Kings Bronze Sepia

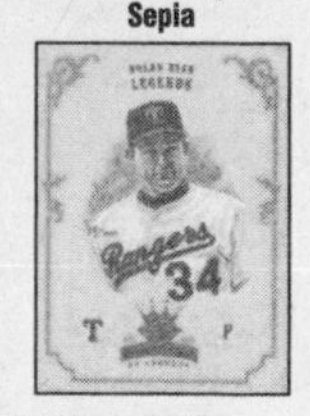

*BRONZE SEPIA: 1.25X TO 3X BASIC
STATED PRINT RUN 100 SERIAL #'d SETS

2004 Diamond Kings Platinum

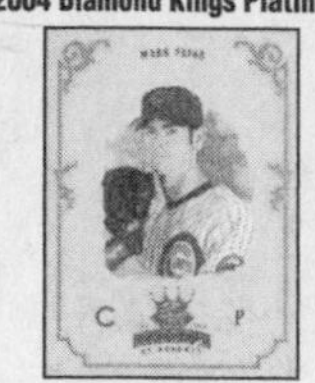

STATED PRINT RUN 1 SERIAL #'d SET
NO PRICING DUE TO SCARCITY

2004 Diamond Kings Platinum Sepia

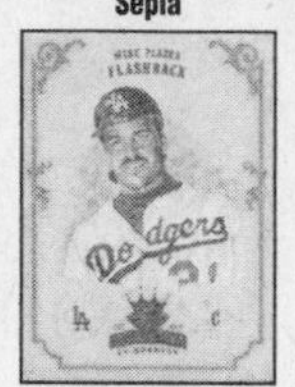

STATED PRINT RUN 1 SERIAL #'d SET
NO PRICING DUE TO SCARCITY

2004 Diamond Kings Silver

*SILVER 1-150: 5X TO 12X BASIC
*SILVER 151-175: 2X TO 5X BASIC
STATED PRINT RUN 50 SERIAL #'d SETS

2004 Diamond Kings Silver Sepia

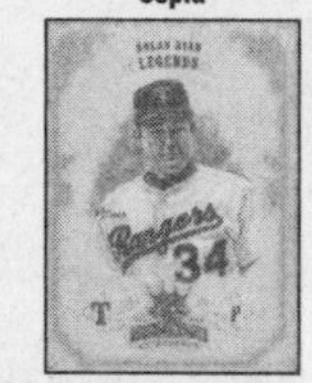

*SILVER SEPIA: 2X TO 5X BASIC
STATED PRINT RUN 50 SERIAL #'d SETS

2004 Diamond Kings Framed Platinum Grey

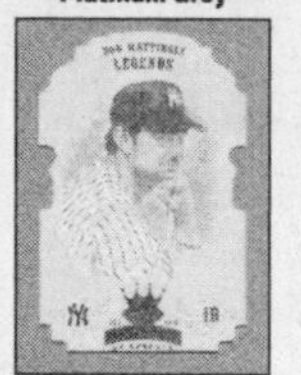

STATED PRINT RUN 1 SERIAL #'d SET
NO PRICING DUE TO SCARCITY

2004 Diamond Kings Framed Bronze

*FRAMED BRZ 1-150: 1.5X TO 4X BASIC
*FRAMED BRZ 151-175: .75X TO 2X BASIC
STATED ODDS 1:6

2004 Diamond Kings Framed Bronze Sepia

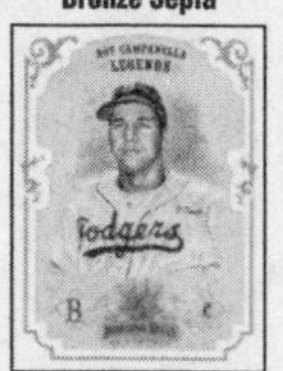

*FRAMED BRZ.SEPIA: .75X TO 2X BASIC
STATED ODDS 1:6

2004 Diamond Kings Framed Gold

*FRAMED GOLD 1-150: 10X TO 25X BASIC
*FRAMED GOLD 150-175: 4X TO 10X BASIC
STATED PRINT RUN 25 SERIAL #'d SETS

2004 Diamond Kings Framed Gold Sepia

*FRAMED GOLD SEPIA: 4X TO 10X BASIC
STATED PRINT RUN 25 SERIAL #'d SETS

2004 Diamond Kings Framed Platinum Black

STATED PRINT RUN 1 SERIAL #'d SET
NO PRICING DUE TO SCARCITY

2004 Diamond Kings Framed Platinum Black Sepia

STATED PRINT RUN 1 SERIAL #'d SET
NO PRICING DUE TO SCARCITY

2004 Diamond Kings Framed Platinum Grey Sepia

STATED PRINT RUN 1 SERIAL #'d SET
NO PRICING DUE TO SCARCITY

2004 Diamond Kings Framed Platinum White

STATED PRINT RUN 1 SERIAL #'d SET
NO PRICING DUE TO SCARCITY

2004 Diamond Kings Framed Platinum White Sepia

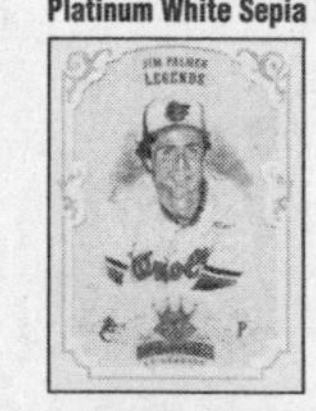

STATED PRINT RUN 1 SERIAL #'d SET
NO PRICING DUE TO SCARCITY

2004 Diamond Kings Framed Silver

*FRAMED SLV 1-150: 4X TO 10X BASIC
*FRAMED SLV 151-175: 1.5X TO 4X BASIC
STATED PRINT RUN 100 SERIAL #'d SETS

2004 Diamond Kings Framed Silver Sepia

*FRAMED SLV SEPIA: 1.5X TO 4X BASIC
STATED PRINT RUN 100 SERIAL #'d SETS

2004 Diamond Kings DK Combos Bronze

RANDOM INSERTS IN PACKS
PRINT RUNS B/WN 1-30 COPIES PER
NO PRICING ON QTY OF 10 OR LESS

26 Marlon Byrd Bat-Jsy/30	12.50	30.00
32 Rich Harden Jsy-Jsy/15	20.00	50.00
35 Brandon Webb Bat-Jsy/15	15.00	40.00
41 Aubrey Huff Bat-Jsy/15	20.00	50.00
53 Eric Hinske Bat-Jsy/30	12.50	30.00
57 Joe Thurston Bat-Jsy/25	12.50	30.00
59 Jay Gibbons Jsy-Jsy/15	15.00	40.00
62 Walter Young Bat-Bat/15	15.00	40.00
65 Bob Abreu Bat-Jsy/15	20.00	50.00
71 Jason Lane Bat-Hat/15	20.00	50.00
73 Run Hernandez Jsy-Jsy/15	15.00	40.00
74 Aramis Ramirez Bat-Bat/15	40.00	80.00
77 Chris Snelling Bat-Bat/15	15.00	40.00
81 Joe Borchard Bat-Jsy/15	15.00	40.00
92 Junior Spivey Bat-Jsy/15	15.00	40.00
98 Dan Haren Bat-Jsy/15	15.00	40.00
101 Lyle Overbay Bat-Jsy/30	12.50	30.00
103 Miguel Cabrera Bat-Jsy/30	30.00	60.00
108 Angel Berroa Bat-Pants/30	12.50	30.00
109 Hank Blalock Bat-Jsy/30	15.00	40.00
111 Jose Castillo Bat-Bat/15	15.00	40.00
121 Morgan Ensberg Bat-Jsy/30	15.00	40.00
123 Orlando Hudson Bat-Jsy/30	12.50	30.00
126 Adam LaRoche Bat-Bat/30	12.50	30.00
127 Hong-Chih Kuo Bat-Bat/15	75.00	150.00
130 Luis Castillo Bat-Jsy/30	12.50	30.00
133 Freddy Sanchez Bat-Bat/15	15.00	40.00
136 Alfredo Amezaga Bat-Jsy/15	15.00	40.00
143 Travis Hafner Bat-Jsy/30	15.00	40.00
147 Chad Gaudin Jsy-Jsy/25	12.50	30.00

2004 Diamond Kings DK Combos Bronze Sepia

PRINT RUNS B/WN 1-5 COPIES PER
NO PRICING DUE TO SCARCITY

2004 Diamond Kings DK Combos Gold

PRINT RUNS B/WN 1-5 COPIES PER
NO PRICING DUE TO SCARCITY

2004 Diamond Kings DK Combos Gold Sepia

STATED PRINT RUN 1 SERIAL #'d SET
NO PRICING DUE TO SCARCITY

2004 Diamond Kings DK Combos Platinum

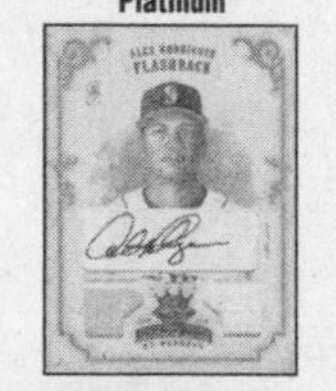

STATED PRINT RUN 1 SERIAL #'d SET
NO PRICING DUE TO SCARCITY

2004 Diamond Kings DK Combos Platinum Sepia

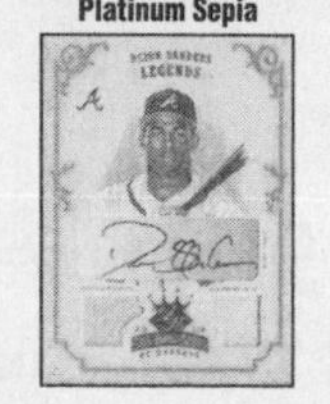

STATED PRINT RUN RUN 1 SERIAL #'d SET
NO PRICING DUE TO SCARCITY

2004 Diamond Kings DK Combos Silver

PRINT RUNS B/WN 1-15 COPIES PER
NO PRICING ON QTY OF 10 OR LESS

26 Marlon Byrd Bat-Jsy/15	15.00	40.00
101 Lyle Overbay Bat-Jsy/15	15.00	40.00
103 Miguel Cabrera Bat-Jsy/15	40.00	80.00
108 Angel Berroa Bat-Pants/15	15.00	40.00
109 Hank Blalock Bat-Jsy/15	20.00	50.00
121 Morgan Ensberg Bat-Jsy/15	20.00	50.00
123 Orlando Hudson Bat-Jsy/15	15.00	40.00
126 Adam LaRoche Bat-Bat/15	15.00	40.00
130 Luis Castillo Bat-Jsy/15	15.00	40.00
143 Travis Hafner Bat-Jsy/15	20.00	50.00

2004 Diamond Kings DK Combos Silver Sepia

PRINT RUNS B/WN 1-3 COPIES PER
NO PRICING DUE TO SCARCITY

2004 Diamond Kings DK Combos Framed Bronze

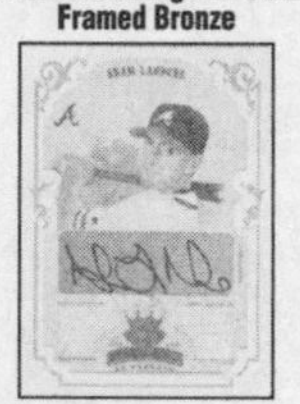

RANDOM INSERTS IN PACKS
PRINT RUNS B/WN 1-25 COPIES PER
NO PRICING ON QTY OF 10 OR LESS

26 Marlon Byrd Bat-Jsy/25	10.00	25.00
35 Brandon Webb Bat-Jsy/25	10.00	25.00
53 Eric Hinske Bat-Jsy/25	10.00	25.00
57 Joe Thurston Bat-Jsy/25	10.00	25.00
59 Jay Gibbons Jsy-Jsy/25	10.00	25.00
62 Walter Young Bat-Bat/25	10.00	25.00
65 Bob Abreu Bat-Jsy/25	15.00	40.00
71 Jason Lane Bat-Hat/25	15.00	40.00
74 Aramis Ramirez Bat-Bat/25	20.00	50.00
77 Chris Snelling Bat-Bat/25	10.00	25.00
81 Joe Borchard Bat-Jsy/25	10.00	25.00
92 Junior Spivey Bat-Jsy/25	10.00	25.00
97 Antonio Perez Bat-Pants/25	10.00	25.00
98 Dan Haren Bat-Jsy/25	10.00	25.00
101 Lyle Overbay Bat-Jsy/25	10.00	25.00
103 Miguel Cabrera Bat-Jsy/25	20.00	50.00
107 Nic Jackson Bat-Bat/25	10.00	25.00
108 Angel Berroa Bat-Pants/25	10.00	25.00
109 Hank Blalock Bat-Jsy/25	15.00	40.00
110 Ryan Klesko Bat-Jsy/15	20.00	50.00
111 Jose Castillo Bat-Bat/25	10.00	25.00
112 Paul Konerko Bat-Jsy/15	30.00	60.00
121 Morgan Ensberg Bat-Jsy/25	15.00	40.00
123 Orlando Hudson Bat-Jsy/25	10.00	25.00
126 Adam LaRoche Bat-Bat/25	10.00	25.00
127 Hong-Chih Kuo Bat-Bat/25	20.00	50.00
130 Luis Castillo Bat-Jsy/25	10.00	25.00
133 Freddy Sanchez Bat-Bat/15	12.50	30.00
136 Alfredo Amezaga Bat-Jsy/15	12.50	30.00
143 Travis Hafner Bat-Jsy/15	20.00	50.00
147 Chad Gaudin Jsy-Jsy/25	10.00	25.00

2004 Diamond Kings DK Combos Framed Bronze Sepia

PRINT RUNS B/WN 1-5 COPIES PER
NO PRICING DUE TO SCARCITY

2004 Diamond Kings DK Combos Framed Gold

PRINT RUNS B/WN 1-5 COPIES PER
NO PRICING DUE TO SCARCITY

2004 Diamond Kings DK Combos Framed Gold Sepia

PRINT RUNS B/WN 1-5 COPIES PER
NO PRICING DUE TO SCARCITY

2004 Diamond Kings DK Combos Framed Platinum Black

STATED PRINT RUN 1 SERIAL #'d SET
NO PRICING DUE TO SCARCITY

2004 Diamond Kings DK Combos Framed Platinum Black Sepia

STATED PRINT RUN 1 SERIAL #'d SET
NO PRICING DUE TO SCARCITY

2004 Diamond Kings DK Combos Framed Platinum Grey

STATED PRINT RUN 1 SERIAL #'d SET
NO PRICING DUE TO SCARCITY

2004 Diamond Kings DK Combos Framed Platinum Grey Sepia

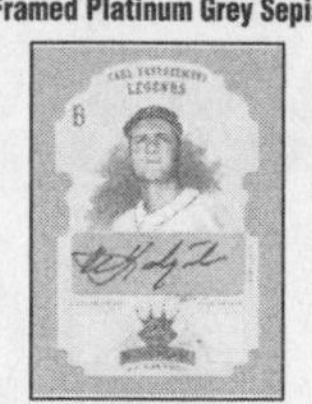

STATED PRINT RUN 1 SERIAL #'d SET
NO PRICING DUE TO SCARCITY

2004 Diamond Kings DK Combos Framed Platinum White

STATED PRINT RUN 1 SERIAL #'d SET
NO PRICING DUE TO SCARCITY

2004 Diamond Kings DK Combos Framed Platinum White Sepia

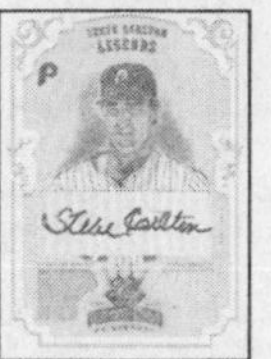

STATED PRINT RUN 1 SERIAL #'d SET
NO PRICING DUE TO SCARCITY

2004 Diamond Kings DK Combos Framed Silver

PRINT RUNS B/WN 1-15 COPIES PER
NO PRICING ON QTY OF 10 OR LESS
110 Ryan Klesko Bat-Jsy/15 20.00 50.00

2004 Diamond Kings DK Combos Framed Silver Sepia

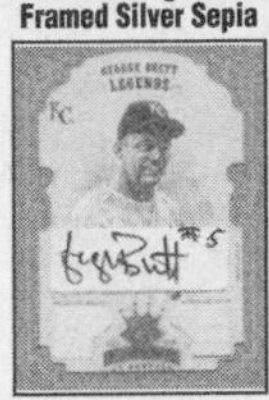

PRINT RUNS B/WN 1-5 COPIES PER
NO PRICING DUE TO SCARCITY

2004 Diamond Kings DK Materials Bronze

PRINT RUNS B/WN 1-150 COPIES PER
NO PRICING ON QTY OF 5 OR LESS
1 Alex Rodriguez Bat-Jsy/150 10.00 25.00
2 Andruw Jones Bat-Jsy/150 6.00 15.00
3 Nomar Garciaparra Bat-Jsy/150 10.00 25.00
4 Kerry Wood Bat-Jsy/150 4.00 10.00
5 Magglio Ordonez Bat-Jsy/150 4.00 10.00
6 Victor Martinez Bat-Bat/100 4.00 10.00
7 Jeremy Bonderman Jsy-Jsy/30 6.00 15.00
8 Josh Beckett Bat-Jsy/150 4.00 10.00
9 Jeff Kent Bat-Jsy/150 4.00 10.00
10 Carlos Beltran Bat-Jsy/150 4.00 10.00
11 Hideo Nomo Bat-Jsy/150 8.00 20.00
12 Richie Sexson Bat-Jsy/150 4.00 10.00
13 Jose Vidro Bat-Jsy/50 4.00 10.00
14 Jae Seo Jsy-Jsy/100 4.00 10.00
15 Alfonso Soriano Bat-Jsy/150 4.00 10.00
16 Barry Zito Bat-Jsy/100 4.00 10.00
17 Brett Myers Jsy-Jsy/30 6.00 15.00
18 Brian Giles Bat-Bat/100 4.00 10.00
19 Edgar Martinez Bat-Jsy/150 6.00 15.00
20 Jim Edmonds Bat-Jsy/150 4.00 10.00
21 Rocco Baldelli Bat-Jsy/100 4.00 10.00
22 Mark Teixeira Bat-Jsy/100 6.00 15.00
23 Carlos Delgado Bat-Jsy/150 4.00 10.00
25 Jose Reyes Bat-Jsy/100 4.00 10.00
26 Marlon Byrd Bat-Jsy/100 4.00 10.00
27 Albert Pujols Bat-Jsy/150 15.00 40.00
28 Vernon Wells Bat-Jsy/150 4.00 10.00
29 Garret Anderson Bat-Jsy/15 10.00 25.00
30 Jerome Williams Jsy-Jsy/100 4.00 10.00
31 Chipper Jones Bat-Jsy/150 8.00 20.00
32 Rich Harden Jsy-Jsy/100 4.00 10.00
33 Manny Ramirez Bat-Jsy/150 6.00 15.00
34 Derek Jeter Base-Base/100 12.50 30.00
35 Brandon Webb Bat-Jsy/100 4.00 10.00
36 Mark Prior Bat-Jsy/100 6.00 15.00
37 Roy Halladay Jsy-Jsy/100 4.00 10.00
38 Frank Thomas Bat-Jsy/150 8.00 20.00
39 Rafael Palmeiro Bat-Jsy/150 6.00 15.00
40 Adam Dunn Bat-Jsy/150 4.00 10.00
41 Aubrey Huff Bat-Jsy/30 6.00 15.00
42 Todd Helton Bat-Jsy/150 6.00 15.00
43 Matt Morris Jsy-Jsy/100 4.00 10.00
44 Dontrelle Willis Bat-Jsy/100 6.00 15.00
45 Lance Berkman Bat-Jsy/150 4.00 10.00
46 Mike Sweeney Bat-Jsy/100 4.00 10.00
47 Kazuhisa Ishii Bat-Jsy/100 4.00 10.00
48 Torii Hunter Bat-Jsy/100 4.00 10.00
49 Vladimir Guerrero Bat-Jsy/100 8.00 20.00
50 Mike Piazza Bat-Jsy/150 10.00 25.00
51 Alexis Rios Bat-Bat/150 4.00 10.00
52 Shannon Stewart Bat-Bat/100 4.00 10.00
53 Eric Hinske Bat-Jsy/100 4.00 10.00
54 Jason Jennings Bat-Jsy/150 4.00 10.00
55 Jason Giambi Bat-Jsy/150 4.00 10.00
56 Brandon Claussen Fld Glv-Shoe/5
57 Joe Thurston Bat-Jsy/150 4.00 10.00
58 Ramon Nivar Bat-Jsy/100 4.00 10.00
59 Jay Gibbons Jsy-Jsy/100 4.00 10.00
60 Eric Chavez Bat-Jsy/150 4.00 10.00
62 Walter Young Bat-Bat/100 4.00 10.00
63 Mark Grace Bat-Jsy/150 6.00 15.00
64 Austin Kearns Bat-Jsy/150 4.00 10.00
65 Bob Abreu Bat-Jsy/150 4.00 10.00
66 Hee Seop Choi Bat-Jsy/100 4.00 10.00
67 Brandon Phillips Bat-Bat/100 4.00 10.00
68 Rickie Weeks Bat-Bat/100 4.00 10.00
69 Luis Gonzalez Bat-Jsy/150 4.00 10.00
70 Mariano Rivera Jsy-Jsy/100 8.00 20.00
71 Jason Lane Bat-Hat/15 10.00 25.00
72 Xavier Nady Bat-Hat/5
73 Run Hernandez Jsy-Jsy/30 6.00 15.00
74 Aramis Ramirez Bat-Bat/1
75 Ichiro Suzuki Ball-Base/15 50.00 100.00
77 Chris Snelling Bat-Bat/30 6.00 15.00
79 Miguel Tejada Bat-Jsy/150 4.00 10.00
80 Juan Gonzalez Bat-Jsy/150 4.00 10.00
81 Joe Borchard Bat-Jsy/15 10.00 25.00
82 Gary Sheffield Bat-Jsy/150 4.00 10.00
83 Wade Miller Bat-Jsy/50 4.00 10.00
84 Jeff Bagwell Bat-Jsy/150 6.00 15.00
86 Adrian Beltre Bat-Jsy/100 4.00 10.00
87 Jeff Baker Bat-Bat/100 4.00 10.00
89 Bernie Williams Bat-Jsy/150 6.00 15.00
90 Pedro Martinez Bat-Jsy/100 6.00 15.00
92 Junior Spivey Bat-Jsy/100 4.00 10.00
93 Tim Hudson Bat-Jsy/150 4.00 10.00
94 Troy Glaus Bat-Jsy/100 4.00 10.00
95 Ken Griffey Jr. Base-Base/100 8.00 20.00
96 Alexis Gomez Bat-Bat/30 6.00 15.00
97 Antonio Perez Bat-Pants/100 4.00 10.00
98 Dan Haren Bat-Jsy/100 4.00 10.00
99 Ivan Rodriguez Bat-Jsy/150 6.00 15.00
100 Randy Johnson Bat-Jsy/100 8.00 20.00
101 Lyle Overbay Bat-Jsy/100 4.00 10.00
103 Miguel Cabrera Bat-Jsy/100 6.00 15.00
104 Scott Rolen Bat-Jsy/100 6.00 15.00
105 Roger Clemens Bat-Jsy/100 12.50 30.00
107 Nic Jackson Bat-Bat/100 4.00 10.00
108 Angel Berroa Bat-Pants/30 6.00 15.00
109 Hank Blalock Bat-Jsy/100 4.00 10.00
110 Ryan Klesko Bat-Jsy/100 4.00 10.00
111 Jose Castillo Bat-Bat/100 4.00 10.00
112 Paul Konerko Bat-Jsy/100 4.00 10.00
113 Greg Maddux Bat-Jsy/100 10.00 25.00
114 Mark Mulder Bat-Jsy/100 4.00 10.00
115 Pat Burrell Bat-Jsy/100 4.00 10.00
116 Garrett Atkins Jsy-Jsy/100 4.00 10.00
118 Orlando Cabrera Bat-Jsy/100 4.00 10.00
119 Nick Johnson Bat-Jsy/100 4.00 10.00
120 Tom Glavine Bat-Jsy/100 6.00 15.00
121 Morgan Ensberg Bat-Jsy/100 4.00 10.00
122 Sean Casey Bat-Hat/15 10.00 25.00
123 Orlando Hudson Bat-Jsy/100 4.00 10.00
124 Hideki Matsui Ball-Base/15 40.00 80.00
125 Craig Biggio Bat-Jsy/100 6.00 15.00
126 Adam LaRoche Bat-Bat/100 4.00 10.00
127 Hong-Chih Kuo Bat-Bat/100 4.00 10.00
128 Paul LoDuca Bat-Jsy/100 4.00 10.00
129 Shawn Green Bat-Jsy/100 4.00 10.00
130 Luis Castillo Bat-Jsy/100 4.00 10.00
131 Joe Crede Bat-Btg Glv/5
132 Ken Harvey Bat-Bat/100 4.00 10.00
133 Freddy Sanchez Bat-Bat/100 4.00 10.00
134 Roy Oswalt Bat-Jsy/100 4.00 10.00
135 Curt Schilling Bat-Jsy/100 6.00 15.00
136 Alfredo Amezaga Bat-Jsy/15 10.00 25.00
138 Barry Larkin Bat-Jsy/15 15.00 40.00
139 Trot Nixon Bat-Bat/100 4.00 10.00
140 Jim Thome Bat-Jsy/100 6.00 15.00
141 Bret Boone Bat-Jsy/100 4.00 10.00
142 Jacque Jones Bat-Jsy/100 4.00 10.00
143 Travis Hafner Bat-Jsy/100 4.00 10.00
144 Sammy Sosa Bat-Jsy/100 8.00 20.00
145 Mike Mussina Bat-Jsy/100 6.00 15.00
147 Chad Gaudin Jsy-Jsy/100 4.00 10.00
149 Mike Lowell Bat-Jsy/100 4.00 10.00
150 R.Henderson Bat-Jsy/100 8.00 20.00
151 R.Clemens FB Bat-Jsy/100 12.50 30.00
152 Mark Grace FB Bat-Jsy/15 15.00 40.00
153 R.Henderson FB Bat-Jsy/30 12.50 30.00
154 A.Rodriguez FB Bat-Jsy/100 10.00 25.00
155 R.Palmeiro FB Bat-Jsy/100 6.00 15.00
156 G.Maddux FB Bat-Bat/100 10.00 25.00
157 Mike Piazza FB Bat-Jsy/100 10.00 25.00
158 M.Mussina FB Bat-Jsy/100 6.00 15.00
159 Dale Murphy LGD Bat-Jsy/30 10.00 25.00
160 Cal Ripken LGD Bat-Jsy/100 20.00 50.00
161 C.Yaz LGD Bat-Jsy/100 10.00 25.00
162 M.Marion LGD Jsy-Jsy/30 6.00 15.00
163 D.Mattingly LGD Bat-Jsy/100 15.00 40.00
164 R.Yount LGD Bat-Jsy/100 8.00 20.00
165 A.Dawson LGD Bat-Jsy/30 6.00 15.00
166 Jim Palmer LGD Jsy-Jsy/5
167 George Brett LGD Bat-Jsy/30 30.00 60.00
168 W.Ford LGD Jsy-Pants/30 10.00 25.00
169 R.Campy LGD Bat-Pants/15 20.00 50.00
170 R.Maris LGD Bat-Jsy/15 60.00 120.00
171 Duke Snider LGD Bat-Jsy/4
172 S.Carlton LGD Bat-Jsy/100 4.00 10.00
173 Stan Musial LGD Bat-Jsy/30 20.00 50.00
174 Nolan Ryan LGD Bat-Jsy/30 30.00 60.00
175 D.Sanders LGD Bat-Jsy/100 6.00 15.00

2004 Diamond Kings DK Materials Bronze Sepia

RANDOM INSERTS IN PACKS
PRINT RUNS B/WN 4-50 COPIES PER
NO PRICING ON QTY OF 5 OR LESS
151 R.Clemens FB Bat-Jsy/30 20.00 50.00
152 Mark Grace FB Bat-Jsy/15 15.00 40.00
153 R.Henderson FB Bat-Jsy/15 20.00 50.00
154 A.Rodriguez FB Bat-Jsy/30 20.00 50.00
155 R.Palmeiro FB Bat-Jsy/50 6.00 15.00
156 G.Maddux FB Bat-Bat/50 15.00 40.00
157 Mike Piazza FB Bat-Jsy/50 15.00 40.00
158 M.Mussina FB Bat-Jsy/50 6.00 15.00
159 Dale Murphy LGD Bat-Jsy/15 15.00 40.00
160 Cal Ripken LGD Bat-Jsy/50 40.00 80.00
161 C.Yaz LGD Bat-Jsy/50 15.00 40.00
162 M.Marion LGD Jsy-Jsy/15 10.00 25.00
163 D.Mattingly LGD Bat-Jsy/50 20.00 50.00
164 R.Yount LGD Bat-Jsy/50 10.00 25.00
165 A.Dawson LGD Bat-Jsy/15 10.00 25.00
166 Jim Palmer LGD Jsy-Jsy/5
167 G.Brett LGD Bat-Jsy/15 50.00 100.00
168 W.Ford LGD Jsy-Pants/15 15.00 40.00
169 R.Campy LGD Bat-Pants/15 20.00 50.00
170 R.Maris LGD Bat-Jsy/15 60.00 120.00
171 Duke Snider LGD Bat-Jsy/4
172 S.Carlton LGD Bat-Jsy/50 4.00 10.00
173 Stan Musial LGD Bat-Jsy/15 40.00 80.00
174 Nolan Ryan LGD Bat-Jsy/15 50.00 100.00
175 D.Sanders LGD Bat-Jsy/50 6.00 15.00

2004 Diamond Kings DK Materials Gold

RANDOM INSERTS IN PACKS
PRINT RUNS B/WN 1-50 COPIES PER
NO PRICING ON QTY OF 5 OR LESS
1 Alex Rodriguez Bat-Jsy/25 20.00 50.00
2 Andruw Jones Bat-Jsy/25 10.00 25.00
3 Nomar Garciaparra Bat-Jsy/25 20.00 50.00
4 Kerry Wood Bat-Jsy/25 6.00 15.00
5 Magglio Ordonez Bat-Jsy/25 6.00 15.00
6 Victor Martinez Bat-Bat/50 4.00 10.00
7 Jeremy Bonderman Jsy-Jsy/5
8 Josh Beckett Bat-Jsy/25 6.00 15.00
9 Jeff Kent Bat-Jsy/25 6.00 15.00
10 Carlos Beltran Bat-Jsy/25 6.00 15.00
11 Hideo Nomo Bat-Jsy/25 12.50 30.00
12 Richie Sexson Bat-Jsy/25 6.00 15.00
13 Jose Vidro Bat-Jsy/25 6.00 15.00
14 Jae Seo Jsy-Jsy/25 6.00 15.00
15 Alfonso Soriano Bat-Jsy/25 6.00 15.00
16 Barry Zito Bat-Jsy/25 6.00 15.00
17 Brett Myers Jsy-Jsy/5
18 Brian Giles Bat-Bat/25 6.00 15.00
19 Edgar Martinez Bat-Jsy/25 10.00 25.00
20 Jim Edmonds Bat-Jsy/25 6.00 15.00
21 Rocco Baldelli Bat-Jsy/25 6.00 15.00
22 Mark Teixeira Bat-Jsy/25 10.00 25.00
23 Carlos Delgado Bat-Jsy/25
25 Jose Reyes Bat-Jsy/25 6.00 15.00
26 Marlon Byrd Bat-Jsy/25 6.00 15.00
27 Albert Pujols Bat-Jsy/25 30.00 60.00
28 Vernon Wells Bat-Jsy/25 6.00 15.00
29 Garret Anderson Bat-Jsy/3
30 Jerome Williams Jsy-Jsy/50 4.00 10.00
31 Chipper Jones Bat-Jsy/25 12.50 30.00
32 Rich Harden Jsy-Jsy/50 4.00 10.00
33 Manny Ramirez Bat-Jsy/25 10.00 25.00
34 Derek Jeter Base-Base/50 15.00 40.00
35 Brandon Webb Bat-Jsy/50 4.00 10.00
36 Mark Prior Bat-Jsy/25 10.00 25.00
37 Roy Halladay Jsy-Jsy/25 6.00 15.00
38 Frank Thomas Bat-Jsy/25 12.50 30.00
39 Rafael Palmeiro Bat-Jsy/50 6.00 15.00
40 Adam Dunn Bat-Jsy/25 6.00 15.00
41 Aubrey Huff Bat-Jsy/5
42 Todd Helton Bat-Jsy/25 10.00 25.00
43 Matt Morris Jsy-Jsy/25 6.00 15.00
44 Dontrelle Willis Bat-Jsy/25 10.00 25.00
45 Lance Berkman Bat-Jsy/25 6.00 15.00
46 Mike Sweeney Bat-Jsy/25 6.00 15.00
47 Kazuhisa Ishii Bat-Jsy/25 6.00 15.00
48 Torii Hunter Bat-Jsy/25 6.00 15.00
49 Vladimir Guerrero Bat-Jsy/25 12.50 30.00
50 Mike Piazza Bat-Jsy/25 20.00 50.00
51 Alexis Rios Bat-Bat/25 6.00 15.00
52 Shannon Stewart Bat-Bat/50 4.00 10.00
53 Eric Hinske Bat-Jsy/50 4.00 10.00
54 Jason Jennings Bat-Jsy/25 6.00 15.00
55 Jason Giambi Bat-Jsy/25 6.00 15.00
56 Brandon Claussen Fld Glv-Shoe/1
57 Joe Thurston Bat-Jsy/50 4.00 10.00
58 Ramon Nivar Bat-Jsy/50 4.00 10.00
59 Jay Gibbons Jsy-Jsy/25 6.00 15.00
60 Eric Chavez Bat-Jsy/25 6.00 15.00
62 Walter Young Bat-Bat/50 4.00 10.00
63 Mark Grace Bat-Jsy/25 10.00 25.00
64 Austin Kearns Bat-Jsy/25 6.00 15.00
65 Bob Abreu Bat-Jsy/25 6.00 15.00
66 Hee Seop Choi Bat-Jsy/25 6.00 15.00
67 Brandon Phillips Bat-Bat/50 4.00 10.00
68 Rickie Weeks Bat-Bat/50 4.00 10.00
69 Luis Gonzalez Bat-Jsy/25 6.00 15.00
70 Mariano Rivera Jsy-Jsy/50 10.00 25.00
71 Jason Lane Bat-Hat/3
72 Xavier Nady Bat-Hat/2
73 Run Hernandez Jsy-Jsy/5
74 Aramis Ramirez Bat-Bat/1
75 Ichiro Suzuki Ball-Base/3
77 Chris Snelling Bat-Bat/5
79 Miguel Tejada Bat-Jsy/50 4.00 10.00
80 Juan Gonzalez Bat-Jsy/25 6.00 15.00
81 Joe Borchard Bat-Jsy/3
82 Gary Sheffield Bat-Jsy/25 6.00 15.00
83 Wade Miller Bat-Jsy/3
84 Jeff Bagwell Bat-Jsy/25 10.00 25.00
86 Adrian Beltre Bat-Jsy/25 6.00 15.00
87 Jeff Baker Bat-Bat/50 4.00 10.00
89 Bernie Williams Bat-Jsy/25 10.00 25.00
90 Pedro Martinez Bat-Jsy/25 10.00 25.00
92 Junior Spivey Bat-Jsy/25 6.00 15.00
93 Tim Hudson Bat-Jsy/25 6.00 15.00
94 Troy Glaus Bat-Jsy/25 6.00 15.00
95 Ken Griffey Jr. Base-Base/50 12.50 30.00
96 Alexis Gomez Bat-Bat/5
97 Antonio Perez Bat-Pants/50 4.00 10.00
98 Dan Haren Bat-Jsy/25 6.00 15.00
99 Ivan Rodriguez Bat-Jsy/25 10.00 25.00
100 Randy Johnson Bat-Jsy/25 12.50 30.00
101 Lyle Overbay Bat-Jsy/50 4.00 10.00
103 Miguel Cabrera Bat-Jsy/25 10.00 25.00
104 Scott Rolen Bat-Jsy/25 10.00 25.00
105 Roger Clemens Bat-Jsy/25 20.00 50.00
107 Nic Jackson Bat-Bat/30 6.00 15.00
108 Angel Berroa Bat-Pants/3
109 Hank Blalock Bat-Jsy/25 6.00 15.00
110 Ryan Klesko Bat-Jsy/25 6.00 15.00
111 Jose Castillo Bat-Bat/50 4.00 10.00
112 Paul Konerko Bat-Jsy/25 6.00 15.00
113 Greg Maddux Bat-Jsy/25 20.00 50.00
114 Mark Mulder Bat-Jsy/25 6.00 15.00
115 Pat Burrell Bat-Jsy/25 6.00 15.00
116 Garrett Atkins Jsy-Jsy/50 4.00 10.00
118 Orlando Cabrera Bat-Jsy/25 6.00 15.00
119 Nick Johnson Bat-Jsy/25 6.00 15.00
120 Tom Glavine Bat-Jsy/25 10.00 25.00
121 Morgan Ensberg Bat-Jsy/25 6.00 15.00
122 Sean Casey Bat-Hat/3
123 Orlando Hudson Bat-Jsy/25 6.00 15.00
124 Hideki Matsui Ball-Base/3
125 Craig Biggio Bat-Jsy/25 10.00 25.00
126 Adam LaRoche Bat-Bat/50 4.00 10.00
127 Hong-Chih Kuo Bat-Bat/50 4.00 10.00
128 Paul LoDuca Bat-Jsy/25 6.00 15.00
129 Shawn Green Bat-Jsy/25 6.00 15.00
130 Luis Castillo Bat-Jsy/25 6.00 15.00
131 Joe Crede Bat-Btg Glv/1
132 Ken Harvey Bat-Bat/50 4.00 10.00
133 Freddy Sanchez Bat-Bat/50 4.00 10.00
134 Roy Oswalt Bat-Jsy/50 4.00 10.00
135 Curt Schilling Bat-Jsy/25 10.00 25.00
136 Alfredo Amezaga Bat-Jsy/3
138 Barry Larkin Bat-Jsy/3
139 Trot Nixon Bat-Bat/25 6.00 15.00
140 Jim Thome Bat-Jsy/25 10.00 25.00
141 Bret Boone Bat-Jsy/5
142 Jacque Jones Bat-Jsy/50 4.00 10.00
143 Travis Hafner Bat-Jsy/50 4.00 10.00
144 Sammy Sosa Bat-Jsy/25 12.50 30.00
145 Mike Mussina Bat-Jsy/50 6.00 15.00
147 Chad Gaudin Jsy-Jsy/25 6.00 15.00
149 Mike Lowell Bat-Jsy/25 6.00 15.00
150 R.Henderson Bat-Jsy/25 12.50 30.00
151 R.Clemens FB Bat-Jsy/25 20.00 50.00
152 Mark Grace FB Bat-Jsy/3
153 R.Henderson FB Bat-Jsy/5
154 A.Rodriguez FB Bat-Jsy/25 20.00 50.00
155 R.Palmeiro FB Bat-Jsy/50 10.00 25.00
156 G.Maddux FB Bat-Bat/50 15.00 40.00
157 Mike Piazza FB Bat-Jsy/50 15.00 40.00
158 M.Mussina FB Bat-Jsy/50 10.00 25.00
159 Dale Murphy LGD Bat-Jsy/5
160 Cal Ripken LGD Bat-Jsy/50 40.00 80.00
161 C.Yaz LGD Bat-Jsy/50 15.00 40.00
162 M.Marion LGD Jsy-Jsy/5
163 D.Mattingly LGD Bat-Jsy/50 20.00 50.00
164 R.Yount LGD Bat-Jsy/50 10.00 25.00
165 A.Dawson LGD Bat-Jsy/5
166 Jim Palmer LGD Jsy-Jsy/2
167 George Brett LGD Bat-Jsy/5
168 W.Ford LGD Jsy-Pants/5
169 R.Campy LGD Bat-Pants/3
170 Roger Maris LGD Bat-Jsy/3
171 Duke Snider LGD Bat-Jsy/1
172 S.Carlton LGD Bat-Jsy/50 4.00 10.00
173 Stan Musial LGD Bat-Jsy/5
174 Nolan Ryan LGD Bat-Jsy/5
175 D.Sanders LGD Bat-Jsy/50 6.00 15.00

2004 Diamond Kings DK Materials Gold Sepia

PRINT RUNS B/WN 1-15 COPIES PER
NO PRICING ON QTY OF 5 OR LESS
151 R.Clemens FB Bat-Jsy/5
152 Mark Grace FB Bat-Jsy/3
153 R.Henderson FB Bat-Jsy/3
154 A.Rodriguez FB Bat-Jsy/5
155 R.Palmeiro FB Bat-Jsy/15 15.00 40.00
156 G.Maddux FB Bat-Bat/15 30.00 60.00
157 Mike Piazza FB Bat-Jsy/15 30.00 60.00
158 M.Mussina FB Bat-Jsy/15 15.00 40.00
159 Dale Murphy LGD Bat-Jsy/3
160 Cal Ripken LGD Bat-Jsy/15 75.00 150.00
161 C.Yaz LGD Bat-Jsy/15 40.00 80.00
162 M.Marion LGD Jsy-Jsy/3
163 D.Mattingly LGD Bat-Jsy/15 50.00 100.00
164 R.Yount LGD Bat-Jsy/15 20.00 50.00
165 A.Dawson LGD Bat-Jsy/3
166 Jim Palmer LGD Jsy-Jsy/2
167 George Brett LGD Bat-Jsy/3
168 W.Ford LGD Jsy-Pants/3
169 R.Campy LGD Bat-Pants/3
170 Roger Maris LGD Bat-Jsy/3
171 Duke Snider LGD Bat-Jsy/1
172 S.Carlton LGD Bat-Jsy/15 10.00 25.00
173 Stan Musial LGD Bat-Jsy/3
174 Nolan Ryan LGD Bat-Jsy/3
175 D.Sanders LGD Bat-Jsy/15 15.00 40.00

2004 Diamond Kings DK Materials Platinum

STATED PRINT RUN 1 SERIAL #'d SET
NO PRICING DUE TO SCARCITY

2004 Diamond Kings DK Materials Platinum Sepia

STATED PRINT RUN 1 SERIAL #'d SET
NO PRICING DUE TO SCARCITY

2004 Diamond Kings DK Materials Silver

RANDOM INSERTS IN PACKS
PRINT RUNS B/WN 1-50 COPIES PER
NO PRICING ON QTY OF 6 OR LESS
1 Alex Rodriguez Bat-Jsy/50 15.00 40.00
2 Andruw Jones Bat-Jsy/50 6.00 15.00
3 Nomar Garciaparra Bat-Jsy/50 15.00 40.00
4 Kerry Wood Bat-Jsy/50 4.00 10.00
5 Magglio Ordonez Bat-Jsy/50 4.00 10.00
6 Victor Martinez Bat-Bat/50 4.00 10.00
7 Jeremy Bonderman Jsy-Jsy/15 10.00 25.00
8 Josh Beckett Bat-Jsy/50 4.00 10.00
9 Jeff Kent Bat-Jsy/50 4.00 10.00
10 Carlos Beltran Bat-Jsy/50 4.00 10.00
11 Hideo Nomo Bat-Jsy/50 10.00 25.00
12 Richie Sexson Bat-Jsy/50 4.00 10.00
13 Jose Vidro Bat-Jsy/30 6.00 15.00
14 Jae Seo Jsy-Jsy/50 4.00 10.00
15 Alfonso Soriano Bat-Jsy/50 4.00 10.00
16 Barry Zito Bat-Jsy/50 4.00 10.00
17 Brett Myers Jsy-Jsy/15 10.00 25.00
18 Brian Giles Bat-Bat/50 4.00 10.00
19 Edgar Martinez Bat-Jsy/50 6.00 15.00
20 Jim Edmonds Bat-Jsy/50 4.00 10.00
21 Rocco Baldelli Bat-Jsy/50 4.00 10.00
22 Mark Teixeira Bat-Jsy/50 6.00 15.00
23 Carlos Delgado Bat-Jsy/50 4.00 10.00
25 Jose Reyes Bat-Jsy/50 4.00 10.00
26 Marlon Byrd Bat-Jsy/50 4.00 10.00
27 Albert Pujols Bat-Jsy/50 20.00 50.00
28 Vernon Wells Bat-Jsy/50 4.00 10.00
29 Garret Anderson Bat-Jsy/6
30 Jerome Williams Jsy-Jsy/50 4.00 10.00
31 Chipper Jones Bat-Jsy/50 10.00 25.00
32 Rich Harden Jsy-Jsy/50 4.00 10.00
33 Manny Ramirez Bat-Jsy/50 6.00 15.00
34 Derek Jeter Base-Base/50 15.00 40.00
35 Brandon Webb Bat-Jsy/50 4.00 10.00
36 Mark Prior Bat-Jsy/50 6.00 15.00
37 Roy Halladay Jsy-Jsy/50 4.00 10.00
38 Frank Thomas Bat-Jsy/50 10.00 25.00
39 Rafael Palmeiro Bat-Jsy/50 6.00 15.00
40 Adam Dunn Bat-Jsy/50 4.00 10.00
41 Aubrey Huff Bat-Jsy/15 10.00 25.00
42 Todd Helton Bat-Jsy/50 6.00 15.00
43 Matt Morris Jsy-Jsy/50 4.00 10.00
44 Dontrelle Willis Bat-Jsy/50 6.00 15.00
45 Lance Berkman Bat-Jsy/50 4.00 10.00
46 Mike Sweeney Bat-Jsy/50 4.00 10.00
47 Kazuhisa Ishii Bat-Jsy/50 4.00 10.00
48 Torii Hunter Bat-Jsy/50 4.00 10.00
49 Vladimir Guerrero Bat-Jsy/50 10.00 25.00
50 Mike Piazza Bat-Jsy/50 15.00 40.00
51 Alexis Rios Bat-Bat/50 4.00 10.00
52 Shannon Stewart Bat-Bat/50 4.00 10.00
53 Eric Hinske Bat-Jsy/50 4.00 10.00
54 Jason Jennings Bat-Jsy/50 4.00 10.00
55 Jason Giambi Bat-Jsy/50 4.00 10.00
56 Brandon Claussen Fld Glv-Shoe/1
57 Joe Thurston Bat-Jsy/50 4.00 10.00
58 Ramon Nivar Bat-Jsy/50 4.00 10.00
59 Jay Gibbons Jsy-Jsy/50 4.00 10.00
60 Eric Chavez Bat-Jsy/50 4.00 10.00
62 Walter Young Bat-Bat/50 4.00 10.00
63 Mark Grace Bat-Jsy/50 6.00 15.00
64 Austin Kearns Bat-Jsy/50 4.00 10.00
65 Bob Abreu Bat-Jsy/50 4.00 10.00
66 Hee Seop Choi Bat-Jsy/50 4.00 10.00
67 Brandon Phillips Bat-Bat/50 4.00 10.00
68 Rickie Weeks Bat-Bat/50 4.00 10.00
69 Luis Gonzalez Bat-Jsy/50 4.00 10.00
70 Mariano Rivera Jsy-Jsy/50 10.00 25.00
71 Jason Lane Bat-Hat/6
72 Xavier Nady Bat-Hat/3
73 Run Hernandez Jsy-Jsy/15 10.00 25.00
74 Aramis Ramirez Bat-Bat/1
75 Ichiro Suzuki Ball-Base/6
77 Chris Snelling Bat-Bat/15 10.00 25.00
79 Miguel Tejada Bat-Jsy/50 4.00 10.00
80 Juan Gonzalez Bat-Jsy/50 4.00 10.00
81 Joe Borchard Bat-Jsy/6
82 Gary Sheffield Bat-Jsy/50 4.00 10.00
83 Wade Miller Bat-Jsy/6
84 Jeff Bagwell Bat-Jsy/50 6.00 15.00
86 Adrian Beltre Bat-Jsy/50 4.00 10.00
87 Jeff Baker Bat-Bat/50 4.00 10.00
89 Bernie Williams Bat-Jsy/50 6.00 15.00
90 Pedro Martinez Bat-Jsy/50 6.00 15.00
92 Junior Spivey Bat-Jsy/50 4.00 10.00
93 Tim Hudson Bat-Jsy/50 4.00 10.00
94 Troy Glaus Bat-Jsy/50 4.00 10.00
95 Ken Griffey Jr. Base-Base/50 12.50 30.00
96 Alexis Gomez Bat-Bat/15 10.00 25.00
97 Antonio Perez Bat-Pants/50 4.00 10.00
98 Dan Haren Bat-Jsy/50 4.00 10.00
99 Ivan Rodriguez Bat-Jsy/50 6.00 15.00
100 Randy Johnson Bat-Jsy/50 10.00 25.00
101 Lyle Overbay Bat-Jsy/50 4.00 10.00
103 Miguel Cabrera Bat-Jsy/50 6.00 15.00
104 Scott Rolen Bat-Jsy/50 6.00 15.00
105 Roger Clemens Bat-Jsy/50 15.00 40.00
107 Nic Jackson Bat-Bat/50 4.00 10.00
108 Angel Berroa Bat-Pants/6
109 Hank Blalock Bat-Jsy/50 4.00 10.00
110 Ryan Klesko Bat-Jsy/50 4.00 10.00
111 Jose Castillo Bat-Bat/50 4.00 10.00
112 Paul Konerko Bat-Jsy/50 4.00 10.00
113 Greg Maddux Bat-Jsy/50 15.00 40.00
114 Mark Mulder Bat-Jsy/50 4.00 10.00
115 Pat Burrell Bat-Jsy/50 4.00 10.00
116 Garrett Atkins Jsy-Jsy/50 4.00 10.00
118 Orlando Cabrera Bat-Jsy/50 4.00 10.00
119 Nick Johnson Bat-Jsy/50 4.00 10.00
120 Tom Glavine Bat-Jsy/50 6.00 15.00
121 Morgan Ensberg Bat-Jsy/50 4.00 10.00
122 Sean Casey Bat-Hat/6
123 Orlando Hudson Bat-Jsy/50 4.00 10.00
124 Hideki Matsui Ball-Base/6
125 Craig Biggio Bat-Jsy/50 6.00 15.00
126 Adam LaRoche Bat-Bat/50 4.00 10.00
127 Hong-Chih Kuo Bat-Bat/50 4.00 10.00
128 Paul LoDuca Bat-Jsy/50 4.00 10.00
129 Shawn Green Bat-Jsy/50 4.00 10.00
130 Luis Castillo Bat-Jsy/50 4.00 10.00
131 Joe Crede Bat-Btg Glv/1
132 Ken Harvey Bat-Bat/50 4.00 10.00
133 Freddy Sanchez Bat-Bat/50 4.00 10.00
134 Roy Oswalt Bat-Jsy/50 4.00 10.00
135 Curt Schilling Bat-Jsy/50 6.00 15.00
136 Alfredo Amezaga Bat-Jsy/6
138 Barry Larkin Bat-Jsy/6
139 Trot Nixon Bat-Bat/50 4.00 10.00
140 Jim Thome Bat-Jsy/50 6.00 15.00
141 Bret Boone Bat-Jsy/50 4.00 10.00
142 Jacque Jones Bat-Jsy/50 4.00 10.00
143 Travis Hafner Bat-Jsy/50 4.00 10.00
144 Sammy Sosa Bat-Jsy/50 10.00 25.00
145 Mike Mussina Bat-Jsy/50 6.00 15.00
147 Chad Gaudin Jsy-Jsy/50 4.00 10.00
149 Mike Lowell Bat-Jsy/50 4.00 10.00
150 R.Henderson Bat-Jsy/50 10.00 25.00
151 R.Clemens FB Bat-Jsy/50 15.00 40.00
152 Mark Grace FB Bat-Jsy/6
153 R.Henderson FB Bat-Jsy/15 20.00 50.00
154 A.Rodriguez FB Bat-Jsy/30 20.00 50.00
155 R.Palmeiro FB Bat-Jsy/50 6.00 15.00
156 G.Maddux FB Bat-Bat/50 15.00 40.00
157 Mike Piazza FB Bat-Jsy/50 15.00 40.00
158 M.Mussina FB Bat-Jsy/50 6.00 15.00
159 Dale Murphy LGD Bat-Jsy/15
160 Cal Ripken LGD Bat-Jsy/50 40.00 80.00
161 C.Yaz LGD Bat-Jsy/50 15.00 40.00
162 M.Marion LGD Jsy-Jsy/15 10.00 25.00
163 D.Mattingly LGD Bat-Jsy/50 20.00 50.00
164 R.Yount LGD Bat-Jsy/50 10.00 25.00
165 A.Dawson LGD Bat-Jsy/15 10.00 25.00
166 Jim Palmer LGD Jsy-Jsy/3
167 G.Brett LGD Bat-Jsy/15 50.00 100.00
168 W.Ford LGD Jsy-Pants/15 15.00 40.00
169 R.Campy LGD Bat-Pants/6
170 Roger Maris LGD Bat-Jsy/6
171 Duke Snider LGD Bat-Jsy/1
172 S.Carlton LGD Bat-Jsy/50 4.00 10.00
173 Stan Musial LGD Bat-Jsy/15 40.00 80.00
174 Nolan Ryan LGD Bat-Jsy/15 50.00 100.00
175 D.Sanders LGD Bat-Jsy/50 6.00 15.00

2004 Diamond Kings DK Materials Silver Sepia

RANDOM INSERTS IN PACKS
PRINT RUNS B/WN 1-30 COPIES PER
NO PRICING ON QTY OF 6 OR LESS
151 R.Clemens FB Bat-Jsy/15 30.00 60.00
152 Mark Grace FB Bat-Jsy/6
153 R.Henderson FB Bat-Jsy/6
154 A.Rodriguez FB Bat-Jsy/15 30.00 60.00
155 R.Palmeiro FB Bat-Jsy/30 10.00 25.00
156 G.Maddux FB Bat-Bat/30 20.00 50.00
157 Mike Piazza FB Bat-Jsy/30 20.00 50.00
158 M.Mussina FB Bat-Jsy/30 10.00 25.00
159 Dale Murphy LGD Bat-Jsy/6
160 Cal Ripken LGD Bat-Jsy/30 50.00 100.00
161 C.Yaz LGD Bat-Jsy/30 20.00 50.00
162 M.Marion LGD Jsy-Jsy/6
163 D.Mattingly LGD Bat-Jsy/30 30.00 60.00
164 R.Yount LGD Bat-Jsy/30 12.50 30.00
165 A.Dawson LGD Bat-Jsy/6
166 Jim Palmer LGD Jsy-Jsy/3
167 George Brett LGD Bat-Jsy/6
168 W.Ford LGD Jsy-Pants/6
169 R.Campy LGD Bat-Pants/6
170 Roger Maris LGD Bat-Jsy/6
171 Duke Snider LGD Bat-Jsy/1
172 S.Carlton LGD Bat-Jsy/30 6.00 15.00
173 Stan Musial LGD Bat-Jsy/6
174 Nolan Ryan LGD Bat-Jsy/6
175 D.Sanders LGD Bat-Jsy/30 10.00 25.00

2004 Diamond Kings DK Materials Framed Bronze

RANDOM INSERTS IN PACKS
PRINT RUNS B/WN 1-100 COPIES PER
NO PRICING ON QTY OF 10 OR LESS
1 Alex Rodriguez Bat-Jsy/100 10.00 25.00
2 Andruw Jones Bat-Jsy/100 6.00 15.00
3 Nomar Garciaparra Bat-Jsy/100 10.00 25.00
4 Kerry Wood Bat-Jsy/100 4.00 10.00
5 Magglio Ordonez Bat-Jsy/100 4.00 10.00
6 Victor Martinez Bat-Bat/100 4.00 10.00
7 Jeremy Bonderman Jsy-Jsy/25 6.00 15.00
8 Josh Beckett Bat-Jsy/100 4.00 10.00
9 Jeff Kent Bat-Jsy/100 4.00 10.00
10 Carlos Beltran Bat-Jsy/100 4.00 10.00
11 Hideo Nomo Bat-Jsy/100 8.00 20.00
12 Richie Sexson Bat-Jsy/100 4.00 10.00
13 Jose Vidro Bat-Jsy/50 4.00 10.00
14 Jae Seo Jsy-Jsy/100 4.00 10.00
15 Alfonso Soriano Bat-Jsy/100 4.00 10.00
16 Barry Zito Bat-Jsy/100 4.00 10.00
17 Brett Myers Jsy-Jsy/25 6.00 15.00
18 Brian Giles Bat-Bat/100 4.00 10.00
19 Edgar Martinez Bat-Jsy/100 6.00 15.00
20 Jim Edmonds Bat-Jsy/100 4.00 10.00
21 Rocco Baldelli Bat-Jsy/100 4.00 10.00
22 Mark Teixeira Bat-Jsy/100 6.00 15.00
23 Carlos Delgado Bat-Jsy/100 4.00 10.00
25 Jose Reyes Bat-Jsy/100 4.00 10.00
26 Marlon Byrd Bat-Jsy/100 4.00 10.00
27 Albert Pujols Bat-Jsy/100 15.00 40.00
28 Vernon Wells Bat-Jsy/100 4.00 10.00
29 Garret Anderson Bat-Jsy/25 6.00 15.00
30 Jerome Williams Jsy-Jsy/100 4.00 10.00
31 Chipper Jones Bat-Jsy/100 8.00 20.00
32 Rich Harden Jsy-Jsy/100 4.00 10.00
33 Manny Ramirez Bat-Jsy/100 6.00 15.00
34 Derek Jeter Base-Base/100 12.50 30.00
35 Brandon Webb Bat-Jsy/100 4.00 10.00
36 Mark Prior Bat-Jsy/100 6.00 15.00
37 Roy Halladay Jsy-Jsy/75 4.00 10.00
38 Frank Thomas Bat-Jsy/100 8.00 20.00
39 Rafael Palmeiro Bat-Jsy/100 6.00 15.00
40 Adam Dunn Bat-Jsy/100 4.00 10.00
41 Aubrey Huff Bat-Jsy/25 6.00 15.00
42 Todd Helton Bat-Jsy/100 6.00 15.00
43 Matt Morris Jsy-Jsy/100 4.00 10.00
44 Dontrelle Willis Bat-Jsy/100 6.00 15.00
45 Lance Berkman Bat-Jsy/100 4.00 10.00
46 Mike Sweeney Bat-Jsy/100 4.00 10.00
47 Kazuhisa Ishii Bat-Jsy/100 4.00 10.00
48 Torii Hunter Bat-Jsy/100 4.00 10.00
49 Vladimir Guerrero Bat-Jsy/100 8.00 20.00
50 Mike Piazza Bat-Jsy/100 10.00 25.00
51 Alexis Rios Bat-Bat/100 4.00 10.00
52 Shannon Stewart Bat-Bat/100 4.00 10.00
53 Eric Hinske Bat-Jsy/100 4.00 10.00
54 Jason Jennings Bat-Jsy/100 4.00 10.00
55 Jason Giambi Bat-Jsy/100 4.00 10.00
56 Brandon Claussen Fld Glv-Shoe/5
57 Joe Thurston Bat-Jsy/100 4.00 10.00
58 Ramon Nivar Bat-Jsy/100 4.00 10.00
59 Jay Gibbons Jsy-Jsy/100 4.00 10.00
60 Eric Chavez Bat-Jsy/100 4.00 10.00
62 Walter Young Bat-Bat/100 4.00 10.00
63 Mark Grace Bat-Jsy/100 6.00 15.00
64 Austin Kearns Bat-Jsy/50 4.00 10.00
65 Bob Abreu Bat-Jsy/100 4.00 10.00
66 Hee Seop Choi Bat-Jsy/100 4.00 10.00
67 Brandon Phillips Bat-Bat/100 4.00 10.00
68 Rickie Weeks Bat-Bat/100 4.00 10.00
69 Luis Gonzalez Bat-Jsy/100 4.00 10.00
70 Mariano Rivera Jsy-Jsy/100 8.00 20.00
71 Jason Lane Bat-Hat/25 6.00 15.00
72 Xavier Nady Bat-Hat/10
73 Run Hernandez Jsy-Jsy/50 4.00 10.00
74 Aramis Ramirez Bat-Bat/1
75 Ichiro Suzuki Ball-Base/25 40.00 80.00
77 Chris Snelling Bat-Bat/25 6.00 15.00
79 Miguel Tejada Bat-Jsy/100 4.00 10.00
80 Juan Gonzalez Bat-Jsy/100 10.00 25.00
81 Joe Borchard Bat-Jsy/25 6.00 15.00
82 Gary Sheffield Bat-Jsy/100 4.00 10.00
83 Wade Miller Bat-Jsy/25 6.00 15.00
84 Jeff Bagwell Bat-Jsy/100 6.00 15.00
86 Adrian Beltre Bat-Jsy/100 4.00 10.00
87 Jeff Baker Bat-Bat/100 4.00 10.00
89 Bernie Williams Bat-Jsy/100 6.00 15.00
90 Pedro Martinez Bat-Jsy/100 6.00 15.00
92 Junior Spivey Bat-Jsy/100 4.00 10.00
93 Tim Hudson Bat-Jsy/100 4.00 10.00
94 Troy Glaus Bat-Jsy/100 4.00 10.00
95 Ken Griffey Jr. Base-Base/100 8.00 20.00
96 Alexis Gomez Bat-Bat/30 6.00 15.00
97 Antonio Perez Bat-Pants/100 4.00 10.00
98 Dan Haren Bat-Jsy/100 4.00 10.00
99 Ivan Rodriguez Bat-Jsy/100 6.00 15.00
100 Randy Johnson Bat-Jsy/100 8.00 20.00
101 Lyle Overbay Bat-Jsy/100 4.00 10.00
103 Miguel Cabrera Bat-Jsy/100 6.00 15.00
104 Scott Rolen Bat-Jsy/100 6.00 15.00
105 Roger Clemens Bat-Jsy/100 12.50 30.00
107 Nic Jackson Bat-Bat/100 4.00 10.00
108 Angel Berroa Bat-Pants/25 6.00 15.00
109 Hank Blalock Bat-Jsy/100 4.00 10.00
110 Ryan Klesko Bat-Jsy/100 4.00 10.00
111 Jose Castillo Bat-Bat/100 4.00 10.00
112 Paul Konerko Bat-Jsy/50 4.00 10.00
113 Greg Maddux Bat-Jsy/100 10.00 25.00
114 Mark Mulder Bat-Jsy/100 4.00 10.00
115 Pat Burrell Bat-Jsy/100 4.00 10.00
116 Garrett Atkins Jsy-Jsy/100 4.00 10.00
118 Orlando Cabrera Bat-Jsy/100 4.00 10.00
119 Nick Johnson Bat-Jsy/100
120 Tom Glavine Bat-Jsy/100 6.00 15.00
121 Morgan Ensberg Bat-Jsy/100 4.00 10.00
122 Sean Casey Bat-Hat/25 6.00 15.00
123 Orlando Hudson Bat-Jsy/100 4.00 10.00
124 Hideki Matsui Ball-Base/25 30.00 60.00
125 Craig Biggio Bat-Jsy/25 10.00 25.00
126 Adam LaRoche Bat-Bat/100 4.00 10.00
127 Hong-Chih Kuo Bat-Bat/100 4.00 10.00
128 Paul LoDuca Bat-Jsy/100 4.00 10.00
129 Shawn Green Bat-Jsy/100 4.00 10.00
130 Luis Castillo Bat-Jsy/100 4.00 10.00
131 Joe Crede Bat-Btg Glv/5
132 Ken Harvey Bat-Bat/100 4.00 10.00
133 Freddy Sanchez Bat-Bat/100 4.00 10.00
134 Roy Oswalt Bat-Jsy/100 4.00 10.00
135 Curt Schilling Bat-Jsy/100 6.00 15.00
136 Alfredo Amezaga Bat-Jsy/25 6.00 15.00
138 Barry Larkin Bat-Jsy/25 10.00 25.00
139 Trot Nixon Bat-Bat/100 4.00 10.00
140 Jim Thome Bat-Jsy/100 6.00 15.00
141 Bret Boone Bat-Jsy/100 4.00 10.00
142 Jacque Jones Bat-Jsy/100 4.00 10.00
143 Travis Hafner Bat-Jsy/100 4.00 10.00
144 Sammy Sosa Bat-Jsy/100 8.00 20.00
145 Mike Mussina Bat-Jsy/100 6.00 15.00
147 Chad Gaudin Jsy-Jsy/50 4.00 10.00
149 Mike Lowell Bat-Jsy/100 4.00 10.00
150 R.Henderson Bat-Jsy/100 8.00 20.00
151 R.Clemens FB Bat-Jsy/25 20.00 50.00
152 Mark Grace FB Bat-Jsy/25 10.00 25.00
153 R.Henderson FB Bat-Jsy/25 12.50 30.00
154 A.Rodriguez FB Bat-Jsy/25 20.00 50.00
155 R.Palmeiro FB Bat-Jsy/100 6.00 15.00
156 G.Maddux FB Bat-Bat/100 10.00 25.00
157 Mike Piazza FB Bat-Jsy/100 10.00 25.00
158 M.Mussina FB Bat-Jsy/100 6.00 15.00
159 Dale Murphy LGD Bat-Jsy/25 10.00 25.00
160 Cal Ripken LGD Bat-Jsy/100 20.00 50.00
161 C.Yaz LGD Bat-Jsy/100 10.00 25.00
162 M.Marion LGD Jsy-Jsy/25 6.00 15.00
163 D.Mattingly LGD Bat-Jsy/100 15.00 40.00

164 R.Yount LGD Bat-Jsy/100 8.00 20.00
165 A.Dawson LGD Bat-Jsy/25 6.00 15.00
166 Jim Palmer LGD Jsy-Jsy/5
167 George Brett LGD Bat-Jsy/25 30.00 60.00
168 W.Ford LGD Jsy-Pants/25 10.00 25.00
169 R.Campy LGD Bat-Pants/25 12.50 30.00
170 R. Maris LGD Bat-Jsy/25 50.00 100.00
171 Duke Snider LGD Bat-Jsy/4
172 S.Carlton LGD Bat-Jsy/100 4.00 10.00
173 Stan Musial LGD Bat-Jsy/25 20.00 50.00
174 Nolan Ryan LGD Bat-Jsy/25 30.00 60.00
175 D.Sanders LGD Bat-Jsy/100 6.00 15.00

2004 Diamond Kings DK Materials Framed Bronze Sepia

RANDOM INSERTS IN PACKS
PRINT RUNS B/WN 4-50 COPIES PER
NO PRICING ON QTY OF 5 OR LESS
151 R.Clemens FB Bat-Jsy/25 20.00 50.00
152 Mark Grace FB Bat-Jsy/25 10.00 25.00
153 R.Henderson FB Bat-Jsy/25 12.50 30.00
154 A.Rodriguez FB Bat-Jsy/25 20.00 50.00
155 R.Palmeiro FB Bat-Jsy/50 6.00 15.00
156 G.Maddux FB Bat-Bat/50 15.00 40.00
157 Mike Piazza FB Bat-Jsy/50 15.00 40.00
158 M.Mussina FB Bat-Jsy/50 6.00 15.00
159 Dale Murphy LGD Bat-Jsy/15 10.00 25.00
160 Cal Ripken LGD Bat-Jsy/50 40.00 80.00
161 C.Yaz LGD Bat-Jsy/50 15.00 40.00
162 M.Marion LGD Jsy-Jsy/15 10.00 25.00
163 D.Mattingly LGD Bat-Jsy/50 20.00 50.00
164 R.Yount LGD Bat-Jsy/50 10.00 25.00
165 A.Dawson LGD Bat-Jsy/15 10.00 25.00
166 Jim Palmer LGD Jsy-Jsy/5
167 G.Brett LGD Bat-Jsy/15 50.00 100.00
168 W.Ford LGD Jsy-Pants/15 15.00 40.00
169 R.Campy LGD Bat-Pants/15 20.00 50.00
170 R.Maris LGD Bat-Jsy/15 60.00 120.00
171 Duke Snider LGD Bat-Jsy/5
172 S.Carlton LGD Bat-Jsy/15 10.00 25.00
173 Stan Musial LGD Bat-Jsy/15 40.00 80.00
174 Nolan Ryan LGD Bat-Jsy/15 50.00 100.00
175 D.Sanders LGD Bat-Jsy/50 6.00 15.00

2004 Diamond Kings DK Materials Framed Gold

RANDOM INSERTS IN PACKS
PRINT RUNS B/WN 1-50 COPIES PER
NO PRICING ON QTY OF 10 OR LESS
6 Victor Martinez Bat-Bat/50 4.00 10.00
26 Marlon Byrd Bat-Jsy/25 6.00 15.00
32 Rich Harden Jsy-Jsy/50 4.00 10.00
34 Derek Jeter Base-Base/50 15.00 40.00
35 Brandon Webb Bat-Jsy/50 4.00 10.00
39 Rafael Palmeiro Bat-Jsy/50 6.00 15.00
50 Mike Piazza Bat-Jsy/50 15.00 40.00
51 Alexis Rios Bat-Bat/50 4.00 10.00
52 Shannon Stewart Bat-Bat/50 4.00 10.00
53 Eric Hinske Bat-Jsy/50 4.00 10.00
57 Joe Thurston Bat-Jsy/50 4.00 10.00
58 Ramon Nivar Bat-Jsy/50 4.00 10.00
62 Walter Young Bat-Bat/50 4.00 10.00
67 Brandon Phillips Bat-Jsy/50 4.00 10.00
68 Rickie Weeks Bat-Bat/50 4.00 10.00
69 Luis Gonzalez Bat-Jsy/10
70 Mariano Rivera Jsy-Jsy/50 10.00 25.00
79 Miguel Tejada Bat-Jsy/50 4.00 10.00
87 Jeff Baker Bat-Bat/50 4.00 10.00
95 Ken Griffey Jr. Base-Base/50 12.50 30.00
97 Antonio Perez Bat-Pants/50 4.00 10.00
98 Dan Haren Bat-Jsy/50 4.00 10.00
101 Lyle Overbay Bat-Jsy/50 4.00 10.00
107 Nic Jackson Bat-Bat/30 6.00 15.00
111 Jose Castillo Bat-Bat/50 4.00 10.00
116 Garrett Atkins Jsy-Jsy/50 4.00 10.00
127 Hong-Chih Kuo Bat-Jsy/50 4.00 10.00
132 Ken Harvey Bat-Bat/50 4.00 10.00
133 Freddy Sanchez Bat-Bat/50 4.00 10.00
134 Roy Oswalt Bat-Jsy/50 4.00 10.00
142 Jacque Jones Bat-Jsy/50 4.00 10.00
143 Travis Hafner Bat-Jsy/50 4.00 10.00
145 Mike Mussina Bat-Jsy/50 6.00 15.00
155 R.Palmeiro FB Bat-Jsy/50 6.00 15.00
156 G.Maddux FB Bat-Bat/50 15.00 40.00
157 Mike Piazza FB Bat-Jsy/50 15.00 40.00
158 M.Mussina FB Bat-Jsy/50 6.00 15.00
160 Cal Ripken LGD Bat-Jsy/50 40.00 80.00
161 C.Yaz LGD Bat-Jsy/50 15.00 40.00
163 D.Mattingly LGD Bat-Jsy/50 20.00 50.00
164 R.Yount LGD Bat-Jsy/50 10.00 25.00
172 S.Carlton LGD Bat-Jsy/15 10.00 25.00
175 D.Sanders LGD Bat-Jsy/50 6.00 15.00

2004 Diamond Kings DK Materials Framed Gold Sepia

PRINT RUNS B/WN 1-15 COPIES PER
NO PRICING ON QTY OF 5 OR LESS
151 R.Clemens FB Bat-Jsy/5
152 Mark Grace FB Bat-Jsy/5
153 R.Henderson FB Bat-Jsy/5
154 A.Rodriguez FB Bat-Jsy/5
155 R.Palmeiro FB Bat-Jsy/15 15.00 40.00
156 G.Maddux FB Bat-Bat/15 30.00 60.00
157 Mike Piazza FB Bat-Jsy/15 30.00 60.00
158 M.Mussina FB Bat-Jsy/15 15.00 40.00
159 Dale Murphy LGD Bat-Jsy/5
160 Cal Ripken LGD Bat-Jsy/15 75.00 150.00
161 C.Yaz LGD Bat-Jsy/15 40.00 80.00
162 M.Marion LGD Jsy-Jsy/5
163 D.Mattingly LGD Bat-Jsy/15 50.00 100.00
164 R.Yount LGD Bat-Jsy/15
165 A.Dawson LGD Bat-Jsy/5
166 Jim Palmer LGD Jsy-Jsy/5
167 George Brett LGD Bat-Jsy/5
168 W.Ford LGD Jsy-Pants/5
169 R.Campy LGD Bat-Pants/5
170 Roger Maris LGD Bat-Jsy/5
171 Duke Snider LGD Bat-Jsy/1
172 S.Carlton LGD Bat-Jsy/5
173 Stan Musial LGD Bat-Jsy/5
174 Nolan Ryan LGD Bat-Jsy/5
175 D.Sanders LGD Bat-Jsy/15 15.00 40.00

2004 Diamond Kings DK Materials Framed Platinum Black

STATED PRINT RUN 1 SERIAL #'d SET
NO PRICING DUE TO SCARCITY

2004 Diamond Kings DK Materials Framed Platinum Black Sepia

STATED PRINT RUN 1 SERIAL #'d SET
NO PRICING DUE TO SCARCITY

2004 Diamond Kings DK Materials Framed Platinum Grey

STATED PRINT RUN 1 SERIAL #'d SET
NO PRICING DUE TO SCARCITY

2004 Diamond Kings DK Materials Framed Platinum Grey Sepia

STATED PRINT RUN 1 SERIAL #'d SET
NO PRICING DUE TO SCARCITY

2004 Diamond Kings DK Materials Framed Platinum White

STATED PRINT RUN 1 SERIAL #'d SET
NO PRICING DUE TO SCARCITY

2004 Diamond Kings DK Materials Framed Platinum White Sepia

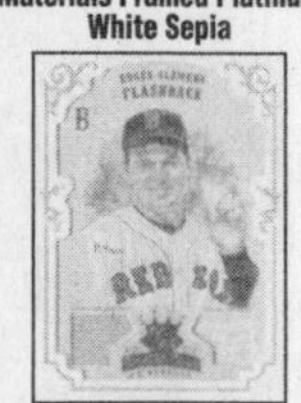

STATED PRINT RUN 1 SERIAL #'d SET
NO PRICING DUE TO SCARCITY

2004 Diamond Kings DK Materials Framed Silver

RANDOM INSERTS IN PACKS
PRINT RUNS B/WN 1-75 COPIES PER
NO PRICING ON QTY OF 10 OR LESS
1 Alex Rodriguez Bat-Jsy/25 20.00 50.00
2 Andruw Jones Bat-Jsy/25 10.00 25.00
3 Nomar Garciaparra Bat-Jsy/25 20.00 50.00
4 Kerry Wood Bat-Jsy/25 6.00 15.00
5 Magglio Ordonez Bat-Jsy/25 6.00 15.00
6 Victor Martinez Bat-Bat/50 4.00 10.00
7 Jeremy Bonderman Jsy-Jsy/10
8 Josh Beckett Bat-Jsy/25 6.00 15.00
9 Jeff Kent Bat-Jsy/25 6.00 15.00
10 Carlos Beltran Bat-Jsy/25 6.00 15.00
11 Hideo Nomo Bat-Jsy/25 12.50 30.00
12 Richie Sexson Bat-Jsy/25 6.00 15.00
13 Jose Vidro Bat-Jsy/25 6.00 15.00
14 Jae Seo Jsy-Jsy/25 6.00 15.00
15 Alfonso Soriano Bat-Jsy/25 6.00 15.00
16 Barry Zito Bat-Jsy/25 6.00 15.00
17 Brett Myers Jsy-Jsy/10
18 Brian Giles Bat-Bat/25 6.00 15.00
19 Edgar Martinez Bat-Jsy/25 10.00 25.00
20 Jim Edmonds Bat-Jsy/25 6.00 15.00
21 Rocco Baldelli Bat-Jsy/25 6.00 15.00
22 Mark Teixeira Bat-Jsy/25 10.00 25.00
23 Carlos Delgado Bat-Jsy/25 6.00 15.00
25 Jose Reyes Bat-Jsy/25 6.00 15.00
26 Marlon Byrd Bat-Jsy/50 4.00 10.00
27 Albert Pujols Bat-Jsy/25 30.00 60.00
28 Vernon Wells Bat-Jsy/25 6.00 15.00
29 Garret Anderson Bat-Jsy/25 6.00 15.00
31 Chipper Jones Bat-Jsy/25 12.50 30.00
32 Rich Harden Jsy-Jsy/50 4.00 10.00
33 Manny Ramirez Bat-Jsy/25 10.00 25.00
34 Derek Jeter Base-Base/50 15.00 40.00
35 Brandon Webb Bat-Jsy/50 4.00 10.00
36 Mark Prior Bat-Jsy/25 10.00 25.00
37 Roy Halladay Jsy-Jsy/10
38 Frank Thomas Bat-Jsy/25 12.50 30.00
39 Rafael Palmeiro Bat-Jsy/50 6.00 15.00
40 Adam Dunn Bat-Jsy/25 6.00 15.00
41 Aubrey Huff Bat-Jsy/10
42 Todd Helton Bat-Jsy/25 10.00 25.00
43 Matt Morris Jsy-Jsy/25 6.00 15.00
44 Dontrelle Willis Bat-Jsy/25 10.00 25.00
45 Lance Berkman Bat-Jsy/25 6.00 15.00
46 Mike Sweeney Bat-Jsy/25
47 Kazuhisa Ishii Bat-Jsy/25 6.00 15.00
48 Torii Hunter Bat-Jsy/25 6.00 15.00
49 Vladimir Guerrero Bat-Jsy/25 12.50 30.00
50 Mike Piazza Bat-Jsy/50 15.00 40.00
51 Alexis Rios Bat-Bat/50 4.00 10.00
52 Shannon Stewart Bat-Bat/50 4.00 10.00
53 Eric Hinske Bat-Jsy/50 4.00 10.00
54 Jason Jennings Bat-Jsy/25 6.00 15.00
55 Jason Giambi Bat-Jsy/25 6.00 15.00
56 Brandon Claussen Fld Glv-Shoe/5
57 Joe Thurston Bat-Jsy/50 4.00 10.00
58 Ramon Nivar Bat-Jsy/50 4.00 10.00
59 Jay Gibbons Jsy-Jsy/25 6.00 15.00
60 Eric Chavez Bat-Jsy/25 6.00 15.00
62 Walter Young Bat-Bat/50 4.00 10.00
63 Mark Grace Bat-Jsy/25 10.00 25.00
64 Austin Kearns Bat-Jsy/25 6.00 15.00
65 Bob Abreu Bat-Jsy/25 6.00 15.00
66 Hee Seop Choi Bat-Jsy/25 6.00 15.00
67 Brandon Phillips Bat-Bat/50 4.00 10.00
68 Rickie Weeks Bat-Bat/50 4.00 10.00
69 Luis Gonzalez Bat-Jsy/25 6.00 15.00
70 Mariano Rivera Jsy-Jsy/75 10.00 25.00
71 Jason Lane Bat-Hat/25 6.00 15.00
72 Xavier Nady Bat-Hat/10
73 Run Hernandez Jsy-Jsy/10
74 Aramis Ramirez Bat/1
75 Ichiro Suzuki Ball-Base/10
77 Chris Snelling Bat-Hat/10
79 Miguel Tejada Bat-Jsy/50 4.00 10.00
80 Juan Gonzalez Bat-Jsy/25 6.00 15.00
81 Joe Borchard Bat-Jsy/25 6.00 15.00
82 Gary Sheffield Bat-Jsy/25 6.00 15.00
83 Wade Miller Bat-Jsy/25 6.00 15.00
84 Jeff Bagwell Bat-Jsy/25 10.00 25.00
86 Adrian Beltre Bat-Jsy/25 6.00 15.00
87 Jeff Baker Bat-Bat/50 4.00 10.00
89 Bernie Williams Bat-Jsy/25 10.00 25.00
90 Pedro Martinez Bat-Jsy/25 10.00 25.00
92 Junior Spivey Bat-Jsy/25 6.00 15.00
93 Tim Hudson Bat-Jsy/25 6.00 15.00
94 Troy Glaus Bat-Jsy/25 6.00 15.00
95 Ken Griffey Jr. Base-Base/50 12.50 30.00
96 Alexis Gomez Bat-Bat/15
97 Antonio Perez Bat-Pants/50 4.00 10.00
98 Dan Haren Bat-Jsy/50 4.00 10.00
99 Ivan Rodriguez Bat-Jsy/25 10.00 25.00
100 Randy Johnson Bat-Jsy/25 12.50 30.00
101 Lyle Overbay Bat-Jsy/50 4.00 10.00
103 Miguel Cabrera Bat-Jsy/25 10.00 25.00
104 Scott Rolen Bat-Jsy/25 10.00 25.00
105 Roger Clemens Bat-Jsy/25 20.00 50.00
107 Nic Jackson Bat-Bat/50 4.00 10.00
108 Angel Berroa Bat-Pants/25 6.00 15.00
109 Hank Blalock Bat-Jsy/25 6.00 15.00
110 Ryan Klesko Bat-Jsy/25 6.00 15.00
111 Jose Castillo Bat-Bat/50 4.00 10.00
112 Paul Konerko Bat-Jsy/25 6.00 15.00
113 Greg Maddux Bat-Jsy/25 20.00 50.00
114 Mark Mulder Bat-Jsy/25 6.00 15.00
115 Pat Burrell Bat-Jsy/25 6.00 15.00
116 Garrett Atkins Jsy-Jsy/50 4.00 10.00
118 Orlando Cabrera Bat-Jsy/25 6.00 15.00
119 Nick Johnson Bat-Jsy/25 6.00 15.00
120 Tom Glavine Bat-Jsy/25 10.00 25.00
121 Morgan Ensberg Bat-Jsy/25 6.00 15.00
122 Sean Casey Bat-Hat/25 6.00 15.00
123 Orlando Hudson Bat-Jsy/25 6.00 15.00
124 Hideki Matsui Ball-Base/10
125 Craig Biggio Bat-Jsy/25 10.00 25.00
126 Adam LaRoche Bat-Jsy/50 4.00 10.00
127 Hong-Chih Kuo Bat-Bat/50 4.00 10.00
128 Paul LoDuca Bat-Jsy/25 6.00 15.00
129 Shawn Green Bat-Jsy/25 6.00 15.00
130 Luis Castillo Bat-Jsy/25 6.00 15.00
131 Joe Crede Bat-Btg Glv/5
132 Ken Harvey Bat-Bat/50 4.00 10.00
133 Freddy Sanchez Bat-Bat/50 4.00 10.00
134 Roy Oswalt Bat-Jsy/50 4.00 10.00
135 Curt Schilling Bat-Jsy/25 10.00 25.00
136 Alfredo Amezaga Bat-Jsy/25 6.00 15.00
138 Barry Larkin Bat-Jsy/25 10.00 25.00
139 Trot Nixon Bat-Bat/25 6.00 15.00
140 Jim Thome Bat-Jsy/25 10.00 25.00
141 Bret Boone Bat-Jsy/50 4.00 10.00
142 Jacque Jones Bat-Jsy/50 4.00 10.00
143 Travis Hafner Bat-Jsy/50 4.00 10.00
144 Sammy Sosa Bat-Jsy/25 12.50 30.00
145 Mike Mussina Bat-Jsy/25 6.00 15.00
147 Chad Gaudin Jsy-Jsy/25 6.00 15.00
149 Mike Lowell Bat-Jsy/25 6.00 15.00
150 R.Henderson Bat-Jsy/25 12.50 30.00
151 R.Clemens FB Bat-Jsy/15 30.00 60.00
152 Mark Grace FB Bat-Jsy/15 15.00 40.00
153 R.Henderson FB Bat-Jsy/15 10.00 25.00
154 A.Rodriguez FB Bat-Jsy/15 30.00 60.00
155 R.Palmeiro FB Bat-Jsy/50 6.00 15.00
156 G.Maddux FB Bat-Bat/50 15.00 40.00
157 Mike Piazza FB Bat-Jsy/50 15.00 40.00
158 M.Mussina FB Bat-Jsy/50 6.00 15.00
159 Dale Murphy LGD Bat-Jsy/15 15.00 40.00
160 Cal Ripken LGD Bat-Jsy/50 40.00 80.00
161 C.Yaz LGD Bat-Jsy/50 15.00 40.00
162 M.Marion LGD Jsy-Jsy/15 10.00 25.00
163 D.Mattingly LGD Bat-Jsy/50 20.00 50.00
164 R.Yount LGD Bat-Jsy/50 10.00 25.00
165 A.Dawson LGD Bat-Jsy/15 10.00 25.00
166 Jim Palmer LGD Jsy-Jsy/5
167 G.Brett LGD Bat-Jsy/15 50.00 100.00
168 W.Ford LGD Jsy-Pants/15 15.00 40.00
169 R.Campy LGD Bat-Pants/15 20.00 50.00
170 R.Maris LGD Bat-Jsy/15 60.00 120.00
171 Duke Snider LGD Bat-Jsy/1
172 S.Carlton LGD Bat-Jsy/50 4.00 10.00
173 Stan Musial LGD Bat-Jsy/15 40.00 80.00
174 Nolan Ryan LGD Bat-Jsy/15 50.00 100.00
175 D.Sanders LGD Bat-Jsy/50 6.00 15.00

2004 Diamond Kings DK Materials Framed Silver Sepia

RANDOM INSERTS IN PACKS
PRINT RUNS B/WN 1-30 COPIES PER
NO PRICING ON QTY OF 10 OR LESS
151 R.Clemens FB Bat-Jsy/15 30.00 60.00
152 Mark Grace FB Bat-Jsy/15 15.00 40.00
153 R.Henderson FB Bat-Jsy/15 20.00 50.00
154 A.Rodriguez FB Bat-Jsy/15 30.00 60.00
155 R.Palmeiro FB Bat-Jsy/30 10.00 25.00
156 G.Maddux FB Bat-Bat/30 20.00 50.00
157 Mike Piazza FB Bat-Jsy/30 20.00 50.00
158 M.Mussina FB Bat-Jsy/30 10.00 25.00
159 Dale Murphy LGD Bat-Jsy/10
160 Cal Ripken LGD Bat-Jsy/30 50.00 100.00
161 C.Yaz LGD Bat-Jsy/30 20.00 50.00
162 M.Marion LGD Jsy-Jsy/10
163 D.Mattingly LGD Bat-Jsy/30 30.00 60.00
164 R.Yount LGD Bat-Jsy/30 12.50 30.00
175 D.Sanders LGD Bat-Jsy/30 10.00 25.00

2004 Diamond Kings DK Signatures Bronze

RANDOM INSERTS IN PACKS
PRINT RUNS B/WN 1-200 COPIES PER
NO PRICING ON QTY OF 10 OR LESS
6 Victor Martinez/200 6.00 15.00
13 Jose Vidro/200 4.00 10.00
14 Jae Seo/200 6.00 15.00
17 Brett Myers/200 6.00 15.00
19 Edgar Martinez/25 30.00 60.00
26 Marlon Byrd/200 4.00 10.00
32 Rich Harden/200 6.00 15.00
35 Brandon Webb/25 6.00 15.00
41 Aubrey Huff/100 6.00 15.00
44 Dontrelle Willis/15 20.00 50.00
48 Torii Hunter/100 6.00 15.00
51 Alexis Rios/200 6.00 15.00
52 Shannon Stewart/200 6.00 15.00
53 Eric Hinske/25 6.00 15.00
54 Jason Jennings/15 10.00 25.00
56 Brandon Claussen/200 4.00 10.00
57 Joe Thurston/200 4.00 10.00
58 Ramon Nivar/100 4.00 10.00
59 Jay Gibbons/25 6.00 15.00
61 Jimmy Gobble/100 4.00 10.00
62 Walter Young/200 4.00 10.00
65 Bob Abreu/15 12.50 30.00
67 Brandon Phillips/100 4.00 10.00
68 Rickie Weeks/30 10.00 25.00
71 Jason Lane/200 6.00 15.00
73 Runelvys Hernandez/50 5.00 12.00
74 Aramis Ramirez/100 6.00 15.00
76 Cliff Lee/200 15.00 40.00
77 Chris Snelling/200 4.00 10.00
78 Ryan Wagner/100 4.00 10.00
81 Joe Borchard/200 4.00 10.00
85 Ryan Church/200 4.00 10.00
87 Jeff Baker/100 6.00 15.00
88 Adam Loewen/100 4.00 10.00
91 Carlos Rivera/100 4.00 10.00
92 Junior Spivey/25 6.00 15.00
96 Alexis Gomez/200 4.00 10.00
97 Antonio Perez/46 5.00 12.00
98 Dan Haren/100 4.00 10.00
101 Lyle Overbay/200 4.00 10.00
102 Oliver Perez/200 6.00 15.00
103 Miguel Cabrera/100 10.00 25.00
106 Brian Tallet/200 4.00 10.00
107 Nic Jackson/200 4.00 10.00
108 Angel Berroa/25 6.00 15.00
109 Hank Blalock/25 10.00 25.00
111 Jose Castillo/200 4.00 10.00
114 Mark Mulder/25 10.00 25.00
116 Garrett Atkins/100 4.00 10.00
117 Jeremy Guthrie/200 4.00 10.00
118 Orlando Cabrera/75 8.00 20.00
121 Morgan Ensberg/200 6.00 15.00
123 Orlando Hudson/100 4.00 10.00
126 Adam LaRoche/100 4.00 10.00
127 Hong-Chih Kuo/25 40.00 80.00
130 Luis Castillo/25 6.00 15.00
131 Joe Crede/100 6.00 15.00
132 Ken Harvey/200 4.00 10.00
133 Freddy Sanchez/50 6.00 15.00
136 Alfredo Amezaga/90 4.00 10.00
137 Chien-Ming Wang/25 125.00 200.00
139 Trot Nixon/15 12.50 30.00
142 Jacque Jones/25 10.00 25.00
143 Travis Hafner/200 6.00 15.00
146 Vinny Chulk/200 4.00 10.00
147 Chad Gaudin/100 4.00 10.00
148 Delmon Young/25 15.00 40.00
149 Mike Lowell/25 10.00 25.00
162 Marty Marion LGD/15 12.50 30.00

2004 Diamond Kings DK Signatures Bronze Sepia

PRINT RUNS B/WN 1-15 COPIES PER
NO PRICING ON QTY OF 1 OR LESS
162 Marty Marion LGD/15 12.50 30.00

2004 Diamond Kings DK Signatures Gold

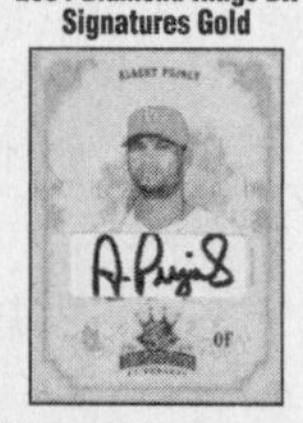

RANDOM INSERTS IN PACKS
PRINT RUNS B/WN 1-50 COPIES PER
NO PRICING ON QTY OF 12 OR LESS
26 Marlon Byrd/15 10.00 25.00
32 Rich Harden/50 8.00 20.00
51 Alexis Rios/50 8.00 20.00
56 Brandon Claussen/50 5.00 12.00
57 Joe Thurston/50 5.00 12.00
62 Walter Young/50 5.00 12.00
71 Jason Lane/40 8.00 20.00
77 Chris Snelling/50 5.00 12.00
81 Joe Borchard/50 5.00 12.00
85 Ryan Church/50 8.00 20.00
96 Alexis Gomez/50 5.00 12.00
101 Lyle Overbay/50 5.00 12.00
102 Oliver Perez/50 8.00 20.00
106 Brian Tallet/50 5.00 12.00
107 Nic Jackson/50 5.00 12.00
121 Morgan Ensberg/48 8.00 20.00
146 Vinny Chulk/50 5.00 12.00

2004 Diamond Kings DK Signatures Gold Sepia

PRINT RUNS B/WN 1-3 COPIES PER
NO PRICING DUE TO SCARCITY

2004 Diamond Kings DK Signatures Platinum

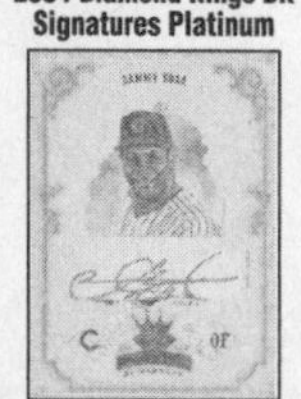

STATED PRINT RUN 1 SERIAL #'d SET
NO PRICING DUE TO SCARCITY

2004 Diamond Kings DK Signatures Platinum Sepia

STATED PRINT RUN 1 SERIAL #'d SET
NO PRICING DUE TO SCARCITY

2004 Diamond Kings DK Signatures Silver

RANDOM INSERTS IN PACKS
PRINT RUNS B/WN 1-100 COPIES PER
NO PRICING ON QTY OF 10 OR LESS
6 Victor Martinez/49 8.00 20.00
13 Jose Vidro/20 8.00 20.00
14 Jae Seo/80 6.00 15.00
17 Brett Myers/90 6.00 15.00
19 Edgar Martinez/15 40.00 80.00
26 Marlon Byrd/100 4.00 10.00
32 Rich Harden/100 6.00 15.00
35 Brandon Webb/15 10.00 25.00
41 Aubrey Huff/40 10.00 25.00
48 Torii Hunter/30 10.00 25.00
51 Alexis Rios/100 6.00 15.00
52 Shannon Stewart/30 8.00 20.00
53 Eric Hinske/15 10.00 25.00
56 Brandon Claussen/100 4.00 10.00
57 Joe Thurston/100 4.00 10.00
58 Ramon Nivar/30 6.00 15.00
59 Jay Gibbons/15 10.00 25.00
61 Jimmy Gobble/30 6.00 15.00
62 Walter Young/100 4.00 10.00
67 Brandon Phillips/30 6.00 15.00
68 Rickie Weeks/20 10.00 25.00
71 Jason Lane/100 6.00 15.00
73 Runelvys Hernandez/30 6.00 15.00
74 Aramis Ramirez/30 10.00 25.00
76 Cliff Lee/100 12.50 30.00
77 Chris Snelling/100 4.00 10.00
78 Ryan Wagner/30 6.00 15.00
81 Joe Borchard/100 4.00 10.00
85 Ryan Church/100 6.00 15.00
87 Jeff Baker/30 6.00 15.00
88 Adam Loewen/30 6.00 15.00
92 Junior Spivey/15 10.00 25.00
96 Alexis Gomez/100 4.00 10.00
97 Antonio Perez/15 10.00 25.00
98 Dan Haren/30 6.00 15.00
101 Lyle Overbay/100 4.00 10.00
102 Oliver Perez/100 6.00 15.00
103 Miguel Cabrera/30 15.00 40.00
106 Brian Tallet/100 4.00 10.00
107 Nic Jackson/100 4.00 10.00
109 Hank Blalock/30 10.00 25.00
111 Jose Castillo/100 4.00 10.00
114 Mark Mulder/15 12.50 30.00
116 Garrett Atkins/30 6.00 15.00
117 Jeremy Guthrie/30 6.00 15.00
118 Orlando Cabrera/15 12.50 30.00
121 Morgan Ensberg/50 8.00 20.00
123 Orlando Hudson/30 6.00 15.00
126 Adam LaRoche/30 6.00 15.00
127 Hong-Chih Kuo/15 60.00 120.00
128 Paul LoDuca/1
130 Luis Castillo/15 10.00 25.00
131 Joe Crede/35 6.00 15.00
132 Ken Harvey/30 6.00 15.00
133 Freddy Sanchez/15 10.00 25.00
136 Alfredo Amezaga/30 6.00 15.00
137 Chien-Ming Wang/15 150.00 250.00
143 Travis Hafner/30 10.00 25.00
146 Vinny Chulk/100 4.00 10.00
147 Chad Gaudin/30 6.00 15.00
149 Mike Lowell/15 12.50 30.00

2004 Diamond Kings DK Signatures Silver Sepia

PRINT RUNS B/WN 1-10 COPIES PER
NO PRICING DUE TO SCARCITY

2004 Diamond Kings DK Signatures Framed Bronze

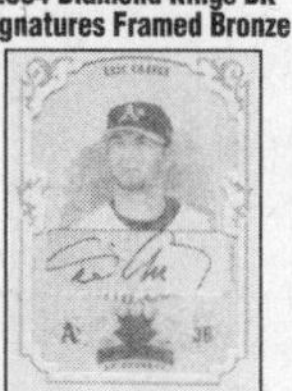

PRINT RUNS B/WN 1-50 COPIES PER
NO PRICING ON QTY OF 10 OR LESS
6 Victor Martinez/50 8.00 20.00
13 Jose Vidro/25 8.00 20.00
14 Jae Seo/50 8.00 20.00
17 Brett Myers/25 10.00 25.00
19 Edgar Martinez/25 30.00 60.00
21 Rocco Baldelli/25 10.00 25.00
26 Marlon Byrd/50 5.00 12.00
28 Vernon Wells/25 10.00 25.00
32 Rich Harden/50 8.00 20.00
35 Brandon Webb/25 8.00 20.00
40 Adam Dunn/25 15.00 40.00
41 Aubrey Huff/25 10.00 25.00
44 Dontrelle Willis/25 15.00 40.00
48 Torii Hunter/25 10.00 25.00
51 Alexis Rios/50 8.00 20.00
52 Shannon Stewart/25 10.00 25.00
53 Eric Hinske/25 8.00 20.00
54 Jason Jennings/25 8.00 20.00
56 Brandon Claussen/50 5.00 12.00
57 Joe Thurston/50 5.00 12.00
58 Ramon Nivar/25 8.00 20.00
59 Jay Gibbons/25 8.00 20.00
60 Eric Chavez/10
61 Jimmy Gobble/50 5.00 12.00
62 Walter Young/50 5.00 12.00
63 Mark Grace/1
64 Austin Kearns/5
65 Bob Abreu/25 10.00 25.00
67 Brandon Phillips/50 5.00 12.00
68 Rickie Weeks/25 10.00 25.00
70 Mariano Rivera /10
71 Jason Lane/25 10.00 25.00
72 Xavier Nady/1
73 Runelvys Hernandez/25 8.00 20.00
74 Aramis Ramirez/25 10.00 25.00
76 Cliff Lee/50 20.00 50.00
77 Chris Snelling/50 5.00 12.00
78 Ryan Wagner/25 8.00 20.00
81 Joe Borchard/50 5.00 12.00
85 Ryan Church/25 8.00 20.00
86 Adrian Beltre/10
87 Jeff Baker/25 8.00 20.00
88 Adam Loewen/25 8.00 20.00
90 Pedro Martinez/1
91 Carlos Rivera/50 5.00 12.00
92 Junior Spivey/25
93 Tim Hudson/10
94 Troy Glaus/25 15.00 40.00
96 Alexis Gomez/50 5.00 12.00
97 Antonio Perez/25 8.00 20.00
98 Dan Haren/25 8.00 20.00
99 Ivan Rodriguez/5
100 Randy Johnson/1
101 Lyle Overbay/50 5.00 12.00
102 Oliver Perez/50 8.00 20.00
103 Miguel Cabrera/50 12.50 30.00
104 Scott Rolen/5
106 Brian Tallet/50 5.00 12.00
107 Nic Jackson/50 5.00 12.00
108 Angel Berroa/25 8.00 20.00
109 Hank Blalock/25 10.00 25.00
110 Ryan Klesko/5
111 Jose Castillo/50 5.00 12.00
112 Paul Konerko/15 20.00 50.00
113 Greg Maddux/1
114 Mark Mulder/25 10.00 25.00
116 Garrett Atkins/50 5.00 12.00
117 Jeremy Guthrie/25 8.00 20.00
118 Orlando Cabrera/25 10.00 25.00
120 Tom Glavine/5
121 Morgan Ensberg/50 8.00 20.00
122 Sean Casey/5
123 Orlando Hudson/50 5.00 12.00
125 Craig Biggio/5
126 Adam LaRoche/50 5.00 12.00
127 Hong-Chih Kuo/25 40.00 80.00
128 Paul LoDuca/1
130 Luis Castillo/25 8.00 20.00
131 Joe Crede/50 8.00 20.00
132 Ken Harvey/25 8.00 20.00
133 Freddy Sanchez/25 8.00 20.00
134 Roy Oswalt/20 10.00 25.00
135 Curt Schilling/1
136 Alfredo Amezaga/25 8.00 20.00
137 Chien-Ming Wang/25 125.00 200.00
139 Trot Nixon/25 10.00 25.00
142 Jacque Jones/25 10.00 25.00
143 Travis Hafner/25 10.00 25.00
144 Sammy Sosa/1
145 Mike Mussina/1
146 Vinny Chulk/50 5.00 12.00
147 Chad Gaudin/25 8.00 20.00
148 Delmon Young/25 15.00 40.00
149 Mike Lowell/25 10.00 25.00
162 Marty Marion LGD/25 10.00 25.00

2004 Diamond Kings DK Signatures Framed Bronze Sepia

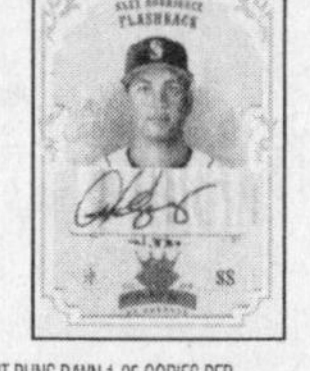

PRINT RUNS B/WN 1-25 COPIES PER
NO PRICING ON QTY OF 1 OR LESS
162 Marty Marion LGD/25 10.00 25.00

2004 Diamond Kings DK Signatures Framed Gold

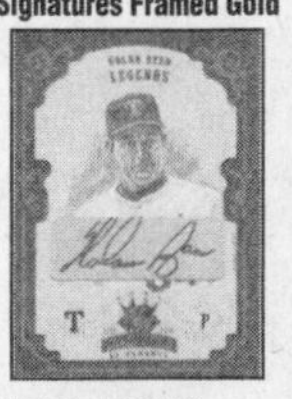

PRINT RUNS B/WN 1-5 COPIES PER
NO PRICING DUE TO SCARCITY

2004 Diamond Kings DK Signatures Framed Gold Sepia

PRINT RUNS B/WN 1-5 COPIES PER
NO PRICING DUE TO SCARCITY

2004 Diamond Kings DK Signatures Framed Platinum Black

STATED PRINT RUN 1 SERIAL #'d SET
NO PRICING DUE TO SCARCITY

2004 Diamond Kings DK Signatures Framed Platinum Black Sepia

STATED PRINT RUN 1 SERIAL #'d SET
NO PRICING DUE TO SCARCITY

2004 Diamond Kings DK Signatures Framed Platinum Grey

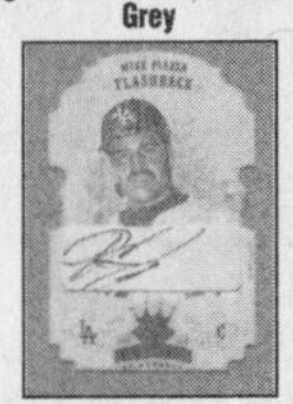

STATED PRINT RUN 1 SERIAL #'d SET
NO PRICING DUE TO SCARCITY

2004 Diamond Kings DK Signatures Framed Platinum Grey Sepia

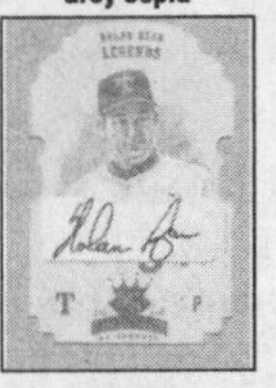

STATED PRINT RUN 1 SERIAL #'d SET
NO PRICING DUE TO SCARCITY

2004 Diamond Kings DK Signatures Framed Platinum White

STATED PRINT RUN 1 SERIAL #'d SET
NO PRICING DUE TO SCARCITY

2004 Diamond Kings DK Signatures Framed Platinum White Sepia

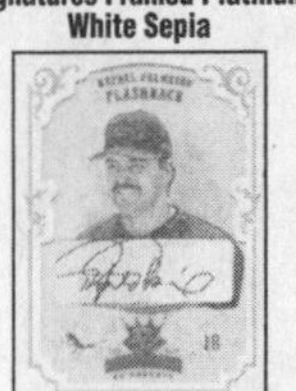

STATED PRINT RUN 1 SERIAL #'d SET
NO PRICING DUE TO SCARCITY

2004 Diamond Kings DK Signatures Framed Silver

RANDOM INSERTS IN PACKS
PRINT RUNS B/WN 1-25 COPIES PER
NO PRICING ON QTY OF 10 OR LESS

6 Victor Martinez/15 12.50 30.00
14 Jae Seo/15 12.50 30.00
21 Rocco Baldelli/15 12.50 30.00
22 Mark Teixeira/1
26 Marlon Byrd/15 10.00 25.00
32 Rich Harden/25 10.00 25.00
35 Brandon Webb/15 10.00 25.00
51 Alexis Rios/25 10.00 25.00
56 Brandon Claussen/25 8.00 20.00
57 Joe Thurston/25 8.00 20.00
58 Ramon Nivar/15 10.00 25.00
59 Jay Gibbons/15 10.00 25.00
61 Jimmy Gobble/15 10.00 25.00
62 Walter Young/25 8.00 20.00
67 Brandon Phillips/15 10.00 25.00
73 Runelvys Hernandez/15 10.00 25.00
76 Cliff Lee/15 30.00 60.00
77 Chris Snelling/25 8.00 20.00
81 Joe Borchard/25 8.00 20.00
85 Ryan Church/25 10.00 25.00
91 Carlos Rivera/15 10.00 25.00
96 Alexis Gomez/25 8.00 20.00
101 Lyle Overbay/25 8.00 20.00
102 Oliver Perez/25 10.00 25.00
106 Brian Tallet/25 8.00 20.00
107 Nic Jackson/25 8.00 20.00
111 Jose Castillo/15 10.00 25.00
121 Morgan Ensberg/15 12.50 30.00
123 Orlando Hudson/15 10.00 25.00
126 Adam LaRoche/15 10.00 25.00
130 Luis Castillo/15 10.00 25.00
133 Freddy Sanchez/15 10.00 25.00
136 Alfredo Amezaga/15 10.00 25.00
137 Chien-Ming Wang/15 150.00 250.00
146 Vinny Chulk/25 8.00 20.00
147 Chad Gaudin/15 10.00 25.00
149 Mike Lowell/15 12.50 30.00

2004 Diamond Kings DK Signatures Framed Silver Sepia

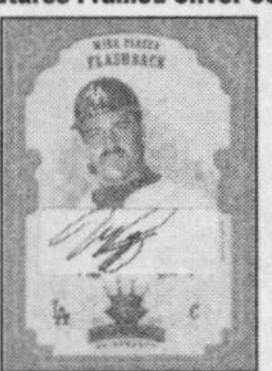

PRINT RUNS B/WN 1-10 COPIES PER
NO PRICING DUE TO SCARCITY

2004 Diamond Kings Diamond Cut Bats

RANDOM INSERTS IN PACKS
PRINT RUNS B/WN 1-100 COPIES PER
NO PRICING ON QTY OF 1 OR LESS

1 Alex Rodriguez/100 10.00 25.00
2 Nomar Garciaparra/100 10.00 25.00
3 Hideo Nomo/100 6.00 15.00
4 Alfonso Soriano/100 4.00 10.00
6 Edgar Martinez/100 6.00 15.00
7 Rocco Baldelli/100 4.00 10.00
8 Mark Teixeira/100 6.00 15.00
9 Albert Pujols/100 12.50 30.00
10 Vernon Wells/100 4.00 10.00
11 Garret Anderson/100 4.00 10.00
14 Brandon Webb/100 4.00 10.00
15 Mark Prior/100 6.00 15.00
16 Rafael Palmeiro/100 6.00 15.00
17 Adam Dunn/100 4.00 10.00
18 Dontrelle Willis/100 6.00 15.00
19 Kazuhisa Ishii/100 4.00 10.00
20 Torii Hunter/100 4.00 10.00
21 Vladimir Guerrero/100 6.00 15.00
22 Mike Piazza/100 10.00 25.00
23 Jason Giambi/100 4.00 10.00
26 Bob Abreu/100 4.00 10.00
27 Hee Seop Choi/100 4.00 10.00
28 Rickie Weeks/100 4.00 10.00
30 Troy Glaus/100 4.00 10.00
31 Ivan Rodriguez/100 6.00 15.00
32 Hank Blalock/100 4.00 10.00
33 Greg Maddux/100 10.00 25.00
34 Nick Johnson/100 4.00 10.00
35 Shawn Green/100 4.00 10.00
36 Sammy Sosa/100 6.00 15.00
37 Dale Murphy/50 10.00 25.00
38 Cal Ripken/50 30.00 60.00
39 Carl Yastrzemski/100 10.00 25.00
41 Don Mattingly/100 12.50 30.00
43 George Brett/50 15.00 40.00
45 Duke Snider/1
46 Steve Carlton/50 6.00 15.00
47 Stan Musial/25 20.00 50.00
48 Nolan Ryan/50 20.00 50.00
49 Deion Sanders/50 10.00 25.00
50 Roberto Clemente/25 75.00 150.00

2004 Diamond Kings Diamond Cut Combos Material

RANDOM INSERTS IN PACKS
PRINT RUNS B/WN 1-50 COPIES PER
NO PRICING ON QTY OF 8 OR LESS

1 Alex Rodriguez Bat-Jsy/50 15.00 40.00
2 Nomar Garciaparra Bat-Jsy/50 15.00 40.00
3 Hideo Nomo Bat-Jsy/25 15.00 40.00
4 Alfonso Soriano Bat-Jsy/50 6.00 15.00
6 Edgar Martinez Bat-Jsy/25 15.00 40.00
7 Rocco Baldelli Bat-Jsy/25 10.00 25.00
8 Mark Teixeira Bat-Jsy/25 15.00 40.00
9 Albert Pujols Bat-Jsy/50 20.00 50.00
10 Vernon Wells Bat-Jsy/25 10.00 25.00
11 Garret Anderson Bat-Jsy/25 10.00 25.00
14 Brandon Webb Bat-Jsy/25 10.00 25.00
15 Mark Prior Bat-Jsy/50 10.00 25.00
16 Rafael Palmeiro Bat-Jsy/25 15.00 40.00
17 Adam Dunn Bat-Jsy/25 10.00 25.00
18 Dontrelle Willis Bat-Jsy/25 15.00 40.00
19 Kazuhisa Ishii Bat-Jsy/25 10.00 25.00
20 Torii Hunter Bat-Jsy/25 10.00 25.00
21 Vladimir Guerrero Bat-Jsy/25 15.00 40.00
22 Mike Piazza Bat-Jsy/50 15.00 40.00
23 Jason Giambi Bat-Jsy/25 10.00 25.00
26 Bob Abreu Bat-Jsy/50 6.00 15.00
27 Hee Seop Choi Bat-Jsy/50 6.00 15.00
30 Troy Glaus Bat-Jsy/25 10.00 25.00
31 Ivan Rodriguez Bat-Jsy/25 15.00 40.00
32 Hank Blalock Bat-Jsy/25 10.00 25.00
33 Greg Maddux Bat-Jsy/50 15.00 40.00
34 Nick Johnson Bat-Jsy/25 10.00 25.00
35 Shawn Green Bat-Jsy/25 10.00 25.00
36 Sammy Sosa Bat-Jsy/50 10.00 25.00
37 Dale Murphy Bat-Jsy/3
38 Cal Ripken Bat-Jsy/8
39 Carl Yastrzemski Bat-Jsy/8
41 Don Mattingly Bat-Jsy/23 40.00 80.00
42 Jim Palmer Jsy-Jsy/22 12.50 30.00
43 George Brett Bat-Jsy/5
44 Whitey Ford Jsy-Pants/16 20.00 50.00
45 Duke Snider Bat-Jsy/1
46 Steve Carlton Bat-Jsy/32 10.00 25.00
47 Stan Musial Bat-Jsy/6
48 Nolan Ryan Bat-Jsy/34 30.00 60.00
49 Deion Sanders Bat-Jsy/24 20.00 50.00
50 Roberto Clemente Bat-Jsy/21

2004 Diamond Kings Diamond Cut Combos Signature

RANDOM INSERTS IN PACKS
PRINT RUNS B/WN 1-32 COPIES PER
NO PRICING ON QTY OF 10 OR LESS

40 Marty Marion Jsy/25 15.00 40.00
41 Don Mattingly Jsy/23 75.00 150.00
42 Jim Palmer Jsy/22 20.00 50.00
44 Whitey Ford Jsy/16 40.00 80.00
46 Steve Carlton Jsy/32 15.00 40.00

2004 Diamond Kings Diamond Cut Jerseys

RANDOM INSERTS IN PACKS
PRINT RUNS B/WN 10-100 COPIES PER
NO PRICING ON QTY OF 10 OR LESS

1 Alex Rodriguez/100 10.00 25.00
2 Nomar Garciaparra/100 10.00 25.00
3 Hideo Nomo/50 10.00 25.00
4 Alfonso Soriano/100 4.00 10.00
5 Brett Myers/50 6.00 15.00
6 Edgar Martinez/100 6.00 15.00
7 Rocco Baldelli/100 4.00 10.00
8 Mark Teixeira/100 6.00 15.00
9 Albert Pujols/100 12.50 30.00
10 Vernon Wells/100 4.00 10.00
11 Garret Anderson/50 6.00 15.00
12 Jerome Williams/100 4.00 10.00
13 Rich Harden/100 4.00 10.00
14 Brandon Webb/100 4.00 10.00
15 Mark Prior/100 6.00 15.00
16 Rafael Palmeiro/100 6.00 15.00
17 Adam Dunn/100 4.00 10.00
18 Dontrelle Willis/100 6.00 15.00
19 Kazuhisa Ishii/100 4.00 10.00
20 Torii Hunter/100 4.00 10.00
21 Vladimir Guerrero/50 10.00 25.00
22 Mike Piazza/100 10.00 25.00
23 Jason Giambi/100 4.00 10.00
25 Ramon Nivar/100 4.00 10.00
26 Bob Abreu/100 4.00 10.00
27 Hee Seop Choi/100 4.00 10.00
30 Troy Glaus/100 4.00 10.00
31 Ivan Rodriguez/100 6.00 15.00
32 Hank Blalock/100 4.00 10.00
33 Greg Maddux/100 10.00 25.00
34 Nick Johnson/100 4.00 10.00
35 Shawn Green/100 4.00 10.00
36 Sammy Sosa/100 6.00 15.00
37 Dale Murphy/50 10.00 25.00
38 Cal Ripken/50 30.00 60.00
39 Carl Yastrzemski/100 10.00 25.00
40 Marty Marion/50 6.00 15.00
41 Don Mattingly/100 12.50 30.00
42 Jim Palmer/25 10.00 25.00
43 George Brett/50 15.00 40.00
44 Whitey Ford/25 15.00 40.00
45 Duke Snider/10
46 Steve Carlton/50 6.00 15.00
47 Stan Musial/10
48 Nolan Ryan/50 20.00 50.00
49 Deion Sanders/50 10.00 25.00
50 Roberto Clemente/10

2004 Diamond Kings Diamond Cut Signatures

RANDOM INSERTS IN PACKS
PRINT RUNS B/WN 1-50 COPIES PER
NO PRICING ON QTY OF 10 OR LESS

7 Rocco Baldelli/25 10.00 25.00
8 Mark Teixeira/25 15.00 40.00
13 Rich Harden/50 8.00 20.00
14 Brandon Webb/50 6.00 15.00
20 Torii Hunter/25 15.00 40.00
24 Ryan Wagner/50 6.00 15.00
25 Ramon Nivar/50 6.00 15.00
28 Rickie Weeks/50 8.00 20.00
29 Adam Loewen/50 6.00 15.00
32 Hank Blalock/25 10.00 25.00
40 Marty Marion/25 10.00 25.00
41 Don Mattingly/23 60.00 120.00
42 Jim Palmer/22 12.50 30.00
44 Whitey Ford/16 20.00 50.00
46 Steve Carlton/32 15.00 40.00
48 Nolan Ryan/34 75.00 150.00

2004 Diamond Kings Gallery of Stars

STATED ODDS 1:37

1 Nolan Ryan 4.00 10.00
2 Cal Ripken 5.00 12.00
3 George Brett 2.50 6.00
4 Don Mattingly 2.50 6.00
5 Deion Sanders .75 2.00
6 Mike Piazza 1.25 3.00
7 Hideo Nomo 1.25 3.00
8 Rickey Henderson 1.25 3.00
9 Roger Clemens 1.50 4.00
10 Greg Maddux 2.00 5.00
11 Albert Pujols 3.00 8.00
12 Alex Rodriguez 2.00 5.00
13 Dale Murphy .75 2.00
14 Mark Prior .75 2.00
15 Dontrelle Willis .50 1.25

2004 Diamond Kings Gallery of Stars Signatures

PRINT RUNS B/WN 1-10 COPIES PER
NO PRICING DUE TO SCARCITY

2004 Diamond Kings Heritage Collection

1 Dale Murphy .75 2.00
2 Cal Ripken 5.00 12.00
3 Carl Yastrzemski 1.25 3.00
4 Don Mattingly 2.50 6.00
5 Jim Palmer .50 1.25
6 Andre Dawson .75 2.00
7 Roy Campanella 1.25 3.00
8 George Brett 2.50 6.00
9 Duke Snider .75 2.00
10 Marty Marion .50 1.25
11 Deion Sanders .75 2.00
12 Whitey Ford .75 2.00
13 Stan Musial 2.00 5.00
14 Nolan Ryan 4.00 10.00
15 Steve Carlton .50 1.25
16 Robin Yount 1.25 3.00
17 Albert Pujols 3.00 8.00
18 Alex Rodriguez 2.00 5.00
19 Mike Piazza 1.25 3.00
20 Roger Clemens 1.50 4.00
21 Hideo Nomo 1.25 3.00
22 Mark Prior .75 2.00
23 Roger Maris 1.25 3.00
24 Greg Maddux 2.00 5.00
25 Mark Grace .75 2.00

2004 Diamond Kings Heritage Collection Bats

RANDOM INSERTS IN PACKS
PRINT RUNS B/WN 1-50 COPIES PER
NO PRICING ON QTY OF 1 OR LESS

1 Dale Murphy/50 10.00 25.00
2 Cal Ripken/50 30.00 60.00
3 Carl Yastrzemski/50 12.50 30.00
4 Don Mattingly/50 15.00 40.00
6 Andre Dawson/25 10.00 25.00
7 Roy Campanella/25 15.00 40.00
8 George Brett/25 30.00 60.00
9 Duke Snider/1
11 Deion Sanders/50 10.00 25.00
13 Stan Musial/25 20.00 50.00
14 Nolan Ryan/25 30.00 60.00
15 Steve Carlton/25 10.00 25.00
16 Robin Yount/50 10.00 25.00
17 Albert Pujols/50 15.00 40.00
18 Alex Rodriguez/50 12.50 30.00
19 Mike Piazza/50 12.50 30.00
20 Roger Clemens/50 12.50 30.00
21 Hideo Nomo/50 10.00 25.00
22 Mark Prior/50 10.00 25.00
23 Roger Maris/25 40.00 80.00
24 Greg Maddux/50 12.50 30.00
25 Mark Grace/50 10.00 25.00

2004 Diamond Kings Heritage Collection Jerseys

RANDOM INSERTS IN PACKS
PRINT RUNS B/WN 10-50 COPIES PER
NO PRICING ON QTY OF 10 OR LESS

1 Dale Murphy/50 10.00 25.00
2 Cal Ripken/50 30.00 60.00
3 Carl Yastrzemski/50 12.50 30.00
4 Don Mattingly/50 15.00 40.00
5 Jim Palmer/10
6 Andre Dawson/25 10.00 25.00
7 Roy Campanella Pants/25 15.00 40.00
8 George Brett/25 30.00 60.00
9 Duke Snider/10
10 Marty Marion/50 6.00 15.00
11 Deion Sanders/50 10.00 25.00
12 Whitey Ford/25 15.00 40.00
13 Stan Musial/10
14 Nolan Ryan/25 30.00 60.00
15 Steve Carlton/25 10.00 25.00
16 Robin Yount/50 10.00 25.00
17 Albert Pujols/50 15.00 40.00
18 Alex Rodriguez/50 15.00 40.00
19 Mike Piazza/50 12.50 30.00
20 Roger Clemens/50 12.50 30.00
21 Hideo Nomo/50 10.00 25.00
22 Mark Prior/50 10.00 25.00
23 Roger Maris/25 40.00 80.00
24 Greg Maddux/50 12.50 30.00
25 Mark Grace/50 10.00 25.00

2004 Diamond Kings Heritage Collection Signatures

PRINT RUNS B/WN 1-16 COPIES PER
NO PRICING ON QTY OF 10 OR LESS

12 Whitey Ford/16 20.00 50.00

2004 Diamond Kings HOF Heroes

RANDOM INSERTS IN PACKS
PRINT RUNS B/WN 100-1000 COPIES PER

1 George Brett #45/1000 2.50 6.00
2 George Brett #45/500 4.00 10.00
3 George Brett #45/250 6.00 15.00
4 Mike Schmidt #46/1000 2.00 5.00
5 Mike Schmidt #46/250 5.00 12.00
6 Nolan Ryan #47/1000 4.00 10.00
7 Nolan Ryan #47/500 6.00 15.00
8 Nolan Ryan #47/250 10.00 25.00
9 Roberto Clemente #48/1000 3.00 8.00
10 Roberto Clemente #48/500 5.00 12.00
11 Roberto Clemente #48/250 8.00 20.00
12 Roberto Clemente #48/100 12.00 30.00
13 Carl Yastrzemski #49/1000 1.25 3.00
14 Robin Yount #50/1000 1.25 3.00
15 Whitey Ford #51/1000 .75 2.00
16 Duke Snider #52/1000 .75 2.00
17 Duke Snider #52/250 2.00 5.00
18 Carlton Fisk #53/1000 .75 2.00
19 Ozzie Smith #54/1000 2.00 5.00
20 Kirby Puckett #55/1000 1.25 3.00
21 Bobby Doerr #56/1000 .50 1.25
22 Frank Robinson #57/1000 .75 2.00
23 Ralph Kiner #58/1000 .75 2.00
24 Al Kaline #59/1000 1.25 3.00
25 Bob Feller #60/1000 .50 1.25
26 Yogi Berra #61/1000 1.25 3.00
27 Stan Musial #62/1000 2.00 5.00
28 Stan Musial #62/500 3.00 8.00
29 Stan Musial #62/250 5.00 12.00
30 Jim Palmer #63/1000 .50 1.25
31 Johnny Bench #64/1000 1.25 3.00
32 Steve Carlton #65/1000 .50 1.25
33 Gary Carter #66/1000 .50 1.25
34 Roy Campanella #67/1000 1.25 3.00
35 Roy Campanella #67/250 3.00 8.00

2004 Diamond Kings HOF Heroes Bats

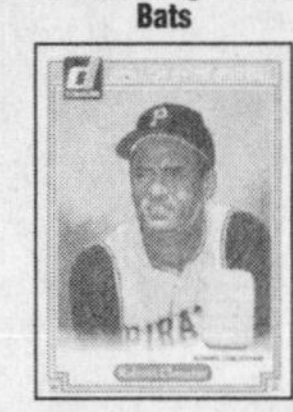

PRINT RUNS B/WN 1-25 COPIES PER
NO PRICING ON QTY OF 5 OR LESS

1 George Brett #45/25 20.00 50.00
2 George Brett #45/25 20.00 50.00
3 George Brett #45/25 20.00 50.00
4 Mike Schmidt #46/25 20.00 50.00
5 Mike Schmidt #46/25 20.00 50.00
6 Nolan Ryan #47/25 30.00 60.00
7 Nolan Ryan #47/25 30.00 60.00
8 Nolan Ryan #47/25 30.00 60.00
9 Roberto Clemente #48/5
10 Roberto Clemente #48/5
11 Roberto Clemente #48/5
12 Roberto Clemente #48/5
13 Carl Yastrzemski #49/25 20.00 50.00
14 Robin Yount #50/25 15.00 40.00
16 Duke Snider #52/1
17 Duke Snider #52/1
18 Carlton Fisk #53/25 15.00 40.00
19 Ozzie Smith #54/25 20.00 50.00
20 Kirby Puckett #55/25 15.00 40.00
21 Bobby Doerr #56/25 10.00 25.00
22 Frank Robinson #57/25 10.00 25.00
23 Ralph Kiner #58/25 10.00 25.00
24 Al Kaline #59/25 15.00 40.00
26 Yogi Berra #61/5
27 Stan Musial #62/5
28 Stan Musial #62/5
29 Stan Musial #62/5
31 Johnny Bench #64/25 15.00 40.00
32 Steve Carlton #65/25 10.00 25.00
33 Gary Carter #66/25 10.00 25.00
34 Roy Campanella #67/25 15.00 40.00
35 Roy Campanella #67/25 15.00 40.00

2004 Diamond Kings HOF Heroes Combos

PRINT RUNS B/WN 1-25 COPIES PER
NO PRICING ON QTY OF 10 OR LESS

1 George Brett #45 Bat-Jsy/25 30.00 60.00
2 George Brett #45 Bat-Jsy/25 30.00 60.00
3 George Brett #45 Bat-Jsy/25 30.00 60.00
4 Mike Schmidt #46 Bat-Jsy/25 30.00 60.00
5 Mike Schmidt #46 Bat-Jsy/25 30.00 60.00
6 Nolan Ryan #47 Bat-Jsy/25 40.00 80.00
7 Nolan Ryan #47 Bat-Jsy/25 40.00 80.00
8 Nolan Ryan #47 Bat-Jsy/25 40.00 80.00
9 Roberto Clemente #48 Bat-Jsy/5
10 Roberto Clemente #48 Bat-Jsy/5
11 Roberto Clemente #48 Bat-Jsy/5
12 Roberto Clemente #48 Bat-Jsy/5
13 C.Yastrzemski #49 Bat-Jsy/25 30.00 60.00
14 Robin Yount #50 Bat-Jsy/25 20.00 50.00
15 Whitey Ford #51 Jsy-Pants/25 20.00 50.00
16 Duke Snider #52 Bat-Jsy/1
17 Duke Snider #52 Bat-Jsy/1
18 Carlton Fisk #53 Bat-Jsy/25 20.00 50.00
19 Ozzie Smith #54 Bat-Jsy/25 30.00 60.00
20 Kirby Puckett #55 Bat-Jsy/25 20.00 50.00
21 Bobby Doerr #56 Bat-Jsy/25 12.50 30.00
22 Frank Robinson #57 Bat-Jsy/10
23 Ralph Kiner #58 Bat-Bat/25 12.50 30.00
24 Al Kaline #59 Bat-Jsy/25 20.00 50.00
25 Bob Feller #60 Jsy-Jsy/10
26 Yogi Berra #61 Bat-Jsy/5
27 Stan Musial #62 Bat-Jsy/5
28 Stan Musial #62 Bat-Jsy/5
29 Stan Musial #62 Bat-Jsy/5
30 Jim Palmer #63 Jsy-Jsy/5
31 Johnny Bench #64 Bat-Jsy/1
32 Steve Carlton #65 Bat-Jsy/25 12.50 30.00
33 Gary Carter #66 Bat-Jsy/25 12.50 30.00
34 R.Campy #67 Bat-Pants/25 20.00 50.00
35 R.Campy #67 Bat-Pants/25 20.00 50.00

2004 Diamond Kings HOF Heroes Jerseys

PRINT RUNS B/WN 1-25 COPIES PER
NO PRICING ON QTY OF 10 OR LESS

1 George Brett #45/25 20.00 50.00
2 George Brett #45/25 20.00 50.00
3 George Brett #45/25 20.00 50.00
4 Mike Schmidt #46/25 20.00 50.00
5 Mike Schmidt #46/25 20.00 50.00
6 Nolan Ryan #47/25 30.00 60.00
7 Nolan Ryan #47/25 30.00 60.00
8 Nolan Ryan #47/25 30.00 60.00
9 Roberto Clemente #48/5
10 Roberto Clemente #48/5
11 Roberto Clemente #48/5
12 Roberto Clemente #48/5
13 Carl Yastrzemski #49/25 20.00 50.00
14 Robin Yount #50/25 15.00 40.00
15 Whitey Ford #51/25 15.00 40.00
16 Duke Snider #52/10
17 Duke Snider #52/10
18 Carlton Fisk #53/25 15.00 40.00
19 Ozzie Smith #54/25 20.00 50.00
20 Kirby Puckett #55/25 15.00 40.00
21 Bobby Doerr #56/25 10.00 25.00
22 Frank Robinson #57/10
24 Al Kaline #59/25 15.00 40.00
25 Bob Feller #60/10
26 Yogi Berra #61/5
27 Stan Musial #62/5
28 Stan Musial #62/5
29 Stan Musial #62/5
30 Jim Palmer #63/5
31 Johnny Bench #64/1
32 Steve Carlton #65/25 10.00 25.00
33 Gary Carter #66/25 10.00 25.00
34 Roy Campanella #67 Pants/25 15.00 40.00
35 Roy Campanella #67 Pants/25 15.00 40.00

2004 Diamond Kings HOF Heroes Signatures

RANDOM INSERTS IN PACKS
PRINT RUNS B/WN 4-32 COPIES PER
NO PRICING ON QTY OF 10 OR LESS

1 George Brett #45/5
2 George Brett #45/5
3 George Brett #45/5
6 Nolan Ryan #47/5
7 Nolan Ryan #47/5
8 Nolan Ryan #47/5
13 Carl Yastrzemski #49/8
14 Robin Yount #50/19 50.00 100.00
15 Whitey Ford #51/16 20.00 50.00
16 Duke Snider #52/4
17 Duke Snider #52/4
18 Carlton Fisk #53/5
19 Ozzie Smith #54/5
20 Kirby Puckett #55/5
21 Bobby Doerr #56/10
22 Frank Robinson #57/20 20.00 50.00
23 Ralph Kiner #58/4
24 Al Kaline #59/6
25 Bob Feller #60/19 12.50 30.00
26 Yogi Berra #61/8
27 Stan Musial #62/6
28 Stan Musial #62/6
29 Stan Musial #62/6
30 Jim Palmer #63/22 12.50 30.00
31 Johnny Bench #64/5
32 Steve Carlton #65/32 10.00 25.00
33 Gary Carter #66/5

2004 Diamond Kings Recollection Autographs

PRINT RUNS B/WN 1-159 COPIES PER
NO PRICING ON QTY OF 14 OR LESS

1 Sandy Alomar Jr. 91 DK/8
2 Rich Aurilia 02 DK/2
3 Jeff Bagwell 93 TP Gall/1
4 Jeff Bagwell 02 DK/2
5 Jeff Bagwell 03 DK/1
6 Clint Barmes 03 DK Black/82 5.00 12.00
7 Clint Barmes 03 DK Blue/72 6.00 15.00
8 Carlos Beltran 02 DK/23 10.00 25.00
9 Carlos Beltran 03 DK/99 6.00 15.00
10 Adrian Beltre 02 DK/40 8.00 20.00
11 Johnny Bench 83 DK/3
12 Johnny Bench 01 DK Rep/1
13 Yogi Berra 83 HOF/4
14 Craig Biggio 91 DK/10
15 Craig Biggio 03 DK/1
16 Wade Boggs 84 DK/13
17 George Brett 03 DK/1

18 John Buck 02 DK/13
19 Chris Burke 03 DK/150 6.00 15.00
20 Marlon Byrd 02 DK/23 6.00 15.00
21 Marlon Byrd 03 DK/100 4.00 10.00
22 Rod Carew 01 DK Rep/1
23 Steve Carlton 01 DK Rep/6
24 Kevin Cash 03 DK/103 4.00 10.00
25 Jose Cruz 85 DK/59 5.00 12.00
26 J.D. Durbin 03 DK/151 4.00 10.00
27 Jim Edmonds 03 DK/24 15.00 40.00
28 Bob Feller 84 HOF/8
29 Bob Feller 03 DK HOF/18 15.00 40.00
30 Carlton Fisk 02 DK/13
31 Carlton Fisk 02 DK Her/5
32 Julio Franco 87 DK/25 10.00 25.00
33 Freddy Garcia 03 DK/50 8.00 20.00
34 Jay Gibbons 03 DK/100 4.00 10.00
35 Juan Gonzalez 03 DK/10
36 Mark Grace 02 DK/5
37 Mark Grace 03 DK/7
38 Shawn Green 02 DK/2
39 Brendan Harris 03 DK/150 4.00 10.00
40 Rickey Henderson 02 DK/1
41 Rickey Henderson 03 DK/2
42 Ru.Hernandez 02 DK/100 4.00 10.00
43 Eric Hinske 03 DK/20 6.00 15.00
44 Tim Hudson 02 DK/25 15.00 40.00
45 Tim Hudson 03 DK/25 15.00 40.00
46 Aubrey Huff 03 DK/99 6.00 15.00
47 Monte Irvin 84 HOF/7
48 Bo Jackson 02 DK/5
49 Jason Jennings 03 DK/50 5.00 12.00
50 Tommy John 88 DK Black/62 8.00 20.00
51 Tommy John 88 DK Blue/7
52 Howard Johnson 90 DK/52 5.00 12.00
53 Andruw Jones 03 DK/14
54 Austin Kearns 02 DK/25 6.00 15.00
55 Austin Kearns 03 DK/25 6.00 15.00
56 Ralph Kiner 83 HOF/5
57 Carney Lansford 85 DK Black/12
58 Carney Lansford 85 DK Blue/4
59 P.Larrison 03 DK Black/74 8.00 20.00
60 P.Larrison 03 DK Blue/77 8.00 20.00
61 Greg Maddux 02 DK/1
62 Greg Maddux 03 DK/2
63 Don Mattingly 85 DK/4
64 Don Mattingly 89 DK/5
65 Don Mattingly 02 DK Time/1
66 Don Mattingly 03 DK/5
67 Dustin McGowan 03 DK/159 4.00 10.00
68 Paul Molitor 02 DK Her/5
69 Melvin Mora 03 DK/101 6.00 15.00
70 Joe Morgan 01 DK Rep/2
71 Jack Morris 03 DK/60 8.00 20.00
72 Jack Morris 03 DK Her/19 15.00 40.00
73 Dale Murphy 03 DK Black/3
74 Dale Murphy 03 DK Blue/47 12.50 30.00
75 Dale Murphy 03 DK Her Black/8
76 Dale Murphy 03 DK Her Blue/10
77 Dale Murphy 03 DK Time/18 30.00 60.00
78 Stan Musial 83 HOF/3
79 Stan Musial 03 DK/2
80 Mike Mussina 03 DK/1
81 Phil Niekro 82 DK/10
82 Magglio Ordonez 03 DK/25 15.00 40.00
83 Magglio Ordonez 03 DK Ins/10
84 Roy Oswalt 03 DK/10
85 Dave Parker 82 DK/20 10.00 25.00
86 Dave Parker 90 DK/18 15.00 40.00
87 Tony Pena 85 DK/7
88 Jorge Posada 02 DK/25 15.00 40.00
89 Mark Prior 03 DK/25 10.00 25.00
90 Cal Ripken 02 DK/2
91 Cal Ripken 03 DK/3
92 Mike Rivera 02 DK/24 6.00 15.00
93 Robin Roberts 84 HOF Black/6
94 Robin Roberts 84 HOF Blue/1
95 Frank Robinson 83 HOF/8
96 Alex Rodriguez 03 DK/1
97 Ivan Rodriguez 03 DK/22 30.00 60.00
98 Scott Rolen 02 DK/5
99 Scott Rolen 03 DK/2
100 Rodrigo Rosario 02 DK/50 5.00 12.00
101 Nolan Ryan 02 DK/3
102 Nolan Ryan 03 DK/5
103 Nolan Ryan 03 DK Bronze/1
104 Nolan Ryan 03 DK Evol/1
105 Ron Santo 02 DK/29 15.00 40.00
106 Richie Sexson 02 DK/25 10.00 25.00
107 Richie Sexson 03 DK/25 10.00 25.00
108 Gary Sheffield 03 DK/11
109 Chris Snelling 02 DK/46 5.00 12.00
110 Duke Snider 83 HOF/4
111 J.T. Snow 93 TP Gall Black/1
112 J.T. Snow 93 TP Gall Blue/1
113 Sammy Sosa 99 Retro DK/2
114 Sammy Sosa 01 DK/2
115 Sammy Sosa 03 DK/3
116 Sammy Sosa 03 DK Ins/1
117 Junior Spivey 03 DK Black/12
118 Junior Spivey 03 DK Blue/13
119 Shannon Stewart 02 DK/50 8.00 20.00
120 S.Stewart 03 DK Black/92 6.00 15.00
121 Shannon Stewart 03 DK Blue/9
122 Frank Thomas 01 DK Black/1
123 Frank Thomas 01 DK Blue/1
124 Frank Thomas 00 Retro DK Black/2
125 Frank Thomas 00 Retro DK Blue/2
126 G.Thomas 82 DK Black/22 6.00 15.00
127 G.Thomas 82 DK Blue/20 6.00 15.00
128 Alan Trammell 02 DK/29 10.00 25.00
129 Alan Trammell 02 DK Her/25 10.00 25.00
130 Robin Ventura 02 DK/25 10.00 25.00
131 Jose Vidro 03 DK/25 6.00 15.00
132 Rickie Weeks 03 DK/52 12.50 30.00
133 Kevin Youkilis 03 DK/153 6.00 15.00
134 Barry Zito 03 DK/5

2004 Diamond Kings Team Timeline

STATED ODDS 1:29
1 Deion Sanders .50 1.25
Andruw Jones
2 Rickie Weeks 1.25 3.00
Robin Yount
3 Don Mattingly 2.50 6.00
Whitey Ford
4 Chipper Jones .75 2.00
Dale Murphy
5 Nomar Garciaparra .50 1.25
Bobby Doerr

6 Mark Prior 1.25 3.00
Sammy Sosa
7 Hideo Nomo 1.25 3.00
Kazuhisa Ishii
8 Andre Dawson .75 2.00
Mark Grace
9 Roger Clemens 1.50 4.00
Carl Yastrzemski
10 Mike Mussina 5.00 12.00
Cal Ripken
11 Stan Musial 3.00 8.00
Albert Pujols
12 Jim Palmer .75 2.00
Mike Mussina
13 Marty Marion 2.00 5.00
Stan Musial
14 George Brett 2.50 6.00
Mike Sweeney
15 Roger Clemens 1.50 4.00
Roger Maris
16 Duke Snider .75 2.00
Shawn Green
17 Jim Thome 2.00 5.00
Mike Schmidt
18 Nolan Ryan 4.00 10.00
Alex Rodriguez
19 Roy Campanella 1.25 3.00
Mike Piazza

2004 Diamond Kings Team Timeline Bats

STATED PRINT RUN 25 SERIAL #'d SETS
SNIDER/GREEN PRINT 1 SERIAL #'d CARD
SNIDER/GREEN TOO SCARCE TO PRICE
1 Deion Sanders 12.50 30.00
Andruw Jones
2 Rickie Weeks 20.00 50.00
Robin Yount
3 Don Mattingly 50.00 100.00
Whitey Ford
4 Chipper Jones 30.00 60.00
Dale Murphy
5 Nomar Garciaparra 20.00 50.00
Bobby Doerr
6 Mark Prior 20.00 50.00
Sammy Sosa
7 Hideo Nomo 30.00 60.00
Kazuhisa Ishii
8 Andre Dawson 12.50 30.00
Mark Grace
9 Roger Clemens 30.00 60.00
Carl Yastrzemski
10 Mike Mussina 60.00 120.00
Cal Ripken
11 Stan Musial 50.00 100.00
Albert Pujols
12 Jim Palmer 12.50 30.00
Mike Mussina
13 Marty Marion
Stan Musial
14 George Brett 20.00 50.00
Mike Sweeney
15 Roger Clemens 50.00 100.00
Roger Maris
16 Duke Snider/1
Shawn Green
17 Jim Thome 30.00 60.00
Mike Schmidt
18 Nolan Ryan 40.00 80.00
Alex Rodriguez
19 Roy Campanella 30.00 60.00
Mike Piazza

2004 Diamond Kings Team Timeline Jerseys

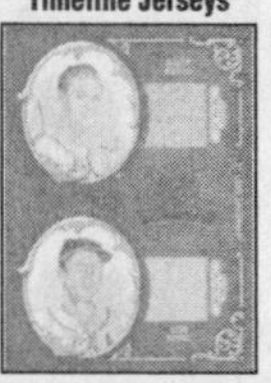

PRINT RUNS B/WN 10-25 COPIES PER
NO PRICING ON QTY OF 10 OR LESS
PRIME PRINT RUN 1 SERIAL #'d SET
NO PRIME PRICING DUE TO SCARCITY
RANDOM INSERTS IN PACKS
R.WEEKS IS A BAT SWATCH
R.CAMPANELLA IS A PANTS SWATCH
1 Deion Sanders/25 12.50 30.00
Andruw Jones
2 Rickie Weeks/25 20.00 50.00
Robin Yount
3 Don Mattingly/25 50.00 100.00
Whitey Ford
4 Chipper Jones/25 30.00 60.00
Dale Murphy
5 Nomar Garciaparra/25 20.00 50.00
Bobby Doerr
6 Mark Prior/25 20.00 50.00
Sammy Sosa
7 Hideo Nomo/25 30.00 60.00
Kazuhisa Ishii
8 Andre Dawson/25 12.50 30.00
Mark Grace
9 Roger Clemens/25 30.00 60.00
Carl Yastrzemski
10 Mike Mussina/25 60.00 120.00
Cal Ripken
11 Stan Musial/10
Albert Pujols
12 Jim Palmer/10
Mike Mussina
13 Marty Marion/10
Stan Musial
14 George Brett/25 20.00 50.00
Mike Sweeney
15 Roger Clemens/25 50.00 100.00
Roger Maris
16 Duke Snider/10
Shawn Green
17 Jim Thome/25 30.00 60.00
Mike Schmidt
18 Nolan Ryan/25 40.00 80.00
Alex Rodriguez
19 Roy Campanella Pants/25 30.00 60.00
Mike Piazza

2004 Diamond Kings Timeline

STATED ODDS 1:92
1 Roger Clemens 1.50 4.00
2 Mark Grace .75 2.00
3 Mike Mussina .75 2.00
4 Mike Piazza 1.25 3.00
5 Nolan Ryan 4.00 10.00
6 Rickey Henderson 1.25 3.00

2004 Diamond Kings Timeline Bats

STATED PRINT RUN 25 SERIAL #'d SETS
1 Roger Clemens Sox-Yanks 20.00 50.00
2 Mark Grace Cubs-D'backs 15.00 40.00
3 Mike Mussina O's-Yanks 15.00 40.00
4 Mike Piazza Dodgers-Mets 20.00 50.00
5 Nolan Ryan Astros-Rangers 40.00 80.00
6 Rickey Henderson A's-Dodgers 15.00 40.00

2004 Diamond Kings Timeline Jerseys

STATED PRINT RUN 25 SERIAL #'d SETS
PRIME PRINT RUN 1 SERIAL #'d SET
NO PRIME PRICING DUE TO SCARCITY
RANDOM INSERTS IN PACKS
1 Roger Clemens Sox-Yanks 30.00 60.00
2 Mark Grace Cubs-D'backs 20.00 50.00
3 Mike Mussina O's-Yanks 20.00 50.00
4 Mike Piazza Dodgers-Mets 30.00 60.00
5 Nolan Ryan Astros-Rangers 50.00 100.00
6 Rickey Henderson A's-Dodgers 20.00 50.00

2005 Diamond Kings

This 300-card first series was released in February, 2005. The series was issued in five card packs with an $6 SRP which came 12 packs to a box and 16 boxes to a case. Although there are no short prints in this set, cards numbered 281-300 feature retired greats. An 150-card update set was released in July, 2005. The second series was also issued in five-card packs with $6 SRP which came 12 packs to a box and 16 boxes to a case.

COMPLETE SET (450) 90.00 180.00
COMP.SERIES 1 SET (300) 60.00 120.00
COMP.SERIES 2 SET (150) 30.00 60.00
COMMON CARD .20 .50
COMMON RC .20 .50
COMMON RETIRED .20 .50
COMP.SET DOES NOT CONTAIN ANY SP's
1 Garret Anderson .20 .50
2 Vladimir Guerrero .50 1.25
3 Jose Guillen .20 .50
4 Troy Glaus UER .20 .50
Previous Diamond King appearences in wrong years
5 Tim Salmon .20 .50
6 Casey Kotchman .20 .50
7 Chone Figgins .20 .50
8 Robb Quinlan .20 .50
9 Francisco Rodriguez .30 .75
10 Troy Percival .20 .50
11 Randy Johnson .50 1.25
12 Brandon Webb .30 .75
13 Richie Sexson .20 .50
14 Shea Hillenbrand .20 .50
15 Chad Tracy .20 .50
16 Alex Cintron .20 .50
17 Luis Gonzalez .20 .50
18 Rafael Furcal .20 .50
19 Andruw Jones .20 .50
20 Marcus Giles .20 .50
21 John Smoltz .50 1.25
22 Adam LaRoche .20 .50
23 Russ Ortiz .20 .50
24 J.D. Drew .20 .50
25 Chipper Jones .50 1.25
26 Nick Green .20 .50
27 Rafael Palmeiro O's .30 .75
28 Miguel Tejada .30 .75
29 Javy Lopez .20 .50
30 Luis Matos .20 .50
31 Larry Bigbie .20 .50
32 Rodrigo Lopez .20 .50
33 Brian Roberts .20 .50
34 Melvin Mora .20 .50
35 Adam Loewen .20 .50
36 Manny Ramirez .50 1.25
37 Jason Varitek .50 1.25
38 Trot Nixon .20 .50
39 Curt Schilling .30 .75
40 Keith Foulke .20 .50
41 Pedro Martinez .30 .75
42 Johnny Damon .30 .75
43 Kevin Youkilis .20 .50
44 Orlando Cabrera Sox .20 .50
45 Abe Alvarez .20 .50
46 David Ortiz .50 1.25
47 Kerry Wood .20 .50
48 Mark Prior .30 .75
49 Aramis Ramirez .20 .50
50 Greg Maddux Cubs .75 2.00
51 Carlos Zambrano .30 .75
52 Derrek Lee .20 .50
53 Corey Patterson .20 .50
54 Moises Alou .20 .50
55 Matt Clement .20 .50
56 Sammy Sosa .50 1.25
57 Nomar Garciaparra Cubs .50 1.25
58 Todd Walker .20 .50
59 Angel Guzman .20 .50
60 Magglio Ordonez .30 .75
61 Carlos Lee .20 .50
62 Joe Crede .20 .50
63 Paul Konerko .30 .75
64 Shingo Takatsu .20 .50
65 Frank Thomas .50 1.25
66 Freddy Garcia .20 .50
67 Aaron Rowand .20 .50
68 Jose Contreras .20 .50
69 Adam Dunn .30 .75
70 Austin Kearns .20 .50
71 Barry Larkin .30 .75
72 Ken Griffey Jr. .75 2.00
73 Ryan Wagner .20 .50
74 Sean Casey .20 .50
75 Danny Graves .20 .50
76 C.C. Sabathia .30 .75
77 Jody Gerut .20 .50
78 Omar Vizquel .30 .75
79 Victor Martinez .30 .75
80 Matt Lawton .20 .50
81 Jake Westbrook .20 .50
82 Kazuhito Tadano .20 .50
83 Travis Hafner .20 .50
84 Todd Helton .30 .75
85 Preston Wilson .20 .50
86 Matt Holliday .50 1.25
87 Jeromy Burnitz .20 .50
88 Vinny Castilla .20 .50
89 Jeremy Bonderman .20 .50
90 Ivan Rodriguez Tigers .30 .75
91 Carlos Guillen .20 .50
92 Brandon Inge .20 .50
93 Rondell White .20 .50
94 Dontrelle Willis .20 .50
95 Miguel Cabrera .50 1.25
96 Josh Beckett .30 .75
97 Mike Lowell .20 .50
98 Luis Castillo .20 .50
99 Juan Pierre .20 .50
100 Paul LoDuca Marlins .20 .50
101 Guillermo Mota .20 .50
102 Craig Biggio .30 .75
103 Lance Berkman .30 .75
104 Roy Oswalt .30 .75
105 Roger Clemens Astros .60 1.50
106 Jeff Kent .20 .50
107 Morgan Ensberg .20 .50
108 Jeff Bagwell .30 .75
109 Carlos Beltran Astros .30 .75
110 Angel Berroa .20 .50
111 Mike Sweeney .20 .50
112 Jeremy Affeldt .20 .50
113 Zack Greinke .50 1.25
114 Juan Gonzalez .20 .50
115 Andres Blanco .20 .50
116 Shawn Green .20 .50
117 Milton Bradley .20 .50
118 Adrian Beltre .20 .50
119 Hideo Nomo .50 1.25
120 Steve Finley .20 .50
121 Eric Gagne .20 .50
122 Brad Penny Dgr .20 .50
123 Scott Podsednik .20 .50
124 Ben Sheets .20 .50
125 Lyle Overbay .20 .50
126 Junior Spivey .20 .50
127 Bill Hall .20 .50
128 Rickie Weeks .30 .75
129 Jacque Jones .20 .50
130 Torii Hunter .20 .50
131 Johan Santana .50 1.25
132 Lew Ford .20 .50
133 Joe Mauer .50 1.25
134 Justin Morneau .50 1.25
135 Jason Kubel .20 .50
136 Jose Vidro .20 .50
137 Chad Cordero .20 .50
138 Brad Wilkerson .20 .50
139 Nick Johnson .20 .50
140 Livan Hernandez .20 .50
141 Tom Glavine .30 .75
142 Jae Weong Seo .20 .50
143 Jose Reyes .30 .75
144 Al Leiter .20 .50
145 Mike Piazza .50 1.25
146 Kazuo Matsui .20 .50
147 Richard Hidalgo Mets .20 .50
148 David Wright .75 2.00
149 Mariano Rivera .50 1.25
150 Mike Mussina .30 .75
151 Alex Rodriguez .75 2.00
152 Derek Jeter 1.25 3.00
153 Jorge Posada .30 .75
154 Jason Giambi .20 .50
155 Gary Sheffield .20 .50
156 Bubba Crosby .20 .50
157 Javier Vazquez .20 .50
158 Kevin Brown .20 .50
159 Tom Gordon .20 .50
160 Esteban Loaiza Yanks .20 .50
161 Hideki Matsui .75 2.00
162 Eric Chavez .20 .50
163 Mark Mulder .20 .50
164 Barry Zito .20 .50
165 Tim Hudson .30 .75
166 Jermaine Dye .20 .50
167 Octavio Dotel .20 .50
168 Bobby Crosby .20 .50
169 Mark Kotsay .20 .50
170 Scott Hatteberg .20 .50
171 Jim Thome Phils .30 .75
172 Bobby Abreu .20 .50
173 Kevin Millwood .20 .50
174 Mike Lieberthal .20 .50
175 Jimmy Rollins .30 .75
176 Chase Utley .30 .75
177 Randy Wolf .20 .50
178 Craig Wilson .20 .50
179 Jason Kendall .20 .50
180 Jack Wilson .20 .50
181 Jose Castillo .20 .50
182 Rob Mackowiak .20 .50
183 Oliver Perez .20 .50
184 Jason Bay .20 .50
185 Sean Burroughs .20 .50
186 Jay Payton .20 .50
187 Brian Giles .20 .50
188 Akinori Otsuka .20 .50
189 Jake Peavy .20 .50
190 Phil Nevin .20 .50
191 Mark Loretta .20 .50
192 Khalil Greene .20 .50
193 Trevor Hoffman .30 .75
194 Freddy Guzman .20 .50
195 Jerome Williams .20 .50
196 Jason Schmidt .20 .50
197 Todd Linden .20 .50
198 Merkin Valdez .20 .50
199 J.T. Snow .20 .50
200 A.J. Pierzynski .20 .50
201 Edgar Martinez .30 .75
202 Ichiro Suzuki .75 2.00
203 Raul Ibanez .20 .50
204 Bret Boone .20 .50
205 Shigetoshi Hasegawa .20 .50
206 Miguel Olivo .20 .50
207 Bucky Jacobsen .20 .50
208 Jamie Moyer .20 .50
209 Jim Edmonds .30 .75
210 Scott Rolen .30 .75
211 Edgar Renteria .20 .50
212 Dan Haren .20 .50
213 Matt Morris .20 .50
214 Albert Pujols 1.25 3.00
215 Larry Walker Cards .30 .75
216 Jason Isringhausen .20 .50
217 Chris Carpenter .50 1.25
218 Jason Marquis .20 .50
219 Jeff Suppan .20 .50
220 Aubrey Huff .20 .50
221 Carl Crawford .30 .75
222 Rocco Baldelli .20 .50
223 Fred McGriff .30 .75
224 Dewon Brazelton .20 .50
225 B.J. Upton .20 .50
226 Joey Gathright .20 .50
227 Scott Kazmir .50 1.25
228 Hank Blalock .20 .50
229 Mark Teixeira .50 1.25
230 Michael Young .20 .50
231 Adrian Gonzalez .30 .75
232 Laynce Nix .20 .50
233 Alfonso Soriano Rgr .30 .75
234 Rafael Palmeiro Rgr .30 .75
235 Kevin Mench .20 .50
236 David Dellucci .20 .50
237 Francisco Cordero .20 .50
238 Kenny Rogers .20 .50
239 Roy Halladay .50 1.25
240 Carlos Delgado .20 .50
241 Alexis Rios .30 .75
242 Vernon Wells .20 .50
243 Yadier Molina .30 .75
244 Rene Rivera .20 .50
245 Logan Kensing .20 .50
246 Gavin Floyd .20 .50
247 Russ Adams .20 .50
248 Dioner Navarro .20 .50
249 Ryan Howard 1.00 2.50
250 Ryan Church .20 .50
251 Jeff Francis .20 .50
252 John VanBenschoten .20 .50
253 Yhency Brazoban .20 .50
254 Dave Krynzel .20 .50
255 Victor Diaz .20 .50
256 Jairo Garcia .20 .50
257 Scott Proctor .20 .50
258 Shawn Hill .20 .50
259 Jeff Baker .20 .50
260 Matt Peterson .20 .50
261 Josh Kroeger .20 .50
262 Grady Sizemore .20 .50
263 Clint Nageotte .20 .50
264 Andy Green .20 .50
265 Justin Verlander RC 4.00 10.00
266 Jim Thome Indians .30 .75
267 Larry Walker Rockies .30 .75
268 Ivan Rodriguez Rgr .30 .75
269 Brad Penny Marlins .20 .50
270 Carlos Beltran Royals .20 .50
271 Paul LoDuca Dgr .20 .50
272 Orlando Cabrera Expos .20 .50
273 Nomar Garciaparra Sox .50 1.25
274 Esteban Loaiza Sox .20 .50
275 Richard Hidalgo Astros .20 .50
276 John Olerud .20 .50
277 Greg Maddux Braves .75 2.00
278 Roger Clemens Yanks .60 1.50
279 Alfonso Soriano Yanks .30 .75
280 Dale Murphy .20 .50
281 Cal Ripken 2.00 5.00
282 Dwight Evans .30 .75
283 Ron Santo .30 .75
284 Andre Dawson .30 .75
285 Harold Baines .20 .50
286 Jack Morris .20 .50
287 Kirk Gibson .20 .50
288 Bo Jackson .50 1.25
289 Orel Hershiser .20 .50
290 Maury Wills .20 .50
291 Tony Oliva .20 .50
292 Darryl Strawberry .20 .50
293 Roger Maris .50 1.25
294 Don Mattingly 1.00 2.50
295 Rickey Henderson .30 .75
296 Dave Stewart .20 .50
297 Dave Parker .20 .50
298 Steve Garvey .20 .50
299 Matt Williams .20 .50
300 Keith Hernandez .20 .50
301 John Lackey .20 .50
302 Vladimir Guerrero Angels .50 1.25
303 Garret Anderson .20 .50
304 Dallas McPherson .20 .50
305 Orlando Cabrera .20 .50
306 Steve Finley Angels .20 .50
307 Luis Gonzalez .20 .50
308 Randy Johnson D'backs .50 1.25
309 Scott Hairston .20 .50
310 Shawn Green .20 .50
311 Troy Glaus .20 .50
312 Javier Vazquez .20 .50
313 Russ Ortiz .20 .50
314 Chipper Jones .50 1.25
315 Johnny Estrada .20 .50
316 Andruw Jones .20 .50
317 Tim Hudson .30 .75
318 Danny Kolb .20 .50
319 Jay Gibbons .20 .50
320 Melvin Mora .20 .50
321 Rafael Palmeiro O's .30 .75
322 Val Majewski .20 .50
323 David Ortiz .50 1.25
324 Manny Ramirez .50 1.25
325 Edgar Renteria .20 .50
326 Matt Clement .20 .50
327 Curt Schilling Sox .30 .75
328 Sammy Sosa Cubs .50 1.25
329 Mark Prior .30 .75
330 Greg Maddux .75 2.00
331 Nomar Garciaparra .50 1.25
332 Frank Thomas .50 1.25
333 Mark Buehrle .30 .75
334 Jermaine Dye .20 .50
335 Scott Podsednik .20 .50
336 Sean Casey .20 .50
337 Adam Dunn .30 .75
338 Ken Griffey Jr. .75 2.00
339 Travis Hafner .20 .50
340 Victor Martinez .30 .75
341 Cliff Lee .30 .75
342 Todd Helton .30 .75
343 Preston Wilson .20 .50
344 Ivan Rodriguez Tigers .30 .75
345 Dmitri Young .20 .50
346 Nate Robertson .20 .50
347 Miguel Cabrera .50 1.25
348 Jeff Bagwell .30 .75
349 Andy Pettitte .30 .75
350 Roger Clemens Astros .60 1.50
351 Ken Harvey .20 .50
352 Denny Bautista .20 .50
353 Hideo Nomo .50 1.25
354 Kazuhisa Ishii .20 .50
355 Edwin Jackson .20 .50
356 J.D. Drew .20 .50
357 Jeff Kent .20 .50
358 Geoff Jenkins .20 .50
359 Carlos Lee .20 .50
360 Shannon Stewart .20 .50
361 Joe Nathan .20 .50
362 Johan Santana .50 1.25
363 Mike Piazza Mets .50 1.25
364 Kazuo Matsui .20 .50
365 Carlos Beltran .30 .75
366 Pedro Martinez .30 .75
367 Ambiorix Concepcion RC .20 .50
368 Hideki Matsui .75 2.00
369 Bernie Williams .30 .75
370 Gary Sheffield Yanks .20 .50
371 Randy Johnson Yanks .50 1.25
372 Jaret Wright .20 .50
373 Carl Pavano .20 .50
374 Derek Jeter 1.25 3.00
375 Alex Rodriguez .75 2.00
376 Eric Byrnes .20 .50
377 Rich Harden .20 .50
378 Mark Mulder A's .20 .50
379 Nick Swisher .50 1.25
380 Eric Chavez .20 .50
381 Jason Kendall .20 .50
382 Marlon Byrd .20 .50
383 Pat Burrell .20 .50
384 Brett Myers .20 .50
385 Jim Thome .30 .75
386 Jason Bay .20 .50
387 Jake Peavy .20 .50
388 Moises Alou .20 .50
389 Omar Vizquel .30 .75
390 Travis Blackley .20 .50
391 Jose Lopez .20 .50
392 Jeremy Reed .20 .50
393 Adrian Beltre .20 .50
394 Richie Sexson .20 .50
395 Wladimir Balentien RC .30 .75
396 Ichiro Suzuki .75 2.00
397 Albert Pujols 1.25 3.00
398 Scott Rolen Cards .30 .75
399 Mark Mulder Cards .20 .50
400 David Eckstein .20 .50
401 Delmon Young .50 1.25
402 Aubrey Huff .20 .50
403 Alfonso Soriano .30 .75
404 Hank Blalock .20 .50
405 Richard Hidalgo .20 .50
406 Vernon Wells .20 .50
407 Orlando Hudson .20 .50
408 Alexis Rios .30 .75
409 Shea Hillenbrand .20 .50
410 Jose Guillen .20 .50
411 Vinny Castilla .20 .50
412 Jose Vidro .20 .50
413 Nick Johnson .20 .50
414 Livan Hernandez .20 .50
415 Miguel Tejada .30 .75
416 Gary Sheffield Braves .30 .75
417 Curt Schilling D'backs .30 .75
418 Rafael Palmeiro Rgr .30 .75
419 Scott Rolen Phils .30 .75
420 Aramis Ramirez .20 .50
421 Vladimir Guerrero Expos .50 1.25
422 Steve Finley D'backs .20 .50
423 Roger Clemens Sox .60 1.50
424 Mike Piazza Dgr .50 1.25
425 Ivan Rodriguez M's .30 .75
426 David Justice .50 1.25
427 Mark Grace .30 .75
428 Alan Trammell .20 .50
429 Bert Blyleven .20 .50
430 Dwight Gooden .20 .50
431 Deion Sanders .30 .75
432 Joe Torre MG .30 .75
433 Jose Canseco .30 .75
434 Tony Gwynn .60 1.50
435 Will Clark .30 .75
436 Marty Marion .20 .50
437 Nolan Ryan 1.25 3.00
438 Billy Martin .30 .75
439 Carlos Delgado .20 .50
440 Magglio Ordonez .30 .75
441 Sammy Sosa O's .50 1.25
442 Keiichi Yabu RC .20 .50
443 Yuniesky Betancourt RC .75 2.00
444 Jeff Niemann RC .50 1.25
445 Brandon McCarthy RC .30 .75
446 Phil Humber RC .50 1.25
447 Tadahito Iguchi RC .30 .75
448 Cal Ripken 2.00 5.00
449 Ryne Sandberg 1.00 2.50
450 Willie Mays 1.00 2.50

2005 Diamond Kings B/W

*B/W: .6X TO 1.5X BASIC
SER.2 STATED ODDS 1:2

2005 Diamond Kings Non-Canvas

STATED PRINT RUN 20 SETS
PRINT RUN INFO PROVIDED BY DONRUSS
NO PRICING DUE TO SCARCITY

2005 Diamond Kings Non-Canvas B/W

STATED PRINT RUN 20 SETS
PRINT RUN INFO PROVIDED BY DONRUSS
NO PRICING DUE TO SCARCITY

2005 Diamond Kings Bronze

*BRONZE 1-300: 2X TO 5X BASIC
*BRONZE 1-300: 1.25X TO 3X BASIC RC's
1-300 INSERT ODDS 10 PER SER.1 BOX
1-300 PRINT RUN 100 SERIAL #'d SETS
*BRONZE 301-450: 2.5X TO 6X BASIC
*BRONZE 301-450: 1.5X TO 4X BASIC RC's
301-450 INSERT ODDS 12 PER SER.2 BOX
301-450 PRINT RUN 50 SERIAL #'d SETS

2005 Diamond Kings Bronze B/W

*BRONZE B/W: 2X TO 5X BASIC
OVERALL INSERT ODDS 12 PER SER.2 BOX
STATED PRINT RUN 100 SERIAL #'d SETS

2005 Diamond Kings Gold

*GOLD 1-300: 4X TO 10X BASIC
1-300 INSERT ODDS 10 PER SER.1 BOX
1-300 PRINT RUN 25 SERIAL #'d SETS
NO PRICING ON CARD 265 VERLANDER
301-450 INSERT ODDS 12 PER SER.2 BOX
301-450 PRINT RUN 10 SERIAL #'d SETS
301-450 NO PRICING DUE TO SCARCITY

2005 Diamond Kings Gold B/W

*GOLD B/W: 4X TO 10X BASIC
OVERALL INSERT ODDS 12 PER SER.2 BOX
STATED PRINT RUN 25 SERIAL #'d SETS

2005 Diamond Kings Platinum

1-300 INSERT ODDS 10 PER SER.1 BOX
301-450 INSERT ODDS 12 PER SER.2 BOX
STATED PRINT RUN 1 SERIAL #'d SET
NO PRICING DUE TO SCARCITY

2005 Diamond Kings Platinum B/W

OVERALL INSERT ODDS 12 PER SER.2 BOX
STATED PRINT RUN 1 SERIAL #'d SET
NO PRICING DUE TO SCARCITY

2005 Diamond Kings Silver

*SILVER 1-300: 2.5X TO 6X BASIC
*SILVER 1-300: 1.5X TO 4X BASIC RC's
1-300 INSERT ODDS 10 PER SER.1 BOX
1-300 PRINT RUN 50 SERIAL #'d SETS
*SILVER: 4X TO 10X BASIC
301-450 INSERT ODDS 12 PER SER.2 BOX
301-450 PRINT RUN 25 SERIAL #'d SETS
301-450 NO RC PRICING DUE TO SCARCITY

2005 Diamond Kings Silver B/W

*SILVER B/W: 2.5X TO 6X BASIC
OVERALL INSERT ODDS 12 PER SER.2 BOX
STATED PRINT RUN 50 SERIAL #'d SETS

2005 Diamond Kings Framed Black

*BLACK: 5X TO 12X BASIC
STATED PRINT RUN 25 SERIAL #'d SETS
NO RC PRICING DUE TO SCARCITY
PLATINUM PRINT RUN 1 SERIAL #'d SET
NO PLAT.PRICING DUE TO SCARCITY
OVERALL INSERT ODDS 10 PER SER.1 BOX
OVERALL INSERT ODDS 12 PER SER.2 BOX

2005 Diamond Kings Framed Black B/W

*BLACK: 5X TO 12X BASIC
STATED PRINT RUN 25 SERIAL #'d SETS
PLATINUM PRINT RUN 1 SERIAL #'d SET
NO PLAT.PRICING DUE TO SCARCITY
OVERALL INSERT ODDS 12 PER SER.2 BOX

2005 Diamond Kings Framed Blue

*BLUE: 2.5X TO 6X BASIC
*BLUE: 1.5X TO 4X BASIC RC's
STATED PRINT RUN 100 SERIAL #'d SETS
PLATINUM PRINT RUN 1 SERIAL #'d SET
NO PLAT.PRICING DUE TO SCARCITY
1-300 INSERT ODDS 10 PER SER.1 BOX
301-450 INSERT ODDS 12 PER SER.2 BOX

2005 Diamond Kings Framed Blue B/W

*BLUE B/W: 2.5X TO 6X BASIC
STATED PRINT RUN 100 SERIAL #'d SETS
PLATINUM PRINT RUN 1 SERIAL #'d SET
NO PLAT.PRICING DUE TO SCARCITY
OVERALL INSERT ODDS 12 PER SER.2 BOX

2005 Diamond Kings Framed Green

*GREEN: 3X TO 8X BASIC
*GREEN: 2X TO 5X BASIC RC's
STATED PRINT RUN 50 SERIAL #'d SETS
PLATINUM PRINT RUN 1 SERIAL #'d SET
NO PLAT.PRICING DUE TO SCARCITY
1-300 INSERT ODDS 10 PER SER.1 BOX
301-450 INSERT ODDS 12 PER SER.2 BOX

2005 Diamond Kings Framed Green B/W

*GREEN B/W: 3X TO 8X BASIC
STATED PRINT RUN 50 SERIAL #'d SETS
PLATINUM PRINT RUN 1 SERIAL #'d SET
NO PLAT.PRICING DUE TO SCARCITY
OVERALL INSERT ODDS 12 PER SER.2 BOX

2005 Diamond Kings Framed Red

*RED: 1X TO 2.5X BASIC
*RED: .6X TO 1.5X BASIC RC's
1-300 SER.1 STATED ODDS 1:3
301-450 SER.2 STATED ODDS 1:3
PLAT.1-300: INSERTS 10 PER SER.1 BOX
PLAT.301-450: INSERTS 12 PER SER.2 BOX
PLATINUM PRINT RUN 1 SERIAL #'d SET
NO PLAT.PRICING DUE TO SCARCITY

2005 Diamond Kings Framed Red B/W

*RED: 1X TO 2.5X BASIC
OVERALL FRAMED RED ODDS 1:3
PLAT: INSERT ODDS 12 PER SER.2 BOX

PLATINUM PRINT RUN 1 SERIAL #'d SET
NO PLAT.PRICING DUE TO SCARCITY

2005 Diamond Kings Materials Bronze

OVERALL AU-GU ODDS 1:6
PRINT RUNS B/WN 10-200 COPIES PER
NO PRICING ON QTY OF 10 OR LESS
1 G.Anderson Bat-Jsy/200 2.50 6.00
2 Vlad Guerrero Bat-Jsy/200 4.00 10.00
4 Troy Glaus Bat-Jsy/200 2.50 6.00
5 Tim Salmon Bat-Jsy/200 3.00 8.00
7 Chone Figgins Bat-Jsy/200 2.50 6.00
10 Troy Percival Jsy-Jsy/200 2.50 6.00
11 Randy Johnson Bat-Bat/10
12 B.Webb Bat-Pants/200 2.50 6.00
13 Richie Sexson Bat-Bat/200 2.50 6.00
17 Luis Gonzalez Jsy-Jsy/200 2.50 6.00
18 Rafael Furcal Bat-Jsy/200 2.50 6.00
19 Andruw Jones Bat-Jsy/200 3.00 8.00
21 John Smoltz Jsy-Jsy/200 3.00 8.00
24 J.D. Drew Bat-Bat/200 2.50 6.00
25 Chipper Jones Bat-Jsy/200 4.00 10.00
27 R.Palmeiro O's Bat-Jsy/200 3.00 8.00
28 Miguel Tejada Bat-Jsy/200 2.50 6.00
29 Javy Lopez Bat-Jsy/25 5.00 12.00
30 Luis Matos Jsy-Jsy/100 3.00 8.00
31 Larry Bigbie Jsy-Jsy/200 2.50 6.00
32 Rodrigo Lopez Jsy-Jsy/200 2.50 6.00
34 Melvin Mora Bat-Jsy/200 2.50 6.00
36 Manny Ramirez Bat-Jsy/200 3.00 8.00
38 Trot Nixon Bat-Bat/200 3.00 8.00
39 Curt Schilling Bat-Jsy/200 3.00 8.00
41 Pedro Martinez Bat-Jsy/200 3.00 8.00
42 Johnny Damon Bat-Bat/200 3.00 8.00
43 Kevin Youkilis Bat-Bat/200 2.50 6.00
46 David Ortiz Bat-Jsy/200 4.00 10.00
47 Kerry Wood Jsy-Pants/200 2.50 6.00
48 Mark Prior Bat-Jsy/200 3.00 8.00
49 Aramis Ramirez Bat-Jsy/200 2.50 6.00
50 G.Madd Cubs Bat-Jsy/100 6.00 15.00
51 C.Zambrano Jsy-Jsy/200 2.50 6.00
52 Derrek Lee Bat-Bat/200 3.00 8.00
54 Moises Alou Bat-Bat/200 2.50 6.00
56 Sammy Sosa Bat-Jsy/200 4.00 10.00
57 N.G'parra Cubs Bat-Bat/200 4.00 10.00
60 M.Ordonez Bat-Jsy/200 2.50 6.00
61 Carlos Lee Bat-Jsy/200 2.50 6.00
62 Joe Crede Bat-Bat/200 2.50 6.00
65 Frank Thomas Bat-Jsy/200 4.00 10.00
69 Adam Dunn Bat-Jsy/200 2.50 6.00
70 Austin Kearns Bat-Bat/200 2.50 6.00
74 Sean Casey Jsy-Pants/200 2.50 6.00
76 C.C. Sabathia Jsy-Jsy/200 2.50 6.00
77 Jody Gerut Bat-Jsy/200 2.50 6.00
78 Omar Vizquel Bat-Jsy/200 3.00 8.00
79 Victor Martinez Bat-Jsy/200 2.50 6.00
80 Matt Lawton Bat-Bat/200 2.50 6.00
84 Todd Helton Bat-Jsy/200 3.00 8.00
85 Preston Wilson Bat-Jsy/200 2.50 6.00
90 I.Rod Tigers Bat-Jsy/200 3.00 8.00
92 Brandon Inge Bat-Jsy/200 2.50 6.00
94 Dontrelle Willis Jsy-Jsy/200 2.50 6.00
95 Miguel Cabrera Bat-Jsy/200 3.00 8.00
96 Josh Beckett Bat-Bat/100 3.00 8.00
97 Mike Lowell Bat-Jsy/100 3.00 8.00
98 Luis Castillo Bat-Bat/200 2.50 6.00
99 Juan Pierre Bat-Bat/200 2.50 6.00
100 P.LoDuca M's Bat-Bat/200 2.50 6.00
102 Craig Biggio Bat-Pants/200 3.00 8.00
103 L.Berkman Bat-Jsy/200 2.50 6.00
104 Roy Oswalt Jsy-Jsy/200 2.50 6.00
105 R.Clem Astros Bat-Jsy/200 5.00 12.00
106 Jeff Kent Bat-Jsy/100 3.00 8.00
108 Jeff Bagwell Bat-Jsy/200 3.00 8.00
109 C.Belt Astros Bat-Jsy/200 2.50 6.00
110 Angel Berroa Bat-Bat/200 2.50 6.00
111 Mike Sweeney Bat-Jsy/200 2.50 6.00
112 J.Affeldt Pants-Pants/200 2.50 6.00
114 Juan Gonzalez Bat-Jsy/200 2.50 6.00
116 Shawn Green Bat-Jsy/200 2.50 6.00
118 Adrian Beltre Bat-Jsy/200 2.50 6.00
119 Hideo Nomo Bat-Jsy/200 4.00 10.00
123 S.Podsednik Jsy-Jsy/200 2.50 6.00
124 Ben Sheets Bat-Pants/200 2.50 6.00
125 Lyle Overbay Jsy-Jsy/200 2.50 6.00
126 Junior Spivey Jsy-Jsy/200 2.50 6.00
127 Bill Hall Bat-Jsy/200 2.50 6.00
129 Jacque Jones Bat-Jsy/200 2.50 6.00
130 Torii Hunter Bat-Jsy/200 2.50 6.00
131 Johan Santana Jsy-Jsy/200 4.00 10.00
132 Lew Ford Bat-Jsy/200 2.50 6.00
136 Jose Vidro Bat-Jsy/200 2.50 6.00
138 Brad Wilkerson Bat-Bat/100 3.00 8.00
139 Nick Johnson Bat-Bat/100 3.00 8.00
140 L.Hernandez Jsy-Jsy/25 5.00 12.00
141 Tom Glavine Bat-Bat/200 3.00 8.00
143 Jose Reyes Bat-Jsy/200 2.50 6.00
144 Al Leiter Jsy-Jsy/200 2.50 6.00
145 Mike Piazza Jsy-Jsy/100 5.00 12.00
146 Kazuo Matsui Bat-Jsy/200 2.50 6.00
147 R.Hidalgo Mets Bat-Bat/200 2.50 6.00
149 Mariano Rivera Jsy-Jsy/100 5.00 12.00
150 Mike Mussina Bat-Jsy/200 3.00 8.00
153 Jorge Posada Bat-Jsy/200 3.00 8.00
154 Jason Giambi Bat-Jsy/200 2.50 6.00
155 Gary Sheffield Bat-Jsy/200 2.50 6.00
158 Kevin Brown Bat-Bat/100 3.00 8.00
160 E.Loaiza Yanks Bat-Bat/100 3.00 8.00
161 H.Matsui Jsy-Pants/200 6.00 15.00
162 Eric Chavez Bat-Jsy/200 2.50 6.00
163 Mark Mulder Bat-Bat/25 5.00 12.00
164 Barry Zito Bat-Jsy/200 2.50 6.00
165 Tim Hudson Bat-Jsy/200 2.50 6.00
166 Jermaine Dye Bat-Jsy/200 2.50 6.00
168 Bobby Crosby Jsy-Jsy/200 2.50 6.00
171 J.Thome Phils Bat-Jsy/200 3.00 8.00
172 Bobby Abreu Jsy-Jsy/200 2.50 6.00
173 Kevin Millwood Jsy-Jsy/200 2.50 6.00
178 Craig Wilson Bat-Jsy/200 2.50 6.00
180 Jack Wilson Bat-Bat/200 2.50 6.00
181 Jose Castillo Bat-Bat/200 2.50 6.00
184 Jason Bay Bat-Jsy/200 2.50 6.00
185 S.Burroughs Bat-Jsy/200 2.50 6.00
187 Brian Giles Bat-Bat/100 3.00 8.00
193 Trevor Hoffman Jsy-Jsy/200 2.50 6.00
199 J.T. Snow Jsy-Jsy/25 5.00 12.00
200 A.J. Pierzynski Jsy-Jsy/100 3.00 8.00
201 Edgar Martinez Bat-Bat/200 3.00 8.00
204 Bret Boone Jsy-Jsy/200 2.50 6.00
208 Jamie Moyer Jsy-Jsy/50 4.00 10.00
209 Jim Edmonds Bat-Jsy/200 2.50 6.00
210 Scott Rolen Bat-Jsy/200 3.00 8.00
211 Edgar Renteria Bat-Jsy/200 2.50 6.00
212 Dan Haren Bat-Jsy/100 3.00 8.00
213 Matt Morris Jsy-Jsy/100 3.00 8.00
214 Albert Pujols Bat-Jsy/200 8.00 20.00
215 L.Walker Cards Bat-Bat/200 3.00 8.00
220 Aubrey Huff Bat-Bat/100 3.00 8.00
221 Carl Crawford Jsy-Jsy/200 2.50 6.00
222 Rocco Baldelli Bat-Jsy/200 2.50 6.00
223 Fred McGriff Bat-Jsy/200 3.00 8.00
224 D.Brazelton Jsy-Jsy/200 2.50 6.00
225 B.J. Upton Bat-Bat/200 3.00 8.00
226 Joey Gathright Bat-Jsy/200 2.50 6.00
228 Hank Blalock Bat-Jsy/100 3.00 8.00
229 Mark Teixeira Bat-Jsy/200 3.00 8.00
230 Michael Young Bat-Jsy/200 2.50 6.00
232 Laynce Nix Bat-Jsy/200 2.50 6.00
233 A.Soriano Rgr Bat-Jsy/200 2.50 6.00
234 R.Palmeiro Rgr Bat-Jsy/200 3.00 8.00
235 Kevin Mench Bat-Jsy/200 2.50 6.00
236 David Dellucci Jsy-Jsy/200 4.00 10.00
237 F.Cordero Jsy-Jsy/200 2.50 6.00
239 Roy Halladay Jsy-Jsy/200 2.50 6.00
240 Carlos Delgado Bat-Jsy/200 2.50 6.00
242 Vernon Wells Bat-Jsy/200 2.50 6.00
267 L.Walk Rockies Jsy-Jsy/200 2.50 6.00
268 I.Rodriguez Rgr Jsy-Jsy/200 3.00 8.00
269 B.Penny M's Bat-Jsy/200 2.50 6.00
270 C.Belt Royals Bat-Jsy/200 2.50 6.00
271 P.LoDuca Dgr Bat-Jsy/200 2.50 6.00
273 N.G'parra Sox Bat-Bat/100 5.00 12.00
274 E.Loaiza Sox Bat-Bat/100 3.00 8.00
275 R.Hidal Astros Jkt-Pants/200 2.50 6.00
276 John Olerud Bat-Jsy/200 2.50 6.00
277 G.Madd Braves Jsy-Jsy/200 5.00 12.00
278 R.Clem Yanks Bat-Jsy/200 5.00 12.00
279 A.Sor Yanks Bat-Jsy/200 2.50 6.00
280 Dale Murphy Jsy-Jsy/200 4.00 10.00
281 Cal Ripken Bat-Jsy/200 12.50 30.00
282 Dwight Evans Bat-Jsy/200 4.00 10.00
283 Ron Santo Bat-Bat/200 4.00 10.00
284 Andre Dawson Bat-Jsy/100 4.00 10.00
285 Harold Baines Bat-Jsy/200 3.00 8.00
286 Jack Morris Jsy-Jsy/100 4.00 10.00
287 Kirk Gibson Bat-Jsy/200 3.00 8.00
288 Bo Jackson Bat-Jsy/200 5.00 12.00
289 Orel Hershiser Jsy-Jsy/50 5.00 12.00
290 Maury Wills Jsy-Jsy/10
291 Tony Oliva Bat-Jsy/200 3.00 8.00
292 D.Strawberry Bat-Jsy/100 4.00 10.00
293 Roger Maris Bat-Jsy/100 20.00 50.00
294 Don Mattingly Bat-Jsy/100 10.00 25.00
295 R.Henderson Bat-Jsy/100 6.00 15.00
297 Dave Parker Bat-Jsy/200 3.00 8.00
298 Steve Garvey Bat-Jsy/200 3.00 8.00
299 Matt Williams Jsy-Jsy/200 3.00 8.00
300 K.Hernandez Bat-Jsy/200 3.00 8.00
302 V.Guer Angels Jsy-Jsy/200 4.00 10.00
303 G.Anderson Bat-Jsy/200 2.50 6.00
307 Luis Gonzalez Jsy-Jsy/200 2.50 6.00
308 Randy Johnson D'backs Bat-Jsy/1
310 Shawn Green Bat-Bat/200 2.50 6.00
311 Troy Glaus Bat-Bat/200 2.50 6.00
314 Chipper Jones Jsy-Jsy/100 5.00 12.00
315 Johnny Estrada Jsy-Jsy/200 2.50 6.00
316 Andruw Jones Bat-Jsy/200 3.00 8.00
319 Jay Gibbons Bat-Bat/200 2.50 6.00
320 Melvin Mora Jsy-Jsy/200 2.50 6.00
321 R.Palmeiro O's Bat-Jsy/200 3.00 8.00
323 David Ortiz Bat-Jsy/200 4.00 10.00
324 M.Ramirez Bat-Jsy/200 3.00 8.00
327 C.Schill Sox Jsy-Jsy/200 3.00 8.00
328 S.Sosa Cubs Bat-Jsy/100 5.00 12.00
329 Mark Prior Bat-Jsy/200 3.00 8.00
330 Greg Maddux Jsy-Jsy/25 10.00 25.00
332 F.Thomas Bat-Pants/200 4.00 10.00
333 Mark Buehrle Bat-Jsy/200 2.50 6.00
336 Sean Casey Bat-Jsy/200 2.50 6.00
337 Adam Dunn Bat-Jsy/200 2.50 6.00
339 Travis Hafner Jsy-Jsy/100 3.00 8.00
340 Victor Martinez Bat-Jsy/100 3.00 8.00
341 Cliff Lee Jsy-Jsy/200 2.50 6.00
342 Todd Helton Bat-Jsy/25 6.00 15.00
343 P.Wilson Jsy-Jsy/200 2.50 6.00
344 I.Rod Tigers Bat-Jsy/200 3.00 8.00
347 M.Cabrera Bat-Jsy/200 3.00 8.00
348 Jeff Bagwell Bat-Jsy/200 3.00 8.00
349 Andy Pettitte Bat-Jsy/200 3.00 8.00
350 R.Clem Astros Bat-Jsy/100 6.00 15.00
351 Ken Harvey Jsy-Jsy/200 2.50 6.00
353 Hideo Nomo Bat-Jsy/200 4.00 10.00
354 Kazuhisa Ishii Jsy-Jsy/200 2.50 6.00
355 E.Jackson Jsy-Jsy/200 2.50 6.00
356 J.D. Drew Bat-Bat/200 2.50 6.00
357 Jeff Kent Bat-Bat/25 5.00 12.00
358 G.Jenkins Jsy-Pants/200 2.50 6.00
359 Carlos Lee Bat-Bat/200 2.50 6.00
360 S.Stewart Jsy-Jsy/200 2.50 6.00
362 J.Santana Jsy-Jsy/100 4.00 10.00
363 M.Piaz Mets Jsy-Jsy/100 5.00 12.00
364 Kazuo Matsui Jsy-Jsy/100 3.00 8.00
365 Carlos Beltran Bat-Bat/10
366 P.Martinez Bat-Bat/100 4.00 10.00
368 Hideki Matsui Bat-Jsy/100 6.00 15.00
369 B.Williams Bat-Jsy/200 3.00 8.00
370 G.Shef Yanks Bat-Jsy/100 3.00 8.00
371 R.John Yanks Bat-Bat/25 8.00 20.00
378 M.Mulder A's Bat-Bat/50 4.00 10.00
380 Eric Chavez Jsy-Jsy/100 3.00 8.00
382 Marlon Byrd Bat-Jsy/200 2.50 6.00
383 Pat Burrell Jsy-Jsy/200 2.50 6.00
385 Jim Thome Bat-Bat/200 3.00 8.00
386 Jason Bay Bat-Jsy/1
388 Moises Alou Bat-Bat/200 2.50 6.00
393 Adrian Beltre Bat-Bat/50 4.00 10.00
394 R.Sexson Bat-Bat/200 2.50 6.00
397 Albert Pujols Bat-Jsy/200 8.00 20.00
398 S.Rolen Cards Bat-Jsy/200 3.00 8.00
401 D.Young Bat-Bat/200 3.00 8.00
402 Aubrey Huff Bat-Bat/50 4.00 10.00
403 A.Soriano Bat-Jsy/200 2.50 6.00
404 Hank Blalock Bat-Jsy/200 2.50 6.00
405 R.Hidalgo Bat-Bat/200 2.50 6.00
406 Vernon Wells Bat-Jsy/200 2.50 6.00
407 O.Hudson Bat-Bat/200 2.50 6.00
412 Jose Vidro Bat-Jsy/5
415 M.Tejada Bat-Jsy/200 2.50 6.00
416 G.Shef Braves Bat-Bat/200 2.50 6.00
417 C.Schil D'back J-J/200 2.50 6.00
418 R.Palm Rgr Bat-Pants/50 5.00 12.00
419 S.Rolen Phils Bat-Jsy/200 3.00 8.00
420 A.Ramirez Jsy-Jsy/200 2.50 6.00
421 V.Guer Guerrero Expos Bat-Bat/200 4.00 10.00
422 S.Finley D'backs J-J/200 2.50 6.00
423 R.Clem Sox Bat-Jsy/200 5.00 12.00
424 M.Piaz Dgr Jsy-Jsy/200 4.00 10.00
425 I.Rod M's Bat-Jsy/200 3.00 8.00
426 David Justice Jsy-Jsy/200 5.00 12.00
427 Mark Grace Bat-Jsy/25 8.00 20.00
428 Alan Trammell Bat-Jsy/100 4.00 10.00
429 Bert Blyleven Jsy-Jsy/1
430 D.Gooden Bat-Jsy/200 3.00 8.00
431 D.Sanders Bat-Jsy/200 4.00 10.00
432 Joe Torre MG Bat-Bat/100 5.00 12.00
433 Jose Canseco Jsy-Jsy/100 6.00 15.00
434 T.Gwynn Bat-Pants/200 5.00 12.00
435 Will Clark Bat-Jsy/100 5.00 12.00
436 Marty Marion Jsy-Jsy/1
437 Nolan Ryan Bat-Jsy/50 12.50 30.00
438 Billy Martin Jsy-Pants/200 4.00 10.00
439 C.Delgado Bat-Bat/100 3.00 8.00
440 M.Ordonez Bat-Bat/200 2.50 6.00
441 S.Sosa O's Bat-Bat/25 8.00 20.00
449 R.Sandberg Bat-Jsy/100 8.00 20.00
450 Willie Mays Bat-Pants/5

2005 Diamond Kings Materials Bronze B/W

*BRZ B/W p/r 100: .5X TO 1.2X BRZ p/r 200
*BRZ B/W p/r 100: .4X TO 1X BRZ p/r 100
*BRZ B/W p/r 50: .6X TO 1.5X BRZ p/r 200
*BRZ B/W p/r 50: .5X TO 1.2X BRZ p/r 100
OVERALL AU-GU ODDS 1:6
PRINT RUNS B/WN 10-100 COPIES PER
NO PRICING ON QTY OF 10
73 Ryan Wagner Jsy-Jsy/100 3.00 8.00

2005 Diamond Kings Materials Gold

*GOLD p/r 50: .6X TO 1.5X BRZ p/r 200
*GOLD p/r 50: .5X TO 1.2X BRZ p/r 100
*GOLD p/r 50: .4X TO 1X BRZ p/r 50
*GOLD p/r 50: .3X TO .8X BRZ p/r 25
*GOLD p/r 25: .75X TO 2X BRZ p/r 200
*GOLD p/r 25: .6X TO 1.5X BRZ p/r 100
*GOLD p/r 25: .5X TO 1.2X BRZ p/r 50
*GOLD p/r 25: .4X TO 1X BRZ p/r 25
OVERALL AU-GU ODDS 1:6
PRINT RUNS B/WN 25-50 COPIES PER
6 C.Kotchman Jsy-Jsy/50 4.00 10.00
9 Francisco Rodriguez Jsy-Jsy/50 4.00 10.00
11 Randy Johnson Bat-Bat/25 8.00 20.00
20 Marcus Giles Jsy-Jsy/50 4.00 10.00
26 Nick Green Bat-Jsy/50 4.00 10.00
33 Brian Roberts Jsy-Jsy/50 4.00 10.00
55 Matt Clement Jsy-Jsy/50 4.00 10.00
73 Ryan Wagner Jsy-Jsy/50 4.00 10.00
89 J.Bonderman Jsy-Jsy/50 4.00 10.00
107 Morgan Ensberg Jsy-Jsy/50 4.00 10.00

2005 Diamond Kings Materials Gold B/W

*GOLD B/W p/r 50: .6X TO 1.5X BRZ p/r 200
*GOLD B/W p/r 50: .5X TO 1.2X BRZ p/r 100
*GOLD B/W p/r 25: .75X TO 2X BRZ p/r 200
OVERALL AU-GU ODDS 1:6
PRINT RUNS B/WN 25-50 COPIES PER
11 Randy Johnson Bat-Bat/25 8.00 20.00
73 Ryan Wagner Jsy-Jsy/50 4.00 10.00

2005 Diamond Kings Materials Platinum

OVERALL AU-GU ODDS 1:6
STATED PRINT RUN 1 SERIAL #'d SET
NO PRICING DUE TO SCARCITY

2005 Diamond Kings Materials Platinum B/W

OVERALL AU-GU ODDS 1:6
STATED PRINT RUN 1 SERIAL #'d SET
NO PRICING DUE TO SCARCITY

2005 Diamond Kings Materials Silver

*SILV p/r 100: .5X TO 1.2X BRZ p/r 200
*SILV p/r 100: .4X TO 1X BRZ p/r 100
*SILV p/r 100: .25X TO .6X BRZ p/r 25
*SILV p/r 50: .6X TO 1.5X BRZ p/r 200
*SILV p/r 50: .5X TO 1.2X BRZ p/r 100
*SILV p/r 50: .4X TO 1X BRZ p/r 50
*SILV p/r 25: .6X TO 1.5X BRZ p/r 100
*SILV p/r 25: .5X TO 1.2X BRZ p/r 50
*SILV p/r 25: .4X TO 1X BRZ p/r 25
OVERALL AU-GU ODDS 1:6
PRINT RUNS B/WN 1-100 COPIES PER
NO PRICING ON QTY OF 10 OR LESS
6 C.Kotchman Jsy-Jsy/100 3.00 8.00
9 F.Rodriguez Jsy-Jsy/100 3.00 8.00
11 Randy Johnson Bat-Bat/25 8.00 20.00
20 Marcus Giles Jsy-Jsy/100 3.00 8.00
26 Nick Green Bat-Jsy/100 3.00 8.00
33 Brian Roberts Jsy-Jsy/100 3.00 8.00
37 Jason Varitek Bat-Bat/50 6.00 15.00
55 Matt Clement Jsy-Jsy/100 3.00 8.00
71 Barry Larkin Bat-Bat/50 5.00 12.00
73 Ryan Wagner Jsy-Jsy/100 3.00 8.00
83 Travis Hafner Jsy-Jsy/50 4.00 10.00
89 J.Bonderman Jsy-Jsy/100 3.00 8.00
107 Morgan Ensberg Jsy-Jsy/100 3.00 8.00

2005 Diamond Kings Materials Silver B/W

*SILV B/W p/r 100: .5X TO 1.2X BRZ p/r 200
*SILV B/W p/r 100: .4X TO 1X BRZ p/r 100
*SILV B/W p/r 50: .6X TO 1.5X BRZ p/r 200
*SILV B/W p/r 50: .5X TO 1.2X BRZ p/r 100
*SILV B/W p/r 25: .75X TO 2X BRZ p/r 200
*SILV B/W p/r 25: .6X TO 1.5X BRZ p/r 100
OVERALL AU-GU ODDS 1:6
PRINT RUNS B/WN 25-100 COPIES PER
11 Randy Johnson Bat-Bat/25 8.00 20.00
73 Ryan Wagner Jsy-Jsy/100 3.00 8.00

2005 Diamond Kings Materials Framed Black

1-300 PRINT RUN 10 SERIAL #'d SETS
301-450 PRINT RUN 1 SERIAL #'d SET
PLATINUM PRINT RUN 1 SERIAL #'d SET
OVERALL AU-GU ODDS 1:6
NO PRICING DUE TO SCARCITY

2005 Diamond Kings Materials Framed Black B/W

STATED PRINT RUN 1 SERIAL #'d SET
PLATINUM PRINT RUN 1 SERIAL #'d SET
OVERALL AU-GU ODDS 1:6
NO PRICING DUE TO SCARCITY

2005 Diamond Kings Materials Framed Blue

*BLUE p/r 100: .5X TO 1.2X BRZ p/r 200
*BLUE p/r 100: .4X TO 1X BRZ p/r 100
*BLUE p/r 100: .3X TO .8X BRZ p/r 50
*BLUE p/r 100: .25X TO .6X BRZ p/r 25
*BLUE p/r 50: .6X TO 1.5X BRZ p/r 200
*BLUE p/r 50: .5X TO 1.2X BRZ p/r 100
*BLUE p/r 50: .4X TO 1X BRZ p/r 50
*BLUE p/r 50: .3X TO .8X BRZ p/r 25
*BLUE p/r 25: .75X TO 2X BRZ p/r 200
*BLUE p/r 25: .4X TO 1X BRZ p/r 25
1-300 PRINT RUN 50 SERIAL #'d SETS
301-450 PRINT RUNS B/WN 1-100 PER
301-450 NO PRICE ON QTY OF 10 OR LESS
PLATINUM PRINT RUN 1 SERIAL #'d SET
NO PLAT.PRICING DUE TO SCARCITY
OVERALL AU-GU ODDS 1:6 PACKS

2005 Diamond Kings Materials Framed Blue B/W

*BLUE B/W p/r 25: .75X TO 2X BRZ p/r 200
*BLUE B/W p/r 25: .6X TO 1.5X BRZ p/r 100
STATED PRINT RUN 25 SERIAL #'d SETS
PLATINUM PRINT RUN 1 SERIAL #'d SET
NO PLAT.PRICING DUE TO SCARCITY
OVERALL AU-GU ODDS 1:6
73 Ryan Wagner Jsy-Jsy/25 5.00 12.00

2005 Diamond Kings Materials Framed Green

*GREEN p/r 25: .75X TO 2X BRZ p/r 200
*GREEN p/r 25: .6X TO 1.5X BRZ p/r 100
*GREEN p/r 25: .5X TO 1.2X BRZ p/r 50
*GREEN p/r 25: .4X TO 1X BRZ p/r 25
1-300 PRINT RUN 25 SERIAL #'d SETS
301-450 PRINT RUNS B/WN 1-25 PER
301-450 NO PRICES ON QTY OF 10 OR LESS
PLATINUM PRINT RUN 1 SERIAL #'d SET
NO PLAT.PRICING DUE TO SCARCITY
OVERALL AU-GU ODDS 1:6
11 Randy Johnson Bat-Jsy 8.00 20.00

2005 Diamond Kings Materials Framed Green B/W

*GRN B/W p/r 25: .75X TO 2X BRZ p/r 200
*GRN B/W p/r 25: .6X TO 1.5X BRZ p/r 100
STATED PRINT RUN 25 SERIAL #'d SETS
PLATINUM PRINT RUN 1 SERIAL #'d SET
NO PLAT.PRICING DUE TO SCARCITY
OVERALL AU-GU ODDS 1:6
73 Ryan Wagner Jsy-Jsy/25 5.00 12.00

2005 Diamond Kings Materials Framed Red

*RED p/r 200: .4X TO 1X BRZ p/r 200
*RED p/r 200: .3X TO .8X BRZ p/r 100
*RED p/r 100: .5X TO 1.2X BRZ p/r 200
*RED p/r 100: .4X TO 1X BRZ p/r 100
*RED p/r 100: .3X TO .8X BRZ p/r 50
*RED p/r 100: .25X TO .6X BRZ p/r 25
*RED p/r 50: .6X TO 1.5X BRZ p/r 200
*RED p/r 50: .5X TO 1.2X BRZ p/r 100
*RED p/r 50: .4X TO 1X BRZ p/r 50
*RED p/r 50: .3X TO .8X BRZ p/r 25
*RED p/r 25: .75X TO 2X BRZ p/r 200
*RED p/r 25: .6X TO 1.5X BRZ p/r 100
*RED p/r 25: .4X TO 1X BRZ p/r 25
PRINT RUNS B/WN 25-100 COPIES PER
PLATINUM PRINT RUN 1 SERIAL #'d SET
NO PLAT.PRICING DUE TO SCARCITY
OVERALL AU-GU ODDS 1:6
6 C.Kotchman Jsy-Jsy/100 3.00 8.00
9 F.Rodriguez Jsy-Jsy/100 3.00 8.00
11 Randy Johnson Bat-Bat/50 6.00 15.00
20 Marcus Giles Jsy-Jsy/100 3.00 8.00
26 Nick Green Bat-Jsy/100 3.00 8.00
33 Brian Roberts Jsy-Jsy/100 3.00 8.00
37 Jason Varitek Bat-Bat/25 8.00 20.00
55 Matt Clement Jsy-Jsy/100 3.00 8.00
71 Barry Larkin Bat-Bat/100 4.00 10.00
73 Ryan Wagner Jsy-Jsy/100 3.00 8.00
83 Travis Hafner Jsy-Jsy/50 4.00 10.00
89 J.Bonderman Jsy-Jsy/100 3.00 8.00
107 Morg Ensberg Jsy-Jsy/100 3.00 8.00
190 Phil Nevin Jsy-Jsy/50 4.00 10.00
195 Jerome Williams Jsy-Jsy/50 4.00 10.00
266 J.Thome Indians Bat-Bat/25 6.00 15.00
272 O.Cabrera Expos Bat-Bat/50 4.00 10.00
290 Maury Wills Jsy-Jsy/25 5.00 12.00
365 Carlos Beltran Bat-Bat/25 5.00 12.00
412 Jose Vidro Bat-Jsy/25 5.00 12.00

2005 Diamond Kings Materials Framed Red B/W

*RED B/W p/r 100: .5X TO 1.2X BRZ p/r 200
*RED B/W p/r 100: .4X TO 1X BRZ p/r 100
*RED B/W p/r 50: .6X TO 1.5X BRZ p/r 200
*RED B/W p/r 50: .5X TO 1.2X BRZ p/r 100
*RED B/W p/r 25: .6X TO 1.5X BRZ p/r 100

PRINT RUNS B/WN 25-100 COPIES PER
PLATINUM PRINT RUN 1 SERIAL #'d SET
NO PLAT.PRICING DUE TO SCARCITY
OVERALL AU-GU ODDS 1:6
73 Ryan Wagner Jsy-Jsy/100 3.00 8.00

2005 Diamond Kings Signature Black

OVERALL AU-GU ODDS 1:6
STATED PRINT RUN 1 SERIAL #'d SET
NO PRICING DUE TO SCARCITY

2005 Diamond Kings Signature Bronze

OVERALL AU-GU ODDS 1:6
PRINT RUNS B/WN 1-100 COPIES PER
NO PRICING ON QTY OF 10 OR LESS
NO RC YR PRICING ON QTY OF 25 OR LESS
1 Garret Anderson/10
3 Jose Guillen/100 6.00 15.00
5 Tim Salmon/100 10.00 25.00
6 Casey Kotchman/100 6.00 15.00
7 Chone Figgins/100 6.00 15.00
8 Robb Quinlan/100 4.00 10.00
9 Francisco Rodriguez/50 12.50 30.00
10 Troy Percival/50 8.00 20.00
11 Randy Johnson/1
12 Brandon Webb/10
14 Shea Hillenbrand/100 6.00 15.00
15 Chad Tracy/100 4.00 10.00
16 Alex Cintron/100 4.00 10.00
18 Rafael Furcal/10
19 Andruw Jones/1
22 Adam LaRoche/50 5.00 12.00
23 Russ Ortiz/50 5.00 12.00
24 J.D. Drew/1
25 Chipper Jones/1
26 Nick Green/100 4.00 10.00
27 Rafael Palmeiro O's/1
30 Luis Matos/100 4.00 10.00
31 Larry Bigbie/100 6.00 15.00
32 Rodrigo Lopez/100 4.00 10.00
33 Brian Roberts/100 6.00 15.00
34 Melvin Mora/100 6.00 15.00
36 Manny Ramirez/1
38 Trot Nixon/10
39 Curt Schilling/1
40 Keith Foulke/50 12.50 30.00
41 Pedro Martinez/1
43 Kevin Youkilis/100 4.00 10.00
44 Orlando Cabrera Sox/50 8.00 20.00
45 Abe Alvarez/100 6.00 15.00
46 David Ortiz/10
47 Kerry Wood/1
48 Mark Prior/1
49 Aramis Ramirez/10
50 Greg Maddux Cubs/1
51 Carlos Zambrano/50 12.50 30.00
52 Derrek Lee/10
55 Matt Clement/5
56 Sammy Sosa/1
58 Todd Walker/50 5.00 12.00
59 Angel Guzman/100 4.00 10.00
60 Magglio Ordonez/5
61 Carlos Lee/100 6.00 15.00
63 Paul Konerko/10
64 Shingo Takatsu/10
65 Frank Thomas/1
68 Jose Contreras/1
69 Adam Dunn/1
70 Austin Kearns/5
71 Barry Larkin/1
73 Ryan Wagner/100 4.00 10.00
74 Sean Casey/5
75 Danny Graves/100 4.00 10.00
76 C.C. Sabathia/50 8.00 20.00
77 Jody Gerut/100 4.00 10.00
78 Omar Vizquel/5
79 Victor Martinez/50 8.00 20.00
82 Kazuhito Tadano/100 6.00 15.00
83 Travis Hafner/100 6.00 15.00
84 Todd Helton/1
89 Jeremy Bonderman/100 6.00 15.00
92 Brandon Inge/100 4.00 10.00
94 Dontrelle Willis/1
95 Miguel Cabrera/10
96 Josh Beckett/1
97 Mike Lowell/5
100 Paul LoDuca Marlins/5
101 Guillermo Mota/50 5.00 12.00
102 Craig Biggio/1
103 Lance Berkman/1
104 Roy Oswalt/5
105 Roger Clemens Astros/1
107 Morgan Ensberg/100 6.00 15.00
108 Jeff Bagwell/1
109 Carlos Beltran Astros/1
110 Angel Berroa/10
112 Jeremy Affeldt/100 4.00 10.00
114 Juan Gonzalez/5
116 Shawn Green/1
117 Milton Bradley/100 6.00 15.00
118 Adrian Beltre/5
119 Hideo Nomo/1
120 Steve Finley/10
122 Brad Penny Dgr/100 4.00 10.00
123 Scott Podsednik/50 12.50 30.00
124 Ben Sheets/5
125 Lyle Overbay/100 4.00 10.00
127 Bill Hall/100 4.00 10.00
128 Rickie Weeks/5
129 Jacque Jones/10
130 Torii Hunter/5
131 Johan Santana/10
132 Lew Ford/100 4.00 10.00
135 Jason Kubel/100 4.00 10.00
136 Jose Vidro/10
137 Chad Cordero/100 6.00 15.00
139 Nick Johnson/10
140 Livan Hernandez/25 10.00 25.00
141 Tom Glavine/1
142 Jae Weong Seo/10
145 Mike Piazza/1
148 David Wright/10
150 Mike Mussina/1
155 Gary Sheffield/1
156 Bubba Crosby/100 4.00 10.00
159 Tom Gordon/25 10.00 25.00
160 Esteban Loaiza Yanks/100 6.00 15.00
162 Eric Chavez/1
163 Mark Mulder/1
164 Barry Zito/1
165 Tim Hudson/1
166 Jermaine Dye/50 8.00 20.00
167 Octavio Dotel/50 8.00 20.00
168 Bobby Crosby/100 6.00 15.00
174 Mike Lieberthal/100 6.00 15.00
177 Randy Wolf/100 6.00 15.00
178 Craig Wilson/100 4.00 10.00
180 Jack Wilson/100 6.00 15.00
181 Jose Castillo/100 4.00 10.00
184 Jason Bay/100 6.00 15.00
185 Sean Burroughs/10
186 Jay Payton/50 5.00 12.00
188 Akinori Otsuka/10
189 Jake Peavy/50 12.50 30.00
194 Freddy Guzman/100 4.00 10.00
195 Jerome Williams/10
197 Todd Linden/50 5.00 12.00
198 Merkin Valdez/100 6.00 15.00
199 J.T. Snow/10
201 Edgar Martinez/5
203 Raul Ibanez/100 10.00 25.00
205 Shigetoshi Hasegawa/5
206 Miguel Olivo/100 4.00 10.00
207 Bucky Jacobsen/100 4.00 10.00
208 Jamie Moyer/50 8.00 20.00
209 Jim Edmonds/1
210 Scott Rolen/1
211 Edgar Renteria/5
212 Dan Haren/100 4.00 10.00
214 Albert Pujols/1
219 Jeff Suppan/100 6.00 15.00
220 Aubrey Huff/50 8.00 20.00
221 Carl Crawford/25 10.00 25.00
223 Fred McGriff/5
224 Dewon Brazelton/100 4.00 10.00
225 B.J. Upton/5
226 Joey Gathright/100 4.00 10.00
227 Scott Kazmir/25 10.00 25.00
228 Hank Blalock/5
229 Mark Teixeira/5
230 Michael Young/50 8.00 20.00
231 Adrian Gonzalez/100 10.00 25.00
232 Laynce Nix/100 4.00 10.00
233 Alfonso Soriano Rgr/1
234 Rafael Palmeiro Rgr/1
236 David Dellucci/100 12.50 30.00
237 Francisco Cordero/100 6.00 15.00
239 Roy Halladay/1
241 Alexis Rios/100 6.00 15.00
242 Vernon Wells/5
243 Yadier Molina/5
248 Dioner Navarro/100 6.00 15.00
253 Yhency Brazoban/100 4.00 10.00
257 Scott Proctor/100 4.00 10.00
260 Matt Peterson/100 4.00 10.00
269 Brad Penny Marlins/50 5.00 12.00
270 Carlos Beltran Royals/1
271 Paul LoDuca Dgr/5
272 Orlando Cabrera Expos/50 8.00 20.00
274 Esteban Loaiza Sox/100 6.00 15.00
277 Greg Maddux Braves/1
278 Roger Clemens Yanks/1
279 Alfonso Soriano Yanks/1
280 Dale Murphy/10
281 Cal Ripken/1
282 Dwight Evans/10
283 Ron Santo/10
284 Andre Dawson/50 8.00 20.00
285 Harold Baines/100 6.00 15.00
286 Jack Morris/100 6.00 15.00
287 Kirk Gibson/5
288 Bo Jackson/1
289 Orel Hershiser/1
290 Maury Wills/100 6.00 15.00
291 Tony Oliva/10
292 Darryl Strawberry/100 6.00 15.00
294 Don Mattingly/1
295 Rickey Henderson/1
296 Dave Stewart/10
297 Dave Parker/100 6.00 15.00
298 Steve Garvey/10
299 Matt Williams/25 15.00 40.00
300 Keith Hernandez/10
303 Garret Anderson/50 8.00 20.00
304 Dallas McPherson/100 4.00 10.00
305 Orlando Cabrera/25 10.00 25.00
306 Steve Finley Angels/50 8.00 20.00
310 Shawn Green/1
313 Russ Ortiz/50 5.00 12.00
314 Chipper Jones/1
315 Johnny Estrada/100 4.00 10.00
317 Tim Hudson/25 15.00 40.00
318 Danny Kolb/100 4.00 10.00
319 Jay Gibbons/50 5.00 12.00
320 Melvin Mora/50 8.00 20.00
323 David Ortiz/10
324 Manny Ramirez/1
325 Edgar Renteria/50 8.00 20.00
326 Matt Clement/10
327 Curt Schilling Sox/1
329 Mark Prior/10
330 Greg Maddux/1
332 Frank Thomas/10
333 Mark Buehrle/50 10.00 25.00
336 Sean Casey/25 10.00 25.00
339 Travis Hafner/50 8.00 20.00
340 Victor Martinez/50 8.00 20.00
341 Cliff Lee/100 10.00 25.00
342 Todd Helton/1
343 Preston Wilson/50 8.00 20.00
347 Miguel Cabrera/10
348 Jeff Bagwell/1
350 Roger Clemens Astros/1
351 Ken Harvey/100 4.00 10.00
353 Hideo Nomo/1
354 Kazuhisa Ishii/5
355 Edwin Jackson/100 4.00 10.00
359 Carlos Lee/100 6.00 15.00
360 Shannon Stewart/25 10.00 25.00
361 Joe Nathan/100 6.00 15.00
362 Johan Santana/10
365 Carlos Beltran/10
366 Pedro Martinez/1
370 Gary Sheffield Yanks/1
371 Randy Johnson Yanks/1
376 Eric Byrnes/100 4.00 10.00
377 Rich Harden/100 6.00 15.00
378 Mark Mulder A's/25 10.00 25.00
380 Eric Chavez/25 10.00 25.00
382 Marlon Byrd/100 4.00 10.00
384 Brett Myers/100 6.00 15.00
386 Jason Bay/50 8.00 20.00
387 Jake Peavy/50 12.50 30.00
389 Omar Vizquel/10
393 Adrian Beltre/1
397 Albert Pujols/1
398 Scott Rolen Cards/10
399 Mark Mulder Cards/10
401 Delmon Young/10
402 Aubrey Huff/50 8.00 20.00
403 Alfonso Soriano/10
406 Vernon Wells/5
407 Orlando Hudson/25 6.00 15.00
408 Alexis Rios/5
410 Jose Guillen/25 10.00 25.00
412 Jose Vidro/1
413 Nick Johnson/5
414 Livan Hernandez/5
416 Gary Sheffield Braves/1
417 Curt Schilling D'backs/1
419 Scott Rolen Phils/5
422 Steve Finley D'backs/5
423 Roger Clemens Sox/1
427 Mark Grace/1
428 Alan Trammell/5
429 Bert Blyleven/50 8.00 20.00
430 Dwight Gooden/50 8.00 20.00
431 Deion Sanders/1
432 Joe Torre MG/5
433 Jose Canseco/1
434 Tony Gwynn/1
435 Will Clark/1
436 Marty Marion/50 8.00 20.00
437 Nolan Ryan/1
440 Magglio Ordonez/5
444 Jeff Niemann/25
445 Brandon McCarthy/25
446 Phil Humber/25
449 Ryne Sandberg/5
450 Willie Mays/1

2005 Diamond Kings Signature Bronze B/W

*BRZ B/W p/r 100: .4X TO 1X BRZ p/r 100
*BRZ B/W p/r 50: .4X TO 1X BRZ p/r 50
*BRZ B/W p/r 25: .4X TO 1X BRZ p/r 25
OVERALL AU-GU ODDS 1:6
PRINT RUNS B/WN 1-100 COPIES PER
NO PRICING ON QTY OF 10 OR LESS
185 Sean Burroughs/25 6.00 15.00

2005 Diamond Kings Signature Gold

*GOLD p/r 50: .5X TO 1.2X BRZ p/r 100
*GOLD p/r 25: .6X TO 1.5X BRZ p/r 100
*GOLD p/r 25: .5X TO 1.2X BRZ p/r 50
*GOLD p/r 25: .4X TO 1X BRZ p/r 25
OVERALL AU-GU ODDS 1:6
PRINT RUNS B/WN 1-50 COPIES PER
NO PRICING ON QTY OF 10 OR LESS
115 Andres Blanco/25 6.00 15.00
325 Edgar Renteria/25 10.00 25.00

2005 Diamond Kings Signature Gold B/W

*GOLD B/W p/r 25: .6X TO 1.5X BRZ p/r 100
OVERALL AU-GU ODDS 1:6
PRINT RUNS B/WN 1-25 COPIES PER
NO PRICING ON QTY OF 10 OR LESS
185 Sean Burroughs/25 6.00 15.00

2005 Diamond Kings Signature Platinum

OVERALL AU-GU ODDS 1:6
STATED PRINT RUN 1 SERIAL #'d SET
NO PRICING DUE TO SCARCITY

2005 Diamond Kings Signature Platinum B/W

OVERALL AU-GU ODDS 1:6
STATED PRINT RUN 1 SERIAL #'d SET
NO PRICING DUE TO SCARCITY

2005 Diamond Kings Signature Silver

*SILV p/r 100: .4X TO 1X BRZ p/r 100
*SILV p/r 50: .5X TO 1.2X BRZ p/r 100
*SILV p/r 50: .4X TO 1X BRZ p/r 50
*SILV p/r 25: .6X TO 1.5X BRZ p/r 100
*SILV p/r 25: .5X TO 1.2X BRZ p/r 50
*SILV p/r 25: .4X TO 1X BRZ p/r 25
OVERALL AU-GU ODDS 1:6
PRINT RUNS B/WN 1-100 COPIES PER
NO PRICING ON QTY OF 10 OR LESS
115 Andres Blanco/50 5.00 12.00

2005 Diamond Kings Signature Silver B/W

*SILV B/W p/r 50: .5X TO 1.2X BRZ p/r 100
*SILV B/W p/r 25: .6X TO 1.5X BRZ p/r 100
OVERALL AU-GU ODDS 1:6
PRINT RUNS B/WN 1-50 COPIES PER
NO PRICING ON QTY OF 10 OR LESS

2005 Diamond Kings Signature Framed Black

STATED PRINT RUN 1 SERIAL #'d SET
NO PRICING DUE TO SCARCITY
PLATINUM PRINT RUN 1 #'d SET
NO PLAT.PRICING DUE TO SCARCITY
OVERALL AU-GU ODDS 1:6

2005 Diamond Kings Signature Framed Black B/W

STATED PRINT RUN 1 SERIAL #'d SET
PLATINUM PRINT RUN 1 SERIAL #'d SET
OVERALL AU-GU ODDS 1:6
NO PRICING DUE TO SCARCITY

2005 Diamond Kings Signature Framed Blue

*BLUE p/r 50: .5X TO 1.2X BRZ p/r 100
*BLUE p/r 25: .6X TO 1.5X BRZ p/r 100
PRINT RUNS B/WN 1-50 COPIES PER
NO PRICING ON QTY OF 10 OR LESS
PLATINUM PRINT RUN 1 SERIAL #'d SET
NO PLAT.PRICING DUE TO SCARCITY
OVERALL AU-GU ODDS 1:6
115 Andres Blanco/25 6.00 15.00

2005 Diamond Kings Signature Framed Blue B/W

*BLUE B/W p/r 50: .5X TO 1.2X BRZ p/r 100
*BLUE B/W p/r 25: .6X TO 1.5X BRZ p/r 100
PRINT RUNS B/WN 1-50 COPIES PER
NO PRICING ON QTY OF 10 OR LESS
PLATINUM PRINT RUN 1 SERIAL #'d SET
NO PLAT.PRICING DUE TO SCARCITY
OVERALL AU-GU ODDS 1:6

2005 Diamond Kings Signature Framed Green

*GRN p/r 25: .6X TO 1.5X BRZ p/r 100
PRINT RUNS B/WN 1-25 COPIES PER
NO PRICING ON QTY OF 10 OR LESS
PLATINUM PRINT RUN 1 SERIAL #'d SET
NO PLATINUM PRICING DUE TO SCARCITY
OVERALL AU-GU ODDS 1:6

2005 Diamond Kings Signature Framed Green B/W

*GREEN B/W p/r 25: .6X TO 1.5X BRZ p/r 100
PRINT RUNS B/WN 1-25 COPIES PER
NO PRICING ON QTY OF 10 OR LESS
PLATINUM PRINT RUN 1 SERIAL #'d SET
NO PLAT.PRICING DUE TO SCARCITY
OVERALL AU-GU ODDS 1:6

2005 Diamond Kings Signature Framed Red

*RED p/r 100: .4X TO 1X BRZ p/r 100
*RED p/r 50: .5X TO 1.2X BRZ p/r 100
*RED p/r 50: .4X TO 1X BRZ p/r 50
*RED p/r 25: .6X TO 1.5X BRZ p/r 100
*RED p/r 25: .5X TO 1.2X BRZ p/r 50
*RED p/r 25: .4X TO 1X BRZ p/r 25

PRINT RUNS B/WN 1-100 COPIES PER
NO PRICING ON QTY OF 14 OR LESS
PLATINUM PRINT RUN 1 SERIAL #'d SET
NO PLAT.PRICING DUE TO SCARCITY
OVERALL AU-GU ODDS 1:6

2005 Diamond Kings Signature Framed Red B/W

*RED B/W p/r 100: .4X TO 1X BRZ p/r 100
*RED B/W p/r 50: .5X TO 1.2X BRZ p/r 100
*RED B/W p/r 50: .4X TO 1X BRZ p/r 50
*RED B/W p/r 25: .6X TO 1.5X BRZ p/r 100
*RED B/W p/r 25: .5X TO 1.2X BRZ p/r 50
*RED B/W p/r 25: .4X TO 1X BRZ p/r 25
PRINT RUNS B/WN 1-100 COPIES PER
NO PRICING ON QTY OF 10 OR LESS
PLATINUM PRINT RUN 1 SERIAL #'d SET
NO PLAT.PRICING DUE TO SCARCITY
OVERALL AU-GU ODDS 1:6

2005 Diamond Kings Signature Materials Black

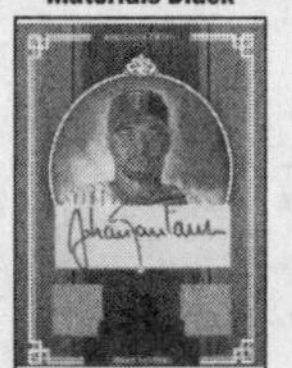

OVERALL AU-GU ODDS 1:6
STATED PRINT RUN 1 SERIAL #'d SET
NO PRICING DUE TO SCARCITY

2005 Diamond Kings Signature Materials Bronze

OVERALL AU-GU ODDS 1:6
PRINT RUNS B/WN 1-200 COPIES PER
NO PRICING ON QTY OF 10 OR LESS
1 Garret Anderson Bat-Jsy/50 10.00 25.00
7 Chone Figgins Bat-Jsy/200 6.00 15.00
18 Rafael Furcal Bat-Jsy/50 10.00 25.00
19 Andruw Jones Bat-Jsy/25 20.00 50.00
25 Chipper Jones Bat-Jsy/10
27 R.Palmeiro O's Bat-Jsy/10
31 Larry Bigbie Jsy-Jsy/200 6.00 15.00
32 Rodrigo Lopez Jsy-Jsy/200 4.00 10.00
38 Trot Nixon Jsy-Jsy/100 12.50 30.00
39 Curt Schilling Bat-Jsy/5
41 Pedro Martinez Bat-Jsy/5
46 David Ortiz Bat-Jsy/100 15.00 40.00
47 Kerry Wood Jsy-Pants/10
48 Mark Prior Bat-Jsy/25 15.00 40.00
49 A.Ramirez Bat-Jsy/100 8.00 20.00
50 Greg Maddux Cubs Jsy-Jsy/5
51 C.Zambrano Jsy-Jsy/200 10.00 25.00
52 Derrek Lee Bat-Bat/100 12.50 30.00
56 Sammy Sosa Bat-Jsy/5
60 Magglio Ordonez Bat-Jsy/10
61 Carlos Lee Bat-Jsy/100 5.00 12.00
69 Adam Dunn Bat-Jsy/10
74 Sean Casey Jsy-Pants/10
76 C.C. Sabathia Jsy-Jsy/100 12.50 30.00
78 Omar Vizquel Jsy-Jsy/25 20.00 50.00
84 Todd Helton Bat-Jsy/1
94 Dontrelle Willis Jsy-Jsy/10
95 Miguel Cabrera Bat-Jsy/25 20.00 50.00
97 Mike Lowell Bat-Jsy/10
100 P.LoDuca Marlins Bat-Bat/10
102 Craig Biggio Bat-Pants/10
103 Lance Berkman Bat-Jsy/5
105 R.Clemens Astros Bat-Jsy/1
108 Jeff Bagwell Bat-Jsy/5
109 C.Belt Astros Bat-Jsy/50 10.00 25.00
110 Angel Berroa Bat-Bat/10
112 J.Affeldt Pants-Pants/100 5.00 12.00
114 Juan Gonzalez Bat-Jsy/10
116 Shawn Green Bat-Jsy/1
127 Bill Hall Bat-Bat/100 5.00 12.00
129 Jacque Jones Bat-Jsy/50 10.00 25.00
130 Torii Hunter Bat-Jsy/10
131 Johan Santana Jsy-Jsy/50 15.00 40.00
132 Lew Ford Bat-Jsy/200 4.00 10.00
139 Nick Johnson Bat-Bat/50 10.00 25.00
141 Tom Glavine Bat-Bat/5
145 Mike Piazza Bat-Jsy/1
150 Mike Mussina Bat-Jsy/5
153 Jorge Posada Bat-Jsy/25 20.00 50.00
155 Gary Sheffield Bat-Bat/10
162 Eric Chavez Bat-Jsy/25 12.50 30.00
164 Barry Zito Bat-Jsy/10
165 Tim Hudson Bat-Jsy/10
178 Craig Wilson Bat-Jsy/200 4.00 10.00
185 S.Burroughs Bat-Jsy/100 5.00 12.00
201 Edgar Martinez Bat-Bat/25 20.00 50.00
209 Jim Edmonds Bat-Jsy/10
211 Edgar Renteria Bat-Jsy/50 10.00 25.00
214 Albert Pujols Jsy-Jsy/5
221 Carl Crawford Jsy-Jsy/200 6.00 15.00
223 Fred McGriff Bat-Jsy/10
229 Mark Teixeira Bat-Jsy/25 20.00 50.00
230 Michael Young Bat-Jsy/100 8.00 20.00
232 Laynce Nix Bat-Jsy/200 4.00 10.00
233 A.Soriano Rgr Bat-Jsy/25 12.50 30.00
234 R.Palmeiro Rgr Bat-Jsy/10
239 Roy Halladay Jsy-Jsy/25 12.50 30.00
269 B.Penny M's Bat-Jsy/100 5.00 12.00
277 G. Maddux Braves Jsy-Jsy/5
278 R.Clemens Yanks Bat-Jsy/5
280 Dale Murphy Jsy-Jsy/50 15.00 40.00
281 Cal Ripken Bat-Jsy/5
282 Dwight Evans Bat-Jsy/50 15.00 40.00
283 Ron Santo Bat-Bat/100 15.00 40.00
284 Andre Dawson Bat-Jsy/100 8.00 20.00
286 Jack Morris Jsy-Jsy/100 8.00 20.00
287 Kirk Gibson Bat-Jsy/25 12.50 30.00
289 Orel Hershiser Jsy-Jsy/25 12.50 30.00
291 Tony Oliva Bat-Jsy/100 8.00 20.00
294 Don Mattingly Bat-Jsy/25 40.00 80.00
295 R.Henderson Bat-Jsy/10
297 Dave Parker Bat-Jsy/100 8.00 20.00
298 Steve Garvey Bat-Jsy/50 10.00 25.00
300 K.Hernandez Bat-Jsy/100 8.00 20.00
303 G.Anderson Bat-Jsy/50 10.00 25.00
310 Shawn Green Bat-Bat/1
314 Chipper Jones Bat-Jsy/1
315 Johnny Estrada Jsy-Jsy/50 6.00 15.00
317 Tim Hudson Bat-Bat/10
319 Jay Gibbons Bat-Bat/50 6.00 15.00
320 Melvin Mora Jsy-Jsy/50 10.00 25.00
321 Rafael Palmeiro O's Bat-Jsy/1
323 David Ortiz Jsy-Jsy/25 30.00 60.00
324 Manny Ramirez Bat-Jsy/1
327 Curt Schilling Sox Jsy-Jsy/5
329 Mark Prior Bat-Jsy/10
330 Greg Maddux Bat-Jsy/1
332 Frank Thomas Bat-Jsy/10
333 Mark Buehrle Jsy-Jsy/25 15.00 40.00
336 Sean Casey Bat-Jsy/10
339 Travis Hafner Jsy-Jsy/25 12.50 30.00
340 Victor Martinez Jsy-Jsy/25 12.50 30.00
341 Cliff Lee Jsy-Jsy/25 10.00 25.00
342 Todd Helton Bat-Bat/5
343 P.Wilson Bat-Jsy/25 12.50 30.00
347 Miguel Cabrera Bat-Jsy/10
348 Jeff Bagwell Bat-Jsy/5
350 Roger Clemens Astros Bat-Jsy/1
351 Ken Harvey Jsy-Jsy/25 8.00 20.00
353 Hideo Nomo Bat-Jsy/1
360 Shannon Stewart Jsy-Jsy/10
362 Johan Santana Jsy-Jsy/10
365 Carlos Beltran Bat-Bat/1
366 Pedro Martinez Bat-Bat/1
370 Gary Sheffield Yanks Bat-Jsy/1
371 Randy Johnson Yanks Bat-Bat/1
378 Mark Mulder A's Jsy-Jsy/10
380 Eric Chavez Bat-Jsy/10
382 Marlon Byrd Bat-Jsy/50 6.00 15.00
386 Jason Bay Bat-Jsy/1
393 Adrian Beltre Bat-Bat/1
397 Albert Pujols Bat-Jsy/1
398 Scott Rolen Cards Bat-Jsy/10
401 Delmon Young Bat-Bat/25 20.00 50.00
402 Aubrey Huff Bat-Bat/10
403 Alfonso Soriano Jsy-Jsy/10
406 Vernon Wells Jsy-Jsy/10
407 O.Hudson Bat-Bat/25 8.00 20.00
416 Gary Sheffield Braves Bat-Jsy/5
417 Curt Schilling D'backs Jsy-Jsy/5
419 S.Rolen Phils Bat-Jsy/25 20.00 50.00
422 Steve Finley D'backs Jsy-Jsy/10
423 Roger Clemens Sox Bat-Jsy/1
426 David Justice Bat-Jsy/1
427 Mark Grace Bat-Jsy/10
428 Alan Trammell Bat-Jsy/25 12.50 30.00
429 Bert Blyleven Jsy-Jsy/1
430 D.Gooden Bat-Jsy/25 12.50 30.00
431 Deion Sanders Bat-Jsy/1
432 Joe Torre MG Bat-Bat/10
434 Tony Gwynn Bat-Jsy/25 30.00 60.00
435 Will Clark Bat-Jsy/10
436 Marty Marion Jsy-Jsy/1
437 Nolan Ryan Bat-Jsy/10
440 Magglio Ordonez Bat-Bat/10
441 Sammy Sosa O's Bat-Bat/1
449 Ryne Sandberg Jsy-Jsy/5
450 Willie Mays Bat-Jsy/1

2005 Diamond Kings Signature Materials Bronze B/W

*BRZ B/W p/r 100: .5X TO 1.2X BRZ p/r 200
*BRZ B/W p/r 50: .5X TO 1.2X BRZ p/r 100
*BRZ B/W p/r 25: .75X TO 2X BRZ p/r 200
*BRZ B/W p/r 25: .6X TO 1.5X BRZ p/r 100
OVERALL AU-GU ODDS 1:6
PRINT RUNS B/WN 1-100 COPIES PER
NO PRICING ON QTY OF 10 OR LESS
73 Ryan Wagner Jsy-Jsy/50 6.00 15.00
97 Mike Lowell Jsy-Jsy/25 8.00 20.00
136 Jose Vidro Bat-Bat/50 6.00 15.00
180 Jack Wilson Bat-Bat/100 5.00 12.00
271 P.Lo Duca Dgr Bat-Bat/25 12.50 30.00
285 Harold Baines Bat-Jsy/50 10.00 25.00

2005 Diamond Kings Signature Materials Gold

*GOLD p/r 50: .6X TO 1.5X BRZ p/r 200
*GOLD p/r 50: .5X TO 1.2X BRZ p/r 100
*GOLD p/r 50: .4X TO 1X BRZ p/r 50
*GOLD p/r 25: .5X TO 1.2X BRZ p/r 50
*GOLD p/r 25: .4X TO 1X BRZ p/r 25
OVERALL AU-GU ODDS 1:6
PRINT RUNS B/WN 1-50 COPIES PER
NO PRICING ON QTY OF 10 OR LESS
104 Roy Oswalt Jsy-Jsy/50 10.00 25.00
285 Harold Baines Bat-Jsy/50 10.00 25.00
299 Matt Williams Jsy-Jsy/25 20.00 50.00

2005 Diamond Kings Signature Materials Gold B/W

*GOLD B/W p/r 25: .75X TO 2X BRZ p/r 200
*GOLD B/W p/r 25: .6X TO 1.5X BRZ p/r 100
OVERALL AU-GU ODDS 1:6
PRINT RUNS B/WN 1-25 COPIES PER
NO PRICING ON QTY OF 10 OR LESS
73 Ryan Wagner Jsy-Jsy/25 8.00 20.00
97 Mike Lowell Jsy-Jsy/25 8.00 20.00
136 Jose Vidro Bat-Bat/25 8.00 20.00
180 Jack Wilson Bat-Bat/25 8.00 20.00
271 P.Lo Duca Dgr Bat-Bat/25 12.50 30.00
285 Harold Baines Bat-Jsy/25 12.50 30.00

2005 Diamond Kings Signature Materials Platinum

OVERALL AU-GU ODDS 1:6
STATED PRINT RUN 1 SERIAL #'d SET
NO PRICING DUE TO SCARCITY

2005 Diamond Kings Signature Materials Platinum B/W

OVERALL AU-GU ODDS 1:6
STATED PRINT RUN 1 SERIAL #'d SET
NO PRICING DUE TO SCARCITY

2005 Diamond Kings Signature Materials Silver

*SILV p/r 100: .5X TO 1.2X BRZ p/r 200
*SILV p/r 100: .4X TO 1X BRZ p/r 100
*SILV p/r 50: .5X TO 1.2X BRZ p/r 100
*SILV p/r 50: .4X TO 1X BRZ p/r 50
*SILV p/r 25: .5X TO 1.2X BRZ p/r 50
*SILV p/r 25: .4X TO 1X BRZ p/r 25
OVERALL AU-GU ODDS 1:6
PRINT RUNS B/WN 1-100 COPIES PER
NO PRICING ON QTY OF 10 OR LESS
104 Roy Oswalt Jsy-Jsy/50 10.00 25.00
285 Harold Baines Bat-Jsy/50 10.00 25.00
299 Matt Williams Jsy-Jsy/25 20.00 50.00
354 Kazuhisa Ishii Jsy-Jsy/25 12.50 30.00

2005 Diamond Kings Signature Materials Silver B/W

*SILV B/W p/r 50: .6X TO 1.5X BRZ p/r 200
*SILV B/W p/r 50: .5X TO 1.2X BRZ p/r 100
*SILV B/W p/r 25: .75X TO 2X BRZ p/r 200
*SILV B/W p/r 25: .6X TO 1.5X BRZ p/r 100
OVERALL AU-GU ODDS 1:6
PRINT RUNS B/WN 1-50 COPIES PER
NO PRICING ON QTY OF 10 OR LESS
73 Ryan Wagner Jsy-Jsy/50 6.00 15.00
97 Mike Lowell Jsy-Jsy/25 8.00 20.00
136 Jose Vidro Bat-Bat/50 6.00 15.00
180 Jack Wilson Bat-Bat/50 6.00 15.00
271 P.Lo Duca Dgr Bat-Bat/25 12.50 30.00
285 Harold Baines Bat-Jsy/25 12.50 30.00

2005 Diamond Kings Signature Materials Framed Black

PRINT RUNS B/WN 1-10 COPIES PER
PLATINUM PRINT RUN 1 SERIAL #'d SET
OVERALL AU-GU ODDS 1:6
NO PRICING DUE TO SCARCITY

2005 Diamond Kings Signature Materials Framed Black B/W

STATED PRINT RUN 1 SERIAL #'d SET
PLATINUM PRINT RUN 1 SERIAL #'d SET
OVERALL AU-GU ODDS 1:6
NO PRICING DUE TO SCARCITY

2005 Diamond Kings Signature Materials Framed Blue

*BLUE p/r 50: .6X TO 1.5X BRZ p/r 200
*BLUE p/r 50: .5X TO 1.2X BRZ p/r 100
*BLUE p/r 50: .4X TO 1X BRZ p/r 50
*BLUE p/r 25: .5X TO 1.2X BRZ p/r 50
PRINT RUNS B/WN 1-50 COPIES PER
NO PRICING ON QTY OF 10 OR LESS
PLATINUM PRINT RUN 1 SERIAL #'d SET
NO PLAT.PRICING DUE TO SCARCITY
OVERALL AU-GU ODDS 1:6

2005 Diamond Kings Signature Materials Framed Blue B/W

*BLUE B/W p/r 25: .75X TO 2X BRZ p/r 200
*BLUE B/W p/r 25: .6X TO 1.5X BRZ p/r 100
PRINT RUNS B/WN 1-25 COPIES PER
NO PRICING ON QTY OF 10 OR LESS
PLATINUM PRINT RUN 1 SERIAL #'d SET
NO PLAT.PRICING DUE TO SCARCITY
OVERALL AU-GU ODDS 1:6
73 Ryan Wagner Jsy-Jsy/25 8.00 20.00
97 Mike Lowell Jsy-Jsy/25 8.00 20.00
180 Jack Wilson Bat-Bat/25 8.00 20.00
271 P.Lo Duca Dgr Bat-Bat/25 12.50 30.00

2005 Diamond Kings Signature Materials Framed Green

*GRN p/r 25: .75X TO 2X BRZ p/r 200
*GRN p/r 25: .6X TO 1.5X BRZ p/r 100
*GRN p/r 25: .5X TO 1.2X BRZ p/r 50
PRINT RUNS B/WN 1-25 COPIES PER
NO PRICING ON QTY OF 10 OR LESS
PLATINUM PRINT RUN 1 SERIAL #'d SET
NO PLAT.PRICING DUE TO SCARCITY
OVERALL AU-GU ODDS 1:6
299 Matt Williams Jsy-Jsy/25 20.00 50.00

2005 Diamond Kings Signature Materials Framed Green B/W

*GREEN B/W p/r 25: .75X TO 2X BRZ p/r 200
*GREEN B/W p/r 25: .6X TO 1.5X BRZ p/r 100
PRINT RUNS B/WN 1-25 COPIES PER
NO PRICING ON QTY OF 10 OR LESS
PLATINUM PRINT RUN 1 SERIAL #'d SET
NO PLAT.PRICING DUE TO SCARCITY
OVERALL AU-GU ODDS 1:6
73 Ryan Wagner Jsy-Jsy/25 8.00 20.00
97 Mike Lowell Jsy-Jsy/25 8.00 20.00
180 Jack Wilson Bat-Bat/25 8.00 20.00
271 P.Lo Duca Dgr Bat-Bat/25 12.50 30.00
285 Harold Baines Bat-Jsy/25 12.50 30.00

2005 Diamond Kings Signature Materials Framed Red

*RED p/r 100: .5X TO 1.2X BRZ p/r 200
*RED p/r 100: .4X TO 1X BRZ p/r 100
*RED p/r 50: .5X TO 1.2X BRZ p/r 100
*RED p/r 50: .4X TO 1X BRZ p/r 50
*RED p/r 25: .5X TO 1.2X BRZ p/r 50
PRINT RUNS B/WN 1-100 COPIES PER
NO PRICING ON QTY OF 10 OR LESS
PLATINUM PRINT RUN 1 SERIAL #'d SET
NO PLAT.PRICING DUE TO SCARCITY
OVERALL AU-GU ODDS 1:6

2005 Diamond Kings Signature Materials Framed Red B/W

*RED B/W p/r 25: .75X TO 2X BRZ p/r 200
*RED B/W p/r 25: .6X TO 1.5X BRZ p/r 100
PRINT RUNS B/WN 1-50 COPIES PER
NO PRICING ON QTY OF 10 OR LESS
PLATINUM PRINT RUN 1 SERIAL #'d SET
NO PLAT.PRICING DUE TO SCARCITY
OVERALL AU-GU ODDS 1:6

2005 Diamond Kings Diamond Cuts Bat

*BAT p/r 200: .4X TO 1X JSY p/r 200
*BAT p/r 200: .4X TO 1X JSY p/r 100
*BAT p/r 200: .3X TO .8X JSY p/r 50
*BAT p/r 100: .5X TO 1.2X JSY p/r 200
*BAT p/r 100: .3X TO .8X JSY p/r 50
*BAT p/r 50: .6X TO 1.5X JSY p/r 200
*BAT p/r 50: .5X TO 1.2X JSY p/r 100
*BAT p/r 50: .4X TO 1X JSY p/r 50
OVERALL AU-GU ODD 1:6
PRINT RUNS B/WN 50-200 COPIES PER
16 Derrek Lee/200 2.50 6.00
47 Tim Salmon/200 2.50 6.00
49 Torii Hunter/200 2.00 5.00

2005 Diamond Kings Diamond Cuts Combos

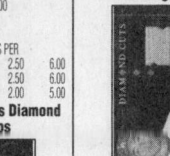

*COMBO p/r 200: .5X TO 1.2X JSY p/r 200
*COMBO p/r 100: .6X TO 1.5X JSY p/r 200
*COMBO p/r 100: .5X TO 1.2X JSY p/r 100
*COMBO p/r 100: .4X TO 1X JSY p/r 50
*COMBO p/r 50: .75X TO 2X JSY p/r 200
*COMBO p/r 50: .6X TO 1.5X JSY p/r 100
*COMBO p/r 50: .5X TO 1.2X JSY p/r 50
PRINT RUNS B/WN 25-200 COPIES PER
PRIME PRINT RUN 1 SERIAL #'d SET
NO PRIME PRICING DUE TO SCARCITY
OVERALL AU-GU ODDS 1:6
49 Torii Hunter Bat-Jsy/25 5.00 12.00

2005 Diamond Kings Diamond Cuts Jersey

PRINT RUNS B/WN 50-200 COPIES PER
PRIME PRINT RUN 1 SERIAL #'d SET
NO PRIME PRICING DUE TO SCARCITY
OVERALL AU-GU ODDS 1:6
1 Adam Dunn/50 3.00 8.00
2 Adrian Beltre/200 2.00 5.00
3 Alfonso Soriano/50 3.00 8.00
4 Andruw Jones/200 2.50 6.00
5 Andy Pettitte/100 3.00 8.00
6 Aramis Ramirez/200 2.00 5.00
7 Brian Giles/200 2.00 5.00
8 C.C. Sabathia/200 2.00 5.00
9 Carl Crawford/200 2.00 5.00
10 Carlos Beltran/200 2.00 5.00
11 Carlos Lee/200 2.00 5.00
12 Craig Wilson/200 2.00 5.00
13 Curt Schilling/50 4.00 10.00
14 Darin Erstad/200 2.00 5.00
17 Fred McGriff/200 2.50 6.00
18 Greg Maddux/50 6.00 15.00
19 Ivan Rodriguez/200 2.50 6.00
20 Jason Bay/200 2.00 5.00
21 Jason Giambi/200 2.00 5.00
22 Jay Gibbons/100 2.50 6.00
23 Jeff Kent/200 2.00 5.00
24 John Olerud/200 2.00 5.00
25 Juan Gonzalez Pants/200 2.00 5.00
26 Junior Spivey/200 2.00 5.00
27 Kazuhisa Ishii/200 2.00 5.00
28 Kevin Brown/200 2.00 5.00
29 Larry Walker Rockies/200 2.00 5.00
30 Lyle Overbay/200 2.00 5.00
31 Mark Teixeira/100 3.00 8.00
32 Melvin Mora/200 2.00 5.00
33 Michael Young/200 2.00 5.00
34 Miguel Tejada/200 2.00 5.00
35 Mike Mussina/100 3.00 8.00
36 Paul LoDuca/50 3.00 8.00
37 Preston Wilson/200 2.00 5.00
38 Randy Johnson/200 3.00 8.00
39 Richie Sexson/200 2.00 5.00
40 Roger Clemens/50 6.00 15.00
41 Scott Rolen/50 4.00 10.00
42 Sean Burroughs/200 2.00 5.00
43 Sean Casey/200 2.00 5.00
44 Shannon Stewart/100 2.50 6.00
45 Shawn Green/200 2.00 5.00
46 Steve Finley/200 2.00 5.00
48 Tom Glavine/200 2.50 6.00
50 Travis Hafner/100 2.50 6.00

2005 Diamond Kings Diamond Cuts Signature

*SIG p/r 100: .3X TO .8X SIG.JSY p/r 100
*SIG p/r 100: .25X TO .6X SIG.JSY p/r 50
*SIG p/r 50: .3X TO .8X SIG.JSY p/r 50
*SIG p/r 25: .5X TO 1.2X SIG.JSY p/r 100
*SIG p/r 25: .3X TO .8X SIG.JSY p/r 25
OVERALL AU-GU ODDS 1:6
PRINT RUNS B/WN 1-100 COPIES PER
NO PRICING ON QTY OF 10 OR LESS
20 Jason Bay/100 6.00 15.00
22 Jay Gibbons/100 4.00 10.00
47 Tim Salmon/100 10.00 25.00

2005 Diamond Kings Diamond Cuts Signature Bat

*SIG.BAT p/r 100: .4X TO 1X SIG.JSY p/r 100
*SIG.BAT p/r 50: .5X TO 1.2X SIG.JSY p/r 100
*SIG.BAT p/r 25: .4X TO 1X SIG.JSY p/r 25
OVERALL AU-GU ODDS 1:6
PRINT RUNS B/WN 1-100 COPIES PER
NO PRICING ON QTY OF 10 OR LESS
1 Adam Dunn/25 20.00 50.00
10 Carlos Beltran/50 10.00 25.00
16 Derrek Lee/100 12.50 30.00
17 Fred McGriff/25 30.00 60.00
22 Jay Gibbons/100 5.00 12.00
49 Torii Hunter/25 12.50 30.00
53 Carlos Beltran/25 12.50 30.00

2005 Diamond Kings Diamond Cuts Signature Combos

*SIG.COM p/r 100: .4X TO 1X SIG.JSY p/r 100
*SIG.COM p/r 50: .5X TO 1.2X SIG.JSY p/r 100
*SIG.COM p/r 25: .6X TO 1.5X SIG.JSY p/r 100
*SIG.COM p/r 25: .5X TO 1.2X SIG.JSY p/r 50
*SIG.COM p/r 25: .4X TO 1X SIG.JSY p/r 25
PRINT RUNS B/WN 1-100 COPIES PER
NO PRICING ON QTY OF 10 OR LESS
PRIME PRINT RUN 1 SERIAL #'d SET
NO PRIME PRICING DUE TO SCARCITY
OVERALL AU-GU ODDS 1:6
1 Adam Dunn Bat-Jsy/25 20.00 50.00
17 Fred McGriff Bat-Jsy/25 30.00 60.00
22 Jay Gibbons Bat-Bat/50 6.00 15.00
25 Juan Gonzalez Bat-Jsy/100 8.00 20.00
49 Torii Hunter Bat-Jsy/25 12.50 30.00
51 Aramis Ramirez Jsy-Jsy/24 12.50 30.00
54 Craig Biggio Bat-Pants/25 20.00 50.00

2005 Diamond Kings Diamond Cuts Signature Jersey

PRINT RUNS B/WN 5-100 COPIES PER
NO PRICING ON QTY OF 10 OR LESS
PRIME PRINT RUN 1 SERIAL #'d SET
NO PRIME PRICING DUE TO SCARCITY
OVERALL AU-GU ODDS 1:6
1 Adam Dunn/10
2 Adrian Beltre/100 8.00 20.00
3 Alfonso Soriano/10
4 Andruw Jones/10
5 Andy Pettitte/10
6 Aramis Ramirez/100 8.00 20.00
8 C.C. Sabathia/100 8.00 20.00
9 Carl Crawford/50 10.00 25.00
11 Carlos Lee/100 8.00 20.00
12 Craig Wilson/100 5.00 12.00
13 Curt Schilling/5
17 Fred McGriff/10
18 Greg Maddux/5
25 Juan Gonzalez Pants/10
27 Kazuhisa Ishii/10
30 Lyle Overbay/100 5.00 12.00
31 Mark Teixeira/25 20.00 50.00
32 Melvin Mora/50 10.00 25.00
33 Michael Young/100 8.00 20.00
35 Mike Mussina/5
36 Paul LoDuca/25 12.50 30.00
38 Randy Johnson/5
40 Roger Clemens/5
41 Scott Rolen/10
42 Sean Burroughs/50 6.00 15.00
43 Sean Casey/25 12.50 30.00
44 Shannon Stewart/25 12.50 30.00
45 Shawn Green/5
46 Steve Finley/25 12.50 30.00
50 Travis Hafner/50 10.00 25.00
51 Aramis Ramirez/10
54 Craig Biggio Pants/10
55 Jim Edmonds/5
56 Johan Santana/25 20.00 50.00
57 Mark Mulder/25 12.50 30.00
59 Tim Hudson/10
60 Victor Martinez/25 12.50 30.00

2005 Diamond Kings Gallery of Stars

SER.2 STATED ODDS 1:8
1 Andre Dawson .75 2.00
2 Bob Feller .50 1.25
3 Bobby Doerr .50 1.25
4 C.C. Sabathia .75 2.00
5 Carl Crawford .75 2.00
6 Dale Murphy .50 1.25
7 Danny Kolb .50 1.25
8 Darryl Strawberry .50 1.25
9 Dave Parker .50 1.25
10 David Ortiz 1.25 3.00
11 Dwight Gooden .50 1.25
12 Garret Anderson .50 1.25
13 Jack Morris .50 1.25
14 Jacque Jones .50 1.25
15 Jim Palmer .50 1.25
16 Johan Santana 1.25 3.00
17 Ken Harvey .50 1.25
18 Lyle Overbay .50 1.25
19 Marty Marion .50 1.25
20 Melvin Mora .50 1.25
21 Michael Young .75 2.00
22 Miguel Cabrera 1.25 3.00
23 Preston Wilson .50 1.25
24 Sean Casey .50 1.25
25 Victor Martinez .75 2.00

2005 Diamond Kings Gallery of Stars Bat

*BAT p/r 200: .3X TO .8X JSY p/r 100
*BAT p/r 100: .4X TO 1X JSY p/r 100
*BAT p/r 100: .3X TO .8X JSY p/r 50
*BAT p/r 100: .25X TO .6X JSY p/r 25
*BAT p/r 50: .5X TO 1.2X JSY p/r 100
OVERALL AU-GU ODDS 1:6
PRINT RUNS B/WN 50-200 COPIES PER

2005 Diamond Kings Gallery of Stars Combos

*COMBO p/r 200: .3X TO .8X JSY p/r 100
*COMBO p/r 100: .5X TO 1.2X JSY p/r 100
*COMBO p/r 100: .4X TO 1X JSY p/r 50
*COMBO p/r 100: .3X TO .8X JSY p/r 25
*COMBO p/r 50: .6X TO 1.5X JSY p/r 100
*COMBO p/r 50: .5X TO 1.2X JSY p/r 50
PRINT RUNS B/WN 50-200 COPIES PER
PRIME PRINT RUN 1 SERIAL #'d SET
NO PRIME PRICING DUE TO SCARCITY
OVERALL AU-GU ODDS 1:6

2005 Diamond Kings Gallery of Stars Jersey

PRINT RUNS B/WN 25-100 COPIES PER
PRIME PRINT RUN 1 SERIAL #'d SET
NO PRIME PRICING DUE TO SCARCITY
OVERALL AU-GU ODDS 1:6
1 Andre Dawson/100 3.00 8.00
2 Bob Feller Pants/50 5.00 12.00
3 Bobby Doerr Pants/100 3.00 8.00
4 C.C. Sabathia/100 2.50 6.00
5 Carl Crawford/100 2.50 6.00
6 Dale Murphy/100 4.00 10.00
8 Darryl Strawberry/25 5.00 12.00
9 Dave Parker/100 3.00 8.00
10 David Ortiz/100 3.00 8.00
11 Dwight Gooden/25 5.00 12.00
12 Garret Anderson/50 3.00 8.00
13 Jack Morris/100 3.00 8.00
14 Jacque Jones/100 2.50 6.00
15 Jim Palmer Pants/50 4.00 10.00
17 Ken Harvey/100 2.50 6.00
18 Lyle Overbay/100 2.50 6.00
20 Melvin Mora/100 2.50 6.00
21 Michael Young/100 2.50 6.00
22 Miguel Cabrera/100 3.00 8.00
23 Preston Wilson/100 2.50 6.00
24 Sean Casey/100 2.50 6.00
25 Victor Martinez/25 4.00 10.00

2005 Diamond Kings Gallery of Stars Signature

*SIG p/r 100: .3X TO .8X SIG.JSY p/r 100
*SIG p/r 100: .25X TO .6X SIG.JSY p/r 50
*SIG p/r 50: .2X TO .5X SIG.JSY p/r 25
*SIG p/r 50: .4X TO 1X SIG.JSY p/r 100
*SIG p/r 50: .25X TO .6X SIG.JSY p/r 25
*SIG p/r 25: .5X TO 1.2X SIG.JSY p/r 100
*SIG p/r 25: .3X TO .8X SIG.JSY p/r 25
OVERALL AU-GU ODDS 1:6
PRINT RUNS B/WN 5-100 COPIES PER
NO PRICING ON QTY OF 10 OR LESS
7 Danny Kolb/100 4.00 10.00
8 Darryl Strawberry/100 6.00 15.00

2005 Diamond Kings Gallery of Stars Signature Bat

*BAT p/r 200: .3X TO .8X SIG.JSY p/r 100
*BAT p/r 100: .3X TO .8X SIG.JSY p/r 50
*BAT p/r 100: .25X TO .6X SIG.JSY p/r 25
*BAT p/r 50: .3X TO .8X SIG.JSY p/r 25
*BAT p/r 25: .6X TO 1.5X SIG.JSY p/r 100
*BAT p/r 25: .4X TO 1X SIG.JSY p/r 25
OVERALL AU-GU ODDS 1:6
PRINT RUNS B/WN 25-200 COPIES PER
21 Michael Young/100 8.00 20.00
22 Miguel Cabrera/50 15.00 40.00

2005 Diamond Kings Gallery of Stars Signature Combos

*SIG.COM p/r 200: .5X TO 1.2X SIG.JSYp/r100
*SIG.COM p/r 100: .4X TO 1X SIG.JSY p/r 100
*SIG.COM p/r 100: .3X TO .8X SIG.JSY p/r 50
*SIG.COM p/r 50: .4X TO 1X SIG.JSY p/r 50
*SIG.COM p/r 50: .3X TO .8X SIG.JSY p/r 25
*SIG.COM p/r 25: .6X TO 1.5X SIG.JSY p/r 100
*SIG.COM p/r 25: .4X TO 1X SIG.JSY p/r 25
PRINT RUNS B/WN 25-200 COPIES PER
PRIME PRINT RUN 1 SERIAL #'d SET
NO PRIME PRICING DUE TO SCARCITY
OVERALL AU-GU ODDS 1:6
21 Michael Young Bat-Jsy/50 10.00 25.00
22 Miguel Cabrera Bat-Jsy/50 15.00 40.00

2005 Diamond Kings Gallery of Stars Signature Jersey

PRINT RUNS B/WN 25-100 COPIES PER
PRIME PRINT RUN 1 SERIAL #'d SET
NO PRIME PRICING DUE TO SCARCITY
OVERALL AU-GU ODDS 1:6
1 Andre Dawson/25 12.50 30.00
2 Bob Feller Pants/50 15.00 40.00
3 Bobby Doerr Pants/100 8.00 20.00
4 C.C. Sabathia/100 8.00 20.00
5 Carl Crawford/50 10.00 25.00
6 Dale Murphy/50 15.00 40.00
9 Dave Parker/100 8.00 20.00
10 David Ortiz/50 20.00 50.00
11 Dwight Gooden/50 10.00 25.00
12 Garret Anderson/50 10.00 25.00
13 Jack Morris/50 10.00 25.00
14 Jacque Jones/25 12.50 30.00
15 Jim Palmer Pants/25 12.50 30.00
17 Ken Harvey/100 5.00 12.00
18 Lyle Overbay/100 5.00 12.00
19 Marty Marion/25 12.50 30.00
20 Melvin Mora/100 8.00 20.00
24 Sean Casey/25 12.50 30.00
25 Victor Martinez/100 8.00 20.00

2005 Diamond Kings Heritage Collection

1-25 STATED ODDS 1:21 SER.1 PACKS
26-35 STATED ODDS 1:76 SER.2 PACKS
1 Andre Dawson 1.00 2.50
2 Bob Gibson 1.00 2.50
3 Cal Ripken 6.00 15.00
4 Dale Murphy .60 1.50
5 Darryl Strawberry .60 1.50
6 Dennis Eckersley .60 1.50
7 Don Mattingly 3.00 8.00
8 Duke Snider 1.00 2.50
9 Dwight Gooden .60 1.50
10 Eddie Murray 1.50 4.00
11 Frank Robinson 1.00 2.50
12 Gary Carter .60 1.50
13 George Brett 3.00 8.00
14 Harmon Killebrew 1.50 4.00
15 Jack Morris .60 1.50
16 Jim Palmer .60 1.50
17 Lou Brock 1.00 2.50
18 Mike Schmidt 3.00 8.00
19 Nolan Ryan 4.00 10.00
20 Ozzie Smith 2.50 6.00
21 Phil Niekro .60 1.50
22 Rod Carew 1.00 2.50
23 Rollie Fingers .60 1.50
24 Steve Carlton .60 1.50
25 Tony Gwynn 2.00 5.00
26 Curt Schilling 1.00 2.50
27 Bobby Doerr .60 1.50
28 Edgar Martinez 1.00 2.50
29 Jim Thorpe 2.50 6.00
30 Mark Grace 1.00 2.50
31 Matt Williams 1.00 2.50
32 Paul Molitor 1.50 4.00
33 Robin Yount 1.50 4.00
34 Ryne Sandberg 3.00 8.00
35 Will Clark 1.00 2.50

2005 Diamond Kings Heritage Collection Bat

*BAT p/r 100: .4X TO 1X JSY p/r 100
*BAT p/r 100: .3X TO .8X JSY p/r 50
*BAT p/r 50: .5X TO 1.2X JSY p/r 100
*BAT p/r 50: .4X TO 1X JSY p/r 50
*BAT p/r 50: .3X TO .8X JSY p/r 25
OVERALL AU-GU ODDS 1:6
PRINT RUNS B/WN 50-100 COPIES PER
11 Frank Robinson/50 4.00 10.00

2005 Diamond Kings Heritage Collection Combos

*COMBO p/r 100: .5X TO 1.2X JSY p/r 100
*COMBO p/r 100: .4X TO 1X JSY p/r 50
*COMBO p/r 50: .6X TO 1.5X JSY p/r 100
*COMBO p/r 50: .5X TO 1.2X JSY p/r 50
*COMBO p/r 25: .75X TO 2X JSY p/r 100
*COMBO p/r 25: .6X TO 1.5X JSY p/r 50
PRINT RUNS B/WN 25-100 COPIES PER
PRIME PRINT RUN 1 SERIAL #'d SET
NO PRIME PRICING DUE TO SCARCITY
OVERALL AU-GU ODDS 1:6

2005 Diamond Kings Heritage Collection Jersey

PRINT RUNS B/WN 25-100 COPIES PER
PRIME PRINT RUN 1 SERIAL #'d SET
NO PRIME PRICING DUE TO SCARCITY
OVERALL AU-GU ODDS 1:6
1 Andre Dawson/100 3.00 8.00
2 Bob Gibson/50 5.00 12.00
3 Cal Ripken/100 12.50 30.00
4 Dale Murphy/100 4.00 10.00
5 Darryl Strawberry/25 5.00 12.00
6 Dennis Eckersley/100 3.00 8.00
7 Don Mattingly/100 8.00 20.00
8 Duke Snider/50 5.00 12.00
9 Dwight Gooden/100 3.00 8.00
10 Eddie Murray/100 5.00 12.00
12 Gary Carter/100 3.00 8.00
13 George Brett/50 10.00 25.00
14 Harmon Killebrew/100 5.00 12.00
15 Jack Morris/100 3.00 8.00
16 Jim Palmer/100 3.00 8.00
17 Lou Brock/100 4.00 10.00
18 Mike Schmidt Jkt/100 8.00 20.00
19 Nolan Ryan/100 8.00 20.00
20 Ozzie Smith Pants/100 6.00 15.00
21 Phil Niekro/50 4.00 10.00
22 Rod Carew/100 4.00 10.00
23 Rollie Fingers/50 4.00 10.00
24 Steve Carlton/50 4.00 10.00
25 Tony Gwynn/100 5.00 12.00

2005 Diamond Kings Heritage Collection Signature

*SIG p/r 50: .4X TO 1X SIG.JSY p/r 100
*SIG p/r 25: .5X TO 1.2X SIG.JSY p/r 100
*SIG p/r 25: .4X TO 1X SIG.JSY p/r 50
OVERALL AU-GU ODDS 1:6
PRINT RUNS B/WN 1-50 COPIES PER
NO PRICING ON QTY OF 10 OR LESS

2005 Diamond Kings Heritage Collection Signature Bat

*SIG.BAT p/r 100: .4X TO 1X SIG.JSY p/r 100
*SIG.BAT p/r 50: .5X TO 1.2X SIG.JSY p/r 100
*SIG.BAT p/r 50: .4X TO 1X SIG.JSY p/r 50
*SIG.BATp/r20-25: .5X TO 1.2X SIG.JSYp/r50
*SIG.BAT p/r 20-25: .4X TO 1X SIG.JSY p/r 25
OVERALL AU-GU ODDS 1:6
PRINT RUNS B/WN 5-100 COPIES PER
NO PRICING ON QTY OF 10 OR LESS
11 Frank Robinson/25 20.00 50.00
25 Tony Gwynn/25 30.00 60.00

2005 Diamond Kings Heritage Collection Signature Combos

*SIG.COM p/r 100: .4X TO 1X SIG.JSY p/r 100
*SIG.COM p/r 50: .5X TO 1.2X SIG.JSY p/r 100
*SIG.COM p/r 50: .4X TO 1X SIG.JSY p/r 50
*SIG.COM p/r 50: .3X TO .8X SIG.JSY p/r 25
*SIG.COM p/r 25: .6X TO 1.5X SIG.JSY p/r 100
*SIG.COM p/r 25: .5X TO 1.2X SIG.JSY p/r 50
*SIG.COM p/r 25: .4X TO 1X SIG.JSY p/r 25
PRINT RUNS B/WN 5-100 COPIES PER
NO PRICING ON QTY OF 10 OR LESS
PRIME PRINT RUN 1 SERIAL #'d SET
NO PRIME PRICING DUE TO SCARCITY
OVERALL AU-GU ODDS 1:6
25 Tony Gwynn Bat-Jsy/25 30.00 60.00

2005 Diamond Kings Heritage Collection Signature Jersey

PRINT RUNS B/WN 5-100 COPIES PER
NO PRICING ON QTY OF 10 OR LESS
PRIME PRINT RUN 1 SERIAL #'d SET
NO PRIME PRICING DUE TO SCARCITY
OVERALL AU-GU ODDS 1:6
1 Andre Dawson/100 8.00 20.00
2 Bob Gibson/25 20.00 50.00
3 Cal Ripken/5
4 Dale Murphy/50 15.00 40.00
5 Darryl Strawberry Pants/100 8.00 20.00
6 Dennis Eckersley/50 10.00 25.00
7 Don Mattingly/25 40.00 80.00
8 Duke Snider/50 15.00 40.00
9 Dwight Gooden/100 8.00 20.00
10 Eddie Murray/5
11 Frank Robinson/25 20.00 50.00
12 Gary Carter/50 10.00 25.00
13 George Brett/5
14 Harmon Killebrew/50 30.00 60.00
15 Jack Morris/100 8.00 20.00
16 Jim Palmer/25 12.50 30.00
17 Lou Brock/50 15.00 40.00
18 Mike Schmidt Jkt/5
19 Nolan Ryan/10
20 Ozzie Smith/25 30.00 60.00
21 Phil Niekro/25 12.50 30.00
22 Rod Carew/25 20.00 50.00
23 Rollie Fingers/25 12.50 30.00
24 Steve Carlton/25 12.50 30.00
25 Tony Gwynn/10
26 Curt Schilling/10
27 Bobby Doerr Pants/25 12.50 30.00
28 Edgar Martinez/25 20.00 50.00
30 Mark Grace/10
31 Matt Williams/25 20.00 50.00
32 Paul Molitor/10
33 Robin Yount/10
34 Ryne Sandberg/5
35 Will Clark/25 20.00 50.00

2005 Diamond Kings HOF Heroes

1-50 STATED ODDS 1:5 SER.1 PACKS
51-100 STATED ODDS 1:7 SER.2 PACKS
NON CANVAS RANDOM IN PACKS
NON-CANVAS PRINT RUN 20 SETS
NON-CANVAS PRINT RUN INFO BY DONRUSS
NO NON-CANVAS PRICING AVAILABLE
*BRONZE 1-50: .75X TO 2X BASIC
*BRONZE 51-100: 1X TO 2.5X BASIC

BRONZE 1-50 PRINT RUN 100 #'d SETS
BRONZE 51-100 PRINT RUN 50 #'d SETS
*GOLD 1-50: 1.5X TO 4X BASIC
GOLD 1-50 PRINT RUN 25 #'d SETS
GOLD 51-100 PRINT RUN 10 #'d SETS
GOLD 51-100 NO PRICING AVAILABLE
PLATINUM PRINT RUN 1 SERIAL #'d SET
NO PLATINUM PRICING DUE TO SCARCITY
*SILVER 1-50: 1.25X TO 3X BASIC
*SILVER 51-100: 2X TO 5X BASIC
SILVER 1-50 PRINT RUN 50 #'d SETS
SILVER 51-100 PRINT RUN 25 #'d SETS
*FRAME BLK: 2X TO 5X BASIC
FRAME BLK PRINT RUN 25 #'d SETS
FRAME BLK PLAT.PRINT RUN 1 #'d SET
NO FRAME BLK PLAT.PRICING AVAIL.
*FRAME BLUE: 1X TO 2.5X BASIC
FRAME BLUE PRINT RUN 100 #'d SETS
FRAME BLUE PLAT.PRINT RUN 1 #'d SET
NO FRAME BLUE PLAT.PRICING AVAIL.
*FRAME GRN: 1.25X TO 3X BASIC
FRAME GRN PRINT RUN 50 #'d SETS
FRAME GRN PLAT.PRINT RUN 1 #'d SET
NO FRAME GRN PLAT.PRICING AVAIL.
*FRAME RED: .6X TO 1.5X BASIC
FRAME RED STATED ODDS 1:18
FRAME RED PLAT.PRINT RUN 1 #'d SET
NO FRAME RED PLAT.PRICING AVAIL.
OVERALL INSERT ODDS 10 PER SER.1 BOX
OVERALL INSERT ODDS 12 PER SER.2 BOX

1 Phil Niekro	.50	1.25
2 Brooks Robinson	.75	2.00
3 Jim Palmer	.50	1.25
4 Carl Yastrzemski	1.50	4.00
5 Ted Williams	2.50	6.00
6 Duke Snider	.75	2.00
7 Burleigh Grimes	.75	2.00
8 Don Sutton	.50	1.25
9 Nolan Ryan	3.00	8.00
10 Fergie Jenkins	.50	1.25
11 Carlton Fisk	.75	2.00
12 Tom Seaver	.75	2.00
13 Bob Feller	.50	1.25
14 Nolan Ryan	3.00	8.00
15 George Brett	2.50	6.00
16 Warren Spahn	.75	2.00
17 Paul Molitor	1.25	3.00
18 Rod Carew	.75	2.00
19 Harmon Killebrew	1.25	3.00
20 Monte Irvin	.50	1.25
21 Gary Carter	.50	1.25
22 Phil Rizzuto	.75	2.00
23 Babe Ruth	3.00	8.00
24 Reggie Jackson	1.25	3.00
25 Mike Schmidt	2.50	6.00
26 Roberto Clemente	3.00	8.00
27 Juan Marichal	.50	1.25
28 Willie McCovey	.75	2.00
29 Stan Musial	2.00	5.00
30 Ozzie Smith	2.00	5.00
31 Dennis Eckersley	.50	1.25
32 Phil Niekro	.50	1.25
33 Jim Palmer	.50	1.25
34 Carl Yastrzemski	1.50	4.00
35 Duke Snider	.75	2.00
36 Don Sutton	.50	1.25
37 Nolan Ryan	3.00	8.00
38 Carlton Fisk	.75	2.00
39 Tom Seaver	.75	2.00
40 Bob Feller	.50	1.25
41 Nolan Ryan	3.00	8.00
42 George Brett	2.50	6.00
43 Harmon Killebrew	1.25	3.00
44 Gary Carter	.50	1.25
45 Mike Schmidt	2.50	6.00
46 Stan Musial	2.00	5.00
47 Ozzie Smith	2.00	5.00
48 Dennis Eckersley	.50	1.25
49 Fergie Jenkins	.50	1.25
50 Brooks Robinson	.75	2.00
51 Eddie Murray	1.25	3.00
52 Frank Robinson	.75	2.00
53 Carlton Fisk	.75	2.00
54 Ted Williams	2.50	6.00
55 Rod Carew	.75	2.00
56 Ernie Banks	1.25	3.00
57 Luis Aparicio	.50	1.25
58 Johnny Bench	1.25	3.00
59 Al Kaline	1.25	3.00
60 George Kell	.50	1.25
61 Robin Yount	1.25	3.00
62 Nolan Ryan	3.00	8.00
63 Whitey Ford	.75	2.00
64 Reggie Jackson	1.25	3.00
65 Babe Ruth	3.00	8.00
66 Rollie Fingers	.50	1.25
67 Steve Carlton	.50	1.25
68 Robin Roberts	.50	1.25
69 Ralph Kiner	.50	1.25
70 Willie Stargell	.75	2.00
71 Roberto Clemente	3.00	8.00
72 Gaylord Perry	.50	1.25
73 Bob Gibson	.75	2.00
74 Lou Brock	.75	2.00
75 Frankie Frisch	.75	2.00
76 Eddie Murray	1.25	3.00
77 Frank Robinson	.75	2.00
78 Carlton Fisk	.75	2.00
79 Ted Williams	2.50	6.00
80 Rod Carew	.75	2.00
81 Ernie Banks	1.25	3.00
82 Luis Aparicio	.50	1.25
83 Johnny Bench	1.25	3.00
84 Al Kaline	1.25	3.00
85 Willie Mays	2.50	6.00
86 Robin Yount	1.25	3.00
87 Nolan Ryan	3.00	8.00
88 Whitey Ford	.75	2.00
89 Reggie Jackson	1.25	3.00
90 Babe Ruth	3.00	8.00
91 Rollie Fingers	.50	1.25
92 Steve Carlton	.50	1.25
93 Wade Boggs Yanks	.75	2.00
94 Wade Boggs Sox	.75	2.00
95 Willie Stargell	.75	2.00
96 Roberto Clemente	3.00	8.00
97 Gaylord Perry	.50	1.25
98 Bob Gibson	.75	2.00
99 Lou Brock	.75	2.00
100 Frankie Frisch	.75	2.00

2005 Diamond Kings HOF Heroes Materials Bronze

OVERALL AU-GU ODDS 1:6 PACKS
PRINT RUNS B/WN 1-100 COPIES PER
NO PRICING ON QTY OF 10 OR LESS

1 Phil Niekro Bat-Jsy/100	4.00	10.00
2 B.Robinson Bat-Jsy/100	5.00	12.00
3 Jim Palmer Jsy-Pants/100	4.00	10.00
4 C.Yastrzemski Bat-Pants/50	10.00	25.00
5 Ted Williams Bat-Jsy/1		
6 Duke Snider Jsy-Pants/50	6.00	15.00
7 B.Grimes Pants-Pants/25	25.00	60.00
8 Don Sutton Jsy-Jsy/100	4.00	10.00
9 Nolan Ryan Bat-Jkt/50	12.50	30.00
10 F.Jenkins Pants-Pants/100	4.00	10.00
11 Carlton Fisk Bat-Jkt/100	5.00	12.00
12 Tom Seaver Jsy-Pants/50	6.00	15.00
13 Bob Feller Pants-Pants/25	8.00	20.00
14 Nolan Ryan Bat-Jsy/50	12.50	30.00
15 George Brett Bat-Bat/25	15.00	40.00
16 W.Spahn Jsy-Pants/25	10.00	25.00
17 Paul Molitor Bat-Jsy/100	4.00	10.00
18 Rod Carew Bat-Jsy/50	6.00	15.00
19 H.Killebrew Bat-Jsy/50	8.00	20.00
21 Gary Carter Bat-Jsy/100	4.00	10.00
23 Babe Ruth Bat-Pants/25	200.00	350.00
24 R.Jackson Bat-Jkt/100	6.00	15.00
25 Mike Schmidt Bat-Jkt/50	12.50	30.00
26 R.Clemente Bat-Bat/50	25.00	60.00
27 J.Marichal Pants-Pants/25	6.00	15.00
28 W.McCovey Jsy-Pants/100	5.00	12.00
29 Stan Musial Bat-Bat/25	12.50	30.00
30 Ozzie Smith Bat-Pants/100	8.00	20.00
31 D.Eckersley Jsy-Jsy/100	4.00	10.00
32 Phil Niekro Bat-Jsy/100	4.00	10.00
33 Jim Palmer Jsy-Pants/25	6.00	15.00
34 C.Yaz Bat-Pants/25	12.50	30.00
35 Duke Snider Jsy-Pants/25	8.00	20.00
36 Don Sutton Jsy-Jsy/100	4.00	10.00
37 Nolan Ryan Bat-Jkt/25	15.00	40.00
38 Carlton Fisk Bat-Jkt/100	5.00	12.00
39 Tom Seaver Bat-Jsy/25	8.00	20.00
40 Bob Feller Pants-Pants/25	8.00	20.00
41 Nolan Ryan Bat-Jkt/25	15.00	40.00
42 George Brett Bat-Bat/25	15.00	40.00
43 H.Killebrew Bat-Jsy/25	10.00	25.00
44 Gary Carter Bat-Jsy/100	4.00	10.00
45 Mike Schmidt Bat-Jsy/25	15.00	40.00
46 Stan Musial Bat-Bat/25	12.50	30.00
47 Ozzie Smith Bat-Pants/100	8.00	20.00
48 D.Eckersley Jsy-Jsy/100	4.00	10.00
49 F.Jenkins Pants-Pants/25	6.00	15.00
50 B.Robinson Bat-Jsy/25	8.00	20.00
51 Eddie Murray Bat-Pants/50	8.00	20.00
52 Frank Robinson Bat-Bat/50	5.00	12.00
53 Carlton Fisk Bat-Bat/50	5.00	12.00
54 Ted Williams Bat-Bat/50	25.00	60.00
55 Rod Carew Bat-Jkt/Jsy/50	6.00	15.00
56 Ernie Banks Bat-Pants/50	8.00	20.00
57 Luis Aparicio Bat-Bat/50	5.00	12.00
58 Johnny Bench Bat-Jsy/50	8.00	20.00
59 Al Kaline Bat-Bat/25	10.00	25.00
61 Robin Yount Bat-Jsy/50	8.00	20.00
62 Nolan Ryan Bat-Jsy/25	15.00	40.00
63 Whitey Ford Jsy-Jsy/25	10.00	25.00
64 R.Jackson Pants-Pants/50	6.00	15.00
65 Babe Ruth Bat-Pants/25	200.00	350.00
66 Rollie Fingers Jsy-Jsy/50	5.00	12.00
67 Steve Carlton Bat-Jsy/50	5.00	12.00
70 Willie Stargell Bat-Jsy/50	6.00	15.00
71 R.Clemente Bat-Bat/25	30.00	80.00
72 Gaylord Perry Jsy-Jsy/50	5.00	12.00
73 Bob Gibson Jsy-Jsy/25	8.00	20.00
74 Lou Brock Bat-Jsy/50	6.00	15.00
75 Frankie Frisch Jkt-Jkt/50	8.00	20.00
76 Eddie Murray Bat-Bat/50	8.00	20.00
77 Frank Robinson Bat-Bat/50	5.00	12.00
78 Carlton Fisk Bat-Bat/50	5.00	12.00
79 Ted Williams Bat-Bat/25	30.00	80.00
80 Rod Carew Bat-Jkt/50	6.00	15.00
81 Ernie Banks Bat-Jsy/25	10.00	25.00
82 Luis Aparicio Bat-Bat/50	5.00	12.00
83 Johnny Bench Bat-Jsy/50	8.00	20.00
84 Al Kaline Bat-Bat/10		
86 Robin Yount Bat-Jsy/50	8.00	20.00
87 Nolan Ryan Bat-Jsy/25	15.00	40.00
88 Whitey Ford Jsy-Jsy/25	10.00	25.00
89 R.Jackson Pants-Pants/50	6.00	15.00
90 Babe Ruth Bat-Pants/10		
91 Rollie Fingers Jsy-Jsy/50	5.00	12.00
92 Steve Carlton Bat-Jsy/50	5.00	12.00
95 Willie Stargell Jsy-Jsy/50	6.00	15.00
96 Roberto Clemente Bat-Bat/10		
97 Gaylord Perry Jsy-Jsy/50	5.00	12.00
98 Bob Gibson Jsy-Jsy/10		
99 Lou Brock Bat-Jsy/50	6.00	15.00
100 Frankie Frisch Jkt-Jkt/50	8.00	20.00

2005 Diamond Kings HOF Heroes Materials Gold

*GOLD p/r 25: .6X TO 1.5X BRZ p/r 100
*GOLD p/r 25: .5X TO 1.2X BRZ p/r 50
*GOLD p/r 25: .4X TO 1X BRZ p/r 25
OVERALL AU-GU ODDS 1:6
PRINT RUNS B/WN 1-25 COPIES PER
NO PRICING ON QTY OF 10 OR LESS

96 R.Clemente Bat-Bat/25	30.00	80.00
98 Bob Gibson Jsy-Jsy/25	8.00	20.00

2005 Diamond Kings HOF Heroes Materials Platinum

OVERALL AU-GU ODDS 1:6
STATED PRINT RUN 1 SERIAL #'d SET
NO PRICING DUE TO SCARCITY

2005 Diamond Kings HOF Heroes Materials Silver

*SILV p/r 50: .5X TO 1.2X BRZ p/r 100
*SILV p/r 50: .4X TO 1X BRZ p/r 50
*SILV p/r 50: .3X TO .8X BRZ p/r 25
*SILV p/r 25: .6X TO 1.5X BRZ p/r 100
*SILV p/r 25: .5X TO 1.2X BRZ p/r 50
*SILV p/r 25: .4X TO 1X BRZ p/r 25
OVERALL AU-GU ODDS 1:6
PRINT RUNS B/WN 10-50 COPIES PER
NO PRICING ON QTY OF 10

65 Babe Ruth Pants-Pants/25	200.00	350.00

2005 Diamond Kings HOF Heroes Materials Framed Black

PRINT RUNS B/WN 1-10 COPIES PER
PLATINUM PRINT RUN 1 SERIAL #'d SET
OVERALL AU-GU ODDS 1:6
NO PRICING DUE TO SCARCITY

2005 Diamond Kings HOF Heroes Materials Framed Blue

*BLUE p/r 25: .6X TO 1.5X BRZ p/r 100
*BLUE p/r 25: .5X TO 1.2X BRZ p/r 50
*BLUE p/r 25: .4X TO 1X BRZ p/r 25
PRINT RUNS B/WN 1-25 COPIES PER
NO PRICING ON QTY OF 10 OR LESS
PLATINUM PRINT RUN 1 SERIAL #'d SET
NO PLAT.PRICING DUE TO SCARCITY
OVERALL AU-GU ODDS 1:6

65 Babe Ruth Pants-Pants/25	200.00	350.00

2005 Diamond Kings HOF Heroes Materials Framed Green

PRINT RUNS B/WN 1-10 COPIES PER
PLATINUM PRINT RUN 1 SERIAL #'d SET
OVERALL AU-GU ODDS 1:6
NO PRICING DUE TO SCARCITY

2005 Diamond Kings HOF Heroes Materials Framed Red

*RED p/r 50: .5X TO 1.2X BRZ p/r 100
*RED p/r 50: .4X TO 1X BRZ p/r 50
*RED p/r 50: .3X TO .8X BRZ p/r 25
*RED p/r 25: .6X TO 1.5X BRZ p/r 100
*RED p/r 25: .5X TO 1.2X BRZ p/r 50
*RED p/r 25: .4X TO 1X BRZ p/r 25
PRINT RUNS B/WN 5-50 COPIES PER
NO PRICING ON QTY OF 10 OR LESS
PLATINUM PRINT RUN 1 SERIAL #'d SET
NO PLATINUM PRICING DUE TO SCARCITY
OVERALL AU-GU ODDS 1:6

5 Ted Williams Bat-Jsy/50	25.00	60.00
65 Babe Ruth Pants-Pants/50	175.00	300.00
90 Babe Ruth Bat-Pants/50	175.00	300.00
96 R.Clemente Bat-Bat/50	25.00	60.00

2005 Diamond Kings HOF Heroes Signature Bronze

OVERALL AU-GU ODDS 1:6
PRINT RUNS B/WN 1-25 COPIES PER
NO PRICING ON QTY OF 10 OR LESS

1 Phil Niekro/5		
2 Brooks Robinson/5		
3 Jim Palmer/5		
4 Carl Yastrzemski/1		
6 Duke Snider/1		
8 Don Sutton/5		
9 Nolan Ryan/1		
10 Fergie Jenkins/10		
11 Carlton Fisk/1		
12 Tom Seaver/1		
13 Bob Feller/25	15.00	40.00
14 Nolan Ryan/1		
15 George Brett/1		
17 Paul Molitor/1		
18 Rod Carew/1		
19 Harmon Killebrew/5		
20 Monte Irvin/5		
21 Gary Carter/5		
22 Phil Rizzuto/5		
24 Reggie Jackson/1		
25 Mike Schmidt/1		
27 Juan Marichal/5		
28 Willie McCovey/1		
29 Stan Musial/1		
30 Ozzie Smith/1		
31 Dennis Eckersley/5		
32 Phil Niekro/5		
33 Jim Palmer/5		
34 Carl Yastrzemski/1		
35 Duke Snider/1		
36 Don Sutton/5		
37 Nolan Ryan/1		
38 Carlton Fisk/1		
39 Tom Seaver/1		
40 Bob Feller/25	15.00	40.00
41 Nolan Ryan/1		
42 George Brett/1		
43 Harmon Killebrew/5		
44 Gary Carter/5		
45 Mike Schmidt/1		
46 Stan Musial/1		
47 Ozzie Smith/1		
48 Dennis Eckersley/5		
49 Fergie Jenkins/10		
50 Brooks Robinson/5		
52 Frank Robinson/25	15.00	40.00
53 Carlton Fisk/10		
55 Rod Carew/10		
56 Ernie Banks/5		
57 Luis Aparicio/25	10.00	25.00
58 Johnny Bench/10		
59 Al Kaline/25	20.00	50.00
60 George Kell/25	15.00	40.00
61 Robin Yount/5		
62 Nolan Ryan/5		
63 Whitey Ford/5		
64 Reggie Jackson/5		
66 Rollie Fingers/25	10.00	25.00
67 Steve Carlton/25	10.00	25.00
68 Robin Roberts/25	10.00	25.00
69 Ralph Kiner/25	20.00	50.00
72 Gaylord Perry/25	10.00	25.00
73 Bob Gibson/5		
74 Lou Brock/25	15.00	40.00
77 Frank Robinson/10		
78 Carlton Fisk/5		
80 Rod Carew/10		
81 Ernie Banks/5		
82 Luis Aparicio/25	10.00	25.00
83 Johnny Bench/5		
84 Al Kaline/25	20.00	50.00
85 Willie Mays/25		
86 Robin Yount/5		
87 Nolan Ryan/5		
88 Whitey Ford/5		
89 Reggie Jackson/5		
91 Rollie Fingers/25	10.00	25.00
92 Steve Carlton/25	10.00	25.00
93 Wade Boggs Yanks/25	15.00	40.00
94 Wade Boggs Sox/25	15.00	40.00
97 Gaylord Perry/25	10.00	25.00
98 Bob Gibson/5		
99 Lou Brock/25	15.00	40.00

2005 Diamond Kings HOF Heroes Signature Gold

OVERALL AU-GU ODDS 1:6
PRINT RUNS B/WN 1-10 COPIES PER
NO PRICING DUE TO SCARCITY

2005 Diamond Kings HOF Heroes Signature Platinum

OVERALL AU-GU ODDS 1:6
STATED PRINT RUN 1 SERIAL #'d SET
NO PRICING DUE TO SCARCITY

2005 Diamond Kings HOF Heroes Signature Silver

*SILV p/r 25: .4X TO 1X BRZ p/r 25
OVERALL AU-GU ODDS 1:6
PRINT RUNS B/WN 1-25 COPIES PER
NO PRICING ON QTY OF 10 OR LESS
85 Willie Mays/25

2005 Diamond Kings HOF Heroes Signature Framed Black

STATED PRINT RUN 1 SERIAL #'d SET
PLATINUM PRINT RUN 1 SERIAL #'d SET
OVERALL AU-GU ODDS 1:6
NO PRICING DUE TO SCARCITY

2005 Diamond Kings HOF Heroes Signature Framed Blue

PRINT RUNS B/WN 1-10 COPIES PER
PLATINUM PRINT RUN 1 SERIAL #'d SET
OVERALL AU-GU ODDS 1:6
NO PRICING DUE TO SCARCITY

2005 Diamond Kings HOF Heroes Signature Framed Green

PRINT RUNS B/WN 1-10 COPIES PER
PLATINUM PRINT RUN 1 SERIAL #'d SET
OVERALL AU-GU ODDS 1:6
NO PRICING DUE TO SCARCITY

2005 Diamond Kings HOF Heroes Signature Framed Red

*SILV p/r 25: .4X TO 1X BRZ p/r 25
PRINT RUNS B/WN 1-25 COPIES PER
NO PRICING ON QTY OF 10 OR LESS
PLATINUM PRINT RUN 1 SERIAL #'d SET
NO PLAT.PRICING DUE TO SCARCITY
OVERALL AU-GU ODDS 1:6
85 Willie Mays/25

2005 Diamond Kings HOF Heroes Signature Materials Bronze

OVERALL AU-GU ODDS 1:6
PRINT RUNS B/WN 5-50 COPIES PER
NO PRICING ON QTY OF 10 OR LESS

2 B.Robinson Bat-Jsy/25	20.00	50.00
3 Jim Palmer Jsy-Pants/25	12.50	30.00
4 C.Yastrzemski Bat-Pants/5		
6 Duke Snider Jsy-Pants/25	20.00	50.00
8 Don Sutton Jsy-Jsy/25	12.50	30.00
9 Nolan Ryan Jkt-Jsy/10		
10 F.Jenkins Pants-Pants/25	12.50	30.00
11 Carlton Fisk Bat-Jkt/10		
12 Tom Seaver Bat-Jsy/10		
13 Bob Feller Pants-Pants/50	15.00	40.00
14 Nolan Ryan Jkt-Jsy/10		
15 George Brett Bat-Bat/5		
17 Paul Molitor Bat-Jsy/10		
18 Rod Carew Bat-Jsy/50	15.00	40.00
19 H.Killebrew Bat-Jsy/25	40.00	80.00
21 Gary Carter Bat-Jsy/50	10.00	25.00
24 Reggie Jackson Bat-Jkt/10		
25 Mike Schmidt Bat-Jsy/10		
27 J.Marichal Pants-Pants/25	12.50	30.00
28 W.McCovey Jsy-Pants/25	20.00	50.00
29 Stan Musial Bat-Bat/25	50.00	100.00
30 Ozzie Smith Bat-Pants/25	30.00	60.00
31 D.Eckersley Jsy-Jsy/25	12.50	30.00
32 Phil Niekro Bat-Jsy/25	12.50	30.00
33 Jim Palmer Jsy-Pants/25	12.50	30.00
34 C.Yastrzemski Bat-Pants/5		
35 Duke Snider Jsy-Pants/25	20.00	50.00
36 Don Sutton Jsy-Jsy/25	12.50	30.00
37 Nolan Ryan Bat-Jkt/10		
38 Carlton Fisk Bat-Jkt/10		
39 Tom Seaver Jsy-Pants/10		
40 Bob Feller Pants-Pants/50	15.00	40.00
41 Nolan Ryan Jsy-Jsy/10		
42 George Brett Bat-Bat/5		
43 H.Killebrew Bat-Jsy/50	30.00	60.00
44 Gary Carter Bat-Jsy/50	10.00	25.00
45 Mike Schmidt Bat-Jkt/5		
46 Stan Musial Bat-Bat/10		
47 Ozzie Smith Bat-Pants/25	30.00	60.00
48 D.Eckersley Jsy-Jsy/50	10.00	25.00
49 F.Jenkins Pants-Pants/25	12.50	30.00
50 B.Robinson Bat-Jsy/25	20.00	50.00
53 Carlton Fisk Bat-Jsy/5		
55 Rod Carew Bat-Jkt/10		
58 Johnny Bench Bat-Jsy/10		
61 Robin Yount Bat-Jsy/25	30.00	60.00
62 Nolan Ryan Bat-Jsy/5		
63 Whitey Ford Jsy-Jsy/5		
64 Reggie Jackson Bat-Pants/5		
66 Rollie Fingers Jsy-Jsy/50	10.00	25.00
67 Steve Carlton Bat-Jsy/10		
72 Gaylord Perry Jsy-Jsy/50	10.00	25.00
74 Lou Brock Jsy-Jsy/50	15.00	40.00
77 Frank Robinson Bat-Bat/10		
78 Carlton Fisk Bat-Jsy/5		
80 Rod Carew Bat-Jsy/50	15.00	40.00
83 Johnny Bench Bat-Jsy/5		
86 Robin Yount Bat-Jsy/10		
87 Nolan Ryan Bat-Jsy/5		
88 Whitey Ford Jsy-Jsy/5		
89 Reggie Jackson Bat-Pants/5		
91 Rollie Fingers Jsy-Jsy/10		
92 Steve Carlton Bat-Jsy/10		
99 Lou Brock Bat-Jsy/25	20.00	50.00

2005 Diamond Kings HOF Heroes Signature Materials Gold

*GOLD: p/r 25: .5X TO 1.2X BRZ p/r 50
*GOLD: p/r 25: .4X TO 1X BRZ p/r 25
OVERALL AU-GU ODDS 1:6
PRINT RUNS B/WN 5-25 COPIES PER
NO PRICING ON QTY OF 10 OR LESS

91 Rollie Fingers Jsy-Jsy/25	12.50	30.00

2005 Diamond Kings HOF Heroes Signature Materials Platinum

OVERALL AU-GU ODDS 1:6
STATED PRINT RUN 1 SERIAL #'d SET
NO PRICING DUE TO SCARCITY

2005 Diamond Kings HOF Heroes Signature Materials Silver

*SILV p/r 50: .4X TO 1X BRZ p/r 50
*SILV p/r 25: .5X TO 1.2X BRZ p/r 50
*SILV p/r 25: .4X TO 1X BRZ p/r 25
OVERALL AU-GU ODDS 1:6
PRINT RUNS B/WN 5-50 COPIES PER
NO PRICING ON QTY OF 10 OR LESS

91 Rollie Fingers Jsy-Jsy/50	10.00	25.00

2005 Diamond Kings HOF Heroes Signature Materials Framed Black

PRINT RUNS B/WN 5-10 COPIES PER
PLATINUM PRINT RUN 1 SERIAL #'d SET
OVERALL AU-GU ODDS 1:6
NO PRICING DUE TO SCARCITY

2005 Diamond Kings HOF Heroes Signature Materials Framed Blue

*BLUE p/r 25: .5X TO 1.2X BRZ p/r 50
*BLUE p/r 25: .4X TO 1X BRZ p/r 25
PRINT RUNS B/WN 5-25 COPIES PER
NO PRICING ON QTY OF 10 OR LESS
PLATINUM PRINT RUN 1 SERIAL #'d SET
NO PLAT.PRICING DUE TO SCARCITY
OVERALL AU-GU ODDS 1:6

53 Carlton Fisk Bat-Jsy/25	12.50	30.00
55 Rod Carew Bat-Jkt/25	20.00	50.00
58 Johnny Bench Bat-Jsy/25	30.00	60.00
62 Nolan Ryan Bat-Jsy/25	60.00	120.00
63 Whitey Ford Jsy-Jsy/25	20.00	50.00
64 R.Jackson Bat-Pants/25	30.00	60.00
67 Steve Carlton Bat-Jsy/25	12.50	30.00
77 Frank Robinson Bat-Bat/25	20.00	50.00
78 Carlton Fisk Bat-Bat/25	12.50	30.00
83 Johnny Bench Bat-Jsy/25	30.00	60.00
86 Robin Yount Bat-Jsy/25	30.00	60.00
87 Nolan Ryan Bat-Jsy/25	60.00	120.00
88 Whitey Ford Jsy-Jsy/25	20.00	50.00
89 R.Jackson Bat-Pants/25	30.00	60.00
91 Rollie Fingers Jsy-Jsy/25	12.50	30.00
92 Steve Carlton Jsy-Pants/25	12.50	30.00

2005 Diamond Kings HOF Heroes Signature Materials Framed Green

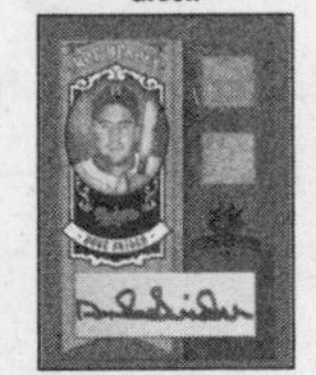

PRINT RUNS B/WN 5-10 COPIES PER
PLATINUM PRINT RUN 1 SERIAL #'d SET
OVERALL AU-GU ODDS 1:6
NO PRICING DUE TO SCARCITY

2005 Diamond Kings HOF Heroes Signature Materials Framed Red

*RED p/r 50: .4X TO 1X BRZ p/r 50
*RED p/r 25: .5X TO 1.2X BRZ p/r 50
*RED p/r 25: .4X TO 1X BRZ p/r 25
PRINT RUNS B/WN 5-50 COPIES PER
NO PRICING ON QTY OF 10 OR LESS
PLATINUM PRINT RUN 1 SERIAL #'d SET
NO PLAT.PRICING DUE TO SCARCITY
OVERALL AU-GU ODDS 1:6

91 Rollie Fingers Jsy-Jsy/50	10.00	25.00

2005 Diamond Kings HOF Sluggers

RANDOM INSERTS IN SER.2 PACKS

1 Duke Snider	.75	2.00
2 Eddie Murray	1.25	3.00
3 Frank Robinson	.75	2.00
4 George Brett	2.50	6.00
5 Harmon Killebrew	1.25	3.00
6 Mike Schmidt	2.50	6.00
7 Reggie Jackson	1.25	3.00

8 Roberto Clemente 3.00 8.00
9 Stan Musial 2.00 5.00
10 Willie Mays 2.50 6.00

2005 Diamond Kings HOF Sluggers Bat

*BAT p/r 50: .4X TO 1X JSY p/r 25
*BAT p/r 50: .3X TO .8X JSY p/r 25
OVERALL AU-GU ODDS 1:6
PRINT RUNS B/WN 10-50 COPIES PER
NO PRICING ON QTY OF 10
3 Frank Robinson/50 4.00 10.00
4 George Brett/50 10.00 25.00
8 Roberto Clemente/50 20.00 50.00

2005 Diamond Kings HOF Sluggers Combos

*COMBO p/r 50: .5X TO 1.2X JSY p/r 50
*COMBO p/r 25: .6X TO 1.5X JSY p/r 50
OVERALL AU-GU ODDS 1:6
PRINT RUNS B/WN 5-50 COPIES PER
NO PRICING ON QTY OF 10 OR LESS
4 George Brett Bat-Hat/50 12.50 30.00

2005 Diamond Kings HOF Sluggers Jersey

OVERALL AU-GU ODDS 1:6
PRINT RUNS B/WN 5-50 COPIES PER
NO PRICING ON QTY OF 5
1 Duke Snider Pants/25 6.00 15.00
2 Eddie Murray/50 6.00 15.00
5 Harmon Killebrew/25 8.00 20.00
6 Mike Schmidt/50 10.00 25.00
7 Reggie Jackson Pants/50 5.00 12.00
8 Roberto Clemente/5
9 Stan Musial Pants/25 12.50 30.00
10 Willie Mays Pants/50 12.50 30.00

2005 Diamond Kings Masters of the Game

RANDOM INSERTS IN SER.2 PACKS
1 Albert Pujols 3.00 8.00
2 Cal Ripken 5.00 12.00
3 Don Mattingly 2.50 6.00
4 Greg Maddux 2.00 5.00
5 Jim Thorpe 2.00 5.00
6 Nolan Ryan 3.00 8.00
7 Randy Johnson 1.25 3.00
8 Roberto Clemente 3.00 8.00
9 Roger Clemens 1.50 4.00
10 Willie Mays 2.50 6.00

2005 Diamond Kings Masters of the Game Bat

*BAT p/r 100: .3X TO .8X JSY p/r 50
*BAT p/r 50: .3X TO .8X JSY p/r 25
*BAT p/r 25: .4X TO 1X JSY p/r 25
OVERALL AU-GU ODDS 1:6
PRINT RUNS B/WN 25-100 COPIES PER
8 Roberto Clemente/50 20.00 50.00

2005 Diamond Kings Masters of the Game Combos

*COMBO p/r 50: .5X TO 1.2X JSY p/r 50
*COMBO p/r 25: .5X TO 1.2X JSY p/r 25
OVERALL AU-GU ODDS 1:6
PRINT RUNS B/WN 25-50 COPIES PER

2005 Diamond Kings Masters of the Game Jersey

OVERALL AU-GU ODDS 1:6
PRINT RUNS B/WN 25-50 COPIES PER
1 Albert Pujols/50 10.00 25.00
2 Cal Ripken/50 15.00 40.00
3 Don Mattingly/25 12.50 30.00
4 Greg Maddux/50 6.00 15.00
5 Jim Thorpe/25 125.00 200.00
6 Nolan Ryan/50 10.00 25.00
7 Randy Johnson/25 6.00 15.00
9 Roger Clemens/50 6.00 15.00
10 Willie Mays Pants/25 15.00 40.00

2005 Diamond Kings Recollection Autographs Gold

RANDOM INSERTS IN PACKS
STATED PRINT RUN 1 SERIAL #'d SET
NO PRICING DUE TO SCARCITY

2005 Diamond Kings Recollection Autographs Platinum

RANDOM INSERTS IN PACKS
STATED PRINT RUN 1 SERIAL #'d SET
NO PRICING DUE TO SCARCITY

2005 Diamond Kings Recollection Autographs Silver

RANDOM INSERTS IN PACKS
STATED PRINT RUN 1 SERIAL #'d SET
NO PRICING DUE TO SCARCITY

2005 Diamond Kings Team Timeline

1-25 STATED ODDS 1:21 SER.1 PACKS
26-30 RANDOM INSERTS IN SER.2 PACKS
1 Albert Pujols 4.00 10.00
Scott Rolen
2 Roger Clemens 2.00 5.00
Andy Pettitte
3 Tim Hudson 1.00 2.50
Mark Mulder
4 Hank Blalock 1.50 4.00
Mark Teixeira
5 Miguel Cabrera 1.50 4.00
Mike Lowell
6 Greg Maddux 2.50 6.00
Sammy Sosa
7 Miguel Tejada 1.00 2.50
Cal Ripken
8 Vladimir Guerrero 1.50 4.00
Reggie Jackson
9 Mike Schmidt 3.00 8.00
Jim Thome
10 Chipper Jones 2.50 6.00
Greg Maddux
11 George Brett 3.00 8.00
Ken Harvey
12 Don Mattingly 3.00 8.00
Hideki Matsui
13 Torii Hunter 1.50 4.00
Johan Santana
14 Carlos Delgado .60 1.50
Vernon Wells
15 Todd Helton 1.00 2.50
Larry Walker
16 Duke Snider 1.00 2.50
Adrian Beltre
17 Al Kaline 1.50 4.00
Ivan Rodriguez
18 Rafael Palmeiro 1.50 4.00
Eddie Murray
19 Manny Ramirez 1.50 4.00
Carl Yastrzemski
20 Ralph Kiner .60 1.50
Jason Bay
21 Johnny Bench 1.00 2.50
Adam Dunn
22 Robin Yount 1.50 4.00
Lyle Overbay
23 Nolan Ryan 4.00 10.00
Randy Johnson
24 Gary Carter 1.50 4.00
Mike Piazza
25 Carlton Fisk 1.50 4.00
Frank Thomas
26 Nolan Ryan 4.00 10.00
Mike Piazza
27 Roger Clemens 2.00 5.00
Jeff Bagwell
28 Cal Ripken 6.00 15.00
Sammy Sosa
29 Willie Mays 3.00 8.00
Jim Thorpe
30 Albert Pujols 4.00 10.00
Stan Musial

2005 Diamond Kings Team Timeline Materials Bat

*BAT p/r 75-100: .4X TO 1X JSY p/r 100
*BAT p/r 50: .5X TO 1.2X JSY p/r 100
*BAT p/r 50: .3X TO .8X JSY p/r 25
*BAT p/r 25: .6X TO 1.5X JSY p/r 100
*BAT p/r 25: .5X TO 1.2X JSY p/r 50
*BAT p/r 25: .4X TO 1X JSY p/r 25
OVERALL AU-GU ODDS 1:6
PRINT RUNS B/WN 25-100 COPIES PER
5 Miguel Cabrera 6.00 15.00
Mike Lowell/100
17 Al Kaline 12.50 30.00
Ivan Rodriguez/25
28 Cal Ripken 25.00 60.00
Sammy Sosa/50

2005 Diamond Kings Team Timeline Materials Jersey

PRINT RUNS B/WN 25-100 COPIES PER
PRIME PRINT RUN 1 SERIAL #'d SET
NO PRIME PRICING DUE TO SCARCITY
OVERALL AU-GU ODDS 1:6
1 Albert Pujols 12.50 30.00
Scott Rolen/100
2 Roger Clemens 10.00 25.00
Andy Pettitte/100
3 Tim Hudson 5.00 12.00
Mark Mulder/100
4 Hank Blalock 6.00 15.00
Mark Teixeira/100
7 Miguel Tejada 20.00 50.00
Cal Ripken/100
8 Vladimir Guerrero 8.00 20.00
Reggie Jackson/100
9 Mike Schmidt Jkt 15.00 40.00
Jim Thome/100
10 Chipper Jones 15.00 40.00
Greg Maddux/100
12 Don Mattingly Jkt 20.00 50.00
Hideki Matsui/100
14 Carlos Delgado 5.00 12.00
Vernon Wells/100
15 Todd Helton 6.00 15.00
Larry Walker/100
16 Duke Snider 5.00 12.00
Adrian Beltre/100
18 Rafael Palmeiro 8.00 20.00
Eddie Murray/100
19 Manny Ramirez 15.00 40.00
Carl Yastrzemski/100
21 Johnny Bench 8.00 20.00
Adam Dunn/100
22 Robin Yount 8.00 20.00
Lyle Overbay/100
23 Nolan Ryan 15.00 40.00
Randy Johnson/100
24 Gary Carter 8.00 20.00
Mike Piazza/100
25 Carlton Fisk 8.00 20.00
Frank Thomas/100
26 Nolan Ryan 15.00 40.00
Mike Piazza/50
27 Roger Clemens 10.00 25.00
Jeff Bagwell/25
29 Willie Mays 125.00 200.00
Jim Thorpe/25
30 Albert Pujols 25.00 60.00
Stan Musial/25

2005 Diamond Kings Timeline

1-25 STATED ODDS 1:21 SER.1 PACKS
26-30 RANDOM INSERTS IN SER.2 PACKS
1 Roger Clemens Sox-Yanks 2.00 5.00
2 Nolan Ryan Angels-Astros 4.00 10.00
3 Carlos Beltran Royals-Astros .60 1.50
4 Ivan Rodriguez Rgr-M's 1.00 2.50
5 Jim Thome Indians-Phils 1.00 2.50
6 Mike Piazza Dgr-Mets 1.50 4.00
7 Miguel Tejada A's-O's 1.00 2.50
8 Rafael Palmeiro O's-Rgr 1.00 2.50
9 Greg Maddux Braves-Cubs 2.50 6.00
10 Tom Glavine Braves-Mets 1.00 2.50
11 Vlad Guerrero Expos-Angels 1.50 4.00
12 Curt Schilling D'backs-Sox 1.00 2.50
13 Mike Mussina O's-Yanks 1.00 2.50
14 Rickey Henderson A's-Dgr 1.00 2.50
15 Scott Rolen Phils-Cards 1.00 2.50
16 Alfonso Soriano Yanks-Rgr 1.00 2.50
17 Gary Sheffield Braves-Yanks .60 1.50
18 Carlton Fisk R.Sox-W.Sox 1.00 2.50
19 Aramis Ramirez Pirates-Cubs .60 1.50
20 Mark Grace Cubs-D'backs 1.00 2.50
21 Jason Giambi A's-Yanks .60 1.50
22 Juan Gonzalez Rgr-Royals .60 1.50
23 Brad Penny M's-Dgr .60 1.50
24 N.Garciaparra Sox-Cubs 1.50 4.00
25 Larry Walker Rockies-Cards 1.00 2.50
26 Curt Schilling Phils-D'backs 1.00 2.50
27 R.Jackson Angels-Yanks 1.50 4.00
28 Gary Carter Expos-Mets .60 1.50
29 Roger Clemens Sox-Astros 2.00 5.00
30 Nolan Ryan Mets-Astros 4.00 10.00

2005 Diamond Kings Timeline Materials Bat

*BAT p/r 100: .5X TO 1.2X JSY p/r 200
*BAT p/r 100: .4X TO 1X JSY p/r 100
*BAT p/r 50: .4X TO 1X JSY p/r 50
*BAT p/r 50: .3X TO .8X JSY p/r 25
*BAT p/r 25: .6X TO 1.5X JSY p/r 100
*BAT p/r 25: .5X TO 1.2X JSY p/r 50
OVERALL AU-GU ODDS 1:6
PRINT RUNS B/WN 25-100 COPIES PER
5 J.Thome Indians-Phils/25 10.00 25.00
10 T.Glavine Braves-Mets/100 6.00 15.00
17 G.Sheff Braves-Yanks/100 5.00 12.00
20 M.Grace Cubs-D'backs/100 6.00 15.00
25 L.Walk Rockies-Cards/100 5.00 12.00

2005 Diamond Kings Timeline Materials Jersey

PRINT RUNS B/WN 25-200 COPIES PER
PRIME PRINT RUN 1 SERIAL #'d SET
NO PRIME PRICING DUE TO SCARCITY
OVERALL AU-GU ODDS 1:6
1 R.Clemens Sox-Yanks/50 12.50 30.00
2 N.Ryan Angels-Astros/50 25.00 60.00
3 C.Belt Royals-Astros/100 5.00 12.00
4 I.Rodriguez Rgr-M's/200 5.00 12.00
6 M.Piazza Dgr-Mets/100 8.00 20.00
7 M.Tejada A's-O's/100 5.00 12.00
8 R.Palmeiro O's-Rgr/100 6.00 15.00
9 G.Madd Braves-Cubs/50 12.50 30.00
11 V.Guer Expos-Angels/100 8.00 20.00
12 C.Schilling D'backs-Sox/100 6.00 15.00
13 M.Mussina O's-Yanks/100 6.00 15.00
14 R.Henderson A's-Dgr/100 10.00 25.00
15 S.Rolen Phils-Cards/100 6.00 15.00
16 A.Soriano Yanks-Rgr/50 6.00 15.00
18 C.Fisk R.Sox-W.Sox/100 6.00 15.00
19 A.Ramirez Pirates-Cubs/100 5.00 12.00
21 J.Giambi A's-Yanks/100 5.00 12.00
22 J.Gonzalez Rgr-Royals/100 5.00 12.00
26 C.Schill Phils-D'backs/50 6.00 15.00
27 R.Jack Ang-Yank Pants/50 10.00 25.00
28 G.Carter Expos-Mets/25 10.00 25.00
29 R.Clemens Sox-Astros/50 12.50 30.00
30 N.Ryan Mets-Astros/25 30.00 80.00

1934-36 Diamond Stars

The cards in this 108-card set measure approximately 2 3/8" by 2 7/8". The Diamond Stars set, produced by National Chicle from 1934-36, is also commonly known by its catalog designation, R327. The year of production can be determined by the statistics contained on the back of the card. There are 170 possible front/back combinations counting blue (B) and green (G) backs over all three years. The last twelve cards are repeat players and are quite scarce. The checklist below lists the year(s) and back color(s) for the cards. Cards 32 through 72 were issued only in 1935 with green ink on back. Cards 73 through 84 were issued three ways: 35B, 35G, and 36B. Card numbers 85 through 108 were issued only in 1936 with blue ink on back. The complete set price below refers to the set of all variations listed explicitly below. A blank-backed proof sheet of 12 additional (never-issued) cards was discovered in 1980.

COMPLETE SET (119) 9000.00 15000.00
COMMON CARD (1-31) 30.00 50.00
COMMON CARD (32-84) 35.00 60.00
COMMON CARD (85-96) 60.00 100.00
COMMON CARD (97-108) 125.00 200.00
WRAP.(1-CENT, BLUE) 200.00 250.00
WRAP.(1-CENT, YELLOW) 150.00 200.00
WRAP.(1-CENT, CLEAR) 150.00 200.00
1 Lefty Grove 450.00 750.00
34G, 35G
2A Al Simmons 90.00 150.00
34G, 35G
Sox on uniform
2B Al Simmons 125.00 200.00
36B
No name on uniform
3 Rabbit Maranville 90.00 150.00
34G, 35G
4 Buddy Myer 35.00 60.00
34G, 35G, 36B
5 Tommy Bridges 35.00 60.00
34G, 35G, 36B
6 Max Bishop 35.00 60.00
34G, 35G
7 Lew Fonseca 35.00 60.00
34G, 35G
8 Joe Vosmik XRC (34G,35G,36B) 30.00 50.00
9 Mickey Cochrane 100.00 175.00
34G, 35G, 36B
10A Leroy Mahaffey 30.00 50.00
34G, 35G
A's on uniform
10B Leroy Mahaffey 50.00 80.00
36B
No name on uniform
11 Bill Dickey 125.00 200.00
34G, 35G
12A Fred Walker XRC (34G) 50.00 80.00
12B Fred Walker 35G 50.00 80.00
(Ruth to Boston
mentioned on back
12C Fred Walker 36B 60.00 100.00
13 George Blaeholder 30.00 50.00
34G, 35G
14 Bill Terry 100.00 175.00
34G, 35G
15A Dick Bartell 34G 60.00 100.00
Philadelphia Nationals
on card back
15B Dick Bartell 35G 50.00 80.00
New York Giants
on card back
16 Lloyd Waner 75.00 125.00
34G, 35G, 36B
17 Frankie Frisch 75.00 125.00
34G, 35G
18 Chick Hafey XRC (34G,35G) 75.00 125.00
19 Van Mungo XRC (34G,35G) 50.00 80.00
20 Frank Hogan 35.00 60.00
34G, 35G
21A Johnny Vergez 34G 50.00 80.00
New York Giants
on card back
21B Johnny Vergez 35G 35.00 60.00
Philadelphia Phillies
on card back
22 Jimmy Wilson 35.00 60.00
34G, 35G, 36B
23 Bill Hallahan 30.00 50.00
34G, 35G
24 Earl Adams 30.00 50.00
34G, 35G
25 Wally Berger 35G 35.00 60.00
26 Pepper Martin 50.00 80.00
35G, 36B
27 Pie Traynor 35G 90.00 150.00
28 Al Lopez 35G 90.00 150.00
29 Red Rolfe 35G 50.00 80.00
30A Heinie Manush 35G 90.00 150.00
W on sleeve
30B Heinie Manush 36B 125.00 200.00
No W on sleeve
31A Kiki Cuyler 35G 75.00 125.00
Chicago Cubs
31B Kiki Cuyler 36B 100.00 175.00
Cincinnati Reds
32 Sam Rice (35G) 75.00 125.00
33 Schoolboy Rowe (35G) 50.00 80.00
34 Stan Hack (35G) 50.00 80.00
35 Earl Averill (35G) 75.00 125.00
36A Earnie Lombardi 175.00 300.00
(Sic, Ernie)
36B Ernie Lombardi (35G) 125.00 200.00
37 Billy Urbanski (35G) 35.00 60.00
38 Ben Chapman (35G) 50.00 80.00
39 Carl Hubbell (35G) 125.00 200.00
40 Blondy Ryan (35G) 35.00 60.00
41 Harvey Hendrick XRC (35G) 35.00 60.00
42 Jimmy Dykes (35G) 50.00 80.00
43 Ted Lyons (35G) 75.00 125.00
44 Rogers Hornsby (35G) 250.00 400.00
45 Jo Jo White XRC (35G) 35.00 60.00
46 Red Lucas (35G) 35.00 60.00
47 Bob Bolton XRC (35G) 35.00 60.00
48 Rick Ferrell (35G) 75.00 125.00
49 Buck Jordan (35G) 35.00 60.00
50 Mel Ott (35G) 175.00 300.00
51 John Whitehead XRC (35G) 35.00 60.00
52 Tuck Stainback XRC (35G) 35.00 60.00
53 Oscar Melillo (35G) 35.00 60.00
54A Hank Greenburg 350.00 600.00
(Sic, Greenberg)
54B Hank Greenberg (35G) 250.00 400.00
55 Tony Cuccinello (35G) 50.00 80.00
56 Gus Suhr (35G) 35.00 60.00
57 Cy Blanton (35G) 35.00 60.00
58 Glenn Myatt (35G) 35.00 60.00
59 Jim Bottomley (35G) 75.00 125.00
60 Red Ruffing (35G) 90.00 150.00
61 Bill Werber (35G) 50.00 80.00
62 Fred Frankhouse (35G) 35.00 60.00
63 Travis Jackson (35G) 75.00 125.00
64 Jimmie Foxx (35G) 250.00 400.00
65 Zeke Bonura (35G) 35.00 60.00
66 Ducky Medwick (35G) 125.00 200.00
67 Marvin Owen (35G) 50.00 80.00
68 Sam Leslie (35G) 35.00 60.00
69 Earl Grace (35G) 35.00 60.00
70 Hal Trosky (35G) 50.00 80.00
71 Ossie Bluege (35G) 50.00 80.00
72 Tony Piet (35G) 35.00 60.00
73 Fritz Ostermueller 50.00 80.00
35G, 35B, 36B
74 Tony Lazzeri 125.00 200.00
35G, 35B, 36B
75 Jack Burns 50.00 80.00
35G, 35B, 36B
76 Billy Rogell 50.00 80.00
35G, 35B, 36B
77 Charley Gehringer 100.00 175.00
35G, 35B, 36B
78 Joe Kuhel 50.00 80.00
35G, 35B, 36B
79 Willis Hudlin 50.00 80.00
35G, 35B, 36B
80 Lou Chiozza 50.00 80.00
35G, 35B, 36B
81 Bill Delancey XRC (35G,35B,36B) 35.00 60.00
82A Johnny Babich 50.00 80.00
(Dodgers on uniorm
35G, 35B)
82B Johnny Babich 75.00 125.00
(No name on
uniform; 36B)
83 Paul Waner 90.00 150.00
35G, 35B, 36B
84 Sam Byrd 50.00 80.00
35G, 35B, 36B
85 Moose Solters (36B) 60.00 100.00
86 Frank Crosetti (36B) 90.00 150.00
87 Steve O'Neill MG (36B) 75.00 125.00
88 George Selkirk XRC (36B) 75.00 125.00
89 Joe Stripp (36B) 75.00 125.00
90 Ray Hayworth (36B) 75.00 125.00
91 Bucky Harris MG XRC (36B) 125.00 200.00
92 Ethan Allen (36B) 60.00 100.00
93 General Crowder (36B) 60.00 100.00
94 Wes Ferrell (36B) 90.00 150.00
95 Luke Appling (36B) 150.00 250.00
96 Lew Riggs XRC (36B) 60.00 100.00
97 Al Lopez (36B) 250.00 400.00
98 Schoolboy Rowe (36B) 125.00 200.00
99 Pie Traynor (36B) 300.00 500.00
100 Earl Averill (36B) 250.00 400.00
101 Dick Bartell (36B) 125.00 200.00
102 Van Lingle Mungo (36B) 150.00 250.00
103 Bill Dickey (36B) 400.00 700.00
104 Red Rolfe (36B) 125.00 200.00
105 Ernie Lombardi (36B) 250.00 400.00
106 Red Lucas (36B) 125.00 200.00
107 Stan Hack (36B) 125.00 200.00
108 Wally Berger (36B) 175.00 300.00

1981 Donruss

In 1981 Donruss launched itself into the baseball card market with a 600-card set. Wax packs contained 15 cards as well as a piece of gum. This would be the only year that Donruss was allowed to have any confectionary product in their packs. The standard-size cards are printed on thin stock and more than one pose exists for several popular players. Numerous errors of the first print run were later corrected by the company. These are marked P1 and P2 in our checklist below. According to published reports at the time, approximately 500 sets were made available in uncut sheet form. The key Rookie Cards in this set are Danny Ainge, Tim Raines, and Jeff Reardon.

COMPLETE SET (605) 20.00 50.00
COMMON CARD (1-605) .02 .10
COMMON RC .05 .15
1 Ozzie Smith 1.25 3.00
2 Rollie Fingers .08 .25
3 Rick Wise .02 .10
4 Gene Richards .02 .10
5 Alan Trammell .20 .50
6 Tom Brookens .02 .10
7A Duffy Dyer P1 .08 .25
(1980 batting average
has decimal
7B Duffy Dyer P2 .02 .10
(1980 batting average
has no decim
8 Mark Fidrych .08 .25
9 Dave Rozema .02 .10
10 Ricky Peters RC .02 .10
11 Mike Schmidt 1.00 2.50
12 Willie Stargell .20 .50
13 Tim Foli .02 .10
14 Manny Sanguillen .08 .25
15 Grant Jackson .02 .10
16 Eddie Solomon .02 .10
17 Omar Moreno .02 .10
18 Joe Morgan .20 .50
19 Rafael Landestoy .02 .10
20 Bruce Bochy .02 .10
21 Joe Sambito .02 .10
22 Manny Trillo .02 .10
23A Dave Smith P1 .20 .50
Line box around stats
is not complete
23B Dave Smith RC .20 .50
P2 Box totally encloses
stats at top
24 Terry Puhl .02 .10
25 Bump Wills .02 .10
26A John Ellis P1 ERR .20 .50
(Photo on front
shows Danny Wa
26B John Ellis P2 COR .08 .25
27 Jim Kern .02 .10
28 Richie Zisk .02 .10
29 John Mayberry .02 .10
30 Bob Davis .02 .10
31 Jackson Todd .02 .10
32 Alvis Woods .02 .10
33 Steve Carlton .20 .50
34 Lee Mazzilli .08 .25
35 John Stearns .02 .10
36 Roy Lee Jackson RC .02 .10
37 Mike Scott .08 .25
38 Lamar Johnson .02 .10
39 Kevin Bell .02 .10
40 Ed Farmer .02 .10
41 Ross Baumgarten .02 .10
42 Leo Sutherland RC .02 .10
43 Dan Meyer .02 .10
44 Ron Reed .02 .10
45 Mario Mendoza .02 .10
46 Rick Honeycutt .02 .10
47 Glenn Abbott .02 .10
48 Leon Roberts .02 .10
49 Rod Carew .20 .50
50 Bert Campaneris .08 .25
51A Tom Donahue P1 ERR .08 .25
(Name on front
misspelled Don
51B Tom Donohue RC .02 .10
P2 COR
52 Dave Frost .02 .10
53 Ed Halicki .02 .10
54 Dan Ford .02 .10
55 Garry Maddox .02 .10
56A Steve Garvey P1 .08 .25
Surpassed 25 HR
56B Steve Garvey P2 21HR .08 .25
57 Bill Russell .08 .25
58 Don Sutton .08 .25
59 Reggie Smith .08 .25
60 Rick Monday .08 .25
61 Ray Knight .08 .25
62 Johnny Bench .40 1.00
63 Mario Soto .08 .25
64 Doug Bair .02 .10
65 George Foster .08 .25
66 Jeff Burroughs .08 .25
67 Keith Hernandez .08 .25
68 Tom Herr .02 .10
69 Bob Forsch .02 .10
70 John Fulgham .02 .10
71A Bobby Bonds P1 ERR .40 1.00
986 lifetime HR
71B Bobby Bonds P2 COR .20 .50
326 lifetime HR
72A Rennie Stennett P1 .08 .25
Breaking broke leg
72B Rennie Stennett P2 .02 .10
Word broke deleted
73 Joe Strain .02 .10
74 Ed Whitson .02 .10
75 Tom Griffin .02 .10
76 Billy North .02 .10
77 Gene Garber .02 .10
78 Mike Hargrove .02 .10
79 Dave Rosello .02 .10
80 Ron Hassey .02 .10
81 Sid Monge .02 .10
82A Joe Charboneau P1 .40 1.00
'78 highlights
For some reason
82B Joe Charboneau RC .40 1.00
P2 Phrase For some reason deleted
83 Cecil Cooper .08 .25
84 Sal Bando .08 .25
85 Moose Haas .02 .10
86 Mike Caldwell .02 .10
87A Larry Hisle P1 .08 .25
('77 highlights& line
ends with %
87B Larry Hisle P2 .02 .10
Correct line 28 HR
88 Luis Gomez .02 .10
89 Larry Parrish .02 .10
90 Gary Carter .20 .50
91 Bill Gullickson RC .20 .50
92 Fred Norman .02 .10
93 Tommy Hutton .02 .10
94 Carl Yastrzemski .60 1.50
95 Glenn Hoffman RC .02 .10
96 Dennis Eckersley .20 .50
97A Tom Burgmeier P1 .08 .25
ERR Throws: Right
97B Tom Burgmeier P2 .02 .10
COR Throws: Left
98 Win Remmerswaal RC .02 .10
99 Bob Horner .08 .25
100 George Brett 1.00 2.50
101 Dave Chalk .02 .10
102 Dennis Leonard .02 .10
103 Renie Martin .02 .10
104 Amos Otis .08 .25
105 Graig Nettles .08 .25
106 Eric Soderholm .02 .10
107 Tommy John .08 .25
108 Tom Underwood .02 .10
109 Lou Piniella .08 .25
110 Mickey Klutts .02 .10
111 Bobby Murcer .08 .25
112 Eddie Murray .60 1.50

113 Rick Dempsey .02 .10
114 Scott McGregor .02 .10
115 Ken Singleton .08 .25
116 Gary Roenicke .02 .10
117 Dave Revering .02 .10
118 Mike Norris .02 .10
119 Rickey Henderson 2.50 6.00
120 Mike Heath .02 .10
121 Dave Cash .02 .10
122 Randy Jones .08 .25
123 Eric Rasmussen .02 .10
124 Jerry Mumphrey .02 .10
125 Richie Hebner .02 .10
126 Mark Wagner .02 .10
127 Jack Morris .20 .50
128 Dan Petry .02 .10
129 Bruce Robbins .02 .10
130 Champ Summers .02 .10
131 Pete Rose P1 1.25 3.00
Last line ends with
see card 251
131B Pete Rose P2 .75 2.00
132 Willie Stargell .20 .50
133 Ed Ott .02 .10
134 Jim Bibby .02 .10
135 Bert Blyleven .08 .25
136 Dave Parker .08 .25
137 Bill Robinson .02 .10
138 Enos Cabell .02 .10
139 Dave Bergman .02 .10
140 J.R. Richard .08 .25
141 Ken Forsch .02 .10
142 Larry Bowa UER .08 .25
143 Frank LaCorte UER .02 .10
Photo actually Randy Niemann
144 Denny Walling .02 .10
145 Buddy Bell .08 .25
146 Fergie Jenkins .08 .25
147 Dannny Darwin .08 .25
148 John Grubb .02 .10
149 Alfredo Griffin .02 .10
150 Jerry Garvin .02 .10
151 Paul Mirabella RC .02 .10
152 Rick Bosetti .02 .10
153 Dick Ruthven .02 .10
154 Frank Taveras .02 .10
155 Craig Swan .02 .10
156 Jeff Reardon RC .40 1.00
157 Steve Henderson .02 .10
158 Jim Morrison .02 .10
159 Glenn Borgmann .02 .10
160 LaMarr Hoyt RC .20 .50
161 Rich Wortham .02 .10
162 Thad Bosley .02 .10
163 Julio Cruz .02 .10
164A Del Unser P1 .08 .25
No 3B heading
164B Del Unser P2 .02 .10
(Batting record on back
corrected (
165 Jim Anderson .02 .10
166 Jim Beattie .02 .10
167 Shane Rawley .02 .10
168 Joe Simpson .02 .10
169 Rod Carew .20 .50
170 Fred Patek .02 .10
171 Frank Tanana .08 .25
172 Alfredo Martinez RC .02 .10
173 Chris Knapp .02 .10
174 Joe Rudi .08 .25
175 Greg Luzinski .08 .25
176 Steve Garvey .20 .50
177 Joe Ferguson .02 .10
178 Bob Welch .08 .25
179 Dusty Baker .08 .25
180 Rudy Law .02 .10
181 Dave Concepcion .08 .25
182 Johnny Bench .40 1.00
183 Mike LaCoss .02 .10
184 Ken Griffey .08 .25
185 Dave Collins .02 .10
186 Brian Asselstine .02 .10
187 Garry Templeton .08 .25
188 Mike Phillips .02 .10
189 Pete Vuckovich .02 .10
190 John Urrea .02 .10
191 Tony Scott .02 .10
192 Darrell Evans .08 .25
193 Milt May .02 .10
194 Bob Knepper .02 .10
195 Randy Moffitt .02 .10
196 Larry Herndon .02 .10
197 Rick Camp .02 .10
198 Andre Thornton .08 .25
199 Tom Veryzer .02 .10
200 Gary Alexander .02 .10
201 Rick Waits .02 .10
202 Rick Manning .02 .10
203 Paul Molitor .40 1.00
204 Jim Gantner .02 .10
205 Paul Mitchell .02 .10
206 Reggie Cleveland .02 .10
207 Sixto Lezcano .02 .10
208 Bruce Benedict .02 .10
209 Rodney Scott .02 .10
210 John Tamargo .02 .10
211 Bill Lee .08 .25
212 Andre Dawson .20 .50
213 Rowland Office .02 .10
214 Carl Yastrzemski .60 1.50
215 Jerry Remy .02 .10
216 Mike Torrez .02 .10
217 Skip Lockwood .02 .10
218 Fred Lynn .08 .25
219 Chris Chambliss .08 .25
220 Willie Aikens .02 .10
221 John Wathan .02 .10
222 Dan Quisenberry .02 .10
223 Willie Wilson .08 .25
224 Clint Hurdle .02 .10
225 Bob Watson .02 .10
226 Jim Spencer .02 .10
227 Ron Guidry .08 .25
228 Reggie Jackson .40 1.00
229 Oscar Gamble .02 .10
230 Jeff Cox RC .02 .10
231 Luis Tiant .08 .25
232 Rich Dauer .02 .10
233 Dan Graham .02 .10
234 Mike Flanagan .02 .10
235 John Lowenstein .02 .10

236 Benny Ayala .02 .10
237 Wayne Gross .02 .10
238 Rick Langford .02 .10
239 Tony Armas .08 .25
240A Bob Lacy P1 ERR .20 .50
(Name misspelled
Bob Lacy)
240B Bob Lacey P2 COR .02 .10
241 Gene Tenace .08 .25
242 Bob Shirley .02 .10
243 Gary Lucas RC .02 .10
244 Jerry Turner .02 .10
245 John Wockenfuss .02 .10
246 Stan Papi .02 .10
247 Milt Wilcox .02 .10
248 Dan Schatzeder .02 .10
249 Steve Kemp .02 .10
250 Jim Lentine RC .02 .10
251 Pete Rose 1.25 3.00
252 Bill Madlock .08 .25
253 Dale Berra .02 .10
254 Kent Tekulve .02 .10
255 Enrique Romo .02 .10
256 Mike Easler .02 .10
257 Chuck Tanner MG .02 .10
258 Art Howe .02 .10
259 Alan Ashby .02 .10
260 Nolan Ryan 2.00 5.00
261A Vern Ruhle P1 ERR .20 .50
(Photo on front
actually Ken F
261B Vern Ruhle P2 COR .08 .25
262 Bob Boone .08 .25
263 Cesar Cedeno .08 .25
264 Jeff Leonard .08 .25
265 Pat Putnam .02 .10
266 Jon Matlack .02 .10
267 Dave Rajsich .02 .10
268 Billy Sample .02 .10
269 Damaso Garcia RC .02 .10
270 Tom Buskey .02 .10
271 Joey McLaughlin .02 .10
272 Barry Bonnell .02 .10
273 Tug McGraw .08 .25
274 Mike Jorgensen .02 .10
275 Pat Zachry .02 .10
276 Neil Allen .02 .10
277 Joel Youngblood .02 .10
278 Greg Pryor .02 .10
279 Britt Burns RC .02 .10
280 Rich Dotson RC .02 .10
281 Chet Lemon .08 .25
282 Rusty Kuntz RC .02 .10
283 Ted Cox .02 .10
284 Sparky Lyle .08 .25
285 Larry Cox .02 .10
286 Floyd Bannister .02 .10
287 Byron McLaughlin .02 .10
288 Rodney Craig .02 .10
289 Bobby Grich .08 .25
290 Dickie Thon .02 .10
291 Mark Clear .02 .10
292 Dave Lemanczyk .02 .10
293 Jason Thompson .02 .10
294 Rick Miller .02 .10
295 Lonnie Smith .08 .25
296 Ron Cey .08 .25
297 Steve Yeager .08 .25
298 Bobby Castillo .02 .10
299 Manny Mota .08 .25
300 Jay Johnstone .02 .10
301 Dan Driessen .02 .10
302 Joe Nolan RC .02 .10
303 Paul Householder RC .02 .10
304 Harry Spilman .02 .10
305 Cesar Geronimo .02 .10
306A Gary Mathews P1 ERR .20 .50
Name misspelled
306B Gary Matthews P2 .08 .25
COR
307 Ken Reitz .02 .10
308 Ted Simmons .08 .25
309 John Littlefield RC .02 .10
310 George Frazier .02 .10
311 Dane Iorg .02 .10
312 Mike Ivie .02 .10
313 Dennis Littlejohn .02 .10
314 Gary Lavelle .02 .10
315 Jack Clark .08 .25
316 Jim Wohlford .02 .10
317 Rick Matula .02 .10
318 Toby Harrah .08 .25
319A Dwane Kuiper P1 ERR .08 .25
Name misspelled
319B Duane Kuiper P2 COR .02 .10
320 Len Barker .08 .25
321 Victor Cruz .02 .10
322 Dell Alston .02 .10
323 Robin Yount .60 1.50
324 Charlie Moore .02 .10
325 Lary Sorensen .02 .10
326A Gorman Thomas P1 .20 .50
(2nd line on back:
30 HR mark
326B Gorman Thomas P2 .08 .25
(%%30 HR mark 3rd-)
327 Bob Rodgers MG .02 .10
328 Phil Niekro .08 .25
329 Chris Speier .02 .10
330A Steve Rodgers P1 .08 .25
ERR Name misspelled
330B Steve Rogers P2 COR .08 .25
331 Woodie Fryman .02 .10
332 Warren Cromartie .02 .10
333 Jerry White .02 .10
334 Tony Perez .20 .50
335 Carlton Fisk .20 .50
336 Dick Drago .02 .10
337 Steve Renko .02 .10
338 Jim Rice .08 .25
339 Jerry Royster .02 .10
340 Frank White .08 .25
341 Jamie Quirk .02 .10
342A Paul Spittorff P1 ERR .08 .25
Name misspelled
342B Paul Splittorff .02 .10
P2 COR
343 Marty Pattin .02 .10
344 Pete LaCock .02 .10
345 Willie Randolph .08 .25
346 Rick Cerone .02 .10

347 Rich Gossage .08 .25
348 Reggie Jackson .40 1.00
349 Ruppert Jones .02 .10
350 Dave McKay RC .02 .10
351 Yogi Berra CO .40 1.00
352 Doug DeCinces .02 .10
353 Jim Palmer .20 .50
354 Tippy Martinez .02 .10
355 Al Bumbry .02 .10
356 Earl Weaver MG .08 .25
357A Bob Picciolo P1 ERR .08 .25
Name misspelled
357B Rob Picciolo P2 COR .02 .10
358 Matt Keough .02 .10
359 Dwayne Murphy .02 .10
360 Brian Kingman .02 .10
361 Bill Fahey .02 .10
362 Steve Mura .02 .10
363 Dennis Kinney RC .02 .10
364 Dave Winfield .20 .50
365 Lou Whitaker .20 .50
366 Lance Parrish .08 .25
367 Tim Corcoran .02 .10
368 Pat Underwood .02 .10
369 Al Cowens .02 .10
370 Sparky Anderson MG .08 .25
371 Pete Rose 1.25 3.00
372 Phil Garner .08 .25
373 Steve Nicosia .02 .10
374 John Candelaria .08 .25
375 Don Robinson .02 .10
376 Lee Lacy .02 .10
377 John Milner .02 .10
378 Craig Reynolds .02 .10
379A Luis Pujols P1 ERR .08 .25
(Name misspelled)
379B Luis Pujols P2 COR .02 .10
380 Joe Niekro .02 .10
381 Joaquin Andujar .08 .25
382 Keith Moreland RC .02 .10
383 Jose Cruz .08 .25
384 Bill Virdon MG .02 .10
385 Jim Sundberg .08 .25
386 Doc Medich .02 .10
387 Al Oliver .08 .25
388 Jim Norris .02 .10
389 Bob Bailor .02 .10
390 Ernie Whitt .02 .10
391 Otto Velez .02 .10
392 Roy Howell .02 .10
393 Bob Walk RC .20 .50
394 Doug Flynn .02 .10
395 Pete Falcone .02 .10
396 Tom Hausman .02 .10
397 Elliott Maddox .02 .10
398 Mike Squires .02 .10
399 Marvis Foley RC .02 .10
400 Steve Trout .02 .10
401 Wayne Nordhagen .02 .10
402 Tony LaRussa MG .08 .25
403 Bruce Bochte .02 .10
404 Bake McBride .08 .25
405 Jerry Narron .02 .10
406 Rob Dressler .02 .10
407 Dave Heaverlo .02 .10
408 Tom Paciorek .02 .10
409 Carney Lansford .08 .25
410 Brian Downing .08 .25
411 Don Aase .02 .10
412 Jim Barr .02 .10
413 Don Baylor .08 .25
414 Jim Fregosi MG .02 .10
415 Dallas Green MG .02 .10
416 Dave Lopes .08 .25
417 Jerry Reuss .02 .10
418 Rick Sutcliffe .08 .25
419 Derrel Thomas .02 .10
420 Tom Lasorda MG .20 .50
421 Charlie Leibrandt RC .20 .50
422 Tom Seaver .40 1.00
423 Ron Oester .02 .10
424 Junior Kennedy .02 .10
425 Tom Seaver .40 1.00
426 Bobby Cox MG .08 .25
427 Leon Durham RC .20 .50
428 Terry Kennedy .02 .10
429 Silvio Martinez .02 .10
430 George Hendrick .08 .25
431 Red Schoendienst MG .20 .50
432 Johnnie LeMaster .02 .10
433 Vida Blue .08 .25
434 John Montefusco .02 .10
435 Terry Whitfield .02 .10
436 Dave Bristol MG .02 .10
437 Dale Murphy .20 .50
438 Jerry Dybzinski RC .02 .10
439 Jorge Orta .02 .10
440 Wayne Garland .02 .10
441 Miguel Dilone .02 .10
442 Dave Garcia MG .02 .10
443 Don Money .02 .10
444A Buck Martinez P1 ERR .08 .25
Reverse negative
444B Buck Martinez .02 .10
P2 COR
445 Jerry Augustine .02 .10
446 Ben Oglivie .08 .25
447 Jim Slaton .02 .10
448 Doyle Alexander .02 .10
449 Tony Bernazard .02 .10
450 Scott Sanderson .02 .10
451 David Palmer .02 .10
452 Stan Bahnsen .02 .10
453 Dick Williams MG .02 .10
454 Rick Burleson .02 .10
455 Gary Allenson .02 .10
456 Bob Stanley .02 .10
457A John Tudor P1 ERR .40 1.00
Lifetime W-L 9.7
457B John Tudor RC .40 1.00
P2 COR Lifetime W-L 9-7
458 Dwight Evans .20 .50
459 Glenn Hubbard .02 .10
460 U.L. Washington .02 .10
461 Larry Gura .02 .10
462 Rich Gale .02 .10
463 Hal McRae .08 .25
464 Jim Frey MG RC .02 .10
465 Bucky Dent .08 .25
466 Dennis Werth RC .02 .10
467 Ron Davis .02 .10

468 Reggie Jackson .40 1.00
469 Bobby Brown .02 .10
470 Mike Davis RC .20 .50
471 Gaylord Perry .08 .25
472 Mark Belanger .02 .10
473 Jim Palmer .20 .50
474 Sammy Stewart .02 .10
475 Tim Stoddard .02 .10
476 Steve Stone .02 .10
477 Jeff Newman .02 .10
478 Steve McCatty .02 .10
479 Billy Martin MG .20 .50
480 Mitchell Page .02 .10
481 Steve Carlton CY .08 .25
482 Bill Buckner .08 .25
483A Ivan DeJesus P1 ERR .08 .25
Lifetime hits 702
483B Ivan DeJesus P2 COR .02 .10
Lifetime hits 642
484 Cliff Johnson .02 .10
485 Lenny Randle .02 .10
486 Larry Milbourne .02 .10
487 Roy Smalley .02 .10
488 John Castino .02 .10
489 Ron Jackson .02 .10
490A Dave Roberts P1 .08 .25
(Career Highlights:
Showed pop
490B Dave Roberts P2 .02 .10
(%%Declared himself-)
491 George Brett MVP .60 1.50
492 Mike Cubbage .02 .10
493 Rob Wilfong .02 .10
494 Danny Goodwin .02 .10
495 Jose Morales .02 .10
496 Mickey Rivers .02 .10
497 Mike Edwards .02 .10
498 Mike Sadek .02 .10
499 Lenn Sakata .02 .10
500 Gene Michael MG .02 .10
501 Dave Roberts .02 .10
502 Steve Dillard .02 .10
503 Jim Essian .02 .10
504 Rance Mulliniks .02 .10
505 Darrell Porter .02 .10
506 Joe Torre MG .08 .25
507 Terry Crowley .02 .10
508 Bill Travers .02 .10
509 Nelson Norman .02 .10
510 Bob McClure .02 .10
511 Steve Howe RC .20 .50
512 Dave Rader .02 .10
513 Mick Kelleher .02 .10
514 Kiko Garcia .02 .10
515 Larry Biittner .02 .10
516A Willie Norwood P1 .08 .25
(Career Highlights
%%Spent mos
516B Willie Norwood P2 .02 .10
(%%Traded to Seattle-)
517 Bo Diaz .02 .10
518 Juan Beniquez .02 .10
519 Scot Thompson .02 .10
520 Jim Tracy RC .40 1.00
521 Carlos Lezcano RC .02 .10
522 Joe Amalfitano MG .02 .10
523 Preston Hanna .02 .10
524A Ray Burris P1 .08 .25
(Career Highlights:
%%Went on ...-
524B Ray Burris P2 .02 .10
(%%Drafted by ...-)
525 Broderick Perkins .02 .10
526 Mickey Hatcher .02 .10
527 John Goryl MG .02 .10
528 Dick Davis .02 .10
529 Butch Wynegar .02 .10
530 Sal Butera RC .02 .10
531 Jerry Koosman .08 .25
532A Geoff Zahn P1 .08 .25
(Career Highlights:
%%Was 2nd in-)
532B Geoff Zahn P2 .02 .10
(%%Signed a 3 year-)
533 Dennis Martinez .08 .25
534 Gary Thomasson .02 .10
535 Steve Macko .02 .10
536 Jim Kaat .08 .25
537 George Brett .60 1.50
Rod Carew
538 Tim Raines RC 1.00 2.50
539 Keith Smith .02 .10
540 Ken Macha .02 .10
541 Burt Hooton .02 .10
542 Butch Hobson .02 .10
543 Bill Stein .02 .10
544 Dave Stapleton RC .02 .10
545 Bob Pate RC .02 .10
546 Doug Corbett RC .02 .10
547 Darrell Jackson .02 .10
548 Pete Redfern .02 .10
549 Roger Erickson .02 .10
550 Al Hrabosky .08 .25
551 Dick Tidrow .02 .10
552 Dave Ford RC .02 .10
553 Dave Kingman .08 .25
554A Mike Vail P1 .08 .25
(Career Highlights:
%%After two ...
554B Mike Vail P2 .02 .10
(%%Traded to ...-)
555A Jerry Martin P1 .08 .25
(Career Highlights:
%%Overcame a
555B Jerry Martin P2 .02 .10
(%%Traded to ...-)
556A Jesus Figueroa P1 .08 .25
(Career Highlights:
%%Had an .
556B Jesus Figueroa RC .02 .10
(P2 Traded to ...-)
557 Don Stanhouse .02 .10
558 Barry Foote .02 .10
559 Tim Blackwell .02 .10
560 Bruce Sutter .20 .50
561 Rick Reuschel .08 .25
562 Lynn McGlothen .02 .10
563A Bob Owchinko P1 .08 .25
(Career Highlights:
%%Traded to
563B Bob Owchinko P2 .02 .10
(%%Involved in a ...-)
564 John Verhoeven .02 .10
565 Ken Landreaux .02 .10
566A Glen Adams P1 ERR .08 .25
Name misspelled
566B Glenn Adams P2 COR .02 .10
567 Hosken Powell .02 .10
568 Dick Noles .02 .10
569 Danny Ainge RC 1.25 3.00
570 Bobby Mattick MG RC .02 .10
571 Joe Lefebvre RC .02 .10
572 Bobby Clark .02 .10
573 Dennis Lamp .02 .10
574 Randy Lerch .02 .10
575 Mookie Wilson RC 1.25 3.00
576 Ron LeFlore .08 .25
577 Jim Dwyer .02 .10
578 Bill Castro .02 .10
579 Greg Minton .02 .10
580 Mark Littell .02 .10
581 Andy Hassler .02 .10
582 Dave Stieb .08 .25
583 Ken Oberkfell .02 .10
584 Larry Bradford .02 .10
585 Fred Stanley .02 .10
586 Bill Caudill .02 .10
587 Doug Capilla .02 .10
588 George Riley RC .02 .10
589 Willie Hernandez .02 .10
590 Mike Schmidt MVP 1.00 2.50
591 Steve Stone CY .02 .10
592 Rick Sofield .02 .10
593 Bombo Rivera .02 .10
594 Gary Ward .02 .10
595A Dave Edwards P1 .08 .25
(Career Highlights:
%%Sidelined
595B Dave Edwards P2 .02 .10
(%%Traded to ...-)
596 Mike Proly .02 .10
597 Tommy Boggs .02 .10
598 Greg Gross .02 .10
599 Elias Sosa .02 .10
600 Pat Kelly .02 .10
601A Checklist 1-120 P1 .08 .25
ERR Unnumbered
51 Donahue
601B Checklist 1-120 P2 .20 .50
COR Unnumbered
51 Donohue
602 Checklist 121-240 .08 .25
Unnumbered
603A Checklist 241-360 P1 .08 .25
ERR Unnumbered
(306 Mathews
603B Checklist 241-360 P2 .08 .25
COR Unnumbered
(306 Matthew
604A Checklist 361-480 P1 .08 .25
ERR Unnumbered
379 Pujois
604B Checklist 361-480 P2 .08 .25
COR Unnumbered
379 Pujols
605A Checklist 481-600 P1 .08 .25
ERR Unnumbered
(566 Glen Ad
605B Checklist 481-600 P2 .08 .25
COR Unnumbered
(566 Glenn A

1982 Donruss

The 1982 Donruss set contains 653 numbered standard-size cards and seven unnumbered checklists. The first 26 cards of this set are entitled Diamond Kings (DK) and feature the artwork of Dick Perez of Perez-Steele Galleries. The set was marketed with puzzle pieces in 15-card packs rather than with bubble gum. Those 15-card packs with an 30 cent SRP were issued 36 packs to a box and 20 boxes to a case. There are 63 pieces to the puzzle, which, when put together, make a collage of Babe Ruth entitled "Hall of Fame Diamond King." The card stock in this year's Donruss cards is considerably thicker than the 1981 cards. The seven unnumbered checklist cards are arbitrarily assigned numbers 654 through 660 and are listed at the end of the list below. Notable Rookie Cards in this set include Brett Butler, Cal Ripken Jr., Lee Smith and Dave Stewart.

COMPLETE SET (660) 30.00 60.00
COMP.FACT.SET (660) 30.00 60.00
COMP.RUTH PUZZLE 5.00 10.00
1 Pete Rose DK 1.00 2.50
2 Gary Carter DK .07 .20
3 Steve Garvey DK .07 .20
4 Vida Blue DK .07 .20
5 Alan Trammell DK .07 .20
COR
5A Alan Trammel DK ERR .07 .20
(Name misspelled)
6 Len Barker DK .02 .10
7 Dwight Evans DK .15 .40
8 Rod Carew DK .15 .40
9 George Hendrick DK .07 .20
10 Phil Niekro DK .07 .20
11 Richie Zisk DK .02 .10
12 Dave Parker DK .07 .20
13 Nolan Ryan DK 1.50 4.00
14 Ivan DeJesus DK .02 .10
15 George Brett DK .75 2.00
16 Tom Seaver DK .15 .40
17 Dave Kingman DK .07 .20
18 Dave Winfield DK .07 .20
19 Mike Norris DK .02 .10
20 Carlton Fisk DK .15 .40
21 Ozzie Smith DK .60 1.50
22 Roy Smalley DK .02 .10
23 Buddy Bell DK .07 .20
24 Ken Singleton DK .07 .20
25 John Mayberry DK .02 .10
26 Gorman Thomas DK .07 .20
27 Earl Weaver MG .07 .20
28 Rollie Fingers .07 .20
29 Sparky Anderson MG .07 .20
30 Dennis Eckersley .15 .40
31 Dave Winfield .07 .20
32 Burt Hooton .02 .10
33 Rick Waits .02 .10
34 George Brett .75 2.00
35 Steve McCatty .02 .10
36 Steve Rogers .07 .20
37 Bill Stein .02 .10
38 Steve Renko .02 .10
39 Mike Squires .02 .10
40 George Hendrick .07 .20
41 Bob Knepper .02 .10
42 Steve Carlton .15 .40
43 Larry Biittner .02 .10
44 Chris Welsh .02 .10
45 Steve Nicosia .02 .10
46 Jack Clark .07 .20
47 Chris Chambliss .07 .20
48 Ivan DeJesus .02 .10
49 Lee Mazzilli .07 .20
50 Julio Cruz .02 .10
51 Pete Redfern .02 .10
52 Dave Stieb .07 .20
53 Doug Corbett .02 .10
54 Jorge Bell RC .40 1.00
55 Joe Simpson .02 .10
56 Rusty Staub .07 .20
57 Hector Cruz .02 .10
58 Claudell Washington .02 .10
59 Enrique Romo .02 .10
60 Gary Lavelle .02 .10
61 Tim Flannery .02 .10
62 Joe Nolan .02 .10
63 Larry Bowa .07 .20
64 Sixto Lezcano .02 .10
65 Joe Sambito .02 .10
66 Bruce Kison .02 .10
67 Wayne Nordhagen .02 .10
68 Woodie Fryman .02 .10
69 Billy Sample .02 .10
70 Amos Otis .07 .20
71 Matt Keough .02 .10
72 Toby Harrah .07 .20
73 Dave Righetti RC .60 1.50
74 Carl Yastrzemski .50 1.25
75 Bob Welch .07 .20
76 Alan Trammell COR .07 .20
76A Alan Trammel ERR .07 .20
(Name misspelled)
77 Rick Dempsey .02 .10
78 Paul Molitor .07 .20
79 Dennis Martinez .07 .20
80 Jim Slaton .02 .10
81 Champ Summers .02 .10
82 Carney Lansford .07 .20
83 Barry Foote .02 .10
84 Steve Garvey .07 .20
85 Rick Manning .02 .10
86 John Wathan .02 .10
87 Brian Kingman .02 .10
88 Andre Dawson UER .07 .20
(Middle name Fernando
should be Nolan)
89 Jim Kern .02 .10
90 Bobby Grich .07 .20
91 Bob Forsch .02 .10
92 Art Howe .02 .10
93 Marty Bystrom .02 .10
94 Ozzie Smith .60 1.50
95 Dave Parker .07 .20
96 Doyle Alexander .02 .10
97 Al Hrabosky .02 .10
98 Frank Taveras .02 .10
99 Tim Blackwell .02 .10
100 Floyd Bannister .02 .10
101 Alfredo Griffin .02 .10
102 Dave Engle .02 .10
103 Mario Soto .07 .20
104 Ross Baumgarten .02 .10
105 Ken Singleton .07 .20
106 Ted Simmons .07 .20
107 Jack Morris .07 .20
108 Bob Watson .02 .10
109 Dwight Evans .15 .40
110 Tom Lasorda MG .15 .40
111 Bert Blyleven .07 .20
112 Dan Quisenberry .02 .10
113 Rickey Henderson 1.00 2.50
114 Gary Carter .07 .20
115 Brian Downing .07 .20
116 Al Oliver .07 .20
117 LaMarr Hoyt .02 .10
118 Cesar Cedeno .07 .20
119 Keith Moreland .02 .10
120 Bob Shirley .02 .10
121 Terry Kennedy .02 .10
122 Frank Pastore .02 .10
123 Gene Garber .02 .10
124 Tony Pena .07 .20
125 Allen Ripley .02 .10
126 Randy Martz .02 .10
127 Richie Zisk .02 .10
128 Mike Scott .07 .20
129 Lloyd Moseby .02 .10
130 Rob Wilfong .02 .10
131 Tim Stoddard .02 .10
132 Gorman Thomas .07 .20
133 Dan Petry .02 .10
134 Bob Stanley .02 .10
135 Lou Piniella .07 .20
136 Pedro Guerrero .07 .20
137 Len Barker .02 .10
138 Rich Gale .02 .10
139 Wayne Gross .02 .10
140 Tim Wallach RC .40 1.00
141 Gene Mauch MG .02 .10
142 Doc Medich .02 .10
143 Tony Bernazard .02 .10
144 Bill Virdon MG .02 .10
145 John Littlefield .02 .10
146 Dave Bergman .02 .10
147 Dick Davis .02 .10
148 Tom Seaver .30 .75
149 Matt Sinatro .02 .10
150 Chuck Tanner MG .02 .10

151 Leon Durham .02 .10
152 Gene Tenace .07 .20
153 Al Bumbry .02 .10
154 Mark Brouhard .02 .10
155 Rick Peters .02 .10
156 Jerry Remy .02 .10
157 Rick Reuschel .07 .20
158 Steve Howe .02 .10
159 Alan Bannister .02 .10
160 U.L. Washington .02 .10
161 Rick Langford .02 .10
162 Bill Gullickson .02 .10
163 Mark Wagner .02 .10
164 Geoff Zahn .02 .10
165 Ron LeFlore .07 .20
166 Dane Iorg .02 .10
167 Joe Niekro .02 .10
168 Pete Rose 1.00 2.50
169 Dave Collins .02 .10
170 Rick Wise .02 .10
171 Jim Bibby .02 .10
172 Larry Herndon .02 .10
173 Bob Horner .07 .20
174 Steve Dillard .02 .10
175 Mookie Wilson .07 .20
176 Dan Meyer .02 .10
177 Fernando Arroyo .02 .10
178 Jackson Todd .02 .10
179 Darrell Jackson .02 .10
180 Alvis Woods .02 .10
181 Jim Anderson .02 .10
182 Dave Kingman .07 .20
183 Steve Henderson .02 .10
184 Brian Asselstine .02 .10
185 Rod Scurry .02 .10
186 Fred Breining .02 .10
187 Danny Boone .02 .10
188 Junior Kennedy .02 .10
189 Sparky Lyle .07 .20
190 Whitey Herzog MG .07 .20
191 Dave Smith .02 .10
192 Ed Ott .02 .10
193 Greg Luzinski .07 .20
194 Bill Lee .07 .20
195 Don Zimmer MG .07 .20
196 Hal McRae .07 .20
197 Mike Norris .02 .10
198 Duane Kuiper .02 .10
199 Rick Cerone .02 .10
200 Jim Rice .07 .20
201 Steve Yeager .07 .20
202 Tom Brookens .02 .10
203 Jose Morales .02 .10
204 Roy Howell .02 .10
205 Tippy Martinez .02 .10
206 Moose Haas .02 .10
207 Al Cowens .02 .10
208 Dave Stapleton .02 .10
209 Bucky Dent .07 .20
210 Ron Cey .07 .20
211 Jorge Orta .02 .10
212 Jamie Quirk .02 .10
213 Jeff Jones .02 .10
214 Tim Raines .15 .40
215 Jon Matlack .02 .10
216 Rod Carew .15 .40
217 Jim Kaat .07 .20
218 Joe Pittman .02 .10
219 Larry Christenson .02 .10
220 Juan Bonilla RC .05 .15
221 Mike Easler .02 .10
222 Vida Blue .07 .20
223 Rick Camp .02 .10
224 Mike Jorgensen .02 .10
225 Jody Davis .02 .10
226 Mike Parrott .02 .10
227 Jim Clancy .02 .10
228 Hosken Powell .02 .10
229 Tom Hume .02 .10
230 Britt Burns .02 .10
231 Jim Palmer .07 .20
232 Bob Rodgers MG .02 .10
233 Milt Wilcox .02 .10
234 Dave Revering .02 .10
235 Mike Torrez .02 .10
236 Robert Castillo .02 .10
237 Von Hayes RC .20 .50
238 Renie Martin .02 .10
239 Dwayne Murphy .02 .10
240 Rodney Scott .02 .10
241 Fred Patek .02 .10
242 Mickey Rivers .02 .10
243 Steve Trout .02 .10
244 Jose Cruz .07 .20
245 Manny Trillo .02 .10
246 Lary Sorensen .02 .10
247 Dave Edwards .02 .10
248 Dan Driessen .02 .10
249 Tommy Boggs .02 .10
250 Dale Berra .02 .10
251 Ed Whitson .02 .10
252 Lee Smith RC .75 2.00
253 Tom Paciorek .02 .10
254 Pat Zachry .02 .10
255 Luis Leal .02 .10
256 John Castino .02 .10
257 Rich Dauer .02 .10
258 Cecil Cooper .07 .20
259 Dave Rozema .02 .10
260 John Tudor .07 .20
261 Jerry Mumphrey .02 .10
262 Jay Johnstone .02 .10
263 Bo Diaz .02 .10
264 Dennis Leonard .02 .10
265 Jim Spencer .02 .10
266 John Milner .02 .10
267 Don Aase .02 .10
268 Jim Sundberg .07 .20
269 Lamar Johnson .02 .10
270 Frank LaCorte .02 .10
271 Barry Evans .02 .10
272 Enos Cabell .02 .10
273 Del Unser .02 .10
274 George Foster .07 .20
275 Brett Butler RC .40 1.00
276 Lee Lacy .02 .10
277 Ken Reitz .02 .10
278 Keith Hernandez .07 .20
279 Doug DeCinces .02 .10
280 Charlie Moore .02 .10
281 Lance Parrish .07 .20

282 Ralph Houk MG .02 .10
283 Rich Gossage .07 .20
284 Jerry Reuss .02 .10
285 Mike Stanton .02 .10
286 Frank White .07 .20
287 Bob Owchinko .02 .10
288 Scott Sanderson .02 .10
289 Bump Wills .02 .10
290 Dave Frost .02 .10
291 Chet Lemon .07 .20
292 Tito Landrum .02 .10
293 Vern Ruhle .02 .10
294 Mike Schmidt .75 2.00
295 Sam Mejias .02 .10
296 Gary Lucas .02 .10
297 John Candelaria .02 .10
298 Jerry Martin .02 .10
299 Dale Murphy .15 .40
300 Mike Lum .02 .10
301 Tom Hausman .02 .10
302 Glenn Abbott .02 .10
303 Roger Erickson .02 .10
304 Otto Velez .02 .10
305 Danny Goodwin .02 .10
306 John Mayberry .02 .10
307 Lenny Randle .02 .10
308 Bob Bailor .02 .10
309 Jerry Morales .02 .10
310 Rufino Linares .02 .10
311 Kent Tekulve .02 .10
312 Joe Morgan .07 .20
313 John Urrea .02 .10
314 Paul Householder .02 .10
315 Garry Maddox .02 .10
316 Mike Ramsey .02 .10
317 Alan Ashby .02 .10
318 Bob Clark .02 .10
319 Tony LaRussa MG .07 .20
320 Charlie Lea .02 .10
321 Danny Darwin .02 .10
322 Cesar Geronimo .02 .10
323 Tom Underwood .02 .10
324 Andre Thornton .02 .10
325 Rudy May .02 .10
326 Frank Tanana .07 .20
327 Dave Lopes .07 .20
328 Richie Hebner .02 .10
329 Mike Flanagan .02 .10
330 Mike Caldwell .02 .10
331 Scott McGregor .02 .10
332 Jerry Augustine .02 .10
333 Stan Papi .02 .10
334 Rick Miller .02 .10
335 Graig Nettles .07 .20
336 Dusty Baker .07 .20
337 Dave Garcia MG .02 .10
338 Larry Gura .02 .10
339 Cliff Johnson .02 .10
340 Warren Cromartie .02 .10
341 Steve Comer .02 .10
342 Rick Burleson .02 .10
343 John Martin RC .05 .15
344 Craig Reynolds .02 .10
345 Mike Proly .02 .10
346 Ruppert Jones .02 .10
347 Omar Moreno .02 .10
348 Greg Minton .02 .10
349 Rick Mahler .02 .10
350 Alex Trevino .02 .10
351 Mike Krukow .02 .10
352A Shane Rawley ERR .15 .40
(Photo actually
Jim Anderson)
352B Shane Rawley COR .02 .10
353 Garth Iorg .02 .10
354 Pete Mackanin .02 .10
355 Paul Moskau .02 .10
356 Richard Dotson .02 .10
357 Steve Stone .02 .10
358 Larry Hisle .02 .10
359 Aurelio Lopez .02 .10
360 Oscar Gamble .02 .10
361 Tom Burgmeier .02 .10
362 Terry Forster .07 .20
363 Joe Charboneau .07 .20
364 Ken Brett .02 .10
365 Tony Armas .07 .20
366 Chris Speier .02 .10
367 Fred Lynn .07 .20
368 Buddy Bell .07 .20
369 Jim Essian .02 .10
370 Terry Puhl .02 .10
371 Greg Gross .02 .10
372 Bruce Sutter .15 .40
373 Joe Lefebvre .02 .10
374 Ray Knight .07 .20
375 Bruce Benedict .02 .10
376 Tim Foli .02 .10
377 Al Holland .02 .10
378 Ken Kravec .02 .10
379 Jeff Burroughs .02 .10
380 Pete Falcone .02 .10
381 Ernie Whitt .02 .10
382 Brad Havens .02 .10
383 Terry Crowley .02 .10
384 Don Money .02 .10
385 Dan Schatzeder .02 .10
386 Gary Allenson .02 .10
387 Yogi Berra CO .30 .75
388 Ken Landreaux .02 .10
389 Mike Hargrove .02 .10
390 Darryl Motley .02 .10
391 Dave McKay .02 .10
392 Stan Bahnsen .02 .10
393 Ken Forsch .02 .10
394 Mario Mendoza .02 .10
395 Jim Morrison .02 .10
396 Mike Ivie .02 .10
397 Broderick Perkins .02 .10
398 Darrell Evans .07 .20
399 Ron Reed .02 .10
400 Johnny Bench .30 .75
401 Steve Bedrosian RC .20 .50
402 Bill Robinson .02 .10
403 Bill Buckner .07 .20
404 Ken Oberkfell .02 .10
405 Cal Ripken RC 10.00 25.00
406 Jim Gantner .02 .10
407 Kirk Gibson .30 .75
408 Tony Perez .15 .40
409 Tommy John UER .07 .20
(Text says 52-56 as
Yankee, should be
52-26)
410 Dave Stewart RC .60 1.50
411 Dan Spillner .02 .10
412 Willie Aikens .02 .10
413 Mike Heath .02 .10
414 Ray Burris .02 .10
415 Leon Roberts .02 .10
416 Mike Witt .20 .50
417 Bob Molinaro .02 .10
418 Steve Braun .02 .10
419 Nolan Ryan UER 1.50 4.00
(Nisnumbering of
Nolan's no-hitters
on card back)
420 Tug McGraw .07 .20
421 Dave Concepcion .07 .20
422A Juan Eichelberger .15 .40
ERR (Photo actually
Gary Lucas)
422B Juan Eichelberger .02 .10
COR
423 Rick Rhoden .02 .10
424 Frank Robinson MG .15 .40
425 Eddie Miller .02 .10
426 Bill Caudill .02 .10
427 Doug Flynn .02 .10
428 Larry Andersen UER .02 .10
(Misspelled Anderson
on card front)
429 Al Williams .02 .10
430 Jerry Garvin .02 .10
431 Glenn Adams .02 .10
432 Barry Bonnell .02 .10
433 Jerry Narron .02 .10
434 John Stearns .02 .10
435 Mike Tyson .02 .10
436 Glenn Hubbard .02 .10
437 Eddie Solomon .02 .10
438 Jeff Leonard .02 .10
439 Randy Bass .20 .50
440 Mike LaCoss .02 .10
441 Gary Matthews .07 .20
442 Mark Littell .02 .10
443 Don Sutton .07 .20
444 John Harris .02 .10
445 Vada Pinson CO .07 .20
446 Elias Sosa .02 .10
447 Charlie Hough .07 .20
448 Willie Wilson .07 .20
449 Fred Stanley .02 .10
450 Tom Veryzer .02 .10
451 Ron Davis .02 .10
452 Mark Clear .02 .10
453 Bill Russell .07 .20
454 Lou Whitaker .07 .20
455 Dan Graham .02 .10
456 Reggie Cleveland .02 .10
457 Sammy Stewart .02 .10
458 Pete Vuckovich .02 .10
459 John Wockenfuss .02 .10
460 Glenn Hoffman .02 .10
461 Willie Randolph .07 .20
462 Fernando Valenzuela .30 .75
463 Ron Hassey .02 .10
464 Paul Splittorff .02 .10
465 Rob Picciolo .02 .10
466 Larry Parrish .02 .10
467 Johnny Grubb .02 .10
468 Dan Ford .02 .10
469 Silvio Martinez .02 .10
470 Kiko Garcia .02 .10
471 Bob Boone .07 .20
472 Luis Salazar .02 .10
473 Randy Niemann UER .02 .10
Card says Pirate, but in an Astro uniform
474 Tom Griffin .02 .10
475 Phil Niekro .07 .20
476 Hubie Brooks .02 .10
477 Dick Tidrow .02 .10
478 Jim Beattie .02 .10
479 Damaso Garcia .02 .10
480 Mickey Hatcher .02 .10
481 Joe Price .02 .10
482 Ed Farmer .02 .10
483 Eddie Murray .30 .75
484 Ben Oglivie .07 .20
485 Kevin Saucier .02 .10
486 Bobby Murcer .07 .20
487 Bill Campbell .02 .10
488 Reggie Smith .07 .20
489 Wayne Garland .02 .10
490 Jim Wright .02 .10
491 Billy Martin MG .15 .40
492 Jim Fanning MG .02 .10
493 Don Baylor .07 .20
494 Rick Honeycutt .02 .10
495 Carlton Fisk .15 .40
496 Denny Walling .02 .10
497 Bake McBride .07 .20
498 Darrell Porter .02 .10
499 Gene Richards .02 .10
500 Ron Oester .02 .10
501 Ken Dayley .02 .10
502 Jason Thompson .02 .10
503 Milt May .02 .10
504 Doug Bird .02 .10
505 Bruce Bochte .02 .10
506 Neil Allen .02 .10
507 Joey McLaughlin .02 .10
508 Butch Wynegar .02 .10
509 Gary Roenicke .02 .10
510 Robin Yount .50 1.25
511 Dave Tobik .02 .10
512 Rich Gedman .20 .50
513 Gene Nelson .02 .10
514 Rick Monday .07 .20
515 Miguel Dilone .02 .10
516 Clint Hurdle .02 .10
517 Jeff Newman .02 .10
518 Grant Jackson .02 .10
519 Andy Hassler .02 .10
520 Pat Putnam .02 .10
521 Greg Pryor .02 .10
522 Tony Scott .02 .10
523 Steve Mura .02 .10
524 Johnnie LeMaster .02 .10
525 Dick Ruthven .02 .10
526 John McNamara MG .02 .10
527 Larry McWilliams .02 .10
528 Johnny Ray RC .20 .50
529 Pat Tabler .02 .10
530 Tom Herr .02 .10
531A SD Chicken .40 1.00
ERR (Without TM)
531B San Diego Chicken .40 1.00
COR (With TM)
532 Sal Butera .02 .10
533 Mike Griffin .02 .10
534 Kelvin Moore .02 .10
535 Reggie Jackson .15 .40
536 Ed Romero .02 .10
537 Derrel Thomas .02 .10
538 Mike O'Berry .02 .10
539 Jack O'Connor .02 .10
540 Bob Ojeda RC .20 .50
541 Roy Lee Jackson .02 .10
542 Lynn Jones .02 .10
543 Gaylord Perry .07 .20
544A Phil Garner ERR .07 .20
(Reverse negative)
544B Phil Garner COR .07 .20
545 Garry Templeton .07 .20
546 Rafael Ramirez .02 .10
547 Jeff Reardon .07 .20
548 Ron Guidry .07 .20
549 Tim Laudner .02 .10
550 John Henry Johnson .02 .10
551 Chris Bando .02 .10
552 Bobby Brown .02 .10
553 Larry Bradford .02 .10
554 Scott Fletcher RC .20 .50
555 Jerry Royster .02 .10
556 Shooty Babitt UER .02 .10
(Spelled Babbitt
on front)
557 Kent Hrbek RC .40 1.00
558 Ron Guidry .07 .20
Tommy John
559 Mark Bomback .02 .10
560 Julio Valdez .02 .10
561 Buck Martinez .02 .10
562 Mike A. Marshall RC .20 .50
563 Rennie Stennett .02 .10
564 Steve Crawford .02 .10
565 Bob Babcock .02 .10
566 Johnny Podres CO .07 .20
567 Paul Serna .02 .10
568 Harold Baines .07 .20
569 Dave LaRoche .02 .10
570 Lee May .02 .10
571 Gary Ward .02 .10
572 John Denny .02 .10
573 Roy Smalley .02 .10
574 Bob Brenly RC .40 1.00
575 Reggie Jackson .07 .20
Dave Winfield
576 Luis Pujols .02 .10
577 Butch Hobson .02 .10
578 Harvey Kuenn MG .02 .10
579 Cal Ripken Sr. CO .07 .20
580 Juan Berenguer .02 .10
581 Benny Ayala .02 .10
582 Vance Law .02 .10
583 Rick Leach .02 .10
584 George Frazier .02 .10
585 Phillies Finest .60 1.50
Pete Rose
Mike Schmidt
586 Joe Rudi .07 .20
587 Juan Beniquez .02 .10
588 Luis DeLeon .02 .10
589 Craig Swan .02 .10
590 Dave Chalk .02 .10
591 Billy Gardner MG .02 .10
592 Sal Bando .07 .20
593 Bert Campaneris .07 .20
594 Steve Kemp .02 .10
595A Randy Lerch ERR .15 .40
(Braves)
595B Randy Lerch COR .02 .10
(Brewers)
596 Bryan Clark RC .05 .15
597 Dave Ford .02 .10
598 Mike Scioscia .07 .20
599 John Lowenstein .02 .10
600 Rene Lachemann MG .02 .10
601 Mick Kelleher .02 .10
602 Ron Jackson .02 .10
603 Jerry Koosman .07 .20
604 Dave Goltz .02 .10
605 Ellis Valentine .02 .10
606 Lonnie Smith .02 .10
607 Joaquin Andujar .07 .20
608 Garry Hancock .02 .10
609 Jerry Turner .02 .10
610 Bob Bonner .02 .10
611 Jim Dwyer .02 .10
612 Terry Bulling .02 .10
613 Joel Youngblood .02 .10
614 Larry Milbourne .02 .10
615 Gene Roof UER .02 .10
(Name on front
is Phil Roof)
616 Keith Drumwright .02 .10
617 Dave Rosello .02 .10
618 Rickey Keeton .02 .10
619 Dennis Lamp .02 .10
620 Sid Monge .02 .10
621 Jerry White .02 .10
622 Luis Aguayo .02 .10
623 Jamie Easterly .02 .10
624 Steve Sax RC .40 1.00
625 Dave Roberts .02 .10
626 Rick Bosetti .02 .10
627 Terry Francona RC 1.25 3.00
628 Tom Seaver .30 .75
Johnny Bench
629 Paul Mirabella .02 .10
630 Rance Mulliniks .02 .10
631 Kevin Hickey RC .05 .15
632 Reid Nichols .02 .10
633 Dave Geisel .02 .10
634 Ken Griffey .07 .20
635 Bob Lemon MG .15 .40
636 Orlando Sanchez .02 .10
637 Bill Almon .02 .10
638 Danny Ainge .07 .20
639 Willie Stargell .15 .40
640 Bob Sykes .02 .10
641 Ed Lynch .02 .10
642 John Ellis .02 .10
643 Ferguson Jenkins .07 .20
644 Lenn Sakata .02 .10
645 Julio Gonzalez .02 .10
646 Jesse Orosco .02 .10
647 Jerry Dybzinski .02 .10
648 Tommy Davis CO .07 .20
649 Ron Gardenhire RC .20 .50
650 Felipe Alou CO .07 .20
651 Harvey Haddix CO .07 .20
652 Willie Upshaw .20 .50
653 Bill Madlock .07 .20
654A DK Checklist 1-26 .15 .40
ERR (Unnumbered)
(With Trammel)
654B DK Checklist 1-26 .07 .20
COR (Unnumbered)
(With Trammell)
655 Checklist 27-130 .07 .20
(Unnumbered)
656 Checklist 131-234 .07 .20
(Unnumbered)
657 Checklist 235-338 .07 .20
(Unnumbered)
658 Checklist 339-442 .07 .20
(Unnumbered)
659 Checklist 443-544 .07 .20
(Unnumbered)
660 Checklist 545-653 .07 .20
(Unnumbered)

1983 Donruss

The 1983 Donruss baseball set leads off with a 26-card Diamond Kings (DK) series. Of the remaining 634 standard-size cards, two are combination cards, one portrays the San Diego Chicken, one shows the completed Ty Cobb puzzle, and seven are unnumbered checklist cards. The seven unnumbered checklist cards are arbitrarily assigned numbers 654 through 660 and are listed at the end of the list below. All cards measure the standard size. Card fronts feature full color photos around a framed white broder. Several printing variations are available but the complete set price below includes only the more common of each variation pair. Cards were issued in 15-card packs which included a three-piece Ty Cobb puzzle panel (21 different panels were needed to complete the puzzle). Notable Rookie Cards include Wade Boggs, Tony Gwynn and Ryne Sandberg.

COMPLETE SET (660) 30.00 60.00
COMP.FACT.SET (660) 40.00 80.00
COMP.COBB PUZZLE 2.00 5.00
1 Fernando Valenzuela DK .07 .20
2 Rollie Fingers DK .07 .20
3 Reggie Jackson DK .15 .40
4 Jim Palmer DK .07 .20
5 Jack Morris DK .07 .20
6 George Foster DK .07 .20
7 Jim Sundberg DK .07 .20
8 Willie Stargell DK .15 .40
9 Dave Stieb DK .07 .20
10 Joe Niekro DK .02 .10
11 Rickey Henderson DK .60 1.50
12 Dale Murphy DK .15 .40
13 Toby Harrah DK .07 .20
14 Bill Buckner DK .07 .20
15 Willie Wilson DK .07 .20
16 Steve Carlton DK .15 .40
17 Ron Guidry DK .07 .20
18 Steve Rogers DK .07 .20
19 Kent Hrbek DK .07 .20
20 Keith Hernandez DK .07 .20
21 Floyd Bannister DK .02 .10
22 Johnny Bench DK .30 .75
23 Britt Burns DK .02 .10
24 Joe Morgan DK .07 .20
25 Carl Yastrzemski DK .30 .75
26 Terry Kennedy DK .02 .10
27 Gary Roenicke .02 .10
28 Dwight Bernard .02 .10
29 Pat Underwood .02 .10
30 Gary Allenson .02 .10
31 Ron Guidry .07 .20
32 Burt Hooton .02 .10
33 Chris Bando .02 .10
34 Vida Blue .07 .20
35 Rickey Henderson .60 1.50
36 Ray Burris .02 .10
37 John Butcher .02 .10
38 Don Aase .02 .10
39 Jerry Koosman .07 .20
40 Bruce Sutter .15 .40
41 Jose Cruz .07 .20
42 Pete Rose 1.00 2.50
43 Cesar Cedeno .07 .20
44 Floyd Chiffer .02 .10
45 Larry McWilliams .02 .10
46 Alan Fowlkes .02 .10
47 Dale Murphy .15 .40
48 Doug Bird .02 .10
49 Hubie Brooks .02 .10
50 Floyd Bannister .02 .10
51 Jack O'Connor .02 .10
52 Steve Senteney .02 .10
53 Gary Gaetti RC .40 1.00
54 Damaso Garcia .02 .10
55 Gene Nelson .02 .10
56 Mookie Wilson .07 .20
57 Allen Ripley .02 .10
58 Bob Horner .07 .20
59 Tony Pena .02 .10
60 Gary Lavelle .02 .10
61 Tim Lollar .02 .10
62 Frank Pastore .02 .10
63 Garry Maddox .02 .10
64 Bob Forsch .02 .10
65 Harry Spillman .02 .10
66 Geoff Zahn .02 .10
67 Salome Barojas .02 .10
68 David Palmer .02 .10
69 Charlie Hough .07 .20
70 Dan Quisenberry .02 .10
71 Tony Armas .07 .20
72 Rick Sutcliffe .07 .20
73 Steve Balboni .02 .10
74 Jerry Remy .02 .10
75 Mike Scioscia .07 .20
76 John Wockenfuss .02 .10
77 Jim Palmer .07 .20
78 Rollie Fingers .07 .20
79 Joe Nolan .02 .10
80 Pete Vuckovich .02 .10
81 Rick Leach .02 .10
82 Rick Miller .02 .10
83 Graig Nettles .07 .20
84 Ron Cey .07 .20
85 Miguel Dilone .02 .10
86 John Wathan .02 .10
87 Kelvin Moore .02 .10
88A Byrn Smith ERR .07 .20
(Sic, Bryn)
88B Bryn Smith COR .15 .40
89 Dave Hostetler .02 .10
90 Rod Carew .15 .40
91 Lonnie Smith .02 .10
92 Bob Knepper .02 .10
93 Marty Bystrom .02 .10
94 Chris Welsh .02 .10
95 Jason Thompson .02 .10
96 Tom O'Malley .02 .10
97 Phil Niekro .07 .20
98 Neil Allen .02 .10
99 Bill Buckner .07 .20
100 Ed VandeBerg .02 .10
101 Jim Clancy .02 .10
102 Robert Castillo .02 .10
103 Bruce Berenyi .02 .10
104 Carlton Fisk .15 .40
105 Mike Flanagan .02 .10
106 Cecil Cooper .07 .20
107 Jack Morris .07 .20
108 Mike Morgan .02 .10
109 Luis Aponte .02 .10
110 Pedro Guerrero .07 .20
111 Len Barker .02 .10
112 Willie Wilson .07 .20
113 Dave Beard .02 .10
114 Mike Gates .02 .10
115 Reggie Jackson .15 .40
116 George Wright RC .20 .50
117 Vance Law .02 .10
118 Nolan Ryan 1.50 4.00
119 Mike Krukow .02 .10
120 Ozzie Smith .50 1.25
121 Broderick Perkins .02 .10
122 Tom Seaver .30 .75
123 Chris Chambliss .07 .20
124 Chuck Tanner MG .02 .10
125 Johnnie LeMaster .02 .10
126 Mel Hall RC .20 .50
127 Bruce Bochte .02 .10
128 Charlie Puleo .02 .10
129 Luis Leal .02 .10
130 John Pacella .02 .10
131 Glenn Gulliver .02 .10
132 Don Money .02 .10
133 Dave Rozema .02 .10
134 Bruce Hurst .02 .10
135 Rudy May .02 .10
136 Tom Lasorda MG .15 .40
137 Dan Spillner UER .02 .10
(Photo actually
Ed Whitson)
138 Jerry Martin .02 .10
139 Mike Norris .02 .10
140 Al Oliver .07 .20
141 Daryl Sconiers .02 .10
142 Lamar Johnson .02 .10
143 Harold Baines .07 .20
144 Alan Ashby .02 .10
145 Garry Templeton .07 .20
146 Al Holland .02 .10
147 Bo Diaz .02 .10
148 Dave Concepcion .07 .20
149 Rick Camp .02 .10
150 Jim Morrison .02 .10
151 Randy Martz .02 .10
152 Keith Hernandez .07 .20
153 John Lowenstein .02 .10
154 Mike Caldwell .02 .10
155 Milt Wilcox .02 .10
156 Rich Gedman .02 .10
157 Rich Gossage .07 .20
158 Jerry Reuss .02 .10
159 Ron Hassey .02 .10
160 Larry Gura .02 .10
161 Dwayne Murphy .02 .10
162 Woodie Fryman .02 .10
163 Steve Comer .02 .10
164 Ken Forsch .02 .10
165 Dennis Lamp .02 .10
166 David Green RC .20 .50
167 Terry Puhl .02 .10
168 Mike Schmidt .75 2.00
(Wearing 37
rather than 20)
169 Eddie Milner .02 .10
170 John Curtis .02 .10
171 Don Robinson .02 .10
172 Rich Gale .02 .10
173 Steve Bedrosian .02 .10
174 Willie Hernandez .02 .10
175 Ron Gardenhire .02 .10
176 Jim Beattie .02 .10
177 Tim Laudner .02 .10
178 Buck Martinez .02 .10
179 Kent Hrbek .07 .20
180 Alfredo Griffin .02 .10
181 Larry Andersen .02 .10
182 Pete Falcone .02 .10
183 Jody Davis .02 .10
184 Glenn Hubbard .02 .10
185 Dale Berra .02 .10
186 Greg Minton .02 .10
187 Gary Lucas .02 .10
188 Dave Van Gorder .02 .10
189 Bob Dernier .02 .10
190 Willie McGee RC .60 1.50
191 Dickie Thon .02 .10
192 Bob Boone .07 .20
193 Britt Burns .02 .10
194 Jeff Reardon .07 .20
195 Jon Matlack .02 .10
196 Don Slaught RC .20 .50
197 Fred Stanley .02 .10
198 Rick Manning .02 .10
199 Dave Righetti .07 .20
200 Dave Stapleton .02 .10
201 Steve Yeager .07 .20
202 Enos Cabell .02 .10
203 Sammy Stewart .02 .10
204 Moose Haas .02 .10
205 Lenn Sakata .02 .10
206 Charlie Moore .02 .10
207 Alan Trammell .07 .20
208 Jim Rice .07 .20
209 Roy Smalley .02 .10
210 Bill Russell .07 .20
211 Andre Thornton .02 .10
212 Willie Aikens .02 .10
213 Dave McKay .02 .10
214 Tim Blackwell .02 .10
215 Buddy Bell .07 .20
216 Doug DeCinces .02 .10
217 Tom Herr .02 .10
218 Frank LaCorte .02 .10
219 Steve Carlton .15 .40
220 Terry Kennedy .02 .10
221 Mike Easler .02 .10
222 Jack Clark .07 .20
223 Gene Garber .02 .10
224 Scott Holman .02 .10
225 Mike Proly .02 .10
226 Terry Bulling .02 .10
227 Jerry Garvin .02 .10
228 Ron Davis .02 .10
229 Tom Hume .02 .10
230 Marc Hill .02 .10
231 Dennis Martinez .07 .20
232 Jim Gantner .02 .10
233 Larry Pashnick .02 .10
234 Dave Collins .02 .10
235 Tom Burgmeier .02 .10
236 Ken Landreaux .02 .10
237 John Denny .02 .10
238 Hal McRae .07 .20
239 Matt Keough .02 .10
240 Doug Flynn .02 .10
241 Fred Lynn .07 .20
242 Billy Sample .02 .10
243 Tom Paciorek .02 .10
244 Joe Sambito .02 .10
245 Sid Monge .02 .10
246 Ken Oberkfell .02 .10
247 Joe Pittman UER .02 .10
(Photo actually
Juan Eichelberger)
248 Mario Soto .07 .20
249 Claudell Washington .02 .10
250 Rick Rhoden .02 .10
251 Darrell Evans .07 .20
252 Steve Henderson .02 .10
253 Manny Castillo .02 .10
254 Craig Swan .02 .10
255 Joey McLaughlin .02 .10
256 Pete Redfern .02 .10
257 Ken Singleton .07 .20
258 Robin Yount .50 1.25
259 Elias Sosa .02 .10
260 Bob Ojeda .02 .10
261 Bobby Murcer .07 .20
262 Candy Maldonado RC .20 .50
263 Rick Waits .02 .10
264 Greg Pryor .02 .10
265 Bob Owchinko .02 .10
266 Chris Speier .02 .10
267 Bruce Kison .02 .10
268 Mark Wagner .02 .10
269 Steve Kemp .02 .10
270 Phil Garner .07 .20
271 Gene Richards .02 .10
272 Renie Martin .02 .10
273 Dave Roberts .02 .10
274 Dan Driessen .02 .10
275 Rufino Linares .02 .10
276 Lee Lacy .02 .10
277 Ryne Sandberg RC 4.00 10.00
278 Darrell Porter .02 .10
279 Cal Ripken 2.50 6.00
280 Jamie Easterly .02 .10
281 Bill Fahey .02 .10
282 Glenn Hoffman .02 .10
283 Willie Randolph .07 .20
284 Fernando Valenzuela .07 .20
285 Alan Bannister .02 .10
286 Paul Splittorff .02 .10
287 Joe Rudi .07 .20
288 Bill Gullickson .02 .10
289 Danny Darwin .02 .10
290 Andy Hassler .02 .10
291 Ernesto Escarrega .02 .10
292 Steve Mura .02 .10
293 Tony Scott .02 .10
294 Manny Trillo .02 .10
295 Greg Harris .02 .10
296 Luis DeLeon .02 .10
297 Kent Tekulve .02 .10
298 Atlee Hammaker .02 .10
299 Bruce Benedict .02 .10
300 Fergie Jenkins .07 .20
301 Dave Kingman .07 .20
302 Bill Caudill .02 .10
303 John Castino .02 .10
304 Ernie Whitt .02 .10
305 Randy Johnson .02 .10
306 Garth Iorg .02 .10
307 Gaylord Perry .07 .20
308 Ed Lynch .02 .10
309 Keith Moreland .02 .10
310 Rafael Ramirez .02 .10
311 Bill Madlock .07 .20
312 Milt May .02 .10
313 John Montefusco .02 .10
314 Wayne Krenchicki .02 .10
315 George Vukovich .02 .10
316 Joaquin Andujar .07 .20
317 Craig Reynolds .02 .10
318 Rick Burleson .02 .10
319 Richard Dotson .02 .10
320 Steve Rogers .07 .20
321 Dave Schmidt .02 .10
322 Bud Black RC .20 .50
323 Jeff Burroughs .02 .10
324 Von Hayes .02 .10
325 Butch Wynegar .02 .10
326 Carl Yastrzemski .50 1.25
327 Ron Roenicke .02 .10
328 Howard Johnson RC .40 1.00
329 Rick Dempsey UER .02 .10
(Posing as a left-
handed batter)
330A Jim Slaton .02 .10
(Bio printed
black on white)
330B Jim Slaton .07 .20
(Bio printed
black on yellow)
331 Benny Ayala .02 .10
332 Ted Simmons .07 .20
333 Lou Whitaker .07 .20
334 Chuck Rainey .02 .10
335 Lou Piniella .07 .20
336 Steve Sax .07 .20
337 Toby Harrah .07 .20
338 George Brett .75 2.00
339 Dave Lopes .07 .20
340 Gary Carter .07 .20
341 John Grubb .02 .10
342 Tim Foli .02 .10
343 Jim Kaat .07 .20
344 Mike LaCoss .02 .10
345 Larry Christenson .02 .10
346 Juan Bonilla .02 .10
347 Omar Moreno .02 .10
348 Chili Davis .07 .20
349 Tommy Boggs .02 .10
350 Rusty Staub .07 .20
351 Bump Wills .02 .10
352 Rick Sweet .02 .10
353 Jim Gott RC .20 .50
354 Terry Felton .02 .10
355 Jim Kern .02 .10
356 Bill Almon UER .02 .10
(Expos/Mets in 1983,
not Padres/Mets)
357 Tippy Martinez .02 .10
358 Roy Howell .02 .10
359 Dan Petry .02 .10
360 Jerry Mumphrey .02 .10
361 Mark Clear .02 .10
362 Mike Marshall .02 .10
363 Lary Sorensen .02 .10
364 Amos Otis .07 .20
365 Rick Langford .02 .10
366 Brad Mills .02 .10
367 Brian Downing .07 .20
368 Mike Richardt .02 .10
369 Aurelio Rodriguez .02 .10
370 Dave Smith .02 .10
371 Tug McGraw .07 .20
372 Doug Bair .02 .10
373 Ruppert Jones .02 .10
374 Alex Trevino .02 .10
375 Ken Dayley .02 .10
376 Rod Scurry .02 .10
377 Bob Brenly .02 .10
378 Scot Thompson .02 .10
379 Julio Cruz .02 .10
380 John Stearns .02 .10
381 Dale Murray .02 .10
382 Frank Viola RC .60 1.50
383 Al Bumbry .02 .10
384 Ben Oglivie .07 .20
385 Dave Tobik .02 .10
386 Bob Stanley .02 .10
387 Andre Robertson .02 .10
388 Jorge Orta .02 .10
389 Ed Whitson .02 .10
390 Don Hood .02 .10
391 Tom Underwood .02 .10
392 Tim Wallach .07 .20
393 Steve Renko .02 .10
394 Mickey Rivers .02 .10
395 Greg Luzinski .07 .20
396 Art Howe .02 .10
397 Alan Wiggins .02 .10
398 Jim Barr .02 .10
399 Ivan DeJesus .02 .10
400 Tom Lawless .02 .10
401 Bob Walk .02 .10
402 Jimmy Smith .02 .10
403 Lee Smith .15 .40
404 George Hendrick .07 .20
405 Eddie Murray .30 .75
406 Marshall Edwards .02 .10
407 Lance Parrish .07 .20
408 Carney Lansford .07 .20
409 Dave Winfield .07 .20
410 Bob Welch .07 .20
411 Larry Milbourne .02 .10
412 Dennis Leonard .02 .10
413 Dan Meyer .02 .10
414 Charlie Lea .02 .10
415 Rick Honeycutt .02 .10
416 Mike Witt .02 .10
417 Steve Trout .02 .10
418 Glenn Brummer .02 .10
419 Denny Walling .02 .10
420 Gary Matthews .07 .20
421 Charlie Leibrandt UER .02 .10
(Liebrandt on
front of card)
422 J.Eichelberger UER .02 .10
Photo actually
Joe Pittman
423 Cecilio Guante UER .02 .10
(Listed as Matt
on card)
424 Bill Laskey .02 .10
425 Jerry Royster .02 .10
426 Dickie Noles .02 .10
427 George,Foster .07 .20
428 Mike Moore RC .20 .50
429 Gary Ward .02 .10
430 Barry Bonnell .02 .10
431 Ron Washington RC .10 .25
432 Rance Mulliniks .02 .10
433 Mike Stanton .02 .10
434 Jesse Orosco .02 .10
435 Larry Bowa .07 .20
436 Biff Pocoroba .02 .10

437 Johnny Ray .02 .10
438 Joe Morgan .07 .20
439 Eric Show RC .20 .50
440 Larry Biittner .02 .10
441 Greg Gross .02 .10
442 Gene Tenace .07 .20
443 Danny Heep .02 .10
444 Bobby Clark .02 .10
445 Kevin Hickey .02 .10
446 Scott Sanderson .02 .10
447 Frank Tanana .07 .20
448 Cesar Geronimo .02 .10
449 Jimmy Sexton .02 .10
450 Mike Hargrove .02 .10
451 Doyle Alexander .02 .10
452 Dwight Evans .15 .40
453 Terry Forster .07 .20
454 Tom Brookens .02 .10
455 Rich Dauer .02 .10
456 Rob Picciolo .02 .10
457 Terry Crowley .02 .10
458 Ned Yost .02 .10
459 Kirk Gibson .07 .20
460 Reid Nichols .02 .10
461 Oscar Gamble .02 .10
462 Dusty Baker .07 .20
463 Jack Perconte .02 .10
464 Frank White .07 .20
465 Mickey Klutts .02 .10
466 Warren Cromartie .02 .10
467 Larry Parrish .02 .10
468 Bobby Grich .07 .20
469 Dane Iorg .02 .10
470 Joe Niekro .02 .10
471 Ed Farmer .02 .10
472 Tim Flannery .02 .10
473 Dave Parker .07 .20
474 Jeff Leonard .02 .10
475 Al Hrabosky .02 .10
476 Ron Hodges .02 .10
477 Leon Durham .02 .10
478 Jim Essian .02 .10
479 Roy Lee Jackson .02 .10
480 Brad Havens .02 .10
481 Joe Price .02 .10
482 Tony Bernazard .02 .10
483 Scott McGregor .02 .10
484 Paul Molitor .07 .20
485 Mike Ivie .02 .10
486 Ken Griffey .07 .20
487 Dennis Eckersley .15 .40
488 Steve Garvey .07 .20
489 Mike Fischlin .02 .10
490 U.L. Washington .02 .10
491 Steve McCatty .02 .10
492 Roy Johnson .02 .10
493 Don Baylor .07 .20
494 Bobby Johnson .02 .10
495 Mike Squires .02 .10
496 Bert Roberge .02 .10
497 Dick Ruthven .02 .10
498 Tito Landrum .02 .10
499 Sixto Lezcano .02 .10
500 Johnny Bench .30 .75
501 Larry Whisenton .02 .10
502 Manny Sarmiento .02 .10
503 Fred Breining .02 .10
504 Bill Campbell .02 .10
505 Todd Cruz .02 .10
506 Bob Bailor .02 .10
507 Dave Stieb .07 .20
508 Al Williams .02 .10
509 Dan Ford .02 .10
510 Gorman Thomas .07 .20
511 Chet Lemon .07 .20
512 Mike Torrez .02 .10
513 Shane Rawley .02 .10
514 Mark Belanger .02 .10
515 Rodney Craig .02 .10
516 Onix Concepcion .02 .10
517 Mike Heath .02 .10
518 Andre Dawson UER .07 .20
(Middle name Fernando,
should be Nolan)
519 Luis Sanchez .02 .10
520 Terry Bogener .02 .10
521 Rudy Law .02 .10
522 Ray Knight .07 .20
523 Joe Lefebvre .02 .10
524 Jim Wohlford .02 .10
525 Julio Franco RC 2.50 6.00
526 Ron Oester .02 .10
527 Rick Mahler .02 .10
528 Steve Nicosia .02 .10
529 Junior Kennedy .02 .10
530A Whitey Herzog MG .07 .20
(Bio printed
black on white)
530B Whitey Herzog MG .07 .20
(Bio printed
black on yellow)
531A Don Sutton .07 .20
(Blue border
on photo)
531B Don Sutton .07 .20
(Green border
on photo)
532 Mark Brouhard .02 .10
533A S.Anderson MG .07 .20
Bio printed
black on white
533B S.Anderson MG .07 .20
Bio printed
black on yellow
534 Roger LaFrancois .02 .10
535 George Frazier .02 .10
536 Tom Niedenfuer .02 .10
537 Ed Glynn .02 .10
538 Lee May .02 .10
539 Bob Kearney .02 .10
540 Tim Raines .07 .20
541 Paul Mirabella .02 .10
542 Luis Tiant .07 .20
543 Ron LeFlore .07 .20
544 Dave LaPoint .02 .10
545 Randy Moffitt .02 .10
546 Luis Aguayo .02 .10
547 Brad Lesley .05 .15
548 Luis Salazar .02 .10
549 John Candelaria .02 .10
550 Dave Bergman .02 .10

551 Bob Watson .02 .10
552 Pat Tabler .02 .10
553 Brent Gaff .02 .10
554 Al Cowens .02 .10
555 Tom Brunansky .07 .20
556 Lloyd Moseby .02 .10
557A Pascual Perez ERR .75 2.00
(Twins in glove)
557B Pascual Perez COR .07 .20
(Braves in glove)
558 Willie Upshaw .02 .10
559 Richie Zisk .02 .10
560 Pat Zachry .02 .10
561 Jay Johnstone .02 .10
562 Carlos Diaz RC .05 .15
563 John Tudor .07 .20
564 Frank Robinson MG .15 .40
565 Dave Edwards .02 .10
566 Paul Householder .02 .10
567 Ron Reed .02 .10
568 Mike Ramsey .02 .10
569 Kiko Garcia .02 .10
570 Tommy John .07 .20
571 Tony LaRussa MG .07 .20
572 Joel Youngblood .02 .10
573 Wayne Tolleson .02 .10
574 Keith Creel .02 .10
575 Billy Martin MG .15 .40
576 Jerry Dybzinski .02 .10
577 Rick Cerone .02 .10
578 Tony Perez .15 .40
579 Greg Brock .02 .10
580 Glenn Wilson .20 .50
581 Tim Stoddard .02 .10
582 Bob McClure .02 .10
583 Jim Dwyer .02 .10
584 Ed Romero .02 .10
585 Larry Herndon .02 .10
586 Wade Boggs RC 4.00 10.00
587 Jay Howell .02 .10
588 Dave Stewart .07 .20
589 Bert Blyleven .07 .20
590 Dick Howser MG .02 .10
591 Wayne Gross .02 .10
592 Terry Francona .07 .20
593 Don Werner .02 .10
594 Bill Stein .02 .10
595 Jesse Barfield .07 .20
596 Bob Molinaro .02 .10
597 Mike Vail .02 .10
598 Tony Gwynn RC 6.00 15.00
599 Gary Rajsich .02 .10
600 Jerry Ujdur .02 .10
601 Cliff Johnson .02 .10
602 Jerry White .02 .10
603 Bryan Clark .02 .10
604 Joe Ferguson .02 .10
605 Guy Sularz .02 .10
606A Ozzie Virgil .07 .20
(Green border
on photo)
606B Ozzie Virgil .07 .20
(Orange border
on photo)
607 Terry Harper .02 .10
608 Harvey Kuenn MG .02 .10
609 Jim Sundberg .07 .20
610 Willie Stargell .15 .40
611 Reggie Smith .07 .20
612 Rob Wilfong .02 .10
613 Joe Niekro .07 .20
Phil Niekro
614 Lee Elia MG .02 .10
615 Mickey Hatcher .02 .10
616 Jerry Hairston .02 .10
617 John Martin .02 .10
618 Wally Backman .02 .10
619 Storm Davis RC .20 .50
620 Alan Knicely .02 .10
621 John Stuper .02 .10
622 Matt Sinatro .02 .10
623 Geno Petralli .20 .50
624 Duane Walker .02 .10
625 Dick Williams MG .02 .10
626 Pat Corrales MG .02 .10
627 Vern Ruhle .02 .10
628 Joe Torre MG .07 .20
629 Anthony Johnson .02 .10
630 Steve Howe .02 .10
631 Gary Woods .02 .10
632 LaMarr Hoyt .02 .10
633 Steve Swisher .02 .10
634 Terry Leach .02 .10
635 Jeff Newman .02 .10
636 Brett Butler .07 .20
637 Gary Gray .02 .10
638 Lee Mazzilli .07 .20
639A Ron Jackson ERR 8.00 20.00
(A's in glove)
639B Ron Jackson COR .02 .10
(Angels in glove,
red border
on photo)
639C Ron Jackson COR .15 .40
(Angels in glove,
green border
on photo)
640 Juan Beniquez .02 .10
641 Dave Rucker .02 .10
642 Luis Pujols .02 .10
643 Rick Monday .07 .20
644 Hosken Powell .02 .10
645 The Chicken .15 .40
646 Dave Engle .02 .10
647 Dick Davis .02 .10
648 Frank Robinson .15 .40
Vida Blue
Joe Morgan
649 Al Chambers .02 .10
650 Jesus Vega .02 .10
651 Jeff Jones .02 .10
652 Marvis Foley .02 .10
653 Ty Cobb Puzzle Card .30 .75
654A Dick Perez/Diamond .15 .40
King Checklist 1-26
(Unnumbered) ERR
(Word 'checklist'
omitted from back)
654B Dick Perez/Diamond .15 .40
King Checklist 1-26
(Unnumbered) COR
(Word 'checklist'
is on back)
655 Checklist 27-130 .02 .10
(Unnumbered)
656 Checklist 131-234 .02 .10
(Unnumbered)
657 Checklist 235-338 .02 .10
(Unnumbered)
658 Checklist 339-442 .02 .10
(Unnumbered)
659 Checklist 443-544 .02 .10
(Unnumbered)
660 Checklist 545-653 .02 .10
(Unnumbered)

1984 Donruss

The 1984 Donruss set contains a total of 660 standard-size cards; however, only 658 are numbered. The first 26 cards in the set are again Diamond Kings (DK). A new feature, Rated Rookies (RR), was introduced with this set with Bill Madden's 20 selections comprising numbers 27 through 46. Two "Living Legend" cards designated A (featuring Gaylord Perry and Rollie Fingers) and B (featuring Johnny Bench and Carl Yastrzemski) were issued as bonus cards in wax packs, but were not issued in the factory sets sold to hobby dealers. The seven unnumbered checklist cards are arbitrarily assigned numbers 652 through 658 and are listed at the end of the list below. The attractive card front designs changed considerably from the previous two years. This set has since grown in stature to be recognized as one of the finest produced in the 1980's. The backs contain statistics and are printed in green and black ink. The cards, issued amongst other ways in 15 card packs which had a 30 cent SRP, were distributed with a three-piece puzzle panel of Duke Snider. There are no extra variation cards included in the complete set price below. The variation cards apparently resulted from a different printing for the factory sets as the Darling and Stenhouse no number variations as well as the Perez-Steele errors were corrected in the factory sets which were released later in the year. The factory sets were shipped 15 to a case. The Diamond King cards found in packs spelled Perez-Steele as Perez-Steel. Rookie Cards in this set include Joe Carter, Don Mattingly, Darryl Strawberry, and Andy Van Slyke. The Joe Carter card is almost never found well centered.

COMPLETE SET (660) 70.00 120.00
COMP.FACT.SET (658) 70.00 120.00
COMP.SNIDER PUZZLE 2.00 5.00
1 Robin Yount DK COR 1.00 2.50
1A Robin Yount DK ERR 2.00 5.00
2 Dave Concepcion DK .30 .75
COR
2A Dave Concepcion DK .30 .75
ERR (Perez Steel)
3 Dwayne Murphy DK .08 .25
COR
3A Dwayne Murphy DK .08 .25
ERR (Perez Steel)
4 John Castino DK COR .08 .25
4A John Castino DK ERR .08 .25
(Perez Steel)
5 Leon Durham DK COR .30 .75
5A Leon Durham DK ERR .08 .25
(Perez Steel)
6 Rusty Staub DK COR .30 .75
6A Rusty Staub DK ERR .30 .75
(Perez Steel)
7 Jack Clark DK COR .30 .75
7A Jack Clark DK ERR .30 .75
(Perez Steel)
8 Dave Dravecky DK .08 .25
COR
8A Dave Dravecky DK .08 .25
ERR (Perez Steel)
9 Al Oliver DK COR .30 .75
9A Al Oliver DK ERR .30 .75
(Perez Steel)
10 Dave Righetti DK .30 .75
COR
10A Dave Righetti DK .30 .75
ERR (Perez Steel)
11 Hal McRae DK COR .30 .75
11A Hal McRae DK ERR .30 .75
(Perez Steel)
12 Ray Knight DK COR .30 .75
12A Ray Knight DK ERR .30 .75
(Perez Steel)
13 Bruce Sutter DK COR .60 1.50
13A Bruce Sutter DK ERR .60 1.50
(Perez Steel)
14 Bob Horner DK COR .30 .75
14A Bob Horner DK ERR .30 .75
(Perez Steel)
15 Lance Parrish DK .30 .75
COR
15A Lance Parrish DK .30 .75
ERR (Perez Steel)
16 Matt Young DK COR .30 .75
16A Matt Young DK ERR .30 .75
(Perez Steel)
17 Fred Lynn DK COR .30 .75
17A Fred Lynn DK ERR .30 .75
(Perez Steel)
(A's logo on back
18 Ron Kittle DK COR .08 .25
18A Ron Kittle DK ERR .08 .25
(Perez Steel)
19 Jim Clancy DK COR .08 .25
19A Jim Clancy DK ERR .08 .25
(Perez Steel)
20 Bill Madlock DK COR .30 .75
20A Bill Madlock DK ERR .30 .75
(Perez Steel)
21 Larry Parrish DK .08 .25
COR

21A Larry Parrish DK .08 .25
ERR (Perez Steel)
22 Eddie Murray DK COR 1.25 3.00
22A Eddie Murray DK ERR 1.25 3.00
23 Mike Schmidt DK COR 2.00 5.00
23A M.Schmidt DK ERR 2.00 5.00
24 Pedro Guerrero DK .30 .75
COR
24A Pedro Guerrero DK .30 .75
ERR (Perez Steel)
25 Andre Thornton DK .08 .25
COR
25A Andre Thornton DK .08 .25
ERR (Perez Steel)
26 Wade Boggs DK COR 1.25 3.00
26A Wade Boggs DK ERR 1.25 3.00
27 Joel Skinner RC .08 .25
28 Tommy Dunbar RC .08 .25
29A Mike Stenhouse RC .08 .25
ERR No number on back
29B Mike Stenhouse RR 1.25 3.00
COR Numbered on back
30A Ron Darling RC .75 2.00
ERR No number on back
30B Ron Darling RR COR 1.25 3.00
(Numbered on back)
31 Dion James RC .08 .25
32 Tony Fernandez RC .75 2.00
33 Angel Salazar RC .08 .25
34 Kevin McReynolds RC .75 2.00
35 Dick Schofield RC .40 1.00
36 Brad Komminsk RC .08 .25
37 Tim Teufel RR RC .40 1.00
38 Doug Frobel RC .08 .25
39 Greg Gagne RC .40 1.00
40 Mike Fuentes RC .08 .25
41 Joe Carter RR RC 3.00 8.00
42 Mike C. Brown RC .08 .25
(Angels OF)
43 Mike Jeffcoat RC .08 .25
44 Sid Fernandez RC .75 2.00
45 Brian Dayett RC .08 .25
46 Chris Smith RC .08 .25
47 Eddie Murray 1.25 3.00
48 Robin Yount 2.00 5.00
49 Lance Parrish .60 1.50
50 Jim Rice .30 .75
51 Dave Winfield .30 .75
52 Fernando Valenzuela .30 .75
53 George Brett 3.00 8.00
54 Rickey Henderson 2.00 5.00
55 Gary Carter .30 .75
56 Buddy Bell .30 .75
57 Reggie Jackson .60 1.50
58 Harold Baines .30 .75
59 Ozzie Smith 2.00 5.00
60 Nolan Ryan UER 6.00 15.00
(Text on back refers to 1972 as
the year he struck out 383;
the year was 1973)
61 Pete Rose 4.00 10.00
62 Ron Oester .08 .25
63 Steve Garvey .30 .75
64 Jason Thompson .08 .25
65 Jack Clark .30 .75
66 Dale Murphy .60 1.50
67 Leon Durham .08 .25
68 Darryl Strawberry RC 3.00 8.00
69 Richie Zisk .08 .25
70 Kent Hrbek .30 .75
71 Dave Stieb .30 .75
72 Ken Schrom .08 .25
73 George Bell .30 .75
74 John Moses .08 .25
75 Ed Lynch .08 .25
76 Chuck Rainey .08 .25
77 Biff Pocoroba .08 .25
78 Cecilio Guante .08 .25
79 Jim Barr .08 .25
80 Kurt Bevacqua .08 .25
81 Tom Foley .08 .25
82 Joe Lefebvre .08 .25
83 Andy Van Slyke RC 1.50 4.00
84 Bob Lillis MG .08 .25
85 Ricky Adams .08 .25
86 Jerry Hairston .08 .25
87 Bob James .08 .25
88 Joe Altobelli MG .08 .25
89 Ed Romero .08 .25
90 John Grubb .08 .25
91 John Henry Johnson .08 .25
92 Juan Espino .08 .25
93 Candy Maldonado .08 .25
94 Andre Thornton .08 .25
95 Onix Concepcion .08 .25
96 Donnie Hill UER .08 .25
(Listed as P,
should be 2B)
97 Andre Dawson UER .30 .75
(Wrong middle name,
should be Nolan)
98 Frank Tanana .30 .75
99 Curtis Wilkerson .08 .25
100 Larry Gura .08 .25
101 Dwayne Murphy .08 .25
102 Tom Brennan .08 .25
103 Dave Righetti .30 .75
104 Steve Sax .08 .25
105 Dan Petry .30 .75
106 Cal Ripken 5.00 12.00
107 Paul Molitor UER .30 .75
('83 stats should
say .270 BA, 608 AB,
and 164 hits)
108 Fred Lynn .30 .75
109 Neil Allen .08 .25
110 Joe Niekro .08 .25
111 Steve Carlton .60 1.50
112 Terry Kennedy .08 .25
113 Bill Madlock .30 .75
114 Chili Davis .30 .75
115 Jim Gantner .08 .25
116 Tom Seaver 1.25 3.00
117 Bill Buckner .30 .75
118 Bill Caudill .08 .25
119 Jim Clancy .08 .25
120 John Castino .08 .25
121 Dave Concepcion .30 .75
122 Greg Luzinski .30 .75
123 Mike Boddicker .08 .25
124 Pete Ladd .08 .25

125 Juan Berenguer .08 .25
126 John Montefusco .08 .25
127 Ed Jurak .08 .25
128 Tom Niedenfuer .08 .25
129 Bert Blyleven .30 .75
130 Bud Black .08 .25
131 Gorman Heimueller .08 .25
132 Dan Schatzeder .08 .25
133 Ron Jackson .08 .25
134 Tom Henke RC .75 2.00
135 Kevin Hickey .08 .25
136 Mike Scott .30 .75
137 Bo Diaz .08 .25
138 Glenn Brummer .08 .25
139 Sid Monge .08 .25
140 Rich Gale .08 .25
141 Brett Butler .30 .75
142 Brian Harper RC .40 1.00
143 John Rabb .08 .25
144 Gary Woods .08 .25
145 Pat Putnam .08 .25
146 Jim Acker .08 .25
147 Mickey Hatcher .08 .25
148 Todd Cruz .08 .25
149 Tom Tellmann .08 .25
150 John Wockenfuss .08 .25
151 Wade Boggs UER 3.00 8.00
1983 runs 10; should be 100
152 Don Baylor .30 .75
153 Bob Welch .30 .75
154 Alan Bannister .08 .25
155 Willie Aikens .08 .25
156 Jeff Burroughs .08 .25
157 Bryan Little .08 .25
158 Bob Boone .30 .75
159 Dave Hostetler .08 .25
160 Jerry Dybzinski .08 .25
161 Mike Madden .08 .25
162 Luis DeLeon .08 .25
163 Willie Hernandez .08 .25
164 Frank Pastore .08 .25
165 Rick Camp .08 .25
166 Lee Mazzilli .30 .75
167 Scot Thompson .08 .25
168 Bob Forsch .08 .25
169 Mike Flanagan .08 .25
170 Rick Manning .08 .25
171 Chet Lemon .30 .75
172 Jerry Remy .08 .25
173 Ron Guidry .30 .75
174 Pedro Guerrero .30 .75
175 Willie Wilson .30 .75
176 Carney Lansford .30 .75
177 Al Oliver .30 .75
178 Jim Sundberg .30 .75
179 Bobby Grich .30 .75
180 Rich Dotson .08 .25
181 Joaquin Andujar .30 .75
182 Jose Cruz .30 .75
183 Mike Schmidt 3.00 8.00
184 Gary Redus RC .40 1.00
185 Garry Templeton .30 .75
186 Tony Pena .08 .25
187 Greg Minton .08 .25
188 Phil Niekro .30 .75
189 Ferguson Jenkins .30 .75
190 Mookie Wilson .30 .75
191 Jim Beattie .08 .25
192 Gary Ward .08 .25
193 Jesse Barfield .30 .75
194 Pete Filson .08 .25
195 Roy Lee Jackson .08 .25
196 Rick Sweet .08 .25
197 Jesse Orosco .08 .25
198 Steve Lake .08 .25
199 Ken Dayley .08 .25
200 Manny Sarmiento .08 .25
201 Mark Davis .08 .25
202 Tim Flannery .08 .25
203 Bill Scherrer .08 .25
204 Al Holland .08 .25
205 Dave Von Ohlen .08 .25
206 Mike LaCoss .08 .25
207 Juan Beniquez .08 .25
208 Juan Agosto .08 .25
209 Bobby Ramos .08 .25
210 Al Bumbry .08 .25
211 Mark Brouhard .08 .25
212 Howard Bailey .08 .25
213 Bruce Hurst .08 .25
214 Bob Shirley .08 .25
215 Pat Zachry .08 .25
216 Julio Franco 1.25 3.00
217 Mike Armstrong .08 .25
218 Dave Beard .08 .25
219 Steve Rogers .30 .75
220 John Butcher .08 .25
221 Mike Smithson .08 .25
222 Frank White .30 .75
223 Mike Heath .08 .25
224 Chris Bando .08 .25
225 Roy Smalley .08 .25
226 Dusty Baker .30 .75
227 Lou Whitaker .30 .75
228 John Lowenstein .08 .25
229 Ben Oglivie .30 .75
230 Doug DeCinces .08 .25
231 Lonnie Smith .08 .25
232 Ray Knight .30 .75
233 Gary Matthews .30 .75
234 Juan Bonilla .08 .25
235 Rod Scurry .08 .25
236 Atlee Hammaker .08 .25
237 Mike Caldwell .08 .25
238 Keith Hernandez .30 .75
239 Larry Bowa .30 .75
240 Tony Bernazard .08 .25
241 Damaso Garcia .08 .25
242 Tom Brunansky .08 .25
243 Dan Driessen .08 .25
244 Ron Kittle .08 .25
245 Tim Stoddard .08 .25
246 Bob L. Gibson RC .08 .25
(Brewers Pitcher)
247 Marty Castillo .08 .25
248 Don Mattingly RC 12.50 30.00
UER trailing on back
249 Jeff Newman .08 .25
250 Alejandro Pena RC .75 2.00
251 Toby Harrah .30 .75
252 Cesar Geronimo .08 .25

253 Tom Underwood .08 .25
254 Doug Flynn .08 .25
255 Andy Hassler .08 .25
256 Odell Jones .08 .25
257 Rudy Law .08 .25
258 Harry Spilman .08 .25
259 Marty Bystrom .08 .25
260 Dave Rucker .08 .25
261 Ruppert Jones .08 .25
262 Jeff R. Jones .08 .25
(Reds OF)
263 Gerald Perry .40 1.00
264 Gene Tenace .30 .75
265 Brad Wellman .08 .25
266 Dickie Noles .08 .25
267 Jamie Allen .08 .25
268 Jim Gott .08 .25
269 Ron Davis .08 .25
270 Benny Ayala .08 .25
271 Ned Yost .08 .25
272 Dave Rozema .08 .25
273 Dave Stapleton .08 .25
274 Lou Piniella .30 .75
275 Jose Morales .08 .25
276 Broderick Perkins .08 .25
277 Butch Davis RC .08 .25
278 Tony Phillips RC .75 2.00
279 Jeff Reardon .30 .75
280 Ken Forsch .08 .25
281 Pete O'Brien RC .40 1.00
282 Tom Paciorek .08 .25
283 Frank LaCorte .08 .25
284 Tim Lollar .08 .25
285 Greg Gross .08 .25
286 Alex Trevino .08 .25
287 Gene Garber .08 .25
288 Dave Parker .30 .75
289 Lee Smith .30 .75
290 Dave LaPoint .08 .25
291 John Shelby .08 .25
292 Charlie Moore .08 .25
293 Alan Trammell .30 .75
294 Tony Armas .30 .75
295 Shane Rawley .08 .25
296 Greg Brock .08 .25
297 Hal McRae .30 .75
298 Mike Davis .08 .25
299 Tim Raines .30 .75
300 Bucky Dent .30 .75
301 Tommy John .30 .75
302 Carlton Fisk .60 1.50
303 Darrell Porter .08 .25
304 Dickie Thon .08 .25
305 Garry Maddox .08 .25
306 Cesar Cedeno .30 .75
307 Gary Lucas .08 .25
308 Johnny Ray .08 .25
309 Andy McGaffigan .08 .25
310 Claudell Washington .08 .25
311 Ryne Sandberg 5.00 12.00
312 George Foster .30 .75
313 Spike Owen RC .40 1.00
314 Gary Gaetti .60 1.50
315 Willie Upshaw .08 .25
316 Al Williams .08 .25
317 Jorge Orta .08 .25
318 Orlando Mercado .08 .25
319 Junior Ortiz .08 .25
320 Mike Proly .08 .25
321 Randy Johnson UER .08 .25
('72-'82 stats are
from Twins' Randy John-
son, '83 stats are from
Braves' Randy Johnson)
322 Jim Morrison .08 .25
323 Max Venable .08 .25
324 Tony Gwynn 5.00 12.00
325 Duane Walker .08 .25
326 Ozzie Virgil .08 .25
327 Jeff Lahti .08 .25
328 Bill Dawley .08 .25
329 Rob Wilfong .08 .25
330 Marc Hill .08 .25
331 Ray Burris .08 .25
332 Allan Ramirez .08 .25
333 Chuck Porter .08 .25
334 Wayne Krenchicki .08 .25
335 Gary Allenson .08 .25
336 Bobby Meacham .08 .25
337 Joe Beckwith .08 .25
338 Rick Sutcliffe .30 .75
339 Mark Huismann .08 .25
340 Tim Conroy .08 .25
341 Scott Sanderson .08 .25
342 Larry Biittner .08 .25
343 Dave Stewart .30 .75
344 Darryl Motley .08 .25
345 Chris Codiroli .08 .25
346 Rich Behenna .08 .25
347 Andre Robertson .08 .25
348 Mike Marshall .08 .25
349 Larry Herndon .30 .75
350 Rich Dauer .08 .25
351 Cecil Cooper .30 .75
352 Rod Carew .60 1.50
353 Willie McGee .30 .75
354 Phil Garner .30 .75
355 Joe Morgan .30 .75
356 Luis Salazar .08 .25
357 John Candelaria .08 .25
358 Bill Laskey .08 .25
359 Bob McClure .08 .25
360 Dave Kingman .30 .75
361 Ron Cey .30 .75
362 Matt Young RC .40 1.00
363 Lloyd Moseby .08 .25
364 Frank Viola .60 1.50
365 Eddie Milner .08 .25
366 Floyd Bannister .08 .25
367 Dan Ford .08 .25
368 Moose Haas .08 .25
369 Doug Bair .08 .25
370 Ray Fontenot .08 .25
371 Luis Aponte .08 .25
372 Jack Fimple .08 .25
373 Neal Heaton .08 .25
374 Greg Pryor .08 .25
375 Wayne Gross .08 .25
376 Charlie Lea .08 .25
377 Steve Lubratich .08 .25
378 Jon Matlack .08 .25

379 Julio Cruz .08 .25
380 John Mizerock .08 .25
381 Kevin Gross RC .40 1.00
382 Mike Ramsey .08 .25
383 Doug Gwosdz .08 .25
384 Kelly Paris .08 .25
385 Pete Falcone .08 .25
386 Milt May .08 .25
387 Fred Breining .08 .25
388 Craig Lefferts RC .08 .25
389 Steve Henderson .08 .25
390 Randy Moffitt .08 .25
391 Ron Washington .08 .25
392 Gary Roenicke .08 .25
393 Tom Candiotti RC .75 2.00
394 Larry Pashnick .08 .25
395 Dwight Evans .60 1.50
396 Rich Gossage .30 .75
397 Derrel Thomas .08 .25
398 Juan Eichelberger .08 .25
399 Leon Roberts .08 .25
400 Dave Lopes .30 .75
401 Bill Gullickson .08 .25
402 Geoff Zahn .08 .25
403 Billy Sample .08 .25
404 Mike Squires .08 .25
405 Craig Reynolds .08 .25
406 Eric Show .08 .25
407 John Denny .08 .25
408 Dann Bilardello .08 .25
409 Bruce Benedict .08 .25
410 Kent Tekulve .08 .25
411 Mel Hall .30 .75
412 John Stuper .08 .25
413 Rick Dempsey .08 .25
414 Don Sutton .30 .75
415 Jack Morris .30 .75
416 John Tudor .30 .75
417 Willie Randolph .30 .75
418 Jerry Reuss .08 .25
419 Don Slaught .30 .75
420 Steve McCatty .08 .25
421 Tim Wallach .08 .25
422 Larry Parrish .08 .25
423 Brian Downing .30 .75
424 Britt Burns .08 .25
425 David Green .08 .25
426 Jerry Mumphrey .08 .25
427 Ivan DeJesus .08 .25
428 Mario Soto .30 .75
429 Gene Richards .08 .25
430 Dale Berra .08 .25
431 Darrell Evans .30 .75
432 Glenn Hubbard .08 .25
433 Jody Davis .08 .25
434 Danny Heep .08 .25
435 Ed Nunez RC .08 .25
436 Bobby Castillo .08 .25
437 Ernie Whitt .08 .25
438 Scott Ullger .08 .25
439 Doyle Alexander .08 .25
440 Domingo Ramos .08 .25
441 Craig Swan .08 .25
442 Warren Brusstar .08 .25
443 Len Barker .08 .25
444 Mike Easler .08 .25
445 Renie Martin .08 .25
446 D.Rasmussen RC .40 1.00
447 Ted Power .08 .25
448 Charles Hudson .08 .25
449 Danny Cox RC .08 .25
450 Kevin Bass .08 .25
451 Daryl Sconiers .08 .25
452 Scott Fletcher .08 .25
453 Bryn Smith .08 .25
454 Jim Dwyer .08 .25
455 Rob Picciolo .08 .25
456 Enos Cabell .08 .25
457 Dennis Boyd .30 .75
458 Butch Wynegar .08 .25
459 Burt Hooton .08 .25
460 Ron Hassey .08 .25
461 Danny Jackson RC .40 1.00
462 Bob Kearney .08 .25
463 Terry Francona .30 .75
464 Wayne Tolleson .08 .25
465 Mickey Rivers .08 .25
466 John Wathan .08 .25
467 Bill Almon .08 .25
468 George Vukovich .08 .25
469 Steve Kemp .08 .25
470 Ken Landreaux .08 .25
471 Milt Wilcox .08 .25
472 Tippy Martinez .08 .25
473 Ted Simmons .30 .75
474 Tim Foli .08 .25
475 George Hendrick .30 .75
476 Terry Puhl .08 .25
477 Von Hayes .08 .25
478 Bobby Brown .08 .25
479 Lee Lacy .08 .25
480 Joel Youngblood .08 .25
481 Jim Slaton .08 .25
482 Mike Fitzgerald .08 .25
483 Keith Moreland .08 .25
484 Ron Roenicke .08 .25
485 Luis Leal .08 .25
486 Bryan Oelkers .08 .25
487 Bruce Berenyi .08 .25
488 LaMarr Hoyt .08 .25
489 Joe Nolan .08 .25
490 Marshall Edwards .08 .25
491 Mike Laga .30 .75
492 Rick Cerone .08 .25
493 Rick Miller UER .08 .25
(Listed as Mike
on card front)
494 Rick Honeycutt .08 .25
495 Mike Hargrove .08 .25
496 Joe Simpson .08 .25
497 Keith Atherton .08 .25
498 Chris Welsh .08 .25
499 Bruce Kison .08 .25
500 Bobby Johnson .08 .25
501 Jerry Koosman .30 .75
502 Frank DiPino .08 .25
503 Tony Perez .60 1.50
504 Ken Oberkfell .08 .25
505 Mark Thurmond .08 .25
506 Joe Price .08 .25
507 Pascual Perez .08 .25

508 Marvell Wynne .40 1.00
509 Mike Krukow .08 .25
510 Dick Ruthven .08 .25
511 Al Cowens .08 .25
512 Cliff Johnson .08 .25
513 Randy Bush .08 .25
514 Sammy Stewart .08 .25
515 Bill Schroeder .08 .25
516 Aurelio Lopez .30 .75
517 Mike C. Brown .08 .25
518 Graig Nettles .30 .75
519 Dave Sax .08 .25
520 Jerry Willard .08 .25
521 Paul Splittorff .08 .25
522 Tom Burgmeier .08 .25
523 Chris Speier .08 .25
524 Bobby Clark .08 .25
525 George Wright .08 .25
526 Dennis Lamp .08 .25
527 Tony Scott .08 .25
528 Ed Whitson .08 .25
529 Ron Reed .08 .25
530 Charlie Puleo .08 .25
531 Jerry Royster .08 .25
532 Don Robinson .08 .25
533 Steve Trout .08 .25
534 Bruce Sutter .60 1.50
535 Bob Horner .30 .75
536 Pat Tabler .08 .25
537 Chris Chambliss .30 .75
538 Bob Ojeda .08 .25
539 Alan Ashby .08 .25
540 Jay Johnstone .08 .25
541 Bob Dernier .08 .25
542 Brook Jacoby .40 1.00
543 U.L. Washington .08 .25
544 Danny Darwin .08 .25
545 Kiko Garcia .08 .25
546 Vance Law UER .08 .25
(Listed as P
on card front)
547 Tug McGraw .30 .75
548 Dave Smith .08 .25
549 Len Matuszek .08 .25
550 Tom Hume .08 .25
551 Dave Dravecky .08 .25
552 Rick Rhoden .08 .25
553 Duane Kuiper .08 .25
554 Rusty Staub .30 .75
555 Bill Campbell .08 .25
556 Mike Torrez .08 .25
557 Dave Henderson .30 .75
558 Len Whitehouse .08 .25
559 Barry Bonnell .08 .25
560 Rick Lysander .08 .25
561 Garth Iorg .08 .25
562 Bryan Clark .08 .25
563 Brian Giles .08 .25
564 Vern Ruhle .08 .25
565 Steve Bedrosian .08 .25
566 Larry McWilliams .08 .25
567 Jeff Leonard UER .08 .25
(Listed as P
on card front)
568 Alan Wiggins .08 .25
569 Jeff Russell RC .40 1.00
570 Salome Barojas .08 .25
571 Dane Iorg .08 .25
572 Bob Knepper .08 .25
573 Gary Lavelle .08 .25
574 Gorman Thomas .30 .75
575 Manny Trillo .08 .25
576 Jim Palmer .30 .75
577 Dale Murray .08 .25
578 Tom Brookens .30 .75
579 Rich Gedman .08 .25
580 Bill Doran RC .40 1.00
581 Steve Yeager .30 .75
582 Dan Spillner .08 .25
583 Dan Quisenberry .08 .25
584 Rance Mulliniks .08 .25
585 Storm Davis .08 .25
586 Dave Schmidt .08 .25
587 Bill Russell .30 .75
588 Pat Sheridan .08 .25
589 Rafael Ramirez .08 .25
UER (A's on front)
590 Bud Anderson .08 .25
591 George Frazier .08 .25
592 Lee Tunnell .08 .25
593 Kirk Gibson 1.25 3.00
594 Scott McGregor .08 .25
595 Bob Bailor .08 .25
596 Tom Herr .08 .25
597 Luis Sanchez .08 .25
598 Dave Engle .08 .25
599 Craig McMurtry .08 .25
600 Carlos Diaz .08 .25
601 Tom O'Malley .08 .25
602 Nick Esasky .08 .25
603 Ron Hodges .08 .25
604 Ed VandeBerg .08 .25
605 Alfredo Griffin .08 .25
606 Glenn Hoffman .08 .25
607 Hubie Brooks .08 .25
608 Richard Barnes UER .08 .25
(Photo actually
Neal Heaton)
609 Greg Walker .40 1.00
610 Ken Singleton .30 .75
611 Mark Clear .08 .25
612 Buck Martinez .08 .25
613 Ken Griffey .30 .75
614 Reid Nichols .08 .25
615 Doug Sisk .08 .25
616 Bob Brenly .08 .25
617 Joey McLaughlin .08 .25
618 Glenn Wilson .30 .75
619 Bob Stoddard .08 .25
620 Lenn Sakata UER .08 .25
(Listed as Len
on card front)
621 Mike Young RC .08 .25
622 John Stefero .08 .25
623 Carmelo Martinez .08 .25
624 Dave Bergman .08 .25
625 Runnin' Reds UER 1.25 3.00
(Sic, Redbirds)
David Green
Willie McGee
Lonnie Smith
Ozzie Smith
626 Rudy May .08 .25
627 Matt Keough .08 .25
628 Jose DeLeon RC .40 1.00
629 Jim Essian .08 .25
630 Darnell Coles RC .40 1.00
631 Mike Warren .08 .25
632 Del Crandall MG .08 .25
633 Dennis Martinez .30 .75
634 Mike Moore .08 .25
635 Lary Sorensen .08 .25
636 Ricky Nelson .08 .25
637 Omar Moreno .08 .25
638 Charlie Hough .30 .75
639 Dennis Eckersley .60 1.50
640 Walt Terrell .08 .25
641 Denny Walling .08 .25
642 Dave Anderson RC .08 .25
643 Jose Oquendo RC .40 1.00
644 Bob Stanley .08 .25
645 Dave Geisel .08 .25
646 Scott Garrelts .08 .25
647 Gary Pettis .08 .25
648 Duke Snider .60 1.50
Puzzle Card
649 Johnnie LeMaster .08 .25
650 Dave Collins .08 .25
651 The Chicken .60 1.50
652 DK Checklist 1-26 .30 .75
(Unnumbered)
653 Checklist 27-130 .08 .25
(Unnumbered)
654 Checklist 131-234 .08 .25
(Unnumbered)
655 Checklist 235-338 .08 .25
(Unnumbered)
656 Checklist 339-442 .08 .25
(Unnumbered)
657 Checklist 443-546 .08 .25
(Unnumbered)
658 Checklist 547-651 .08 .25
(Unnumbered)
A Living Legends A 1.00 2.50
Gaylord Perry
Rollie Fingers
B Living Legends B 2.00 5.00
Carl Yastrzemski
Johnny Bench

1985 Donruss

The 1985 Donruss set consists of 660 standard-size cards. The wax packs, packed 36 packs to a box and 20 boxes to a case, contained 15 cards and a Lou Gehrig puzzle panel. The fronts feature full color photos framed by jet black borders (making the cards condition sensitive). The first 26 cards of the set feature Diamond Kings (DK), for the fourth year in a row; the artwork on the Diamond Kings was again produced by the Perez-Steele Galleries. Cards 27-46 feature Rated Rookies (RR). The unnumbered checklist cards are arbitrarily numbered below as numbers 654 through 660. Rookie Cards in this set include Roger Clemens, Eric Davis, Shawon Dunston, Dwight Gooden, Orel Hershiser, Jimmy Key, Terry Pendleton, Kirby Puckett and Bret Saberhagen.

COMPLETE SET (660) 30.00 60.00
COMP.FACT.SET (660) 50.00 100.00
COMP.GEHRIG PUZZLE 1.50 4.00
1 Ryne Sandberg DK .50 1.25
2 Doug DeCinces DK .05 .15
3 Richard Dotson DK .05 .15
4 Bert Blyleven DK .15 .40
5 Lou Whitaker DK .15 .40
6 Dan Quisenberry DK .05 .15
7 Don Mattingly DK 1.00 2.50
8 Carney Lansford DK .15 .40
9 Frank Tanana DK .15 .40
10 Willie Upshaw DK .05 .15
11 C.Washington DK .05 .15
12 Mike Marshall DK .05 .15
13 Joaquin Andujar DK .15 .40
14 Cal Ripken DK 1.00 2.50
15 Jim Rice DK .15 .40
16 Don Sutton DK .15 .40
17 Frank Viola DK .15 .40
18 Alvin Davis DK .15 .40
19 Mario Soto DK .15 .40
20 Jose Cruz DK .15 .40
21 Charlie Lea DK .05 .15
22 Jesse Orosco DK .05 .15
23 Juan Samuel DK .05 .15
24 Tony Pena DK .05 .15
25 Tony Gwynn DK .50 1.25
26 Bob Brenly DK .05 .15
27 Danny Tartabull RC .40 1.00
28 Mike Bielecki RC .08 .25
29 Steve Lyons RC .20 .50
30 Jeff Reed RC .08 .25
31 Tony Brewer RC .08 .25
32 John Morris RC .08 .25
33 Daryl Boston RC .08 .25
34 Al Pulido RC .08 .25
35 Steve Kiefer RC .08 .25
36 Larry Sheets RC .08 .25
37 Scott Bradley RC .08 .25
38 Calvin Schiraldi RC .20 .50
39 Shawon Dunston RC .40 1.00
40 Charlie Mitchell RC .08 .25
41 Billy Hatcher RC .20 .50
42 Russ Stephans RC .08 .25
43 Alejandro Sanchez RC .08 .25
44 Steve Jeltz RC .08 .25
45 Jim Traber RC .08 .25
46 Doug Loman RC .08 .25
47 Eddie Murray .50 1.25
48 Robin Yount .75 2.00
49 Lance Parrish .15 .40
50 Jim Rice .15 .40
51 Dave Winfield .15 .40
52 Fernando Valenzuela .15 .40
53 George Brett 1.25 3.00
54 Dave Kingman .15 .40
55 Gary Carter .15 .40
56 Buddy Bell .15 .40
57 Reggie Jackson .30 .75
58 Harold Baines .15 .40
59 Ozzie Smith .75 2.00
60 Nolan Ryan UER 2.50 6.00
(Set strikeout record
in 1973, not 1972)
61 Mike Schmidt 1.25 3.00
62 Dave Parker .15 .40
63 Tony Gwynn 1.00 2.50
64 Tony Pena .05 .15
65 Jack Clark .15 .40
66 Dale Murphy .30 .75
67 Ryne Sandberg 1.00 2.50
68 Keith Hernandez .15 .40
69 Alvin Davis RC .20 .50
70 Kent Hrbek .15 .40
71 Willie Upshaw .05 .15
72 Dave Engle .05 .15
73 Alfredo Griffin .05 .15
74A Jack Perconte .05 .15
(Career Highlights
takes four lines)
74B Jack Perconte .05 .15
(Career Highlights
takes three lines)
75 Jesse Orosco .05 .15
76 Jody Davis .05 .15
77 Bob Horner .15 .40
78 Larry McWilliams .05 .15
79 Joel Youngblood .05 .15
80 Alan Wiggins .05 .15
81 Ron Oester .05 .15
82 Ozzie Virgil .05 .15
83 Ricky Horton .05 .15
84 Bill Doran .05 .15
85 Rod Carew .30 .75
86 LaMarr Hoyt .05 .15
87 Tim Wallach .05 .15
88 Mike Flanagan .05 .15
89 Jim Sundberg .15 .40
90 Chet Lemon .15 .40
91 Bob Stanley .05 .15
92 Willie Randolph .15 .40
93 Bill Russell .15 .40
94 Julio Franco .15 .40
95 Dan Quisenberry .05 .15
96 Bill Caudill .05 .15
97 Bill Gullickson .05 .15
98 Danny Darwin .05 .15
99 Curtis Wilkerson .05 .15
100 Bud Black .05 .15
101 Tony Phillips .05 .15
102 Tony Bernazard .05 .15
103 Jay Howell .05 .15
104 Burt Hooton .05 .15
105 Milt Wilcox .05 .15
106 Rich Dauer .05 .15
107 Don Sutton .15 .40
108 Mike Witt .05 .15
109 Bruce Sutter .15 .40
110 Enos Cabell .05 .15
111 John Denny .05 .15
112 Dave Dravecky .05 .15
113 Marvell Wynne .05 .15
114 Johnnie LeMaster .05 .15
115 Chuck Porter .05 .15
116 John Gibbons RC .05 .15
117 Keith Moreland .05 .15
118 Darnell Coles .05 .15
119 Dennis Lamp .05 .15
120 Ron Davis .05 .15
121 Nick Esasky .05 .15
122 Vance Law .05 .15
123 Gary Roenicke .05 .15
124 Bill Schroeder .05 .15
125 Dave Rozema .05 .15
126 Bobby Meacham .05 .15
127 Marty Barrett .05 .15
128 R.J. Reynolds .05 .15
129 Ernie Camacho UER .05 .15
(Photo actually
Rich Thompson)
130 Jorge Orta .05 .15
131 Lary Sorensen .05 .15
132 Terry Francona .15 .40
133 Fred Lynn .15 .40
134 Bob Jones .05 .15
135 Jerry Hairston .05 .15
136 Kevin Bass .05 .15
137 Garry Maddox .05 .15
138 Dave LaPoint .05 .15
139 Kevin McReynolds .15 .40
140 Wayne Krenchicki .05 .15
141 Rafael Ramirez .05 .15
142 Rod Scurry .05 .15
143 Greg Minton .05 .15
144 Tim Stoddard .05 .15
145 Steve Henderson .05 .15
146 George Bell .15 .40
147 Dave Meier .05 .15
148 Sammy Stewart .05 .15
149 Mark Brouhard .05 .15
150 Larry Herndon .05 .15
151 Oil Can Boyd .05 .15
152 Brian Dayett .05 .15
153 Tom Niedenfuer .05 .15
154 Brook Jacoby .05 .15
155 Onix Concepcion .05 .15
156 Tim Conroy .05 .15
157 Joe Hesketh .05 .15
158 Brian Downing .15 .40
159 Tommy Dunbar .05 .15
160 Marc Hill .05 .15
161 Phil Garner .15 .40
162 Jerry Davis .05 .15
163 Bill Campbell .05 .15
164 John Franco RC .40 1.00
165 Len Barker .05 .15
166 Benny Distefano .05 .15
167 George Frazier .05 .15
168 Tito Landrum .05 .15
169 Cal Ripken 2.00 5.00
170 Cecil Cooper .15 .40
171 Alan Trammell .15 .40
172 Wade Boggs .50 1.25
173 Don Baylor .15 .40
174 Pedro Guerrero .15 .40
175 Frank White .15 .40
176 Rickey Henderson .60 1.50
177 Charlie Lea .05 .15
178 Pete O'Brien .05 .15
179 Doug DeCinces .05 .15
180 Ron Kittle .05 .15
181 George Hendrick .15 .40
182 Joe Niekro .05 .15
183 Juan Samuel .05 .15
184 Mario Soto .15 .40
185 Rich Gossage .15 .40
186 Johnny Ray .05 .15
187 Bob Brenly .05 .15
188 Craig McMurtry .05 .15
189 Leon Durham .05 .15
190 Dwight Gooden RC 1.25 3.00
191 Barry Bonnell .05 .15
192 Tim Teufel .05 .15
193 Dave Stieb .15 .40
194 Mickey Hatcher .05 .15
195 Jesse Barfield .15 .40
196 Al Cowens .05 .15
197 Hubie Brooks .05 .15
198 Steve Trout .05 .15
199 Glenn Hubbard .05 .15
200 Bill Madlock .15 .40
201 Jeff D. Robinson .05 .15
202 Eric Show .05 .15
203 Dave Concepcion .15 .40
204 Ivan DeJesus .05 .15
205 Neil Allen .05 .15
206 Jerry Mumphrey .05 .15
207 Mike C. Brown .05 .15
208 Carlton Fisk .30 .75
209 Bryn Smith .05 .15
210 Tippy Martinez .05 .15
211 Dion James .05 .15
212 Willie Hernandez .05 .15
213 Mike Easler .05 .15
214 Ron Guidry .15 .40
215 Rick Honeycutt .05 .15
216 Brett Butler .15 .40
217 Larry Gura .05 .15
218 Ray Burris .05 .15
219 Steve Rogers .15 .40
220 Frank Tanana UER .15 .40
(Bats Left listed
twice on card back)
221 Ned Yost .05 .15
222 Bret Saberhagen RC .60 1.50
UER 18 career IP on back
223 Mike Davis .05 .15
224 Bert Blyleven .15 .40
225 Steve Kemp .05 .15
226 Jerry Reuss .05 .15
227 Darrell Evans UER .15 .40
(80 homers in 1980)
228 Wayne Gross .05 .15
229 Jim Gantner .05 .15
230 Bob Boone .15 .40
231 Lonnie Smith .05 .15
232 Frank DiPino .05 .15
233 Jerry Koosman .15 .40
234 Graig Nettles .15 .40
235 John Tudor .15 .40
236 John Rabb .05 .15
237 Rick Manning .05 .15
238 Mike Fitzgerald .05 .15
239 Gary Matthews .15 .40
240 Jim Presley .20 .50
241 Dave Collins .05 .15
242 Gary Gaetti .15 .40
243 Dann Bilardello .05 .15
244 Rudy Law .05 .15
245 John Lowenstein .05 .15
246 Tom Tellmann .05 .15
247 Howard Johnson .15 .40
248 Ray Fontenot .05 .15
249 Tony Armas .15 .40
250 Candy Maldonado .05 .15
251 Mike Jeffcoat .05 .15
252 Dane Iorg .05 .15
253 Bruce Bochte .05 .15
254 Pete Rose Expos 1.50 4.00
255 Don Aase .05 .15
256 George Wright .05 .15
257 Britt Burns .05 .15
258 Mike Scott .15 .40
259 Len Matuszek .05 .15
260 Dave Rucker .05 .15
261 Craig Lefferts .05 .15
262 Jay Tibbs .05 .15
263 Bruce Benedict .05 .15
264 Don Robinson .05 .15
265 Gary Lavelle .05 .15
266 Scott Sanderson .05 .15
267 Matt Young .05 .15
268 Ernie Whitt .05 .15
269 Houston Jimenez .05 .15
270 Ken Dixon .05 .15
271 Pete Ladd .05 .15
272 Juan Berenguer .05 .15
273 Roger Clemens RC 8.00 20.00
274 Rick Cerone .05 .15
275 Dave Anderson .05 .15
276 George Vukovich .05 .15
277 Greg Pryor .05 .15
278 Mike Warren .05 .15
279 Bob James .05 .15
280 Bobby Grich .15 .40
281 Mike Mason RC .08 .25
282 Ron Reed .05 .15
283 Alan Ashby .05 .15
284 Mark Thurmond .05 .15
285 Joe Lefebvre .05 .15
286 Ted Power .05 .15
287 Chris Chambliss .15 .40
288 Lee Tunnell .05 .15
289 Rich Bordi .05 .15
290 Glenn Brummer .05 .15
291 Mike Boddicker .05 .15
292 Rollie Fingers .15 .40
293 Lou Whitaker .15 .40
294 Dwight Evans .30 .75
295 Don Mattingly 2.00 5.00
296 Mike Marshall .05 .15
297 Willie Wilson .15 .40
298 Mike Heath .05 .15
299 Tim Raines .15 .40
300 Larry Parrish .05 .15
301 Geoff Zahn .05 .15
302 Rich Dotson .05 .15
303 David Green .05 .15
304 Jose Cruz .15 .40
305 Steve Carlton .15 .40
306 Gary Redus .05 .15
307 Steve Garvey .15 .40
308 Jose DeLeon .05 .15
309 Randy Lerch .05 .15
310 Claudell Washington .05 .15
311 Lee Smith .15 .40
312 Darryl Strawberry .50 1.25
313 Jim Beattie .05 .15
314 John Butcher .05 .15
315 Damaso Garcia .05 .15
316 Mike Smithson .05 .15
317 Luis Leal .05 .15
318 Ken Phelps .05 .15
319 Wally Backman .05 .15
320 Ron Cey .15 .40
321 Brad Komminsk .05 .15
322 Jason Thompson .05 .15
323 Frank Williams .05 .15
324 Tim Lollar .05 .15
325 Eric Davis RC 1.25 3.00
326 Von Hayes .05 .15
327 Andy Van Slyke .30 .75
328 Craig Reynolds .05 .15
329 Dick Schofield .05 .15
330 Scott Fletcher .05 .15
331 Jeff Reardon .15 .40
332 Rick Dempsey .05 .15
333 Ben Oglivie .15 .40
334 Dan Petry .05 .15
335 Jackie Gutierrez .05 .15
336 Dave Righetti .15 .40
337 Alejandro Pena .05 .15
338 Mel Hall .05 .15
339 Pat Sheridan .05 .15
340 Keith Atherton .05 .15
341 David Palmer .05 .15
342 Gary Ward .05 .15
343 Dave Stewart .15 .40
344 Mark Gubicza RC .20 .50
345 Carney Lansford .15 .40
346 Jerry Willard .05 .15
347 Ken Griffey .15 .40
348 Franklin Stubbs .05 .15
349 Aurelio Lopez .05 .15
350 Al Bumbry .05 .15
351 Charlie Moore .05 .15
352 Luis Sanchez .05 .15
353 Darrell Porter .05 .15
354 Bill Dawley .05 .15
355 Charles Hudson .05 .15
356 Garry Templeton .15 .40
357 Cecilio Guante .05 .15
358 Jeff Leonard .05 .15
359 Paul Molitor .15 .40
360 Ron Gardenhire .05 .15
361 Larry Bowa .15 .40
362 Bob Kearney .05 .15
363 Garth Iorg .05 .15
364 Tom Brunansky .05 .15
365 Brad Gulden .05 .15
366 Greg Walker .05 .15
367 Mike Young .05 .15
368 Rick Waits .05 .15
369 Doug Bair .05 .15
370 Bob Shirley .05 .15
371 Bob Ojeda .05 .15
372 Bob Welch .15 .40
373 Neal Heaton .05 .15
374 Danny Jackson UER .05 .15
(Photo actually
Frank Wills)
375 Donnie Hill .05 .15
376 Mike Stenhouse .05 .15
377 Bruce Kison .05 .15
378 Wayne Tolleson .05 .15
379 Floyd Bannister .05 .15
380 Vern Ruhle .05 .15
381 Tim Corcoran .05 .15
382 Kurt Kepshire .05 .15
383 Bobby Brown .05 .15
384 Dave Van Gorder .05 .15
385 Rick Mahler .05 .15
386 Lee Mazzilli .15 .40
387 Bill Laskey .05 .15
388 Thad Bosley .05 .15
389 Al Chambers .05 .15
390 Tony Fernandez .15 .40
391 Ron Washington .05 .15
392 Bill Swaggerty .05 .15
393 Bob L. Gibson .05 .15
394 Marty Castillo .05 .15
395 Steve Crawford .05 .15
396 Clay Christiansen .05 .15
397 Bob Bailor .05 .15
398 Mike Hargrove .05 .15
399 Charlie Leibrandt .05 .15
400 Tom Burgmeier .05 .15
401 Razor Shines .05 .15
402 Rob Wilfong .05 .15
403 Tom Henke .15 .40
404 Al Jones .05 .15
405 Mike LaCoss .05 .15
406 Luis DeLeon .05 .15
407 Greg Gross .05 .15
408 Tom Hume .05 .15
409 Rick Camp .05 .15
410 Milt May .05 .15
411 Henry Cotto RC .08 .25
412 David Von Ohlen .05 .15
413 Scott McGregor .05 .15
414 Ted Simmons .15 .40
415 Jack Morris .15 .40
416 Bill Buckner .15 .40
417 Butch Wynegar .05 .15
418 Steve Sax .05 .15
419 Steve Balboni .05 .15
420 Dwayne Murphy .05 .15
421 Andre Dawson .15 .40
422 Charlie Hough .15 .40
423 Tommy John .15 .40
424A Tom Seaver ERR .30 .75
(Photo actually
Floyd Bannister)
424B Tom Seaver COR 4.00 10.00
425 Tom Herr .05 .15
426 Terry Puhl .05 .15
427 Al Holland .05 .15
428 Eddie Milner .05 .15
429 Terry Kennedy .05 .15
430 John Candelaria .05 .15
431 Manny Trillo .05 .15
432 Ken Oberkfell .05 .15
433 Rick Sutcliffe .15 .40
434 Ron Darling .15 .40
435 Spike Owen .05 .15
436 Frank Viola .15 .40
437 Lloyd Moseby .05 .15
438 Kirby Puckett RC 5.00 12.00
439 Jim Clancy .05 .15
440 Mike Moore .05 .15
441 Doug Sisk .05 .15
442 Dennis Eckersley .30 .75
443 Gerald Perry .05 .15
444 Dale Berra .05 .15
445 Dusty Baker .15 .40
446 Ed Whitson .05 .15
447 Cesar Cedeno .15 .40
448 Rick Schu .05 .15
449 Joaquin Andujar .15 .40
450 Mark Bailey .05 .15
451 Ron Romanick .05 .15
452 Julio Cruz .05 .15
453 Miguel Dilone .05 .15
454 Storm Davis .05 .15
455 Jaime Cocanower .05 .15
456 Barbaro Garbey .05 .15
457 Rich Gedman .05 .15
458 Phil Niekro .15 .40
459 Mike Scioscia .15 .40
460 Pat Tabler .05 .15
461 Darryl Motley .05 .15
462 Chris Codiroli .05 .15
463 Doug Flynn .05 .15
464 Billy Sample .05 .15
465 Mickey Rivers .05 .15
466 John Wathan .05 .15
467 Bill Krueger .05 .15
468 Andre Thornton .05 .15
469 Rex Hudler .05 .15
470 Sid Bream RC .20 .50
471 Kirk Gibson .15 .40
472 John Shelby .05 .15
473 Moose Haas .05 .15
474 Doug Corbett .05 .15
475 Willie McGee .15 .40
476 Bob Knepper .05 .15
477 Kevin Gross .05 .15
478 Carmelo Martinez .05 .15
479 Kent Tekulve .05 .15
480 Chili Davis .15 .40
481 Bobby Clark .05 .15
482 Mookie Wilson .15 .40
483 Dave Owen .05 .15
484 Ed Nunez .05 .15
485 Rance Mulliniks .05 .15
486 Ken Schrom .05 .15
487 Jeff Russell .05 .15
488 Tom Paciorek .05 .15
489 Dan Ford .05 .15
490 Mike Caldwell .05 .15
491 Scottie Earl .05 .15
492 Jose Rijo RC .40 1.00
493 Bruce Hurst .05 .15
494 Ken Landreaux .05 .15
495 Mike Fischlin .05 .15
496 Don Slaught .05 .15
497 Steve McCatty .05 .15
498 Gary Lucas .05 .15
499 Gary Pettis .05 .15
500 Marvis Foley .05 .15
501 Mike Squires .05 .15
502 Jim Pankovits .05 .15
503 Luis Aguayo .05 .15
504 Ralph Citarella .05 .15
505 Bruce Bochy .05 .15
506 Bob Owchinko .05 .15
507 Pascual Perez .05 .15
508 Lee Lacy .05 .15
509 Atlee Hammaker .05 .15
510 Bob Dernier .05 .15
511 Ed VandeBerg .05 .15
512 Cliff Johnson .05 .15
513 Len Whitehouse .05 .15
514 Dennis Martinez .15 .40
515 Ed Romero .05 .15
516 Rusty Kuntz .05 .15
517 Rick Miller .05 .15
518 Dennis Rasmussen .05 .15
519 Steve Yeager .15 .40
520 Chris Bando .05 .15
521 U.L. Washington .05 .15
522 Curt Young .05 .15
523 Angel Salazar .05 .15
524 Curt Kaufman .05 .15
525 Odell Jones .05 .15
526 Juan Agosto .05 .15
527 Denny Walling .05 .15
528 Andy Hawkins .05 .15
529 Sixto Lezcano .05 .15
530 Skeeter Barnes RC .08 .25
531 Randy Johnson .05 .15
532 Jim Morrison .05 .15
533 Warren Brusstar .05 .15
534A Terry Pendleton RC .40 1.00
ERR Wrong first name as Jeff
534B Terry Pendleton COR .40 1.00
535 Vic Rodriguez .05 .15
536 Bob McClure .05 .15
537 Dave Bergman .05 .15
538 Mark Clear .05 .15
539 Mike Pagliarulo .05 .15
540 Terry Whitfield .05 .15
541 Joe Beckwith .05 .15
542 Jeff Burroughs .05 .15
543 Dan Schatzeder .05 .15
544 Donnie Scott .05 .15
545 Jim Slaton .05 .15
546 Greg Luzinski .15 .40
547 Mark Salas .05 .15
548 Dave Smith .05 .15
549 John Wockenfuss .05 .15
550 Frank Pastore .05 .15
551 Tim Flannery .05 .15
552 Rick Rhoden .05 .15
553 Mark Davis .05 .15
554 Jeff Dedmon .05 .15
555 Gary Woods .05 .15
556 Danny Heep .05 .15
557 Mark Langston RC .40 1.00
558 Darrell Brown .05 .15
559 Jimmy Key RC .40 1.00
560 Rick Lysander .05 .15
561 Doyle Alexander .05 .15
562 Mike Stanton .05 .15
563 Sid Fernandez .15 .40
564 Richie Hebner .05 .15
565 Alex Trevino .05 .15
566 Brian Harper .05 .15
567 Dan Gladden RC .20 .50
568 Luis Salazar .05 .15
569 Tom Foley .05 .15
570 Larry Andersen .05 .15
571 Danny Cox .05 .15
572 Joe Sambito .05 .15
573 Juan Beniquez .05 .15
574 Joel Skinner .05 .15
575 Randy St.Claire .05 .15
576 Floyd Rayford .05 .15
577 Roy Howell .05 .15
578 John Grubb .05 .15
579 Ed Jurak .05 .15
580 John Montefusco .05 .15
581 Orel Hershiser RC 1.25 3.00
582 Tom Waddell .05 .15
583 Mark Huismann .05 .15
584 Joe Morgan .15 .40
585 Jim Wohlford .05 .15
586 Dave Schmidt .05 .15
587 Jeff Kunkel .05 .15
588 Hal McRae .15 .40
589 Bill Almon .05 .15
590 Carmelo Castillo .05 .15
591 Omar Moreno .05 .15
592 Ken Howell .05 .15
593 Tom Brookens .05 .15
594 Joe Nolan .05 .15
595 Willie Lozado .05 .15
596 Tom Nieto .05 .15
597 Walt Terrell .05 .15
598 Al Oliver .15 .40
599 Shane Rawley .05 .15
600 Denny Gonzalez .05 .15
601 Mark Grant .05 .15
602 Mike Armstrong .05 .15
603 George Foster .15 .40
604 Dave Lopes .15 .40
605 Salome Barojas .05 .15
606 Roy Lee Jackson .05 .15
607 Pete Filson .05 .15
608 Duane Walker .05 .15
609 Glenn Wilson .05 .15
610 Rafael Santana .05 .15
611 Roy Smith .05 .15
612 Ruppert Jones .05 .15
613 Joe Cowley .05 .15
614 Al Nipper UER .05 .15
(Photo actually
Mike Brown)
615 Gene Nelson .05 .15
616 Joe Carter .50 1.25
617 Ray Knight .15 .40
618 Chuck Rainey .05 .15
619 Dan Driessen .05 .15
620 Daryl Sconiers .05 .15
621 Bill Stein .05 .15
622 Roy Smalley .05 .15
623 Ed Lynch .05 .15
624 Jeff Stone RC .05 .15
625 Bruce Berenyi .05 .15
626 Kelvin Chapman .05 .15
627 Joe Price .05 .15
628 Steve Bedrosian .05 .15
629 Vic Mata .05 .15
630 Mike Krukow .05 .15
631 Phil Bradley .20 .50
632 Jim Gott .05 .15
633 Randy Bush .05 .15
634 Tom Browning RC .20 .50
635 Lou Gehrig .50 1.25
Puzzle Card
636 Reid Nichols .05 .15
637 Dan Pasqua RC .20 .50
638 German Rivera .05 .15
639 Don Schulze .05 .15
640A Mike Jones .05 .15
(Career Highlights,
takes five lines)
640B Mike Jones .05 .15
(Career Highlights,
takes four lines)
641 Pete Rose 1.50 4.00
642 Wade Rowdon .05 .15
643 Jerry Narron .05 .15
644 Darrell Miller .05 .15
645 Tim Hulett RC .08 .25
646 Andy McGaffigan .05 .15
647 Kurt Bevacqua .05 .15
648 John Russell .05 .15
649 Ron Robinson .05 .15
650 Donnie Moore .05 .15
651A Two for the Title .75 2.00
Dave Winfield
Don Mattingly
(Yellow letters)
651B Two for the Title 2.00 5.00
Dave Winfield
Don Mattingly
(White letters)
652 Tim Laudner .05 .15
653 Steve Farr RC .20 .50
654 DK Checklist 1-26 .05 .15
(Unnumbered)
655 Checklist 27-130 .05 .15
(Unnumbered)
656 Checklist 131-234 .05 .15
(Unnumbered)
657 Checklist 235-338 .05 .15
(Unnumbered)
658 Checklist 339-442 .05 .15
(Unnumbered)
659 Checklist 443-546 .05 .15
(Unnumbered)
660 Checklist 547-653 .05 .15
(Unnumbered)

1986 Donruss

The 1986 Donruss set consists of 660 standard-size cards. Wax packs, packed 36 packs to a box and 20 boxes to a case, contained 15 cards plus a Hank Aaron puzzle panel. The card fronts feature blue borders, the standard team logo, player's name, position, and Donruss logo. The first 26 cards of the set are Diamond Kings (DK), for the fifth year in a row; the artwork on the Diamond Kings was again produced by the Perez-Steele Galleries. Cards 27-46 again feature Rated Rookies (RR). The unnumbered checklist cards are arbitrarily numbered below as numbers 654 through 660. Rookie Cards in this set include Jose Canseco, Darren Daulton, Len Dykstra, Cecil Fielder, Andres Galarraga, Fred McGriff and Paul O'Neill.

COMPLETE SET (660) 15.00 40.00
COMP.FACT.SET (660) 15.00 40.00
COMP.AARON PUZZLE .75 2.00
1 Kirk Gibson DK .08 .25
2 Rich Gossage DK .08 .25
3 Willie McGee DK .08 .25
4 George Bell DK .08 .25
5 Tony Armas DK .08 .25
6 Chili Davis DK .08 .25
7 Cecil Cooper DK .08 .25
8 Mike Boddicker DK .05 .15
9 Dave Lopes DK .08 .25
10 Bill Doran DK .05 .15
11 Bret Saberhagen DK .08 .25
12 Brett Butler DK .08 .25
13 Harold Baines DK .08 .25
14 Mike Davis DK .05 .15
15 Tony Perez DK .20 .50
16 Willie Randolph DK .08 .25
17 Bob Boone DK .08 .25
18 Orel Hershiser DK .20 .50
19 Johnny Ray DK .05 .15
20 Gary Ward DK .05 .15
21 Rick Mahler DK .05 .15
22 Phil Bradley DK .05 .15
23 Jerry Koosman DK .08 .25
24 Tom Brunansky DK .05 .15
25 Andre Dawson DK .05 .15
26 Dwight Gooden DK .30 .75
27 Kal Daniels RR .20 .50
28 Fred McGriff RR RC 3.00 8.00
29 Cory Snyder RR .05 .15
30 Jose Guzman RR RC .05 .15
31 Ty Gainey RC .05 .15
32 Johnny Abrego RC .05 .15
33A A.Galarraga RR RC .60 1.50
No accent
33B A.Galarraga RR RC .60 1.50
Accent over e
34 Dave Shipanoff RC .05 .15
35 M.McLemore RR RC .40 1.00
36 Marty Clary RC .05 .15
37 Paul O'Neill RR RC 1.50 4.00
38 Danny Tartabull RR .08 .25
39 Jose Canseco RR RC 4.00 10.00
40 Juan Nieves RC .05 .15
41 Lance McCullers RC .05 .15
42 Rick Surhoff RC .05 .15
43 Todd Worrell RR RC .20 .50
44 Bob Kipper RC .05 .15
45 John Habyan RR RC .05 .15
46 Mike Woodard RC .05 .15
47 Mike Boddicker .05 .15
48 Robin Yount .50 1.25
49 Lou Whitaker .08 .25
50 Oil Can Boyd .05 .15
51 Rickey Henderson .30 .75
52 Mike Marshall .05 .15
53 George Brett .75 2.00
54 Dave Kingman .08 .25
55 Hubie Brooks .05 .15
56 Oddibe McDowell .05 .15
57 Doug DeCinces .05 .15
58 Britt Burns .05 .15
59 Ozzie Smith .50 1.25
60 Jose Cruz .08 .25
61 Mike Schmidt .75 2.00
62 Pete Rose 1.00 2.50
63 Steve Garvey .08 .25
64 Tony Pena .05 .15
65 Chili Davis .08 .25
66 Dale Murphy .20 .50
67 Ryne Sandberg .60 1.50
68 Gary Carter .08 .25
69 Alvin Davis .05 .15
70 Kent Hrbek .08 .25
71 George Bell .08 .25
72 Kirby Puckett .75 2.00
73 Lloyd Moseby .05 .15
74 Bob Kearney .05 .15
75 Dwight Gooden .30 .75
76 Gary Matthews .08 .25
77 Rick Mahler .05 .15
78 Benny Distefano .05 .15
79 Jeff Leonard .05 .15
80 Kevin McReynolds .08 .25
81 Ron Oester .05 .15
82 John Russell .05 .15
83 Tommy Herr .05 .15
84 Jerry Mumphrey .05 .15
85 Ron Romanick .05 .15
86 Daryl Boston .05 .15
87 Andre Dawson .08 .25
88 Eddie Murray .30 .75
89 Dion James .05 .15
90 Chet Lemon .08 .25
91 Bob Stanley .05 .15
92 Willie Randolph .08 .25
93 Mike Scioscia .08 .25
94 Tom Waddell .05 .15
95 Danny Jackson .05 .15
96 Mike Davis .05 .15
97 Mike Fitzgerald .05 .15
98 Gary Ward .05 .15
99 Pete O'Brien .05 .15
100 Bret Saberhagen .08 .25
101 Alfredo Griffin .05 .15
102 Brett Butler .08 .25
103 Ron Guidry .08 .25
104 Jerry Reuss .05 .15
105 Jack Morris .08 .25
106 Rick Dempsey .05 .15
107 Ray Burris .05 .15
108 Brian Downing .08 .25
109 Willie McGee .08 .25
110 Bill Doran .05 .15
111 Kent Tekulve .05 .15
112 Tony Gwynn .50 1.25
113 Marvell Wynne .05 .15
114 David Green .05 .15
115 Jim Gantner .05 .15
116 George Foster .08 .25
117 Steve Trout .05 .15
118 Mark Langston .08 .25
119 Tony Fernandez .05 .15
120 John Butcher .05 .15
121 Ron Robinson .05 .15
122 Dan Spillner .05 .15
123 Mike Young .05 .15
124 Paul Molitor .08 .25
125 Kirk Gibson .08 .25
126 Ken Griffey .08 .25
127 Tony Armas .08 .25
128 Mariano Duncan RC .20 .50
129 Pat Tabler .05 .15
130 Frank White .08 .25
131 Carney Lansford .08 .25
132 Vance Law .05 .15
133 Dick Schofield .05 .15
134 Wayne Tolleson .05 .15
135 Greg Walker .05 .15
136 Denny Walling .05 .15
137 Ozzie Virgil .05 .15
138 Ricky Horton .05 .15
139 LaMarr Hoyt .05 .15
140 Wayne Krenchicki .05 .15
141 Glenn Hubbard .05 .15
142 Cecilio Guante .05 .15
143 Mike Krukow .05 .15
144 Lee Smith .08 .25
145 Edwin Nunez .05 .15
146 Dave Stieb .08 .25
147 Mike Smithson .05 .15
148 Ken Dixon .05 .15
149 Danny Darwin .05 .15
150 Chris Pittaro .05 .15
151 Bill Buckner .08 .25
152 Mike Pagliarulo .05 .15
153 Bill Russell .08 .25
154 Brook Jacoby .05 .15
155 Pat Sheridan .05 .15
156 Mike Gallego RC .05 .15
157 Jim Wohlford .05 .15
158 Gary Pettis .05 .15
159 Toby Harrah .08 .25
160 Richard Dotson .05 .15
161 Bob Knepper .05 .15
162 Dave Dravecky .05 .15
163 Greg Gross .05 .15
164 Eric Davis .30 .75
165 Gerald Perry .05 .15
166 Rick Rhoden .05 .15
167 Keith Moreland .05 .15
168 Jack Clark .08 .25
169 Storm Davis .05 .15
170 Cecil Cooper .08 .25
171 Alan Trammell .08 .25
172 Roger Clemens 2.00 5.00
173 Don Mattingly 1.00 2.50
174 Pedro Guerrero .08 .25
175 Willie Wilson .08 .25
176 Dwayne Murphy .05 .15
177 Tim Raines .08 .25
178 Larry Parrish .05 .15
179 Mike Witt .05 .15
180 Harold Baines .08 .25
181 Vince Coleman RC .40 1.00
UER BA 2.67 on back
182 Jeff Heathcock .05 .15
183 Steve Carlton .08 .25
184 Mario Soto .08 .25
185 Rich Gossage .08 .25
186 Johnny Ray .05 .15
187 Dan Gladden .05 .15
188 Bob Horner .08 .25
189 Rick Sutcliffe .08 .25
190 Keith Hernandez .08 .25
191 Phil Bradley .05 .15
192 Tom Brunansky .05 .15
193 Jesse Barfield .08 .25
194 Frank Viola .08 .25
195 Willie Upshaw .05 .15
196 Jim Beattie .05 .15
197 Darryl Strawberry .20 .50
198 Ron Cey .08 .25
199 Steve Bedrosian .05 .15
200 Steve Kemp .05 .15
201 Manny Trillo .05 .15
202 Garry Templeton .08 .25
203 Dave Parker .08 .25
204 John Denny .05 .15
205 Terry Pendleton .08 .25
206 Terry Puhl .05 .15
207 Bobby Grich .08 .25
208 Ozzie Guillen RC .75 2.00
209 Jeff Reardon .08 .25
210 Cal Ripken 1.25 3.00
211 Bill Schroeder .05 .15
212 Dan Petry .05 .15
213 Jim Rice .08 .25
214 Dave Righetti .08 .25
215 Fernando Valenzuela .08 .25
216 Julio Franco .08 .25
217 Darryl Motley .05 .15
218 Dave Collins .05 .15
219 Tim Wallach .05 .15
220 George Wright .05 .15
221 Tommy Dunbar .05 .15
222 Steve Balboni .05 .15
223 Jay Howell .05 .15
224 Joe Carter .08 .25
225 Ed Whitson .05 .15
226 Orel Hershiser .30 .75
227 Willie Hernandez .05 .15
228 Lee Lacy .05 .15
229 Rollie Fingers .08 .25
230 Bob Boone .08 .25
231 Joaquin Andujar .08 .25
232 Craig Reynolds .05 .15
233 Shane Rawley .05 .15
234 Eric Show .05 .15
235 Jose DeLeon .05 .15
236 Jose Uribe .05 .15
237 Moose Haas .05 .15
238 Wally Backman .05 .15
239 Dennis Eckersley .20 .50
240 Mike Moore .05 .15
241 Damaso Garcia .05 .15
242 Tim Teufel .05 .15
243 Dave Concepcion .08 .25
244 Floyd Bannister .05 .15
245 Fred Lynn .08 .25
246 Charlie Moore .05 .15
247 Walt Terrell .05 .15
248 Dave Winfield .08 .25
249 Dwight Evans .20 .50
250 Dennis Powell .05 .15
251 Andre Thornton .05 .15
252 Onix Concepcion .05 .15
253 Mike Heath .05 .15
254A David Palmer ERR .05 .15
(Position 2B)
254B David Palmer COR .20 .50
(Position P)
255 Donnie Moore .05 .15
256 Curtis Wilkerson .05 .15
257 Julio Cruz .05 .15
258 Nolan Ryan 1.50 4.00
259 Jeff Stone .05 .15
260 John Tudor .08 .25
261 Mark Thurmond .05 .15
262 Jay Tibbs .05 .15
263 Rafael Ramirez .05 .15
264 Larry McWilliams .05 .15
265 Mark Davis .05 .15
266 Bob Dernier .05 .15
267 Matt Young .05 .15
268 Jim Clancy .05 .15
269 Mickey Hatcher .05 .15
270 Sammy Stewart .05 .15
271 Bob L. Gibson .05 .15
272 Nelson Simmons .05 .15
273 Rich Gedman .05 .15
274 Butch Wynegar .05 .15
275 Ken Howell .05 .15
276 Mel Hall .05 .15
277 Jim Sundberg .08 .25
278 Chris Codiroli .05 .15
279 Herm Winningham .05 .15
280 Rod Carew .20 .50
281 Don Slaught .05 .15
282 Scott Fletcher .05 .15
283 Bill Dawley .05 .15
284 Andy Hawkins .05 .15
285 Glenn Wilson .05 .15
286 Nick Esasky .05 .15
287 Claudell Washington .05 .15
288 Lee Mazzilli .08 .25
289 Jody Davis .05 .15
290 Darrell Porter .05 .15
291 Scott McGregor .05 .15
292 Ted Simmons .08 .25
293 Aurelio Lopez .05 .15
294 Marty Barrett .05 .15
295 Dale Berra .05 .15
296 Greg Brock .05 .15
297 Charlie Leibrandt .05 .15
298 Bill Krueger .05 .15
299 Bryn Smith .05 .15
300 Burt Hooton .05 .15
301 Stu Cliburn .05 .15
302 Luis Salazar .05 .15
303 Ken Dayley .05 .15
304 Frank DiPino .05 .15
305 Von Hayes .05 .15
306 Gary Redus .05 .15
307 Craig Lefferts .05 .15
308 Sammy Khalifa .05 .15
309 Scott Garrelts .05 .15
310 Rick Cerone .05 .15
311 Shawon Dunston .08 .25
312 Howard Johnson .08 .25
313 Jim Presley .05 .15
314 Gary Gaetti .08 .25
315 Luis Leal .05 .15
316 Mark Salas .05 .15
317 Bill Caudill .05 .15
318 Dave Henderson .05 .15
319 Rafael Santana .05 .15
320 Leon Durham .05 .15
321 Bruce Sutter .08 .25
322 Jason Thompson .05 .15
323 Bob Brenly .05 .15
324 Carmelo Martinez .05 .15
325 Eddie Milner .05 .15
326 Juan Samuel .05 .15
327 Tom Nieto .05 .15
328 Dave Smith .05 .15
329 Urbano Lugo .05 .15
330 Joel Skinner .05 .15
331 Bill Gullickson .05 .15
332 Floyd Rayford .05 .15
333 Ben Oglivie .08 .25
334 Lance Parrish .08 .25
335 Jackie Gutierrez .05 .15
336 Dennis Rasmussen .05 .15
337 Terry Whitfield .05 .15
338 Neal Heaton .05 .15
339 Jorge Orta .05 .15
340 Donnie Hill .05 .15
341 Joe Hesketh .05 .15
342 Charlie Hough .08 .25
343 Dave Rozema .05 .15
344 Greg Pryor .05 .15
345 Mickey Tettleton RC .20 .50
346 George Vukovich .05 .15
347 Don Baylor .08 .25
348 Carlos Diaz .05 .15
349 Barbaro Garbey .05 .15
350 Larry Sheets .05 .15
351 Ted Higuera RC .20 .50
352 Juan Beniquez .05 .15
353 Bob Forsch .05 .15
354 Mark Bailey .05 .15
355 Larry Andersen .05 .15
356 Terry Kennedy .05 .15
357 Don Robinson .05 .15
358 Jim Gott .05 .15
359 Earnie Riles .05 .15
360 John Christensen .05 .15
361 Ray Fontenot .05 .15
362 Spike Owen .05 .15
363 Jim Acker .05 .15
364 Ron Davis .05 .15
365 Tom Hume .05 .15
366 Carlton Fisk .20 .50
367 Nate Snell .05 .15
368 Rick Manning .05 .15
369 Darrell Evans .08 .25
370 Ron Hassey .05 .15
371 Wade Boggs .20 .50
372 Rick Honeycutt .05 .15
373 Chris Bando .05 .15
374 Bud Black .05 .15
375 Steve Henderson .05 .15
376 Charlie Lea .05 .15
377 Reggie Jackson .20 .50
378 Dave Schmidt .05 .15
379 Bob James .05 .15
380 Glenn Davis .05 .15
381 Tim Corcoran .05 .15
382 Danny Cox .05 .15
383 Tim Flannery .05 .15
384 Tom Browning .05 .15
385 Rick Camp .05 .15
386 Jim Morrison .05 .15
387 Dave LaPoint .05 .15
388 Dave Lopes .08 .25
389 Al Cowens .05 .15
390 Doyle Alexander .05 .15
391 Tim Laudner .05 .15
392 Don Aase .05 .15
393 Jaime Cocanower .05 .15
394 Randy O'Neal .05 .15
395 Mike Easler .05 .15
396 Scott Bradley .05 .15
397 Tom Niedenfuer .05 .15
398 Jerry Willard .05 .15
399 Lonnie Smith .05 .15
400 Bruce Bochte .05 .15
401 Terry Francona .08 .25
402 Jim Slaton .05 .15
403 Bill Stein .05 .15
404 Tim Hulett .05 .15
405 Alan Ashby .05 .15
406 Tim Stoddard .05 .15
407 Garry Maddox .05 .15
408 Ted Power .05 .15
409 Len Barker .05 .15
410 Denny Gonzalez .05 .15
411 George Frazier .05 .15
412 Andy Van Slyke .20 .50
413 Jim Dwyer .05 .15
414 Paul Householder .05 .15
415 Alejandro Sanchez .05 .15
416 Steve Crawford .05 .15
417 Dan Pasqua .05 .15
418 Enos Cabell .05 .15
419 Mike Jones .05 .15
420 Steve Kiefer .05 .15
421 Tim Burke .05 .15
422 Mike Mason .05 .15
423 Ruppert Jones .05 .15
424 Jerry Hairston .05 .15
425 Tito Landrum .05 .15
426 Jeff Calhoun .05 .15
427 Don Carman .05 .15
428 Tony Perez .20 .50
429 Jerry Davis .05 .15
430 Bob Walk .05 .15
431 Brad Wellman .05 .15
432 Terry Forster .08 .25
433 Billy Hatcher .05 .15
434 Clint Hurdle .05 .15
435 Ivan Calderon RC .20 .50
436 Pete Filson .05 .15
437 Tom Henke .08 .25
438 Dave Engle .05 .15
439 Tom Filer .05 .15
440 Gorman Thomas .08 .25
441 Rick Aguilera RC .20 .50
442 Scott Sanderson .05 .15
443 Jeff Dedmon .05 .15
444 Joe Orsulak RC .20 .50
445 Atlee Hammaker .05 .15
446 Jerry Royster .05 .15
447 Buddy Bell .08 .25
448 Dave Rucker .05 .15
449 Ivan DeJesus .05 .15
450 Jim Pankovits .05 .15
451 Jerry Narron .05 .15
452 Bryan Little .05 .15
453 Gary Lucas .05 .15
454 Dennis Martinez .08 .25
455 Ed Romero .05 .15
456 Bob Melvin .05 .15
457 Glenn Hoffman .05 .15
458 Bob Shirley .05 .15
459 Bob Welch .08 .25
460 Carmen Castillo .05 .15
461 Dave Leeper .05 .15
462 Tim Birtsas .05 .15
463 Randy St.Claire .05 .15
464 Chris Welsh .05 .15
465 Greg Harris .05 .15
466 Lynn Jones .05 .15
467 Dusty Baker .08 .25
468 Roy Smith .05 .15
469 Andre Robertson .05 .15
470 Ken Landreaux .05 .15
471 Dave Bergman .05 .15
472 Gary Roenicke .05 .15
473 Pete Vuckovich .05 .15
474 Kirk McCaskill RC .20 .50
475 Jeff Lahti .05 .15
476 Mike Scott .08 .25
477 Darren Daulton RC .40 1.00
478 Graig Nettles .08 .25
479 Bill Almon .05 .15
480 Greg Minton .05 .15
481 Randy Ready .05 .15
482 Len Dykstra RC .60 1.50
483 Thad Bosley .05 .15
484 Harold Reynolds RC .60 1.50
485 Al Oliver .08 .25
486 Roy Smalley .05 .15
487 John Franco .08 .25
488 Juan Agosto .05 .15
489 Al Pardo .05 .15
490 Bill Wegman RC .05 .15
491 Frank Tanana .08 .25
492 Brian Fisher RC .05 .15
493 Mark Clear .05 .15
494 Len Matuszek .05 .15
495 Ramon Romero .05 .15
496 John Wathan .05 .15
497 Rob Picciolo .05 .15
498 U.L. Washington .05 .15
499 John Candelaria .05 .15
500 Duane Walker .05 .15
501 Gene Nelson .05 .15
502 John Mizerock .05 .15
503 Luis Aguayo .05 .15
504 Kurt Kepshire .05 .15
505 Ed Wojna .05 .15
506 Joe Price .05 .15
507 Milt Thompson RC .20 .50
508 Junior Ortiz .05 .15
509 Vida Blue .08 .25
510 Steve Engel .05 .15
511 Karl Best .05 .15
512 Cecil Fielder RC .75 2.00
513 Frank Eufemia .05 .15
514 Tippy Martinez .05 .15
515 Billy Joe Robidoux .05 .15
516 Bill Scherrer .05 .15
517 Bruce Hurst .05 .15
518 Rich Bordi .05 .15
519 Steve Yeager .08 .25
520 Tony Bernazard .05 .15
521 Hal McRae .08 .25
522 Jose Rijo .08 .25
523 Mitch Webster .05 .15
524 Jack Howell .05 .15
525 Alan Bannister .05 .15
526 Ron Kittle .05 .15
527 Phil Garner .08 .25
528 Kurt Bevacqua .05 .15
529 Kevin Gross .05 .15
530 Bo Diaz .05 .15
531 Ken Oberkfell .05 .15
532 Rick Reuschel .08 .25
533 Ron Meridith .05 .15
534 Steve Braun .05 .15
535 Wayne Gross .05 .15
536 Ray Searage .05 .15
537 Tom Brookens .05 .15
538 Al Nipper .05 .15
539 Billy Sample .05 .15
540 Steve Sax .05 .15
541 Dan Quisenberry .05 .15
542 Tony Phillips .05 .15
543 Floyd Youmans .05 .15
544 Steve Buechele RC .20 .50
545 Craig Gerber .05 .15
546 Joe DeSa .05 .15
547 Brian Harper .05 .15
548 Kevin Bass .05 .15
549 Tom Foley .05 .15
550 Dave Van Gorder .05 .15
551 Bruce Bochy .05 .15
552 R.J. Reynolds .05 .15
553 Chris Brown RC .05 .15
554 Bruce Benedict .05 .15
555 Warren Brusstar .05 .15
556 Danny Heep .05 .15
557 Darnell Coles .05 .15
558 Greg Gagne .05 .15
559 Ernie Whitt .05 .15
560 Ron Washington .05 .15
561 Jimmy Key .08 .25
562 Billy Swift .05 .15
563 Ron Darling .08 .25
564 Dick Ruthven .05 .15
565 Zane Smith .05 .15
566 Sid Bream .05 .15
567A J.Youngblood ERR .05 .15
Position P
567B J.Youngblood COR .20 .50
Position IF
568 Mario Ramirez .05 .15
569 Tom Runnells .05 .15
570 Rick Schu .05 .15
571 Bill Campbell .05 .15
572 Dickie Thon .05 .15
573 Al Holland .05 .15
574 Reid Nichols .05 .15
575 Bert Roberge .05 .15
576 Mike Flanagan .05 .15
577 Tim Leary .05 .15
578 Mike Laga .05 .15
579 Steve Lyons .05 .15
580 Phil Niekro .08 .25
581 Gilberto Reyes .05 .15
582 Jamie Easterly .05 .15
583 Mark Gubicza .05 .15
584 Stan Javier RC .20 .50
585 Bill Laskey .05 .15
586 Jeff Russell .05 .15
587 Dickie Noles .05 .15
588 Steve Farr .05 .15
589 Steve Ontiveros RC .05 .15
590 Mike Hargrove .05 .15
591 Marty Bystrom .05 .15
592 Franklin Stubbs .05 .15
593 Larry Herndon .05 .15
594 Bill Swaggerty .05 .15
595 Carlos Ponce .05 .15
596 Pat Perry .05 .15
597 Ray Knight .08 .25
598 Steve Lombardozzi .05 .15
599 Brad Havens .05 .15
600 Pat Clements .05 .15
601 Joe Niekro .05 .15
602 Hank Aaron .30 .75
Puzzle Card
603 Dwayne Henry .05 .15
604 Mookie Wilson .08 .25
605 Buddy Biancalana .05 .15
606 Rance Mulliniks .05 .15
607 Alan Wiggins .05 .15
608 Joe Cowley .05 .15
609 Tom Seaver .20 .50
(Green borders
on name)
609B Tom Seaver .75 2.00
(Yellow borders
on name)
610 Neil Allen .05 .15
611 Don Sutton .08 .25
612 Fred Toliver .05 .15
613 Jay Baller .05 .15
614 Marc Sullivan .05 .15
615 John Grubb .05 .15
616 Bruce Kison .05 .15
617 Bill Madlock .08 .25
618 Chris Chambliss .08 .25
619 Dave Stewart .08 .25
620 Tim Lollar .05 .15
621 Gary Lavelle .05 .15
622 Charles Hudson .05 .15
623 Joel Davis .05 .15
624 Joe Johnson .05 .15
625 Sid Fernandez .05 .15
626 Dennis Lamp .05 .15
627 Terry Harper .05 .15
628 Jack Lazorko .05 .15
629 Roger McDowell RC .20 .50
630 Mark Funderburk .05 .15
631 Ed Lynch .05 .15
632 Rudy Law .05 .15
633 Roger Mason RC .05 .15
634 Mike Felder RC .05 .15
635 Ken Schrom .05 .15
636 Bob Ojeda .05 .15
637 Ed VandeBerg .05 .15
638 Bobby Meacham .05 .15
639 Cliff Johnson .05 .15
640 Garth Iorg .05 .15
641 Dan Driessen .05 .15
642 Mike Brown OF .05 .15
643 John Shelby .05 .15
644 Pete Rose RB .30 .75
645 Phil Niekro .08 .25
Joe Niekro
646 Jesse Orosco .05 .15
647 Billy Beane RC .40 1.00
648 Cesar Cedeno .08 .25
649 Bert Blyleven .08 .25
650 Max Venable .05 .15
651 Vince Coleman .05 .15
Willie McGee
652 Calvin Schiraldi .05 .15
653 Pete Rose KING .30 .75
654 Dia. Kings CL 1-26 .05 .15
Unnumbered
655A CL 1: 27-130 .05 .15
(Unnumbered)
(45 Beane ERR)
655B CL 1: 27-130 .05 .15
(Unnumbered)
(45 Habyan COR)
656 CL 2: 131-234 .05 .15
(Unnumbered)
657 CL 3: 235-338 .05 .15
(Unnumbered)
658 CL 4: 339-442 .05 .15
(Unnumbered)
659 CL 5: 443-546 .05 .15
(Unnumbered)
660 CL 6: 547-653 .05 .15
(Unnumbered)

1986 Donruss Rookies

The 1986 Donruss "The Rookies" set features 56 full-color standard-size cards plus a 15-piece puzzle of Hank Aaron. The set was distributed through hobby dealers, packed in 60-set cases, in a small green, cellophane wrapped factory box. Although the set was wrapped in cellophane, the top card was number one Joyner, resulting in a percentage of the Joyner cards arriving in less than perfect condition. Donruss fixed the problem after it was called to their attention and even went so far as to include a customer service phone number in their second printing. Card fronts are similar in design to the 1986 Donruss regular issue except for the presence of "The Rookies" logo in the lower left corner and a bluish green border instead of a blue border. The key extended Rookie Cards in this set are Barry Bonds, Bobby Bonilla, Will Clark, Bo Jackson, Wally Joyner and John Kruk.

COMP.FACT.SET (56) 10.00 25.00
1 Wally Joyner XRC .40 1.00
2 Tracy Jones .05 .15
3 Allan Anderson XRC .05 .15
4 Ed Correa .05 .15
5 Reggie Williams .05 .15
6 Charlie Kerfeld .05 .15
7 Andres Galarraga .60 1.50
8 Bob Tewksbury XRC .20 .50
9 Al Newman XRC .08 .25
10 Andres Thomas .05 .15
11 Barry Bonds XRC 5.00 12.00
12 Juan Nieves .05 .15
13 Mark Eichhorn .05 .15
14 Dan Plesac XRC .20 .50
15 Cory Snyder .05 .15
16 Kelly Gruber .05 .15
17 Kevin Mitchell XRC .40 1.00
18 Steve Lombardozzi .05 .15
19 Mitch Williams XRC .20 .50
20 John Cerutti .05 .15
21 Todd Worrell .20 .50
22 Jose Canseco 1.50 4.00
23 Pete Incaviglia XRC .20 .50
24 Jose Guzman .05 .15
25 Scott Bailes .05 .15
26 Greg Mathews .05 .15
27 Eric King .05 .15
28 Paul Assenmacher .20 .50
29 Jeff Sellers .05 .15
30 Bobby Bonilla XRC .40 1.00
31 Doug Drabek XRC .40 1.00
32 Will Clark UER .75 2.00
(Listed as throwing
right, should be left) XRC
33 Bip Roberts XRC .20 .50
34 Jim Deshaies XRC .05 .15
35 Mike LaValliere XRC .20 .50
36 Scott Bankhead .05 .15
37 Dale Sveum .05 .15
38 Bo Jackson XRC 2.00 5.00
39 Robby Thompson XRC .20 .50
40 Eric Plunk .05 .15
41 Bill Bathe .05 .15
42 John Kruk XRC .60 1.50
43 Andy Allanson XRC .05 .15
44 Mark Portugal XRC .20 .50
45 Danny Tartabull .08 .25
46 Bob Kipper .05 .15
47 Gene Walter .05 .15
48 Rey Quinones UER .05 .15
(Misspelled Quinonez)
49 Bobby Witt XRC .20 .50
50 Bill Mooneyham .05 .15
51 John Cangelosi .05 .15
52 Ruben Sierra XRC .60 1.50
53 Rob Woodward .05 .15
54 Ed Hearn XRC .05 .15
55 Joel McKeon .05 .15
56 Checklist 1-56 .05 .15

1987 Donruss

This set consists of 660 standard-size cards. Cards were primarily distributed in 15-card wax packs, rack packs and a factory set. All packs included a Roberto Clemente puzzle panel and the factory sets contained a complete puzzle.The regular-issue cards feature a black and gold border on the front. The backs of the cards in the factory sets are oriented differently than cards taken from wax packs, giving the appearance that one version or the other is upside down when sorting from the card backs. There are no premiums or discounts for either version. The popular Diamond King subset returns for the sixth consecutive year. Some of the Diamond King (1-26) selections are repeats from prior years; Perez-Steele Galleries had indicated in 1987 that a five-year rotation would be maintained in order to avoid depleting the pool of available worthy "kings" on some of the teams. The rich selection of Rookie Cards in this set include Barry Bonds, Bobby Bonilla, Kevin Brown, Will Clark, David Cone, Chuck Finley, Bo Jackson, Wally Joyner, Barry Larkin, Greg Maddux and Rafael Palmeiro.

COMPLETE SET (660) 15.00 40.00
COMP.FACT.SET (660) 20.00 50.00
COMP.CLEMENTE PUZZLE .60 1.50
1 Wally Joyner DK .15 .40
2 Roger Clemens DK .75 2.00
3 Dale Murphy DK .08 .25
4 Darryl Strawberry DK .05 .15
5 Ozzie Smith DK .25 .60
6 Jose Canseco DK .40 1.00
7 Charlie Hough DK .05 .15
8 Brook Jacoby DK .02 .10
9 Fred Lynn DK .05 .15
10 Rick Rhoden DK .02 .10
11 Chris Brown DK .02 .10
12 Von Hayes DK .02 .10
13 Jack Morris DK .05 .15
14A Kevin McReynolds DK .15 .40
ERR (Yellow strip
missing on back)
14B Kevin McReynolds DK .02 .10
COR
15 George Brett DK .40 1.00
16 Ted Higuera DK .02 .10
17 Hubie Brooks DK .02 .10
18 Mike Scott DK .05 .15
19 Kirby Puckett DK .30 .75
20 Dave Winfield DK .05 .15
21 Lloyd Moseby DK .02 .10
22A Eric Davis DK ERR .15 .40
(Yellow strip
missing on back)
22B Eric Davis DK COR .08 .25
23 Jim Presley DK .02 .10
24 Keith Moreland DK .02 .10
25A Greg Walker DK ERR .15 .40
(Yellow strip
missing on back)
25B Greg Walker DK COR .02 .10
26 Steve Sax DK .02 .10
27 DK Checklist 1-26 .02 .10
28 B.J. Surhoff RR RC .25 .60
29 Randy Myers RR RC .25 .60
30 Ken Gerhart RC .05 .15
31 Benito Santiago .05 .15
32 Greg Swindell RR RC .15 .40
33 Mike Birkbeck RC .05 .15
34 Terry Steinbach RR RC .25 .60
35 Bo Jackson RR RC 2.00 5.00
36 Greg Maddux UER RC 4.00 10.00
middle name misspelled Allen
37 Jim Lindeman RC .05 .15
38 Devon White RR RC .25 .60
39 Eric Bell RC .05 .15
40 Willie Fraser RC .05 .15
41 Jerry Browne RR RC .05 .15
42 Chris James RR RC .05 .15
43 Rafael Palmeiro RR RC 2.00 5.00
44 Pat Dodson RC .05 .15
45 Duane Ward RR RC .15 .40
46 Mark McGwire RR 3.00 8.00
47 Bruce Fields UER RC .05 .15
(Photo actually
Darnell Coles)
48 Eddie Murray .15 .40
49 Ted Higuera .02 .10
50 Kirk Gibson .05 .15
51 Oil Can Boyd .02 .10
52 Don Mattingly .50 1.25

53 Pedro Guerrero .05 .15
54 George Brett .40 1.00
55 Jose Rijo .05 .15
56 Tim Raines .05 .15
57 Ed Correa .02 .10
58 Mike Witt .02 .10
59 Greg Walker .02 .10
60 Ozzie Smith .25 .60
61 Glenn Davis .02 .10
62 Glenn Wilson .02 .10
63 Tom Browning .02 .10
64 Tony Gwynn .25 .60
65 R.J. Reynolds .02 .10
66 Will Clark RC .60 1.50
67 Ozzie Virgil .02 .10
68 Rick Sutcliffe .05 .15
69 Gary Carter .05 .15
70 Mike Moore .02 .10
71 Bert Blyleven .05 .15
72 Tony Fernandez .02 .10
73 Kent Hrbek .05 .15
74 Lloyd Moseby .02 .10
75 Alvin Davis .02 .10
76 Keith Hernandez .05 .15
77 Ryne Sandberg .30 .75
78 Dale Murphy .08 .25
79 Sid Bream .02 .10
80 Chris Brown .02 .10
81 Steve Garvey .05 .15
82 Mario Soto .05 .15
83 Shane Rawley .02 .10
84 Willie McGee .05 .15
85 Jose Cruz .05 .15
86 Brian Downing .05 .15
87 Ozzie Guillen .08 .25
88 Hubie Brooks .02 .10
89 Cal Ripken .60 1.50
90 Juan Nieves .02 .10
91 Lance Parrish .05 .15
92 Jim Rice .05 .15
93 Ron Guidry .05 .15
94 Fernando Valenzuela .05 .15
95 Andy Allanson RC .02 .10
96 Willie Wilson .05 .15
97 Jose Canseco .40 1.00
98 Jeff Reardon .05 .15
99 Bobby Witt RC .15 .40
100 Checklist 28-133 .02 .10
101 Jose Guzman .02 .10
102 Steve Balboni .02 .10
103 Tony Phillips .02 .10
104 Brook Jacoby .02 .10
105 Dave Winfield .05 .15
106 Orel Hershiser .08 .25
107 Lou Whitaker .05 .15
108 Fred Lynn .05 .15
109 Bill Wegman .02 .10
110 Donnie Moore .02 .10
111 Jack Clark .05 .15
112 Bob Knepper .02 .10
113 Von Hayes .02 .10
114 Bip Roberts RC .15 .40
115 Tony Pena .02 .10
116 Scott Garrelts .02 .10
117 Paul Molitor .05 .15
118 Darryl Strawberry .05 .15
119 Shawon Dunston .02 .10
120 Jim Presley .02 .10
121 Jesse Barfield .05 .15
122 Gary Gaetti .05 .15
123 Kurt Stillwell .02 .10
124 Joel Davis .02 .10
125 Mike Boddicker .02 .10
126 Robin Yount .25 .60
127 Alan Trammell .05 .15
128 Dave Righetti .05 .15
129 Dwight Evans .08 .25
130 Mike Scioscia .05 .15
131 Julio Franco .05 .15
132 Bret Saberhagen .05 .15
133 Mike Davis .02 .10
134 Joe Hesketh .02 .10
135 Wally Joyner RC .25 .60
136 Don Slaught .02 .10
137 Daryl Boston .02 .10
138 Nolan Ryan .75 2.00
139 Mike Schmidt .40 1.00
140 Tommy Herr .02 .10
141 Garry Templeton .05 .15
142 Kal Daniels .02 .10
143 Billy Sample .02 .10
144 Johnny Ray .02 .10
145 Rob Thompson RC .15 .40
146 Bob Dernier .02 .10
147 Danny Tartabull .02 .10
148 Ernie Whitt .02 .10
149 Kirby Puckett .30 .75
150 Mike Young .02 .10
151 Ernest Riles .02 .10
152 Frank Tanana .05 .15
153 Rich Gedman .02 .10
154 Willie Randolph .05 .15
155 Bill Madlock .05 .15
156 Joe Carter .05 .15
157 Danny Jackson .02 .10
158 Carney Lansford .05 .15
159 Bryn Smith .02 .10
160 Gary Pettis .02 .10
161 Oddibe McDowell .02 .10
162 John Cangelosi .02 .10
163 Mike Scott .05 .15
164 Eric Show .02 .10
165 Juan Samuel .02 .10
166 Nick Esasky .02 .10
167 Zane Smith .02 .10
168 Mike C. Brown .02 .10
169 Keith Moreland .02 .10
170 John Tudor .05 .15
171 Ken Dixon .02 .10
172 Jim Gantner .02 .10
173 Jack Morris .05 .15
174 Bruce Hurst .02 .10
175 Dennis Rasmussen .02 .10
176 Mike Marshall .02 .10
177 Dan Quisenberry .02 .10
178 Eric Plunk .02 .10
179 Tim Wallach .02 .10
180 Steve Buechele .02 .10
181 Don Sutton .05 .15
182 Dave Schmidt .02 .10
183 Terry Pendleton .05 .15
184 Jim Deshaies RC .05 .15
185 Steve Bedrosian .02 .10
186 Pete Rose .50 1.25
187 Dave Dravecky .02 .10
188 Rick Reuschel .05 .15
189 Dan Gladden .02 .10
190 Rick Mahler .02 .10
191 Thad Bosley .02 .10
192 Ron Darling .05 .15
193 Matt Young .02 .10
194 Tom Brunansky .02 .10
195 Dave Stieb .05 .15
196 Frank Viola .05 .15
197 Tom Henke .02 .10
198 Karl Best .02 .10
199 Dwight Gooden .08 .25
200 Checklist 134-239 .02 .10
201 Steve Trout .02 .10
202 Rafael Ramirez .02 .10
203 Bob Walk .02 .10
204 Roger Mason .02 .10
205 Terry Kennedy .02 .10
206 Ron Oester .02 .10
207 John Russell .02 .10
208 Greg Mathews .02 .10
209 Charlie Kerfeld .02 .10
210 Reggie Jackson .08 .25
211 Floyd Bannister .02 .10
212 Vance Law .02 .10
213 Rich Bordi .02 .10
214 Dan Plesac .02 .10
215 Dave Collins .02 .10
216 Bob Stanley .02 .10
217 Joe Niekro .02 .10
218 Tom Niedenfuer .02 .10
219 Brett Butler .05 .15
220 Charlie Leibrandt .02 .10
221 Steve Ontiveros .02 .10
222 Tim Burke .02 .10
223 Curtis Wilkerson .02 .10
224 Pete Incaviglia RC .15 .40
225 Lonnie Smith .02 .10
226 Chris Codiroli .02 .10
227 Scott Bailes .02 .10
228 Rickey Henderson .15 .40
229 Ken Howell .02 .10
230 Darnell Coles .02 .10
231 Don Aase .02 .10
232 Tim Leary .02 .10
233 Bob Boone .05 .15
234 Ricky Horton .02 .10
235 Mark Bailey .02 .10
236 Kevin Gross .02 .10
237 Lance McCullers .02 .10
238 Cecilio Guante .02 .10
239 Bob Melvin .02 .10
240 Billy Joe Robidoux .02 .10
241 Roger McDowell .02 .10
242 Leon Durham .02 .10
243 Ed Nunez .02 .10
244 Jimmy Key .05 .15
245 Mike Smithson .02 .10
246 Bo Diaz .02 .10
247 Carlton Fisk .08 .25
248 Larry Sheets .02 .10
249 Juan Castillo RC .05 .15
250 Eric King .02 .10
251 Doug Drabek RC .25 .60
252 Wade Boggs .08 .25
253 Mariano Duncan .02 .10
254 Pat Tabler .02 .10
255 Frank White .05 .15
256 Alfredo Griffin .02 .10
257 Floyd Youmans .02 .10
258 Rob Wilfong .02 .10
259 Pete O'Brien .02 .10
260 Tim Hulett .02 .10
261 Dickie Thon .02 .10
262 Darren Daulton .05 .15
263 Vince Coleman .02 .10
264 Andy Hawkins .02 .10
265 Eric Davis .08 .25
266 Andres Thomas .02 .10
267 Mike Diaz .02 .10
268 Chili Davis .05 .15
269 Jody Davis .02 .10
270 Phil Bradley .02 .10
271 George Bell .05 .15
272 Keith Atherton .02 .10
273 Storm Davis .02 .10
274 Rob Deer .02 .10
275 Walt Terrell .02 .10
276 Roger Clemens .75 2.00
277 Mike Easler .02 .10
278 Steve Sax .02 .10
279 Andre Thornton .02 .10
280 Jim Sundberg .05 .15
281 Bill Bathe .02 .10
282 Jay Tibbs .02 .10
283 Dick Schofield .02 .10
284 Mike Mason .02 .10
285 Jerry Hairston .02 .10
286 Bill Doran .02 .10
287 Tim Flannery .02 .10
288 Gary Redus .02 .10
289 John Franco .05 .15
290 Paul Assenmacher .15 .40
291 Joe Orsulak .02 .10
292 Lee Smith .05 .15
293 Mike Laga .02 .10
294 Rick Dempsey .02 .10
295 Mike Felder .02 .10
296 Tom Brookens .02 .10
297 Al Nipper .02 .10
298 Mike Pagliarulo .02 .10
299 Franklin Stubbs .02 .10
300 Checklist 240-345 .02 .10
301 Steve Farr .02 .10
302 Bill Mooneyham .02 .10
303 Andres Galarraga .05 .15
304 Scott Fletcher .02 .10
305 Jack Howell .02 .10
306 Russ Morman .02 .10
307 Todd Worrell .02 .10
308 Dave Smith .02 .10
309 Jeff Stone .02 .10
310 Ron Robinson .02 .10
311 Bruce Bochy .02 .10
312 Jim Winn .02 .10
313 Mark Davis .02 .10
314 Jeff Dedmon .02 .10
315 Jamie Moyer RC .40 1.00
316 Wally Backman .02 .10
317 Ken Phelps .02 .10
318 Steve Lombardozzi .02 .10
319 Rance Mulliniks .02 .10
320 Tim Laudner .02 .10
321 Mark Eichhorn .02 .10
322 Lee Guetterman .02 .10
323 Sid Fernandez .02 .10
324 Jerry Mumphrey .02 .10
325 David Palmer .02 .10
326 Bill Almon .02 .10
327 Candy Maldonado .02 .10
328 John Kruk RC .40 1.00
329 John Denny .02 .10
330 Milt Thompson .02 .10
331 Mike LaValliere RC .15 .40
332 Alan Ashby .02 .10
333 Doug Corbett .02 .10
334 Ron Karkovice RC .15 .40
335 Mitch Webster .02 .10
336 Lee Lacy .02 .10
337 Glenn Braggs RC .05 .15
338 Dwight Lowry .02 .10
339 Don Baylor .05 .15
340 Brian Fisher .02 .10
341 Reggie Williams .02 .10
342 Tom Candiotti .02 .10
343 Rudy Law .02 .10
344 Curt Young .02 .10
345 Mike Fitzgerald .02 .10
346 Ruben Sierra RC .40 1.00
347 Mitch Williams RC .15 .40
348 Jorge Orta .02 .10
349 Mickey Tettleton .02 .10
350 Ernie Camacho .02 .10
351 Ron Kittle .02 .10
352 Ken Landreaux .02 .10
353 Chet Lemon .05 .15
354 John Shelby .02 .10
355 Mark Clear .02 .10
356 Doug DeCinces .02 .10
357 Ken Dayley .02 .10
358 Phil Garner .05 .15
359 Steve Jeltz .02 .10
360 Ed Whitson .02 .10
361 Barry Bonds RC 5.00 12.00
362 Vida Blue .05 .15
363 Cecil Cooper .05 .15
364 Bob Ojeda .02 .10
365 Dennis Eckersley .08 .25
366 Mike Morgan .02 .10
367 Willie Upshaw .02 .10
368 Allan Anderson RC .02 .10
369 Bill Gullickson .02 .10
370 Bobby Thigpen RC .15 .40
371 Juan Beniquez .02 .10
372 Charlie Moore .02 .10
373 Dan Petry .02 .10
374 Rod Scurry .02 .10
375 Tom Seaver .08 .25
376 Ed VandeBerg .02 .10
377 Tony Bernazard .02 .10
378 Greg Pryor .02 .10
379 Dwayne Murphy .02 .10
380 Andy McGaffigan .02 .10
381 Kirk McCaskill .02 .10
382 Greg Harris .02 .10
383 Rich Dotson .02 .10
384 Craig Reynolds .02 .10
385 Greg Gross .02 .10
386 Tito Landrum .02 .10
387 Craig Lefferts .02 .10
388 Dave Parker .05 .15
389 Bob Horner .05 .15
390 Pat Clements .02 .10
391 Jeff Leonard .02 .10
392 Chris Speier .02 .10
393 John Moses .02 .10
394 Garth Iorg .02 .10
395 Greg Gagne .02 .10
396 Nate Snell .02 .10
397 Bryan Clutterbuck .02 .10
398 Darrell Evans .05 .15
399 Steve Crawford .02 .10
400 Checklist 346-451 .02 .10
401 Phil Lombardi .02 .10
402 Rick Honeycutt .02 .10
403 Ken Schrom .02 .10
404 Bud Black .02 .10
405 Donnie Hill .02 .10
406 Wayne Krenchicki .02 .10
407 Chuck Finley RC .25 .60
408 Toby Harrah .05 .15
409 Steve Lyons .02 .10
410 Kevin Bass .02 .10
411 Marvell Wynne .02 .10
412 Ron Roenicke .02 .10
413 Tracy Jones .02 .10
414 Gene Garber .02 .10
415 Mike Bielecki .02 .10
416 Frank DiPino .02 .10
417 Andy Van Slyke .08 .25
418 Jim Dwyer .02 .10
419 Ben Oglivie .05 .15
420 Dave Bergman .02 .10
421 Joe Sambito .02 .10
422 Bob Tewksbury RC .15 .40
423 Len Matuszek .02 .10
424 Mike Kingery RC .05 .15
425 Dave Kingman .05 .15
426 Al Newman RC .02 .10
427 Gary Ward .02 .10
428 Ruppert Jones .02 .10
429 Harold Baines .05 .15
430 Pat Perry .02 .10
431 Terry Puhl .02 .10
432 Don Carman .02 .10
433 Eddie Milner .02 .10
434 LaMarr Hoyt .02 .10
435 Rick Rhoden .02 .10
436 Jose Uribe .02 .10
437 Ken Oberkfell .02 .10
438 Ron Davis .02 .10
439 Jesse Orosco .02 .10
440 Scott Bradley .02 .10
441 Randy Bush .02 .10
442 John Cerutti .02 .10
443 Roy Smalley .02 .10
444 Kelly Gruber .02 .10
445 Bob Kearney .02 .10
446 Ed Hearn RC .02 .10
447 Scott Sanderson .02 .10
448 Bruce Benedict .02 .10
449 Junior Ortiz .02 .10
450 Mike Aldrete .02 .10
451 Kevin McReynolds .02 .10
452 Rob Murphy .02 .10
453 Kent Tekulve .02 .10
454 Curt Ford .02 .10
455 Dave Lopes .05 .15
456 Bob Grich .05 .15
457 Jose DeLeon .02 .10
458 Andre Dawson .05 .15
459 Mike Flanagan .02 .10
460 Joey Meyer .05 .15
461 Chuck Cary .02 .10
462 Bill Buckner .05 .15
463 Bob Shirley .02 .10
464 Jeff Hamilton .02 .10
465 Phil Niekro .05 .15
466 Mark Gubicza .02 .10
467 Jerry Willard .02 .10
468 Bob Sebra .02 .10
469 Larry Parrish .02 .10
470 Charlie Hough .05 .15
471 Hal McRae .05 .15
472 Dave Leiper .02 .10
473 Mel Hall .02 .10
474 Dan Pasqua .02 .10
475 Bob Welch .05 .15
476 Johnny Grubb .02 .10
477 Jim Traber .02 .10
478 Chris Bosio RC .15 .40
479 Mark McLemore .05 .15
480 John Morris .02 .10
481 Billy Hatcher .02 .10
482 Dan Schatzeder .02 .10
483 Rich Gossage .05 .15
484 Jim Morrison .02 .10
485 Bob Brenly .02 .10
486 Bill Schroeder .02 .10
487 Mookie Wilson .05 .15
488 Dave Martinez RC .15 .40
489 Harold Reynolds .05 .15
490 Jeff Hearron .02 .10
491 Mickey Hatcher .02 .10
492 Barry Larkin RC .60 1.50
493 Bob James .02 .10
494 John Habyan .02 .10
495 Jim Adduci .02 .10
496 Mike Heath .02 .10
497 Tim Stoddard .02 .10
498 Tony Armas .05 .15
499 Dennis Powell .02 .10
500 Checklist 452-557 .02 .10
501 Chris Bando .02 .10
502 David Cone RC .40 1.00
503 Jay Howell .02 .10
504 Tom Foley .02 .10
505 Ray Chadwick .02 .10
506 Mike Loynd RC .05 .15
507 Neil Allen .02 .10
508 Danny Darwin .02 .10
509 Rick Schu .02 .10
510 Jose Oquendo .02 .10
511 Gene Walter .02 .10
512 Terry McGriff .02 .10
513 Ken Griffey .05 .15
514 Benny Distefano .02 .10
515 Terry Mulholland RC .15 .40
516 Ed Lynch .02 .10
517 Bill Swift .02 .10
518 Manny Lee .02 .10
519 Andre David .02 .10
520 Scott McGregor .02 .10
521 Rick Manning .02 .10
522 Willie Hernandez .02 .10
523 Marty Barrett .02 .10
524 Wayne Tolleson .02 .10
525 Jose Gonzalez RC .05 .15
526 Cory Snyder .02 .10
527 Buddy Biancalana .02 .10
528 Moose Haas .02 .10
529 Wilfredo Tejada .02 .10
530 Stu Cliburn .02 .10
531 Dale Mohorcic .02 .10
532 Ron Hassey .02 .10
533 Ty Gainey .02 .10
534 Jerry Royster .02 .10
535 Mike Maddux RC .02 .10
536 Ted Power .02 .10
537 Ted Simmons .05 .15
538 Rafael Belliard RC .15 .40
539 Chico Walker .02 .10
540 Bob Forsch .02 .10
541 John Stefero .02 .10
542 Dale Sveum .02 .10
543 Mark Thurmond .02 .10
544 Jeff Sellers .02 .10
545 Joel Skinner .02 .10
546 Alex Trevino .02 .10
547 Randy Kutcher .02 .10
548 Joaquin Andujar .05 .15
549 Casey Candaele .02 .10
550 Jeff Russell .02 .10
551 John Candelaria .02 .10
552 Joe Cowley .02 .10
553 Danny Cox .02 .10
554 Denny Walling .02 .10
555 Bruce Ruffin RC .05 .15
556 Buddy Bell .05 .15
557 Jimmy Jones RC .05 .15
558 Bobby Bonilla RC .25 .60
559 Jeff D. Robinson .02 .10
560 Ed Olwine .02 .10
561 Glenallen Hill RC .15 .40
562 Lee Mazzilli .05 .15
563 Mike G. Brown P .02 .10
564 George Frazier .02 .10
565 Mike Sharperson RC .05 .15
566 Mark Portugal RC .15 .40
567 Rick Leach .02 .10
568 Mark Langston .02 .10
569 Rafael Santana .02 .10
570 Manny Trillo .02 .10
571 Cliff Speck .02 .10
572 Bob Kipper .02 .10
573 Kelly Downs RC .05 .15
574 Randy Asadoor .02 .10
575 Dave Magadan RC .15 .40
576 Marvin Freeman RC .05 .15
577 Jeff Lahti .02 .10
578 Jeff Calhoun .02 .10
579 Gus Polidor .02 .10
580 Gene Nelson .02 .10
581 Tim Teufel .02 .10
582 Odell Jones .02 .10
583 Mark Ryal .02 .10
584 Randy O'Neal .02 .10
585 Mike Greenwell RC .15 .40
586 Ray Knight .05 .15
587 Ralph Bryant .02 .10
588 Carmen Castillo .02 .10
589 Ed Wojna .02 .10
590 Stan Javier .02 .10
591 Jeff Musselman .02 .10
592 Mike Stanley RC .15 .40
593 Darrell Porter .02 .10
594 Drew Hall .02 .10
595 Rob Nelson .02 .10
596 Bryan Oelkers .02 .10
597 Scott Nielsen .02 .10
598 Brian Holton .02 .10
599 Kevin Mitchell RC .25 .60
600 Checklist 558-660 .02 .10
601 Jackie Gutierrez .02 .10
602 Barry Jones .02 .10
603 Jerry Narron .02 .10
604 Steve Lake .02 .10
605 Jim Pankovits .02 .10
606 Ed Romero .02 .10
607 Dave LaPoint .02 .10
608 Don Robinson .02 .10
609 Mike Krukow .02 .10
610 Dave Valle RC .05 .15
611 Len Dykstra .05 .15
612 R.Clemente PUZ .20 .50
613 Mike Trujillo .02 .10
614 Damaso Garcia .02 .10
615 Neal Heaton .02 .10
616 Juan Berenguer .02 .10
617 Steve Carlton .05 .15
618 Gary Lucas .02 .10
619 Geno Petralli .02 .10
620 Rick Aguilera .02 .10
621 Fred McGriff .30 .75
622 Dave Henderson .02 .10
623 Dave Clark RC .05 .15
624 Angel Salazar .02 .10
625 Randy Hunt .02 .10
626 John Gibbons .02 .10
627 Kevin Brown RC .60 1.50
628 Bill Dawley .02 .10
629 Aurelio Lopez .02 .10
630 Charles Hudson .02 .10
631 Ray Soff .02 .10
632 Ray Hayward .02 .10
633 Spike Owen .02 .10
634 Glenn Hubbard .02 .10
635 Kevin Elster RC .15 .40
636 Mike LaCoss .02 .10
637 Dwayne Henry .02 .10
638 Rey Quinones .02 .10
639 Jim Clancy .02 .10
640 Larry Andersen .02 .10
641 Calvin Schiraldi .02 .10
642 Stan Jefferson .02 .10
643 Marc Sullivan .02 .10
644 Mark Grant .02 .10
645 Cliff Johnson .02 .10
646 Howard Johnson .05 .15
647 Dave Sax .02 .10
648 Dave Stewart .05 .15
649 Danny Heep .02 .10
650 Joe Johnson .02 .10
651 Bob Brower .02 .10
652 Rob Woodward .02 .10
653 John Mizerock .02 .10
654 Tim Pyznarski .02 .10
655 Luis Aquino .02 .10
656 Mickey Brantley .02 .10
657 Doyle Alexander .02 .10
658 Sammy Stewart .02 .10
659 Jim Acker .02 .10
660 Pete Ladd .02 .10

1987 Donruss Rookies

The 1987 Donruss "The Rookies" set features 56 full-color standard-size cards plus a 15-piece puzzle of Roberto Clemente. The set was distributed in factory set form packaged in a small green and black box through hobby dealers. Card fronts are similar in design to the 1987 Donruss regular issue except for the presence of "The Rookies" logo in the lower left corner and a green border instead of a black border. The key extended Rookie Cards in this set are Ellis Burks and Matt Williams. The second Donruss-issued cards of Greg Maddux and Rafael Palmeiro are also in this set. Because it's the first card in the set (of which came in a tightly-sealed cello wrap, the Mark McGwire card is quite condition sensitive.

COMP.FACT.SET (56) 10.00 25.00
1 Mark McGwire 4.00 10.00
2 Eric Bell .05 .15
3 Mark Williamson .02 .10
4 Mike Greenwell .15 .40
5 Ellis Burks XRC .25 .60
6 DeWayne Buice .02 .10
7 Mark McLemore .08 .25
8 Devon White .25 .60
9 Willie Fraser .05 .15
10 Les Lancaster .02 .10
11 Ken Williams XRC .02 .10
12 Matt Nokes XRC .15 .40
13 Jeff M. Robinson .02 .10
14 Bo Jackson 2.00 5.00
15 Kevin Seitzer XRC .15 .40
16 Billy Ripken XRC .15 .40
17 B.J. Surhoff .25 .60
18 Chuck Crim .02 .10
19 Mike Birkbeck .05 .15
20 Chris Bosio .15 .40
21 Les Straker .02 .10
22 Mark Davidson .02 .10
23 Gene Larkin XRC .15 .40
24 Ken Gerhart .02 .10
25 Luis Polonia XRC .15 .40
26 Terry Steinbach .25 .60
27 Mickey Brantley .02 .10
28 Mike Stanley .10 .10
29 Jerry Browne .05 .15
30 Todd Benzinger XRC .15 .40
31 Fred McGriff .60 1.50
32 Mike Henneman XRC .15 .40
33 Casey Candaele .02 .10
34 Dave Magadan .15 .40
35 David Cone .40 1.00
36 Mike Jackson XRC .15 .40
37 John Mitchell XRC .05 .15
38 Mike Dunne .02 .10
39 John Smiley XRC .15 .40
40 Joe Magrane XRC .05 .15
41 Jim Lindeman .05 .15
42 Shane Mack .02 .10
43 Stan Jefferson .02 .10
44 Benito Santiago .08 .25
45 Matt Williams XRC 1.00 2.50
46 Dave Meads .02 .10
47 Rafael Palmeiro 2.00 5.00
48 Bill Long .02 .10
49 Bob Brower .02 .10
50 James Steels .02 .10
51 Paul Noce .02 .10
52 Greg Maddux 3.00 8.00
53 Jeff Musselman .02 .10
54 Brian Holton .02 .10
55 Chuck Jackson .02 .10
56 Checklist 1-56 .02 .10

1987 Donruss Opening Day

This innovative set of 272 standard-size cards features a card for each of the players in the starting line-ups of all the teams on Opening Day 1987. The set was packaged in a specially designed box. Cards are very similar in design to the 1987 regular Donruss issue except that these "OD" cards have a maroon border instead of a black border. Teams in the same city share a checklist card. A 15-piece puzzle of Roberto Clemente is also included with every complete set. The error on Barry Bonds (picturing Johnny Ray by mistake) was corrected very early in the press run; supposedly less than one percent of the sets have the error. Players in this set in their Rookie Card year include Will Clark, Bo Jackson, Wally Joyner and Barry Larkin.

COMP.FACT. SET (272) 15.00 40.00
163A LISTED IN NEAR MINT CONDITION
1 Doug DeCinces .02 .10
2 Mike Witt .02 .10
3 George Hendrick .05 .15
4 Dick Schofield .02 .10
5 Devon White .25 .60
6 Butch Wynegar .02 .10
7 Wally Joyner .08 .25
8 Mark McLemore .05 .15
9 Brian Downing .05 .15
10 Gary Pettis .02 .10
11 Bill Doran .02 .10
12 Phil Garner .05 .15
13 Jose Cruz .05 .15
14 Kevin Bass .02 .10
15 Mike Scott .05 .15
16 Glenn Davis .02 .10
17 Alan Ashby .02 .10
18 Billy Hatcher .02 .10
19 Craig Reynolds .02 .10
20 Carney Lansford .05 .15
21 Mike Davis .02 .10
22 Reggie Jackson .08 .25
23 Mickey Tettleton .02 .10
24 Jose Canseco .60 1.50
25 Rob Nelson .02 .10
26 Tony Phillips .02 .10
27 Dwayne Murphy .02 .10
28 Alfredo Griffin .02 .10
29 Curt Young .02 .10
30 Willie Upshaw .02 .10
31 Mike Sharperson .02 .10
32 Rance Mulliniks .02 .10
33 Ernie Whitt .02 .10
34 Jesse Barfield .05 .15
35 Tony Fernandez .02 .10
36 Lloyd Moseby .02 .10
37 Jimmy Key .05 .15
38 Fred McGriff .30 .75
39 George Bell .05 .15
40 Dale Murphy .08 .25
41 Rick Mahler .02 .10
42 Ken Griffey .05 .15
43 Andres Thomas .02 .10
44 Dion James .02 .10
45 Ozzie Virgil .02 .10
46 Ken Oberkfell .02 .10
47 Gary Roenicke .02 .10
48 Glenn Hubbard .02 .10
49 Bill Schroeder .02 .10
50 Greg Brock .02 .10
51 Billy Joe Robidoux .02 .10
52 Glenn Braggs .05 .15
53 Jim Gantner .02 .10
54 Paul Molitor .05 .15
55 Dale Sveum .02 .10
56 Ted Higuera .02 .10
57 Rob Deer .02 .10
58 Robin Yount .25 .60
59 Jim Lindeman .05 .15
60 Vince Coleman .02 .10
61 Tommy Herr .02 .10
62 Terry Pendleton .05 .15
63 John Tudor .05 .15
64 Tony Pena .02 .10
65 Ozzie Smith .25 .60
66 Tito Landrum .02 .10
67 Jack Clark .05 .15
68 Bob Dernier .02 .10
69 Rick Sutcliffe .05 .15
70 Andre Dawson .05 .15
71 Keith Moreland .02 .10
72 Jody Davis .02 .10
73 Brian Dayett .02 .10
74 Leon Durham .02 .10
75 Ryne Sandberg .30 .75
76 Shawon Dunston .02 .10
77 Mike Marshall .02 .10
78 Bill Madlock .05 .15
79 Orel Hershiser .08 .25
80 Mike Ramsey .02 .10
81 Ken Landreaux .02 .10
82 Mike Scioscia .05 .15
83 Franklin Stubbs .02 .10
84 Mariano Duncan .02 .10
85 Steve Sax .02 .10
86 Mitch Webster .02 .10
87 Reid Nichols .02 .10
88 Tim Wallach .02 .10
89 Floyd Youmans .02 .10
90 Andres Galarraga .05 .15
91 Hubie Brooks .02 .10
92 Jeff Reed .02 .10
93 Alonzo Powell .02 .10
94 Vance Law .02 .10
95 Bob Brenly .02 .10
96 Will Clark .75 2.00
97 Chili Davis .05 .15
98 Mike Krukow .02 .10
99 Jose Uribe .02 .10
100 Chris Brown .02 .10
101 Robby Thompson .15 .40
102 Candy Maldonado .02 .10
103 Jeff Leonard .02 .10
104 Tom Candiotti .02 .10
105 Chris Bando .02 .10
106 Cory Snyder .02 .10
107 Pat Tabler .02 .10
108 Andre Thornton .02 .10
109 Joe Carter .05 .15
110 Tony Bernazard .02 .10
111 Julio Franco .05 .15
112 Brook Jacoby .02 .10
113 Brett Butler .05 .15
114 Donell Nixon .02 .10
115 Alvin Davis .02 .10
116 Mark Langston .02 .10
117 Harold Reynolds .05 .15
118 Ken Phelps .02 .10
119 Mike Kingery .05 .15
120 Dave Valle .05 .15
121 Rey Quinones .02 .10
122 Phil Bradley .02 .10
123 Jim Presley .02 .10
124 Keith Hernandez .05 .15
125 Kevin McReynolds .02 .10
126 Rafael Santana .02 .10
127 Bob Ojeda .02 .10
128 Darryl Strawberry .05 .15
129 Mookie Wilson .05 .15
130 Gary Carter .05 .15
131 Tim Teufel .02 .10
132 Howard Johnson .05 .15
133 Cal Ripken .60 1.50
134 Rick Burleson .02 .10
135 Fred Lynn .05 .15
136 Eddie Murray .15 .40
137 Ray Knight .05 .15
138 Alan Wiggins .02 .10
139 John Shelby .02 .10
140 Mike Boddicker .02 .10
141 Ken Gerhart .02 .10
142 Terry Kennedy .02 .10
143 Steve Garvey .05 .15
144 Marvell Wynne .02 .10
145 Kevin Mitchell .08 .25
146 Tony Gwynn .25 .60
147 Joey Cora .15 .40
148 Benito Santiago .05 .15
149 Eric Show .02 .10
150 Garry Templeton .05 .15
151 Carmelo Martinez .02 .10
152 Von Hayes .02 .10
153 Lance Parrish .05 .15
154 Milt Thompson .02 .10
155 Mike Easler .02 .10
156 Juan Samuel .02 .10
157 Steve Jeltz .02 .10
158 Glenn Wilson .02 .10
159 Shane Rawley .02 .10
160 Mike Schmidt .40 1.00
161 Andy Van Slyke .08 .25
162 Johnny Ray .02 .10
163A Barry Bonds ERR 175.00 300.00
(Photo actually
Johnny Ray wearing
a black shirt)
163B Barry Bonds COR 5.00 12.00
164 Junior Ortiz .02 .10
165 Rafael Belliard .15 .40
166 Bob Patterson .02 .10
167 Bobby Bonilla .25 .60
168 Sid Bream .02 .10
169 Jim Morrison .02 .10
170 Jerry Browne .05 .15
171 Scott Fletcher .02 .10
172 Ruben Sierra .40 1.00
173 Larry Parrish .02 .10
174 Pete O'Brien .02 .10
175 Pete Incaviglia .15 .40
176 Don Slaught .02 .10
177 Oddibe McDowell .02 .10
178 Charlie Hough .05 .15
179 Steve Buechele .02 .10
180 Bob Stanley .02 .10
181 Wade Boggs .08 .25
182 Jim Rice .05 .15
183 Bill Buckner .05 .15
184 Dwight Evans .08 .25
185 Spike Owen .02 .10
186 Don Baylor .05 .15
187 Marc Sullivan .02 .10

188 Marty Barrett .02 .10
189 Dave Henderson .02 .10
190 Bo Diaz .02 .10
191 Barry Larkin .75 2.00
192 Kal Daniels .02 .10
193 Terry Francona .05 .15
194 Tom Browning .02 .10
195 Ron Oester .02 .10
196 Buddy Bell .05 .15
197 Eric Davis .08 .25
198 Dave Parker .05 .15
199 Steve Balboni .02 .10
200 Danny Tartabull .02 .10
201 Ed Hearn .02 .10
202 Buddy Biancalana .02 .10
203 Danny Jackson .02 .10
204 Frank White .05 .15
205 Bo Jackson 2.00 5.00
206 George Brett .40 1.00
207 Kevin Seitzer .05 .15
208 Willie Wilson .05 .15
209 Orlando Mercado .02 .10
210 Darrell Evans .05 .15
211 Larry Herndon .02 .10
212 Jack Morris .05 .15
213 Chet Lemon .05 .15
214 Mike Heath .02 .10
215 Darnell Coles .02 .10
216 Alan Trammell .05 .15
217 Terry Harper .02 .10
218 Lou Whitaker .05 .15
219 Gary Gaetti .05 .15
220 Tom Nieto .02 .10
221 Kirby Puckett .30 .75
222 Tom Brunansky .02 .10
223 Greg Gagne .02 .10
224 Dan Gladden .02 .10
225 Mark Davidson .02 .10
226 Bert Blyleven .05 .15
227 Steve Lombardozzi .02 .10
228 Kent Hrbek .05 .15
229 Gary Redus .02 .10
230 Ivan Calderon .02 .10
231 Tim Hulett .02 .10
232 Carlton Fisk .08 .25
233 Greg Walker .02 .10
234 Ron Karkovice .15 .40
235 Ozzie Guillen .08 .25
236 Harold Baines .05 .15
237 Donnie Hill .02 .10
238 Rich Dotson .02 .10
239 Mike Pagliarulo .02 .10
240 Joel Skinner .02 .10
241 Don Mattingly .50 1.25
242 Gary Ward .02 .10
243 Dave Winfield .05 .15
244 Dan Pasqua .02 .10
245 Wayne Tolleson .02 .10
246 Willie Randolph .05 .15
247 Dennis Rasmussen .02 .10
248 Rickey Henderson .15 .40
249 Angels Logo .01 .05
250 Astros Logo .01 .05
251 A's Logo .01 .05
252 Blue Jays Logo .01 .05
253 Braves Logo .01 .05
254 Brewers Logo .01 .05
255 Cardinals Logo .01 .05
256 Dodgers Logo .01 .05
257 Expos Logo .01 .05
258 Giants Logo .01 .05
259 Indians Logo .01 .05
260 Mariners Logo .01 .05
261 Orioles Logo .01 .05
262 Padres Logo .01 .05
263 Phillies Logo .01 .05
264 Pirates Logo .01 .05
265 Rangers Logo .01 .05
266 Red Sox Logo .01 .05
267 Reds Logo .01 .05
268 Royals Logo .01 .05
269 Tigers Logo .01 .05
270 Twins Logo .01 .05
271 Chicago Logos .01 .05
272 New York Logos .01 .05

1988 Donruss

This set consists of 660 standard-size cards. For the seventh straight year, wax packs consisted of 15 cards plus a puzzle panel (featuring Stan Musial this time around). Cards were also distributed in rack packs and retail and hobby factory sets. Card fronts feature a distinctive black and blue border on the front. The card front border design pattern of the factory set card fronts is oriented differently from that of the regular wax pack cards. No premium or discount exists for either version. Subsets include Diamond Kings (1-27) and Rated Rookies (28-47). Cards marked as SP (short printed) from 648-660 are more difficult to find than the other 13 SP's in the lower 600s. These 26 cards listed as SP were apparently pulled from the printing sheet to make room for the 26 Bonus MVP cards. Six of the checklist cards were done two different ways to reflect the inclusion or exclusion of the Bonus MVP cards in the wax packs. In the checklist below, the A variations (for the checklist cards) are from the wax packs and the B variations are from the factory-collated sets. The key Rookie Cards in this set are Roberto Alomar, Jay Bell, Jay Buhner, Ellis Burks, Ken Caminiti, Tom Glavine, Mark Grace and Matt Williams. There was also a Kirby Puckett card issued as the package back of Donruss blister packs; it uses a different photo from both of Kirby's regular and Bonus MVP cards and is unnumbered on the back.

COMPLETE SET (660) 4.00 10.00
COMP.FACT.SET (660) 6.00 15.00
COMMON CARD (1-660) .01 .05
COMMON SP (648-660) .02 .10

1 Mark McGwire DK .30 .75
2 Tim Raines DK .02 .10
3 Benito Santiago DK .02 .10
4 Alan Trammell DK .02 .10
5 Danny Tartabull DK .01 .05
6 Ron Darling DK .02 .10
7 Paul Molitor DK .02 .10
8 Devon White DK .02 .10
9 Andre Dawson DK .01 .05
10 Julio Franco DK .02 .10
11 Scott Fletcher DK .01 .05
12 Tony Fernandez DK .01 .05
13 Shane Rawley DK .01 .05
14 Kal Daniels DK .01 .05
15 Jack Clark DK .02 .10
16 Dwight Evans DK .05 .15
17 Tommy John DK .02 .10
18 Andy Van Slyke DK .05 .15
19 Gary Gaetti DK .02 .10
20 Mark Langston DK .01 .05
21 Will Clark DK .07 .20
22 Glenn Hubbard DK .01 .05
23 Billy Hatcher DK .01 .05
24 Bob Welch DK .02 .10
25 Ivan Calderon DK .01 .05
26 Cal Ripken DK .15 .40
27 DK Checklist 1-26 .01 .05
28 Mackey Sasser RR RC .08 .25
29 Jeff Treadway RR RC .08 .25
30 Mike Campbell RR .01 .05
31 Lance Johnson RR RC .08 .25
32 Nelson Liriano RR .01 .05
33 Shawn Abner RR .01 .05
34 Roberto Alomar RR RC .75 2.00
35 Shawn Hillegas RR .01 .05
36 Joey Meyer RR .01 .05
37 Kevin Elster RR .01 .05
38 Jose Lind RR RC .08 .25
39 Kirt Manwaring RR RC .08 .25
40 Mark Grace RR RC .75 2.00
41 Jody Reed RR RC .08 .25
42 John Farrell RR RC .02 .10
43 Al Leiter RR RC .30 .75
44 Gary Thurman RR .01 .05
45 Vicente Palacios RR .01 .05
46 Eddie Williams RR RC .02 .10
47 Jack McDowell RR RC .15 .40
48 Ken Dixon .01 .05
49 Mike Birkbeck .01 .05
50 Eric King .01 .05
51 Roger Clemens .40 1.00
52 Pat Clements .01 .05
53 Fernando Valenzuela .02 .10
54 Mark Gubicza .01 .05
55 Jay Howell .01 .05
56 Floyd Youmans .01 .05
57 Ed Correa .01 .05
58 DeWayne Buice .01 .05
59 Jose DeLeon .01 .05
60 Danny Cox .01 .05
61 Nolan Ryan .40 1.00
62 Steve Bedrosian .01 .05
63 Tom Browning .01 .05
64 Mark Davis .01 .05
65 R.J. Reynolds .01 .05
66 Kevin Mitchell .02 .10
67 Ken Oberkfell .01 .05
68 Rick Sutcliffe .02 .10
69 Dwight Gooden .02 .10
70 Scott Bankhead .01 .05
71 Bert Blyleven .02 .10
72 Jimmy Key .02 .10
73 Les Straker .01 .05
74 Jim Clancy .01 .05
75 Mike Moore .01 .05
76 Ron Darling .02 .10
77 Ed Lynch .01 .05
78 Dale Murphy .05 .15
79 Doug Drabek .01 .05
80 Scott Garrelts .01 .05
81 Ed Whitson .01 .05
82 Rob Murphy .01 .05
83 Shane Rawley .01 .05
84 Greg Mathews .01 .05
85 Jim Deshaies .01 .05
86 Mike Witt .01 .05
87 Donnie Hill .01 .05
88 Jeff Reed .01 .05
89 Mike Boddicker .01 .05
90 Ted Higuera .01 .05
91 Walt Terrell .01 .05
92 Bob Stanley .01 .05
93 Dave Righetti .02 .10
94 Orel Hershiser .02 .10
95 Chris Bando .01 .05
96 Bret Saberhagen .02 .10
97 Curt Young .01 .05
98 Tim Burke .01 .05
99 Charlie Hough .02 .10
100A Checklist 28-137 .01 .05
100B Checklist 28-133 .01 .05
101 Bobby Witt .01 .05
102 George Brett .20 .50
103 Mickey Tettleton .01 .05
104 Scott Bailes .01 .05
105 Mike Pagliarulo .01 .05
106 Mike Scioscia .02 .10
107 Tom Brookens .01 .05
108 Ray Knight .02 .10
109 Dan Plesac .01 .05
110 Wally Joyner .02 .10
111 Bob Forsch .01 .05
112 Mike Scott .02 .10
113 Kevin Gross .01 .05
114 Benito Santiago .02 .10
115 Bob Kipper .01 .05
116 Mike Krukow .01 .05
117 Chris Bosio .01 .05
118 Sid Fernandez .01 .05
119 Jody Davis .01 .05
120 Mike Morgan .01 .05
121 Mark Eichhorn .01 .05
122 Jeff Reardon .02 .10
123 John Franco .02 .10
124 Richard Dotson .01 .05
125 Eric Bell .01 .05
126 Juan Nieves .01 .05
127 Jack Morris .02 .10
128 Rick Rhoden .01 .05
129 Rich Gedman .01 .05
130 Ken Howell .01 .05

131 Brook Jacoby .01 .05
132 Danny Jackson .01 .05
133 Gene Nelson .01 .05
134 Neal Heaton .01 .05
135 Willie Fraser .01 .05
136 Jose Guzman .01 .05
137 Ozzie Guillen .02 .10
138 Bob Knepper .01 .05
139 Mike Jackson RC .08 .25
140 Joe Magrane RC .08 .25
141 Jimmy Jones .01 .05
142 Ted Power .01 .05
143 Ozzie Virgil .01 .05
144 Felix Fermin .01 .05
145 Kelly Downs .01 .05
146 Shawon Dunston .01 .05
147 Scott Bradley .01 .05
148 Dave Stieb .02 .10
149 Frank Viola .02 .10
150 Terry Kennedy .01 .05
151 Bill Wegman .01 .05
152 Matt Nokes RC .08 .25
153 Wade Boggs .05 .15
154 Wayne Tolleson .01 .05
155 Mariano Duncan .01 .05
156 Julio Franco .02 .10
157 Charlie Leibrandt .01 .05
158 Terry Steinbach .02 .10
159 Mike Fitzgerald .01 .05
160 Jack Lazorko .01 .05
161 Mitch Williams .01 .05
162 Greg Walker .01 .05
163 Alan Ashby .01 .05
164 Tony Gwynn .10 .30
165 Bruce Ruffin .01 .05
166 Ron Robinson .01 .05
167 Zane Smith .01 .05
168 Junior Ortiz .01 .05
169 Jamie Moyer .02 .10
170 Tony Pena .01 .05
171 Cal Ripken .30 .75
172 B.J. Surhoff .02 .10
173 Lou Whitaker .02 .10
174 Ellis Burks RC .15 .40
175 Ron Guidry .02 .10
176 Steve Sax .01 .05
177 Danny Tartabull .01 .05
178 Carney Lansford .02 .10
179 Casey Candaele .01 .05
180 Scott Fletcher .01 .05
181 Mark McLemore .01 .05
182 Ivan Calderon .01 .05
183 Jack Clark .02 .10
184 Glenn Davis .01 .05
185 Luis Aguayo .01 .05
186 Bo Diaz .01 .05
187 Stan Jefferson .01 .05
188 Sid Bream .01 .05
189 Bob Brenly .01 .05
190 Dion James .01 .05
191 Leon Durham .01 .05
192 Jesse Orosco .01 .05
193 Alvin Davis .01 .05
194 Gary Gaetti .02 .10
195 Fred McGriff .07 .20
196 Steve Lombardozzi .01 .05
197 Rance Mulliniks .01 .05
198 Rey Quinones .01 .05
199 Gary Carter .02 .10
200A Checklist 138-247 .01 .05
200B Checklist 134-239 .01 .05
201 Keith Moreland .01 .05
202 Ken Griffey .02 .10
203 Tommy Gregg .01 .05
204 Will Clark .07 .20
205 John Kruk .02 .10
206 Buddy Bell .02 .10
207 Von Hayes .01 .05
208 Tommy Herr .01 .05
209 Craig Reynolds .01 .05
210 Gary Pettis .01 .05
211 Harold Baines .02 .10
212 Vance Law .01 .05
213 Ken Gerhart .01 .05
214 Jim Gantner .01 .05
215 Chet Lemon .02 .10
216 Dwight Evans .05 .15
217 Don Mattingly .25 .60
218 Franklin Stubbs .01 .05
219 Pat Tabler .01 .05
220 Bo Jackson .07 .20
221 Tony Phillips .01 .05
222 Tim Wallach .01 .05
223 Ruben Sierra .02 .10
224 Steve Buechele .01 .05
225 Frank White .02 .10
226 Alfredo Griffin .01 .05
227 Greg Swindell .01 .05
228 Willie Randolph .02 .10
229 Mike Marshall .01 .05
230 Alan Trammell .02 .10
231 Eddie Murray .07 .20
232 Dale Sveum .01 .05
233 Dick Schofield .01 .05
234 Jose Oquendo .01 .05
235 Bill Doran .01 .05
236 Milt Thompson .01 .05
237 Marvell Wynne .01 .05
238 Bobby Bonilla .02 .10
239 Chris Speier .01 .05
240 Glenn Braggs .01 .05
241 Wally Backman .01 .05
242 Ryne Sandberg .15 .40
243 Phil Bradley .01 .05
244 Kelly Gruber .01 .05
245 Tom Brunansky .01 .05
246 Ron Oester .01 .05
247 Bobby Thigpen .01 .05
248 Fred Lynn .02 .10
249 Paul Molitor .02 .10
250 Darrell Evans .02 .10
251 Gary Ward .01 .05
252 Bruce Hurst .01 .05
253 Bob Welch .02 .10
254 Joe Carter .02 .10
255 Willie Wilson .02 .10
256 Mark McGwire .60 1.50
257 Mitch Webster .01 .05
258 Brian Downing .02 .10
259 Mike Stanley .01 .05
260 Carlton Fisk .05 .15

261 Billy Hatcher .01 .05
262 Glenn Wilson .01 .05
263 Ozzie Smith .10 .30
264 Randy Ready .01 .05
265 Kurt Stillwell .01 .05
266 David Palmer .01 .05
267 Mike Diaz .01 .05
268 Robby Thompson .01 .05
269 Andre Dawson .02 .10
270 Lee Guetterman .01 .05
271 Willie Upshaw .01 .05
272 Randy Bush .01 .05
273 Larry Sheets .01 .05
274 Rob Deer .01 .05
275 Kirk Gibson .07 .20
276 Marty Barrett .01 .05
277 Rickey Henderson .07 .20
278 Pedro Guerrero .02 .10
279 Brett Butler .02 .10
280 Kevin Seitzer .01 .05
281 Mike Davis .01 .05
282 Andres Galarraga .02 .10
283 Devon White .02 .10
284 Pete O'Brien .01 .05
285 Jerry Hairston .01 .05
286 Kevin Bass .01 .05
287 Carmelo Martinez .01 .05
288 Juan Samuel .01 .05
289 Kal Daniels .01 .05
290 Albert Hall .01 .05
291 Andy Van Slyke .05 .15
292 Lee Smith .02 .10
293 Vince Coleman .01 .05
294 Tom Niedenfuer .01 .05
295 Robin Yount .10 .30
296 Jeff M. Robinson .01 .05
297 Todd Benzinger RC .08 .25
298 Dave Winfield .02 .10
299 Mickey Hatcher .01 .05
300A Checklist 248-357 .01 .05
300B Checklist 240-345 .01 .05
301 Bud Black .01 .05
302 Jose Canseco .20 .50
303 Tom Foley .01 .05
304 Pete Incaviglia .01 .05
305 Bob Boone .02 .10
306 Bill Long .01 .05
307 Willie McGee .02 .10
308 Ken Caminiti RC .75 2.00
309 Darren Daulton .02 .10
310 Tracy Jones .01 .05
311 Greg Booker .01 .05
312 Mike LaValliere .01 .05
313 Chili Davis .02 .10
314 Glenn Hubbard .01 .05
315 Paul Noce .01 .05
316 Keith Hernandez .02 .10
317 Mark Langston .01 .05
318 Keith Atherton .01 .05
319 Tony Fernandez .01 .05
320 Kent Hrbek .02 .10
321 John Cerutti .01 .05
322 Mike Kingery .01 .05
323 Dave Magadan .01 .05
324 Rafael Palmeiro .15 .40
325 Jeff Dedmon .01 .05
326 Barry Bonds .75 2.00
327 Jeffrey Leonard .01 .05
328 Tim Flannery .01 .05
329 Dave Concepcion .02 .10
330 Mike Schmidt .20 .50
331 Bill Dawley .01 .05
332 Larry Andersen .01 .05
333 Jack Howell .01 .05
334 Ken Williams RC .01 .05
335 Bryn Smith .01 .05
336 Bill Ripken RC .08 .25
337 Greg Brock .01 .05
338 Mike Heath .01 .05
339 Mike Greenwell .01 .05
340 Claudell Washington .01 .05
341 Jose Gonzalez .01 .05
342 Mel Hall .01 .05
343 Jim Eisenreich .01 .05
344 Tony Bernazard .01 .05
345 Tim Raines .02 .10
346 Bob Brower .01 .05
347 Larry Parrish .01 .05
348 Thad Bosley .01 .05
349 Dennis Eckersley .05 .15
350 Cory Snyder .01 .05
351 Rick Cerone .01 .05
352 John Shelby .01 .05
353 Larry Herndon .01 .05
354 John Habyan .01 .05
355 Chuck Crim .01 .05
356 Gus Polidor .01 .05
357 Ken Dayley .01 .05
358 Danny Darwin .01 .05
359 Lance Parrish .02 .10
360 James Steels .01 .05
361 Al Pedrique .01 .05
362 Mike Aldrete .01 .05
363 Juan Castillo .01 .05
364 Len Dykstra .02 .10
365 Luis Quinones .01 .05
366 Jim Presley .01 .05
367 Lloyd Moseby .01 .05
368 Kirby Puckett .07 .20
369 Eric Davis .02 .10
370 Gary Redus .01 .05
371 Dave Schmidt .01 .05
372 Mark Clear .01 .05
373 Dave Bergman .01 .05
374 Charles Hudson .01 .05
375 Calvin Schiraldi .01 .05
376 Alex Trevino .01 .05
377 Tom Candiotti .01 .05
378 Steve Farr .01 .05
379 Mike Gallego .01 .05
380 Andy McGaffigan .01 .05
381 Kirk McCaskill .01 .05
382 Oddibe McDowell .01 .05
383 Floyd Bannister .01 .05
384 Denny Walling .01 .05
385 Don Carman .01 .05
386 Todd Worrell .01 .05
387 Eric Show .01 .05
388 Dave Parker .02 .10
389 Rick Mahler .01 .05
390 Mike Dunne .01 .05

391 Candy Maldonado .01 .05
392 Bob Dernier .01 .05
393 Dave Valle .01 .05
394 Ernie Whitt .01 .05
395 Juan Berenguer .01 .05
396 Mike Young .01 .05
397 Mike Felder .01 .05
398 Willie Hernandez .01 .05
399 Jim Rice .02 .10
400A Checklist 358-467 .01 .05
400B Checklist 346-451 .01 .05
401 Tommy John .02 .10
402 Brian Holton .01 .05
403 Carmen Castillo .01 .05
404 Jamie Quirk .01 .05
405 Dwayne Murphy .01 .05
406 Jeff Parrett .01 .05
407 Don Sutton .02 .10
408 Jerry Browne .01 .05
409 Jim Winn .01 .05
410 Dave Smith .01 .05
411 Shane Mack .01 .05
412 Greg Gross .01 .05
413 Nick Esasky .01 .05
414 Damaso Garcia .01 .05
415 Brian Fisher .01 .05
416 Brian Dayett .01 .05
417 Curt Ford .01 .05
418 Mark Williamson .01 .05
419 Bill Schroeder .01 .05
420 Mike Henneman RC .08 .25
421 John Marzano .01 .05
422 Ron Kittle .01 .05
423 Matt Young .01 .05
424 Steve Balboni .01 .05
425 Luis Polonia RC .08 .25
426 Randy St.Claire .01 .05
427 Greg Harris .01 .05
428 Johnny Ray .01 .05
429 Ray Searage .01 .05
430 Ricky Horton .01 .05
431 Gerald Young .01 .05
432 Rick Schu .01 .05
433 Paul O'Neill .05 .15
434 Rich Gossage .02 .10
435 John Cangelosi .01 .05
436 Mike LaCoss .01 .05
437 Gerald Perry .01 .05
438 Dave Martinez .01 .05
439 Darryl Strawberry .02 .10
440 John Moses .01 .05
441 Greg Gagne .01 .05
442 Jesse Barfield .02 .10
443 George Frazier .01 .05
444 Garth Iorg .01 .05
445 Ed Nunez .01 .05
446 Rick Aguilera .01 .05
447 Jerry Mumphrey .01 .05
448 Rafael Ramirez .01 .05
449 John Smiley RC .08 .25
450 Atlee Hammaker .01 .05
451 Lance McCullers .01 .05
452 Guy Hoffman .01 .05
453 Chris James .01 .05
454 Terry Pendleton .02 .10
455 Dave Meads .01 .05
456 Bill Buckner .02 .10
457 John Pawlowski .01 .05
458 Bob Sebra .01 .05
459 Jim Dwyer .01 .05
460 Jay Aldrich .01 .05
461 Frank Tanana .02 .10
462 Oil Can Boyd .01 .05
463 Dan Pasqua .01 .05
464 Tim Crews RC .08 .25
465 Andy Allanson .01 .05
466 Bill Pecota RC .02 .10
467 Steve Ontiveros .01 .05
468 Hubie Brooks .01 .05
469 Paul Kilgus .01 .05
470 Dale Mohorcic .01 .05
471 Dan Quisenberry .01 .05
472 Dave Stewart .02 .10
473 Dave Clark .01 .05
474 Joel Skinner .01 .05
475 Dave Anderson .01 .05
476 Dan Petry .01 .05
477 Carl Nichols .01 .05
478 Ernest Riles .01 .05
479 George Hendrick .02 .10
480 John Morris .01 .05
481 Manny Hernandez .01 .05
482 Jeff Stone .01 .05
483 Chris Brown .01 .05
484 Mike Bielecki .01 .05
485 Dave Dravecky .01 .05
486 Rick Manning .01 .05
487 Bill Almon .01 .05
488 Jim Sundberg .02 .10
489 Ken Phelps .01 .05
490 Tom Henke .01 .05
491 Dan Gladden .01 .05
492 Barry Larkin .05 .15
493 Fred Manrique .01 .05
494 Mike Griffin .01 .05
495 Mark Knudson .01 .05
496 Bill Madlock .02 .10
497 Tim Stoddard .01 .05
498 Sam Horn RC .07 .20
499 Tracy Woodson RC .02 .10
500A Checklist 468-577 .01 .05
500B Checklist 452-557 .01 .05
501 Ken Schrom .01 .05
502 Angel Salazar .01 .05
503 Eric Plunk .01 .05
504 Joe Hesketh .01 .05
505 Greg Minton .01 .05
506 Geno Petralli .01 .05
507 Bob James .01 .05
508 Robbie Wine .01 .05
509 Jeff Calhoun .01 .05
510 Steve Lake .01 .05
511 Mark Grant .01 .05
512 Frank Williams .01 .05
513 Jeff Blauser RC .08 .25
514 Bob Walk .01 .05
515 Craig Lefferts .01 .05
516 Manny Trillo .01 .05
517 Jerry Reed .01 .05
518 Rick Leach .01 .05
519 Mark Davidson .01 .05

520 Jeff Ballard .01 .05
521 Dave Stapleton .01 .05
522 Pat Sheridan .01 .05
523 Al Nipper .01 .05
524 Steve Trout .01 .05
525 Jeff Hamilton .01 .05
526 Tommy Hinzo .01 .05
527 Lonnie Smith .01 .05
528 Greg Cadaret .01 .05
529 Bob McClure UER .01 .05
(Rob on front)
530 Chuck Finley .02 .10
531 Jeff Russell .01 .05
532 Steve Lyons .01 .05
533 Terry Puhl .01 .05
534 Eric Nolte .01 .05
535 Kent Tekulve .01 .05
536 Pat Pacillo .01 .05
537 Charlie Puleo .01 .05
538 Tom Prince .01 .05
539 Greg Maddux .40 1.00
540 Jim Lindeman .01 .05
541 Pete Stanicek .01 .05
542 Steve Kiefer .01 .05
543A Jim Morrison ERR .05 .15
(No decimal before lifetime average)
543B Jim Morrison COR .01 .05
544 Spike Owen .01 .05
545 Jay Buhner RC .20 .50
546 Mike Devereaux RC .08 .25
547 Jerry Don Gleaton .01 .05
548 Jose Rijo .02 .10
549 Dennis Martinez .02 .10
550 Mike Loynd .01 .05
551 Darrell Miller .01 .05
552 Dave LaPoint .01 .05
553 John Tudor .02 .10
554 Rocky Childress .01 .05
555 Wally Ritchie .01 .05
556 Terry McGriff .01 .05
557 Dave Leiper .01 .05
558 Jeff D. Robinson .01 .05
559 Jose Uribe .01 .05
560 Ted Simmons .02 .10
561 Les Lancaster .01 .05
562 Keith A. Miller RC .08 .25
563 Harold Reynolds .02 .10
564 Gene Larkin RC .08 .25
565 Cecil Fielder .02 .10
566 Roy Smalley .01 .05
567 Duane Ward .01 .05
568 Bill Wilkinson .01 .05
569 Howard Johnson .02 .10
570 Frank DiPino .01 .05
571 Pete Smith RC .02 .10
572 Darnell Coles .01 .05
573 Don Robinson .01 .05
574 Rob Nelson UER .01 .05
(Career 0 RBI, but 1 RBI in '87)
575 Dennis Rasmussen .01 .05
576 Steve Jeltz UER .01 .05
(Photo actually Juan Samuel; Samuel noted for one batting glove and black bat)
577 Tom Pagnozzi RC .02 .10
578 Ty Gainey .01 .05
579 Gary Lucas .01 .05
580 Ron Hassey .01 .05
581 Herm Winningham .01 .05
582 Rene Gonzales RC .02 .10
583 Brad Komminsk .01 .05
584 Doyle Alexander .01 .05
585 Jeff Sellers .01 .05
586 Bill Gullickson .01 .05
587 Tim Belcher .01 .05
588 Doug Jones RC .08 .25
589 Melido Perez RC .08 .25
590 Rick Honeycutt .01 .05
591 Pascual Perez .01 .05
592 Curt Wilkerson .01 .05
593 Steve Howe .01 .05
594 John Davis .01 .05
595 Storm Davis .01 .05
596 Sammy Stewart .01 .05
597 Neil Allen .01 .05
598 Alejandro Pena .01 .05
599 Mark Thurmond .01 .05
600A Checklist 578-660 .01 .05
BC1-BC26
600B Checklist 558-660 .01 .05
601 Jose Mesa RC .08 .25
602 Don August .01 .05
603 Terry Leach SP .02 .10
604 Tom Newell .01 .05
605 Randall Byers SP .02 .10
606 Jim Gott .01 .05
607 Harry Spilman .01 .05
608 John Candelaria .01 .05
609 Mike Brumley .01 .05
610 Mickey Brantley .01 .05
611 Jose Nunez SP .02 .10
612 Tom Nieto .01 .05
613 Rick Reuschel .01 .05
614 Lee Mazzilli SP .02 .10
615 Scott Lusader .01 .05
616 Bobby Meacham .01 .05
617 Kevin McReynolds SP .02 .10
618 Gene Garber .01 .05
619 Barry Lyons SP .02 .10
620 Randy Myers .02 .10
621 Donnie Moore .01 .05
622 Domingo Ramos .01 .05
623 Ed Romero .01 .05
624 Greg Myers RC .08 .25
625 Ripken Family .15 .40
Cal Ripken Sr.
Cal Ripken Jr.
Billy Ripken
626 Pat Perry .01 .05
627 Andres Thomas SP .02 .10
628 Matt Williams SP RC .30 .75
629 Dave Hengel .01 .05
630 Jeff Musselman SP .02 .10
631 Tim Laudner .01 .05
632 Bob Ojeda SP .02 .10
633 Rafael Santana .01 .05
634 Wes Gardner .01 .05
635 Roberto Kelly SP RC .08 .25

636 Mike Flanagan SP .02 .10
637 Jay Bell RC .15 .40
638 Bob Melvin .01 .05
639 D.Berryhill RC UER .08 .25
Bats: Swithch
640 David Wells SP RC .40 1.00
641 Stan Musial PUZ .07 .20
642 Doug Sisk .01 .05
643 Keith Hughes .01 .05
644 Tom Glavine RC 1.00 2.50
645 Al Newman .01 .05
646 Scott Sanderson .01 .05
647 Scott Terry .01 .05
648 Tim Teufel SP .02 .10
649 Garry Templeton SP .02 .10
650 Manny Lee SP .02 .10
651 Roger McDowell SP .02 .10
652 Mookie Wilson SP .02 .10
653 David Cone SP .02 .10
654 Ron Gant SP RC .15 .40
655 Joe Price SP .02 .10
656 George Bell SP .02 .10
657 Gregg Jefferies SP RC .08 .25
658 Todd Stottlemyre SP RC .08 .25
659 Geronimo Berroa SP RC .08 .25
660 Jerry Royster SP .02 .10
XX Kirby Puckett .50 1.25
Blister Pack

1988 Donruss Rookies

The 1988 Donruss "The Rookies" set features 56 standard-size full-color cards plus a 15-piece puzzle of Stan Musial. This set was distributed exclusively in factory set form in a small, cellophane-wrapped, green and black through hobby dealers. Card fronts are similar in design to the 1988 Donruss regular issue except for the presence of "The Rookies" logo in the lower right corner and a green and black border instead of a blue and black border on the fronts. Extended Rookie Cards in this set include Brady Anderson, Edgar Martinez, and Walt Weiss. Notable early cards were issued of Roberto Alomar, Mark Grace and Jay Buhner.

COMP.FACT.SET (56) 4.00 10.00
1 Mark Grace .75 2.00
2 Mike Campbell .05 .15
3 Todd Frohwirth .05 .15
4 Dave Stapleton .05 .15
5 Shawn Abner .05 .15
6 Jose Cecena .05 .15
7 Dave Gallagher .05 .15
8 Mark Parent .05 .15
9 Cecil Espy XRC .05 .15
10 Pete Smith .05 .15
11 Jay Buhner .40 1.00
12 Pat Borders XRC .20 .50
13 Doug Jennings .05 .15
14 Brady Anderson XRC .30 .75
15 Pete Stanicek .05 .15
16 Roberto Kelly .20 .50
17 Jeff Treadway .05 .15
18 Walt Weiss XRC .30 .75
19 Paul Gibson .05 .15
20 Tim Crews .05 .15
21 Melido Perez .05 .15
22 Steve Peters .05 .15
23 Craig Worthington .05 .15
24 John Trautwein .05 .15
25 DeWayne Vaughn .05 .15
26 David Wells .60 1.50
27 Al Leiter .40 1.00
28 Tim Belcher .05 .15
29 Johnny Paredes .05 .15
30 Chris Sabo XRC .15 .40
31 Damon Berryhill .05 .15
32 Randy Milligan XRC .08 .25
33 Gary Thurman .05 .15
34 Kevin Elster .05 .15
35 Roberto Alomar 1.50 4.00
36 Edgar Martinez XRC 2.00 5.00
UER Photo actually Edwin Nunez
37 Todd Stottlemyre .05 .15
38 Joey Meyer .05 .15
39 Carl Nichols .05 .15
40 Jack McDowell .30 .75
41 Jose Bautista XRC .08 .25
42 Sil Campusano .05 .15
43 John Dopson .05 .15
44 Jody Reed .20 .50
45 Darrin Jackson XRC .08 .25
46 Mike Capel .05 .15
47 Ron Gant .30 .75
48 John Davis .05 .15
49 Kevin Coffman .05 .15
50 Cris Carpenter XRC .08 .25
51 Mackey Sasser .05 .15
52 Luis Alicea XRC .20 .50
53 Bryan Harvey XRC .10 .30
54 Steve Ellsworth .05 .15
55 Mike Macfarlane XRC .20 .50
56 Checklist 1-56 .05 .15

1989 Donruss

This set consists of 660 standard-size cards. The cards were primarily issued in 15-card wax packs, rack packs and hobby and retail factory sets. Each wax pack also contained a puzzle panel (featuring Warren Spahn this year). The wax packs were issued 36 packs to a box and 20 boxes to a case. The cards feature a distinctive black side border with an alternating coating. Subsets include Diamond Kings (1-27) and Rated Rookies (28-47). There are two variations that occur throughout most of the set. On the card backs "Denotes Led League" can be found with one asterisk to the left or with an asterisk on each side. On the card fronts the horizontal lines on the left and right borders can be glossy or non-glossy. Since both of these variation types are relatively minor and seem equally common, there is no premium value for either type. Rather than short-printing 26 cards in order to make room for printing the Bonus MVP's this year, Donruss apparently chose to double print 106 cards. These double prints are listed below by DP. Rookie Cards in this set include Sandy Alomar Jr., Brady Anderson, Dante Bichette, Craig Biggio, Ken Griffey Jr., Randy Johnson, Curt Schilling, Gary Sheffield and John Smoltz. Similar to the 1988 Donruss set, a special card was issued on blister packs, and features the card number as "Bonus Card".

COMPLETE SET (660)	10.00	25.00
COMP.FACT.SET (672)	10.00	25.00
1 Mike Greenwell DK	.01	.05
2 Bobby Bonilla DK DP	.02	.10
3 Pete Incaviglia DK	.01	.05
4 Chris Sabo DK DP	.02	.10
5 Robin Yount DK	.15	.40
6 Tony Gwynn DK DP	.05	.15
7 Carlton Fisk DK UER	.05	.15
(OF on back)		
8 Cory Snyder DK	.01	.05
9 David Cone DK UER	.02	.10
('hurdlers')		
10 Kevin Seitzer DK	.01	.05
11 Rick Reuschel DK	.02	.10
12 Johnny Ray DK	.01	.05
13 Dave Schmidt DK	.01	.05
14 Andres Galarraga DK	.02	.10
15 Kirk Gibson DK	.02	.10
16 Fred McGriff DK	.05	.15
17 Mark Grace DK	.08	.25
18 Jeff M. Robinson DK	.01	.05
19 Vince Coleman DK DP	.01	.05
20 Dave Henderson DK	.01	.05
21 Harold Reynolds DK	.02	.10
22 Gerald Perry DK	.01	.05
23 Frank Viola DK	.02	.10
24 Steve Bedrosian DK	.01	.05
25 Glenn Davis DK	.01	.05
26 Don Mattingly DK UER	.10	.30
(Doesn't mention Don's previous DK in 1985)		
27 DK Checklist 1-26 DP	.01	.05
28 S.Alomar Jr. RR RC	.15	.40
29 Steve Searcy RR	.01	.05
30 Cameron Drew RR	.01	.05
31 Gary Sheffield RR RC	.60	1.50
32 Erik Hanson RR RC	.08	.25
33 Ken Griffey Jr. RR RC	3.00	8.00
34 Greg W. Harris RR RC	.02	.10
35 Gregg Jefferies RR	.01	.05
36 Luis Medina RR	.01	.05
37 Carlos Quintana RR RC	.02	.10
38 Felix Jose RR RC	.02	.10
39 Cris Carpenter RR RC*	.02	.10
40 Ron Jones RR	.02	.10
41 Dave West RR RC	.02	.10
42 R.Johnson RC RR UER	.75	2.00
Card says born in 1964 he was born in 1963		
43 Mike Harkey RR RC	.02	.10
44 P.Harnisch RR DP RC	.08	.25
45 Tom Gordon RR DP RC	.20	.50
46 Gregg Olson RC RR DP	.08	.25
47 Alex Sanchez RR DP	.01	.05
48 Ruben Sierra	.02	.10
49 Rafael Palmeiro	.08	.25
50 Ron Gant	.02	.10
51 Cal Ripken	.30	.75
52 Wally Joyner	.02	.10
53 Gary Carter	.02	.10
54 Andy Van Slyke	.05	.15
55 Robin Yount	.15	.40
56 Pete Incaviglia	.01	.05
57 Greg Brock	.01	.05
58 Melido Perez	.01	.05
59 Craig Lefferts	.01	.05
60 Gary Pettis	.01	.05
61 Danny Tartabull	.01	.05
62 Guillermo Hernandez	.01	.05
63 Ozzie Smith	.15	.40
64 Gary Gaetti	.02	.10
65 Mark Davis	.01	.05
66 Lee Smith	.02	.10
67 Dennis Eckersley	.05	.15
68 Wade Boggs	.05	.15
69 Mike Scott	.02	.10
70 Fred McGriff	.05	.15
71 Tom Browning	.01	.05
72 Claudell Washington	.01	.05
73 Mel Hall	.01	.05
74 Don Mattingly	.25	.60
75 Steve Bedrosian	.01	.05
76 Juan Samuel	.01	.05
77 Mike Scioscia	.02	.10
78 Dave Righetti	.02	.10
79 Alfredo Griffin	.01	.05
80 Eric Davis UER	.02	.10
(165 games in 1988, should be 135)		
81 Juan Berenguer	.01	.05
82 Todd Worrell	.01	.05
83 Joe Carter	.02	.10
84 Steve Sax	.01	.05
85 Frank White	.02	.10
86 John Kruk	.02	.10
87 Rance Mulliniks	.01	.05
88 Alan Ashby	.01	.05
89 Charlie Leibrandt	.01	.05
90 Frank Tanana	.02	.10
91 Jose Canseco	.08	.25
92 Barry Bonds	.60	1.50
93 Harold Reynolds	.02	.10
94 Mark McLemore	.01	.05
95 Mark McGwire	.40	1.00
96 Eddie Murray	.08	.25
97 Tim Raines	.02	.10
98 Robby Thompson	.01	.05
99 Kevin McReynolds	.01	.05
100 Checklist 28-137	.01	.05
101 Carlton Fisk	.05	.15
102 Dave Martinez	.01	.05
103 Glenn Braggs	.01	.05
104 Dale Murphy	.05	.15
105 Ryne Sandberg	.15	.40
106 Dennis Martinez	.02	.10
107 Pete O'Brien	.01	.05
108 Dick Schofield	.01	.05
109 Henry Cotto	.01	.05
110 Mike Marshall	.01	.05
111 Keith Moreland	.01	.05
112 Tom Brunansky	.01	.05
113 Kelly Gruber UER	.01	.05
(Wrong birthdate)		
114 Brook Jacoby	.01	.05
115 Keith Brown	.01	.05
116 Matt Nokes	.01	.05
117 Keith Hernandez	.02	.10
118 Bob Forsch	.01	.05
119 Bert Blyleven UER	.02	.10
(... 3000 strikeouts in 1987, should be 1986)		
120 Willie Wilson	.02	.10
121 Tommy Gregg	.01	.05
122 Jim Rice	.02	.10
123 Bob Knepper	.01	.05
124 Danny Jackson	.01	.05
125 Eric Plunk	.01	.05
126 Brian Fisher	.01	.05
127 Mike Pagliarulo	.01	.05
128 Tony Gwynn	.10	.30
129 Lance McCullers	.01	.05
130 Andres Galarraga	.02	.10
131 Jose Uribe	.01	.05
132 Kirk Gibson UER	.02	.10
(Wrong birthdate)		
133 David Palmer	.01	.05
134 R.J. Reynolds	.01	.05
135 Greg Walker	.01	.05
136 Kirk McCaskill UER	.01	.05
(Wrong birthdate)		
137 Shawon Dunston	.01	.05
138 Andy Allanson	.01	.05
139 Rob Murphy	.01	.05
140 Mike Aldrete	.01	.05
141 Terry Kennedy	.01	.05
142 Scott Fletcher	.01	.05
143 Steve Balboni	.01	.05
144 Bret Saberhagen	.02	.10
145 Ozzie Virgil	.01	.05
146 Dale Sveum	.01	.05
147 Darryl Strawberry	.02	.10
148 Harold Baines	.02	.10
149 George Bell	.02	.10
150 Dave Parker	.02	.10
151 Bobby Bonilla	.02	.10
152 Mookie Wilson	.02	.10
153 Ted Power	.01	.05
154 Nolan Ryan	.40	1.00
155 Jeff Reardon	.02	.10
156 Tim Wallach	.01	.05
157 Jamie Moyer	.02	.10
158 Rich Gossage	.02	.10
159 Dave Winfield	.02	.10
160 Von Hayes	.01	.05
161 Willie McGee	.02	.10
162 Rich Gedman	.01	.05
163 Tony Pena	.01	.05
164 Mike Morgan	.01	.05
165 Charlie Hough	.02	.10
166 Mike Stanley	.01	.05
167 Andre Dawson	.02	.10
168 Joe Boever	.01	.05
169 Pete Stanicek	.01	.05
170 Bob Boone	.02	.10
171 Ron Darling	.02	.10
172 Bob Walk	.01	.05
173 Rob Deer	.01	.05
174 Steve Buechele	.01	.05
175 Ted Higuera	.01	.05
176 Ozzie Guillen	.02	.10
177 Candy Maldonado	.01	.05
178 Doyle Alexander	.01	.05
179 Mark Gubicza	.01	.05
180 Alan Trammell	.02	.10
181 Vince Coleman	.01	.05
182 Kirby Puckett	.08	.25
183 Chris Brown	.01	.05
184 Marty Barrett	.01	.05
185 Stan Javier	.01	.05
186 Mike Greenwell	.01	.05
187 Billy Hatcher	.01	.05
188 Jimmy Key	.02	.10
189 Nick Esasky	.01	.05
190 Don Slaught	.01	.05
191 Cory Snyder	.01	.05
192 John Candelaria	.01	.05
193 Mike Schmidt	.20	.50
194 Kevin Gross	.01	.05
195 John Tudor	.02	.10
196 Neil Allen	.01	.05
197 Orel Hershiser	.02	.10
198 Kal Daniels	.01	.05
199 Kent Hrbek	.02	.10
200 Checklist 138-247	.01	.05
201 Joe Magrane	.01	.05
202 Scott Bailes	.01	.05
203 Tim Belcher	.01	.05
204 George Brett	.25	.60
205 Benito Santiago	.02	.10
206 Tony Fernandez	.01	.05
207 Gerald Young	.01	.05
208 Bo Jackson	.08	.25
209 Chet Lemon	.02	.10
210 Storm Davis	.01	.05
211 Doug Drabek	.01	.05
212 Mickey Brantley UER	.01	.05
(Photo actually Nelson Simmons)		
213 Devon White	.02	.10
214 Dave Stewart	.02	.10
215 Dave Schmidt	.01	.05
216 Bryn Smith	.01	.05
217 Brett Butler	.02	.10
218 Bob Ojeda	.01	.05
219 Steve Rosenberg	.01	.05
220 Hubie Brooks	.01	.05
221 B.J. Surhoff	.02	.10
222 Rick Mahler	.01	.05
223 Rick Sutcliffe	.02	.10
224 Neal Heaton	.01	.05
225 Mitch Williams	.01	.05
226 Chuck Finley	.02	.10
227 Mark Langston	.01	.05
228 Jesse Orosco	.01	.05
229 Ed Whitson	.01	.05
230 Terry Pendleton	.02	.10
231 Lloyd Moseby	.01	.05
232 Greg Swindell	.01	.05
233 John Franco	.02	.10
234 Jack Morris	.02	.10
235 Howard Johnson	.02	.10
236 Glenn Davis	.01	.05
237 Frank Viola	.02	.10
238 Kevin Seitzer	.01	.05
239 Gerald Perry	.01	.05
240 Dwight Evans	.05	.15
241 Jim Deshaies	.01	.05
242 Bo Diaz	.01	.05
243 Carney Lansford	.02	.10
244 Mike LaValliere	.01	.05
245 Rickey Henderson	.08	.25
246 Roberto Alomar	.08	.25
247 Jimmy Jones	.01	.05
248 Pascual Perez	.01	.05
249 Will Clark	.05	.15
250 Fernando Valenzuela	.02	.10
251 Shane Rawley	.01	.05
252 Sid Bream	.01	.05
253 Steve Lyons	.01	.05
254 Brian Downing	.02	.10
255 Mark Grace	.08	.25
256 Tom Candiotti	.01	.05
257 Barry Larkin	.05	.15
258 Mike Krukow	.01	.05
259 Billy Ripken	.01	.05
260 Cecilio Guante	.01	.05
261 Scott Bradley	.01	.05
262 Floyd Bannister	.01	.05
263 Pete Smith	.01	.05
264 Jim Gantner UER	.01	.05
(Wrong birthdate)		
265 Roger McDowell	.01	.05
266 Bobby Thigpen	.01	.05
267 Jim Clancy	.01	.05
268 Terry Steinbach	.02	.10
269 Mike Dunne	.01	.05
270 Dwight Gooden	.02	.10
271 Mike Heath	.01	.05
272 Dave Smith	.01	.05
273 Keith Atherton	.01	.05
274 Tim Burke	.01	.05
275 Damon Berryhill	.01	.05
276 Vance Law	.01	.05
277 Rich Dotson	.01	.05
278 Lance Parrish	.02	.10
279 Denny Walling	.01	.05
280 Roger Clemens	.40	1.00
281 Greg Mathews	.01	.05
282 Tom Niedenfuer	.01	.05
283 Paul Kilgus	.01	.05
284 Jose Guzman	.01	.05
285 Calvin Schiraldi	.01	.05
286 Charlie Puleo UER	.01	.05
(Career ERA 4.24, should be 4.23)		
287 Joe Orsulak	.01	.05
288 Jack Howell	.01	.05
289 Kevin Elster	.01	.05
290 Jose Lind	.01	.05
291 Paul Molitor	.02	.10
292 Cecil Espy	.01	.05
293 Bill Wegman	.01	.05
294 Dan Pasqua	.01	.05
295 Scott Garrelts UER	.01	.05
(Wrong birthdate)		
296 Walt Terrell	.01	.05
297 Ed Hearn	.01	.05
298 Lou Whitaker	.02	.10
299 Ken Dayley	.01	.05
300 Checklist 248-357	.01	.05
301 Tommy Herr	.01	.05
302 Mike Brumley	.01	.05
303 Ellis Burks	.02	.10
304 Curt Young UER	.01	.05
(Wrong birthdate)		
305 Jody Reed	.01	.05
306 Bill Doran	.01	.05
307 David Wells	.02	.10
308 Ron Robinson	.01	.05
309 Rafael Santana	.01	.05
310 Julio Franco	.02	.10
311 Jack Clark	.02	.10
312 Chris James	.01	.05
313 Milt Thompson	.01	.05
314 John Shelby	.01	.05
315 Al Leiter	.08	.25
316 Mike Davis	.01	.05
317 Chris Sabo RC *	.15	.40
318 Greg Gagne	.01	.05
319 Jose Oquendo	.01	.05
320 John Farrell	.01	.05
321 Franklin Stubbs	.01	.05
322 Kurt Stillwell	.01	.05
323 Shawn Abner	.01	.05
324 Mike Flanagan	.01	.05
325 Kevin Bass	.01	.05
326 Pat Tabler	.01	.05
327 Mike Henneman	.01	.05
328 Rick Honeycutt	.01	.05
329 John Smiley	.01	.05
330 Rey Quinones	.01	.05
331 Johnny Ray	.01	.05
332 Bob Welch	.02	.10
333 Larry Sheets	.01	.05
334 Jeff Parrett	.01	.05
335 Rick Reuschel UER	.02	.10
(For Don Robinson& should be Jeff)		
336 Randy Myers	.02	.10
337 Ken Williams	.01	.05
338 Andy McGaffigan	.01	.05
339 Joey Meyer	.01	.05
340 Dion James	.01	.05
341 Les Lancaster	.01	.05
342 Tom Foley	.01	.05
343 Geno Petralli	.01	.05
344 Dan Petry	.01	.05
345 Alvin Davis	.01	.05
346 Mickey Hatcher	.01	.05
347 Marvell Wynne	.01	.05
348 Danny Cox	.01	.05
349 Dave Stieb	.02	.10
350 Jay Bell	.02	.10
351 Jeff Treadway	.01	.05
352 Luis Salazar	.01	.05
353 Len Dykstra	.02	.10
354 Juan Agosto	.01	.05
355 Gene Larkin	.01	.05
356 Steve Farr	.01	.05
357 Paul Assenmacher	.01	.05
358 Todd Benzinger	.01	.05
359 Larry Andersen	.01	.05
360 Paul O'Neill	.05	.15
361 Ron Hassey	.01	.05
362 Jim Gott	.01	.05
363 Ken Phelps	.01	.05
364 Tim Flannery	.01	.05
365 Randy Ready	.01	.05
366 Nelson Santovenia	.01	.05
367 Kelly Downs	.01	.05
368 Danny Heep	.01	.05
369 Phil Bradley	.01	.05
370 Jeff D. Robinson	.01	.05
371 Ivan Calderon	.01	.05
372 Mike Witt	.01	.05
373 Greg Maddux	.20	.50
374 Carmen Castillo	.01	.05
375 Jose Rijo	.02	.10
376 Joe Price	.01	.05
377 Rene Gonzales	.01	.05
378 Oddibe McDowell	.01	.05
379 Jim Presley	.01	.05
380 Brad Wellman	.01	.05
381 Tom Glavine	.08	.25
382 Dan Plesac	.01	.05
383 Wally Backman	.01	.05
384 Dave Gallagher	.01	.05
385 Tom Henke	.01	.05
386 Luis Polonia	.01	.05
387 Junior Ortiz	.01	.05
388 David Cone	.02	.10
389 Dave Bergman	.01	.05
390 Danny Darwin	.01	.05
391 Dan Gladden	.01	.05
392 John Dopson	.01	.05
393 Frank DiPino	.01	.05
394 Al Nipper	.01	.05
395 Willie Randolph	.02	.10
396 Don Carman	.01	.05
397 Scott Terry	.01	.05
398 Rick Cerone	.01	.05
399 Tom Pagnozzi	.01	.05
400 Checklist 358-467	.01	.05
401 Mickey Tettleton	.01	.05
402 Curtis Wilkerson	.01	.05
403 Jeff Russell	.01	.05
404 Pat Perry	.01	.05
405 Jose Alvarez RC	.02	.10
406 Rick Schu	.01	.05
407 Sherman Corbett	.01	.05
408 Dave Magadan	.01	.05
409 Bob Kipper	.01	.05
410 Don August	.01	.05
411 Bob Brower	.01	.05
412 Chris Bosio	.01	.05
413 Jerry Reuss	.01	.05
414 Atlee Hammaker	.01	.05
415 Jim Walewander	.01	.05
416 Mike Macfarlane RC *	.08	.25
417 Pat Sheridan	.01	.05
418 Pedro Guerrero	.02	.10
419 Allan Anderson	.01	.05
420 Mark Parent	.01	.05
421 Bob Stanley	.01	.05
422 Mike Gallego	.01	.05
423 Bruce Hurst	.01	.05
424 Dave Meads	.01	.05
425 Jesse Barfield	.02	.10
426 Rob Dibble RC	.15	.40
427 Joel Skinner	.01	.05
428 Ron Kittle	.01	.05
429 Rick Rhoden	.01	.05
430 Bob Dernier	.01	.05
431 Steve Jeltz	.01	.05
432 Rick Dempsey	.01	.05
433 Roberto Kelly	.01	.05
434 Dave Anderson	.01	.05
435 Herm Winningham	.01	.05
436 Al Newman	.01	.05
437 Jose DeLeon	.01	.05
438 Doug Jones	.01	.05
439 Brian Holton	.01	.05
440 Jeff Montgomery	.01	.05
441 Dickie Thon	.01	.05
442 Cecil Fielder	.02	.10
443 John Fishel	.01	.05
444 Jerry Don Gleaton	.01	.05
445 Paul Gibson	.01	.05
446 Walt Weiss	.01	.05
447 Glenn Wilson	.01	.05
448 Mike Moore	.01	.05
449 Chili Davis	.02	.10
450 Dave Henderson	.01	.05
451 Jose Bautista RC	.02	.10
452 Rex Hudler	.01	.05
453 Bob Brenly	.01	.05
454 Mackey Sasser	.01	.05
455 Daryl Boston	.01	.05
456 Mike R. Fitzgerald	.01	.05
457 Jeffrey Leonard	.01	.05
458 Bruce Sutter	.02	.10
459 Mitch Webster	.01	.05
460 Joe Hesketh	.01	.05
461 Bobby Witt	.01	.05
462 Stu Cliburn	.01	.05
463 Scott Bankhead	.01	.05
464 Ramon Martinez RC	.08	.25
465 Dave Leiper	.01	.05
466 Luis Alicea RC *	.08	.25
467 John Cerutti	.01	.05
468 Ron Washington	.01	.05
469 Jeff Reed	.01	.05
470 Jeff M. Robinson	.01	.05
471 Sid Fernandez	.01	.05
472 Terry Puhl	.01	.05
473 Charlie Lea	.01	.05
474 Israel Sanchez	.01	.05
475 Bruce Benedict	.01	.05
476 Oil Can Boyd	.01	.05
477 Craig Reynolds	.01	.05
478 Frank Williams	.01	.05
479 Greg Cadaret	.01	.05
480 Randy Kramer	.01	.05
481 Dave Eiland	.01	.05
482 Eric Show	.01	.05
483 Garry Templeton	.02	.10
484 Wallace Johnson	.01	.05
485 Kevin Mitchell	.02	.10
486 Tim Crews	.01	.05
487 Mike Maddux	.01	.05
488 Dave LaPoint	.01	.05
489 Fred Manrique	.01	.05
490 Greg Minton	.01	.05
491 Doug Dascenzo UER	.01	.05
(Photo actually Damon Berryhill)		
492 Willie Upshaw	.01	.05
493 Jack Armstrong RC *	.08	.25
494 Kirt Manwaring	.01	.05
495 Jeff Ballard	.01	.05
496 Jeff Kunkel	.01	.05
497 Mike Campbell	.01	.05
498 Gary Thurman	.01	.05
499 Zane Smith	.01	.05
500 Checklist 468-577 DP	.01	.05
501 Mike Birkbeck	.01	.05
502 Terry Leach	.01	.05
503 Shawn Hillegas	.01	.05
504 Manny Lee	.01	.05
505 Doug Jennings	.01	.05
506 Ken Oberkfell	.01	.05
507 Tim Teufel	.01	.05
508 Tom Brookens	.01	.05
509 Rafael Ramirez	.01	.05
510 Fred Toliver	.01	.05
511 Brian Holman RC *	.02	.10
512 Mike Bielecki	.01	.05
513 Jeff Pico	.01	.05
514 Charles Hudson	.01	.05
515 Bruce Ruffin	.01	.05
516 L.McWilliams UER	.01	.05
New Richland, should be North Richland		
517 Jeff Sellers	.01	.05
518 John Costello	.01	.05
519 Brady Anderson RC	.15	.40
520 Craig McMurtry	.01	.05
521 Ray Hayward DP	.01	.05
522 Drew Hall DP	.01	.05
523 Mark Lemke DP RC	.15	.40
524 Oswald Peraza DP	.01	.05
525 Bryan Harvey DP RC *	.08	.25
526 Rick Aguilera DP	.01	.05
527 Tom Prince DP	.01	.05
528 Mark Clear DP	.01	.05
529 Jerry Browne DP	.01	.05
530 Juan Castillo DP	.01	.05
531 Jack McDowell DP	.02	.10
532 Chris Speier DP	.01	.05
533 Darrell Evans DP	.02	.10
534 Luis Aquino DP	.01	.05
535 Eric King DP	.01	.05
536 Ken Hill DP RC	.08	.25
537 Randy Bush DP	.01	.05
538 Shane Mack DP	.01	.05
539 Tom Bolton DP	.01	.05
540 Gene Nelson DP	.01	.05
541 Wes Gardner DP	.01	.05
542 Ken Caminiti DP	.05	.15
543 Duane Ward DP	.01	.05
544 Norm Charlton DP RC	.08	.25
545 Hal Morris DP RC	.08	.25
546 Rich Yett DP	.01	.05
547 H.Meulens DP RC	.02	.10
548 Greg A. Harris DP	.01	.05
549 Darren Daulton DP	.02	.10
(Posing as right-handed hitter)		
550 Jeff Hamilton DP	.01	.05
551 Luis Aguayo DP	.01	.05
552 Tim Leary DP	.01	.05
(Resembles M.Marshall)		
553 Ron Oester DP	.01	.05
554 S.Lombardozzi DP	.01	.05
555 Tim Jones DP	.01	.05
556 Bud Black DP	.01	.05
557 Alejandro Pena DP	.01	.05
558 Jose DeJesus DP	.01	.05
559 D.Rasmussen DP	.01	.05
560 Pat Borders DP RC*	.08	.25
561 Craig Biggio DP RC	1.25	3.00
562 Luis DeLosSantos DP	.01	.05
563 Fred Lynn DP	.02	.10
564 Todd Burns DP	.01	.05
565 Felix Fermin DP	.01	.05
566 Darnell Coles DP	.01	.05
567 Willie Fraser DP	.01	.05
568 Glenn Hubbard DP	.01	.05
569 Craig Worthington DP	.01	.05
570 Johnny Paredes DP	.01	.05
571 Don Robinson DP	.01	.05
572 Barry Lyons DP	.01	.05
573 Bill Long DP	.01	.05
574 Tracy Jones DP	.01	.05
575 Juan Nieves DP	.01	.05
576 Andres Thomas DP	.01	.05
577 Rolando Roomes DP	.01	.05
578 Luis Rivera UER DP	.01	.05
(Wrong birthdate)		
579 Chad Kreuter DP RC	.08	.25
580 Tony Armas DP	.02	.10
581 Jay Buhner	.02	.10
582 Ricky Horton DP	.01	.05
583 Andy Hawkins DP	.01	.05
584 Sil Campusano	.01	.05
585 Dave Clark	.01	.05
586 Van Snider DP	.01	.05
587 Todd Frohwirth DP	.01	.05
588 W.Spahn DP PUZ	.05	.15
589 William Brennan	.01	.05
590 German Gonzalez	.01	.05
591 Ernie Whitt DP	.01	.05
592 Jeff Blauser	.01	.05
593 Spike Owen DP	.01	.05
594 Matt Williams	.08	.25
595 Lloyd McClendon DP	.01	.05
596 Steve Ontiveros	.01	.05
597 Scott Medvin	.01	.05
598 Hipolito Pena DP	.01	.05
599 Jerald Clark DP RC	.02	.10
600A CL 578-660 DP	.01	.05
635 Kurt Schilling		
600B CL 578-660 DP	.01	.05
635 Curt Schilling; MVP's not listed on checklist card		
600C CL 578-660 DP	.01	.05
635 Curt Schilling; MVP's listed following 660		
601 Carmelo Martinez DP	.01	.05
602 Mike LaCoss	.01	.05
603 Mike Devereaux	.01	.05
604 Alex Madrid DP	.01	.05
605 Gary Redus DP	.01	.05
606 Lance Johnson	.01	.05
607 Terry Clark DP	.01	.05
608 Manny Trillo DP	.01	.05
609 Scott Jordan RC	.08	.25
610 Jay Howell DP	.01	.05
611 Francisco Melendez	.01	.05
612 Mike Boddicker	.01	.05
613 Kevin Brown DP	.08	.25
614 Dave Valle	.01	.05
615 Tim Laudner DP	.01	.05
616 Andy Nezelek UER	.01	.05
(Wrong birthdate)		
617 Chuck Crim	.01	.05
618 Jack Savage DP	.01	.05
619 Adam Peterson	.01	.05
620 Todd Stottlemyre	.01	.05
621 Lance Blankenship RC	.02	.10
622 Miguel Garcia DP	.01	.05
623 Keith A. Miller DP	.01	.05
624 Ricky Jordan DP RC*	.08	.25
625 Ernest Riles DP	.01	.05
626 John Moses DP	.01	.05
627 Nelson Liriano DP	.01	.05
628 Mike Smithson DP	.01	.05
629 Scott Sanderson	.01	.05
630 Dale Mohorcic	.01	.05
631 Marvin Freeman DP	.01	.05
632 Mike Young DP	.01	.05
633 Dennis Lamp	.01	.05
634 Dante Bichette DP RC	.15	.40
635 Curt Schilling DP RC	1.50	4.00
636 Scott May DP	.01	.05
637 Mike Schooler	.01	.05
638 Rick Leach	.01	.05
639 Tom Lampkin UER	.01	.05
(Throws Left, should be Throws Right)		
640 Brian Meyer	.01	.05
641 Brian Harper	.01	.05
642 John Smoltz RC	.60	1.50
643 Jose Canseco	.08	.25
(40/40 Club)		
644 Bill Schroeder	.01	.05
645 Edgar Martinez	.08	.25
646 Dennis Cook RC	.08	.25
647 Barry Jones	.01	.05
648 Orel Hershiser	.02	.10
(59 and Counting)		
649 Rod Nichols	.01	.05
650 Jody Davis	.01	.05
651 Bob Milacki	.01	.05
652 Mike Jackson	.01	.05
653 Derek Lilliquist RC	.02	.10
654 Paul Mirabella	.01	.05
655 Mike Diaz	.01	.05
656 Jeff Musselman	.01	.05
657 Jerry Reed	.01	.05
658 Kevin Blankenship	.01	.05
659 Wayne Tolleson	.01	.05
660 Eric Hetzel	.01	.05
BC Jose Canseco	.75	2.00
Blister Pack		

1989 Donruss Rookies

The 1989 Donruss Rookies set contains 56 standard-size cards. The cards were distributed exclusively in factory set form in small, emerald green, cellophane-wrapped boxes through hobby dealers. The cards are almost identical in design to regular 1989 Donruss except for the green borders. Rookie Cards in this set include Jim Abbott, Steve Finley, Kenny Rogers and Deion Sanders. Ken Griffey Jr. and Randy Johnson are also featured on a card within the set.

COMP.FACT.SET (56)	6.00	15.00
1 Gary Sheffield	.75	2.00
2 Gregg Jefferies	.02	.10
3 Ken Griffey Jr.	4.00	10.00
4 Tom Gordon	.08	.25
5 Billy Spiers RC	.08	.25
6 Deion Sanders RC	.60	1.50
7 Donn Pall	.01	.05
8 Steve Carter	.01	.05
9 Francisco Oliveras	.01	.05
10 Steve Wilson RC	.02	.10
11 Bob Geren RC	.01	.05
12 Tony Castillo RC	.02	.10
13 Kenny Rogers RC	1.00	2.50
14 Carlos Martinez RC	.02	.10
15 Edgar Martinez	.08	.25
16 Jim Abbott RC	.40	1.00
17 Torey Lovullo RC	.02	.10
18 Mark Carreon	.01	.05
19 Geronimo Berroa	.01	.05
20 Luis Medina	.01	.05
21 Sandy Alomar Jr.	.05	.15
22 Bob Milacki	.01	.05
23 Joe Girardi RC	.15	.40
24 German Gonzalez	.01	.05
25 Craig Worthington	.01	.05
26 Jerome Walton RC	.08	.25
27 Gary Wayne	.01	.05
28 Tim Jones	.01	.05
29 Dante Bichette	.05	.15
30 Alexis Infante RC	.01	.05
31 Ken Hill	.08	.25
32 Dwight Smith RC	.08	.25
33 Luis de los Santos	.01	.05
34 Eric Yelding	.01	.05
35 Gregg Olson	.08	.25
36 Phil Stephenson	.01	.05
37 Ken Patterson	.01	.05
38 Rick Wrona	.01	.05
39 Mike Brumley	.01	.05
40 Cris Carpenter	.01	.05
41 Jeff Brantley RC	.08	.25
42 Ron Jones	.01	.05
43 Randy Johnson	.75	2.00
44 Kevin Brown	.08	.25
45 Ramon Martinez	.02	.10
46 Greg W.Harris	.01	.05
47 Steve Finley RC	.30	.75
48 Randy Kramer	.01	.05
49 Erik Hanson	.02	.10
50 Matt Merullo	.01	.05
51 Mike Devereaux	.01	.05
52 Clay Parker	.01	.05
53 Omar Vizquel RC	.40	1.00
54 Derek Lilliquist	.01	.05
55 Junior Felix RC	.02	.10
56 Checklist 1-56	.01	.05

1990 Donruss

The 1990 Donruss set contains 716 standard-size cards. Cards were issued in wax packs and hobby and retail factory sets. The card fronts feature bright red borders. Subsets include Diamond Kings (1-27) and Rated Rookies (28-47). The set was the largest ever produced by Donruss, unfortunately it also had a large number of errors which were corrected after the cards were released. Most of these feature minor printing flaws and insignificant variations that collectors have found unworthy of price differentials. There are several double-printed cards indicated in our checklist with the set indicated with a "DP" coding. Rookie Cards of note include Juan Gonzalez, David Justice, John Olerud, Dean Palmer, Sammy Sosa, Larry Walker and Bernie Williams.

COMPLETE SET (716)	6.00	15.00
COMP.FACT.SET (728)	6.00	15.00
COMP.YAZ PUZZLE	.40	1.00
1 Bo Jackson DK	.05	.15
2 Steve Sax DK	.01	.05
3A Ruben Sierra DK ERR	.02	.10
(No small line on top border on card back)		
3B Ruben Sierra DK COR	.02	.10
4 Ken Griffey Jr. DK	.15	.40
5 Mickey Tettleton DK	.01	.05
6 Dave Stewart DK	.01	.05
7 Jim Deshaies DK DP	.01	.05
8 John Smoltz DK	.08	.25
9 Mike Bielecki DK	.01	.05
10A Brian Downing DK	.05	.15
ERR (Reverse neg-on card front)		
10B Brian Downing DK COR	.01	.05
11 Kevin Mitchell DK	.01	.05
12 Kelly Gruber DK	.01	.05
13 Joe Magrane DK	.01	.05
14 John Franco DK	.02	.10
15 Ozzie Guillen DK	.02	.10
16 Lou Whitaker DK	.01	.05
17 John Smiley DK	.01	.05
18 Howard Johnson DK	.01	.05
19 Willie Randolph DK	.02	.10
20 Chris Bosio DK	.01	.05
21 Tommy Herr DK DP	.01	.05
22 Dan Gladden DK	.01	.05
23 Ellis Burks DK	.02	.10
24 Pete O'Brien DK	.01	.05
25 Bryn Smith DK	.01	.05
26 Ed Whitson DK DP	.01	.05
27 DK Checklist 1-27 DP	.01	.05
(Comments on Perez-Steele on back)		
28 Robin Ventura RR	.08	.25
29 Todd Zeile RR	.02	.10
30 Sandy Alomar Jr.	.02	.10
31 Kent Mercker RC	.08	.25
32 B.McDonald RC UER	.08	.25
Middle name Benard not Benjamin		
33A J.Gonzalez ERR RC	.75	2.00
Reverse negative		
33B J.Gonzalez COR RC	.40	1.00
34 Eric Anthony RC	.02	.10
35 Mike Fetters RC	.08	.25
36 Marquis Grissom RC	.15	.40
37 Greg Vaughn RR	.01	.05
38 Brian DuBois RC	.02	.10
39 Steve Avery RR UER	.01	.05
(Born in MI, not NJ)		
40 Mark Gardner RC	.02	.10
41 Andy Benes	.02	.10
42 Delino DeShields RC	.08	.25
43 Scott Coolbaugh RC	.02	.10
44 Pat Combs DP	.01	.05
45 Alex Sanchez DP	.01	.05
46 Kelly Mann DP RC	.02	.10
47 Julio Machado RC	.02	.10
48 Pete Incaviglia	.01	.05
49 Shawon Dunston	.01	.05
50 Jeff Treadway	.01	.05
51 Jeff Ballard	.01	.05
52 Claudell Washington	.01	.05
53 Juan Samuel	.01	.05
54 John Smiley	.01	.05
55 Rob Deer	.01	.05
56 Geno Petralli	.01	.05
57 Chris Bosio	.01	.05
58 Carlton Fisk	.05	.15

59 Kirt Manwaring .01 .05
60 Chet Lemon .01 .05
61 Bo Jackson .08 .25
62 Doyle Alexander .01 .05
63 Pedro Guerrero .01 .05
64 Allan Anderson .01 .05
65 Greg W. Harris .01 .05
66 Mike Greenwell .01 .05
67 Walt Weiss .01 .05
68 Wade Boggs .05 .15
69 Jim Clancy .01 .05
70 Junior Felix .01 .05
71 Barry Larkin .05 .15
72 Dave LaPoint .01 .05
73 Joel Skinner .01 .05
74 Jesse Barfield .01 .05
75 Tommy Herr .01 .05
76 Ricky Jordan .01 .05
77 Eddie Murray .08 .25
78 Steve Sax .01 .05
79 Tim Belcher .01 .05
80 Danny Jackson .01 .05
81 Kent Hrbek .02 .10
82 Milt Thompson .01 .05
83 Brook Jacoby .01 .05
84 Mike Marshall .01 .05
85 Kevin Seitzer .01 .05
86 Tony Gwynn .10 .30
87 Dave Stieb .02 .10
88 Dave Smith .01 .05
89 Bret Saberhagen .02 .10
90 Alan Trammell .02 .10
91 Tony Phillips .01 .05
92 Doug Drabek .01 .05
93 Jeffrey Leonard .01 .05
94 Wally Joyner .02 .10
95 Carney Lansford .02 .10
96 Cal Ripken .30 .75
97 Andres Galarraga .02 .10
98 Kevin Mitchell .01 .05
99 Howard Johnson .01 .05
100A Checklist 28-129 .01 .05
100B Checklist 28-125 .01 .05
101 Melido Perez .01 .05
102 Spike Owen .01 .05
103 Paul Molitor .02 .10
104 Geronimo Berroa .01 .05
105 Ryne Sandberg .15 .40
106 Bryn Smith .01 .05
107 Steve Buechele .01 .05
108 Jim Abbott .05 .15
109 Alvin Davis .01 .05
110 Lee Smith .02 .10
111 Roberto Alomar .05 .15
112 Rick Reuschel .01 .05
113A Kelly Gruber ERR .01 .05
(Born 2/22)
113B Kelly Gruber COR .01 .05
(Born 2/26; corrected in factory sets)
114 Joe Carter .02 .10
115 Jose Rijo .01 .05
116 Greg Minton .01 .05
117 Bob Ojeda .01 .05
118 Glenn Davis .01 .05
119 Jeff Reardon .02 .10
120 Kurt Stillwell .01 .05
121 John Smoltz .08 .25
122 Dwight Evans .05 .15
123 Eric Yelding RC .01 .05
124 John Franco .02 .10
125 Jose Canseco .05 .15
126 Barry Bonds .40 1.00
127 Lee Guetterman .01 .05
128 Jack Clark .02 .10
129 Dave Valle .01 .05
130 Hubie Brooks .01 .05
131 Ernest Riles .01 .05
132 Mike Morgan .01 .05
133 Steve Jeltz .01 .05
134 Jeff D. Robinson .01 .05
135 Ozzie Guillen .02 .10
136 Chili Davis .02 .10
137 Mitch Webster .01 .05
138 Jerry Browne .01 .05
139 Bo Diaz .01 .05
140 Robby Thompson .01 .05
141 Craig Worthington .01 .05
142 Julio Franco .02 .10
143 Brian Holman .01 .05
144 George Brett .25 .60
145 Tom Glavine .05 .15
146 Robin Yount .15 .40
147 Gary Carter .02 .10
148 Ron Kittle .01 .05
149 Tony Fernandez .01 .05
150 Dave Stewart .02 .10
151 Gary Gaetti .02 .10
152 Kevin Elster .01 .05
153 Gerald Perry .01 .05
154 Jesse Orosco .01 .05
155 Wally Backman .01 .05
156 Dennis Martinez .02 .10
157 Rick Sutcliffe .02 .10
158 Greg Maddux .15 .40
159 Andy Hawkins .01 .05
160 John Kruk .02 .10
161 Jose Oquendo .01 .05
162 John Dopson .01 .05
163 Joe Magrane .01 .05
164 Bill Ripken .01 .05
165 Fred Manrique .01 .05
166 Nolan Ryan UER .40 1.00
(Did not lead NL in K's in '89 as he was in AL in '89)
167 Damon Berryhill .01 .05
168 Dale Murphy .05 .15
169 Mickey Tettleton .01 .05
170A Kirk McCaskill ERR .01 .05
(Born 4/19)
170B Kirk McCaskill COR .01 .05
(Born 4/9; corrected in factory sets)
171 Dwight Gooden .02 .10
172 Jose Lind .01 .05
173 B.J. Surhoff .02 .10
174 Ruben Sierra .02 .10
175 Dan Plesac .01 .05
176 Dan Pasqua .01 .05
177 Kelly Downs .01 .05
178 Matt Nokes .01 .05
179 Luis Aquino .01 .05
180 Frank Tanana .01 .05
181 Tony Pena .01 .05
182 Dan Gladden .01 .05
183 Bruce Hurst .01 .05
184 Roger Clemens .40 1.00
185 Mark McGwire .40 1.00
186 Rob Murphy .01 .05
187 Jim Deshaies .01 .05
188 Fred McGriff .08 .25
189 Rob Dibble .02 .10
190 Don Mattingly .25 .60
191 Felix Fermin .01 .05
192 Roberto Kelly .01 .05
193 Dennis Cook .01 .05
194 Darren Daulton .02 .10
195 Alfredo Griffin .01 .05
196 Eric Plunk .01 .05
197 Orel Hershiser .02 .10
198 Paul O'Neill .05 .15
199 Randy Bush .01 .05
200A Checklist 130-231 .01 .05
200B Checklist 126-223 .01 .05
201 Ozzie Smith .15 .40
202 Pete O'Brien .01 .05
203 Jay Howell .01 .05
204 Mark Gubicza .01 .05
205 Ed Whitson .01 .05
206 George Bell .01 .05
207 Mike Scott .01 .05
208 Charlie Leibrandt .01 .05
209 Mike Heath .01 .05
210 Dennis Eckersley .02 .10
211 Mike LaValliere .01 .05
212 Darnell Coles .01 .05
213 Lance Parrish .01 .05
214 Mike Moore .01 .05
215 Steve Finley .02 .10
216 Tim Raines .02 .10
217A Scott Garrelts ERR .01 .05
(Born 10/20)
217B Scott Garrelts COR .01 .05
(Born 10/30; corrected in factory sets)
218 Kevin McReynolds .01 .05
219 Dave Gallagher .01 .05
220 Tim Wallach .01 .05
221 Chuck Crim .01 .05
222 Lonnie Smith .01 .05
223 Andre Dawson .02 .10
224 Nelson Santovenia .01 .05
225 Rafael Palmeiro .05 .15
226 Devon White .02 .10
227 Harold Reynolds .02 .10
228 Ellis Burks .05 .15
229 Mark Parent .01 .05
230 Will Clark .05 .15
231 Jimmy Key .02 .10
232 John Farrell .01 .05
233 Eric Davis .02 .10
234 Johnny Ray .01 .05
235 Darryl Strawberry .02 .10
236 Bill Doran .01 .05
237 Greg Gagne .01 .05
238 Jim Eisenreich .01 .05
239 Tommy Gregg .01 .05
240 Marty Barrett .01 .05
241 Rafael Ramirez .01 .05
242 Chris Sabo .01 .05
243 Dave Henderson .01 .05
244 Andy Van Slyke .05 .15
245 Alvaro Espinoza .01 .05
246 Garry Templeton .01 .05
247 Gene Harris .01 .05
248 Kevin Gross .01 .05
249 Brett Butler .02 .10
250 Willie Randolph .02 .10
251 Roger McDowell .01 .05
252 Rafael Belliard .01 .05
253 Steve Rosenberg .01 .05
254 Jack Howell .01 .05
255 Marvell Wynne .01 .05
256 Tom Candiotti .01 .05
257 Todd Benzinger .01 .05
258 Don Robinson .01 .05
259 Phil Bradley .01 .05
260 Cecil Espy .01 .05
261 Scott Bankhead .01 .05
262 Frank White .02 .10
263 Andres Thomas .01 .05
264 Glenn Braggs .01 .05
265 David Cone .02 .10
266 Bobby Thigpen .01 .05
267 Nelson Liriano .01 .05
268 Terry Steinbach .01 .05
269 Kirby Puckett UER .08 .25
(Back doesn't consider Joe Torre's .363 in '71)
270 Gregg Jefferies .02 .10
271 Jeff Blauser .01 .05
272 Cory Snyder .01 .05
273 Roy Smith .01 .05
274 Tom Foley .01 .05
275 Mitch Williams .01 .05
276 Paul Kilgus .01 .05
277 Don Slaught .01 .05
278 Von Hayes .01 .05
279 Vince Coleman .01 .05
280 Mike Boddicker .01 .05
281 Ken Dayley .01 .05
282 Mike Devereaux .01 .05
283 Kenny Rogers .02 .10
284 Jeff Russell .01 .05
285 Jerome Walton .01 .05
286 Derek Lilliquist .01 .05
287 Joe Orsulak .01 .05
288 Dick Schofield .01 .05
289 Ron Darling .01 .05
290 Bobby Bonilla .02 .10
291 Jim Gantner .01 .05
292 Bobby Witt .01 .05
293 Greg Brock .01 .05
294 Ivan Calderon .01 .05
295 Steve Bedrosian .01 .05
296 Mike Henneman .01 .05
297 Tom Gordon .02 .10
298 Lou Whitaker .02 .10
299 Terry Pendleton .02 .10
300A Checklist 232-333 .01 .05
300B Checklist 224-321 .01 .05
301 Juan Berenguer .01 .05
302 Mark Davis .01 .05
303 Nick Esasky .01 .05
304 Rickey Henderson .08 .25
305 Rick Cerone .01 .05
306 Craig Biggio .08 .25
307 Duane Ward .01 .05
308 Tom Browning .01 .05
309 Walt Terrell .01 .05
310 Greg Swindell .01 .05
311 Dave Righetti .01 .05
312 Mike Maddux .01 .05
313 Len Dykstra .02 .10
314 Jose Gonzalez .01 .05
315 Steve Balboni .01 .05
316 Mike Scioscia .01 .05
317 Ron Oester .01 .05
318 Gary Wayne .01 .05
319 Todd Worrell .01 .05
320 Doug Jones .01 .05
321 Jeff Hamilton .01 .05
322 Danny Tartabull .01 .05
323 Chris James .01 .05
324 Mike Flanagan .01 .05
325 Gerald Young .01 .05
326 Bob Boone .02 .10
327 Frank Williams .01 .05
328 Dave Parker .02 .10
329 Sid Bream .01 .05
330 Mike Schooler .01 .05
331 Bert Blyleven .02 .10
332 Bob Welch .01 .05
333 Bob Milacki .01 .05
334 Tim Burke .01 .05
335 Jose Uribe .01 .05
336 Randy Myers .02 .10
337 Eric King .01 .05
338 Mark Langston .01 .05
339 Teddy Higuera .01 .05
340 Oddibe McDowell .01 .05
341 Lloyd McClendon .01 .05
342 Pascual Perez .01 .05
343 Kevin Brown UER .02 .10
(Signed is misspelled as signed on back)
344 Chuck Finley .02 .10
345 Erik Hanson .01 .05
346 Rich Gedman .01 .05
347 Bip Roberts .01 .05
348 Matt Williams .02 .10
349 Tom Henke .01 .05
350 Brad Komminsk .01 .05
351 Jeff Reed .01 .05
352 Brian Downing .01 .05
353 Frank Viola .01 .05
354 Terry Puhl .01 .05
355 Brian Harper .01 .05
356 Steve Farr .01 .05
357 Joe Boever .01 .05
358 Danny Heep .01 .05
359 Larry Andersen .01 .05
360 Rolando Roomes .01 .05
361 Mike Gallego .01 .05
362 Bob Kipper .01 .05
363 Clay Parker .01 .05
364 Mike Pagliarulo .01 .05
365 Ken Griffey Jr. UER .30 .75
(Signed through 1990, should be 1991)
366 Rex Hudler .01 .05
367 Pat Sheridan .01 .05
368 Kirk Gibson .02 .10
369 Jeff Parrett .01 .05
370 Bob Walk .01 .05
371 Ken Patterson .01 .05
372 Bryan Harvey .01 .05
373 Mike Bielecki .01 .05
374 Tom Magrann RC .01 .05
375 Rick Mahler .01 .05
376 Craig Lefferts .01 .05
377 Gregg Olson .02 .10
378 Jamie Moyer .02 .10
379 Randy Johnson .20 .50
380 Jeff Montgomery .02 .10
381 Marty Clary .01 .05
382 Bill Spiers .01 .05
383 Dave Magadan .01 .05
384 Greg Hibbard RC .02 .10
385 Ernie Whitt .01 .05
386 Rick Honeycutt .01 .05
387 Dave West .01 .05
388 Keith Hernandez .02 .10
389 Jose Alvarez .01 .05
390 Joey Belle .08 .25
391 Rick Aguilera .02 .10
392 Mike Fitzgerald .01 .05
393 Dwight Smith .01 .05
394 Steve Wilson .01 .05
395 Bob Geren .01 .05
396 Randy Ready .01 .05
397 Ken Hill .02 .10
398 Jody Reed .01 .05
399 Tom Brunansky .01 .05
400A Checklist 334-435 .01 .05
400B Checklist 322-419 .01 .05
401 Rene Gonzales .01 .05
402 Harold Baines .02 .10
403 Cecilio Guante .01 .05
404 Joe Girardi .05 .15
405A Sergio Valdez ERR RC .01 .05
(Card front shows black line crossing S in Sergio)
405B Sergio Valdez COR .01 .05
406 Mark Williamson .01 .05
407 Glenn Hoffman .01 .05
408 Jeff Innis RC .01 .05
409 Randy Kramer .01 .05
410 Charlie O'Brien .01 .05
411 Charlie Hough .02 .10
412 Gus Polidor .01 .05
413 Ron Karkovice .01 .05
414 Trevor Wilson .01 .05
415 Kevin Ritz RC .01 .05
416 Gary Thurman .01 .05
417 Jeff M. Robinson .01 .05
418 Scott Terry .01 .05
419 Tim Laudner .01 .05
420 Dennis Rasmussen .01 .05
421 Luis Rivera .01 .05
422 Jim Corsi .01 .05
423 Dennis Lamp .01 .05
424 Ken Caminiti .02 .10
425 David Wells .02 .10
426 Norm Charlton .01 .05
427 Deion Sanders .08 .25
428 Dion James .01 .05
429 Chuck Cary .01 .05
430 Ken Howell .01 .05
431 Steve Lake .01 .05
432 Kal Daniels .01 .05
433 Lance McCullers .01 .05
434 Lenny Harris .01 .05
435 Scott Scudder .01 .05
436 Gene Larkin .01 .05
437 Dan Quisenberry .01 .05
438 Steve Olin RC .08 .25
439 Mickey Hatcher .01 .05
440 Willie Wilson .01 .05
441 Mark Grant .01 .05
442 Mookie Wilson .02 .10
443 Alex Trevino .01 .05
444 Pat Tabler .01 .05
445 Dave Bergman .01 .05
446 Todd Burns .01 .05
447 R.J. Reynolds .01 .05
448 Jay Buhner .02 .10
449 Lee Stevens .02 .10
450 Ron Hassey .01 .05
451 Bob Melvin .01 .05
452 Dave Martinez .01 .05
453 Greg Litton .01 .05
454 Mark Carreon .01 .05
455 Scott Fletcher .01 .05
456 Otis Nixon .01 .05
457 Tony Fossas RC .01 .05
458 John Russell .01 .05
459 Paul Assenmacher .01 .05
460 Zane Smith .01 .05
461 Jack Daugherty RC .01 .05
462 Rich Monteleone .01 .05
463 Greg Briley .01 .05
464 Mike Smithson .01 .05
465 Benito Santiago .02 .10
466 Jeff Brantley .01 .05
467 Jose Nunez .01 .05
468 Scott Bailes .01 .05
469 Ken Griffey Sr. .02 .10
470 Bob McClure .01 .05
471 Mackey Sasser .01 .05
472 Glenn Wilson .01 .05
473 Kevin Tapani RC .08 .25
474 Bill Buckner .02 .10
475 Ron Gant .02 .10
476 Kevin Romine .01 .05
477 Juan Agosto .01 .05
478 Herm Winningham .01 .05
479 Storm Davis .01 .05
480 Jeff King .01 .05
481 Kevin Mmahat RC .01 .05
482 Carmelo Martinez .01 .05
483 Omar Vizquel .08 .25
484 Jim Dwyer .01 .05
485 Bob Knepper .01 .05
486 Dave Anderson .01 .05
487 Ron Jones .01 .05
488 Jay Bell .02 .10
489 Sammy Sosa RC 1.00 2.50
490 Kent Anderson .01 .05
491 Domingo Ramos .01 .05
492 Dave Clark .01 .05
493 Tim Birtsas .01 .05
494 Ken Oberkfell .01 .05
495 Larry Sheets .01 .05
496 Jeff Kunkel .01 .05
497 Jim Presley .01 .05
498 Mike Macfarlane .01 .05
499 Pete Smith .01 .05
500A Checklist 436-537 DP .01 .05
500B Checklist 420-517 .01 .05
501 Gary Sheffield .08 .25
502 Terry Bross RC .01 .05
503 Jerry Kutzler RC .01 .05
504 Lloyd Moseby .01 .05
505 Curt Young .01 .05
506 Al Newman .01 .05
507 Keith Miller .01 .05
508 Mike Stanton RC .08 .25
509 Rich Yett .01 .05
510 Tim Drummond RC .01 .05
511 Joe Hesketh .01 .05
512 Rick Wrona .01 .05
513 Luis Salazar .01 .05
514 Hal Morris .01 .05
515 Terry Mulholland .01 .05
516 John Morris .01 .05
517 Carlos Quintana .01 .05
518 Frank DiPino .01 .05
519 Randy Milligan .01 .05
520 Chad Kreuter .01 .05
521 Mike Jeffcoat .01 .05
522 Mike Harkey .01 .05
523A Andy Nezelek ERR .01 .05
(Wrong birth year)
523B Andy Nezelek COR .05 .15
(Finally corrected in factory sets)
524 Dave Schmidt .01 .05
525 Tony Armas .01 .05
526 Barry Lyons .01 .05
527 Rick Reed RC .08 .25
528 Jerry Reuss .01 .05
529 Dean Palmer RC .08 .25
530 Jeff Peterek RC .01 .05
531 Carlos Martinez .01 .05
532 Atlee Hammaker .01 .05
533 Mike Brumley .01 .05
534 Terry Leach .01 .05
535 Doug Strange RC .01 .05
536 Jose DeLeon .01 .05
537 Shane Rawley .01 .05
538 Joey Cora .02 .10
539 Eric Hetzel .01 .05
540 Gene Nelson .01 .05
541 Wes Gardner .01 .05
542 Mark Portugal .01 .05
543 Al Leiter .08 .25
544 Jack Armstrong .01 .05
545 Greg Cadaret .01 .05
546 Rod Nichols .01 .05
547 Luis Polonia .01 .05
548 Charlie Hayes .01 .05
549 Dickie Thon .01 .05
550 Tim Crews .01 .05
551 Dave Winfield .02 .10
552 Mike Davis .01 .05
553 Ron Robinson .01 .05
554 Carmen Castillo .01 .05
555 John Costello .01 .05
556 Bud Black .01 .05
557 Rick Dempsey .01 .05
558 Jim Acker .01 .05
559 Eric Show .01 .05
560 Pat Borders .01 .05
561 Danny Darwin .01 .05
562 Rick Luecken RC .01 .05
563 Edwin Nunez .01 .05
564 Felix Jose .01 .05
565 John Cangelosi .01 .05
566 Bill Swift .01 .05
567 Bill Schroeder .01 .05
568 Stan Javier .01 .05
569 Jim Traber .01 .05
570 Wallace Johnson .01 .05
571 Donell Nixon .01 .05
572 Sid Fernandez .01 .05
573 Lance Johnson .01 .05
574 Andy McGaffigan .01 .05
575 Mark Knudson .01 .05
576 Tommy Greene RC .02 .10
577 Mark Grace .05 .15
578 Larry Walker RC .40 1.00
579 Mike Stanley .01 .05
580 Mike Witt DP .01 .05
581 Scott Bradley .01 .05
582 Greg A. Harris .01 .05
583A Kevin Hickey ERR .08 .25
583B Kevin Hickey COR .01 .05
584 Lee Mazzilli .01 .05
585 Jeff Pico .01 .05
586 Joe Oliver .01 .05
587 Willie Fraser DP .01 .05
588 Carl Yastrzemski .08 .25
Puzzle Card DP
589 Kevin Bass DP .01 .05
590 John Moses DP .01 .05
591 Tom Pagnozzi DP .01 .05
592 Tony Castillo DP .01 .05
593 Jerald Clark DP .01 .05
594 Dan Schatzeder .01 .05
595 Luis Quinones DP .01 .05
596 Pete Harnisch DP .01 .05
597 Gary Redus .01 .05
598 Mel Hall .01 .05
599 Rick Schu .01 .05
600A Checklist 538-639 .01 .05
600B Checklist 518-617 .01 .05
601 Mike Kingery DP .01 .05
602 Terry Kennedy DP .01 .05
603 Mike Sharperson DP .01 .05
604 Don Carman DP .01 .05
605 Jim Gott .01 .05
606 Donn Pall DP .01 .05
607 Rance Mulliniks .01 .05
608 Curt Wilkerson DP .01 .05
609 Mike Felder DP .01 .05
610 G.Hernandez DP .01 .05
611 Candy Maldonado DP .01 .05
612 Mark Thurmond DP .01 .05
613 Rick Leach DP RC .01 .05
614 Jerry Reed DP .01 .05
615 Franklin Stubbs .01 .05
616 Billy Hatcher DP .01 .05
617 Don August DP .01 .05
618 Tim Teufel .01 .05
619 Shawn Hillegas DP .01 .05
620 Manny Lee .01 .05
621 Gary Ward DP .01 .05
622 Mark Guthrie DP RC .01 .05
623 Jeff Musselman DP .01 .05
624 Mark Lemke DP .01 .05
625 Fernando Valenzuela .02 .10
626 Paul Sorrento DP RC .08 .25
627 Glenallen Hill DP .01 .05
628 Les Lancaster DP .01 .05
629 Vance Law DP .01 .05
630 Randy Velarde DP .01 .05
631 Todd Frohwirth DP .01 .05
632 Willie McGee .02 .10
633 Dennis Boyd DP .01 .05
634 Cris Carpenter DP .01 .05
635 Brian Holton .01 .05
636 Tracy Jones DP .01 .05
637A Terry Steinbach AS .01 .05
(Recent Major League Performance)
637B Terry Steinbach AS .01 .05
(All-Star Game Performance)
638 Brady Anderson .02 .10
639A Jack Morris ERR .02 .10
(Card front shows black line crossing J in Jack)
639B Jack Morris COR .02 .10
640 Jaime Navarro .01 .05
641 Darrin Jackson .01 .05
642 Mike Dyer RC .01 .05
643 Mike Schmidt .20 .50
644 Henry Cotto .01 .05
645 John Cerutti .01 .05
646 Francisco Cabrera .01 .05
647 Scott Sanderson .01 .05
648 Brian Meyer .01 .05
649 Ray Searage .01 .05
650A Bo Jackson AS .08 .25
(Recent Major League Performance)
650B Bo Jackson AS .08 .25
(All-Star Game Performance)
651 Steve Lyons .01 .05
652 Mike LaCoss .01 .05
653 Ted Power .01 .05
654A Howard Johnson AS .01 .05
(Recent Major League Performance)
654B Howard Johnson AS .01 .05
(All-Star Game Performance)
655 Mauro Gozzo RC .01 .05
656 Mike Blowers RC .02 .10
657 Paul Gibson .01 .05
658 Neal Heaton .01 .05
659 Nolan Ryan 5000K .20 .50
COR (Still an error as Ryan did not lead AL in K's in '75)
659A Nolan Ryan 5000K .60 1.50
(665 King of Kings back) ERR
660A Harold Baines AS .30 .75
(Black line through star on front; Recent Major League Performance)
660B Harold Baines AS .40 1.00
(Black line through star on front; All-Star Game Performance)
660C Harold Baines AS .08 .25
(Black line behind star on front; Recent Major League Performance)
660D Harold Baines AS .01 .05
(Black line behind star on front; All-Star Game Performance)
661 Gary Pettis .01 .05
662 Clint Zavaras RC .01 .05
663A Rick Reuschel AS .01 .05
(Recent Major League Performance)
663B Rick Reuschel AS .01 .05
(All-Star Game Performance)
664 Alejandro Pena .01 .05
665 N.Ryan KING COR .20 .50
665A Nolan Ryan KING .60 1.50
(659 5000 K back) ERR
665C N.Ryan KING ERR .30 .75
No number on back in factory sets
666 Ricky Horton .01 .05
667 Curt Schilling .40 1.00
668 Bill Landrum .01 .05
669 Todd Stottlemyre .02 .10
670 Tim Leary .01 .05
671 John Wetteland .08 .25
672 Calvin Schiraldi .01 .05
673A Ruben Sierra AS .01 .05
(Recent Major League Performance)
673B Ruben Sierra AS .01 .05
(All-Star Game Performance)
674A Pedro Guerrero AS .01 .05
(Recent Major League Performance)
674B Pedro Guerrero AS .01 .05
(All-Star Game Performance)
675 Ken Phelps .01 .05
676A Cal Ripken AS .15 .40
(All-Star Game Performance)
676B Cal Ripken AS .30 .75
(Recent Major League Performance)
677 Denny Walling .01 .05
678 Goose Gossage .02 .10
679 Gary Mielke RC .01 .05
680 Bill Bathe .01 .05
681 Tom Lawless .01 .05
682 Xavier Hernandez RC .01 .05
683A Kirby Puckett AS .05 .15
(Recent Major League Performance)
683B Kirby Puckett AS .05 .15
(All-Star Game Performance)
684 Mariano Duncan .01 .05
685 Ramon Martinez .01 .05
686 Tim Jones .01 .05
687 Tom Filer .01 .05
688 Steve Lombardozzi .01 .05
689 Bernie Williams RC .60 1.50
690 Chip Hale RC .01 .05
691 Beau Allred RC .01 .05
692A Ryne Sandberg AS .08 .25
(Recent Major League Performance)
692B Ryne Sandberg AS .08 .25
(All-Star Game Performance)
693 Jeff Huson RC .02 .10
694 Curt Ford .01 .05
695A Eric Davis AS .01 .05
(Recent Major League Performance)
695B Eric Davis AS .01 .05
(All-Star Game Performance)
696 Scott Lusader .01 .05
697A Mark McGwire AS .20 .50
(Recent Major League Performance)
697B Mark McGwire AS .20 .50
(All-Star Game Performance)
698 Steve Cummings RC .01 .05
699 George Canale RC .01 .05
700A Checklist 640-715 .08 .25
and BC1-BC26
700B Checklist 640-716 .02 .10
and BC1-BC26
700C Checklist 618-716 .01 .05
701A Julio Franco AS .01 .05
(Recent Major League Performance)
701B Julio Franco AS .01 .05
(All-Star Game Performance)
702 Dave Wayne Johnson RC .01 .05
703A Dave Stewart AS .01 .05
(Recent Major League Performance)
703B Dave Stewart AS .01 .05
(All-Star Game Performance)
704 Dave Justice RC .20 .50
705 Tony Gwynn AS .05 .15
(All-Star Game Performance)
705A Tony Gwynn AS .05 .15
(Recent Major League Performance)
706 Greg Myers .01 .05
707A Will Clark AS .05 .15
(Recent Major League Performance)
707B Will Clark AS .05 .15
(All-Star Game Performance)
708A Benito Santiago AS .01 .05
(Recent Major League Performance)
708B Benito Santiago AS .01 .05
(All-Star Game Performance)
709 Larry McWilliams .01 .05
710A Ozzie Smith AS .08 .25
(Recent Major League Performance)
710B Ozzie Smith AS Perf .08 .25
711 John Olerud RC .20 .50
712A Wade Boggs AS .02 .10
(Recent Major League Performance)
712B Wade Boggs AS .02 .10
(All-Star Game Performance)
713 Gary Eave RC .01 .05
714 Bob Tewksbury .01 .05
715A Kevin Mitchell AS .01 .05
(Recent Major League Performance)
715B Kevin Mitchell AS .01 .05
(All-Star Game Performance)
716 B.Giamatti COMM .08 .25
In Memoriam

1990 Donruss Rookies

The 1990 Donruss Rookies set marked the fifth consecutive year that Donruss issued a boxed set at season's end honoring the best rookies of the season. This set, which used the 1990 Donruss design but featured a green border, was issued exclusively through the Donruss dealer network to hobby dealers. This 56-card, standard size set came in its own box and the words "The Rookies" are featured prominently on the front of the cards. There are no notable Rookie Cards in this set.

COMP.FACT.SET (56) .75 2.00
1 Sandy Alomar Jr. UER .02 .10
(No stitches on baseball on Donruss logo on card front)
2 John Olerud .20 .50
3 Pat Combs .01 .05
4 Brian DuBois .01 .05
5 Felix Jose .01 .05
6 Delino DeShields .08 .25
7 Mike Stanton .01 .05
8 Mike Munoz RC .01 .05
9 Craig Grebeck RC .02 .10
10 Joe Kraemer RC .01 .05
11 Jeff Huson .01 .05
12 Bill Sampen RC .01 .05
13 Brian Bohanon RC .02 .10
14 Dave Justice .20 .50
15 Robin Ventura .08 .25
16 Greg Vaughn .01 .05
17 Wayne Edwards RC .01 .05
18 Shawn Boskie RC .02 .10
19 Carlos Baerga RC .08 .25
20 Mark Gardner .01 .05
21 Kevin Appier .02 .10
22 Mike Harkey .01 .05
23 Tim Layana RC .01 .05
24 Glenallen Hill .01 .05
25 Jerry Kutzler .01 .05
26 Mike Blowers .02 .10
27 Scott Ruskin RC .01 .05
28 Dana Kiecker RC .01 .05
29 Willie Blair RC .02 .10
30 Ben McDonald .02 .10
31 Todd Zeile .02 .10
32 Scott Coolbaugh RC .01 .05
33 Xavier Hernandez .01 .05
34 Mike Hartley RC .01 .05
35 Kevin Tapani .08 .25
36 Kevin Wickander .01 .05
37 Carlos Hernandez RC .08 .25
38 Brian Traxler RC .02 .10
39 Marty Brown .01 .05
40 Scott Radinsky RC .02 .10
41 Julio Machado .01 .05
42 Steve Avery .01 .05
43 Mark Lemke .01 .05
44 Alan Mills RC .02 .10
45 Marquis Grissom .08 .25
46 Greg Olson (C) RC .02 .10
47 Dave Hollins RC .08 .25
48 Jerald Clark .01 .05
49 Eric Anthony .01 .05
50 Tim Drummond .01 .05
51 John Burkett .01 .05
52 Brent Knackert RC .02 .10
53 Jeff Shaw .01 .05
54 John Orton RC .02 .10
55 Terry Shumpert RC .01 .05
56 Checklist 1-56 .01 .05

1991 Donruss

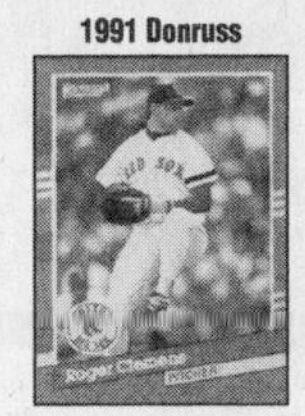

The 1991 Donruss set was issued in two series of 386 and 384 for a total of 770 standard-size cards. This set marked the first time Donruss issued cards in multiple series. The second series was issued approximately three months after the first series was issued. Cards were issued in wax packs and factory sets. As a separate promotion, wax packs were also given away with six and 12-packs of Coke and Diet Coke. First series cards feature blue borders and second series green borders with some stripes and the players name in white against a red background. Subsets include Diamond Kings (1-27), Rated Rookies (28-47/413-432), AL All-Stars (48-56), MVP's (387-412) and NL All-Stars (433-441). There were also special cards to honor the award winners and the heroes of the World Series. On cards 60, 70, 127, 182, 239, 294, 355, 368, and 377, the border stripes are red and yellow. There are no notable Rookie Cards in this set.

COMPLETE SET (770) 3.00 8.00
COMP.FACT.w/LEAF PREV 4.00 10.00
COMP.FACT.w/STUD. PREV 4.00 10.00
COMP.STARGELL PUZZLE .40 1.00
1 Dave Stieb DK .01 .05
2 Craig Biggio DK .02 .10
3 Cecil Fielder DK .01 .05
4 Barry Bonds DK .20 .50
5 Barry Larkin DK .02 .10
6 Dave Parker DK .01 .05
7 Len Dykstra DK .01 .05
8 Bobby Thigpen DK .01 .05
9 Roger Clemens DK .15 .40
10 Ron Gant DK UER .02 .10
(No trademark on team logo on back)
11 Delino DeShields DK .01 .05
12 Roberto Alomar DK UER .02 .10
No trademark on team logo on back
13 Sandy Alomar Jr. DK .01 .05
14 Ryne Sandberg DK UER .08 .25
Was DK in '85, not '83 as shown
15 Ramon Martinez DK .01 .05
16 Edgar Martinez DK .05 .15
17 Dave Magadan DK .01 .05
18 Matt Williams DK .01 .05
19 Rafael Palmeiro DK .02 .10
UER (No trademark on team logo on back)
20 Bob Welch DK .01 .05
21 Dave Righetti DK .01 .05
22 Brian Harper DK .01 .05
23 Gregg Olson DK .01 .05
24 Kurt Stillwell DK .01 .05
25 Pedro Guerrero DK UER .01 .05
No trademark on team logo on back
26 Chuck Finley DK UER .02 .10
(No trademark on team logo on back)
27 DK Checklist 1-27 .01 .05
28 Tino Martinez RR .08 .25
29 Mark Lewis RR .01 .05
30 Bernard Gilkey RR .01 .05
31 Hensley Meulens RR .01 .05
32 Derek Bell RR .02 .10
33 Jose Offerman RR .01 .05
34 Terry Bross RR .01 .05
35 Leo Gomez RR .01 .05
36 Derrick May RR .01 .05
37 Kevin Morton RR RC .01 .05
38 Moises Alou RR .02 .10
39 Julio Valera RR .01 .05
40 Milt Cuyler RR .01 .05
41 Phil Plantier RR RC .08 .25
42 Scott Chiamparino RR .01 .05
43 Ray Lankford RR .02 .10
44 Mickey Morandini RR .01 .05
45 Dave Hansen RR .01 .05
46 Kevin Belcher RR RC .01 .05
47 Darrin Fletcher RR .01 .05
48 Steve Sax AS .01 .05
49 Ken Griffey Jr. AS .08 .25
50A J.Canseco AS ERR .02 .10
Team in stat box should be AL, not A's
50B J.Canseco AS COR .05 .15
51 Sandy Alomar Jr. AS .01 .05
52 Cal Ripken AS .15 .40
53 Rickey Henderson AS .05 .15
54 Bob Welch AS .01 .05
55 Wade Boggs AS .02 .10
56 Mark McGwire AS .15 .40
57A Jack McDowell ERR .08 .25
(Career stats do not include 1990)
57B Jack McDowell COR .20 .50
(Career stats do not include 1990)
58 Jose Lind .01 .05
59 Alex Fernandez .01 .05
60 Pat Combs .01 .05
61 Mike Walker .01 .05
62 Juan Samuel .01 .05
63 Mike Blowers UER .01 .05
(Last line has aseball, not baseball)
64 Mark Guthrie .01 .05
65 Mark Salas .01 .05
66 Tim Jones .01 .05
67 Tim Leary .01 .05
68 Andres Galarraga .02 .10
69 Bob Milacki .01 .05
70 Tim Belcher .01 .05
71 Todd Zeile .01 .05
72 Jerome Walton .01 .05
73 Kevin Seitzer .01 .05
74 Jerald Clark .01 .05
75 John Smoltz UER .05 .15
(Born in Detroit, not Warren)
76 Mike Henneman .01 .05
77 Ken Griffey Jr. .20 .50
78 Jim Abbott .05 .15
79 Gregg Jefferies .01 .05
80 Kevin Reimer .01 .05
81 Roger Clemens .30 .75
82 Mike Fitzgerald .01 .05
83 Bruce Hurst UER .01 .05
(Middle name is Lee, not Vee)
84 Eric Davis .02 .10
85 Paul Molitor .02 .10
86 Will Clark .05 .15
87 Mike Bielecki .01 .05
88 Bret Saberhagen .02 .10
89 Nolan Ryan .40 1.00
90 Bobby Thigpen .01 .05
91 Dickie Thon .01 .05
92 Duane Ward .01 .05
93 Luis Polonia .01 .05
94 Terry Kennedy .01 .05
95 Kent Hrbek .02 .10
96 Danny Jackson .01 .05
97 Sid Fernandez .01 .05
98 Jimmy Key .02 .10
99 Franklin Stubbs .01 .05
100 Checklist 28-103 .01 .05
101 R.J. Reynolds .01 .05
102 Dave Stewart .02 .10
103 Dan Pasqua .01 .05
104 Dan Plesac .01 .05
105 Mark McGwire .30 .75
106 John Farrell .01 .05
107 Don Mattingly .25 .60
108 Carlton Fisk .05 .15
109 Ken Oberkfell .01 .05
110 Darrel Akerfelds .01 .05
111 Gregg Olson .01 .05
112 Mike Scioscia .01 .05
113 Bryn Smith .01 .05
114 Bob Geren .01 .05
115 Tom Candiotti .01 .05
116 Kevin Tapani .01 .05
117 Jeff Treadway .01 .05
118 Alan Trammell .02 .10
119 Pete O'Brien UER .01 .05
(Blue shading goes through stats)
120 Joel Skinner .01 .05
121 Mike LaValliere .01 .05
122 Dwight Evans .05 .15
123 Jody Reed .01 .05
124 Lee Guetterman .01 .05
125 Tim Burke .01 .05
126 Dave Johnson .01 .05
127 Fernando Valenzuela UER .02 .10
(Lower large stripe in yellow instead of blue)
128 Jose DeLeon .01 .05
129 Andre Dawson .02 .10
130 Gerald Perry .01 .05
131 Greg W. Harris .01 .05
132 Tom Glavine .05 .15
133 Lance McCullers .01 .05
134 Randy Johnson .10 .30
135 Lance Parrish UER .02 .10
(Born in McKeesport, not Clairton)
136 Mackey Sasser .01 .05
137 Geno Petralli .01 .05
138 Dennis Lamp .01 .05
139 Dennis Martinez .02 .10
140 Mike Pagliarulo .01 .05
141 Hal Morris .01 .05
142 Dave Parker .02 .10
143 Brett Butler .02 .10
144 Paul Assenmacher .01 .05
145 Mark Gubicza .01 .05
146 Charlie Hough .01 .05
147 Sammy Sosa .08 .25
148 Randy Ready .01 .05
149 Kelly Gruber .01 .05
150 Devon White .02 .10
151 Gary Carter .02 .10
152 Gene Larkin .01 .05
153 Chris Sabo .01 .05
154 David Cone .02 .10
155 Todd Stottlemyre .01 .05
156 Glenn Wilson .01 .05
157 Bob Walk .01 .05
158 Mike Gallego .01 .05
159 Greg Hibbard .01 .05
160 Chris Bosio .01 .05
161 Mike Moore .01 .05
162 Jerry Browne UER .01 .05
(Born Christiansted, should be St. Croix)
163 Steve Sax UER .01 .05
(No asterisk next to his 1989 At Bats)
164 Melido Perez .01 .05
165 Danny Darwin .01 .05
166 Roger McDowell .01 .05
167 Bill Ripken .01 .05
168 Mike Sharperson .01 .05
169 Lee Smith .02 .10
170 Matt Nokes .01 .05
171 Jesse Orosco .01 .05
172 Rick Aguilera .02 .10
173 Jim Presley .01 .05
174 Lou Whitaker .02 .10
175 Harold Reynolds .02 .10
176 Brook Jacoby .01 .05
177 Wally Backman .01 .05
178 Wade Boggs .05 .15
179 Chuck Cary UER .01 .05
(Comma after DOB, not on other cards)
180 Tom Foley .01 .05
181 Pete Harnisch .01 .05
182 Mike Morgan .01 .05
183 Bob Tewksbury .01 .05
184 Joe Girardi .01 .05
185 Storm Davis .01 .05
186 Ed Whitson .01 .05
187 Steve Avery UER .01 .05
(Born in New Jersey, should be Michigan)
188 Lloyd Moseby .01 .05
189 Scott Bankhead .01 .05
190 Mark Langston .01 .05
191 Kevin McReynolds .01 .05
192 Julio Franco .02 .10
193 John Dopson .01 .05
194 Dennis Boyd .01 .05
195 Bip Roberts .01 .05
196 Billy Hatcher .01 .05
197 Edgar Diaz .01 .05
198 Greg Litton .01 .05
199 Mark Grace .05 .15
200 Checklist 104-179 .01 .05
201 George Brett .25 .60
202 Jeff Russell .01 .05
203 Ivan Calderon .01 .05
204 Ken Howell .01 .05
205 Tom Henke .01 .05
206 Bryan Harvey .01 .05
207 Steve Bedrosian .01 .05
208 Al Newman .01 .05
209 Randy Myers .01 .05
210 Daryl Boston .01 .05
211 Manny Lee .01 .05
212 Dave Smith .01 .05
213 Don Slaught .01 .05
214 Walt Weiss .01 .05
215 Donn Pall .01 .05
216 Jaime Navarro .01 .05
217 Willie Randolph .02 .10
218 Rudy Seanez .01 .05
219 Jim Leyritz .01 .05
220 Ron Karkovice .01 .05
221 Ken Caminiti .02 .10
222 Von Hayes .01 .05
223 Cal Ripken .30 .75
224 Lenny Harris .01 .05
225 Milt Thompson .01 .05
226 Alvaro Espinoza .01 .05
227 Chris James .01 .05
228 Dan Gladden .01 .05
229 Jeff Blauser .01 .05
230 Mike Heath .01 .05
231 Omar Vizquel .05 .15
232 Doug Jones .01 .05
233 Jeff King .01 .05
234 Luis Rivera .01 .05
235 Ellis Burks .02 .10
236 Greg Cadaret .01 .05
237 Dave Martinez .01 .05
238 Mark Williamson .01 .05
239 Stan Javier .01 .05
240 Ozzie Smith .15 .40
241 Shawn Boskie .01 .05
242 Tom Gordon .01 .05
243 Tony Gwynn .10 .30
244 Tommy Gregg .01 .05
245 Jeff M. Robinson .01 .05
246 Keith Comstock .01 .05
247 Jack Howell .01 .05
248 Keith Miller .01 .05
249 Bobby Witt .01 .05
250 Rob Murphy UER .01 .05
(Shown as on Reds in '89 in stats, should be Red Sox)
251 Spike Owen .01 .05
252 Garry Templeton .01 .05
253 Glenn Braggs .01 .05
254 Ron Robinson .01 .05
255 Kevin Mitchell .01 .05
256 Les Lancaster .01 .05
257 Mel Stottlemyre Jr. .01 .05
258 Kenny Rogers UER .02 .10
(IP listed as 171, should be 172)
259 Lance Johnson .01 .05
260 John Kruk .02 .10
261 Fred McGriff .05 .15
262 Dick Schofield .01 .05
263 Trevor Wilson .01 .05
264 David West .01 .05
265 Scott Scudder .01 .05
266 Dwight Gooden .02 .10
267 Willie Blair .01 .05
268 Mark Portugal .01 .05
269 Doug Drabek .01 .05
270 Dennis Eckersley .02 .10
271 Eric King .01 .05
272 Robin Yount .15 .40
273 Carney Lansford .02 .10
274 Carlos Baerga .01 .05
275 Dave Righetti .02 .10
276 Scott Fletcher .01 .05
277 Eric Yelding .01 .05
278 Charlie Hayes .01 .05
279 Jeff Ballard .01 .05
280 Orel Hershiser .02 .10
281 Jose Oquendo .01 .05
282 Mike Witt .01 .05
283 Mitch Webster .01 .05
284 Greg Gagne .01 .05
285 Greg Olson .01 .05
286 Tony Phillips UER .01 .05
(Born 4/15 should be 4/25)
287 Scott Bradley .01 .05
288 Cory Snyder UER .01 .05
(In text, led is repeated Inglewood is misspelled as Englewood)
289 Jay Bell UER .02 .10
(Born in Pensacola, not Eglin AFB)
290 Kevin Romine .01 .05
291 Jeff D. Robinson .01 .05
292 Steve Frey UER .01 .05
(Bats left, should be right)
293 Craig Worthington .01 .05
294 Tim Crews .01 .05
295 Joe Magrane .01 .05
296 Hector Villanueva .01 .05
297 Terry Shumpert .01 .05
298 Joe Carter .02 .10
299 Kent Mercker UER .01 .05
(IP listed as 53, should be 52)
300 Checklist 180-255 .01 .05
301 Chet Lemon .01 .05
302 Mike Schooler .01 .05
303 Dante Bichette .02 .10
304 Kevin Elster .01 .05
305 Jeff Huson .01 .05
306 Greg A. Harris .01 .05
307 Marquis Grissom UER .02 .10
(Middle name Deon, should be Dean)
308 Calvin Schiraldi .01 .05
309 Mariano Duncan .01 .05
310 Bill Spiers .01 .05
311 Scott Garrelts .01 .05
312 Mitch Williams .01 .05
313 Mike Macfarlane .01 .05
314 Kevin Brown .02 .10
315 Robin Ventura .02 .10
316 Darren Daulton .02 .10
317 Pat Borders .01 .05
318 Mark Eichhorn .01 .05
319 Jeff Brantley .01 .05
320 Shane Mack .01 .05
321 Rob Dibble .02 .10
322 John Franco .02 .10
323 Junior Felix .01 .05
324 Casey Candaele .01 .05
325 Bobby Bonilla .02 .10
326 Dave Henderson .01 .05
327 Wayne Edwards .01 .05
328 Mark Knudson .01 .05
329 Terry Steinbach .01 .05
330 Colby Ward UER RC .01 .05
(No comma between city and state)
331 Oscar Azocar .01 .05
332 Scott Radinsky .01 .05
333 Eric Anthony .01 .05
334 Steve Lake .01 .05
335 Bob Melvin .01 .05
336 Kal Daniels .01 .05
337 Tom Pagnozzi .01 .05
338 Alan Mills .01 .05
339 Steve Olin .01 .05
340 Juan Berenguer .01 .05
341 Francisco Cabrera .01 .05
342 Dave Bergman .01 .05
343 Henry Cotto .01 .05
344 Sergio Valdez .01 .05
345 Bob Patterson .01 .05
346 John Marzano .01 .05
347 Dana Kiecker .01 .05
348 Dion James .01 .05
349 Hubie Brooks .01 .05
350 Bill Landrum .01 .05
351 Bill Sampen .01 .05
352 Greg Briley .01 .05
353 Paul Gibson .01 .05
354 Dave Eiland .01 .05
355 Steve Finley .02 .10
356 Bob Boone .02 .10
357 Steve Buechele .01 .05
358 Chris Hoiles .01 .05
359 Larry Walker .08 .25
360 Frank DiPino .01 .05
361 Mark Grant .01 .05
362 Dave Magadan .01 .05
363 Robby Thompson .01 .05
364 Lonnie Smith .01 .05
365 Steve Farr .01 .05
366 Dave Valle .01 .05
367 Tim Naehring .01 .05
368 Jim Acker .01 .05
369 Jeff Reardon UER .02 .10
(Born in Pittsfield, not Dalton)
370 Tim Teufel .01 .05
371 Juan Gonzalez .08 .25
372 Luis Salazar .01 .05
373 Rick Honeycutt .01 .05
374 Greg Maddux .15 .40
375 Jose Uribe UER .01 .05
(Middle name Elta, should be Alta)
376 Donnie Hill .01 .05
377 Don Carman .01 .05
378 Craig Grebeck .01 .05
379 Willie Fraser .01 .05
380 Glenallen Hill .01 .05
381 Joe Oliver .01 .05
382 Randy Bush .01 .05
383 Alex Cole .01 .05
384 Norm Charlton .01 .05
385 Gene Nelson .01 .05
386 Checklist 256-331 .01 .05
387 R. Henderson MVP .05 .15
388 Lance Parrish MVP .01 .05
389 Fred McGriff MVP .02 .10
390 Dave Parker MVP .01 .05
391 C. Maldonado MVP .01 .05
392 Ken Griffey Jr. MVP .08 .25
393 Gregg Olson MVP .01 .05
394 Rafael Palmeiro MVP .02 .10
395 Roger Clemens MVP .15 .40
396 George Brett MVP .08 .25
397 Cecil Fielder MVP .01 .05
398 Brian Harper MVP .01 .05
UER Major League Performance, should be Career
399 Bobby Thigpen MVP .01 .05
400 Roberto Kelly MVP .01 .05
UER (Second Base on front and OF on back)
401 Danny Darwin MVP .01 .05
402 Dave Justice MVP .01 .05
403 Lee Smith MVP .01 .05
404 Ryne Sandberg MVP .08 .25
405 Eddie Murray MVP .05 .15
406 Tim Wallach MVP .01 .05
407 Kevin Mitchell MVP .01 .05
408 D. Strawberry MVP .01 .05
409 Joe Carter MVP .01 .05
410 Len Dykstra MVP .01 .05
411 Doug Drabek MVP .01 .05
412 Chris Sabo MVP .01 .05
413 Paul Marak RR RC .01 .05
414 Tim McIntosh RR .01 .05
415 Brian Barnes RR RC .02 .10
416 Eric Gunderson RR .01 .05
417 Mike Gardiner RR RC .01 .05
418 Steve Carter RR .01 .05
419 Gerald Alexander RR RC .01 .05
420 Rich Garces RR RC .02 .10
421 Chuck Knoblauch RR .02 .10
422 Scott Aldred RR .01 .05
423 W.Chamberlain RR RC .08 .25
424 Lance Dickson RR RC .02 .10
425 Greg Colbrunn RR RC .08 .25
426 Rich DeLucia RR UER RC .01 .05
(Misspelled Delucia on card)
427 Jeff Conine RR RC .10 .10
428 Steve Decker RR RC .01 .05
429 Turner Ward RR RC .08 .25
430 Mo Vaughn RR .02 .10
431 Steve Chitren RR RC .01 .05
432 Mike Benjamin RR .01 .05
433 Ryne Sandberg AS .08 .25
434 Len Dykstra AS .01 .05
435 Andre Dawson AS .01 .05
436A Mike Scioscia AS .01 .05
(White star by name)
436B Mike Scioscia AS .01 .05
(Yellow star by name)
437 Ozzie Smith AS .08 .25
438 Kevin Mitchell AS .01 .05
439 Jack Armstrong AS .01 .05
440 Chris Sabo AS .01 .05
441 Will Clark AS .02 .10
442 Mel Hall .01 .05
443 Mark Gardner .01 .05
444 Mike Devereaux .01 .05
445 Kirk Gibson .02 .10
446 Terry Pendleton .02 .10
447 Mike Harkey .01 .05
448 Jim Eisenreich .01 .05
449 Benito Santiago .02 .10
450 Oddibe McDowell .01 .05
451 Cecil Fielder .02 .10
452 Ken Griffey Sr. .02 .10
453 Bert Blyleven .02 .10
454 Howard Johnson .01 .05
455 Monty Fariss UER .01 .05
(Misspelled Farris on card)
456 Tony Pena .01 .05
457 Tim Raines .02 .10
458 Dennis Rasmussen .01 .05
459 Luis Quinones .01 .05
460 B.J. Surhoff .02 .10
461 Ernest Riles .01 .05
462 Rick Sutcliffe .02 .10
463 Danny Tartabull .01 .05
464 Pete Incaviglia .01 .05
465 Carlos Martinez .01 .05
466 Ricky Jordan .01 .05
467 John Cerutti .01 .05
468 Dave Winfield .02 .10
469 Francisco Oliveras .01 .05
470 Roy Smith .01 .05
471 Barry Larkin .05 .15
472 Ron Darling .01 .05
473 David Wells .02 .10
474 Glenn Davis .01 .05
475 Neal Heaton .01 .05
476 Ron Hassey .01 .05
477 Frank Thomas .08 .25
478 Greg Vaughn .01 .05
479 Todd Burns .01 .05
480 Candy Maldonado .01 .05
481 Dave LaPoint .01 .05
482 Alvin Davis .01 .05
483 Mike Scott .01 .05
484 Dale Murphy .05 .15
485 Ben McDonald .01 .05
486 Jay Howell .01 .05
487 Vince Coleman .01 .05
488 Alfredo Griffin .01 .05
489 Sandy Alomar Jr. .01 .05
490 Kirby Puckett .08 .25
491 Andres Thomas .01 .05
492 Jack Morris .02 .10
493 Matt Young .01 .05
494 Greg Myers .01 .05
495 Barry Bonds .40 1.00
496 Scott Cooper UER .01 .05
(No BA for 1990 and career)
497 Dan Schatzeder .01 .05
498 Jesse Barfield .01 .05
499 Jerry Goff .01 .05
500 Checklist 332-408 .01 .05
501 Anthony Telford RC .01 .05
502 Eddie Murray .08 .25
503 Omar Olivares RC .08 .25
504 Ryne Sandberg .15 .40
505 Jeff Montgomery .01 .05
506 Mark Parent .01 .05
507 Ron Gant .02 .10
508 Frank Tanana .01 .05
509 Jay Buhner .02 .10
510 Max Venable .01 .05
511 Wally Whitehurst .01 .05
512 Gary Pettis .01 .05
513 Tom Brunansky .01 .05
514 Tim Wallach .01 .05
515 Craig Lefferts .01 .05
516 Tim Layana .01 .05
517 Darryl Hamilton .01 .05
518 Rick Reuschel .01 .05
519 Steve Wilson .01 .05
520 Kurt Stillwell .01 .05
521 Rafael Palmeiro .05 .15
522 Ken Patterson .01 .05
523 Len Dykstra .02 .10
524 Tony Fernandez .01 .05
525 Kent Anderson .01 .05
526 Mark Leonard RC .01 .05
527 Allan Anderson .01 .05
528 Tom Browning .01 .05
529 Frank Viola .02 .10
530 John Olerud .02 .10
531 Juan Agosto .01 .05
532 Zane Smith .01 .05
533 Scott Sanderson .01 .05
534 Barry Jones .01 .05
535 Mike Felder .01 .05
536 Jose Canseco .05 .15
537 Felix Fermin .01 .05
538 Roberto Kelly .01 .05
539 Brian Holman .01 .05
540 Mark Davidson .01 .05
541 Terry Mulholland .01 .05
542 Randy Milligan .01 .05
543 Jose Gonzalez .01 .05
544 Craig Wilson RC .01 .05
545 Mike Hartley .01 .05
546 Greg Swindell .01 .05
547 Gary Gaetti .02 .10
548 Dave Justice .02 .10
549 Steve Searcy .01 .05
550 Erik Hanson .01 .05
551 Dave Stieb .01 .05
552 Andy Van Slyke .05 .15
553 Mike Greenwell .01 .05
554 Kevin Maas .01 .05
555 Delino DeShields .02 .10
556 Curt Schilling .08 .25
557 Ramon Martinez .01 .05
558 Pedro Guerrero .02 .10
559 Dwight Smith .01 .05
560 Mark Davis .01 .05
561 Shawn Abner .01 .05
562 Charlie Leibrandt .01 .05
563 John Shelby .01 .05
564 Bill Swift .01 .05
565 Mike Fetters .01 .05
566 Alejandro Pena .01 .05
567 Ruben Sierra .02 .10
568 Carlos Quintana .01 .05
569 Kevin Gross .01 .05
570 Derek Lilliquist .01 .05
571 Jack Armstrong .01 .05
572 Greg Brock .01 .05
573 Mike Kingery .01 .05
574 Greg Smith .01 .05
575 Brian McRae RC .08 .25
576 Jack Daugherty .01 .05
577 Ozzie Guillen .02 .10
578 Joe Boever .01 .05
579 Luis Sojo .01 .05
580 Chili Davis .02 .10
581 Don Robinson .01 .05
582 Brian Harper .01 .05
583 Paul O'Neill .05 .15
584 Bob Ojeda .01 .05
585 Mookie Wilson .02 .10
586 Rafael Ramirez .01 .05
587 Gary Redus .01 .05
588 Jamie Quirk .01 .05
589 Shawn Hillegas .01 .05
590 Tom Edens RC .01 .05
591 Joe Klink .01 .05
592 Charles Nagy .01 .05
593 Eric Plunk .01 .05
594 Tracy Jones .01 .05
595 Craig Biggio .05 .15
596 Jose DeJesus .01 .05
597 Mickey Tettleton .01 .05
598 Chris Gwynn .01 .05
599 Rex Hudler .01 .05
600 Checklist 409-506 .01 .05
601 Jim Gott .01 .05
602 Jeff Manto .01 .05
603 Nelson Liriano .01 .05
604 Mark Lemke .01 .05
605 Clay Parker .01 .05
606 Edgar Martinez .05 .15
607 Mark Whiten .01 .05
608 Ted Power .01 .05
609 Tom Bolton .01 .05
610 Tom Herr .01 .05
611 Andy Hawkins UER .01 .05
Pitched No-Hitter on 7/1, not 7/2
612 Scott Ruskin .01 .05
613 Ron Kittle .01 .05
614 John Wetteland .02 .10
615 Mike Perez RC .02 .10
616 Dave Clark .01 .05
617 Brent Mayne .01 .05
618 Jack Clark .02 .10
619 Marvin Freeman .01 .05
620 Edwin Nunez .01 .05
621 Russ Swan .01 .05
622 Johnny Ray .01 .05
623 Charlie O'Brien .01 .05
624 Joe Bitker RC .01 .05
625 Mike Marshall .01 .05
626 Otis Nixon .01 .05
627 Andy Benes .01 .05
628 Ron Oester .01 .05
629 Ted Higuera .01 .05
630 Kevin Bass .01 .05
631 Damon Berryhill .01 .05
632 Bo Jackson .08 .25
633 Brad Arnsberg .01 .05
634 Jerry Willard .01 .05
635 Tommy Greene .01 .05
636 Bob MacDonald RC .01 .05
637 Kirk McCaskill .01 .05
638 John Burkett .01 .05
639 Paul Abbott RC .01 .05
640 Todd Benzinger .01 .05
641 Todd Hundley .01 .05
642 George Bell .01 .05
643 Javier Ortiz .01 .05
644 Sid Bream .01 .05
645 Bob Welch .01 .05
646 Phil Bradley .01 .05
647 Bill Krueger .01 .05
648 Rickey Henderson .08 .25
649 Kevin Wickander .01 .05
650 Steve Balboni .01 .05
651 Gene Harris .01 .05
652 Jim Deshaies .01 .05
653 Jason Grimsley .01 .05
654 Joe Orsulak .01 .05
655 Jim Poole .01 .05
656 Felix Jose .01 .05
657 Denis Cook .01 .05
658 Tom Brookens .01 .05
659 Junior Ortiz .01 .05
660 Jeff Parrett .01 .05
661 Jerry Don Gleaton .01 .05
662 Brent Knackert .01 .05
663 Rance Mulliniks .01 .05
664 John Smiley .01 .05
665 Larry Andersen .01 .05
666 Willie McGee .02 .10
667 Chris Nabholz .01 .05
668 Brady Anderson .02 .10
669 Darren Holmes UER RC .08 .25
19 CG's, should be 0)
670 Ken Hill .01 .05
671 Gary Varsho .01 .05
672 Bill Pecota .01 .05
673 Fred Lynn .01 .05
674 Kevin D. Brown .01 .05
675 Dan Petry .01 .05
676 Mike Jackson .01 .05
677 Wally Joyner .02 .10
678 Danny Jackson .01 .05
679 Bill Haselman RC .01 .05
680 Mike Boddicker .01 .05
681 Mel Rojas .01 .05
682 Roberto Alomar .05 .15
683 Dave Justice ROY .01 .05
684 Chuck Crim .01 .05
685 Matt Williams .02 .10
686 Shawon Dunston .01 .05
687 Jeff Schulz RC .01 .05
688 John Barfield .01 .05
689 Gerald Young .01 .05
690 Luis Gonzalez RC .20 .50
691 Frank Wills .01 .05
692 Chuck Finley .02 .10
693 S.Alomar Jr. ROY .01 .05
694 Tim Drummond .01 .05
695 Herm Winningham .01 .05
696 Darryl Strawberry .02 .10
697 Al Leiter .02 .10
698 Karl Rhodes .01 .05
699 Stan Belinda .01 .05
700 Checklist 507-604 .01 .05
701 Lance Blankenship .01 .05
702 Willie Stargell PUZ .05 .15
703 Jim Gantner .01 .05
704 Reggie Harris .01 .05
705 Rob Ducey .01 .05
706 Tim Hulett .01 .05
707 Atlee Hammaker .01 .05
708 Xavier Hernandez .01 .05
709 Chuck McElroy .01 .05
710 John Mitchell .01 .05
711 Carlos Hernandez .01 .05
712 Geronimo Pena .01 .05
713 Jim Neidlinger RC .01 .05
714 John Orton .01 .05
715 Terry Leach .01 .05
716 Mike Stanton .01 .05
717 Walt Terrell .01 .05
718 Luis Aquino .01 .05
719 Bud Black UER .01 .05
Blue Jays uniform, but Giants logo
720 Bob Kipper .01 .05
721 Jeff Gray RC .01 .05
722 Jose Rijo .01 .05
723 Curt Young .01 .05
724 Jose Vizcaino .01 .05
725 Randy Tomlin RC .02 .10
726 Junior Noboa .01 .05
727 Bob Welch CY .01 .05
728 Gary Ward .01 .05
729 Rob Deer UER .01 .05
(Brewers uniform, but Tigers logo)
730 David Segui .01 .05
731 Mark Carreon .01 .05
732 Vicente Palacios .01 .05
733 Sam Horn .01 .05
734 Howard Farmer .01 .05
735 Ken Dayley UER .01 .05
(Cardinals uniform, but Blue Jays logo)
736 Kelly Mann .01 .05
737 Joe Grahe RC .02 .10
738 Kelly Downs .01 .05
739 Jimmy Kremers .01 .05
740 Kevin Appier .02 .10
741 Jeff Reed .01 .05
742 Jose Rijo WS .01 .05
743 Dave Rohde .01 .05
744 Len Dykstra .05 .15
Dale Murphy UER (No '91 Donruss logo on card front)
745 Paul Sorrento .01 .05
746 Thomas Howard .01 .05
747 Matt Stark RC .01 .05
748 Harold Baines .02 .10
749 Doug Dascenzo .01 .05
750 Doug Drabek CY .01 .05
751 Gary Sheffield .02 .10
752 Terry Lee RC .01 .05
753 Jim Vatcher RC .01 .05
754 Lee Stevens .01 .05
755 Randy Veres .01 .05
756 Bill Doran .01 .05
757 Gary Wayne .01 .05
758 Pedro Munoz RC .02 .10
759 Chris Hammond .01 .05
760 Checklist 605-702 .01 .05
761 R.Henderson MVP .05 .15
762 Barry Bonds MVP .20 .50
763 Billy Hatcher WS .01 .05
UER (Line 13, on should be one)
764 Julio Machado .01 .05
765 Jose Mesa .01 .05
766 Willie Randolph WS .01 .05
767 Scott Erickson .01 .05
768 Travis Fryman .02 .10
769 Rich Rodriguez RC .01 .05
770 Checklist 703-770/BC1-BC22 .01 .05

1991 Donruss Rookies

The 56-card 1991 Donruss Rookies set was issued exclusively in factory set form through hobby dealers. The cards measure the standard size and a mini puzzle featuring Hall of Famer Willie Stargell was included with the set. The fronts feature color action player photos, with white and red borders. Rookie Cards include Jeff Bagwell and Ivan Rodriguez.

COMP.FACT.SET (56) 2.00 5.00
1 Pat Kelly RC .02 .10
2 Rich DeLucia .02 .10
3 Wes Chamberlain .02 .10
4 Scott Leius .02 .10
5 Darryl Kile .08 .25
6 Milt Cuyler .02 .10
7 Todd Van Poppel RC .02 .10
8 Ray Lankford .08 .25
9 Brian R. Hunter RC .08 .25
10 Tony Perezchica .02 .10
11 Ced Landrum RC .02 .10
12 Dave Burba RC .08 .25
13 Ramon Garcia RC .02 .10
14 Ed Sprague .02 .10
15 Warren Newson RC .02 .10
16 Paul Faries RC .02 .10
17 Luis Gonzalez .20 .50
18 Charles Nagy .02 .10
19 Chris Hammond .02 .10
20 Frank Castillo RC .08 .25
21 Pedro Munoz .02 .10
22 Orlando Merced RC .02 .10
23 Jose Melendez RC .02 .10
24 Kirk Dressendorfer RC .02 .10
25 Heathcliff Slocumb RC .08 .25
26 Doug Simons RC .02 .10
27 Mike Timlin RC .08 .25
28 Jeff Fassero RC .08 .25
29 Mark Leiter RC .02 .10
30 Jeff Bagwell RC .60 1.50
31 Brian McRae .08 .25
32 Mark Whiten .02 .10
33 Ivan Rodriguez RC .75 2.00
34 Wade Taylor RC .02 .10
35 Darren Lewis .02 .10
36 Mo Vaughn .08 .25
37 Mike Remlinger .02 .10
38 Rick Wilkins RC .02 .10
39 Chuck Knoblauch .08 .25
40 Kevin Morton .02 .10
41 Carlos Rodriguez RC .02 .10
42 Mark Lewis .02 .10
43 Brent Mayne .02 .10
44 Chris Haney RC .02 .10
45 Denis Boucher RC .02 .10
46 Mike Gardiner .02 .10
47 Jeff Johnson RC .02 .10
48 Dean Palmer .08 .25
49 Chuck McElroy .02 .10
50 Chris Jones RC .02 .10
51 Scott Kamieniecki RC .02 .10
52 Al Osuna RC .02 .10
53 Rusty Meacham RC .02 .10
54 Chito Martinez RC .02 .10
55 Reggie Jefferson .02 .10
56 Checklist 1-56 .02 .10

1992 Donruss

The 1992 Donruss set contains 784 standard-size cards issued in two separate series of 396. Cards were issued in first and second series foil wrapped packs in addition to hobby and retail factory sets. One of 21 different puzzle panels featuring Hall of Famer Rod Carew was inserted into each pack. The basic card design features glossy color player photos with white borders. Two-toned blue stripes overlay the top and bottom of the picture. Subsets include Rated Rookies (1-20, 397-421), All-Stars (21-30/422-431) and Highlights (33, 94, 154, 215, 276, 434, 495, 555, 616, 677). The only notable Rookie Card in the set features Scott Brosius.

COMPLETE SET (784) 4.00 10.00
COMP.HOBBY SET (788) 4.00 10.00
COMP.RETAIL SET (788) 4.00 10.00
COMP. SERIES 1 (396) 2.00 5.00
COMP. SERIES 2 (388) 2.00 5.00
COMP.CAREW PUZZLE .40 1.00
1 Mark Wohlers RR .01 .05
2 Wil Cordero RR .01 .05
3 Kyle Abbott RR .01 .05
4 Dave Nilsson RR .01 .05
5 Kenny Lofton RR .05 .15
6 Luis Mercedes RR .01 .05
7 Roger Salkeld RR .01 .05
8 Eddie Zosky RR .01 .05
9 Todd Van Poppel RR .01 .05
10 Frank Seminara RR RC .02 .10
11 Andy Ashby RR .01 .05
12 Reggie Jefferson RR .01 .05
13 Ryan Klesko RR .02 .10
14 Carlos Garcia RR .01 .05
15 John Ramos RR .01 .05
16 Eric Karros RR .02 .10
17 Patrick Lennon RR .01 .05
18 Eddie Taubensee RR RC .08 .25
19 Roberto Hernandez RR .01 .05
20 D.J. Dozier RR .01 .05
21 Dave Henderson AS .01 .05
22 Cal Ripken AS .15 .40
23 Wade Boggs AS .02 .10
24 Ken Griffey Jr. AS .08 .25
25 Jack Morris AS .01 .05
26 Danny Tartabull AS .01 .05
27 Cecil Fielder AS .01 .05
28 Roberto Alomar AS .02 .10
29 Sandy Alomar Jr. AS .01 .05
30 Rickey Henderson AS .05 .15
31 Ken Hill .01 .05
32 John Habyan .01 .05
33 Otis Nixon HL .01 .05
34 Tim Wallach .01 .05
35 Cal Ripken .30 .75
36 Gary Carter .02 .10
37 Juan Agosto .01 .05
38 Doug Dascenzo .01 .05
39 Kirk Gibson .02 .10
40 Benito Santiago .02 .10
41 Otis Nixon .01 .05
42 Andy Allanson .01 .05
43 Brian Holman .01 .05
44 Dick Schofield .01 .05
45 Dave Magadan .01 .05
46 Rafael Palmeiro .05 .15
47 Jody Reed .01 .05
48 Ivan Calderon .01 .05
49 Greg W. Harris .01 .05
50 Chris Sabo .01 .05
51 Paul Molitor .02 .10
52 Robby Thompson .01 .05
53 Dave Smith .01 .05
54 Mark Davis .01 .05
55 Kevin Brown .02 .10
56 Donn Pall .01 .05
57 Len Dykstra .02 .10
58 Roberto Alomar .05 .15
59 Jeff D. Robinson .01 .05
60 Willie McGee .02 .10
61 Jay Buhner .02 .10
62 Mike Pagliarulo .01 .05
63 Paul O'Neill .05 .15
64 Hubie Brooks .01 .05
65 Kelly Gruber .01 .05
66 Ken Caminiti .02 .10
67 Gary Redus .01 .05
68 Harold Baines .02 .10
69 Charlie Hough .02 .10
70 B.J. Surhoff .02 .10
71 Walt Weiss .01 .05
72 Shawn Hillegas .01 .05
73 Roberto Kelly .01 .05
74 Jeff Ballard .01 .05
75 Craig Biggio .05 .15
76 Pat Combs .01 .05
77 Jeff M. Robinson .01 .05
78 Tim Belcher .01 .05
79 Cris Carpenter .01 .05
80 Checklist 1-79 .01 .05
81 Steve Avery .01 .05
82 Chris James .01 .05
83 Brian Harper .01 .05
84 Charlie Leibrandt .01 .05
85 Mickey Tettleton .01 .05
86 Pete O'Brien .01 .05
87 Danny Darwin .01 .05
88 Bob Walk .01 .05
89 Jeff Reardon .02 .10
90 Bobby Rose .01 .05
91 Danny Jackson .01 .05
92 John Morris .01 .05
93 Bud Black .01 .05
94 Tommy Greene HL .01 .05
95 Rick Aguilera .02 .10
96 Gary Gaetti .02 .10
97 David Cone .02 .10
98 John Olerud .02 .10
99 Joel Skinner .01 .05
100 Jay Bell .02 .10
101 Bob Milacki .01 .05
102 Norm Charlton .01 .05
103 Chuck Crim .01 .05
104 Terry Steinbach .01 .05
105 Juan Samuel .01 .05
106 Steve Howe .01 .05
107 Rafael Belliard .01 .05
108 Joey Cora .01 .05
109 Tommy Greene .01 .05
110 Gregg Olson .01 .05
111 Frank Tanana .01 .05
112 Lee Smith .02 .10
113 Greg A. Harris .01 .05
114 Dwayne Henry .01 .05
115 Chili Davis .02 .10
116 Kent Mercker .01 .05
117 Brian Barnes .01 .05
118 Rich DeLucia .01 .05
119 Andre Dawson .02 .10
120 Carlos Baerga .01 .05
121 Mike LaValliere .01 .05
122 Jeff Gray .01 .05
123 Bruce Hurst .01 .05
124 Alvin Davis .01 .05
125 John Candelaria .01 .05
126 Matt Nokes .01 .05
127 George Bell .01 .05
128 Bret Saberhagen .02 .10
129 Jeff Russell .01 .05
130 Jim Abbott .05 .15
131 Bill Gullickson .01 .05
132 Todd Zeile .01 .05
133 Dave Winfield .02 .10
134 Wally Whitehurst .01 .05
135 Matt Williams .02 .10
136 Tom Browning .01 .05
137 Marquis Grissom .02 .10
138 Erik Hanson .01 .05
139 Rob Dibble .02 .10
140 Don August .01 .05
141 Tom Henke .01 .05
142 Dan Pasqua .01 .05
143 George Brett .25 .60
144 Jerald Clark .01 .05
145 Robin Ventura .02 .10
146 Dale Murphy .05 .15
147 Dennis Eckersley .02 .10
148 Eric Yelding .01 .05
149 Mario Diaz .01 .05
150 Casey Candaele .01 .05
151 Steve Olin .01 .05
152 Luis Salazar .01 .05
153 Kevin Maas .01 .05
154 Nolan Ryan HL .20 .50
155 Barry Jones .01 .05
156 Chris Hoiles .01 .05
157 Bob Ojeda .01 .05
158 Pedro Guerrero .02 .10
159 Paul Assenmacher .01 .05
160 Checklist 80-157 .01 .05
161 Mike Macfarlane .01 .05
162 Craig Lefferts .01 .05
163 Brian Hunter .01 .05
164 Alan Trammell .02 .10
165 Ken Griffey Jr. .15 .40
166 Lance Parrish .02 .10
167 Brian Downing .01 .05
168 John Barfield .01 .05
169 Jack Clark .02 .10
170 Chris Nabholz .01 .05
171 Tim Teufel .01 .05
172 Chris Hammond .01 .05
173 Robin Yount .15 .40
174 Dave Righetti .02 .10
175 Joe Girardi .01 .05
176 Mike Boddicker .01 .05
177 Dean Palmer .02 .10
178 Greg Hibbard .01 .05
179 Randy Ready .01 .05
180 Devon White .02 .10
181 Mark Eichhorn .01 .05
182 Mike Felder .01 .05
183 Joe Klink .01 .05
184 Steve Bedrosian .01 .05
185 Barry Larkin .05 .15
186 John Franco .02 .10
187 Ed Sprague .01 .05
188 Mark Portugal .01 .05
189 Jose Lind .01 .05
190 Bob Welch .01 .05
191 Alex Fernandez .01 .05
192 Gary Sheffield .02 .10
193 Rickey Henderson .08 .25
194 Rod Nichols .01 .05
195 Scott Kamieniecki .01 .05
196 Mike Flanagan .01 .05
197 Steve Finley .02 .10
198 Darren Daulton .02 .10
199 Leo Gomez .01 .05
200 Mike Morgan .01 .05
201 Bob Tewksbury .01 .05
202 Sid Bream .01 .05
203 Sandy Alomar Jr. .01 .05
204 Greg Gagne .01 .05
205 Juan Berenguer .01 .05
206 Cecil Fielder .02 .10
207 Randy Johnson .08 .25
208 Tony Pena .01 .05
209 Doug Drabek .01 .05
210 Wade Boggs .05 .15
211 Bryan Harvey .01 .05
212 Jose Vizcaino .01 .05
213 Alonzo Powell .01 .05
214 Will Clark .05 .15
215 Rickey Henderson HL .05 .15
216 Jack Morris .02 .10
217 Junior Felix .01 .05
218 Vince Coleman .01 .05
219 Jimmy Key .02 .10
220 Alex Cole .01 .05
221 Bill Landrum .01 .05
222 Randy Milligan .01 .05
223 Jose Rijo .01 .05
224 Greg Vaughn .01 .05
225 Dave Stewart .02 .10
226 Lenny Harris .01 .05
227 Scott Sanderson .01 .05
228 Jeff Blauser .01 .05
229 Ozzie Guillen .02 .10
230 John Kruk .02 .10
231 Bob Melvin .01 .05
232 Milt Cuyler .01 .05
233 Felix Jose .01 .05
234 Ellis Burks .02 .10
235 Pete Harnisch .01 .05
236 Kevin Tapani .01 .05
237 Terry Pendleton .02 .10
238 Mark Gardner .01 .05
239 Harold Reynolds .02 .10
240 Checklist 158-237 .01 .05
241 Mike Harkey .01 .05
242 Felix Fermin .01 .05
243 Barry Bonds .40 1.00
244 Roger Clemens .20 .50
245 Dennis Rasmussen .01 .05
246 Jose DeLeon .01 .05
247 Orel Hershiser .02 .10
248 Mel Hall .01 .05
249 Rick Wilkins .01 .05
250 Tom Gordon .01 .05
251 Kevin Reimer .01 .05
252 Luis Polonia .01 .05
253 Mike Henneman .01 .05
254 Tom Pagnozzi .01 .05
255 Chuck Finley .02 .10
256 Mackey Sasser .01 .05
257 John Burkett .01 .05
258 Hal Morris .01 .05
259 Larry Walker .05 .15
260 Bill Swift .01 .05
261 Joe Oliver .01 .05
262 Julio Machado .01 .05
263 Todd Stottlemyre .01 .05
264 Matt Merullo .01 .05
265 Brent Mayne .01 .05
266 Thomas Howard .01 .05
267 Lance Johnson .01 .05
268 Terry Mulholland .01 .05
269 Rick Honeycutt .01 .05
270 Luis Gonzalez .02 .10
271 Jose Guzman .01 .05
272 Jimmy Jones .01 .05
273 Mark Lewis .01 .05
274 Rene Gonzales .01 .05
275 Jeff Johnson .01 .05
276 Dennis Martinez HL .01 .05
277 Delino DeShields .01 .05
278 Sam Horn .01 .05
279 Kevin Gross .01 .05
280 Jose Oquendo .01 .05
281 Mark Grace .05 .15
282 Mark Gubicza .01 .05
283 Fred McGriff .05 .15
284 Ron Gant .02 .10
285 Lou Whitaker .02 .10
286 Edgar Martinez .05 .15
287 Ron Tingley .01 .05
288 Kevin McReynolds .01 .05
289 Ivan Rodriguez .08 .25
290 Mike Gardiner .01 .05
291 Chris Haney .01 .05
292 Darrin Jackson .01 .05
293 Bill Doran .01 .05
294 Ted Higuera .01 .05
295 Jeff Brantley .01 .05
296 Les Lancaster .01 .05
297 Jim Eisenreich .01 .05
298 Ruben Sierra .02 .10
299 Scott Radinsky .01 .05
300 Jose DeJesus .01 .05
301 Mike Timlin .01 .05
302 Luis Sojo .01 .05
303 Kelly Downs .01 .05
304 Scott Bankhead .01 .05
305 Pedro Munoz .01 .05
306 Scott Scudder .01 .05
307 Kevin Elster .01 .05
308 Duane Ward .01 .05
309 Darryl Kile .02 .10
310 Orlando Merced .01 .05
311 Dave Henderson .01 .05
312 Tim Raines .02 .10
313 Mark Lee .01 .05
314 Mike Gallego .01 .05
315 Charles Nagy .01 .05
316 Jesse Barfield .01 .05
317 Todd Frohwirth .01 .05
318 Al Osuna .01 .05
319 Darrin Fletcher .01 .05
320 Checklist 238-316 .01 .05
321 David Segui .01 .05
322 Stan Javier .01 .05
323 Bryn Smith .01 .05
324 Jeff Treadway .01 .05
325 Mark Whiten .01 .05
326 Kent Hrbek .02 .10
327 Dave Justice .02 .10
328 Tony Phillips .01 .05
329 Rob Murphy .01 .05
330 Kevin Morton .01 .05
331 John Smiley .01 .05
332 Luis Rivera .01 .05
333 Wally Joyner .02 .10
334 Heathcliff Slocumb .01 .05
335 Rick Cerone .01 .05
336 Mike Remlinger .01 .05
337 Mike Moore .01 .05
338 Lloyd McClendon .01 .05
339 Al Newman .01 .05
340 Kirk McCaskill .01 .05
341 Howard Johnson .01 .05
342 Greg Myers .01 .05
343 Kal Daniels .01 .05
344 Bernie Williams .05 .15
345 Shane Mack .01 .05
346 Gary Thurman .01 .05
347 Dante Bichette .02 .10
348 Mark McGwire .25 .60
349 Travis Fryman .02 .10
350 Ray Lankford .02 .10
351 Mike Jeffcoat .01 .05
352 Jack McDowell .01 .05
353 Mitch Williams .01 .05
354 Mike Devereaux .01 .05
355 Andres Galarraga .02 .10
356 Henry Cotto .01 .05
357 Scott Bailes .01 .05
358 Jeff Bagwell .08 .25
359 Scott Leius .01 .05
360 Zane Smith .01 .05
361 Bill Pecota .01 .05
362 Tony Fernandez .01 .05
363 Glenn Braggs .01 .05
364 Bill Spiers .01 .05
365 Vicente Palacios .01 .05
366 Tim Burke .01 .05
367 Randy Tomlin .01 .05
368 Kenny Rogers .02 .10
369 Brett Butler .02 .10
370 Pat Kelly .01 .05
371 Bip Roberts .01 .05
372 Gregg Jefferies .01 .05
373 Kevin Bass .01 .05
374 Ron Karkovice .01 .05
375 Paul Gibson .01 .05
376 Bernard Gilkey .01 .05
377 Dave Gallagher .01 .05
378 Bill Wegman .01 .05
379 Pat Borders .01 .05
380 Ed Whitson .01 .05
381 Gilberto Reyes .01 .05
382 Russ Swan .01 .05
383 Andy Van Slyke .05 .15
384 Wes Chamberlain .01 .05
385 Steve Chitren .01 .05
386 Greg Olson .01 .05
387 Brian McRae .01 .05
388 Rich Rodriguez .01 .05
389 Steve Decker .01 .05
390 Chuck Knoblauch .02 .10
391 Bobby Witt .01 .05
392 Eddie Murray .08 .25
393 Juan Gonzalez .05 .15
394 Scott Ruskin .01 .05
395 Jay Howell .01 .05
396 Checklist 317-396 .01 .05
397 Royce Clayton RR .01 .05
398 John Jaha RR RC .08 .25
399 Dan Wilson RR .01 .05
400 Archie Corbin RR .01 .05
401 Barry Manuel RR .01 .05
402 Kim Batiste RR .01 .05
403 Pat Mahomes RR RC .08 .25
404 Dave Fleming RR .01 .05
405 Jeff Juden RR .01 .05
406 Jim Thome RR .08 .25
407 Sam Militello RR .01 .05
408 Jeff Nelson RR RC .15 .40
409 Anthony Young RR .01 .05
410 Tino Martinez RR .05 .15
411 Jeff Mutis RR .01 .05
412 Rey Sanchez RR RC .08 .25
413 Chris Gardner RR .01 .05
414 John Vander Wal RR .01 .05
415 Reggie Sanders RR .02 .10
416 Brian Williams RR RC .02 .10
417 Mo Sanford RR .01 .05
418 David Weathers RR RC .15 .40
419 Hector Fajardo RR RC .02 .10
420 Steve Foster RR .01 .05
421 Lance Dickson RR .01 .05
422 Andre Dawson AS .01 .05
423 Ozzie Smith AS .08 .25
424 Chris Sabo AS .01 .05
425 Tony Gwynn AS .05 .15
426 Tom Glavine AS .02 .10
427 Bobby Bonilla AS .01 .05
428 Will Clark AS .02 .10
429 Ryne Sandberg AS .08 .25
430 Benito Santiago AS .01 .05
431 Ivan Calderon AS .01 .05
432 Ozzie Smith .15 .40
433 Tim Leary .01 .05
434 Bret Saberhagen HL .01 .05
435 Mel Rojas .01 .05
436 Ben McDonald .01 .05
437 Tim Crews .01 .05
438 Rex Hudler .01 .05
439 Chico Walker .01 .05
440 Kurt Stillwell .01 .05
441 Tony Gwynn .10 .30
442 John Smoltz .05 .15
443 Lloyd Moseby .01 .05
444 Mike Schooler .01 .05
445 Joe Grahe .01 .05
446 Dwight Gooden .02 .10
447 Oil Can Boyd .01 .05
448 John Marzano .01 .05
449 Bret Barberie .01 .05
450 Mike Maddux .01 .05
451 Jeff Reed .01 .05
452 Dale Sveum .01 .05
453 Jose Uribe .01 .05
454 Bob Scanlan .01 .05
455 Kevin Appier .02 .10
456 Jeff Huson .01 .05
457 Ken Patterson .01 .05
458 Ricky Jordan .01 .05
459 Tom Candiotti .01 .05
460 Lee Stevens .01 .05
461 Rod Beck RC .08 .25
462 Dave Valle .01 .05
463 Scott Erickson .01 .05
464 Chris Jones .01 .05
465 Mark Carreon .01 .05
466 Rob Ducey .01 .05
467 Jim Corsi .01 .05
468 Jeff King .01 .05
469 Curt Young .01 .05
470 Bo Jackson .08 .25
471 Chris Bosio .01 .05
472 Jamie Quirk .01 .05
473 Jesse Orosco .01 .05
474 Alvaro Espinoza .01 .05
475 Joe Orsulak .01 .05
476 Checklist 397-477 .01 .05
477 Gerald Young .01 .05
478 Wally Backman .01 .05
479 Juan Bell .01 .05
480 Mike Scioscia .01 .05
481 Omar Olivares .01 .05
482 Francisco Cabrera .01 .05
483 Greg Swindell UER .01 .05
(Shown on Indians,
but listed on Reds)
484 Terry Leach .01 .05
485 Tommy Gregg .01 .05
486 Scott Aldred .01 .05
487 Greg Briley .01 .05
488 Phil Plantier .01 .05
489 Curtis Wilkerson .01 .05
490 Tom Brunansky .01 .05
491 Mike Fetters .01 .05
492 Frank Castillo .01 .05
493 Joe Boever .01 .05
494 Kirt Manwaring .01 .05
495 Wilson Alvarez HL .01 .05
496 Gene Larkin .01 .05
497 Gary DiSarcina .01 .05
498 Frank Viola .02 .10
499 Manuel Lee .01 .05
500 Albert Belle .02 .10
501 Stan Belinda .01 .05
502 Dwight Evans .05 .15
503 Eric Davis .02 .10
504 Darren Holmes .01 .05
505 Mike Bordick .01 .05
506 Dave Hansen .01 .05
507 Lee Guetterman .01 .05
508 Keith Mitchell .01 .05
509 Melido Perez .01 .05
510 Dickie Thon .01 .05
511 Mark Williamson .01 .05
512 Mark Salas .01 .05
513 Milt Thompson .01 .05
514 Mo Vaughn .02 .10
515 Jim Deshaies .01 .05
516 Rich Garces .01 .05
517 Lonnie Smith .01 .05
518 Spike Owen .01 .05
519 Tracy Jones .01 .05
520 Greg Maddux .15 .40
521 Carlos Martinez .01 .05
522 Neal Heaton .01 .05
523 Mike Greenwell .01 .05
524 Andy Benes .01 .05
525 Jeff Schaefer UER .01 .05
(Photo actually
Tino Martinez)
526 Mike Sharperson .01 .05
527 Wade Taylor .01 .05
528 Jerome Walton .01 .05
529 Storm Davis .01 .05
530 Jose Hernandez RC .08 .25
531 Mark Langston .01 .05
532 Rob Deer .01 .05
533 Geronimo Pena .01 .05
534 Juan Guzman .01 .05
535 Pete Schourek .01 .05
536 Todd Benzinger .01 .05
537 Billy Hatcher .01 .05
538 Tom Foley .01 .05
539 Dave Cochrane .01 .05
540 Mariano Duncan .01 .05
541 Edwin Nunez .01 .05
542 Rance Mulliniks .01 .05
543 Carlton Fisk .05 .15
544 Luis Aquino .01 .05
545 Ricky Bones .01 .05
546 Craig Grebeck .01 .05
547 Charlie Hayes .01 .05
548 Jose Canseco .05 .15
549 Andujar Cedeno .01 .05
550 Geno Petralli .01 .05
551 Javier Ortiz .01 .05
552 Rudy Seanez .01 .05
553 Rich Gedman .01 .05
554 Eric Plunk .01 .05
555 Nolan Ryan HL .15 .40
(With Rich Gossage)
556 Checklist 478-555 .01 .05
557 Greg Colbrunn .01 .05
558 Chito Martinez .01 .05
559 Darryl Strawberry .02 .10
560 Luis Alicea .01 .05
561 Dwight Smith .01 .05
562 Terry Shumpert .01 .05
563 Jim Vatcher .01 .05
564 Deion Sanders .05 .15
565 Walt Terrell .01 .05
566 Dave Burba .01 .05
567 Dave Howard .01 .05
568 Todd Hundley .01 .05
569 Jack Daugherty .01 .05
570 Scott Cooper .01 .05
571 Bill Sampen .01 .05
572 Jose Melendez .01 .05
573 Freddie Benavides .01 .05
574 Jim Gantner .01 .05
575 Trevor Wilson .01 .05
576 Ryne Sandberg .15 .40
577 Kevin Seitzer .01 .05
578 Gerald Alexander .01 .05
579 Mike Huff .01 .05
580 Von Hayes .01 .05
581 Derek Bell .02 .10
582 Mike Stanley .01 .05
583 Kevin Mitchell .01 .05
584 Mike Jackson .01 .05
585 Dan Gladden .01 .05
586 Ted Power UER .01 .05
(Wrong year given for
signing with Reds)
587 Jeff Innis .01 .05
588 Bob MacDonald .01 .05
589 Jose Tolentino .01 .05
590 Bob Patterson .01 .05
591 Scott Brosius RC .15 .40
592 Frank Thomas .08 .25
593 Darryl Hamilton .01 .05
594 Kirk Dressendorfer .01 .05
595 Jeff Shaw .01 .05
596 Don Mattingly .25 .60
597 Glenn Davis .01 .05
598 Andy Mota .01 .05
599 Jason Grimsley .01 .05
600 Jim Poole .01 .05
601 Jim Gott .01 .05
602 Stan Royer .01 .05
603 Marvin Freeman .01 .05
604 Denis Boucher .01 .05
605 Denny Neagle .02 .10
606 Mark Lemke .01 .05
607 Jerry Don Gleaton .01 .05
608 Brent Knackert .01 .05
609 Carlos Quintana .01 .05
610 Bobby Bonilla .02 .10
611 Joe Hesketh .01 .05
612 Daryl Boston .01 .05
613 Shawon Dunston .01 .05
614 Danny Cox .01 .05
615 Darren Lewis .01 .05
616 Braves No-Hitter UER .01 .05
Kent Mercker
(Misspelled Merker
on card front)
Alejandro Pena
Mark Wohlers
617 Kirby Puckett .08 .25
618 Franklin Stubbs .01 .05
619 Chris Donnels .01 .05
620 David Wells UER .02 .10
(Career Highlights
in black not red)
621 Mike Aldrete .01 .05
622 Bob Kipper .01 .05
623 Anthony Telford .01 .05
624 Randy Myers .01 .05
625 Willie Randolph .02 .10
626 Joe Slusarski .01 .05
627 John Wetteland .02 .10
628 Greg Cadaret .01 .05
629 Tom Glavine .05 .15
630 Wilson Alvarez .01 .05
631 Wally Ritchie .01 .05
632 Mike Mussina .08 .25
633 Mark Leiter .01 .05
634 Gerald Perry .01 .05
635 Matt Young .01 .05
636 Checklist 556-635 .01 .05
637 Scott Hemond .01 .05
638 David West .01 .05
639 Jim Clancy .01 .05
640 Doug Piatt UER .01 .05
(Not born in 1955 as
on card; incorrect info
on How Acquired)
641 Omar Vizquel .05 .15
642 Rick Sutcliffe .02 .10
643 Glenallen Hill .01 .05
644 Gary Varsho .01 .05
645 Tony Fossas .01 .05
646 Jack Howell .01 .05
647 Jim Campanis .01 .05
648 Chris Gwynn .01 .05
649 Jim Leyritz .01 .05
650 Chuck McElroy .01 .05
651 Sean Berry .01 .05
652 Donald Harris .01 .05
653 Don Slaught .01 .05
654 Rusty Meacham .01 .05
655 Scott Terry .01 .05
656 Ramon Martinez .01 .05
657 Keith Miller .01 .05
658 Ramon Garcia .01 .05
659 Milt Hill .01 .05
660 Steve Frey .01 .05
661 Bob McClure .01 .05
662 Ced Landrum .01 .05
663 Doug Henry RC .02 .10
664 Candy Maldonado .01 .05
665 Carl Willis .01 .05
666 Jeff Montgomery .01 .05
667 Craig Shipley .01 .05
668 Warren Newson .01 .05
669 Mickey Morandini .01 .05
670 Brook Jacoby .01 .05
671 Ryan Bowen .01 .05
672 Bill Krueger .01 .05
673 Rob Mallicoat .01 .05
674 Doug Jones .01 .05
675 Scott Livingstone .01 .05
676 Danny Tartabull .01 .05
677 Joe Carter HL .01 .05
678 Cecil Espy .01 .05
679 Randy Velarde .01 .05
680 Bruce Ruffin .01 .05
681 Ted Wood .01 .05
682 Dan Plesac .01 .05
683 Eric Bullock .01 .05
684 Junior Ortiz .01 .05
685 Dave Hollins .01 .05
686 Dennis Martinez .02 .10
687 Larry Andersen .01 .05
688 Doug Simons .01 .05
689 Tim Spehr .01 .05
690 Calvin Jones .01 .05
691 Mark Guthrie .01 .05
692 Alfredo Griffin .01 .05
693 Joe Carter .02 .10
694 Terry Mathews .01 .05
695 Pascual Perez .01 .05
696 Gene Nelson .01 .05
697 Gerald Williams .01 .05
698 Chris Cron .01 .05
699 Steve Buechele .01 .05
700 Paul McClellan .01 .05
701 Jim Lindeman .01 .05
702 Francisco Oliveras .01 .05
703 Rob Maurer .01 .05
704 Pat Hentgen .01 .05
705 Jaime Navarro .01 .05
706 Mike Magnante RC .02 .10
707 Nolan Ryan .40 1.00
708 Bobby Thigpen .01 .05
709 John Cerutti .01 .05
710 Steve Wilson .01 .05
711 Hensley Meulens .01 .05
712 Rheal Cormier .01 .05
713 Scott Bradley .01 .05
714 Mitch Webster .01 .05
715 Roger Mason .01 .05
716 Checklist 636-716 .01 .05
717 Jeff Fassero .01 .05
718 Cal Eldred .01 .05
719 Sid Fernandez .01 .05
720 Bob Zupcic RC .02 .10
721 Jose Offerman .01 .05
722 Cliff Brantley .01 .05
723 Ron Darling .01 .05
724 Dave Stieb .01 .05
725 Hector Villanueva .01 .05
726 Mike Hartley .01 .05
727 Arthur Rhodes .01 .05
728 Randy Bush .01 .05
729 Steve Sax .01 .05
730 Dave Otto .01 .05
731 John Wehner .01 .05
732 Dave Martinez .01 .05
733 Ruben Amaro .01 .05
734 Billy Ripken .01 .05
735 Steve Farr .01 .05
736 Shawn Abner .01 .05
737 Gil Heredia RC .08 .25
738 Ron Jones .01 .05
739 Tony Castillo .01 .05
740 Sammy Sosa .08 .25
741 Julio Franco .02 .10
742 Tim Naehring .01 .05
743 Steve Wapnick .01 .05
744 Craig Wilson .01 .05
745 Darrin Chapin .01 .05
746 Chris George .01 .05
747 Mike Simms .01 .05
748 Rosario Rodriguez .01 .05
749 Skeeter Barnes .01 .05
750 Roger McDowell .01 .05
751 Dann Howitt .01 .05
752 Paul Sorrento .01 .05
753 Braulio Castillo .01 .05
754 Yorkis Perez .01 .05
755 Willie Fraser .01 .05
756 Jeremy Hernandez RC .02 .10
757 Curt Schilling .05 .15
758 Steve Lyons .01 .05
759 Dave Anderson .01 .05
760 Willie Banks .01 .05
761 Mark Leonard .01 .05
762 Jack Armstrong .01 .05
(Listed on Indians,
but shown on Reds)
763 Scott Servais .01 .05
764 Ray Stephens .01 .05
765 Junior Noboa .01 .05
766 Jim Olander .01 .05
767 Joe Magrane .01 .05
768 Lance Blankenship .01 .05
769 Mike Humphreys .01 .05
770 Jarvis Brown .01 .05
771 Damon Berryhill .01 .05
772 Alejandro Pena .01 .05
773 Jose Mesa .01 .05
774 Gary Cooper .01 .05
775 Carney Lansford .02 .10
776 Mike Bielecki .01 .05
Shown on Cubs,
but listed on Braves
777 Charlie O'Brien .01 .05
778 Carlos Hernandez .01 .05
779 Howard Farmer .01 .05
780 Mike Stanton .01 .05
781 Reggie Harris .01 .05
782 Xavier Hernandez .01 .05
783 Bryan Hickerson RC .02 .10
784 Checklist 717-784 .01 .05
and BC1-BC8

1992 Donruss Rookies

After six years of issuing "The Rookies" as a 56-card boxed set, Donruss expanded it to a 132-card standard-size set and distributed the cards in hobby and retail foil packs. The card design is the same as the 1992 Donruss regular issue except that the two-tone blue color bars have been replaced by green, as in the previous six Donruss Rookies sets. The cards are arranged in alphabetical order and numbered on the back. Rookie Cards in this set include Jeff Kent, Manny Ramirez and Eric Young. In addition an early card of Pedro Martinez is featured.

COMPLETE SET (132)	4.00	10.00
1 Kyle Abbott	.01	.05
2 Troy Afenir	.01	.05
3 Rich Amaral RC	.02	.10
4 Ruben Amaro	.01	.05
5 Billy Ashley RC	.02	.10
6 Pedro Astacio RC	.08	.25
7 Jim Austin	.01	.05
8 Robert Ayrault	.01	.05
9 Kevin Baez	.01	.05
10 Esteban Beltre	.01	.05
11 Brian Bohanon	.01	.05
12 Kent Bottenfield RC	.08	.25
13 Jeff Branson	.01	.05
14 Brad Brink	.01	.05
15 John Briscoe	.01	.05
16 Doug Brocail RC	.02	.10
17 Rico Brogna	.01	.05
18 J.T. Bruett	.01	.05
19 Jacob Brumfield	.01	.05
20 Jim Bullinger	.01	.05
21 Kevin Campbell	.01	.05
22 Pedro Castellano RC	.02	.10
23 Mike Christopher	.01	.05
24 Archi Cianfrocco RC	.02	.10
25 Mark Clark RC	.02	.10
26 Craig Colbert	.01	.05
27 Victor Cole RC	.01	.05
28 Steve Cooke RC	.02	.10
29 Tim Costo	.01	.05
30 Chad Curtis RC	.08	.25
31 Doug Davis	.01	.05
32 Gary DiSarcina	.01	.05
33 John Doherty RC	.02	.10
34 Mike Draper	.01	.05
35 Monty Fariss	.01	.05
36 Bien Figueroa	.01	.05
37 John Flaherty	.01	.05
38 Tim Fortugno	.01	.05
39 Eric Fox RC	.02	.10
40 Jeff Frye RC	.02	.10
41 Ramon Garcia	.01	.05
42 Brent Gates RC	.02	.10
43 Tom Goodwin	.01	.05
44 Buddy Groom RC	.02	.10
45 Jeff Grotewold	.01	.05
46 Juan Guerrero	.01	.05
47 Johnny Guzman RC	.02	.10
48 Shawn Hare RC	.02	.10
49 Ryan Hawblitzel RC	.02	.10
50 Bert Heffernan	.01	.05
51 Butch Henry	.01	.05
52 Cesar Hernandez RC	.02	.10
53 Vince Horsman	.01	.05
54 Steve Hosey	.01	.05
55 Pat Howell	.01	.05
56 Peter Hoy	.01	.05
57 Jonathan Hurst RC	.02	.10
58 Mark Hutton RC	.02	.10
59 Shawn Jeter RC	.02	.10
60 Joel Johnston	.01	.05
61 Jeff Kent RC	1.00	2.50
62 Kurt Knudsen RC	.02	.10
63 Kevin Koslofski	.01	.05
64 Danny Leon	.01	.05
65 Jesse Levis	.01	.05
66 Tom Marsh	.01	.05
67 Ed Martel	.01	.05
68 Al Martin RC	.08	.25
69 Pedro Martinez	.75	2.00
70 Derrick May	.01	.05
71 Matt Maysey	.01	.05
72 Russ McGinnis	.01	.05
73 Tim McIntosh	.01	.05
74 Jim McNamara	.01	.05
75 Jeff McNeely	.01	.05
76 Rusty Meacham	.01	.05
77 Tony Menendez	.01	.05
78 Henry Mercedes	.01	.05
79 Paul Miller	.01	.05
80 Joe Millette	.01	.05
81 Blas Minor	.01	.05
82 Dennis Moeller	.01	.05
83 Raul Mondesi	.02	.10
84 Rob Natal	.01	.05
85 Troy Neel RC	.02	.10
86 David Nied RC	.02	.10
87 Jerry Nielson	.01	.05
88 Donovan Osborne	.01	.05
89 John Patterson RC	.02	.10
90 Roger Pavlik RC	.02	.10
91 Dan Peltier	.01	.05
92 Jim Pena	.01	.05
93 William Pennyfeather	.01	.05
94 Mike Perez	.01	.05
95 Hipolito Pichardo RC	.02	.10
96 Greg Pirkl RC	.02	.10
97 Harvey Pulliam	.01	.05
98 Manny Ramirez RC	1.50	4.00
99 Pat Rapp RC	.02	.10
100 Jeff Reboulet	.01	.05
101 Darren Reed	.01	.05
102 Shane Reynolds RC	.08	.25
103 Bill Risley	.01	.05
104 Ben Rivera	.01	.05
105 Henry Rodriguez	.01	.05
106 Rico Rossy	.01	.05
107 Johnny Ruffin	.01	.05
108 Steve Scarsone	.01	.05
109 Tim Scott	.01	.05
110 Steve Shifflett	.01	.05
111 Dave Silvestri	.01	.05
112 Matt Stairs RC	.08	.25
113 William Suero	.01	.05
114 Jeff Tackett	.01	.05
115 Eddie Taubensee	.02	.10
116 Rick Trlicek RC	.02	.10
117 Scooter Tucker	.01	.05
118 Shane Turner	.01	.05
119 Julio Valera	.01	.05
120 Paul Wagner RC	.02	.10
121 Tim Wakefield RC	1.25	3.00
122 Mike Walker	.01	.05
123 Bruce Walton	.01	.05
124 Lenny Webster	.01	.05
125 Bob Wickman	.08	.25
126 Mike Williams RC	.08	.25
127 Kerry Woodson	.01	.05
128 Eric Young RC	.08	.25
129 Kevin Young RC	.08	.25
130 Pete Young	.01	.05
131 Checklist 1-66	.01	.05
132 Checklist 67-132	.01	.05

1993 Donruss

The 792-card 1993 Donruss set was issued in two series, each with 396 standard-size cards. Cards were distributed in foil packs. The basic card fronts feature glossy color action photos with white borders. At the bottom of the picture, the team logo appears in a team color-coded diamond with the player's name in a color-coded bar extending to the right. A Rated Rookies (RR) subset, sprinkled throughout the set, spotlights 20 young prospects. There are no key Rookie Cards in this set.

COMPLETE SET (792)	12.00	30.00
COMP.SERIES 1 (396)	6.00	15.00
COMP.SERIES 2 (396)	6.00	15.00
1 Craig Lefferts	.02	.10
2 Kent Mercker	.02	.10
3 Phil Plantier	.02	.10
4 Alex Arias	.02	.10
5 Julio Valera	.02	.10
6 Dan Wilson	.07	.20
7 Frank Thomas	.20	.50
8 Eric Anthony	.02	.10
9 Derek Lilliquist	.02	.10
10 Rafael Bournigal	.02	.10
11 Manny Alexander RR	.02	.10
12 Bret Barberie	.02	.10
13 Mickey Tettleton	.02	.10
14 Anthony Young	.02	.10
15 Tim Spehr	.02	.10
16 Bob Ayrault	.02	.10
17 Bill Wegman	.02	.10
18 Jay Bell	.07	.20
19 Rick Aguilera	.02	.10
20 Todd Zeile	.02	.10
21 Steve Farr	.02	.10
22 Andy Benes	.02	.10
23 Lance Blankenship	.02	.10
24 Ted Wood	.02	.10
25 Omar Vizquel	.10	.30
26 Steve Avery	.02	.10
27 Brian Bohanon	.02	.10
28 Rick Wilkins	.02	.10
29 Devon White	.07	.20
30 Bobby Ayala RC	.02	.10
31 Leo Gomez	.02	.10
32 Mike Simms	.02	.10
33 Ellis Burks	.07	.20
34 Steve Wilson	.02	.10
35 Jim Abbott	.10	.30
36 Tim Wallach	.02	.10
37 Wilson Alvarez	.02	.10
38 Daryl Boston	.02	.10
39 Sandy Alomar Jr.	.02	.10
40 Mitch Williams	.02	.10
41 Rico Brogna	.02	.10
42 Gary Varsho	.02	.10
43 Kevin Appier	.07	.20
44 Eric Wedge RR RC	.02	.10
45 Dante Bichette	.07	.20
46 Jose Oquendo	.02	.10
47 Mike Trombley	.02	.10
48 Dan Walters	.02	.10
49 Gerald Williams	.02	.10
50 Bud Black	.02	.10
51 Bobby Witt	.02	.10
52 Mark Davis	.02	.10
53 Shawn Barton RC	.02	.10
54 Paul Assenmacher	.02	.10
55 Kevin Reimer	.02	.10
56 Billy Ashley RR	.02	.10
57 Eddie Zosky	.02	.10
58 Chris Sabo	.02	.10
59 Billy Ripken	.02	.10
60 Scooter Tucker	.02	.10
61 Tim Wakefield RR	.20	.50
62 Mitch Webster	.02	.10
63 Jack Clark	.07	.20
64 Mark Gardner	.02	.10
65 Lee Stevens	.02	.10
66 Todd Hundley	.02	.10
67 Bobby Thigpen	.02	.10
68 Dave Hollins	.02	.10
69 Jack Armstrong	.02	.10
70 Alex Cole	.02	.10
71 Mark Carreon	.02	.10
72 Todd Worrell	.02	.10
73 Steve Shifflett	.02	.10
74 Jerald Clark	.02	.10
75 Paul Molitor	.07	.20
76 Larry Carter RC	.02	.10
77 Rich Rowland RR	.02	.10
78 Damon Berryhill	.02	.10
79 Willie Banks	.02	.10
80 Hector Villanueva	.02	.10
81 Mike Gallego	.02	.10
82 Tim Belcher	.02	.10
83 Mike Bordick	.02	.10
84 Craig Biggio	.10	.30
85 Lance Parrish	.07	.20
86 Brett Butler	.07	.20
87 Mike Timlin	.02	.10
88 Brian Barnes	.02	.10
89 Brady Anderson	.07	.20
90 D.J. Dozier	.02	.10
91 Frank Viola	.07	.20
92 Darren Daulton	.07	.20
93 Chad Curtis	.02	.10
94 Zane Smith	.02	.10
95 George Bell	.02	.10
96 Rex Hudler	.02	.10
97 Mark Whiten	.02	.10
98 Tim Teufel	.02	.10
99 Kevin Ritz	.02	.10
100 Jeff Brantley	.02	.10
101 Jeff Conine	.07	.20
102 Vinny Castilla	.20	.50
103 Greg Vaughn	.02	.10
104 Steve Buechele	.02	.10
105 Darren Reed	.02	.10
106 Bip Roberts	.02	.10
107 John Habyan	.02	.10
108 Scott Servais	.02	.10
109 Walt Weiss	.02	.10
110 J.T. Snow RR RC	.10	.30
111 Jay Buhner	.07	.20
112 Darryl Strawberry	.07	.20
113 Roger Pavlik	.02	.10
114 Chris Nabholz	.02	.10
115 Pat Borders	.02	.10
116 Pat Howell	.02	.10
117 Gregg Olson	.02	.10
118 Curt Schilling	.07	.20
119 Roger Clemens	.40	1.00
120 Victor Cole	.02	.10
121 Gary DiSarcina	.02	.10
122 Gary Carter CL Kirt Manwaring	.02	.10
123 Steve Sax	.02	.10
124 Chuck Carr	.02	.10
125 Mark Lewis	.02	.10
126 Tony Gwynn	.25	.60
127 Travis Fryman	.07	.20
128 Dave Burba	.02	.10
129 Wally Joyner	.07	.20
130 John Smoltz	.10	.30
131 Cal Eldred	.02	.10
132 Roberto Alomar CL Devon White	.07	.20
133 Arthur Rhodes	.02	.10
134 Jeff Blauser	.02	.10
135 Scott Cooper	.02	.10
136 Doug Strange	.02	.10
137 Luis Sojo	.02	.10
138 Jeff Branson	.02	.10
139 Alex Fernandez	.02	.10
140 Ken Caminiti	.07	.20
141 Charles Nagy	.02	.10
142 Tom Candiotti	.02	.10
143 Willie Greene RR	.02	.10
144 John Vander Wal	.02	.10
145 Kurt Knudsen	.02	.10
146 John Franco	.07	.20
147 Eddie Pierce RC	.02	.10
148 Kim Batiste	.02	.10
149 Darren Holmes	.02	.10
150 Steve Cooke	.02	.10
151 Terry Jorgensen	.02	.10
152 Mark Clark	.02	.10
153 Randy Velarde	.02	.10
154 Greg W. Harris	.02	.10
155 Kevin Campbell	.02	.10
156 John Burkett	.02	.10
157 Kevin Mitchell	.02	.10
158 Deion Sanders	.10	.30
159 Jose Canseco	.10	.30
160 Jeff Hartsock	.02	.10
161 Tom Quinlan RC	.02	.10
162 Tim Pugh RC	.02	.10
163 Glenn Davis	.02	.10
164 Shane Reynolds	.02	.10
165 Jody Reed	.02	.10
166 Mike Sharperson	.02	.10
167 Scott Lewis	.02	.10
168 Dennis Martinez	.07	.20
169 Scott Radinsky	.02	.10
170 Dave Gallagher	.02	.10
171 Jim Thome	.10	.30
172 Terry Mulholland	.02	.10
173 Milt Cuyler	.02	.10
174 Bob Patterson	.02	.10
175 Jeff Montgomery	.02	.10
176 Tim Salmon RR	.10	.30
177 Franklin Stubbs	.02	.10
178 Donovan Osborne	.02	.10
179 Jeff Reboulet	.02	.10
180 Jeremy Hernandez	.02	.10
181 Charlie Hayes	.02	.10
182 Matt Williams	.07	.20
183 Mike Raczka	.02	.10
184 Francisco Cabrera	.02	.10
185 Rich DeLucia	.02	.10
186 Sammy Sosa	.20	.50
187 Ivan Rodriguez	.10	.30
188 Bret Boone RR	.07	.20
189 Juan Guzman	.02	.10
190 Tom Browning	.02	.10
191 Randy Milligan	.02	.10
192 Steve Finley	.07	.20
193 John Patterson RR	.02	.10
194 Kip Gross	.02	.10
195 Tony Fossas	.02	.10
196 Ivan Calderon	.02	.10
197 Junior Felix	.02	.10
198 Pete Schourek	.02	.10
199 Craig Grebeck	.02	.10
200 Juan Bell	.02	.10
201 Glenallen Hill	.02	.10
202 Danny Jackson	.02	.10
203 John Kiely	.02	.10
204 Bob Tewksbury	.02	.10
205 Kevin Koslofski	.02	.10
206 Craig Shipley	.02	.10
207 John Jaha	.02	.10
208 Royce Clayton	.02	.10
209 Mike Piazza RR	1.25	3.00
210 Ron Gant	.07	.20
211 Scott Erickson	.02	.10
212 Doug Dascenzo	.02	.10
213 Andy Stankiewicz	.02	.10
214 Geronimo Berroa	.02	.10
215 Dennis Eckersley	.07	.20
216 Al Osuna	.02	.10
217 Tino Martinez	.10	.30
218 Henry Rodriguez	.02	.10
219 Ed Sprague	.02	.10
220 Ken Hill	.02	.10
221 Chito Martinez	.02	.10
222 Bret Saberhagen	.07	.20
223 Mike Greenwell	.02	.10
224 Mickey Morandini	.02	.10
225 Chuck Finley	.07	.20
226 Denny Neagle	.07	.20
227 Kirk McCaskill	.02	.10
228 Rheal Cormier	.02	.10
229 Paul Sorrento	.02	.10
230 Darrin Jackson	.02	.10
231 Rob Deer	.02	.10
232 Bill Swift	.02	.10
233 Kevin McReynolds	.02	.10
234 Terry Pendleton	.07	.20
235 Dave Nilsson	.02	.10
236 Chuck McElroy	.02	.10
237 Derek Parks	.02	.10
238 Norm Charlton	.02	.10
239 Matt Nokes	.02	.10
240 Juan Guerrero	.02	.10
241 Jeff Parrett	.02	.10
242 Ryan Thompson RR	.02	.10
243 Dave Fleming	.02	.10
244 Dave Hansen	.02	.10
245 Monty Fariss	.02	.10
246 Archi Cianfrocco	.02	.10
247 Pat Hentgen	.02	.10
248 Bill Pecota	.02	.10
249 Ben McDonald	.02	.10
250 Cliff Brantley	.02	.10
251 John Valentin	.02	.10
252 Jeff King	.02	.10
253 Reggie Williams	.02	.10
254 Damon Berryhill CL Alex Arias	.02	.10
255 Ozzie Guillen	.07	.20
256 Mike Perez	.02	.10
257 Thomas Howard	.02	.10
258 Kurt Stillwell	.02	.10
259 Mike Henneman	.02	.10
260 Steve Decker	.02	.10
261 Brent Mayne	.02	.10
262 Otis Nixon	.02	.10
263 Mark Kiefer	.02	.10
264 Don Mattingly CL Mike Bordick)	.10	.30
265 Richie Lewis RC	.02	.10
266 Pat Gomez RC	.02	.10
267 Scott Taylor	.02	.10
268 Shawon Dunston	.02	.10
269 Greg Myers	.02	.10
270 Tim Costo	.02	.10
271 Greg Hibbard	.02	.10
272 Pete Harnisch	.02	.10
273 Dave Mlicki	.02	.10
274 Orel Hershiser	.07	.20
275 Sean Berry RR	.02	.10
276 Doug Simons	.02	.10
277 John Doherty	.02	.10
278 Eddie Murray	.20	.50
279 Chris Haney	.02	.10
280 Stan Javier	.02	.10
281 Jaime Navarro	.02	.10
282 Orlando Merced	.02	.10
283 Kent Hrbek	.07	.20
284 Bernard Gilkey	.02	.10
285 Russ Springer	.02	.10
286 Mike Maddux	.02	.10
287 Eric Fox	.02	.10
288 Mark Leonard	.02	.10
289 Tim Leary	.02	.10
290 Brian Hunter	.02	.10
291 Donald Harris	.02	.10
292 Bob Scanlan	.02	.10
293 Turner Ward	.02	.10
294 Hal Morris	.02	.10
295 Jimmy Poole	.02	.10
296 Doug Jones	.02	.10
297 Tony Pena	.02	.10
298 Ramon Martinez	.02	.10
299 Tim Fortugno	.02	.10
300 Marquis Grissom	.07	.20
301 Lance Johnson	.02	.10
302 Jeff Kent	.20	.50
303 Reggie Jefferson	.02	.10
304 Wes Chamberlain	.02	.10
305 Shawn Hare	.02	.10
306 Mike LaValliere	.02	.10
307 Gregg Jefferies	.02	.10
308 Troy Neel RR	.02	.10
309 Pat Listach	.02	.10
310 Geronimo Pena	.02	.10
311 Pedro Munoz	.02	.10
312 Guillermo Velasquez	.02	.10
313 Roberto Kelly	.02	.10
314 Mike Jackson	.02	.10
315 Rickey Henderson	.20	.50
316 Mark Lemke	.02	.10
317 Erik Hanson	.02	.10
318 Derrick May	.02	.10
319 Geno Petralli	.02	.10
320 Melvin Nieves RR	.02	.10
321 Doug Linton	.02	.10
322 Rob Dibble	.07	.20
323 Chris Hoiles	.02	.10
324 Jimmy Jones	.02	.10
325 Dave Staton RR	.02	.10
326 Pedro Martinez	.40	1.00
327 Paul Quantrill	.02	.10
328 Greg Colbrunn	.02	.10
329 Hilly Hathaway RC	.02	.10
330 Jeff Innis	.02	.10
331 Ron Karkovice	.02	.10
332 Keith Shepherd RC	.02	.10
333 Alan Embree	.02	.10
334 Paul Wagner	.02	.10
335 Dave Haas	.02	.10
336 Ozzie Canseco	.02	.10
337 Bill Sampen	.02	.10
338 Rich Rodriguez	.02	.10
339 Dean Palmer	.07	.20
340 Greg Litton	.02	.10
341 Jim Tatum RR RC	.02	.10
342 Todd Haney RC	.02	.10
343 Larry Casian	.02	.10
344 Ryne Sandberg	.30	.75
345 Sterling Hitchcock RC	.07	.20
346 Chris Hammond	.02	.10
347 Vince Horsman	.02	.10
348 Butch Henry	.02	.10
349 Dann Howitt	.02	.10
350 Roger McDowell	.02	.10
351 Jack Morris	.07	.20
352 Bill Krueger	.02	.10
353 Cris Colon	.02	.10
354 Joe Vitko	.02	.10
355 Willie McGee	.07	.20
356 Jay Baller	.02	.10
357 Pat Mahomes	.02	.10
358 Roger Mason	.02	.10
359 Jerry Nielsen	.02	.10
360 Tom Pagnozzi	.02	.10
361 Kevin Baez	.02	.10
362 Tim Scott	.02	.10
363 Domingo Martinez RC	.02	.10
364 Kirt Manwaring	.02	.10
365 Rafael Palmeiro	.10	.30
366 Ray Lankford	.07	.20
367 Tim McIntosh	.02	.10
368 Jessie Hollins	.02	.10
369 Scott Leius	.02	.10
370 Bill Doran	.02	.10
371 Sam Militello	.02	.10
372 Ryan Bowen	.02	.10
373 Dave Henderson	.02	.10
374 Dan Smith RR	.02	.10
375 Steve Reed RR RC	.02	.10
376 Jose Offerman	.02	.10
377 Kevin Brown	.07	.20
378 Darrin Fletcher	.02	.10
379 Duane Ward	.02	.10
380 Wayne Kirby RR	.02	.10
381 Steve Scarsone	.02	.10
382 Mariano Duncan	.02	.10
383 Ken Ryan RC	.02	.10
384 Lloyd McClendon	.02	.10
385 Brian Holman	.02	.10
386 Braulio Castillo	.02	.10
387 Danny Leon	.02	.10
388 Omar Olivares	.02	.10
389 Kevin Wickander	.02	.10
390 Fred McGriff	.10	.30
391 Phil Clark	.02	.10
392 Darren Lewis	.02	.10
393 Phil Hiatt	.02	.10
394 Mike Morgan	.02	.10
395 Shane Mack	.02	.10
396 Dennis Eckersley CL Art Kusnyer CO	.07	.20
397 David Segui	.02	.10
398 Rafael Belliard	.02	.10
399 Tim Naehring	.02	.10
400 Frank Castillo	.02	.10
401 Joe Grahe	.02	.10
402 Reggie Sanders	.07	.20
403 Roberto Hernandez	.02	.10
404 Luis Gonzalez	.07	.20
405 Carlos Baerga	.02	.10
406 Carlos Hernandez	.02	.10
407 Pedro Astacio RR	.02	.10
408 Mel Rojas	.02	.10
409 Scott Livingstone	.02	.10
410 Chico Walker	.02	.10
411 Brian McRae	.02	.10
412 Ben Rivera	.02	.10
413 Ricky Bones	.02	.10
414 Andy Van Slyke	.10	.30
415 Chuck Knoblauch	.07	.20
416 Luis Alicea	.02	.10
417 Bob Wickman	.02	.10
418 Doug Brocail	.02	.10
419 Scott Brosius	.07	.20
420 Rod Beck	.02	.10
421 Edgar Martinez	.10	.30
422 Ryan Klesko	.07	.20
423 Nolan Ryan	.75	2.00
424 Rey Sanchez	.02	.10
425 Roberto Alomar	.10	.30
426 Barry Larkin	.10	.30
427 Mike Mussina	.10	.30
428 Jeff Bagwell	.10	.30
429 Mo Vaughn	.07	.20
430 Eric Karros	.07	.20
431 John Orton	.02	.10
432 Wil Cordero	.02	.10
433 Jack McDowell	.02	.10
434 Howard Johnson	.02	.10
435 Albert Belle	.07	.20
436 John Kruk	.07	.20
437 Skeeter Barnes	.02	.10
438 Don Slaught	.02	.10
439 Rusty Meacham	.02	.10
440 Tim Laker RR RC	.02	.10
441 Robin Yount	.30	.75
442 Brian Jordan	.07	.20
443 Kevin Tapani	.02	.10
444 Gary Sheffield	.07	.20
445 Rich Monteleone	.02	.10
446 Will Clark	.10	.30
447 Jerry Browne	.02	.10
448 Jeff Treadway	.02	.10
449 Mike Schooler	.02	.10
450 Mike Harkey	.02	.10
451 Julio Franco	.07	.20
452 Kevin Young RR	.07	.20
453 Kelly Gruber	.02	.10
454 Jose Rijo	.02	.10
455 Mike Devereaux	.02	.10
456 Andujar Cedeno	.02	.10
457 Damion Easley RR	.02	.10
458 Kevin Gross	.02	.10
459 Matt Young	.02	.10
460 Matt Stairs	.02	.10
461 Luis Polonia	.02	.10
462 Dwight Gooden	.07	.20
463 Warren Newson	.02	.10
464 Jose DeLeon	.02	.10
465 Jose Mesa	.02	.10
466 Danny Cox	.02	.10
467 Dan Gladden	.02	.10
468 Gerald Perry	.02	.10
469 Mike Boddicker	.02	.10
470 Jeff Gardner	.02	.10
471 Doug Henry	.02	.10
472 Mike Benjamin	.02	.10
473 Dan Peltier RR	.02	.10
474 Mike Stanton	.02	.10
475 John Smiley	.02	.10
476 Dwight Smith	.02	.10
477 Jim Leyritz	.02	.10
478 Dwayne Henry	.02	.10
479 Mark McGwire	.50	1.25
480 Pete Incaviglia	.02	.10
481 Dave Cochrane	.02	.10
482 Eric Davis	.07	.20
483 John Olerud	.07	.20
484 Kent Bottenfield	.02	.10
485 Mark McLemore	.02	.10
486 Dave Magadan	.02	.10
487 John Marzano	.02	.10
488 Ruben Amaro	.02	.10
489 Rob Ducey	.02	.10
490 Stan Belinda	.02	.10
491 Dan Pasqua	.02	.10
492 Joe Magrane	.02	.10
493 Brook Jacoby	.02	.10
494 Gene Harris	.02	.10
495 Mark Leiter	.02	.10
496 Bryan Hickerson	.02	.10
497 Tom Gordon	.02	.10
498 Pete Smith	.02	.10
499 Chris Bosio	.02	.10
500 Shawn Boskie	.02	.10
501 Dave West	.02	.10
502 Milt Hill	.02	.10
503 Pat Kelly	.02	.10
504 Joe Boever	.02	.10
505 Terry Steinbach	.02	.10
506 Butch Huskey RR	.02	.10
507 David Valle	.02	.10
508 Mike Scioscia	.02	.10
509 Kenny Rogers	.07	.20
510 Moises Alou	.07	.20
511 David Wells	.07	.20
512 Mackey Sasser	.02	.10
513 Todd Frohwirth	.02	.10
514 Ricky Jordan	.02	.10
515 Mike Gardiner	.02	.10
516 Gary Redus	.02	.10
517 Gary Gaetti	.07	.20
518 Checklist	.02	.10
519 Carlton Fisk	.10	.30
520 Ozzie Smith	.30	.75
521 Rod Nichols	.02	.10
522 Benito Santiago	.07	.20
523 Bill Gullickson	.02	.10
524 Robby Thompson	.02	.10
525 Mike Macfarlane	.02	.10
526 Sid Bream	.02	.10
527 Darryl Hamilton	.02	.10
528 Checklist	.02	.10
529 Jeff Tackett	.02	.10
530 Greg Olson	.02	.10
531 Bob Zupcic	.02	.10
532 Mark Grace	.10	.30
533 Steve Frey	.02	.10
534 Dave Martinez	.02	.10
535 Robin Ventura	.07	.20
536 Casey Candaele	.02	.10
537 Kenny Lofton	.07	.20
538 Jay Howell	.02	.10
539 Fern.Ramsey RR RC	.02	.10
540 Larry Walker	.07	.20
541 Cecil Fielder	.07	.20
542 Lee Guetterman	.02	.10
543 Keith Miller	.02	.10
544 Len Dykstra	.07	.20
545 B.J. Surhoff	.07	.20
546 Bob Walk	.02	.10
547 Brian Harper	.02	.10
548 Lee Smith	.07	.20
549 Danny Tartabull	.02	.10
550 Frank Seminara	.02	.10
551 Henry Mercedes	.02	.10
552 Dave Righetti	.07	.20
553 Ken Griffey Jr.	.30	.75
554 Tom Glavine	.10	.30
555 Juan Gonzalez	.07	.20
556 Jim Bullinger	.02	.10
557 Derek Bell	.02	.10
558 Cesar Hernandez	.02	.10
559 Cal Ripken	.60	1.50
560 Eddie Taubensee	.02	.10
561 John Flaherty	.02	.10
562 Todd Benzinger	.02	.10
563 Hubie Brooks	.02	.10
564 Delino DeShields	.02	.10
565 Tim Raines	.07	.20
566 Sid Fernandez	.02	.10
567 Steve Olin	.02	.10
568 Tommy Greene	.02	.10
569 Buddy Groom	.02	.10
570 Randy Tomlin	.02	.10
571 Hipolito Pichardo	.02	.10
572 Rene Arocha RR RC	.07	.20
573 Mike Fetters	.02	.10
574 Felix Jose	.02	.10
575 Gene Larkin	.02	.10
576 Bruce Hurst	.02	.10
577 Bernie Williams	.10	.30
578 Trevor Wilson	.02	.10
579 Bob Welch	.02	.10
580 David Justice	.07	.20
581 Randy Johnson	.20	.50
582 Jose Vizcaino	.02	.10
583 Jeff Huson	.02	.10
584 Rob Maurer RR	.02	.10
585 Todd Stottlemyre	.02	.10
586 Joe Oliver	.02	.10
587 Bob Milacki	.02	.10
588 Rob Murphy	.02	.10
589 Greg Pirkl RR	.02	.10
590 Lenny Harris	.02	.10
591 Luis Rivera	.02	.10
592 John Wetteland	.07	.20
593 Mark Langston	.02	.10
594 Bobby Bonilla	.07	.20
595 Esteban Beltre	.02	.10
596 Mike Hartley	.02	.10
597 Felix Fermin	.02	.10
598 Carlos Garcia	.02	.10
599 Frank Tanana	.02	.10
600 Pedro Guerrero	.07	.20
601 Terry Shumpert	.02	.10
602 Wally Whitehurst	.02	.10
603 Kevin Seitzer	.02	.10
604 Chris James	.02	.10
605 Greg Gohr RR	.02	.10
606 Mark Wohlers	.02	.10
607 Kirby Puckett	.20	.50
608 Greg Maddux	.30	.75
609 Don Mattingly	.50	1.25
610 Greg Cadaret	.02	.10
611 Dave Stewart	.07	.20
612 Mark Portugal	.02	.10
613 Pete O'Brien	.02	.10
614 Bob Ojeda	.02	.10
615 Joe Carter	.07	.20
616 Pete Young	.02	.10
617 Sam Horn	.02	.10
618 Vince Coleman	.02	.10
619 Wade Boggs	.10	.30
620 Todd Pratt RC	.07	.20
621 Ron Tingley	.02	.10
622 Doug Drabek	.02	.10
623 Scott Hemond	.02	.10
624 Tim Jones	.02	.10
625 Dennis Cook	.02	.10
626 Jose Melendez	.02	.10
627 Mike Munoz	.02	.10
628 Jim Pena	.02	.10
629 Gary Thurman	.02	.10
630 Charlie Leibrandt	.02	.10
631 Scott Fletcher	.02	.10
632 Andre Dawson	.07	.20
633 Greg Gagne	.02	.10
634 Greg Swindell	.02	.10
635 Kevin Maas	.02	.10
636 Xavier Hernandez	.02	.10
637 Ruben Sierra	.07	.20
638 Dmitri Young RR	.07	.20
639 Harold Reynolds	.07	.20
640 Tom Goodwin	.02	.10
641 Todd Burns	.02	.10
642 Jeff Fassero	.02	.10
643 Dave Winfield	.07	.20
644 Willie Randolph	.07	.20
645 Luis Mercedes	.02	.10
646 Dale Murphy	.10	.30
647 Danny Darwin	.02	.10
648 Dennis Moeller	.02	.10
649 Chuck Crim	.02	.10
650 Checklist	.02	.10
651 Shawn Abner	.02	.10
652 Tracy Woodson	.02	.10
653 Scott Scudder	.02	.10
654 Tom Lampkin	.02	.10
655 Alan Trammell	.07	.20
656 Cory Snyder	.02	.10
657 Chris Gwynn	.02	.10
658 Lonnie Smith	.02	.10
659 Jim Austin	.02	.10
660 Rob Picciolo CL	.02	.10
661 Tim Hulett	.02	.10
662 Marvin Freeman	.02	.10
663 Greg A. Harris	.02	.10
664 Heathcliff Slocumb	.02	.10
665 Mike Butcher	.02	.10
666 Steve Foster	.02	.10
667 Donn Pall	.02	.10
668 Darryl Kile	.07	.20
669 Jesse Levis	.02	.10
670 Jim Gott	.02	.10
671 Mark Hutton RR	.02	.10
672 Brian Drahman	.02	.10
673 Chad Kreuter	.02	.10
674 Tony Fernandez	.02	.10
675 Jose Lind	.02	.10
676 Kyle Abbott	.02	.10
677 Dan Plesac	.02	.10
678 Barry Bonds	.60	1.50
679 Chili Davis	.07	.20
680 Stan Royer	.02	.10
681 Scott Kamieniecki	.02	.10
682 Carlos Martinez	.02	.10
683 Mike Moore	.02	.10
684 Candy Maldonado	.02	.10
685 Jeff Nelson	.02	.10
686 Lou Whitaker	.07	.20
687 Jose Guzman	.02	.10
688 Manuel Lee	.02	.10
689 Bob MacDonald	.02	.10
690 Scott Bankhead	.02	.10
691 Alan Mills	.02	.10
692 Brian Williams	.02	.10
693 Tom Brunansky	.02	.10
694 Lenny Webster	.02	.10
695 Greg Briley	.02	.10
696 Paul O'Neill	.10	.30
697 Joey Cora	.02	.10
698 Charlie O'Brien	.02	.10
699 Junior Ortiz	.02	.10
700 Ron Darling	.02	.10
701 Tony Phillips	.02	.10
702 William Pennyfeather	.02	.10
703 Mark Gubicza	.02	.10
704 Steve Hosey RR	.02	.10
705 Henry Cotto	.02	.10
706 David Hulse RC	.02	.10
707 Mike Pagliarulo	.02	.10
708 Dave Stieb	.02	.10
709 Melido Perez	.02	.10
710 Jimmy Key	.07	.20
711 Jeff Russell	.02	.10
712 David Cone	.07	.20
713 Russ Swan	.02	.10
714 Mark Guthrie	.02	.10
715 Checklist	.02	.10
716 Al Martin RR	.02	.10
717 Randy Knorr	.02	.10
718 Mike Stanley	.02	.10
719 Rick Sutcliffe	.07	.20
720 Terry Leach	.02	.10
721 Chipper Jones RR	.20	.50
722 Jim Eisenreich	.02	.10
723 Tom Henke	.02	.10
724 Jeff Frye	.02	.10
725 Harold Baines	.07	.20
726 Scott Sanderson	.02	.10
727 Tom Foley	.02	.10
728 Bryan Harvey	.02	.10
729 Tom Edens	.02	.10
730 Eric Young	.02	.10
731 Dave Weathers	.02	.10
732 Spike Owen	.02	.10
733 Scott Aldred	.02	.10
734 Cris Carpenter	.02	.10
735 Dion James	.02	.10
736 Joe Girardi	.02	.10
737 Nigel Wilson RR	.02	.10
738 Scott Champarino	.02	.10
739 Jeff Reardon	.07	.20

740 Willie Blair .02 .10
741 Jim Corsi .02 .10
742 Ken Patterson .02 .10
743 Andy Ashby .02 .10
744 Rob Natal .02 .10
745 Kevin Bass .02 .10
746 Freddie Benavides .02 .10
747 Chris Donnels .02 .10
748 Kerry Woodson .02 .10
749 Calvin Jones .02 .10
750 Gary Scott .02 .10
751 Joe Orsulak .02 .10
752 Armando Reynoso .02 .10
753 Monty Fariss .02 .10
754 Billy Hatcher .02 .10
755 Denis Boucher .02 .10
756 Walt Weiss .02 .10
757 Mike Fitzgerald .02 .10
758 Rudy Seanez .02 .10
759 Bret Barberie .02 .10
760 Mo Sanford .02 .10
761 Pedro Castellano .02 .10
762 Chuck Carr .02 .10
763 Steve Howe .02 .10
764 Andres Galarraga .07 .20
765 Jeff Conine .07 .20
766 Ted Power .02 .10
767 Butch Henry .02 .10
768 Steve Decker .02 .10
769 Storm Davis .02 .10
770 Vinny Castilla .20 .50
771 Junior Felix .02 .10
772 Walt Terrell .02 .10
773 Brad Ausmus .20 .50
774 Jamie McAndrew .02 .10
775 Milt Thompson .02 .10
776 Charlie Hayes .02 .10
777 Jack Armstrong .02 .10
778 Dennis Rasmussen .02 .10
779 Darren Holmes .02 .10
780 Alex Arias .02 .10
781 Randy Bush .02 .10
782 Javy Lopez .10 .30
783 Dante Bichette .07 .20
784 John Johnstone RC .02 .10
785 Rene Gonzales .02 .10
786 Alex Cole .02 .10
787 Jeromy Burnitz RR .07 .20
788 Michael Huff .02 .10
789 Anthony Telford .02 .10
790 Jerald Clark .02 .10
791 Joel Johnston .02 .10
792 David Nied RR .02 .10

1994 Donruss

The 1994 Donruss set was issued in two separate series of 330 standard-size cards for a total of 660. Cards were issued in foil wrapped packs. The fronts feature borderless color player action photos on front. There are no notable Rookie Cards in this set.

COMPLETE SET (660) 12.00 30.00
COMP.SERIES 1 (330) 6.00 15.00
COMP.SERIES 2 (330) 6.00 15.00
1 Nolan Ryan 1.50 4.00
2 Mike Piazza .60 1.50
3 Moises Alou .10 .30
4 Ken Griffey Jr. .50 1.25
5 Gary Sheffield .10 .30
6 Roberto Alomar .20 .50
7 John Kruk .10 .30
8 Gregg Olson .05 .15
9 Gregg Jefferies .05 .15
10 Tony Gwynn .40 1.00
11 Chad Curtis .05 .15
12 Craig Biggio .20 .50
13 John Burkett .05 .15
14 Carlos Baerga .05 .15
15 Robin Yount .50 1.25
16 Dennis Eckersley .10 .30
17 Dwight Gooden .10 .30
18 Ryne Sandberg .50 1.25
19 Rickey Henderson .30 .75
20 Jack McDowell .05 .15
21 Jay Bell .10 .30
22 Kevin Brown .10 .30
23 Robin Ventura .10 .30
24 Paul Molitor .10 .30
25 David Justice .10 .30
26 Rafael Palmeiro .20 .50
27 Cecil Fielder .10 .30
28 Chuck Knoblauch .10 .30
29 Dave Hollins .05 .15
30 Jimmy Key .10 .30
31 Mark Langston .05 .15
32 Darryl Kile .10 .30
33 Ruben Sierra .10 .30
34 Ron Gant .10 .30
35 Ozzie Smith .50 1.25
36 Wade Boggs .20 .50
37 Marquis Grissom .10 .30
38 Will Clark .20 .50
39 Kenny Lofton .10 .30
40 Cal Ripken 1.00 2.50
41 Steve Avery .05 .15
42 Mo Vaughn .10 .30
43 Brian McRae .05 .15
44 Mickey Tettleton .05 .15
45 Barry Larkin .20 .50
46 Charlie Hayes .05 .15
47 Kevin Appier .10 .30
48 Robby Thompson .05 .15
49 Juan Gonzalez .10 .30
50 Paul O'Neill .20 .50
51 Marcos Armas .05 .15
52 Mike Butcher .05 .15
53 Ken Caminiti .10 .30
54 Pat Borders .05 .15
55 Pedro Munoz .05 .15
56 Tim Belcher .05 .15
57 Paul Assenmacher .05 .15
58 Damon Berryhill .05 .15
59 Ricky Bones .05 .15
60 Rene Arocha .05 .15
61 Shawn Boskie .05 .15
62 Pedro Astacio .05 .15
63 Frank Bolick .05 .15
64 Bud Black .05 .15
65 Sandy Alomar Jr. .05 .15
66 Rich Amaral .05 .15
67 Luis Aquino .05 .15
68 Kevin Baez .05 .15
69 Mike Devereaux .05 .15
70 Andy Ashby .05 .15
71 Larry Andersen .05 .15
72 Steve Cooke .05 .15
73 Mario Diaz .05 .15
74 Rob Deer .05 .15
75 Bobby Ayala .05 .15
76 Freddie Benavides .05 .15
77 Stan Belinda .05 .15
78 John Doherty .05 .15
79 Willie Banks .05 .15
80 Spike Owen .05 .15
81 Mike Bordick .05 .15
82 Chili Davis .10 .30
83 Luis Gonzalez .10 .30
84 Ed Sprague .05 .15
85 Jeff Reboulet .05 .15
86 Jason Bere .05 .15
87 Mark Hutton .05 .15
88 Jeff Blauser .05 .15
89 Cal Eldred .05 .15
90 Bernard Gilkey .05 .15
91 Frank Castillo .05 .15
92 Jim Gott .05 .15
93 Greg Colbrunn .05 .15
94 Jeff Brantley .05 .15
95 Jeremy Hernandez .05 .15
96 Norm Charlton .05 .15
97 Alex Arias .05 .15
98 John Franco .10 .30
99 Chris Hoiles .05 .15
100 Brad Ausmus .20 .50
101 Wes Chamberlain .05 .15
102 Mark Dewey .05 .15
103 Benji Gil .05 .15
104 John Dopson .05 .15
105 John Smiley .05 .15
106 David Nied .05 .15
107 George Brett .75 2.00
108 Kirk Gibson .10 .30
109 Larry Casian .05 .15
110 Ryne Sandberg CL .30 .75
111 Brent Gates .05 .15
112 Damion Easley .05 .15
113 Pete Harnisch .05 .15
114 Danny Cox .05 .15
115 Kevin Tapani .05 .15
116 Roberto Hernandez .05 .15
117 Domingo Jean .05 .15
118 Sid Bream .05 .15
119 Doug Henry .05 .15
120 Omar Olivares .05 .15
121 Mike Harkey .05 .15
122 Carlos Hernandez .05 .15
123 Jeff Fassero .05 .15
124 Dave Burba .05 .15
125 Wayne Kirby .05 .15
126 John Cummings .05 .15
127 Bret Barberie .05 .15
128 Todd Hundley .05 .15
129 Tim Hulett .05 .15
130 Phil Clark .05 .15
131 Danny Jackson .05 .15
132 Tom Foley .05 .15
133 Donald Harris .05 .15
134 Scott Fletcher .05 .15
135 Johnny Ruffin .05 .15
136 Jerald Clark .05 .15
137 Billy Brewer .05 .15
138 Dan Gladden .05 .15
139 Eddie Guardado .10 .30
140 Cal Ripken CL .30 .75
141 Scott Hemond .05 .15
142 Steve Frey .05 .15
143 Xavier Hernandez .05 .15
144 Mark Eichhorn .05 .15
145 Ellis Burks .10 .30
146 Jim Leyritz .05 .15
147 Mark Lemke .05 .15
148 Pat Listach .05 .15
149 Donovan Osborne .05 .15
150 Glenallen Hill .05 .15
151 Orel Hershiser .10 .30
152 Darrin Fletcher .05 .15
153 Royce Clayton .05 .15
154 Derek Lilliquist .05 .15
155 Mike Felder .05 .15
156 Jeff Conine .10 .30
157 Ryan Thompson .05 .15
158 Ben McDonald .05 .15
159 Ricky Gutierrez .05 .15
160 Terry Mulholland .05 .15
161 Carlos Garcia .05 .15
162 Tom Henke .05 .15
163 Mike Greenwell .05 .15
164 Thomas Howard .05 .15
165 Joe Girardi .05 .15
166 Hubie Brooks .05 .15
167 Greg Gohr .05 .15
168 Chip Hale .05 .15
169 Rick Honeycutt .05 .15
170 Hilly Hathaway .05 .15
171 Todd Jones .05 .15
172 Tony Fernandez .05 .15
173 Bo Jackson .30 .75
174 Bobby Munoz .05 .15
175 Greg McMichael .05 .15
176 Graeme Lloyd .05 .15
177 Tom Pagnozzi .05 .15
178 Derrick May .05 .15
179 Pedro Martinez .30 .75
180 Ken Hill .05 .15
181 Bryan Hickerson .05 .15
182 Jose Mesa .05 .15
183 Dave Fleming .05 .15
184 Henry Cotto .05 .15
185 Jeff Kent .20 .50
186 Mark McLemore .05 .15
187 Trevor Hoffman .20 .50
188 Todd Pratt .05 .15
189 Blas Minor .05 .15
190 Charlie Leibrandt .05 .15
191 Tony Pena .05 .15
192 Larry Luebbers RC .05 .15
193 Greg W. Harris .05 .15
194 David Cone .10 .30
195 Bill Gullickson .05 .15
196 Brian Harper .05 .15
197 Steve Karsay .05 .15
198 Greg Myers .05 .15
199 Mark Portugal .05 .15
200 Pat Hentgen .05 .15
201 Mike LaValliere .05 .15
202 Mike Stanley .05 .15
203 Kent Mercker .05 .15
204 Dave Nilsson .05 .15
205 Erik Pappas .05 .15
206 Mike Morgan .05 .15
207 Roger McDowell .05 .15
208 Mike Lansing .05 .15
209 Kirt Manwaring .05 .15
210 Randy Milligan .05 .15
211 Erik Hanson .05 .15
212 Orestes Destrade .05 .15
213 Mike Maddux .05 .15
214 Alan Mills .05 .15
215 Tim Mauser .05 .15
216 Ben Rivera .05 .15
217 Don Slaught .05 .15
218 Bob Patterson .05 .15
219 Carlos Quintana .05 .15
220 Tim Raines CL .05 .15
221 Hal Morris .05 .15
222 Darren Holmes .05 .15
223 Chris Gwynn .05 .15
224 Chad Kreuter .05 .15
225 Mike Hartley .05 .15
226 Scott Lydy .05 .15
227 Eduardo Perez .05 .15
228 Greg Swindell .05 .15
229 Al Leiter .10 .30
230 Scott Radinsky .05 .15
231 Bob Wickman .05 .15
232 Otis Nixon .05 .15
233 Kevin Reimer .05 .15
234 Geronimo Pena .05 .15
235 Kevin Roberson .05 .15
236 Jody Reed .05 .15
237 Kirk Rueter .05 .15
238 Willie McGee .10 .30
239 Charles Nagy .05 .15
240 Tim Leary .05 .15
241 Carl Everett .10 .30
242 Charlie O'Brien .05 .15
243 Mike Pagliarulo .05 .15
244 Kerry Taylor .05 .15
245 Kevin Stocker .05 .15
246 Joel Johnston .05 .15
247 Geno Petralli .05 .15
248 Jeff Russell .05 .15
249 Joe Oliver .05 .15
250 Roberto Mejia .05 .15
251 Chris Haney .05 .15
252 Bill Krueger .05 .15
253 Shane Mack .05 .15
254 Terry Steinbach .05 .15
255 Luis Polonia .05 .15
256 Eddie Taubensee .05 .15
257 Dave Stewart .10 .30
258 Tim Raines .10 .30
259 Bernie Williams .20 .50
260 John Smoltz .20 .50
261 Kevin Seitzer .05 .15
262 Bob Tewksbury .05 .15
263 Bob Scanlan .05 .15
264 Henry Rodriguez .05 .15
265 Tim Scott .05 .15
266 Scott Sanderson .05 .15
267 Eric Plunk .05 .15
268 Edgar Martinez .20 .50
269 Charlie Hough .10 .30
270 Joe Orsulak .05 .15
271 Harold Reynolds .10 .30
272 Tim Teufel .05 .15
273 Bobby Thigpen .05 .15
274 Randy Tomlin .05 .15
275 Gary Redus .05 .15
276 Ken Ryan .05 .15
277 Tim Pugh .05 .15
278 Jayhawk Owens .05 .15
279 Phil Hiatt .05 .15
280 Alan Trammell .10 .30
281 Dave McCarty .05 .15
282 Bob Welch .05 .15
283 J.T. Snow .10 .30
284 Brian Williams .05 .15
285 Devon White .10 .30
286 Steve Sax .05 .15
287 Tony Tarasco .05 .15
288 Bill Spiers .05 .15
289 Allen Watson .05 .15
290 Rickey Henderson CL .20 .50
291 Jose Vizcaino .05 .15
292 Darryl Strawberry .10 .30
293 John Wetteland .10 .30
294 Bill Swift .05 .15
295 Jeff Treadway .05 .15
296 Tino Martinez .20 .50
297 Richie Lewis .05 .15
298 Bret Saberhagen .10 .30
299 Arthur Rhodes .05 .15
300 Guillermo Velasquez .05 .15
301 Milt Thompson .05 .15
302 Doug Strange .05 .15
303 Aaron Sele .05 .15
304 Bip Roberts .05 .15
305 Bruce Ruffin .05 .15
306 Jose Lind .05 .15
307 David Wells .10 .30
308 Bobby Witt .05 .15
309 Mark Wohlers .05 .15
310 B.J. Surhoff .10 .30
311 Mark Whiten .05 .15
312 Turk Wendell .05 .15
313 Raul Mondesi .10 .30
314 Brian Turang RC .05 .15
315 Chris Hammond .05 .15
316 Tim Bogar .05 .15
317 Brad Pennington .05 .15
318 Tim Worrell .05 .15
319 Mitch Williams .05 .15
320 Rondell White .10 .30
321 Frank Viola .10 .30
322 Manny Ramirez .30 .75
323 Gary Wayne .05 .15
324 Mike Macfarlane .05 .15
325 Russ Springer .05 .15
326 Tim Wallach .05 .15
327 Salomon Torres .05 .15
328 Omar Vizquel .20 .50
329 Andy Tomberlin RC .05 .15
330 Chris Sabo .05 .15
331 Mike Mussina .20 .50
332 Andy Benes .05 .15
333 Darren Daulton .10 .30
334 Orlando Merced .05 .15
335 Mark McGwire .75 2.00
336 Dave Winfield .10 .30
337 Sammy Sosa .30 .75
338 Eric Karros .10 .30
339 Greg Vaughn .05 .15
340 Don Mattingly .75 2.00
341 Frank Thomas .30 .75
342 Fred McGriff .20 .50
343 Kirby Puckett .30 .75
344 Roberto Kelly .05 .15
345 Wally Joyner .10 .30
346 Andres Galarraga .10 .30
347 Bobby Bonilla .10 .30
348 Benito Santiago .10 .30
349 Barry Bonds .75 2.00
350 Delino DeShields .05 .15
351 Albert Belle .10 .30
352 Randy Johnson .30 .75
353 Tim Salmon .20 .50
354 John Olerud .10 .30
355 Dean Palmer .10 .30
356 Roger Clemens .60 1.50
357 Jim Abbott .20 .50
358 Mark Grace .20 .50
359 Ozzie Guillen .10 .30
360 Lou Whitaker .10 .30
361 Jose Rijo .05 .15
362 Jeff Montgomery .05 .15
363 Chuck Finley .10 .30
364 Tom Glavine .20 .50
365 Jeff Bagwell .20 .50
366 Joe Carter .10 .30
367 Ray Lankford .10 .30
368 Ramon Martinez .05 .15
369 Jay Buhner .10 .30
370 Matt Williams .10 .30
371 Larry Walker .10 .30
372 Jose Canseco .20 .50
373 Lenny Dykstra .10 .30
374 Bryan Harvey .05 .15
375 Andy Van Slyke .20 .50
376 Ivan Rodriguez .20 .50
377 Kevin Mitchell .05 .15
378 Travis Fryman .10 .30
379 Duane Ward .05 .15
380 Greg Maddux .50 1.25
381 Scott Servais .05 .15
382 Greg Olson .05 .15
383 Rey Sanchez .05 .15
384 Tom Kramer .05 .15
385 David Valle .05 .15
386 Eddie Murray .30 .75
387 Kevin Higgins .05 .15
388 Dan Wilson .05 .15
389 Todd Frohwirth .05 .15
390 Gerald Williams .05 .15
391 Hipolito Pichardo .05 .15
392 Pat Meares .05 .15
393 Luis Lopez .05 .15
394 Ricky Jordan .05 .15
395 Bob Walk .05 .15
396 Sid Fernandez .05 .15
397 Todd Worrell .05 .15
398 Darryl Hamilton .05 .15
399 Randy Myers .05 .15
400 Rod Brewer .05 .15
401 Lance Blankenship .05 .15
402 Steve Finley .10 .30
403 Phil Leftwich RC .05 .15
404 Juan Guzman .05 .15
405 Anthony Young .05 .15
406 Jeff Gardner .05 .15
407 Ryan Bowen .05 .15
408 Fernando Valenzuela .10 .30
409 David West .05 .15
410 Kenny Rogers .10 .30
411 Bob Zupcic .05 .15
412 Eric Young .05 .15
413 Bret Boone .10 .30
414 Danny Tartabull .05 .15
415 Bob MacDonald .05 .15
416 Ron Karkovice .05 .15
417 Scott Cooper .05 .15
418 Dante Bichette .10 .30
419 Tripp Cromer .05 .15
420 Billy Ashley .05 .15
421 Roger Smithberg .05 .15
422 Dennis Martinez .10 .30
423 Mike Blowers .05 .15
424 Darren Lewis .05 .15
425 Junior Ortiz .05 .15
426 Butch Huskey .05 .15
427 Jimmy Poole .05 .15
428 Walt Weiss .05 .15
429 Scott Bankhead .05 .15
430 Deion Sanders .20 .50
431 Scott Bullett .05 .15
432 Jeff Huson .05 .15
433 Tyler Green .05 .15
434 Billy Hatcher .05 .15
435 Bob Hamelin .05 .15
436 Reggie Sanders .10 .30
437 Scott Erickson .05 .15
438 Steve Reed .05 .15
439 Randy Velarde .05 .15
440 Tony Gwynn CL .20 .50
441 Terry Leach .05 .15
442 Danny Bautista .05 .15
443 Kent Hrbek .10 .30
444 Rick Wilkins .05 .15
445 Tony Phillips .05 .15
446 Dion James .05 .15
447 Joey Cora .05 .15
448 Andre Dawson .10 .30
449 Pedro Castellano .05 .15
450 Tom Gordon .05 .15
451 Rob Dibble .10 .30
452 Ron Darling .05 .15
453 Chipper Jones .30 .75
454 Joe Grahe .05 .15
455 Domingo Cedeno .05 .15
456 Tom Edens .05 .15
457 Mitch Webster .05 .15
458 Jose Bautista .05 .15
459 Troy O'Leary .05 .15
460 Todd Zeile .05 .15
461 Sean Berry .05 .15
462 Brad Holman RC .05 .15
463 Dave Martinez .05 .15
464 Mark Lewis .05 .15
465 Paul Carey .05 .15
466 Jack Armstrong .05 .15
467 David Telgheder .05 .15
468 Gene Harris .05 .15
469 Danny Darwin .05 .15
470 Kim Batiste .05 .15
471 Tim Wakefield .20 .50
472 Craig Lefferts .05 .15
473 Jacob Brumfield .05 .15
474 Lance Painter .05 .15
475 Milt Cuyler .05 .15
476 Melido Perez .05 .15
477 Derek Parks .05 .15
478 Gary DiSarcina .05 .15
479 Steve Bedrosian .05 .15
480 Eric Anthony .05 .15
481 Julio Franco .10 .30
482 Tommy Greene .05 .15
483 Pat Kelly .05 .15
484 Nate Minchey .05 .15
485 William Pennyfeather .05 .15
486 Harold Baines .10 .30
487 Howard Johnson .05 .15
488 Angel Miranda .05 .15
489 Scott Sanders .05 .15
490 Shawon Dunston .05 .15
491 Mel Rojas .05 .15
492 Jeff Nelson .05 .15
493 Archi Cianfrocco .05 .15
494 Al Martin .05 .15
495 Mike Gallego .05 .15
496 Mike Henneman .05 .15
497 Armando Reynoso .05 .15
498 Mickey Morandini .05 .15
499 Rick Renteria .05 .15
500 Rick Sutcliffe .10 .30
501 Bobby Jones .05 .15
502 Gary Gaetti .10 .30
503 Rick Aguilera .05 .15
504 Todd Stottlemyre .05 .15
505 Mike Mohler .05 .15
506 Mike Stanton .05 .15
507 Jose Guzman .05 .15
508 Kevin Rogers .05 .15
509 Chuck Carr .05 .15
510 Chris Jones .05 .15
511 Brent Mayne .05 .15
512 Greg Harris .05 .15
513 Dave Henderson .05 .15
514 Eric Hillman .05 .15
515 Dan Peltier .05 .15
516 Craig Shipley .05 .15
517 John Valentin .05 .15
518 Wilson Alvarez .05 .15
519 Andujar Cedeno .05 .15
520 Troy Neel .05 .15
521 Tom Candiotti .05 .15
522 Matt Mieske .05 .15
523 Jim Thome .20 .50
524 Lou Frazier .05 .15
525 Mike Jackson .05 .15
526 Pedro Martinez RC .05 .15
527 Roger Pavlik .05 .15
528 Kent Bottenfield .05 .15
529 Felix Jose .05 .15
530 Mark Guthrie .05 .15
531 Steve Farr .05 .15
532 Craig Paquette .05 .15
533 Doug Jones .05 .15
534 Luis Alicea .05 .15
535 Cory Snyder .05 .15
536 Paul Sorrento .05 .15
537 Nigel Wilson .05 .15
538 Jeff King .05 .15
539 Willie Greene .05 .15
540 Kirk McCaskill .05 .15
541 Al Osuna .05 .15
542 Greg Hibbard .05 .15
543 Brett Butler .10 .30
544 Jose Valentin .05 .15
545 Wil Cordero .05 .15
546 Chris Bosio .05 .15
547 Jamie Moyer .10 .30
548 Jim Eisenreich .05 .15
549 Vinny Castilla .10 .30
550 Dave Winfield CL .05 .15
551 John Roper .05 .15
552 Lance Johnson .05 .15
553 Scott Kamieniecki .05 .15
554 Mike Moore .05 .15
555 Steve Buechele .05 .15
556 Terry Pendleton .10 .30
557 Todd Van Poppel .05 .15
558 Rob Butler .05 .15
559 Zane Smith .05 .15
560 David Hulse .05 .15
561 Tim Costo .05 .15
562 John Habyan .05 .15
563 Terry Jorgensen .05 .15
564 Matt Nokes .05 .15
565 Kevin McReynolds .05 .15
566 Phil Plantier .05 .15
567 Chris Turner .05 .15
568 Carlos Delgado .20 .50
569 John Jaha .05 .15
570 Dwight Smith .05 .15
571 John Vander Wal .05 .15
572 Trevor Wilson .05 .15
573 Felix Fermin .05 .15
574 Marc Newfield .05 .15
575 Jeromy Burnitz .10 .30
576 Leo Gomez .05 .15
577 Curt Schilling .10 .30
578 Kevin Young .05 .15
579 Jerry Spradlin RC .05 .15
580 Curt Leskanic .05 .15
581 Carl Willis .05 .15
582 Alex Fernandez .05 .15
583 Mark Holzemer .05 .15
584 Domingo Martinez .05 .15
585 Pete Smith .05 .15
586 Brian Jordan .10 .30
587 Kevin Gross .05 .15
588 J.R. Phillips .05 .15
589 Chris Nabholz .05 .15
590 Bill Wertz .05 .15
591 Derek Bell .05 .15
592 Brady Anderson .10 .30
593 Matt Turner .05 .15
594 Pete Incaviglia .05 .15
595 Greg Gagne .05 .15
596 John Flaherty .05 .15
597 Scott Livingstone .05 .15
598 Rod Bolton .05 .15
599 Mike Perez .05 .15
600 Roger Clemens CL .30 .75
601 Tony Castillo .05 .15
602 Henry Mercedes .05 .15
603 Mike Fetters .05 .15
604 Rod Beck .05 .15
605 Damon Buford .05 .15
606 Matt Whiteside .05 .15
607 Shawn Green .30 .75
608 Midre Cummings .05 .15
609 Jeff McNeely .05 .15
610 Danny Sheaffer .05 .15
611 Paul Wagner .05 .15
612 Torey Lovullo .05 .15
613 Javier Lopez .10 .30
614 Mariano Duncan .05 .15
615 Doug Brocail .05 .15
616 Dave Hansen .05 .15
617 Ryan Klesko .10 .30
618 Eric Davis .10 .30
619 Scott Ruffcorn .05 .15
620 Mike Trombley .05 .15
621 Jaime Navarro .05 .15
622 Rheal Cormier .05 .15
623 Jose Offerman .05 .15
624 David Segui .05 .15
625 Robb Nen .10 .30
626 Dave Gallagher .05 .15
627 Julian Tavarez RC .10 .30
628 Chris Gomez .05 .15
629 Jeffrey Hammonds .05 .15
630 Scott Brosius .10 .30
631 Willie Blair .05 .15
632 Doug Drabek .05 .15
633 Bill Wegman .05 .15
634 Jeff McKnight .05 .15
635 Rich Rodriguez .05 .15
636 Steve Trachsel .05 .15
637 Buddy Groom .05 .15
638 Sterling Hitchcock .05 .15
639 Chuck McElroy .05 .15
640 Rene Gonzales .05 .15
641 Dan Plesac .05 .15
642 Jeff Branson .05 .15
643 Darrell Whitmore .05 .15
644 Paul Quantrill .05 .15
645 Rich Rowland .05 .15
646 Curtis Pride RC .10 .30
647 Erik Plantenberg RC .05 .15
648 Albie Lopez .05 .15
649 Rich Batchelor RC .05 .15
650 Lee Smith .10 .30
651 Cliff Floyd .10 .30
652 Pete Schourek .05 .15
653 Reggie Jefferson .05 .15
654 Bill Haselman .05 .15
655 Steve Hosey .05 .15
656 Mark Clark .05 .15
657 Mark Davis .05 .15
658 Dave Magadan .05 .15
659 Candy Maldonado .05 .15
660 Mark Langston CL .05 .15

1995 Donruss

The 1995 Donruss set consists of 550 standard-size cards. The first series had 330 cards while 220 cards comprised the second series. The fronts feature borderless color action player photos. A second, smaller color player photo in a homeplate shape with team color-coded borders appears in the lower left corner. There are no key Rookie Cards in this set. To preview the product prior to it's public release, Donruss printed up additional quantities of cards 5, 8, 20, 42, 55, 275, 331 and 340 and mailed them to dealers and hobby media.

COMPLETE SET (550) 12.00 30.00
COMP.SERIES 1 (330) 8.00 20.00
COMP.SERIES 2 (220) 4.00 10.00
1 David Justice .10 .30
2 Rene Arocha .05 .15
3 Sandy Alomar Jr. .05 .15
4 Luis Lopez .05 .15
5 Mike Piazza .50 1.25
6 Bobby Jones .05 .15
7 Damion Easley .05 .15
8 Barry Bonds .75 2.00
9 Mike Mussina .20 .50
10 Kevin Seitzer .05 .15
11 John Smiley .05 .15
12 Wm.VanLandingham .05 .15
13 Ron Darling .05 .15
14 Walt Weiss .05 .15
15 Mike Lansing .05 .15
16 Allen Watson .05 .15
17 Aaron Sele .05 .15
18 Randy Johnson .30 .75
19 Dean Palmer .10 .30
20 Jeff Bagwell .20 .50
21 Curt Schilling .10 .30
22 Darrell Whitmore .05 .15
23 Steve Trachsel .05 .15
24 Dan Wilson .05 .15
25 Steve Finley .10 .30
26 Bret Boone .10 .30
27 Charles Johnson .10 .30
28 Mike Stanton .05 .15
29 Ismael Valdes .05 .15
30 Salomon Torres .05 .15
31 Eric Anthony .05 .15
32 Spike Owen .05 .15
33 Joey Cora .05 .15
34 Robert Eenhoorn .05 .15
35 Rick White .05 .15
36 Omar Vizquel .20 .50
37 Carlos Delgado .10 .30
38 Eddie Williams .05 .15
39 Shawon Dunston .05 .15
40 Darrin Fletcher .05 .15
41 Leo Gomez .05 .15
42 Juan Gonzalez .10 .30
43 Luis Alicea .05 .15
44 Ken Ryan .05 .15
45 Lou Whitaker .10 .30
46 Mike Blowers .05 .15
47 Willie Blair .05 .15
48 Todd Van Poppel .05 .15
49 Roberto Alomar .20 .50
50 Ozzie Smith .50 1.25
51 Sterling Hitchcock .05 .15
52 Mo Vaughn .10 .30
53 Rick Aguilera .05 .15
54 Kent Mercker .05 .15
55 Don Mattingly .75 2.00
56 Bob Scanlan .05 .15
57 Wilson Alvarez .05 .15
58 Jose Mesa .05 .15
59 Scott Kamieniecki .05 .15
60 Todd Jones .05 .15
61 John Kruk .10 .30
62 Mike Stanley .05 .15
63 Tino Martinez .20 .50
64 Eddie Zambrano .05 .15
65 Todd Hundley .05 .15
66 Jamie Moyer .10 .30
67 Rich Amaral .05 .15
68 Jose Valentin .05 .15
69 Alex Gonzalez .05 .15
70 Kurt Abbott .05 .15
71 Delino DeShields .05 .15
72 Brian Anderson .05 .15
73 John Vander Wal .05 .15
74 Turner Ward .05 .15
75 Tim Raines .10 .30
76 Mark Acre .05 .15
77 Jose Offerman .05 .15
78 Jimmy Key .10 .30
79 Mark Whiten .05 .15
80 Mark Gubicza .05 .15
81 Darren Hall .05 .15
82 Travis Fryman .10 .30
83 Cal Ripken 1.00 2.50
84 Geronimo Berroa .05 .15
85 Bret Barberie .05 .15
86 Andy Ashby .05 .15
87 Steve Avery .05 .15
88 Rich Becker .05 .15
89 John Valentin .05 .15
90 Glenallen Hill .05 .15
91 Carlos Garcia .05 .15
92 Dennis Martinez .10 .30
93 Pat Kelly .05 .15
94 Orlando Miller .05 .15
95 Felix Jose .05 .15
96 Mike Kingery .05 .15
97 Jeff Kent .10 .30
98 Pete Incaviglia .05 .15
99 Chad Curtis .05 .15
100 Thomas Howard .05 .15
101 Hector Carrasco .05 .15
102 Tom Pagnozzi .05 .15
103 Danny Tartabull .05 .15
104 Donnie Elliott .05 .15
105 Danny Jackson .05 .15
106 Steve Dunn .05 .15
107 Roger Salkeld .05 .15
108 Jeff King .05 .15
109 Cecil Fielder .10 .30
110 Paul Molitor CL .05 .15
111 Denny Neagle .10 .30
112 Troy Neel .05 .15
113 Rod Beck .05 .15
114 Alex Rodriguez .75 2.00
115 Joey Eischen .05 .15
116 Tom Candiotti .05 .15
117 Ray McDavid .05 .15
118 Vince Coleman .05 .15
119 Pete Harnisch .05 .15
120 David Nied .05 .15
121 Pat Rapp .05 .15
122 Sammy Sosa .30 .75
123 Steve Reed .05 .15
124 Jose Oliva .05 .15
125 Ricky Bottalico .05 .15
126 Jose DeLeon .05 .15
127 Pat Hentgen .05 .15
128 Will Clark .20 .50
129 Mark Dewey .05 .15
130 Greg Vaughn .05 .15
131 Darren Dreifort .05 .15
132 Ed Sprague .05 .15
133 Lee Smith .10 .30
134 Charles Nagy .05 .15
135 Phil Plantier .05 .15
136 Jason Jacome .05 .15
137 Jose Lima .05 .15
138 J.R. Phillips .05 .15
139 J.T. Snow .10 .30
140 Michael Huff .05 .15
141 Billy Brewer .05 .15
142 Jeromy Burnitz .10 .30
143 Ricky Bones .05 .15
144 Carlos Rodriguez .05 .15
145 Luis Gonzalez .10 .30
146 Mark Lemke .05 .15
147 Al Martin .05 .15
148 Mike Bordick .05 .15
149 Robb Nen .10 .30
150 Wil Cordero .05 .15
151 Edgar Martinez .20 .50
152 Gerald Williams .05 .15

153 Esteban Beltre .05 .15
154 Mike Moore .05 .15
155 Mark Langston .05 .15
156 Mark Clark .05 .15
157 Bobby Ayala .05 .15
158 Rick Wilkins .05 .15
159 Bobby Munoz .05 .15
160 Brett Butler CL .05 .15
161 Scott Erickson .05 .15
162 Paul Molitor .10 .30
163 Jon Lieber .05 .15
164 Jason Grimsley .05 .15
165 Norberto Martin .05 .15
166 Javier Lopez .10 .30
167 Brian McRae .05 .15
168 Gary Sheffield .10 .30
169 Marcus Moore .05 .15
170 John Hudek .05 .15
171 Kelly Stinnett .05 .15
172 Chris Gomez .05 .15
173 Rey Sanchez .05 .15
174 Juan Guzman .05 .15
175 Chan Ho Park .10 .30
176 Terry Shumpert .05 .15
177 Steve Ontiveros .05 .15
178 Brad Ausmus .10 .30
179 Tim Davis .05 .15
180 Billy Ashley .05 .15
181 Vinny Castilla .10 .30
182 Bill Spiers .05 .15
183 Randy Knorr .05 .15
184 Brian Hunter .05 .15
185 Pat Meares .05 .15
186 Steve Buechele .05 .15
187 Kirt Manwaring .05 .15
188 Tim Naehring .05 .15
189 Matt Mieske .05 .15
190 Josias Manzanillo .05 .15
191 Greg McMichael .05 .15
192 Chuck Carr .05 .15
193 Midre Cummings .05 .15
194 Darryl Strawberry .10 .30
195 Greg Gagne .05 .15
196 Steve Cooke .05 .15
197 Woody Williams .05 .15
198 Ron Karkovice .05 .15
199 Phil Leftwich .05 .15
200 Jim Thome .20 .50
201 Brady Anderson .10 .30
202 Pedro A.Martinez .05 .15
203 Steve Karsay .05 .15
204 Reggie Sanders .10 .30
205 Bill Risley .05 .15
206 Jay Bell .10 .30
207 Kevin Brown .10 .30
208 Tim Scott .05 .15
209 Lenny Dykstra .10 .30
210 Willie Greene .05 .15
211 Jim Eisenreich .05 .15
212 Cliff Floyd .10 .30
213 Otis Nixon .05 .15
214 Eduardo Perez .05 .15
215 Manuel Lee .05 .15
216 Armando Benitez .05 .15
217 Dave McCarty .05 .15
218 Scott Livingstone .05 .15
219 Chad Kreuter .05 .15
220 Don Mattingly CL .40 1.00
221 Brian Jordan .10 .30
222 Matt Whiteside .05 .15
223 Jim Edmonds .20 .50
224 Tony Gwynn .40 1.00
225 Jose Lind .05 .15
226 Marvin Freeman .05 .15
227 Ken Hill .05 .15
228 David Hulse .05 .15
229 Joe Hesketh .05 .15
230 Roberto Petagine .05 .15
231 Jeffrey Hammonds .05 .15
232 John Jaha .05 .15
233 John Burkett .05 .15
234 Hal Morris .05 .15
235 Tony Castillo .05 .15
236 Ryan Bowen .05 .15
237 Wayne Kirby .05 .15
238 Brent Mayne .05 .15
239 Jim Bullinger .05 .15
240 Mike Lieberthal .10 .30
241 Barry Larkin .20 .50
242 David Segui .05 .15
243 Jose Bautista .05 .15
244 Hector Fajardo .05 .15
245 Orel Hershiser .10 .30
246 James Mouton .05 .15
247 Scott Leius .05 .15
248 Tom Glavine .20 .50
249 Danny Bautista .05 .15
250 Jose Mercedes .05 .15
251 Marquis Grissom .10 .30
252 Charlie Hayes .05 .15
253 Ryan Klesko .10 .30
254 Vicente Palacios .05 .15
255 Matias Carrillo .05 .15
256 Gary DiSarcina .05 .15
257 Kirk Gibson .10 .30
258 Garey Ingram .05 .15
259 Alex Fernandez .05 .15
260 John Mabry .05 .15
261 Chris Howard .05 .15
262 Miguel Jimenez .05 .15
263 Heathcliff Slocumb .05 .15
264 Albert Belle .10 .30
265 Dave Clark .05 .15
266 Joe Orsulak .05 .15
267 Joey Hamilton .05 .15
268 Mark Portugal .05 .15
269 Kevin Tapani .05 .15
270 Sid Fernandez .05 .15
271 Steve Dreyer .05 .15
272 Denny Hocking .05 .15
273 Troy O'Leary .05 .15
274 Milt Cuyler .05 .15
275 Frank Thomas .30 .75
276 Jorge Fabregas .05 .15
277 Mike Gallego .05 .15
278 Mickey Morandini .05 .15
279 Roberto Hernandez .05 .15
280 Henry Rodriguez .05 .15
281 Garret Anderson .10 .30
282 Bob Wickman .05 .15
283 Gar Finnvold .05 .15
284 Paul O'Neill .20 .50
285 Royce Clayton .05 .15
286 Chuck Knoblauch .10 .30
287 Johnny Ruffin .05 .15
288 Dave Nilsson .05 .15
289 David Cone .10 .30
290 Chuck McElroy .05 .15
291 Kevin Stocker .05 .15
292 Jose Rijo .05 .15
293 Sean Berry .05 .15
294 Ozzie Guillen .10 .30
295 Chris Hoiles .05 .15
296 Kevin Foster .05 .15
297 Jeff Frye .05 .15
298 Lance Johnson .05 .15
299 Mike Kelly .05 .15
300 Ellis Burks .10 .30
301 Roberto Kelly .05 .15
302 Dante Bichette .10 .30
303 Alvaro Espinoza .05 .15
304 Alex Cole .05 .15
305 Rickey Henderson .30 .75
306 Dave Weathers .05 .15
307 Shane Reynolds .05 .15
308 Bobby Bonilla .10 .30
309 Junior Felix .05 .15
310 Jeff Fassero .05 .15
311 Darren Lewis .05 .15
312 John Doherty .05 .15
313 Scott Servais .05 .15
314 Rick Helling .05 .15
315 Pedro Martinez .20 .50
316 Wes Chamberlain .05 .15
317 Bryan Eversgerd .05 .15
318 Trevor Hoffman .10 .30
319 John Patterson .05 .15
320 Matt Walbeck .05 .15
321 Jeff Montgomery .05 .15
322 Mel Rojas .05 .15
323 Eddie Taubensee .05 .15
324 Ray Lankford .10 .30
325 Jose Vizcaino .05 .15
326 Carlos Baerga .05 .15
327 Jack Voigt .05 .15
328 Julio Franco .10 .30
329 Brent Gates .05 .15
330 Kirby Puckett CL .20 .50
331 Greg Maddux .50 1.25
332 Jason Bere .05 .15
333 Bill Wegman .05 .15
334 Tuffy Rhodes .05 .15
335 Kevin Young .05 .15
336 Andy Benes .05 .15
337 Pedro Astacio .05 .15
338 Reggie Jefferson .05 .15
339 Tim Belcher .05 .15
340 Ken Griffey Jr. .50 1.25
341 Mariano Duncan .05 .15
342 Andres Galarraga .10 .30
343 Rondell White .10 .30
344 Cory Bailey .05 .15
345 Bryan Harvey .05 .15
346 John Franco .10 .30
347 Greg Swindell .05 .15
348 David West .05 .15
349 Fred McGriff .20 .50
350 Jose Canseco .20 .50
351 Orlando Merced .05 .15
352 Rheal Cormier .05 .15
353 Carlos Pulido .05 .15
354 Terry Steinbach .05 .15
355 Wade Boggs .20 .50
356 B.J. Surhoff .10 .30
357 Rafael Palmeiro .20 .50
358 Anthony Young .05 .15
359 Tom Brunansky .05 .15
360 Todd Stottlemyre .05 .15
361 Chris Turner .05 .15
362 Joe Boever .05 .15
363 Jeff Blauser .05 .15
364 Derek Bell .05 .15
365 Matt Williams .10 .30
366 Jeremy Hernandez .05 .15
367 Joe Girardi .05 .15
368 Mike Devereaux .05 .15
369 Jim Abbott .20 .50
370 Manny Ramirez .20 .50
371 Kenny Lofton .10 .30
372 Mark Smith .05 .15
373 Dave Fleming .05 .15
374 Dave Stewart .10 .30
375 Roger Pavlik .05 .15
376 Hipolito Pichardo .05 .15
377 Bill Taylor .05 .15
378 Robin Ventura .10 .30
379 Bernard Gilkey .05 .15
380 Kirby Puckett .30 .75
381 Steve Howe .05 .15
382 Devon White .10 .30
383 Roberto Mejia .05 .15
384 Darrin Jackson .05 .15
385 Mike Morgan .05 .15
386 Rusty Meacham .05 .15
387 Bill Swift .05 .15
388 Lou Frazier .05 .15
389 Andy Van Slyke .20 .50
390 Brett Butler .10 .30
391 Bobby Witt .05 .15
392 Jeff Conine .10 .30
393 Tim Hyers .05 .15
394 Terry Pendleton .10 .30
395 Ricky Jordan .05 .15
396 Eric Plunk .05 .15
397 Melido Perez .05 .15
398 Darryl Kile .10 .30
399 Mark McLemore .05 .15
400 Greg W.Harris .05 .15
401 Jim Leyritz .05 .15
402 Doug Strange .05 .15
403 Tim Salmon .20 .50
404 Terry Mulholland .05 .15
405 Robby Thompson .05 .15
406 Ruben Sierra .10 .30
407 Tony Phillips .05 .15
408 Moises Alou .10 .30
409 Felix Fermin .05 .15
410 Pat Listach .05 .15
411 Kevin Bass .05 .15
412 Ben McDonald .05 .15
413 Scott Cooper .05 .15
414 Jody Reed .05 .15
415 Deion Sanders .20 .50
416 Ricky Gutierrez .05 .15
417 Gregg Jefferies .05 .15
418 Jack McDowell .05 .15
419 Al Leiter .10 .30
420 Tony Longmire .05 .15
421 Paul Wagner .05 .15
422 Geronimo Pena .05 .15
423 Ivan Rodriguez .20 .50
424 Kevin Gross .05 .15
425 Kirk McCaskill .05 .15
426 Greg Myers .05 .15
427 Roger Clemens .60 1.50
428 Chris Hammond .05 .15
429 Randy Myers .05 .15
430 Roger Mason .05 .15
431 Bret Saberhagen .10 .30
432 Jeff Reboulet .05 .15
433 John Olerud .10 .30
434 Bill Gullickson .05 .15
435 Eddie Murray .30 .75
436 Pedro Munoz .05 .15
437 Charlie O'Brien .05 .15
438 Jeff Nelson .05 .15
439 Mike Macfarlane .05 .15
440 Don Mattingly CL .40 1.00
441 Derrick May .05 .15
442 John Roper .05 .15
443 Darryl Hamilton .05 .15
444 Dan Miceli .05 .15
445 Tony Eusebio .05 .15
446 Jerry Browne .05 .15
447 Wally Joyner .10 .30
448 Brian Harper .05 .15
449 Scott Fletcher .05 .15
450 Bip Roberts .05 .15
451 Pete Smith .05 .15
452 Chili Davis .10 .30
453 Dave Hollins .05 .15
454 Tony Pena .05 .15
455 Butch Henry .05 .15
456 Craig Biggio .20 .50
457 Zane Smith .05 .15
458 Ryan Thompson .05 .15
459 Mike Jackson .05 .15
460 Mark McGwire .75 2.00
461 John Smoltz .20 .50
462 Steve Scarsone .05 .15
463 Greg Colbrunn .05 .15
464 Shawn Green .10 .30
465 David Wells .10 .30
466 Jose Hernandez .05 .15
467 Chip Hale .05 .15
468 Tony Tarasco .05 .15
469 Kevin Mitchell .05 .15
470 Billy Hatcher .05 .15
471 Jay Buhner .10 .30
472 Ken Caminiti .10 .30
473 Tom Henke .05 .15
474 Todd Worrell .05 .15
475 Mark Eichhorn .05 .15
476 Bruce Ruffin .05 .15
477 Chuck Finley .10 .30
478 Marc Newfield .05 .15
479 Paul Shuey .05 .15
480 Bob Tewksbury .05 .15
481 Ramon J.Martinez .05 .15
482 Melvin Nieves .05 .15
483 Todd Zeile .05 .15
484 Benito Santiago .10 .30
485 Stan Javier .05 .15
486 Kirk Rueter .05 .15
487 Andre Dawson .10 .30
488 Eric Karros .10 .30
489 Dave Magadan .05 .15
490 Joe Carter CL .05 .15
491 Randy Velarde .05 .15
492 Larry Walker .10 .30
493 Cris Carpenter .05 .15
494 Tom Gordon .05 .15
495 Dave Burba .05 .15
496 Darren Bragg .05 .15
497 Darren Daulton .10 .30
498 Don Slaught .05 .15
499 Pat Borders .05 .15
500 Lenny Harris .05 .15
501 Joe Ausanio .05 .15
502 Alan Trammell .10 .30
503 Mike Fetters .05 .15
504 Scott Ruffcorn .05 .15
505 Rich Rowland .05 .15
506 Juan Samuel .05 .15
507 Bo Jackson .30 .75
508 Jeff Branson .05 .15
509 Bernie Williams .20 .50
510 Paul Sorrento .05 .15
511 Dennis Eckersley .10 .30
512 Pat Mahomes .05 .15
513 Rusty Greer .10 .30
514 Luis Polonia .05 .15
515 Willie Banks .05 .15
516 John Wetteland .10 .30
517 Mike LaValliere .05 .15
518 Tommy Greene .05 .15
519 Mark Grace .20 .50
520 Bob Hamelin .05 .15
521 Scott Sanderson .05 .15
522 Joe Carter .10 .30
523 Jeff Brantley .05 .15
524 Andrew Lorraine .05 .15
525 Rico Brogna .05 .15
526 Shane Mack .05 .15
527 Mark Wohlers .05 .15
528 Scott Sanders .05 .15
529 Chris Bosio .05 .15
530 Andujar Cedeno .05 .15
531 Kenny Rogers .10 .30
532 Doug Drabek .05 .15
533 Curt Leskanic .05 .15
534 Craig Shipley .05 .15
535 Craig Grebeck .05 .15
536 Cal Eldred .05 .15
537 Mickey Tettleton .05 .15
538 Harold Baines .10 .30
539 Tim Wallach .05 .15
540 Damon Buford .05 .15
541 Lenny Webster .05 .15
542 Kevin Appier .10 .30
543 Raul Mondesi .10 .30
544 Eric Young .05 .15
545 Russ Davis .05 .15
546 Mike Benjamin .05 .15
547 Mike Greenwell .05 .15
548 Scott Brosius .10 .30
549 Brian Dorsett .05 .15
550 Chili Davis CL .05 .15

1996 Donruss

The 1996 Donruss set was issued in two series of 330 and 220 cards respectively, for a total of 550. The 12-card packs had a suggested retail price of $1.79. The full-bleed fronts feature full-color action photos with the player's name is in white ink in the upper right. The horizontal backs feature season and career stats, text, vital stats and another photo. Rookie Cards in this set include Mike Cameron.

COMPLETE SET (550) 16.00 40.00
COMP.SERIES 1 (330) 10.00 25.00
COMP.SERIES 2 (220) 6.00 15.00
1 Frank Thomas .30 .75
2 Jason Bates .10 .30
3 Steve Sparks .10 .30
4 Scott Servais .10 .30
5 Angelo Encarnacion RC .10 .30
6 Scott Sanders .10 .30
7 Billy Ashley .10 .30
8 Alex Rodriguez .60 1.50
9 Sean Bergman .10 .30
10 Brad Radke .10 .30
11 Andy Van Slyke .20 .50
12 Joe Girardi .10 .30
13 Mark Grudzielanek .10 .30
14 Rick Aguilera .10 .30
15 Randy Veres .10 .30
16 Tim Bogar .10 .30
17 Dave Veres .10 .30
18 Kevin Stocker .10 .30
19 Marquis Grissom .10 .30
20 Will Clark .20 .50
21 Jay Bell .10 .30
22 Allen Battle .10 .30
23 Frank Rodriguez .10 .30
24 Terry Steinbach .10 .30
25 Gerald Williams .10 .30
26 Sid Roberson .10 .30
27 Greg Zaun .10 .30
28 Ozzie Timmons .10 .30
29 Vaughn Eshelman .10 .30
30 Ed Sprague .10 .30
31 Gary DiSarcina .10 .30
32 Joe Boever .10 .30
33 Steve Avery .10 .30
34 Brad Ausmus .10 .30
35 Kirt Manwaring .10 .30
36 Gary Sheffield .10 .30
37 Jason Bere .10 .30
38 Jeff Manto .10 .30
39 David Cone .10 .30
40 Manny Ramirez .20 .50
41 Sandy Alomar Jr. .10 .30
42 Curtis Goodwin .10 .30
43 Tino Martinez .20 .50
44 Woody Williams .10 .30
45 Dean Palmer .10 .30
46 Hipolito Pichardo .10 .30
47 Jason Giambi .10 .30
48 Lance Johnson .10 .30
49 Bernard Gilkey .10 .30
50 Kirby Puckett .30 .75
51 Tony Fernandez .10 .30
52 Alex Gonzalez .10 .30
53 Bret Saberhagen .10 .30
54 Lyle Mouton .10 .30
55 Brian McRae .10 .30
56 Mark Gubicza .10 .30
57 Sergio Valdez .10 .30
58 Darrin Fletcher .10 .30
59 Steve Parris .10 .30
60 Johnny Damon .20 .50
61 Rickey Henderson .30 .75
62 Darrell Whitmore .10 .30
63 Roberto Petagine .10 .30
64 Trenidad Hubbard .10 .30
65 Heathcliff Slocumb .10 .30
66 Steve Finley .10 .30
67 Mariano Rivera .60 1.50
68 Brian L.Hunter .10 .30
69 Jamie Moyer .10 .30
70 Ellis Burks .10 .30
71 Pat Kelly .10 .30
72 Mickey Tettleton .10 .30
73 Garret Anderson .10 .30
74 Andy Pettitte .20 .50
75 Glenallen Hill .10 .30
76 Brent Gates .10 .30
77 Lou Whitaker .10 .30
78 David Segui .10 .30
79 Dan Wilson .10 .30
80 Pat Listach .10 .30
81 Jeff Bagwell .20 .50
82 Ben McDonald .10 .30
83 John Valentin .10 .30
84 John Jaha .10 .30
85 Pete Schourek .10 .30
86 Bryce Florie .10 .30
87 Brian Jordan .10 .30
88 Ron Karkovice .10 .30
89 Al Leiter .10 .30
90 Tony Longmire .10 .30
91 Nelson Liriano .10 .30
92 David Bell .10 .30
93 Kevin Gross .10 .30
94 Tom Candiotti .10 .30
95 Dave Martinez .10 .30
96 Greg Myers .10 .30
97 Rheal Cormier .10 .30
98 Chris Hammond .10 .30
99 Randy Myers .10 .30
100 Bill Pulsipher .10 .30
101 Jason Isringhausen .10 .30
102 Dave Stevens .10 .30
103 Roberto Alomar .20 .50
104 Bob Higginson .10 .30
105 Eddie Murray .30 .75
106 Matt Walbeck .10 .30
107 Mark Wohlers .10 .30
108 Jeff Nelson .10 .30
109 Tom Goodwin .10 .30
110 Cal Ripken CL .50 1.25
111 Rey Sanchez .10 .30
112 Hector Carrasco .10 .30
113 B.J. Surhoff .10 .30
114 Dan Miceli .10 .30
115 Dean Hartgraves .10 .30
116 John Burkett .10 .30
117 Gary Gaetti .10 .30
118 Ricky Bones .10 .30
119 Mike Macfarlane .10 .30
120 Bip Roberts .10 .30
121 Dave Mlicki .10 .30
122 Chili Davis .10 .30
123 Mark Whiten .10 .30
124 Herbert Perry .10 .30
125 Butch Henry .10 .30
126 Derek Bell .10 .30
127 Al Martin .10 .30
128 John Franco .10 .30
129 W. VanLandingham .10 .30
130 Mike Bordick .10 .30
131 Mike Mordecai .10 .30
132 Robby Thompson .10 .30
133 Greg Colbrunn .10 .30
134 Domingo Cedeno .10 .30
135 Chad Curtis .10 .30
136 Jose Hernandez .10 .30
137 Scott Klingenbeck .10 .30
138 Ryan Klesko .10 .30
139 John Smiley .10 .30
140 Charlie Hayes .10 .30
141 Jay Buhner .10 .30
142 Doug Drabek .10 .30
143 Roger Pavlik .10 .30
144 Todd Worrell .10 .30
145 Cal Ripken 1.00 2.50
146 Steve Reed .10 .30
147 Chuck Finley .10 .30
148 Mike Blowers .10 .30
149 Orel Hershiser .10 .30
150 Allen Watson .10 .30
151 Ramon Martinez .10 .30
152 Melvin Nieves .10 .30
153 Tripp Cromer .10 .30
154 Yorkis Perez .10 .30
155 Stan Javier .10 .30
156 Mel Rojas .10 .30
157 Aaron Sele .10 .30
158 Eric Karros .10 .30
159 Robb Nen .10 .30
160 Raul Mondesi .10 .30
161 John Wetteland .10 .30
162 Tim Scott .10 .30
163 Kenny Rogers .10 .30
164 Melvin Bunch .10 .30
165 Rod Beck .10 .30
166 Andy Benes .10 .30
167 Lenny Dykstra .10 .30
168 Orlando Merced .10 .30
169 Tomas Perez .10 .30
170 Xavier Hernandez .10 .30
171 Ruben Sierra .10 .30
172 Alan Trammell .10 .30
173 Mike Fetters .10 .30
174 Wilson Alvarez .10 .30
175 Erik Hanson .10 .30
176 Travis Fryman .10 .30
177 Jim Abbott .20 .50
178 Bret Boone .10 .30
179 Sterling Hitchcock .10 .30
180 Pat Mahomes .10 .30
181 Mark Acre .10 .30
182 Charles Nagy .10 .30
183 Rusty Greer .10 .30
184 Mike Stanley .10 .30
185 Jim Bullinger .10 .30
186 Shane Andrews .10 .30
187 Brian Keyser .10 .30
188 Tyler Green .10 .30
189 Mark Grace .20 .50
190 Bob Hamelin .10 .30
191 Luis Ortiz .10 .30
192 Joe Carter .10 .30
193 Eddie Taubensee .10 .30
194 Brian Anderson .10 .30
195 Edgardo Alfonzo .10 .30
196 Pedro Munoz .10 .30
197 David Justice .10 .30
198 Trevor Hoffman .10 .30
199 Bobby Ayala .10 .30
200 Tony Eusebio .10 .30
201 Jeff Russell .10 .30
202 Mike Hampton .10 .30
203 Walt Weiss .10 .30
204 Joey Hamilton .10 .30
205 Roberto Hernandez .10 .30
206 Greg Vaughn .10 .30
207 Felipe Lira .10 .30
208 Harold Baines .10 .30
209 Tim Wallach .10 .30
210 Manny Alexander .10 .30
211 Tim Laker .10 .30
212 Chris Haney .10 .30
213 Brian Maxcy .10 .30
214 Eric Young .10 .30
215 Darryl Strawberry .10 .30
216 Barry Bonds .75 2.00
217 Tim Naehring .10 .30
218 Scott Brosius .10 .30
219 Reggie Sanders .10 .30
220 Eddie Murray CL .20 .50
221 Luis Alicea .10 .30
222 Albert Belle .10 .30
223 Benji Gil .10 .30
224 Dante Bichette .10 .30
225 Bobby Bonilla .10 .30
226 Todd Stottlemyre .10 .30
227 Jim Edmonds .10 .30
228 Todd Jones .10 .30
229 Shawn Green .10 .30
230 Javier Lopez .10 .30
231 Ariel Prieto .10 .30
232 Tony Phillips .10 .30
233 James Mouton .10 .30
234 Jose Oquendo .10 .30
235 Royce Clayton .10 .30
236 Chuck Carr .10 .30
237 Doug Jones .10 .30
238 Mark McLemore .10 .30
239 Bill Swift .10 .30
240 Scott Leius .10 .30
241 Russ Davis .10 .30
242 Ray Durham .10 .30
243 Matt Mieske .10 .30
244 Brent Mayne .10 .30
245 Thomas Howard .10 .30
246 Troy O'Leary .10 .30
247 Jacob Brumfield .10 .30
248 Mickey Morandini .10 .30
249 Todd Hundley .10 .30
250 Chris Bosio .10 .30
251 Omar Vizquel .20 .50
252 Mike Lansing .10 .30
253 John Mabry .10 .30
254 Mike Perez .10 .30
255 Delino DeShields .10 .30
256 Wil Cordero .10 .30
257 Mike James .10 .30
258 Todd Van Poppel .10 .30
259 Joey Cora .10 .30
260 Andre Dawson .10 .30
261 Jerry DiPoto .10 .30
262 Rick Krivda .10 .30
263 Glenn Dishman .10 .30
264 Mike Mimbs .10 .30
265 John Ericks .10 .30
266 Jose Canseco .20 .50
267 Jeff Branson .10 .30
268 Curt Leskanic .10 .30
269 Jon Nunnally .10 .30
270 Scott Stahoviak .10 .30
271 Jeff Montgomery .10 .30
272 Hal Morris .10 .30
273 Esteban Loaiza .10 .30
274 Rico Brogna .10 .30
275 Dave Winfield .10 .30
276 J.R. Phillips .10 .30
277 Todd Zeile .10 .30
278 Tom Pagnozzi .10 .30
279 Mark Lemke .10 .30
280 Dave Magadan .10 .30
281 Greg McMichael .10 .30
282 Mike Morgan .10 .30
283 Moises Alou .10 .30
284 Dennis Martinez .10 .30
285 Jeff Kent .10 .30
286 Mark Johnson .10 .30
287 Darren Lewis .10 .30
288 Brad Clontz .10 .30
289 Chad Fonville .10 .30
290 Paul Sorrento .10 .30
291 Lee Smith .10 .30
292 Tom Glavine .20 .50
293 Antonio Osuna .10 .30
294 Kevin Foster .10 .30
295 Sandy Martinez .10 .30
296 Mark Leiter .10 .30
297 Julian Tavarez .10 .30
298 Mike Kelly .10 .30
299 Joe Oliver .10 .30
300 John Flaherty .10 .30
301 Don Mattingly .75 2.00
302 Pat Meares .10 .30
303 John Doherty .10 .30
304 Joe Vitiello .10 .30
305 Vinny Castilla .10 .30
306 Jeff Brantley .10 .30
307 Mike Greenwell .10 .30
308 Midre Cummings .10 .30
309 Curt Schilling .10 .30
310 Ken Caminiti .10 .30
311 Scott Erickson .10 .30
312 Carl Everett .10 .30
313 Charles Johnson .10 .30
314 Alex Diaz .10 .30
315 Jose Mesa .10 .30
316 Mark Carreon .10 .30
317 Carlos Perez .10 .30
318 Ismael Valdes .10 .30
319 Frank Castillo .10 .30
320 Tom Henke .10 .30
321 Spike Owen .10 .30
322 Joe Orsulak .10 .30
323 Paul Menhart .10 .30
324 Pedro Borbon .10 .30
325 Paul Molitor CL .10 .30
326 Jeff Cirillo .10 .30
327 Edwin Hurtado .10 .30
328 Orlando Miller .10 .30
329 Steve Ontiveros .10 .30
330 Kirby Puckett CL .20 .50
331 Scott Bullett .10 .30
332 Andres Galarraga .10 .30
333 Cal Eldred .10 .30
334 Sammy Sosa .30 .75
335 Don Slaught .10 .30
336 Jody Reed .10 .30
337 Roger Cedeno .10 .30
338 Ken Griffey Jr. .50 1.25
339 Todd Hollandsworth .10 .30
340 Mike Trombley .10 .30
341 Gregg Jefferies .10 .30
342 Larry Walker .10 .30
343 Pedro Martinez .20 .50
344 Dwayne Hosey .10 .30
345 Terry Pendleton .10 .30
346 Pete Harnisch .10 .30
347 Tony Castillo .10 .30
348 Paul Quantrill .10 .30
349 Fred McGriff .20 .50
350 Ivan Rodriguez .20 .50
351 Butch Huskey .10 .30
352 Ozzie Smith .50 1.25
353 Marty Cordova .10 .30
354 John Wasdin .10 .30
355 Wade Boggs .20 .50
356 Dave Nilsson .10 .30
357 Rafael Palmeiro .20 .50
358 Luis Gonzalez .10 .30
359 Reggie Jefferson .10 .30
360 Carlos Delgado .10 .30
361 Orlando Palmeiro .10 .30
362 Chris Gomez .10 .30
363 John Smoltz .20 .50
364 Marc Newfield .10 .30
365 Matt Williams .10 .30
366 Jesus Tavarez .10 .30
367 Bruce Ruffin .10 .30
368 Sean Berry .10 .30
369 Randy Velarde .10 .30
370 Tony Pena .10 .30
371 Jim Thome .20 .50
372 Jeffrey Hammonds .10 .30
373 Bob Wolcott .10 .30
374 Juan Guzman .10 .30
375 Juan Gonzalez .10 .30
376 Michael Tucker .10 .30
377 Doug Johns .10 .30
378 Mike Cameron RC .25 .60
379 Ray Lankford .10 .30
380 Jose Parra .10 .30
381 Jimmy Key .10 .30
382 John Olerud .10 .30
383 Kevin Ritz .10 .30
384 Tim Raines .10 .30
385 Rich Amaral .10 .30
386 Keith Lockhart .10 .30
387 Steve Scarsone .10 .30
388 Cliff Floyd .10 .30
389 Rich Aude .10 .30
390 Hideo Nomo .30 .75
391 Geronimo Berroa .10 .30
392 Pat Rapp .10 .30
393 Dustin Hermanson .10 .30
394 Greg Maddux .50 1.25
395 Darren Daulton .10 .30
396 Kenny Lofton .10 .30
397 Ruben Rivera .10 .30
398 Billy Wagner .10 .30
399 Kevin Brown .10 .30
400 Mike Kingery .10 .30
401 Bernie Williams .20 .50
402 Otis Nixon .10 .30
403 Damion Easley .10 .30
404 Paul O'Neill .20 .50
405 Deion Sanders .20 .50
406 Dennis Eckersley .10 .30
407 Tony Clark .10 .30
408 Rondell White .10 .30
409 Luis Sojo .10 .30
410 David Hulse .10 .30
411 Shane Reynolds .10 .30
412 Chris Hoiles .10 .30
413 Lee Tinsley .10 .30
414 Scott Karl .10 .30
415 Ron Gant .10 .30
416 Brian Johnson .10 .30
417 Jose Oliva .10 .30
418 Jack McDowell .10 .30
419 Paul Molitor .10 .30
420 Ricky Bottalico .10 .30
421 Paul Wagner .10 .30
422 Terry Bradshaw .10 .30
423 Bob Tewksbury .10 .30
424 Mike Piazza .50 1.25
425 Luis Andujar .10 .30
426 Mark Langston .10 .30
427 Stan Belinda .10 .30
428 Kurt Abbott .10 .30
429 Shawon Dunston .10 .30
430 Bobby Jones .10 .30
431 Jose Vizcaino .10 .30
432 Matt Lawton RC .15 .40
433 Pat Hentgen .10 .30
434 Cecil Fielder .10 .30
435 Carlos Baerga .10 .30
436 Rich Becker .10 .30
437 Chipper Jones .30 .75
438 Bill Risley .10 .30
439 Kevin Appier .10 .30
440 Wade Boggs CL .10 .30
441 Jaime Navarro .10 .30
442 Barry Larkin .20 .50
443 Jose Valentin .10 .30
444 Bryan Rekar .10 .30
445 Rick Wilkins .10 .30
446 Quilvio Veras .10 .30
447 Greg Gagne .10 .30
448 Mark Kiefer .10 .30
449 Bobby Witt .10 .30
450 Andy Ashby .10 .30
451 Alex Ochoa .10 .30
452 Jorge Fabregas .10 .30
453 Gene Schall .10 .30
454 Ken Hill .10 .30
455 Tony Tarasco .10 .30
456 Donnie Wall .10 .30
457 Carlos Garcia .10 .30
458 Ryan Thompson .10 .30
459 Marvin Benard RC .15 .40
460 Jose Herrera .10 .30
461 Jeff Blauser .10 .30
462 Chris Hook .10 .30
463 Jeff Conine .10 .30
464 Devon White .10 .30
465 Danny Bautista .10 .30
466 Steve Trachsel .10 .30
467 C.J. Nitkowski .10 .30
468 Mike Devereaux .10 .30
469 David Wells .10 .30
470 Jim Eisenreich .10 .30
471 Edgar Martinez .20 .50
472 Craig Biggio .20 .50
473 Jeff Frye .10 .30
474 Karim Garcia .10 .30
475 Jimmy Haynes .10 .30
476 Darren Holmes .10 .30
477 Tim Salmon .20 .50
478 Randy Johnson .30 .75
479 Eric Plunk .10 .30
480 Scott Cooper .10 .30
481 Chan Ho Park .10 .30
482 Ray McDavid .10 .30
483 Mark Petkovsek .10 .30
484 Greg Swindell .10 .30
485 George Williams .10 .30
486 Yamil Benitez .10 .30
487 Tim Wakefield .10 .30
488 Kevin Tapani .10 .30
489 Derrick May .10 .30
490 Ken Griffey Jr. CL .30 .75
491 Derek Jeter .75 2.00
492 Jeff Fassero .10 .30
493 Benito Santiago .10 .30

494 Tom Gordon .10 .30
495 Jamie Brewington RC .10 .30
496 Vince Coleman .10 .30
497 Kevin Jordan .10 .30
498 Jeff King .10 .30
499 Mike Simms .10 .30
500 Jose Rijo .10 .30
501 Denny Neagle .10 .30
502 Jose Lima .10 .30
503 Kevin Seitzer .10 .30
504 Alex Fernandez .10 .30
505 Mo Vaughn .10 .30
506 Phil Nevin .10 .30
507 J.T. Snow .10 .30
508 Andujar Cedeno .10 .30
509 Ozzie Guillen .10 .30
510 Mark Clark .10 .30
511 Mark McGwire .75 2.00
512 Jeff Reboulet .10 .30
513 Armando Benitez .10 .30
514 LaTroy Hawkins .10 .30
515 Brett Butler .10 .30
516 Tavo Alvarez .10 .30
517 Chris Snopek .10 .30
518 Mike Mussina .20 .50
519 Darryl Kile .10 .30
520 Wally Joyner .10 .30
521 Willie McGee .10 .30
522 Kent Mercker .10 .30
523 Mike Jackson .10 .30
524 Troy Percival .10 .30
525 Tony Gwynn .40 1.00
526 Ron Coomer .10 .30
527 Darryl Hamilton .10 .30
528 Phil Plantier .10 .30
529 Norm Charlton .10 .30
530 Craig Paquette .10 .30
531 Dave Burba .10 .30
532 Mike Henneman .10 .30
533 Terrell Wade .10 .30
534 Eddie Williams .10 .30
535 Robin Ventura .10 .30
536 Chuck Knoblauch .10 .30
537 Les Norman .10 .30
538 Brady Anderson .10 .30
539 Roger Clemens .60 1.50
540 Mark Portugal .10 .30
541 Mike Matheny .10 .30
542 Jeff Parrett .10 .30
543 Roberto Kelly .10 .30
544 Damon Buford .10 .30
545 Chad Ogea .10 .30
546 Jose Offerman .10 .30
547 Brian Barber .10 .30
548 Danny Tartabull .10 .30
549 Duane Singleton .10 .30
550 Tony Gwynn CL .20 .50

1997 Donruss

The 1997 Donruss set was issued in two separate series of 270 and 180 cards respectively. Both first series and Update cards were distributed in 10-card packs carrying a suggested retail price of $1.99 each. Card fronts feature color action player photos while the backs carry another color player photo with player information and career statistics. The following subsets are included within the set: Checklists (267-270/448-450), Rookies (353-397), Hit List (398-422), King of the Hill (423-437) and Interleague Showdown (438-447). Rookie Cards in this set include Jose Cruz Jr., Brian Giles and Hideki Irabu.

COMPLETE SET (450) 20.00 50.00
COMP. SERIES 1 (270) 10.00 25.00
COMPLETE UPDATE (180) 10.00 25.00
1 Juan Gonzalez .10 .30
2 Jim Edmonds .10 .30
3 Tony Gwynn .40 1.00
4 Andres Galarraga .10 .30
5 Joe Carter .10 .30
6 Raul Mondesi .10 .30
7 Greg Maddux .50 1.25
8 Travis Fryman .10 .30
9 Brian Jordan .10 .30
10 Henry Rodriguez .10 .30
11 Manny Ramirez .20 .50
12 Mark McGwire .75 2.00
13 Marc Newfield .10 .30
14 Craig Biggio .20 .50
15 Sammy Sosa .30 .75
16 Brady Anderson .10 .30
17 Wade Boggs .20 .50
18 Charles Johnson .10 .30
19 Matt Williams .10 .30
20 Denny Neagle .10 .30
21 Ken Griffey Jr. .50 1.25
22 Robin Ventura .10 .30
23 Barry Larkin .20 .50
24 Todd Zeile .10 .30
25 Chuck Knoblauch .10 .30
26 Todd Hundley .10 .30
27 Roger Clemens .60 1.50
28 Michael Tucker .10 .30
29 Rondell White .10 .30
30 Osvaldo Fernandez .10 .30
31 Ivan Rodriguez .20 .50
32 Alex Fernandez .10 .30
33 Jason Isringhausen .10 .30
34 Chipper Jones .30 .75
35 Paul O'Neill .20 .50
36 Hideo Nomo .30 .75
37 Roberto Alomar .20 .50
38 Derek Bell .10 .30
39 Paul Molitor .10 .30
40 Andy Benes .10 .30
41 Steve Trachsel .10 .30
42 J.T. Snow .10 .30
43 Jason Kendall .10 .30
44 Alex Rodriguez .50 1.25
45 Joey Hamilton .10 .30
46 Carlos Delgado .10 .30
47 Jason Giambi .10 .30
48 Larry Walker .10 .30
49 Derek Jeter .75 2.00
50 Kenny Lofton .10 .30
51 Devon White .10 .30
52 Matt Mieske .10 .30
53 Melvin Nieves .10 .30
54 Jose Canseco .20 .50
55 Tino Martinez .20 .50
56 Rafael Palmeiro .20 .50
57 Edgardo Alfonzo .10 .30
58 Jay Buhner .10 .30
59 Shane Reynolds .10 .30
60 Steve Finley .10 .30
61 Bobby Higginson .10 .30
62 Dean Palmer .10 .30
63 Terry Pendleton .10 .30
64 Marquis Grissom .10 .30
65 Mike Stanley .10 .30
66 Moises Alou .10 .30
67 Ray Lankford .10 .30
68 Marty Cordova .10 .30
69 John Olerud .10 .30
70 David Cone .10 .30
71 Benito Santiago .10 .30
72 Ryne Sandberg .50 1.25
73 Rickey Henderson .30 .75
74 Roger Cedeno .10 .30
75 Wilson Alvarez .10 .30
76 Tim Salmon .20 .50
77 Orlando Merced .10 .30
78 Vinny Castilla .10 .30
79 Ismael Valdes .10 .30
80 Dante Bichette .10 .30
81 Kevin Brown .10 .30
82 Andy Pettitte .20 .50
83 Scott Stahoviak .10 .30
84 Mickey Tettleton .10 .30
85 Jack McDowell .10 .30
86 Tom Glavine .20 .50
87 Gregg Jefferies .10 .30
88 Chili Davis .10 .30
89 Randy Johnson .30 .75
90 John Mabry .10 .30
91 Billy Wagner .10 .30
92 Jeff Cirillo .10 .30
93 Trevor Hoffman .10 .30
94 Juan Guzman .10 .30
95 Geronimo Berroa .10 .30
96 Bernard Gilkey .10 .30
97 Danny Tartabull .10 .30
98 Johnny Damon .20 .50
99 Charlie Hayes .10 .30
100 Reggie Sanders .10 .30
101 Robby Thompson .10 .30
102 Bobby Bonilla .10 .30
103 Reggie Jefferson .10 .30
104 John Smoltz .20 .50
105 Jim Thome .20 .50
106 Ruben Rivera .10 .30
107 Darren Oliver .10 .30
108 Mo Vaughn .10 .30
109 Roger Pavlik .10 .30
110 Terry Steinbach .10 .30
111 Jermaine Dye .10 .30
112 Mark Grudzielanek .10 .30
113 Rick Aguilera .10 .30
114 Jamey Wright .10 .30
115 Eddie Murray .30 .75
116 Brian L. Hunter .10 .30
117 Hal Morris .10 .30
118 Tom Pagnozzi .10 .30
119 Mike Mussina .20 .50
120 Mark Grace .20 .50
121 Cal Ripken 1.00 2.50
122 Tom Goodwin .10 .30
123 Paul Sorrento .10 .30
124 Jay Bell .10 .30
125 Todd Hollandsworth .10 .30
126 Edgar Martinez .20 .50
127 George Arias .10 .30
128 Greg Vaughn .10 .30
129 Roberto Hernandez .10 .30
130 Delino DeShields .10 .30
131 Bill Pulsipher .10 .30
132 Joey Cora .10 .30
133 Mariano Rivera .30 .75
134 Mike Piazza .50 1.25
135 Carlos Baerga .10 .30
136 Jose Mesa .10 .30
137 Will Clark .20 .50
138 Frank Thomas .30 .75
139 John Wetteland .10 .30
140 Shawn Estes .10 .30
141 Garret Anderson .10 .30
142 Andre Dawson .10 .30
143 Eddie Taubensee .10 .30
144 Ryan Klesko .10 .30
145 Rocky Coppinger .10 .30
146 Jeff Bagwell .20 .50
147 Donovan Osborne .10 .30
148 Greg Myers .10 .30
149 Brant Brown .10 .30
150 Kevin Elster .10 .30
151 Bob Wells .10 .30
152 Wally Joyner .10 .30
153 Rico Brogna .10 .30
154 Dwight Gooden .10 .30
155 Jermaine Allensworth .10 .30
156 Ray Durham .10 .30
157 Cecil Fielder .10 .30
158 John Burkett .10 .30
159 Gary Sheffield .10 .30
160 Albert Belle .10 .30
161 Tomas Perez .10 .30
162 David Doster .10 .30
163 John Valentin .10 .30
164 Danny Graves .10 .30
165 Jose Paniagua .10 .30
166 Brian Giles RC .60 1.50
167 Barry Bonds .75 2.00
168 Sterling Hitchcock .10 .30
169 Bernie Williams .20 .50
170 Fred McGriff .20 .50
171 George Williams .10 .30
172 Amaury Telemaco .10 .30
173 Ken Caminiti .10 .30
174 Ron Gant .10 .30
175 Dave Justice .10 .30
176 James Baldwin .10 .30
177 Pat Hentgen .10 .30
178 Ben McDonald .10 .30
179 Tim Naehring .10 .30
180 Jim Eisenreich .10 .30
181 Ken Hill .10 .30
182 Paul Wilson .10 .30
183 Marvin Benard .10 .30
184 Alan Benes .10 .30
185 Ellis Burks .10 .30
186 Scott Servais .10 .30
187 David Segui .10 .30
188 Scott Brosius .10 .30
189 Jose Offerman .10 .30
190 Eric Davis .10 .30
191 Brett Butler .10 .30
192 Curtis Pride .10 .30
193 Yamil Benitez .10 .30
194 Chan Ho Park .10 .30
195 Bret Boone .10 .30
196 Omar Vizquel .20 .50
197 Orlando Miller .10 .30
198 Ramon Martinez .10 .30
199 Harold Baines .10 .30
200 Eric Young .10 .30
201 Fernando Vina .10 .30
202 Alex Gonzalez .10 .30
203 Fernando Valenzuela .10 .30
204 Steve Avery .10 .30
205 Ernie Young .10 .30
206 Kevin Appier .10 .30
207 Randy Myers .10 .30
208 Jeff Suppan .10 .30
209 James Mouton .10 .30
210 Russ Davis .10 .30
211 Al Martin .10 .30
212 Troy Percival .10 .30
213 Al Leiter .10 .30
214 Dennis Eckersley .10 .30
215 Mark Johnson .10 .30
216 Eric Karros .10 .30
217 Royce Clayton .10 .30
218 Tony Phillips .10 .30
219 Tim Wakefield .10 .30
220 Alan Trammell .10 .30
221 Eduardo Perez .10 .30
222 Butch Huskey .10 .30
223 Tim Belcher .10 .30
224 Jamie Moyer .10 .30
225 F.P. Santangelo .10 .30
226 Rusty Greer .10 .30
227 Jeff Brantley .10 .30
228 Mark Langston .10 .30
229 Ray Montgomery .10 .30
230 Rich Becker .10 .30
231 Ozzie Smith .50 1.25
232 Rey Ordonez .10 .30
233 Ricky Otero .10 .30
234 Mike Cameron .10 .30
235 Mike Sweeney .10 .30
236 Mark Lewis .10 .30
237 Luis Gonzalez .10 .30
238 Marcus Jensen .10 .30
239 Ed Sprague .10 .30
240 Jose Valentin .10 .30
241 Jeff Frye .10 .30
242 Charles Nagy .10 .30
243 Carlos Garcia .10 .30
244 Mike Hampton .10 .30
245 B.J. Surhoff .10 .30
246 Wilton Guerrero .10 .30
247 Frank Rodriguez .10 .30
248 Gary Gaetti .10 .30
249 Lance Johnson .10 .30
250 Darren Bragg .10 .30
251 Darryl Hamilton .10 .30
252 John Jaha .10 .30
253 Craig Paquette .10 .30
254 Jaime Navarro .10 .30
255 Shawon Dunston .10 .30
256 Mark Loretta .10 .30
257 Tim Belk .10 .30
258 Jeff Darwin .10 .30
259 Ruben Sierra .10 .30
260 Chuck Finley .10 .30
261 Darryl Strawberry .10 .30
262 Shannon Stewart .10 .30
263 Pedro Martinez .20 .50
264 Neifi Perez .10 .30
265 Jeff Conine .10 .30
266 Orel Hershiser .10 .30
267 Eddie Murray CL .20 .50
268 Paul Molitor CL .10 .30
269 Barry Bonds CL .40 1.00
270 Mark McGwire CL .40 1.00
271 Matt Williams .10 .30
272 Todd Zeile .10 .30
273 Roger Clemens .60 1.50
274 Michael Tucker .10 .30
275 J.T. Snow .10 .30
276 Kenny Lofton .10 .30
277 Jose Canseco .20 .50
278 Marquis Grissom .10 .30
279 Moises Alou .10 .30
280 Benito Santiago .10 .30
281 Willie McGee .10 .30
282 Chili Davis .10 .30
283 Ron Coomer .10 .30
284 Orlando Merced .10 .30
285 Delino DeShields .10 .30
286 John Wetteland .10 .30
287 Darren Daulton .10 .30
288 Lee Stevens .10 .30
289 Albert Belle .10 .30
290 Sterling Hitchcock .10 .30
291 David Justice .10 .30
292 Eric Davis .10 .30
293 Brian Hunter .10 .30
294 Darryl Hamilton .10 .30
295 Steve Avery .10 .30
296 Joe Vitiello .10 .30
297 Jaime Navarro .10 .30
298 Eddie Murray .30 .75
299 Randy Myers .10 .30
300 Francisco Cordova .10 .30
301 Javier Lopez .10 .30
302 Geronimo Berroa .10 .30
303 Jeffrey Hammonds .10 .30
304 Deion Sanders .20 .50
305 Jeff Fassero .10 .30
306 Curt Schilling .10 .30
307 Robb Nen .10 .30
308 Mark McLemore .10 .30
309 Jimmy Key .10 .30
310 Quilvio Veras .10 .30
311 Bip Roberts .10 .30
312 Esteban Loaiza .10 .30
313 Andy Ashby .10 .30
314 Sandy Alomar Jr. .10 .30
315 Shawn Green .10 .30
316 Luis Castillo .10 .30
317 Benji Gil .10 .30
318 Otis Nixon .10 .30
319 Aaron Sele .10 .30
320 Brad Ausmus .10 .30
321 Troy O'Leary .10 .30
322 Terrell Wade .10 .30
323 Jeff King .10 .30
324 Kevin Seitzer .10 .30
325 Mark Wohlers .10 .30
326 Edgar Renteria .10 .30
327 Dan Wilson .10 .30
328 Brian McRae .10 .30
329 Rod Beck .10 .30
330 Julio Franco .10 .30
331 Dave Nilsson .10 .30
332 Glenallen Hill .10 .30
333 Kevin Elster .10 .30
334 Joe Girardi .10 .30
335 David Wells .10 .30
336 Jeff Blauser .10 .30
337 Darryl Kile .10 .30
338 Jeff Kent .10 .30
339 Jim Leyritz .10 .30
340 Todd Stottlemyre .10 .30
341 Tony Clark .10 .30
342 Chris Hoiles .10 .30
343 Mike Lieberthal .10 .30
344 Matt Lawton .10 .30
345 Alex Ochoa .10 .30
346 Chris Snopek .10 .30
347 Rudy Pemberton .10 .30
348 Eric Owens .10 .30
349 Joe Randa .10 .30
350 John Olerud .10 .30
351 Steve Karsay .10 .30
352 Mark Whiten .10 .30
353 Bob Abreu .20 .50
354 Bartolo Colon .10 .30
355 Vladimir Guerrero .30 .75
356 Darin Erstad .10 .30
357 Scott Rolen .20 .50
358 Andruw Jones .20 .50
359 Scott Spiezio .10 .30
360 Karim Garcia .10 .30
361 Hideki Irabu RC .15 .40
362 Nomar Garciaparra .50 1.25
363 Dmitri Young .10 .30
364 Bubba Trammell RC .15 .40
365 Kevin Orie .10 .30
366 Jose Rosado .10 .30
367 Jose Guillen .10 .30
368 Brooks Kieschnick .10 .30
369 Pokey Reese .10 .30
370 Glendon Rusch .10 .30
371 Jason Dickson .10 .30
372 Todd Walker .10 .30
373 Justin Thompson .10 .30
374 Todd Greene .10 .30
375 Jeff Suppan .10 .30
376 Trey Beamon .10 .30
377 Damon Mashore .10 .30
378 Wendell Magee .10 .30
379 S. Hasegawa RC .20 .50
380 Bill Mueller RC .50 1.25
381 Chris Widger .10 .30
382 Tony Graffanino .10 .30
383 Derrek Lee .20 .50
384 Brian Moehler RC .15 .40
385 Quinton McCracken .10 .30
386 Matt Morris .10 .30
387 Marvin Benard .10 .30
388 Deivi Cruz RC .15 .40
389 Javier Valentin .10 .30
390 Todd Dunwoody .10 .30
391 Derrick Gibson .10 .30
392 Raul Casanova .10 .30
393 George Arias .10 .30
394 Tony Womack RC .15 .40
395 Antone Williamson .10 .30
396 Jose Cruz Jr. RC .15 .40
397 Desi Relaford .10 .30
398 Frank Thomas HIT .20 .50
399 Ken Griffey Jr. HIT .30 .75
400 Cal Ripken HIT .50 1.25
401 Chipper Jones HIT .20 .50
402 Mike Piazza HIT .30 .75
403 Gary Sheffield HIT .10 .30
404 Alex Rodriguez HIT .30 .75
405 Wade Boggs HIT .10 .30
406 Juan Gonzalez HIT .10 .30
407 Tony Gwynn HIT .20 .50
408 Edgar Martinez HIT .10 .30
409 Jeff Bagwell HIT .10 .30
410 Larry Walker HIT .10 .30
411 Kenny Lofton HIT .10 .30
412 Manny Ramirez HIT .10 .30
413 Mark McGwire HIT .40 1.00
414 Roberto Alomar HIT .10 .30
415 Derek Jeter HIT .40 1.00
416 Brady Anderson HIT .10 .30
417 Paul Molitor HIT .10 .30
418 Dante Bichette HIT .10 .30
419 Jim Edmonds HIT .10 .30
420 Mo Vaughn HIT .10 .30
421 Barry Bonds HIT .40 1.00
422 Rusty Greer HIT .10 .30
423 Greg Maddux KING .30 .75
424 Andy Pettitte KING .10 .30
425 John Smoltz KING .10 .30
426 Randy Johnson KING .20 .50
427 Hideo Nomo KING .10 .30
428 Roger Clemens KING .30 .75
429 Tom Glavine KING .10 .30
430 Pat Hentgen KING .10 .30
431 Kevin Brown KING .10 .30
432 Mike Mussina KING .10 .30
433 Alex Fernandez KING .10 .30
434 Kevin Appier KING .10 .30
435 David Cone KING .10 .30
436 Jeff Fassero KING .10 .30
437 John Wetteland KING .10 .30
438 Barry Bonds IS .40 1.00
Ivan Rodriguez
439 Ken Griffey Jr. IS .30 .75
Andres Galarraga
440 Fred McGriff IS .10 .30
Rafael Palmeiro
441 Barry Larkin IS .20 .50
Jim Thome
442 Sammy Sosa IS .20 .50
Albert Belle
443 Bernie Williams IS .10 .30
Todd Hundley
444 Chuck Knoblauch IS .10 .30
Brian Jordan
445 Mo Vaughn IS .10 .30
Jeff Conine
446 Ken Caminiti IS .10 .30
Jason Giambi
447 Raul Mondesi IS .10 .30
Tim Salmon
448 Cal Ripken CL .50 1.25
449 Greg Maddux CL .30 .75
450 Ken Griffey Jr. CL .30 .75

1998 Donruss

The 1998 Donruss set was issued in two series (series one numbers 1-170, series two numbers 171-420) and was distributed in 10-card packs with a suggested retail price of $1.99. The fronts feature color player photos with player information on the backs. The set contains the topical subsets: Fan Club (156-165), Hit List (346-375), The Untouchables (376-385), Spirit of the Game (386-415) and Checklists (416-420). Each Fan Club card carried instructions on how the fan could vote for their favorite players to be included in the 1998 Donruss Update set. Rookie Cards include Kevin Millwood and Magglio Ordonez. Sadly, after an eighteen year run, this was the last Donruss set to be issued due to card manufacturer Pinnacle's bankruptcy in 1998. In 2001, however, Donruss/Playoff procured a license to produce baseball cards and the Donruss brand was reinstituted after a two year break.

COMPLETE SET (420) 20.00 50.00
COMP.SERIES 1 (170) 8.00 20.00
COMPLETE UPDATE (250) 12.50 30.00
1 Paul Molitor .08 .25
2 Juan Gonzalez .08 .25
3 Darryl Kile .08 .25
4 Randy Johnson .25 .60
5 Tom Glavine .15 .40
6 Pat Hentgen .08 .25
7 David Justice .08 .25
8 Kevin Brown .15 .40
9 Mike Mussina .15 .40
10 Ken Caminiti .08 .25
11 Todd Hundley .08 .25
12 Frank Thomas .25 .60
13 Ray Lankford .08 .25
14 Justin Thompson .08 .25
15 Jason Dickson .08 .25
16 Kenny Lofton .08 .25
17 Ivan Rodriguez .15 .40
18 Pedro Martinez .15 .40
19 Brady Anderson .08 .25
20 Barry Larkin .15 .40
21 Chipper Jones .25 .60
22 Tony Gwynn .30 .75
23 Roger Clemens .50 1.25
24 Sandy Alomar Jr. .08 .25
25 Tino Martinez .15 .40
26 Jeff Bagwell .15 .40
27 Shawn Estes .08 .25
28 Ken Griffey Jr. .40 1.00
29 Javier Lopez .08 .25
30 Denny Neagle .08 .25
31 Mike Piazza .40 1.00
32 Andres Galarraga .08 .25
33 Larry Walker .08 .25
34 Alex Rodriguez .40 1.00
35 Greg Maddux .40 1.00
36 Albert Belle .08 .25
37 Barry Bonds .60 1.50
38 Mo Vaughn .08 .25
39 Kevin Appier .08 .25
40 Wade Boggs .15 .40
41 Garret Anderson .08 .25
42 Jeffrey Hammonds .08 .25
43 Marquis Grissom .08 .25
44 Jim Edmonds .08 .25
45 Brian Jordan .08 .25
46 Raul Mondesi .08 .25
47 John Valentin .08 .25
48 Brad Radke .08 .25
49 Ismael Valdes .08 .25
50 Matt Stairs .08 .25
51 Matt Williams .08 .25
52 Reggie Jefferson .08 .25
53 Alan Benes .08 .25
54 Charles Johnson .08 .25
55 Chuck Knoblauch .08 .25
56 Edgar Martinez .15 .40
57 Nomar Garciaparra .40 1.00
58 Craig Biggio .15 .40
59 Bernie Williams .15 .40
60 David Cone .08 .25
61 Cal Ripken .75 2.00
62 Mark McGwire .60 1.50
63 Roberto Alomar .15 .40
64 Fred McGriff .15 .40
65 Eric Karros .08 .25
66 Robin Ventura .08 .25
67 Darin Erstad .08 .25
68 Michael Tucker .08 .25
69 Jim Thome .15 .40
70 Mark Grace .15 .40
71 Lou Collier .08 .25
72 Karim Garcia .08 .25
73 Alex Fernandez .08 .25
74 J.T. Snow .08 .25
75 Reggie Sanders .08 .25
76 John Smoltz .15 .40
77 Tim Salmon .15 .40
78 Paul O'Neill .15 .40
79 Vinny Castilla .08 .25
80 Rafael Palmeiro .15 .40
81 Jaret Wright .08 .25
82 Jay Buhner .08 .25
83 Brett Butler .08 .25
84 Todd Greene .08 .25
85 Scott Rolen .15 .40
86 Sammy Sosa .25 .60
87 Jason Giambi .08 .25
88 Carlos Delgado .08 .25
89 Deion Sanders .15 .40
90 Wilton Guerrero .08 .25
91 Andy Pettitte .15 .40
92 Brian Giles .08 .25
93 Dmitri Young .08 .25
94 Ron Coomer .08 .25
95 Mike Cameron .08 .25
96 Edgardo Alfonzo .08 .25
97 Jimmy Key .08 .25
98 Ryan Klesko .08 .25
99 Andy Benes .08 .25
100 Derek Jeter .60 1.50
101 Jeff Fassero .08 .25
102 Neifi Perez .08 .25
103 Hideo Nomo .25 .60
104 Andruw Jones .15 .40
105 Todd Helton .15 .40
106 Livan Hernandez .08 .25
107 Brett Tomko .08 .25
108 Shannon Stewart .08 .25
109 Bartolo Colon .08 .25
110 Matt Morris .08 .25
111 Miguel Tejada .25 .60
112 Pokey Reese .08 .25
113 Fernando Tatis .08 .25
114 Todd Dunwoody .08 .25
115 Jose Cruz Jr. .08 .25
116 Chan Ho Park .08 .25
117 Kevin Young .08 .25
118 Rickey Henderson .25 .60
119 Hideki Irabu .08 .25
120 Francisco Cordova .08 .25
121 Al Martin .08 .25
122 Tony Clark .08 .25
123 Curt Schilling .08 .25
124 Rusty Greer .08 .25
125 Jose Canseco .15 .40
126 Edgar Renteria .08 .25
127 Todd Walker .08 .25
128 Wally Joyner .08 .25
129 Bill Mueller .08 .25
130 Jose Guillen .08 .25
131 Manny Ramirez .15 .40
132 Bobby Higginson .08 .25
133 Kevin Orie .08 .25
134 Will Clark .15 .40
135 Dave Nilsson .08 .25
136 Jason Kendall .08 .25
137 Ivan Cruz .08 .25
138 Gary Sheffield .08 .25
139 Bubba Trammell .08 .25
140 Vladimir Guerrero .25 .60
141 Dennis Reyes .08 .25
142 Bobby Bonilla .08 .25
143 Ruben Rivera .08 .25
144 Ben Grieve .08 .25
145 Moises Alou .08 .25
146 Tony Womack .08 .25
147 Eric Young .08 .25
148 Paul Konerko .08 .25
149 Dante Bichette .08 .25
150 Joe Carter .08 .25
151 Rondell White .08 .25
152 Chris Holt .08 .25
153 Shawn Green .08 .25
154 Mark Grudzielanek .08 .25
UER back rudzielanek
155 Jermaine Dye .08 .25
156 Ken Griffey Jr. FC .25 .60
157 Frank Thomas FC .15 .40
158 Chipper Jones FC .15 .40
159 Mike Piazza FC .25 .60
160 Cal Ripken FC .40 1.00
161 Greg Maddux FC .25 .60
162 Juan Gonzalez FC .08 .25
163 Alex Rodriguez FC .25 .60
164 Mark McGwire FC .30 .75
165 Derek Jeter FC .30 .75
166 Larry Walker CL .08 .25
167 Tony Gwynn CL .15 .40
168 Tino Martinez CL .08 .25
169 Scott Rolen CL .08 .25
170 Nomar Garciaparra CL .25 .60
171 Mike Sweeney .08 .25
172 Dustin Hermanson .08 .25
173 Darren Dreifort .08 .25
174 Ron Gant .08 .25
175 Todd Hollandsworth .08 .25
176 John Jaha .08 .25
177 Kerry Wood .10 .30
178 Chris Stynes .08 .25
179 Kevin Elster .08 .25
180 Derek Bell .08 .25
181 Darryl Strawberry .08 .25
182 Damion Easley .08 .25
183 Jeff Cirillo .08 .25
184 John Thomson .08 .25
185 Dan Wilson .08 .25
186 Jay Bell .08 .25
187 Bernard Gilkey .08 .25
188 Marc Valdes .08 .25
189 Ramon Martinez .08 .25
190 Charles Nagy .08 .25
191 Derek Lowe .08 .25
192 Andy Benes .08 .25
193 Delino DeShields .08 .25
194 Ryan Jackson RC .08 .25
195 Kenny Lofton .08 .25
196 Chuck Knoblauch .08 .25
197 Andres Galarraga .08 .25
198 Jose Canseco .15 .40
199 John Olerud .08 .25
200 Lance Johnson .08 .25
201 Darryl Kile .08 .25
202 Luis Castillo .08 .25
203 Joe Carter .08 .25
204 Dennis Eckersley .08 .25
205 Steve Finley .08 .25
206 Esteban Loaiza .08 .25
207 R.Christenson RC UER .08 .25
birthdate says 1988
208 Deivi Cruz .08 .25
209 Mariano Rivera .25 .60
210 Mike Judd RC .10 .30
211 Billy Wagner .08 .25
212 Scott Spiezio .08 .25
213 Russ Davis .08 .25
214 Jeff Suppan .08 .25
215 Doug Glanville .08 .25
216 Dmitri Young .08 .25
217 Rey Ordonez .08 .25
218 Cecil Fielder .08 .25
219 Masato Yoshii RC .10 .30
220 Raul Casanova .08 .25
221 Rolando Arrojo RC .10 .30
222 Ellis Burks .08 .25
223 Butch Huskey .08 .25
224 Brian Hunter .08 .25
225 Marquis Grissom .08 .25
226 Kevin Brown .15 .40
227 Joe Randa .08 .25
228 Henry Rodriguez .08 .25
229 Omar Vizquel .15 .40
230 Fred McGriff .15 .40
231 Matt Williams .08 .25
232 Moises Alou .08 .25
233 Travis Fryman .08 .25
234 Wade Boggs .15 .40
235 Pedro Martinez .15 .40
236 Rickey Henderson .25 .60
237 Bubba Trammell .08 .25
238 Mike Caruso .08 .25
239 Wilson Alvarez .08 .25
240 Geronimo Berroa .08 .25
241 Eric Milton .08 .25
242 Scott Erickson .08 .25
243 Todd Erdos RC .08 .25
244 Bobby Hughes .08 .25
245 Dave Hollins .08 .25
246 Dean Palmer .08 .25
247 Carlos Baerga .08 .25
248 Jose Silva .08 .25
249 Jose Cabrera RC .08 .25
250 Tom Evans .08 .25
251 Marty Cordova .08 .25
252 Hanley Frias RC .08 .25
253 Javier Valentin .08 .25
254 Mario Valdez .08 .25
255 Joey Cora .08 .25
256 Mike Lansing .08 .25
257 Jeff Kent .08 .25
258 Dave Dellucci RC .20 .50
259 Curtis King RC .08 .25
260 David Segui .08 .25
261 Royce Clayton .08 .25
262 Jeff Blauser .08 .25
263 Manny Aybar RC .08 .25
264 Mike Cather RC .08 .25
265 Todd Zeile .08 .25
266 Richard Hidalgo .08 .25
267 Dante Powell .08 .25
268 Mike DeJean RC .08 .25
269 Ken Cloude .08 .25
270 Danny Klassen .08 .25
271 Sean Casey .08 .25
272 A.J. Hinch .08 .25
273 Rich Butler RC .08 .25
274 Ben Ford RC .08 .25
275 Billy McMillon .08 .25
276 Wilson Delgado .08 .25
277 Orlando Cabrera .08 .25
278 Geoff Jenkins .08 .25
279 Enrique Wilson .08 .25
280 Derrek Lee .15 .40
281 Marc Pisciotta RC .08 .25
282 Abraham Nunez .08 .25
283 Aaron Boone .08 .25
284 Brad Fullmer .08 .25
285 Rob Stanifer RC .08 .25
286 Preston Wilson .08 .25
287 Greg Norton .08 .25
288 Bobby Smith .08 .25
289 Josh Booty .08 .25
290 Russell Branyan .08 .25
291 Jeremi Gonzalez .08 .25
292 Michael Coleman .08 .25
293 Cliff Politte .08 .25
294 Eric Ludwick .08 .25
295 Rafael Medina .08 .25
296 Jason Varitek .25 .60
297 Ron Wright .08 .25
298 Mark Kotsay .08 .25
299 David Ortiz .30 .75
300 Frank Catalanotto RC .20 .50
301 Robinson Checo .08 .25
302 Kevin Millwood RC .30 .75
303 Jacob Cruz .08 .25
304 Javier Vazquez .08 .25
305 Magglio Ordonez RC 1.00 2.50
306 Kevin Witt .08 .25
307 Derrick Gibson .08 .25
308 Shane Monahan .08 .25
309 Brian Rose .08 .25
310 Bobby Estalella .08 .25
311 Felix Heredia .08 .25
312 Desi Relaford .08 .25
313 Esteban Yan RC .10 .30
314 Ricky Ledee .08 .25
315 Steve Woodard .08 .25
316 Pat Watkins .08 .25
317 Damian Moss .08 .25
318 Bob Abreu .08 .25
319 Jeff Abbott .08 .25
320 Miguel Cairo .08 .25
321 Rigo Beltran RC .08 .25
322 Tony Saunders .08 .25
323 Randall Simon .08 .25
324 Hiram Bocachica .08 .25
325 Richie Sexson .08 .25
326 Karim Garcia .08 .25
327 Mike Lowell RC .50 1.25
328 Pat Cline .08 .25
329 Matt Clement .08 .25
330 Scott Elarton .08 .25
331 Manuel Barrios RC .08 .25
332 Bruce Chen .08 .25
333 Juan Encarnacion .08 .25

334 Travis Lee .08 .25
335 Wes Helms .08 .25
336 Chad Fox RC .08 .25
337 Donnie Sadler .08 .25
338 Carlos Mendoza RC .08 .25
339 Damian Jackson .08 .25
340 Julio Ramirez RC .08 .25
341 John Halama RC .10 .30
342 Edwin Diaz .08 .25
343 Felix Martinez .08 .25
344 Eli Marrero .08 .25
345 Carl Pavano .08 .25
346 Vladimir Guerrero HL .15 .40
347 Barry Bonds HL .30 .75
348 Darin Erstad HL .08 .25
349 Albert Belle HL .08 .25
350 Kenny Lofton HL .08 .25
351 Mo Vaughn HL .08 .25
352 Jose Cruz Jr. HL .08 .25
353 Tony Clark HL .08 .25
354 Roberto Alomar HL .08 .25
355 Manny Ramirez HL .08 .25
356 Paul Molitor HL .08 .25
357 Jim Thome HL .08 .25
358 Tino Martinez HL .08 .25
359 Tim Salmon HL .08 .25
360 David Justice HL .08 .25
361 Raul Mondesi HL .08 .25
362 Mark Grace HL .08 .25
363 Craig Biggio HL .08 .25
364 Larry Walker HL .08 .25
365 Mark McGwire HL .30 .75
366 Juan Gonzalez HL .08 .25
367 Derek Jeter HL .30 .75
368 Chipper Jones HL .15 .40
369 Frank Thomas HL .15 .40
370 Alex Rodriguez HL .25 .60
371 Mike Piazza HL .25 .60
372 Tony Gwynn HL .15 .40
373 Jeff Bagwell HL .08 .25
374 N.Garciaparra HL .25 .60
375 Ken Griffey Jr. HL .25 .60
376 Livan Hernandez UN .08 .25
377 Chan Ho Park UN .08 .25
378 Mike Mussina UN .08 .25
379 Andy Pettitte UN .08 .25
380 Greg Maddux UN .25 .60
381 Hideo Nomo UN .15 .40
382 Roger Clemens UN .25 .60
383 Randy Johnson UN .15 .40
384 Pedro Martinez UN .15 .40
385 Jaret Wright UN .08 .25
386 Ken Griffey Jr. SG .25 .60
387 Todd Helton SG .08 .25
388 Paul Konerko SG .08 .25
389 Cal Ripken SG .40 1.00
390 Larry Walker SG .08 .25
391 Ken Caminiti SG .08 .25
392 Jose Guillen SG .08 .25
393 Jim Edmonds SG .08 .25
394 Barry Larkin SG .08 .25
395 Bernie Williams SG .08 .25
396 Tony Clark SG .08 .25
397 Jose Cruz Jr. SG .08 .25
398 Ivan Rodriguez SG .08 .25
399 Darin Erstad SG .08 .25
400 Scott Rolen SG .08 .25
401 Mark McGwire SG .30 .75
402 Andruw Jones SG .08 .25
403 Juan Gonzalez SG .08 .25
404 Derek Jeter SG .30 .75
405 Chipper Jones SG .15 .40
406 Greg Maddux SG .25 .60
407 Frank Thomas SG .15 .40
408 Alex Rodriguez SG .25 .60
409 Mike Piazza SG .25 .60
410 Tony Gwynn SG .15 .40
411 Jeff Bagwell SG .08 .25
412 N.Garciaparra SG .25 .60
413 Hideo Nomo SG .15 .40
414 Barry Bonds SG .30 .75
415 Ben Grieve SG .08 .25
416 Barry Bonds CL .30 .75
417 Mark McGwire CL .30 .75
418 Roger Clemens CL .25 .60
419 Livan Hernandez CL .08 .25
420 Ken Griffey Jr. CL .25 .60

2001 Donruss

The 2001 Donruss product was released in early May, 2001. The 220-card base set was broken into tiers as follows: Base Veterans (1-150), short-printed Rated Rookies (151-200) serial numbered to 2001, and Fan Club cards (201-220) inserted approximately one per box. Exchange cards with a redemption deadline of May 1st, 2003 was seeded into packs for card 156 Albert Pujols and 159 Ben Sheets. Each pack contained five cards, and a one card retro pack. Packs carried a suggested retail price of $1.99. Please note that 1999 Retro packs were inserted in Hobby packs, while 2000 Retro packs were inserted into Retail packs. One in every 720 packs contained an exchange card good for a complete set of 2001 Donruss Baseball's Best. One in every 72 packs contained and exchange card good for a complete set of 2001 Donruss the Rookies. The redemption deadline for both exchange cards was January 20th, 2002. The original exchange deadline was November 1st, 2001 but the manufacturer lengthened the redemption period.

COMP.SET w/o SP's (150) 10.00 25.00
COMMON CARD (1-150) .10 .30
COMMON (151-200) 3.00 8.00
COMMON (201-220) 1.00 2.50
1 Alex Rodriguez .50 1.25
2 Barry Bonds .75 2.00
3 Cal Ripken 1.00 2.50
4 Chipper Jones .30 .75
5 Derek Jeter .75 2.00
6 Troy Glaus .10 .30
7 Frank Thomas .30 .75
8 Greg Maddux .50 1.25
9 Ivan Rodriguez .20 .50
10 Jeff Bagwell .20 .50
11 Jose Canseco .20 .50
12 Todd Helton .20 .50
13 Ken Griffey Jr. .50 1.25
14 Manny Ramirez Sox .20 .50
15 Mark McGwire .75 2.00
16 Mike Piazza .50 1.25
17 Nomar Garciaparra .50 1.25
18 Pedro Martinez .20 .50
19 Randy Johnson .30 .75
20 Rick Ankiel .10 .30
21 Rickey Henderson .30 .75
22 Roger Clemens .60 1.50
23 Sammy Sosa .30 .75
24 Tony Gwynn .40 1.00
25 Vladimir Guerrero .30 .75
26 Eric Davis .10 .30
27 Roberto Alomar .10 .30
28 Mark Mulder .10 .30
29 Pat Burrell .10 .30
30 Harold Baines .10 .30
31 Carlos Delgado .10 .30
32 J.D. Drew .10 .30
33 Jim Edmonds .10 .30
34 Darin Erstad .10 .30
35 Jason Giambi .10 .30
36 Tom Glavine .20 .50
37 Juan Gonzalez .10 .30
38 Mark Grace .20 .50
39 Shawn Green .10 .30
40 Tim Hudson .10 .30
41 Andruw Jones .20 .50
42 David Justice .10 .30
43 Jeff Kent .10 .30
44 Barry Larkin .20 .50
45 Pokey Reese .10 .30
46 Mike Mussina .20 .50
47 Hideo Nomo .30 .75
48 Rafael Palmeiro .20 .50
49 Adam Piatt .10 .30
50 Scott Rolen .20 .50
51 Gary Sheffield .10 .30
52 Bernie Williams .20 .50
53 Bob Abreu .10 .30
54 Edgardo Alfonzo .10 .30
55 Jermaine Clark RC .20 .50
56 Albert Belle .10 .30
57 Craig Biggio .20 .50
58 Andres Galarraga .10 .30
59 Edgar Martinez .20 .50
60 Fred McGriff .20 .50
61 Magglio Ordonez .10 .30
62 Jim Thome .20 .50
63 Matt Williams .10 .30
64 Kerry Wood .10 .30
65 Moises Alou .10 .30
66 Brady Anderson .10 .30
67 Garret Anderson .10 .30
68 Tony Armas Jr. .10 .30
69 Tony Batista .10 .30
70 Jose Cruz Jr. .10 .30
71 Carlos Beltran .10 .30
72 Adrian Beltre .10 .30
73 Kris Benson .10 .30
74 Lance Berkman .10 .30
75 Kevin Brown .10 .30
76 Jay Buhner .10 .30
77 Jeromy Burnitz .10 .30
78 Ken Caminiti .10 .30
79 Sean Casey .10 .30
80 Luis Castillo .10 .30
81 Eric Chavez .10 .30
82 Jeff Cirillo .10 .30
83 Bartolo Colon .10 .30
84 David Cone .10 .30
85 Freddy Garcia .10 .30
86 Johnny Damon .20 .50
87 Ray Durham .10 .30
88 Jermaine Dye .10 .30
89 Juan Encarnacion .10 .30
90 Terrence Long .10 .30
91 Carl Everett .10 .30
92 Steve Finley .10 .30
93 Cliff Floyd .10 .30
94 Brad Fullmer .10 .30
95 Brian Giles .10 .30
96 Luis Gonzalez .10 .30
97 Rusty Greer .10 .30
98 Jeffrey Hammonds .10 .30
99 Mike Hampton .10 .30
100 Orlando Hernandez .10 .30
101 Richard Hidalgo .10 .30
102 Geoff Jenkins .10 .30
103 Jacque Jones .10 .30
104 Brian Jordan .10 .30
105 Gabe Kapler .10 .30
106 Eric Karros .10 .30
107 Jason Kendall .10 .30
108 Adam Kennedy .10 .30
109 Byung-Hyun Kim .10 .30
110 Ryan Klesko .10 .30
111 Chuck Knoblauch .10 .30
112 Paul Konerko .10 .30
113 Carlos Lee .10 .30
114 Kenny Lofton .10 .30
115 Javy Lopez .10 .30
116 Tino Martinez .20 .50
117 Ruben Mateo .10 .30
118 Kevin Millwood .10 .30
119 Ben Molina .10 .30
120 Raul Mondesi .10 .30
121 Trot Nixon .10 .30
122 John Olerud .10 .30
123 Paul O'Neill .20 .50
124 Chan Ho Park .10 .30
125 Andy Pettitte .20 .50
126 Jorge Posada .20 .50
127 Mark Quinn .10 .30
128 Aramis Ramirez .10 .30
129 Mariano Rivera .30 .75
130 Tim Salmon .20 .50
131 Curt Schilling .10 .30
132 Richie Sexson .10 .30
133 John Smoltz .20 .50
134 J.T. Snow .10 .30
135 Jay Payton .10 .30
136 Shannon Stewart .10 .30
137 B.J. Surhoff .10 .30
138 Mike Sweeney .10 .30
139 Fernando Tatis .10 .30
140 Miguel Tejada .10 .30
141 Jason Varitek .30 .75
142 Greg Vaughn .10 .30
143 Mo Vaughn .10 .30
144 Robin Ventura UER .10 .30
Listed as playing for Yankees last 2 years
Also Bat and Throw information is wrong
145 Jose Vidro .10 .30
146 Omar Vizquel .20 .50
147 Larry Walker .10 .30
148 David Wells .10 .30
149 Rondell White .10 .30
150 Preston Wilson .10 .30
151 Brent Abernathy RR 3.00 8.00
152 Cory Aldridge RR RC 3.00 8.00
153 Gene Altman RR RC 3.00 8.00
154 Josh Beckett RR 4.00 10.00
155 W. Betemit RR RC 4.00 10.00
156 A.Pujols RR/500 RC 60.00 120.00
157 Joe Crede RR 4.00 10.00
158 Jack Cust RR 3.00 8.00
159 Ben Sheets RR/500 15.00 40.00
160 Alex Escobar RR 3.00 8.00
161 A. Hernandez RR RC 3.00 8.00
162 Pedro Feliz RR 3.00 8.00
163 Nate Frese RR RC 3.00 8.00
164 Carlos Garcia RR RC 3.00 8.00
165 Marcus Giles RR 3.00 8.00
166 Alexis Gomez RR RC 3.00 8.00
167 Jason Hart RR 3.00 8.00
168 Eric Hinske RR RC 4.00 10.00
169 Cesar Izturis RR 3.00 8.00
170 Nick Johnson RR 3.00 8.00
171 Mike Young RR 4.00 10.00
172 B. Lawrence RR RC 3.00 8.00
173 Steve Lomasney RR 3.00 8.00
174 Nick Maness RR 3.00 8.00
175 Jose Mieses RR RC 3.00 8.00
176 Greg Miller RR RC 3.00 8.00
177 Eric Munson RR 3.00 8.00
178 Xavier Nady RR 3.00 8.00
179 Blaine Neal RR RC 3.00 8.00
180 Abraham Nunez RR 3.00 8.00
181 Jose Ortiz RR 3.00 8.00
182 Jeremy Owens RR RC 3.00 8.00
183 Pablo Ozuna RR 3.00 8.00
184 Corey Patterson RR 3.00 8.00
185 Carlos Pena RR 3.00 8.00
186 Wily Mo Pena RR 3.00 8.00
187 Timo Perez RR 3.00 8.00
188 A. Pettyjohn RR RC 3.00 8.00
189 Luis Rivas RR 3.00 8.00
190 J. Melian RR RC 3.00 8.00
191 Wilken Ruan RR RC 3.00 8.00
192 D. Sanchez RR RC 3.00 8.00
193 Alfonso Soriano RR 4.00 10.00
194 Rafael Soriano RR RC 3.00 8.00
195 Ichiro Suzuki RR RC 30.00 60.00
196 Billy Sylvester RR RC 3.00 8.00
197 Juan Uribe RR RC 4.00 10.00
198 Eric Valent RR 3.00 8.00
199 C.Valderrama RR RC 3.00 8.00
200 Matt White RR RC 3.00 8.00
201 Alex Rodriguez FC 2.50 6.00
202 Barry Bonds FC 4.00 10.00
203 Cal Ripken FC 5.00 12.00
204 Chipper Jones FC 1.50 4.00
205 Derek Jeter FC 4.00 10.00
206 Troy Glaus FC 1.00 2.50
207 Frank Thomas FC 1.50 4.00
208 Greg Maddux FC 2.50 6.00
209 Ivan Rodriguez FC 1.00 2.50
210 Jeff Bagwell FC 1.00 2.50
211 Todd Helton FC 1.00 2.50
212 Ken Griffey Jr. FC 2.50 6.00
213 Manny Ramirez Sox FC 1.00 2.50
214 Mark McGwire FC 4.00 10.00
215 Mike Piazza FC 2.50 6.00
216 Pedro Martinez FC 1.00 2.50
217 Sammy Sosa FC 1.50 4.00
218 Tony Gwynn FC 2.00 5.00
219 Vladimir Guerrero FC 1.50 4.00
220 Nomar Garciaparra FC 2.50 6.00
NNO BB Best Coupon .75 2.00
NNO The Rookies Coupon .20 .50

2001 Donruss Stat Line Career

Randomly inserted into 2001 Donruss packs, this 220-card insert parallels the 2001 Donruss base set. Each card is individually serial numbered to a career stat of the given players. Please note that print runs are listed in our checklist. Exchange cards for Albert Pujols and Ben Sheets with a redemption deadline of May 1st, 2003 were seeded into packs. A special autographed version of Albert Pujols' Stat Line Career card was printed in response to an error in production whereby more Stat Line Career Pujols exchange cards were seeded into packs than the 154 copies intended for release. To honor their commitment to collectors redeeming the exchange card, Donruss had Pujols sign a special non-serial numbered version of the card and sent it out to collectors redeeming the exchange card. Cards with a print run of 25 or fewer are not priced due to market scarcity.

*1-150 P/R b/wn 251-400: 2.5X TO 6X
*1-150 P/R b/wn 201-250: 2.5X TO 6X
*1-150 P/R b/wn 151-200: 3X TO 8X
*1-150 P/R b/wn 121-150: 3X TO 8X
*1-150 P/R b/wn 81-120: 4X TO 10X
*1-150 P/R b/wn 66-80: 5X TO 12X
*1-150 P/R b/wn 51-65: 5X TO 12X
*1-150 P/R b/wn 36-50: 6X TO 15X
*1-150 P/R b/wn 26-35: 8X TO 20X
*201-220 P/R b/wn 251-400 .5X TO 1.2X
*201-220 P/R b/wn 201-250 .5X TO 1.2X
*201-220 P/R b/wn 151-200 .6X TO 1.5X
*201-220 P/R b/wn 121-150 .6X TO 1.5X
*201-220 P/R b/wn 81-120 .75X TO 2X
*201-220 P/R b/wn 36-50 1.25X TO 3X
NO PRICING ON QTY OF 25 OR LESS
151 B. Abernathy RR/22
152 Cory Aldridge RR/33 4.00 10.00
153 Gene Altman RR/351 .75 2.00
154 Josh Beckett RR/212 1.00 2.50
155 Wilson Betemit RR/15
156 Albert Pujols RR/154 125.00 200.00
156D Albert Pujols RR AU
157 Joe Crede RR/357 1.25 3.00
158 Jack Cust RR/66 2.00 5.00
159 Ben Sheets RR/159 6.00 15.00
159B Ben Sheets RR AU
160 Alex Escobar RR/45 3.00 8.00
161 A. Hernandez RR/86 2.00 5.00
162 Pedro Feliz RR/286 .75 2.00
163 Nate Frese RR/119 2.00 5.00
164 Carlos Garcia RR/106 2.00 5.00
165 Marcus Giles RR/320 .75 2.00
166 Alexis Gomez RR/34 4.00 10.00
167 Jason Hart RR/303 .75 2.00
168 Eric Hinske RR/332 1.00 2.50
169 Cesar Izturis RR/60 2.50 6.00
170 Nick Johnson RR/308 .75 2.00
171 Mike Young RR/37 5.00 12.00
172 B. Lawrence RR/281 .75 2.00
173 S. Lomasney RR/229 1.00 2.50
174 Nick Maness RR/25
175 Jose Mieses RR/265 .75 2.00
176 Greg Miller RR/328 .75 2.00
177 Eric Munson RR/3
178 Xavier Nady RR/1
179 Blaine Neal RR/296 .75 2.00
180 A. Nunez RR/38 3.00 8.00
181 Jose Ortiz RR/7
182 J. Owens RR/273 .75 2.00
183 Pablo Ozuna RR/333 .75 2.00
184 Corey Patterson RR/11
185 Carlos Pena RR/52 2.50 6.00
186 Wily Mo Pena RR/114 2.00 5.00
187 Timo Perez RR/49 3.00 8.00
188 A. Pettyjohn RR/20
189 Luis Rivas RR/310 .75 2.00
190 J. Melian RR/26 4.00 10.00
191 Wilken Ruan RR/215 1.00 2.50
192 D. Sanchez RR/19
193 A. Soriano RR/50 3.00 8.00
194 Rafael Soriano RR/13
195 Ichiro Suzuki RR/106 60.00 120.00
196 Billy Sylvester RR/11
197 Juan Uribe RR/157 1.25 3.00
198 Eric Valent RR/342 .75 2.00
199 Carlos Valderrama RR/13
200 Matt White RR/31 4.00 10.00

2001 Donruss Stat Line Season

Randomly inserted into 2001 Donruss packs, this 220-card insert parallels the 2001 Donruss base set. Each card is individually serial numbered to a season stat of the given players. Please note that the print runs are listed in our checklist. Exchange cards for Albert Pujols and Ben Sheets with a redemption deadline of May 1st, 2003 were seeded into packs. Autographed versions of Pujols and Sheets were made available due to an error in production whereby more than the stated amount of Stat Line Season cards for each player were produced. To honor their commitment to collectors - Donruss contracted with the two athletes to sign special non-serial numbered versions of their Stat Line Season card and sent them out to collectors that redeemed the exchange cards. Cards with a print run of 25 or fewer are not priced due to market scarcity.

*1-150 P/R b/wn 151-200: 3X TO 8X
*1-150 P/R b/wn 121-150: 3X TO 8X
*1-150 P/R b/wn 81-120: 4X TO 10X
*1-150 P/R b/wn 66-80: 5X TO 12X
*1-150 P/R b/wn 51-65: 5X TO 12X
*1-150 P/R b/wn 36-50: 6X TO 15X
*1-150 P/R b/wn 26-35: 8X TO 20X
*201-220 P/R b/wn 151-200 .6X TO 1.5X
*201-220 P/R b/wn 121-150 .6X TO 1.5X
*201-220 P/R b/wn 81-120 .75X TO 2X
*201-220 P/R b/wn 66-80 1X TO 2.5X
*201-220 P/R b/wn 36-50 1.25X TO 3X
*201-220 P/R b/wn 26-35 1.5X TO 4X
SEE BECKETT.COM FOR PRINT RUNS
NO PRICING ON QTY OF 25 OR LESS
151 B. Abernathy RR/130 1.50 4.00
152 Cory Aldridge RR/100 2.00 5.00
153 Gene Altman RR/6
154 Josh Beckett RR/61 2.50 6.00
155 Wilson Betemit RR/89 6.00 15.00
156 Albert Pujols RR/17
156B Albert Pujols RR AU 500.00 800.00
157 Joe Crede RR/5
158 Jack Cust RR/131 1.50 4.00
159 Ben Sheets RR/8
159B Ben Sheets RR AU 30.00 60.00
160 Alex Escobar RR/126 1.50 4.00
161 Adrian Hernandez RR/8
162 Pedro Feliz RR/2
163 Nate Frese RR/126 1.50 4.00
164 Carlos Garcia RR/14
165 Marcus Giles RR/133 1.50 4.00
166 Alexis Gomez RR/117 2.00 5.00
167 Jason Hart RR/31 4.00 10.00
168 Eric Hinske RR/20
169 Cesar Izturis RR/95 2.00 5.00
170 Nick Johnson RR/145 1.50 4.00
171 Mike Young RR/155 2.00 5.00
172 B. Lawrence RR/165 1.25 3.00
173 Steve Lomasney RR/8
174 Nick Maness RR/127 1.50 4.00
175 Jose Mieses RR/17
176 Greg Miller RR/10
177 Eric Munson RR/1
178 Xavier Nady RR/1
179 Blaine Neal RR/65 2.50 6.00
180 A. Nunez RR/51 2.50 6.00
181 Jose Ortiz RR/2
182 Jeremy Owens RR/16
183 Pablo Ozuna RR/8
184 Corey Patterson RR/2
185 Carlos Pena RR/117 2.00 5.00
186 Wily Mo Pena RR/10
187 Timo Perez RR/14
188 A. Pettyjohn RR/00 2.00 3.00
189 Luis Rivas RR/18
190 J. Melian RR/73 2.00 5.00
191 Wilken Ruan RR/165 1.25 3.00
192 D.Sanchez RR/121 1.50 4.00
193 Alfonso Soriano RR/2
194 Rafael Soriano RR/90 2.00 5.00
195 Ichiro Suzuki RR/153 50.00 100.00
196 Billy Sylvester RR/16
197 Juan Uribe RR/22
198 Eric Valent RR/22
199 C.Valderrama RR/137 1.50 4.00
200 Matt White RR/126 1.50 4.00

2001 Donruss 1999 Retro

Inserted into hobby packs at one per hobby pack, this 100-card insert features cards that Donruss would have released in 1999 had they been producing baseball cards at the time. The set is broken into tiers as follows: Base Veterans (1-80), and Short-printed Prospects (81-100) serial numbered to 1999. Please note that these cards have a 2001 copyright, thus, are listed under the 2001 products.

COMPLETE SET (100) 75.00 150.00
COMP.SET w/o SP's (80) 20.00 50.00
COMMON CARD (1-80) .25 .60
COMMON CARD (81-100) 2.00 5.00
1 Ken Griffey Jr. 1.00 2.50
2 Nomar Garciaparra 1.00 2.50
3 Alex Rodriguez 1.00 2.50
4 Mark McGwire 1.50 4.00
5 Sammy Sosa .60 1.50
6 Chipper Jones .60 1.50
7 Mike Piazza 1.00 2.50
8 Barry Larkin .40 1.00
9 Andruw Jones .40 1.00
10 Albert Belle .25 .60
11 Jeff Bagwell .40 1.00
12 Tony Gwynn .75 2.00
13 Manny Ramirez .40 1.00
14 Mo Vaughn .25 .60
15 Barry Bonds 1.50 4.00
16 Frank Thomas .60 1.50
17 Vladimir Guerrero .60 1.50
18 Derek Jeter 1.50 4.00
19 Randy Johnson .60 1.50
20 Greg Maddux 1.00 2.50
21 Pedro Martinez .40 1.00
22 Cal Ripken 2.00 5.00
23 Ivan Rodriguez .40 1.00
24 Matt Williams .25 .60
25 Javy Lopez .25 .60
26 Tim Salmon .40 1.00
27 Raul Mondesi .25 .60
28 Todd Helton .40 1.00
29 Magglio Ordonez .25 .60
30 Sean Casey .25 .60
31 Jeromy Burnitz .25 .60
32 Jeff Kent .25 .60
33 Jim Edmonds .25 .60
34 Jim Thome .40 1.00
35 Dante Bichette .25 .60
36 Larry Walker .25 .60
37 Will Clark .40 1.00
38 Omar Vizquel .40 1.00
39 Mike Mussina .40 1.00
40 Eric Karros .25 .60
41 Kenny Lofton .25 .60
42 David Justice .25 .60
43 Craig Biggio .40 1.00
44 J.D. Drew .25 .60
45 Rickey Henderson .60 1.50
46 Bernie Williams .40 1.00
47 Brian Giles .25 .60
48 Paul O'Neill .40 1.00
49 Orlando Hernandez .25 .60
50 Jason Giambi .25 .60
51 Curt Schilling .25 .60
52 Scott Rolen .40 1.00
53 Mark Grace .40 1.00
54 Moises Alou .25 .60
55 Jason Kendall .25 .60
56 Ray Lankford .25 .60
57 Kerry Wood .25 .60
58 Gary Sheffield .25 .60
59 Ruben Mateo .25 .60
60 Darin Erstad .25 .60
61 Troy Glaus .25 .60
62 Jose Canseco .40 1.00
63 Wade Boggs .40 1.00
64 Tom Glavine .40 1.00
65 Gabe Kapler .25 .60
66 Juan Gonzalez .25 .60
67 Rafael Palmeiro .40 1.00
68 Richie Sexson .25 .60
69 Carl Everett .25 .60
70 David Wells .25 .60
71 Carlos Delgado .25 .60
72 Eric Davis .25 .60
73 Shawn Green .25 .60
74 Andres Galarraga .25 .60
75 Edgar Martinez .40 1.00
76 Roberto Alomar .40 1.00
77 John Olerud .25 .60
78 Luis Gonzalez .25 .60
79 Kevin Brown .25 .60
80 Roger Clemens 1.25 3.00
81 Josh Beckett SP 3.00 8.00
82 Alfonso Soriano SP 3.00 8.00
83 Alex Escobar SP 2.00 5.00
84 Pat Burrell SP 2.00 5.00
85 Eric Chavez SP 2.00 5.00
86 Erubiel Durazo SP 2.00 5.00
87 Abraham Nunez SP 2.00 5.00
88 Carlos Pena SP 2.00 5.00
89 Nick Johnson SP 2.00 5.00
90 Eric Munson SP 2.00 5.00
91 Corey Patterson SP 2.00 5.00
92 Wily Mo Pena SP 2.00 5.00
93 Rafael Furcal SP 2.00 5.00
94 Eric Valent SP 2.00 5.00
95 Mark Mulder SP 2.00 5.00
96 Chad Hutchinson SP 2.00 5.00
97 Freddy Garcia SP 2.00 5.00
98 Tim Hudson SP 2.00 5.00
99 Rick Ankiel SP 2.00 5.00
100 Kip Wells SP 2.00 5.00

2001 Donruss 1999 Retro Stat Line Career

Randomly inserted into 1999 Retro packs, this 100-card insert parallels the 1999 Retro base set. Each card is individually serial numbered to a career stat of the given players. Please note that the print runs are listed in our checklist. Cards with a print run of 25 or fewer are not priced due to market scarcity.

*1-80 P/R b/wn 251-400: 1.25X TO 3X
*1-80 P/R b/wn 201-250: 1.25X TO 3X
*1-80 P/R b/wn 151-200: 1.5X TO 4X
*1-80 P/R b/wn 121-150: 1.5X TO 4X
*1-80 P/R b/wn 81-120: 2X TO 5X
*1-80 P/R b/wn 66-80: 2.5X TO 6X
*1-80 P/R b/wn 51-65: 2.5X TO 6X
*1-80 P/R b/wn 36-50: 3X TO 8X
*1-80 P/R b/wn 26-35: 4X TO 10X
81 Josh Beckett/13
82 Alfonso Soriano/113 1.50 4.00
83 Alex Escobar/181 1.00 2.50
84 Pat Burrell/303 .75 2.00
85 Eric Chavez/314 .75 2.00
86 Erubiel Durazo/147 1.25 3.00
87 Abraham Nunez/106 1.50 4.00
88 Carlos Pena/46 2.50 6.00
89 Nick Johnson/259 .75 2.00
90 Eric Munson/392 .75 2.00
91 Corey Patterson/117 1.50 4.00
92 Wily Mo Pena/247 .75 2.00
93 Rafael Furcal/137 1.25 3.00
94 Eric Valent/53 2.00 5.00
95 Mark Mulder/340 .75 2.00
96 Chad Hutchinson/2
97 Freddy Garcia/397 .75 2.00
98 Tim Hudson/17
99 Rick Ankiel/222 .75 2.00
100 Kip Wells/371 .75 2.00

2001 Donruss 1999 Retro Stat Line Season

Randomly inserted into 1999 Retro packs, this 100-card insert parallels the 1999 Retro base set. Each card is individually serial numbered to a season stat of the given players. Please note that the print runs are listed in our checklist. Cards with a print run of 25 or fewer are not priced due to market scarcity.

*1-80 P/R b/wn 251-400: 1.25X TO 3X
*1-80 P/R b/wn 201-250: 1.25X TO 3X
*1-80 P/R b/wn 151-200: 1.5X TO 4X
*1-80 P/R b/wn 121-150: 1.5X TO 4X
*1-80 P/R b/wn 81-120: 2X TO 5X
*1-80 P/R b/wn 66-80: 2.5X TO 6X
*1-80 P/R b/wn 51-65: 2.5X TO 6X
*1-80 P/R b/wn 36-50: 3X TO 8X
*1-80 P/R b/wn 26-35: 4X TO 10X
81 Josh Beckett/178 1.00 2.50
82 Alfonso Soriano/7
83 Alex Escobar/27 3.00 8.00
84 Pat Burrell/7
85 Eric Chavez/33 3.00 8.00
86 Erubiel Durazo/19
87 Abraham Nunez/95 1.50 4.00
88 Carlos Pena/319 .75 2.00
89 Nick Johnson/17
90 Eric Munson/16
91 Corey Patterson/22
92 Wily Mo Pena/7
93 Rafael Furcal/88 1.50 4.00
94 Eric Valent/13
95 Mark Mulder/113 1.50 4.00
96 Chad Hutchinson/51 2.00 5.00
97 Freddy Garcia/10
98 Tim Hudson/152 1.00 2.50
99 Rick Ankiel/12
100 Kip Wells/135 1.00 2.50

2001 Donruss 1999 Retro Diamond Kings

Randomly inserted into 1999 Retro packs, this 5-card insert set features the "Diamond King" cards that Donruss would have produced had they been producing baseball cards in 1999. Each card is individually serial numbered to 2500.

COMPLETE SET (5) 30.00 60.00
*STUDIO: .75X TO 2X BASIC RETRO DK
STUDIO PRINT RUN 250 SERIAL #'d SETS
1 Scott Rolen 4.00 10.00
2 Sammy Sosa 4.00 10.00
3 Juan Gonzalez 4.00 10.00
4 Ken Griffey Jr. 5.00 12.00
5 Derek Jeter 8.00 20.00

2001 Donruss 2000 Retro

Inserted into retail packs at one per retail pack, this 100-card insert features cards that Donruss would have released in 2000 had they been producing baseball cards at the time. The set is broken into tiers as follows: Base Veterans (1-80), and Short-printed Prospects (81-100) serial numbered to 2000. Please note that these cards have a 2001 copyright, thus, are listed under the 2001 products. Exchange cards originally intended for number 82 C.C. Sabathia and number 95 Ben Sheets were both issued in packs with an expiration date of 05/01/03. It's believed, however, two separate cards were made available for redemption card 95 ... Ben Sheets and Ichiro Suzuki. It's not known at this time exactly which player was featured on the exchange card number 82.

COMPLETE SET (100) 125.00 250.00
COMP.SET w/o SP's (80) 40.00 80.00
COMMON CARD (1-80) .25 .60
COMMON CARD (81-100) 2.00 5.00
SP * 82/95 WERE AVAIL.ONLY VIA MAIL
1 Vladimir Guerrero .60 1.50
2 Alex Rodriguez 1.00 2.50
3 Ken Griffey Jr. 1.00 2.50
4 Nomar Garciaparra 1.00 2.50
5 Mike Piazza 1.00 2.50
6 Mark McGwire 1.50 4.00
7 Sammy Sosa .60 1.50
8 Chipper Jones .60 1.50
9 Jim Edmonds .25 .60
10 Tony Gwynn .75 2.00
11 Andruw Jones .25 .60
12 Albert Belle .25 .60
13 Jeff Bagwell .40 1.00
14 Manny Ramirez .40 1.00
15 Mo Vaughn .25 .60
16 Barry Bonds 1.50 4.00
17 Frank Thomas .60 1.50
18 Ivan Rodriguez .40 1.00
19 Derek Jeter 1.50 4.00
20 Randy Johnson .60 1.50
21 Greg Maddux 1.00 2.50
22 Pedro Martinez .40 1.00
23 Cal Ripken 2.00 5.00
24 Mark Grace .40 1.00
25 Javy Lopez .25 .60
26 Ray Durham .25 .60
27 Todd Helton .40 1.00
28 Magglio Ordonez .25 .60
29 Sean Casey .25 .60
30 Darin Erstad .25 .60
31 Barry Larkin .40 1.00
32 Will Clark .40 1.00
33 Jim Thome .40 1.00
34 Dante Bichette .25 .60
35 Larry Walker .25 .60
36 Ken Caminiti .25 .60
37 Omar Vizquel .40 1.00
38 Miguel Tejada .25 .60
39 Eric Karros .25 .60
40 Gary Sheffield .25 .60
41 Jeff Cirillo .25 .60
42 Rondell White .25 .60
43 Rickey Henderson .60 1.50
44 Bernie Williams .40 1.00
45 Brian Giles .25 .60
46 Paul O'Neill .40 1.00
47 Orlando Hernandez .25 .60
48 Ben Grieve .25 .60
49 Jason Giambi .25 .60
50 Curt Schilling .25 .60
51 Scott Rolen .40 1.00
52 Bobby Abreu .25 .60
53 Jason Kendall .25 .60
54 Fernando Tatis .25 .60
55 Jeff Kent .25 .60
56 Mike Mussina .40 1.00
57 Troy Glaus .25 .60
58 Jose Canseco .40 1.00
59 Wade Boggs .40 1.00
60 Fred McGriff .25 .60
61 Juan Gonzalez .25 .60
62 Rafael Palmeiro .40 1.00
63 Rusty Greer .25 .60
64 Carl Everett .25 .60
65 David Wells .25 .60
66 Carlos Delgado .25 .60
67 Shawn Green .25 .60

68 David Justice .25 .60
69 Edgar Martinez .40 1.00
70 Andres Galarraga .25 .60
71 Roberto Alomar .40 1.00
72 Jermaine Dye .25 .60
73 John Olerud .25 .60
74 Luis Gonzalez .25 .60
75 Craig Biggio .40 1.00
76 Kevin Millwood .25 .60
77 Kevin Brown .25 .60
78 John Smoltz .40 1.00
79 Roger Clemens 1.25 3.00
80 Mike Hampton .25 .60
81 Tomas De La Rosa SP 2.00 5.00
82 C.C. Sabathia SP * 6.00 15.00
83 Ryan Christenson SP 2.00 5.00
84 Pedro Feliz SP 2.00 5.00
85 Jose Ortiz SP 2.00 5.00
86 Xavier Nady SP 2.00 5.00
87 Julio Zuleta SP 2.00 5.00
88 Jason Hart SP 2.00 5.00
89 Keith Ginter SP 2.00 5.00
90 Brent Abernathy SP 2.00 5.00
91 Timo Perez SP 2.00 5.00
92 Juan Pierre SP 2.00 5.00
93 Tike Redman SP 2.00 5.00
94 Mike Lamb SP 2.00 5.00
95A Ben Sheets SP * 6.00 15.00
95B Ichiro Suzuki SP * 20.00 50.00
96 Kazuhiro Sasaki SP 2.00 5.00
97 Barry Zito SP 3.00 8.00
98 Adam Bernero SP 2.00 5.00
99 Chad Durbin SP 2.00 5.00
100 Matt Ginter SP 2.00 5.00

2001 Donruss 2000 Retro Stat Line Career

Randomly inserted into 2000 Retro packs, this 100-card insert parallels the 2000 Retro base set. Each card is individually serial numbered to a career stat of the given players. Please note that the print runs are listed in our checklist. Cards issued to a stated print run of 25 or fewer are not priced due to market scarcity. Exchange cards were seeded into packs for cards 82 and 95. These cards were originally intended to be redeemed for C.C. Sabathia and Ben Sheets. It's since been discovered that Ichiro Suzuki cards were actually redeemed for card 95.

*1-80 P/R b/wn 251-400: 1.25X TO 3X
*1-80 P/R b/wn 201-250: 1.25X TO 3X
*1-80 P/R b/wn 151-200: 1.5X TO 4X
*1-80 P/R b/wn 121-150: 1.5X TO 4X
*1-80 P/R b/wn 81-120: 2X TO 5X
*1-80 P/R b/wn 66-80: 2.5X TO 6X
*1-80 P/R b/wn 51-65: 2.5X TO 6X
*1-80 P/R b/wn 36-50: 3X TO 8X
*1-80 P/R b/wn 26-35: 4X TO 10X
19 Derek Jeter/63 10.00 25.00
81 Tomas De La Rosa/76 2.00 5.00
82 C.C. Sabathia/6
83 Ryan Christenson/9
84 Pedro Feliz/45 2.00 5.00
85 Jose Ortiz/90 1.50 4.00
86 Xavier Nady/175 1.00 2.50
87 Julio Zuleta/295 .75 2.00
88 Jason Hart/19
89 Keith Ginter/188 1.00 2.50
90 Brent Abernathy/254 .75 2.00
91 Timo Perez/5
92 Juan Pierre/104 1.50 4.00
93 Tike Redman/151 1.00 2.50
94 Mike Lamb/240 .75 2.00
95 Ichiro Suzuki/159 10.00 25.00
96 Kazuhiro Sasaki/229 .75 2.00
97 Barry Zito/6
98 Adam Bernero/254 .75 2.00
99 Chad Durbin/3
100 Matt Ginter/300 .75 2.00

2001 Donruss 2000 Retro Stat Line Season

Randomly inserted into 2000 Retro packs, this 100-card insert parallels the 2000 Retro base set. Each card is individually serial numbered to a season stat of the given players. Please note that the print runs are listed in our checklist. Cards printed to a stated print run of 25 or fewer are not printed due to market scarcity. Exchange cards were seeded into packs for cards 82 and 95. These cards were originally intended to be redeemed for C.C. Sabathia and Ben Sheets. It's since been discovered that Ichiro Suzuki cards were actually redeemed for card 95.

*1-80 P/R b/wn 251-400: 1.25X TO 3X
*1-80 P/R b/wn 201-250: 1.25X TO 3X
*1-80 P/R b/wn 151-200: 1.5X TO 4X
*1-80 P/R b/wn 121-150: 1.5X TO 4X
*1-80 P/R b/wn 81-120: 2X TO 5X
*1-80 P/R b/wn 66-80: 2.5X TO 6X
*1-80 P/R b/wn 51-65: 2.5X TO 6X
*1-80 P/R b/wn 36-50: 3X TO 8X
*1-80 P/R b/wn 26-35: 4X TO 10X
19 Derek Jeter/37 12.50 30.00
81 Tomas De La Rosa/122 1.00 2.50
82 C.C. Sabathia/76 10.00 25.00
83 Ryan Christenson/56 2.00 5.00
84 Pedro Feliz/13
85 Jose Ortiz/107 1.50 4.00
86 Xavier Nady/23
87 Julio Zuleta/21
88 Jason Hart/168 1.00 2.50
89 Keith Ginter/13
90 Brent Abernathy/168 1.00 2.50
91 Timo Perez/4
92 Juan Pierre/187 1.00 2.50
93 Tike Redman/143 1.00 2.50
94 Mike Lamb/177 1.00 2.50
95 Ichiro Suzuki/8
96 Kazuhiro Sasaki/34 3.00 8.00
97 Barry Zito/97 1.50 4.00
98 Adam Bernero/80 2.00 5.00
99 Chad Durbin/3
100 Matt Ginter/66 2.00 5.00

2001 Donruss 2000 Retro Diamond Kings

Randomly inserted into 2000 Retro packs, this 5-card insert set features the "Diamond King" cards that Donruss would have produced had they been producing baseball cards in 2000. Each card is individually serial numbered to 2500. Card backs carry a "DK" prefix.

COMPLETE SET (5) 30.00 60.00
*STUDIO: .75X TO 2X BASIC RETRO DK
STUDIO PRINT RUN 250 SERIAL #'d SETS
DK1 Frank Thomas 4.00 10.00
DK2 Greg Maddux 5.00 12.00
DK3 Alex Rodriguez 5.00 12.00
DK4 Jeff Bagwell 4.00 10.00
DK5 Manny Ramirez 4.00 10.00

2001 Donruss 2000 Retro Diamond Kings Studio Series Autograph

An exchange card for an Alex Rodriguez autograph with a redemption deadline of May 1st, 2003 was randomly inserted in 2001 Donruss retro 2000 retail packs. The card is a signed version of A-Rod's basic Diamond King Studio Series insert and only 250 serial numbered copies were produced.

DK3 Alex Rodriguez 100.00 200.00

2001 Donruss All-Time Diamond Kings

Randomly inserted into 2001 Donruss packs, this 10-card insert features some of the greatest players to have ever grace the front of a "Diamond Kings" card. Card backs carry a "ATDK" prefix. There were 2500 serial numbered sets produced. The Willie Mays and Hank Aaron cards both packed out as exchange cards with a redemption deadline of May 1st, 2003. The Mays card was originally intended to be card number ATDK-9 within this set, but was erroneously numbered ATDK-1 (the same number as the Frank Robinson card) when it was sent out by Donruss. Thus, this set has two card #1's and no card #9.

COMPLETE SET (10) 75.00 150.00
*STUDIO: 1X TO 2.5X BASIC ALL-TIME DK
STUDIO PRINT RUN 200 SERIAL #'d SETS
STUDIO CARDS ARE SERIAL #'d 51-250
ATDK1 Willie Mays 10.00 25.00
ATDK1 Frank Robinson 4.00 10.00
ATDK2 Harmon Killebrew 5.00 12.00
ATDK3 Mike Schmidt 8.00 20.00
ATDK4 Reggie Jackson 4.00 10.00
ATDK5 Nolan Ryan 15.00 40.00
ATDK6 George Brett 8.00 20.00
ATDK7 Tom Seaver 4.00 10.00
ATDK8 Hank Aaron 10.00 25.00
ATDK10 Stan Musial 8.00 20.00

2001 Donruss All-Time Diamond Kings Studio Series Autograph

Randomly inserted into 2001 Donruss packs, this 10-card insert is a complete autographed parallel of the 2001 Donruss All-Time Diamond Kings. Card backs carry a "ATDK" prefix. Please note that the serial #ing for these cards is as follows: cards #'d 1/250 through 50/250 are from this Autograph set and cards #'d 51/250 to 250/250 are from the ATDK Studio Series (non-autographed set). Exchange cards with a redemption deadline of May 1st, 2003 were seeded into packs for Hank Aaron, Willie Mays and Nolan Ryan.

AU CARDS ARE #'d 1/250 TO 50/250
ATDK1 Willie Mays 150.00 250.00
ATDK1 Frank Robinson 40.00 80.00
ATDK2 Harmon Killebrew 75.00 150.00
ATDK3 Mike Schmidt 100.00 175.00
ATDK4 Reggie Jackson 60.00 120.00
ATDK5 Nolan Ryan 150.00 250.00
ATDK6 George Brett 125.00 200.00
ATDK7 Tom Seaver 50.00 100.00
ATDK8 Hank Aaron 150.00 250.00
ATDK10 Stan Musial 75.00 150.00

2001 Donruss Anniversary Originals Autograph

Each of these BGS graded cards were randomly inserted as box-toppers in boxes of 2001 Donruss. Unfortunately, exchange cards with a redemption deadline of May 1st, 2003 were seeded into packs for almost the entire set. Of the twelve cards featured in the set - only autograph cards for Tony Gwynn, David Justice and Ryne Sandberg actually made their way into packs. Since each card was signed to a different print run, we have included that information in our checklist.

82405 Cal Ripken/23
83277 Ryne Sandberg/24
83279 Cal Ripken/2
83586 Wade Boggs/25
83598 Tony Gwynn/24
84248 Don Mattingly/25
8736 Greg Maddux/25
8743 Rafael Palmeiro/250 30.00 60.00
87361 Barry Bonds/25
8834 Roberto Alomar/250 20.00 50.00
88644 Tom Glavine/250 30.00 60.00
8942 Randy Johnson/25
90704 David Justice/24

2001 Donruss Bat Kings

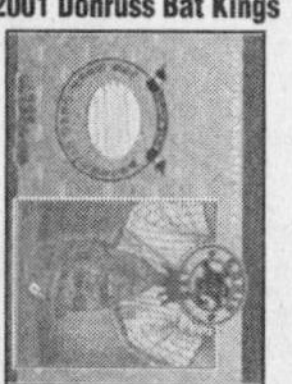

Randomly inserted into packs, this 10-card insert features swatches of actual game-used bat. Card backs carry a "BK" prefix. Each card is individually serial numbered to 200. An exchange card with a redemption deadline of May 1st, 2003 was seeded into packs for Hank Aaron.

BK1 Ivan Rodriguez 10.00 25.00
BK2 Tony Gwynn 15.00 40.00
BK3 Barry Bonds 40.00 80.00
BK4 Todd Helton 10.00 25.00
BK5 Troy Glaus 10.00 25.00
BK6 Mike Schmidt 30.00 60.00
BK7 Reggie Jackson 10.00 25.00
BK8 Harmon Killebrew 10.00 25.00
BK9 Frank Robinson 10.00 25.00
BK10 Hank Aaron 50.00 100.00

2001 Donruss Bat Kings Autograph

Randomly inserted into packs, this 10-card insert features swatches of actual game-used bat, as well as, an autograph from the depicted player. Card backs carry a "BK" prefix. Each card is individually serial numbered to 50. Exchange cards with a redemption deadline of May 1st, 2003 were seeded into packs for Barry Bonds, Troy Glaus, Todd Helton and Ivan Rodriguez. Unfortunately, Donruss was not able to get Barry Bonds to sign his Bat King cards - thus a non-autographed version of Bonds' card was sent out to collectors. Bonds did, however, agree to sign 100 of his vintage Donruss cards (1988 - 25 copies, 1989 -25 copies and 1990 - 50 copies). These 100 cards were stamped with a "Recollection Collection" logo and sent out to collectors - along with the unsigned Bonds Bat King card.

BK1 Ivan Rodriguez 60.00 120.00
BK2 Tony Gwynn 75.00 150.00
BK3 B.Bonds Bat NO AU 30.00 60.00
BK4 Todd Helton 50.00 100.00
BK5 Troy Glaus 50.00 100.00
BK6 Mike Schmidt 100.00 175.00
BK7 Reggie Jackson 60.00 120.00
BK8 Harmon Killebrew 75.00 150.00
BK9 Frank Robinson 150.00 250.00
BK10 Hank Aaron 175.00 300.00

2001 Donruss Diamond Kings Hawaii Promos

This card was given out to people who attended the 2001 Kit Young Hawaii Trade Conference. The card is gold-bordered and stamped with "Hawaii 2001" in gold lettering on the card front. Card back carries a "DK" prefix.

COMPLETE SET (1) 100.00 200.00
HDK1 Alex Rodriguez 4.00 10.00
Has 'Sample' stamped on back and "2001 Hawaii" stamp on card front.
HDK1 Alex Rodriguez 100.00 200.00

Has neither the 'Hawaii 2001' stamp or 'Sample' stamp on front.
HDK1 Alex Rodriguez 4.00 10.00
Does not have 'Sample' stamp on card back

2001 Donruss Diamond Kings

Randomly inserted into 2001 Donruss packs, this 20-card insert features players that are leaders on and off the baseball field. Card backs carry a "DK" prefix. Each card is individually serial numbered to 2500.

COMPLETE SET (20) 125.00 250.00
*STUDIO: .75X TO 2X BASIC DK
STUDIO NO AU PLAYER PRINT 250 #'d SETS
STUDIO AU PLAYER PRINT 200 #'d SETS
DK1 Alex Rodriguez 5.00 12.00
DK2 Cal Ripken 10.00 25.00
DK3 Mark McGwire 8.00 20.00
DK4 Ken Griffey Jr. 5.00 12.00
DK5 Derek Jeter 8.00 20.00
DK6 Nomar Garciaparra 5.00 12.00
DK7 Mike Piazza 5.00 12.00
DK8 Roger Clemens 6.00 15.00
DK9 Greg Maddux 5.00 12.00
DK10 Chipper Jones 4.00 10.00
DK11 Tony Gwynn 4.00 10.00
DK12 Barry Bonds 8.00 20.00
DK13 Sammy Sosa 4.00 10.00
DK14 Vladimir Guerrero 4.00 10.00
DK15 Frank Thomas 4.00 10.00
DK16 Troy Glaus 4.00 10.00
DK17 Todd Helton 4.00 10.00
DK18 Ivan Rodriguez 4.00 10.00
DK19 Pedro Martinez 4.00 10.00
DK20 Carlos Delgado 4.00 10.00

2001 Donruss Diamond Kings Studio Series Autograph

Randomly inserted into 2001 Donruss packs, this 11-card insert is a partial parallel of the 2001 Diamond Kings insert. Each of these autographed cards were serial numbered to 50. Exchange cards with a redemption deadline of May 1st, 2003 were seeded into packs for Barry Bonds, Roger Clemens, Troy Glaus, Vladimir Guerrero, Todd Helton, Chipper Jones, Alex Rodriguez and Ivan Rodriguez.

DK1 Alex Rodriguez 75.00 150.00
DK2 Cal Ripken 150.00 300.00
DK8 Roger Clemens 100.00 175.00
DK9 Greg Maddux 100.00 200.00
DK10 Chipper Jones 60.00 120.00
DK11 Tony Gwynn 60.00 120.00
DK12 Barry Bonds
DK14 Vladimir Guerrero 30.00 60.00
DK16 Troy Glaus 30.00 60.00
DK17 Todd Helton 50.00 100.00
DK18 I. Rodriguez EXCH 40.00 80.00

2001 Donruss Diamond Kings Reprints

Randomly inserted into 2001 Donruss packs, this 20-card insert features reprints of past "Diamond King" cards. Card backs carry a "DKR" prefix. Print runs are listed in our checklist. An exchange card with a redemption deadline of May 1st, 2003 was seeded into packs for Will Clark.

COMPLETE SET (20) 100.00 200.00
DKR1 Rod Carew/1982 4.00 10.00
DKR2 Nolan Ryan/1982 10.00 25.00
DKR3 Tom Seaver/1982 4.00 10.00
DKR4 Carlton Fisk/1982 4.00 10.00
DKR5 R.Jackson/1983 4.00 10.00
DKR6 S. Carlton/1983 4.00 10.00
DKR7 Johnny Bench/1983 4.00 10.00
DKR8 Joe Morgan/1983 4.00 10.00
DKR9 Mike Schmidt/1984 8.00 20.00
DKR10 Wade Boggs/1984 4.00 10.00
DKR11 Cal Ripken/1985 10.00 25.00
DKR12 Tony Gwynn/1985 5.00 12.00
DKR13 A.Dawson/1986 4.00 10.00
DKR14 Ozzie Smith/1987 6.00 15.00
DKR15 George Brett/1987 8.00 20.00
DKR16 D.Winfield/1987 4.00 10.00
DKR17 Paul Molitor/1988 4.00 10.00
DKR18 Will Clark/1988 6.00 15.00
DKR19 Robin Yount/1989 4.00 10.00
DKR20 K.Griffey Jr./1989 6.00 15.00

2001 Donruss Diamond Kings Reprints Autographs

Randomly inserted into 2001 Donruss packs, this 20-card insert features autographed reprints of past "Diamond King" cards. Card backs carry a "DKR" prefix. Print runs are listed below. Exchange cards with a redemption deadline of May 1st, 2003 were seeded into packs for Wade Boggs, Rod Carew, Steve Carlton, Will Clark, Andre Dawson, Carlton Fisk, Cal Ripken, Nolan Ryan, Ozzie Smith, Dave Winfield and Robin Yount. Ken Griffey Jr. had a card issued serial #'d of 89 copies but he was the only player featured in the set to not sign any of his cards.

DKR1 Rod Carew/82 20.00 50.00
DKR2 Nolan Ryan/82 100.00 200.00
DKR3 Tom Seaver/82 40.00 80.00
DKR4 Carlton Fisk/82 20.00 50.00
DKR5 Reggie Jackson/83 40.00 80.00
DKR6 Steve Carlton/83 15.00 40.00
DKR7 Johnny Bench/83 40.00 80.00
DKR8 Joe Morgan/83 20.00 50.00
DKR9 Mike Schmidt/84 75.00 150.00
DKR10 Wade Boggs/84 20.00 50.00
DKR11 Cal Ripken/85 125.00 250.00
DKR12 Tony Gwynn/85 50.00 100.00
DKR13 Andre Dawson/86 15.00 40.00
DKR14 Ozzie Smith/87 50.00 100.00
DKR15 George Brett/87 75.00 150.00
DKR16 Dave Winfield/87 20.00 50.00
DKR17 Paul Molitor/88 15.00 40.00
DKR18 Will Clark/88 20.00 50.00
DKR19 Robin Yount/89 40.00 80.00
DKR20 Ken Griffey Jr. 15.00 40.00
NO AU/89

2001 Donruss Elite Series

Randomly inserted into 2001 Donruss packs, this 20-card insert features many of the Major Leagues elite players. Card backs carry an "ES" prefix. Each card is individually serial numbered to 2500.

COMPLETE SET (20) 75.00 150.00
*DOMINATORS: 6X TO 15X BASIC ELITE
DOMINATORS PRINT RUN 25 SERIAL #'d SETS
ES1 Vladimir Guerrero 2.00 5.00
ES2 Cal Ripken 6.00 15.00
ES3 Greg Maddux 3.00 8.00
ES4 Alex Rodriguez 3.00 8.00
ES5 Barry Bonds 5.00 12.00
ES6 Chipper Jones 2.00 5.00
ES7 Derek Jeter 5.00 12.00
ES8 Ivan Rodriguez 1.50 4.00
ES9 Ken Griffey Jr. 3.00 8.00
ES10 Mark McGwire 5.00 12.00
ES11 Mike Piazza 3.00 8.00
ES12 Nomar Garciaparra 3.00 8.00
ES13 Pedro Martinez 1.50 4.00
ES14 Randy Johnson 2.00 5.00
ES15 Roger Clemens 4.00 10.00
ES16 Sammy Sosa 2.00 5.00
ES17 Tony Gwynn 2.50 6.00
ES18 Darin Erstad 1.50 4.00
ES19 Andruw Jones 1.50 4.00
ES20 Bernie Williams 1.50 4.00

2001 Donruss Jersey Kings

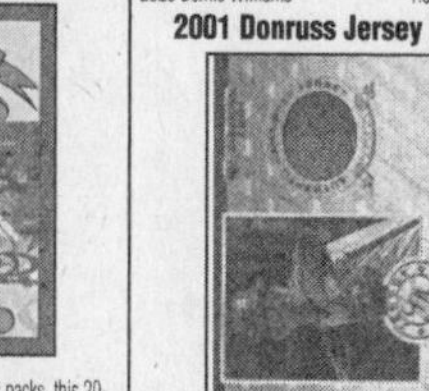

Randomly inserted into packs, this 10-card insert features swatches of actual game-used jerseys. Card backs carry a "JK" prefix. Each card is individually serial numbered to 250. Chipper Jones and Ozzie Smith were available only via mail redemption. Exchange cards with a redemption deadline of May 1st, 2003 for "to be determined" players were seeded originally into packs and many months passed before Chipper Jones and Ozzie Smith were revealed as the players that would be used to fulfill these cards.

JK1 Vladimir Guerrero 10.00 25.00
JK2 Cal Ripken 60.00 120.00
JK3 Greg Maddux 20.00 50.00
JK4 Chipper Jones 10.00 25.00
JK5 Roger Clemens 30.00 60.00
JK6 George Brett 20.00 50.00
JK7 Tom Seaver 10.00 25.00
JK8 Nolan Ryan 60.00 120.00
JK9 Stan Musial 30.00 60.00
JK10 Ozzie Smith 15.00 40.00

2001 Donruss Jersey Kings Autograph

Randomly inserted into packs, this 10-card insert features swatches of actual game-used jerseys, as well as, an autograph from the depicted player. Card backs carry a "JK" prefix. Each card is individually serial numbered to 50. The following players players did not return their cards in time for inclusion in packs: Vladimir Guerrero, Cal Ripken, Chipper Jones, Roger Clemens, Nolan Ryan and Ozzie Smith. Exchange cards with a redemption deadline of May 1st, 2003 were seeded into packs for these players.

JK1 Vladimir Guerrero 75.00 150.00
JK2 Cal Ripken 175.00 300.00
JK3 Greg Maddux 125.00 200.00
JK4 Chipper Jones 75.00 150.00
JK5 Roger Clemens 125.00 200.00
JK6 George Brett 125.00 200.00
JK7 Tom Seaver 50.00 100.00
JK8 Nolan Ryan 150.00 250.00
JK9 Stan Musial 125.00 200.00
JK10 Ozzie Smith 75.00 150.00

2001 Donruss Longball Leaders

Randomly inserted into packs, this 20-card insert features some of the Major Leagues top power hitters. Card backs carry a "LL" prefix. Each card is individually serial numbered to 1000.

COMPLETE SET (20) 75.00 150.00
LL1 Vladimir Guerrero 3.00 8.00
LL2 Alex Rodriguez 5.00 12.00
LL3 Barry Bonds 8.00 20.00
LL4 Troy Glaus 1.50 4.00
LL5 Frank Thomas 3.00 8.00
LL6 Jeff Bagwell 2.00 5.00
LL7 Todd Helton 2.00 5.00
LL8 Ken Griffey Jr. 5.00 12.00
LL9 Manny Ramirez Sox 2.00 5.00
LL10 Mike Piazza 5.00 12.00
LL11 Sammy Sosa 3.00 8.00
LL12 Carlos Delgado 1.50 4.00
LL13 Jim Edmonds 1.50 4.00
LL14 Jason Giambi 1.50 4.00
LL15 David Justice 1.50 4.00
LL16 Rafael Palmeiro 2.00 5.00
LL17 Gary Sheffield 1.50 4.00
LL18 Jim Thome 2.00 5.00
LL19 Tony Batista 1.50 4.00
LL20 Richard Hidalgo 1.50 4.00

2001 Donruss Production Line

Randomly inserted into packs, this 60-card insert features some of the Major League's most feared hitters. Card backs carry a "PL" prefix. Each card is individually serial numbered to one of three offensive categories: OBP, SLG, and PI. Print runs are listed in our checklist.

COMPLETE SET (60) 200.00 400.00
COMMON SLG (21-40) 1.25 3.00
COMMON PI (41-60) 1.00 2.50
*DIE CUT OBP 1-20: .75X TO 2X BASIC PL
*DIE CUT SLG 21-40: 1X TO 2.5X BASIC PL
*DIE CUT PI 41-60: 1.25X TO 3X BASIC PL
DIE CUT PRINT RUN 100 SERIAL #'d SETS
PL1 J.Giambi OBP/476 1.50 4.00
PL2 C.Delgado OBP/470 1.50 4.00
PL3 Todd Helton OBP/463 2.50 6.00
PL4 M.Ramirez Sox OBP/457 2.50 6.00
PL5 Barry Bonds OBP/440 10.00 25.00
PL6 G.Sheffield OBP/438 1.50 4.00
PL7 F.Thomas OBP/436 4.00 10.00
PL8 N.Garciaparra OBP/434 6.00 15.00
PL9 Brian Giles OBP/432 1.50 4.00
PL10 E.Alfonzo OBP/425 1.50 4.00
PL11 Jeff Kent OBP/424 1.50 4.00
PL12 J.Bagwell OBP/424 2.50 6.00
PL13 E.Martinez OBP/423 2.50 6.00
PL14 A.Rodriguez OBP/420 6.00 15.00
PL15 L.Castillo OBP/418 1.50 4.00
PL16 Will Clark OBP/418 2.50 6.00
PL17 J.Posada OBP/417 2.50 6.00
PL18 Derek Jeter OBP/416 10.00 25.00
PL19 Bob Abreu OBP/416 1.50 4.00
PL20 M.Alou OBP/416 1.50 4.00
PL21 T.Helton SLG/698 2.00 5.00
PL22 M.Ramirez Sox SLG/697 2.00 5.00
PL23 B.Bonds SLG/688 8.00 20.00
PL24 C.Delgado SLG/664 1.25 3.00
PL25 V.Guerrero SLG/664 3.00 8.00
PL26 J.Giambi SLG/647 1.25 3.00
PL27 G.Sheffield SLG/643 1.25 3.00
PL28 R.Hidalgo SLG/636 1.25 3.00
PL29 S. Sosa SLG/634 3.00 8.00
PL30 F. Thomas SLG/625 3.00 8.00
PL31 M. Alou SLG/623 1.25 3.00
PL32 J.Bagwell SLG/615 2.00 5.00
PL33 M. Piazza SLG/614 5.00 12.00
PL34 A. Rodriguez SLG/606 5.00 12.00
PL35 Troy Glaus SLG/604 1.25 3.00
PL36 N.Garciaparra SLG/599 5.00 12.00
PL37 Jeff Kent SLG/596 1.25 3.00
PL38 Brian Giles SLG/594 1.25 3.00
PL39 G. Jenkins SLG/588 1.25 3.00
PL40 Carl Everett SLG/587 1.25 3.00
PL41 Todd Helton PI/1161 1.50 4.00
PL42 M. Ramirez Sox PI/1154 1.50 4.00
PL43 C. Delgado PI/1134 1.00 2.50
PL44 Barry Bonds PI/1128 6.00 15.00
PL45 J.Giambi PI/1123 1.00 2.50
PL46 G.Sheffield PI/1081 1.00 2.50
PL47 V.Guerrero PI/1074 2.50 6.00
PL48 F.Thomas PI/1061 2.50 6.00
PL49 S.Sosa PI/1040 2.50 6.00
PL50 Moises Alou PI/1039 1.00 2.50
PL51 Jeff Bagwell PI/1039 1.50 4.00
PL52 N.Garciaparra PI/1033 4.00 10.00
PL53 R.Hidalgo PI/1027 1.00 2.50
PL54 A.Rodriguez PI/1026 4.00 10.00
PL55 Brian Giles PI/1026 1.00 2.50
PL56 Jeff Kent PI/1020 1.00 2.50
PL57 Mike Piazza PI/1012 4.00 10.00
PL58 Troy Glaus PI/1008 1.00 2.50
PL59 E.Martinez PI/1002 1.50 4.00
PL60 J.Edmonds PI/994 1.50 4.00

2001 Donruss Recollection Autographs

Two different players signed cards for this program. Barry Bonds and Alex Rodriguez each signed 100 total cards. The Rodriguez cards were randomly inserted in packs as exchange cards and the Bonds cards were issued as concessionary cards for collectors that redeemed a Bat Kings Autograph Bonds. According to representatives at Donruss, Bonds refused to sign the memorabilia bat cards, but did approve signing these Recollection buybacks. The exchange deadline for the Rodriguez cards was May 1st, 2003. The Rodriguez exchange cards that went into packs were numbered RC1-RC4, but the actual autograph cards are not numbered as such. For simplicity's sake we have kept the original RC1-RC4 checklisting.

BB1 Barry Bonds 88/25
BB2 Barry Bonds 89/25
BB3 Barry Bonds 90/50
RC1 Alex Rodriguez 97 Don Hit/10
RC2 Alex Rodriguez 98 Don/20
RC3 Alex Rodriguez 01 Retro/30 60.00 120.00
RC4 Alex Rodriguez 01 Don/40 60.00 120.00
RR25 Tom Glavine 88/6

2001 Donruss Rookie Reprints

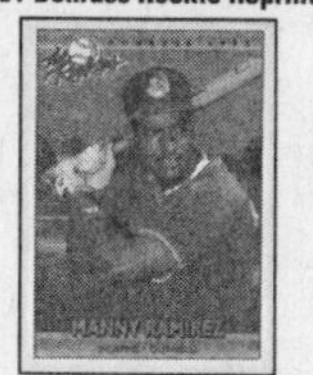

Randomly inserted into packs, this 40-card insert features reprinted Donruss rookie cards from the 80's-90s. Card backs carry a "RR" prefix. Please note that there was an error in production, and there are two number 39's, no number 40. Print runs are listed in our checklist.

COMPLETE SET (40) 150.00 300.00
RR1 Cal Ripken/1982 10.00 25.00
RR2 Wade Boggs/1983 2.00 5.00
RR3 Tony Gwynn/1983 5.00 12.00
RR4 Ryne Sandberg/1983 6.00 15.00
RR5 Don Mattingly/1984 10.00 25.00
RR6 Joe Carter/1984 2.00 5.00
RR7 Roger Clemens/1985 8.00 20.00
RR8 Kirby Puckett/1985 3.00 8.00
RR9 Orel Hershiser/1985 2.00 5.00
RR10 A.Galarraga/1986 2.00 5.00
RR11 Jose Canseco/1986 2.00 5.00
RR12 Fred McGriff/1986 2.00 5.00
RR13 Paul O'Neill/1986 2.00 5.00
RR14 Mark McGwire/1987 8.00 20.00
RR15 Barry Bonds/1987 8.00 20.00
RR16 Kevin Brown/1987 2.00 5.00
RR17 David Cone/1987 2.00 5.00
RR18 R.Palmeiro/1987 2.00 5.00
RR19 Barry Larkin/1987 2.00 5.00
RR20 Bo Jackson/1987 3.00 8.00
RR21 Greg Maddux/1987 5.00 12.00
RR22 R. Alomar/1988 2.00 5.00
RR23 Mark Grace/1988 2.00 5.00
RR24 David Wells/1988 2.00 5.00
RR25 Tom Glavine/1988 2.00 5.00
RR26 Matt Williams/1988 2.00 5.00
RR27 Ken Griffey Jr./1989 5.00 12.00
RR28 R. Johnson/1989 3.00 8.00
RR29 Gary Sheffield/1989 2.00 5.00
RR30 Craig Biggio/1989 2.00 5.00
RR31 Curt Schilling/1989 2.00 5.00
RR32 Larry Walker/1990 2.00 5.00
RR33 B. Williams/1990 2.00 5.00
RR34 Sammy Sosa/1990 3.00 8.00
RR35 Juan Gonzalez/1990 2.00 5.00

RR36 David Justice/1990 2.00 5.00
RR37 I.Rodriguez/1991 2.00 5.00
RR38 Jeff Bagwell/1991 2.00 5.00
RR39 Jeff Kent/1992 UER 2.00 5.00
Should have been RR40
RR39 M.Ramirez/1991 2.00 5.00

2001 Donruss Rookie Reprints Autograph

Randomly inserted into packs, this 26-card skip-numbered insert features autographed reprinted Donruss rookie cards from the 80's-90s. Card backs carry a "RR" prefix. Print runs are listed in our checklist. Nearly all of these cards packed out in the form of exchange cards - of which carried a May 1st, 2003 redemption deadline. Only autograph cards for Joe Carter, Tony Gwynn, David Justice, Greg Maddux and Ryne Sandberg actually made it into packs. Card RR24 was originally announced as a 1988 Donruss David Wells Reprint (with a print run of 88 copies) but due to contractual problems with the athlete the manufacturer substituted Diamondbacks outfielder Luis Gonzalez (reprinting 91 copies of his 1991 Donruss the Rookies RC).

RR1 Cal Ripken/82 125.00 200.00
RR2 W.Boggs/83 EXCH 30.00 60.00
RR3 Tony Gwynn/83 50.00 100.00
RR4 Ryne Sandberg/83 125.00 250.00
RR5 D.Mattingly/84 EXCH 60.00 120.00
RR6 Joe Carter/84 15.00 40.00
RR7 R.Clemens/85 EXCH 175.00 300.00
RR8 K.Puckett/85 EXCH 100.00 200.00
RR9 O.Hershiser/85 EXCH 30.00 60.00
RR10 A.Galarraga/86 EXCH 30.00 60.00
RR15 B.Bonds/87 EXCH 125.00 200.00
RR16 K. Brown/87 EXCH 15.00 40.00
RR17 D.Cone/87 EXCH 15.00 40.00
RR18 R.Palmeiro/87 EXCH 30.00 60.00
RR20 B.Jackson/87 EXCH 60.00 120.00
RR21 Greg Maddux/87 150.00 300.00
RR22 R.Alomar/88 EXCH 50.00 100.00
RR24 D.Wells/88 EXCH 15.00 40.00
RR25 T.Glavine/88 EXCH 20.00 50.00
RR28 R.Johnson/89 EXCH 100.00 175.00
RR29 G.Sheffield/89 EXCH 40.00 80.00
RR31 C.Schilling/89 EXCH 60.00 120.00
RR35 J.Gonzalez/90 EXCH 15.00 40.00
RR36 David Justice/90 15.00 40.00
RR37 I.Rodriguez/91 EXCH 30.00 60.00
RR39 M.Ramirez/92 EXCH 75.00 150.00

2001 Donruss Rookies

This 110-card redemption set was issued via coupons in the 2001 Donruss product. The coupons were issued in packs at a rate of 1:72 and were good for a complete factory sealed set of 2001 Donruss the Rookies. Collector's were to send the coupon along with $24.99 to Playoff by January 20th, 2002. The set also came with one additional Diamond King card (106-110).

COMP.FACT.SET (106) 60.00 100.00
COMP.SET w/o SP's (105) 30.00 60.00
R1 Adam Dunn .30 .75
R2 Ryan Drese RC .30 .75
R3 Bud Smith RC .15 .40
R4 Tsuyoshi Shinjo RC .30 .75
R5 Roy Oswalt .40 1.00
R6 Wilmy Caceres RC .20 .50
R7 Willie Harris RC .20 .50
R8 Andres Torres RC .15 .40
R9 Brandon Knight RC .15 .40
R10 Horacio Ramirez RC .30 .75
R11 Benito Baez RC .15 .40
R12 Jeremy Affeldt RC .20 .50
R13 Ryan Jensen RC .20 .50
R14 Casey Fossum RC .15 .40
R15 Ramon Vazquez RC .20 .50
R16 Dustan Mohr RC .15 .40
R17 Saul Rivera RC .20 .50
R18 Zach Day RC .20 .50
R19 Erik Hiljus RC .15 .40
R20 Cesar Crespo RC .15 .40
R21 Wilson Guzman RC .20 .50
R22 Travis Hafner RC 2.00 5.00
R23 Grant Balfour RC .15 .40
R24 Johnny Estrada RC .20 .50
R25 Morgan Ensberg RC .75 2.00
R26 Jack Wilson RC .30 .75
R27 Aubrey Huff .20 .50
R28 Endy Chavez RC .30 .75
R29 Delvin James RC .15 .40
R30 Michael Cuddyer .15 .40
R31 Jason Michaels RC .20 .50
R32 Martin Vargas RC .20 .50
R33 Donaldo Mendez RC .15 .40
R34 Jorge Julio RC .20 .50
R35 T.Spooneybarger RC .15 .40
R36 Kurt Ainsworth .15 .40
R37 Josh Fogg RC .20 .50
R38 Brian Reith RC .15 .40
R39 Rick Bauer RC .15 .40
R40 Tim Redding .15 .40
R41 Erick Almonte RC .15 .40
R42 Juan A.Pena RC .15 .40
R43 Ken Harvey .15 .40
R44 David Brous RC .15 .40
R45 Kevin Olsen RC .20 .50
R46 Henry Mateo RC .15 .40
R47 Nick Neugebauer .15 .40
R48 Mike Penney RC .20 .50
R49 Jay Gibbons RC .30 .75
R50 Tim Christman RC .15 .40
R51 B.Duckworth RC .15 .40
R52 Brett Jodie RC .15 .40
R53 Christian Parker RC .15 .40
R54 Carlos Hernandez .15 .40
R55 Brandon Larson RC .15 .40
R56 Nick Punto RC .20 .50
R57 Elpidio Guzman RC .15 .40
R58 Joe Beimel RC .15 .40
R59 Junior Spivey RC .30 .75
R60 Will Ohman RC .20 .50
R61 Brandon Lyon RC .15 .40
R62 Stubby Clapp RC .15 .40
R63 J.Duchscherer RC .20 .50
R64 Jimmy Rollins .20 .50
R65 David Williams RC .15 .40
R66 Craig Monroe RC 1.00 2.50
R67 Jose Acevedo RC .15 .40
R68 Jason Jennings .15 .40
R69 Josh Phelps .15 .40
R70 Brian Roberts RC .75 2.00
R71 Claudio Vargas RC .15 .40
R72 Adam Johnson .15 .40
R73 Bart Miadich RC .15 .40
R74 Juan Rivera .15 .40
R75 Brad Voyles RC .15 .40
R76 Nate Cornejo .15 .40
R77 Juan Moreno RC .20 .50
R78 Brian Rogers RC .15 .40
R79 R.Rodriguez RC .20 .50
R80 Geronimo Gil RC .15 .40
R81 Joe Kennedy RC .30 .75
R82 Kevin Joseph RC .20 .50
R83 Josue Perez RC .20 .50
R84 Victor Zambrano RC .30 .75
R85 Josh Towers RC .30 .75
R86 Mike Rivera RC .20 .50
R87 Mark Prior RC 2.00 5.00
R88 Juan Cruz RC .20 .50
R89 Dewon Brazelton RC .20 .50
R90 Angel Berroa RC .30 .75
R91 Mark Teixeira RC 4.00 10.00
R92 Cody Ransom RC .15 .40
R93 Angel Santos RC .15 .40
R94 Corky Miller RC .15 .40
R95 Brandon Berger RC .15 .40
R96 Corey Patterson UPD .15 .40
R97 A. Pujols UPD UER 20.00 50.00
Homers and RBI Stats wrong
R98 Josh Beckett UPD .30 .75
R99 C.C. Sabathia UPD .20 .50
R100 A. Soriano UPD .30 .75
R101 Ben Sheets UPD .30 .75
R102 Rafael Soriano UPD .20 .50
R103 Wilson Betemit UPD .75 2.00
R104 Ichiro Suzuki UPD 5.00 12.00
R105 Jose Ortiz UPD .15 .40

2001 Donruss Rookies Diamond Kings

Inserted one per Donruss Rookies set, these five cards feature some of the leading 2001 rookies in a special Diamond King format.

COMPLETE SET (5) 30.00 60.00
RDK1 C.C. Sabathia DK 3.00 8.00
RDK2 T.Shinjo DK 4.00 10.00
RDK3 Albert Pujols DK 30.00 60.00
RDK4 Roy Oswalt DK 4.00 10.00
RDK5 Ichiro Suzuki DK 10.00 25.00

2002 Donruss Samples

Issued one per sealed copy of Beckett Baseball Card Monthly issue number 204, this is a partial parallel to the 2002 Leaf Set. Only the first 150 cards of this set were issued in this format.

*SAMPLES: 1.5X TO 4X BASIC CARDS
ONE PER SEALED BBCM 204
*GOLD SAMPLES: 1.5X TO 4X LISTED PRICE

2002 Donruss

This 220 card set was issued in four card packs which had an SRP of $1.99 per pack and were issued 24 to a box and 20 boxes to a case. Cards numbered 151-200 featured leading rookie prospect and were inserted at stated odds of one in four. Card numbered 201-220 were Fan Club subset cards and were inserted at stated odds of one in eight.

COMPLETE SET (220) 60.00 150.00
COMP.SET w/o SP'S (150) 10.00 25.00
COMMON CARD (1-150) .10 .30
COMMON CARD (151-200) 1.25 3.00
COMMON CARD (201-220) .60 1.50
1 Alex Rodriguez .50 1.25
2 Barry Bonds .75 2.00
3 Derek Jeter .75 2.00
4 Robert Fick .10 .30
5 Juan Pierre .10 .30
6 Torii Hunter .10 .30
7 Todd Helton .20 .50
8 Cal Ripken 1.00 2.50
9 Manny Ramirez .20 .50
10 Johnny Damon .20 .50
11 Mike Piazza .50 1.25
12 Nomar Garciaparra .50 1.25
13 Pedro Martinez .20 .50
14 Brian Giles .10 .30
15 Albert Pujols .60 1.50
16 Roger Clemens .60 1.50
17 Sammy Sosa .30 .75
18 Vladimir Guerrero .30 .75
19 Tony Gwynn .40 1.00
20 Pat Burrell .10 .30
21 Carlos Delgado .10 .30
22 Tino Martinez .20 .50
23 Jim Edmonds .10 .30
24 Jason Giambi .10 .30
25 Tom Glavine .20 .50
26 Mark Grace .20 .50
27 Tony Armas Jr. .10 .30
28 Andruw Jones .20 .50
29 Ben Sheets .10 .30
30 Jeff Kent .10 .30
31 Barry Larkin .20 .50
32 Joe Mays .10 .30
33 Mike Mussina .20 .50
34 Hideo Nomo .30 .75
35 Rafael Palmeiro .20 .50
36 Scott Brosius .10 .30
37 Scott Rolen .20 .50
38 Gary Sheffield .10 .30
39 Bernie Williams .20 .50
40 Bob Abreu .10 .30
41 Edgardo Alfonzo .10 .30
42 C.C. Sabathia .10 .30
43 Jeremy Giambi .10 .30
44 Craig Biggio .20 .50
45 Andres Galarraga .10 .30
46 Edgar Martinez .20 .50
47 Fred McGriff .20 .50
48 Magglio Ordonez .10 .30
49 Jim Thome .20 .50
50 Matt Williams .10 .30
51 Kerry Wood .10 .30
52 Moises Alou .10 .30
53 Brady Anderson .10 .30
54 Garret Anderson .10 .30
55 Juan Gonzalez .10 .30
56 Bret Boone .10 .30
57 Jose Cruz Jr. .10 .30
58 Carlos Beltran .10 .30
59 Adrian Beltre .10 .30
60 Joe Kennedy .10 .30
61 Lance Berkman .10 .30
62 Kevin Brown .10 .30
63 Tim Hudson .10 .30
64 Jeromy Burnitz .10 .30
65 Jarrod Washburn .10 .30
66 Sean Casey .10 .30
67 Eric Chavez .10 .30
68 Bartolo Colon .10 .30
69 Freddy Garcia .10 .30
70 Jermaine Dye .10 .30
71 Terrence Long .10 .30
72 Cliff Floyd .10 .30
73 Luis Gonzalez .10 .30
74 Ichiro Suzuki .60 1.50
75 Mike Hampton .10 .30
76 Richard Hidalgo .10 .30
77 Geoff Jenkins .10 .30
78 Gabe Kapler .10 .30
79 Ken Griffey Jr. .50 1.25
80 Jason Kendall .10 .30
81 Josh Towers .10 .30
82 Ryan Klesko .10 .30
83 Paul Konerko .10 .30
84 Carlos Lee .10 .30
85 Kenny Lofton .10 .30
86 Josh Beckett .10 .30
87 Raul Mondesi .10 .30
88 Trot Nixon .10 .30
89 John Olerud .10 .30
90 Paul O'Neill .20 .50
91 Chan Ho Park .10 .30
92 Andy Pettitte .20 .50
93 Jorge Posada .20 .50
94 Mark Quinn .10 .30
95 Aramis Ramirez .10 .30
96 Curt Schilling .10 .30
97 Richie Sexson .10 .30
98 John Smoltz .20 .50
99 Wilson Betemit .10 .30
100 Shannon Stewart .10 .30
101 Alfonso Soriano .10 .30
102 Mike Sweeney .10 .30
103 Miguel Tejada .10 .30
104 Greg Vaughn .10 .30
105 Robin Ventura .10 .30
106 Jose Vidro .10 .30
107 Larry Walker .10 .30
108 Preston Wilson .10 .30
109 Corey Patterson .10 .30
110 Mark Mulder .10 .30
111 Tony Clark .10 .30
112 Roy Oswalt .10 .30
113 Jimmy Rollins .10 .30
114 Kazuhiro Sasaki .10 .30
115 Barry Zito .10 .30
116 Javier Vazquez .10 .30
117 Mike Cameron .10 .30
118 Phil Nevin .10 .30
119 Bud Smith .10 .30
120 Cristian Guzman .10 .30
121 Al Leiter .10 .30
122 Brad Radke .10 .30
123 Bobby Higginson .10 .30
124 Robert Person .10 .30
125 Adam Dunn .10 .30
126 Ben Grieve .10 .30
127 Rafael Furcal .10 .30
128 Jay Gibbons .10 .30
129 Paul LoDuca .10 .30
130 Wade Miller .10 .30
131 Tsuyoshi Shinjo .10 .30
132 Eric Milton .10 .30
133 Rickey Henderson .30 .75
134 Roberto Alomar .20 .50
135 Darin Erstad .10 .30
136 J.D. Drew .10 .30
137 Shawn Green .10 .30
138 Randy Johnson .30 .75
139 Austin Kearns .10 .30
140 Jose Canseco .20 .50
141 Jeff Bagwell .20 .50
142 Greg Maddux .50 1.25
143 Mark Buehrle .10 .30
144 Ivan Rodriguez .20 .50
145 Frank Thomas .30 .75
146 Rich Aurilia .10 .30
147 Troy Glaus .10 .30
148 Ryan Dempster .10 .30
149 Chipper Jones .30 .75
150 Matt Morris .10 .30
151 Marlon Byrd RR 1.25 3.00
152 Ben Howard RR RC 1.25 3.00
153 Brandon Backe RR RC 1.25 3.00
154 Jorge De La Rosa RR RC 1.25 3.00
155 Corky Miller RR 1.25 3.00
156 Dennis Tankersley RR 1.25 3.00
157 Kyle Kane RR RC 1.25 3.00
158 Justin Duchscherer RR 1.25 3.00
159 Brian Mallette RR RC 1.25 3.00
160 Chris Baker RR RC 1.25 3.00
161 Jason Lane RR 1.25 3.00
162 Hee Seop Choi RR 1.25 3.00
163 Juan Cruz RR 1.25 3.00
164 Rodrigo Rosario RR RC 1.25 3.00
165 Matt Guerrier RR 1.25 3.00
166 Anderson Machado RR RC 1.25 3.00
167 Geronimo Gil RR 1.25 3.00
168 Dewon Brazelton RR 1.25 3.00
169 Mark Prior RR 1.50 4.00
170 Bill Hall RR 1.25 3.00
171 Jorge Padilla RR RC 1.25 3.00
172 Jose Cueto RR RC 1.25 3.00
173 Allan Simpson RR RC 1.25 3.00
174 Doug Devore RR RC 1.25 3.00
175 Josh Pearce RR 1.25 3.00
176 Angel Berroa RR 1.25 3.00
177 Steve Bechler RR RC 1.25 3.00
178 Antonio Perez RR 1.25 3.00
179 Mark Teixeira RR 1.50 4.00
180 Erick Almonte RR 1.25 3.00
181 Orlando Hudson RR 1.25 3.00
182 Michael Rivera RR 1.25 3.00
183 Raul Chavez RR RC 1.25 3.00
184 Juan Pena RR 1.25 3.00
185 Travis Hughes RR RC 1.25 3.00
186 Ryan Ludwick RR 1.25 3.00
187 Ed Rogers RR 1.25 3.00
188 Andy Pratt RR RC 1.25 3.00
189 Nick Neugebauer RR 1.25 3.00
190 Tom Shearn RR RC 1.25 3.00
191 Eric Cyr RR 1.25 3.00
192 Victor Martinez RR 1.50 4.00
193 Brandon Berger RR 1.25 3.00
194 Erik Bedard RR 1.25 3.00
195 Fernando Rodney RR 1.25 3.00
196 Joe Thurston RR 1.25 3.00
197 John Buck RR 1.25 3.00
198 Jeff Deardorff RR 1.25 3.00
199 Ryan Jamison RR 1.25 3.00
200 Alfredo Amezaga RR 1.25 3.00
201 Luis Gonzalez FC .60 1.50
202 Roger Clemens FC 2.00 5.00
203 Barry Zito FC .60 1.50
204 Bud Smith FC .60 1.50
205 Magglio Ordonez FC .60 1.50
206 Kerry Wood FC .60 1.50
207 Freddy Garcia FC .60 1.50
208 Adam Dunn FC .60 1.50
209 Curt Schilling FC .60 1.50
210 Lance Berkman FC .60 1.50
211 Rafael Palmeiro FC .60 1.50
212 Ichiro Suzuki FC 2.00 5.00
213 Bob Abreu FC .60 1.50
214 Mark Mulder FC .60 1.50
215 Roy Oswalt FC .60 1.50
216 Mike Sweeney FC .60 1.50
217 Paul LoDuca FC .60 1.50
218 Aramis Ramirez FC .60 1.50
219 Randy Johnson FC 1.00 2.50
220 Albert Pujols FC 2.00 5.00

2002 Donruss Autographs

Inserted randomly in packs, these 19 cards feature signatures of players in the Fan Club subset. Since the cards have different stated print runs, we have listed those print runs in our checklist. Cards with a print run of 25 or fewer are not priced due to market scarcity.

201 Luis Gonzalez FC/25
202 Roger Clemens FC/25
203 Barry Zito FC/200 15.00 40.00
204 Bud Smith FC/200 10.00 25.00
205 Magglio Ordonez FC/200 10.00 25.00
206 Kerry Wood FC/200 15.00 40.00
207 Freddy Garcia FC/200 10.00 25.00
208 Adam Dunn FC/200 15.00 40.00
209 Curt Schilling FC/25
210 Lance Berkman FC/175 15.00 40.00
211 Rafael Palmeiro FC/25
213 Bob Abreu FC/200 10.00 25.00
214 Mark Mulder FC/200 10.00 25.00
215 Roy Oswalt FC/200 10.00 25.00
216 Mike Sweeney FC/200 10.00 25.00
217 Paul LoDuca FC/200 10.00 25.00
218 Aramis Ramirez FC/200 10.00 25.00
219 Randy Johnson FC/10
220 Albert Pujols FC/200 150.00 250.00

2002 Donruss Stat Line Career

Randomly inserted into packs, this is a parallel to the basic Donruss set. These cards feature cards printed on foil-board with silver holo-foil stamping. Each card has a stated print run to a unique career stat. Please note that is a card has a stated print run of 15 or less, no pricing is provided.

*1-150 P/R b/wn 251-400: 2.5X TO 6X
*1-150 P/R b/wn 201-250: 2.5X TO 6X
*1-150 P/R b/wn 151-200: 3X TO 8X
*1-150 P/R b/wn 121-150: 3X TO 8X
*1-150 P/R b/wn 81-120: 4X TO 10X
*1-150 P/R b/wn 66-80: 5X TO 12X
*1-150 P/R b/wn 51-65: 5X TO 12X
*1-150 P/R b/wn 36-50: 6X TO 15X
*201-220 P/R b/wn 251-400 .5X TO 1.2X
*201-220 P/R b/wn 201-250 .6X TO 1.5X
*201-220 P/R b/wn 151-200 .75X TO 2X
*201-220 P/R b/wn 121-150 1X TO 2.5X
*201-220 P/R b/wn 51-65 1.5X TO 4X
SEE BECKETT.COM FOR PRINT RUNS
151 Marlon Byrd RR/232 1.00 2.50
152 Ben Howard RR/283 .75 2.00
153 Brandon Backe RR/94 2.00 5.00
154 Jorge De La Rosa RR/54 2.50 6.00
155 Corky Miller RR/184 1.25 3.00
156 Dennis Tankersley RR/253 .75 2.00
157 Kyle Kane RR/179 1.25 3.00
158 Justin Duchscherer RR/11
159 Brian Mallette RR/273 .75 2.00
160 Chris Baker RR/270 .75 2.00
161 Jason Lane RR/302 .75 2.00
162 Hee Seop Choi RR/286 .75 2.00
163 Juan Cruz RR/322 .75 2.00
164 Rodrigo Rosario RR/313 .75 2.00
165 Matt Guerrier RR/280 .75 2.00
166 Anderson Machado RR/252 .75 2.00
167 Geronimo Gil RR/293 .75 2.00
168 Dewon Brazelton RR/335 .75 2.00
169 Mark Prior RR/303 1.25 3.00
170 Bill Hall RR/373 .75 2.00
171 Jorge Padilla RR/273 .75 2.00
172 Jose Cueto RR/156 1.25 3.00
173 Allan Simpson RR/204 1.00 2.50
174 Doug Devore RR/287 .75 2.00
175 Josh Pearce RR/315 .75 2.00
176 Angel Berroa RR/268 .75 2.00
177 Steve Bechler RR/25
178 Antonio Perez RR/143 1.50 4.00
179 Mark Teixeira RR/165 2.00 5.00
180 Erick Almonte RR/4
181 Orlando Hudson RR/283 .75 2.00
182 Michael Rivera RR/333 .75 2.00
183 Raul Chavez RR/253 .75 2.00
184 Juan Pena RR/293 .75 2.00
185 Travis Hughes RR/174 1.25 3.00
186 Ryan Ludwick RR/264 .75 2.00
187 Ed Rogers RR/270 .75 2.00
188 Andy Pratt RR/203 1.00 2.50
189 Nick Neugebauer RR/11
190 Tom Shearn RR/251 .75 2.00
191 Eric Cyr RR/161 1.25 3.00
192 Victor Martinez RR/305 1.25 3.00
193 Brandon Berger RR/313 .75 2.00
194 Erik Bedard RR/279 .75 2.00
195 Fernando Rodney RR/309 .75 2.00
196 Joe Thurston RR/284 .75 2.00
197 John Buck RR/271 .75 2.00
198 Jeff Deardorff RR/201 1.00 2.50
199 Ryan Jamison RR/273 .75 2.00
200 Alfredo Amezaga RR/290 .75 2.00

2002 Donruss Stat Line Season

Randomly inserted into packs, this is a parallel to the basic Donruss set. These cards feature cards printed on foil-board with silver holo-foil stamping. Each card has a stated print run to a unique seasonal stat. Please note that is a card has a stated print run of 15 or less, no pricing is provided.

*1-150 P/R b/wn 151-200: 3X TO 8X
*1-150 P/R b/wn 121-150: 3X TO 8X
*1-150 P/R b/wn 81-120: 4X TO 10X
*1-150 P/R b/wn 66-80: 5X TO 12X
*1-150 P/R b/wn 51-65: 5X TO 12X
*1-150 P/R b/wn 36-50: 6X TO 15X
*1-150 P/R b/wn 26-35: 8X TO 20X
*201-220 P/R b/wn 81-120 1.25X TO 3X
*201-220 P/R b/wn 66-80 1.5X TO 4X
*201-220 P/R b/wn 51-65 1.5X TO 4X
*201-220 P/R b/wn 36-50 2X TO 5X
*201-220 P/R b/wn 26-35 2.5X TO 6X
SEE BECKETT.COM FOR PRINT RUNS
NO PRICING ON QTY OF 25 OR LESS
151 Marlon Byrd RR/89 2.00 5.00
152 Ben Howard RR/29 4.00 10.00
153 Brandon Backe RR/39 3.00 8.00
154 Jorge De La Rosa RR/32 4.00 10.00
155 Corky Miller RR/7
156 Dennis Tankersley RR/30 4.00 10.00
157 Kyle Kane RR/75 2.50 6.00
158 Justin Duchscherer RR/20
159 Brian Mallette RR/94 2.00 5.00
160 Chris Baker RR/121 1.50 4.00
161 Jason Lane RR/38 3.00 8.00
162 Hee Seop Choi RR/45 3.00 8.00
163 Juan Cruz RR/39 3.00 8.00
164 Rodrigo Rosario RR/131 1.50 4.00
165 Matt Guerrier RR/118 2.00 5.00
166 Anderson Machado RR/36 3.00 8.00
167 Geronimo Gil RR/17
168 Dewon Brazelton RR/13
169 Mark Prior RR/14
170 Bill Hall RR/65 2.50 6.00
171 Jorge Padilla RR/66 2.50 6.00
172 Jose Cueto RR/62 2.50 6.00
173 Allan Simpson RR/77 2.50 6.00
174 Doug Devore RR/74 2.50 6.00
175 Josh Pearce RR/132 1.50 4.00
176 Angel Berroa RR/63 2.50 6.00
177 Steve Bechler RR/135 1.50 4.00
178 Antonio Perez RR/143 1.50 4.00
179 Mark Teixeira RR/20
180 Erick Almonte RR/8
181 Orlando Hudson RR/79 2.50 6.00
182 Michael Rivera RR/4
183 Raul Chavez RR/5
184 Juan Pena RR/106 2.00 5.00
185 Travis Hughes RR/86 2.00 5.00
186 Ryan Ludwick RR/103 2.00 5.00
187 Ed Rogers RR/54 2.50 6.00
188 Andy Pratt RR/132 1.50 4.00
189 Nick Neugebauer RR/5
190 Tom Shearn RR/136 1.50 4.00
191 Eric Cyr RR/131 1.50 4.00
192 Victor Martinez RR/57 4.00 10.00
193 Brandon Berger RR/16
194 Erik Bedard RR/137 1.50 4.00
195 Fernando Rodney RR/52 2.50 6.00
196 Joe Thurston RR/46 3.00 8.00
197 John Buck RR/73 2.50 6.00
198 Jeff Deardorff RR/100 2.00 5.00
199 Ryan Jamison RR/95 2.00 5.00
200 Alfredo Amezaga RR/37 3.00 8.00

2002 Donruss All-Time Diamond Kings

Randomly inserted in packs, these 10 cards feature legendary baseball superstars reproduced on conventional stock with bronze foil. These cards have a stated print run of 2,500 copies.

*STUDIO: 1X TO 2.5X BASIC ALL-TIME DK
STUDIO PRINT RUN 250 SERIAL #'d SETS
1 Ted Williams UER 6.00 15.00
Rogers Hornsby also won the triple crown twice
2 Cal Ripken 12.50 30.00
3 Lou Gehrig 6.00 15.00
4 Babe Ruth 10.00 25.00
5 Roberto Clemente 8.00 20.00
6 Don Mattingly 10.00 25.00
7 Kirby Puckett 4.00 10.00
8 Stan Musial 6.00 15.00
9 Yogi Berra 4.00 10.00
10 Ernie Banks 4.00 10.00

2002 Donruss Bat Kings

Randomly inserted in packs, these five cards feature a mix of active and retired superstars along with a sliver of each player's game-used bat. The active players have a stated print run of 250 copies while the retired players have a stated print run of 125 copies.

*STUDIO 1-3: .75X TO 2X BASIC BAT KING
STUDIO 1-3 PRINT RUN 50 SERIAL #'d SETS
STUDIO 4-5 PRINT RUN 25 SERIAL #'d SETS
1 Jason Giambi 6.00 15.00
2 Alex Rodriguez 10.00 25.00
3 Mike Piazza 10.00 25.00
4 Roberto Clemente/125 50.00 100.00
5 Babe Ruth/125 100.00 200.00

2002 Donruss Diamond Kings Inserts

Randomly inserted in packs, these 20 cards feature leading players with silver foil stamping and stated sequential serial numbering to 2500.

*STUDIO: .75X TO 2X BASIC DK'S
STUDIO PRINT RUN 250 SERIAL #'d SETS
1 Nomar Garciaparra 5.00 12.00
2 Shawn Green 4.00 10.00
3 Randy Johnson 4.00 10.00
4 Derek Jeter 8.00 20.00
5 Curt Schilling 4.00 10.00
6 Roger Clemens 6.00 15.00
7 Jeff Bagwell 4.00 10.00
8 Vladimir Guerrero 4.00 10.00
9 Luis Gonzalez 4.00 10.00
10 Mike Piazza 5.00 12.00
11 Ichiro Suzuki 6.00 15.00
12 Pedro Martinez 4.00 10.00
13 Todd Helton 4.00 10.00
14 Sammy Sosa 4.00 10.00
15 Ivan Rodriguez 4.00 10.00
16 Barry Bonds 8.00 20.00
17 Albert Pujols 6.00 15.00
18 Jim Thome 4.00 10.00
19 Alex Rodriguez 5.00 12.00
20 Jason Giambi 4.00 10.00

2002 Donruss Elite Series

Randomly inserted in packs, these 20 cards feature some of today's most storied performers. These cards are printed on metalized film board and are sequentially numbered to 2,500.

1 Barry Bonds 5.00 12.00
2 Lance Berkman 1.50 4.00
3 Jason Giambi 1.50 4.00
4 Nomar Garciaparra 3.00 8.00
5 Curt Schilling 1.50 4.00
6 Vladimir Guerrero 2.00 5.00
7 Shawn Green 1.50 4.00
8 Troy Glaus 1.50 4.00
9 Jeff Bagwell 1.50 4.00
10 Manny Ramirez 1.50 4.00
11 Eric Chavez 1.50 4.00
12 Carlos Delgado 1.50 4.00
13 Mike Sweeney 1.50 4.00
14 Todd Helton 1.50 4.00
15 Luis Gonzalez 1.50 4.00
16 Enos Slaughter LGD 1.50 4.00
17 Frank Robinson LGD 1.50 4.00
18 Bob Gibson LGD 1.50 4.00
19 Warren Spahn LGD 1.50 4.00
20 Whitey Ford LGD 1.50 4.00

2002 Donruss Elite Series Signatures

16 Enos Slaughter LGD/250 15.00 40.00
17 Frank Robinson LGD/250 30.00 60.00
18 Bob Gibson LGD/250 15.00 40.00
19 Warren Spahn LGD/250 30.00 60.00
20 Whitey Ford LGD/250 15.00 40.00

2002 Donruss Jersey Kings

Randomly inserted in packs, these 15 cards feature game-worn jersey swatches of a mix all-time greats and active superstars. The active players have a stated print run of 250 serial numbered sets while the retired players have a stated print run of 125 sets.

*STUDIO 1-12: .75X TO 2X BASIC JSY KINGS
STUDIO 1-12 PRINT RUN 50 SERIAL #'d SETS
STUDIO 13-15 PRINT RUN 25 SERIAL #'d SETS
STUDIO 13-15 TOO SCARCE TO PRICE
1 Alex Rodriguez 10.00 25.00
2 Jason Giambi 6.00 15.00
3 Carlos Delgado 6.00 15.00
4 Barry Bonds 15.00 40.00
5 Randy Johnson 10.00 25.00
6 Jim Thome 10.00 25.00
7 Shawn Green 6.00 15.00
8 Pedro Martinez 10.00 25.00
9 Jeff Bagwell 10.00 25.00
10 Vladimir Guerrero 10.00 25.00
11 Ivan Rodriguez 10.00 25.00
12 Nomar Garciaparra 10.00 25.00
13 Don Mattingly/125 15.00 40.00
14 Ted Williams/125 50.00 100.00
15 Lou Gehrig/125 125.00 200.00

2002 Donruss Longball Leaders

Randomly inserted in packs, these 20 cards feature the majors most powerful hitters and they are featured on metalized film board and have a stated print run of 1,000 sequentially numbered sets.

1 Barry Bonds 8.00 20.00
2 Sammy Sosa 3.00 8.00
3 Luis Gonzalez 1.50 4.00
4 Alex Rodriguez 5.00 12.00
5 Shawn Green 1.50 4.00
6 Todd Helton 2.00 5.00
7 Jim Thome 2.00 5.00
8 Rafael Palmeiro 2.00 5.00
9 Richie Sexson 1.50 4.00
10 Troy Glaus 1.50 4.00
11 Manny Ramirez 2.00 5.00
12 Phil Nevin 1.50 4.00
13 Jeff Bagwell 2.00 5.00
14 Carlos Delgado 1.50 4.00
15 Jason Giambi 1.50 4.00
16 Chipper Jones 3.00 8.00
17 Larry Walker 1.50 4.00
18 Albert Pujols 6.00 15.00
19 Brian Giles 1.50 4.00
20 Bret Boone 1.50 4.00

2002 Donruss Production Line

Randomly inserted in packs, these 60 cards feature the msot productive sluggers in three categories: On-Base Percentage, Slugging Percentage and OPS. Cards numbered 1-20 feature On-Base Percentage, while cards numbered 21-40 feature Slugging Percentage and cards numbered 41-60 feature OPS. Since all the cards have different stated print runs, we have listed that information next to the card in our checklist.

COMMON OBP (1-20) 1.50 4.00
COMMON SLG (21-40) 1.25 3.00
COMMON OPS (41-60) 1.00 2.50
*DIE CUT OBP 1-20: .75X TO 2X BASIC PL
*DIE CUT SLG 21-40: 1X TO 2.5X BASIC PL
*DIE CUT OPS 41-60: 1.25X TO 3X BASIC PL
DIE CUT PRINT RUN 100 SERIAL #'d SETS
DC's ARE 1ST 100 #'d OF EACH PLAYER
1 Barry Bonds OBP/415 10.00 25.00
2 Jason Giambi OBP/377 1.50 4.00
3 Larry Walker OBP/349 1.50 4.00
4 Sammy Sosa OBP/337 4.00 10.00
5 Todd Helton OBP/332 2.50 6.00
6 Lance Berkman OBP/330 1.50 4.00
7 Luis Gonzalez OBP/329 1.50 4.00
8 Chipper Jones OBP/327 4.00 10.00
9 Edgar Martinez OBP/323 2.50 6.00
10 Gary Sheffield OBP/317 1.50 4.00
11 Jim Thome OBP/316 2.50 6.00
12 Roberto Alomar OBP/315 2.50 6.00
13 J.D. Drew OBP/314 1.50 4.00
14 Jim Edmonds OBP/310 1.50 4.00
15 Carlos Delgado OBP/308 1.50 4.00
16 Manny Ramirez OBP/305 2.50 6.00
17 Brian Giles OBP/304 1.50 4.00
18 Albert Pujols OBP/303 8.00 20.00
19 John Olerud OBP/301 1.50 4.00
20 Alex Rodriguez OBP/299 6.00 15.00
21 Barry Bonds SLG/763 8.00 20.00
22 Sammy Sosa SLG/637 4.00 10.00
23 Luis Gonzalez SLG/588 1.25 3.00
24 Todd Helton SLG/685 2.00 5.00
25 Larry Walker SLG/562 1.25 3.00
26 Jason Giambi SLG/560 1.25 3.00
27 Jim Thome SLG/524 2.00 5.00
28 Alex Rodriguez SLG/522 5.00 12.00
29 Lance Berkman SLG/520 1.25 3.00
30 J.D. Drew SLG/513 1.25 3.00
31 Albert Pujols SLG/510 6.00 15.00
32 Manny Ramirez SLG/509 2.00 5.00
33 Chipper Jones SLG/505 3.00 8.00
34 Shawn Green SLG/498 1.25 3.00
35 Brian Giles SLG/490 1.25 3.00
36 Juan Gonzalez SLG/490 1.25 3.00
37 Phil Nevin SLG/488 1.25 3.00
38 Gary Sheffield SLG/483 1.25 3.00
39 Bret Boone SLG/478 1.25 3.00
40 Cliff Floyd SLG/478 1.25 3.00
41 Barry Bonds OPS/1278 6.00 15.00
42 Sammy Sosa OPS/1074 4.00 10.00
43 Jason Giambi OPS/1037 1.00 2.50
44 Todd Helton OPS/1017 1.50 4.00
45 Luis Gonzalez OPS/1017 1.00 2.50
46 Larry Walker OPS/1011 1.00 2.50
47 Lance Berkman OPS/950 1.00 2.50
48 Jim Thome OPS/940 1.50 4.00
49 Chipper Jones OPS/932 2.50 6.00
50 J.D. Drew OPS/927 1.00 2.50
51 Alex Rodriguez OPS/921 4.00 10.00
52 Manny Ramirez OPS/914 1.50 4.00
53 Albert Pujols OPS/913 5.00 12.00
54 Gary Sheffield OPS/900 1.00 2.50
55 Brian Giles OPS/894 1.00 2.50
56 Phil Nevin OPS/876 1.00 2.50
57 Jim Edmonds OPS/874 1.00 2.50
58 Shawn Green OPS/870 1.00 2.50
59 Cliff Floyd OPS/868 1.00 2.50
60 Edgar Martinez OPS/866 1.50 4.00

2002 Donruss Recollection Autographs

Randomly inserted in packs, these 47 cards feature players who signed repurchased copies of their original cards for inclusion in the 2002 Donruss set. Since each player signed a different amount of cards, we have noted that information in our checklist. Please note that due to market scarcity, not all cards can be priced.

8 Gary Carter 87/100 10.00 25.00
9 Gary Carter 89/100 10.00 25.00
11 Joe Carter 87/45
13 Andre Dawson 81/50
14 Andre Dawson 83/50
16 Andre Dawson 87/45
17 Dennis Eckersley 81/45
24 Steve Garvey 87/75 15.00 40.00
46 Tom Seaver 87/60
47 Don Sutton 87/200 10.00 25.00

2002 Donruss Rookie Year Materials Bats

Randomly inserted into packs, these four cards feature a sliver of a game-used bat from the player's rookie season which includes silver holo-foil and are sequentially numbered a stated print run of 250 sequentially numbered sets.

1 Barry Bonds 20.00 50.00
2 Cal Ripken 30.00 60.00
3 Kirby Puckett 10.00 25.00
4 Johnny Bench 15.00 40.00

2002 Donruss Rookie Year Materials Bats ERA

These cards parallel the "Rookie Year Material Bats" insert set. These cards have gold holo-foil and have a stated print run sequentially numbered to the player's debut year. Since those years are all different, we have notated that information in our checklist.

1 Barry Bonds/86 50.00 100.00
2 Cal Ripken/81 60.00 120.00
3 Kirby Puckett/84 25.00 50.00
4 Johnny Bench/68 40.00 80.00

2002 Donruss Rookie Year Materials Jersey

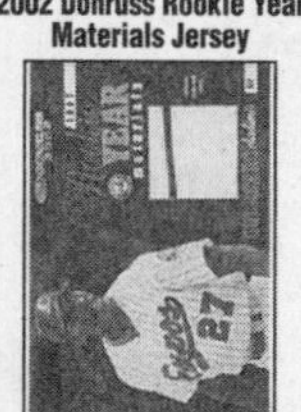

Randomly inserted into packs, these four cards feature a swatch of a game-used jersey from the player's rookie season which includes silver holo-foil and are sequentially numbered to a stated print run of either 250 or 50 sequentially numbered sets. The active players have the print run of 250 while the retired players have the print run of 50 sets.

1 Nomar Garciaparra 10.00 25.00
2 Randy Johnson 10.00 25.00
3 Ivan Rodriguez 10.00 25.00
4 Vladimir Guerrero 10.00 25.00
5 Stan Musial/50 40.00 80.00
6 Yogi Berra/50 40.00 80.00

2002 Donruss Rookie Year Materials Jersey Numbers

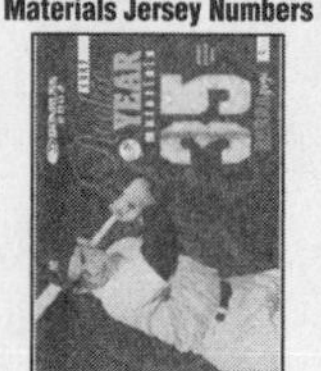

These cards parallel the "Rookie Year Material Jerseys" insert set. These cards have gold holo-foil and have a stated print run sequentially numbered to the player's jersey number his rookie season. We have notated that specific stated print information in our checklist.

1 Nomar Garciaparra/5
2 Randy Johnson/51
3 Ivan Rodriguez/7
4 Vladimir Guerrero/27
5 Stan Musial/6
6 Yogi Berra/35

2002 Donruss Rookies

This 110 card set was released in December, 2002. These cards were issued in five-card packs which came 24 packs to a box and 16 boxes to a case with an SRP of $3.29 per pack. This set features the top rookies and prospects of the 2002 season.

COMPLETE SET (110) 10.00 25.00
1 Kazuhisa Ishii RC .20 .50
2 P.J. Bevis RC .15 .40
3 Jason Simontacchi RC .15 .40
4 John Lackey .08 .25
5 Travis Driskill RC .15 .40
6 Carl Sadler RC .15 .40
7 Tim Kalita RC .15 .40
8 Nelson Castro RC .15 .40
9 Francis Beltran RC .15 .40
10 So Taguchi RC .20 .50
11 Ryan Bukvich RC .15 .40
12 Brian Fitzgerald RC .15 .40
13 Kevin Frederick RC .15 .40
14 Chone Figgins RC .60 1.50
15 Marlon Byrd .08 .25
16 Ron Calloway RC .15 .40
17 Jason Lane .15 .40
18 Satoru Komiyama RC .15 .40
19 John Ennis RC .15 .40
20 Juan Brito RC .15 .40
21 Gustavo Chacin RC .30 .75
22 Josh Bard RC .15 .40
23 Brett Myers .15 .40
24 Mike Smith RC .15 .40
25 Eric Hinske .08 .25
26 Jake Peavy .20 .50
27 Todd Donovan RC .15 .40
28 Luis Ugueto RC .15 .40
29 Corey Thurman RC .15 .40
30 Takahito Nomura RC .15 .40
31 Andy Shibilo RC .15 .40
32 Mike Crudale RC .15 .40
33 Earl Snyder RC .15 .40
34 Brian Tallet RC .15 .40
35 Miguel Asencio RC .15 .40
36 Felix Escalona RC .15 .40
37 Drew Henson .08 .25
38 Steve Kent RC .15 .40
39 Rene Reyes RC .15 .40
40 Edwin Almonte RC .15 .40
41 Chris Snelling RC .25 .60
42 Franklyn German RC .15 .40
43 Jeriome Robertson RC .15 .40
44 Colin Young RC .15 .40
45 Jeremy Lambert RC .15 .40
46 Kirk Saarloos RC .15 .40
47 Matt Childers RC .15 .40
48 Justin Wayne .08 .25
49 Jose Valverde RC .15 .40
50 Wily Mo Pena .15 .40
51 Victor Alvarez RC .15 .40
52 Julius Matos RC .15 .40
53 Aaron Cook RC .15 .40
54 Jeff Austin RC .15 .40
55 Adrian Burnside RC .15 .40
56 Brandon Puffer RC .15 .40
57 Jeremy Hill RC .15 .40
58 Jaime Cerda RC .15 .40
59 Aaron Guiel RC .15 .40
60 Ron Chiavacci .08 .25
61 Kevin Cash RC .15 .40
62 Elio Serrano RC .15 .40
63 Julio Mateo RC .15 .40
64 Cam Esslinger RC .15 .40
65 Ken Huckaby RC .15 .40
66 Will Nieves RC .15 .40
67 Luis Martinez RC .15 .40
68 Scotty Layfield RC .15 .40
69 Jeremy Guthrie RC .30 .75
70 Hansel Izquierdo RC .15 .40
71 Shane Nance RC .15 .40
72 Jeff Baker RC .40 1.00
73 Cliff Bartosh RC .15 .40
74 Mitch Wylie RC .15 .40
75 Oliver Perez RC .30 .75
76 Matt Thornton RC .15 .40
77 John Foster RC .15 .40
78 Joe Borchard .08 .25
79 Eric Junge RC .15 .40
80 Jorge Sosa RC .20 .50
81 Runelvys Hernandez RC .15 .40
82 Kevin Mench .08 .25
83 Ben Kozlowski RC .15 .40
84 Trey Hodges RC .15 .40
85 Reed Johnson RC .30 .75
86 Eric Eckenstahler RC .15 .40
87 Franklin Nunez RC .15 .40
88 Victor Martinez .30 .75
89 Kevin Gryboski RC .15 .40
90 Jason Jennings .08 .25
91 Jim Rushford RC .15 .40
92 Jeremy Ward RC .15 .40
93 Adam Walker RC .15 .40
94 Freddy Sanchez RC .75 2.00
95 Wilson Valdez RC .15 .40
96 Lee Gardner RC .15 .40
97 Eric Good RC .15 .40
98 Hank Blalock .20 .50
99 Mark Corey RC .15 .40
100 Jason Davis RC .15 .40
101 Mike Gonzalez RC .15 .40
102 David Ross RC .25 .60
103 Tyler Yates RC .15 .40
104 Cliff Lee RC 3.00 8.00
105 Mike Moriarty RC .15 .40
106 Josh Hancock RC .20 .50
107 Jason Beverlin RC .15 .40
108 Clay Condrey RC .15 .40
109 Shawn Sedlacek RC .15 .40
110 Sean Burroughs .08 .25

2002 Donruss Rookies Autographs

Randomly inserted into packs, this is a partial parallel to the Donruss Rookies set. Each players signed between 15 and 100 cards for insertion in this product and cards with a stated print run of 25 or fewer are not priced due to market scarcity.

1 Kazuhisa Ishii/25
2 P.J. Bevis/50 10.00 25.00
7 Tim Kalita/25
9 Francis Beltran/100 4.00 10.00
10 So Taguchi/15
13 Kevin Frederick/100 4.00 10.00
14 Chone Figgins/100 10.00 25.00
15 Marlon Byrd/100 4.00 10.00
17 Jason Lane/100 6.00 15.00
18 Satoru Komiyama/25
19 John Ennis/100 4.00 10.00
22 Josh Bard/100 4.00 10.00
25 Eric Hinske/100 4.00 10.00
28 Luis Ugueto/100 4.00 10.00
29 Corey Thurman/100 4.00 10.00
30 Takahito Nomura/100 10.00 25.00
33 Earl Snyder/100 4.00 10.00
34 Brian Tallet/100 4.00 10.00
36 Felix Escalona/25
37 Drew Henson/50 6.00 15.00
39 Rene Reyes/50 10.00 25.00
40 Edwin Almonte/50 10.00 25.00
41 Chris Snelling/50 12.50 30.00
42 Franklyn German/100 4.00 10.00
45 Jeremy Lambert/100 4.00 10.00
46 Kirk Saarloos/50 6.00 15.00
47 Matt Childers/100 4.00 10.00
50 Wily Mo Pena/100 6.00 15.00
51 Victor Alvarez/100 4.00 10.00
61 Kevin Cash/100 4.00 10.00
62 Elio Serrano/100 4.00 10.00
64 Cam Esslinger/100 4.00 10.00
69 Jeremy Guthrie/100 10.00 25.00
71 Shane Nance/100 4.00 10.00
72 Jeff Baker/100 10.00 25.00
75 Oliver Perez/25
76 Matt Thornton/100 4.00 10.00
78 Joe Borchard/100 4.00 10.00
79 Eric Junge/25
82 Kevin Mench/100 6.00 15.00
83 Ben Kozlowski/100 4.00 10.00
84 Trey Hodges/100 4.00 10.00
85 Reed Johnson/100 6.00 15.00
88 Victor Martinez/100 15.00 40.00
90 Jason Jennings/100 4.00 10.00
95 Wilson Valdez/100 4.00 10.00
97 Eric Good/100 4.00 10.00
98 Hank Blalock/100 6.00 15.00
104 Cliff Lee/100 75.00 150.00
110 Sean Burroughs/50 6.00 15.00

2002 Donruss Rookies Crusade

Randomly inserted into packs, these 50 cards, which were printed on metalized holo-foil board, were printed to a stated print run of 1500 serial numbered sets.

1 Corky Miller 1.50 4.00
2 Jack Cust 1.50 4.00
3 Erik Bedard 1.50 4.00
4 Andres Torres 1.50 4.00
5 Geronimo Gil 1.50 4.00
6 Rafael Soriano 1.50 4.00
7 Johnny Estrada 1.50 4.00
8 Steve Bechler 1.50 4.00
9 Adam Johnson 1.50 4.00
10 So Taguchi 1.50 4.00
11 Dee Brown 1.50 4.00
12 Kevin Frederick 1.50 4.00
13 Allan Simpson 1.50 4.00
14 Ricardo Rodriguez 1.50 4.00
15 Jason Hart 1.50 4.00
16 Matt Childers 1.50 4.00
17 Jason Jennings 1.50 4.00
18 Anderson Machado 1.50 4.00
19 Fernando Rodney 1.50 4.00
20 Brandon Larson 1.50 4.00
21 Satoru Komiyama 1.50 4.00
22 Francis Beltran 1.50 4.00
23 Joe Thurston 1.50 4.00
24 Josh Pearce 1.50 4.00
25 Carlos Hernandez 1.50 4.00
26 Ben Howard 1.50 4.00
27 Wilson Valdez 1.50 4.00
28 Victor Alvarez 1.50 4.00
29 Cesar Izturis 1.50 4.00
30 Endy Chavez 1.50 4.00
31 Michael Cuddyer 1.50 4.00
32 Bobby Hill 1.50 4.00
33 Willie Harris 1.50 4.00
34 Joe Crede 1.50 4.00
35 Jorge Padilla 1.50 4.00
36 Brandon Backe 1.50 4.00
37 Franklyn German 1.50 4.00
38 Xavier Nady 1.50 4.00
39 Raul Chavez 1.50 4.00
40 Shane Nance 1.50 4.00
41 Brandon Claussen 1.50 4.00
42 Tom Shearn 1.50 4.00
43 Freddy Sanchez 3.00 8.00
44 Chone Figgins 2.00 5.00
45 Cliff Lee 3.00 8.00
46 Brian Mallette 1.50 4.00
47 Mike Rivera 1.50 4.00
48 Elio Serrano 1.50 4.00
49 Rodrigo Rosario 1.50 4.00
50 Earl Snyder 1.50 4.00

2002 Donruss Rookies Crusade Autographs

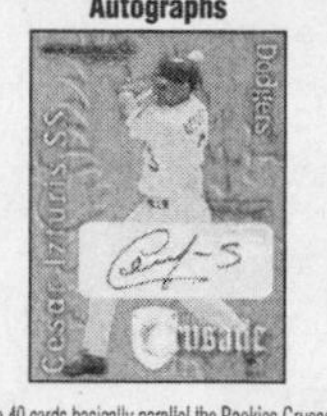

These 49 cards basically parallel the Rookies Crusade set. These cards were issued to a stated print run of anywhere from 15 to 500 copies per. Cards with a print run of 25 or fewer are not priced due to market scarcity.

COMMON CARD p/r 300+ 4.00 10.00
COMMON ROOKIE p/r 300+ 4.00 10.00
COMMON CARD p/r 150-250 4.00 10.00
COMMON CARD p/r 100 4.00 10.00
1 Corky Miller/500 4.00 10.00
2 Jack Cust/500 4.00 10.00
3 Erik Bedard/100 4.00 10.00
4 Andres Torres/500 4.00 10.00
5 Geronimo Gil/500 4.00 10.00
6 Rafael Soriano/500 4.00 10.00
7 Johnny Estrada/400 4.00 10.00
8 Steve Bechler/500 4.00 10.00
9 Adam Johnson/500 4.00 10.00
10 So Taguchi/15
11 Dee Brown/500 4.00 10.00
12 Kevin Frederick/150 4.00 10.00
13 Allan Simpson/150 4.00 10.00
14 Ricardo Rodriguez/500 4.00 10.00
15 Jason Hart/500 4.00 10.00
16 Matt Childers/150 4.00 10.00
17 Jason Jennings/500 4.00 10.00
18 Anderson Machado/500 4.00 10.00
19 Fernando Rodney/500 4.00 10.00
20 Brandon Larson/400 4.00 10.00
21 Satoru Komiyama/25
22 Francis Beltran/500 4.00 10.00
23 Joe Thurston/500 4.00 10.00
24 Josh Pearce/500 4.00 10.00
25 Carlos Hernandez/500 4.00 10.00
26 Ben Howard/500 4.00 10.00
27 Wilson Valdez/500 4.00 10.00
28 Victor Alvarez/500 4.00 10.00
29 Cesar Izturis/500 4.00 10.00
30 Endy Chavez/500 4.00 10.00
31 Michael Cuddyer/375 4.00 10.00
32 Bobby Hill/250 4.00 10.00
33 Willie Harris/300 4.00 10.00
34 Joe Crede/100 4.00 10.00
35 Jorge Padilla/475 4.00 10.00
36 Brandon Backe/350 6.00 15.00
37 Franklyn German/500 4.00 10.00
38 Xavier Nady/500 4.00 10.00
39 Raul Chavez/500 4.00 10.00
40 Shane Nance/500 4.00 10.00
41 Brandon Claussen/150 4.00 10.00
42 Tom Shearn/500 4.00 10.00
44 Chone Figgins/500 6.00 15.00
45 Cliff Lee/500 60.00 120.00
46 Brian Mallette/150 4.00 10.00
47 Mike Rivera/500 4.00 10.00
48 Elio Serrano/500 4.00 10.00
49 Rodrigo Rosario/100 4.00 10.00
50 Earl Snyder/100 4.00 10.00

2002 Donruss Rookies Phenoms

Randomly inserted into packs, these 25 cards, which are set on shimmering double rainbow holo-foil board were sequentially numbered to 1000 serial numbered sets.

1 Kazuhisa Ishii 2.00 5.00
2 Eric Hinske 2.00 5.00
3 Jason Lane 2.00 5.00
4 Victor Martinez 3.00 8.00
5 Mark Prior 2.00 5.00
6 Antonio Perez 2.00 5.00
7 John Buck 2.00 5.00
8 Joe Borchard 2.00 5.00
9 Alexis Gomez 2.00 5.00
10 Sean Burroughs 2.00 5.00
11 Carlos Pena 2.00 5.00
12 Bill Hall 2.00 5.00
13 Alfredo Amezaga 2.00 5.00
14 Ed Rogers 2.00 5.00
15 Mark Teixeira 3.00 8.00
16 Chris Snelling 2.50 6.00
17 Nick Johnson 2.00 5.00
18 Angel Berroa 2.00 5.00
19 Orlando Hudson 2.00 5.00
20 Drew Henson 2.00 5.00
21 Austin Kearns 2.00 5.00
22 Dewon Brazelton 2.00 5.00
23 Dennis Tankersley 2.00 5.00
24 Josh Beckett 2.00 5.00
25 Marlon Byrd 2.00 5.00

2002 Donruss Rookies Phenoms Autographs

These cards parallel the Phenoms insert set. Each of these cards were issued to a stated print run of between 25 and 500 signed copies. As the Ishii was produced to a stated print run of 25 sets, no pricing is provided for that card.

COMMON CARD p/r 300+ 4.00 10.00
COMMON CARD p/r 150-250 4.00 10.00
1 Kazuhisa Ishii/25
2 Eric Hinske/500 4.00 10.00
3 Jason Lane/500 6.00 15.00
4 Victor Martinez/225 10.00 25.00
5 Mark Prior/100 10.00 25.00
6 Antonio Perez/500 4.00 10.00
7 John Buck/100 4.00 10.00
8 Joe Borchard/100 4.00 10.00
9 Alexis Gomez/400 4.00 10.00
10 Sean Burroughs/150 4.00 10.00
11 Carlos Pena/150 4.00 10.00
12 Bill Hall/200 6.00 15.00
13 Alfredo Amezaga/500 4.00 10.00
14 Ed Rogers/500 4.00 10.00
15 Mark Teixeira/100 15.00 40.00
16 Chris Snelling/100 8.00 20.00
17 Nick Johnson/250 6.00 15.00
18 Angel Berroa/500 4.00 10.00
19 Orlando Hudson/400 4.00 10.00
20 Drew Henson/500 4.00 10.00
21 Austin Kearns/75 4.00 10.00
22 Dewon Brazelton/350 4.00 10.00
23 Dennis Tankersley/500 4.00 10.00
24 Josh Beckett/125 10.00 25.00
25 Marlon Byrd/500 4.00 10.00

2003 Donruss Samples

Issued as a one per in an issue of Beckett Baseball Card Monthly, these cards previewed the 2003 Donruss set. These cards have the word sample printed in silver on the back.

*SAMPLES: 1.5X TO 4X BASIC CARDS
ONE PER BBCM MAGAZINE

2003 Donruss

This 400 card set was released in December, 2002. The set was issued in 13 card packs with an SRP of $2.29 which were packed 24 packs to a box and 20 boxes to a case. Subsets in this set include cards numbered Diamond Kings (1-20) and Rated Rookies (21-70). For the first time since Donruss/Playoff returned to card production, this was a baseball set without short printed base cards.

COMPLETE SET (400) 25.00 50.00
COMMON CARD (71-400) .10 .30
COMMON CARD (1-20) .20 .50
COMMON CARD (21-70) .20 .50
1 Vladimir Guerrero DK .30 .75
2 Derek Jeter DK .75 2.00
3 Adam Dunn DK .20 .50
4 Greg Maddux DK .50 1.25
5 Lance Berkman DK .20 .50
6 Ichiro Suzuki DK .60 1.50
7 Mike Piazza DK .50 1.25
8 Alex Rodriguez DK .50 1.25
9 Tom Glavine DK .20 .50
10 Randy Johnson DK .30 .75
11 Nomar Garciaparra DK .50 1.25
12 Jason Giambi DK .20 .50
13 Sammy Sosa DK .30 .75
14 Barry Zito DK .20 .50
15 Chipper Jones DK .30 .75
16 Magglio Ordonez DK .20 .50
17 Larry Walker DK .20 .50
18 Alfonso Soriano DK .20 .50
19 Curt Schilling DK .20 .50
20 Barry Bonds DK .75 2.00
21 Joe Borchard RR .20 .50
22 Chris Snelling RR .20 .50
23 Brian Tallet RR .20 .50
24 Cliff Lee RR 1.25 3.00
25 Freddy Sanchez RR .20 .50
26 Chone Figgins RR .20 .50
27 Kevin Cash RR .20 .50
28 Josh Bard RR .20 .50
29 Jeriome Robertson RR .20 .50
30 Jeremy Hill RR .20 .50
31 Shane Nance RR .20 .50
32 Jake Peavy RR .20 .50
33 Trey Hodges RR .20 .50
34 Eric Eckenstahler RR .20 .50
35 Jim Rushford RR .20 .50
36 Oliver Perez RR .20 .50
37 Kirk Saarloos RR .20 .50
38 Hank Blalock RR .20 .50
39 Francisco Rodriguez RR .20 .50
40 Runelvys Hernandez RR .20 .50
41 Aaron Cook RR .20 .50
42 Josh Hancock RR .20 .50
43 P.J. Bevis RR .20 .50
44 Jon Adkins RR .20 .50
45 Tim Kalita RR .20 .50
46 Nelson Castro RR .20 .50
47 Colin Young RR .20 .50
48 Adrian Burnside RR .20 .50
49 Luis Martinez RR .20 .50
50 Pete Zamora RR .20 .50
51 Todd Donovan RR .20 .50
52 Jeremy Ward RR .20 .50
53 Wilson Valdez RR .20 .50
54 Eric Good RR .20 .50
55 Jeff Baker RR .20 .50
56 Mitch Wylie RR .20 .50
57 Ron Calloway RR .20 .50
58 Jose Valverde RR .20 .50
59 Jason Davis RR .20 .50
60 Scotty Layfield RR .20 .50
61 Matt Thornton RR .20 .50
62 Adam Walker RR .20 .50
63 Gustavo Chacin RR .20 .50
64 Ron Chiavacci RR .20 .50
65 Wiki Nieves RR .20 .50
66 Cliff Bartosh RR .20 .50
67 Mike Gonzalez RR .20 .50
68 Justin Wayne RR .20 .50
69 Eric Junge RR .20 .50
70 Ben Kozlowski RR .20 .50
71 Darin Erstad .10 .30
72 Garret Anderson .10 .30
73 Troy Glaus .10 .30
74 David Eckstein .10 .30
75 Adam Kennedy .10 .30
76 Kevin Appier .10 .30
77 Jarrod Washburn .10 .30
78 Scott Spiezio .10 .30
79 Tim Salmon .10 .30
80 Ramon Ortiz .10 .30
81 Bengie Molina .10 .30
82 Brad Fullmer .10 .30
83 Troy Percival .10 .30
84 David Segui .10 .30
85 Jay Gibbons .10 .30
86 Tony Batista .10 .30
87 Scott Erickson .10 .30
88 Jeff Conine .10 .30
89 Melvin Mora .10 .30
90 Buddy Groom .10 .30
91 Rodrigo Lopez .10 .30
92 Marty Cordova .10 .30
93 Geronimo Gil .10 .30
94 Kenny Lofton .10 .30
95 Shea Hillenbrand .10 .30
96 Manny Ramirez .20 .50
97 Pedro Martinez .20 .50
98 Nomar Garciaparra .50 1.25
99 Rickey Henderson .30 .75
100 Johnny Damon .20 .50
101 Trot Nixon .10 .30
102 Derek Lowe .10 .30
103 Hee Seop Choi .10 .30
104 Mark Teixeira .20 .50
105 Tim Wakefield .10 .30
106 Jason Varitek .30 .75
107 Frank Thomas .30 .75
108 Joe Crede .10 .30
109 Magglio Ordonez .10 .30
110 Ray Durham .10 .30
111 Mark Buehrle .10 .30
112 Paul Konerko .10 .30
113 Jose Valentin .10 .30
114 Carlos Lee .10 .30
115 Royce Clayton .10 .30
116 C.C. Sabathia .10 .30
117 Ellis Burks .10 .30
118 Omar Vizquel .20 .50
119 Jim Thome .20 .50
120 Matt Lawton .10 .30
121 Travis Fryman .10 .30
122 Earl Snyder .10 .30
123 Ricky Gutierrez .10 .30
124 Einar Diaz .10 .30
125 Danys Baez .10 .30
126 Robert Fick .10 .30
127 Bobby Higginson .10 .30
128 Steve Sparks .10 .30
129 Mike Rivera .10 .30
130 Wendell Magee .10 .30
131 Randall Simon .10 .30
132 Carlos Pena .10 .30
133 Mark Redman .10 .30
134 Juan Acevedo .10 .30
135 Mike Sweeney .10 .30
136 Aaron Guiel .10 .30
137 Carlos Beltran .10 .30
138 Joe Randa .10 .30
139 Paul Byrd .10 .30
140 Shawn Sedlacek .10 .30
141 Raul Ibanez .10 .30
142 Michael Tucker .10 .30
143 Torii Hunter .10 .30
144 Jacque Jones .10 .30
145 David Ortiz .30 .75
146 Corey Koskie .10 .30
147 Brad Radke .10 .30
148 Doug Mientkiewicz .10 .30
149 A.J. Pierzynski .10 .30
150 Dustan Mohr .10 .30
151 Michael Cuddyer .10 .30
152 Eddie Guardado .10 .30
153 Cristian Guzman .10 .30
154 Derek Jeter .75 2.00
155 Bernie Williams .20 .50
156 Roger Clemens .60 1.50
157 Mike Mussina .20 .50
158 Jorge Posada .20 .50
159 Alfonso Soriano .10 .30
160 Jason Giambi .10 .30
161 Robin Ventura .10 .30
162 Andy Pettitte .20 .50
163 David Wells .10 .30
164 Nick Johnson .10 .30
165 Jeff Weaver .10 .30
166 Raul Mondesi .10 .30

167 Rondell White .10 .30
168 Tim Hudson .10 .30
169 Barry Zito .10 .30
170 Mark Mulder .10 .30
171 Miguel Tejada .10 .30
172 Eric Chavez .10 .30
173 Billy Koch .10 .30
174 Jermaine Dye .10 .30
175 Scott Hatteberg .10 .30
176 Terrence Long .10 .30
177 David Justice .10 .30
178 Ramon Hernandez .10 .30
179 Ted Lilly .10 .30
180 Ichiro Suzuki .60 1.50
181 Edgar Martinez .20 .50
182 Mike Cameron .10 .30
183 John Olerud .10 .30
184 Bret Boone .10 .30
185 Dan Wilson .10 .30
186 Freddy Garcia .10 .30
187 Jamie Moyer .10 .30
188 Carlos Guillen .10 .30
189 Ruben Sierra .10 .30
190 Kazuhiro Sasaki .10 .30
191 Mark McLemore .10 .30
192 John Halama .10 .30
193 Joel Pineiro .10 .30
194 Jeff Cirillo .10 .30
195 Rafael Soriano .10 .30
196 Ben Grieve .10 .30
197 Aubrey Huff .10 .30
198 Steve Cox .10 .30
199 Toby Hall .10 .30
200 Randy Winn .10 .30
201 Brent Abernathy .10 .30
202 Chris Gomez .10 .30
203 John Flaherty .10 .30
204 Paul Wilson .10 .30
205 Chan Ho Park .10 .30
206 Alex Rodriguez .50 1.25
207 Juan Gonzalez .10 .30
208 Rafael Palmeiro .20 .50
209 Ivan Rodriguez .20 .50
210 Rusty Greer .10 .30
211 Kenny Rogers .10 .30
212 Ismael Valdes .10 .30
213 Frank Catalanotto .10 .30
214 Hank Blalock .10 .30
215 Michael Young .20 .50
216 Kevin Mench .10 .30
217 Herbert Perry .10 .30
218 Gabe Kapler .10 .30
219 Carlos Delgado .10 .30
220 Shannon Stewart .10 .30
221 Eric Hinske .10 .30
222 Roy Halladay .10 .30
223 Felipe Lopez .10 .30
224 Vernon Wells .10 .30
225 Josh Phelps .10 .30
226 Jose Cruz .10 .30
227 Curt Schilling .10 .30
228 Randy Johnson .30 .75
229 Luis Gonzalez .10 .30
230 Mark Grace .20 .50
231 Junior Spivey .10 .30
232 Tony Womack .10 .30
233 Matt Williams .10 .30
234 Steve Finley .10 .30
235 Byung-Hyun Kim .10 .30
236 Craig Counsell .10 .30
237 Greg Maddux .50 1.25
238 Tom Glavine .20 .50
239 John Smoltz .20 .50
240 Chipper Jones .30 .75
241 Gary Sheffield .10 .30
242 Andruw Jones .20 .50
243 Vinny Castilla .10 .30
244 Damian Moss .10 .30
245 Rafael Furcal .10 .30
246 Javy Lopez .10 .30
247 Kevin Millwood .10 .30
248 Kerry Wood .10 .30
249 Fred McGriff .20 .50
250 Sammy Sosa .30 .75
251 Alex Gonzalez .10 .30
252 Corey Patterson .10 .30
253 Moises Alou .10 .30
254 Juan Cruz .10 .30
255 Jon Lieber .10 .30
256 Matt Clement .10 .30
257 Mark Prior .20 .50
258 Ken Griffey Jr. .50 1.25
259 Barry Larkin .20 .50
260 Adam Dunn .10 .30
261 Sean Casey .10 .30
262 Jose Rijo .10 .30
263 Elmer Dessens .10 .30
264 Austin Kearns .10 .30
265 Corky Miller .10 .30
266 Todd Walker .10 .30
267 Chris Reitsma .10 .30
268 Ryan Dempster .10 .30
269 Aaron Boone .10 .30
270 Danny Graves .10 .30
271 Brandon Larson .10 .30
272 Larry Walker .10 .30
273 Todd Helton .20 .50
274 Juan Uribe .10 .30
275 Juan Pierre .10 .30
276 Mike Hampton .10 .30
277 Todd Zeile .10 .30
278 Todd Hollandsworth .10 .30
279 Jason Jennings .10 .30
280 Josh Beckett .10 .30
281 Mike Lowell .10 .30
282 Derrek Lee .20 .50
283 A.J. Burnett .10 .30
284 Luis Castillo .10 .30
285 Tim Raines .10 .30
286 Preston Wilson .10 .30
287 Juan Encarnacion .10 .30
288 Charles Johnson .10 .30
289 Jeff Bagwell .20 .50
290 Craig Biggio .20 .50
291 Lance Berkman .10 .30
292 Daryle Ward .10 .30
293 Roy Oswalt .10 .30
294 Richard Hidalgo .10 .30
295 Octavio Dotel .10 .30
296 Wade Miller .10 .30
297 Julio Lugo .10 .30
298 Billy Wagner .10 .30
299 Shawn Green .10 .30
300 Adrian Beltre .10 .30
301 Paul Lo Duca .10 .30
302 Eric Karros .10 .30
303 Kevin Brown .10 .30
304 Hideo Nomo .30 .75
305 Odalis Perez .10 .30
306 Eric Gagne .10 .30
307 Brian Jordan .10 .30
308 Cesar Izturis .10 .30
309 Mark Grudzielanek .10 .30
310 Kazuhisa Ishii .10 .30
311 Geoff Jenkins .10 .30
312 Richie Sexson .10 .30
313 Jose Hernandez .10 .30
314 Ben Sheets .10 .30
315 Ruben Quevedo .10 .30
316 Jeffrey Hammonds .10 .30
317 Alex Sanchez .10 .30
318 Eric Young .10 .30
319 Takahito Nomura .10 .30
320 Vladimir Guerrero .30 .75
321 Jose Vidro .10 .30
322 Orlando Cabrera .10 .30
323 Michael Barrett .10 .30
324 Javier Vazquez .10 .30
325 Tony Armas Jr. .10 .30
326 Andres Galarraga .10 .30
327 Tomo Ohka .10 .30
328 Bartolo Colon .10 .30
329 Fernando Tatis .10 .30
330 Brad Wilkerson .10 .30
331 Masato Yoshii .10 .30
332 Mike Piazza .50 1.25
333 Jeromy Burnitz .10 .30
334 Roberto Alomar .20 .50
335 Mo Vaughn .10 .30
336 Al Leiter .10 .30
337 Pedro Astacio .10 .30
338 Edgardo Alfonzo .10 .30
339 Armando Benitez .10 .30
340 Timo Perez .10 .30
341 Jay Payton .10 .30
342 Roger Cedeno .10 .30
343 Rey Ordonez .10 .30
344 Steve Trachsel .10 .30
345 Satoru Komiyama .10 .30
346 Scott Rolen .20 .50
347 Pat Burrell .10 .30
348 Bobby Abreu .10 .30
349 Mike Lieberthal .10 .30
350 Brandon Duckworth .10 .30
351 Jimmy Rollins .10 .30
352 Marlon Anderson .10 .30
353 Travis Lee .10 .30
354 Vicente Padilla .10 .30
355 Randy Wolf .10 .30
356 Jason Kendall .10 .30
357 Brian Giles .10 .30
358 Aramis Ramirez .10 .30
359 Pokey Reese .10 .30
360 Kip Wells .10 .30
361 Josh Fogg .10 .30
362 Mike Williams .10 .30
363 Jack Wilson .10 .30
364 Craig Wilson .10 .30
365 Kevin Young .10 .30
366 Ryan Klesko .10 .30
367 Phil Nevin .10 .30
368 Brian Lawrence .10 .30
369 Mark Kotsay .10 .30
370 Brett Tomko .10 .30
371 Trevor Hoffman .10 .30
372 Deivi Cruz .10 .30
373 Bubba Trammell .10 .30
374 Sean Burroughs .10 .30
375 Barry Bonds .75 2.00
376 Jeff Kent .10 .30
377 Rich Aurilia .10 .30
378 Tsuyoshi Shinjo .10 .30
379 Benito Santiago .10 .30
380 Kirk Rueter .10 .30
381 Livan Hernandez .10 .30
382 Russ Ortiz .10 .30
383 David Bell .10 .30
384 Jason Schmidt .10 .30
385 Reggie Sanders .10 .30
386 J.T. Snow .10 .30
387 Robb Nen .10 .30
388 Ryan Jensen .10 .30
389 Jim Edmonds .10 .30
390 J.D. Drew .10 .30
391 Albert Pujols .60 1.50
392 Fernando Vina .10 .30
393 Tino Martinez .20 .50
394 Edgar Renteria .10 .30
395 Matt Morris .10 .30
396 Woody Williams .10 .30
397 Jason Isringhausen .10 .30
398 Placido Polanco .10 .30
399 Eli Marrero .10 .30
400 Jason Simontacchi .10 .30

2003 Donruss Chicago Collection

These cards were distributed in March 2003 at the Chicago Sportsfest at the Donruss-Playoff corporate booth. Any collector that opened three Donruss/Playoff packs at the Donruss booth received one of these cards as a redemption for the wrappers. Only five serial-numbered sets were produced, thus the cards are too scarce to price. They can be easily identified by the large silver-foil "Chicago Collection" logo and serial-numbering stamped on the front of each card.

DISTRIBUTED AT CHICAGO SPORTSFEST
STATED PRINT RUN 5 SERIAL #'d SETS
NO PRICING DUE TO SCARCITY

2003 Donruss Stat Line Career

Randomly inserted into packs, this is a parallel to the 2003 Donruss set. Each card is printed to a number matching some career statistic and the cards are serial numbered to that amount. For those cards with a print run of 25 or fewer, no pricing is provided due to market scarcity.

*STAT LINE 1-20: 2.5X TO 6X BASIC
*21-70 P/R b/wn 251-400: 1.25X TO 3X
*21-70 P/R b/wn 201-250: 1.25X TO 3X
*21-70 P/R b/wn 151-200 1.5X TO 4X
*21-70 P/R b/wn 121-150: 2X TO 5X
*21-70 P/R b/wn 81-120: 2.5X TO 6X
*21-70 P/R b/wn 51-65: 3X TO 8X
*21-70 P/R b/wn 36-50: 4X TO 10X
*21-70 P/R b/wn 26-35: 5X TO 12X
*71-400 P/R b/wn 251-400: 2.5X TO 6X
*71-400 P/R b/wn 201-250: 2.5X TO 6X
*71-400 P/R b/wn 151-200 3X TO 8X
*71-400 P/R b/wn 121-150: 3X TO 8X
*71-400 P/R b/wn 81-120: 4X TO 10X
*71-400 P/R b/wn 66-80: 5X TO 12X
*71-400 P/R b/wn 51-65: 5X TO 12X
*71-400 P/R b/wn 36-50: 6X TO 15X
*71-400 P/R b/wn 26-35: 8X TO 20X
SEE BECKETT.COM FOR FOR PRINT RUNS
NO PRICING ON QTY OF 25 OR LESS

2003 Donruss Stat Line Season

Randomly inserted into packs, this is a parallel to the 2003 Donruss set. Each card is printed to a number matching some seasonal statistic and the cards are serial numbered to that amount. For those cards with a print run of 25 or fewer, no pricing is provided due to market scarcity.

*1-20 P/R b/wn 121-150 3X TO 8X
*1-20 P/R b/wn 81-120 4X TO 10X
*1-20 P/R b/wn 66-80 5X TO 12X
*1-20 P/R b/wn 51-65 5X TO 12X
*1-20 P/R b/wn 36-50 6X TO 15X
*1-20 P/R b/wn 26-35 8X TO 20X
*21-70 P/R b/wn 81-120 2.5X TO 6X
*21-70 P/R b/wn 66-80 3X TO 8X
*21-70 P/R b/wn 51-65 3X TO 8X
*21-70 P/R b/wn 36-50 4X TO 10X
*21-70 P/R b/wn 26-35 5X TO 12X
*71-400 P/R b/wn 81-120 4X TO 10X
*71-400 P/R b/wn 66-80 5X TO 12X
*71-400 P/R b/wn 51-65 5X TO 12X
*71-400 P/R b/wn 36-50 6X TO 15X
*71-400 P/R b/wn 26-35 8X TO 20X
SEE BECKETT.COM FOR PRINT RUNS
NO PRICING ON QTY OF 25 OR LESS

2003 Donruss All-Stars

Issued at a stated rate of one in 12 retail packs, these 10 cards feature players who are projected to be mainstays on the All-Star team.

1 Ichiro Suzuki 2.50 6.00
2 Alex Rodriguez 2.00 5.00
3 Nomar Garciaparra 2.00 5.00
4 Derek Jeter 3.00 8.00
5 Manny Ramirez 1.25 3.00
6 Barry Bonds 3.00 8.00
7 Adam Dunn 1.25 3.00
8 Mike Piazza 2.00 5.00
9 Sammy Sosa 1.25 3.00
10 Todd Helton 1.25 3.00

2003 Donruss Anniversary 1983

Issued at a stated rate of one in 12, this 20 card set features players who were among the most important players of that era. These cards use the 1983 Donruss design and photos.

COMPLETE SET (20) 20.00 50.00
1 Dale Murphy 1.25 3.00
2 Jim Palmer 1.25 3.00
3 Nolan Ryan 3.00 8.00
4 Ozzie Smith 2.00 5.00
5 Tom Seaver 1.25 3.00
6 Mike Schmidt 2.50 6.00
7 Steve Carlton 1.25 3.00
8 Robin Yount 1.25 3.00
9 Ryne Sandberg 2.00 5.00
10 Cal Ripken 4.00 10.00
11 Fernando Valenzuela 1.25 3.00
12 Andre Dawson 1.25 3.00
13 George Brett 2.50 6.00
14 Eddie Murray 1.25 3.00
15 Dave Winfield 1.25 3.00
16 Johnny Bench 1.25 3.00
17 Wade Boggs 1.25 3.00
18 Tony Gwynn 2.50 6.00
19 San Diego Chicken 1.25 3.00
20 Ty Cobb 2.00 5.00

2003 Donruss Bat Kings

Randomly inserted into packs, these 20 cards feature a game bat chip long with a reproduction of a previously used Diamond King card. Cards numbered 1 through 10 have a stated print run of 250 serial numbered sets while cards numbered 11 through 20 have a stated print run of 100 serial numbered sets.

1-10 PRINT RUN 250 SERIAL #'d SETS
11-20 PRINT RUN 100 SERIAL #'d SETS
*STUDIO 1-10: .75X TO 2X BASIC BAT KING
STUDIO 1-10 PRINT RUN 50 SERIAL #'d SETS
STUDIO 11-20 PRINT RUN 25 SERIAL #'d SETS
STUDIO 11-20 NO PRICING DUE TO SCARCITY
1 Scott Rolen 99 DK/250 8.00 20.00
2 Frank Thomas 00 DK/250 8.00 20.00
3 Chipper Jones 01 DK/250 8.00 20.00
4 Ivan Rodriguez 01 DK/250 8.00 20.00
5 Stan Musial 01 ATDK/100 20.00 50.00
6 Nomar Garciaparra 02 DK/250 10.00 25.00
7 Vladimir Guerrero 03 DK/250 8.00 20.00
8 Adam Dunn 03 DK/250 6.00 15.00
9 Lance Berkman 03 DK/250 6.00 15.00
10 Magglio Ordonez 03 DK/250 6.00 15.00
11 Ernie Banks 02 ATDK/50
12 Manny Ramirez 95 DK/100 10.00 25.00
13 Mike Piazza 94 DK/100 15.00 40.00
14 Alex Rodriguez 97 DK/100 15.00 40.00
15 Todd Helton 97 RDK/100 10.00 25.00
16 Andre Dawson 85 DK/100 8.00 20.00
17 Cal Ripken 87 DK/100 40.00 80.00
18 Tony Gwynn 88 DK/100 12.50 30.00
19 Don Mattingly 02 ATDK/100 15.00 40.00
20 Ryne Sandberg 90 DK/100 30.00 60.00

2003 Donruss Diamond Kings Inserts

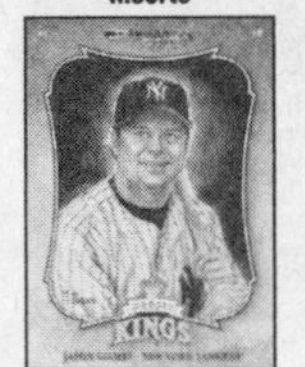

Randomly inserted into packs, these cards parallel the first 20 cards of the regular Donruss set except they are serial numbered to a stated print run of 2500 serial numbered sets. These cards can be easily seperated from the cards inserted into the regular packs as they were printed with a foil stamp.

*STUDIO: .75X TO 2X BASIC DK
STUDIO PRINT RUN 250 SERIAL #'d SETS
1 Vladimir Guerrero 4.00 10.00
2 Derek Jeter 8.00 20.00
3 Adam Dunn 4.00 10.00
4 Greg Maddux 5.00 12.00
5 Lance Berkman 4.00 10.00
6 Ichiro Suzuki 6.00 15.00
7 Mike Piazza 5.00 12.00
8 Alex Rodriguez 5.00 12.00
9 Tom Glavine 4.00 10.00
10 Randy Johnson 4.00 10.00
11 Nomar Garciaparra 5.00 12.00
12 Jason Giambi 4.00 10.00
13 Sammy Sosa 4.00 10.00
14 Barry Zito 4.00 10.00
15 Chipper Jones 4.00 10.00
16 Magglio Ordonez 4.00 10.00
17 Larry Walker 4.00 10.00
18 Alfonso Soriano 4.00 10.00
19 Curt Schilling 4.00 10.00
20 Barry Bonds 8.00 20.00

2003 Donruss Elite Series

Randomly inserted into packs, this 15 card set, which is issued on metalized film board, features the elite 15 players in baseball. These cards were issued to a stated print run of 2500 serial numbered sets.

DOMINATORS PR.RUN 25 SERIAL #'d SETS
DOMINATORS NO PRICE DUE TO SCARCITY
1 Alex Rodriguez 3.00 8.00
2 Barry Bonds 5.00 12.00
3 Ichiro Suzuki 4.00 10.00
4 Vladimir Guerrero 2.00 5.00
5 Randy Johnson 2.00 5.00
6 Pedro Martinez 1.50 4.00
7 Adam Dunn 1.50 4.00
8 Sammy Sosa 2.00 5.00
9 Jim Edmonds 1.50 4.00
10 Greg Maddux 3.00 8.00
11 Kazuhisa Ishii 1.50 4.00
12 Jason Giambi 1.50 4.00
13 Nomar Garciaparra 3.00 8.00
14 Tom Glavine 1.50 4.00
15 Todd Helton 1.50 4.00

2003 Donruss Gamers

Randomly inserted in DLP (Donruss/Leaf/Playoff) rookie packs, these 50 cards have game-worn memorabilia swatches of the featured players.

STATED PRINT RUN 500 SERIAL #'d SETS
*JSY NUM: .6X TO 1.5X BASIC
JSY NUM PRINT RUN 100 SERIAL #'d SETS
*POSITION: .6X TO 1.5X BASIC
POSITION PRINT RUN 100 SERIAL #'d SETS
PRIME PRINT RUN 25 SERIAL #'d SETS
NO PRIME PRICING DUE TO SCARCITY
REWARDS PRINT RUN 10 SERIAL #'d SETS
NO REWARDS PRICING DUE TO SCARCITY
1 Nomar Garciaparra 6.00 15.00
2 Alex Rodriguez 4.00 10.00
3 Mike Piazza 4.00 10.00
4 Greg Maddux 4.00 10.00
5 Roger Clemens 6.00 15.00
6 Sammy Sosa 3.00 8.00
7 Randy Johnson 3.00 8.00
8 Albert Pujols 6.00 15.00
9 Alfonso Soriano 2.00 5.00
10 Chipper Jones 3.00 8.00
11 Mark Prior 3.00 8.00
12 Hideo Nomo 3.00 8.00
13 Adam Dunn 2.00 5.00
14 Juan Gonzalez 2.00 5.00
15 Vladimir Guerrero 3.00 8.00
16 Pedro Martinez 3.00 8.00
17 Jim Thome 3.00 8.00
18 Brandon Webb/200 4.00 10.00
19 Mike Mussina 3.00 8.00
20 Mark Teixeira 3.00 8.00
21 Barry Larkin 3.00 8.00
22 Ivan Rodriguez 3.00 8.00
23 Hank Blalock 2.00 5.00
24 Rafael Palmeiro 3.00 8.00
25 Curt Schilling 2.00 5.00
26 Troy Glaus 2.00 5.00
27 Bernie Williams 3.00 8.00
28 Scott Rolen 3.00 8.00
29 Torii Hunter 2.00 5.00
30 Nick Johnson 2.00 5.00
31 Kazuhisa Ishii 2.00 5.00
32 Shawn Green 2.00 5.00
33 Jeff Bagwell 3.00 8.00
34 Lance Berkman 2.00 5.00
35 Roy Oswalt 2.00 5.00
36 Kerry Wood 2.00 5.00
37 Todd Helton 3.00 8.00
38 Manny Ramirez 3.00 8.00
39 Andruw Jones 3.00 8.00
40 Frank Thomas 3.00 8.00
41 Gary Sheffield 2.00 5.00
42 Magglio Ordonez 2.00 5.00
43 Mike Sweeney 2.00 5.00
44 Carlos Beltran 2.00 5.00
45 Richie Sexson 2.00 5.00
46 Jeff Kent 2.00 5.00
47 Carlos Delgado 2.00 5.00
48 Vernon Wells 2.00 5.00
49 Dontrelle Willis 3.00 8.00
50 Jae Weong Seo 2.00 5.00

2003 Donruss Gamers Autographs

PRINT RUNS B/WN 5-50 COPIES PER
NO PRICING ON QTY OF 25 OR LESS
2 Alex Rodriguez/5
3 Mike Piazza/5
4 Greg Maddux/5
5 Roger Clemens/5
7 Randy Johnson/5
8 Albert Pujols/5
9 Alfonso Soriano/5
10 Chipper Jones/10
11 Mark Prior/25
12 Hideo Nomo/5
13 Adam Dunn/25
14 Juan Gonzalez/25
15 Vladimir Guerrero/5
16 Pedro Martinez/5
18 Brandon Webb/25
19 Mike Mussina/5
20 Mark Teixeira/50 10.00 25.00
22 Ivan Rodriguez/5
23 Hank Blalock/50 12.50 30.00
24 Rafael Palmeiro/10
25 Curt Schilling/25
26 Troy Glaus/25
27 Bernie Williams/5
28 Scott Rolen/25
29 Torii Hunter/50 12.50 30.00
30 Nick Johnson/25
31 Kazuhisa Ishii/5
32 Shawn Green/5
33 Jeff Bagwell/5
34 Lance Berkman/10
35 Roy Oswalt/50 12.50 30.00
36 Kerry Wood/25
37 Todd Helton/10
39 Andruw Jones/25
40 Frank Thomas/10
41 Gary Sheffield/25
42 Magglio Ordonez/25
43 Mike Sweeney/50 12.50 30.00
44 Carlos Beltran/25
45 Richie Sexson/25
46 Jeff Kent/12
48 Vernon Wells/30 15.00 40.00
49 Dontrelle Willis/50 10.00 25.00
50 Jae Weong Seo/50 12.50 30.00

2003 Donruss Jersey Kings

Randomly inserted into packs, this set features cards which parallel previously issued Diamond King cards along with a game-worn jersey swatch. Cards were printed to a stated print run of either 100 or 250 serial numbered cards and we have put that information next to the player's name in our checklist.

*STUDIO 1-10: .75X TO 2X BASIC JSY KINGS
STUDIO 1-10 PRINT RUN 50 SERIAL #'d SETS
STUDIO 11-20 PRINT RUN 25 SERIAL #'d SETS
STUDIO 11-20 NO PRICE DUE TO SCARCITY
1 Juan Gonzalez 99 DK/250 6.00 15.00
2 Greg Maddux 00 DK/250 8.00 20.00
3 Nomar Garciaparra 01 DK/250 10.00 25.00
4 Troy Glaus 01 DK/250 6.00 15.00
5 Reggie Jackson 01 ATDK/100 10.00 25.00
6 Alex Rodriguez 01 DK/250 10.00 25.00
7 Alfonso Soriano 03 DK/250 6.00 15.00
8 Curt Schilling 03 DK/250 6.00 15.00
9 Vladimir Guerrero 03 DK/250 6.00 15.00
10 Adam Dunn 03 DK/250 6.00 15.00
11 Mark Grace 88 DK/100 10.00 25.00
12 Roger Clemens 90 DK/100 15.00 40.00
13 Jeff Bagwell 91 DK/100 10.00 25.00
14 Tom Glavine 92 DK/100 10.00 25.00
15 Mike Piazza 94 DK/100 12.50 30.00
16 Rod Carew 82 DK/100 10.00 25.00
17 Rickey Henderson 82 DK/100 10.00 25.00
18 Mike Schmidt 83 DK/100 15.00 40.00
19 Cal Ripken 85 DK/100 40.00 80.00
20 Dale Murphy 86 DK/100 10.00 25.00

2003 Donruss Longball Leaders

Randomly inserted into packs, these 10 cards, honoring some of the leading home run hitters, were printed on metalized film board and were issued to a stated print run of 1000 serial numbered sets.

*SEASON SUM: 1.5X TO 4X BASIC LL
SEASON PRINT RUN BASED ON 02 HR'S
1 Alex Rodriguez 5.00 12.00
2 Alfonso Soriano 2.00 5.00
3 Rafael Palmeiro 2.00 5.00
4 Jim Thome 2.00 5.00
5 Jason Giambi 2.00 5.00
6 Sammy Sosa 3.00 8.00
7 Barry Bonds 8.00 20.00
8 Lance Berkman 2.00 5.00
9 Shawn Green 2.00 5.00
10 Vladimir Guerrero 3.00 8.00

2003 Donruss Production Line

Randomly inserted into packs, these 30 cards feature players who excel in either on base percentage, slugging percentage, batting average or total bases. Each card is printed on metalized film board and was issued to that player's statistical information.

*DIE CUT OPS: 1.25X TO 3X BASIC PL
*DIE CUT OBP/SLG: 1X TO 2.5X BASIC PL
*DIE CUT AVG/TB: .75X TO 2X BASIC PL
DIE CUT PRINT RUN 100 SERIAL #'d SETS
1 Alex Rodriguez OPS/1015 4.00 10.00
2 Jim Thome OPS/1122 1.50 4.00
3 Lance Berkman OPS/982 1.00 2.50
4 Barry Bonds OPS/1381 6.00 15.00
5 Sammy Sosa OPS/993 2.50 6.00
6 Vladimir Guerrero OPS/1010 2.50 6.00
7 Barry Bonds OBP/582 8.00 20.00
8 Jason Giambi OBP/435 1.25 3.00
9 Vladimir Guerrero OBP/417 3.00 8.00
10 Adam Dunn OBP/400 1.25 3.00
11 Chipper Jones OBP/435 3.00 8.00
12 Todd Helton OBP/429 2.00 5.00
13 Rafael Palmeiro SLG/571 2.00 5.00
14 Sammy Sosa SLG/594 3.00 8.00
15 Alex Rodriguez SLG/623 5.00 12.00
16 Larry Walker SLG/602 1.25 3.00
17 Lance Berkman SLG/578 1.25 3.00
18 Alfonso Soriano SLG/547 1.25 3.00
19 Ichiro Suzuki AVG/321 6.00 15.00
20 Mike Sweeney AVG/340 1.50 4.00
21 Manny Ramirez AVG/349 2.50 6.00
22 Larry Walker AVG/338 1.50 4.00
23 Barry Bonds AVG/370 10.00 25.00
24 Jim Edmonds AVG/311 1.50 4.00
25 Alfonso Soriano TB/381 1.50 4.00
26 Jason Giambi TB/335 1.50 4.00
27 Miguel Tejada TB/336 1.50 4.00
28 Brian Giles TB/309 1.50 4.00
29 Vladimir Guerrero TB/364 4.00 10.00
30 Pat Burrell TB/319 1.50 4.00

2003 Donruss Timber and Threads

Randomly inserted into packs, these 50 cards feature either a game-used jersey swatch or a game-use bat chip of the featured player. Since these cards have different stated print runs we have put that information next to the player's name in our checklist.

1 Al Kaline Bat/125 10.00 25.00
2 Alex Rodriguez Bat/350 8.00 20.00
3 Carlos Delgado Bat/250 4.00 10.00
4 Cliff Floyd Bat/250 4.00 10.00
5 Eddie Mathews Bat/125 10.00 25.00
6 Edgar Martinez Bat/125 10.00 25.00
7 Ernie Banks Bat/50 15.00 40.00
8 Ivan Rodriguez Bat/125 10.00 25.00
9 J.D. Drew Bat/125 6.00 15.00
10 Jorge Posada Bat/300 6.00 15.00
11 Lou Brock Bat/125 10.00 25.00
12 Mike Piazza Bat/125 10.00 25.00
13 Mike Schmidt Bat/125 15.00 40.00
14 Reggie Jackson Bat/125 10.00 25.00
15 Rickey Henderson Bat/125 10.00 25.00
16 Robin Yount Bat/125 10.00 25.00
17 Rod Carew Bat/125 10.00 25.00
18 Scott Rolen Bat/125 10.00 25.00
19 Shawn Green Bat/200 4.00 10.00
20 Willie Stargell Bat/125 10.00 25.00
21 Alex Rodriguez Jsy/175 12.50 30.00
22 Andruw Jones Jsy/275 6.00 15.00
23 Brooks Robinson Jsy/150 10.00 25.00
24 Chipper Jones Jsy/150 10.00 25.00
25 Greg Maddux Jsy/175 8.00 20.00
26 Hideo Nomo Jsy/300 15.00 40.00
27 Ivan Rodriguez Jsy/225 6.00 15.00
28 Jack Morris Jsy/150 6.00 15.00
29 J.D. Drew Jsy/150 6.00 15.00
30 Jeff Bagwell Jsy/500 6.00 15.00
31 Jim Thome Jsy/200 6.00 15.00
32 John Smoltz Jsy/175 6.00 15.00
33 John Olerud Jsy/450 4.00 10.00
34 Kerry Wood Jsy/200 4.00 10.00
35 Harmon Killebrew Jsy/50
36 Larry Walker Jsy/500 4.00 10.00
37 Magglio Ordonez Jsy/150 6.00 15.00
38 Manny Ramirez Jsy/500 6.00 15.00
39 Mike Piazza Jsy/300 6.00 15.00
40 Mike Sweeney Jsy/200 4.00 10.00
41 Nomar Garciaparra Jsy/200 10.00 25.00
42 Paul Konerko Jsy/500 4.00 10.00
43 Pedro Martinez Jsy/175 6.00 15.00
44 Randy Johnson Jsy/175 6.00 15.00
45 Roger Clemens Jsy/350 10.00 25.00
46 Shawn Green Jsy/250 4.00 10.00
47 Todd Helton Jsy/175 6.00 15.00
48 Tom Glavine Jsy/225 6.00 15.00
49 Tony Gwynn Jsy/150 10.00 25.00
50 Vladimir Guerrero Jsy/450 6.00 15.00

2003 Donruss Rookies

This 65-card set was released in December, 2003. This set was issued as part of the DLP (Donruss/Leaf/Playoff) Rookie Update product in which many of the products issued earlier in the year had Rookie Cards added. Each pack, contained eight cards and were sold at an $5 SRP with 24 packs in a box and 12 boxes in a case. In this Rookies set, cards 1-60 feature Rookie Cards while cards numbered 61-65 feature some of the most important players who changed teams during the 2003 season. As mentioned cards from the following DLP products were inserted into these packs: Donruss, Donruss Champions, Donruss Classics, Donruss Diamond Kings, Donruss Elite, Donruss Signature, Donruss Team Heroes, Leaf, Leaf Certified Materials, Leaf Limited, Playoff Absolute Memorablia, Playoff Prestige and Studio.

COMPLETE SET (65) 8.00 20.00
COMMON CARD (1-65) .07 .20
COMMON RC .08 .25
1 Jeremy Bonderman RC .75 2.00
2 Adam Loewen RC .20 .50
3 Dan Haren RC .20 .50
4 Jose Contreras RC .20 .50
5 Hideki Matsui RC .75 2.00
6 Arnie Munoz RC .08 .25

7 Miguel Cabrera .20 .50
8 Andrew Brown RC .15 .40
9 Josh Hall RC .08 .25
10 Josh Stewart RC .08 .25
11 Clint Barmes RC .30 .75
12 Luis Ayala RC .08 .25
13 Brandon Webb RC .60 1.50
14 Greg Aquino RC .08 .25
15 Chien-Ming Wang RC 1.00 2.50
16 Rickie Weeks RC .60 1.50
17 Edgar Gonzalez RC .08 .25
18 Dontrelle Willis .20 .50
19 Bo Hart RC .08 .25
20 Rosman Garcia RC .08 .25
21 Jeremy Griffiths RC .08 .25
22 Craig Brazell RC .08 .25
23 Daniel Cabrera RC .20 .50
24 Fernando Cabrera RC .08 .25
25 Termel Sledge RC .08 .25
26 Ramon Nivar RC .08 .25
27 Rob Hammock RC .08 .25
28 Francisco Rosario RC .08 .25
29 Cory Stewart RC .08 .25
30 Felix Sanchez RC .08 .25
31 Jorge Cordova RC .08 .25
32 Rocco Baldelli .07 .20
33 Beau Kemp RC .08 .25
34 Mike Nakamura RC .08 .25
35 Rett Johnson RC .08 .25
36 Guillermo Quiroz RC .08 .25
37 Hong-Chih Kuo RC .75 2.00
38 Ian Ferguson RC .08 .25
39 Franklin Perez RC .08 .25
40 Tim Olson RC .08 .25
41 Jerome Williams .07 .20
42 Rich Fischer RC .08 .25
43 Phil Seibel RC .08 .25
44 Aaron Looper RC .08 .25
45 Jae Weong Seo .07 .20
46 Chad Gaudin RC .08 .25
47 Matt Kata RC .08 .25
48 Ryan Wagner RC .08 .25
49 Michel Hernandez RC .08 .25
50 Diegomar Markwell RC .08 .25
51 Doug Waechter RC .15 .40
52 Mike Nicolas RC .08 .25
53 Prentice Redman RC .08 .25
54 Shane Bazzell RC .08 .25
55 Delmon Young RC 1.25 3.00
56 Brian Stokes RC .08 .25
57 Matt Bruback RC .08 .25
58 Nook Logan RC .15 .40
59 Oscar Villarreal RC .08 .25
60 Pete LaForest RC .08 .25
61 Shea Hillenbrand .07 .20
62 Aramis Ramirez .07 .20
63 Aaron Boone .07 .20
64 Roberto Alomar .10 .30
65 Rickey Henderson .20 .50

2003 Donruss Rookies Autographs

PRINT RUNS B/WN 10-1000 COPIES PER
NO PRICING ON QTY OF 25 OR LESS
1 Jeremy Bonderman/50 20.00 50.00
2 Adam Loewen/500 6.00 15.00
3 Dan Haren/100 10.00 25.00
4 Jose Contreras/100 12.50 30.00
6 Arnie Munoz/584 4.00 10.00
7 Miguel Cabrera/50 50.00 100.00
8 Andrew Brown/584 6.00 15.00
9 Josh Hall/1000 4.00 10.00
10 Josh Stewart/300 4.00 10.00
11 Clint Barmes/129 6.00 15.00
12 Luis Ayala/1000 4.00 10.00
13 Brandon Webb/100 12.50 30.00
14 Greg Aquino/1000 4.00 10.00
15 Chien-Ming Wang/100 60.00 120.00
16 Rickie Weeks/10
17 Edgar Gonzalez/400 4.00 10.00
18 Dontrelle Willis/25
19 Bo Hart/150 4.00 10.00
20 Rosman Garcia/250 4.00 10.00
21 Jeremy Griffiths/812 4.00 10.00
22 Craig Brazell/205 4.00 10.00
23 Daniel Cabrera/383 10.00 25.00
24 Fernando Cabrera/1000 4.00 10.00
25 Termel Sledge/250 4.00 10.00
26 Ramon Nivar/100 4.00 10.00
27 Rob Hammock/201 4.00 10.00
28 Francisco Rosario/25
29 Cory Stewart/1000 4.00 10.00
30 Felix Sanchez/1000 4.00 10.00
31 Jorge Cordova/1000 4.00 10.00
32 Rocco Baldelli/25
33 Beau Kemp/1000 4.00 10.00
34 Mike Nakamura/1000 4.00 10.00
35 Rett Johnson/1000 4.00 10.00
36 Guillermo Quiroz/90 4.00 10.00
37 Hong-Chih Kuo/50 100.00 200.00
38 Ian Ferguson/1000 4.00 10.00
39 Franklin Perez/1000 4.00 10.00
40 Tim Olson/150 4.00 10.00
41 Jerome Williams/50 6.00 15.00
42 Rich Fischer/734 4.00 10.00
43 Phil Seibel/1000 4.00 10.00
44 Aaron Looper/513 4.00 10.00
45 Jae Weong Seo/50 10.00 25.00
46 Chad Gaudin/19
47 Matt Kata/203 4.00 10.00
48 Ryan Wagner/100 4.00 10.00
49 Michel Hernandez/41
50 Diegomar Markwell/1000 4.00 10.00
51 Doug Waechter/583 6.00 15.00
52 Mike Nicolas/1000 4.00 10.00
53 Prentice Redman/425 4.00 10.00
54 Shane Bazzell/1000 4.00 10.00
55 Delmon Young/75 100.00 200.00
56 Brian Stokes/1000 4.00 10.00
57 Matt Bruback/513 4.00 10.00
58 Nook Logan/150 6.00 15.00
59 Oscar Villarreal/150 6.00 15.00
60 Pete LaForest/250 4.00 10.00

2003 Donruss Rookies Stat Line Career

*SLC P/R b/wn 201+: 4X TO 10X
*SLC P/R b/wn 121-200: 5X TO 12X
*SLC P/R b/wn 81-120: 6X TO 15X
*SLC P/R b/wn 66-80: 8X TO 20X
*SLC P/R b/wn 51-65: 8X TO 20X
*SLC RC's P/R b/wn 201+: 4X TO 10X
*SLC RC's P/R b/wn 121-200: 4X TO 10X
*SLC RC's P/R b/wn 81-120: 4X TO 10X
*SLC RC's P/R b/wn 66-80: 5X TO 12X
*SLC RC's P/R b/wn 51-65: 5X TO 12X
*SLC RC's P/R b/wn 36-50: 6X TO 15X
*SLC RC's P/R b/wn 26-35: 8X TO 20X
PRINT RUNS B/WN 1-245 COPIES PER
NO PRICING ON QTY OF 25 OR LESS
15 Chien-Ming Wang/212 12.50 30.00
37 Hong-Chih Kuo/45 30.00 60.00

2003 Donruss Rookies Stat Line Season

*SLS P/R b/wn 201+: 4X TO 10X
*SLS P/R b/wn 121-200: 5X TO 12X
*SLS P/R b/wn 66-80: 8X TO 20X
*SLS P/R b/wn 36-50: 10X TO 25X
*SLS P/R b/wn 26-35: 12.5X TO 30X
*SLS RC's P/R b/wn 81-120: 4X TO 10X
*SLS RC's P/R b/wn 66-80: 5X TO 12X
*SLS RC's P/R b/wn 51-65: 5X TO 12X
*SLS RC's P/R b/wn 36-50: 6X TO 15X
*SLS RC's P/R b/wn 26-35: 8X TO 20X
PRINT RUNS B/WN 1-130 COPIES PER
NO PRICING ON QTY OF 25 OR LESS
15 Chien-Ming Wang/64 20.00 50.00

2003 Donruss Rookies Recollection Autographs

PRINT RUNS B/WN 1-75 COPIES PER
NO PRICING ON QTY OF 5 OR LESS
1 Sandy Alomar Jr. 89 DR/2
2 Sandy Alomar Jr. 90 Black/5
3 Sandy Alomar Jr. 90 Blue/5
4 Jay Buhner 88 DR/5
5 Jose Canseco 86/1
6 Sid Fernandez 84/5
7 Jack McDowell 88/75 10.00 25.00
8 Paul O'Neill 86/5
9 Gary Sheffield 89/5
10 Ruben Sierra 86 DR/1
11 J.T. Snow 93/5
12 Robby Thompson 86 DR/5
13 Matt Williams 87 DR/5

2004 Donruss

This 400-card standard-size set was released in November, 2003. This set was issued in 10 card packs with an $1.99 SRP and those cards came 24 packs to a box and 16 boxes to a case. Please note the following subsets were issued as part of this product: Diamond King (1-25); Rated Rookies (26-70) and Team Checklists (371-400).

COMPLETE SET (400) 75.00 150.00
COMP.SET w/o SP's (300) 10.00 25.00
COMMON CARD (71-370) .12 .30
COMMON CARD (1-25/371-400) .25 .60
COMMON CARD (26-70) .60 1.50
1-70/370-400 RANDOM INSERTS IN PACKS
1 Derek Jeter DK 1.50 4.00
2 Greg Maddux DK 1.00 2.50
3 Albert Pujols DK 1.50 4.00
4 Ichiro Suzuki DK 1.00 2.50
5 Alex Rodriguez DK 1.00 2.50
6 Roger Clemens DK .75 2.00
7 Andruw Jones DK .25 .60
8 Barry Bonds DK 1.25 3.00
9 Jeff Bagwell DK .40 1.00
10 Randy Johnson DK .60 1.50
11 Scott Rolen DK .40 1.00
12 Lance Berkman DK .40 1.00
13 Barry Zito DK .25 .60
14 Manny Ramirez DK .60 1.50
15 Carlos Delgado DK .25 .60
16 Alfonso Soriano DK .25 .60
17 Todd Helton DK .40 1.00
18 Mike Mussina DK .40 1.00
19 Austin Kearns DK .25 .60
20 Nomar Garciaparra DK .60 1.50
21 Chipper Jones DK .60 1.50
22 Mark Prior DK .40 1.00
23 Jim Thome DK .40 1.00
24 Vladimir Guerrero DK .60 1.50
25 Pedro Martinez DK .40 1.00
26 Sergio Mitre RR .60 1.50
27 Adam Loewen RR .60 1.50
28 Alfredo Gonzalez RR .60 1.50
29 Miguel Ojeda RR .60 1.50
30 Rosman Garcia RR .60 1.50
31 Arnie Munoz RR .60 1.50
32 Andrew Brown RR .60 1.50
33 Josh Hall RR .60 1.50
34 Josh Stewart RR .60 1.50
35 Clint Barmes RR 1.00 2.50
36 Brandon Webb RR .60 1.50
37 Chien-Ming Wang RR 3.00 8.00
38 Edgar Gonzalez RR .60 1.50
39 Alejandro Machado RR .60 1.50
40 Jeremy Griffiths RR .60 1.50
41 Craig Brazell RR .60 1.50
42 Daniel Cabrera RR .60 1.50
43 Fernando Cabrera RR .60 1.50
44 Termel Sledge RR .60 1.50
45 Rob Hammock RR .60 1.50
46 Francisco Rosario RR .60 1.50
47 Francisco Cruceta RR .60 1.50
48 Rett Johnson RR .60 1.50
49 Guillermo Quiroz RR .60 1.50
50 Hong-Chih Kuo RR .60 1.50
51 Ian Ferguson RR .60 1.50
52 Tim Olson RR .60 1.50
53 Todd Wellemeyer RR .60 1.50
54 Rich Fischer RR .60 1.50
55 Phil Seibel RR .60 1.50
56 Joe Valentine RR .60 1.50
57 Matt Kata RR .60 1.50
58 Michael Hessman RR .60 1.50
59 Michel Hernandez RR .60 1.50
60 Doug Waechter RR .60 1.50
61 Prentice Redman RR .60 1.50
62 Nook Logan RR .60 1.50
63 Oscar Villarreal RR .60 1.50
64 Pete LaForest RR .60 1.50
65 Matt Bruback RR .60 1.50
66 Dan Haren RR .60 1.50
67 Greg Aquino RR .60 1.50
68 Lew Ford RR .60 1.50
69 Jeff Duncan RR .60 1.50
70 Ryan Wagner RR .60 1.50
71 Bengie Molina .12 .30
72 Brad Fullmer .12 .30
73 Darin Erstad .12 .30
74 David Eckstein .12 .30
75 Garret Anderson .12 .30
76 Jarrod Washburn .12 .30
77 Kevin Appier .12 .30
78 Scott Spiezio .12 .30
79 Tim Salmon .12 .30
80 Troy Glaus .12 .30
81 Troy Percival .12 .30
82 Jason Johnson .12 .30
83 Jay Gibbons .12 .30
84 Melvin Mora .12 .30
85 Sidney Ponson .12 .30
86 Tony Batista .12 .30
87 Bill Mueller .12 .30
88 Byung-Hyun Kim .12 .30
89 David Ortiz .30 .75
90 Derek Lowe .12 .30
91 Johnny Damon .20 .50
92 Casey Fossum .12 .30
93 Manny Ramirez .30 .75
94 Nomar Garciaparra .30 .75
95 Pedro Martinez .20 .50
96 Todd Walker .12 .30
97 Trot Nixon .12 .30
98 Bartolo Colon .12 .30
99 Carlos Lee .12 .30
100 D'Angelo Jimenez .12 .30
101 Esteban Loaiza .12 .30
102 Frank Thomas .30 .75
103 Joe Crede .12 .30
104 Jose Valentin .12 .30
105 Magglio Ordonez .20 .50
106 Mark Buehrle .20 .50
107 Paul Konerko .20 .50
108 Brandon Phillips .12 .30
109 C.C Sabathia .20 .50
110 Ellis Burks .12 .30
111 Jeremy Guthrie .12 .30
112 Josh Bard .12 .30
113 Matt Lawton .12 .30
114 Milton Bradley .12 .30
115 Omar Vizquel .20 .50
116 Travis Hafner .12 .30
117 Bobby Higginson .12 .30
118 Carlos Pena .20 .50
119 Dmitri Young .12 .30
120 Eric Munson .12 .30
121 Jeremy Bonderman .12 .30
122 Nate Cornejo .12 .30
123 Omar Infante .12 .30
124 Ramon Santiago .12 .30
125 Angel Berroa .12 .30
126 Carlos Beltran .12 .30
127 Desi Relaford .12 .30
128 Jeremy Affeldt .12 .30
129 Joe Randa .12 .30
130 Ken Harvey .12 .30
131 Mike MacDougal .12 .30
132 Michael Tucker .12 .30
133 Mike Sweeney .12 .30
134 Raul Ibanez .12 .30
135 Runelvys Hernandez .12 .30
136 A.J. Pierzynski .12 .30
137 Brad Radke .12 .30
138 Corey Koskie .12 .30
139 Cristian Guzman .12 .30
140 Doug Mientkiewicz .12 .30
141 Dustan Mohr .12 .30
142 Jacque Jones .12 .30
143 Kenny Rogers .12 .30
144 Bobby Kielty .12 .30
145 Kyle Lohse .12 .30
146 Luis Rivas .12 .30
147 Torii Hunter .12 .30
148 Alfonso Soriano .12 .30
149 Andy Pettitte .20 .50
150 Bernie Williams .20 .50
151 David Wells .12 .30
152 Derek Jeter .75 2.00
153 Hideki Matsui .50 1.25
154 Jason Giambi .12 .30
155 Jorge Posada .20 .50
156 Jose Contreras .12 .30
157 Mike Mussina .20 .50
158 Nick Johnson .12 .30
159 Robin Ventura .12 .30
160 Roger Clemens .40 1.00
161 Barry Zito .12 .30
162 Chris Singleton .12 .30
163 Eric Byrnes .12 .30
164 Eric Chavez .12 .30
165 Erubiel Durazo .12 .30
166 Keith Foulke .12 .30
167 Mark Ellis .12 .30
168 Miguel Tejada .20 .50
169 Mark Mulder .12 .30
170 Ramon Hernandez .12 .30
171 Ted Lilly .12 .30
172 Terrence Long .12 .30
173 Tim Hudson .20 .50
174 Bret Boone .12 .30
175 Carlos Guillen .12 .30
176 Dan Wilson .12 .30
177 Edgar Martinez .20 .50
178 Freddy Garcia .12 .30
179 Gil Meche .12 .30
180 Ichiro Suzuki .50 1.25
181 Jamie Moyer .12 .30
182 Joel Pineiro .12 .30
183 John Olerud .12 .30
184 Mike Cameron .12 .30
185 Randy Winn .12 .30
186 Ryan Franklin .12 .30
187 Kazuhiro Sasaki .12 .30
188 Aubrey Huff .12 .30
189 Carl Crawford .20 .50
190 Joe Kennedy .12 .30
191 Marlon Anderson .12 .30
192 Rey Ordonez .12 .30
193 Rocco Baldelli .12 .30
194 Toby Hall .12 .30
195 Travis Lee .12 .30
196 Alex Rodriguez .50 1.25
197 Carl Everett .12 .30
198 Chan Ho Park .20 .50
199 Einar Diaz .12 .30
200 Hank Blalock .12 .30
201 Ismael Valdes .12 .30
202 Juan Gonzalez .12 .30
203 Mark Teixeira .30 .75
204 Mike Young .12 .30
205 Rafael Palmeiro .20 .50
206 Carlos Delgado .12 .30
207 Kelvim Escobar .12 .30
208 Eric Hinske .12 .30
209 Frank Catalanotto .12 .30
210 Josh Phelps .12 .30
211 Orlando Hudson .12 .30
212 Roy Halladay .30 .75
213 Shannon Stewart .12 .30
214 Vernon Wells .12 .30
215 Carlos Baerga .12 .30
216 Curt Schilling .20 .50
217 Junior Spivey .12 .30
218 Luis Gonzalez .12 .30
219 Lyle Overbay .12 .30
220 Mark Grace .20 .50
221 Matt Williams .12 .30
222 Randy Johnson .30 .75
223 Shea Hillenbrand .12 .30
224 Steve Finley .12 .30
225 Andruw Jones .12 .30
226 Chipper Jones .30 .75
227 Gary Sheffield .12 .30
228 Greg Maddux .50 1.25
229 Javy Lopez .12 .30
230 John Smoltz .30 .75
231 Marcus Giles .12 .30
232 Mike Hampton .12 .30
233 Rafael Furcal .12 .30
234 Robert Fick .12 .30
235 Russ Ortiz .12 .30
236 Alex Gonzalez .12 .30
237 Carlos Zambrano .20 .50
238 Corey Patterson .12 .30
239 Hee Seop Choi .12 .30
240 Kerry Wood .12 .30
241 Mark Bellhorn .12 .30
242 Mark Prior .20 .50
243 Moises Alou .12 .30
244 Sammy Sosa .30 .75
245 Aaron Boone .12 .30
246 Adam Dunn .20 .50
247 Austin Kearns .12 .30
248 Barry Larkin .20 .50
249 Felipe Lopez .12 .30
250 Jose Guillen .12 .30
251 Ken Griffey Jr. .50 1.25
252 Jason LaRue .12 .30
253 Scott Williamson .12 .30
254 Sean Casey .12 .30
255 Shawn Chacon .12 .30
256 Chris Stynes .12 .30
257 Jason Jennings .12 .30
258 Jay Payton .12 .30
259 Jose Hernandez .12 .30
260 Larry Walker .20 .50
261 Preston Wilson .12 .30
262 Ronnie Belliard .12 .30
263 Todd Helton .20 .50
264 A.J. Burnett .20 .50
265 Alex Gonzalez .12 .30
266 Brad Penny .12 .30
267 Derrek Lee .12 .30
268 Ivan Rodriguez .20 .50
269 Josh Beckett .20 .50
270 Juan Encarnacion .12 .30
271 Juan Pierre .12 .30
272 Luis Castillo .12 .30
273 Mike Lowell .12 .30
274 Todd Hollandsworth .12 .30
275 Billy Wagner .12 .30
276 Brad Ausmus .12 .30
277 Craig Biggio .20 .50
278 Jeff Bagwell .20 .50
279 Jeff Kent .12 .30
280 Lance Berkman .20 .50
281 Richard Hidalgo .12 .30
282 Roy Oswalt .20 .50
283 Wade Miller .12 .30
284 Adrian Beltre .12 .30
285 Brian Jordan .12 .30
286 Cesar Izturis .12 .30
287 Dave Roberts .12 .30
288 Eric Gagne .12 .30
289 Fred McGriff .12 .30
290 Hideo Nomo .30 .75
291 Kazuhisa Ishii .12 .30
292 Kevin Brown .12 .30
293 Paul Lo Duca .12 .30
294 Shawn Green .12 .30
295 Ben Sheets .12 .30
296 Geoff Jenkins .12 .30
297 Rey Sanchez .12 .30
298 Richie Sexson .12 .30
299 Wes Helms .12 .30
300 Brad Wilkerson .12 .30
301 Claudio Vargas .12 .30
302 Endy Chavez .12 .30
303 Fernando Tatis .12 .30
304 Javier Vazquez .12 .30
305 Jose Vidro .12 .30
306 Michael Barrett .12 .30
307 Orlando Cabrera .12 .30
308 Tony Armas Jr. .12 .30
309 Vladimir Guerrero .30 .75
310 Zach Day .12 .30
311 Al Leiter .12 .30
312 Cliff Floyd .12 .30
313 Jae Weong Seo .12 .30
314 Jeromy Burnitz .12 .30
315 Mike Piazza .30 .75
316 Mo Vaughn .12 .30
317 Roberto Alomar .20 .50
318 Roger Cedeno .12 .30
319 Tom Glavine .20 .50
320 Jose Reyes .20 .50
321 Bobby Abreu .12 .30
322 Brett Myers .12 .30
323 David Bell .12 .30
324 Jim Thome .20 .50
325 Jimmy Rollins .20 .50
326 Kevin Millwood .12 .30
327 Marlon Byrd .12 .30
328 Mike Lieberthal .12 .30
329 Pat Burrell .12 .30
330 Randy Wolf .12 .30
331 Aramis Ramirez .12 .30
332 Brian Giles .12 .30
333 Jason Kendall .12 .30
334 Kenny Lofton .12 .30
335 Kip Wells .12 .30
336 Kris Benson .12 .30
337 Randall Simon .12 .30
338 Reggie Sanders .12 .30
339 Albert Pujols .75 2.00
340 Edgar Renteria .12 .30
341 Fernando Vina .12 .30
342 J.D. Drew .12 .30
343 Jim Edmonds .20 .50
344 Matt Morris .12 .30
345 Mike Matheny .12 .30
346 Scott Rolen .20 .50
347 Tino Martinez .20 .50
348 Woody Williams .12 .30
349 Brian Lawrence .12 .30
350 Mark Kotsay .12 .30
351 Mark Loretta .12 .30
352 Ramon Vazquez .12 .30
353 Rondell White .12 .30
354 Ryan Klesko .12 .30
355 Sean Burroughs .12 .30
356 Trevor Hoffman .20 .50
357 Xavier Nady .12 .30
358 Andres Galarraga .12 .30
359 Barry Bonds .60 1.50
360 Benito Santiago .12 .30
361 Deivi Cruz .12 .30
362 Edgardo Alfonzo .12 .30
363 J.T. Snow .12 .30
364 Jason Schmidt .12 .30
365 Kirk Rueter .12 .30
366 Kurt Ainsworth .12 .30
367 Marquis Grissom .12 .30
368 Ray Durham .12 .30
369 Rich Aurilia .12 .30
370 Tim Worrell .12 .30
371 Troy Glaus TC .25 .60
372 Melvin Mora TC .25 .60
373 Nomar Garciaparra TC .60 1.50
374 Magglio Ordonez TC .40 1.00
375 Omar Vizquel TC .40 1.00
376 Dmitri Young TC .25 .60
377 Mike Sweeney TC .25 .60
378 Torii Hunter TC .25 .60
379 Derek Jeter TC 1.50 4.00
380 Barry Zito TC .25 .60
381 Ichiro Suzuki TC 1.00 2.50
382 Rocco Baldelli TC .25 .60
383 Alex Rodriguez TC 1.00 2.50
384 Carlos Delgado TC .25 .60
385 Randy Johnson TC .60 1.50
386 Greg Maddux TC 1.00 2.50
387 Sammy Sosa TC .60 1.50
388 Ken Griffey Jr. TC 1.00 2.50
389 Todd Helton TC .40 1.00
390 Ivan Rodriguez TC .40 1.00
391 Jeff Bagwell TC .40 1.00
392 Hideo Nomo TC .60 1.50
393 Richie Sexson TC .25 .60
394 Vladimir Guerrero TC .60 1.50
395 Mike Piazza TC .60 1.50
396 Jim Thome TC .40 1.00
397 Jason Kendall TC .25 .60
398 Albert Pujols TC 1.50 4.00
399 Ryan Klesko TC .25 .60
400 Barry Bonds TC 1.25 3.00

2004 Donruss Autographs

RANDOM INSERTS IN PACKS
#'d CARD PRINTS B/WN 5-141 COPIES PER
NO PRICING ON QTY OF 12 OR LESS
51 Ian Ferguson 4.00 10.00
73 Darin Erstad/5
106 Mark Buehrle/141 12.50 30.00
112 Josh Bard 4.00 10.00
123 Omar Infante 4.00 10.00
172 Terrence Long 4.00 10.00
188 Aubrey Huff/143 6.00 15.00
194 Toby Hall 4.00 10.00
217 Junior Spivey/132 4.00 10.00
234 Robert Fick 4.00 10.00
312 Cliff Floyd/12
349 Brian Lawrence 4.00 10.00

2004 Donruss Press Proofs Black

STATED PRINT RUN 10 SERIAL #'d SETS
NO PRICING DUE TO SCARCITY

2004 Donruss Press Proofs Blue

*PP BLUE 71-370: 4X TO 10X BASIC
*PP BLUE 1-25/371-400: 1.5X TO 4X BASIC
*PP BLUE 26-70: .75X TO 2X BASIC
STATED PRINT RUN 100 SERIAL #'d SETS

2004 Donruss Press Proofs Gold

STATED PRINT RUN 25 SERIAL #'d SETS
NO PRICING DUE TO SCARCITY

2004 Donruss Press Proofs Red

*PP RED 71-370: 2.5X TO 6X BASIC
*PP RED 1-25/371-400: 1X TO 2.5X BASIC
*PP RED 26-70: .5X TO 1.2X BASIC
STATED ODDS 1:12 RETAIL

2004 Donruss Stat Line Career

*71-370 p/r 200-443 2.5X TO 6X
*71-370 p/r 121-200: 3X TO 8X
*71-370 p/r 81-120: 4X TO 10X
*71-370 p/r 66-80: 5X TO 12X
*71-370 p/r 51-65: 5X TO 12X
*71-370 p/r 36-50: 6X TO 15X
*71-370 p/r 26-35: 8X TO 20X
*1-25/371-400 p/r 200-500: 1X TO 2.5X
*1-25/371-400 p/r 121-200: 1.25X TO 3X
*1-25/371-400 p/r 81-120: 1.5X TO 4X
*1-25/371-400 p/r 66-80: 2X TO 5X
*1-25/371-400 p/r 51-65: 2X TO 5X
*1-25/371-400 p/r 36-50: 2.5X TO 6X
*1-25/371-400 p/r 26-35: 3X TO 8X
*26-70 p/r 200-491: .5X TO 1.2X
*26-70 p/r 121-200: .6X TO 1.5X
*26-70 p/r 81-120: .75X TO 2X
*26-70 p/r 66-80: 1X TO 2.5X
*26-70 p/r 51-65: 1X TO 2.5X
*26-70 p/r 36-50: 1.25X TO 3X
*26-70 p/r 26-35: 1.5X TO 4X
RANDOM INSERTS IN PACKS
PRINT RUNS B/WN 6-500 COPIES PER
NO PRICING ON QTY OF 25 OR LESS

2004 Donruss Stat Line Season

*71-370 p/r 121-193: 3X TO 8X
*71-370 p/r 81-120: 4X TO 10X
*71-370 p/r 66-80: 5X TO 12X
*71-370 p/r 51-65: 5X TO 12X
*71-370 p/r 36-50: 6X TO 15X
*71-370 p/r 26-35: 8X TO 20X
*1-25/371-400 p/r 201-225:1X TO 2.5X
*1-25/371-400 p/r 121-200: 1.25X TO 3X
*1-25/371-400 p/r 81-120: 1.5X TO 4X
*1-25/371-400 p/r 66-80: 2X TO 5X
*1-25/371-400 p/r 51-65: 2X TO 5X
*1-25/371-400 p/r 36-50: 2.5X TO 6X
*1-25/371-400 p/r 26-35: 3X TO 8X
*26-70 p/r 201-261: .5X TO 1.2X
*26-70 p/r 121-200: .6X TO 1.5X
*26-70 p/r 81-120: .75X TO 2X
*26-70 p/r 66-80: 1X TO 2.5X
*26-70 p/r 51-65: 1X TO 2.5X
*26-70 p/r 36-50: 1.25X TO 3X
*26-70 p/r 26-35: 1.5X TO 4X
RANDOM INSERTS IN PACKS
PRINT RUNS B/WN 1-261 COPIES PER
NO PRICING ON QTY OF 25 OR LESS

2004 Donruss All-Stars American League

STATED PRINT RUN 1000 SERIAL #'d SETS
*BLACK: .6X TO 1.5X BASIC
BLACK PRINT RUN 250 SERIAL #'d SETS
RANDOM INSERTS IN PACKS
1 Alex Rodriguez 2.50 6.00
2 Roger Clemens 2.00 5.00
3 Ichiro Suzuki 2.50 6.00
4 Barry Zito .60 1.50
5 Garret Anderson .60 1.50
6 Derek Jeter 4.00 10.00
7 Manny Ramirez 1.50 4.00
8 Pedro Martinez 1.00 2.50
9 Alfonso Soriano .60 1.50
10 Carlos Delgado .60 1.50

2004 Donruss All-Stars National League

STATED PRINT RUN 1000 SERIAL #'d SETS
*BLACK: .6X TO 1.5X BASIC
BLACK PRINT RUN 250 SERIAL #'d SETS
RANDOM INSERTS IN PACKS
1 Barry Bonds 3.00 8.00
2 Andruw Jones .60 1.50
3 Scott Rolen 1.00 2.50
4 Austin Kearns .60 1.50
5 Mark Prior 1.00 2.50
6 Vladimir Guerrero 1.50 4.00
7 Jeff Bagwell 1.00 2.50
8 Mike Piazza 1.50 4.00
9 Albert Pujols 4.00 10.00
10 Randy Johnson 1.50 4.00

2004 Donruss Bat Kings

1-4 PRINT RUN 250 SERIAL #'d SETS
5-8 PRINT RUN 100 SERIAL #'d SETS
*STUDIO 1-4: .75X TO 2X BASIC
STUDIO 1-4 PRINT RUN 50 SERIAL #'d SETS
STUDIO 5-8 PRINT RUN 25 SERIAL #'d SETS
STUDIO 5-8 NO PRICING DUE TO SCARCITY
1 Alex Rodriguez 03 8.00 20.00
2 Albert Pujols 03 10.00 25.00
3 Chipper Jones 03 6.00 15.00
4 Lance Berkman 03 4.00 10.00
5 Cal Ripken 88 40.00 80.00
6 George Brett 87 15.00 40.00
7 Don Mattingly 89 15.00 40.00
8 Roberto Clemente 02 50.00 100.00

2004 Donruss Craftsmen

STATED PRINT RUN 2000 SERIAL #'d SETS
*BLACK: 1X TO 2.5X BASIC
BLACK PRINT RUN 275 SERIAL #'d SETS
*MASTER: 1.25X TO 3X BASIC
MASTER PRINT RUN 150 SERIAL #'d SETS
RANDOM INSERTS IN PACKS
1 Alex Rodriguez 1.50 4.00
2 Mark Prior .60 1.50
3 Ichiro Suzuki 1.50 4.00
4 Barry Bonds 2.00 5.00
5 Ken Griffey Jr. 1.50 4.00
6 Alfonso Soriano .40 1.00
7 Mike Piazza 1.00 2.50
8 Chipper Jones 1.00 2.50
9 Derek Jeter 2.50 6.00
10 Randy Johnson 1.00 2.50
11 Sammy Sosa 1.00 2.50
12 Roger Clemens 1.25 3.00
13 Nomar Garciaparra 1.00 2.50
14 Greg Maddux 1.50 4.00
15 Albert Pujols 2.50 6.00

2004 Donruss Diamond Kings Inserts

STATED PRINT RUN 2500 SERIAL #'d SETS
*BLACK: .75X TO 2X BASIC
BLACK PRINT RUN 100 SERIAL #'d SETS
*STUDIO: .6X TO 1.5X BASIC
STUDIO PRINT RUN 250 SERIAL #'d SETS
1 Derek Jeter 5.00 12.00
2 Greg Maddux 3.00 8.00
3 Albert Pujols 5.00 12.00
4 Ichiro Suzuki 3.00 8.00
5 Alex Rodriguez 3.00 8.00
6 Roger Clemens 2.50 6.00
7 Andruw Jones .75 2.00
8 Barry Bonds 4.00 10.00
9 Jeff Bagwell 1.25 3.00
10 Randy Johnson 2.00 5.00
11 Scott Rolen 1.25 3.00
12 Lance Berkman 1.25 3.00
13 Barry Zito .75 2.00
14 Manny Ramirez 2.00 5.00
15 Carlos Delgado .75 2.00
16 Alfonso Soriano .75 2.00
17 Todd Helton 1.25 3.00
18 Mike Mussina 1.25 3.00
19 Austin Kearns .75 2.00
20 Nomar Garciaparra 2.00 5.00
21 Chipper Jones 2.00 5.00
22 Mark Prior 1.25 3.00
23 Jim Thome 1.25 3.00
24 Vladimir Guerrero 2.00 5.00
25 Pedro Martinez 1.25 3.00

2004 Donruss Elite Series

STATED PRINT RUN 1500 SERIAL #'d SETS
*BLACK: 1X TO 2.5X BASIC
BLACK PRINT RUN 150 SERIAL #'d SETS
DOMINATORS PRINT 25 SERIAL #'d SETS
DOMINATORS NO PRICE DUE TO SCARCITY
1 Albert Pujols 4.00 10.00
2 Barry Zito .60 1.50
3 Gary Sheffield .60 1.50
4 Mike Mussina 1.00 2.50
5 Lance Berkman 1.00 2.50
6 Alfonso Soriano .60 1.50
7 Randy Johnson 1.50 4.00
8 Nomar Garciaparra 1.50 4.00
9 Austin Kearns .60 1.50
10 Manny Ramirez 1.50 4.00
11 Mark Prior 1.00 2.50
12 Alex Rodriguez 2.50 6.00
13 Derek Jeter 4.00 10.00
14 Barry Bonds 3.00 8.00
15 Roger Clemens 2.00 5.00

2004 Donruss Inside View

STATED PRINT RUN 1250 SERIAL #'d SETS
1 Derek Jeter 3.00 8.00
2 Greg Maddux 2.00 5.00
3 Albert Pujols 3.00 8.00
4 Ichiro Suzuki 2.00 5.00
5 Alex Rodriguez 2.00 5.00
6 Roger Clemens 1.50 4.00
7 Andruw Jones .50 1.25
8 Barry Bonds 2.50 6.00
9 Jeff Bagwell .75 2.00
10 Randy Johnson 1.25 3.00
11 Scott Rolen .75 2.00
12 Lance Berkman .75 2.00
13 Barry Zito .50 1.25
14 Manny Ramirez 1.25 3.00
15 Carlos Delgado .50 1.25
16 Alfonso Soriano .50 1.25
17 Todd Helton .75 2.00
18 Mike Mussina .75 2.00
19 Austin Kearns .50 1.25
20 Nomar Garciaparra 1.25 3.00
21 Chipper Jones 1.25 3.00
22 Mark Prior .75 2.00
23 Jim Thome .75 2.00
24 Vladimir Guerrero 1.25 3.00
25 Pedro Martinez .75 2.00

2004 Donruss Jersey Kings

1-6 PRINT RUN 250 SERIAL #'d SETS
7-12 PRINT RUN 100 SERIAL #'d SETS
*STUDIO 1-6: .75X TO 2X BASIC JSY KINGS
STUDIO 1-6 PRINT RUN 50 SERIAL #'d SETS
STUDIO 7-12 PRINT RUN 25 SERIAL #'d SETS
STUDIO 7-12 NO PRICING DUE TO SCARCITY
1 Alfonso Soriano 03 4.00 10.00
2 Sammy Sosa 03 6.00 15.00
3 Roger Clemens 03 10.00 25.00
4 Nomar Garciaparra 03 8.00 20.00
5 Mark Prior 03 6.00 15.00
6 Vladimir Guerrero 03 6.00 15.00
7 Don Mattingly 89 15.00 40.00
8 Roberto Clemente 02 50.00 100.00
9 George Brett 87 15.00 40.00
10 Nolan Ryan 01 20.00 50.00
11 Cal Ripken 01 40.00 80.00
12 Mike Schmidt 01 15.00 40.00

2004 Donruss Longball Leaders

STATED PRINT RUN 1500 SERIAL #'d SETS
*BLACK: .75X TO 2X BASIC LL
BLACK PRINT RUN 250 SERIAL #'d SETS
*DIE CUT: 1.25X TO 3X BASIC LL
DIE CUT PRINT RUN 50 SERIAL #'d SETS
1 Barry Bonds 2.50 6.00
2 Alfonso Soriano .50 1.25
3 Adam Dunn .75 2.00
4 Alex Rodriguez 2.00 5.00
5 Jim Thome .75 2.00
6 Garret Anderson .50 1.25
7 Juan Gonzalez .50 1.25
8 Jeff Bagwell .75 2.00
9 Gary Sheffield .50 1.25
10 Sammy Sosa 1.25 3.00

2004 Donruss Mound Marvels

STATED PRINT RUN 750 SERIAL #'d SETS
*BLACK: .75X TO 2X BASIC MM
BLACK PRINT RUN 175 SERIAL #'d SETS
RANDOM INSERTS IN PACKS
1 Mark Prior 1.25 3.00
2 Curt Schilling 1.25 3.00
3 Mike Mussina 1.25 3.00
4 Kevin Brown .75 2.00
5 Pedro Martinez 1.25 3.00
6 Mark Mulder .75 2.00
7 Kerry Wood .75 2.00
8 Greg Maddux 3.00 8.00
9 Kevin Millwood .75 2.00
10 Barry Zito .75 2.00
11 Roger Clemens 2.50 6.00
12 Randy Johnson 2.00 5.00
13 Hideo Nomo 2.00 5.00
14 Tim Hudson 1.25 3.00
15 Tom Glavine 1.25 3.00

2004 Donruss Power Alley Red

STATED PRINT RUN 2500 SERIAL #'d SETS
BLACK DC PRINT RUN 1 SERIAL #'d SET
BLACK DC NO PRICING DUE TO SCARCITY
*BLUE: .6X TO 1.5X BASIC RED
BLUE PRINT RUN 1000 SERIAL #'d SETS
*BLUE DC: 1.25X TO 3X BASIC RED
BLUE DC PRINT RUN 100 SERIAL #'d SETS
GREEN PRINT RUN 25 SERIAL #'d SETS

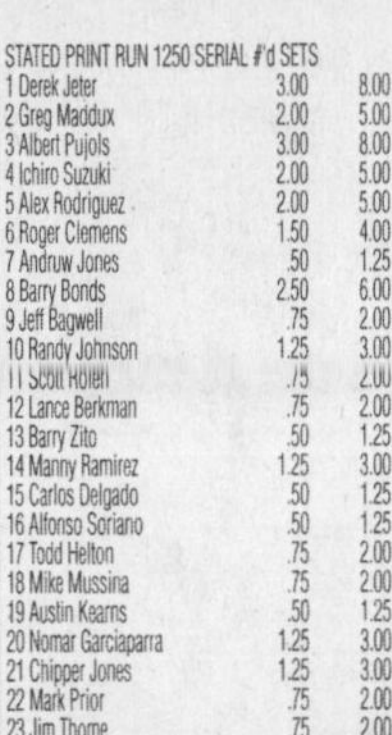

GREEN NO PRICING DUE TO SCARCITY
GREEN DC 5 SERIAL #'d SETS
GREEN DC NO PRICING DUE TO SCARCITY
*PURPLE: 1X TO 2.5X BASIC RED
PURPLE PRINT RUN 250 SERIAL #'d SETS
PURPLE DC PRINT RUN 25 SERIAL #'d SETS
PURPLE DC NO PRICING DUE TO SCARCITY
*RED DC: 1X TO 2.5X BASIC RED
RED DC PRINT RUN 250 SERIAL #'d SETS
*YELLOW: 1.25X TO 3X BASIC RED
YELLOW PRINT RUN 100 SERIAL #'d SETS
YELLOW DC PRINT RUN 10 SERIAL #'d SETS
YELLOW DC NO PRICING DUE TO SCARCITY
1 Albert Pujols 2.50 6.00
2 Mike Piazza 1.00 2.50
3 Carlos Delgado .40 1.00
4 Barry Bonds 2.00 5.00
5 Jim Edmonds .60 1.50
6 Nomar Garciaparra 1.00 2.50
7 Alfonso Soriano .40 1.00
8 Alex Rodriguez 1.50 4.00
9 Lance Berkman .60 1.50
10 Scott Rolen .60 1.50
11 Manny Ramirez 1.00 2.50
12 Rafael Palmeiro .60 1.50
13 Sammy Sosa 1.00 2.50
14 Adam Dunn .60 1.50
15 Andruw Jones .40 1.00
16 Jim Thome .60 1.50
17 Jason Giambi .40 1.00
18 Jeff Bagwell .60 1.50
19 Juan Gonzalez .40 1.00
20 Austin Kearns .40 1.00

2004 Donruss Production Line Average

PRINT RUNS B/WN 300-359 COPIES PER
*BLACK: .75X TO 2X BASIC AVG
BLACK PRINT RUN 35 SERIAL #'d SETS
*DIE CUT: .5X TO 1.2X BASIC AVG
DIE CUT PRINT RUN 100 SERIAL #'d SETS
1 Gary Sheffield/330 1.00 2.50
2 Ichiro Suzuki/312 4.00 10.00
3 Todd Helton/358 1.50 4.00
4 Manny Ramirez/325 2.50 6.00
5 Garret Anderson/315 1.00 2.50
6 Barry Bonds/341 5.00 12.00
7 Albert Pujols/359 6.00 15.00
8 Derek Jeter/324 6.00 15.00
9 Nomar Garciaparra/301 2.50 6.00
10 Hank Blalock/300 1.00 2.50

2004 Donruss Production Line OBP

PRINT RUNS B/WN 396-529 COPIES PER
*BLACK: 1X TO 2.5X BASIC OBP
BLACK PRINT RUN 40 SERIAL #'d SETS
*DIE CUT: .6X TO 1.5X BASIC OBP
DIE CUT PRINT RUN 100 SERIAL #'d SETS
1 Todd Helton/458 1.25 3.00
2 Albert Pujols/439 5.00 12.00
3 Larry Walker/422 1.25 3.00
4 Barry Bonds/529 4.00 10.00
5 Chipper Jones/402 2.00 5.00
6 Manny Ramirez/427 2.00 5.00
7 Gary Sheffield/419 .75 2.00
8 Lance Berkman/412 1.25 3.00
9 Alex Rodriguez/396 3.00 8.00
10 Jason Giambi/412 .75 2.00

2004 Donruss Production Line OPS

PRINT RUNS B/WN 910-1278 COPIES PER
*BLACK: .75X TO 2X BASIC OPS
BLACK PRINT RUN 125 SERIAL #'d SETS
*DIE CUT: .75X TO 2X BASIC OPS
DIE CUT PRINT RUN 100 SERIAL #'d SETS
1 Albert Pujols/1106 4.00 10.00
2 Barry Bonds/1278 3.00 8.00
3 Gary Sheffield/1023 .60 1.50
4 Todd Helton/1088 1.00 2.50
5 Scott Rolen/910 1.00 2.50
6 Manny Ramirez/1014 1.50 4.00
7 Alex Rodriguez/995 2.50 6.00
8 Jim Thome/958 1.00 2.50
9 Jason Giambi/939 .60 1.50
10 Frank Thomas/952 1.50 4.00

2004 Donruss Production Line Slugging

PRINT RUNS B/WN 541-749 COPIES PER
*BLACK: .75X TO 2X BASIC SLG
BLACK PRINT RUN 75 SERIAL #'d SETS
*DIE CUT: .6X TO 1.5X BASIC SLG
DIE CUT PRINT RUN 100 SERIAL #'d SETS
1 Alex Rodriguez/600 3.00 8.00
2 Frank Thomas/562 2.00 5.00
3 Garret Anderson/541 .75 2.00
4 Albert Pujols/667 5.00 12.00
5 Sammy Sosa/553 2.00 5.00
6 Gary Sheffield/604 .75 2.00
7 Manny Ramirez/587 2.00 5.00
8 Jim Edmonds/617 1.25 3.00
9 Barry Bonds/749 4.00 10.00
10 Todd Helton/630 1.25 3.00

2004 Donruss Recollection Autographs

PRINT RUNS B/WN 1-100 COPIES PER
NO PRICING ON QTY OF 50 OR LESS
27 John Candelaria 88 Black/83 6.00 15.00
39 Jack Clark 87/67 8.00 20.00
40 Jack Clark 88/75 6.00 15.00
69 Sid Fernandez 86/52 8.00 20.00
72 Sid Fernandez 88/58 8.00 20.00
83 George Foster 83/50 8.00 20.00
84 George Foster 84/70 8.00 20.00
85 George Foster 85/50 8.00 20.00
86 George Foster 86/83 6.00 15.00
91 Cliff Lee 03/100 15.00 40.00
92 Terrence Long 01/90 4.00 10.00
93 Melvin Mora 03/50 8.00 20.00
100 Jesse Orosco 86 Blue/65 5.00 12.00
102 Jesse Orosco 87 Blue/90 4.00 10.00
115 Jose Vidro 01/89 4.00 10.00

2004 Donruss Timber and Threads

STATED ODDS 1:40
*STUDIO: .75X TO 2X BASIC TT
STUDIO RANDOM INSERTS IN PACKS
STUDIO PRINT RUN 50 SERIAL #'d SETS
1 Adam Dunn Jsy 3.00 8.00
2 Alex Rodriguez Blue Jsy 6.00 15.00
3 Alex Rodriguez White Jsy 6.00 15.00
4 Andruw Jones Jsy 4.00 10.00
5 Austin Kearns Jsy 3.00 8.00
6 Carlos Beltran Jsy 3.00 8.00
7 Carlos Lee Jsy 3.00 8.00
8 Frank Thomas Jsy 4.00 10.00
9 Greg Maddux Jsy 4.00 10.00
10 Hideo Nomo Jsy 4.00 10.00
11 Jeff Bagwell Jsy 4.00 10.00
12 Lance Berkman Jsy 3.00 8.00
13 Magglio Ordonez Jsy 3.00 8.00
14 Mike Sweeney Jsy 3.00 8.00
15 Randy Johnson Jsy 4.00 10.00
16 Rocco Baldelli Jsy 3.00 8.00
17 Roger Clemens Jsy 6.00 15.00
18 Sammy Sosa Jsy 4.00 10.00
19 Shawn Green Jsy 3.00 8.00
20 Tom Glavine Jsy 4.00 10.00
21 Adam Dunn Bat 3.00 8.00
22 Andruw Jones Bat 4.00 10.00
23 Bobby Abreu Bat 3.00 8.00
24 Hank Blalock Bat 3.00 8.00
25 Ivan Rodriguez Bat 4.00 10.00
26 Jim Edmonds Bat 3.00 8.00
27 Josh Phelps Bat 3.00 8.00
28 Juan Gonzalez Bat 3.00 8.00
29 Lance Berkman Bat 3.00 8.00
30 Larry Walker Bat 3.00 8.00
31 Magglio Ordonez Bat 3.00 8.00
32 Manny Ramirez Bat 4.00 10.00
33 Mike Piazza Bat 4.00 10.00
34 Nomar Garciaparra Bat 6.00 15.00
35 Paul Lo Duca Bat 3.00 8.00
36 Roberto Alomar Bat 4.00 10.00
37 Rocco Baldelli Bat 3.00 8.00
38 Sammy Sosa Bat 4.00 10.00
39 Vernon Wells Bat 3.00 8.00
40 Vladimir Guerrero Bat 4.00 10.00

2004 Donruss Timber and Threads Autographs

RANDOM INSERTS IN PACKS
PRINT RUNS B/WN 5-50 COPIES PER
NO PRICING ON QTY OF 34 OR LESS
2 Alex Rodriguez Blue Jsy/5
5 Austin Kearns Jsy/19
6 Carlos Beltran Jsy/34
7 Carlos Lee Jsy/25
8 Frank Thomas Jsy/5
9 Greg Maddux Jsy/5
10 Hideo Nomo Jsy/5
11 Jeff Bagwell Jsy/5
12 Lance Berkman Jsy/5
13 Magglio Ordonez Jsy/30
14 Mike Sweeney Jsy/25
17 Roger Clemens Jsy/5
19 Shawn Green Jsy/5
20 Tom Glavine Jsy/5
21 Adam Dunn Bat/5
22 Andruw Jones Bat/5
23 Bobby Abreu Bat/50 10.00 25.00
24 Hank Blalock Bat/50 10.00 25.00
25 Ivan Rodriguez Bat/7
26 Jim Edmonds Bat/5
27 Josh Phelps Bat/50 10.00 25.00
28 Juan Gonzalez Bat/5
31 Magglio Ordonez Bat/30
32 Manny Ramirez Bat/5
35 Paul Lo Duca Bat/50 10.00 25.00
36 Roberto Alomar Bat/10
37 Rocco Baldelli Bat/15
40 Vladimir Guerrero Bat/50 30.00 60.00

2004 Donruss-Playoff Hawaii Fans of the Game Gandolfini

These cards, which were issued to select attendees of the 2004 Hawaii Trade Conference feature Sopranos star James Gandolfini. The cards were issued to promote the 2004 Donruss/Playoff initiative of having celebrity signatures within their 2004 products.

FG1 James Gandolfini/300
FG1A James Gandolfini AU/50

2005 Donruss

This 400-card set was released in November, 2004. The set was issued in 10-card packs with an $2 SRP which came 24 packs to a box and 16 boxes to a case. Subsets included: Diamond Kings (1-25), Rated Rookies (26-70), Team Checklists (371-400). All of these subets were issued at a stated rate of one in six.

COMPLETE SET (400) 75.00 150.00
COMP.SET w/o SP's (300) 10.00 25.00
COMMON CARD (71-3 .10 .30
COMMON (1-25/371-400) .40 1.00
COMMON CARD (26-70) .75 2.00
1-25 STATED ODDS 1:6
26-70 STATED ODDS 1:6
371-400 STATED ODDS 1:6
1 Garret Anderson DK .40 1.00
2 Vladimir Guerrero DK 1.00 2.50
3 Manny Ramirez DK 1.00 2.50
4 Kerry Wood DK .40 1.00
5 Sammy Sosa DK 1.00 2.50
6 Magglio Ordonez DK .60 1.50
7 Adam Dunn DK .60 1.50
8 Todd Helton DK .60 1.50
9 Josh Beckett DK .60 1.50
10 Miguel Cabrera DK 1.00 2.50
11 Lance Berkman DK .60 1.50
12 Carlos Beltran DK .40 1.00
13 Shawn Green DK .40 1.00
14 Roger Clemens DK 1.25 3.00
15 Mike Piazza DK 1.00 2.50
16 Alex Rodriguez DK 1.50 4.00
17 Derek Jeter DK 2.50 6.00
18 Mark Mulder DK .40 1.00
19 Jim Thome DK .60 1.50
20 Albert Pujols DK 2.50 6.00
21 Scott Rolen DK .60 1.50
22 Aubrey Huff DK .40 1.00
23 Alfonso Soriano DK .60 1.50
24 Hank Blalock DK .40 1.00
25 Vernon Wells DK .40 1.00
26 Kazuo Matsui RR .75 2.00
27 B.J. Upton RR 1.25 3.00
28 Charles Thomas RR .75 2.00
29 Akinori Otsuka RR .75 2.00
30 David Aardsma RR .75 2.00
31 Travis Blackley RR .75 2.00
32 Brad Halsey RR .75 2.00
33 David Wright RR 3.00 8.00
34 Kazuhito Tadano RR .75 2.00
35 Casey Kotchman RR .75 2.00
36 Khalil Greene RR .75 2.00
37 Adrian Gonzalez RR 1.25 3.00
38 Zack Greinke RR 1.25 3.00
39 Chad Cordero RR .75 2.00
40 Scott Kazmir RR 2.00 5.00
41 Jeremy Guthrie RR 1.25 3.00
42 Noah Lowry RR .75 2.00
43 Chase Utley RR 1.25 3.00
44 Billy Traber RR .75 2.00
45 Aaron Baldiris RR .75 2.00
46 Abe Alvarez RR .75 2.00
47 Angel Chavez RR .75 2.00
48 Joe Mauer RR 2.00 5.00
49 Joey Gathright RR .75 2.00
50 John Gall RR .75 2.00
51 Ronald Belisario RR .75 2.00
52 Ryan Wing RR .75 2.00
53 Scott Proctor RR .75 2.00
54 Yadier Molina RR 1.25 3.00
55 Carlos Hines RR .75 2.00
56 Frankie Francisco RR .75 2.00
57 Graham Koonce RR .75 2.00
58 Jake Woods RR .75 2.00
59 Jason Bartlett RR .75 2.00
60 Mike Rouse RR .75 2.00
61 Phil Stockman RR .75 2.00
62 Renyel Pinto RR .75 2.00
63 Roberto Novoa RR .75 2.00
64 Ryan Meaux RR .75 2.00
65 Dave Crouthers RR .75 2.00
66 Justin Knoedler RR .75 2.00
67 Justin Leone RR .75 2.00
68 Nick Regilio RR .75 2.00
69 Mike Gosling RR .75 2.00
70 Onil Joseph RR .75 2.00
71 Bartolo Colon .12 .30
72 Brad Fullmer .12 .30
73 Chone Figgins .12 .30
74 Darin Erstad .12 .30
75 Francisco Rodriguez .20 .50
76 Garret Anderson .12 .30
77 Jarrod Washburn .12 .30
78 John Lackey .12 .30
79 Jose Guillen .12 .30
80 Robb Quinlan .12 .30
81 Tim Salmon .12 .30
82 Troy Glaus .12 .30
83 Troy Percival .12 .30
84 Vladimir Guerrero .30 .75
85 Brandon Webb .20 .50
86 Casey Fossum .12 .30
87 Luis Gonzalez .12 .30
88 Randy Johnson .30 .75
89 Richie Sexson .12 .30
90 Robby Hammock .12 .30
91 Roberto Alomar .20 .50
92 Adam LaRoche .12 .30
93 Andruw Jones .12 .30
94 Bubba Nelson .12 .30
95 Chipper Jones .30 .75
96 J.D. Drew .12 .30
97 John Smoltz .30 .75
98 Johnny Estrada .12 .30
99 Marcus Giles .12 .30
100 Mike Hampton .12 .30
101 Nick Green .12 .30
102 Rafael Furcal .12 .30
103 Russ Ortiz .12 .30
104 Adam Loewen .12 .30
105 Brian Roberts .12 .30
106 Javy Lopez .12 .30
107 Jay Gibbons .12 .30
108 Larry Bigbie UER .12 .30
Player pictured is Brian Roberts
109 Luis Matos .12 .30
110 Melvin Mora .12 .30
111 Miguel Tejada .20 .50
112 Rafael Palmeiro .20 .50
113 Rodrigo Lopez .12 .30
114 Sidney Ponson .12 .30
115 Bill Mueller .12 .30
116 Byung-Hyun Kim .12 .30
117 Curt Schilling .20 .50
118 David Ortiz .30 .75
119 Derek Lowe .12 .30
120 Doug Mientkiewicz .12 .30
121 Jason Varitek .30 .75
122 Johnny Damon .20 .50
123 Keith Foulke .12 .30
124 Kevin Youkilis .12 .30
125 Manny Ramirez .30 .75
126 Orlando Cabrera .12 .30
127 Pedro Martinez .20 .50
128 Trot Nixon .12 .30
129 Aramis Ramirez .12 .30
130 Carlos Zambrano .20 .50
131 Corey Patterson .12 .30
132 Derrek Lee .12 .30
133 Greg Maddux .50 1.25
134 Kerry Wood .12 .30
135 Mark Prior .20 .50
136 Matt Clement .12 .30
137 Moises Alou .12 .30
138 Nomar Garciaparra .30 .75
139 Sammy Sosa .30 .75
140 Todd Walker .12 .30
141 Angel Guzman .12 .30
142 Billy Koch .12 .30
143 Carlos Lee .12 .30
144 Frank Thomas .30 .75
145 Magglio Ordonez .20 .50
146 Mark Buehrle .20 .50
147 Paul Konerko .20 .50
148 Wilson Valdez .12 .30
149 Adam Dunn .20 .50
150 Austin Kearns .12 .30
151 Barry Larkin .20 .50
152 Benito Santiago .12 .30
153 Jason LaRue .12 .30
154 Ken Griffey Jr. .50 1.25
155 Ryan Wagner .12 .30
156 Sean Casey .12 .30
157 Brandon Phillips .12 .30
158 Brian Tallet .12 .30
159 C.C. Sabathia .20 .50
160 Cliff Lee .20 .50
161 Jeremy Guthrie .20 .50
162 Jody Gerut .12 .30
163 Matt Lawton .12 .30
164 Omar Vizquel .20 .50
165 Travis Hafner .12 .30
166 Victor Martinez .20 .50
167 Charles Johnson .12 .30
168 Garrett Atkins .12 .30
169 Jason Jennings .12 .30
170 Jay Payton .12 .30
171 Jeromy Burnitz .12 .30
172 Joe Kennedy .12 .30
173 Larry Walker .20 .50
174 Preston Wilson .12 .30
175 Todd Helton .20 .50
176 Vinny Castilla .12 .30
177 Bobby Higginson .12 .30
178 Brandon Inge .12 .30
179 Carlos Guillen UER .12 .30
Photo is Alex Sanchez
180 Carlos Pena .20 .50
181 Craig Monroe .12 .30
182 Dmitri Young .12 .30
183 Eric Munson .12 .30
184 Fernando Vina .12 .30
185 Ivan Rodriguez .20 .50
186 Jeremy Bonderman .12 .30
187 Rondell White .12 .30
188 A.J. Burnett .20 .50
189 Dontrelle Willis .12 .30
190 Guillermo Mota .12 .30
191 Hee Seop Choi .12 .30
192 Jeff Conine .12 .30
193 Josh Beckett .20 .50
194 Juan Encarnacion .12 .30
195 Juan Pierre .12 .30
196 Luis Castillo .12 .30
197 Miguel Cabrera .30 .75
198 Mike Lowell .12 .30
199 Paul Lo Duca .12 .30
200 Andy Pettitte .20 .50
201 Brad Ausmus .12 .30
202 Carlos Beltran .12 .30
203 Chris Burke .12 .30
204 Craig Biggio .20 .50
205 Jeff Bagwell .20 .50
206 Jeff Kent .12 .30
207 Lance Berkman .20 .50
208 Morgan Ensberg .12 .30
209 Octavio Dotel .12 .30
210 Roger Clemens .40 1.00
211 Roy Oswalt .20 .50
212 Tim Redding .12 .30
213 Angel Berroa .12 .30
214 Juan Gonzalez .12 .30
215 Ken Harvey .12 .30
216 Mike Sweeney .12 .30
217 Adrian Beltre .12 .30
218 Brad Penny .12 .30
219 Eric Gagne .12 .30
220 Hideo Nomo .30 .75
221 Hong-Chih Kuo .12 .30
222 Jeff Weaver .12 .30
223 Kazuhisa Ishii .12 .30
224 Milton Bradley .12 .30
225 Shawn Green .12 .30
226 Steve Finley .12 .30
227 Danny Kolb .12 .30
228 Geoff Jenkins .12 .30
229 Junior Spivey .12 .30
230 Lyle Overbay .12 .30
231 Rickie Weeks .20 .50
232 Scott Podsednik .12 .30
233 Brad Radke .12 .30
234 Corey Koskie .12 .30
235 Cristian Guzman .12 .30
236 Dustan Mohr .12 .30
237 Eddie Guardado .12 .30
238 J.D. Durbin .12 .30
239 Jacque Jones .12 .30
240 Joe Nathan .12 .30
241 Johan Santana .30 .75
242 Lew Ford .12 .30
243 Michael Cuddyer .12 .30
244 Shannon Stewart .12 .30
245 Torii Hunter .12 .30
246 Brad Wilkerson .12 .30
247 Carl Everett .12 .30
248 Jeff Fassero .12 .30
249 Jose Vidro .12 .30
250 Livan Hernandez .12 .30
251 Michael Barrett .12 .30
252 Tony Batista .12 .30
253 Zach Day .12 .30
254 Al Leiter .12 .30
255 Cliff Floyd .12 .30
256 Jae Weong Seo .12 .30
257 John Olerud .12 .30
258 Jose Reyes .20 .50
259 Mike Cameron .12 .30
260 Mike Piazza .30 .75
261 Richard Hidalgo .12 .30
262 Tom Glavine .20 .50
263 Vance Wilson .12 .30
264 Alex Rodriguez .50 1.25
265 Armando Benitez .12 .30
266 Bernie Williams .20 .50
267 Bubba Crosby .12 .30
268 Chien-Ming Wang .50 1.25
269 Derek Jeter .75 2.00
270 Esteban Loaiza .12 .30
271 Gary Sheffield .12 .30
272 Hideki Matsui .50 1.25
273 Jason Giambi .12 .30
274 Javier Vazquez .12 .30
275 Jorge Posada .20 .50
276 Jose Contreras .12 .30
277 Kenny Lofton .12 .30
278 Kevin Brown .12 .30
279 Mariano Rivera .30 .75
280 Mike Mussina .20 .50
281 Barry Zito .12 .30
282 Bobby Crosby .12 .30
283 Eric Byrnes .12 .30
284 Eric Chavez .12 .30
285 Erubiel Durazo .12 .30
286 Jermaine Dye .12 .30
287 Mark Kotsay .12 .30
288 Mark Mulder .12 .30
289 Rich Harden .12 .30
290 Tim Hudson .20 .50
291 Billy Wagner .12 .30
292 Bobby Abreu .12 .30
293 Brett Myers .12 .30

294 Eric Milton .12 .30
295 Jim Thome .20 .50
296 Jimmy Rollins .20 .50
297 Kevin Millwood .12 .30
298 Marlon Byrd .12 .30
299 Mike Lieberthal .12 .30
300 Pat Burrell .12 .30
301 Randy Wolf .12 .30
302 Craig Wilson .12 .30
303 Jack Wilson .12 .30
304 Jacob Cruz .12 .30
305 Jason Bay .12 .30
306 Jason Kendall .12 .30
307 Jose Castillo .12 .30
308 Kip Wells .12 .30
309 Brian Giles .12 .30
310 Brian Lawrence .12 .30
311 Chris Oxspring .12 .30
312 David Wells .12 .30
313 Freddy Guzman .12 .30
314 Jake Peavy .12 .30
315 Mark Loretta .12 .30
316 Ryan Klesko .12 .30
317 Sean Burroughs .12 .30
318 Trevor Hoffman .20 .50
319 Xavier Nady .12 .30
320 A.J. Pierzynski .12 .30
321 Edgardo Alfonzo .12 .30
322 J.T. Snow .12 .30
323 Jason Schmidt .12 .30
324 Jerome Williams .12 .30
325 Kirk Rueter .12 .30
326 Bret Boone .12 .30
327 Bucky Jacobsen .12 .30
328 Edgar Martinez .20 .50
329 Freddy Garcia .12 .30
330 Ichiro Suzuki .50 1.25
331 Jamie Moyer .12 .30
332 Joel Pineiro .12 .30
333 Scott Spiezio .12 .30
334 Shigetoshi Hasegawa .12 .30
335 Albert Pujols .75 2.00
336 Edgar Renteria .12 .30
337 Jason Isringhausen .12 .30
338 Jim Edmonds .20 .50
339 Matt Morris .12 .30
340 Mike Matheny .12 .30
341 Reggie Sanders .12 .30
342 Scott Rolen .20 .50
343 Woody Williams .12 .30
344 Jeff Suppan .12 .30
345 Aubrey Huff .12 .30
346 Carl Crawford .20 .50
347 Chad Gaudin .12 .30
348 Delmon Young .30 .75
349 Dewon Brazelton .12 .30
350 Jose Cruz Jr. .12 .30
351 Rocco Baldelli .12 .30
352 Tino Martinez .20 .50
353 Toby Hall .12 .30
354 Alfonso Soriano .20 .50
355 Brian Jordan .12 .30
356 Francisco Cordero .12 .30
357 Hank Blalock .12 .30
358 Kenny Rogers .12 .30
359 Kevin Mench .12 .30
360 Laynce Nix .12 .30
361 Mark Teixeira .30 .75
362 Michael Young .20 .50
363 Alex S. Gonzalez .12 .30
364 Alexis Rios .20 .50
365 Carlos Delgado .12 .30
366 Eric Hinske .12 .30
367 Frank Catalanotto .12 .30
368 Josh Phelps .12 .30
369 Roy Halladay .30 .75
370 Vernon Wells .12 .30
371 Vladimir Guerrero TC 1.00 2.50
372 Randy Johnson TC 1.00 2.50
373 Chipper Jones TC 1.00 2.50
374 Miguel Tejada TC .60 1.50
375 Pedro Martinez TC .60 1.50
376 Sammy Sosa TC 1.00 2.50
377 Frank Thomas TC 1.00 2.50
378 Ken Griffey Jr. TC 1.50 4.00
379 Victor Martinez TC .60 1.50
380 Todd Helton TC .60 1.50
381 Ivan Rodriguez TC .60 1.50
382 Miguel Cabrera TC 1.00 2.50
383 Roger Clemens TC 1.25 3.00
384 Ken Harvey TC .40 1.00
385 Eric Gagne TC .40 1.00
386 Lyle Overbay TC .40 1.00
387 Shannon Stewart TC .40 1.00
388 Brad Wilkerson TC .40 1.00
389 Mike Piazza TC 1.00 2.50
390 Alex Rodriguez TC 1.50 4.00
391 Mark Mulder TC .40 1.00
392 Jim Thome TC .60 1.50
393 Jack Wilson TC .40 1.00
394 Khalil Greene TC .40 1.00
395 Jason Schmidt TC .40 1.00
396 Ichiro Suzuki TC 1.50 4.00
397 Albert Pujols TC 2.50 6.00
398 Rocco Baldelli TC .40 1.00
399 Alfonso Soriano TC .60 1.50
400 Vernon Wells TC .40 1.00

2005 Donruss 25th Anniversary

*25th ANN 71-370: 10X TO 25X BASIC
*25th ANN 1-25/371-400: 4X TO 10X BASIC
*25th ANN 26-70: 2X TO 5X BASIC
STATED PRINT RUN 25 SERIAL #'d SETS

2005 Donruss Press Proofs Black

STATED PRINT RUN 10 SERIAL #'d SETS
NO PRICING DUE TO SCARCITY

2005 Donruss Press Proofs Blue

*BLUE 71-370: 4X TO 10X BASIC
*BLUE 1-25/371-400: 1.5X TO 4X BASIC
*BLUE 26-70: .75X TO 2X BASIC
STATED PRINT RUN 100 SERIAL #'d SETS

2005 Donruss Press Proofs Gold

*GOLD 71-370: 10X TO 25X BASIC
*GOLD 1-25/371-400: 4X TO 10X BASIC
*GOLD 26-70: 2X TO 5X BASIC
STATED PRINT RUN 25 SERIAL #'d SETS

2005 Donruss Press Proofs Red

*RED 71-370: X TO X BASIC
*RED 1-25/371-400: 1X TO 2.5X BASIC
*RED 26-70: .5X TO 1.2X BASIC
STATED PRINT RUN 200 SERIAL #'d SETS

2005 Donruss Stat Line Career

*71-370 p/r 200-394 2.5X TO 6X
*71-370 p/r 121-200: 3X TO 8X
*71-370 p/r 81-120: 4X TO 10X
*71-370 p/r 51-80: 5X TO 12X
*71-370 p/r 36-50: 6X TO 15X
*71-370 p/r 26-35: 8X TO 20X
*71-370 p/r 16-25: 10X TO 25X
*1-25/371-400 p/r 200-574:1X TO 2.5X
*1-25/371-400 p/r 121-200: 1.25X TO 3X
*1-25/371-400 p/r 81-120: 1.5X TO 4X
*1-25/371-400 p/r 51-80: 2X TO 5X
*1-25/371-400 p/r 36-50: 2.5X TO 6X
*1-25/371-400 p/r 26-35: 3X TO 8X
*26-70 p/r 200-263: .5X TO 1.2X
*26-70 p/r 121-200: .6X TO 1.5X
*26-70 p/r 81-120: .75X TO 2X
*26-70 p/r 51-80: 1X TO 2.5X
*26-70 p/r 36-50: 1.25X TO 3X
*26-70 p/r 26-35: 1.5X TO 4X
*26-70 p/r 16-25: 2X TO 5X
RANDOM INSERTS IN PACKS
PRINT RUNS B/WN 6-500 COPIES PER
NO PRICING ON QTY OF 15 OR LESS

2005 Donruss Stat Line Season

*71-370 p/r 121-158: 3X TO 8X
*71-370 p/r 81-120: 4X TO 10X
*71-370 p/r 51-80: 5X TO 12X
*71-370 p/r 36-50: 6X TO 15X
*71-370 p/r 26-35: 8X TO 20X
*71-370 p/r 16-25: 10X TO 25X
*1-25/371-400 p/r 81-120: 1.5X TO 4X
*1-25/371-400 p/r 51-80: 2X TO 5X
*1-25/371-400 p/r 36-50: 2.5X TO 6X
*1-25/371-400 p/r 26-35: 3X TO 8X
*1-25/371-400 p/r 16-25: 4X TO 10X
*26-70 p/r 121-200: .6X TO 1.5X
*26-70 p/r 81-120: .75X TO 2X
*26-70 p/r 51-80: 1X TO 2.5X
*26-70 p/r 36-50: 1.25X TO 3X
*26-70 p/r 26-35: 1.5X TO 4X
*26-70 p/r 16-25: 2X TO 5X
RANDOM INSERTS IN PACKS
PRINT RUNS B/WN 1-158 COPIES PER
NO PRICING ON QTY OF 15 OR LESS

2005 Donruss Autographs

80 Robb Quinlan 4.00 10.00
101 Nick Green 4.00 10.00
141 Angel Guzman 4.00 10.00
148 Wilson Valdez 4.00 10.00
172 Joe Kennedy 4.00 10.00
178 Brandon Inge 6.00 15.00
181 Craig Monroe 4.00 10.00
263 Vance Wilson 4.00 10.00
304 Jacob Cruz 4.00 10.00
327 Bucky Jacobsen 4.00 10.00
344 Jeff Suppan 6.00 15.00

2005 Donruss '85 Reprints

STATED PRINT RUN 1985 SERIAL #'d SETS
1 Eddie Murray 2.00 5.00
2 George Brett 4.00 10.00
3 Nolan Ryan 5.00 12.00
4 Mike Schmidt 4.00 10.00
5 Tony Gwynn 2.50 6.00
7 Cal Ripken 8.00 20.00
8 Dwight Gooden .75 2.00
9 Roger Clemens 2.50 6.00
10 Don Mattingly 4.00 10.00
11 Kirby Puckett 2.00 5.00
12 Orel Hershiser .75 2.00

2005 Donruss '85 Reprints Material

STATED PRINT RUN 85 SERIAL #'d SETS
1 Eddie Murray Jsy 10.00 25.00
2 George Brett Jsy 15.00 40.00
3 Nolan Ryan Jkt 15.00 40.00
4 Mike Schmidt Jkt 15.00 40.00
5 Tony Gwynn Jsy 10.00 25.00
7 Cal Ripken Jsy 30.00 60.00
8 Dwight Gooden Jsy 6.00 15.00
9 Roger Clemens Jsy 15.00 40.00
10 Don Mattingly Jsy 15.00 40.00
11 Kirby Puckett Jsy 10.00 25.00
12 Orel Hershiser Jsy 6.00 15.00

2005 Donruss All-Stars AL

STATED PRINT RUN 1000 SERIAL #'d SETS
*GOLD: .75X TO 2X BASIC
GOLD PRINT RUN 100 SERIAL #'d SETS
RANDOM INSERTS IN PACKS
1 Alex Rodriguez 3.00 8.00
2 Alfonso Soriano 1.25 3.00
3 Curt Schilling 1.25 3.00
4 Derek Jeter 5.00 12.00
5 Hank Blalock .75 2.00
6 Hideki Matsui 3.00 8.00
7 Ichiro Suzuki 3.00 8.00
8 Ivan Rodriguez 1.25 3.00
9 Jason Giambi .75 2.00
10 Manny Ramirez 2.00 5.00
11 Mark Mulder .75 2.00
12 Michael Young 1.25 3.00
13 Tim Hudson 1.25 3.00
14 Victor Martinez 1.25 3.00
15 Vladimir Guerrero 2.00 5.00

2005 Donruss All-Stars NL

STATED PRINT RUN 1000 SERIAL #'d SETS
*GOLD: .75X TO 2X BASIC
GOLD PRINT RUN 100 SERIAL #'d SETS
RANDOM INSERTS IN PACKS

1 Albert Pujols 5.00 12.00
2 Ben Sheets .75 2.00
3 Edgar Renteria .75 2.00
4 Eric Gagne .75 2.00
5 Jack Wilson .75 2.00
6 Jason Schmidt .75 2.00
7 Jeff Kent .75 2.00
8 Jim Thome 1.25 3.00
9 Ken Griffey Jr. 3.00 8.00
10 Mike Piazza 2.00 5.00
11 Roger Clemens 2.50 6.00
12 Sammy Sosa 2.00 5.00
13 Scott Rolen 1.25 3.00
14 Sean Casey .75 2.00
15 Todd Helton 1.25 3.00

2005 Donruss Bat Kings

RANDOM INSERTS IN PACKS
PRINT RUNS B/WN 100-250 COPIES PER
1 Garret Anderson/250 3.00 8.00
2 Vladimir Guerrero/250 4.00 10.00
3 Cal Ripken/100 30.00 60.00
4 Manny Ramirez/250 4.00 10.00
5 Kerry Wood/250 3.00 8.00
6 Sammy Sosa/250 4.00 10.00
7 Magglio Ordonez/250 3.00 8.00
8 Adam Dunn/250 3.00 8.00
9 Todd Helton/250 4.00 10.00
10 Josh Beckett/250 3.00 8.00
11 Miguel Cabrera/250 4.00 10.00
12 Lance Berkman/250 3.00 8.00
13 Carlos Beltran/250 3.00 8.00
14 Shawn Green/250 3.00 8.00
15 Roger Clemens/100 8.00 20.00
16 Mike Piazza/250 4.00 10.00
17 Nolan Ryan/100 20.00 50.00
18 Mark Mulder/250 3.00 8.00
19 Jim Thome/250 4.00 10.00
20 Albert Pujols/250 8.00 20.00
21 Scott Rolen/250 4.00 10.00
22 Aubrey Huff/250 3.00 8.00
23 Alfonso Soriano/250 3.00 8.00

2005 Donruss Bat Kings Signatures

PRINT RUNS B/WN 5-10 COPIES PER
NO PRICING DUE TO SCARCITY

2005 Donruss Craftsmen

STATED PRINT RUN 2000 SERIAL #'d SETS
*BLACK: 1.25X TO 3X BASIC
BLACK PRINT RUN 100 SERIAL #'d SETS
*MASTER: 1X TO 2.5X BASIC
MASTER PRINT RUN 250 SERIAL #'d SETS
MASTER BLACK PRINT RUN 10 #'d SETS
NO MASTER BLACK PRICING AVAILABLE
RANDOM INSERTS IN PACKS
1 Albert Pujols 2.50 6.00
2 Alex Rodriguez 1.50 4.00
3 Alfonso Soriano .60 1.50
4 Andruw Jones .40 1.00
5 Carlos Beltran .40 1.00
6 Derek Jeter 2.50 6.00
7 Greg Maddux 1.50 4.00
8 Hank Blalock .40 1.00
9 Ichiro Suzuki 1.50 4.00
10 Jeff Bagwell .60 1.50
11 Jim Thome .60 1.50
12 Josh Beckett .60 1.50
13 Ken Griffey Jr. 1.50 4.00
14 Manny Ramirez 1.00 2.50
15 Mark Mulder .40 1.00
16 Mark Prior .60 1.50
17 Mark Teixeira 1.00 2.50
18 Miguel Tejada .60 1.50
19 Mike Mussina .60 1.50
20 Mike Piazza 1.00 2.50
21 Nomar Garciaparra 1.00 2.50
22 Pedro Martinez .60 1.50
23 Rafael Palmeiro .60 1.50
24 Randy Johnson 1.00 2.50
25 Roger Clemens 1.25 3.00
26 Sammy Sosa 1.00 2.50
27 Scott Rolen .60 1.50
28 Tim Hudson .60 1.50
29 Vernon Wells .40 1.00
30 Vladimir Guerrero 1.00 2.50

2005 Donruss Diamond Kings Inserts

STATED PRINT RUN 2005 SERIAL #'d SETS
*STUDIO: 1X TO 2.5X BASIC
STUDIO PRINT RUN 250 SERIAL #'d SETS
*STUDIO BLACK: 1.25X TO 3X BASIC
STUDIO BLACK PRINT RUN 100 #'d SETS
RANDOM INSERTS IN PACKS
1 Garret Anderson .40 1.00
2 Vladimir Guerrero 1.00 2.50
3 Manny Ramirez 1.00 2.50
4 Kerry Wood .40 1.00
5 Sammy Sosa 1.00 2.50
6 Magglio Ordonez .60 1.50
7 Adam Dunn .60 1.50
8 Todd Helton .60 1.50
9 Josh Beckett .60 1.50
10 Miguel Cabrera 1.00 2.50
11 Lance Berkman .60 1.50
12 Carlos Beltran .40 1.00
13 Shawn Green .40 1.00
14 Roger Clemens 1.25 3.00
15 Mike Piazza 1.00 2.50
16 Alex Rodriguez 1.50 4.00
17 Derek Jeter 2.50 6.00
18 Mark Mulder .40 1.00
19 Jim Thome .60 1.50
20 Albert Pujols 2.50 6.00
21 Scott Rolen .60 1.50
22 Aubrey Huff .40 1.00
23 Alfonso Soriano .60 1.50
24 Hank Blalock .40 1.00
25 Vernon Wells .40 1.00

2005 Donruss Elite Series

STATED PRINT RUN 1500 SERIAL #'d SETS
*BLACK: .75X TO 2X BASIC
BLACK PRINT RUN 100 SERIAL #'d SETS
*DOMINATOR: .6X TO 1.5X BASIC
DOMINATOR PRINT RUN 250 #'d SETS
*DOM.BLACK: 1.5X TO 4X BASIC
DOM.BLACK PRINT RUN 25 #'d SETS
RANDOM INSERTS IN PACKS
1 Albert Pujols 4.00 10.00
2 Alex Rodriguez 2.50 6.00
3 Alfonso Soriano 1.00 2.50
4 Derek Jeter 4.00 10.00
5 Hank Blalock .60 1.50
6 Ichiro Suzuki 2.50 6.00
7 Ivan Rodriguez 1.00 2.50
8 Jim Thome 1.00 2.50
9 Ken Griffey Jr. 2.50 6.00
10 Manny Ramirez 1.50 4.00
11 Mark Mulder .60 1.50
12 Mark Prior 1.00 2.50
13 Michael Young 1.00 2.50
14 Miguel Cabrera 1.50 4.00
15 Miguel Tejada 1.00 2.50
16 Mike Piazza 1.50 4.00
17 Nomar Garciaparra 1.50 4.00
18 Rafael Palmeiro 1.00 2.50
19 Randy Johnson 1.50 4.00
20 Roger Clemens 2.00 5.00
21 Sammy Sosa 1.50 4.00
22 Scott Rolen 1.00 2.50
23 Tim Hudson 1.00 2.50
24 Todd Helton 1.00 2.50
25 Vladimir Guerrero 1.50 4.00

2005 Donruss Fans of the Game

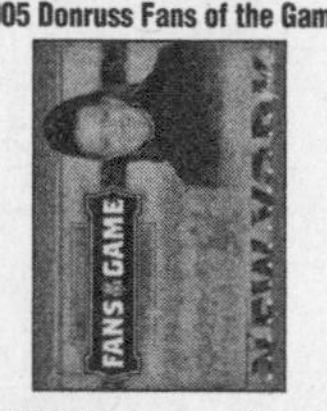

COMPLETE SET (5) 4.00 10.00
1 Jesse Ventura 1.25 3.00
2 John C. McGinley .75 2.00
3 Susie Essman .75 2.00
4 Dean Cain .75 2.00
5 Meat Loaf 1.25 3.00

2005 Donruss Fans of the Game Autographs

RANDOM INSERTS IN PACKS
SP PRINT RUNS PROVIDED BY DONRUSS
SP'S ARE NOT SERIAL-NUMBERED
1 Jesse Ventura 25.00 50.00
2 John C. McGinley SP/300 20.00 50.00
3 Susie Essman 20.00 50.00
4 Dean Cain SP/250 40.00 80.00
5 Meat Loaf 30.00 60.00

2005 Donruss Inside View

NO PRICING DUE TO SCARCITY
NOT INTENDED FOR PUBLIC RELEASE
1 Alex Rodriguez
2 Austin Kearns
3 Barry Larkin
4 C.C. Sabathia
5 Carlos Delgado
6 Chipper Jones
7 Craig Biggio
8 Derek Jeter
9 Derrek Lee
10 Edgar Martinez
11 Garret Anderson
12 Hideo Nomo
13 Ichiro Suzuki
14 Javier Vazquez
15 Javy Lopez
16 Ken Griffey Jr.
17 Magglio Ordonez
18 Rafael Palmeiro
19 Rocco Baldelli
20 Torii Hunter

2005 Donruss Jersey Kings

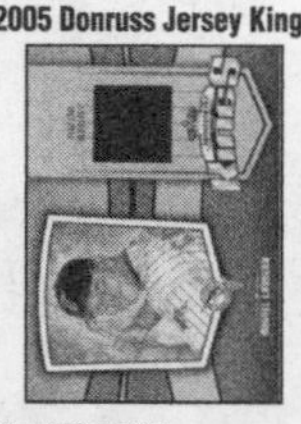

RANDOM INSERTS IN PACKS
PRINT RUNS B/WN 100-250 COPIES PER
1 Garret Anderson/250 3.00 8.00
2 Vladimir Guerrero/250 4.00 10.00
3 Cal Ripken/100 30.00 60.00
4 Manny Ramirez/250 4.00 10.00
5 Kerry Wood/250 3.00 8.00
6 Sammy Sosa/250 4.00 10.00
7 Magglio Ordonez/250 3.00 8.00
8 Adam Dunn/250 3.00 8.00
9 Todd Helton/250 4.00 10.00
10 Josh Beckett/250 3.00 8.00
11 Miguel Cabrera/250 4.00 10.00
12 Lance Berkman/250 3.00 8.00
13 Carlos Beltran/250 3.00 8.00
14 Shawn Green/250 3.00 8.00
15 Roger Clemens/250 6.00 15.00
16 Mike Piazza/250 4.00 10.00
17 Nolan Ryan/100 20.00 50.00
18 Mark Mulder/250 3.00 8.00
19 Jim Thome/250 4.00 10.00
20 Albert Pujols/250 8.00 20.00
21 Scott Rolen/250 4.00 10.00
22 Aubrey Huff/250 3.00 8.00
23 Alfonso Soriano/250 3.00 8.00
24 Hank Blalock/250 3.00 8.00
25 Vernon Wells/250 3.00 8.00

2005 Donruss Jersey Kings Signatures

PRINT RUNS B/WN 5-10 COPIES PER
NO PRICING DUE TO SCARCITY

2005 Donruss Longball Leaders

STATED PRINT RUN 1500 SERIAL #'d SETS
*BLACK: .75X TO 2X BASIC
BLACK PRINT RUN 250 SERIAL #'d SETS
*DIE CUT: 1.25X TO 3X BASIC
DIE CUT PRINT RUN 50 SERIAL #'d SETS
BLACK DC PRINT RUN 10 SERIAL #'d SETS
NO BLACK DC PRICING DUE TO SCARCITY
RANDOM INSERTS IN PACKS
1 Adam Dunn .75 2.00
2 Adrian Beltre .50 1.25
3 Albert Pujols 3.00 8.00
4 Alex Rodriguez 2.00 5.00
5 David Ortiz 1.25 3.00
6 Hank Blalock .50 1.25
7 J.D. Drew .50 1.25
8 Jeromy Burnitz .50 1.25
9 Jim Edmonds .75 2.00
10 Jim Thome .75 2.00
11 Manny Ramirez 1.25 3.00
12 Mark Teixeira 1.25 3.00
13 Moises Alou .50 1.25
14 Paul Konerko .75 2.00
15 Steve Finley .50 1.25

2005 Donruss Mound Marvels

STATED PRINT RUN 1000 SERIAL #'d SETS
BLACK PRINT RUN 10 SERIAL #'d SETS
NO BLACK PRICING DUE TO SCARCITY
RANDOM INSERTS IN PACKS
1 Curt Schilling 1.00 2.50
2 Dontrelle Willis .60 1.50
3 Eric Gagne .60 1.50
4 Greg Maddux 2.50 6.00
5 John Smoltz 1.50 4.00
6 Kenny Rogers .60 1.50
7 Kerry Wood .60 1.50
8 Mariano Rivera 1.50 4.00
9 Mark Mulder .60 1.50
10 Mark Prior 1.00 2.50
11 Mike Mussina 1.00 2.50
12 Pedro Martinez 1.00 2.50
13 Randy Johnson 1.50 4.00
14 Roger Clemens 2.00 5.00
15 Tim Hudson 1.00 2.50

2005 Donruss Power Alley Red

STATED PRINT RUN 2500 SERIAL #'d SETS
BLACK PRINT RUN 10 SERIAL #'d SETS
NO BLACK PRICING DUE TO SCARCITY
BLACK DC PRINT RUN 5 SERIAL #'d SETS
NO BLACK DC PRICING DUE TO SCARCITY
*BLUE: .6X TO 1.5X RED
BLUE PRINT RUN 1000 SERIAL #'d SETS
*BLUE DC: 1.25X TO 3X RED
BLUE DC PRINT RUN 100 SERIAL #'d SETS
*GREEN: 2.5X TO 6X RED
GREEN PRINT RUN 25 SERIAL #'d SETS
GREEN DC PRINT RUN 10 SERIAL #'d SETS
NO GREEN DC PRICING DUE TO SCARCITY
*PURPLE: 1X TO 2.5X RED
PURPLE PRINT RUN 250 SERIAL #'d SETS
*PURPLE DC: 1.5X TO 4X RED
PURPLE DC PRINT RUN 50 SERIAL #'d SETS
*RED DC: 1X TO 2.5X RED
RED DC PRINT RUN 250 SERIAL #'d SETS
*YELLOW: 1.25X TO 3X RED
YELLOW PRINT RUN 100 SERIAL #'d SETS
*YELLOW DC: 2.5X TO 6X RED
YELLOW DC PRINT RUN 25 #'d SETS
1 Adam Dunn .60 1.50
2 Adrian Beltre .40 1.00
3 Albert Pujols 2.50 6.00
4 Alex Rodriguez 1.50 4.00
5 Alfonso Soriano .60 1.50
6 Gary Sheffield .40 1.00
7 Hank Blalock .40 1.00
8 Hideki Matsui 1.50 4.00
9 J.D. Drew .40 1.00
10 Jeromy Burnitz .40 1.00
11 Jim Edmonds .60 1.50
12 Jim Thome .60 1.50
13 Ken Griffey Jr. 1.50 4.00
14 Manny Ramirez 1.00 2.50
15 Mark Teixeira 1.00 2.50
16 Miguel Cabrera 1.00 2.50
17 Miguel Tejada .60 1.50
18 Mike Lowell .40 1.00
19 Mike Piazza 1.00 2.50
20 Moises Alou .40 1.00
21 Paul Konerko .60 1.50
22 Sammy Sosa 1.00 2.50
23 Scott Rolen .60 1.50
24 Todd Helton .60 1.50
25 Vladimir Guerrero 1.00 2.50

2005 Donruss Production Line BA

PRINT RUNS B/WN 324-372 COPIES PER
*BLACK: 1X TO 2.5X BASIC PL
BLACK PRINT RUN 25 SERIAL #'d SETS
*DIE CUT: .5X TO 1.2X BASIC PL
DIE CUT PRINT RUN 100 SERIAL #'d SETS
BLACK DC PRINT RUN 10 SERIAL #'d SETS
NO BLACK DC PRICING DUE TO SCARCITY
RANDOM INSERTS IN PACKS
1 Ichiro Suzuki/372 4.00 10.00
2 Ivan Rodriguez/334 1.50 4.00
3 Juan Pierre/326 1.00 2.50
4 Adrian Beltre/334 1.00 2.50
5 Albert Pujols/331 6.00 15.00
6 Mark Loretta/335 1.00 2.50
7 Melvin Mora/340 1.00 2.50
8 Sean Casey/324 1.00 2.50
9 Todd Helton/347 1.50 4.00
10 Vladimir Guerrero/337 2.50 6.00

2005 Donruss Production Line OBP

PRINT RUNS B/WN 397-469 COPIES PER
*BLACK: 1.25X TO 3X BASIC PL
BLACK PRINT RUN 25 SERIAL #'d SETS
*DIE CUT: .6X TO 1.5X BASIC PL
DIE CUT PRINT RUN 100 SERIAL #'d SETS
BLACK DC PRINT RUN 10 SERIAL #'d SETS
NO BLACK DC PRICING DUE TO SCARCITY
RANDOM INSERTS IN PACKS

1 Albert Pujols/415 5.00 12.00
2 Bobby Abreu/428 .75 2.00
3 Lance Berkman/450 1.25 3.00
4 J.D. Drew/436 .75 2.00
5 Jorge Posada/400 1.25 3.00
6 Ichiro Suzuki/414 3.00 8.00
7 Manny Ramirez/397 2.00 5.00
8 Melvin Mora/419 .75 2.00
9 Todd Helton/469 1.25 3.00
10 Travis Hafner/410 .75 2.00

2005 Donruss Production Line OPS

PRINT RUNS B/WN 977-1088 COPIES PER
*BLACK: 1X TO 2.5X BASIC PL
BLACK PRINT RUN 50 SERIAL #'d SETS
*DIE CUT: .75X TO 2X BASIC PL
DIE CUT PRINT RUN 100 SERIAL #'d SETS
*BLACK DC: 1.5X TO 4X BASIC PL
BLACK DC PRINT RUN 25 SERIAL #'d SETS
RANDOM INSERTS IN PACKS

1 Albert Pujols/1072 4.00 10.00
2 David Ortiz/983 1.50 4.00
3 Adrian Beltre/1017 .60 1.50
4 J.D. Drew/1006 .60 1.50
5 Jim Thome/977 1.00 2.50
6 Lance Berkman/1016 1.00 2.50
7 Manny Ramirez/1009 1.50 4.00
8 Scott Rolen/1007 1.00 2.50
9 Todd Helton/1088 1.00 2.50
10 Travis Hafner/993 .60 1.50

2005 Donruss Production Line Slugging

PRINT RUNS B/WN 569-657 COPIES PER
*BLACK: .75X TO 2X BASIC PL
BLACK PRINT RUN 50 SERIAL #'d SETS
*DIE CUT: .6X TO 1.5X BASIC PL
DIE CUT PRINT RUN 100 SERIAL #'d SETS
*BLACK DC: 1.2X TO 3X BASIC PL
BLACK DC PRINT RUN 25 SERIAL #'d SETS
RANDOM INSERTS IN PACKS

1 Adrian Beltre/629 .75 2.00
2 Albert Pujols/657 5.00 12.00
3 Todd Helton/620 1.25 3.00
4 J.D. Drew/569 .75 2.00
5 Jim Edmonds/643 1.25 3.00
6 Jim Thome/581 1.25 3.00
7 Vladimir Guerrero/598 2.00 5.00
8 Manny Ramirez/613 2.00 5.00
9 Scott Rolen/598 1.25 3.00
10 Travis Hafner/583 .75 2.00

2005 Donruss Recollection Autographs

RANDOM INSERTS IN PACKS
PRINT RUNS B/WN 1-5 COPIES PER
NO PRICING DUE TO SCARCITY

2005 Donruss Rookies

STATED ODDS 1:23
BLACK PRINT RUN 10 SERIAL #'d SETS
NO BLACK PRICING DUE TO SCARCITY
*BLUE: .5X TO 1.2X BASIC
BLUE PRINT RUN 100 SERIAL #'d SETS
*GOLD: 1.25X TO 3X BASIC
GOLD PRINT RUN 25 SERIAL #'d SETS
*RED: .4X TO 1X BASIC
RED PRINT RUN 200 SERIAL #'d SETS

1 Fernando Nieve .40 1.00
2 Frankie Francisco .40 1.00

3 Jorge Vasquez .40 1.00
4 Travis Blackley .40 1.00
5 Joey Gathright .40 1.00
6 Kazuhito Tadano .40 1.00
7 Edwin Moreno .40 1.00
8 Lance Cormier .40 1.00
9 Justin Knoedler .40 1.00
10 Orlando Rodriguez .40 1.00
11 Renyel Pinto .40 1.00
12 Justin Leone .40 1.00
13 Dennis Sarfate .40 1.00
14 Sam Narron .40 1.00
15 Yadier Molina .60 1.50
16 Carlos Vasquez .40 1.00
17 Ryan Wing .40 1.00
18 Brad Halsey .40 1.00
19 Ryan Meaux .40 1.00
20 Michael Wuertz .40 1.00
21 Shawn Camp .40 1.00
22 Ruddy Yan .40 1.00
23 Don Kelly .40 1.00
24 Jake Woods .40 1.00
25 Colby Miller .40 1.00
26 Abe Alvarez .40 1.00
27 Mike Rouse .40 1.00
28 Phil Stockman .40 1.00
29 Kevin Cave .40 1.00
30 Chris Shelton .40 1.00
31 Tim Bittner .40 1.00
32 Mariano Gomez .40 1.00
33 Angel Chavez .40 1.00
34 Carlos Hines .40 1.00
35 Aarom Baldiris .40 1.00
36 Kazuo Matsui .40 1.00
37 Nick Regilio .40 1.00
38 Ivan Ochoa .40 1.00
39 Graham Koonce .40 1.00
40 Merkin Valdez .40 1.00
41 Greg Dobbs .40 1.00
42 Chris Oxspring .40 1.00
43 Dave Crouthers .40 1.00
44 Freddy Guzman .40 1.00
45 Akinori Otsuka .40 1.00
46 Jesse Crain .40 1.00
47 Casey Daigle .40 1.00
48 Roberto Novoa .40 1.00
49 Eddy Rodriguez .40 1.00
50 Jason Bartlett .40 1.00

2005 Donruss Rookies Stat Line Career

*SLC p/r 201-316: .4X TO 1X
*SLC p/r 121-200: .4X TO 1X
*SLC p/r 81-120: .5X TO 1.2X
*SLC p/r 51-80: .6X TO 1.5X
*SLC p/r 36-50: .75X TO 2X
*SLC p/r 26-35: 1X TO 2.5X
*SLC p/r 16-25: 1.25X TO 3X
RANDOM INSERTS IN DLP R/T PACKS
PRINT RUNS B/WN 1-316 COPIES PER
NO PRICING ON QTY OF 15 OR LESS

2005 Donruss Rookies Stat Line Season

*SLS p/r 121-200: .4X TO 1X
*SLS p/r 81-120: .5X TO 1.2X
*SLS p/r 51-80: .6X TO 1.5X
*SLS p/r 36-50: .75X TO 2X
*SLS p/r 26-35: 1X TO 2.5X
*SLS p/r 16-25: 1.25X TO 3X
PRINT RUNS B/WN 1-188 COPIES PER
NO PRICING ON QTY OF 15 OR LESS

2005 Donruss Rookies Autographs

COMMON SP 4.00 10.00
RANDOM INSERTS IN PACKS
6/12/14/21/36/40-41/44-47 DO NOT EXIST
SP INFO PROVIDED BY DONRUSS

1 Fernando Nieve 3.00 8.00
2 Frankie Francisco 3.00 8.00
3 Jorge Vasquez 3.00 8.00
4 Travis Blackley 3.00 8.00
5 Joey Gathright 4.00 10.00
7 Edwin Moreno 3.00 8.00
8 Lance Cormier 3.00 8.00
9 Justin Knoedler 3.00 8.00
10 Orlando Rodriguez 3.00 8.00
11 Renyel Pinto 3.00 8.00
13 Dennis Sarfate 3.00 8.00
15 Yadier Molina 12.50 30.00
16 Carlos Vasquez
17 Ryan Wing SP 4.00 10.00
18 Brad Halsey 4.00 10.00
19 Ryan Meaux 3.00 8.00
20 Michael Wuertz 3.00 8.00
22 Ruddy Yan 3.00 8.00
23 Don Kelly 3.00 8.00
24 Jake Woods 3.00 8.00
25 Colby Miller 3.00 8.00
26 Abe Alvarez 4.00 10.00
27 Mike Rouse SP 4.00 10.00
28 Phil Stockman 3.00 8.00
29 Kevin Cave 3.00 8.00
30 Chris Shelton SP 10.00 25.00
31 Tim Bittner 3.00 8.00
32 Mariano Gomez 3.00 8.00
33 Angel Chavez 3.00 8.00
34 Carlos Hines 3.00 8.00
35 Aarom Baldiris 3.00 8.00
37 Nick Regilio 3.00 8.00
38 Ivan Ochoa 3.00 8.00
39 Graham Koonce 3.00 8.00
42 Chris Oxspring 3.00 8.00
43 Dave Crouthers 3.00 8.00
48 Roberto Novoa 3.00 8.00
49 Eddy Rodriguez 3.00 8.00
50 Jason Bartlett 3.00 8.00

2005 Donruss Timber and Threads Bat

RANDOM INSERTS IN PACKS

1 Albert Pujols 6.00 15.00
2 Alfonso Soriano 3.00 8.00
3 Andre Dawson 3.00 8.00
4 Austin Kearns 3.00 8.00
5 Brad Penny 3.00 8.00
6 Carlos Beltran 3.00 8.00
7 Carlos Lee 3.00 8.00
8 Chipper Jones 4.00 10.00
9 Dale Murphy 4.00 10.00
10 Don Mattingly 8.00 20.00
11 Frank Thomas 4.00 10.00
12 Garret Anderson 3.00 8.00
13 Gary Carter 3.00 8.00
14 Hank Blalock 3.00 8.00
15 Jacque Jones 3.00 8.00
17 Jay Gibbons 3.00 8.00
18 Jeff Bagwell 4.00 10.00
20 Jermaine Dye 3.00 8.00
21 Jim Thome 4.00 10.00
22 Jose Vidro 3.00 8.00
23 Lance Berkman 3.00 8.00
24 Laynce Nix 3.00 8.00
25 Magglio Ordonez 3.00 8.00
26 Marcus Giles 3.00 8.00
27 Mark Prior 4.00 10.00
28 Mark Teixeira 4.00 10.00
29 Melvin Mora 3.00 8.00
30 Michael Young 3.00 8.00
31 Miguel Cabrera 4.00 10.00
32 Mike Lowell 3.00 8.00
33 Roy Oswalt 3.00 8.00
34 Sammy Sosa 4.00 10.00
35 Scott Rolen 4.00 10.00
36 Sean Burroughs 3.00 8.00
37 Sean Casey 3.00 8.00
38 Shannon Stewart 3.00 8.00
39 Torii Hunter 3.00 8.00
40 Travis Hafner 3.00 8.00

2005 Donruss Timber and Threads Bat Signature

PRINT RUNS B/WN 5-10 COPIES PER
NO PRICING DUE TO SCARCITY

2005 Donruss Timber and Threads Combo

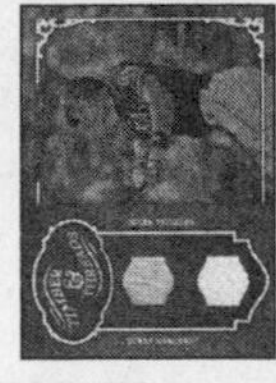

*COMBO: .6X TO 1.5X BAT

2005 Donruss Timber and Threads Combo Signature

PRINT RUNS B/WN 5-10 COPIES PER
NO PRICING DUE TO SCARCITY

2005 Donruss Timber and Threads Jersey

*JSY: .4X TO 1X BAT
19 Jeremy Bonderman 3.00 8.00

2005 Donruss Timber and Threads Jersey Signature

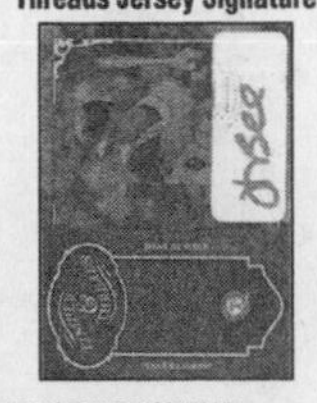

PRINT RUNS B/WN 5-10 COPIES PER
NO PRICING DUE TO SCARCITY

2001 Donruss Baseball's Best Bronze

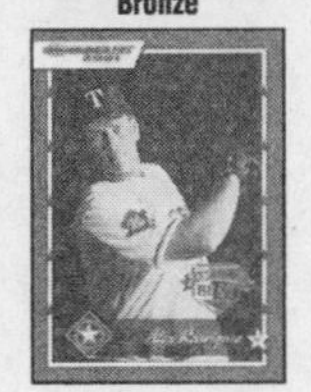

These 220 cards were available via a coupon randomly seeded into 2001 Donruss baseball packs at stated odds of 1:720. Consumers that pulled the Baseball's Best coupon (or bought it off the secondary market) then had to mail it into Donruss along with a check or money order for $105 prior to the January 20th, 2002 deadline to receive a factory sealed set 330-card set (of which contained the 220-card Baseball's Best set plus the 110-card Baseball's Best "The Rookies" set. The consumer did not know upon mailing in the coupon whether he or she would be receiving the Bronze, Silver or Gold version of the set of which were disseminated randomly. The 330 cards are glossy-coated parallels of the 220-card basic 2001 Donruss set and the 110-card 2001 Donruss the Rookies set. Only 999 Bronze sets were created, with each factory set box carrying serial-numbering (though the cards themselves are not numbered).

COMP.FACT.SET (330) 125.00 200.00
*STARS 1-150: 1.5X TO 4X BASIC CARDS
*ROOKIES 151-200: .2X TO .5X BASIC
*FAN CLUB 201-220: .4X TO 1X BASIC
5 Derek Jeter 8.00 20.00
156 Albert Pujols RR 40.00 80.00
195 Ichiro Suzuki RR 8.00 20.00
205 Derek Jeter FC 8.00 20.00

2001 Donruss Baseball's Best Bronze Rookies

Issued as a redemption "update" set to the basic 2001 Donruss set, these 105 cards were available via a coupon which could be mailed into Donruss. There were only 999 bronze sets produced.

*BRONZE: .6X TO 1.5X BASIC ROOKIES

2001 Donruss Baseball's Best Bronze Rookies Diamond Kings

Inserted one per Donruss Baseball's Best Bronze, these five cards parallel the Donruss Rookies Diamond Kings.

*BRONZE DK'S: .4X TO 1X BASIC DK'S
RDK3 Albert Pujols DK 40.00 80.00

2001 Donruss Baseball's Best Gold

These 220 cards were available via a coupon randomly seeded into 2001 Donruss baseball packs at stated odds of 1:720. Consumers that pulled the Baseball's Best coupon (or bought it off the secondary market) then had to mail it into Donruss along with a check or money order for $105 prior to the January 20th, 2002 deadline to receive a factory sealed set 330-card set (of which contained the 220-card Baseball's Best set plus the 110-card Baseball's Best "The Rookies" set. The consumer did not know upon mailing in the coupon whether he or she would be receiving the Bronze, Silver or Gold version of the set of which were disseminated randomly. The 330 cards are glossy-coated parallels of the 220-card basic 2001 Donruss set and the 110-card 2001 Donruss the Rookies set. Only 99 Gold sets were created, with each factory set box card carrying serial-numbering (though the cards themselves are not numbered).

COMP.FACT.SET (330) 350.00 600.00
*STARS 1-150: 4X TO 10X BASIC CARDS
*ROOKIES 151-200: .4X TO 1X BASIC
*FAN CLUB 201-220: 1X TO 2.5X BASIC
5 Derek Jeter 20.00 50.00
205 Derek Jeter FC 20.00 50.00

2001 Donruss Baseball's Best Gold Rookies

Issued as a redemption "update" set to the basic 2001 Donruss set, these 105 cards were available via a coupon which could be mailed into Donruss for these 110 cards. There were only 99 gold sets produced.

*GOLD: 2X TO 5X BASIC ROOKIES

2001 Donruss Baseball's Best Gold Rookies Diamond Kings

Inserted one per Donruss Baseball's Best Gold set, these five card parallel the Donruss Rookies Diamond Kings set.

*GOLD DK'S: 1.25X TO 3X BASIC DK'S
RDK3 Albert Pujols DK 90.00 150.00

2001 Donruss Baseball's Best Silver

These 220 cards were available via a coupon randomly seeded into 2001 Donruss baseball packs at stated odds of 1:720. Consumers that pulled the Baseball's Best coupon (or bought it off the secondary market) then had to mail it into Donruss along with a check or money order for $105 prior to the January 20th, 2002 deadline to receive a factory sealed set 330-card set (of which contained the 220-card Baseball's Best set plus the 110-card Baseball's Best "The Rookies" set. The consumer did not know upon mailing in the coupon whether he or she would be receiving the Bronze, Silver or Gold version of the set of which were disseminated randomly. The 330 cards are glossy-coated parallels of the 220-card basic 2001 Donruss set and the 110-card 2001 Donruss the Rookies set. Only 499 Silver sets were created, with each factory set box carrying serial-numbering on it (though the actual cards are not serial-numbered at all).

COMP.FACT.SET (330) 175.00 300.00
*STARS 1-150: 2.5X TO 6X BASIC CARDS
*ROOKIES 151-200: .3X TO .8X BASIC
*FAN CLUB 201-220: .6X TO 1.5X BASIC
5 Derek Jeter 12.50 30.00
205 Derek Jeter FC 12.50 30.00

2001 Donruss Baseball's Best Silver Rookies

Issued as a redemption "update" set to the basic 2001 Donruss set, these 105 cards were available via a coupon which could be mailed into Donruss for these 110 cards. There were only 499 silver sets produced.

*SILVER: 1X TO 2.5X BASIC ROOKIES

2001 Donruss Baseball's Best Silver Rookies Diamond Kings

Inserted one per Donruss Baseball's Best Silver set, these five cards parallel the Donruss Rookies Diamond Kings set. These cards were issued to a stated print run of 499 serial numbered sets.

*SILVER DK'S: .6X TO 1.5X BASIC DK'S

2003 Donruss Champions

This 309 card set was issued in two separate releases. The primary Donruss Champions product - containing cards 1-301 within the basic set - was released in April, 2003. The set was issued in eight card packs with an $5 SRP. These packs were issued in 24 pack boxes which came 20 boxes to a case. This primary set was originally supposed to be capped at 300 cards but a late addition of Hideki Matsui (card number 301) brought the complete set to 301 cards. In December, 2003, eight additional cards (302-309) were seeded within packs of DLP Rookies and Traded.

COMP.LO SET (301) 20.00 50.00
COMP.UPDATE SET (8) 3.00 8.00
COMMON CARD (302-309) .20 .50
1 Adam Kennedy .10 .30
2 Alfredo Amezaga .10 .30
3 Chone Figgins .10 .30
4 Darin Erstad .20 .50
5 David Eckstein .20 .50
6 Garret Anderson .20 .50
7 Jarrod Washburn .10 .30
8 Nolan Ryan Angels 1.25 3.00
9 Tim Salmon .30 .75
10 Troy Glaus .20 .50
11 Troy Percival .20 .50
12 Curt Schilling .20 .50
13 Junior Spivey .10 .30
14 Luis Gonzalez .20 .50
15 Mark Grace .30 .75
16 Randy Johnson .50 1.25
17 Steve Finley .20 .50
18 Andruw Jones .30 .75
19 Chipper Jones .50 1.25
20 Dale Murphy .30 .75
21 Gary Sheffield .20 .50
22 Greg Maddux .75 2.00
23 John Smoltz .30 .75
24 Andy Pratt .10 .30
25 Adam LaRoche .10 .30
26 Trey Hodges .10 .30
27 Warren Spahn .30 .75
28 Cal Ripken 1.50 4.00
29 Ed Rogers .10 .30
30 Brian Roberts .20 .50
31 Geronimo Gil .10 .30
32 Jay Gibbons .10 .30
33 Josh Towers .10 .30
34 Casey Fossum .10 .30
35 Cliff Floyd .20 .50
36 Derek Lowe .20 .50
37 Fred Lynn .20 .50
38 Freddy Sanchez .10 .30
39 Manny Ramirez .30 .75
40 Nomar Garciaparra .75 2.00
41 Pedro Martinez .30 .75
42 Rickey Henderson .50 1.25
43 Shea Hillenbrand .20 .50
44 Trot Nixon .20 .50
45 Bobby Hill .10 .30
46 Corey Patterson .10 .30
47 Fred McGriff .30 .75
48 Hee Seop Choi .10 .30
49 Juan Cruz .10 .30
50 Kerry Wood .20 .50
51 Mark Prior .30 .75
52 Moises Alou .20 .50
53 Nic Jackson .10 .30
54 Ryne Sandberg 1.00 2.50
55 Sammy Sosa .50 1.25
56 Carlos Lee .20 .50
57 Corwin Malone .10 .30
58 Frank Thomas .50 1.25
59 Joe Borchard .10 .30
60 Joe Crede .20 .50
61 Magglio Ordonez .20 .50
62 Mark Buehrle .20 .50
63 Paul Konerko .20 .50
64 Tim Hummel .10 .30
65 Jon Adkins .10 .30
66 Adam Dunn .20 .50
67 Austin Kearns .10 .30
68 Barry Larkin .30 .75
69 Jose Acevedo .10 .30
70 Corky Miller .10 .30
71 Eric Davis .20 .50
72 Ken Griffey Jr. .75 2.00
73 Sean Casey .20 .50
74 Wily Mo Pena .20 .50
75 Bob Feller .20 .50
76 Brian Tallet .10 .30
77 C.C. Sabathia .20 .50
78 Cliff Lee .10 .30
79 Earl Snyder .10 .30
80 Ellis Burks .20 .50
81 Jeremy Guthrie .10 .30
82 Travis Hafner .20 .50
83 Luis Garcia .10 .30
84 Omar Vizquel .30 .75
85 Ricardo Rodriguez .10 .30
86 Ryan Church .20 .50
87 Victor Martinez .30 .75
88 Brandon Phillips .10 .30
89 Jack Cust .10 .30
90 Jason Jennings .10 .30
91 Jeff Baker .10 .30
92 Garrett Atkins .10 .30
93 Juan Uribe .10 .30
94 Larry Walker .20 .50
95 Rene Reyes .10 .30
96 Todd Helton .30 .75
97 Alan Trammell .20 .50
98 Fernando Rodney .10 .30
99 Carlos Pena .10 .30
100 Jack Morris .20 .50
101 Bobby Higginson .20 .50
102 Mike Maroth .10 .30
103 Robert Fick .10 .30
104 Jesus Medrano .10 .30
105 Josh Beckett .20 .50
106 Luis Castillo .10 .30
107 Mike Lowell .20 .50
108 Juan Pierre .20 .50
109 Josh Wilson .10 .30
110 Tim Redding .10 .30
111 Carlos Hernandez .10 .30
112 Craig Biggio .30 .75
113 Henri Stanley .10 .30
114 Jason Lane .10 .30
115 Jeff Bagwell .30 .75
116 John Buck .10 .30
117 Kirk Saarloos .10 .30
118 Lance Berkman .20 .50
119 Nolan Ryan Astros 1.25 3.00
120 Richard Hidalgo .10 .30
121 Rodrigo Rosario .10 .30
122 Roy Oswalt .20 .50
123 Tommy Whiteman .10 .30
124 Wade Miller .10 .30
125 Alexis Gomez .10 .30
126 Angel Berroa .10 .30
127 Brandon Berger .10 .30
128 Carlos Beltran .20 .50
129 George Brett 1.00 2.50
130 Jimmy Gobble .10 .30
131 Dee Brown .10 .30
132 Mike Sweeney .20 .50
133 Raul Ibanez .10 .30
134 Runelvys Hernandez .10 .30
135 Adrian Beltre .20 .50
136 Brian Jordan .20 .50
137 Cesar Izturis .10 .30
138 Victor Alvarez .10 .30
139 Hideo Nomo .50 1.25
140 Joe Thurston .10 .30
141 Kazuhisa Ishii .20 .50
142 Kevin Brown .20 .50
143 Odalis Perez .10 .30
144 Paul Lo Duca .20 .50
145 Shawn Green .20 .50
146 Ben Sheets .20 .50
147 Bill Hall .10 .30
148 Nick Neugebauer .10 .30
149 Richie Sexson .20 .50
150 Robin Yount .50 1.25
151 Shane Nance .10 .30
152 Takahito Nomura .10 .30
153 A.J. Pierzynski .20 .50
154 Joe Mays .10 .30
155 Kirby Puckett .50 1.25
156 Adam Johnson .10 .30
157 Rob Bowen .10 .30
158 Torii Hunter .20 .50
159 Andres Galarraga .20 .50
160 Endy Chavez .10 .30
161 Javier Vazquez .20 .50
162 Jose Vidro .10 .30
163 Vladimir Guerrero .50 1.25
164 Dwight Gooden .20 .50
165 Mike Piazza .75 2.00
166 Roberto Alomar .30 .75
167 Tom Glavine .30 .75
168 Alfonso Soriano .20 .50
169 Bernie Williams .30 .75
170 Brandon Claussen .10 .30
171 Derek Jeter 1.25 3.00
172 Don Mattingly 1.00 2.50
173 Drew Henson .10 .30
174 Jason Giambi .20 .50
175 Joe Torre MG .30 .75
176 Jorge Posada .30 .75
177 Mike Mussina .30 .75
178 Nick Johnson .20 .50
179 Roger Clemens 1.00 2.50
180 Whitey Ford .30 .75
181 Adam Morrissey .10 .30
182 Barry Zito .20 .50
183 David Justice .20 .50
184 Eric Chavez .20 .50
185 Jermaine Dye .20 .50
186 Mark Mulder .20 .50
187 Miguel Tejada .20 .50
188 Reggie Jackson .30 .75
189 Terrence Long .10 .30
190 Tim Hudson .20 .50
191 Anderson Machado .10 .30

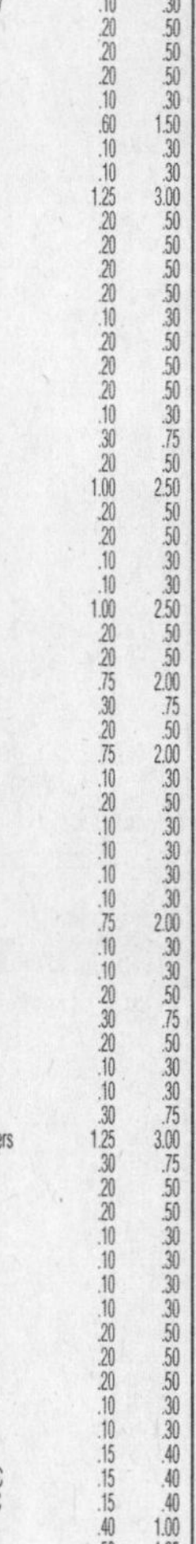

192 Bobby Abreu .20 .50
193 Brandon Duckworth .10 .30
194 Jim Thome .30 .75
195 Eric Junge .10 .30
196 Jeremy Giambi .10 .30
197 Johnny Estrada .10 .30
198 Jorge Padilla .10 .30
199 Marlon Byrd .10 .30
200 Mike Schmidt 1.00 2.50
201 Pat Burrell .20 .50
202 Steve Carlton .20 .50
203 Aramis Ramirez .20 .50
204 Brian Giles .20 .50
205 Carlos Rivera .10 .30
206 Craig Wilson .10 .30
207 Dave Williams .10 .30
208 Jack Wilson .10 .30
209 Jose Castillo .10 .30
210 Kip Wells .10 .30
211 Roberto Clemente 1.25 3.00
212 Walter Young .10 .30
213 Ben Howard .10 .30
214 Brian Lawrence .10 .30
215 Cliff Bartosh .10 .30
216 Dennis Tankersley .10 .30
217 Oliver Perez .20 .50
218 Phil Nevin .20 .50
219 Ryan Klesko .20 .50
220 Sean Burroughs .10 .30
221 Tony Gwynn .60 1.50
222 Xavier Nady .10 .30
223 Mike Rivera .10 .30
224 Barry Bonds 1.25 3.00
225 Benito Santiago .20 .50
226 Jason Schmidt .20 .50
227 Jeff Kent .20 .50
228 Kenny Lofton .20 .50
229 Rich Aurilia .10 .30
230 Robb Nen .20 .50
231 Tsuyoshi Shinjo .20 .50
232 Bret Boone .20 .50
233 Chris Snelling .10 .30
234 Edgar Martinez .30 .75
235 Freddy Garcia .20 .50
236 Ichiro Suzuki 1.00 2.50
237 John Olerud .20 .50
238 Kazuhiro Sasaki .20 .50
239 Mike Cameron .10 .30
240 Rafael Soriano .10 .30
241 Albert Pujols 1.00 2.50
242 J.D. Drew .20 .50
243 Jim Edmonds .20 .50
244 Ozzie Smith .75 2.00
245 Scott Rolen .30 .75
246 So Taguchi .20 .50
247 Stan Musial .75 2.00
248 Antonio Perez .10 .30
249 Aubrey Huff .20 .50
250 Dewon Brazelton .10 .30
251 Delvin James .10 .30
252 Joe Kennedy .10 .30
253 Toby Hall .10 .30
254 Alex Rodriguez .75 2.00
255 Ben Kozlowski .10 .30
256 Gerald Laird .10 .30
257 Hank Blalock .20 .50
258 Ivan Rodriguez .30 .75
259 Juan Gonzalez .20 .50
260 Kevin Mench .10 .30
261 Mario Ramos .10 .30
262 Mark Teixeira .30 .75
263 Nolan Ryan Rangers 1.25 3.00
264 Rafael Palmeiro .30 .75
265 Alexis Rios .20 .50
266 Carlos Delgado .20 .50
267 Eric Hinske .10 .30
268 Josh Phelps .10 .30
269 Kevin Cash .10 .30
270 Orlando Hudson .10 .30
271 Roy Halladay .20 .50
272 Shannon Stewart .20 .50
273 Vernon Wells .20 .50
274 Vinny Chulk .10 .30
275 Jason Anderson .10 .30
276 Craig Brazell RC .15 .40
277 Termel Sledge RC .15 .40
278 Ryan Cameron RC .15 .40
279 Clint Barmes RC .40 1.00
280 Jhonny Peralta .50 1.25
281 Todd Wellemeyer RC .15 .40
282 John Leicester RC .15 .40
283 Brandon Webb RC .75 2.00
284 Tim Olson RC .15 .40
285 Matt Kata RC .15 .40
286 Rob Hammock RC .15 .40
287 Pete LaForest RC .15 .40
288 Nook Logan RC .20 .50
289 Prentice Redman RC .15 .40
290 Joe Valentine RC .15 .40
291 Jose Contreras RC .30 .75
292 Josh Stewart RC .15 .40
293 Mike Nicolas RC .15 .40
294 Marshall McDougall .10 .30
295 Travis Chapman .10 .30
296 Jose Morban .10 .30
297 Michael Hessman RC .15 .40
298 Buddy Hernandez RC .15 .40
299 Shane Victorino RC .40 1.00
300 Jason Dubois .10 .30
301 Hideki Matsui RC 2.00 5.00
302 Ryan Wagner RC .20 .50
303 Adam Loewen RC .20 .50
304 Chien-Ming Wang RC .60 1.50
305 Hong-Chih Kuo RC .75 2.00
306 Delmon Young RC 1.25 3.00
307 Dan Haren RC .20 .50
308 Rickie Weeks RC .60 1.50
309 Ramon Nivar RC .20 .50

2003 Donruss Champions Autographs

Cards checklisted 1-300 from this set were randomly inserted into Donruss Champions packs. Cards 302-309 were randomly inserted into packs of DLP Rookies and Traded. These cards were issued to different stated print runs and we have notated that information next to the player's name in our checklist. Please note that for cards with stated print runs of 45 or fewer cards we have not priced these cards due to market scarcity.

2 Alfredo Amezaga/325 4.00 10.00
3 Chone Figgins/375 6.00 15.00

4 Darin Erstad/9
8 Nolan Ryan Angels/4
10 Troy Glaus/20
12 Curt Schilling/5
13 Junior Spivey/45 6.00 15.00
14 Luis Gonzalez/5
18 Andruw Jones/20
19 Chipper Jones/10
20 Dale Murphy/20
21 Gary Sheffield/10
24 Andy Pratt/475 4.00 10.00
25 Adam LaRoche/400 4.00 10.00
26 Trey Hodges/305 4.00 10.00
28 Cal Ripken/5
29 Ed Rogers/305 4.00 10.00
30 Brian Roberts/500 10.00 25.00
31 Geronimo Gil/150 4.00 10.00
32 Jay Gibbons/475 4.00 10.00
33 Josh Towers/500 4.00 10.00
34 Casey Fossum/160 4.00 10.00
35 Cliff Floyd/70 10.00 25.00
37 Fred Lynn/80 15.00 40.00
38 Freddy Sanchez/400 6.00 15.00
39 Manny Ramirez/5
40 Nomar Garciaparra/5
41 Pedro Martinez/5
42 Rickey Henderson/5
45 Bobby Hill/5
46 Corey Patterson/100 6.00 15.00
49 Juan Cruz/250 4.00 10.00
50 Kerry Wood/20
51 Mark Prior/50 12.50 30.00
53 Nic Jackson/100 6.00 15.00
56 Carlos Lee/25
57 Corwin Malone/400 4.00 10.00
58 Frank Thomas/5
59 Joe Borchard/215 4.00 10.00
60 Joe Crede/5
61 Magglio Ordonez/25
62 Mark Buehrle/15
64 Tim Hummel/400 4.00 10.00
65 Jon Adkins/400 4.00 10.00
66 Adam Dunn/100 15.00 40.00
67 Austin Kearns/50 6.00 15.00
68 Barry Larkin/9
69 Jose Acevedo/315 4.00 10.00
70 Corky Miller/295 4.00 10.00
71 Eric Davis/45 15.00 40.00
73 Sean Casey/10
74 Wily Mo Pena/450 6.00 15.00
75 Bob Feller/20
76 Brian Tallet/250 4.00 10.00
77 C.C. Sabathia/25
78 Cliff Lee/330 30.00 60.00
79 Earl Snyder/225 4.00 10.00
81 Jeremy Guthrie/400 6.00 15.00
83 Luis Garcia/395 4.00 10.00
86 Ryan Church/395 6.00 15.00
87 Victor Martinez/250 10.00 25.00
88 Brandon Phillips/375 4.00 10.00
89 Jack Cust/498 4.00 10.00
90 Jason Jennings/375 4.00 10.00
91 Jeff Baker/400 4.00 10.00
92 Garrett Atkins/400 4.00 10.00
95 Rene Reyes/350 4.00 10.00
96 Todd Helton/5
97 Alan Trammell/25
98 Fernando Rodney/500 4.00 10.00
100 Jack Morris/50 15.00 40.00
102 Mike Maroth/400 4.00 10.00
103 Robert Fick/15
104 Jesus Medrano/500 4.00 10.00
105 Josh Beckett/14
109 Josh Wilson/400 4.00 10.00
110 Tim Redding/375 4.00 10.00
111 Carlos Hernandez/250 4.00 10.00
112 Craig Biggio/20
113 Henri Stanley/390 4.00 10.00
114 Jason Lane/250 6.00 15.00
117 Kirk Saarloos/149 4.00 10.00
118 Lance Berkman/10
119 Nolan Ryan Astros/4
120 Richard Hidalgo/120 4.00 10.00
121 Rodrigo Rosario/500 4.00 10.00
122 Roy Oswalt/100 10.00 25.00
123 Tommy Whiteman/375 4.00 10.00
124 Wade Miller/125 4.00 10.00
126 Angel Berroa/400 4.00 10.00
127 Brandon Berger/325 4.00 10.00
128 Carlos Beltran/10
129 George Brett/9
130 Jimmy Gobble/400 4.00 10.00
131 Dee Brown/500 4.00 10.00
132 Mike Sweeney/45 10.00 25.00
134 Runelvys Hernandez/400 4.00 10.00
135 Adrian Beltre/20
138 Victor Alvarez/308 4.00 10.00
141 Kazuhisa Ishii/20
142 Kevin Brown/30
144 Paul Lo Duca/45 10.00 25.00
145 Shawn Green/5
146 Ben Sheets/50 10.00 25.00
147 Bill Hall/450 4.00 10.00
148 Nick Neugebauer/375 4.00 10.00
149 Richie Sexson/25
150 Robin Yount/5
151 Shane Nance/150 4.00 10.00
152 Takahito Nomura/50 10.00 25.00
153 A.J. Pierzynski/250 6.00 15.00
154 Joe Mays/5
155 Kirby Puckett/10
156 Adam Johnson/500 4.00 10.00
157 Rob Bowen/375 4.00 10.00
158 Torii Hunter/45 10.00 25.00
159 Andres Galarraga/25
160 Endy Chavez/280 4.00 10.00
161 Javier Vazquez/50 10.00 25.00
162 Jose Vidro/45 6.00 15.00
163 Vladimir Guerrero/20
164 Dwight Gooden/45 15.00 40.00
166 Roberto Alomar/15
167 Tom Glavine/15
168 Alfonso Soriano/10
169 Bernie Williams/10
170 Brandon Claussen/475 4.00 10.00
172 Don Mattingly/20
173 Drew Henson/20
175 Joe Torre/20
177 Mike Mussina/5
178 Nick Johnson/500 6.00 15.00
179 Roger Clemens/5
180 Whitey Ford/10
181 Adam Morrissey/395 4.00 10.00
182 Barry Zito/25
183 David Justice/10
184 Eric Chavez/10
185 Jermaine Dye/125 6.00 15.00
186 Mark Mulder/25
187 Miguel Tejada/15
188 Reggie Jackson/9
189 Terrence Long/250 4.00 10.00
190 Tim Hudson/20
191 Anderson Machado/500 4.00 10.00
192 Bobby Abreu/25
193 Brandon Duckworth/100 6.00 15.00
194 Jim Thome/15
195 Eric Junge/279 4.00 10.00
196 Jeremy Giambi/195 4.00 10.00
198 Jorge Padilla/11
199 Marlon Byrd/10
200 Mike Schmidt/20
202 Steve Carlton/25
203 Aramis Ramirez/20
204 Brian Giles/25
205 Carlos Rivera/400 4.00 10.00
206 Craig Wilson/245 4.00 10.00
207 Dave Williams/265 4.00 10.00
208 Jack Wilson/500 6.00 15.00
209 Jose Castillo/400 4.00 10.00
210 Kip Wells/500 4.00 10.00
212 Walter Young/400 4.00 10.00
213 Ben Howard/500 4.00 10.00
214 Brian Lawrence/500 4.00 10.00
215 Cliff Bartosh/400 4.00 10.00
216 Dennis Tankersley/25
217 Oliver Perez/5
219 Ryan Klesko/20
220 Sean Burroughs/19
221 Tony Gwynn/15
222 Xavier Nady/250 4.00 10.00
223 Mike Rivera/90 6.00 15.00
228 Kenny Lofton/25
233 Chris Snelling/200 4.00 10.00
234 Edgar Martinez/20
235 Freddy Garcia/10
240 Rafael Soriano/500 4.00 10.00
241 Albert Pujols/10
242 J.D. Drew/5
243 Jim Edmonds/10
244 Ozzie Smith/20
245 Scott Rolen/10
246 So Taguchi/10
247 Stan Musial/15
248 Antonio Perez/500 4.00 10.00
249 Aubrey Huff/475 6.00 15.00
250 Dewon Brazelton/50 6.00 15.00
251 Delvin James/400 4.00 10.00
252 Joe Kennedy/250 4.00 10.00
253 Toby Hall/500 4.00 10.00
254 Alex Rodriguez/5
255 Ben Kozlowski/400 4.00 10.00
256 Gerald Laird/450 4.00 10.00
257 Hank Blalock/50 10.00 25.00
258 Ivan Rodriguez/5
259 Juan Gonzalez/20
260 Kevin Mench/475 6.00 15.00
261 Mario Ramos/475 4.00 10.00
262 Mark Teixeira/40 15.00 40.00
263 Nolan Ryan Rangers/4
264 Rafael Palmeiro/5
265 Alexis Rios/400 8.00 20.00
267 Eric Hinske/390 4.00 10.00
268 Josh Phelps/5
269 Kevin Cash/375 4.00 10.00
272 Shannon Stewart/25
274 Vinny Chulk/100 6.00 15.00
275 Jason Anderson/493 10.00 25.00
277 Termel Sledge/500 4.00 10.00
278 Ryan Cameron/475 4.00 10.00
279 Clint Barmes/475 5.00 12.00
280 Jhonny Peralta/500 6.00 15.00
281 Todd Wellemeyer/477 4.00 10.00
282 John Leicester/480 4.00 10.00
283 Brandon Webb/500 10.00 25.00
284 Tim Olson/500 4.00 10.00
285 Matt Kata/487 4.00 10.00
286 Rob Hammock/486 4.00 10.00
287 Pete LaForest/500 4.00 10.00
288 Nook Logan/500 6.00 15.00
289 Prentice Redman/488 4.00 10.00
290 Joe Valentine/475 4.00 10.00
291 Jose Contreras/100 12.50 30.00
292 Josh Stewart/485 4.00 10.00
293 Mike Nicolas/500 4.00 10.00
295 Travis Chapman/100 6.00 15.00
296 Jose Morban/475 4.00 10.00
297 Michael Hessman/500 4.00 10.00
298 Buddy Hernandez/500 4.00 10.00
299 Shane Victorino/480 10.00 25.00
300 Jason Dubois/480 4.00 10.00
302 Ryan Wagner/100 4.00 10.00
303 Adam Loewen/100 10.00 25.00
304 Chien-Ming Wang/100 50.00 100.00
305 Hong-Chih Kuo/100 50.00 100.00
306 Delmon Young/25
307 Dan Haren/100 6.00 15.00
308 Rickie Weeks/10
309 Ramon Nivar/100 4.00 10.00

2003 Donruss Champions Metalized

Randomly inserted into packs, this is a parallel to the Donruss Champions set. Cards 302-309 were randomly seeded within packs of DLP Rookies and Traded. These cards were issued with a special metalized film board and were issued to a stated print run of 100 serial numbered sets.

*METALIZED ACTIVE 1-301: 4X TO 10X
*METALIZED RETIRED 1-301: 8X TO 20X

*METALIZED RC'S 1-301: 1.5X TO 4X
*METALIZED RC'S 302-309: 3X TO 8X
304 Chien-Ming Wang 10.00 25.00
305 Hong-Chih Kuo 15.00 40.00

2003 Donruss Champions Call to the Hall

Randomly inserted into packs, these 10 cards feature players who have already been elected to the Hall of Fame. These cards were issued to a stated print run of 2500 serial numbered sets.

HOLO-FOIL PRINT RUN 25 #'d SETS
NO HOLO-FOIL PRICING DUE TO SCARCITY
*METALIZED: 2.5X TO 6X BASIC CALL
METALIZED PRINT RUN 100 #'d SETS
1 Nolan Ryan 4.00 10.00
2 Tom Seaver 2.00 5.00
3 Phil Rizzuto 2.00 5.00
4 Orlando Cepeda 1.25 3.00
5 Al Kaline 2.00 5.00
6 Hoyt Wilhelm 1.25 3.00
7 Luis Aparicio 1.25 3.00
8 Billy Williams 1.25 3.00
9 Jim Palmer 1.25 3.00
10 Mike Schmidt 3.00 8.00

2003 Donruss Champions Grand Champions

Issued at a stated rate of one in 18 hobby and one in 23 retail, this 25 card sets features a mix of Hall of Famers as well as guaranteed HOFers among active players.

HOLO-FOIL PRINT RUN 25 #'d SETS
NO HOLO-FOIL PRICING DUE TO SCARCITY
*METALIZED: 2X TO 5X BASIC GRAND
METALIZED PRINT RUN 100 SERIAL #'d SETS
1 Stan Musial 3.00 8.00
2 Bob Feller 1.25 3.00
3 Reggie Jackson 2.00 5.00
4 George Brett 4.00 10.00
5 Jim Palmer 1.25 3.00
6 Harmon Killebrew 2.00 5.00
7 Ernie Banks 2.00 5.00
8 Frank Robinson 2.00 5.00
9 Greg Maddux 3.00 8.00
10 Whitey Ford 2.00 5.00
11 Bob Gibson 2.00 5.00
12 Mike Schmidt 4.00 10.00
13 Nolan Ryan 5.00 12.00
14 Warren Spahn 2.00 5.00
15 Rod Carew 2.00 5.00
16 Hoyt Wilhelm 1.25 3.00
17 Duke Snider 2.00 5.00
18 Tom Seaver 2.00 5.00
19 Steve Carlton 1.25 3.00
20 Yogi Berra 2.00 5.00
21 Cal Ripken 6.00 15.00
22 Tony Gwynn 2.50 6.00
23 Wade Boggs 2.00 5.00
24 Rickey Henderson 2.00 5.00
25 Roger Clemens 4.00 10.00

2003 Donruss Champions Statistical Champs

Inserted at a stated rate of one in 10 hobby and one in 23 retail, this 30 card set features a mix of active and retired players who have led the league in various offensive categories.

1 Alex Rodriguez 2.50 6.00
2 Alfonso Soriano 1.25 3.00
3 Curt Schilling 1.25 3.00
4 Eddie Mathews 2.00 5.00
5 Fred Lynn 1.25 3.00
6 Harmon Killebrew 2.00 5.00
7 Hideo Nomo 1.50 4.00
8 Jim Thome 1.50 4.00
9 Kirby Puckett 1.50 4.00
10 Luis Gonzalez 1.25 3.00
11 Manny Ramirez 1.50 4.00
12 Jason Giambi 1.25 3.00
13 Mike Schmidt 4.00 10.00
14 Nomar Garciaparra 2.50 6.00
15 Lou Brock 2.00 5.00
16 Randy Johnson 1.50 4.00
17 Reggie Jackson 2.00 5.00
18 Rickey Henderson 1.50 4.00
19 Roberto Clemente 5.00 12.00
20 Barry Zito 1.25 3.00
21 Todd Helton 1.50 4.00
22 Tom Seaver 2.00 5.00
23 Tony Gwynn 2.50 6.00
24 Torii Hunter 1.25 3.00
25 Troy Glaus 1.25 3.00
26 Wade Boggs 2.00 5.00
27 Rod Carew 2.00 5.00
28 Juan Gonzalez 1.25 3.00
29 Sammy Sosa 1.50 4.00
30 Warren Spahn 2.00 5.00

2003 Donruss Champions Statistical Champs Materials

Randomly inserted into packs, this is a parallel to the Statistical Champs insert set. These cards basically feature game-used jersey pieces and were issued to different print runs. We have notated that print run information next to the player's name in our checklist.

1 Alex Rodriguez Jsy/250 10.00 25.00
2 Alfonso Soriano Jsy/25
3 Curt Schilling Jsy/225 4.00 10.00
4 Eddie Mathews Jsy/200 10.00 25.00
5 Fred Lynn Jsy/50 15.00 40.00
6 Harmon Killebrew Jsy/250 10.00 25.00
7 Hideo Nomo Jsy/110 30.00 60.00
8 Jim Thome Jsy/250 6.00 15.00
9 Kirby Puckett Jsy/250 10.00 25.00
10 Luis Gonzalez Jsy/250 4.00 10.00
11 Manny Ramirez Jsy/155 6.00 15.00
12 Jason Giambi Jsy/250 4.00 10.00
13 Mike Schmidt Jsy/250 15.00 40.00
14 Nomar Garciaparra Jsy/99 15.00 40.00
15 Lou Brock Jsy/250 10.00 25.00
16 Randy Johnson Jsy/100 10.00 25.00
17 Reggie Jackson Jsy/200 10.00 25.00
18 Rickey Henderson Jsy/184 6.00 15.00
19 Roberto Clemente Jsy/64
20 Barry Zito Jsy/100 6.00 15.00
21 Todd Helton Jsy/250 6.00 15.00
22 Tom Seaver Jsy/100 15.00 40.00
23 Tony Gwynn Jsy/250 10.00 25.00
24 Torii Hunter Jsy/250 4.00 10.00
25 Troy Glaus Jsy/125 6.00 15.00
26 Wade Boggs Jsy/250 10.00 25.00
27 Rod Carew Hat/150 10.00 25.00
28 Juan Gonzalez Jsy/250 4.00 10.00
29 Sammy Sosa Jsy/250 6.00 15.00
30 Warren Spahn Jsy/150 10.00 25.00

2003 Donruss Champions Team Colors

Issued at a stated rate of one in 10 hobby and one in 23 retail, these 30 cards feature star players from a team set against background colors of the teams colors.

1 Miguel Tejada 1.25 3.00
2 Mike Schmidt 4.00 10.00
3 George Brett 4.00 10.00
4 Magglio Ordonez 1.25 3.00
5 Ryne Sandberg 4.00 10.00
6 Adam Dunn 1.25 3.00
7 Mark Prior 1.50 4.00
8 Tony Gwynn 2.50 6.00
9 Troy Glaus 1.25 3.00
10 Stan Musial 3.00 8.00
11 Kirby Puckett 1.50 4.00
12 Don Mattingly 4.00 10.00
13 Bobby Abreu 1.25 3.00
14 Ichiro Suzuki 3.00 8.00
15 Cal Ripken 6.00 15.00
16 Chipper Jones 1.50 4.00
17 Carlos Beltran 1.25 3.00
18 Alfonso Soriano 1.25 3.00
19 Albert Pujols 3.00 8.00
20 Andruw Jones 1.50 4.00
21 Bernie Williams 1.50 4.00
22 Todd Helton 1.50 4.00
23 Roberto Clemente 5.00 12.00
24 Jim Thome 1.50 4.00
25 Carlos Delgado 1.25 3.00
26 Derek Jeter 4.00 10.00
27 Garret Anderson 1.25 3.00
28 Nomar Garciaparra 2.50 6.00
29 Torii Hunter 1.25 3.00
30 Vladimir Guerrero 1.50 4.00

2003 Donruss Champions Team Colors Materials

Randomly inserted in packs, this is a parallel to the Team Colors insert set. These cards feature a memorabilia piece associated with the player's career. Since each card is serial numbered to a different amount, we have notated that information next to the player's name in our checklist.

1 Miguel Tejada Jsy/50 6.00 15.00
2 Mike Schmidt Jsy/200 15.00 40.00
3 George Brett Jsy/200 15.00 40.00
4 Magglio Ordonez Jsy/100 4.00 10.00

5 Ryne Sandberg Jsy/200 15.00 40.00
6 Adam Dunn Jsy/44 6.00 15.00
7 Mark Prior Jsy/200 4.00 10.00
8 Tony Gwynn Jsy/200 8.00 20.00
9 Troy Glaus Jsy/200 3.00 8.00
10 Stan Musial Jsy/200 15.00 40.00
11 Kirby Puckett Jsy/200 6.00 15.00
12 Don Mattingly Jsy/200 15.00 40.00
13 Bobby Abreu Jsy/200 3.00 8.00
14 Ichiro Suzuki Base/200 10.00 25.00
15 Cal Ripken Jsy/200 30.00 60.00
16 Chipper Jones Jsy/200 4.00 10.00
17 Carlos Beltran Jsy/200 3.00 8.00
18 Alfonso Soriano Jsy/25
19 Albert Pujols Base/200 6.00 15.00
20 Andruw Jones Jsy/200 4.00 10.00
21 Bernie Williams Jsy/200 4.00 10.00
22 Todd Helton Jsy/200 4.00 10.00
23 Roberto Clemente Jsy/200 50.00 100.00
24 Jim Thome Jsy/200 4.00 10.00
25 Carlos Delgado Jsy/200 3.00 8.00
26 Derek Jeter Base/200 10.00 25.00
27 Garret Anderson Jsy/50 6.00 15.00
28 Nomar Garciaparra Jsy/200 10.00 25.00
29 Torii Hunter Jsy/200 3.00 8.00
30 Vladimir Guerrero Jsy/200 4.00 10.00

2003 Donruss Champions Total Game

Inserted at a stated rate of one in nine hobby and one in 12 retail, these 40 cards feature position players who have well-rounded games.

1 Vladimir Guerrero 1.50 4.00
2 Nomar Garciaparra 2.50 6.00
3 Magglio Ordonez 1.25 3.00
4 Garret Anderson 1.25 3.00
5 Derek Jeter 4.00 10.00
6 Jim Thome 1.50 4.00
7 Torii Hunter 1.25 3.00
8 Todd Helton 1.50 4.00
9 Andruw Jones 1.50 4.00
10 Alfonso Soriano 1.25 3.00
11 Luis Gonzalez 1.25 3.00
12 Manny Ramirez 1.50 4.00
13 Paul Konerko 1.25 3.00
14 Alex Rodriguez 2.50 6.00
15 Carlos Beltran 1.25 3.00
16 Bernie Williams 1.50 4.00
17 Barry Bonds 4.00 10.00
18 Miguel Tejada 1.25 3.00
19 Jason Giambi 1.25 3.00
20 Ichiro Suzuki 3.00 8.00
21 Ivan Rodriguez 1.50 4.00
22 Rafael Palmeiro 1.50 4.00
23 Carlos Delgado 1.25 3.00
24 Vernon Wells 1.25 3.00
25 Sammy Sosa 1.50 4.00
26 Chipper Jones 1.50 4.00
27 Adam Dunn 1.25 3.00
28 Larry Walker 1.25 3.00
29 Shawn Green 1.25 3.00
30 Richie Sexson 1.25 3.00
31 Jose Vidro 1.25 3.00
32 Mike Piazza 2.50 6.00
33 Roberto Alomar 1.50 4.00
34 Bobby Abreu 1.25 3.00
35 Pat Burrell 1.25 3.00
36 Brian Giles 1.25 3.00
37 Albert Pujols 3.00 8.00
38 Lance Berkman 1.25 3.00
39 Ryan Klesko 1.25 3.00
40 Jeff Kent 1.25 3.00

2003 Donruss Champions Total Game Materials

Randomly inserted into packs, this is a parallel to the Total Game insert set. Each player has a game-used swatch of some item attached to their career. Since each card is serial numbered to a differing amount of cards, we have notated that information next to the player's name in our checklist.

1 Vladimir Guerrero Jsy/200 6.00 15.00
2 Nomar Garciaparra Jsy/200 10.00 25.00
3 Magglio Ordonez Jsy/100 6.00 15.00
4 Garret Anderson Jsy/50 8.00 20.00
5 Derek Jeter Base/200 10.00 25.00
6 Jim Thome Jsy/200 6.00 15.00
7 Torii Hunter Jsy/200 4.00 10.00
8 Todd Helton Jsy/200 6.00 15.00
9 Andruw Jones Jsy/200 6.00 15.00
10 Alfonso Soriano Jsy/25
11 Luis Gonzalez Jsy/200 4.00 10.00
12 Manny Ramirez Jsy/200 6.00 15.00
13 Paul Konerko Jsy/200 4.00 10.00
14 Alex Rodriguez Jsy/200 10.00 25.00
15 Carlos Beltran Jsy/200 4.00 10.00
16 Bernie Williams Jsy/200 6.00 15.00
17 Barry Bonds Base/200 10.00 25.00
18 Miguel Tejada Jsy/50 8.00 20.00
19 Jason Giambi Base/200 4.00 10.00
20 Ichiro Suzuki Base/200 10.00 25.00
21 Ivan Rodriguez Jsy/100 10.00 25.00
22 Rafael Palmeiro Jsy/200 6.00 15.00
23 Carlos Delgado Jsy/200 4.00 10.00
24 Vernon Wells Jsy/200 4.00 10.00
25 Sammy Sosa Jsy/200 6.00 15.00
26 Chipper Jones Jsy/200 6.00 15.00
27 Adam Dunn Jsy/44 8.00 20.00
28 Larry Walker Jsy/200 4.00 10.00
29 Shawn Green Jsy/100 6.00 15.00
30 Richie Sexson Jsy/200 4.00 10.00
31 Jose Vidro Jsy/200 4.00 10.00
32 Mike Piazza Jsy/50 40.00 80.00
33 Roberto Alomar Jsy/100 10.00 25.00
34 Bobby Abreu Jsy/200 4.00 10.00
35 Pat Burrell Jsy/200 4.00 10.00
36 Brian Giles Jsy/200 4.00 10.00
37 Albert Pujols Base/200 6.00 15.00
38 Lance Berkman Jsy/50 8.00 20.00
39 Ryan Klesko Jsy/200 4.00 10.00
40 Jeff Kent Jsy/200 4.00 10.00

2003 Donruss Champions World Series Champs Samples

Randomly inserted into Beckett Baseball Collector magazines, these cards parallel the World Series Champs insert set. These cards were issued to a stated print run of 40 sets and are notated by the word "Sample" printed on the back.

STATED PRINT RUN 40 SETS
*GOLD: 1.5X TO 4X BASIC SAMPLES
GOLD STATED PRINT RUN 10 SETS

2003 Donruss Champions World Series Champs

Randomly inserted into packs, this 15 card set honors key members of the 2002 Anaheim Angels. These cards were issued to a stated print run of 2,002 serial numbered sets.

HOLO-FOIL PRINT RUN 25 #'d SETS
NO HOLO-FOIL PRICING DUE TO SCARCITY
*METALIZED: 1.25X TO 3X BASIC WS
METALIZED PRINT RUN 100 #'d SETS
1 Troy Glaus 1.25 3.00
2 Jarrod Washburn 1.25 3.00
3 Darin Erstad 1.25 3.00
4 Troy Percival 1.25 3.00
5 David Eckstein 1.25 3.00
6 Francisco Rodriguez 1.25 3.00
7 Garret Anderson 1.25 3.00
8 John Lackey 1.25 3.00
9 Tim Salmon 2.00 5.00
10 Chone Figgins 1.25 3.00
11 Adam Kennedy 1.25 3.00
12 Scott Spiezio 1.25 3.00
13 Ben Molina 1.25 3.00
14 Brad Fullmer 1.25 3.00
15 Troy Glaus MVP 1.25 3.00

2003 Donruss Champions Atlantic City National

Collectors who opened a set number of Champions packs at the 2003 Atlantic City National were rewarded with a card from that set with a special Atlantic City National Logo on the front and serial numbering to five on the back. Due to market scarcity, no pricing is provided for these cards.

PRINT RUN 5 SERIAL #'d SETS

2005 Donruss Champions

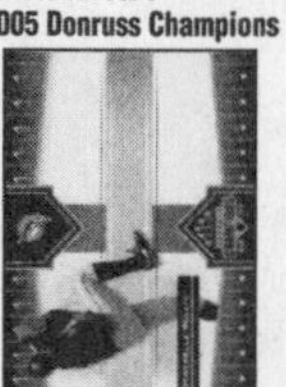

This 450-card swet was released in December, 2005. The set was issued in eight-card hobby packs with an $4 SRP which came 24 packs to a box and 20 boxes to a case.

COMPLETE SET (450) 40.00 80.00
COMMON CARD (1-450) .20 .50
COMMON RC (1-450) .20 .50
PRESS PLATES RANDOM IN PACKS
PLATE PRINT RUN 1 SET PER COLOR
BLACK-CYAN-MAGENTA-YELLOW ISSUED
NO PLATE PRICING DUE TO SCARCITY
1 Adam Dunn .30 .75
2 Albert Pujols 1.25 3.00
3 Albert Pujols 1.25 3.00
4 Ichiro Suzuki .75 2.00
5 Alex Rodriguez .75 2.00
6 Andruw Jones .20 .50
7 Carlos Beltran Royals .20 .50
8 Derrek Lee .20 .50
9 Hideki Matsui .75 2.00
10 Ichiro Suzuki .75 2.00
11 Ichiro Suzuki .75 2.00
12 Jeff Kent Giants .20 .50
13 Ken Griffey Jr. .75 2.00
14 Ken Griffey Jr. .75 2.00
15 Sammy Sosa .50 1.25
16 Sean Casey Reds .20 .50

17 Troy Glaus Angels .20 .50
18 Derek Jeter 1.25 3.00
19 Cal Ripken 2.00 5.00
20 Roberto Alomar Indians .30 .75
21 B.J. Surhoff .20 .50
22 Brian Jordan .20 .50
23 Corey Koskie .20 .50
24 Doug Davis .20 .50
25 Jason Varitek .50 1.25
26 Jim Edmonds .30 .75
27 Kevin Mench .20 .50
28 Roberto Alomar O's .30 .75
29 Tony Armas Jr. .20 .50
30 Ramon Ortiz .20 .50
31 Rodrigo Lopez .20 .50
32 Andres Galarraga Giants .20 .50
33 Brian Lawrence .20 .50
34 Jay Payton .20 .50
35 Ryan Ludwick .20 .50
36 Hee Seop Choi .20 .50
37 J.D. Drew Cards .20 .50
38 Raul Mondesi .20 .50
39 Brian Jordan .20 .50
40 Luis Matos .20 .50
41 Russell Branyan .20 .50
42 Tony Gwynn .60 1.50
43 Francisco Rodriguez .30 .75
44 Frank Robinson .30 .75
45 Jeff Bagwell .30 .75
46 Tony Gwynn .60 1.50
47 Tony Gwynn .60 1.50
48 Will Clark .30 .75
49 Antonio Perez .20 .50
50 Rickey Henderson Yanks .30 .75
51 Brian Lawrence .20 .50
52 Carlos Beltran Mets .20 .50
53 Chris Snelling .20 .50
54 Darryl Strawberry Dgr .20 .50
55 Doug Mientkiewicz Mets .20 .50
56 Edgardo Alfonzo .20 .50
57 Eric Chavez .20 .50
58 Eric Davis .20 .50
59 Guillermo Quiroz .20 .50
60 J.D. Drew Braves .20 .50
61 J.D. Drew Dgr .20 .50
62 Walter Young .20 .50
63 John Kruk .20 .50
64 Jose Reyes .30 .75
65 Jose Vidro .20 .50
66 Josh Phelps .20 .50
67 Larry Walker Expos .30 .75
68 Lyle Overbay .20 .50
69 Manny Ramirez .50 1.25
70 Marlon Byrd Phils .20 .50
71 Matt Williams .30 .75
72 Melvin Mora .20 .50
73 Nook Logan .20 .50
74 Orlando Hudson .20 .50
75 Orlando Hudson .20 .50
76 Orlando Hudson .20 .50
77 Paul Konerko .30 .75
78 Raul Mondesi .20 .50
79 Reed Johnson .20 .50
80 Ryan Ludwick .20 .50
81 So Taguchi .20 .50
82 Toby Hall .20 .50
83 Todd Helton .30 .75
84 Tommy John Dgr .20 .50
85 Tony Clark .20 .50
86 Victor Martinez .30 .75
87 Vladimir Guerrero Angels .50 1.25
88 Wade Boggs .30 .75
89 Roberto Clemente 1.25 3.00
90 Angel Berroa .20 .50
91 Termel Sledge .20 .50
92 Andres Galarraga Rockies .20 .50
93 Brooks Robinson .30 .75
94 Brooks Robinson .30 .75
95 Dennis Tankersley .20 .50
96 Don Mattingly 1.00 2.50
97 Ricardo Rodriguez Rgr .20 .50
98 Deivi Cruz Nats .20 .50
99 Deivi Cruz Giants .20 .50
100 Pete LaForest .20 .50
101 Roger Clemens Sox .60 1.50
102 Frankie Francisco .20 .50
103 Kevin Millwood Phils .20 .50
104 Tony Womack .20 .50
105 Jeff Bagwell .30 .75
106 Billy Martin .30 .75
107 J.T. Snow .20 .50
108 Juan Uribe .20 .50
109 Ryan Dempster .20 .50
110 Toby Hall .20 .50
111 Dennis Tankersley .20 .50
112 Freddy Garcia .20 .50
113 Garrett Atkins .20 .50
114 Troy Glaus Angels .20 .50
115 Gabe Kapler .20 .50
116 Jeff Kent Jays .20 .50
117 Rondell White .20 .50
118 C.C. Sabathia .30 .75
119 Javier Vazquez .20 .50
120 Mike Cameron .20 .50
121 Pat Burrell .20 .50
122 Lew Ford .20 .50
123 Brad Radke .20 .50
124 Preston Wilson .20 .50
125 Ray Durham .20 .50
126 Vernon Wells .20 .50
127 Bo Jackson Sox .50 1.25
128 Dmitri Young .20 .50
129 Doug Davis .20 .50
130 Brandon Duckworth .20 .50
131 Brandon Backe .20 .50
132 Juan Encarnacion Tigers .20 .50
133 Mike Maroth .20 .50
134 Sean Casey Indians .20 .50
135 Travis Hafner Rgr .20 .50
136 Wes Helms .20 .50
137 Randy Johnson M's .50 1.25
138 Larry Walker Cards .30 .75
139 Luis Gonzalez .20 .50
140 John Olerud M's .20 .50
141 Kazuhisa Ishii .20 .50
142 Mike Lowell .20 .50
143 Kevin Millwood Braves .20 .50
144 Chad Gaudin .20 .50
145 Bret Boone .20 .50
146 Cliff Floyd M's .20 .50
147 Dale Murphy .20 .50
148 Rickey Henderson M's .30 .75
149 Ricardo Rodriguez Indians .20 .50
150 Richard Hidalgo Astros .20 .50
151 Joe Kennedy Rockies .20 .50
152 Juan Pierre Rockies .20 .50
153 Juan Pierre M's .20 .50
154 Lance Berkman .30 .75
155 Joe Borchard .20 .50
156 Craig Monroe .20 .50
157 Abraham Nunez .20 .50
158 Willie Wilson .20 .50
159 Carlos Lee Brewers .20 .50
160 Carl Everett .20 .50
161 Frank White .20 .50
162 Craig Biggio .30 .75
163 Jason Varitek .50 1.25
164 Magglio Ordonez .30 .75
165 Carlos Delgado M's .20 .50
166 Casey Kotchman .20 .50
167 Kenny Lofton Braves .20 .50
168 Gil Hodges .30 .75
169 Rafael Furcal .20 .50
170 Ramon Vazquez .20 .50
171 Jeff Bagwell .30 .75
172 Jason Lane .20 .50
173 Nomar Garciaparra .50 1.25
174 Willie Harris .20 .50
175 Adam Dunn .30 .75
176 Jose Cruz Jr. D'backs .20 .50
177 Robin Ventura Sox .20 .50
178 Al Oliver Rgr .20 .50
179 Wily Mo Pena .20 .50
180 Erubiel Durazo .20 .50
181 Joey Gathright .20 .50
182 Luis Castillo .20 .50
183 Mark Teixeira .50 1.25
184 Delmon Young .50 1.25
185 Esteban Loaiza .20 .50
186 Bo Jackson Royals .50 1.25
187 Freddy Sanchez .20 .50
188 Jason Bay .20 .50
189 Rickey Henderson A's .30 .75
190 Shawn Green D'backs .20 .50
191 Roger Cedeno Mets .20 .50
192 Hideki Matsui .75 2.00
193 Andruw Jones .20 .50
194 David Wright .75 2.00
195 Cesar Izturis Dgr .20 .50
196 Chipper Jones .50 1.25
197 Troy Glaus D'backs .20 .50
198 Cliff Floyd Mets .20 .50
199 Jason Jennings .20 .50
200 Mike Lowell .20 .50
201 Johnny Damon .30 .75
202 Aramis Ramirez Cubs .20 .50
203 John Smoltz .50 1.25
204 Alan Trammell .20 .50
205 Moises Alou Astros .20 .50
206 Randy Johnson Expos .50 1.25
207 Reggie Sanders .20 .50
208 Rickey Henderson Dgr .30 .75
209 Runelvys Hernandez .20 .50
210 Ryan Klesko .20 .50
211 Casey Fossum .20 .50
212 Robert Fick Tigers .20 .50
213 Al Oliver Dgr .20 .50
214 Kazuo Matsui .20 .50
215 Pedro Martinez Dgr .30 .75
216 Roberto Alomar Sox .30 .75
217 Greg Maddux .75 2.00
218 Mark Ellis .20 .50
219 Shawn Green Dgr .20 .50
220 Shawn Green Jays .20 .50
221 Willie McCovey .30 .75
222 Rafael Furcal .20 .50
223 Richie Ashburn .30 .75
224 Edgar Martinez .30 .75
225 Carlos Delgado Jays .20 .50
226 David Justice Braves .50 1.25
227 Jose Cruz .20 .50
228 Larry Walker Rockies .30 .75
229 Miguel Tejada .30 .75
230 Andres Galarraga Braves .20 .50
231 Trot Nixon .20 .50
232 Willie Mays Mets 1.00 2.50
233 Dennis Eckersley .20 .50
234 Michael Barrett .20 .50
235 Jose Cruz Jr. Jays .20 .50
236 Nolan Ryan Astros UER 1.25 3.00
Wrong location for third 19 strikeout game
237 Hal Newhouser .30 .75
238 Roger Clemens Yanks .60 1.50
239 Victor Martinez .30 .75
240 Sean Burroughs .20 .50
241 Andres Galarraga Rgr .20 .50
242 Cal Ripken 2.00 5.00
243 Doug Mientkiewicz Twins .20 .50
244 Hank Aaron 1.00 2.50
245 Vladimir Guerrero Expos .50 1.25
246 Reggie Jackson .50 1.25
247 Terrence Long .20 .50
248 Tommy Lasorda .20 .50
249 Bert Blyleven .20 .50
250 Ken Boyer .30 .75
251 Maury Wills .20 .50
252 Lou Brock .30 .75
253 Don Sutton .20 .50
254 Enos Slaughter .20 .50
255 Ernie Banks .50 1.25
256 Gaylord Perry .20 .50
257 Joe Carter Jays .20 .50
258 Keith Hernandez .20 .50
259 Orlando Cabrera .20 .50
260 Phil Niekro Braves .20 .50
261 Robin Ventura Yanks .20 .50
262 Rod Carew .30 .75
263 Rollie Fingers .20 .50
264 Sammy Sosa .50 1.25
265 Byung-Hyun Kim .20 .50
266 Zach Day .20 .50
267 Richie Ashburn .30 .75
268 Mike Piazza .50 1.25
269 Tommy John Yanks .20 .50
270 Craig Biggio .30 .75
271 Hideki Matsui .75 2.00
272 Cesar Izturis Jays .20 .50
273 Paul Molitor Brewers .50 1.25
274 Steve Carlton Phils .20 .50
275 Justin Morneau .50 1.25
276 Albert Pujols 1.25 3.00
277 John Olerud Jays .20 .50
278 Austin Kearns .20 .50
279 Travis Hafner Indians .20 .50
280 Charles Johnson M's .20 .50
281 Craig Wilson .20 .50
282 Joe Carter Indians .20 .50
283 Josh Beckett .30 .75
284 Dale Murphy .20 .50
285 Robert Fick Padres .20 .50
286 David Justice Yanks .50 1.25
287 Kirby Puckett .50 1.25
288 Juan Encarnacion M's .20 .50
289 Moises Alou Giants .20 .50
290 Shannon Stewart Twins .20 .50
291 Alfonso Soriano Rgr .30 .75
292 Jacque Jones .20 .50
293 Pee Wee Reese .30 .75
294 Deion Sanders .30 .75
295 Richard Hidalgo Rgr .20 .50
296 Rocco Baldelli .20 .50
297 Bill Hall .20 .50
298 Mike Sweeney .20 .50
299 Paul Molitor Twins .50 1.25
300 Will Clark .30 .75
301 Torii Hunter .20 .50
302 Jim Thome .30 .75
303 Kevin Mench .20 .50
304 John Buck .20 .50
305 Joe Morgan .20 .50
306 Wilson Betemit .20 .50
307 Ivan Rodriguez .30 .75
308 Michael Young .30 .75
309 Moises Alou Cubs .20 .50
310 So Taguchi .20 .50
311 Rickey Henderson Padres .30 .75
312 Kenny Lofton Indians .20 .50
313 Rickey Henderson Sox .30 .75
314 Shannon Stewart Jays .20 .50
315 Fred Lynn .20 .50
316 Mark Prior .30 .75
317 Tony Perez .20 .50
318 Dontrelle Willis .20 .50
319 Xavier Nady .20 .50
320 Juan Uribe .20 .50
321 Chipper Jones .50 1.25
322 Joe Crede .20 .50
323 Kerry Wood .20 .50
324 Eric Hinske .20 .50
325 Carlos Lee Sox .20 .50
326 Joe Borchard .20 .50
327 Sean Casey Indians .20 .50
328 Joe Kennedy Rays .20 .50
329 Brandon Duckworth .20 .50
330 Willie Mays NY Giants 1.00 2.50
331 Andruw Jones .20 .50
332 Brandon Claussen .20 .50
333 Brandon Claussen .20 .50
334 Brian Giles .20 .50
335 Gary Sheffield .20 .50
336 Mark Grace .30 .75
337 Ryne Sandberg 1.00 2.50
338 Sammy Sosa .50 1.25
339 Steve Carlton Cards .20 .50
340 Vernon Wells .20 .50
341 Wade Miller .20 .50
342 Andre Dawson .30 .75
343 Darryl Strawberry Mets .20 .50
344 Nolan Ryan Angels 1.25 3.00
345 Curt Schilling .30 .75
346 Bo Jackson Royals .50 1.25
347 Darin Erstad .20 .50
348 Alfonso Soriano Yanks .30 .75
349 A.J. Burnett .30 .75
350 David Ortiz Sox .50 1.25
351 George Foster .20 .50
352 Rafael Palmeiro .30 .75
353 Alan Trammell .20 .50
354 Willie Mays SF Giants 1.00 2.50
355 Bernie Williams .30 .75
356 Phil Niekro Yanks .20 .50
357 Hank Blalock .20 .50
358 Miguel Cabrera .50 1.25
359 Carl Yastrzemski .60 1.50
360 Aramis Ramirez Pirates .20 .50
361 Frank Thomas .50 1.25
362 Tony Oliva .20 .50
363 Roger Clemens Astros .60 1.50
364 Adam Loewen .20 .50
365 Alex Cintron .20 .50
366 Alfredo Simon .20 .50
367 Angel Guzman .20 .50
368 Anthony Lerew .20 .50
369 Ben Hendrickson .20 .50
370 Brandon McCarthy RC .30 .75
371 Bubba Nelson .20 .50
372 Clint Nageotte .20 .50
373 Eddy Rodriguez .20 .50
374 Edwin Moreno .20 .50
375 J.J. Putz .20 .50
376 Jake Woods .20 .50
377 Jeff Suppan .20 .50
378 Jeremy Affeldt .20 .50
379 Jose Castillo .20 .50
380 Justin Leone .20 .50
381 Justin Verlander RC 4.00 10.00
382 Marlon Byrd Nats .20 .50
383 Mike Gosling .20 .50
384 Prince Fielder RC 1.00 2.50
385 Randy Wolf .20 .50
386 Raul Ibanez .20 .50
387 Raul Tablado RC .20 .50
388 Rick Dempsey .20 .50
389 Roberto Novoa .20 .50
390 Russ Ortiz .20 .50
391 Ryan Wing .20 .50
392 Scot Shields .20 .50
393 Steve Stone .20 .50
394 Tadahito Iguchi RC .30 .75
395 Todd Wellemeyer .20 .50
396 Travis Blackley .20 .50
397 Troy Percival .20 .50
398 Wilson Valdez .20 .50
399 Kevin Youkilis .20 .50
400 Jose Guillen .20 .50
401 Duke Snider .30 .75
402 Jeff Niemann RC .50 1.25
403 Johan Santana .50 1.25
404 Nellie Fox .30 .75
405 Nellie Fox .30 .75
406 Marlon Byrd Nats .20 .50
407 Mike Piazza .50 1.25
408 Bobby Higginson .20 .50
409 Don Mattingly 1.00 2.50
410 Jayson Werth .30 .75
411 Al Kaline .50 1.25
412 Bobby Higginson .20 .50
413 Roger Cedeno Cards .20 .50
414 Roger Cedeno Mets .20 .50
415 Roger Cedeno Tigers .20 .50
416 Roger Cedeno Astros .20 .50
417 Roger Cedeno Dgr .20 .50
418 Magglio Ordonez .30 .75
419 Don Mattingly 1.00 2.50
420 Morgan Ensberg .20 .50
421 Charles Johnson Sox .20 .50
422 Albert Pujols 1.25 3.00
423 Dave Righetti .20 .50
424 Roy Halladay .50 1.25
425 Tom Seaver .30 .75
426 Early Wynn .20 .50
427 Bob Gibson .30 .75
428 Doug Mientkiewicz Sox .20 .50
429 Jason Varitek .50 1.25
430 Tom Glavine .30 .75
431 Erik Bedard .20 .50
432 Pedro Martinez Sox .30 .75
433 David Ortiz Twins .50 1.25
434 Kazuhisa Ishii .20 .50
435 Trevor Hoffman .30 .75
436 Paul Molitor Twins .50 1.25
437 Derrek Lee .20 .50
438 Fergie Jenkins .20 .50
439 Tony Gwynn .60 1.50
440 Jeff Bagwell .30 .75
441 Steve Carlton Giants .20 .50
442 Adam Dunn .30 .75
443 Sean Casey Reds .20 .50
444 Geoff Jenkins .20 .50
445 Derek Jeter 1.25 3.00
446 J.T. Snow .20 .50
447 Kenny Lofton Giants .20 .50
448 Benito Santiago .20 .50
449 Tim Salmon .20 .50
450 Ichiro Suzuki .75 2.00

2005 Donruss Champions Impressions

*IMP: 1.25X TO 3X BASIC
*IMP: .75X TO 2X BASIC RC
STATED ODDS 1:3

2005 Donruss Champions Impressions Black

STATED PRINT RUN 5 SERIAL #'d SETS
NO PRICING DUE TO SCARCITY

2005 Donruss Champions Impressions Blue

*IMP BLUE: 2X TO 5X BASIC
*IMP BLUE: 1.25X TO 3X BASIC RC
STATED PRINT RUN 100 SERIAL #'d SETS

2005 Donruss Champions Impressions Gold

*IMP GOLD: 2.5X TO 6X BASIC
*IMP GOLD: 1.5X TO 4X BASIC RC
STATED PRINT RUN 50 SERIAL #'d SETS

2005 Donruss Champions Impressions Green

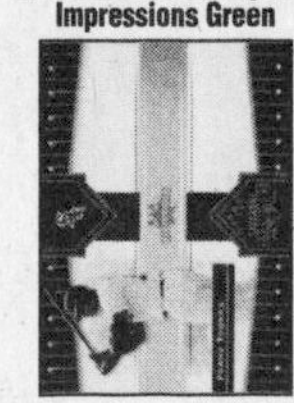

*IMP GREEN: 3X TO 8X BASIC
STATED PRINT RUN 25 SERIAL #'d SETS
NO RC YR PRICING DUE TO SCARCITY

2005 Donruss Champions Impressions Orange

*IMP ORANGE: 2X TO 5X BASIC
*IMP ORANGE: 1.25X TO 3X BASIC RC
STATED PRINT RUN 75 SERIAL #'d SETS

2005 Donruss Champions Impressions Red

*IMP RED: 1.5X TO 4X BASIC
*IMP RED: 1X TO 2.5X BASIC RC
STATED PRINT RUN 250 SERIAL #'d SETS

2005 Donruss Champions Impressions Autograph

STATED ODDS 1:46
ASTERISK PRINT RUNS B/WN 1-94 PER
TIER 1 PRINT RUNS B/WN 101-250 PER
TIER 2 PRINT RUNS B/WN 251-500 PER
TIER 3 PRINT RUNS B/WN 501-800 PER
TIER 4 PRINT RUNS B/WN 801-1200 PER
TIER 5 PRINT RUNS B/WN 1201-1500 PER
CARDS ARE NOT SERIAL-NUMBERED
PRINT RUN INFO PROVIDED BY DONRUSS
NO PRICING ON QTY OF 19 OR LESS
1 Adam Dunn/1 *
2 Albert Pujols/11 *
19 Cal Ripken/65 * 75.00 150.00
26 Jim Edmonds/6 *
31 Rodrigo Lopez/5 *
34 Jay Payton/3 *
42 Tony Gwynn/65 * 15.00 40.00
44 Frank Robinson/59 * 12.50 30.00
46 Tony Gwynn/65 * 15.00 40.00
47 Tony Gwynn/61 * 15.00 40.00
48 Will Clark/2 *
53 Chris Snelling/12 *
57 Eric Chavez/8 *
65 Jose Vidro/1 *
68 Lyle Overbay/15 *
72 Melvin Mora/1 *
74 Orlando Hudson/1 *
77 Paul Konerko/8 *
86 Victor Martinez/4 *
90 Angel Berroa/18 *
102 Frankie Francisco/6 *
126 Vernon Wells/1 *
130 Brandon Duckworth/13 *
135 Travis Hafner Rgr/19 *
142 Mike Lowell/2 *
159 Carlos Lee Brewers/10 *
162 Craig Biggio/7 *
164 Magglio Ordonez/6 *
172 Jason Lane/1 *
181 Joey Gathright/19 *
183 Mark Teixeira/1 *
185 Esteban Loaiza/1 *
188 Jason Bay/13 *
194 David Wright/16 *
202 Aramis Ramirez Cubs/5 *
206 Randy Johnson Expos/62 * 40.00 80.00
224 Edgar Martinez/1 *
226 David Justice Braves/8 *
229 Miguel Tejada/3 *
232 Willie Mays Mets/1 *
239 Victor Martinez/4 *
242 Cal Ripken/25 * 125.00 200.00
246 Reggie Jackson/18 *
253 Dennis Eckersley/10 *
255 Ernie Banks/11 *
256 Gaylord Perry/9 *
258 Keith Hernandez/9 *
259 Orlando Cabrera/4 *
262 Rod Carew/37 * 12.50 30.00
275 Justin Morneau/18 *
279 Travis Hafner Indians/49 * 8.00 20.00
290 Shannon Stewart Twins/1 *
297 Bill Hall/52 * 5.00 12.00
300 Will Clark/1 *
305 Joe Morgan/4 *
306 Wilson Betemit/7 *
314 Shannon Stewart Jays/1 *
315 Fred Lynn/10 *
319 Xavier Nady/1 *
322 Joe Crede/34 * 10.00 25.00
343 Darryl Strawberry Mets/5 *
354 Willie Mays SF Giants/1 *
361 Frank Thomas/2 *
364 Adam Loewen T1 4.00 10.00
365 Alex Cintron T1 4.00 10.00
366 Alfredo Simon T2 4.00 10.00
367 Angel Guzman T2 4.00 10.00
369 Ben Hendrickson T3 4.00 10.00
371 Bubba Nelson T2 4.00 10.00
372 Clint Nageotte T2 4.00 10.00
373 Eddy Rodriguez/89 * 4.00 10.00
374 Edwin Moreno/55 * 5.00 12.00
375 J.J. Putz T3 4.00 10.00
376 Jake Woods T1 4.00 10.00
377 Jeff Suppan T4 4.00 10.00
378 Jeremy Affeldt T1 4.00 10.00
379 Jose Castillo T1 4.00 10.00
380 Justin Leone T2 4.00 10.00
381 Justin Verlander/12 *
382 Marlon Byrd Nats T1 4.00 10.00
383 Mike Gosling/93 * 4.00 10.00
385 Randy Wolf T1 4.00 10.00
386 Raul Ibanez T1 8.00 20.00
387 Raul Tablado/74 * 4.00 10.00
388 Rick Dempsey T4 4.00 10.00
389 Roberto Novoa T2 4.00 10.00
390 Russ Ortiz/49 * 5.00 12.00
391 Ryan Wing T1 4.00 10.00
392 Scot Shields T5 4.00 10.00
393 Steve Stone/65 * 8.00 20.00
395 Todd Wellemeyer/92 * 4.00 10.00
396 Travis Blackley/87 * 4.00 10.00
397 Troy Percival T1 6.00 15.00
398 Wilson Valdez T5 4.00 10.00
399 Kevin Youkilis T2 6.00 15.00
401 Duke Snider/30 * 15.00 40.00
402 Jeff Niemann/77 * 6.00 15.00
403 Johan Santana/29 * 15.00 40.00
418 Magglio Ordonez/6 *
423 Dave Righetti T1 6.00 15.00
424 Roy Halladay/19 *
425 Tom Seaver/28 * 15.00 40.00
430 Tom Glavine/1 *
438 Fergie Jenkins/2 *

2005 Donruss Champions Impressions Ball

*BALL p/r 75-100: .5X TO 1.2X MAT T1-T5
*BALL p/r 37-65: .6X TO 1.5X MAT T1-T5
*BALL p/r 25-31: .75X TO 2X MAT T1-T5
RANDOM INSERTS IN PACKS
PRINT RUNS B/WN 1-100 COPIES PER
NO PRICING ON QTY OF 24 OR LESS
192 Hideki Matsui/40 15.00 40.00
316 Mark Prior/31 5.00 12.00
348 Alfonso Soriano Yanks/75 2.50 6.00
352 Rafael Palmeiro/65 4.00 10.00
390 Russ Ortiz/50 3.00 8.00

2005 Donruss Champions Impressions Batting Glove

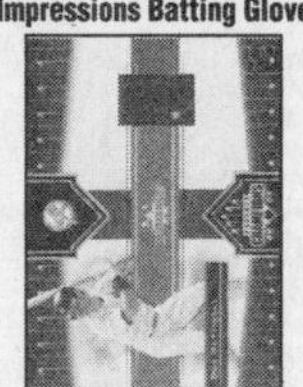

RANDOM INSERTS IN PACKS
PRINT RUNS B/WN 44-145 COPIES PER
306 Wilson Betemit/145 2.00 5.00
320 Juan Uribe/125 2.00 5.00
322 Joe Crede/89 2.50 6.00
325 Carlos Lee Sox/71 2.50 6.00
334 Brian Giles/44 3.00 8.00
419 Don Mattingly/125 6.00 15.00

2005 Donruss Champions Impressions Button

PRINT RUNS B/WN 1-16 COPIES PER
PRICING DUE TO SCARCITY

2005 Donruss Champions Impressions Fielding Glove

PRINT RUNS B/WN 26-250 COPIES PER
317 Tony Perez/49 4.00 10.00
319 Xavier Nady/97 2.50 6.00
321 Chipper Jones/26 15.00 40.00
328 Joe Kennedy Rays/130 2.00 5.00
331 Andruw Jones/82 3.00 8.00
332 Brandon Claussen/250 2.00 5.00
336 Mark Grace/186 3.00 8.00
337 Ryne Sandberg/64 10.00 25.00
339 Steve Carlton Cards/86 3.00 8.00
341 Wade Miller/117 2.00 5.00
420 Morgan Ensberg/87 2.50 6.00

2005 Donruss Champions Impressions Hat

RANDOM INSERTS IN PACKS
PRINT RUNS B/WN 1-250 COPIES PER
NO PRICING ON QTY OF 1
313 Rickey Henderson Sox/219 4.00 10.00
314 Shannon Stewart Jays/250 2.00 5.00
316 Mark Prior/250 2.50 6.00
329 Brandon Duckworth/157 2.00 5.00
332 Brandon Claussen/250 2.00 5.00
340 Vernon Wells/26 4.00 10.00
409 Don Mattingly/1

2005 Donruss Champions Impressions Material

STATED ODDS 1:8
ASTERISK PRINT RUNS B/WN 2-90 PER
TIER 1 PRINT RUNS B/WN 101-250 PER
TIER 2 PRINT RUNS B/WN 251-500 PER
TIER 3 PRINT RUNS B/WN 501-800 PER
TIER 4 PRINT RUNS B/WN 801-1200 PER
TIER 5 PRINT RUNS B/WN 1201-1500 PER
CARDS ARE NOT SERIAL-NUMBERED
PRINT RUN INFO PROVIDED BY DONRUSS
NO PRICING ON QTY OF 24 OR LESS
21 B.J. Surhoff Jsy T5 2.00 5.00
22 Brian Jordan Jsy T5 2.00 5.00
23 Corey Koskie Jsy T5 2.00 5.00
24 Doug Davis Jsy T5 2.00 5.00
25 Jason Varitek Jsy T5 3.00 8.00
26 Jim Edmonds Jsy/65 * 3.00 8.00
27 Kevin Mench Jsy T5 2.00 5.00
28 Roberto Alomar O's Jsy T5 2.50 6.00
29 Tony Armas Jr. Jsy T5 2.00 5.00
30 Ramon Ortiz Jsy T5 2.00 5.00
31 Rodrigo Lopez Jsy T5 2.00 5.00
32 A.Galarraga Giants Jsy T4 3.00 8.00
33 Brian Lawrence Jsy T5 2.00 5.00
34 Jay Payton Jsy T5 2.00 5.00
36 Hee Seop Choi Jsy T5 2.00 5.00
37 J.D. Drew Cards Jsy T4 2.00 5.00
38 Raul Mondesi Jsy T4 2.00 5.00
39 Brian Jordan Jsy T4 2.00 5.00
40 Luis Matos Jsy T5 2.00 5.00
41 Russell Branyan Jsy T4 2.00 5.00
42 Tony Gwynn Jsy T4 4.00 10.00
43 Francisco Rodriguez Jsy T4 2.00 5.00
44 Frank Robinson Jkt T5 2.50 6.00
45 Jeff Bagwell Pants T5 2.50 6.00
46 Tony Gwynn Pants T5 4.00 10.00
47 Tony Gwynn Pants T5 4.00 10.00
48 Will Clark Pants T5 3.00 8.00
50 R.Henderson Yanks Jkt T3 4.00 10.00
51 Brian Lawrence Bat T4 2.00 5.00
52 Carlos Beltran Mets Bat T5 2.00 5.00
53 Chris Snelling Bat T5 2.00 5.00
54 D.Strawberry Dgr Bat/50 * 4.00 10.00
55 D.Mientkiewicz Mets Bat T5 2.00 5.00
56 Edgardo Alfonzo Bat T5 2.00 5.00
57 Eric Chavez Bat T5 2.00 5.00
58 Eric Davis Bat T5 3.00 8.00
59 Guillermo Quiroz Bat T5 2.00 5.00
60 J.D. Drew Braves Bat T5 2.00 5.00
61 J.D. Drew Dgr Bat T5 2.00 5.00
62 Walter Young Bat T4 2.00 5.00
63 John Kruk Bat T5 2.50 6.00
64 Jose Reyes Bat T5 2.00 5.00
65 Jose Vidro Bat T5 2.00 5.00
66 Josh Phelps Bat T5 2.00 5.00
67 Larry Walker Expos Bat T5 2.00 5.00
68 Lyle Overbay Bat T5 2.00 5.00
69 Manny Ramirez Bat T1 2.50 6.00
70 Marlon Byrd Phils Bat T5 2.00 5.00
71 Matt Williams Bat T5 3.00 8.00
72 Melvin Mora Bat T5 2.00 5.00
73 Nook Logan Bat T5 2.00 5.00
74 Orlando Hudson Bat T5 2.00 5.00
75 Orlando Hudson Bat T5 2.00 5.00
76 Orlando Hudson Bat T5 2.00 5.00
77 Paul Konerko Bat T5 2.00 5.00
78 Raul Mondesi Bat T4 2.00 5.00
79 Reed Johnson Bat T5 2.00 5.00
81 So Taguchi Bat T4 2.00 5.00
82 Toby Hall Bat T5 2.00 5.00
83 Todd Helton Bat T2 2.50 6.00
84 Tommy John Dgr Bat T5 2.50 6.00
85 Tony Clark Bat T4 2.00 5.00
86 Victor Martinez Bat T5 2.00 5.00
87 V.Guerrero Angels Bat/51 * 5.00 12.00
88 Wade Boggs Bat T5 2.50 6.00
89 Roberto Clemente Bat T5 15.00 40.00
90 Angel Berroa Bat T5 2.00 5.00
91 Termel Sledge Bat T5 2.00 5.00
92 A.Galarraga Rockies Bat T4 3.00 8.00
93 Brooks Robinson Bat T5 3.00 8.00
94 Brooks Robinson Bat T4 3.00 8.00
95 Dennis Tankersley Bat T4 2.00 5.00
96 Don Mattingly Bat T4 5.00 12.00
97 R.Rodriguez Rgr Bat T4 2.00 5.00
98 Deivi Cruz Nats Bat T5 2.00 5.00
99 Deivi Cruz Giants Bat T3 2.00 5.00
100 Pete LaForest Bat T4 2.00 5.00

101 R.Clemens Sox Jsy T1 6.00 15.00
102 Frankie Francisco Jsy T4 2.00 5.00
103 Kevin Millwood Phils Jsy T4 2.00 5.00
104 Tony Womack Jsy T4 2.00 5.00
105 Jeff Bagwell Jsy T4 2.50 6.00
106 Billy Martin Jsy T3 4.00 10.00
107 J.T. Snow Jsy T3 2.00 5.00
108 Juan Uribe Jsy T4 2.00 5.00
109 Ryan Dempster Jsy T3 2.00 5.00
110 Toby Hall Jsy T4 2.00 5.00
111 Dennis Tankersley Jsy T3 2.00 5.00
112 Freddy Garcia Jsy T4 2.00 5.00
113 Garrett Atkins Jsy T4 2.00 5.00
114 Troy Glaus Angels Jsy T3 2.00 5.00
115 Gabe Kapler Jsy T4 2.00 5.00
116 Jeff Kent Jays Jsy T4 2.00 5.00
117 Rondell White Jsy T3 2.00 5.00
118 C.C. Sabathia Jsy T3 2.00 5.00
119 Javier Vazquez Jsy T4 2.00 5.00
120 Mike Cameron Jsy T3 2.00 5.00
121 Pat Burrell Jsy T3 2.00 5.00
122 Lew Ford Jsy T3 2.00 5.00
123 Brad Radke Jsy T3 2.00 5.00
124 Preston Wilson Jsy T3 2.00 5.00
125 Ray Durham Jsy T3 2.00 5.00
126 Vernon Wells Jsy T3 2.00 5.00
127 Bo Jackson Sox Jsy T3 4.00 10.00
128 Dmitri Young Jsy T3 2.00 5.00
129 Doug Davis Jsy T3 2.00 5.00
130 Brandon Duckworth Jsy T3 2.00 5.00
131 Brandon Backe Jsy T3 2.00 5.00
132 J.Encarn Tigers Jsy T3 2.00 5.00
133 Mike Maroth Jsy T3 2.00 5.00
134 Sean Casey Indians Jsy T4 2.00 5.00
135 Travis Hafner Rgr Jsy T3 2.00 5.00
136 Wes Helms Jsy T3 2.00 5.00
137 Randy Johnson M's Jsy T3 3.00 8.00
138 Larry Walker Cards Jsy T2 2.50 6.00
139 Luis Gonzalez Jsy T2 2.00 5.00
140 John Olerud M's Jsy T1 2.00 5.00
141 Kazuhisa Ishii Jsy T4 2.00 5.00
142 Mike Lowell Jsy T2 2.00 5.00
143 K.Millwood Braves Jsy T2 2.00 5.00
144 Chad Gaudin Jsy T2 2.00 5.00
145 Bret Boone Jsy T2 2.00 5.00
146 Cliff Floyd M's Jsy T2 2.00 5.00
147A Dale Murphy Jsy T3 3.00 8.00
147B Dale Murphy Bat 3.00 8.00
148 R.Henderson M's Pants T4 4.00 10.00
149 R.Rod Indians Pants T2 2.00 5.00
150 Richard Hidalgo Pants T3 2.00 5.00
151 J.Kennedy Rockies Bat T4 2.00 5.00
152 Juan Pierre Rockies Bat T4 2.00 5.00
153 Juan Pierre M's Bat T4 2.00 5.00
154 Lance Berkman Bat T4 2.00 5.00
155 Joe Borchard Bat T4 2.00 5.00
156 Craig Monroe Bat T4 2.00 5.00
157 Abraham Nunez Bat T1 2.00 5.00
158 Willie Wilson Bat T4 2.50 6.00
159 Carlos Lee Brewers Bat T3 2.00 5.00
160 Carl Everett Bat T4 2.00 5.00
161 Frank White Bat T4 2.50 6.00
162 Craig Biggio Bat T4 2.50 6.00
163 Jason Varitek Bat T4 3.00 8.00
164 Magglio Ordonez Bat T4 2.00 5.00
165 Carlos Delgado M's Bat T4 2.00 5.00
166 Casey Kotchman Bat T4 2.00 5.00
167 Kenny Lofton Braves Bat T4 2.50 6.00
168 Gil Hodges Bat T4 6.00 15.00
169 Rafael Furcal Bat T3 2.00 5.00
170 Ramon Vazquez Bat T3 2.00 5.00
171 Jeff Bagwell Bat T3 2.50 6.00
172 Jason Lane Bat T3 2.00 5.00
173 Nomar Garciaparra Bat T3 3.00 8.00
174 Willie Harris Bat T3 2.00 5.00
175 Adam Dunn Bat T3 2.00 5.00
176 J.Cruz Jr. D'backs Bat T3 2.00 5.00
177 Robin Ventura Sox Bat T3 2.50 6.00
178 Al Oliver Rgr Bat T3 2.50 6.00
179 Wily Mo Pena Bat T3 2.00 5.00
180 Erubiel Durazo Bat T3 2.00 5.00
181 Joey Gathright Bat T3 2.00 5.00
182 Luis Castillo Bat T3 2.00 5.00
183 Mark Teixeira Bat T3 2.50 6.00
184 Delmon Young Bat T3 2.00 5.00
185 Esteban Loaiza Bat T3 2.00 5.00
186 Bo Jackson Royals Bat T3 4.00 10.00
187 Freddy Sanchez Bat T3 2.00 5.00
188 Jason Bay Bat T3 2.00 5.00
189 R.Henderson A's Bat T3 4.00 10.00
190 S.Green D'backs Bat T2 2.00 5.00
191 Roger Cedeno Mets Bat T4 2.00 5.00
192 Hideki Matsui Bat T3 6.00 15.00
193 Andruw Jones Bat T3 2.50 6.00
194 David Wright Bat T3 4.00 10.00
195 Cesar Izturis Dgr Bat T2 2.00 5.00
196 Chipper Jones Bat T3 3.00 8.00
197 Troy Glaus D'backs Bat T3 2.00 5.00
198 Cliff Floyd Mets Bat T3 2.00 5.00
199 Jason Jennings Bat T2 2.00 5.00
200 Mike Lowell Bat T2 2.00 5.00
201 Johnny Damon Jsy T2 2.50 6.00
202 Aramis Ramirez Cubs Jsy T1 2.00 5.00
203 John Smoltz Jsy T2 2.50 6.00
204 Alan Trammell Jsy T2 2.50 6.00
205 Moises Alou Astros Jsy T2 2.00 5.00
206 R.Johnson Expos Jsy T2 3.00 8.00
207 Reggie Sanders Jsy T2 2.00 5.00
208 R.Henderson Dgr Jsy T2 4.00 10.00
209 Ru.Hernandez Jsy T2 2.00 5.00
210 Ryan Klesko Jsy T2 2.00 5.00
211 Casey Fossum Jsy T2 2.00 5.00
212 Robert Fick Tigers Jsy T2 2.00 5.00
213 Al Oliver Dgr Jsy T2 2.50 6.00
214 Kazuo Matsui Jsy T2 2.00 5.00
215 Pedro Martinez Dgr Jsy T2 2.50 6.00
216 Roberto Alomar Sox Jsy T1 2.50 6.00
217 Greg Maddux Jsy T1 4.00 10.00
218 Mark Ellis Jsy T2 2.00 5.00
219 Shawn Green Dgr Jsy T1 2.00 5.00
220 Shawn Green Jays Jsy T1 2.00 5.00
221 Willie McCovey Jsy T2 3.00 8.00
222 Rafael Furcal Jsy T1 2.00 5.00
223 Richie Ashburn Jsy T1 4.00 10.00
224 Edgar Martinez Jsy/15 *
225 Carlos Delgado Jays Jsy T2 2.00 5.00
226 D.Justice Braves Jsy T2 3.00 8.00
227 Jose Cruz Jsy T2 2.50 6.00
228 L.Walker Rockies Jsy T1 2.00 5.00
229 Miguel Tejada Jsy T1 2.00 5.00
230 A.Galarraga Braves Jsy T1 3.00 8.00
231 Trot Nixon Jsy T1 2.00 5.00
232 Willie Mays Mets Jsy T2 10.00 25.00
233 Dennis Eckersley Jsy T1 2.50 6.00
234 Michael Barrett Jsy T1 2.00 5.00
235 Jose Cruz Jr. Jays Jsy T1 2.00 5.00
236 Nolan Ryan Astros Jsy T1 10.00 25.00
237 Hal Newhouser Jsy T1 2.50 6.00
238 R.Clemens Yanks Jsy T1 6.00 15.00
239 Victor Martinez Jsy/50 * 3.00 8.00
240 Sean Burroughs Jsy/90 * 2.50 6.00
241 A.Galarraga Rgr Jsy/84 * 4.00 10.00
242 Cal Ripken Jsy T1 15.00 40.00
243 D.Mient Twins Jsy/68 * 2.50 6.00
244 Hank Aaron Jsy/60 * 15.00 40.00
245 V.Guerrero Expos Jsy/17 *
246 Reggie Jackson Jsy/35 * 6.00 15.00
247 Terrence Long Jsy/73 * 2.50 6.00
248 Tommy Lasorda Jsy/24 *
250 Ken Boyer Jsy/20 *
251 Maury Wills Jsy/19 *
252 Lou Brock Jsy/2 *
253 Don Sutton Jsy/11 *
256 Gaylord Perry Jsy/2 *
257 Joe Carter Jays Jsy/4 *
262 Rod Carew Jsy/7 *
265 Byung-Hyun Kim Jsy T2 3.00 8.00
266 Zach Day Pants T2 2.00 5.00
267 Richie Ashburn Pants T2 4.00 10.00
268 Mike Piazza Pants T2 3.00 8.00
269 T.John Yanks Pants T1 2.50 6.00
270 Craig Biggio Pants T1 2.50 6.00
271 Hideki Matsui Pants T1 6.00 15.00
272 Cesar Izturis Jays Pants T1 2.00 5.00
273 P.Molitor Brewers Pants T1 2.50 6.00
274 S.Carlton Phils Pants/40 * 4.00 10.00
275 Justin Morneau Bat T2 2.00 5.00
276 Albert Pujols Bat T2 6.00 15.00
277 John Olerud Jays Bat T2 2.00 5.00
278 Austin Kearns Bat T2 2.00 5.00
279 T.Hafner Indians Bat T2 2.00 5.00
280 Charles Johnson M's Bat T2 2.00 5.00
281 Craig Wilson Bat T2 2.00 5.00
282 Joe Carter Indians Bat T2 3.00 8.00
283 Josh Beckett Bat T2 2.00 5.00
284 Dale Murphy Bat/42 * 5.00 12.00
285 Robert Fick Padres Bat T2 2.00 5.00
286 David Justice Yanks Bat T2 3.00 8.00
287 Kirby Puckett Bat T2 3.00 8.00
288 J.Encarnacion M's Bat T2 2.00 5.00
289 Moises Alou Giants Bat T2 2.00 5.00
290 S.Stewart Twins Bat T2 2.00 5.00
291 Alfonso Soriano Rgr Bat T2 2.00 5.00
292 Jacque Jones Bat T2 2.00 5.00
293 Pee Wee Reese Bat T2 3.00 8.00
294 Deion Sanders Bat/81 * 4.00 10.00
295 R.Hidalgo Rgr Bat T2 2.00 5.00
296 Rocco Baldelli Bat T2 2.00 5.00
297 Bill Hall Bat T2 2.00 5.00
298 Mike Sweeney Bat T1 2.00 5.00
299 Paul Molitor Twins Bat T2 2.50 6.00
300 Will Clark Bat T1 3.00 8.00
301 Torii Hunter Bat T1 2.00 5.00
304 John Buck Bat/20 *
305 Joe Morgan Bat/95 * 3.00 8.00
308 Michael Young Bat/1 *
309 Moises Alou Cubs Bat/1 *
311 R.Henderson Padres Bat T1 4.00 10.00
315 Fred Lynn Bat/40 * 4.00 10.00
318 Dontrelle Willis Bat/51 * 3.00 8.00
342 Andre Dawson Bat/25 * 5.00 12.00
349 A.J. Burnett Bat/1 *
350 David Ortiz Sox Bat T1 2.50 6.00
351 George Foster Bat T1 2.50 6.00
353 Alan Trammell Bat T1 2.50 6.00
354 W.Mays SF Giants Bat T1 12.50 30.00
355 Bernie Williams Bat T1 2.50 6.00
356 Phil Niekro Yanks Bat T1 2.50 6.00
357 Hank Blalock Bat T1 2.00 5.00
358 Miguel Cabrera Bat T1 2.50 6.00
359 Carl Yastrzemski Bat/47 * 8.00 20.00
360 A.Ramirez Pirates Bat/57 * 3.00 8.00
361 Frank Thomas Bat T1 3.00 8.00
363 R.Clemens Astros Bat/10 *
404 Nellie Fox Bat T5 6.00 15.00
405 Nellie Fox Bat T5 6.00 15.00
406 Marlon Byrd Nats Bat T5 2.00 5.00
407 Mike Piazza Bat T2 3.00 8.00
408 Bobby Higginson Bat T4 2.00 5.00
410 Jayson Werth Bat T5 2.00 5.00
411 Al Kaline Bat T4 4.00 10.00
412 Bobby Higginson Bat T3 2.00 5.00
413 R.Cedeno Cards Bat T4 2.00 5.00
414 R.Cedeno Mets Bat T4 2.00 5.00
415 R.Cedeno Tigers Bat T4 2.00 5.00
416 R.Cedeno Astros Bat T4 2.00 5.00
417 R.Cedeno Dgr Bat T4 2.00 5.00
418 Magglio Ordonez Bat T5 2.00 5.00
423 Dave Righetti Jsy/7 *
424 Roy Halladay Jsy/89 * 2.50 6.00
425 Tom Seaver Jsy/13 *
426 Early Wynn Jsy T1 3.00 8.00
427 Bob Gibson Jsy/36 * 5.00 12.00
428 D.Mientkiewicz Sox Jsy T5 2.00 5.00
429 Jason Varitek Jsy T2 3.00 8.00
430 Tom Glavine Jsy T1 2.50 6.00
431 Erik Bedard Jsy T2 2.00 5.00
432 Pedro Martinez Sox Jsy T2 2.50 6.00
433 David Ortiz Twins Jsy T3 2.50 6.00
434 Kazuhisa Ishii Jsy T2 2.00 5.00
435 Trevor Hoffman Jsy T2 2.00 5.00
436 Paul Molitor Twins Jsy T1 2.50 6.00
437 Derrek Lee Jsy T1 2.50 6.00
439 Tony Gwynn Pants T5 4.00 10.00
440 Jeff Bagwell Pants T4 2.50 6.00
441 S.Carlton Giants Jsy/14 *

2005 Donruss Champions Impressions Material Prime

*PRIME p/r 101-250: .6X TO 1.5X MAT T1-T5
*PRIMEp/r101-250: .5X TO 1.2X MATp/r68-95
*PRM.RETp/r101-250: .6XTO1.5X MAT T1-T5
*PRM.RETp/r101-250:.5XTO1.2XMATp/r68-95
*PRIME p/r 68-98: .75XTO 2X MAT T1-T5
*PRM.RET p/r 68-98: .75X TO 2X MAT T1-T5
*PRIME p/r 36-65: 1X TO 2.5X MAT T1-T5
*PRIME p/r 36-65: .75X TO 2X MAT p/r 68-95
*PRM.RET p/r 36-65: 1X TO 2.5X MAT T1-T5
*PRM.RETp/r36-65: .6X TO 1.5X MATp/r36-65
*PRIME p/r 25-34: 1.25X TO 3X MAT T1-T5
*PRIME p/r 25-34: 1X TO 2.5X MAT p/r 68-95
*PRM.RET p/r 25-34: 1.25X TO 3X MAT T1-T5
PRINT RUNS B/WN 1-250 COPIES PER
NO PRICING ON QTY OF 24 OR LESS
245 V.Guerrero Expos Jsy/250 5.00 12.00
248 Tommy Lasorda Jsy/186 5.00 12.00
249 Bert Blyleven Jsy/150 4.00 10.00
250 Ken Boyer Jsy/141 15.00 40.00
251 Maury Wills Jsy/37 6.00 15.00
252 Lou Brock Jsy/73 6.00 15.00
253 Don Sutton Jsy/108 4.00 10.00
254 Enos Slaughter Jsy/61 10.00 25.00
256 Gaylord Perry Jsy/127 4.00 10.00
257 Joe Carter Jays Jsy/153 5.00 12.00
258 Keith Hernandez Jsy/93 5.00 12.00
259 Orlando Cabrera Jsy/157 3.00 8.00
260 Phil Niekro Braves Jsy/82 5.00 12.00
261 R.Ventura Yanks Jsy/173 5.00 12.00
262 Rod Carew Jsy/86 6.00 15.00
263 Rollie Fingers Jsy/197 4.00 10.00
264 Sammy Sosa Jsy/250 5.00 12.00
438 Fergie Jenkins Pants/75 5.00 12.00
441 Steve Carlton Giants Jsy/54 6.00 15.00

2005 Donruss Champions Impressions MLB Logo Patch

PRINT RUNS B/WN 1-7 COPIES PER
PRICING DUE TO SCARCITY

2005 Donruss Champions Impressions Shoe

RANDOM INSERTS IN PACKS
PRINT RUNS B/WN 2-226 COPIES PER
NO PRICING ON QTY OF 15 OR LESS
307 Ivan Rodriguez/10
310 So Taguchi/226 2.00 5.00
312 Kenny Lofton Indians/103 2.50 6.00
323 Kerry Wood/89 2.50 6.00
324 Eric Hinske/133 2.00 5.00
326 Joe Borchard/200 2.00 5.00
327 Sean Casey Indians/51 3.00 8.00
330 Willie Mays NY Giants TBD
338 Sammy Sosa/75 4.00 10.00
348 Alfonso Soriano Yanks/5
352 Rafael Palmeiro/2
421 Charles Johnson Sox/196 2.00 5.00
422 Albert Pujols/15

2005 Donruss Champions Impressions Combos

PRINT RUNS B/WN 1-210 COPIES PER
A/B VARIATION INFO ISSUED BY DONRUSS
NO PRICING ON QTY OF 19 OR LESS
302A Jim Thome Jsy-Jsy/105 3.00 8.00
302B Jim Thome Bat-Jsy/45 * 5.00 12.00
303 Kevin Mench Bat-Jsy/175 2.50 6.00
304 J.Buck Bat-Chest Prot/150 2.50 6.00
305 Joe Morgan Bat-Jsy/80 4.00 10.00
306A W.Betemit Bat-Hat/210 2.50 6.00
306B W.Betemit Hat-Shoe/65 * 4.00 10.00
307A I.Rod Bat-Chest Prot/175 3.00 8.00
307B I.Rod Chest Prot-Jsy/35 * 6.00 15.00
308A Michael Young Bat-Jsy/180 2.50 6.00
308B Michael Young Jsy-Jsy/50 * 4.00 10.00
310 So Taguchi Bat-Jsy/150 2.50 6.00
311 R.Henderson Hat-Pants/40 8.00 20.00
312 Kenny Lofton Bat-Shoe/1
313 R.Henderson Bat-Jsy/85 6.00 12.00
314 S.Stewart Hat-Jsy/1
315A Fred Lynn Bat-Jsy/60 5.00 12.00
315B Fred Lynn Jsy-Jsy/10 *
316A Mark Prior Bat-Fld Glv/53 5.00 12.00
316B Mark Prior Jsy-Shoe/13 *
317 Tony Perez Bat-Jsy/62 5.00 12.00
318A Dontrelle Willis Jsy-Jsy/2
318B Dontrelle Willis Bat-Jsy/1 *
319A X.Nady Btg Glv-Hat/50 4.00 10.00
319B X.Nady Bat-Btg Glv/5 *
320 Juan Uribe Bat-Shoe/59 4.00 10.00
321A C.Jones Jsy-Jsy/2
321B C.Jones Fld Glv-Jsy/1 *
322A J.Crede Hat-Shoe/190 2.50 6.00
322B J.Crede Bat-Btg Glv/40 * 4.00 10.00
323A K.Wood Hat-Jsy/33 5.00 12.00
323B K.Wood Fld Glv-Pants/10 *
324A Eric Hinske Jsy-Jsy/132 2.50 6.00
324B Eric Hinske Hat-Jsy TBD
325A Carlos Lee Hat-Jsy/52 4.00 10.00
325B Carlos Lee Fld Glv-Jsy/2 *
326A Joe Borchard Jsy-Jsy/57 4.00 10.00
326B Joe Borchard Fld Glv-Jsy/7 *
328 Joe Kennedy Fld Glv-Jsy/6
330 W.Mays Bat-Btg Glv TBD
331A Andruw Jones Hat-Jsy/19
331B Andruw Jones Jsy-Shoe/4 *
332A B.Clauss Fld Glv-Shoe/165 2.50 6.00
332B B.Clauss Fld Glv-Hat/15 *
333 B.Claussen Hat-Shoe/15
334A Brian Giles Fld Glv-Jsy/90 3.00 8.00
334B Brian Giles Hat-Jsy TBD *
337 Ryne Sandberg Hat-Jsy/8
338 Sammy Sosa Bat-Hat/10
340 Vernon Wells Hat-Jsy/14
341 Wade Miller Hat-Jsy/3
342A A.Dawson Bat-Pants/165 3.00 8.00
342B A.Dawson Jsy-Pants/50 * 5.00 12.00
343 D.Strawberry Jsy-Pants/73 4.00 10.00
344 Nolan Ryan Jkt-Jsy/9
345 Curt Schilling Jsy-Jsy/89 4.00 10.00
347 Darin Erstad Jsy-Jsy/7
348A A.Soriano Btg Glv-Jsy/10
348B A.Soriano Hat-Jsy/3 *
349 A.J. Burnett Bat-Jsy/19
350A David Ortiz Bat-Jsy/53 5.00 12.00
350B David Ortiz Bat-Shoe TBD *
352 R.Palmeiro Bat-Jsy/201 3.00 8.00
353 Alan Trammell Bat-Jsy/4
354 Willie Mays Bat-Jsy/6
355 B.Williams Bat-Jsy/43 5.00 12.00
356 Phil Niekro Bat-Jsy/19
357 Hank Blalock Bat-Jsy/47 4.00 10.00
359 C.Yastrzemski Bat-Jsy/73 12.50 30.00
360 Aramis Ramirez Bat-Jsy/7
362 Tony Oliva Bat-Jsy/93 4.00 10.00
363 R.Clemens Bat-Jsy/10

2005 Donruss Champions Impressions Combos Prime

*PRM.RETp/r39-50: .6XTO1.5X COMp/r73-93
*PRM.RETp/r39-50: .5XTO1.2X COMp/r40-62
*PRIMEp/r25-33: 1X TO 2.5X COMp/r105-210
RANDOM INSERTS IN PACKS
PRINT RUNS B/WN 1-50 COPIES PER
NO PRICING ON QTY OF 24 OR LESS
301 Torii Hunter Hat-Bat/40 5.00 12.00
302 Jim Thome Jsy-Bat/40 6.00 15.00
306 W.Betemit Hat-Hat/25 6.00 15.00
309 Moises Alou Jsy-Bat/50 5.00 12.00
314 S.Stewart Jsy-Jsy/30 6.00 15.00
315 Fred Lynn Jsy-Jsy/39 6.00 15.00
318 D.Willis Jsy-Jsy/31 6.00 15.00
326 Joe Borchard Jsy-Jsy/50 5.00 12.00
328 Joe Kennedy Jsy-Jsy/50 5.00 12.00
335 G.Sheffield Jsy-Fld Glv/47 5.00 12.00
338 Sammy Sosa Jsy-Hat/49 8.00 20.00
340 Vernon Wells Jsy-Jsy/50 5.00 12.00
346 Bo Jackson Jsy-Jsy/50 10.00 25.00
347 Darin Erstad Jsy-Bat/33 6.00 15.00
349 A.J. Burnett Jsy-Jsy/39 5.00 12.00
351 G.Foster Jsy-Bat/50 6.00 15.00
360 A.Ramirez Jsy-Bat/50 5.00 12.00
363 R.Clemens Jsy-Jsy/26 15.00 40.00

2005 Donruss Champions Recollection Autographs

RANDOM INSERTS IN PACKS
PRINT RUNS B/WN 1-319 COPIES PER
NO PRICING ON QTY OF 23 OR LESS
AD1 Andre Dawson 81 D/7
AD2 Andre Dawson 83 D/2
AD3 Andre Dawson 87 D/3
AR1 Aramis Ramirez 02 D/2
AR2 Aramis Ramirez 02 DK/34 10.00 25.00
AR3 Aramis Ramirez 04 DK/33 10.00 25.00
BBR1 Brian Bruney 03 DK/151 4.00 10.00
BB1 Brandon Berger 01 Eli ED/19
BG1 Bobby Grich 82 D/1
BG2 Bobby Grich 85 Leaf/1
BG3 Bobby Grich 87 D/68 4.00 10.00
BJ1 B.J. Surhoff 91 Leaf/2
BJ2 B.J. Surhoff 91 Stu/5
BL1 Barry Larkin 03 DK/33 15.00 40.00
BM1 Bill Madlock 81 D/15
BM2 Bill Madlock 82 D/10
BM3 Bill Madlock 83 D/10
BM4 Bill Madlock 83 DK/35 10.00 25.00
BM5 Bill Madlock 84 D/10
BM6 Bill Madlock 85 D/7
BM7 Bill Madlock 86 D/10
BM8 Bill Madlock 87 D/10
BM9 Bill Madlock 88 D/10
BN1 Bubba Nelson 03 DK/147 4.00 10.00
BO1 Ben Oglivie 81 D/44 8.00 20.00
BO2 Ben Oglivie 82 D/81 6.00 15.00
BO3 Ben Oglivie 83 D/28 10.00 25.00
BO4 Ben Oglivie 84 D/17
BO5 Ben Oglivie 85 D/4
BO6 Ben Oglivie 86 D/62 8.00 20.00
BO7 Ben Oglivie 87 D/132 6.00 15.00
BW1 Brandon Webb 03 D/15
BW2 Brandon Webb 03 DK/51 8.00 20.00
BZ1 Barry Zito 03 D DK/4
BZ2 Barry Zito 03 DK/4
CF1 Chone Figgins 03 D/20
CF2 Chone Figgins 03 DK/68 6.00 15.00
CLE1 Cliff Lee 03 D/5
CLE2 Cliff Lee 03 DK/73 6.00 15.00
CL1 Carlos Lee 01 LRS/4
CL2 Carlos Lee 01 Stu/8
CS1 Chris Snelling 02 DK/47 5.00 12.00
DC1 David Cone 87 D/25 10.00 25.00
DC2 David Cone 89 DK/116 6.00 15.00
DC3 David Cone 97 PP/2
DC4 David Cone 01 D/5
DD1 Darren Daulton 91 Stu/3
DH1 Dan Haren 03 DK/146 4.00 10.00
EA1 Erick Almonte 01 Eli ED/29 6.00 15.00
EC1 Eric Chavez 02 DK/4
EC2 Eric Chavez 03 DK/33 10.00 25.00
EM1 Edgar Martinez 91 Stu/11
EM2 Edgar Martinez 98 LRS/1
EM3 Edgar Martinez 01 Eli/35 15.00 40.00
EM4 Edgar Martinez 01 LRS/4
EM5 Edgar Martinez 01 Stu/11
EM6 Edgar Martinez 02 DK/3
EM7 Edgar Martinez 02 Eli/15
EM8 Edgar Martinez 02 Eli AS/5
EM9 Edgar Martinez 03 DK/33 15.00 40.00
FM1 Fred McGriff 87 D/4
FM2 Fred McGriff 88 D/3
FM3 Fred McGriff 88 OD/1
FM4 Fred McGriff 89 D/2
FM5 Fred McGriff 89 DK/12
FM6 Fred McGriff 89 MVP/3
FM7 Fred McGriff 96 D/1
FM8 Fred McGriff 97 D/3
FM9 Fred McGriff 98 D/1
FM10 Fred McGriff 98 Eli Asp/1
FM11 Fred McGriff 03 DK/16
GA1 Garret Anderson 03 DK/14
GG1 Geronimo Gil 01 Eli/40 5.00 12.00
GK1 Gabe Kapler 01 LRS/5
GK2 Gabe Kapler 01 Stu/8
GQ1 Guillermo Quiroz 03 DK/149 4.00 10.00
GS1 Greg Swindell 89 D/1
GT1 Gorman Thomas 82 D/1
JB1 Jesse Barfield 89 Score/1
JD1 Jermaine Dye 00 D/25 10.00 25.00
JD2 Jermaine Dye 01 D/25 10.00 25.00
JD3 Jermaine Dye 02 D/6
JD4 Jermaine Dye 03 DK/33 10.00 25.00
JF1 John Franco 87 Leaf/1
JGI1 Jay Gibbons 03 DK/27 6.00 15.00
JGU1 Jose Guillen 04 D/35 10.00 25.00
JG1 Jason Giambi 99 D/25 15.00 40.00
JG2 Jason Giambi 00 D/25 15.00 40.00
JG3 Jason Giambi 01 D/25 15.00 40.00
JJ1 Jacque Jones 01 20A/5
JJ2 Jacque Jones 03 DK/32 10.00 25.00
JK1 Jason Kubel 03 DK/151 4.00 10.00
JMC1 Jack McDowell 91 Stu/3
JMO1 Jamie Moyer 87 D/20
JM1 Jack Morris 82 D/6
JM2 Jack Morris 87 DK/1
JM3 Jack Morris 88 D/9
JM4 Jack Morris 91 D/5
JM5 Jack Morris 91 Stu/7
JM6 Jack Morris 03 DK/74 6.00 15.00
JP1 Jake Peavy 03 D/17
JS1 Jae Weong Seo 04 DK/33 10.00 25.00
JV1 Jose Vidro 01 LRS/21
JV2 Jose Vidro 03 DK/71 6.00 15.00
JW1 Jack Wilson 01 DR/18
JW2 Jack Wilson 03 D/20
KI1 Kazuhisa Ishii 03 DK/4
KW1 Kerry Wood 02 DK/3
LF1 Lew Ford 04 D/4
MB1 Marlon Byrd 01 Eli ED/319 4.00 10.00
MB2 Marlon Byrd 03 D Sig Fld/25 6.00 15.00
MB3 Marlon Byrd 03 D Sig Hit/25 6.00 15.00
MB4 Marlon Byrd 03 DK/23
MB5 Marlon Byrd 04 DK/35 6.00 15.00
MLO1 Mike Lowell 03 DK/33 10.00 25.00
ML1 Mike Lieberthal 03 D/20
ML2 Mike Lieberthal 03 DK/27 10.00 25.00
ML3 Mike Lieberthal 04 D/20
MO1 Magglio Ordonez 99 D/10
MO2 Magglio Ordonez 00 D/10
MO3 Magglio Ordonez 01 D/10
MO4 M.Ordonez 03 Don DK/33 10.00 25.00
MO5 Magglio Ordonez 03 DK/33 10.00 25.00
MW1 Mitch Williams 89 D/1
OV1 Omar Vizquel 89 D/2
OV2 Omar Vizquel 98 PPS/1
OV3 Omar Vizquel 99 D/5
OV4 Omar Vizquel 00 D/5
PK1 Paul Konerko 04 DK/33 15.00 40.00
PL1 Paul Lo Duca 03 DK/13
RA1 Roberto Alomar 01 Stu/9
RD1 Rob Dibble 89 D/33 6.00 15.00
RD2 Rob Dibble 90 D/20
RD3 Rob Dibble 91 D/3
RD4 Rob Dibble 91 Stu/1
RD5 Rob Dibble 92 D/15
RD6 Rob Dibble 93 D/28 6.00 15.00
RD7 Rob Dibble 94 D/1
RHA1 Rich Harden 04 DK/33 10.00 25.00
RHO1 Ryan Howard 03 DK/150 60.00 120.00
RH1 Roy Halladay 03 DK/4
RI1 Raul Ibanez 03 DK/72 8.00 20.00
RK1 Ryan Klesko 97 Stu/1
RK2 Ryan Klesko 98 LRS/1
RK3 Ryan Klesko 98 Stu/1
RK4 Ryan Klesko 01 LRS/14
RK5 Ryan Klesko 01 Stu/16
RO1 Roy Oswalt 02 DK/73 6.00 15.00
RO2 Roy Oswalt 03 DK/13
RR1 R.Rodriguez 01 Eli ED/63 5.00 12.00
RWA1 Ryan Wagner 04 DK/12
RW1 Randy Wolf 03 D/20
RW2 Randy Wolf 04 D/20
SA1 Sandy Alomar Jr. 91 Stu/1
SB1 Sean Burroughs 03 DK/72 4.00 10.00
SGR1 Shawn Green 03 Eli/2
SG1 Steve Garvey 82 DK/13
SH1 Shea Hillenbrand 03 D/14
SS1 Shannon Stewart 02 DK/75 6.00 15.00
THU1 Torii Hunter 02 D/10
THU2 Torii Hunter 03 DK/72 6.00 15.00
THU3 Torii Hunter 04 DK/3
TH1 Tim Hudson 01 D/5
TH2 Tim Hudson 01 Stu/10
TH3 Tim Hudson 02 DK/4
TH4 Tim Hudson 03 DK/4
TN1 Trot Nixon 04 DK/33 10.00 25.00
TSP1 T.Spooney 01 Eli ED/14
TS1 Tim Salmon 93 D/8
TS2 Tim Salmon 95 D/4
TS3 Tim Salmon 96 D/2
TS4 Tim Salmon 99 D/5
TS5 Tim Salmon 01 D/10
TW1 Todd Wellemeyer 03 DK/146 4.00 10.00
VW1 Vernon Wells 03 DK/33 10.00 25.00
VW2 Vernon Wells 03 PC/49 8.00 20.00
WM1 Wade Miller 02 D/1
WM2 Wade Miller 03 DK/89 4.00 10.00

2001 Donruss Class of 2001

This product was released in mid-December 2001, and featured a 300-card base set that was broken into tiers as follows: 100 Base Veterans, 100 Rookies/Prospects serial numbered to 1875, and an additional 100 Rookies/Prospects serial numbered to 625. Each pack contained three cards, and carried a suggested retail price of $3.99. Due to an error in printing, two different players were checklisted as card 252 (John Buck and Adam Johnson) - thus, a total of 301 cards exist for the set, though it's numbering runs from 1-300. Both Buck and Johnson's cards are serial numbered "of 625" on back.

COMP.SET w/o SP's (100) 10.00 25.00
COMMON CARD (1-100) .15 .40
COMMON (101-200) 1.50 4.00
COMMON (201-300) 2.50 6.00
1 Alex Rodriguez .60 1.50
2 Barry Bonds 1.00 2.50
3 Vladimir Guerrero .40 1.00
4 Jim Edmonds .15 .40
5 Derek Jeter 1.00 2.50
6 Jose Canseco .25 .60
7 Rafael Furcal .15 .40
8 Cal Ripken 1.25 3.00
9 Brad Radke .15 .40
10 Miguel Tejada .15 .40
11 Pat Burrell .15 .40
12 Ken Griffey Jr. .60 1.50
13 Cliff Floyd .15 .40
14 Luis Gonzalez .15 .40
15 Frank Thomas .40 1.00
16 Mike Sweeney .15 .40
17 Paul LoDuca .15 .40
18 Lance Berkman .15 .40
19 Tony Gwynn .50 1.25
20 Chipper Jones .40 1.00
21 Eric Chavez .15 .40
22 Kerry Wood .15 .40
23 Jorge Posada .25 .60
24 J.D. Drew .15 .40
25 Garret Anderson .15 .40
26 Mike Piazza .60 1.50
27 Kenny Lofton .15 .40
28 Mike Mussina .25 .60
29 Paul Konerko .15 .40
30 Bernie Williams .25 .60
31 Eric Milton .15 .40
32 Shawn Green .15 .40
33 Paul O'Neill .25 .60
34 Juan Gonzalez .15 .40
35 Andres Galarraga .15 .40
36 Gary Sheffield .15 .40
37 Ben Grieve .15 .40
38 Scott Rolen .25 .60
39 Mark Grace .25 .60
40 Hideo Nomo .40 1.00
41 Barry Zito .25 .60
42 Edgar Martinez .25 .60
43 Jarrod Washburn .15 .40
44 Greg Maddux .60 1.50
45 Mark Buehrle .25 .60
46 Larry Walker .15 .40
47 Trot Nixon .15 .40
48 Nomar Garciaparra .60 1.50
49 Robert Fick .15 .40
50 Sean Casey .15 .40
51 Joe Mays .15 .40
52 Roger Clemens .75 2.00
53 Chan Ho Park .15 .40
54 Carlos Delgado .15 .40
55 Phil Nevin .15 .40
56 Jason Giambi .15 .40
57 Raul Mondesi .15 .40
58 Roberto Alomar .25 .60
59 Ryan Klesko .15 .40
60 Andruw Jones .25 .60
61 Gabe Kapler .15 .40
62 Darin Erstad .15 .40
63 Cristian Guzman .15 .40
64 Kazuhiro Sasaki .15 .40
65 Doug Mientkiewicz .15 .40
66 Sammy Sosa .40 1.00
67 Mike Hampton .15 .40
68 Rickey Henderson .40 1.00
69 Mark Mulder .15 .40
70 Mark McGwire 1.00 2.50
71 Freddy Garcia .15 .40
72 Ivan Rodriguez .25 .60
73 Terrence Long .15 .40
74 Jeff Bagwell .25 .60
75 Moises Alou .15 .40
76 Todd Helton .25 .60
77 Preston Wilson .15 .40
78 Pedro Martinez .25 .60
79 Bobby Abreu .15 .40
80 Manny Ramirez Sox .25 .60
81 Jose Vidro .15 .40
82 Randy Johnson .40 1.00
83 Richie Sexson .15 .40
84 Troy Glaus .15 .40
85 Kevin Brown .15 .40
86 Carlos Lee .15 .40
87 Adrian Beltre .15 .40
88 Brian Giles .15 .40
89 Jermaine Dye .15 .40
90 Craig Biggio .25 .60
91 Richard Hidalgo .15 .40
92 Magglio Ordonez .15 .40
93 Aramis Ramirez .15 .40
94 Jeff Kent .15 .40
95 Curt Schilling .15 .40
96 Tim Hudson .15 .40
97 Fred McGriff .25 .60
98 Barry Larkin .25 .60
99 Jim Thome .25 .60
100 Tom Glavine .25 .60
101 S.Douglass/1875 RC 1.50 4.00
102 R.MacKowiak/1875 RC 2.50 6.00
103 J.Fikac/1875 RC 1.50 4.00
104 Henry Mateo/1875 RC 1.50 4.00
105 G. Gil/1875 RC 1.50 4.00
106 R. Vazquez/1875 RC 1.50 4.00
107 P. Santana/1875 RC 1.50 4.00
108 Ryan Jensen/1875 RC 1.50 4.00
109 Paul Phillips/1625 RC 1.50 4.00
110 Saul Rivera/1875 RC 1.50 4.00
111 Larry Bigbie/1875 1.50 4.00
112 Josh Phelps/1875 1.50 4.00
113 Justin Kaye/1875 RC 1.50 4.00
114 Kris Keller/1625 RC 1.50 4.00
115 Adam Bernero/1625 1.50 4.00
116 V.Zambrano/1875 RC 2.50 6.00
117 Felipe Lopez/1875 1.50 4.00
118 B.Roberts/1875 RC 4.00 10.00
119 Kurt Ainsworth/1875 1.50 4.00
120 G.Perez/1625 RC 1.50 4.00
121 W.Guzman/1875 RC 1.50 4.00
122 D.Lewis/1875 RC 1.50 4.00
123 Nate Teut/1625 RC 1.50 4.00
124 M. Vargas/1625 RC 1.50 4.00
125 Brandon Inge/1875 1.50 4.00
126 T. Phelps/1875 RC 1.50 4.00
127 Les Walrond/1625 RC 1.50 4.00
128 J. Atchley/1875 RC 1.50 4.00
129 S. Clapp/1875 RC 1.50 4.00
130 Bret Prinz/1875 RC 1.50 4.00
131 Bert Snow/1875 RC 1.50 4.00
132 Joe Crede/1625 2.50 6.00
133 Nick Punto/1875 RC 1.50 4.00
134 C. Hernandez/1875 1.50 4.00
135 Ken Vining/1875 RC 1.50 4.00
136 Luis Pineda/1875 RC 1.50 4.00
137 W. Abreu/1625 RC 1.50 4.00
138 Matt Ginter/1625 1.50 4.00
139 Jason Smith/1875 RC 1.50 4.00
140 Gene Altman/1625 RC 1.50 4.00
141 B. Rogers/1875 RC 1.50 4.00
142 M.Cuddyer/1625 1.50 4.00
143 Mike Penney/1625 RC 1.50 4.00
144 S.Podsednik/1875 RC 6.00 15.00
145 Esix Snead/1625 RC 1.50 4.00
146 S.Watkins/1875 RC 1.50 4.00
147 O.Woodards/1625 RC 1.50 4.00
148 J.Deardorff/1775 RC 1.50 4.00
149 Eric Cyr/1875 RC 1.50 4.00
150 Blaine Neal/1625 RC 1.50 4.00
151 Ben Sheets/1875 2.50 6.00
152 S.Stewart/1875 RC 1.50 4.00
153 M.Koplove/1875 RC 1.50 4.00
154 Kyle Lohse/1875 RC 2.50 6.00
155 F. Rodney/1875 RC 1.50 4.00
156 Aubrey Huff/1625 1.50 4.00
157 Pablo Ozuna/1625 1.50 4.00
158 Bill Ortega/1625 RC 1.50 4.00
159 Toby Hall/1875 1.50 4.00
160 Kevin Olsen/1625 RC 1.50 4.00
161 Will Ohman/1625 RC 1.50 4.00
162 Nate Cornejo/1875 1.50 4.00
163 Jack Cust/1625 1.50 4.00
164 Juan Rivera/1875 1.50 4.00
165 J. Riggan/1875 RC 1.50 4.00
166 D.Mohr/1875 RC 1.50 4.00
167 Doug Nickle/1875 RC 1.50 4.00
168 C.Monroe/1625 RC 3.00 8.00
169 Jason Jennings/1625 1.50 4.00
170 Bart Miadich/1875 RC 1.50 4.00
171 Luis Rivas/1625 1.50 4.00
172 T. Christman/1875 RC 1.50 4.00
173 L. Hudson/1625 RC 1.50 4.00
174 Brett Jodie/1875 RC 1.50 4.00
175 Jorge Julio/1875 RC 1.50 4.00
176 David Espinosa/1625 1.50 4.00
177 Mike Maroth/1625 RC 2.50 6.00
178 Keith Ginter/1625 1.50 4.00
179 J. Moreno/1875 RC 1.50 4.00
180 B. Knight/1875 RC 1.50 4.00
181 Steve Lomasney/1625 1.50 4.00
182 J. Grabow/1625 RC 1.50 4.00
183 Steve Green/1875 RC 1.50 4.00
185 Bob File/1875 RC 1.50 4.00
186 Brent Abernathy/1625 1.50 4.00
187 M.Ensberg/1875 RC 4.00 10.00
188 Wily Mo Pena/1625 1.50 4.00
189 Ken Harvey/1875 1.50 4.00
190 Josh Pearce/1875 RC 1.50 4.00
191 Cesar Izturis/1625 1.50 4.00
192 Eric Hinske/1625 RC 2.50 6.00
193 Joe Beimel/1875 RC 1.50 4.00
194 Timo Perez/1775 1.50 4.00
195 Troy Mattes/1875 RC 1.50 4.00
196 Eric Valent/1625 1.50 4.00
197 Ed Rogers/1875 RC 1.50 4.00
198 G.Balfour/1875 RC 1.50 4.00
199 Benito Baez/1875 RC 1.50 4.00
200 Vernon Wells/1875 1.50 4.00
201 J.Kennedy PH/525 RC 4.00 10.00
202 W.Betemit PH/525 RC 4.00 10.00
203 C.Parker PH/525 RC 2.50 6.00
204 J.Gibbons PH/525 RC 4.00 10.00
205 C.Garcia PH/425 RC 2.50 6.00
206 J.Wilson PH/525 RC 4.00 10.00
207 J.Estrada PH/425 RC 4.00 10.00
208 W.Ruan PH/425 RC 2.50 6.00
209 B.Duckworth PH/525 RC 2.50 6.00
210 W.Harris PH/625 RC 2.50 6.00
211 M.Byrd PH/525 RC 2.50 6.00
212 C.C. Sabathia PH/600 2.50 6.00
213 D.Tankersley PH/525 RC 2.50 6.00
214 B.Larson PH/425 RC 2.50 6.00
215 A.Gomez PH/425 RC 2.50 6.00

216 Bill Hall PH/525 RC	6.00	15.00
217 A.Perez PH/525 RC	4.00	10.00
218 J.Affeldt PH/425 RC	2.50	6.00
219 J.Spivey PH/625 RC	4.00	10.00
220 C.Fossum PH/425 RC	2.50	6.00
221 B.Lyon PH/625 RC	2.50	6.00
222 A.Santos PH/625 RC	2.50	6.00
223 L.Davis PH/625 RC	2.50	6.00
224 Zach Day PH/425 RC	2.50	6.00
225 D.Williams PH/425 RC	2.50	6.00
226 C.Crespo PH/625 RC	2.50	6.00
227 J.Acevedo PH/425 RC	2.50	6.00
228 I.Hafner PH/625 RC	8.00	20.00
229 O.Hudson PH/525 RC	4.00	10.00
230 J.Mieses PH/425 RC	2.50	6.00
231 R.Rodriguez PH/425 RC	2.50	6.00
232 A.Soriano PH/525	4.00	10.00
233 Jason Hart PH/525	2.50	6.00
234 E.Chavez PH/425 RC	2.50	6.00
235 D.James PH/525 RC	2.50	6.00
236 R.Drese PH/625 RC	4.00	10.00
237 J.Owens PH/425 RC	2.50	6.00
238 B.Voyles PH/425 RC	2.50	6.00
239 Nate Frese PH/425 RC	2.50	6.00
240 Josh Beckett PH/600	4.00	10.00
241 Roy Oswalt PH/525	4.00	10.00
242 J.Uribe PH/475 RC	4.00	10.00
243 C.Aldridge PH/425 RC	2.50	6.00
244 Adam Dunn PH/525	4.00	10.00
245 Bud Smith PH/525 RC	2.50	6.00
246 A.Hernandez PH/525 RC	2.50	6.00
247 M.Guerrier PH/625 RC	2.50	6.00
248 J.Rollins PH/625	2.50	6.00
249 W.Caceres PH/425 RC	2.50	6.00
250 J.Michaels PH/425 RC	2.50	6.00
251 I.Suzuki PH/625 RC	20.00	50.00
252 John Buck PH/525 RC	4.00	10.00
252 Adam Johnson PH/625	2.50	6.00
253 A.Torres PH/525 RC	2.50	6.00
254 A.Amezaga PH/625 RC	2.50	6.00
255 C.Miller PH/525 RC	2.50	6.00
256 Rafael Soriano PH/425 RC	2.50	6.00
257 Donaldo Mendez PH/425 RC	2.50	6.00
258 V.Martinez PH/625 RC	15.00	40.00
259 Corey Patterson PH/525	2.50	6.00
260 H.Ramirez PH/425 RC	4.00	10.00
261 Elpidio Guzman PH/425 RC	2.50	6.00
262 Juan Diaz PH/425 RC	2.50	6.00
263 Mike Rivera PH/625 RC	2.50	6.00
264 Brian Lawrence PH/425 RC	2.50	6.00
265 Josue Perez PH/425 RC	2.50	6.00
266 Jose Nunez PH/425 RC	2.50	6.00
267 E.Bedard PH/625 RC	10.00	25.00
268 A.Pujols PH/525 RC	125.00	175.00
269 Duaner Sanchez PH/425 RC	2.50	6.00
270 Cody Ransom PH/625 RC	2.50	6.00
271 Greg Miller PH/425 RC	2.50	6.00
272 Adam Pettyjohn PH/425 RC	2.50	6.00
273 T.Shinjo PH/625 RC	4.00	10.00
274 Claudio Vargas PH/425 RC	2.50	6.00
275 Just Duchscherer PH/625 RC	2.50	6.00
276 T.Spooneybarger PH/625 RC	2.50	6.00
277 Rick Bauer PH/625 RC	2.50	6.00
278 Josh Fogg PH/625 RC	2.50	6.00
279 Brian Reith PH/425 RC	2.50	6.00
280 Scott MacRae PH/625 RC	2.50	6.00
281 Ryan Ludwick PH/625 RC	6.00	15.00
282 Erick Almonte PH/625 RC	2.50	6.00
283 J.Towers PH/525 RC	4.00	10.00
284 Juan A.Pena PH/625 RC	2.50	6.00
285 David Brous PH/425 RC	2.50	6.00
286 Erik Hiljus PH/625 RC	2.50	6.00
287 N.Neugebauer PH/525	2.50	6.00
288 J.Melian PH/625 RC	2.50	6.00
289 B.Sylvester PH/425 RC	2.50	6.00
290 C Valderrama PH/425 RC	2.50	6.00
291 J.Cueto PH/625 RC	2.50	6.00
292 M.White PH/425 RC	2.50	6.00
293 N.Maness PH/425 RC	2.50	6.00
294 J.Lane PH/625 RC	2.50	6.00
295 B.Berger PH/625 RC	2.50	6.00
296 A.Berroa PH/525 RC	4.00	10.00
297 Juan Cruz PH/525 RC	2.50	6.00
298 D.Brazelton PH/525 RC	2.50	6.00
299 M.Prior PH/525 RC	10.00	25.00
300 M.Teixeira PH/525 RC	10.00	25.00

2001 Donruss Class of 2001 First Class

Randomly inserted into packs, this 284-card skip-numbered set parallels the Donruss Class of 2001 base set. Each card was produced with a special holographic foil. Please note that a few of the players were short-printed and are marked accordingly. Cards 1-100 were serial numbered to 100, while cards 101-300 were serial numbered to 50.

*1ST CLASS 1-100: 6X TO 15X BASIC
*1ST CLASS 101-200: .75X TO 2X BASIC
*1ST CLASS 201-300: .6X TO 1.5X BASIC

1 Alex Rodriguez SP/75	10.00	25.00
3 Vladimir Guerrero SP/75	6.00	15.00
10 Miguel Tejada SP/25		
14 Luis Gonzalez SP/75	2.50	6.00
15 Frank Thomas SP/75	6.00	15.00
18 Lance Berkman SP/75	2.50	6.00
20 Chipper Jones SP/75	6.00	15.00
22 Kerry Wood SP/75	2.50	6.00
24 J.D. Drew SP/75	2.50	6.00
27 Kenny Lofton SP/75	2.50	6.00
28 Mike Mussina SP/75	4.00	10.00
30 Bernie Williams SP/75	4.00	10.00
32 Shawn Green SP/85	2.50	6.00
34 Juan Gonzalez SP/75	2.50	6.00
35 Andres Galarraga SP/75	2.50	6.00
36 Gary Sheffield SP/75	2.50	6.00
38 Scott Rolen SP/75	4.00	10.00
44 Greg Maddux SP/75	10.00	25.00
48 Nomar Garciaparra SP/85	10.00	25.00
52 Roger Clemens SP/75	12.50	30.00
53 Chan Ho Park SP/85	2.50	6.00
58 Roberto Alomar SP/85	4.00	10.00
59 Ryan Klesko SP/50	2.50	6.00
62 Darin Erstad SP/75	2.50	6.00
72 Ivan Rodriguez SP/75	4.00	10.00
74 Jeff Bagwell SP/85	4.00	10.00
75 Moises Alou SP/75	2.50	6.00
76 Todd Helton SP/75	4.00	10.00
78 Pedro Martinez SP/85	4.00	10.00
80 Manny Ramirez Sox SP/85	4.00	10.00
82 Randy Johnson SP/85	6.00	15.00
85 Kevin Brown SP/75	2.50	6.00
88 Brian Giles SP/75	2.50	6.00
90 Craig Biggio SP/85	4.00	10.00
95 Curt Schilling SP/75	2.50	6.00
98 Barry Larkin SP/85	4.00	10.00
100 Tom Glavine SP/75	4.00	10.00
258 Victor Martinez PH	30.00	60.00

2001 Donruss Class of 2001 First Class Autographs

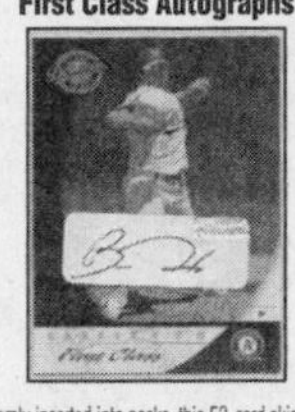

Randomly inserted into packs, this 53-card skip-numbered insert features authentic autographs from some of the hottest players in Major League Baseball. Individual print runs are listed in our checklist.

1 Alex Rodriguez/25		
3 Vladimir Guerrero/25		
10 Miguel Tejada/75	15.00	40.00
14 Luis Gonzalez/25		
15 Frank Thomas/25		
17 Paul LoDuca/100	10.00	25.00
18 Lance Berkman/25		
20 Chipper Jones/25		
21 Eric Chavez/100	10.00	25.00
22 Kerry Wood/25		
24 J.D. Drew/25		
27 Kenny Lofton/25		
28 Mike Mussina/25		
30 Bernie Williams/25		
32 Shawn Green/15		
34 Juan Gonzalez/25		
35 Andres Galarraga/25		
36 Gary Sheffield/25		
38 Scott Rolen/25		
41 Barry Zito/100	15.00	40.00
44 Greg Maddux/25		
45 Mark Buehrle/100	20.00	50.00
48 Nomar Garciaparra/15		
49 Robert Fick/100	10.00	25.00
50 Sean Casey/100	10.00	25.00
51 Joe Mays/100	10.00	25.00
52 Roger Clemens/25		
53 Chan Ho Park/15		
58 Roberto Alomar/15		
59 Ryan Klesko/50		
62 Darin Erstad/25		
69 Mark Mulder/100	10.00	25.00
72 Ivan Rodriguez/25		
73 Terrence Long/100	10.00	25.00
74 Jeff Bagwell/15		
75 Moises Alou/25		
76 Todd Helton/25		
78 Pedro Martinez/15		
80 Manny Ramirez Sox/15		
81 Jose Vidro/100	10.00	25.00
82 Randy Johnson/15		
83 Richie Sexson/100	10.00	25.00
84 Troy Glaus/100	10.00	25.00
85 Kevin Brown/25		
88 Brian Giles/25		
89 Jermaine Dye/100	10.00	25.00
90 Craig Biggio/15		
91 Richard Hidalgo/100	10.00	25.00
93 Aramis Ramirez/100	10.00	25.00
95 Curt Schilling/25		
96 Tim Hudson/100	15.00	40.00
98 Barry Larkin/15		
100 Tom Glavine/25		

2001 Donruss Class of 2001 Rookie Autographs

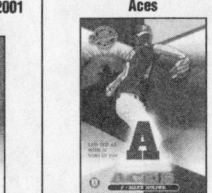

Randomly inserted into packs, this 109-card insert features authentic autographs from some of the hottest young talent in the Minor Leagues. Individual print runs are listed in our checklist.

109 Paul Phillips/250	4.00	10.00
114 Kris Keller/250	4.00	10.00
115 Adam Bernero/250	4.00	10.00
120 George Perez/250	4.00	10.00
123 Nate Teut/250	4.00	10.00
124 Martin Vargas/250	4.00	10.00
127 Les Walrond/250	4.00	10.00
132 Joe Crede/250	10.00	25.00
137 Winston Abreu/250	4.00	10.00
138 Matt Ginter/250	4.00	10.00
140 Gene Altman/250	4.00	10.00
142 Michael Cuddyer/250	10.00	25.00
143 Mike Penney/250	4.00	10.00
145 Esix Snead/250	4.00	10.00
147 O.Woodards/250	4.00	10.00
148 Jeff Deardorff/100	6.00	15.00
150 Blaine Neal/250	4.00	10.00
156 Aubrey Huff/250	6.00	15.00
157 Pablo Ozuna/250	4.00	10.00
158 Bill Ortega/250	4.00	10.00
160 Kevin Olsen/250	4.00	10.00
161 Will Ohman/250	4.00	10.00
163 Jack Cust/250	4.00	10.00
168 Craig Monroe/250	12.50	30.00
169 Jason Jennings/250	4.00	10.00
171 Luis Rivas/250	4.00	10.00
173 Luke Hudson/250	4.00	10.00
176 David Espinosa/250	4.00	10.00
177 Mike Maroth/250	6.00	15.00
178 Keith Ginter/250	4.00	10.00
181 Steve Lomasney/250	4.00	10.00
182 John Grabow/250	4.00	10.00
184 Jason Karnuth/250	4.00	10.00
186 Brent Abernathy/250	4.00	10.00
188 Wily Mo Pena/250	6.00	15.00
191 Cesar Izturis/250	4.00	10.00
192 Eric Hinske/250	6.00	15.00
194 Timo Perez/100	6.00	15.00
196 Eric Valent/250	4.00	10.00
201 Joe Kennedy PH/100	6.00	15.00
202 W.Betemit PH/100	10.00	25.00
203 C.Parker PH/100	6.00	15.00
204 Jay Gibbons PH/100	6.00	15.00
205 Carlos Garcia PH/200	4.00	10.00
206 Jack Wilson PH/100	6.00	15.00
207 J.Estrada PH/200	6.00	15.00
208 Wilkin Ruan PH/200	4.00	10.00
209 B.Duckworth PH/100	6.00	15.00
211 Marlon Byrd PH/100	6.00	15.00
212 C.C. Sabathia PH/25		
213 D.Tankersley PH/100	6.00	15.00
214 B.Larson PH/200	4.00	10.00
215 Alexis Gomez PH/200	4.00	10.00
216 Bill Hall PH/100	30.00	60.00
217 Antonio Perez PH/100	6.00	15.00
218 J. Affeldt PH/200	4.00	10.00
220 C. Fossum PH/200	4.00	10.00
224 Zach Day PH/200	4.00	10.00
225 D. Williams PH/200	4.00	10.00
227 Jose Acevedo PH/200	4.00	10.00
229 O.Hudson PH/100	6.00	15.00
230 Jose Mieses PH/200	4.00	10.00
231 Ric Rodriguez PH/200	4.00	10.00
232 A. Soriano PH/100	15.00	40.00
233 Jason Hart PH/100	6.00	15.00
234 Endy Chavez PH/200	4.00	10.00
235 Delvin James PH/100	6.00	15.00
237 J. Owens PH/200	4.00	10.00
238 Brad Voyles PH/200	4.00	10.00
239 Nate Frese PH/200	4.00	10.00
240 Josh Beckett PH/25		
241 Roy Oswalt PH/100	15.00	40.00
242 Juan Uribe PH/150	6.00	15.00
243 Cory Aldridge PH/200	4.00	10.00
244 Adam Dunn PH/100	15.00	40.00
245 Bud Smith PH/100	6.00	15.00
246 A.Hernandez PH/100	6.00	15.00
249 W. Caceres PH/200	4.00	10.00
250 J.Michaels PH/200	4.00	10.00
252 John Buck PH/100	6.00	15.00
253 Andres Torres PH/100	6.00	15.00
255 Corky Miller PH/100	6.00	15.00
256 R. Soriano PH/200	6.00	15.00
257 D. Mendez PH/200	4.00	10.00
259 C.Patterson PH/100	6.00	15.00
260 H.Ramirez PH/200	6.00	15.00
261 E.Guzman PH/200	4.00	10.00
262 Juan Diaz PH/200	4.00	10.00
264 B.Lawrence PH/200	4.00	10.00
265 Josue Perez PH/200	4.00	10.00
266 Jose Nunez PH/200	4.00	10.00
268 Albert Pujols PH/100	400.00	600.00
269 D.Sanchez PH/200	4.00	10.00
271 Greg Miller PH/200	4.00	10.00
272 A.Pettyjohn PH/200	4.00	10.00
274 C.Vargas PH/200	4.00	10.00
279 Brian Reith PH/200	4.00	10.00
283 Josh Towers PH/100	6.00	15.00
285 David Brous PH/200	4.00	10.00
287 N.Neugebauer PH/100	6.00	15.00
289 Billy Sylvester PH/200	4.00	10.00
290 C.Valderrama PH/200	4.00	10.00
292 Matt White PH/200	4.00	10.00
293 Nick Maness PH/200	4.00	10.00
296 Angel Berroa PH/100	6.00	15.00
297 Juan Cruz PH/100	6.00	15.00
298 D.Brazelton PH/100	6.00	15.00
299 Mark Prior PH/100	75.00	150.00
300 Mark Teixeira PH/100	60.00	120.00

2001 Donruss Class of 2001 Aces

Randomly inserted into packs at one in 30, this 20-card insert features baseball's most prized pitchers. Card backs carry an "A" prefix.

COMPLETE SET (20)	50.00	100.00
A1 Roger Clemens	5.00	12.00
A2 Randy Johnson	2.50	6.00
A3 Freddy Garcia	2.00	5.00
A4 Greg Maddux	4.00	10.00
A5 Tim Hudson	2.00	5.00
A6 Curt Schilling	2.00	5.00
A7 Mark Buehrle	2.00	5.00
A8 Matt Morris	2.00	5.00
A9 Joe Mays	2.00	5.00
A10 Javier Vazquez	2.00	5.00
A11 Mark Mulder	2.00	5.00
A12 Wade Miller	2.00	5.00
A13 Barry Zito	2.00	5.00
A14 Pedro Martinez	2.00	5.00
A15 Al Leiter	2.00	5.00
A16 Chan Ho Park	2.00	5.00
A17 John Burkett	2.00	5.00
A18 C.C. Sabathia	2.00	5.00
A19 Jamie Moyer	2.00	5.00
A20 Mike Mussina	2.00	5.00

2001 Donruss Class of 2001 Diamond Aces

This 19-card set is a parallel to the more common Aces insert card. Randomly inserted into packs at an unspecified ratio, each Diamond Aces card features a swatch of game-used memorabilia. All cards utilize jersey swatches except card number A20 Mike Mussina of whom has a Hat swatch instead. Card number A8 was intended to feature Matt Morris, but the card was pulled from the set due to complications in obtaining game-used equipment featuring Morris.

A1 Roger Clemens/200	15.00	40.00
A2 Randy Johnson/750	6.00	15.00
A3 Freddy Garcia/350	4.00	10.00
A4 Greg Maddux/750	10.00	25.00
A5 Tim Hudson/550	4.00	10.00
A6 Curt Schilling/525	4.00	10.00
A7 Mark Buehrle/750	6.00	15.00
A9 Joe Mays/750	4.00	10.00
A10 Javier Vazquez/500	4.00	10.00
A11 Mark Mulder/300	4.00	10.00
A12 Wade Miller/525	4.00	10.00
A13 Barry Zito/550	6.00	15.00
A14 Pedro Martinez/550	6.00	15.00
A15 Al Leiter/525	4.00	10.00
A16 Chan Ho Park/400	4.00	10.00
A17 John Burkett/700	4.00	10.00
A18 C.C. Sabathia/550	4.00	10.00
A19 Jamie Moyer/700	4.00	10.00
A20 Mike Mussina Hat/75		

2001 Donruss Class of 2001 BobbleHead

Each box of Donruss Class of 2001 featured one randomly inserted BobbleHead Doll. There were 2000 of each regular doll produced, and 1000 of each ROY doll.

1 Ichiro Suzuki	15.00	40.00
2 Cal Ripken	15.00	40.00
3 Derek Jeter	12.50	30.00
4 Mark McGwire	15.00	40.00
5 Albert Pujols	20.00	50.00
6 Ken Griffey Jr.	8.00	20.00
7 Nomar Garciaparra	8.00	20.00
8 Mike Piazza	8.00	20.00
9 Alex Rodriguez	7.50	20.00
10 Manny Ramirez Sox	6.00	15.00
11 Tsuyoshi Shinjo	6.00	15.00
12 Hideo Nomo	6.00	15.00
13 Chipper Jones	6.00	15.00
14 Sammy Sosa	6.00	15.00
15 Roger Clemens	10.00	25.00
16 Tony Gwynn	6.00	15.00
17 Barry Bonds	12.50	30.00
18 Kazuhiro Sasaki	4.00	10.00
19 Pedro Martinez	6.00	15.00
20 Jeff Bagwell	6.00	15.00
21 Ichiro Suzuki ROY	12.50	30.00
22 Albert Pujols ROY	20.00	50.00

2001 Donruss Class of 2001 BobbleHead Cards

The cards were inserted in with the 2001 Donruss BobbleHead dolls, the 22-card set features some of baseball's most prized players. Please note that there were only 2000 of each card product, except for the two ROY cards numbered to 1000 each.

COMPLETE SET (22)	40.00	100.00
1 Ichiro Suzuki	10.00	25.00
2 Cal Ripken	8.00	20.00
3 Derek Jeter	6.00	15.00
4 Mark McGwire	8.00	20.00
5 Albert Pujols	12.50	30.00
6 Ken Griffey Jr.	4.00	10.00
7 Nomar Garciaparra	4.00	10.00
8 Mike Piazza	4.00	10.00
9 Alex Rodriguez	4.00	10.00
10 Manny Ramirez Sox	3.00	8.00
11 Tsuyoshi Shinjo	3.00	8.00
12 Hideo Nomo	4.00	10.00
13 Chipper Jones	3.00	8.00
14 Sammy Sosa	3.00	8.00
15 Roger Clemens	5.00	12.00
16 Tony Gwynn	3.00	8.00
17 Barry Bonds	6.00	15.00
18 Kazuhiro Sasaki	2.00	5.00
19 Pedro Martinez	3.00	8.00
20 Jeff Bagwell	3.00	8.00
21 Ichiro Suzuki ROY	12.50	30.00
22 Albert Pujols ROY	12.50	30.00

2001 Donruss Class of 2001 Crusade

Randomly inserted into packs, this 50-card insert features players on a mission. Card backs carry a "C" prefix. Individual print runs are listed in our checklist.

C1 Roger Clemens/275	10.00	25.00
C2 Luis Gonzalez/275	3.00	8.00
C3 Troy Glaus/275	3.00	8.00
C4 Freddy Garcia/300	3.00	8.00
C5 Sean Casey/285	3.00	8.00
C6 Bobby Abreu/300	3.00	8.00
C7 Matt Morris/300	3.00	8.00
C8 Cal Ripken/275	15.00	40.00
C9 Miguel Tejada/285	3.00	8.00
C10 V.Guerrero/275	5.00	12.00
C11 Mark Buehrle/100	3.00	8.00
C12 Mike Sweeney/300	3.00	8.00
C13 Ivan Rodriguez/275	3.00	8.00
C14 Jeff Bagwell/275	3.00	8.00
C15 Joe Mays/250	3.00	8.00
C16 Cliff Floyd/300	3.00	8.00
C17 Lance Berkman/300	3.00	8.00
C18 Aramis Ramirez/100	3.00	8.00
C19 Tony Gwynn/300	6.00	15.00
C20 S.Stewart/100	3.00	8.00
C21 Todd Helton/275	3.00	8.00
C22 Chipper Jones/275	5.00	12.00
C23 Javier Vazquez/100	3.00	8.00
C24 Shawn Green/275	3.00	8.00
C25 Barry Bonds/300	12.50	30.00
C26 Albert Pujols/250	60.00	120.00
C27 Wilson Betemit/100	3.00	8.00
C28 C.C. Sabathia/290	3.00	8.00
C29 Roy Oswalt/100	4.00	10.00
C30 Johnny Estrada/100	3.00	8.00
C31 Nick Johnson/100	3.00	8.00
C32 Aubrey Huff/100	3.00	8.00
C33 Corey Patterson/200	3.00	8.00
C34 Jay Gibbons/100	3.00	8.00
C35 Marcus Giles/100	3.00	8.00
C36 Juan Cruz/100	3.00	8.00
C37 Tsuyoshi Shinjo/300	3.00	8.00
C38 Ben Sheets/285	3.00	8.00
C39 Bud Smith/100	3.00	8.00
C40 Alex Escobar/100	3.00	8.00
C41 Joe Kennedy/100	3.00	8.00
C42 Alexis Gomez/100	3.00	8.00
C43 Jimmy Rollins/300	3.00	8.00
C44 Josh Towers/100	3.00	8.00
C45 Joe Crede/100	4.00	10.00
C46 B.Duckworth/100	3.00	8.00
C47 Ichiro Suzuki/300	30.00	60.00
C48 Jose Ortiz/100	3.00	8.00
C49 Casey Fossum/100	3.00	8.00
C50 Adam Dunn/200	3.00	8.00

2001 Donruss Class of 2001 Crusade Autographs

Randomly inserted into packs, this 39-card insert features authentic autographs from veterans like Cal Ripken and Chipper Jones. Card backs carry a "C" prefix. Individual print runs are listed in our checklist.

C1 Roger Clemens/25		
C2 Luis Gonzalez/25		
C3 Troy Glaus/25		
C5 Sean Casey/15		
C8 Cal Ripken/25		
C9 Miguel Tejada/15		
C10 Vladimir Guerrero/25		
C11 Mark Buehrle/200	12.50	30.00
C13 Ivan Rodriguez/25		
C14 Jeff Bagwell/25		
C15 Joe Mays/50		
C18 Aramis Ramirez/200	6.00	15.00
C20 S. Stewart/200	6.00	15.00
C21 Todd Helton/25		
C22 Chipper Jones/25		
C23 Javier Vazquez/200	6.00	15.00
C24 Shawn Green/25		
C26 Albert Pujols/50	400.00	700.00
C27 Wilson Betemit/200	10.00	25.00
C28 C.C. Sabathia/10		
C29 Roy Oswalt/200	15.00	40.00
C30 Johnny Estrada/200	10.00	25.00
C31 Nick Johnson/200	6.00	15.00
C32 Aubrey Huff/200	6.00	15.00
C33 Corey Patterson/100	4.00	10.00
C34 Jay Gibbons/200	10.00	25.00
C35 Marcus Giles/200	6.00	15.00
C36 Juan Cruz/200	6.00	15.00
C38 Ben Sheets/15		
C39 Bud Smith/200	4.00	10.00
C40 Alex Escobar/200	4.00	10.00
C41 Joe Kennedy/200	10.00	25.00
C42 Alexis Gomez/200	4.00	10.00
C44 Josh Towers/200	10.00	25.00
C45 Joe Crede/200	10.00	25.00
C46 B. Duckworth/200	4.00	10.00
C48 Jose Ortiz/200	4.00	10.00
C49 Casey Fossum/200	6.00	15.00
C50 Adam Dunn/100	15.00	40.00

2001 Donruss Class of 2001 Dominators

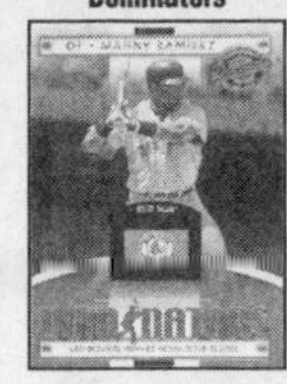

Randomly inserted into packs at one in 20, this 30-card insert features players that dominate their opponents. Card backs carry a "DM" prefix.

COMPLETE SET (30)	75.00	150.00
DM1 Manny Ramirez Sox	2.00	5.00
DM2 Lance Berkman	2.00	5.00
DM3 Juan Gonzalez	2.00	5.00
DM4 Albert Pujols	15.00	40.00
DM5 Jason Giambi	2.00	5.00
DM6 Mike Sweeney	2.00	5.00
DM7 Rafael Palmeiro	2.00	5.00
DM8 Luis Gonzalez	2.00	5.00
DM9 Ichiro Suzuki	6.00	15.00
DM10 Cliff Floyd	2.00	5.00
DM11 Roberto Alomar	2.00	5.00
DM12 Paul LoDuca	2.00	5.00
DM13 Shannon Stewart	2.00	5.00
DM14 Barry Bonds	6.00	15.00
DM15 Larry Walker	2.00	5.00
DM16 Shawn Green	2.00	5.00
DM17 Moises Alou	2.00	5.00
DM18 Cal Ripken	8.00	20.00
DM19 Brian Giles	2.00	5.00
DM20 Magglio Ordonez	2.00	5.00
DM21 Jose Vidro	2.00	5.00
DM22 Edgar Martinez	2.00	5.00
DM23 Aramis Ramirez	2.00	5.00
DM24 Tony Gwynn	3.00	8.00
DM25 Richie Sexson	2.00	5.00
DM26 Todd Helton	2.00	5.00
DM27 Garret Anderson	2.00	5.00
DM28 Chipper Jones	2.50	6.00
DM29 Troy Glaus	2.00	5.00
DM30 Jeff Bagwell	2.00	5.00

2001 Donruss Class of 2001 Diamond Dominators

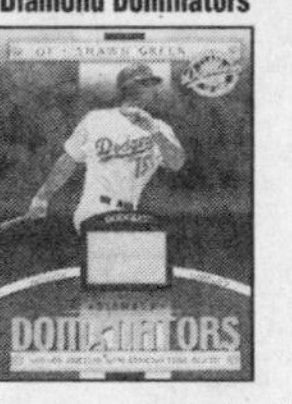

Randomly inserted into packs, this 30-card insert is a complete parallel of the Donruss Class of 2001 Dominators insert each featuring a game-used piece of memorabilia. Card backs carry a "DM" prefix. Individual print runs are listed below.

DM1 Manny Ramirez Sox Bat/725	6.00	15.00
DM2 Lance Berkman Bat/725	4.00	10.00
DM3 Juan Gonzalez Bat/500	4.00	10.00
DM4 Albert Pujols Bat/125	60.00	120.00
DM5 Jason Giambi Bat/250	4.00	10.00
DM6 Mike Sweeney Jsy/325	4.00	10.00
DM7 Rafael Palmeiro Bat/550	6.00	15.00
DM8 Luis Gonzalez Bat/725	4.00	10.00
DM9 Ichiro Suzuki Ball/50	50.00	100.00
DM10 Cliff Floyd Jsy/725	4.00	10.00
DM11 Roberto Alomar Bat/200	6.00	15.00
DM12 Paul LoDuca Jsy/600	4.00	10.00
DM13 Shannon Stewart Bat/725	4.00	10.00
DM14 Barry Bonds Bat/250	10.00	25.00
DM15 Larry Walker Bat/725	4.00	10.00
DM16 Shawn Green Bat/500	4.00	10.00
DM17 Moises Alou Bat/550	4.00	10.00
DM18 Cal Ripken Bat/250	15.00	40.00
DM19 Brian Giles Bat/725	4.00	10.00
DM20 Magglio Ordonez Bat/725	4.00	10.00
DM21 Jose Vidro Jsy/725	4.00	10.00
DM22 Edgar Martinez Jsy/200	6.00	15.00
DM23 Aramis Ramirez Bat/200	4.00	10.00
DM24 Tony Gwynn Bat/500	6.00	15.00
DM25 Richie Sexson Bat/725	4.00	10.00
DM26 Todd Helton Bat/725	6.00	15.00
DM27 Garret Anderson Bat/725	4.00	10.00
DM28 Chipper Jones Bat/725	6.00	15.00
DM29 Troy Glaus Jsy/200	4.00	10.00
DM30 Jeff Bagwell Jsy/325	6.00	15.00

2001 Donruss Class of 2001 Rewards

Randomly inserted into packs at one in 212, this 10-card insert features award winning players. Card backs carry a "RW" prefix.

RW1 Jason Giambi MVP	4.00	10.00
RW2 Ichiro Suzuki MVP	12.50	30.00
RW3 Roger Clemens CY	12.50	30.00
RW4 Freddy Garcia CY	4.00	10.00
RW5 Ichiro Suzuki ROY	12.50	30.00
RW6 Albert Pujols ROY	20.00	50.00
RW7 Barry Bonds MVP	12.50	30.00
RW8 Albert Pujols MVP	20.00	50.00
RW9 Randy Johnson CY	6.00	15.00
RW10 Matt Morris CY	4.00	10.00

2001 Donruss Class of 2001 Final Rewards

Randomly inserted into packs, this nine-card insert is a partial parallel of the Donruss Class of 2001 Rewards insert. Each card includes a a swatch of game-used memorabilia. Individual print runs are listed below.

RW1 Jason Giambi MVP Jsy/250	4.00	10.00
RW2 Ichiro Suzuki MVP Ball/50	50.00	100.00
RW3 Roger Clemens CY Jsy/200	8.00	20.00
RW4 Freddy Garcia CY Jsy/250	4.00	10.00
RW5 Ichiro Suzuki ROY Ball/50	50.00	100.00
RW6 Albert Pujols ROY Bat/125	70.00	120.00
RW7 Barry Bonds MVP Jsy/200	10.00	25.00
RW8 Albert Pujols MVP Bat/125	70.00	120.00
RW9 Randy Johnson CY Jsy/250	6.00	15.00

2001 Donruss Class of 2001 Rookie Team

Randomly inserted into packs at one in 83, this 15-card insert features top rookies from the 2001 season. Card backs carry a " RT" prefix.

COMPLETE SET (15)	75.00	150.00
RT1 Jay Gibbons	3.00	8.00
RT2 Alfonso Soriano	3.00	8.00
RT3 Jimmy Rollins	2.00	5.00
RT4 Wilson Betemit	3.00	8.00
RT5 Albert Pujols	20.00	50.00
RT6 Johnny Estrada	3.00	8.00
RT7 Ichiro Suzuki	10.00	25.00
RT8 Tsuyoshi Shinjo	3.00	8.00
RT9 Adam Dunn	3.00	8.00
RT10 C.C. Sabathia	2.00	5.00
RT11 Ben Sheets	3.00	8.00
RT12 Roy Oswalt	3.00	8.00
RT13 Bud Smith	2.00	5.00
RT14 Josh Towers	3.00	8.00
RT15 Juan Cruz	2.00	5.00

2001 Donruss Class of 2001 Rookie Team Materials

Randomly inserted into packs, this 15-card insert is a parallel of the Donruss Class of 2001 Rookie Team insert. Each card contains a swatch of game-used memorabilia. Individual print runs are listed in our checklist.

RT1 Jay Gibbons Btg Glv/100	8.00	20.00
RT2 Alfonso Soriano Btg Glv/100	8.00	20.00
RT3 J.Rollins Jsy/200	4.00	10.00
RT4 Wilson Betemit Hat/100	8.00	20.00
RT5 Albert Pujols Bat/100	90.00	150.00
RT6 Johnny Estrada Shoes/100	6.00	15.00
RT7 Ichiro Suzuki Ball/50	50.00	100.00
RT8 T.Shinjo Shoes/200	6.00	15.00

RT9 Adam Dunn Bat/200	6.00	15.00
RT10 C.C. Sabathia Jsy/200	4.00	10.00
RT11 Ben Sheets Bat/200	6.00	15.00
RT12 Roy Oswalt Btg Glv/50	10.00	25.00
RT13 Bud Smith Jsy/250	4.00	10.00
RT14 J.Towers Pants/200	6.00	15.00
RT15 Juan Cruz Jsy/200	4.00	10.00

2001 Donruss Class of 2001 Yearbook

Randomly inserted into packs at one in 24, this 25-card insert features players that had outstanding seasons in 2001. Card backs carry a "YB" prefix.

COMPLETE SET (25)	75.00	150.00
YB1 Barry Bonds	6.00	15.00
YB2 Mark Mulder	1.50	4.00
YB3 Luis Gonzalez	1.50	4.00
YB4 Lance Berkman	1.50	4.00
YB5 Matt Morris	1.50	4.00
YB6 Roy Oswalt	2.50	6.00
YB7 Todd Helton	1.50	4.00
YB8 Tsuyoshi Shinjo	1.50	4.00
YB9 C.C. Sabathia	1.50	4.00
YB10 Curt Schilling	1.50	4.00
YB11 Rickey Henderson	2.50	6.00
YB12 Jamie Moyer	1.50	4.00
YB13 Shawn Green	1.50	4.00
YB14 Randy Johnson	2.50	6.00
YB15 Jim Thome	1.50	4.00
YB16 Larry Walker	1.50	4.00
YB17 Jimmy Rollins	1.50	4.00
YB18 Kazuhiro Sasaki	1.50	4.00
YB19 Hideo Nomo	2.50	6.00
YB20 Roger Clemens	5.00	12.00
YB21 Bud Smith	1.50	4.00
YB22 Ichiro Suzuki	6.00	15.00
YB23 Albert Pujols	12.50	30.00
YB24 Cal Ripken	8.00	20.00
YB25 Tony Gwynn	3.00	8.00

2001 Donruss Class of 2001 Scrapbook

Randomly inserted into packs, this 24-card insert is a partial parallel of the Donruss Class of 2001 Yearbook insert. Each card contains a swatch of game-used memorabilia. Individual print runs are listed below.

SB1 B.Bonds Pants/525	10.00	25.00
SB2 Mark Mulder/500	4.00	10.00
SB3 Luis Gonzalez/500	4.00	10.00
SB4 Lance Berkman/525	4.00	10.00
SB6 Roy Oswalt/150	6.00	15.00
SB7 Todd Helton/525	6.00	15.00
SB8 Tsuyoshi Shinjo/75	6.00	15.00
SB9 C.C. Sabathia/500	4.00	10.00
SB10 Curt Schilling/525	4.00	10.00
SB11 R.Henderson Bat/200	6.00	15.00
SB12 Jamie Moyer/500	4.00	10.00
SB13 Shawn Green/525	4.00	10.00
SB14 R.Johnson/500	6.00	15.00
SB15 Jim Thome/400	6.00	15.00
SB16 Larry Walker/500	4.00	10.00
SB17 Jimmy Rollins Base/25		
SB18 K.Sasaki/500	4.00	10.00
SB19 Hideo Nomo/150	10.00	25.00
SB20 Roger Clemens/475	10.00	25.00
SB21 Bud Smith/525	4.00	10.00
SB22 Ichiro Suzuki Ball/75	40.00	80.00
SB23 A.Pujols Bat/150	70.00	120.00
SB24 Cal Ripken/525	15.00	40.00
SB25 T.Gwynn Pants/500	6.00	15.00

2001 Donruss Classics

This 200-card set was distributed in six-card packs with a suggested retail price of $11.99. The set features color photos of stars of the game from the past, present, and future highlighted with silver tint and foil. Cards 101-150 display color photos of rookies and are sequentially numbered to 585. Cards 151-200 consisting of retired players are sequentailly numbered to 1755 and are highlighted with gold tint and foil. Cards 162 (Sandy Koufax LGD) and 185 (Robin Roberts LGD) were not intended for public release but a handful of copies made their way into packs despite the manufacturers efforts to physically pull them from the production process. It's rumored that some Koufax cards were issued to dealers as sample cards along with wholesale order forms prior to the product's release but the scarcity of the card likely belies any truth to that statement. Due to their scarcity, the set is considered complete at 198 cards and pricing is unavailable on them individually.

COMP.SET w/o SP's (100)	10.00	25.00
COMMON CARD (1-100)	.25	.60
COMMON (101-150)	2.00	5.00
COMMON (151-200)	1.50	4.00
1 Alex Rodriguez	1.00	2.50
2 Barry Bonds	1.50	4.00
3 Cal Ripken	2.00	5.00
4 Chipper Jones	.60	1.50
5 Derek Jeter	1.50	4.00
6 Troy Glaus	.25	.60
7 Frank Thomas	.60	1.50
8 Greg Maddux	1.00	2.50
9 Ivan Rodriguez	.40	1.00
10 Jeff Bagwell	.40	1.00
11 Cliff Floyd	.25	.60
12 Todd Helton	.40	1.00
13 Ken Griffey Jr.	1.00	2.50
14 Manny Ramirez Sox	.40	1.00
15 Mark McGwire	1.50	4.00
16 Mike Piazza	1.00	2.50
17 Nomar Garciaparra	1.00	2.50
18 Pedro Martinez	.40	1.00
19 Randy Johnson	.60	1.50
20 Rick Ankiel	.25	.60
21 Rickey Henderson	.60	1.50
22 Roger Clemens	1.25	3.00
23 Sammy Sosa	.60	1.50
24 Tony Gwynn	.75	2.00
25 Vladimir Guerrero	.60	1.50
26 Kazuhiro Sasaki	.25	.60
27 Roberto Alomar	.40	1.00
28 Barry Zito	.40	1.00
29 Pat Burrell	.25	.60
30 Harold Baines	.25	.60
31 Carlos Delgado	.25	.60
32 J.D. Drew	.25	.60
33 Jim Edmonds	.25	.60
34 Darin Erstad	.25	.60
35 Jason Giambi	.25	.60
36 Tom Glavine	.40	1.00
37 Juan Gonzalez	.25	.60
38 Mark Grace	.40	1.00
39 Shawn Green	.25	.60
40 Tim Hudson	.25	.60
41 Andruw Jones	.40	1.00
42 Jeff Kent	.25	.60
43 Barry Larkin	.40	1.00
44 Rafael Furcal	.25	.60
45 Mike Mussina	.40	1.00
46 Hideo Nomo	.60	1.50
47 Rafael Palmeiro	.40	1.00
48 Scott Rolen	.40	1.00
49 Gary Sheffield	.25	.60
50 Bernie Williams	.40	1.00
51 Bob Abreu	.25	.60
52 Edgardo Alfonzo	.25	.60
53 Edgar Martinez	.40	1.00
54 Magglio Ordonez	.25	.60
55 Kerry Wood	.25	.60
56 Adrian Beltre	.25	.60
57 Lance Berkman	.25	.60
58 Kevin Brown	.25	.60
59 Sean Casey	.25	.60
60 Eric Chavez	.25	.60
61 Bartolo Colon	.25	.60
62 Johnny Damon	.40	1.00
63 Jermaine Dye	.25	.60
64 Juan Encarnacion	.25	.60
65 Carl Everett	.25	.60
66 Brian Giles	.25	.60
67 Mike Hampton	.25	.60
68 Richard Hidalgo	.25	.60
69 Geoff Jenkins	.25	.60
70 Jacque Jones	.25	.60
71 Jason Kendall	.25	.60
72 Ryan Klesko	.25	.60
73 Chan Ho Park	.25	.60
74 Richie Sexson	.25	.60
75 Mike Sweeney	.25	.60
76 Fernando Tatis	.25	.60
77 Miguel Tejada	.25	.60
78 Jose Vidro	.25	.60
79 Larry Walker	.25	.60
80 Preston Wilson	.25	.60
81 Craig Biggio	.40	1.00
82 Fred McGriff	.40	1.00
83 Jim Thome	.40	1.00
84 Garret Anderson	.25	.60
85 Russell Branyan	.25	.60
86 Tony Batista	.25	.60
87 Terrence Long	.25	.60
88 Brad Fullmer	.25	.60
89 Rusty Greer	.25	.60
90 Orlando Hernandez	.25	.60
91 Gabe Kapler	.25	.60
92 Paul Konerko	.25	.60
93 Carlos Lee	.25	.60
94 Kenny Lofton	.25	.60
95 Raul Mondesi	.25	.60
96 Jorge Posada	.40	1.00
97 Tim Salmon	.40	1.00
98 Greg Vaughn	.25	.60
99 Mo Vaughn	.25	.60
100 Omar Vizquel	.40	1.00
101 Aubrey Huff SP	2.00	5.00
102 Jimmy Rollins SP	2.00	5.00
103 Cory Aldridge SP RC	2.00	5.00
104 Wilmy Caceres SP RC	2.00	5.00
105 Josh Beckett SP	3.00	8.00
106 Wilson Betemit SP RC	3.00	8.00
107 Timo Perez SP	2.00	5.00
108 Albert Pujols SP RC	150.00	250.00
109 Bud Smith SP RC	2.00	5.00
110 Jack Wilson SP RC	3.00	8.00
111 Alex Escobar SP	2.00	5.00
112 J. Estrada SP RC	3.00	8.00
113 Pedro Feliz SP	2.00	5.00
114 Nate Frese SP RC	2.00	5.00
115 Carlos Garcia SP RC	2.00	5.00
116 Brandon Larson SP RC	2.00	5.00
117 Alexis Gomez SP RC	2.00	5.00
118 Jason Hart SP	2.00	5.00
119 Adam Dunn SP	3.00	8.00
120 Marcus Giles SP	2.00	5.00
121 C. Parker SP RC	2.00	5.00
122 J.Melian SP RC	2.00	5.00
123 Endy Chavez SP RC	2.00	5.00
124 A.Hernandez SP RC	2.00	5.00
125 Joe Kennedy SP RC	3.00	8.00
126 Jose Mieses SP RC	2.00	5.00
127 C.C. Sabathia SP	2.00	5.00
128 Eric Munson SP	2.00	5.00
129 Xavier Nady SP	2.00	5.00
130 H. Ramirez SP RC	3.00	8.00
131 Abraham Nunez SP	2.00	5.00
132 Jose Ortiz SP	2.00	5.00
133 Jeremy Owens SP RC	2.00	5.00
134 Claudio Vargas SP RC	2.00	5.00
135 Corey Patterson SP	2.00	5.00
136 Andres Torres SP RC	2.00	5.00
137 Ben Sheets SP	3.00	8.00
138 Joe Crede SP	3.00	8.00
139 A.Pettyjohn SP RC	2.00	5.00
140 E.Guzman SP RC	2.00	5.00
141 Jay Gibbons SP RC	3.00	8.00
142 Wilkin Ruan SP RC	2.00	5.00
143 Tsuyoshi Shinjo SP RC	3.00	8.00
144 Alfonso Soriano SP	3.00	8.00
145 Nick Johnson SP	2.00	5.00
146 Ichiro Suzuki SP RC	40.00	80.00
147 Juan Uribe SP RC	3.00	8.00
148 Jack Cust SP	2.00	5.00
149 C.Valderrama SP RC	2.00	5.00
150 Matt White SP RC	2.00	5.00
151 Hank Aaron LGD	4.00	10.00
152 Ernie Banks LGD	2.00	5.00
153 Johnny Bench LGD	2.00	5.00
154 George Brett LGD	4.00	10.00
155 Lou Brock LGD	2.00	5.00
156 Rod Carew LGD	2.00	5.00
157 Steve Carlton LGD	1.50	4.00
158 Bob Feller LGD	1.50	4.00
159 Bob Gibson LGD	2.00	5.00
160 Reggie Jackson LGD	2.00	5.00
161 Al Kaline LGD	2.00	5.00
162 Sandy Koufax LGD SP		
163 Don Mattingly LGD	4.00	10.00
164 Willie Mays LGD	4.00	10.00
165 Willie McCovey LGD	1.50	4.00
166 Joe Morgan LGD	1.50	4.00
167 Stan Musial LGD	3.00	8.00
168 Jim Palmer LGD	1.50	4.00
169 Brooks Robinson LGD	2.00	5.00
170 Frank Robinson LGD	2.00	5.00
171 Nolan Ryan LGD	5.00	12.00
172 Mike Schmidt LGD	4.00	10.00
173 Tom Seaver LGD	2.00	5.00
174 Warren Spahn LGD	2.00	5.00
175 Robin Yount LGD	2.00	5.00
176 Wade Boggs LGD	2.00	5.00
177 Ty Cobb LGD	3.00	8.00
178 Lou Gehrig LGD	4.00	10.00
179 Luis Aparicio LGD	1.50	4.00
180 Babe Ruth LGD	6.00	15.00
181 Ryne Sandberg LGD	4.00	10.00
182 Yogi Berra LGD	2.00	5.00
183 R.Clemente LGD	5.00	12.00
184 Eddie Murray LGD	2.00	5.00
185 Robin Roberts LGD SP		
186 Duke Snider LGD	2.00	5.00
187 Orlando Cepeda LGD	1.50	4.00
188 Billy Williams LGD	1.50	4.00
189 Juan Marichal LGD	1.50	4.00
190 Harmon Killebrew LGD	2.00	5.00
191 Kirby Puckett LGD	2.00	5.00
192 Carlton Fisk LGD	2.00	5.00
193 Dave Winfield LGD	1.50	4.00
194 Whitey Ford LGD	2.00	5.00
195 Paul Molitor LGD	1.50	4.00
196 Tony Perez LGD	1.50	4.00
197 Ozzie Smith LGD	3.00	8.00
198 Ralph Kiner LGD	2.00	5.00
199 Fergie Jenkins LGD	1.50	4.00
200 Phil Rizzuto LGD	2.00	5.00

2001 Donruss Classics Significant Signatures

Randomly inserted into packs at the rate of one in 18, this 83-card set is a partial parallel version of the base set. Each card is autographed and displays a rookie/prospect or retired player with platinum tint and holographic foil. Please note, the following cards packed out as redemption cards with an expiration date of September 10th, 2003: Hank Aaron, Luis Aparicio, Ernie Banks, Josh Beckett, Yogi Berra, Rod Carew, Steve Carlton, Orlando Cepeda, Adam Dunn, Johnny Estrada, Bob Feller, Carlton Fisk, Whitey Ford, Bob Gibson, Reggie Jackson, Nick Johnson, Juan Marichal, Willie Mays, Paul Molitor, Joe Morgan, Eddie Murray, Jim Palmer, Corey Patterson, Tony Perez, Kirby Puckett, Phil Rizzuto, Brooks Robinson, Frank Robinson, Nolan Ryan (Astros), C.C. Sabathia, Ryne Sandberg, Ron Santo, Mike Schmidt, Ben Sheets, Ozzie Smith, Billy Williams, Dave Winfield and Robin Yount. Exchange card 162 was originally intended to feature Sandy Koufax but in late 2002 representatives at Donruss switched the redemption to a Nolan Ryan Mets card (Ryan's basic card 171 in the set pictures him as a member of the Texas Rangers). In addition, exchange card 185 was originally intended to feature Robin Roberts but the redemption was switched in late 2002 to Ron Santo.

101 Aubrey Huff	4.00	10.00
103 Cory Aldridge	3.00	8.00
105 Josh Beckett SP	10.00	25.00
106 Wilson Betemit	10.00	25.00
107 Timo Perez	4.00	10.00
108 Albert Pujols	300.00	500.00
110 Jack Wilson	6.00	15.00
111 Alex Escobar	3.00	8.00
112 Johnny Estrada	6.00	15.00
113 Pedro Feliz	3.00	8.00
114 Nate Frese	4.00	10.00
115 Carlos Garcia	3.00	8.00
116 Brandon Larson	3.00	8.00
118 Jason Hart	3.00	8.00
119 Adam Dunn SP	10.00	25.00
120 Marcus Giles	4.00	10.00
121 Christian Parker	3.00	8.00
126 Jose Mieses	4.00	10.00
127 C.C.Sabathia SP	6.00	15.00
129 Xavier Nady	6.00	15.00
130 Horacio Ramirez	6.00	15.00
131 Abraham Nunez	3.00	8.00
132 Jose Ortiz	3.00	8.00
133 Jeremy Owens	4.00	10.00
134 Claudio Vargas	4.00	10.00
135 Corey Patterson SP	4.00	10.00
136 Andres Torres	3.00	8.00
137 Ben Sheets SP	10.00	25.00
138 Joe Crede	6.00	15.00
139 Adam Pettyjohn	3.00	8.00
140 Elpidio Guzman	3.00	8.00
141 Jay Gibbons	6.00	15.00
142 Wilkin Ruan	4.00	10.00
144 Alfonso Soriano SP	15.00	40.00
145 Nick Johnson SP	6.00	15.00
147 Juan Uribe	8.00	20.00
149 Carlos Valderrama	3.00	8.00
151 Hank Aaron SP	400.00	500.00
152 Ernie Banks	20.00	50.00
153 Johnny Bench SP	40.00	80.00
154 George Brett SP	75.00	150.00
155 Lou Brock	10.00	25.00
156 Rod Carew	15.00	40.00
157 Steve Carlton	12.50	30.00
158 Bob Feller	12.50	30.00
159 Bob Gibson	10.00	25.00
160 Reggie Jackson SP	40.00	80.00
161 Al Kaline	15.00	40.00
162A Nolan Ryan Astros SP	125.00	200.00
162B Sandy Koufax No Auto		
163 Don Mattingly	40.00	80.00
164 Willie Mays SP	125.00	200.00
165 Willie McCovey	10.00	25.00
166 Joe Morgan	8.00	20.00
167 Stan Musial SP	50.00	100.00
168 Jim Palmer	8.00	20.00
169 B. Robinson EXCH	15.00	40.00
170 Frank Robinson	10.00	25.00
171 Nolan Ryan Rangers SP	125.00	200.00
172 Mike Schmidt	20.00	50.00
173 Tom Seaver	15.00	40.00
174 Warren Spahn	20.00	50.00
175 Robin Yount SP	100.00	175.00
176 Wade Boggs SP	30.00	60.00
179 Luis Aparicio	8.00	20.00
180 Babe Ruth No Auto		
181 Ryne Sandberg	30.00	60.00
182 Yogi Berra	30.00	60.00
183 Roberto Clemente No Auto		
184 Eddie Murray	30.00	60.00
185 Ron Santo	12.50	30.00
186 Duke Snider	20.00	50.00
187 Orlando Cepeda	8.00	20.00
188 Billy Williams	12.50	30.00
189 Juan Marichal	8.00	20.00
190 Harmon Killebrew	20.00	50.00
191 Kirby Puckett SP	75.00	150.00
192 Carlton Fisk	20.00	50.00
193 Dave Winfield SP	30.00	60.00
194 Whitey Ford	20.00	50.00
195 Paul Molitor SP	15.00	40.00
196 Tony Perez	8.00	20.00
197 Ozzie Smith SP	40.00	80.00
198 Ralph Kiner	12.50	30.00
199 Fergie Jenkins	8.00	20.00
200 Phil Rizzuto	30.00	60.00

2001 Donruss Classics Timeless Tributes

Randomly inserted in packs, this 198-card set is a parallel version of the base set featuring silver or gold holo-foil highlights. The cards are sequentially numbered to 100. Cards 162 and 185 were not intended for production due to contractual problems with the featured athletes (Sandy Koufax for card 162 and Robin Roberts for card 185). The manufacturer made the effort to pull and destroy all copies found within the print run during the packout process. A handful of copies of the basic versions of these cards have been confirmed to exist but pricing is unavailable due to lack of sales information.

*TRIBUTE 1-100: 2.5X TO 6X BASIC
*TRIBUTE 101-150: .5X TO 1.2X BASIC
*TRIBUTE 151-200: 1.25X TO 3X BASIC

108 Albert Pujols	100.00	200.00
146 Ichiro Suzuki	50.00	100.00

2001 Donruss Classics Benchmarks

Randomly inserted in hobby packs at the rate of one in 18 and in retail packs at the rate of one in 72, this 25-card set features color player photos with game-used bench swatches embedded in the cards. Hank Aaron, Willie Stargell and card BM19 were only available as exchange cards. Those cards could be redeemed until September 10, 2003.

CARDS 11, 19 AND 24 WERE EXCHANGE
NO EXCH.PRICING DUE TO SCARCITY

BM1 Todd Helton	6.00	15.00
BM2 Roberto Clemente	20.00	50.00
BM3 Mark McGwire	15.00	40.00
BM4 Barry Bonds	12.50	30.00
BM5 Bob Gibson	6.00	15.00
BM6 Ken Griffey Jr.	8.00	20.00
BM7 Frank Robinson	6.00	15.00
BM8 Greg Maddux	8.00	20.00
BM9 Reggie Jackson	6.00	15.00
BM10 Sammy Sosa	6.00	15.00
BM11 Willie Stargell	50.00	100.00
BM12 Vladimir Guerrero	6.00	15.00
BM13 Johnny Bench	6.00	15.00
BM14 Tony Gwynn	6.00	15.00
BM15 Mike Schmidt	10.00	25.00
BM16 Ivan Rodriguez	6.00	15.00
BM17 Jeff Bagwell	6.00	15.00
BM18 Cal Ripken	15.00	40.00
BM20 Kirby Puckett	6.00	15.00
BM21 Frank Thomas	6.00	15.00
BM22 Joe Morgan	4.00	10.00
BM23 Mike Piazza	8.00	20.00
BM24 Hank Aaron	40.00	80.00
BM25 Andruw Jones	6.00	15.00

2001 Donruss Classics Combos

Randomly inserted in packs, this 45-card set features color action photos of baseball legends. Some cards consist of one player while others display a pairing of two great players. Each card has two or four swatches of game-worn/used memorabilia. One player cards are sequentially numbered to 100 while two player cards are sequentially numbered to 50. The following cards were issued in packs as exchange cards with a redemption deadline of Septemer 10th, 2003: Hank Aaron, Ernie Banks, Wade Boggs, Lou Brock, Steve Carlton, Andre Dawson, Don Mattingly, Jackie Robinson, Ryne Sandberg, Willie Stargell and Billy Williams. In addition, the following dual-player cards packed out as exchange cards (with the same redemption deadline as detailed above): Banks/Williams, Carlton/Schmidt, Clemente/Stargell, Dawson/Sandberg, Mattingly/Boggs, Musial/Brock and Robinson/Snider.

1 R.Clemente/100	30.00	60.00
2 Willie Stargell/100	15.00	40.00
3 Babe Ruth/100	250.00	400.00
4 Lou Gehrig/100	125.00	250.00
5 Hank Aaron/100	40.00	80.00
6 Eddie Mathews/100	10.00	25.00
7 Johnny Bench/100	20.00	50.00
8 Joe Morgan/100	10.00	25.00
9 Robin Yount/100	10.00	25.00
10 Paul Molitor/100	10.00	25.00
11 S.Carlton/85 EXCH	10.00	25.00
12 Mike Schmidt/85	12.50	30.00
13 Stan Musial/100	12.50	30.00
14 Lou Brock/100	15.00	40.00
15 Yogi Berra/100	30.00	60.00
16 Phil Rizzuto/100	10.00	25.00
17 Ernie Banks/85	10.00	25.00
18 B. Williams/85 EXCH	10.00	25.00
19 Don Mattingly/100	12.50	30.00
20 Wade Boggs/100	15.00	40.00
21 Jackie Robinson/100	50.00	100.00
22 Duke Snider/100	30.00	60.00
23 Frank Robinson/85	15.00	40.00
24 Brooks Robinson/85	15.00	40.00
25 Orlando Cepeda/100	10.00	25.00
26 Willie McCovey/100	10.00	25.00
27 Ryne Sandberg/100	10.00	25.00
28 Andre Dawson/100	10.00	25.00
29 H.Killebrew/100	20.00	50.00
30 Rod Carew/100	15.00	40.00
31 Roberto Clemente Willie Stargell/50	60.00	120.00
32 Babe Ruth Lou Gehrig	600.00	1000.00
33 Hank Aaron Eddie Mathews	30.00	60.00
34 Johnny Bench Joe Morgan	20.00	50.00
35 Robin Yount Paul Molitor	60.00	120.00
36 Steve Carlton Mike Schmidt/40	20.00	50.00
37 Stan Musial Lou Brock/50	20.00	50.00
38 Yogi Berra Phil Rizzuto/50	75.00	150.00
39 Ernie Banks Billy Williams/40	20.00	50.00
40 Don Mattingly Wade Boggs/50	20.00	50.00
41 Jackie Robinson Jacket-Jsy Duke Snider Bat-Jsy/50	40.00	80.00
42 Brooks Robinson Frank Robinson	20.00	50.00
43 Orlando Cepeda Willie McCovey/50	30.00	60.00
44 Andre Dawson Ryne Sandberg/50	30.00	60.00
45 Harmon Killebrew Rod Carew	30.00	60.00

2001 Donruss Classics Legendary Lumberjacks

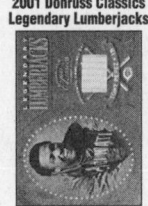

Randomly inserted in hobby packs at the rate of one in 18 and in retail packs at the rate of one in 72, this 50-card set features color photos of the most skilled sluggers in Baseball. A swatch of a game-used bat was embedded in each card. The following cards packed out as exchange cards with a redemption deadline of September 10th, 2003: Hack Wilson, Hank Aaron, Ernie Banks, Nellie Fox, Jimmie Foxx, Rogers Horsnby, Roger Maris, Willie Stargell and Ted Williams.

STATED ODDS 1:18 HOBBY, 1:72 RETAIL
SP PRINT RUNS PROVIDED BY DONRUSS
SP'S ARE NOT SERIAL-NUMBERED

LL1 Hack Wilson SP/244 *	40.00	80.00
LL2 Chipper Jones	10.00	25.00
LL3 Rogers Hornsby SP/301 *	50.00	100.00
LL4 Nellie Fox SP/300 *	50.00	100.00
LL5 Ivan Rodriguez	6.00	15.00
LL6 Jimmie Foxx SP/300 *	20.00	50.00
LL7 Hank Aaron	20.00	50.00
LL8 Yogi Berra SP/400 *	20.00	50.00
LL9 Ernie Banks SP/300 *	15.00	40.00
LL10 George Brett	15.00	40.00
LL11 Ty Cobb SP/100 *	100.00	200.00
LL12 R. Clemente SP	100.00	200.00
LL13 Carlton Fisk	6.00	15.00
LL14 Reggie Jackson	6.00	15.00
LL15 Al Kaline	10.00	25.00
LL16 Harmon Killebrew	10.00	25.00
LL17 Ralph Kiner	6.00	15.00
LL18 Roger Maris SP/275 *	30.00	60.00
LL19 Eddie Mathews SP/400 *	12.50	30.00
LL20 Ted Williams SP/300 *	20.00	50.00
LL21 Willie McCovey	6.00	15.00
LL22 Eddie Murray	10.00	25.00
LL23 Joe Morgan SP/268 *	10.00	25.00
LL24 Frank Robinson	6.00	15.00
LL25 Tony Perez	4.00	10.00
LL26 Mike Schmidt	15.00	40.00
LL27 Ryne Sandberg	15.00	40.00
LL28 Duke Snider SP/300 *		
LL29 Willie Stargell SP/500 *	30.00	60.00
LL30 Billy Williams	4.00	10.00
LL31 Dave Winfield	4.00	10.00
LL32 Robin Yount	10.00	25.00
LL33 Barry Bonds	20.00	50.00
LL34 Stan Musial SP/300 *	20.00	50.00
LL35 Johnny Bench SP/300 *		
LL36 Orlando Cepeda	4.00	10.00
LL37 Todd Helton	6.00	15.00
LL38 Frank Thomas	10.00	25.00
LL39 Juan Gonzalez SP/400 *		
LL40 Cal Ripken SP/500 *	12.50	30.00
LL41 Rafael Palmeiro	6.00	15.00
LL42 Troy Glaus SP/100 *		
LL43 Vladimir Guerrero	10.00	25.00
LL44 Paul Molitor SP/400 *		
LL45 Tony Gwynn	6.00	15.00
LL46 Rod Carew	6.00	15.00
LL47 Lou Brock	6.00	15.00
LL48 Wade Boggs	6.00	15.00
LL49 Babe Ruth SP/60 *	125.00	250.00
LL50 Lou Gehrig SP/100 *	100.00	200.00

2001 Donruss Classics Stadium Stars

Randomly inserted in hobby packs at the rate of one in 18 and in retail packs at the rate of one in 72, this 25-card set features color action player photos with swatches of stadium seats taken from some of the most heralded ballparks embedded in the cards. An exchange card with a redemption deadline of September 10th, 2003 was seeded into packs for Honus Wagner's card.

SS1 Babe Ruth SP	30.00	60.00
SS2 Cal Ripken	10.00	25.00
SS3 Brooks Robinson	4.00	10.00
SS4 Tony Gwynn SP	6.00	15.00
SS5 Ty Cobb	12.50	30.00
SS6 Vladimir Guerrero SP	6.00	15.00
SS7 Lou Gehrig SP	20.00	50.00
SS8 Nomar Garciaparra	6.00	15.00
SS9 Sammy Sosa SP	6.00	15.00
SS10 Reggie Jackson SP	6.00	15.00
SS11 Alex Rodriguez	6.00	15.00
SS12 Derek Jeter	15.00	40.00
SS13 Willie McCovey SP	4.00	10.00
SS14 Mark McGwire	10.00	25.00
SS15 Chipper Jones	4.00	10.00
SS16 Honus Wagner	15.00	40.00
SS17 Ken Griffey Jr.	6.00	15.00
SS18 Frank Robinson	4.00	10.00
SS19 Barry Bonds SP	10.00	25.00
SS20 Yogi Berra SP	6.00	15.00
SS21 Mike Piazza SP	6.00	15.00
SS22 Roger Clemens	6.00	15.00
SS23 Duke Snider SP	6.00	15.00
SS24 Frank Thomas	4.00	10.00
SS25 Andruw Jones	4.00	10.00

2001 Donruss Classics Timeless Treasures

Randomly inserted in hobby packs at the rate of one in 420, and in retail packs at the rate of one in 1680, this five-card set features pictures of great players with swatches of memorabilia from five famous events in baseball history.

TT1 M. McGwire Ball SP	125.00	200.00
TT2 Babe Ruth Seat	30.00	60.00
TT3 H. Killebrew Bat SP	20.00	50.00
TT4 Derek Jeter Base	20.00	50.00
TT5 Barry Bonds Ball SP	30.00	60.00

2002 Donruss Classics Samples

This partial parallel to the Donruss Classics set was issued as inserts in Beckett Baseball Card Monthly issue number 209. Only the first 100 cards of this set were created for this project.

*SAMPLES: .75X TO 2X BASIC CARDS
*GOLD: 1.5X TO 4X BASIC SAMPLES

2002 Donruss Classics

This 200 card standard-size was issued in June, 2002. An additional 25 update cards were seeded into Donruss the Rookies packs distributed in December, 2002. The basic set was released in six card packs which came in two nine-pack mini boxes per full box. The full boxes were issued four boxes to a case and had an SRP of $6 per pack. Cards 1-100 feature veteran active players, while cards 101-150 feature rookies and prospects and cards 151-200 feature retired greats. Cards numbered 101-200 were all printed to a stated print run of 1500 sets and were released two cards per mini-box (or 4 per full box of 18 packs). Update cards 201-225 were also serial-numbered to 1500.

COMP.SET w/o SP's (100)	10.00	25.00
COMMON CARD (1-100)	.25	.60
COMMON (101-150/201-225)	1.50	4.00
COMMON CARD (151-200)	1.50	4.00
1 Alex Rodriguez	1.00	2.50
2 Barry Bonds	1.50	4.00
3 C.C. Sabathia	.25	.60
4 Chipper Jones	.60	1.50
5 Derek Jeter	1.50	4.00
6 Troy Glaus	.25	.60
7 Frank Thomas	.60	1.50
8 Greg Maddux	1.00	2.50
9 Ivan Rodriguez	.40	1.00
10 Jeff Bagwell	.40	1.00
11 Mark Buehrle	.25	.60
12 Todd Helton	.40	1.00
13 Ken Griffey Jr.	1.00	2.50
14 Manny Ramirez	.40	1.00
15 Brad Penny	.25	.60
16 Mike Piazza	1.00	2.50
17 Nomar Garciaparra	1.00	2.50
18 Pedro Martinez	.40	1.00
19 Randy Johnson	.60	1.50
20 Bud Smith	.25	.60
21 Rickey Henderson	.60	1.50
22 Roger Clemens	1.25	3.00
23 Sammy Sosa	.60	1.50
24 Brandon Duckworth	.25	.60
25 Vladimir Guerrero	.60	1.50
26 Kazuhiro Sasaki	.25	.60
27 Roberto Alomar	.40	1.00
28 Barry Zito	.25	.60
29 Rich Aurilia	.25	.60
30 Ben Sheets	.25	.60
31 Carlos Delgado	.25	.60
32 J.D. Drew	.25	.60
33 Jermaine Dye	.25	.60
34 Darin Erstad	.25	.60
35 Jason Giambi	.25	.60
36 Tom Glavine	.40	1.00
37 Juan Gonzalez	.25	.60
38 Luis Gonzalez	.25	.60
39 Shawn Green	.25	.60
40 Tim Hudson	.25	.60
41 Andruw Jones	.40	1.00
42 Shannon Stewart	.25	.60
43 Barry Larkin	.40	1.00
44 Wade Miller	.25	.60
45 Mike Mussina	.40	1.00
46 Hideo Nomo	.60	1.50
47 Rafael Palmeiro	.40	1.00
48 Scott Rolen	.40	1.00
49 Gary Sheffield	.25	.60
50 Bernie Williams	.40	1.00
51 Bob Abreu	.25	.60
52 Javier Vazquez	.25	.60
53 Edgar Martinez	.40	1.00
54 Magglio Ordonez	.25	.60
55 Kerry Wood	.25	.60
56 Adrian Beltre	.25	.60
57 Lance Berkman	.25	.60
58 Kevin Brown	.25	.60
59 Sean Casey	.25	.60
60 Eric Chavez	.25	.60
61 Robert Person	.25	.60
62 Jeremy Giambi	.25	.60
63 Freddy Garcia	.25	.60
64 Alfonso Soriano	.25	.60
65 Doug Davis	.25	.60
66 Brian Giles	.25	.60
67 Moises Alou	.25	.60
68 Richard Hidalgo	.25	.60
69 Paul LoDuca	.25	.60
70 Aramis Ramirez	.25	.60
71 Andres Galarraga	.25	.60
72 Ryan Klesko	.25	.60
73 Chan Ho Park	.25	.60

74 Richie Sexson .25 .60
75 Mike Sweeney .25 .60
76 Aubrey Huff .25 .60
77 Miguel Tejada .25 .60
78 Jose Vidro .25 .60
79 Larry Walker .25 .60
80 Roy Oswalt .25 .60
81 Craig Biggio .40 1.00
82 Juan Pierre .25 .60
83 Jim Thome .40 1.00
84 Josh Towers .25 .60
85 Alex Escobar .25 .60
86 Cliff Floyd .25 .60
87 Terrence Long .25 .60
88 Curt Schilling .25 .60
89 Carlos Beltran .25 .60
90 Albert Pujols 1.25 3.00
91 Gabe Kapler .25 .60
92 Mark Mulder .25 .60
93 Carlos Lee .25 .60
94 Robert Fick .25 .60
95 Raul Mondesi .25 .60
96 Ichiro Suzuki 1.25 3.00
97 Adam Dunn .25 .60
98 Corey Patterson .25 .60
99 Tsuyoshi Shinjo .25 .60
100 Joe Mays .25 .60
101 Juan Cruz ROO 1.50 4.00
102 Marlon Byrd ROO 1.50 4.00
103 Luis Garcia ROO 1.50 4.00
104 Jorge Padilla ROO RC 1.50 4.00
105 Dennis Tankersley ROO 1.50 4.00
106 Josh Pearce ROO 1.50 4.00
107 Ramon Vazquez ROO 1.50 4.00
108 Chris Baker ROO RC 1.50 4.00
109 Eric Cyr ROO 1.50 4.00
110 Reed Johnson ROO RC 2.00 5.00
111 Ryan Jamison ROO 1.50 4.00
112 Antonio Perez ROO 1.50 4.00
113 Satoru Komiyama ROO RC 1.50 4.00
114 Austin Kearns ROO 1.50 4.00
115 Juan Pena ROO 1.50 4.00
116 Orlando Hudson ROO 1.50 4.00
117 Kazuhisa Ishii ROO RC 2.00 5.00
118 Erik Bedard ROO 1.50 4.00
119 Luis Ugueto ROO RC 1.50 4.00
120 Ben Howard ROO RC 1.50 4.00
121 Morgan Ensberg ROO 1.50 4.00
122 Doug Devore ROO RC 1.50 4.00
123 Josh Phelps ROO 1.50 4.00
124 Angel Berroa ROO 1.50 4.00
125 Ed Rogers ROO 1.50 4.00
126 Takahito Nomura ROO RC 1.50 4.00
127 John Ennis ROO RC 1.50 4.00
128 Bill Hall ROO 1.50 4.00
129 Dewon Brazelton ROO 1.50 4.00
130 Hank Blalock ROO 2.00 5.00
131 So Taguchi ROO RC 1.50 4.00
132 Jorge De La Rosa ROO RC 1.50 4.00
133 Matt Thornton ROO RC 1.50 4.00
134 Brandon Backe ROO RC 2.00 5.00
135 Jeff Deardorff ROO 1.50 4.00
136 Steve Smyth ROO 1.50 4.00
137 An. Machado ROO RC 1.50 4.00
138 John Buck ROO 1.50 4.00
139 Mark Prior ROO 2.00 5.00
140 Sean Burroughs ROO 1.50 4.00
141 Alex Herrera ROO 1.50 4.00
142 Francis Beltran ROO RC 1.50 4.00
143 Jason Romano ROO 1.50 4.00
144 Michael Cuddyer ROO 1.50 4.00
145 Steve Bechler ROO RC 1.50 4.00
146 Alfredo Amezaga ROO 1.50 4.00
147 Ryan Ludwick ROO 1.50 4.00
148 Martin Vargas ROO 1.50 4.00
149 Allan Simpson ROO RC 1.50 4.00
150 Mark Teixeira ROO 2.00 5.00
151 Dale Murphy LGD 2.00 5.00
152 Ernie Banks LGD 2.00 5.00
153 Johnny Bench LGD 2.00 5.00
154 George Brett LGD 3.00 8.00
155 Lou Brock LGD 2.00 5.00
156 Rod Carew LGD 2.00 5.00
157 Steve Carlton LGD 1.50 4.00
158 Joe Torre LGD 1.50 4.00
159 Dennis Eckersley LGD 1.50 4.00
160 Reggie Jackson LGD 2.00 5.00
161 Al Kaline LGD 2.00 5.00
162 Dave Parker LGD 1.50 4.00
163 Don Mattingly LGD 3.00 8.00
164 Tony Gwynn LGD 2.00 5.00
165 Willie McCovey LGD 1.50 4.00
166 Joe Morgan LGD 1.50 4.00
167 Stan Musial LGD 2.50 6.00
168 Jim Palmer LGD 1.50 4.00
169 Brooks Robinson LGD 2.00 5.00
170 Bo Jackson LGD 2.00 5.00
171 Nolan Ryan LGD 4.00 10.00
172 Mike Schmidt LGD 3.00 8.00
173 Tom Seaver LGD 2.00 5.00
174 Cal Ripken LGD 5.00 12.00
175 Robin Yount LGD 2.00 5.00
176 Wade Boggs LGD 2.00 5.00
177 Gary Carter LGD 1.50 4.00
178 Ron Santo LGD 2.00 5.00
179 Luis Aparicio LGD 1.50 4.00
180 Bobby Doerr LGD 1.50 4.00
181 Ryne Sandberg LGD 3.00 8.00
182 Yogi Berra LGD 2.00 5.00
183 Will Clark LGD 2.00 5.00
184 Eddie Murray LGD 2.00 5.00
185 Andre Dawson LGD 1.50 4.00
186 Duke Snider LGD 2.00 5.00
187 Orlando Cepeda LGD 1.50 4.00
188 Billy Williams LGD 1.50 4.00
189 Juan Marichal LGD 1.50 4.00
190 Harmon Killebrew LGD 2.00 5.00
191 Kirby Puckett LGD 2.00 5.00
192 Carlton Fisk LGD 2.00 5.00
193 Dave Winfield LGD 1.50 4.00
194 Alan Trammell LGD 1.50 4.00
195 Paul Molitor LGD 1.50 4.00
196 Tony Perez LGD 1.50 4.00
197 Ozzie Smith LGD 2.50 6.00
198 Ralph Kiner LGD 1.50 4.00
199 Fergie Jenkins LGD 1.50 4.00
200 Phil Rizzuto LGD 2.00 5.00
201 Oliver Perez ROO RC 2.00 5.00
202 Aaron Cook ROO RC 1.50 4.00
203 Eric Junge ROO RC 1.50 4.00
204 Freddy Sanchez ROO RC 2.00 5.00
205 Cliff Lee ROO RC 6.00 15.00
206 Run. Hernandez ROO RC 1.50 4.00
207 Chone Figgins ROO RC 2.00 5.00
208 Rodrigo Rosario ROO RC 1.50 4.00
209 Kevin Cash ROO RC 1.50 4.00
210 Josh Bard ROO RC 1.50 4.00
211 Felix Escalona ROO RC 1.50 4.00
212 Jer. Robertson ROO RC 1.50 4.00
213 J. Simontacchi ROO RC 1.50 4.00
214 Shane Nance ROO RC 1.50 4.00
215 Ben Kozlowski ROO RC 1.50 4.00
216 Brian Tallet ROO RC [illegible] [illegible]
217 Earl Snyder ROO RC 1.50 4.00
218 Andy Pratt ROO RC 1.50 4.00
219 Trey Hodges ROO RC 1.50 4.00
220 Kirk Saarloos ROO RC 1.50 4.00
221 Rene Reyes ROO RC 1.50 4.00
222 Joe Borchard ROO 1.50 4.00
223 Wilson Valdez ROO RC 1.50 4.00
224 Miguel Asencio ROO RC 1.50 4.00
225 Chris Snelling ROO RC 1.50 4.00

2002 Donruss Classics National

ISSUED AT '02 NATIONAL CONVENTION
STATED PRINT RUN 5 SERIAL #'d SETS
NO PRICING DUE TO SCARCITY

2002 Donruss Classics Significant Signatures

101 Juan Cruz ROO/400 4.00 10.00
102 Marlon Byrd ROO/500 4.00 10.00
103 Luis Garcia ROO/500 4.00 10.00
104 Jorge Padilla ROO/500 4.00 10.00
105 Dennis Tankersley ROO/250 6.00 15.00
106 Josh Pearce ROO/500 4.00 10.00
107 Ramon Vazquez ROO/500 4.00 10.00
108 Chris Baker ROO/500 4.00 10.00
109 Eric Cyr ROO/500 4.00 10.00
110 Reed Johnson ROO/500 6.00 15.00
111 Ryan Jamison ROO/500 4.00 10.00
112 Antonio Perez ROO/500 4.00 10.00
113 Satoru Komiyama ROO/50 15.00 40.00
114 Austin Kearns ROO/500 4.00 10.00
115 Juan Pena ROO/500 4.00 10.00
116 Orlando Hudson ROO/400 4.00 10.00
117 Kazuhisa Ishii ROO/50 15.00 40.00
118 Erik Bedard ROO/500 6.00 15.00
119 Luis Ugueto ROO/250 4.00 10.00
120 Ben Howard ROO/500 4.00 10.00
121 Morgan Ensberg ROO/500 6.00 15.00
122 Doug Devore ROO/500 4.00 10.00
123 Josh Phelps ROO/500 4.00 10.00
124 Angel Berroa ROO/500 4.00 10.00
125 Ed Rogers ROO/500 4.00 10.00
126 Takahito Nomura ROO/25
127 John Ennis ROO/500 4.00 10.00
128 Bill Hall ROO/400 6.00 15.00
129 Dewon Brazelton ROO/400 4.00 10.00
130 Hank Blalock ROO/100 6.00 15.00
131 So Taguchi ROO/150 12.50 30.00
132 Jorge De La Rosa ROO/500 4.00 10.00
133 Matt Thornton ROO/500 4.00 10.00
134 Brandon Backe ROO/500 6.00 15.00
135 Jeff Deardorff ROO/500 4.00 10.00
136 Steve Smyth ROO/500 4.00 10.00
137 Anderson Machado ROO/500 4.00 10.00
138 John Buck ROO/500 4.00 10.00
139 Mark Prior ROO/250 6.00 15.00
140 Sean Burroughs ROO/50 10.00 25.00
141 Alex Herrera ROO/500 4.00 10.00
142 Francis Beltran ROO/500 4.00 10.00
143 Jason Romano ROO/500 4.00 10.00
144 Michael Cuddyer ROO/400 4.00 10.00
145 Steve Bechler ROO/500 4.00 10.00
146 Alfredo Amezaga ROO/500 4.00 10.00
147 Ryan Ludwick ROO/25 30.00 60.00
148 Martin Vargas ROO/500 4.00 10.00
149 Allan Simpson ROO/500 4.00 10.00
150 Mark Teixeira ROO/200 10.00 25.00
151 Dale Murphy LGD/25
152 Ernie Banks LGD/25
153 Johnny Bench LGD/25
154 George Brett LGD/25
155 Lou Brock LGD/100 15.00 40.00
156 Rod Carew LGD/25
157 Steve Carlton LGD/125 10.00 25.00
158 Joe Torre LGD/25
159 Dennis Eckersley LGD/500 6.00 15.00
160 Reggie Jackson LGD/25
161 Al Kaline LGD/125 20.00 50.00
162 Dave Parker LGD/500 6.00 15.00
163 Don Mattingly LGD/50 50.00 100.00
164 Tony Gwynn LGD/25
165 Willie McCovey LGD/25
166 Joe Morgan LGD/25
167 Stan Musial LGD/25
168 Jim Palmer LGD/125 10.00 25.00
169 Brooks Robinson LGD/125 15.00 40.00
170 Bo Jackson LGD/25
171 Nolan Ryan LGD/25
172 Mike Schmidt LGD/25
173 Tom Seaver LGD/25
174 Cal Ripken LGD/25
175 Robin Yount LGD/25
176 Wade Boggs LGD/25
177 Gary Carter LGD/150 8.00 20.00
178 Ron Santo LGD/500 12.50 30.00
179 Luis Aparicio LGD/400 6.00 15.00
180 Bobby Doerr LGD/500 10.00 25.00
181 Ryne Sandberg LGD/25
182 Yogi Berra LGD/25
183 Will Clark LGD/50
184 Eddie Murray LGD/25
185 Andre Dawson LGD/200 8.00 20.00
186 Duke Snider LGD/25
187 Orlando Cepeda LGD/125 10.00 25.00
188 Billy Williams LGD/200 8.00 20.00
189 Juan Marichal LGD/500 6.00 15.00
190 Harmon Killebrew LGD/100 30.00 60.00
191 Kirby Puckett LGD/25
192 Carlton Fisk LGD/25
193 Dave Winfield LGD/25
194 Alan Trammell LGD/200 8.00 20.00
195 Paul Molitor LGD/25
196 Tony Perez LGD/150 8.00 20.00
197 Ozzie Smith LGD/25
198 Ralph Kiner LGD/125 10.00 25.00
199 Fergie Jenkins LGD/200 8.00 20.00
200 Phil Rizzuto LGD/125 15.00 40.00
201 Oliver Perez ROO/50 30.00 60.00
[illegible] Eric Junge ROO/[illegible] [illegible] [illegible]
205 Cliff Lee ROO/100 150.00 300.00
207 Chone Figgins ROO/100 10.00 25.00
208 Rodrigo Rosario ROO/250 4.00 10.00
209 Kevin Cash ROO/100 4.00 10.00
210 Josh Bard ROO/100 4.00 10.00
211 Felix Escalona ROO/25
214 Shane Nance ROO/200 4.00 10.00
215 Ben Kozlowski ROO/200 4.00 10.00
216 Brian Tallet ROO/100 4.00 10.00
217 Earl Snyder ROO/100 4.00 10.00
218 Andy Pratt ROO/250 4.00 10.00
219 Trey Hodges ROO/250 4.00 10.00
220 Kirk Saarloos ROO/100 4.00 10.00
221 Rene Reyes ROO/50 6.00 15.00
222 Joe Borchard ROO/100 6.00 15.00
223 Wilson Valdez ROO/100 4.00 10.00
225 Chris Snelling ROO/100 4.00 10.00

2002 Donruss Classics Timeless Tributes

Cards 1-200 were randomly inserted in Donruss Classics packs and cards 201-225 in Donruss the Rookies packs. This is a parallel to the Donruss Classics set. The set is issued to a stated print run of 100 serial-numbered sets.

*TRIBUTE 1-100: 2.5X TO 6X BASIC
*TRIB.101-150/201-225: .6X TO 1.5X BASIC
*TRIB.151-200: 1.25X TO 3X BASIC

2002 Donruss Classics Classic Singles

Randomly inserted into packs, these 30 cards feature both a veteran great as well as a game-used memorabilia piece. As these cards have varying print runs, we have notated that information next to the player's name as well as the information as to what memorabilia piece is used.

1 Cal Ripken Jsy/100 20.00 50.00
2 Eddie Murray Jsy/100 6.00 15.00
3 George Brett Jsy/100 10.00 25.00
4 Bo Jackson Jsy/100 6.00 15.00
5 Ted Williams Bat/50 50.00 100.00
6 Jimmie Foxx Sox Bat/50 40.00 80.00
7 Steve Carlton Jsy/50 6.00 15.00
8 Reg Jackson Yanks Jsy/100 6.00 15.00
9 Mel Ott Jsy/50 40.00 80.00
10 Catfish Hunter Jsy/100 6.00 15.00
11 Nolan Ryan Jsy/100 20.00 50.00
12 Rickey Henderson Jsy /100 6.00 15.00
13 Robin Yount Jsy/100 6.00 15.00
14 Orlando Cepeda Jsy/100 4.00 10.00
15 Ty Cobb Bat/50 75.00 150.00
16 Babe Ruth Bat/50 125.00 250.00
17 Dave Parker Jsy/100 4.00 10.00
18 Willie Stargell Jsy/100 6.00 15.00
19 Ernie Banks Bat/100 6.00 15.00
20 Mike Schmidt Jsy/100 10.00 25.00
21 Duke Snider Jsy/50 10.00 25.00
22 Jackie Robinson Jsy/50 50.00 100.00
23 Rickey Henderson Bat/100 6.00 15.00
24 Dale Murphy Bat/100 6.00 15.00
25 Lou Gehrig Bat/50 125.00 200.00
26 Jimmie Foxx A's Bat/50 40.00 80.00
27 Reggie Jackson A's Jsy/100 6.00 15.00
28 Tony Gwynn Bat/100 10.00 25.00
29 Bobby Doerr Jsy/100 4.00 10.00
30 Joe Torre Jsy/100 6.00 15.00

2002 Donruss Classics Legendary Hats

Randomly inserted into packs, this five-card set features not only a retired great but a game-worn swatch of a cap. Each card was printed to a stated print run of 50 serial numbered sets.

1 Don Mattingly 60.00 120.00
2 George Brett 60.00 120.00
3 Wade Boggs 20.00 50.00
4 Reggie Jackson 20.00 50.00
5 Ryne Sandberg 60.00 120.00

2002 Donruss Classics Legendary Leather

Randomly inserted into packs, this five-card set features not only a retired great but a game-worn swatch of a glove. Each card was printed to a stated print run of 50 serial numbered sets.

1 Don Mattingly Btg Glv 60.00 120.00
2 Wade Boggs Btg Glv 20.00 50.00
3 Tony Gwynn Fld Glv 50.00 100.00
4 Kirby Puckett Fld Glv 40.00 80.00
5 Mike Schmidt Fld Glv 60.00 120.00

2002 Donruss Classics Legendary Lumberjacks

Randomly inserted in packs, this 35 card set features great players of the past along with a game-used bat piece. Since this set was printed to different amounts of cards printed, we have notated the stated print run information next to the player's name.

1 Don Mattingly/500 10.00 25.00
2 George Brett/400 10.00 25.00
3 Stan Musial/100 20.00 50.00
4 Lou Gehrig/50 125.00 200.00
5 Mike Piazza/500 6.00 15.00
6 Mel Ott/50 40.00 80.00
7 Ted Williams/50 50.00 100.00
8 Bo Jackson/500 6.00 15.00
9 Kirby Puckett/500 6.00 15.00
10 Rafael Palmeiro/500 6.00 15.00
11 Andre Dawson/500 4.00 10.00
12 Ozzie Smith/500 6.00 15.00
13 Paul Molitor/500 4.00 10.00
14 Babe Ruth/50 125.00 250.00
15 Carlton Fisk/500 6.00 15.00
16 Rickey Henderson/500 6.00 15.00
17 Gary Carter/500 4.00 10.00
18 Cal Ripken/100 15.00 40.00
19 Eddie Mathews/100 10.00 25.00
20 Luis Aparicio/500 4.00 10.00
21 Al Kaline/100 10.00 25.00
22 Eddie Murray/500 6.00 15.00
23 Yogi Berra/100 10.00 25.00
24 Alex Rodriguez/500 6.00 15.00
25 Tony Gwynn/500 6.00 15.00
26 Roberto Clemente/100 50.00 100.00
27 Mike Schmidt/100 10.00 25.00
28 Reggie Jackson/500 6.00 15.00
29 Ryne Sandberg/500 10.00 25.00
30 Joe Morgan/400 4.00 10.00
31 Joe Torre/500 6.00 15.00
32 Gary Sheffield/500 4.00 10.00
33 Nomar Garciaparra/500 6.00 15.00
34 Jeff Bagwell/500 6.00 15.00
35 Manny Ramirez/500 6.00 15.00

2002 Donruss Classics Legendary Spikes

Randomly inserted into packs, this five-card set features not only a retired great but a game-worn piece of a pair of spikes. Each card was printed to a stated print run of 50 serial numbered sets.

1 Don Mattingly 60.00 120.00
2 Eddie Murray 30.00 60.00
3 Paul Molitor 15.00 40.00
4 Harmon Killebrew 30.00 60.00
5 Mike Schmidt 60.00 120.00

2002 Donruss Classics New Millennium Classics

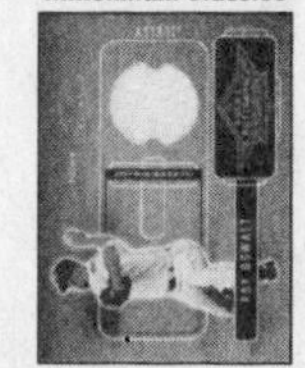

Randomly inserted into packs, these 60 cards feature both an active star as well as a game-used memorabilia piece. As these cards have varying print runs, we have notated that information next to the player's name as well as the information as to what memorabilia piece is used. The Ishii and Taguchi jersey cards were not ready as Donruss went to press and those cards were issued as exchange cards with an deadline of June 1, 2004 to redeem those cards.

*MULTI-COLOR PATCH: 1.25X TO 3X BASIC
1 Curt Schilling Jsy/500 3.00 8.00
2 Vladimir Guerrero Jsy/100 6.00 15.00
3 Jim Thome Jsy/500 4.00 10.00
4 Troy Glaus Jsy/400 3.00 8.00
5 Ivan Rodriguez Jsy/200 6.00 15.00
6 Todd Helton Jsy/400 4.00 10.00
7 Sean Casey Jsy/500 3.00 8.00
8 Scott Rolen Jsy/475 4.00 10.00
9 Ken Griffey Jr. Base/150 6.00 15.00
10 Hideo Nomo Jsy/100 10.00 25.00
11 Tom Glavine Jsy/350 4.00 10.00
12 Pedro Martinez Jsy/100 6.00 15.00
13 Cliff Floyd Jsy/500 3.00 8.00
14 Shawn Green Jsy/125 4.00 10.00
15 Rafael Palmeiro Jsy/250 4.00 10.00
16 Luis Gonzalez Jsy/100 4.00 10.00
17 Lance Berkman Jsy/100 4.00 10.00
18 Frank Thomas Jsy/500 4.00 10.00
19 Randy Johnson Jsy/400 4.00 10.00
20 Moises Alou Jsy/500 3.00 8.00
21 Chipper Jones Jsy/500 4.00 10.00
22 Larry Walker Jsy/300 3.00 8.00
23 Mike Sweeney Jsy/500 3.00 8.00
24 Juan Gonzalez Jsy/300 3.00 8.00
25 Roger Clemens Jsy/100 10.00 25.00
26 Albert Pujols Base/300 6.00 15.00
27 Magglio Ordonez Jsy/500 3.00 8.00
28 Alex Rodriguez Jsy/400 6.00 15.00
29 Jeff Bagwell Jsy/125 6.00 15.00
30 Kazuhiro Sasaki Jsy/500 3.00 8.00
31 Barry Larkin Jsy/300 4.00 10.00
32 Andruw Jones Jsy/350 4.00 10.00
33 Kerry Wood Jsy/200 4.00 10.00
34 Rickey Henderson Jsy/100 6.00 15.00
35 Greg Maddux Jsy/100 10.00 25.00
36 Brian Giles Jsy/400 3.00 8.00
37 Craig Biggio Jsy/100 6.00 15.00
38 Roberto Alomar Jsy/400 4.00 10.00
39 Mike Piazza Jsy/400 6.00 15.00
40 Bernie Williams Jsy/100 6.00 15.00
41 Ichiro Suzuki Ball/100 15.00 40.00
42 Kenny Lofton Jsy/450 3.00 8.00
43 Mark Mulder Jsy/500 3.00 8.00
44 Kazuhisa Ishii Jsy/100 6.00 15.00
45 Darin Erstad Jsy/500 3.00 8.00
46 Jose Vidro Jsy/500 3.00 8.00
47 Miguel Tejada Jsy/475 3.00 8.00
48 Roy Oswalt Jsy/500 3.00 8.00
49 So Taguchi Jsy/100 6.00 15.00
50 Barry Zito Jsy/500 3.00 8.00
51 Manny Ramirez Jsy/400 4.00 10.00
52 Nomar Garciaparra Jsy/400 6.00 15.00
53 C.C. Sabathia Jsy/500 3.00 8.00
54 Carlos Delgado Jsy/500 3.00 8.00
55 Gary Sheffield Jsy/500 3.00 8.00
56 J.D. Drew Jsy/500 3.00 8.00
57 Barry Bonds Ball/150 15.00 40.00
58 Derek Jeter Ball/150 15.00 40.00
59 Edgar Martinez Jsy/400 4.00 10.00
60 Sammy Sosa Ball/150 6.00 15.00

2002 Donruss Classics Timeless Treasures

Randomly inserted into packs, these 17 cards feature all-time greats along with key pieces of their memorabilia. These cards have different print runs which we have put next to their names. Those cards with a stated print run of 25 or less are not priced due to market scarcity.

1 Ted Williams .406 Avg Jsy/25
2 Ted Williams The Kid Jsy/10
3 Ted Williams Ballgame Jsy/10
4 Ted Williams Splinter Jsy/10
5 Ted Williams Crown Bat/42 50.00 100.00
6 Ted Williams Crown Bat/47 50.00 100.00
7 Ted Williams MVP Bat/46 50.00 100.00
8 Ted Williams MVP Bat/49 50.00 100.00
9 Ted Williams Jsy/9
10 Cal Ripken Iron Man Jsy/98 20.00 50.00
11 Cal Ripken ROY Jsy/82 40.00 80.00
12 Cal Ripken MVP Jsy/83 40.00 80.00
13 Cal Ripken MVP Jsy/91 40.00 80.00
14 Cal Ripken
Lou Gehrig Jsy/25
15 Cal Ripken 2131 Jsy/25
16 Cal Ripken 3000 Hits Jsy/25
17 Cal Ripken Jsy/8

2003 Donruss Classics Samples

Inserted at a stated rate of one per sealed Beckett Baseball Collector Magazine, these cards parallel the basic Donruss Classic cards and can be differentiated by the word "Sample" printed in silver on the back.

*SAMPLES: 1.5X TO 4X BASIC CARDS
ONE PER SEALED BBC MAGAZINE
*GOLD: 1.5X TO 4X BASIC SAMPLES

2003 Donruss Classics

This 211-card set was released in two separate series. The primary Donruss Classics product - containing cards 1-200 from the basic set - was released in April, 2003. This set was issued in seven-card packs with an $6 SRP which were packed 18 to a box and 12 boxes to a case. Cards 201-211 were randomly seeded within packs of DLP Rookies and Traded of which was distributed in December, 2003. The first 100 cards feature active veterans, while cards 101-150 feature retired legends and cards 151-211 feature rookies and leading prospects. Please note that cards 101-200 were issued at a stated rate of one in nine and were issued to a stated print run of 1500 serial numbered sets. Cards 201-211 were serial-numbered to 1000 copies each.

COMP.LO SET w/o SP's (100) 10.00 25.00
COMMON CARD (1-100) .25 .60
COMMON CARD (101-150) 1.50 4.00
COMMON CARD (151-200) 1.50 4.00
COIMMON CARD (201-211) 1.50 4.00
1 Troy Glaus .25 .60
2 Barry Bonds 1.50 4.00
3 Miguel Tejada .25 .60
4 Randy Johnson .60 1.50
5 Eric Hinske .25 .60
6 Barry Zito .25 .60
7 Jason Jennings .25 .60
8 Derek Jeter 1.50 4.00
9 Vladimir Guerrero .60 1.50
10 Corey Patterson .25 .60
11 Manny Ramirez .40 1.00
12 Edgar Martinez .40 1.00
13 Roy Oswalt .25 .60
14 Andruw Jones .40 1.00
15 Alex Rodriguez 1.00 2.50
16 Mark Mulder .25 .60
17 Kazuhisa Ishii .25 .60
18 Gary Sheffield .25 .60
19 Jay Gibbons .25 .60
20 Roberto Alomar .40 1.00
21 A.J. Pierzynski .25 .60
22 Eric Chavez .25 .60
23 Roger Clemens 1.25 3.00
24 C.C. Sabathia .25 .60
25 Jose Vidro .25 .60
26 Shannon Stewart .25 .60
27 Mark Teixeira .40 1.00
28 Joe Thurston .25 .60
29 Josh Beckett .25 .60
30 Jeff Bagwell .40 1.00
31 Geronimo Gil .25 .60
32 Curt Schilling .25 .60
33 Frank Thomas .60 1.50
34 Lance Berkman .25 .60
35 Adam Dunn .25 .60
36 Christian Parker .25 .60
37 Jim Thome .40 1.00
38 Shawn Green .25 .60
39 Drew Henson .25 .60
40 Chipper Jones .60 1.50
41 Kevin Mench .25 .60
42 Hideo Nomo .60 1.50
43 Andres Galarraga .25 .60
44 Doug Davis .25 .60
45 Mark Prior .40 1.00
46 Sean Casey .25 .60
47 Magglio Ordonez .25 .60
48 Tom Glavine .40 1.00
49 Marlon Byrd .25 .60
50 Albert Pujols 1.25 3.00
51 Mark Buehrle .25 .60
52 Aramis Ramirez .25 .60
53 Pat Burrell .25 .60
54 Craig Biggio .40 1.00
55 Alfonso Soriano .25 .60
56 Kerry Wood .25 .60
57 Wade Miller .25 .60
58 Hank Blalock .25 .60
59 Cliff Floyd .25 .60
60 Jason Giambi .25 .60
61 Carlos Beltran .25 .60
62 Brian Roberts .25 .60
63 Paul Lo Duca .25 .60
64 Tim Redding .25 .60
65 Sammy Sosa .60 1.50
66 Joe Borchard .25 .60
67 Ryan Klesko .25 .60
68 Richie Sexson .25 .60
69 Carlos Lee .25 .60
70 Rickey Henderson .60 1.50
71 Brian Tallet .25 .60
72 Luis Gonzalez .25 .60
73 Satoru Komiyama .25 .60
74 Tim Hudson .25 .60
75 Ken Griffey Jr. 1.00 2.50
76 Adam Johnson .25 .60
77 Bobby Abreu .25 .60
78 Adrian Beltre .25 .60
79 Rafael Palmeiro .40 1.00
80 Ichiro Suzuki 1.25 3.00
81 Kenny Lofton .25 .60
82 Brian Giles .25 .60
83 Barry Larkin .40 1.00
84 Robert Fick .25 .60
85 Ben Sheets .25 .60
86 Scott Rolen .40 1.00
87 Nomar Garciaparra 1.00 2.50
88 Brandon Phillips .25 .60
89 Ben Kozlowski .25 .60
90 Bernie Williams .40 1.00
91 Pedro Martinez .40 1.00
92 Todd Helton .40 1.00
93 Jermaine Dye .25 .60
94 Carlos Delgado .25 .60
95 Mike Piazza 1.00 2.50
96 Junior Spivey .25 .60
97 Torii Hunter .25 .60
98 Mike Sweeney .25 .60
99 Ivan Rodriguez .40 1.00
100 Greg Maddux 1.00 2.50
101 Ernie Banks LGD 2.00 5.00
102 Steve Garvey LGD 1.50 4.00
103 George Brett LGD 3.00 8.00
104 Lou Brock LGD 2.00 5.00
105 Hoyt Wilhelm LGD 1.50 4.00
106 Steve Carlton LGD 1.50 4.00
107 Joe Torre LGD 1.50 4.00
108 Dennis Eckersley LGD 1.50 4.00
109 Reggie Jackson LGD 2.00 5.00
110 Al Kaline LGD 2.00 5.00
111 Harold Reynolds LGD 1.50 4.00
112 Don Mattingly LGD 3.00 8.00
113 Tony Gwynn LGD 2.00 5.00
114 Willie McCovey LGD 1.50 4.00
115 Joe Morgan LGD 1.50 4.00
116 Stan Musial LGD 2.50 6.00
117 Jim Palmer LGD 1.50 4.00
118 Brooks Robinson LGD 2.00 5.00
119 Don Sutton LGD 1.50 4.00
120 Nolan Ryan LGD 4.00 10.00
121 Mike Schmidt LGD 3.00 8.00
122 Tom Seaver LGD 2.00 5.00
123 Cal Ripken LGD 5.00 12.00
124 Robin Yount LGD 2.00 5.00
125 Bob Feller LGD 1.50 4.00
126 Joe Carter LGD 1.50 4.00
127 Jack Morris LGD 1.50 4.00
128 Luis Aparicio LGD 1.50 4.00
129 Bobby Doerr LGD 1.50 4.00
130 Dave Parker LGD 1.50 4.00
131 Yogi Berra LGD 2.00 5.00
132 Will Clark LGD 2.00 5.00
133 Fred Lynn LGD 1.50 4.00
134 Andre Dawson LGD 1.50 4.00
135 Duke Snider LGD 2.00 5.00
136 Orlando Cepeda LGD 1.50 4.00
137 Billy Williams LGD 1.50 4.00
138 Dale Murphy LGD 2.00 5.00
139 Harmon Killebrew LGD 2.00 5.00
140 Kirby Puckett LGD 2.00 5.00
141 Carlton Fisk LGD 2.00 5.00
142 Eric Davis LGD 1.50 4.00
143 Alan Trammell LGD 1.50 4.00
144 Paul Molitor LGD 1.50 4.00
145 Jose Canseco LGD 2.00 5.00
146 Ozzie Smith LGD 2.50 6.00
147 Ralph Kiner LGD 1.50 4.00
148 Dwight Gooden LGD 1.50 4.00
149 Phil Rizzuto LGD 2.00 5.00
150 Lenny Dykstra LGD 1.50 4.00
151 Adam LaRoche ROO 1.50 4.00
152 Tim Hummel ROO 1.50 4.00
153 Matt Kata ROO RC 1.50 4.00
154 Jeff Baker ROO 1.50 4.00
155 Josh Stewart ROO RC 1.50 4.00
156 Marshall McDougall ROO 1.50 4.00
157 Jhonny Peralta ROO 2.00 5.00
158 Mike Nicolas ROO RC 1.50 4.00
159 Jeremy Guthrie ROO 1.50 4.00
160 Craig Brazell ROO RC 1.50 4.00
161 Joe Valentine ROO RC 1.50 4.00
162 Buddy Hernandez ROO RC 1.50 4.00
163 Freddy Sanchez ROO 1.50 4.00
164 Shane Victorino ROO RC 2.50 6.00
165 Corwin Malone ROO 1.50 4.00
166 Jason Dubois ROO 1.50 4.00
167 Josh Wilson ROO 1.50 4.00
168 Tim Olson ROO RC 1.50 4.00
169 Cliff Bartosh ROO 1.50 4.00
170 Michael Hessman ROO RC 1.50 4.00
171 Ryan Church ROO 1.50 4.00
172 Garrett Atkins ROO 1.50 4.00
173 Jose Morban ROO 1.50 4.00
174 Ryan Cameron ROO RC 1.50 4.00
175 Todd Wellemeyer ROO RC 1.50 4.00
176 Travis Chapman ROO 1.50 4.00
177 Jason Anderson ROO 1.50 4.00
178 Adam Morrissey ROO 1.50 4.00
179 Jose Contreras ROO RC 2.00 5.00
180 Nic Jackson ROO 1.50 4.00
181 Rob Hammock ROO RC 1.50 4.00
182 Carlos Rivera ROO 1.50 4.00
183 Vinny Chulk ROO 1.50 4.00
184 Pete LaForest ROO RC 1.50 4.00
185 Jon Leicester ROO RC 1.50 4.00
186 Terrmel Sledge ROO RC 1.50 4.00
187 Jose Castillo ROO 1.50 4.00
188 Gerald Laird ROO 1.50 4.00
189 Nook Logan ROO RC 2.00 5.00
190 Clint Barmes ROO RC 1.25 3.00
191 Jesus Medrano ROO 1.50 4.00
192 Henri Stanley ROO 1.50 4.00
193 Hideki Matsui ROO RC 4.00 10.00
194 Walter Young ROO 1.50 4.00
195 Jon Adkins ROO 1.50 4.00
196 Tommy Whiteman ROO 1.50 4.00
197 Rob Bowen ROO 1.50 4.00
198 Brandon Webb ROO RC 4.00 10.00
199 Prentice Redman ROO RC 1.50 4.00
200 Jimmy Gobble ROO 1.50 4.00
201 J.Bonderman ROO RC 4.00 10.00
202 Adam Loewen ROO RC 2.00 5.00
203 Chien-Ming Wang ROO RC 6.00 15.00
204 Hong-Chih Kuo ROO RC 6.00 15.00
205 Ryan Wagner ROO RC 1.50 4.00
206 Dan Haren ROO RC 2.00 5.00
207 Dontrelle Willis ROO 2.00 5.00
208 Rickie Weeks ROO RC 3.00 8.00
209 Ramon Nivar ROO RC 1.50 4.00
210 Chad Gaudin ROO RC 1.50 4.00
211 Delmon Young ROO RC 6.00 15.00

2003 Donruss Classics Significant Signatures

Randomly inserted into packs, this is an almost complete parallel to the basic set. Please note, cards 201-211 were randomly inserted within packs of DLP Rookies and Traded. Each of the these cards feature an authentic "sticker" autograph of the featured player on them. Please note that these players signed a different amount of cards ranging between 5-500 copies per and that information is next to the player's name in our checklist. Please note that if the print run is 25 or fewer, no pricing is provided due to market scarcity. Also please note that Hoyt Wilhelm, since he had signed stickers, is able to have signed cards in this set despite having passed on the previous year.

1 Troy Glaus/10
3 Miguel Tejada/5
5 Eric Hinske/250 4.00 10.00
6 Barry Zito/25
7 Jason Jennings/250 4.00 10.00
9 Vladimir Guerrero/5
10 Corey Patterson/100 6.00 15.00
11 Manny Ramirez/5
12 Edgar Martinez/20
13 Roy Oswalt/100 10.00 25.00
14 Andruw Jones/10
15 Alex Rodriguez/5
16 Mark Mulder/100 6.00 15.00
17 Kazuhisa Ishii/5
18 Gary Sheffield/5
19 Jay Gibbons/250 4.00 10.00
20 Roberto Alomar/5
21 A.J. Pierzynski/75 10.00 25.00
22 Eric Chavez/20
23 Roger Clemens/5
24 C.C. Sabathia/5
25 Jose Vidro/75 6.00 15.00
26 Shannon Stewart/25
27 Mark Teixeira/50 15.00 40.00
29 Josh Beckett/5
31 Geronimo Gil/50 6.00 15.00
32 Curt Schilling/5
33 Frank Thomas/5
34 Lance Berkman/5
35 Adam Dunn/100 15.00 40.00
36 Christian Parker/250 4.00 10.00
37 Jim Thome/5
38 Shawn Green/5
39 Drew Henson/100 6.00 15.00
40 Chipper Jones/5
41 Kevin Mench/250 6.00 15.00
43 Andres Galarraga/5
44 Doug Davis/15
45 Mark Prior/50 12.50 30.00
46 Sean Casey/5
47 Magglio Ordonez/5
48 Tom Glavine/10
49 Marlon Byrd/10
50 Albert Pujols/10
51 Mark Buehrle/25
52 Aramis Ramirez/10
53 Pat Burrell/10
54 Craig Biggio/5
55 Alfonso Soriano/5
56 Kerry Wood/15
57 Wade Miller/200 4.00 10.00
58 Hank Blalock/50 10.00 25.00
59 Cliff Floyd/20
61 Carlos Beltran/20
62 Brian Roberts/250 10.00 25.00
63 Paul Lo Duca/100 10.00 25.00
64 Tim Redding/250 4.00 10.00
66 Joe Borchard/100 6.00 15.00
67 Ryan Klesko/20
68 Richie Sexson/20
69 Carlos Lee/25
70 Rickey Henderson/5
71 Brian Tallet/25
72 Luis Gonzalez/5
73 Satoru Komiyama/124 10.00 25.00
74 Tim Hudson/20
76 Adam Johnson/200 4.00 10.00
77 Bobby Abreu/10
78 Adrian Beltre/10
79 Rafael Palmeiro/5
81 Kenny Lofton/5
82 Brian Giles/25
83 Barry Larkin/5
84 Robert Fick/50 6.00 15.00
85 Ben Sheets/20
86 Scott Rolen/5
88 Brandon Phillips/250 4.00 10.00
89 Ben Kozlowski/150 4.00 10.00
90 Bernie Williams/5
91 Pedro Martinez/5
92 Todd Helton/5
93 Jermaine Dye/100 10.00 25.00
96 Junior Spivey/100 6.00 15.00
97 Torii Hunter/50 10.00 25.00
98 Mike Sweeney/25
99 Ivan Rodriguez/5
100 Greg Maddux/5
101 Ernie Banks LGD/5
102 Steve Garvey LGD/100 10.00 25.00
103 George Brett LGD/5
104 Lou Brock LGD/20
105 Hoyt Wilhelm LGD/25
106 Steve Carlton LGD/20
107 Joe Torre LGD/5
108 Dennis Eckersley LGD/50 15.00 40.00
109 Reggie Jackson LGD/5
110 Al Kaline LGD/20
111 Harold Reynolds LGD/50 15.00 40.00
112 Don Mattingly LGD/15
113 Tony Gwynn LGD/5
114 Willie McCovey LGD/5
115 Joe Morgan LGD/5
116 Stan Musial LGD/25
117 Jim Palmer LGD/20
118 Brooks Robinson LGD/20
119 Don Sutton LGD/100 10.00 25.00
120 Nolan Ryan LGD/50 150.00 250.00
121 Mike Schmidt LGD/15
122 Tom Seaver LGD/5
123 Cal Ripken LGD/50 75.00 150.00
124 Robin Yount LGD/5
125 Bob Feller LGD/25
126 Joe Carter LGD/100 10.00 25.00
127 Jack Morris LGD/100 10.00 25.00
128 Luis Aparicio LGD/50 15.00 40.00
129 Bobby Doerr LGD/25
130 Dave Parker LGD/10
131 Yogi Berra LGD/10
132 Will Clark LGD/20
133 Fred Lynn LGD/50 15.00 40.00
134 Andre Dawson LGD/50 15.00 40.00
135 Duke Snider LGD/5
136 Orlando Cepeda LGD/100 10.00 25.00
137 Billy Williams LGD/100 10.00 25.00
138 Dale Murphy LGD/20
139 Harmon Killebrew LGD/15
140 Kirby Puckett LGD/5
141 Carlton Fisk LGD/5
142 Eric Davis LGD/50 15.00 40.00
143 Alan Trammell LGD/50 15.00 40.00
144 Paul Molitor LGD/10
145 Jose Canseco LGD/15
146 Ozzie Smith LGD/5
147 Ralph Kiner LGD/20
148 Dwight Gooden LGD/50 15.00 40.00
149 Phil Rizzuto LGD/20
150 Lenny Dykstra LGD/50 15.00 40.00
151 Adam LaRoche ROO/250 4.00 10.00
152 Tim Hummel ROO/500 4.00 10.00
153 Matt Kata ROO/500 4.00 10.00
154 Jeff Baker ROO/500 4.00 10.00
155 Josh Stewart ROO/177 4.00 10.00
156 Marshall McDougall ROO/500 4.00 10.00
157 Jhonny Peralta ROO/500 6.00 15.00
158 Mike Nicolas ROO/500 4.00 10.00
159 Jeremy Guthrie ROO/500 4.00 10.00
160 Craig Brazell ROO/500 4.00 10.00
161 Joe Valentine ROO/172 4.00 10.00
162 Buddy Hernandez ROO/500 4.00 10.00
163 Freddy Sanchez ROO/500 6.00 15.00
164 Shane Victorino ROO/351 20.00 50.00
165 Corwin Malone ROO/500 4.00 10.00
166 Jason Dubois ROO/500 4.00 10.00
167 Josh Wilson ROO/500 4.00 10.00
168 Tim Olson ROO/500 4.00 10.00
169 Cliff Bartosh ROO/500 4.00 10.00
170 Michael Hessman ROO/427 4.00 10.00
171 Ryan Church ROO/500 6.00 15.00
172 Garrett Atkins ROO/500 4.00 10.00
173 Jose Morban ROO/500 4.00 10.00
174 Ryan Cameron ROO/500 4.00 10.00
175 Todd Wellemeyer ROO/500 4.00 10.00
176 Travis Chapman ROO/477 4.00 10.00
177 Jason Anderson ROO/500 6.00 15.00
178 Adam Morrissey ROO/500 4.00 10.00
179 Jose Contreras ROO/100 12.50 30.00
180 Nic Jackson ROO/500 4.00 10.00
181 Rob Hammock ROO/500 4.00 10.00
182 Carlos Rivera ROO/500 4.00 10.00
183 Vinny Chulk ROO/500 4.00 10.00
184 Pete LaForest ROO/177 4.00 10.00
185 John Leicester ROO/500 4.00 10.00
186 Termel Sledge ROO/500 4.00 10.00
187 Jose Castillo ROO/500 4.00 10.00
188 Gerald Laird ROO/500 4.00 10.00
189 Nook Logan ROO/427 6.00 15.00
190 Clint Barmes ROO/100 8.00 20.00
191 Jesus Medrano ROO/500 4.00 10.00
192 Henri Stanley ROO/500 4.00 10.00
194 Walter Young ROO/500 4.00 10.00
195 Jon Adkins ROO/500 4.00 10.00
196 Tommy Whiteman ROO/500 4.00 10.00
197 Rob Bowen ROO/500 4.00 10.00
198 Brandon Webb ROO/500 12.50 30.00
199 Prentice Redman ROO/127 4.00 10.00
200 Jimmy Gobble ROO/500 4.00 10.00
201 Jeremy Bonderman ROO/100 15.00 40.00
202 Adam Loewen ROO/100 10.00 25.00
203 Chien-Ming Wang ROO/50 60.00 120.00
204 Hong-Chih Kuo ROO/25
205 Ryan Wagner ROO/100 4.00 10.00
206 Dan Haren ROO/100 12.50 30.00
207 Dontrelle Willis ROO/25
208 Rickie Weeks ROO/10
209 Ramon Nivar ROO/100 4.00 10.00
210 Chad Gaudin ROO/25
211 Delmon Young ROO/25

2003 Donruss Classics Timeless Tributes

Randomly inserted into packs, this is a complete parallel of the basic Classics set. Please note, cards 201-211 were randomly inserted into packs of DLP Rookies and Traded. Each of these cards were issued to a stated print run of 100 serial numbered sets.

*TRIBUTE 1-100: 2.5X TO 6X BASIC
*TRIB.101-150: 1.25X TO 3X BASIC
*TRIBUTE 151-200: .6X TO 1.5X BASIC
*TRIBUTE 201-211: .6X TO 1.5X BASIC
203 Chien-Ming Wang ROO 12.50 30.00
204 Hong-Chih Kuo ROO 15.00 40.00

2003 Donruss Classics Classic Combos

Randomly inserted in packs, this 15 card set features two players along with game-used memorabilia of each player. We have noted the print run information next to the player's name in our checklist. Please note that if a card has a stated print run of 25 or fewer we have not priced the card due to market scarcity.

1 Babe Ruth Jsy 400.00 600.00
Lou Gehrig Jsy/50
2 Jackie Robinson Jsy 50.00 100.00
Pee Wee Reese Jsy/50
3 Bobby Doerr Jsy
Fred Lynn Jsy/25
4 Honus Wagner Seat 125.00 200.00
Roberto Clemente Jsy/50
5 Kirby Puckett Jsy
Torri Hunter Jsy/25
6 Ryne Sandberg Jsy
Sammy Sosa Jsy/25
7 Hideo Nomo Jsy
Kazuhisa Ishii Jsy/25
8 Mike Schmidt Jsy
Steve Carlton Jsy/25
9 Paul Molitor Jsy
Robin Yount Jsy/25
10 Duke Snider Jsy
Mike Piazza Jsy/25
11 Al Kaline Jsy
Ty Cobb Bat/25
12 Don Mattingly Jsy
Jason Giambi Jsy/25
13 Ozzie Smith Jsy
Stan Musial Jsy/25
14 Pedro Martinez Jsy
Roger Clemens Jsy/25
15 Thurman Munson Jsy
Yogi Berra Jsy/25

2003 Donruss Classics Classic Singles

Randomly inserted into packs, this 30-card set features a mix of active and retired players along with a memorabilia piece about that player. We have noted the stated print run information next to the player's name in our checklist and if a card was issued to a stated print run of 25 or fewer, there is no pricing due to market scarcity.

1 Babe Ruth Jsy/100 250.00 400.00
2 Lou Gehrig Jsy/80 150.00 250.00
3 Jackie Robinson Jsy/80 50.00 100.00
4 Pee Wee Reese Jsy/25
5 Bobby Doerr Jsy/100 8.00 20.00
6 Fred Lynn Jsy/100 8.00 20.00
7 Honus Wagner Seat/100 20.00 50.00
8 Roberto Clemente Jsy/80 60.00 120.00
9 Kirby Puckett Jsy/100 15.00 40.00
10 Torii Hunter Jsy/100 6.00 15.00
11 Sammy Sosa Jsy/100 10.00 25.00
12 Ryne Sandberg Jsy/100 30.00 60.00
13 Hideo Nomo Jsy/50 60.00 120.00
14 Kazuhisa Ishii Jsy/50 10.00 25.00
15 Mike Schmidt Jsy/100 30.00 60.00
16 Steve Carlton Jsy/100 8.00 20.00
17 Robin Yount Jsy/100 15.00 40.00
18 Paul Molitor Jsy/100 8.00 20.00
19 Mike Piazza Jsy/100 10.00 25.00
20 Duke Snider Jsy/50 15.00 40.00
21 Al Kaline Jsy/50 30.00 60.00
22 Ty Cobb Bat/25
23 Don Mattingly Jsy/100 30.00 60.00
24 Jason Giambi Jsy/100 6.00 15.00
25 Stan Musial Jsy/25
26 Ozzie Smith Jsy/100 15.00 40.00
27 Roger Clemens Jsy/100 12.50 30.00
28 Pedro Martinez Jsy/100 8.00 20.00
29 Thurman Munson Jsy/50 30.00 60.00
30 Yogi Berra Jsy/25

2003 Donruss Classics Dress Code

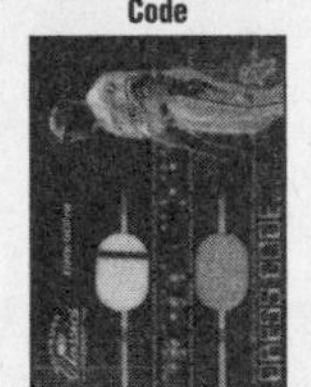

Randomly inserted into pack, this 75-card set features anywhere from one to four swatches of game-worn/used materials. Each card was issued to different quantities and we have notated that information next to the card in our checklist.

1 Roger Clemens Yanks Jsy/500 6.00 15.00
2 Miguel Tejada Bat-Hat-Jsy/250 8.00 20.00
3 Vladimir Guerrero Jsy/425 4.00 10.00
4 Kazuhisa Ishii Jsy/250 3.00 8.00
5 Chipper Jones Jsy/425 4.00 10.00
6 Troy Glaus Jsy/425 3.00 8.00
7 Rafael Palmeiro Jsy/425 4.00 10.00
8 R.Henderson R.Sox Jsy/250 4.00 10.00
9 Pedro Martinez Jsy/425 4.00 10.00
10 Andruw Jones Jsy/425 4.00 10.00
11 Nomar Garciaparra Jsy/500 6.00 15.00
12 Carlos Delgado Jsy/500 3.00 8.00
13 R.Hend Padres Hat-Jsy/250 8.00 20.00
14 Kerry Wood Hat-Jsy/250 6.00 15.00
15 Lance Berkman Hat-Jsy/50 10.00 25.00
16 Tony Gwynn 40.00 80.00
Hat-Jsy-Pants-Shoe/100
17 Mark Mulder Jsy/425 3.00 8.00
18 Jim Thome Jsy/500 4.00 10.00
19 Mike Piazza Jsy/500 6.00 15.00
20 Mike Mussina Jsy/500 4.00 10.00
21 Luis Gonzalez Jsy/500 3.00 8.00
22 Ryan Klesko Jsy/500 3.00 8.00
23 Richie Sexson Jsy/500 3.00 8.00
24 Curt Schilling Jsy/200 3.00 8.00
25 Alex Rodriguez Rgr Jsy/500 6.00 15.00
26 Bernie Williams Jsy/425 4.00 10.00
27 Cal Ripken Jsy/500 15.00 40.00
28 C.C. Sabathia Jsy/500 3.00 8.00
29 Mike Piazza Bat-Jsy/200 15.00 40.00
30 R.Hend Mets Hat-Jsy/250 8.00 20.00
31 Torii Hunter Jsy/425 3.00 8.00
32 Mark Teixeira Jsy/425 4.00 10.00
33 Dale Murphy Bat-Jsy/300 6.00 15.00
34 Todd Helton Jsy/425 4.00 10.00
35 Eric Chavez Jsy/425 3.00 8.00
36 Vernon Wells Jsy/425 3.00 8.00
37 Jeff Bagwell Hat-Jsy/100 12.50 30.00
38 Nick Johnson Jsy/425 3.00 8.00
39 Tim Hudson Hat-Jsy/250 6.00 15.00
40 Shawn Green Jsy/425 3.00 8.00
41 Mark Buehrle Jsy/500 3.00 8.00
42 Garret Anderson Jsy/100 4.00 10.00
43 Alex Rodriguez M's Jsy/500 6.00 15.00
44 Jason Giambi Jsy/500 3.00 8.00
45 Carlos Beltran Jsy/500 3.00 8.00
46 Adam Dunn Hat-Jsy/100 8.00 20.00
47 Jorge Posada Jsy/425 4.00 10.00
48 Roy Oswalt Hat-Jsy/200 6.00 15.00
49 Rich Aurilia Jsy/500 3.00 8.00
50 Jason Jennings 8.00 20.00
Bat-Hat-Jsy-Shoe/250
51 Mark Prior 15.00 40.00
Fld Glv-Hat-Jsy-Shoe/250
52 Jim Edmonds Jsy/500 3.00 8.00
53 Fred McGriff Jsy/500 4.00 10.00
54 A.Soriano Jsy-Shoe/100 4.00 10.00
55 Jeff Kent Jsy/425 3.00 8.00
56 Hideo Nomo R.Sox Jsy/200 15.00 40.00
57 Manny Ramirez Jsy/425 4.00 10.00
58 Jose Canseco Bat-Jsy/350 6.00 15.00
59 Magglio Ordonez Jsy/500 3.00 8.00
60 Alan Trammell Bat-Jsy/250 6.00 15.00
61 Bobby Abreu Jsy/500 3.00 8.00
62 Rickey Henderson 8.00 20.00
A's Hat-Jsy/200
63 Josh Beckett Jsy/500 3.00 8.00
64 Barry Larkin Jsy/500 4.00 10.00
65 Randy Johnson Jsy/200 4.00 10.00
66 Juan Gonzalez Jsy/500 3.00 8.00
67 Barry Zito Hat-Jsy/125 8.00 20.00
68 Roger Clemens R.Sox Jsy/500 6.00 15.00
69 R.Henderson M's Hat-Jsy/100 12.50 30.00
70 Hideo Nomo Mets Jsy/100 30.00 60.00
71 Paul Konerko Jsy/400 3.00 8.00
72 Pat Burrell Jsy/100 4.00 10.00
73 Frank Thomas Jsy-Pants/500 6.00 15.00
74 Sammy Sosa Jsy/500 4.00 10.00
75 Greg Maddux Btg Glv-Jsy/50 40.00 80.00

2003 Donruss Classics Legendary Hats

Randomly inserted in packs, this five-card set features a game-worn hat swatch of the featured player. The Roberto Clemente card was issued to a stated print run of 80 serial numbered sets.

1 Roberto Clemente/80 50.00 100.00
2 Kirby Puckett 30.00 60.00
3 Mike Schmidt 60.00 120.00
4 Tony Gwynn 50.00 100.00
5 Rickey Henderson 30.00 60.00

2003 Donruss Classics Legendary Leather

Randomly inserted into packs, this five-card set features a game-used glove piece. Each of these cards were issued to a stated print run of 25 serial numbered sets and there is no pricing due to market scarcity.

1 Nolan Ryan Fld Glv/80 60.00 120.00
2 Jimmie Foxx Fld Glv
3 Steve Carlton Fld Glv
4 Don Mattingly Btg Glv
5 Mike Schmidt Btg Glv

2003 Donruss Classics Legendary Lumberjacks

Randomly inserted into packs, this 35-card set feature retired players along with a game-used bat swatch. These cards were issued to different stated print runs and we have notated that information next to their name in our checklist. Please note that for cards with a stated print run of 25 or fewer, there is no pricing due to market scarcity.

1 Babe Ruth/100 100.00 200.00
2 Lou Gehrig/80 75.00 150.00
3 George Brett/250 12.50 30.00
4 Duke Snider/250 10.00 25.00
5 Roberto Clemente/25
6 Ryne Sandberg/400 12.50 30.00
7 Robin Yount/300 8.00 20.00
8 Harmon Killebrew/250 10.00 25.00
9 Al Kaline/250 10.00 25.00
10 Eddie Mathews/225 10.00 25.00
11 Brooks Robinson/400 8.00 20.00
12 Stan Musial/11
13 Kirby Puckett/375 8.00 20.00
14 Jose Canseco/400 8.00 20.00
15 Nellie Fox/325 8.00 20.00
16 Don Mattingly/400 12.50 30.00
17 Joe Torre/250 6.00 15.00
18 Cal Ripken/250 20.00 50.00
19 Richie Ashburn/250 10.00 25.00
20 Mike Schmidt/250 12.50 30.00
21 Dale Murphy/250 10.00 25.00
22 Thurman Munson/400 8.00 20.00
23 Tony Gwynn/400 8.00 20.00
24 Orlando Cepeda/225 6.00 15.00
25 Ty Cobb/25
26 Paul Molitor/325 6.00 15.00
27 Ralph Kiner/200 6.00 15.00
28 Frank Robinson/225 10.00 25.00
29 Yogi Berra/50 30.00 60.00
30 Reggie Jackson/375 8.00 20.00
31 Rod Carew/325 8.00 20.00
32 Carlton Fisk/325 8.00 20.00
33 Rogers Hornsby/50 40.00 80.00
34 Mel Ott/125 15.00 40.00
35 Jimmie Foxx/50 40.00 80.00

2003 Donruss Classics Legendary Spikes

Randomly inserted into packs, this five-card set featureds game-used spike pieces of the featured players. These cards were issued to a stated print run of 50 serial numbered sets.

1 Kirby Puckett 30.00 60.00
2 Tony Gwynn 50.00 100.00
3 Don Mattingly 75.00 150.00
4 Frank Robinson 20.00 50.00
5 Gary Carter 15.00 40.00

2003 Donruss Classics Legends of the Fall

Randomly inserted into packs, this 10 card set featured players who were stars of at least one World Series they played in. Each of these cards were issued to a stated print run of 2500 serial numbered sets.

1 Reggie Jackson 1.50 4.00
2 Duke Snider 1.50 4.00
3 Roberto Clemente 5.00 12.00
4 Mel Ott 2.00 5.00
5 Yogi Berra 2.00 5.00
6 Jackie Robinson 2.00 5.00
7 Enos Slaughter 1.50 4.00
8 Willie Stargell 1.50 4.00
9 Bobby Doerr 1.50 4.00
10 Thurman Munson 2.00 5.00

2003 Donruss Classics Legends of the Fall Fabrics

Randomly inserted into packs, this is a parallel to the Legends of the Fall insert set. Each of these cards features a game-worn/used memorabilia swatch sequentially numbered to varying quantities. Please note that we have put that stated print run information next to the player's name in our checklist and if the print run is 25 or fewer, no pricing is provided due to market scarcity.

1 Reggie Jackson/100 10.00 25.00
2 Duke Snider/25
3 Roberto Clemente/50 75.00 150.00
4 Mel Ott/25
5 Yogi Berra/15
6 Jackie Robinson/50 50.00 100.00
7 Enos Slaughter/25
8 Willie Stargell/100 10.00 25.00
9 Bobby Doerr/100 8.00 20.00
10 Thurman Munson/25

2003 Donruss Classics Membership

Randomly inserted into packs, this 15-card set feature members of some of the most prestigious stat groups. Each of these cards were issued to a stated print run of 2500 serial numbered sets.

1 Babe Ruth 6.00 15.00
2 Steve Carlton 1.50 4.00
3 Honus Wagner 3.00 8.00
4 Warren Spahn 1.50 4.00
5 Eddie Mathews 2.00 5.00
6 Nolan Ryan 5.00 12.00
7 Rogers Hornsby 1.50 4.00
8 Ernie Banks 2.00 5.00
9 Harmon Killebrew 2.00 5.00
10 Tom Seaver 1.50 4.00
11 Jimmie Foxx 2.00 5.00
12 Ty Cobb 3.00 8.00
13 Frank Robinson 1.50 4.00
14 Mel Ott 2.00 5.00
15 Lou Gehrig 4.00 10.00

2003 Donruss Classics Membership VIP Memorabilia

Randomly inserted in packs, this is a parallel to the Membership insert set. Each of these cards feature a game worn/used memorabilia swatch. Each of these cards were issued to a varying sequential numbering and we have put that information next to the player's name in our checklist. Please note that if a card has a print run of 25 or fewer, no pricing is provided due to market scarcity.

1 Babe Ruth Bat/29
2 Steve Carlton Jsy/81 10.00 25.00
3 Honus Wagner Seat/14
4 Warren Spahn Jsy/61 30.00 60.00
5 Eddie Mathews Bat/67 30.00 60.00
6 Nolan Ryan Jsy/80 50.00 100.00
7 Rogers Hornsby Bat/31
8 Ernie Banks Jsy/70 30.00 60.00
9 Harmon Killebrew Jsy/71 30.00 60.00
10 Tom Seaver Jsy/81 15.00 40.00
11 Jimmie Foxx Bat/40 40.00 80.00
12 Ty Cobb Bat/21
13 Frank Robinson Jsy/71 20.00 50.00
14 Mel Ott Jsy/45 40.00 80.00
15 Lou Gehrig Bat/31

2003 Donruss Classics Timeless Treasures

Randomly inserted into packs, these five cards featured some of the game's most legendary players along with two swatches of game-worn/used material sequentially numbered to varying quantities. Please note that for cards with stated print runs of 25 or fewer, no pricing is provided due to market scarcity.

1 Stan Musial Jsy 75.00 150.00
Tony Gwynn Jsy/50
2 Alex Rodriguez Jsy
Cal Ripken Jsy/25
3 Roberto Clemente Jsy 75.00 150.00
Vladimir Guerrero Jsy/50
4 Ernie Banks Jsy
Sammy Sosa Jsy/25
5 Don Mattingly Jsy 60.00 120.00
Jason Giambi Jsy/50

2003 Donruss Classics Atlantic City National

Collectors who opened a stated number of Donruss Classic packs at the Donruss booth at the Atlantic City National were rewarded with these cards. The fronts of these cards had a special Atlantic City embossed logo while the backs show serial numbering to five.

PRINT RUN 5 SERIAL #'d SETS

2004 Donruss Classics

This 213-card set was released in April, 2004. The set was issued in six card packs with an $6 SRP which came 18 packs to a box and 14 boxes to a case. The first 150 cards in this set are active veterans while cards 151-175 and 206-211 featured retired greats and cards number 176-205 feature leading prospects. All those cards were printed to a print run of 1999 serial numbered sets. The set closes with three cards featuring leading players who switched teams in the off-season and those cards were issued at a stated rate of one in 18.

COMP.SET w/o SP's (153) 10.00 25.00
COMMON CARD (1-150) .25 .60
COMMON (151-175/206-210) .60 1.50
COMMON CARD (176-205) 1.25 3.00
COMMON CARD (211-213) .40 1.00
1 Albert Pujols 1.50 4.00
2 Derek Jeter 1.50 4.00
3 Hank Blalock .25 .60
4 Shannon Stewart .25 .60
5 Jason Giambi .25 .60
6 Carlos Lee .25 .60
7 Trot Nixon .25 .60
8 Bret Boone .25 .60
9 Mark Mulder .25 .60
10 Mariano Rivera .60 1.50
11 Scott Podsednik .25 .60
12 Jim Edmonds .40 1.00
13 Mike Lowell .25 .60
14 Robin Ventura .25 .60
15 Brian Giles .25 .60
16 Jose Vidro .25 .60
17 Manny Ramirez .60 1.50
18 Alex Rodriguez Rgr 1.00 2.50
19 Carlos Beltran .25 .60
20 Hideki Matsui 1.00 2.50
21 Johan Santana .60 1.50
22 Richie Sexson .25 .60
23 Chipper Jones .60 1.50
24 Steve Finley .25 .60
25 Mark Prior .40 1.00
26 Alexis Rios .40 1.00
27 Rafael Palmeiro .40 1.00
28 Jorge Posada .40 1.00
29 Barry Zito .25 .60
30 Jamie Moyer .25 .60
31 Preston Wilson .25 .60
32 Miguel Cabrera .60 1.50
33 Pedro Martinez .40 1.00
34 Curt Schilling .40 1.00
35 Hee Seop Choi .25 .60
36 Dontrelle Willis .25 .60
37 Rafael Soriano .25 .60
38 Richard Fischer .25 .60
39 Brian Tallet .25 .60
40 Jose Castillo .25 .60
41 Wade Miller .25 .60
42 Jose Contreras .25 .60
43 Runelvys Hernandez .25 .60
44 Joe Borchard .25 .60
45 Kazuhisa Ishii .25 .60
46 Jose Reyes .40 1.00
47 Adam Dunn .40 1.00
48 Randy Johnson .60 1.50
49 Brandon Phillips .25 .60
50 Scott Rolen .40 1.00
51 Ken Griffey Jr. 1.00 2.50
52 Tom Glavine .40 1.00
53 Cliff Lee .40 1.00
54 Chien-Ming Wang 1.25 3.00
55 Roy Oswalt .40 1.00
56 Austin Kearns .25 .60
57 Jhonny Peralta .25 .60
58 Greg Maddux Braves 1.00 2.50
59 Mark Grace .40 1.00
60 Jae Weong Seo .25 .60
61 Nic Jackson .25 .60
62 Roger Clemens .75 2.00
63 Jimmy Gobble .25 .60
64 Travis Hafner .25 .60
65 Paul Konerko .40 1.00
66 Jerome Williams .25 .60
67 Ryan Klesko .25 .60
68 Alexis Gomez .25 .60
69 Omar Vizquel .40 1.00
70 Zach Day .25 .60
71 Rickey Henderson .60 1.50
72 Morgan Ensberg .25 .60
73 Josh Beckett .40 1.00
74 Garrett Atkins .25 .60
75 Sean Casey .25 .60
76 Julio Franco .25 .60
77 Lyle Overbay .25 .60
78 Josh Phelps .25 .60
79 Juan Gonzalez .25 .60
80 Rich Harden .25 .60
81 Bernie Williams .40 1.00
82 Torii Hunter .25 .60
83 Angel Berroa .25 .60
84 Jody Gerut .25 .60
85 Roberto Alomar .40 1.00
86 Byung-Hyun Kim .25 .60
87 Jay Gibbons .25 .60
88 Chone Figgins .25 .60
89 Fred McGriff .25 .60
90 Rich Aurilia .25 .60
91 Xavier Nady .25 .60
92 Marlon Byrd .25 .60
93 Mike Piazza .60 1.50
94 Vladimir Guerrero .60 1.50
95 Shawn Green .25 .60
96 Jeff Kent .25 .60
97 Ivan Rodriguez .40 1.00
98 Jay Payton .25 .60
99 Barry Larkin .40 1.00
100 Mike Sweeney .25 .60
101 Adrian Beltre .25 .60
102 Robby Hammock .25 .60
103 Orlando Hudson .25 .60
104 Mark Teixeira .60 1.50
105 Hong-Chih Kuo .25 .60
106 Eric Chavez .25 .60
107 Nick Johnson .25 .60
108 Jacque Jones .25 .60
109 Ken Harvey .25 .60
110 Aramis Ramirez .25 .60
111 Victor Martinez .40 1.00
112 Joe Crede .25 .60
113 Jason Varitek .60 1.50
114 Troy Glaus .25 .60
115 Billy Wagner .25 .60
116 Kerry Wood .25 .60
117 Hideo Nomo .60 1.50
118 Brandon Webb .25 .60
119 Craig Biggio .40 1.00
120 Orlando Cabrera .25 .60
121 Sammy Sosa .60 1.50
122 Bobby Abreu .25 .60
123 Andruw Jones .25 .60
124 Jeff Bagwell .40 1.00
125 Jim Thome .40 1.00
126 Javy Lopez .25 .60
127 Luis Castillo .25 .60
128 Todd Helton .40 1.00
129 Roy Halladay .60 1.50
130 Mike Mussina .40 1.00
131 Eric Byrnes .25 .60

132 Eric Hinske	.25	.60
133 Nomar Garciaparra	.60	1.50
134 Edgar Martinez	.40	1.00
135 Rocco Baldelli	.25	.60
136 Miguel Tejada	.40	1.00
137 Alfonso Soriano Yanks	.25	.60
138 Carlos Delgado	.25	.60
139 Rafael Furcal	.25	.60
140 Ichiro Suzuki	1.00	2.50
141 Aubrey Huff	.25	.60
142 Garret Anderson	.25	.60
143 Vernon Wells	.25	.60
144 Magglio Ordonez	.40	1.00
145 Brett Myers	.25	.60
146 Luis Gonzalez	.25	.60
147 Lance Berkman	.40	1.00
148 Frank Thomas	.60	1.50
149 Gary Sheffield	.25	.60
150 Tim Hudson	.40	1.00
151 Duke Snider LGD	1.00	2.50
152 Carl Yastrzemski LGD	1.50	4.00
153 Whitey Ford LGD	1.00	2.50
154 Cal Ripken LGD	6.00	15.00
155 Dwight Gooden LGD	.60	1.50
156 Warren Spahn LGD	1.00	2.50
157 Bob Gibson LGD	1.00	2.50
158 Don Mattingly LGD	3.00	8.00
159 Jack Morris LGD	.60	1.50
160 Jim Bunning LGD	.60	1.50
161 Fergie Jenkins LGD	.60	1.50
162 Brooks Robinson LGD	1.00	2.50
163 George Kell LGD	.60	1.50
164 Darryl Strawberry LGD	.60	1.50
165 Robin Roberts LGD	.60	1.50
166 Monte Irvin LGD	.60	1.50
167 Ernie Banks LGD	1.50	4.00
168 Wade Boggs LGD	1.00	2.50
169 Gaylord Perry LGD	.60	1.50
170 Keith Hernandez LGD	.60	1.50
171 Lou Brock LGD	1.00	2.50
172 Frank Robinson LGD	1.00	2.50
173 Nolan Ryan LGD	5.00	12.00
174 Stan Musial LGD	2.50	6.00
175 Eddie Murray LGD	1.50	4.00
176 Byron Gettis ROO	1.25	3.00
177 Merkin Valdez ROO RC	1.25	3.00
178 Rickie Weeks ROO	1.25	3.00
179 Akinori Otsuka ROO RC	1.25	3.00
180 Brian Bruney ROO	1.25	3.00
181 Freddy Guzman ROO RC	1.25	3.00
182 Brendan Harris ROO	1.25	3.00
183 John Gall ROO RC	1.25	3.00
184 Jason Kubel ROO	1.25	3.00
185 Delmon Young ROO	2.00	5.00
186 Ryan Howard ROO UER	4.00	10.00
Stat headers are for a pitcher		
187 Adam Loewen ROO	1.25	3.00
188 J.D. Durbin ROO	1.25	3.00
189 Dan Haren ROO	1.25	3.00
190 Dustin McGowan ROO	1.25	3.00
191 Chad Gaudin ROO	1.25	3.00
192 Preston Larrison ROO	1.25	3.00
193 Ramon Nivar ROO	1.25	3.00
194 Ronald Belisario ROO RC	1.25	3.00
195 Mike Gosling ROO RC	1.25	3.00
196 Kevin Youkilis ROO	2.00	5.00
197 Ryan Wagner ROO	1.25	3.00
198 Bubba Nelson ROO	1.25	3.00
199 Edwin Jackson ROO	1.25	3.00
200 Chris Burke ROO	1.25	3.00
201 Carlos Hines ROO RC	1.25	3.00
202 Greg Dobbs ROO RC	1.25	3.00
203 Jamie Brown ROO RC	1.25	3.00
204 Dave Crouthers ROO RC	1.25	3.00
205 Ian Snell ROO RC	1.25	3.00
206 Gary Carter LGD	.60	1.50
207 Dale Murphy LGD	1.00	2.50
208 Ryne Sandberg LGD	3.00	8.00
209 Phil Niekro LGD	.60	1.50
210 Don Sutton LGD	.60	1.50
211 Alex Rodriguez Yanks SP	1.50	4.00
212 Alfonso Soriano Rgr SP	.40	1.00
213 Greg Maddux Cubs SP	1.50	4.00

2004 Donruss Classics Significant Signatures Green

PRINT RUNS B/WN 1-100 COPIES PER
NO PRICING ON QTY OF 15 OR LESS

3 Hank Blalock/25	10.00	25.00
4 Shannon Stewart/50	8.00	20.00
6 Carlos Lee/10		
7 Trot Nixon/25	10.00	25.00
9 Mark Mulder/10		
10 Mariano Rivera/5		
12 Jim Edmonds/10		
13 Mike Lowell/25	10.00	25.00
14 Robin Ventura/25	10.00	25.00
16 Jose Vidro/10		
17 Manny Ramirez/5		
18 Alex Rodriguez Rgr/1		
19 Carlos Beltran/25	10.00	25.00
21 Johan Santana/50	12.50	30.00
22 Richie Sexson/5		
23 Chipper Jones/1		
24 Steve Finley/25	15.00	40.00
25 Mark Prior/5		
26 Alexis Rios/100	6.00	15.00
27 Rafael Palmeiro/10		
28 Jorge Posada/10		
29 Barry Zito/10		
30 Jamie Moyer/5		
32 Miguel Cabrera/50	12.50	30.00
33 Pedro Martinez/1		
34 Curt Schilling/1		
36 Dontrelle Willis/25	15.00	40.00
37 Rafael Soriano/100	4.00	10.00
38 Richard Fischer/100	4.00	10.00
39 Brian Tallet/100	4.00	10.00
40 Jose Castillo/100	4.00	10.00
41 Wade Miller/25	6.00	15.00
42 Jose Contreras/10		
43 Runelvys Hernandez/20	6.00	15.00
44 Joe Borchard/50	5.00	12.00
47 Adam Dunn/25	15.00	40.00
48 Randy Johnson/1		
49 Brandon Phillips/50	5.00	12.00
50 Scott Rolen/10		
52 Tom Glavine/5		
53 Cliff Lee/50	8.00	20.00
54 Chien-Ming Wang/50	100.00	200.00
55 Roy Oswalt/10		
56 Austin Kearns/10		
57 Jhonny Peralta/100	6.00	15.00
58 Greg Maddux Braves/1		
59 Mark Grace/5		
60 Jae Weong Seo/50	8.00	20.00
61 Nic Jackson/100	4.00	10.00
62 Roger Clemens/1		
63 Jimmy Gobble/45	5.00	12.00
64 Travis Hafner/50	8.00	20.00
65 Paul Konerko/10		
66 Jerome Williams/50	5.00	12.00
67 Ryan Klesko/5		
68 Alexis Gomez/50	5.00	12.00
70 Zach Day/50	5.00	12.00
72 Morgan Ensberg/50	8.00	20.00
73 Josh Beckett/5		
74 Garrett Atkins/99	4.00	10.00
75 Sean Casey/10		
76 Julio Franco/10		
77 Lyle Overbay/100	4.00	10.00
78 Josh Phelps/25	6.00	15.00
79 Juan Gonzalez/25	10.00	25.00
80 Rich Harden/50	8.00	20.00
82 Torii Hunter/10		
83 Angel Berroa/5		
84 Jody Gerut/50	5.00	12.00
85 Roberto Alomar/5		
87 Jay Gibbons/50	5.00	12.00
88 Chone Figgins/50	8.00	20.00
89 Fred McGriff/5		
90 Rich Aurilia/10		
91 Xavier Nady/5		
92 Marlon Byrd/10		
93 Mike Piazza/1		
94 Vladimir Guerrero/5		
95 Shawn Green/1		
97 Ivan Rodriguez/5		
98 Jay Payton/50	5.00	12.00
99 Barry Larkin/25	15.00	40.00
100 Mike Sweeney/1		
101 Adrian Beltre/5		
102 Robby Hammock/50	5.00	12.00
103 Orlando Hudson/50	5.00	12.00
104 Mark Teixeira/10		
105 Hong-Chih Kuo/50	30.00	60.00
106 Eric Chavez/25	10.00	25.00
107 Nick Johnson/10		
108 Jacque Jones/50	8.00	20.00
109 Ken Harvey/100	4.00	10.00
110 Aramis Ramirez/50	8.00	20.00
111 Victor Martinez/50	8.00	20.00
112 Joe Crede/50	8.00	20.00
113 Jason Varitek/25	20.00	50.00
114 Troy Glaus/10		
116 Kerry Wood/5		
117 Hideo Nomo/1		
118 Brandon Webb/25	6.00	15.00
119 Craig Biggio/10		
120 Orlando Cabrera/10		
121 Sammy Sosa/21	50.00	100.00
122 Bobby Abreu/10		
123 Andruw Jones/10		
124 Jeff Bagwell/5		
127 Luis Castillo/25	6.00	15.00
128 Todd Helton/1		
130 Mike Mussina/1		
131 Eric Byrnes/10		
132 Eric Hinske/10		
134 Edgar Martinez/25	20.00	50.00
135 Rocco Baldelli/10		
136 Miguel Tejada/5		
141 Aubrey Huff/5		
142 Garret Anderson/5		
143 Vernon Wells/10		
144 Magglio Ordonez/10		
145 Brett Myers/50	8.00	20.00
147 Lance Berkman/5		
148 Frank Thomas/5		
149 Gary Sheffield/25	15.00	40.00
150 Tim Hudson/10		
151 Duke Snider LGD/25	20.00	50.00
152 Carl Yastrzemski LGD/5		
153 Whitey Ford LGD/25	20.00	50.00
154 Cal Ripken LGD/5		
155 Dwight Gooden LGD/50	10.00	25.00
156 Warren Spahn LGD/10		
157 Bob Gibson LGD/5		
158 Don Mattingly LGD/25	75.00	150.00
159 Jack Morris LGD/50	6.00	15.00
160 Jim Bunning LGD/25	30.00	60.00
161 Fergie Jenkins LGD/50	10.00	25.00
162 Brooks Robinson LGD/10		
163 George Kell LGD/50	15.00	40.00
164 Darryl Strawberry LGD/50	10.00	25.00
165 Robin Roberts LGD/25	12.50	30.00
166 Monte Irvin LGD/25	12.50	30.00
167 Ernie Banks LGD/25	30.00	60.00
168 Wade Boggs LGD/25	30.00	60.00
169 Gaylord Perry LGD/50	6.00	15.00
170 Keith Hernandez LGD/50	10.00	25.00
171 Lou Brock LGD/10		
172 Frank Robinson LGD/25	20.00	50.00
173 Nolan Ryan LGD/25	75.00	150.00
174 Stan Musial LGD/25	40.00	80.00
175 Eddie Murray LGD/25	50.00	100.00
176 Byron Gettis ROO/100	4.00	10.00
177 Merkin Valdez ROO/100	4.00	10.00
178 Rickie Weeks ROO/25	10.00	25.00
180 Brian Bruney ROO/100	4.00	10.00
181 Freddy Guzman ROO/100	4.00	10.00
182 Brendan Harris ROO/100	4.00	10.00
183 John Gall ROO/100	4.00	10.00
184 Jason Kubel ROO/100	4.00	10.00
185 Delmon Young ROO/50	20.00	50.00
186 Ryan Howard ROO/100	40.00	80.00
187 Adam Loewen ROO/100	4.00	10.00
188 J.D. Durbin ROO/100	4.00	10.00
189 Dan Haren ROO/100	4.00	10.00
190 Dustin McGowan ROO/100	4.00	10.00
191 Chad Gaudin ROO/100	4.00	10.00
192 Preston Larrison ROO/100	4.00	10.00
193 Ramon Nivar ROO/100	4.00	10.00
195 Mike Gosling ROO/100	4.00	10.00
196 Kevin Youkilis ROO/100	4.00	10.00
197 Ryan Wagner ROO/100	4.00	10.00
198 Bubba Nelson ROO/100	4.00	10.00
199 Edwin Jackson ROO/100	6.00	15.00
200 Chris Burke ROO/100	6.00	15.00
201 Carlos Hines ROO/100	4.00	10.00
202 Greg Dobbs ROO/50	5.00	12.00
203 Jamie Brown ROO/100	4.00	10.00
204 Dave Crouthers ROO/100		
205 Ian Snell ROO/100	6.00	15.00
206 Gary Carter LGD/50	10.00	25.00
207 Dale Murphy LGD/50	15.00	40.00
208 Ryne Sandberg LGD/50	40.00	80.00
209 Phil Niekro LGD/50	15.00	40.00
210 Don Sutton LGD/50	10.00	25.00
211 Alex Rodriguez Yanks/1		
213 Greg Maddux Cubs/1		

2004 Donruss Classics Significant Signatures Platinum

STATED PRINT RUN 1 SERIAL #'d SET
NO PRICING DUE TO SCARCITY

2004 Donruss Classics Significant Signatures Red

PRINT RUNS B/WN 1-250 COPIES PER
NO PRICING ON QTY OF 15 OR LESS

3 Hank Blalock/50	8.00	20.00
4 Shannon Stewart/100	6.00	15.00
6 Carlos Lee/25	10.00	25.00
7 Trot Nixon/50	8.00	20.00
9 Mark Mulder/25	10.00	25.00
10 Mariano Rivera/5		
12 Jim Edmonds/25	15.00	40.00
13 Mike Lowell/50	8.00	20.00
14 Robin Ventura/50	8.00	20.00
16 Jose Vidro/25	6.00	15.00
17 Manny Ramirez/5		
18 Alex Rodriguez Rgr/5		
19 Carlos Beltran/25	10.00	25.00
21 Johan Santana/100	10.00	25.00
22 Richie Sexson/10		
23 Chipper Jones/5		
24 Steve Finley/100	10.00	25.00
25 Mark Prior/10		
26 Alexis Rios/250	6.00	15.00
27 Rafael Palmeiro/25	50.00	100.00
28 Jorge Posada/25	15.00	40.00
29 Barry Zito/10		
30 Jamie Moyer/5		
32 Miguel Cabrera/100	10.00	25.00
33 Pedro Martinez/5		
34 Curt Schilling/5		
36 Dontrelle Willis/100	10.00	25.00
37 Rafael Soriano/250	4.00	10.00
38 Richard Fischer/250	4.00	10.00
39 Brian Tallet/250	4.00	10.00
40 Jose Castillo/250	4.00	10.00
41 Wade Miller/92	4.00	10.00
42 Jose Contreras/25	10.00	25.00
43 Runelvys Hernandez/50	5.00	12.00
44 Joe Borchard/250	4.00	10.00
47 Adam Dunn/25	15.00	40.00
48 Randy Johnson/3		
49 Brandon Phillips/70	4.00	10.00
50 Scott Rolen/25	15.00	40.00
52 Tom Glavine/10		
53 Cliff Lee/100	12.50	30.00
54 Chien-Ming Wang/250	60.00	120.00
55 Roy Oswalt/25	10.00	25.00
56 Austin Kearns/25	6.00	15.00
57 Jhonny Peralta/250	6.00	15.00
58 Greg Maddux Braves/5		
59 Mark Grace/5		
60 Jae Weong Seo/100	6.00	15.00
61 Nic Jackson/250	4.00	10.00
62 Roger Clemens/1		
63 Jimmy Gobble/200	4.00	10.00
64 Travis Hafner/100	6.00	15.00
65 Paul Konerko/25	15.00	40.00
66 Jerome Williams/250	4.00	10.00
67 Ryan Klesko/5		
68 Alexis Gomez/100	4.00	10.00
70 Zach Day/100	4.00	10.00
72 Morgan Ensberg/100	6.00	15.00
73 Josh Beckett/5		
74 Garrett Atkins/245	4.00	10.00
75 Sean Casey/10		
76 Julio Franco/25	10.00	25.00
77 Lyle Overbay/250	4.00	10.00
78 Josh Phelps/50	5.00	12.00
79 Juan Gonzalez/25	10.00	25.00
80 Rich Harden/150	6.00	15.00
82 Torii Hunter/25	10.00	25.00
83 Angel Berroa/10		
84 Jody Gerut/100	4.00	10.00
85 Roberto Alomar/10		
87 Jay Gibbons/100	4.00	10.00
88 Chone Figgins/100	6.00	15.00
89 Fred McGriff/5		
90 Rich Aurilia/25	6.00	15.00
91 Xavier Nady/10		
92 Marlon Byrd/25	6.00	15.00
93 Mike Piazza/10		
94 Vladimir Guerrero/10		
95 Shawn Green/1		
97 Ivan Rodriguez/10		
98 Jay Payton/100	4.00	10.00
99 Barry Larkin/25	15.00	40.00
100 Mike Sweeney/1		
101 Adrian Beltre/5		
102 Robby Hammock/150	4.00	10.00
103 Orlando Hudson/100	4.00	10.00
104 Mark Teixeira/10		
105 Hong-Chih Kuo/100	20.00	50.00
106 Eric Chavez/25	10.00	25.00
107 Nick Johnson/25	10.00	25.00
108 Jacque Jones/100	6.00	15.00
109 Ken Harvey/250	4.00	10.00
110 Aramis Ramirez/100	6.00	15.00
111 Victor Martinez/99	6.00	15.00
112 Joe Crede/250	6.00	15.00
113 Jason Varitek/50	20.00	50.00
114 Troy Glaus/25	15.00	40.00
116 Kerry Wood/10		
117 Hideo Nomo/1		
118 Brandon Webb/50	5.00	12.00
119 Craig Biggio/25	15.00	40.00
120 Orlando Cabrera/50	8.00	20.00
121 Sammy Sosa/25	50.00	100.00
122 Bobby Abreu/25	10.00	25.00
123 Andruw Jones/25	15.00	40.00
124 Jeff Bagwell/25	40.00	80.00
127 Luis Castillo/50	5.00	12.00
128 Todd Helton/5		
130 Mike Mussina/5		
131 Eric Byrnes/25	6.00	15.00
132 Eric Hinske/25	6.00	15.00
134 Edgar Martinez/50	20.00	50.00
135 Rocco Baldelli/25	10.00	25.00
136 Miguel Tejada/5		
141 Aubrey Huff/5		
142 Garret Anderson/5		
143 Vernon Wells/25	10.00	25.00
144 Magglio Ordonez/25	15.00	40.00
145 Brett Myers/100	6.00	15.00
147 Lance Berkman/5		
148 Frank Thomas/5		
149 Gary Sheffield/50	12.50	30.00
150 Tim Hudson/25	15.00	40.00
151 Duke Snider LGD/50	15.00	40.00
152 Carl Yastrzemski LGD/10		
153 Whitey Ford LGD/50	15.00	40.00
154 Cal Ripken LGD/10		
155 Dwight Gooden LGD/100	8.00	20.00
156 Warren Spahn LGD/25	30.00	60.00
157 Bob Gibson LGD/15		
158 Don Mattingly LGD/25	75.00	150.00
159 Jack Morris LGD/100	6.00	15.00
160 Jim Bunning LGD/100	15.00	40.00
161 Fergie Jenkins LGD/100	8.00	20.00
162 Brooks Robinson LGD/20	50.00	100.00
163 George Kell LGD/100	12.50	30.00
164 Darryl Strawberry LGD/100	8.00	20.00
165 Robin Roberts LGD/100	6.00	15.00
166 Monte Irvin LGD/100	8.00	20.00
167 Ernie Banks LGD/50	20.00	50.00
168 Wade Boggs LGD/50	20.00	50.00
169 Gaylord Perry LGD/100	6.00	15.00
170 Keith Hernandez LGD/100	8.00	20.00
171 Lou Brock LGD/25	20.00	50.00
172 Frank Robinson LGD/50	15.00	40.00
173 Nolan Ryan LGD/50	60.00	120.00
174 Stan Musial LGD/50	30.00	60.00
175 Eddie Murray LGD/50	40.00	80.00
176 Byron Gettis ROO/250	4.00	10.00
177 Merkin Valdez ROO/250	4.00	10.00
178 Rickie Weeks ROO/50	8.00	20.00
180 Brian Bruney ROO/250	4.00	10.00
181 Freddy Guzman ROO/250	4.00	10.00
182 Brendan Harris ROO/250	4.00	10.00
183 John Gall ROO/250	4.00	10.00
184 Jason Kubel ROO/250	4.00	10.00
185 Delmon Young ROO/100	20.00	50.00
186 Ryan Howard ROO/250	30.00	60.00
187 Adam Loewen ROO/250	4.00	10.00
188 J.D. Durbin ROO/250	4.00	10.00
189 Dan Haren ROO/250	4.00	10.00
190 Dustin McGowan ROO/250	4.00	10.00
191 Chad Gaudin ROO/250	4.00	10.00
192 Preston Larrison ROO/250	4.00	10.00
193 Ramon Nivar ROO/250	4.00	10.00
195 Mike Gosling ROO/250	4.00	10.00
196 Kevin Youkilis ROO/250	4.00	10.00
197 Ryan Wagner ROO/250	4.00	10.00
198 Bubba Nelson ROO/250	4.00	10.00
199 Edwin Jackson ROO/250	6.00	15.00
200 Chris Burke ROO/250	6.00	15.00
201 Carlos Hines ROO/250	4.00	10.00
202 Greg Dobbs ROO/100	4.00	10.00
203 Jamie Brown ROO/250	4.00	10.00
204 Dave Crouthers ROO/250	4.00	10.00
205 Ian Snell ROO/250	6.00	15.00
206 Gary Carter LGD/100	8.00	20.00
207 Dale Murphy LGD/50	15.00	40.00
208 Ryne Sandberg LGD/25	50.00	100.00
209 Phil Niekro LGD/100	10.00	25.00
210 Don Sutton LGD/100	8.00	20.00
211 Alex Rodriguez Yanks/5		
213 Greg Maddux Cubs/5		

2004 Donruss Classics Timeless Tributes Green

*GREEN 1-150: 3X TO 8X BASIC
*GREEN 151-175/206-210: 1.5X TO 4X BASIC
*GREEN 176-205: .75X TO 2X BASIC
*GREEN 211-213: 2X TO 5X BASIC
STATED PRINT RUN 50 SERIAL #'d SETS

2004 Donruss Classics Timeless Tributes Platinum

STATED PRINT RUN 1 SERIAL #'d SET
NO PRICING DUE TO SCARCITY

2004 Donruss Classics Timeless Tributes Red

*RED 1-150: 2.5X TO 6X BASIC
*RED 151-175/206-210: 1.25X TO 3X BASIC
*RED 176-205: .6X TO 1.5X BASIC
*RED 211-213: 1.5X TO 4X BASIC
STATED PRINT RUN 100 SERIAL #'d SETS

2004 Donruss Classics Classic Combos Bat

RANDOM INSERTS IN PACKS
PRINT RUNS B/WN 25-50 COPIES PER
ALL CARDS FEATURE BAT-BAT COMBOS

1 Babe Ruth	200.00	350.00
Lou Gehrig/25		
2 Roy Campanella	15.00	40.00
Pee Wee Reese/50		
3 Ted Williams	125.00	200.00
Carl Yastrzemski/25		
4 Roberto Clemente	75.00	150.00
Willie Stargell/25		
5 Eddie Murray	40.00	80.00
Cal Ripken/50		
6 Roger Maris	50.00	100.00
Yogi Berra/25		
10 Nolan Ryan	20.00	50.00
Rod Carew/50		
11 Don Mattingly	30.00	60.00
Rickey Henderson/50		
15 Robin Yount	15.00	40.00
Paul Molitor/50		
16 Mark Grace	15.00	40.00
Sammy Sosa/50		
17 Ted Williams	75.00	150.00
Bobby Doerr/25		
18 Reggie Jackson	15.00	40.00
Rod Carew/50		

2004 Donruss Classics Classic Combos Jersey

PRINT RUNS B/WN
NO PRICING ON QTY OF 10 OR LESS
PRIME PRINT RUN 1 SERIAL #'d SET
NO PRIME PRICING DUE TO SCARCITY
RANDOM INSERTS IN PACKS
ALL ARE JSY-JSY COMBOS UNLESS NOTED

1 Babe Ruth Pants		
Lou Gehrig Pants/15		
2 Roy Campanella Pants	20.00	50.00
Pee Wee Reese/25		
3 Ted Williams	175.00	300.00
Carl Yastrzemski/15		
4 Roberto Clemente	75.00	150.00
Willie Stargell/25		
5 Eddie Murray	60.00	120.00
Cal Ripken/25		
6 Roger Maris	50.00	100.00
Yogi Berra/25		
7 Stan Musial		
Bob Gibson/10		
8 Whitey Ford	20.00	50.00
Yogi Berra/25		
9 Marty Marion	30.00	60.00
Stan Musial/25		
10 Nolan Ryan	30.00	60.00
Rod Carew/25		
11 Don Mattingly	30.00	60.00
Rickey Henderson/50		
12 Jack Morris	10.00	25.00
Alan Trammell/50		
13 Whitey Ford	20.00	50.00
Phil Rizzuto/25		
14 Marty Marion	15.00	40.00
Red Schoendienst/25		
15 Robin Yount	15.00	40.00
Paul Molitor/50		
16 Mark Grace	15.00	40.00
Sammy Sosa/50		
17 Ted Williams	150.00	250.00
Bobby Doerr/15		
18 Reggie Jackson	15.00	40.00
Rod Carew/50		

2004 Donruss Classics Classic Combos Quad

NO PRICING ON QTY OF 5 OR LESS
PRIME PRINT RUN 1 SERIAL #'d SET
NO PRIME PRICING DUE TO SCARCITY

1 Babe Ruth Bat-Pants		
Lou Gehrig Bat-Pants/5		
2 Roy Campanella Bat-Pants	50.00	100.00
Pee Wee Reese Bat-Jsy/25		
3 Ted Williams Bat-Jsy	250.00	400.00
Carl Yastrzemski Bat-Jsy/15		
4 Roberto Clemente Bat-Jsy	175.00	300.00
Willie Stargell Bat-Jsy/25		
5 Eddie Murray Bat-Jsy	125.00	200.00
Cal Ripken Bat-Jsy/25		
6 Roger Maris Bat-Jsy	150.00	250.00
Yogi Berra Bat-Jsy/15		
10 Nolan Ryan Bat-Jsy	60.00	120.00
Rod Carew Bat-Jsy/25		
11 Don Mattingly Bat-Jsy	75.00	150.00
Rickey Henderson Bat-Jsy/25		
15 Robin Yount Bat-Jsy	50.00	100.00
Paul Molitor Bat-Jsy/25		
16 Mark Grace Bat-Jsy	50.00	100.00
Sammy Sosa Bat-Jsy/25		
17 Ted Williams Bat-Jsy	175.00	300.00
Bobby Doerr Bat-Jsy/15		
18 Reggie Jackson Bat-Jsy	40.00	80.00
Rod Carew Bat-Jsy/25		

2004 Donruss Classics Classic Singles Bat

RANDOM INSERTS IN PACKS
PRINT RUNS B/WN 10-50 COPIES PER
NO PRICING ON QTY OF 10 OR LESS

1 Babe Ruth/15	250.00	400.00
2 Nolan Ryan/10		
3 Stan Musial/25	20.00	50.00
4 Ted Williams/25	60.00	120.00
5 Lou Gehrig/50	75.00	150.00
6 Eddie Murray/50	12.50	30.00
7 Roy Campanella/50	12.50	30.00
8 Robin Yount/50	12.50	30.00
9 Roberto Clemente/25	50.00	100.00
10 Don Mattingly/50	20.00	50.00
12 Carl Yastrzemski/50	15.00	40.00
13 Mark Grace/50	10.00	25.00
15 Rickey Henderson/50	12.50	30.00
16 Reggie Jackson/50	10.00	25.00
17 Pee Wee Reese/50	10.00	25.00
20 Roger Maris/25	30.00	60.00
21 Cal Ripken/50	40.00	80.00
23 Willie Stargell/50	10.00	25.00
24 Paul Molitor/50	6.00	15.00
26 Alan Trammell/50	6.00	15.00
27 Sammy Sosa/50	12.50	30.00
28 Bobby Doerr/50	6.00	15.00
29 Rod Carew/50	10.00	25.00
30 Yogi Berra/25	15.00	40.00
32 George Brett/50	20.00	50.00

2004 Donruss Classics Classic Singles Jersey

PRINT RUNS B/WN 10-100 COPIES PER
NO PRICING ON QTY FO 10 OR LESS
PRIME PRINT RUN 1 SERIAL #'d SET
NO PRIME PRICING DUE TO SCARCITY
RANDOM INSERTS IN PACKS

1 Babe Ruth Pants/10		
2 Nolan Ryan/50	20.00	50.00
3 Stan Musial/15	30.00	60.00
4 Ted Williams/10		
5 Lou Gehrig Pants/10		
6 Eddie Murray/100	8.00	20.00
7 Roy Campanella Pants/50	12.50	30.00
8 Robin Yount/100	8.00	20.00
9 Roberto Clemente/25	60.00	120.00
10 Don Mattingly/100	15.00	40.00
11 Bob Gibson/15	15.00	40.00
12 Carl Yastrzemski/50	15.00	40.00
13 Mark Grace/25	12.50	30.00
14 Jack Morris/100	4.00	10.00
15 Rickey Henderson/25	15.00	40.00
16 Reggie Jackson/50	10.00	25.00
17 Pee Wee Reese/25	12.50	30.00
18 Marty Marion/100	4.00	10.00
19 Tommy John/100	4.00	10.00
20 Roger Maris/25	30.00	60.00
21 Cal Ripken/25	60.00	120.00
22 Red Schoendienst/25	8.00	20.00
23 Willie Stargell/100	6.00	15.00
24 Paul Molitor/100	4.00	10.00
25 Whitey Ford/50	10.00	25.00
26 Alan Trammell/100	4.00	10.00
27 Sammy Sosa/50	8.00	20.00
28 Bobby Doerr/50	6.00	15.00
29 Rod Carew/100	6.00	15.00
30 Yogi Berra/15	20.00	50.00
31 Phil Rizzuto/25	12.50	30.00
32 George Brett/25	30.00	60.00

2004 Donruss Classics Classic Singles Jersey-Bat

PRINT RUNS B/WN 5-25 COPIES PER
NO PRICING ON QTY OF 10 OR LESS
PRIME PRINT RUN 1 SERIAL #'d SET
NO PRIME PRICING DUE TO SCARCITY
ALL ARE JSY-BAT COMBOS UNLESS NOTED

1 Babe Ruth Pants/5		
2 Nolan Ryan/25	30.00	60.00
3 Stan Musial/15	40.00	80.00
4 Ted Williams/10		
5 Lou Gehrig Pants/10		
6 Eddie Murray/25	20.00	50.00
7 Roy Campanella Pants/25	20.00	50.00
8 Robin Yount/25	20.00	50.00
9 Roberto Clemente/25	125.00	200.00
10 Don Mattingly/25	40.00	80.00
12 Carl Yastrzemski/25	30.00	60.00
13 Mark Grace/25	15.00	40.00
15 Rickey Henderson/25	20.00	50.00
16 Reggie Jackson/25	15.00	40.00
17 Pee Wee Reese/25	15.00	40.00
20 Roger Maris/15	60.00	120.00
21 Cal Ripken/25	75.00	150.00
23 Willie Stargell/25	15.00	40.00
24 Paul Molitor/25	10.00	25.00
26 Alan Trammell/25	10.00	25.00
27 Sammy Sosa/25	20.00	50.00
28 Bobby Doerr/25	10.00	25.00
29 Rod Carew/25	15.00	40.00
30 Yogi Berra/15	30.00	60.00
32 George Brett/25	40.00	80.00

2004 Donruss Classics Dress Code Bat

STATED PRINT RUN 50 SERIAL #'d SETS
S.STEWART PRINT 10 SERIAL #'d CARDS
*DC COMBO MTRL: .5X TO 1.2X BASIC
DC COMBO MTRL PRINT 50 SERIAL #'d SETS
DC COMBO MTRL STEWART 10 #'d CARDS
RANDOM INSERTS IN PACKS
NO S.STEWART PRICING DUE TO SCARCITY

1 Derek Jeter	15.00	40.00
2 Kerry Wood	4.00	10.00
3 Nomar Garciaparra	8.00	20.00
4 Jacque Jones	4.00	10.00
5 Mark Teixeira	6.00	15.00
6 Troy Glaus	4.00	10.00
7 Todd Helton	6.00	15.00
8 Miguel Tejada	4.00	10.00
9 Mike Piazza	8.00	20.00
11 Mike Sweeney	4.00	10.00
12 Albert Pujols	10.00	25.00
13 Rickey Henderson	6.00	15.00
14 Chipper Jones	6.00	15.00
15 Don Mattingly	20.00	50.00
16 Shawn Green	4.00	10.00
17 Mark Grace	6.00	15.00
18 Jason Giambi	4.00	10.00
19 Barry Zito	4.00	10.00
20 Sammy Sosa	6.00	15.00
22 Rafael Palmeiro	6.00	15.00
23 Frank Thomas	6.00	15.00
24 Manny Ramirez	6.00	15.00
25 Mike Mussina	6.00	15.00
26 Magglio Ordonez	4.00	10.00
27 Rocco Baldelli	4.00	10.00
28 Andruw Jones	6.00	15.00
29 Torii Hunter	4.00	10.00
30 Ivan Rodriguez	6.00	15.00
31 Jeff Bagwell	6.00	15.00
32 Mark Mulder	4.00	10.00
33 Trot Nixon	4.00	10.00
34 Cal Ripken	40.00	80.00
35 Dontrelle Willis	6.00	15.00
36 Hank Blalock	4.00	10.00
37 Brandon Webb	4.00	10.00
38 Miguel Cabrera	6.00	15.00
39 Hideo Nomo	6.00	15.00
40 Shannon Stewart/10		
41 Tim Hudson	4.00	10.00
42 Pedro Martinez	6.00	15.00
43 Hee Seop Choi	4.00	10.00
44 Randy Johnson	6.00	15.00
45 Tony Gwynn	10.00	25.00
46 Mark Prior	6.00	15.00
47 Eric Chavez	4.00	10.00
48 Alex Rodriguez	6.00	15.00
50 Alfonso Soriano	4.00	10.00

2004 Donruss Classics Dress Code Combos Signature

PRINT RUNS B/WN 1-25 COPIES PER
NO PRICING ON QTY OF 10 OR LESS
PRIME PRINT RUN 1 SERIAL #'d SET
NO PRIME PRICING DUE TO SCARCITY
RANDOM INSERTS IN PACKS
2 Kerry Wood Jsy/5
4 Jacque Jones Jsy/25 10.00 25.00
5 Mark Teixeira Jsy/5
6 Troy Glaus Jsy/5
7 Todd Helton Jsy/5
8 Miguel Tejada Jsy/5
9 Mike Piazza Jsy/5
11 Mike Sweeney Jsy/5
13 Rickey Henderson Jsy/5
14 Chipper Jones Jsy/5
15 Don Mattingly Jsy/5
16 Shawn Green Jsy/1
17 Mark Grace Jsy/5
19 Barry Zito Jsy/5
20 Sammy Sosa Jsy/5
21 Jay Gibbons Jsy/25 10.00 25.00
22 Rafael Palmeiro Jsy/5
23 Frank Thomas Jsy/5
25 Mike Mussina Jsy/5
26 Magglio Ordonez Jsy/5
27 Rocco Baldelli Jsy/10
28 Andruw Jones Jsy/5
29 Torii Hunter Jsy/10
30 Ivan Rodriguez Jsy/5
31 Jeff Bagwell Jsy/5
32 Mark Mulder Jsy/25 10.00 25.00
33 Trot Nixon Jsy/25 10.00 25.00
34 Cal Ripken Jsy/5
35 Dontrelle Willis Jsy/25 15.00 40.00
36 Hank Blalock Jsy/10
37 Brandon Webb Jsy/10
38 Miguel Cabrera Jsy/25 15.00 40.00
39 Hideo Nomo Jsy/5
40 Shannon Stewart Jsy/25 10.00 25.00
41 Tim Hudson Jsy/10
42 Pedro Martinez Jsy/5
44 Randy Johnson Jsy/5
45 Tony Gwynn Jsy/5
46 Mark Prior Jsy/10
47 Eric Chavez Jsy/10
48 Alex Rodriguez Jsy/5
49 Johan Santana Jsy/25 15.00 40.00

2004 Donruss Classics Dress Code Jersey

STATED PRINT RUN 100 SERIAL #'d SETS
RIPKEN PRINT RUN 25 SERIAL #'d CARDS
*NUMBER: .4X TO 1X BASIC
*NUMBER RIPKEN: .15X TO .4X BASIC RIPKEN
NUMBER PRINT RUN 100 SERIAL #'d SETS
*PRIME: 1.5X TO 4X BASIC
*PRIME MATTINGLY: .75X TO 2X BASIC MATT
*PRIME RIPKEN: .6X TO 1.2X BASIC RIPKEN
PRIME PRINT RUN 25 SERIAL #'d SETS
PRIME SORIANO PRINT 12 #'d CARDS
NO PRIME SORIANO PRICING AVAILABLE
1 Derek Jeter 12.50 30.00
2 Kerry Wood 3.00 8.00
3 Nomar Garciaparra 6.00 15.00
4 Jacque Jones 3.00 8.00
5 Mark Teixeira 4.00 10.00
6 Troy Glaus 3.00 8.00
7 Todd Helton 4.00 10.00
8 Miguel Tejada 3.00 8.00
9 Mike Piazza 6.00 15.00
11 Mike Sweeney 3.00 8.00
12 Albert Pujols 8.00 20.00
13 Rickey Henderson 4.00 10.00
14 Chipper Jones 4.00 10.00
15 Don Mattingly 15.00 40.00
16 Shawn Green 3.00 8.00
17 Mark Grace 4.00 10.00
18 Jason Giambi 3.00 8.00
19 Barry Zito 3.00 8.00
20 Sammy Sosa 4.00 10.00
21 Jay Gibbons 3.00 8.00
22 Rafael Palmeiro 4.00 10.00
23 Frank Thomas 4.00 10.00
24 Manny Ramirez 4.00 10.00
25 Mike Mussina 4.00 10.00
26 Magglio Ordonez 3.00 8.00
27 Rocco Baldelli 3.00 8.00
28 Andruw Jones 4.00 10.00
29 Torii Hunter 3.00 8.00
30 Ivan Rodriguez 4.00 10.00
31 Jeff Bagwell 4.00 10.00
32 Mark Mulder 3.00 8.00
33 Trot Nixon 3.00 8.00
34 Cal Ripken/25 60.00 120.00
35 Dontrelle Willis 4.00 10.00
36 Hank Blalock 3.00 8.00
37 Brandon Webb 3.00 8.00
38 Miguel Cabrera 4.00 10.00
39 Hideo Nomo 4.00 10.00
40 Shannon Stewart 3.00 8.00
41 Tim Hudson 3.00 8.00
42 Pedro Martinez 4.00 10.00
43 Hee Seop Choi 3.00 8.00
44 Randy Johnson 4.00 10.00
45 Tony Gwynn 8.00 20.00
46 Mark Prior 4.00 10.00
47 Eric Chavez 3.00 8.00
48 Alex Rodriguez 4.00 10.00
49 Johan Santana 4.00 10.00
50 Alfonso Soriano 3.00 8.00

2004 Donruss Classics Famous Foursomes

STATED PRINT RUN 99 SERIAL #'d SETS
1 Roy Campanella 4.00 10.00
Pee Wee Reese
Jackie Robinson
Duke Snider
2 Stan Musial 10.00 25.00
Bob Gibson
Red Schoendienst
Ken Boyer

2004 Donruss Classics Famous Foursomes Jersey

STATED PRINT RUN 10 SERIAL #'d SETS
PRIME PRINT RUN 1 SERIAL #'d SET
NO PRIME PRICING DUE TO SCARCITY
RANDOM INSERTS IN PACKS
ALL ARE QUAD JSY CARDS UNLESS NOTED
1 Roy Campanella Pants
Pee Wee Reese
Jackie Robinson
Duke Snider
2 Stan Musial
Bob Gibson
Red Schoendienst
Ken Boyer

2004 Donruss Classics Legendary Hats Material

PRINT RUNS B/WN 5-25 COPIES PER
NO PRICING ON QTY OF 10 OR LESS
1 Tony Gwynn/10
2 Mike Schmidt/25 40.00 80.00
6 George Brett/25 40.00 80.00
14 Cal Ripken/25 75.00 150.00
16 Kirby Puckett/25 20.00 50.00
20 Reggie Jackson Yanks/25 15.00 40.00
21 Roberto Clemente/5
22 Ernie Banks/25 20.00 50.00
29 Dave Winfield/25 10.00 25.00
40 Wade Boggs/25 15.00 40.00
42 Rickey Henderson A's/25 20.00 50.00
49 Reggie Jackson Angels/25 15.00 40.00
51 Rafael Palmeiro/25 15.00 40.00
52 Sammy Sosa/25 20.00 50.00
55 Steve Carlton/25 10.00 25.00
56 Rod Carew Angels/25 15.00 40.00
60 R.Henderson Angels/25 20.00 50.00

2004 Donruss Classics Legendary Jackets Material

STATED PRINT RUN 100 SERIAL #'d SETS
2 Mike Schmidt 15.00 40.00
8 Reggie Jackson A's 6.00 15.00
17 Don Mattingly 15.00 40.00
32 Gary Carter 4.00 10.00
54 Nolan Ryan 20.00 50.00
56 Rod Carew Angels 6.00 15.00

2004 Donruss Classics Legendary Jerseys Material

PRINT RUNS B/WN 5-50 COPIES PER
NO PRICING ON QTY OF 10 OR LESS
PRIME PRINT RUN 1 SERIAL #'d SET
NO PRIME PRICING DUE TO SCARCITY
1 Tony Gwynn/50 10.00 25.00
2 Mike Schmidt/25 30.00 60.00
3 Johnny Bench/50 10.00 25.00
4 Roger Maris Yanks/10
5 Ted Williams/10
6 George Brett/25 30.00 60.00
7 Carlton Fisk/50 10.00 25.00
8 Reggie Jackson A's/25 12.50 30.00
9 Joe Morgan/25 8.00 20.00
10 Bo Jackson/25 15.00 40.00
11 Stan Musial/10
12 Andre Dawson/50 6.00 15.00
13 R.Henderson Yanks/25 15.00 40.00
14 Cal Ripken/25 60.00 120.00
15 Dale Murphy/25 12.50 30.00
16 Kirby Puckett/50 12.50 30.00
17 Don Mattingly/50 20.00 50.00
18 Brooks Robinson/50 10.00 25.00
19 Orlando Cepeda/50 6.00 15.00
20 Reggie Jackson Yanks/25 12.50 30.00
21 Roberto Clemente/25 60.00 120.00
22 Ernie Banks/10
23 Frank Robinson/50 6.00 15.00
24 Harmon Killebrew/50 12.50 30.00
25 Willie Stargell/50 10.00 25.00
26 Al Kaline/15 20.00 50.00
27 Carl Yastrzemski/50 15.00 40.00
28 Duke Snider/10
29 Dave Winfield/50 6.00 15.00
30 Eddie Murray/50 12.50 30.00
31 Eddie Mathews/25 15.00 40.00
32 Gary Carter/50 6.00 15.00
33 Rod Carew Twins/25 12.50 30.00
35 Mel Ott/10
36 Paul Molitor/50 6.00 15.00
37 Thurman Munson/15 20.00 50.00
39 Robin Yount/50 12.50 30.00
40 Wade Boggs/50 10.00 25.00
41 Jackie Robinson/5
42 Rickey Henderson A's/25 15.00 40.00
44 Yogi Berra/15 20.00 50.00
46 Luis Aparicio/50 6.00 15.00
47 Phil Rizzuto/25 12.50 30.00
48 Roger Maris A's/25 30.00 60.00
49 Reggie Jackson Angels/50 10.00 25.00
50 Lou Gehrig/5
51 Rafael Palmeiro/50 10.00 25.00
52 Sammy Sosa/50 12.50 30.00
53 Roger Clemens/50 12.50 30.00
54 Nolan Ryan/50 20.00 50.00
55 Steve Carlton/50 6.00 15.00
56 Rod Carew Angels/50 10.00 25.00
57 Whitey Ford/25 12.50 30.00
59 Babe Ruth/5

2004 Donruss Classics Legendary Jerseys Material Number

*NUMBER p/r 50: .4X TO 1X BASIC p/r 50
*NUMBER p/r 25: .5X TO 1.2X BASIC p/r 50
*NUMBER p/r 25: .4X TO 1X BASIC p/r 25
*NUMBER p/r 15: .5X TO 1.2X BASIC p/r 25
*NUMBER p/r 15: .4X TO 1X BASIC p/r 15
PRINT RUNS B/WN 3-50 COPIES PER
NO PRICNG ON QTY OF 10 OR LESS
45 Roy Campanella Pants/25 15.00 40.00
58 Fergie Jenkins Pants/25 8.00 20.00

2004 Donruss Classics Legendary Leather Material

PRINT RUNS B/WN 5-25 COPIES PER
NO PRICING ON QTY OF 10 OR LESS
1 Tony Gwynn Fld Glv/10
2 Mike Schmidt Fld Glv/10
16 Kirby Puckett Fld Glv/25 20.00 50.00
17 Don Mattingly Btg Glv/10
29 Dave Winfield Fld Glv/10
32 Gary Carter Fld Glv/25 10.00 25.00
34 Jimmie Foxx Fld Glv/10
51 Rafael Palmeiro Fld Glv/25 15.00 40.00
52 Sammy Sosa Btg Glv/25 20.00 50.00
54 Nolan Ryan Fld Glv/5
55 Steve Carlton Fld Glv/25 10.00 25.00
58 Fergie Jenkins Fld Glv/25 10.00 25.00

2004 Donruss Classics Legendary Lumberjacks

STATED PRINT RUN 1000 SERIAL #'d SETS
*HATS: 1.5X TO 4X LUMBERJACKS
HATS PRINT RUN 50 SERIAL #'d SETS
*JACKETS: 1.5X TO 4X LUMBERJACKS
JACKET PRINT RUN 50 SERIAL #'d SETS
*JERSEYS: .6X TO 1.5X LUMBERJACKS
JERSEY PRINT RUN 500 SERIAL #'d SETS
*LEATHER: 1.2X TO 3X LUMBERJACKS
LEATHER PRINT RUN 100 SERIAL #'d SETS
*PANTS: 1.5X TO 4X LUMBERJACKS
PANTS PRINT RUN 50 SERIAL #'d SETS
*SPIKES: 1.25X TO 3X LUMBERJACKS
SPIKES PRINT RUN 100 SERIAL #'d SETS
1 Tony Gwynn 1.25 3.00
2 Mike Schmidt 2.00 5.00
3 Johnny Bench 1.25 3.00
4 Roger Maris Yanks 1.25 3.00
5 Ted Williams 3.00 8.00
6 George Brett 2.50 6.00
7 Carlton Fisk .75 2.00
8 Reggie Jackson A's .75 2.00
9 Joe Morgan .50 1.25
10 Bo Jackson 1.25 3.00
11 Stan Musial 2.00 5.00
12 Andre Dawson .75 2.00
13 Rickey Henderson Yanks 1.25 3.00
14 Cal Ripken 5.00 12.00
15 Dale Murphy .75 2.00
16 Kirby Puckett 1.25 3.00
17 Don Mattingly 2.50 6.00
18 Brooks Robinson .75 2.00
19 Orlando Cepeda .50 1.25
20 Reggie Jackson Yanks .75 2.00
21 Roberto Clemente 3.00 8.00
22 Ernie Banks 1.25 3.00
23 Frank Robinson .75 2.00
24 Harmon Killebrew 1.25 3.00
25 Willie Stargell .75 2.00
26 Al Kaline 1.25 3.00
27 Carl Yastrzemski 1.25 3.00
28 Duke Snider .75 2.00
29 Dave Winfield .50 1.25
30 Eddie Murray 1.25 3.00
31 Eddie Mathews 1.25 3.00
32 Gary Carter .50 1.25
33 Rod Carew Twins .75 2.00
34 Jimmie Foxx 1.25 3.00
35 Mel Ott 1.25 3.00
36 Paul Molitor 1.25 3.00
37 Thurman Munson 1.25 3.00
38 Rogers Hornsby .75 2.00
39 Robin Yount 1.25 3.00
40 Wade Boggs .75 2.00
41 Jackie Robinson 1.25 3.00
42 Rickey Henderson A's 1.25 3.00
43 Ty Cobb 2.00 5.00
44 Yogi Berra 1.25 3.00
45 Roy Campanella 1.25 3.00
46 Luis Aparicio .50 1.25
47 Phil Rizzuto .75 2.00
48 Roger Maris A's 1.25 3.00
49 Reggie Jackson Angels .75 2.00
50 Lou Gehrig 2.50 6.00
51 Rafael Palmeiro .75 2.00
52 Sammy Sosa 1.25 3.00
53 Roger Clemens 1.50 4.00
54 Nolan Ryan 4.00 10.00
55 Steve Carlton .50 1.25
56 Rod Carew Angels .75 2.00
57 Whitey Ford .75 2.00
58 Fergie Jenkins .50 1.25
59 Babe Ruth 3.00 8.00
60 R.Henderson Angels 1.25 3.00

2004 Donruss Classics Legendary Lumberjacks Material

RANDOM INSERTS IN PACKS
PRINT RUNS B/WN 10-100 COPIES PER
NO PRICING ON QTY OF 10 OR LESS
1 Tony Gwynn/100 8.00 20.00
2 Mike Schmidt/100 10.00 25.00
3 Johnny Bench/100 6.00 15.00
4 Roger Maris Yanks/25 30.00 60.00
5 Ted Williams/25 60.00 120.00
6 George Brett/100 10.00 25.00
7 Carlton Fisk/100 6.00 15.00
8 Reggie Jackson A's/100 6.00 15.00
9 Joe Morgan/100 4.00 10.00
10 Bo Jackson/100 8.00 20.00
11 Stan Musial/25 20.00 50.00
12 Andre Dawson/100 4.00 10.00
13 R.Henderson Yanks/100 8.00 20.00
14 Cal Ripken/100 20.00 50.00
15 Dale Murphy/100 6.00 15.00
16 Kirby Puckett/100 8.00 20.00
17 Don Mattingly/100 10.00 25.00
18 Brooks Robinson/100 6.00 15.00
19 Orlando Cepeda/100 4.00 10.00
20 Reggie Jackson Yanks/100 6.00 15.00
21 Roberto Clemente/25 50.00 100.00
22 Ernie Banks/100 8.00 20.00
23 Frank Robinson/100 4.00 10.00
24 Harmon Killebrew/100 8.00 20.00
25 Willie Stargell/100 6.00 15.00
26 Al Kaline/100 8.00 20.00
27 Carl Yastrzemski/100 12.50 30.00
28 Duke Snider/10
29 Dave Winfield/100 4.00 10.00
30 Eddie Murray/100 8.00 20.00
31 Eddie Mathews/50 12.50 30.00
32 Gary Carter/100 4.00 10.00
33 Rod Carew Twins/100 6.00 15.00
34 Jimmie Foxx/10
35 Mel Ott/25 15.00 40.00
36 Paul Molitor/100 4.00 10.00
37 Thurman Munson/50 10.00 25.00
38 Rogers Hornsby/25 40.00 80.00
39 Robin Yount/100 8.00 20.00
40 Wade Boggs/100 6.00 15.00
42 Rickey Henderson A's/50 12.50 30.00
43 Ty Cobb/10
44 Yogi Berra/25 15.00 40.00
45 Roy Campanella/25 15.00 40.00
46 Luis Aparicio/100 4.00 10.00
48 Roger Maris A's/25 30.00 60.00
49 Reggie Jackson Angels/100 6.00 15.00
50 Lou Gehrig/25 125.00 200.00
51 Rafael Palmeiro/100 6.00 15.00
52 Sammy Sosa/100 8.00 20.00
56 Rod Carew Angels/100 6.00 15.00
59 Babe Ruth/10
60 R.Henderson Angels/100 8.00 20.00

2004 Donruss Classics Legendary Pants Material

RANDOM INSERTS IN PACKS
PRINT RUNS B/WN 3-50 COPIES PER
NO PRICING ON QTY OF 10 OR LESS
1 Tony Gwynn/25 15.00 40.00
12 Andre Dawson/25 8.00 20.00
24 Harmon Killebrew/50 12.50 30.00
26 Al Kaline/50 12.50 30.00
35 Mel Ott/10
43 Ty Cobb/5

45 Roy Campanella/25 15.00 40.00
46 Luis Aparicio/50 6.00 15.00
47 Phil Rizzuto/50 10.00 25.00
48 Roger Maris A's/25 30.00 60.00
50 Lou Gehrig/4
51 Rafael Palmeiro/25 12.50 30.00
56 Rod Carew Angels/50 10.00 25.00
57 Whitey Ford/25 12.50 30.00
58 Fergie Jenkins/25 8.00 20.00
59 Babe Ruth/3

2004 Donruss Classics Legendary Spikes Material

RANDOM INSERTS IN PACKS
NO PRICING ON QTY OF 10 OR LESS
13 R.Henderson Yanks/25 20.00 50.00
17 Don Mattingly/50 40.00 80.00
29 Dave Winfield/50 8.00 20.00
42 Rickey Henderson A's/25 20.00 50.00
51 Rafael Palmeiro/25 15.00 40.00
52 Sammy Sosa/50 15.00 40.00
56 Rod Carew Angels/10
60 R.Henderson Angels/25 20.00 50.00

2004 Donruss Classics Membership

STATED PRINT RUN 2499 SERIAL #'d SETS
1 Stan Musial 1.50 4.00
2 Ted Williams 2.50 6.00
3 Early Wynn .40 1.00
4 Roberto Clemente 2.50 6.00
5 Al Kaline 1.00 2.50
6 Bob Gibson .60 1.50
7 Lou Brock .60 1.50
8 Carl Yastrzemski 1.00 2.50
9 Gaylord Perry .40 1.00
10 Fergie Jenkins .40 1.00
11 Steve Carlton .40 1.00
12 Reggie Jackson .60 1.50
13 Rod Carew .60 1.50
14 Bert Blyleven .40 1.00
15 Mike Schmidt 1.50 4.00
16 Nolan Ryan 3.00 8.00
17 Robin Yount 1.00 2.50
18 George Brett 2.00 5.00
19 Eddie Murray 1.00 2.50
20 Tony Gwynn 1.00 2.50
21 Cal Ripken 4.00 10.00
22 Randy Johnson 1.00 2.50
23 Sammy Sosa 1.00 2.50
24 Rafael Palmeiro .60 1.50
25 Roger Clemens 1.25 3.00

2004 Donruss Classics Membership VIP Bat

PRINT RUNS B/WN 10-25 COPIES PER
NO PRICING ON QTY OF 10 OR LESS
1 Stan Musial/25 20.00 50.00
2 Ted Williams/25 60.00 120.00
4 Roberto Clemente/25 50.00 100.00
5 Al Kaline/25 15.00 40.00
7 Lou Brock/25 12.50 30.00
8 Carl Yastrzemski/25 20.00 50.00
11 Steve Carlton/25 8.00 20.00
12 Reggie Jackson/25 12.50 30.00
13 Rod Carew/25 12.50 30.00
15 Mike Schmidt/25 30.00 60.00
16 Nolan Ryan/10
17 Robin Yount/25 15.00 40.00
18 George Brett/10
19 Eddie Murray/25 15.00 40.00
20 Tony Gwynn/25 15.00 40.00
21 Cal Ripken/10
22 Randy Johnson/25 15.00 40.00
23 Sammy Sosa/25 15.00 40.00
24 Rafael Palmeiro/25 12.50 30.00
25 Roger Clemens/25 15.00 40.00

2004 Donruss Classics Membership VIP Combos Material

PRINT RUNS B/WN 9-25 COPIES PER
NO PRICING ON QTY OF 10 OR LESS
PRIME PRINT RUN 1 SERIAL #'d SET
NO PRIME PRICING DUE TO SCARCITY
RANDOM INSERTS IN PACKS
1 Stan Musial Bat-Jsy/15 40.00 80.00
2 Ted Williams Bat-Jsy/9
4 Rob Clemente Bat-Jsy/25 125.00 200.00
5 Al Kaline Bat-Pants/25 20.00 50.00
7 Lou Brock Bat-Jsy/10
8 Carl Yastrzemski Bat-Jsy/25 30.00 60.00
10 F.Jenkins Fld Glv-Pants/25 10.00 25.00
11 Steve Carlton Bat-Jsy/25 10.00 25.00
12 Reggie Jackson Bat-Jsy/25 15.00 40.00
13 Rod Carew Bat-Pants/25 15.00 40.00
15 Mike Schmidt Bat-Jsy/25 40.00 80.00
16 Nolan Ryan Bat-Jsy/25 30.00 60.00
17 Robin Yount Bat-Jsy/25 20.00 50.00
18 George Brett Bat-Jsy/25 40.00 80.00
19 Eddie Murray Bat-Jsy/25 20.00 50.00
20 Tony Gwynn Bat-Jsy/25 30.00 60.00
21 Cal Ripken Bat-Jsy/25 75.00 150.00
22 Randy Johnson Bat-Jsy/25 20.00 50.00
23 Sammy Sosa Bat-Jsy/25 20.00 50.00
24 Rafael Palmeiro Bat-Jsy/25 15.00 40.00
25 Roger Clemens Bat-Jsy/25 20.00 50.00

2004 Donruss Classics Membership VIP Combos Signature

PRINT RUNS B/WN 1-50 COPIES PER
NO PRICING ON QTY OF 5 OR LESS
PRIME PRINT RUN 1 SERIAL #'d SET
NO PRIME PRICING DUE TO SCARCITY
1 Stan Musial Jsy/5
5 Al Kaline Pants/25 60.00 120.00
6 Bob Gibson Jsy/5
7 Lou Brock Jsy/5
8 Carl Yastrzemski Jsy/5
9 Gaylord Perry Jsy/50 10.00 25.00
10 Fergie Jenkins Pants/50 15.00 40.00
11 Steve Carlton Jsy/25 20.00 50.00
12 Reggie Jackson Jsy/5
13 Rod Carew Pants/5
14 Bert Blyleven Jsy/50 10.00 25.00
16 Nolan Ryan Jsy/5
17 Robin Yount Jsy/5
18 George Brett Jsy/5
19 Eddie Murray Jsy/5
20 Tony Gwynn Jsy/5
21 Cal Ripken Jsy/5
22 Randy Johnson Jsy/5
23 Sammy Sosa Jsy/5
24 Rafael Palmeiro Jsy/5
25 Roger Clemens Jsy/1

2004 Donruss Classics Membership VIP Jersey

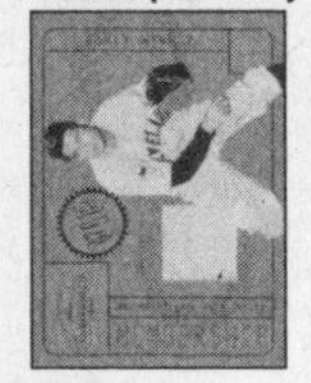

PRINT RUNS B/WN 9-25 COPIES PER
NO PRICING ON QTY OF 10 OR LESS
PRIME PRINT RUN 1 SERIAL #'d SET
NO PRIME PRICING DUE TO SCARCITY
RANDOM INSERTS IN PACKS
1 Stan Musial/15 30.00 60.00
2 Ted Williams/9
3 Early Wynn/10
4 Roberto Clemente/25 60.00 120.00
5 Al Kaline Pants/25 15.00 40.00
6 Bob Gibson/10
7 Lou Brock/10
8 Carl Yastrzemski/25 20.00 50.00
9 Gaylord Perry/25 8.00 20.00
10 Fergie Jenkins Pants/25 8.00 20.00
11 Steve Carlton/25 8.00 20.00
12 Reggie Jackson/25 12.50 30.00
13 Rod Carew/25 12.50 30.00
14 Bert Blyleven/25 8.00 20.00
15 Mike Schmidt/25 30.00 60.00
16 Nolan Ryan/25 30.00 60.00
17 Robin Yount/25 15.00 40.00
18 George Brett/25 30.00 60.00
19 Eddie Murray/25 15.00 40.00
20 Tony Gwynn/25 15.00 40.00
21 Cal Ripken/25 60.00 120.00
22 Randy Johnson/25 15.00 40.00
23 Sammy Sosa/25 15.00 40.00
24 Rafael Palmeiro/25 12.50 30.00
25 Roger Clemens/25 15.00 40.00

2004 Donruss Classics Membership VIP Signatures

RANDOM INSERTS IN PACKS
PRINT RUNS B/WN 1-50 COPIES PER
NO PRICING ON QTY OF 5 OR LESS
1 Stan Musial/5
5 Al Kaline/20 40.00 80.00
6 Bob Gibson/5
7 Lou Brock/5
8 Carl Yastrzemski/5
9 Gaylord Perry/50 6.00 15.00
10 Fergie Jenkins/50 10.00 25.00
11 Steve Carlton/20 12.50 30.00
12 Reggie Jackson/5
13 Rod Carew/5
14 Bert Blyleven/50 6.00 15.00
16 Nolan Ryan/5
17 Robin Yount/5
18 George Brett/5
19 Eddie Murray/5
20 Tony Gwynn/5
21 Cal Ripken/5
22 Randy Johnson/5
23 Sammy Sosa/5
24 Rafael Palmeiro/5
25 Roger Clemens/1

2004 Donruss Classics October Heroes

STATED PRINT RUN 2499 SERIAL #'d SETS
1 Reggie Jackson 1.00 2.50
2 Bob Gibson 1.00 2.50
3 Carlton Fisk 1.00 2.50
4 Whitey Ford 1.00 2.50
5 George Brett 3.00 8.00
6 Roberto Clemente 4.00 10.00
7 Roy Campanella 1.50 4.00
8 Babe Ruth 4.00 10.00

2004 Donruss Classics October Heroes Bat

PRINT RUNS B/WN 10-25 COPIES PER
NO PRICING 0ON QTY OF 10 OR LESS
1 Reggie Jackson/25 12.50 30.00
3 Carlton Fisk/25 12.50 30.00
5 George Brett/10
6 Roberto Clemente/25 50.00 100.00
7 Roy Campanella/25 15.00 40.00
8 Babe Ruth/10

2004 Donruss Classics October Heroes Combos Material

PRINT RUNS B/WN 3-25 COPIES PER
NO PRICING ON QTY OF 5 OR LESS
PRIME PRINT RUN 1 SERIAL #'d SET
NO PRIME PRICING DUE TO SCARCITY
RANDOM INSERTS IN PACKS
1 Reggie Jackson Bat-Hat/25 15.00 40.00
3 Carlton Fisk Bat-Jsy/25 15.00 40.00
5 George Brett Bat-Jsy/25 40.00 80.00
6 Roberto Clemente Bat-Jsy/5
7 R.Campanella Bat-Pants/25 20.00 50.00
8 Babe Ruth Bat-Pants/3

2004 Donruss Classics October Heroes Combos Signature

PRINT RUNS B/WN 5-50 COPIES PER
NO PRICING ON QTY OF 5 OR LESS
PRIME PRINT RUN 1 SERIAL #'d SET
NO PRIME PRICING DUE TO SCARCITY
RANDOM INSERTS IN PACKS
1 Reggie Jackson Bat/5
2 Bob Gibson Jsy/5
3 Carlton Fisk Jsy/5
4 Whitey Ford Jsy/50 30.00 60.00
5 George Brett Jsy/5

2004 Donruss Classics October Heroes Fabric

PRINT RUNS B/WN 5-25 COPIES PER
NO PRICING ON QTY OF 5 OR LESS
PRIME PRINT RUN 1 SERIAL #'d SET
NO PRIME PRICING DUE TO SCARCITY
2 Bob Gibson Jsy/15 15.00 40.00
3 Carlton Fisk Jsy/25 12.50 30.00
4 Whitey Ford Jsy/25 12.50 30.00
5 George Brett Jsy/25 30.00 60.00
6 Roberto Clemente Jsy/5
7 Roy Campanella Pants/25 15.00 40.00
8 Babe Ruth Pants/5

2004 Donruss Classics October Heroes Signature

PRINT RUNS B/WN 5-50 COPIES PER
NO PRICING ON QTY OF 5 OR LESS

1 Reggie Jackson/5
2 Bob Gibson/5
3 Carlton Fisk/5
4 Whitey Ford/50 15.00 40.00
5 George Brett/5

2004 Donruss Classics Team Colors Bat

RANDOM INSERTS IN PACKS
PRINT RUNS B/WN 10-50 COPIES PER
NO PRICING ON QTY OF 10 OR LESS
2 Steve Garvey/50 6.00 15.00
3 Eric Davis/25 12.50 30.00
4 Al Oliver/50 4.00 10.00
5 Nolan Ryan/10
6 Bobby Doerr/25 8.00 20.00
7 Paul Molitor/50 6.00 15.00
8 Dale Murphy/50 10.00 25.00
11 Jose Canseco/50 10.00 25.00
12 Jim Rice/50 6.00 15.00
13 Will Clark/50 20.00 50.00
14 Alan Trammell/50 6.00 15.00
16 Dwight Evans/50 10.00 25.00
18 Dave Parker Pirates/25 8.00 20.00
21 Andre Dawson Expos/50 6.00 15.00
22 Darryl Strawberry Dgr/50 6.00 15.00
23 George Foster/50 4.00 10.00
26 Bo Jackson/50 12.50 30.00
27 Cal Ripken/50 40.00 80.00
28 Deion Sanders/25 12.50 30.00
29 Don Mattingly/50 20.00 50.00
30 Mark Grace/50 10.00 25.00
31 Fred Lynn/50 4.00 10.00
33 Ernie Banks/25 15.00 40.00
34 Gary Carter/50 6.00 15.00
35 Roger Maris/25 30.00 60.00
36 Ron Santo/50 10.00 25.00
38 Tony Gwynn/50 10.00 25.00
40 Red Schoendienst/25 8.00 20.00
41 Steve Carlton/25 8.00 20.00
42 Wade Boggs/25 12.50 30.00
44 Luis Aparicio/25 8.00 20.00
46 Andre Dawson Cubs/25 8.00 20.00
48 Darryl Strawberry Mets/50 6.00 15.00
49 Dave Parker Reds/50 6.00 15.00

2004 Donruss Classics Team Colors Combos Material

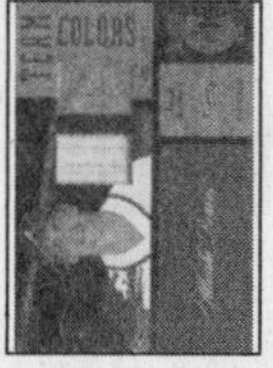

STATED PRINT RUN 25 SERIAL #'d SETS
MARIS PRINT RUN 10 SERIAL #'d CARDS
NO MARIS PRICING DUE TO SCARCITY
PRIME PRINT RUN 1 SERIAL #'d SET
NO PRIME PRICING DUE TO SCARCITY
RANDOM INSERTS IN PACKS
2 Steve Garvey Bat-Jsy 10.00 25.00
3 Eric Davis Bat-Jsy 15.00 40.00
5 Nolan Ryan Bat-Jsy 30.00 60.00
6 Bobby Doerr Bat-Jsy 10.00 25.00
7 Paul Molitor Bat-Jsy 10.00 25.00
8 Dale Murphy Bat-Jsy 15.00 40.00
11 Jose Canseco Bat-Jsy 15.00 40.00
12 Jim Rice Bat-Jsy 10.00 25.00
13 Will Clark Bat-Jsy 40.00 80.00
14 Alan Trammell Bat-Jsy 10.00 25.00
16 Dwight Evans Bat-Jsy 15.00 40.00
18 Dave Parker Pirates Bat-Jsy 10.00 25.00
21 Andre Dawson Expos Bat-Jsy 10.00 25.00
22 Darryl Strawberry Dgr Bat-Jsy 10.00 25.00
23 George Foster Bat-Jsy 8.00 20.00
26 Bo Jackson Bat-Jsy 20.00 50.00
27 Cal Ripken Bat-Jsy 75.00 150.00
28 Deion Sanders Bat-Jsy 15.00 40.00
29 Don Mattingly Bat-Jsy 40.00 80.00
30 Mark Grace Bat-Jsy 15.00 40.00
33 Ernie Banks Bat-Jsy 20.00 50.00
34 Gary Carter Bat-Jacket 10.00 25.00
35 Roger Maris Bat-Jsy/10
38 Tony Gwynn Bat-Jsy 30.00 60.00
40 Red Schoendienst Bat-Jsy 10.00 25.00
41 Steve Carlton Bat-Jsy 10.00 25.00
42 Wade Boggs Bat-Jsy 15.00 40.00
44 Luis Aparicio Bat-Jsy 10.00 25.00
46 Andre Dawson Cubs Bat-Jsy 10.00 25.00
48 D.Strawberry Mets Bat-Jsy 10.00 25.00
49 Dave Parker Reds Bat-Jsy 10.00 25.00

2004 Donruss Classics Team Colors Combos Signature

PRINT RUNS B/WN 2-100 COPIES PER
NO PRICING ON QTY OF 10 OR LESS
PRIME PRINT RUN 1 SERIAL #'d SET
NO PRIME PRICING DUE TO SCARCITY
RANDOM INSERTS IN PACKS
1 L.Dykstra Mets Fld Glv/100 10.00 25.00
2 Steve Garvey Jsy/100 10.00 25.00
3 Eric Davis Jsy/100 15.00 40.00
4 Al Oliver Bat/100 10.00 25.00
5 Nolan Ryan Jsy/5
6 Bobby Doerr Jsy/100 10.00 25.00
7 Paul Molitor Jsy/10
8 Dale Murphy Jsy/10
9 Harold Baines Jsy/100 10.00 25.00
10 Dwight Gooden Jsy/100 10.00 25.00
11 Jose Canseco Jsy/10
12 Jim Rice Jsy/100 10.00 25.00
13 Will Clark Jsy/10
14 Alan Trammell Jsy/100 10.00 25.00
15 Lee Smith Jsy/100 10.00 25.00
16 Dwight Evans Jsy/100 15.00 40.00
17 Tony Oliva Jsy/100 10.00 25.00
18 Dave Parker Pirates Jsy/100 10.00 25.00
19 Jack Morris Jsy/100 10.00 25.00
20 Luis Tiant Jsy/100 10.00 25.00
21 Andre Dawson Expos Jsy/50 15.00 40.00
22 D.Strawberry Dgr Jsy/100 10.00 25.00
23 George Foster Jsy/100 10.00 25.00
24 Marty Marion Jsy/100 10.00 25.00
25 Dennis Eckersley Jsy/100 15.00 40.00
26 Bo Jackson Jsy/10
27 Cal Ripken Jsy/5
28 Deion Sanders Jsy/5
29 Don Mattingly Jacket/10
30 Mark Grace Jsy/10
31 Fred Lynn Jsy/100 10.00 25.00
32 Enos Slaughter Jsy/2
33 Ernie Banks Jsy/25 60.00 120.00
34 Gary Carter Jacket/50 15.00 40.00
36 Ron Santo Bat/25 20.00 50.00
37 Keith Hernandez Jsy/25 20.00 50.00
38 Tony Gwynn Jsy/5
39 Jim Palmer Jsy/50 15.00 40.00
40 Red Schoendienst Jsy/100 10.00 25.00
41 Steve Carlton Jsy/50 15.00 40.00
42 Wade Boggs Jsy/5
43 Tommy John Jsy/100 10.00 25.00
44 Luis Aparicio Jsy/100 10.00 25.00
45 Bob Feller Jsy/100 10.00 25.00
46 Andre Dawson Cubs Jsy/50 15.00 40.00
47 Bert Blyleven Jsy/100 10.00 25.00
48 D.Strawberry Mets Jsy/100 10.00 25.00
49 Dave Parker Reds Jsy/100 10.00 25.00
50 L.Dykstra Phils Btg Glv/30 20.00 50.00

2004 Donruss Classics Team Colors Jersey

PRINT RUNS B/WN 10-100 COPIES PER
NO PRICING ON QTY OF 10 OR LESS
PRIME PRINT RUN 1 SERIAL #'d SET
NO PRIME PRICING DUE TO SCARCITY
RANDOM INSERTS IN PACKS
1 L.Dykstra Mets Fld Glv/25 8.00 20.00
2 Steve Garvey/100 4.00 10.00
3 Eric Davis/25 12.50 30.00
5 Nolan Ryan/50 20.00 50.00
6 Bobby Doerr/25 8.00 20.00
7 Paul Molitor/100 4.00 10.00
8 Dale Murphy/50 10.00 25.00
9 Harold Baines/100 6.00 15.00
10 Dwight Gooden/50 6.00 15.00
11 Jose Canseco/100 6.00 15.00
12 Jim Rice/100 4.00 10.00
13 Will Clark/50 20.00 50.00
14 Alan Trammell/100 4.00 10.00
15 Lee Smith/100 4.00 10.00
16 Dwight Evans/50 10.00 25.00
17 Tony Oliva/100 4.00 10.00
18 Dave Parker Pirates/25 8.00 20.00
19 Jack Morris/100 4.00 10.00
20 Luis Tiant/100 4.00 10.00
21 Andre Dawson Expos/100 4.00 10.00
22 Darryl Strawberry Dgr/100 4.00 10.00
23 George Foster/100 4.00 10.00
24 Marty Marion/50 6.00 15.00
25 Dennis Eckersley/100 4.00 10.00
26 Bo Jackson/50 12.50 30.00
27 Cal Ripken/100 20.00 50.00
28 Deion Sanders/50 10.00 25.00
29 Don Mattingly Jacket/100 15.00 40.00
30 Mark Grace/50 10.00 25.00
31 Fred Lynn/50 6.00 15.00
32 Enos Slaughter/10
33 Ernie Banks/25 15.00 40.00
34 Gary Carter Jacket/100 4.00 10.00
35 Roger Maris/10
37 Keith Hernandez/25 8.00 20.00
38 Tony Gwynn/50 10.00 25.00
39 Jim Palmer/25 8.00 20.00
40 Red Schoendienst/25 8.00 20.00
41 Steve Carlton/25 8.00 20.00
42 Wade Boggs/25 12.50 30.00
43 Tommy John/100 4.00 10.00
44 Luis Aparicio/25 8.00 20.00
45 Bob Feller/10
46 Andre Dawson Cubs/25 8.00 20.00
47 Bert Blyleven/100 4.00 10.00
48 Darryl Strawberry Mets/100 4.00 10.00
49 Dave Parker Reds/100 4.00 10.00

2004 Donruss Classics Team Colors Signatures

RANDOM INSERTS IN PACKS
PRINT RUNS B/WN 1-50 COPIES PER
NO PRICING ON QTY OF 10 OR LESS
1 Len Dykstra Mets/50 10.00 25.00
2 Steve Garvey/50 10.00 25.00
3 Eric Davis/50 15.00 40.00
4 Al Oliver/50 6.00 15.00
5 Nolan Ryan/5
6 Bobby Doerr/50 10.00 25.00
7 Paul Molitor/5
8 Dale Murphy/5
9 Harold Baines/50 10.00 25.00

10 Dwight Gooden/50 10.00 25.00
11 Jose Canseco/5
12 Jim Rice/50 10.00 25.00
13 Will Clark/5
14 Alan Trammell/50 10.00 25.00
15 Lee Smith/50 10.00 25.00
16 Dwight Evans/50 15.00 40.00
17 Tony Oliva/50 10.00 25.00
18 Dave Parker Pirates/50 10.00 25.00
19 Jack Morris/50 6.00 15.00
20 Luis Tiant/50 6.00 15.00
21 Andre Dawson Expos/25 12.50 30.00
22 Darryl Strawberry Dgr/50 10.00 25.00
23 George Foster/50 6.00 15.00
24 Marty Marion/50 10.00 25.00
25 Dennis Eckersley/50 15.00 40.00
26 Bo Jackson/5
27 Cal Ripken/5
28 Deion Sanders/5
29 Don Mattingly/5
30 Mark Grace/5
31 Fred Lynn/50 6.00 15.00
32 Enos Slaughter/1
33 Ernie Banks/10
34 Gary Carter/20 12.50 30.00
36 Ron Santo/10
37 Keith Hernandez/25 12.50 30.00
38 Tony Gwynn/5
39 Jim Palmer/20 12.50 30.00
40 Red Schoendienst/50 10.00 25.00
41 Steve Carlton/20 12.50 30.00
42 Wade Boggs/5
43 Tommy John/50 6.00 15.00
44 Luis Aparicio/50 10.00 25.00
45 Bob Feller/50 10.00 25.00
46 Andre Dawson Cubs/25 12.50 30.00
47 Bert Blyleven/50 10.00 25.00
48 Darryl Strawberry Mets/50 10.00 25.00
49 Dave Parker Reds/50 10.00 25.00
50 Len Dykstra Phils/50 10.00 25.00

2004 Donruss Classics Timeless Triples

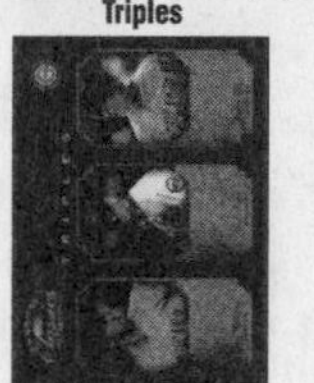

STATED PRINT RUN 500 SERIAL #'d SETS
1 Ted Williams 5.00 12.00
Carl Yastrzemski
Carlton Fisk
2 Lou Gehrig 2.00 5.00
Roger Maris
Thurman Munson
3 Brooks Robinson 1.25 3.00
Frank Robinson
Cal Ripken
4 Roger Clemens 1.25 3.00
Andy Pettitte
Roy Oswalt
5 Greg Maddux 3.00 8.00
Mark Prior
Kerry Wood
6 Alex Rodriguez 5.00 12.00
Derek Jeter
Gary Sheffield

2004 Donruss Classics Timeless Triples Bat

1 Ted Williams 150.00 250.00
Carl Yastrzemski
Carlton Fisk
2 Lou Gehrig 175.00 300.00
Roger Maris
Thurman Munson
3 Brooks Robinson 100.00 175.00
Frank Robinson
Cal Ripken

2004 Donruss Classics Timeless Triples Jersey

PRINT RUNS B/WN 10-25 COPIES PER
NO PRICING ON QTY OF 10 OR LESS
ALL ARE JSY SWATCHES UNLESS NOTED
GEHRIG IS PANTS SWATCH
PRIME PRINT RUN 1 SERIAL #'d SET
NO PRIME PRICING DUE TO SCARCITY
RANDOM INSERTS IN PACKS
1 Ted Williams
Carl Yastrzemski
Carlton Fisk/10
2 Lou Gehrig Pants
Roger Maris
Thurman Munson/10
3 Brooks Robinson 125.00 200.00
Frank Robinson
Cal Ripken/25

2005 Donruss Classics

This 242-card set was released in March, 2005. The set was issued in five card packs with a $6 SRP which came 18 packs to a box and 16 boxes to a case. The first 200 cards in the set features active veterans while cards 201-225 feature autographed Rookie Cards and cards 226 through 250 feature cards of retired supestars. Please note that cards 203, 209, 211, 212, 214, 216, 220 and 222 were never produced. The Rookie cards are signed and issued to a different amount of cards while the retired veterans were issued to a state print run of 1000 serial numbered sets.

COMP.SET w/o SP's (200) 15.00 40.00
COMMON CARD (1-200) .25 .60
COM AU p/r 1200-1500 3.00 8.00
COM AU p/r 750-785 3.00 8.00
COM AU p/r 400 4.00 10.00
AU 201-225 OVERALL AU-GU ODDS 1:6
AU 201-225 PRINT RUN B/WN 400-1500 PER
COMMON CARD (226-250) .75 2.00
226-250 OVERALL INSERT ODDS 1:2
226-250 PRINT RUN 1000 SERIAL #'d SETS
1 Scott Rolen .40 1.00
2 Derek Jeter 1.50 4.00
3 Jose Vidro .25 .60
4 Johnny Damon .40 1.00
5 Nomar Garciaparra .60 1.50
6 Jose Guillen .25 .60
7 Trot Nixon .25 .60
8 Mark Loretta .25 .60
9 Jody Gerut .25 .60
10 Miguel Tejada .40 1.00
11 Barry Larkin .40 1.00
12 Jeff Kent .25 .60
13 Carl Crawford .40 1.00
14 Paul Konerko .40 1.00
15 Jim Edmonds .40 1.00
16 Garret Anderson .25 .60
17 Jay Gibbons .25 .60
18 Moises Alou .25 .60
19 Mike Lowell .25 .60
20 Mark Mulder .25 .60
21 Josh Beckett .40 1.00
22 Tim Salmon .25 .60
23 Shannon Stewart .25 .60
24 Miguel Cabrera .60 1.50
25 Jim Thome .40 1.00
26 Kevin Youkilis .25 .60
27 Justin Morneau .60 1.50
28 Austin Kearns .25 .60
29 Cliff Lee .40 1.00
30 Ken Griffey Jr. 1.00 2.50
31 Mike Piazza .60 1.50
32 Roy Halladay .60 1.50
33 Larry Walker .40 1.00
34 David Ortiz .60 1.50
35 Dontrelle Willis .25 .60
36 Craig Wilson .25 .60
37 Jeff Suppan .25 .60
38 Curt Schilling .40 1.00
39 Larry Bigbie .25 .60
40 Rich Harden .25 .60
41 Victor Martinez .40 1.00
42 Jorge Posada .40 1.00
43 Joey Gathright .25 .60
44 Adam Dunn .40 1.00
45 Pedro Martinez .40 1.00
46 Dallas McPherson .25 .60
47 Tom Glavine .40 1.00
48 Torii Hunter .25 .60
49 Angel Berroa .25 .60
50 Mark Prior .40 1.00
51 Ichiro Suzuki 1.00 2.50
52 C.C. Sabathia .40 1.00
53 Bobby Abreu .25 .60
54 Shigetoshi Hasegawa .25 .60
55 Brandon Webb .40 1.00
56 Mark Buehrle .40 1.00
57 Johan Santana .60 1.50
58 Francisco Rodriguez .40 1.00
59 Roy Oswalt .40 1.00
60 Mike Sweeney .25 .60
61 Jake Peavy .25 .60
62 Akinori Otsuka .25 .60
63 Dioner Navarro .25 .60
64 Kazuhito Tadano .25 .60
65 Ryan Wagner .25 .60
66 Abe Alvarez .25 .60
67 Mark Teixeira .60 1.50
68 Jermaine Dye .25 .60
69 Todd Walker .25 .60
70 Octavio Dotel .25 .60
71 Frank Thomas .60 1.50
72 Javy Lopez .25 .60
73 Scott Podsednik .25 .60
74 B.J. Upton .40 1.00
75 Barry Zito .25 .60
76 Raul Ibanez .25 .60
77 Orlando Cabrera .25 .60
78 Sean Burroughs .25 .60
79 Esteban Loaiza .25 .60
80 Jason Schmidt .25 .60
81 Vinny Castilla .25 .60
82 Shingo Takatsu .25 .60
83 Juan Pierre .25 .60
84 David Dellucci .25 .60
85 Travis Blackley .25 .60
86 Brad Penny .25 .60
87 Nick Johnson .25 .60
88 Brian Roberts .25 .60
89 Kazuo Matsui .25 .60
90 Mike Lieberthal .25 .60
91 Craig Biggio .40 1.00
92 Sean Casey .25 .60
93 Andy Pettitte .40 1.00
94 Milton Bradley .25 .60
95 Rocco Baldelli .25 .60
96 Adrian Gonzalez .40 1.00
97 Chad Tracy .25 .60
98 Chad Cordero .25 .60
99 Albert Pujols 1.50 4.00
100 Jason Kubel .25 .60
101 Rafael Furcal .25 .60
102 Jack Wilson .25 .60
103 Eric Chavez .25 .60
104 Casey Kotchman .25 .60
105 Jeff Bagwell .40 1.00
106 Melvin Mora .25 .60
107 Bobby Crosby .25 .60
108 Preston Wilson .25 .60
109 Hank Blalock .25 .60
110 Vernon Wells .25 .60
111 Francisco Cordero .25 .60
112 Steve Finley .25 .60
113 Omar Vizquel .40 1.00
114 Eric Byrnes .25 .60
115 Tim Hudson .40 1.00
116 Aramis Ramirez .25 .60
117 Lance Berkman .40 1.00
118 Shea Hillenbrand .25 .60
119 Aubrey Huff .25 .60
120 Lew Ford .25 .60
121 Sammy Sosa .60 1.50
122 Marcus Giles .25 .60
123 Rickie Weeks .40 1.00
124 Manny Ramirez .60 1.50
125 Jason Giambi .25 .60
126 Adam LaRoche .25 .60
127 Vladimir Guerrero .60 1.50
128 Ken Harvey .25 .60
129 Adrian Beltre .25 .60
130 Magglio Ordonez .40 1.00
131 Greg Maddux 1.00 2.50
132 Russ Ortiz .25 .60
133 Jason Varitek .60 1.50
134 Kerry Wood .25 .60
135 Mike Mussina .40 1.00
136 Joe Nathan .25 .60
137 Troy Glaus .25 .60
138 Carlos Zambrano .40 1.00
139 Ben Sheets .25 .60
140 Jae Weong Seo .25 .60
141 Derrek Lee .25 .60
142 Carlos Beltran .25 .60
143 John Lackey .25 .60
144 Aaron Rowand .25 .60
145 Dewon Brazelton .25 .60
146 Jason Bay .25 .60
147 Alfonso Soriano .40 1.00
148 Travis Hafner .25 .60
149 Ryan Church .25 .60
150 Bret Boone .25 .60
151 Bernie Williams .40 1.00
152 Wade Miller .25 .60
153 Zack Greinke .40 1.00
154 Scott Kazmir .60 1.50
155 Hideki Matsui 1.00 2.50
156 Livan Hernandez .25 .60
157 Jose Capellan .25 .60
158 David Wright 1.00 2.50
159 Chone Figgins .25 .60
160 Jeremy Reed .25 .60
161 J.D. Drew .25 .60
162 Hideo Nomo .60 1.50
163 Merkin Valdez .25 .60
164 Shawn Green .25 .60
165 Alexis Rios .40 1.00
166 Johnny Estrada .25 .60
167 Danny Graves .25 .60
168 Carlos Lee .25 .60
169 John Van Benschoten .25 .60
170 Randy Johnson .60 1.50
171 Randy Wolf .25 .60
172 Luis Gonzalez .25 .60
173 Chipper Jones .60 1.50
174 Delmon Young .60 1.50
175 Edwin Jackson .25 .60
176 Carlos Delgado .25 .60
177 Matt Clement .25 .60
178 Jacque Jones .25 .60
179 Gary Sheffield .25 .60
180 Laynce Nix .25 .60
181 Tom Gordon .25 .60
182 Jose Castillo .25 .60
183 Andruw Jones .25 .60
184 Brian Giles .25 .60
185 Paul Lo Duca .25 .60
186 Roger Clemens .75 2.00
187 Todd Helton .40 1.00
188 Keith Foulke .25 .60
189 Jeremy Bonderman .25 .60
190 Troy Percival .25 .60
191 Michael Young .40 1.00
192 Carlos Guillen .25 .60
193 Rafael Palmeiro .40 1.00
194 Brett Myers .25 .60
195 Carl Pavano .25 .60
196 Alex Rodriguez 1.00 2.50
197 Lyle Overbay .25 .60
198 Ivan Rodriguez .40 1.00
199 Khalil Greene .25 .60
200 Edgar Renteria .25 .60
201 Justin Verlander AU/400 RC 20.00 50.00
202 Miguel Negron AU/1300 RC 4.00 10.00
204 Paul Reynoso AU/1200 RC 3.00 8.00
205 Colter Bean AU/1200 RC 4.00 10.00
206 Raul Tablado AU/1200 RC 3.00 8.00
207 M.McLemore AU/1500 RC 3.00 8.00
208 Russ Rohlicek AU/1200 RC 3.00 8.00
210 Chris Seddon AU/785 RC 3.00 8.00
213 Mike Morse AU/1200 RC 4.00 10.00
215 R.Messenger AU/1200 RC 3.00 8.00
217 Carlos Ruiz AU/1200 RC 4.00 10.00
218 Chris Roberson AU/1200 RC 3.00 8.00
219 Ryan Speier AU/1200 RC 3.00 8.00
223 Dave Gassner AU/1200 RC 3.00 8.00
224 Sean Tracey AU/1200 RC 3.00 8.00
225 C.Rogowski AU/1500 RC 4.00 10.00
226 Billy Williams LGD .75 2.00
227 Ralph Kiner LGD .75 2.00
228 Ozzie Smith LGD 3.00 8.00
229 Rod Carew LGD 1.25 3.00
230 Nolan Ryan LGD 5.00 12.00
231 Fergie Jenkins LGD .75 2.00
232 Paul Molitor LGD 2.00 5.00
233 Carlton Fisk LGD 1.25 3.00
234 Rollie Fingers LGD .75 2.00
235 Lou Brock LGD 1.25 3.00
236 Gaylord Perry LGD .75 2.00
237 Don Mattingly LGD 4.00 10.00
238 Maury Wills LGD .75 2.00
239 Luis Aparicio LGD .75 2.00
240 George Brett LGD 4.00 10.00
241 Mike Schmidt LGD 4.00 10.00
242 Joe Morgan LGD .75 2.00
243 Dennis Eckersley LGD .75 2.00
244 Reggie Jackson LGD 2.00 5.00
245 Bobby Doerr LGD .75 2.00
246 Bob Feller LGD .75 2.00
247 Cal Ripken LGD 8.00 20.00
248 Harmon Killebrew LGD 2.00 5.00
249 Frank Robinson LGD 1.25 3.00
250 Stan Musial LGD 3.00 8.00

2005 Donruss Classics Significant Signatures Gold

*GOLD p/r 100: .5X TO 1.2X SILV p/r 200
*GOLD p/r 50: .6X TO 1.5X SILV p/r 200
*GOLD p/r 50: .5X TO 1.2X SILV p/r 100
*GOLD p/r 25: .5X TO 1.2X SILV p/r 50
OVERALL AU-GU ODDS 1:6
PRINT RUNS B/WN 1-100 COPIES PER
NO PRICING ON QTY OF 10 OR LESS

2005 Donruss Classics Significant Signatures Platinum

OVERALL AU-GU ODDS 1:6
STATED PRINT RUN 1 SERIAL #'d SET
NO PRICING DUE TO SCARCITY

2005 Donruss Classics Significant Signatures Silver

OVERALL AU-GU ODDS 1:6
PRINT RUNS B/WN 1-200 COPIES PER
1-200/226-250 NO PRICING ON 10 OR LESS
201-225 NO PRICING ON QTY OF 25
1 Scott Rolen/1
3 Jose Vidro/10
6 Jose Guillen/10
7 Trot Nixon/10
8 Mark Loretta/10
9 Jody Gerut/10
11 Barry Larkin/1
14 Paul Konerko/10
15 Jim Edmonds/1
16 Garret Anderson/10
17 Jay Gibbons/25 6.00 15.00
19 Mike Lowell/1
21 Josh Beckett/1
22 Tim Salmon/100 10.00 25.00
23 Shannon Stewart/10
24 Miguel Cabrera/10
26 Kevin Youkilis/25 6.00 15.00
28 Austin Kearns/10
29 Cliff Lee/200 8.00 20.00
32 Roy Halladay/1
34 David Ortiz/10
35 Dontrelle Willis/1
36 Craig Wilson/1
37 Jeff Suppan/200 6.00 15.00
38 Curt Schilling/1
39 Larry Bigbie/100 6.00 15.00
40 Rich Harden/100 6.00 15.00
41 Victor Martinez/25 10.00 25.00
43 Joey Gathright/100 4.00 10.00
44 Adam Dunn/5
45 Pedro Martinez/1
47 Tom Glavine/1
48 Torii Hunter/5
49 Angel Berroa/10
50 Mark Prior/1
52 C.C. Sabathia/10
54 Shigetoshi Hasegawa/10
55 Brandon Webb/10
56 Mark Buehrle/10
57 Johan Santana/10
58 Francisco Rodriguez/10
61 Jake Peavy/25 15.00 40.00
62 Akinori Otsuka/10
63 Dioner Navarro/100 6.00 15.00
64 Kazuhito Tadano/100 10.00 25.00
65 Ryan Wagner/50 5.00 12.00
66 Abe Alvarez/100 6.00 15.00
68 Jermaine Dye/25 10.00 25.00
69 Todd Walker/25 6.00 15.00
70 Octavio Dotel/25 10.00 25.00
71 Frank Thomas/1
73 Scott Podsednik/25 15.00 40.00
74 B.J. Upton/10
75 Barry Zito/1
77 Orlando Cabrera/25 10.00 25.00
78 Sean Burroughs/10
79 Esteban Loaiza/50 8.00 20.00
82 Shingo Takatsu/10
84 David Dellucci/50 12.50 30.00
85 Travis Blackley/200 4.00 10.00
86 Brad Penny/25 6.00 15.00
87 Nick Johnson/10
88 Brian Roberts/100 6.00 15.00
90 Mike Lieberthal/25 10.00 25.00
91 Craig Biggio/1
92 Sean Casey/10
94 Milton Bradley/100 6.00 15.00
96 Adrian Gonzalez/200 10.00 25.00
97 Chad Tracy/100 4.00 10.00
98 Chad Cordero/100 6.00 15.00
99 Albert Pujols/1
100 Jason Kubel/200 4.00 10.00
101 Rafael Furcal/10
102 Jack Wilson/100 6.00 15.00
103 Eric Chavez/1
104 Casey Kotchman/100 6.00 15.00
105 Jeff Bagwell/1
106 Melvin Mora/100 6.00 15.00
107 Bobby Crosby/100 6.00 15.00
110 Vernon Wells/1
111 Francisco Cordero/50 8.00 20.00
112 Steve Finley/10
113 Omar Vizquel/10
114 Eric Byrnes/50 5.00 12.00
115 Tim Hudson/1
116 Aramis Ramirez/10
117 Lance Berkman/1
118 Shea Hillenbrand/25 10.00 25.00
119 Aubrey Huff/25 10.00 25.00
120 Lew Ford/25 6.00 15.00
121 Sammy Sosa/1
123 Rickie Weeks/10
124 Manny Ramirez/1
126 Adam LaRoche/25 6.00 15.00
128 Ken Harvey/50 5.00 12.00
129 Adrian Beltre/10
130 Magglio Ordonez/10
131 Greg Maddux/1
132 Russ Ortiz/25 6.00 15.00
134 Kerry Wood/1
135 Mike Mussina/1
136 Joe Nathan/100 10.00 25.00
138 Carlos Zambrano/25 15.00 40.00
139 Ben Sheets/10
140 Jae Weong Seo/10
141 Derrek Lee/10
143 John Lackey/200 6.00 15.00
145 Dewon Brazelton/200 4.00 10.00
146 Jason Bay/25 10.00 25.00
147 Alfonso Soriano/1
148 Travis Hafner/100 6.00 15.00
152 Wade Miller/50 5.00 12.00
154 Scott Kazmir/25 10.00 25.00
156 Livan Hernandez/25 10.00 25.00
157 Jose Capellan/10
158 David Wright/25 60.00 120.00
159 Chone Figgins/50 5.00 12.00
162 Hideo Nomo/1
163 Merkin Valdez/200 4.00 10.00
164 Shawn Green/1
165 Alexis Rios/50 8.00 20.00
166 Johnny Estrada/200 4.00 10.00
167 Danny Graves/50 5.00 12.00
168 Carlos Lee/25 10.00 25.00
170 Randy Johnson/1
171 Randy Wolf/25 10.00 25.00
173 Chipper Jones/1
174 Delmon Young/10
175 Edwin Jackson/25 6.00 15.00
177 Matt Clement/10
178 Jacque Jones/25 10.00 25.00
179 Gary Sheffield/1
180 Laynce Nix/200 4.00 10.00
181 Tom Gordon/25 10.00 25.00
182 Jose Castillo/100 4.00 10.00
185 Paul Lo Duca/10
186 Roger Clemens/1
187 Todd Helton/1
188 Keith Foulke/25 15.00 40.00
189 Jeremy Bonderman/50 8.00 20.00
190 Troy Percival/25 10.00 25.00
191 Michael Young/10
193 Rafael Palmeiro/1
194 Brett Myers/50 8.00 20.00
197 Lyle Overbay/25 6.00 15.00
200 Edgar Renteria/10
201 Justin Verlander/25
202 Miguel Negron/100 5.00 12.00
204 Paulino Reynoso/100 4.00 10.00
205 Colter Bean/100 5.00 12.00
206 Raul Tablado/100 4.00 10.00
207 Mark McLemore/100 4.00 10.00
208 Russ Rohlicek/100 4.00 10.00
210 Chris Seddon/100 4.00 10.00
213 Mike Morse/100 5.00 12.00
217 Carlos Ruiz/100 5.00 12.00
218 Chris Roberson/100 4.00 10.00
219 Ryan Speier/100 4.00 10.00
221 Ambiorix Burgos/100 4.00 10.00
223 Dave Gassner/100 4.00 10.00
224 Sean Tracey/100 4.00 10.00
225 Casey Rogowski/100 5.00 12.00
226 Billy Williams LGD/10
227 Ralph Kiner LGD/10
228 Ozzie Smith LGD/10
229 Rod Carew LGD/5
230 Nolan Ryan LGD/5
231 Fergie Jenkins LGD/10
232 Paul Molitor LGD/10
233 Carlton Fisk LGD/5
234 Rollie Fingers LGD/10
235 Lou Brock LGD/10
236 Gaylord Perry LGD/25 10.00 25.00
237 Don Mattingly LGD/5
238 Maury Wills LGD/10
239 Luis Aparicio LGD/10
240 George Brett LGD/5
241 Mike Schmidt LGD/5
243 Dennis Eckersley LGD/10
244 Reggie Jackson LGD/5
245 Bobby Doerr LGD/25 10.00 25.00
246 Bob Feller LGD/25 15.00 40.00
247 Cal Ripken LGD/5
248 Harmon Killebrew LGD/10
249 Frank Robinson LGD/10
250 Stan Musial LGD/5

2005 Donruss Classics Timeless Tributes Gold

*GOLD 1-200: 3X TO 8X BASIC
*GOLD 226-250: 1.5X TO 4X BASIC
OVERALL INSERT ODDS 1:2
STATED PRINT RUN 50 SERIAL #'d SETS

2005 Donruss Classics Timeless Tributes Platinum

OVERALL INSERT ODDS 1:2
STATED PRINT RUN 1 SERIAL #'d SET
NO PRICING DUE TO SCARCITY

2005 Donruss Classics Timeless Tributes Silver

*SILV 1-200: 2X TO 5X BASIC
*SILV 201-225: .15X TO .4X AU p/r 1200-1500
*SILV 201-225: .15X TO .4X AU p/r 750-785
*SILV 201-225: .12X TO .3X AU p/r 400
*SILV 226-250: 1X TO 2.5X BASIC
OVERALL INSERT ODDS 1:2
STATED PRINT RUN 100 SERIAL #'d SETS

2005 Donruss Classics Classic Combos

STATED PRINT RUN 400 SERIAL #'d SETS
*GOLD: 1.5X TO 4X BASIC
GOLD PRINT RUN 25 SERIAL #'d SETS
PLATINUM PRINT RUN 1 SERIAL #'d SET
NO PLATINUM PRICING DUE TO SCARCITY
OVERALL INSERT ODDS 1:2
33 Babe Ruth 6.00 15.00
Ted Williams
34 Roberto Clemente 6.00 15.00
Vladimir Guerrero
35 Willie Mays 5.00 12.00
Willie McCovey
36 Yogi Berra 2.50 6.00
Mike Piazza
37 Sandy Koufax 8.00 20.00
Nolan Ryan
38 Harmon Killebrew 5.00 12.00
Mike Schmidt
39 Whitey Ford 2.50 6.00
Randy Johnson
40 Cal Ripken 10.00 25.00
George Brett
41 Hank Aaron 5.00 12.00
Stan Musial
42 Carl Yastrzemski 1.50 4.00
Frank Robinson
43 Bob Feller 3.00 8.00
Roger Clemens
44 Bob Gibson 1.50 4.00
Tom Seaver
45 Roger Maris 2.50 6.00
Jim Thome
46 Albert Pujols 6.00 15.00
Don Mattingly
47 Duke Snider 2.50 6.00
Sammy Sosa
48 Rickey Henderson 2.50 6.00
Bo Jackson
49 Ernie Banks 2.50 6.00
Reggie Jackson
50 Burleigh Grimes 4.00 10.00
Greg Maddux

2005 Donruss Classics Classic Combos Bat

OVERALL AU-GU ODDS 1:6
STATED PRINT RUN 5 SERIAL #'d SETS
NO PRICING DUE TO SCARCITY

2005 Donruss Classics Classic Combos Jersey

PRINT RUNS B/WN 5-50 COPIES PER
NO PRICING ON QTY OF 10 OR LESS
PRIME PRINT RUNS B/WN 1-5 COPIES PER
NO PRIME PRICING DUE TO SCARCITY
OVERALL AU-GU ODDS 1:6
33 Babe Ruth
Ted Williams/5
34 Roberto Clemente
Vladimir Guerrero/5
35 Willie Mays
Willie McCovey/10
36 Yogi Berra
Mike Piazza/10
37 Sandy Koufax
Nolan Ryan/10
38 Harmon Killebrew 15.00 40.00
Mike Schmidt/50
39 Whitey Ford 12.50 30.00
Randy Johnson/25
40 Cal Ripken 40.00 80.00
George Brett/50
41 Hank Aaron
Stan Musial/10
43 Bob Feller Pants
Roger Clemens/10
45 Roger Maris 30.00 60.00
Jim Thome/25
46 Albert Pujols 20.00 50.00
Don Mattingly/50
47 Duke Snider 12.50 30.00
Sammy Sosa/25
48 Rickey Henderson 10.00 25.00
Bo Jackson/50
49 Ernie Banks
Reggie Jackson/10
50 Burleigh Grimes Pants
Greg Maddux/10

2005 Donruss Classics Classic Combos Materials

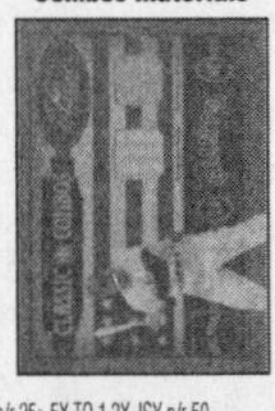

*MTL p/r 25: .5X TO 1.2X JSY p/r 50
PRINT RUNS B/WN 1-25 COPIES PER
NO PRICING ON QTY OF 10 OR LESS
ALL ARE BAT-JSY COMBOS UNLESS NOTED
PRIME PRINT RUN 5 SERIAL #'d SETS
NO PRIME PRICING DUE TO SCARCITY
OVERALL AU-GU ODDS 1:6

2005 Donruss Classics Classic Combos Materials HR

*MTL HR p/r 25: .5X TO 1.2X JSY p/r 50
OVERALL AU-GU ODDS 1:6
PRINT RUNS B/WN 1-25 COPIES PER
ALL ARE BAT-JSY COMBOS UNLESS NOTED
NO PRICING ON QTY OF 10 OR LESS

2005 Donruss Classics Classic Combos Signature

OVERALL AU-GU ODDS 1:6
STATED PRINT RUN 1 SERIAL #'d SET
NO PRICING DUE TO SCARCITY

2005 Donruss Classics Classic Combos Signature Bat

OVERALL AU-GU ODDS 1:6
STATED PRINT RUN 1 SERIAL #'d SET
NO PRICING DUE TO SCARCITY

2005 Donruss Classics Classic Combos Signature Jersey

PRINT RUNS B/WN 1-5 COPIES PER
NO PRICING DUE TO SCARCITY
PRIME PRINT RUN 1 SERIAL #'d SET
NO PRIME PRICING DUE TO SCARCITY
OVERALL AU-GU ODDS 1:6

2005 Donruss Classics Classic Combos Signature Materials

STATED PRINT RUN 1 SERIAL #'d SET
ALL ARE BAT-JSY COMBOS UNLESS NOTED
HR PRINT RUN 1 SERIAL #'d SET
PRIME PRINT RUN 1 SERIAL #'d SET
OVERALL AU-GU ODDS 1:6
NO PRICING DUE TO SCARCITY

2005 Donruss Classics Classic Singles

STATED PRINT RUN 400 SERIAL #'d SETS
*GOLD: 1.5X TO 4X BASIC
GOLD PRINT RUN 25 SERIAL #'d SETS
PLATINUM PRINT RUN 1 SERIAL #'d SET
NO PLATINUM PRICING DUE TO SCARCITY
OVERALL INSERT ODDS 1:2
1 Hank Aaron 5.00 12.00
2 Tom Seaver 1.50 4.00
3 Harmon Killebrew 2.50 6.00
4 Paul Molitor 2.50 6.00
5 Brooks Robinson 1.50 4.00
6 Stan Musial 4.00 10.00
7 Bobby Doerr 1.00 2.50
8 Cal Ripken 10.00 25.00
9 Phil Niekro 1.00 2.50
10 Eddie Murray 2.50 6.00
11 Randy Johnson 2.50 6.00
12 Steve Carlton 1.00 2.50
13 Rickey Henderson 1.50 4.00
14 Ernie Banks 2.50 6.00
15 Curt Schilling 1.50 4.00
16 Whitey Ford 1.50 4.00
17 Al Kaline 2.50 6.00
18 Gary Carter 1.00 2.50
19 Robin Yount 2.50 6.00
20 Johnny Bench 2.50 6.00
21 Bob Feller 1.00 2.50
22 Jim Palmer 1.00 2.50
23 Don Mattingly 5.00 12.00
24 Willie Mays 5.00 12.00
25 Dave Righetti 1.00 2.50
26 Roger Clemens 3.00 8.00
27 Juan Marichal 1.00 2.50
28 Tony Gwynn 3.00 8.00
29 Nolan Ryan 6.00 15.00
30 Carlton Fisk 1.50 4.00
31 Greg Maddux 4.00 10.00
32 Sandy Koufax 8.00 20.00

2005 Donruss Classics Classic Singles Bat

*BAT p/r 50: .5X TO 1.2X JSY p/r 100
*BAT p/r 50: .4X TO 1X JSY p/r 50
*BAT p/r 50: .3X TO .8X JSY p/r 25
*BAT p/r 25: .6X TO 1.5X JSY p/r 100
*BAT p/r 25: .5X TO 1.2X JSY p/r 50
*BAT p/r 25: .4X TO 1X JSY p/r 25
OVERALL AU-GU ODDS 1:6
PRINT RUNS B/WN 25-50 COPIES PER
1 Hank Aaron/25 20.00 50.00
6 Stan Musial/25 12.50 30.00
17 Al Kaline/25 10.00 25.00
24 Willie Mays/25 20.00 50.00

2005 Donruss Classics Classic Singles Jersey

PRINT RUNS B/WN 10-100 COPIES PER
NO PRICING ON QTY OF 10
PRIME PRINT RUNS B/WN 1-5 COPIES PER
NO PRIME PRICING DUE TO SCARCITY
OVERALL AU-GU ODDS 1:6
1 Hank Aaron/10
2 Tom Seaver/25 8.00 20.00
3 Harmon Killebrew/25 10.00 25.00
4 Paul Molitor/50 4.00 10.00
5 Brooks Robinson/50 6.00 15.00
6 Stan Musial/10
7 Bobby Doerr Pants/100 3.00 8.00
8 Cal Ripken/25 40.00 80.00
9 Phil Niekro/50 4.00 10.00
10 Eddie Murray/50 8.00 20.00
11 Randy Johnson/100 6.00 15.00
12 Steve Carlton/25 5.00 12.00
13 Rickey Henderson/100 6.00 15.00
14 Ernie Banks/25 10.00 25.00
15 Curt Schilling/100 5.00 12.00
16 Whitey Ford/25 8.00 20.00
18 Gary Carter/100 3.00 8.00
19 Robin Yount/50 8.00 20.00
20 Johnny Bench/50 8.00 20.00
21 Bob Feller Pants/25 8.00 20.00
22 Jim Palmer/100 3.00 8.00
23 Don Mattingly/100 10.00 25.00
24 Willie Mays/25
25 Dave Righetti/50 4.00 10.00
26 Roger Clemens/25 10.00 25.00
27 Juan Marichal/50 4.00 10.00
28 Tony Gwynn/100 6.00 15.00
29 Nolan Ryan/50 15.00 40.00
30 Carlton Fisk/25 8.00 20.00
31 Greg Maddux/100 6.00 15.00
32 Sandy Koufax/25 75.00 150.00

2005 Donruss Classics Classic Singles Materials

*MTL p/r 25: .75X TO 2X JSY p/r 100
*MTL p/r 25: .6X TO 1.5X JSY p/r 50
*MTL p/r 25: .5X TO 1.2X JSY p/r 25
PRINT RUNS B/WN 10-25 COPIES PER
NO PRICING ON QTY OF 10
PRIME PRINT RUNS B/WN 1-5 COPIES PER
NO PRIME PRICING DUE TO SCARCITY
OVERALL AU-GU ODDS 1:6

2005 Donruss Classics Classic Singles Materials HR

*MTL HR p/r 25: .75X TO 2X JSY p/r 100
*MTL HR p/r 25: .6X TO 1.5X JSY p/r 50
*MTL HR p/r 25: .5X TO 1.2X JSY p/r 25
OVERALL AU-GU ODDS 1:6
PRINT RUNS B/WN 10-25 COPIES PER
NO PRICING ON QTY OF 10

2005 Donruss Classics Classic Singles Signature

OVERALL AU-GU ODDS 1:6
PRINT RUNS B/WN 1-5 COPIES PER
NO PRICING DUE TO SCARCITY

2005 Donruss Classics Classic Singles Signature Bat

OVERALL AU-GU ODDS 1:6
PRINT RUNS B/WN 1-10 COPIES PER
NO PRICING DUE TO SCARCITY

2005 Donruss Classics Classic Singles Signature Jersey

PRINT RUNS B/WN 1-5 COPIES PER
PRIME PRINT RUN 1 SERIAL #'d SET
OVERALL AU-GU ODDS 1:6
NO PRICING DUE TO SCARCITY

2005 Donruss Classics Classic Singles Signature Materials

PRINT RUNS B/WN 1-10 COPIES PER
PRIME PRINT RUNS B/WN 1-5 COPIES PER
OVERALL AU-GU ODDS 1:6
NO PRICING DUE TO SCARCITY

2005 Donruss Classics Classic Singles Signature Materials HR

OVERALL AU-GU ODDS 1:6
PRINT RUNS B/WN 1-10 COPIES PER
NO PRICING DUE TO SCARCITY

2005 Donruss Classics Dress Code Bat

*BAT p/r 100: .3X TO .8X MTL p/r 100
*BAT p/r 50: .3X TO .8X MTL p/r 50
OVERALL AU-GU ODDS 1:6
PRINT RUNS B/WN 50-100 COPIES PER
14 Mark Prior/50 5.00 12.00

2005 Donruss Classics Dress Code Jersey Number

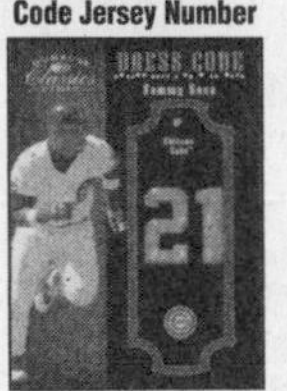

*JSY NBR p/r 38-57: .4X TO 1X MTL p/r 100
*JSY NBR p/r 38-57: .3X TO .8X MTL p/r 50
*JSY NBR p/r 20-34: .5X TO 1.2X MTL p/r 100
*JSY NBR p/r 15-17: .6X TO 1.5X MTL p/r 100
*JSY NBR p/r 15-17: .5X TO 1.2X MTL p/r 50
OVERALL AU-GU ODDS 1:6
PRINT RUNS B/WN 5-57 COPIES PER
NO PRICING ON QTY OF 13 OR LESS
12 Johan Santana/57 5.00 12.00
13 Mark Mulder/20 4.00 10.00
14 Mark Prior/22 6.00 15.00
20 Randy Johnson Pants/51 6.00 15.00
21 Roger Clemens/23 10.00 25.00
24 Tim Hudson/15 5.00 12.00

2005 Donruss Classics Dress Code Jersey Prime

*PRIME: .75X TO 2X MTL p/r 100
*PRIME: .6X TO 1.5X MTL p/r 50
OVERALL AU-GU ODDS 1:6
STATED PRINT RUN 25 SERIAL #'d SETS
3 Carl Crawford 6.00 15.00
12 Johan Santana 10.00 25.00
13 Mark Mulder 6.00 15.00
14 Mark Prior 10.00 25.00
20 Randy Johnson 12.50 30.00
21 Roger Clemens 15.00 40.00
24 Tim Hudson 6.00 15.00

2005 Donruss Classics Dress Code Materials

PRINT RUNS B/WN 5-100 COPIES PER
NO PRICING ON QTY OF 5
PRIME PRINT RUN 5 SERIAL #'d SETS
NO PRIME PRICING DUE TO SCARCITY
OVERALL AU-GU ODDS 1:6
1 Albert Pujols Bat-Jsy/100 10.00 25.00
2 Bernie Williams Bat-Jsy/50 6.00 15.00
4 C.Beltran Bat-Bat/Jsy/100 3.00 8.00
5 Chipper Jones Bat-Jsy/100 6.00 15.00
6 Curt Schilling Bat-Jsy/50 6.00 15.00
7 David Ortiz Bat-Hat/100 5.00 12.00
8 Hank Blalock Bat-Jsy/100 3.00 8.00
9 Hideki Matsui Bat-Jsy/100 15.00 40.00
10 Jim Edmonds Bat-Jsy/100 3.00 8.00
11 Jim Thome Jsy-Jsy/100 5.00 12.00
15 Mark Teixeira Bat-Jsy/100 5.00 12.00
16 Miguel Cabrera Jsy-Jsy/100 5.00 12.00
17 Miguel Tejada Bat-Jsy/100 3.00 8.00
18 Mike Piazza Bat-Jsy/100 6.00 15.00
19 Pedro Martinez Bat-Jsy/100 5.00 12.00
21 Roger Clemens Bat-Jsy/5
22 Sammy Sosa Bat-Jsy/100 6.00 15.00
23 Scott Rolen Bat-Jsy/100 5.00 12.00
25 Todd Helton Jsy-Jsy/50 6.00 15.00
26 Torii Hunter Bat-Jsy/100 3.00 8.00
27 Travis Hafner Jsy-Shoes/50 4.00 10.00
28 Vernon Wells Jsy-Jsy/50 4.00 10.00
29 Victor Martinez Jsy-Jsy/50 4.00 10.00
30 V.Guerrero Bat-Jsy/100 6.00 15.00

2005 Donruss Classics Dress Code Signature Bat

*BAT p/r 25: .4X TO 1X JSY p/r 25
OVERALL AU-GU ODDS 1:6
PRINT RUNS B/WN 1-25 COPIES PER
NO PRICING ON QTY OF 5 OR LESS

2005 Donruss Classics Dress Code Signature Jersey

PRINT RUNS B/WN 5-25 COPIES PER
NO PRICING ON QTY OF 10 OR LESS
PRIME PRINT RUNS B/WN 1-5 COPIES PER
NO PRIME PRICING DUE TO SCARCITY
OVERALL AU-GU ODDS 1:6
1 Albert Pujols/5
5 Chipper Jones/5
6 Curt Schilling/5
7 David Ortiz/25 30.00 60.00
8 Hank Blalock/25 12.50 30.00
10 Jim Edmonds/5
12 Johan Santana/25 20.00 50.00
14 Mark Prior/10
16 Miguel Cabrera/25 20.00 50.00
19 Pedro Martinez/5
20 Randy Johnson/5
21 Roger Clemens/5
22 Sammy Sosa/5
23 Scott Rolen/10
24 Tim Hudson/10
25 Todd Helton/5
26 Torii Hunter/25 12.50 30.00
27 Travis Hafner/25 12.50 30.00
28 Vernon Wells/25 12.50 30.00
29 Victor Martinez/25 12.50 30.00

2005 Donruss Classics Dress Code Signature Jersey Number

*NBR p/r 25: .4X TO 1X JSY p/r 25
OVERALL AU-GU ODDS 1:6
PRINT RUNS B/WN 1-25 COPIES PER
NO PRICING ON QTY OF 10 OR LESS

2005 Donruss Classics Dress Code Signature Materials

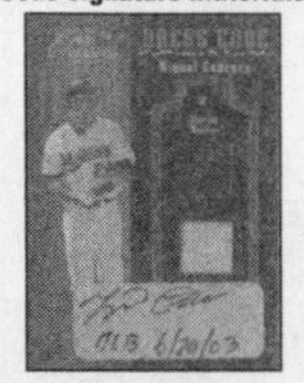

PRINT RUNS B/WN 1-5 COPIES PER
PRIME PRINT RUNS B/WN 1-5 COPIES PER
OVERALL AU-GU ODDS 1:6
NO PRICING DUE TO SCARCITY

2005 Donruss Classics Home Run Heroes

STATED PRINT RUN 1000 SERIAL #'d SETS
*GOLD: 1.5X TO 4X BASIC
GOLD PRINT RUN 50 SERIAL #'d SETS
PLATINUM PRINT RUN 1 SERIAL #'d SET
NO PLATINUM PRICING DUE TO SCARCITY
OVERALL INSERT ODDS 1:2
1 Mike Schmidt 3.00 8.00
2 Ken Griffey Jr. 2.50 6.00
3 Babe Ruth 4.00 10.00
4 Duke Snider 1.00 2.50
5 Johnny Bench 1.50 4.00
6 Stan Musial 2.50 6.00
7 Willie McCovey 1.00 2.50
8 Willie Stargell 1.00 2.50
9 Ted Williams 3.00 8.00
10 Frank Thomas 1.50 4.00
11 Gary Sheffield .60 1.50
12 Jim Thome 1.00 2.50
13 Harmon Killebrew 1.50 4.00
14 Ernie Banks 1.50 4.00
15 George Foster .60 1.50
16 Albert Pujols 4.00 10.00
17 Tony Perez .60 1.50
18 Richie Sexson .60 1.50
19 Juan Gonzalez .60 1.50
20 Frank Robinson 1.00 2.50
21 Sammy Sosa 1.50 4.00
22 Jeff Bagwell 1.00 2.50
23 Mark Teixeira 1.50 4.00
24 Willie Mays 3.00 8.00
25 Rafael Palmeiro 1.00 2.50
26 Billy Williams .60 1.50
27 Vladimir Guerrero 1.50 4.00
28 Gary Carter .60 1.50
29 Fred McGriff 1.00 2.50
30 Orlando Cepeda .60 1.50
31 Dave Winfield .60 1.50
32 Shawn Green .60 1.50
33 Jose Canseco 1.00 2.50
34 Hideki Matsui 2.50 6.00
35 Roger Maris 1.50 4.00
36 Andre Dawson 1.00 2.50
37 Paul Konerko 1.00 2.50
38 Darryl Strawberry .60 1.50
39 Dave Parker .60 1.50
40 Adam Dunn 1.00 2.50
41 Ralph Kiner .60 1.50
42 Miguel Tejada 1.00 2.50
43 Dale Murphy .60 1.50
44 Hank Aaron 3.00 8.00
45 Mike Piazza 1.50 4.00
46 Reggie Jackson 1.50 4.00
47 Adrian Beltre .60 1.50
48 Cal Ripken 6.00 15.00
49 Manny Ramirez 1.50 4.00
50 Alex Rodriguez 2.50 6.00

2005 Donruss Classics Home Run Heroes Bat

*BAT p/r 36-66: .4X TO 1X JSY p/r 38-66
*BAT p/r 36-66: .3X TO .8X JSY p/r 25
*BAT p/r 36-66: .4X TO 1X JSY p/r 38-66
*BAT p/r 19: .4X TO 1X JSY p/r 19

OVERALL AU-GU ODDS 1:6
PRINT RUNS B/WN 4-66 COPIES PER
NO PRICING ON QTY OF 14 OR LESS
3 Babe Ruth/25 125.00 200.00
6 Stan Musial/39 10.00 25.00
17 Tony Perez/24 5.00 12.00
20 Frank Robinson/49 4.00 10.00

2005 Donruss Classics Home Run Heroes Jersey HR

PRINT RUNS B/WN 1-66 COPIES PER
NO PRICING ON QTY OF 14 OR LESS
PRIME PRINT RUN 1 SERIAL #'d SET
NO PRIME PRICING DUE TO SCARCITY
OVERALL AU-GU ODDS 1:6
1 Mike Schmidt/48 12.50 30.00
3 Babe Ruth/25 175.00 300.00
4 Duke Snider Pants/14
5 Johnny Bench/45 8.00 20.00
6 Stan Musial/6
7 Willie McCovey/23 8.00 20.00
8 Willie Stargell/48 6.00 15.00
9 Ted Williams/43 30.00 60.00
10 Frank Thomas/43 6.00 15.00
11 Gary Sheffield/36 3.00 8.00
12 Jim Thome/47 5.00 12.00
13 Harmon Killebrew/49 8.00 20.00
14 Ernie Banks Pants/47 8.00 20.00
15 George Foster/25 5.00 12.00
16 Albert Pujols/46 15.00 40.00
18 Richie Sexson/45 3.00 8.00
19 Juan Gonzalez/47 3.00 8.00
20 Frank Robinson/1
21 Sammy Sosa/66 6.00 15.00
22 Jeff Bagwell/47 5.00 12.00
23 Mark Teixeira/38 5.00 12.00
24 Willie Mays/51 30.00 60.00
25 Rafael Palmeiro/47 5.00 12.00
26 Billy Williams/26 5.00 12.00
27 Vladimir Guerrero/44 6.00 15.00
28 Gary Carter/31 5.00 12.00
29 Fred McGriff/32 6.00 15.00
30 Orlando Cepeda Pants/46 4.00 10.00
31 Dave Winfield/34 5.00 12.00
32 Shawn Green/49 3.00 8.00
33 Jose Canseco/44 8.00 20.00
34 Hideki Matsui Pants/31 30.00 60.00
35 Roger Maris Pants/19 30.00 60.00
36 Andre Dawson/49 4.00 10.00
37 Paul Konerko/14
38 Darryl Strawberry/24 5.00 12.00
39 Dave Parker/34 5.00 12.00
40 Adam Dunn/46 3.00 8.00
42 Miguel Tejada/34 4.00 10.00
43 Dale Murphy/44 6.00 15.00
44 Hank Aaron/47 30.00 60.00
45 Mike Piazza/40 6.00 15.00
46 Reggie Jackson/39 6.00 15.00
47 Adrian Beltre/48 3.00 8.00
48 Cal Ripken/34 30.00 60.00
49 Manny Ramirez/43 5.00 12.00

2005 Donruss Classics Home Run Heroes Materials

*MTL p/r 36-66: .5X TO 1.2X JSY p/r 36-66
*MTL p/r 36-66: .4X TO 1X JSY p/r 25
*MTL p/r 23-34: .5X TO 1.2X JSY p/r 23-34
*MTL p/r 19: .5X TO 1.2X JSY p/r 19
PRINT RUNS B/WN 1-66 COPIES PER
NO PRICING ON QTY OF 14 OR LESS
PRIME PRINT RUN 1 SERIAL #'d SET
NO PRIME PRICING DUE TO SCARCITY
OVERALL AU-GU ODDS 1:6
3 Babe Ruth Bat-Jsy/25 250.00 400.00
17 Tony Perez Bat-Fld Glv/24 6.00 15.00

2005 Donruss Classics Home Run Heroes Signature

OVERALL AU-GU ODDS 1:6
PRINT RUNS B/WN 1-10 COPIES PER
NO PRICING DUE TO SCARCITY

2005 Donruss Classics Home Run Heroes Signature Materials

PRINT RUNS B/WN 1-10 COPIES PER
PRIME PRINT RUN 1 SERIAL #'d SET
OVERALL AU-GU ODDS 1:6
NO PRICING DUE TO SCARCITY

2005 Donruss Classics Legendary Lumberjacks Bat

OVERALL AU-GU ODDS 1:6
PRINT RUNS B/WN 1-50 COPIES PER
NO PRICING ON QTY OF 6 OR LESS
1 Al Kaline/6
2 Babe Ruth/25 125.00 200.00
6 Brooks Robinson/50 6.00 15.00
7 Cal Ripken/50 20.00 50.00
8 Carlton Fisk/50 6.00 15.00
10 Don Mattingly/50 12.50 30.00
12 Eddie Murray/50 8.00 20.00
13 Ernie Banks/50 8.00 20.00
15 Frank Robinson/50 4.00 10.00
17 George Brett/50 12.50 30.00
19 Harmon Killebrew/50 8.00 20.00
21 Joe Morgan/50 4.00 10.00
22 Johnny Bench/50 8.00 20.00
24 Lou Brock/50 6.00 15.00
26 Mike Schmidt/50 12.50 30.00
28 Ozzie Smith/50 10.00 25.00
29 Paul Molitor/50 4.00 10.00
30 Pee Wee Reese/50 6.00 15.00
34 Reggie Jackson/50 6.00 15.00
35 Rickey Henderson/50 8.00 20.00
36 Roberto Clemente/50 40.00 80.00
37 Robin Yount/50 8.00 20.00
38 Rod Carew/50 6.00 15.00
39 Roger Maris/25 20.00 50.00
40 Stan Musial/25 12.50 30.00
42 Ted Williams/25 30.00 60.00
44 Tony Gwynn/50 8.00 20.00
45 Tony Perez/1
46 Wade Boggs/50 6.00 15.00
49 Willie McCovey/50 6.00 15.00
50 Yogi Berra/25 10.00 25.00

2005 Donruss Classics Legendary Lumberjacks Jersey

*JSY p/r 50: .4X TO 1X BAT p/r 50
*JSY p/r 25: .5X TO 1.2X BAT p/r 50
OVERALL AU-GU ODDS 1:6
PRINT RUNS B/WN 1-50 COPIES PER
NO PRICING ON QTY OF 10 OR LESS
3 Billy Williams/25 5.00 12.00
25 Maury Wills/25 5.00 12.00

2005 Donruss Classics Legendary Lumberjacks Jersey HR

*JSY HR p/r 25: .5X TO 1.2X BAT p/r 50
OVERALL AU-GU ODDS 1:6
PRINT RUNS B/WN 1-25 COPIES PER
NO PRICING ON QTY OF 10 OR LESS
45 Tony Perez/25 5.00 12.00

2005 Donruss Classics Legendary Lumberjacks Materials

*MTL p/r 44-50: .5X TO 1.2X BAT p/r 50
OVERALL AU-GU ODDS 1:6
PRINT RUNS B/WN - COPIES PER
NO PRICING ON QTY OF 10 OR LESS
*MTL p/r 25: .6X TO 1.5X BAT p/r 50
2 Babe Ruth Bat-Jsy/25 250.00 400.00

2005 Donruss Classics Legendary Players

STATED PRINT RUN 800 SERIAL #'d SETS
*GOLD: 1.25X TO 3X BASIC
GOLD PRINT RUN 75 SERIAL #'d SETS
PLATINUM PRINT RUN 1 SERIAL #'d SET
NO PLATINUM PRICING DUE TO SCARCITY
*LUMBERJACK: .6X TO 1.5X BASIC
LUMBERJACK PRINT RUN 400 #'d SETS
OVERALL INSERT ODDS 1:2
1 Al Kaline 1.50 4.00
2 Babe Ruth 4.00 10.00
3 Billy Williams .60 1.50
4 Bob Feller .60 1.50
5 Bob Gibson 1.00 2.50
6 Brooks Robinson 1.00 2.50
7 Cal Ripken 6.00 15.00
8 Carlton Fisk 1.00 2.50
9 Dennis Eckersley .60 1.50
10 Don Mattingly 3.00 8.00
11 Duke Snider 1.00 2.50
12 Eddie Murray 1.50 4.00
13 Ernie Banks 1.50 4.00
14 Fergie Jenkins .60 1.50
15 Frank Robinson 1.00 2.50
16 Gaylord Perry .60 1.50
17 George Brett 3.00 8.00
18 George Kell .60 1.50
19 Harmon Killebrew 1.50 4.00
20 Jim Palmer .60 1.50
21 Joe Morgan .60 1.50
22 Johnny Bench 1.50 4.00
23 Juan Marichal .60 1.50
24 Lou Brock 1.00 2.50
25 Maury Wills .60 1.50
26 Mike Schmidt 3.00 8.00
27 Nolan Ryan 4.00 10.00
28 Ozzie Smith 2.50 6.00
29 Paul Molitor 1.50 4.00
30 Pee Wee Reese 1.00 2.50
31 Phil Niekro .60 1.50
32 Phil Rizzuto 1.00 2.50
33 Ralph Kiner .60 1.50
34 Reggie Jackson 1.50 4.00
35 Rickey Henderson 1.00 2.50
36 Roberto Clemente 4.00 10.00
37 Robin Yount 1.50 4.00
38 Rod Carew 1.00 2.50
39 Roger Maris 1.50 4.00
40 Stan Musial 2.50 6.00
41 Steve Carlton .60 1.50
42 Ted Williams 3.00 8.00
43 Tom Seaver 1.00 2.50
44 Tony Gwynn 2.00 5.00
45 Tony Perez .60 1.50
46 Wade Boggs 1.00 2.50
47 Warren Spahn 1.00 2.50
48 Whitey Ford 1.00 2.50
49 Willie McCovey 1.00 2.50
50 Yogi Berra 1.50 4.00

2005 Donruss Classics Legendary Players Hat

*HAT p/r 25: .4X TO 1X JSY NBR p/r 20-35
*HAT p/r 25: .3X TO .8X JSY NBR p/r 16-19
OVERALL AU-GU ODDS 1:6
PRINT RUNS B/WN 1-25 COPIES PER
NO PRICING ON QTY OF 10 OR LESS
13 Ernie Banks/25 10.00 25.00
17 George Brett/25 15.00 40.00
28 Ozzie Smith/25 12.50 30.00

2005 Donruss Classics Legendary Players Jacket

*JKT: .6X TO 1.5X JSY NBR p/r 72
*JKT: .5X TO 1.2X JSY NBR p/r 36-44
*JKT: .4X TO 1X JSY NBR p/r 20-34
OVERALL AU-GU ODDS 1:6
STATED PRINT RUN 25 SERIAL #'d SETS
7 Cal Ripken 40.00 80.00
34 Reggie Jackson 8.00 20.00
42 Ted Williams 40.00 80.00

2005 Donruss Classics Legendary Players Jersey Number

PRINT RUNS B/WN 1-72 COPIES PER
NO PRICING ON QTY OF 14 OR LESS
PRIME PRINT RUN 1 SERIAL #'d SET

NO PRIME PRICING DUE TO SCARCITY
OVERALL AU-GU ODDS 1:6
2 Babe Ruth/3
3 Billy Williams/26 5.00 12.00
4 Bob Feller/1
6 Brooks Robinson/5
7 Cal Ripken/8
8 Carlton Fisk/72 4.00 10.00
9 Dennis Eckersley/43 4.00 10.00
10 Don Mattingly/23 15.00 40.00
11 Duke Snider/4
12 Eddie Murray/33 10.00 25.00
13 Ernie Banks/14
16 Gaylord Perry/36 4.00 10.00
17 George Brett/5
19 Harmon Killebrew/3
20 Jim Palmer/22 5.00 12.00
21 Joe Morgan/1
22 Johnny Bench/5
23 Juan Marichal/27 5.00 12.00
24 Lou Brock/20 8.00 20.00
25 Maury Wills/30 5.00 12.00
26 Mike Schmidt/20 15.00 40.00
27 Nolan Ryan/34 20.00 50.00
28 Ozzie Smith/1
29 Paul Molitor/4
30 Pee Wee Reese/1
31 Phil Niekro/35 5.00 12.00
32 Phil Rizzuto Pants/1
34 Reggie Jackson/9
35 Rickey Henderson/24 10.00 25.00
36 Roberto Clemente/1
37 Robin Yount/19 12.50 30.00
38 Rod Carew/29 8.00 20.00
39 Roger Maris/9
40 Stan Musial/6
41 Steve Carlton/32 5.00 12.00
42 Ted Williams/9
43 Tom Seaver/41 6.00 15.00
44 Tony Gwynn/19 12.50 30.00
45 Tony Perez/24 5.00 12.00
46 Wade Boggs/26 8.00 20.00
47 Warren Spahn/24 8.00 20.00
48 Whitey Ford/16 10.00 25.00
49 Willie McCovey/44 6.00 15.00
50 Yogi Berra/8

2005 Donruss Classics Legendary Players Leather

*LTR p/r 25: .6X TO 1.5X JSY p/r 20-34
*LTR p/r 25: .5X TO 1.2X JSY p/r 16-19
OVERALL AU-GU ODDS 1:6
PRINT RUNS B/WN 10-25 COPIES PER
NO PRICING ON QTY OF 10
14 Fergie Jenkins Fld Glv/25 8.00 20.00

2005 Donruss Classics Legendary Players Pants

*PNTp/r24-25: .5X TO 1.2X JSY NUMp/r36-44
*PNTp/r24-25: .4X TO 1X JSY NUM p/r 20-34
*PNTp/r24-25: .3X TO .8X JSY NUM p/r 16-19
OVERALL AU-GU ODDS 1:6
PRINT RUNS B/WN 1-25 COPIES PER
NO PRICING ON QTY OF 10 OR LESS
4 Bob Feller/19 10.00 25.00
7 Cal Ripken/25 40.00 80.00
11 Duke Snider/25 8.00 20.00
14 Fergie Jenkins/25 5.00 12.00
22 Johnny Bench/25 10.00 25.00
28 Ozzie Smith/25 12.50 30.00
29 Paul Molitor/25 5.00 12.00
39 Roger Maris/25 20.00 50.00

2005 Donruss Classics Legendary Players Spikes

*SPK p/r 25: .5X TO 1.2X JSY NUM p/r 16-19
OVERALL AU-GU ODDS 1:6
PRINT RUNS B/WN 1-25 COPIES PER
NO PRICING ON QTY OF 10 OR LESS
15 Frank Robinson/25 8.00 20.00

2005 Donruss Classics Legendary Players Signature

OVERALL AU-GU ODDS 1:6
PRINT RUNS B/WN 1-10 COPIES PER
NO PRICING DUE TO SCARCITY

2005 Donruss Classics Membership

STATED PRINT RUN 1000 SERIAL #'d SETS
*GOLD: 1.5X TO 4X BASIC
GOLD PRINT RUN 50 SERIAL #'d SETS
PLATINUM PRINT RUN 1 SERIAL #'d SET
NO PLATINUM PRICING DUE TO SCARCITY
OVERALL INSERT ODDS 1:2
1 Bobby Doerr .60 1.50
2 Tom Seaver 1.00 2.50
3 Cal Ripken 6.00 15.00
4 Paul Molitor 1.50 4.00
5 Brooks Robinson 1.00 2.50
6 Al Kaline 1.50 4.00
7 Steve Carlton .60 1.50
8 Carl Yastrzemski 2.00 5.00
9 Bob Feller .60 1.50
10 Fred Lynn .60 1.50
11 Luis Aparicio .60 1.50
12 Hank Aaron 3.00 8.00
13 Willie Mays 3.00 8.00
14 Bob Gibson 1.00 2.50
15 Joe Morgan .60 1.50
16 Whitey Ford 1.00 2.50
17 Don Sutton .60 1.50
18 Harmon Killebrew 1.50 4.00
19 Tony Gwynn 2.00 5.00
20 Lou Brock 1.00 2.50
21 Dennis Eckersley .60 1.50
22 Jim Palmer .60 1.50
23 Don Mattingly 3.00 8.00
24 Carlton Fisk 1.00 2.50
25 Gaylord Perry .60 1.50
26 Mike Schmidt 3.00 8.00
27 Nolan Ryan 4.00 10.00
28 Sandy Koufax 5.00 12.00
29 Rod Carew 1.00 2.50
30 Maury Wills .60 1.50

2005 Donruss Classics Membership VIP Bat

*BAT p/r 25: .5X TO 1.2X JSY p/r 50
*BAT p/r 25: .4X TO 1X JSY p/r 25
OVERALL AU-GU ODDS 1:6
STATED PRINT RUN 25 SERIAL #'d SETS
1 Bobby Doerr 5.00 12.00
2 Tom Seaver 8.00 20.00
3 Cal Ripken 40.00 80.00
4 Paul Molitor 5.00 12.00
5 Brooks Robinson 8.00 20.00
6 Al Kaline 10.00 25.00
8 Carl Yastrzemski 8.00 20.00
12 Hank Aaron 20.00 50.00
13 Willie Mays 20.00 50.00
18 Harmon Killebrew 10.00 25.00

2005 Donruss Classics Membership VIP Jersey

PRINT RUNS B/WN 5-50 COPIES PER
NO PRICING ON QTY OF 10 OR LESS
PRIME PRINT RUN 1 SERIAL #'d SET
NO PRIME PRICING DUE TO SCARCITY
OVERALL AU-GU ODDS 1:6
1 Bobby Doerr Pants/10
2 Tom Seaver/10
3 Cal Ripken/10
4 Paul Molitor/10
5 Brooks Robinson/10
7 Steve Carlton/25 5.00 12.00
8 Carl Yastrzemski/10
9 Bob Feller Pants/10
10 Fred Lynn/25 5.00 12.00
11 Luis Aparicio/25 5.00 12.00
12 Hank Aaron/10
13 Willie Mays/10
14 Bob Gibson/5
15 Joe Morgan/25 5.00 12.00
16 Whitey Ford/10
17 Don Sutton/50 4.00 10.00
18 Harmon Killebrew/10
19 Tony Gwynn/50 8.00 20.00
20 Lou Brock/25 8.00 20.00
21 Dennis Eckersley/50 4.00 10.00
22 Jim Palmer/25 5.00 12.00
23 Don Mattingly/25 15.00 40.00
24 Carlton Fisk/25 8.00 20.00
25 Gaylord Perry/50 4.00 10.00
26 Mike Schmidt/50 12.50 30.00
27 Nolan Ryan/25 20.00 50.00
28 Sandy Koufax/5
29 Rod Carew/50 6.00 15.00
30 Maury Wills/10

2005 Donruss Classics Membership VIP Materials

*MTL p/r 25: .6X TO 1.5X JSY p/r 50
*MTL p/r 25: .5X TO 1.2X JSY p/r 25
PRINT RUNS B/WN 5-25 COPIES PER
NO PRICING ON QTY OF 10 OR LESS
PRIME PRINT RUN 1 SERIAL #'d SET
NO PRIME PRICING DUE TO SCARCITY
OVERALL AU-GU ODDS 1:6
1 Bobby Doerr Bat-Pants/25 6.00 15.00
2 Tom Seaver Bat-Jsy/25 10.00 25.00
3 Cal Ripken Bat-Jsy/25 50.00 100.00
4 Paul Molitor Bat-Jsy/25 6.00 15.00
5 Brooks Robinson Bat-Jsy/25 10.00 25.00
18 Harmon Killebrew Bat-Jsy/25 12.50 30.00

2005 Donruss Classics Membership VIP Materials Awards

OVERALL AU-GU ODDS 1:6
PRINT RUNS B/WN 5-10 COPIES PER
NO PRICING DUE TO SCARCITY

2005 Donruss Classics Membership VIP Materials HOF

OVERALL AU-GU ODDS 1:6
STATED PRINT RUN 10 SERIAL #'d SETS
NO PRICING DUE TO SCARCITY

2005 Donruss Classics Membership VIP Materials HR

*MTL HR p/r 37-49: .5X TO 1.2X JSY p/r 50
*MTL HR p/r 37-49: .4X TO 1X JSY p/r 25
*MTL HR p/r 21-35: .5X TO 1.2X JSY p/r 25
*MTL HR p/r 17: .75X TO 2X JSY p/r 50
OVERALL AU-GU ODDS 1:6
PRINT RUNS B/WN 6-49 COPIES PER
NO PRICING ON QTY OF 14 OR LESS
1 Bobby Doerr Jsy-Pants/27 6.00 15.00
3 Cal Ripken Jsy-Pants/34 40.00 80.00
4 Paul Molitor Bat-Jsy/22 6.00 15.00
8 Carl Yastrzemski Bat-Jsy/44 15.00 40.00
12 Hank Aaron Bat-Jsy/47 40.00 80.00
18 Harmon Killebrew Bat-Jsy/49 10.00 25.00

2005 Donruss Classics Membership VIP Materials Stats

OVERALL AU-GU ODDS 1:6
STATED PRINT RUN 10 SERIAL #'d SETS
NO PRICING DUE TO SCARCITY

2005 Donruss Classics Membership VIP Signature

OVERALL AU-GU ODDS 1:6
PRINT RUNS B/WN 1-5 COPIES PER
NO PRICING DUE TO SCARCITY

2005 Donruss Classics Membership VIP Signature Bat

OVERALL AU-GU ODDS 1:6
PRINT RUNS B/WN 1-10 COPIES PER
NO PRICING DUE TO SCARCITY

2005 Donruss Classics Membership VIP Signature Jersey

PRINT RUNS B/WN 1-10 COPIES PER
PRIME PRINT RUN 1 SERIAL #'d SET
OVERALL AU-GU ODDS 1:6
NO PRICING DUE TO SCARCITY

2005 Donruss Classics Membership VIP Signature Materials

PRINT RUNS B/WN 1-25 COPIES PER
NO PRICING ON QTY OF 10 OR LESS
PRIME PRINT RUN 1 SERIAL #'d SET
NO PRIME PRICING DUE TO SCARCITY
OVERALL AU-GU ODDS 1:6
1 Bobby Doerr Bat-Pants/25 15.00 40.00
2 Tom Seaver Bat-Jsy/5
3 Cal Ripken Bat-Jsy/1
4 Paul Molitor Bat-Jsy/5
5 Brooks Robinson Bat-Jsy/5
7 Steve Carlton Bat-Jsy/5
8 Carl Yastrzemski Bat-Jsy/1
10 Fred Lynn Bat-Jsy/25 15.00 40.00
11 Luis Aparicio Bat-Jsy/25 15.00 40.00
12 Hank Aaron Bat-Jsy/5
13 Willie Mays Bat-Jsy/1
18 Harmon Killebrew Bat-Jsy/10
19 Tony Gwynn Bat-Jsy/10
20 Lou Brock Bat-Jsy/25 30.00 60.00
23 Don Mattingly Bat-Jsy/10
24 Carlton Fisk Bat-Jsy/5
27 Nolan Ryan Bat-Jsy/5
29 Rod Carew Bat-Jsy/5

2005 Donruss Classics Membership VIP Signature Materials Awards

OVERALL AU-GU ODDS 1:6
PRINT RUNS B/WN 1-10 COPIES PER
NO PRICING DUE TO SCARCITY

2005 Donruss Classics Membership VIP Signature Materials HOF

OVERALL AU-GU ODDS 1:6
PRINT RUNS B/WN 1-10 COPIES PER
NO PRICING DUE TO SCARCITY

2005 Donruss Classics Membership VIP Signature Materials HR

OVERALL AU-GU ODDS 1:6
PRINT RUNS B/WN 1-10 COPIES PER
NO PRICING DUE TO SCARCITY

2005 Donruss Classics Membership VIP Signature Materials Stats

OVERALL AU-GU ODDS 1:6
PRINT RUNS B/WN 5-10 COPIES PER
NO PRICING DUE TO SCARCITY

2005 Donruss Classics Stars of Summer

STATED PRINT RUN 1000 SERIAL #'d SETS
*GOLD: 1.5X TO 4X BASIC
GOLD PRINT RUN 50 SERIAL #'d SETS
PLATINUM PRINT RUN 1 SERIAL #'d SET
NO PLATINUM PRICING DUE TO SCARCITY
OVERALL INSERT ODDS 1:2

1 Andre Dawson 1.00 2.50
2 Bert Blyleven .60 1.50
3 Bill Madlock .60 1.50
4 Dale Murphy .60 1.50
5 Darryl Strawberry .60 1.50
6 Dave Parker .60 1.50
7 Dave Righetti .60 1.50
8 Dwight Evans 1.00 2.50
9 Dwight Gooden .60 1.50
10 Fred Lynn .60 1.50
11 George Foster .60 1.50
12 Harold Baines .60 1.50
13 Jack Morris .60 1.50
14 Jim Rice .60 1.50
15 Keith Hernandez .60 1.50
16 Kirk Gibson .60 1.50
17 Luis Aparicio .60 1.50
18 Mark Grace 1.00 2.50
19 Marty Marion .60 1.50
20 Orel Hershiser .60 1.50
21 Ron Guidry .60 1.50
22 Ron Santo 1.00 2.50
23 Steve Garvey .60 1.50
24 Tony Oliva .60 1.50
25 Will Clark 1.00 2.50

2005 Donruss Classics Stars of Summer Material

OVERALL AU-GU ODDS 1:6
PRINT RUNS B/WN 100-250 COPIES PER

1 Andre Dawson Jsy/250 3.00 8.00
2 Bert Blyleven Jsy/150 3.00 8.00
3 Bill Madlock Bat/250 3.00 8.00
4 Dale Murphy Jsy/100 5.00 12.00
5 Darryl Strawberry Jsy/250 3.00 8.00
6 Dave Parker Jsy/100 3.00 8.00
7 Dave Righetti Jsy/150 3.00 8.00
8 Dwight Evans Bat/250 5.00 12.00
9 Dwight Gooden Bat/150 3.00 8.00
10 Fred Lynn Jsy/100 3.00 8.00
11 George Foster Bat/250 3.00 8.00
12 Harold Baines Jsy/250 3.00 8.00
13 Jack Morris Jsy/100 3.00 8.00
14 Jim Rice Pants/250 3.00 8.00
15 Keith Hernandez Bat/100 3.00 8.00
16 Kirk Gibson Jsy/250 3.00 8.00
17 Luis Aparicio Bat/250 3.00 8.00
18 Mark Grace Bat/250 5.00 12.00
22 Ron Santo Bat/150 5.00 12.00
23 Steve Garvey Jsy/250 3.00 8.00
24 Tony Oliva Jsy/250 3.00 8.00
25 Will Clark Bat/250 5.00 12.00

2005 Donruss Classics Stars of Summer Signature

*SIG p/r 50: .4X TO 1X MTL.SIG p/r 100
*SIG p/r 50: .3X TO .8X MTL.SIG p/r 50
*SIG p/r 50: .25X TO .6X MTL.SIG p/r 25
*SIG p/r 25: .4X TO 1X MTL.SIG p/r 50
*SIG p/r 25: .3X TO .8X MTL.SIG p/r 25
OVERALL AU-GU ODDS 1:6
PRINT RUNS B/WN 10-100 COPIES PER
NO PRICING ON QTY OF 10

5 Darryl Strawberry/100 6.00 15.00
19 Marty Marion/50 8.00 20.00
21 Ron Guidry/25 15.00 40.00

2005 Donruss Classics Stars of Summer Signature Material

OVERALL AU-GU ODDS 1:6
PRINT RUNS B/WN 25-100 COPIES PER

1 Andre Dawson Jsy/100 8.00 20.00
2 Bert Blyleven Jsy/50 10.00 25.00
3 Bill Madlock Bat/100 8.00 20.00
4 Dale Murphy Jsy/25 20.00 50.00
6 Dave Parker Jsy/50 10.00 25.00
7 Dave Righetti Jsy/50 10.00 25.00
8 Dwight Evans Jsy/50 15.00 40.00
9 Dwight Gooden Bat/25 12.50 30.00
10 Fred Lynn Jsy/100 8.00 20.00
11 George Foster Bat/50 10.00 25.00
12 Harold Baines Jsy/100 8.00 20.00
13 Jack Morris Jsy/100 8.00 20.00
14 Jim Rice Pants/50 10.00 25.00
15 Keith Hernandez Jsy/50 10.00 25.00
16 Kirk Gibson Jsy/25 12.50 30.00
17 Luis Aparicio Bat/50 10.00 25.00
18 Mark Grace Bat/25 20.00 50.00
22 Ron Santo Bat/50 15.00 40.00
23 Steve Garvey Jsy/50 10.00 25.00
24 Tony Oliva Jsy/50 10.00 25.00
25 Will Clark Bat/25 20.00 50.00

2005 Donruss Classics Team Colors

STATED PRINT RUN 800 SERIAL #'d SETS
*GOLD: 1.5X TO 4X BASIC
GOLD PRINT RUN 50 SERIAL #'d SETS
PLATINUM PRINT RUN 1 SERIAL #'d SET
NO PLATINUM PRICING DUE TO SCARCITY
OVERALL INSERT ODDS 1:2

1 Adam Dunn 1.00 2.50
2 Albert Pujols 4.00 10.00
3 Andruw Jones .60 1.50
4 Aramis Ramirez .60 1.50
5 Aubrey Huff .60 1.50
6 Bobby Abreu .60 1.50
7 Cal Ripken 6.00 15.00
8 Carlos Lee .60 1.50
9 Craig Biggio 1.00 2.50
10 Derrek Lee .60 1.50
11 Garret Anderson .60 1.50
12 Gary Carter .60 1.50
13 Geoff Jenkins .60 1.50
14 Greg Maddux 2.50 6.00
15 Hank Blalock .60 1.50
16 Hideki Matsui 2.50 6.00
17 Jake Peavy .60 1.50
18 Jim Edmonds 1.00 2.50
19 Jim Palmer .60 1.50
20 Jose Guillen .60 1.50
21 Jose Vidro .60 1.50
22 Juan Pierre .60 1.50
23 Lew Ford .60 1.50
24 Lyle Overbay .60 1.50
25 Manny Ramirez 1.50 4.00
26 Mark Loretta .60 1.50
27 Mark Teixeira 1.50 4.00
28 Melvin Mora .60 1.50
29 Michael Young 1.00 2.50
30 Miguel Cabrera 1.50 4.00
31 Mike Lowell .60 1.50
32 Mike Mussina 1.00 2.50
33 Milton Bradley .60 1.50
34 Randy Johnson 1.50 4.00
35 Roger Clemens 2.00 5.00
36 Sean Casey .60 1.50
37 Shawn Green .60 1.50
38 Steve Carlton .60 1.50
39 Todd Helton 1.00 2.50
40 Travis Hafner .60 1.50

2005 Donruss Classics Team Colors Bat

OVERALL AU-GU ODDS 1:6
STATED PRINT RUN 100 SERIAL #'d SETS

1 Adam Dunn 2.50 6.00
2 Albert Pujols 8.00 20.00
3 Andruw Jones 4.00 10.00
4 Aramis Ramirez 2.50 6.00
7 Cal Ripken 15.00 40.00
9 Craig Biggio 4.00 10.00
10 Derrek Lee 4.00 10.00
11 Garret Anderson 2.50 6.00
12 Gary Carter 2.50 6.00
15 Hank Blalock 2.50 6.00
16 Hideki Matsui 15.00 40.00
18 Jim Edmonds 2.50 6.00
21 Jose Vidro 2.50 6.00
22 Juan Pierre 2.50 6.00
23 Lew Ford 2.50 6.00
27 Mark Teixeira 4.00 10.00
28 Melvin Mora 2.50 6.00
29 Michael Young 2.50 6.00
30 Miguel Cabrera 4.00 10.00
31 Mike Lowell 2.50 6.00
36 Sean Casey 2.50 6.00
37 Shawn Green 2.50 6.00

2005 Donruss Classics Team Colors Jersey Prime

*JSY PRIME p/r 25: 1X TO 2.5X BAT p/r 100
OVERALL AU-GU ODDS 1:6
PRINT RUNS B/WN 5-25 COPIES PER
NO PRICING ON QTY OF 5

5 Aubrey Huff/25 5.00 12.00
6 Bobby Abreu/25 5.00 12.00
8 Carlos Lee/25 5.00 12.00
13 Geoff Jenkins/25 5.00 12.00
24 Lyle Overbay/25 5.00 12.00
32 Mike Mussina/25 8.00 20.00
34 Randy Johnson/25 10.00 25.00
35 Roger Clemens/25 15.00 40.00
38 Steve Carlton/25 5.00 12.00
39 Todd Helton/25 8.00 20.00
40 Travis Hafner/25 5.00 12.00

2005 Donruss Classics Team Colors Materials

*MTL p/r 100: .5X TO 1.2X BAT p/r 100
*MTL p/r 50: .6X TO 1.5X BAT p/r 100
PRINT RUNS B/WN 25-100 COPIES PER
PRIME PRINT RUN 5 SERIAL #'d SETS
NO PRIME PRICING DUE TO SCARCITY
OVERALL AU-GU ODDS 1:6

6 Bobby Abreu Jsy-Jsy/100 3.00 8.00
8 Carlos Lee Jsy-Jsy/100 3.00 8.00
13 Geoff Jenkins Jsy-Pants/100 3.00 8.00
19 Jim Palmer Jsy-Pants/25 5.00 12.00
25 Manny Ramirez Jsy-Jsy/100 5.00 12.00
39 Todd Helton Jsy-Jsy/50 6.00 15.00

2005 Donruss Classics Team Colors Signature

*SIG p/r 25: .3X TO .8X SIG JSY p/r 25
OVERALL AU-GU ODDS 1:6
PRINT RUNS B/WN 1-25 COPIES PER
NO PRICING ON QTY OF 10 OR LESS

17 Jake Peavy/25 15.00 40.00
20 Jose Guillen/25 10.00 25.00
26 Mark Loretta/25 6.00 15.00
33 Milton Bradley/25 10.00 25.00

2005 Donruss Classics Team Colors Signature Bat

*SIG BAT p/r 25: .4X TO 1X SIG JSY p/r 25
OVERALL AU-GU ODDS 1:6
PRINT RUNS B/WN 5-25 COPIES PER
NO PRICING ON QTY OF 10 OR LESS

10 Derrek Lee/25 20.00 50.00

2005 Donruss Classics Team Colors Signature Jersey

PRINT RUNS B/WN 1-25 COPIES PER
NO PRICING ON QTY OF 10 OR LESS
PRIME PRINT RUN 1 SERIAL #'d SET
NO PRIME PRICING DUE TO SCARCITY
OVERALL AU-GU ODDS 1:6

1 Adam Dunn/25 20.00 50.00
2 Albert Pujols/1
4 Aramis Ramirez/25 12.50 30.00
5 Aubrey Huff/25 12.50 30.00
7 Cal Ripken/1
8 Carlos Lee/25 12.50 30.00
9 Craig Biggio/10
11 Garret Anderson/25 12.50 30.00
12 Gary Carter/25 12.50 30.00
14 Greg Maddux/1
15 Hank Blalock/25 12.50 30.00
18 Jim Edmonds/10
19 Jim Palmer/10
21 Jose Vidro/25 12.50 30.00
23 Lew Ford/25 8.00 20.00
24 Lyle Overbay/25 8.00 20.00
25 Manny Ramirez/1
28 Melvin Mora/25 12.50 30.00
29 Michael Young/25 12.50 30.00
30 Miguel Cabrera/10
32 Mike Mussina/1
34 Randy Johnson/1
35 Roger Clemens/1
36 Sean Casey/10
37 Shawn Green/5
38 Steve Carlton/10
39 Todd Helton/5
40 Travis Hafner/25 12.50 30.00

2005 Donruss Classics Team Colors Signature Materials

*SIG MTL p/r 25: .5X TO 1.2X SIG JSY p/r 25
PRINT RUNS B/WN 5-25 COPIES PER
NO PRICING ON QTY OF 10 OR LESS
PRIME PRINT RUN 1 SERIAL #'d SET
NO PRIME PRICING DUE TO SCARCITY
OVERALL AU-GU ODDS 1:6

1998 Donruss Collections Samples

This 200 card standard-size set was issued one per dealer order form or one per media release to herald the release of the 1998 Donruss Prized Collections set. The cards are similar to the regular 1998 Donruss Prized Collections except the backs have the word "Sample" printed on them in big capital black letters.

COMPLETE SET (200) 480.00 1200.00
1 Paul Molitor 5.00 12.00
2 Juan Gonzalez 4.00 10.00
3 Darryl Kile .75 2.00
4 Randy Johnson 6.00 15.00
5 Tom Glavine 3.00 8.00
6 Pat Hentgen .75 2.00
7 David Justice 1.50 4.00
8 Kevin Brown 2.50 6.00
9 Mike Mussina 3.00 8.00
10 Ken Caminiti 1.50 4.00
11 Todd Hundley 1.50 4.00
12 Frank Thomas 5.00 12.00
13 Ray Lankford 1.50 4.00
14 Justin Thompson .75 2.00
15 Jason Dickson .75 2.00
16 Kenny Lofton 2.50 6.00
17 Ivan Rodriguez 5.00 12.00
18 Pedro Martinez 5.00 12.00
19 Brady Anderson 1.50 4.00
20 Barry Larkin 3.00 8.00
21 Chipper Jones 10.00 25.00
22 Tony Gwynn 8.00 20.00
23 Roger Clemens 8.00 20.00
24 Sandy Alomar Jr. 1.50 4.00
25 Tino Martinez 1.50 4.00
26 Jeff Bagwell 5.00 12.00
27 Shawn Estes .75 2.00
28 Ken Griffey Jr. 16.00 30.00
29 Javier Lopez 1.50 4.00
30 Denny Neagle .75 2.00
31 Mike Piazza 12.50 25.00
32 Andres Galarraga 3.00 8.00
33 Larry Walker 1.50 4.00
34 Alex Rodriguez 12.50 25.00
35 Greg Maddux 10.00 25.00
36 Albert Belle 1.50 4.00
37 Barry Bonds 8.00 20.00
38 Mo Vaughn .75 2.00
39 Kevin Appier 1.50 4.00
40 Wade Boggs 5.00 12.00
41 Garret Anderson 1.50 4.00
42 Jeffrey Hammonds .75 2.00
43 Marquis Grissom 1.50 4.00
44 Jim Edmonds 3.00 8.00
45 Brian Jordan 1.50 4.00
46 Raul Mondesi 1.50 4.00
47 John Valentin .75 2.00
48 Brad Radke 1.50 4.00
49 Ismael Valdes .75 2.00
50 Matt Stairs .75 2.00
51 Matt Williams 2.50 6.00
52 Reggie Jefferson .80 2.00
53 Alan Benes .75 2.00
54 Charles Johnson .75 2.00
55 Chuck Knoblauch 1.50 4.00
56 Edgar Martinez 2.50 6.00
57 Nomar Garciaparra 12.50 25.00
58 Craig Biggio 2.50 6.00
59 Bernie Williams 3.00 8.00
60 David Cone 2.50 6.00
61 Cal Ripken 16.00 40.00
62 Mark McGwire 16.00 30.00
63 Roberto Alomar 3.00 8.00
64 Fred McGriff 2.50 6.00
65 Eric Karros 1.50 4.00
66 Robin Ventura 1.50 4.00
67 Darin Erstad 3.00 8.00
68 Michael Tucker .75 2.00
69 Jim Thome 3.00 8.00
70 Mark Grace 3.00 8.00
71 Lou Collier .75 2.00
72 Karim Garcia 2.50 6.00
73 Alex Fernandez .75 2.00
74 J.T. Snow 1.50 4.00
75 Reggie Sanders 1.50 4.00
76 John Smoltz 1.50 4.00
77 Tim Salmon 2.50 6.00
78 Paul O'Neill 1.50 4.00
79 Vinny Castilla 1.50 4.00
80 Rafael Palmeiro 3.00 8.00
81 Jaret Wright .75 2.00
82 Jay Buhner 1.50 4.00
83 Brett Butler 1.50 4.00
84 Todd Greene .75 2.00
85 Scott Rolen 3.00 8.00
86 Sammy Sosa 8.00 20.00
87 Jason Giambi 4.00 10.00
88 Carlos Delgado 3.00 8.00
89 Deion Sanders 1.50 4.00
90 Wilton Guerrero .75 2.00
91 Andy Pettitte 1.50 4.00
92 Brian Giles 2.50 6.00
93 Dmitri Young 1.50 4.00
94 Ron Coomer .75 2.00
95 Mike Cameron 1.50 4.00
96 Edgardo Alfonzo 3.20 8.00
97 Jimmy Key .75 2.00
98 Ryan Klesko 1.50 4.00
99 Andy Benes .75 2.00
100 Derek Jeter 16.00 40.00
101 Jeff Fassero .75 2.00
102 Neifi Perez .75 2.00
103 Hideo Nomo 10.00 25.00
104 Andruw Jones 3.00 8.00
105 Todd Helton 5.00 12.00
106 Livan Hernandez .75 2.00
107 Brett Tomko .75 2.00
108 Shannon Stewart 1.50 4.00
109 Bartolo Colon 1.50 4.00
110 Matt Morris 2.50 6.00
111 Miguel Tejada 4.00 10.00
112 Pokey Reese .75 2.00
113 Fernando Tatis 1.50 4.00
114 Todd Dunwoody .75 2.00
115 Jose Cruz Jr. 1.50 4.00
116 Chan Ho Park 1.50 4.00
117 Kevin Young .75 2.00
118 Rickey Henderson 8.00 20.00
119 Hideki Irabu .75 2.00
120 Francisco Cordova .75 2.00
121 Al Martin .75 2.00
122 Tony Clark .75 2.00
123 Curt Schilling 4.00 10.00
124 Rusty Greer 1.50 4.00
125 Jose Canseco 5.00 12.00
126 Edgar Renteria 2.50 6.00
127 Todd Walker 1.50 4.00
128 Wally Joyner 1.50 4.00
129 Bill Mueller 2.50 6.00
130 Jose Guillen 2.50 6.00
131 Manny Ramirez 5.00 12.00
132 Bobby Higginson 1.50 4.00
133 Kevin Orie .75 2.00
134 Will Clark 6.00 15.00
135 Dave Nilsson .75 2.00
136 Jason Kendall 1.50 4.00
137 Ivan Cruz .75 2.00
138 Gary Sheffield 4.00 10.00
139 Bubba Trammell .75 2.00
140 Vladimir Guerrero 6.00 15.00
141 Dennis Reyes .75 2.00
142 Bobby Bonilla .75 2.00
143 Ruben Rivera .75 2.00
144 Ben Grieve 1.50 4.00
145 Moises Alou 1.50 4.00
146 Tony Womack .75 2.00
147 Eric Young .75 2.00
148 Paul Konerko 1.50 4.00
149 Dante Bichette 1.50 4.00
150 Joe Carter 1.50 4.00
151 Rondell White 1.50 4.00
152 Chris Holt .75 2.00
153 Shawn Green 3.00 8.00
154 Mark Grudzielanek .75 2.00
155 Jermaine Dye 1.50 4.00
156 Ken Griffey Jr. FC 6.00 15.00
157 Frank Thomas FC 3.00 8.00
158 Chipper Jones FC 3.00 8.00
159 Mike Piazza FC 6.00 15.00
160 Cal Ripken FC 8.00 20.00
161 Greg Maddux FC 4.00 10.00
162 Juan Gonzalez FC 1.50 4.00
163 Alex Rodriguez FC 5.00 12.00
164 Mark McGwire FC 6.00 15.00
165 Derek Jeter FC 8.00 20.00
166 Larry Walker CL 1.50 4.00
167 Tony Gwynn CL 4.00 10.00
168 Tino Martinez CL .75 2.00
169 Scott Rolen CL 2.50 6.00
170 Nomar Garciaparra CL 6.00 12.00
171 Mark Kotsay RR 1.50 4.00
172 Neifi Perez RR .75 2.00
173 Paul Konerko RR 1.50 4.00
174 Jose Cruz RR 1.50 4.00
175 Hideki Irabu RR .75 2.00
176 Mike Cameron RR 1.50 4.00
177 Jeff Suppan RR .75 2.00
178 Kevin Orie RR .75 2.00
179 Pokey Reese RR .75 2.00
180 Todd Dunwoody RR .75 2.00
181 Miguel Tejada RR 4.00 10.00
182 Jose Guillen RR 2.50 6.00
183 Bartolo Colon RR 3.00 8.00
184 Derrek Lee RR .75 2.00
185 A.Williamson RR .75 2.00
186 Wilton Guerrero RR .75 2.00
187 Jaret Wright RR .75 2.00
188 Todd Helton RR 5.00 12.00
189 Shannon Stewart RR 1.50 4.00
190 N.Garciaparra RR 12.50 30.00
191 Brett Tomko RR .75 2.00
192 Fernando Tatis RR 1.50 4.00
193 Raul Ibanez RR 1.50 4.00
194 Dennis Reyes RR .75 2.00
195 Bobby Estalella RR .75 2.00
196 Lou Collier RR .75 2.00
197 Bubba Trammell RR .75 2.00
198 Ben Grieve RR 1.50 4.00
199 Ivan Cruz RR .75 2.00
200 Karim Garcia RR 2.50 6.00

1998 Donruss Collections Donruss

The Donruss Collections set was issued in one series totalling 200 cards and inserted at a rate of two cards per pack. The five-card packs retailed for $4.99 each. The set contains the subsets: Fan Club (156-165), Rated Rookie (176-205), and Checklists (166-170). The fronts feature color action photography surrounded by a background of blue and silver stars.

COMPLETE SET (200) 60.00 120.00
1 Paul Molitor .25 .60
2 Juan Gonzalez .25 .60
3 Darryl Kile .25 .60
4 Randy Johnson .60 1.50
5 Tom Glavine .40 1.00
6 Pat Hentgen .15 .40
7 David Justice .25 .60
8 Kevin Brown .40 1.00
9 Mike Mussina .40 1.00
10 Ken Caminiti .25 .60
11 Todd Hundley .15 .40
12 Frank Thomas .60 1.50
13 Ray Lankford .25 .60
14 Justin Thompson .15 .40
15 Jason Dickson .15 .40
16 Kenny Lofton .25 .60
17 Ivan Rodriguez .40 1.00
18 Pedro Martinez .40 1.00
19 Brady Anderson .25 .60
20 Barry Larkin .40 1.00
21 Chipper Jones .60 1.50
22 Tony Gwynn .75 2.00
23 Roger Clemens 1.25 3.00
24 Sandy Alomar Jr. .15 .40
25 Tino Martinez .40 1.00
26 Jeff Bagwell .40 1.00
27 Shawn Estes .15 .40
28 Ken Griffey Jr. 1.00 2.50
29 Javier Lopez .25 .60
30 Denny Neagle .15 .40
31 Mike Piazza 1.00 2.50
32 Andres Galarraga .25 .60
33 Larry Walker .25 .60
34 Alex Rodriguez 1.00 2.50
35 Greg Maddux 1.00 2.50
36 Albert Belle .25 .60
37 Barry Bonds 1.50 4.00
38 Mo Vaughn .25 .60
39 Kevin Appier .25 .60
40 Wade Boggs .40 1.00
41 Garret Anderson .25 .60
42 Jeffrey Hammonds .15 .40
43 Marquis Grissom .25 .60
44 Jim Edmonds .25 .60
45 Brian Jordan .25 .60
46 Raul Mondesi .25 .60
47 John Valentin .15 .40
48 Brad Radke .25 .60
49 Ismael Valdes .15 .40
50 Matt Stairs .15 .40
51 Matt Williams .25 .60
52 Reggie Jefferson .15 .40
53 Alan Benes .15 .40
54 Charles Johnson .25 .60
55 Chuck Knoblauch .25 .60
56 Edgar Martinez .40 1.00
57 Nomar Garciaparra 1.00 2.50
58 Craig Biggio .40 1.00
59 Bernie Williams .40 1.00
60 David Cone .25 .60
61 Cal Ripken 2.00 5.00
62 Mark McGwire 1.50 4.00
63 Roberto Alomar .40 1.00
64 Fred McGriff .40 1.00
65 Eric Karros .25 .60
66 Robin Ventura .25 .60
67 Darin Erstad .25 .60
68 Michael Tucker .15 .40
69 Jim Thome .40 1.00
70 Mark Grace .40 1.00
71 Lou Collier .15 .40
72 Karim Garcia .15 .40
73 Alex Fernandez .15 .40
74 J.T. Snow .25 .60
75 Reggie Sanders .25 .60
76 John Smoltz .40 1.00
77 Tim Salmon .40 1.00
78 Paul O'Neill .40 1.00
79 Vinny Castilla .25 .60
80 Rafael Palmeiro .40 1.00
81 Jaret Wright .15 .40
82 Jay Buhner .25 .60
83 Brett Butler .25 .60
84 Todd Greene .15 .40
85 Scott Rolen .40 1.00
86 Sammy Sosa .60 1.50
87 Jason Giambi .25 .60
88 Carlos Delgado .25 .60
89 Deion Sanders .40 1.00
90 Wilton Guerrero .15 .40
91 Andy Pettitte .40 1.00
92 Brian Giles .25 .60
93 Dmitri Young .25 .60
94 Ron Coomer .15 .40
95 Mike Cameron .15 .40
96 Edgardo Alfonzo .15 .40
97 Jimmy Key .25 .60
98 Ryan Klesko .25 .60
99 Andy Benes .15 .40
100 Derek Jeter 1.50 4.00
101 Jeff Fassero .15 .40
102 Neifi Perez .15 .40
103 Hideo Nomo .60 1.50
104 Andruw Jones .40 1.00
105 Todd Helton .40 1.00
106 Livan Hernandez .25 .60
107 Brett Tomko .15 .40
108 Shannon Stewart .25 .60
109 Bartolo Colon .25 .60
110 Matt Morris .25 .60
111 Miguel Tejada .60 1.50
112 Pokey Reese .15 .40
113 Fernando Tatis .15 .40
114 Todd Dunwoody .15 .40
115 Jose Cruz Jr. .15 .40
116 Chan Ho Park .25 .60
117 Kevin Young .25 .60
118 Rickey Henderson .60 1.50
119 Hideki Irabu .15 .40
120 Francisco Cordova .15 .40
121 Al Martin .15 .40
122 Tony Clark .15 .40
123 Curt Schilling .25 .60
124 Rusty Greer .25 .60
125 Jose Canseco .40 1.00
126 Edgar Renteria .25 .60
127 Todd Walker .15 .40
128 Wally Joyner .25 .60
129 Bill Mueller .25 .60
130 Jose Guillen .25 .60
131 Manny Ramirez .40 1.00
132 Bobby Higginson .25 .60
133 Kevin Orie .15 .40
134 Will Clark .40 1.00
135 Dave Nilsson .15 .40
136 Jason Kendall .25 .60
137 Ivan Cruz .15 .40
138 Gary Sheffield .25 .60
139 Bubba Trammell .15 .40
140 Vladimir Guerrero .60 1.50
141 Dennis Reyes .15 .40
142 Bobby Bonilla .25 .60
143 Ruben Rivera .15 .40
144 Ben Grieve .15 .40
145 Moises Alou .25 .60
146 Tony Womack .15 .40
147 Eric Young .15 .40
148 Paul Konerko .25 .60
149 Dante Bichette .25 .60
150 Joe Carter .25 .60
151 Rondell White .25 .60
152 Chris Holt .15 .40
153 Shawn Green .25 .60
154 Mark Grudzielanek .15 .40
155 Jermaine Dye .25 .60
156 Ken Griffey Jr. FC .60 1.50
157 Frank Thomas FC .40 1.00
158 Chipper Jones FC .40 1.00
159 Mike Piazza FC .60 1.50
160 Cal Ripken FC 1.00 2.50
161 Greg Maddux FC .60 1.50
162 Juan Gonzalez FC .15 .40
163 Alex Rodriguez FC .60 1.50
164 Mark McGwire FC .75 2.00
165 Derek Jeter FC .75 2.00
166 Larry Walker CL .15 .40
167 Tony Gwynn CL .40 1.00
168 Tino Martinez CL .25 .60
169 Scott Rolen CL .25 .60
170 Nomar Garciaparra CL .60 1.50
176 Mark Kotsay RR .25 .60
177 Neifi Perez RR .15 .40
178 Paul Konerko RR .25 .60
179 Jose Cruz Jr. RR .15 .40
180 Hideki Irabu RR .15 .40
181 Mike Cameron RR .15 .40
182 Jeff Suppan RR .15 .40
183 Kevin Orie RR .15 .40
184 Pokey Reese RR .15 .40
185 Todd Dunwoody RR .15 .40
186 Miguel Tejada RR .60 1.50
187 Jose Guillen RR .25 .60
188 Bartolo Colon RR .25 .60
189 Derrek Lee RR .40 1.00
190 A.Williamson RR .15 .40
191 Wilton Guerrero RR .15 .40
192 Jaret Wright RR .15 .40

193 Todd Helton RR .40 1.00
194 Shannon Stewart RR .25 .60
195 N.Garciaparra RR 1.00 2.50
196 Brett Tomko RR .15 .40
197 Fernando Tatis RR .15 .40
198 Raul Ibanez RR .15 .40
199 Dennis Reyes RR .15 .40
200 Bobby Estalella RR .15 .40
201 Lou Collier RR .15 .40
202 Bubba Trammell RR .15 .40
203 Ben Grieve RR .15 .40
204 Ivan Cruz RR .15 .40
205 Karim Garcia RR .15 .40

1998 Donruss Prized Collections Donruss

These cards parallel the 1998 Donruss set. According to published reports, less than 560 sets were produced.

*STARS: 1.25X TO 3X BASIC DONRUSS COLL.

1998 Donruss Collections Elite

These cards were issued one card per Donruss Collection pack. These cards parallel the Donruss Elite set and have the same checklist and subsets as the regular Donruss cards.

401 Ken Griffey Jr. 1.50 4.00
402 Frank Thomas 1.00 2.50
403 Alex Rodriguez 1.50 4.00
404 Mike Piazza 1.50 4.00
405 Greg Maddux 1.50 4.00
406 Cal Ripken 3.00 8.00
407 Chipper Jones 1.00 2.50
408 Derek Jeter 2.50 6.00
409 Tony Gwynn 1.25 3.00
410 Andruw Jones .60 1.50
411 Juan Gonzalez .40 1.00
412 Jeff Bagwell .60 1.50
413 Mark McGwire 2.50 6.00
414 Roger Clemens 2.00 5.00
415 Albert Belle .40 1.00
416 Barry Bonds 2.50 6.00
417 Kenny Lofton .40 1.00
418 Ivan Rodriguez .60 1.50
419 Manny Ramirez .60 1.50
420 Jim Thome .60 1.50
421 Chuck Knoblauch .40 1.00
422 Paul Molitor .40 1.00
423 Barry Larkin .60 1.50
424 Andy Pettitte .60 1.50
425 John Smoltz .60 1.50
426 Randy Johnson 1.00 2.50
427 Bernie Williams .60 1.50
428 Larry Walker .40 1.00
429 Mo Vaughn .40 1.00
430 Bobby Higginson .40 1.00
431 Edgardo Alfonzo .25 .60
432 Justin Thompson .25 .60
433 Jeff Suppan .25 .60
434 Roberto Alomar .60 1.50
435 Hideo Nomo 1.00 2.50
436 Rusty Greer .40 1.00
437 Tim Salmon .60 1.50
438 Jim Edmonds .40 1.00
439 Gary Sheffield .40 1.00
440 Ken Caminiti .40 1.00
441 Sammy Sosa 1.00 2.50
442 Tony Womack .25 .60
443 Matt Williams .40 1.00
444 Andres Galarraga .40 1.00
445 Garret Anderson .40 1.00
446 Rafael Palmeiro .60 1.50
447 Mike Mussina .60 1.50
448 Craig Biggio .60 1.50
449 Wade Boggs .60 1.50
450 Tom Glavine .60 1.50
451 Jason Giambi .40 1.00
452 Will Clark .60 1.50
453 David Justice .40 1.00
454 Sandy Alomar Jr. .25 .60
455 Edgar Martinez .60 1.50
456 Brady Anderson .40 1.00
457 Eric Young .25 .60
458 Ray Lankford .40 1.00
459 Kevin Brown .60 1.50
460 Raul Mondesi .40 1.00
461 Bobby Bonilla .40 1.00
462 Javier Lopez .40 1.00
463 Fred McGriff .60 1.50
464 Rondell White .40 1.00
465 Todd Hundley .25 .60
466 Mark Grace .60 1.50
467 Alan Benes .25 .60
468 Jeff Abbott .25 .60
469 Bob Abreu .40 1.00
470 Deion Sanders .60 1.50
471 Tino Martinez .60 1.50
472 Shannon Stewart .40 1.00
473 Homer Bush .25 .60
474 Carlos Delgado .40 1.00
475 Raul Ibanez .25 .60
476 Hideki Irabu .25 .60
477 Jose Cruz Jr. .25 .60
478 Tony Clark .25 .60
479 Wilton Guerrero .25 .60
480 Vladimir Guerrero 1.00 2.50
481 Scott Rolen .60 1.50
482 Nomar Garciaparra 1.50 4.00
483 Darin Erstad .40 1.00
484 Chan Ho Park .40 1.00
485 Mike Cameron .25 .60
486 Todd Walker .25 .60
487 Todd Dunwoody .25 .60
488 Neifi Perez .25 .60
489 Brett Tomko .25 .60
490 Jose Guillen .40 1.00
491 Matt Morris .40 1.00
492 Bartolo Colon .40 1.00
493 Jaret Wright .25 .60
494 Shawn Estes .25 .60
495 Livan Hernandez .40 1.00
496 Bobby Estalella .25 .60
497 Ben Grieve .25 .60
498 Paul Konerko .40 1.00
499 David Ortiz 1.25 3.00
500 Todd Helton .60 1.50
501 Juan Encarnacion .25 .60
502 Bubba Trammell .25 .60
503 Miguel Tejada 1.00 2.50
504 Jacob Cruz .25 .60
505 Todd Greene .25 .60
506 Kevin Orie .25 .60
507 Mark Kotsay .40 1.00
508 Fernando Tatis .25 .60
509 Jay Payton .25 .60
510 Pokey Reese .25 .60
511 Derrek Lee .60 1.50
512 Richard Hidalgo .25 .60
513 Ricky Ledee .25 .60
514 Lou Collier .25 .60
515 Ruben Rivera .25 .60
516 Shawn Green .40 1.00
517 Moises Alou .40 1.00
518 Ken Griffey Jr. GEN 1.00 2.50
519 Frank Thomas GEN .60 1.50
520 Alex Rodriguez GEN 1.00 2.50
521 Mike Piazza GEN 1.00 2.50
522 Greg Maddux GEN 1.00 2.50
523 Cal Ripken GEN 1.50 4.00
524 Chipper Jones GEN .60 1.50
525 Derek Jeter GEN 1.25 3.00
526 Tony Gwynn GEN .60 1.50
527 Andruw Jones GEN .40 1.00
528 Juan Gonzalez GEN .25 .60
529 Jeff Bagwell GEN .40 1.00
530 Mark McGwire GEN 1.25 3.00
531 Roger Clemens GEN 1.00 2.50
532 Albert Belle GEN .25 .60
533 Barry Bonds GEN 1.00 2.50
534 Kenny Lofton GEN .25 .60
535 Ivan Rodriguez GEN .40 1.00
536 Manny Ramirez GEN .60 1.50
537 Jim Thome GEN .40 1.00
538 C.Knoblauch GEN .25 .60
539 Paul Molitor GEN .25 .60
540 Barry Larkin GEN .40 1.00
541 Mo Vaughn GEN .25 .60
542 Hideki Irabu GEN .25 .60
543 Jose Cruz Jr. GEN .25 .60
544 Tony Clark GEN .25 .60
545 V.Guerrero GEN .60 1.50
546 Scott Rolen GEN .60 1.50
547 N.Garciaparra GEN 1.00 2.50
548 Nomar Garciaparra CL 1.00 2.50
549 Larry Walker CL .25 .60
550 Tino Martinez CL .40 1.00

1998 Donruss Prized Collections Elite

These cards parallel the already paralleled Donruss Elite set. According to published reports, less than 220 sets were produced.

*STARS: 1.5X TO 4X BASIC ELITE COLL.

1998 Donruss Collections Leaf

The Donruss Collections Leaf set contains 200 cards and inserted at a rate of two cards per pack. The set contains the subsets: Curtain Calls (347-356), Gold Leaf Stars (357-376), Gold Leaf Rookies (377-396), and Checklists (397-399).

201 Rusty Greer .30 .75
202 Tino Martinez .50 1.25
203 Bobby Bonilla .30 .75
204 Jason Giambi .30 .75
205 Matt Morris .30 .75
206 Craig Counsell .20 .50
207 Reggie Jefferson .20 .50
208 Brian Rose .20 .50
209 Ruben Rivera .20 .50
210 Shawn Estes .20 .50
211 Tony Gwynn 1.00 2.50
212 Jeff Abbott .20 .50
213 Jose Cruz Jr. .20 .50
214 Francisco Cordova .20 .50
215 Ryan Klesko .30 .75
216 Tim Salmon .50 1.25
217 Brett Tomko .20 .50
218 Matt Williams .30 .75
219 Joe Carter .30 .75
220 Harold Baines .30 .75
221 Gary Sheffield .30 .75
222 Charles Johnson .30 .75
223 Aaron Boone .30 .75
224 Eddie Murray .75 2.00
225 Matt Stairs .20 .50
226 David Cone .30 .75
227 Jon Nunnally .20 .50
228 Chris Stynes .20 .50
229 Enrique Wilson .20 .50
230 Randy Johnson .75 2.00
231 Garret Anderson .30 .75
232 Manny Ramirez .50 1.25
233 Jeff Suppan .20 .50
234 Rickey Henderson .75 2.00
235 Scott Spiezio .20 .50
236 Rondell White .30 .75
237 Todd Greene .20 .50
238 Delino DeShields .20 .50
239 Kevin Brown .50 1.25
240 Chili Davis .30 .75
241 Jimmy Key .30 .75
242 Mike Mussina .50 1.25
243 Joe Randa .30 .75
244 Chan Ho Park .30 .75
245 Brad Radke .30 .75
246 Geronimo Berroa .20 .50
247 Wade Boggs .50 1.25
248 Kevin Appier .30 .75
249 Moises Alou .30 .75
250 David Justice .30 .75
251 Ivan Rodriguez .50 1.25
252 J.T. Snow .30 .75
253 Brian Giles .30 .75
254 Will Clark .50 1.25
255 Justin Thompson .20 .50
256 Javier Lopez .30 .75
257 Hideki Irabu .20 .50
258 Mark Grudzielanek .20 .50
259 Abraham Nunez .20 .50
260 Todd Hollandsworth .20 .50
261 Jay Bell .30 .75
262 Nomar Garciaparra 1.25 3.00
263 Vinny Castilla .30 .75
264 Lou Collier .20 .50
265 Kevin Orie .20 .50
266 John Valentin .20 .50
267 Robin Ventura .30 .75
268 Denny Neagle .20 .50
269 Tony Womack .20 .50
270 Dennis Reyes .20 .50
271 Wally Joyner .30 .75
272 Kevin Brown .50 1.25
273 Ray Durham .30 .75
274 Mike Cameron .20 .50
275 Dante Bichette .30 .75
276 Jose Guillen .30 .75
277 Carlos Delgado .30 .75
278 Paul Molitor .30 .75
279 Jason Kendall .30 .75
280 Mark Bellhorn .30 .75
281 Damian Jackson .20 .50
282 Bill Mueller .30 .75
283 Kevin Young .30 .75
284 Curt Schilling .30 .75
285 Jeffrey Hammonds .20 .50
286 Sandy Alomar Jr. .20 .50
287 Bartolo Colon .30 .75
288 Wilton Guerrero .20 .50
289 Bernie Williams .50 1.25
290 Deion Sanders .50 1.25
291 Mike Piazza 1.25 3.00
292 Butch Huskey .20 .50
293 Edgardo Alfonzo .20 .50
294 Alan Benes .20 .50
295 Craig Biggio .50 1.25
296 Mark Grace .50 1.25
297 Shawn Green .30 .75
298 Derrek Lee .50 1.25
299 Ken Griffey Jr. 1.25 3.00
300 Tim Raines .30 .75
301 Pokey Reese .20 .50
302 Lee Stevens .20 .50
303 Shannon Stewart .30 .75
304 John Smoltz .50 1.25
305 Frank Thomas .75 2.00
306 Jeff Fassero .20 .50
307 Jay Buhner .30 .75
308 Jose Canseco .50 1.25
309 Omar Vizquel .50 1.25
310 Travis Fryman .30 .75
311 Dave Nilsson .20 .50
312 John Olerud .30 .75
313 Larry Walker .30 .75
314 Jim Edmonds .30 .75
315 Bobby Higginson .30 .75
316 Todd Hundley .20 .50
317 Paul O'Neill .50 1.25
318 Bip Roberts .20 .50
319 Ismael Valdes .20 .50
320 Pedro Martinez .50 1.25
321 Jeff Cirillo .20 .50
322 Andy Benes .20 .50
323 Bobby Jones .20 .50
324 Brian Hunter .20 .50
325 Darryl Kile .30 .75
326 Pat Hentgen .20 .50
327 Marquis Grissom .30 .75
328 Eric Davis .30 .75
329 Chipper Jones .75 2.00
330 Edgar Martinez .50 1.25
331 Andy Pettitte .50 1.25
332 Cal Ripken 2.50 6.00
333 Scott Rolen .50 1.25
334 Ron Coomer .20 .50
335 Luis Castillo .20 .50
336 Fred McGriff .50 1.25
337 Neifi Perez .20 .50
338 Eric Karros .30 .75
339 Alex Fernandez .20 .50
340 Jason Dickson .20 .50
341 Lance Johnson .20 .50
342 Ray Lankford .30 .75
343 Sammy Sosa .75 2.00
344 Eric Young .20 .50
345 Bubba Trammell .20 .50
346 Todd Walker .20 .50
347 Mo Vaughn CC .20 .50
348 Jeff Bagwell CC .30 .75
349 Kenny Lofton CC .20 .50
350 Raul Mondesi CC .20 .50
351 Mike Piazza CC .75 2.00
352 Chipper Jones CC .50 1.25
353 Larry Walker CC .20 .50
354 Greg Maddux CC .75 2.00
355 Ken Griffey Jr. CC .75 2.00
356 Frank Thomas CC .50 1.25
357 Darin Erstad GLS .20 .50
358 Roberto Alomar GLS .30 .75
359 Albert Belle GLS .20 .50
360 Jim Thome GLS .30 .75
361 Tony Clark GLS .20 .50
362 Chuck Knoblauch GLS .20 .50
363 Derek Jeter GLS 1.00 2.50
364 Alex Rodriguez GLS .75 2.00
365 Tony Gwynn GLS .50 1.25
366 Roger Clemens GLS .75 2.00
367 Barry Larkin GLS .30 .75
368 Andres Galarraga GLS .20 .50
369 V.Guerrero GLS .50 1.25
370 Mark McGwire GLS 1.00 2.50
371 Barry Bonds GLS .75 2.00
372 Juan Gonzalez GLS .20 .50
373 Andruw Jones GLS .30 .75
374 Paul Molitor GLS .20 .50
375 Hideo Nomo GLS .50 1.25
376 Cal Ripken GLS 1.25 3.00
377 Brad Fullmer GLR .20 .50
378 Jaret Wright GLR .20 .50
379 Bobby Estalella GLR .20 .50
380 Ben Grieve GLR .20 .50
381 Paul Konerko GLR .30 .75
382 David Ortiz GLR 1.00 2.50
383 Todd Helton GLR .50 1.25
384 J.Encarnacion GLR .20 .50
385 Miguel Tejada GLR .75 2.00
386 Jacob Cruz GLR .20 .50
387 Mark Kotsay GLR .30 .75
388 Fernando Tatis GLR .20 .50
389 Ricky Ledee GLR .20 .50
390 Richard Hidalgo GLR .20 .50
391 Richie Sexson GLR .30 .75
392 Luis Ordaz GLR .20 .50
393 Eli Marrero GLR .20 .50
394 Livan Hernandez GLR .30 .75
395 Homer Bush GLR .20 .50
396 Raul Ibanez GLR .20 .50
397 Nomar Garciaparra CL .75 2.00
398 Scott Rolen CL .30 .75
399 Jose Cruz Jr. CL .20 .50
400 Al Martin .20 .50

1998 Donruss Prized Collections Leaf

These cards parallel the already parallelled Leaf set. According to published reports, less than 400 sets were produced.

*STARS: 1.25X TO 3X BASIC LEAF COLL.

1998 Donruss Collections Preferred

These cards, which parallel the regular Donruss Preferred set were issued one every two packs. According to published reports, less than 1400 sets were produced. Again, the checklist matches the regular Donruss Preferred set.

551 Ken Griffey Jr. EX 5.00 12.00
552 Frank Thomas EX 3.00 8.00
553 Cal Ripken EX 10.00 25.00
554 Alex Rodriguez EX 5.00 12.00
555 Greg Maddux EX 5.00 12.00
556 Mike Piazza EX 5.00 12.00
557 Chipper Jones EX 3.00 8.00
558 Tony Gwynn FB 4.00 10.00
559 Derek Jeter FB 8.00 20.00
560 Jeff Bagwell EX 2.00 5.00
561 Juan Gonzalez EX 1.25 3.00
562 Nomar Garciaparra EX 5.00 12.00
563 Andruw Jones FB 2.00 5.00
564 Hideo Nomo FB 3.00 8.00
565 Roger Clemens FB 6.00 15.00
566 Mark McGwire FB 8.00 20.00
567 Scott Rolen FB 2.00 5.00
568 Vladimir Guerrero FB 3.00 8.00
569 Barry Bonds FB 8.00 20.00
570 Darin Erstad FB 1.25 3.00
571 Albert Belle FB 1.25 3.00
572 Kenny Lofton FB 1.25 3.00
573 Mo Vaughn FB 1.25 3.00
574 Tony Clark FB .75 2.00
575 Ivan Rodriguez FB 2.00 5.00
576 Larry Walker CB 1.25 3.00
577 Eddie Murray CB 3.00 8.00
578 Andy Pettitte CB 2.00 5.00
579 Roberto Alomar CB 2.00 5.00
580 Randy Johnson CB 3.00 8.00
581 Manny Ramirez CB 2.00 5.00
582 Paul Molitor FB 1.25 3.00
583 Mike Mussina CB 2.00 5.00
584 Jim Thome FB 2.00 5.00
585 Tino Martinez CB 2.00 5.00
586 Gary Sheffield CB 1.25 3.00
587 Chuck Knoblauch CB 1.25 3.00
588 Bernie Williams CB 2.00 5.00
589 Tim Salmon CB 2.00 5.00
590 Sammy Sosa CB 3.00 8.00
591 Wade Boggs GS 2.00 5.00
592 Will Clark GS 2.00 5.00
593 Andres Galarraga CB 1.25 3.00
594 Raul Mondesi CB 1.25 3.00
595 Rickey Henderson GS 3.00 8.00
596 Jose Canseco GS 2.00 5.00
597 Pedro Martinez GS 2.00 5.00
598 Jay Buhner GS 1.25 3.00
599 Ryan Klesko GS 1.25 3.00
600 Barry Larkin CB 2.00 5.00
601 Charles Johnson GS 1.25 3.00
602 Tom Glavine GS 2.00 5.00
603 Edgar Martinez CB 2.00 5.00
604 Fred McGriff GS 2.00 5.00
605 Moises Alou ME 1.25 3.00
606 Dante Bichette GS 1.25 3.00
607 Jim Edmonds CB 1.25 3.00
608 Mark Grace ME 2.00 5.00
609 Chan Ho Park ME 1.25 3.00
610 Justin Thompson ME .75 2.00
611 John Smoltz ME 2.00 5.00
612 Craig Biggio CB 2.00 5.00
613 Ken Caminiti ME 1.25 3.00
614 Deion Sanders ME 2.00 5.00
615 Carlos Delgado GS 1.25 3.00
616 David Justice CB 1.25 3.00
617 J.T. Snow GS 1.25 3.00
618 Jason Giambi CB 1.25 3.00
619 Garret Anderson ME 1.25 3.00
620 Rondell White ME 1.25 3.00
621 Matt Williams ME 1.25 3.00
622 Brady Anderson ME 1.25 3.00
623 Eric Karros GS 1.25 3.00
624 Javier Lopez GS 1.25 3.00
625 Pat Hentgen GS .75 2.00
626 Todd Hundley GS .75 2.00
627 Ray Lankford GS 1.25 3.00
628 Denny Neagle GS .75 2.00
629 Henry Rodriguez GS .75 2.00
630 Sandy Alomar Jr. ME .75 2.00
631 Rafael Palmeiro ME 2.00 5.00
632 Robin Ventura GS 1.25 3.00
633 John Olerud GS 1.25 3.00
634 Omar Vizquel GS 2.00 5.00
635 Joe Randa GS 1.25 3.00
636 Lance Johnson GS .75 2.00
637 Kevin Brown GS 2.00 5.00
638 Curt Schilling GS 1.25 3.00
639 Ismael Valdes GS .75 2.00
640 Francisco Cordova GS .75 2.00
641 David Cone GS 1.25 3.00
642 Paul O'Neill GS 2.00 5.00
643 Jimmy Key GS 1.25 3.00
644 Brad Radke GS 1.25 3.00
645 Kevin Appier GS 1.25 3.00
646 Al Martin GS .75 2.00
647 Rusty Greer ME 1.25 3.00
648 Reggie Jefferson GS .75 2.00
649 Ron Coomer GS .75 2.00
650 Vinny Castilla GS 1.25 3.00
651 Bobby Bonilla ME 1.25 3.00
652 Eric Young GS .75 2.00
653 Tony Womack GS .75 2.00
654 Jason Kendall GS 1.25 3.00
655 Jeff Suppan GS .75 2.00
656 Shawn Estes ME .75 2.00
657 Shawn Green GS 1.25 3.00
658 Edgardo Alfonzo ME .75 2.00
659 Alan Benes ME .75 2.00
660 Bobby Higginson GS 1.25 3.00
661 Mark Grudzielanek GS .75 2.00
662 Wilton Guerrero GS .75 2.00
663 Todd Greene ME .75 2.00
664 Pokey Reese GS .75 2.00
665 Jose Guillen CB 1.25 3.00
666 Neifi Perez ME .75 2.00
667 Luis Castillo GS .75 2.00
668 Edgar Renteria GS 1.25 3.00
669 Karim Garcia GS .75 2.00
670 Butch Huskey GS .75 2.00
671 Michael Tucker GS .75 2.00
672 Jason Dickson GS .75 2.00
673 Todd Walker ME .75 2.00
674 Brian Jordan GS 1.25 3.00
675 Joe Carter GS 1.25 3.00
676 Matt Morris ME 1.25 3.00
677 Brett Tomko ME .75 2.00
678 Mike Cameron CB .75 2.00
679 Russ Davis GS .75 2.00
680 Shannon Stewart ME 1.25 3.00
681 Kevin Orie GS .75 2.00
682 Scott Spiezio GS .75 2.00
683 Brian Giles GS 1.25 3.00
684 Raul Casanova GS .75 2.00
685 Jose Cruz Jr. CB .75 2.00
686 Hideki Irabu GS .75 2.00
687 Bubba Trammell GS .75 2.00
688 Richard Hidalgo CB .75 2.00
689 Paul Konerko CB 1.25 3.00
690 Todd Helton FB 2.00 5.00
691 Miguel Tejada CB 3.00 8.00
692 Fernando Tatis ME .75 2.00
693 Ben Grieve FB .75 2.00
694 Travis Lee FB .75 2.00
695 Mark Kotsay CB 1.25 3.00
696 Eli Marrero ME .75 2.00
697 David Ortiz CB 4.00 10.00
698 Juan Encarnacion ME .75 2.00
699 Jaret Wright ME .75 2.00
700 Livan Hernandez CB 1.25 3.00
701 Ruben Rivera GS .75 2.00
702 Brad Fullmer ME .75 2.00
703 Dennis Reyes GS .75 2.00
704 Enrique Wilson ME .75 2.00
705 Todd Dunwoody ME .75 2.00
706 Derrick Gibson ME .75 2.00
707 Aaron Boone ME 1.25 3.00
708 Ron Wright ME .75 2.00
709 Preston Wilson ME 1.25 3.00
710 Abraham Nunez GS .75 2.00
711 Shane Monahan GS .75 2.00
712 Carl Pavano GS 1.25 3.00
713 Derrek Lee GS 2.00 5.00
714 Jeff Abbott GS .75 2.00
715 Wes Helms ME .75 2.00
716 Brian Rose GS .75 2.00
717 Bobby Estalella GS .75 2.00
718 Ken Griffey Jr. PP GS 3.00 8.00
719 Frank Thomas PP GS 2.00 5.00
720 Cal Ripken PP GS 5.00 12.00
721 Alex Rodriguez PP GS 3.00 8.00
722 Greg Maddux PP GS 3.00 8.00
723 Mike Piazza PP GS 3.00 8.00
724 Chipper Jones PP GS 2.00 5.00
725 Tony Gwynn PP GS 2.00 5.00
726 Derek Jeter PP GS 4.00 10.00
727 Jeff Bagwell PP GS 1.25 3.00
728 Juan Gonzalez PP GS 1.25 3.00
729 N. Garciaparra PP GS 3.00 8.00
730 Andruw Jones PP GS 1.25 3.00
731 Hideo Nomo PP GS 2.00 5.00
732 R.Clemens PP GS 3.00 8.00
733 Mark McGwire PP GS 4.00 10.00
734 Scott Rolen PP GS 2.00 5.00
735 Barry Bonds PP GS 3.00 8.00
736 Darin Erstad PP GS .75 2.00
737 Mo Vaughn PP GS .75 2.00
738 Ivan Rodriguez PP GS 2.00 5.00
739 Larry Walker PP ME 1.25 3.00
740 Andy Pettitte PP GS 1.25 3.00
741 R.Johnson PP ME 2.00 5.00
742 Paul Molitor PP GS .75 2.00
743 Jim Thome PP GS 1.25 3.00
744 Tino Martinez PP ME 1.25 3.00
745 Gary Sheffield PP GS .75 2.00
746 Albert Belle PP GS .75 2.00
747 Jose Cruz Jr. PP GS .75 2.00
748 Todd Helton CL GS 1.25 3.00
749 Ben Grieve CL GS .75 2.00
750 Paul Konerko CL GS .75 2.00

1998 Donruss Prized Collections Preferred

These cards parallel the already parallelled Donruss Preferred set. According to published reports, less than 55 sets were produced.

*STARS: 1.25X TO 3X BASIC PREF.COLL.

1997 Donruss Elite

The 1997 Donruss Elite set was issued in one series totalling 150 cards. The product was distributed exclusively to hobby dealers around February, 1997. Each foil-wrapped pack contained eight cards and carried a suggested retail price of $3.49. Player selection was limited to the top stars (plus three player checklist cards) and card design is very similar to the Donruss Elite hockey set that was released one year earlier. Strangely enough, the backs only provide career statistics neglecting statistics from the previous season.

COMPLETE SET (150) 10.00 25.00
1 Juan Gonzalez .15 .40
2 Alex Rodriguez .60 1.50
3 Frank Thomas .40 1.00
4 Greg Maddux .60 1.50
5 Ken Griffey Jr. .60 1.50
6 Cal Ripken 1.25 3.00
7 Mike Piazza .60 1.50
8 Chipper Jones .40 1.00
9 Albert Belle .15 .40
10 Andruw Jones .25 .60
11 Vladimir Guerrero .40 1.00
12 Mo Vaughn .15 .40
UER front Gonzales
13 Ivan Rodriguez .25 .60
14 Andy Pettitte .25 .60
15 Tony Gwynn .50 1.25
16 Barry Bonds 1.00 2.50
17 Jeff Bagwell .25 .60
18 Manny Ramirez .25 .60
19 Kenny Lofton .15 .40
20 Roberto Alomar .25 .60
21 Mark McGwire 1.00 2.50
22 Ryan Klesko .15 .40
23 Tim Salmon .25 .60
24 Derek Jeter 1.00 2.50
25 Eddie Murray .40 1.00
26 Jermaine Dye .15 .40
27 Ruben Rivera .15 .40
28 Jim Edmonds .15 .40
29 Mike Mussina .25 .60
30 Randy Johnson .40 1.00
31 Sammy Sosa .40 1.00
32 Hideo Nomo .40 1.00
33 Chuck Knoblauch .15 .40
34 Paul Molitor .15 .40
35 Rafael Palmeiro .25 .60
36 Brady Anderson .15 .40
37 Will Clark .25 .60
38 Craig Biggio .25 .60
39 Jason Giambi .15 .40
40 Roger Clemens .75 2.00
41 Jay Buhner .15 .40
42 Edgar Martinez .25 .60
43 Gary Sheffield .15 .40
44 Fred McGriff .25 .60
45 Bobby Bonilla .15 .40
46 Tom Glavine .25 .60
47 Wade Boggs .25 .60
48 Jeff Conine .15 .40
49 John Smoltz .25 .60
50 Jim Thome .25 .60
51 Billy Wagner .15 .40
52 Jose Canseco .25 .60
53 Javy Lopez .15 .40
54 Cecil Fielder .15 .40
55 Garret Anderson .15 .40
56 Alex Ochoa .15 .40
57 Scott Rolen .25 .60
58 Darin Erstad .15 .40
59 Rey Ordonez .15 .40
60 Dante Bichette .15 .40
61 Joe Carter .15 .40
62 Moises Alou .15 .40
63 Jason Isringhausen .15 .40
64 Karim Garcia .15 .40
65 Brian Jordan .15 .40
66 Ruben Sierra .15 .40
67 Todd Hollandsworth .15 .40
68 Paul Wilson .15 .40
69 Ernie Young .15 .40
70 Ryne Sandberg .60 1.50
71 Raul Mondesi .15 .40
72 George Arias .15 .40
73 Ray Durham .15 .40
74 Dean Palmer .15 .40
75 Shawn Green .15 .40
76 Eric Young .15 .40
77 Jason Kendall .15 .40
78 Greg Vaughn .15 .40
79 Terrell Wade .15 .40
80 Bill Pulsipher .15 .40
81 Bobby Higginson .15 .40
82 Mark Grudzielanek .15 .40
83 Ken Caminiti .15 .40
84 Todd Greene .15 .40
85 Carlos Delgado .15 .40
86 Mark Grace .25 .60
87 Rondell White .15 .40
88 Barry Larkin .25 .60
89 J.T. Snow .15 .40
90 Alex Gonzalez .15 .40
91 Raul Casanova .15 .40
92 Marc Newfield .15 .40
93 Jermaine Allensworth .15 .40
94 John Mabry .15 .40
95 Kirby Puckett .40 1.00
96 Travis Fryman .15 .40
97 Kevin Brown .15 .40
98 Andres Galarraga .15 .40
99 Marty Cordova .15 .40
100 Henry Rodriguez .15 .40
101 Sterling Hitchcock .15 .40
102 Trey Beamon .15 .40
103 Brett Butler .15 .40
104 Rickey Henderson .40 1.00
105 Tino Martinez .25 .60
106 Kevin Appier .15 .40
107 Brian Hunter .15 .40
108 Eric Karros .15 .40
109 Andre Dawson .15 .40
110 Darryl Strawberry .15 .40
111 James Baldwin .15 .40
112 Chad Mottola .15 .40
113 Dave Nilsson .15 .40
114 Carlos Baerga .15 .40
115 Chan Ho Park .15 .40
116 John Jaha .15 .40
117 Alan Benes .15 .40
118 Mariano Rivera .40 1.00
119 Ellis Burks .15 .40
120 Tony Clark .15 .40
121 Todd Walker .15 .40
122 Dwight Gooden .15 .40
123 Ugueth Urbina .15 .40
124 David Cone .15 .40
125 Ozzie Smith .60 1.50
126 Kimera Bartee .15 .40
127 Rusty Greer .15 .40
128 Pat Hentgen .15 .40
129 Charles Johnson .15 .40
130 Quinton McCracken .15 .40
131 Troy Percival .15 .40
132 Shane Reynolds .15 .40
133 Charles Nagy .15 .40
134 Tom Goodwin .15 .40
135 Ron Gant .15 .40
136 Dan Wilson .15 .40
137 Matt Williams .15 .40
138 LaTroy Hawkins .15 .40
139 Kevin Seitzer .15 .40
140 Michael Tucker .15 .40
141 Todd Hundley .15 .40
142 Alex Fernandez .15 .40
143 Marquis Grissom .15 .40
144 Steve Finley .15 .40
145 Curtis Pride .15 .40
146 Derek Bell .15 .40
147 Butch Huskey .15 .40
148 Dwight Gooden CL .15 .40
149 Al Leiter CL .15 .40
150 Hideo Nomo CL .15 .40

1997 Donruss Elite Gold Stars

Randomly seeded into one in every nine packs, cards from this set parallel the 150-card base issue. The distinctive gold foil fronts easily differentiate them from their silver-foiled base-issue brethren. The following cards were erroneously printed with a silver (rather than gold) logo on front: 6, 15, 25, 32, 42, 47, 57, 60, 69 and 70. Corrected gold logo versions of these cards do exist but are in far shorter supply though secondary market trading values remain similar due to general indifference. The set is considered complete with the erroneous silver logo cards.

*STARS: 4X TO 10X BASIC CARDS

1997 Donruss Elite Leather and Lumber

This ten-card insert set features color action veteran player photos printed on two unique materials. The fronts display a player image on real wood card stock with the end of a baseball bat as background. The backs carry another player photo printed on genuine leather card stock with a baseball and glove as background. Only 500 of each card was produced and are sequentially numbered.

1 Ken Griffey Jr.	15.00	40.00
2 Alex Rodriguez	15.00	40.00
3 Frank Thomas	10.00	25.00
4 Chipper Jones	10.00	25.00
5 Ivan Rodriguez	6.00	15.00
6 Cal Ripken	30.00	80.00
7 Barry Bonds	25.00	60.00
8 Chuck Knoblauch	4.00	10.00
9 Manny Ramirez	6.00	15.00
10 Mark McGwire	25.00	60.00

1997 Donruss Elite Passing the Torch

This 12-card insert set features eight players on four double-sided cards. A color portrait of a superstar veteran is displayed on one side with a gold foil background, and a portrait of a rising young star is printed on the flipside. Each of the eight players also has his own card to round out the 12-card set. Only 1500 of this set were produced and are sequentially numbered. However, only 1,350 of each card are available without autographs.

COMPLETE SET (12)	100.00	250.00
1 Cal Ripken	15.00	40.00
2 Alex Rodriguez	8.00	20.00
3 Cal Ripken	20.00	50.00
Alex Rodriguez		
4 Kirby Puckett	5.00	12.00
5 Andruw Jones	3.00	8.00
6 Kirby Puckett	4.00	10.00
Andruw Jones		
7 Cecil Fielder	2.00	5.00
8 Frank Thomas	5.00	12.00
9 Cecil Fielder	4.00	10.00
Frank Thomas		
10 Ozzie Smith	8.00	20.00
11 Derek Jeter	12.50	30.00
12 Ozzie Smith	12.50	30.00
Derek Jeter		

1997 Donruss Elite Passing the Torch Autographs

This 12-card set consists of the first 150 sets of the regular "Passing the Torch" set with each card displaying an authentic player autograph. The set features a double front design which captures eight of the league's top superstars, alternating one of four different megastars on the flipside. An individual card for each of the eight players rounds out the set. Each set is sequentially numbered to 150.

1 Cal Ripken	175.00	300.00
2 Alex Rodriguez	125.00	250.00
3 Cal Ripken	500.00	800.00
Alex Rodriguez		
4 Kirby Puckett	60.00	120.00
5 Andruw Jones	30.00	60.00
6 Kirby Puckett	150.00	300.00
Andruw Jones		
7 Cecil Fielder	20.00	50.00
8 Frank Thomas	50.00	100.00
9 Cecil Fielder	60.00	120.00
Frank Thomas		
10 Ozzie Smith	75.00	150.00
11 Derek Jeter	200.00	400.00
12 Ozzie Smith	200.00	350.00
Derek Jeter		

1997 Donruss Elite Turn of the Century

This 20-card set showcases the stars of the next millennium and features a color player image on a silver-and-black background. The backs display another player photo with a short paragraph about the player. Only 3,500 of this set were produced and are sequentially numbered, but the first 500 sets were devoted to the TOC Die Cuts parallel.

COMPLETE SET (20)	50.00	120.00
*DIE CUTS: 1.25X TO 3X BASIC TURN CENT.		
DC STATED PRINT RUN 500 SERIAL #'d SETS		
RANDOM INSERTS IN PACKS		
1 Alex Rodriguez	6.00	15.00
2 Andruw Jones	2.50	6.00
3 Chipper Jones	4.00	10.00
4 Todd Walker	1.50	4.00
5 Scott Rolen	2.50	6.00
6 Trey Beamon	1.50	4.00
7 Derek Jeter	10.00	25.00
8 Darin Erstad	1.50	4.00
9 Tony Clark	1.50	4.00
10 Todd Greene	1.50	4.00
11 Jason Giambi	1.50	4.00
12 Justin Thompson	1.50	4.00
13 Ernie Young	1.50	4.00
14 Jason Kendall	1.50	4.00
15 Alex Ochoa	1.50	4.00
16 Brooks Kieschnick	1.50	4.00
17 Bobby Higginson	1.50	4.00
18 Ruben Rivera	1.50	4.00
19 Chan Ho Park	1.50	4.00
20 Chad Mottola	1.50	4.00
P5 Scott Rolen PROMO	.75	2.00
P7 Derek Jeter PROMO	1.25	3.00
P20 Chad Mottola PROMO	.40	1.00

1998 Donruss Elite

The 1998 Donruss Elite set was issued in one series totalling 150 cards and distributed in five-card packs with a suggested retail price of $3.99. The fronts feature color player action photos. The backs carry player information. The set contains the topical subset: Generations (118-147). A special embossed Frank Thomas autograph card (parallel to basic issue card number two, except, of course, for Thomas' signature) was available to lucky collectors who pulled a Back to the Future Frank Thomas/David Ortiz card serial numbered between 1 and 100 and redeemed it to Donruss/Leaf.

COMPLETE SET (150)	10.00	25.00
1 Ken Griffey Jr.	.50	1.25
2 Frank Thomas	.30	.75
3 Alex Rodriguez	.50	1.25
4 Mike Piazza	.50	1.25
5 Greg Maddux	.50	1.25
6 Cal Ripken	1.00	2.50
7 Chipper Jones	.30	.75
8 Derek Jeter	.75	2.00
9 Tony Gwynn	.40	1.00
10 Andruw Jones	.20	.50
11 Juan Gonzalez	.10	.30
12 Jeff Bagwell	.20	.50
13 Mark McGwire	.75	2.00
14 Roger Clemens	.60	1.50
15 Albert Belle	.10	.30
16 Barry Bonds	.75	2.00
17 Kenny Lofton	.10	.30
18 Ivan Rodriguez	.20	.50
19 Manny Ramirez	.20	.50
20 Jim Thome	.20	.50
21 Chuck Knoblauch	.10	.30
22 Paul Molitor	.10	.30
23 Barry Larkin	.20	.50
24 Andy Pettitte	.20	.50
25 John Smoltz	.20	.50
26 Randy Johnson	.30	.75
27 Bernie Williams	.20	.50
28 Larry Walker	.10	.30
29 Mo Vaughn	.10	.30
30 Bobby Higginson	.10	.30
31 Edgardo Alfonzo	.10	.30
32 Justin Thompson	.10	.30
33 Jeff Suppan	.10	.30
34 Roberto Alomar	.20	.50
35 Hideo Nomo	.30	.75
36 Rusty Greer	.10	.30
37 Tim Salmon	.20	.50
38 Jim Edmonds	.10	.30
39 Gary Sheffield	.10	.30
40 Ken Caminiti	.10	.30
41 Sammy Sosa	.30	.75
42 Tony Womack	.10	.30
43 Matt Williams	.10	.30
44 Andres Galarraga	.10	.30
45 Garret Anderson	.10	.30
46 Rafael Palmeiro	.20	.50
47 Mike Mussina	.20	.50
48 Craig Biggio	.20	.50
49 Wade Boggs	.20	.50
50 Tom Glavine	.20	.50
51 Jason Giambi	.10	.30
52 Will Clark	.20	.50
53 David Justice	.10	.30
54 Sandy Alomar Jr.	.10	.30
55 Edgar Martinez	.20	.50
56 Brady Anderson	.10	.30
57 Eric Young	.10	.30
58 Ray Lankford	.10	.30
59 Kevin Brown	.20	.50
60 Raul Mondesi	.10	.30
61 Bobby Bonilla	.10	.30
62 Javier Lopez	.10	.30
63 Fred McGriff	.20	.50
64 Rondell White	.10	.30
65 Todd Hundley	.10	.30
66 Mark Grace	.20	.50
67 Alan Benes	.10	.30
68 Jeff Abbott	.10	.30
69 Bob Abreu	.10	.30
70 Deion Sanders	.20	.50
71 Tino Martinez	.20	.50
72 Shannon Stewart	.10	.30
73 Homer Bush	.10	.30
74 Carlos Delgado	.10	.30
75 Raul Ibanez	.10	.30
76 Hideki Irabu	.10	.30
77 Jose Cruz Jr.	.10	.30
78 Tony Clark	.10	.30
79 Wilton Guerrero	.10	.30
80 Vladimir Guerrero	.30	.75
81 Scott Rolen	.20	.50
82 Nomar Garciaparra	.50	1.25
83 Darin Erstad	.10	.30
84 Chan Ho Park	.10	.30
85 Mike Cameron	.10	.30
86 Todd Walker	.10	.30
87 Todd Dunwoody	.10	.30
88 Neifi Perez	.10	.30
89 Brett Tomko	.10	.30
90 Jose Guillen	.10	.30
91 Matt Morris	.10	.30
92 Bartolo Colon	.10	.30
93 Jaret Wright	.10	.30
94 Shawn Estes	.10	.30
95 Livan Hernandez	.10	.30
96 Bobby Estalella	.10	.30
97 Ben Grieve	.10	.30
98 Paul Konerko	.10	.30
99 David Ortiz	.40	1.00
100 Todd Helton	.20	.50
101 Juan Encarnacion	.10	.30
102 Bubba Trammell	.10	.30
103 Miguel Tejada	.30	.75
104 Jacob Cruz	.10	.30
105 Todd Greene	.10	.30
106 Kevin Orie	.10	.30
107 Mark Kotsay	.10	.30
108 Fernando Tatis	.10	.30
109 Jay Payton	.10	.30
110 Pokey Reese	.10	.30
111 Derrek Lee	.20	.50
112 Richard Hidalgo	.10	.30
113 Ricky Ledee	.10	.30
UER front Rickey		
114 Lou Collier	.10	.30
115 Ruben Rivera	.10	.30
116 Shawn Green	.10	.30
117 Moises Alou	.10	.30
118 Ken Griffey Jr. GEN	.30	.75
119 Frank Thomas GEN	.20	.50
120 Alex Rodriguez GEN	.30	.75
121 Mike Piazza GEN	.30	.75
122 Greg Maddux GEN	.30	.75
123 Cal Ripken GEN	.50	1.25
124 Chipper Jones GEN	.20	.50
125 Derek Jeter GEN	.40	1.00
126 Tony Gwynn GEN	.20	.50
127 Andruw Jones GEN	.10	.30
128 Juan Gonzalez GEN	.10	.30
129 Jeff Bagwell GEN	.10	.30
130 Mark McGwire GEN	.40	1.00
131 Roger Clemens GEN	.30	.75
132 Albert Belle GEN	.10	.30
133 Barry Bonds GEN	.40	1.00
134 Kenny Lofton GEN	.10	.30
135 Ivan Rodriguez GEN	.10	.30
136 Manny Ramirez GEN	.20	.50
137 Jim Thome GEN	.10	.30
138 C.Knoblauch GEN	.10	.30
139 Paul Molitor GEN	.10	.30
140 Barry Larkin GEN	.10	.30
141 Mo Vaughn GEN	.10	.30
142 Hideki Irabu GEN	.10	.30
143 Jose Cruz Jr. GEN	.10	.30
144 Tony Clark GEN	.10	.30
145 V.Guerrero GEN	.20	.50
146 Scott Rolen GEN	.10	.30
147 N.Garciaparra GEN	.30	.75
148 Nomar Garciaparra CL	.30	.75
149 Larry Walker CL	.10	.30
150 Tino Martinez CL	.10	.30
AU2 F.Thomas AUTO/100	40.00	80.00

1998 Donruss Elite Aspirations

Randomly inserted in packs, this 150-card set is parallel to the base set. Only 750 of this set were produced and are sequentially numbered.

*ASPIRATION: 3X TO 8X BASIC CARDS

1998 Donruss Elite Status

Randomly inserted in packs, this 150-card set is parallel to the base set. Only 100 of this set were produced and are serially numbered.

*STATUS: 10X TO 25X BASIC

1998 Donruss Elite Back to the Future

Randomly inserted in packs, this eight-card set is double-sided and features color images of top veteran and new players on a tile background. Only 1,500 of each card were produced and sequentially numbered but the first 100 #'d cards were devoted to the Back to the Future Autograph parallel set.

COMPLETE SET (8)	50.00	120.00
1 Cal Ripken	12.50	30.00
Paul Konerko		
2 Jeff Bagwell	2.50	6.00
Todd Helton		
3 Eddie Mathews	4.00	10.00
Chipper Jones		
4 Juan Gonzalez	1.50	4.00
Ben Grieve		
5 Hank Aaron	6.00	15.00
Jose Cruz Jr.		
6 Frank Thomas	5.00	12.00
David Ortiz		
1-100		
7 Nolan Ryan	15.00	40.00
Greg Maddux		
8 Alex Rodriguez	6.00	15.00
Nomar Garciaparra		

1998 Donruss Elite Back to the Future Autographs

Randomly inserted in packs, this seven-card set is a parallel version of the the regular 1998 Donruss Elite Back to the Future insert set and contains the first 100 cards of the regular set signed by both pictured players. Card number six does not exist. Cal Ripken did not sign card number 1 along with Paul Konerko. Ripken eventually signed 200 separate cards. One hundred special redemptions (rather bland black and white text-based cards) were issued for the Ripken card and randomly seeded into packs. In addition, lucky collectors that pulled one of the first 100 serial numbered Back to the Future Konerko autograph cards could exchange it for a Ripken autograph AND still receive their Konerko autograph back. The first 100 of each card were autographed by both players pictured on the card. There is no autographed card number six. Due to problems in obtaining Frank Thomas' autograph prior to the shipping deadline for the parallel signed Back to the Future cards, the manufacturer was forced to make the first 100 serial numbered cards of card number 6 a redemption for a special Frank Thomas autographed card (a basic 1998 Donruss Elite Thomas card, embossed with a special stamp and signed by Thomas on front). Due to Pinnacle's bankruptcy, the exchange program was abruptly halted in late 1998. Prior to this, the serial numbered 1-100 Thomas/Ortiz cards traded for as much as $300. After this date, the premiums disappeared entirely.

1A Cal Ripken	15.00	40.00
Paul Konerko Redeemed/100		
Redeemed card signed only by Konerko		
1B C. Ripken AU/200	125.00	200.00
Redeemed card signed only by Ripken		
2 Jeff Bagwell	75.00	150.00
Todd Helton		
3 Eddie Mathews	150.00	250.00
Chipper Jones		
4 Juan Gonzalez	50.00	100.00
Ben Grieve		
5 Hank Aaron	150.00	250.00
Jose Cruz Jr.		
7 Nolan Ryan	800.00	1200.00
Greg Maddux		
8 Alex Rodriguez	400.00	600.00
Nomar Garciaparra		

1998 Donruss Elite Craftsmen

Randomly inserted in packs, this 30-card set features color photos of players who are the best at what they do. Only 3,500 of this set were produced and are sequentially numbered.

COMPLETE SET (30)	60.00	150.00
*MASTER: 2.5X TO 6X BASIC CRAFTSMEN		
MASTER PRINT RUN 100 SERIAL #'d SETS		
RANDOM INSERTS IN PACKS		
1 Ken Griffey Jr.	4.00	10.00
2 Frank Thomas	2.50	6.00
3 Alex Rodriguez	4.00	10.00
4 Cal Ripken	8.00	20.00
5 Greg Maddux	4.00	10.00
6 Mike Piazza	4.00	10.00
7 Chipper Jones	2.50	6.00
8 Derek Jeter	6.00	15.00
9 Tony Gwynn	3.00	8.00
10 Nomar Garciaparra	4.00	10.00
11 Scott Rolen	1.50	4.00
12 Jose Cruz Jr.	1.00	2.50
13 Tony Clark	1.00	2.50
14 Vladimir Guerrero	2.50	6.00
15 Todd Helton	1.50	4.00
16 Ben Grieve	1.00	2.50
17 Andruw Jones	1.50	4.00
18 Jeff Bagwell	1.50	4.00
19 Mark McGwire	6.00	15.00
20 Juan Gonzalez	1.00	2.50
21 Roger Clemens	5.00	12.00
22 Albert Belle	1.00	2.50
23 Barry Bonds	6.00	15.00
24 Kenny Lofton	1.00	2.50
25 Ivan Rodriguez	1.50	4.00
26 Paul Molitor	1.00	2.50
27 Barry Larkin UER	1.50	4.00
His team was midentified as the Cardinals		
28 Mo Vaughn	1.00	2.50
29 Larry Walker	1.00	2.50
30 Tino Martinez	1.50	4.00

1998 Donruss Elite Prime Numbers Samples

Promotional samples were created for all 36 Prime Numbers inserts and distributed one per wholesale dealer order form. The cards are identical to regular Prime Numbers inserts except for the large "SAMPLE" text running diagonally across the backs and lack of serial numbering.

COMPLETE SET (36)	140.00	350.00
1A Ken Griffey Jr. 2	5.00	12.00
1B Ken Griffey Jr. 9	5.00	12.00
1C Ken Griffey Jr. 4	5.00	12.00
2A Frank Thomas 4	2.50	6.00
2B Frank Thomas 5	2.50	6.00
2C Frank Thomas 6	2.50	6.00
3A Mark McGwire 3	6.00	15.00
3B Mark McGwire 8	6.00	15.00
3C Mark McGwire 7	6.00	15.00
4A Cal Ripken 5	8.00	20.00
4B Cal Ripken 1	8.00	20.00
4C Cal Ripken 7	8.00	20.00
5A Mike Piazza 5	6.00	15.00
5B Mike Piazza 7	6.00	15.00
5C Mike Piazza 6	6.00	15.00
6A Chipper Jones 4	4.00	10.00
6B Chipper Jones 8	4.00	10.00
6C Chipper Jones 9	4.00	10.00
7A Tony Gwynn 3	4.00	10.00
7B Tony Gwynn 7	4.00	10.00
7C Tony Gwynn 2	4.00	10.00
8A Barry Bonds 3	4.00	10.00
8B Barry Bonds 7	4.00	10.00
8C Barry Bonds 4	4.00	10.00
9A Jeff Bagwell 4	2.50	6.00
9B Jeff Bagwell 2	2.50	6.00
9C Jeff Bagwell 5	2.50	6.00
10A Juan Gonzalez 5	2.00	5.00
10B Juan Gonzalez 8	2.00	5.00
10C Juan Gonzalez 9	2.00	5.00
11A Alex Rodriguez 5	6.00	15.00
11B Alex Rodriguez 3	6.00	15.00
11C Alex Rodriguez 4	6.00	15.00
12A Kenny Lofton 3	1.50	4.00
12B Kenny Lofton 5	1.50	4.00
12C Kenny Lofton 4	1.50	4.00

1998 Donruss Elite Prime Numbers

Randomly inserted in packs, this 36-card set features three cards each of 12 top players in the league printed with three different numerical backgrounds (of which form a statistical benchmark when placed together). The total number of each card produced depended on the player's particular statistic. Print runs are included below in parentheses at the end of each card description.

1A Ken Griffey Jr. 2 (94)	20.00	50.00
1B Ken Griffey Jr. 9 (204)	10.00	25.00
1C Ken Griffey Jr. 4 (290)	8.00	20.00
2A Frank Thomas 4 (56)	15.00	40.00
2B Frank Thomas 5 (406)	4.00	10.00
2C Frank Thomas 6 (450)	4.00	10.00
3A Mark McGwire 3 (87)	40.00	100.00
3B Mark McGwire 8 (307)	15.00	40.00
3C Mark McGwire 7 (380)	15.00	40.00
4A Cal Ripken 5 (17)	150.00	400.00
4B Cal Ripken 1 (507)	12.50	30.00
4C Cal Ripken 7 (510)	12.50	30.00
5A Mike Piazza 5 (76)	20.00	50.00
5B Mike Piazza 7 (506)	6.00	15.00
5C Mike Piazza 6 (570)	6.00	15.00
6A Chipper Jones 4 (89)	12.50	30.00
6B Chipper Jones 8 (409)	4.00	10.00
6C Chipper Jones 9 (480)	4.00	10.00
7A Tony Gwynn 3 (72)	15.00	40.00
7B Tony Gwynn 7 (302)	6.00	15.00
7C Tony Gwynn 2 (370)	6.00	15.00
8A Barry Bonds 3 (74)	30.00	80.00
8B Barry Bonds 7 (304)	12.50	30.00
8C Barry Bonds 4 (370)	12.50	30.00
9A Jeff Bagwell 4 (25)	25.00	60.00
9B Jeff Bagwell 2 (405)	2.50	6.00
9C Jeff Bagwell 5 (420)	2.50	6.00
10A Juan Gonzalez 5 (89)	6.00	15.00
10B J.Gonzalez 8 (509)	2.00	5.00
10C J.Gonzalez 9 (580)	2.00	5.00
11A Alex Rodriguez 5 (34)	30.00	80.00
11B A.Rodriguez 3 (504)	6.00	15.00
11C A.Rodriguez 4 (530)	6.00	15.00
12A Kenny Lofton 3 (54)	8.00	20.00
12B Kenny Lofton 5 (304)	2.00	5.00
12C Kenny Lofton 4 (350)	2.00	5.00

1998 Donruss Elite Prime Numbers Die Cuts

Randomly inserted in packs, this 36-card set is a die-cut parallel version to the regular Donruss Elite Prime Numbers set. Print runs are included below in parentheses at the end of each card description. Cards printed in quantites of 10 or less are identified in the checklist but not priced below.

1A Ken Griffey Jr. 2 (200)	10.00	25.00
1B Ken Griffey Jr. 9 (90)	20.00	50.00
1C Ken Griffey Jr. 4 (4)		
2A Frank Thomas 4 (400)	4.00	10.00
2B Frank Thomas 5 (50)	15.00	40.00
2C Frank Thomas 6 (6)		
3A Mark McGwire 3 (300)	15.00	40.00
3B Mark McGwire 8 (80)	40.00	100.00
3C Mark McGwire 7 (7)		
4A Cal Ripken 5 (500)	12.50	30.00
4B Cal Ripken 1 (10)		
4C Cal Ripken 7 (7)		
5A Mike Piazza 5 (500)	6.00	15.00
5B Mike Piazza 7 (70)	20.00	50.00
5C Mike Piazza 6 (6)		
6A Chipper Jones 4 (400)	4.00	10.00
6B Chipper Jones 8 (80)	12.50	30.00
7A Tony Gwynn 3 (300)	6.00	15.00
7B Tony Gwynn 7 (70)	15.00	40.00
7C Tony Gwynn 2 (2)		
8A Barry Bonds 3 (300)	12.50	30.00
8B Barry Bonds 7 (70)	30.00	80.00
8C Barry Bonds 4 (4)		
9A Jeff Bagwell 4 (400)	2.50	6.00
9B Jeff Bagwell 2 (20)	30.00	80.00
9C Jeff Bagwell 5 (5)		
10A J.Gonzalez 5 (500)	2.00	5.00
10B Juan Gonzalez 8 (80)	6.00	15.00
10C Juan Gonzalez 9 (9)		
11A A.Rodriguez 5 (500)	6.00	15.00
11B Alex Rodriguez 3 (30)	40.00	100.00
11C Alex Rodriguez 4 (4)		
12A Kenny Lofton 3 (300)	2.00	5.00
12B Kenny Lofton 5 (50)	8.00	20.00
12C Kenny Lofton 4 (4)		

2001 Donruss Elite

This 200-card hobby only set was distributed in May, 2001 in five-card packs with a suggested retail price of $3.99 and features color photos of some of Baseball's finest players and hot rookies. The low series rookie cards are sequentially numbered to 1000 with the first 100 labeled "Turn of the Century." Cards 201-250 were issued as exchange coupons for unspecified rookies and prospects and randomly seeded into packs at a rate of 1:14. Specific players for each exchange card were announced on Donruss' website in late October, 2001 (and about 15 players were dropped and updated with new players about a month later). The deadline to redeem the coupons was originally 11/01/01 but it was extended to January 20th, 2002. Each coupon carried a cost of $5.99 to redeem. In April of 2002 representatives at Donruss-Playoff released explicit quantities for each of these exchange cards, of which ranged from as few as 377 to as many as 556. All of these cards are actually serial-numbered "XXX/1000" on back but were mailed out in non-sequential order, thus cards serial-numbered as high as 900/1000 etc are in existence but it doesn't mean that 900+ copies were distributed. When the January 20th deadline passed, according to representatives at Donruss-Playoff, the remaining cards were destroyed. Please see our checklist for specific quantities of each card produced.

COMP.SET w/o SP's (150)	10.00	25.00
COMMON CARD (1-150)	.10	.30
COMMON (151-200)	3.00	8.00
COMMON CARD (201-250)	4.00	10.00
1 Alex Rodriguez	.50	1.25
2 Barry Bonds	.75	2.00
3 Cal Ripken	1.00	2.50
4 Chipper Jones	.30	.75
5 Derek Jeter	.75	2.00
6 Troy Glaus	.10	.30
7 Frank Thomas	.30	.75
8 Greg Maddux	.50	1.25
9 Ivan Rodriguez	.20	.50
10 Jeff Bagwell	.20	.50
11 Jose Canseco	.20	.50
12 Todd Helton	.20	.50
13 Ken Griffey Jr.	.50	1.25
14 Manny Ramirez Sox	.20	.50
15 Mark McGwire	.75	2.00
16 Mike Piazza	.50	1.25
17 Nomar Garciaparra	.50	1.25
18 Pedro Martinez	.20	.50
19 Randy Johnson	.30	.75
20 Rick Ankiel	.10	.30
21 Rickey Henderson	.30	.75
22 Roger Clemens	.60	1.50
23 Sammy Sosa	.30	.75
24 Tony Gwynn	.40	1.00
25 Vladimir Guerrero	.30	.75
26 Eric Davis	.10	.30
27 Roberto Alomar	.20	.50
28 Mark Mulder	.10	.30
29 Pat Burrell	.10	.30
30 Harold Baines	.10	.30
31 Carlos Delgado	.10	.30
32 J.D. Drew	.10	.30
33 Jim Edmonds	.10	.30
34 Darin Erstad	.10	.30
35 Jason Giambi	.10	.30
36 Tom Glavine	.20	.50
37 Juan Gonzalez	.10	.30
38 Mark Grace	.20	.50
39 Shawn Green	.10	.30
40 Tim Hudson	.10	.30
41 Andruw Jones	.20	.50
42 David Justice	.10	.30
43 Jeff Kent	.10	.30
44 Barry Larkin	.20	.50
45 Pokey Reese	.10	.30
46 Mike Mussina	.20	.50
47 Hideo Nomo	.30	.75
48 Rafael Palmeiro	.20	.50
49 Adam Piatt	.10	.30
50 Scott Rolen	.20	.50
51 Gary Sheffield	.10	.30
52 Bernie Williams	.20	.50
53 Bob Abreu	.10	.30
54 Edgardo Alfonzo	.10	.30
55 Jermaine Clark RC	.30	.75
56 Albert Belle	.10	.30
57 Craig Biggio	.20	.50
58 Andres Galarraga	.10	.30
59 Edgar Martinez	.20	.50
60 Fred McGriff	.20	.50
61 Maggilo Ordonez	.10	.30
62 Jim Thome	.20	.50
63 Matt Williams	.10	.30
64 Kerry Wood	.10	.30
65 Moises Alou	.10	.30
66 Brady Anderson	.10	.30
67 Garret Anderson	.10	.30
68 Tony Armas Jr.	.10	.30
69 Tony Batista	.10	.30
70 Jose Cruz Jr.	.10	.30
71 Carlos Beltran	.10	.30
72 Adrian Beltre	.10	.30
73 Kris Benson	.10	.30
74 Lance Berkman	.10	.30
75 Kevin Brown	.10	.30
76 Jay Buhner	.10	.30
77 Jeromy Burnitz	.10	.30
78 Ken Caminiti	.10	.30
79 Sean Casey	.10	.30
80 Luis Castillo	.10	.30
81 Eric Chavez	.10	.30
82 Jeff Cirillo	.10	.30
83 Bartolo Colon	.10	.30
84 David Cone	.10	.30
85 Freddy Garcia	.10	.30
86 Johnny Damon	.20	.50
87 Ray Durham	.10	.30
88 Jermaine Dye	.10	.30
89 Juan Encarnacion	.10	.30
90 Terrence Long	.10	.30
91 Carl Everett	.10	.30
92 Steve Finley	.10	.30
93 Cliff Floyd	.10	.30
94 Brad Fullmer	.10	.30
95 Brian Giles	.10	.30
96 Luis Gonzalez	.10	.30
97 Rusty Greer	.10	.30
98 Jeffrey Hammonds	.10	.30
99 Mike Hampton	.10	.30
100 Orlando Hernandez	.10	.30
101 Richard Hidalgo	.10	.30
102 Geoff Jenkins	.10	.30
103 Jacque Jones	.10	.30
104 Brian Jordan	.10	.30
105 Gabe Kapler	.10	.30
106 Eric Karros	.10	.30
107 Jason Kendall	.10	.30
108 Adam Kennedy	.10	.30
109 Byung-Hyun Kim	.10	.30
110 Ryan Klesko	.10	.30
111 Chuck Knoblauch	.10	.30
112 Paul Konerko	.10	.30
113 Carlos Lee	.10	.30
114 Kenny Lofton	.10	.30
115 Javy Lopez	.10	.30
116 Tino Martinez	.20	.50
117 Ruben Mateo	.10	.30
118 Kevin Millwood	.10	.30
119 Ben Molina	.10	.30
120 Raul Mondesi	.10	.30
121 Trot Nixon	.10	.30
122 John Olerud	.10	.30
123 Paul O'Neill	.20	.50
124 Chan Ho Park	.10	.30
125 Andy Pettitte	.20	.50
126 Jorge Posada	.20	.50
127 Mark Quinn	.10	.30
128 Aramis Ramirez	.10	.30
129 Mariano Rivera	.30	.75
130 Tim Salmon	.20	.50
131 Curt Schilling	.10	.30
132 Richie Sexson	.10	.30
133 John Smoltz	.20	.50
134 J.T. Snow	.10	.30
135 Jay Payton	.10	.30
136 Shannon Stewart	.10	.30
137 B.J. Surhoff	.10	.30
138 Mike Sweeney	.10	.30
139 Fernando Tatis	.10	.30
140 Miguel Tejada	.10	.30
141 Jason Varitek	.30	.75
142 Greg Vaughn	.10	.30
143 Mo Vaughn	.10	.30
144 Robin Ventura UER	.10	.30
Listed as playing for Yankees last 2 years,		
Also Bat and Throw information is wrong		
145 Jose Vidro	.10	.30

146 Omar Vizquel .20 .50
147 Larry Walker .10 .30
148 David Wells .10 .30
149 Rondell White .10 .30
150 Preston Wilson .10 .30
151 Brent Abernathy SP 3.00 8.00
152 Cory Aldridge SP RC 3.00 8.00
153 Gene Altman SP RC 3.00 8.00
154 Josh Beckett SP 4.00 10.00
155 Wilson Betemit SP RC 4.00 10.00
156 Albert Pujols SP RC 400.00 600.00
157 Joe Crede SP 4.00 10.00
158 Jack Cust SP 3.00 8.00
159 Ben Sheets SP 4.00 10.00
160 Alex Escobar SP 3.00 8.00
161 A. Hernandez SP RC 3.00 8.00
162 Pedro Feliz SP 3.00 8.00
163 Nate Frese SP RC 3.00 8.00
164 Carlos Garcia SP RC 3.00 8.00
165 Marcus Giles SP 3.00 8.00
166 Alexis Gomez SP RC 3.00 8.00
167 Jason Hart SP 3.00 8.00
168 Aubrey Huff SP 3.00 8.00
169 Cesar Izturis SP 3.00 8.00
170 Nick Johnson SP 3.00 8.00
171 Jack Wilson SP RC 4.00 10.00
172 B.Lawrence SP RC 3.00 8.00
173 C. Parker SP RC 3.00 8.00
174 Nick Maness SP RC 3.00 8.00
175 Jose Mieses SP RC 3.00 8.00
176 Greg Miller SP RC 3.00 8.00
177 Eric Munson SP 3.00 8.00
178 Xavier Nady SP 3.00 8.00
179 Blaine Neal SP RC 3.00 8.00
180 Abraham Nunez SP 3.00 8.00
181 Jose Ortiz SP 3.00 8.00
182 Jeremy Owens SP RC 3.00 8.00
183 Jay Gibbons SP RC 4.00 10.00
184 Corey Patterson SP 3.00 8.00
185 Carlos Pena SP 3.00 8.00
186 C.C. Sabathia SP 3.00 8.00
187 Timo Perez SP 3.00 8.00
188 A. Pettyjohn SP RC 3.00 8.00
189 D. Mendez SP RC 3.00 8.00
190 J. Melian SP RC 3.00 8.00
191 Wilkin Ruan SP RC 3.00 8.00
192 D. Sanchez SP RC 3.00 8.00
193 Alfonso Soriano SP 4.00 10.00
194 Rafael Soriano SP RC 3.00 8.00
195 Ichiro Suzuki SP RC 40.00 80.00
196 Billy Sylvester SP RC 3.00 8.00
197 Juan Uribe SP RC 4.00 10.00
198 T. Shinjo SP RC 4.00 10.00
199 C. Valderrama SP RC 3.00 8.00
200 Matt White SP RC 3.00 8.00
201 Adam Dunn/468 6.00 15.00
202 Joe Kennedy/465 XRC 6.00 15.00
203 Mike Rivera/427 XRC 4.00 10.00
204 Erick Almonte/401 XRC 4.00 10.00
205 Bran Duckworth EXCH 4.00 10.00
206 Victor Martinez/410 XRC 15.00 40.00
207 Rick Bauer/390 XRC 4.00 10.00
208 Jeff Deardorff/396 XRC 4.00 10.00
209 Antonio Perez/448 XRC 6.00 15.00
210 Bill Hall/404 XRC 15.00 40.00
211 D. Tankersley EXCH 4.00 10.00
212 Jeremy Affeldt/386 XRC 4.00 10.00
213 Junior Spivey/377 XRC 6.00 15.00
214 Casey Fossum/393 XRC 4.00 10.00
215 Brandon Lyon/402 XRC 4.00 10.00
216 Angel Santos/408 XRC 4.00 10.00
217 Cody Ransom/404 XRC 4.00 10.00
218 Jason Lane/424 XRC 6.00 15.00
219 David Williams/408 XRC 4.00 10.00
220 Alex Herrera/405 XRC 4.00 10.00
221 Ryan Drese/378 XRC 6.00 15.00
222 Travis Hafner/419 XRC 30.00 60.00
223 Bud Smith/468 XRC 4.00 10.00
224 Johnny Estrada/415 XRC 6.00 15.00
225 R. Rodriguez EXCH 4.00 10.00
226 Brandon Berger/428 XRC 4.00 10.00
227 Claudio Vargas/395 XRC 4.00 10.00
228 Luis Garcia/438 XRC 4.00 10.00
229 Marlon Byrd/452 XRC 4.00 10.00
230 Hee Seop Choi/479 XRC 6.00 15.00
231 Corky Miller/431 XRC 4.00 10.00
232 J. Duchscherer EXCH 4.00 10.00
233 T. Spooneybarger EXCH 4.00 10.00
234 Roy Oswalt/427 6.00 15.00
235 Willie Harris/418 XRC 4.00 10.00
236 Josh Towers/437 XRC 6.00 15.00
237 Juan A.Pena/400 XRC 4.00 10.00
238 A. Amezaga EXCH 4.00 10.00
239 Geronimo Gil/396 XRC 4.00 10.00
240 Juan Cruz/489 XRC 4.00 10.00
241 Ed Rogers/429 XRC 4.00 10.00
242 Joe Thurston/420 XRC 4.00 10.00
243 O.Hudson EXCH 6.00 15.00
244 John Buck/416 XRC 6.00 15.00
245 Martin Vargas/400 XRC 4.00 10.00
246 David Brous/399 XRC 4.00 10.00
247 D. Brazelton EXCH 4.00 10.00
248 Mark Prior/556 XRC 15.00 40.00
249 Angel Berroa/420 XRC 6.00 15.00
250 Mark Teixeira/543 XRC 15.00 40.00

2001 Donruss Elite Aspirations

Randomly inserted in packs at the rate of one in 62, this 200-card set is a parallel version of the base set printed on holo-foil board with red foil and red tint. Each card was sequentially numbered to the remaining number after subtracting the player's jersey number from 100. Cards with a print run of 25 or fewer are not priced due to market scarcity.

*1-150 PRINT RUN b/wn 81-100: 4X TO 10X
*1-150 PRINT RUN b/wn 66-80: 5X TO 12X
*1-150 PRINT RUN b/wn 51-65: 5X TO 12X
*1-150 PRINT RUN b/wn 36-50: 6X TO 15X
*1-150 PRINT RUN b/wn 26-35: 8X TO 20X
COMMON (151-200) p/r 81-100 1.50 4.00
MINOR 151-200 p/r 81-100 2.50 6.00
UNLISTED 151-200 p/r 81-100 6.00 15.00
MINOR 151-200 p/r 66-80 3.00 8.00
SEMISTARS 151-200 p/r 66-80 5.00 12.00
UNLISTED 151-200 p/r 66-80 8.00 20.00
MINOR 151-200 p/r 51-65 4.00 10.00
UNLISTED 151-200 p/r 51-65 10.00 25.00
COMMON (151-200) p/r 36-50 3.00 8.00
MINOR 151-200 p/r 36-50 5.00 12.00
SEMISTARS 151-200 p/r 36-50 8.00 20.00
UNLISTED 151-200 p/r 36-50 12.50 30.00
COMMON (151-200) p/r 26-35 4.00 10.00
MINOR 151-200 p/r 26-35 6.00 15.00
UNLISTED 151-200 p/r 26-35 15.00 40.00
UNLISTED 151-200 p/r 21-25 20.00 50.00
MINOR 151-200 p/r 16-20 10.00 25.00
SEE BECKETT.COM FOR PRINT RUNS
PRINTS b/wn 1-15 TOO SCARCE TO PRICE
RC'S OF 25 OR LESS TOO SCARCE TO PRICE

2001 Donruss Elite Status

Randomly inserted in packs at the rate of one in 163, this 200-card set is a parallel version of the base set printed on holo-foil board with gold foil and gold tint. Each card is sequentially numbered to the player's jersey number. Cards issued to a stated print run of 25 or fewer are not priced due to market scarcity.

*1-150 PRINT RUN b/wn 81-100: 4X TO 10X
*1-150 PRINT RUN b/wn 66-80: 5X TO 12X
*1-150 PRINT RUN b/wn 51-65: 5X TO 12X
*1-150 PRINT RUN b/wn 36-50: 6X TO 15X
*1-150 PRINT RUN b/wn 26-35: 8X TO 20X
*1-150 PRINT RUN b/wn 21-25: 10X TO 25X
*1-150 PRINT RUN b/wn 16-20: 12.5X TO 30X
MINOR 151-200 p/r 81-100 2.50 6.00
COMMON (151-200) p/r 66-80 2.00 5.00
MINOR 151-200 p/r 66-80 3.00 8.00
UNLISTED 151-200 p/r 66-80 8.00 20.00
COMMON (151-200) p/r 51-65 2.50 6.00
MINOR 151-200 p/r 51-65 4.00 10.00
SEMISTARS 151-200 p/r 51-65 6.00 15.00
UNLISTED 151-200 p/r 51-65 10.00 25.00
MINOR 151-200 p/r 36-50 5.00 12.00
SEMISTARS 151-200 p/r 36-50 8.00 20.00
MINOR 151-200 p/r 21-25 8.00 20.00
UNLISTED 151-200 p/r 21-25 20.00 50.00
MINOR 151-200 p/r 16-20 10.00 25.00
SEMISTARS 151-200 p/r 16-20 15.00 40.00
UNLISTED 151-200 p/r 16-20 25.00 60.00
SEE BECKETT.COM FOR PRINT RUNS
PRINTS b/wn 1-15 TOO SCARCE TO PRICE

2001 Donruss Elite Extra Edition Autographs

These certified autograph cards were made available as a compensation by Donruss-Playoff to collectors for autograph exchange cards that the manufacturer was unable to fulfill in the 2001 season. Each card is serial-numbered of 100 on front. Unlike most Donruss-Playoff autograph cards from 2001, the athletes signed the actual card rather than signing a sticker (of which was then affixed to the card at a later date). The cards first started to appear on the secondary market in April, 2002 but are catalogued as 2001 cards to avoid confusion for collectors looking to reference them.

234 Roy Oswalt 30.00 60.00
238 Alfredo Amezaga 6.00 15.00
241 Ed Rogers 6.00 15.00

2001 Donruss Elite Turn of the Century Autographs

Randomly inserted in packs, these 50 cards feature prospects who signed their cards for the Donruss Elite product. Each card had a stated print run of 100 sets though they are cumulatively serial-numbered to 1000 (only the first 100 numbered copies of each card Turn of the Century Autographs - the last 900 numbered copies of each card are basic Elite cards). Some players did not return their cards in time for inclusion in the product and these cards had an redemption deadline of May 1, 2003. Cards number 195 and 198 at first were not believed to exist, but subsequently were issued without autographs.

151 Brent Abernathy 6.00 15.00
152 Cory Aldridge 4.00 10.00
153 Gene Altman 4.00 10.00
154 Josh Beckett 40.00 80.00
155 Wilson Betemit 20.00 50.00
156 Albert Pujols 900.00 1200.00
157 Joe Crede 15.00 40.00
158 Jack Cust 6.00 15.00
159 Ben Sheets 15.00 40.00
160 Alex Escobar 6.00 15.00
161 Adrian Hernandez 4.00 10.00
162 Pedro Feliz 6.00 15.00
163 Nate Frese 6.00 15.00
164 Carlos Garcia 4.00 10.00
165 Marcus Giles 10.00 25.00
166 Alexis Gomez 4.00 10.00
167 Jason Hart 6.00 15.00
168 Aubrey Huff 10.00 25.00
169 Cesar Izturis 6.00 15.00
170 Nick Johnson 10.00 25.00
171 Jack Wilson 10.00 25.00
172 Brandon Lawrence 6.00 15.00
173 Christian Parker 4.00 10.00
174 Nick Maness 6.00 15.00
175 Jose Mieses 6.00 15.00
176 Greg Miller 4.00 10.00
177 Eric Munson 6.00 15.00
178 Xavier Nady 15.00 40.00
179 Blaine Neal 4.00 10.00
180 Abraham Nunez 6.00 15.00
181 Jose Ortiz 6.00 15.00
182 Jeremy Owens 6.00 15.00
183 Jay Gibbons 10.00 25.00
184 Corey Patterson 6.00 15.00
185 Carlos Pena 6.00 15.00
186 C.C. Sabathia 10.00 25.00
187 Timo Perez 6.00 15.00
188 Adam Pettyjohn 4.00 10.00
189 Donaldo Mendez 4.00 10.00
190 Jackson Melian 4.00 10.00
191 Wilkin Ruan 6.00 15.00
192 Duaner Sanchez 4.00 10.00
193 Alfonso Soriano 15.00 40.00
194 Rafael Soriano 6.00 15.00
195 Ichiro Suzuki NO AU
196 Billy Sylvester 4.00 10.00
197 Juan Uribe 10.00 25.00
198 Tsuyoshi Shinjo NO AU
199 Carlos Valderrama 4.00 10.00
200 Matt White 6.00 15.00

2001 Donruss Elite Back 2 Back Jacks

Randomly inserted in packs, this double-sided 45-card set features color photos of one or two players with game-used bat pieces embedded in the cards. Cards with single players are sequentially numbered to 100 while those with doubles were numbered to 50. Exchange cards with a redemption deadline of May 1st, 2003 were seeded into packs for Eddie Mathews, Frank Thomas, Mathews/Glaus combo and F.Robinson/Thomas combo.

BB1 Ernie Banks SP/75 10.00 25.00
BB2 Ryne Sandberg SP/75 20.00 50.00
BB3 Babe Ruth 100.00 200.00
BB4 Lou Gehrig 75.00 150.00
BB5 Eddie Mathews 10.00 25.00
BB6 Troy Glaus SP/50 10.00 25.00
BB7 Don Mattingly SP/50 30.00 60.00
BB8 Todd Helton 10.00 25.00
BB9 Wade Boggs 10.00 25.00
BB10 Tony Gwynn 10.00 25.00
BB11 Robin Yount 10.00 25.00
BB12 Paul Molitor SP/50 10.00 25.00
BB13 Mike Schmidt SP/50 20.00 50.00
BB14 Scott Rolen SP/75 10.00 25.00
BB15 Reggie Jackson 10.00 25.00
BB16 Dave Winfield 6.00 15.00
BB17 J. Bench SP/50 15.00 40.00
BB18 Joe Morgan 6.00 15.00
BB19 B. Robinson SP/50 15.00 40.00
BB20 Cal Ripken 20.00 50.00
BB21 Ty Cobb 60.00 120.00
BB22 Al Kaline SP/50 15.00 40.00
BB23 F. Robinson SP/50 15.00 40.00
BB24 Frank Thomas 10.00 25.00
BB25 Roberto Clemente 50.00 100.00
BB26 V. Guerrero SP/50 15.00 40.00
BB27 H.Killebrew SP/50 15.00 40.00
BB28 Kirby Puckett 10.00 25.00
BB29 Yogi Berra SP/75 15.00 40.00
BB30 Phil Rizzuto SP/75 15.00 40.00
BB31 Ernie Banks / Ryne Sandberg 50.00 100.00
BB32 Babe Ruth / Lou Gehrig 250.00 400.00
BB33 Eddie Mathews / Troy Glaus 30.00 60.00
BB34 Don Mattingly / Todd Helton 50.00 100.00
BB35 Wade Boggs / Tony Gwynn 40.00 80.00
BB36 Robin Yount / Paul Molitor 30.00 60.00
BB37 Mike Schmidt / Scott Rolen 50.00 100.00
BB38 Reggie Jackson / Dave Winfield 15.00 40.00
BB39 Johnny Bench / Joe Morgan 30.00 60.00
BB40 Brooks Robinson / Cal Ripken 60.00 120.00
BB41 Ty Cobb / Al Kaline 100.00 200.00
BB42 Frank Robinson / Frank Thomas 30.00 60.00
BB43 Roberto Clemente / Vladimir Guerrero 60.00 120.00
BB44 Harmon Killebrew / Kirby Puckett 30.00 60.00
BB45 Yogi Berra / Phil Rizzuto SP/25

2001 Donruss Elite Back 2 Back Jacks Autograph

Randomly inserted in packs, this 16-card set is a partial parallel autographed version of the regular insert set. Almost every card in the set packed out as an exchange card with a redemption deadline of May 1st, 2003. Only Johnny Bench, Al Kaline and Harmon Killebrew signed cards in time to be seeded directly into packs. Cards with a print run of 25 copies are not priced due to scarcity.

BB1 Ernie Banks/25
BB2 Ryne Sandberg/25
BB6 Troy Glaus/50 40.00 80.00
BB7 Don Mattingly/50 100.00 200.00
BB12 Paul Molitor/50 30.00 60.00
BB13 Mike Schmidt/50 60.00 120.00
BB14 Scott Rolen/25
BB17 Johnny Bench/50 60.00 120.00
BB19 Brooks Robinson/50 40.00 80.00
BB22 Al Kaline/50 60.00 120.00
BB23 Frank Robinson/50 40.00 80.00
BB26 Vladimir Guerrero/50 60.00 120.00
BB27 Harmon Killebrew/50 75.00 150.00
BB29 Yogi Berra/25
BB30 Phil Rizzuto/25
BB45 Yogi Berra / Phil Rizzuto/25

2001 Donruss Elite Passing the Torch

Randomly inserted in packs, this 24-card set features color action photos of legendary players and up-and-coming phenoms printed on holo-foil board. Cards with single players were sequentially numbered to 1000 while those with two players were numbered to 500.

PT1 Stan Musial 5.00 12.00
PT2 Tony Gwynn 4.00 10.00
PT3 Willie Mays 6.00 15.00
PT4 Barry Bonds 8.00 20.00
PT5 Mike Schmidt 6.00 15.00
PT6 Scott Rolen 2.00 5.00
PT7 Cal Ripken 10.00 25.00
PT8 Alex Rodriguez 5.00 12.00
PT9 Hank Aaron 6.00 15.00
PT10 Andruw Jones 2.00 5.00
PT11 Nolan Ryan 8.00 20.00
PT12 Pedro Martinez 2.00 5.00
PT13 Wade Boggs 2.00 5.00
PT14 Nomar Garciaparra 5.00 12.00
PT15 Don Mattingly 6.00 15.00
PT16 Todd Helton 2.00 5.00
PT17 Stan Musial / Tony Gwynn 8.00 20.00
PT18 Willie Mays / Barry Bonds 10.00 25.00
PT19 Mike Schmidt / Scott Rolen 8.00 20.00
PT20 Cal Ripken / Alex Rodriguez 15.00 40.00
PT21 Hank Aaron / Andruw Jones 10.00 25.00
PT22 Nolan Ryan / Pedro Martinez 12.50 30.00
PT23 Wade Boggs / Nomar Garciaparra 8.00 20.00
PT24 Don Mattingly / Todd Helton 8.00 20.00

2001 Donruss Elite Passing the Torch Autographs

Randomly inserted in packs, this 22-card set is a partial autographed parallel version of the regular insert set printed on double-sided holo-foil board. Cards with single players were sequentially numbered to 100 while those with dual players were numbered to 50. Nearly all of these cards were not available in time for insertion into packs and collectors had until May 1st, 2003 to redeem them. Wade Boggs, Todd Helton, Stan Musial and Nolan Ryan were the only players to return their cards in time for them to be seeded into packs. Cards PT22, PT23 and PT24 were actually 2001 Donruss Elite football exchange cards that were erroneously placed into baseball packs. To honor their commitment to collectors that pulled these cards - the manufacturer created three additional dual autograph baseball cards. These cards are tagged in our checklist with an "FB" status to indicate their origin. The set contains two separate cards numbered PT22 because of this same football snafu - whereby it's theorized that the baseball was originally intended to be complete at 22 cards. The three additional football exchange cards expanded the set to 25 cards and also created two separate PT22 cards.

PT1 Stan Musial 60.00 120.00
PT2 Tony Gwynn 40.00 80.00
PT3 Willie Mays 175.00 300.00
PT4 Barry Bonds 175.00 300.00
PT5 Mike Schmidt 60.00 120.00
PT6 Scott Rolen 30.00 60.00
PT7 Cal Ripken 125.00 200.00
PT8 Alex Rodriguez 100.00 175.00
PT9 Hank Aaron 175.00 300.00
PT10 Andruw Jones 30.00 60.00
PT11 Nolan Ryan 75.00 150.00
PT12 P.Martinez EXCH 75.00 150.00
PT13 Wade Boggs 30.00 60.00
PT14 N.Garciaparra EXCH 40.00 80.00
PT15 Don Mattingly 60.00 120.00
PT16 Todd Helton 30.00 60.00
PT17 Stan Musial / Tony Gwynn 250.00 500.00
PT18 Willie Mays / Barry Bonds 900.00 1200.00
PT19 Mike Schmidt / Scott Rolen 125.00 200.00
PT20 Cal Ripken / Alex Rodriguez 500.00 800.00
PT21 Hank Aaron / Andruw Jones 250.00 400.00
PT22A Nolan Ryan / Roger Clemens FB 250.00 500.00
PT22B Nolan Ryan / Pedro Martinez BB 250.00 400.00
PT23 Wade Boggs / Nomar Garciaparra FB 175.00 300.00
PT24 Don Mattingly / Todd Helton FB 150.00 250.00

2001 Donruss Elite Primary Colors Red

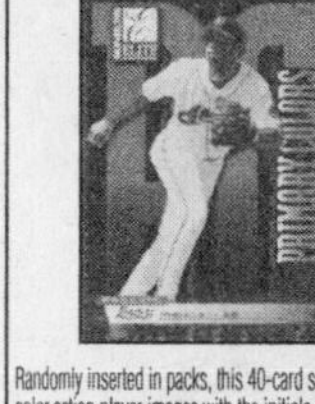

Randomly inserted in packs, this 40-card set features color action player images with the initials "PC" on a red background. The cards are sequentially numbered to 975. A die-cut holo-foil parallel version of this set was produced and sequentially numbered to 25. A Blue parallel version numbered to 200 and a Yellow one numbered to 25 were also printed. Holo-foil, die-cut parallel versions of both of these sets were produced with the Blue sequentially numbered to 50 and the Yellow to 75.

COMPLETE SET (40) 200.00 400.00
*BLUE: .6X TO 1.5X BASIC RED
BLUE PRINT RUN 200 SERIAL #'d SETS
*BLUE DIE CUT: 1.25X TO 3X BASIC RED
BLUE DC PRINT RUN 50 SERIAL #'d SETS
*RED DIE CUT: 2X TO 5X BASIC RED
RED DC PRINT RUN 25 SERIAL #'d SETS
*YELLOW: 2X TO 5X BASIC RED
YELLOW PRINT RUN 25 SERIAL #'d SETS
*YELLOW DIE CUT: 1X TO 2.5X BASIC RED
YELLOW DC PRINT RUN 75 SERIAL #'d SETS
PC1 Alex Rodriguez 6.00 15.00
PC2 Barry Bonds 8.00 20.00
PC3 Cal Ripken 12.50 30.00
PC4 Chipper Jones 4.00 10.00
PC5 Derek Jeter 4.00 10.00
PC6 Troy Glaus 2.00 5.00
PC7 Frank Thomas 4.00 10.00
PC8 Greg Maddux 6.00 15.00
PC9 Ivan Rodriguez 2.50 6.00
PC10 Jeff Bagwell 2.50 6.00
PC11 Todd Helton 2.50 6.00
PC12 Ken Griffey Jr. 6.00 15.00
PC13 Manny Ramirez Sox 2.50 6.00
PC14 Mark McGwire 10.00 25.00
PC15 Mike Piazza 6.00 15.00
PC16 Nomar Garciaparra 6.00 15.00
PC17 Pedro Martinez 2.50 6.00
PC18 Randy Johnson 4.00 10.00
PC19 Rick Ankiel 2.00 5.00
PC20 Roger Clemens 8.00 20.00
PC21 Sammy Sosa 4.00 10.00
PC22 Tony Gwynn 5.00 12.00
PC23 Vladimir Guerrero 4.00 10.00
PC24 Carlos Delgado 2.00 5.00
PC25 Jason Giambi 2.00 5.00
PC26 Andruw Jones 2.50 6.00
PC27 Bernie Williams 2.50 6.00
PC28 Roberto Alomar 2.50 6.00
PC29 Shawn Green 2.00 5.00
PC30 Barry Larkin 2.50 6.00
PC31 Scott Rolen 2.50 6.00
PC32 Gary Sheffield 2.00 5.00
PC33 Rafael Palmeiro 2.50 6.00
PC34 Albert Belle 2.00 5.00
PC35 Magglio Ordonez 2.00 5.00
PC36 Jim Thome 2.50 6.00
PC37 Jim Edmonds 2.00 5.00
PC38 Darin Erstad 2.00 5.00
PC39 Kris Benson 2.00 5.00
PC40 Sean Casey 2.00 5.00

2001 Donruss Elite Prime Numbers

Randomly inserted in packs at the rate of one in 84, this 30-card set features color action images of 10 stellar performers. Each player has three cards highlighted by a single digit from his high average. The cards are sequentially numbered to the base total of the digit displayed.

PN1A Alex Rodriguez/300 8.00 20.00
PN1B Alex Rodriguez/50 20.00 50.00
PN1C Alex Rodriguez/8
PN2A Ken Griffey Jr./400 8.00 20.00
PN2B Ken Griffey Jr./30 25.00 60.00
PN2C Ken Griffey Jr./8
PN3A Mark McGwire/500 12.50 30.00
PN3B Mark McGwire/50 30.00 80.00
PN3C Mark McGwire/4
PN4A Cal Ripken/400 15.00 40.00
PN4B Cal Ripken/10
PN4C Cal Ripken/7
PN5A Derek Jeter/300 12.50 30.00
PN5B Derek Jeter/20 125.00 250.00
PN5C Derek Jeter/2
PN6A Mike Piazza/300 8.00 20.00
PN6B Mike Piazza/60 15.00 40.00
PN6C Mike Piazza/2
PN7A N.Garciaparra/300 8.00 20.00
PN7B N.Garciaparra/70 12.50 30.00
PN7C Nomar Garciaparra/7
PN8A Sammy Sosa/300 6.00 15.00
PN8B Sammy Sosa/80 10.00 25.00
PN8C Sammy Sosa/6
PN9A V.Guerrero/300 5.00 12.00
PN9B V.Guerrero/40 12.50 30.00
PN9C Vladimir Guerrero/5
PN10A Tony Gwynn/300 6.00 15.00
PN10B Tony Gwynn/90 8.00 20.00
PN10C Tony Gwynn/4

2001 Donruss Elite Throwback Threads

Randomly inserted into packs, this 45-card set features past and present greats with swatches of game-worn jerseys displayed on the cards. Cards with single players are sequentially numbered to 100 while those with doubles are numbered to 50. Exchange cards with a redemption deadline of May 1st, 2003 were seeded into packs for Ernie Banks, Lou Brock, Pedro Martinez, Ozzie Smith and Frank Thomas. In addition, exchange cards packed out for the following dual-player cards: Brock/Ozzie, Banks/Sandberg, F.Robinson/Thomas and Clemens/Pedro. Pricing is not available for cards with a print run of 25 copies due to scarcity.

TT1 Stan Musial SP/75 30.00 60.00
TT2 Tony Gwynn SP/75 15.00 40.00
TT3 Willie McCovey 6.00 15.00
TT4 Barry Bonds 20.00 50.00
TT5 Babe Ruth 175.00 300.00
TT6 Lou Gehrig 150.00 250.00
TT7 Mike Schmidt SP/75 20.00 50.00
TT8 Scott Rolen 10.00 25.00
TT9 H.Killebrew SP/75 15.00 40.00
TT10 Kirby Puckett 10.00 25.00
TT11 Al Kaline SP/75 15.00 40.00
TT12 Eddie Mathews 15.00 40.00
TT13 Hank Aaron SP/75 40.00 80.00
TT14 Andruw Jones SP/50 15.00 40.00
TT15 Lou Brock 10.00 25.00
TT16 Ozzie Smith 10.00 25.00
TT17 Ernie Banks SP/75
TT18 Ryne Sandberg 20.00 50.00
TT19 Roberto Clemente 50.00 100.00
TT20 V. Guerrero SP/50 15.00 40.00
TT21 F.Robinson SP/50 15.00 40.00
TT22 Frank Thomas SP/50 15.00 40.00
TT23 B.Robinson SP/50 15.00 40.00
TT24 Cal Ripken 20.00 50.00
TT25 Roger Clemens 10.00 25.00
TT26 Pedro Martinez 10.00 25.00
TT27 Reggie Jackson 10.00 25.00
TT28 Dave Winfield 6.00 15.00
TT29 Don Mattingly SP/50 30.00 60.00
TT30 Todd Helton 10.00 25.00
TT32 Willie McCovey / Barry Bonds 50.00 100.00
TT33 Babe Ruth / Lou Gehrig 350.00 600.00
TT34 Mike Schmidt / Scott Rolen SP/25
TT35 Harmon Killebrew / Kirby Puckett 40.00 80.00
TT36 Al Kaline / Eddie Mathews 50.00 100.00
TT37 Hank Aaron / Andruw Jones 20.00 50.00
TT38 Lou Brock / Ozzie Smith 40.00 80.00
TT39 Ernie Banks / Ryne Sandberg SP/25
TT40 Roberto Clemente / Vladimir Guerrero 60.00 120.00
TT41 Frank Robinson / Frank Thomas 30.00 60.00
TT42 Brooks Robinson / Cal Ripken 50.00 100.00
TT43 Roger Clemens / Pedro Martinez 40.00 80.00
TT44 Reggie Jackson / Dave Winfield 15.00 40.00
TT45 Don Mattingly / Todd Helton 40.00 80.00

2001 Donruss Elite Throwback Threads Autographs

TT14 Andruw Jones/50 40.00 80.00
TT20 Vladimir Guerrero/50 50.00 100.00
TT21 Frank Robinson/50 FB 40.00 80.00
TT22 Frank Thomas/50 FB 50.00 100.00
TT23 Brooks Robinson/50 40.00 80.00
TT29 Don Mattingly/50 75.00 150.00

2001 Donruss Elite Title Waves

Randomly inserted in packs, this 30-card set features the game's most decorated performers highlighted in five different title-winning categories and sequentially numbered to the year they won the title.

COMPLETE SET (30) 125.00 250.00
*HOLO: 1.5X TO 4X BASIC WAVES
HOLO-FOIL PRINT RUN 100 SERIAL #'d SETS
TW1 Tony Gwynn/1994 3.00 8.00
TW2 Todd Helton/2000 1.50 4.00
TW3 N.Garciaparra/2000 4.00 10.00
TW4 Frank Thomas/1997 2.50 6.00
TW5 Alex Rodriguez/1996 4.00 10.00
TW6 Jeff Bagwell/1994 1.50 4.00
TW7 Mark McGwire/1998 6.00 15.00
TW8 Sammy Sosa/2000 2.50 6.00
TW9 Ken Griffey Jr./1997 4.00 10.00
TW10 Albert Belle/1995 1.25 3.00
TW11 Barry Bonds/1993 6.00 15.00
TW12 Jose Canseco/1991 1.50 4.00
TW13 M.Ramirez Sox/1999 1.50 4.00
TW14 Sammy Sosa/1998 2.50 6.00
TW15 A.Galarraga/1996 1.25 3.00
TW16 Todd Helton/2000 1.50 4.00
TW17 Ken Griffey Jr./1997 4.00 10.00
TW18 Jeff Bagwell/1994 1.50 4.00
TW19 Mike Piazza/1995 4.00 10.00
TW20 A.Rodriguez/1995 4.00 10.00
TW21 Jason Giambi/2000 1.25 3.00
TW22 I.Rodriguez/1999 1.50 4.00
TW23 Greg Maddux/1997 4.00 10.00
TW24 P.Martinez/1994 1.50 4.00
TW25 Derek Jeter/2000 6.00 15.00
TW26 B.Williams/1998 1.50 4.00
TW27 R.Clemens/1999 5.00 12.00
TW28 Chipper Jones/1995 2.50 6.00
TW29 M.McGwire/1990 6.00 15.00
TW30 Cal Ripken/1983 8.00 20.00

2002 Donruss Elite Samples

Issued one per sealed copy of Beckett Baseball Card Monthly issue number 207, this is a partial parallel to the 2002 Donruss Elite Set. Only the first 100 cards of this set were issued in this format.

*SAMPLES: 1.5X TO 4X BASIC CARDS
ONE PER SEALED BBCM 207
*GOLD: 4X TO 10X BASIC SAMPLES
GOLD 10% OF PRESS RUN

2002 Donruss Elite

This 268-card set highlights baseball's premier performers. The standard-size set is made up of 100 veteran players, 50 STAR veteran subset cards and 50 rookie players. The fronts feature full color action shots. The STAR subset cards (101-150) were seeded into packs at a rate of 1:10. The rookie cards (151-200) are sequentially numbered to 1500 but only 1350 of each were actually produced. The first 150 of each rookie card is die-cut and labeled "Turn of the Century" with varying quantities of some autographed. These cards were issued in 5 card packs with a $3.99 SRP which came 20 packs to a box and 20 boxes to a case. Cards 256, 263 and 267-271 were never released.

COMP.LO SET w/o SP's (100) 8.00 20.00
COMMON CARD (1-100) .10 .30
COMMON CARD (101-150) .75 2.00
COMMON CARD (151-200) 2.00 5.00
COMMON CARD (201-275) 2.00 5.00
1 Vladimir Guerrero .30 .75
2 Bernie Williams .20 .50
3 Ichiro Suzuki .60 1.50
4 Roger Clemens .60 1.50
5 Greg Maddux .50 1.25
6 Fred McGriff .20 .50
7 Jermaine Dye .10 .30
8 Ken Griffey Jr. .50 1.25
9 Todd Helton .20 .50
10 Torii Hunter .10 .30
11 Pat Burrell .10 .30
12 Chipper Jones .30 .75
13 Ivan Rodriguez .20 .50
14 Roy Oswalt .10 .30
15 Shannon Stewart .10 .30
16 Magglio Ordonez .10 .30
17 Lance Berkman .10 .30
18 Mark Mulder .10 .30
19 Al Leiter .10 .30
20 Sammy Sosa .30 .75
21 Scott Rolen .20 .50
22 Aramis Ramirez .10 .30
23 Alfonso Soriano .10 .30

24 Phil Nevin .10 .30
25 Barry Bonds .75 2.00
26 Joe Mays .10 .30
27 Jeff Kent .10 .30
28 Mark Quinn .10 .30
29 Adrian Beltre .10 .30
30 Freddy Garcia .10 .30
31 Pedro Martinez .20 .50
32 Darryl Kile .10 .30
33 Mike Cameron .10 .30
34 Frank Catalanotto .10 .30
35 Jose Vidro .10 .30
36 Jim Thome .20 .50
37 Javy Lopez .10 .30
38 Paul Konerko .10 .30
39 Jeff Bagwell .20 .50
40 Curt Schilling .10 .30
41 Miguel Tejada .10 .30
42 Jim Edmonds .10 .30
43 Ellis Burks .10 .30
44 Mark Grace .20 .50
45 Robb Nen .10 .30
46 Jeff Conine .10 .30
47 Derek Jeter .75 2.00
48 Mike Lowell .10 .30
49 Javier Vazquez .10 .30
50 Manny Ramirez .20 .50
51 Bartolo Colon .10 .30
52 Carlos Beltran .10 .30
53 Tim Hudson .10 .30
54 Rafael Palmeiro .20 .50
55 Jimmy Rollins .10 .30
56 Andruw Jones .20 .50
57 Orlando Cabrera .10 .30
58 Dean Palmer .10 .30
59 Bret Boone .10 .30
60 Carlos Febles .10 .30
61 Ben Grieve .10 .30
62 Richie Sexson .10 .30
63 Alex Rodriguez .50 1.25
64 Juan Pierre .10 .30
65 Bobby Higginson .10 .30
66 Barry Zito .10 .30
67 Raul Mondesi .10 .30
68 Albert Pujols .60 1.50
69 Omar Vizquel .20 .50
70 Bobby Abreu .10 .30
71 Corey Koskie .10 .30
72 Tom Glavine .20 .50
73 Paul LoDuca .10 .30
74 Terrence Long .10 .30
75 Matt Morris .10 .30
76 Andy Pettitte .20 .50
77 Rich Aurilia .10 .30
78 Todd Walker .10 .30
79 John Olerud UER .10 .30
Career Header stats are those for a pitcher
80 Mike Sweeney .10 .30
81 Ray Durham .10 .30
82 Fernando Vina .10 .30
83 Nomar Garciaparra .50 1.25
84 Mariano Rivera .30 .75
85 Mike Piazza .50 1.25
86 Mark Buehrle .10 .30
87 Adam Dunn .10 .30
88 Luis Gonzalez .10 .30
89 Richard Hidalgo .10 .30
90 Brad Radke .10 .30
91 Russ Ortiz .10 .30
92 Brian Giles .10 .30
93 Billy Wagner .10 .30
94 Cliff Floyd .10 .30
95 Eric Milton .10 .30
96 Bud Smith .10 .30
97 Wade Miller .10 .30
98 Jon Lieber .10 .30
99 Derrek Lee .20 .50
100 Jose Cruz Jr. .10 .30
101 Dmitri Young STAR .75 2.00
102 Mo Vaughn STAR .75 2.00
103 Tino Martinez STAR 1.25 3.00
104 Larry Walker STAR .75 2.00
105 Chuck Knoblauch STAR .75 2.00
106 Troy Glaus STAR .75 2.00
107 Jason Giambi STAR .75 2.00
108 Travis Fryman STAR .75 2.00
109 Josh Beckett STAR .75 2.00
110 Edgar Martinez STAR 1.25 3.00
111 Tim Salmon STAR 1.25 3.00
112 C.C. Sabathia STAR .75 2.00
113 Randy Johnson STAR 2.00 5.00
114 Juan Gonzalez STAR .75 2.00
115 Carlos Delgado STAR .75 2.00
116 Hideo Nomo STAR 2.00 5.00
117 Kerry Wood STAR .75 2.00
118 Brian Jordan STAR .75 2.00
119 Carlos Pena STAR .75 2.00
120 Roger Cedeno STAR .75 2.00
121 Chan Ho Park STAR .75 2.00
122 Rafael Furcal STAR .75 2.00
123 Frank Thomas STAR 2.00 5.00
124 Mike Mussina STAR 1.25 3.00
125 Rickey Henderson STAR 2.00 5.00
126 Sean Casey STAR .75 2.00
127 Barry Larkin STAR 1.25 3.00
128 Kazuhiro Sasaki STAR .75 2.00
129 Moises Alou STAR .75 2.00
130 Jeff Cirillo STAR .75 2.00
131 Jason Kendall STAR .75 2.00
132 Gary Sheffield STAR .75 2.00
133 Ryan Klesko STAR .75 2.00
134 Kevin Brown STAR .75 2.00
135 Darin Erstad STAR .75 2.00
136 Roberto Alomar STAR 1.25 3.00
137 Brad Fullmer STAR .75 2.00
138 Eric Chavez STAR .75 2.00
139 Ben Sheets STAR .75 2.00
140 Trot Nixon STAR .75 2.00
141 Garret Anderson STAR .75 2.00
142 Shawn Green STAR .75 2.00
143 Troy Percival STAR .75 2.00
144 Craig Biggio STAR 1.25 3.00
145 Jorge Posada STAR 1.25 3.00
146 J.D. Drew STAR .75 2.00
147 Johnny Damon STAR 1.25 3.00
148 Jeromy Burnitz STAR .75 2.00
149 Robin Ventura STAR .75 2.00
150 Aaron Sele STAR .75 2.00
151 Cam Esslinger ROO RC 2.00 5.00
152 Ben Howard ROO RC 2.00 5.00
153 Brandon Backe ROO RC 3.00 8.00
154 Jorge De La Rosa ROO RC 2.00 5.00
155 Austin Kearns ROO 2.00 5.00
156 Carlos Zambrano ROO 2.00 5.00
157 Kyle Kane ROO RC 2.00 5.00
158 So Taguchi ROO RC 3.00 8.00
159 Brian Mallette ROO RC 2.00 5.00
160 Brett Jodie ROO 2.00 5.00
161 Elio Serrano ROO RC 2.00 5.00
162 Joe Thurston ROO 2.00 5.00
163 Kevin Olsen ROO 2.00 5.00
164 Rodrigo Rosario ROO RC 2.00 5.00
165 Matt Guerrier ROO 2.00 5.00
166 And. Machado ROO RC 2.00 5.00
167 Bert Snow ROO 2.00 5.00
168 Franklyn German ROO RC 2.00 5.00
169 Brandon Claussen ROO 2.00 5.00
170 Jason Romano ROO 2.00 5.00
171 Jorge Padilla ROO RC 2.00 5.00
172 Jose Cueto ROO 2.00 5.00
173 Allan Simpson ROO RC 2.00 5.00
174 Doug Devore ROO RC 2.00 5.00
175 Justin Duchscherer ROO 2.00 5.00
176 Josh Pearce ROO 2.00 5.00
177 Steve Bechler ROO RC 2.00 5.00
178 Josh Phelps ROO 2.00 5.00
179 Juan Diaz ROO 2.00 5.00
180 Victor Alvarez ROO RC 2.00 5.00
181 Ramon Vazquez ROO 2.00 5.00
182 Mike Rivera ROO 2.00 5.00
183 Kazuhisa Ishii ROO RC 3.00 8.00
184 Henry Mateo ROO 2.00 5.00
185 Travis Hughes ROO RC 2.00 5.00
186 Zach Day ROO 2.00 5.00
187 Brad Voyles ROO 2.00 5.00
188 Sean Douglass ROO 2.00 5.00
189 Nick Neugebauer ROO 2.00 5.00
190 Tom Shearn ROO RC 2.00 5.00
191 Eric Cyr ROO 2.00 5.00
192 Adam Johnson ROO 2.00 5.00
193 Michael Cuddyer ROO 2.00 5.00
194 Erik Bedard ROO 2.00 5.00
195 Mark Ellis ROO 2.00 5.00
196 Carlos Hernandez ROO 2.00 5.00
197 Deivis Santos ROO 2.00 5.00
198 Morgan Ensberg ROO 2.00 5.00
199 Ryan Jamison ROO 2.00 5.00
200 Cody Ransom ROO 2.00 5.00
201 Chris Snelling ROO RC 2.00 5.00
202 Satoru Komiyama ROO RC 2.00 5.00
203 Jas. Simontacchi ROO RC 2.00 5.00
204 Tim Kalita ROO RC 2.00 5.00
205 Run. Hernandez ROO RC 2.00 5.00
206 Kirk Saarloos ROO RC 2.00 5.00
207 Aaron Cook ROO RC 2.00 5.00
208 Luis Ugueto ROO RC 2.00 5.00
209 Gustavo Chacin ROO RC 3.00 8.00
210 Francis Beltran ROO RC 2.00 5.00
211 Takahito Nomura ROO RC 2.00 5.00
212 Oliver Perez ROO RC 4.00 10.00
213 Miguel Asencio ROO RC 2.00 5.00
214 Rene Reyes ROO RC 2.00 5.00
215 Jeff Baker ROO RC 3.00 8.00
216 Jon Adkins ROO RC 2.00 5.00
217 Carlos Rivera ROO RC 2.00 5.00
218 Corey Thurman ROO RC 2.00 5.00
219 Earl Snyder ROO RC 2.00 5.00
220 Felix Escalona ROO RC 2.00 5.00
221 Jeremy Guthrie ROO RC 2.00 5.00
222 Josh Hancock ROO RC 2.50 6.00
223 Ben Kozlowski ROO RC 2.00 5.00
224 Eric Good ROO RC 2.00 5.00
225 Eric Junge ROO RC 2.00 5.00
226 Andy Pratt ROO RC 2.00 5.00
227 Matt Thornton ROO RC 2.00 5.00
228 Jorge Sosa ROO RC 3.00 8.00
229 Mike Smith ROO RC 2.00 5.00
230 Mitch Wylie ROO RC 2.00 5.00
231 John Ennis ROO RC 2.00 5.00
232 Reed Johnson ROO RC 3.00 8.00
233 Joe Borchard ROO 2.00 5.00
234 Ron Calloway ROO RC 2.00 5.00
235 Brian Tallet ROO RC 2.00 5.00
236 Chris Baker ROO RC 2.00 5.00
237 Cliff Lee ROO RC 10.00 25.00
238 Matt Childers ROO RC 2.00 5.00
239 Freddy Sanchez ROO RC 4.00 10.00
240 Chone Figgins ROO RC 3.00 8.00
241 Kevin Cash ROO RC 2.00 5.00
242 Josh Bard ROO RC 2.00 5.00
243 Jer. Robertson ROO RC 2.00 5.00
244 Jeremy Hill ROO RC 2.00 5.00
245 Shane Nance ROO RC 2.00 5.00
246 Wes Obermueller ROO RC 2.00 5.00
247 Trey Hodges ROO RC 2.00 5.00
248 Eric Eckenstahler ROO RC 2.00 5.00
249 Jim Rushford ROO RC 2.00 5.00
250 Jose Castillo ROO RC 6.00 15.00
251 Garrett Atkins ROO RC 6.00 15.00
252 Alexis Rios ROO RC 10.00 25.00
253 Ryan Church ROO RC 3.00 8.00
254 Jimmy Gobble ROO RC 2.00 5.00
255 Corwin Malone ROO RC 2.00 5.00
257 Nic Jackson ROO RC 2.00 5.00
258 Tommy Whiteman ROO RC 2.00 5.00
259 Mario Ramos ROO RC 2.00 5.00
260 Rob Bowen ROO RC 2.00 5.00
261 Josh Wilson ROO RC 2.00 5.00
262 Tim Hummel ROO RC 2.00 5.00
264 Gerald Laird ROO RC 3.00 8.00
265 Vinny Chulk ROO RC 2.00 5.00
266 Jesus Medrano ROO RC 2.00 5.00
272 Adam LaRoche ROO RC 20.00 50.00
273 Adam Morrissey ROO RC 2.00 5.00
274 Henri Stanley ROO RC 2.00 5.00
275 Walter Young ROO RC 3.00 8.00

2002 Donruss Elite Aspirations

Randomly inserted into packs, this 200-card set is a parallel to the base set. The cards are standard-size and die-cut on holo-foil board with blue tint and blue foil stamping sequentially numbered to the featured player's jersey number. Due to market scarcity, cards with a print run of less than 25 are not priced.

*1-100 PRINT RUN b/wn 26-35 8X TO 20X
*1-100 PRINT RUN b/wn 36-50 6X TO 15X
*1-100 PRINT RUN b/wn 51-65 5X TO 12X
*1-100 PRINT RUN b/wn 66-80 5X TO 12X
*101-150 PRINT RUN b/wn 26-35 1.25X TO 3X
*101-150 PRINT RUN b/wn 36-50 1X TO 2.5X
*101-150 PRINT RUN b/wn 51-65 .75X TO 2X
UNLISTED 151-200 p/r 81-99 6.00 15.00
COMMON (151-200) p/r 66-80 3.00 8.00
SEMIS 151-200 p/r 66-80 5.00 12.00
UNLISTED 151-200 p/r 66-80 8.00 20.00
COMMON (151-200) p/r 51-65 4.00 10.00
SEMIS 151-200 p/r 51-65 6.00 15.00
UNLISTED 151-200 p/r 51-65 10.00 25.00
COMMON (151-200) p/r 36-50 5.00 12.00
SEMIS 151-200 p/r 36-50 5.00 20.00
UNLISTED 151-200 p/r 36-50 12.50 30.00
COMMON (151-200) p/r 26-35 6.00 15.00
SEMIS 151-200 p/r 26-35 10.00 25.00
UNLISTED 151-200 p/r 26-35 15.00 40.00
SEE BECKETT.COM FOR PRINT RUNS
NO PRICING ON QUANTITIES OF 25 OR LESS

2002 Donruss Elite Status

Randomly inserted into packs, this 200-card set is a parallel to the base set. The cards are die-cut on holo-foil board with platinum tint and platinum foil stamping sequentially numbered to the remaining number out of 100 as reduced from the Donruss Elite Aspirations parallel (of which was serial numbered to the featured player's jersey number). We have listed the stated print run next to the player's name in our checklist. Cards with a stated print run of 25 or fewer are not printed due to market scarcity.

*1-100 PRINT RUN b/wn 36-50 6X TO 15X
*1-100 PRINT RUN b/wn 51-65 5X TO 12X
*1-100 PRINT RUN b/wn 66-80 5X TO 12X
*1-100 PRINT RUN b/wn 81-98 4X TO 10X
*101-150 PRINT RUN b/wn 36-50 1X TO 2.5X
*101-150 PRINT RUN b/wn 51-65 .75X TO 2X
*101-150 PRINT RUN b/wn 66-80 .75X TO 2X
*101-150 PRINT RUN b/wn 81-99 .6X TO 1.5X
COMMON (151-200) p/r 81-99 2.50 6.00
SEMIS 151-200 p/r 81-99 4.00 10.00
UNLISTED 151-200 p/r 81-99 6.00 15.00
COMMON (151-200) p/r 66-80 3.00 8.00
SEMIS 151-200 p/r 66-80 5.00 12.00
UNLISTED 151-200 p/r 66-80 8.00 20.00
COMMON (151-200) p/r 51-65 4.00 10.00
SEMIS 151-200 p/r 51-65 6.00 15.00
UNLISTED 151-200 p/r 51-65 10.00 25.00
COMMON (151-200) p/r 36-50 5.00 12.00
SEMIS 151-200 p/r 36-50 8.00 20.00
UNLISTED 151-200 p/r 36-50 12.50 30.00
COMMON (151-200) p/r 26-35 6.00 15.00
SEMIS 151-200 p/r 26-35 10.00 25.00
UNLISTED 151-200 p/r 26-35 15.00 40.00
SEE BECKETT.COM FOR PRINT RUNS
NO PRICING ON QUANTITIES OF 25 OR LESS

2002 Donruss Elite Turn of the Century

Randomly inserted in packs of Elite and Donruss the Rookies, these 71 cards partially parallel the prospect cards in 2002 Donruss Elite. Cards checklisted between 151-200 were distributed in Elite packs and 201-275 in Donruss the Rookies packs. The Turn of the Century parallels are easily identified from basic issue cards by their rounded corners. It's important to note that Turn of the Centruy cards were cumulatively serial-numbered, intermingling the basic Elite cards and the Turn of the Century Autograph cards. For example, card 201 Chris Snelling features serial numbering to 1000. The first 100 numbered copies were devoted to the Turn of the Century sets with Snelling signing cards "1 of 1000" through "50 of 1000". The last 900 numbered cards are his basic Elite Rookie Card. Some players signed all of their Turn of the Century cards and others signed none. We have notated the stated print run next to the player's name in our checklist and cards with a print run of less than 25 are not priced due to market scarcity.

*TOC p/r 100-150: .6X TO 1.5X BASIC
*TOC p/r 50-75: .75X TO 2X BASIC
CARDS DISPLAY CUMULATIVE PRINT RUNS
SEE BECKETT.COM FOR PRINT RUNS
PRINT RUNS B/WN 25-150 COPIES PER
151-200 DIE CUTS ARE 1ST 150 #'d OF 1500
201-275 DIE CUTS ARE 1ST 100 #'d OF 1000
SKIP-NUMBERED 72-CARD SET
NO PRICING ON QTY OF 25 OR LESS
252 Alexis Rios/100 15.00 40.00

2002 Donruss Elite Turn of the Century Autographs

Randomly inserted into packs of Elite and Donruss the Rookies, these 95 cards basically parallel the prospect cards in 2002 Donruss Elite. Cards 151-200 were distributed in Elite packs and cards 201-275 in Donruss the Rookies. These cards are all signed by the featured player and we have notated the stated print run information next to the player's name in our checklist. Please note, the cards are serial numbered cumulatively out of 1,500 for cards 151-200 and 1,000 for cards 201-275 - intermingling the basic issue Elite set, the Turn of the Century parallel die cuts and the Turn of the Century Autographs. Actual print runs for the autographs are listed below.

151 Cam Esslinger/150 6.00 15.00
152 Ben Howard/150 6.00 15.00
153 Brandon Backe/150 10.00 25.00
154 Jorge De La Rosa/100 6.00 15.00
155 Austin Kearns/150 6.00 15.00
156 Carlos Zambrano/100 10.00 25.00
157 Kyle Kane/100 6.00 15.00
158 So Taguchi/125 10.00 25.00
159 Brian Mallette/100 6.00 15.00
160 Brett Jodie/100 6.00 15.00
161 Elio Serrano/150 6.00 15.00
162 Joe Thurston/150 6.00 15.00
163 Kevin Olsen/150 6.00 15.00
164 Rodrigo Rosario/150 6.00 15.00
165 Matt Guerrier/100 6.00 15.00
166 Anderson Machado/150 6.00 15.00
167 Bert Snow/150 6.00 15.00
168 Franklyn German/100 6.00 15.00
169 Brandon Claussen/100 6.00 15.00
170 Jason Romano/150 6.00 15.00
171 Jorge Padilla/100 6.00 15.00
172 Jose Cueto/100 6.00 15.00
173 Allan Simpson/150 6.00 15.00
174 Doug Devore/150 6.00 15.00
175 Justin Duchscherer/150 12.50 30.00
176 Josh Pearce/100 6.00 15.00
177 Steve Bechler/100 6.00 15.00
178 Josh Phelps/100 6.00 15.00
179 Juan Diaz/150 6.00 15.00
180 Victor Alvarez/100 6.00 15.00
181 Ramon Vazquez/150 6.00 15.00
182 Michael Rivera/100 6.00 15.00
183 Kazuhisa Ishii/25
184 Henry Mateo/100 6.00 15.00
185 Travis Hughes/150 6.00 15.00
186 Zach Day/100 6.00 15.00
187 Brad Voyles/150 6.00 15.00
188 Sean Douglass/150 6.00 15.00
189 Nick Neugebauer/50 10.00 25.00
190 Tom Shearn/150 6.00 15.00
191 Eric Cyr/150 6.00 15.00
192 Adam Johnson/25
193 Michael Cuddyer/100 6.00 15.00
194 Erik Bedard/150 6.00 15.00
195 Mark Ellis/125 6.00 15.00
197 Deivis Santos/150 6.00 15.00
198 Morgan Ensberg/100 6.00 15.00
199 Ryan Jamison/150 6.00 15.00
201 Chris Snelling/50 15.00 40.00
202 Satoru Komiyama/25
204 Tim Kalita/25
206 Kirk Saarloos/50 10.00 25.00
208 Luis Ugueto/25
210 Francis Beltran/25
211 Takahito Nomura/25
212 Oliver Perez/25
214 Rene Reyes/25
215 Jeff Baker/100 15.00 40.00
216 Jon Adkins/100 6.00 15.00
217 Carlos Rivera/100 6.00 15.00
218 Corey Thurman/25
219 Earl Snyder/25
220 Felix Escalona/25
221 Jeremy Guthrie/100 10.00 25.00
223 Ben Kozlowski/100 6.00 15.00
224 Eric Good/100 6.00 15.00
225 Eric Junge/25
226 Andy Pratt/25
227 Matt Thornton/25
231 John Ennis/25
232 Reed Johnson/25
233 Joe Borchard/25
235 Brian Tallet/25
236 Chris Baker/25
237 Cliff Lee/25
238 Matt Childers/25
240 Chone Figgins/100 15.00 40.00
241 Kevin Cash/100 6.00 15.00
242 Josh Bard/25
245 Shane Nance/25
247 Trey Hodges/100 6.00 15.00
251 Garrett Atkins/100 20.00 50.00
253 Ryan Church/100 15.00 40.00
254 Jimmy Gobble/100 6.00 15.00
255 Corwin Malone/100 6.00 15.00
258 Tommy Whiteman/100 6.00 15.00
259 Mario Ramos/100 6.00 15.00
260 Rob Bowen/100 6.00 15.00
261 Josh Wilson/100 6.00 15.00
262 Tim Hummel/100 6.00 15.00
264 Gerald Laird/100 10.00 25.00
266 Jesus Medrano/100 6.00 15.00
272 Adam LaRoche/100 60.00 120.00
273 Adam Morrissey/100 6.00 15.00
274 Henri Stanley/100 6.00 15.00

2002 Donruss Elite All-Star Salutes

Randomly inserted into packs, this 25-card insert set spotlights on the most heralded players. The fronts of the standard-size cards feature full color action shots set on metalized film board with foil and is sequentially numbered to the year the featured player shined in the All-Star Game.

COMPLETE SET (25) 75.00 150.00
*CENTURY: 1.25X TO 3X BASIC AS SALUTE
CENTURY PRINT RUN 100 SERIAL #'d SETS
1 Ichiro Suzuki/2001 5.00 12.00
2 Tony Gwynn/2001 3.00 8.00
3 Magglio Ordonez/2001 1.50 4.00
4 Cal Ripken/2001 8.00 20.00
5 Roger Clemens/1998 5.00 12.00
6 Kazuhiro Sasaki/2001 1.50 4.00
7 Freddy Garcia/2001 1.50 4.00
8 Luis Gonzalez/2001 1.50 4.00
9 Lance Berkman/2001 1.50 4.00
10 Derek Jeter/2000 6.00 15.00
11 Chipper Jones/2000 2.50 6.00
12 Randy Johnson/2000 2.50 6.00
13 Andruw Jones/2000 1.50 4.00
14 Pedro Martinez/1999 1.50 4.00
15 Jim Thome/1999 1.50 4.00
16 Rafael Palmeiro/1999 1.50 4.00
17 Barry Larkin/1999 1.50 4.00
18 Ivan Rodriguez/1998 1.50 4.00
19 Omar Vizquel/1998 1.50 4.00
20 Edgar Martinez/1997 1.50 4.00
21 Larry Walker/1997 1.50 4.00
22 Javy Lopez/1997 1.50 4.00
23 Mariano Rivera/1997 2.50 6.00
24 Frank Thomas/1995 2.50 6.00
25 Greg Maddux/1994 4.00 10.00

2002 Donruss Elite Back 2 Back Jacks

Randomly inserted into pack, this 30-card insert set showcases both retired and present-day stars. The standard-size fronts are full color action shots that are featured with one or two swatches of game-used bats. Cards featuring one player have a stated print run of 150 sets while cards featuring two players have a stated print run of 75 sets.

1 Ivan Rodriguez 15.00 40.00
Alex Rodriguez
2 Kirby Puckett 20.00 50.00
Dave Winfield
3 Ted Williams 50.00 100.00
Nomar Garciaparra
4 Jeff Bagwell 20.00 50.00
Craig Biggio
5 Eddie Murray 50.00 100.00
Cal Ripken
6 Andruw Jones 20.00 50.00
Chipper Jones
7 Roberto Clemente 60.00 120.00
Willie Stargell
8 Lou Gehrig 100.00 200.00
Don Mattingly
9 Larry Walker 20.00 50.00
Todd Helton
10 Manny Ramirez 20.00 50.00
Trot Nixon
11 Ivan Rodriguez 10.00 25.00
12 Alex Rodriguez 10.00 25.00
13 Kirby Puckett 15.00 40.00
14 Dave Winfield 10.00 25.00
15 Ted Williams 50.00 100.00
16 Nomar Garciaparra 10.00 25.00
17 Jeff Bagwell 10.00 25.00
18 Craig Biggio 10.00 25.00
19 Eddie Murray 15.00 40.00
20 Cal Ripken 20.00 50.00
21 Andruw Jones 10.00 25.00
22 Chipper Jones 10.00 25.00
23 Roberto Clemente 50.00 100.00
24 Willie Stargell 10.00 25.00
25 Lou Gehrig 75.00 150.00
26 Don Mattingly 15.00 40.00
27 Larry Walker 6.00 15.00
28 Todd Helton 10.00 25.00
29 Manny Ramirez 10.00 25.00
30 Trot Nixon 6.00 15.00

2002 Donruss Elite Back to the Future

Randomly inserted into packs, this 22-card insert set matches both current and future stars on the fronts and backs respectively. The standard-size card fronts/backs feature full color action shots on metalized film board. 500 serial-numbered copies of each dual-player card were produced and 1000 serial-numbered copies of each single-player card were produced. Card number 6 was originally intended to feature Cardinals rookie So Taguchi paired up with Jim Edmonds and card number 20 was to feature Taguchi by himself, but both cards were pulled from the set before production was finalized, thus this set is complete at 22 cards. Cards featuring one player had a stated print run of 1000 sets and cards featuring two players had a stated print run of 500 sets.

COMPLETE SET (23) 60.00 120.00
1 Scott Rolen 2.50 6.00
Marlon Byrd
2 Joe Crede 1.50 4.00
Frank Thomas
3 Lance Berkman 2.50 6.00
Jeff Bagwell
4 Marcus Giles 2.50 6.00
Chipper Jones
5 Shawn Green 2.00 5.00
Paul LoDuca
7 Kerry Wood 2.00 5.00
Juan Cruz
8 Vladimir Guerrero 2.50 6.00
Orlando Cabrera
9 Scott Rolen 1.50 4.00
10 Marlon Byrd 1.50 4.00
11 Frank Thomas 2.00 5.00
12 Joe Crede 1.50 4.00
13 Jeff Bagwell 1.50 4.00
14 Lance Berkman 1.50 4.00
15 Chipper Jones 2.00 5.00
16 Marcus Giles 1.50 4.00
17 Shawn Green 1.50 4.00
18 Paul LoDuca 1.50 4.00
19 Jim Edmonds 1.50 4.00
21 Kerry Wood 1.50 4.00
22 Juan Cruz 1.50 4.00
23 Vladimir Guerrero 2.00 5.00
24 Orlando Cabrera 1.50 4.00

2002 Donruss Elite Back to the Future Threads

Randomly inserted into packs, this 24-card insert set is a parallel to Donruss Elite Back to the Future. It matches both current and future stars on the fronts and backs respectively. The standard-size card fronts/backs feature full color action shots on metalized film board. The fronts differ by offering one or two swatches of game-worn jerseys. Autograph exchange cards for the Edmonds/Taguchi dual card and So Taguchi's stand alone card were seeded into packs. Please note that only Taguchi was contracted to sign the Edmonds/Taguchi combo card. Both cards had a redemption deadline of October 10th, 2003. Cards featuring one player had a stated print run of 100 sets and cards featuring two players have a stated print run of 50 sets.

1 Scott Rolen Jsy 15.00 40.00
Marlon Byrd Jsy
2 Frank Thomas Jsy 6.00 15.00
Joe Crede Hat
3 Jeff Bagwell Jsy 15.00 40.00
Lance Berkman Jsy
4 Chipper Jones Jsy 15.00 40.00
Marcus Giles Jsy
5 Shawn Green Jsy 10.00 25.00
Paul LoDuca Jsy
6 So Taguchi Jsy AU 20.00 50.00
Jim Edmonds Jsy
7 Kerry Wood Jsy 10.00 25.00
Juan Cruz Jsy
8 Vladimir Guerrero Jsy 15.00 40.00
Orlando Cabrera Jsy
9 Scott Rolen 10.00 25.00
10 Marlon Byrd 6.00 15.00
11 Frank Thomas 15.00 40.00
12 Joe Crede Shoes 6.00 15.00
13 Jeff Bagwell 10.00 25.00
14 Lance Berkman 6.00 15.00
15 Chipper Jones 15.00 40.00
16 Marcus Giles 6.00 15.00
17 Shawn Green 6.00 15.00
18 Paul LoDuca 6.00 15.00
19 Jim Edmonds 6.00 15.00
20 So Taguchi AU 50.00 100.00
21 Kerry Wood 6.00 15.00
22 Juan Cruz 6.00 15.00
23 Vladimir Guerrero 15.00 40.00
24 Orlando Cabrera 6.00 15.00

2002 Donruss Elite Career Best

Randomly inserted into packs, this 40-card insert set spotlights on players who established career statistical highs in 2001. Each card is serial numbered to a specific statistical achievement and the cards were randomly seeded into packs. The standard-size card fronts feature color action shots on metalized film board with silver holo-foil stamping. Cards with a stated print run of less than 25 copies are not priced due to market scarcity.

1 Albert Pujols OPS/1013 5.00 12.00
2 Alex Rodriguez HR/52 10.00 25.00
3 Alex Rodriguez RBI/135 8.00 20.00
4 Andruw Jones RBI/104 3.00 8.00
5 Barry Bonds HR/73 15.00 40.00
6 Barry Bonds OPS/1379 6.00 15.00
7 Barry Bonds BB/177 12.50 30.00
8 C.C. Sabathia K/171 3.00 8.00
9 Carlos Beltran OPS/876 1.50 4.00
10 Chipper Jones BA/330 3.00 8.00
11 Derek Jeter SB/900 6.00 15.00
12 Eric Chavez RBI/114 3.00 8.00
13 Frank Catalanotto BA/330 2.00 5.00
14 Ichiro Suzuki OPS/838 5.00 12.00
15 Ichiro Suzuki RUN/127 10.00 25.00
16 Ichiro Suzuki 3B/8
17 J.D. Drew HR/27 12.50 30.00
18 J.D. Drew OPS/1027 1.50 4.00
19 Jason Giambi SLG/660 1.50 4.00
20 Jim Thome HR/49 12.50 30.00
21 Jim Thome SLG/624 1.50 4.00
22 Jorge Posada RBI/95 6.00 15.00
23 Jose Cruz Jr. SLG/856 1.50 4.00
24 Kazuhiro Sasaki SV/45 12.50 30.00
25 Kerry Wood ERA/336 2.00 5.00
26 Lance Berkman OPS/1050 1.50 4.00
27 Magglio Ordonez OB/382 2.00 5.00
28 Mark Mulder ERA/345 2.00 5.00
29 Pat Burrell HR/27 12.50 30.00
30 Pat Burrell SLG/469 2.00 5.00
31 Randy Johnson K/372 3.00 8.00
32 Randy Johnson WIN/21
33 Richie Sexson SLG/547 1.50 4.00
34 Roberto Alomar OPS/956 1.50 4.00
35 Sammy Sosa RBI/160 5.00 12.00
36 Sammy Sosa OPS/1174 2.50 6.00
37 Shawn Green RBI/125 3.00 8.00
38 Tsuyoshi Shinjo RUN/10
39 Trot Nixon HIT/150 3.00 8.00
40 Troy Glaus RBI/108 3.00 8.00

2002 Donruss Elite Passing the Torch

Randomly inserted into packs, this 24-card insert set presents baseball legends and rising stars on double-sided holo-foil board. The front/back of these standard-size cards feature color photos of the players. 500 serial-numbered copies of each dual-player card were produced. 1000 serial-numbered copies of single player card were produced.

COMPLETE SET (24) 125.00 250.00
1 Fergie Jenkins 3.00 8.00
Mark Prior
2 Nolan Ryan 12.50 30.00
Roy Oswalt
3 Ozzie Smith 6.00 15.00
J.D. Drew
4 George Brett 10.00 25.00
Carlos Beltran
5 Kirby Puckett 4.00 10.00
Michael Cuddyer
6 Johnny Bench 4.00 10.00
Adam Dunn
7 Duke Snider 4.00 10.00
Paul LoDuca
8 Tony Gwynn 6.00 15.00
Xavier Nady
9 Fergie Jenkins 2.00 5.00
10 Mark Prior 2.00 5.00
11 Nolan Ryan 8.00 20.00
12 Roy Oswalt 2.00 5.00
13 Ozzie Smith 5.00 12.00
14 J.D. Drew 2.00 5.00
15 George Brett 8.00 20.00
16 Carlos Beltran 2.00 5.00
17 Kirby Puckett 3.00 8.00
18 Michael Cuddyer 2.00 5.00
19 Johnny Bench 3.00 8.00
20 Adam Dunn 2.00 5.00
21 Duke Snider 2.00 5.00
22 Paul LoDuca 2.00 5.00
23 Tony Gwynn 4.00 10.00
24 Xavier Nady 2.00 5.00

2002 Donruss Elite Passing the Torch Autographs

Randomly inserted into packs, this 24-card autograph set is a parallel to the Donruss Elite Passing the Torch insert set. It presents baseball legends and rising stars on double-sided holo-foil board. The front/back of these standard-size cards also feature color photos of the players, but differ by using color highlight overlays. We have notated the stated print runs next to the player's name in our checklist.

1 Fergie Jenkins 30.00 60.00
Mark Prior/50
2 Nolan Ryan 60.00 120.00
Roy Oswalt/50
3 Ozzie Smith 60.00 120.00
J.D. Drew/50
4 George Brett
Carlos Beltran/25
5 Kirby Puckett 60.00 120.00
Michael Cuddyer/50
6 Johnny Bench 50.00 100.00
Adam Dunn/50
7 Duke Snider 50.00 100.00
Paul LoDuca/50
8 Tony Gwynn 50.00 100.00
Xavier Nady/50
9 Fergie Jenkins/50 20.00 50.00
10 Mark Prior/100 10.00 25.00
11 Nolan Ryan/100 60.00 120.00
12 Roy Oswalt/100 10.00 25.00
13 Ozzie Smith/25
14 J.D. Drew/100 10.00 25.00
15 George Brett/25
16 Carlos Beltran/100 10.00 25.00
17 Kirby Puckett/25
18 Michael Cuddyer/100 10.00 25.00
19 Johnny Bench/100 30.00 60.00
20 Adam Dunn/50 30.00 60.00
21 Duke Snider/100 15.00 40.00
22 Paul LoDuca/100 10.00 25.00

23 Tony Gwynn/100 30.00 60.00
24 Xavier Nady/100 10.00 25.00

2002 Donruss Elite Recollection Autographs

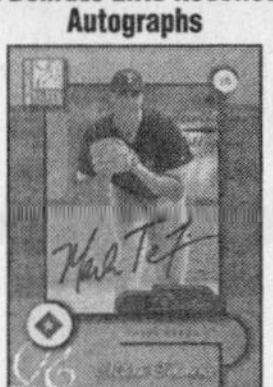

Randomly inserted into packs, these 23 cards featured signed copies of the player's 2001 Donruss Elite card. We have notated the stated print run next to the player's name and cards with a stated print run of 25 or less are not priced due to market scarcity.

1 Jeremy Affeldt 01/25
2 Alfredo Amezaga 01/50 8.00 20.00
3 Angel Berroa 01/25
4 Dewon Brazelton 01/25
5 John Buck 01/25
6 Marlon Byrd 01/25
7 Juan Cruz 01/25
8 Brandon Duckworth 01/10
9 Brandon Duckworth 01/15
10 Casey Fossum 01/25
11 Luis Garcia 01/25
12 Tony Gwynn 01/10
13 Bill Hall 01/25
14 Orlando Hudson 01/50 8.00 20.00
15 Ryan Klesko 01/5
16 Jason Lane 01/24
17 Corky Miller 01/25
18 Roy Oswalt 01/25
19 Antonio Perez 01/50 8.00 20.00
20 Mark Prior 01/25
21 Mike Rivera 01/50 8.00 20.00
22 Mark Teixeira 01/25
23 Claudio Vargas 01/50 8.00 20.00
24 Martin Vargas 01/50 8.00 20.00

2002 Donruss Elite Throwback Threads

Randomly inserted into packs, this 64-card insert set offers standard-size cards that display one or two swatches of game-used jerseys from retired legends or current stars. The card front/back features a white border background with color action shots. Card number 28 (intended to be a Rickey Henderson Red Sox card) does not exist in unsigned form. The legendary speedster signed all 100 copies produced and this card can be referenced in the Throwback Threads Autographs parallel set. Cards featuring one player have a stated print run of 100 sets while cards featuring two players have a stated print run of 50 sets.

1 Ted Williams / Manny Ramirez 50.00 100.00
2 Carlton Fisk / Mike Piazza 15.00 40.00
3 Bo Jackson / George Brett 40.00 80.00
4 Curt Schilling / Randy Johnson 20.00 50.00
5 Don Mattingly / Lou Gehrig 150.00 250.00
6 Bernie Williams / Dave Winfield 20.00 50.00
7 Rickey Henderson / Ricky Henderson 20.00 50.00
8 Robin Yount / Paul Molitor 20.00 50.00
9 Stan Musial / J.D. Drew 40.00 80.00
10 Andre Dawson / Ryne Sandberg 30.00 60.00
11 Babe Ruth / Reggie Jackson 250.00 400.00
12 Brooks Robinson / Cal Ripken 50.00 100.00
13 Ted Williams / Nomar Garciaparra 50.00 100.00
14 Jackie Robinson / Shawn Green 40.00 80.00
15 Cal Ripken / Tony Gwynn 50.00 100.00
16 Ted Williams 40.00 80.00
17 Manny Ramirez 10.00 25.00
18 Carlton Fisk Red Sox 15.00 40.00
19 Mike Piazza 10.00 25.00
20 Bo Jackson 15.00 40.00
21 George Brett 15.00 40.00
22 Curt Schilling 6.00 15.00
23 Randy Johnson 10.00 25.00
24 Don Mattingly 15.00 40.00
25 Lou Gehrig 100.00 200.00
26 Bernie Williams 10.00 25.00
27 Dave Winfield 10.00 25.00
29 Rickey Henderson Mariners 10.00 25.00
30 Robin Yount 15.00 40.00
31 Paul Molitor 10.00 25.00
32 Stan Musial 30.00 60.00
33 J.D. Drew 6.00 15.00
34 Andre Dawson 10.00 25.00
35 Ryne Sandberg 20.00 50.00
36 Babe Ruth 175.00 300.00
37 Reggie Jackson 15.00 40.00
38 Brooks Robinson 15.00 40.00
39 Cal Ripken Running 40.00 80.00
40 Nomar Garciaparra
41 Jackie Robinson 40.00 80.00
42 Shawn Green 6.00 15.00
43 Pedro Martinez Grey 10.00 25.00
44 Nolan Ryan Astros 30.00 60.00
45 Kazuhiro Sasaki 6.00 15.00
46 Tony Gwynn 15.00 40.00
47 Carlton Fisk White Sox 15.00 40.00
48 Cal Ripken Batting 40.00 80.00
49 Rod Carew Angels 15.00 40.00
50 Nolan Ryan Rangers 30.00 60.00
51 Alex Rodriguez 10.00 25.00
52 Greg Maddux 10.00 25.00
53 Pedro Martinez White 10.00 25.00
54 Rickey Henderson Padres 10.00 25.00
55 Rod Carew Twins 15.00 40.00
56 Roberto Clemente 50.00 100.00
57 Hideo Nomo 10.00 25.00
58 Rickey Henderson Mets 10.00 25.00
59 Dave Parker 10.00 25.00
60 Eddie Mathews 15.00 40.00
61 Eddie Murray 15.00 40.00
62 Nolan Ryan Angels 30.00 60.00
63 Tom Seaver 15.00 40.00
64 Roger Clemens 15.00 40.00
65 Rickey Henderson A's 10.00 25.00

2002 Donruss Elite Throwback Threads Autographs

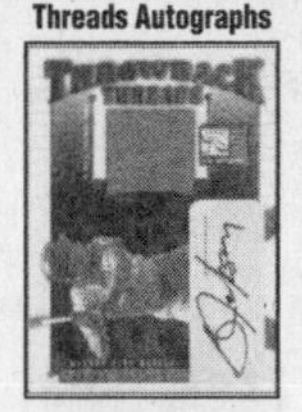

28 R.Henderson/100 75.00 150.00

2003 Donruss Elite

This 200 card set was released in June, 2003. The first 180 cards consist of veterans while the final 20 cards are either rookies or leading prospects. This product was issued in five card packs which came 20 packs to a box and 20 boxes to a case with an $5 SRP. The final 20 cards consists of rookies and leading prospects, which were randomly inserted into packs and printed to a stated print run of 1750 serial numbered sets.

COMP.SET w/o SP's (180) 8.00 20.00
COMMON CARD (1-180) .10 .30
COMMON CARD (181-200) 1.50 4.00
1 Darin Erstad .10 .30
2 David Eckstein .10 .30
3 Garret Anderson .10 .30
4 Jarrod Washburn .10 .30
5 Tim Salmon .20 .50
6 Troy Glaus .10 .30
7 Marty Cordova .10 .30
8 Melvin Mora .10 .30
9 Rodrigo Lopez .10 .30
10 Tony Batista .10 .30
11 Derek Lowe .10 .30
12 Johnny Damon .20 .50
13 Manny Ramirez .20 .50
14 Nomar Garciaparra .50 1.25
15 Pedro Martinez .20 .50
16 Shea Hillenbrand .10 .30
17 Carlos Lee .10 .30
18 Joe Crede .10 .30
19 Frank Thomas .30 .75
20 Magglio Ordonez .10 .30
21 Mark Buehrle .10 .30
22 Paul Konerko .10 .30
23 C.C. Sabathia .10 .30
24 Ellis Burks .10 .30
25 Omar Vizquel .20 .50
26 Brian Tallet .10 .30
27 Bobby Higginson .10 .30
28 Carlos Pena .10 .30
29 Mark Redman .10 .30
30 Steve Sparks .10 .30
31 Carlos Beltran .20 .50
32 Joe Randa .10 .30
33 Mike Sweeney .10 .30
34 Raul Ibanez .10 .30
35 Runelvys Hernandez .10 .30
36 Brad Radke .10 .30
37 Corey Koskie .10 .30
38 Cristian Guzman .10 .30
39 David Ortiz .30 .75
40 Doug Mientkiewicz .10 .30
41 Jacque Jones .10 .30
42 Torii Hunter .10 .30
43 Alfonso Soriano .20 .50
44 Andy Pettitte .20 .50
45 Bernie Williams .20 .50
46 David Wells .10 .30
47 Derek Jeter .75 2.00
48 Jason Giambi .10 .30
49 Jeff Weaver .10 .30
50 Jorge Posada .20 .50
51 Mike Mussina .20 .50
52 Roger Clemens .60 1.50
53 Barry Zito .10 .30
54 Eric Chavez .10 .30
55 Jermaine Dye .10 .30
56 Mark Mulder .10 .30
57 Miguel Tejada .10 .30
58 Tim Hudson .10 .30
59 Bret Boone .10 .30
60 Chris Snelling .10 .30
61 Edgar Martinez .20 .50
62 Freddy Garcia .10 .30
63 Ichiro Suzuki .60 1.50
64 Jamie Moyer .10 .30
65 John Olerud .10 .30
66 Kazuhiro Sasaki .10 .30
67 Aubrey Huff .10 .30
68 Joe Kennedy .10 .30
69 Paul Wilson .10 .30
70 Alex Rodriguez .50 1.25
71 Chan Ho Park .10 .30
72 Hank Blalock .10 .30
73 Juan Gonzalez .10 .30
74 Kevin Mench .10 .30
75 Rafael Palmeiro .20 .50
76 Carlos Delgado .10 .30
77 Eric Hinske .10 .30
78 Josh Phelps .10 .30
79 Roy Halladay .10 .30
80 Shannon Stewart .10 .30
81 Vernon Wells .10 .30
82 Curt Schilling .10 .30
83 Junior Spivey .10 .30
84 Luis Gonzalez .10 .30
85 Mark Grace .20 .50
86 Randy Johnson .30 .75
87 Steve Finley .10 .30
88 Andruw Jones .20 .50
89 Chipper Jones .30 .75
90 Gary Sheffield .10 .30
91 Greg Maddux .50 1.25
92 John Smoltz .20 .50
93 Corey Patterson .10 .30
94 Kerry Wood .10 .30
95 Mark Prior .20 .50
96 Moises Alou .10 .30
97 Sammy Sosa .30 .75
98 Adam Dunn .10 .30
99 Austin Kearns .10 .30
100 Barry Larkin .20 .50
101 Ken Griffey Jr. .50 1.25
102 Sean Casey .10 .30
103 Jason Jennings .10 .30
104 Jay Payton .10 .30
105 Larry Walker .10 .30
106 Todd Helton .20 .50
107 A.J. Burnett .10 .30
108 Josh Beckett .10 .30
109 Juan Encarnacion .10 .30
110 Mike Lowell .10 .30
111 Craig Biggio .20 .50
112 Daryle Ward .10 .30
113 Jeff Bagwell .20 .50
114 Lance Berkman .10 .30
115 Roy Oswalt .10 .30
116 Jason Lane .10 .30
117 Adrian Beltre .10 .30
118 Hideo Nomo .30 .75
119 Kazuhisa Ishii .10 .30
120 Kevin Brown .10 .30
121 Odalis Perez .10 .30
122 Paul Lo Duca .10 .30
123 Shawn Green .10 .30
124 Ben Sheets .10 .30
125 Jeffrey Hammonds .10 .30
126 Jose Hernandez .10 .30
127 Richie Sexson .10 .30
128 Bartolo Colon .10 .30
129 Brad Wilkerson .10 .30
130 Javier Vazquez .10 .30
131 Jose Vidro .10 .30
132 Michael Barrett .10 .30
133 Vladimir Guerrero .30 .75
134 Al Leiter .10 .30
135 Mike Piazza .50 1.25
136 Mo Vaughn .10 .30
137 Pedro Astacio .10 .30
138 Roberto Alomar .20 .50
139 Pat Burrell .10 .30
140 Vicente Padilla .10 .30
141 Jimmy Rollins .10 .30
142 Bobby Abreu .10 .30
143 Marlon Byrd .10 .30
144 Brian Giles .10 .30
145 Jason Kendall .10 .30
146 Aramis Ramirez .10 .30
147 Josh Fogg .10 .30
148 Ryan Klesko .10 .30
149 Phil Nevin .10 .30
150 Sean Burroughs .10 .30
151 Mark Kotsay .10 .30
152 Barry Bonds .75 2.00
153 Damian Moss .10 .30
154 Jason Schmidt .10 .30
155 Benito Santiago .10 .30
156 Rich Aurilia .10 .30
157 Scott Rolen .20 .50
158 J.D. Drew .10 .30
159 Jim Edmonds .10 .30
160 Matt Morris .10 .30
161 Tino Martinez .20 .50
162 Albert Pujols .60 1.50
163 Russ Ortiz .10 .30
164 Rey Ordonez .10 .30
165 Paul Byrd .10 .30
166 Kenny Lofton .10 .30
167 Kenny Rogers .10 .30
168 Rickey Henderson .30 .75
169 Fred McGriff .20 .50
170 Charles Johnson .10 .30
171 Mike Hampton .10 .30
172 Jim Thome .20 .50
173 Travis Hafner .10 .30
174 Ivan Rodriguez .20 .50
175 Ray Durham .10 .30
176 Jeremy Giambi .10 .30
177 Jeff Kent .10 .30
178 Cliff Floyd .10 .30
179 Kevin Millwood .10 .30
180 Tom Glavine .20 .50
181 Hideki Matsui ROO RC 4.00 10.00
182 Jose Contreras ROO RC 2.00 5.00
183 Termel Sledge ROO RC 1.50 4.00
184 Lew Ford ROO RC 2.00 5.00
185 Jhonny Peralta ROO 2.00 5.00
186 Alexis Rios ROO 3.00 8.00
187 Jeff Baker ROO 1.50 4.00
188 Jeremy Guthrie ROO 1.50 4.00
189 Jose Castillo ROO 1.50 4.00
190 Garrett Atkins ROO 1.50 4.00
191 Jer. Bonderman ROO RC 2.50 6.00
192 Adam LaRoche ROO 1.50 4.00
193 Vinny Chulk ROO 1.50 4.00
194 Walter Young ROO 1.50 4.00
195 Jimmy Gobble ROO 1.50 4.00
196 Prentice Redman ROO RC 1.50 4.00
197 Jason Anderson ROO 1.50 4.00
198 Nic Jackson ROO 1.50 4.00
199 Travis Chapman ROO 1.50 4.00
200 Shane Victorino ROO RC 2.50 6.00

2003 Donruss Elite Aspirations

*1-180 PRINT RUN b/wn 36-50 6X TO 15X
*1-180 PRINT RUN b/wn 51-65: 5X TO 12X
*1-180 PRINT RUN b/wn 66-80 5X TO 12X
*1-180 PRINT RUN b/wn 81-99 4X TO 10X
COMMON (181-200) p/r 81-99 2.50 6.00
SEMIS 181-200 p/r 81-99 4.00 10.00
COMMON (181-200) p/r 51-65 4.00 10.00
SEMIS 181-200 p/r 51-65 6.00 15.00
COMMON (181-200) p/r 36-50 4.00 10.00
COMMON (181-200) p/r 26-35 5.00 12.00
SEMIS 181-200 p/r 26-35 8.00 20.00
SEE BECKETT.COM FOR PRINT RUNS
NO PRICING ON QTY OF 25 OR LESS

2003 Donruss Elite Aspirations Gold

STATED PRINT RUN 1 SERIAL #'d SET
NO PRICING DUE TO SCARCITY

2003 Donruss Elite Atlantic City National

Collectors who opened Donruss Elite product while at the Donruss corporate booth at the 2003 Atlantic City National were eligible to receive these specially produced cards. The fronts of these cards have special stamping with the Atlantic City National logo and the backs are serially numbered to a stated print run of five copies. Due to market scarcity, no pricing is provided for these cards.

PRINT RUN 5 SERIAL #'d SETS

2003 Donruss Elite Status

*1-180 PRINT RUN b/wn 26-35: 8X TO 20X
*1-180 PRINT RUN b/wn 36-50: 6X TO 15X
*1-180 PRINT RUN b/wn 51-65: 5X TO 12X
*1-180 PRINT RUN b/wn 66-80: 5X TO 12X
*1-180 PRINT RUN b/wn 81-99: 4X TO 10X
COMMON (181-200) p/r 66-80 3.00 8.00
COMMON (181-200) p/r 51-65 4.00 10.00
COMMON (181-200) p/r 36-50 4.00 10.00
NO PRICING ON QTY OF 25 OR LESS

2003 Donruss Elite Status Gold

STATED PRINT RUN 24 SERIAL #'d SETS
NO PRICING DUE TO SCARCITY

2003 Donruss Elite Turn of the Century Autographs

Randomly inserted into packs, this is a partial parallel to the Donruss Elite set and features just the rookie cards with the exception of Hideki Matsui who was under an exclusive contract to Upper Deck. These cards are signed by the player and were issued to a stated print run of 50 serial numbered sets.

182 Jose Contreras ROO 15.00 40.00
183 Termel Sledge ROO 6.00 15.00
184 Lew Ford ROO 10.00 25.00
185 Jhonny Peralta ROO 15.00 40.00
186 Alexis Rios ROO 15.00 40.00
187 Jeff Baker ROO 6.00 15.00
188 Jeremy Guthrie ROO 6.00 15.00
189 Jose Castillo ROO 6.00 15.00
190 Garrett Atkins ROO 6.00 15.00
191 Jeremy Bonderman ROO 40.00 80.00
192 Adam LaRoche ROO 6.00 15.00
193 Vinny Chulk ROO 6.00 15.00
194 Walter Young ROO 6.00 15.00
195 Jimmy Gobble ROO 6.00 15.00
196 Prentice Redman ROO 6.00 15.00
197 Jason Anderson ROO 6.00 15.00
198 Nic Jackson ROO 6.00 15.00
199 Travis Chapman ROO 6.00 15.00
200 Shane Victorino ROO 40.00 80.00

2003 Donruss Elite All-Time Career Best

STATED ODDS 1:9
*PARALLEL 1-25 p/r 211-239: 1X TO 2.5X
*PARALLEL 1-25 p/r 105-140: 1.25X TO 3X
*PARALLEL 1-25 p/r 53-60: 2X TO 5X
*PARALLEL 1-25 p/r 39-49: 2.5X TO 6X
*PARALLEL 1-25 p/r 29-31: 3X TO 8X
*PARALLEL 26-50 p/r 393: .6X TO 1.5X
*PARALLEL 26-50 p/r 130-137: 1X TO 2.5X
*PARALLEL 26-50 p/r 55-66: 1.5X TO 4X
*PARALLEL 26-50 p/r 37-49: 2X TO 5X
*PARALLEL 26-50 p/r 35: 2.5X TO 6X
PARALLEL PRINTS B/WN 1-393 COPIES PER
NO PARALLEL PRICING ON QTY OF 25 OR LESS
1 Babe Ruth 5.00 12.00
2 Ty Cobb 3.00 8.00
3 Jackie Robinson 1.50 4.00
4 Lou Gehrig 3.00 8.00
5 Thurman Munson 1.50 4.00
6 Nolan Ryan 5.00 12.00
7 Mike Schmidt 3.00 8.00
8 Don Mattingly 3.00 8.00
9 Yogi Berra 1.50 4.00
10 Rod Carew 1.25 3.00
11 Reggie Jackson 1.50 4.00
12 Al Kaline 1.50 4.00
13 Harmon Killebrew 1.50 4.00
14 Eddie Mathews 1.50 4.00
15 Stan Musial 2.50 6.00
16 Jim Palmer 1.25 3.00
17 Phil Rizzuto 1.25 3.00
18 Brooks Robinson 1.25 3.00
19 Tom Seaver 1.25 3.00
20 Robin Yount 1.50 4.00
21 Carlton Fisk 1.25 3.00
22 Dale Murphy 1.25 3.00
23 Cal Ripken 5.00 12.00
24 Tony Gwynn 2.00 5.00
25 Andre Dawson 1.25 3.00
26 Derek Jeter 4.00 10.00
27 Ken Griffey Jr. 2.50 6.00
28 Albert Pujols 3.00 8.00
29 Sammy Sosa 1.50 4.00
30 Jason Giambi 1.25 3.00
31 Randy Johnson 1.50 4.00
32 Greg Maddux 2.50 6.00
33 Rickey Henderson 1.50 4.00
34 Pedro Martinez 1.25 3.00
35 Jeff Bagwell 1.25 3.00
36 Alex Rodriguez 2.50 6.00
37 Vladimir Guerrero 1.50 4.00
38 Chipper Jones 1.50 4.00
39 Shawn Green 1.25 3.00
40 Tom Glavine 1.25 3.00
41 Curt Schilling 1.25 3.00
42 Todd Helton 1.25 3.00
43 Roger Clemens 3.00 8.00
44 Lance Berkman 1.25 3.00
45 Nomar Garciaparra 2.50 6.00

2003 Donruss Elite All-Time Career Best Materials

Randomly inserted into packs, this is a parallel to the All-Time Career Best insert set. Each of these cards feature not only the player but also a piece of game-used memorabilia from their career. We have printed what type of material as well as the stated print run next to the player's name in our checklist. Please note that for cards with a stated print run of 25 or fewer, there is no pricing due to market scarcity.

*MULTI-COLOR PATCH: 1.5X TO 4X HI COL
1 Babe Ruth Bat/25
2 Ty Cobb Bat/25
3 Jackie Robinson Jkt/50 40.00 80.00
4 Lou Gehrig Bat/100 75.00 150.00
5 Thurman Munson Bat/200 10.00 25.00
6 Nolan Ryan Jkt/400 20.00 50.00
7 Mike Schmidt Jkt/400 15.00 40.00
8 Don Mattingly Hat/250 15.00 40.00
9 Yogi Berra Bat/100 12.50 30.00
10 Rod Carew Bat/400 6.00 15.00
11 Reggie Jackson Bat/400 6.00 15.00
12 Al Kaline Bat/400 8.00 20.00
13 Harmon Killebrew Pants/400 8.00 20.00
14 Eddie Mathews Bat/200 10.00 25.00
15 Stan Musial Bat/100 20.00 50.00
16 Jim Palmer Jsy/200 8.00 20.00
17 Phil Rizzuto Bat/400 6.00 15.00
18 Brooks Robinson Bat/400 6.00 15.00
19 Tom Seaver Jsy/400 6.00 15.00
20 Robin Yount Bat/400 8.00 20.00
21 Carlton Fisk Bat/400 6.00 15.00
22 Dale Murphy Bat/400 6.00 15.00
23 Cal Ripken Bat/400 15.00 40.00
24 Tony Gwynn Pants/400 6.00 15.00
25 Andre Dawson Bat/400 4.00 10.00
26 Derek Jeter Base/400 10.00 25.00
27 Ken Griffey Jr. Base/400 6.00 15.00
28 Albert Pujols Base/400 6.00 15.00
29 Sammy Sosa Bat/400 4.00 10.00
30 Jason Giambi Bat/400 3.00 8.00
31 Randy Johnson Jsy/400 4.00 10.00
32 Greg Maddux Jsy/400 4.00 10.00
33 Rickey Henderson Bat/400 4.00 10.00
34 Pedro Martinez Jsy/400 4.00 10.00
35 Jeff Bagwell Pants/400 4.00 10.00
36 Alex Rodriguez Bat/400 6.00 15.00
37 Vladimir Guerrero Bat/400 4.00 10.00
38 Chipper Jones Bat/400 4.00 10.00
39 Shawn Green Bat/400 3.00 8.00
40 Tom Glavine Jsy/400 4.00 10.00
41 Curt Schilling Jsy/400 3.00 8.00
42 Todd Helton Bat/400 4.00 10.00
43 Roger Clemens Jsy/400 8.00 20.00
44 Lance Berkman Bat/400 3.00 8.00
45 Nomar Garciaparra Bat/400 6.00 15.00

2003 Donruss Elite All-Time Career Best Materials Parallel

PRINT RUNS B/WN 1-393 COPIES PER
NO PRICING ON QTY OF 25 OR LESS
1 Babe Ruth Bat/60 75.00 150.00
2 Ty Cobb Bat/24
3 Jackie Robinson Jkt/19
4 Lou Gehrig Bat/49 75.00 150.00
5 Thurman Munson Bat/105 15.00 40.00
6 Nolan Ryan Jkt/22
7 Mike Schmidt Jkt/48 40.00 80.00
8 Don Mattingly Hat/53 40.00 80.00
9 Yogi Berra Bat/30 30.00 60.00
10 Rod Carew Bat/239 6.00 15.00
11 Reggie Jackson Bat/39 15.00 40.00
12 Al Kaline Bat/29 30.00 60.00
13 Harmon Killebrew Pants/140 10.00 25.00
14 Eddie Mathews Bat/31 30.00 60.00
15 Stan Musial Bat/39 50.00 100.00
16 Jim Palmer Jsy/23
17 Phil Rizzuto Bat/10
18 Brooks Robinson Bat/118 10.00 25.00
19 Tom Seaver Jsy/7
20 Robin Yount Bat/49 20.00 50.00
21 Carlton Fisk Bat/107 10.00 25.00
22 Dale Murphy Bat/44 15.00 40.00
23 Cal Ripken Bat/211 20.00 50.00
24 Tony Gwynn Pants/220 8.00 20.00
25 Andre Dawson Bat/49 10.00 25.00
26 Derek Jeter Base/24
27 Ken Griffey Jr. Base/56 15.00 40.00
28 Albert Pujols Base/37 20.00 50.00
29 Sammy Sosa Bat/66 10.00 25.00
30 Jason Giambi Bat/137 4.00 10.00
31 Randy Johnson Jsy/12
32 Greg Maddux Jsy/20
33 Rickey Henderson Bat/130 6.00 15.00
34 Pedro Martinez Jsy/23
35 Jeff Bagwell Pants/47 10.00 25.00
36 Alex Rodriguez Bat/393 6.00 15.00
37 Vladimir Guerrero Bat/44 15.00 40.00
38 Chipper Jones Bat/45 15.00 40.00
39 Shawn Green Bat/49 6.00 15.00
40 Tom Glavine Jsy/22
41 Curt Schilling Jsy/35 6.00 15.00
42 Todd Helton Bat/59 10.00 25.00
43 Roger Clemens Jsy/1
44 Lance Berkman Bat/55 6.00 15.00
45 Nomar Garciaparra Bat/35 40.00 80.00

2003 Donruss Elite Back to Back Jacks

Randomly inserted into packs, these 50 cards feature game use bat pieces on them. These cards were issued to different print runs depending on what the card number is and we have notated that information in our headers to this set.

1-25 PRINT RUN 250 SERIAL #'d SETS
26-35 PRINT RUN 125 SERIAL #'d SETS
36-40 PRINT RUN 100 SERIAL #'d SETS
41-45 PRINT RUN 75 SERIAL #'d SETS
46-50 PRINT RUN 50 SERIAL #'d SETS
1 Adam Dunn 3.00 8.00
2 Alex Rodriguez 6.00 15.00
3 Alfonso Soriano 3.00 8.00
4 Andruw Jones 4.00 10.00
5 Chipper Jones 4.00 10.00
6 Jason Giambi 3.00 8.00
7 Jeff Bagwell 4.00 10.00
8 Jim Thome 4.00 10.00
9 Juan Gonzalez 3.00 8.00
10 Lance Berkman 3.00 8.00
11 Magglio Ordonez 3.00 8.00
12 Manny Ramirez 4.00 10.00
13 Miguel Tejada 3.00 8.00
14 Mike Piazza 6.00 15.00
15 Nomar Garciaparra 6.00 15.00
16 Rafael Palmeiro 4.00 10.00
17 Rickey Henderson 4.00 10.00
18 Sammy Sosa 4.00 10.00
19 Scott Rolen 4.00 10.00
20 Shawn Green 3.00 8.00
21 Todd Helton 4.00 10.00
22 Vladimir Guerrero 4.00 10.00
23 Ivan Rodriguez 4.00 10.00
24 Eric Chavez 3.00 8.00
25 Larry Walker 3.00 8.00
26 Garret Anderson / Troy Glaus 8.00 20.00
27 Adam Dunn / Austin Kearns 8.00 20.00
28 Alex Rodriguez / Rafael Palmeiro 12.50 30.00
29 Miguel Tejada / Eric Chavez 8.00 20.00
30 Magglio Ordonez / Frank Thomas 10.00 25.00
31 Lance Berkman / Jeff Bagwell 8.00 20.00
32 Nomar Garciaparra / Manny Ramirez 15.00 40.00
33 Vladimir Guerrero / Jose Vidro 10.00 25.00
34 Mike Piazza / Roberto Alomar 10.00 25.00
35 Todd Helton / Larry Walker 8.00 20.00
36 Babe Ruth 75.00 150.00
37 Cal Ripken 40.00 80.00
38 Don Mattingly 20.00 50.00
39 Kirby Puckett 10.00 25.00
40 Roberto Clemente 30.00 60.00
41 Alfonso Soriano / Phil Rizzuto 12.50 30.00
42 Sammy Sosa / Andre Dawson 15.00 40.00
43 Ozzie Smith / Scott Rolen 30.00 60.00
44 Don Mattingly / Jason Giambi 30.00 60.00
45 Rickey Henderson / Ty Cobb 75.00 150.00
46 Joe Morgan / Johnny Bench 30.00 60.00
47 Cal Ripken / Brooks Robinson 75.00 150.00
48 George Brett / Bo Jackson 50.00 100.00
49 Babe Ruth / Lou Gehrig 250.00 400.00
50 Yogi Berra / Thurman Munson 30.00 60.00

2003 Donruss Elite Back to the Future

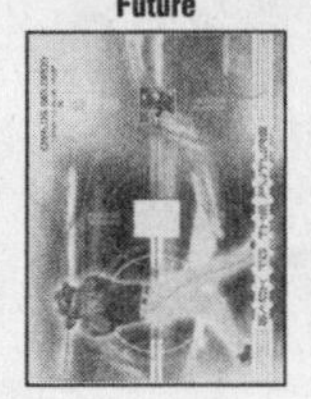

1-10 PRINT RUN 1000 SERIAL #'d SETS
11-15 PRINT RUN 500 SERIAL #'d SETS
1 Kerry Wood 1.50 4.00
2 Mark Prior 1.50 4.00
3 Magglio Ordonez 1.50 4.00
4 Joe Borchard 1.50 4.00
5 Lance Berkman 1.50 4.00
6 Jason Lane 1.50 4.00
7 Rafael Palmeiro 1.50 4.00
8 Mark Teixeira 1.50 4.00
9 Carlos Delgado 1.50 4.00
10 Josh Phelps 1.50 4.00
11 Kerry Wood / Mark Prior 2.50 6.00
12 Magglio Ordonez / Joe Borchard 2.50 6.00
13 Lance Berkman / Jason Lane 2.50 6.00
14 Rafael Palmeiro / Mark Teixeira 2.50 6.00
15 Carlos Delgado / John Phelps 2.50 6.00

2003 Donruss Elite Back to the Future Threads

*MULTI-COLOR PATCH: .75X TO 2X HI COL
1-10 PRINT RUN 250 SERIAL #'d SETS
11-15 PRINT RUN 125 SERIAL #'d SETS
1 Kerry Wood 3.00 8.00
2 Mark Prior 4.00 10.00
3 Magglio Ordonez 3.00 8.00
4 Joe Borchard 3.00 8.00
5 Lance Berkman 3.00 8.00
6 Jason Lane 3.00 8.00
7 Rafael Palmeiro 4.00 10.00
8 Mark Teixeira 4.00 10.00
9 Carlos Delgado 3.00 8.00
10 Josh Phelps 3.00 8.00
11 Kerry Wood / Mark Prior 6.00 15.00
12 Magglio Ordonez / Joe Borchard 6.00 15.00
13 Lance Berkman / Jason Lane 6.00 15.00
14 Rafael Palmeiro / Mark Teixeira 6.00 15.00
15 Carlos Delgado / John Phelps 6.00 15.00

2003 Donruss Elite Career Bests

PRINT RUNS B/WN 4-417 COPIES PER
NO PRICING ON QTY OF 25 OR LESS
1 Randy Johnson WIN/24
2 Curt Schilling WIN/23
3 Garret Anderson 2B/56 4.00 10.00
4 Andruw Jones BB/83 4.00 10.00
5 Kerry Wood CG/4
6 Magglio Ordonez HR/38 5.00 12.00
7 Magglio Ordonez RBI/135 2.50 6.00
8 Adam Dunn HR/26 6.00 15.00
9 Roy Oswalt WIN/19
10 Lance Berkman HR/42 5.00 12.00
11 Lance Berkman RBI/128 2.50 6.00
12 Shawn Green OBP/385 2.00 5.00
13 Alfonso Soriano HR/39 5.00 12.00
14 Alfonso Soriano AVG/300 2.00 5.00
15 Jason Giambi RUN/120 2.50 6.00
16 Derek Jeter SB/32 25.00 60.00
17 Vladimir Guerrero SB/40 8.00 20.00
18 Vladimir Guerrero OBP/417 3.00 8.00
19 Barry Zito WIN/23
20 Miguel Tejada HR/34 6.00 15.00
21 Barry Bonds BB/198 10.00 25.00
22 Barry Bonds AVG/370 8.00 20.00
23 Ichiro Suzuki OBP/388 6.00 15.00
24 Alex Rodriguez HR/57 12.50 30.00
25 Alex Rodriguez RBI/142 8.00 20.00

2003 Donruss Elite Career Bests Materials

STATED PRINT RUN 500 SERIAL #'d SETS
1 Randy Johnson WIN Jsy 4.00 10.00
2 Curt Schilling WIN Jsy 3.00 8.00
3 Garret Anderson 2B Bat 3.00 8.00
4 Andruw Jones BB Bat 4.00 10.00
5 Kerry Wood CG Shoe 4.00 10.00
6 Magglio Ordonez HR Bat 3.00 8.00
7 Magglio Ordonez RBI Bat 3.00 8.00
8 Adam Dunn HR Bat 3.00 8.00
9 Roy Oswalt WIN Jsy 3.00 8.00
10 Lance Berkman HR Bat 3.00 8.00
11 Lance Berkman RBI Bat 3.00 8.00
12 Shawn Green OBP Bat 3.00 8.00
13 Alfonso Soriano HR Bat 3.00 8.00
14 Alfonso Soriano AVG Bat 3.00 8.00
15 Jason Giambi RUN Bat 3.00 8.00
16 Derek Jeter SB Base 8.00 20.00
17 Vladimir Guerrero SB Bat 4.00 10.00
18 Vladimir Guerrero OBP Bat 4.00 10.00
19 Barry Zito WIN Jsy 3.00 8.00
20 Miguel Tejada HR Bat 3.00 8.00
21 Barry Bonds BB Base 8.00 20.00
22 Barry Bonds AVG Base 8.00 20.00
23 Ichiro Suzuki OBP Base 10.00 25.00
24 Alex Rodriguez HR Jsy 6.00 15.00
25 Alex Rodriguez RBI Jsy 6.00 15.00

2003 Donruss Elite Career Bests Materials Autographs

PRINT RUNS B/WN 5-250 COPIES PER
NO PRICING ON QTY OF 25 OR LESS
2 Curt Schilling WIN Jsy/5
3 Garret Anderson 2B Bat/75 20.00 50.00
4 Andruw Jones BB Bat/10
5 Kerry Wood CG Shoe/15
6 Magglio Ordonez HR Bat/10
7 Magglio Ordonez RBI Bat/10
8 Adam Dunn HR Bat/100 30.00 60.00
9 Roy Oswalt WIN Jsy/250 15.00 40.00
10 Lance Berkman HR Bat/25
11 Lance Berkman RBI Bat/25
13 Alfonso Soriano HR Bat/5
14 Alfonso Soriano AVG Bat/5
17 Vlad Guerrero SB Bat/50 50.00 100.00
18 Vlad Guerrero OBP Bat/50 50.00 100.00
19 Barry Zito WIN Jsy/75 30.00 60.00
20 Miguel Tejada HR Bat/25
24 Alex Rodriguez HR Jsy/5
25 Alex Rodriguez RBI Jsy/5

2003 Donruss Elite Highlights

STATED PRINT RUN 500 SERIAL #'d SETS
1 Sammy Sosa 500 HR 3.00 8.00
2 Rafael Palmeiro 500 HR 3.00 8.00
3 Hideki Matsui Debut 4.00 10.00
4 Jose Contreras Debut 3.00 8.00
5 Kevin Millwood No-Hit 2.00 5.00

2003 Donruss Elite Highlights Autographs

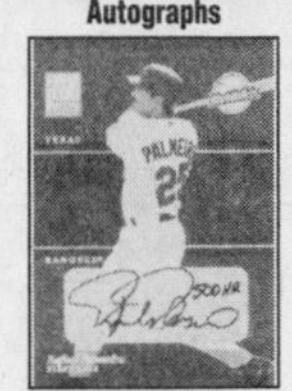

STATED PRINT RUN 50 SERIAL #'d SETS
2 Rafael Palmeiro 500 HR 50.00 100.00
4 Jose Contreras Debut 15.00 40.00

2003 Donruss Elite Passing the Torch

1-10 PRINT RUN 1000 SERIAL #'d SETS
11-15 PRINT RUN 500 SERIAL #'d SETS
1 Stan Musial 4.00 10.00
2 Jim Edmonds 1.50 4.00
3 Dale Murphy 2.50 6.00
4 Andruw Jones 2.50 6.00
5 Roger Clemens 5.00 12.00
6 Mark Prior 2.50 6.00
7 Tom Seaver 2.50 6.00
8 Tom Glavine 2.50 6.00
9 Mike Schmidt 5.00 12.00
10 Pat Burrell 1.50 4.00
11 Stan Musial / Jim Edmonds 6.00 15.00
12 Dale Murphy / Andruw Jones 4.00 10.00
13 Roger Clemens / Mark Prior 6.00 15.00
14 Tom Seaver / Tom Glavine 4.00 10.00
15 Mike Schmidt / Pat Burrell 8.00 20.00

2003 Donruss Elite Passing the Torch Autographs

Randomly inserted into packs, these cards feature the continuation of the popular Passing the Torch Autograph insert set. The first 10 cards feature individual autographs while the final five cards feature dual autographs of the players.

1-10 PRINT RUN 50 SERIAL #'d SETS
11-15 PRINT RUN 25 SERIAL #'d SETS
NO 11-15 PRICING DUE TO SCARCITY
1 Stan Musial 60.00 120.00
2 Jim Edmonds 40.00 80.00
3 Dale Murphy 40.00 80.00
4 Andruw Jones 40.00 80.00
5 Roger Clemens 100.00 200.00
6 Mark Prior 20.00 50.00
7 Tom Seaver 40.00 80.00
8 Tom Glavine 40.00 80.00
9 Mike Schmidt 75.00 150.00
10 Pat Burrell 20.00 50.00
11 Stan Musial / Jim Edmonds
12 Dale Murphy / Andruw Jones
13 Roger Clemens / Mark Prior
14 Tom Seaver / Tom Glavine
15 Mike Schmidt / Pat Burrell

2003 Donruss Elite Recollection Autographs

Randomly inserted into packs, these 65 cards feature cards prepared for previous Donruss Elite products and they feature both autographs and a recollection collection stamp on all the cards. Please note that we have notated the stated print run next to the player's name and specific card in our checklist. For cards with print runs of 25 or fewer, no pricing is available due to market scarcity.

1 Jeremy Affeldt 01/75 4.00 10.00
2 Erick Almonte 01/75 4.00 10.00
3 Jeff Bagwell 02/1
4 Adrian Beltre 02/36 10.00 25.00
5 Adrian Beltre 02 Asp/5
6 Adrian Beltre 02 Sta/3
7 Brandon Berger 01/83 4.00 10.00
8 Angel Berroa 01/28 10.00 25.00
9 John Buck 01/25
10 Mark Buehrle 02/23
11 Marlon Byrd 01/24
12 Jose Castillo 02/23
13 Jeff Deardorff 01/53 4.00 10.00
14 Ryan Drese 01/100 6.00 15.00
15 J.D. Drew 01/15
16 J.D. Drew 02/10
17 J.D. Drew 02 CB/5
18 Jim Edmonds 01/15
19 Jim Edmonds 02/5
20 Jim Edmonds 02 BTF/5
21 Luis Garcia 01/28 6.00 15.00
22 Geronimo Gil 01/75 4.00 10.00
23 Mark Grace 02/2
24 Shawn Green 01/2
25 Shawn Green 02/2
26 Shawn Green 02 BTF/2
27 Shawn Green 02 CB/2
28 Travis Hafner 01 Black/52 10.00 25.00
29 Travis Hafner 01 Blue/23
30 Bill Hall 01/27 10.00 25.00
31 Orlando Hudson 01 Black/12
32 Orlando Hudson 01 Blue /13
33 Tim Hudson 01/25
34 Tim Hudson 02/25
35 Gerald Laird 02/46 6.00 15.00
36 Jason Lane 01/27 10.00 25.00
37 Adam LaRoche 02/25
38 Cliff Lee 01/25
39 Kenny Lofton 01/25
40 Greg Maddux 01/5
41 Greg Maddux 01 TW/5
42 Greg Maddux 02/10
43 Greg Maddux 02 AS/5
44 Victor Martinez 01/52 60.00 120.00
45 Corky Miller 01/25
46 Roy Oswalt 01 Black/61 6.00 15.00
47 Roy Oswalt 01 Blue/9
48 Roy Oswalt 02/24
49 Mark Prior 01/10
50 Mike Rivera 01/3
51 Ricardo Rodriguez 01/75 4.00 10.00
52 Freddy Sanchez 02/25
53 Gary Sheffield 01/25
54 Gary Sheffield 02/14
55 Bud Smith 01/50 6.00 15.00
56 Bud Smith 02/28 6.00 15.00
57 Chris Snelling 02/25
58 Junior Spivey 01/45 6.00 15.00
59 Tim Spooneybarger 01/100 4.00 10.00
60 Shannon Stewart 01/24
61 Shannon Stewart 02/35 10.00 25.00
62 Dennis Tankersley 01/15
63 Mark Teixeira 01/19
64 Claudio Vargas 01/51 4.00 10.00
65 Martin Vargas 01/10

2003 Donruss Elite Throwback Threads

Randomly inserted into packs, these 100 cards feature not only the player's featured but also a game-worn uniform piece from during their career. Please note that the final 10 cards in the checklist feature either two different pieces from a player's career or two pieces from players who have something in common.

1-45 PRINT RUN 250 SERIAL #'d SETS
46-75 PRINT RUN 125 SERIAL #'d SETS
76-90 PRINT RUN 100 SERIAL #'d SETS
91-95 PRINT RUN 75 SERIAL #'d SETS
96-100 PRINT RUN RUN 50 SERIAL #'d SETS
*MULTI-COLOR PATCH: .75X TO 2X HI COL
1 Randy Johnson D'backs 4.00 10.00
2 Randy Johnson M's 4.00 10.00
3 Roger Clemens Yanks 10.00 25.00
4 Roger Clemens Red Sox 10.00 25.00
5 Manny Ramirez 4.00 10.00
6 Greg Maddux 6.00 15.00
7 Jason Giambi Yanks 3.00 8.00
8 Jason Giambi A's 3.00 8.00
9 Alex Rodriguez Rgr 6.00 15.00
10 Alex Rodriguez M's 6.00 15.00
11 Miguel Tejada 3.00 8.00
12 Alfonso Soriano 3.00 8.00
13 Nomar Garciaparra 6.00 15.00
14 Pedro Martinez Red Sox 4.00 10.00
15 Pedro Martinez Expos 4.00 10.00
16 Andruw Jones 4.00 10.00
17 Chipper Jones 4.00 10.00
18 Barry Zito 3.00 8.00
19 Mark Mulder 3.00 8.00
20 Lance Berkman 3.00 8.00
21 Magglio Ordonez 3.00 8.00
22 Mike Piazza Mets 6.00 15.00
23 Mike Piazza Dodgers 6.00 15.00
24 Rickey Henderson Padres 4.00 10.00
25 Rickey Henderson Mets 4.00 10.00
26 Rickey Henderson M's 4.00 10.00
27 Sammy Sosa 4.00 10.00
28 Shawn Green 3.00 8.00
29 Troy Glaus 3.00 8.00
30 Vladimir Guerrero 4.00 10.00
31 Adam Dunn 3.00 8.00
32 Jeff Bagwell 4.00 10.00
33 Curt Schilling 3.00 8.00
34 Hideo Nomo Dodgers 15.00 40.00
35 Hideo Nomo Red Sox 15.00 40.00
36 Hideo Nomo Mets 15.00 40.00
37 Kerry Wood 3.00 8.00
38 Mark Prior 4.00 10.00
39 Roberto Alomar 4.00 10.00
40 Todd Helton 4.00 10.00
41 Jim Thome 4.00 10.00
42 Rafael Palmeiro 4.00 10.00
43 Juan Gonzalez 3.00 8.00
44 Vernon Wells 3.00 8.00
45 Torii Hunter 3.00 8.00
46 Randy Johnson D'backs / Randy Johnson M's 10.00 25.00
47 Roger Clemens Yankees / Roger Clemens Red Sox 20.00 50.00
48 Jason Giambi Yankees / Jason Giambi A's 8.00 20.00
49 Alex Rodriguez Rangers / Alex Rodriguez M's 15.00 40.00
50 Pedro Martinez Red Sox / Pedro Martinez Expos 10.00 25.00
51 Mike Piazza Mets / Mike Piazza Dodgers 15.00 40.00
52 Rickey Henderson A's / Rickey Henderson M's 10.00 25.00
53 Rickey Henderson Padres / Rickey Henderson Mets 10.00 25.00
54 Rickey Henderson Angels / Rickey Henderson Padres 10.00 25.00
55 Hideo Nomo Dodgers / Hideo Nomo Red Sox 20.00 50.00
56 Randy Johnson D'backs / Randy Johnson Expos 10.00 25.00
57 Randy Johnson / Curt Schilling 10.00 25.00
58 Alfonso Soriano / Jason Giambi 8.00 20.00
59 Barry Zito / Mark Mulder 8.00 20.00
60 Andruw Jones / Chipper Jones 10.00 25.00
61 Greg Maddux / Tom Glavine 30.00 60.00
62 Lance Berkman / Jeff Bagwell 10.00 25.00
63 Roger Clemens / Mark Prior 12.50 30.00
64 Alex Rodriguez / Rafael Palmeiro 12.50 30.00
65 Jim Thome / Roberto Alomar 10.00 25.00
66 Mike Piazza / Roberto Alomar 10.00 25.00
67 Sammy Sosa / Mark Grace 10.00 25.00
68 Todd Helton / Larry Walker 10.00 25.00
69 Adam Dunn / Austin Kearns 8.00 20.00
70 Alex Rodriguez / Ivan Rodriguez 10.00 25.00
71 Bobby Abreu / Marlon Byrd 8.00 20.00
72 Miguel Tejada / Eric Chavez 8.00 20.00
73 Greg Maddux / John Smoltz 15.00 40.00
74 Kerry Wood / Mark Prior 4.00 10.00
75 Barry Zito / {Tim Hudson 8.00 20.00
76 Babe Ruth 250.00 400.00
77 Ty Cobb 60.00 120.00
78 Jackie Robinson 50.00 100.00
79 Lou Gehrig 100.00 200.00
80 Thurman Munson 20.00 50.00
81 Nolan Ryan Astros 20.00 50.00
82 Don Mattingly 15.00 40.00
83 Mike Schmidt 15.00 40.00
84 Reggie Jackson 10.00 25.00
85 George Brett 15.00 40.00
86 Cal Ripken 30.00 60.00
87 Tony Gwynn 10.00 25.00
88 Yogi Berra 10.00 25.00
89 Stan Musial 20.00 50.00
90 Jim Palmer 8.00 20.00
91 Thurman Munson / Jorge Posada 30.00 60.00
92 Dale Murphy / Chipper Jones 20.00 50.00
93 Don Mattingly / Jason Giambi 40.00 80.00
94 Andre Dawson / Sammy Sosa 15.00 40.00
95 Nolan Ryan / Mark Prior 40.00 80.00
96 Babe Ruth / Lou Gehrig 300.00 500.00
97 Tom Seaver / Joe Morgan 30.00 60.00
98 Harmon Killebrew / Rod Carew 30.00 60.00
99 Nolan Ryan Rangers / Nolan Ryan Angels 60.00 120.00
100 Reggie Jackson Yankees / Reggie Jackson A's 30.00 60.00

2003 Donruss Elite Throwback Threads Autographs

Randomly inserted into packs, this is a quasi-parallel to the Throwback Threads insert set. These cards were signed by the player featured and issued to stated print runs of between five and 75 copies per. Please note that if a player signed 25 or fewer copies, there is no pricing due to market scarcity.

3 Roger Clemens Yanks/15
4 Roger Clemens Red Sox/5
6 Greg Maddux/5
9 Alex Rodriguez Rgr/5
10 Alex Rodriguez M's/5
12 Alfonso Soriano/5
14 Pedro Martinez Red Sox/5
15 Pedro Martinez Expos/5
16 Andruw Jones/25
17 Chipper Jones/20
18 Barry Zito/25
19 Mark Mulder/10
20 Lance Berkman/25
21 Magglio Ordonez/15
24 Rickey Henderson Padres/10
25 Rickey Henderson Mets/5
26 Rickey Henderson M's/5
27 Sammy Sosa/15
29 Troy Glaus/15
30 Vladimir Guerrero/50 50.00 100.00
31 Adam Dunn/50 10.00 25.00
37 Kerry Wood/50 15.00 40.00
38 Mark Prior/75 30.00 60.00
39 Roberto Alomar/50 50.00 100.00
40 Todd Helton/15
41 Jim Thome/25
45 Torii Hunter/25
81 Nolan Ryan Angels/25
82 Don Mattingly/25
83 Mike Schmidt/25
84 Reggie Jackson/25
85 George Brett/15
86 Cal Ripken/15
87 Tony Gwynn/25
88 Yogi Berra/25
89 Stan Musial/25
90 Jim Palmer/25

2003 Donruss Elite Throwback Threads Prime

1-45 PRINT RUN 25 SERIAL #'d SETS
46-75 PRINT RUN 15 SERIAL #'d SETS
76-95 PRINT RUN 10 SERIAL #'d SETS
96-100 PRINT RUN 5 SERIAL #'d SETS

2003 Donruss Elite Extra Edition

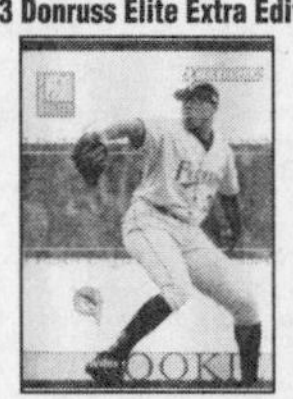

These cards were also inserted as part of the overall DLP Rookie/Traded Packs. Each of these cards feature Rookie Cards and are all issued to a stated print run of 900 serial numbered sets. Please note that cards numbered 42, 51, 54 and 56 do not exist for this set.

1 Adam Loewen RC 2.00 5.00
2 Brandon Webb RC 4.00 10.00
3 Chien-Ming Wang RC 8.00 20.00
4 Hong-Chih Kuo RC 8.00 20.00
5 Clint Barmes RC 2.00 5.00
6 Guillermo Quiroz RC 1.50 4.00
7 Edgar Gonzalez RC 1.50 4.00
8 Todd Wellemeyer RC 2.00 5.00
9 Alfredo Gonzalez RC 1.50 4.00
10 Craig Brazell RC 1.50 4.00
11 Tim Olson RC 1.50 4.00
12 Rich Fischer RC 1.50 4.00
13 Daniel Cabrera RC 2.00 5.00
14 Francisco Rosario RC 1.50 4.00
15 Francisco Cruceta RC 1.50 4.00
16 Alejandro Machado RC 1.50 4.00
17 Andrew Brown RC 2.00 5.00
18 Rob Hammock RC 1.50 4.00
19 Arnie Munoz RC 1.50 4.00
20 Felix Sanchez RC 1.50 4.00
21 Nook Logan RC 2.00 5.00
22 Cory Stewart RC 1.50 4.00
23 Michel Hernandez RC 1.50 4.00
24 Rett Johnson RC 1.50 4.00
25 Josh Hall RC 1.50 4.00
26 Doug Waechter RC 2.00 5.00
27 Matt Kata RC 1.50 4.00
28 Dan Haren RC 2.00 5.00
29 Dontrelle Willis 2.00 5.00
30 Ramon Nivar RC 1.50 4.00
31 Chad Gaudin RC 1.50 4.00
32 Rickie Weeks RC 4.00 10.00
33 Ryan Wagner RC 1.50 4.00
34 Kevin Correia RC 1.50 4.00
35 Bo Hart RC 1.50 4.00
36 Oscar Villarreal RC 1.50 4.00
37 Josh Willingham RC 3.00 8.00
38 Jeff Duncan RC 1.50 4.00
39 David DeJesus RC 2.00 5.00
40 Dustin McGowan RC 2.00 5.00
41 Preston Larrison RC 2.00 5.00
43 Kevin Youkilis RC 3.00 8.00
44 Bubba Nelson RC 2.00 5.00
45 Chris Burke RC 2.00 5.00
46 J.D. Durbin RC 1.50 4.00
47 Ryan Howard RC 12.50 30.00
48 Jason Kubel RC 2.00 5.00
49 Brendan Harris RC 2.00 5.00
50 Brian Bruney RC 2.00 5.00
52 Byron Gettis RC 1.50 4.00
53 Edwin Jackson RC 2.00 5.00
55 Daniel Garcia RC 1.50 4.00
57 Chad Cordero RC 3.00 8.00
58 Delmon Young RC 10.00 25.00

2003 Donruss Elite Extra Edition Aspirations

*ASP P/R b/wn 51-65: 1X TO 2.5X
*ASP RC's P/R b/wn 81-120: .6X TO 1.5X
*ASP RC's P/R b/wn 66-80: .75X TO 2X
*ASP RC's P/R b/wn 51-65: .75X TO 2X
*ASP RC's P/R b/wn 36-50: 1X TO 2.5X
*ASP RC's P/R b/wn 26-35: 1.25X TO 3X
PRINT RUNS B/WN 24-98 COPIES PER
NO PRICING ON QTY OF 25 OR LESS
CARDS 42/51/54/56 DO NOT EXIST
4 Hong-Chih Kuo/32 50.00 100.00
32 Rickie Weeks/89 12.50 30.00
47 Ryan Howard/43 75.00 150.00
58 Delmon Young/70 15.00 40.00

2003 Donruss Elite Extra Edition Aspirations Gold

STATED PRINT RUN 1 SERIAL #'d SET
NO PRICING DUE TO SCARCITY
CARDS 42/51/54/56 DO NOT EXIST

2003 Donruss Elite Extra Edition Status

*STATUS P/R b/wn 26-35: 1.5X TO 4X
*STATUS RC's P/R b/wn 66-80: .75X TO 2X
*STATUS RC's P/R b/wn 51-65: .75X TO 2X
*STATUS RC's P/R b/wn 36-50: 1X TO 2.5X
*STATUS RC's P/R b/wn 26-35: 1.25X TO 3X
PRINT RUNS B/WN 2-76 COPIES PER
NO PRICING ON QTY OF 25 OR LESS
CARDS 42/51/54/56 DO NOT EXIST
3 Chien-Ming Wang/76 15.00 40.00
4 Hong-Chih Kuo/68 30.00 60.00
47 Ryan Howard/57 75.00 150.00

2003 Donruss Elite Extra Edition Status Gold

STATED PRINT RUN 24 SERIAL #'d SETS
NO PRICING DUE TO SCARCITY
CARDS 42/51/54/56 DO NOT EXIST

2003 Donruss Elite Extra Edition Turn of the Century

*TOC P/R b/wn 66-80: .75X TO 2X
*TOC RC's P/R b/wn 66-80: .75X TO 2X
PRINT RUNS B/WN 75-100 COPIES PER

2003 Donruss Elite Extra Edition Turn of the Century Autographs

STATED PRINT RUN 100 SERIAL #'d SETS
CARDS 29/32/34 PRINT RUN 25 #'d SETS
NO PRICING ON QTY OF 25 OR LESS
1 Adam Loewen 10.00 25.00
2 Brandon Webb 40.00 80.00
3 Chien-Ming Wang 75.00 150.00
4 Hong-Chih Kuo 100.00 200.00
5 Clint Barmes 4.00 10.00
6 Guillermo Quiroz 4.00 10.00
7 Edgar Gonzalez 4.00 10.00
8 Todd Wellemeyer 4.00 10.00
9 Alfredo Gonzalez 4.00 10.00
10 Craig Brazell 4.00 10.00
11 Tim Olson 4.00 10.00
12 Rich Fischer 4.00 10.00
13 Daniel Cabrera 15.00 40.00
14 Francisco Rosario 4.00 10.00
15 Francisco Cruceta 4.00 10.00
16 Alejandro Machado 4.00 10.00
17 Andrew Brown 6.00 15.00
18 Rob Hammock 4.00 10.00
19 Arnie Munoz 4.00 10.00
20 Felix Sanchez 4.00 10.00
21 Nook Logan 6.00 15.00
22 Cory Stewart 4.00 10.00
23 Michel Hernandez 4.00 10.00
24 Rett Johnson 4.00 10.00
25 Josh Hall 4.00 10.00
26 Doug Waechter 6.00 15.00
27 Matt Kata 4.00 10.00
28 Dan Haren 20.00 50.00
29 Dontrelle Willis/25
30 Ramon Nivar 4.00 10.00
31 Chad Gaudin 4.00 10.00
32 Rickie Weeks/25
33 Ryan Wagner 4.00 10.00
34 Kevin Correia/25
35 Bo Hart 4.00 10.00
36 Oscar Villarreal 6.00 15.00
37 Josh Willingham 15.00 40.00
38 Jeff Duncan 4.00 10.00
40 Dustin McGowan 6.00 15.00
41 Preston Larrison 4.00 10.00
43 Kevin Youkilis 50.00 100.00
44 Bubba Nelson 4.00 10.00
45 Chris Burke 15.00 40.00
46 J.D. Durbin 4.00 10.00
47 Ryan Howard 300.00 500.00
48 Jason Kubel 15.00 40.00
49 Brendan Harris 6.00 15.00
50 Brian Bruney 6.00 15.00
52 Byron Gettis 4.00 10.00
53 Edwin Jackson 8.00 20.00
55 Daniel Garcia 4.00 10.00
58 Delmon Young 100.00 200.00

2004 Donruss Elite

This 205 card set was released in May, 2004. The set was issued in five card packs with an $5 SRP which came 20 packs to a box and 12 boxes to a case. The first 150 cards of this set featured veterans while cards numbered 151 through 180 featured rookie cards printed to varying print runs. We have notated those specfic print runs next to the players name in our checklist. Cards numbered 181 through 200 feature retired greats which were randomly inserted into packs and those cards were issued to a stated print run of 1000 serial numbered sets. Please note, that although there is two separate numberings (including 201-205) for the Fans of the Game insert set, we have moved those cards into an insert set listing. Card number 169 was not issued.

COMP.SET w/o SP's (150) 10.00 25.00
COMMON CARD 1-150 .12 .30
COMMON AUTO (151-180) 3.00 8.00
151-180 RANDOM INSERTS IN PACKS
151-180 PRINT RUN B/WN 750-1000 #'d PER
COMMON CARD (181-200) .40 1.00
181-200 RANDOM INSERTS IN PACKS
181-200 PRINT RUN 1000 SERIAL #'d SETS
CARD NUMBER 169 DOES NOT EXIST
1 Troy Glaus .12 .30
2 Darin Erstad .12 .30
3 Garret Anderson .12 .30
4 Tim Salmon .12 .30
5 Bartolo Colon .12 .30
6 Jose Guillen .12 .30
7 Miguel Tejada .20 .50
8 Adam Loewen .12 .30
9 Jay Gibbons .12 .30
10 Melvin Mora .12 .30
11 Javy Lopez .12 .30
12 Pedro Martinez .20 .50
13 Curt Schilling .20 .50
14 David Ortiz .30 .75
15 Keith Foulke .12 .30
16 Nomar Garciaparra .30 .75
17 Magglio Ordonez .20 .50
18 Frank Thomas .30 .75
19 Carlos Lee .12 .30
20 Paul Konerko .20 .50
21 Mark Buehrle .20 .50
22 Jody Gerut .12 .30
23 Victor Martinez .20 .50
24 C.C. Sabathia .20 .50
25 Ellis Burks .12 .30
26 Bobby Higginson .12 .30
27 Jeremy Bonderman .12 .30
28 Fernando Vina .12 .30
29 Carlos Pena .20 .50
30 Dmitri Young .12 .30
31 Carlos Beltran .12 .30
32 Benito Santiago .12 .30
33 Mike Sweeney .12 .30
34 Angel Berroa .12 .30
35 Runelvys Hernandez .12 .30
36 Johan Santana .30 .75
37 Doug Mientkiewicz .12 .30
38 Shannon Stewart .12 .30
39 Torii Hunter .12 .30
40 Derek Jeter .75 2.00
41 Jason Giambi .12 .30
42 Bernie Williams .20 .50
43 Alfonso Soriano .12 .30
44 Gary Sheffield .12 .30
45 Mike Mussina .20 .50
46 Jorge Posada .20 .50
47 Hideki Matsui .50 1.25
48 Kevin Brown .12 .30
49 Javier Vazquez .12 .30
50 Mariano Rivera .30 .75
51 Eric Chavez .12 .30
52 Tim Hudson .20 .50
53 Mark Mulder .12 .30
54 Barry Zito .12 .30
55 Ichiro Suzuki .50 1.25
56 Edgar Martinez .20 .50
57 Bret Boone .12 .30
58 John Olerud .12 .30
59 Scott Spiezio .12 .30
60 Aubrey Huff .12 .30
61 Rocco Baldelli .12 .30
62 Jose Cruz Jr. .12 .30
63 Delmon Young .20 .50
64 Mark Teixeira .30 .75
65 Hank Blalock .12 .30
66 Michael Young .12 .30
67 Alex Rodriguez .50 1.25
68 Carlos Delgado .12 .30
69 Eric Hinske .12 .30
70 Roy Halladay .30 .75
71 Vernon Wells .12 .30
72 Randy Johnson .30 .75
73 Richie Sexson .12 .30
74 Brandon Webb .12 .30
75 Luis Gonzalez .12 .30
76 Steve Finley .12 .30
77 Chipper Jones .30 .75
78 Andruw Jones .12 .30
79 Marcus Giles .12 .30
80 Rafael Furcal .12 .30
81 J.D. Drew .12 .30

82 Sammy Sosa .30 .75
83 Kerry Wood .12 .30
84 Mark Prior .20 .50
85 Derrek Lee .12 .30
86 Moises Alou .12 .30
87 Corey Patterson .12 .30
88 Ken Griffey Jr. .50 1.25
89 Austin Kearns .12 .30
90 Adam Dunn .20 .50
91 Barry Larkin .20 .50
92 Todd Helton .20 .50
93 Larry Walker .20 .50
94 Preston Wilson .12 .30
95 Charles Johnson .12 .30
96 Luis Castillo .12 .30
97 Josh Beckett .20 .50
98 Mike Lowell .12 .30
99 Miguel Cabrera .30 .75
100 Juan Pierre .12 .30
101 Dontrelle Willis .12 .30
102 Andy Pettitte .20 .50
103 Wade Miller .12 .30
104 Jeff Bagwell .20 .50
105 Craig Biggio .20 .50
106 Lance Berkman .20 .50
107 Jeff Kent .12 .30
108 Roy Oswalt .20 .50
109 Hideo Nomo .30 .75
110 Adrian Beltre .12 .30
111 Paul Lo Duca .12 .30
112 Shawn Green .12 .30
113 Fred McGriff .12 .30
114 Eric Gagne .12 .30
115 Geoff Jenkins .12 .30
116 Rickie Weeks .12 .30
117 Scott Podsednik .12 .30
118 Nick Johnson .12 .30
119 Orlando Cabrera .12 .30
120 Jose Vidro .12 .30
121 Kazuo Matsui RC .20 .50
122 Tom Glavine .20 .50
123 Al Leiter .12 .30
124 Mike Piazza .30 .75
125 Jose Reyes .20 .50
126 Mike Cameron .12 .30
127 Pat Burrell .12 .30
128 Jim Thome .20 .50
129 Mike Lieberthal .12 .30
130 Bobby Abreu .12 .30
131 Kip Wells .12 .30
132 Jack Wilson .12 .30
133 Pokey Reese .12 .30
134 Brian Giles .12 .30
135 Sean Burroughs .12 .30
136 Ryan Klesko .12 .30
137 Trevor Hoffman .20 .50
138 Jason Schmidt .12 .30
139 J.T. Snow .12 .30
140 A.J. Pierzynski .12 .30
141 Ray Durham .12 .30
142 Jim Edmonds .20 .50
143 Albert Pujols .75 2.00
144 Edgar Renteria .12 .30
145 Scott Rolen .20 .50
146 Matt Morris .12 .30
147 Ivan Rodriguez .20 .50
148 Vladimir Guerrero .30 .75
149 Greg Maddux .50 1.25
150 Kevin Millwood .12 .30
151 Hector Gimenez AU/750 RC 3.00 8.00
152 Willy Taveras AU/750 RC 8.00 20.00
153 Ruddy Yan AU/750 3.00 8.00
154 Graham Koonce AU/750 3.00 8.00
155 Jose Capellan AU/750 RC 3.00 8.00
156 Onil Joseph AU/750 RC 3.00 8.00
157 John Gall AU/1000 RC 3.00 8.00
158 Carlos Hines AU/750 RC 3.00 8.00
159 Jerry Gil AU/750 RC 3.00 8.00
160 Mike Gosling AU/750 RC 3.00 8.00
161 Jason Frasor AU/750 RC 3.00 8.00
162 Justin Knoedler AU/750 RC 3.00 8.00
163 Merkin Valdez AU/500 RC 3.00 8.00
164 Angel Chavez AU/1000 RC 3.00 8.00
165 Ivan Ochoa AU/750 RC 3.00 8.00
166 Greg Dobbs AU/750 RC 3.00 8.00
167 Ronald Belisario AU/750 RC 3.00 8.00
168 Aarom Baldiris AU/750 RC 3.00 8.00
170 Dave Crouthers AU/750 RC 3.00 8.00
171 Freddy Guzman AU/750 RC 3.00 8.00
172 Akinori Otsuka AU/250 RC 12.50 30.00
173 Ian Snell AU/750 RC 6.00 15.00
174 Nick Regilio AU/1000 RC 3.00 8.00
175 Jamie Brown AU/750 RC 3.00 8.00
176 Jerome Gamble AU/750 RC 3.00 8.00
177 Roberto Novoa AU/1000 RC 3.00 8.00
178 Sean Henn AU/1000 RC 3.00 8.00
179 Ramon Ramirez AU/1000 RC 3.00 8.00
180 Jason Bartlett AU/1000 RC 4.00 10.00
181 Bob Gibson RET .60 1.50
182 Cal Ripken RET 4.00 10.00
183 Carl Yastrzemski RET 1.00 2.50
184 Dale Murphy RET .60 1.50
185 Don Mattingly RET 2.00 5.00
186 Eddie Murray RET 1.00 2.50
187 George Brett RET 2.00 5.00
188 Jackie Robinson RET 1.00 2.50
189 Jim Palmer RET .40 1.00
190 Lou Gehrig RET 2.00 5.00
191 Mike Schmidt RET 1.50 4.00
192 Ozzie Smith RET 1.50 4.00
193 Nolan Ryan RET 3.00 8.00
194 Reggie Jackson RET .60 1.50
195 Roberto Clemente RET 2.50 6.00
196 Robin Yount RET 1.00 2.50
197 Stan Musial RET 1.50 4.00
198 Ted Williams RET 2.50 6.00
199 Tony Gwynn RET 1.00 2.50
200 Ty Cobb RET 1.50 4.00

2004 Donruss Elite Aspirations

*1-150 PRINT RUN b/wn 81-99: 4X TO 10X
*1-150 PRINT RUN b/wn 66-80: 5X TO 12X
*1-150 PRINT RUN b/wn 51-65: 5X TO 12X
*1-150 PRINT RUN b/wn 36-50: 6X TO 15X
*1-150 PRINT RUN b/wn 26-35: 8X TO 20X
*1-150 PRINT RUN b/wn 16-25: 10X TO 25X
COMMON CARD (151-180) 2.50 6.00
SEMISTARS 151-180 4.00 10.00
UNLISTED STARS 151-180 6.00 15.00
*181-200 P/R b/wn 81-99: 1.25X TO 3X
*181-200 P/R b/wn 66-80: 1.5X TO 4X
*181-200 P/R b/wn 51-65: 1.5X TO 4X
RANDOM INSERTS IN PACKS
PRINT RUNS B/WN 19-99 COPIES PER
1-150/181-200 NO PRICING ON 15 OR LESS
151-180 NO PRICING ON 25 OR LESS
121 Kazuo Matsui/75
151 Hector Gimenez ROO/30 2.50 6.00
152 Willy Taveras ROO/99 6.00 15.00
153 Ruddy Yan ROO/38 2.50 6.00
154 Graham Koonce ROO/82 2.50 6.00
155 Jose Capellan ROO/29 2.50 6.00
156 Onil Joseph ROO/24 2.50 6.00
157 John Gall ROO/19 2.50 6.00
158 Carlos Hines ROO/31 2.50 6.00
159 Jerry Gil ROO/38 2.50 6.00
160 Mike Gosling ROO/56 2.50 6.00
161 Jason Frasor ROO/22 2.50 6.00
162 Justin Knoedler ROO/40 2.50 6.00
163 Merkin Valdez ROO/39 2.50 6.00
164 Angel Chavez ROO/41 2.50 6.00
165 Ivan Ochoa ROO/26 2.50 6.00
166 Greg Dobbs ROO/40 2.50 6.00
167 Ronald Belisario ROO/29 2.50 6.00
168 Aarom Baldiris ROO/35 2.50 6.00
169 Kazuo Matsui ROO/75 4.00 10.00
170 Dave Crouthers ROO/30 2.50 6.00
171 Freddy Guzman ROO/35 2.50 6.00
172 Akinori Otsuka ROO/84 2.50 6.00
173 Ian Snell ROO/51 2.50 6.00
174 Nick Regilio ROO/36 2.50 6.00
175 Jamie Brown ROO/48 2.50 6.00
176 Jerome Gamble ROO/38 2.50 6.00
177 Roberto Novoa ROO/49 2.50 6.00
178 Sean Henn ROO/37 2.50 6.00
179 Ramon Ramirez ROO/34 2.50 6.00
180 Jason Bartlett ROO/20 8.00 20.00

2004 Donruss Elite Status

*1-150 PRINT RUN b/wn 66-80: 5X TO 12X
*1-150 PRINT RUN b/wn 51-65: 5X TO 12X
*1-150 PRINT RUN b/wn 36-50: 6X TO 15X
*1-150 PRINT RUN b/wn 26-35: 8X TO 20X
*1-150 PRINT RUN b/wn 16-25: 10X TO 25X
COMMON CARD (151-180) 2.50 6.00
SEMISTARS 151-180 4.00 10.00
UNLISTED STARS 151-180 6.00 15.00
*181-200 P/R b/wn 36-50: 2X TO 5X
*181-200 P/R b/wn 26-35: 2.5X TO 6X
*181-200 P/R b/wn 16-25: 3X TO 8X
RANDOM INSERTS IN PACKS
PRINT RUNS B/WN 1-81 COPIES PER
1-120/122-50/181-200 NO PRICE 15 OR LESS
121/151-180 NO PRICING ON 25 OR LESS
151 Hector Gimenez ROO/70 2.50 6.00
152 Willy Taveras ROO/1
153 Ruddy Yan ROO/62 2.50 6.00
154 Graham Koonce ROO/18 2.50 6.00
155 Jose Capellan ROO/71 2.50 6.00
156 Onil Joseph ROO/76 2.50 6.00
157 John Gall ROO/81 2.50 6.00
158 Carlos Hines ROO/69 2.50 6.00
159 Jerry Gil ROO/62 2.50 6.00
160 Mike Gosling ROO/44 2.50 6.00
161 Jason Frasor ROO/78 2.50 6.00
162 Justin Knoedler ROO/60 2.50 6.00
163 Merkin Valdez ROO/61 2.50 6.00
164 Angel Chavez ROO/59 2.50 6.00
165 Ivan Ochoa ROO/74 2.50 6.00
166 Greg Dobbs ROO/60 2.50 6.00
167 Ronald Belisario ROO/71 2.50 6.00
168 Aarom Baldiris ROO/65 2.50 6.00
169 Kazuo Matsui ROO/25 4.00 10.00
170 Dave Crouthers ROO/70 2.50 6.00
171 Freddy Guzman ROO/65 2.50 6.00
172 Akinori Otsuka ROO/16 2.50 6.00
173 Ian Snell ROO/49 2.50 6.00
174 Nick Regilio ROO/52 2.50 6.00
175 Jamie Brown ROO/52 2.50 6.00
176 Jerome Gamble ROO/62 2.50 6.00
177 Roberto Novoa ROO/51 2.50 6.00
178 Sean Henn ROO/63 2.50 6.00
179 Ramon Ramirez ROO/66 2.50 6.00
180 Jason Bartlett ROO/80 8.00 20.00

2004 Donruss Elite Status Gold

*GOLD 1-120/122-150: 10X TO 25X BASIC
*GOLD 181-200: 3X TO 8X BASIC
STATED PRINT RUN 24 SERIAL #'d SETS
121/151-180 NO PRICING DUE TO SCARCITY

2004 Donruss Elite Turn of the Century

*TOC 1-120/122-150: 1.5X TO 4X BASIC
*TOC 121: 1.25X TO 3X BASIC
1-150 PRINT RUN 750 SERIAL #'d SETS
*TOC 181-200: .75X TO 2X BASIC
181-200 PRINT RUN 250 SERIAL #'d SETS
RANDOM INSERTS IN PACKS
CARDS 151-180 DO NOT EXIST

2004 Donruss Elite Back 2 Back Jacks

RANDOM INSERTS IN PACKS
SINGLE PRINT RUNS B/WN 25-125 PER
DUAL PRINT RUNS B/WN 25-50 PER
1 Albert Pujols/125 6.00 15.00
2 Alex Rodriguez Rgr/125 4.00 10.00
3 Alfonso Soriano/125 3.00 8.00
4 Andruw Jones/125 4.00 10.00
5 Chipper Jones/125 4.00 10.00
6 Derek Jeter/125 8.00 20.00
7 Frank Thomas/125 4.00 10.00
8 Miguel Cabrera/125 4.00 10.00
9 Jason Giambi/125 3.00 8.00
10 Jim Thome/125 4.00 10.00
11 Mike Piazza/125 4.00 10.00
12 Nomar Garciaparra/25 10.00 25.00
13 Sammy Sosa/125 4.00 10.00
14 Shawn Green/125 3.00 8.00
15 Vladimir Guerrero/125 4.00 10.00
16 Andruw Jones 10.00 25.00
Chipper Jones/50
17 Alfonso Soriano 15.00 40.00
Derek Jeter/50
18 Jeff Bagwell 10.00 25.00
Lance Berkman/50
19 Alex Rodriguez 10.00 25.00
Rafael Palmeiro/50
20 Adam Dunn 8.00 20.00
Austin Kearns/25
21 Al Kaline/100 6.00 15.00
22 Babe Ruth/50 100.00 175.00
23 Cal Ripken/100 15.00 40.00
24 Dale Murphy/100 6.00 15.00
25 Don Mattingly/100 6.00 15.00
26 George Brett/100 6.00 15.00
27 Lou Gehrig/100 50.00 100.00
28 Mike Schmidt/100 6.00 15.00
29 Roberto Clemente/100 15.00 40.00
30 Roy Campanella/100 6.00 15.00
31 Babe Ruth 150.00 250.00
Roger Maris /25
32 Harmon Killebrew 15.00 40.00
Kirby Puckett /50
33 Paul Molitor 10.00 25.00
Robin Yount /50
34 Reggie Jackson 10.00 25.00
Reggie Jackson /50
35 Lou Gehrig 125.00 200.00
Ty Cobb /50
36 Don Mattingly 12.50 30.00
Jason Giambi /50
37 Ted Williams 40.00 80.00
Nomar Garciaparra /50
38 Andre Dawson 10.00 25.00
Sammy Sosa /50
39 Dale Murphy 10.00 25.00
Chipper Jones /50
40 Stan Musial 12.50 30.00
Jim Edmonds /50

2004 Donruss Elite Back 2 Back Jacks Combos

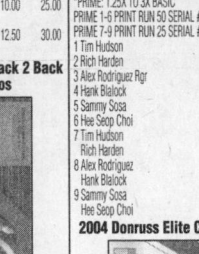

*COMBO 1-15: .75X TO 2X B2B p/r 125
*COMBO 1-15: .4X TO 1X B2B p/r 25
*COMBO 16-20: .6X TO 1.5X B2B p/r 50
*COMBO 16-20: .5X TO 1.2X B2B p/r 25
*COMBO 21-30 p/r 50: .6X TO 1.5X BTB p/r 100
*COMBO 21-30 p/r 25: 1X TO 2.5X BTB p/r 100
*COMBO 21-30 p/r 25: .6X TO 1.5X BTB p/r 50
*COMBO 31-40 p/r 25: .6X TO 1.5X B2B p/r 50
SINGLE PRINT RUNS B/WN 25-50 PER
DUAL PRINT RUNS B/WN 10-25 PER
NO PRICING ON QTY OF 10 OR LESS
12 N.Garciaparra Bat-Jsy/25 10.00 25.00
22 Babe Ruth Bat-Jsy/25 250.00 400.00
27 Lou Gehrig Bat-Jsy/25 150.00 250.00
35 Lou Gehrig Bat-Jsy 250.00 400.00
Ty Cobb Bat-Jsy/25
37 Ted Williams Bat-Jsy 75.00 150.00
Nomar Garciaparra Bat-Jsy/25

2004 Donruss Elite Back to the Future

COMMON CARD (1-6) .60 1.50
SEMISTARS 1-6 1.00 2.50
UNLISTED STARS 1-6 1.50 4.00
1-6 PRINT RUN 500 SERIAL #'d SETS
COMMON CARD (6-9) .75 2.00
SEMISTARS 6-9 1.25 3.00
UNLISTED STARS 6-9 2.00 5.00
6-9 PRINT RUN 250 SERIAL #'d SETS
*BLACK 1-6: 1X TO 2.5X BASIC
*BLACK 7-9: 1.25X TO 3X BASIC
BLACK 1-6 PRINT RUN 50 SERIAL #'d SETS
BLACK 7-9 PRINT RUN 25 SERIAL #'d SETS
*GOLD 1-6: .6X TO 1.5X BASIC
*GOLD 7-9: .75X TO 2X BASIC
GOLD 1-6 PRINT RUN 100 SERIAL #'d SETS
GOLD 7-9 PRINT RUN 50 SERIAL #'d SETS
*RED 1-6: .5X TO 1.2X BASIC
*RED 7-9: .5X TO 1.2X BASIC
RED 1-6 PRINT RUN 250 SERIAL #'d SETS
RED 7-9 PRINT RUN 125 SERIAL #'d SETS
RANDOM INSERTS IN PACKS
1 Tim Hudson 1.00 2.50
2 Rich Harden .60 1.50
3 Alex Rodriguez Rgr 2.50 6.00
4 Hank Blalock .60 1.50
5 Sammy Sosa 1.50 4.00
6 Hee Seop Choi .60 1.50
7 Tim Hudson 1.25 3.00
Rich Harden
8 Alex Rodriguez 3.00 8.00
Hank Blalock
9 Sammy Sosa 2.00 5.00
Hee Seop Choi

2004 Donruss Elite Back to the Future Bats

1-6 PRINT RUN 200 SERIAL #'d SETS
8-9 PRINT RUN 100 SERIAL #'d SETS
RANDOM INSERTS IN PACKS
1 Tim Hudson 2.50 6.00
3 Alex Rodriguez Rgr 4.00 10.00
4 Hank Blalock 2.50 6.00
5 Sammy Sosa 3.00 8.00
6 Hee Seop Choi 2.50 6.00
8 Alex Rodriguez 6.00 15.00
Hank Blalock
9 Sammy Sosa 5.00 12.00
Hee Seop Choi

2004 Donruss Elite Back to the Future Jerseys

1-6 PRINT RUN 200 SERIAL #'d SETS
7-9 PRINT RUN 100 SERIAL #'d SETS
*PRIME: 1.25X TO 3X BASIC
PRIME 1-6 PRINT RUN 50 SERIAL #'d SETS
PRIME 7-9 PRINT RUN 25 SERIAL #'d SETS
1 Tim Hudson 2.50 6.00
2 Rich Harden 2.50 6.00
3 Alex Rodriguez Rgr 4.00 10.00
4 Hank Blalock 2.50 6.00
5 Sammy Sosa 3.00 8.00
6 Hee Seop Choi 2.50 6.00
7 Tim Hudson 4.00 10.00
Rich Harden
8 Alex Rodriguez 6.00 15.00
Hank Blalock
9 Sammy Sosa 5.00 12.00
Hee Seop Choi

2004 Donruss Elite Career Best

STATED PRINT RUN 1000 SERIAL #'d SETS
*BLACK: 1.25X TO 3X BASIC
BLACK PRINT RUN 100 SERIAL #'d SETS
*GOLD p/r 220-390: 1X TO 2.5X BASIC
*GOLD p/r 130-193: 1X TO 2.5X BASIC
*GOLD p/r 113-116: 1.25X TO 3X BASIC
*GOLD p/r 40-57: 2X TO 5X BASIC
*GOLD p/r 23-33: 3X TO 8X BASIC
*GOLD p/r 18-20: 4X TO 10X BASIC
GOLD PRINT RUNS B/WN 14-393 PER
NO GOLD PRICING ON QTY OF 14 OR LESS
RANDOM INSERTS IN PACKS
1 Albert Pujols 2.50 6.00
2 Alex Rodriguez Rgr 1.50 4.00
3 Alfonso Soriano .40 1.00
4 Andruw Jones .40 1.00
5 Barry Zito .40 1.00
6 Cal Ripken 4.00 10.00
7 Chipper Jones 1.00 2.50
8 Curt Schilling .60 1.50
9 Derek Jeter 2.50 6.00
10 Don Mattingly 2.00 5.00
11 Dontrelle Willis .40 1.00
12 Doc Gooden .40 1.00
13 Eddie Murray 1.00 2.50
14 Frank Thomas 1.00 2.50
15 Gary Sheffield .40 1.00
16 George Brett 2.00 5.00
17 Greg Maddux 1.50 4.00
18 Hideo Nomo 1.00 2.50
19 Ichiro Suzuki 1.50 4.00
20 Ivan Rodriguez .60 1.50
21 Jason Giambi .40 1.00
22 Jeff Bagwell .60 1.50
23 Jim Thome .60 1.50
24 Kerry Wood .40 1.00
25 Lance Berkman .60 1.50
26 Magglio Ordonez .60 1.50
27 Mark Prior .60 1.50
28 Mike Piazza 1.00 2.50
29 Mike Schmidt 1.50 4.00
30 Nomar Garciaparra 1.00 2.50
31 Pedro Martinez .60 1.50
32 Randy Johnson 1.00 2.50
33 Roger Clemens 1.25 3.00
34 Sammy Sosa 1.00 2.50
35 Tony Gwynn 1.00 2.50

2004 Donruss Elite Career Best Bats

PRINT RUNS B/WN 100-200 COPIES PER
*COMBO p/r 50: 1X TO 2.5X BASIC p/r 200
*COMBO p/r 50: .75X TO 2X BASIC p/r 100
*COMBO p/r 25: 1.25X TO 3X BASIC p/r 200
COMBO PRINT RUNS B/WN 25-50 PER
RANDOM INSERTS IN PACKS
1 Albert Pujols/200 6.00 15.00
2 Alex Rodriguez Rgr/200 4.00 10.00
3 Alfonso Soriano/200 2.50 6.00
4 Andruw Jones/200 3.00 8.00
5 Barry Zito/200 2.50 6.00
6 Cal Ripken/200 15.00 40.00
7 Chipper Jones/200 3.00 8.00
8 Curt Schilling/200 2.50 6.00
9 Derek Jeter/200 6.00 15.00
10 Don Mattingly/200 6.00 15.00
11 Dontrelle Willis/100 4.00 10.00
12 Doc Gooden/200 3.00 8.00
13 Eddie Murray/200 4.00 10.00
14 Frank Thomas/200 3.00 8.00
15 Gary Sheffield/200 2.50 6.00
16 George Brett/200 6.00 15.00
17 Greg Maddux/100 5.00 12.00
18 Hideo Nomo/100 4.00 10.00
20 Ivan Rodriguez/200 3.00 8.00
21 Jason Giambi/200 2.50 6.00
22 Jeff Bagwell/200 3.00 8.00
23 Jim Thome/200 3.00 8.00
24 Kerry Wood/200 3.00 8.00
25 Lance Berkman/200 2.50 6.00
26 Magglio Ordonez/200 2.50 6.00
27 Mark Prior/100 4.00 10.00
28 Mike Piazza/200 4.00 10.00
29 Mike Schmidt/200 6.00 15.00
30 Nomar Garciaparra/200 4.00 10.00
31 Pedro Martinez/200 3.00 8.00
32 Randy Johnson/200 3.00 8.00
33 Roger Clemens/200 6.00 15.00
34 Sammy Sosa/200 3.00 8.00
35 Tony Gwynn/200 6.00 15.00

2004 Donruss Elite Career Best Jerseys

PRINT RUNS B/WN 50-200 COPIES PER
*PRIME p/r 50: 1.25X TO 3X BASIC p/r 200
*PRIME p/r 25: 1.5X TO 4X BASIC p/r 200
*PRIME p/r 25: 1X TO 2.5X BASIC p/r 100
*PRIME p/r 25: 1X TO 2.5X BASIC p/r 50
PRIME PRINT RUNS B/WN 25-50 COPIES PER
1 Albert Pujols/200 6.00 15.00
2 Alex Rodriguez/200 4.00 10.00
3 Alfonso Soriano/200 2.50 6.00
4 Andruw Jones/200 3.00 8.00
5 Barry Zito/200 2.50 6.00
6 Cal Ripken/50 30.00 60.00
7 Chipper Jones/200 3.00 8.00
8 Curt Schilling/200 2.50 6.00
9 Derek Jeter/200 6.00 15.00
10 Don Mattingly/50 12.50 30.00
11 Dontrelle Willis/200 3.00 8.00
12 Doc Gooden/200 3.00 8.00
13 Eddie Murray/200 4.00 10.00
14 Frank Thomas/200 3.00 8.00
15 Gary Sheffield/200 2.50 6.00
16 George Brett/50 12.50 30.00
17 Greg Maddux/200 4.00 10.00
18 Hideo Nomo/200 4.00 10.00
20 Ivan Rodriguez/200 3.00 8.00
21 Jason Giambi/200 2.50 6.00
22 Jeff Bagwell/200 3.00 8.00
23 Jim Thome/200 3.00 8.00
24 Kerry Wood/200 3.00 8.00
25 Lance Berkman/200 2.50 6.00
26 Magglio Ordonez/200 2.50 6.00
27 Mark Prior/200 3.00 8.00
28 Mike Piazza/200 4.00 10.00
29 Mike Schmidt/100 10.00 25.00
30 Nomar Garciaparra/200 4.00 10.00
31 Pedro Martinez/200 3.00 8.00
32 Randy Johnson/200 3.00 8.00
33 Roger Clemens/200 6.00 15.00
34 Sammy Sosa/200 3.00 8.00
35 Tony Gwynn/50 10.00 25.00

2004 Donruss Elite Fans of the Game

201 James Gandolfini 1.25 3.00
202 Freddy Adu 1.25 3.00
203 Summer Sanders .75 2.00
204 Janet Evans .75 2.00
205 Brandi Chastain 1.25 3.00

2004 Donruss Elite Fans of the Game Autographs

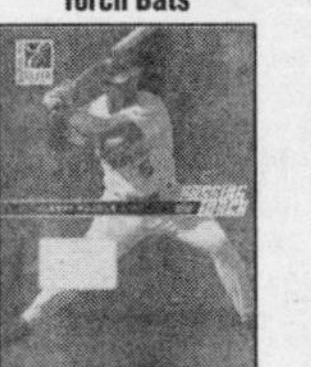

This five card insert set, which was randomly inserted into packs, was the lead-off insert of inserting autograph cards of living celebrities from other fields into major sport mainstream packs. Among the players in these packs were teenage soccer sensation Freddy Adu and star of Television show "The Sopranos" James Gandolfini.

RANDOM INSERTS IN PACKS
SP PRINT RUNS PROVIDED BY DONRUSS
SP'S ARE NOT SERIAL-NUMBERED
201 James Gandolfini 30.00 60.00
202 Freddy Adu 20.00 50.00
203 Summer Sanders SP/250 20.00 50.00
204 Janet Evans SP/250 15.00 40.00
205 Brandi Chastain SP/250 20.00 50.00

2004 Donruss Elite Passing the Torch

1-30 PRINT RUN 1000 SERIAL #'d SETS
31-45 PRINT RUN 500 SERIAL #'d SETS
*BLACK 1-30: .75X TO 2X BASIC
*BLACK 31-45: 1X TO 2.5X BASIC
BLACK 1-30 PRINT RUN 100 #'d SETS
BLACK 31-45 PRINT RUN 50 #'d SETS
*BLUE 1-30: .6X TO 1.5X BASIC
*BLUE 31-45: .6X TO 1.5X BASIC
BLUE 1-30 PRINT RUN 250 #'d SETS
BLUE 31-45 PRINT RUN 125 #'d SETS
*GOLD 1-30: 1.25X TO 3X BASIC
*GOLD 31-45: 1.5X TO 4X BASIC
GOLD 1-30 PRINT RUN 50 #'d SETS
GOLD 31-45 PRINT RUN 25 #'d SETS
*GREEN 1-30: .5X TO 1.2X BASIC
*GREEN 31-45: .5X TO 1.2X BASIC
GREEN 1-30 PRINT RUN 500 #'d SETS
GREEN 31-45 PRINT RUN 250 #'d SETS
1 Whitey Ford .75 2.00
2 Andy Pettitte .75 2.00
3 Willie McCovey .75 2.00
4 Will Clark .75 2.00
5 Stan Musial 2.00 5.00
6 Albert Pujols 3.00 8.00
7 Andre Dawson .75 2.00
8 Vladimir Guerrero 1.25 3.00
9 Dale Murphy .75 2.00
10 Chipper Jones 1.25 3.00
11 Joe Morgan .50 1.25
12 Barry Larkin .75 2.00
13 Catfish Hunter .50 1.25
14 Tim Hudson .75 2.00
15 Jim Rice .75 2.00
16 Manny Ramirez 1.25 3.00
17 Greg Maddux 2.00 5.00
18 Mark Prior .75 2.00
19 Don Mattingly 2.50 6.00
20 Jason Giambi .50 1.25
21 Roy Campanella 1.25 3.00
22 Mike Piazza 1.25 3.00
23 Ozzie Smith 2.00 5.00
24 Scott Rolen .75 2.00
25 Roger Clemens 1.50 4.00
26 Mike Mussina .75 2.00
27 Babe Ruth 3.00 8.00
28 Roger Maris 1.25 3.00
29 Nolan Ryan 4.00 10.00
30 Roy Oswalt .75 2.00
31 Whitey Ford 1.00 2.50
Andy Pettitte
32 Willie McCovey 1.00 2.50
Will Clark
33 Stan Musial 4.00 10.00
Albert Pujols
34 Andre Dawson 1.50 4.00
Vladimir Guerrero
35 Dale Murphy 1.00 2.50
Chipper Jones
36 Joe Morgan 1.00 2.50
Barry Larkin
37 Catfish Hunter 1.00 2.50
Tim Hudson
38 Jim Rice 1.50 4.00
Manny Ramirez
39 Greg Maddux 2.50 6.00
Mark Prior
40 Don Mattingly 3.00 8.00
Jason Giambi
41 Roy Campanella 1.50 4.00
Mike Piazza
42 Ozzie Smith 2.50 6.00
Scott Rolen
43 Roger Clemens 2.00 5.00
Mike Mussina
44 Babe Ruth 4.00 10.00
Roger Maris
45 Nolan Ryan 5.00 12.00
Roy Oswalt

2004 Donruss Elite Passing the Torch Autographs

RANDOM INSERTS IN PACKS
SINGLE PRINT RUNS B/WN 5-50 PER
DUAL PRINT RUNS B/WN 1-5 COPIES PER
NO PRICING ON QTY OF 10 OR LESS
1 Whitey Ford/10
3 Willie McCovey/10
4 Will Clark/15 75.00 150.00
6 Stan Musial/10
7 Andre Dawson/50 8.00 20.00
8 Vladimir Guerrero/5
9 Dale Murphy/50 10.00 25.00
10 Chipper Jones/5
11 Joe Morgan/15 15.00 40.00
12 Barry Larkin/10
14 Tim Hudson/15 30.00 60.00
15 Jim Rice/50 8.00 20.00
16 Manny Ramirez/5
17 Greg Maddux/5
18 Mark Prior/15 20.00 50.00
19 Don Mattingly/10
22 Mike Piazza/5
23 Ozzie Smith/5
24 Scott Rolen/15 30.00 60.00
25 Roger Clemens/5
26 Mike Mussina/5
29 Nolan Ryan/5
30 Roy Oswalt/50 8.00 20.00
32 Willie McCovey
Will Clark/5
33 Stan Musial
Albert Pujols/5
34 Andre Dawson
Vladimir Guerrero/5
35 Dale Murphy
Chipper Jones/5
36 Joe Morgan
Barry Larkin/5
38 Jim Rice
Manny Ramirez/5
39 Greg Maddux
Mark Prior/5
42 Ozzie Smith
Scott Rolen/5
43 Roger Clemens
Mike Mussina/5
44 Babe Ruth
Roger Maris/1
45 Nolan Ryan
Roy Oswalt/5

2004 Donruss Elite Passing the Torch Bats

1-30 PRINT RUNS B/WN 25-200 COPIES PER
31-45 PRINT RUNS B/WN 25-50 COPIES PER
2 Andy Pettitte/200 3.00 8.00
3 Willie McCovey/100 4.00 10.00
4 Will Clark/100 6.00 15.00
5 Stan Musial/100 12.50 30.00
6 Albert Pujols/200 6.00 15.00
7 Andre Dawson/100 4.00 10.00
8 Vladimir Guerrero/200 3.00 8.00
9 Dale Murphy/100 6.00 15.00
10 Chipper Jones/200 3.00 8.00
11 Joe Morgan/200 3.00 8.00
12 Barry Larkin/200 3.00 8.00
14 Tim Hudson/200 2.50 6.00
15 Jim Rice/200 3.00 8.00
16 Manny Ramirez/200 3.00 8.00
17 Greg Maddux/200 4.00 10.00
18 Mark Prior/200 3.00 8.00
19 Don Mattingly/100 8.00 20.00
20 Jason Giambi/200 2.50 6.00
21 Roy Campanella/50 12.50 30.00
22 Mike Piazza/200 4.00 10.00
23 Ozzie Smith/200 6.00 15.00
24 Scott Rolen/200 3.00 8.00
25 Roger Clemens/200 6.00 15.00
26 Mike Mussina/200 3.00 8.00
27 Babe Ruth/25 100.00 200.00
28 Roger Maris/50 20.00 50.00
29 Nolan Ryan/100 10.00 25.00
30 Roy Oswalt/200 2.50 6.00
32 Willie McCovey 10.00 25.00
Will Clark /50
33 Stan Musial 20.00 50.00
Albert Pujols /50
34 Andre Dawson 10.00 25.00
Vladimir Guerrero /50
35 Dale Murphy 10.00 25.00
Chipper Jones /50
36 Joe Morgan 10.00 25.00
Barry Larkin /50
38 Jim Rice 10.00 25.00
Manny Ramirez /50
39 Greg Maddux 15.00 40.00
Mark Prior /50
40 Don Mattingly 15.00 40.00
Jason Giambi /50
41 Roy Campanella 15.00 40.00
Mike Piazza /25
42 Ozzie Smith 12.50 30.00

2004 Donruss Elite Passing the Torch Bats

Scott Rolen /50
43 Roger Clemens 12.50 30.00
Mike Mussina /50
44 Babe Ruth 150.00 250.00
Roger Maris /25
45 Nolan Ryan 15.00 40.00
Roy Oswalt /50

2004 Donruss Elite Passing the Torch Jerseys

1-30 PRINT RUNS B/WN 25-200 COPIES PER
31-45 PRINT RUNS B/WN 25-50 COPIES PER
1 Whitey Ford/100 6.00 15.00
2 Andy Pettitte/200 3.00 8.00
3 Willie McCovey/100 4.00 10.00
4 Will Clark/100 6.00 15.00
5 Stan Musial/100 12.50 30.00
6 Albert Pujols/200 6.00 15.00
7 Andre Dawson/200 3.00 8.00
8 Vladimir Guerrero/200 3.00 8.00
9 Dale Murphy/100 6.00 15.00
10 Chipper Jones/200 3.00 8.00
11 Joe Morgan/100 4.00 10.00
12 Barry Larkin/200 3.00 8.00
13 Catfish Hunter/100 6.00 15.00
14 Tim Hudson/200 2.50 6.00
15 Jim Rice/200 3.00 8.00
16 Manny Ramirez/200 3.00 8.00
18 Mark Prior/200 3.00 8.00
19 Don Mattingly/100 10.00 25.00
20 Jason Giambi/200 2.50 6.00
21 Roy Campanella/50 12.50 30.00
22 Mike Piazza/200 4.00 10.00
23 Ozzie Smith/100 8.00 20.00
24 Scott Rolen/200 3.00 8.00
25 Roger Clemens/200 6.00 15.00
26 Mike Mussina/200 3.00 8.00
27 Babe Ruth/25 250.00 400.00
28 Roger Maris/50 30.00 60.00
29 Nolan Ryan/100 12.50 30.00
30 Roy Oswalt/200 2.50 6.00
31 Whitey Ford 10.00 25.00
Andy Pettitte/50
32 Willie McCovey 10.00 25.00
Will Clark/50
33 Stan Musial 20.00 50.00
Albert Pujols/50
34 Andre Dawson 10.00 25.00
Vladimir Guerrero/50
35 Dale Murphy 10.00 25.00
Chipper Jones/50
36 Joe Morgan 10.00 25.00
Barry Larkin/50
37 Catfish Hunter 10.00 25.00
Tim Hudson/50
38 Jim Rice 10.00 25.00
Manny Ramirez/50
40 Don Mattingly 15.00 40.00
Jason Giambi/50
41 Roy Campanella 20.00 50.00
Mike Piazza/25
42 Ozzie Smith 12.50 30.00
Scott Rolen/50
43 Roger Clemens 12.50 30.00
Mike Mussina/50
44 Babe Ruth
Roger Maris/25
45 Nolan Ryan 20.00 50.00
Roy Oswalt/50

2004 Donruss Elite Recollection Autographs

RANDOM INSERTS IN PACKS
PRINT RUNS B/WN 1-95 COPIES PER
NO PRICING ON QTY OF 14 OR LESS
1 Jeremy Affeldt 01/25 8.00 20.00
2 Erick Almonte 01/25 6.00 15.00
3 Rich Aurilia 02/2
4 Jeff Baker 02/25 15.00 40.00
5 Brandon Berger 01/25 6.00 15.00
6 Marlon Byrd 01/24 8.00 20.00
7 Juan Cruz 01/5
8 Ryan Drese 02/45 6.00 15.00
9 Brandon Duckworth 01/16 6.00 15.00
10 Casey Fossum 01/23 8.00 20.00
11 Geronimo Gil 01/25 6.00 15.00
12 Mark Grace 02/2
13 Jeremy Guthrie 02/25 8.00 20.00
14 Nic Jackson 02/95 4.00 10.00
15 Barry Larkin 01 PCRD/4
16 Greg Maddux 01 Ser/1
17 Antonio Perez 01/3
18 Mark Prior 01/14
19 Ivan Rodriguez 01 Ser/3
20 Ivan Rodriguez 01 SerDom/3
21 Ricardo Rodriguez 01/25 6.00 15.00
22 Ruben Sierra 97 GS/1
23 Bud Smith 01/25 6.00 15.00
24 Sammy Sosa 01/1
25 Junior Spivey 01/20 8.00 20.00
26 Tim Spooneybarger 01/25 6.00 15.00
27 Mark Teixeira 01/6
28 Martin Vargas 01/37 4.00 10.00

2004 Donruss Elite Team

STATED PRINT RUN 1500 SERIAL #'d SETS
*BLACK: 1X TO 2.5X BASIC
BLACK PRINT RUN 150 SERIAL #'d SETS
*GOLD: .75X TO 2X BASIC
GOLD PRINT RUN 250 SERIAL #'d SETS
RANDOM INSERTS IN PACKS
1 Cal Ripken 4.00 10.00
Eddie Murray
Jim Palmer
2 Derek Jeter 2.50 6.00
Roger Clemens
Bernie Williams
Andy Pettitte
3 Johnny Bench .40 1.00
Tony Perez
George Foster
Dave Concepcion
4 Josh Beckett .40 1.00
Dontrelle Willis
Ivan Rodriguez
5 Randy Johnson 1.00 2.50
Curt Schilling
Luis Gonzalez
Mark Grace
6 Derek Jeter 2.50 6.00
Wade Boggs
Darryl Strawberry
7 Chipper Jones 1.50 4.00
Tom Glavine
Greg Maddux
Ryan Klesko
8 Doc Gooden .40 1.00
Gary Carter
Darryl Strawberry
9 Jackie Robinson 1.00 2.50
Roy Campanella
Duke Snider
10 Phil Rizzuto 1.00 2.50
Yogi Berra
Whitey Ford
11 Stan Musial 1.50 4.00
Red Schoendienst
Marty Marion
Enos Slaughter

2004 Donruss Elite Team Bats

RANDOM INSERTS IN PACKS
STATED PRINT RUN 100 SERIAL #'d SETS
2 Derek Jeter 15.00 40.00
Roger Clemens
Bernie Williams
Andy Pettitte
3 Johnny Bench 20.00 50.00
Tony Perez
George Foster
Dave Concepcion
4 Josh Beckett 6.00 15.00
Dontrelle Willis
Ivan Rodriguez
5 Randy Johnson 10.00 25.00
Curt Schilling
Luis Gonzalez
Mark Grace
6 Derek Jeter 12.50 30.00
Wade Boggs
Darryl Strawberry
7 Chipper Jones 12.50 30.00
Tom Glavine
Greg Maddux
Ryan Klesko
8 Doc Gooden 6.00 15.00
Gary Carter
Darryl Strawberry

2004 Donruss Elite Team Jerseys

RANDOM INSERTS IN PACKS
STATED PRINT RUN 100 SERIAL #'d SETS
JACKIE/CAMPY/SNIDER PRINT 50 #'d CARDS
ROY CAMPANELLA SWATCH IS PANTS
1 Cal Ripken 30.00 60.00
Eddie Murray
Jim Palmer
2 Derek Jeter 15.00 40.00
Roger Clemens
Bernie Williams
Andy Pettitte
4 Josh Beckett 6.00 15.00
Dontrelle Willis
Ivan Rodriguez
5 Randy Johnson 10.00 25.00
Curt Schilling
Luis Gonzalez
Mark Grace
6 Derek Jeter 12.50 30.00
Wade Boggs
Darryl Strawberry
7 Chipper Jones 12.50 30.00
Tom Glavine
Greg Maddux
Ryan Klesko
9 Jackie Robinson 40.00 80.00
Roy Campanella Pants
Duke Snider/50
10 Phil Rizzuto 15.00 40.00
Yogi Berra
Whitey Ford
11 Stan Musial 30.00 60.00
Red Schoendienst
Marty Marion
Enos Slaughter

2004 Donruss Elite Throwback Threads

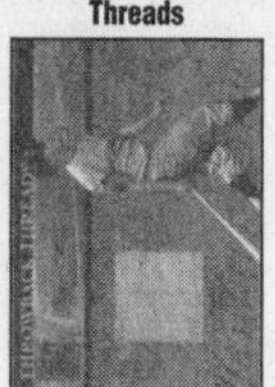

1-20 PRINT RUN 150 SERIAL #'d SETS
21-30 PRINT RUN 75 SERIAL #'d SETS
RUTH 31 PRINT RUN 50 #'d CARDS
32-50 PRINT RUN 100 SERIAL #'d SETS
RUTH/GEHRIG 51 PRINT 25 #'d CARDS
52-60 PRINT RUN 50 SERIAL #'d SETS
*PRIME 1-20: 1.5X TO 4X BASIC 1-20
*PRIME 21-30: 1X TO 2.5X BASIC 21-30
*PRIME 31-50: 1.25X TO 3X BASIC 31-50
PRIME SINGLE PRINTS B/WN 10-25 PER
PRIME DUAL PRINTS B/WN 5-15 PER
NO PRIME PRICING ON QTY OF 10 OR LESS
CARD NUMBER 3 DOES NOT EXIST
1 Albert Pujols/150 6.00 15.00
2 Alex Rodriguez Rgr/150 4.00 10.00
4 Chipper Jones/150 3.00 8.00
5 Derek Jeter/150 6.00 15.00
6 Greg Maddux/150 4.00 10.00
7 Hideo Nomo/150 4.00 10.00
8 Miguel Cabrera/150 3.00 8.00
9 Ivan Rodriguez/150 3.00 8.00
10 Jason Giambi/150 2.50 6.00
11 Jeff Bagwell/150 3.00 8.00
12 Lance Berkman/150 2.50 6.00
13 Mark Prior/150 3.00 8.00
14 Mike Piazza/150 4.00 10.00
15 Nomar Garciaparra/150 4.00 10.00
16 Pedro Martinez/150 3.00 8.00
17 Randy Johnson/150 3.00 8.00
18 Sammy Sosa/150 3.00 8.00
19 Shawn Green/150 2.50 6.00
20 Vladimir Guerrero/150 3.00 8.00
21 Adam Dunn 6.00 15.00
Austin Kearns /75
22 Barry Zito 6.00 15.00
Mark Mulder /75
23 Curt Schilling 6.00 15.00
Curt Schilling /75
24 Derek Jeter 12.50 30.00
Jason Giambi /75
25 Dontrelle Willis 8.00 20.00
Josh Beckett /75
26 Frank Thomas 8.00 20.00
Magglio Ordonez /75
27 Jim Thome 8.00 20.00
Jim Thome /75
28 Kerry Wood 6.00 15.00
Mark Prior /75
29 Hank Blalock 8.00 20.00
Mark Teixeira /75
30 Albert Pujols 15.00 40.00
Scott Rolen /75
31 Babe Ruth/50 200.00 300.00
32 Cal Ripken/100 20.00 50.00
33 Carl Yastrzemski/100 10.00 25.00
34 Deion Sanders/100 6.00 15.00
35 Don Mattingly/100 10.00 25.00
36 George Brett/100 10.00 25.00
37 Jim Palmer/100 4.00 10.00
38 Kirby Puckett/100 6.00 15.00
39 Lou Gehrig/100 125.00 200.00
40 Mark Grace/100 6.00 15.00
41 Mike Schmidt/100 10.00 25.00
42 Nolan Ryan/100 12.50 30.00
43 Ozzie Smith/100 8.00 20.00
44 Reggie Jackson/100 6.00 15.00
45 Rickey Henderson/100 6.00 15.00
46 Roberto Clemente/100 40.00 80.00
47 Roger Clemens/100 8.00 20.00
48 Roger Maris/100 20.00 50.00
49 Roy Campanella Pants/100 10.00 25.00
50 Tony Gwynn/100 8.00 20.00
51 Babe Ruth 300.00 500.00
Lou Gehrig /25
52 Cal Ripken 30.00 60.00
Eddie Murray /50
53 Ted Williams 50.00 100.00
Carl Yastrzemski /50
54 Andre Dawson 8.00 20.00
Gary Carter /50
55 Reggie Jackson 10.00 25.00
Rod Carew /50
56 Derek Jeter 20.00 50.00
Phil Rizzuto /50
57 Nolan Ryan 20.00 50.00
Roy Oswalt /50
58 Roger Clemens 12.50 30.00
Mike Mussina /50
59 Albert Pujols 20.00 50.00
Stan Musial /50
60 Nomar Garciaparra 50.00 100.00
Ted Williams /50

2004 Donruss Elite Throwback Threads Autographs

STATED PRINT RUN 25 SERIAL #'d SETS
PRIME PRINT RUNS B/WN 5-10 COPIES PER
NO PRIME PRICING DUE TO SCARCITY
9 Ivan Rodriguez/25 40.00 80.00
13 Mark Prior/25 20.00 50.00
18 Sammy Sosa/25 50.00 100.00
35 Don Mattingly/25 75.00 150.00
37 Jim Palmer/25 20.00 50.00

2004 Donruss Elite Extra Edition

This 286-card set was released in December, 2004. The set was issued in five card packs with an $6 SRP which came 12 packs to a box and 32 boxes to a case. Cards numbered 1-150 featured active veterans while cards numbered 206 through 215 feature retired players and cards 216 through 355 are all Rookie Cards including many players drafted in 2004. This is the set in which Donruss had the right to picture any player drafted and later signed from the 2004 amateur draft. Each company, which the exception of Topps (who signs their players individually), was allowed to have one product with a full run of 2004 amateur draft in it. This was Donruss' product for that purpose.

COMP.SET w/o SP's (150) 10.00 25.00
COMMON CARD (1-150) .12 .30
COMMON CARD (206-215) .40 1.00
206-215 RANDOM INSERTS IN PACKS
206-215 PRINT RUN 1000 SERIAL #'d SETS
COMMON NO AU (234-254) .75 2.00
NO AU 234-254 RANDOM IN PACKS
NO AU 234-254 PRINT RUN 1000 #'d SETS
COMMON AU p/r 803-1195 3.00 8.00
COMMON AU p/r 522-799 3.00 8.00
COMMON AU p/r 350-493 4.00 10.00
COMMON AU p/r 260 5.00 12.00
216-355 OVERALL AU-GU ODDS 1:4
216-355 PRINT RUNS B/WN 260-1617 PER
DO NOT EXIST: 151-205/232/236-238/240
DO NOT EXIST: 241/245/248-249/251/255
DO NOT EXIST: 274/339
1 Troy Glaus .12 .30
2 John Lackey .12 .30
3 Garret Anderson .12 .30
4 Francisco Rodriguez .20 .50
5 Casey Kotchman .12 .30
6 Jose Guillen .12 .30
7 Miguel Tejada .20 .50
8 Rafael Palmeiro .20 .50
9 Jay Gibbons .12 .30
10 Melvin Mora .12 .30
11 Javy Lopez .12 .30
12 Pedro Martinez .20 .50
13 Curt Schilling .20 .50
14 David Ortiz .30 .75
15 Manny Ramirez .30 .75
16 Nomar Garciaparra .30 .75
17 Magglio Ordonez .20 .50
18 Frank Thomas .30 .75
19 Esteban Loaiza .12 .30
20 Paul Konerko .20 .50
21 Mark Buehrle .20 .50
22 Jody Gerut .12 .30
23 Victor Martinez .20 .50
24 C.C. Sabathia .20 .50
25 Travis Hafner .12 .30
26 Cliff Lee .20 .50
27 Jeremy Bonderman .12 .30
28 Dallas McPherson .12 .30
29 Jermaine Dye .12 .30
30 Carlos Guillen .12 .30
31 Carlos Beltran .12 .30
32 Ken Harvey .12 .30
33 Mike Sweeney .12 .30
34 Angel Berroa .12 .30
35 Joe Nathan .12 .30
36 Johan Santana .30 .75
37 Jacque Jones .12 .30
38 Shannon Stewart .12 .30
39 Torii Hunter .12 .30
40 Derek Jeter .75 2.00
41 Jason Giambi .12 .30
42 Danny Graves .12 .30
43 Alfonso Soriano .12 .30
44 Gary Sheffield .12 .30
45 Mike Mussina .20 .50
46 Jorge Posada .20 .50
47 Hideki Matsui .50 1.25
48 Francisco Cordero .12 .30
49 Javier Vazquez .12 .30
50 Mariano Rivera .30 .75
51 Eric Chavez .12 .30
52 Tim Hudson .20 .50
53 Mark Mulder .12 .30
54 Barry Zito .12 .30
55 Ichiro Suzuki .50 1.25
56 Edgar Martinez .20 .50
57 Bret Boone .12 .30
58 Lew Ford .12 .30
59 B.J. Upton .20 .50
60 Aubrey Huff .12 .30
61 Rocco Baldelli .12 .30
62 Carl Crawford .20 .50
63 Delmon Young .20 .50
64 Mark Teixeira .30 .75
65 Hank Blalock .12 .30
66 Michael Young .12 .30
67 Alex Rodriguez .50 1.25
68 Carlos Delgado .12 .30
69 Milton Bradley .12 .30
70 Roy Halladay .30 .75
71 Vernon Wells .12 .30
72 Randy Johnson .30 .75
73 Bobby Crosby .12 .30
74 Lyle Overbay .12 .30
75 Luis Gonzalez .12 .30
76 Steve Finley .12 .30
77 Chipper Jones .30 .75
78 Andruw Jones .12 .30
79 Marcus Giles .12 .30
80 Rafael Furcal .12 .30
81 J.D. Drew .12 .30
82 Sammy Sosa .30 .75
83 Kerry Wood .12 .30
84 Mark Prior .20 .50
85 Derrek Lee .12 .30
86 Moises Alou .12 .30
87 Carlos Zambrano .20 .50
88 Ken Griffey Jr. .50 1.25
89 Austin Kearns .12 .30
90 Adam Dunn .20 .50
91 Barry Larkin .20 .50
92 Todd Helton .20 .50
93 Larry Walker Cards .20 .50
94 Preston Wilson .12 .30
95 Sean Casey .12 .30
96 Luis Castillo .12 .30
97 Josh Beckett .20 .50
98 Mike Lowell .12 .30
99 Miguel Cabrera .30 .75
100 Brad Penny .12 .30
101 Dontrelle Willis .12 .30
102 Andy Pettitte .20 .50
103 Wade Miller .12 .30
104 Jeff Bagwell .20 .50
105 Craig Biggio .20 .50
106 Lance Berkman .20 .50
107 Jeff Kent .12 .30
108 Roy Oswalt .20 .50
109 Hideo Nomo .30 .75
110 Adrian Beltre .12 .30
111 Paul Lo Duca .12 .30
112 Shawn Green .12 .30
113 Roger Clemens .40 1.00
114 Eric Gagne .12 .30
115 Danny Kolb .12 .30
116 Rickie Weeks .12 .30
117 Scott Podsednik .12 .30
118 Livan Hernandez .12 .30
119 Orlando Cabrera .12 .30
120 Jose Vidro .12 .30
121 David Wright .50 1.25
122 Tom Glavine .20 .50
123 Al Leiter .12 .30
124 Mike Piazza .30 .75
125 Jose Reyes .20 .50
126 Richard Hidalgo .12 .30
127 Eric Milton .12 .30
128 Jim Thome .20 .50
129 Mike Lieberthal .12 .30
130 Bobby Abreu .12 .30
131 Kip Wells .12 .30
132 Jack Wilson .12 .30
133 Jason Bay .20 .50
134 Brian Giles .12 .30
135 Sean Burroughs .12 .30
136 Khalil Greene .20 .50
137 Jake Peavy .12 .30
138 Jason Schmidt .12 .30
139 J.T. Snow .12 .30
140 Craig Wilson .12 .30
141 Chase Utley .30 .75
142 Jim Edmonds .20 .50
143 Albert Pujols .75 2.00
144 Edgar Renteria .12 .30
145 Scott Rolen .20 .50
146 Matt Morris .12 .30
147 Ivan Rodriguez .20 .50
148 Vladimir Guerrero .30 .75
149 Greg Maddux .50 1.25
150 Ben Sheets .12 .30
206 Will Clark RET .60 1.50
207 Nolan Ryan RET 3.00 8.00
208 Bob Feller RET .40 1.00
209 Red Schoendienst RET .40 1.00
210 Brooks Robinson RET .60 1.50
211 Al Kaline RET 1.00 2.50
212 Ozzie Smith RET 1.50 4.00
213 Maury Wills RET .40 1.00
214 Steve Carlton RET .40 1.00
215 Duke Snider RET .60 1.50
216 Scott Lewis AU/603 RC 8.00 20.00
217 Josh Johnson AU/597 RC 4.00 10.00
218 Jeff Fiorentino AU/597 RC 5.00 12.00
219 Grant Hansen AU/599 RC 3.00 8.00
220 Yov Gallardo AU/803 RC 15.00 40.00
221 Eddie Prasch AU/603 RC 4.00 10.00
222 Danny Hill AU/603 RC 3.00 8.00
223 Chuck Lofgren AU/803 RC 6.00 15.00
224 Blake Johnson AU/811 RC 4.00 10.00
225 Cory Dunlap AU/599 RC 6.00 15.00
226 Carlos Vasquez AU/869 RC 3.00 8.00
227 Jesse Crain AU/1000 RC 3.00 8.00
228 Yhency Brazoban AU/1000 3.00 8.00
229 Abe Alvarez AU/1000 RC 4.00 10.00
230 Scott Kazmir AU/350 RC 15.00 40.00
231 J.A. Happ AU/1195 RC 12.50 30.00
233 Mark Jecmen AU/1047 RC 3.00 8.00
234 Kameron Loe/1000 RC .75 2.00
235 Ervin Santana/1000 RC 2.00 5.00
239 Josh Karp/1000 RC .75 2.00
242 Alberto Callaspo/1000 RC 2.00 5.00
243 Jesse Hoover AU/1191 RC 4.00 10.00
246 Just Hoyman AU/1124 RC 4.00 10.00
247 Juan Cedeno/1000 RC .75 2.00
250 Jake Dittler/1000 RC .75 2.00
252 Ben Zobrist AU/1178 RC 6.00 15.00
253 Jeff Salazar/1000 RC .75 2.00
254 Fausto Carmona/1000 RC 1.25 3.00
256 Jor Vasquez AU/1000 RC 3.00 8.00
257 Raf Gonzalez AU/603 RC 3.00 8.00
258 Andrew Dobies AU/601 RC 10.00 25.00
259 Colby Miller AU/997 RC 3.00 8.00
260 K.C. Herren AU/735 RC 3.00 8.00
261 Ryan Meaux AU/546 RC 3.00 8.00
262 Dust Pedroia AU/1114 RC 50.00 100.00
263 Fern Nieve AU/1000 RC 3.00 8.00
264 Mar Gomez AU/1000 RC 3.00 8.00
265 Eric Campbell AU/260 RC 70.00 120.00
266 Billy Killian AU/703 RC 4.00 10.00
267 Mike Rouse AU/999 RC 3.00 8.00
268 Kyle Bono AU/1203 RC 3.00 8.00
269 M.Einertson AU/1047 RC 6.00 15.00
270 Scott Proctor AU/1000 RC 3.00 8.00
271 Tim Bittner AU/1000 RC 3.00 8.00
272 Christian Garcia AU/799 RC 4.00 10.00
273 Yadier Molina AU/1000 RC 15.00 40.00
275 C.Thomas AU/907 RC 3.00 8.00
276 Trav Blackley AU/1000 RC 3.00 8.00
277 F.Francisco AU/1000 RC 3.00 8.00
278 Dion Navarro AU/1000 RC 3.00 8.00
279 Joey Gathright AU/1000 RC 3.00 8.00
280 Kaz Tadano AU/1000 RC 4.00 10.00
281 Matt Bush AU/1100 RC 6.00 15.00
282 David Haehnel AU/865 RC 4.00 10.00
283 Tommy Hottovy AU/825 RC 4.00 10.00
284 Chris Carter AU/973 RC 5.00 12.00
285 Mark Rogers AU/578 RC 8.00 20.00
286 Jeremy Sowers AU/537 RC 15.00 30.00
287 Homer Bailey AU/1571 RC 6.00 15.00
288 Mike Butia AU/825 RC 3.00 8.00
289 Chris Nelson AU/465 RC 15.00 30.00
290 T.Diamond AU/1055 RC 6.00 15.00
291 Neil Walker AU/1343 RC 8.00 20.00
292 Sean Gamble AU/1229 RC 3.00 8.00
293 Bill Bray AU/1073 RC 3.00 8.00
294 Reid Brignac AU/522 RC 8.00 20.00
295 R.Klosterman AU/865 RC 3.00 8.00
296 David Purcey AU/1485 RC 3.00 8.00
297 Scott Elbert AU/1617 RC 8.00 20.00
298 Josh Fields AU/961 RC 15.00 30.00
299 Chris Lambert AU/954 RC 4.00 10.00
300 Trevor Plouffe AU/1329 RC 4.00 10.00
301 Greg Golson AU/1334 RC 4.00 10.00
302 Josh Baker AU/525 RC 3.00 8.00
303 Philip Hughes AU/1485 RC 12.50 30.00
304 Matt Macri AU/979 RC 4.00 10.00
305 Kyle Waldrop AU/823 RC 6.00 15.00
306 Rich Robnett AU/1575 RC 4.00 10.00
307 T.Tankersley AU/1073 RC 4.00 10.00
308 Blake DeWitt AU/1562 RC 8.00 20.00
309 Daryl Jones AU/575 RC 12.50 30.00
310 Eric Hurley AU/1021 RC 10.00 25.00
311 J.P. Howell AU/1453 RC 4.00 10.00
312 Zach Jackson AU/1069 RC 3.00 8.00
313 Justin Orenduff AU/473 RC 12.50 30.00
314 Tyler Lumsden AU/473 RC 4.00 10.00
315 Matt Fox AU/473 RC 4.00 10.00
316 Danny Putnam AU/473 RC 4.00 10.00
317 Jon Poterson AU/464 RC 6.00 10.00
318 Gio Gonzalez AU/473 RC 10.00 25.00
319 Jay Rainville AU/823 RC 10.00 25.00
320 Huston Street AU/709 RC 10.00 25.00
321 Jeff Marquez AU/493 RC 4.00 10.00
322 Eric Beattie AU/930 RC 4.00 10.00
323 B.Szymanski AU/1327 RC 4.00 10.00
324 Seth Smith AU/1065 RC 4.00 10.00
325 Rob Johnson AU/790 RC 4.00 10.00
326 Wes Whisler AU/473 RC 4.00 10.00
327 Billy Buckner AU/673 RC 4.00 10.00
328 Jon Zeringue AU/473 RC 3.00 8.00
329 Curtis Thigpen AU/673 RC 12.50 30.00
330 Donny Lucy AU/573 RC 3.00 8.00
331 Mike Ferris AU/558 RC 4.00 10.00
332 A.Swarzak AU/370 RC 10.00 25.00
333 Jason Jaramillo AU/573 RC 4.00 10.00
334 Hunter Pence AU/672 RC 30.00 60.00
335 Mike Rozier AU/628 RC 4.00 10.00
336 Kurt Suzuki AU/473 RC 6.00 15.00
337 Jason Vargas AU/621 RC 8.00 20.00
338 Brian Bixler AU/665 RC 10.00 25.00
340 Dexter Fowler AU/623 RC 20.00 50.00
341 Mark Trumbo AU/1321 RC 12.50 30.00
342 Jeff Frazier AU/423 RC 4.00 10.00
343 Steve Register AU/673 RC 3.00 8.00
344 M.Schlact AU/477 RC 4.00 10.00
345 Garrett Mock AU/471 RC 4.00 10.00
346 Eric Haberer AU/473 RC 4.00 10.00
347 M.Tuiasosopo AU/473 RC 10.00 25.00
348 Jason Windsor AU/473 RC 10.00 25.00
349 Grant Johnson AU/815 RC 4.00 10.00
350 J.C. Holt AU/673 RC 4.00 10.00
351 Joe Bauserman AU/472 RC 4.00 10.00
352 Jamar Walton AU/481 RC 4.00 10.00
353 Eric Patterson AU/1571 RC 6.00 15.00
354 Tyler Johnson AU/775 RC 6.00 15.00
355 Nick Adenhart AU/653 RC 10.00 25.00

2004 Donruss Elite Extra Edition Aspirations

*1-150 p/r 81-99: 4X TO 10X
*1-150 p/r 51-80: 5X TO 12X
*1-150 p/r 36-50: 6X TO 15X
*1-150 p/r 26-35: 8X TO 20X
*1-150 p/r 16-25: 10X TO 25X
*206-215 p/r 81-99: 1.25X TO 3X
*206-215 p/r 51-80: 1.5X TO 4X
*216-355 p/r 51-80: .6X TO 1.5X NO AU
*216-355 p/r 36-50: .75X TO 2X NO AU
*216-355p/r81-99: .3X TO .8X AUp/r803-1617
*216-355p/r81-99: .25X TO .6X AUp/r522-799
*216-355p/r81-99: .2X TO .5X AU p/r 350-493
*216-355p/r51-80: .4X TO 1X AU p/r 803-1617
*216-355p/r51-80: .3X TO .8X AU p/r 522-799
*216-355p/r51-80: .25X TO .6X AUp/r350-493
*216-355 p/r 51-80: .15X TO .4X AU p/r 260
*216-355p/r36-50:.5X TO 1.2X AUp/r803-1617
*216-355 p/r 36-50: .4X TO 1X AU p/r 522-799
*216-355p/r36-50: .3X TO .8X AU p/r 350-493
*216-355 p/r 26-35: .4X TO 1X AU p/r 350-493
PRINT RUNS B/WN 4-99 COPIES PER
NO PRICING ON QTY OF 13 OR LESS

2004 Donruss Elite Extra Edition Aspirations Gold

*ASP.GOLD 1-150: 10X TO 25X
*ASP.GOLD 206-215: 3X TO 8X
RANDOM INSERTS IN PACKS
STATED PRINT RUN 25 SERIAL #'d SETS
216-355 NO PRICING DUE TO SCARCITY

2004 Donruss Elite Extra Edition Status

*1-150 p/r 51-80: 5X TO 12X
*1-150 p/r 36-50: 6X TO 15X
*1-150 p/r 26-35: 8X TO 20X
*1-150 p/r 16-25: 10X TO 25X
*206-215 p/r 26-35: 2.5X TO 6X
*206-215 p/r 16-25: 3X TO 8X
*216-355 p/r 36-50: .75X TO 2X NO AU
*216-355p/r81-96: .3X TO .8X AUp/r803-1617
*216-355p/r51-80: .4X TO 1X AU p/r 803-1617
*216-355p/r51-80: .3X TO .8X AU p/r 522-799
*216-355p/r51-80: .25X TO .6X AUp/r350-493
*216-355p/r36-50:.5X TO 1.2X AUp/r803-1617
*216-355 p/r 36-50: .4X TO 1X AU p/r 522-799
*216-355p/r36-50: .3X TO .8X AU p/r 350-493
*216-355p/r26-35:.6X TO 1.5X AUp/r803-1617
*216-355p/r26-35: .5X TO 1.2X AUp/r 522-799
*216-355 p/r 26-35: .4X TO 1X AU p/r 350-493
*216-355 p/r 26-35: .25X TO .6X AU p/r 260
PRINT RUNS B/WN 1-96 COPIES PER
1-215 NO PRICING ON QTY OF 15 OR LESS
216-355 NO PRICING ON QTY 25 OR LESS

2004 Donruss Elite Extra Edition Status Gold

STATED PRINT RUN 10 SERIAL #'d SETS
NO PRICING DUE TO SCARCITY

2004 Donruss Elite Extra Edition Turn of the Century

*1-150: 2.5X TO 6X BASIC
1-150 PRINT RUN 250 SERIAL #'d SETS
*206-215: 1.25X TO 3X BASIC
*216-355: .5X TO 1.2X NO AU p/r 1000
206-355 PRINT RUN 100 SERIAL #'d SETS
RANDOM INSERTS IN PACKS

2004 Donruss Elite Extra Edition Signature

*216-355 p/r 50: 1X TO 2.5X AU p/r 803-1617
OVERALL AU-GU ODDS 1:4
PRINT RUNS B/WN 1-50 #'d COPIES PER
NO PRICING ON QTY OF 10 OR LESS
132 Jack Wilson/25 12.50 30.00
133 Jason Bay/25 12.50 30.00
234 Kameron Loe ROO/50 10.00 25.00
235 Ervin Santana ROO/50 20.00 50.00
239 Josh Karp ROO/50 8.00 20.00
247 Juan Cedeno ROO/50 8.00 20.00
253 Jeff Salazar ROO/50 10.00 25.00
254 Fausto Carmona ROO/50 40.00 80.00

2004 Donruss Elite Extra Edition Signature Aspirations

*216-355 p/r 100: .6X TO 1.5X p/r 803-1617
*216-355 p/r 100: .6X TO 1.5X p/r 522-799
*216-355 p/r 100: .5X TO 1.2X p/r 350-493
*216-355 p/r 49-50: 1.25X TO 3X p/r 803-1617
*216-355 p/r 49-50: 1X TO 2.5X p/r 522-799

*216-355 p/r 49-50: .75X TO 2X p/r 350-493
OVERALL AU-GU ODDS 1:4
PRINT RUNS B/WN 1-100 COPIES PER
NO PRICING ON QTY OF 10 OR LESS
220 Yovani Gallardo ROO/50 40.00 80.00
274 Justin Leone ROO/50 10.00 25.00
281 Matt Bush DP/100 12.50 30.00
303 Philip Hughes DP/100 30.00 60.00
334 Hunter Pence DP/50 100.00 175.00
340 Dexter Fowler DP/50 50.00 100.00
347 Matt Tuiasosopo DP/100 20.00 40.00
355 Nick Adenhart DP/100 12.50 30.00

2004 Donruss Elite Extra Edition Signature Aspirations Gold

OVERALL AU-GU ODDS 1:4
PRINT RUNS B/WN 1-25 COPIES PER
NO PRICING DUE TO SCARCITY

2004 Donruss Elite Extra Edition Signature Status

*216-355 p/r 50: 1.25X TO 3X p/r 803-1617
*216-355 p/r 50: 1X TO 2.5X p/r 522-799
*216-355 p/r 50: .75X TO 2X p/r 350-493
*216-355 p/r 50: .5X TO 1.2X p/r 260
OVERALL AU-GU ODDS 1:4
PRINT RUNS B/WN 1-50 COPIES PER
NO PRICING ON QTY OF 25 OR LESS
281 Matt Bush DP/50 15.00 40.00
289 Chris Nelson DP/50 30.00 60.00
303 Philip Hughes DP/50 50.00 100.00
308 Blake DeWitt DP/50 15.00 40.00
318 Gio Gonzalez DP/50 20.00 50.00
334 Hunter Pence DP/50 40.00 80.00
340 Dexter Fowler DP/50 30.00 60.00
347 Matt Tuiasosopo DP/50 30.00 60.00
355 Nick Adenhart DP/50 15.00 40.00

2004 Donruss Elite Extra Edition Signature Status Gold

OVERALL AU-GU ODDS 1:4
PRINT RUNS B/WN 1-10 COPIES PER
NO PRICING DUE TO SCARCITY

2004 Donruss Elite Extra Edition Signature Turn of the Century

*216-355p/r150-250: .6X TO 1.5X p/r803-1617
*216-355p/r150-250: .5X TO 1.2X p/r 522-799
*216-355p/r150-250: .4X TO 1X p/r 350-493
*216-355 p/r 100: .75X TO 2X p/r 803-1617
*216-355 p/r 100: .6X TO 1.5X p/r 522-799
*216-355 p/r 100: .5X TO 1.2X p/r 350-493
*216-355 p/r 50: .75X TO 2X p/r 350-493
OVERALL AU-GU ODDS 1:4
PRINT RUNS B/WN 1-250 COPIES PER
NO PRICING ON QTY OF 25 OR LESS
220 Yovani Gallardo ROO/100 30.00 60.00
252 Ben Zobrist DP/150 15.00 40.00
274 Justin Leone ROO/100 6.00 15.00
281 Matt Bush DP/250 8.00 20.00
285 Mark Rogers DP/100 12.50 30.00
287 Homer Bailey DP/250 5.00 12.00
303 Philip Hughes DP/250 20.00 50.00
308 Blake DeWitt DP/250 10.00 25.00
310 Eric Hurley DP/250 12.50 30.00
334 Hunter Pence DP/200 40.00 80.00
340 Dexter Fowler DP/250 15.00 40.00
347 Matt Tuiasosopo DP/250 15.00 30.00
355 Nick Adenhart DP/100 12.50 30.00

2004 Donruss Elite Extra Edition Back to Back Picks Signature

OVERALL AU-GU ODDS 1:4
1-10 PRINT RUNS B/WN 10-50 COPIES PER
11-20 PRINT RUNS B/WN 100-250 PER
NO PRICING ON QTY OF 10 OR LESS
1 Delmon Young 30.00 60.00
Rickie Weeks/25
2 George Brett
Mike Schmidt/10
3 Adam Dunn 30.00 60.00
Austin Kearns/25
4 Bubba Crosby
Lance Berkman/10
5 Michael Young 30.00 60.00
Vernon Wells/25
6 Brian Roberts 15.00 40.00
Larry Bigbie/50
7 Ron Cey 20.00 50.00
Steve Garvey/50
8 Bill Madlock 40.00 80.00
Dave Parker/50
9 Derrek Lee 30.00 60.00
Torii Hunter
Trot Nixon/50
10 Barry Zito
Ben Sheets
Brett Myers/10
11 Chris Nelson 25.00 60.00
Matt Bush
Reid Brignac/250
12 B.J. Szymanski 15.00 40.00
Greg Golson
Jeff Frazier/250
13 Mark Trumbo 40.00 80.00
Nick Adenhart
Tyler Johnson/100
14 Chris Carter 15.00 40.00
Danny Putnam
Mark Jecmen/100
15 Billy Killian 15.00 40.00
Daryl Jones
Matt Bush/100
16 Blake DeWitt 12.50 30.00
Justin Orenduff
Scott Elbert/250
17 Jay Rainville 20.00 50.00
Kyle Waldrop
Trevor Plouffe/250
18 Jeff Marquez 30.00 60.00
Jon Poterson
Philip Hughes/100
19 Gio Gonzalez 20.00 50.00
Tyler Lumsden
Wes Whisler/100
20 Curtis Thigpen 12.50 30.00
David Purcey
Zach Jackson/100

2004 Donruss Elite Extra Edition Career Best All-Stars

STATED PRINT RUN 500 SERIAL #'d SETS
1 Randy Johnson 1.50 4.00
2 David Ortiz 1.50 4.00
3 Edgar Renteria .60 1.50
4 Victor Martinez 1.00 2.50
5 Albert Pujols 4.00 10.00
6 Hideki Matsui 2.50 6.00
7 Mariano Rivera 1.50 4.00
8 Carlos Zambrano 1.00 2.50
9 Hank Blalock .60 1.50
10 Michael Young .60 1.50
11 Mike Piazza 1.50 4.00
12 Alfonso Soriano .60 1.50
13 Carl Crawford 1.00 2.50
14 Scott Rolen 1.00 2.50
15 Vladimir Guerrero 1.50 4.00
16 Lance Berkman 1.00 2.50
17 Todd Helton 1.00 2.50
18 Curt Schilling 1.00 2.50
19 Francisco Cordero .60 1.50
20 Mark Mulder .60 1.50
21 Sammy Sosa 1.50 4.00
22 Roger Clemens 2.00 5.00
23 Miguel Cabrera 1.50 4.00
24 Manny Ramirez 1.50 4.00
25 Jim Thome 1.00 2.50

2004 Donruss Elite Extra Edition Career Best All-Stars Jersey

STATED PRINT RUN 50 SERIAL #'d SETS
*PRIME p/r 25: .75X TO 2X BASIC
PRIME PRINT RUN B/WN 5-25 COPIES PER
NO PRIME PRICING ON QTY OF 5
OVERALL AU-GU ODDS 1:4
1 Randy Johnson 6.00 15.00
2 David Ortiz 6.00 15.00
3 Edgar Renteria 4.00 10.00
4 Victor Martinez 4.00 10.00
5 Albert Pujols 10.00 25.00
6 Hideki Matsui 12.50 30.00
7 Mariano Rivera 6.00 15.00
8 Carlos Zambrano 4.00 10.00
9 Hank Blalock 4.00 10.00
10 Michael Young 4.00 10.00
11 Mike Piazza 8.00 20.00
12 Alfonso Soriano 4.00 10.00
13 Carl Crawford 4.00 10.00
14 Scott Rolen 6.00 15.00
15 Vladimir Guerrero 6.00 15.00
16 Lance Berkman 4.00 10.00
17 Todd Helton 6.00 15.00
18 Curt Schilling 6.00 15.00
19 Francisco Cordero 4.00 10.00
20 Mark Mulder 4.00 10.00
21 Sammy Sosa 6.00 15.00
22 Roger Clemens 8.00 20.00
23 Miguel Cabrera 6.00 15.00
24 Manny Ramirez 6.00 15.00
25 Jim Thome 6.00 15.00

2004 Donruss Elite Extra Edition Career Best All-Stars Signature Jersey Gold

PRINT RUNS B/WN 1-25 COPIES PER
NO PRICING ON QTY OF 10 OR LESS
SIG BLACK PRINT RUN B/WN 1-5 PER
NO SIG BLACK PRICING DUE TO SCARCITY
SIG GOLD PRINT RUN B/WN 1-10 PER
NO SIG GOLD PRICING DUE TO SCARCITY
SIG JSY PRIME PRINT RUN B/WN 1-10 PER
NO SIG JSY PRIME PRICING AVAILABLE
OVERALL AU-GU ODDS 1:4
1 Randy Johnson/1
2 David Ortiz/25 40.00 80.00
3 Edgar Renteria/25 15.00 40.00
4 Victor Martinez/25 15.00 40.00
5 Albert Pujols/1
8 Carlos Zambrano/25 15.00 40.00
9 Hank Blalock/10
10 Michael Young/25 15.00 40.00
11 Mike Piazza/1
12 Alfonso Soriano/5
13 Carl Crawford/25 15.00 40.00
16 Lance Berkman/5
17 Todd Helton/5
18 Curt Schilling/1
19 Francisco Cordero/25 10.00 25.00
20 Mark Mulder/10
21 Sammy Sosa/1
22 Roger Clemens/1
23 Miguel Cabrera/10
24 Manny Ramirez/1

2004 Donruss Elite Extra Edition Draft Class

RANDOM INSERTS IN PACKS
STATED PRINT RUN 500 SERIAL #'d SETS
1 Johnny Bench 5.00 12.00
Nolan Ryan
2 Bert Blyleven .60 1.50
Dwight Evans
3 Jim Rice 1.00 2.50
Keith Hernandez
4 Dennis Eckersley .60 1.50
Gary Carter
5 Fred Lynn 1.50 4.00
Robin Yount
6 Andre Dawson 1.00 2.50
Lee Smith
7 Alan Trammell .60 1.50
Jack Morris
8 Harold Baines 1.50 4.00
Paul Molitor
9 Cal Ripken 6.00 15.00
Kirk Gibson
10 Don Mattingly 3.00 8.00
Orel Hershiser
11 Darryl Strawberry .60 1.50
Eric Davis
12 Dwight Gooden 1.00 2.50
Jose Canseco
13 Rafael Palmeiro 1.50 4.00
Randy Johnson
14 Curt Schilling 1.00 2.50
Gary Sheffield
15 Mike Piazza 1.50 4.00
Robin Ventura
16 Frank Thomas 1.50 4.00
Jeff Bagwell
17 Chipper Jones 1.50 4.00
Mike Mussina
18 Garret Anderson 1.00 2.50
Jorge Posada
19 Scott Rolen 1.00 2.50
Torii Hunter
20 Kerry Wood 1.00 2.50
Todd Helton
21 Eric Chavez 1.00 2.50
Roy Oswalt
22 Johnny Estrada .60 1.50
Vernon Wells
23 Lance Berkman 1.00 2.50
Tim Hudson
24 Mark Buehrle 1.00 2.50
Mark Mulder
25 C.C. Sabathia 1.00 2.50
Sean Burroughs
26 Albert Pujols 4.00 10.00
Barry Zito
27 Rich Harden .60 1.50
Rocco Baldelli
28 Bobby Crosby 1.50 4.00
Mark Teixeira
29 Casey Kotchman 1.00 2.50
Mark Prior
30 Dewon Brazelton .60 1.50
Jeremy Bonderman
31 J.C. Holt .60 1.50
Jon Zeringue
32 Kyle Bono .60 1.50
Matt Fox
33 Dexter Fowler 3.00 8.00
Mike Rozier
34 Huston Street 1.50 4.00
J.P. Howell
35 Grant Johnson .60 1.50
Matt Macri
36 Eric Beattie .60 1.50
Jeff Frazier
37 Jason Windsor .60 1.50
Kurt Suzuki
38 Josh Fields 1.50 4.00
Matt Tuiasosopo
39 Joe Bauserman .60 1.50
K.C. Herren
40 Chris Lambert .60 1.50
Eric Haberer

2004 Donruss Elite Extra Edition Draft Class Signature

OVERALL AU-GU ODDS 1:4
1-30 PRINT RUNS B/WN 5-50 COPIES PER
31-40 PRINT RUNS B/WN 100-250 PER
NO PRICING ON QTY OF 10 OR LESS
1 Johnny Bench
Nolan Ryan/10
2 Bert Blyleven 20.00 50.00
Dwight Evans/50
3 Jim Rice 15.00 40.00
Keith Hernandez/50
4 Dennis Eckersley 30.00 60.00
Gary Carter/25
5 Fred Lynn
Robin Yount/10
6 Andre Dawson 15.00 40.00
Lee Smith/50
7 Alan Trammell 15.00 40.00
Jack Morris/50
8 Harold Baines 20.00 50.00
Paul Molitor/25
9 Cal Ripken
Kirk Gibson/10
10 Don Mattingly
Orel Hershiser/10
11 Darryl Strawberry 15.00 40.00
Eric Davis/50
12 Dwight Gooden 50.00 100.00
Jose Canseco/25
13 Rafael Palmeiro
Randy Johnson/5
14 Curt Schilling
Gary Sheffield/5
15 Mike Piazza
Robin Ventura/5
16 Frank Thomas
Jeff Bagwell/10
17 Chipper Jones
Mike Mussina/10
18 Garret Anderson
Jorge Posada/10
20 Kerry Wood
Todd Helton/5
21 Eric Chavez 20.00 50.00
Roy Oswalt/25
22 Johnny Estrada 20.00 50.00
Vernon Wells/25
23 Lance Berkman
Tim Hudson/10
24 Mark Buehrle
Mark Mulder/10
25 C.C. Sabathia 10.00 25.00
Sean Burroughs/50
26 Albert Pujols
Barry Zito/5
28 Bobby Crosby 30.00 60.00
Mark Teixeira/25
29 Casey Kotchman 20.00 50.00
Mark Prior/25
30 Dewon Brazelton 15.00 40.00
Jeremy Bonderman/50
31 J.C. Holt 10.00 25.00
Jon Zeringue/100
32 Kyle Bono 8.00 20.00
Matt Fox/100
33 Dexter Fowler 10.00 25.00
Mike Rozier/250
34 Huston Street 10.00 25.00
J.P. Howell/100
35 Grant Johnson 8.00 20.00
Matt Macri/100
36 Eric Beattie 8.00 20.00
Jeff Frazier/100
37 Jason Windsor 10.00 25.00
Kurt Suzuki/100
38 Josh Fields 20.00 50.00
Matt Tuiasosopo/100
39 Joe Bauserman 8.00 20.00
K.C. Herren/100
40 Chris Lambert 8.00 20.00
Eric Haberer/100

2004 Donruss Elite Extra Edition Passing the Torch

STATED PRINT RUN 500 SERIAL #'d SETS
1 Dennis Eckersley 1.50 4.00
Huston Street
2 Matt Bush 1.50 4.00
Tony Gwynn
3 Homer Bailey 1.00 2.50
Tom Seaver
4 Bob Feller .60 1.50
Jeremy Sowers
5 Josh Fields 1.00 2.50
Robin Ventura
6 Nolan Ryan 5.00 12.00
Thomas Diamond
7 Eric Patterson 3.00 8.00
Ryne Sandberg
8 Richie Robnett 1.50 4.00
Rickey Henderson
9 Mike Ferris 2.50 6.00
Stan Musial
10 Bobby Doerr 3.00 8.00
Dustin Pedroia

2004 Donruss Elite Extra Edition Passing the Torch Autograph Gold

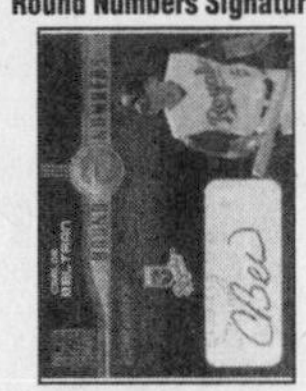

PRINT RUNS B/WN 5-25 COPIES PER
BLACK PRINT RUNS B/WN 5-10 PER
OVERALL AU-GU ODDS 1:4
NO PRICING DUE TO SCARCITY

2004 Donruss Elite Extra Edition Round Numbers

RANDOM INSERTS IN PACKS
STATED PRINT RUN 500 SERIAL #'d SETS
1 Ozzie Smith 2.50 6.00
2 Derek Jeter 4.00 10.00
3 Alex Rodriguez 2.50 6.00
4 Paul Molitor 1.50 4.00
5 George Brett 3.00 8.00
6 Delmon Young 1.00 2.50
7 Dontrelle Willis .60 1.50
8 Gary Carter .60 1.50
9 Reggie Jackson 1.00 2.50
10 Andre Dawson 1.00 2.50
11 Neil Walker 3.00 8.00
12 Laynce Nix .60 1.50
13 Matt Bush 1.00 2.50
14 Lyle Overbay .60 1.50
15 Carlos Beltran .60 1.50
16 Todd Helton 1.00 2.50
17 Mark Grace 1.00 2.50
18 Fred Lynn .60 1.50
19 Robin Yount 1.50 4.00
20 Mike Schmidt 2.50 6.00
21 Roger Clemens 2.00 5.00
22 Will Clark 1.00 2.50
23 Don Mattingly 3.00 8.00
24 Blake DeWitt 2.50 6.00
25 Rafael Palmeiro 1.00 2.50
26 Wade Boggs 1.00 2.50
27 Mark Rogers 1.00 2.50
28 Billy Buckner .60 1.50
29 Jeff Baker .60 1.50
30 Nolan Ryan 5.00 12.00
31 Mike Piazza 1.50 4.00
32 Alexis Rios 1.00 2.50
33 Eddie Murray 1.50 4.00
34 Jose Canseco 1.00 2.50
35 Mike Mussina 1.00 2.50
36 Eric Beattie .60 1.50
37 Keith Hernandez .60 1.50
38 Michael Young .60 1.50
39 Dwight Evans .60 1.50
40 Scott Elbert .60 1.50
41 Adrian Gonzalez 1.00 2.50
42 Johnny Bench 1.50 4.00
43 Dennis Eckersley .60 1.50
44 Dale Murphy 1.00 2.50
45 Ryne Sandberg 3.00 8.00
46 David Wright 2.50 6.00
47 Hank Blalock .60 1.50
48 Orel Hershiser .60 1.50
49 Sean Casey .60 1.50
50 Albert Pujols 4.00 10.00

2004 Donruss Elite Extra Edition Round Numbers Signature

OVERALL AU-GU ODDS 1:4
PRINT RUNS B/WN 5-250 COPIES PER
NO PRICING ON QTY OF 10 OR LESS
1 Ozzie Smith/25 40.00 80.00
4 Paul Molitor/25 10.00 25.00
5 George Brett/5
6 Delmon Young/50 12.50 30.00
7 Dontrelle Willis/25 15.00 40.00
8 Gary Carter/50 8.00 20.00
9 Reggie Jackson/5
10 Andre Dawson/50 8.00 20.00
11 Neil Walker/250 8.00 20.00
12 Laynce Nix/50 5.00 12.00
13 Matt Bush/100 12.50 30.00
14 Lyle Overbay/50 5.00 12.00
15 Carlos Beltran/25 10.00 25.00
16 Todd Helton/5
17 Mark Grace/25 15.00 40.00
18 Fred Lynn/50 5.00 12.00
19 Robin Yount/5
20 Mike Schmidt/25 50.00 100.00
21 Roger Clemens/5
22 Will Clark/20 15.00 40.00
23 Don Mattingly/25 50.00 100.00
24 Blake DeWitt/250 6.00 15.00
25 Rafael Palmeiro/5
26 Wade Boggs/5
27 Mark Rogers/100 12.50 30.00
28 Billy Buckner/100 6.00 15.00
29 Jeff Baker/6
30 Nolan Ryan/10
31 Mike Piazza/5
32 Alexis Rios/50 8.00 20.00
33 Eddie Murray/5
34 Jose Canseco/25 15.00 40.00
35 Mike Mussina/5
36 Eric Beattie/100 6.00 15.00
37 Keith Hernandez/50 8.00 20.00
38 Michael Young/50 8.00 20.00
39 Dwight Evans/50 12.50 30.00
40 Scott Elbert/250 6.00 15.00
41 Adrian Gonzalez/50 10.00 25.00
42 Johnny Bench/5
43 Dennis Eckersley/50 12.50 30.00
44 Dale Murphy/50 12.50 30.00
45 Ryne Sandberg/5
46 David Wright/25 50.00 100.00
47 Hank Blalock/25 8.00 20.00
48 Orel Hershiser/5
49 Sean Casey/25 8.00 20.00
50 Albert Pujols/5

2004 Donruss Elite Extra Edition Throwback Threads

OVERALL AU-GU ODDS 1:4
1 Roger Maris 30.00 60.00
2 Ted Williams 40.00 80.00
3 Cal Ripken 40.00 80.00
4 Duke Snider 10.00 25.00
5 George Brett 15.00 40.00

2004 Donruss Elite Extra Edition Throwback Threads Autograph

OVERALL AU-GU ODDS 1:4
PRINT RUNS B/WN 5-10 COPIES PER
NO PRICING DUE TO SCARCITY
3 Cal Ripken/8
4 Duke Snider/10
5 George Brett/5

2004 Donruss Elite Ripken World Serie

These standard-size cards were issued as part of a special promotion for the 2004 Cal Ripken League World Series. Each of these cards issued have a special 2004 Cal Ripken World Series logo embossed on the card. Although representatives at Donruss had no specific record of which regular Elite cards were stamped for this promotion they did issue a special Passing the Torch set for the project.

COMPLETE SET

2005 Donruss Elite

This 200-card set was released in May, 2005. The set was issued in five-card packs with an $5 SRP which were issued 20 packs to a box and 12 boxes to a case. Cards numbered 1-150 feature active veterans while cards numbered 151 through 170 feature retired greats and cards numbered 171-200 (with the exception of 188 and 189) feature autographed Rookie Cards. Cards numbered 151 through 170 were issued to a stated print run of 1250 serial numbered sets and were randomly inserted into packs. Cards numbered 171 through 200 were issued to varying print runs which have been notated in our checklist.

COMP.SET w/o SP's (150) 10.00 25.00
COMMON CARD (1-150) .10 .30
COMMON CARD (151-170) .40 1.00
151-170 RANDOM INSERTS IN PACKS
151-170 PRINT RUN 1250 SERIAL #'d SETS
COMMON CARD (188-189) .60 1.50
COMMON AUTO p/r 1000+ 3.00 8.00
COMMON AUTO p/r 500-671 3.00 8.00
171-200: OVERALL AU-GU ODDS 3 PER BOX
171-200 PRINT RUNS B/WN 500-1500 PER
CARD 185 DOES NOT EXIST
1 Bartolo Colon .12 .30
2 Casey Kotchman .12 .30
3 Chone Figgins .12 .30
4 Darin Erstad .12 .30
5 Garret Anderson .12 .30
6 Jose Guillen .12 .30
7 Vladimir Guerrero .30 .75
8 Luis Gonzalez .12 .30
9 Randy Johnson .30 .75
10 Troy Glaus .12 .30
11 Andruw Jones .12 .30
12 Chipper Jones .30 .75
13 J.D. Drew .12 .30
14 John Smoltz .30 .75
15 Johnny Estrada .12 .30
16 Marcus Giles .12 .30
17 Rafael Furcal .12 .30
18 Javy Lopez .12 .30
19 Jay Gibbons .12 .30
20 Melvin Mora .12 .30
21 Miguel Tejada .20 .50
22 Rafael Palmeiro .20 .50
23 Sidney Ponson .12 .30
24 Curt Schilling .20 .50
25 David Ortiz .30 .75
26 Derek Lowe .12 .30
27 Jason Varitek .30 .75
28 Johnny Damon .20 .50
29 Manny Ramirez .30 .75
30 Pedro Martinez .20 .50
31 Aramis Ramirez .12 .30
32 Carlos Zambrano .20 .50
33 Corey Patterson .12 .30
34 Derrek Lee .12 .30
35 Greg Maddux .50 1.25
36 Kerry Wood .12 .30
37 Mark Prior .20 .50
38 Moises Alou .12 .30
39 Nomar Garciaparra .30 .75
40 Sammy Sosa .30 .75
41 Carlos Lee .12 .30
42 Frank Thomas .30 .75
43 Jermaine Dye .12 .30
44 Magglio Ordonez .20 .50
45 Mark Buehrle .20 .50
46 Paul Konerko .20 .50
47 Adam Dunn .20 .50
48 Austin Kearns .12 .30
49 Barry Larkin .20 .50
50 Ken Griffey Jr. .50 1.25
51 Sean Casey .12 .30
52 C.C. Sabathia .20 .50
53 Cliff Lee .20 .50
54 Travis Hafner .12 .30
55 Victor Martinez .20 .50
56 Jeromy Burnitz .12 .30
57 Preston Wilson .12 .30
58 Todd Helton .20 .50
59 Brandon Inge .12 .30
60 Ivan Rodriguez .20 .50
61 Jeremy Bonderman .12 .30
62 Troy Percival .12 .30
63 Dontrelle Willis .12 .30
64 Josh Beckett .20 .50
65 Juan Pierre .12 .30
66 Miguel Cabrera .30 .75
67 Mike Lowell .12 .30
68 Paul Lo Duca .12 .30
69 Andy Pettitte .20 .50
70 Brad Ausmus .12 .30
71 Carlos Beltran. .12 .30
72 Craig Biggio .20 .50
73 Jeff Bagwell .20 .50
74 Lance Berkman .20 .50
75 Roger Clemens .40 1.00
76 Roy Oswalt .20 .50
77 Juan Gonzalez .12 .30
78 Mike Sweeney .12 .30
79 Zack Greinke .20 .50
80 Adrian Beltre .12 .30
81 Hideo Nomo .30 .75
82 Jeff Kent .12 .30
83 Milton Bradley .12 .30
84 Shawn Green .12 .30
85 Steve Finley .12 .30
86 Ben Sheets .12 .30

87 Lyle Overbay .12 .30
88 Scott Podsednik .12 .30
89 Lew Ford .12 .30
90 Shannon Stewart .12 .30
91 Torii Hunter .12 .30
92 David Wright .50 1.25
93 Jose Reyes .20 .50
94 Kazuo Matsui .12 .30
95 Mike Piazza .30 .75
96 Tom Glavine .20 .50
97 Alex Rodriguez .50 1.25
98 Bernie Williams .20 .50
99 Derek Jeter .75 2.00
100 Gary Sheffield .12 .30
101 Hideki Matsui .50 1.25
102 Jason Giambi .12 .30
103 Kevin Brown .12 .30
104 Mike Mussina .20 .50
105 Barry Zito .12 .30
106 Bobby Crosby .12 .30
107 Eric Chavez .12 .30
108 Jason Kendall .12 .30
109 Mark Mulder .12 .30
110 Bobby Abreu .12 .30
111 Jim Thome .20 .50
112 Kevin Millwood .12 .30
113 Pat Burrell .12 .30
114 Craig Wilson .12 .30
115 Jack Wilson .12 .30
116 Jason Bay .12 .30
117 Brian Giles .12 .30
118 Khalil Greene .12 .30
119 Mark Loretta .12 .30
120 Ryan Klesko .12 .30
121 Sean Burroughs .12 .30
122 Edgardo Alfonzo .12 .30
123 J.T. Snow .12 .30
124 Jason Schmidt .12 .30
125 Omar Vizquel .20 .50
126 Ichiro Suzuki .50 1.25
127 Jamie Moyer .12 .30
128 Bret Boone .12 .30
129 Richie Sexson .12 .30
130 Albert Pujols .75 2.00
131 Edgar Renteria .12 .30
132 Jeff Suppan .12 .30
133 Jim Edmonds .20 .50
134 Larry Walker .20 .50
135 Scott Rolen .20 .50
136 Aubrey Huff .12 .30
137 B.J. Upton .20 .50
138 Carl Crawford .20 .50
139 Rocco Baldelli .12 .30
140 Alfonso Soriano .20 .50
141 Hank Blalock .12 .30
142 Kenny Rogers .12 .30
143 Laynce Nix .12 .30
144 Mark Teixeira .30 .75
145 Michael Young .20 .50
146 Carlos Delgado .12 .30
147 Eric Hinske .12 .30
148 Roy Halladay .30 .75
149 Vernon Wells .12 .30
150 Jose Vidro .12 .30
151 Bob Gibson RET .60 1.50
152 Brooks Robinson RET .60 1.50
153 Cal Ripken RET 4.00 10.00
154 Carl Yastrzemski RET 1.25 3.00
155 Don Mattingly RET 2.00 5.00
156 Eddie Murray RET 1.00 2.50
157 Ernie Banks RET 1.00 2.50
158 Frank Robinson RET .60 1.50
159 George Brett RET 2.00 5.00
160 Harmon Killebrew RET 1.00 2.50
161 Johnny Bench RET 1.00 2.50
162 Mike Schmidt RET 2.00 5.00
163 Nolan Ryan RET 2.50 6.00
164 Paul Molitor RET 1.00 2.50
165 Stan Musial RET 1.50 4.00
166 Steve Carlton RET .40 1.00
167 Tony Gwynn RET 1.25 3.00
168 Warren Spahn RET .60 1.50
169 Willie Mays RET 2.00 5.00
170 Willie McCovey RET .60 1.50
171 Miguel Negron AU/1500 RC 4.00 10.00
172 Mike Morse AU/1000 RC 4.00 10.00
173 W.Balentien AU/1500 RC 10.00 25.00
174 A.Concepcion AU/651 RC 3.00 8.00
175 Ubaldo Jimenez AU/500 RC 10.00 25.00
176 Justin Verlander AU/500 RC 50.00 100.00
177 Ryan Speier AU/1000 RC 3.00 8.00
178 Geovany Soto AU/500 RC 30.00 60.00
179 M.McLemore AU/1200 RC 3.00 8.00
180 Ambiorix Burgos AU/599 RC 3.00 8.00
181 C.Roberson AU/1000 RC 3.00 8.00
182 Colter Bean AU/625 RC 4.00 10.00
183 Erick Threets AU/500 RC 3.00 8.00
184 Carlos Ruiz AU/1000 RC 8.00 20.00
186 J.Gothreaux AU/1500 RC 3.00 8.00
187 L.Hernandez AU/1000 RC 3.00 8.00
188 Agustin Montero/1000 RC .40 1.00
189 Paulino Reynoso/1000 RC .40 1.00
190 Garrett Jones AU/500 RC 10.00 25.00
191 S.Thompson AU/500 RC 3.00 8.00
192 Matt Lindstrom AU/1500 RC 3.00 8.00
193 Nate McLouth AU/500 RC 8.00 20.00
194 Luke Scott AU/671 RC 10.00 25.00
195 John Hattig AU/1500 RC 3.00 8.00
196 Jason Hammel AU/1500 RC 3.00 8.00
197 Danny Rueckel AU/671 RC 3.00 8.00
198 Justin Wechsler AU/500 RC 3.00 8.00
199 Chris Resop AU/500 RC 4.00 10.00
200 Jeff Miller AU/500 RC 3.00 8.00

2005 Donruss Elite Aspirations

*1-150 p/r 81-99: 5X TO 12X
*1-150 p/r 51-80: 5X TO 12X
*1-150 p/r 36-50: 5X TO 12X
*1-150 p/r 16-25: 10X TO 25X
*151-170 p/r 51-80: 1.25X TO 3X
RANDOM INSERTS IN PACKS
PRINT RUNS B/WN 15-99 COPIES PER
NO PRICING ON QTY OF 15
171 Miguel Negron/81 2.50 6.00
172 Mike Morse/63 4.00 10.00
173 Wladimir Balentien/62 2.50 6.00
174 Ambiorix Concepcion/40 1.50 4.00
175 Ubaldo Jimenez/59 5.00 12.00
176 Justin Verlander/41 30.00 80.00
177 Ryan Speier/77 1.50 4.00
178 Geovany Soto/47 8.00 20.00
179 Mark McLemore/38 1.50 4.00
180 Ambiorix Burgos/50 1.50 4.00
181 Chris Roberson/80 1.50 4.00
182 Colter Bean/29 1.50 4.00
183 Erick Threets/19 1.50 4.00
184 Carlos Ruiz/78 1.50 4.00
186 Jared Gothreaux/40 1.50 4.00
187 Luis Hernandez/25 1.50 4.00
190 Garrett Jones/50 2.50 6.00
191 Sean Thompson/27 1.50 4.00
192 Matt Lindstrom/33 1.50 4.00
193 Nate McLouth/36 2.50 6.00
194 Luke Scott/70 4.00 10.00
195 John Hattig/75 1.50 4.00
196 Jason Hammel/27 1.50 4.00
197 Danny Rueckel/40 1.50 4.00
198 Justin Wechsler/36 1.50 4.00
199 Chris Resop/28 1.50 4.00
200 Jeff Miller/38 1.50 4.00

2005 Donruss Elite Status

*1-150 p/r 51-80: 6X TO 15X
*1-150 p/r 36-50: 6X TO 15X
*1-150 p/r 26-35: 6X TO 15X
*1-150 p/r 16-25: 6X TO 15X
*151-170 p/r 36-50: 2X TO 5X
*151-170 p/r 26-35: 2X TO 5X
*151-170 p/r 16-25: 2X TO 5X
*171-200 p/r 51-80: .3X TO .8X AU 1000+
*171-200 p/r 36-50: .4X TO 1X AU 1000+
COMMON (171-200) 1.50 4.00
SEMISTARS 2.50 6.00
UNLISTED STARS 4.00 10.00
*188-189 p/r 51-80: .75X TO 2X BASIC
*188-189 p/r 36-50: .75X TO 2X BASIC
RANDOM INSERTS IN PACKS
PRINT RUNS B/WN 1-81 COPIES PER
NO PRICING ON QTY OF 15 OR LESS
171 Miguel Negron/19 2.50 6.00
172 Mike Morse/37 4.00 10.00
173 Wladimir Balentien/38 2.50 6.00
174 Ambiorix Concepcion/60 1.50 4.00
175 Ubaldo Jimenez/41 5.00 12.00
176 Justin Verlander/59 30.00 80.00
177 Ryan Speier/23 1.50 4.00
178 Geovany Soto/53 8.00 20.00
179 Mark McLemore/62 1.50 4.00
180 Ambiorix Burgos/50 1.50 4.00
181 Chris Roberson/20 1.50 4.00
182 Colter Bean/71 1.50 4.00
183 Erick Threets/81 1.50 4.00
184 Carlos Ruiz/22 1.50 4.00
186 Jared Gothreaux/60 1.50 4.00
187 Luis Hernandez/75 1.50 4.00
188 Agustin Montero/50 1.25 3.00
189 Paulino Reynoso/61 1.25 3.00
190 Garrett Jones/50 2.50 6.00
191 Sean Thompson/73 1.50 4.00
192 Matt Lindstrom/67 1.50 4.00
193 Nate McLouth/64 2.50 6.00
194 Luke Scott/30 4.00 10.00
195 John Hattig/25 1.50 4.00
196 Jason Hammel/73 1.50 4.00
197 Danny Rueckel/60 1.50 4.00
198 Justin Wechsler/64 1.50 4.00
199 Chris Resop/72 1.50 4.00
200 Jeff Miller/62 1.50 4.00

2005 Donruss Elite Status Gold

*GOLD 1-150: 10X TO 25X BASIC
*GOLD 151-170: 2.5X TO 6X BASIC
STATED PRINT RUN 24 SERIAL #'d SETS
171-200 NO PRICING DUE TO SCARCITY

2005 Donruss Elite Turn of the Century

*TOC 1-150: 1.5X TO 4X BASIC
1-150 PRINT RUN 750 SERIAL #'d SETS
*TOC 151-170: .6X TO 1.5X BASIC
151-170 PRINT RUN 250 SERIAL #'d SETS
COMMON CARD (171-200) .60 1.50
SEMIS 171-200 1.00 2.50
UNLISTED 171-200 1.50 4.00
*TOC 171-200: .15X TO .4X AU 1000+
*TOC 171-200: .15X TO .4X AU 500-671
*TOC 188-189: .4X TO 1X BASIC 1000
171-200 PRINT RUN 500 SERIAL #'d SETS
RANDOM INSERTS IN PACKS
175 Ubaldo Jimenez 6.00 15.00

2005 Donruss Elite Back 2 Back Jacks

1-30 PRINT RUNS B/WN 25-200 COPIES PER
31-36 PRINT RUN 50 SERIAL #'d SETS
OVERALL AU-GU ODDS THREE PER BOX
1 Adam Dunn/200 2.50 6.00
3 Albert Pujols/100 6.00 15.00
4 Babe Ruth/50 100.00 175.00
5 Cal Ripken/100 12.50 30.00
6 David Ortiz/200 3.00 8.00
7 Eddie Murray/150 4.00 10.00
8 Ernie Banks/50 6.00 15.00
9 Frank Robinson/50 4.00 10.00
10 Gary Sheffield/200 2.50 6.00
11 George Foster/125 3.00 8.00
12 Don Mattingly/100 6.00 15.00
13 Hideki Matsui/25 12.50 30.00
14 Jason Giambi/50 4.00 10.00
16 Jim Rice/125 3.00 8.00
17 Jim Thome/200 3.00 8.00
18 Johnny Bench/125 5.00 12.00
19 Lance Berkman/200 2.50 6.00
20 Manny Ramirez/200 3.00 8.00
21 Mike Piazza/200 3.00 8.00
22 Mike Schmidt/125 6.00 15.00
23 Rafael Palmeiro/200 3.00 8.00
24 Reggie Jackson/125 4.00 10.00
25 Sammy Sosa/100 4.00 10.00
26 Scott Rolen/200 3.00 8.00
27 Stan Musial/125 6.00 15.00
28 Willie Mays/50 20.00 50.00
29 Kirk Gibson/125 3.00 8.00
30 Will Clark/125 4.00 10.00
31 Willie Mays 30.00 60.00
Sammy Sosa/50
32 Eddie Murray 6.00 15.00
Mike Piazza/50
33 Mike Schmidt 15.00 40.00
Jim Thome/50
34 Rafael Palmeiro 6.00 15.00
Kirk Gibson/50
35 Jim Rice 6.00 15.00
Manny Ramirez/50
36 Adrian Beltre 6.00 15.00
Will Clark/50
37 Reggie Jackson 6.00 15.00
David Ortiz/50
38 Johnny Bench 8.00 20.00
Adam Dunn/50

2005 Donruss Elite Back 2 Back Jacks Combos

*1-30 p/r 100: .6X TO 1.5X B2B p/r 200
*1-30 p/r 100: .5X TO 1.2X B2B p/r 100
*1-30 p/r 50: .75X TO 2X B2B p/r 150-200
*1-30 p/r 50: .6X TO 1.5X B2B p/r 100-125
*1-30 p/r 50: .5X TO 1.2X B2B p/r 50
*1-30 p/r 25: .5X TO 1.2X B2B p/r 25
1-30 PRINT RUNS B/WN 25-100 COPIES PER
*31-36 p/r 50: .5X TO 1.2X B2B p/r 50
*31-36 p/r 25: .6X TO 1.5X B2B p/r 50
31-36 PRINT RUNS B/WN 10-50 COPIES PER
31-36 ARE ALL DUAL BAT-JSY COMBOS
OVERALL AU-GU ODDS THREE PER BOX
2 Adrian Beltre Bat-Jsy/100 4.00 10.00
4 Babe Ruth Bat-Pants/25 250.00 400.00
15 Jim Edmonds Bat-Jsy/100 4.00 10.00
40 Cal Ripken Bat-Jsy 60.00 120.00
Albert Pujols Bat-Jsy/25

2005 Donruss Elite Career Best

STATED PRINT RUN 1500 SERIAL #'d SETS
*BLACK: 1X TO 2.5X BASIC
BLACK PRINT RUN 150 SERIAL #'d SETS
*BLUE: .75X TO 2X BASIC
BLUE PRINT RUN 250 SERIAL #'d SETS
*GOLD: .6X TO 1.5X BASIC
GOLD PRINT RUN 500 SERIAL #'d SETS
1 Adam Dunn .60 1.50
2 Adrian Beltre .40 1.00
3 Albert Pujols 2.50 6.00
4 Andruw Jones .40 1.00
5 Ben Sheets .40 1.00
6 Bo Jackson 1.00 2.50
7 Brooks Robinson .60 1.50
8 Cal Ripken 4.00 10.00
9 Dale Murphy .40 1.00
10 Don Mattingly 2.00 5.00
11 Eddie Murray 1.00 2.50
12 George Brett 2.00 5.00
13 Hank Blalock .40 1.00
14 Ichiro Suzuki 1.50 4.00
15 Jim Thome .60 1.50
16 Kerry Wood .40 1.00
17 Lance Berkman .60 1.50
18 Mark Prior .60 1.50
19 Mark Teixeira 1.00 2.50
20 Mike Schmidt 2.00 5.00
21 Pedro Martinez .60 1.50
22 Randy Johnson 1.00 2.50
23 Rickey Henderson .60 1.50
24 Sammy Sosa 1.00 2.50
25 Tony Gwynn 1.25 3.00

2005 Donruss Elite Career Best Bats

*BAT p/r 150-250: .4X TO 1X JSY p/r 150-250
*BAT p/r 150-250: .3X TO .8X JSY p/r 100
*BAT p/r 150-250: .25X TO .6X JSY p/r 50
*BAT p/r 100: .5X TO 1.2X JSY p/r 150-250
*BAT p/r 100: .4X TO 1X JSY p/r 100
OVERALL AU-GU ODDS THREE PER BOX
PRINT RUNS B/WN 50-250 COPIES PER

2005 Donruss Elite Career Best Jerseys

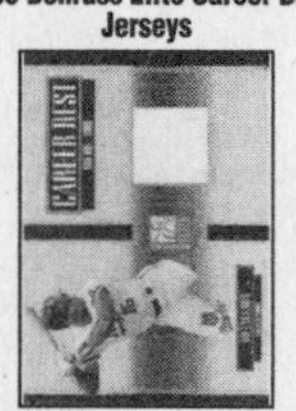

OVERALL AU-GU ODDS THREE PER BOX
PRINT RUNS B/WN 50-250 COPIES PER
1 Adam Dunn/250 2.50 6.00
2 Adrian Beltre/250 2.50 6.00
3 Albert Pujols/250 6.00 15.00
4 Andruw Jones/250 3.00 8.00
5 Ben Sheets/250 2.50 6.00
6 Bo Jackson/250 4.00 10.00
7 Brooks Robinson/50 5.00 12.00
8 Cal Ripken/150 10.00 25.00
9 Dale Murphy/100 4.00 10.00
10 Don Mattingly/150 5.00 12.00
11 Eddie Murray/150 5.00 12.00
12 George Brett/100 6.00 15.00
13 Hank Blalock/250 2.50 6.00
15 Jim Thome/250 3.00 8.00
16 Kerry Wood/250 2.50 6.00
17 Lance Berkman/250 2.50 6.00
18 Mark Prior/250 3.00 8.00
19 Mark Teixeira/250 3.00 8.00
20 Mike Schmidt/100 6.00 15.00
21 Pedro Martinez/250 3.00 8.00
22 Randy Johnson/100 4.00 10.00
23 Rickey Henderson/50 6.00 15.00
24 Sammy Sosa/250 3.00 8.00
25 Tony Gwynn/250 4.00 10.00

2005 Donruss Elite Career Best Combos

*COMBO p/r 150: .5X TO 1.2X JSY p/r 150-250
*COMBO p/r 125: .6X TO 1.5X JSY p/r 150-250
*COMBO p/r 25: 1X TO 2.5X JSY p/r 150-250
*COMBO p/r 25: .75X TO 2X JSY p/r 100
*COMBO p/r 25: .6X TO 1.5X JSY p/r 50
OVERALL AU-GU ODDS THREE PER BOX
PRINT RUNS B/WN 25-150 COPIES PER

2005 Donruss Elite Face 2 Face

STATED PRINT RUN 1500 SERIAL #'d SETS
*BLACK: .6X TO 1.5X BASIC
BLACK PRINT RUN 500 SERIAL #'d SETS
*GOLD: 1X TO 2.5X BASIC
GOLD PRINT RUN 250 SERIAL #'d SETS
*RED: .5X TO 1.2X BASIC
RED PRINT RUN 750 SERIAL #'d SETS
RANDOM INSERTS IN PACKS
1 Roger Clemens 1.25 3.00
Scott Rolen
2 Greg Maddux 1.50 4.00
Jeff Bagwell
3 Mark Prior 1.00 2.50
Mike Piazza
4 Mike Mussina .60 1.50
Ivan Rodriguez
5 Josh Beckett .60 1.50
Sammy Sosa
6 Roy Oswalt 1.00 2.50
Miguel Cabrera
7 Roger Clemens 2.50 6.00
Albert Pujols
8 Pedro Martinez 1.00 2.50
Vladimir Guerrero
9 Randy Johnson 1.00 2.50
Jim Edmonds
10 Curt Schilling 2.50 6.00
Derek Jeter
11 Kerry Wood .60 1.50
Lance Berkman
12 Tim Hudson .60 1.50
Garret Anderson
13 Pedro Martinez .60 1.50
Gary Sheffield
14 Barry Zito .60 1.50
Magglio Ordonez
15 Kerry Wood .40 1.00
Shawn Green
16 Mike Mussina .60 1.50
Miguel Tejada
17 Randy Johnson 2.50 6.00
Albert Pujols
18 Nolan Ryan 2.50 6.00
George Brett
19 Tom Seaver 2.00 5.00
Mike Schmidt
20 Jim Palmer 1.00 2.50
Harmon Killebrew

2005 Donruss Elite Face 2 Face Bats

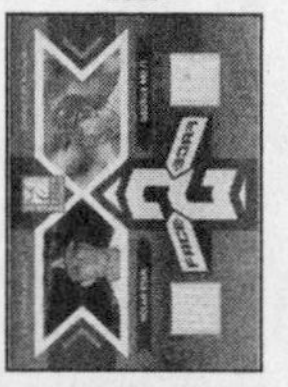

*BAT p/r 150: .4X TO 1X JSY p/r 200
*BAT p/r 150: .3X TO .8X JSY p/r 75
*BAT p/r 150: .25X TO .6X JSY p/r 50
*BAT p/r 100: .5X TO 1.2X JSY p/r 200
*BAT p/r 100: .25X TO .6X JSY p/r 25
*BAT p/r 50: .6X TO 1.5X JSY p/r 200
*BAT p/r 50: .5X TO 1.2X JSY p/r 75
*BAT p/r 25: .75X TO 2X JSY p/r 200
OVERALL AU-GU ODDS THREE PER BOX
PRINT RUNS B/WN 25-150 COPIES PER
9 Randy Johnson 6.00 15.00
Jim Edmonds/50

2005 Donruss Elite Face 2 Face Jerseys

OVERALL AU-GU ODDS THREE PER BOX
PRINT RUNS B/WN 25-200 COPIES PER
1 Roger Clemens 4.00 10.00
Scott Rolen/200
2 Greg Maddux 5.00 12.00
Jeff Bagwell/75
3 Mark Prior 4.00 10.00
Mike Piazza/200
4 Mike Mussina 4.00 10.00
Ivan Rodriguez/200
5 Josh Beckett 4.00 10.00
Sammy Sosa/200
6 Roy Oswalt 4.00 10.00
Miguel Cabrera/200
7 Roger Clemens 10.00 25.00
Albert Pujols/200
8 Pedro Martinez 5.00 12.00
Vladimir Guerrero/75
11 Kerry Wood 3.00 8.00
Lance Berkman/200
12 Tim Hudson 4.00 10.00
Garret Anderson/75
13 Pedro Martinez 5.00 12.00
Gary Sheffield/75
14 Barry Zito 3.00 8.00
Magglio Ordonez/200
15 Kerry Wood 3.00 8.00
Shawn Green/200
16 Mike Mussina 4.00 10.00
Miguel Tejada/200
17 Randy Johnson 10.00 25.00
Albert Pujols/75
18 Nolan Ryan 30.00 60.00
George Brett/25
19 Tom Seaver 10.00 25.00
Mike Schmidt/50
20 Jim Palmer 10.00 25.00
Harmon Killebrew/25

2005 Donruss Elite Face 2 Face Combos

*COMBO p/r 250: .4X TO 1X JSY p/r 200
*COMBO p/r 75-100: .5X TO 1.2X JSY p/r 200
*COMBO p/r 75-100: .4X TO 1X JSY p/r 75
*COMBO p/r 50: .4X TO 1X JSY p/r 50
*COMBO p/r 25: .4X TO 1X JSY p/r 25
OVERALL AU-GU ODDS THREE PER BOX
PRINT RUNS B/WN 25-250 COPIES PER

2005 Donruss Elite Passing the Torch

1-30 PRINT RUN 1000 SERIAL #'d SETS
31-45 PRINT RUN 500 SERIAL #'d SETS
*BLACK 1-30: 1.25X TO 3X BASIC
*BLACK 31-45: 1.5X TO 4X BASIC
BLACK 1-30 PRINT RUN 50 #'d SETS
BLACK 31-45 PRINT RUN 25 #'d SETS
*GOLD 1-30: .75X TO 2X BASIC
*GOLD 31-45: 1X TO 2.5X BASIC
GOLD 1-30 PRINT RUN 100 #'d SETS
GOLD 31-45 PRINT RUN 50 #'d SETS
*GREEN 1-30: .6X TO 1.5X BASIC
*GREEN 31-45: .6X TO 1.5X BASIC
GREEN 1-30 PRINT RUN 250 #'d SETS
GREEN 31-45 PRINT RUN 125 #'d SETS
*RED 1-30: .5X TO 1.2X BASIC
*RED 31-45: .5X TO 1.2X BASIC
RED 1-30 PRINT RUN 500 #'d SETS
RED 31-45 PRINT RUN 250 #'d SETS
1 Adrian Beltre .40 1.00
2 Albert Pujols 2.50 6.00
3 Alex Rodriguez 1.50 4.00
4 Andruw Jones .40 1.00
5 Babe Ruth 2.50 6.00
6 Ben Sheets .40 1.00
7 Brooks Robinson .60 1.50
8 Cal Ripken 4.00 10.00
9 Carl Yastrzemski 1.25 3.00
10 Dale Murphy .40 1.00
11 David Ortiz 1.00 2.50
12 Derek Jeter 2.50 6.00
13 Don Mattingly 2.00 5.00
14 George Brett 2.00 5.00
15 Greg Maddux 1.50 4.00
16 Hank Blalock .40 1.00
17 Jeff Bagwell .60 1.50
18 Johnny Bench 1.00 2.50
19 Magglio Ordonez .60 1.50
20 Mark Prior .60 1.50
21 Mark Teixeira 1.00 2.50
22 Miguel Cabrera 1.00 2.50
23 Mike Schmidt 2.00 5.00
24 Nolan Ryan 2.50 6.00
25 Pedro Martinez .60 1.50
26 Sammy Sosa 1.00 2.50
27 Scott Rolen .60 1.50
28 Tom Seaver .60 1.50
29 Vladimir Guerrero 1.00 2.50
30 Willie Mays 2.00 5.00
31 Carlton Fisk 1.25 3.00
Magglio Ordonez
32 Nolan Ryan 5.00 12.00
Ben Sheets
33 Babe Ruth 5.00 12.00
Alex Rodriguez
34 Cal Ripken 8.00 20.00
B.J. Upton
35 Willie Mays .75 2.00
Andruw Jones
36 George Brett 4.00 10.00
Hank Blalock
37 Greg Maddux 3.00 8.00
Whitey Ford
38 Harmon Killebrew 2.00 5.00
Adrian Beltre
39 Tom Seaver 1.25 3.00
Mark Prior
40 Don Mattingly 4.00 10.00
Mark Teixeira
41 Stan Musial 3.00 8.00
Carlos Beltran
42 Dale Murphy 1.25 3.00
Lance Berkman
43 Willie McCovey 1.25 3.00
Jeff Bagwell
44 Andre Dawson 2.00 5.00
Miguel Cabrera
45 Brooks Robinson 1.25 3.00
Scott Rolen

2005 Donruss Elite Passing the Torch Autographs

1-30 SINGLE PRINT RUNS B/WN 5-100 PER
31-45 DUAL PRINT RUNS B/WN 5-25 PER
NO PRICING ON QTY OF 10 OR LESS
1 Adrian Beltre/75 6.00 15.00
2 Albert Pujols/5
6 Ben Sheets/75 6.00 15.00
7 Brooks Robinson/100 15.00 40.00
8 Cal Ripken/10
9 Carl Yastrzemski/5
10 Dale Murphy/100 10.00 25.00
13 Don Mattingly/50 20.00 50.00
14 George Brett/5
16 Hank Blalock/50 10.00 25.00
17 Jeff Bagwell/5
18 Johnny Bench/25 20.00 50.00
19 Magglio Ordonez/75 6.00 15.00
20 Mark Prior/25 12.50 30.00
21 Mark Teixeira/75 10.00 25.00
22 Miguel Cabrera/75 10.00 25.00
23 Mike Schmidt/25 30.00 60.00
24 Nolan Ryan/10
25 Pedro Martinez/5
26 Sammy Sosa/5
27 Scott Rolen/25 15.00 40.00
28 Tom Seaver/25 20.00 50.00
30 Willie Mays/10
31 Carlton Fisk 30.00 60.00
Magglio Ordonez/25
32 Nolan Ryan 125.00 200.00
Ben Sheets/25
34 Cal Ripken
B.J. Upton/5
36 George Brett
Hank Blalock/5
38 Harmon Killebrew
Adrian Beltre/10
39 Tom Seaver
Mark Prior/10
40 Don Mattingly
Mark Teixeira/10
43 Willie McCovey
Jeff Bagwell/5
44 Andre Dawson 30.00 60.00
Miguel Cabrera/25
45 Brooks Robinson 40.00 80.00
Scott Rolen/25

2005 Donruss Elite Passing the Torch Bats

*1-30 p/r 150-250: .4X TO 1X JSY p/r 150-250
*1-30 p/r 150-250: .25X TO .6X JSY p/r 50
*1-30 p/r 150-250: .2X TO .5X JSY p/r 25
*1-30 p/r 50: .6X TO 1.5X JSY p/r 150-250
*1-30 p/r 50: .4X TO 1X JSY p/r 50
*1-30 p/r 50: .3X TO .8X JSY p/r 25
1-30 PRINT RUNS B/WN 25-250 PER
*31-45 p/r 150-250: .4X TO 1X JSY p/r 150
*31-45 p/r 150-250: .3X TO .8X JSY p/r 100
*31-45 p/r 150-250: .25X TO .6X JSY p/r 50
*31-45 p/r 150-250: .2X TO .5X JSY p/r 25
*31-45 p/r 50: .6X TO 1.5X JSY p/r 150
*31-45 p/r 50: .4X TO 1X JSY p/r 50
*31-45 p/r 25: .5X TO 1.2X JSY p/r 50
*31-45 p/r 25: .4X TO 1X JSY p/r 25
31-45 PRINT RUNS B/WN 25-250 PER
OVERALL AU-GU ODDS THREE PER BOX
5 Babe Ruth/25 125.00 200.00

2005 Donruss Elite Passing the Torch Jerseys

31-45 PRINT RUNS B/WN 25-150 PER
OVERALL AU-GU ODDS THREE PER BOX
1 Adrian Beltre/250 2.50 6.00
2 Albert Pujols/250 6.00 15.00
4 Andruw Jones/250 3.00 8.00
5 Babe Ruth Pants/25 150.00 250.00
6 Ben Sheets/250 2.50 6.00
7 Brooks Robinson/25 6.00 15.00
8 Cal Ripken/250 10.00 25.00
9 Carl Yastrzemski Pants/50 6.00 15.00
10 Dale Murphy/250 3.00 8.00
11 David Ortiz/250 3.00 8.00
13 Don Mattingly/150 5.00 12.00
14 George Brett/50 8.00 20.00
15 Greg Maddux/250 4.00 10.00
16 Hank Blalock/250 2.50 6.00
17 Jeff Bagwell/250 3.00 8.00
18 Johnny Bench Pants/150 4.00 10.00
19 Magglio Ordonez/250 2.50 6.00
20 Mark Prior/250 3.00 8.00
21 Mark Teixeira/250 3.00 8.00
22 Miguel Cabrera/250 3.00 8.00
23 Mike Schmidt/150 5.00 12.00
24 Nolan Ryan/50 10.00 25.00
25 Pedro Martinez/250 3.00 8.00
26 Sammy Sosa/250 3.00 8.00
27 Scott Rolen/250 3.00 8.00
28 Tom Seaver/50 5.00 12.00
29 Vladimir Guerrero/250 3.00 8.00
30 Willie Mays/25 30.00 60.00
31 Carlton Fisk 5.00 12.00
Magglio Ordonez/250
32 Nolan Ryan 15.00 40.00
Ben Sheets/50
34 Cal Ripken 30.00 60.00
B.J. Upton/50
35 Willie Mays 30.00 60.00
Andruw Jones/50
36 George Brett 10.00 25.00
Hank Blalock/50
37 Greg Maddux 15.00 40.00
Whitey Ford/25
38 Harmon Killebrew 8.00 20.00
Adrian Beltre/50
39 Tom Seaver 8.00 20.00
Mark Prior/25
40 Don Mattingly 8.00 20.00
Mark Teixeira/100
41 Stan Musial Pants 12.50 30.00
Carlos Beltran/25
42 Dale Murphy 4.00 10.00
Lance Berkman/150
43 Willie McCovey 6.00 15.00
Jeff Bagwell/250
44 Andre Dawson 4.00 10.00
Miguel Cabrera/150
45 Brooks Robinson 8.00 20.00
Scott Rolen/25

2005 Donruss Elite Teams

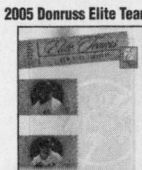

STATED PRINT RUN 1500 SERIAL #'d SETS
*BLACK: .75X TO 2X BASIC
BLACK PRINT RUN 250 SERIAL #'d SETS
*BLUE: .4X TO 1X BASIC
BLUE PRINT RUN 1000 SERIAL #'d SETS
*GOLD: 1.25X TO 3X BASIC
GOLD PRINT RUN 100 SERIAL #'d SETS
*GREEN: .5X TO 1.2X BASIC
GREEN PRINT RUN 750 SERIAL #'d SETS
*RED: .6X TO 1.5X BASIC
RED PRINT RUN 500 SERIAL #'d SETS
1 Manny Ramirez 1.25 3.00
Pedro Martinez
David Ortiz
2 Albert Pujols 3.00 8.00
Scott Rolen
Jim Edmonds
3 Roger Clemens 1.50 4.00
Jeff Bagwell
Lance Berkman
Craig Biggio
4 Miguel Cabrera 1.25 3.00
Josh Beckett
Mike Lowell
5 Kerry Wood 2.00 5.00
Mark Prior
Sammy Sosa
Greg Maddux
6 Adrian Beltre 1.25 3.00
Shawn Green
Hideo Nomo
Kazuhisa Ishii
7 Cal Ripken 5.00 12.00
Eddie Murray
Jim Palmer
8 George Brett 2.50 6.00
Bo Jackson
Frank White
9 Roger Clemens .75 2.00
Mike Mussina
Alfonso Soriano
Bernie Williams
10 Tom Glavine 2.00 5.00
Greg Maddux
Ryan Klesko
David Justice

2005 Donruss Elite Teams Bats

*BAT p/r 100: .5X TO 1.2X JSY p/r 150
*BAT p/r 100: .3X TO .8X JSY p/r 50
*BAT p/r 50: .6X TO 1.5X JSY p/r 150
*BAT p/r 50: .4X TO 1X JSY p/r 50
OVERALL AU-GU ODDS THREE PER BOX
PRINT RUNS B/WN 50-100 COPIES PER
8 George Brett 12.50 30.00
Bo Jackson
Frank White/100

2005 Donruss Elite Teams Jerseys

OVERALL AU-GU ODDS THREE PER BOX
PRINT RUNS B/WN 50-150 COPIES PER
1 Manny Ramirez 6.00 15.00
Pedro Martinez
David Ortiz/150
2 Albert Pujols 12.50 30.00
Scott Rolen
Jim Edmonds/150
3 Roger Clemens 10.00 25.00
Jeff Bagwell
Lance Berkman
Craig Biggio/150
4 Miguel Cabrera 6.00 15.00
Josh Beckett
Mike Lowell/50
5 Kerry Wood 12.50 30.00
Mark Prior
Sammy Sosa
Greg Maddux/150
6 Adrian Beltre 10.00 25.00
Shawn Green
Hideo Nomo
Kazuhisa Ishii/50
7 Cal Ripken 20.00 50.00
Eddie Murray
Jim Palmer/100
9 Roger Clemens 10.00 25.00
Mike Mussina
Alfonso Soriano
Bernie Williams/100
10 Tom Glavine 15.00 40.00
Greg Maddux
Ryan Klesko
David Justice/100

2005 Donruss Elite Throwback Threads

1-40 PRINT RUNS B/WN 10-200 PER
1-40 NO PRICING ON QTY OF 10
41-60 PRINT RUNS B/WN 5-150 PER
41-60 NO PRICING ON QTY OF 5
OVERALL AU-GU ODDS THREE PER BOX
1 Albert Pujols/200 6.00 15.00
2 Babe Ruth Pants/25 150.00 250.00
3 Bert Blyleven/200 2.50 6.00
4 Bobby Doerr Pants/200 2.50 6.00
5 Brooks Robinson/25 6.00 15.00
6 Cal Ripken/150 10.00 25.00
7 Carl Yastrzemski Pants/150 5.00 12.00
8 Dale Murphy/150 3.00 8.00
9 Dennis Eckersley/50 4.00 10.00
10 Don Mattingly/200 5.00 12.00
11 Don Sutton/100 3.00 8.00
12 Duke Snider Pants/25 6.00 15.00
13 Early Wynn/50 4.00 10.00
14 Eddie Murray/100 5.00 12.00
15 George Brett/25 10.00 25.00
16 Greg Maddux/150 4.00 10.00
17 Harmon Killebrew/100 5.00 12.00
18 Hoyt Wilhelm/150 2.50 6.00
19 Jim Edmonds/200 2.50 6.00
20 Jim Palmer/25 5.00 12.00
21 Lou Boudreau/50 4.00 10.00
22 Lou Brock/100 4.00 10.00
23 Miguel Cabrera/200 3.00 8.00
24 Mike Mussina/150 3.00 8.00
25 Mike Piazza/150 3.00 8.00
26 Mike Schmidt/150 5.00 12.00
27 Nolan Ryan/50 10.00 25.00
28 Phil Niekro/100 3.00 8.00
29 Randy Johnson/150 3.00 8.00
30 Rickey Henderson/150 4.00 10.00
31 Sammy Sosa/150 3.00 8.00
32 Scott Rolen/200 3.00 8.00
33 Stan Musial/10
34 Steve Carlton/100 3.00 8.00
35 Ted Williams/25 50.00 100.00
36 Tommy John/150 2.50 6.00
37 Vladimir Guerrero/200 3.00 8.00
38 Whitey Ford/25 6.00 15.00
39 Willie Mays/50 20.00 50.00
40 Willie McCovey/150 3.00 8.00
41 Babe Ruth Pants
Don Mattingly/25
42 Whitey Ford 15.00 40.00
Roger Clemens/25
43 Stan Musial
Jim Edmonds/5
44 Ted Williams 60.00 120.00
Tony Gwynn/25
45 Willie Mays Pants 30.00 60.00
Miguel Cabrera/25
46 Lou Brock 5.00 12.00
Rickey Henderson/100
47 Brooks Robinson 30.00 60.00
George Brett/25
48 Willie McCovey 8.00 20.00
David Ortiz/25
49 Bo Jackson 4.00 10.00
Deion Sanders/150
50 Nolan Ryan 12.50 30.00
Curt Schilling/100
51 Don Sutton 6.00 15.00
Greg Maddux/100
52 Harmon Killebrew 5.00 12.00
Rafael Palmeiro/100
53 Dale Murphy 4.00 10.00
Dwight Evans/150
54 Steve Carlton 8.00 20.00
Randy Johnson/25
55 Carl Yastrzemski 8.00 20.00
Vladimir Guerrero/50
56 Eddie Murray 5.00 12.00
Mike Piazza/100
57 Johnny Bench 6.00 15.00
Ivan Rodriguez/50
58 Jim Palmer 5.00 12.00
Tim Hudson/50
59 Cal Ripken 20.00 50.00
Hank Blalock/50
60 Jim Rice 5.00 12.00
Manny Ramirez/100

2005 Donruss Elite Throwback Threads Prime

*1-40 p/r 25: 1.5X TO 4X TT p/r 150-200
*1-40 p/r 25: 1.25X TO 3X TT p/r 100
*1-40 p/r 25: 1X TO 2.5X TT p/r 50
*1-40 p/r 25: .75X TO 2X TT p/r 25
1-40 PRINT RUNS B/WN 5-25 COPIES PER
*41-60 p/r 25: 2X TO 5X TT p/r 150-200
*41-60 p/r 25: 1.5X TO 4X TT p/r 100
*41-60 p/r 25: 1.25X TO 3X TT p/r 50
*41-60 p/r 25: 1X TO 2.5X TT p/r 25
41-60 PRINT RUNS B/WN 1-25 COPIES PER
OVERALL AU-GU ODDS THREE PER BOX
NO PRICDING ON QTY OF 10 OR LESS
59 Cal Ripken 60.00 120.00
Hank Blalock/25

2005 Donruss Elite Throwback Threads Autographs

PRINT RUNS B/WN 5-100 COPIES PER
NO PRICING ON QTY OF 10 OR LESS
PRIME PRINT RUNS B/WN 1-10 PER
NO PRIME PRICING DUE TO SCARCITY
OVERALL AU-GU ODDS THREE PER BOX
3 Bert Blyleven/100 8.00 20.00
4 Bobby Doerr Pants/100 8.00 20.00
5 Brooks Robinson/50 15.00 40.00
6 Cal Ripken/5
8 Dale Murphy/100 12.50 30.00
9 Dennis Eckersley/75 10.00 25.00
10 Don Mattingly/25 40.00 80.00
11 Don Sutton/50 10.00 25.00
12 Duke Snider/10
15 George Brett/5
17 Harmon Killebrew/75 20.00 50.00
19 Jim Edmonds/5
20 Jim Palmer/75 8.00 20.00
22 Lou Brock Jkt/75 12.50 30.00
23 Miguel Cabrera/75 12.50 30.00
24 Mike Mussina/5
26 Mike Schmidt/5
27 Nolan Ryan/5
32 Scott Rolen/5
33 Stan Musial/5
38 Whitey Ford/5
39 Willie Mays/5
40 Willie McCovey/25 20.00 50.00

2010 Donruss Elite National Convention

ANNOUNCED PRINT RUN 499 SETS
49 Cito Culver 4.00 10.00
50 Bryan Holaday 3.00 8.00
51 Cole Leonida 3.00 8.00
52 Chris Sale 6.00 15.00

2010 Donruss Elite National Convention Aspirations

*ASPIRATIONS: .8X TO 2X BASIC CARDS
ANNOUNCED PRINT RUN 50

2010 Donruss Elite National Convention Green

STATED PRINT RUN 10 SER. #'d SETS
UNPRICED DUE TO SCARCITY

2010 Donruss Elite National Convention Status

*STATUS: .8X TO 2X BASIC CARDS
ANNOUNCED PRINT RUN 25

2007 Donruss Elite Extra Edition

COMPLETE SET (142)
COMP.SET w/o AU's (92) 8.00 20.00
COMMON CARD (1-92) .20 .50
COMMON AU (92-142) 4.00 10.00
OVERALL AUTO/MEM ODDS 1:5
AU PRINT RUNS B/WN 374-999 COPIES PER
EXCHANGE DEADLINE 07/01/2009
1 Andrew Brackman .60 1.50
2 Austin Gallagher .20 .50
3 Brett Cecil .20 .50
4 Darwin Barney .50 1.25
5 David Price 2.00 5.00
6 J. P. Arencibia .40 1.00
7 Josh Donaldson .20 .50
8 Brandon Hicks .20 .50
9 Brian Rike .20 .50
10 Bryan Morris .20 .50
11 Cale Iorg .20 .50
12 Casey Weathers .20 .50
13 Corey Kluber .20 .50
14 Daniel Moskos .20 .50
15 Danny Payne .20 .50
16 David Kopp .20 .50
17 Dellin Betances .60 1.50
18 Derrick Robinson .20 .50
19 Drew Stubbs .20 .50
20 Eric Eiland .20 .50
21 Francisco Pena .20 .50
22 Greg Reynolds .20 .50
23 Jeff Samardzija 1.25 3.00
24 Jess Todd .20 .50
25 John Tolisano .20 .50
26 Jordan Zimmerman UER .50 1.25
Last name misspelled
27 Julian Sampson .20 .50
28 Luke Hochevar .50 1.25
29 Mat Latos .75 2.00
30 Matt Mangini .20 .50
31 Matt Spencer .30 .75
32 Matthew Sweeney .50 1.25
33 Max Scherzer .75 2.00
34 Mitch Canham .20 .50
35 Nick Schmidt .20 .50
36 Paul Kelly .20 .50
37 Ryan Pope .30 .75
38 Sam Runion .20 .50
39 Steven Souza .20 .50
40 Travis Mattair .20 .50
41 Trystan Magnuson .20 .50
42 Will Middlebrooks .30 .75
43 Zack Cozart .20 .50
44 James Adkins .20 .50
45 Cory Luebke .20 .50
46 Aaron Poreda .20 .50
47 Clayton Mortensen .20 .50
48 Bradley Suttle .30 .75
49 Tony Butler .30 .75
50 Zach Britton 1.25 3.00
51 Scott Cousins .20 .50
52 Wendell Fairley .50 1.25
53 Eric Sogard .20 .50
54 Jonathan Lucroy .30 .75
55 Lars Davis .20 .50
77 Jennie Finch .50 1.25
91 Charlie Culberson .60 1.50
92 Jacob Smolinski .20 .50
93 Blake Beaven AU/719 5.00 12.00
94 Brad Chalk AU/613 4.00 10.00
95 Brett Anderson AU/549 20.00 50.00
96 Chris Withrow AU/700 4.00 10.00
97 Clay Fuller AU/674 4.00 10.00
98 Damon Sublett AU/674 8.00 20.00
99 Devin Mesoraco AU/674 10.00 25.00
100 Drew Cumberland AU/744 4.00 10.00
101 Jack McGeary AU/674 6.00 15.00
102 Jake Arrieta AU/949 10.00 25.00
103 James Simmons AU/624 EXCH 4.00 10.00
104 Jarrod Parker AU/499 10.00 25.00
105 Jason Dominguez AU/744 4.00 10.00
106 Jason Heyward AU/750 30.00 60.00
107 Joe Savery AU/750 5.00 12.00
108 Jon Gilmore AU/819 3.00 8.00
109 Jordan Walden AU/794 4.00 10.00
110 Josh Smoker AU/719 10.00 25.00
111 Josh Vitters AU/769 10.00 25.00
112 Julio Borbon AU/594 8.00 20.00
113 Justin Jackson AU/850 4.00 10.00
114 Kellen Kulbacki AU/549 5.00 12.00
115 Kevin Ahrens AU/794 8.00 20.00
116 Kyle Lotzkar AU/611 4.00 10.00
117 Madison Bumgarner AU/794 15.00 40.00
118 Matt Dominguez AU/769 10.00 25.00
119 Matt LaPorta AU/594 30.00 60.00
120 Matt Wieters AU/799 20.00 50.00
121 Michael Burgess AU/672 4.00 10.00
122 Michael Main AU/794 5.00 12.00
123 Mike Moustakas AU/999 30.00 60.00
124 Nathan Vineyard AU/700 5.00 12.00
125 Neil Ramirez AU/774 6.00 15.00
126 Nick Hagadone AU/544 4.00 10.00
127 Pete Kozma AU/719 4.00 10.00
128 Phillippe Aumont AU/674 15.00 40.00
129 Preston Mattingly AU/519 10.00 25.00
130 Mystery EXCH 40.00 80.00
131 Ross Detwiler AU/650 5.00 12.00
132 Tim Alderson AU/719 8.00 20.00
133 Todd Frazier AU/774 8.00 20.00
134 Wes Roemer AU/694 5.00 12.00
135 Ben Revere AU/700 6.00 15.00
136 Chris Davis AU/374 EXCH 60.00 120.00
138 Bryan Anderson AU/474 EXCH 4.00 10.00
141 Austin Jackson AU/794 12.50 30.00
142 Beau Mills AU/624 EXCH 8.00 20.00
149 Tommy Hunter AU/474 15.00 40.00

2007 Donruss Elite Extra Edition Aspirations

*ASP 1-92: 3X TO 8X BASIC
OVERALL INSERT ODDS 1:4
STATED PRINT RUN 100 SER.#'d SETS
5 David Price 30.00 60.00
23 Jeff Samardzija 8.00 20.00
33 Max Scherzer 30.00 60.00
92 Jacob Smolinski 1.50 4.00
93 Blake Beaven 1.50 4.00
94 Brad Chalk 1.50 4.00
95 Brett Anderson 2.50 6.00
96 Chris Withrow 1.50 4.00
97 Clay Fuller 1.50 4.00
98 Damon Sublett 2.50 6.00
99 Devin Mesoraco 2.00 5.00
100 Drew Cumberland 1.50 4.00
101 Jack McGeary 2.00 5.00
102 Jake Arrieta 1.50 4.00
103 James Simmons 1.50 4.00
104 Jarrod Parker 8.00 20.00
105 Jason Dominguez 1.50 4.00
106 Jason Heyward 50.00 100.00
107 Joe Savery 2.00 5.00
108 Jon Gilmore 2.00 5.00
109 Jordan Walden 2.50 6.00
110 Josh Smoker 2.50 6.00
111 Josh Vitters 5.00 12.00
112 Julio Borbon 2.00 5.00
113 Justin Jackson 1.50 4.00
114 Kellen Kulbacki 2.00 5.00
115 Kevin Ahrens 2.00 5.00
116 Kyle Lotzkar 1.50 4.00
117 Madison Bumgarner 6.00 15.00
118 Matt Dominguez 6.00 15.00
119 Matt LaPorta 8.00 20.00
120 Matt Wieters 6.00 15.00
121 Michael Burgess 6.00 15.00
122 Michael Main 2.00 5.00
123 Mike Moustakas 6.00 15.00
124 Nathan Vineyard 2.00 5.00
125 Neil Ramirez 1.50 4.00
126 Nick Hagadone 2.50 6.00
127 Pete Kozma 1.50 4.00
128 Phillippe Aumont 5.00 12.00
129 Preston Mattingly 4.00 10.00
131 Ross Detwiler 2.50 6.00
132 Tim Alderson 2.50 6.00
133 Todd Frazier 2.00 5.00
134 Wes Roemer 1.50 4.00
135 Ben Revere 2.50 6.00
141 Austin Jackson 10.00 25.00
142 Beau Mills 4.00 10.00
149 Tommy Hunter

2007 Donruss Elite Extra Edition Signature Aspirations

OVERALL AU/MEM ODDS 1:5
PRINT RUNS B/WN 5-100 COPIES PER
NO PRICING ON QTY 25 OR LESS
EXCHANGE DEADLINE 07/01/2007
1 Andrew Brackman/100 10.00 25.00
2 Austin Gallagher/100 12.50 30.00
3 Brett Cecil /100 10.00 25.00
4 Danny Worth/100 EXCH 6.00 15.00
5 David Price/100 50.00 100.00
6 J. P. Arencibia/100 20.00 50.00
7 Josh Donaldson/100 8.00 20.00
8 Brandon Hicks/100 4.00 10.00
9 Brian Rike/100 4.00 10.00
10 Bryan Morris/100 4.00 10.00
11 Cale Iorg/100 12.50 30.00
12 Casey Weathers/100 6.00 15.00
13 Corey Kluber/100 4.00 10.00
14 Daniel Moskos/100 4.00 10.00
15 Danny Payne/50 6.00 15.00
16 David Kopp/36 6.00 15.00
17 Dellin Betances/50 30.00 60.00
18 Derrick Robinson/100 4.00 10.00
19 Drew Stubbs/100 15.00 40.00
20 Eric Eiland/100 6.00 15.00
21 Francisco Pena/100 8.00 20.00
22 Greg Reynolds/100 4.00 10.00
23 Jeff Samardzija/15
24 Jess Todd/50 12.50 30.00
25 John Tolisano/100 10.00 25.00
26 Jordan Zimmerman/75 20.00 50.00
27 Julian Sampson/50 4.00 10.00
28 Luke Hochevar/25
29 Mat Latos/34 50.00 100.00
30 Matt Mangini/80 10.00 25.00
31 Matt Spencer/30 6.00 15.00
32 Matthew Sweeney/100 EXCH 8.00 20.00
34 Mitch Canham/25
35 Nick Schmidt/25
36 Paul Kelly/100 4.00 10.00
37 Ryan Pope/100 12.50 30.00
38 Sam Runion/50 6.00 15.00
39 Steven Souza/100 6.00 15.00
40 Travis Mattair/50 6.00 15.00
41 Trystan Magnuson/50 4.00 10.00
42 Will Middlebrooks/25
43 Zack Cozart/25
44 James Adkins/100 10.00 25.00
45 Cory Luebke/100 4.00 10.00
46 Aaron Poreda/100 6.00 15.00
47 Clayton Mortensen/100 6.00 15.00
48 Bradley Suttle/100 12.50 30.00
49 Tony Butler/100 4.00 10.00
50 Zach Britton/100 20.00 50.00
51 Scott Cousins /50 6.00 15.00
52 Wendell Fairley/100 12.50 30.00
53 Eric Sogard/100 4.00 10.00
54 Jonathan Lucroy/100 8.00 20.00
55 Lars Davis/100 4.00 10.00
56 Tony Thomas/100 EXCH 4.00 10.00
59 Nick Noonan/100 EXCH 4.00 10.00
60 Henry Sosa/100 EXCH 4.00 10.00
73 Corey Brown/5 EXCH
77 Jennie Finch/50 40.00 80.00
91 Charlie Culberson/100 15.00 40.00
92 Jacob Smolinski/100 8.00 20.00
93 Blake Beaven/100 4.00 10.00
94 Brad Chalk/100 4.00 10.00
95 Brett Anderson/100 15.00 40.00
96 Chris Withrow/100 6.00 15.00
97 Clay Fuller/100 6.00 15.00
98 Damon Sublett/50 15.00 40.00
99 Devin Mesoraco/100 15.00 40.00
100 Drew Cumberland/100 5.00 12.00
101 Jack McGeary/100 6.00 15.00
102 Jake Arrieta/100 8.00 20.00
103 James Simmons/50 EXCH 4.00 10.00
104 Jarrod Parker/50 20.00 50.00
105 Jason Dominguez/100 5.00 12.00
106 Jason Heyward/100 75.00 150.00
107 Joe Savery/100 5.00 12.00
108 Jon Gilmore/100 6.00 15.00
109 Jordan Walden/50 15.00 40.00
110 Josh Smoker/100 30.00 60.00
111 Josh Vitters/100 15.00 40.00
112 Julio Borbon/100 10.00 25.00
113 Justin Jackson/50 10.00 25.00
114 Kellen Kulbacki/100 8.00 20.00
115 Kevin Ahrens/50 15.00 40.00
116 Kyle Lotzkar/100 12.50 30.00
117 Madison Bumgarner/50 20.00 50.00
118 Matt Dominguez/50 40.00 80.00
119 Matt LaPorta/100 40.00 80.00
120 Matt Wieters/50 200.00 400.00
121 Michael Burgess/50 30.00 60.00
122 Michael Main/50 12.50 30.00
123 Mike Moustakas/100 60.00 120.00
124 Nathan Vineyard/100 5.00 12.00
125 Neil Ramirez/100 8.00 20.00
126 Nick Hagadone/50 12.50 30.00
127 Pete Kozma/100 10.00 25.00
128 Phillippe Aumont/100 40.00 80.00
129 Preston Mattingly/50 30.00 60.00
131 Ross Detwiler/100 10.00 25.00
132 Tim Alderson/100 15.00 40.00
133 Todd Frazier/100 20.00 50.00
134 Wes Roemer/100 6.00 15.00
135 Ben Revere/100 10.00 25.00
136 Chris Davis/50 EXCH 150.00 200.00
138 Bryan Anderson/50 EXCH 4.00 10.00
141 Austin Jackson/50 20.00 50.00
142 Beau Mills/50 EXCH 6.00 15.00
149 Tommy Hunter/50

2007 Donruss Elite Extra Edition Signature Status

OVERALL AU/MEM ODDS 1:5
PRINT RUNS B/WN 1-50 COPIES PER
NO PRICING ON QTY 25 OR LESS
EXCHANGE DEADLINE 07/01/2007
1 Andrew Brackman/50 15.00 40.00
2 Austin Gallagher/50 20.00 50.00
3 Brett Cecil /50 20.00 50.00
4 Danny Worth/50 EXCH 8.00 20.00
5 David Price/50 150.00 250.00
6 J. P. Arencibia/50 30.00 60.00
7 Josh Donaldson/50 12.50 30.00
8 Brandon Hicks/50 6.00 15.00
9 Brian Rike/50 6.00 15.00
10 Bryan Morris/50 6.00 15.00
11 Cale Iorg/50 12.50 30.00
12 Casey Weathers/50 10.00 25.00
13 Corey Kluber/50 6.00 15.00
14 Daniel Moskos/50 6.00 15.00
15 Danny Payne/25
16 David Kopp/25
17 Dellin Betances/25
18 Derrick Robinson/50 6.00 15.00
19 Drew Stubbs/50 15.00 40.00
20 Eric Eiland/50 10.00 25.00
21 Francisco Pena/50 12.50 30.00
22 Greg Reynolds/50 6.00 15.00
23 Jeff Samardzija/10
24 Jess Todd/25
25 John Tolisano/50 15.00 40.00
26 Jordan Zimmerman/25
27 Julian Sampson/25
28 Luke Hochevar/10
29 Mat Latos/25
30 Matt Mangini/50 15.00 40.00
31 Matt Spencer/15
32 Matthew Sweeney/50 EXCH 12.50 30.00
33 Max Scherzer/12
34 Mitch Canham/10
35 Nick Schmidt/10
36 Paul Kelly/50 6.00 15.00
37 Ryan Pope/50 20.00 50.00
38 Sam Runion/25
39 Steven Souza/50 10.00 25.00
40 Travis Mattair/25
41 Trystan Magnuson/25
42 Will Middlebrooks/10
43 Zack Cozart/10
44 James Adkins/50 6.00 15.00
45 Cory Luebke/50 6.00 15.00
46 Aaron Poreda/50 10.00 25.00
47 Clayton Mortensen/50 10.00 25.00
48 Bradley Suttle/50 20.00 50.00
49 Tony Butler/50 6.00 15.00
50 Zach Britton/50 40.00 80.00
51 Scott Cousins /19
52 Wendell Fairley/50 20.00 50.00
53 Eric Sogard/50 6.00 15.00
54 Jonathan Lucroy/50 10.00 25.00
55 Lars Davis/50 6.00 15.00
56 Tony Thomas/50 EXCH 6.00 15.00
59 Nick Noonan/50 EXCH 6.00 15.00
60 Henry Sosa/50 EXCH 6.00 15.00
73 Corey Brown/1 EXCH
77 Jennie Finch/25
91 Charlie Culberson/50 30.00 60.00
92 Jacob Smolinski/50 12.50 30.00
93 Blake Beaven/50 6.00 15.00
94 Brad Chalk/50 6.00 15.00
95 Brett Anderson/50 60.00 120.00
96 Chris Withrow/50 10.00 25.00
97 Clay Fuller/50 10.00 25.00
98 Damon Sublett/25
99 Devin Mesoraco/50 25.00 60.00
100 Drew Cumberland/50 8.00 20.00
101 Jack McGeary/50 10.00 25.00
102 Jake Arrieta/50 12.50 30.00
103 James Simmons/25 EXCH
104 Jarrod Parker/25
105 Jason Dominguez/50 8.00 20.00
106 Jason Heyward/50 125.00 250.00
107 Joe Savery/50 8.00 20.00
108 Jon Gilmore/50 10.00 25.00
109 Jordan Walden/25
110 Josh Smoker/50 50.00 100.00
111 Josh Vitters/50 40.00 80.00
112 Julio Borbon/50 12.50 30.00
113 Justin Jackson/25
114 Kellen Kulbacki/50 12.50 30.00
115 Kevin Ahrens/25
116 Kyle Lotzkar/50 10.00 25.00
117 Madison Bumgarner/25
118 Matt Dominguez/25
119 Matt LaPorta/50 150.00 300.00
120 Matt Wieters/25
121 Michael Burgess/25
122 Michael Main/25
123 Mike Moustakas/50 100.00 200.00
124 Nathan Vineyard/50 8.00 20.00
125 Neil Ramirez/50 12.50 30.00
126 Nick Hagadone/25
127 Pete Kozma/50 10.00 25.00
128 Phillippe Aumont/50 60.00 120.00
129 Preston Mattingly/25
131 Ross Detwiler/50 15.00 40.00
132 Tim Alderson/50 30.00 60.00
133 Todd Frazier/50 40.00 80.00
134 Wes Roemer/50 10.00 25.00
135 Ben Revere/50 15.00 40.00
136 Chris Davis/25 EXCH
138 Bryan Anderson/25 EXCH
141 Austin Jackson/25
142 Beau Mills/25 EXCH
149 Tommy Hunter/25

2007 Donruss Elite Extra Edition Signature Status Black

OVERALL AUTO/MEM ODDS 1:5
STATED PRINT RUN 1 SER.#'d SET
NO PRICING DUE TO SCARCITY
EXCHANGE DEADLINE 07/01/2009
149 Tommy Hunter

2007 Donruss Elite Extra Edition Signature Status Gold

OVERALL AUTO/MEM ODDS 1:5
STATED PRINT RUN 5 SER.#'d SETS
NO PRICING DUE TO SCARCITY
EXCHANGE DEADLINE 07/01/2009
149 Tommy Hunter

2007 Donruss Elite Extra Edition Signature Turn of the Century

OVERALL AU/MEM ODDS 1:5
PRINT RUNS B/WN 10-500 COPIES PER
NO PRICING ON QTY 25 OR LESS
EXCHANGE DEADLINE 07/01/2007
1 Andrew Brackman/500 8.00 20.00
2 Austin Gallagher/500 10.00 25.00
3 Brett Cecil /500 8.00 20.00
4 Danny Worth/500 EXCH 6.00 15.00
5 David Price/500 15.00 40.00
6 J. P. Arencibia/500 8.00 20.00
7 Josh Donaldson/500 4.00 10.00
8 Brandon Hicks/419 5.00 12.00
9 Brian Rike/500 5.00 12.00
10 Bryan Morris/500 4.00 10.00
11 Cale Iorg/397 6.00 15.00
12 Casey Weathers/500 5.00 12.00
13 Corey Kluber/419 4.00 10.00
14 Daniel Moskos/500 4.00 10.00
15 Danny Payne/394 4.00 10.00
16 David Kopp/449 4.00 10.00
17 Dellin Betances/494 12.50 30.00
18 Derrick Robinson/500 4.00 10.00
19 Drew Stubbs/494 6.00 15.00
20 Eric Eiland/419 6.00 15.00
21 Francisco Pena/396 6.00 15.00
22 Greg Reynolds/500 4.00 10.00
23 Jeff Samardzija/219 12.50 30.00
24 Jess Todd/394 12.50 30.00
25 John Tolisano/419 6.00 15.00
26 Jordan Zimmerman/469 12.50 30.00
27 Julian Sampson/494 4.00 10.00
28 Luke Hochevar/158 12.50 30.00
29 Mat Latos/499 15.00 40.00
30 Matt Mangini/500 5.00 12.00
31 Matt Spencer/500 4.00 10.00
32 Matthew Sweeney/500 EXCH 6.00 15.00
33 Max Scherzer/250 40.00 80.00
34 Mitch Canham/209 5.00 12.00
35 Nick Schmidt/409 4.00 10.00
36 Paul Kelly/500 4.00 10.00
37 Ryan Pope/500 6.00 15.00
38 Sam Runion/494 5.00 12.00
39 Steven Souza/500 6.00 15.00
40 Travis Mattair/494 6.00 15.00
41 Trystan Magnuson/246 4.00 10.00
42 Will Middlebrooks/409 12.50 30.00
43 Zack Cozart/409 4.00 10.00
44 James Adkins/500 4.00 10.00
45 Cory Luebke/469 4.00 10.00
46 Aaron Poreda/500 5.00 12.00
47 Clayton Mortensen/500 4.00 10.00
48 Bradley Suttle/500 5.00 12.00
49 Tony Butler/419 4.00 10.00
50 Zach Britton/437 20.00 50.00
51 Scott Cousins /500 5.00 12.00
52 Wendell Fairley/500 10.00 25.00
53 Eric Sogard/500 5.00 12.00
54 Jonathan Lucroy/500 12.50 30.00
55 Lars Davis/500 4.00 10.00
56 Tony Thomas/300 EXCH 4.00 10.00
59 Nick Noonan/300 EXCH 4.00 10.00
60 Henry Sosa/300 EXCH 5.00 12.00
73 Corey Brown/10 EXCH
77 Jennie Finch/119 30.00 60.00
91 Charlie Culberson/500 6.00 15.00
92 Jacob Smolinski/500 6.00 15.00
93 Blake Beaven/100 6.00 15.00
94 Brad Chalk/100 5.00 12.00
95 Brett Anderson/145 15.00 40.00
96 Chris Withrow/168 6.00 15.00
97 Clay Fuller/145 5.00 12.00
98 Damon Sublett/220 10.00 25.00
99 Devin Mesoraco/145 12.50 30.00
100 Drew Cumberland/125 5.00 12.00
101 Jack McGeary/145 6.00 15.00
102 Jake Arrieta/145 5.00 12.00
103 James Simmons/100 EXCH 5.00 12.00
104 Jarrod Parker/55 20.00 50.00
105 Jason Dominguez/100 5.00 12.00
106 Jason Heyward/169 50.00 100.00
107 Joe Savery/119 6.00 15.00
108 Jon Gilmore/100 6.00 15.00
109 Jordan Walden/100 10.00 25.00
110 Josh Smoker/200 15.00 40.00
111 Josh Vitters/150 8.00 20.00
112 Julio Borbon/100 10.00 25.00
113 Justin Jackson/100 6.00 15.00
114 Kellen Kulbacki/145 5.00 12.00
115 Kevin Ahrens/100 10.00 25.00
116 Kyle Lotzkar/100 6.00 15.00
117 Madison Bumgarner/100 20.00 50.00
118 Matt Dominguez/100 10.00 25.00
119 Matt LaPorta/100 50.00 100.00
120 Matt Wieters/100 100.00 200.00
121 Michael Burgess/100 15.00 40.00
122 Michael Main/100 6.00 15.00
123 Mike Moustakas/345 30.00 60.00
124 Nathan Vineyard/119 6.00 15.00
125 Neil Ramirez/145 6.00 15.00
126 Nick Hagadone/100 6.00 15.00
127 Pete Kozma/100 5.00 12.00
128 Phillippe Aumont/120 20.00 50.00
129 Preston Mattingly/100 15.00 40.00
131 Ross Detwiler/119 10.00 25.00
132 Tim Alderson/100 15.00 40.00
133 Todd Frazier/145 12.50 30.00
134 Wes Roemer/100 5.00 12.00
135 Ben Revere/119 10.00 25.00
136 Chris Davis/100 EXCH 60.00 120.00
138 Bryan Anderson/100 EXCH 4.00 10.00
139 Marc Gasol EXCH 4.00 10.00
141 Austin Jackson/100 20.00 50.00
142 Beau Mills/100 EXCH 12.50 30.00
149 Tommy Hunter 12.50 30.00

2007 Donruss Elite Extra Edition Status

*STATUS 1-92: 4X TO 10X BASIC
OVERALL INSERT ODDS 1:4
STATED PRINT RUN 50 SER.#'d SETS
92 Jacob Smolinski 2.00 5.00
93 Blake Beaven 2.00 5.00
94 Brad Chalk 2.00 5.00
95 Brett Anderson 3.00 8.00
96 Chris Withrow 2.00 5.00
97 Clay Fuller 2.00 5.00
98 Damon Sublett 3.00 8.00
99 Devin Mesoraco 2.50 6.00
100 Drew Cumberland 2.00 5.00
101 Jack McGeary 2.50 6.00
102 Jake Arrieta 2.00 5.00
103 James Simmons 2.00 5.00
104 Jarrod Parker 10.00 25.00
105 Jason Dominguez 2.00 5.00
106 Jason Heyward 60.00 120.00
107 Joe Savery 2.00 5.00
108 Jon Gilmore 2.00 5.00
109 Jordan Walden 3.00 8.00
110 Josh Smoker 3.00 8.00
111 Josh Vitters 6.00 15.00
112 Julio Borbon 2.50 6.00
113 Justin Jackson 2.00 5.00
114 Kellen Kulbacki 2.50 6.00
115 Kevin Ahrens 2.00 5.00
116 Kyle Lotzkar 2.00 5.00
117 Madison Bumgarner 8.00 20.00
118 Matt Dominguez 8.00 20.00
119 Matt LaPorta 10.00 25.00
120 Matt Wieters 6.00 15.00
121 Michael Burgess 8.00 20.00
122 Michael Main 2.50 6.00
123 Mike Moustakas 8.00 20.00
124 Nathan Vineyard 2.50 6.00
125 Neil Ramirez 2.00 5.00
126 Nick Hagadone 3.00 8.00
127 Pete Kozma 2.00 5.00
128 Phillippe Aumont 6.00 15.00
129 Preston Mattingly 5.00 12.00
131 Ross Detwiler 3.00 8.00
132 Tim Alderson 3.00 8.00
133 Todd Frazier 2.50 6.00
134 Wes Roemer 2.00 5.00
135 Ben Revere 3.00 8.00
141 Austin Jackson 12.50 30.00
142 Beau Mills 5.00 12.00

2007 Donruss Elite Extra Edition Status Gold

OVERALL INSERT ODDS 1:4
STATED PRINT RUN 25 SER.#'d SETS
NO PRICING DUE TO SCARCITY

2007 Donruss Elite Extra Edition College Ties

STATED PRINT RUN 1500 SER.#'d SETS
*GOLD: .6X TO 1.5X BASIC
GOLD PRINT RUN 500 SER.#'d SETS
*RED: 1X TO 2.5X BASIC
RED PRINT RUN 100 SER.#'d SETS
OVERALL INSERT ODDS 1:4

Card	Low	High
1 Daniel Moskos	.75	2.00
David Kopp		
2 Nick Schmidt	.75	2.00
Jess Todd		
3 J. P. Arencibia	.75	2.00
Julio Borbon		
4 David Price	1.50	4.00
Casey Weathers		
5 Taurean Green	1.25	3.00
Matt LaPorta		
6 Jennie Finch	1.50	4.00
Amanda Beard		
7 Jim Boeheim	.75	2.00
Demetris Nichols		
8 Danny Payne	1.50	4.00
Matt Wieters		
9 Darwin Barney	.75	2.00
Mitch Canham		
10 Luke Hochevar	.75	2.00
James Adkins		
11 Daequan Cook	.75	2.00
Cory Luebke		
12 D. J. Strawberry	.75	2.00
Brett Cecil		

2007 Donruss Elite Extra Edition College Ties Autographs

OVERALL AUTO/MEM ODDS 1:5
PRINT RUNS B/WN 50-100 COPIES PER
EXCHANGE DEADLINE 07/01/2009

Card	Low	High
1 Daniel Moskos	6.00	15.00
David Kopp		
2 Nick Schmidt	6.00	15.00
Jess Todd		
3 J. P. Arencibia	30.00	60.00
Julio Borbon		
4 David Price	15.00	40.00
Casey Weathers		
5 Taurean Green	10.00	25.00
Matt LaPorta		
6 Jennie Finch	60.00	120.00
Amanda Beard		
7 Jim Boeheim	6.00	15.00
Demetris Nichols EXCH		
8 Danny Payne	60.00	120.00
Matt Wieters		
9 Darwin Barney	6.00	15.00
Mitch Canham EXCH		
10 Luke Hochevar	15.00	40.00
James Adkins		
11 Daequan Cook	10.00	25.00
Cory Luebke		
12 D. J. Strawberry	6.00	15.00
Brett Cecil EXCH		

2007 Donruss Elite Extra Edition College Ties Jerseys

OVERALL AUTO/MEM ODDS 1:5
PRINT RUNS B/WN 50-500 COPIES PER

Card	Low	High
1 Daniel Moskos	4.00	10.00
David Kopp/75		
6 Jennie Finch	6.00	15.00
Amanda Beard/50		
9 Darwin Barney	3.00	8.00
Mitch Canham/500		

2007 Donruss Elite Extra Edition College Ties Jerseys Prime

OVERALL AU/MEM ODDS 1:5
PRINT RUNS B/WN 5-50 COPIES PER
NO PRICING ON QTY 25 OR LESS

Card	Low	High
1 Daniel Moskos		
David Kopp/5		
6 Jennie Finch		
Amanda Beard/25		
9 Darwin Barney	4.00	10.00
Mitch Canham/50		

2007 Donruss Elite Extra Edition Collegiate Patches

OVERALL AUTO/MEM ODDS 1:5
PRINT RUNS B/WN 25-250 COPIES PER
NO PRICING ON QTY 25 OR LESS

Card	Low	High
10 Jennie Finch/249	30.00	60.00
19 Josh Donaldson/250	6.00	15.00
25 Drew Stubbs/250	10.00	25.00
26 Andrew Brackman/250	6.00	15.00
27 Casey Weathers/250	10.00	25.00
28 Daniel Moskos/250	6.00	15.00
29 David Price/250	12.50	30.00
30 Greg Reynolds/250	6.00	15.00
31 J. P. Arencibia/249	10.00	25.00
32 Jeff Samardzija/150	40.00	80.00
33 Julio Borbon/250	6.00	15.00
34 Luke Hochevar/100	12.50	30.00
35 Matt LaPorta/250	30.00	60.00
36 Matt Mangini/250	6.00	15.00
37 Matt Wieters/250 EXCH	20.00	50.00
38 Max Scherzer/182	10.00	25.00
39 Mitch Canham/250	6.00	15.00
40 Nick Schmidt/250	6.00	15.00
41 James Adkins/250	6.00	15.00
42 Tony Thomas/250 EXCH	6.00	15.00
45 Tommy Hunter/250	8.00	20.00
52 Cale Iorg/250	6.00	15.00
54 Nick Hagadone/250	6.00	15.00
55 Trystan Magnuson/248	6.00	15.00
64 Matt Spencer/249	6.00	15.00
65 Corey Brown/250 EXCH	6.00	15.00
67 Connie Mack III/100	6.00	15.00

2007 Donruss Elite Extra Edition School Colors

OVERALL INSERT ODDS 1:4
STATED PRINT RUN 1500 SER.#'d SETS

Card	Low	High
1 David Price	2.00	5.00
2 Daniel Moskos	.75	2.00
3 Greg Reynolds	.75	2.00
4 Matt LaPorta	1.25	3.00
5 Matt Wieters	3.00	8.00
6 Luke Hochevar	.75	2.00
7 Max Scherzer	.75	2.00
26 Nick Schmidt	.75	2.00
29 Beau Mills	.75	2.00
30 James Simmons	.75	2.00
31 Joe Savery	.75	2.00
32 Ross Detwiler	.75	2.00
33 J. P. Arencibia	.75	2.00
34 Drew Stubbs	.75	2.00

2007 Donruss Elite Extra Edition School Colors Autographs

OVERALL AUTO/MEM ODDS 1:5
PRINT RUNS B/WN 10-50 COPIES PER
NO PRICING ON QTY 25 OR LESS
EXCHANGE DEADLINE 07/01/2009

Card	Low	High
1 David Price/50	30.00	60.00
2 Daniel Moskos/50	6.00	15.00
3 Greg Reynolds/50	6.00	15.00
4 Matt LaPorta/50	30.00	60.00
5 Matt Wieters/50	90.00	150.00
6 Luke Hochevar/50	10.00	25.00
7 Max Scherzer/50	75.00	150.00
26 Nick Schmidt/50	6.00	15.00
29 Beau Mills/50 EXCH	10.00	25.00
30 James Simmons/50 EXCH	6.00	15.00
31 Joe Savery/50	6.00	15.00
32 Ross Detwiler/50	10.00	25.00
33 J. P. Arencibia/50	30.00	60.00
34 Drew Stubbs/50	15.00	40.00
35 Josh Vitters/50	12.50	30.00

2007 Donruss Elite Extra Edition Throwback Threads

OVERALL AUTO/MEM ODDS 1:5
PRINT RUNS B/WN 44-500 COPIES PER

Card	Low	High
3 Drew Stubbs/500	3.00	8.00
4 Drew Cumberland/500	3.00	8.00
6 Mat Latos/500	6.00	15.00
7 Brett Cecil /500	3.00	8.00
9 Brett Anderson/500	3.00	8.00
10 Casey Weathers/75	4.00	10.00
11 Daniel Moskos/500	3.00	8.00
12 Darwin Barney/500	6.00	15.00
13 Kellen Kulbacki/500	3.00	8.00
14 Matt Dominguez/500	3.00	8.00
15 Matt Mangini/500	3.00	8.00
16 Mitch Canham/500	3.00	8.00
18 Will Middlebrooks/500	3.00	8.00
23 Nick Schmidt/500	3.00	8.00
24 Zack Cozart/500	3.00	8.00

2007 Donruss Elite Extra Edition Throwback Threads Prime

*PRIME: .75X TO 2X BASIC
OVERALL AUTO/MEM ODDS 1:5
PRINT RUNS B/WN 3-50 COPIES PER
NO PRICING ON QTY 25 OR LESS

10 Casey Weathers/3

2007 Donruss Elite Extra Edition Throwback Threads Autographs

OVERALL AUTO/MEM ODDS 1:5
PRINT RUNS B/WN 50-100 COPIES PER
EXCHANGE DEADLINE 07/01/2009

Card	Low	High
3 Drew Stubbs/100	20.00	50.00
4 Drew Cumberland/100	6.00	15.00
6 Mat Latos/100	20.00	50.00
9 Brett Anderson/100	15.00	40.00
10 Casey Weathers/100	10.00	25.00
11 Daniel Moskos/100	6.00	15.00
12 Josh Vitters/100	10.00	25.00
13 Kellen Kulbacki/100	6.00	15.00
14 Matt Dominguez/100	20.00	50.00
15 Matt Mangini/100	10.00	25.00
16 Mitch Canham/100	6.00	15.00
18 Will Middlebrooks/100	6.00	15.00
23 Nick Schmidt/100	6.00	15.00
24 Zack Cozart/100	10.00	25.00

2007 Donruss Elite Extra Edition Throwback Threads Autographs Prime

OVERALL AUTO/MEM ODDS 1:5
PRINT RUNS B/WN 1-25 COPIES PER
NO PRICING DUE TO SCARCITY
EXCHANGE DEADLINE 07/01/2009

2008 Donruss Elite Extra Edition

This set was released on November 26, 2008. The base set consists of 199 cards.

Card	Low	High
COMP.SET w/o AU's (100)	10.00	25.00
COMMON CARD (1-100)	.20	.50
COMMON AU (101-200)	3.00	8.00

RANDOM INSERTS IN PACKS
PRINT RUNS B/WN 99-1495
EXCH DEADLINE 5/26/2010

Card	Low	High
1 Aaron Cunningham	.20	.50
2 Aaron Pribanic	.20	.50
3 Aaron Shafer	.20	.50
4 Adam Mills	.20	.50
5 Adam Moore	.20	.50
6 Beamer Weems	.20	.50
7 Beau Mills	.20	.50
8 Blake Tekotte	.30	.75
9 Bobby Lanigan	.20	.50
10 Brad Hand	.30	.75
11 Brandon Crawford	.30	.75
12 Brandon Waring	.60	1.50
13 Brent Morel	.30	.75
14 Brett Jacobson	.20	.50
15 Caleb Gindl	.20	.50
16 Carlos Peguero	.30	.75
17 Charlie Blackmon	.20	.50
18 Charlie Furbush	.20	.50
19 Chris Davis	.50	1.25
20 Chris Valaika	.20	.50
21 Clark Murphy	.30	.75
22 Clayton Cook	.30	.75
23 Cody Adams	.30	.75
24 Cody Satterwhite	.30	.75
25 Cole St. Clair	.20	.50
26 Corey Young	.20	.50
27 Curtis Petersen	.20	.50
28 Danny Rams	.30	.75
29 Dennis Raben	.30	.75
30 Derek Norris	.30	.75
31 Tyson Brummett	.20	.50
32 Dusty Coleman	.20	.50
33 Edgar Olmos	.20	.50
34 Engel Beltre	.60	1.50
35 Eric Beaulac	.20	.50
36 Geison Aguasviva	.20	.50
37 Gerardo Parra	.20	.50
38 Graham Hicks	.30	.75
39 Greg Halman	.30	.75
40 Hector Gomez	.50	1.25
41 J.D. Alfaro	.20	.50
42 Jack Egbert	.30	.75
43 James Darnell	.30	.75
44 Jay Austin	.20	.50
45 Jeremy Beckham	.30	.75
46 Jeremy Farrell	.20	.50
47 Jeremy Hamilton	.20	.50
48 Jericho Jones	.20	.50
49 Jesse Darcy	.20	.50
50 Jeudy Valdez	.30	.75
51 Jharmidy De Jesus	.20	.50
52 Joba Chamberlain	.30	.75
53 Johnny Giavotella	.60	1.50
54 Jon Mark Owings	.30	.75
55 Jordan Meaker	.30	.75
56 Jose Duran	.30	.75
57 Josh Harrison	.30	.75
58 Josh Lindblom	.30	.75
59 Josh Reddick	.60	1.50
60 Juan Carlos Sulbaran	.20	.50
61 Justin Bristow	.20	.50
62 Kenny Gilbert	.20	.50
63 Kirk Nieuwenhuis	.20	.50
64 Kyle Hudson	.20	.50
65 Kyle Russell	.20	.50
66 Kyle Weiland	.50	1.25
67 L. J. Hoes	.50	1.25
68 Mark Cohoon	.30	.75
69 Mark Sobolewski	.50	1.25
70 Mat Gamel	.50	1.25
71 Matt Harrison	.20	.50
72 Max Ramirez	.20	.50
73 Tony Delmonico	.30	.75
74 Mike Stanton	2.50	6.00
75 Mitch Abeita	.20	.50
76 Neftali Feliz	.60	1.50
77 Neftali Soto	.30	.75
78 Niko Vasquez	.50	1.25
79 Omar Aguilar	.30	.75
80 Petey Paramore	.30	.75
81 Ray Kruml	.20	.50
82 Rolando Gomez	.30	.75
83 Ryan Chaffee	.30	.75
84 Ryan Pressly	.20	.50
85 Sam Freeman	.50	1.25
86 Sawyer Carroll	.30	.75
87 Scott Green	.20	.50
88 Sean Ratliff	.20	.50
89 Shane Peterson	.30	.75
90 T.J. Steele	.30	.75
91 Tim Federowicz	.30	.75
92 Tyler Chatwood	.30	.75
93 Tyler Cline	.20	.50
94 Tyler Ladendorf	.30	.75
95 Tyler Yockey	.20	.50
96 Wilmer Flores	.75	2.00
97 Wilson Ramos	.60	1.50
98 Zach McAllister	.30	.75
99 Zachary Stewart	.20	.50
100 Zeke Spruill	.50	1.25
101 Adrian Nieto AU/521	4.00	10.00
102 Alan Horne AU/349	6.00	15.00
103 Andrew Cashner AU/685	6.00	15.00
104 Anthony Hewitt AU/920	6.00	15.00
105 Brad Holt AU/432	5.00	12.00
106 Bryan Petersen AU/319	3.00	8.00
107 Bryan Price AU/572	4.00	10.00
108 Bud Norris AU/1095	3.00	8.00
109 Carlos Gutierrez AU/202	5.00	12.00
110 Chase D'Arnaud AU/1218	4.00	10.00
111 Chris Johnson AU/99	40.00	80.00
112 Christian Friedrich AU/402	8.00	20.00
113 Christian Marrero AU/662	4.00	10.00
114 Clayton Conner AU/819	3.00	8.00
115 Cole Rohrbough AU/719	4.00	10.00
116 Collin DeLome AU/819	3.00	8.00
117 Daniel Cortes AU/680	3.00	8.00
118 Daniel Schlereth AU/570	3.00	8.00
119 Denny Almonte AU/821	3.00	8.00
120 Allan Dykstra AU/1069	4.00	10.00
121 Dominic Brown AU/996	20.00	50.00
122 Evan Fredrickson AU/922	3.00	8.00
123 Gordon Beckham AU/710	6.00	15.00
124 Greg Veloz AU/819	3.00	8.00
125 Ike Davis AU/995	10.00	25.00
126 Isaac Galloway AU/1099	3.00	8.00
127 Jacob Jefferies AU/819	3.00	8.00
128 Michael Kohn AU/199	3.00	8.00
129 Jared Goedert AU/819	3.00	8.00
130 Jason Knapp AU/999	4.00	10.00
131 Jhoulys Chacin AU/821	4.00	10.00
132 Jordy Mercer AU/483	3.00	8.00
133 Jorge Bucardo AU/819	4.00	10.00
134 Jose Ceda AU/1470	3.00	8.00
135 Jose Martinez AU/868	3.00	8.00
136 Josh Roenicke AU/829	3.00	8.00
137 Juan Francisco AU/1495	5.00	12.00
138 Justin Parker AU/719	3.00	8.00
139 Kyle Ginley AU/819	3.00	8.00
140 Lance Lynn AU/570	6.00	15.00
141 Logan Forsythe AU/162	3.00	8.00
142 Logan Morrison AU/360	12.50	30.00
143 Logan Schafer AU/793	3.00	8.00
144 Lorenzo Cain AU/817	6.00	15.00
145 Lucas Duda AU/124	10.00	25.00
146 Matt Mitchell AU/719	3.00	8.00
147 Danny Espinosa AU/443	12.50	30.00
148 Michael Taylor AU/720	20.00	50.00
149 Michel Inoa AU/1199	6.00	15.00
150 Mike Montgomery AU/922	6.00	15.00
151 Cord Phelps AU/693	5.00	12.00
152 Pablo Sandoval AU/819	20.00	50.00
153 Quincy Latimore AU/819	3.00	8.00
154 R. J. Seidel AU/819	3.00	8.00
155 Rayner Contreras AU/1349	3.00	8.00
156 Rick Porcello AU/1299	10.00	25.00
157 Robert Hernandez AU/859	3.00	8.00
158 Ryan Kalish AU/1129	8.00	20.00
159 Ryan Perry AU/745	4.00	10.00
160 Shelby Ford AU/819	3.00	8.00
161 Shooter Hunt AU/397	8.00	20.00
162 Tyler Kolodny AU/819	4.00	10.00
163 Tyler Sample AU/619	4.00	10.00
164 Tyson Ross AU/999	3.00	8.00
166 Waldis Joaquin AU/819	3.00	8.00
167 Welington Castillo AU/1319	3.00	8.00
168 Wilin Rosario AU/1099	3.00	8.00
169 Xavier Avery AU/199	10.00	25.00
170 Zach Collier AU/217	10.00	25.00
171 Zach Putnam AU/444	3.00	8.00
172 Anthony Gose AU/519	4.00	10.00
173 Roger Kieschnick AU/569	6.00	15.00
174 Andrew Liebel AU/219	5.00	12.00
175 Tim Murphy AU/244	4.00	10.00
176 Vance Worley AU/219	30.00	60.00
177 Buster Posey AU/934	50.00	100.00
178 Kenn Kasparek AU/694	3.00	8.00
179 J.P. Ramirez AU/719	5.00	12.00
180 Evan Bigley AU/819	3.00	8.00
181 Trey Haley AU/719	3.00	8.00
182 Robbie Grossman AU/719	3.00	8.00
183 Jordan Danks AU/254 EXCH	12.50	30.00
184 Brett Hunter AU/269	4.00	10.00
185 Rafael Rodriguez AU/999	5.00	12.00
186 Yeicok Calderon AU/819	6.00	15.00
187 Gustavo Pierre AU/719	4.00	10.00
188 Will Smith AU/719	3.00	8.00
189 Daniel Thomas AU/719	3.00	8.00
190 Carson Blair AU/719	3.00	8.00
191 Chris Hicks AU/719	4.00	10.00
192 Rashun Dixon AU/199 EXCH	10.00	25.00
193 Marcus Lemon AU/199	5.00	12.00
194 Kyle Nicholson AU/719	3.00	8.00
195 Mike Cisco AU/719	3.00	8.00
196 Jarek Cunningham AU/719	3.00	8.00
197 Cat Osterman AU/719	12.50	30.00
198 Derrick Rose AU/99	125.00	250.00
199 Michael Beasley AU/99	30.00	60.00
200 O.J. Mayo AU/99	40.00	80.00

2008 Donruss Elite Extra Edition Aspirations

*ASP 1-100: 2.5X TO 6X BASIC
RANDOM INSERTS IN PACKS
STATED PRINT RUN 150 SER.#'d SETS

Card	Low	High
101 Adrian Nieto	1.25	3.00
102 Alan Horne	1.25	3.00
103 Andrew Cashner	3.00	8.00
104 Anthony Hewitt	1.25	3.00
105 Brad Holt	1.25	3.00
106 Bryan Petersen	1.25	3.00
107 Bryan Price	1.25	3.00
108 Bud Norris	1.25	3.00
109 Carlos Gutierrez	3.00	8.00
110 Chase D'Arnaud	1.25	3.00
111 Chris Johnson	5.00	12.00
112 Christian Friedrich	4.00	10.00
113 Christian Marrero	2.00	5.00
114 Clayton Conner	1.25	3.00
115 Cole Rohrbough	1.25	3.00
116 Collin DeLome	2.00	5.00
117 Daniel Cortes	3.00	8.00
118 Daniel Schlereth	1.25	3.00
119 Denny Almonte	2.00	5.00
120 Allan Dykstra	1.25	3.00
121 Dominic Brown	15.00	40.00
122 Evan Fredrickson	1.25	3.00
123 Gordon Beckham	3.00	8.00
124 Greg Veloz	1.25	3.00
125 Ike Davis	5.00	12.00
126 Isaac Galloway	2.00	5.00
127 Jacob Jefferies	1.25	3.00
128 Michael Kohn	1.25	3.00
129 Jared Goedert	1.25	3.00
130 Jason Knapp	1.25	3.00
131 Jhoulys Chacin	6.00	15.00
132 Jordy Mercer	1.25	3.00
133 Jorge Bucardo	1.25	3.00
134 Jose Ceda	1.25	3.00
135 Jose Martinez	1.25	3.00
136 Josh Roenicke	1.25	3.00
137 Juan Francisco	6.00	15.00
138 Justin Parker	1.25	3.00
139 Kyle Ginley	1.25	3.00
140 Lance Lynn	2.00	5.00
141 Logan Forsythe	1.25	3.00
142 Logan Morrison	8.00	20.00
143 Logan Schafer	1.25	3.00
144 Lorenzo Cain	3.00	8.00
145 Lucas Duda	2.00	5.00
146 Matt Mitchell	1.25	3.00
147 Danny Espinosa	2.00	5.00
148 Michael Taylor	3.00	8.00
149 Michel Inoa	3.00	8.00
150 Mike Montgomery	2.00	5.00
151 Cord Phelps	1.25	3.00
152 Pablo Sandoval	8.00	20.00
153 Quincy Latimore	1.25	3.00
154 R. J. Seidel	1.25	3.00
155 Rayner Contreras	1.25	3.00
156 Rick Porcello	5.00	12.00
157 Robert Hernandez	1.25	3.00
158 Ryan Kalish	3.00	8.00
159 Ryan Perry	2.00	5.00
160 Shelby Ford	2.00	5.00
161 Shooter Hunt	1.25	3.00
162 Tyler Kolodny	3.00	8.00
163 Tyler Sample	1.25	3.00
164 Tyson Ross	2.00	5.00
166 Waldis Joaquin	1.25	3.00
167 Welington Castillo	1.25	3.00
168 Wilin Rosario	2.00	5.00
169 Xavier Avery	3.00	8.00
170 Zach Collier	2.00	5.00
171 Zach Putnam	1.25	3.00
172 Anthony Gose	2.00	5.00
173 Roger Kieschnick	2.00	5.00
174 Andrew Liebel	1.25	3.00
175 Tim Murphy	1.25	3.00
176 Vance Worley	6.00	15.00
177 Buster Posey	4.00	10.00
178 Kenn Kasparek	3.00	8.00
179 J.P. Ramirez	1.25	3.00
180 Evan Bigley	1.25	3.00
181 Trey Haley	1.25	3.00
182 Robbie Grossman	2.00	5.00
183 Jordan Danks	3.00	8.00
184 Brett Hunter	1.25	3.00
185 Rafael Rodriguez	1.25	3.00
186 Yeicok Calderon	1.25	3.00
187 Gustavo Pierre	1.25	3.00
188 Will Smith	1.25	3.00
189 Daniel Thomas	1.25	3.00
190 Carson Blair	1.25	3.00
191 Chris Hicks	1.25	3.00
192 Rashun Dixon	1.25	3.00
193 Marcus Lemon	1.25	3.00
194 Kyle Nicholson	1.25	3.00
195 Mike Cisco	1.25	3.00
196 Jarek Cunningham	1.25	3.00
197 Cat Osterman	4.00	10.00
198 Derrick Rose	20.00	50.00
199 Michael Beasley	6.00	15.00
200 O.J. Mayo	3.00	8.00

2008 Donruss Elite Extra Edition Status

*STATUS 1-100: 4X TO 10X BASIC
*STATUS 101-200: .6X TO 1.5X ASP
RANDOM INSERTS IN PACKS
STATED PRINT RUN 50 SER.#'d SETS

Card	Low	High
101 Adrian Nieto	2.00	5.00
102 Alan Horne	2.00	5.00
103 Andrew Cashner	5.00	12.00
104 Anthony Hewitt	2.00	5.00
105 Brad Holt	2.00	5.00
106 Bryan Petersen	2.00	5.00
107 Bryan Price	2.00	5.00
108 Bud Norris	2.00	5.00
109 Carlos Gutierrez	5.00	12.00
110 Chase D'Arnaud	2.00	5.00
111 Chris Johnson	8.00	20.00
112 Christian Friedrich	6.00	15.00
113 Christian Marrero	3.00	8.00
114 Clayton Conner	2.00	5.00
115 Cole Rohrbough	2.00	5.00
116 Collin DeLome	3.00	8.00
117 Daniel Cortes	5.00	12.00
118 Daniel Schlereth	2.00	5.00
119 Denny Almonte	3.00	8.00
120 Allan Dykstra	2.00	5.00
121 Dominic Brown	25.00	60.00
122 Evan Fredrickson	2.00	5.00
123 Gordon Beckham	5.00	12.00
124 Greg Veloz	2.00	5.00
125 Ike Davis	8.00	20.00
126 Isaac Galloway	3.00	8.00
127 Jacob Jefferies	2.00	5.00
128 Michael Kohn	2.00	5.00
129 Jared Goedert	2.00	5.00
130 Jason Knapp	2.00	5.00
131 Jhoulys Chacin	10.00	25.00
132 Jordy Mercer	2.00	5.00
133 Jorge Bucardo	2.00	5.00
134 Jose Ceda	2.00	5.00
135 Jose Martinez	2.00	5.00
136 Josh Roenicke	2.00	5.00
137 Juan Francisco	4.00	10.00
138 Justin Parker	2.00	5.00
139 Kyle Ginley	2.00	5.00
140 Lance Lynn	3.00	8.00
141 Logan Forsythe	2.00	5.00
142 Logan Morrison	12.00	30.00
143 Logan Schafer	2.00	5.00
144 Lorenzo Cain	5.00	12.00
145 Lucas Duda	3.00	8.00
146 Matt Mitchell	2.00	5.00
147 Danny Espinosa	3.00	8.00
148 Michael Taylor	5.00	12.00
149 Michel Inoa	5.00	12.00
150 Mike Montgomery	3.00	8.00
151 Cord Phelps	2.00	5.00
152 Pablo Sandoval	12.00	30.00
153 Quincy Latimore	2.00	5.00
154 R. J. Seidel	2.00	5.00
155 Rayner Contreras	2.00	5.00
156 Rick Porcello	8.00	20.00
157 Robert Hernandez	2.00	5.00
158 Ryan Kalish	5.00	12.00
159 Ryan Perry	3.00	8.00
160 Shelby Ford	3.00	8.00
161 Shooter Hunt	2.00	5.00
162 Tyler Kolodny	5.00	12.00
163 Tyler Sample	2.00	5.00
164 Tyson Ross	3.00	8.00
166 Waldis Joaquin	2.00	5.00
167 Welington Castillo	2.00	5.00
168 Wilin Rosario	3.00	8.00
169 Xavier Avery	5.00	12.00
170 Zach Collier	3.00	8.00
171 Zach Putnam	2.00	5.00
172 Anthony Gose	3.00	8.00
173 Roger Kieschnick	3.00	8.00
174 Andrew Liebel	2.00	5.00
175 Tim Murphy	2.00	5.00
176 Vance Worley	10.00	25.00
177 Buster Posey	50.00	100.00
178 Kenn Kasparek	5.00	12.00
179 J.P. Ramirez	2.00	5.00
180 Evan Bigley	2.00	5.00
181 Trey Haley	2.00	5.00
182 Robbie Grossman	3.00	8.00
183 Jordan Danks	5.00	12.00
184 Brett Hunter	2.00	5.00
185 Rafael Rodriguez	2.00	5.00
186 Yeicok Calderon	2.00	5.00
187 Gustavo Pierre	2.00	5.00
188 Will Smith	2.00	5.00
189 Daniel Thomas	2.00	5.00
190 Carson Blair	2.00	5.00
191 Chris Hicks	2.00	5.00
192 Rashun Dixon	2.00	5.00
193 Marcus Lemon	2.00	5.00
194 Kyle Nicholson	2.00	5.00
195 Mike Cisco	2.00	5.00
196 Jarek Cunningham	2.00	5.00
197 Cat Osterman	6.00	15.00
198 Derrick Rose	40.00	80.00
199 Michael Beasley	10.00	25.00
200 O.J. Mayo	6.00	15.00

2008 Donruss Elite Extra Edition Status Gold

RANDOM INSERTS IN PACKS
STATED PRINT RUN 25 SER.#'d SETS
NO PRICING DUE TO SCARCITY

2008 Donruss Elite Extra Edition Signature Aspirations

OVERALL AUTO/MEM ODDS 1:5
PRINT RUN B/WN 5-100 COPIES PER
NO PRICING ON QTY 25 OR LESS
EXCH DEADLINE 5/26/2010

Card	Low	High
1 Aaron Cunningham/50	6.00	15.00
2 Aaron Pribanic/100	5.00	12.00
3 Aaron Shafer/100	4.00	10.00
4 Adam Mills/100	4.00	10.00
5 Adam Moore/100	8.00	20.00
6 Beamer Weems/100	4.00	10.00
7 Beau Mills/50	6.00	15.00
8 Blake Tekotte/25		
9 Bobby Lanigan/100	4.00	10.00
10 Brad Hand/50	20.00	50.00
11 Brandon Crawford/50	8.00	20.00
12 Brandon Waring/100	5.00	12.00
13 Brent Morel/100	6.00	15.00
14 Brett Jacobson/100	5.00	12.00
15 Caleb Gindl/100	8.00	20.00
16 Carlos Peguero/100	12.50	30.00
17 Charlie Blackmon/50	4.00	10.00
18 Charlie Furbush/100	5.00	12.00
19 Chris Davis/100	10.00	25.00
20 Chris Valaika/100	4.00	10.00
21 Clark Murphy/50	4.00	10.00
22 Clayton Cook/100	4.00	10.00
23 Cody Adams/50	4.00	10.00
24 Cody Satterwhite/50	10.00	25.00
25 Cole St. Clair/100	5.00	12.00
26 Corey Young/100	4.00	10.00
27 Curtis Petersen/100	4.00	10.00
28 Danny Rams/100	5.00	12.00
29 Dennis Raben/50	8.00	20.00
30 Derek Norris/50	15.00	40.00
31 Tyson Brummett/100	4.00	10.00
32 Dusty Coleman/50	5.00	12.00
33 Edgar Olmos/100	4.00	10.00
34 Engel Beltre/5		
35 Eric Beaulac/100	4.00	10.00
36 Geison Aguasviva/100	4.00	10.00
37 Gerardo Parra/100	5.00	12.00
38 Graham Hicks/100	4.00	10.00
39 Greg Halman/100	12.00	30.00
40 Hector Gomez/100	5.00	12.00
41 J.D. Alfaro/100	4.00	10.00
42 Jack Egbert/100	4.00	10.00
43 James Darnell/50	6.00	15.00
44 Jay Austin/50	5.00	12.00
45 Jeremy Beckham/100 EXCH	6.00	15.00
46 Jeremy Farrell/100	4.00	10.00
47 Jeremy Hamilton/100	4.00	10.00
48 Jericho Jones/100	8.00	20.00
49 Jesse Darcy/100	5.00	12.00
50 Jeudy Valdez/100	4.00	10.00
51 Jharmidy De Jesus/50	12.50	30.00
52 Joba Chamberlain/25		
53 Johnny Giavotella/100	10.00	25.00
54 Jon Mark Owings/100	5.00	12.00
55 Jordan Meaker/100	4.00	10.00
56 Jose Duran/100	12.50	30.00
57 Josh Harrison/100	5.00	12.00
58 Josh Lindblom/50	4.00	10.00
59 Josh Reddick/100	20.00	50.00
60 Juan Carlos Sulbaran/100	5.00	12.00
61 Justin Bristow/100	4.00	10.00
62 Kenny Gilbert/100	4.00	10.00
63 Kirk Nieuwenhuis/100	10.00	25.00
64 Kyle Hudson/50	5.00	12.00
65 Kyle Russell/50	5.00	12.00
66 Kyle Weiland/50	5.00	12.00
67 L. J. Hoes/50	5.00	12.00
68 Mark Cohoon/100	5.00	12.00
69 Mark Sobolewski/100	15.00	40.00
70 Mat Gamel/50	30.00	60.00
71 Matt Harrison/100	10.00	25.00
72 Max Ramirez/100	8.00	20.00
73 Tony Delmonico/50	6.00	15.00
74 Mike Stanton/25		
75 Mitch Abeita/100	4.00	10.00
76 Neftali Feliz/50	20.00	50.00
77 Neftali Soto/50	20.00	50.00
78 Niko Vasquez/50	6.00	15.00
79 Omar Aguilar/100	4.00	10.00
80 Petey Paramore/100	4.00	10.00
81 Ray Kruml/100	5.00	12.00
82 Rolando Gomez/50	4.00	10.00
83 Ryan Chaffee/100	5.00	12.00
84 Ryan Pressly/100	4.00	10.00
85 Sam Freeman/100	5.00	12.00
86 Sawyer Carroll/100	4.00	10.00
87 Scott Green/100	6.00	15.00
88 Sean Ratliff/100	8.00	20.00
89 Shane Peterson/50	8.00	20.00
90 T.J. Steele/50	8.00	20.00
91 Tim Federowicz/100	6.00	15.00
92 Tyler Chatwood/50	8.00	20.00
93 Tyler Cline/100	4.00	10.00
94 Tyler Ladendorf/50	5.00	12.00
95 Tyler Yockey/100	6.00	15.00
96 Wilmer Flores/50 EXCH	50.00	100.00
97 Wilson Ramos/100	12.50	30.00
98 Zach McAllister/100	6.00	15.00
99 Zachary Stewart/100	5.00	12.00
100 Zeke Spruill/50 EXCH	12.50	30.00
101 Adrian Nieto/25		
102 Alan Horne/100	10.00	25.00
103 Andrew Cashner/25		
104 Anthony Hewitt/25		
105 Brad Holt/25		
106 Bryan Petersen/50	4.00	10.00
107 Bryan Price/25		
108 Bud Norris/50	4.00	10.00
109 Carlos Gutierrez/25		
110 Chase D'Arnaud/25		
111 Chris Johnson/25		
112 Christian Friedrich/25		
113 Christian Marrero/50	5.00	12.00
114 Clayton Conner/50	4.00	10.00
115 Cole Rohrbough/25		
116 Collin DeLome/50	5.00	12.00
117 Daniel Cortes/25		
118 Daniel Schlereth/25		
119 Denny Almonte/50	4.00	10.00
120 Allan Dykstra/25		
121 Dominic Brown/50	100.00	200.00
122 Evan Fredrickson/25		
123 Gordon Beckham/25		
124 Greg Veloz/50	4.00	10.00
125 Ike Davis/25		
126 Isaac Galloway/25		
127 Jacob Jefferies/50	4.00	10.00
128 Michael Kohn/25		
129 Jared Goedert/50	4.00	10.00
130 Jason Knapp/50	15.00	40.00
131 Jhoulys Chacin/50	10.00	25.00
132 Jordy Mercer/75	4.00	10.00
133 Jorge Bucardo/50	5.00	12.00
134 Jose Ceda/100	5.00	12.00
135 Jose Martinez/75	4.00	10.00
136 Josh Roenicke/50	4.00	10.00
137 Juan Francisco/100 EXCH	10.00	25.00
138 Justin Parker/25		
139 Kyle Ginley/50	4.00	10.00
140 Lance Lynn/25		
141 Logan Forsythe/10		
142 Logan Morrison/25		
143 Logan Schafer/50	4.00	10.00
144 Lorenzo Cain/50	30.00	60.00
145 Lucas Duda/20		
146 Matt Mitchell/25		
147 Danny Espinosa/25		
148 Michael Taylor/50	50.00	100.00
149 Michel Inoa/25		
150 Mike Montgomery/25		
151 Cord Phelps/25		
152 Pablo Sandoval/50	50.00	100.00
153 Quincy Latimore/50	4.00	10.00
154 R. J. Seidel/50	4.00	10.00
155 Rayner Contreras/100	4.00	10.00
156 Rick Porcello/25		
157 Robert Hernandez/50	4.00	10.00
158 Ryan Kalish/50	20.00	50.00
159 Ryan Perry/25		
160 Shelby Ford/50	4.00	10.00
161 Shooter Hunt/25		
162 Tyler Kolodny/50	10.00	25.00
163 Tyler Sample/25		
164 Tyson Ross/25		
166 Waldis Joaquin/50	4.00	10.00
167 Welington Castillo/50	4.00	10.00
168 Wilin Rosario/25		
169 Xavier Avery/25		
170 Zach Collier/25		
171 Zach Putnam/25		
172 Anthony Gose/25		
173 Roger Kieschnick/50	10.00	25.00
174 Andrew Liebel/25		
175 Tim Murphy/25		
176 Vance Worley/25		
177 Buster Posey/25		
178 Kenn Kasparek/25		
179 J.P. Ramirez/25		
180 Evan Bigley/50	6.00	15.00
181 Trey Haley/25		
182 Robbie Grossman/25		
183 Jordan Danks/25 EXCH		
184 Brett Hunter/25		
185 Rafael Rodriguez/25		
186 Yeicok Calderon/50	12.50	30.00
187 Gustavo Pierre/25		
188 Will Smith/25		
189 Daniel Thomas/25		
190 Carson Blair/25		
191 Chris Hicks/25		
192 Rashun Dixon/10 EXCH		
193 Marcus Lemon/25		
194 Kyle Nicholson/25		
195 Mike Cisco/25		
196 Jarek Cunningham/25		
197 Cat Osterman/10		
198 Derrick Rose/10		
199 Michael Beasley/10		
200 O.J. Mayo/25		

2008 Donruss Elite Extra Edition Signature Status

OVERALL AUTO/MEM ODDS 1:5
PRINT RUN B/WN 5-50 COPIES PER
NO PRICING ON QTY 25 OR LESS
EXCH DEADLINE 5/26/2010
1 Aaron Cunningham/25
2 Aaron Pribanic/50 6.00 15.00
3 Aaron Shafer/50 4.00 10.00
4 Adam Mills/50 4.00 10.00
5 Adam Moore/50 8.00 20.00
6 Beamer Weems/50 4.00 10.00
7 Beau Mills/25
8 Blake Tekotte/10
9 Bobby Lanigan/50 4.00 10.00
10 Brad Hand/10
11 Brandon Crawford/25
12 Brandon Waring/50 5.00 12.00
13 Brent Morel/50 8.00 20.00
14 Brett Jacobson/50 5.00 12.00
15 Caleb Gindl/50 8.00 20.00
16 Carlos Peguero/50 12.50 30.00
17 Charlie Blackmon/25
18 Charlie Furbush/50 5.00 12.00
19 Chris Davis/50 10.00 25.00
20 Chris Valaika/50 4.00 10.00
21 Clark Murphy/25
22 Clayton Cook/50 4.00 10.00
23 Cody Adams/25
24 Cody Satterwhite/25
25 Cole St. Clair/50 5.00 12.00
26 Corey Young/50 4.00 10.00
27 Curtis Petersen/50 4.00 10.00
28 Danny Rams/50 5.00 12.00
29 Dennis Raben/25
30 Derek Norris/25
31 Tyson Brummett/50 5.00 12.00
32 Dusty Coleman/25
33 Edgar Olmos/50 4.00 10.00
34 Engel Beltre/5
35 Eric Beaulac/50 4.00 10.00
36 Geison Aguasviva/50 4.00 10.00
37 Gerardo Parra/50 5.00 12.00
38 Graham Hicks/50 4.00 10.00
39 Greg Halman/50 15.00 40.00
40 Hector Gomez/50 5.00 12.00
41 J.D. Alfaro/50 4.00 10.00
42 Jack Egbert/50 4.00 10.00
43 James Darnell/25
44 Jay Austin/25
45 Jeremy Beckham/50 EXCH 6.00 15.00
46 Jeremy Farrell/50 4.00 10.00
47 Jeremy Hamilton/50 4.00 10.00
48 Jericho Jones/50 8.00 20.00
49 Jesse Darcy/50 5.00 12.00
50 Jeudy Valdez/50 4.00 10.00
51 Jharmidy De Jesus/25
52 Joba Chamberlain/10
53 Johnny Giavotella/50 12.50 30.00
54 Jon Mark Owings/50 5.00 12.00
55 Jordan Meaker/50 4.00 10.00
56 Jose Duran/50 12.50 30.00
57 Josh Harrison/50 5.00 12.00
58 Josh Lindblom/25
59 Josh Reddick/50 20.00 50.00
60 Juan Carlos Sulbaran/50 5.00 12.00
61 Justin Bristow/50 4.00 10.00
62 Kenny Gilbert/50 4.00 10.00
63 Kirk Nieuwenhuis/50 12.50 30.00
64 Kyle Hudson/25
65 Kyle Russell/25
66 Kyle Weiland/25
67 L. J. Hoes/25
68 Mark Cohoon/50 5.00 12.00
69 Mark Sobolewski/50 15.00 40.00
70 Mat Gamel/25
71 Matt Harrison/50 12.50 30.00
72 Max Ramirez/50 8.00 20.00
73 Tony Delmonico/25
74 Mike Stanton/10
75 Mitch Abeita/50 4.00 10.00
76 Neftali Feliz/25
77 Neftali Soto/25
78 Niko Vasquez/25
79 Omar Aguilar/50 4.00 10.00
80 Petey Paramore/50 4.00 10.00
81 Ray Kruml/50 5.00 12.00
82 Rolando Gomez/25
83 Ryan Chaffee/50 5.00 12.00
84 Ryan Pressly/50 4.00 10.00
85 Sam Freeman/50 5.00 12.00
86 Sawyer Carroll/50 4.00 10.00
87 Scott Green/50 6.00 15.00
88 Sean Ratliff/50 8.00 20.00
89 Shane Peterson/25
90 T.J. Steele/25
91 Tim Federowicz/50 6.00 15.00
92 Tyler Chatwood/25
93 Tyler Cline/50 4.00 10.00
94 Tyler Ladendorf/25
95 Tyler Yockey/50 6.00 15.00
96 Wilmer Flores/25 EXCH
97 Wilson Ramos/50 15.00 40.00
98 Zach McAllister/50 6.00 15.00
99 Zachary Stewart/50 5.00 12.00
132 Jordy Mercer/40 5.00 12.00
133 Jorge Bucardo/25
134 Jose Ceda/50 5.00 12.00
135 Jose Martinez/50 4.00 10.00

2008 Donruss Elite Extra Edition Signature Status Black

OVERALL AUTO/MEM ODDS 1:5
STATED PRINT RUN 1 SER.#'d SET
NO PRICING DUE TO SCARCITY
EXCH DEADLINE 5/26/2010

2008 Donruss Elite Extra Edition Signature Status Gold

OVERALL AUTO/MEM ODDS 1:5
STATED PRINT RUN 5 SER.#'d SETS
NO PRICING DUE TO SCARCITY
EXCH DEADLINE 5/26/2010

2008 Donruss Elite Extra Edition Signature Turn of the Century

OVERALL AUTO/MEM ODDS 1:5
PRINT RUNS B/WN 8-999 COPIES PER
EXCH DEADLINE 5/26/2010
1 Aaron Cunningham/150 5.00 12.00
2 Aaron Pribanic/269 4.00 10.00
3 Aaron Shafer/117 4.00 10.00
4 Adam Mills/841 3.00 8.00
5 Adam Moore/844 4.00 10.00
6 Beamer Weems/844 3.00 8.00
7 Beau Mills/64 6.00 15.00
8 Blake Tekotte/194 4.00 10.00
9 Bobby Lanigan/594 3.00 8.00
10 Brad Hand/447 4.00 10.00
11 Brandon Crawford/718 4.00 10.00
12 Brandon Waring/369 4.00 10.00
13 Brent Morel/269 4.00 10.00
14 Brett Jacobson/488 4.00 10.00
15 Caleb Gindl/245 3.00 8.00
16 Carlos Peguero/344 4.00 10.00
17 Charlie Blackmon/122 3.00 8.00
18 Charlie Furbush/469 3.00 8.00
19 Chris Davis/399 12.50 30.00
20 Chris Valaika/309 3.00 8.00
21 Clark Murphy/644 3.00 8.00
22 Clayton Cook/844 3.00 8.00
23 Cody Adams/447 3.00 8.00
24 Cody Satterwhite/322 6.00 15.00
25 Cole St. Clair/342 4.00 10.00
26 Corey Young/594 3.00 8.00
27 Curtis Petersen/199 3.00 8.00
28 Danny Rams/594 3.00 8.00
29 Dennis Raben/172 6.00 15.00
30 Derek Norris/744 8.00 20.00
31 Tyson Brummett/919 3.00 8.00
32 Dusty Coleman/719 3.00 8.00
33 Edgar Olmos/594 3.00 8.00
34 Engel Beltre/8
35 Eric Beaulac/594 3.00 8.00
36 Geison Aguasviva/368 3.00 8.00
37 Gerardo Parra/421 5.00 12.00
38 Graham Hicks/594 3.00 8.00
39 Greg Halman/429 5.00 12.00
40 Hector Gomez/320 4.00 10.00
41 J.D. Alfaro/790 3.00 8.00
42 Jack Egbert/844 3.00 8.00
43 James Darnell/89 5.00 12.00
44 Jay Austin/207 4.00 10.00
45 Jeremy Beckham/199 EXCH 5.00 12.00
46 Jeremy Farrell/844 3.00 8.00
47 Jeremy Hamilton/844 3.00 8.00
48 Jericho Jones/844 6.00 15.00
49 Jesse Darcy/594 3.00 8.00
50 Jeudy Valdez/374 3.00 8.00
51 Jharmidy De Jesus/269 10.00 25.00
52 Joba Chamberlain/39 30.00 60.00
53 Johnny Giavotella/844 6.00 15.00
54 Jon Mark Owings/844 4.00 10.00
55 Jordan Meaker/844 3.00 8.00
56 Jose Duran/262 10.00 25.00
57 Josh Harrison/844 4.00 10.00
58 Josh Lindblom/131 3.00 8.00
59 Josh Reddick/320 8.00 20.00
60 Juan Carlos Sulbaran/844 4.00 10.00
61 Justin Bristow/594 3.00 8.00
62 Kenny Gilbert/842 3.00 8.00
63 Kirk Nieuwenhuis/844 5.00 12.00
64 Kyle Hudson/419 4.00 10.00
65 Kyle Russell/594 4.00 10.00
66 Kyle Weiland/394 4.00 10.00
67 L. J. Hoes/494 5.00 12.00
68 Mark Cohoon/844 3.00 8.00
69 Mark Sobolewski/269 12.50 30.00
70 Mat Gamel/145 20.00 50.00
71 Matt Harrison/244 3.00 8.00
72 Max Ramirez/604 5.00 12.00
73 Tony Delmonico/744 5.00 12.00
74 Mike Stanton/100 150.00 300.00
75 Mitch Abeita/769 3.00 8.00
76 Neftali Feliz/999 8.00 20.00
77 Neftali Soto/645 5.00 12.00
78 Niko Vasquez/494 5.00 12.00
79 Omar Aguilar/594 4.00 10.00
80 Petey Paramore/519 3.00 8.00
81 Ray Kruml/844 4.00 10.00
82 Rolando Gomez/544 3.00 8.00
83 Ryan Chaffee/594 4.00 10.00
84 Ryan Pressly/844 3.00 8.00
85 Sam Freeman/819 3.00 8.00
86 Sawyer Carroll/544 3.00 8.00
87 Scott Green/294 3.00 8.00
88 Sean Ratliff/544 3.00 8.00
89 Shane Peterson/132 6.00 15.00
90 T.J. Steele/122 6.00 15.00
91 Tim Federowicz/844 4.00 10.00
92 Tyler Chatwood/257 5.00 12.00
93 Tyler Cline/594 3.00 8.00
94 Tyler Ladendorf/227 4.00 10.00
95 Tyler Yockey/844 3.00 8.00
96 Wilmer Flores/99 EXCH 75.00 150.00
97 Wilson Ramos/745 6.00 15.00
98 Zach McAllister/844 3.00 8.00
99 Zachary Stewart/294 4.00 10.00
100 Zeke Spruill/99 EXCH 10.00 25.00
101 Adrian Nieto/50 10.00 25.00
102 Alan Horne/125 10.00 25.00
103 Andrew Cashner/50 15.00 40.00
104 Anthony Hewitt/50 8.00 20.00
105 Brad Holt/50 10.00 25.00
106 Bryan Petersen/100 4.00 10.00
107 Bryan Price/50 4.00 10.00
108 Bud Norris/100 4.00 10.00
109 Carlos Gutierrez/50 6.00 15.00
110 Chase D'Arnaud/50 5.00 12.00
111 Chris Johnson/50 8.00 20.00
112 Christian Friedrich/50 12.50 30.00
113 Christian Marrero/100 5.00 12.00
114 Clayton Conner/100 4.00 10.00
115 Cole Rohrbough/50 10.00 25.00
116 Collin DeLome/100 5.00 12.00
117 Daniel Cortes/50 8.00 20.00
118 Daniel Schlereth/50 4.00 10.00
119 Denny Almonte/100 4.00 10.00
120 Allan Dykstra/50 12.50 30.00
121 Dominic Brown/100 40.00 80.00
122 Evan Fredrickson/50 4.00 10.00
123 Gordon Beckham/50 12.50 30.00
124 Greg Veloz/100 4.00 10.00
125 Ike Davis/50 40.00 80.00
126 Isaac Galloway/50 10.00 25.00
127 Jacob Jefferies/100 4.00 10.00
128 Michael Kohn/40 4.00 10.00
129 Jared Goedert/100 4.00 10.00
130 Jason Knapp/125 10.00 25.00
131 Jhoulys Chacin/50 10.00 25.00
132 Jordy Mercer/50 5.00 12.00
133 Jorge Bucardo/100 5.00 12.00
134 Jose Ceda/250 4.00 10.00
135 Jose Martinez/100 4.00 10.00
136 Josh Roenicke/100 4.00 10.00
137 Juan Francisco/250 10.00 25.00
138 Justin Parker/50 5.00 12.00
139 Kyle Ginley/100 4.00 10.00
140 Lance Lynn/50 10.00 25.00
141 Logan Forsythe/25
142 Logan Morrison/50 50.00 100.00
143 Logan Schafer/125 4.00 10.00
144 Lorenzo Cain/100 12.50 30.00
145 Lucas Duda/25
146 Matt Mitchell/50 4.00 10.00
147 Danny Espinosa/50 50.00 100.00
148 Michael Taylor/100 20.00 50.00
149 Michel Inoa/50 12.50 30.00
150 Mike Montgomery/50 20.00 50.00
151 Cord Phelps/50 6.00 15.00
152 Pablo Sandoval/100 40.00 80.00
153 Quincy Latimore/100 4.00 10.00
154 R. J. Seidel/100 4.00 10.00
155 Rayner Contreras/250 4.00 10.00
156 Rick Porcello/50 60.00 120.00
157 Robert Hernandez/100 4.00 10.00
158 Ryan Kalish/100 5.00 12.00
159 Ryan Perry/50 8.00 20.00
160 Shelby Ford/100 4.00 10.00
161 Shooter Hunt/50 15.00 40.00
162 Tyler Kolodny/100 10.00 25.00
163 Tyler Sample/50 5.00 12.00
164 Tyson Ross/50 4.00 10.00
166 Waldis Joaquin/100 4.00 10.00
167 Welington Castillo/100 4.00 10.00
168 Wilin Rosario/50 6.00 15.00
169 Xavier Avery/50 3.00 8.00
170 Zach Collier/50 12.50 30.00
171 Zach Putnam/50 5.00 12.00
172 Anthony Gose/50 12.50 30.00
173 Roger Kieschnick/50 10.00 25.00
174 Andrew Liebel/50 6.00 15.00
175 Tim Murphy/50 5.00 12.00
176 Vance Worley/50 40.00 80.00
177 Buster Posey/50 125.00 250.00
178 Kenn Kasparek/50 4.00 10.00
179 J.P. Ramirez/50 10.00 25.00
180 Evan Bigley/100 6.00 15.00
181 Trey Haley/50 6.00 15.00
182 Robbie Grossman/50 6.00 15.00
183 Jordan Danks/40 EXCH 20.00 50.00
184 Brett Hunter/50 5.00 12.00
185 Rafael Rodriguez/50 20.00 50.00
186 Yeicok Calderon/100 12.50 30.00
187 Gustavo Pierre/50 6.00 15.00
188 Will Smith/50 4.00 10.00
189 Daniel Thomas/50 4.00 10.00
190 Carson Blair/50 8.00 20.00
191 Chris Hicks/50 8.00 20.00
192 Rashun Dixon/25 EXCH
193 Marcus Lemon/40 6.00 15.00
194 Kyle Nicholson/50 10.00 25.00
195 Mike Cisco/50 4.00 10.00
196 Jarek Cunningham/50 4.00 10.00
197 Cat Osterman/50 20.00 50.00
198 Derrick Rose/25 125.00 250.00
199 Michael Beasley/25 30.00 80.00
200 O.J. Mayo/25 30.00 80.00

2008 Donruss Elite Extra Edition College Ties Green

STATED PRINT RUN 1500 SER.#'d SETS
*GOLD: .75X TO 2X BASIC
OVERALL INSERT ODDS 1:2
GOLD PRINT RUN 100 SER.#'d SETS
*RED: 1.2X TO 3X BASIC
OVERALL INSERT ODDS 1:2
RED PRINT RUN 50 SER.#'d SETS
1 Cord Phelps#[Sean Ratliff .75 2.00
2 Ryan Perry#[T.J. Steele 1.25 3.00
3 Mitch Abeita#[Aaron Pribanic .75 2.00
4 Ryan Perry#[Daniel Schlereth 1.25 3.00
5 Daniel Schlereth#[T.J. Steele 1.25 3.00
6 Matt Mangini#[Jordy Mercer .75 2.00
7 Blake Tekotte#[Mark Sobolewski 1.25 3.00
8 Nick Schmidt#[Logan Forsythe .75 2.00
9 Matt Wieters#[Charlie Blackmon 2.50 6.00
10 Mitch Abeita#[Joba Chamberlain .75 2.00
11 Andrew Cashner#[Andrew Walker 2.00 5.00
12 Sawyer Carroll#[Scott Green .75 2.00
13 Taylor Teagarden#[Kyle Russell .75 2.00
14 Carlos Gutierrez#[Dennis Raben 1.25 3.00
15 Lance Lynn#[Cody Satterwhite .75 2.00
16 Jordan Danks#[Cat Osterman 1.25 3.00
17 Dusty Coleman#[Aaron Shafer .75 2.00
18 Joba Chamberlain#[Aaron Pribanic .75 2.00
19 Bryan Price#[Cole St. Clair .75 2.00
20 Cat Osterman#[Kenn Kasparek 1.25 3.00
21 Jose Duran#[Brandon Hicks .75 2.00
22 Roger Kieschnick#[Zachary Stewart .75 2.00
23 Shane Peterson#[Danny Espinosa 1.25 3.00
24 David Price#[Brett Jacobson 1.25 3.00
25 Joe Savery#[Bryan Price .75 2.00
26 Petey Paramore#[Ike Davis 2.00 5.00
27 Brent Morel#[Logan Schafer 1.25 3.00
28 Dennis Raben#[Mark Sobolewski 1.25 3.00
29 Andrew Liebel#[Shane Peterson 1.25 3.00
30 Buster Posey#[Tony Thomas 2.00 5.00
31 Joe Savery#[Cole St. Clair .75 2.00
32 Cat Osterman#[Bradley Suttle .75 2.00
33 Dennis Raben#[Blake Tekotte 1.25 3.00
34 Carlos Gutierrez#[Mark Sobolewski 1.25 3.00
35 Carlos Gutierrez#[Blake Tekotte 2.00 5.00

2008 Donruss Elite Extra Edition College Ties Autographs

OVERALL AUTO/MEM ODDS 1:5
PRINT RUNS B/N 20-44 COPIES PER
NO PRICING ON QTY 25 OR LESS
EXCH DEADLINE 5/26/2010
24 David Price 10.00 25.00
Brett Jacobson/44

2008 Donruss Elite Extra Edition College Ties Jerseys

OVERALL AU/MEM ODDS 1:5
PRINT RUNS B/WN 100-500 COPIES PER
6 Matt Mangini#[Jordy Mercer/500 3.00 8.00
8 Nick Schmidt#[Logan Forsythe/500 3.00 8.00
11 Andrew Cashner#[Andrew Walker/500 3.00 8.00
15 Lance Lynn#[Cody Satterwhite/500 3.00 8.00
16 Jordan Danks#[Cat Osterman/100 5.00 12.00
20 Cat Osterman#[Kenn Kasparek/100 6.00 15.00
21 Jose Duran#[Brandon Hicks/100 4.00 10.00
30 Buster Posey#[Tony Thomas/500 10.00 25.00
32 Cat Osterman#[Bradley Suttle/500

2008 Donruss Elite Extra Edition College Ties Jerseys Prime

OVERALL AU/MEM ODDS 1:5
STATED PRINT RUN 25 SER.#'d SETS
NO PRICING DUE TO SCARCITY
6 Matt Mangini#[Jordy Mercer/25
8 Nick Schmidt#[Logan Forsythe/25
11 Andrew Cashner#[Andrew Walker/25
15 Lance Lynn#[Cody Satterwhite/25
21 Jose Duran#[Brandon Hicks/25
30 Buster Posey#[Tony Thomas/25

2008 Donruss Elite Extra Edition Collegiate Patches Autographs

OVERALL AUTO/MEM ODDS 1:5
PRINT RUNS B/WN 20-255 COPIES PER
NO PRICING ON QTY 25 OR LESS
EXCH DEADLINE 5/26/2010
1 Ryan Patterson/250 4.00 10.00
2 Mark Melancon/250 8.00 20.00
3 Buster Posey/250 50.00 100.00
4 O.J. Mayo/50 20.00 50.00
5 Gordon Beckham/250 10.00 25.00
6 Josh Roenicke/250 4.00 10.00
7 Michael Beasley/100 15.00 40.00
8 Jack Egbert/249 4.00 10.00
10 Joba Chamberlain/20
11 Tyson Brummett/250 4.00 10.00
12 Ike Davis/250 20.00 50.00
13 Andrew Cashner/250 10.00 25.00
14 Charlie Furbush/250 5.00 12.00
15 Ryan Perry/248 4.00 10.00
16 Sean Doolittle/250 4.00 10.00
17 Alan Horne/250 EXCH 8.00 20.00
18 Daniel Schlereth/250 4.00 10.00
19 Carlos Gutierrez/249 8.00 20.00
20 Shooter Hunt/250 10.00 25.00
21 Cat Osterman/250 20.00 50.00
22 Lance Lynn/249 8.00 20.00
23 Byron Wiley/248 4.00 10.00
24 Brad Mills/249 4.00 10.00
25 Bryan Price/249 4.00 10.00
26 Logan Forsythe/249 8.00 20.00
27 Brian Duensing/50
28 Tyson Ross/255 5.00 12.00
29 Shane Peterson/250 6.00 15.00
30 Josh Lindblom/249 6.00 15.00
31 Aaron Shafer/250 4.00 10.00
32 Dennis Raben/250 4.00 10.00
33 Cody Satterwhite/250 8.00 20.00
34 James Darnell/250 6.00 15.00
35 Charlie Blackmon/240 5.00 12.00
36 Blake Wood/250 4.00 10.00
37 Jordan Danks/250 EXCH 6.00 15.00
38 Jordy Mercer/247 5.00 12.00
39 Roger Kieschnick/250 5.00 12.00
40 Zachary Stewart/250 4.00 10.00
41 Daniel McCutchen/250 4.00 10.00
42 Brent Morel/250 4.00 10.00
43 Kyle Hudson/249 5.00 12.00
44 Tim Murphy/250 4.00 10.00
45 Petey Paramore/250 4.00 10.00
46 Kyle Russell/250 5.00 12.00
47 Logan Schafer/250 4.00 10.00
48 Andrew Liebel/248 6.00 15.00
49 Aaron Pribanic/250 4.00 10.00
50 Scott Green/250 6.00 15.00
51 Blake Tekotte/248 5.00 12.00
52 Vance Worley/250 20.00 50.00
53 Taylor Teagarden/250 5.00 12.00
54 Cord Phelps/250 4.00 10.00
55 Kyle Weiland/250 10.00 25.00
56 Allan Dykstra/250 5.00 12.00
57 Danny Espinosa/250 12.50 30.00
58 James Caan/30
59 Zach Putnam/244 4.00 10.00
60 Mark Sobolewski/250 10.00 25.00
61 Regis Philbin/50 50.00 100.00
62 Randy Couture/50 50.00 100.00
63 Jose Duran/250 4.00 10.00
64 Lucas Duda/249 4.00 10.00
65 Ashley Judd/29

2008 Donruss Elite Extra Edition School Colors

OVERALL INSERT ODDS 1:2
STATED PRINT RUN 1500 SER.#'d SET
1 T.J. Steele 1.25 3.00
2 Brett Jacobson .50 1.25
3 Buster Posey 3.00 8.00
4 O.J. Mayo 1.25 3.00
5 Gordon Beckham 1.50 4.00
6 Sean Ratliff .75 2.00
7 Michael Beasley 1.25 3.00
8 Jose Duran .75 2.00
9 Derrick Rose 5.00 12.00
10 Joba Chamberlain 1.25 3.00
11 Sam Freeman 1.25 3.00
12 Ike Davis 3.00 8.00
13 Andrew Cashner 2.00 5.00
14 Chase D'Arnaud .75 2.00
15 Ryan Perry 1.25 3.00
16 Blake Tekotte 1.25 3.00
17 Cole St. Clair .75 2.00
18 Daniel Schlereth .75 2.00
19 Carlos Gutierrez 1.25 3.00
20 Shooter Hunt .75 2.00
21 Zach Putnam .75 2.00
22 Lance Lynn .75 2.00
23 Mitch Abeita .75 2.00
24 Jordan Danks 1.25 3.00
25 Bryan Price .75 2.00
26 Logan Forsythe .75 2.00
27 Brandon Crawford 1.25 3.00
28 Tyson Ross .75 2.00
29 Shane Peterson 1.25 3.00
30 Josh Lindblom .75 2.00
31 Aaron Shafer .75 2.00
32 Dennis Raben 1.25 3.00
33 Cody Satterwhite .75 2.00
34 James Darnell 1.25 3.00
35 Charlie Blackmon .75 2.00
36 Sawyer Carroll .75 2.00
37 Cat Osterman 2.00 5.00
38 Jordy Mercer .75 2.00
39 Roger Kieschnick .75 2.00
40 Zachary Stewart .75 2.00
41 Kyle Weiland 2.00 5.00
42 Brent Morel 1.25 3.00
43 Lucas Duda .75 2.00
44 Tim Murphy .75 2.00
45 Petey Paramore .75 2.00
46 Kyle Russell .75 2.00
47 Logan Schafer .75 2.00
48 Andrew Liebel .75 2.00
49 Aaron Pribanic .75 2.00
50 Scott Green .75 2.00

2008 Donruss Elite Extra Edition School Colors Autographs

OVERALL AUTO/MEM ODDS 1:5
PRINT RUNS B/WN 25-50 COPIES PER
NO PRICING ON QTY 25 OR LESS
EXCH DEADLINE 5/26/2010
1 T.J. Steele/25
2 Brett Jacobson/25
3 Buster Posey/50 60.00 120.00
4 O.J. Mayo/25
5 Gordon Beckham/50 12.50 30.00
6 Sean Ratliff/25
7 Michael Beasley/25
8 Jose Duran/50 4.00 10.00
9 Derrick Rose/25
10 Joba Chamberlain/25
11 Sam Freeman/25
12 Ike Davis/50 20.00 50.00
13 Andrew Cashner/50 10.00 25.00
14 Chase D'Arnaud/50 5.00 12.00
15 Ryan Perry/50 4.00 10.00
16 Blake Tekotte/50 4.00 10.00
17 Cole St. Clair/25
18 Daniel Schlereth/50 4.00 10.00
19 Carlos Gutierrez/25
20 Shooter Hunt/25
21 Zach Putnam/25
22 Lance Lynn/50 5.00 12.00
23 Mitch Abeita/25
24 Jordan Danks/25 EXCH
25 Bryan Price/50 5.00 12.00
26 Logan Forsythe/25
27 Brandon Crawford/25
28 Tyson Ross/25
29 Shane Peterson/25
30 Josh Lindblom/25
31 Aaron Shafer/50 4.00 10.00
32 Dennis Raben/50 10.00 25.00
33 Cody Satterwhite/50 8.00 20.00
34 James Darnell/25
35 Charlie Blackmon/50 5.00 12.00
36 Sawyer Carroll/25
37 Cat Osterman/25
38 Jordy Mercer/25
39 Roger Kieschnick/25
40 Zachary Stewart/25
41 Kyle Weiland/25
42 Brent Morel/50 10.00 25.00
43 Lucas Duda/25
44 Tim Murphy/25
45 Petey Paramore/50
46 Kyle Russell/50 8.00 20.00
47 Logan Schafer/50 4.00 10.00
48 Andrew Liebel/25
49 Aaron Pribanic/25
50 Scott Green/25

2008 Donruss Elite Extra Edition School Colors Materials

OVERALL AU/MEM ODDS 1:5
STATED PRINT RUN 100 SER.#'d SETS
3 Buster Posey 6.00 15.00
4 O.J. Mayo 6.00 15.00
5 Gordon Beckham 4.00 10.00
7 Michael Beasley 6.00 15.00
8 Jose Duran 4.00 10.00
9 Derrick Rose 20.00 50.00
13 Andrew Cashner 4.00 10.00
33 Cody Satterwhite 6.00 15.00
37 Cat Osterman 8.00 20.00

2008 Donruss Elite Extra Edition School Colors Materials Prime

OVERALL AU/MEM ODDS 1:5
STATED PRINT RUN 25 SER.#'d SETS
NO PRICING DUE TO SCARCITY

2008 Donruss Elite Extra Edition Throwback Threads

OVERALL AU/MEM ODDS 1:5
PRINT RUNS B/WN 15-500 COPIES PER
NO PRICING ON QTY 25 OR LESS
1 Rick Porcello/500 6.00 15.00
2 Gordon Beckham/500 4.00 10.00
3 Andrew Cashner/500 4.00 10.00
5 Xavier Avery/15
6 Cody Satterwhite/500 6.00 15.00
8 Logan Morrison/25
9 Jose Duran/500 3.00 8.00
10 Derrick Rose/500 12.50 30.00
11 Michael Beasley/500 8.00 20.00
12 O.J. Mayo/400 6.00 15.00
13 Buster Posey/250 10.00 25.00
15 Luis Exposito/25
20 Cat Osterman/100 6.00 15.00
24 Tim Alderson/500 3.00 8.00
25 Michael Burgess/500 3.00 8.00

2008 Donruss Elite Extra Edition Throwback Threads Prime

OVERALL AU/MEM ODDS 1:5
PRINT RUNS B/WN 1-50 COPIES PER
NO PRICING ON QTY 10 OR LESS
1 Rick Porcello/10
2 Gordon Beckham/10
3 Andrew Cashner/10
6 Cody Satterwhite/10
9 Jose Duran/10
10 Derrick Rose/10
11 Michael Beasley/10
12 O.J. Mayo/10
13 Buster Posey/10
21 Mark Melancon/1
24 Tim Alderson/50 6.00 15.00
25 Michael Burgess/50 6.00 15.00

2008 Donruss Elite Extra Edition Throwback Threads Autographs

OVERALL AUTO/MEM ODDS 1:5
PRINT RUNS B/WN 4-100 COPIES PER
NO PRICING ON QTY 25 OR LESS
EXCH DEADLINE 5/26/2010
1 Rick Porcello/100 40.00 80.00
2 Gordon Beckham/100 20.00 50.00
3 Andrew Cashner/100 12.50 30.00
5 Xavier Avery/35 20.00 50.00
6 Cody Satterwhite/100
8 Logan Morrison/25
9 Jose Duran/100 10.00 25.00
10 Derrick Rose/25
11 Michael Beasley/25
12 O.J. Mayo/25
13 Buster Posey/100 100.00 175.00
15 Luis Exposito/25
20 Cat Osterman/50 30.00 60.00
21 Mark Melancon/4
22 Madison Bumgarner/4
23 Nick Hagadone/15
24 Tim Alderson/40 10.00 25.00
25 Michael Burgess/5

2008 Donruss Elite Extra Edition Throwback Threads Autographs Prime

OVERALL AUTO/MEM ODDS 1:5
PRINT RUNS B/WN 1-25 COPIES PER
NO PRICING DUE TO SCARCITY
EXCH DEADLINE 5/26/2010

2009 Donruss Elite Extra Edition

COMP.SET w/o AU's (50) 6.00 15.00
COMMON CARD (1-50) .20 .50
COMMON AU (51-150) 3.00 8.00
OVERALL AUTO ODDS 1:5 HOBBY
AU PRINT RUNS B/WN 99-999 COPIES PER
EXCHANGE DEADLINE 7/20/2011
1 Bobby Borchering .30 .75
2 Blake Smith .20 .50
3 Drew Storen .30 .75
4 J.R. Murphy .20 .50
5 Zack Wheeler .30 .75
6 Nolan Arenado .60 1.50
7 Matt Bashore .20 .50
8 Josh Phegley .20 .50
9 Jacob Turner .60 1.50
10 Mike Leake .60 1.50
11 Kelly Dugan .20 .50
12 Bill Bullock .20 .50
13 Shelby Miller .75 2.00
14 Alex Wilson .20 .50
15 Ben Paulsen .20 .50
16 Max Stassi .30 .75
17 A.J. Pollock .20 .50
18 Aaron Miller .20 .50
19 Brooks Pounders .30 .75
20 Shaver Hansen .20 .50
21 Tyler Skaggs .30 .75
22 Jiovanni Mier .30 .75
23 Everett Williams .20 .50
24 Rich Poythress .20 .50
25 Chad Jenkins .20 .50
26 Rey Fuentes .20 .50
27 Ryan Jackson .20 .50
28 Eric Arnett .30 .75
29 Chris Owings .20 .50
30 Garrett Gould .20 .50
31 Tyler Matzek .30 .75
32 Donnie Joseph .20 .50
33 Brandon Belt 1.00 2.50
34 Jon Gaston .20 .50
35 Tracye Thompson .30 .75
36 Marc Krauss .20 .50
37 Kyrell Hudson .30 .75
38 Ben Tootle .20 .50
39 Jake Marisnick .20 .50
40 Aaron Baker .20 .50
41 Kent Matthes .20 .50
42 Andrew Oliver .20 .50
43 Cameron Garfield .20 .50
44 Adam Warren .20 .50
45 Dustin Dickerson .30 .75
46 James Jones .20 .50
47 Brooks Raley .20 .50
48 Jenrry Mejia .30 .75
49 Brock Holt .20 .50
50 Wes Hatton .20 .50
51 Dustin Ackley AU/899 20.00 50.00
52 Donavan Tate AU/999 6.00 15.00
53 Tony Sanchez AU/435 8.00 20.00
54 Matt Hobgood AU/681 5.00 12.00
55 Alex White AU/599 5.00 12.00
56 Jared Mitchell AU/370 6.00 15.00
57 Mike Trout AU/495 40.00 80.00
58 Brett Jackson AU/534 12.50 30.00
59 Mike Minor AU/570 6.00 15.00
60 Slade Heathcott AU/754 6.00 15.00
61 Tom Mendonca AU/569 4.00 10.00
62 Wil Myers AU/799 10.00 25.00
63 Jason Kipnis AU/319 10.00 25.00
64 Robert Stock AU/569 6.00 15.00
65 Tim Wheeler AU/794 5.00 12.00
66 Mychal Givens AU/794 EXCH 5.00 12.00
67 Grant Green AU/444 6.00 15.00
68 D.J. LeMahieu AU/645 6.00 15.00
69 Rex Brothers AU/699 3.00 8.00
70 Thomas Joseph AU/99 40.00 80.00
71 Wade Gaynor AU/730 3.00 8.00
72 Ryan Wheeler AU/690 5.00 12.00
73 Kyle Heckathorn AU/599 4.00 10.00
74 Chad James AU/99 15.00 40.00
75 Victor Black AU/694 4.00 10.00
76 Todd Glaesmann AU/494 4.00 10.00
77 Tyler Kehrer AU/99 15.00 40.00
78 Steve Baron AU/700 3.00 8.00

79 Matt Davidson AU/599 4.00 10.00
80 Jeff Kobernus AU/570 3.00 8.00
81 Kentrail Davis AU/655 4.00 10.00
82 Kyle Gibson AU/645 8.00 20.00
83 Garrett Richards AU/470 4.00 10.00
84 Brad Boxberger AU/550 4.00 10.00
85 Evan Chambers AU/695 3.00 8.00
86 Telvin Nash AU/725 3.00 8.00
87 Austin Kirk AU/599 3.00 8.00
88 Marquise Cooper AU/99 EXCH 10.00 25.00
89 Jason Christian AU/730 3.00 8.00
90 Randal Grichuk AU/770 4.00 10.00
91 Nick Franklin AU/724 12.50 30.00
92 Eric Smith AU/99 12.50 30.00
93 Jeremy Hazelbaker AU/640 4.00 10.00
94 Zach Dotson AU/699 3.00 8.00
95 Josh Fellhauer AU/494 4.00 10.00
96 Jeff Malm AU/650 4.00 10.00
97 Caleb Cotham AU/549 5.00 12.00
98 Trevor Holder AU/649 3.00 8.00
99 Joe Kelly AU/690 4.00 10.00
100 Robbie Shields AU/749 3.00 8.00
101 Kyle Bellamy AU/695 3.00 8.00
102 Braxton Lane AU/710 3.00 8.00
103 Justin Marks AU/99 EXCH 3.00 8.00
104 Ryan Goins AU/599 3.00 8.00
105 Chase Anderson AU/619 3.00 8.00
106 Kyle Seager AU/744 3.00 8.00
107 Colton Cain AU/99 20.00 50.00
108 David Renfroe AU/695 6.00 15.00
109 Travis Banwart AU/645 3.00 8.00
110 Joe Testa AU/699 3.00 8.00
111 Brandon Jacobs AU/725 3.00 8.00
112 Brett Brach AU/699 3.00 8.00
113 Brad Brach AU/695 3.00 8.00
114 Keon Broxton AU/675 3.00 8.00
115 Nathan Karns AU/734 4.00 10.00
116 Kendal Volz AU/695 3.00 8.00
117 Charles Ruiz AU/594 3.00 8.00
118 Mike Spina AU/580 4.00 10.00
119 Jamie Johnson AU/619 3.00 8.00
120 Bryan Mitchell AU/699 4.00 10.00
121 Chad Bell AU/744 3.00 8.00
122 Dan Taylor AU/650 3.00 8.00
123 Khris Davis AU/150 EXCH
124 Ashur Tolliver AU/99 30.00 60.00
125 Cody Rogers AU/690 4.00 10.00
126 Trent Stevenson AU/744 3.00 8.00
127 Dean Weaver AU/599 3.00 8.00
128 Matt Helm AU/790 5.00 12.00
129 Andrew Doyle AU/640 3.00 8.00
130 Matt Graham AU/690 3.00 8.00
131 Kevan Hess AU/719 3.00 8.00
132 Luke Bailey AU/475 3.00 8.00
133 Steve Matz AU/790 5.00 12.00
134 Tanner Bushue AU/652 4.00 10.00
135 Neil Medchill AU/710 6.00 15.00
136 Edward Paredes AU/725 3.00 8.00
137 A.J. Jimenez AU/695 3.00 8.00
138 Grant Desme AU/744 5.00 12.00
139 Zack Von Rosenberg AU/770 4.00 10.00
140 Daniel Fields AU/749 5.00 12.00
141 Graham Stoneburner AU/719 3.00 8.00
142 David Holmberg AU/710 5.00 12.00
143 Chris Dominguez AU/719 4.00 10.00
144 Luke Murton AU/750 4.00 10.00
145 Danny Rosenbaum AU/695 3.00 8.00
146 Tyler Townsend AU/99 20.00 50.00
147 Louis Coleman AU/597 3.00 8.00
148 Patrick Schuster AU/695 3.00 8.00
149 Jeff Hunt AU/99 15.00 40.00
150 Aroldis Chapman AU/695 20.00 50.00

2009 Donruss Elite Extra Edition Aspirations

*ASP 1-50: 2.5X TO 6X BASIC
RANDOM INSERTS IN PACKS
STATED PRINT RUN 150 SER.#'d SETS
51 Dustin Ackley 6.00 15.00
52 Donavan Tate 3.00 8.00
53 Tony Sanchez 3.00 8.00
54 Matt Hobgood 3.00 8.00
55 Alex White 3.00 8.00
56 Jared Mitchell 2.00 5.00
57 Mike Trout 10.00 25.00
58 Brett Jackson 4.00 10.00
59 Mike Minor 2.00 5.00
60 Slade Heathcott 3.00 8.00
61 Tom Mendonca 2.00 5.00
62 Wil Myers 6.00 15.00
63 Jason Kipnis 3.00 8.00
64 Robert Stock 2.00 5.00
65 Tim Wheeler 2.00 5.00
66 Mychal Givens 2.00 5.00
67 Grant Green 1.25 3.00
68 D.J. LeMahieu 2.00 5.00
69 Rex Brothers 2.00 5.00
70 Thomas Joseph 1.25 3.00
71 Wade Gaynor 1.25 3.00
72 Ryan Wheeler 1.25 3.00
73 Kyle Heckathorn 2.00 5.00
74 Chad James 2.00 5.00
75 Victor Black 2.00 5.00
76 Todd Glaesmann 1.25 3.00
77 Tyler Kehrer 2.00 5.00
78 Steve Baron 2.00 5.00
79 Matt Davidson 2.00 5.00
80 Jeff Kobernus 2.00 5.00
81 Kentrail Davis 2.00 5.00
82 Kyle Gibson 3.00 8.00
83 Garrett Richards 1.25 3.00
84 Brad Boxberger 2.00 5.00
85 Evan Chambers 1.25 3.00
86 Telvin Nash 2.00 5.00
87 Austin Kirk 1.25 3.00
88 Marquise Cooper 2.00 5.00
89 Jason Christian 1.25 3.00
90 Randal Grichuk 2.00 5.00
91 Nick Franklin 3.00 8.00
92 Eric Smith 2.00 5.00
93 Jeremy Hazelbaker 2.00 5.00
94 Zach Dotson 1.25 3.00
95 Josh Fellhauer 1.25 3.00
96 Jeff Malm 1.25 3.00
97 Caleb Cotham 2.00 5.00
98 Trevor Holder 1.25 3.00
99 Joe Kelly 1.25 3.00
100 Robbie Shields 1.25 3.00
101 Kyle Bellamy 1.25 3.00
102 Braxton Lane 1.25 3.00
103 Justin Marks 1.25 3.00
104 Ryan Goins 1.25 3.00
105 Chase Anderson 1.25 3.00
106 Kyle Seager 1.25 3.00
107 Colton Cain 2.00 5.00
108 David Renfroe 1.25 3.00
109 Travis Banwart 1.25 3.00
110 Joe Testa 1.25 3.00
111 Brandon Jacobs 2.00 5.00
112 Brett Brach 1.25 3.00
113 Brad Brach 1.25 3.00
114 Keon Broxton 1.25 3.00
115 Nathan Karns 1.25 3.00
116 Kendal Volz 2.00 5.00
117 Charles Ruiz 1.25 3.00
118 Mike Spina 1.25 3.00
119 Jamie Johnson 1.25 3.00
120 Bryan Mitchell 1.25 3.00
121 Chad Bell 1.25 3.00
122 Dan Taylor 1.25 3.00
123 Khris Davis 2.00 5.00
124 Ashur Tolliver 2.00 5.00
125 Cody Rogers 2.00 5.00
126 Trent Stevenson 1.25 3.00
127 Dean Weaver 1.25 3.00
128 Matt Helm 2.00 5.00
129 Andrew Doyle 1.25 3.00
130 Matt Graham 1.25 3.00
131 Kevan Hess 1.25 3.00
132 Luke Bailey 1.25 3.00
133 Steve Matz 2.00 5.00
134 Tanner Bushue 2.00 5.00
135 Neil Medchill 2.00 5.00
136 Edward Paredes 1.25 3.00
137 A.J. Jimenez 1.25 3.00
138 Grant Desme 1.25 3.00
139 Zack Von Rosenberg 1.25 3.00
140 Daniel Fields 1.25 3.00
141 Graham Stoneburner 1.25 3.00
142 David Holmberg 3.00 8.00
143 Chris Dominguez 1.25 3.00
144 Luke Murton 1.25 3.00
145 Danny Rosenbaum 1.25 3.00
146 Tyler Townsend 2.00 5.00
147 Louis Coleman 1.25 3.00
148 Patrick Schuster 1.25 3.00
149 Jeff Hunt 3.00 8.00
150 Aroldis Chapman 5.00 12.00

2009 Donruss Elite Extra Edition Status

*STATUS 1-50: 4X TO 10X BASIC
*STATUS 51-150: .6X TO 1.5X ASP
RANDOM INSERTS IN PACKS
STATED PRINT RUN 100 SER.#'d SETS

2009 Donruss Elite Extra Edition Status Gold

*STAT.GOLD 1-50: 5X TO 12X BASIC
*STAT.GOLD 51-150: .75X TO 2X ASP
RANDOM INSERTS IN PACKS
STATED PRINT RUN 50 SER.#'d SETS

2009 Donruss Elite Extra Edition Signature Aspirations

OVERALL AUTO ODDS 1:4 HOBBY
STATED PRINT RUN 100 SER.#'d SETS
EXCHANGE DEADLINE 7/20/2011
1 Bobby Borchering 10.00 25.00
2 Blake Smith 4.00 10.00
3 Drew Storen 6.00 15.00
4 J.R. Murphy 10.00 25.00
5 Zack Wheeler 12.50 30.00
6 Nolan Arenado 20.00 50.00
7 Matt Bashore 4.00 10.00
8 Josh Phegley 4.00 10.00
9 Jacob Turner 20.00 50.00
10 Mike Leake 12.50 30.00
11 Kelly Dugan 6.00 15.00
12 Bill Bullock 4.00 10.00
13 Shelby Miller 15.00 40.00
14 Alex Wilson 6.00 15.00
15 Ben Paulsen 3.00 8.00
16 Max Stassi 8.00 20.00
17 A.J. Pollock 6.00 15.00
18 Aaron Miller 6.00 15.00
19 Brooks Pounders 4.00 10.00
20 Shaver Hansen 3.00 8.00
21 Tyler Skaggs 15.00 40.00
22 Jiovanni Mier 6.00 15.00
23 Everett Williams 8.00 20.00
25 Chad Jenkins 6.00 15.00
27 Ryan Jackson 8.00 20.00
28 Eric Arnett 3.00 8.00
29 Chris Owings 6.00 15.00
30 Garrett Gould 8.00 20.00
32 Donnie Joseph 3.00 8.00
33 Brandon Belt 50.00 100.00
34 Jon Gaston 5.00 12.00
35 Tracye Thompson 10.00 25.00
36 Marc Krauss 6.00 15.00
38 Ben Tootle 3.00 8.00
39 Jake Marisnick 12.50 30.00
40 Aaron Baker 3.00 8.00
41 Kent Matthes 4.00 10.00
42 Andrew Oliver 5.00 12.00
43 Cameron Garfield 5.00 12.00
44 Adam Warren 8.00 20.00
45 Dustin Dickerson 4.00 10.00
47 Brooks Raley 4.00 10.00
48 Jenrry Mejia 15.00 40.00
49 Brock Holt 3.00 8.00
50 Wes Hatton 4.00 10.00
51 Dustin Ackley 50.00 100.00
52 Donavan Tate 10.00 25.00
53 Tony Sanchez 12.50 30.00
54 Matt Hobgood 8.00 20.00
55 Alex White 10.00 25.00
56 Jared Mitchell 6.00 15.00
57 Mike Trout 60.00 120.00
58 Brett Jackson 20.00 50.00
59 Mike Minor 8.00 20.00
60 Slade Heathcott 20.00 50.00
61 Tom Mendonca 8.00 20.00
62 Wil Myers 60.00 120.00
63 Jason Kipnis 15.00 40.00
64 Robert Stock 10.00 25.00
65 Tim Wheeler 10.00 25.00
66 Mychal Givens 12.50 30.00
67 Grant Green 20.00 50.00
68 D.J. LeMahieu 6.00 15.00
69 Rex Brothers 5.00 12.00
71 Wade Gaynor 5.00 12.00
72 Ryan Wheeler 10.00 25.00
73 Kyle Heckathorn 5.00 12.00
75 Victor Black 4.00 10.00
76 Todd Glaesmann 5.00 12.00
78 Steve Baron 3.00 8.00
79 Matt Davidson 8.00 20.00
80 Jeff Kobernus 5.00 12.00
81 Kentrail Davis 10.00 25.00
82 Kyle Gibson 12.50 30.00
83 Garrett Richards 8.00 20.00
84 Brad Boxberger 10.00 25.00
85 Evan Chambers 3.00 8.00
86 Telvin Nash 4.00 10.00
87 Austin Kirk 4.00 10.00
89 Jason Christian 3.00 8.00
90 Randal Grichuk 8.00 20.00
91 Nick Franklin 20.00 50.00
93 Jeremy Hazelbaker 5.00 12.00
94 Zach Dotson 4.00 10.00
95 Josh Fellhauer 4.00 10.00
96 Jeff Malm 8.00 20.00
97 Caleb Cotham 10.00 25.00
98 Trevor Holder 3.00 8.00
99 Joe Kelly 8.00 20.00
100 Robbie Shields 3.00 8.00
101 Kyle Bellamy 4.00 10.00
102 Braxton Lane 5.00 12.00
104 Ryan Goins 3.00 8.00
105 Chase Anderson 3.00 8.00
106 Kyle Seager 3.00 8.00
108 David Renfroe 15.00 40.00
109 Travis Banwart 3.00 8.00
110 Joe Testa 6.00 15.00
111 Brandon Jacobs 5.00 12.00
112 Brett Brach 3.00 8.00
113 Brad Brach 3.00 8.00
114 Keon Broxton 5.00 12.00
115 Nathan Karns 4.00 10.00
116 Kendal Volz 5.00 12.00
117 Charles Ruiz 3.00 8.00
118 Mike Spina 8.00 20.00
119 Jamie Johnson 4.00 10.00
120 Bryan Mitchell 8.00 20.00
121 Chad Bell 3.00 8.00
122 Dan Taylor 3.00 8.00
125 Cody Rogers 6.00 15.00
126 Trent Stevenson 5.00 12.00
127 Dean Weaver 4.00 10.00
128 Matt Helm 10.00 25.00
129 Andrew Doyle 3.00 8.00
130 Matt Graham 4.00 10.00
131 Kevan Hess 4.00 10.00
132 Luke Bailey 5.00 12.00
133 Steve Matz 10.00 25.00
134 Tanner Bushue 6.00 15.00
135 Neil Medchill 10.00 25.00
136 Edward Paredes 4.00 10.00
137 A.J. Jimenez 3.00 8.00
138 Grant Desme 5.00 12.00
139 Zack Von Rosenberg 6.00 15.00
140 Daniel Fields 8.00 20.00
141 Graham Stoneburner 4.00 10.00
142 David Holmberg 8.00 20.00
143 Chris Dominguez 12.50 30.00
144 Luke Murton 8.00 20.00
145 Danny Rosenbaum 3.00 8.00
147 Louis Coleman 4.00 10.00
148 Patrick Schuster 4.00 10.00
150 Aroldis Chapman 50.00 100.00

2009 Donruss Elite Extra Edition Signature Status

OVERALL AUTO ODDS 1:4 HOBBY
STATED PRINT RUN 100 SER.#'d SETS
EXCHANGE DEADLINE 7/20/2011
1 Bobby Borchering 12.50 30.00
2 Blake Smith
3 Drew Storen 10.00 25.00
4 J.R. Murphy 12.50 30.00
5 Zack Wheeler 20.00 50.00
6 Nolan Arenado 30.00 60.00
7 Matt Bashore 5.00 12.00
8 Josh Phegley 6.00 15.00
9 Jacob Turner 30.00 60.00
10 Mike Leake 15.00 40.00
11 Kelly Dugan 6.00 15.00
12 Bill Bullock 10.00 25.00
13 Shelby Miller 40.00 80.00
14 Alex Wilson 5.00 12.00
15 Ben Paulsen 4.00 10.00
16 Max Stassi 10.00 25.00
17 A.J. Pollock 8.00 20.00
18 Aaron Miller 15.00 40.00
19 Brooks Pounders 6.00 15.00
20 Shaver Hansen 3.00 8.00
21 Tyler Skaggs 12.50 30.00
22 Jiovanni Mier 12.50 30.00
23 Everett Williams 12.50 30.00
25 Chad Jenkins 10.00 25.00
27 Ryan Jackson 5.00 12.00
28 Eric Arnett 4.00 10.00
29 Chris Owings 12.50 30.00
30 Garrett Gould 12.50 30.00
32 Donnie Joseph 4.00 10.00
33 Brandon Belt 100.00 200.00
34 Jon Gaston 15.00 40.00
35 Tracye Thompson 20.00 50.00
36 Marc Krauss 10.00 25.00
38 Ben Tootle 3.00 8.00
39 Jake Marisnick 12.50 30.00
40 Aaron Baker 3.00 8.00
41 Kent Matthes 3.00 8.00
42 Andrew Oliver 8.00 20.00
43 Cameron Garfield 10.00 25.00
44 Adam Warren 12.50 30.00
45 Dustin Dickerson 4.00 10.00
47 Brooks Raley 5.00 12.00
48 Jenrry Mejia 20.00 50.00
49 Brock Holt 4.00 10.00
50 Wes Hatton 5.00 12.00
51 Dustin Ackley 100.00 175.00
52 Donavan Tate 12.50 30.00
53 Tony Sanchez 12.50 30.00
54 Matt Hobgood 15.00 40.00
55 Alex White 12.50 30.00
56 Jared Mitchell 30.00 60.00
57 Mike Trout 75.00 150.00
58 Brett Jackson 30.00 60.00
59 Mike Minor 12.50 30.00
60 Slade Heathcott 30.00 60.00
61 Tom Mendonca 5.00 12.00
62 Wil Myers 75.00 150.00
63 Jason Kipnis 20.00 50.00
64 Robert Stock 12.50 30.00
65 Tim Wheeler 10.00 25.00
66 Mychal Givens 15.00 40.00
67 Grant Green 30.00 60.00
68 D.J. LeMahieu 10.00 25.00
69 Rex Brothers 12.50 30.00
71 Wade Gaynor 10.00 25.00
72 Ryan Wheeler 10.00 25.00
73 Kyle Heckathorn 12.50 30.00
75 Victor Black 10.00 25.00
76 Todd Glaesmann 8.00 20.00
78 Steve Baron 5.00 12.00
79 Matt Davidson 15.00 40.00
80 Jeff Kobernus 4.00 10.00
81 Kentrail Davis 30.00 60.00
82 Kyle Gibson 20.00 50.00
83 Garrett Richards 10.00 25.00
84 Brad Boxberger 15.00 40.00
85 Evan Chambers 4.00 10.00
86 Telvin Nash 5.00 12.00
87 Austin Kirk 4.00 10.00
89 Jason Christian 4.00 10.00
90 Randal Grichuk 12.50 30.00
91 Nick Franklin 30.00 60.00
93 Jeremy Hazelbaker 8.00 20.00
94 Zach Dotson 6.00 15.00
95 Josh Fellhauer 8.00 20.00
96 Jeff Malm 15.00 40.00
97 Caleb Cotham 10.00 25.00
98 Trevor Holder 3.00 8.00
99 Joe Kelly 10.00 25.00
100 Robbie Shields 5.00 12.00
101 Kyle Bellamy 3.00 8.00
102 Braxton Lane 10.00 25.00
104 Ryan Goins 4.00 10.00
105 Chase Anderson 3.00 8.00
106 Kyle Seager 3.00 8.00
108 David Renfroe 30.00 60.00
109 Travis Banwart 3.00 8.00
110 Joe Testa 5.00 12.00
111 Brandon Jacobs 8.00 20.00
112 Brett Brach 10.00 25.00
113 Brad Brach 3.00 8.00
114 Keon Broxton 10.00 25.00
115 Nathan Karns 4.00 10.00
116 Kendal Volz 8.00 20.00
117 Charles Ruiz 3.00 8.00
118 Mike Spina 6.00 15.00
119 Jamie Johnson 4.00 10.00
120 Bryan Mitchell 12.50 30.00
121 Chad Bell 5.00 12.00
122 Dan Taylor 12.50 30.00
125 Cody Rogers 10.00 25.00
126 Trent Stevenson
127 Dean Weaver 4.00 10.00
128 Matt Helm 6.00 15.00
129 Andrew Doyle 3.00 8.00
130 Matt Graham 4.00 10.00
131 Kevan Hess 6.00 15.00
132 Luke Bailey 6.00 15.00
133 Steve Matz 20.00 50.00
134 Tanner Bushue 12.50 30.00
135 Neil Medchill 15.00 40.00
136 Edward Paredes 4.00 10.00
137 A.J. Jimenez 4.00 10.00
138 Grant Desme 15.00 40.00
139 Zack Von Rosenberg 10.00 25.00
140 Daniel Fields 15.00 40.00
141 Graham Stoneburner 10.00 25.00
142 David Holmberg 10.00 25.00
143 Chris Dominguez 30.00 60.00
144 Luke Murton 10.00 25.00
145 Danny Rosenbaum 4.00 10.00
147 Louis Coleman 4.00 10.00
148 Patrick Schuster 8.00 20.00
150 Aroldis Chapman 100.00 200.00

2009 Donruss Elite Extra Edition Signature Status Black

OVERALL AUTO ODDS 1:5 HOBBY
STATED PRINT RUN 1 SER.#'d SET
NO PRICING DUE TO SCARCITY

2009 Donruss Elite Extra Edition Signature Status Gold

OVERALL AUTO ODDS 1:5 HOBBY
STATED PRINT RUN 5 SER.#'d SETS
NO PRICING DUE TO SCARCITY

2009 Donruss Elite Extra Edition Signature Turn of the Century

OVERALL AUTO ODDS 1:5 HOBBY
AU PRINT RUNS B/WN 10-844 COPIES PER
EXCHANGE DEADLINE 7/20/2011
1 Bobby Borchering AU/799 5.00 12.00
2 Blake Smith AU/794 3.00 8.00
3 Drew Storen AU/519 4.00 10.00
4 J.R. Murphy AU/840 5.00 12.00
5 Zack Wheeler AU/744 6.00 15.00
6 Nolan Arenado AU/844 10.00 25.00
7 Matt Bashore AU/655 3.00 8.00
8 Josh Phegley AU/613 4.00 10.00
9 Jacob Turner AU/799 20.00 50.00
10 Mike Leake AU/356 10.00 25.00
11 Kelly Dugan AU/799 3.00 8.00
12 Bill Bullock AU/370 3.00 8.00
13 Shelby Miller AU/690 10.00 25.00
14 Alex Wilson AU/710 3.00 8.00
15 Ben Paulsen AU/599 3.00 8.00
16 Max Stassi AU/810 5.00 12.00
17 A.J. Pollock AU/499 5.00 12.00
18 Aaron Miller AU/650 4.00 10.00
19 Brooks Pounders AU/844 3.00 8.00
20 Shaver Hansen AU/425 3.00 8.00
21 Tyler Skaggs AU/820 10.00 25.00
22 Jiovanni Mier AU/825 4.00 10.00
23 Everett Williams AU/799 4.00 10.00
24 Rich Poythress AU/150 10.00 25.00
25 Chad Jenkins AU/785 3.00 8.00
26 Rey Fuentes AU/99 EXCH 15.00 40.00
27 Ryan Jackson AU/558 3.00 8.00
28 Eric Arnett AU/669 3.00 8.00
29 Chris Owings AU/799 4.00 10.00
30 Garrett Gould AU/799 3.00 8.00
31 Tyler Matzek AU/125 EXCH 15.00 40.00
32 Donnie Joseph AU/699 3.00 8.00
33 Brandon Belt AU/610 30.00 60.00
34 Jon Gaston AU/725 3.00 8.00
35 Tracye Thompson AU/699 6.00 15.00
36 Marc Krauss AU/619 3.00 8.00
37 Kyrell Hudson AU/99 EXCH 20.00 50.00
38 Ben Tootle AU/825 3.00 8.00
39 Jake Marisnick AU/799 10.00 25.00
40 Aaron Baker AU/359 3.00 8.00
41 Kent Matthes AU/619 3.00 8.00
42 Andrew Oliver AU/710 3.00 8.00
43 Cameron Garfield AU/844 3.00 8.00
44 Adam Warren AU/675 4.00 10.00
45 Dustin Dickerson AU/650 3.00 8.00
46 James Jones AU/99 10.00 25.00
47 Brooks Raley AU/494 3.00 8.00
48 Jenrry Mejia AU/844 12.50 30.00
49 Brock Holt AU/619 3.00 8.00
50 Wes Hatton AU/790 3.00 8.00
51 Dustin Ackley AU/75 50.00 100.00
52 Donavan Tate AU/225 8.00 20.00
53 Tony Sanchez AU/50 20.00 50.00
54 Matt Hobgood AU/75 8.00 20.00
55 Alex White AU/70 6.00 15.00
56 Jared Mitchell AU/60 10.00 25.00
57 Mike Trout AU/149 40.00 80.00
58 Brett Jackson AU/49 30.00 60.00
59 Mike Minor AU/10
60 Slade Heathcott AU/40 20.00 50.00
61 Tom Mendonca AU/50 10.00 25.00
62 Wil Myers AU/50 50.00 100.00
63 Jason Kipnis AU/25 EXCH
64 Robert Stock AU/50 15.00 40.00
65 Tim Wheeler AU/25
66 Mychal Givens AU/299 5.00 12.00
67 Grant Green AU/25
68 D.J. LeMahieu AU/15
69 Rex Brothers AU/100 5.00 12.00
71 Wade Gaynor AU/110 3.00 8.00
72 Ryan Wheeler AU/150 5.00 12.00
73 Kyle Heckathorn AU/99 6.00 15.00
75 Victor Black AU/100 4.00 10.00
76 Todd Glaesmann AU/50 4.00 10.00
78 Steve Baron AU/125 4.00 10.00
79 Matt Davidson AU/125 5.00 12.00
80 Jeff Kobernus AU/99 5.00 12.00
81 Kentrail Davis AU/50 20.00 50.00
82 Kyle Gibson AU/99 12.50 30.00
83 Garrett Richards AU/99 6.00 15.00
84 Brad Boxberger AU/110 5.00 12.00
85 Evan Chambers AU/149 3.00 8.00
86 Telvin Nash AU/100 4.00 10.00
87 Austin Kirk AU/199 4.00 10.00
89 Jason Christian AU/111 3.00 8.00
90 Randal Grichuk AU/50 12.50 30.00
91 Nick Franklin AU/120 15.00 40.00
93 Jeremy Hazelbaker AU/204 4.00 10.00
94 Zach Dotson AU/100 3.00 8.00
95 Josh Fellhauer AU/125 4.00 10.00
96 Jeff Malm AU/149 10.00 25.00
97 Caleb Cotham AU/50 10.00 25.00
98 Trevor Holder AU/100 3.00 8.00
99 Joe Kelly AU/99 4.00 10.00
100 Robbie Shields AU/99 3.00 8.00
101 Kyle Bellamy AU/149 3.00 8.00
102 Braxton Lane AU/125 3.00 8.00
104 Ryan Goins AU/150 5.00 12.00
105 Chase Anderson AU/25
106 Kyle Seager AU/100 4.00 10.00
108 David Renfroe AU/149 8.00 20.00
109 Travis Banwart AU/199 3.00 8.00
110 Joe Testa AU/125 4.00 10.00
111 Brandon Jacobs AU/100 5.00 12.00
112 Brett Brach AU/75 3.00 8.00
113 Brad Brach AU/100 3.00 8.00
114 Keon Broxton AU/114 3.00 8.00
115 Nathan Karns AU/110 3.00 8.00
116 Kendal Volz AU/99 4.00 10.00
117 Charles Ruiz AU/125 3.00 8.00
118 Mike Spina AU/115 3.00 8.00
119 Jamie Johnson AU/100 4.00 10.00
120 Bryan Mitchell AU/125 4.00 10.00
121 Chad Bell AU/100 3.00 8.00
122 Dan Taylor AU/175 3.00 8.00
125 Cody Rogers AU/150 4.00 10.00
126 Trent Stevenson AU/100 3.00 8.00
127 Dean Weaver AU/199 3.00 8.00
128 Matt Helm AU/50 6.00 15.00
129 Andrew Doyle AU/155 3.00 8.00
130 Matt Graham AU/150 4.00 10.00
131 Kevan Hess AU/125 3.00 8.00
132 Luke Bailey AU/100 5.00 12.00
133 Steve Matz AU/50 15.00 40.00
134 Tanner Bushue AU/190 4.00 10.00
135 Neil Medchill AU/125 10.00 25.00
136 Edward Paredes AU/110 3.00 8.00
137 A.J. Jimenez AU/149 3.00 8.00
138 Grant Desme AU/100 6.00 15.00
139 Zack Von Rosenberg AU/50 8.00 20.00
140 Daniel Fields AU/90 15.00 40.00
141 Graham Stoneburner AU/125 4.00 10.00
142 David Holmberg AU/110 8.00 20.00
143 Chris Dominguez AU/125 8.00 20.00
144 Luke Murton AU/90 6.00 15.00
145 Danny Rosenbaum AU/149 3.00 8.00
147 Louis Coleman AU/199 4.00 10.00
148 Patrick Schuster AU/149 4.00 10.00
150 Aroldis Chapman AU/149 50.00 100.00

2009 Donruss Elite Extra Edition Back to Back Materials

RANDOM INSERTS IN PACKS
PRINT RUNS B/WN 35-250 COPIES PER
1 Ike Davis 5.00 12.00
Reggie Jackson
2 Jason Kipnis 4.00 10.00
Reggie Jackson
3 Robbie Grossman 3.00 8.00
Quincy Latimore
4 Buster Posey 15.00 40.00
Will Clark

2009 Donruss Elite Extra Edition Back to the Future Signatures

OVERALL AUTO ODDS 1:5 HOBBY
PRINT RUNS B/WN 1-99 COPIES PER
NO PRICING ON QTY 25 OR LESS
1 Allan Dykstra/99 3.00 8.00
2 Alan Horne/99 3.00 8.00
3 Jim Palmer/49 8.00 20.00
4 Andrew Cashner/99 4.00 10.00
5 Andrew Lambo/99 5.00 12.00
6 Anthony Hewitt/99 4.00 10.00
8 Brandon Crawford/99 3.00 8.00
9 Brett Hunter/99 3.00 8.00
10 Bryan Price/99 3.00 8.00
11 Buster Posey/99 20.00 50.00
12 Chase D'Arnaud/99 3.00 8.00
14 Christian Friedrich/99 6.00 15.00
16 Dwight Gooden/99 4.00 10.00
17 Don Mattingly/23
18 Evan Frederickson/99 4.00 10.00
19 Mark Fidrych/49 15.00 40.00
20 George Brett/30 40.00 80.00
22 Ike Davis/99 15.00 40.00
23 Jason Knapp/99 3.00 8.00
25 Jordan Danks/1
26 Logan Schafer/99 3.00 8.00
27 Michael Ynoa/99 4.00 10.00
28 Mike Cisco/50 3.00 8.00
29 Mike Schmidt/20
31 Paul Molitor/20
32 Pete Rose/99 40.00 80.00
33 Rafael Rodriguez/99 15.00 40.00
34 Reggie Jackson/20
35 Robin Yount/49 15.00 40.00
37 Steve Garvey/50 15.00 40.00
38 Wade Boggs/25
39 Zach McAllister/99 4.00 10.00
40 Zeke Spruill/99 3.00 8.00

2009 Donruss Elite Extra Edition College Ties Green

COMPLETE SET (10) 8.00 20.00
RANDOM INSERTS IN PACKS
*GOLD: .6X TO 1.5X BASIC
GOLD RANDOMLY INSERTED
GOLD PRINT RUN 100 SER.#'d SETS
RED RANDOMLY INSERTED
RED PRINT RUN 25 SER.#'d SETS
NO RED PRICING AVAILABLE
1 Dustin Ackley 2.00 5.00
Alex White
2 Mike Leake 1.25 3.00
Jason Kipnis
3 Mike Minor .60 1.50
Caleb Cotham
4 Jason Kipnis 1.00 2.50
Ike Davis
5 Brad Boxberger .60 1.50
Robert Stock
6 Garrett Richards .40 1.00
Jamie Johnson
7 Chase Anderson .40 1.00
Aaron Baker
8 Shaver Hansen .60 1.50
Dustin Dickerson
9 Kendal Volz .60 1.50
Aaron Miller
10 Brooks Raley .60 1.50
Jose Duran
11 Robert Stock .60 1.50
Grant Green
12 Chad Jenkins .60 1.50
Kyle Heckathorn
13 Eric Arnett .60 1.50
Josh Phegley
14 Matt Bashore .40 1.00
Josh Phegley
15 Jared Mitchell .60 1.50
D.J. LeMahieu
16 Victor Black .60 1.50
Ryan Goins
17 Brett Jackson 1.25 3.00
Jeff Kobernus
18 Brett Jackson 1.25 3.00
Blake Smith
19 Trevor Holder .40 1.00
Rich Poythress
20 Jordan Danks 2.00 5.00
Brandon Belt

2009 Donruss Elite Extra Edition College Ties Autographs

OVERALL AUTO ODDS 1:5 HOBBY
PRINT RUNS B/WN 4-50 COPIES PER
NO PRICING ON QTY 25 OR LESS
EXCHANGE DEADLINE 7/20/2011
1 Dustin Ackley 20.00 50.00
Alex White/50
2 Mike Leake 10.00 25.00
Jason Kipnis/50 EXCH
3 Mike Minor 10.00 25.00
Caleb Cotham/50
4 Jason Kipnis 12.50 30.00
Ike Davis/50 EXCH
5 Brad Boxberger 8.00 20.00
Robert Stock/50
6 Garrett Richards
Jamie Johnson/25
7 Chase Anderson 5.00 12.00
Aaron Baker/50
8 Shaver Hansen 5.00 12.00
Dustin Dickerson/50
9 Kendal Volz 5.00 12.00
Aaron Miller/50
10 Brooks Raley
Jose Duran/50
11 Robert Stock 8.00 20.00
Grant Green/50
12 Chad Jenkins 6.00 15.00
Kyle Heckathorn/50
13 Eric Arnett 10.00 25.00
Josh Phegley/50
14 Matt Bashore 8.00 20.00
Josh Phegley/50
15 Jared Mitchell
D.J. LeMahieu/20
16 Victor Black 6.00 15.00
Ryan Goins/50
17 Brett Jackson 12.50 30.00
Jeff Kobernus/50
18 Brett Jackson 10.00 25.00
Blake Smith/50
19 Trevor Holder 5.00 12.00
Rich Poythress/50
20 Jordan Danks
Brandon Belt/4

2009 Donruss Elite Extra Edition College Ties Jerseys

RANDOM INSERTS IN PACKS
STATED PRINT RUN 250 SER.#'d SETS
7 Chase Anderson 3.00 8.00
Aaron Baker
10 Brooks Raley 3.00 8.00
Jose Duran

2009 Donruss Elite Extra Edition College Ties Jerseys Prime

RANDOM INSERTS IN PACKS
PRINT RUNS B/WN 12-25 COPIES PER
NO PRICING DUE TO SCARCITY

2009 Donruss Elite Extra Edition Collegiate Patches Autographs

OVERALL AUTO ODDS 1:5 HOBBY
PRINT RUNS B/WN 104-125 COPIES PER
EXCHANGE DEADLINE 7/20/2011
1 Dustin Ackley/118 40.00 80.00
2 Tony Sanchez/125 10.00 25.00
3 Mike Minor/125 8.00 20.00
4 Mike Leake/125 20.00 50.00
5 Drew Storen/125 8.00 20.00
6 Grant Green/125 8.00 20.00
7 Alex White/124 12.50 30.00
8 A.J. Pollock/123 10.00 25.00
9 Jared Mitchell/125 10.00 25.00
10 Eric Arnett/125 6.00 15.00
11 Brett Jackson/125 10.00 25.00
12 Aaron Miller/117 5.00 12.00
13 Josh Phegley/125 5.00 12.00
14 Kentrail Davis/125 8.00 20.00
15 Garrett Richards/104 4.00 10.00
16 Brad Boxberger/125 8.00 20.00
17 Matt Bashore/124 5.00 12.00
18 Jeff Kobernus/125 6.00 15.00
19 Rich Poythress/124 15.00 40.00
20 Blake Smith/125 6.00 15.00
21 Andrew Oliver/125 6.00 15.00
22 Tom Mendonca/125 12.50 30.00
23 Jason Kipnis/125 EXCH 15.00 40.00
24 Marc Krauss/120 8.00 20.00
25 Robert Stock/125 8.00 20.00
26 Bill Bullock/125 5.00 12.00
27 Alex Wilson/125 4.00 10.00
28 D.J. LeMahieu/125 10.00 25.00
29 Trevor Holder/125 4.00 10.00
30 Donnie Joseph/125 4.00 10.00
31 Ben Paulsen/125 5.00 12.00
32 Kent Matthes/125 5.00 12.00
33 Adam Warren/125 8.00 20.00
34 Brandon Belt/125 40.00 80.00
35 Ryan Jackson/125 6.00 15.00
36 Caleb Cotham/125 10.00 25.00
37 Shaver Hansen/124 6.00 15.00
38 Josh Fellhauer/125 4.00 10.00
39 Jamie Johnson/125 4.00 10.00
40 Khris Davis/125 EXCH 4.00 10.00
41 Dustin Dickerson/125 4.00 10.00
42 Brock Holt/125 5.00 12.00
43 Charles Ruiz/125 4.00 10.00
44 Aaron Baker/125 5.00 12.00
45 Mike Spina/125 5.00 12.00
46 Jim Abbott/125 EXCH 20.00 50.00
47 Fred Lynn/125 6.00 15.00
48 John Olerud/125 EXCH 10.00 25.00
49 Robin Ventura/125 12.50 30.00

2009 Donruss Elite Extra Edition Elite Series

RANDOM INSERTS IN PACKS
1 Dustin Ackley 2.50 6.00
2 Donavan Tate 1.25 3.00
3 Mike Leake 1.50 4.00
4 Tony Sanchez 1.25 3.00
5 Al Kaline 1.25 3.00
6 Mike Minor .75 2.00
7 A.J. Pollock .50 1.25
8 Nolan Ryan 4.00 10.00
9 Will Clark .75 2.00
10 Albert Pujols 3.00 8.00

2009 Donruss Elite Extra Edition Elite Series Autographs

OVERALL AUTO ODDS 1:5 HOBBY
PRINT RUNS B/WN 20-199 COPIES PER
NO PRICING ON QTY 20 OR LESS
1 Dustin Ackley/100 20.00 50.00
2 Donavan Tate/199 10.00 25.00
3 Mike Leake/100 15.00 40.00
4 Tony Sanchez/100 8.00 20.00
5 Al Kaline/100 10.00 25.00
6 Mike Minor/40 10.00 25.00
7 A.J. Pollock/100 8.00 20.00
8 Nolan Ryan/50 50.00 100.00
9 Will Clark/52 15.00 40.00
10 Albert Pujols/20

2009 Donruss Elite Extra Edition Passing the Torch Autographs

OVERALL AUTO ODDS 1:5 HOBBY
PRINT RUNS B/WN 5-100 COPIES PER
NO PRICING ON QTY 25 OR LESS
1 Buster Posey 30.00 60.00
Tony Sanchez/100
2 Will Clark
Dustin Ackley/25
3 Jordan Danks
Brandon Belt/5
4 Andre Dawson
Donavan Tate/100
5 Jim Palmer
Matt Hobgood/100

2009 Donruss Elite Extra Edition Private Signings

OVERALL AUTO ODDS 1:5 HOBBY
PRINT RUNS B/WN 5-250 COPIES PER
NO PRICING ON QTY 25 OR LESS
EXCHANGE DEADLINE 7/20/2011
1 Al Kaline/20
2 Barry Larkin/10
3 Bobby Borchering/50 12.50 30.00
4 Dave Winfield/5
5 Don Mattingly/5
6 Donavan Tate/245 8.00 20.00
7 Drew Storen/100 12.50 30.00
8 Dustin Ackley/250 30.00 60.00
9 Frank Howard/25
10 Grant Green/50 12.50 30.00
11 Jacob Turner/100 30.00 60.00
12 Jim Rice/20
13 Kyle Gibson/50 20.00 50.00
14 Mark Fidrych/20
15 Matt Hobgood/100 20.00 50.00
16 Mike Leake/50 20.00 50.00
17 Nolan Ryan/10
18 Mike Minor/50 8.00 20.00
19 Robin Roberts/10
20 Slade Heathcott/50 20.00 50.00

21 Steve Garvey/20
22 Tony Gwynn/5
23 Tony Sanchez/50 15.00 40.00
24 Tyler Matzek/100 EXCH 20.00 50.00
25 Zack Wheeler/100 15.00 40.00

2009 Donruss Elite Extra Edition School Colors

COMPLETE SET (20) 8.00 20.00
RANDOM INSERTS IN PACKS
1 Dustin Ackley 2.00 5.00
2 Grant Green .40 1.00
3 Mike Leake 1.25 3.00
4 Drew Storen .60 1.50
5 Jared Mitchell .60 1.50
6 Ryan Jackson .40 1.00
7 Tom Mendonca .60 1.50
8 Josh Phegley .40 1.00
9 A.J. Pollock .40 1.00
10 Tony Sanchez 1.00 2.50
11 Marc Krauss .40 1.00
12 Garrett Richards .40 1.00
13 Shaver Hansen .40 1.00
14 Josh Fellhauer .40 1.00
15 Brandon Belt 2.00 5.00
16 Bill Bullock .40 1.00
17 Mike Minor .60 1.50
18 Kent Matthes .40 1.00
19 Ben Paulsen .40 1.00
20 Aaron Baker .40 1.00

2009 Donruss Elite Extra Edition School Colors Autographs

OVERALL AUTO ODDS 1:5 HOBBY
PRINT RUNS B/WN 20-100 COPIES PER
NO PRICING ON QTY 20 OR LESS
1 Dustin Ackley/100 12.50 30.00
2 Grant Green/100 12.50 30.00
3 Mike Leake/100 20.00 50.00
4 Drew Storen/100 6.00 15.00
5 Jared Mitchell/100 12.50 30.00
6 Ryan Jackson/100 4.00 10.00
7 Tom Mendonca/100 10.00 25.00
8 Josh Phegley/50
9 A.J. Pollock/100 8.00 20.00
10 Tony Sanchez/100 8.00 20.00
11 Marc Krauss/100 4.00 10.00
12 Garrett Richards/100 3.00 8.00
13 Shaver Hansen/100 3.00 8.00
14 Josh Fellhauer/100 3.00 8.00
15 Brandon Belt/100 30.00 60.00
16 Bill Bullock/100 3.00 8.00
17 Mike Minor/20
18 Kent Matthes/100 6.00 15.00
19 Ben Paulsen/100 3.00 8.00
20 Aaron Baker/100 3.00 8.00

2009 Donruss Elite Extra Edition School Colors Materials

RANDOM INSERTS IN PACKS
STATED PRINT RUN 250 SER.#'d SETS
5 Jared Mitchell 3.00 8.00
13 Shaver Hansen 3.00 8.00
16 Bill Bullock 3.00 8.00
17 Mike Minor 3.00 8.00
20 Aaron Baker 3.00 8.00

2009 Donruss Elite Extra Edition School Colors Materials Prime

RANDOM INSERTS IN PACKS
PRINT RUNS B/WN 16-25 COPIES PER
NO PRICING DUE TO SCARCITY

2009 Donruss Elite Extra Edition Throwback Threads

RANDOM INSERTS IN PACKS
PRINT RUNS B/WN 50-250 COPIES PER
1 Mike Trout/250 15.00 40.00
2 Shelby Miller/250 6.00 15.00
3 Mike Minor/250 3.00 8.00
4 Jason Kipnis/250 4.00 10.00
5 Bill Bullock/250 3.00 8.00
6 Jared Mitchell/250 3.00 8.00
9 Kyle Russell/250 3.00 8.00
10 Jose Duran/250 3.00 8.00
11 Buster Posey/149 8.00 20.00
14 Pete Rose/250 10.00 25.00
16 Robbie Grossman/250 3.00 8.00
17 Shaver Hansen/250 3.00 8.00
18 Tim Wheeler/250 3.00 8.00
19 Josh Vitters/50 4.00 10.00
20 Todd Glaesmann/250 3.00 8.00
21 Mike Cisco/250 3.00 8.00
22 Aaron Baker/250 3.00 8.00
23 Chase Anderson/250 3.00 8.00
24 Brooks Raley/250 3.00 8.00

2009 Donruss Elite Extra Edition Throwback Threads Prime

RANDOM INSERTS IN PACKS
PRINT RUNS B/WN 1-10 COPIES PER
NO PRICING DUE TO SCARCITY

2009 Donruss Elite Extra Edition Throwback Threads Autographs

OVERALL AUTO ODDS 1:5 HOBBY
PRINT RUNS B/WN 5-250 COPIES PER
NO PRICING ON QTY 25 OR LESS
EXCHANGE DEADLINE 7/20/2011
1 Mike Trout/100 20.00 50.00
2 Shelby Miller/100 30.00 60.00
3 Mike Minor/53 12.50 30.00
4 Jason Kipnis/100 EXCH 6.00 15.00
5 Bill Bullock/199 4.00 10.00
6 Jared Mitchell/149 12.50 30.00
10 Jose Duran/40
11 Buster Posey/25
14 Pete Rose/149 60.00 120.00
17 Shaver Hansen/100
18 Tim Wheeler/10
19 Josh Vitters/5
20 Todd Glaesmann/250 4.00 10.00
21 Mike Cisco/250 4.00 10.00
22 Aaron Baker/100
23 Chase Anderson/100 4.00 10.00
24 Brooks Raley/250 4.00 10.00

2009 Donruss Elite Extra Edition Throwback Threads Autographs Prime

*PRIME: .6X TO 1.5X BASIC
OVERALL AUTO ODDS 1:5 HOBBY
PRINT RUNS B/WN 1-50 COPIES PER
NO PRICING ON QTY 25 OR LESS

2010 Donruss Elite Extra Edition

COMP.SET w/o AU's (100) 10.00 25.00
COMMON CARD (1-100) .20 .50
COMMON AUTO (101-200) 3.00 8.00
OVERALL AUTO ODDS 6 PER BOX
AUTO PRINT RUNS B/WN 99-825 COPIES PER
EXCHANGE DEADLINE 4/6/2012
1 Bryce Brentz .50 1.25
2 Drew Vettleson .30 .75
3 Mike Olt .50 1.25
4 Tyrell Jenkins .50 1.25
5 Delino DeShields Jr. .30 .75
6 Asher Wojciechowski .50 1.25
7 Bobby Doran .20 .50
8 Hunter Morris .50 1.25
9 J.R. Bradley .20 .50
10 Nick Castellanos .60 1.50
11 Chad Bettis .20 .50
12 Drew Robinson .20 .50
13 Aaron Sanchez .30 .75
14 Brandon Workman .20 .50
15 Matt Moore 2.50 6.00
16 Cole Leonida .20 .50
17 Seth Rosin .30 .75
18 Josh Rutledge .20 .50
19 Vincent Velasquez .30 .75
20 Matt den Dekker .30 .75
21 Rett Varner .20 .50
22 Reggie Golden .20 .50
23 Derek Dietrich .60 1.50
24 Robbie Aviles .20 .50
25 DeAngelo Mack .30 .75
26 Alex Wimmers .30 .75
28 Mike Antonio .20 .50
29 Andy Wilkins .20 .50
30 Cody Buckel .20 .50
31 Kevin Munson .20 .50
32 Chris Hawkins .20 .50
33 Drew Smyly .30 .75
34 Gary Sanchez .60 1.50
35 Dan Klein .20 .50
36 Yordy Cabrera .30 .75
37 Ralston Cash .20 .50
38 Jonathan Galvez .20 .50
39 Sam Dyson .20 .50
40 Rob Segedin .30 .75
41 Jimmy Nelson .20 .50
42 Daniel Tillman .20 .50
43 Raoul Torrez .20 .50
44 Sammy Solis .50 1.25
45 Austin Wates .20 .50
46 Matt Harvey .75 2.00
47 Connor Narron .30 .75
48 Bryan Morgado .30 .75
49 Chris Hernandez .20 .50
50 Hayden Simpson .30 .75
51 Brooks Hall .30 .75
52 Devin Lohman .20 .50
53 Pat Dean .50 1.25
54 Gary Brown .50 1.25
55 Stetson Allie .30 .75
56 Griffin Murphy .30 .75
57 Jake Thompson .20 .50
58 Cody Wheeler .20 .50
59 Niko Goodrum .30 .75
60 Rob Brantly .20 .50
61 Austin Ross .20 .50
62 Kevin Rath .20 .50
63 A.J. Cole .30 .75
64 Scott Lawson .30 .75
65 Logan Bawcom .20 .50
66 Connor Powers .20 .50
67 Mike Nesseth .30 .75
68 Jose Vinicio .30 .75
69 Ryan Casteel .20 .50
70 Rick Hague .20 .50
71 Kyle Blair .20 .50
72 Jordan Swagerty .50 1.25
73 Jake Anderson .20 .50
74 Brian Garman .20 .50
75 Mark Canha .20 .50
76 Perci Garner .30 .75
77 Edinson Rincon .20 .50
78 Jonathan Jones .20 .50
79 Ross Wilson .20 .50
80 Mel Rojas Jr. .20 .50
81 Luke Jackson .30 .75
82 Cole Nelson .20 .50
83 David Filak .20 .50
84 Kyle Bellows .20 .50
85 Sam Tuivailala .30 .75
86 Cole Cook .20 .50
87 Jesse Hahn .20 .50
88 A.J. Griffin .20 .50
89 Max Walla .20 .50
90 Jurickson Profar 1.00 2.50
91 Zach Cates .20 .50
92 Ronald Torreyes .20 .50
93 Marcus Littlewood .30 .75
94 Parker Bridwell .30 .75
95 Tyler Austin .20 .50
96 Rob Rasmussen .20 .50
97 Seth Blair .30 .75
98 Tyler Holt .20 .50
99 Micah Gibbs .30 .75
100 Pamela Anderson .50 1.25
101 Michael Choice AU/470 8.00 20.00
102 Christian Colon AU/432 10.00 25.00
103 Chris Sale AU/655 4.00 10.00
104 Jake Skole AU/675 5.00 12.00
105 Mike Foltynewicz AU/653 4.00 10.00
106 Kolbrin Vitek AU/542 10.00 25.00
107 Kellin Deglan AU/640 3.00 8.00
108 Jesse Biddle AU/800 6.00 15.00
109 Justin O'Conner AU/794 4.00 10.00
110 Cito Culver AU/589 8.00 20.00
111 Mike Kvasnicka AU/530 3.00 8.00
112 Matt Lipka AU/722 5.00 12.00
113 Noah Syndergaard AU/809 4.00 10.00
114 Ryan LaMarre AU/564 4.00 10.00
115 Josh Sale AU/536 12.50 30.00
116 Zack Cox AU/478 8.00 20.00
117 Bryan Holaday AU/500 4.00 10.00
118 Todd Cunningham AU/699 4.00 10.00
119 Jarrett Parker AU/580 8.00 20.00
120 Leon Landry AU/550 4.00 10.00
121 Cam Bedrosian AU/652 4.00 10.00
122 Ryan Bolden AU/799 3.00 8.00
123 Cameron Rupp AU/498 4.00 10.00
124 Jedd Gyorko AU/675 5.00 12.00
125 Matt Curry AU/209 3.00 8.00
126 Drew Pomeranz AU/527 8.00 20.00
127 Yasmani Grandal AU/395 10.00 25.00
128 Deck McGuire AU/441 10.00 25.00
129 Chevez Clarke AU/799 5.00 12.00
130 Jameson Taillon AU/699 15.00 40.00
131 Kaleb Cowart AU/750 6.00 15.00
132 Manny Machado AU/425 40.00 80.00
133 Tony Thompson AU/199 4.00 10.00
134 Dee Gordon AU/310 8.00 20.00
135 Chance Ruffin AU/550 3.00 8.00
136 J.T. Realmuto AU/99 6.00 15.00
137 Kevin Chapman AU/694 3.00 8.00
138 Kyle Roller AU/810 3.00 8.00
139 Stephen Pryor AU/819 3.00 8.00
140 Jonathan Singleton AU/699 12.50 30.00
141 Drew Cisco AU/399 4.00 10.00
142 Blake Forsythe AU/401 4.00 10.00
143 Kellen Sweeney AU/819 3.00 8.00
144 Brett Eibner AU/545 5.00 12.00
145 Martin Perez AU/494 8.00 20.00
146 Jean Segura AU/811 12.50 30.00
147 Christian Yelich AU/815 6.00 15.00
148 Robby Rowland AU/799 3.00 8.00
149 Trent Mummey AU/694 3.00 8.00
150 Zach Lee AU/650 8.00 20.00
151 Jason Mitchell AU/600 3.00 8.00
152 Nick Longmire AU/819 4.00 10.00
153 Robbie Erlin AU/699 6.00 15.00
154 Addison Reed AU/601 4.00 10.00
155 Austin Reed AU/499 4.00 10.00
156 Tyler Thornburg AU/819 8.00 20.00
157 Ty Linton AU/99 5.00 12.00
158 Chris Balcom-Miller AU/819 3.00 8.00
159 Wes Mugarian AU/799 3.00 8.00
160 Tony Wolters AU/99
161 Justin Grimm AU/99 10.00 25.00
162 Alex Lavisky AU/499 4.00 10.00
163 Taijuan Walker AU/819 8.00 20.00
164 Arodys Vizcaino AU/770 6.00 15.00
165 Brody Colvin AU/819 6.00 15.00
166 Christian Carmichael AU/815 3.00 8.00
167 Josh Spence AU/699 3.00 8.00
168 Joc Pederson AU/799 3.00 8.00
169 Justin Nicolino AU/399 5.00 12.00
170 Nick Tepesch AU/550 3.00 8.00
171 Joe Gardner AU/819 3.00 8.00
172 Taylor Morton AU/815 4.00 10.00
173 Jason Martinson AU/815 3.00 8.00
174 Matt Miller AU/585 3.00 8.00
175 Justin Bloxom AU/790 3.00 8.00
176 Matt Suschak AU/780 3.00 8.00
177 Zach Neal AU/750 3.00 8.00
178 Ben Gamel AU/801 4.00 10.00
179 Jimmy Reyes AU/810 3.00 8.00
180 Matt Price AU/699 3.00 8.00
181 Aaron Shipman AU/701 3.00 8.00
182 Hector Noesi AU/819 6.00 15.00
183 Peter Tago AU/649 3.00 8.00
184 Kyle Knudson AU/825 3.00 8.00
185 Matt Kirkland AU/99 5.00 12.00
186 Mickey Wiswall AU/499 3.00 8.00
187 Steve Geltz AU/599 3.00 8.00
188 Shawn Tolleson AU/815 3.00 8.00
189 Greg Holle AU/810 3.00 8.00
190 Erik Goeddel AU/810 3.00 8.00
191 Paul Goldschmidt AU/820 20.00 50.00
192 LeVon Washington AU/199 6.00 15.00
193 Trey McNutt AU/249 8.00 20.00
194 Henry Rodriguez AU/620 3.00 8.00
195 Adrian Sanchez AU/620 4.00 10.00
196 Daniel Bibona AU/420 3.00 8.00
197 Chad Lewis AU/799 3.00 8.00
198 Brodie Greene AU/625 3.00 8.00
199 Carter Jurica AU/685 3.00 8.00
200 Anthony Ranaudo AU/150 40.00 80.00

2010 Donruss Elite Extra Edition Aspirations

*ASP 1-100: 2X TO 5X BASIC
RANDOM INSERTS IN PACKS
STATED PRINT RUN 200 SER.#'d SETS
100 Pamela Anderson 8.00 20.00
101 Michael Choice 1.50 4.00
102 Christian Colon 1.50 4.00
103 Chris Sale 2.50 6.00
104 Jake Skole 1.50 4.00
105 Mike Foltynewicz 1.50 4.00
106 Kolbrin Vitek 2.50 6.00
107 Kellin Deglan 1.00 2.50
108 Jesse Biddle 4.00 10.00
109 Justin O'Conner 1.00 2.50
110 Cito Culver 1.50 4.00
111 Mike Kvasnicka 1.50 4.00
112 Matt Lipka 4.00 10.00
113 Noah Syndergaard 1.50 4.00
114 Ryan LaMarre 1.50 4.00
115 Josh Sale 3.00 8.00
116 Zack Cox 3.00 8.00
117 Bryan Holaday 2.50 6.00
118 Todd Cunningham 1.50 4.00
119 Jarrett Parker 2.50 6.00
120 Leon Landry 2.50 6.00
121 Cam Bedrosian 1.50 4.00
122 Ryan Bolden 1.00 2.50
123 Cameron Rupp 1.50 4.00
124 Jedd Gyorko 1.50 4.00
125 Matt Curry 1.50 4.00
126 Drew Pomeranz 3.00 8.00
127 Yasmani Grandal 2.50 6.00
128 Deck McGuire 1.50 4.00
129 Chevez Clarke 1.50 4.00
130 Jameson Taillon 4.00 10.00
131 Kaleb Cowart 1.50 4.00
132 Manny Machado 8.00 20.00
133 Tony Thompson 1.00 2.50
134 Dee Gordon 1.50 4.00
135 Chance Ruffin 1.00 2.50
136 J.T. Realmuto 1.00 2.50
137 Kevin Chapman 1.00 2.50
138 Kyle Roller 1.50 4.00
139 Stephen Pryor 1.00 2.50
140 Jonathan Singleton 1.50 4.00
141 Drew Cisco 1.50 4.00
142 Blake Forsythe 1.00 2.50
143 Kellen Sweeney 1.50 4.00
144 Brett Eibner 2.50 6.00
145 Martin Perez 1.50 4.00
146 Jean Segura 2.50 6.00
147 Christian Yelich 1.50 4.00
148 Robby Rowland 1.00 2.50
149 Trent Mummey 1.00 2.50
150 Zach Lee 2.50 6.00
151 Jason Mitchell 1.00 2.50
152 Nick Longmire 1.50 4.00
153 Robbie Erlin 2.50 6.00
154 Addison Reed 1.00 2.50
155 Austin Reed 1.00 2.50
156 Tyler Thornburg 1.50 4.00
157 Ty Linton 1.50 4.00
158 Chris Balcom-Miller 1.50 4.00
159 Wes Mugarian 1.00 2.50
160 Tony Wolters 1.50 4.00
161 Justin Grimm 1.50 4.00
162 Alex Lavisky 1.50 4.00
163 Taijuan Walker 3.00 8.00
164 Arodys Vizcaino 1.50 4.00
165 Brody Colvin 1.50 4.00
166 Christian Carmichael 1.50 4.00
167 Josh Spence 1.00 2.50
168 Joc Pederson 1.50 4.00
169 Justin Nicolino 1.50 4.00
170 Nick Tepesch 1.00 2.50
171 Joe Gardner 1.00 2.50
172 Taylor Morton 2.50 6.00
173 Jason Martinson 1.00 2.50
174 Matt Miller 1.00 2.50
175 Justin Bloxom 1.00 2.50
176 Matt Suschak 1.00 2.50
177 Zach Neal 1.00 2.50
178 Ben Gamel 1.50 4.00
179 Jimmy Reyes 1.00 2.50
180 Matt Price 1.00 2.50
181 Aaron Shipman 1.50 4.00
182 Hector Noesi 1.50 4.00
183 Peter Tago 1.50 4.00
184 Kyle Knudson 1.00 2.50
185 Matt Kirkland 1.00 2.50
186 Mickey Wiswall 1.00 2.50
187 Steve Geltz 1.00 2.50
188 Shawn Tolleson 1.00 2.50
189 Greg Holle 1.50 4.00
190 Erik Goeddel 1.00 2.50
191 Paul Goldschmidt 8.00 20.00
192 LeVon Washington 1.50 4.00
193 Trey McNutt 1.00 2.50
194 Henry Rodriguez 1.00 2.50
195 Adrian Sanchez 1.00 2.50
196 Daniel Bibona 1.50 4.00
197 Chad Lewis 1.50 4.00
198 Brodie Greene 1.00 2.50
199 Carter Jurica 1.00 2.50
200 Anthony Ranaudo 5.00 12.00

2010 Donruss Elite Extra Edition Status

*STATUS 1-100: 2.5X TO 6X BASIC
RANDOM INSERTS IN PACKS
STATED PRINT RUN 100 SER.#'d SETS
100 Pamela Anderson 10.00 25.00
101 Michael Choice 2.00 5.00
102 Christian Colon 2.00 5.00
103 Chris Sale 3.00 8.00
104 Jake Skole 2.00 5.00
105 Mike Foltynewicz 2.00 5.00
106 Kolbrin Vitek 3.00 8.00
107 Kellin Deglan 1.25 3.00
108 Jesse Biddle 5.00 12.00
109 Justin O'Conner 1.25 3.00
110 Cito Culver 2.00 5.00
111 Mike Kvasnicka 2.00 5.00
112 Matt Lipka 5.00 12.00
113 Noah Syndergaard 2.00 5.00
114 Ryan LaMarre 2.00 5.00
115 Josh Sale 4.00 10.00
116 Zack Cox 4.00 10.00
117 Bryan Holaday 3.00 8.00
118 Todd Cunningham 2.00 5.00
119 Jarrett Parker 3.00 8.00
120 Leon Landry 3.00 8.00
121 Cam Bedrosian 2.00 5.00
122 Ryan Bolden 1.25 3.00
123 Cameron Rupp 2.00 5.00
124 Jedd Gyorko 2.00 5.00
125 Matt Curry 2.00 5.00
126 Drew Pomeranz 4.00 10.00
127 Yasmani Grandal 3.00 8.00
128 Deck McGuire 2.00 5.00
129 Chevez Clarke 2.00 5.00
130 Jameson Taillon 5.00 12.00
131 Kaleb Cowart 2.00 5.00
132 Manny Machado 10.00 25.00
133 Tony Thompson 1.25 3.00
134 Dee Gordon 2.00 5.00
135 Chance Ruffin 1.25 3.00
136 J.T. Realmuto 1.25 3.00
137 Kevin Chapman 1.25 3.00
138 Kyle Roller 2.00 5.00
139 Stephen Pryor 1.25 3.00
140 Jonathan Singleton 2.00 5.00
141 Drew Cisco 2.00 5.00
142 Blake Forsythe 1.25 3.00
143 Kellen Sweeney 2.00 5.00
144 Brett Eibner 3.00 8.00
145 Martin Perez 2.00 5.00
146 Jean Segura 3.00 8.00
147 Christian Yelich 2.00 5.00
148 Robby Rowland 1.25 3.00
149 Trent Mummey 1.25 3.00
150 Zach Lee 3.00 8.00
151 Jason Mitchell 1.25 3.00
152 Nick Longmire 2.00 5.00
153 Robbie Erlin 3.00 8.00
154 Addison Reed 1.25 3.00
155 Austin Reed 1.25 3.00
156 Tyler Thornburg 2.00 5.00
157 Ty Linton 2.00 5.00
158 Chris Balcom-Miller 2.00 5.00
159 Wes Mugarian 1.25 3.00
160 Tony Wolters 2.00 5.00
161 Justin Grimm 2.00 5.00
162 Alex Lavisky 2.00 5.00
163 Taijuan Walker 4.00 10.00
164 Arodys Vizcaino 2.00 5.00
165 Brody Colvin 2.00 5.00
166 Christian Carmichael 2.00 5.00
167 Josh Spence 1.25 3.00
168 Joc Pederson 2.00 5.00
169 Justin Nicolino 2.00 5.00
170 Nick Tepesch 1.25 3.00
171 Joe Gardner 1.25 3.00
172 Taylor Morton 3.00 8.00
173 Jason Martinson 1.25 3.00
174 Matt Miller 1.25 3.00
175 Justin Bloxom 1.25 3.00
176 Matt Suschak 1.25 3.00
177 Zach Neal 1.25 3.00
178 Ben Gamel 2.00 5.00
179 Jimmy Reyes 1.25 3.00
180 Matt Price 1.25 3.00
181 Aaron Shipman 2.00 5.00
182 Hector Noesi 2.00 5.00
183 Peter Tago 2.00 5.00
184 Kyle Knudson 1.25 3.00
185 Matt Kirkland 1.25 3.00
186 Mickey Wiswall 1.25 3.00
187 Steve Geltz 1.25 3.00
188 Shawn Tolleson 1.25 3.00
189 Greg Holle 2.00 5.00
190 Erik Goeddel 1.25 3.00
191 Paul Goldschmidt 10.00 25.00
192 LeVon Washington 2.00 5.00
193 Trey McNutt 1.25 3.00
194 Henry Rodriguez 1.25 3.00
195 Adrian Sanchez 1.25 3.00
196 Daniel Bibona 2.00 5.00
197 Chad Lewis 2.00 5.00
198 Brodie Greene 1.25 3.00
199 Carter Jurica 1.25 3.00
200 Anthony Ranaudo 6.00 15.00

2010 Donruss Elite Extra Edition Status Emerald

RANDOM INSERTS IN PACKS
STATED PRINT RUN 25 SER.#'d SETS
NO PRICING DUE TO SCARCITY

2010 Donruss Elite Extra Edition Status Gold

RANDOM INSERTS IN PACKS
STATED PRINT RUN 10 SER.#'d SETS
NO PRICING DUE TO SCARCITY

2010 Donruss Elite Extra Edition Signature Aspirations

OVERALL AUTO ODDS SIX PER BOX
STATED PRINT RUN 100 SER.#'d SETS
EXCHANGE DEADLINE 4/6/2012
1 Bryce Brentz 15.00 40.00
2 Drew Vettleson 10.00 25.00
3 Mike Olt 10.00 25.00
4 Tyrell Jenkins 6.00 15.00
5 Delino DeShields Jr. 8.00 20.00
6 Asher Wojciechowski 8.00 20.00
7 Bobby Doran 3.00 8.00
8 Hunter Morris 6.00 15.00
9 J.R. Bradley 4.00 10.00
10 Nick Castellanos 20.00 50.00
11 Chad Bettis 5.00 12.00
12 Drew Robinson 3.00 8.00
13 Aaron Sanchez 6.00 15.00
14 Brandon Workman 6.00 15.00
15 Matt Moore 75.00 150.00
16 Cole Leonida 5.00 12.00
17 Seth Rosin 3.00 8.00
18 Josh Rutledge 3.00 8.00
19 Vincent Velasquez 4.00 10.00
20 Matt den Dekker 8.00 20.00
21 Rett Varner 3.00 8.00
22 Reggie Golden 8.00 20.00
23 Derek Dietrich 12.50 30.00
24 Robbie Aviles 6.00 15.00
25 DeAngelo Mack 10.00 25.00
26 Alex Wimmers 12.50 30.00
28 Mike Antonio 5.00 12.00
29 Andy Wilkins 5.00 12.00
30 Cody Buckel 4.00 10.00
31 Kevin Munson 4.00 10.00
32 Chris Hawkins 10.00 25.00
33 Drew Smyly 8.00 20.00
34 Gary Sanchez 15.00 40.00
35 Dan Klein 3.00 8.00
36 Yordy Cabrera 8.00 20.00
37 Ralston Cash 4.00 10.00
38 Jonathan Galvez 3.00 8.00
39 Sam Dyson 4.00 10.00
40 Rob Segedin 8.00 20.00
41 Jimmy Nelson 3.00 8.00
42 Daniel Tillman 4.00 10.00
43 Raoul Torrez 3.00 8.00
44 Sammy Solis 4.00 10.00
45 Austin Wates 5.00 12.00
46 Matt Harvey 15.00 40.00
47 Connor Narron 4.00 10.00
48 Bryan Morgado 4.00 10.00
49 Chris Hernandez 4.00 10.00
50 Hayden Simpson 10.00 25.00
51 Brooks Hall
52 Devin Lohman 4.00 10.00
53 Pat Dean 3.00 8.00
54 Gary Brown 15.00 40.00
55 Stetson Allie 15.00 40.00
56 Griffin Murphy 8.00 20.00
57 Jake Thompson 4.00 10.00
58 Cody Wheeler 3.00 8.00
59 Niko Goodrum 4.00 10.00
60 Rob Brantly 4.00 10.00
61 Austin Ross 4.00 10.00
62 Kevin Rath 3.00 8.00
63 A.J. Cole 6.00 15.00
64 Scott Lawson 3.00 8.00
65 Logan Bawcom 3.00 8.00
66 Connor Powers 3.00 8.00
67 Mike Nesseth 3.00 8.00
68 Jose Vinicio 5.00 12.00
69 Ryan Casteel 4.00 10.00
70 Rick Hague 4.00 10.00
71 Kyle Blair 4.00 10.00
72 Jordan Swagerty UER 30.00 60.00
Magic Johnson Auto
73 Jake Anderson 5.00 12.00
74 Brian Garman 3.00 8.00
75 Mark Canha 4.00 10.00
76 Perci Garner 4.00 10.00
77 Edinson Rincon 4.00 10.00
78 Jonathan Jones 5.00 12.00
79 Ross Wilson 3.00 8.00
80 Mel Rojas Jr. 5.00 12.00
81 Luke Jackson 6.00 15.00
82 Cole Nelson 4.00 10.00
83 David Filak 4.00 10.00
84 Kyle Bellows 4.00 10.00
85 Sam Tuivailala 4.00 10.00
86 Cole Cook 4.00 10.00
87 Jesse Hahn 3.00 8.00
88 A.J. Griffin 4.00 10.00
89 Max Walla 8.00 20.00
90 Jurickson Profar 25.00 60.00
91 Zach Cates 4.00 10.00
92 Ronald Torreyes 12.50 30.00
93 Marcus Littlewood 6.00 15.00
94 Parker Bridwell 10.00 25.00
95 Tyler Austin 6.00 15.00
96 Rob Rasmussen 4.00 10.00
97 Seth Blair 8.00 20.00
98 Tyler Holt 6.00 15.00
99 Micah Gibbs 6.00 15.00
101 Michael Choice 12.50 30.00
102 Christian Colon 10.00 25.00
103 Chris Sale 8.00 20.00
104 Jake Skole 5.00 12.00
105 Mike Foltynewicz 5.00 12.00
106 Kolbrin Vitek 12.50 30.00
107 Kellin Deglan 3.00 8.00
108 Jesse Biddle 12.50 30.00
109 Justin O'Conner 5.00 12.00
110 Cito Culver 12.50 30.00
111 Mike Kvasnicka 5.00 12.00
112 Matt Lipka 8.00 20.00
113 Noah Syndergaard 5.00 12.00
114 Ryan LaMarre 6.00 15.00
115 Josh Sale 15.00 40.00
116 Zack Cox 8.00 20.00
117 Bryan Holaday 6.00 15.00
118 Todd Cunningham 6.00 15.00
119 Jarrett Parker 12.50 30.00
120 Leon Landry 10.00 25.00
121 Cam Bedrosian 4.00 10.00
122 Ryan Bolden 5.00 12.00
123 Cameron Rupp 6.00 15.00
124 Jedd Gyorko 20.00 50.00
125 Matt Curry 10.00 25.00
126 Drew Pomeranz 15.00 40.00
127 Yasmani Grandal 8.00 20.00
128 Deck McGuire 8.00 20.00
129 Chevez Clarke 5.00 12.00
130 Jameson Taillon 30.00 60.00
131 Kaleb Cowart 12.50 30.00
132 Manny Machado EXCH 50.00 100.00
133 Tony Thompson 4.00 10.00
134 Dee Gordon 10.00 25.00
135 Chance Ruffin 4.00 10.00
136 J.T. Realmuto 3.00 8.00
137 Kevin Chapman 4.00 10.00
138 Kyle Roller 6.00 15.00
139 Stephen Pryor 5.00 12.00
140 Jonathan Singleton 20.00 50.00
141 Drew Cisco 6.00 15.00
142 Blake Forsythe 4.00 10.00
143 Kellen Sweeney 10.00 25.00
144 Brett Eibner 8.00 20.00
145 Martin Perez 8.00 20.00
146 Jean Segura 15.00 40.00
147 Christian Yelich 8.00 20.00
148 Robby Rowland 4.00 10.00
149 Trent Mummey 4.00 10.00
150 Zach Lee 10.00 25.00
151 Jason Mitchell 3.00 8.00
152 Nick Longmire 6.00 15.00
153 Robbie Erlin 12.50 30.00
154 Addison Reed 5.00 12.00
155 Austin Reed 3.00 8.00
156 Tyler Thornburg 10.00 25.00
157 Ty Linton 5.00 12.00
158 Chris Balcom-Miller 5.00 12.00
159 Wes Mugarian 3.00 8.00
160 Tony Wolters 4.00 10.00
161 Justin Grimm 3.00 8.00
162 Alex Lavisky 6.00 15.00
163 Taijuan Walker 15.00 40.00
164 Arodys Vizcaino 12.50 30.00
165 Brody Colvin 10.00 25.00
166 Christian Carmichael 4.00 10.00
167 Josh Spence 5.00 12.00
168 Joc Pederson 5.00 12.00
169 Justin Nicolino 8.00 20.00
170 Nick Tepesch 4.00 10.00
171 Joe Gardner 4.00 10.00
172 Taylor Morton 8.00 20.00
173 Jason Martinson 3.00 8.00
174 Matt Miller 3.00 8.00
175 Justin Bloxom 4.00 10.00
176 Matt Suschak 3.00 8.00
177 Zach Neal 4.00 10.00
178 Ben Gamel 6.00 15.00
179 Jimmy Reyes 3.00 8.00
180 Matt Price 3.00 8.00
181 Aaron Shipman 5.00 12.00
182 Hector Noesi 10.00 25.00
183 Peter Tago 5.00 12.00
184 Kyle Knudson 4.00 10.00
185 Matt Kirkland 3.00 8.00
186 Mickey Wiswall 3.00 8.00
187 Steve Geltz 3.00 8.00
188 Shawn Tolleson 4.00 10.00
189 Greg Holle 5.00 12.00
190 Erik Goeddel 4.00 10.00
191 Paul Goldschmidt 60.00 100.00
192 LeVon Washington 6.00 15.00
193 Trey McNutt 8.00 20.00
194 Henry Rodriguez 5.00 12.00
195 Adrian Sanchez 4.00 10.00
196 Daniel Bibona 3.00 8.00
197 Chad Lewis 5.00 12.00
198 Brodie Greene 4.00 10.00
199 Carter Jurica
200 Anthony Ranaudo 50.00 100.00

2010 Donruss Elite Extra Edition Signature Status

OVERALL AUTO ODDS SIX PER BOX
STATED PRINT RUN 50 SER.#'d SETS
EXCHANGE DEADLINE 4/6/2012
1 Bryce Brentz 15.00 40.00
2 Drew Vettleson 20.00 50.00
3 Mike Olt 12.50 30.00
4 Tyrell Jenkins 8.00 20.00
5 Delino DeShields Jr. 10.00 25.00
6 Asher Wojciechowski 10.00 25.00
7 Bobby Doran 4.00 10.00
8 Hunter Morris 8.00 20.00
9 J.R. Bradley 5.00 12.00
10 Nick Castellanos 30.00 60.00
11 Chad Bettis 10.00 25.00
12 Drew Robinson 4.00 10.00
13 Aaron Sanchez 8.00 20.00
14 Brandon Workman 15.00 40.00
15 Matt Moore 150.00 250.00
16 Cole Leonida 6.00 15.00
17 Seth Rosin 4.00 10.00
18 Josh Rutledge 4.00 10.00
19 Vincent Velasquez 5.00 12.00
20 Matt den Dekker 10.00 25.00
21 Rett Varner 4.00 10.00
22 Reggie Golden 10.00 25.00
23 Derek Dietrich 15.00 40.00
24 Robbie Aviles 8.00 20.00
25 DeAngelo Mack 12.50 30.00
26 Alex Wimmers 15.00 40.00
28 Mike Antonio 6.00 15.00
29 Andy Wilkins 6.00 15.00
30 Cody Buckel 5.00 12.00
31 Kevin Munson 5.00 12.00
32 Chris Hawkins 12.50 30.00
33 Drew Smyly 12.50 30.00
34 Gary Sanchez 20.00 50.00
35 Dan Klein 4.00 10.00
36 Yordy Cabrera 10.00 25.00
37 Ralston Cash 5.00 12.00
38 Jonathan Galvez 10.00 25.00
39 Sam Dyson 12.50 30.00
40 Rob Segedin 10.00 25.00
41 Jimmy Nelson 4.00 10.00
42 Daniel Tillman 8.00 20.00
43 Raoul Torrez 4.00 10.00
44 Sammy Solis 10.00 25.00
45 Austin Wates 6.00 15.00
46 Matt Harvey 20.00 50.00
47 Connor Narron 5.00 12.00
48 Bryan Morgado 5.00 12.00
49 Chris Hernandez 10.00 25.00
50 Hayden Simpson 12.50 30.00
51 Brooks Hall 6.00 15.00
52 Devin Lohman 8.00 20.00
53 Pat Dean 6.00 15.00
54 Gary Brown 20.00 50.00
55 Stetson Allie 20.00 50.00
56 Griffin Murphy 10.00 25.00
57 Jake Thompson 5.00 12.00
58 Cody Wheeler 4.00 10.00
59 Niko Goodrum 5.00 12.00
60 Rob Brantly 5.00 12.00
61 Austin Ross 5.00 12.00
62 Kevin Rath 4.00 10.00
63 A.J. Cole 15.00 40.00
64 Scott Lawson 6.00 15.00
65 Logan Bawcom 4.00 10.00
66 Connor Powers 4.00 10.00
67 Mike Nesseth 4.00 10.00
68 Jose Vinicio 6.00 15.00
69 Ryan Casteel 5.00 12.00
70 Rick Hague 5.00 12.00
71 Kyle Blair 5.00 12.00
72 Jordan Swagerty UER 40.00 80.00
Magic Johnson Auto
73 Jake Anderson 6.00 15.00
74 Brian Garman 4.00 10.00
75 Mark Canha 5.00 12.00
76 Perci Garner 5.00 12.00
77 Edinson Rincon 10.00 25.00
78 Jonathan Jones 6.00 15.00
79 Ross Wilson 4.00 10.00
80 Mel Rojas Jr. 6.00 15.00
81 Luke Jackson 8.00 20.00
82 Cole Nelson 5.00 12.00
83 David Filak 5.00 12.00
84 Kyle Bellows 5.00 12.00
85 Sam Tuivailala 5.00 12.00
86 Cole Cook 5.00 12.00
87 Jesse Hahn 4.00 10.00
88 A.J. Griffin 5.00 12.00
89 Max Walla 10.00 25.00
90 Jurickson Profar 75.00 150.00
91 Zach Cates 6.00 15.00
92 Ronald Torreyes 10.00 25.00

93 Marcus Littlewood 8.00 20.00
94 Parker Bridwell 12.50 30.00
95 Tyler Austin 12.50 30.00
96 Rob Rasmussen 10.00 25.00
97 Seth Blair 10.00 25.00
98 Tyler Holt 8.00 20.00
99 Micah Gibbs 8.00 20.00
101 Michael Choice 30.00 60.00
102 Christian Colon 12.50 30.00
103 Chris Sale 10.00 25.00
104 Jake Skole 10.00 25.00
105 Mike Foltynewicz 10.00 25.00
106 Kolbrin Vitek 15.00 40.00
107 Kellin Deglan 4.00 10.00
108 Jesse Biddle 15.00 40.00
109 Justin O'Conner 10.00 25.00
110 Cito Culver 20.00 50.00
111 Mike Kvasnicka 6.00 15.00
112 Matt Lipka 10.00 25.00
113 Noah Syndergaard 6.00 15.00
114 Ryan LaMarre 8.00 20.00
115 Josh Sale 20.00 50.00
116 Zack Cox 15.00 40.00
117 Bryan Holaday 8.00 20.00
118 Todd Cunningham 8.00 20.00
119 Jarrett Parker 15.00 40.00
120 Leon Landry 12.50 30.00
121 Cam Bedrosian EXCH 5.00 12.00
122 Ryan Bolden 6.00 15.00
123 Cameron Rupp 8.00 20.00
124 Jedd Gyorko 30.00 60.00
125 Matt Curry 12.50 30.00
126 Drew Pomeranz 20.00 50.00
127 Yasmani Grandal 10.00 25.00
128 Deck McGuire 20.00 50.00
129 Chevez Clarke 12.50 30.00
130 Jameson Taillon 60.00 120.00
131 Kaleb Cowart 15.00 40.00
132 Manny Machado EXCH 75.00 150.00
133 Tony Thompson 5.00 12.00
134 Dee Gordon 12.50 30.00
135 Chance Ruffin 5.00 12.00
136 J.T. Realmuto 6.00 10.00
137 Kevin Chapman 5.00 12.00
138 Kyle Roller 10.00 25.00
139 Stephen Pryor 10.00 25.00
140 Jonathan Singleton 50.00 100.00
141 Drew Cisco 8.00 20.00
142 Blake Forsythe 8.00 20.00
143 Kellen Sweeney 12.50 30.00
144 Brett Eibner 15.00 40.00
145 Martin Perez 10.00 25.00
146 Jean Segura 20.00 50.00
147 Christian Yelich 20.00 50.00
148 Robby Rowland 5.00 12.00
149 Trent Mummey 5.00 12.00
150 Zach Lee 15.00 40.00
151 Jason Mitchell 4.00 10.00
152 Nick Longmire 8.00 20.00
153 Robbie Erlin 20.00 50.00
154 Addison Reed 6.00 15.00
155 Austin Reed 4.00 10.00
156 Tyler Thornburg 12.50 30.00
157 Ty Linton 10.00 25.00
158 Chris Balcom-Miller 10.00 25.00
159 Wes Mugarian 4.00 10.00
160 Tony Wolters 5.00 12.00
161 Justin Grimm 4.00 10.00
162 Alex Lavisky 8.00 20.00
163 Taijuan Walker 20.00 50.00
164 Arodys Vizcaino 15.00 40.00
165 Brody Colvin 20.00 50.00
166 Christian Carmichael 5.00 12.00
167 Josh Spence 6.00 15.00
168 Joc Pederson 6.00 15.00
169 Justin Nicolino 6.00 15.00
170 Nick Tepesch 5.00 12.00
171 Joe Gardner 5.00 12.00
172 Taylor Morton 10.00 25.00
173 Jason Martinson 4.00 10.00
174 Matt Miller 4.00 10.00
175 Justin Bloxom 5.00 12.00
176 Matt Suschak 4.00 10.00
177 Zach Neal 5.00 12.00
178 Ben Gamel 12.50 30.00
179 Jimmy Reyes 4.00 10.00
180 Matt Price 4.00 10.00
181 Aaron Shipman 6.00 15.00
182 Hector Noesi 12.50 30.00
183 Peter Tago 6.00 15.00
184 Kyle Knudson 5.00 12.00
185 Matt Kirkland 6.00 15.00
186 Mickey Wiswall 4.00 10.00
187 Steve Geltz 4.00 10.00
188 Shawn Tolleson 5.00 12.00
189 Greg Holle 6.00 15.00
190 Erik Goeddel 12.50 30.00
191 Paul Goldschmidt 60.00 120.00
192 LeVon Washington 8.00 20.00
193 Trey McNutt 15.00 40.00
194 Henry Rodriguez 6.00 15.00
195 Adrian Sanchez 5.00 12.00
196 Daniel Bibona 4.00 10.00
197 Chad Lewis 6.00 15.00
198 Brodie Greene 5.00 12.00
199 Carter Jurica
200 Anthony Ranaudo 60.00 120.00

2010 Donruss Elite Extra Edition Signature Status Black

OVERALL AUTO ODDS 6 PER BOX
STATED PRINT RUN 1 SER.#'d SET
NO PRICING DUE TO SCARCITY

2010 Donruss Elite Extra Edition Signature Status Emerald

OVERALL AUTO ODDS 6 PER BOX
STATED PRINT RUN 25 SER.#'d SETS
NO PRICING DUE TO SCARCITY

2010 Donruss Elite Extra Edition Signature Status Gold

OVERALL AUTO ODDS 6 PER BOX
STATED PRINT RUN 5 SER.#'d SETS
NO PRICING DUE TO SCARCITY

2010 Donruss Elite Extra Edition Back to the Future Signatures

OVERALL AUTO ODDS 6 PER BOX
PRINT RUNS B/WN 5-249 COPIES PER
NO PRICING ON QTY 15 OR LESS
EXCHANGE DEADLINE 4/6/2012
1 Pedro Baez/249 3.00 8.00
2 Colton Cain/249 3.00 8.00
3 Tyler Townsend/249 3.00 8.00
4 James Jones/249 3.00 8.00
5 Ashur Tolliver/249 4.00 10.00
6 Jeff Hunt/95 3.00 8.00
7 Aaron Baker/235 3.00 8.00
8 Tyler Matzek/150 8.00 20.00
9 Reymond Fuentes/249 3.00 8.00
10 Thomas Joseph/249 4.00 10.00
11 Chad James/244 3.00 8.00
12 Khris Davis/249 4.00 10.00
13 Eric Smith/249 3.00 8.00
14 Tyler Kehrer/249 3.00 8.00
15 Frank Robinson/5
16 Sparky Anderson/5
17 Bob Gibson/50 12.50 30.00
18 Tom Seaver/15
19 Don Sutton/49 4.00 10.00
20 Frank Howard/30 12.50 30.00

2010 Donruss Elite Extra Edition College Ties

COMPLETE SET (10) 10.00 25.00
RANDOM INSERTS IN PACKS
1 Zack Cox 1.25 3.00
Brett Eibner
2 Brandon Workman .40 1.00
Chance Ruffin
3 Matt Curry .60 1.50
Bryan Holaday
4 Micah Gibbs .60 1.50
Leon Landry
5 Christian Colon 1.00 2.50
Gary Brown
6 Michael Choice .60 1.50
Rett Varner
7 Deck McGuire 1.25 3.00
Derek Dietrich
8 Ryan LaMarre .60 1.50
Matt Miller
9 Dan Klein .40 1.00
Rob Rasmussen
10 Chad Bettis .40 1.00
Bobby Doran

2010 Donruss Elite Extra Edition College Ties Autographs

OVERALL AUTO ODDS 6 PER BOX
STATED PRINT RUN 50 SER.#'d SETS
EXCHANGE DEADLINE 4/6/2012
1 Zack Cox 20.00 50.00
Brett Eibner
2 Brandon Workman 8.00 20.00
Chance Ruffin
3 Matt Curry 8.00 20.00
Bryan Holaday
4 Micah Gibbs
Leon Landry
5 Christian Colon 20.00 50.00
Gary Brown
6 Michael Choice 10.00 25.00
Rett Varner
7 Deck McGuire 30.00 60.00
Derek Dietrich
8 Ryan LaMarre 8.00 20.00
Matt Miller
9 Dan Klein 8.00 20.00
Rob Rasmussen
10 Chad Bettis 12.50 30.00
Bobby Doran

2010 Donruss Elite Extra Edition Collegiate Patches Autographs

OVERALL AUTO ODDS 6 PER BOX
PRINT RUNS B/WN 49-150 COPIES PER
EXCHANGE DEADLINE 4/6/2012
AR Anthony Ranaudo/125 15.00 40.00
AW Alex Wimmers/125 10.00 25.00
BD Bobby Doran/125 5.00 12.00
BE Brett Eibner/125 8.00 20.00
BF Blake Forsythe/125 10.00 25.00
BG Brodie Greene/125 4.00 10.00
BH Bryan Holaday/125 8.00 20.00
BW Brandon Workman/125 5.00 12.00
CB Chad Bettis/125 4.00 10.00
CH Chris Hernandez/125 5.00 12.00
CJ Carter Jurica/125 4.00 10.00
CL Cole Leonida/140 4.00 10.00
CR Chance Ruffin/125 5.00 12.00
DD Derek Dietrich/125 12.50 30.00
DK Dan Klein/125 4.00 10.00
DL Devin Lohman/125 4.00 10.00
DM Deck McGuire/125 6.00 15.00
DP Drew Pomeranz/125 12.50 30.00
GB Gary Brown/49 12.50 30.00
HM Hunter Morris/150 8.00 20.00
JG Jedd Gyorko/125 6.00 15.00
JJ Jonathan Jones/125 EXCH
JN Jimmy Nelson/125 4.00 8.00
JP Jarrett Parker/125 8.00 20.00
JS Josh Spence/125 6.00 15.00
JT Jake Thompson/125 4.00 10.00
KB Kyle Blair/125 4.00 10.00
KC Kevin Chapman/125 8.00 20.00
KG Kirk Gibson/125 12.50 30.00
LL Leon Landry/125 10.00 25.00
MC Matt Curry/125 4.00 10.00
MD Matt den Dekker/125 6.00 15.00
MG Micah Gibbs/125 10.00 25.00
MH Matt Harvey/125 15.00 40.00
MK Mike Kvasnicka/125 6.00 15.00
MN Mike Nesseth/125 4.00 10.00
MO Mike Olt/125 6.00 15.00
PD Pat Dean/125 5.00 12.00
PI Pete Incaviglia/125 EXCH 5.00 12.00
RH Rick Hague/125 4.00 10.00
RL Ryan LaMarre/125 5.00 12.00
RR Rob Rasmussen/125 5.00 12.00
SB Seth Blair/125 8.00 20.00
SD Sam Dyson/125 6.00 15.00
SS Sammy Solis/125 5.00 12.00
TH Tyler Holt/125 5.00 12.00
TM Trent Mummey/125 6.00 15.00
YG Yasmani Grandal/125 12.50 30.00
ZC Zack Cox/125 12.50 30.00
ANW Andy Wilkins/125 5.00 12.00
AUW Austin Wates/125 10.00 25.00
BJS B.J. Surhoff/125 6.00 15.00
BMC Ben McDonald/125 10.00 25.00
CAR Cameron Rupp/124 5.00 12.00
JOS Jordan Swagerty/125 UER 50.00 100.00
Magic Johnson Auto
JUG Justin Grimm/125 5.00 12.00

2010 Donruss Elite Extra Edition Draft Hits Autographs

OVERALL AUTO ODDS 6 PER BOX
PRINT RUNS B/WN 5-299 COPIES PER
NO PRICING ON QTY 23 OR LESS
1 Rick Monday/99 EXCH 4.00 10.00
2 Dale Murphy/99 15.00 40.00
3 Craig Biggio/35
4 Randy Johnson/20 EXCH
5 Paul Molitor/20
6 Bo Jackson/10
7 Alan Trammell/40 40.00 80.00
8 B.J. Surhoff/299 4.00 10.00
9 Jack Morris/150 3.00 8.00
10 Nomar Garciaparra/20
11 Kirk Gibson/23
12 Robin Ventura/99 8.00 20.00
13 Cal Ripken Jr./5
14 Pete Incaviglia/99 4.00 10.00
15 Ben McDonald/299 5.00 12.00
16 Ron Blomberg/299 3.00 8.00
17 Jeff Bagwell/35 EXCH 20.00 50.00
18 Jay Buhner/99 30.00 60.00
19 Tino Martinez/99 20.00 50.00
20 Reggie Jackson/10

2010 Donruss Elite Extra Edition Elite Series

RANDOM INSERTS IN PACKS
1 Kaleb Cowart .60 1.50
2 Christian Colon .60 1.50
3 Brandon Workman .40 1.00
4 Michael Choice .60 1.50
5 Delino DeShields Jr. .60 1.50
6 Jarrett Parker 1.00 2.50
7 Kolbrin Vitek 1.00 2.50
8 Manny Machado 3.00 8.00
9 Dave Winfield .40 1.00
10 Yasmani Grandal 1.00 2.50
11 Chance Ruffin .40 1.00
12 Cito Culver .60 1.50
13 Zach Lee 1.00 2.50
14 Zack Cox 1.25 3.00
15 Drew Pomeranz 1.25 3.00
16 Josh Sale 1.25 3.00
17 Matt Harvey 1.50 4.00
18 Mike Olt 1.00 2.50
19 Jameson Taillon 1.50 4.00
20 Nick Castellanos 1.25 3.00

2010 Donruss Elite Extra Edition Elite Series Autographs

OVERALL AUTO ODDS 6 PER BOX
PRINT RUNS B/WN 19-100 COPIES PER
NO PRICING ON QTY 25 OR LESS
1 Kaleb Cowart/19
2 Christian Colon/25
3 Brandon Workman/95 8.00 20.00
4 Michael Choice/100 6.00 15.00
5 Delino DeShields Jr./75 8.00 20.00
6 Jarrett Parker/100 10.00 25.00
7 Kolbrin Vitek/100 8.00 20.00
8 Manny Machado/25 EXCH
9 Dave Winfield/20
10 Yasmani Grandal/100 10.00 25.00
11 Chance Ruffin/25
12 Cito Culver/25
13 Zach Lee/50 12.50 30.00
14 Zack Cox/49 40.00 80.00
15 Drew Pomeranz/49 12.50 30.00
16 Josh Sale/25
17 Matt Harvey/25
18 Mike Olt/100 10.00 25.00
19 Jameson Taillon/49 40.00 80.00
20 Nick Castellanos/50 20.00 50.00

2010 Donruss Elite Extra Edition Franchise Futures Signatures

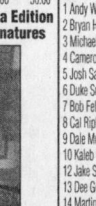

OVERALL AUTO ODDS 6 PER BOX
PRINT RUNS B/WN 49-150 COPIES PER
EXCHANGE DEADLINE 4/6/2012
1 Bryce Brentz/719 8.00 20.00
2 Drew Vettleson/690 4.00 10.00
3 Mike Olt/399 6.00 15.00
4 Tyrell Jenkins/599 4.00 10.00
5 Delino DeShields Jr./499 6.00 15.00
6 Asher Wojciechowski/675 5.00 12.00
7 Bobby Doran/644 4.00 10.00
8 Hunter Morris/619 4.00 10.00
9 J.R. Bradley/625 3.00 8.00
10 Nick Castellanos/699 12.50 30.00
11 Chad Bettis/635 4.00 10.00
12 Drew Robinson/550 3.00 8.00
13 Aaron Sanchez/499 5.00 12.00
14 Brandon Workman/450 5.00 12.00
15 Matt Moore/819 50.00 100.00
16 Cole Leonida/669 3.00 8.00
17 Seth Rosin/710 3.00 8.00
18 Josh Rutledge/595 3.00 8.00
19 Vincent Velasquez/799 3.00 8.00
20 Matt den Dekker/694 4.00 10.00
21 Rett Varner/650 3.00 8.00
22 Reggie Golden/819 5.00 12.00
23 Derek Dietrich/490 6.00 15.00
24 Robbie Aviles/810 3.00 8.00
25 DeAngelo Mack/819 3.00 8.00
26 Alex Wimmers/199 12.50 30.00
28 Mike Antonio/99 10.00 25.00
29 Andy Wilkins/494 3.00 8.00
30 Cody Buckel/816 3.00 8.00
31 Kevin Munson/819 3.00 8.00
32 Chris Hawkins/99 10.00 25.00
33 Drew Smyly/799 8.00 20.00
34 Gary Sanchez/669 8.00 20.00
35 Dan Klein/599 4.00 10.00
36 Yordy Cabrera/818 4.00 10.00
37 Ralston Cash/819 3.00 8.00
38 Jonathan Galvez/810 3.00 8.00
39 Sam Dyson/199 6.00 15.00
40 Rob Segedin/816 4.00 10.00
41 Jimmy Nelson/640 3.00 8.00
42 Daniel Tillman/816 3.00 8.00
43 Raoul Torrez/325 3.00 8.00
44 Sammy Solis/699 3.00 8.00
45 Austin Wates/99 12.50 30.00
46 Matt Harvey/149 12.50 30.00
47 Connor Narron/835 3.00 8.00
48 Bryan Morgado/601 4.00 10.00
49 Chris Hernandez/690 3.00 8.00
50 Hayden Simpson/599 5.00 12.00
51 Brooks Hall/819 4.00 10.00
52 Devin Lohman/694 3.00 8.00
53 Pat Dean/525 4.00 10.00
54 Gary Brown/199 12.50 30.00
55 Stetson Allie/599 6.00 15.00
56 Griffin Murphy/775 3.00 8.00
57 Jake Thompson/699 3.00 8.00
58 Cody Wheeler/815 3.00 8.00
59 Niko Goodrum/819 3.00 8.00
60 Rob Brantly/819 4.00 10.00
61 Austin Ross/819 3.00 8.00
62 Kevin Rath/820 3.00 8.00
63 A.J. Cole/819 4.00 10.00
64 Scott Lawson/694 3.00 8.00
65 Logan Bawcom/790 3.00 8.00
66 Connor Powers/811 3.00 8.00
67 Mike Nesseth/590 3.00 8.00
68 Jose Vinicio/99 5.00 12.00
69 Ryan Casteel/817 3.00 8.00
70 Rick Hague/490 3.00 8.00
71 Kyle Blair/749 4.00 10.00
72 Jordan Swagerty/450 UER 20.00 50.00
Magic Johnson Auto
73 Jake Anderson/810 4.00 10.00
74 Brian Garman/810 3.00 8.00
75 Mark Canha/799 3.00 8.00
76 Perci Garner/799 3.00 8.00
77 Edinson Rincon/819 3.00 8.00
78 Jonathan Jones/694 3.00 8.00
79 Ross Wilson/815 3.00 8.00
80 Mel Rojas Jr./819 4.00 10.00
81 Luke Jackson/99
82 Cole Nelson/819 3.00 8.00
83 David Filak/817 3.00 8.00
84 Kyle Bellows/819 3.00 8.00
85 Sam Tuivailala/820 3.00 8.00
86 Cole Cook/840 3.00 8.00
87 Jesse Hahn/99 12.50 30.00
88 A.J. Griffin/99 4.00 10.00
89 Max Walla/819 3.00 8.00
90 Jurickson Profar/390 20.00 50.00
91 Zach Cates/816 3.00 8.00
92 Ronald Torreyes/599 5.00 12.00
93 Marcus Littlewood/825 4.00 10.00
94 Parker Bridwell/99 12.50 30.00
95 Tyler Austin/811 4.00 10.00
96 Rob Rasmussen/658 3.00 8.00
97 Seth Blair/99 4.00 10.00
98 Tyler Holt/694 4.00 10.00
99 Micah Gibbs/390 4.00 10.00
100 Pamela Anderson/35 300.00 400.00

2010 Donruss Elite Extra Edition Private Signings

OVERALL AUTO ODDS 6 PER BOX
PRINT RUNS B/WN 8-149 COPIES PER
NO PRICING ON QTY 20 OR LESS
1 Andy Wilkins/149 10.00 25.00
2 Bryan Holaday/50 30.00 60.00
3 Michael Choice/99 12.50 30.00
4 Cameron Rupp/50 8.00 20.00
5 Josh Sale/125 10.00 25.00
6 Duke Snider/20
7 Bob Feller/20
8 Cal Ripken Jr./8
9 Dale Murphy/15
10 Kaleb Cowart/49 40.00 80.00
12 Jake Skole/125 5.00 12.00
13 Dee Gordon/100 10.00 25.00
14 Martin Perez/125 8.00 20.00
15 Hayden Simpson/125 6.00 15.00
16 Brandon Workman/99 10.00 25.00
17 Tom Seaver/10
18 Kolbrin Vitek/100 12.50 30.00
19 Rett Varner/99 3.00 8.00
20 Matt Lipka/100 8.00 20.00
21 Chris Sale/125 6.00 15.00
22 Cam Bedrosian/149 8.00 20.00
23 Cito Culver/149 12.50 30.00
24 Tyrell Jenkins/125 6.00 15.00
25 Mike Olt/125 8.00 20.00
26 Bryce Brentz/100 15.00 40.00
27 Asher Wojciechowski/125 EXCH 8.00 20.00
28 Zack Cox/99 10.00 25.00
29 Drew Vettleson/149 6.00 15.00
30 Gary Sanchez/149 20.00 50.00
31 Brett Eibner/99 8.00 20.00
32 J.R. Bradley/149 5.00 12.00
33 Micah Gibbs/99 8.00 20.00
34 Kellin Deglan/149 10.00 25.00
35 Dennis Eckersley/20
36 Matt Curry/100 6.00 15.00
37 Drew Pomeranz/100 10.00 25.00
38 Mike Foltynewicz/149 6.00 15.00
39 Aaron Sanchez/125 8.00 20.00
40 Zach Lee/110 10.00 25.00

2010 Donruss Elite Extra Edition School Colors

COMPLETE SET (20) 10.00 25.00
RANDOM INSERTS IN PACKS
1 Jordan Swagerty 1.00 2.50
2 Christian Colon .60 1.50
3 Michael Choice .60 1.50
4 Zack Cox 1.25 3.00
5 Yasmani Grandal 1.00 2.50
6 Kolbrin Vitek 1.00 2.50
7 Ryan LaMarre .60 1.50
8 Drew Pomeranz 1.25 3.00
9 Jarrett Parker 1.00 2.50
10 Blake Forsythe .40 1.00
11 Josh Rutledge .40 1.00
12 Sam Dyson .40 1.00
13 Hunter Morris 1.00 2.50
14 Deck McGuire .60 1.50
15 Mike Kvasnicka .60 1.50
16 Cameron Rupp .60 1.50
17 Todd Cunningham .60 1.50
18 Micah Gibbs .60 1.50
19 Alex Wimmers .60 1.50
20 Derek Dietrich 1.25 3.00

2010 Donruss Elite Extra Edition School Colors Autographs

OVERALL AUTO ODDS 6 PER BOX
PRINT RUNS B/WN 19-299 COPIES PER
NO PRICING ON QTY 20 OR LESS
1 Jordan Swagerty/149 UER 30.00 60.00
Magic Johnson Auto
2 Christian Colon/49 EXCH
3 Michael Choice/99 10.00 25.00
4 Zack Cox/20
5 Yasmani Grandal/99 6.00 15.00
6 Kolbrin Vitek/68 10.00 25.00
7 Ryan LaMarre/90 5.00 12.00
8 Drew Pomeranz/20
9 Jarrett Parker/19
10 Blake Forsythe/49 6.00 15.00
11 Josh Rutledge/99 3.00 8.00
12 Sam Dyson/49 5.00 12.00
13 Hunter Morris/50 6.00 15.00
14 Deck McGuire/49 6.00 15.00
15 Mike Kvasnicka/165 4.00 10.00
16 Cameron Rupp/70 5.00 12.00
17 Todd Cunningham/82 3.00 8.00
18 Micah Gibbs/149 8.00 20.00
19 Alex Wimmers/49 EXCH 10.00 25.00
20 Derek Dietrich/199 12.50 30.00

2005 Donruss Greats

This product was released in November, 2005. The 150-card set was issued in eight-card packs with an $10 SRP which came 15 packs to a box and 16 boxes to a case. The first 100 cards in this set were retired players while the final 50 cards were active players. Cards 101 through 140 featured active stars, cards 141 and 142 feature Rookie Cards and cards 143 through 150 feature active stars in uniforms they wore previously.

COMPLETE SET (150) 20.00 50.00
COMMON CARD (1-100) .25 .60
COMMON CARD (101-150) .25 .60
COMMON RC (101-150) .25 .60
1 Al Kaline .60 1.50
2 Alan Trammell .25 .60
3 Andre Dawson .40 1.00
4 Barry Larkin .40 1.00
5 Bert Blyleven .25 .60
6 Billy Williams .25 .60
7 Bo Jackson .60 1.50
8 Bob Feller .25 .60
9 Bobby Doerr .25 .60
10 Brooks Robinson .40 1.00
11 Cal Ripken 2.50 6.00
12 Dale Murphy .25 .60
13 Darryl Strawberry .25 .60
14 Dave Parker .25 .60
15 Dave Stewart .25 .60
16 David Cone .25 .60
17 Dennis Eckersley .25 .60
18 Don Larsen .25 .60
19 Don Mattingly 1.25 3.00
20 Don Sutton .25 .60
21 Duke Snider .40 1.00
22 Dwight Evans .40 1.00
23 Dwight Gooden .25 .60
24 Earl Weaver .25 .60
25 Fergie Jenkins .25 .60
26 Frank Robinson .40 1.00
27 Fred Lynn .25 .60
28 Gary Carter .25 .60
29 Gaylord Perry .25 .60
30 George Brett 1.25 3.00
31 George Foster .25 .60
32 George Kell .25 .60
33 Harmon Killebrew .60 1.50
34 Harold Baines .25 .60
35 Harold Reynolds .25 .60
36 Jack Morris .25 .60
37 Jim Abbott .25 .60
38 Jim Bunning .25 .60
39 Jim Palmer .25 .60
40 Jim Rice .25 .60
41 Jim Leyritz .25 .60
42 Joe Morgan Swing .25 .60
43 John Kruk .25 .60
44 Johnny Bench .60 1.50
45 Johnny Podres .25 .60
46 Jose Canseco .40 1.00
47 Juan Marichal .25 .60
48 Keith Hernandez .25 .60
49 Kent Hrbek .25 .60
50 Kirby Puckett .60 1.50
51 Lee Smith .25 .60
52 Lenny Dykstra .25 .60
53 Luis Aparicio .25 .60
54 Luis Tiant .25 .60
55 Mark Grace .40 1.00
56 Marty Marion .25 .60
57 Matt Williams .40 1.00
58 Maury Wills .25 .60
59 Mike Schmidt 1.25 3.00
60 Minnie Minoso .25 .60
61 Nolan Ryan 1.50 4.00
62 Ozzie Smith 1.00 2.50
63 Paul Molitor .60 1.50
64 Phil Rizzuto .40 1.00
65 Ralph Kiner .25 .60
66 Randy Jones .25 .60
67 Red Schoendienst .25 .60
68 Rich Gossage .25 .60
69 Rob Dibble .25 .60
70 Robin Roberts .25 .60
71 Rod Carew .40 1.00
72 Rollie Fingers .25 .60
73 Ron Guidry .25 .60
74 Ron Santo .40 1.00
75 Ryne Sandberg 1.25 3.00
76 Stan Musial 1.00 2.50
77 Steve Carlton .25 .60
78 Steve Garvey .25 .60
79 Steve Stone .25 .60
80 Terry Pendleton .25 .60
81 Terry Steinbach .25 .60
82 Tom Seaver .40 1.00
83 Tommy John .25 .60
84 Tony Gwynn .75 2.00
85 Tony Oliva .25 .60
86 Whitey Ford .40 1.00
87 Will Clark .40 1.00
88 Willie Mays 1.25 3.00
89 Willie McCovey .40 1.00
90 Roberto Clemente 1.50 4.00
91 Roger Maris .60 1.50
92 Bob Gibson .40 1.00
93 Carl Yastrzemski .75 2.00
94 Catfish Hunter .25 .60
95 Warren Spahn .40 1.00
96 Reggie Jackson .60 1.50
97 Lou Brock .40 1.00
98 Joe Morgan Stand .25 .60
99 Carlton Fisk .40 1.00
100 Eddie Murray .60 1.50
101 Roger Clemens Astros .75 2.00
102 Greg Maddux Cubs 1.00 2.50
103 Derek Jeter 1.50 4.00
104 Albert Pujols 1.50 4.00
105 Ken Griffey Jr. Reds 1.00 2.50
106 Alex Rodriguez Yanks 1.00 2.50
107 Mike Piazza .60 1.50
108 Manny Ramirez .60 1.50
109 Sammy Sosa .60 1.50
110 Rafael Palmeiro .40 1.00
111 Randy Johnson Yanks .60 1.50
112 Vladimir Guerrero Angels .60 1.50
113 Ichiro Suzuki 1.00 2.50
114 David Ortiz .60 1.50
115 Miguel Cabrera .60 1.50
116 Frank Thomas .60 1.50
117 Pedro Martinez Mets .40 1.00
118 Chipper Jones .60 1.50
119 Todd Helton .40 1.00
120 Alfonso Soriano .40 1.00
121 Ivan Rodriguez .40 1.00
122 Carlos Delgado .25 .60
123 Carlos Beltran .25 .60
124 Jeff Kent .25 .60
125 Curt Schilling .40 1.00
126 Derrek Lee .25 .60
127 Jason Bay .25 .60
128 Mark Teixeira .60 1.50
129 Craig Biggio .40 1.00
130 Miguel Tejada .40 1.00
131 Johan Santana .60 1.50
132 Jim Thome .40 1.00
133 Tim Hudson .40 1.00
134 Barry Zito .25 .60
135 Mark Mulder .25 .60
136 Hideki Matsui 1.00 2.50
137 John Smoltz .60 1.50
138 Mark Prior .40 1.00
139 Andruw Jones .25 .60
140 Adam Dunn .40 1.00
141 Prince Fielder RC 1.25 3.00
142 Tadahito Iguchi RC .40 1.00
143 Randy Johnson D'backs .60 1.50
144 Pedro Martinez Sox .40 1.00
145 Alex Rodriguez M's 1.00 2.50
146 Roger Clemens Yanks .75 2.00
147 Vladimir Guerrero Expos .60 1.50
148 Greg Maddux Braves 1.00 2.50
149 Ken Griffey Jr. M's 1.00 2.50
150 Roger Clemens Sox .75 2.00

2005 Donruss Greats Gold HoloFoil

*GOLD 1-100: 2.5X TO 6X BASIC
*GOLD 101-150: 2.5X TO 6X BASIC
*GOLD 101-150: 2X TO 5X BASIC RC
ONE GOLD OR PLAT PER 15-PACK BOX
GOLD PRINT RUN 100 SERIAL #'d SETS

2005 Donruss Greats Platinum HoloFoil

*PLAT 1-100: 3X TO 8X BASIC
*PLAT 101-150: 3X TO 8X BASIC
*PLAT 101-150: 2.5X TO 6X BASIC RC
ONE PLAT OR PLAT PER 15-PACK BOX
PLAT PRINT RUN 50 SERIAL #'d SETS

2005 Donruss Greats Silver HoloFoil

*SILVER 1-100: .75X TO 2X BASIC
*SILVER 101-150: .75X TO 2X BASIC
*SILVER 101-150: .75X TO 2X BASIC RC
STATED ODDS 1:3

2005 Donruss Greats Signature Gold HoloFoil

OVERALL AU ODDS 2 PER 15-PACK BOX
TIER 1 QTY B/WN 1-50 COPIES PER
TIER 2 QTY B/WN 51-100 COPIES PER
TIER 3 QTY B/WN 101-250 COPIES PER
TIER 4 QTY B/WN 251-800 COPIES PER
TIER 5 QTY B/WN 801-1200 COPIES PER
TIER 6 QTY B/WN 1201-2000 COPIES PER
CARDS ARE NOT SERIAL-NUMBERED
PRINT RUN INFO PROVIDED BY DONRUSS
1 Al Kaline T2 15.00 40.00
2 Alan Trammell T3 6.00 15.00
3 Andre Dawson T5 4.00 10.00
4 Barry Larkin T2/55 * 15.00 40.00
5 Bert Blyleven T4 4.00 10.00
6 Billy Williams T2/55 * 8.00 20.00
7 Bo Jackson T1/35 * 20.00 50.00
8 Bob Feller T6 6.00 15.00
9 Bobby Doerr T5 4.00 10.00
10 Brooks Robinson T2 12.50 30.00
11 Cal Ripken T3 60.00 120.00
12 Dale Murphy T3 10.00 25.00
13 Darryl Strawberry T6 4.00 10.00
14 Dave Parker T3 6.00 15.00
15 Dave Stewart T4 4.00 10.00
16 David Cone T2 8.00 20.00
17 Dennis Eckersley T2 8.00 20.00
18 Don Larsen T4 6.00 15.00
19 Don Mattingly T1/45 * 40.00 80.00
20 Don Sutton T3 6.00 15.00
21 Duke Snider T2/55 * 12.50 30.00
22 Dwight Evans T3 6.00 15.00
23 Dwight Gooden T4 4.00 10.00
24 Earl Weaver T4 4.00 10.00
25 Fergie Jenkins T3 6.00 15.00
26 Frank Robinson T2 8.00 20.00
27 Fred Lynn T4 4.00 10.00
28 Gary Carter T2/55 * 8.00 20.00
29 Gaylord Perry T3 6.00 15.00
30 George Brett T1/35 * 40.00 80.00
31 George Foster T5 4.00 10.00
32 George Kell T6 8.00 20.00
33 Harmon Killebrew T2/55 * 15.00 40.00
34 Harold Baines T4 4.00 10.00
35 Harold Reynolds T4 4.00 10.00
36 Jack Morris T5 4.00 10.00
37 Jim Abbott T4 4.00 10.00
38 Jim Bunning T2 12.50 30.00
39 Jim Palmer T3 6.00 15.00
40 Jim Rice T2 8.00 20.00
41 Jim Leyritz T3 4.00 10.00
42 Joe Morgan Swing T1/35 * 10.00 25.00
43 John Kruk T2 8.00 20.00
44 Johnny Bench T1/35 * 20.00 50.00
45 Johnny Podres T6 4.00 10.00
46 Jose Canseco T1/45 * 20.00 50.00
47 Juan Marichal T2 8.00 20.00
48 Keith Hernandez T5 4.00 10.00
49 Kent Hrbek T5 4.00 10.00
50 Kirby Puckett T1/35 * 50.00 100.00
51 Lee Smith T5 4.00 10.00
52 Lenny Dykstra T4 4.00 10.00
53 Luis Aparicio T3 6.00 15.00
54 Luis Tiant T3 4.00 10.00
55 Mark Grace T1/45 * 15.00 40.00
56 Marty Marion T4 6.00 15.00
57 Matt Williams T5 6.00 15.00
58 Maury Wills T4 4.00 10.00
59 Mike Schmidt T1/35 * 30.00 60.00
60 Minnie Minoso T5 10.00 25.00
61 Nolan Ryan T2/75 * 40.00 80.00
62 Ozzie Smith T2/55 * 15.00 40.00
63 Paul Molitor T2/55 * 8.00 20.00
64 Phil Rizzuto T2/55 * 12.50 30.00

65 Ralph Kiner T5 10.00 25.00
66 Randy Jones T4 4.00 10.00
67 Red Schoendienst T3 6.00 15.00
68 Rich Gossage T3 10.00 25.00
69 Rob Dibble T4 3.00 8.00
70 Robin Roberts T2 20.00 50.00
71 Rod Carew T2/55 * 12.50 30.00
72 Rollie Fingers T3 6.00 15.00
73 Ron Guidry T3 10.00 25.00
74 Ron Santo T3 12.50 30.00
75 Ryne Sandberg T1/35 * 30.00 60.00
76 Stan Musial T1/35 * 30.00 60.00
77 Steve Carlton T2 8.00 20.00
78 Steve Garvey T3 6.00 15.00
79 Steve Stone T5 4.00 10.00
81 Terry Steinbach T3 4.00 10.00
82 Tom Seaver T1/35 * 20.00 50.00
83 Tommy John T6 4.00 10.00
84 Tony Gwynn T1/45 * 20.00 50.00
85 Tony Oliva T5 8.00 20.00
86 Whitey Ford T1/35 * 15.00 40.00
87 Will Clark T2/55 * 12.50 30.00
88 Willie Mays T2 100.00 200.00
89 Willie McCovey T1/45 * 15.00 40.00

2005 Donruss Greats Signature Platinum HoloFoil

*PLAT: .75X TO 2X GOLD T5-T6
*PLAT: .75X TO 2X GOLD T4
*PLAT: .6X TO 1.5X GOLD T3
OVERALL AU ODDS 2 PER 15-PACK BOX
TIER 1 QTY B/WN 1-50 COPIES PER
CARDS ARE NOT SERIAL-NUMBERED
PRINT RUN INFO PROVIDED BY DONRUSS
NO PRICING ON QTY OF 10 OR LESS
SEE BECKETT.COM FOR ALL PRINT RUNS

2005 Donruss Greats Dodger Blues Brooklyn Material

TIER 1 QTY B/WN 1-50 COPIES PER
TIER 4 QTY B/WN 251-800 COPIES PER
OVERALL GU ODDS 1:5
CARDS ARE NOT SERIAL-NUMBERED
PRINT RUN INFO PROVIDED BY DONRUSS
1 Sandy Koufax Jsy T1/43 * 75.00 150.00
2 Duke Snider Pants T1/27 * 15.00 40.00
3 Burleigh Grimes Pants T4 20.00 50.00
4 Tommy Lasorda Jsy T4 4.00 10.00

2005 Donruss Greats Dodger Blues Brooklyn Material Prime

OVERALL GAME-USED ODDS 1:5
TIER 1 QTY B/WN 1-50 COPIES PER
CARDS ARE NOT SERIAL-NUMBERED
PRINT RUN INFO PROVIDED BY DONRUSS
NO PRICING DUE TO SCARCITY
4 Tommy Lasorda Jsy T1/10 *

2005 Donruss Greats Dodger Blues Brooklyn Signature Material

TIER 1 QTY B/WN 1-50 COPIES PER
NO PRICING ON QTY OF 10
OVERALL AU ODDS 2 PER 15-PACK BOX
CARDS ARE NOT SERIAL-NUMBERED
PRINT RUN INFO PROVIDED BY DONRUSS
1 Sandy Koufax Jsy T1/37 *
2 Duke Snider Jsy T1/10 *

2005 Donruss Greats Dodger Blues Brooklyn Signature Material Prime

OVERALL AU ODDS 2 PER 15-PACK BOX
TIER 1 QTY B/WN 1-50 COPIES PER
CARDS ARE NOT SERIAL-NUMBERED
PRINT RUN INFO PROVIDED BY DONRUSS
NO PRICING DUE TO SCARCITY
1 Sandy Koufax Jsy T1/1 *

2005 Donruss Greats Dodger Blues LA Material

TIER 1 QTY B/WN 1-50 COPIES PER
TIER 2 QTY B/WN 51-100 COPIES PER
TIER 3 QTY B/WN 101-250 COPIES PER
TIER 5 QTY B/WN 801-1200 COPIES PER
OVERALL GU ODDS 1:5
CARDS ARE NOT SERIAL-NUMBERED
PRINT RUN INFO PROVIDED BY DONRUSS
1 Sandy Koufax Jsy T1/43 * 75.00 150.00
2 Duke Snider Pants T2/55 * 12.50 30.00
4 Tommy Lasorda Jsy T5 4.00 10.00
5 Orel Hershiser Jsy T3 8.00 20.00
6 Don Sutton Jsy T3 8.00 20.00

2005 Donruss Greats Dodger Blues LA Material Prime

OVERALL GAME-USED ODDS 1:5
TIER 1 QTY B/WN 1-50 COPIES PER
CARDS ARE NOT SERIAL-NUMBERED
PRINT RUN INFO PROVIDED BY DONRUSS
NO PRICING DUE TO SCARCITY
1 Sandy Koufax Jsy T1/1 *
4 Tommy Lasorda Jsy T1/10 *
5 Orel Hershiser Jsy T1/5 *
6 Don Sutton Jsy T1/1 *

2005 Donruss Greats Dodger Blues LA Signature Material

TIER 1 QTY B/WN 1-50 COPIES PER
NO PRICING ON QTY OF 10
OVERALL AU ODDS 2 PER 15-PACK BOX
CARDS ARE NOT SERIAL-NUMBERED
PRINT RUN INFO PROVIDED BY DONRUSS
1 Sandy Koufax Jsy T1/37 *
2 Duke Snider Jsy T1/10 *
5 Orel Hershiser Jsy T1/10 *
6 Don Sutton Jsy T1/10 *

2005 Donruss Greats Dodger Blues LA Signature Material Prime

OVERALL AU ODDS 2 PER 15-PACK BOX
TIER 1 QTY B/WN 1-50 COPIES PER
CARDS ARE NOT SERIAL-NUMBERED
PRINT RUN INFO PROVIDED BY DONRUSS
NO PRICING DUE TO SCARCITY
1 Sandy Koufax Jsy T1/1 *
5 Orel Hershiser Jsy T1/5 *
6 Don Sutton Jsy T1/1 *

2005 Donruss Greats Hall of Fame Souvenirs

OVERALL INSERT ODDS 2 PER 15-PACK BOX
1 Willie Mays Giants 2.50 6.00
2 Hank Aaron Mil 2.50 6.00
3 Hank Aaron Atl 2.50 6.00
4 Willie Mays Mets 2.50 6.00
5 Nolan Ryan 3.00 8.00
6 R.Clemente Kneeling 3.00 8.00
7 Nellie Fox .75 2.00
8 Pee Wee Reese .75 2.00
9 Babe Ruth 3.00 8.00
10 Bobby Doerr .50 1.25
11 Brooks Robinson .75 2.00
12 Carlton Fisk .75 2.00
13 Eddie Murray 1.25 3.00
14 Ernie Banks 1.25 3.00
15 Frank Robinson .75 2.00
16 Gary Carter .50 1.25
17 Hack Wilson .75 2.00
18 Harmon Killebrew 1.25 3.00
19 Joe Morgan .50 1.25
20 Kirby Puckett 1.25 3.00
21 Lou Brock .75 2.00
22 Orlando Cepeda .50 1.25
23 Red Schoendienst .50 1.25
24 Richie Ashburn .75 2.00
25 Stan Musial 2.00 5.00
26 R.Clemente Standing 3.00 8.00
27 Wade Boggs Sox .75 2.00
28 Wade Boggs Yanks .75 2.00

2005 Donruss Greats Hall of Fame Souvenirs Material Bat

OVERALL GU ODDS 1:5
TIER 1 QTY B/WN 1-50 COPIES PER
TIER 3 QTY B/WN 101-250 COPIES PER
TIER 4 QTY B/WN 251-800 COPIES PER
TIER 5 QTY B/WN 801-1200 COPIES PER
TIER 6 QTY B/WN 1201-2000 COPIES PER
CARDS ARE NOT SERIAL-NUMBERED
PRINT RUN INFO PROVIDED BY DONRUSS
1 Willie Mays Giants T3 10.00 25.00
2 Hank Aaron Mil T3 10.00 25.00
3 Hank Aaron Atl T3 10.00 25.00
4 Willie Mays Mets T3 10.00 25.00
5 Nolan Ryan T1/30 * 10.00 25.00
6 R.Clemente Kneeling T6 15.00 40.00
7 Nellie Fox T5 4.00 10.00
8 Pee Wee Reese T4 4.00 10.00
9 Babe Ruth T4 90.00 150.00
11 Brooks Robinson T5 3.00 8.00
12 Carlton Fisk T5 3.00 8.00
13 Eddie Murray T5 4.00 10.00
14 Ernie Banks T5 5.00 12.00
15 Frank Robinson T4 2.50 6.00
16 Gary Carter T5 2.50 6.00
17 Hack Wilson T4 12.50 30.00
18 Harmon Killebrew T4 4.00 10.00
19 Joe Morgan T5 2.50 6.00
20 Kirby Puckett T5 4.00 10.00
21 Lou Brock T6 3.00 8.00
22 Orlando Cepeda T5 2.50 6.00
23 Red Schoendienst T4 3.00 8.00
24 Richie Ashburn T5 4.00 10.00
25 Stan Musial T4 6.00 15.00
26 R.Clemente Standing T6 15.00 40.00
27 Wade Boggs Sox T6 3.00 8.00
28 Wade Boggs Yanks T6 3.00 8.00

2005 Donruss Greats Hall of Fame Souvenirs Material Combo

OVERALL GU ODDS 1:5
TIER 1 QTY B/WN 1-50 COPIES PER
TIER 3 QTY B/WN 101-250 COPIES PER
TIER 4 QTY B/WN 251-800 COPIES PER
CARDS ARE NOT SERIAL-NUMBERED
PRINT RUN INFO PROVIDED BY DONRUSS
NO PRICING ON QTY OF 24 OR LESS
1 W.Mays Giants B-J T1/25 * 20.00 50.00
2 H.Aaron Mil Bat-Jsy T1/25 * 20.00 50.00
3 H.Aaron Atl Bat-Jsy T1/25 * 20.00 50.00

4 W.Mays Mets B-J T1/25 * 20.00 50.00
5 N.Ryan Bat-Jsy T1/25 * 15.00 40.00
6 R.Clemente Knee Bat-Jsy T1/13 *
8 P.Reese Bat-Jsy T1/38 * 12.50 30.00
9 B.Ruth Bat-Pants T1/50 * 200.00 300.00
10 B.Doerr Bat-Pants T4 4.00 10.00
11 B.Rob Bat-Hat T1/29 * 10.00 25.00
12 C.Fisk Bat-Jsy T4 5.00 12.00
13 E.Murray Bat-Jsy T4 6.00 15.00
14 E.Banks Bat-Jsy T3 10.00 25.00
16 G.Carter Bat-Pants T4 4.00 10.00
18 H.Killebrew Bat-Jsy T4 6.00 15.00
22 O.Cepeda Bat-Jsy T1/24 *
24 R.Ashburn Bat-Pants T4 6.00 15.00
25 S.Musial Bat-Pants T3 12.50 30.00
26 R.Clem Stand Bat-Hat T3 40.00 80.00
27 W.Boggs Sox Bat-Jsy T3 6.00 15.00

2005 Donruss Greats Hall of Fame Souvenirs Material Jersey

OVERALL GU ODDS 1:5
TIER 1 QTY B/WN 1-50 COPIES PER
TIER 3 QTY B/WN 101-250 COPIES PER
TIER 4 QTY B/WN 251-800 COPIES PER
CARDS ARE NOT SERIAL-NUMBERED
PRINT RUN INFO PROVIDED BY DONRUSS
NO PRICING ON QTY OF 22
1 Willie Mays Giants T1/25 * 15.00 40.00
2 Hank Aaron Mil T1/25 * 15.00 40.00
3 Hank Aaron Atl T1/25 * 15.00 40.00
4 Willie Mays Mets T1/25 * 15.00 40.00
5 Nolan Ryan T1/25 * 10.00 25.00
9 Babe Ruth Pants T1/25 * 150.00 250.00
10 Bobby Doerr Pants T3 3.00 8.00
12 Carlton Fisk Jkt T4 3.00 8.00
22 O.Cepeda Pants T1/22 *
24 Richie Ashburn Pants T3 5.00 12.00
25 Stan Musial T1/50 * 12.50 30.00
27 Wade Boggs Sox T4 3.00 8.00

2005 Donruss Greats Hall of Fame Souvenirs Signature

OVERALL AU ODDS 2 PER 15-PACK BOX
TIER 1 QTY B/WN 1-50 COPIES PER
CARDS ARE NOT SERIAL-NUMBERED
PRINT RUN INFO PROVIDED BY DONRUSS
NO PRICING DUE TO SCARCITY
1 Willie Mays Giants T1/10 *
2 Hank Aaron Mil T1/10 *
3 Hank Aaron Atl T1/10 *
4 Willie Mays Mets T1/10 *
5 Nolan Ryan T1/10 *

2005 Donruss Greats Hall of Fame Souvenirs Signature Material Bat

OVERALL AU ODDS 2 PER 15-PACK BOX
TIER 1 QTY B/WN 1-50 COPIES PER
TIER 2 QTY B/WN 51-100 COPIES PER
TIER 3 QTY B/WN 101-250 COPIES PER
CARDS ARE NOT SERIAL-NUMBERED
PRINT RUN INFO PROVIDED BY DONRUSS
NO PRICING ON QTY OF 22 OR LESS
1 Willie Mays Giants T1/10 *
2 Hank Aaron Mil T1/10 *
3 Hank Aaron Atl T1/10 *
4 Willie Mays Mets T1/10 *
5 Nolan Ryan T1/10 *
10 Bobby Doerr T2 8.00 20.00
11 Brooks Robinson T2 12.50 30.00
12 Carlton Fisk T2 12.50 30.00
15 Frank Robinson T2 8.00 20.00
16 Gary Carter T2 8.00 20.00
18 Harmon Killebrew T2 30.00 60.00
19 Joe Morgan T2 8.00 20.00
20 Kirby Puckett T2/52 * 50.00 100.00
21 Lou Brock T2 12.50 30.00
22 Orlando Cepeda T2 8.00 20.00
23 Red Schoendienst T3 10.00 25.00
25 Stan Musial T2/50 * 30.00 60.00
27 Wade Boggs Sox T1/22 *
28 Wade Boggs Yanks T1/22 *

2005 Donruss Greats Hall of Fame Souvenirs Signature Material Combo

OVERALL AU ODDS 2 PER 15-PACK BOX
TIER 1 QTY B/WN 1-50 COPIES PER
TIER 2 QTY B/WN 51-100 COPIES PER
TIER 3 QTY B/WN 101-250 COPIES PER
CARDS ARE NOT SERIAL-NUMBERED
PRINT RUN INFO PROVIDED BY DONRUSS
NO PRICING ON QTY OF 10 OR LESS
1 W.Mays Giants B-J T1/10 *
2 H.Aaron Mil Bat-Jsy T1/10 *
3 H.Aaron Atl Bat-Jsy T1/10 *
4 W.Mays Mets Bat-Jsy T1/10 *
5 N.Ryan Bat-Jsy T1/10 *
10 B.Doerr Bat-Pants T3 8.00 20.00
11 B.Robinson Bat-Hat T2 15.00 40.00
12 C.Fisk Bat-Hat T1/50 * 20.00 50.00
15 F.Rob Bat-Shoes T1/39 * 12.50 30.00
16 G.Carter Bat-Jsy T3 8.00 20.00
18 H.Killebrew Bat-Jsy T3 30.00 60.00
19 J.Morgan Bat-Jsy T1/23 * 12.50 30.00
20 K.Puckett Bat-Jsy T1/45 * 60.00 150.00
22 O.Cepeda Bat-Pants T2 10.00 25.00
25 S.Musial Bat-Jsy T2 30.00 80.00
27 W.Boggs Sox B-J T1/50 * 15.00 40.00
28 W.Boggs Yanks B-H T1/31 * 15.00 40.00

2005 Donruss Greats Hall of Fame Souvenirs Signature Material Jersey

OVERALL AU ODDS 2 PER 15-PACK BOX
TIER 1 QTY B/WN 1-50 COPIES PER
TIER 2 QTY B/WN 51-100 COPIES PER
TIER 3 QTY B/WN 101-250 COPIES PER
CARDS ARE NOT SERIAL-NUMBERED
PRINT RUN INFO PROVIDED BY DONRUSS
NO PRICING ON QTY OF 16 OR LESS
1 Willie Mays Giants T1/10 *
2 Hank Aaron Mil T1/10 *
3 Hank Aaron Atl T1/10 *
4 Willie Mays Mets T1/10 *
5 Nolan Ryan T1/10 *
10 Bobby Doerr Pants T3 6.00 15.00
11 Brooks Robinson T1/5 *
12 Carlton Fisk Jkt T2 12.50 30.00
15 Frank Robinson T1/27 * 10.00 25.00
16 Gary Carter T2/63 * 8.00 20.00
18 Harmon Killebrew T2 30.00 60.00
20 Kirby Puckett T1/16 *
22 O.Cepeda Pants T2/68 * 8.00 20.00
23 Red Schoendienst Hat T3 10.00 25.00
25 Stan Musial T2 25.00 60.00
27 Wade Boggs Sox T1/50 * 15.00 40.00
28 Wade Boggs Yanks T1/3 *

2005 Donruss Greats Redbirds Material

OVERALL GU ODDS 1:5
TIER 2 QTY B/WN 51-100 COPIES PER
TIER 3 QTY B/WN 101-250 COPIES PER
TIER 4 QTY B/WN 251-800 COPIES PER
CARDS ARE NOT SERIAL-NUMBERED
PRINT RUN INFO PROVIDED BY DONRUSS
1 S.Musial w/Glove Jsy T2 15.00 40.00
2 Ozzie Smith Jkt T4 8.00 20.00
3 Enos Slaughter Jsy T4 8.00 20.00
4 Frankie Frisch Jkt T3 10.00 25.00
5 Lou Brock Jsy T2 15.00 40.00
6 Bob Gibson Jsy T2 15.00 40.00
7 Ken Boyer Jsy T3 15.00 40.00
8 Lee Smith Jsy T4 3.00 8.00
9 Albert Pujols Jsy T2 15.00 40.00
10 S.Musial w/Bat Pants T2 15.00 40.00

2005 Donruss Greats Redbirds Material Prime

*PRIME T1 p/r 25: .75X TO 2X BAT T3
OVERALL GAME-USED ODDS 1:5
TIER 1 QTY B/WN 1-50 COPIES PER
CARDS ARE NOT SERIAL-NUMBERED
PRINT RUN INFO PROVIDED BY DONRUSS
NO PRICING ON QTY OF 5 OR LESS
1 S.Musial w/Glove Jsy T1/1 *
2 Ozzie Smith Jkt T1/5 *
3 Enos Slaughter Jsy T1/5 *
5 Lou Brock Jsy T1/5 *
6 Bob Gibson Jsy T1/5 *
7 Ken Boyer Jsy T1/25 * 30.00 80.00
8 Lee Smith Jsy T1/5 *

2005 Donruss Greats Redbirds Signature Material

TIER 1 QTY B/WN 1-50 COPIES PER
NO PRICING ON QTY OF 10 OR LESS
OVERALL AU ODDS 2 PER 15-PACK BOX
CARDS ARE NOT SERIAL-NUMBERED
PRINT RUN INFO PROVIDED BY DONRUSS
1 S.Musial w/Glove Jsy T1/5 *
2 Ozzie Smith Jkt T1/10 *
5 Lou Brock Jsy T1/10 *
6 Bob Gibson Jsy T1/10 *
8 Lee Smith Jsy T1/50 * 10.00 25.00
10 S.Musial w/Bat Pants T1/5 *

2005 Donruss Greats Redbirds Signature Material Prime

OVERALL AU ODDS 2 PER 15-PACK BOX
TIER 1 QTY B/WN 1-50 COPIES PER
CARDS ARE NOT SERIAL-NUMBERED
PRINT RUN INFO PROVIDED BY DONRUSS
NO PRICING DUE TO SCARCITY
1 S.Musial w/Glove Jsy T1/1 *
2 Ozzie Smith Jkt T1/5 *
5 Lou Brock Jsy T1/5 *
6 Bob Gibson Jsy T1/5 *
8 Lee Smith Jsy T1/5 *

2005 Donruss Greats Souvenirs

OVERALL INSERT ODDS 2 PER 15-PACK BOX
1 Jim Thorpe 2.00 5.00
2 Joe Carter .50 1.25
3 Will Clark .75 2.00
4 Cal Ripken 5.00 12.00
5 Dwight Evans .75 2.00
6 George Foster .50 1.25
7 Steve Garvey .50 1.25
8 Don Mattingly 2.50 6.00
9 Deion Sanders .75 2.00
10 Ron Santo .75 2.00
11 Alan Trammell .50 1.25
12 Robin Ventura .50 1.25
13 Matt Williams .75 2.00

2005 Donruss Greats Souvenirs Material Bat

OVERALL GU ODDS 1:5
TIER 5 QTY B/WN 801-1200 COPIES PER
CARDS ARE NOT SERIAL-NUMBERED
PRINT RUN INFO PROVIDED BY DONRUSS
2 Joe Carter T5 2.50 6.00
3 Will Clark T5 3.00 8.00
5 Dwight Evans T5 3.00 8.00
6 George Foster T5 2.50 6.00
7 Steve Garvey T5 2.50 6.00
8 Don Mattingly T5 6.00 15.00
9 Deion Sanders T5 3.00 8.00
10 Ron Santo T5 3.00 8.00
11 Alan Trammell T5 2.50 6.00
12 Robin Ventura T5 2.50 6.00
13 Matt Williams T5 3.00 8.00

2005 Donruss Greats Souvenirs Material Combo

OVERALL GU ODDS 1:5
TIER 1 QTY B/WN 1-50 COPIES PER
TIER 2 QTY B/WN 51-100 COPIES PER
CARDS ARE NOT SERIAL-NUMBERED
PRINT RUN INFO PROVIDED BY DONRUSS
2 Joe Carter Bat-Jsy T1/50 * 5.00 12.00
3 Will Clark Bat-Jsy T2 5.00 12.00
9 Deion Sanders Bat-Jsy T2 5.00 12.00
11 Alan Trammell Bat-Jsy T2 4.00 10.00
13 Matt Williams Bat-Jsy T2 5.00 12.00

2005 Donruss Greats Souvenirs Material Jersey

OVERALL GU ODDS 1:5
TIER 1 QTY B/WN 1-50 COPIES PER
TIER 2 QTY B/WN 51-100 COPIES PER
TIER 3 QTY B/WN 101-250 COPIES PER
TIER 4 QTY B/WN 251-800 COPIES PER
TIER 5 QTY B/WN 801-1200 COPIES PER
CARDS ARE NOT SERIAL-NUMBERED
PRINT RUN INFO PROVIDED BY DONRUSS
NO PRICING ON QTY OF 7 OR LESS
1 Jim Thorpe T4 75.00 150.00
2 Joe Carter T1/7 *
3 Will Clark T2 5.00 12.00
4 Cal Ripken T4 10.00 25.00
6 George Foster T1/4 *
9 Deion Sanders T5 3.00 8.00
11 Alan Trammell T2/68 * 4.00 10.00
12 Robin Ventura T1/48 * 5.00 12.00
13 Matt Williams T3 4.00 10.00

2005 Donruss Greats Souvenirs Signature

OVERALL AU ODDS 2 PER 15-PACK BOX
TIER 1 QTY B/WN 1-50 COPIES PER
TIER 2 QTY B/WN 51-100 COPIES PER
CARDS ARE NOT SERIAL-NUMBERED
PRINT RUN INFO PROVIDED BY DONRUSS
NO PRICING ON QTY OF 10
3 Will Clark T2 12.50 30.00
4 Cal Ripken T1/10 *
5 Dwight Evans T1/25 * 10.00 25.00
7 Steve Garvey T2 8.00 20.00
8 Don Mattingly T1/25 *
10 Ron Santo T2 12.50 30.00
11 Alan Trammell T2 8.00 20.00

2005 Donruss Greats Souvenirs Signature Material Bat

OVERALL AU ODDS 2 PER 15-PACK BOX
TIER 2 QTY B/WN 51-100 COPIES PER
CARDS ARE NOT SERIAL-NUMBERED
PRINT RUN INFO PROVIDED BY DONRUSS
3 Will Clark T2 12.50 30.00
5 Dwight Evans T2 8.00 20.00
7 Steve Garvey T2 8.00 20.00
10 Ron Santo T2 20.00 50.00
11 Alan Trammell T2 8.00 20.00
12 Robin Ventura T2 8.00 20.00

2005 Donruss Greats Souvenirs Signature Material Combo

OVERALL AU ODDS 2 PER 15-PACK BOX
TIER 1 QTY B/WN 1-50 COPIES PER
TIER 2 QTY B/WN 51-100 COPIES PER
TIER 3 QTY B/WN 101-250 COPIES PER
CARDS ARE NOT SERIAL-NUMBERED
PRINT RUN INFO PROVIDED BY DONRUSS
NO PRICING ON QTY OF 10 OR LESS
2 Joe Carter Bat-Jsy T1/3 *
3 Will Clark Bat-Jsy T2 15.00 40.00
5 D.Evans Bat-Jsy T1/10 *
7 Steve Garvey Bat-Jsy T2 10.00 25.00
11 Alan Trammell Bat-Jsy T2 10.00 25.00

2005 Donruss Greats Souvenirs Signature Material Jersey

OVERALL AU ODDS 2 PER 15-PACK BOX
TIER 1 QTY B/WN 1-50 COPIES PER
TIER 2 QTY B/WN 51-100 COPIES PER
TIER 3 QTY B/WN 101-250 COPIES PER
CARDS ARE NOT SERIAL-NUMBERED
PRINT RUN INFO PROVIDED BY DONRUSS
NO PRICING ON QTY OF 5 OR LESS
3 Will Clark T3 10.00 25.00
4 Cal Ripken T1/5 *
5 Dwight Evans T1/42 * 10.00 25.00
7 Steve Garvey T3 6.00 15.00
8 Don Mattingly T1/5 *
11 Alan Trammell T2 8.00 20.00
12 Robin Ventura T1/1 *

2005 Donruss Greats Sox Nation Material

TIER 2 QTY B/WN 51-100 COPIES PER
TIER 3 QTY B/WN 101-250 COPIES PER
TIER 4 QTY B/WN 251-800 COPIES PER
TIER 5 QTY B/WN 801-1200 COPIES PER
OVERALL GU ODDS 1:5
CARDS ARE NOT SERIAL-NUMBERED
PRINT RUN INFO PROVIDED BY DONRUSS
1 Ted Williams Jsy T3 40.00 80.00
2 Bobby Doerr Pants T3 8.00 20.00
3 Roger Clemens Jsy T2/55 * 20.00 50.00
4 Carl Yastrzemski Pants T4 10.00 25.00
5 Carl Yastrzemski Jsy T3 12.50 30.00
6 Jim Rice Left Pants T3 6.00 15.00
7 Jim Rice Right Jsy T3 6.00 15.00
8 J.Cronin Standing Pants T5 4.00 10.00
9 Joe Cronin Left Jsy T5 4.00 10.00
10 Carlton Fisk Jsy T2/55 * 15.00 40.00
11 Fred Lynn Jsy T3 6.00 15.00
12 W.Boggs Away Jsy T3 6.00 15.00
13 W.Boggs Home Jsy T2/55 * 15.00 40.00

2005 Donruss Greats Sox Nation Material Prime

OVERALL GAME-USED ODDS 1:5
TIER 1 QTY B/WN 1-50 COPIES PER
CARDS ARE NOT SERIAL-NUMBERED
PRINT RUN INFO PROVIDED BY DONRUSS
NO PRICING DUE TO SCARCITY
3 Roger Clemens Jsy T1/10 *
7 Jim Rice Right Jsy T1/5 *
9 Joe Cronin Left Jsy T1/1 *
11 Fred Lynn Jsy T1/1 *
13 W.Boggs Home Jsy T1/1 *

2005 Donruss Greats Sox Nation Signature Material

TIER 1 QTY B/WN 1-50 COPIES PER
NO PRICING ON QTY OF 5
OVERALL AU ODDS 2 PER 15-PACK BOX
CARDS ARE NOT SERIAL-NUMBERED
PRINT RUN INFO PROVIDED BY DONRUSS
2 Bobby Doerr Pants T1/50 * 10.00 25.00
6 Jim Rice Left Pants T1/50 * 10.00 25.00
7 Jim Rice Right Jsy T1/50 * 10.00 25.00
10 Carlton Fisk Jsy T1/5 *
11 Fred Lynn Jsy T1/50 * 10.00 25.00
12 W.Boggs Away Jsy T1/5 *
13 W.Boggs Home Jsy T1/5 *

2005 Donruss Greats Sox Nation Signature Material Prime

OVERALL AU ODDS 2 PER 15-PACK BOX
TIER 1 QTY B/WN 1-50 COPIES PER
CARDS ARE NOT SERIAL-NUMBERED
PRINT RUN INFO PROVIDED BY DONRUSS
NO PRICING DUE TO SCARCITY
7 Jim Rice Right Jsy T1/5 *
11 Fred Lynn Jsy T1/5 *
13 W.Boggs Home Jsy T1/1 *

2005 Donruss Greats Yankee Clippings Material

OVERALL GU ODDS 1:5
TIER 1 QTY B/WN 1-50 COPIES PER
TIER 2 QTY B/WN 51-100 COPIES PER
TIER 3 QTY B/WN 100-250 COPIES PER
TIER 4 QTY B/WN 250-800 COPIES PER
TIER 5 QTY B/WN 801-1200 COPIES PER
TIER 6 QTY B/WN 1201-2000 COPIES PER
CARDS ARE NOT SERIAL-NUMBERED
PRINT RUN INFO PROVIDED BY DONRUSS
1 B.Ruth w/o Bat Jsy T1/30 *
2 Babe Ruth Look Up Jsy T2 250.00 400.00
3 B.Martin Fielding Pants T3 30.00 60.00
4 B.Martin Kneeling Jsy T3 30.00 60.00
5 Bobby Murcer Pants T5 6.00 15.00
6 Bucky Dent Pants T5 4.00 10.00
7 C.Hunter w/Glove Pants T4 4.00 10.00
8 C.Hunter w/o Glove Jsy T5 4.00 10.00
9 Darryl Strawberry Jsy T2 10.00 25.00
10 Dave Righetti Jsy T5 4.00 10.00
11 Dave Winfield Pants T6 4.00 10.00
12 D.Sanders w/Helmet Jsy T5 6.00 15.00
13 D.Sand w/o Helmet Pants T4 6.00 15.00
14 Don Mattingly Jsy T2 15.00 40.00
15 Elston Howard Pants T5 6.00 15.00
16 Graig Nettles Pants T5 4.00 10.00
17 Roger Clemens Jsy T1/43 * 50.00 100.00
18 Luis Tiant Pants T4 4.00 10.00
19 Mickey Rivers Pants T5 4.00 10.00
20 Phil Rizzuto Jsy T4 6.00 15.00
21 Reggie Jackson Pants T3 10.00 25.00
22 Rickey Henderson Pants T5 6.00 15.00
23 R.Maris w/Bat Jsy T2 50.00 100.00
24 R.Maris w/o Bat Pants T2 50.00 100.00
25 Ron Guidry Pants T4 6.00 15.00
26 Sparky Lyle Pants T5 4.00 10.00
27 Phil Niekro Jsy T1/49 * 15.00 40.00
28 Tommy John Jsy T2 10.00 25.00
29 Whitey Ford Jsy T2 20.00 50.00
30 Yogi Berra Pants T2 20.00 50.00

2005 Donruss Greats Yankee Clippings Material Prime

OVERALL GAME-USED ODDS 1:5
TIER 1 QTY B/WN 1-50 COPIES PER
CARDS ARE NOT SERIAL-NUMBERED
PRINT RUN INFO PROVIDED BY DONRUSS
NO PRICING ON QTY OF 8 OR LESS
27 Phil Niekro Jsy T1/33 * 20.00 50.00

2005 Donruss Greats Yankee Clippings Signature Material

TIER 1 QTY B/WN 1-50 COPIES PER
NO PRICING ON QTY OF 10 OR LESS
OVERALL AU ODDS 2 PER 15-PACK BOX
CARDS ARE NOT SERIAL-NUMBERED
PRINT RUN INFO PROVIDED BY DONRUSS
9 D.Strawberry Jsy T1/25 * 15.00 40.00
18 Luis Tiant Pants T1/50 * 15.00 40.00
20 Phil Rizzuto Jsy T1/25 * 30.00 60.00
25 Ron Guidry Pants T1/25 * 30.00 60.00
27 Phil Niekro Jsy T1/1 *
28 Tommy John Jsy T1/25 * 15.00 40.00
29 Whitey Ford Jsy T1/5 *

2005 Donruss Greats Yankee Clippings Signature Material Prime

OVERALL AU ODDS 2 PER 15-PACK BOX
TIER 1 QTY B/WN 1-50 COPIES PER
CARDS ARE NOT SERIAL-NUMBERED
PRINT RUN INFO PROVIDED BY DONRUSS
NO PRICING DUE TO SCARCITY
10 Dave Righetti Jsy T1/1 *
13 D.Sand w/o Helmet Jsy T1/1 *
20 Phil Rizzuto Jsy T1/1 *
28 Tommy John Jsy T1/5 *
29 Whitey Ford Jsy T1/5 *

1997 Donruss Signature

Distributed in five-card packs with one authentic autographed card per pack, this 100-card set was issued in two series. However, these regular cards were issued with both series and one could make sets from either series. These packs carried a suggested retail price of $14.99. The fronts feature color player photos with player information on the backs. The only Rookie Cards of note in this set are Jose Cruz Jr. and Mark Kotsay.

COMPLETE SET (100) 25.00 50.00
1 Mark McGwire 1.25 3.00
2 Kenny Lofton .20 .50
3 Tony Gwynn .60 1.50
4 Tony Clark .20 .50
5 Tim Salmon .30 .75
6 Ken Griffey Jr. .75 2.00
7 Mike Piazza .75 2.00
8 Greg Maddux .75 2.00
9 Roberto Alomar .30 .75
10 Andres Galarraga .20 .50
11 Roger Clemens 1.00 2.50
12 Bernie Williams .30 .75
13 Rondell White .20 .50
14 Kevin Appier .20 .50
15 Ray Lankford .20 .50
16 Frank Thomas .50 1.25
17 Will Clark .30 .75
18 Chipper Jones .50 1.25
19 Jeff Bagwell .30 .75
20 Manny Ramirez .30 .75
21 Ryne Sandberg .75 2.00
22 Paul Molitor .20 .50
23 Gary Sheffield .20 .50
24 Jim Edmonds .20 .50
25 Barry Larkin .30 .75
26 Rafael Palmeiro .30 .75
27 Alan Benes .20 .50
28 Dave Justice .20 .50
29 Randy Johnson .50 1.25
30 Barry Bonds 1.25 3.00
31 Mo Vaughn .20 .50
32 Michael Tucker .20 .50
33 Larry Walker .20 .50
34 Tino Martinez .30 .75
35 Jose Guillen .20 .50
36 Carlos Delgado .20 .50
37 Jason Dickson .20 .50
38 Tom Glavine .30 .75
39 Raul Mondesi .20 .50
40 Jose Cruz Jr. RC .20 .50
41 Johnny Damon .30 .75
42 Mark Grace .30 .75
43 Juan Gonzalez .20 .50
44 Vladimir Guerrero .50 1.25
45 Kevin Brown .20 .50
46 Justin Thompson .20 .50
47 Eric Young .20 .50
48 Ron Coomer .20 .50
49 Mark Kotsay RC .50 1.25
50 Scott Rolen .30 .75
51 Derek Jeter 1.25 3.00
52 Jim Thome .30 .75
53 Fred McGriff .30 .75
54 Albert Belle .20 .50

55 Garret Anderson	.20	.50
56 Wilton Guerrero	.20	.50
57 Jose Canseco	.30	.75
58 Cal Ripken	1.50	4.00
59 Sammy Sosa	.50	1.25
60 Dmitri Young	.20	.50
61 Alex Rodriguez	.75	2.00
62 Javier Lopez	.20	.50
63 Sandy Alomar Jr.	.20	.50
64 Joe Carter	.20	.50
65 Dante Bichette	.20	.50
66 Al Martin	.20	.50
67 Darin Erstad	.20	.50
68 Pokey Reese	.20	.50
69 Brady Anderson	.20	.50
70 Andruw Jones	.30	.75
71 Ivan Rodriguez	.30	.75
72 Nomar Garciaparra	.75	2.00
73 Moises Alou	.20	.50
74 Andy Pettitte	.30	.75
75 Jay Buhner	.20	.50
76 Craig Biggio	.30	.75
77 Wade Boggs	.30	.75
78 Shawn Estes	.20	.50
79 Neifi Perez	.20	.50
80 Rusty Greer	.20	.50
81 Pedro Martinez	.30	.75
82 Mike Mussina	.30	.75
83 Jason Giambi	.20	.50
84 Hideo Nomo	.50	1.25
85 Todd Hundley	.20	.50
86 Deion Sanders	.30	.75
87 Mike Cameron	.20	.50
88 Bobby Bonilla	.20	.50
89 Todd Greene	.20	.50
90 Kevin Orie	.20	.50
91 Ken Caminiti	.20	.50
92 Chuck Knoblauch	.20	.50
93 Matt Morris	.20	.50
94 Matt Williams	.20	.50
95 Pat Hentgen	.20	.50
96 John Smoltz	.30	.75
97 Edgar Martinez	.30	.75
98 Jason Kendall	.20	.50
99 Ken Griffey Jr. CL	.50	1.25
100 Frank Thomas CL	.30	.75

1997 Donruss Signature Platinum Press Proofs

Randomly inserted in packs, this set is a holo foil parallel version of the base set. Only 150 of this set were produced. Each card is numbered "1 of 150" on the back. Some cards were mistakenly printed with the "1 of 150 backs" but did not have the platinum press proof front. These cards are valued at approximately the same price as the values below.

*STARS: 10X TO 25X BASIC CARDS
*ROOKIES: 4X TO 10X BASIC CARDS

1997 Donruss Signature Autographs

Inserted one per pack, this 117-card set features color player autographed photos. The first 100 cards each player signed were blue, sequentially numbered to 100, and designated as "Century Marks." The next 100 cards signed were green, sequentially numbered 101-1100, and designated as "Millenium Marks." Player autographs surpassing 1100 were red and were not numbered. Some autographed signature cards were not available at first and were designated by blank-backed redemption cards which could be redeemed by mail for the player's autograph card. The cards are checklisted below in alphabetical order. Asterisk cards were found in both Series A and B. Print runs for how many cards each player signed is noted next to the players name. Exchange cards for Raul Mondesi and Edgar Renteria were seeded into packs. Notable cards of players in their Rookie Card seasons include Brian Giles and Miguel Tejada. The Miguel Tejada and David Ortiz cards were signed in either black or blue ink. At this time, there is no price differential for either version of these cards.

1 Jeff Abbott/3900	2.00	5.00
2 Bob Abreu/3900	5.00	12.00
3 Edgardo Alfonzo/3900	2.00	5.00
4 Roberto Alomar/150 *	20.00	50.00
5 Sandy Alomar Jr./1400	6.00	15.00
6 Moises Alou/900	6.00	15.00
7 Garret Anderson/3900	4.00	10.00
8 Andy Ashby/3900	2.00	5.00
9 Trey Beamon/3900	2.00	5.00
10 Alan Benes/3900	2.00	5.00
11 Geronimo Berroa/3900	2.00	5.00
12 Wade Boggs/150 *	60.00	120.00
13 Kevin Brown C/3900	2.00	5.00
14 Brett Butler/1400	6.00	15.00
15 Mike Cameron/3900	4.00	10.00
16 Giovanni Carrara/2900	2.00	5.00
17 Luis Castillo/3900	4.00	10.00
18 Tony Clark/3900	2.00	5.00
19 Will Clark/1400	8.00	20.00
20 Lou Collier/3900	2.00	5.00
21 Bartolo Colon/3900	4.00	10.00
22 Ron Coomer/3900	2.00	5.00
23 Marty Cordova/3900	2.00	5.00
24 Jacob Cruz/3900 *	2.00	5.00
25 Jose Cruz Jr./900 *	3.00	8.00
26 Russ Davis/3900	2.00	5.00
27 Jason Dickson/3900	2.00	5.00
28 Todd Dunwoody/3900	2.00	5.00
29 Jermaine Dye/3900	4.00	10.00
30 Jim Edmonds/3900	6.00	15.00
31 Darin Erstad/900 *	4.00	10.00
32 Bobby Estalella/3900	2.00	5.00
33 Shawn Estes/3900	2.00	5.00
34 Jeff Fassero/3900	2.00	5.00
35 Andres Galarraga/900	8.00	20.00
36 Karim Garcia/3900	2.00	5.00
37 Derrick Gibson/3900	2.00	5.00
38 Brian Giles/3900	6.00	15.00
39 Tom Glavine/150	40.00	80.00
40 Rick Gorecki/900	3.00	8.00
41 Shawn Green/1900	6.00	15.00
42 Todd Greene/3900	2.00	5.00
43 Rusty Greer/3900	4.00	10.00
44 Ben Grieve/3900	2.00	5.00
45 M.Grudzielanek/3900	4.00	10.00
46 V.Guerrero/1900 *	8.00	20.00
47 Wilton Guerrero/2150	2.00	5.00
48 Jose Guillen/2900	4.00	10.00
49 J.Hammonds/2150	2.00	5.00
50 Todd Helton/1400	10.00	25.00
51 T.Hollandsworth/2900	2.00	5.00
52 Trenidad Hubbard/900	3.00	8.00
53 Todd Hundley/1400	6.00	15.00
54 Bobby Jones/3900	2.00	5.00
55 Brian Jordan/1400	6.00	15.00
56 David Justice/900	6.00	15.00
57 Eric Karros/650	6.00	15.00
58 Jason Kendall/3900	4.00	10.00
59 Jimmy Key/3900	4.00	10.00
60 B.Kieschnick/3900	2.00	5.00
61 Ryan Klesko/225	5.00	12.00
62 Paul Konerko/3900	6.00	15.00
63 Mark Kotsay/2400	6.00	15.00
64 Ray Lankford/3900	4.00	10.00
65 Barry Larkin/150 *	20.00	50.00
66 Derrek Lee/3900	6.00	15.00
67 Esteban Loaiza/3900	2.00	5.00
68 Javier Lopez/1400	6.00	15.00
69 Edgar Martinez/150 *	12.50	30.00
70 Pedro Martinez/900	30.00	60.00
71 Rafael Medina/3900	2.00	5.00
72 Raul Mondesi/650	6.00	15.00
73 Matt Morris/3900	4.00	10.00
74 Paul O'Neill/900	10.00	25.00
75 Kevin Orie/3900	2.00	5.00
76 David Ortiz/3900	15.00	40.00
77 Rafael Palmeiro/900	12.50	30.00
78 Jay Payton/3900	2.00	5.00
79 Neifi Perez/3900	2.00	5.00
80 Manny Ramirez/900	10.00	25.00
81 Joe Randa/3900	4.00	10.00
82 Pokey Reese/3900	4.00	10.00
83 Edgar Renteria SP	10.00	25.00
84 Dennis Reyes/3900	2.00	5.00
85 Henry Rodriguez/3900	2.00	5.00
86 Scott Rolen/1900 *	6.00	15.00
87 Kirk Rueter/2900	2.00	5.00
88 Ryne Sandberg/400	30.00	60.00
89 Dwight Smith/2900	2.00	5.00
90 J.T. Snow/900	4.00	10.00
91 Scott Spiezio/3900	2.00	5.00
92 Shannon Stewart/2900	4.00	10.00
93 Jeff Suppan/1900	4.00	10.00
94 Mike Sweeney/3900	4.00	10.00
95 Miguel Tejada/3900	6.00	15.00
96 Justin Thompson/2400	2.00	5.00
97 Brett Tomko/3900	2.00	5.00
98 Bubba Trammell/3900	3.00	8.00
99 Michael Tucker/3900	4.00	10.00
100 Javier Valentin/3900	2.00	5.00
101 Mo Vaughn/150 *	15.00	40.00
102 Robin Ventura/1400	6.00	15.00
103 Terrell Wade/3900	2.00	5.00
104 Billy Wagner/3900	4.00	10.00
105 Larry Walker/900	12.50	30.00
106 Todd Walker/2400	2.00	5.00
107 Rondell White/3900	2.00	5.00
108 Kevin Wickander/900	2.00	5.00
109 Chris Widger/3900	2.00	5.00
110 Matt Williams/150 *	12.50	30.00
111 A.Williamson/3900	2.00	5.00
112 Dan Wilson/3900	2.00	5.00
113 Tony Womack/3900	3.00	8.00
114 Jaret Wright/3900	3.00	8.00
115 Dmitri Young/3900	4.00	10.00
116 Eric Young/3900	2.00	5.00
117 Kevin Young/3900	2.00	5.00
NNO F.Thomas Sample Fascimile Autograph	.75	2.00

1997 Donruss Signature Autographs Century

Randomly inserted in packs, this set, identified with blue card fronts, features the first 100 cards signed by each player. The cards are sequentially numbered. Raul Mondesi, Eddie Murray, Edgar Renteria and Jim Thome were seeded in packs as exchange cards. The cards are checklisted below in alphabetical order. A number of Nomar Garciaparra Century marks were lost or destroyed during packaging and only 62 of these cards were inserted into packs.

1 Jeff Abbott	12.50	30.00
2 Bob Abreu	30.00	60.00
3 Edgardo Alfonzo	20.00	50.00
4 Roberto Alomar *	40.00	80.00
5 Sandy Alomar Jr.	20.00	50.00
6 Moises Alou	20.00	50.00
7 Garret Anderson	20.00	50.00
8 Andy Ashby	12.50	30.00
9 Jeff Bagwell	75.00	150.00
10 Trey Beamon	12.50	30.00
11 Albert Belle	20.00	50.00
12 Alan Benes	12.50	30.00
13 Geronimo Berroa	12.50	30.00
14 Wade Boggs *	50.00	100.00
15 Barry Bonds	225.00	350.00
16 Bobby Bonilla *	20.00	50.00
17 Kevin Brown	20.00	50.00
18 Kevin Brown C	12.50	30.00
19 Jay Buhner	20.00	50.00
20 Brett Butler	20.00	50.00
21 Mike Cameron	20.00	50.00
22 Giovanni Carrara	12.50	30.00
23 Luis Castillo	20.00	50.00
24 Tony Clark	12.50	30.00
25 Will Clark	40.00	80.00
26 Roger Clemens *	175.00	300.00
27 Lou Collier	12.50	30.00
28 Bartolo Colon	20.00	50.00
29 Ron Coomer	12.50	30.00
30 Marty Cordova	12.50	30.00
31 Jacob Cruz *	12.50	30.00
32 Jose Cruz Jr. *	12.50	30.00
33 Russ Davis	12.50	30.00
34 Jason Dickson	12.50	30.00
35 Todd Dunwoody	12.50	30.00
36 Jermaine Dye	20.00	50.00
37 Jim Edmonds	60.00	120.00
38 Darin Erstad *	20.00	50.00
39 Bobby Estalella	12.50	30.00
40 Shawn Estes	12.50	30.00
41 Jeff Fassero	12.50	30.00
42 Andres Galarraga	20.00	50.00
43 Karim Garcia	12.50	30.00
44 N. Garciaparra SP62 *	125.00	200.00
45 Derrick Gibson	12.50	30.00
46 Brian Giles	30.00	60.00
47 Tom Glavine	50.00	100.00
48 Juan Gonzalez	10.00	25.00
49 Rick Gorecki	12.50	30.00
50 Shawn Green	40.00	80.00
51 Todd Greene	12.50	30.00
52 Rusty Greer	20.00	50.00
53 Ben Grieve	12.50	30.00
54 Mark Grudzielanek	20.00	50.00
55 Vladimir Guerrero *	75.00	150.00
56 Wilton Guerrero	12.50	30.00
57 Jose Guillen	20.00	50.00
58 Tony Gwynn *	60.00	120.00
59 Jeffrey Hammonds	12.50	30.00
60 Todd Helton	40.00	80.00
61 Todd Hollandsworth	12.50	30.00
62 Trenidad Hubbard	12.50	30.00
63 Todd Hundley	12.50	30.00
64 Derek Jeter *	250.00	400.00
65 Andruw Jones *	50.00	100.00
66 Bobby Jones	12.50	30.00
67 Chipper Jones *	200.00	300.00
68 Brian Jordan	20.00	50.00
69 David Justice	20.00	50.00
70 Eric Karros	20.00	50.00
71 Jason Kendall	20.00	50.00
72 Jimmy Key	20.00	50.00
73 Brooks Kieschnick	12.50	30.00
74 Ryan Klesko	20.00	50.00
75 Chuck Knoblauch *	20.00	50.00
76 Paul Konerko	40.00	80.00
77 Mark Kotsay	20.00	50.00
78 Ray Lankford	20.00	50.00
79 Barry Larkin *	40.00	80.00
80 Derrek Lee	40.00	80.00
81 Esteban Loaiza	12.50	30.00
82 Javier Lopez	20.00	50.00
83 Greg Maddux *	175.00	300.00
84 Edgar Martinez *	50.00	100.00
85 Pedro Martinez	75.00	150.00
86 Tino Martinez *	75.00	150.00
87 Rafael Medina	12.50	30.00
88 Raul Mondesi	20.00	50.00
89 Matt Morris	20.00	50.00
90 Eddie Murray EXCH*	60.00	120.00
91 Mike Mussina	40.00	80.00
92 Paul O'Neill	40.00	80.00
93 Kevin Orie	12.50	30.00
94 David Ortiz	400.00	600.00
95 Rafael Palmeiro	50.00	100.00
96 Jay Payton	12.50	30.00
97 Neifi Perez	12.50	30.00
98 Andy Pettitte *	100.00	200.00
99 Manny Ramirez	60.00	120.00
100 Joe Randa	20.00	50.00
101 Pokey Reese	20.00	50.00
102 Edgar Renteria	40.00	80.00
103 Dennis Reyes	12.50	30.00
104 Cal Ripken	125.00	250.00
105 Alex Rodriguez	600.00	800.00
106 Henry Rodriguez	12.50	30.00
107 Ivan Rodriguez	50.00	100.00
108 Scott Rolen *	40.00	80.00
109 Kirk Rueter	12.50	30.00
110 Ryne Sandberg	90.00	150.00
111 Gary Sheffield *	40.00	80.00
112 Dwight Smith	12.50	30.00
113 J.T. Snow	20.00	50.00
114 Scott Spiezio	12.50	30.00
115 Shannon Stewart	20.00	50.00
116 Jeff Suppan	20.00	50.00
117 Mike Sweeney	20.00	50.00
118 Miguel Tejada	75.00	150.00
119 Frank Thomas	50.00	100.00
120 Jim Thome	50.00	100.00
121 Justin Thompson	12.50	30.00
122 Brett Tomko	12.50	30.00
123 Bubba Trammell	12.50	30.00
124 Michael Tucker	20.00	50.00
125 Javier Valentin	12.50	30.00
126 Mo Vaughn *	20.00	50.00
127 Robin Ventura	20.00	50.00
128 Terrell Wade	12.50	30.00
129 Billy Wagner	40.00	80.00
130 Larry Walker	60.00	120.00
131 Todd Walker	12.50	30.00
132 Rondell White	20.00	50.00
133 Kevin Wickander	12.50	30.00
134 Chris Widger	12.50	30.00
135 Bernie Williams	60.00	120.00
136 Matt Williams *	40.00	80.00
137 Antone Williamson	12.50	30.00
138 Dan Wilson	12.50	30.00
139 Tony Womack	12.50	30.00
140 Jaret Wright	12.50	30.00
141 Dmitri Young	20.00	50.00
142 Eric Young	12.50	30.00
143 Kevin Young	12.50	30.00

1997 Donruss Signature Autographs Millennium

Randomly inserted in packs, this set, identified with green card fronts, features the second group of 100 cards signed by each player. The cards are sequentially numbered 101-1,100 (except for some shortprinted cards in quantities of 400, 650 or 900) and are checklisted in alphabetical order. It has been noted that there are some cards in circulation that lack serial numbering. Edgar Renteria was seeded into packs as an exchange card and has been verified by representatives at Donruss as being a short-print. Eddie Murray, Raul Mondesi and Jim Thome were also exchange cards.

1 Jeff Abbott	3.00	8.00
2 Bob Abreu	4.00	10.00
3 Edgardo Alfonzo	3.00	8.00
4 Roberto Alomar *	15.00	40.00
5 Sandy Alomar Jr.	6.00	15.00
6 Moises Alou	6.00	15.00
7 Garret Anderson	6.00	15.00
8 Andy Ashby	3.00	8.00
9 Jeff Bagwell/400	30.00	60.00
10 Trey Beamon	3.00	8.00
11 Albert Belle/400	10.00	25.00
12 Alan Benes	3.00	8.00
13 Geronimo Berroa	3.00	8.00
14 Wade Boggs *	15.00	40.00
15 Barry Bonds/400	50.00	100.00
16 Bobby Bonilla/900 *	6.00	15.00
17 Kevin Brown/900	6.00	15.00
18 Kevin Brown C	3.00	8.00
19 Jay Buhner/900	10.00	25.00
20 Brett Butler	6.00	15.00
21 Mike Cameron	6.00	15.00
22 Giovanni Carrara	3.00	8.00
23 Luis Castillo	6.00	15.00
24 Tony Clark	3.00	8.00
25 Will Clark	10.00	25.00
26 Roger Clemens/400 *	30.00	60.00
27 Lou Collier	3.00	8.00
28 Bartolo Colon	6.00	15.00
29 Ron Coomer	3.00	8.00
30 Marty Cordova	3.00	8.00
31 Jacob Cruz	3.00	8.00
32 Jose Cruz Jr. *	4.00	10.00
33 Russ Davis	3.00	8.00
34 Jason Dickson	3.00	8.00
35 Todd Dunwoody	3.00	8.00
36 Jermaine Dye	6.00	15.00
37 Jim Edmonds	10.00	25.00
38 Darin Erstad *	6.00	15.00
39 Bobby Estalella	3.00	8.00
40 Shawn Estes	3.00	8.00
41 Jeff Fassero	3.00	8.00
42 Andres Galarraga	6.00	15.00
43 Karim Garcia	3.00	8.00
44 N.Garciaparra/650 *	50.00	100.00
45 Derrick Gibson	3.00	8.00
46 Brian Giles	10.00	25.00
47 Tom Glavine	15.00	40.00
48 Juan Gonzalez/900	15.00	40.00
49 Rick Gorecki	3.00	8.00
50 Shawn Green	10.00	25.00
51 Todd Greene	3.00	8.00
52 Rusty Greer	6.00	15.00
53 Ben Grieve	3.00	8.00
54 Mark Grudzielanek	6.00	15.00
55 Vladimir Guerrero *	8.00	20.00
56 Wilton Guerrero	3.00	8.00
57 Jose Guillen	6.00	15.00
58 Tony Gwynn/900 *	15.00	40.00
59 Jeffrey Hammonds	3.00	8.00
60 Todd Helton	6.00	15.00
61 Todd Hundley	3.00	8.00
62 Todd Hollandsworth	3.00	8.00
63 Trenidad Hubbard	3.00	8.00
64 Derek Jeter/400 *	100.00	175.00
65 Andruw Jones/900 *	8.00	20.00
66 Bobby Jones	3.00	8.00
67 Chipper Jones/900 *	20.00	50.00
68 Brian Jordan	6.00	15.00
69 David Justice	6.00	15.00
70 Eric Karros	6.00	15.00
71 Jason Kendall	3.00	8.00
72 Jimmy Key	6.00	15.00
73 Brooks Kieschnick	3.00	8.00
74 Ryan Klesko	6.00	15.00
75 C.Knoblauch/900 *	6.00	15.00
76 Paul Konerko	8.00	20.00
77 Mark Kotsay	8.00	20.00
78 Ray Lankford	6.00	15.00
79 Barry Larkin *	10.00	25.00
80 Derrek Lee	10.00	25.00
81 Esteban Loaiza	3.00	8.00
82 Javier Lopez	6.00	15.00
83 Greg Maddux/400 *	60.00	120.00
84 Edgar Martinez *	15.00	40.00
85 Pedro Martinez	30.00	60.00
86 Tino Martinez/900 *	15.00	40.00
87 Rafael Medina	3.00	8.00
88 Raul Mondesi	6.00	15.00
89 Matt Morris	6.00	15.00
90 Eddie Murray/900 *	20.00	50.00
91 Mike Mussina/900	10.00	25.00
92 Paul O'Neill	10.00	25.00
93 Kevin Orie	3.00	8.00
94 David Ortiz	30.00	60.00
95 Rafael Palmeiro	20.00	50.00
96 Jay Payton	3.00	8.00
97 Neifi Perez	3.00	8.00
98 Andy Pettitte/900 *	30.00	60.00
99 Manny Ramirez	15.00	40.00
100 Joe Randa	6.00	15.00
101 Pokey Reese	6.00	15.00
102 Edgar Renteria SP	10.00	25.00
103 Dennis Reyes	3.00	8.00
104 Cal Ripken/400	75.00	150.00
105 Alex Rodriguez/400	60.00	120.00
106 Henry Rodriguez	3.00	8.00
107 Ivan Rodriguez/900	10.00	25.00
108 Scott Rolen *	10.00	25.00
109 Kirk Rueter	3.00	8.00
110 Ryne Sandberg	20.00	50.00
111 Gary Sheffield/400 *	15.00	40.00
112 Dwight Smith	3.00	8.00
113 J.T. Snow	6.00	15.00
114 Scott Spiezio	3.00	8.00
115 Shannon Stewart	6.00	15.00
116 Jeff Suppan	6.00	15.00
117 Mike Sweeney	6.00	15.00
118 Miguel Tejada	10.00	25.00
119 Frank Thomas/400	30.00	60.00
120 Jim Thome/900	40.00	80.00
121 Justin Thompson	3.00	8.00
122 Brett Tomko	3.00	8.00
123 Bubba Trammell	4.00	10.00
124 Michael Tucker	6.00	15.00
125 Javier Valentin	3.00	8.00
126 Mo Vaughn *	6.00	15.00
127 Robin Ventura	6.00	15.00
128 Terrell Wade	3.00	8.00
129 Billy Wagner	4.00	10.00
130 Larry Walker	10.00	25.00
131 Todd Walker	3.00	8.00
132 Rondell White	6.00	15.00
133 Kevin Wickander	3.00	8.00
134 Chris Widger	3.00	8.00
135 Bernie Williams/400	60.00	120.00
136 Matt Williams *	10.00	25.00
137 Antone Williamson	3.00	8.00
138 Dan Wilson	3.00	8.00
139 Tony Womack	4.00	10.00
140 Jaret Wright	4.00	10.00
141 Dmitri Young	6.00	15.00
142 Eric Young	3.00	8.00
143 Kevin Young	3.00	8.00

1997 Donruss Signature Notable Nicknames

Randomly inserted in packs, this 10-card set features photos of players with notable nicknames. Only 200 of this serial numbered set were produced. The cards are unnumbered and checklisted in alphabetical order. Roger Clemens signed a good deal of his cards without using his "Rocket" nickname. In addition, some Frank Thomas cards have been seen signed without "The Big Hurt" nickname. There is no difference in value between the two versions.

1 Ernie Banks Mr. Cub	100.00	200.00
2 Tony Clark The Tiger	20.00	50.00
3 Roger Clemens The Rocket	300.00	600.00
4 Reggie Jackson Mr. October	100.00	200.00
5 Randy Johnson The Big Unit	250.00	500.00
6 Stan Musial The Man	150.00	300.00
7 Ivan Rodriguez Pudge	100.00	200.00
9 Frank Thomas The Big Hurt	100.00	200.00
10 Mo Vaughn The Hit Dog	20.00	50.00
11 Billy Wagner The Kid	75.00	150.00

1997 Donruss Signature Significant Signatures

Randomly inserted in packs, this 22-card set features photos with autographs of legendary Hall of Fame players. Only 2000 of each card was produced and serially numbered. The cards are checklisted below in alphabetical order. Reggie Jackson signed his cards in 2 different color inks. The cards he signed in silver are in shorter supply and are valued higher.

1 Ernie Banks	20.00	50.00
2 Johnny Bench	15.00	40.00
3 Yogi Berra	15.00	40.00
4 George Brett	30.00	60.00
5 Lou Brock	15.00	40.00
6 Rod Carew	12.50	30.00
7 Steve Carlton	10.00	25.00
8 Larry Doby	30.00	60.00
9 Carlton Fisk	10.00	25.00
10 Bob Gibson	10.00	25.00
11 Reggie Jackson	15.00	40.00
11A R.Jackson Silver Ink	100.00	200.00
12 Al Kaline	15.00	40.00
13 Harmon Killebrew	20.00	50.00
14 Don Mattingly	20.00	50.00
15 Stan Musial	20.00	50.00
16 Jim Palmer	10.00	25.00
17 Brooks Robinson	8.00	20.00
18 Frank Robinson	10.00	25.00
19 Mike Schmidt	20.00	50.00
20 Tom Seaver	15.00	40.00
21 Duke Snider	10.00	25.00
22 Carl Yastrzemski	20.00	50.00

1998 Donruss Signature

The 140-card 1998 Donruss Signature set was distributed in five-card packs with one authentic autographed card per pack and a suggested retail price of $14.99. The fronts feature color action player photos in white borders. The backs carry player information and career statistics. Due to Pinnacle's bankruptcy, these cards were later released by Playoff. This set was released in very late December, 1998. Notable Rookie Cards in this set include J.D. Drew, Troy Glaus, Orlando Hernandez, Gabe Kapler, Kevin Millwood and Magglio Ordonez.

COMPLETE SET (140)	20.00	50.00
1 David Justice	.15	.40
2 Derek Jeter	1.00	2.50
3 Nomar Garciaparra	.60	1.50
4 Ryan Klesko	.15	.40
5 Jeff Bagwell	.25	.60
6 Dante Bichette	.15	.40
7 Ivan Rodriguez	.25	.60
8 Albert Belle	.15	.40
9 Cal Ripken	1.25	3.00
10 Craig Biggio	.25	.60
11 Barry Larkin	.25	.60
12 Jose Guillen	.15	.40
13 Will Clark	.25	.60
14 J.T. Snow	.15	.40
15 Chuck Knoblauch	.15	.40
16 Todd Walker	.15	.40
17 Scott Rolen	.25	.60
18 Rickey Henderson	.40	1.00
19 Juan Gonzalez	.15	.40
20 Justin Thompson	.15	.40
21 Roger Clemens	.75	2.00
22 Ray Lankford	.15	.40
23 Jose Cruz Jr.	.15	.40
24 Ken Griffey Jr.	.60	1.50
25 Andruw Jones	.25	.60
26 Darin Erstad	.15	.40
27 Jim Thome	.25	.60
28 Wade Boggs	.25	.60
29 Ken Caminiti	.15	.40
30 Todd Hundley	.15	.40
31 Mike Piazza	.60	1.50
32 Sammy Sosa	.40	1.00
33 Larry Walker	.15	.40
34 Matt Williams	.15	.40
35 Frank Thomas	.40	1.00
36 Gary Sheffield	.15	.40
37 Alex Rodriguez	.60	1.50
38 Hideo Nomo	.40	1.00
39 Kenny Lofton	.15	.40
40 John Smoltz	.25	.60
41 Mo Vaughn	.15	.40
42 Edgar Martinez	.25	.60
43 Paul Molitor	.15	.40
44 Rafael Palmeiro	.25	.60
45 Barry Bonds	1.00	2.50
46 Vladimir Guerrero	.40	1.00
47 Carlos Delgado	.15	.40
48 Bobby Higginson	.15	.40
49 Greg Maddux	.60	1.50
50 Jim Edmonds	.15	.40
51 Randy Johnson	.40	1.00
52 Mark McGwire	1.00	2.50
53 Rondell White	.15	.40
54 Raul Mondesi	.15	.40
55 Manny Ramirez	.25	.60
56 Pedro Martinez	.25	.60
57 Tim Salmon	.25	.60
58 Moises Alou	.15	.40
59 Fred McGriff	.25	.60
60 Garret Anderson	.15	.40
61 Sandy Alomar Jr.	.15	.40
62 Chan Ho Park	.15	.40
63 Mark Kotsay	.15	.40
64 Mike Mussina	.25	.60
65 Tom Glavine	.25	.60
66 Tony Clark	.15	.40
67 Mark Grace	.25	.60
68 Tony Gwynn	.50	1.25
69 Tino Martinez	.25	.60
70 Kevin Brown	.25	.60
71 Todd Greene	.15	.40
72 Andy Pettitte	.25	.60
73 Livan Hernandez	.15	.40
74 Curt Schilling	.15	.40
75 Andres Galarraga	.15	.40
76 Rusty Greer	.15	.40
77 Jay Buhner	.15	.40
78 Bobby Bonilla	.15	.40
79 Chipper Jones	.40	1.00
80 Eric Young	.15	.40
81 Jason Giambi	.15	.40
82 Javy Lopez	.15	.40
83 Roberto Alomar	.25	.60
84 Bernie Williams	.25	.60
85 A.J. Hinch	.15	.40
86 Kerry Wood	.20	.50
87 Juan Encarnacion	.15	.40
88 Brad Fullmer	.15	.40
89 Ben Grieve	.15	.40
90 Magglio Ordonez RC	2.00	5.00
91 Todd Helton	.25	.60
92 Richard Hidalgo	.15	.40
93 Paul Konerko	.15	.40
94 Aramis Ramirez	.15	.40
95 Ricky Ledee	.15	.40
96 Derrek Lee	.25	.60
97 Travis Lee	.15	.40
98 Matt Anderson RC	.15	.40
99 Jaret Wright	.15	.40
100 David Ortiz	.50	1.25
101 Carl Pavano	.15	.40
102 O.Hernandez RC	.75	2.00
103 Fernando Tatis	.15	.40
104 Miguel Tejada	.40	1.00
105 Rolando Arrojo RC	.25	.60
106 Kevin Millwood RC	.60	1.50
107 Ken Griffey Jr. CL	.40	1.00
108 Frank Thomas CL	.25	.60
109 Cal Ripken CL	.60	1.50
110 Greg Maddux CL	.40	1.00
111 John Olerud	.15	.40
112 David Cone	.15	.40
113 Vinny Castilla	.15	.40
114 Jason Kendall	.15	.40
115 Brian Jordan	.15	.40
116 Hideki Irabu	.15	.40
117 Bartolo Colon	.15	.40
118 Greg Vaughn	.15	.40
119 David Segui	.15	.40
120 Bruce Chen	.15	.40
121 Julio Ramirez RC	.15	.40
122 Troy Glaus RC	1.50	4.00
123 Jeremy Giambi RC	.25	.60
124 Ryan Minor RC	.15	.40
125 Richie Sexson	.15	.40
126 Dermal Brown	.15	.40
127 Adrian Beltre	.15	.40
128 Eric Chavez	.15	.40
129 J.D. Drew RC	1.25	3.00
130 Gabe Kapler RC	.40	1.00
131 Masato Yoshii RC	.25	.60
132 Mike Lowell RC	1.00	2.50
133 Jim Parque RC	.25	.60
134 Roy Halladay	.75	2.00
135 Carlos Lee RC	1.25	3.00
136 Jin Ho Cho RC	.15	.40
137 Michael Barrett	.15	.40
138 F.Seguignol RC	.15	.40
139 Odalis Perez RC UER Back pictures John Rocker	.60	1.50
140 Mark McGwire CL	.50	1.25

1998 Donruss Signature Proofs

Randomly inserted in packs, this 140-card set is a holo-foil treated parallel version of the base set. Only 150 sets were produced and numbered "1 of 150."

*STARS: 6X TO 15X BASIC CARDS
*RC's: 2X TO 5X BASIC CARDS

1998 Donruss Signature Autographs

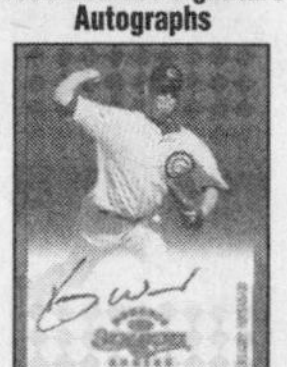

Inserted one per pack, this 98-card set features color action player images on a red foil background with the player's autograph in the lower portion of the card. The numbers following the player's name in our checklist indicate how many cards that player signed. The first 100 cards signed by each player are blue, sequentially-numbered and designated as "Century Marks." The next 1,000 signed are green, sequentially numbered and designated as "Millennium Marks." The cards are unnumbered and checklisted below in alphabetical order. An unnumbered Travis Lee sample card was distributed many months prior to the product's release. It's important to note that sample card features a facsimile autograph of Lee's.

1 Roberto Alomar/150	15.00	40.00
2 Sandy Alomar Jr./700	6.00	15.00
3 Moises Alou/900	6.00	15.00
4 Gabe Alvarez/2900	2.00	5.00
5 Wilson Alvarez/1600	2.00	5.00
6 Jay Bell/1500	2.00	5.00
7 Adrian Beltre/1900	8.00	20.00
8 Andy Benes/2600	2.00	5.00
9 Aaron Boone/3400	6.00	15.00
10 Russell Branyan/1650	3.00	8.00
11 Orlando Cabrera/3100	6.00	15.00
12 Mike Cameron/1150	2.00	5.00
13 Joe Carter/400	6.00	15.00
14 Sean Casey/2275	6.00	15.00
15 Bruce Chen/150	6.00	15.00
16 Tony Clark/2275	2.00	5.00
17 Will Clark/1400	8.00	20.00
18 Matt Clement/1400	6.00	15.00
19 Pat Cline/1400	2.00	5.00
20 Ken Cloude/3400	2.00	5.00
21 Michael Coleman/2800	2.00	5.00
22 David Cone/25		
23 Jeff Conine/1400	6.00	15.00
24 Jacob Cruz/3200	2.00	5.00
25 Russ Davis/3500	2.00	5.00
26 Jason Dickson/1400	2.00	5.00
27 Todd Dunwoody/3500	2.00	5.00
28 Juan Encarnacion/3400	6.00	15.00
29 Darin Erstad/700	6.00	15.00
30 Bobby Estalella/3400	2.00	5.00
31 Jeff Fassero/3400	2.00	5.00
32 John Franco/1800	6.00	15.00
33 Brad Fullmer/3100	2.00	5.00
34 Jason Giambi/3100	10.00	25.00
35 Derrick Gibson/1200	2.00	5.00
36 Todd Greene/1400	2.00	5.00
37 Ben Grieve/1400	2.00	5.00
38 M.Grudzielanek/3200	2.00	5.00
39 V.Guerrero/2100	10.00	25.00
40 Wilton Guerrero/1900	2.00	5.00
41 Jose Guillen/2400	6.00	15.00
42 Todd Helton/1300	10.00	25.00

43 Richard Hidalgo/3400 2.00 5.00
44 A.J. Hinch/2900 2.00 5.00
45 Butch Huskey/1900 2.00 5.00
46 Raul Ibanez/3300 6.00 15.00
47 Damian Jackson/900 2.00 5.00
48 Geoff Jenkins/3100 6.00 15.00
49 Eric Karros/650 6.00 15.00
50 Ryan Klesko/400 6.00 15.00
51 Mark Kotsay/3600 6.00 15.00
52 Ricky Ledee/2200 2.00 5.00
53 Derrek Lee/3400 8.00 20.00
54 Travis Lee/150 6.00 15.00
55 Javier Lopez/650 6.00 15.00
56 Mike Lowell/3500 6.00 15.00
57 Greg Maddux/12
58 Eli Marrero/3400 2.00 5.00
59 Al Martin/1300 2.00 5.00
60 Rafael Medina/1400 2.00 5.00
61 Scott Morgan/900 3.00 8.00
62 Abraham Nunez/3500 2.00 5.00
63 Paul O'Neill/1000 10.00 25.00
64 Luis Ordaz/2700 2.00 5.00
65 Magglio Ordonez/3200 8.00 20.00
66 Kevin Orie/1350 2.00 5.00
67 David Ortiz/3400 12.50 30.00
68 Rafael Palmeiro/1000 12.50 30.00
69 Carl Pavano/2600 6.00 15.00
70 Neifi Perez/3300 2.00 5.00
71 Dante Powell/3050 2.00 5.00
72 Aramis Ramirez/2800 6.00 15.00
73 Mariano Rivera/900 60.00 120.00
74 Felix Rodriguez/1400 2.00 5.00
75 Henry Rodriguez/3400 2.00 5.00
76 Scott Rolen/1900 6.00 15.00
77 Brian Rose/1400 2.00 5.00
78 Curt Schilling/900 10.00 25.00
79 Richie Sexson/3500 6.00 15.00
80 Randall Simon/3500 2.00 5.00
81 J.T. Snow/400 6.00 15.00
82 Jeff Suppan/1400 6.00 15.00
83 Fernando Tatis/3900 2.00 5.00
84 Miguel Tejada/3800 5.00 12.00
85 Brett Tomko/3400 2.00 5.00
86 Bubba Trammell/3900 10.00 25.00
87 Ismael Valdes/1900 2.00 5.00
88 Robin Ventura/1400 6.00 15.00
89 Billy Wagner/3900 10.00 25.00
90 Todd Walker/1900 6.00 15.00
91 Daryle Ward/400 3.00 8.00
92 Rondell White/3400 6.00 15.00
93 A.Williamson/3350 2.00 5.00
94 Dan Wilson/2400 2.00 5.00
95 Enrique Wilson/3400 2.00 5.00
96 Preston Wilson/2100 6.00 15.00
97 Tony Womack/3500 2.00 5.00
98 Kerry Wood/3400 6.00 15.00
NNO Travis Lee Sample Facsimile Autograph .40 1.00

1998 Donruss Signature Autographs Century

Randomly inserted in packs, this 122-card set is a sequentially numbered, blue parallel version of the Signature Autographs insert set and features the first 100 cards signed by each pictured player. The cards are unnumbered and checklisted in alphabetical order.

1 Roberto Alomar 75.00 150.00
2 Sandy Alomar Jr. 12.50 30.00
3 Moises Alou 20.00 50.00
4 Gabe Alvarez 12.50 30.00
5 Wilson Alvarez 12.50 30.00
6 Brady Anderson 20.00 50.00
7 Jay Bell 20.00 50.00
8 Albert Belle 20.00 50.00
9 Adrian Beltre 25.00 60.00
10 Andy Benes 12.50 30.00
11 Wade Boggs 50.00 100.00
12 Barry Bonds 225.00 350.00
13 Aaron Boone 20.00 50.00
14 Russell Branyan 12.50 30.00
15 Jay Buhner 20.00 50.00
16 Ellis Burks 20.00 50.00
17 Orlando Cabrera 20.00 50.00
18 Mike Cameron 20.00 50.00
19 Ken Caminiti 20.00 50.00
20 Joe Carter 20.00 50.00
21 Sean Casey 20.00 50.00
22 Bruce Chen 12.50 30.00
23 Tony Clark 12.50 30.00
24 Will Clark 40.00 80.00
25 Roger Clemens 175.00 300.00
26 Matt Clement 20.00 50.00
27 Pat Cline 12.50 30.00
28 Ken Cloude 12.50 30.00
29 Michael Coleman 12.50 30.00
30 David Cone 40.00 80.00
31 Jeff Conine 20.00 50.00
32 Jacob Cruz 12.50 30.00
33 Jose Cruz Jr. 12.50 30.00
34 Russ Davis 12.50 30.00
35 Jason Dickson 12.50 30.00
36 Todd Dunwoody 12.50 30.00
37 Scott Elarton 12.50 30.00
38 Darin Erstad 20.00 50.00
39 Bobby Estalella 12.50 30.00
40 Jeff Fassero 12.50 30.00
41 John Franco 20.00 50.00
42 Brad Fullmer 12.50 30.00
43 Andres Galarraga 20.00 50.00
44 Nomar Garciaparra 60.00 120.00
45 Jason Giambi 40.00 80.00
46 Derrick Gibson 12.50 30.00
47 Tom Glavine 50.00 100.00
48 Juan Gonzalez 20.00 50.00
49 Todd Greene 12.50 30.00
50 Ben Grieve 12.50 30.00
51 Mark Grudzielanek 12.50 30.00
52 Vladimir Guerrero 60.00 120.00
53 Wilton Guerrero 12.50 30.00
54 Jose Guillen 20.00 50.00
55 Tony Gwynn 60.00 120.00
56 Todd Helton 40.00 80.00
57 Richard Hidalgo 12.50 30.00
58 A.J. Hinch 12.50 30.00
59 Butch Huskey 12.50 30.00
60 Raul Ibanez 30.00 60.00
61 Damian Jackson 12.50 30.00
62 Geoff Jenkins 20.00 50.00
63 Derek Jeter 300.00 500.00
64 Randy Johnson 150.00 250.00
65 Chipper Jones 250.00 350.00
66 Eric Karros/50 20.00 50.00
67 Ryan Klesko 20.00 50.00
68 Chuck Knoblauch 20.00 50.00
69 Mark Kotsay 20.00 50.00
70 Ricky Ledee 12.50 30.00
71 Derrek Lee 40.00 80.00
72 Travis Lee 12.50 30.00
73 Javier Lopez 20.00 50.00
74 Mike Lowell 50.00 100.00
75 Greg Maddux 350.00 500.00
76 Eli Marrero 12.50 30.00
77 Al Martin 12.50 30.00
78 Rafael Medina 12.50 30.00
79 Paul Molitor 20.00 50.00
80 Scott Morgan 12.50 30.00
81 Mike Mussina 40.00 80.00
82 Abraham Nunez 12.50 30.00
83 Paul O'Neill 40.00 80.00
84 Luis Ordaz 12.50 30.00
85 Magglio Ordonez 40.00 80.00
86 Kevin Orie 12.50 30.00
87 David Ortiz 50.00 100.00
88 Rafael Palmeiro 60.00 120.00
89 Carl Pavano 20.00 50.00
90 Neifi Perez 12.50 30.00
91 Andy Pettitte 40.00 80.00
92 Aramis Ramirez 40.00 80.00
93 Cal Ripken 200.00 350.00
94 Mariano Rivera 100.00 200.00
95 Alex Rodriguez 175.00 350.00
96 Felix Rodriguez 12.50 30.00
97 Henry Rodriguez 12.50 30.00
98 Ivan Rodriguez 50.00 100.00
99 Scott Rolen 20.00 50.00
100 Brian Rose 12.50 30.00
101 Curt Schilling 50.00 100.00
102 Richie Sexson 20.00 50.00
103 Randall Simon 12.50 30.00
104 J.T. Snow 20.00 50.00
105 Darryl Strawberry 125.00 200.00
106 Jeff Suppan 20.00 50.00
107 Fernando Tatis 12.50 30.00
108 Brett Tomko 12.50 30.00
109 Bubba Trammell 12.50 30.00
110 Ismael Valdes 12.50 30.00
111 Robin Ventura 20.00 50.00
112 Billy Wagner 40.00 80.00
113 Todd Walker 20.00 50.00
114 Daryle Ward 20.00 50.00
115 Rondell White 20.00 50.00
116 Matt Williams/80 20.00 50.00
117 Antone Williamson 12.50 30.00
118 Dan Wilson 12.50 30.00
119 Enrique Wilson 12.50 30.00
120 Preston Wilson 20.00 50.00
121 Tony Womack 12.50 30.00
122 Kerry Wood 60.00 120.00

1998 Donruss Signature Autographs Millennium

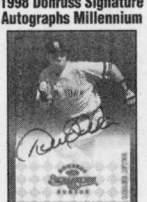

Randomly inserted in packs, this 125-card set is a sequentially numbered, green foil parallel version of the Signature Autographs insert set and features the next 1,000 cards signed by each pictured player after the initial 100. In numerous cases, players signed less than 1,000 cards. Print runs for these short-prints are specified after the player's name in the checklist. The cards are unnumbered and checklisted below in alphabetical order.

1 Roberto Alomar 10.00 25.00
2 Sandy Alomar Jr. 3.00 8.00
3 Moises Alou 6.00 15.00
4 Gabe Alvarez 3.00 8.00
5 Wilson Alvarez 3.00 8.00
6 Brady Anderson/800 6.00 15.00
7 Jay Bell 6.00 15.00
8 Albert Belle/400 10.00 25.00
9 Adrian Beltre 8.00 20.00
10 Andy Benes 3.00 8.00
11 Wade Boggs/900 6.00 15.00
12 Barry Bonds/400 100.00 175.00
13 Aaron Boone 6.00 15.00
14 Russell Branyan 3.00 8.00
15 Jay Buhner/400 15.00 40.00
16 Ellis Burks/900 4.00 10.00
17 Orlando Cabrera 6.00 15.00
18 Mike Cameron 6.00 15.00
19 Ken Caminiti/900 15.00 40.00
20 Joe Carter 10.00 25.00
21 Sean Casey 6.00 15.00
22 Bruce Chen 3.00 8.00
23 Tony Clark 3.00 8.00
24 Will Clark 10.00 25.00
25 Roger Clemens/400 40.00 80.00
26 Matt Clement/900 6.00 15.00
27 Pat Cline 3.00 8.00
28 Ken Cloude 3.00 8.00
29 Michael Coleman 3.00 8.00
30 David Cone 10.00 25.00
31 Jeff Conine 6.00 15.00
32 Jacob Cruz 3.00 8.00
33 Jose Cruz Jr./850 3.00 8.00
34 Russ Davis/950 3.00 8.00
35 Jason Dickson/950 3.00 8.00
36 Todd Dunwoody 3.00 8.00
37 Scott Elarton/900 3.00 8.00
38 Juan Encarnacion 6.00 15.00
39 Darin Erstad 6.00 15.00
40 Bobby Estalella 3.00 8.00
41 Jeff Fassero 3.00 8.00
42 John Franco/950 6.00 15.00
43 Brad Fullmer 3.00 8.00
44 Andres Galarraga/900 6.00 15.00
45 Nomar Garciaparra/400 40.00 80.00
46 Jason Giambi 10.00 25.00
47 Derrick Gibson 3.00 8.00
48 Tom Glavine/700 10.00 25.00
49 Juan Gonzalez 15.00 40.00
50 Todd Greene 3.00 8.00
51 Ben Grieve 3.00 8.00
52 Mark Grudzielanek 3.00 8.00
53 Vladimir Guerrero 10.00 25.00
54 Wilton Guerrero 3.00 8.00
55 Jose Guillen 6.00 15.00
56 Tony Gwynn/900 15.00 40.00
57 Todd Helton 8.00 20.00
58 Richard Hidalgo 3.00 8.00
59 A.J. Hinch 3.00 8.00
60 Butch Huskey 3.00 8.00
61 Raul Ibanez 12.50 30.00
62 Damian Jackson 3.00 8.00
63 Geoff Jenkins 6.00 15.00
64 Derek Jeter/400 175.00 350.00
65 Randy Johnson/800 40.00 80.00
66 Chipper Jones/900 30.00 60.00
67 Eric Karros 6.00 15.00
68 Ryan Klesko 6.00 15.00
69 Chuck Knoblauch/900 6.00 15.00
70 Mark Kotsay 6.00 15.00
71 Ricky Ledee 3.00 8.00
72 Derrek Lee 10.00 25.00
73 Travis Lee 3.00 8.00
74 Javier Lopez/800 6.00 15.00
75 Mike Lowell 12.50 30.00
76 Greg Maddux/400 60.00 120.00
77 Eli Marrero 3.00 8.00
78 Al Martin/950 3.00 8.00
79 Rafael Medina/850 3.00 8.00
80 Paul Molitor/900 15.00 40.00
81 Scott Morgan 3.00 8.00
82 Mike Mussina/900 10.00 25.00
83 Abraham Nunez 3.00 8.00
84 Paul O'Neill/900 10.00 25.00
85 Luis Ordaz 3.00 8.00
86 Magglio Ordonez 15.00 40.00
87 Kevin Orie 3.00 8.00
88 David Ortiz 15.00 40.00
89 Rafael Palmeiro/900 20.00 50.00
90 Carl Pavano 6.00 15.00
91 Neifi Perez 3.00 8.00
92 Andy Pettitte/900 20.00 50.00
93 Dante Powell/950 3.00 8.00
94 Aramis Ramirez 10.00 25.00
95 Cal Ripken/375 75.00 150.00
96 Mariano Rivera 60.00 120.00
97 Alex Rodriguez/350 60.00 120.00
98 Felix Rodriguez 3.00 8.00
99 Henry Rodriguez 3.00 8.00
100 Ivan Rodriguez 10.00 25.00
101 Scott Rolen 6.00 15.00
102 Brian Rose 3.00 8.00
103 Curt Schilling 20.00 50.00
104 Richie Sexson 6.00 15.00
105 Randall Simon 3.00 8.00
106 J.T. Snow 6.00 15.00
107 Darryl Strawberry/900 12.50 30.00
108 Jeff Suppan 3.00 8.00
109 Fernando Tatis 6.00 15.00
110 Miguel Tejada 15.00 40.00
111 Brett Tomko 3.00 8.00
112 Bubba Trammell 3.00 8.00
113 Ismael Valdes 3.00 8.00
114 Robin Ventura 6.00 15.00
115 Billy Wagner/900 10.00 25.00
116 Todd Walker 6.00 15.00
117 Daryle Ward 3.00 8.00
118 Rondell White 6.00 15.00
119 Matt Williams/820 10.00 25.00
120 Antone Williamson 3.00 8.00
121 Dan Wilson 3.00 8.00
122 Enrique Wilson 3.00 8.00
123 Preston Wilson/400 15.00 40.00
124 Tony Womack 3.00 8.00
125 Kerry Wood 8.00 20.00

1998 Donruss Signature Significant Signatures

Randomly inserted in packs, this 18-card set features color photos with autographs of some of baseball's all-time great players. Only 2,000 of this sequentially-numbered set were produced. Sandy Koufax was on the original checklist but his cards were not returned in time for the pack out. Thus, officials at Donruss made the Billy Williams card an exchange card. Each collector that pulled a Billy Williams card could send it in to Donruss for a Koufax card. In addition, the signed Williams card was sent back too. Special exchange cards were created for Nolan Ryan and Ozzie Smith. The cards were randomly seeded into packs and then redeemed to Donruss for the real autograph cards. The exchange deadline for cards R1-R3 was December 31st, 1999. All three "R-Series" exchange cards (Ryan, Koufax and Smith) feature refractive, shiny fronts whereas the other cards seeded in packs are printed on basic foilboard. For pricing on these R1-R3 cards, please see the 1998 Donruss Signature Significant Signatures Refractors listing. At some point in time after the product's release, non-refractive versions of the Koufax (#'d of 2000), Ozzie (#'[d of 2000) and Ryan (#'d of 1000) cards made their way into the secondary market. Each card features a different card front image than the Refractor versions (most notably with Koufax wearing a Brooklyn cap). Representatives at Donruss-Playoff were unable to provide us with information on this matter given that the company was technically owned by Pinnacle in 1998 and then purchased out of bankruptcy in 2001 by the new Donruss-Playoff Corporation. The Catfish Hunter card was signed in either blue or blank ink. Only 1,000 serial #'d copies of Phil Rizzuto's card were produced.

KOUFAX NOT MEANT FOR PUBLIC RELEASE
OZZIE NOT MEANT FOR PUBLIC RELEASE
RYAN NOT MEANT FOR PUBLIC RELEASE
1 Ernie Banks/2000 20.00 50.00
2 Yogi Berra/2000 20.00 50.00
3 George Brett/2000 20.00 50.00
4 Catfish Hunter/2000 20.00 50.00
5 Al Kaline/2000 12.50 30.00
6 Harmon Killebrew/2000 20.00 50.00
7 Ralph Kiner/2000 10.00 25.00
9 Eddie Mathews/2000 20.00 50.00
10 Don Mattingly/2000 30.00 60.00
11 Willie McCovey/2000 15.00 40.00
12 Stan Musial/2000 30.00 60.00
13 Phil Rizzuto/1000 15.00 40.00
14 Nolan Ryan No Auto 6.00 15.00
15 Ozzie Smith No Auto 2.00 5.00
16 Duke Snider/2000 10.00 25.00
17 Don Sutton/2000 10.00 25.00
18 Billy Williams/2000 10.00 25.00
18A Billy Williams No Auto 2.00 5.00
SP Nolan Ryan/1000 50.00 100.00
NNO S.Koufax Brooklyn/2000 100.00 175.00
NNO Ozzie Smith/2000 15.00 40.00

1998 Donruss Signature Significant Signatures Refractors

AVAILABLE VIA MAIL EXCHANGE
STATED PRINT RUN 2000 SERIAL #'d SETS
R1 Nolan Ryan 40.00 80.00
R2 Ozzie Smith 20.00 50.00
R3 Sandy Koufax LA 175.00 250.00

2001 Donruss Signature

This 311 card set was issued 25 cards to a "gift" box. The 25 card boxes had a SRP of $49.99 per box and the boxes were issued eight to a mini case. Cards numbered from 111 through 165 were inserted at an approximate rate of one per box and were serial numbered to 330. Cards numbered 166 to 311 were issued at an approximate rate of two per box and were serial numbered to 800.

COMP.SET w/o SP'S (110) 20.00 50.00
COMMON CARD (1-110) .40 1.00
COMMON (111-165) 4.00 10.00
COMMON AU RC (111-165) 4.00 10.00
COMMON NO AU (111-165) 3.00 8.00
COMMON (166-311) 2.00 5.00
COMMON RC (166-311) 2.00 5.00
1 Alex Rodriguez 1.50 4.00
2 Barry Bonds 2.50 6.00
3 Cal Ripken 3.00 8.00
4 Chipper Jones 1.00 2.50
5 Derek Jeter 2.50 6.00
6 Troy Glaus .40 1.00
7 Frank Thomas 1.00 2.50
8 Greg Maddux 1.50 4.00
9 Ivan Rodriguez .60 1.50
10 Jeff Bagwell .60 1.50
11 John Olerud .40 1.00
12 Todd Helton .60 1.50
13 Ken Griffey Jr. 1.50 4.00
14 Manny Ramirez Sox .60 1.50
15 Mark McGwire 2.50 6.00
16 Mike Piazza 1.50 4.00
17 Nomar Garciaparra 1.50 4.00
18 Moises Alou .40 1.00
19 Aramis Ramirez .40 1.00
20 Curt Schilling .40 1.00
21 Pat Burrell .40 1.00
22 Doug Mientkiewicz .40 1.00
23 Carlos Delgado .40 1.00
24 J.D. Drew .40 1.00
25 Cliff Floyd .40 1.00
26 Freddy Garcia .40 1.00
27 Roberto Alomar .60 1.50
28 Barry Zito .60 1.50
29 Juan Encarnacion .40 1.00
30 Paul Konerko .40 1.00
31 Mark Mulder .40 1.00
32 Andy Pettitte .60 1.50
33 Jim Edmonds .40 1.00
34 Darin Erstad .40 1.00
35 Jason Giambi .40 1.00
36 Tom Glavine .60 1.50
37 Juan Gonzalez .40 1.00
38 Fred McGriff .60 1.50
39 Shawn Green .40 1.00
40 Tim Hudson .40 1.00
41 Andruw Jones .60 1.50
42 Jeff Kent .40 1.00
43 Barry Larkin .60 1.50
44 Brad Radke .40 1.00
45 Mike Mussina .60 1.50
46 Hideo Nomo 1.00 2.50
47 Rafael Palmeiro .60 1.50
48 Scott Rolen .60 1.50
49 Gary Sheffield .40 1.00
50 Bernie Williams .60 1.50
51 Bob Abreu .40 1.00
52 Edgardo Alfonzo .40 1.00
53 Edgar Martinez .60 1.50
54 Magglio Ordonez .40 1.00
55 Kerry Wood .40 1.00
56 Adrian Beltre .40 1.00
57 Lance Berkman .40 1.00
58 Kevin Brown 1.00 2.50
59 Sean Casey .40 1.00
60 Eric Chavez .40 1.00
61 Bartolo Colon .40 1.00
62 Sammy Sosa 1.00 2.50
63 Jermaine Dye .40 1.00
64 Tony Gwynn 1.25 3.00
65 Carl Everett .40 1.00
66 Brian Giles .40 1.00
67 Mike Hampton .40 1.00
68 Richard Hidalgo .40 1.00
69 Geoff Jenkins .40 1.00
70 Tony Clark .40 1.00
71 Roger Clemens 2.00 5.00
72 Ryan Klesko .40 1.00
73 Chan Ho Park .40 1.00
74 Richie Sexson .40 1.00
75 Mike Sweeney .40 1.00
76 Kazuhiro Sasaki .40 1.00
77 Miguel Tejada .40 1.00
78 Jose Vidro .40 1.00
79 Larry Walker .40 1.00
80 Preston Wilson .40 1.00
81 Craig Biggio .60 1.50
82 Andres Galarraga .40 1.00
83 Jim Thome .60 1.50
84 Vladimir Guerrero 1.00 2.50
85 Rafael Furcal .40 1.00
86 Cristian Guzman .40 1.00
87 Terrence Long .40 1.00
88 Bret Boone .40 1.00
89 Wade Miller .40 1.00
90 Eric Milton .40 1.00
91 Gabe Kapler .40 1.00
92 Johnny Damon .60 1.50
93 Carlos Lee .40 1.00
94 Kenny Lofton .40 1.00
95 Raul Mondesi .40 1.00
96 Jorge Posada .60 1.50
97 Mark Grace .60 1.50
98 Robert Fick .40 1.00
99 Joe Mays .40 1.00
100 Aaron Sele .40 1.00
101 Ben Grieve .40 1.00
102 Luis Gonzalez .40 1.00
103 Ray Durham .40 1.00
104 Mark Quinn .40 1.00
105 Jose Canseco .60 1.50
106 David Justice .40 1.00
107 Pedro Martinez .60 1.50
108 Randy Johnson 1.00 2.50
109 Phil Nevin .40 1.00
110 Rickey Henderson 1.00 2.50
111 Alex Escobar AU 4.00 10.00
112 J.Estrada AU RC 6.00 15.00
113 Pedro Feliz AU 4.00 10.00
114 Nate Frese AU RC 4.00 10.00
115 R. Rodriguez AU RC 4.00 10.00
116 B.Larson AU RC 4.00 10.00
117 Alexis Gomez AU RC 4.00 10.00
118 Jason Hart AU 4.00 10.00
119 C.C. Sabathia AU 15.00 40.00
120 Endy Chavez AU RC 4.00 10.00
121 C.Parker AU RC 4.00 10.00
122 Jackson Melian RC 3.00 8.00
123 Joe Kennedy AU RC 6.00 15.00
124 A.Hernandez AU RC 4.00 10.00
125 Cesar Izturis AU 4.00 10.00
126 Jose Mieses AU RC 4.00 10.00
127 Roy Oswalt AU 10.00 25.00
128 Eric Munson AU 4.00 10.00
129 Xavier Nady AU 6.00 15.00
130 H.Ramirez AU RC 6.00 15.00
131 Abraham Nunez AU 4.00 10.00
132 Jose Ortiz AU 4.00 10.00
133 Jeremy Owens AU RC 4.00 10.00
134 Claudio Vargas AU RC 4.00 10.00
135 Corey Patterson AU 4.00 10.00
136 Carlos Pena 3.00 8.00
137 Bud Smith AU RC 4.00 10.00
138 Adam Dunn AU 10.00 25.00
139 A.Pettyjohn AU RC 4.00 10.00
140 E.Guzman AU RC 4.00 10.00
141 Jay Gibbons AU RC 6.00 15.00
142 Wilkin Ruan AU RC 4.00 10.00
143 Tsuyoshi Shinjo RC 4.00 10.00
144 Alfonso Soriano AU 10.00 25.00
145 Marcus Giles AU 6.00 15.00
146 Ichiro Suzuki RC 40.00 80.00
147 Juan Uribe AU RC 10.00 25.00
148 David Williams AU RC 4.00 10.00
149 C. Valderrama AU RC 4.00 10.00
150 Matt White AU RC 4.00 10.00
151 Albert Pujols AU RC 400.00 800.00
152 D.Mendez AU RC 4.00 10.00
153 Cory Aldridge AU RC 4.00 10.00
154 B. Duckworth AU RC 4.00 10.00
155 Josh Beckett AU 12.50 30.00
156 W.Betemit AU RC 10.00 25.00
157 Ben Sheets AU 10.00 25.00
158 Andres Torres AU RC 10.00 25.00
159 Aubrey Huff AU 6.00 15.00
160 Jack Wilson AU RC 6.00 15.00
161 Rafael Soriano AU RC 6.00 15.00
162 Nick Johnson AU 6.00 15.00
163 Carlos Garcia AU RC 4.00 10.00
164 Josh Towers AU RC 6.00 15.00
165 J.Michaels AU RC 4.00 10.00
166 Ryan Drese RC 3.00 8.00
167 Dewon Brazelton RC 2.00 5.00
168 Kevin Olsen RC 2.00 5.00
169 Benito Baez RC 2.00 5.00
170 Mark Prior RC 10.00 25.00
171 Wilmy Caceres RC 2.00 5.00
172 Mark Teixeira RC 12.50 30.00
173 Willie Harris RC 2.00 5.00
174 Mike Koplove RC 2.00 5.00
175 Brandon Knight RC 2.00 5.00
176 John Grabow RC 2.00 5.00
177 Jeremy Affeldt RC 2.00 5.00
178 Brandon Inge 2.00 5.00
179 Casey Fossum RC 2.00 5.00
180 Scott Stewart RC 2.00 5.00
181 Luke Hudson RC 2.00 5.00
182 Ken Vining RC 2.00 5.00
183 Toby Hall 2.00 5.00
184 Eric Knott RC 2.00 5.00
185 Kris Foster RC 2.00 5.00
186 David Brous RC 2.00 5.00
187 Roy Smith RC 2.00 5.00
188 Grant Balfour RC 2.00 5.00
189 Jeremy Fikac RC 2.00 5.00
190 Morgan Ensberg RC 3.00 8.00
191 Ryan Freel RC 3.00 8.00
192 Ryan Jensen RC 2.00 5.00
193 Lance Davis RC 2.00 5.00
194 Delvin James RC 2.00 5.00
195 Timo Perez 2.00 5.00
196 Michael Cuddyer 2.00 5.00
197 Bob File RC 2.00 5.00
198 Martin Vargas RC 2.00 5.00
199 Kris Keller RC 2.00 5.00
200 T.Spooneybarger RC 2.00 5.00
201 Adam Everett 2.00 5.00
202 Josh Fogg RC 2.00 5.00
203 Kip Wells 2.00 5.00
204 Rick Bauer RC 2.00 5.00
205 Brent Abernathy 2.00 5.00
206 Erick Almonte RC 2.00 5.00
207 Pedro Santana RC 2.00 5.00
208 Ken Harvey 2.00 5.00
209 Jerrod Riggan RC 2.00 5.00
210 Nick Punto RC 2.00 5.00
211 Steve Green RC 2.00 5.00
212 Nick Neugebauer 2.00 5.00
213 Chris George 2.00 5.00
214 Mike Penney RC 2.00 5.00
215 Bret Prinz RC 2.00 5.00
216 Tim Christman RC 2.00 5.00
217 Sean Douglass RC 2.00 5.00
218 Brett Jodie RC 2.00 5.00
219 Juan Diaz RC 2.00 5.00
220 Carlos Hernandez 2.00 5.00
221 Alex Cintron 2.00 5.00
222 Juan Cruz RC 2.00 5.00
223 Larry Bigbie 2.00 5.00
224 Junior Spivey RC 3.00 8.00
225 Luis Rivas 2.00 5.00
226 Brandon Lyon RC 2.00 5.00
227 Tony Cogan RC 2.00 5.00
228 J.Duchscherer RC 2.00 5.00
229 Tike Redman 2.00 5.00
230 Jimmy Rollins 2.00 5.00
231 Scott Podsednik RC 8.00 20.00
232 Jose Acevedo RC 2.00 5.00
233 Luis Pineda RC 2.00 5.00
234 Josh Phelps 2.00 5.00
235 Paul Phillips RC 2.00 5.00
236 Brian Roberts RC 3.00 8.00
237 O.Woodards RC 2.00 5.00
238 Bart Miadich RC 2.00 5.00
239 Les Walrond RC 2.00 5.00
240 Brad Voyles RC 2.00 5.00
241 Joe Crede 3.00 8.00
242 Juan Moreno RC 2.00 5.00
243 Matt Ginter 2.00 5.00
244 Brian Rogers RC 2.00 5.00
245 Pablo Ozuna 2.00 5.00
246 Geronimo Gil RC 2.00 5.00
247 Mike Maroth RC 3.00 8.00
248 Josue Perez RC 2.00 5.00
249 Dee Brown 2.00 5.00
250 Victor Zambrano RC 3.00 8.00
251 Nick Maness RC 2.00 5.00
252 Kyle Lohse RC 3.00 8.00
253 Greg Miller RC 2.00 5.00
254 Henry Mateo RC 2.00 5.00
255 Duaner Sanchez RC 2.00 5.00
256 Rob MacKowiak RC 3.00 8.00
257 Steve Lomasney 2.00 5.00
258 Angel Santos RC 2.00 5.00
259 Winston Abreu RC 2.00 5.00
260 Brandon Berger RC 2.00 5.00
261 Tomas De La Rosa 2.00 5.00
262 Ramon Vazquez RC 2.00 5.00
263 Mickey Callaway RC 2.00 5.00
264 Corky Miller RC 2.00 5.00
265 Keith Ginter 2.00 5.00
266 Cody Ransom RC 2.00 5.00
267 Doug Nickle RC 2.00 5.00
268 Derrick Lewis RC 2.00 5.00
269 Eric Hinske RC 3.00 8.00
270 Travis Phelps RC 2.00 5.00
271 Eric Valent 2.00 5.00
272 Michael Rivera RC 2.00 5.00
273 Esix Snead RC 2.00 5.00
274 Troy Mattes RC 2.00 5.00
275 Jermaine Clark RC 2.00 5.00
276 Nate Cornejo 2.00 5.00
277 George Perez RC 2.00 5.00
278 Juan Rivera 2.00 5.00
279 Justin Atchley RC 2.00 5.00
280 Adam Johnson 2.00 5.00
281 Gene Altman RC 2.00 5.00
282 Jason Jennings 2.00 5.00
283 Scott MacRae RC 2.00 5.00
284 Craig Monroe RC 3.00 8.00
285 Bert Snow RC 2.00 5.00
286 Stubby Clapp RC 2.00 5.00
287 Jack Cust 2.00 5.00
288 Will Ohman RC 2.00 5.00
289 Wily Mo Pena 2.00 5.00
290 Joe Beimel RC 2.00 5.00
291 Jason Karnuth RC 2.00 5.00
292 Bill Ortega RC 2.00 5.00
293 Nate Teut RC 2.00 5.00
294 Erik Hiljus RC 2.00 5.00
295 Jason Smith RC 2.00 5.00
296 Juan A.Pena RC 2.00 5.00
297 David Espinosa 2.00 5.00
298 Tim Redding 2.00 5.00
299 Brian Lawrence RC 2.00 5.00
300 Brian Reith RC 2.00 5.00
301 Chad Durbin 2.00 5.00
302 Kurt Ainsworth 2.00 5.00
303 Blaine Neal RC 2.00 5.00
304 Jorge Julio RC 2.00 5.00
305 Adam Bernero 2.00 5.00
306 Travis Hafner RC 8.00 20.00
307 Dustan Mohr RC 2.00 5.00
308 Cesar Crespo RC 2.00 5.00
309 Billy Sylvester RC 2.00 5.00
310 Zach Day RC 2.00 5.00
311 Angel Berroa RC 3.00 8.00

2001 Donruss Signature Proofs

Randomly inserted in gift boxes, these 311 cards parallel the Donruss Signature set. Cards numbered 1-110 were issued to a print run of 175 sets while cards numbered 111-311 were issued to a print run of 25 sets. Please note that all cards numbered between 111 and 165 were autographed in addition to a few other scattered cards throughout the set. Due to market scarcity, no pricing is provided for cards numbered 111-311.

*PROOFS 1-110: 1.5X TO 4X BASIC

2001 Donruss Signature Award Winning Signatures

Randomly inserted in gift boxes, these cards feature signature from various players who won awards and the cards have stated print runs to that year they won an award. Please see our checklist for specific print run information.

1 Jeff Bagwell/94 50.00 100.00
2 Carlos Beltran/99 10.00 25.00
3 Johnny Bench/68 50.00 100.00
4 Yogi Berra/55 30.00 60.00
5 Craig Biggio/97 20.00 50.00
6 Barry Bonds/93 60.00 120.00
7 Rod Carew/77 40.00 80.00
8 Orlando Cepeda/67 12.50 30.00
9 Andre Dawson/77 12.50 30.00
10 D.Eckersley CY/92 12.50 30.00
11 D.Eckersley MVP/92 12.50 30.00
12 Whitey Ford/61 30.00 60.00
13 Jason Giambi/100 10.00 25.00
14 Bob Gibson/68 20.00 50.00
15 Juan Gonzalez/96 10.00 25.00
16 Orel Hershiser/88 15.00 40.00
17 Al Kaline/67 50.00 100.00
18 Fred Lynn/75 MVP 12.50 30.00
19 Fred Lynn/75 ROY 12.50 30.00
20 Jim Palmer/76 12.50 30.00
21 Cal Ripken/83 75.00 150.00
22 Phil Rizzuto/50 20.00 50.00
23 Brooks Robinson/64 20.00 50.00
24 Scott Rolen/97 15.00 40.00
25 Ryne Sandberg/84 60.00 120.00
26 Warren Spahn/57 30.00 60.00
27 Frank Thomas/94 20.00 50.00
28 Billy Williams/61 12.50 30.00
29 Kerry Wood/98 15.00 40.00
30 Robin Yount/89 40.00 80.00

2001 Donruss Signature Award Winning Signatures Masters Series

Randomly inserted in gift boxes, these cards feature various award winners who signed cards relating to various awards they won during their career.

1 Jeff Bagwell
2 Carlos Beltran 10.00 25.00
3 Johnny Bench
4 Yogi Berra
5 Craig Biggio 20.00 50.00
6 Barry Bonds
7 Rod Carew
8 Orlando Cepeda 10.00 25.00
9 Andre Dawson 10.00 25.00
10 Dennis Eckersley CY 10.00 25.00
11 Dennis Eckersley MVP 10.00 25.00
12 Whitey Ford 40.00 80.00
13 Jason Giambi
14 Bob Gibson 15.00 40.00
15 Juan Gonzalez
16 Orel Hershiser 50.00 100.00
17 Al Kaline 40.00 80.00
18 Fred Lynn MVP 10.00 25.00
19 Fred Lynn ROY 10.00 25.00
20 Jim Palmer 10.00 25.00
21 Cal Ripken
22 Phil Rizzuto 15.00 40.00
23 Brooks Robinson 15.00 40.00
24 Scott Rolen 15.00 40.00
25 Ryne Sandberg
26 Warren Spahn 30.00 60.00
27 Frank Thomas
28 Billy Williams 10.00 25.00
29 Kerry Wood 15.00 40.00
30 Robin Yount

2001 Donruss Signature Century Marks

Randomly inserted in gift boxes, these 48 cards feature signed cards of the featured players to various amounts. Please see our checklist to get the specific information on how many cards each player signed for this part of the promotion.

1 Brent Abernathy/184 4.00 10.00
2 Roberto Alomar/102 15.00 40.00
3 Rick Ankiel/119 10.00 25.00
4 Lance Berkman/121 10.00 25.00
5 Mark Buehrle/224 12.50 30.00
6 Wilmy Caceres/194 4.00 10.00
7 Eric Chavez/170 6.00 15.00
8 Joe Crede/154 10.00 25.00
9 Jack Cust/178 4.00 10.00
10 B. Duckworth/183 4.00 10.00
11 David Espinosa/199 4.00 10.00
12 Johnny Estrada/198 6.00 15.00
13 Pedro Feliz/180 4.00 10.00
14 Robert Fick/232 4.00 10.00
15 Cliff Floyd/146 6.00 15.00
16 Casey Fossum/100 4.00 10.00
17 Jay Gibbons/175 6.00 15.00
18 Keith Ginter/163 4.00 10.00
19 Troy Glaus/144 10.00 25.00
20 Luis Gonzalez/101 6.00 15.00
21 Vladimir Guerrero/187 15.00 40.00
22 Richard Hidalgo/173 4.00 10.00
23 Tim Hudson/145 10.00 25.00
24 Adam Johnson/130 4.00 10.00
25 Gabe Kapler/150 6.00 15.00
26 Joe Kennedy/219 6.00 15.00
27 Ryan Klesko/176 6.00 15.00
28 Carlos Lee/179 6.00 15.00
29 Terrence Long/180 4.00 10.00
30 Edgar Martinez/110 15.00 40.00
31 Joe Mays/209 4.00 10.00
32 Greg Miller/194 4.00 10.00
33 Wade Miller/180 4.00 10.00
34 Mark Mulder/203 6.00 15.00
35 Xavier Nady/180 6.00 15.00
36 Magglio Ordonez/104 6.00 15.00
37 Jose Ortiz/187 4.00 10.00
38 Roy Oswalt/192 15.00 40.00
39 Wily Mo Pena/203 6.00 15.00
40 Brad Penny/198 4.00 10.00
41 Aramis Ramirez/241 6.00 15.00
42 Luis Rivas/163 4.00 10.00
43 Alex Rodriguez/110 60.00 120.00
44 Scott Rolen/106 10.00 25.00
45 Mike Sweeney/99 6.00 15.00
46 Eric Valent/163 4.00 10.00
47 Kip Wells/223 4.00 10.00
48 Kerry Wood/109 10.00 25.00

2001 Donruss Signature Century Marks Masters Series

Randomly inserted in packs, these cards were signed by the players.

1 Brent Abernathy 4.00 10.00
2 Roberto Alomar 20.00 50.00
3 Rick Ankiel 10.00 25.00
4 Lance Berkman 10.00 25.00
5 Mark Buehrle 12.50 30.00
6 Wilmy Caceres 4.00 10.00
7 Eric Chavez 6.00 15.00
8 Joe Crede 10.00 25.00
9 Jack Cust 4.00 10.00
10 Brandon Duckworth 4.00 10.00
11 David Espinosa 4.00 10.00
12 Johnny Estrada 6.00 15.00
13 Pedro Feliz 4.00 10.00
14 Robert Fick 4.00 10.00
15 Cliff Floyd 6.00 15.00
16 Casey Fossum 4.00 10.00
17 Jay Gibbons 6.00 15.00
18 Keith Ginter 4.00 10.00
19 Troy Glaus 15.00 40.00
20 Luis Gonzalez
21 Vladimir Guerrero
22 Richard Hidalgo 4.00 10.00
23 Tim Hudson 10.00 25.00
24 Adam Johnson 4.00 10.00
25 Gabe Kapler 6.00 15.00
26 Joe Kennedy 6.00 15.00
27 Ryan Klesko 6.00 15.00
28 Carlos Lee 6.00 15.00
29 Terrence Long 4.00 10.00
30 Edgar Martinez 15.00 40.00
31 Joe Mays 4.00 10.00
32 Greg Miller 4.00 10.00
33 Wade Miller 4.00 10.00
34 Mark Mulder 6.00 15.00
35 Xavier Nady 6.00 15.00
36 Magglio Ordonez 6.00 15.00
37 Jose Ortiz 4.00 10.00
38 Roy Oswalt 15.00 40.00
39 Wily Mo Pena 6.00 15.00
40 Brad Penny 4.00 10.00
41 Aramis Ramirez 6.00 15.00
42 Luis Rivas 4.00 10.00
43 Alex Rodriguez
44 Scott Rolen

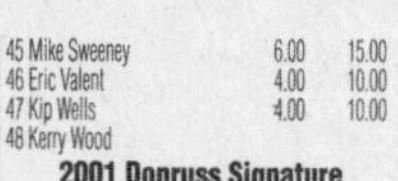

45 Mike Sweeney 6.00 15.00
46 Eric Valent 4.00 10.00
47 Kip Wells 4.00 10.00
48 Kerry Wood

2001 Donruss Signature Milestone Marks

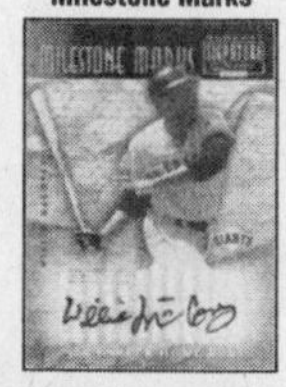

Randomly inserted in gift boxes, these 36 cards feature players autographs on a card related to specific highlights from each player's career. Since each player signed a different number of cards, please see our checklist for more detailed information on how many of each card was signed.

1 Ernie Banks/285 20.00 50.00
2 Yogi Berra/120 30.00 60.00
3 Wade Boggs/98 60.00 120.00
4 Barry Bonds/55 100.00 175.00
5 G. Brett 3000 Hits/27
6 George Brett 1500 RBI/23
7 Lou Brock/83 12.50 30.00
8 Rod Carew/110 20.00 50.00
9 Steve Carlton/75 8.00 20.00
10 Gary Carter/213 8.00 20.00
11 Bobby Doerr/192 8.00 20.00
12 Bob Feller/202 8.00 20.00
13 Whitey Ford/186 12.50 30.00
14 Steve Garvey/175 8.00 20.00
15 Tony Gwynn/99 30.00 60.00
16 Fergie Jenkins/149 8.00 20.00
17 Al Kaline/149 30.00 60.00
18 Harmon Killebrew/127 30.00 60.00
19 Ralph Kiner/105 8.00 20.00
20 Willie McCovey/20
21 Paul Molitor/96 20.00 50.00
22 E. Murray 3000 Hits/46 75.00 150.00
23 Eddie Murray 1500 RBI/17
24 Stan Musial/109 40.00 80.00
25 Phil Niekro/300 8.00 20.00
26 Tony Perez/146 8.00 20.00
27 Cal Ripken/25
28 Frank Robinson/136 12.50 30.00
29 M. Schmidt 500 HR/40
30 Mike Schmidt 1500 RBI/23
31 Enos Slaughter/117 12.50 30.00
32 Warren Spahn/300 20.00 50.00
33 Alan Trammell/154 8.00 20.00
34 Hoyt Wilhelm/227 12.50 30.00
35 D.Winfield Padres/31
36 Dave Winfield Yankees/15

2001 Donruss Signature Milestone Marks Masters Series

Randomly inserted in packs, these cards were signed by the players. Card number one does not exist for this set.

1 Does Not Exist
2 Yogi Berra
3 Wade Boggs
4 Barry Bonds
5 George Brett 3000 Hits
6 George Brett 1500 RBI
7 Lou Brock 12.50 30.00
8 Rod Carew 12.50 30.00
9 Steve Carlton 12.50 20.00
10 Gary Carter 12.50 20.00
11 Bobby Doerr 12.50 20.00
12 Bob Feller 12.50 20.00
13 Whitey Ford 40.00 80.00
14 Steve Garvey 12.50 20.00
15 Tony Gwynn 12.50 30.00
16 Fergie Jenkins 12.50 20.00
17 Al Kaline 50.00 100.00
18 Harmon Killebrew 50.00 100.00
19 Ralph Kiner 12.50 20.00
20 Willie McCovey
21 Paul Molitor 40.00 80.00
22 Eddie Murray 3000 Hits
23 Eddie Murray 1500 RBI
24 Stan Musial
25 Phil Niekro 12.50 20.00
26 Tony Perez 12.50 20.00
27 Cal Ripken
28 Frank Robinson 12.50 30.00
29 Mike Schmidt 500 HR
30 Mike Schmidt 1500 RBI
31 Enos Slaughter 12.50 30.00
32 Warren Spahn
33 Alan Trammell 12.50 20.00
34 Hoyt Wilhelm 12.50 30.00
35 Dave Winfield Padres
36 Dave Winfield Yankees

2001 Donruss Signature Notable Nicknames

Randomly inserted in gift boxes, these 18 cards feature players along with their nickname. Each player signed 100 of these cards for inclusion in this product.

1 Ernie Banks 60.00 120.00
Mr. Cub
2 Orlando Cepeda 30.00 60.00
Baby Bull
3 Will Clark 50.00 100.00
The Thrill
4 Roger Clemens 300.00 500.00
The Rocket

5 Andre Dawson 30.00 60.00
The Hawk
6 Bob Feller 30.00 60.00
Rapid Robert
7 Carlton Fisk 50.00 100.00
Pudge
8 Andres Galarraga 50.00 100.00
Big Cat
9 Luis Gonzalez 30.00 60.00
4
10 Reggie Jackson 60.00 120.00
Mr. October
11 Harmon Killebrew 75.00 150.00
Killer
12 Stan Musial 75.00 150.00
The Man
13 Brooks Robinson 50.00 100.00
Hoover
14 Nolan Ryan 250.00 400.00
The Express
15 Ryne Sandberg 125.00 200.00
Ryno
16 Enos Slaughter 50.00 100.00
Country
17 Duke Snider 50.00 100.00
4
18 Frank Thomas 60.00 120.00
MVP

2001 Donruss Signature Notable Nicknames Masters Series

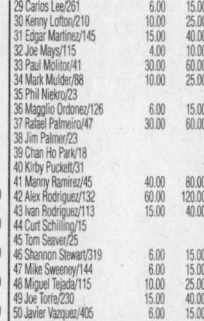

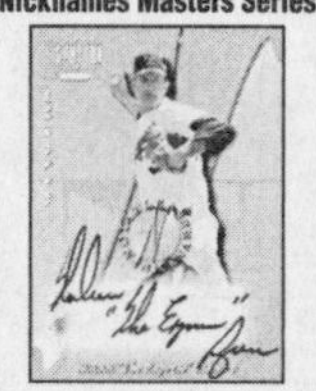

Randomly inserted into gift boxes, these 18 cards featured signed cards of star players along with their nicknames.

1 Ernie Banks 75.00 150.00
Mr. Cub
2 Orlando Cepeda 40.00 80.00
Baby Bull
3 Will Clark 30.00 60.00
The Thrill
4 Roger Clemens
The Rocket
5 Andre Dawson 40.00 80.00
The Hawk
6 Bob Feller 40.00 80.00
Rapid Robert
7 Carlton Fisk 60.00 120.00
Pudge
8 Andres Galarraga 60.00 120.00
Big Cat
9 Luis Gonzalez 40.00 80.00
4
10 Reggie Jackson
Mr. October
11 Harmon Killebrew 100.00 200.00
Killer
12 Stan Musial
The Man
13 Brooks Robinson 60.00 120.00
Hoover
14 Nolan Ryan 300.00 500.00
The Express
15 Ryne Sandberg 175.00 300.00
Rhino
16 Enos Slaughter 60.00 120.00
Country
17 Duke Snider
4
18 Frank Thomas 125.00 250.00
MVP

2001 Donruss Signature Stats

Randomly inserted into gift boxes, these 52 cards feature players who signed cards relating to a key stat in their career. Since each card is signed to a different amount, please see our checklist for specific information about each card.

1 Roberto Alomar/120 15.00 40.00
2 Moises Alou/124 6.00 15.00
3 Luis Aparicio/313 6.00 15.00
4 Lance Berkman/297 10.00 25.00
5 Wade Boggs/51 75.00 150.00
6 Lou Brock/118 10.00 25.00
7 Gary Carter/32
8 Joe Carter/121 6.00 15.00
9 Sean Casey/103 6.00 15.00
10 Darin Erstad/100 6.00 15.00
11 Bob Feller/26
12 Cliff Floyd/45 6.00 15.00
13 Whitey Ford/72 30.00 60.00
14 Andres Galarraga/150 6.00 15.00
15 Bob Gibson/112 10.00 25.00
16 Brian Giles/123 6.00 15.00
17 Troy Glaus/102 10.00 25.00
18 Luis Gonzalez/114 6.00 15.00
19 Vladimir Guerrero/131 15.00 40.00
20 Tony Gwynn/17
21 Richard Hidalgo/314 4.00 10.00
22 Bo Jackson/32
23 Fergie Jenkins/25
24 Randy Johnson/20
25 Al Kaline/128 30.00 60.00
26 Gabe Kapler/302 6.00 15.00
27 Ralph Kiner/54 15.00 40.00
28 Ryan Klesko/23
29 Carlos Lee/261 6.00 15.00
30 Kenny Lofton/210 10.00 25.00
31 Edgar Martinez/145 15.00 40.00
32 Joe Mays/115 4.00 10.00
33 Paul Molitor/41 30.00 60.00
34 Mark Mulder/88 10.00 25.00
35 Phil Niekro/23
36 Magglio Ordonez/126 6.00 15.00
37 Rafael Palmeiro/47 30.00 60.00
38 Jim Palmer/23
39 Chan Ho Park/18
40 Kirby Puckett/31
41 Manny Ramirez/45 40.00 80.00
42 Alex Rodriguez/132 60.00 120.00
43 Ivan Rodriguez/113 15.00 40.00
44 Curt Schilling/15
45 Tom Seaver/25
46 Shannon Stewart/319 6.00 15.00
47 Mike Sweeney/144 6.00 15.00
48 Miguel Tejada/115 10.00 25.00
49 Joe Torre/230 15.00 40.00
50 Javier Vazquez/405 6.00 15.00
51 Jose Vidro/330 4.00 10.00
52 Hoyt Wilhelm/243 10.00 25.00

2001 Donruss Signature Stats Masters Series

Randomly inserted into gift boxes, these 52 cards featured signed cards of star players along with information about a key stat.

1 Roberto Alomar 30.00 60.00
2 Moises Alou 6.00 15.00
3 Luis Aparicio 6.00 15.00
4 Lance Berkman 10.00 25.00
5 Wade Boggs
6 Lou Brock 40.00 80.00
7 Gary Carter 6.00 15.00
8 Joe Carter 6.00 15.00
9 Sean Casey 6.00 15.00
10 Darin Erstad 30.00 60.00
11 Bob Feller 6.00 15.00
12 Cliff Floyd 6.00 15.00
13 Whitey Ford 40.00 80.00
14 Andres Galarraga 30.00 60.00
15 Bob Gibson 20.00 50.00
16 Brian Giles 6.00 15.00
17 Troy Glaus 12.50 30.00
18 Luis Gonzalez
19 Vladimir Guerrero
20 Tony Gwynn
21 Richard Hidalgo 4.00 10.00
22 Bo Jackson 40.00 80.00
23 Fergie Jenkins 6.00 15.00
24 Randy Johnson
25 Al Kaline 40.00 80.00
26 Gabe Kapler 6.00 15.00
27 Ralph Kiner 10.00 25.00
28 Ryan Klesko 6.00 15.00
29 Carlos Lee 6.00 15.00
30 Kenny Lofton 10.00 25.00
31 Edgar Martinez 20.00 50.00
32 Joe Mays 4.00 10.00
33 Paul Molitor
34 Mark Mulder 6.00 15.00
35 Phil Niekro 6.00 15.00
36 Magglio Ordonez 6.00 15.00
37 Rafael Palmeiro
38 Jim Palmer 15.00 40.00
39 Chan Ho Park 125.00 200.00
40 Kirby Puckett
41 Manny Ramirez
42 Alex Rodriguez
43 Ivan Rodriguez
44 Curt Schilling 30.00 60.00
45 Tom Seaver
46 Shannon Stewart 6.00 15.00
47 Mike Sweeney 6.00 15.00
48 Miguel Tejada 6.00 15.00
49 Joe Torre 50.00 100.00
50 Javier Vazquez 6.00 15.00
51 Jose Vidro 4.00 10.00
52 Hoyt Wilhelm

2001 Donruss Signature Team Trademarks

Randomly inserted into gift boxes, these 58 cards feature signed cards of a player as well as information about the team they played for. Since each player signed a different amount of cards for this promotion, we have included detailed information in our checklist.

2 Rick Ankiel/179 10.00 25.00
3 Ernie Banks/180 30.00 60.00
4 Johnny Bench/20
5 Yogi Berra/124 30.00 60.00
6 Wade Boggs/89 60.00 120.00
7 Barry Bonds/77 100.00 175.00
8 Lou Brock/29
9 Steve Carlton/174 6.00 15.00
10 Sean Casey/123 6.00 15.00
11 Orlando Cepeda/100 6.00 15.00
12 Roger Clemens RS/30
13 Roger Clemens Yankees/21
14 Andre Dawson/176 6.00 15.00
15 Bobby Doerr/193 10.00 25.00
16 Whitey Ford/94 20.00 50.00
17 Steve Garvey/182 6.00 15.00
18 Bob Gibson/98 15.00 40.00
19 Juan Gonzalez/70 20.00 50.00
20 Shawn Green/109 10.00 25.00
21 Orel Hershiser/210 20.00 50.00
22 Reggie Jackson/73 40.00 80.00
23 Fergie Jenkins/213 6.00 15.00
24 Chipper Jones/74 40.00 80.00
25 Pedro Martinez/27
26 Don Mattingly/72 75.00 150.00
27 Willie Mays/197 75.00 150.00
28 Willie McCovey/26 40.00 80.00
29 Joe Morgan/33
30 Eddie Murray/45 60.00 120.00
31 Stan Musial/65 50.00 100.00
32 Mike Mussina Balt./85 40.00 80.00
33 M.Mussina Yanks/95 40.00 80.00
34 Phil Niekro/187 6.00 15.00
35 Rafael Palmeiro/99 20.00 50.00
36 Jim Palmer/142 6.00 15.00
37 Tony Perez/73 6.00 15.00
38 Manny Ramirez Sox/57 60.00 120.00
39 Cal Ripken/47 150.00 300.00
40 Phil Rizzuto/98 20.00 50.00
41 Brooks Robinson/146 10.00 25.00
42 F.Robinson Orioles/118 10.00 25.00
43 F.Robinson Reds/116 10.00 25.00
44 Alex Rodriguez/100 60.00 120.00
45 Ivan Rodriguez/62 40.00 80.00
46 Scott Rolen/39
47 Nolan Ryan/153 75.00 150.00
48 Ryne Sandberg/52 75.00 150.00
49 Curt Schilling/63 15.00 40.00
50 Mike Schmidt/107 50.00 100.00
51 Tom Seaver/25
52 Gary Sheffield/194 10.00 25.00
53 Enos Slaughter/215 10.00 25.00
54 Duke Snider/47 40.00 80.00
55 Warren Spahn/140 15.00 40.00
56 Joe Torre/90 30.00 60.00
57 Billy Williams/194 6.00 15.00
58 Kerry Wood/52 30.00 60.00

2001 Donruss Signature Team Trademarks Masters Series

Randomly inserted into gift boxes, these 56 cards featured signed cards of star players along with information about the team they played for. Card number 27 does not exist in this set.

1 Hank Aaron
2 Rick Ankiel
3 Does Not Exist
4 Johnny Bench
5 Yogi Berra
6 Wade Boggs
7 Barry Bonds
8 Lou Brock
9 Steve Carlton 6.00 15.00
10 Sean Casey
11 Orlando Cepeda 6.00 15.00
12 Roger Clemens Red Sox
13 Roger Clemens Yankees
14 Andre Dawson 6.00 15.00
15 Bobby Doerr 6.00 15.00
16 Whitey Ford
17 Nomar Garciaparra 60.00 120.00
18 Steve Garvey 6.00 15.00
19 Bob Gibson 30.00 60.00
20 Juan Gonzalez
21 Shawn Green
22 Orel Hershiser 40.00 80.00
23 Reggie Jackson
24 Fergie Jenkins 6.00 15.00
25 Chipper Jones
26 Pedro Martinez
27 Don Mattingly 75.00 150.00
28 Does Not Exist
29 Willie McCovey
30 Joe Morgan
31 Eddie Murray
32 Stan Musial
33 Mike Mussina Orioles
34 Mike Mussina Yankees
35 Phil Niekro 6.00 15.00
36 Rafael Palmeiro
37 Jim Palmer 10.00 25.00
38 Tony Perez 6.00 15.00
39 Manny Ramirez Sox
40 Cal Ripken
41 Phil Rizzuto 20.00 50.00
42 Brooks Robinson 20.00 50.00
43 Frank Robinson Orioles 40.00 80.00
44 Frank Robinson Reds
45 Alex Rodriguez
46 Ivan Rodriguez
47 Scott Rolen
48 Nolan Ryan 75.00 150.00
49 Ryne Sandberg
50 Curt Schilling 15.00 40.00
51 Mike Schmidt
52 Tom Seaver 30.00 60.00
53 Gary Sheffield 8.00 20.00
54 Enos Slaughter 8.00 20.00
55 Duke Snider
56 Warren Spahn 20.00 50.00
57 Joe Torre
58 Billy Williams 6.00 15.00
59 Kerry Wood

2003 Donruss Signature

This 150 card set was released in August, 2003. This set was issued in four card packs issued in a special "box". These pack/boxes had a $50 SRP. Cards numbered 1-100 feature veterans in team alphabetical order while cards numbered 111 through 150 feature rookies. Unlike most Donruss/Playoff products, these rookie cards were not shortprinted.

COMMON CARD (1-100) .40 1.00

COMMON CARD (101-150) .40 1.00
1 Garret Anderson .40 1.00
2 Tim Salmon .60 1.50
3 Troy Glaus .40 1.00
4 Curt Schilling .40 1.00
5 Luis Gonzalez .40 1.00
6 Mark Grace .60 1.50
7 Matt Williams .40 1.00
8 Randy Johnson 1.00 2.50
9 Andruw Jones .60 1.50
10 Chipper Jones 1.00 2.50
11 Gary Sheffield .40 1.00
12 Greg Maddux 1.50 4.00
13 Johnny Damon .60 1.50
14 Manny Ramirez .60 1.50
15 Nomar Garciaparra 1.50 4.00
16 Pedro Martinez .60 1.50
17 Corey Patterson .40 1.00
18 Kerry Wood .40 1.00
19 Mark Prior .60 1.50
20 Sammy Sosa 1.00 2.50
21 Bartolo Colon .40 1.00
22 Frank Thomas 1.00 2.50
23 Magglio Ordonez .40 1.00
24 Paul Konerko .40 1.00
25 Adam Dunn .40 1.00
26 Austin Kearns .40 1.00
27 Barry Larkin .60 1.50
28 Ken Griffey Jr. 1.50 4.00
29 C.C. Sabathia .40 1.00
30 Omar Vizquel .60 1.50
31 Larry Walker .40 1.00
32 Todd Helton .60 1.50
33 Ivan Rodriguez .60 1.50
34 Josh Beckett .40 1.00
35 Craig Biggio .60 1.50
36 Jeff Bagwell .60 1.50
37 Jeff Kent .40 1.00
38 Lance Berkman .40 1.00
39 Richard Hidalgo .40 1.00
40 Roy Oswalt .40 1.00
41 Carlos Beltran .40 1.00
42 Mike Sweeney .40 1.00
43 Runelvys Hernandez .40 1.00
44 Hideo Nomo 1.00 2.50
45 Kazuhisa Ishii .40 1.00
46 Paul Lo Duca .40 1.00
47 Shawn Green .40 1.00
48 Ben Sheets .40 1.00
49 Richie Sexson .40 1.00
50 A.J. Pierzynski .40 1.00
51 Torii Hunter .40 1.00
52 Javier Vazquez .40 1.00
53 Jose Vidro .40 1.00
54 Vladimir Guerrero 1.00 2.50
55 Cliff Floyd .40 1.00
56 David Cone .40 1.00
57 Mike Piazza 1.50 4.00
58 Roberto Alomar .60 1.50
59 Tom Glavine .60 1.50
60 Alfonso Soriano .40 1.00
61 Derek Jeter 2.50 6.00
62 Drew Henson .40 1.00
63 Jason Giambi .40 1.00
64 Mike Mussina .60 1.50
65 Nick Johnson .40 1.00
66 Roger Clemens 2.00 5.00
67 Barry Zito .40 1.00
68 Eric Chavez .40 1.00
69 Mark Mulder .40 1.00
70 Miguel Tejada .40 1.00
71 Tim Hudson .40 1.00
72 Bobby Abreu .40 1.00
73 Jim Thome .60 1.50
74 Kevin Millwood .40 1.00
75 Pat Burrell .40 1.00
76 Brian Giles .40 1.00
77 Jason Kendall .40 1.00
78 Kenny Lofton .40 1.00
79 Phil Nevin .40 1.00
80 Ryan Klesko .40 1.00
81 Andres Galarraga .40 1.00
82 Barry Bonds 2.50 6.00
83 Rich Aurilia .40 1.00
84 Edgar Martinez .60 1.50
85 Freddy Garcia .40 1.00
86 Ichiro Suzuki 2.00 5.00
87 Albert Pujols 2.00 5.00
88 Jim Edmonds .40 1.00
89 Scott Rolen .60 1.50
90 So Taguchi .40 1.00
91 Rocco Baldelli .40 1.00
92 Alex Rodriguez 1.50 4.00
93 Hank Blalock .40 1.00
94 Juan Gonzalez .40 1.00
95 Mark Teixeira .60 1.50
96 Rafael Palmeiro .60 1.50
97 Carlos Delgado .40 1.00
98 Eric Hinske .40 1.00
99 Roy Halladay .40 1.00
100 Vernon Wells .40 1.00
101 Hideki Matsui ROO RC 4.00 10.00
102 Jose Contreras ROO RC 1.00 2.50
103 Jer. Bonderman ROO RC 3.00 8.00
104 Bernie Castro ROO RC .40 1.00
105 Alfredo Gonzalez ROO RC .40 1.00
106 Arnie Munoz ROO RC .40 1.00
107 Andrew Brown ROO RC .60 1.50
108 Josh Hall ROO RC .40 1.00
109 Josh Stewart ROO RC .40 1.00
110 Clint Barmes ROO RC 1.25 3.00
111 Brandon Webb ROO RC 3.00 8.00
112 Chien-Ming Wang ROO RC 2.50 6.00
113 Edgar Gonzalez ROO RC .40 1.00
114 Al. Machado ROO RC .40 1.00
115 Jeremy Griffiths ROO RC .40 1.00
116 Craig Brazell ROO RC .40 1.00
117 Shane Bazzell ROO RC .40 1.00
118 Fernando Cabrera ROO RC .40 1.00
119 Termel Sledge ROO RC .40 1.00
120 Rob Hammock ROO RC .40 1.00
121 Francisco Rosario ROO RC .40 1.00
122 Francisco Cruceta ROO RC .40 1.00
123 Rett Johnson ROO RC .40 1.00
124 Guillermo Quiroz ROO RC .40 1.00
125 Hong-Chih Kuo ROO RC 3.00 8.00
126 Ian Ferguson ROO RC .40 1.00
127 Tim Olson ROO RC .40 1.00
128 Todd Wellemeyer ROO RC .40 1.00
129 Rich Fischer ROO RC .40 1.00
130 Phil Seibel ROO RC .40 1.00
131 Joe Valentine ROO RC .40 1.00
132 Matt Kata ROO RC .40 1.00
133 Michael Hessman ROO RC .40 1.00
134 Michel Hernandez ROO RC .40 1.00
135 Doug Waechter ROO RC .60 1.50
136 Prentice Redman ROO RC .40 1.00
137 Nook Logan ROO RC .60 1.50
138 Oscar Villarreal ROO RC .40 1.00
139 Pete LaForest ROO RC .40 1.00
140 Matt Bruback ROO RC .40 1.00
141 Dontrelle Willis ROO 1.00 2.50
142 Greg Aquino ROO RC .40 1.00
143 Lew Ford ROO RC .60 1.50
144 Jeff Duncan ROO RC .40 1.00
145 Dan Haren ROO RC 1.00 2.50
146 Miguel Ojeda ROO RC .40 1.00
147 Rosman Garcia ROO RC .40 1.00
148 Felix Sanchez ROO RC .40 1.00
149 Jon Leicester ROO RC .40 1.00
150 Roger Deago ROO RC .40 1.00

2003 Donruss Signature Century Proofs

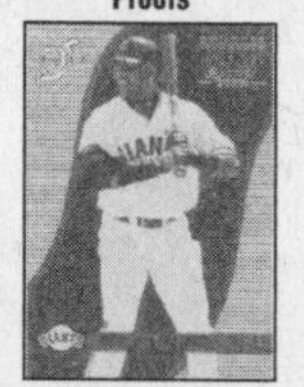

*CENTURY 1-100: 2X TO 5X BASIC
*CENTURY 101-150: 1X TO 2.5X BASIC
STATED PRINT RUN 100 SERIAL #'d SETS
112 Chien-Ming Wang ROO 12.50 30.00
125 Hong-Chih Kuo ROO 15.00 40.00

2003 Donruss Signature Decade Proofs

STATED PRINT RUN 10 SERIAL #'d SETS
NO PRICING DUE TO SCARCITY

2003 Donruss Signature Autographs

Randomly inserted into packs; these 50 cards parallel the basic set and feature autographs of the featured players. The first 47 of these cards (checklisted from 1-102) are not serial numbered but we are giving print run information in our checklist provided by Donruss/Playoff. Cards 151-153 were distributed as random inserts within packs of DLP Rookies and Traded and each is serial numbered to 200. No pricing is provided for cards with print runs of 28 or fewer due to scarcity.

1 Garret Anderson 6.00 15.00
6 Mark Grace SP/141 15.00 40.00
7 Matt Williams 10.00 25.00
8 Randy Johnson SP/50 40.00 80.00
10 Chipper Jones SP/50 40.00 80.00
12 Greg Maddux SP/25
14 Manny Ramirez SP/50 20.00 50.00
16 Pedro Martinez SP/5
27 Barry Larkin SP/159 15.00 40.00
32 Todd Helton SP/5
33 Ivan Rodriguez SP/50 20.00 50.00
36 Jeff Bagwell SP/25
38 Lance Berkman SP/75 10.00 25.00
39 Richard Hidalgo 4.00 10.00
40 Roy Oswalt SP/150 10.00 25.00
42 Mike Sweeney 6.00 15.00
44 Hideo Nomo SP/25
45 Kazuhisa Ishii SP/25
50 A.J. Pierzynski 6.00 15.00
51 Torii Hunter 6.00 15.00
53 Jose Vidro 6.00 15.00
54 Vladimir Guerrero 8.00 20.00
55 Cliff Floyd 6.00 15.00
56 David Cone SP/35 10.00 25.00
57 Mike Piazza SP/5
58 Roberto Alomar SP/50 15.00 40.00
62 Drew Henson SP/28
64 Mike Mussina SP/5
65 Nick Johnson 6.00 15.00
67 Barry Zito SP/150 6.00 15.00
68 Eric Chavez 6.00 15.00
69 Mark Mulder SP/50 10.00 25.00
72 Bobby Abreu 6.00 15.00
78 Kenny Lofton SP/229 10.00 25.00

80 Ryan Klesko SP/150 6.00 15.00
81 Andres Galarraga 6.00 15.00
83 Rich Aurilia SP/122 4.00 10.00
84 Edgar Martinez 15.00 40.00
88 Jim Edmonds SP/25
89 Scott Rolen SP/200 10.00 25.00
90 So Taguchi SP/220 6.00 15.00
92 Alex Rodriguez SP/25
95 Mark Teixeira SP/150 10.00 25.00
96 Rafael Palmeiro SP/25
100 Vernon Wells 6.00 15.00
102 Jose Contreras ROO 8.00 20.00
141 D.Willis ROO SP/150 8.00 20.00
151 Delmon Young ROO 40.00 80.00
152 Rickie Weeks ROO 10.00 25.00
153 Edwin Jackson ROO 4.00 10.00

2003 Donruss Signature Autographs Century

1-102 PRINT RUN 100 SERIAL #'d SETS
151-154 PRINT RUN 21 SERIAL #'d SETS
NO PRICING ON QTY OF 25 OR LESS
CARD 154 IS NOT SIGNED
1 Garret Anderson 10.00 25.00
7 Matt Williams 15.00 40.00
27 Barry Larkin 15.00 40.00
39 Richard Hidalgo 6.00 15.00
42 Mike Sweeney 10.00 25.00
50 A.J. Pierzynski 10.00 25.00
51 Torii Hunter 10.00 25.00
53 Jose Vidro 6.00 15.00
54 Vladimir Guerrero 8.00 20.00
55 Cliff Floyd 10.00 25.00
62 Drew Henson 6.00 15.00
65 Nick Johnson 10.00 25.00
69 Mark Mulder 10.00 25.00
72 Bobby Abreu 10.00 25.00
78 Kenny Lofton 15.00 40.00
81 Andres Galarraga 10.00 25.00
84 Edgar Martinez 15.00 40.00
09 Scott Rolen 15.00 40.00
90 So Taguchi 10.00 25.00
100 Vernon Wells 10.00 25.00
102 Jose Contreras ROO 12.50 30.00
151 Delmon Young ROO/21
152 Rickie Weeks ROO/21
153 Edwin Jackson ROO/21

2003 Donruss Signature Autographs Decade

STATED PRINT RUN 10 SERIAL #'d SETS
NO PRICING DUE TO SCARCITY
CARD 154 IS NOT SIGNED

2003 Donruss Signature Autographs Notations

Randomly inserted into packs, these cards feature not only authentic autographs from the featured player but also a special "notation" next to their name in the checklist. Since each card has a different print run we have put that information next to the card in our checklist. Please note that for cards with print runs of 30 or fewer, no pricing is provided.

1A Garret Anderson #16/75 10.00 25.00
1B Garret Anderson 7-27-94/45 12.50 30.00
1C Garret Anderson WSC 02/75 10.00 25.00
6 Mark Grace Amazing/5
7A Matt Williams #9/250 10.00 25.00
7B Matt Williams 01 WS/50 20.00 50.00
10A Chipper Jones 96-01 AS/25
10B Chipper Jones MVP 99/25
32 Todd Helton 02 AS/15
33 Ivan Rodriguez #7/5
36 Jeff Bagwell Baggy/5
38A Lance Berkman #17/15
38B Lance Berkman #22/5
38C Lance Berkman #27/1
38D Lance Berkman 02/1
38E Lance Berkman Rice Owls/5
38F Lance Berkman Rice Univ./5
38G Lance Berkman William/1
40 Roy Oswalt #44/25
45 Kazuhisa Ishii #17/35 12.50 30.00
50 A.J. Pierzynski 02 AS/200 6.00 15.00
51A Torii Hunter 02 AS/25
51B Torii Hunter #48/20
53A Jose Vidro #3/40 8.00 20.00
53B Jose Vidro AS 00/15
53C Jose Vidro 2X AS/6
55 Cliff Floyd #30/5
57A Mike Piazza #31/5
57B Mike Piazza ROY 93/1
62A Drew Henson UM #7/2
62B Drew Henson QB #7/24
62C Drew Henson DH #7/73 6.00 15.00
68A Eric Chavez #3/50 12.50 30.00
68B Eric Chavez Chavy/25
69 Mark Mulder MSU/30
78 Kenny Lofton #7/150 10.00 25.00
80 Ryan Klesko #30/75 10.00 25.00
83 Rich Aurilia #35/61 8.00 20.00
84A Edgar Martinez #11/250 10.00 25.00
84B E.Martinez BT 92-95/60 20.00 50.00
92A Alex Rodriguez #3/5
92B Alex Rodriguez WCS 93/5
92C Alex Rodriguez Westminster/1
96 Rafael Palmeiro 500 HR/25
100 Vernon Wells #10/75 10.00 25.00

2003 Donruss Signature Autographs Notations Century

STATED PRINT RUN 100 SERIAL #'d SETS
1A Garret Anderson #16 10.00 25.00
1B Garret Anderson 7-27-94 10.00 25.00
7A Matt Williams #9 15.00 40.00
7B Matt Williams 01 WS 15.00 40.00
50 A.J. Pierzynski 02 AS 10.00 25.00
68A Eric Chavez #3 10.00 25.00
78 Kenny Lofton #7 15.00 40.00
84A Edgar Martinez #11 15.00 40.00

2003 Donruss Signature Autographs Notations Decade

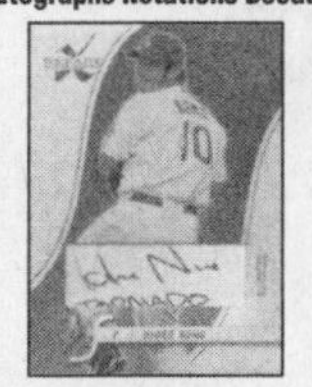

STATED PRINT RUN 10 SERIAL #'d SETS
NO PRICING DUE TO SCARCITY

2003 Donruss Signature Cuts

Randomly inserted into packs, these 15 cards feature "cut" signatures from the featured player. Each of these cards have different print runs and we have notated that print run information in our checklist. Please note for cards with 25 or fewer copies, no pricing is provided.

4 Curt Schilling/7
8 Randy Johnson/40 40.00 80.00
10 Chipper Jones/9
33 Ivan Rodriguez/122 15.00 40.00
54 Vladimir Guerrero/34 10.00 25.00
58 Roberto Alomar/100 15.00 40.00
59 Tom Glavine/9
64 Mike Mussina/82 20.00 50.00
66 Roger Clemens/9
73 Jim Thome/127 15.00 40.00
80 Ryan Klesko/35 12.50 30.00
81 Andres Galarraga/51 12.50 30.00
89 Scott Rolen/36 20.00 50.00
94 Juan Gonzalez/9
96 Rafael Palmeiro/13

2003 Donruss Signature Cuts Decade

STATED PRINT RUN 10 SERIAL #'d SETS
NO PRICING DUE TO SCARCITY

2003 Donruss Signature Authentic Cuts

Randomly inserted into packs, these three cards feature cut signatures of the most legendary players in baseball history. We have notated the print run next to the player's name in our checklist and due to market scarcity, no pricing is provided for these cards.

1 Ty Cobb/3
2 Babe Ruth/1
3 Lou Gehrig/1

2003 Donruss Signature INKredible Three

Randomly inserted into packs, these five cards feature three signatures on each card from players with a common team allegiance. Each of these cards were issued to a stated print run of 50 serial numbered sets.

1 Barry Zito 150.00 250.00
Mark Mulder
Tim Hudson
2 Greg Maddux 250.00 400.00
Chipper Jones
Andruw Jones
3 Kerry Wood 125.00 250.00
Mark Prior
Ernie Banks
4 Kirby Puckett 200.00 400.00
Harmon Killebrew
Torii Hunter
5 Vladimir Guerrero 90.00 150.00
Jose Vidro
Javier Vazquez

2003 Donruss Signature INKredible Four

Randomly inserted into packs, these 10 cards feature four signatures from players with a common team allegiance. Each of these cards were issued to a stated print run of 25 serial numbered sets and no pricing is provided due to market scarcity.

2003 Donruss Signature INKredible Six

Randomly inserted into packs, these five cards feature six signatures on each card with a common thread tying together all the players. Each of these cards were issued to a stated print run of 10 serial numbered sets and no pricing is provided due to market scarcity.

2003 Donruss Signature Legends of Summer

Randomly inserted into packs, these 40 cards feature some of the best retired players. Each of these cards were issued to a stated print run of 250 serial numbered sets.

*CENTURY: .6X TO 1.5X BASIC
CENTURY PRINT RUN 100 SERIAL #'d SETS
DECADE PRINT RUN 10 SERIAL #'d SETS
NO DECADE PRICING DUE TO SCARCITY
1 Al Kaline 3.00 8.00
2 Alan Trammell 2.00 5.00
3 Andre Dawson 2.00 5.00
4 Babe Ruth 6.00 15.00
5 Billy Williams 2.00 5.00
6 Bo Jackson 3.00 8.00
7 Bob Feller 2.00 5.00
8 Bobby Doerr 2.00 5.00
9 Brooks Robinson 2.00 5.00
10 Dale Murphy 2.00 5.00
11 Dennis Eckersley 2.00 5.00
12 Don Mattingly 5.00 12.00
13 Duke Snider 2.00 5.00
14 Eric Davis 2.00 5.00
15 Frank Robinson 2.00 5.00
16 Fred Lynn 2.00 5.00
17 Gary Carter 2.00 5.00
18 Harmon Killebrew 3.00 8.00
19 Jack Morris 2.00 5.00
20 Jim Palmer 2.00 5.00
21 Jim Abbott 2.00 5.00
22 Joe Morgan 2.00 5.00
23 Joe Torre 2.00 5.00
24 Johnny Bench 3.00 8.00
25 Jose Canseco 2.00 5.00
26 Kirby Puckett 3.00 8.00
27 Lenny Dykstra 2.00 5.00
28 Lou Brock 2.00 5.00
29 Ralph Kiner 2.00 5.00
30 Mike Schmidt 5.00 12.00
31 Nolan Ryan Rgr 6.00 15.00
32 Nolan Ryan Angels 6.00 15.00
33 Orel Hershiser 2.00 5.00
34 Phil Rizzuto 2.00 5.00
35 Orlando Cepeda 2.00 5.00
36 Ryne Sandberg 5.00 12.00
37 Stan Musial 4.00 10.00
38 Steve Garvey 2.00 5.00
39 Tony Perez 2.00 5.00
40 Ty Cobb 4.00 10.00

2003 Donruss Signature Legends of Summer Autographs

Randomly inserted into packs, this is a partial parallel of the Legends of Summer set. A few cards were issued in smaller quantities and we have notated that information (as provided by Donruss/Playoff) in our checklist.

1 Al Kaline 10.00 25.00
2 Alan Trammell 6.00 15.00
3 Andre Dawson 6.00 15.00
5 Billy Williams 6.00 15.00
6 Bo Jackson SP/100 30.00 60.00
7 Bob Feller 6.00 15.00
8 Bobby Doerr 6.00 15.00
9 Brooks Robinson 10.00 25.00
10 Dale Murphy SP/75 15.00 40.00
11 Dennis Eckersley 6.00 15.00
12 Don Mattingly SP/50 50.00 100.00
13 Duke Snider SP/225 10.00 25.00
14 Eric Davis 6.00 15.00
15 Frank Robinson 6.00 15.00
16 Fred Lynn 6.00 15.00
17 Gary Carter 6.00 15.00
18 Harmon Killebrew SP/171 12.50 30.00
19 Jack Morris 6.00 15.00
20 Jim Palmer 6.00 15.00
21 Jim Abbott 6.00 15.00
22 Joe Morgan SP/125 10.00 25.00
23 Joe Torre 10.00 25.00
24 Johnny Bench SP/75 15.00 40.00
25 Jose Canseco SP/75 15.00 40.00
26 Kirby Puckett SP/75 50.00 100.00
27 Lenny Dykstra 6.00 15.00
28 Lou Brock 10.00 25.00
29 Ralph Kiner 10.00 25.00
30 Mike Schmidt SP/75 40.00 80.00
31 Nolan Ryan Rgr SP/75 75.00 150.00
33 Orel Hershiser 10.00 25.00
34 Phil Rizzuto 10.00 25.00
35 Orlando Cepeda 6.00 15.00
36 Ryne Sandberg SP/75 40.00 80.00
37 Stan Musial SP/200 30.00 60.00
38 Steve Garvey 6.00 15.00
39 Tony Perez 6.00 15.00

2003 Donruss Signature Legends of Summer Autographs Century

STATED PRINT RUN 100 SERIAL #'d SETS
1 Al Kaline 15.00 40.00
2 Alan Trammell 10.00 25.00
3 Andre Dawson 10.00 25.00
5 Billy Williams 10.00 25.00
6 Bo Jackson 30.00 60.00
7 Bob Feller 10.00 25.00
8 Bobby Doerr 10.00 25.00
9 Brooks Robinson 15.00 40.00
11 Dennis Eckersley 10.00 25.00
12 Don Mattingly 40.00 80.00
14 Eric Davis 10.00 25.00
15 Frank Robinson 10.00 25.00
16 Fred Lynn 10.00 25.00
17 Gary Carter 10.00 25.00
19 Jack Morris 10.00 25.00
20 Jim Palmer 10.00 25.00
21 Jim Abbott 10.00 25.00
23 Joe Torre 10.00 25.00
27 Lenny Dykstra 10.00 25.00
28 Lou Brock 15.00 40.00
29 Ralph Kiner 10.00 25.00
33 Orel Hershiser 40.00 80.00
34 Phil Rizzuto 15.00 40.00
35 Orlando Cepeda 10.00 25.00
36 Ryne Sandberg 40.00 80.00
37 Stan Musial 30.00 60.00
38 Steve Garvey 10.00 25.00
39 Tony Perez 10.00 25.00

2003 Donruss Signature Legends of Summer Autographs Decade

STATED PRINT RUN 10 SERIAL #'d SETS
NO PRICING DUE TO SCARCITY

2003 Donruss Signature Legends of Summer Autographs Notations

This parallel to the Legends of Summer insert set features not only authentic autographs from some of the featured players but also special notations added by the player. Since there are varying print runs on these cards we have provided that information next to the player's name in our checklist. Please note that cards with a print run of 25 or fewer are not priced due to market scarcity.

1A Al Kaline #6/200 10.00 25.00
1B Al Kaline HOF '80/200 12.50 30.00
1C Al Kaline Mr. Tiger/200 12.50 30.00
2 A.Trammell 84 WS MVP/250 6.00 15.00
3A Andre Dawson #8/165 6.00 15.00
3B Andre Dawson 87 MVP/250 6.00 15.00
5B Billy Williams 61 ROY/250 6.00 15.00
5C Billy Williams 87 HOF/150 6.00 15.00
7A Bob Feller #19/250 6.00 15.00
7B Bob Feller HOF 62/250 6.00 15.00
7C Bob Feller Triple Crown/200
8A Bobby Doerr #1/250 6.00 15.00
8B Bobby Doerr HOF 86/250 6.00 15.00
8C Bobby Doerr MVP 44/250 6.00 15.00
9A B.Robinson 64 MVP/150 10.00 25.00
9B B.Robinson 70 WS MVP/50 20.00 50.00
10A Dale Murphy MVP 82/50 20.00 50.00
10B Dale Murphy MVP 83/50 20.00 50.00
11A D.Eckersley 92 CY/250 6.00 15.00
11B D.Eckersley 92 CY-MVP/250 6.00 15.00
11C D.Eckersley 92 MVP/250 6.00 15.00
13 Duke Snider HOF 80/25
14A Eric Davis #44/250 6.00 15.00
14B Eric Davis 87 AS/150 6.00 15.00
14C Eric Davis 90 WS/200 6.00 15.00
16A Fred Lynn 75 MVP-ROY/240 6.00 15.00
16B Fred Lynn 75-83 AS/250 6.00 15.00
17 Gary Carter The Kid/5
18A H.Killebrew #3/75 20.00 50.00
18B H.Killebrew 69 MVP/50 30.00 60.00
18C H.Killebrew 573 HR/50 30.00 60.00
18D H.Killebrew HOF 84/125 20.00 50.00
19A J.Morris 91 WS MVP/250 6.00 15.00
19B Jack Morris 92 WS/250 6.00 15.00
20A Jim Palmer 73 CY/190 6.00 15.00
20B Jim Palmer 75 CY/140 6.00 15.00
20C Jim Palmer 76 CY/50 12.50 30.00
21A Jim Abbott 4-8-89/200 6.00 15.00
21B Jim Abbott 9-4-93/100 10.00 25.00
21C Jim Abbott 6-15-99/75 10.00 25.00
21D Jim Abbott U of Mich/50 12.50 30.00
21E Jim Abbott Yanks/25
24A Johnny Bench #5/20
24B Johnny Bench HOF/1
24C Johnny Bench HOF 89/5
24D Johnny Bench MVP 70/1
24E Johnny Bench MVP 72/1
27 Lenny Dykstra 86 WS/226 6.00 15.00
28A Lou Brock SB 938/25
28B Lou Brock HOF 85/50 20.00 50.00
29A Ralph Kiner #4/150 6.00 15.00
29B Ralph Kiner 48-53 AS/25
29C Ralph Kiner HOF/200 6.00 15.00
29D Ralph Kiner HOF 75/100 10.00 25.00
31 Nolan Ryan Rgr 5714 SO/25
35A O.Cepeda Baby Bull/75 20.00 50.00
35B O.Cepeda MVP 67/40 12.50 30.00
35C O.Cepeda 58 ROY/40 12.50 30.00
35D O.Cepeda 67 WS/40 12.50 30.00
35E O.Cepeda 68 WS/40 12.50 30.00
36A Ryne Sandberg #23/5
36B Ryne Sandberg Cubs/20
36C Ryne Sandberg 84 MVP/25
38A Steve Garvey #6/150 6.00 15.00
38B Steve Garvey 74 MVP/25
38C Steve Garvey 78 AS MVP/50 12.50 30.00
38D Steve Garvey 81 WS/75 10.00 25.00
39A Tony Perez #24/250 6.00 15.00
39B Tony Perez HOF 02/175 6.00 15.00
39C Tony Perez WS 75/125 10.00 25.00
39D Tony Perez WS 76/75 10.00 25.00

2003 Donruss Signature Legends of Summer Autographs Notations Century

STATED PRINT RUN 100 SERIAL #'d SETS
1A Al Kaline #6 15.00 40.00
1B Al Kaline HOF 80 15.00 40.00
1C Al Kaline Mr. Tiger 15.00 40.00
2 Alan Trammell 84 WS MVP 10.00 25.00
3A Andre Dawson #8 10.00 25.00
3B Andre Dawson 87 MVP 10.00 25.00
5A Billy Williams #26 10.00 25.00
5B Billy Williams 61 ROY 10.00 25.00
5C Billy Williams 87 HOF 10.00 25.00
7A Bob Feller #19 10.00 25.00
7B Bob Feller HOF 62 10.00 25.00
7C Bob Feller Triple Crown 10.00 25.00
8A Bobby Doerr #1 10.00 25.00
8B Bobby Doerr HOF 86 10.00 25.00
8C Bobby Doerr MVP 44 10.00 25.00
11A Dennis Eckersley 92 CY 10.00 25.00
11B D.Eckersley 92 CY-MVP 10.00 25.00
11C Dennis Eckersley 92 MVP 10.00 25.00
14A Eric Davis #44 10.00 25.00
14B Eric Davis 87 AS 10.00 25.00
14C Eric Davis 90 WS 10.00 25.00
16A Fred Lynn 75 MVP-ROY 10.00 25.00
16B Fred Lynn 75-83 AS 10.00 25.00
19A Jack Morris 91 WS MVP 10.00 25.00
19B Jack Morris 92 WS 10.00 25.00
20A Jim Palmer 73 CY 10.00 25.00
20B Jim Palmer 75 CY 10.00 25.00
20C Jim Palmer 76 CY 10.00 25.00
21A Jim Abbott 4-8-89 10.00 25.00
21B Jim Abbott 9-4-93 10.00 25.00
21C Jim Abbott 6-15-99 10.00 25.00
21D Jim Abbott U of Mich 10.00 25.00
21E Jim Abbott Yanks 10.00 25.00
27 Lenny Dykstra 86 WS 10.00 25.00
29A Ralph Kiner #4 10.00 25.00
29B Ralph Kiner 48-53 AS 10.00 25.00
29C Ralph Kiner HOF 10.00 25.00
29D Ralph Kiner HOF 75 10.00 25.00
38A Steve Garvey #6 10.00 25.00
38B Steve Garvey 74 MVP 10.00 25.00
38C Steve Garvey 78 AS MVP 10.00 25.00
38D Steve Garvey 81 WS 10.00 25.00
39A Tony Perez #24 10.00 25.00
39B Tony Perez HOF 02 10.00 25.00
39C Tony Perez WS 75 10.00 25.00
39D Tony Perez WS 76 10.00 25.00

2003 Donruss Signature Legends of Summer Autographs Notations Decade

STATED PRINT RUN 10 SERIAL #'d SETS
NO PRICING DUE TO SCARCITY

2003 Donruss Signature Notable Nicknames

Randomly inserted into packs, these 20 cards players who are commonly known by a nickname. Each of these cards were issued to a stated print run of 750 serial numbered sets.

*CENTURY: .6X TO 1.5X BASIC
CENTURY PRINT RUN 100 SERIAL #'d SETS
DECADE PRINT RUN 10 SERIAL #'d SETS
NO DECADE PRICING DUE TO SCARCITY

1 Andre Dawson 2.00 5.00
2 Torii Hunter 2.00 5.00
3 Brooks Robinson 2.00 5.00
4 Carlton Fisk 2.00 5.00
5 Mike Mussina 2.00 5.00
6 Don Mattingly 5.00 12.00
7 Duke Snider 2.00 5.00
8 Eric Davis 2.00 5.00
9 Frank Thomas 2.50 6.00
10 Randy Johnson 2.50 6.00
11 Lenny Dykstra 2.00 5.00
12 Ivan Rodriguez 2.00 5.00
13 Nolan Ryan 6.00 15.00
14 Phil Rizzuto 2.00 5.00
15 Reggie Jackson 2.00 5.00
16 Roger Clemens 5.00 12.00
17 Ryne Sandberg 5.00 12.00
18 Stan Musial 4.00 10.00
19 Luis Gonzalez 2.00 5.00
20 Will Clark 2.00 5.00

2003 Donruss Signature Notable Nicknames Century

STATED PRINT RUN 100 SERIAL #'d SETS

2003 Donruss Signature Notable Nicknames Decade

STATED PRINT RUN 10 SERIAL #'d SETS
NO PRICING DUE TO SCARCITY

2003 Donruss Signature Notable Nicknames Autographs

Randomly inserted in packs, these cards parallel the regular Notable Nickname set but also include an authentic autograph from the featured player as well as his nickname. Most of these cards were issued to a stated print run of 100 copies but a few were issued in smaller quantities and that information is notated in our checklist. For those cards with a print run of 25 or fewer, no pricing is provided due to market scarcity.

1 Andre Dawson 20.00 50.00
2 Torii Hunter 20.00 50.00
3 Brooks Robinson 40.00 80.00
4 Carlton Fisk 40.00 80.00
5 Mike Mussina 50.00 100.00
6 Don Mattingly 75.00 150.00
7 Duke Snider 40.00 80.00
8 Eric Davis/40 40.00 80.00
9 Frank Thomas 60.00 120.00
10 Randy Johnson 60.00 120.00
11 Lenny Dykstra 12.50 30.00
12 Ivan Rodriguez/75 40.00 80.00
13 Nolan Ryan/15
14 Phil Rizzuto 40.00 80.00
15 Reggie Jackson 40.00 80.00
16 Roger Clemens 125.00 200.00
17 Ryne Sandberg 50.00 100.00
18 Stan Musial 60.00 120.00
19 Luis Gonzalez 20.00 50.00
20 Will Clark 40.00 80.00

2003 Donruss Signature Notable Nicknames Autographs Decade

STATED PRINT RUN 10 SERIAL #'d SETS
NO PRICING DUE TO SCARCITY

2003 Donruss Signature Player Collection Autographs

Randomly inserted in packs, these cards feature authentic autographs on "player collection" cards. Since each of these cards were issued to a different print run, we have notated that information next to the player's name in our checklist.

1 Roberto Alomar/75 15.00 40.00
2 Adrian Beltre/104 10.00 25.00
3 Lance Berkman/50 20.00 50.00
4 Craig Biggio Btg/26
5 Craig Biggio Fldg/26
6 Joe Borchard/53 8.00 20.00
7 Roger Clemens Pitch/9
8 Roger Clemens Stretch/4
9 J.D. Drew/52 12.50 30.00
10 Jim Edmonds/52 20.00 50.00
11 Tony Gwynn/11
12 Todd Helton/50 20.00 50.00
13 Jason Jennings/49 8.00 20.00
14 Andruw Jones Away/25
15 Andruw Jones Home/25
16 Chipper Jones/51 30.00 60.00
17 Paul Konerko/26
18 Paul Lo Duca/227 6.00 15.00
19 Magglio Ordonez/102 10.00 25.00
20 Roy Oswalt/10
21 Rafael Palmeiro/25
22 Mark Prior/27 20.00 50.00
23 Cal Ripken/22
24 Alex Rodriguez M's/24
25 Alex Rodriguez Rgr/25
26 Ivan Rodriguez/52 20.00 50.00
27 Richie Sexson/50 12.50 30.00
28 Alfonso Soriano/11
29A Matt Williams/19
29B Matt Williams/483 10.00 25.00

2003 Donruss Signature Team Trademarks

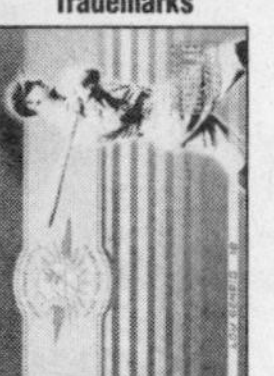

Randomly inserted into packs, these cards feature the term "team trademark" on the card. Each of these cards were issued to a stated print run of 500 serial numbered sets.

*CENTURY: .75X TO 2X BASIC
CENTURY PRINT RUN 100 SERIAL #'d SETS
DECADE PRINT RUN 10 SERIAL #'d SETS
NO DECADE PRICING DUE TO SCARCITY
1 Adam Dunn 1.50 4.00
2 Andre Dawson 1.50 4.00
3 Babe Ruth 5.00 12.00
4 Barry Bonds 5.00 12.00
5 Brooks Robinson 1.50 4.00
6 Cal Ripken 6.00 15.00
7 Derek Jeter 5.00 12.00
8 Don Mattingly 4.00 10.00
9 Frank Robinson 1.50 4.00
10 Fred Lynn 1.50 4.00
11 Gary Carter 1.50 4.00
12 George Brett 4.00 10.00
13 Greg Maddux 3.00 8.00
14 Ichiro Suzuki 4.00 10.00
15 Jim Palmer 1.50 4.00
16 Jose Contreras 2.00 5.00
17 Kerry Wood 1.50 4.00
18 Lou Gehrig 3.00 8.00
19 Magglio Ordonez 1.50 4.00
20 Mark Grace 1.50 4.00
21 Mike Schmidt 4.00 10.00
22 Nolan Ryan Rgr 5.00 12.00
23 Nolan Ryan Astros 5.00 12.00
24 Reggie Jackson 1.50 4.00
25 Rickey Henderson 2.00 5.00
26 Roberto Clemente 4.00 10.00
27 Roger Clemens Sox 4.00 10.00
28 Roger Clemens Yanks 4.00 10.00
29 Ryne Sandberg 4.00 10.00
30 Sammy Sosa 2.00 5.00
31 Stan Musial 3.00 8.00
32 Steve Carlton 1.50 4.00
33 Tim Hudson 1.50 4.00
34 Tom Glavine 1.50 4.00
35 Tom Seaver 1.50 4.00
36 Tony Gwynn 2.50 6.00
37 Torii Hunter 1.50 4.00
38 Ty Cobb 3.00 8.00
39 Vladimir Guerrero 2.00 5.00
40 Will Clark 1.50 4.00

2003 Donruss Signature Team Trademarks Autographs

Randomly inserted into packs, these cards partially parallel the Team Trademark insert set. Each of these cards feature an authentic autograph from the featured player. Since there are some different print runs we have notated that information in our checklist next to the player's name. For those cards with print runs of 25 or fewer, no pricing is provided due to market scarcity.

1 Adam Dunn/50 20.00 50.00
2 Andre Dawson/250 6.00 15.00
5 Brooks Robinson/250 10.00 25.00
6 Cal Ripken/50 125.00 200.00
8 Don Mattingly/75 50.00 100.00
10 Fred Lynn/250 6.00 15.00
11 Gary Carter/250 6.00 15.00
12 George Brett/50 60.00 120.00
13 Greg Maddux/50 60.00 120.00
16 Jose Contreras/250 8.00 20.00
17 Kerry Wood/50 20.00 50.00
19 Magglio Ordonez/75 10.00 25.00
20 Mark Grace/25
23 Nolan Ryan Astros/50 75.00 150.00
24 Reggie Jackson/75 15.00 40.00
25 Rickey Henderson/50 50.00 100.00
27 Roger Clemens Sox/50 75.00 150.00
28 Roger Clemens Yanks/50 75.00 150.00
29 Ryne Sandberg/100 40.00 80.00
31 Stan Musial/200 30.00 60.00
32 Steve Carlton/150 6.00 15.00
33 Tim Hudson/100 15.00 40.00
34 Tom Glavine/50 20.00 50.00
35 Tom Seaver/50 20.00 50.00
36 Tony Gwynn/50 40.00 80.00
37 Torii Hunter/250 6.00 15.00
39 Vladimir Guerrero/250 10.00 25.00
40 Will Clark/125 15.00 40.00

2003 Donruss Signature Team Trademarks Autographs Century

STATED PRINT RUN 100 SERIAL #'d SETS
1 Andre Dawson 10.00 25.00
5 Brooks Robinson 15.00 40.00
9 Frank Robinson 10.00 25.00
10 Fred Lynn 10.00 25.00
11 Gary Carter 10.00 25.00
15 Jim Palmer 10.00 25.00
16 Jose Contreras 12.50 30.00
20 Mark Grace 30.00 60.00
29 Ryne Sandberg 40.00 80.00
31 Stan Musial 30.00 60.00
32 Steve Carlton 10.00 25.00
34 Tom Glavine 15.00 40.00
37 Torii Hunter 10.00 25.00
39 Vladimir Guerrero 15.00 40.00

2003 Donruss Signature Team Trademarks Autographs Decade

STATED PRINT RUN 10 SERIAL #'d SETS
NO PRICING DUE TO SCARCITY

2003 Donruss Signature Team Trademarks Autographs Notations

Randomly inserted into packs, these cards feature not only authentic autographs from the featured player as well as a special notation added to that autographs. Each of these cards have varying print runs and we have added that information in our checklist next to the player's name. For those cards with a stated print run of 25 or fewer copies, no pricing is provided due to market scarcity.

2A Andre Dawson #10/250 6.00 15.00
2B Andre Dawson ROY 77/150 6.00 15.00
5A B.Robinson 64 MVP/75 20.00 50.00
5B B.Robinson 70 WS MVP/125 15.00 40.00
10A Fred Lynn 75-83 AS/50 12.50 30.00
11 Gary Carter The Kid/25
12 George Brett #5/25
15A Jim Palmer 73 CY/32 12.50 30.00
15B Jim Palmer 75 CY/128 10.00 25.00
15C Jim Palmer 76 CY/150 6.00 15.00
17 Kerry Wood ROY 98/25
24A Reggie Jackson #44/5
24B Reggie Jackson 99/20
29A Ryne Sandberg #23/40 60.00 120.00
29B Ryne Sandberg Cubs/5
29C Ryne Sandberg 84 MVP/55 50.00 100.00
32A Steve Carlton 72 CY/50 12.50 30.00
32B Steve Carlton 77 CY/50 12.50 30.00
32C Steve Carlton 80 CY/50 12.50 30.00
32D Steve Carlton 82 CY/50 12.50 30.00
33A Tim Hudson Black Angus/5
33B Tim Hudson Huddy/50 20.00 50.00
37A Torii Hunter #48/20
40A Will Clark 89 MVP/52 40.00 80.00
40B Will Clark 89 WS/52 40.00 80.00

2003 Donruss Signature Team Trademarks Autographs Notations Century

STATED PRINT RUN 100 SERIAL #'d SETS
2A Andre Dawson #10 10.00 25.00
2B Andre Dawson ROY 77 10.00 25.00
10A Fred Lynn 75-83 AS 10.00 25.00
10B Fred Lynn 75 MVP-ROY 10.00 25.00
15A Jim Palmer 73 CY 10.00 25.00
15B Jim Palmer 75 CY 10.00 25.00
15C Jim Palmer 76 CY 10.00 25.00

2003 Donruss Signature Team Trademarks Autographs Notations Decade

STATED PRINT RUN 10 SERIAL #'d SETS
NO PRICING DUE TO SCARCITY

2005 Donruss Signature

This 159-card set was released in November, 2005. The set was issued in five-card packs with an $10 SRP which came four packs to a box and four boxes to a case. Cards numbered 1-150 feature a mix of current stars, prospects and retired stars while cards numbered 151 through 159 feature two or more rookies or prospects with common teams and those cards were issued at different stated odds which we have notated in our set detail.

COMMON CARD (1-150) .60 1.50
COMMON RC (1-150) .60 1.50
COM.DUAL AU T3-T6 4.00 10.00
151-156 DUAL AU STATED ODDS 1:14
COMMON TRI AU T4 6.00 15.00
COMMON TRI AU T2 8.00 20.00
157-158 TRIPLE AU STATED ODDS 1:51
COMMON QUAD AU T2 10.00 25.00
159 QUAD AU STATED ODDS 1:626
151-159 TIER 1 QTY B/WN 1-50 PER
151-159 TIER 2 QTY B/WN 51-100 PER
151-159 TIER 3 QTY B/WN 101-250 PER
151-159 TIER 4 QTY B/WN 251-800 PER
151-159 TIER 6 QTY B/WN 1201-2000 PER
151-159 ARE NOT SERIAL-NUMBERED
151-159 QTY INFO PROVIDED BY DONRUSS
155-156 NOT PRICED DUE TO SCARCITY
1 Scot Shields .60 1.50
2 Tim Salmon .60 1.50
3 Chone Figgins .60 1.50
4 Dallas McPherson .60 1.50
5 John Lackey .60 1.50
6 Ervin Santana .60 1.50
7 Casey Kotchman .60 1.50
8 Steve Finley .60 1.50
9 Brandon Webb 1.00 2.50
10 Chad Tracy .60 1.50
11 Russ Ortiz .60 1.50
12 Alex Cintron .60 1.50
13 Marcus Giles .60 1.50
14 Ichiro Suzuki 2.50 6.00
15 Tadahito Iguchi RC 1.00 2.50
16 Chipper Jones 1.50 4.00
17 Cal Ripken 6.00 15.00
18 Rick Dempsey .60 1.50
19 Adam Loewen .60 1.50
20 Eric Byrnes .60 1.50
21 Luis Matos .60 1.50
22 Miguel Tejada 1.00 2.50
23 Brooks Robinson 1.00 2.50
24 Kevin Youkilis .60 1.50
25 Keith Foulke .60 1.50
26 Trot Nixon .60 1.50
27 Edgar Renteria .60 1.50
28 Luis Tiant .60 1.50
29 Todd Walker .60 1.50
30 Mark Grace 1.00 2.50
31 Steve Stone .60 1.50
32 Ron Santo 1.00 2.50
33 Michael Wuertz .60 1.50
34 Russ Rohlicek RC .60 1.50
35 Ryne Sandberg 3.00 8.00
36 Andre Dawson 1.00 2.50
37 Aramis Ramirez .60 1.50
38 Derrek Lee .60 1.50
39 Paulino Reynoso RC .60 1.50
40 Jose Contreras .60 1.50
41 Freddy Garcia .60 1.50
42 Mark Buehrle 1.00 2.50
43 Bubba Nelson .60 1.50
44 Eric Davis .60 1.50
45 Adam Dunn 1.00 2.50
46 Travis Hafner .60 1.50
47 Larry Bigbie .60 1.50
48 Todd Helton 1.00 2.50
49 Chris Shelton .60 1.50
50 Willie Mays 3.00 8.00
51 Craig Monroe .60 1.50
52 Ivan Rodriguez 1.00 2.50
53 Miguel Cabrera 1.50 4.00
54 Chris Resop RC .60 1.50
55 Paul Lo Duca .60 1.50
56 Luke Scott RC 1.50 4.00
57 Brandon Backe .60 1.50
58 Mark McLemore RC .60 1.50
59 Devon Lowery RC .60 1.50
60 Jeremy Affeldt .60 1.50
61 Duke Snider 1.00 2.50
62 Johnny Podres .60 1.50
63 Rickie Weeks 1.00 2.50
64 Ben Sheets .60 1.50
65 Carlos Lee .60 1.50
66 Lew Ford .60 1.50
67 Travis Bowyer RC .60 1.50
68 Garrett Jones RC 1.00 2.50
69 Joe Nathan .60 1.50
70 Kent Hrbek .60 1.50
71 J.D. Durbin .60 1.50
72 Shannon Stewart .60 1.50
73 Torii Hunter .60 1.50
74 Kirby Puckett 1.50 4.00
75 Danny Graves .60 1.50
76 Jae Weong Seo .60 1.50
77 Matt Lindstrom RC .60 1.50
78 Dwight Gooden .60 1.50
79 Carlos Beltran .60 1.50
80 Mike Piazza 1.50 4.00
81 Tom Gordon .60 1.50
82 Adam LaRoche .60 1.50
83 Dave Righetti .60 1.50
84 Joe Pepitone .60 1.50
85 Gary Sheffield .60 1.50
86 Jim Leyritz .60 1.50
87 Rich Gossage .60 1.50
88 Don Larsen .60 1.50
89 Bernie Williams 1.00 2.50
90 Jorge Posada 1.00 2.50
91 Octavio Dotel .60 1.50
92 Rollie Fingers .60 1.50
93 Dennis Eckersley .60 1.50
94 Rich Harden .60 1.50
95 Art Howe .60 1.50
96 Jose Canseco 1.00 2.50
97 Barry Zito .60 1.50
98 Eric Chavez .60 1.50
99 Rickey Henderson 1.00 2.50
100 Chris Roberson RC .60 1.50
101 Eude Brito RC .60 1.50
102 Randy Wolf .60 1.50
103 Mike Lieberthal .60 1.50
104 John Kruk .60 1.50
105 Lenny Dykstra .60 1.50
106 Carlos Ruiz RC .60 1.50
107 Bobby Abreu .60 1.50
108 Bill Madlock .60 1.50
109 Mike Johnston .60 1.50
110 Ian Snell .60 1.50
111 Freddy Sanchez .60 1.50
112 Jose Castillo .60 1.50
113 Jeff Miller RC .60 1.50
114 John Candelaria .60 1.50
115 Jason Bay .60 1.50
116 Mark Loretta .60 1.50
117 Sean Thompson RC .60 1.50
118 Akinori Otsuka .60 1.50
119 Omar Vizquel 1.00 2.50
120 Will Clark 1.00 2.50
121 Clint Nageotte .60 1.50
122 J.J. Putz .60 1.50
123 Raul Ibanez .60 1.50
124 Wladimir Balentien RC 1.00 2.50
125 Jamie Moyer .60 1.50
126 Adrian Beltre .60 1.50
127 Richie Sexson .60 1.50
128 Edgar Martinez 1.00 2.50
129 Jeff Suppan .60 1.50
130 Marty Marion .60 1.50
131 Keith Hernandez .60 1.50
132 Ozzie Smith 2.50 6.00
133 Mark Mulder .60 1.50
134 Lee Smith .60 1.50
135 Jim Edmonds 1.00 2.50
136 Nomar Garciaparra 1.50 4.00
137 Delmon Young 1.50 4.00
138 Jason Hammel RC .60 1.50
139 Agustin Montero RC .60 1.50
140 Francisco Cordero .60 1.50
141 Michael Young 1.00 2.50
142 Al Oliver .60 1.50
143 David Dellucci .60 1.50
144 Nolan Ryan 4.00 10.00
145 Rafael Palmeiro 1.00 2.50
146 Alexis Rios 1.00 2.50
147 Jose Guillen .60 1.50
148 Danny Rueckel RC .60 1.50
149 Jose Vidro .60 1.50
150 Preston Wilson .60 1.50
151 Rickie Weeks 60.00 100.00
Prince Fielder RC T3
152 Hayden Penn RC 8.00 20.00
Adam Loewen T4
153 Akinori Otsuka 10.00 25.00
Keiichi Yabu RC T4
154 Brandon McCarthy RC 12.50 30.00
Anibal Sanchez RC T6
155 Norihiro Nakamura RC
Keiichi Yabu T1/35 *
156 Mike Morse RC
Yuniesky Betancourt RC T1/49 *
157 Jeff Niemann RC 15.00 40.00
Justin Verlander RC
Phil Humber RC T4
158 Wladimir Balentien 12.50 30.00
Ambiorix Concepcion RC
Miguel Negron RC T2/77 *
159 Justin Verlander 100.00 200.00
Jeff Niemann
Tony Pena RC
Ubaldo Jimenez RC T2/74 *

2005 Donruss Signature Century Proofs Gold

*GOLD: 1.5X TO 4X BASIC
STATED PRINT RUN 25 SERIAL #'d SETS
NO RC PRICING DUE TO SCARCITY

2005 Donruss Signature Century Proofs Platinum

STATED PRINT RUN 10 SERIAL #'d SETS
NO PRICING DUE TO SCARCITY

2005 Donruss Signature Century Proofs Silver

*SILVER: 1X TO 2.5X BASIC
*SILVER: 1X TO 2.5X BASIC RC
STATED PRINT RUN 75 SERIAL #'d SETS

2005 Donruss Signature Autograph Gold MS

*GOLD p/r 25-50: .6X TO 1.5X SILV T5-T6
*GOLD p/r 25-50: .6X TO 1.5X SILV T4
*GOLD p/r 25-50: .6X TO 1.5X SILV T3
*GOLD p/r 25-50: .5X TO 1.2X SILV T2
*GOLD p/r 25-50: 1X TO 1X SILV T1
RANDOM INSERTS IN PACKS
PRINT RUNS B/WN 3-50 COPIES PER
NO PRICING ON QTY OF 21 OR LESS
NO RC YR PRICING ON QTY OF 25 OR LESS
17 Cal Ripken/50 60.00 120.00
21 Luis Matos/50 6.00 15.00
49 Chris Shelton/43 12.50 30.00
88 Don Larsen/25 10.00 25.00
93 Dennis Eckersley/50 10.00 25.00
110 Ian Snell/34 6.00 15.00
142 Al Oliver/25 10.00 25.00
143 David Dellucci/25 10.00 25.00

2005 Donruss Signature Autograph Platinum MS

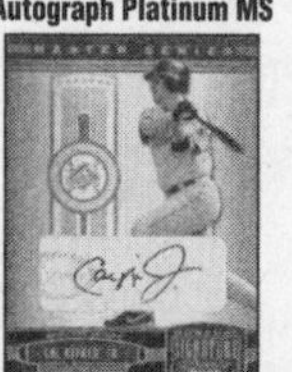

*PLAT p/r 25: .6X TO 1.5X SILV T5-T6
*PLAT p/r 25: .6X TO 1.5X SILV T4
*PLAT p/r 25: .6X TO 1.5X SILV T3
*PLAT p/r 25: .5X TO 1.2X SILV T2
*PLAT p/r 25: .4X TO 1X SILV T1
RANDOM INSERTS IN PACKS
PRINT RUNS B/WN 1-25 COPIES PER
NO PRICING ON QTY OF 22 OR LESS
NO RC YR PRICING DUE TO SCARCITY
17 Cal Ripken/25 75.00 150.00

2005 Donruss Signature Autograph Silver

STATED ODDS 1:2
TIER 1 QTY B/WN 1-50 COPIES PER
TIER 2 QTY B/WN 51-100 COPIES PER
TIER 3 QTY B/WN 101-250 COPIES PER
TIER 4 QTY B/WN 251-800 COPIES PER
TIER 5 QTY B/WN 801-1200 COPIES PER
TIER 6 QTY B/WN 1201-2000 COPIES PER
CARDS ARE NOT SERIAL-NUMBERED
PRINT RUN INFO PROVIDED BY DONRUSS
NO PRICING ON QTY OF 21 OR LESS
1 Scot Shields T6 4.00 10.00
2 Tim Salmon T4 6.00 15.00
3 Chone Figgins T3 6.00 15.00
4 Dallas McPherson T3 4.00 10.00
5 John Lackey T3 6.00 15.00
6 Ervin Santana T1/25 * 10.00 25.00
8 Steve Finley T1/14 *
9 Brandon Webb T5 4.00 10.00
10 Chad Tracy T4 4.00 10.00
11 Russ Ortiz T4 4.00 10.00
12 Alex Cintron T4 4.00 10.00
16 Chipper Jones T1/15 *
17 Cal Ripken T5 50.00 100.00
18 Rick Dempsey T6 4.00 10.00
19 Adam Loewen T5 4.00 10.00
20 Eric Byrnes T4 4.00 10.00
24 Kevin Youkilis T6 4.00 10.00
25 Keith Foulke T5 6.00 15.00
26 Trot Nixon T4 6.00 15.00
27 Edgar Renteria T4 6.00 15.00
28 Luis Tiant T3 6.00 15.00
29 Todd Walker T5 4.00 10.00
30 Mark Grace T4 10.00 25.00
31 Steve Stone T3 6.00 15.00
32 Ron Santo T3 10.00 25.00
33 Michael Wuertz T3 4.00 10.00
34 Russ Rohlicek T2/60 * 5.00 12.00
35 Ryne Sandberg T4 20.00 50.00
36 Andre Dawson T1/11 *
39 Paulino Reynoso T2/86 * 5.00 12.00
40 Jose Contreras T1/19 *
43 Bubba Nelson T3 4.00 10.00
47 Larry Bigbie T2/92 * 8.00 20.00
53 Miguel Cabrera T4 10.00 25.00
54 Chris Resop T4 3.00 8.00
56 Luke Scott T3 8.00 20.00
58 Mark McLemore T1/43 * 6.00 15.00
59 Devon Lowery T4 3.00 8.00
61 Duke Snider T4 10.00 25.00
62 Johnny Podres T2/99 * 8.00 20.00
63 Rickie Weeks T4 6.00 15.00
64 Ben Sheets T4 6.00 15.00
66 Lew Ford T5 4.00 10.00
67 Travis Bowyer T5 3.00 8.00
68 Garrett Jones T4 5.00 12.00
69 Joe Nathan T4 6.00 15.00
70 Kent Hrbek T4 6.00 15.00
71 J.D. Durbin T1/39 * 6.00 15.00
75 Danny Graves T5 4.00 10.00
76 Jae Weong Seo T4 6.00 15.00
77 Matt Lindstrom T4 3.00 8.00
79 Carlos Beltran T1/37 * 10.00 25.00
81 Tom Gordon T5 4.00 10.00
82 Adam LaRoche T2/53 * 8.00 20.00
83 Dave Righetti T4 6.00 15.00
84 Joe Pepitone T3 6.00 15.00
85 Gary Sheffield T3 10.00 25.00
86 Jim Leyritz T2/93 * 8.00 20.00
87 Rich Gossage T2/65 * 8.00 20.00
91 Octavio Dotel T4 4.00 10.00
92 Rollie Fingers T4 6.00 15.00
94 Rich Harden T3 6.00 15.00
96 Jose Canseco T1/8 *
97 Barry Zito T1/26 * 10.00 25.00
100 Chris Roberson T4 3.00 8.00
101 Eude Brito T4 3.00 8.00
102 Randy Wolf T4 4.00 10.00
103 Mike Lieberthal T4 6.00 15.00
104 John Kruk T3 6.00 15.00
105 Lenny Dykstra T1/21 *
106 Carlos Ruiz T1/11 *
109 Mike Johnston T3 4.00 10.00
112 Jose Castillo T1/20 *
113 Jeff Miller T1/49 * 6.00 15.00
114 John Candelaria T1/43 * 10.00 25.00
116 Mark Loretta T5 4.00 10.00
117 Sean Thompson T3 4.00 10.00
118 Akinori Otsuka T2/52 * 8.00 20.00
119 Omar Vizquel T2/100 * 12.50 30.00
121 Clint Nageotte T5 4.00 10.00
122 J.J. Putz T6 4.00 10.00
123 Raul Ibanez T6 6.00 15.00
124 Wladimir Balentien T4 5.00 12.00
125 Jamie Moyer T4 6.00 15.00
129 Jeff Suppan T6 4.00 10.00
130 Marty Marion T5 6.00 15.00
131 Keith Hernandez T4 6.00 15.00
132 Ozzie Smith T2/94 * 20.00 50.00
133 Mark Mulder T3 6.00 15.00
134 Lee Smith T1/6 *
137 Delmon Young T2/99 * 12.50 30.00
138 Jason Hammel T2/57 * 5.00 12.00
139 Agustin Montero T3 4.00 10.00
140 Francisco Cordero T3 4.00 10.00
141 Michael Young T1/6 *
142 Al Oliver T1/7 *
144 Nolan Ryan T2/62 * 50.00 100.00
145 Rafael Palmeiro T1/6 *
146 Alexis Rios T3 6.00 15.00
147 Jose Guillen T6 4.00 10.00
148 Danny Rueckel T4 3.00 8.00
149 Jose Vidro T1/18 *

2005 Donruss Signature Autograph Silver Notation

*NT T4: .5X TO 1.2X SILV T5-T6
*NT T3: .5X TO 1.2X SILV T5-T6
*NT T2: .6X TO 1.5X SILV T4
*NT T1 p/r 25-41: .75X TO 2X SILV T4
RANDOM INSERTS IN PACKS
TIER 1 QTY B/WN 1-50 COPIES PER
TIER 2 QTY B/WN 51-100 COPIES PER
TIER 3 QTY B/WN 101-250 COPIES PER
TIER 4 QTY B/WN 251-800 COPIES PER
CARDS ARE NOT SERIAL-NUMBERED
PRINT RUN INFO PROVIDED BY DONRUSS
NO PRICING ON QTY OF 24 OR LESS
17 Cal Ripken T1/25 * 75.00 150.00
105 Lenny Dykstra T1/41 * 12.50 30.00

2005 Donruss Signature Autograph Material Bat Gold

*BAT p/r 25-50: .6X TO 1.5X SILV T5-T6
*BAT p/r 25-50: .6X TO 1.5X SILV T3
*BAT p/r 25-50: .5X TO 1.2X SILV T2
RANDOM INSERTS IN PACKS
PRINT RUNS B/WN 1-50 COPIES PER
NO PRICING ON QTY OF 15 OR LESS
7 Casey Kotchman/25 10.00 25.00
24 Kevin Youkilis/25 6.00 15.00
65 Carlos Lee/25 10.00 25.00
108 Bill Madlock/50 10.00 25.00
111 Freddy Sanchez/42 6.00 15.00

2005 Donruss Signature Autograph Material Bat Platinum

*BAT p/r 25: .6X TO 1.5X SILV T3
*BAT p/r 25: .5X TO 1.2X SILV T2
RANDOM INSERTS IN PACKS
PRINT RUNS B/WN 1-25 COPIES PER
NO PRICING ON QTY OF 21 OR LESS
108 Bill Madlock/25 10.00 25.00
111 Freddy Sanchez/25 6.00 15.00

2005 Donruss Signature Autograph Material Bat Silver

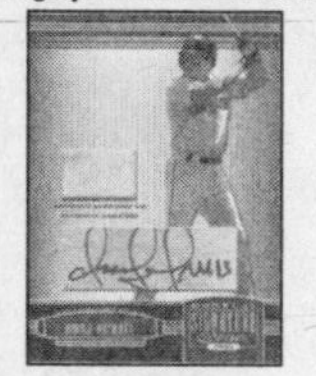

*BAT T1 p/r 50: .6X TO 1.5X SILV T3
RANDOM INSERTS IN PACKS
TIER 1 QTY B/WN 1-50 COPIES PER
TIER 3 QTY B/WN 101-250 COPIES PER
CARDS ARE NOT SERIAL-NUMBERED
PRINT RUN INFO PROVIDED BY DONRUSS
NO PRICING ON QTY OF 22 OR LESS
108 Bill Madlock T3 6.00 15.00
119 Omar Vizquel T3 10.00 25.00

2005 Donruss Signature Autograph Material Button Platinum

PRINT RUNS B/WN 1-6 COPIES PER
NO PRICING DUE TO SCARCITY

2005 Donruss Signature Autograph Material Jersey Silver

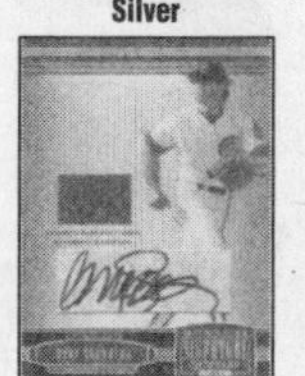

*JSY T3: .4X TO 1X SILV T4 10.00 25.00
*JSY T2: .5X TO 1.2X SILV T4
*JSY T1 p/r 36-50: .6X TO 1.5X SILV T5-T6
TIER 1 QTY B/WN 1-50 COPIES PER
TIER 2 QTY B/WN 51-100 COPIES PER
TIER 3 QTY B/WN 101-250 COPIES PER
CARDS ARE NOT SERIAL-NUMBERED
PRINT RUN INFO PROVIDED BY DONRUSS
NO PRICING ON QTY OF 22 OR LESS
21 Luis Matos T3 4.00 10.00
60 Jeremy Affeldt Pants T1/36 * 6.00 15.00
93 Dennis Eckersley T1/50 * 10.00 25.00

2005 Donruss Signature Autograph Material Jersey Number Platinum

*JSY NP p/r 25: .6X TO 1.5X SILV T5-T6
*JSY NP p/r 25: .6X TO 1.5X SILV T4
PRINT RUNS B/WN 1-25 COPIES PER
NO PRICING ON QTY OF 14 OR LESS
21 Luis Matos/25 6.00 15.00
57 Brandon Backe/25 6.00 15.00
93 Dennis Eckersley/25 10.00 25.00

2005 Donruss Signature Autograph Material Jersey Position Gold

*JSY JP p/r 25-50: .6X TO 1.5X SILV T5-T6
*JSY JP p/r 25-50: .6X TO 1.5X SILV T4
RANDOM INSERTS IN PACKS
PRINT RUNS B/WN 1-50 COPIES PER
NO PRICING ON QTY OF 10 OR LESS

21 Luis Matos/50 6.00 15.00
57 Brandon Backe/50 6.00 15.00
93 Dennis Eckersley/50 10.00 25.00

2005 Donruss Signature Autograph Material Combo Gold

*COMBO p/r 25-46: .75X TO 2X SILV T4
RANDOM INSERTS IN PACKS
PRINT RUNS B/WN 1-46 COPIES PER
NO PRICING ON QTY OF 10 OR LESS

17 C.Ripken Bat-Pants/46 75.00 150.00

2005 Donruss Signature Autograph Material Combo Platinum

RANDOM INSERTS IN PACKS
PRINT RUNS B/WN 1-25 COPIES PER
NO PRICING ON QTY OF 10 OR LESS

44 Eric Davis Bat-Jsy/25 40.00 80.00
50 Willie Mays Bat-Jsy/25 75.00 150.00
78 D.Gooden Bat-Jsy/25 12.50 30.00

2005 Donruss Signature Autograph Material Combo Silver

*COMBO p/r 50: .75X TO 2X SILV T4
RANDOM INSERTS IN PACKS
TIER 1 QTY B/WN 1-50 COPIES PER
TIER 2 QTY B/WN 51-100 COPIES PER
CARDS ARE NOT SERIAL-NUMBERED
PRINT RUN INFO PROVIDED BY DONRUSS
NO PRICING ON QTY OF 22 OR LESS

17 C.Rip Bat-Pants T2/100 * 60.00 120.00

2005 Donruss Signature Club Autograph Barrel

RANDOM INSERTS IN PACKS
PRINT RUNS B/WN 1-4 COPIES PER
CARDS ARE NOT SERIAL-NUMBERED
PRINT RUN INFO PROVIDED BY DONRUSS
NO PRICING DUE TO SCARCITY

2005 Donruss Signature Club Autograph Bat

STATED ODDS 1:20
TIER 1 QTY B/WN 1-50 COPIES PER
TIER 2 QTY B/WN 51-100 COPIES PER
TIER 3 QTY B/WN 101-250 COPIES PER
TIER 4 QTY B/WN 251-800 COPIES PER
CARDS ARE NOT SERIAL-NUMBERED
PRINT RUN INFO PROVIDED BY DONRUSS
NO PRICING ON QTY OF 2

1 Paul O'Neill T1/32 * 15.00 40.00
2 Alan Trammell T2/70 * 8.00 20.00
3 Barry Larkin T3 10.00 25.00
4 Carlton Fisk T1/34 * 15.00 40.00
5 Dale Murphy T2/100 * 12.50 30.00
6 Frank Thomas T3 15.00 40.00
7 Magglio Ordonez T4 6.00 15.00
8 Mark Teixeira T2/100 * 12.50 30.00
10 Omar Vizquel T4 10.00 25.00
11 Steve Garvey T4 6.00 15.00
12 Willie Mays T1/2 *

2005 Donruss Signature Hall of Fame

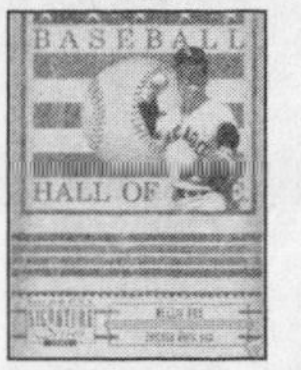

STATED ODDS 1:3

1 Al Kaline 2.00 5.00
2 Billy Williams .75 2.00
3 Bobby Doerr .75 2.00
4 Gaylord Perry .75 2.00
5 George Brett 4.00 10.00
6 Hank Aaron 4.00 10.00
7 Mike Schmidt 4.00 10.00
8 Nolan Ryan 5.00 12.00
9 Robin Roberts .75 2.00
10 Phil Niekro .75 2.00
11 Phil Rizzuto 1.25 3.00
12 Ralph Kiner .75 2.00
13 Rod Carew 1.25 3.00
14 Ryne Sandberg 4.00 10.00
15 Stan Musial 3.00 8.00
16 Steve Carlton .75 2.00
17 Tom Seaver 1.25 3.00
18 Willie McCovey 1.25 3.00
19 Willie Mays 4.00 10.00
20 Duke Snider 1.25 3.00
21 Rollie Fingers .75 2.00
22 Monte Irvin .75 2.00
23 Ozzie Smith 3.00 8.00
24 Johnny Bench 2.00 5.00
25 Luis Aparicio .75 2.00
26 Whitey Ford 1.25 3.00
27 Orlando Cepeda .75 2.00
28 Jim Bunning .75 2.00
29 Earl Weaver .75 2.00
30 Frank Robinson 1.25 3.00
31 Babe Ruth Yanks 5.00 12.00
32 Yogi Berra 2.00 5.00
33 Wade Boggs 1.25 3.00
34 Ted Williams 4.00 10.00
35 Roberto Clemente 5.00 12.00
36 Nellie Fox 1.25 3.00
37 Joe Morgan .75 2.00
38 Harmon Killebrew 2.00 5.00
39 Carlton Fisk 1.25 3.00
40 Babe Ruth Sox 5.00 12.00

2005 Donruss Signature Hall of Fame Material Bat

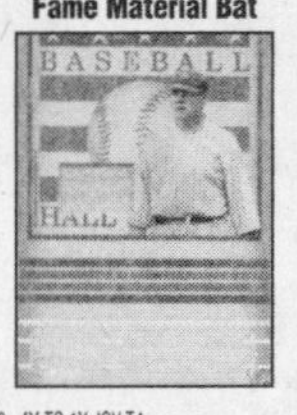

*BAT T3: .4X TO 1X JSY T4
*BAT T3: .4X TO 1X JSY T3
STATED ODDS 1:20
TIER 2 QTY B/WN 51-100 COPIES PER
TIER 3 QTY B/WN 101-250 COPIES PER
TIER 4 QTY B/WN 251-800 COPIES PER
TIER 5 QTY B/WN 801-1200 COPIES PER
CARDS ARE NOT SERIAL-NUMBERED
PRINT RUN INFO PROVIDED BY DONRUSS

31 Babe Ruth Yanks T3 90.00 150.00
33 Wade Boggs T4 4.00 10.00
35 Roberto Clemente T5 15.00 40.00
40 Babe Ruth Sox T2/55 *

2005 Donruss Signature Hall of Fame Material Jersey

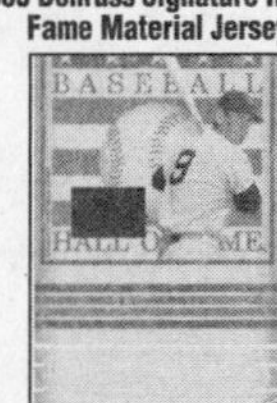

STATED ODDS 1:21
TIER 1 QTY B/WN 1-50 COPIES PER
TIER 2 QTY B/WN 51-100 COPIES PER
TIER 3 QTY B/WN 101-250 COPIES PER
TIER 4 QTY B/WN 251-800 COPIES PER
CARDS ARE NOT SERIAL-NUMBERED
PRINT RUN INFO PROVIDED BY DONRUSS
NO PRICING ON QTY OF 17 OR LESS

2 Billy Williams T1/25 * 5.00 12.00
3 Bobby Doerr T2/100 * 4.00 10.00
4 Gaylord Perry T3 3.00 8.00
6 Hank Aaron T3 10.00 25.00
8 Nolan Ryan T1/30 * 20.00 50.00
10 Phil Niekro T3 3.00 8.00
11 Phil Rizzuto T3 4.00 10.00
13 Rod Carew T3 4.00 10.00
14 Ryne Sandberg T1/11 *
15 Stan Musial T2/66 * 8.00 20.00
16 Steve Carlton Pants T3 3.00 8.00
18 Willie McCovey T1/17 *
19 Willie Mays Pants T4 10.00 25.00
21 Rollie Fingers T1/33 * 5.00 12.00
23 Ozzie Smith T1/47 * 8.00 20.00
24 J.Bench Pants T2/51 * 6.00 15.00
26 Whitey Ford T1/13 *
34 Ted Williams Jkt T4 15.00 40.00

2005 Donruss Signature Hall of Fame Material Combo

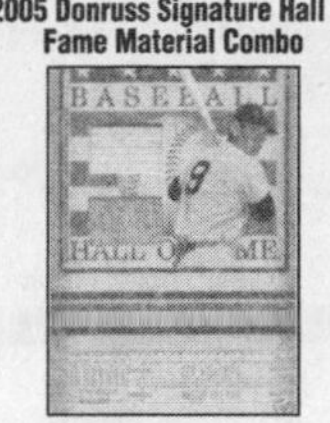

*COMBO T3: .6X TO 1.5X JSY T4
*COMBO T3: .6X TO 1.5X JSY T3
STATED ODDS 1:49
TIER 2 QTY B/WN 51-100 COPIES PER
TIER 3 QTY B/WN 101-250 COPIES PER
CARDS ARE NOT SERIAL-NUMBERED
PRINT RUN INFO PROVIDED BY DONRUSS

31 B.Ruth Yank Bat-Jsy T2/79 * 200.00 300.00

2005 Donruss Signature Hall of Fame Autograph

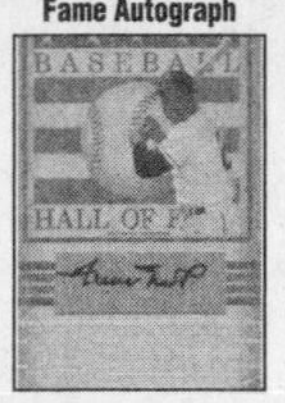

STATED ODDS 1:16
TIER 1 QTY B/WN 1-50 COPIES PER
TIER 2 QTY B/WN 51-100 COPIES PER
TIER 3 QTY B/WN 101-250 COPIES PER
TIER 4 QTY B/WN 251-800 COPIES PER
CARDS ARE NOT SERIAL-NUMBERED
PRINT RUN INFO PROVIDED BY DONRUSS
NO PRICING ON QTY OF 22 OR LESS

1 Al Kaline T2/82 * 15.00 40.00
2 Billy Williams T1/42 * 10.00 25.00
3 Bobby Doerr T1/25 * 10.00 25.00
4 Gaylord Perry T3 10.00 25.00
5 George Brett T1/2 *
6 Hank Aaron T1/5 *
7 Mike Schmidt T1/4 *
8 Nolan Ryan T1/25 * 60.00 120.00
9 Robin Roberts T4 10.00 25.00
11 Phil Rizzuto T3 20.00 50.00
12 Ralph Kiner T1/3 *
13 Rod Carew T1/4 *
14 Ryne Sandberg T2/55 * 30.00 60.00
15 Stan Musial T2/56 * 30.00 60.00
16 Steve Carlton T1/5 *
17 Tom Seaver T1/10 *
18 Willie McCovey T3 10.00 25.00
19 Willie Mays T1/2 *
20 Duke Snider T4 12.50 30.00
21 Rollie Fingers T4 6.00 15.00
22 Monte Irvin T4 6.00 15.00
23 Ozzie Smith T4 15.00 40.00
24 Johnny Bench T3 15.00 40.00
25 Luis Aparicio T1/1 *
26 Whitey Ford T1/6 *
27 Orlando Cepeda T1/30 * 10.00 25.00
28 Jim Bunning T1/25 * 15.00 40.00
29 Earl Weaver T1/22 *
30 Frank Robinson T1/1 *

2005 Donruss Signature Hall of Fame Autograph MS

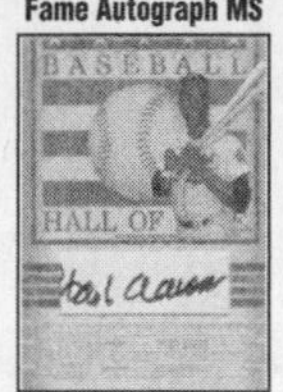

*AUTO MS p/r 25: .6X TO 1.5X AUTO T4
*AUTO MS p/r 25: .6X TO 1.5X AUTO T3
*AUTO MS p/r 25: .5X TO 1.2X AUTO T2
*AUTO MS p/r 25: .4X TO 1X AUTO T1
RANDOM INSERTS IN PACKS
PRINT RUNS B/WN 1-25 COPIES PER
NO PRICING ON QTY OF 23 OR LESS

26 Whitey Ford/25 15.00 40.00
29 Earl Weaver/25 10.00 25.00

2005 Donruss Signature Hall of Fame Autograph Material Bat

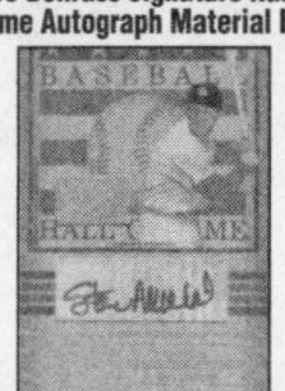

STATED ODDS 1:63
TIER 1 QTY B/WN 1-50 COPIES PER
TIER 2 QTY B/WN 51-100 COPIES PER
CARDS ARE NOT SERIAL-NUMBERED
PRINT RUN INFO PROVIDED BY DONRUSS
NO PRICING ON QTY OF 10 OR LESS

12 Ralph Kiner T2/97 * 12.50 30.00
25 Luis Aparicio T2/100 * 8.00 20.00
33 Wade Boggs T2/56 * 12.50 30.00

2005 Donruss Signature Hall of Fame Autograph Material Jersey

*AU JSY T2: .5X TO 1.2X AU T4
*AU JSY T2: .5X TO 1.2X AU T3
*AU JSY T1: .6X TO 1.5X AU T3

*AU JSY T1: .5X TO 1.2X AU T2
*AU JSY T1: .4X TO 1X AU T1
TIER 1 QTY B/WN 1-50 COPIES PER
TIER 2 QTY B/WN 51-100 COPIES PER
CARDS ARE NOT SERIAL-NUMBERED
PRINT RUN INFO PROVIDED BY DONRUSS
NO PRICING ON QTY OF 20 OR LESS

6 Hank Aaron T1/25 * 125.00 200.00
16 Steve Carlton Pants T1/25 * 10.00 25.00
17 Tom Seaver T1/25 * 15.00 40.00
26 Whitey Ford T1/33 * 15.00 40.00

2005 Donruss Signature Hall of Fame Autograph Material Combo

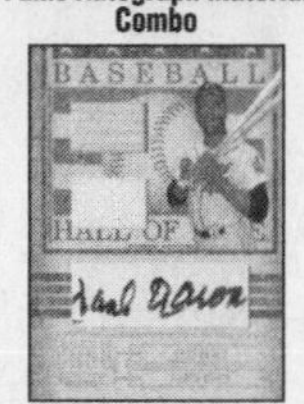

*AU COM T2: .6X TO 1.5X AU T3
*AU COM T2: .5X TO 1.2X AU T2
*AU COM T1: .75X TO 2X AU T3
TIER 1 QTY B/WN 1-50 COPIES PER
TIER 2 QTY B/WN 51-100 COPIES PER
CARDS ARE NOT SERIAL-NUMBERED
PRINT RUN INFO PROVIDED BY DONRUSS
NO PRICING ON QTY OF 20 OR LESS

6 Hank Aaron Bat-Jsy T1/50 * 125.00 200.00
16 S.Carlton Bat-Pants T1/50 * 12.50 30.00
17 T.Seaver Jsy-Pants T1/50 * 20.00 50.00

2005 Donruss Signature HOF Combos Autograph

STATED ODDS 1:41
TIER 1 QTY B/WN 1-50 COPIES PER
TIER 2 QTY B/WN 51-100 COPIES PER
TIER 3 QTY B/WN 101-250 COPIES PER
CARDS ARE NOT SERIAL-NUMBERED
PRINT RUN INFO PROVIDED BY DONRUSS
NO PRICING ON QTY OF 10

41 Harmon Killebrew 60.00 120.00
Rod Carew T1/25 *
42 Ryne Sandberg 40.00 80.00
Wade Boggs T2/100 *
43 Nolan Ryan 75.00 150.00
George Brett T1/36 *
44 Steve Carlton 20.00 50.00
Phil Rizzuto T2/100 *
45 Tom Seaver 20.00 50.00
Rollie Fingers T2/100 *
46 Jim Palmer 20.00 50.00
Joe Morgan T1/25 *
47 Bobby Doerr 15.00 40.00
Willie McCovey T2/51 *
48 Luis Aparicio 50.00 100.00
Harmon Killebrew T1/25 *
49 Al Kaline 40.00 80.00
Duke Snider T1/25 *
50 Jim Palmer 20.00 50.00
Frank Robinson T1/25 *
51 Bobby Doerr 30.00 60.00
Carlton Fisk T1/25 *
52 Johnny Bench 40.00 80.00
Joe Morgan T1/25 *
53 Duke Snider 20.00 50.00
Don Sutton T2/100 *
54 Whitey Ford 30.00 60.00
Phil Rizzuto T2/57 *
55 Johnny Bench 40.00 80.00
Carlton Fisk T1/25 *
56 Willie Mays
Duke Snider T1/10 *
57 Whitey Ford 30.00 60.00
Steve Carlton T1/25 *
58 Jim Palmer 30.00 60.00
Tom Seaver T1/32 *
59 Reggie Jackson 40.00 80.00
Rollie Fingers T1/49 *
60 Duke Snider 50.00 100.00
Stan Musial T3

2005 Donruss Signature HOF Trios Autograph

STATED ODDS 1:80
TIER 1 QTY B/WN 1-50 COPIES PER
TIER 2 QTY B/WN 51-100 COPIES PER
CARDS ARE NOT SERIAL-NUMBERED
PRINT RUN INFO PROVIDED BY DONRUSS
NO PRICING ON QTY OF 15

61 Billy Williams 60.00 120.00
Fergie Jenkins
Ryne Sandberg T2/100 *
62 Tony Perez
Joe Morgan
Johnny Bench T2/61 *
63 Rod Carew
Gaylord Perry
Fergie Jenkins T1/25 *
64 Bobby Doerr 50.00 100.00
Joe Morgan
Ryne Sandberg T2/63 *
65 Luis Aparicio 50.00 100.00
Phil Rizzuto
Ozzie Smith T1/50 *
66 Wade Boggs
George Brett
Mike Schmidt T1/25 *
67 Frank Robinson 50.00 100.00
Reggie Jackson
Ralph Kiner T1/25 *
68 Gaylord Perry 40.00 80.00
Fergie Jenkins
Bob Gibson T1/50 *
69 Ozzie Smith 75.00 150.00
Stan Musial
Bob Gibson T2/100 *
70 Willie Mays
Juan Marichal
Willie McCovey T1/15 *

2005 Donruss Signature HOF Quads Autograph

STATED ODDS 1:147
TIER 1 QTY B/WN 1-50 COPIES PER
TIER 2 QTY B/WN 51-100 COPIES PER
CARDS ARE NOT SERIAL-NUMBERED
PRINT RUN INFO PROVIDED BY DONRUSS
NO PRICING ON QTY OF 15

71 Gaylord Perry 40.00 80.00
Juan Marichal
Monte Irvin
Willie McCovey T2/85 *
72 Mike Schmidt
Robin Roberts
Jim Bunning
Steve Carlton T1/38 *
73 Juan Marichal
Willie Mays
Willie McCovey
Gaylord Perry T1/15 *
74 Lou Brock 50.00 100.00
Monte Irvin
Ralph Kiner
Billy Williams T1/41 *
75 Bob Gibson 60.00 120.00
Fergie Jenkins
Gaylord Perry
Tom Seaver T1/50 *
76 Nolan Ryan 125.00 200.00
Steve Carlton
Tom Seaver
Don Sutton T1/50 *

2005 Donruss Signature HOF Six Autograph

STATED ODDS 1:579
TIER 1 QTY B/WN 1-50 COPIES PER
CARDS ARE NOT SERIAL-NUMBERED
PRINT RUN INFO PROVIDED BY DONRUSS
NO PRICING ON QTY OF 5 OR LESS

2005 Donruss Signature INKcredible Combos

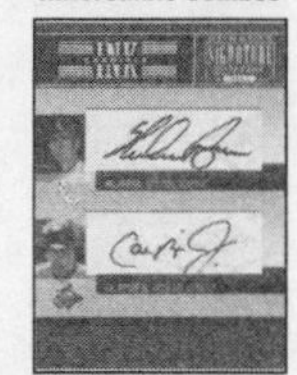

STATED ODDS 1:7
TIER 1 QTY B/WN 1-50 COPIES PER
TIER 2 QTY B/WN 51-100 COPIES PER
TIER 3 QTY B/WN 101-250 COPIES PER
TIER 4 QTY B/WN 251-800 COPIES PER
CARDS ARE NOT SERIAL-NUMBERED
PRINT RUN INFO PROVIDED BY DONRUSS
NO PRICING ON QTY OF 21 OR LESS

1 Troy Percival 12.50 30.00
Francisco Rodriguez T3
2 Scot Shields 8.00 20.00
Francisco Rodriguez T3
3 Scot Shields 6.00 15.00
Troy Percival T4
5 Adam LaRoche
Chipper Jones T1/1 *
6 Rickie Weeks 12.50 30.00
Paul Molitor T1/28 *
7 Ozzie Smith 30.00 60.00
Marty Marion T2/100 *
8 Jeff Suppan 6.00 15.00
{Mark Mulder T4
9 Ron Cey 30.00 60.00
Ron Santo T1/25 *
10 Greg Maddux
Mark Prior T1/11 *
11 Steve Garvey 15.00 40.00
Don Sutton T2/100 *
12 Cal Ripken 50.00 100.00
Billy Ripken T4
13 Jim Palmer 10.00 25.00
Rick Dempsey T2/100 *
14 Jeff Bagwell
Craig Biggio T1/3 *
15 Mark Loretta 4.00 10.00
Sean Burroughs T4
16 David Ortiz
Jason Varitek T1/3 *
17 Brett Myers 5.00 12.00
Randy Wolf T3
18 Andruw Jones
Chipper Jones T1/5 *
19 Justin Morneau 12.50 30.00
Kent Hrbek T1/36 *
20 Frank Thomas 30.00 60.00
Paul Konerko T1/50 *
21 Luis Aparicio 10.00 25.00
Minnie Minoso T4
22 Cal Ripken 75.00 150.00
Tony Gwynn T2/100 *
23 Cal Ripken
Roger Clemens T1/4 *
24 Jose Guillen 6.00 15.00
Tim Salmon T4
25 Kevin Youkilis 6.00 15.00
Dallas McPherson T4
26 Esteban Loaiza 6.00 15.00
Jose Guillen T4
27 Nolan Ryan
Roger Clemens T1/4 *
28 Nolan Ryan
Cal Ripken T1/21 *
29 Chan Ho Park
Jae Weong Seo T1/1 *
30 Nolan Ryan
Randy Johnson T1/29 *
31 Lew Ford 5.00 12.00
Jason Kubel T3
32 Danny Graves 5.00 12.00
Matt Lindstrom T3
33 Tim Salmon 12.50 30.00
Garret Anderson T3
34 Clint Nageotte 4.00 10.00
J.J. Putz T4

2005 Donruss Signature INKcredible Trios

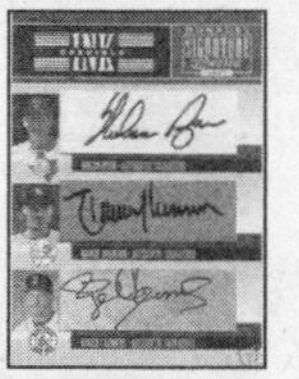

STATED ODDS 1:23
TIER 1 QTY B/WN 1-50 COPIES PER
TIER 2 QTY B/WN 51-100 COPIES PER
TIER 3 QTY B/WN 101-250 COPIES PER
TIER 4 QTY B/WN 251-800 COPIES PER
CARDS ARE NOT SERIAL-NUMBERED
PRINT RUN INFO PROVIDED BY DONRUSS
NO PRICING ON QTY OF 16 OR LESS

35 Scot Shields 15.00 40.00
Troy Percival
Francisco Rodriguez T3
36 Barry Zito 60.00 120.00
Mark Mulder
Tim Hudson T1/37 *
37 Mike Mussina
Mariano Rivera
Jorge Posada T1/1 *
38 Roy Halladay 20.00 50.00
Vernon Wells
Alexis Rios T1/39 *
39 Greg Maddux
Mark Grace
Ryne Sandberg T1/25 *
40 Duke Snider 30.00 60.00
Johnny Podres
Maury Wills T2/100 *
41 Josh Beckett
Dontrelle Willis
Miguel Cabrera T1/2 *
42 Keith Hernandez 20.00 50.00
Lenny Dykstra
Jesse Orosco T2/80 *
43 Esteban Loaiza 15.00 40.00
Jose Guillen
Marlon Byrd T4
44 Cal Ripken 75.00 150.00
Jim Palmer
Rick Dempsey T2/80 *
45 Brett Myers 15.00 40.00
Randy Wolf
Mike Lieberthal T3
46 Jacque Jones 15.00 40.00
Lew Ford
Jason Kubel T2/91 *
47 Randy Jones 50.00 100.00
Ozzie Smith
Rollie Fingers T1/36 *
48 Ron Guidry 20.00 50.00
Rich Gossage
Luis Tiant T3
49 Ron Guidry 20.00 50.00
Rich Gossage
Dave Righetti T3
50 Ozzie Smith 125.00 200.00
Cal Ripken
Alan Trammell T2/99 *
51 Wade Boggs 75.00 150.00
Ryne Sandberg
Tony Gwynn T2/95 *
52 Earl Weaver 75.00 150.00
Cal Ripken
Frank Robinson T1/38 *
53 Harmon Killebrew 75.00 150.00
Rod Carew
Kent Hrbek T1/28 *
54 Minnie Minoso 40.00 80.00
Luis Aparicio
Carlton Fisk T1/25 *
55 Jeff Bagwell
Craig Biggio
Lance Berkman T1/5 *
56 Nolan Ryan
Randy Johnson
Roger Clemens T1/4 *
57 Hideo Nomo
Shigetoshi Hasegawa
Akinori Otsuka T1/16 *
58 David Ortiz
Jason Varitek
Manny Ramirez T1/1 *

2005 Donruss Signature INKcredible Quads

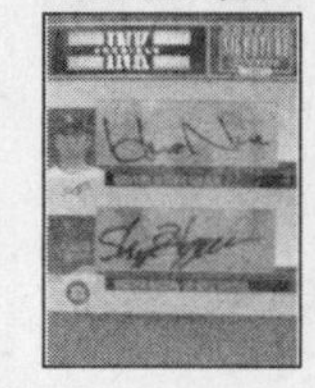

STATED ODDS 1:105
TIER 1 QTY B/WN 1-50 COPIES PER
TIER 2 QTY B/WN 51-100 COPIES PER
TIER 3 QTY B/WN 101-250 COPIES PER
CARDS ARE NOT SERIAL-NUMBERED
PRINT RUN INFO PROVIDED BY DONRUSS
NO PRICING ON QTY OF 11 OR LESS

59 Michael Young
Bobby Crosby
Mike Morse
Orlando Cabrera T1/1 *
60 Jose Guillen 30.00 60.00
Esteban Loaiza
Marlon Byrd
Junior Spivey T3
61 Marlon Byrd 30.00 60.00
Jose Guillen
Livan Hernandez
Esteban Loaiza T3
62 Alfonso Soriano
David Dellucci
Mark Teixeira
Michael Young T1/50 *
63 Dwight Evans 60.00 120.00
Jim Rice
Luis Tiant
Carlton Fisk T2/73 *
64 Phil Rizzuto
Whitey Ford
Don Mattingly
Ron Guidry T1/25 *
65 Hideo Nomo 200.00 350.00
Shigetoshi Hasegawa
So Taguchi
Akinori Otsuka T1/45 *
66 Shigetoshi Hasegawa
Akinori Otsuka
Shingo Takatsu
Keiichi Yabu T1/11 *

2005 Donruss Signature INKcredible Six

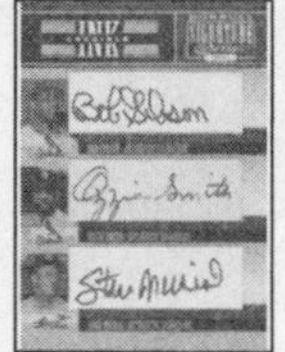

STATED ODDS 1:188
TIER 1 QTY B/WN 1-50 COPIES PER

TIER 2 QTY B/WN 51-100 COPIES PER
TIER 3 QTY B/WN 101-250 COPIES PER
CARDS ARE NOT SERIAL-NUMBERED
PRINT RUN INFO PROVIDED BY DONRUSS
NO PRICING ON QTY OF 1
67 Bob Gibson 150.00 250.00
Ozzie Smith
Stan Musial
Lou Brock
Red Schoendienst
Marty Marion T3
68 Livan Hernandez 50.00 100.00
Jose Guillen
Esteban Loaiza
Jose Vidro
Marlon Byrd
Junior Spivey T2/70 *
69 Cal Ripken
Wade Boggs
Tony Gwynn
Ryne Sandberg
Don Mattingly
Ozzie Smith T1/25 *
70 Hideo Nomo
Kazuhisa Ishii
Shigetoshi Hasegawa
So Taguchi
Akinori Otsuka
Shingo Takatsu T1/1 *
71 Shigetoshi Hasegawa
So Taguchi
Akinori Otsuka
Shingo Takatsu
Keiichi Yabu
Hideo Nomo T1/1 *
72 Hideo Nomo
Shigetoshi Hasegawa
So Taguchi
Akinori Otsuka
Shingo Takatsu
Norihiro Nakamura T1/1 *
73 Andruw Jones
Albert Pujols
Derrek Lee
Adam Dunn
Morgan Ensberg
Aramis Ramirez T1/1 *

2005 Donruss Signature K-Force

STATED ODDS 1:7
1 Nolan Ryan 5.00 12.00
2 Steve Carlton .75 2.00
3 Roger Clemens 2.50 6.00
4 Randy Johnson 2.00 5.00
5 Tom Seaver 1.25 3.00
6 Don Sutton .75 2.00
7 Gaylord Perry .75 2.00
8 Fergie Jenkins .75 2.00
9 Bob Gibson 1.25 3.00
10 Greg Maddux 3.00 8.00
11 David Cone .75 2.00
12 Bob Feller .75 2.00
13 Johan Santana 2.00 5.00
14 Roy Halladay 2.00 5.00
15 Juan Marichal .75 2.00

2005 Donruss Signature K-Force Autograph

RANDOM INSERTS IN PACKS
TIER 1 QTY B/WN 1-50 COPIES PER
TIER 2 QTY B/WN 51-100 COPIES PER
TIER 3 QTY B/WN 101-250 COPIES PER
CARDS ARE NOT SERIAL-NUMBERED
PRINT RUN INFO PROVIDED BY DONRUSS
NO PRICING ON QTY OF 20 OR LESS
1 Nolan Ryan T3 40.00 80.00
2 Steve Carlton T1/33 * 10.00 25.00
3 Roger Clemens T1/1 *
4 Randy Johnson T1/5 *
5 Tom Seaver T1/5 *
6 Don Sutton T3 6.00 15.00
7 Gaylord Perry T2/75 * 8.00 20.00
8 Fergie Jenkins T2/55 * 8.00 20.00
9 Bob Gibson T1/20 *
10 Greg Maddux T1/25 * 50.00 100.00
11 David Cone T3 6.00 15.00
12 Bob Feller T1/39 * 10.00 25.00
13 Johan Santana T2/55 * 12.50 30.00
14 Roy Halladay T1/11 *
15 Juan Marichal T3 6.00 15.00

2005 Donruss Signature K-Force Autograph MS

*AU MS p/r 25: .6X TO 1.5X AU T3
*AU MS p/r 25: .5X TO 1.2X AU T2
*AU MS p/r 25: .4X TO 1X AU T1
PRINT RUNS B/WN 1-25 COPIES PER
NO PRICING ON QTY OF 20 OR LESS

2005 Donruss Signature K-Force Autograph Material

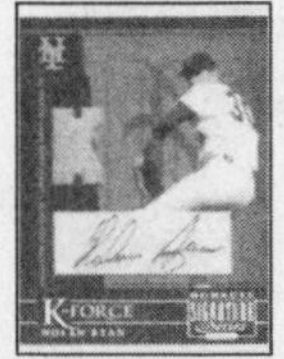

*AU MAT T3: .4X TO 1X AU T3
*AU MAT T3: .25X TO .6X AU T1
*AU MAT T2: .5X TO 1.2X AU T3
*AU MAT T1: .5X TO 1.2X AU T2
*AU MAT T1: .4X TO 1X AU T1
STATED ODDS 1:54
TIER 1 QTY B/WN 1-50 COPIES PER
TIER 2 QTY B/WN 51-100 COPIES PER
TIER 3 QTY B/WN 101-250 COPIES PER
CARDS ARE NOT SERIAL-NUMBERED
PRINT RUN INFO PROVIDED BY DONRUSS
NO PRICING ON QTY OF 7 OR LESS
9 Bob Gibson Jsy T1/41 * 15.00 40.00

2005 Donruss Signature Milestone Marks

STATED ODDS 1:10
CARD 8 DOES NOT EXIST
1 Duke Snider 1.25 3.00
2 Nolan Ryan 5.00 12.00
3 Gaylord Perry .75 2.00
4 Johnny Bench 2.00 5.00
5 Willie McCovey 1.25 3.00
6 Stan Musial 3.00 8.00
7 Randy Johnson 2.00 5.00
8 Warren Spahn
9 Gary Carter .75 2.00
10 Tony Gwynn 2.50 6.00

2005 Donruss Signature Milestone Marks Autograph

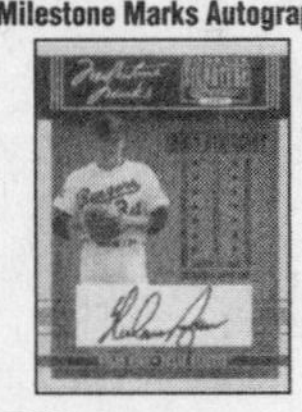

STATED ODDS 1:41
TIER 1 QTY B/WN 1-50 COPIES PER
TIER 3 QTY B/WN 101-250 COPIES PER
CARDS ARE NOT SERIAL-NUMBERED
PRINT RUN INFO PROVIDED BY DONRUSS
NO PRICING ON QTY OF 6 OR LESS
1 Duke Snider T3 10.00 25.00
2 Nolan Ryan T3 40.00 80.00
3 Gaylord Perry T3 6.00 15.00
The milestone mark celebrated was when Perry was a Mariner
4 Johnny Bench T3 12.50 30.00
5 Willie McCovey T1/44 * 15.00 40.00
6 Stan Musial T3 20.00 50.00
9 Gary Carter T1/1 *
10 Tony Gwynn T1/6 *

2005 Donruss Signature Milestone Marks Autograph MS

*AU MS: .6X TO 1.5X AU T3
*AU MS: .4X TO 1X AU T1
RANDOM INSERTS IN PACKS
PRINT RUNS B/WN 20-25 COPIES PER
NO PRICING ON QTY OF 20
10 Tony Gwynn/25 20.00 50.00

2005 Donruss Signature Milestone Marks Autograph Material Bat

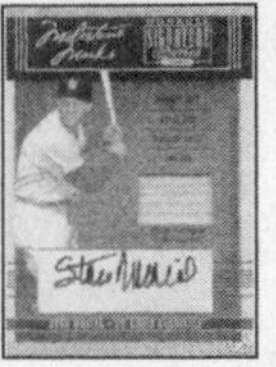

*AU BAT T1 p/r 25: .6X TO 1.5X AU T3
STATED ODDS 1:1524
TIER 1 QTY B/WN 1-50 COPIES PER
CARDS ARE NOT SERIAL-NUMBERED
PRINT RUN INFO PROVIDED BY DONRUSS
NO PRICING ON QTY OF 5

2005 Donruss Signature Milestone Marks Autograph Material Jersey

*AU JSY T3: .4X TO 1X AU T3
*AU JSY T2: .3X TO .8X AU T1
STATED ODDS 1:134
TIER 1 QTY B/WN 1-50 COPIES PER
TIER 2 QTY B/WN 51-100 COPIES PER
TIER 3 QTY B/WN 101-250 COPIES PER
CARDS ARE NOT SERIAL-NUMBERED
PRINT RUN INFO PROVIDED BY DONRUSS
NO PRICING ON QTY OF 21
10 Tony Gwynn T2/75 * 15.00 40.00

2005 Donruss Signature Milestone Marks Autograph Material Combo

STATED ODDS 1:210
TIER 1 QTY B/WN 1-50 COPIES PER
TIER 3 QTY B/WN 101-250 COPIES PER
CARDS ARE NOT SERIAL-NUMBERED
PRINT RUN INFO PROVIDED BY DONRUSS
NO PRICING ON QTY OF 17 OR LESS
7 R.John Fld Glv-Jsy T1/25 * 40.00 80.00
10 T.Gwynn Jsy-Pants T3 30.00 60.00

2005 Donruss Signature Notable Nicknames 01

STATED PRINT RUN 100 SERIAL #'d SETS
NON #'d MASTER SERIES CARDS ISSUED
NO MAST.SER.PRICING DUE TO SCARCITY
RANDOM INSERTS IN PACKS
I-ROD AUTO IS NOT NOTATED
OZZIE AUTO IS NOT NOTATED
GM Greg Maddux Bulldog 250.00 400.00
IR Ivan Rodriguez Pudge 20.00 50.00
OS Ozzie Smith Wizard
PR Phil Rizzuto Scooter 30.00 60.00

2005 Donruss Signature Recollection Autographs

STATED ODDS 1:116
NO PRICING DUE TO SCARCITY

2005 Donruss Signature Stamps Material Centennial

PRINT RUNS B/WN 40-100 COPIES PER
*PRO BALL: .4X TO 1X CENTENNIAL
PRO BALL PRINT RUNS B/WN 40-100 PER
RANDOM INSERTS IN PACKS
1 Babe Ruth Pants/40
2 Cal Ripken Pants/50 20.00 50.00
5 Harmon Killebrew Bat/70 6.00 15.00
8 Adrian Beltre Shoes/100 4.00 10.00
10 Cal Ripken Pants/50 20.00 50.00
11 Jim Thorpe Jsy/68 90.00 150.00
12 Willie Mays Jsy/100 20.00 50.00
13 Roger Maris Pants/100 20.00 50.00

2005 Donruss Signature Stamps Autograph Centennial

PRINT RUNS B/WN 3-81 COPIES PER
*PRO BALL: .4X TO 1X CENTENNIAL
PRO BALL PRINT RUNS B/WN 3-81 PER
RANDOM INSERTS IN PACKS
NO PRICING ON QTY OF 17 OR LESS
2 Cal Ripken/50 75.00 150.00
3 Sandy Koufax/17
4 Duke Snider/81 12.50 30.00
5 Harmon Killebrew/5
6 Orlando Cepeda/48 10.00 25.00
7 Don Larsen/50 10.00 25.00
8 Adrian Beltre/5
9 Jim Palmer/3
10 Cal Ripken/50 75.00 150.00

2005 Donruss Signature Stamps Autograph Material Centennial

PRINT RUNS B/WN 2-50 COPIES PER
*PRO BALL: .4X TO 1X CENTENNIAL
PRO BALL PRINT RUNS B/WN 1-50 PER
RANDOM INSERTS IN PACKS
NO PRICING ON QTY OF 20 OR LESS
1 Babe Ruth Jsy/2
2 Cal Ripken Pants/50 75.00 150.00
3 Sandy Koufax Jsy/10
5 Harmon Killebrew Bat/33 20.00 50.00
8 Adrian Beltre Shoes/20
10 Cal Ripken Pants/50 75.00 150.00

2005 Donruss Signature Stamps Centennial Autograph

RANDOM INSERTS IN PACKS
PRINT RUNS B/WN 1-2 COPIES PER
NO PRICING DUE TO SCARCITY

2005 Donruss Signature Stars Autograph

STATED ODDS 1:47
TIER 1 QTY B/WN 1-50 COPIES PER
TIER 2 QTY B/WN 51-100 COPIES PER
TIER 3 QTY B/WN 101-250 COPIES PER
CARDS ARE NOT SERIAL-NUMBERED
PRINT RUN INFO PROVIDED BY DONRUSS
1 Mark Teixeira T1/42 * 15.00 40.00
2 Scott Rolen T3 10.00 25.00
3 Roy Oswalt T2/85 * 5.00 12.00
5 Morgan Ensberg T3 6.00 15.00
6 Mark Grace T2/86 * 12.50 30.00
7 Gary Sheffield T2/82 * 12.50 30.00
8 Sean Casey T3 6.00 15.00
10 Ryne Sandberg T3 20.00 50.00

2005 Donruss Signature Stars Autograph MS

*AU MS p/r 25: .6X TO 1.5X AU T3
*AU MS p/r 25: .5X TO 1.2X AU T2
*AU MS p/r 25: .4X TO 1X AU T1
PRINT RUNS B/WN 1-25 COPIES PER
NO PRICING ON QTY OF 5 OR LESS
14 Barry Larkin/25 15.00 40.00

2005 Donruss Signature Stars Autograph Material Bat

*AU BAT T3: .3X TO .8X AU T2
*AU BAT T2: .3X TO .8X AU T1
STATED ODDS 1:35
TIER 1 QTY B/WN 1-50 COPIES PER
TIER 2 QTY B/WN 51-100 COPIES PER
TIER 3 QTY B/WN 101-250 COPIES PER
CARDS ARE NOT SERIAL-NUMBERED
PRINT RUN INFO PROVIDED BY DONRUSS
NO PRICING ON QTY OF 9
4 Hideo Nomo T1/36 * 175.00 300.00
11 Stan Musial T1/38 * 40.00 80.00
12 Joe Torre T1/44 * 15.00 40.00
13 Wade Boggs T1/40 * 15.00 40.00
14 Barry Larkin T3 10.00 25.00
15 Dale Murphy T2/100 * 12.50 30.00

2005 Donruss Signature Stars Autograph Material Jersey

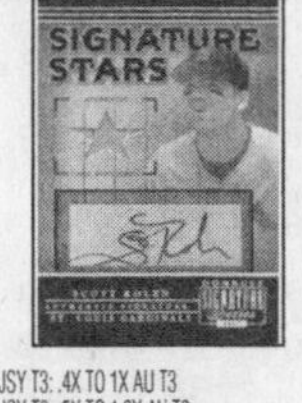

*AU JSY T3: .4X TO 1X AU T3
*AU JSY T2: .5X TO 1.2X AU T3
*AU JSY T1: .5X TO 1.2X AU T2
STATED ODDS 1:64
TIER 1 QTY B/WN 1-50 COPIES PER
TIER 2 QTY B/WN 51-100 COPIES PER
TIER 3 QTY B/WN 101-250 COPIES PER
CARDS ARE NOT SERIAL-NUMBERED
PRINT RUN INFO PROVIDED BY DONRUSS
NO PRICING ON QTY OF 19 OR LESS
4 Hideo Nomo Pants T1/50 * 175.00 300.00
11 Stan Musial T1/44 * 40.00 80.00
12 Joe Torre T1/50 * 15.00 40.00
15 Dale Murphy T3 10.00 25.00

2005 Donruss Signature Stats Autograph

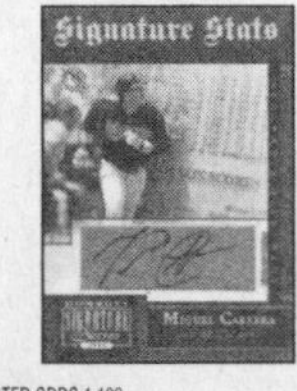

STATED ODDS 1:102
TIER 1 QTY B/WN 1-50 COPIES PER
TIER 3 QTY B/WN 101-250 COPIES PER
CARDS ARE NOT SERIAL-NUMBERED
PRINT RUN INFO PROVIDED BY DONRUSS
NO PRICING ON QTY OF 16 OR LESS
1 Tony Gwynn T1/6 *
2 Johan Santana T1/13 *
3 Orel Hershiser T1/16 *
4 Alfonso Soriano T3 6.00 15.00
5 Don Mattingly T1/6 *
6 Curt Schilling T1/2 *
8 Victor Martinez T1/9 *
9 Miguel Cabrera T3 8.00 20.00
10 Mark Teixeira T1/41 * 15.00 40.00

2005 Donruss Signature Stats Autograph MS

*AU MS p/r 25: .6X TO 1.5X AU T3
*AU MS p/r 25: .4X TO 1X AU T1
PRINT RUNS B/WN 1-25 COPIES PER
NO PRICING ON QTY OF 15 OR LESS
1 Tony Gwynn/25 20.00 50.00
2 Johan Santana/25 15.00 40.00
3 Orel Hershiser/25 10.00 25.00
5 Don Mattingly/25 40.00 80.00
8 Victor Martinez/25 10.00 25.00

2005 Donruss Signature Stats Autograph Material Bat

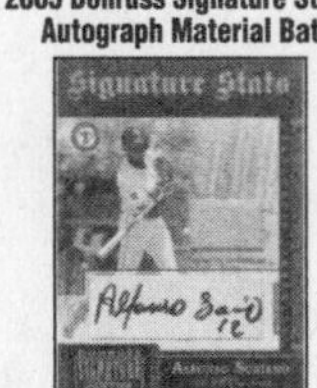

*AU BAT T4: .3X TO .8X AU T3
*AU BAT T3: .25X TO .6X AU T1
RANDOM INSERTS IN PACKS
TIER 1 QTY B/WN 1-50 COPIES PER
TIER 3 QTY B/WN 101-250 COPIES PER
TIER 4 QTY B/WN 251-800 COPIES PER
CARDS ARE NOT SERIAL-NUMBERED
PRINT RUN INFO PROVIDED BY DONRUSS
NO PRICING ON QTY OF 15
5 Don Mattingly T1/25 * 40.00 80.00

2005 Donruss Signature Stats Autograph Material Jersey

STATED ODDS 1:238
TIER 1 QTY B/WN 1-50 COPIES PER
TIER 2 QTY B/WN 51-100 COPIES PER
CARDS ARE NOT SERIAL-NUMBERED
PRINT RUN INFO PROVIDED BY DONRUSS
NO PRICING ON QTY OF 17 OR LESS
1 Tony Gwynn T1/25 * 20.00 50.00
2 Johan Santana T2/100 * 12.50 30.00

3 Orel Hershiser T1/25 * 10.00 25.00
8 Victor Martinez T1/25 * 10.00 25.00

2005 Donruss Signature Stats Autograph Material Combo

*AU COM T1: .75X TO 2X AU T3
STATED ODDS 1:186
TIER 1 QTY B/WN 1-50 COPIES PER
TIER 3 QTY B/WN 101-250 COPIES PER
CARDS ARE NOT SERIAL-NUMBERED
PRINT RUN INFO PROVIDED BY DONRUSS
NO PRICING ON QTY OF 14 OR LESS
1 T.Gwynn Jsy-Pants T3 15.00 40.00

2008 Donruss Sports Legends

This set was released on December 10, 2008. The base set consists of 144 cards and features cards of players from various sports.

COMPLETE SET (144) 40.00 100.00
1 Ted Williams 1.25 3.00
5 Willie Mays 1.25 3.00
10 Hank Aaron 1.25 3.00
15 Nolan Ryan 1.25 3.00
20 Stan Musial .75 2.00
30 Satchel Paige .60 1.50
35 Don Mattingly 1.25 3.00
40 Bob Gibson .50 1.25
45 Roberto Clemente 1.25 3.00
50 Joe Jackson 1.25 3.00
60 Yogi Berra .60 1.50
63 Pete Rose 1.25 3.00
65 Bob Feller .50 1.25
70 Brooks Robinson .50 1.25
75 Cal Ripken Jr. 2.00 5.00
80 Carl Yastrzemski .75 2.00
85 Carlton Fisk .50 1.25
90 Duke Snider .50 1.25
95 Eddie Murray .60 1.50
100 Frank Robinson .40 1.00
105 Jim Palmer .40 1.00
110 Johnny Bench .60 1.50
115 Juan Marichal .50 1.25
120 Mike Schmidt 1.00 2.50
122 Whitey Ford .50 1.25
125 Paul Molitor .60 1.50
128 Tony Gwynn .60 1.50
130 Reggie Jackson .60 1.50
135 Ryne Sandberg 1.00 2.50
140 Nolan Ryan 1.25 3.00
143 Willie McCovey .50 1.25
145 Al Kaline .60 1.50
150 Pete Rose 1.25 3.00

2008 Donruss Sports Legends Mirror Blue

*BLUE/100: 2X TO 5X BASIC CARDS
STATED PRINT RUN 100 SER.#'d SETS

2008 Donruss Sports Legends Mirror Emerald

UNPRICED MIRROR EMERALD PRINT RUN 5

2008 Donruss Sports Legends Mirror Gold

*GOLD/25: 3X TO 8X BASIC CARDS
STATED PRINT RUN 25 SER.#'d SETS

2008 Donruss Sports Legends Mirror Red

*RED/250: 1.5X TO 4X BASIC CARDS
STATED PRINT RUN 250 SER.#'d SETS

2008 Donruss Sports Legends Mirror Black

UNPRICED MIRROR BLACK PRINT RUN 1

2008 Donruss Sports Legends Champions

SILVER PRINT RUN 1000 SER.#'d SETS
*GOLD/100: .6X TO 1.5X SILVER/1000
GOLD PRINT RUN 100 SER.#'d SETS
3 Whitey Ford 1.25 3.00
6 Bob Gibson 1.25 3.00
9 Pete Rose 3.00 8.00
11 Reggie Jackson 1.50 4.00
14 Don Larsen 1.00 2.50

2008 Donruss Sports Legends Champions Materials

STATED PRINT RUN 10-250
3 Whitey Ford Jsy/10
6 Bob Gibson Jsy/10
9 Pete Rose Jsy/25
11 Reggie Jackson Jsy/150 5.00 12.00

2008 Donruss Sports Legends Champions Signatures

STATED PRINT RUN 1-100
SERIAL #'d UNDER 25 NOT PRICED
3 Whitey Ford/25 25.00 50.00
6 Bob Gibson/25 12.00 30.00
9 Pete Rose/25 75.00 135.00
11 Reggie Jackson/10
14 Don Larsen/9

2008 Donruss Sports Legends College Heroes

SILVER PRINT RUN 1000 SER.#'d SETS
*GOLD/100: .6X TO 1.5X SILVER/1000
GOLD PRINT RUN 100 SER.#'d SETS
5 Gordon Beckham 2.00 5.00
8 Buster Posey 2.50 6.00

2008 Donruss Sports Legends College Heroes Materials

STATED PRINT RUN 50-250
5 Gordon Beckham Jsy/50 5.00 12.00
8 Buster Posey Jsy/50 5.00 12.00

2008 Donruss Sports Legends College Heroes Signatures

STATED PRINT RUN 25-100
5 Gordon Beckham/100 20.00 40.00
8 Buster Posey/50 40.00 80.00

2008 Donruss Sports Legends Collegiate Legends Patch Autographs

STATED PRINT RUN 25-250
1 Tom Seaver/50 30.00 60.00
2 Reggie Jackson/51 30.00 60.00
3 Robin Roberts/48

2008 Donruss Sports Legends Legends of the Game Combos

STATED PRINT RUN 25-100
UNPRICED PRIME PRINT RUN 1-10
2 Pete Rose Jsy 150.00 250.00
Joe Jackson Bat
5 Dan Fouts Jsy 12.00 30.00
Tony Gwynn Jsy
6 Ted Williams Jsy 30.00 60.00
Larry Bird Jsy/25
7 Nolan Ryan Jsy 20.00 50.00
Troy Aikman Jsy
9 Hank Aaron Bat 8.00 20.00
Dominique Wilkins Jsy
11 Nolan Ryan Jsy 12.00 30.00
Earl Campbell Jsy
12 Willie Mays Jsy 30.00 60.00
Joe Montana Jsy/50
15 Cal Ripken Jr. Bat 25.00 50.00
Raymond Berry Jsy

2008 Donruss Sports Legends Materials Mirror Blue

*MIRROR BLUE: .5X TO 1.2X MIRROR RED
MIRROR BLUE PRINT RUN 5-250
SERIAL #'d UNDER 15 NOT PRICED
30 Satchel Paige/25 15.00 40.00
35 Don Mattingly Jsy/25 12.00 30.00
50 Joe Jackson/25 125.00 250.00
85 Carlton Fisk Jsy/50 6.00 15.00
95 Eddie Murray/25 8.00 20.00
122 Whitey Ford/25 8.00 20.00
143 Willie McCovey/25 8.00 20.00

2008 Donruss Sports Legends Materials Mirror Gold

*GOLD/25: .8X TO 2X MIRROR RED
GOLD PRINT RUN 1-25 SER.#'d SETS
SERIAL #'d UNDER 20 NOT PRICED
5 Willie Mays/10
30 Satchel Paige/10
35 Don Mattingly/10
40 Bob Gibson/10
60 Yogi Berra/10
70 Brooks Robinson/25 8.00 20.00
80 Carl Yastrzemski/10
85 Carlton Fisk/25 10.00 25.00
95 Eddie Murray/10
105 Jim Palmer/10
110 Johnny Bench/10
115 Juan Marichal/10
122 Whitey Ford/10
135 Ryne Sandberg/10
143 Willie McCovey/10

2008 Donruss Sports Legends Materials Mirror Red

MIRROR RED PRINT RUN 10-500
SERIAL #'d UNDER 25 NOT PRICED
*GOLD/25: .8X TO 2X MIRROR RED
UNPRICED MIRROR EMERALD PRINT RUN 1-5
UNPRICED MIRROR BLACK PRINT RUN 1
1 Ted Williams Bat/100 12.00 30.00
10 Hank Aaron Bat/100 10.00 25.00
15 Nolan Ryan Jsy/250 8.00 20.00
45 Roberto Clemente Bat/250 10.00 25.00
50 Joe Jackson Bat/50 75.00 150.00
63 Pete Rose Jsy/250 12.00 30.00
75 Cal Ripken Jr. Jsy/100 12.00 30.00
100 Frank Robinson Jsy/100 3.00 8.00
120 Mike Schmidt Bat/250 6.00 15.00
125 Paul Molitor Jsy/50 5.00 12.00
128 Tony Gwynn Jsy/500 4.00 10.00
130 Reggie Jackson Bat/250 5.00 12.00
140 Nolan Ryan Jsy/100 8.00 20.00
150 Pete Rose Jsy/250 12.00 30.00

2008 Donruss Sports Legends Museum Collection

SILVER PRINT RUN 1000 SER.#'d SETS
*GOLD/100: .6X TO 1.5X SILVER/1000
GOLD PRINT RUN 100 SER.#'d SETS
1 Hank Aaron 3.00 8.00
5 Joe Jackson 3.00 8.00
7 Don Drysdale 1.25 3.00
11 Ted Williams 3.00 8.00
12 Cal Ripken Jr. 5.00 12.00
13 Satchel Paige 1.50 4.00
17 Willie Mays 3.00 8.00
21 Casey Stengel 1.25 3.00
22 Eddie Mathews 1.50 4.00
25 Pete Rose 3.00 8.00

2008 Donruss Sports Legends Museum Collection Materials

STATED PRINT RUN 25-250
*PRIME/25: .6X TO 1.5X BASIC MATERIAL
PRIME PRINT RUN 1-25
SERIAL #'d UNDER 25 NOT PRICED
1 Hank Aaron/100 10.00 25.00
5 Joe Jackson/100 75.00 150.00
7 Don Drysdale/50 5.00 12.00
11 Ted Williams/250 15.00 40.00
12 Cal Ripken Jr./100 15.00 40.00
13 Satchel Paige/50 15.00 40.00
17 Willie Mays/25 12.00 30.00
21 Casey Stengel/100 4.00 10.00
22 Eddie Mathews/25 8.00 20.00
25 Pete Rose/250 12.00 30.00

2008 Donruss Sports Legends Museum Collection Signatures
STATED PRINT RUN 1-250
SERIAL #'d UNDER 25 NOT PRICED
1 Hank Aaron/10
12 Cal Ripken Jr./8
17 Willie Mays/25 90.00 150.00
25 Pete Rose/25 75.00 135.00

2008 Donruss Sports Legends Museum Collection Signatures Materials
STATED PRINT RUN 1-50
SERIAL #'d UNDER 25 NOT PRICED
1 Hank Aaron/5
12 Cal Ripken Jr./5
17 Willie Mays/10
25 Pete Rose/10

2008 Donruss Sports Legends Museum Curator Collection Materials
STATED PRINT RUN 10-100
*PRIME/25: .6X TO 1.5X BASIC MATERIAL
PRIME PRINT RUN 1-25
SERIAL #'d UNDER 25 NOT PRICED
1 Hank Aaron/10
5 Joe Jackson/50 125.00 250.00
7 Don Drysdale/25 6.00 15.00
11 Ted Williams/25 25.00 60.00
12 Cal Ripken Jr./25 25.00 60.00
13 Satchel Paige/25 20.00 50.00
17 Willie Mays/10
21 Casey Stengel/25 6.00 15.00
22 Eddie Mathews/100 5.00 12.00
25 Pete Rose/100 15.00 40.00

2008 Donruss Sports Legends Museum Curator Collection Signatures Materials
STATED PRINT RUN 1-25
SERIAL #'d UNDER 25 NOT PRICED
1 Hank Aaron
12 Cal Ripken Jr.
17 Willie Mays/5
25 Pete Rose/5

2008 Donruss Sports Legends Signature Connection Combos
STATED PRINT RUN 25-100
2 Cal Ripken Jr. 150.00 250.00
John Riggins
3 Dan Fouts 60.00 100.00
Tony Gwynn
4 Nolan Ryan 100.00 175.00
Troy Aikman
7 Bob Feller 40.00 80.00
Jim Brown

2008 Donruss Sports Legends Signature Connection Triples
STATED PRINT RUN 25-250
3 Lynette Woodard 30.00 60.00
Marques Haynes
Bob Gibson/50

2008 Donruss Sports Legends Signatures Mirror Blue
MIRROR BLUE PRINT RUN 2-250
SERIAL #'d UNDER 10 NOT PRICED
UNPRICED MIRROR EMERALD PRINT RUN 1-5
UNPRICED MIRROR BLACK PRINT RUN 1
5 Willie Mays/25 90.00 150.00
10 Hank Aaron/25 125.00 200.00
15 Nolan Ryan/25 40.00 80.00
20 Stan Musial/25 30.00 60.00
35 Don Mattingly/25 30.00 60.00
40 Bob Gibson/25 12.00 30.00
60 Yogi Berra/25 30.00 60.00
63 Pete Rose/50 75.00 125.00
65 Bob Feller/50 12.00 30.00
70 Brooks Robinson/25 15.00 40.00
75 Cal Ripken Jr./25 60.00 120.00
80 Carl Yastrzemski/25 15.00 40.00
85 Carlton Fisk/25 15.00 40.00
90 Duke Snider/25 15.00 40.00
95 Eddie Murray/25 15.00 40.00
100 Frank Robinson/25 15.00 40.00
105 Jim Palmer/25 10.00 25.00
110 Johnny Bench/25 40.00 80.00
115 Juan Marichal/25 15.00 40.00
120 Mike Schmidt/25 15.00 40.00
122 Whitey Ford/25 25.00 50.00
125 Paul Molitor/25 10.00 25.00
128 Tony Gwynn/25 15.00 40.00
130 Reggie Jackson/25 15.00 40.00
135 Ryne Sandberg/25 30.00 60.00
140 Nolan Ryan/25 40.00 80.00
143 Willie McCovey/25 25.00 50.00
145 Al Kaline/25 15.00 40.00
150 Pete Rose/50 75.00 125.00

2008 Donruss Sports Legends Signatures Mirror Gold
MIRROR GOLD PRINT RUN 4-25
SERIAL #'d UNDER 10 NOT PRICED
5 Willie Mays/10 100.00 175.00
10 Hank Aaron/10 175.00 300.00
15 Nolan Ryan/10 50.00 100.00
20 Stan Musial/10 30.00 80.00
35 Don Mattingly/10 30.00 80.00
40 Bob Gibson/10 15.00 40.00
60 Yogi Berra/10 30.00 80.00
63 Pete Rose/25 75.00 135.00
65 Bob Feller/25 15.00 40.00
70 Brooks Robinson/10 20.00 50.00
75 Cal Ripken Jr./10 125.00 200.00
80 Carl Yastrzemski/10 20.00 50.00
85 Carlton Fisk/10 20.00 50.00
90 Duke Snider/10 20.00 50.00
95 Eddie Murray/10 20.00 50.00
100 Frank Robinson/10 20.00 50.00
105 Jim Palmer/10 12.00 30.00
110 Johnny Bench/10 50.00 100.00
115 Juan Marichal/10 20.00 50.00
120 Mike Schmidt/10 20.00 50.00
122 Whitey Ford/10 25.00 60.00
125 Paul Molitor/10 12.00 30.00
128 Tony Gwynn/10 20.00 50.00
130 Reggie Jackson/10 20.00 50.00
135 Ryne Sandberg/10 30.00 80.00
140 Nolan Ryan/10 50.00 100.00
143 Willie McCovey/10 25.00 60.00
145 Al Kaline/25 20.00 50.00
150 Pete Rose/25 75.00 135.00

2008 Donruss Sports Legends Signatures Mirror Red
*MIRROR RED: .3X TO .8X MIRROR BLUE
MIRROR RED PRINT RUN 25-1370
40 Bob Gibson/55 10.00 25.00
65 Bob Feller/100 10.00 25.00
100 Frank Robinson/25 15.00 40.00
122 Whitey Ford/50 15.00 40.00
123 Paul Molitor/30 8.00 20.00
145 Al Kaline/100 12.00 30.00

2008 Donruss Threads
This set was released on October 22, 2008. The base set consists of 184 cards.

COMP.SET w/o AU's (100) 10.00 25.00
COMMON CARD (1-50) .15 .40
COMMON CARD (51-100) .30 .75
COMMON AUTO (101-184) 3.00 8.00
AUTOS RANDOMLY INSERTED
AU PRINT RUN B/WN 99-199 COPIES
EXCHANGE DEADLINE 4/22/2010
1 Hank Aaron .75 2.00
2 Dale Murphy .25 .60
3 Brooks Robinson .25 .60
4 Cal Ripken Jr. 1.50 4.00
5 Eddie Murray .40 1.00
6 Carl Yastrzemski .60 1.50
7 Carlton Fisk .25 .60
8 Wade Boggs .25 .60
9 Joe Jackson 1.25 3.00
10 Johnny Pesky .15 .40
11 Jim Rice .15 .40
12 Fred Lynn .15 .40
13 Duke Snider .25 .60
14 Carl Erskine .15 .40
15 Ernie Banks .40 1.00
16 Ryne Sandberg .75 2.00
17 Don Sutton .15 .40
18 Luis Aparicio .15 .40
19 Tom Seaver .25 .60
20 Tony Perez .25 .60
21 Pete Rose 1.25 3.00
22 Bob Feller .25 .60
23 Al Kaline .40 1.00
24 Mark Fidrych .15 .40
25 Kirk Gibson .15 .40
26 Alan Trammell .15 .40
27 George Brett .75 2.00
28 Steve Garvey .15 .40
29 Robin Yount .40 1.00
30 Harmon Killebrew .40 1.00
31 Paul Molitor .40 1.00
32 Gary Carter .25 .60
34 Don Larsen .15 .40
35 Don Mattingly .75 2.00
36 Reggie Jackson .25 .60
37 Tim Raines .15 .40
38 Mike Schmidt .60 1.50
39 Steve Carlton .25 .60
40 Tony Gwynn .40 1.00
41 Juan Marichal .25 .60
42 Willie Mays .75 2.00
43 Willie McCovey .25 .60
44 Will Clark .25 .60
45 Bob Gibson .25 .60
46 Dennis Eckersley .15 .40
47 Red Schoendienst .15 .40
48 Stan Musial .60 1.50
49 Nolan Ryan 1.00 2.50
50 Frank Howard .15 .40
51 Austin Romine .50 1.25
52 Chris Carter .50 1.25
53 Jordan Schafer .60 1.50
54 Michael Burgess .50 1.25
55 John Raynor .30 .75
56 Lars Anderson .75 2.00
57 Josh Reddick .30 .75
58 Luis Esposito .30 .75
59 Aneury Rodriguez .75 2.00
60 Nick Weglarz .30 .75
61 Hector Gomez .30 .75
62 Jon Still .30 .75
63 Brandon Hamilton .50 1.25
64 Bud Norris .30 .75
65 Danny Duffy .50 1.25
66 Jovan Rosa .50 1.25
67 Sean O'Sullivan .30 .75
68 Edilio Colina .30 .75
69 Ryan Patterson .30 .75
70 Brent Brewer .30 .75
71 David Bromberg .30 .75
72 Bryan Petersen .50 1.25
73 Lucas Duda .50 1.25
74 Ruben Tejada .50 1.25
75 Andrew Lambo .75 2.00
76 Jeff Corsaletti .30 .75
77 Alexis Oliveras .30 .75
78 Fernando Garcia .30 .75
79 Jairo Heredia .30 .75
80 Jesus Montero .75 2.00
81 Jose Tabata .30 .75
82 Carlos Gonzalez .50 1.25
83 Patrick Ryan .30 .75
84 Sean Doolittle .30 .75
85 Carlos Carrasco .50 1.25
86 Luis Cruz .50 1.25
87 Yefri Carvajal .30 .75
88 Stolmy Pimentel .30 .75
89 Wilber Bucardo .30 .75
90 Angel Villalona .75 2.00
91 Madison Bumgarner 1.00 2.50
92 Danny Carroll .30 .75
93 Juan Ramirez .30 .75
94 Lou Marson .30 .75
95 Josh Vitters .50 1.25
96 Desmond Jennings .50 1.25
97 Abraham Almonte .30 .75
98 Mat Gamel .50 1.25
99 Andrew LeFave .30 .75
100 Elvis Andrus .50 1.25
101 Emilio Bonifacio AU/1874 5.00 12.00
102 Wilin Rosario AU/999 4.00 10.00
103 Carlos Peguero AU/465 8.00 20.00
104 Tyler Flowers AU/999 10.00 25.00
105 Tyler Henson AU/999 4.00 10.00
106 Nevin Griffith AU/999 3.00 8.00
107 Caleb Gindl AU/465 5.00 12.00
108 Jose Ceda AU/999 3.00 8.00
109 Brandon Waring AU/465 6.00 15.00
110 Neftali Soto AU/500 10.00 25.00
111 Ryan Miller AU/999 3.00 8.00
112 Jack Egbert AU/999 3.00 8.00
113 Juan Silverio AU/999 5.00 12.00
114 Jhoulys Chacin AU/1999 4.00 10.00
115 Charlie Furbush AU/465 4.00 10.00
116 Hector Correa AU/999 3.00 8.00
117 Brad James AU/1999 3.00 8.00
118 Keaton Hayenga AU/999 4.00 10.00
120 Brent Fisher AU/1058 3.00 8.00
121 Juan Francisco AU/999 8.00 20.00
122 Andrew Romine AU/875 3.00 8.00
123 Mason Tobin AU/999 3.00 8.00
124 Anel De Los Santos AU/999 3.00 8.00
125 Andrew Walker AU/99 EXCH 6.00 15.00
126 Alfredo Silverio AU/999 3.00 8.00
127 Mario Martinez AU/1375 5.00 12.00
128 Taylor Green AU/999 4.00 10.00
129 D.J. Jones AU/399 4.00 10.00
130 Wilson Ramos AU/999 8.00 20.00
131 Trevor Reckling AU/875 4.00 10.00
132 Engel Beltre AU/465 8.00 20.00
133 Scott Moviel AU/1000 4.00 10.00
134 Josh Tomlin AU/875 6.00 15.00
135 Dominic Brown AU/999 30.00 60.00
136 Neftali Feliz AU/465 8.00 20.00
137 Brian Friday AU/1249 3.00 8.00
138 Drew Miller AU/1999 3.00 8.00
139 Steve Garrison AU/1999 3.00 8.00
140 Mike McBryde AU/950 3.00 8.00
141 Brian Duensing AU/575 3.00 8.00
142 Greg Halman AU/465 4.00 10.00
143 Jharmidy De Jesus AU/465 8.00 20.00
144 Mike Stanton AU/465 40.00 80.00
145 Wilmer Flores AU/99 EXCH 50.00 100.00
146 Heath Rollins AU/999 3.00 8.00
147 Alex Cobb AU/999 3.00 8.00
148 Omar Poveda AU/999 3.00 8.00
149 Yohermyn Chavez AU/999 4.00 10.00
150 Gerardo Parra AU/999 4.00 10.00
151 Clayton Conner AU/240 4.00 10.00
152 Tyler Kolodny AU/280 6.00 15.00
153 Ryan Kalish AU/240 10.00 25.00
154 Rick Porcello AU/240 30.00 60.00
155 Shane Peterson AU/240 5.00 12.00
156 Tyler Ladendorf AU/269 4.00 10.00
157 Josh Lindblom AU/240 5.00 12.00
158 Tyler Chatwood AU/240 5.00 12.00
159 Logan Morrison AU/240 10.00 25.00
160 Collin DeLome AU/240 6.00 15.00
161 Daniel Cortes AU/240 6.00 15.00
162 Chris Johnson AU/280 EXCH 20.00 50.00
163 Matt Mitchell AU/240 5.00 12.00
164 Denny Almonte AU/280 6.00 15.00
165 Greg Veloz AU/250 8.00 20.00
166 R. J. Seidel AU/240 5.00 12.00
167 Xavier Avery AU/250 8.00 20.00
168 Quincy Latimore AU/240 6.00 15.00
169 Aaron Shafer AU/280 EXCH 5.00 12.00
170 Rayner Contreras AU/270 5.00 12.00
171 Waldis Joaquin AU/280 5.00 12.00
172 Jorge Bucardo AU/240 5.00 12.00
173 James Darnell AU/280 8.00 20.00
174 Logan Forsythe AU/239 6.00 15.00
175 Kyle Gibson AU/240 5.00 12.00
176 Ike Davis AU/250 30.00 60.00
177 Max Ramirez AU/244 6.00 15.00
178 Chris Davis AU/250 12.50 30.00
180 Jay Austin AU/240 5.00 12.00
181 Brad Holt AU/240 4.00 10.00
182 Carlos Gutierrez AU/270 6.00 15.00
183 Christian Friedrich AU/270 EXCH 6.00 15.00
184 Zach Collier AU/280 10.00 25.00
186 Robert Hernandez AU/269 6.00 15.00
187 Christian Marrero AU/280 6.00 15.00

2008 Donruss Threads Century Proof Gold
*GOLD 1-50: 3X TO 8X BASIC
*GOLD 51-100: 3X TO 8X BASIC
*GOLD 101-150: 1.2X TO 3X GREEN
RANDOM INSERTS IN PACKS
STATED PRINT RUN 50 SER.#'d SETS
144 Mike Stanton 30.00 60.00

2008 Donruss Threads Century Proof Green
*GRN 1-50: 1X TO 2.5X BASIC
*GRN 51-100: 1X TO 2.5X BASIC
RANDOM INSERTS IN PACKS
STATED PRINT RUN 250 SER.#'d SETS
101 Emilio Bonifacio 1.50 4.00
102 Wilin Rosario 1.00 2.50
103 Carlos Peguero .75 2.00
104 Tyler Flowers 1.00 2.50
105 Tyler Henson 1.00 2.50
106 Nevin Griffith .75 2.00
107 Caleb Gindl .75 2.00
108 Jose Ceda .75 2.00
109 Brandon Waring 2.00 5.00
110 Neftali Soto 2.00 5.00
111 Ryan Miller .75 2.00
112 Jack Egbert .75 2.00
113 Juan Silverio 1.25 3.00
114 Jhoulys Chacin 2.50 6.00
115 Charlie Furbush 1.00 2.50
116 Hector Correa .75 2.00
117 Brad James .75 2.00
118 Devon Torrence
119 Keaton Hayenga 1.00 2.50
120 Brent Fisher .75 2.00
121 Juan Francisco 1.25 3.00
122 Andrew Romine .75 2.00
123 Mason Tobin .75 2.00
124 Anel De Los Santos .75 2.00
125 Andrew Walker .75 2.00
126 Alfredo Silverio .75 2.00
127 Mario Martinez 1.50 4.00
128 Taylor Green 1.00 2.50
129 D.J. Jones 1.00 2.50
130 Wilson Ramos 1.00 2.50
131 Trevor Reckling 1.00 2.50
132 Engel Beltre 1.00 2.50
133 Scott Moviel 1.00 2.50
134 Josh Tomlin .75 2.00
135 Dominic Brown 1.50 4.00
136 Neftali Feliz 3.00 8.00
137 Brian Friday .75 2.00
138 Drew Miller .75 2.00
139 Steve Garrison .75 2.00
140 Mike McBryde .75 2.00
141 Brian Duensing .75 2.00
142 Greg Halman 2.00 5.00
143 Jharmidy De Jesus 2.00 5.00
144 Mike Stanton 12.50 30.00
145 Wilmer Flores 3.00 8.00
146 Heath Rollins .75 2.00
147 Alex Cobb .75 2.00
148 Omar Poveda .75 2.00
149 Yohermyn Chavez 1.00 2.50
150 Gerardo Parra .75 2.00

2008 Donruss Threads Century Proof Platinum
RANDOM INSERTS IN PACKS
STATED PRINT RUN 25 SER.#'d SETS
NO PRICING DUE TO SCARCITY

2008 Donruss Threads Century Proof Silver
*SILVER 1-50: 1.5X TO 4X BASIC
*SILVER 51-100: 1.5X TO 4X BASIC
*SILVER 101-150: .6X TO 1.5X GREEN
RANDOM INSERTS IN PACKS
STATED PRINT RUN 100 SER.#'d SETS
144 Mike Stanton 15.00 40.00

2008 Donruss Threads Baseball Americana
RANDOM INSERTS IN PACKS
STATED PRINT RUN 500 SER.#'d SETS
3 Don Mattingly 2.50 6.00
4 Eddie Murray 1.25 3.00
5 Ryne Sandberg 2.00 5.00
6 Pete Rose 4.00 10.00
7 Cal Ripken Jr. 4.00 10.00
8 Ernie Banks 2.00 5.00
9 George Brett 2.50 6.00
10 Mike Schmidt 2.00 5.00
11 Johnny Bench 1.50 4.00
12 Carlton Fisk 1.50 4.00
13 Tony Gwynn 1.50 4.00
14 Hank Aaron 2.00 5.00
15 Willie Mays 2.00 5.00
16 Joe Jackson 4.00 10.00
17 Ted Williams 2.00 5.00
18 Stan Musial 2.00 5.00
19 Nolan Ryan 3.00 8.00
20 Bob Feller 1.50 4.00
41 Bob Gibson 1.50 4.00
42 Dennis Eckersley 1.50 4.00
43 Carl Yastrzemski 1.50 4.00
44 Don Drysdale 1.50 4.00
45 Satchel Paige 2.00 5.00
46 Casey Stengel 1.50 4.00
47 Eddie Mathews 1.50 4.00
48 Early Wynn 1.50 4.00

2008 Donruss Threads Baseball Americana Materials
RANDOM INSERTS IN PACKS
PRINT RUNS B/WN 1-500 PER
NO PRICING ON QTY 25 OR LESS
1 Bud Abbott/500 6.00 15.00
2 Lou Costello/250 8.00 20.00
3 Don Mattingly/100 6.00 15.00
4 Eddie Murray/150 5.00 12.00
5 Ryne Sandberg/25
6 Pete Rose/250 20.00 50.00
7 Cal Ripken Jr./100 20.00 50.00
8 Ernie Banks/1
9 George Brett/75 6.00 15.00
10 Mike Schmidt/100 6.00 15.00
11 Johnny Bench/50 12.50 30.00
12 Carlton Fisk/75 4.00 10.00
13 Tony Gwynn/250 3.00 8.00
14 Hank Aaron/5
15 Willie Mays/15
17 Ted Williams/100 20.00 50.00
18 Stan Musial/25
19 Nolan Ryan/100 10.00 25.00
20 Bob Feller/5
41 Bob Gibson/100 3.00 8.00
42 Dennis Eckersley/100 4.00 10.00
43 Carl Yastrzemski/100 3.00 8.00
44 Don Drysdale/100 5.00 12.00
45 Satchel Paige/100 15.00 40.00
46 Casey Stengel/500 6.00 15.00
47 Eddie Mathews/100 8.00 20.00
48 Early Wynn/100 4.00 10.00

2008 Donruss Threads Baseball Americana Materials Position
RANDOM INSERTS IN PACKS
PRINT RUNS B/WN 1-250 PER
NO PRICING ON QTY 25 OR LESS
1 Bud Abbott/200 6.00 15.00
2 Lou Costello/100 8.00 20.00
3 Don Mattingly/50 8.00 20.00
4 Eddie Murray/50 6.00 15.00
5 Ryne Sandberg/25
6 Pete Rose/100 20.00 50.00
7 Cal Ripken Jr./25
8 Ernie Banks/5
9 George Brett/75 6.00 15.00
10 Mike Schmidt/100 6.00 15.00
11 Johnny Bench/25
12 Carlton Fisk/75 4.00 10.00
13 Tony Gwynn/100 4.00 10.00
14 Hank Aaron/5
15 Willie Mays/100
17 Ted Williams/50 30.00 60.00
18 Stan Musial/25
19 Nolan Ryan/50 12.50 30.00
20 Bob Feller/5
41 Bob Gibson/100 3.00 8.00
42 Dennis Eckersley/100 4.00 10.00
43 Carl Yastrzemski/100 3.00 8.00
44 Don Drysdale/100 5.00 12.00
45 Satchel Paige/100 15.00 40.00
46 Casey Stengel/250 6.00 15.00
47 Eddie Mathews/100 8.00 20.00
48 Early Wynn/100 4.00 10.00

2008 Donruss Threads Baseball Americana Signatures Materials
RANDOM INSERTS IN PACKS
PRINT RUNS B/WN 3-100 COPIES
NO PRICING ON QTY 25 OR LESS
3 Don Mattingly/25
4 Eddie Murray/5
5 Ryne Sandberg/5
6 Pete Rose/50 100.00 200.00
7 Cal Ripken Jr./25
8 Ernie Banks/3
9 George Brett/5
10 Mike Schmidt/25
11 Johnny Bench/50 30.00 60.00
12 Carlton Fisk/50 10.00 25.00
13 Tony Gwynn/50 15.00 40.00
14 Hank Aaron/5
15 Willie Mays/25
18 Stan Musial/25
19 Nolan Ryan/25
20 Bob Feller/10
41 Bob Gibson/50 12.50 30.00
42 Dennis Eckersley/25
43 Carl Yastrzemski/25

2008 Donruss Threads Bats
RANDOM INSERTS IN PACKS
PRINT RUNS B/WN 1-500 PER
NO PRICING ON QTY 20 OR LESS
1 Hank Aaron/500 10.00 25.00
9 Joe Jackson/100 100.00 200.00
25 Kirk Gibson/10
28 Steve Garvey/20
31 Paul Molitor/1
35 Don Mattingly/250 5.00 12.00
36 Reggie Jackson/500 4.00 10.00
38 Mike Schmidt/500 5.00 12.00
39 Steve Carlton/3
42 Willie Mays/50 10.00 25.00
52 Chris Carter/500 3.00 8.00
53 Jordan Schafer/500 3.00 8.00
54 Michael Burgess/500 3.00 8.00
70 Brent Brewer/500 3.00 8.00
81 Jose Tabata/500 3.00 8.00
84 Sean Doolittle/500 3.00 8.00
92 Danny Carroll/500 3.00 8.00
96 Desmond Jennings/500 4.00 10.00
128 Taylor Green/500 3.00 8.00
142 Greg Halman/500 3.00 8.00
143 Jharmidy De Jesus/500 3.00 8.00

2008 Donruss Threads Century Collection Materials
RANDOM INSERTS IN PACKS
PRINT RUNS B/WN 10-100 PER
NO MAYS PRICING AVAILABLE
1 Cal Ripken Jr./100 12.50 30.00
2 Ryne Sandberg/75 6.00 15.00
3 Pete Rose/100 20.00 50.00
4 Fred Lynn/100 3.00 8.00
5 Tom Seaver/100 3.00 8.00
6 George Brett/50 10.00 25.00
7 Don Mattingly/75 6.00 15.00
8 Mike Schmidt/100 6.00 15.00
9 Tony Gwynn/100 4.00 10.00
10 Willie Mays/10
11 Nolan Ryan/100 8.00 20.00
12 Dale Murphy/100 6.00 15.00
13 Pete Rose/100 20.00 50.00
15 Dave Winfield/100 3.00 8.00
16 Paul Molitor/100 3.00 8.00
17 Barry Larkin/100 4.00 10.00
18 Kirk Gibson/100 5.00 12.00
19 Pete Rose/100 20.00 50.00
20 Steve Garvey/100 5.00 12.00
21 Wade Boggs/100 3.00 8.00
22 Ted Williams/100 15.00 40.00
23 Steve Carlton/100 3.00 8.00
24 Robin Yount/100 4.00 10.00
25 Luis Aparicio/100 3.00 8.00
26 Jim Rice/100 3.00 8.00
27 Jim Palmer/100 3.00 8.00
28 Harmon Killebrew/100 5.00 12.00
29 Gaylord Perry/100 3.00 8.00
30 Gary Carter/100 4.00 10.00
31 Eddie Murray/50 4.00 10.00
32 Don Drysdale/100 4.00 10.00
33 Satchel Paige/100 15.00 40.00
34 Casey Stengel/100 6.00 15.00
35 Eddie Mathews/100 8.00 20.00
36 Dennis Eckersley/100 3.00 8.00
37 Carlton Fisk/100 4.00 10.00
38 Carl Yastrzemski/100 4.00 10.00
39 Early Wynn/100 4.00 10.00
40 Lefty Grove/50 75.00 150.00

2008 Donruss Threads Century Collection Materials Prime
RANDOM INSERTS IN PACKS
PRINT RUNS B/WN 3-10 COPIES PER
NO PRICING DUE TO SCARCITY

2008 Donruss Threads Century Legends
RANDOM INSERTS IN PACKS
*CENTURY PROOF: .75X TO 2X BASIC
CENTRUY RANDOMLY INSERTED
CENTURY PRINT RUN 100 SER.#'d SETS
1 Stan Musial 2.00 5.00
2 Willie Mays 2.00 5.00
3 Hank Aaron 2.00 5.00
4 Ted Williams 2.00 5.00
5 Whitey Ford .75 2.00
6 Bob Gibson .75 2.00
7 Joe Jackson 3.00 8.00
8 Duke Snider 1.25 3.00
9 Ernie Banks 1.25 3.00
10 Bob Feller .75 2.00
11 Nolan Ryan 2.50 6.00
12 Mike Schmidt 1.50 4.00
13 Carl Yastrzemski 1.25 3.00
14 Pete Rose 3.00 8.00
15 Harmon Killebrew 1.25 3.00

2008 Donruss Threads Century Legends Materials
RANDOM INSERTS IN PACKS
PRINT RUNS B/WN 1-100 COPIES
NO PRICING ON QTY 25 OR LESS
1 Stan Musial/25
2 Willie Mays/10
4 Ted Williams/50 20.00 50.00
5 Whitey Ford/1
6 Bob Gibson/50 5.00 12.00
9 Ernie Banks/10
10 Bob Feller/10
11 Nolan Ryan/100 6.00 15.00
12 Mike Schmidt/100 6.00 15.00
13 Carl Yastrzemski/100 5.00 12.00
14 Pete Rose/100 20.00 50.00
15 Harmon Killebrew/100 5.00 12.00

2008 Donruss Threads Century Legends Materials Prime
RANDOM INSERTS IN PACKS
PRINT RUNS B/WN 1-25 COPIES PER
NO PRICING DUE TO SCARCITY
1 Stan Musial/1
2 Willie Mays/5
4 Ted Williams/5
5 Whitey Ford/1
6 Bob Gibson/3
9 Ernie Banks/10
11 Nolan Ryan/10
12 Mike Schmidt/25
13 Carl Yastrzemski/1
14 Pete Rose/25
15 Harmon Killebrew/1

2008 Donruss Threads Century Stars Materials
RANDOM INSERTS IN PACKS
PRINT RUNS B/WN 50-100 PER
1 Carlton Fisk/100 4.00 10.00
2 Harmon Killebrew/100 3.00 8.00
3 Ryne Sandberg/50 15.00 40.00
4 Cal Ripken Jr./100 15.00 40.00
5 Mike Schmidt/100 6.00 15.00
6 Tony Gwynn/100 3.00 8.00
7 Pete Rose/100 20.00 50.00
9 Dale Murphy/100 3.00 8.00
10 Steve Carlton/100 3.00 8.00
11 Bob Gibson/100 3.00 8.00
12 Nolan Ryan/100 8.00 20.00
13 Robin Yount/100 3.00 8.00
14 Paul Molitor/100 3.00 8.00
15 Kirk Gibson/50 3.00 8.00

2008 Donruss Threads Century Stars Materials Prime
RANDOM INSERTS IN PACKS
PRINT RUNS B/WN 1-10 COPIES PER
NO PRICING DUE TO SCARCITY

2008 Donruss Threads College Greats
RANDOM INSERTS IN PACKS
1 Tom Seaver 1.50 4.00
2 Reggie Jackson 1.50 4.00
3 Frank Howard 1.00 2.50
4 Dave Winfield 1.00 2.50
5 Paul Molitor 1.00 2.50
6 Barry Larkin 1.00 2.50
7 Kirk Gibson 1.00 2.50
8 Robin Roberts 1.00 2.50
9 Will Clark 1.50 4.00
10 Bob Gibson 1.50 4.00
11 Steve Garvey 1.00 2.50
12 Fred Lynn 1.00 2.50

2008 Donruss Threads College Greats Signatures
RANDOM INSERTS IN PACKS
PRINT RUNS B/WN 5-50 COPIES PER
NO PRICING ON QTY 25 OR LESS
1 Tom Seaver/25
2 Reggie Jackson/25
3 Frank Howard/50 10.00 25.00
4 Dave Winfield/25
5 Paul Molitor/25
6 Barry Larkin/50 30.00 60.00
7 Kirk Gibson/25
8 Robin Roberts/40 10.00 25.00
9 Will Clark/25
10 Bob Gibson/50 12.50 30.00
11 Steve Garvey/20
12 Fred Lynn/50 10.00 25.00

2008 Donruss Threads College Greats Signatures Combos
RANDOM INSERTS IN PACKS
STATED PRINT RUN 25 SER.#'d SETS
NO PRICING DUE TO SCARCITY

2008 Donruss Threads Diamond Kings
RANDOM INSERTS IN PACKS
*GOLD: .6X TO 1.5X BASIC
GOLD RANDOMLY INSERTED
GOLD PRINT RUN 100 SER.#'d SETS
FRM.BLK.RANDOMLY INSERTED
FRM.BLK.PRINT RUN 10 SER.#'d SETS
NO FRM.BLK PRINCING AVAILABLE
*FRM.BLUE: .75X TO 2X BASIC
FRM.BLUE RANDOMLY INSERTS
FRM.BLUE PRINT RUN 50 SER.#'d SETS
FRM.GRN.RANDOMLY INSERTED
FRM.GRN.PRINT RUN 25 SER.#'d SETS
NO FRM.GRN PRINCING AVAILABLE
*FRM.RED: .6X TO 1.5X BASIC
FRM.RED RANDOMLY INSERTS
FRM.RED PRINT RUN 100 SER.#'d SETS
PLAT.RANDOMLY INSERTED
PLAT.PRINT RUN 25 SER.#'d SETS
NO PLAT.PRINCING AVAILABLE
*SILVER: .5X TO 1.2X BASIC
SILVER RANDOMLY INSERTS
SILVER PRINT RUN 250 SER.#'d SETS
1 Jordan Schafer 1.00 2.50
2 Nolan Reimold 1.00 2.50
3 Matt McBride 1.00 2.50
4 Lars Anderson 1.25 3.00
5 Blake Wood 1.00 2.50
6 Josh Vitters 1.00 2.50
7 Chris Valaika 1.00 2.50
8 Mark Melancon 1.00 2.50
9 Drew Stubbs 1.00 2.50
10 Rick Porcello 2.50 6.00
11 Anthony Rizzo 1.00 2.50
12 Jon Jay 1.00 2.50
13 Clay Fuller 1.00 2.50
14 Damon Sublett 1.00 2.50
15 Brett Anderson 1.00 2.50
16 Matt Spencer 1.00 2.50
17 Drew Cumberland 1.00 2.50
18 Tim Alderson 1.00 2.50
19 Madison Bumgarner 1.00 2.50
20 Jess Todd 1.00 2.50
21 Michael Hollimon 1.00 2.50
22 Taylor Teagarden 1.00 2.50
23 Daniel McCutchen 1.00 2.50
24 Trystan Magnuson 1.00 2.50
25 Michael Burgess 1.00 2.50
26 Hank Aaron 2.50 6.00
27 Cal Ripken Jr. 3.00 8.00
28 Jim Palmer 1.00 2.50
29 Bobby Doerr 1.00 2.50
30 Duke Snider 1.25 3.00
31 Rod Carew 1.00 2.50
32 Ernie Banks 1.50 4.00
33 Ryne Sandberg 2.50 6.00
34 Billy Williams 1.00 2.50
35 Fergie Jenkins 1.00 2.50
36 Pete Rose 3.00 8.00
37 George Kell 1.00 2.50
38 George Brett 2.50 6.00
39 Reggie Jackson 1.25 3.00
40 Don Mattingly 2.50 6.00
41 Phil Niekro 1.00 2.50
42 Whitey Ford 1.25 3.00
43 Yogi Berra 1.50 4.00
44 Mike Schmidt 2.00 5.00
45 Tony Gwynn 1.50 4.00
46 Willie Mays 2.50 6.00
47 Gaylord Perry 1.00 2.50
48 Stan Musial 2.00 5.00
49 Lou Brock 1.25 3.00
50 Nolan Ryan 2.50 6.00
51 Joe Jackson 2.50 6.00
52 Gordon Beckham 2.50 6.00
56 Pete Rose 3.00 8.00
57 Rick Porcello 2.50 6.00
58 Nolan Ryan 2.50 6.00

2008 Donruss Threads Diamond Kings Materials
RANDOM INSERTS IN PACKS
PRINT RUNS B/WN 1-250 PER
NO PRICING ON QTY 25 OR LESS
1 Jordan Schafer/250 5.00 12.00
6 Josh Vitters/250 3.00 8.00
8 Mark Melancon/125 3.00 8.00
9 Drew Stubbs/250 3.00 8.00
10 Rick Porcello/250 5.00 12.00
13 Clay Fuller/250 3.00 8.00
14 Damon Sublett/250 5.00 12.00
15 Brett Anderson/250 3.00 8.00
16 Matt Spencer/250 3.00 8.00
17 Drew Cumberland/250 3.00 8.00
18 Tim Alderson/250 3.00 8.00
19 Madison Bumgarner/125 6.00 15.00
20 Jess Todd/250 3.00 8.00
24 Trystan Magnuson/250 3.00 8.00
25 Michael Burgess/250 3.00 8.00
26 Hank Aaron/10
27 Cal Ripken Jr./200 12.50 30.00
28 Jim Palmer/50 5.00 12.00
29 Bobby Doerr/5
31 Rod Carew/5
32 Ernie Banks/1
33 Ryne Sandberg/50 12.50 30.00
36 Pete Rose/250 20.00 50.00
38 George Brett/75 8.00 20.00
39 Reggie Jackson/5
40 Don Mattingly/150 10.00 25.00
42 Whitey Ford/5
43 Yogi Berra/25
44 Mike Schmidt/75 8.00 20.00
45 Tony Gwynn/250 5.00 12.00
46 Willie Mays/50 20.00 50.00
48 Stan Musial/25
49 Lou Brock/100 6.00 15.00
50 Nolan Ryan/50 12.50 30.00
51 Joe Jackson/25
56 Pete Rose/100 20.00 50.00
57 Rick Porcello/250 5.00 12.00
58 Nolan Ryan/50 12.50 30.00

2008 Donruss Threads Diamond Kings Materials Prime
RANDOM INSERTS IN PACKS
PRINT RUNS B/WN 1-25 COPIES PER
NO PRICING DUE TO SCARCITY

2008 Donruss Threads Diamond Kings Signatures
RANDOM INSERTS IN PACKS
PRINT RUNS B/WN 5-500 COPIES PER
NO PRICING ON QTY 25 OR LESS
1 Jordan Schafer/199 15.00 40.00
2 Nolan Reimold/500 8.00 20.00
3 Matt McBride/500 4.00 10.00
4 Lars Anderson/474 8.00 20.00
5 Blake Wood/500 4.00 10.00
6 Josh Vitters/10
7 Chris Valaika/500 5.00 12.00
8 Mark Melancon/238 6.00 15.00
9 Drew Stubbs/465 6.00 15.00
10 Rick Porcello/300 12.50 30.00
11 Anthony Rizzo/500 20.00 50.00
12 Jon Jay/10
14 Damon Sublett/14
15 Brett Anderson/315 4.00 10.00
18 Tim Alderson/215 5.00 12.00
19 Madison Bumgarner/223 10.00 25.00
21 Michael Hollimon/500 4.00 10.00
22 Taylor Teagarden/475 4.00 10.00
23 Daniel McCutchen/500 4.00 10.00
24 Trystan Magnuson/215 4.00 10.00
25 Michael Burgess/182 5.00 12.00
26 Hank Aaron/5
27 Cal Ripken Jr./5
28 Jim Palmer/100 8.00 20.00
29 Bobby Doerr/250 6.00 15.00
30 Duke Snider/50 15.00 40.00
31 Rod Carew/5
32 Ernie Banks/5
33 Ryne Sandberg/5
34 Billy Williams/5
35 Fergie Jenkins/100 8.00 20.00
36 Pete Rose/50 90.00 150.00
37 George Kell/5
38 George Brett/5
39 Reggie Jackson/25
40 Don Mattingly/25
41 Phil Niekro/50 10.00 25.00
42 Whitey Ford/100 20.00 50.00

43 Yogi Berra/5
44 Mike Schmidt/25
45 Tony Gwynn/5
46 Willie Mays/5
47 Gaylord Perry/150 5.00 12.00
48 Stan Musial/25
49 Lou Brock/50 10.00 25.00
50 Nolan Ryan/25
56 Pete Rose/25
57 Rick Porcello/25
58 Nolan Ryan/25

2008 Donruss Threads Diamond Kings Signatures Materials

RANDOM INSERTS IN PACKS
PRINT RUNS B/WN 5-100 COPIES PER
NO PRICING ON MOST DUE TO SCARCITY
10 Rick Porcello/25 40.00 80.00
36 Pete Rose/25 125.00 250.00
49 Lou Brock/100 12.50 30.00
50 Nolan Ryan/25
56 Pete Rose/25 125.00 250.00
57 Rick Porcello/25 40.00 80.00
58 Nolan Ryan/10

2008 Donruss Threads Diamond Kings Signatures Materials Prime

RANDOM INSERTS IN PACKS
PRINT RUNS B/WN 1-10 COPIES PER
NO PRICING DUE TO SCARCITY

2008 Donruss Threads Dynasty

RANDOM INSERTS IN PACKS
*CENTURY PROOF: .75X TO 2X BASIC
CENTRUY RANDOMLY INSERTED
CENTURY PRINT RUN 100 SER.#'d SETS
1 Cal Ripken Jr./Jim Palmer/Eddie Murray 2.50 6.00
2 Johnny Bench/Pete Rose/Joe Morgan 3.00 8.00
3 Juan Marichal/Willie Mays/Willie McCovey 2.00 5.00

2008 Donruss Threads Dynasty Materials

RANDOM INSERTS IN PACKS
PRINT RUN B/WN 50-100 COPIES PER
1 Cal Ripken Jr./Jim Palmer/Eddie Murray/50 12.50 30.00
2 Johnny Bench/Pete Rose/Joe Morgan/100 40.00 80.00

2008 Donruss Threads Dynasty Materials Prime

RANDOM INSERTS IN PACKS
STATED PRINT RUN 10 SER.#'d SETS
NO PRICING DUE TO SCARCITY

2008 Donruss Threads Generations

RANDOM INSERTS IN PACKS
*CENTURY PROOF: .75X TO 2X BASIC
CENTRUY RANDOMLY INSERTED
CENTURY PRINT RUN 100 SER.#'d SETS
1 Hank Aaron 2.50 6.00
Dale Murphy
2 Eddie Murray 3.00 8.00
Cal Ripken Jr.
3 Ernie Banks 3.00 8.00
Ryne Sandberg
4 Willie Mays 2.50 6.00
Willie McCovey
5 Rod Carew 2.00 5.00
Paul Molitor

2008 Donruss Threads Generations Materials

RANDOM INSERTS IN PACKS
PRINT RUNS B/WN 10-100 COPIES PER
NO PRICING ON QTY 15 OR LESS
1 Hank Aaron
Dale Murphy
10
2 Eddie Murray 15.00 40.00
Cal Ripken Jr.
100
3 Ernie Banks
Ryne Sandberg
15
4 Willie Mays
Willie McCovey
10

2008 Donruss Threads Generations Materials Prime

RANDOM INSERTS IN PACKS
PRINT RUN B/WN 5-10 COPIES PER
NO PRICING DUE TO SCARCITY

2008 Donruss Threads Jerseys

RANDOM INSERTS IN PACKS
PRINT RUNS B/WN 5-500 PER
NO PRICING ON QTY 25 OR LESS
1 Hank Aaron/10
2 Dale Murphy/350 5.00 12.00
3 Brooks Robinson/250 5.00 12.00
4 Cal Ripken Jr./350 6.00 15.00
5 Eddie Murray/250 3.00 8.00
6 Carl Yastrzemski/400 3.00 8.00
7 Carlton Fisk/150 3.00 8.00
8 Wade Boggs/500 3.00 8.00
11 Jim Rice/350 3.00 8.00
12 Fred Lynn/350 3.00 8.00
15 Ernie Banks/10
16 Ryne Sandberg/150 5.00 12.00
18 Luis Aparicio/200 3.00 8.00
19 Tom Seaver/350 3.00 8.00
21 Pete Rose/100 20.00 50.00
22 Bob Feller/15
22 Bob Feller/15
25 Kirk Gibson/250 3.00 8.00
26 Alan Trammell/250 3.00 8.00
27 George Brett/250 5.00 12.00
28 Steve Garvey/150 4.00 10.00
29 Robin Yount/500 4.00 10.00
30 Harmon Killebrew/150 5.00 12.00
31 Paul Molitor/300 3.00 8.00
32 Gary Carter/450 3.00 8.00
35 Don Mattingly/150 6.00 15.00
36 Reggie Jackson/350 3.00 8.00
38 Mike Schmidt/350 4.00 10.00
39 Steve Carlton/250 4.00 10.00
40 Tony Gwynn/500 3.00 8.00
42 Willie Mays/5
43 Willie McCovey/500 3.00 8.00
44 Will Clark/500 3.00 8.00
45 Bob Gibson/100 4.00 10.00
46 Dennis Eckersley/250 3.00 8.00
47 Red Schoendienst/300 4.00 10.00
48 Stan Musial/25
49 Nolan Ryan/250 8.00 20.00
54 Michael Burgess/500 3.00 8.00
55 John Raynor/50 4.00 10.00
58 Luis Exposito/100 4.00 10.00
91 Madison Bumgarner/100 5.00 12.00
95 Josh Vitters/500 3.00 8.00
104 Tyler Flowers/95 4.00 10.00
105 Tyler Henson/50 3.00 8.00
146 Heath Rollins/50 3.00 8.00
147 Alex Cobb/95 3.00 8.00

2008 Donruss Threads Jerseys Prime

RANDOM INSERTS IN PACKS
PRINT RUN B/WN 1-25 COPIES PER
NO PRICING DUE TO SCARCITY

2008 Donruss Threads Signatures Gold

RANDOM INSERTS IN PACKS
PRINT RUNS B/WN 10-999 COPIES PER
NO PRICING ON QTY 25 OR LESS
1 Hank Aaron/10
2 Dale Murphy/10
3 Brooks Robinson/50 10.00 25.00
4 Cal Ripken Jr./50 50.00 100.00
5 Eddie Murray/25
6 Carl Yastrzemski/50 20.00 50.00
7 Carlton Fisk/50 12.50 30.00
8 Wade Boggs/10
10 Johnny Pesky/100 5.00 12.00
11 Jim Rice/100 6.00 15.00
12 Fred Lynn/50 5.00 12.00
13 Duke Snider/50 12.50 30.00
14 Carl Erskine/75 5.00 12.00
15 Ernie Banks/10
16 Ryne Sandberg/50 20.00 50.00
17 Don Sutton/100 5.00 12.00
18 Luis Aparicio/50 5.00 12.00
19 Tom Seaver/50 15.00 40.00
20 Tony Perez/25
21 Pete Rose/75 90.00 150.00
22 Bob Feller/100 12.50 30.00
23 Al Kaline/50 12.50 30.00
24 Mark Fidrych/100 20.00 50.00
25 Kirk Gibson/10
26 Alan Trammell/75 5.00 12.00
27 George Brett/10
28 Steve Garvey/45 10.00 25.00
29 Robin Yount/50 15.00 40.00
30 Harmon Killebrew/10
31 Paul Molitor/50 6.00 15.00
32 Gary Carter/50 10.00 25.00
34 Don Larsen/50 8.00 20.00
35 Don Mattingly/50 12.50 30.00
36 Reggie Jackson/50 12.50 30.00
37 Tim Raines/25
38 Mike Schmidt/50 20.00 50.00
39 Steve Carlton/50 20.00 50.00
40 Tony Gwynn/50 15.00 40.00
41 Juan Marichal/50 10.00 25.00
42 Willie Mays/50 75.00 150.00
43 Willie McCovey/50 15.00 40.00
44 Will Clark/15
45 Bob Gibson/50 8.00 20.00
46 Dennis Eckersley/50 6.00 15.00
47 Red Schoendienst/100 8.00 20.00
48 Stan Musial/50 40.00 80.00
49 Nolan Ryan/50 40.00 80.00
50 Frank Howard/75 6.00 15.00
51 Austin Romine/725 5.00 12.00
52 Chris Carter/499 8.00 20.00
53 Jordan Schafer/275 15.00 40.00
54 Michael Burgess/25
55 John Raynor/575 4.00 10.00
56 Lars Anderson/499 10.00 25.00
57 Josh Reddick/499 10.00 25.00
58 Luis Exposito/971 4.00 10.00
59 Aneury Rodriguez/975 4.00 10.00
60 Nick Weglarz/999 4.00 10.00
61 Hector Gomez/499 5.00 12.00
62 Jon Still/725 4.00 10.00
63 Brandon Hamilton/972 4.00 10.00
64 Bud Norris/499 4.00 10.00
65 Danny Duffy/499 10.00 25.00
66 Jovan Rosa/973 4.00 10.00
67 Sean O'Sullivan/499 4.00 10.00
68 Edilio Colina/975 4.00 10.00
69 Ryan Patterson/775 4.00 10.00
70 Brent Brewer/470 5.00 12.00
71 David Bromberg/999 4.00 10.00
72 Bryan Petersen/475 4.00 10.00
73 Lucas Duda/250 6.00 15.00
74 Ruben Tejada/999 5.00 12.00
75 Andrew Lambo/25
76 Jeff Corsaletti/975 4.00 10.00
77 Alexis Oliveras/975 4.00 10.00
78 Fernando Garcia/975 4.00 10.00
79 Jairo Heredia/999 4.00 10.00
80 Jesus Montero/975 15.00 40.00
81 Jose Tabata/975 10.00 25.00
82 Carlos Gonzalez/975 15.00 40.00
83 Patrick Ryan/499 4.00 10.00
84 Sean Doolittle/249 10.00 25.00
85 Carlos Carrasco/999 4.00 10.00
86 Luis Cruz/975 4.00 10.00
87 Yefri Carvajal/999 4.00 10.00
88 Stolmy Pimentel/975 4.00 10.00
89 Wilber Bucardo/420 4.00 10.00
90 Angel Villalona/25
91 Madison Bumgarner/250 12.50 30.00
92 Danny Carroll/999 4.00 10.00
93 Juan Ramirez/999 4.00 10.00
94 Lou Marson/725 5.00 12.00
95 Josh Vitters/25
96 Desmond Jennings/749 20.00 50.00
97 Abraham Almonte/975 4.00 10.00
98 Mat Gamel/25
99 Andrew LeFave/975 4.00 10.00
100 Elvis Andrus/749 8.00 20.00
101 Emilio Bonifacio/100 6.00 15.00
102 Wilin Rosario/100 5.00 12.00
103 Carlos Peguero/25
104 Tyler Flowers/100 20.00 50.00
105 Tyler Henson/100 4.00 10.00
106 Nevin Griffith/100 4.00 10.00
107 Caleb Gindl/25
108 Jose Ceda/100 4.00 10.00
109 Brandon Waring/25
110 Neftali Soto/100 20.00 50.00
111 Ryan Miller/100 4.00 10.00
112 Jack Egbert/100 6.00 15.00
113 Juan Silverio/100 6.00 15.00
114 Jhoulys Chacin/100 10.00 25.00
115 Charlie Furbush/25
116 Hector Correa/100 4.00 10.00
117 Brad James/100 4.00 10.00
119 Keaton Hayenga/100 4.00 10.00
120 Brent Fisher/100 4.00 10.00
121 Juan Francisco/100 8.00 20.00
122 Andrew Romine/100 4.00 10.00
123 Mason Tobin/100 4.00 10.00
124 Anel De Los Santos/100 4.00 10.00
125 Andrew Walker/25
126 Alfredo Silverio/100 4.00 10.00
127 Mario Martinez/100 5.00 12.00
128 Taylor Green/100 5.00 12.00
129 D.J. Jones/100 4.00 10.00
130 Wilson Ramos/100 10.00 25.00
131 Trevor Reckling/100 8.00 20.00
132 Engel Beltre/25
133 Scott Moviel/100 4.00 10.00
134 Josh Tomlin/100 8.00 20.00
135 Dominic Brown/100 75.00 150.00
136 Neftali Feliz/25
137 Brian Friday/100 4.00 10.00
138 Drew Miller/100 4.00 10.00
139 Steve Garrison/100 4.00 10.00
140 Mike McBryde/100 4.00 10.00
141 Brian Duensing/100 4.00 10.00
142 Greg Halman/25
143 Jharmidy De Jesus/25
144 Mike Slanton/25
145 Wilmer Flores/25
146 Heath Rollins/100 4.00 10.00
147 Alex Cobb/100 4.00 10.00
148 Omar Poveda/100 4.00 10.00
149 Yohermyn Chavez/100 4.00 10.00
150 Gerardo Parra/100 10.00 25.00

2008 Donruss Threads Signatures Platinum

RANDOM INSERTS IN PACKS
PRINT RUNS B/WN 5-25 COPIES PER
NO PRICING DUE TO SCARCITY

1997 E-X2000

This 100-card set (produced by Fleer/SkyBox) was distributed in two-card foil packs with a suggested retail price of $3.99. An oversized Alex Rodriguez card shipped in its own holder was mailed to dealers who ordered E-X 2000 cases. They are numbered out of 3,000 and priced below. Also priced below is the redemption card for a baseball signed by Rodriguez. 100 of these cards were produced and the redemption deadline was May 1, 1998.

COMPLETE SET (100) 30.00 80.00
1 Jim Edmonds .30 .75
2 Darin Erstad .30 .75
3 Eddie Murray .75 2.00
4 Roberto Alomar .50 1.25
5 Brady Anderson .30 .75
6 Mike Mussina .50 1.25
7 Rafael Palmeiro .50 1.25
8 Cal Ripken 2.50 6.00
9 Steve Avery .30 .75
10 Nomar Garciaparra 1.25 3.00
11 Mo Vaughn .30 .75
12 Albert Belle .30 .75
13 Mike Cameron .30 .75
14 Ray Durham .30 .75
15 Frank Thomas .75 2.00
16 Robin Ventura .30 .75
17 Manny Ramirez .50 1.25
18 Jim Thome .50 1.25
19 Matt Williams .30 .75
20 Tony Clark .30 .75
21 Travis Fryman .30 .75
22 Bob Higginson .30 .75
23 Kevin Appier .30 .75
24 Johnny Damon .50 1.25
25 Jermaine Dye .30 .75
26 Jeff Cirillo .30 .75
27 Ben McDonald .30 .75
28 Chuck Knoblauch .30 .75
29 Paul Molitor .30 .75
30 Todd Walker .30 .75
31 Wade Boggs .50 1.25
32 Cecil Fielder .30 .75
33 Derek Jeter 2.00 5.00
34 Andy Pettitte .50 1.25
35 Ruben Rivera .30 .75
36 Bernie Williams .50 1.25
37 Jose Canseco .50 1.25
38 Mark McGwire 2.00 5.00
39 Jay Buhner .30 .75
40 Ken Griffey Jr. 1.25 3.00
41 Randy Johnson .75 2.00
42 Edgar Martinez .50 1.25
43 Alex Rodriguez 1.25 3.00
44 Dan Wilson .30 .75
45 Will Clark .50 1.25
46 Juan Gonzalez .30 .75
47 Ivan Rodriguez .50 1.25
48 Joe Carter .30 .75
49 Roger Clemens 1.50 4.00
50 Juan Guzman .30 .75
51 Pat Hentgen .30 .75
52 Tom Glavine .50 1.25
53 Andruw Jones .50 1.25
54 Chipper Jones .75 2.00
55 Ryan Klesko .30 .75
56 Kenny Lofton .30 .75
57 Greg Maddux 1.25 3.00
58 Fred McGriff .50 1.25
59 John Smoltz .50 1.25
60 Mark Wohlers .30 .75
61 Mark Grace .50 1.25
62 Ryne Sandberg 1.25 3.00
63 Sammy Sosa .75 2.00
64 Barry Larkin .50 1.25
65 Deion Sanders .50 1.25
66 Reggie Sanders .30 .75
67 Dante Bichette .30 .75
68 Ellis Burks .30 .75
69 Andres Galarraga .30 .75
70 Moises Alou .30 .75
71 Kevin Brown .30 .75
72 Cliff Floyd .30 .75
73 Edgar Renteria .30 .75
74 Gary Sheffield .30 .75
75 Bob Abreu .50 1.25
76 Jeff Bagwell .50 1.25
77 Craig Biggio .50 1.25
78 Todd Hollandsworth .30 .75
79 Eric Karros .30 .75
80 Raul Mondesi .30 .75
81 Hideo Nomo .75 2.00
82 Mike Piazza 1.25 3.00
83 Vladimir Guerrero .75 2.00
84 Henry Rodriguez .30 .75
85 Todd Hundley .30 .75
86 Alex Ochoa .30 .75
87 Rey Ordonez .30 .75
88 Gregg Jefferies .30 .75
89 Scott Rolen .50 1.25
90 Jermaine Allensworth .30 .75
91 Jason Kendall .30 .75
92 Ken Caminiti .30 .75
93 Tony Gwynn 1.00 2.50
94 Rickey Henderson .75 2.00
95 Barry Bonds 2.00 5.00
96 J.T. Snow .30 .75
97 Dennis Eckersley .30 .75
98 Ron Gant .30 .75
99 Brian Jordan .30 .75
100 Ray Lankford .30 .75
101 Checklist .30 .75
102 Checklist .30 .75
P43 Alex Rodriguez .60 1.50
Three card promo strip
S43 Alex Rodriguez Sample/3000 4.00 10.00
NNO A.Rod AU Ball/100 6.00 15.00

1997 E-X2000 Credentials

Randomly inserted in packs at the approximate rate of one in 60, this 100-card set is parallel to the base set with an etched holofoil border. 299 serial-numbered sets were issued.

*STARS: 3X TO 8X BASIC CARDS

1997 E-X2000 Essential Credentials

Randomly inserted in packs at the rate of one in 200, this 100-card set is parallel to the base set with an etched refractive holographic foil border. 99 serial-numbered sets were issued.

*STARS: 8X TO 20X BASIC CARDS

1997 E-X2000 A Cut Above

Randomly inserted in packs at the rate of one in 288, this 10-card set features color images of "power hitters" on a holographic foil, die-cut sawblade background.

COMPLETE SET (10) 125.00 250.00
STATED ODDS 1:288
1 Frank Thomas 8.00 20.00
2 Ken Griffey Jr. 12.50 30.00
3 Alex Rodriguez 12.50 30.00
4 Albert Belle 3.00 8.00
5 Juan Gonzalez 3.00 8.00
6 Mark McGwire 20.00 50.00
7 Mo Vaughn 3.00 8.00
8 Manny Ramirez 5.00 12.00
9 Barry Bonds 20.00 50.00
10 Fred McGriff 5.00 12.00

1997 E-X2000 Emerald Autographs

This six-card set features autographed color player photos of some of the hottest young stars in baseball. In addition to an authentic black-ink autograph, each card is embossed with a SkyBox logo about the size of a quarter. These cards were obtained by exchanging a redemption card by mail before the May 1, 1998, deadline.

*EXCH.CARDS: .1X TO .25X BASIC AUTO
EXCH.CARDS STATED ODDS 1:500 PACKS
2 Darin Erstad 6.00 15.00
30 Todd Walker 6.00 15.00
43 Alex Rodriguez 60.00 120.00
78 Todd Hollandsworth 6.00 15.00
86 Alex Ochoa 6.00 15.00
89 Scott Rolen 10.00 25.00

1997 E-X2000 Hall or Nothing

Randomly inserted in packs at the rate of one in 20, this 20-card set features color images of future Cooperstown Hall of Fame candidates printed on 30-pt. acrylic card stock with etched copper foil borders and gold foil stamping.

COMPLETE SET (20) 50.00 120.00
STATED ODDS 1:20
1 Frank Thomas 2.00 5.00
2 Ken Griffey Jr. 3.00 8.00
3 Eddie Murray 2.00 5.00
4 Cal Ripken 6.00 15.00
5 Ryne Sandberg 3.00 8.00
6 Wade Boggs 1.25 3.00
7 Roger Clemens 4.00 10.00
8 Tony Gwynn 2.50 6.00
9 Alex Rodriguez 3.00 8.00
10 Mark McGwire 5.00 12.00
11 Barry Bonds 5.00 12.00
12 Greg Maddux 3.00 8.00
13 Juan Gonzalez .75 2.00
14 Albert Belle .75 2.00
15 Mike Piazza 3.00 8.00
16 Jeff Bagwell 1.25 3.00
17 Dennis Eckersley .75 2.00
18 Mo Vaughn .75 2.00
19 Roberto Alomar 1.25 3.00
20 Kenny Lofton .75 2.00

1997 E-X2000 Star Date 2000

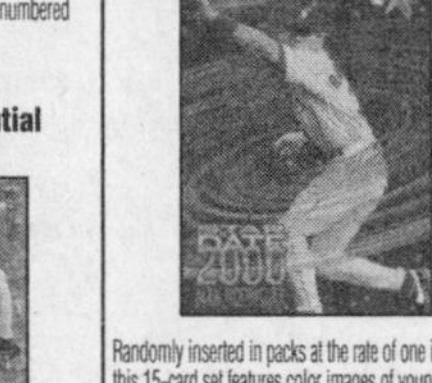

Randomly inserted in packs at the rate of one in nine, this 15-card set features color images of young star players printed on holographic foil with swirls of spot glitter coating.

COMPLETE SET (15) 12.50 30.00
STATED ODDS 1:9
1 Alex Rodriguez 2.00 5.00
2 Andruw Jones .75 2.00
3 Andy Pettitte .75 2.00
4 Brooks Kieschnick .50 1.25
5 Chipper Jones 1.25 3.00
6 Darin Erstad .50 1.25
7 Derek Jeter 3.00 8.00
8 Jason Kendall .50 1.25
9 Jermaine Dye .50 1.25
10 Neifi Perez .50 1.25
11 Scott Rolen .75 2.00
12 Todd Hollandsworth .50 1.25
13 Todd Walker .50 1.25
14 Tony Clark .50 1.25
15 Vladimir Guerrero 1.25 3.00

1998 E-X2001 Rodriguez Hawaii XIII Promo

This card was distributed to industry leaders at the 13th Annual Hawaii Trade Show in late February, 1998. It previewed the upcoming 1998 E-X2001 baseball release. A small gold foil "Hawaii XIII" stamp with a palm tree on the left-hand side of the card front distinguishes the card. According to informed sources, Fleer/SkyBox produced approximately 200 of these cards.

NNO Alex Rodriguez 10.00 25.00

1998 E-X2001

The 1998 E-X2001 set (made by Fleer/SkyBox) was issued in one series totalling 100 cards and distributed exclusively to hobby outlets. Cards were issued in two-card packs carrying a $3.99 suggested retail price. The cards are stunningly attractive, featuring full color action shots printed on clear acetate stock with sparkling foil backgrounds. An unnumbered Kerry Wood exchange card was randomly seeded into 1 in every 50 packs (the same pull rate as any other basic issue card). Unlike the acetate stock basic cards, this Wood exchange card was printed on paper stock and could be redeemed until March 31st, 1999 for a real E-X2001 acetate stock Wood card (number 101). In addition, an Alex Rodriguez sample card was issued a few months prior to the product's release. This sample card was distributed to dealers and hobby media to preview the upcoming release. The card is identical to a standard Alex Rodriguex E-X2001 except for the text "PROMOTIONAL SAMPLE" printed diagonally across the card back. There are no key Rookie Cards in this set.

COMPLETE SET (100) 30.00 80.00
1 Alex Rodriguez 1.25 3.00
2 Barry Bonds 2.00 5.00
3 Greg Maddux 1.25 3.00
4 Roger Clemens 1.50 4.00
5 Juan Gonzalez .30 .75
6 Chipper Jones .75 2.00
7 Derek Jeter 2.00 5.00
8 Frank Thomas .75 2.00
9 Cal Ripken 2.50 6.00
10 Ken Griffey Jr. 1.25 3.00
11 Mark McGwire 2.00 5.00
12 Hideo Nomo .75 2.00
13 Tony Gwynn 1.00 2.50
14 Ivan Rodriguez .50 1.25
15 Mike Piazza 1.25 3.00
16 Roberto Alomar .50 1.25
17 Jeff Bagwell .50 1.25
18 Andruw Jones .50 1.25
19 Albert Belle .30 .75
20 Mo Vaughn .30 .75
21 Kenny Lofton .30 .75
22 Gary Sheffield .30 .75
23 Tony Clark .20 .50
24 Mike Mussina .50 1.25
25 Barry Larkin .50 1.25
26 Moises Alou .30 .75
27 Brady Anderson .30 .75
28 Andy Pettitte .50 1.25
29 Sammy Sosa .75 2.00
30 Raul Mondesi .30 .75
31 Andres Galarraga .30 .75
32 Chuck Knoblauch .30 .75
33 Jim Thome .50 1.25
34 Craig Biggio .50 1.25
35 Jay Buhner .30 .75
36 Rafael Palmeiro .50 1.25
37 Curt Schilling .30 .75
38 Tino Martinez .50 1.25
39 Pedro Martinez .50 1.25
40 Jose Canseco .50 1.25
41 Jeff Cirillo .20 .50
42 Dean Palmer .30 .75
43 Tim Salmon .50 1.25
44 Jason Giambi .30 .75
45 Bobby Higginson .30 .75
46 Jim Edmonds .30 .75
47 David Justice .30 .75
48 John Olerud .30 .75
49 Ray Lankford .30 .75
50 Al Martin .20 .50
51 Mike Lieberthal .20 .50
52 Henry Rodriguez .20 .50
53 Edgar Renteria .30 .75
54 Eric Karros .30 .75
55 Marquis Grissom .20 .50
56 Wilson Alvarez .20 .50
57 Darryl Kile .20 .50
58 Jeff King .20 .50
59 Shawn Estes .20 .50
60 Tony Womack .20 .50
61 Willie Greene .20 .50
62 Ken Caminiti .30 .75
63 Vinny Castilla .30 .75
64 Mark Grace .50 1.25
65 Ryan Klesko .30 .75
66 Robin Ventura .30 .75
67 Todd Hundley .20 .50
68 Travis Fryman .30 .75
69 Edgar Martinez .50 1.25
70 Matt Williams .30 .75
71 Paul Molitor .30 .75
72 Kevin Brown .50 1.25
73 Randy Johnson .75 2.00
74 Bernie Williams .50 1.25
75 Manny Ramirez .50 1.25
76 Fred McGriff .50 1.25
77 Tom Glavine .50 1.25
78 Carlos Delgado .30 .75
79 Larry Walker .30 .75
80 Hideki Irabu .20 .50
81 Ryan McGuire .20 .50
82 Justin Thompson .20 .50
83 Kevin Orie .20 .50
84 Jon Nunnally .20 .50
85 Mark Kotsay .20 .50
86 Todd Walker .20 .50
87 Jason Dickson .20 .50
88 Fernando Tatis .20 .50
89 Karim Garcia .20 .50
90 Ricky Ledee .20 .50
91 Paul Konerko .30 .75
92 Jaret Wright .20 .50
93 Darin Erstad .30 .75
94 Livan Hernandez .20 .50
95 Nomar Garciaparra 1.25 3.00
96 Jose Cruz Jr. .20 .50
97 Scott Rolen .50 1.25
98 Ben Grieve .20 .50
99 Vladimir Guerrero .75 2.00
100 Travis Lee .20 .50
101 Kerry Wood 1.50 4.00
NNO Kerry Wood .75 2.00
NNO A.Rodriguez Sample .60 1.50

1998 E-X2001 Essential Credentials Future

These cards were randomly inserted in E-X2001 packs. For this parallel version, the amount of cards produced is inverse to the card number. Each card is individually serial numbered on the lower edge of the card back. For conveniece, the amount of each player produced is listed next to their listing. Cards between 76 and 100 are not priced due to scarcity.

1 Alex Rodriguez/100 25.00 60.00
2 Barry Bonds/99 40.00 100.00
3 Greg Maddux/98 25.00 60.00
4 Roger Clemens/97 30.00 80.00
5 Juan Gonzalez/96 10.00 25.00
6 Chipper Jones/95 15.00 40.00
7 Derek Jeter/94 40.00 100.00
8 Frank Thomas/93 15.00 40.00
9 Cal Ripken/92 50.00 120.00
10 Ken Griffey Jr./91 25.00 60.00
11 Mark McGwire/90 40.00 100.00
12 Hideo Nomo/89 15.00 40.00
13 Tony Gwynn/88 20.00 50.00
14 Ivan Rodriguez/87 10.00 25.00
15 Mike Piazza/86 25.00 60.00
16 Roberto Alomar/85 10.00 25.00
17 Jeff Bagwell/84 10.00 25.00
18 Andruw Jones/83 10.00 25.00
19 Albert Belle/82 10.00 25.00
20 Mo Vaughn/81 10.00 25.00
21 Kenny Lofton/80 10.00 25.00
22 Gary Sheffield/79 10.00 25.00
23 Tony Clark/78 6.00 15.00
24 Mike Mussina/77 10.00 25.00
25 Barry Larkin/76 10.00 25.00
26 Moises Alou/75 10.00 25.00
27 Brady Anderson/74 10.00 25.00
28 Andy Pettitte/73 10.00 25.00
29 Sammy Sosa/72 15.00 40.00
30 Raul Mondesi/71 10.00 25.00
31 Andres Galarraga/70 10.00 25.00
32 Chuck Knoblauch/69 8.00 20.00
33 Jim Thome/68 12.50 30.00
34 Craig Biggio/67 12.50 30.00
35 Jay Buhner/66 8.00 20.00
36 Rafael Palmeiro/65 12.50 30.00
37 Curt Schilling/64 8.00 20.00
38 Tino Martinez/63 12.50 30.00
39 Pedro Martinez/62 12.50 30.00
40 Jose Canseco/61 12.50 30.00
41 Jeff Cirillo/60 5.00 12.00
42 Dean Palmer/59 8.00 20.00
43 Tim Salmon/58 12.50 30.00
44 Jason Giambi/57 8.00 20.00
45 Bobby Higginson/56 8.00 20.00
46 Jim Edmonds/55 8.00 20.00
47 David Justice/54 8.00 20.00
48 John Olerud/53 8.00 20.00
49 Ray Lankford/52 8.00 20.00
50 Al Martin/51 5.00 12.00
51 Mike Lieberthal/50 10.00 25.00
52 Henry Rodriguez/49 6.00 15.00
53 Edgar Renteria/48 10.00 25.00
54 Eric Karros/47 10.00 25.00
55 Marquis Grissom/46 10.00 25.00
56 Wilson Alvarez/45 6.00 15.00
57 Darryl Kile/44 10.00 25.00
58 Jeff King/43 6.00 15.00
59 Shawn Estes/42 6.00 15.00
60 Tony Womack/41 6.00 15.00
61 Willie Greene/40 6.00 15.00
62 Ken Caminiti/39 10.00 25.00
63 Vinny Castilla/38 10.00 25.00
64 Mark Grace/37 15.00 40.00
65 Ryan Klesko/36 10.00 25.00
66 Robin Ventura/35 15.00 40.00
67 Todd Hundley/34 12.50 30.00
68 Travis Fryman/33 15.00 40.00
69 Edgar Martinez/32 20.00 50.00
70 Matt Williams/31 15.00 40.00
71 Paul Molitor/30 15.00 40.00
72 Kevin Brown/29 20.00 50.00
73 Randy Johnson/28 30.00 80.00
74 Bernie Williams/27 20.00 50.00
75 Manny Ramirez/26 20.00 50.00

1998 E-X2001 Essential Credentials Now

26 Moises Alou/26 15.00 40.00
27 Brady Anderson/27 15.00 40.00
28 Andy Pettitte/28 20.00 50.00
29 Sammy Sosa/29 40.00 80.00
30 Raul Mondesi/30 15.00 40.00
31 Andres Galarraga/31 15.00 40.00
32 Chuck Knoblauch/32 15.00 40.00
33 Jim Thome/33 20.00 50.00
34 Craig Biggio/34 20.00 50.00
35 Jay Buhner/35 15.00 40.00
36 Rafael Palmeiro/36 15.00 40.00
37 Curt Schilling/37 10.00 25.00
38 Tino Martinez/38 15.00 40.00
39 Pedro Martinez/39 15.00 40.00
40 Jose Canseco/40 15.00 40.00
41 Jeff Cirillo/41 8.00 20.00
42 Dean Palmer/42 10.00 25.00

43 Tim Salmon/43 15.00 40.00
44 Jason Giambi/44 10.00 25.00
45 Bobby Higginson/45 10.00 25.00
46 Jim Edmonds/46 10.00 25.00
47 David Justice/47 10.00 25.00
48 John Olerud/48 10.00 25.00
49 Ray Lankford/49 10.00 25.00
50 Al Martin/50 6.00 15.00
51 Mike Lieberthal/51 8.00 20.00
52 Henry Rodriguez/52 5.00 12.00
53 Edgar Renteria/53 8.00 20.00
54 Eric Karros/54 8.00 20.00
55 Marquis Grissom/55 8.00 20.00
56 Wilson Alvarez/56 5.00 12.00
57 Darryl Kile/57 8.00 20.00
58 Jeff King/58 5.00 12.00
59 Shawn Estes/59 5.00 12.00
60 Tony Womack/60 5.00 12.00
61 Willie Greene/61 5.00 12.00
62 Ken Caminiti/62 8.00 20.00
63 Vinny Castilla/63 8.00 20.00
64 Mark Grace/64 10.00 25.00
65 Ryan Klesko/65 8.00 20.00
66 Robin Ventura/66 8.00 20.00
67 Todd Hundley/67 5.00 12.00
68 Travis Fryman/68 8.00 20.00
69 Edgar Martinez/69 10.00 25.00
70 Matt Williams/70 8.00 20.00
71 Paul Molitor/71 6.00 15.00
72 Kevin Brown/72 10.00 25.00
73 Randy Johnson/73 15.00 40.00
74 Bernie Williams/74 10.00 25.00
75 Manny Ramirez/75 15.00 40.00
76 Fred McGriff/76 10.00 25.00
77 Tom Glavine/77 10.00 25.00
78 Carlos Delgado/78 6.00 15.00
79 Larry Walker/79 6.00 15.00
80 Hideki Irabu/80 4.00 10.00
81 Ryan McGuire/81 4.00 10.00
82 Justin Thompson/82 4.00 10.00
83 Kevin Orie/83 4.00 10.00
84 Jon Nunnally/84 4.00 10.00
85 Mark Kotsay/85 6.00 15.00
86 Todd Walker/86 4.00 10.00
87 Jason Dickson/87 4.00 10.00
88 Fernando Tatis/88 4.00 10.00
89 Karim Garcia/89 4.00 10.00
90 Ricky Ledee/90 4.00 10.00
91 Paul Konerko/91 6.00 15.00
92 Jaret Wright/92 4.00 10.00
93 Darin Erstad/93 6.00 15.00
94 Livan Hernandez/94 6.00 15.00
95 Nomar Garciaparra/95 25.00 60.00
96 Jose Cruz Jr./96 4.00 10.00
97 Scott Rolen/97 10.00 25.00
98 Ben Grieve/98 4.00 10.00
99 Vladimir Guerrero/99 15.00 40.00
100 Travis Lee/100 4.00 10.00

1998 E-X2001 Cheap Seat Treats

Randomly inserted in packs at a rate of one in 24, this 20-card set is an insert to the SkyBox E-X2001 brand. Each die-cut card is shaped like a folding chair with silver foil stamping and features a color player photo of some of today's greatest sluggers.

COMPLETE SET (20) 40.00 100.00
STATED ODDS 1:24
1 Frank Thomas 3.00 8.00
2 Ken Griffey Jr. 5.00 12.00
3 Mark McGwire 8.00 20.00
4 Tino Martinez 2.00 5.00
5 Larry Walker 1.25 3.00
6 Juan Gonzalez 1.25 3.00
7 Mike Piazza 5.00 12.00
8 Jeff Bagwell 2.00 5.00
9 Tony Clark .75 2.00
10 Albert Belle 1.25 3.00
11 Andres Galarraga 1.25 3.00
12 Jim Thome 2.00 5.00
13 Mo Vaughn 1.25 3.00
14 Barry Bonds 8.00 20.00
15 Vladimir Guerrero 3.00 8.00
16 Scott Rolen 2.00 5.00
17 Travis Lee .75 2.00
18 David Justice 1.25 3.00
19 Jose Cruz Jr. .75 2.00
20 Andruw Jones 2.00 5.00

1998 E-X2001 Destination Cooperstown

Randomly inserted in packs at a rate of one in 720, this 15-card set is an insert to the SkyBox E-X2001 brand. Each card is designed to resemble a luggage destination tag including a piece of string tied to a hole at the top of each card and honors future Hall-of Famers with color player photos. The cards also provide the featured player's name, team, and position.

STATED ODDS 1:720
1 Alex Rodriguez 15.00 40.00
2 Frank Thomas 10.00 25.00
3 Cal Ripken 30.00 80.00
4 Roger Clemens 20.00 50.00
5 Greg Maddux 15.00 40.00
6 Chipper Jones 10.00 25.00
7 Ken Griffey Jr. 15.00 40.00
8 Mark McGwire 25.00 60.00
9 Tony Gwynn 12.50 30.00
10 Mike Piazza 15.00 40.00
11 Jeff Bagwell 6.00 15.00
12 Jose Cruz Jr. 4.00 10.00
13 Derek Jeter 25.00 60.00
14 Hideo Nomo 15.00 40.00
15 Ivan Rodriguez 6.00 15.00

1998 E-X2001 Signature 2001

Randomly inserted in packs at a rate of one in 60, this 17-card set is an insert to the SkyBox E-X2001 brand. The exclusive insert features color action photos and autographs signed by some of MLB's brightest young stars.

COMPLETE SET (17) 100.00 250.00
STATED ODDS 1:60
1 Ricky Ledee 4.00 10.00
2 Derrick Gibson 4.00 10.00
3 Mark Kotsay 6.00 15.00
4 Kevin Millwood 10.00 25.00
5 Brad Fullmer 4.00 10.00
6 Todd Walker 6.00 15.00
7 Ben Grieve 4.00 10.00
8 Tony Clark 4.00 10.00
9 Jaret Wright 4.00 10.00
10 Randall Simon 4.00 10.00
11 Paul Konerko 6.00 15.00
12 Todd Helton 10.00 25.00
13 David Ortiz 15.00 40.00
14 Alex Gonzalez 4.00 10.00
15 Bobby Estalella 4.00 10.00
16 Alex Rodriguez SP 50.00 100.00
17 Mike Lowell 12.50 30.00

1998 E-X2001 Star Date 2001

Randomly inserted in packs at a rate of one in 12, this 15-card set is an insert to the SkyBox E-X2001 brand. The fronts feature a background of space-age graphics and gold-foil stamping on plastic stock. The color action photos showcase some of the hottest up-and-coming stars in the MLB.

COMPLETE SET (15) 6.00 15.00
STATED ODDS 1:12
1 Travis Lee .40 1.00
2 Jose Cruz Jr. .40 1.00
3 Paul Konerko .40 1.00
4 Bobby Estalella .40 1.00
5 Magglio Ordonez 1.25 3.00
6 Juan Encarnacion .40 1.00
7 Richard Hidalgo .40 1.00
8 Abraham Nunez .40 1.00
9 Sean Casey .40 1.00
10 Todd Helton .60 1.50
11 Brad Fullmer .40 1.00
12 Ben Grieve .40 1.00
13 Livan Hernandez .40 1.00
14 Jaret Wright .40 1.00
15 Todd Dunwoody .40 1.00

1999 E-X Century

This 120-card set features color action player photos silhouetted on extra thick transparent plastic card stock. Each pack contained three cards and carried a suggested retail price of $5.99. The set contains a 30-card Rookie short-printed subset (91-120) with an insertion rate of 1:2 packs. A promotional sample card featuring Ben Grieve was distributed to dealer accounts and hobby media shortly before the product's national release. This card can be easily identified by the "PROMOTIONAL SAMPLE" text running across the back. Notable Rookie Cards include Pat Burrell.

COMPLETE SET (120) 30.00 80.00
COMP.SET w/o SP's (90) 15.00 40.00
COMMON CARD (1-90) .20 .50
COMMON SP (91-120) .40 1.00
1 Scott Rolen .50 1.25
2 Nomar Garciaparra 1.25 3.00
3 Mike Piazza 1.25 3.00
4 Tony Gwynn 1.00 2.50
5 Sammy Sosa 1.25 3.00
6 Alex Rodriguez 1.25 3.00
7 Vladimir Guerrero .75 2.00
8 Chipper Jones .75 2.00
9 Derek Jeter 2.00 5.00
10 Kerry Wood .30 .75
11 Juan Gonzalez .30 .75
12 Frank Thomas .75 2.00
13 Mo Vaughn .30 .75
14 Greg Maddux 1.25 3.00
15 Jeff Bagwell .50 1.25
16 Mark McGwire 2.00 5.00
17 Ken Griffey Jr. 1.25 3.00
18 Roger Clemens 1.50 4.00
19 Cal Ripken 2.50 6.00
20 Travis Lee .20 .50
21 Todd Helton .50 1.25
22 Darin Erstad .30 .75
23 Pedro Martinez .50 1.25
24 Barry Bonds 2.00 5.00
25 Andruw Jones .50 1.25
26 Larry Walker .30 .75
27 Albert Belle .30 .75
28 Ivan Rodriguez .50 1.25
29 Magglio Ordonez .30 .75
30 Andres Galarraga .30 .75
31 Mike Mussina .50 1.25
32 Randy Johnson .75 2.00
33 Tom Glavine .50 1.25
34 Barry Larkin .50 1.25
35 Jim Thome .50 1.25
36 Gary Sheffield .30 .75
37 Bernie Williams .50 1.25
38 Carlos Delgado .30 .75
39 Rafael Palmeiro .50 1.25
40 Edgar Renteria .30 .75
41 Brad Fullmer .20 .50
42 David Wells .30 .75
43 Dante Bichette .30 .75
44 Jaret Wright .20 .50
45 Ricky Ledee .20 .50
46 Ray Lankford .30 .75
47 Mark Grace .50 1.25
48 Jeff Cirillo .20 .50
49 Rondell White .30 .75
50 Jeromy Burnitz .30 .75
51 Sean Casey .30 .75
52 Rolando Arrojo .20 .50
53 Jason Giambi .30 .75
54 John Olerud .30 .75
55 Will Clark .50 1.25
56 Raul Mondesi .30 .75
57 Scott Brosius .30 .75
58 Bartolo Colon .30 .75
59 Steve Finley .30 .75
60 Javy Lopez .30 .75
61 Tim Salmon .50 1.25
62 Roberto Alomar .50 1.25
63 Vinny Castilla .30 .75
64 Craig Biggio .50 1.25
65 Jose Guillen .30 .75
66 Greg Vaughn .20 .50
67 Jose Canseco .50 1.25
68 Shawn Green .30 .75
69 Curt Schilling .30 .75
70 Orlando Hernandez .30 .75
71 Jose Cruz Jr. .20 .50
72 Alex Gonzalez .20 .50
73 Tino Martinez .50 1.25
74 Todd Hundley .20 .50
75 Brian Giles .30 .75
76 Cliff Floyd .30 .75
77 Paul O'Neill .50 1.25
78 Ken Caminiti .30 .75
79 Ron Gant .30 .75
80 Juan Encarnacion .20 .50
81 Ben Grieve .20 .50
82 Brian Jordan .30 .75
83 Rickey Henderson .75 2.00
84 Tony Clark .20 .50
85 Shannon Stewart .30 .75
86 Robin Ventura .30 .75
87 Todd Walker .20 .50
88 Kevin Brown .50 1.25
89 Moises Alou .30 .75
90 Manny Ramirez .50 1.25
91 Gabe Alvarez SP .40 1.00
92 Jeremy Giambi SP .40 1.00
93 Adrian Beltre SP .40 1.00
94 George Lombard SP .40 1.00
95 Ryan Minor SP .40 1.00
96 Kevin Witt SP .40 1.00
97 Scott Hunter SP RC .40 1.00
98 Carlos Guillen SP .40 1.00
99 Derrick Gibson SP .40 1.00
100 Trot Nixon SP .40 1.00
101 Troy Glaus SP .40 1.00
102 Armando Rios SP .40 1.00
103 Preston Wilson SP .40 1.00
104 Pat Burrell SP RC 1.25 3.00
105 J.D. Drew SP .40 1.00
106 Bruce Chen SP .40 1.00
107 Matt Clement SP .40 1.00
108 Carlos Beltran SP .40 1.00
109 Carlos Febles SP .40 1.00
110 Rob Fick SP .40 1.00
111 Russell Branyan SP .40 1.00
112 R.Brown SP RC .40 1.00
113 Corey Koskie SP .40 1.00
114 M.Encarnacion SP RC .40 1.00
115 Peter Tucci SP .40 1.00
116 Eric Chavez SP .40 1.00
117 Gabe Kapler SP .40 1.00
118 Marlon Anderson SP .40 1.00
119 A.J. Burnett SP RC .60 1.50
120 Ryan Bradley SP .40 1.00
P81 Ben Grieve Sample .40 1.00

1999 E-X Century Essential Credentials Future

Randomly inserted into packs, this 120-card set is a sequentially numbered gold foil parallel version of the E-X Century base set. The print run for each card follows the player's name in the checklist below.

1 Scott Rolen/120 8.00 20.00
2 Nomar Garciaparra/119 20.00 50.00
3 Mike Piazza/118 20.00 50.00
4 Tony Gwynn (117) 15.00 40.00
5 Sammy Sosa/116 8.00 20.00
6 Alex Rodriguez/115 20.00 50.00
7 Vladimir Guerrero/114 8.00 20.00
8 Chipper Jones/113 8.00 20.00
9 Derek Jeter/112 30.00 80.00
10 Kerry Wood/111 6.00 15.00
11 Juan Gonzalez/110 6.00 15.00
12 Frank Thomas/109 8.00 20.00
13 Mo Vaughn/108 6.00 15.00
14 Greg Maddux/107 20.00 50.00
15 Jeff Bagwell/106 8.00 20.00
16 Mark McGwire/105 30.00 80.00
17 Ken Griffey Jr./104 20.00 50.00
18 Roger Clemens/103 25.00 60.00
19 Cal Ripken/102 40.00 100.00
20 Travis Lee/101 5.00 12.00
21 Todd Helton/100 8.00 20.00
22 Darin Erstad/99 5.00 12.00
23 Pedro Martinez/98 8.00 20.00
24 Barry Bonds/97 40.00 100.00
25 Andruw Jones/96 8.00 20.00
26 Larry Walker/95 5.00 12.00
27 Albert Belle/94 5.00 12.00
28 Ivan Rodriguez/93 8.00 20.00
29 Magglio Ordonez/92 5.00 12.00
30 Andres Galarraga/91 5.00 12.00
31 Mike Mussina/90 8.00 20.00
32 Randy Johnson/89 12.50 30.00
33 Tom Glavine/88 8.00 20.00
34 Barry Larkin/87 8.00 20.00
35 Jim Thome/86 8.00 20.00
36 Gary Sheffield/85 5.00 12.00
37 Bernie Williams/84 8.00 20.00
38 Carlos Delgado/83 5.00 12.00
39 Rafael Palmeiro/82 8.00 20.00
40 Edgar Renteria/81 5.00 12.00
41 Brad Fullmer/80 4.00 10.00
42 David Wells/79 5.00 12.00
43 Dante Bichette/78 5.00 12.00
44 Jaret Wright/77 4.00 10.00
45 Ricky Ledee/76 4.00 10.00
46 Ray Lankford/75 5.00 12.00
47 Mark Grace/74 8.00 20.00
48 Jeff Cirillo/73 4.00 10.00
49 Rondell White/72 5.00 12.00
50 Jeromy Burnitz/71 5.00 12.00
51 Sean Casey/70 6.00 15.00
52 Rolando Arrojo/69 5.00 12.00
53 Jason Giambi/68 6.00 15.00
54 John Olerud/67 6.00 15.00
55 Will Clark/66 10.00 25.00
56 Raul Mondesi/65 6.00 15.00
57 Scott Brosius/64 6.00 15.00
58 Bartolo Colon/63 6.00 15.00
59 Steve Finley/62 6.00 15.00
60 Javy Lopez/61 6.00 15.00
61 Tim Salmon/60 10.00 25.00
62 Roberto Alomar/59 10.00 25.00
63 Vinny Castilla/58 6.00 15.00
64 Craig Biggio/57 10.00 25.00
65 Jose Guillen/56 6.00 15.00
66 Greg Vaughn/55 5.00 12.00
67 Jose Canseco/54 10.00 25.00
68 Shawn Green/53 6.00 15.00
69 Curt Schilling/52 6.00 15.00
70 Orlando Hernandez/51 6.00 15.00
71 Jose Cruz Jr./50 5.00 12.00
72 Alex Gonzalez/49 5.00 12.00
73 Tino Martinez/48 12.50 30.00
74 Todd Hundley/47 5.00 12.00
75 Brian Giles/46 8.00 20.00
76 Cliff Floyd/45 8.00 20.00
77 Paul O'Neill/44 12.50 30.00
78 Ken Caminiti/43 8.00 20.00
79 Ron Gant/42 8.00 20.00
80 Juan Encarnacion/41 5.00 12.00
81 Ben Grieve/40 5.00 12.00
82 Brian Jordan/39 8.00 20.00
83 Rickey Henderson/38 20.00 50.00
84 Tony Clark/37 5.00 12.00
85 Shannon Stewart/36 8.00 20.00
86 Robin Ventura/35 10.00 25.00
87 Todd Walker/34 6.00 15.00
88 Kevin Brown/33 15.00 40.00
89 Moises Alou/32 10.00 25.00
90 Manny Ramirez/31 15.00 40.00
91 Gabe Alvarez/30 6.00 15.00
92 Jeremy Giambi/29 6.00 15.00
93 Adrian Beltre/28 10.00 25.00
94 George Lombard/27 6.00 15.00
95 Ryan Minor/26 6.00 15.00

1999 E-X Century Essential Credentials Now

26 Larry Walker/26 15.00 40.00
27 Albert Belle/27 15.00 40.00
28 Ivan Rodriguez/28 20.00 50.00
29 Magglio Ordonez/29 15.00 40.00
30 Andres Galarraga/30 15.00 40.00
31 Mike Mussina/31 20.00 50.00
32 Randy Johnson/32 25.00 60.00
33 Tom Glavine/33 20.00 50.00
34 Barry Larkin/34 20.00 50.00
35 Jim Thome/35 20.00 50.00
36 Gary Sheffield/36 8.00 20.00
37 Bernie Williams/37 12.50 30.00
38 Carlos Delgado/38 8.00 20.00
39 Rafael Palmeiro/39 12.50 30.00
40 Edgar Renteria/40 8.00 20.00
41 Brad Fullmer/41 5.00 12.00
42 David Wells/42 8.00 20.00
43 Dante Bichette/43 8.00 20.00
44 Jaret Wright/44 5.00 12.00
45 Ricky Ledee/45 5.00 12.00
46 Ray Lankford/46 8.00 20.00
47 Mark Grace/47 12.50 30.00
48 Jeff Cirillo/48 5.00 12.00
49 Rondell White/49 8.00 20.00
50 Jeromy Burnitz/50 8.00 20.00
51 Sean Casey/51 6.00 15.00
52 Rolando Arrojo/52 5.00 12.00
53 Jason Giambi/53 6.00 15.00
54 John Olerud/54 6.00 15.00
55 Will Clark/55 10.00 25.00
56 Raul Mondesi/56 6.00 15.00
57 Scott Brosius/57 6.00 15.00
58 Bartolo Colon/58 6.00 15.00
59 Steve Finley/59 6.00 15.00
60 Javy Lopez/60 6.00 15.00
61 Tim Salmon/61 10.00 25.00
62 Roberto Alomar/62 10.00 25.00
63 Vinny Castilla/63 6.00 15.00
64 Craig Biggio/64 10.00 25.00
65 Jose Guillen/65 6.00 15.00
66 Greg Vaughn/66 5.00 12.00
67 Jose Canseco/67 10.00 25.00
68 Shawn Green/68 6.00 15.00
69 Curt Schilling/69 6.00 15.00
70 Orlando Hernandez/70 6.00 15.00
71 Jose Cruz Jr./71 4.00 10.00
72 Alex Gonzalez/72 4.00 10.00
73 Tino Martinez/73 8.00 20.00
74 Todd Hundley/74 4.00 10.00
75 Brian Giles/75 5.00 12.00
76 Cliff Floyd/76 5.00 12.00
77 Paul O'Neill/77 8.00 20.00
78 Ken Caminiti/78 5.00 12.00
79 Ron Gant/79 5.00 12.00
80 Juan Encarnacion/80 4.00 10.00
81 Ben Grieve/81 4.00 10.00
82 Brian Jordan/82 5.00 12.00
83 Rickey Henderson/83 12.50 30.00
84 Tony Clark/84 4.00 10.00
85 Shannon Stewart/85 5.00 12.00
86 Robin Ventura/86 5.00 12.00
87 Todd Walker/87 4.00 10.00
88 Kevin Brown/88 8.00 20.00
89 Moises Alou/89 5.00 12.00
90 Manny Ramirez/90 8.00 20.00
91 Gabe Alvarez (91) 4.00 10.00
92 Jeremy Giambi (92) 4.00 10.00
93 Adrian Beltre (93) 5.00 12.00
94 George Lombard (94) 4.00 10.00
95 Ryan Minor (95) 4.00 10.00
96 Kevin Witt (96) 4.00 10.00
97 Scott Hunter (97) 4.00 10.00
98 Carlos Guillen (98) 5.00 12.00
99 Derrick Gibson (99) 4.00 10.00
100 Trot Nixon (100) 5.00 12.00
101 Troy Glaus (101) 6.00 15.00
102 Armando Rios (102) 2.50 6.00
103 Preston Wilson (103) 4.00 10.00
104 Pat Burrell (104) 20.00 50.00
105 J.D. Drew (105) 4.00 10.00
106 Bruce Chen (106) 2.50 6.00
107 Matt Clement (107) 4.00 10.00
108 Carlos Beltran (108) 6.00 15.00
109 Carlos Febles (109) 2.50 6.00
110 Rob Fick (110) 2.50 6.00
111 Russell Branyan (111) 2.50 6.00
112 Roosevelt Brown (112) 2.50 6.00
113 Corey Koskie (113) 2.50 6.00
114 Mario Encarnacion (114) 2.50 6.00
115 Peter Tucci (115) 2.50 6.00
116 Eric Chavez (116) 4.00 10.00
117 Gabe Kapler (117) 4.00 10.00
118 Marlon Anderson (118) 2.50 6.00
119 A.J. Burnett (119) 10.00 25.00
120 Ryan Bradley (120) 2.50 6.00

1999 E-X Century Authen-Kicks

Randomly inserted into packs, this nine-card set features color cut-outs of top young players with swatches of their game-worn shoes embedded in the cards beside black-and-white head shots of the players in the background. The print run for each card follows the player's name in our checklist.

B1/R1 AU PRINT RUN 8 #'d OF EACH
NO B1/R1 PRICING DUE TO SCARCITY
1 J.D. Drew/160 10.00 25.00
2 Travis Lee/175 6.00 15.00
3 Kevin Millwood/165 10.00 25.00
4 Bruce Chen/205 6.00 15.00
5 Troy Glaus/205 15.00 40.00
6 Todd Helton/205 15.00 40.00
7 Ricky Ledee/180 6.00 15.00
8 Scott Rolen/205 15.00 40.00
9 Jeremy Giambi/205 6.00 15.00
B1 J.D. Drew Black AU/8
R1 J.D. Drew Red AU/8

1999 E-X Century E-X Quisite

Randomly inserted into packs at the rate of one in 18, this 15-card set features color cut-outs of top young players printed on cards with an unique interior die-cut design.

COMPLETE SET (15) 15.00 40.00
STATED ODDS 1:18
1 Troy Glaus .60 1.50
2 J.D. Drew .60 1.50
3 Pat Burrell 1.50 4.00
4 Russell Branyan .60 1.50
5 Kerry Wood 1.00 2.50
6 Eric Chavez .60 1.50
7 Ben Grieve .60 1.50
8 Gabe Kapler .60 1.50
9 Adrian Beltre .60 1.50
10 Todd Helton 1.50 4.00
11 Roosevelt Brown .60 1.50
12 Marlon Anderson .60 1.50
13 Jeremy Giambi .60 1.50
14 Magglio Ordonez 1.00 2.50
15 Travis Lee .60 1.50

1999 E-X Century Favorites for Fenway '99

Randomly inserted into packs at the rate of one in 36, this 20-card set features color cut-outs of All-Star Game starters silhouetted in front of The Green Monster, Fenway Park.

COMPLETE SET (20) 150.00 300.00
STATED ODDS 1:36
1 Mo Vaughn 1.50 4.00
2 Nomar Garciaparra 6.00 15.00
3 Frank Thomas 4.00 10.00
4 Ken Griffey Jr. 6.00 15.00
5 Roger Clemens 8.00 20.00
6 Alex Rodriguez 6.00 15.00
7 Derek Jeter 10.00 25.00
8 Juan Gonzalez 1.50 4.00
9 Cal Ripken 12.50 30.00
10 Ivan Rodriguez 2.50 6.00
11 J.D. Drew 2.00 5.00
12 Barry Bonds 10.00 25.00
13 Tony Gwynn 5.00 12.00
14 Vladimir Guerrero 4.00 10.00
15 Chipper Jones 4.00 10.00
16 Kerry Wood 1.50 4.00
17 Mike Piazza 6.00 15.00
18 Sammy Sosa 6.00 15.00
19 Scott Rolen 2.50 6.00
20 Mark McGwire 10.00 25.00

1999 E-X Century Milestones of the Century

Randomly inserted into packs, this 10-card set features color action photos of players with top statistical performances from the 1998 season printed on a multi-layered card design. Each card is sequentially numbed to the pictured player's 1998 statistical performance and follows the player's name in our checklist.

1 Kerry Wood/20
2 Mark McGwire/70 60.00 120.00
3 Sammy Sosa/66 15.00 40.00
4 Ken Griffey Jr./350 12.50 30.00
5 Roger Clemens/98 30.00 60.00
6 Cal Ripken/17
7 Alex Rodriguez/40 40.00 80.00
8 Barry Bonds/400 15.00 40.00
9 N.Y. Yankees/114 40.00 80.00
10 Travis Lee/98 2.00 5.00

2000 E-X

The 2000 E-X product was released in June, 2000 as a 90-card set. The set featured 60-player cards and 30-short printed prospect cards. Each of the prospect cards were individually serial numbered to 3499. Each pack contained three cards and carried a suggested retail price of $3.99.

COMPLETE SET (90) 40.00 100.00
COMP.SET w/o SP's (60) 8.00 20.00
COMMON CARD (1-60) .15 .40
COMMON PROS (61-90) 1.50 4.00
1 Alex Rodriguez .60 1.50
2 Jeff Bagwell .25 .60
3 Mike Piazza .60 1.50
4 Tony Gwynn .50 1.25
5 Ken Griffey Jr. .60 1.50
6 Juan Gonzalez .15 .40
7 Vladimir Guerrero .40 1.00
8 Cal Ripken 1.25 3.00
9 Mo Vaughn .15 .40
10 Chipper Jones .40 1.00
11 Derek Jeter 1.00 2.50
12 Nomar Garciaparra .60 1.50
13 Mark McGwire 1.00 2.50
14 Sammy Sosa .40 1.00
15 Pedro Martinez .25 .60
16 Greg Maddux .60 1.50
17 Frank Thomas .40 1.00
18 Shawn Green .15 .40
19 Carlos Beltran .15 .40
20 Roger Clemens .75 2.00
21 Randy Johnson .40 1.00
22 Bernie Williams .25 .60
23 Carlos Delgado .15 .40
24 Manny Ramirez .25 .60
25 Freddy Garcia .15 .40
26 Barry Bonds 1.00 2.50
27 Tim Hudson .15 .40
28 Larry Walker .15 .40
29 Raul Mondesi .15 .40
30 Ivan Rodriguez .25 .60
31 Magglio Ordonez .15 .40
32 Scott Rolen .25 .60
33 Mike Mussina .25 .60
34 J.D. Drew .15 .40
35 Tom Glavine .25 .60
36 Barry Larkin .25 .60
37 Jim Thome .25 .60
38 Erubiel Durazo .15 .40
39 Curt Schilling .15 .40
40 Orlando Hernandez .15 .40
41 Rafael Palmeiro .25 .60
42 Gabe Kapler .15 .40
43 Mark Grace .25 .60
44 Jeff Cirillo .15 .40
45 Jeromy Burnitz .15 .40
46 Sean Casey .15 .40
47 Kevin Millwood .15 .40
48 Vinny Castilla .15 .40
49 Jose Canseco .25 .60
50 Roberto Alomar .25 .60
51 Craig Biggio .25 .60
52 Preston Wilson .15 .40
53 Jeff Weaver .15 .40
54 Robin Ventura .15 .40
55 Ben Grieve .15 .40
56 Troy Glaus .15 .40
57 Jacque Jones .15 .40
58 Brian Giles .15 .40
59 Kevin Brown .15 .40
60 Todd Helton .25 .60
61 Ben Petrick PROS 1.50 4.00
62 C.Hermansen PROS 1.50 4.00
63 Kevin Barker PROS 1.50 4.00
64 Matt LeCroy PROS 1.50 4.00
65 Brad Penny PROS 1.50 4.00
66 D.T. Cromer PROS 1.50 4.00
67 Steve Lomasney PROS 1.50 4.00
68 Cole Liniak PROS 1.50 4.00
69 B.J. Ryan PROS 1.50 4.00
70 Wilton Veras PROS 1.50 4.00
71 A.McNeal PROS RC 1.50 4.00
72 Nick Johnson PROS 1.50 4.00
73 Adam Piatt PROS 1.50 4.00
74 Adam Kennedy PROS 1.50 4.00
75 Cesar King PROS 1.50 4.00
76 Peter Bergeron PROS 1.50 4.00
77 Rob Bell PROS 1.50 4.00
78 Wily Pena PROS 1.50 4.00
79 Ruben Mateo PROS 1.50 4.00
80 Kip Wells PROS 1.50 4.00
81 Alex Escobar PROS 1.50 4.00
82 Danys Baez PROS RC 1.50 4.00
83 Travis Dawkins PROS 1.50 4.00
84 Mark Quinn PROS 1.50 4.00
85 Jimmy Anderson PROS 1.50 4.00
86 Rick Ankiel PROS 1.50 4.00
87 Alfonso Soriano PROS 2.00 5.00
88 Pat Burrell PROS 1.50 4.00
89 Eric Munson PROS 1.50 4.00
90 Josh Beckett PROS 2.00 5.00

2000 E-X Essential Credentials Future

Randomly inserted into packs, this 90-card insert is a complete parallel of the E-X base set. Print runs for each of these cards are provided after the player's name in our checklist.

1 Alex Rodriguez/60 30.00 80.00
2 Jeff Bagwell/59 12.50 30.00
3 Mike Piazza/58 30.00 80.00
4 Tony Gwynn/57 25.00 60.00
5 Ken Griffey Jr./56 30.00 80.00
6 Juan Gonzalez/55 12.50 30.00
7 Vladimir Guerrero/54 15.00 40.00
8 Cal Ripken/53 60.00 150.00
9 Mo Vaughn/52 12.50 30.00
10 Chipper Jones/51 15.00 40.00
11 Derek Jeter/50 50.00 120.00
12 Nomar Garciaparra/49 30.00 80.00
13 Mark McGwire/48 50.00 120.00
14 Sammy Sosa/47 15.00 40.00
15 Pedro Martinez/46 15.00 40.00
16 Greg Maddux/45 30.00 80.00
17 Frank Thomas/44 15.00 40.00
18 Shawn Green/43 8.00 20.00
19 Carlos Beltran/42 8.00 20.00
20 Roger Clemens/41 40.00 100.00
21 Randy Johnson/40 15.00 40.00
22 Bernie Williams/39 15.00 40.00
23 Carlos Delgado/38 8.00 20.00
24 Manny Ramirez/37 15.00 40.00
25 Freddy Garcia/36 8.00 20.00
26 Barry Bonds/35 60.00 150.00
27 Tim Hudson/34 15.00 40.00
28 Larry Walker/33 15.00 40.00
29 Raul Mondesi/32 15.00 40.00
30 Ivan Rodriguez/31 20.00 50.00
31 Magglio Ordonez/30 15.00 40.00
32 Scott Rolen/29 20.00 50.00
33 Mike Mussina/28 20.00 50.00
34 J.D. Drew/27 15.00 40.00
35 Tom Glavine/26 20.00 50.00
61 Ben Petrick/30 10.00 25.00
62 Chad Hermansen/29 10.00 25.00
63 Kevin Barker/28 10.00 25.00
64 Matt LeCroy/27 10.00 25.00
65 Brad Penny/26 10.00 25.00
66 D.T. Cromer/25

2000 E-X Essential Credentials Now

26 Barry Bonds/26 60.00 150.00
27 Tim Hudson/27
28 Larry Walker/28 15.00 40.00
29 Raul Mondesi/29 15.00 40.00
30 Ivan Rodriguez/30 25.00 60.00
31 Magglio Ordonez/31 15.00 40.00
32 Scott Rolen/32 20.00 50.00
33 Mike Mussina/33 20.00 50.00
34 J.D. Drew/34 15.00 40.00
35 Tom Glavine/35 20.00 50.00
36 Barry Larkin/36 12.50 30.00
37 Jim Thome/37 12.50 30.00
38 Erubiel Durazo/38 8.00 20.00
39 Curt Schilling/39 10.00 25.00
40 Orlando Hernandez/40 10.00 25.00
41 Rafael Palmeiro/41 12.50 30.00
42 Gabe Kapler/42 10.00 25.00
43 Mark Grace/43 12.50 30.00
44 Jeff Cirillo/44 8.00 20.00
45 Jeromy Burnitz/45 10.00 25.00
46 Sean Casey/46 10.00 25.00
47 Kevin Millwood/47 10.00 25.00
48 Vinny Castilla/48 10.00 25.00
49 Jose Canseco/49 12.50 30.00
50 Roberto Alomar/50 12.50 30.00
51 Craig Biggio/51 10.00 25.00
52 Preston Wilson/52 8.00 20.00
53 Jeff Weaver/53 6.00 15.00
54 Robin Ventura/54 8.00 20.00
55 Ben Grieve/55 6.00 15.00
56 Troy Glaus/56 8.00 20.00
57 Jacque Jones/57 8.00 20.00
58 Brian Giles/58 8.00 20.00
59 Kevin Brown/59 10.00 25.00
60 Todd Helton/60 10.00 25.00
86 Rick Ankiel/26 20.00 50.00
87 Alfonso Soriano/27 25.00 60.00
88 Pat Burrell/28 25.00 60.00
89 Eric Munson/29 20.00 50.00
90 Josh Beckett/30 25.00 60.00

2000 E-X E-Xceptional Red

Randomly inserted into packs, this 15-card insert features some of the hottest major league ballplayers. Each card is individually numbered to 1999. Card backs carry a "XC" prefix.

COMPLETE SET (15) 60.00 150.00
*BLUE: 1.25X TO 3X RED
BLUE PRINT RUN 250 SERIAL #'d SETS
*GREEN: .6X TO 1.5X RED
GREEN PRINT RUN 999 SERIAL #'d SETS
XC1 Ken Griffey Jr. 4.00 10.00
XC2 Derek Jeter 6.00 15.00
XC3 Nomar Garciaparra 4.00 10.00
XC4 Mark McGwire 6.00 15.00
XC5 Sammy Sosa 2.50 6.00
XC6 Mike Piazza 4.00 10.00
XC7 Alex Rodriguez 4.00 10.00
XC8 Cal Ripken 8.00 20.00
XC9 Chipper Jones 2.50 6.00
XC10 Pedro Martinez 1.50 4.00
XC11 Jeff Bagwell 1.50 4.00
XC12 Greg Maddux 4.00 10.00
XC13 Roger Clemens 5.00 12.00
XC14 Tony Gwynn 3.00 8.00
XC15 Frank Thomas 2.50 6.00

2000 E-X E-Xciting

Randomly inserted into packs at one in 24, this 10-card insert set features some of the most exciting players in modern major league baseball. Card backs carry a "XT" prefix.

COMPLETE SET (10) 25.00 60.00
XT1 Mark McGwire 4.00 10.00
XT2 Ken Griffey Jr. 2.50 6.00
XT3 Randy Johnson 1.50 4.00
XT4 Sammy Sosa 1.50 4.00
XT5 Manny Ramirez 1.00 2.50
XT6 Jose Canseco 1.00 2.50
XT7 Derek Jeter 4.00 10.00
XT8 Scott Rolen 1.00 2.50
XT9 Juan Gonzalez .60 1.50
XT10 Barry Bonds 4.00 10.00

2000 E-X E-Xplosive

Randomly inserted into packs, this 20-card set features some of the most explosive players in major league baseball. Each card is individually serial numbered to 2499. Card backs carry a "XP" prefix.

COMPLETE SET (20) 80.00 200.00

XP1 Tony Gwynn 3.00 8.00
XP2 Alex Rodriguez 4.00 10.00
XP3 Pedro Martinez 1.50 4.00
XP4 Sammy Sosa 1.50 4.00
XP5 Cal Ripken 8.00 20.00
XP6 Adam Piatt 1.50 4.00
XP7 Pat Burrell 1.50 4.00
XP8 J.D. Drew 1.50 4.00
XP9 Mike Piazza 4.00 10.00
XP10 Shawn Green 1.50 4.00
XP11 Troy Glaus 1.50 4.00
XP12 Randy Johnson 1.50 4.00
XP13 Juan Gonzalez 1.50 4.00
XP14 Chipper Jones 1.50 4.00
XP15 Ivan Rodriguez 1.50 4.00
XP16 Nomar Garciaparra 4.00 10.00
XP17 Ken Griffey Jr. 4.00 10.00
XP18 Nick Johnson 1.50 4.00
XP19 Mark McGwire 6.00 15.00
XP20 Frank Thomas 1.50 4.00

2000 E-X Generation E-X

Randomly inserted into packs at one in eight, this15-card insert set features some of the hottest young talent in major league baseball. Card backs carry a "GX" prefix.

COMPLETE SET (15) 20.00 50.00
GX1 Rick Ankiel 1.50 4.00
GX2 Josh Beckett 1.25 3.00
GX3 Carlos Beltran .60 1.50
GX4 Pat Burrell 1.25 3.00
GX5 Freddy Garcia 1.25 3.00
GX6 Alex Rodriguez 2.50 6.00
GX7 Derek Jeter 4.00 10.00
GX8 Tim Hudson 1.25 3.00
GX9 Shawn Green 1.25 3.00
GX10 Eric Munson 1.25 3.00
GX11 Adam Piatt 1.50 4.00
GX12 Adam Kennedy .60 1.50
GX13 Nick Johnson 1.25 3.00
GX14 Alfonso Soriano 1.25 3.00
GX15 Nomar Garciaparra 2.50 6.00

2000 E-X Genuine Coverage

Randomly inserted into packs at one in 144, this 10-card insert set features swatches from actual game-used jerseys. Cards are numbered based on each player's actual uniform number.

2 Derek Jeter 12.50 30.00
3 Alex Rodriguez 6.00 15.00
8 Cal Ripken 12.50 30.00
10 Chipper Jones 6.00 15.00
11 Edgar Martinez 6.00 15.00
25 Barry Bonds 10.00 25.00
35 Mike Mussina
43 Raul Mondesi 4.00 10.00
47 Tom Glavine 6.00 15.00
52 Tim Hudson 4.00 10.00
NNO Heath Murray 4.00 10.00

2001 E-X

The 2001 E-X product was released in mid-May, 2001, and featured a 130-card base set that was broken into tiers as follows: Base Veterans (1-100), and Rookies/Prospects (101-130) (individually serial numbered). Each pack contained 5 cards, and carried a suggested retail price of $4.99. An additional ten cards (131-140) featuring a selection of top prospects was distributed in late December, 2001 within Fleer Platinum RC packs. Each of these cards is serial-numbered to 499 copies.

COMP.SET w/o SP's (100) 10.00 25.00
COMMON CARD (1-100) .20 .50
COMMON (101-130) 3.00 8.00
COMMON (131-140) 3.00 8.00
1 Jason Kendall .20 .50
2 Derek Jeter 1.25 3.00
3 Greg Vaughn .20 .50
4 Eric Chavez .20 .50
5 Nomar Garciaparra .75 2.00
6 Roberto Alomar .30 .75
7 Barry Larkin .30 .75
8 Matt Lawton .20 .50
9 Larry Walker .20 .50
10 Chipper Jones .50 1.25
11 Scott Rolen .30 .75
12 Carlos Lee .20 .50
13 Adrian Beltre .20 .50
14 Ben Grieve .20 .50
15 Mike Sweeney .20 .50
16 John Olerud .20 .50
17 Gabe Kapler .20 .50
18 Brian Giles .20 .50
19 Luis Gonzalez .20 .50
20 Sammy Sosa .50 1.25
21 Roger Clemens 1.00 2.50
22 Vladimir Guerrero .50 1.25
23 Ken Griffey Jr. .75 2.00
24 Mark McGwire 1.25 3.00
25 Orlando Hernandez .20 .50
26 Shannon Stewart .20 .50
27 Fred McGriff .30 .75
28 Lance Berkman .20 .50
29 Carlos Delgado .20 .50
30 Mike Piazza .75 2.00
31 Juan Encarnacion .20 .50
32 David Justice .20 .50
33 Greg Maddux .75 2.00
34 Frank Thomas .50 1.25
35 Jason Giambi .20 .50
36 Ruben Mateo .20 .50
37 Todd Helton .30 .75
38 Jim Edmonds .20 .50
39 Steve Finley .20 .50
40 Tom Glavine .30 .75
41 Mo Vaughn .20 .50
42 Phil Nevin .20 .50
43 Richie Sexson .20 .50
44 Craig Biggio .30 .75
45 Kerry Wood .20 .50
46 Pat Burrell .20 .50
47 Edgar Martinez .30 .75
48 Jim Thome .30 .75
49 Jeff Bagwell .30 .75
50 Bernie Williams .30 .75
51 Andruw Jones .30 .75
52 Gary Sheffield .20 .50
53 Johnny Damon .30 .75
54 Rondell White .20 .50
55 J.D. Drew .20 .50
56 Tony Batista .20 .50
57 Paul Konerko .20 .50
58 Rafael Palmeiro .30 .75
59 Cal Ripken 1.50 4.00
60 Darin Erstad .20 .50
61 Ivan Rodriguez .30 .75
62 Barry Bonds 1.25 3.00
63 Edgardo Alfonzo .20 .50
64 Ellis Burks .20 .50
65 Mike Lieberthal .20 .50
66 Robin Ventura .20 .50
67 Richard Hidalgo .20 .50
68 Magglio Ordonez .20 .50
69 Kazuhiro Sasaki .20 .50
70 Miguel Tejada .20 .50
71 David Wells .20 .50
72 Troy Glaus .20 .50
73 Jose Vidro .20 .50
74 Shawn Green .20 .50
75 Barry Zito .30 .75
76 Jermaine Dye .20 .50
77 Geoff Jenkins .20 .50
78 Jeff Kent .20 .50
79 Al Leiter .20 .50
80 Delvi Cruz .20 .50
81 Eric Karros .20 .50
82 Albert Belle .20 .50
83 Pedro Martinez .30 .75
84 Raul Mondesi .20 .50
85 Preston Wilson .20 .50
86 Rafael Furcal .20 .50
87 Rick Ankiel .20 .50
88 Randy Johnson .50 1.25
89 Kevin Brown .20 .50
90 Sean Casey .20 .50
91 Mike Mussina .30 .75
92 Alex Rodriguez .75 2.00
93 Andres Galarraga .20 .50
94 Juan Gonzalez .20 .50
95 Manny Ramirez Sox .30 .75
96 Mark Grace .30 .75
97 Carl Everett .20 .50
98 Tony Gwynn .60 1.50
99 Mike Hampton .20 .50
100 Ken Caminiti .20 .50
101 Jason Hart/1749 3.00 8.00
102 Corey Patterson/1199 3.00 8.00
103 Timo Perez/1999 3.00 8.00
104 Marcus Giles/1999 3.00 8.00
105 I. Suzuki/1999 RC 20.00 50.00
106 Aubrey Huff/1499 3.00 8.00
107 Joe Crede/1999 4.00 10.00
108 Larry Barnes/1499 3.00 8.00
109 Esix Snead/1999 RC 3.00 8.00
110 Kenny Kelly/2249 3.00 8.00
111 Justin Miller/2249 3.00 8.00
112 Jack Cust/1999 3.00 8.00
113 Xavier Nady/999 3.00 8.00
114 Eric Munson/1499 3.00 8.00
115 E. Guzman/1749 RC 3.00 8.00
116 Juan Pierre/2189 3.00 8.00
117 W. Abreu/1749 RC 3.00 8.00
118 Keith Ginter/1999 3.00 8.00
119 Jace Brewer/2699 3.00 8.00
120 P. Crawford/2249 3.00 8.00
121 Jason Tyner/2249 3.00 8.00
122 Tike Redman/1999 3.00 8.00
123 John Riedling/2499 3.00 8.00
124 Jose Ortiz/1499 3.00 8.00
125 O. Mairena/2499 3.00 8.00
126 Eric Byrnes/2249 3.00 8.00
127 Brian Cole/999 3.00 8.00
128 Adam Piatt/2249 3.00 8.00
129 Nate Rolison/2499 3.00 8.00
130 Keith McDonald/2249 3.00 8.00
131 Albert Pujols/499 RC 125.00 250.00
132 Bud Smith/499 RC 3.00 8.00
133 T.Shinjo/499 RC 5.00 12.00
134 W.Betemit/499 RC 5.00 12.00
135 A.Hernandez/499 RC 3.00 8.00
136 J.Melian/499 RC 3.00 8.00
137 Jay Gibbons/499 RC 5.00 12.00
138 J.Estrada/499 RC 5.00 12.00
139 M.Ensberg/499 RC 5.00 12.00
140 Drew Henson/499 RC 5.00 12.00
NNO Derek Jeter 75.00 150.00
Base Inks AU/500
MM2 Derek Jeter 5.00 12.00
Monumental Moments
NNO Derek Jeter 60.00 120.00
Monumental Moments AU/96

2001 E-X Prospect Autographs

Randomly inserted into packs, this 29-card insert is actually an autographed parallel of cards 101-130 in the 2001 E-X base set (with exception of card 105). Please note that the print runs are listed below for each card.

101 Jason Hart/250 4.00 10.00
102 Corey Patterson/800 4.00 10.00
103 Timo Perez/1000 4.00 10.00
104 Marcus Giles/500 6.00 15.00
106 Aubrey Huff/500 6.00 15.00
107 Joe Crede/500 10.00 25.00
108 Larry Barnes/500 4.00 10.00
109 Esix Snead/500 4.00 10.00
110 Kenny Kelly/250 4.00 10.00
111 Justin Miller/250 4.00 10.00
112 Jack Cust/1000 4.00 10.00
113 Xavier Nady/1000 4.00 10.00
114 Eric Munson/1500 4.00 10.00
115 Elpidio Guzman/250 4.00 10.00
116 Juan Pierre/810 6.00 15.00
117 Winston Abreu/250 4.00 10.00
118 Keith Ginter/500 4.00 10.00
119 Jace Brewer/300 4.00 10.00
120 Paxton Crawford/250 4.00 10.00
121 Jason Tyner/250 4.00 10.00
122 Tike Redman/250 4.00 10.00
123 John Riedling/500 4.00 10.00
124 Jose Ortiz/500 4.00 10.00
125 Oswaldo Mairena/500 4.00 10.00
126 Eric Byrnes/250 4.00 10.00
127 Brian Cole/2000 6.00 15.00
128 Adam Piatt/250 4.00 10.00
129 Nate Rolison/500 4.00 10.00
130 Keith McDonald/250 4.00 10.00

2001 E-X Essential Credentials

Randomly inserted into packs, this 130-card insert is a complete parallel of the 2001 E-X base set. Please note that cards 1-100 are individually serial numbered to 299, while cards 101-130 are serial numbered to 29.

COMMON CARD (1-100) 2.00 5.00
*STARS 1-100: 5X TO 12X BASIC CARDS
COMMON (101-130) 6.00 15.00

2001 E-X Behind the Numbers Game Jersey

Randomly inserted into packs at one in 33, this 44-card insert features game used jersey swatches for some of the greatest players of all-time. Card backs carry a "BH" prefix.

BH1 Johnny Bench 6.00 15.00
BH2 Wade Boggs 6.00 15.00
BH3 George Brett 10.00 25.00
BH4 Lou Brock 6.00 15.00
BH5 Rollie Fingers 4.00 10.00
BH6 Carlton Fisk 6.00 15.00
BH7 Reggie Jackson 6.00 15.00
BH8 Al Kaline 6.00 15.00
BH9 Willie Mays 30.00 60.00
BH10 Willie McCovey 4.00 10.00
BH11 Paul Molitor 4.00 10.00
BH12 Eddie Murray 6.00 15.00
BH13 Jim Palmer 4.00 10.00
BH14 Ozzie Smith 6.00 15.00
BH15 Nolan Ryan 20.00 50.00
BH16 Mike Schmidt 10.00 25.00
BH17 Tom Seaver 6.00 15.00
BH18 Dave Winfield 4.00 10.00
BH19 Ted Williams 50.00 100.00
BH20 Robin Yount 6.00 15.00
BH21 Brady Anderson 4.00 10.00
BH22 Rick Ankiel 4.00 10.00
BH23 Albert Belle 4.00 10.00
BH24 Adrian Beltre 4.00 10.00
BH25 Barry Bonds 15.00 40.00
BH26 Eric Chavez 4.00 10.00
BH27 J.D. Drew 4.00 10.00
BH28 Darin Erstad 4.00 10.00
BH29 Troy Glaus 4.00 10.00
BH30 Mark Grace 6.00 15.00
BH31 Ben Grieve 4.00 10.00
BH32 Tony Gwynn 8.00 20.00
BH33 Todd Helton 6.00 15.00
BH34 Derek Jeter 15.00 40.00
BH35 Jeff Kent 4.00 10.00
BH36 Jason Kendall 4.00 10.00
BH37 Greg Maddux 8.00 20.00
BH38 John Olerud 4.00 10.00
BH39 Cal Ripken 15.00 40.00
BH40 Chipper Jones 6.00 15.00
BH41 John Smoltz 6.00 15.00
BH42 Frank Thomas 6.00 15.00
BH43 Robin Ventura 4.00 10.00
BH44 Bernie Williams 6.00 15.00

2001 E-X Behind the Numbers Game Jersey Autograph

Randomly inserted into packs, this 42-card insert is a partial parallel of the 2001 E-X Behind the Numbers insert. Each card in this set is autographed, and the stated print run for each card is listed below for your convenience.

1 Brady Anderson/9
2 Rick Ankiel/66 15.00 40.00
3 Albert Belle/88 20.00 50.00
4 Adrian Beltre/29 25.00 60.00
5 Johnny Bench/5
6 Wade Boggs/26 50.00 100.00
7 Barry Bonds/25
8 George Brett/5
9 Lou Brock/20
10 Eric Chavez/3
11 J.D. Drew/7
12 Darin Erstad/17
13 Rollie Fingers/34 20.00 50.00
14 Carlton Fisk/27 50.00 100.00
15 Troy Glaus/25
16 Mark Grace/17
17 Ben Grieve/14
18 Tony Gwynn/19
19 Todd Helton/17
20 Reggie Jackson/44 50.00 100.00
21 Derek Jeter/2
22 Chipper Jones/10
23 Al Kaline/6
24 Jason Kendall/18
25 Jeff Kent/21
26 Greg Maddux/31 175.00 300.00
27 Willie McCovey/44 40.00 80.00
28 Paul Molitor/4
29 Eddie Murray/33 50.00 100.00
30 John Olerud/5
31 Jim Palmer/22
32 Cal Ripken/8
33 Nolan Ryan/34 175.00 300.00
34 Mike Schmidt/20
35 Tom Seaver/41 50.00 100.00
36 Ozzie Smith/1
37 John Smoltz/29 40.00 80.00
38 Frank Thomas/35 50.00 100.00
39 Robin Ventura/4
40 Bernie Williams/51 50.00 100.00
41 Dave Winfield/31 50.00 100.00
42 Robin Yount/19

2001 E-X Extra Innings

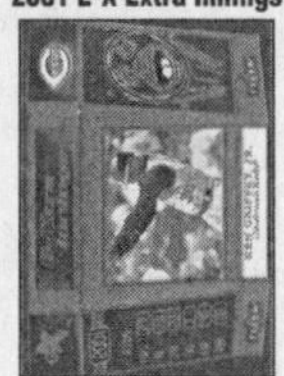

Randomly inserted into retail packs at one in 20, this 10-card insert features players that keep on going long after 9-innings. Card backs carry an "XI" prefix.

COMPLETE SET (10) 50.00 100.00
XI1 Mark McGwire 5.00 12.00
XI2 Sammy Sosa 2.00 5.00
XI3 Chipper Jones 2.00 5.00
XI4 Mike Piazza 3.00 8.00
XI5 Cal Ripken 6.00 15.00
XI6 Ken Griffey Jr. 3.00 8.00
XI7 Alex Rodriguez 3.00 8.00
XI8 Vladimir Guerrero 2.00 5.00
XI9 Nomar Garciaparra 3.00 8.00
XI10 Derek Jeter 5.00 12.00

2001 E-X Wall of Fame

Randomly inserted into packs at one in 24, this 30-card insert features swatches of the outfield walls used in Major League ballparks. Please note that the cards are not numbered, and are listed below in alphabetical order for convenience.

1 Jeff Bagwell 4.00 10.00
2 Barry Bonds 10.00 25.00
3 Pat Burrell 3.00 8.00
4 Roger Clemens 6.00 15.00
5 Nomar Garciaparra 6.00 15.00
6 Jason Giambi 3.00 8.00
7 Troy Glaus 3.00 8.00
8 Juan Gonzalez 3.00 8.00
9 Ken Griffey Jr. 6.00 15.00
10 Vladimir Guerrero 4.00 10.00
11 Tony Gwynn 6.00 15.00
12 Todd Helton 4.00 10.00
13 Geoff Jenkins 3.00 8.00
14 Derek Jeter 10.00 25.00
15 Andruw Jones 4.00 10.00
16 Chipper Jones 4.00 10.00
17 Jason Kendall 3.00 8.00
18 Greg Maddux 4.00 10.00
19 Pedro Martinez 4.00 10.00
20 Mark McGwire 15.00 40.00
21 Paul Molitor 3.00 8.00
22 Mike Piazza 4.00 10.00
23 Manny Ramirez Sox 4.00 10.00
24 Cal Ripken 15.00 40.00
25 Alex Rodriguez 6.00 15.00
26 Ivan Rodriguez 4.00 10.00
27 Scott Rolen 4.00 10.00
28 Sammy Sosa 4.00 10.00
29 Frank Thomas 4.00 10.00
30 Robin Yount 4.00 10.00

2002 E-X

This 139 card set was issued in May, 2002. It was released in four card packs which came 24 packs to a box and four boxes to a case. The price for hobby packs (which had many more inserts) was $5 per pack and the retail packs were $3 per pack. The first 100 cards featured veterans while the last 40 cards featured rookies and prospects. Cards numbered 101 through 125 were printed to specific serial numbers while cards numbered 126-140 were issued at a stated rate of one in 24 hobby or retail packs. Though the set is checklisted 1-140, card 133 does not exist. It was originally intended to feature Yankees prospect Drew Henson, but Fleer's exclusive contract with the ballplayer expired two weeks prior to the release of E-X.

COMP.SET w/o SP's (100) 10.00 25.00
COMMON CARD (1-100) .20 .50
COMMON CARD (101-120) 2.00 5.00
COMMON CARD (121-125) 2.00 5.00
COMMON CARD (126-140) 2.00 5.00
1 Alex Rodriguez .75 2.00
2 Albert Pujols 1.00 2.50
3 Ken Griffey Jr. .75 2.00
4 Vladimir Guerrero .50 1.25
5 Sammy Sosa .50 1.25
6 Ichiro Suzuki 1.00 2.50
7 Jorge Posada .30 .75
8 Matt Williams .20 .50
9 Adrian Beltre .20 .50
10 Pat Burrell .20 .50
11 Roger Cedeno .20 .50
12 Tony Clark .20 .50
13 Steve Finley .20 .50
14 Rafael Furcal .20 .50
15 Rickey Henderson .50 1.25
16 Richard Hidalgo .20 .50
17 Jason Kendall .20 .50
18 Tino Martinez .30 .75
19 Scott Rolen .30 .75
20 Shannon Stewart .20 .50
21 Jose Vidro .20 .50
22 Preston Wilson .20 .50
23 Raul Mondesi .20 .50
24 Lance Berkman .20 .50
25 Rick Ankiel .20 .50
26 Kevin Brown .20 .50
27 Jeromy Burnitz .20 .50
28 Jeff Cirillo .20 .50
29 Carl Everett .20 .50
30 Eric Chavez .20 .50
31 Freddy Garcia .20 .50
32 Mark Grace .30 .75
33 David Justice .20 .50
34 Fred McGriff .30 .75
35 Mike Mussina .30 .75
36 John Olerud .20 .50
37 Magglio Ordonez .20 .50
38 Curt Schilling .20 .50
39 Aaron Sele .20 .50
40 Robin Ventura .20 .50
41 Adam Dunn .20 .50
42 Jeff Bagwell .30 .75
43 Barry Bonds 1.25 3.00
44 Roger Clemens 1.00 2.50
45 Cliff Floyd .20 .50
46 Jason Giambi .20 .50
47 Juan Gonzalez .20 .50
48 Luis Gonzalez .20 .50
49 Cristian Guzman .20 .50
50 Todd Helton .30 .75
51 Derek Jeter 1.25 3.00
52 Rafael Palmeiro .30 .75
53 Mike Sweeney .20 .50
54 Ben Grieve .20 .50
55 Phil Nevin .20 .50
56 Mike Piazza .75 2.00
57 Moises Alou .20 .50
58 Ivan Rodriguez .30 .75
59 Manny Ramirez .30 .75
60 Brian Giles .20 .50
61 Jim Thome .30 .75
62 Larry Walker .20 .50
63 Bobby Abreu .20 .50
64 Troy Glaus .20 .50
65 Garret Anderson .20 .50
66 Roberto Alomar .30 .75
67 Bret Boone .20 .50
68 Marty Cordova .20 .50
69 Craig Biggio .30 .75
70 Omar Vizquel .30 .75
71 Jermaine Dye .20 .50
72 Darin Erstad .20 .50
73 Carlos Delgado .20 .50
74 Nomar Garciaparra .75 2.00
75 Greg Maddux .75 2.00
76 Tom Glavine .30 .75
77 Frank Thomas .50 1.25
78 Shawn Green .20 .50
79 Bobby Higginson .20 .50
80 Jeff Kent .20 .50
81 Chuck Knoblauch .20 .50
82 Paul Konerko .20 .50
83 Carlos Lee .20 .50
84 Jon Lieber .20 .50
85 Paul LoDuca .20 .50
86 Mike Lowell .20 .50
87 Edgar Martinez .30 .75
88 Doug Mientkiewicz .20 .50
89 Pedro Martinez .30 .75
90 Randy Johnson .50 1.25
91 Aramis Ramirez .20 .50
92 J.D. Drew .20 .50
93 Chris Richard .20 .50
94 Jimmy Rollins .20 .50
95 Ryan Klesko .20 .50
96 Gary Sheffield .20 .50
97 Chipper Jones .50 1.25
98 Greg Vaughn .20 .50
99 Mo Vaughn .20 .50
100 Bernie Williams .30 .75
101 John Foster NT/2999 RC 2.00 5.00
102 J. DeLaRosa NT/2999 RC 2.00 5.00
103 Ed. Almonte NT/2999 RC 2.00 5.00
104 Chris Booker NT/2999 RC 2.00 5.00
105 Victor Alvarez NT/2999 RC 2.00 5.00
106 Cliff Bartosh NT/2999 RC 2.00 5.00
107 Felix Escalona NT/2999 RC 2.00 5.00
108 C. Thurman NT/2999 RC 2.00 5.00
109 Kazuhisa Ishii NT/2999 RC 3.00 8.00
110 Mig. Asencio NT/2999 RC 2.00 5.00
111 P.J. Bevis NT/2499 RC 2.00 5.00
112 Gus. Chacin NT/2499 RC 3.00 8.00
113 Steve Kent NT/2499 RC 2.00 5.00
114 Tak. Nomura NT/2499 RC 2.00 5.00
115 Adam Walker NT/2499 RC 2.00 5.00
116 So Taguchi NT/2499 RC 3.00 8.00
117 Reed Johnson NT/2499 RC 3.00 8.00
118 Rod Rosario NT/2499 RC 2.00 5.00
119 Luis Martinez NT/2499 RC 2.00 5.00
120 Sat Komiyama NT/2499 RC 2.00 5.00
121 Sean Burroughs NT/1999 2.00 5.00
122 Hank Blalock NT/1999 3.00 8.00
123 Marlon Byrd NT/1999 2.00 5.00
124 Nick Johnson NT/1999 2.00 5.00
125 Mark Teixeira NT/1999 3.00 8.00
126 David Espinosa NT 2.00 5.00
127 Adrian Burnside NT RC 2.00 5.00
128 Mark Corey NT RC 2.00 5.00
129 Matt Thornton NT RC 2.00 5.00
130 Dane Sardinha NT 2.00 5.00
131 Juan Rivera NT 2.00 5.00
132 Austin Kearns NT 2.00 5.00
134 Ben Broussard NT 2.00 5.00
135 Orlando Hudson NT 2.00 5.00
136 Carlos Pena NT 2.00 5.00
137 Kenny Kelly NT 2.00 5.00
138 Bill Hall NT 2.00 5.00
139 Ron Chiavacci NT 2.00 5.00
140 Mark Prior NT 2.00 5.00

2002 E-X Essential Credentials Future

Randomly inserted in packs, these 125 cards have two distinct patterns of serial numbering. Cards numbered 1 through 60 are inversely numbered and have a game used piece on them while cards numbered 61 through 125 are also inversley numbered.

1 Alex Rodriguez Jsy/60 30.00 60.00
2 Albert Pujols Base/59 30.00 60.00
3 Ken Griffey Jr. Base/58 30.00 60.00
4 Vladimir Guerrero Base/57 15.00 40.00
5 Sammy Sosa Base/56 15.00 40.00
6 Ichiro Suzuki Base/55
7 Jorge Posada Bat/54 12.50 30.00
8 Matt Williams Bat/53 10.00 25.00
9 Adrian Beltre Bat/52 10.00 25.00
10 Pat Burrell Bat/51 10.00 25.00
11 Roger Cedeno Bat/50 10.00 25.00
12 Tony Clark Bat/49 10.00 25.00
13 Steve Finley Bat/48 12.50 30.00
14 Rafael Furcal Bat/47 12.50 30.00
15 Rickey Henderson Bat/46 20.00 50.00
16 Richard Hidalgo Bat/45 10.00 25.00
17 Jason Kendall Bat/44 12.50 30.00
18 Tino Martinez Bat/43 15.00 40.00
19 Scott Rolen Bat/42 15.00 40.00
20 Shannon Stewart Bat/41 12.50 30.00
21 Jose Vidro Bat/40 10.00 25.00
22 Preston Wilson Bat/39 12.50 30.00
23 Raul Mondesi Bat/38 12.50 30.00
24 Lance Berkman Bat/37 12.50 30.00
25 Rick Ankiel Jsy/36 10.00 25.00
26 Kevin Brown Jsy/35 15.00 40.00
27 Jeromy Burnitz Bat/34 15.00 40.00
28 Jeff Cirillo Jsy/33 12.50 30.00
29 Carl Everett Jsy/32 15.00 40.00
30 Eric Chavez Bat/31 15.00 40.00
31 Freddy Garcia Jsy/30 20.00 50.00
32 Mark Grace Jsy/29 20.00 50.00
33 David Justice Jsy/28 15.00 40.00
34 Fred McGriff Jsy/27 20.00 50.00
61 Jim Thome/125 5.00 12.00
62 Larry Walker/124 3.00 8.00
63 Bobby Abreu/123 3.00 8.00
64 Troy Glaus/122 3.00 8.00
65 Garret Anderson/121 3.00 8.00
66 Roberto Alomar/120 5.00 12.00
67 Bret Boone/119 3.00 8.00
68 Marty Cordova/118 3.00 8.00

69 Craig Biggio/117	5.00	12.00
70 Omar Vizquel/116	5.00	12.00
71 Jermaine Dye/115	3.00	8.00
72 Darin Erstad/114	3.00	8.00
73 Carlos Delgado/113	3.00	8.00
74 Nomar Garciaparra/112	12.50	30.00
75 Greg Maddux/111	12.50	30.00
76 Tom Glavine/110	5.00	12.00
77 Frank Thomas/109	8.00	20.00
78 Shawn Green/108	3.00	8.00
79 Bobby Higginson/107	3.00	8.00
80 Jeff Kent/106	3.00	8.00
81 Chuck Knoblauch/105	3.00	8.00
82 Paul Konerko/104	3.00	8.00
83 Carlos Lee/103	3.00	8.00
84 Jon Lieber/102	3.00	8.00
85 Paul LoDuca/101	3.00	8.00
86 Mike Lowell/100	3.00	8.00
87 Edgar Martinez/99	5.00	12.00
88 Doug Mientkiewicz/98	3.00	8.00
89 Pedro Martinez/97	5.00	12.00
90 Randy Johnson/96	8.00	20.00
91 Aramis Ramirez/95	3.00	8.00
92 J.D. Drew/94	3.00	8.00
93 Chris Richard/93	3.00	8.00
94 Jimmy Rollins/92	3.00	8.00
95 Ryan Klesko/91	3.00	8.00
96 Gary Sheffield/90	3.00	8.00
97 Chipper Jones/89	8.00	20.00
98 Greg Vaughn/88	3.00	8.00
99 Mo Vaughn/87	3.00	8.00
100 Bernie Williams/86	5.00	12.00
101 John Foster NT/85	3.00	8.00
102 Jorge De La Rosa NT/84	3.00	8.00
103 Edwin Almonte NT/83	3.00	8.00
104 Chris Booker NT/82	3.00	8.00
105 Victor Alvarez NT/81	3.00	8.00
106 Cliff Bartosh NT/80	4.00	10.00
107 Felix Escalona NT/79	4.00	10.00
108 Corey Thurman NT/78	4.00	10.00
109 Kazuhisa Ishii NT/77	6.00	15.00
110 Miguel Asencio NT/76	4.00	10.00
111 P.J. Bevis NT/75	4.00	10.00
112 Gustavo Chacin NT/74	10.00	25.00
113 Steve Kent NT/73	4.00	10.00
114 Takahito Nomura NT/72	4.00	10.00
115 Adam Walker NT/71	4.00	10.00
116 So Taguchi NT/70	6.00	15.00
117 Reed Johnson NT/69	6.00	15.00
118 Rodrigo Rosario NT/68	4.00	10.00
119 Luis Martinez NT/67	4.00	10.00
120 Satoru Komiyama NT/66	4.00	10.00
121 Sean Burroughs NT/65	5.00	12.00
122 Hank Blalock NT/64	8.00	20.00
123 Marlon Byrd NT/63	5.00	12.00
124 Nick Johnson NT/62	5.00	12.00
125 Mark Teixeira NT/61	12.50	30.00

2002 E-X Essential Credentials Now

26 Kevin Brown Jsy/26	15.00	40.00
27 Jeromy Burnitz Bat/27	15.00	40.00
28 Jeff Cirillo Jsy/28	12.50	30.00
29 Carl Everett Jsy/29	15.00	40.00
30 Eric Chavez Bat/30	15.00	40.00
31 Freddy Garcia Jsy/31	15.00	40.00
32 Mark Grace Jsy/32	20.00	50.00
33 David Justice Jsy/33	15.00	40.00
34 Fred McGriff Jsy/34	20.00	50.00
35 Mike Mussina Jsy/35		
36 John Olerud Jsy/36	12.50	30.00
37 Magglio Ordonez Jsy/37	12.50	30.00
38 Curt Schilling Jsy/38	12.50	30.00
39 Aaron Sele Jsy/39	10.00	25.00
40 Robin Ventura Jsy/40	12.50	30.00
41 Adam Dunn Bat/41	12.50	30.00
42 Jeff Bagwell Jsy/42	15.00	40.00
43 Barry Bonds Pants/43	60.00	120.00
44 Roger Clemens Bat/44	50.00	100.00
45 Cliff Floyd Bat/45	12.50	30.00
46 Jason Giambi Base/46	12.50	30.00
47 Juan Gonzalez Jsy/47	12.50	30.00
48 Luis Gonzalez Base/48	12.50	30.00
49 Cristian Guzman Bat/49	10.00	25.00
50 Todd Helton Base/50	15.00	40.00
51 Derek Jeter Bat/51	60.00	120.00
52 Rafael Palmeiro Bat/52	12.50	30.00
53 Mike Sweeney Bat/53	10.00	25.00
54 Ben Grieve Jsy/54	8.00	20.00
55 Phil Nevin Bat/55	10.00	25.00
56 Mike Piazza Base/56	30.00	60.00
57 Moises Alou Bat/57	10.00	25.00
58 Ivan Rodriguez Jsy/58	12.50	30.00
59 Manny Ramirez Base/59	12.50	30.00
60 Brian Giles Bat/60	10.00	25.00
61 Jim Thome/61	8.00	20.00
62 Larry Walker/62	5.00	12.00
63 Bobby Abreu/63	5.00	12.00
64 Troy Glaus/64	5.00	12.00
65 Garret Anderson/65	5.00	12.00
66 Roberto Alomar/66	6.00	15.00
67 Bret Boone/67	4.00	10.00
68 Marty Cordova/68	4.00	10.00
69 Craig Biggio/69	6.00	15.00
70 Omar Vizquel/70	6.00	15.00
71 Jermaine Dye/71	4.00	10.00
72 Darin Erstad/72	4.00	10.00
73 Carlos Delgado/73	4.00	10.00
74 Nomar Garciaparra/74	15.00	40.00
75 Greg Maddux/75	15.00	40.00
76 Tom Glavine/76	6.00	15.00
77 Frank Thomas/77	10.00	25.00
78 Shawn Green/78	4.00	10.00
79 Bobby Higginson/79	4.00	10.00
80 Jeff Kent/80	4.00	10.00
81 Chuck Knoblauch/81	3.00	8.00
82 Paul Konerko/82	3.00	8.00
83 Carlos Lee/83	3.00	8.00
84 Jon Lieber/84	3.00	8.00
85 Paul LoDuca/85	3.00	8.00
86 Mike Lowell/86	3.00	8.00
87 Edgar Martinez/87	5.00	12.00
88 Doug Mientkiewicz/88	3.00	8.00
89 Pedro Martinez/89	5.00	12.00
90 Randy Johnson/90	8.00	20.00
91 Aramis Ramirez/91	3.00	8.00
92 J.D. Drew/92	3.00	8.00
93 Chris Richard/93	3.00	8.00
94 Jimmy Rollins/94	3.00	8.00
95 Ryan Klesko/95	3.00	8.00
96 Gary Sheffield/96	3.00	8.00
97 Chipper Jones/97	8.00	20.00
98 Greg Vaughn/98	3.00	8.00
99 Mo Vaughn/99	3.00	8.00
100 Bernie Williams/100	5.00	12.00
101 John Foster NT/101	3.00	8.00
102 Jorge De La Rosa NT/102	3.00	8.00
103 Edwin Almonte NT/103	3.00	8.00
104 Chris Booker NT/104	3.00	8.00
105 Victor Alvarez NT/105	3.00	8.00
106 Cliff Bartosh NT/106	3.00	8.00
107 Felix Escalona NT/107	3.00	8.00
108 Corey Thurman NT/108	3.00	8.00
109 Kazuhisa Ishii NT/109	5.00	12.00
110 Miguel Asencio NT/110	3.00	8.00
111 P.J. Bevis NT/111	3.00	8.00
112 Gustavo Chacin NT/112	8.00	20.00
113 Steve Kent NT/113	3.00	8.00
114 Takahito Nomura NT/114	3.00	8.00
115 Adam Walker NT/115	3.00	8.00
116 So Taguchi NT/116	5.00	12.00
117 Reed Johnson NT/117	5.00	12.00
118 Rodrigo Rosario NT/118	3.00	8.00
119 Luis Martinez NT/119	3.00	8.00
120 Satoru Komiyama NT/120	3.00	8.00
121 Sean Burroughs NT/121	3.00	8.00
122 Hank Blalock NT/122	5.00	12.00
123 Marlon Byrd NT/123	3.00	8.00
124 Nick Johnson NT/124	3.00	8.00
125 Mark Teixeira NT/125	8.00	20.00

2002 E-X Behind the Numbers

Inserted at stated odds of one in eight hobby and one in 12 retail, these 35 cards pays tribute to special numbers for hitters and pitchers.

COMPLETE SET (35)	50.00	120.00
1 Ichiro Suzuki	3.00	8.00
2 Jason Giambi	1.00	2.50
3 Mike Piazza	2.50	6.00
4 Brian Giles	1.00	2.50
5 Barry Bonds	4.00	10.00
6 Pedro Martinez	1.00	2.50
7 Nomar Garciaparra	2.50	6.00
8 Randy Johnson	1.50	4.00
9 Craig Biggio	1.00	2.50
10 Manny Ramirez	1.00	2.50
11 Mike Mussina	1.00	2.50
12 Kerry Wood	1.00	2.50
13 Jim Edmonds	1.00	2.50
14 Ivan Rodriguez	1.00	2.50
15 Jeff Bagwell	1.00	2.50
16 Roger Clemens	3.00	8.00
17 Chipper Jones	1.50	4.00
18 Shawn Green	1.00	2.50
19 Albert Pujols	3.00	8.00
20 Andruw Jones	1.00	2.50
21 Luis Gonzalez	1.00	2.50
22 Todd Helton	1.00	2.50
23 Jorge Posada	1.00	2.50
24 Scott Rolen	1.00	2.50
25 Ben Sheets	1.00	2.50
26 Alfonso Soriano	1.00	2.50
27 Greg Maddux	2.50	6.00
28 Gary Sheffield	1.00	2.50
29 Barry Zito	1.00	2.50
30 Alex Rodriguez	2.50	6.00
31 Larry Walker	1.00	2.50
32 Derek Jeter	4.00	10.00
33 Ken Griffey Jr.	2.50	6.00
34 Vladimir Guerrero	1.50	4.00
35 Sammy Sosa	1.50	4.00

2002 E-X Behind the Numbers Game Jersey

This partial parallel, issued at a stated rate of one in 24 hobby packs and one in 130 retail packs, features not only the Behind the Numbers insert card but a swatch of game used memorabilia.

1 Jeff Bagwell	6.00	15.00
2 Craig Biggio Jsy/Pants	6.00	15.00
3 Barry Bonds SP/50		
4 Roger Clemens	10.00	25.00
5 Jim Edmonds	4.00	10.00
6 Brian Giles	4.00	10.00
7 Luis Gonzalez	4.00	10.00
8 Shawn Green	4.00	10.00
9 Todd Helton	6.00	15.00
10 Derek Jeter SP	15.00	40.00
11 Randy Johnson SP	6.00	15.00
12 Andruw Jones	6.00	15.00
13 Chipper Jones	6.00	15.00
14 Greg Maddux	6.00	15.00
15 Pedro Martinez	6.00	15.00
16 Mike Mussina	6.00	15.00
17 Mike Piazza Pants	6.00	15.00
18 Jorge Posada	6.00	15.00
19 Manny Ramirez	6.00	15.00
20 Alex Rodriguez	8.00	20.00
21 Ivan Rodriguez	6.00	15.00
22 Scott Rolen	6.00	15.00
23 Alfonso Soriano SP	4.00	10.00
24 Barry Zito	4.00	10.00

2002 E-X Behind the Numbers Game Jersey Dual

Randomly inserted in packs, these seven cards feature two swatches of jerseys from players who wear the same uniform number. These cards have a stated print run of 25 serial number sets and there is no pricing due to scarcity.

1 Craig Biggio
Ivan Rodriguez
2 Barry Bonds
Andruw Jones
3 Jim Edmonds
Shawn Green
4 Brian Giles
Manny Ramirez
5 Greg Maddux
Mike Piazza
6 Scott Rolen
Todd Helton
7 Alfonso Soriano
Larry Walker

2002 E-X Barry Bonds 4X MVP

Randomly inserted in packs, these four cards have a stated print run to the years in which Barry Bonds won the MVP award.

COMMON CARD (1-4)	4.00	10.00

2002 E-X Game Essentials

Randomly inserted in packs, these 35 cards feature players along with a piece of their game-used gear.

*PATCH PREMIUM: 1.5X TO 3X LISTED PRICE

1 Carlos Beltran Jsy	4.00	10.00
2 Barry Bonds Btg Glv SP		
3 Barry Bonds Wristband SP		
4 Kevin Brown Pants	4.00	10.00
5 Jeromy Burnitz Jsy	4.00	10.00
6 Carlos Delgado Bat	4.00	10.00
7 Jason Hart Bat SP		
8 Rickey Henderson Bat	6.00	15.00
9 Rickey Henderson Jsy	6.00	15.00
10 Drew Henson Bat	4.00	10.00
11 Drew Henson Cleat	4.00	10.00
12 Drew Henson Fld Glv	6.00	15.00
13 Derek Jeter Cleat	20.00	50.00
14 Jason Kendall Jsy	4.00	10.00
15 Jeff Kent Jsy SP		
16 Barry Larkin Fld Glv	10.00	25.00
17 Javy Lopez Jsy	4.00	10.00
18 Raul Mondesi Btg Glv	6.00	15.00
19 Raul Mondesi Jsy	4.00	10.00
20 Rafael Palmeiro Bat	6.00	15.00
21 Rafael Palmeiro Pants	6.00	15.00
22 Adam Piatt Jsy	4.00	10.00
23 Brad Radke Jsy	4.00	10.00
24 Cal Ripken Jsy	15.00	40.00
25 Mariano Rivera Jsy	6.00	15.00
26 Alex Rodriguez Btg Glv	10.00	25.00
27 Alex Rodriguez Cleat SP		
28 Ivan Rodriguez Cleat SP		
29 Kazuhiro Sasaki Jsy	4.00	10.00
30 J.T. Snow Jsy SP		
31 Mo Vaughn Jsy	4.00	10.00
32 Robin Ventura Btg Glv	6.00	15.00
33 Robin Ventura Jsy	4.00	10.00
34 Jose Vidro Jsy	4.00	10.00
35 Matt Williams Jsy	4.00	10.00

2002 E-X HardWear

Inserted in packs at stated odds of one in 72 hobby and one in 216 retail, these 10 cards feature players who play the game with proper aggressiveness.

COMPLETE SET (10)	40.00	100.00
1 Ivan Rodriguez	3.00	8.00
2 Mike Piazza	5.00	12.00
3 Derek Jeter	8.00	20.00
4 Barry Bonds	8.00	20.00
5 Todd Helton	3.00	8.00
6 Roberto Alomar	3.00	8.00
7 Albert Pujols	6.00	15.00
8 Ichiro Suzuki	6.00	15.00
9 Ken Griffey Jr.	5.00	12.00
10 Jason Giambi	3.00	8.00

2002 E-X Hit and Run

Inserted at stated odds of one in 12 hobby and one in 72 retail, these 30 cards feature players who do the best job of hitting a baseball.

COMPLETE SET (30)	40.00	100.00
1 Adam Dunn	1.00	2.50
2 Derek Jeter	4.00	10.00
3 Frank Thomas	1.50	4.00
4 Albert Pujols	3.00	8.00
5 J.D. Drew	1.00	2.50
6 Richard Hidalgo	1.00	2.50
7 John Olerud	1.00	2.50
8 Roberto Alomar	1.00	2.50
9 Pat Burrell	1.00	2.50
10 Darin Erstad	1.00	2.50
11 Mark Grace	1.00	2.50
12 Chipper Jones	1.50	4.00
13 Jose Vidro	1.00	2.50
14 Cliff Floyd	1.00	2.50
15 Mo Vaughn	1.00	2.50
16 Nomar Garciaparra	2.50	6.00
17 Ivan Rodriguez	1.00	2.50
18 Luis Gonzalez	1.00	2.50
19 Jason Giambi	1.00	2.50
20 Bernie Williams	1.00	2.50
21 Mike Piazza	2.50	6.00
22 Barry Bonds	4.00	10.00
23 Jose Ortiz	1.00	2.50
24 Magglio Ordonez	1.00	2.50
25 Troy Glaus	1.00	2.50
26 Alex Rodriguez	2.50	6.00
27 Ichiro Suzuki	3.00	8.00
28 Sammy Sosa	1.50	4.00
29 Ken Griffey Jr.	2.50	6.00
30 Vladimir Guerrero	1.50	4.00

2002 E-X Hit and Run Game Base

Inserted in packs at stated odds of one in 120 hobby and one in 360 retail, this 10-card partial parallel set to the Hit and Run set includes a game base piece.

1 J.D. Drew	3.00	8.00
2 Adam Dunn	3.00	8.00
3 Jason Giambi	3.00	8.00
4 Troy Glaus	3.00	8.00
5 Ken Griffey Jr.	6.00	15.00
6 Vladimir Guerrero	4.00	10.00
7 Albert Pujols	6.00	15.00
8 Sammy Sosa	4.00	10.00
9 Ichiro Suzuki	6.00	15.00
10 Bernie Williams	4.00	10.00

2002 E-X Hit and Run Game Bat

Inserted in packs at a stated rate of one in 24 hobby and one in 130 retail packs, this 19-card partial parallel set features not only players from the Hit and Run insert set but a game bat sliver attached to the card.

1 Roberto Alomar	5.00	12.00
2 J.D. Drew	3.00	8.00
3 Darin Erstad	3.00	8.00
4 Cliff Floyd	3.00	8.00
5 Nomar Garciaparra	10.00	25.00
6 Luis Gonzalez	3.00	8.00
7 Richard Hidalgo	3.00	8.00
8 Derek Jeter	12.50	30.00
9 Chipper Jones	5.00	12.00
10 John Olerud	3.00	8.00
11 Magglio Ordonez	3.00	8.00
12 Jose Ortiz	3.00	8.00
13 Mike Piazza	6.00	15.00
14 Alex Rodriguez	8.00	20.00
15 Ivan Rodriguez	5.00	12.00
16 Frank Thomas	5.00	12.00
17 Mo Vaughn	3.00	8.00
18 Jose Vidro	3.00	8.00
19 Bernie Williams	5.00	12.00

2002 E-X Hit and Run Game Bat and Base

Inserted in packs at a stated rate of one in 240 hobby and one in 720 retail packs, these eight cards are a partial parallel to the Hit and Run insert set. These cards feature both a piece of a game bat and a base used by the featured players.

1 Roberto Alomar	6.00	15.00
2 Barry Bonds SP		
3 Nomar Garciaparra	15.00	40.00
4 Derek Jeter	20.00	50.00
5 Chipper Jones	10.00	25.00
6 Mike Piazza	12.50	30.00
7 Alex Rodriguez	15.00	40.00
8 Mo Vaughn	6.00	15.00

2002 E-X Derek Jeter 4X Champ

Randomly inserted in packs, these four cards honor the four years that Fleer representative Derek Jeter was on a World Series Champion. These cards have a stated print run of the season in which Jeter finished as a champion.

COMMON CARD (1-4)	4.00	10.00

2003 E-X

This 102 card set was issued in October, 2003. This set was issued in three card packs which had an $6 SRP and were issued 20 packs to a box and 12 boxes to a case. The first 72 cards featured common veterans while cards 73 through 82 feature shorter printed veterans and cards numbered 83 through 86 feature 2003 rookies and cards numbered 87 through 102 feature Rookie Cards of the player.

COMP.SET w/o SP's (72)	15.00	40.00
COMMON CARD (1-72)	.20	.50
COMMON CARD (73-82)	1.50	4.00
COMMON CARD (83-86)	1.50	4.00
COMMON CARD (87-102)	1.50	4.00
1 Troy Glaus	.20	.50
2 Darin Erstad	.20	.50
3 Garret Anderson	.20	.50
4 Curt Schilling	.20	.50
5 Randy Johnson	.50	1.25
6 Luis Gonzalez	.20	.50
7 Greg Maddux	.75	2.00
8 Chipper Jones	.50	1.25
9 Andruw Jones	.30	.75
10 Melvin Mora	.20	.50
11 Jay Gibbons	.20	.50
12 Nomar Garciaparra	.75	2.00
13 Pedro Martinez	.30	.75
14 Manny Ramirez	.30	.75
15 Sammy Sosa	.50	1.25
16 Kerry Wood	.20	.50
17 Magglio Ordonez	.20	.50
18 Frank Thomas	.50	1.25
19 Roberto Alomar	.30	.75
20 Barry Larkin	.30	.75
21 Adam Dunn	.20	.50
22 Austin Kearns	.20	.50
23 Omar Vizquel	.30	.75
24 Larry Walker	.20	.50
25 Todd Helton	.30	.75
26 Preston Wilson	.20	.50
27 Dmitri Young	.20	.50
28 Ivan Rodriguez	.30	.75
29 Mike Lowell	.20	.50
30 Jeff Kent	.20	.50
31 Jeff Bagwell	.30	.75
32 Roy Oswalt	.20	.50
33 Craig Biggio	.30	.75
34 Mike Sweeney	.20	.50
35 Carlos Beltran	.20	.50
36 Shawn Green	.20	.50
37 Kazuhisa Ishii	.20	.50
38 Richie Sexson	.20	.50
39 Torii Hunter	.20	.50
40 Jacque Jones	.20	.50
41 Jose Vidro	.20	.50
42 Vladimir Guerrero	.50	1.25
43 Mike Piazza	.75	2.00
44 Tom Glavine	.30	.75
45 Roger Clemens	1.00	2.50
46 Jason Giambi	.20	.50
47 Bernie Williams	.30	.75
48 Alfonso Soriano	.20	.50
49 Mike Mussina	.30	.75
50 Barry Zito	.20	.50
51 Miguel Tejada	.20	.50
52 Eric Chavez	.20	.50
53 Eric Byrnes	.20	.50
54 Jim Thome	.30	.75
55 Kevin Millwood	.20	.50
56 Brian Giles	.20	.50
57 Xavier Nady	.20	.50
58 Barry Bonds	1.25	3.00
59 Bret Boone	.20	.50
60 Edgar Martinez	.30	.75
61 Kazuhiro Sasaki	.20	.50
62 Edgar Renteria	.20	.50
63 J.D. Drew	.20	.50
64 Scott Rolen	.30	.75
65 Jim Edmonds	.20	.50
66 Aubrey Huff	.20	.50
67 Alex Rodriguez	.75	2.00
68 Juan Gonzalez	.20	.50
69 Hank Blalock	.20	.50
70 Mark Teixeira	.30	.75
71 Carlos Delgado	.20	.50
72 Vernon Wells	.20	.50
73 Shea Hillenbrand SP	1.50	4.00
74 Gary Sheffield SP	1.50	4.00
75 Mark Prior SP	2.00	5.00
76 Ken Griffey Jr. SP	5.00	12.00
77 Lance Berkman SP	1.50	4.00
78 Hideo Nomo SP	6.00	15.00
79 Derek Jeter SP	8.00	20.00
80 Ichiro Suzuki SP	6.00	15.00
81 Albert Pujols SP	6.00	15.00
82 Rafael Palmeiro SP	2.00	5.00
83 Jose Reyes ROO SP	1.50	4.00
84 Rocco Baldelli ROO SP	1.50	4.00
85 Hee Seop Choi ROO SP	1.50	4.00
86 Dontrelle Willis ROO SP	2.00	5.00
87 Robb Hammock ROO SP RC	1.50	4.00
88 Brandon Webb ROO SP RC	4.00	10.00
89 Matt Kata ROO SP RC	1.50	4.00
90 T.Wellemeyer ROO SP RC	1.50	4.00
91 Fran Cruceta ROO SP RC	1.50	4.00
92 Clint Barmes ROO SP RC	1.50	4.00
93 Jer Bonderman ROO SP RC	5.00	12.00
94 David Matranga ROO SP RC	1.50	4.00
95 Ryan Wagner ROO SP RC	1.50	4.00
96 Jeremy Griffiths ROO SP RC	1.50	4.00
97 Hideki Matsui ROO SP RC	6.00	15.00
98 Jose Contreras ROO SP RC	2.00	5.00
99 C.Wang ROO SP RC	4.00	10.00
100 Bo Hart ROO SP RC	1.50	4.00
101 Danny Haren ROO SP RC	2.00	5.00
102 Rickie Weeks ROO SP RC	3.00	8.00

2003 E-X Essential Credentials Future

*EC FUTURE 1-22: 4X TO 10X BASIC
*EC FUTURE 23-52: 5X TO 12X BASIC
*EC FUTURE 53-67: 6X TO 15X BASIC
*EC FUTURE 68-72: 8X TO 20X BASIC
*EC FUTURE 73-77: 1.5X TO 4X BASIC
PRINT RUNS B/WN 1-102 COPIES PER
78-102 NOT PRICED DUE TO SCARCITY

2003 E-X Essential Credentials Now

*EC NOW 26-30: 10X TO 25X BASIC
*EC NOW 31-35: 8X TO 20X BASIC
*EC NOW 36-50: 6X TO 15X BASIC
*EC NOW 51-72: 5X TO 12X BASIC
*EC NOW 73-80: .75X TO 2X BASIC
*EC NOW 81-82: .6X TO 1.5X BASIC
*EC NOW 83-102: .75X TO 2X BASIC
*EC NOW 83-102: .75X TO 2X BASIC RC'S
PRINT RUNS B/WN 1-102 COPIES PER
1-25 NO PRICING DUE TO SCARCITY

99 Chien-Ming Wang ROO/99	12.50	30.00

2003 E-X Behind the Numbers

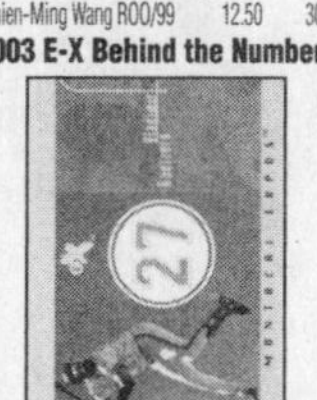

STATED ODDS 1:80

1 Derek Jeter	8.00	20.00
2 Alex Rodriguez	5.00	12.00
3 Randy Johnson	3.00	8.00
4 Chipper Jones	3.00	8.00
5 Jim Thome	3.00	8.00
6 Alfonso Soriano	2.00	5.00
7 Adam Dunn	2.00	5.00
8 Nomar Garciaparra	5.00	12.00
9 Roger Clemens	6.00	15.00
10 Gary Sheffield	2.00	5.00
11 Vladimir Guerrero	3.00	8.00
12 Greg Maddux	5.00	12.00
13 Sammy Sosa	3.00	8.00
14 Mike Piazza	5.00	12.00
15 Troy Glaus	2.00	5.00

2003 E-X Behind the Numbers Game Jersey 500

PRINT RUN 500 SERIAL #'d SETS
*BTN 199: .5X TO 1.2X BTN 500
BTN 199 PRINT RUN 199 #'d SETS
*BTN 99 MULTI-PATCH: 1.25X TO 3X BTN 500
*BTN 99 ONE COLOR: .75X TO 2X BTN 500
BTN 99 PRINT RUN 99 #'d SETS
BTN 99 ARE MOSTLY PATCH CARDS

AD Adam Dunn	2.00	5.00
AR Alex Rodriguez	5.00	12.00
AS Alfonso Soriano	2.00	5.00
BM Brett Myers	2.00	5.00
BZ Barry Zito	2.00	5.00
CJ Chipper Jones	3.00	8.00
DJ Derek Jeter	8.00	20.00
DW Dontrelle Willis	3.00	8.00
GM Greg Maddux	4.00	10.00
GS Gary Sheffield	2.00	5.00
HB Hank Blalock	2.00	5.00
JT Jim Thome	3.00	8.00
LB Lance Berkman	2.00	5.00
MB Marlon Byrd	2.00	5.00
MP Mike Piazza	4.00	10.00
NG Nomar Garciaparra	5.00	12.00
RA Roberto Alomar	3.00	8.00
RB Rocco Baldelli	2.00	5.00
RC Roger Clemens	5.00	12.00
RJ Randy Johnson	3.00	8.00
RP Rafael Palmeiro	3.00	8.00
SS Sammy Sosa	3.00	8.00
TG Troy Glaus	2.00	5.00
TGL Tom Glavine	3.00	8.00
VG Vladimir Guerrero	3.00	8.00

2003 E-X Behind the Numbers Game Jersey Autographs

Please note there is no expiration date to redeem the Marlon Byrd autographs.

PRINT RUNS B/WN 5-35 COPIES PER

DW Dontrelle Willis/35	10.00	25.00
HB Hank Blalock/9		
MB Marlon Byrd/29		
RB Rocco Baldelli/5		

2003 E-X Behind the Numbers Game Jersey Number

PRINT RUNS B/WN 2-75 COPIES PER
NO PRICING ON QTY OF 25 OR LESS

AD Adam Dunn/44	8.00	20.00
AR Alex Rodriguez/3		
AS Alfonso Soriano/12		
BM Brett Myers/39	6.00	15.00
BZ Barry Zito/75	4.00	10.00
CJ Chipper Jones/10		
DJ Derek Jeter/2		
DW Dontrelle Willis/35	10.00	25.00
GM Greg Maddux/31	15.00	40.00
GS Gary Sheffield/11		
HB Hank Blalock/9		
JT Jim Thome/25		
LB Lance Berkman/17		
MB Marlon Byrd/29	8.00	20.00
MP Mike Piazza/31	15.00	40.00
NG Nomar Garciaparra/5		
RA Roberto Alomar/12		
RB Rocco Baldelli/5		
RC Roger Clemens/22		
RJ Randy Johnson/51	6.00	15.00
RP Rafael Palmeiro/25		
SS Sammy Sosa/21		
TG Troy Glaus/25		
TGL Tom Glavine/47	8.00	20.00
VG Vladimir Guerrero/27	10.00	25.00

2003 E-X Diamond Essentials

STATED ODDS 1:480
NO MORE THAN 30 SETS PRODUCED
PRINT RUN INFO PROVIDED BY FLEER
NO PRICING DUE TO SCARCITY

2003 E-X Diamond Essentials Autographs

Please note there is no scheduled expiration date to redeem these Albert Pujols autographs.

PRINT RUNS B/WN 100-299 COPIES PER
AP Albert Pujols/100
DW Dontrelle Willis/265 10.00 25.00
RB Rocco Baldelli/299 6.00 15.00
RW Ryan Wagner/199 6.00 15.00

2003 E-X Diamond Essentials Game Jersey 345

STATED PRINT RUN 345 SERIAL #'d SETS
*DE 245: .5X TO 1.2X DE 345
DE 245 PRINT RUN 245 #'d SETS
*DE 145: .6X TO 1.5X DE 345
DE 145 PRINT RUN 145 #'d SETS
*DE 55 MULTI-PATCH: 1.25X TO 3X DE 345
*DE 55 ONE COLOR: 1X TO 2.5X DE 345
DE 55 PRINT RUN 55 #'d SETS
DE 55 ARE MOSTLY PATCH CARDS
DE 5 PRINT RUN 5 #'d SETS
NO DE 5 PRICING DUE TO SCARCITY
CJ Chipper Jones 3.00 8.00
DJ Derek Jeter 8.00 20.00
JB Jeff Bagwell 3.00 8.00
JG Jason Giambi 2.00 5.00
JR Jose Reyes 2.00 5.00
MP Mike Piazza 5.00 12.00
MP Mark Prior 3.00 8.00
PM Pedro Martinez 3.00 8.00
RJ Randy Johnson 3.00 8.00
SS Sammy Sosa 3.00 8.00

2003 E-X Emerald Essentials

STATED ODDS 1:240
NO PRICING DUE TO SCARCITY

2003 E-X Emerald Essentials Autographs

Please note that there is no expiration date to redeem the Marlon Byrd autographs.

PRINT RUNS B/WN 29-299 COPIES PER
BW Brandon Webb/299 15.00 40.00
HB Hank Blalock/299 6.00 15.00
MB Marlon Byrd/29

2003 E-X Emerald Essentials Game Jersey 375

STATED PRINT RUN 375 SERIAL #'d SETS
*EE 250: .5X TO 1.2X EE 375
EE 250 PRINT RUN 250 #'d SETS
*EE 175: .6X TO 1.5X EE 375
EE 175 PRINT RUN 175 #'d SETS
*EE 60 SWATCH: 1X TO 2.5X EE 375
*EE 60 MULTI-PATCH: 1.25X TO 3X EE 375
EE 60 PRINT RUN 60 #'d SETS
ABOUT HALF OF EE 60'S ARE PATCH CARDS
EE 15 PRINT RUN 15 #'d SETS
NO EE 15 PRICING DUE TO SCARCITY
AD Adam Dunn 2.00 5.00
AK Austin Kearns 2.00 5.00
AR Alex Rodriguez 5.00 12.00
AS Alfonso Soriano 2.00 5.00
HN Hideo Nomo 6.00 15.00
KW Kerry Wood 2.00 5.00
MT Miguel Tejada 2.00 5.00
NG Nomar Garciaparra 5.00 12.00
RC Roger Clemens 5.00 12.00
TG Troy Glaus 2.00 5.00

2003 E-X X-tra Innings

STATED ODDS 1:32
1 Ichiro Suzuki 4.00 10.00
2 Albert Pujols 4.00 10.00
3 Barry Bonds 5.00 12.00
4 Jason Giambi 1.50 4.00
5 Pedro Martinez 2.00 5.00
6 Mark Prior 2.00 5.00
7 Derek Jeter 5.00 12.00
8 Curt Schilling 1.50 4.00
9 Jeff Bagwell 2.00 5.00
10 Alex Rodriguez 3.00 8.00

2004 E-X

This 65-card set was released in late August, 2004. The set was issued in seven -card packs with an $200 SRP which came 12 "packs" to a case. The first 40-cards of this set featured veterans while the final 25 cards feature Rookie Cards and leading prospects which were inserted at a stated rate of one per pack. Those cards (41-65) were issued to a stated print run of 350 serial numbered sets with the first 150 of those cards being die-cut.

COMMON CARD (1-40) .40 1.00
COMMON CARD (41-65) 1.00 2.50
SEE PARALLEL SET FOR DIE CUT PRICES
1 Vladimir Guerrero 1.00 2.50
2 Randy Johnson 1.00 2.50
3 Chipper Jones 1.00 2.50
4 Miguel Tejada .60 1.50
5 Pedro Martinez .60 1.50
6 Nomar Garciaparra 1.00 2.50
7 Sammy Sosa 1.00 2.50
8 Greg Maddux 1.50 4.00
9 Frank Thomas 1.00 2.50
10 Ken Griffey Jr. 1.50 4.00
11 Omar Vizquel .60 1.50
12 Todd Helton .60 1.50
13 Ivan Rodriguez .60 1.50
14 Miguel Cabrera 1.00 2.50
15 Dontrelle Willis .40 1.00
16 Jeff Bagwell .60 1.50
17 Roger Clemens 1.25 3.00
18 Carlos Beltran .40 1.00
19 Hideo Nomo 1.00 2.50
20 Scott Podsednik .40 1.00
21 Torii Hunter .40 1.00
22 Jose Vidro .40 1.00
23 Mike Piazza 1.00 2.50
24 Hideki Matsui 1.50 4.00
25 Alex Rodriguez 1.50 4.00
26 Derek Jeter 2.50 6.00
27 Tim Hudson .60 1.50
28 Jim Thome .60 1.50
29 Craig Wilson .40 1.00
30 Brian Giles .40 1.00
31 Jason Schmidt .40 1.00
32 Ichiro Suzuki 1.50 4.00
33 Scott Rolen .60 1.50
34 Albert Pujols 2.50 6.00
35 Rocco Baldelli .40 1.00
36 Alfonso Soriano .40 1.00
37 Carlos Delgado .40 1.00
38 Curt Schilling .60 1.50
39 Mark Prior .60 1.50
40 Josh Beckett .60 1.50
41 Merkin Valdez ROO RC 1.00 2.50
42 Akinori Otsuka ROO RC 1.00 2.50
43 Ian Snell ROO RC 1.00 2.50
44 Kaz Matsui ROO RC 1.50 4.00
45 Jason Bartlett ROO RC 3.00 8.00
46 Dennis Sarfate ROO RC 1.00 2.50
47 Sean Henn ROO RC 1.00 2.50
48 David Aardsma ROO RC 1.00 2.50
49 Casey Kotchman ROO 1.00 2.50
50 John Gall ROO RC 1.00 2.50
51 William Bergolla ROO RC 1.00 2.50
52 Angel Chavez ROO RC 1.00 2.50
53 Hector Gimenez ROO RC 1.00 2.50
54 Aaron Baldiris ROO RC 1.00 2.50
55 Justin Leone ROO RC 1.00 2.50
56 Onil Joseph ROO RC 1.00 2.50
57 Freddy Guzman ROO RC 1.00 2.50
58 Andres Blanco ROO RC 1.00 2.50
59 Greg Dobbs ROO RC 1.00 2.50
60 Joe Mauer ROO 2.50 6.00
61 Luis Gonzalez ROO RC 1.00 2.50
62 Chris Saenz ROO RC 1.00 2.50
63 Zack Greinke ROO 1.50 4.00
64 Jose Capellan ROO RC 1.00 2.50
65 Brad Halsey ROO RC 1.00 2.50

2004 E-X Die Cuts

*DIE CUTS 41-65: .5X TO 1.2X BASIC
41-65 OVERALL ODDS ONE PER PACK
STATED PRINT RUN 150 SERIAL #'d SETS
DIE CUTS ARE 1ST 150 SERIAL #'d COPIES

2004 E-X Essential Credentials Future

*FUTURE p/r 51-65: 1.5X TO 4X BASIC
*FUTURE p/r 36-50: 2X TO 5X BASIC
*FUTURE p/r 26-35: 2.5X TO 6X BASIC
OVERALL PARALLEL ODDS 1:3
PRINT RUNS B/WN 1-65 COPIES PER
NO PRICING ON QTY OF 25 OR LESS

2004 E-X Essential Credentials Now

*NOW p/r 51-65: .75X TO 2X BASIC
*NOW p/r 41-50: 1X TO 2.5X BASIC
*NOW p/r
*NOW p/r 26-35: 2.5X TO 6X BASIC
*NOW p/r 16-25: 3X TO 8X BASIC
OVERALL PARALLEL ODDS 1:3
PRINT RUNS B/WN 1-65 COPIES PER
NO PRICING ON QTY OF 14 OR LESS

2004 E-X Check Mates

OVERALL AUTO ODDS ONE PER PACK
PRINT RUNS B/WN 1-25 COPIES PER
NO PRICING ON QTY OF 1 COPY PER
EXCHANGE DEADLINE INDEFINITE
APSM Albert Pujols 300.00 400.00
Stan Musial/25
BRLG Babe Ruth
Lou Gehrig/1
CYDS Carl Yastrzemski
Duke Snider/25
EBRS Ernie Banks 125.00 200.00
Ryne Sandberg/25
EMRP Eddie Murray 90.00 150.00
Rafael Palmeiro/25
HWTC Honus Wagner
Ty Cobb/1
MRPM Manny Ramirez
Pedro Martinez/25
RJDM Reggie Jackson 150.00 250.00
Don Mattingly/25
RJGM Randy Johnson
Greg Maddux/25
RYKP Robin Yount
Kirby Puckett/25
WBTG Wade Boggs 100.00 175.00
Tony Gwynn/25
YBJB Yogi Berra
Johnny Bench/25

2004 E-X Classic ConnExions Game Used Double

STATED PRINT RUN 22 SERIAL #'d SETS
DOUBLE EMERALD PRINT RUN 1 #'d SET
NO DOUBLE EMERALD PRICING AVAILABLE
OVERALL GU ODDS ONE PER PACK
BRJF Babe Ruth Bat 150.00 250.00
Jimmie Foxx Bat
CRBR Cal Ripken Jsy 75.00 150.00
Brooks Robinson Bat
CRNR Cal Ripken Jsy 75.00 150.00
Nolan Ryan Jsy
CRRY Cal Ripken Jsy 60.00 120.00
Robin Yount Jsy
DMRJ Don Mattingly Jsy 40.00 80.00
Reggie Jackson Jsy
DMTM Don Mattingly Jsy 50.00 100.00
Thurman Munson Jsy
DWCY Dave Winfield Jsy 20.00 50.00
Carl Yastrzemski Jsy
EMCR Eddie Murray Jsy 75.00 150.00
Cal Ripken Jsy
EMRJ Eddie Murray Jsy 30.00 60.00
Reggie Jackson Jsy
HKAK Harmon Killebrew Pants 30.00 60.00
Al Kaline Pants
HWHG Hack Wilson Bat 50.00 100.00
Hank Greenberg Bat
JBCF Johnny Bench Jsy 30.00 60.00
Carlton Fisk Pants
JCRH Jose Canseco Jsy 30.00 60.00
Rickey Henderson Jsy
KPDM Kirby Puckett Jsy 40.00 80.00
Don Mattingly Jsy
LBRC Lou Brock Jsy 15.00 40.00
Rod Carew Jsy
MSEM Mike Schmidt Jsy 75.00 150.00
Eddie Mathews Pants
NRTS Nolan Ryan Jsy 60.00 120.00
Tom Seaver Jsy
PMRY Paul Molitor Jsy 30.00 60.00
Robin Yount Jsy
RCRJ Rod Carew Jsy 15.00 40.00
Reggie Jackson Jsy
RHLB Rickey Henderson Jsy 30.00 60.00
Lou Brock Jsy
RMBR Roger Maris Bat 175.00 300.00
Babe Ruth Bat
TGRH Tony Gwynn Jsy 40.00 80.00
Rickey Henderson Jsy
TWCY Ted Williams Bat 125.00 200.00
Carl Yastrzemski Bat
WBCY Wade Boggs Bat 30.00 60.00
Carl Yastrzemski Jsy
WBDM Wade Boggs Jsy 30.00 60.00
Don Mattingly Jsy
WBTG Wade Boggs Bat 30.00 60.00
Tony Gwynn Jsy
WMWS Willie McCovey Bat 15.00 40.00
Willie Stargell Bat
WSWF Warren Spahn Jsy 30.00 60.00
Whitey Ford Pants
YBRC Yogi Berra Bat 30.00 60.00
Roy Campanella Bat

2004 E-X Classic ConnExions Game Used Triple

STATED PRINT RUN 13 SERIAL #'d SETS
TRIPLE EMERALD PRINT RUN 1 #'d SET
NO TRIPLE EMERALD PRICING AVAILABLE
OVERALL GU ODDS ONE PER PACK

2004 E-X Clearly Authentics Black Patch

*3-COLOR PATCHES: ADD 20% PREMIUM
*4-COLOR PATCHES: ADD 50% PREMIUM
*5-COLOR PATCHES: ADD 100% PREMIUM
*JSY TAG PATCHES: ADD 100% PREMIUM
OVERALL GU ODDS ONE PER PACK
STATED PRINT RUN 75 SERIAL #'d SETS
AD Adam Dunn 6.00 15.00
AJ Andruw Jones 8.00 20.00
AP Albert Pujols 20.00 50.00
AR Alex Rodriguez 15.00 40.00
AS Alfonso Soriano 6.00 15.00
BG Brian Giles 6.00 15.00
BZ Barry Zito 6.00 15.00
CJ Chipper Jones 10.00 25.00
CR Cal Ripken 40.00 80.00
CS Curt Schilling 8.00 20.00
DM Don Mattingly 20.00 50.00
DW Dontrelle Willis 8.00 20.00
EG Eric Gagne 6.00 15.00
EM Eddie Murray 15.00 40.00
FT Frank Thomas 10.00 25.00
GM Greg Maddux 12.50 30.00
HB Hank Blalock 6.00 15.00
HM Hideki Matsui 30.00 60.00
HN Hideo Nomo 15.00 40.00
IR Ivan Rodriguez 8.00 20.00
JB Jeff Bagwell 8.00 20.00
JB2 Josh Beckett 6.00 15.00
JG2 Jason Giambi 6.00 15.00
JT Jim Thome 8.00 20.00
KM Kaz Matsui 10.00 25.00
KW Kerry Wood 6.00 15.00
LB Lance Berkman 6.00 15.00
MC Miguel Cabrera 8.00 20.00
MO Magglio Ordonez 6.00 15.00
MP Mark Prior 8.00 20.00
MP2 Mike Piazza 15.00 40.00
MR Manny Ramirez 8.00 20.00
MT Mark Teixeira 8.00 20.00
MT2 Miguel Tejada 6.00 15.00
OS Ozzie Smith 15.00 40.00
PB Pat Burrell 6.00 15.00
PM Paul Molitor 6.00 15.00
PR Pedro Martinez 8.00 20.00
RB Rocco Baldelli 6.00 15.00
RC Roger Clemens 15.00 40.00
RC2 Rod Carew 10.00 25.00
RH Rickey Henderson 12.50 30.00
RJ Randy Johnson 10.00 25.00
RP Rafael Palmeiro 8.00 20.00
RW Rickie Weeks 6.00 15.00
SG Shawn Green 6.00 15.00
SR Scott Rolen 8.00 20.00
SS Sammy Sosa 10.00 25.00
TG Troy Glaus 6.00 15.00
TG2 Tony Gwynn 15.00 40.00
TH Todd Helton 8.00 20.00
TH2 Torii Hunter 6.00 15.00
TH3 Tim Hudson 6.00 15.00
VG Vladimir Guerrero 10.00 25.00

2004 E-X Clearly Authentics Bronze Jersey-Patch

*BRONZE JSY-PATCH: .6X TO 1.5X BASIC
*3-COLOR PATCHES: ADD 20% PREMIUM
*4-COLOR PATCHES: ADD 50% PREMIUM
*5-COLOR PATCHES: ADD 100% PREMIUM
*JSY TAG PATCHES: ADD 100% PREMIUM
OVERALL GU ODDS ONE PER PACK
STATED PRINT RUN 35 SERIAL #'d SETS
CY Carl Yastrzemski 25.00 60.00
RJ2 Reggie Jackson 15.00 40.00

2004 E-X Clearly Authentics Burgundy Triple Patch

OVERALL GU ODDS ONE PER PACK
STATED PRINT RUN 13 SERIAL #'d SETS
NO PRICING DUE TO SCARCITY

2004 E-X Clearly Authentics Pewter Bat-Patch

*PEWTER BAT-PATCH: .6X TO 1.5X BASIC
*3-COLOR PATCHES: ADD 20% PREMIUM
*4-COLOR PATCHES: ADD 50% PREMIUM
*5-COLOR PATCHES: ADD 100% PREMIUM
*JSY TAG PATCHES: ADD 100% PREMIUM
OVERALL GU ODDS ONE PER PACK
STATED PRINT RUN 44 SERIAL #'d SETS
CY Carl Yastrzemski 25.00 60.00
RJ2 Reggie Jackson 15.00 40.00

2004 E-X Clearly Authentics Royal Blue Bat-Jersey-Patch

OVERALL GU ODDS ONE PER PACK
STATED PRINT RUN 8 SERIAL #'d SETS
NO PRICING DUE TO SCARCITY

2004 E-X Clearly Authentics Tan Double Patch

*TAN DOUBLE PATCH: .75X TO 2X BASIC
*3-COLOR PATCHES: ADD 20% PREMIUM
*4-COLOR PATCHES: ADD 50% PREMIUM
*5-COLOR PATCHES: ADD 100% PREMIUM
*JSY TAG PATCHES: ADD 100% PREMIUM
OVERALL GU ODDS ONE PER PACK
STATED PRINT RUN 22 SERIAL #'d SETS
CY Carl Yastrzemski 30.00 80.00
RJ2 Reggie Jackson 20.00 50.00

2004 E-X Clearly Authentics Turquoise Nameplate

OVERALL GU ODDS ONE PER PACK
PRINT RUNS B/WN 4-11 COPIES PER
NO PRICING DUE TO SCARCITY

2004 E-X Clearly Authentics Double MLB Logo

OVERALL GU ODDS ONE PER PACK
STATED PRINT RUN 1 SERIAL #'d SET
NO PRICING DUE TO SCARCITY

2004 E-X Clearly Authentics Signature Black Jersey

*3-COLOR PATCHES: ADD 20% PREMIUM
*4-COLOR PATCHES: ADD 50% PREMIUM
*5-COLOR PATCHES: ADD 100% PREMIUM
*JSY TAG PATCHES: ADD 100% PREMIUM
OVERALL AUTO ODDS ONE PER PACK
PRINT RUNS B/WN 17-50 COPIES PER
EXCHANGE DEADLINE INDEFINITE
AP Albert Pujols/50 150.00 250.00
BW Bernie Williams/42 20.00 50.00
BZ Barry Zito/18 15.00 40.00
CJ Chipper Jones/50 30.00 60.00
DW Dontrelle Willis/50 15.00 40.00
FT Frank Thomas/50 30.00 60.00
GM Greg Maddux/37
GS Gary Sheffield/50 15.00 40.00
HB Hank Blalock/50 10.00 25.00
IR Ivan Rodriguez/50 20.00 50.00
JB Josh Beckett/50 15.00 40.00
JD J.D. Drew/50 10.00 25.00
KW Kerry Wood/34 20.00 50.00
MC Miguel Cabrera/50 15.00 40.00
MP1 Mike Piazza/37 60.00 120.00
MR1 Manny Ramirez/50 30.00 60.00
MR2 Mariano Rivera/50 40.00 80.00
PM Pedro Martinez/23 60.00 120.00
RC Roger Clemens/50 75.00 150.00
RJ Randy Johnson/17 40.00 80.00
RO Roy Oswalt/49 10.00 25.00
RP Rafael Palmeiro/43 30.00 60.00
TG Troy Glaus/50 15.00 40.00
TH Todd Helton/50 15.00 40.00
VG Vladimir Guerrero/50 30.00 60.00

2004 E-X Clearly Authentics Signature Burgundy Button

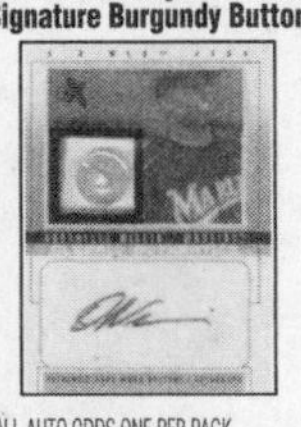

OVERALL AUTO ODDS ONE PER PACK
STATED PRINT RUN 6 SERIAL #'d SETS
NO PRICING DUE TO SCARCITY
EXCHANGE DEADLINE INDEFINITE

2004 E-X Clearly Authentics Signature Emerald MLB Logo

OVERALL AUTO ODDS ONE PER PACK
STATED PRINT RUN 1 SERIAL #'d SET
NO PRICING DUE TO SCARCITY
EXCHANGE DEADLINE INDEFINITE

2004 E-X Clearly Authentics Signature Pewter Jersey

*PTR p/r 36-41: .4X TO 1X BLK p/r 50
*PTR p/r 20-27: .5X TO 1.2X BLK p/r 50
*3-COLOR PATCHES: ADD 20% PREMIUM
*4-COLOR PATCHES: ADD 50% PREMIUM
*5-COLOR PATCHES: ADD 100% PREMIUM
*JSY TAG PATCHES: ADD 100% PREMIUM
OVERALL AUTO ODDS ONE PER PACK
PRINT RUNS B/WN 7-41 COPIES PER
NO PRICING ON QTY OF 10 OR LESS

2004 E-X Clearly Authentics Signature Tan Patch

*TAN p/r 75: .4X TO .1X BLK p/r 18
*TAN p/r 42-51: .6X TO 1.5X BLK p/r 42-50
*TAN p/r 42-51: .4X TO 1X BLK p/r 23
*TAN p/r 42-51: .4X TO 1X BLK p/r 17
*TAN p/r 21-35: .6X TO 1.5X BLK p/r 37-50
*TAN p/r 21-35: .5X TO 1.2X BLK p/r 34
*TAN p/r 17: .75X TO 2X BLK p/r 50
*3-COLOR PATCHES: ADD 20% PREMIUM
*4-COLOR PATCHES: ADD 50% PREMIUM
*5-COLOR PATCHES: ADD 100% PREMIUM
*JSY TAG PATCHES: ADD 100% PREMIUM
OVERALL AUTO ODDS ONE PER PACK
PRINT RUNS B/WN 5-75 COPIES PER
NO PRICING ON QTY OF 11 OR LESS
EXCHANGE DEADLINE INDEFINITE
RC Roger Clemens/22 100.00 200.00

2004 E-X ConnExions Dual Autograph

OVERALL AUTO ODDS ONE PER PACK
PRINT RUNS B/WN 25-50 COPIES PER
EXCHANGE DEADLINE INDEFINITE
ABCB Adrian Beltre 30.00 60.00
Carlos Beltran/25
BBMW Bill Buckner 30.00 60.00
Mookie Wilson/50
BDMT Bucky Dent 20.00 50.00
Mike Torrez/50
BGMG Brian Giles 30.00 60.00
Marcus Giles/25
BJDS Bo Jackson
Deion Sanders/25
BZTH Barry Zito 40.00 80.00
Tim Hudson/25
CKJM Casey Kotchman 50.00 100.00
Joe Mauer/50
CLMO Carlos Lee 30.00 60.00
Magglio Ordonez/25
CWJW Craig Wilson 20.00 50.00
Jack Wilson/25
DWMC Dontrelle Willis 40.00 80.00
Miguel Cabrera/25
EGBW Eric Gagne
Billy Wagner/25
JDTN Johnny Damon 50.00 100.00
Trot Nixon/25
JNPN Joe Niekro 20.00 50.00
Phil Niekro/50
KGDE Kirk Gibson 40.00 80.00
Dennis Eckersley/25
MTHB Mark Teixeira 40.00 80.00
Hank Blalock/25
MYKG Michael Young 40.00 80.00
Khalil Greene/50
RWDY Rickie Weeks 40.00 80.00
Delmon Young/25
SPLO Scott Podsednik 40.00 80.00
Lyle Overbay/25
SSTH Shannon Stewart 30.00 60.00
Torii Hunter/25

2004 E-X Double Barrel

OVERALL GU ODDS ONE PER PACK
STATED PRINT RUN 1 SERIAL #'d SET
NO PRICING DUE TO SCARCITY

2004 E-X Signings of the Times Best Year

OVERALL AUTO ODDS ONE PER PACK
PRINT RUNS B/WN 48-94 COPIES PER
EXCHANGE DEADLINE INDEFINITE
BJ Bo Jackson Jsy/89 30.00 60.00
CY Carl Yastrzemski Bat/67 40.00 80.00
DM Don Mattingly Jsy/85 40.00 80.00
DS Duke Snider Bat/55 20.00 50.00
DS2 Deion Sanders Jsy/92 30.00 60.00
EB Ernie Banks Bat/58 40.00 80.00
EM Eddie Murray Jsy/83 30.00 60.00
GB George Brett Jsy/80 50.00 100.00
JB Johnny Bench Jsy/72 30.00 60.00
JC Jose Canseco Jsy/88 15.00 40.00
KP Kirby Puckett Bat/88 50.00 100.00
MS Mike Schmidt Jsy/80 50.00 100.00
NR Nolan Ryan Jsy/73 75.00 150.00
OS Ozzie Smith Jsy/87 30.00 60.00
RH Rickey Henderson Jsy/90 40.00 80.00
RJ Reggie Jackson Jsy/73 30.00 60.00
RS Ryne Sandberg Bat/90 40.00 80.00
RY Robin Yount Jsy/82
SM Stan Musial Bat/48 40.00 80.00
TG Tony Gwynn Jsy/94 30.00 60.00
TS Tom Seaver Jsy/69 20.00 50.00
WB Wade Boggs Bat/87 15.00 40.00
WC Will Clark Jsy/91 15.00 40.00
YB Yogi Berra Bat/54 50.00 100.00

2004 E-X Signings of the Times Debut Year

*DEBUT p/r 66-89: .4X TO 1X BEST p/r 69-94
*DEBUT p/r 41-61: .4X TO 1X BEST p/r 48-58
OVERALL AUTO ODDS ONE PER PACK
PRINT RUNS B/WN 41-89 COPIES PER
EXCHANGE DEADLINE INDEFINITE

2004 E-X Signings of the Times Emerald

OVERALL AUTO ODDS ONE PER PACK
STATED PRINT RUN 1 SERIAL #'d SET
NO PRICING DUE TO SCARCITY
EXCHANGE DEADLINE INDEFINITE

2004 E-X Signings of the Times HOF Year

*HOF p/r 69-99: .4X TO 1X BEST p/r 67-82
*HOF p/r 69-99: .6X TO .8X BEST p/r 48-58
OVERALL AUTO ODDS ONE PER PACK
PRINT RUNS B/WN 1-99 COPIES PER
NO PRICING ON QTY OF 3 OR LESS
EXCHANGE DEADLINE INDEFINITE
CY Carl Yastrzemski Bat/89 30.00 80.00
DS Duke Snider Bat/80 15.00 40.00
EB Ernie Banks Bat/77 25.00 60.00
EM Eddie Murray Jsy/3
GB George Brett Jsy/99 40.00 100.00
JB Johnny Bench Jsy/89 25.00 60.00
KP Kirby Puckett Bat/1
MS Mike Schmidt Jsy/95 40.00 100.00
NR Nolan Ryan Jsy/99 60.00 150.00
OS Ozzie Smith Jsy/2
RJ Reggie Jackson Jsy/93 25.00 60.00
RY Robin Yount Jsy/99
SM Stan Musial Bat/69 25.00 60.00
TS Tom Seaver Jsy/92 20.00 50.00
YB Yogi Berra Bat/72 50.00 100.00

2004 E-X Signings of the Times Pewter

*PTR p/r 36-60: .5X TO 1.2X BEST p/r 83-92
*PTR p/r 36-60: .4X TO 1X BEST p/r 48
*PTR p/r 21-33: .6X TO 1.5X BEST p/r 85-94
*PTR p/r 21-33: .5X TO 1.2X BEST p/r 54-58
OVERALL AUTO ODDS ONE PER PACK
PRINT RUNS B/WN 21-60 COPIES PER

1939-46 Exhibits Salutation

This collection of exhibit cards shares a common style: the "Personal Greeting" or "Salutation". The specific

greeting varies from card to card -- "Yours truly, Best wishes, etc." -- as does the location of the exhibit identification (lower left, LL, or lower right, LR). Some players appear with different teams and there are occasional misspellings. Each card measures 3 3/8" by 5 3/8". The Bob Feller (Yours Truly), Andy Pafko (Yours Truly) and Ted Williams (Sincerely Yours) cards are relatively quite common as they were still being printed into the middle to late 1950s, i.e., basically until the end of their respective careers. The Jeff Heath small picture variation (26B) is differentiated by measuring the distance between the top of his cap and the top edge of the card; for the small picture variation that distance is approximately 5/8" whereas it is only 3/8" for 26A. There is some doubt about whether Camilli #6B exists. An Andy Pafko sincerely yours card is rumored to exist but has never been verified, while the 50B Pafko is a very tough card since it was printed only in 1960.

COMPLETE SET (84) 4000.00 8000.00
1A Luke Appling LL 15.00 25.00
Sincerely Yours
1B Luke Appling LR 9.00 15.00
Sincerely Yours
2 Earl Averill 500.00 800.00
Very Best Wishes
3 Charles Red Barrett 3.00 5.00
Yours Truly
4 Henry Hank Borowy 3.00 5.00
Sincerely Yours
5 Lou Boudreau 5.00 8.00
Sincerely
6A Adolf Camilli LL 15.00 25.00
Very Truly Yours
6B Adolf Camilli LR 120.00 200.00
Very Truly Yours
7 Phil Cavarretta 3.00 5.00
Cordially Yours
8 Harland Clift 12.00 20.00
Very Truly Yours
9 Tony Cuccinello 25.00 40.00
Very Best Wishes
10 Dizzy Dean 60.00 100.00
Sincerely
11 Paul Derringer 3.00 5.00
Yours Truly
12A Bill Dickey LL 30.00 50.00
Cordially Yours
12B Bill Dickey LR 30.00 50.00
Cordially Yours
13 Joe DiMaggio 70.00 120.00
Cordially
14 Bob Elliott 3.00 5.00
Truly Yours
15A Bob Feller 70.00 120.00
Best Wishes
(portrait)
15B Bob Feller 9.00 15.00
Yours Truly
(pitching pose)
16 Dave Ferriss 3.00 5.00
Best of Luck
17 Jimmy Foxx 120.00 200.00
Sincerely
18 Lou Gehrig 1200.00 2000.00
Sincerely
19 Charlie Gehringer 75.00 125.00
Yours Truly
20 Lefty Gomez 120.00 200.00
21A Joe Gordon 15.00 25.00
(Cleveland)
Sincerely
21B Joe Gordon 3.00 5.00
(New York)
Sincerely
22A Hank Greenberg 20.00 35.00
Truly Yours
22B Henry Greenberg 90.00 150.00
Very Truly Yours
23 Robert Grove 75.00 125.00
Cordially Yours
24 Gabby Hartnett 200.00 350.00
Cordially
25 Buddy Hassett 15.00 25.00
Yours Truly
26A Jeff Heath 15.00 25.00
Best Wishes
26B Jeff Heath 3.00 5.00
(Small Picture)
Best Wishes
27 Kirby Higbe 15.00 25.00
Sincerely
28A Tommy Holmes 120.00 200.00
Sincerely Yours
28B Tommy Holmes 3.00 5.00
Yours Truly
29 Carl Hubbell 60.00 100.00
Best Wishes
30 Bob Johnson 15.00 25.00
Yours Truly
31A Charles Keller LL 15.00 25.00
Best Wishes
31B Charles Keller LR 6.00 10.00
Best Wishes
32 Ken Keltner 30.00 50.00
Sincerly (sic)
33 Chuck Klein 180.00 300.00
Yours Truly
34 Mike Kreevich 150.00 250.00
Sincerely
35 Joe Kuhel 3.00 5.00
Truly Yours
36 Bill Lee 12.00 20.00
Cordially Yours
37A Ernie Lombardi 250.00 400.00
(1/2 B) Cordially
38B Ernie Lombardi 6.00 10.00
Cordially Yours
39 Marty Marion 6.00 10.00
Best Wishes
40 Merrill May 15.00 25.00
Best Wishes
41A Frank McCormick LL 15.00 25.00
Sincerely
41B Frank McCormick LR 3.00 5.00
Sincerely
42A George McQuinn LL 15.00 25.00
Yours Truly
42B George McQuinn LR 3.00 5.00
Yours Truly
43 Joe Medwick 20.00 35.00
Very Best Wishes
44A Johnny Mize LL 25.00 40.00
Yours Truly
44B Johnny Mize LR 9.00 15.00
Yours Truly
45 Hugh Mulcahy 15.00 25.00
Cordially
46 Hal Newhouser 9.00 15.00
Best Wishes
47 Louis (Buck) Newsom 15.00 25.00
Sincerely
48 Buck Newson (sic) 180.00 300.00
Very Best Wishes
49A Mel Ott LL 30.00 50.00
Sincerely Yours
49B Mel Ott LR 25.00 40.00
Sincerely Yours
50A Andy Pafko 3.00 5.00
Yours Truly
50B Andy Pafko 20.00 40.00
Yours Truly
(plain cap)
51 Claude Passeau 3.00 5.00
Sincerely
52A Howard Pollet LL 15.00 25.00
Best Wishes
52B Howard Pollet LR 3.00 5.00
Best Wishes
53A Pete Reiser LL 60.00 100.00
Truly Yours
53B Pete Reiser LR 5.00 8.00
Truly Yours
54 Johnny Rizzo 300.00 500.00
Sincerely Yours
55 Glenn Russell 180.00 300.00
Sincerely
56 George Stirnweiss 3.00 5.00
Yours Truly
57 Cecil Travis 9.00 15.00
Best Wishes
58 Paul Trout 3.00 5.00
Truly Yours
59 Johnny Vander Meer 30.00 50.00
Cordially Yours
60 Arky Vaughan 15.00 25.00
Best Wishes
61A Fred Dixie Walker 3.00 5.00
(D on Hat)
Yours Truly
61B Fred Dixie Walker 40.00 75.00
Cap blanked out
Yours Truly
62 Bucky Walters 3.00 5.00
Sincerely Yours
63 Lon Warneke 12.00 20.00
Very Truly Yours
64A Ted Williams Sincerely #9 Showing 200.00400.00
64B Ted Williams Sincerely Yours #9 Not Showing
45.00 80.00
65 Rudy York 3.00 5.00
Cordially

1947-66 Exhibits

This grouping encompasses a wide time span but displays a common design. The following players have been illegally reprinted in mass quantities on a thinner-than-original cardboard which is also characterized by a dark gray back: Aaron, Ford, Fox, Hodges, Elston Howard, Mantle, Mays, Musial, Newcombe, Reese, Spahn, and Ted Williams. Each card measures 3 3/8" by 5 3/8". In the checklist below SIG refers to signature and SCR refers to script name on card. The abbreviations POR (portrait), BAT (batting), and FIE (fielding) are also used below. There are many levels of scarcity within this "set," essentially based on which year(s) the player's card was printed. The Mickey Mantle portrait card, for example, was only printed in 1966, the last year of production. Those scarce cards which were only produced one or two years are noted parenthetically below by the last two digits of the year(s) of issue. Cards which seem to be especially difficult to obtain are the ones produced only in 1966 which are the aforementioned Mantle Portrait, Ford, Kranepool, Richardson, Skowron (White Sox), Ward and Yastrzemski. Some leading exhibit experts believe that the salutation and these cards should be checklisted together because of the long printing history of some of the salutations.

COMPLETE SET (321) 4000.00 8000.00
1 Hank Aaron 30.00 60.00
(has been reprinted)
2A Joe Adcock SCR 3.00 8.00
2B Joe Adcock SIG 3.00 8.00
3 Max Alvis 66 30.00 60.00
4A Johnny Antonelli 3.00 8.00
(Braves)
4B Johnny Antonelli 3.00 8.00
(Giants)
5A Luis Aparicio POR 4.00 10.00
5B Luis Aparicio BAT 64 40.00 80.00
6 Luke Appling 4.00 10.00
7A Richie Ashburn 30.00 60.00
(Phillies)
7B Ritchie Ashburn 6.00 15.00
(sic, Richie)
7C Richie Ashburn 40.00 80.00
(Cubs) 61
8 Bob Aspromonte 64/66 3.00 8.00
9 Toby Atwell 3.00 8.00
10A Ed Bailey 61 6.00 15.00
(Cincinnati cap)
10B Ed Bailey (no cap) 3.00 8.00
11 Gene Baker 3.00 8.00
12A Ernie Banks SCR 20.00 50.00
12B Ernie Banks SIG 10.00 25.00
12C Ernie Banks POR [illegible] [illegible]
64/66
13 Steve Barber 64/66 3.00 8.00
14 Earl Battey 64/66 3.00 8.00
15 Matt Batts 4.00 10.00
16A Hank Bauer 3.00 8.00
(New York cap)
16B Hank Bauer 61 20.00 50.00
(plain cap)
17 Frank Baumholtz 3.00 8.00
18 Gene Bearden 3.00 8.00
19 Joe Beggs 47 12.50 30.00
20A Yogi Berra 6.00 15.00
20B Larry Yogi Berra 30.00 60.00
64/66
21 Steve Bilko 3.00 8.00
22A Ewell Blackwell 4.00 10.00
(foot up)
22B Ewell Blackwell POR 3.00 8.00
23A Don Blasingame 3.00 8.00
(St. Louis cap)
23B Don Blasingame 4.00 10.00
(plain cap)
24 Ken Boyer 64/66 12.50 30.00
25 Ralph Branca 3.00 8.00
26 Jackie Brandt 61 40.00 80.00
27 Harry Brecheen 3.00 8.00
28 Tom Brewer 61 30.00 60.00
29 Lou Brissie 3.00 8.00
30 Bill Bruton 3.00 8.00
31A Lew Burdette 3.00 8.00
(side view)
31B Lew Burdette 15.00 40.00
(facing) 64
32 Johnny Callison 64/66 4.00 10.00
33 Roy Campanella 30.00 60.00
34A Chico Carrasquel 3.00 8.00
(White Sox)
34B Chico Carrasquel 10.00 25.00
(plain cap)
35 George Case 47 12.50 30.00
36 Hugh Casey 6.00 15.00
37 Norm Cash 64/66 10.00 25.00
38A Orlando Cepeda POR 10.00 25.00
60/61
38B Orlando Cepeda BAT 10.00 25.00
64/66
39A Bob Cerv 60 3.00 8.00
(A's uniform)
39B Bob Cerv 61 30.00 60.00
(plain uniform)
40 Dean Chance 64/66 3.00 8.00
41 Spud Chandler 47 12.50 30.00
42 Tom Cheney 64/66 3.00 8.00
43 Bubba Church 3.00 8.00
44 Roberto Clemente 75.00 150.00
45A Rocky Colavito POR 75.00 150.00
61
45B Rocky Colavito BAT 15.00 40.00
64/66
46 Choo Choo Coleman 64 15.00 40.00
47 Gordy Coleman 66 30.00 60.00
48 Jerry Coleman 3.00 8.00
49 Mort Cooper 47 15.00 40.00
50 Walker Cooper 3.00 8.00
51 Roger Craig 64/66 6.00 15.00
52 Delmar Crandall 3.00 8.00
53A Joe Cunningham POR 4.00 10.00
64/66
53B Joe Cunningham BAT 40.00 80.00
61
54 Guy Curtwright 47 12.50 30.00
(sic, Curtright)
55 Bud Daley 61 30.00 60.00
56A Alvin Dark 6.00 15.00
(Boston cap)
56B Alvin Dark 3.00 8.00
(New York cap)
56C Alvin Dark (Cubs) 60 20.00 50.00
57 Murray Dickson 3.00 8.00
58 Bob Dillinger 6.00 15.00
59 Dom DiMaggio 6.00 15.00
60 Joe Dobson 3.00 8.00
61 Larry Doby 3.00 8.00
62 Bobby Doerr 6.00 15.00
63A Dick Donovan 3.00 8.00
(Braves, plain cap)
63B Dick Donovan 3.00 8.00
(White Sox)
64 Walter Dropo 3.00 8.00
65A Don Drysdale Portrait 30.00 60.00
(circa 1960-61)
65B Don Drysdale Glove at Waist 30.00 60.00
(circa 1964-66)
66 Luke Easter 3.00 8.00
67 Bruce Edwards 6.00 15.00
68 Del Ennis 3.00 8.00
69 Al Evans 3.00 8.00
70 Walter Evers 3.00 8.00
71A Ferris Fain FIE 6.00 15.00
71B Ferris Fain POR 3.00 8.00
72 Dick Farrell 64/66 3.00 8.00
73A Whitey Ford 6.00 15.00
(has been reprinted)
(no glove, throwing)
73B Whitey Ford POR 66 175.00 350.00
73C Ed Whitey Ford 30.00 60.00
(glove on shoulder)
64/66
74 Dick Fowler 3.00 8.00
75 Nelson Fox 10.00 25.00
(has been reprinted)
76 Tito Francona 64/66 3.00 8.00
77 Bob Friend 3.00 8.00
78 Carl Furillo 12.50 30.00
79 Augie Galan 12.50 30.00
80 Jim Gentile 64/66 3.00 8.00
81 Tony Gonzalez 64/66 3.00 8.00
82A Billy Goodman FIE 3.00 8.00
(fielding)
82B Billy Goodman BAT 12.50 30.00
60/61
83 Ted Greengrass 6.00 15.00
(sic, Jim)
84 Dick Groat 3.00 8.00
85 Steve Gromek 6.00 15.00
86 Johnny Groth 3.00 8.00
87 Orval Grove 47 12.50 30.00
88A Frank Gustine 3.00 8.00
(Pirates)
88B Frank Gustine(Cubs) 3.00 8.00
89 [illegible] Haas 12.50 30.00
90 Grady Hatton 3.00 8.00
91 Jim Hegan 3.00 8.00
92 Tommy Henrich 3.00 8.00
93 Ray Herbert 66 30.00 60.00
94 Gene Hermanski 6.00 15.00
95 Whitey Herzog 60/61 6.00 15.00
96 Kirby Higbe 47 12.50 30.00
97 Chuck Hinton 64/66 3.00 8.00
98 Don Hoak 64 15.00 40.00
99A Gil Hodges 6.00 15.00
(Brooklyn cap)
(has been reprinted)
99B Gil Hodges 12.50 30.00
(Los Angeles cap)
100 Johnny Hopp 47 12.50 30.00
101 Elston Howard 3.00 8.00
(has been reprinted)
102 Frank Howard 64/66 10.00 25.00
103 Ken Hubbs 64 75.00 150.00
104 Tex Hughson 47 12.50 30.00
105 Fred Hutchinson 50 6.00 15.00
106 Monte Irvin 6.00 15.00
107 Joey Jay 64/66 3.00 8.00
108 Jackie Jensen 60 40.00 80.00
109 Sam Jethroe 4.00 10.00
110 Bill Johnson 50 4.00 10.00
111 Walter Judnich 47 12.50 30.00
112A Al Kaline SCR 12.50 30.00
(kneeling)
112B Al Kaline SIG POR 10.00 25.00
113 George Kell 6.00 15.00
114 Charley Keller 6.00 15.00
115 Alex Kellner 3.00 8.00
116 Kenn Keltner 12.50 30.00
(sic, Ken)
117A Harmon Killebrew 30.00 60.00
pinstripes, batting)
60/61
117B Harmon Killibrew 40.00 80.00
(sic, Killebrew)
POR 66
117C Harmon Killebrew 15.00 40.00
(throwing) 64/66
118 Ellis Kinder 3.00 8.00
119 Ralph Kiner 6.00 15.00
120 Billy Klaus 60 30.00 60.00
121A Ted Kluszewski(Reds) 12.50 30.00
121B Ted Kluszewski 12.50 30.00
(Pirates)
121C Ted Kluszewski 40.00 80.00
(plain uniform) 60/61
122 Don Kolloway 50 6.00 15.00
123 Jim Konstanty 4.00 10.00
124 Sandy Koufax 64/66 75.00 150.00
125 Ed Kranepool 66 150.00 300.00
126A Tony Kubek 3.00 8.00
(dark background)
126B Tony Kubek 3.00 8.00
(light background)
127A Harvey Kuenn 60 6.00 15.00
(Detroit)
127B Harvey Kuenn 61 30.00 60.00
(plain uniform)
127C Harvey Kuenn 6.00 15.00
(San Francisco) 64/66
128 Whitey Kurowski 50 12.50 30.00
129 Eddie Lake 47 12.50 30.00
130 Jim Landis 64/66 3.00 8.00
131 Don Larsen 3.00 8.00
132A Bob Lemon 4.00 10.00
(left arm not shown)
132B Bob Lemon 40.00 80.00
(left arm extended)
133 Buddy Lewis 47 12.50 30.00
134 Johnny Lindell 50 12.50 30.00
135 Phil Linz 66 30.00 60.00
136 Don Lock 66 30.00 60.00
137 Whitey Lockman 3.00 8.00
138 Johnny Logan 3.00 8.00
139A Dale Long (Pirates) 3.00 8.00
139B Dale Long (Cubs) 61 30.00 60.00
140 Ed Lopat 3.00 8.00
141A Harry Lowery 6.00 15.00
(sic, Lowrey)
141B Harry Lowrey 3.00 8.00
142 Sal Maglie 3.00 8.00
143 Art Mahaffey 64/66 3.00 8.00
144 Hank Majeski 3.00 8.00
145 Frank Malzone 3.00 8.00
146A Mickey Mantle Batting at Waist
White Outline 100.00 200.00
146B Mickey Mantle Batting at Waist No
White Outline 150.00 300.00
146C Mickey Mantle Batting Full
(circa 1964-66) 100.00 200.00
146D Mickey Mantle Portrait
(circa 1966) 400.00 800.00
147 Marty Marion 3.00 8.00
148 Roger Maris 64/66 40.00 80.00
149 Willard Marshall 3.00 8.00
150A Ed Matthews SCR 10.00 25.00
(sic, Mathews)
150B Eddie Mathews SIG 15.00 40.00
151 Ed Mayo 3.00 8.00
152A Willie Mays Batting 30.00 60.00
(New York)
Card has been reprinted
152B Willie Mays 30.00 60.00
(San Francisco)
153A Bill Mazeroski POR 8.00 20.00
60/61
153B Bill Mazeroski BAT 8.00 20.00
64/66
154 Ken McBride 64/66 3.00 8.00
155A Barney McCaskey 15.00 40.00
(sic, McCosky)
155B Barney McCoskey 50.00 100.00
(sic, McCosky)
156 Lindy McDaniel 60/61 3.00 8.00
157 Gil McDougald 3.00 8.00
158 Albert Mele 30.00 60.00
159 Sam Mele 6.00 15.00
160A Minnie Minoso 3.00 8.00
(White Sox)
160B Minnie Minoso 6.00 15.00
(Cleveland)
161 Dale Mitchell 3.00 8.00
162 Wally Moon 3.00 8.00
163 Don Mueller 15.00 40.00
164A Stan Musial 30.00 60.00
(three bats, kneeling)
(has been reprinted)
164B Stan Musial BAT 64 100.00 200.00
165 Charles Neal 64 15.00 40.00
166A Don Newcombe 6.00 15.00
(shaking hands)
166B Don Newcombe 3.00 8.00
(Brooklyn cap)
(has been reprinted)
166C Don Newcombe 10.00 25.00
(plain cap)
167 Hal Newhouser 6.00 15.00
168 Ron Northey 47 15.00 40.00
169 Bill O'Dell 64/66 3.00 8.00
170 Joe Page 50 12.50 30.00
171 Satchel Paige 75.00 150.00
172 Milt Pappas 64/66 3.00 8.00
173 Camilo Pascual 64/66 3.00 8.00
174 Albie Pearson 66 30.00 60.00
175 Johnny Pesky 3.00 8.00
176 Gary Peters 66 30.00 60.00
177 Dave Philley 3.00 8.00
178 Billy Pierce 60/61 3.00 8.00
179 Jimmy Piersall 66 50.00 100.00
180 Vada Pinson 64/66 10.00 25.00
181 Bob Porterfield 3.00 8.00
182 Boog Powell 66 75.00 150.00
183 Vic Raschi 3.00 8.00
184A Harold Peewee Reese 10.00 25.00
(ball visible along
bottom border)
184B Harold Peewee Reese 10.00 25.00
(ball not visible)
(has been reprinted)
185 Del Rice 3.00 8.00
186 Bobby Richardson 66 175.00 350.00
187A Phil Rizzuto 10.00 25.00
(small photo)
187B Phil Rizzuto 6.00 15.00
(larger photo)
188A Robin Roberts SIG 6.00 15.00
188B Robin Roberts SCR 8.00 20.00
189 Brooks Robinson 30.00 60.00
190 Eddie Robinson POR 3.00 8.00
191 Floyd Robinson 66 30.00 60.00
192 Frankie Robinson 30.00 60.00
64/66
193 Jackie Robinson 40.00 80.00
194 Preacher Roe 3.00 8.00
195 Bob Rogers 66 30.00 60.00
(sic, Rodgers)
196 Richard Rollins 66 30.00 60.00
197 Pete Runnels 64 15.00 40.00
198 John Sain 3.00 8.00
199 Ron Santo 64/66 12.50 30.00
200 Henry Sauer 3.00 8.00
201A Carl Sawatski 3.00 8.00
(Milwaukee cap)
201B Carl Sawatski 3.00 8.00
(Philadelphia cap)
201C Carl Sawatski 61 15.00 40.00
(plain cap)
202 Johnny Schmitz 4.00 10.00
203A Red Schoendeinst 15.00 40.00
(one foot shown
catching)
(sic, Schoendienst)
203B Red Schoendeinst 30.00 60.00
(both feet shown
catching)
(sic, Schoendienst)
203C Red Schoendinst BAT 6.00 15.00
(sic, Schoendienst)
204A Herb Score 6.00 15.00
(Cleveland cap)
204B Herb Score 61 30.00 60.00
(plain cap)
205 Andy Seminick 3.00 8.00
206 Rip Sewell 47 15.00 40.00
207 Norm Siebern 3.00 8.00
208A Roy Sievers 51 40.00 80.00
(Browns)
208B Roy Sievers 3.00 8.00
(Senators)
dark background)
208C Roy Sievers 3.00 8.00
(Senators)
light background)
208D Roy Sievers 61 30.00 60.00
(plain uniform)
209 Curt Simmons 3.00 8.00
210 Dick Sisler 3.00 8.00
211A Bill Skowron 3.00 8.00
(New York)
211B Bill Moose Skowron 150.00 300.00
(White Sox) 66
212 Enos Slaughter 6.00 15.00
213A Duke Snider 10.00 25.00
(Brooklyn)
213B Duke Snider 15.00 40.00
(Los Angeles)
214A Warren Spahn 6.00 15.00
(Boston)
(has been reprinted)
214B Warren Spahn 12.50 30.00
(Milwaukee)
215 Stanley Spence 12.50 30.00
216A Ed Stanky 3.00 8.00
(plain uniform)
216B Ed Stanky (Giants) 3.00 8.00
217A Vern Stephens 3.00 8.00
(Browns)
217B Vern Stephens 4.00 10.00
(Red Sox)
218 Ed Stewart 3.00 8.00
219 Snuffy Stirnweiss 15.00 40.00
220 George Birdie Tebbets 10.00 25.00
221A Frankie Thomas BAT 30.00 60.00
(Bob Skinner picture)
59
221B Frank Thomas (Cubs) 30.00 60.00
60/61
222 Lee Thomas 64/66 3.00 8.00
223 Bobby Thomson 6.00 15.00
224A Earl Torgeson 3.00 8.00
(Braves)
224B Earl Torgeson 60/61 3.00 8.00
(plain uniform)
225 Gus Triandos 60/61 6.00 15.00
226 Virgil Trucks 3.00 8.00
227 Johnny Vandermeer 47 40.00 80.00
228 Emil Verban 15.00 40.00
229A Mickey Vernon 3.00 8.00
(throwing)
229B Mickey Vernon BAT 3.00 8.00
230 Bill Voiselle 47 15.00 40.00
231 Leon Wagner 64/66 3.00 8.00
232A Eddie Waitkus BAT 3.00 8.00
(Cub uniform)
232B Eddie Waitkus BAT 3.00 8.00
(plain uniform)
232C Eddie Waitkus POR 30.00 60.00
(Phillies uniform)
233 Dick Wakefield 3.00 8.00
234 Harry Walker 40.00 80.00
235 Bucky Walters 6.00 15.00
236 Pete Ward 66 125.00 250.00
237 Herman Wehmeier 3.00 8.00
238A Vic Wertz (Tigers) 3.00 8.00
238B Vic Wertz(Red Sox) 3.00 8.00
239 Wally Westlake 3.00 8.00
240 Wes Westrum 30.00 60.00
241 Billy Williams 64/66 30.00 60.00
242 Maurice Wills 64/66 12.50 30.00
243A Gene Woodling SCR 3.00 8.00
243B Gene Woodling SIG 3.00 8.00
244 Taffy Wright 47 12.50 30.00
245 Carl Yastrzemski 66 250.00 500.00
246 Al Zarilla 51 6.00 15.00
247A Gus Zernial SCR 3.00 8.00
247B Gus Zernial SIG 3.00 8.00
248 Braves Team 1948
249 Dodgers Team 1949
250 Dodgers Team 1952
251 Dodgers Team 1955
252 Dodgers Team 1956
253 Giants Team 1951
254 Giants Team 1954
255 Indians Team 1948
256 Indians Team 1954
257 Phillies Team 1950
258 Yankees Team 1949
259 Yankees Team 1950
260 Yankees Team 1951
261 Yankees Team 1952
262 Yankees Team 1955
263 Yankees Team 1956

2006 Exquisite Collection

COMMON AU RC (1-90) 8.00 20.00
ISSUED AS EXCH CARDS IN VARIOUS
2006 UPPER DECK PRODUCTS
1-90 PRINT RUN 55 SER.#'d SETS
91-100 PRINT RUN 10 SER.#'d SETS
1-90 FEATURE ROOKIE LOGOS
NO PRICING ON 91-100 DUE TO SCARCITY
1 Melky Cabrera AU (RC)
Jeremy Hermida AU (RC)
2 Craig Hansen AU (RC) 12.50 30.00
Fausto Carmona AU (RC)
3 Andre Ethier AU (RC) 8.00 20.00
Jason Kubel AU (RC)
4 Chad Billingsley AU (RC) 6.00 15.00
Boof Bonser AU (RC)
5 Jeremy Sowers AU (RC) 20.00 50.00
Fausto Carmona AU (RC)
6 Josh Willingham AU (RC) 10.00 25.00
Ronny Paulino AU (RC)
7 Takashi Saito AU RC 20.00 50.00
Andre Ethier AU (RC)
8 Cole Hamels AU (RC) 50.00 100.00
James Shields AU RC
9 Chris Denorfia AU (RC) 10.00 25.00
Carlos Quentin AU (RC)
10 Jason Hammel AU (RC) 10.00 25.00
James Shields AU RC
11 Dan Uggla AU (RC) 10.00 25.00
Ian Kinsler AU (RC)
12 Jeremy Accardo AU RC 15.00 40.00
Matt Cain AU (RC)
13 Jeremy Sowers AU (RC) 10.00 25.00
Paul Maholm AU (RC)
14 Cole Hamels AU (RC) 10.00 25.00
Jeremy Sowers AU (RC)
15 Francisco Liriano AU (RC) 15.00 40.00
Boof Bonser AU (RC)
16 Justin Verlander AU (RC) 20.00 50.00
Joel Zumaya AU (RC)
17 Hanley Ramirez AU (RC) 30.00 60.00
Stephen Drew AU (RC)
18 Alay Soler AU RC 10.00 25.00
Brian Bannister AU (RC)
19 Dave Gassner AU (RC) 10.00 25.00
Boof Bonser AU (RC)
20 Angel Pagan AU (RC) 12.50 30.00
Ryan Theroit AU (RC)
21 Dan Uggla AU (RC) 12.50 30.00
Jeremy Hermida AU (RC)
22 Mike Pelfrey AU RC
Chad Billingsley AU (RC)
23 Fausto Carmona AU (RC) 6.00 15.00
Cole Hamels AU (RC)
24 Takashi Saito AU RC 60.00 120.00
Hong-Chih Kuo AU (RC)
25 Paul Maholm AU (RC) 8.00 20.00
Sean Marshall AU (RC)
26 Howie Kendrick AU (RC) 15.00 40.00
Dan Uggla AU (RC)

27 Josh Johnson AU (RC)	10.00	25.00
Yusmeiro Petit AU (RC)		
28 Matt Cain AU (RC)		
Mike Pelfrey AU RC		
29 Russell Martin AU (RC)	40.00	80.00
Andre Ethier AU (RC)		
30 Francisco Liriano AU (RC)	20.00	50.00
Jered Weaver AU (RC)		
31 Cole Hamels AU (RC)	6.00	15.00
Zach Jackson AU (RC)		
32 Jonathan Papelbon AU (RC)	20.00	50.00
Craig Hansen AU RC		
33 Mike Pelfrey AU RC		
Alay Soler AU RC		
34 Chris Denorfia AU (RC)	12.50	30.00
Jeremy Hermida AU (RC)		
35 Josh Willingham AU (RC)	10.00	25.00
Cody Ross AU (RC)		
36 Stephen Drew AU (RC)	30.00	60.00
Jered Weaver AU (RC)		
37 Melky Cabrera AU (RC)		
Wil Nieves AU (RC)		
38 Scott Dunn AU (RC)	20.00	50.00
James Shields AU RC		
39 Howie Kendrick AU (RC)	10.00	25.00
Kendry Morales AU (RC)		
40 Paul Maholm AU (RC)	10.00	25.00
Matt Capps AU (RC)		
41 Ian Kinsler AU (RC)	10.00	25.00
Howie Kendrick AU (RC)		
42 Matt Cain AU (RC)	20.00	50.00
Alay Soler AU RC		
43 Andre Ethier AU (RC)		
Melky Cabrera AU (RC)		
44 Justin Verlander AU (RC)	30.00	60.00
Jeremy Sowers AU (RC)		
45 Howie Kendrick AU (RC)	10.00	25.00
Jered Weaver AU (RC)		
46 Hanley Ramirez AU (RC)	20.00	50.00
Josh Willingham AU (RC)		
47 Hanley Ramirez AU (RC)	15.00	40.00
Jeremy Hermida AU (RC)		
48 Dan Uggla AU (RC)	12.50	30.00
Josh Willingham AU (RC)		
49 Alay Soler AU RC	6.00	15.00
Cole Hamels AU (RC)		
50 Jason Kubel AU (RC)	10.00	25.00
Boof Bonser AU (RC)		
51 Mike Jacobs AU (RC)	10.00	25.00
Kendry Morales AU (RC)		
52 Takashi Saito AU RC	10.00	25.00
Jonathan Papelbon AU (RC)		
53 Jonathan Papelbon AU (RC)	50.00	100.00
Justin Verlander AU (RC)		
54 Andre Ethier AU (RC)	20.00	50.00
Chad Billingsley AU (RC)		
55 Jeremy Hermida AU (RC)	12.50	30.00
Tony Gwynn Jr. AU (RC)		
56 Ryan Zimmerman AU (RC)	40.00	80.00
Stephen Drew AU (RC)		
57 Tony Gwynn Jr. AU (RC)	12.50	30.00
Josh Barfield AU (RC)		
58 Clay Hensley AU (RC)	10.00	25.00
Mike Thompson AU RC		
59 Justin Verlander AU (RC)	30.00	60.00
Josh Johnson AU (RC)		
60 Justin Verlander AU (RC)	50.00	100.00
Jered Weaver AU (RC)		
61 Tony Gwynn Jr. AU (RC)		
Melky Cabrera AU (RC)		
62 Tony Gwynn Jr. AU (RC)	20.00	50.00
Andre Ethier AU (RC)		
63 Stephen Drew AU (RC)	20.00	50.00
Carlos Quentin AU (RC)		
64 Conor Jackson AU (RC)	20.00	50.00
Carlos Quentin AU (RC)		
65 Ryan Zimmerman AU (RC)	30.00	60.00
Brendan Harris AU (RC)		
66 Takashi Saito AU RC	20.00	50.00
Russell Martin AU (RC)		
67 Mike Jacobs AU (RC)	12.50	30.00
Josh Willingham AU (RC)		
68 Mike Jacobs AU (RC)	15.00	40.00
Hanley Ramiez AU (RC)		
69 Mike Pelfrey AU RC		
Justin Verlander AU (RC)		
70 Mike Pelfrey AU RC		
Jonathan Papelbon AU (RC)		
71 Craig Hansen AU RC	6.00	15.00
Cole Hamels AU (RC)		
72 Hanley Ramirez AU (RC)	12.50	30.00
Freddie Bynum AU (RC)		
73 Tony Gwynn Jr. AU (RC)		
Choo Freeman AU (RC)		
74 Fernando Nieve AU (RC)	8.00	20.00
Taylor Buchholz AU (RC)		
75 Adam Wainwright AU (RC)	60.00	120.00
Josh Johnson AU (RC)		
76 Josh Willingham AU (RC)	20.00	50.00
Russell Martin AU (RC)		
77 Russell Martin AU (RC)	15.00	40.00
Wil Nieves AU (RC)		
78 Ben Johnson AU (RC)	8.00	20.00
Mike Thompson AU RC		
79 Zach Jackson AU (RC)	8.00	20.00
Ben Hendrickson AU (RC)		
80 Jonathan Papelbon AU (RC)	30.00	60.00
Joel Zumaya AU (RC)		
81 Ben Hendrickson AU (RC)	10.00	25.00
Jose Capellan AU (RC)		
82 Joey Devine AU RC	10.00	25.00
Ken Ray AU RC		
83 Mike Pelfrey AU RC		
Anderson Hernandez AU (RC)		
84 Kelly Shoppach AU (RC)	20.00	50.00
Russell Martin AU (RC)		
85 Alay Soler AU RC	8.00	20.00
Josh Johnson AU (RC)		
86 Alay Soler AU RC	10.00	25.00
Craig Hansen AU RC		
87 Craig Hansen AU RC	8.00	20.00
Chad Billingsley AU (RC)		
88 Chad Billingsley AU (RC)	10.00	25.00
Matt Cain AU (RC)		
89 Francisco Liriano AU (RC)	15.00	40.00
Craig Hansen AU RC		
90 Conor Jackson AU (RC)	12.50	30.00
Mike Jacobs AU (RC)		
91 Ken Griffey Jr. AU		
92 Derek Jeter AU		
93 Albert Pujols AU		
94 Roger Clemens AU		
95 Jim Thome AU		
96 Howie Kendrick AU (RC)		
97 Francisco Liriano AU (RC)		
98 Jered Weaver AU (RC)		
99 Justin Verlander AU (RC)		
100 Stephen Drew AU (RC)		

2006 Exquisite Collection Gold

*GOLD 1-90: .5X TO 1.2X BASIC
ISSUED AS EXCH CARDS IN VARIOUS
2006 UPPER DECK PRODUCTS
1-90 PRINT RUN 30 SER.#'d SETS
91-100 PRINT RUN 5 SER.#'d SETS
NO PRICING ON 91-100 DUE TO SCARCITY

2006 Exquisite Collection Platinum

ISSUED AS EXCH CARDS IN VARIOUS
2006 UPPER DECK PRODUCTS
STATED PRINT RUN 1 SER.#'d SET
NO PRICING DUE TO SCARCITY

2006 Exquisite Collection Cuts

ISSUED AS EXCH CARDS IN VARIOUS
2006 UPPER DECK PRODUCTS
PRINT RUNS B/WN 25-65 COPIES PER

AC Al Campanis/65	40.00	80.00
BD Bill Dickey/65	75.00	150.00
BG Burleigh Grimes/65	60.00	120.00
BH Billy Herman/65	50.00	100.00
CG Charlie Gehringer/65	50.00	100.00
CH Carl Hubbell/65	60.00	120.00
DC Dolph Camilli/65	50.00	100.00
DD Dizzy Dean/30		
EA Earl Averill/65	50.00	100.00
EM Eddie Mathews/65	75.00	150.00
ER Edd Roush/65	50.00	100.00
GE George Selkirk/65	75.00	150.00
GH Gabby Hartnett/25		
GS George Sisler/65	200.00	300.00
HG Hank Greenberg/65	125.00	250.00
JC Joe Cronin/65	50.00	100.00
JD Joe DiMaggio/25		
JM Johnny Mize/65	50.00	100.00
LA Luke Appling/65	50.00	100.00
LB Lou Boudreau/65	50.00	100.00
LG Lefty Gomez/65	60.00	120.00
MC Max Carey/65	60.00	120.00
PW Pee Wee Reese/65		
RR Red Ruffing/52		
RS Ray Schalk/30		
SC Stan Coveleski/65	50.00	100.00
VW Vic Wertz/65	50.00	100.00
WG Warren Giles/65	60.00	120.00
WH Waite Hoyt/65	50.00	100.00
WS Warren Spahn/65	60.00	120.00

2006 Exquisite Collection Cuts Dual

ISSUED AS EXCH CARDS IN VARIOUS
2006 UPPER DECK PRODUCTS
STATED PRINT RUN 5 SER.#'d SETS
NO PRICING DUE TO SCARCITY

2006 Exquisite Collection Endorsed Emblems

ISSUED AS EXCH CARDS IN VARIOUS
2006 UPPER DECK PRODUCTS
STATED PRINT RUN 25 SER.#'d SETS

AB A.J. Burnett		
AD Adam Dunn	20.00	50.00
AJ Andruw Jones	30.00	60.00
AR Alex Rios	30.00	60.00
BJ B.J. Upton	20.00	50.00
BR Brian Roberts	30.00	60.00
BS Ben Sheets	30.00	60.00
CB Craig Biggio	60.00	120.00
CC Chris Carpenter		
CL Carlos Lee		
CU Chase Utley	30.00	60.00
CZ Carlos Zambrano		
DJ Derek Jeter		
DL Derrek Lee	50.00	100.00
DO David Ortiz		
FH Felix Hernandez		
FL Francisco Liriano	50.00	100.00
HR Hanley Ramirez		
HS Huston Street	20.00	50.00
JB Jason Bay		
JM Joe Mauer	75.00	150.00
JO Jonathan Papelbon	100.00	150.00
JP Jake Peavy	50.00	100.00
JR Jose Reyes		
JS Jeremy Sowers	20.00	50.00
JT Jim Thome	60.00	120.00
JU Justin Morneau	30.00	60.00
JU2 Justin Morneau	30.00	60.00
JV Justin Verlander	60.00	120.00
JW Jered Weaver	30.00	60.00
KG Ken Griffey Jr.	125.00	250.00
KG2 Ken Griffey Jr.	125.00	250.00
KG3 Ken Griffey Jr.	125.00	250.00
KH Khalil Greene	30.00	60.00
MC Miguel Cabrera	100.00	150.00
MG Marcus Giles	20.00	50.00
MH Matt Holliday	30.00	60.00
MI Miguel Tejada		
MT Mark Teixeira	20.00	50.00
MY Michael Young	20.00	50.00
NS Nick Swisher	30.00	60.00
RO Roy Oswalt		
RW Rickie Weeks	30.00	60.00
SD Stephen Drew	60.00	120.00
SK Scott Kazmir		
SM John Smoltz	100.00	150.00
TH Travis Hafner	50.00	100.00
TI Tadahito Iguchi		
TR Trevor Hoffman	50.00	100.00
VM Victor Martinez		

2006 Exquisite Collection Endorsements

ISSUED AS EXCH CARDS IN VARIOUS
2006 UPPER DECK PRODUCTS
STATED PRINT RUN 40 SER.#'d SETS

AP Albert Pujols		
AS Alay Soler	15.00	40.00
BF Bob Feller	20.00	50.00
BJ B.J. Upton	20.00	50.00
BR Brooks Robinson	30.00	60.00
CC Chris Carpenter	30.00	60.00
CF Carlton Fisk	30.00	60.00
CH Cole Hamels	30.00	60.00
CJ Chipper Jones	60.00	120.00
CR Cal Ripken Jr.	75.00	150.00
DJ Derek Jeter		
DO David Ortiz	40.00	80.00
DW Dontrelle Willis	20.00	50.00
FH Felix Hernandez	50.00	100.00
FL Francisco Liriano	15.00	40.00
FR Frank Robinson	30.00	60.00
GP Gaylord Perry	15.00	40.00
HA Craig Hansen		
HK Howie Kendrick	12.50	30.00
JB Johnny Bench	30.00	60.00
JD Johnny Damon		
JM Joe Mauer	50.00	100.00
JO Jonathan Papelbon	30.00	60.00
JP Jake Peavy	10.00	25.00
JR Jose Reyes	60.00	120.00
JS Jeremy Sowers	20.00	50.00
JT Jim Thome		
JV Justin Verlander	40.00	80.00
JW Jered Weaver	50.00	100.00
KG Ken Griffey Jr.	90.00	150.00
KG2 Ken Griffey Jr.	90.00	150.00
MC Miguel Cabrera	30.00	60.00
MS Mike Schmidt		
MT Mark Teixeira	20.00	50.00
NR Nolan Ryan	100.00	200.00
PM Paul Molitor	15.00	40.00
RC Roger Clemens	60.00	120.00
RJ Reggie Jackson	40.00	80.00
RO Roy Oswalt	12.50	30.00
RS Ryne Sandberg	40.00	80.00
RZ Ryan Zimmerman	30.00	60.00
SD Stephen Drew	30.00	60.00
SK Scott Kazmir	15.00	40.00
SM Stan Musial	40.00	80.00
TG Tony Gwynn		
TH Travis Hafner	30.00	60.00
TI Tadahito Iguchi	30.00	60.00
VG Vladimir Guerrero	40.00	80.00
VM Victor Martinez	15.00	40.00
WC Will Clark	15.00	40.00

2006 Exquisite Collection Ensemble Dual Patches

ISSUED AS EXCH CARDS IN VARIOUS
2006 UPPER DECK PRODUCTS
STATED PRINT RUN 25 SER.#'d SETS
NO PRICING DUE TO SCARCITY

2006 Exquisite Collection Ensemble Endorsements Dual

ISSUED AS EXCH CARDS IN VARIOUS
2006 UPPER DECK PRODUCTS
STATED PRINT RUN 20 SER.#'d SETS
NO PRICING DUE TO SCARCITY

2006 Exquisite Collection Ensemble Endorsements Triple

ISSUED AS EXCH CARDS IN VARIOUS
2006 UPPER DECK PRODUCTS
STATED PRINT RUN 15 SER.#'d SETS
NO PRICING DUE TO SCARCITY

2006 Exquisite Collection Ensemble Endorsements Quad

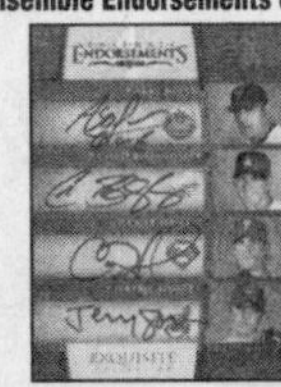

ISSUED AS EXCH CARDS IN VARIOUS
2006 UPPER DECK PRODUCTS
STATED PRINT RUN 10 SER.#'d SETS
NO PRICING DUE TO SCARCITY

2006 Exquisite Collection Ensemble Triple Patches

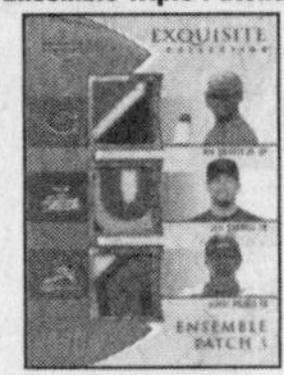

ISSUED AS EXCH CARDS IN VARIOUS
2006 UPPER DECK PRODUCTS
STATED PRINT RUN 15 SER.#'d SETS
NO PRICING DUE TO SCARCITY

2006 Exquisite Collection Ensemble Quad Patches

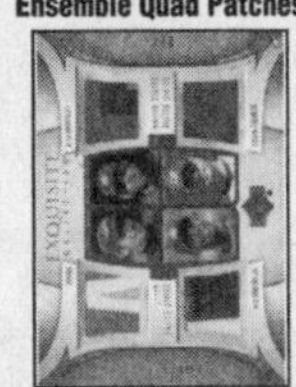

ISSUED AS EXCH CARDS IN VARIOUS
2006 UPPER DECK PRODUCTS
STATED PRINT RUN 10 SER.#'d SETS
NO PRICING DUE TO SCARCITY

2006 Exquisite Collection Legends Memorabilia

ISSUED AS EXCH CARDS IN VARIOUS
2006 UPPER DECK PRODUCTS
STATED PRINT RUN 15 SER.#'d SETS
PLAT.ISSUED AS EXCH CARDS IN VARIOUS
2006 UPPER DECK PRODUCTS
PLATINUM PRINT RUN 1 SER.#'d SET
NO PLATINUM PRICING DUE TO SCARCITY

AK Al Kaline	20.00	50.00
BD Bill Dickey	40.00	80.00
BD2 Bill Dickey	40.00	80.00
BM Bill Mazeroski	30.00	60.00
BM2 Bill Mazeroski	30.00	60.00
BR Babe Ruth	900.00	1200.00
BR2 Babe Ruth	900.00	1200.00
CF Carlton Fisk	20.00	50.00
CR Cal Ripken Jr.	30.00	60.00
CR2 Cal Ripken Jr.	30.00	60.00
CR3 Cal Ripken Jr.	30.00	60.00
DM Don Mattingly	60.00	120.00
FR Frank Robinson	20.00	50.00
JB Johnny Bench	20.00	50.00
JB2 Johnny Bench	20.00	50.00
JC Joe Cronin	20.00	50.00
JD Joe DiMaggio	150.00	250.00
JD2 Joe DiMaggio	150.00	250.00
JF Jimmie Foxx	200.00	300.00
JM Joe Morgan	20.00	50.00
LG Lou Gehrig	300.00	500.00
LG2 Lou Gehrig	300.00	500.00
MO Mel Ott	100.00	175.00
MS Mike Schmidt	20.00	50.00
NR Nolan Ryan	75.00	150.00
NR2 Nolan Ryan	75.00	150.00
OC Orlando Cepeda	20.00	50.00
RC Roberto Clemente	250.00	300.00
RC2 Roberto Clemente	250.00	300.00
RH Rogers Hornsby	75.00	150.00
RH2 Rogers Hornsby	75.00	150.00
RJ Reggie Jackson	40.00	80.00
RJ2 Reggie Jackson	40.00	80.00
RO Brooks Robinson	20.00	50.00
RS Ryne Sandberg	40.00	80.00
SM Stan Musial	40.00	80.00
TG Tony Gwynn	30.00	60.00
TG2 Tony Gwynn	30.00	60.00
TM Thurman Munson	75.00	150.00
TM2 Thurman Munson	75.00	150.00
TW Ted Williams	150.00	250.00
WB Wade Boggs	40.00	80.00

2006 Exquisite Collection Material Cuts

ISSUED AS EXCH CARDS IN VARIOUS
2006 UPPER DECK PRODUCTS
STATED PRINT RUN 2 SER.#'d SETS
NO PRICING DUE TO SCARCITY

2006 Exquisite Collection Maximum Patch

ISSUED AS EXCH CARDS IN VARIOUS
2006 UPPER DECK PRODUCTS
STATED PRINT RUN 25 SER.#'d SETS
PRICING FOR NON-LOGO PATCHES

AD Adam Dunn	40.00	80.00
AP Albert Pujols	150.00	250.00
AS Alfonso Soriano	40.00	80.00
CA Carl Crawford	40.00	80.00
CB Carlos Beltran	50.00	100.00
CC Chris Carpenter	75.00	150.00
CD Carlos Delgado	40.00	80.00
CJ Chipper Jones	75.00	150.00
CR Craig Biggio	50.00	100.00
CS Curt Schilling	40.00	80.00
CU Chase Utley		
CZ Carlos Zambrano		
DJ Derek Jeter	300.00	400.00
DL Derrek Lee		
DO David Ortiz	60.00	120.00
FH Felix Hernandez	75.00	150.00
FL Francisco Liriano	40.00	80.00
FT Frank Thomas	75.00	150.00
JF Jeff Francoeur		
JG Jason Giambi	40.00	80.00
JM Justin Morneau		
JO Jonathan Papelbon	40.00	80.00
JP Jake Peavy	40.00	80.00
JR Jose Reyes		
JS Johan Santana		
JT Jim Thome	40.00	80.00
JV Justin Verlander	40.00	80.00
JW Jered Weaver	40.00	80.00
KG Ken Griffey Jr.	90.00	150.00
MC Miguel Cabrera	40.00	80.00
MI Miguel Tejada	40.00	80.00
MT Mark Teixeira	40.00	80.00
MY Michael Young		
PF Prince Fielder	40.00	80.00
PM Pedro Martinez	50.00	100.00
RH Ryan Howard		
TG Troy Glaus	40.00	80.00
TH Todd Helton	40.00	80.00
TO Tom Glavine		
TR Travis Hafner		
VG Vladimir Guerrero	40.00	80.00
VM Victor Martinez	40.00	80.00

2006 Exquisite Collection Memorabilia

ISSUED AS EXCH CARDS IN VARIOUS
2006 UPPER DECK PRODUCTS
STATED PRINT RUN 45 SER.#'d SETS
MEM.1 ISSUED AS EXCH CARD IN VARIOUS
2006 UPPER DECK PRODUCTS
MEM.1 PRINT RUN 1 SER.#'d SET
NO MEM.1 PRICING DUE TO SCARCITY
*GOLD: .5X TO 1.2X BASIC
GOLD ISSUED AS EXCH CARD IN VARIOUS
2006 UPPER DECK PRODUCTS
GOLD PRINT RUN 25 SER.#'d SETS
PLAT.ISSUED AS EXCH CARD IN VARIOUS
2006 UPPER DECK PRODUCTS
PLAT.PRINT RUN 15 SER.#'d SETS
NO PLAT.PRICING DUE TO SCARCITY

AD Adam Dunn	6.00	15.00
AD2 Adam Dunn	6.00	15.00
AJ Andruw Jones	10.00	25.00
AJ2 Andruw Jones	10.00	25.00
AP Albert Pujols	20.00	50.00
AP2 Albert Pujols	20.00	50.00
AR Alex Rodriguez	20.00	50.00
AS Alfonso Soriano	6.00	15.00
AS2 Alfonso Soriano	6.00	15.00
BR Babe Ruth	350.00	450.00
BR2 Babe Ruth	350.00	450.00
BZ Barry Zito	10.00	25.00
BZ2 Barry Zito	10.00	25.00
CB Carlos Beltran	10.00	25.00
CB2 Carlos Beltran	10.00	25.00
CF Carlton Fisk	10.00	25.00
CF2 Carlton Fisk	10.00	25.00
CJ Chipper Jones	15.00	40.00
CJ2 Chipper Jones	15.00	40.00
CR Cal Ripken Jr.	20.00	50.00
CR2 Cal Ripken Jr.	20.00	50.00
CR3 Cal Ripken Jr.	20.00	50.00
CS Curt Schilling	6.00	15.00
CU Chase Utley	15.00	40.00
CU2 Chase Utley	15.00	40.00
CY Carl Yastrzemski	10.00	25.00
CY2 Carl Yastrzemski	10.00	25.00
DA Daisuke Matsuzaka	150.00	250.00
DJ Derek Jeter	30.00	60.00
DJ2 Derek Jeter	30.00	60.00
DL Derrek Lee	10.00	25.00
DM Don Mattingly	20.00	50.00
DO David Ortiz	10.00	25.00
DO2 David Ortiz	10.00	25.00
FL Francisco Liriano	10.00	25.00
FL2 Francisco Liriano	10.00	25.00
GM Greg Maddux	10.00	25.00
GM2 Greg Maddux	10.00	25.00
HO Ryan Howard	10.00	25.00
HO2 Ryan Howard	10.00	25.00
IS Ichiro Suzuki	200.00	250.00
JA Jason Bay	6.00	15.00
JA2 Jason Bay	6.00	15.00
JB Jeff Bagwell	10.00	25.00
JB2 Jeff Bagwell	10.00	25.00
JD Joe DiMaggio	75.00	150.00
JM Joe Mauer	10.00	25.00
JP Jake Peavy	6.00	15.00
JP2 Jake Peavy	6.00	15.00
JS Johan Santana	10.00	25.00
JS2 Johan Santana	10.00	25.00
JT Jim Thome	10.00	25.00
JT2 Jim Thome	10.00	25.00
JV Justin Verlander	15.00	40.00
JV2 Justin Verlander	15.00	40.00
JW Jered Weaver	6.00	15.00
JW2 Jered Weaver	6.00	15.00
KG Ken Griffey Jr.	15.00	40.00
KG2 Ken Griffey Jr.	15.00	40.00
KG3 Ken Griffey Jr.	15.00	40.00
KJ Kenji Johjima	15.00	40.00
KJ2 Kenji Johjima	15.00	40.00
MA Manny Ramirez	10.00	25.00
MA2 Manny Ramirez	10.00	25.00
MA3 Manny Ramirez	10.00	25.00
MC Miguel Cabrera	10.00	25.00
MC2 Miguel Cabrera	10.00	25.00
MI Miguel Tejada	6.00	15.00
MI2 Miguel Tejada	6.00	15.00
MR Mariano Rivera	15.00	40.00
MR2 Mariano Rivera	15.00	40.00
MS Mike Schmidt	10.00	25.00
MS2 Mike Schmidt	10.00	25.00
MT Mark Teixeira	6.00	15.00
NR Nolan Ryan	20.00	50.00
NR2 Nolan Ryan	20.00	50.00
PE Pedro Martinez	15.00	40.00
PF Prince Fielder	10.00	25.00
PF2 Prince Fielder	10.00	25.00
PM Paul Molitor	6.00	15.00
PM2 Paul Molitor	6.00	15.00
RC Roger Clemens	15.00	40.00
RC2 Roger Clemens	15.00	40.00
RC3 Roger Clemens	15.00	40.00
RE Reggie Jackson	15.00	40.00
RE2 Reggie Jackson	15.00	40.00
RH Roy Halladay	6.00	15.00
RH2 Roy Halladay	6.00	15.00
RJ Randy Johnson	10.00	25.00
RO Roy Oswalt	6.00	15.00
RO2 Roy Oswalt	6.00	15.00
RY Robin Yount	15.00	40.00
RY2 Robin Yount	15.00	40.00
SM Stan Musial	20.00	50.00
SM2 Stan Musial	20.00	50.00
TG Tony Gwynn	20.00	50.00
TH Travis Hafner	6.00	15.00
VG Vladimir Guerrero	10.00	25.00
VG2 Vladimir Guerrero	10.00	25.00
WB Wade Boggs	10.00	25.00

2006 Exquisite Collection Patch

ISSUED AS EXCH CARDS IN VARIOUS
2006 UPPER DECK PRODUCTS
STATED PRINT RUN 25 SER.#'d SETS
NO PRICING ON MOST DUE TO SCARCITY
PATCH 1 ISSUED AS EXCH IN VARIOUS
2006 UPPER DECK PRODUCTS
PATCH 1 PRINT RUN 1 SER.#'d SET
NO PATCH 1 PRICING DUE TO SCARCITY
*PATCH 10: .5X TO 1.2X BASIC
PATCH 10 ISSUED AS EXCH IN VARIOUS
2006 UPPER DECK PRODUCTS
PATCH 10 PRINT RUN 10 SER.#'d SETS
PRICING IS FOR NON-LOGO PATCHES

AD Adam Dunn	15.00	40.00
AD2 Adam Dunn	15.00	40.00
AJ Andruw Jones	20.00	50.00
AJ2 Andruw Jones	20.00	50.00
AP Albert Pujols	75.00	150.00
AP2 Albert Pujols	75.00	150.00
AR Alex Rodriguez		
AS Alfonso Soriano	30.00	60.00
AS2 Alfonso Soriano	30.00	60.00
BR Babe Ruth		
BR2 Babe Ruth		
BZ Barry Zito	15.00	40.00
BZ2 Barry Zito	15.00	40.00
CB Carlos Beltran	30.00	60.00
CB2 Carlos Beltran	30.00	60.00
CF Carlton Fisk	20.00	50.00
CF2 Carlton Fisk	20.00	50.00
CJ Chipper Jones	50.00	100.00
CJ2 Chipper Jones	50.00	100.00
CR Cal Ripken Jr.	75.00	150.00
CR2 Cal Ripken Jr.	75.00	150.00
CR3 Cal Ripken Jr.	75.00	150.00
CS Curt Schilling	20.00	50.00
CU Chase Utley	30.00	60.00
CU2 Chase Utley	30.00	60.00
CY Carl Yastrzemski		
CY2 Carl Yastrzemski		
DA Daisuke Matsuzaka		
DJ Derek Jeter	100.00	200.00
DJ2 Derek Jeter	100.00	200.00
DL Derrek Lee	20.00	50.00
DM Don Mattingly	60.00	120.00
DO David Ortiz	30.00	60.00
DO2 David Ortiz	30.00	60.00
FL Francisco Liriano	20.00	50.00
FL2 Francisco Liriano	20.00	50.00
GM Greg Maddux	40.00	80.00
GM2 Greg Maddux	40.00	80.00
HO Ryan Howard	50.00	100.00
HO2 Ryan Howard	50.00	100.00
IS Ichiro Suzuki		
JA Jason Bay	20.00	50.00
JA2 Jason Bay	20.00	50.00
JB Jeff Bagwell		
JB2 Jeff Bagwell		
JD Joe DiMaggio		
JM Joe Mauer	40.00	80.00
JP Jake Peavy	30.00	60.00
JP2 Jake Peavy	30.00	60.00
JS Johan Santana	30.00	60.00
JS2 Johan Santana	30.00	60.00
JT Jim Thome	20.00	50.00
JT2 Jim Thome	20.00	50.00
JV Justin Verlander	20.00	50.00
JV2 Justin Verlander	20.00	50.00
JW Jered Weaver	30.00	60.00
JW2 Jered Weaver	30.00	60.00
KG Ken Griffey Jr.	75.00	150.00
KG2 Ken Griffey Jr.	75.00	150.00
KG3 Ken Griffey Jr.	75.00	150.00
KJ Kenji Johjima	30.00	60.00
KJ2 Kenji Johjima	30.00	60.00
MA Manny Ramirez	30.00	60.00
MA2 Manny Ramirez	30.00	60.00
MA3 Manny Ramirez	30.00	60.00
MC Miguel Cabrera	30.00	60.00
MC2 Miguel Cabrera	30.00	60.00
MI Miguel Tejada	20.00	50.00
MI2 Miguel Tejada	20.00	50.00
MR Mariano Rivera	40.00	80.00
MR2 Mariano Rivera	40.00	80.00
MS Mike Schmidt	20.00	50.00
MS2 Mike Schmidt	20.00	50.00
MT Mark Teixeira	20.00	50.00
NR Nolan Ryan	60.00	120.00
NR2 Nolan Ryan	60.00	120.00
PE Pedro Martinez	20.00	50.00
PF Prince Fielder	30.00	60.00
PF2 Prince Fielder	30.00	60.00
PM Paul Molitor		
PM2 Paul Molitor		
RC Roger Clemens	40.00	80.00
RC2 Roger Clemens	40.00	80.00
RC3 Roger Clemens	40.00	80.00
RE Reggie Jackson	20.00	50.00
RE2 Reggie Jackson	20.00	50.00
RH Roy Halladay	30.00	60.00
RH2 Roy Halladay	30.00	60.00
RJ Randy Johnson	20.00	50.00
RO Roy Oswalt	20.00	50.00
RO2 Roy Oswalt	20.00	50.00
RY Robin Yount	40.00	80.00
RY2 Robin Yount	40.00	80.00
SM Stan Musial		
SM2 Stan Musial		
TG Tony Gwynn	50.00	100.00
TH Travis Hafner	20.00	50.00
VG Vladimir Guerrero	30.00	60.00
VG2 Vladimir Guerrero	30.00	60.00
WB Wade Boggs	20.00	50.00

2006 Exquisite Collection Signature Patch

ISSUED AS EXCH CARDS IN VARIOUS
2006 UPPER DECK PRODUCTS
STATED PRINT RUN 30 SER.#'d SETS
NO PRICING ON MANY DUE TO SCARCITY

AB A.J. Burnett		
AD Adam Dunn	20.00	50.00

AJ Andruw Jones 40.00 80.00
AR Alex Rios 30.00 60.00
BJ B.J. Upton 30.00 60.00
BR Brian Roberts 20.00 50.00
BS Ben Sheets
CB Craig Biggio 60.00 120.00
CC Chris Carpenter 40.00 80.00
CL Carlos Lee 20.00 50.00
CU Chase Utley 60.00 120.00
CZ Carlos Zambrano 20.00 50.00
DJ Derek Jeter 275.00 350.00
DL Derrek Lee 60.00 120.00
DO David Ortiz
FH Felix Hernandez 100.00 200.00
FL Francisco Liriano
HR Hanley Ramirez
HS Huston Street
JB Jason Bay
JM Joe Mauer
JO Jonathan Papelbon
JP Jake Peavy 30.00 60.00
JR Jose Reyes 100.00 200.00
JS Jeremy Sowers 30.00 60.00
JT Jim Thome
JU Justin Morneau 40.00 80.00
JU2 Justin Morneau 40.00 80.00
JV Justin Verlander
JW Jered Weaver 40.00 80.00
KG Ken Griffey Jr.
KG2 Ken Griffey Jr.
KG3 Ken Griffey Jr.
KH Khalil Greene 60.00 120.00
MC Miguel Cabrera 40.00 80.00
MG Marcus Giles 30.00 60.00
MH Matt Holliday 50.00 100.00
MI Miguel Tejada
MT Mark Teixeira 50.00 100.00
MY Michael Young 20.00 50.00
NS Nick Swisher 30.00 60.00
RO Roy Oswalt 20.00 50.00
RW Rickie Weeks 30.00 60.00
SD Stephen Drew 40.00 80.00
SK Scott Kazmir 40.00 80.00
SM John Smoltz
TH Travis Hafner 30.00 60.00
TI Tadahito Iguchi 30.00 60.00
TR Trevor Hoffman
VM Victor Martinez 30.00 60.00

2006 Exquisite Collection Signature Patch Dual

ISSUED AS EXCH CARDS IN VARIOUS
2006 UPPER DECK PRODUCTS
STATED PRINT RUN 1 SER.#'d SET
NO PRICING DUE TO SCARCITY

2006 Exquisite Collection Signature Patch Triple

ISSUED AS EXCH CARDS IN VARIOUS
2006 UPPER DECK PRODUCTS
STATED PRINT RUN 1 SER.#'d SET
NO PRICING DUE TO SCARCITY

2007 Exquisite Collection Rookie Signatures

This 191-card set was released in January, 2008. The set was issued in six-card packs (which were actually small boxes which came five boxes to a case. The first 100 cards in this set feature veterans while cards 101-191 feature signed 2007 rookies. A few of the cards in that range also have game-used relic pieces as a part of the card. All the cards from 101-191 were issued to stated print runs between 125 and 235 serial numbered copies. The specific print run for each card in notated in our checklist. In addition, a few players did not return their signatures in time for pack out and those cards could be redeemed until December 28, 2009.

COMMON CARD (1-100) 1.50 4.00
ONE BASE CARD PER PACK
1-100 PRINT RUN 99 SER.#'d SETS
COMMON AU RC (101-191) 4.00 10.00
OVERALL FIVE AUTOS PER PACK
AU RC SER.#'d B/WN 150-235 PER
COMMON JSY AU RC (101-191) 6.00 15.00
OVERALL FIVE AUTOS PER PACK
JSY AU RC SER.#'d B/WN 125-199 PER
EXCHANGE DEADLINE 12/28/2009
1 Ichiro Suzuki 6.00 15.00
2 Alex Rodriguez 6.00 15.00
3 David Wright 6.00 15.00
4 Ryan Howard 6.00 15.00
5 Ken Griffey Jr. 6.00 15.00
6 Derek Jeter 8.00 20.00
7 Vladimir Guerrero 4.00 10.00
8 Roger Clemens 4.00 10.00
9 Greg Maddux 6.00 15.00
10 Johan Santana 4.00 10.00
11 Nomar Garciaparra 4.00 10.00
12 Carlos Beltran 1.50 4.00
13 Carlos Delgado 1.50 4.00
14 Manny Ramirez 4.00 10.00
15 John Lackey 1.50 4.00
16 David Ortiz 2.50 6.00
17 Curt Schilling 2.50 6.00
18 Cal Ripken Jr. 12.00 30.00
19 Albert Pujols 8.00 20.00
20 Frank Thomas 4.00 10.00
21 Chris Carpenter 4.00 10.00
22 Prince Fielder 2.50 6.00
23 Justin Morneau 4.00 10.00
24 Joe Mauer 4.00 10.00
25 Torii Hunter 1.50 4.00
26 Jake Peavy 1.50 4.00
27 Roy Oswalt 2.50 6.00
28 Craig Biggio 2.50 6.00
29 Lance Berkman 2.50 6.00
30 Carlos Zambrano 2.50 6.00
31 Derrek Lee 1.50 4.00
32 Aramis Ramirez 1.50 4.00
33 Noah Lowry 1.50 4.00
34 Magglio Ordonez 2.50 6.00
35 Ivan Rodriguez 2.50 6.00
36 Johnny Damon 2.50 6.00
37 Justin Verlander 5.00 12.00
38 John Smoltz 4.00 10.00
39 Chipper Jones 4.00 10.00
40 Jeff Francoeur 4.00 10.00
41 Hanley Ramirez 4.00 10.00
42 Miguel Cabrera 4.00 10.00
43 Josh Beckett 2.50 6.00
44 Cole Hamels 4.00 10.00
45 Chase Utley 4.00 10.00
46 Grady Sizemore 2.50 6.00
47 Travis Hafner 1.50 4.00
48 Victor Martinez 2.50 6.00
49 Russell Martin 1.50 4.00
50 Jason Varitek 4.00 10.00
51 Hideki Matsui 4.00 10.00
52 Carl Crawford 2.50 6.00
53 Scott Kazmir 2.50 6.00
54 Miguel Tejada 2.50 6.00
55 Erik Bedard 1.50 4.00
56 Carlos Lee 1.50 4.00
57 Sammy Sosa 4.00 10.00
58 Mark Teixeira 4.00 10.00
59 Michael Young 2.50 6.00
60 Jim Thome 2.50 6.00
61 Paul Konerko 2.50 6.00
62 Jermaine Dye 1.50 4.00
63 Mark Teahen 1.50 4.00
64 Felix Hernandez 4.00 10.00
65 Andruw Jones 1.50 4.00
66 Pedro Martinez 2.50 6.00
67 Randy Johnson 4.00 10.00
68 Ryan Zimmerman 2.50 6.00
69 Matt Holliday 4.00 10.00
70 Todd Helton 2.50 6.00
71 Brian Bannister 1.50 4.00
72 Jeremy Bonderman 1.50 4.00
73 Adam Dunn 2.50 6.00
74 Aaron Harang 1.50 4.00
75 Jason Bay 2.50 6.00
76 Adam LaRoche 1.50 4.00
77 Freddy Sanchez 1.50 4.00
78 Dan Uggla 2.50 6.00
79 Joe Nathan 1.50 4.00
80 Brad Penny 1.50 4.00
81 Takashi Saito 1.50 4.00
82 Jimmy Rollins 2.50 6.00
83 Jose Reyes 2.50 6.00
84 Jered Weaver 2.50 6.00
85 Chien-Ming Wang 2.50 6.00
86 Jonathan Papelbon 4.00 10.00
87 Mariano Rivera 4.00 10.00
88 Eric Byrnes 1.50 4.00
89 Nick Markakis 4.00 10.00
90 Brian Roberts 1.50 4.00
91 Omar Vizquel 2.50 6.00
92 Vernon Wells 1.50 4.00
93 Dan Haren 1.50 4.00
94 Ben Sheets 1.50 4.00
95 B.J. Upton 1.50 4.00
96 Adrian Gonzalez 2.50 6.00
97 J.J. Hardy 1.50 4.00
98 Mike Piazza 4.00 10.00
99 Roy Halladay 4.00 10.00
100 Alfonso Soriano 2.50 6.00
101 Sean Henn AU/235 (RC) 4.00 10.00
102 Sean White AU/235 RC 4.00 10.00
103 Mike Schultz AU/234 RC 4.00 10.00
104 Michael Bourn AU/234 (RC) 4.00 10.00
105 Matt Chico AU/235 (RC) 4.00 10.00
106 Matt Lindstrom AU/235 (RC) 4.00 10.00
107 Connor Robertson AU/235 RC 4.00 10.00
108 Jay Marshall AU/235 RC 4.00 10.00
109 Jared Burton AU/235 RC 4.00 10.00
110 Juan Perez AU/235 RC 4.00 10.00
111 Scott Moore AU/235 (RC) 4.00 10.00
112 Brad Salmon AU/235 RC 4.00 10.00
113 Danny Putnam AU/235 (RC) 4.00 10.00
114 Kelvin Jimenez AU/235 RC 4.00 10.00
115 Dennis Dove AU/235 (RC) 4.00 10.00
116 Yoel Hernandez AU/234 RC 4.00 10.00
117 Devern Hansack AU/235 RC 4.00 10.00
118 Mike Rabelo AU/235 RC 4.00 10.00
119 Miguel Montero AU/235 (RC) 8.00 20.00
120 Kevin Cameron AU/235 RC 4.00 10.00
121 Joseph Bisenius AU/235 RC 4.00 10.00
122 Ryan Z. Braun AU/234 RC 4.00 10.00
123 Levale Speigner AU/235 RC 4.00 10.00
124 Lee Gardner AU/235 (RC) 4.00 10.00
125 Ryan Rowland-Smith AU/234 RC 4.00 10.00
126 Zack Segovia AU/235 (RC) 4.00 10.00
127 Rick Vanden Hurk AU/235 RC 4.00 10.00
128 Dallas Braden AU/235 RC 30.00 60.00
129 Rocky Cherry AU/234 RC 4.00 10.00
130 Andy Gonzalez AU/235 (RC) 4.00 10.00
131 Neal Musser AU/235 RC 4.00 10.00
132 Garrett Jones AU/235 (RC) 12.50 30.00
133 Ben Francisco AU/235 (RC) 4.00 10.00
134 Jon Coutlangus AU/235 (RC) 4.00 10.00
135 A.J. Murray AU/235 RC 4.00 10.00
136 Brett Carroll AU/235 RC 4.00 10.00
137 John Danks AU/235 RC 8.00 20.00
138 Kyle Kendrick AU/235 RC 6.00 15.00
139 Joaquin Arias AU/235 (RC) 4.00 10.00
140 Matt Brown AU/235 RC 4.00 10.00
141 Kurt Suzuki AU/150 (RC) 10.00 25.00
142 Curtis Thigpen AU/150 (RC) 4.00 10.00
143 Jerry Owens AU/150 (RC) 4.00 10.00
144 Billy Butler AU/150 (RC) 15.00 40.00
145 Kei Igawa AU/150 RC 15.00 40.00
146 Mike Fontenot AU/150 (RC) 10.00 25.00
147 Brandon Wood AU/150 (RC) 10.00 25.00
148 Alexi Casilla AU/150 RC 4.00 10.00
149 Jeff Baker AU/150 (RC) 4.00 10.00
150 Brian Barden AU/150 RC 4.00 10.00
151 Chris Stewart AU/150 RC 4.00 10.00
152 Jon Knott AU/150 (RC) 4.00 10.00
153 Chase Wright AU/150 RC 6.00 15.00
154 Chase Headley AU/150 (RC) 10.00 25.00
155 Jesse Litsch Jsy AU/199 RC 6.00 15.00
156 Tyler Clippard AU/150 (RC) 15.00 40.00
157 Matt DeSalvo AU/150 (RC) 4.00 10.00
158 Kory Casto AU/150 (RC) 4.00 10.00
159 Jarrod Saltalamacchia Jsy AU/199 (RC) 8.00 20.00
160 Glen Perkins AU/150 (RC) 4.00 10.00
161 Ryan Braun Jsy AU/199 (RC) 40.00 80.00
162 Justin Upton Jsy AU/199 RC 20.00 50.00
163 Tim Lincecum Jsy AU/199 RC 150.00 250.00
164 Fred Lewis AU/150 (RC) 6.00 15.00
165 Alex Gordon Jsy AU/199 RC 8.00 20.00
166 Akinori Iwamura Jsy AU/199 RC 10.00 25.00
167 Delmon Young Jsy AU/199 (RC) 12.50 30.00
168 Troy Tulowitzki Jsy AU/199 (RC) 60.00 120.00
169 Daisuke Matsuzaka Jsy AU/199 RC 60.00 120.00
170 Josh Hamilton Jsy AU/199 (RC) 20.00 50.00
171 Kevin Kouzmanoff Jsy AU/199 (RC) 6.00 15.00
172 Hunter Pence Jsy AU/199 (RC) 15.00 40.00
173 Felix Pie Jsy AU/199 (RC) 6.00 15.00
174 Andrew Miller Jsy AU/199 RC 10.00 25.00
175 Yovani Gallardo Jsy AU/199 (RC) 10.00 25.00
176 Ryan Sweeney Jsy AU/199 (RC) 6.00 15.00
177 Josh Fields Jsy AU/199 (RC) 8.00 20.00
178 Mark Reynolds Jsy AU/199 RC 20.00 50.00
180 Homer Bailey AU/150 (RC) 10.00 25.00
182 Joba Chamberlain AU/150 RC 60.00 120.00
184 Travis Metcalf Jsy AU/125 RC 8.00 20.00
185 Kevin Slowey Jsy AU/199 (RC) 12.50 30.00
186 Phil Hughes AU/150 (RC) 12.50 30.00
187 Micah Owings AU/150 (RC) 10.00 25.00
188 Joe Smith AU/150 RC 4.00 10.00
189 Joakim Soria Jsy AU/199 RC 10.00 25.00
190 Adam Lind Jsy AU/199 (RC) 8.00 20.00
191 Andy LaRoche Jsy AU/199 (RC) 8.00 20.00
192 Brandon Morrow Jsy AU/175 RC 15.00 40.00
193 Carlos Gomez Jsy AU/125 RC 8.00 20.00
194 Yunel Escobar AU/150 (RC) 12.50 30.00

2007 Exquisite Collection Rookie Signatures Gold

*1-100 GOLD: .6X TO 1.5X BASIC
ONE BASE OR BASE PARALLEL PER PACK
1-100 PRINT RUN 75 SER.#'d SETS
*101-191 AU GOLD: .6X TO 1.5X BASIC
OVERALL FIVE AUTOS PER PACK
101-191 AU SER.#'d B/WN 25-75 PER
NO PRICING ON QTY 25 OR LESS
*101-191 JSY AU GOLD: .6X TO 1.5X BASIC
101-191 JSY AU SER.#'d B/WN 50-99 PER
EXCHANGE DEADLINE 12/28/2009

2007 Exquisite Collection Rookie Signatures Gold Spectrum Patches

OVERALL FIVE AUTOS PER PACK
STATED PRINT RUN 1 SER.#'d SET
NO PRICING DUE TO SCARCITY
EXCHANGE DEADLINE 12/28/2009

2007 Exquisite Collection Rookie Signatures Silver Spectrum

ONE BASE OR BASE PARALLEL PER PACK
1-100 STATED PRINT RUN 1 SER.#'d SET
OVERALL AU ODDS FIVE PER PACK
101-191 AU PRINT RUN 1 SER.#'d SET
101-191 JSY AU PRINT RUN 25 SER.#'d SETS
NO PRICING DUE TO SCARCITY
EXCHANGE DEADLINE 12/28/2009

2007 Exquisite Collection Rookie Signatures All Rookie Team Autographs

OVERALL FIVE AUTOS PER PACK
STATED PRINT RUN 20 SER.#'d SETS
NO PRICING DUE TO SCARCITY
COPPER SPEC.PRINT RUN 1 SER.#'d SET
NO COPPER SPEC PRICING AVAILABLE
GOLD SPEC. PRINT RUN 5 SER.#'d SETS
NO GOLD SPEC PRICING AVAILABLE
SILVER INK PRINT RUN 1 SER.#'d SET
NO SILVER INK PRICING AVAILABLE
SILVER SPEC PRINT RUN 15 SER.#'d SETS
NO SILVER SPEC PRICING AVAILABLE
EXCHANGE DEADLINE 12/28/2009

2007 Exquisite Collection Rookie Signatures Cal Ripken Jr. All Rookie Team Autographs

OVERALL FIVE AUTOS PER PACK
STATED PRINT RUN 8 SER.#'d SETS
NO PRICING DUE TO SCARCITY
SILVER SPEC PRINT RUN 1 SER.#'d SET
NO SILVER SPEC PRICING AVAILABLE

2007 Exquisite Collection Rookie Signatures College Ties Autographs

OVERALL FIVE AUTOS PER PACK
PRINT RUNS B/WN 10-25 COPIES PER
NO PRICING DUE TO SCARCITY
GOLD PRINT RUN 2 SER.#'d SETS
NO GOLD PRICING AVAILABLE
SILVER SPEC PRINT RUN 1 SER.#'d SET
NO SILVER SPEC PRICING AVAILABLE
EXCHANGE DEADLINE 12/28/2009

2007 Exquisite Collection Rookie Signatures Common Ground Signatures

OVERALL FIVE AUTOS PER PACK
STATED PRINT RUN 25 SER.#'d SETS
NO PRICING DUE TO SCARCITY
GOLD PRINT RUN 2 SER.#'d SETS
NO GOLD PRICING AVAILABLE
SILVER SPEC PRINT RUN 1 SER.#'d SET
NO SILVER SPEC PRICING AVAILABLE
EXCHANGE DEADLINE 12/28/2009

2007 Exquisite Collection Rookie Signatures Common Numbers

OVERALL FIVE AUTOS PER PACK
PRINT RUNS B/WN 2-60 COPIES PER
NO PRICING ON QTY 25 OR LESS
GOLD SPEC. PRINT RUN 1 SER.#'d SET
NO GOLD SPEC PRICING AVAILABLE
SILVER SPEC PRINT RUN 2 SER.#'d SETS
NO SILVER SPEC PRICING AVAILABLE
EXCHANGE DEADLINE 12/28/2009
BB Jason Bay / Jeremy Bonderman/38 10.00 25.00
BC Ryan Z. Braun / Matt Chico/47 6.00 15.00
BR Ryan Braun / Cal Ripken Jr./8
CP Manny Corpas / Glen Perkins/60 6.00 15.00
EC Yunel Escobar / Tyler Clippard/19
EH Andre Ethier / Chase Headley/16
FR Josh Fields / Mark Reynolds/27 8.00 20.00
GH Yovani Gallardo / Philip Humber/49 8.00 20.00
GO Alex Gordon / Jerry Owens/7
GS Jose Garcia / Kevin Slowey/59 8.00 20.00
LC Adam LaRoche / Alexi Casilla/25
LT Derrek Lee / Jim Thome/25
MB Nick Markakis / Billy Butler/21
MS Andrew Miller / Joakim Soria/48 10.00 25.00
PB Hunter Pence / Michael Bourn/9
RJ Hanley Ramirez / Derek Jeter/2
TJ Troy Tulowitzki / Derek Jeter/2
VG Jamie Vermilyea / Sean Gallagher/36 6.00 15.00
VT Justin Verlander / Frank Thomas/35 75.00 150.00
WL Josh Willingham / Fred Lewis/14

2007 Exquisite Collection Rookie Signatures Derek Jeter All Rookie Team Autographs

OVERALL FIVE AUTOS PER PACK
STATED PRINT RUN 2 SER.#'d SETS
NO PRICING DUE TO SCARCITY
SILVER SPEC PRINT RUN 1 SER.#'d SET
NO SILVER SPEC PRICING AVAILABLE

2007 Exquisite Collection Rookie Signatures Draft Choice Autographs

OVERALL FIVE AUTOS PER PACK
STATED PRINT RUN 20 SER.#'d SETS
NO PRICING DUE TO SCARCITY
COPPER SPEC.PRINT RUN 1 SER.#'d SET
NO COPPER SPEC PRICING AVAILABLE
GOLD SPEC. PRINT RUN 5 SER.#'d SETS
NO GOLD SPEC PRICING AVAILABLE
SILVER INK PRINT RUN 15 SER.#'d SETS
NO SILVER INK PRICING AVAILABLE
SILVER SPEC PRINT RUN 15 SER.#'d SETS
NO SILVER SPEC PRICING AVAILABLE
EXCHANGE DEADLINE 12/28/2009

2007 Exquisite Collection Rookie Signatures Draft Duals Autographs

OVERALL FIVE AUTOS PER PACK
STATED PRINT RUN 25 SER.#'d SETS
NO PRICING DUE TO SCARCITY
GOLD PRINT RUN 2 SER.#'d SETS
NO GOLD PRICING AVAILABLE
SILVER SPEC PRINT RUN 1 SER.#'d SET
NO SILVER SPEC PRICING AVAILABLE
EXCHANGE DEADLINE 12/28/2009

2007 Exquisite Collection Rookie Signatures Dual Signatures

OVERALL FIVE AUTOS PER PACK
PRINT RUNS B/WN 10-35 COPIES PER
NO PRICING ON QTY 10 OR LESS
GOLD #'d B/WN 5-25 COPIES PER
NO GOLD PRICING AVAILABLE
SILVER SPEC. #'d B/WN 1-10 COPIES PER
NO SILVER SPEC PRICING AVAILABLE
EXCHANGE DEADLINE 12/28/2009
AC Andrew Miller / Cameron Maybin/35 30.00 60.00
AD Alexi Casilla / Don Kelly/35 6.00 15.00

AJ Aaron Harang / Jeff Keppinger/35 10.00 25.00
AM Joaquin Arias / Travis Metcalf/35 6.00 15.00
BB Ryan Braun / Ryan Z. Braun/35 12.50 30.00
BC Jared Burton / Jon Coutlangus/35 6.00 15.00
BG Jason Bay / Tom Gorzelanny/35 6.00 15.00
BH Brian Burres / Ramon Hernandez/35 6.00 15.00
BI Ryan Braun / Akinori Iwamura/35 30.00 60.00
BJ Bill Hall / Johnny Estrada/35 6.00 15.00
BK Chad Billingsley / Hong-Chih Kuo/35 20.00 50.00
BL Homer Bailey / Tim Lincecum/35 20.00 50.00
BR Brian Barden / Mark Reynolds/35 20.00 50.00
BW Billy Butler / Brandon Wood/35 12.50 30.00
CC Curtis Granderson / Cameron Maybin/35 30.00 60.00
CD Matt Chico / Matt DeSalvo/35 6.00 15.00
CH Joba Chamberlain / Phil Hughes/35 75.00 150.00
CJ Alexi Casilla / Garrett Jones/35 6.00 15.00
CK Cesar Jimenez / Kelvin Jimenez/35 6.00 15.00
CY Carl Crawford / Delmon Young/35 10.00 25.00
DH J.D. Durbin / Yoel Hernandez/35 6.00 15.00
DM Doug Slaten / Mike Schultz/35 6.00 15.00
DO Stephen Drew / Micah Owings/35 10.00 25.00
DW Matt DeSalvo / Chase Wright/35 6.00 15.00
FE Mike Fontenot / Mark Ellis/35 6.00 15.00
FL Prince Fielder / Carlos Lee/35 30.00 60.00
GB Alex Gordon / Ryan Braun/35 20.00 50.00
GC Sean Gallagher / Rocky Cherry/35 6.00 15.00
GG Jose Garcia / Lee Gardner/35 6.00 15.00
GJ Vladimir Guerrero / Andruw Jones/35 30.00 60.00
GK Adrian Gonzalez / Casey Kotchman/35 10.00 25.00
GL Jose Garcia / Matt Lindstrom/35 6.00 15.00
GM Gustavo Molina / Miguel Montero/35 12.50 30.00
GP Carlos Gomez / Felix Pie/35 10.00 25.00
GR Ken Griffey Jr. / Cal Ripken Jr./10
GV Lee Gardner / Rick Vanden Hurk/35 6.00 15.00
HA Homer Bailey / Aaron Harang/35 15.00 40.00
HB Yoel Hernandez / Joseph Bisenius/35 6.00 15.00
HC Sean Henn / Tyler Clippard/35 6.00 15.00
HD Sean Henn / Matt DeSalvo/35 6.00 15.00
HE Ramon Hernandez / Johnny Estrada/35 6.00 15.00
HG Josh Hamilton / Curtis Granderson/35 20.00 50.00
HH Justin Hampson / Chase Headley/35 6.00 15.00
HK Phil Hughes / Hong-Chih Kuo/35 12.50 30.00
HL Phil Hughes / Tim Lincecum/35 50.00 100.00
HM Cole Hamels / Andrew Miller/35 20.00 50.00
HP Homer Bailey / Phil Hughes/35 30.00 60.00
IC Kei Igawa / Tyler Clippard/35 15.00 40.00
IH Kei Igawa / Phil Hughes/35 20.00 50.00
JE Kelly Johnson / Yunel Escobar/35 12.50 30.00
JJ James Shields / Juan Salas/35 6.00 15.00
KB Ian Kinsler / Hank Blalock/35 10.00 25.00
KH Kevin Kouzmanoff / Chase Headley/35 6.00 15.00
KK Howie Kendrick / Casey Kotchman/35 12.50 30.00
KW Howie Kendrick / Brandon Wood/35 12.50 30.00
LA Andy LaRoche / Tony Abreu/35 10.00 25.00
LB Fred Lewis / Michael Bourn/35 6.00 15.00
LE John Lackey / Kelvim Escobar/35 10.00 25.00
LH Jon Lester / Devern Hansack/35 12.50 30.00
LO Tim Lincecum / Roy Oswalt/35 60.00 120.00
LP Carlos Lee / Hunter Pence/35 30.00 60.00
LS Jesse Litsch / Kevin Slowey/35 6.00 15.00
ME Brian McCann / Yunel Escobar/35 12.50 30.00
MH Nick Markakis / Josh Hamilton/35 10.00 25.00
MM Russell Martin / Brian McCann/35 12.50 30.00
MO Andrew Miller / Micah Owings/35 12.50 30.00
MC John Maine / Joe Smith/35 10.00 25.00
NT Nick Swisher / Travis Buck/35 12.50 30.00
OC Micah Owings / Matt Chico/35 12.50 30.00
PH Hunter Pence / Josh Hamilton/35 20.00 50.00
PM Corey Patterson / Nick Markakis/35 12.50 30.00
PO Felix Pie / Jerry Owens/35 6.00 15.00
RB Mark Reynolds / Ryan Braun/35 20.00 50.00
RJ Cal Ripken Jr. / Derek Jeter/10
RM Connor Robertson / Jay Marshall/35 6.00 15.00
RO Mark Reynolds / Micah Owings/35 12.50 30.00
RU Hanley Ramirez / Dan Uggla/35 12.50 30.00
RZ Aramis Ramirez / Carlos Zambrano/35 20.00 50.00
SA Joakim Soria / Jeremy Accardo/35 6.00 15.00
SB Joakim Soria / Ryan Z. Braun/35 6.00 15.00
SG Joe Smith / Carlos Gomez/35 10.00 25.00
SM Kurt Suzuki / Gustavo Molina/35 6.00 15.00
SO Ryan Sweeney / Jerry Owens/35 6.00 15.00
SR Chris Stewart / Mike Rabelo/35 6.00 15.00
SS Joe Smith / Kevin Slowey/35 6.00 15.00
ST Sean Henn / Tyler Clippard/35 6.00 15.00
TB Troy Tulowitzki / Jeff Baker/35 20.00 50.00
TE Yunel Escobar / Ryan Theriot/35 10.00 25.00
TF Ryan Theriot / Mike Fontenot/35 20.00 50.00
TJ Curtis Thigpen / Garrett Jones/35 6.00 15.00
TL Curtis Thigpen / Adam Lind/35 6.00 15.00
TR Travis Hafner / Ryan Garko/35 15.00 40.00
TT Frank Thomas / Jim Thome/35 40.00 80.00
TV Travis Hafner / Victor Martinez/35 8.00 20.00
VL Rick Vanden Hurk / Matt Lindstrom/35 6.00 15.00
VM Justin Verlander / Andrew Miller/35 60.00 120.00
WI Chase Wright / Kei Igawa/35 15.00 40.00
YT Yovani Gallardo / Tim Lincecum/35 50.00 100.00
ZB Ryan Zimmerman / Ryan Braun/35 15.00 40.00
ZG Ryan Zimmerman / Alex Gordon/35 15.00 40.00

2007 Exquisite Collection Rookie Signatures Endorsements Signatures

OVERALL FIVE AUTOS PER PACK
STATED PRINT RUN 50 SER.#'d SETS
GOLD PRINT RUN 15 SER.#'d SETS
NO GOLD PRICING AVAILABLE
SILVER SPEC PRINT RUN 1 SER.#'d SET
NO SILVER SPEC PRICING AVAILABLE
EXCHANGE DEADLINE 12/28/2009
AC Alexi Casilla 4.00 10.00
AE Andre Ethier 20.00 50.00
AL Adam Lind 6.00 15.00
BH Brendan Harris 6.00 15.00
BO Jeremy Bonderman 10.00 25.00
CP Corey Patterson 4.00 10.00
DH Dan Haren 4.00 10.00
DL Derrek Lee 10.00 25.00
DM David Murphy 6.00 15.00
DU Dan Uggla 4.00 10.00
FL Fred Lewis 6.00 15.00
FP Felix Pie 6.00 15.00
GP Glen Perkins 4.00 10.00
HB Homer Bailey 10.00 25.00
HP Hunter Pence 30.00 60.00
HR Hanley Ramirez 10.00 25.00
JB Jason Bay 6.00 15.00
JF Josh Fields 4.00 10.00
JL Jon Lester 15.00 40.00
JP Jonathan Papelbon 10.00 25.00
JS James Shields 4.00 10.00
JV Justin Verlander 20.00 50.00
KI Kei Igawa 15.00 40.00
KS Kevin Slowey 6.00 15.00
LG Luis Gonzalez 6.00 15.00
MH Matt Holliday 15.00 40.00
MO Micah Owings 6.00 15.00
NS Nick Swisher 6.00 15.00
PF Prince Fielder 30.00 60.00
RB Ryan Braun 30.00 60.00
RM Russell Martin 10.00 25.00
RS Ryan Sweeney 4.00 10.00
RT Ryan Theriot 6.00 15.00
RZ Ryan Zimmerman 15.00 40.00
SM Joe Smith 6.00 15.00
TH Travis Hafner 10.00 25.00
TL Tim Lincecum 60.00 120.00
TT Troy Tulowitzki 15.00 40.00
VM Victor Martinez 10.00 25.00
YE Yunel Escobar 10.00 25.00

2007 Exquisite Collection Rookie Signatures Ensemble Quad Signatures

OVERALL FIVE AUTOS PER PACK
STATED PRINT RUN 15 SER.#'d SETS
NO PRICING DUE TO SCARCITY
GOLD SPEC. PRINT RUN 1 SER.#'d SET
NO GOLD SPEC PRICING AVAILABLE
SILVER SPEC PRINT RUN 4 SER.#'d SETS
NO SILVER SPEC PRICING AVAILABLE
EXCHANGE DEADLINE 12/28/2009

2007 Exquisite Collection Rookie Signatures Ensemble Triple Signatures

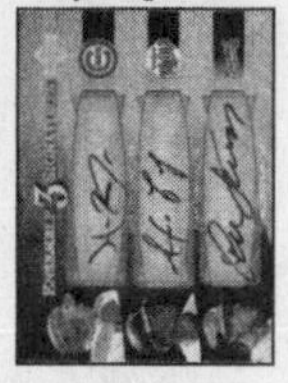

OVERALL FIVE AUTOS PER PACK
PRINT RUNS B/WN 10-35 COPIES PER
NO PRICING ON QTY 10 OR LESS
GOLD SPEC. PRINT RUN 3 SER.#'d SETS
NO GOLD SPEC PRICING AVAILABLE
SILVER SPEC PRINT RUN 1 SER.#'d SET
NO SILVER SPEC PRICING AVAILABLE
EXCHANGE DEADLINE 12/28/2009
BGL Ryan Braun / Alex Gordon / Andy LaRoche/35 30.00 60.00
BLG Michael Bourn / Fred Lewis / Carlos Gomez/35 12.50 30.00
BTY Ryan Braun / Troy Tulowitzki / Delmon Young/35 50.00 100.00
BWL Billy Butler / Brandon Wood / Adam Lind/35 30.00 60.00
CSP Joba Chamberlain / Joakim Soria / Glen Perkins/35 20.00 50.00
FCE Mike Fontenot / Alexi Casilla / Yunel Escobar/35 20.00 50.00
GFC Sean Gallagher / Mike Fontenot / Rocky Cherry/35 12.50 30.00
GIB Alex Gordon / Akinori Iwamura / Ryan Braun/35 50.00 100.00
GJR Ken Griffey Jr. / Derek Jeter / Cal Ripken Jr./10
HHD Phil Hughes / Sean Henn / Matt DeSalvo/35
IGR Akinori Iwamura / Alex Gordon / Mark Reynolds/35 40.00 80.00
KHH Kevin Kouzmanoff / Chase Headley / Justin Hampson/35
LHB Tim Lincecum / Phil Hughes / Homer Bailey/35 40.00 80.00
LLT Adam Lind / Jesse Litsch / Curtis Thigpen/35 12.50 30.00
MKI Andrew Miller / Kyle Kendrick / Kei Igawa/35 30.00 60.00
PHY Hunter Pence / Josh Hamilton / Delmon Young/35 20.00 50.00
SHG Joakim Soria / Justin Hampson / Sean Gallagher/35 12.50 30.00
SMA Jarrod Saltalamacchia / David Murphy / Joaquin Arias/35 15.00 40.00
UBB Justin Upton / Travis Buck / Billy Butler/35 60.00 120.00
WCD Chase Wright / Tyler Clippard / Matt DeSalvo/35

2007 Exquisite Collection Rookie Signatures First Signs Autographs

OVERALL FIVE AUTOS PER PACK
STATED PRINT RUN 20 SER.#'d SETS
NO PRICING DUE TO SCARCITY
COPPER SPEC.PRINT RUN 1 SER.#'d SET
NO COPPER SPEC PRICING AVAILABLE
GOLD SPEC. PRINT RUN 5 SER.#'d SETS
NO GOLD SPEC PRICING AVAILABLE
SILVER INK PRINT RUN 1 SER.#'d SET
NO SILVER INK PRICING AVAILABLE
SILVER SPEC PRINT RUN 15 SER.#'d SETS
NO SILVER SPEC PRICING AVAILABLE
EXCHANGE DEADLINE 12/28/2009

2007 Exquisite Collection Rookie Signatures Futures Autographs

OVERALL FIVE AUTOS PER PACK
STATED PRINT RUN 20 SER.#'d SETS
NO PRICING DUE TO SCARCITY
GOLD SPEC. PRINT RUN 1 SER.#'d SET

NO GOLD SPEC PRICING AVAILABLE
SILVER SPEC PRINT RUN 5 SER.#'d SETS
NO SILVER SPEC PRICING AVAILABLE
EXCHANGE DEADLINE 12/28/2009

2007 Exquisite Collection Rookie Signatures Game Dated Debut Signatures

OVERALL FIVE AUTOS PER PACK
STATED PRINT RUN 20 SER.#'d SETS
NO PRICING DUE TO SCARCITY
GOLD PRINT RUN 5 SER.#'d SETS
NO GOLD SPEC PRICING AVAILABLE
SILVER INK PRINT RUN 1 SER.#'d SET
NO SILVER INK PRICING AVAILABLE
SILVER SPEC PRINT RUN 15 SER.#'d SETS
NO SILVER SPEC PRICING AVAILABLE
EXCHANGE DEADLINE 12/28/2009

2007 Exquisite Collection Rookie Signatures Imagery Autographs

OVERALL FIVE AUTOS PER PACK
STATED PRINT RUN 25 SER.#'d SETS
NO PRICING ON MOST DUE TO SCARCITY
EACG VERSION PRICED EQUALLY
GOLD PRINT RUN 10 SER.#'d SETS
NO GOLD PRICING AVAILABLE
SILVER INK PRINT RUN 1 SER.#'d SET
NO SILVER INK PRICING AVAILABLE
SILVER SPEC PRINT RUN 1 SER.#'d SET
NO SILVER SPEC PRICING AVAILABLE
EXCHANGE DEADLINE 12/28/2009
AC Alexi Casilla
AG Alex Gordon 15.00 40.00
AG2 Alex Gordon 15.00 40.00
AL Adam Lind 10.00 25.00
AL2 Adam Lind 10.00 25.00
BB Billy Butler
BH Bill Hall
BO Michael Bourn 6.00 15.00
BO2 Michael Bourn 6.00 15.00
BR Ryan Z. Braun
BS Brian Stokes
CG Carlos Gomez 12.50 30.00
CG2 Carlos Gomez 12.50 30.00
CG3 Carlos Gomez 12.50 30.00
CH Chase Headley
CT Curtis Thigpen
CW Chase Wright
CZ Carlos Zambrano
DD Dennis Dove
DH Devern Hansack
DM David Murphy 10.00 25.00
DM2 David Murphy 10.00 25.00
FL Fred Lewis 6.00 15.00
FL2 Fred Lewis 6.00 15.00
FL3 Fred Lewis 6.00 15.00
FP Felix Pie 6.00 15.00
FP2 Felix Pie 6.00 15.00
GJ Garrett Jones
GM Gustavo Molina
GP Glen Perkins
HA Justin Hampson
HB Homer Bailey
HP Hunter Pence
HR Hanley Ramirez
JB Jason Bay 6.00 15.00
JB2 Jason Bay 6.00 15.00
JF Josh Fields 6.00 15.00
JF2 Josh Fields 6.00 15.00
JF3 Josh Fields 6.00 15.00
JH Josh Hamilton 5.00 12.00
JH2 Josh Hamilton 5.00 12.00
JL Jesse Litsch
JO Jerry Owens
JS James Shields
JU Justin Upton
JW Josh Willingham 6.00 15.00
JW2 Josh Willingham 6.00 15.00
KE Kyle Kendrick 10.00 25.00
KE2 Kyle Kendrick 10.00 25.00
KI Kei Igawa
KK Kevin Kouzmanoff 6.00 15.00
KK2 Kevin Kouzmanoff 6.00 15.00
KK3 Kevin Kouzmanoff 6.00 15.00
KS Kevin Slowey 6.00 15.00
KS2 Kevin Slowey 6.00 15.00
LA Andy LaRoche
MB Matt Brown
MD Matt DeSalvo
MF Mike Fontenot 6.00 15.00
MF2 Mike Fontenot 6.00 15.00
MF3 Mike Fontenot 6.00 15.00
MH Matt Holliday 20.00 50.00
MH2 Matt Holliday 20.00 50.00
MO Micah Owings 10.00 25.00
MO2 Micah Owings 10.00 25.00
MR Mark Reynolds 10.00 25.00
MR2 Mark Reynolds 10.00 25.00
MT Miguel Tejada
NM Nick Markakis
RB Ryan Braun 20.00 50.00
RB2 Ryan Braun 20.00 50.00
RC Rocky Cherry
RM Russell Martin 8.00 20.00
RM2 Russell Martin 8.00 20.00
RS Ryan Sweeney 6.00 15.00
RS2 Ryan Sweeney 6.00 15.00
RV Rick Vanden Hurk
RZ Ryan Zimmerman 20.00 50.00
RZ2 Ryan Zimmerman 20.00 50.00
SA Jarrod Saltalamacchia
SG Sean Gallagher
SH Sean Henn
SM Joe Smith 6.00 15.00
SM2 Joe Smith 6.00 15.00
TA Tony Abreu
TB Travis Buck 6.00 15.00
TB2 Travis Buck 6.00 15.00
TC Tyler Clippard
TG Tom Gorzelanny
TH Travis Hafner 6.00 15.00
TH2 Travis Hafner 6.00 15.00
TM Travis Metcalf
VM Victor Martinez 6.00 15.00
VM2 Victor Martinez 6.00 15.00
VM3 Victor Martinez 6.00 15.00
YE Yunel Escobar 12.50 30.00
YE2 Yunel Escobar 12.50 30.00
YG Yovani Gallardo
YH Yoel Hernandez
ZS Zack Segovia

2007 Exquisite Collection Rookie Signatures Ken Griffey Jr. All Rookie Team Autographs

OVERALL FIVE AUTOS PER PACK
STATED PRINT RUN 3 SER.#'d SETS
NO PRICING DUE TO SCARCITY
SILVER SPEC PRINT RUN 1 SER.#'d SET
NO SILVER SPEC PRICING AVAILABLE

2007 Exquisite Collection Rookie Signatures Phenoms Autographs

OVERALL FIVE AUTOS PER PACK
STATED PRINT RUN 20 SER.#'d SETS
NO PRICING DUE TO SCARCITY
GOLD PRINT RUN 15 SER.#'d SETS
NO GOLD PRICING AVAILABLE
SILVER INK PRINT RUN 1 SER.#'d SET
NO SILVER INK PRICING AVAILABLE
SILVER SPEC PRINT RUN 15 SER.#'d SETS
NO SILVER SPEC PRICING AVAILABLE
EXCHANGE DEADLINE 12/28/2009

2007 Exquisite Collection Rookie Signatures Reflections Autographs

OVERALL FIVE AUTOS PER PACK
PRINT RUNS B/WN 10-40 COPIES PER
NO PRICING QTY OF 20 OR LESS
GOLD #'d B/WN 5-20 COPIES PER
NO GOLD PRICING AVAILABLE
SILVER INK #'d B/WN 5-20 COPIES PER
NO SILVER INK PRICING AVAILABLE
SILVER SPEC #'d B/WN 1-10 COPIES PER
NO SILVER SPEC PRICING AVAILABLE
AB Alex Gordon 8.00 20.00
Billy Butler/40
AC Joaquin Arias 6.00 15.00
Alexi Casilla/40
AH Aaron Harang 20.00 50.00
Homer Bailey/40
AJ Andrew Miller 10.00 25.00
Jeremy Sowers/40
BA Matt Brown 6.00 15.00
Tony Abreu/40
BB Brian Bannister 6.00 15.00
Boof Bonser/40
BD Brian Bannister 6.00 15.00
John Danks/40
BG Ryan Braun 30.00 60.00
Alex Gordon/40
BH Josh Barfield 10.00 25.00
Travis Hafner/40
BJ Brad Salmon 10.00 25.00
Jared Burton/40
BL Michael Bourn 10.00 25.00
Fred Lewis/40
BS Joseph Bisenius 6.00 15.00
Zack Segovia/40
BT Brian Bannister 10.00 25.00
Mark Teahen/40
BV Jeremy Bonderman 20.00 50.00
Justin Verlander/40
BW Matt Brown 10.00 25.00
Brandon Wood/40
CG Carl Crawford 10.00 25.00
Carlos Gomez/40
CH Kevin Cameron 6.00 15.00
Justin Hampson/40
CK Curtis Thigpen 10.00 25.00
Kurt Suzuki/40
CR Cal Ripken Jr.
Ryan Braun/10
CS Rocky Cherry 6.00 15.00
Joakim Soria/40
DC Matt DeSalvo 6.00 15.00
Matt Chico/40
DH J.D. Durbin 6.00 15.00
Yoel Hernandez/40
DO John Danks 6.00 15.00
Micah Owings/40
DS J.D. Durbin 10.00 25.00
Zack Segovia/40
EC Yunel Escobar 6.00 15.00
Alexi Casilla/40
EL Andre Ethier 20.00 50.00
Fred Lewis/40
EP Mark Ellis 10.00 25.00
Danny Putnam/40
FM Josh Fields 6.00 15.00
Travis Metcalf/40
FO Prince Fielder 30.00 60.00
David Ortiz/40
FY Felix Hernandez 12.50 30.00
Yovani Gallardo/40
GA Glen Perkins 6.00 15.00
Alexi Casilla/40
GB Jeremy Guthrie 10.00 25.00
Brian Burres/40
GC Sean Gallagher 6.00 15.00
Rocky Cherry/40
GG Jeremy Guthrie 6.00 15.00
Tom Gorzelanny/40
GK Alex Gordon 15.00 40.00
Kevin Kouzmanoff/40
GL Lee Gardner 6.00 15.00
Matt Lindstrom/40
GM Gustavo Molina 6.00 15.00
Miguel Montero/40
GT Ken Griffey Jr.
Frank Thomas/20
GV Jose Garcia 6.00 15.00
Rick Vanden Hurk/40
HB Phil Hughes 10.00 25.00
Homer Bailey/40
HC Justin Hampson 6.00 15.00
Jon Coutlangus/40
HD Huston Street 30.00 60.00
Dallas Braden/40
HG Rich Hill 10.00 25.00
Sean Gallagher/40
HH Phil Hughes 20.00 50.00
Sean Henn/40
HK Chase Headley 6.00 15.00
Kevin Kouzmanoff/40
HM Cole Hamels 20.00 50.00
Andrew Miller/40
HP Josh Hamilton 15.00 40.00
Hunter Pence/40
HT Homer Bailey 40.00 80.00
Tim Lincecum/40
HW Jeremy Hermida 6.00 15.00
Josh Willingham/40
IM Kei Igawa 20.00 50.00
Andrew Miller/40
JC James Shields 10.00 25.00
Chad Billingsley/40
JD Kelvin Jimenez 6.00 15.00
Dennis Dove/40
JE Kelly Johnson 12.50 30.00
Yunel Escobar/40
JJ Josh Fields 10.00 25.00
Jerry Owens/40
JK Jarrod Saltalamacchia 10.00 25.00
Kurt Suzuki/40
JL Reed Johnson 6.00 15.00
Adam Lind/40
JM John Danks 6.00 15.00
Matt Chico/40
JR Derek Jeter
Cal Ripken Jr./10
KC Kelvin Jimenez 10.00 25.00
Cesar Jimenez/40
KG Kurt Suzuki 6.00 15.00
Gustavo Molina/40
LA Andy LaRoche 10.00 25.00
Tony Abreu/40
LB Adam Lind 6.00 15.00
Jeff Baker/40
LH Jon Lester 20.00 50.00
Cole Hamels/40
LL Jesse Litsch 10.00 25.00
Adam Lind/40
LO Fred Lewis 6.00 15.00
Jerry Owens/40
MA Mark Ellis 6.00 15.00
Alexi Casilla/40
MB Jay Marshall 6.00 15.00
Dallas Braden/40
MG Nick Markakis 12.50 30.00
Jeremy Guthrie/40
MJ Matt Holliday 10.00 25.00
Jason Bay/40
MK Nick Markakis 10.00 25.00
Jon Knott/40
MM Russell Martin 12.50 30.00
Brian McCann/40
MR Jay Marshall 10.00 25.00
Connor Robertson/40
MS Russell Martin 12.50 30.00
Kurt Suzuki/40
NR Neal Musser 10.00 25.00
Ryan Z. Braun/40
OB Micah Owings 6.00 15.00
Homer Bailey/40
PB Danny Putnam 6.00 15.00
Travis Buck/40
PC Glen Perkins 6.00 15.00
Matt Chico/40
PD Glen Perkins 6.00 15.00
Matt DeSalvo/40
PG Felix Pie 12.50 30.00
Carlos Gomez/40
PO Felix Pie 6.00 15.00
Jerry Owens/40
PR Phil Hughes
Roger Clemens/10
RB Mark Reynolds 20.00 50.00
Ryan Braun/40
RC Ryan Braun 15.00 40.00
Chase Headley/40
RM Mike Rabelo 6.00 15.00
Gustavo Molina/40
RR Ryan Z. Braun 20.00 50.00
Ryan Braun/40
SB Joakim Soria 6.00 15.00
Ryan Z. Braun/40
SG Ben Sheets 20.00 50.00
Yovani Gallardo/40
SH Joe Smith 10.00 25.00
Justin Hampson/40
SM Jarrod Saltalamacchia 10.00 25.00
David Murphy/40
SP Kevin Slowey 10.00 25.00
Glen Perkins/40
SR Kurt Suzuki 6.00 15.00
Shawn Riggans/40
SS Joe Smith 6.00 15.00
Kevin Slowey/40
ST Sean Henn 6.00 15.00
Tyler Clippard/40
TJ Curtis Thigpen 6.00 15.00
Garrett Jones/40
TR Curtis Thigpen 6.00 15.00
Shawn Riggans/40
TS Mark Teahen 6.00 15.00
Angel Sanchez/40
VG Rick Vanden Hurk 6.00 15.00
Lee Gardner/40
WD Chase Wright 6.00 15.00
John Danks/40
WH Josh Willingham 10.00 25.00
Bill Hall/40
ZY Zack Segovia 6.00 15.00
Yoel Hernandez/40

2007 Exquisite Collection Rookie Signatures Retro Rookie Duals Autographs

OVERALL FIVE AUTOS PER PACK
PRINT RUNS B/WN 3-15 COPIES PER
NO PRICING DUE TO SCARCITY
GOLD PRINT RUN 2 SER.#'d SETS
NO GOLD PRICING AVAILABLE
SILVER SPEC PRINT RUN 1 SER.#'d SET
NO SILVER SPEC PRICING AVAILABLE
EXCHANGE DEADLINE 12/28/2009

2007 Exquisite Collection Rookie Signatures Rookie Biography Autographs

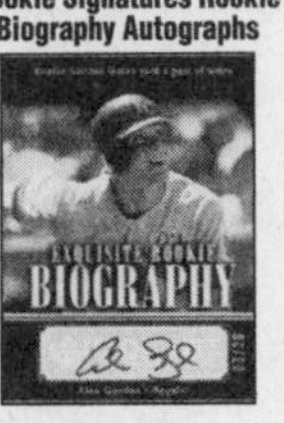

OVERALL FIVE AUTOS PER PACK
STATED PRINT RUN 20 SER.#'d SETS
NO PRICING DUE TO SCARCITY
BLUE.SPEC PRINT RUN 1 SER.#'d SET
NO BLUE SPEC PRICING AVAILABLE
GOLD PRINT RUN 15 SER.#'d SETS
NO GOLD PRICING AVAILABLE
GOLD SPEC. PRINT RUN 1 SER.#'d SET
NO GOLD SPEC PRICING AVAILABLE
SILVER INK PRINT RUN 1 SER.#'d SET
NO SILVER INK PRICING AVAILABLE
SILVER SPEC PRINT RUN 10 SER.#'d SETS
NO SILVER SPEC PRICING AVAILABLE
EXCHANGE DEADLINE 12/28/2009

2007 Exquisite Collection Rookie Signatures Rookie Heroes Autographs

OVERALL FIVE AUTOS PER PACK
STATED PRINT RUN 25 SER.#'d SETS
EACH VERSION PRICED EQUALLY
*GOLD: .6X TO 1.5X BASIC
GOLD PRINT RUN 15 SER.#'d SETS
GOLD SPEC. PRINT RUN 1 SER.#'d SET
NO GOLD SPEC PRICING AVAILABLE
SILVER INK PRINT RUN 1 SER.#'d SET
NO SILVER INK PRICING AVAILABLE
*SILVER SPEC: .75X TO 2X BASIC
SILVER SPEC PRINT RUN 10 SER.#'d SETS
EXCHANGE DEADLINE 12/28/2009
AI1 Akinori Iwamura 10.00 25.00
AI2 Akinori Iwamura 10.00 25.00
AI3 Akinori Iwamura 10.00 25.00
AI4 Akinori Iwamura 10.00 25.00
AI5 Akinori Iwamura 10.00 25.00
AM1 Andrew Miller 6.00 15.00
AM2 Andrew Miller 6.00 15.00
AM3 Andrew Miller 6.00 15.00
AM4 Andrew Miller 6.00 15.00
AM5 Andrew Miller 6.00 15.00
BB1 Billy Butler 10.00 25.00
BB2 Billy Butler 10.00 25.00
BB3 Billy Butler 10.00 25.00
BB4 Billy Butler 10.00 25.00
BB5 Billy Butler 10.00 25.00
CG1 Carlos Gomez 10.00 25.00
CG2 Carlos Gomez 10.00 25.00
CG3 Carlos Gomez 10.00 25.00
CG4 Carlos Gomez 10.00 25.00
CG5 Carlos Gomez 10.00 25.00
FL1 Fred Lewis 6.00 15.00
FL2 Fred Lewis 6.00 15.00
FL3 Fred Lewis 6.00 15.00
FL4 Fred Lewis 6.00 15.00
FL5 Fred Lewis 6.00 15.00
FP1 Felix Pie 6.00 15.00
FP2 Felix Pie 6.00 15.00
FP3 Felix Pie 6.00 15.00
FP4 Felix Pie 6.00 15.00
FP5 Felix Pie 6.00 15.00
HB1 Homer Bailey 6.00 15.00
HB2 Homer Bailey 6.00 15.00
HB3 Homer Bailey 6.00 15.00
HB4 Homer Bailey 6.00 15.00
HB5 Homer Bailey 6.00 15.00
HP1 Hunter Pence 15.00 40.00
HP2 Hunter Pence 15.00 40.00
HP3 Hunter Pence 15.00 40.00
HP4 Hunter Pence 15.00 40.00
HP5 Hunter Pence 15.00 40.00
JD1 John Danks 8.00 20.00
JD2 John Danks 8.00 20.00
JD3 John Danks 8.00 20.00
JD4 John Danks 8.00 20.00
JD5 John Danks 8.00 20.00
JS1 Jarrod Saltalamacchia 6.00 15.00
JS2 Jarrod Saltalamacchia 6.00 15.00
JS3 Jarrod Saltalamacchia 6.00 15.00
JS4 Jarrod Saltalamacchia 6.00 15.00
JS5 Jarrod Saltalamacchia 6.00 15.00
KE1 Kyle Kendrick 10.00 25.00
KE2 Kyle Kendrick 10.00 25.00
KE3 Kyle Kendrick 10.00 25.00
KE4 Kyle Kendrick 10.00 25.00
KE5 Kyle Kendrick 10.00 25.00
KK1 Kevin Kouzmanoff 6.00 15.00
KK2 Kevin Kouzmanoff 6.00 15.00
KK3 Kevin Kouzmanoff 6.00 15.00
KK4 Kevin Kouzmanoff 6.00 15.00
KK5 Kevin Kouzmanoff 6.00 15.00
KS1 Kevin Slowey 6.00 15.00
KS2 Kevin Slowey 6.00 15.00
KS3 Kevin Slowey 6.00 15.00
KS4 Kevin Slowey 6.00 15.00
KS5 Kevin Slowey 6.00 15.00
MR1 Mark Reynolds 40.00 80.00
MR2 Mark Reynolds 40.00 80.00
MR3 Mark Reynolds 40.00 80.00
MR4 Mark Reynolds 40.00 80.00
MR5 Mark Reynolds 40.00 80.00
RB1 Ryan Braun 30.00 60.00
RB2 Ryan Braun 30.00 60.00
RB3 Ryan Braun 30.00 60.00
RB4 Ryan Braun 30.00 60.00
RB5 Ryan Braun 30.00 60.00
SO1 Joakim Soria 6.00 15.00
SO2 Joakim Soria 6.00 15.00
SO3 Joakim Soria 6.00 15.00
SO4 Joakim Soria 6.00 15.00
SO5 Joakim Soria 6.00 15.00
TB1 Travis Buck 6.00 15.00
TB2 Travis Buck 6.00 15.00
TB3 Travis Buck 6.00 15.00
TB4 Travis Buck 6.00 15.00
TB5 Travis Buck 6.00 15.00
TL1 Tim Lincecum 75.00 150.00
TL2 Tim Lincecum 75.00 150.00
TL3 Tim Lincecum 75.00 150.00
TL4 Tim Lincecum 75.00 150.00
TL5 Tim Lincecum 75.00 150.00
TT1 Troy Tulowitzki 30.00 60.00
TT2 Troy Tulowitzki 30.00 60.00
TT3 Troy Tulowitzki 30.00 60.00
TT4 Troy Tulowitzki 30.00 60.00
TT5 Troy Tulowitzki 30.00 60.00
YE1 Yunel Escobar 10.00 25.00
YE2 Yunel Escobar 10.00 25.00
YE3 Yunel Escobar 10.00 25.00
YE4 Yunel Escobar 10.00 25.00
YE5 Yunel Escobar 10.00 25.00

2007 Exquisite Collection Rookie Signatures Signature Materials

OVERALL FIVE AUTOS PER PACK
PRINT RUNS B/WN 25-85 COPIES PER
NO PRICING ON QTY 25 OR LESS
*GOLD: .5X TO 1.2X BASIC
GOLD SER.#'d B/WN 15-50 COPIES PER
NO PRICING ON QTY 15 OR LESS
GOLD SPEC. PRINT RUN 1 SER.#'d SET
NO GOLD SPEC PRICING AVAILABLE
SILVER SPEC #'d B/WN 10-25 COPIES PER
NO SILVER SPEC PRICING AVAILABLE
EXCHANGE DEADLINE 12/28/2009
AD Adam Dunn/85 10.00 25.00
AG Adrian Gonzalez/85 10.00 25.00
AH Aaron Harang/85 5.00 12.00
AR Aramis Ramirez/85 6.00 15.00
BA Bronson Arroyo/85 5.00 12.00
BH Bill Hall/85 6.00 15.00
BL Joe Blanton/85 5.00 12.00
BO Jeremy Bonderman/85 10.00 25.00
BR Brian Roberts/85 6.00 15.00
BS Ben Sheets/85 5.00 12.00
BU B.J. Upton/85 8.00 20.00
CC Carl Crawford/85 6.00 15.00
CH Cole Hamels/85 15.00 40.00
CL Carlos Lee/85 5.00 12.00
CR Cal Ripken Jr./85 60.00 120.00
CZ Carlos Zambrano/85 10.00 25.00
DH Dan Haren/85 6.00 15.00
DJ Derek Jeter/25
DL Derrek Lee/85 10.00 25.00
DU Dan Uggla/85 5.00 12.00
DW Dontrelle Willis/85 5.00 12.00
FH Felix Hernandez/85 15.00 40.00
FT Frank Thomas/85 30.00 60.00
HA Travis Hafner/85 10.00 25.00
HK Howie Kendrick/85 10.00 25.00
HR Hanley Ramirez/85 15.00 40.00
HS Huston Street/85 5.00 12.00
IK Ian Kinsler/85 10.00 25.00
JB Jason Bay/85 10.00 25.00
JM John Maine/85 6.00 15.00
JO Josh Barfield/85 5.00 12.00
JP Jonathan Papelbon/85 15.00 40.00
JV Justin Verlander/85 12.50 30.00
JW Josh Willingham/85 5.00 12.00
KG Ken Griffey Jr./25
LS Luke Scott/85 5.00 12.00
MC Matt Cain/85 12.50 30.00
MO Justin Morneau/85 10.00 25.00
MT Mark Teixeira/85 20.00 50.00
NM Nick Markakis/85 10.00 25.00
NS Nick Swisher/85 6.00 15.00
PF Prince Fielder/85 20.00 50.00
RC Roger Clemens/25
RH Rich Harden/85 5.00 12.00
RM Russell Martin/85 10.00 25.00
RW Rickie Weeks/85 6.00 15.00
RZ Ryan Zimmerman/85 12.50 30.00
SD Stephen Drew/85 10.00 25.00
TH Torii Hunter/85 6.00 15.00
VM Victor Martinez/85 6.00 15.00

2007 Exquisite Collection Rookie Signatures The Future Autographs

OVERALL FIVE AUTOS PER PACK
STATED PRINT RUN 20 SER.#'d SETS
NO PRICING DUE TO SCARCITY
GOLD PRINT RUN 15 SER.#'d SETS
NO GOLD PRICING AVAILABLE
SILVER INK PRINT RUN 1 SER.#'d SET
NO SILVER INK PRICING AVAILABLE
SILVER SPEC PRINT RUN 1 SER.#'d SET
NO SILVER SPEC PRICING AVAILABLE
EXCHANGE DEADLINE 12/28/2009

2007 Exquisite Collection Rookie Signatures The Next Generation Signatures

OVERALL FIVE AUTOS PER PACK
STATED PRINT RUN 20 SER.#'d SETS
NO PRICING DUE TO SCARCITY
GOLD PRINT RUN 15 SER.#'d SETS
NO GOLD PRICING AVAILABLE
SILVER INK PRINT RUN 1 SER.#'d SET
NO SILVER INK PRICING AVAILABLE
SILVER SPEC PRINT RUN 1 SER.#'d SET
NO SILVER SPEC PRICING AVAILABLE
EXCHANGE DEADLINE 12/28/2009

2009 Fathead Tradeables

1 Dustin Pedroia 2.00 5.00
2 Albert Pujols 4.00 10.00
3 Chase Utley 1.50 4.00
4 Evan Longoria 2.00 5.00
5 David Wright 2.00 5.00
6 Derek Jeter 4.00 10.00
7 Alfonso Soriano 1.00 2.50
8 Justin Morneau 1.50 4.00
9 Ryan Braun 2.00 5.00
10 Cliff Lee 1.00 2.50
11 Tim Lincecum 2.50 6.00
12 Ervin Santana .60 1.50
13 Ronnie Belliard .60 1.50
14 Michael Young 1.00 2.50
15 Andre Ethier 1.00 2.50
16 Adrian Beltre .60 1.50
17 Jair Jurrjens .60 1.50
18 Aubrey Huff .60 1.50
19 Edinson Volquez .60 1.50
20 Jack Cust .60 1.50
21 Josh Johnson 1.00 2.50
22 Chris Young .60 1.50
23 Alex Rios 1.00 2.50
24 Troy Tulowitzki 1.50 4.00
25 Ryan Doumit .60 1.50
26 Alex Gordon 1.00 2.50
27 Curtis Granderson 1.00 2.50
28 Dan Haren .60 1.50
29 Daisuke Matsuzaka 1.50 4.00
30 Brad Ziegler .60 1.50
31 Brad Lidge .60 1.50
32 Mark Buehrle 1.00 2.50
33 Miguel Tejada 1.00 2.50
34 Bengie Molina .60 1.50
35 Andy Pettitte 1.00 2.50
36 Victor Martinez 1.00 2.50
37 Yadier Molina 1.00 2.50
38 Carlos Zambrano 1.00 2.50
39 Joba Chamberlain 1.00 2.50
40 Roy Halladay 1.50 4.00
41 Todd Helton 1.00 2.50
42 Russell Martin .60 1.50
43 Scott Kazmir .60 1.50
44 Jason Bay 1.00 2.50
45 Chad Billingsley .60 1.50
46 Joe Nathan .60 1.50
47 Melvin Mora .60 1.50
48 Johan Santana 1.50 4.00
49 Mike Lowell .60 1.50
50 Carlos Delgado .60 1.50
51 Justin Upton 1.00 2.50
52 Geovany Soto 1.00 2.50
53 Lance Berkman 1.00 2.50
54 Yuniesky Betancourt .60 1.50
55 Jermaine Dye .60 1.50
56 Jose Guillen .60 1.50
57 James Shields .60 1.50
58 Felix Hernandez 1.50 4.00
59 Kyle Lohse .60 1.50
60 Ricky Nolasco .60 1.50
61 John Lackey .60 1.50
62 Jacoby Ellsbury 1.50 4.00
63 Travis Hafner .60 1.50
64 Magglio Ordonez 1.00 2.50
65 Paul Konerko 1.00 2.50
66 Brian Wilson 1.50 4.00
67 Hunter Pence 1.00 2.50
68 Derrek Lee .60 1.50
69 Brandon Webb 1.00 2.50
70 Manny Ramirez 1.50 4.00
71 Hanley Ramirez 1.50 4.00
72 Corey Hart .60 1.50
73 Torii Hunter .60 1.50
74 Josh Hamilton 1.50 4.00
75 Carl Crawford 1.00 2.50
76 Brian McCann 1.00 2.50
77 Troy Glaus .60 1.50
78 Cristian Guzman .60 1.50
79 Brandon Phillips .60 1.50
80 Brad Hawpe .60 1.50
81 Justin Verlander 2.00 5.00
82 Carlos Marmol 1.00 2.50
83 Joe Saunders .60 1.50
84 Kevin Youkilis 1.00 2.50
85 Delmon Young 1.00 2.50
86 Alex Rodriguez 2.50 6.00
87 Roy Oswalt 1.00 2.50
88 Mike Cameron .60 1.50
89 Kosuke Fukudome 1.50 4.00
90 Aaron Rowand .60 1.50
91 Dan Uggla 1.00 2.50
92 Mariano Rivera 1.50 4.00
93 Vladimir Guerrero 1.50 4.00
94 J.D. Drew .60 1.50
95 Placido Polanco .60 1.50
96 Robinson Cano 1.50 4.00
97 J.J. Hardy .60 1.50
98 Jonathan Papelbon 1.00 2.50
99 James Loney 1.00 2.50
100 Adrian Gonzalez 1.00 2.50
101 Nate McLouth .60 1.50
102 Garrett Atkins .60 1.50
103 Ryan Zimmerman 1.00 2.50
104 Jim Thome 1.00 2.50
105 Carlos Lee .60 1.50
106 Josh Beckett 1.00 2.50
107 Jay Bruce 1.00 2.50
108 Ichiro Suzuki 2.50 6.00
109 Ryan Dempster .60 1.50
110 Hideki Matsui 1.50 4.00
111 Jayson Werth 1.00 2.50
112 Rafael Furcal .60 1.50
113 Vernon Wells .60 1.50
114 Ryan Howard 2.00 5.00
115 Chris Young .60 1.50
116 Grady Sizemore 1.00 2.50
117 Brian Roberts .60 1.50
118 Ian Kinsler 1.00 2.50
119 Carlos Pena 1.00 2.50
120 Jon Lester 1.50 4.00
121 David DeJesus .60 1.50
122 Miguel Cabrera 1.50 4.00
123 Freddy Sanchez .60 1.50
124 Carlos Beltran .60 1.50
125 Joe Mauer 1.50 4.00
126 Carlos Quentin 1.00 2.50
127 Jason Varitek 1.50 4.00
128 Jose Reyes 1.00 2.50
129 Jimmy Rollins 1.00 2.50
130 Chris Davis .60 1.50
131 Jake Peavy .60 1.50
132 Cole Hamels 1.50 4.00
133 Fausto Carmona .60 1.50
134 David Ortiz 1.00 2.50
135 Francisco Liriano .60 1.50
136 Prince Fielder 1.00 2.50
137 Johnny Damon 1.00 2.50
138 Stephen Drew .60 1.50
139 Adam LaRoche .60 1.50
140 Nick Markakis 1.50 4.00
141 A.J. Pierzynski .60 1.50
142 Jeremy Guthrie .60 1.50
143 Jorge Posada 1.00 2.50
144 Ryan Ludwick 1.00 2.50
145 Aramis Ramirez .60 1.50
146 Chien-Ming Wang 1.00 2.50
147 Shane Victorino .60 1.50
148 Justin Duchscherer .60 1.50
149 Chipper Jones 1.50 4.00
150 B.J. Upton 1.00 2.50

2009 Fat Head Tradeables Logos

L1 Arizona Diamondbacks .60 1.50
L2 Atlanta Braves .60 1.50
L3 Baltimore Orioles .60 1.50
L4 Boston Red Sox 1.50 4.00
L5 Chicago Cubs .60 1.50
L6 Chicago White Sox .60 1.50
L7 Cincinnati Reds .60 1.50
L8 Cleveland Indians .60 1.50
L9 Colorado Rockies .60 1.50
L10 Detroit Tigers .60 1.50
L11 Florida Marlins .60 1.50
L12 Houston Astros .60 1.50
L13 Kansas City Royals .60 1.50
L14 Los Angels Dodgers .60 1.50
L15 Los Angeles Angels .60 1.50
L16 Milwaukee Brewers .60 1.50
L17 Minnesota Twins .60 1.50
L18 New York Mets .60 1.50
L19 New York Yankees 1.50 4.00
L20 Oakland Athletics .60 1.50
L21 Philadelphia Phillies .60 1.50
L22 Pittsburgh Pirates .60 1.50
L23 San Diego Padres .60 1.50
L24 San Francisco Giants .60 1.50
L25 Seattle Mariners .60 1.50
L26 St. Louis Cardinals .60 1.50
L27 Tampa Bay Rays .60 1.50
L28 Texas Rangers .60 1.50
L29 Toronto Blue Jays .60 1.50
L30 Washington Nationals .60 1.50

2010 Fathead Tradeables

1 Derek Jeter 4.00 10.00
2 Chase Utley 1.50 4.00
3 Albert Pujols 4.00 10.00
4 Joe Mauer 1.50 4.00
5 Tim Lincecum 2.50 6.00
6 Zack Greinke 1.00 2.50
7 Shin-Soo Choo 1.00 2.50
8 Ryan Braun 2.00 5.00
9 Jimmy Rollins 1.00 2.50
10 Ichiro Suzuki 2.50 6.00
11 Brian Roberts .60 1.50
12 Josh Hamilton 1.50 4.00
13 C.C. Sabathia 1.00 2.50
14 David Ortiz 1.00 2.50
15 Mark Buehrle 1.00 2.50
16 Rick Porcello .60 1.50
17 Johan Santana 1.50 4.00
18 Adam Dunn 1.00 2.50
19 Felix Hernandez 1.50 4.00
20 Nate McLouth .60 1.50
21 James Loney 1.00 2.50
22 Pablo Sandoval 1.00 2.50
23 Chris Coghlan .60 1.50
24 Andrew Bailey .60 1.50
25 Hanley Ramirez 1.50 4.00
26 Justin Verlander 2.00 5.00
27 Matt Holliday 1.50 4.00
28 Aramis Ramirez .60 1.50
29 Adam Lind 1.00 2.50
30 Torii Hunter .60 1.50
31 Ryan Theriot .60 1.50
32 Curtis Granderson 1.00 2.50
33 Mark Teixeira 1.50 4.00
34 Heath Bell 1.00 2.50
35 Bobby Abreu .60 1.50
36 Carlos Lee .60 1.50
37 Colby Rasmus 1.50 4.00
38 Jayson Werth 1.00 2.50
39 Justin Morneau 1.50 4.00
40 Kurt Suzuki .60 1.50
41 Michael Young 1.00 2.50
42 Nick Markakis 1.50 4.00
43 Prince Fielder 1.00 2.50
44 Ryan Zimmerman 1.00 2.50
45 Jacoby Ellsbury 1.50 4.00
46 Dustin Pedroia 2.00 5.00
47 Chipper Jones 1.50 4.00
48 Francisco Rodriguez 1.00 2.50
49 Troy Tulowitzki 1.50 4.00
50 Jose Reyes 1.00 2.50
51 David Wright 2.00 5.00
52 Chris Carpenter 1.50 4.00
53 A. J. Pierzynski .60 1.50
54 Alfonso Soriano 1.00 2.50
55 Kendry Morales .60 1.50
56 Miguel Cabrera 1.50 4.00
57 Paul Konerko 1.00 2.50
58 Carlos Zambrano 1.00 2.50
59 Andrew McCutchen 1.50 4.00
60 Adam Wainwright 1.00 2.50
61 Aaron Hill .60 1.50
62 Joey Votto 1.50 4.00
63 Lance Berkman 1.00 2.50
64 Nelson Cruz 1.00 2.50

65 Shane Victorino 1.00 2.50
66 Kevin Youkilis 1.00 2.50
67 Jered Weaver .60 1.50
68 Yadier Molina 1.00 2.50
69 Evan Longoria 2.00 5.00
70 Dan Haren .60 1.50
71 Carl Crawford 1.00 2.50
72 Carlos Beltran .60 1.50
73 Grady Sizemore 1.00 2.50
74 Ian Kinsler 1.00 2.50
75 Jake Peavy .60 1.50
76 Matt Kemp 1.00 2.50
77 Matt Cain 1.00 2.50
78 Raul Ibanez 1.00 2.50
79 Michael Cuddyer .60 1.50
80 Derrek Lee .60 1.50
81 Carlos Pena 1.00 2.50
82 Chad Billingsley .60 1.50
83 Jason Bartlett .60 1.50
84 Josh Johnson 1.00 2.50
85 Justin Upton 1.00 2.50
86 Jonathan Papelbon 1.00 2.50
87 Mark Reynolds .60 1.50
88 Manny Ramirez 1.50 4.00
89 Mariano Rivera 1.50 4.00
90 Ryan Howard 2.00 5.00
91 Adam Jones 1.00 2.50
92 Adrian Gonzalez 1.00 2.50
93 Josh Beckett 1.00 2.50
94 Andre Ethier 1.00 2.50
95 Brian McCann 1.00 2.50
96 Alex Rodriguez 2.50 6.00
97 Brandon Phillips .60 1.50
98 Andy LaRoche .60 1.50
99 Billy Butler .60 1.50
100 Todd Helton 1.00 2.50

2011 Fathead Tradeables

1 Buster Posey 2.00 5.00
2 Josh Hamilton 1.50 4.00
3 Roy Halladay 1.50 4.00
4 Felix Hernandez 1.50 4.00
5 Joey Votto 1.50 4.00
6 David Wright 2.00 5.00
7 Brian Wilson 1.50 4.00
8 Joe Mauer 1.50 4.00
9 Kevin Youkilis 1.00 2.50
10 C.C. Sabathia 1.00 2.50
11 Jason Heyward 2.00 5.00
12 Paul Konerko 1.00 2.50
13 Prince Fielder 1.00 2.50
14 Ubaldo Jimenez 1.00 2.50
15 Joakim Soria .60 1.50
16 Alex Rodriguez 2.50 6.00
17 Brandon Phillips .60 1.50
18 Johan Santana 1.50 4.00
19 Garrett Jones .60 1.50
20 Jon Lester 1.50 4.00
21 Albert Pujols 4.00 10.00
22 Matt Kemp 1.00 2.50
23 Jose Bautista 1.00 2.50
24 Jimmy Rollins 1.00 2.50
25 Jason Kubel .60 1.50
26 Neftali Feliz .60 1.50
27 Jose Reyes 1.00 2.50
28 David Price 1.50 4.00
29 Stephen Strasburg 3.00 8.00
30 Torii Hunter .60 1.50
31 Kevin Kouzmanoff .60 1.50
32 Matt Cain 1.00 2.50
33 Chase Utley 1.50 4.00
34 Alfonso Soriano 1.00 2.50
35 Elvis Andrus 1.00 2.50
36 Mark Teixeira 1.50 4.00
37 Ike Davis 1.00 2.50
38 Matt Holliday 1.50 4.00
39 Justin Morneau 1.50 4.00
40 Shane Victorino 1.00 2.50
41 Carlos Santana 1.50 4.00
42 Justin Verlander 2.00 5.00
43 Nelson Cruz 1.00 2.50
44 Carlos Lee .60 1.50
45 Clayton Kershaw 1.50 4.00
46 Adam Wainwright 1.50 4.00
47 Tim Lincecum 1.50 4.00
48 Troy Tulowitzki 1.50 4.00
49 Scott Rolen 1.00 2.50
50 Corey Hart .60 1.50
51 Carlos Gonzalez 1.00 2.50
52 Hanley Ramirez 1.50 4.00
53 Mariano Rivera 1.50 4.00
54 Mat Latos .60 1.50
55 Shin-Soo Choo 1.00 2.50
56 Miguel Cabrera 1.50 4.00
57 Derek Jeter 4.00 10.00
58 Josh Johnson 1.00 2.50
59 Cliff Lee 1.50 4.00
60 Brian McCann 1.00 2.50
61 Andrew Bailey .60 1.50
62 Starlin Castro 1.50 4.00
63 Evan Longoria 2.00 5.00
64 Dustin Pedroia 2.00 5.00
65 Hunter Pence 1.00 2.50
66 Andrew McCutchen 1.50 4.00
67 Michael Young 1.00 2.50
68 Chris Young .60 1.50
69 Austin Jackson .60 1.50
70 Nick Markakis 1.50 4.00
71 Ichiro Suzuki 2.50 6.00
72 Colby Rasmus 1.50 4.00
73 Ervin Santana .60 1.50
74 Mark Buehrle 1.00 2.50
75 Chipper Jones 1.50 4.00
76 Billy Butler .60 1.50
77 Andre Ethier 1.00 2.50
78 Aubrey Huff .60 1.50
79 Michael Bourn .60 1.50
80 Chris Carpenter 1.50 4.00
81 Martin Prado 1.00 2.50
82 Gordon Beckham 1.00 2.50
83 Marlon Byrd .60 1.50
84 Robinson Cano 1.50 4.00
85 Adam Jones 1.00 2.50
86 Justin Upton 1.00 2.50
87 Jered Weaver .60 1.50
88 Bobby Abreu .60 1.50
89 Ryan Howard 2.00 5.00
90 Jay Bruce 1.00 2.50
91 Clay Buchholz 1.00 2.50
92 Ryan Zimmerman 1.00 2.50
93 Jonathan Broxton .60 1.50
94 Nick Swisher 1.50 4.00
95 Denard Span .60 1.50
96 Ryan Braun 2.00 5.00
97 Ian Kinsler 1.00 2.50
98 Aramis Ramirez .60 1.50
99 David Ortiz 1.00 2.50
100 Heath Bell 1.00 2.50

1993 Finest

This 199-card standard-size single series set is widely recognized as one of the most important issues of the 1990's. The Finest brand was Topps first attempt at the super-premium card market. Production was announced at 4,000 cases and cards were distributed exclusively through hobby dealers in the fall of 1993. This was the first time in the history of the hobby that a major manufacturer publicly released production figures. Cards were issued in seven-card foil finwrapped packs that carried a suggested retail price of $3.99. The product was a smashing success upon release with pack prices immediately soaring well above suggested retail prices. The popularity of the product has continued to grow throughout the years as it's place in hobby lore is now well solidified. The cards have silver-blue metallic finishes on their fronts and feature color player action photos. The set's title appears at the top, and the player's name is shown at the bottom. J.T. Snow is the only Rookie Card of note in this set.

COMPLETE SET (199) 50.00 100.00
1 David Justice 1.00 2.50
2 Lou Whitaker 1.00 2.50
3 Bryan Harvey .60 1.50
4 Carlos Garcia .60 1.50
5 Sid Fernandez .60 1.50
6 Brett Butler 1.00 2.50
7 Scott Cooper .60 1.50
8 B.J. Surhoff .60 1.50
9 Steve Finley 1.00 2.50
10 Curt Schilling 1.00 2.50
11 Jeff Bagwell 1.50 4.00
12 Alex Cole .60 1.50
13 John Olerud 1.00 2.50
14 John Smiley .60 1.50
15 Bip Roberts .60 1.50
16 Albert Belle 1.00 2.50
17 Duane Ward .60 1.50
18 Alan Trammell 1.00 2.50
19 Andy Benes .60 1.50
20 Reggie Sanders 1.00 2.50
21 Todd Zeile .60 1.50
22 Rick Aguilera .60 1.50
23 Dave Hollins .60 1.50
24 Jose Rijo .60 1.50
25 Matt Williams 1.00 2.50
26 Sandy Alomar Jr. .60 1.50
27 Alex Fernandez .60 1.50
28 Ozzie Smith 4.00 10.00
29 Ramon Martinez .60 1.50
30 Bernie Williams 1.50 4.00
31 Gary Sheffield 1.00 2.50
32 Eric Karros 1.00 2.50
33 Frank Viola 1.00 2.50
34 Kevin Young 1.00 2.50
35 Ken Hill .60 1.50
36 Tony Fernandez .60 1.50
37 Tim Wakefield 2.50 6.00
38 John Kruk 1.00 2.50
39 Chris Sabo .60 1.50
40 Marquis Grissom 1.00 2.50
41 Glenn Davis .60 1.50
42 Jeff Montgomery .60 1.50
43 Kenny Lofton 1.00 2.50
44 John Burkett .60 1.50
45 Darryl Hamilton .60 1.50
46 Jim Abbott 1.50 4.00
47 Ivan Rodriguez 1.50 4.00
48 Eric Young .60 1.50
49 Mitch Williams .60 1.50
50 Harold Reynolds 1.00 2.50
51 Brian Harper .60 1.50
52 Rafael Palmeiro 1.50 4.00
53 Bret Saberhagen 1.00 2.50
54 Jeff Conine 1.00 2.50
55 Ivan Calderon .60 1.50
56 Juan Guzman .60 1.50
57 Carlos Baerga .60 1.50
58 Charles Nagy .60 1.50
59 Wally Joyner 1.00 2.50
60 Charlie Hayes .60 1.50
61 Shane Mack .60 1.50
62 Pete Harnisch .60 1.50
63 George Brett 6.00 15.00
64 Lance Johnson .60 1.50
65 Ben McDonald .60 1.50
66 Bobby Bonilla 1.00 2.50
67 Terry Steinbach .60 1.50
68 Ron Gant 1.00 2.50
69 Doug Jones .60 1.50
70 Paul Molitor 1.00 2.50
71 Brady Anderson 1.00 2.50
72 Chuck Finley 1.00 2.50
73 Mark Grace 1.50 4.00
74 Mike Devereaux .60 1.50
75 Tony Phillips .60 1.50
76 Chuck Knoblauch 1.00 2.50
77 Tony Gwynn 3.00 8.00
78 Kevin Appier 1.00 2.50
79 Sammy Sosa 2.50 6.00
80 Mickey Tettleton .60 1.50
81 Felix Jose .60 1.50
82 Mark Langston .60 1.50
83 Gregg Jefferies .60 1.50
84 Andre Dawson AS 1.00 2.50
85 Greg Maddux AS 4.00 10.00
86 Rickey Henderson AS 2.50 6.00
87 Tom Glavine AS 1.00 2.50
88 Roberto Alomar AS 1.50 4.00
89 Darryl Strawberry AS 1.00 2.50
90 Wade Boggs AS 1.50 4.00
91 Bo Jackson AS 2.50 6.00
92 Mark McGwire AS 6.00 15.00
93 Robin Ventura AS 1.00 2.50
94 Joe Carter AS 1.00 2.50
95 Lee Smith AS 1.00 2.50
96 Cal Ripken AS 8.00 20.00
97 Larry Walker AS 1.00 2.50
98 Don Mattingly AS 6.00 15.00
99 Jose Canseco AS 1.50 4.00
100 Dennis Eckersley AS 1.00 2.50
101 Terry Pendleton AS 1.00 2.50
102 Frank Thomas AS 2.50 6.00
103 Barry Bonds AS 6.00 15.00
104 Roger Clemens AS 5.00 12.00
105 Ryne Sandberg AS 4.00 10.00
106 Fred McGriff AS 1.50 4.00
107 Nolan Ryan AS 10.00 25.00
108 Will Clark AS 1.50 4.00
109 Pat Listach AS .60 1.50
110 Ken Griffey Jr. AS 4.00 10.00
111 Cecil Fielder AS 1.00 2.50
112 Kirby Puckett AS 2.50 6.00
113 Dwight Gooden AS 1.00 2.50
114 Barry Larkin AS 1.50 4.00
115 David Cone AS 1.00 2.50
116 Juan Gonzalez AS 1.00 2.50
117 Kent Hrbek 1.00 2.50
118 Tim Wallach .60 1.50
119 Craig Biggio 1.50 4.00
120 Roberto Kelly .60 1.50
121 Gregg Olson .60 1.50
122 Eddie Murray UER 2.50 6.00
122 career strikeouts
should be 1224
123 Wil Cordero .60 1.50
124 Jay Buhner 1.00 2.50
125 Carlton Fisk 1.50 4.00
126 Eric Davis 1.00 2.50
127 Doug Drabek .60 1.50
128 Ozzie Guillen 1.00 2.50
129 John Wetteland 1.00 2.50
130 Andres Galarraga 1.00 2.50
131 Ken Caminiti 1.00 2.50
132 Tom Candiotti .60 1.50
133 Pat Borders .60 1.50
134 Kevin Brown 1.00 2.50
135 Travis Fryman 1.00 2.50
136 Kevin Mitchell .60 1.50
137 Greg Swindell .60 1.50
138 Benito Santiago 1.00 2.50
139 Reggie Jefferson .60 1.50
140 Chris Bosio .60 1.50
141 Deion Sanders 1.50 4.00
142 Scott Erickson .60 1.50
143 Howard Johnson .60 1.50
144 Orestes Destrade .60 1.50
145 Jose Guzman .60 1.50
146 Chad Curtis .60 1.50
147 Cal Eldred .60 1.50
148 Willie Greene .60 1.50
149 Tommy Greene .60 1.50
150 Erik Hanson .60 1.50
151 Bob Welch .60 1.50
152 John Jaha .60 1.50
153 Harold Baines 1.00 2.50
154 Randy Johnson 2.50 6.00
155 Al Martin .60 1.50
156 J.T. Snow RC 1.50 4.00
157 Mike Mussina 1.50 4.00
158 Ruben Sierra 1.00 2.50
159 Dean Palmer 1.00 2.50
160 Steve Avery .60 1.50
161 Julio Franco 1.00 2.50
162 Dave Winfield 1.00 2.50
163 Tim Salmon 1.50 4.00
164 Tom Henke .60 1.50
165 Mo Vaughn 1.00 2.50
166 John Smoltz 1.50 4.00
167 Danny Tartabull .60 1.50
168 Delino DeShields .60 1.50
169 Charlie Hough 1.00 2.50
170 Paul O'Neill 1.00 2.50
171 Darren Daulton 1.00 2.50
172 Jack McDowell .60 1.50
173 Junior Felix .60 1.50
174 Jimmy Key 1.00 2.50
175 George Bell .60 1.50
176 Mike Stanton .60 1.50
177 Len Dykstra 1.00 2.50
178 Norm Charlton .60 1.50
179 Eric Anthony .60 1.50
180 Rob Dibble 1.00 2.50
181 Otis Nixon .60 1.50
182 Randy Myers .60 1.50
183 Tim Raines 1.00 2.50
184 Orel Hershiser 1.00 2.50
185 Andy Van Slyke 1.50 4.00
186 Mike Lansing RC 1.00 2.50
187 Ray Lankford 1.00 2.50
188 Mike Morgan .60 1.50
189 Moises Alou 1.00 2.50
190 Edgar Martinez 1.50 4.00
191 John Franco 1.00 2.50
192 Robin Yount 4.00 10.00
193 Bob Tewksbury .60 1.50
194 Jay Bell 1.00 2.50
195 Luis Gonzalez 1.00 2.50
196 Dave Fleming .60 1.50
197 Mike Greenwell .60 1.50
198 David Nied .60 1.50
199 Mike Piazza 6.00 15.00

1993 Finest Refractors

Randomly inserted in packs at a rate of one in 18, these 199 standard-size cards are identical to the regular-issue 1993 Topps Finest except that their fronts have been laminated with a plastic diffraction grating that gives the card a colorful 3-D appearance. Because of the known production numbers, these cards are believed to have a print run of 241 of each card. It is believed that there might be short printed cards in this set. Topps, however, has never publicly released any verification of shortprinted singles, but some of the singles are accepted as being tough to find due to poor regional distribution and hoarding. Due to their high value, these cards are extremely condition sensitive, with much attention paid to centering and minor scratches on the card fronts.

STATED ODDS 1:18
28 Ozzie Smith 60.00 120.00
41 Glenn Davis* 60.00 120.00
47 Ivan Rodriguez * 75.00 150.00
63 George Brett 125.00 200.00
77 Tony Gwynn 60.00 120.00
79 Sammy Sosa * 100.00 200.00
81 Felix Jose* 40.00 80.00
85 Greg Maddux AS 100.00 200.00
88 Roberto Alomar AS 40.00 80.00
91 Bo Jackson AS 50.00 100.00
92 Mark McGwire AS 175.00 300.00
96 Cal Ripken AS 200.00 400.00
98 Don Mattingly AS 125.00 250.00
99 Jose Canseco AS 40.00 80.00
102 Frank Thomas AS 150.00 300.00
103 Barry Bonds AS 250.00 400.00
104 Roger Clemens AS 125.00 200.00
105 Ryne Sandberg AS 75.00 150.00
107 Nolan Ryan AS 300.00 500.00
108 Will Clark AS 40.00 80.00
110 Ken Griffey Jr. AS 200.00 400.00
112 Kirby Puckett AS 60.00 120.00
114 Barry Larkin AS 40.00 80.00
116 Juan Gonzalez AS * 150.00 250.00
122 Eddie Murray UER 60.00 120.00
122 career strikeouts
should be 1224
154 Randy Johnson 75.00 150.00
157 Mike Mussina 40.00 80.00
192 Robin Yount 60.00 120.00
199 Mike Piazza 100.00 200.00

1993 Finest Jumbos

These oversized (approximately 4" by 6") cards were inserted one per sealed box of 1993 Topps Finest packs and feature reproductions of 33 players from that set's All-Star subset (84-116). Some hobby dealers believe because of the known production numbers that slightly less than 1,500 of each of these cards were produced.

*STARS: 1X TO 2.5X BASIC CARDS
ONE CARD PER SEALED BOX

1994 Finest

The 1994 Topps Finest baseball set consists of two series of 220 cards each, for a total of 440 standard-size cards. Each series includes 40 special design Finest cards: 20 top 1993 rookies (1-20), 20 top 1994 rookies (421-440) and 40 top veterans (201-240). It's believed that these subset cards are in slightly shorter supply than the basic issue cards, but the manufacturer has never confirmed this. These glossy and metallic cards have a color photo on front with green and gold borders. A color photo on back is accompanied by statistics and a "Finest Moment" note. Some series 2 packs contained either one or two series 1 cards. The only notable Rookie Card is Chan Ho Park.

COMPLETE SET (440) 50.00 120.00
COMP. SERIES 1 (220) 25.00 60.00
COMP. SERIES 2 (220) 25.00 60.00
1 Mike Piazza FIN 2.50 6.00
2 Kevin Stocker FIN .30 .75
3 Greg McMichael FIN .30 .75
4 Jeff Conine FIN .50 1.25
5 Rene Arocha FIN .30 .75
6 Aaron Sele FIN .30 .75
7 Brent Gates FIN .30 .75
8 Chuck Carr FIN .30 .75
9 Kirk Rueter FIN .30 .75
10 Mike Lansing FIN .30 .75
11 Al Martin FIN .30 .75
12 Jason Bere FIN .30 .75
13 Troy Neel FIN .30 .75
14 Armando Reynoso FIN .30 .75
15 Jeromy Burnitz FIN .50 1.25
16 Rich Amaral FIN .30 .75
17 David McCarty FIN .30 .75
18 Tim Salmon FIN .75 2.00
19 Steve Cooke FIN .30 .75
20 Wil Cordero FIN .30 .75
21 Kevin Tapani .30 .75
22 Deion Sanders .75 2.00
23 Jose Offerman .30 .75
24 Mark Langston .30 .75
25 Ken Hill .30 .75
26 Alex Fernandez .30 .75
27 Jeff Blauser .30 .75
28 Royce Clayton .30 .75
29 Brad Ausmus .75 2.00
30 Ryan Bowen .30 .75
31 Steve Finley .50 1.25
32 Charlie Hayes .30 .75
33 Jeff Kent .75 2.00
34 Mike Henneman .30 .75
35 Andres Galarraga .50 1.25
36 Wayne Kirby .30 .75
37 Joe Oliver .30 .75
38 Terry Steinbach .30 .75
39 Ryan Thompson .30 .75
40 Luis Alicea .30 .75
41 Randy Velarde .30 .75
42 Bob Tewksbury .30 .75
43 Reggie Sanders .50 1.25
44 Brian Williams .30 .75
45 Joe Orsulak .30 .75
46 Jose Lind .30 .75
47 Dave Hollins .30 .75
48 Graeme Lloyd .30 .75
49 Jim Gott .30 .75
50 Andre Dawson .50 1.25
51 Steve Buechele .30 .75
52 David Cone .50 1.25
53 Ricky Gutierrez .30 .75
54 Lance Johnson .30 .75
55 Tino Martinez .75 2.00
56 Phil Hiatt .30 .75
57 Carlos Garcia .30 .75
58 Danny Darwin .30 .75
59 Dante Bichette .50 1.25
60 Scott Kamieniecki .30 .75
61 Orlando Merced .30 .75
62 Brian McRae .30 .75
63 Pat Kelly .30 .75
64 Tom Henke .30 .75
65 Jeff King .30 .75
66 Mike Mussina .75 2.00
67 Tim Pugh .30 .75
68 Robby Thompson .30 .75
69 Paul O'Neill .75 2.00
70 Hal Morris .30 .75
71 Ron Karkovice .30 .75
72 Joe Girardi .30 .75
73 Eduardo Perez .30 .75
74 Raul Mondesi .50 1.25
75 Mike Gallego .30 .75
76 Mike Stanley .30 .75
77 Kevin Roberson .30 .75
78 Mark McGwire 3.00 8.00
79 Pat Listach .30 .75
80 Eric Davis .50 1.25
81 Mike Bordick .30 .75
82 Dwight Gooden .50 1.25
83 Mike Moore .30 .75
84 Phil Plantier .30 .75
85 Darren Lewis .30 .75
86 Rick Wilkins .30 .75
87 Darryl Strawberry .50 1.25
88 Rob Dibble .50 1.25
89 Greg Vaughn .30 .75
90 Jeff Russell .30 .75
91 Mark Lewis .30 .75
92 Gregg Jefferies .30 .75
93 Jose Guzman .30 .75
94 Kenny Rogers .50 1.25
95 Mark Lemke .30 .75
96 Mike Morgan .30 .75
97 Andujar Cedeno .30 .75
98 Orel Hershiser .50 1.25
99 Greg Swindell .30 .75
100 John Smoltz .75 2.00
101 Pedro A.Martinez RC .30 .75
102 Jim Thome .75 2.00
103 David Segui .30 .75
104 Charles Nagy .30 .75
105 Shane Mack .30 .75
106 John Jaha .30 .75
107 Tom Candiotti .30 .75
108 David Wells .50 1.25
109 Bobby Jones .30 .75
110 Bob Hamelin .30 .75
111 Bernard Gilkey .30 .75
112 Chili Davis .50 1.25
113 Todd Stottlemyre .30 .75
114 Derek Bell .30 .75
115 Mark McLemore .30 .75
116 Mark Whiten .30 .75
117 Mike Devereaux .30 .75
118 Terry Pendleton .50 1.25
119 Pat Meares .30 .75
120 Pete Harnisch .30 .75
121 Moises Alou .50 1.25
122 Jay Buhner .50 1.25
123 Wes Chamberlain .30 .75
124 Mike Perez .30 .75
125 Devon White .50 1.25
126 Ivan Rodriguez .75 2.00
127 Don Slaught .30 .75
128 John Valentin .30 .75
129 Jaime Navarro .30 .75
130 Dave Magadan .30 .75
131 Brady Anderson .50 1.25
132 Juan Guzman .30 .75
133 John Wetteland .50 1.25
134 Dave Stewart .50 1.25
135 Scott Servais .30 .75
136 Ozzie Smith 2.00 5.00
137 Darrin Fletcher .30 .75
138 Jose Mesa .30 .75
139 Wilson Alvarez .30 .75
140 Pete Incaviglia .30 .75
141 Chris Hoiles .30 .75
142 Darryl Hamilton .30 .75
143 Chuck Finley .50 1.25
144 Archi Cianfrocco .30 .75
145 Bill Wegman .30 .75
146 Joey Cora .30 .75
147 Darrell Whitmore .30 .75
148 David Hulse .30 .75
149 Jim Abbott .75 2.00
150 Curt Schilling .50 1.25
151 Bill Swift .30 .75
152 Tommy Greene .30 .75
153 Roberto Mejia .30 .75
154 Edgar Martinez .75 2.00
155 Roger Pavlik .30 .75
156 Randy Tomlin .30 .75
157 J.T. Snow .50 1.25
158 Bob Welch .30 .75
159 Alan Trammell .50 1.25
160 Ed Sprague .30 .75
161 Ben McDonald .30 .75
162 Derrick May .30 .75
163 Roberto Kelly .30 .75
164 Bryan Harvey .30 .75
165 Ron Gant .50 1.25
166 Scott Erickson .30 .75
167 Anthony Young .30 .75
168 Scott Cooper .30 .75
169 Rod Beck .30 .75
170 John Franco .50 1.25
171 Gary DiSarcina .30 .75
172 Dave Fleming .30 .75
173 Wade Boggs .75 2.00
174 Kevin Appier .50 1.25
175 Jose Bautista .30 .75
176 Wally Joyner .50 1.25
177 Dean Palmer .50 1.25
178 Tony Phillips .30 .75
179 John Smiley .30 .75
180 Charlie Hough .50 1.25
181 Scott Fletcher .30 .75
182 Todd Van Poppel .30 .75
183 Mike Blowers .30 .75
184 Willie McGee .50 1.25
185 Paul Sorrento .30 .75
186 Eric Young .30 .75
187 Bret Barberie .30 .75
188 Manuel Lee .30 .75
189 Jeff Branson .30 .75
190 Jim Deshaies .30 .75
191 Ken Caminiti .50 1.25
192 Tim Raines .50 1.25
193 Joe Grahe .30 .75
194 Hipolito Pichardo .30 .75
195 Denny Neagle .50 1.25
196 Jeff Gardner .30 .75
197 Mike Benjamin .30 .75
198 Milt Thompson .30 .75
199 Bruce Ruffin .30 .75
200 Chris Hammond UER .30 .75
(Back of card has Mariners;
should be Marlins)
201 Tony Gwynn FIN 1.50 4.00
202 Robin Ventura FIN .50 1.25
203 Frank Thomas FIN 1.25 3.00
204 Kirby Puckett FIN 1.25 3.00
205 Roberto Alomar FIN .75 2.00
206 Dennis Eckersley FIN .50 1.25
207 Joe Carter FIN .50 1.25
208 Albert Belle FIN .50 1.25
209 Greg Maddux FIN 2.00 5.00
210 Ryne Sandberg FIN 2.00 5.00
211 Juan Gonzalez FIN .50 1.25
212 Jeff Bagwell FIN .75 2.00
213 Randy Johnson FIN 1.25 3.00
214 Matt Williams FIN .50 1.25
215 Dave Winfield FIN .50 1.25
216 Larry Walker FIN .50 1.25
217 Roger Clemens FIN 2.50 6.00
218 Kenny Lofton FIN .50 1.25
219 Cecil Fielder FIN .50 1.25
220 Darren Daulton FIN .50 1.25
221 John Olerud FIN .50 1.25
222 Jose Canseco FIN .75 2.00
223 Rickey Henderson FIN 1.25 3.00
224 Fred McGriff FIN .75 2.00
225 Gary Sheffield FIN .50 1.25
226 Jack McDowell FIN .30 .75
227 Rafael Palmeiro FIN .75 2.00
228 Travis Fryman FIN .50 1.25
229 Marquis Grissom FIN .50 1.25
230 Barry Bonds FIN 3.00 8.00
231 Carlos Baerga FIN .30 .75
232 Ken Griffey Jr. FIN 2.00 5.00
233 David Justice FIN .50 1.25
234 Bobby Bonilla FIN .50 1.25
235 Cal Ripken FIN 4.00 10.00
236 Sammy Sosa FIN 1.25 3.00
237 Len Dykstra FIN .50 1.25
238 Will Clark FIN .75 2.00
239 Paul Molitor FIN .50 1.25
240 Barry Larkin FIN .75 2.00
241 Bo Jackson 1.25 3.00
242 Mitch Williams .30 .75
243 Ron Darling .30 .75
244 Darryl Kile .50 1.25
245 Geronimo Berroa .30 .75
246 Gregg Olson .30 .75
247 Brian Harper .30 .75
248 Rheal Cormier .30 .75
249 Rey Sanchez .30 .75
250 Jeff Fassero .30 .75
251 Sandy Alomar Jr. .30 .75
252 Chris Bosio .30 .75
253 Andy Stankiewicz .30 .75
254 Harold Baines .50 1.25
255 Andy Ashby .30 .75
256 Tyler Green .30 .75
257 Kevin Brown .50 1.25
258 Mo Vaughn .50 1.25
259 Mike Harkey .30 .75
260 Dave Henderson .30 .75
261 Kent Hrbek .50 1.25
262 Darrin Jackson .30 .75
263 Bob Wickman .30 .75
264 Spike Owen .30 .75
265 Todd Jones .30 .75
266 Pat Borders .30 .75
267 Tom Glavine .75 2.00
268 Dave Nilsson .30 .75
269 Rich Batchelor .30 .75
270 Delino DeShields .30 .75
271 Felix Fermin .30 .75
272 Orestes Destrade .30 .75
273 Mickey Morandini .30 .75
274 Otis Nixon .30 .75
275 Ellis Burks .50 1.25
276 Greg Gagne .30 .75
277 John Doherty .30 .75
278 Julio Franco .50 1.25
279 Bernie Williams .75 2.00
280 Rick Aguilera .30 .75
281 Mickey Tettleton .30 .75
282 David Nied .30 .75
283 Johnny Ruffin .30 .75
284 Dan Wilson .30 .75
285 Omar Vizquel .75 2.00
286 Willie Banks .30 .75
287 Erik Pappas .30 .75
288 Cal Eldred .30 .75
289 Bobby Witt .30 .75
290 Luis Gonzalez .50 1.25
291 Greg Pirkl .30 .75
292 Alex Cole .30 .75
293 Ricky Bones .30 .75
294 Denis Boucher .30 .75
295 John Burkett .30 .75
296 Steve Trachsel .30 .75
297 Ricky Jordan .30 .75
298 Mark Dewey .30 .75
299 Jimmy Key .50 1.25
300 Mike Macfarlane .30 .75
301 Tim Belcher .30 .75
302 Carlos Reyes .30 .75
303 Greg A. Harris .30 .75
304 Brian Anderson RC .50 1.25
305 Terry Mulholland .30 .75
306 Felix Jose .30 .75
307 Darren Holmes .30 .75
308 Jose Rijo .30 .75
309 Paul Wagner .30 .75
310 Bob Scanlan .30 .75
311 Mike Jackson .30 .75
312 Jose Vizcaino .30 .75
313 Rob Butler .30 .75
314 Kevin Seitzer .30 .75
315 Geronimo Pena .30 .75
316 Hector Carrasco .30 .75
317 Eddie Murray 1.25 3.00
318 Roger Salkeld .30 .75
319 Todd Hundley .30 .75
320 Danny Jackson .30 .75
321 Kevin Young .30 .75
322 Mike Greenwell .30 .75
323 Kevin Mitchell .30 .75
324 Chuck Knoblauch .50 1.25
325 Danny Tartabull .30 .75
326 Vince Coleman .30 .75
327 Marvin Freeman .30 .75
328 Andy Benes .30 .75
329 Mike Kelly .30 .75
330 Karl Rhodes .30 .75
331 Allen Watson .30 .75
332 Damion Easley .30 .75
333 Reggie Jefferson .30 .75
334 Kevin McReynolds .30 .75
335 Arthur Rhodes .30 .75
336 Brian R. Hunter .30 .75
337 Tom Browning .30 .75
338 Pedro Munoz .30 .75
339 Billy Ripken .30 .75
340 Gene Harris .30 .75
341 Fernando Vina .30 .75
342 Sean Berry .30 .75
343 Pedro Astacio .30 .75
344 B.J. Surhoff .50 1.25
345 Doug Drabek .30 .75
346 Jody Reed .30 .75
347 Ray Lankford .50 1.25
348 Steve Farr .30 .75
349 Eric Anthony .30 .75
350 Pete Smith .30 .75
351 Lee Smith .50 1.25
352 Mariano Duncan .30 .75
353 Doug Strange .30 .75
354 Tim Bogar .30 .75
355 Dave Weathers .30 .75
356 Eric Karros .50 1.25
357 Randy Myers .30 .75
358 Chad Curtis .30 .75
359 Steve Avery .30 .75
360 Brian Jordan .50 1.25
361 Tim Wallach .30 .75
362 Pedro Martinez 1.25 3.00
363 Bip Roberts .30 .75
364 Lou Whitaker .50 1.25
365 Luis Polonia .30 .75
366 Benito Santiago .50 1.25
367 Brett Butler .50 1.25
368 Shawon Dunston .30 .75
369 Kelly Stinnett RC .50 1.25
370 Chris Turner .30 .75
371 Ruben Sierra .50 1.25
372 Greg A. Harris .30 .75
373 Xavier Hernandez .30 .75
374 Howard Johnson .30 .75
375 Duane Ward .30 .75
376 Roberto Hernandez .30 .75
377 Scott Leius .30 .75
378 Dave Valle .30 .75
379 Sid Fernandez .30 .75
380 Doug Jones .30 .75
381 Zane Smith .30 .75
382 Craig Biggio .75 2.00
383 Rick White RC .30 .75
384 Tom Pagnozzi .30 .75
385 Chris James .30 .75
386 Bret Boone .50 1.25
387 Jeff Montgomery .30 .75
388 Chad Kreuter .30 .75
389 Greg Hibbard .30 .75
390 Mark Grace .75 2.00
391 Phil Leftwich RC .30 .75
392 Don Mattingly 3.00 8.00
393 Ozzie Guillen .50 1.25
394 Gary Gaetti .50 1.25
395 Erik Hanson .30 .75
396 Scott Brosius .50 1.25
397 Tom Gordon .30 .75
398 Bill Gullickson .30 .75
399 Matt Mieske .30 .75
400 Pat Hentgen .30 .75
401 Walt Weiss .30 .75
402 Greg Blosser .30 .75
403 Stan Javier .30 .75
404 Doug Henry .30 .75
405 Ramon Martinez .30 .75
406 Frank Viola .50 1.25
407 Mike Hampton .50 1.25
408 Andy Van Slyke .75 2.00
409 Bobby Ayala .30 .75
410 Todd Zeile .30 .75
411 Jay Bell .50 1.25
412 Dennis Martinez .50 1.25
413 Mark Portugal .30 .75
414 Bobby Munoz .30 .75
415 Kirt Manwaring .30 .75
416 John Kruk .50 1.25
417 Trevor Hoffman .75 2.00
418 Chris Sabo .30 .75
419 Bret Saberhagen .50 1.25
420 Chris Nabholz .30 .75
421 James Mouton FIN .30 .75
422 Tony Tarasco FIN .30 .75
423 Carlos Delgado FIN .75 2.00

424 Rondell White FIN .50 1.25
425 Javier Lopez FIN .50 1.25
426 Chan Ho Park FIN RC .75 2.00
427 Cliff Floyd FIN .50 1.25
428 Dave Staton FIN .30 .75
429 J.R. Phillips FIN .30 .75
430 Manny Ramirez FIN 1.25 3.00
431 Kurt Abbott FIN RC .30 .75
432 Melvin Nieves FIN .30 .75
433 Alex Gonzalez FIN .30 .75
434 Rick Helling FIN .30 .75
435 Danny Bautista FIN .30 .75
436 Matt Walbeck FIN .30 .75
437 Ryan Klesko FIN .50 1.25
438 Steve Karsay FIN .30 .75
439 Salomon Torres FIN .30 .75
440 Scott Ruffcorn FIN .30 .75

1994 Finest Refractors

The 1994 Topps Finest Refractors baseball set consists of two series of 220 cards each, for a total of 440 cards. These special cards were inserted at a rate of one in every nine packs. They are identical to the basic Finest card except for a more intense luster and 3-D appearance.

*STARS: 2.5X TO 6X BASIC CARDS
*ROOKIES: 1.5X TO 4X BASIC CARDS
STATED ODDS 1:9

1994 Finest Jumbos

Inserted one per Finest box, this 80-card over-sized set (3 1/2" by 5") was issued in two series of 40. Each of the 80 cards is identical in design to the special "Finest" cards from the basic Finest set except for the size. The "Finest" subset was designated to showcase top rookies, prospects and veterans. The card numbering is the same as the corresponding basic issue cards. Hence, the first series comprises of cards 1-20 and 201-220. The second series is cards 221-240 and 421-440.

*JUMBOS: 1.25X TO 3X BASIC CARDS

1995 Finest

Consisting of 330 standard-size cards, this set (produced by Topps) was issued in series of 220 and 110. A protective film, designed to keep the card from scratching and to maintain original gloss, covers the front. With the Finest logo at the top, a silver baseball diamond design surrounded by green (field) form the background to an action photo. Horizontally designed backs have a photo to the right with statistical information to the left. A Finest Moment, or career highlight, is also included. Rookie Cards in this set include Bobby Higginson and Hideo Nomo.

COMPLETE SET (330) 25.00 60.00
COMP. SERIES 1 (220) 20.00 50.00
COMP. SERIES 2 (110) 6.00 15.00
1 Raul Mondesi .40 1.00
2 Kurt Abbott .20 .50
3 Chris Gomez .20 .50
4 Manny Ramirez .60 1.50
5 Rondell White .40 1.00
6 William VanLandingham .20 .50
7 Jon Lieber .20 .50
8 Ryan Klesko .40 1.00
9 John Hudek .20 .50
10 Joey Hamilton .20 .50
11 Bob Hamelin .20 .50
12 Brian Anderson .20 .50
13 Mike Lieberthal .40 1.00
14 Rico Brogna .20 .50
15 Rusty Greer .40 1.00
16 Carlos Delgado .40 1.00
17 Jim Edmonds .60 1.50
18 Steve Trachsel .20 .50
19 Matt Walbeck .20 .50
20 Armando Benitez .20 .50
21 Steve Karsay .20 .50
22 Jose Oliva .20 .50
23 Cliff Floyd .40 1.00
24 Kevin Foster .20 .50
25 Javier Lopez .40 1.00
26 Jose Valentin .20 .50
27 James Mouton .20 .50
28 Hector Carrasco .20 .50
29 Orlando Miller .20 .50
30 Garret Anderson .40 1.00
31 Marvin Freeman .20 .50
32 Brett Butler .40 1.00
33 Roberto Kelly .20 .50
34 Rod Beck .20 .50
35 Jose Rijo .20 .50
36 Edgar Martinez .60 1.50
37 Jim Thome .60 1.50
38 Rick Wilkins .20 .50
39 Wally Joyner .40 1.00
40 Wil Cordero .20 .50
41 Tommy Greene .20 .50
42 Travis Fryman .40 1.00
43 Don Slaught .20 .50
44 Brady Anderson .40 1.00
45 Matt Williams .40 1.00
46 Rene Arocha .20 .50
47 Rickey Henderson 1.00 2.50
48 Mike Mussina .60 1.50
49 Greg McMichael .20 .50
50 Jody Reed .20 .50
51 Tino Martinez .60 1.50
52 Dave Clark .20 .50
53 John Valentin .20 .50
54 Bret Boone .40 1.00
55 Walt Weiss .20 .50
56 Kenny Lofton .40 1.00
57 Scott Leius .20 .50
58 Eric Karros .40 1.00
59 John Olerud .40 1.00
60 Chris Hoiles .20 .50
61 Sandy Alomar Jr. .20 .50
62 Tim Wallach .20 .50
63 Cal Eldred .20 .50
64 Tom Glavine .60 1.50
65 Mark Grace .60 1.50
66 Rey Sanchez .20 .50
67 Bobby Ayala .20 .50
68 Dante Bichette .40 1.00
69 Andres Galarraga .40 1.00
70 Chuck Carr .20 .50
71 Bobby Witt .20 .50
72 Steve Avery .20 .50
73 Bobby Jones .20 .50
74 Delino DeShields .20 .50
75 Kevin Tapani .20 .50
76 Randy Johnson 1.00 2.50
77 David Nied .20 .50
78 Pat Hentgen .20 .50
79 Tim Salmon .60 1.50
80 Todd Zeile .20 .50
81 John Wetteland .40 1.00
82 Albert Belle .40 1.00
83 Ben McDonald .20 .50
84 Bobby Munoz .20 .50
85 Bip Roberts .20 .50
86 Mo Vaughn .40 1.00
87 Chuck Finley .40 1.00
88 Chuck Knoblauch .40 1.00
89 Frank Thomas 1.00 2.50
90 Danny Tartabull .20 .50
91 Dean Palmer .40 1.00
92 Len Dykstra .40 1.00
93 J.R. Phillips .20 .50
94 Tom Candiotti .20 .50
95 Marquis Grissom .40 1.00
96 Barry Larkin .60 1.50
97 Bryan Harvey .20 .50
98 David Justice .40 1.00
99 David Cone .40 1.00
100 Wade Boggs .60 1.50
101 Jason Bere .20 .50
102 Hal Morris .20 .50
103 Fred McGriff .60 1.50
104 Bobby Bonilla .40 1.00
105 Jay Buhner .40 1.00
106 Allen Watson .20 .50
107 Mickey Tettleton .20 .50
108 Kevin Appier .40 1.00
109 Ivan Rodriguez .60 1.50
110 Carlos Garcia .20 .50
111 Andy Benes .20 .50
112 Eddie Murray 1.00 2.50
113 Mike Piazza 1.50 4.00
114 Greg Vaughn .20 .50
115 Paul Molitor .40 1.00
116 Terry Steinbach .20 .50
117 Jeff Bagwell .60 1.50
118 Ken Griffey Jr. 1.50 4.00
119 Gary Sheffield .40 1.00
120 Cal Ripken 3.00 8.00
121 Jeff Kent .40 1.00
122 Jay Bell .40 1.00
123 Will Clark .60 1.50
124 Cecil Fielder .40 1.00
125 Alex Fernandez .20 .50
126 Don Mattingly 2.50 6.00
127 Reggie Sanders .40 1.00
128 Moises Alou .40 1.00
129 Craig Biggio .60 1.50
130 Eddie Williams .20 .50
131 John Franco .40 1.00
132 John Kruk .40 1.00
133 Jeff King .20 .50
134 Royce Clayton .20 .50
135 Doug Drabek .20 .50
136 Ray Lankford .40 1.00
137 Roberto Alomar .60 1.50
138 Todd Hundley .20 .50
139 Alex Cole .20 .50
140 Shawon Dunston .20 .50
141 John Roper .20 .50
142 Mark Langston .20 .50
143 Tom Pagnozzi .20 .50
144 Wilson Alvarez .20 .50
145 Scott Cooper .20 .50
146 Kevin Mitchell .20 .50
147 Mark Whiten .20 .50
148 Jeff Conine .40 1.00
149 Chili Davis .40 1.00
150 Luis Gonzalez .40 1.00
151 Juan Guzman .20 .50
152 Mike Greenwell .20 .50
153 Mike Henneman .20 .50
154 Rick Aguilera .20 .50
155 Dennis Eckersley .40 1.00
156 Darrin Fletcher .20 .50
157 Darren Lewis .20 .50
158 Juan Gonzalez .40 1.00
159 Dave Hollins .20 .50
160 Jimmy Key .40 1.00
161 Roberto Hernandez .20 .50
162 Randy Myers .20 .50
163 Joe Carter .40 1.00
164 Darren Daulton .40 1.00
165 Mike Macfarlane .20 .50
166 Bret Saberhagen .40 1.00
167 Kirby Puckett 1.00 2.50
168 Lance Johnson .20 .50
169 Mark McGwire 2.50 6.00
170 Jose Canseco .60 1.50
171 Mike Stanley .20 .50
172 Lee Smith .40 1.00
173 Robin Ventura .40 1.00
174 Greg Gagne .20 .50
175 Brian McRae .20 .50
176 Mike Bordick .20 .50
177 Rafael Palmeiro .60 1.50
178 Kenny Rogers .40 1.00
179 Chad Curtis .20 .50
180 Devon White .40 1.00
181 Paul O'Neill .60 1.50
182 Ken Caminiti .40 1.00
183 Dave Nilsson .20 .50
184 Tim Naehring .20 .50
185 Roger Clemens 2.00 5.00
186 Otis Nixon .20 .50
187 Tim Raines .40 1.00
188 Denny Martinez .40 1.00
189 Pedro Martinez .60 1.50
190 Jim Abbott .60 1.50
191 Ryan Thompson .20 .50
192 Barry Bonds 2.50 6.00
193 Joe Girardi .20 .50
194 Steve Finley .40 1.00
195 John Jaha .20 .50
196 Tony Gwynn 1.25 3.00
197 Sammy Sosa 1.00 2.50
198 John Burkett .20 .50
199 Carlos Baerga .20 .50
200 Ramon Martinez .20 .50
201 Aaron Sele .20 .50
202 Eduardo Perez .20 .50
203 Alan Trammell .40 1.00
204 Orlando Merced .20 .50
205 Deion Sanders .60 1.50
206 Robb Nen .40 1.00
207 Jack McDowell .20 .50
208 Ruben Sierra .40 1.00
209 Bernie Williams .60 1.50
210 Kevin Seitzer .20 .50
211 Charles Nagy .20 .50
212 Tony Phillips .20 .50
213 Greg Maddux 1.50 4.00
214 Jeff Montgomery .20 .50
215 Larry Walker .40 1.00
216 Andy Van Slyke .60 1.50
217 Ozzie Smith 1.50 4.00
218 Geronimo Pena .20 .50
219 Gregg Jefferies .20 .50
220 Lou Whitaker .40 1.00
221 Chipper Jones 1.00 2.50
222 Benji Gil .20 .50
223 Tony Phillips .20 .50
224 Trevor Wilson .20 .50
225 Tony Tarasco .20 .50
226 Roberto Petagine .20 .50
227 Mike Macfarlane .20 .50
228 Hideo Nomo RC UER 4.00 10.00
(In 3rd line against)
229 Mark McLemore .20 .50
230 Ron Gant .40 1.00
231 Andujar Cedeno .20 .50
232 Mike Mimbs RC .20 .50
233 Jim Abbott .60 1.50
234 Ricky Bones .20 .50
235 Marty Cordova .20 .50
236 Mark Johnson RC .50 1.25
237 Marquis Grissom .40 1.00
238 Tom Henke .20 .50
239 Terry Pendleton .40 1.00
240 John Wetteland .40 1.00
241 Lee Smith .40 1.00
242 Jaime Navarro .20 .50
243 Luis Alicea .20 .50
244 Scott Cooper .20 .50
245 Gary Gaetti .40 1.00
246 Edgardo Alfonzo UER .20 .50
(Incomplete career BA)
247 Brad Clontz .20 .50
248 Dave Mlicki .20 .50
249 Dave Winfield .40 1.00
250 Mark Grudzielanek RC .75 2.00
251 Alex Gonzalez .20 .50
252 Kevin Brown .40 1.00
253 Esteban Loaiza .20 .50
254 Vaughn Eshelman .20 .50
255 Bill Swift .20 .50
256 Brian McRae .20 .50
257 Bobby Higginson RC .75 2.00
258 Jack McDowell .20 .50
259 Scott Stahoviak .20 .50
260 Jon Nunnally .20 .50
261 Charlie Hayes .20 .50
262 Jacob Brumfield .20 .50
263 Chad Curtis .20 .50
264 Heathcliff Slocumb .20 .50
265 Mark Whiten .20 .50
266 Mickey Tettleton .20 .50
267 Jose Mesa .20 .50
268 Doug Jones .20 .50
269 Trevor Hoffman .40 1.00
270 Paul Sorrento .20 .50
271 Shane Andrews .20 .50
272 Brett Butler .40 1.00
273 Curtis Goodwin .20 .50
274 Larry Walker .40 1.00
275 Phil Plantier .20 .50
276 Ken Hill .20 .50
277 Vinny Castilla UER .40 1.00
Rockies spelled Rockie
278 Billy Ashley .20 .50
279 Derek Jeter 2.50 6.00
280 Bob Tewksbury .20 .50
281 Jose Offerman .20 .50
282 Glenallen Hill .20 .50
283 Tony Fernandez .20 .50
284 Mike Devereaux .20 .50
285 John Burkett .20 .50
286 Geronimo Berroa .20 .50
287 Quilvio Veras .20 .50
288 Jason Bates .20 .50
289 Lee Tinsley .20 .50
290 Derek Bell .20 .50
291 Jeff Fassero .20 .50
292 Ray Durham .40 1.00
293 Chad Ogea .20 .50
294 Bill Pulsipher .20 .50
295 Phil Nevin .40 1.00
296 Carlos Perez RC .50 1.25
297 Roberto Kelly .20 .50
298 Tim Wakefield .40 1.00
299 Jeff Manto .20 .50
300 Brian Hunter .20 .50
301 C.J. Nitkowski .20 .50
302 Dustin Hermanson .20 .50
303 John Mabry .20 .50
304 Orel Hershiser .40 1.00
305 Ron Villone .20 .50
306 Sean Bergman .20 .50
307 Tom Goodwin .20 .50
308 Al Reyes .20 .50
309 Todd Stottlemyre .20 .50
310 Rich Becker .20 .50
311 Joey Cora .20 .50
312 Ed Sprague .20 .50
313 John Smoltz UER .60 1.50
(3rd line; from spelled as form)
314 Frank Castillo .20 .50
315 Chris Hammond .20 .50
316 Ismael Valdes .20 .50
317 Pete Harnisch .20 .50
318 Bernard Gilkey .20 .50
319 John Kruk .40 1.00
320 Marc Newfield .20 .50
321 Brian Johnson .20 .50
322 Mark Portugal .20 .50
323 David Hulse .20 .50
324 Luis Ortiz UER .20 .50
(Below spelled beloe)
325 Mike Benjamin .20 .50
326 Brian Jordan .40 1.00
327 Shawn Green .40 1.00
328 Joe Oliver .20 .50
329 Felipe Lira .20 .50
330 Andre Dawson .40 1.00

1995 Finest Refractors

This set is a parallel to the basic Finest set, including the use of protective coating, the difference can be found in the refractive sheen. The cards were inserted at a rate of one in 12 packs.

*STARS: 4X TO 10X BASIC CARDS
*ROOKIES: 3X TO 8X BASIC CARDS
STATED ODDS 1:12

1995 Finest Flame Throwers

Randomly inserted in first series packs at a rate of 1:48, this nine-card set showcases strikeout leaders who bring on the heat. With a protective coating, a player photo is superimposed over a fiery orange background.

COMPLETE SET (9) 15.00 40.00
SER.1 STATED ODDS 1:48
FT1 Jason Bere 1.25 3.00
FT2 Roger Clemens 12.50 30.00
FT3 Juan Guzman 1.25 3.00
FT4 John Hudek 1.25 3.00
FT5 Randy Johnson 6.00 15.00
FT6 Pedro Martinez 4.00 10.00
FT7 Jose Rijo 1.25 3.00
FT8 Bret Saberhagen 2.50 6.00
FT9 John Wetteland 2.50 6.00

1995 Finest Power Kings

Randomly inserted in series one packs at a rate of one in 24, Power Kings is an 18-card set highlighting top sluggers. With a protective coating, the fronts feature chromium technology that allows the player photo to be further enhanced as if to jump out from a blue lightning bolt background.

COMPLETE SET (18) 60.00 150.00
SER.1 STATED ODDS 1:24
PK1 Bob Hamelin 1.00 2.50
PK2 Raul Mondesi 2.00 5.00
PK3 Ryan Klesko 2.00 5.00
PK4 Carlos Delgado 2.00 5.00
PK5 Manny Ramirez 3.00 8.00
PK6 Mike Piazza 8.00 20.00
PK7 Jeff Bagwell 3.00 8.00
PK8 Mo Vaughn 2.00 5.00
PK9 Frank Thomas 5.00 12.00
PK10 Ken Griffey Jr. 8.00 20.00
PK11 Albert Belle 2.00 5.00
PK12 Sammy Sosa 5.00 12.00
PK13 Dante Bichette 2.00 5.00
PK14 Gary Sheffield 2.00 5.00
PK15 Matt Williams 2.00 5.00
PK16 Fred McGriff 3.00 8.00
PK17 Barry Bonds 12.50 30.00
PK18 Cecil Fielder 2.00 5.00

1995 Finest Bronze

Available exclusively direct from Topps, this six-card set features 1994 league leaders. The fronts feature chromium metallized graphics, mounted on bronze and factory sealed in clear resin. The cards are numbered on the back "X of 6."

COMPLETE SET (6) 40.00 80.00
1 Matt Williams 3.00 8.00
2 Tony Gwynn 10.00 25.00
3 Jeff Bagwell 6.00 15.00
4 Ken Griffey Jr. 12.50 30.00
5 Paul O'Neill 2.00 5.00
6 Frank Thomas 6.00 15.00

1996 Finest

The 1996 Finest set (produced by Topps) was issued in two series of 191 cards and 168 cards respectively, for a total of 359 cards. The six-card foil packs originally retailed for $5.00 each. A protective film, designed to keep the card from scratching and to maintain original gloss, covers the front. This product provides collectors with the opportunity to complete a number of sets within sets, each with a different degree of insertion. Each card is numbered twice to indicate the set count and the theme count. Series 1 set covers four distinct themes: Finest Phenoms, Finest Intimidators, Finest Gamers and Finest Sterling. Within the first three themes, some players will be common (bronze trim), some uncommon (silver) and some rare (gold). Finest Sterling consists of star players included within one of the other three themes, but featured with a new design and different photography. The breakdown for the player selection of common, uncommon and rare cards is completely random. There are 110 common, 55 uncommon (1:4 packs) and 25 rare cards (1:24 packs). Series 2 covers four distict themes also with common, uncommon and rare cards seeded at the same ratio. The four themes are: Finest Franchises which features 36 team leaders and bonafide superstars, Finest Additions which features 47 players who have switched teams in '96, Finest Prodigies which features 45 best up-and-coming players, and Finest Sterling with 39 top stars. In addition to the cards' special borders, each card will also have either "common," "uncommon", or "rare" written within the numbering box on the card backs to let collectors know which type of card they hold.

COMP.BRONZE SER.1 (110) 10.00 25.00
COMP.BRONZE SER.2 (110) 10.00 25.00
COMMON BRONZE .20 .50
COMMON GOLD 2.00 5.00
COMMON G RC 2.00 5.00
COMMON SILVER 1.00 2.50
B5 Roberto Hernandez B .20 .50
B8 Terry Pendleton B .20 .50
B12 Ken Caminiti B .20 .50
B15 Dan Miceli B .20 .50
B16 Chipper Jones B .50 1.25
B17 John Wetteland B .20 .50
B19 Tim Naehring B .20 .50
B21 Eddie Murray B .50 1.25
B23 Kevin Appier B .20 .50
B24 Ken Griffey Jr. B .75 2.00
B26 Brian McRae B .20 .50
B27 Pedro Martinez B .30 .75
B28 Brian Jordan B .20 .50
B29 Mike Fetters B .20 .50
B30 Carlos Delgado B .20 .50
B31 Shane Reynolds B .20 .50
B32 Terry Steinbach B .20 .50
B34 Mark Leiter B .20 .50
B36 David Segui B .20 .50
B40 Fred McGriff B .30 .75
B44 Glenallen Hill B .20 .50
B45 Brady Anderson B .20 .50
B47 Jim Thome B .30 .75
B48 Frank Thomas B .50 1.25
B49 Chuck Knoblauch B .20 .50
B50 Len Dykstra B .20 .50
B53 Tom Pagnozzi B .20 .50
B55 Ricky Bones B .20 .50
B56 David Justice B .20 .50
B57 Steve Avery B .20 .50
B58 Robby Thompson B .20 .50
B61 Tony Gwynn B .60 1.50
B63 Denny Neagle B .20 .50
B67 Robin Ventura B .20 .50
B70 Kevin Seitzer B .20 .50
B71 Ramon Martinez B .20 .50
B75 Brian L.Hunter B .20 .50
B76 Alan Benes B .20 .50
B80 Ozzie Guillen B .20 .50
B82 Benji Gil B .20 .50
B85 Todd Hundley B .20 .50
B87 Pat Hentgen B .20 .50
B89 Chuck Finley B .20 .50
B92 Derek Jeter B 1.25 3.00
B93 Paul O'Neill B .30 .75
B94 Darrin Fletcher B .20 .50
B96 Delino DeShields B .20 .50
B97 Tim Salmon B .30 .75
B98 John Olerud B .20 .50
B101 Tim Wakefield B .20 .50
B103 Dave Stevens B .20 .50
B104 Orlando Merced B .20 .50
B106 Jay Bell B .20 .50
B107 John Burkett B .20 .50
B108 Chris Hoiles B .20 .50
B110 Dave Nilsson B .20 .50
B111 Rod Beck B .20 .50
B113 Mike Piazza B .75 2.00
B114 Mark Langston B .20 .50
B116 Rico Brogna B .20 .50
B118 Tom Goodwin B .20 .50
B119 Bryan Rekar B .20 .50
B120 David Cone B .20 .50
B122 Andy Pettitte B .30 .75
B123 Chili Davis B .20 .50
B124 John Smoltz B .30 .75
B125 H.Slocumb B .20 .50
B126 Dante Bichette B .20 .50
B128 Alex Gonzalez B .20 .50
B129 Jeff Montgomery B .20 .50
B131 Denny Martinez B .20 .50
B132 Mel Rojas B .20 .50
B133 Derek Bell B .20 .50
B134 Trevor Hoffman B .20 .50
B136 Darren Daulton B .20 .50
B137 Pete Schourek B .20 .50
B138 Phil Nevin B .20 .50
B139 Andres Galarraga B .20 .50
B140 Chad Fonville B .20 .50
B144 J.T. Snow B .20 .50
B146 Barry Bonds B 1.25 3.00
B147 Orel Hershiser B .20 .50
B148 Quilvio Veras B .20 .50
B149 Will Clark B .30 .75
B150 Jose Rijo B .20 .50
B152 Travis Fryman B .20 .50
B154 Alex Fernandez B .20 .50
B155 Wade Boggs B .30 .75
B156 Troy Percival B .20 .50
B157 Moises Alou B .20 .50
B158 Javy Lopez B .20 .50
B159 Jason Giambi B .20 .50
B162 Mark McGwire B 1.25 3.00
B163 Eric Karros B .20 .50
B166 Mickey Tettleton B .20 .50
B167 Barry Larkin B .30 .75
B169 Ruben Sierra B .20 .50
B170 Bill Swift B .20 .50
B172 Chad Curtis B .20 .50
B173 Dean Palmer B .20 .50
B175 Bobby Bonilla B .20 .50
B176 Greg Colbrunn B .20 .50
B177 Jose Mesa B .20 .50
B178 Mike Greenwell B .20 .50
B181 Doug Drabek B .20 .50
B183 Wilson Alvarez B .20 .50
B184 Marty Cordova B .20 .50
B185 Hal Morris B .20 .50
B187 Carlos Garcia B .20 .50
B190 Marquis Grissom B .20 .50
B193 Will Clark B .30 .75
B194 Paul Molitor B .20 .50
B195 Kenny Rogers B .20 .50
B196 Reggie Sanders B .20 .50
B199 Raul Mondesi B .20 .50
B200 Lance Johnson B .20 .50
B201 Alvin Morman B .20 .50
B203 Jack McDowell B .20 .50
B204 Randy Myers B .20 .50
B205 Harold Baines B .20 .50
B206 Marty Cordova B .20 .50
B207 Rich Hunter B RC .20 .50
B208 Al Leiter B .20 .50
B209 Greg Gagne B .20 .50
B210 Ben McDonald B .20 .50
B212 Terry Adams B .20 .50
B213 Paul Sorrento B .20 .50
B214 Albert Belle B .20 .50
B215 Mike Blowers B .20 .50
B216 Jim Edmonds B .20 .50
B217 Felipe Crespo B .20 .50
B219 Shawon Dunston B .20 .50
B220 Jimmy Haynes B .20 .50
B221 Jose Canseco B .30 .75
B222 Eric Davis B .20 .50
B224 Tim Raines B .20 .50
B225 Tony Phillips B .20 .50
B226 Charlie Hayes B .20 .50
B227 Eric Owens B .20 .50
B228 Roberto Alomar B .20 .50
B233 Kenny Lofton B .20 .50
B236 Mark McGwire B 1.25 3.00
B237 Jay Buhner B .20 .50
B238 Craig Biggio B .30 .75
B240 Barry Bonds B 1.25 3.00
B244 Ron Gant B .20 .50
B245 Paul Wilson B .20 .50
B246 T.Hollandsworth B .20 .50
B247 Todd Zeile B .20 .50
B248 David Justice B .20 .50
B250 Moises Alou B .20 .50
B251 Bob Wolcott B .20 .50
B252 David Wells B .20 .50
B253 Juan Gonzalez B .20 .50
B254 Andres Galarraga B .20 .50
B255 Dave Hollins B .20 .50
B257 Sammy Sosa B .50 1.25
B258 Ivan Rodriguez B .30 .75
B259 Bip Roberts B .20 .50
B260 Tino Martinez B .30 .75
B262 Mike Stanley B .20 .50
B264 Butch Huskey B .20 .50
B265 Jeff Conine B .20 .50
B267 Mark Grace B .30 .75
B268 Jason Schmidt B .30 .75
B269 Otis Nixon B .20 .50
B271 Kirby Puckett B .50 1.25
B273 Andy Benes B .20 .50
B275 Mike Piazza B .75 2.00
B276 Rey Ordonez B .20 .50
B278 Gary Gaetti B .20 .50
B280 Robin Ventura B .20 .50
B281 Cal Ripken B 1.50 4.00
B282 Carlos Baerga B .20 .50
B283 Roger Cedeno B .20 .50
B285 Terrell Wade B .20 .50
B286 Kevin Brown B .20 .50
B287 Rafael Palmeiro B .30 .75
B288 Mo Vaughn B .20 .50
B292 Bob Tewksbury B .20 .50
B297 T.J. Mathews B .20 .50
B298 Manny Ramirez B .30 .75
B299 Jeff Bagwell B .30 .75
B301 Wade Boggs B .30 .75
B303 Steve Gibralter B .20 .50
B304 B.J. Surhoff B .20 .50
B306 Royce Clayton B .20 .50
B307 Sal Fasano B .20 .50
B309 Gary Sheffield B .20 .50
B310 Ken Hill B .20 .50
B311 Joe Girardi B .20 .50
B312 Matt Lawton B RC .20 .50
B314 Julio Franco B .20 .50
B315 Joe Carter B .20 .50
B316 Brooks Kieschnick B .20 .50
B318 H.Slocumb B .20 .50
B319 Barry Larkin B .30 .75
B320 Tony Gwynn B .60 1.50
B322 Frank Thomas B .50 1.25
B323 Edgar Martinez B .30 .75
B325 Henry Rodriguez B .20 .50
B326 Marvin Benard B RC .20 .50
B329 Ugueth Urbina B .20 .50
B331 Roger Salkeld B .20 .50
B332 Edgar Renteria B .20 .50
B333 Ryan Klesko B .20 .50
B334 Ray Lankford B .20 .50
B336 Justin Thompson B .20 .50
B339 Mark Clark B .20 .50
B340 Ruben Rivera B .20 .50
B342 Matt Williams B .20 .50
B343 F.Cordova B RC .20 .50
B344 Cecil Fielder B .20 .50
B348 Mark Grudzielanek B .20 .50
B349 Ron Coomer B .20 .50
B351 Rich Aurilia B RC .20 .50
B352 Jose Herrera B .20 .50
B356 Tony Clark B .20 .50
B358 Dan Naulty B .20 .50
B359 Checklist B .20 .50
G4 Marty Cordova G 2.00 5.00
G6 Tony Gwynn G 6.00 15.00
G9 Albert Belle G 2.00 5.00
G18 Kirby Puckett G 5.00 12.00
G20 Karim Garcia G 2.00 5.00
G25 Cal Ripken G 15.00 40.00
G33 Hideo Nomo G 5.00 12.00
G39 Ryne Sandberg G 8.00 20.00
G42 Jeff Bagwell G 1.50 4.00
G51 Jason Isringhausen G 2.00 5.00
G64 Mo Vaughn G 2.00 5.00
G66 Dante Bichette G 2.00 5.00
G74 Mark McGwire G 12.50 30.00
G81 Kenny Lofton G 2.00 5.00
G83 Jim Edmonds G 2.00 5.00
G90 Mike Mussina G 3.00 8.00
G100 Jeff Conine G 2.00 5.00
G102 Johnny Damon G 3.00 8.00
G105 Barry Bonds G 12.50 30.00
G117 Jose Canseco G 3.00 8.00
G135 Ken Griffey Jr. G 8.00 20.00
G141 Chipper Jones G 5.00 12.00
G145 Greg Maddux G 8.00 20.00
G164 Jay Buhner G 2.00 5.00
G186 Frank Thomas G 5.00 12.00
G191 Checklist G 2.00 5.00
G192 Chipper Jones G 5.00 12.00
G197 Roberto Alomar G 3.00 8.00
G198 Dennis Eckersley G 2.00 5.00
G202 George Arias G 2.00 5.00
G232 Hideo Nomo G 5.00 12.00
G243 Chris Snopek G 2.00 5.00
G249 Tim Salmon G 3.00 8.00
G266 Matt Williams G 2.00 5.00
G270 Randy Johnson G 5.00 12.00
G279 Paul Molitor G 2.00 5.00
G290 Cecil Fielder G 2.00 5.00
G294 L.Hernandez G RC 4.00 10.00
G300 Marty Janzen G RC 2.00 5.00
G308 Ron Gant G 2.00 5.00
G321 Ryan Klesko G 2.00 5.00
G324 Jermaine Dye G 2.00 5.00
G330 Jason Giambi G 2.00 5.00
G335 Edgar Martinez G 3.00 8.00
G338 Rey Ordonez G 2.00 5.00
G347 Sammy Sosa G 5.00 12.00
G354 Juan Gonzalez G 2.00 5.00
G355 Craig Biggio G 3.00 8.00
S1 Greg Maddux S UER 4.00 10.00
95 stats listed as Mariners
S2 Bernie Williams S 1.50 4.00
S3 Ivan Rodriguez S 1.50 4.00
S7 Barry Larkin S 1.50 4.00
S10 Ray Lankford S 1.00 2.50
S11 Mike Piazza S 4.00 10.00
S13 Larry Walker S 1.00 2.50
S14 Matt Williams S 1.00 2.50
S22 Tim Salmon S 1.50 4.00
S35 Edgar Martinez S 1.50 4.00
S37 Gregg Jefferies S 1.00 2.50
S38 Bill Pulsipher S 1.00 2.50
S41 Shawn Green S 1.00 2.50
S43 Jim Abbott S 1.50 4.00
S46 Roger Clemens S 5.00 12.00
S52 Rondell White S 1.00 2.50
S54 Dennis Eckersley S 1.00 2.50
S59 Hideo Nomo S 2.50 6.00
S60 Gary Sheffield S 1.00 2.50
S62 Will Clark S 1.50 4.00
S65 Bret Boone S 1.00 2.50
S68 Rafael Palmeiro S 1.50 4.00
S69 Carlos Baerga S 1.00 2.50
S72 Tom Glavine S 1.50 4.00
S73 Garret Anderson S 1.00 2.50
S77 Randy Johnson S 2.50 6.00
S78 Jeff King S 1.00 2.50
S79 Kirby Puckett S 2.50 6.00
S84 Cecil Fielder S 1.00 2.50
S86 Reggie Sanders S 1.00 2.50
S88 Ryan Klesko S 1.00 2.50
S91 John Valentin S 1.00 2.50
S95 Manny Ramirez S 1.50 4.00
S99 Vinny Castilla S 1.00 2.50
S109 Carlos Perez S 1.00 2.50
S112 Craig Biggio S 1.50 4.00
S115 Juan Gonzalez S 1.00 2.50
S121 Ray Durham S 1.00 2.50
S127 C.J. Nitkowski S 1.00 2.50
S130 Raul Mondesi S 1.00 2.50
S142 Lee Smith S 1.00 2.50
S143 Joe Carter S 1.00 2.50
S151 Mo Vaughn S 1.00 2.50
S153 Frank Rodriguez S 1.00 2.50

S160 Steve Finley S	1.00	2.50
S161 Jeff Bagwell S	1.50	4.00
S165 Cal Ripken S	8.00	20.00
S168 Lyle Mouton S	1.00	2.50
S171 Sammy Sosa S	2.50	6.00
S174 John Franco S	1.00	2.50
S179 Greg Vaughn S	1.00	2.50
S180 Mark Wohlers S	1.00	2.50
S182 Paul O'Neill S	1.50	4.00
S188 Albert Belle S	1.00	2.50
S189 Mark Grace S	1.50	4.00
S211 Ernie Young S	1.00	2.50
S216 Fred McGriff S	1.50	4.00
S223 Kimera Bartee S	1.00	2.50
S229 Rickey Henderson S	2.50	6.00
S230 Sterling Hitchcock S	1.00	2.50
S231 Bernard Gilkey S	1.00	2.50
S234 Ryne Sandberg S	4.00	10.00
S235 Greg Maddux S	4.00	10.00
S239 Todd Stottlemyre S	1.00	2.50
S241 Jason Kendall S	1.00	2.50
S242 Paul O'Neill S	1.50	4.00
S256 Devon White S	1.00	2.50
S261 Chuck Knoblauch S	1.00	2.50
S263 Wally Joyner S	1.00	2.50
S272 Andy Fox S	1.00	2.50
S274 Sean Berry S	1.00	2.50
S277 Benito Santiago S	1.00	2.50
S284 Chad Mottola S	1.00	2.50
S289 Dante Bichette S	1.00	2.50
S291 Dwight Gooden S	1.00	2.50
S293 Kevin Mitchell S	1.00	2.50
S295 Russ Davis S	1.00	2.50
S296 Chan Ho Park S	1.00	2.50
S302 Larry Walker S	1.00	2.50
S305 Ken Griffey Jr. S	4.00	10.00
S313 Billy Wagner S	1.00	2.50
S317 Mike Grace S RC	1.00	2.50
S327 Kenny Lofton S	1.00	2.50
S328 Derek Bell S	1.00	2.50
S337 Gary Sheffield S	1.00	2.50
S341 Mark Grace S	1.50	4.00
S345 Andres Galarraga S	1.00	2.50
S346 Brady Anderson S	1.00	2.50
S350 Derek Jeter S	5.00	12.00
S353 Jay Buhner S	1.00	2.50
S357 Tino Martinez S	1.50	4.00

1996 Finest Refractors

This 359-card set is parallel to the basic 1996 Finest set. The first 191 cards are parallel to the regular Series 1 with the second 168 cards parallel to regular Series 2. The word "refractor" is printed above the numbers on the card backs. The rate of insertion is one in 12 for a Bronze refractor (common), one in 48 for a Silver refractor (uncommon), and one in 288 for a Gold refractor (rare).

*BRONZE STARS: 4X to 10X BASIC CARDS
BRONZE STATED ODDS 1:12
*GOLD STARS: .75X TO 2X BASIC CARDS
GOLD STATED ODDS 1:288
*SILVER STARS: 1.25X TO 3X BASIC CARDS
SILVER STATED ODDS 1:48

1996 Finest Landmark

This four-card limited edition medallion set came with a Certificate of Authenticity and was produced by Topps. Only 2,000 sets were made. The fronts feature color action player photos on a gold ball and star metallic background. The backs carry player biographical and career information including batting records.

COMPLETE SET (4)	40.00	100.00
1 Greg Maddux	12.50	30.00
2 Albert Belle	4.00	10.00
3 Cal Ripken	25.00	60.00
4 Eddie Murray	6.00	15.00

1997 Finest

The 1997 Finest set (produced by Topps) was issued in two series of 175 cards each and was distributed in six-card packs with a suggested retail price of $5.00. The fronts feature a borderless action player photo while the backs carry player information with another player photo. Series one is divided into five distinct themes: Finest Hurlers (top pitchers), Finest Blue Chips (up-and-coming future stars), Finest Power (long-ball hitters), Finest Warriors (superstar players), and Finest Masters (hottest players). Series two is also divided into five distinct themes: Finest Power (power hitters and pitchers), Finest Masters (top players), Finest Blue Chips (top new players), Finest Competitors (hottest players), and Finest Acquisitions (latest trades and new signings). All five themes of each series have common cards (1-100 and 176-275) designated with bronze trim, uncommon (101-150 and 276-325) with silver trim and an insertion rate of one in four for both series, and rare (151-175 and 326-350) with gold trim and an insertion rate of one in 24 for both series. The cards are numbered on the backs within the whole set and within the theme set. Notable Rookie Cards include Brian Giles.

COMP.BRONZE SER.1 (100)	12.50	30.00
COMP.BRONZE SER.2 (100)	12.50	30.00
COM.BRON.(1-100/176-275)	.20	.50
COMP.SILVER SER.1 (50)		
COMP.SILVER SER.2 (50)		
COM.SILV.(101-150/276-325)	.75	2.00
COMP.GOLD SER.1 (25)		
COMP.GOLD SER.2 (25)		
COM.GOLD (151-175/326-350)	2.00	5.00
BICHETTE/JETER BOTH NUMBERED 155		
BICHETTE UER SHOULD BE NUMBER 5		
1 Barry Bonds B	1.25	3.00
2 Ryne Sandberg B	.75	2.00
3 Brian Jordan B	.20	.50
4 Rocky Coppinger B	.20	.50
5 Dante Bichette B UER	.20	.50
Card is erroneously numbered 155		
6 Al Martin B	.20	.50
7 Charles Nagy B	.20	.50
8 Otis Nixon B	.20	.50
9 Mark Johnson B	.20	.50
10 Jeff Bagwell B	.30	.75
11 Ken Hill B	.20	.50
12 Willie Adams B	.20	.50
13 Raul Mondesi B	.20	.50
14 Reggie Sanders B	.20	.50
15 Derek Jeter B	1.25	3.00
16 Jermaine Dye B	.20	.50
17 Edgar Renteria B	.20	.50
18 Travis Fryman B	.20	.50
19 Roberto Hernandez B	.20	.50
20 Sammy Sosa B	.50	1.25
21 Garret Anderson B	.20	.50
22 Rey Ordonez B	.20	.50
23 Glenallen Hill B	.20	.50
24 Dave Nilsson B	.20	.50
25 Kevin Brown B	.20	.50
26 Brian McRae B	.20	.50
27 Joey Hamilton B	.20	.50
28 Jamey Wright B	.20	.50
29 Frank Thomas B	.50	1.25
30 Mark McGwire B	1.25	3.00
31 Ramon Martinez B	.20	.50
32 Jaime Bluma B	.20	.50
33 Frank Rodriguez B	.20	.50
34 Andy Benes B	.20	.50
35 Jay Buhner B	.20	.50
36 Justin Thompson B	.20	.50
37 Darin Erstad B	.20	.50
38 Gregg Jefferies B	.20	.50
39 Jeff D'Amico B	.20	.50
40 Pedro Martinez B	.30	.75
41 Nomar Garciaparra B	.75	2.00
42 Jose Valentin B	.20	.50
43 Pat Hentgen B	.20	.50
44 Will Clark B	.30	.75
45 Bernie Williams B	.30	.75
46 Luis Castillo B	.20	.50
47 B.J. Surhoff B	.20	.50
48 Greg Gagne B	.20	.50
49 Pete Schourek B	.20	.50
50 Mike Piazza B	.75	2.00
51 Dwight Gooden B	.20	.50
52 Javy Lopez B	.20	.50
53 Chuck Finley B	.20	.50
54 James Baldwin B	.20	.50
55 Jack McDowell B	.20	.50
56 Royce Clayton B	.20	.50
57 Carlos Delgado B	.20	.50
58 Neifi Perez B	.20	.50
59 Eddie Taubensee B	.20	.50
60 Rafael Palmeiro B	.30	.75
61 Marty Cordova B	.20	.50
62 Wade Boggs B	.30	.75
63 Rickey Henderson B	.50	1.25
64 Mike Hampton B	.20	.50
65 Troy Percival B	.20	.50
66 Barry Larkin B	.30	.75
67 J.Allensworth B	.20	.50
68 Mark Clark B	.20	.50
69 Mike Lansing B	.20	.50
70 Mark Grudzielanek B	.20	.50
71 Todd Stottlemyre B	.20	.50
72 Juan Guzman B	.20	.50
73 John Burkett B	.20	.50
74 Wilson Alvarez B	.20	.50
75 Ellis Burks B	.20	.50
76 Bobby Higginson B	.20	.50
77 Ricky Bottalico B	.20	.50
78 Omar Vizquel B	.30	.75
79 Paul Sorrento B	.20	.50
80 Denny Neagle B	.20	.50
81 Roger Pavlik B	.20	.50
82 Mike Lieberthal B	.20	.50
83 Devon White B	.20	.50
84 John Olerud B	.20	.50
85 Kevin Appier B	.20	.50
86 Joe Girardi B	.20	.50
87 Paul O'Neill B	.30	.75
88 Mike Sweeney B	.20	.50
89 John Smiley B	.20	.50
90 Ivan Rodriguez B	.30	.75
91 Randy Myers B	.20	.50
92 Bip Roberts B	.20	.50
93 Jose Mesa B	.20	.50
94 Paul Wilson B	.20	.50
95 Mike Mussina B	.30	.75
96 Ben McDonald B	.20	.50
97 John Mabry B	.20	.50
98 Tom Goodwin B	.20	.50
99 Edgar Martinez B	.30	.75
100 Andruw Jones B	.30	.75
101 Jose Canseco S	1.25	3.00
102 Billy Wagner S	.75	2.00
103 Dante Bichette S	.75	2.00
104 Curt Schilling S	.75	2.00
105 Dean Palmer S	.75	2.00
106 Larry Walker S	.75	2.00
107 Bernie Williams S	1.25	3.00
108 Chipper Jones S	2.00	5.00
109 Gary Sheffield S	.75	2.00
110 Randy Johnson S	2.00	5.00
111 Roberto Alomar S	1.25	3.00
112 Todd Walker S	.75	2.00
113 Sandy Alomar Jr. S	.75	2.00
114 John Jaha S	.75	2.00
115 Ken Caminiti S UER	.75	2.00
Card is numbered 135		
116 Ryan Klesko S	.75	2.00
117 Mariano Rivera S	2.00	5.00
118 Jason Giambi S	.75	2.00
119 Lance Johnson S	.75	2.00
120 Robin Ventura S	.75	2.00
121 Todd Hollandsworth S	.75	2.00
122 Johnny Damon S	1.25	3.00
123 W. VanLandingham S	.75	2.00
124 Jason Kendall S	.75	2.00
125 Vinny Castilla S	.75	2.00
126 Harold Baines S	.75	2.00
127 Joe Carter S	.75	2.00
128 Craig Biggio S	1.25	3.00
129 Tony Clark S	.75	2.00
130 Ron Gant S	.75	2.00
131 David Segui S	.75	2.00
132 Steve Trachsel S	.75	2.00
133 Scott Rolen S	1.25	3.00
134 Mike Stanley S	.75	2.00
135 Cal Ripken S	6.00	15.00
136 John Smoltz S	1.25	3.00
137 Bobby Jones S	.75	2.00
138 Manny Ramirez S	1.25	3.00
139 Ken Griffey Jr. S	3.00	8.00
140 Chuck Knoblauch S	.75	2.00
141 Mark Grace S	1.25	3.00
142 Chris Snopek S	.75	2.00
143 Hideo Nomo S	2.00	5.00
144 Tim Salmon S	1.25	3.00
145 David Cone S	.75	2.00
146 Eric Young S	.75	2.00
147 Jeff Brantley S	.75	2.00
148 Jim Thome S	1.25	3.00
149 Trevor Hoffman S	.75	2.00
150 Juan Gonzalez S	.75	2.00
151 Mike Piazza G	8.00	20.00
152 Ivan Rodriguez G	3.00	8.00
153 Mo Vaughn G	2.00	5.00
154 Brady Anderson G	2.00	5.00
155 Mark McGwire G	12.50	30.00
156 Rafael Palmeiro G	3.00	8.00
157 Barry Larkin G	3.00	8.00
158 Greg Maddux G	8.00	20.00
159 Jeff Bagwell G	3.00	8.00
160 Frank Thomas G	5.00	12.00
161 Ken Caminiti G	2.00	5.00
162 Andruw Jones G	3.00	8.00
163 Dennis Eckersley G	2.00	5.00
164 Jeff Conine G	2.00	5.00
165 Jim Edmonds G	2.00	5.00
166 Derek Jeter G	12.50	30.00
167 Vladimir Guerrero G	5.00	12.00
168 Sammy Sosa G	5.00	12.00
169 Tony Gwynn G	6.00	15.00
170 Andres Galarraga G	2.00	5.00
171 Todd Hundley G	2.00	5.00
172 Jay Buhner G UER	2.00	5.00
Card is numbered 164		
173 Paul Molitor G	2.00	5.00
174 Kenny Lofton G	2.00	5.00
175 Barry Bonds G	12.50	30.00
176 Gary Sheffield B	.20	.50
177 Dmitri Young B	.20	.50
178 Jay Bell B	.20	.50
179 David Wells B	.20	.50
180 Walt Weiss B	.20	.50
181 Paul Molitor B	.20	.50
182 Jose Guillen B	.20	.50
183 Al Leiter B	.20	.50
184 Mike Fetters B	.20	.50
185 Mark Langston B	.20	.50
186 Fred McGriff B	.30	.75
187 Darrin Fletcher B	.20	.50
188 Brant Brown B	.20	.50
189 Geronimo Berroa B	.20	.50
190 Jim Thome B	.30	.75
191 Jose Vizcaino B	.20	.50
192 Andy Ashby B	.20	.50
193 Rusty Greer B	.20	.50
194 Brian Hunter B	.20	.50
195 Chris Hoiles B	.20	.50
196 Orlando Merced B	.20	.50
197 Brett Butler B	.20	.50
198 Derek Bell B	.20	.50
199 Bobby Bonilla B	.20	.50
200 Alex Ochoa B	.20	.50
201 Wally Joyner B	.20	.50
202 Mo Vaughn B	.20	.50
203 Doug Drabek B	.20	.50
204 Tino Martinez B	.30	.75
205 Roberto Alomar B	.30	.75
206 Brian Giles B RC	1.25	3.00
207 Todd Worrell B	.20	.50
208 Alan Benes B	.20	.50
209 Jim Leyritz B	.20	.50
210 Darryl Hamilton B	.20	.50
211 Jimmy Key B	.20	.50
212 Juan Gonzalez B	.20	.50
213 Vinny Castilla B	.20	.50
214 Chuck Knoblauch B	.20	.50
215 Tony Phillips B	.20	.50
216 Jeff Cirillo B	.20	.50
217 Carlos Garcia B	.20	.50
218 Brooks Kieschnick B	.20	.50
219 Marquis Grissom B	.20	.50
220 Dan Wilson B	.20	.50
221 Greg Vaughn B	.20	.50
222 John Wetteland B	.20	.50
223 Andres Galarraga B	.20	.50
224 Ozzie Guillen B	.20	.50
225 Kevin Elster B	.20	.50
226 Bernard Gilkey B	.20	.50
227 Mike Macfarlane B	.20	.50
228 Heathcliff Slocumb B	.20	.50
229 Wendell Magee Jr. B	.20	.50
230 Carlos Baerga B	.20	.50
231 Kevin Seitzer B	.20	.50
232 Henry Rodriguez B	.20	.50
233 Roger Clemens B	1.00	2.50
234 Mark Wohlers B	.20	.50
235 Eddie Murray B	.50	1.25
236 Todd Zeile B	.20	.50
237 J.T. Snow B	.20	.50
238 Ken Griffey Jr. B	.75	2.00
239 Sterling Hitchcock B	.20	.50
240 Albert Belle B	.20	.50
241 Terry Steinbach B	.20	.50
242 Robb Nen B	.20	.50
243 Mark McLemore B	.20	.50
244 Jeff King B	.20	.50
245 Tony Clark B	.20	.50
246 Tim Salmon B	.30	.75
247 Benito Santiago B	.20	.50
248 Robin Ventura B	.20	.50
249 Bubba Trammell B RC	.20	.50
250 Chili Davis B	.20	.50
251 John Valentin B	.20	.50
252 Cal Ripken B	1.50	4.00
253 Matt Williams B	.20	.50
254 Jeff Kent B	.20	.50
255 Eric Karros B	.20	.50
256 Ray Lankford B	.20	.50
257 Ed Sprague B	.20	.50
258 Shane Reynolds B	.20	.50
259 Jaime Navarro B	.20	.50
260 Eric Davis B	.20	.50
261 Orel Hershiser B	.20	.50
262 Mark Grace B	.30	.75
263 Rod Beck B	.20	.50
264 Ismael Valdes B	.20	.50
265 Manny Ramirez B	.30	.75
266 Ken Caminiti B	.20	.50
267 Tim Naehring B	.20	.50
268 Jose Rosado B	.20	.50
269 Greg Colbrunn B	.20	.50
270 Dean Palmer B	.20	.50
271 David Justice B	.20	.50
272 Scott Spiezio B	.20	.50
273 Chipper Jones B	.50	1.25
274 Mel Rojas B	.20	.50
275 Bartolo Colon B	.20	.50
276 Darin Erstad S	.75	2.00
277 Sammy Sosa S	2.00	5.00
278 Rafael Palmeiro S	1.25	3.00
279 Frank Thomas S	2.00	5.00
280 Ruben Rivera S	.75	2.00
281 Hal Morris S	.75	2.00
282 Jay Buhner S	.75	2.00
283 Kenny Lofton S	.75	2.00
284 Jose Canseco S	1.25	3.00
285 Alex Fernandez S	.75	2.00
286 Todd Helton S	2.00	5.00
287 Andy Pettitte S	1.25	3.00
288 John Franco S	.75	2.00
289 Ivan Rodriguez S	1.25	3.00
290 Ellis Burks S	.75	2.00
291 Julio Franco S	.75	2.00
292 Mike Piazza S	3.00	8.00
293 Brian Jordan S	.75	2.00
294 Greg Maddux S	3.00	8.00
295 Bob Abreu S	1.25	3.00
296 Rondell White S	.75	2.00
297 Moises Alou S	.75	2.00
298 Tony Gwynn S	2.50	6.00
299 Deion Sanders S	1.25	3.00
300 Jeff Montgomery S	.75	2.00
301 Ray Durham S	.75	2.00
302 John Wasdin S	.75	2.00
303 Ryne Sandberg S	3.00	8.00
304 Delino DeShields S	.75	2.00
305 Mark McGwire S	5.00	12.00
306 Andruw Jones S	1.25	3.00
307 Kevin Orie S	.75	2.00
308 Matt Williams S	.75	2.00
309 Karim Garcia S	.75	2.00
310 Derek Jeter S	5.00	12.00
311 Mo Vaughn S	.75	2.00
312 Brady Anderson S	.75	2.00
313 Barry Bonds S	5.00	12.00
314 Steve Finley S	.75	2.00
315 Vladimir Guerrero S	2.00	5.00
316 Matt Morris S	.75	2.00
317 Tom Glavine S	1.25	3.00
318 Jeff Bagwell S	1.25	3.00
319 Albert Belle S	.75	2.00
320 Hideki Irabu S RC	.75	2.00
321 Andres Galarraga S	.75	2.00
322 Cecil Fielder S	.75	2.00
323 Barry Larkin S	1.25	3.00
324 Todd Hundley S	.75	2.00
325 Fred McGriff S	1.25	3.00
326 Gary Sheffield G	3.00	8.00
327 Craig Biggio G	3.00	8.00
328 Raul Mondesi G	2.00	5.00
329 Edgar Martinez G	3.00	8.00
330 Chipper Jones G	5.00	12.00
331 Bernie Williams G	3.00	8.00
332 Juan Gonzalez G	2.00	5.00
333 Ron Gant G	2.00	5.00
334 Cal Ripken G	15.00	40.00
335 Larry Walker G	2.00	5.00
336 Matt Williams G	2.00	5.00
337 Jose Cruz Jr. G RC	2.00	5.00
338 Joe Carter G	2.00	5.00
339 Wilton Guerrero G	2.00	5.00
340 Cecil Fielder G	2.00	5.00
341 Todd Walker G	2.00	5.00
342 Ken Griffey Jr. G	8.00	20.00
343 Ryan Klesko G	2.00	5.00
344 Roger Clemens G	10.00	25.00
345 Hideo Nomo G	5.00	12.00
346 Dante Bichette G	2.00	5.00
347 Albert Belle G	2.00	5.00
348 Randy Johnson G	5.00	12.00
349 Manny Ramirez G	3.00	8.00
350 John Smoltz G	3.00	8.00

1997 Finest Embossed

This 150-card set is parallel to regular set numbers 101-175 of Finest Series 1 and 276-350 of Finest Series 2. There is an embossed version of cards 101-150 and 276-325 with an insertion rate of one in 16 for each series. There is an embossed die-cut version of cards 151-175 and 326-350 with an insertion rate of one in 96 packs for each series.

*SILV.STARS: .60X TO 1.5X BASIC CARD
*SILVER ROOKIES: .5X TO 1.25X BASIC
SILVER STATED ODDS 1:16
*GOLD STARS: .75X TO 2X BASIC CARD
*GOLD ROOKIES: .5X TO 1.2X BASIC CARD
GOLD STATED ODDS 1:96

1997 Finest Embossed Refractors

This 150-card set is a parallel version of the regular Finest Embossed set and is similar in design. The difference is found in the refractive quality of the cards.

*SILVER STARS: 2.5X TO 6X BASIC CARDS
*SILVER ROOKIES: 2X TO 5X BASIC CARDS
SILVER STATED ODDS 1:192
*SER.1 GOLD STARS: 2X TO 5X BASIC
*SER.2 GOLD STARS: 2X TO 5X BASIC
*SER.2 GOLD RC'S: 1.25X TO 3X BASIC
GOLD STATED ODDS 1:1152

1997 Finest Refractors

This 350-card set is parallel and similar in design to the regular Finest set. The distinction is in the refractive quality of the card. Cards 1-100 and 176-275 have an insertion rate of one in 12 in each series packs. Cards 101-150 and 276-325 have an insertion rate of one in 48 in each series packs. Cards 151-175 and 326-350 have an insertion rate of one in 288.

*BRONZE STARS: 4X TO 10X BASIC CARD
*BRONZE RC'S: 1.25X TO 3X BASIC CARD
BRONZE STATED ODDS 1:12
*SILVER STARS: 1.25X TO 3X BASIC CARD
*SILVER ROOKIES: 1X TO 2.5X BASIC CARD
SILVER STATED ODDS 1:48
*GOLD STARS: 1.25X TO 3X BASIC CARD
*GOLD ROOKIES: .75X TO 2X BASIC CARD
GOLD STATED ODDS 1:288

1998 Finest

This 275-card set (produced by Topps) was distributed in first and second series six-card packs with a suggested retail price of $5. Series one contains cards 1-150 and series two contains cards 151-275. Each card features action color player photos printed on 26 pt. card stock with each position identified by a different card design. The backs carry player information and career statistics.

COMPLETE SET (275)	20.00	50.00
COMP.SERIES 1 (150)	10.00	25.00
COMP.SERIES 2 (125)	10.00	25.00
1 Larry Walker	.15	.40
2 Andruw Jones	.25	.60
3 Ramon Martinez	.08	.25
4 Geronimo Berroa	.08	.25
5 David Justice	.15	.40
6 Rusty Greer	.15	.40
7 Chad Ogea	.08	.25
8 Tom Goodwin	.08	.25
9 Tino Martinez	.25	.60
10 Jose Guillen	.15	.40
11 Jeffrey Hammonds	.08	.25
12 Brian McRae	.08	.25
13 Jeremi Gonzalez	.08	.25
14 Craig Counsell	.08	.25
15 Mike Piazza	.60	1.50
16 Greg Maddux	.60	1.50
17 Todd Greene	.08	.25
18 Rondell White	.15	.40
19 Kirk Rueter	.08	.25
20 Tony Clark	.08	.25
21 Brad Radke	.15	.40
22 Jaret Wright	.08	.25
23 Carlos Delgado	.15	.40
24 Dustin Hermanson	.08	.25
25 Gary Sheffield	.15	.40
26 Jose Canseco	.25	.60
27 Kevin Young	.15	.40
28 David Wells	.15	.40
29 Mariano Rivera	.40	1.00
30 Reggie Sanders	.15	.40
31 Mike Cameron	.08	.25
32 Bobby Witt	.08	.25
33 Kevin Orie	.08	.25
34 Royce Clayton	.08	.25
35 Edgar Martinez	.25	.60
36 Neifi Perez	.08	.25
37 Kevin Appier	.15	.40
38 Darryl Hamilton	.08	.25
39 Michael Tucker	.08	.25
40 Roger Clemens	.75	2.00
41 Carl Everett	.15	.40
42 Mike Sweeney	.15	.40
43 Pat Meares	.08	.25
44 Brian Giles	.15	.40
45 Matt Morris	.15	.40
46 Jason Dickson	.08	.25
47 Rich Loiselle RC	.15	.40
48 Joe Girardi	.08	.25
49 Steve Trachsel	.08	.25
50 Ben Grieve	.08	.25
51 Brian Johnson	.08	.25
52 Hideki Irabu	.08	.25
53 J.T. Snow	.15	.40
54 Mike Hampton	.15	.40
55 Dave Nilsson	.08	.25
56 Alex Fernandez	.08	.25
57 Brett Tomko	.08	.25
58 Wally Joyner	.15	.40
59 Kelvim Escobar	.08	.25
60 Roberto Alomar	.25	.60
61 Todd Jones	.08	.25
62 Paul O'Neill	.25	.60
63 Jamie Moyer	.15	.40
64 Mark Wohlers	.08	.25
65 Jose Cruz Jr.	.08	.25
66 Troy Percival	.15	.40
67 Rick Reed	.08	.25
68 Will Clark	.25	.60
69 Jamey Wright	.08	.25
70 Mike Mussina	.25	.60
71 David Cone	.15	.40
72 Ryan Klesko	.15	.40
73 Scott Hatteberg	.08	.25
74 James Baldwin	.08	.25
75 Tony Womack	.08	.25
76 Carlos Perez	.08	.25
77 Charles Nagy	.08	.25
78 Jeromy Burnitz	.15	.40
79 Shane Reynolds	.08	.25
80 Cliff Floyd	.15	.40
81 Jason Kendall	.15	.40
82 Chad Curtis	.08	.25
83 Matt Karchner	.08	.25
84 Ricky Bottalico	.08	.25
85 Sammy Sosa	.40	1.00
86 Javy Lopez	.15	.40
87 Jeff Kent	.15	.40
88 Shawn Green	.15	.40
89 Joey Cora	.08	.25
90 Tony Gwynn	.50	1.25
91 Bob Tewksbury	.08	.25
92 Derek Jeter	1.00	2.50
93 Eric Davis	.15	.40
94 Jeff Fassero	.08	.25
95 Denny Neagle	.08	.25
96 Ismael Valdes	.08	.25
97 Tim Salmon	.25	.60
98 Mark Grudzielanek	.08	.25
99 Curt Schilling	.15	.40
100 Ken Griffey Jr.	.60	1.50
101 Edgardo Alfonzo	.08	.25
102 Vinny Castilla	.15	.40
103 Jose Rosado	.08	.25
104 Scott Erickson	.08	.25
105 Alan Benes	.08	.25
106 Shannon Stewart	.15	.40
107 Delino DeShields	.08	.25
108 Mark Loretta	.08	.25
109 Todd Hundley	.08	.25
110 Chuck Knoblauch	.15	.40
111 Todd Helton	.25	.60
112 F.P. Santangelo	.08	.25
113 Jeff Cirillo	.08	.25
114 Omar Vizquel	.25	.60
115 John Valentin	.08	.25
116 Damion Easley	.08	.25
117 Matt Lawton	.08	.25
118 Jim Thome	.25	.60
119 Sandy Alomar Jr.	.08	.25
120 Albert Belle	.15	.40
121 Chris Stynes	.08	.25
122 Butch Huskey	.08	.25
123 Shawn Estes	.08	.25
124 Terry Adams	.08	.25
125 Ivan Rodriguez	.25	.60
126 Ron Gant	.15	.40
127 John Mabry	.08	.25
128 Jeff Shaw	.08	.25
129 Jeff Montgomery	.08	.25
130 Justin Thompson	.08	.25
131 Livan Hernandez	.15	.40
132 Ugueth Urbina	.08	.25
133 Scott Servais	.08	.25
134 Troy O'Leary	.08	.25
135 Cal Ripken	1.25	3.00
136 Quilvio Veras	.08	.25
137 Pedro Astacio	.08	.25
138 Willie Greene	.08	.25
139 Lance Johnson	.08	.25
140 Nomar Garciaparra	.60	1.50
141 Jose Offerman	.08	.25
142 Scott Rolen	.25	.60
143 Derek Bell	.08	.25
144 Johnny Damon	.25	.60
145 Mark McGwire	1.00	2.50
146 Chan Ho Park	.15	.40
147 Edgar Renteria	.15	.40
148 Eric Young	.08	.25
149 Craig Biggio	.25	.60
150 Checklist (1-150)	.08	.25
151 Frank Thomas	.40	1.00
152 John Wetteland	.15	.40
153 Mike Lansing	.08	.25
154 Pedro Martinez	.25	.60
155 Rico Brogna	.08	.25
156 Kevin Brown	.25	.60
157 Alex Rodriguez	.60	1.50
158 Wade Boggs	.25	.60
159 Richard Hidalgo	.08	.25
160 Mark Grace	.25	.60
161 Jose Mesa	.08	.25
162 John Olerud	.15	.40
163 Tim Belcher	.08	.25
164 Chuck Finley	.15	.40
165 Brian Hunter	.08	.25
166 Joe Carter	.15	.40
167 Stan Javier	.08	.25
168 Jay Bell	.15	.40
169 Ray Lankford	.15	.40
170 John Smoltz	.25	.60
171 Ed Sprague	.08	.25
172 Jason Giambi	.15	.40
173 Todd Walker	.08	.25
174 Paul Konerko	.15	.40
175 Rey Ordonez	.08	.25
176 Dante Bichette	.15	.40
177 Bernie Williams	.25	.60
178 Jon Nunnally	.08	.25
179 Rafael Palmeiro	.25	.60
180 Jay Buhner	.15	.40
181 Devon White	.15	.40
182 Jeff D'Amico	.08	.25
183 Walt Weiss	.15	.40
184 Scott Spiezio	.08	.25
185 Moises Alou	.15	.40
186 Carlos Baerga	.08	.25
187 Todd Zeile	.15	.40
188 Gregg Jefferies	.08	.25
189 Mo Vaughn	.15	.40
190 Terry Steinbach	.08	.25
191 Ray Durham	.15	.40
192 Robin Ventura	.15	.40
193 Jeff Reed	.08	.25
194 Ken Caminiti	.15	.40
195 Eric Karros	.15	.40
196 Wilson Alvarez	.08	.25
197 Gary Gaetti	.15	.40
198 Andres Galarraga	.15	.40
199 Alex Gonzalez	.08	.25
200 Garret Anderson	.15	.40
201 Andy Benes	.15	.40
202 Harold Baines	.15	.40
203 Ron Coomer	.08	.25
204 Dean Palmer	.15	.40
205 Reggie Jefferson	.08	.25
206 John Burkett	.08	.25
207 Jermaine Allensworth	.08	.25
208 Bernard Gilkey	.08	.25
209 Jeff Bagwell	.25	.60
210 Kenny Lofton	.15	.40
211 Bobby Jones	.08	.25
212 Bartolo Colon	.15	.40
213 Jim Edmonds	.15	.40
214 Pat Hentgen	.08	.25
215 Matt Williams	.15	.40
216 Bob Abreu	.15	.40
217 Jorge Posada	.25	.60
218 Marty Cordova	.08	.25
219 Ken Hill	.08	.25
220 Steve Finley	.15	.40
221 Jeff King	.08	.25
222 Quinton McCracken	.08	.25
223 Matt Stairs	.08	.25
224 Darin Erstad	.15	.40
225 Fred McGriff	.25	.60
226 Marquis Grissom	.15	.40
227 Doug Glanville	.08	.25
228 Tom Glavine	.25	.60
229 John Franco	.15	.40
230 Darren Bragg	.08	.25
231 Barry Larkin	.25	.60
232 Trevor Hoffman	.15	.40
233 Brady Anderson	.15	.40
234 Al Martin	.08	.25
235 B.J. Surhoff	.15	.40
236 Ellis Burks	.15	.40
237 Randy Johnson	.40	1.00
238 Mark Clark	.08	.25
239 Tony Saunders	.08	.25
240 Hideo Nomo	.40	1.00
241 Brad Fullmer	.08	.25
242 Chipper Jones	.40	1.00
243 Jose Valentin	.08	.25
244 Manny Ramirez	.25	.60
245 Derrek Lee	.25	.60
246 Jimmy Key	.15	.40
247 Tim Naehring	.08	.25
248 Bobby Higginson	.15	.40
249 Charles Johnson	.15	.40
250 Chili Davis	.15	.40
251 Tom Gordon	.08	.25
252 Mike Lieberthal	.15	.40
253 Billy Wagner	.15	.40
254 Juan Guzman	.08	.25
255 Todd Stottlemyre	.08	.25
256 Brian Jordan	.15	.40
257 Barry Bonds	1.00	2.50
258 Dan Wilson	.08	.25
259 Paul Molitor	.15	.40
260 Juan Gonzalez	.15	.40
261 Francisco Cordova	.08	.25
262 Cecil Fielder	.15	.40
263 Travis Lee	.08	.25
264 Kevin Tapani	.08	.25
265 Raul Mondesi	.15	.40
266 Travis Fryman	.15	.40
267 Armando Benitez	.08	.25
268 Pokey Reese	.08	.25
269 Rick Aguilera	.08	.25
270 Andy Pettitte	.25	.60
271 Jose Vizcaino	.08	.25
272 Kerry Wood	.20	.50
273 Vladimir Guerrero	.40	1.00
274 John Smiley	.08	.25
275 Checklist (151-275)	.08	.25

1998 Finest No-Protectors

Randomly inserted in retail packs at the rate of one in two and one in every HTA pack, this 275-card set is parallel to the base set only without the Finest Protector covering and features double-sided Finest technology.

COMPLETE SET (275)	175.00	350.00
COMP. SERIES 1 (150)	100.00	200.00
COMP. SERIES 2 (125)	75.00	150.00

*STARS: 2X TO 4X BASIC CARDS
STATED ODDS 1:2, 1 PER HTA

1998 Finest Oversize

These sixteen 3" by 5" cards were inserted one every three hobby boxes. Though not actually on the cards, first series cards have been assigned an A prefix and second series a B prefix to clarify our listing. The cards are parallel to the regular Finest cards except numbering "of 8". They were issued as chiptoppers in the boxes.

COMPLETE SERIES 1 (8)	50.00	120.00
COMPLETE SERIES 2 (8)	30.00	80.00
STATED ODDS 1:3 HOBBY/HTA BOXES		
*REFRACTORS: .75X TO 2X BASIC OVERSIZE		
REF.ODDS 1:6 HOBBY/HTA BOXES		
A1 Mark McGwire	6.00	15.00
A2 Cal Ripken	8.00	20.00
A3 Nomar Garciaparra	4.00	10.00
A4 Mike Piazza	4.00	10.00
A5 Greg Maddux	4.00	10.00
A6 Jose Cruz Jr.	.60	1.50
A7 Roger Clemens	5.00	12.00
A8 Ken Griffey Jr.	4.00	10.00
B1 Frank Thomas	2.50	6.00
B2 Bernie Williams	1.50	4.00
B3 Randy Johnson	2.50	6.00
B4 Chipper Jones	2.50	6.00
B5 Manny Ramirez	1.50	4.00
B6 Barry Bonds	6.00	15.00
B7 Juan Gonzalez	1.00	2.50
B8 Jeff Bagwell	1.50	4.00

1998 Finest Refractors

Randomly inserted in retail packs at the rate of one in 12 and in HTA packs at the rate of one in five, this 275-card set is parallel to the base set. The difference is found in the refractive quality of the card.

*STARS: 5X TO 12X BASIC CARDS
STATED ODDS 1:12, 1:5 HTA
NO-PROTECTOR REF.ODDS 1:24, 1:10 HTA

1998 Finest Centurions

Randomly inserted in Series one hobby packs at a rate of 1:153 and Home Team Advantage packs at a rate of 1:71, cards from this 20-card set feature action color photos of top players who will lead the game into the next century. Each card is sequentially numbered on back to 500. Unfortunately, an unknown quantity of unnumbered Centurions made their way into the secondary market in 1999. It's believed that these cards were quality control extras. To further compound this situation, some unscrupulous parties attempted to serial-number the cards. The fake cards have flat gold foil numbering. The real cards have bright foil numbering.

COMPLETE SET (20)	40.00	100.00
SER.1 ODDS 1:153 HOBBY, 1:71 HTA		
*REF: 2X TO 5X BASIC CENTURIONS		
SER.1 REF.ODDS 1:1020 HOBBY, 1:471 HTA		
REFRACTOR PR.RUN 75 SERIAL #'d SETS		
C1 Andruw Jones	1.25	3.00
C2 Vladimir Guerrero	2.00	5.00
C3 Nomar Garciaparra	3.00	8.00
C4 Scott Rolen	1.25	3.00
C5 Ken Griffey Jr.	3.00	8.00
C6 Jose Cruz Jr.	.50	1.25
C7 Barry Bonds	5.00	12.00
C8 Mark McGwire	5.00	12.00
C9 Juan Gonzalez	.75	2.00
C10 Jeff Bagwell	1.25	3.00
C11 Frank Thomas	2.00	5.00
C12 Paul Konerko	.75	2.00
C13 Alex Rodriguez	3.00	8.00
C14 Mike Piazza	3.00	8.00
C15 Travis Lee	.50	1.25
C16 Chipper Jones	2.00	5.00
C17 Larry Walker	.75	2.00
C18 Mo Vaughn	.75	2.00
C19 Livan Hernandez	.75	2.00
C20 Jaret Wright	.50	1.25

1998 Finest The Man

Randomly inserted in packs at a rate of one in 119, this 20-card set is an insert to the 1998 Finest base set. The entire set is sequentially numbered to 500.

COMPLETE SET (20)	150.00	400.00
SER.2 STATED ODDS 1:119		
*REF: 1X TO 2.5X BASIC THE MAN		
REF.SER.2 ODDS 1:793		
REFRACTOR PR.RUN 75 SERIAL #'d SETS		
TM1 Ken Griffey Jr.	10.00	25.00
TM2 Barry Bonds	15.00	40.00
TM3 Frank Thomas	6.00	15.00
TM4 Chipper Jones	6.00	15.00
TM5 Cal Ripken	20.00	50.00
TM6 Nomar Garciaparra	10.00	25.00
TM7 Mark McGwire	15.00	40.00
TM8 Mike Piazza	10.00	25.00
TM9 Derek Jeter	15.00	40.00
TM10 Alex Rodriguez	10.00	25.00
TM11 Jose Cruz Jr.	1.50	4.00
TM12 Larry Walker	2.50	6.00
TM13 Jeff Bagwell	4.00	10.00
TM14 Tony Gwynn	8.00	20.00
TM15 Travis Lee	1.50	4.00
TM16 Juan Gonzalez	2.50	6.00
TM17 Scott Rolen	4.00	10.00
TM18 Randy Johnson	6.00	15.00
TM19 Roger Clemens	12.50	30.00
TM20 Greg Maddux	10.00	25.00

1998 Finest Mystery Finest 1

Randomly inserted in first series hobby packs at the rate of one in 36 and Home Team Advantage packs at the rate of one in 15, cards from this 50-card set feature color action photos of 20 top players on double-sided cards. Each player is matched with three different players on the opposite side or another photo of himself. Each side is covered with the Finest opaque protector.

SER.1 ODDS 1:36 HOBBY, 1:15 HTA		
*REFRACTOR: 1X TO 2.5X BASIC MYSTERY		
REF.SER.1 ODDS 1:144 HOBBY, 1:64 HTA		
M1 Frank Thomas Ken Griffey Jr.	6.00	15.00
M2 Frank Thomas Mike Piazza	4.00	10.00
M3 Frank Thomas Mark McGwire	10.00	25.00
M4 Frank Thomas Frank Thomas	4.00	10.00
M5 Ken Griffey Jr. Mike Piazza	6.00	15.00
M6 Ken Griffey Jr. Mark McGwire	10.00	25.00
M7 Ken Griffey Jr. Ken Griffey Jr.	6.00	15.00
M8 Mike Piazza Mark McGwire	10.00	25.00
M9 Mike Piazza Mike Piazza	8.00	20.00
M10 Mark McGwire Mark McGwire	12.50	30.00
M11 Nomar Garciaparra Jose Cruz Jr.	6.00	15.00
M12 Nomar Garciaparra Derek Jeter	8.00	20.00
M13 Nomar Garciaparra Andruw Jones	6.00	15.00
M14 Nomar Garciaparra Nomar Garciaparra	8.00	20.00
M15 Jose Cruz Jr. Derek Jeter	10.00	25.00
M16 Jose Cruz Jr. Andruw Jones	2.50	6.00
M17 Jose Cruz Jr. Jose Cruz Jr.	1.50	4.00
M18 Derek Jeter Andruw Jones	10.00	25.00
M19 Derek Jeter Derek Jeter	12.50	30.00
M20 Andruw Jones Andruw Jones	2.50	6.00
M21 Cal Ripken Tony Gwynn	10.00	25.00
M22 Cal Ripken Barry Bonds	12.50	30.00
M23 Cal Ripken Greg Maddux	12.50	30.00
M24 Cal Ripken Cal Ripken	15.00	40.00
M25 Tony Gwynn Barry Bonds	12.50	30.00
M26 Tony Gwynn Greg Maddux	6.00	15.00
M27 Tony Gwynn Tony Gwynn	6.00	15.00
M28 Barry Bonds Greg Maddux	12.50	30.00
M29 Barry Bonds Barry Bonds	12.50	30.00
M30 Greg Maddux Greg Maddux	8.00	20.00
M31 Juan Gonzalez Larry Walker	1.50	4.00
M32 Juan Gonzalez Andres Galarraga	1.50	4.00
M33 Juan Gonzalez Chipper Jones	4.00	10.00
M34 Juan Gonzalez Juan Gonzalez	1.50	4.00
M35 Larry Walker Andres Galarraga	1.50	4.00
M36 Larry Walker Chipper Jones	4.00	10.00
M37 Larry Walker Larry Walker	1.50	4.00
M38 Andres Galarraga Chipper Jones	4.00	10.00
M39 Andres Galarraga Andres Galarraga	1.50	4.00
M40 Chipper Jones Chipper Jones	4.00	10.00
M41 Gary Sheffield Sammy Sosa	4.00	10.00
M42 Gary Sheffield Jeff Bagwell	2.50	6.00
M43 Gary Sheffield Tino Martinez	2.50	6.00
M44 Gary Sheffield Gary Sheffield	1.50	4.00
M45 Sammy Sosa Jeff Bagwell	8.00	20.00
M46 Sammy Sosa Tino Martinez	4.00	10.00
M47 Sammy Sosa Sammy Sosa	4.00	10.00
M48 Jeff Bagwell Tino Martinez	2.50	6.00
M49 Jeff Bagwell Jeff Bagwell	2.50	6.00
M50 Tino Martinez Tino Martinez	2.50	6.00

1998 Finest Mystery Finest 2

Randomly inserted in second series hobby packs at the rate of one in 36 and Home Team Advantage packs at the rate of one in 15, cards from this 50-card set feature color action photos of 20 top players on double-sided cards. Each player is matched with three different players on the opposite side or another photo of himself. Each side is covered with the Finest opaque protector.

COMPLETE SET (40)	125.00	300.00
SER.2 STATED ODDS 1:36		
*REFRACTOR: 1X TO 2.5X BASIC MYSTERY		
REF.SER.2 ODDS 1:144		
M1 Nomar Garciaparra Frank Thomas	4.00	10.00
M2 Nomar Garciaparra Albert Belle	4.00	10.00
M3 Nomar Garciaparra Scott Rolen	6.00	15.00
M4 Frank Thomas Albert Belle	4.00	10.00
M5 Frank Thomas Scott Rolen	4.00	10.00
M6 Albert Belle Scott Rolen	2.50	6.00
M7 Ken Griffey Jr. Jose Cruz Jr.	6.00	15.00
M8 Ken Griffey Jr. Alex Rodriguez	6.00	15.00
M9 Ken Griffey Jr. Roger Clemens	8.00	20.00
M10 Jose Cruz Jr. Alex Rodriguez	6.00	15.00
M11 Jose Cruz Jr. Roger Clemens	8.00	20.00
M12 Alex Rodriguez Roger Clemens	6.00	15.00
M13 Mike Piazza Barry Bonds	12.50	30.00
M14 Mike Piazza Derek Jeter	10.00	25.00
M15 Mike Piazza Bernie Williams	6.00	15.00
M16 Barry Bonds Derek Jeter	12.50	30.00
M17 Barry Bonds Bernie Williams	6.00	15.00
M18 Deter Jeter Bernie Williams	10.00	25.00
M19 Mark McGwire Jeff Bagwell	10.00	25.00
M20 Mark McGwire Mo Vaughn	10.00	25.00
M21 Mark McGwire Jim Thome	10.00	25.00
M22 Jeff Bagwell Mo Vaughn	2.50	6.00
M23 Jeff Bagwell Jim Thome	2.50	6.00
M24 Mo Vaughn Jim Thome	2.50	6.00
M25 Juan Gonzalez Travis Lee	1.50	4.00
M26 Juan Gonzalez Ben Grieve	1.50	4.00
M27 Juan Gonzalez Fred McGriff	2.50	6.00
M28 Travis Lee Ben Grieve	1.50	4.00
M29 Travis Lee Fred McGriff	2.50	6.00
M30 Ben Grieve Fred McGriff	2.50	6.00
M31 Albert Belle Albert Belle	1.50	4.00
M32 Scott Rolen Scott Rolen	2.50	6.00
M33 Alex Rodriguez Alex Rodriguez	8.00	20.00
M34 Roger Clemens Roger Clemens	8.00	20.00
M35 Bernie Williams Bernie Williams	2.50	6.00
M36 Mo Vaughn Mo Vaughn	1.50	4.00
M37 Jim Thome Jim Thome	2.50	6.00
M38 Travis Lee Travis Lee	1.50	4.00
M39 Fred McGriff Fred McGriff	2.50	6.00
M40 Ben Grieve Ben Grieve	1.50	4.00

1998 Finest Mystery Finest Oversize

One of these three different cards was randomly seeded as chiptoppers (lying on top of the packs, but within the sealed box) at a rate of 1:6 series two Home Team Collector boxes. Besides the obvious difference in size, these cards are also numbered differently than the standard-sized cards, but beyond that they're essentially straight parallels of their standard sized siblings.

COMPLETE SET (3)	15.00	40.00
SER.2 STATED ODDS 1:6 HTA BOXES		
*REFRACTOR: .75X TO 2X OVERSIZE		
SER.2 REF.STATED ODDS 1:12 HTA BOXES		
1 Ken Griffey Jr. Alex Rodriguez	4.00	10.00
2 Derek Jeter Bernie Williams	6.00	15.00
3 Mark McGwire Jeff Bagwell	6.00	15.00

1998 Finest Power Zone

Randomly inserted in series one hobby packs at the rate of one in 72 and in series one Home Team Advantage packs at the rate of one in 32, this 20-card set features color action photos of top players printed with new "Flop Inks" technology which actually changes the color of the card when it is held at different angles.

COMPLETE SET (20)	80.00	200.00
SER.1 STAT.ODDS 1:72 HOBBY, 1:32 HTA		
P1 Ken Griffey Jr.	8.00	20.00
P2 Jeff Bagwell	3.00	8.00
P3 Jose Cruz Jr.	1.25	3.00
P4 Barry Bonds	12.50	30.00
P5 Mark McGwire	12.50	30.00
P6 Jim Thome	3.00	8.00
P7 Mo Vaughn	2.00	5.00
P8 Gary Sheffield	2.00	5.00
P9 Andres Galarraga	2.00	5.00
P10 Nomar Garciaparra	8.00	20.00
P11 Rafael Palmeiro	3.00	8.00
P12 Sammy Sosa	5.00	12.00
P13 Jay Buhner	2.00	5.00
P14 Tony Clark	1.25	3.00
P15 Mike Piazza	8.00	20.00
P16 Larry Walker	2.00	5.00
P17 Albert Belle	2.00	5.00
P18 Tino Martinez	3.00	8.00
P19 Juan Gonzalez	2.00	5.00
P20 Frank Thomas	5.00	12.00

1998 Finest Stadium Stars

Randomly inserted in packs at a rate of one in 72, this 24-card set features a selection of the majors top hitters set against an attractive foil-glowing stadium background.

COMPLETE SET (24)	125.00	300.00
SER.2 STATED ODDS 1:72		
JUMBOS: RANDOM IN SER.2 JUMBO BOXES		
SS1 Ken Griffey Jr.	8.00	20.00
SS2 Alex Rodriguez	8.00	20.00
SS3 Mo Vaughn	2.00	5.00
SS4 Nomar Garciaparra	8.00	20.00
SS5 Frank Thomas	5.00	12.00
SS6 Albert Belle	2.00	5.00
SS7 Derek Jeter	12.50	30.00
SS8 Chipper Jones	5.00	12.00
SS9 Cal Ripken	15.00	40.00
SS10 Jim Thome	3.00	8.00
SS11 Mike Piazza	8.00	20.00
SS12 Juan Gonzalez	2.00	5.00
SS13 Jeff Bagwell	3.00	8.00
SS14 Sammy Sosa	5.00	12.00
SS15 Jose Cruz Jr.	1.25	3.00
SS16 Gary Sheffield	2.00	5.00
SS17 Larry Walker	2.00	5.00
SS18 Tony Gwynn	6.00	15.00
SS19 Mark McGwire	12.50	30.00
SS20 Barry Bonds	12.50	30.00
SS21 Tino Martinez	3.00	8.00
SS22 Manny Ramirez	3.00	8.00
SS23 Ken Caminiti	2.00	5.00
SS24 Andres Galarraga	2.00	5.00

1999 Finest

This 300-card set (produced by Topps) was distributed in first and second series six-card packs with a suggested retail price of $5. The fronts feature color action player photos printed on 27 pt. card stock using Chromium technology. The backs carry player information. The set includes the following subsets: Gems (101-120), Sensations (121-130) Rookies (131-150/277-299), Sterling (251-265) and Gamers (266-276). Card number 300 is a special Hank Aaron/Mark McGwire tribute. Cards numbered from 101 through 150 and 251 through 300 were short printed and seeded at a rate of one per hobby, one per retail and two per Home Team Advantage pack. Notable Rookie Cards include Pat Burrell, Sean Burroughs, Nick Johnson, Austin Kearns, Corey Patterson and Alfonso Soriano.

COMPLETE SET (300)	30.00	80.00
COMP.SERIES 1 (150)	15.00	40.00
COMP.SERIES 2 (150)	15.00	40.00
COMP.SER.1 w/o SP's (100)	6.00	15.00
COMP.SER.2 w/o SP's (100)	6.00	15.00
COMMON (1-100/151-250)	.15	.40
COMMON (101-150/251-300)	.20	.50
1 Darin Erstad	.15	.40
2 Javy Lopez	.15	.40
3 Vinny Castilla	.15	.40
4 Jim Thome	.25	.60
5 Tino Martinez	.25	.60
6 Mark Grace	.25	.60
7 Shawn Green	.15	.40
8 Dustin Hermanson	.15	.40
9 Kevin Young	.15	.40
10 Tony Clark	.15	.40
11 Scott Brosius	.15	.40
12 Craig Biggio	.25	.60
13 Brian McRae	.15	.40
14 Chan Ho Park	.15	.40
15 Manny Ramirez	.25	.60
16 Chipper Jones	.40	1.00
17 Rico Brogna	.15	.40
18 Quinton McCracken	.15	.40
19 J.T. Snow	.15	.40
20 Tony Gwynn	.50	1.25
21 Juan Guzman	.15	.40
22 John Valentin	.15	.40
23 Rick Helling	.15	.40
24 Sandy Alomar Jr.	.15	.40
25 Frank Thomas	.40	1.00
26 Jorge Posada	.25	.60
27 Dmitri Young	.15	.40
28 Rick Reed	.15	.40
29 Kevin Tapani	.15	.40
30 Troy Glaus	.25	.60
31 Kenny Rogers	.15	.40
32 Jeromy Burnitz	.15	.40
33 Mark Grudzielanek	.15	.40
34 Mike Mussina	.25	.60
35 Scott Rolen	.25	.60
36 Neifi Perez	.15	.40
37 Brad Radke	.15	.40
38 Darryl Strawberry	.15	.40
39 Robb Nen	.15	.40
40 Moises Alou	.15	.40
41 Eric Young	.15	.40
42 Livan Hernandez	.15	.40
43 John Wetteland	.15	.40
44 Matt Lawton	.15	.40
45 Ben Grieve	.15	.40
46 Fernando Tatis	.15	.40
47 Travis Fryman	.15	.40
48 David Segui	.15	.40
49 Bob Abreu	.15	.40
50 Nomar Garciaparra	.60	1.50
51 Paul O'Neill	.25	.60
52 Jeff King	.15	.40
53 Francisco Cordova	.15	.40
54 John Olerud	.15	.40
55 Vladimir Guerrero	.40	1.00
56 Fernando Vina	.15	.40
57 Shane Reynolds	.15	.40
58 Chuck Finley	.15	.40
59 Rondell White	.15	.40
60 Greg Vaughn	.15	.40
61 Ryan Minor	.15	.40
62 Tom Gordon	.15	.40
63 Damion Easley	.15	.40
64 Ray Durham	.15	.40
65 Orlando Hernandez	.15	.40
66 Bartolo Colon	.15	.40
67 Jaret Wright	.15	.40
68 Royce Clayton	.15	.40
69 Tim Salmon	.25	.60
70 Mark McGwire	1.00	2.50
71 Alex Gonzalez	.15	.40
72 Tom Glavine	.25	.60
73 David Justice	.15	.40
74 Omar Vizquel	.25	.60
75 Juan Gonzalez	.15	.40
76 Bobby Higginson	.15	.40
77 Todd Walker	.15	.40
78 Dante Bichette	.15	.40
79 Kevin Millwood	.15	.40
80 Roger Clemens	.75	2.00
81 Kerry Wood	.15	.40
82 Cal Ripken	1.25	3.00
83 Jay Bell	.15	.40
84 Barry Bonds	1.00	2.50
85 Alex Rodriguez	.60	1.50
86 Doug Glanville	.15	.40
87 Jason Kendall	.15	.40
88 Sean Casey	.15	.40
89 Aaron Sele	.15	.40
90 Derek Jeter	1.00	2.50
91 Andy Ashby	.15	.40
92 Rusty Greer	.15	.40
93 Rod Beck	.15	.40
94 Matt Williams	.15	.40
95 Mike Piazza	.60	1.50
96 Wally Joyner	.15	.40
97 Barry Larkin	.25	.60
98 Eric Milton	.15	.40
99 Gary Sheffield	.15	.40
100 Greg Maddux	.60	1.50
101 Ken Griffey Jr. GEM	1.00	2.50
102 Frank Thomas GEM	.60	1.50
103 N.Garciaparra GEM	1.00	2.50
104 Mark McGwire GEM	1.50	4.00
105 Alex Rodriguez GEM	1.00	2.50
106 Tony Gwynn GEM	.75	2.00
107 Juan Gonzalez GEM	.25	.60
108 Jeff Bagwell GEM	.40	1.00
109 Sammy Sosa GEM	.60	1.50
110 V.Guerrero GEM	.60	1.50
111 Roger Clemens GEM	1.25	3.00
112 Barry Bonds GEM	1.50	4.00
113 Darin Erstad GEM	.25	.60
114 Mike Piazza GEM	1.00	2.50
115 Derek Jeter GEM	1.50	4.00
116 Chipper Jones GEM	.60	1.50
117 Larry Walker GEM	.25	.60
118 Scott Rolen GEM	.40	1.00
119 Cal Ripken GEM	2.00	5.00
120 Greg Maddux GEM	1.00	2.50
121 Troy Glaus SENS	.40	1.00
122 Ben Grieve SENS	.20	.50
123 Ryan Minor SENS	.20	.50
124 Kerry Wood SENS	.25	.60
125 Travis Lee SENS	.20	.50
126 Adrian Beltre SENS	.25	.60
127 Brad Fullmer SENS	.20	.50
128 Aramis Ramirez SENS	.25	.60
129 Eric Chavez SENS	.25	.60
130 Todd Helton SENS	.40	1.00
131 Pat Burrell RC	1.25	3.00
132 Ryan Mills RC	.20	.50
133 Austin Kearns RC	1.25	3.00
134 Josh McKinley RC	.20	.50
135 Adam Everett RC	.40	1.00
136 Marlon Anderson	.20	.50
137 Bruce Chen	.20	.50
138 Matt Clement	.25	.60
139 Alex Gonzalez	.20	.50
140 Roy Halladay	.25	.60
141 Calvin Pickering	.20	.50
142 Randy Wolf	.20	.50
143 Ryan Anderson	.20	.50
144 Ruben Mateo	.20	.50
145 Alex Escobar RC	.25	.60
146 Jeremy Giambi	.20	.50
147 Lance Berkman	.25	.60
148 Michael Barrett	.20	.50
149 Preston Wilson	.25	.60
150 Gabe Kapler	.25	.60
151 Roger Clemens	.75	2.00
152 Jay Buhner	.15	.40
153 Brad Fullmer	.15	.40
154 Ray Lankford	.15	.40
155 Jim Edmonds	.15	.40
156 Jason Giambi	.15	.40
157 Bret Boone	.15	.40
158 Jeff Cirillo	.15	.40
159 Rickey Henderson	.40	1.00
160 Edgar Martinez	.25	.60
161 Ron Gant	.15	.40
162 Mark Kotsay	.15	.40
163 Trevor Hoffman	.15	.40
164 Jason Schmidt	.15	.40
165 Brett Tomko	.15	.40
166 David Ortiz	.40	1.00
167 Dean Palmer	.15	.40
168 Hideki Irabu	.15	.40
169 Mike Cameron	.15	.40
170 Pedro Martinez	.25	.60
171 Tom Goodwin	.15	.40
172 Brian Hunter	.15	.40
173 Al Leiter	.15	.40
174 Charles Johnson	.15	.40
175 Curt Schilling	.15	.40
176 Robin Ventura	.15	.40
177 Travis Lee	.15	.40
178 Jeff Shaw	.15	.40
179 Ugueth Urbina	.15	.40
180 Roberto Alomar	.25	.60
181 Cliff Floyd	.15	.40
182 Adrian Beltre	.15	.40
183 Tony Womack	.15	.40
184 Brian Jordan	.15	.40
185 Randy Johnson	.40	1.00
186 Mickey Morandini	.15	.40
187 Todd Hundley	.15	.40
188 Jose Valentin	.15	.40
189 Eric Davis	.15	.40
190 Ken Caminiti	.15	.40
191 David Wells	.15	.40
192 Ryan Klesko	.15	.40
193 Garret Anderson	.15	.40
194 Eric Karros	.15	.40
195 Ivan Rodriguez	.25	.60
196 Aramis Ramirez	.15	.40
197 Mike Lieberthal	.15	.40
198 Will Clark	.25	.60
199 Rey Ordonez	.15	.40
200 Ken Griffey Jr.	.60	1.50
201 Jose Guillen	.15	.40
202 Scott Erickson	.15	.40
203 Paul Konerko	.15	.40
204 Johnny Damon	.25	.60
205 Larry Walker	.15	.40
206 Denny Neagle	.15	.40
207 Jose Offerman	.15	.40
208 Andy Pettitte	.25	.60
209 Bobby Jones	.15	.40
210 Kevin Brown	.25	.60
211 John Smoltz	.25	.60
212 Henry Rodriguez	.15	.40
213 Tim Belcher	.15	.40
214 Carlos Delgado	.15	.40
215 Andruw Jones	.25	.60
216 Andy Benes	.15	.40
217 Fred McGriff	.25	.60
218 Edgar Renteria	.15	.40
219 Miguel Tejada	.15	.40
220 Bernie Williams	.25	.60
221 Justin Thompson	.15	.40
222 Marty Cordova	.15	.40
223 Delino DeShields	.15	.40
224 Ellis Burks	.15	.40
225 Kenny Lofton	.15	.40
226 Steve Finley	.15	.40
227 Eric Chavez	.15	.40
228 Jose Cruz Jr.	.15	.40
229 Marquis Grissom	.15	.40
230 Jeff Bagwell	.25	.60
231 Jose Canseco	.25	.60
232 Edgardo Alfonzo	.15	.40
233 Richie Sexson	.15	.40
234 Jeff Kent	.15	.40
235 Rafael Palmeiro	.25	.60
236 David Cone	.15	.40
237 Gregg Jefferies	.15	.40
238 Mike Lansing	.15	.40
239 Mariano Rivera	.40	1.00
240 Albert Belle	.15	.40
241 Chuck Knoblauch	.15	.40
242 Derek Bell	.15	.40
243 Pat Hentgen	.15	.40
244 Andres Galarraga	.15	.40
245 Mo Vaughn	.15	.40
246 Wade Boggs	.25	.60
247 Devon White	.15	.40
248 Todd Helton	.25	.60
249 Raul Mondesi	.15	.40
250 Sammy Sosa	.40	1.00
251 Nomar Garciaparra ST	1.00	2.50
252 Mark McGwire ST	1.50	4.00
253 Alex Rodriguez ST	1.00	2.50
254 Juan Gonzalez ST	.25	.60
255 Vladimir Guerrero ST	.60	1.50
256 Ken Griffey Jr. ST	1.00	2.50
257 Mike Piazza ST	1.00	2.50
258 Derek Jeter ST	1.50	4.00
259 Albert Belle ST	.25	.60
260 Greg Vaughn ST	.20	.50
261 Sammy Sosa ST	.60	1.50
262 Greg Maddux ST	1.00	2.50
263 Frank Thomas ST	.60	1.50
264 Mark Grace ST	.40	1.00
265 Ivan Rodriguez ST	.40	1.00
266 Roger Clemens GM	1.25	3.00
267 Mo Vaughn GM	.25	.60
268 Jim Thome GM	.40	1.00
269 Darin Erstad GM	.25	.60
270 Chipper Jones GM	.60	1.50
271 Larry Walker GM	.25	.60
272 Cal Ripken GM	2.00	5.00
273 Scott Rolen GM	.40	1.00
274 Randy Johnson GM	.60	1.50
275 Tony Gwynn GM	.75	2.00
276 Barry Bonds GM	1.50	4.00
277 Sean Burroughs RC	.40	1.00
278 J.M. Gold RC	.20	.50
279 Carlos Lee	.25	.60
280 George Lombard	.20	.50
281 Carlos Beltran	.40	1.00
282 Fernando Seguignol	.20	.50
283 Eric Chavez	.25	.60
284 Carlos Pena RC	.30	.75
285 Corey Patterson RC	.60	1.50
286 Alfonso Soriano RC	3.00	8.00
287 Nick Johnson RC	.60	1.50
288 Jorge Toca RC	.25	.60
289 A.J. Burnett RC	.60	1.50
290 Andy Brown RC	.20	.50
291 D.Mientkiewicz RC	.40	1.00
292 Bobby Seay RC	.20	.50
293 Chip Ambres RC	.20	.50
294 C.C. Sabathia RC	1.50	4.00
295 Choo Freeman RC	.25	.60
296 Eric Valent RC	.25	.60
297 Matt Belisle RC	.20	.50
298 Jason Tyner RC	.20	.50
299 Masao Kida RC	.25	.60
300 Hank Aaron Mark McGwire	1.25	3.00

1999 Finest Gold Refractors

This 300-card set is a die-cut gold foil parallel version of the base set. Only 100 serially numbered sets were produced. Cards were randomly inserted in hobby and retail packs. Series one packs were at the rate of one in 82 and HTA packs at a rate of one in 38. Series 2 packs were at the rate of one in 57 and HTA packs at a rate of one in 26.

*STARS 1-100/151-250: 10X TO 25X BASIC		
*STARS 101-150/251-300: 6X TO 15X BAS.		
*ROOKIES: 4X TO 10X BASIC		
SER.1 ODDS 1:82 HOB/RET, 1:38 HTA		
SER.2 ODDS 1:57 HOB/RET, 1:26 HTA		
294 C.C. Sabathia	50.00	100.00

1999 Finest Refractors

Randomly inserted in series one and two packs at the rate of one in 12 hobby/retail and one in five HTA, this 300-card set is a parallel version of the base set and is similar in design. The difference is found in the refractive quality of the card.

*STARS 1-100/151-250: 3X TO 8X BASIC
*STARS 101-150/251-300: 2X TO 5X BASIC
*ROOKIES: 1.5X TO 4X BASIC
STATED ODDS 1:12 HOB/RET, 1:5 HTA

1999 Finest Aaron Award Contenders

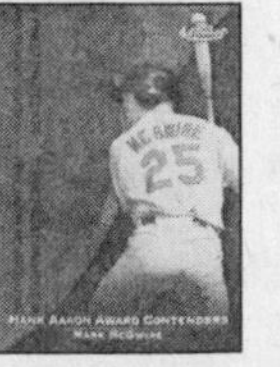

Randomly inserted into Series two packs at different rates depending on the player, this nine-card set features color action photos of players vying for the Hank Aaron Award.

COMPLETE SET (9)	30.00	60.00
HA1 SER.2 ODDS 1:216, 1:108 HTA		

HA2 SER.2 ODDS 1:108, 1:54 HTA
HA3 SER.2 ODDS 1:72, 1:36 HTA
HA4 SER.2 ODDS 1:54, 1:27 HTA
HA5 SER.2 ODDS 1:43, 1:21 HTA
HA6 SER.2 ODDS 1:36, 1:18 HTA
HA7 SER.2 ODDS 1:31, 1:15 HTA
HA8 SER.2 ODDS 1:27, 1:13 HTA
HA9 SER.2 ODDS 1:24, 1:12 HTA
*REFRACTORS: 1.5X TO 4X BASIC AARON AW
REF HA1 SER.2 ODDS 1:1728, 1:864 HTA
REF HA2 SER.2 ODDS 1:864, 1:432 HTA
REF HA3 SER.2 ODDS 1:576, 1:288 HTA
REF HA4 SER.2 ODDS 1:432, 1:216 HTA
REF HA5 SER.2 ODDS 1:344, 1:172 HTA
REF HA6 SER.2 ODDS 1:288, 1:144 HTA
REF HA7 SER.2 ODDS 1:248, 1:124 HTA
REF HA8 SER.2 ODDS 1:216, 1:108 HTA
REF HA9 SER.2 ODDS 1:192, 1:96 HTA

Card	Low	High
HA1 Juan Gonzalez	2.00	5.00
HA2 Vladimir Guerrero	4.00	10.00
HA3 Nomar Garciaparra	5.00	12.00
HA4 Albert Belle	2.00	5.00
HA5 Frank Thomas	2.00	5.00
HA6 Sammy Sosa	2.00	5.00
HA7 Alex Rodriguez	2.00	5.00
HA8 Ken Griffey Jr.	1.50	4.00
HA9 Mark McGwire	2.00	5.00

1999 Finest Complements

Randomly inserted into Series two packs at the rate of one in 56, this seven-card set features color action photos of 14 stars who complement each other's skills and share a common bond paired together on cards printed with advanced "Split Screen" technology which combines Refractor and Non-Refractor technology on the same card. Each card has three variations as follows: 1) Non-Refractor/Refractor, 2) Refractor/Non-Refractor, and 3) Refractor/Refractor.

COMPLETE SET (7) 25.00 50.00
SER.2 STATED ODDS 1:56, 1:27 HTA
RIGHT/LEFT REF.VARIATIONS EQUAL VALUE
*DUAL REF: 1.25X TO 3X BASIC COMP.
DUAL REF.SER.2 ODDS 1:168, 1:81 HTA

Card	Low	High
C1 Mike Piazza Ivan Rodriguez	2.50	6.00
C2 Tony Gwynn Wade Boggs	2.00	5.00
C3 Kerry Wood Roger Clemens	3.00	8.00
C4 Juan Gonzalez Sammy Sosa	1.50	4.00
C5 Derek Jeter Nomar Garciaparra	4.00	10.00
C6 Mark McGwire Frank Thomas	4.00	10.00
C7 Vladimir Guerrero Andruw Jones	1.50	4.00

1999 Finest Double Feature

Randomly inserted into Series two packs at the rate of one in 56, this seven-card set features color photos of fourteen paired teammates printed on cards using Split Screen technology combining Refractor and Non-Refractor technology on the same card. There are three different versions of each card as follows: 1) Non-Refractor/Refractor, 2) Refractor/Non-Refractor, and 3) Refractor/Refractor.

COMPLETE SET (7) 20.00 40.00
SER.2 STATED ODDS 1:56, 1:27 HTA
RIGHT/LEFT REF.VARIATIONS EQUAL VALUE
*DUAL REF: 1.25X TO 3X BASIC DOUB.FEAT.
*DUAL REF BURRELL: 1.25X TO 3X HI COLUMN
DUAL REF.SER.2 ODDS 1:168, 1:81 HTA

Card	Low	High
DF1 Ken Griffey Jr. Alex Rodriguez	2.50	6.00
DF2 Chipper Jones Andruw Jones	1.50	4.00
DF3 Darin Erstad Mo Vaughn	.60	1.50
DF4 Craig Biggio Jeff Bagwell	1.00	2.50
DF5 Ben Grieve Eric Chavez	.60	1.50
DF6 Albert Belle Cal Ripken	5.00	12.00
DF7 Scott Rolen Pat Burrell	1.25	3.00

1999 Finest Franchise Records

Randomly inserted into Series two packs at the rate of one in 129, this ten-card set features color action photos of all-time and single-season franchise statistic holders. A refractive parallel version of this set was also produced and inserted in Series two packs at the rate of one in 378.

COMPLETE SET (10) 75.00 150.00
SER.2 STATED ODDS 1:129, 1:64 HTA
*REFRACTORS: .75X TO 2X BASIC FRAN.REC.
REF.SER.2 ODDS 1:378, 1:189 HTA

Card	Low	High
FR1 Frank Thomas	4.00	10.00
FR2 Ken Griffey Jr.	6.00	15.00
FR3 Mark McGwire	10.00	25.00
FR4 Juan Gonzalez	1.50	4.00
FR5 Nomar Garciaparra	[illegible]	10.00
FR6 Mike Piazza	6.00	15.00
FR7 Cal Ripken	12.50	30.00
FR8 Sammy Sosa	4.00	10.00
FR9 Barry Bonds	10.00	25.00
FR10 Tony Gwynn	5.00	12.00

1999 Finest Future's Finest

Randomly inserted into Series two packs at the rate of one in 171, this 10-card set features color photos of top young stars printed on card stock using Refractive Finest technology. The cards are sequentially numbered to 500.

COMPLETE SET (10) 50.00 100.00
SER.2 STATED ODDS 1:171, 1:79 HTA

Card	Low	High
FF1 Pat Burrell	6.00	15.00
FF2 Troy Glaus	4.00	10.00
FF3 Eric Chavez	4.00	10.00
FF4 Ryan Anderson	4.00	10.00
FF5 Ruben Mateo	4.00	10.00
FF6 Gabe Kapler	4.00	10.00
FF7 Alex Gonzalez	4.00	10.00
FF8 Michael Barrett	4.00	10.00
FF9 Adrian Beltre	4.00	10.00
FF10 Fernando Seguignol	4.00	10.00

1999 Finest Leading Indicators

Randomly inserted in Series one packs at the rate of one in 24, this 10-card set features color action photos highlighting the 1998 home run totals of superstar players and printed on cards using a heat-sensitive, thermal-ink technology. When a collector touched the baseball field background in left, center, or right field, the heat from his finger revealed the pictured player's '98 home run totals in that direction.

COMPLETE SET (10) 20.00 50.00
SER.1 ODDS 1:24 HOB/RET, 1:11 HTA

Card	Low	High
L1 Mark McGwire	4.00	10.00
L2 Sammy Sosa	1.50	4.00
L3 Ken Griffey Jr.	2.50	6.00
L4 Greg Vaughn	.60	1.50
L5 Albert Belle	.60	1.50
L6 Juan Gonzalez	.60	1.50
L7 Andres Galarraga	.60	1.50
L8 Alex Rodriguez	2.50	6.00
L9 Barry Bonds	4.00	10.00
L10 Jeff Bagwell	1.00	2.50

1999 Finest Milestones

Randomly inserted into packs at the rate of one in 29, this 40-card set features color photos of players who have the highest statistics in four categories: Hits, Home Runs, RBI's and Doubles. The cards are printed with Refractor technology and sequentially numbered based on the category as follows: Hits to 3,000, Home Runs to 500, RBIs to 1,400, and Doubles to 500.

HIT SER.2 ODDS 1:29, 1:13 HTA
HR SER.2 ODDS 1:171, 1:79 HTA
RBI SER.2 ODDS 1:61, 1:28 HTA
2B SER.2 ODDS 1:171, 1:79 HTA

Card	Low	High
M1 Tony Gwynn HIT	2.00	5.00
M2 Cal Ripken HIT	5.00	12.00
M3 Wade Boggs HIT	1.00	2.50
M4 Ken Griffey Jr. HIT	2.50	6.00
M5 Frank Thomas HIT	1.50	4.00
M6 Barry Bonds HIT	4.00	10.00
M7 Travis Lee HIT	.60	1.50
M8 Alex Rodriguez HIT	2.50	6.00
M9 Derek Jeter HIT	4.00	10.00
M10 V.Guerrero HIT	1.50	4.00
M11 Mark McGwire HR	12.50	30.00
M12 Ken Griffey Jr. HR	8.00	20.00
M13 Vladimir Guerrero HR	5.00	12.00
M14 Alex Rodriguez HR	8.00	20.00
M15 Barry Bonds HR	12.50	30.00
M16 Sammy Sosa HR	5.00	12.00
M17 Albert Belle HR	2.00	5.00
M18 Frank Thomas HR	5.00	12.00
M19 Jose Canseco HR	3.00	8.00
M20 Mike Piazza HR	8.00	20.00
M21 Jeff Bagwell RBI	1.50	4.00
M22 Barry Bonds RBI	6.00	15.00
M23 Ken Griffey Jr. RBI	4.00	10.00
M24 Albert Belle RBI	1.00	2.50
M25 Juan Gonzalez RBI	1.00	2.50
M26 Vinny Castilla RBI	1.00	2.50
M27 Mark McGwire RBI	6.00	15.00
M28 Alex Rodriguez RBI	4.00	10.00
M29 N.Garciaparra RBI	4.00	10.00
M30 Frank Thomas RBI	2.50	6.00
M31 Barry Bonds 2B	12.50	30.00
M32 Albert Belle 2B	2.00	5.00
M33 Ben Grieve 2B	2.00	5.00
M34 Craig Biggio 2B	3.00	8.00
M35 Vladimir Guerrero 2B	5.00	12.00
M36 N.Garciaparra 2B	8.00	20.00
M37 Alex Rodriguez 2B	8.00	20.00
M38 Derek Jeter 2B	12.50	30.00
M39 Ken Griffey Jr. 2B	8.00	20.00
M40 Brad Fullmer 2B	2.00	5.00

1999 Finest Peel and Reveal Sparkle

Randomly inserted in Series one packs at the rate of one in 30, this 20-card set features color action player images on a sparkle background. This set was considered Common and the protective coating had to be peeled from the card front and back to reveal the level.

COMPLETE SET (20) 60.00 120.00
SER.1 STATED ODDS 1:30 HOB/RET, 1:15 HTA
*HYPERPLAID: .6X TO 1.5X SPARKLE
HYPERPLAID SER.1 ODDS 1:60 H/R, 1:30 HTA
*STADIUM STARS: 1.25X TO 3X SPARKLE
STAD.STAR SER.1 ODDS 1:120 H/R, 1:60 HTA

Card	Low	High
1 Kerry Wood	.75	2.00
2 Mark McGwire	5.00	12.00
3 Sammy Sosa	2.00	5.00
4 Ken Griffey Jr.	3.00	8.00
5 Nomar Garciaparra	3.00	8.00
6 Greg Maddux	3.00	8.00
7 Derek Jeter	5.00	12.00
8 Andres Galarraga	.75	2.00
9 Alex Rodriguez	3.00	8.00
10 Frank Thomas	2.00	5.00
11 Roger Clemens	4.00	10.00
12 Juan Gonzalez	.75	2.00
13 Ben Grieve	.75	2.00
14 Jeff Bagwell	1.25	3.00
15 Todd Helton	1.25	3.00
16 Chipper Jones	2.00	5.00
17 Barry Bonds	5.00	12.00
18 Travis Lee	.75	2.00
19 Vladimir Guerrero	2.00	5.00
20 Pat Burrell	1.50	4.00

1999 Finest Prominent Figures

Randomly inserted in Series one packs with various insertion rates, this 50-card set features color action photos of ten superstars in each of five statistical categories and printed with refractor technology. The categories are: Home Runs (with an insertion rate of 1:1,749) and sequentially numbered to 70, Slugging Percentage (1:145) numbered to 847, Batting Average (1:289) numbered to 424, Runs Batted In (1:644) numbered to 190, and Total Bases (1:268) numbered to 457.

HR SER.1 ODDS 1:1749 HOB/RET, 1:807 HTA
SLUGGING SER.1 ODDS 1:145 H/R, 1:67 HTA
BAT SER.1 ODDS 1:289 HOB/RET, 1:133 HTA
RBI SER.1 ODDS 1:644 HOB/RET, 1:297 HTA
TOT.BASES SER.1 ODDS 1:268 H/R, 1:124 HTA

Card	Low	High
PF1 Mark McGwire HR	40.00	100.00
PF2 Sammy Sosa HR	15.00	40.00
PF3 Ken Griffey Jr. HR	25.00	60.00
PF4 Mike Piazza HR	25.00	60.00
PF5 Juan Gonzalez HR	6.00	15.00
PF6 Greg Vaughn HR	6.00	15.00
PF7 Alex Rodriguez HR	25.00	60.00
PF8 Manny Ramirez HR	10.00	25.00
PF9 Jeff Bagwell HR	10.00	25.00
PF10 Andres Galarraga HR	6.00	15.00
PF11 Mark McGwire SLG	8.00	20.00
PF12 Sammy Sosa SLG	3.00	8.00
PF13 Juan Gonzalez SLG	1.25	3.00
PF14 Ken Griffey Jr. SLG	5.00	12.00
PF15 Barry Bonds SLG	8.00	20.00
PF16 Greg Vaughn SLG	1.25	3.00
PF17 Larry Walker SLG	1.25	3.00
PF18 A.Galarraga SLG	1.25	3.00
PF19 Jeff Bagwell SLG	2.00	5.00
PF20 Albert Belle SLG	1.25	3.00
PF21 Tony Gwynn BAT	1.25	3.00
PF22 Mike Piazza BAT	6.00	15.00
PF23 Larry Walker BAT	1.50	4.00
PF24 Alex Rodriguez BAT	6.00	15.00
PF25 John Olerud BAT	1.50	4.00
PF26 Frank Thomas BAT	4.00	10.00
PF27 Bernie Williams BAT	2.50	6.00
PF28 Chipper Jones BAT	4.00	10.00
PF29 Jim Thome BAT	2.50	6.00
PF30 Barry Bonds BAT	10.00	25.00
PF31 Juan Gonzalez RBI	2.50	6.00
PF32 Sammy Sosa RBI	6.00	15.00
PF33 Mark McGwire RBI	15.00	40.00
PF34 Albert Belle RBI	2.50	6.00
PF35 Ken Griffey Jr. RBI	10.00	25.00
PF36 Jeff Bagwell RBI	4.00	10.00
PF37 Chipper Jones RBI	6.00	15.00
PF38 Vinny Castilla RBI	2.50	6.00
PF39 Alex Rodriguez RBI	10.00	25.00
PF40 A.Galarraga RBI	2.50	6.00
PF41 Sammy Sosa TB	4.00	10.00
PF42 Mark McGwire TB	10.00	25.00
PF43 Albert Belle TB	1.50	4.00
PF44 Ken Griffey Jr. TB	6.00	15.00
PF45 Jeff Bagwell TB	2.50	6.00
PF46 Juan Gonzalez TB	1.50	4.00
PF47 Barry Bonds TB	10.00	25.00
PF48 V.Guerrero TB	4.00	10.00
PF49 Larry Walker TB	1.50	4.00
PF50 Alex Rodriguez TB	6.00	15.00

1999 Finest Split Screen

Randomly inserted in Series one packs at the rate of one in 28, this 14-card set features action color photos of two players paired together on the same card and printed using a special refractor and non-refractor technology. Each card was printed with right/left refractor variations.

COMPLETE SET (14) 50.00 100.00
SER.1 STATED ODDS 1:28 HOB/RET, 1:14 HTA
RIGHT/LEFT REF.VARIATIONS EQUAL VALUE
*DUAL REF: 1.25X TO 3X BASIC SCREEN
DUAL REF.SER.1 ODDS 1:82 H/R, 1:42 HTA

Card	Low	High
SS1 Mark McGwire Sammy Sosa	4.00	10.00
SS2 Ken Griffey Jr. Alex Rodriguez	2.50	6.00
SS3 Nomar Garciaparra Derek Jeter	4.00	10.00
SS4 Barry Bonds Albert Belle	4.00	10.00
SS5 C.Ripken REF/T.Gwynn	5.00	12.00
SS6 Manny Ramirez Juan Gonzalez	1.00	2.50
SS7 Frank Thomas Andres Galarraga	1.50	4.00
SS8 Scott Rolen Chipper Jones	1.50	4.00
SS9 Ivan Rodriguez Mike Piazza	2.50	6.00
SS10 Kerry Wood Roger Clemens	3.00	8.00
SS11 Greg Maddux Tom Glavine	2.50	6.00
SS12 Troy Glaus Eric Chavez	1.00	2.50
SS13 Ben Grieve Todd Helton	1.00	2.50
SS14 Travis Lee Pat Burrell	1.25	3.00

1999 Finest Team Finest Blue

Randomly inserted in Series one and Series two packs at the rate of one in 82 first series and one in 57 second series. Also distributed in HTA packs at a rate of one in 38 first series and one in 26 second series. This 20-card set features color action player images printed using prismatic Chromium technology with blue highlights and is sequentially numbered to 1500. Cards 1-10 were distributed in first series packs and 11-20 in second series packs.

COMP.BLUE SET (20) 75.00 150.00
COMP.BLUE SER.2 (10) 30.00 70.00
BLUE SER.1 ODDS 1:82 HOB/RET, 1:38 HTA
BLUE SER.2 ODDS 1:57 HOB/RET, 1:26 HTA
*BLUE REF: .75X TO 2X BASIC BLUE
BLUE REF.SER.1 ODDS 1:816 HOB, 1:377 HTA
BLUE REF.SER.2 ODDS 1:571 HOB, 1:263 HTA
BLUE REF.PRINT RUN 150 SERIAL #'d SETS
*RED: .5X TO 1.2X BASIC BLUE
RED SER.2 ODDS 1:18 HTA
RED SER.1 ODDS 1:25 HTA
RED PRINT RUN 500 SERIAL #'d SETS
*RED REF: 2.5X TO 6X BASIC BLUE
RED REF.SER.1 ODDS 1:254 HTA
RED REF.SER.2 ODDS 1:184 HTA
RED REF.PRINT RUN 50 SERIAL #'d SETS
*GOLD: .6X TO 1.5X BASIC BLUE
GOLD SER.1 ODDS 1:51 HTA
GOLD SER.2 ODDS 1:37 HTA
GOLD PRINT RUN 250 SERIAL #'d SETS
*GOLD REF: 4X TO 10X BASIC BLUE
GOLD REF.SER.1 ODDS 1:510 HTA
GOLD REF.SER.2 ODDS 1:369 HTA
GOLD REF.PRINT RUN 25 SERIAL #'d SETS

Card	Low	High
TF1 Greg Maddux	2.50	6.00
TF2 Mark McGwire	4.00	10.00
TF3 Sammy Sosa	1.50	4.00
TF4 Juan Gonzalez	.75	2.00
TF5 Alex Rodriguez	2.50	6.00
TF6 Travis Lee	.75	2.00
TF7 Roger Clemens	3.00	8.00
TF8 Darin Erstad	.75	2.00
TF9 Todd Helton	1.00	2.50
TF10 Mike Piazza	2.50	6.00
TF11 Kerry Wood	.75	2.00
TF12 Ken Griffey Jr.	2.50	6.00
TF13 Frank Thomas	1.50	4.00
TF14 Jeff Bagwell	1.00	2.50
TF15 Nomar Garciaparra	2.50	6.00
TF16 Derek Jeter	4.00	10.00
TF17 Chipper Jones	1.50	4.00
TF18 Barry Bonds	4.00	10.00
TF19 Tony Gwynn	2.00	5.00
TF20 Ben Grieve	.75	2.00

2000 Finest

Produced by Topps, the 2000 Finest Series one product was released in April, 2000 as a 147-card set. The Finest Series two product was released in July, 2000 as a 140-card set. Each hobby and retail pack contained six cards and carried a suggested retail price of $4.99. Each HTA pack contained 13 cards and carried a suggested retail price of $10.00. The set includes 179-player cards, 20 first series Rookie Cards (cards 101-120) each serial numbered to 2000 and 20 second series Rookie Cards (cards 247-266) each serial numbered to 3000, 15 Features subset cards (cards 121-135), 10 Counterparts subset cards (numbers 267-276), and 20 Gems subset cards (numbers 136-145 and 277-286). The set also includes two versions of card number 146 Ken Griffey Jr. wearing his Reds uniform (a portrait and action shot). Rookie Cards were seeded at a rate of 1:23 hobby/retail packs and 1:6 HTA packs. Features and Counterparts subset cards were inserted one every eight hobby and retail packs and one every three HTA packs. Gems subset cards were inserted one every 24 hobby and retail packs and one every nine HTA packs. Finally, 20 "Graded Gems" exchange cards were randomly seeded into packs (10 per series). The lucky handful of collectors that found these cards could send them into Topps for a complete Gems subset, each of which was professionally graded "Gem Mint 10" by PSA.

Card	Low	High
COMP.SERIES 1 w/o SP's (100)	10.00	25.00
COMP.SERIES 2 w/o SP's (100)	10.00	25.00
COMMON (1-100/147-246)	.15	.40
COMMON (101-120)	2.00	5.00
COMMON (121-135)	.60	1.50
COMMON (136-145/277-286)	.75	2.00
COMMON (247-266)	2.00	5.00
COMMON (267-276)	.40	1.00
1 Nomar Garciaparra	.60	1.50
2 Chipper Jones	.40	1.00
3 Erubiel Durazo	.15	.40
4 Robin Ventura	.25	.60
5 Garret Anderson	.15	.40
6 Dean Palmer	.15	.40
7 Mariano Rivera	.40	1.00
8 Rusty Greer	.15	.40
9 Jim Thome	.25	.60
10 Jeff Bagwell	.25	.60
11 Jason Giambi	.15	.40
12 Jeromy Burnitz	.15	.40
13 Mark Grace	.25	.60
14 Russ Ortiz	.15	.40
15 Kevin Brown	.25	.60
16 Kevin Millwood	.15	.40
17 Scott Williamson	.15	.40
18 Orlando Hernandez	.15	.40
19 Todd Walker	.15	.40
20 Carlos Beltran	.15	.40
21 Ruben Rivera	.15	.40
22 Curt Schilling	.15	.40
23 Brian Giles	.15	.40
24 Eric Karros	.15	.40
25 Preston Wilson	.15	.40
26 Al Leiter	.15	.40
27 Juan Encarnacion	.15	.40
28 Tim Salmon	.25	.60
29 B.J. Surhoff	.15	.40
30 Bernie Williams	.25	.60
31 Lee Stevens	.15	.40
32 Pokey Reese	.15	.40
33 Mike Sweeney	.15	.40
34 Corey Koskie	.15	.40
35 Roberto Alomar	.25	.60
36 Tim Hudson	.15	.40
37 Tom Glavine	.25	.60
38 Jeff Kent	.15	.40
39 Mike Lieberthal	.15	.40
40 Barry Larkin	.25	.60
41 Paul O'Neill	.25	.60
42 Rico Brogna	.15	.40
43 Brian Daubach	.15	.40
44 Rich Aurilia	.15	.40
45 Vladimir Guerrero	.40	1.00
46 Luis Castillo	.15	.40
47 Bartolo Colon	.15	.40
48 Kevin Appier	.15	.40
49 Mo Vaughn	.15	.40
50 Alex Rodriguez	.60	1.50
51 Randy Johnson	.40	1.00
52 Kris Benson	.15	.40
53 Tony Clark	.15	.40
54 Chad Allen	.15	.40
55 Larry Walker	.15	.40
56 Freddy Garcia	.15	.40
57 Paul Konerko	.15	.40
58 Edgardo Alfonzo	.15	.40
59 Brady Anderson	.15	.40
60 Derek Jeter	1.00	2.50
61 John Smoltz	.25	.60
62 Doug Glanville	.15	.40
63 Shannon Stewart	.15	.40
64 Greg Maddux	.60	1.50
65 Mark McGwire	1.00	2.50
66 Gary Sheffield	.15	.40
67 Kevin Young	.15	.40
68 Tony Gwynn	.50	1.25
69 Rey Ordonez	.15	.40
70 Cal Ripken	1.25	3.00
71 Todd Helton	.25	.60
72 Brian Jordan	.15	.40
73 Jose Canseco	.25	.60
74 Luis Gonzalez	.15	.40
75 Barry Bonds	1.00	2.50
76 Jermaine Dye	.15	.40
77 Jose Offerman	.15	.40
78 Maggilo Ordonez	.15	.40
79 Fred Mcgriff	.25	.60
80 Ivan Rodriguez	.25	.60
81 Josh Hamilton	.75	2.00
82 Vernon Wells	.15	.40
83 Mark Mulder	.15	.40
84 John Patterson	.15	.40
85 Nick Johnson	.15	.40
86 Pablo Ozuna	.15	.40
87 A.J. Burnett	.15	.40
88 Jack Cust	.15	.40
89 Adam Piatt	.15	.40
90 Rob Ryan	.15	.40
91 Sean Burroughs	.15	.40
92 D'Angelo Jimenez	.15	.40
93 Chad Hermansen	.15	.40
94 Robert Fick	.15	.40
95 Ruben Mateo	.15	.40
96 Alex Escobar	.15	.40
97 Wily Pena	.15	.40
98 Corey Patterson	.15	.40
99 Eric Munson	.15	.40
100 Pat Burrell	.15	.40
101 Michael Tejera RC	2.00	5.00
102 Bobby Bradley RC	2.00	5.00
103 Larry Bigbie RC	3.00	8.00
104 B.J. Garbe RC	2.00	5.00
105 Josh Kalinowski RC	2.00	5.00
106 Brett Myers RC	3.00	8.00
107 Chris Mears RC	2.00	5.00
108 Aaron Rowand RC	4.00	10.00
109 Corey Myers RC	2.00	5.00
110 John Sneed RC	2.00	5.00
111 Ryan Christianson RC	2.00	5.00
112 Kyle Snyder	2.00	5.00
113 Mike Paradis	2.00	5.00
114 Chance Caple RC	2.00	5.00
115 Ben Christensen RC	2.00	5.00
116 Brad Baker RC	2.00	5.00
117 Rob Purvis RC	2.00	5.00
118 Rick Asadoorian RC	2.00	5.00
119 Ruben Salazar RC	2.00	5.00
120 Julio Zuleta RC	2.00	5.00
121 Alex Rodriguez Ken Griffey Jr.	1.00	2.50
122 Nomar Garciaparra Derek Jeter	1.25	3.00
123 Mark Mcgwire Sammy Sosa	1.50	4.00
124 Randy Johnson Pedro Martinez	1.00	2.50
125 Ivan Rodriguez Mike Piazza	1.00	2.50
126 Manny Ramirez Roberto Alomar	.60	1.50
127 Chipper Jones Andruw Jones	1.00	2.50
128 Cal Ripken Tony Gwynn	2.00	5.00
129 Jeff Bagwell Craig Biggio	.60	1.50
130 Barry Bonds Vladimir Guerrero	1.50	4.00
131 Nick Johnson Alfonso Soriano	1.00	2.50
132 Josh Hamilton Pat Burrell	4.00	10.00
133 Corey Patterson Ruben Mateo	.60	1.50
134 Larry Walker Todd Helton	.60	1.50
135 Rey Ordonez Edgardo Alfonzo	.60	1.50
136 Derek Jeter GEM	3.00	8.00
137 Alex Rodriguez GEM	2.00	5.00
138 Chipper Jones GEM	2.00	5.00
139 Mike Piazza GEM	2.00	5.00
140 Mark McGwire GEM	3.00	8.00
141 Ivan Rodriguez GEM	1.25	3.00
142 Cal Ripken GEM	4.00	10.00
143 V.Guerrero GEM	2.00	5.00
144 Randy Johnson GEM	2.00	5.00
145 Jeff Bagwell GEM	1.25	3.00
146 K.Griffey Jr. ACTION	.60	1.50
146A Ken Griffey Jr. PORT	.60	1.50
147 Andruw Jones	.25	.60
148 Kerry Wood	.15	.40
149 Jim Edmonds	.15	.40
150 Pedro Martinez	.25	.60
151 Warren Morris	.15	.40
152 Trevor Hoffman	.15	.40
153 Ryan Klesko	.15	.40
154 Andy Pettitte	.25	.60
155 Frank Thomas	.40	1.00
156 Damion Easley	.15	.40
157 Cliff Floyd	.15	.40
158 Ben Davis	.15	.40
159 John Valentin	.15	.40
160 Rafael Palmeiro	.25	.60
161 Andy Ashby	.15	.40
162 J.D. Drew	.15	.40
163 Jay Bell	.15	.40
164 Adam Kennedy	.15	.40
165 Manny Ramirez	.25	.60
166 John Halama	.15	.40
167 Octavio Dotel	.15	.40
168 Darin Erstad	.15	.40
169 Jose Lima	.15	.40
170 Andres Galarraga	.15	.40
171 Scott Rolen	.25	.60
172 Delino DeShields	.15	.40
173 J.T. Snow	.15	.40
174 Tony Womack	.15	.40
175 John Olerud	.15	.40
176 Jason Kendall	.15	.40
177 Carlos Lee	.15	.40
178 Eric Milton	.15	.40
179 Jeff Cirillo	.15	.40
180 Gabe Kapler	.15	.40
181 Greg Vaughn	.15	.40
182 Denny Neagle	.15	.40
183 Tino Martinez	.25	.60
184 Doug Mientkiewicz	.15	.40
185 Juan Gonzalez	.15	.40
186 Ellis Burks	.15	.40
187 Mike Hampton	.15	.40
188 Royce Clayton	.15	.40
189 Mike Mussina	.25	.60
190 Carlos Delgado	.15	.40
191 Ben Grieve	.15	.40
192 Fernando Tatis	.15	.40
193 Matt Williams	.15	.40
194 Rondell White	.15	.40
195 Shawn Green	.15	.40
196 Hideki Irabu	.15	.40
197 Troy Glaus	.15	.40
198 Roger Cedeno	.15	.40
199 Ray Lankford	.15	.40
200 Sammy Sosa	.40	1.00
201 Kenny Lofton	.15	.40
202 Edgar Martinez	.25	.60
203 Mark Kotsay	.15	.40
204 David Wells	.15	.40
205 Craig Biggio	.25	.60
206 Ray Durham	.15	.40
207 Troy O'Leary	.15	.40
208 Rickey Henderson	.40	1.00
209 Bob Abreu	.15	.40
210 Neifi Perez	.15	.40
211 Carlos Febles	.15	.40
212 Chuck Knoblauch	.15	.40
213 Moises Alou	.15	.40
214 Omar Vizquel	.25	.60
215 Vinny Castilla	.15	.40
216 Javy Lopez	.15	.40
217 Johnny Damon	.25	.60
218 Roger Clemens	.75	2.00
219 Miguel Tejada	.15	.40
220 Carl Everett	.15	.40
221 Matt Lawton	.15	.40
222 Albert Belle	.15	.40
223 Adrian Beltre	.15	.40
224 Dante Bichette	.15	.40
225 Raul Mondesi	.15	.40
226 Mike Piazza	.60	1.50
227 Brad Penny	.15	.40
228 Kip Wells	.15	.40
229 Adam Everett	.15	.40
230 Eddie Yarnall	.15	.40
231 Matt LeCroy	.15	.40
232 Jason Tyner	.15	.40
233 Rick Ankiel	.15	.40
234 Lance Berkman	.15	.40
235 Rafael Furcal	.15	.40
236 Dee Brown	.15	.40
237 Gookie Dawkins	.15	.40
238 Eric Valent	.15	.40
239 Peter Bergeron	.15	.40
240 Alfonso Soriano	.40	1.00
241 Adam Dunn	.40	1.00
242 Jorge Toca	.15	.40
243 Ryan Anderson	.15	.40
244 Jason Dellaero	.15	.40
245 Jason Grilli	.15	.40
246 Milton Bradley	.15	.40
247 Scott Downs RC	2.00	5.00
248 Keith Reed RC	2.00	5.00
249 Edgar Cruz RC	2.00	5.00
250 Wes Anderson RC	2.00	5.00
251 Lyle Overbay RC	3.00	8.00
252 Mike Lamb RC	3.00	8.00
253 Vince Faison RC	2.00	5.00
254 Chad Alexander	2.00	5.00
255 Chris Wakeland RC	2.00	5.00
256 Aaron McNeal RC	2.00	5.00
257 Tomo Ohka RC	2.00	5.00
258 Ty Howington RC	2.00	5.00
259 Javier Colina RC	2.00	5.00
260 Jason Jennings	2.00	5.00
261 Ramon Santiago RC	2.00	5.00
262 Johan Santana RC	12.50	30.00
263 Quincy Foster RC	2.00	5.00
264 Junior Brignac RC	2.00	5.00
265 Rico Washington RC	2.00	5.00
266 Scott Sobkowiak RC	2.00	5.00
267 Pedro Martinez Rick Ankiel	.60	1.50
268 Manny Ramirez Vladimir Guerrero	1.00	2.50
269 A.J.Burnett Mark Mulder	.40	1.00
270 Mike Piazza Eric Munson	1.00	2.50
271 Josh Hamilton Corey Patterson	1.25	3.00
272 Ken Griffey Jr. Sammy Sosa	.75	2.00
273 Derek Jeter Alfonso Soriano	1.50	4.00
274 Mark McGwire Pat Burrell	1.50	4.00
275 Chipper Jones Cal Ripken	1.50	4.00
276 Nomar Garciaparra Alex Rodriguez	1.00	2.50
277 Pedro Martinez GEM	1.25	3.00
278 Tony Gwynn GEM	1.50	4.00
279 Barry Bonds GEM	3.00	8.00
280 Juan Gonzalez GEM	.75	2.00
281 Larry Walker GEM	.75	2.00
282 N.Garciaparra GEM	2.00	5.00
283 Ken Griffey Jr. GEM	2.00	5.00
284 Manny Ramirez GEM	1.25	3.00
285 Shawn Green GEM	.75	2.00
286 Sammy Sosa GEM	2.00	5.00

2000 Finest Gold Refractors

Randomly inserted in packs, this 287-card set parallels the base set. The set includes 179-player cards, 40 Rookie Cards (numbers 101-120 and 247-266) each serial numbered to 100, 15 Features subset cards (numbers 121-135), 10 Counterparts subset cards (numbers 267-276), and 20 Gems subset cards (numbers 136-145 and 277-286). The set also includes two versions of card number 146 Ken Griffey Jr. wearing his Reds uniform (a portrait and action shot). Rookie/Veteran Cards were seeded at a rate of 1:240 hobby/retail packs and TBD HTA packs. Features and Counterparts subset cards were inserted one every 960 hobby and retail packs and one every 400 HTA packs. Gems subset cards were inserted one every 2880 hobby and retail packs and one every 1200 HTA packs. All cards are featured on gold die-cut technology.

*STARS 1-100/146-246: 20X TO 50X BASIC
*ROOKIES 101-120: 2.5X TO 6X BASIC
*ROOKIES 247-266: 2.5X TO 6X BASIC
*FEATURES 121-135: 4X TO 10X BASIC
*GEMS 136-145/277-286: 4X TO 10X BASIC
*COUNTER 267-276: 4X TO 10X BASIC
262 Johan Santana 175.00 350.00

2000 Finest Refractors

Randomly inserted in packs, this 146-card set parallels the base set. The set includes 179-player cards, 40 Rookie Cards (numbers 101-120 serial numbered to 500 and and 247-266 serial-numbered to 1,000), 15 Features subset cards (numbers 121-135), 10 Counterparts subset cards (numbers 267-276), and 20 Gems subset cards (numbers 136-145 and 277-286). The set also includes two versions of card number 146 Ken Griffey Jr. wearing his Reds uniform (a portrait and action shot). Rookie/Veteran Cards were seeded at a rate of 1:24 hobby/retail packs and 1:6 HTA packs. Features and Counterparts subset cards were inserted one every 96 hobby and retail packs and one every 40 HTA packs. Gems subset cards were inserted one every 288 hobby and retail packs and one every 120 HTA packs.

*STARS 1-100/146-246: 6X TO 15X BASIC
*ROOKIES 101-120: 1X TO 2.5X BASIC
*FEATURES 121-135: 1.5X TO 4X BASIC
*GEMS 136-145/277-286: 1.5X TO 4X BASIC
*ROOKIES 247-266: 1X TO 2.5X BASIC RC'S
*COUNTER 267-276: 1.5X TO 4X BASIC

2000 Finest Gems Oversize

Randomly inserted as a "box-topper", this 20-card oversized set features some of the best players in major league baseball. Please note that cards 1-10 were inserted into series one boxes, and cards 11-20 were inserted into series two boxes.

COMPLETE SERIES 1 (10) 30.00 60.00
COMPLETE SERIES 2 (10) 20.00 50.00
*REF: .4X TO 1X BASIC GEMS OVERSIZE
REFRACTORS ONE PER HTA CHIP-TOPPER
1 Derek Jeter 4.00 10.00
2 Alex Rodriguez 2.50 6.00
3 Chipper Jones 1.50 4.00
4 Mike Piazza 2.50 6.00
5 Mark McGwire 4.00 10.00
6 Ivan Rodriguez 1.00 2.50
7 Cal Ripken 5.00 12.00
8 Vladimir Guerrero 1.50 4.00
9 Randy Johnson 1.50 4.00
10 Jeff Bagwell 1.00 2.50
11 Nomar Garciaparra 2.50 6.00
12 Ken Griffey Jr. 2.50 6.00
13 Manny Ramirez 1.00 2.50
14 Shawn Green .60 1.50
15 Sammy Sosa 1.50 4.00
16 Pedro Martinez 1.00 2.50
17 Tony Gwynn 2.00 5.00
18 Barry Bonds 4.00 10.00
19 Juan Gonzalez .60 1.50
20 Larry Walker .60 1.50

2000 Finest Ballpark Bounties

Randomly inserted into first and second series packs at one in 24 hobby/retail and 1:12 HTA, this insert set features 30 MLB players who are "wanted" for their pure talent. Card backs carry a "BB" prefix. Please note that cards 1-15 were inserted into series one packs, while cards 16-30 were inserted into series two packs.

COMPLETE SERIES 1 (15) 30.00 80.00
COMPLETE SERIES 2 (15) 40.00 100.00
BB1 Chipper Jones 2.00 5.00
BB2 Mike Piazza 3.00 8.00
BB3 Vladimir Guerrero 2.00 5.00
BB4 Sammy Sosa 2.00 5.00
BB5 Nomar Garciaparra 3.00 8.00
BB6 Manny Ramirez 1.25 3.00
BB7 Jeff Bagwell 1.25 3.00
BB8 Scott Rolen 1.25 3.00
BB9 Carlos Beltran .75 2.00
BB10 Pedro Martinez 1.25 3.00
BB11 Greg Maddux 3.00 8.00
BB12 Josh Hamilton 2.00 5.00
BB13 Adam Piatt .75 2.00
BB14 Pat Burrell .75 2.00
BB15 Alfonso Soriano 2.00 5.00
BB16 Alex Rodriguez 3.00 8.00
BB17 Derek Jeter 5.00 12.00
BB18 Cal Ripken 6.00 15.00
BB19 Larry Walker .75 2.00
BB20 Barry Bonds 5.00 12.00
BB21 Ken Griffey Jr. 3.00 8.00
BB22 Mark McGwire 5.00 12.00
BB23 Ivan Rodriguez 1.25 3.00
BB24 Andruw Jones 1.25 3.00
BB25 Todd Helton 1.25 3.00
BB26 Randy Johnson 2.00 5.00
BB27 Ruben Mateo .75 2.00
BB28 Corey Patterson .75 2.00
BB29 Sean Burroughs .75 2.00
BB30 Eric Munson .75 2.00

2000 Finest Dream Cast

Randomly inserted into series two packs at one in 36 hobby/retail packs and one in 13 HTA packs, this 10-card insert features players that have skills people dream about having. Card backs carry a "DC" prefix.

COMPLETE SET (10) 40.00 100.00
DC1 Mark McGwire 6.00 15.00
DC2 Roberto Alomar 1.50 4.00
DC3 Chipper Jones 2.50 6.00
DC4 Derek Jeter 6.00 15.00
DC5 Barry Bonds 6.00 15.00
DC6 Ken Griffey Jr. 4.00 10.00
DC7 Sammy Sosa 2.50 6.00
DC8 Mike Piazza 4.00 10.00
DC9 Pedro Martinez 1.50 4.00
DC10 Randy Johnson 2.50 6.00

2000 Finest For the Record

Randomly inserted in first series packs at a rate of 1:71 hobby or retail and 1:33 HTA, this insert set features 30 serial-numbered cards. Each player has three versions that are sequentially numbered to the distance of the left, center, and right field walls of their home ballpark. Card backs carry a "FR" prefix.

FR1A Derek Jeter/318 12.50 30.00
FR1B Derek Jeter/408 12.50 30.00
FR1C Derek Jeter/314 12.50 30.00
FR2A Mark McGwire/330 12.50 30.00
FR2B Mark McGwire/402 12.50 30.00
FR2C Mark McGwire/330 12.50 30.00
FR3A Ken Griffey Jr./331 6.00 15.00
FR3B Ken Griffey Jr./405 6.00 15.00
FR3C Ken Griffey Jr./327 6.00 15.00
FR4A Alex Rodriguez/331 8.00 20.00
FR4B Alex Rodriguez/405 8.00 20.00
FR4C Alex Rodriguez/327 8.00 20.00
FR5A N.Garciaparra/310 6.00 15.00
FR5B N.Garciaparra/390 6.00 15.00
FR5C N.Garciaparra/302 6.00 15.00
FR6A Cal Ripken/333 15.00 40.00
FR6B Cal Ripken/410 15.00 40.00
FR6C Cal Ripken/318 15.00 40.00
FR7A Sammy Sosa/355 4.00 10.00
FR7B Sammy Sosa/400 4.00 10.00
FR7C Sammy Sosa/353 4.00 10.00
FR8A Manny Ramirez/325 4.00 10.00
FR8B Manny Ramirez/410 4.00 10.00
FR8C Manny Ramirez/325 4.00 10.00
FR9A Mike Piazza/338 6.00 15.00
FR9B Mike Piazza/410 6.00 15.00
FR9C Mike Piazza/338 6.00 15.00
FR10A Chipper Jones/335 4.00 10.00
FR10B Chipper Jones/401 4.00 10.00
FR10C Chipper Jones/330 4.00 10.00

2000 Finest Going the Distance

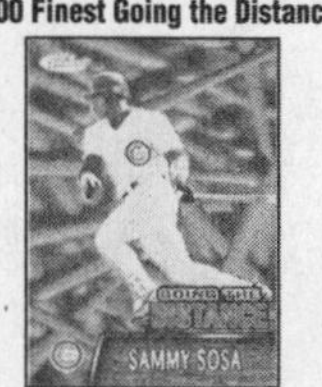

Randomly inserted in first series hobby and retail packs at one in 24 and HTA packs at a rate of one in 12, this 12-card insert set features some of the best hitters in major league baseball. Card backs carry a "GTD" prefix.

COMPLETE SET (12) 30.00 80.00
GTD1 Tony Gwynn 2.00 5.00
GTD2 Alex Rodriguez 2.50 6.00
GTD3 Derek Jeter 4.00 10.00
GTD4 Chipper Jones 1.50 4.00
GTD5 Nomar Garciaparra 2.50 6.00
GTD6 Sammy Sosa 1.50 4.00
GTD7 Ken Griffey Jr. 2.50 6.00
GTD8 Vladimir Guerrero 1.50 4.00
GTD9 Mark McGwire 4.00 10.00
GTD10 Mike Piazza 2.50 6.00
GTD11 Manny Ramirez 1.00 2.50
GTD12 Cal Ripken 5.00 12.00

2000 Finest Moments

Randomly inserted into series two hobby and retail packs at one in nine, and HTA packs at one in four, this four-card insert features great moments from the 1999 baseball season. Card backs carry a "FM" prefix.

COMPLETE SET (4) 2.50 6.00
*REFRACTORS: .75X TO 2X BASIC MOMENTS
SER.2 REF.ODDS 1:20 H/R 1:9 HTA
FM1 Chipper Jones .60 1.50
FM2 Ivan Rodriguez .40 1.00
FM3 Tony Gwynn .75 2.00
FM4 Wade Boggs .60 1.50

2000 Finest Moments Refractors Autograph

Randomly inserted into series two hobby/retail packs at one in 425, and in HTA packs at one in 196, this four-card set is a complete parallel of the Finest Moments insert. This set is autographed by the player depicted on the card. Card backs carry a "FM" prefix.

FM1 Chipper Jones 20.00 50.00
FM2 Ivan Rodriguez 15.00 40.00
FM3 Tony Gwynn 20.00 50.00
FM4 Wade Boggs 15.00 40.00

2001 Finest

This 140-card set was distributed in six-card hobby packs with a suggested retail price of $6. Printed on 27 pt. card stock, the set features color action photos of 100 veteran players, 30 draft picks and prospects printed with the "Rookie Card" logo and sequentially numbered to 999, and 10 standout veterans sequentially numbered to 1999.

COMP.SET w/o SP's 10.00 25.00
COMMON CARD (1-110) .15 .40
COMMON SP 4.00 10.00
COMMON (111-140) 4.00 10.00
1 Mike Piazza SP 8.00 20.00
2 Andruw Jones .25 .60
3 Jason Giambi .15 .40
4 Fred McGriff .25 .60
5 Vladimir Guerrero SP 4.00 10.00
6 Adrian Gonzalez 1.00 2.50
7 Pedro Martinez .25 .60
8 Mike Lieberthal .15 .40
9 Warren Morris .15 .40
10 Juan Gonzalez .15 .40
11 Jose Canseco .25 .60
12 Jose Valentin .15 .40
13 Jeff Cirillo .15 .40
14 Pokey Reese .15 .40
15 Scott Rolen .25 .60
16 Greg Maddux .60 1.50
17 Carlos Delgado .15 .40
18 Rick Ankiel .15 .40
19 Steve Finley .15 .40
20 Shawn Green .15 .40
21 Orlando Cabrera .15 .40
22 Roberto Alomar .25 .60
23 John Olerud .15 .40
24 Albert Belle .15 .40
25 Edgardo Alfonzo .15 .40
26 Rafael Palmeiro .25 .60
27 Mike Sweeney .15 .40
28 Bernie Williams .25 .60
29 Larry Walker .15 .40
30 Barry Bonds SP 10.00 25.00
31 Orlando Hernandez .15 .40
32 Randy Johnson .40 1.00
33 Shannon Stewart .15 .40
34 Mark Grace .25 .60
35 Alex Rodriguez SP 10.00 25.00
36 Tino Martinez .25 .60
37 Carlos Febles .15 .40
38 Al Leiter .15 .40
39 Omar Vizquel .25 .60
40 Chuck Knoblauch .15 .40
41 Tim Salmon .25 .60
42 Brian Jordan .15 .40
43 Edgar Renteria .15 .40
44 Preston Wilson .15 .40
45 Mariano Rivera .40 1.00
46 Gabe Kapler .15 .40
47 Jason Kendall .15 .40
48 Rickey Henderson .40 1.00
49 Luis Gonzalez .15 .40
50 Tom Glavine .25 .60
51 Jeromy Burnitz .15 .40
52 Garret Anderson .15 .40
53 Craig Biggio .25 .60
54 Vinny Castilla .15 .40
55 Jeff Kent .15 .40
56 Gary Sheffield .15 .40
57 Jorge Posada .25 .60
58 Sean Casey .15 .40
59 Johnny Damon .25 .60
60 Dean Palmer .15 .40
61 Todd Helton .25 .60
62 Barry Larkin .25 .60
63 Robin Ventura .15 .40
64 Kenny Lofton .15 .40
65 Sammy Sosa SP 4.00 10.00
66 Rafael Furcal .15 .40
67 Jay Bell .15 .40
68 J.T. Snow .15 .40
69 Jose Vidro .15 .40
70 Ivan Rodriguez .25 .60
71 Jermaine Dye .15 .40
72 Chipper Jones SP 4.00 10.00
73 Fernando Vina .15 .40
74 Ben Grieve .15 .40
75 Mark McGwire SP 10.00 25.00
76 Matt Williams .15 .40
77 Mark Grudzielanek .15 .40
78 Mike Hampton .15 .40
79 Brian Giles .15 .40
80 Tony Gwynn .50 1.25
81 Carlos Beltran .15 .40
82 Ray Durham .15 .40
83 Brad Radke .15 .40
84 David Justice .15 .40
85 Frank Thomas .40 1.00
86 Todd Zeile .15 .40
87 Pat Burrell .15 .40
88 Jim Thome .25 .60
89 Greg Vaughn .15 .40
90 Ken Griffey Jr. SP 6.00 15.00
91 Mike Mussina .25 .60
92 Magglio Ordonez .15 .40
93 Bob Abreu .15 .40
94 Alex Gonzalez .15 .40
95 Kevin Brown .15 .40
96 Jay Buhner .15 .40
97 Roger Clemens .75 2.00
98 Nomar Garciaparra SP 6.00 15.00
99 Derrek Lee .25 .60
100 Derek Jeter SP 10.00 25.00
101 Adrian Beltre .15 .40
102 Geoff Jenkins .15 .40
103 Javy Lopez .15 .40
104 Raul Mondesi .15 .40
105 Troy Glaus .15 .40
106 Jeff Bagwell .25 .60
107 Eric Karros .15 .40
108 Mo Vaughn .15 .40
109 Cal Ripken 1.25 3.00
110 Manny Ramirez Sox .25 .60
111 Scott Heard PROS 4.00 10.00
112 L. Montanez PROS RC 4.00 10.00
113 Ben Diggins PROS 4.00 10.00
114 Shaun Boyd PROS RC 4.00 10.00
115 Sean Burnett PROS 4.00 10.00
116 Carmen Cali PROS RC 4.00 10.00
117 D.Thompson PROS 4.00 10.00
118 D.Parrish PROS RC 4.00 10.00
119 D.Rich PROS RC 4.00 10.00
120 Chad Petty PROS RC 4.00 10.00
121 S.Smyth PROS RC 4.00 10.00
122 John Lackey PROS 4.00 10.00
123 M.Galante PROS RC 4.00 10.00
124 D.Borrell PROS RC 4.00 10.00
125 Bob Keppel PROS RC 4.00 10.00
126 J.Wayne PROS RC 4.00 10.00
127 J.R. House PROS 4.00 10.00
128 Brian Sellier PROS RC 4.00 10.00
129 Dan Moylan PROS RC 4.00 10.00
130 Scott Pratt PROS RC 4.00 10.00
131 Victor Hall PROS RC 4.00 10.00
132 Joel Pineiro PROS 4.00 10.00
133 J.Axelson PROS RC 4.00 10.00
134 Jose Reyes PROS RC 30.00 60.00
135 G. Runser PROS RC 4.00 10.00
136 B. Hebson PROS RC 4.00 10.00
137 S.Serrano PROS RC 4.00 10.00
138 K. Joseph PROS RC 4.00 10.00
139 J. Richardson PROS RC 4.00 10.00
140 M. Fischer PROS RC 4.00 10.00

2001 Finest Refractors

This 140-card set is a parallel version of the base set and is distinguished by the refractive quality of the cards. The 100 veteran cards are sequentially numbered to 499, the 30 draft picks and prospects to 241, and the 10 standout veterans to 399.

*1-110 REF: 4X TO 10X BASIC 1-110
*SP REF: .5X TO 1.2X BASIC SP
*111-140 REF: .75X TO 2X BASIC 111-140

2001 Finest All-Stars

Randomly inserted in packs at the rate of one in five, this 10-card set features color photos of the preeminent players at their respective postions. A refractive parallel version of this insert set was also produced and inserted in packs at the rate of one in 20.

COMPLETE SET (10) 30.00 60.00
*REF: 1X TO 2.5X BASIC ALL-STARS
REFRACTOR ODDS 1:40 HOBBY, 1:20 HTA
FAS1 Mark McGwire 4.00 10.00
FAS2 Derek Jeter 4.00 10.00
FAS3 Alex Rodriguez 2.50 6.00
FAS4 Chipper Jones 1.50 4.00
FAS5 Nomar Garciaparra 2.50 6.00
FAS6 Sammy Sosa 1.50 4.00
FAS7 Mike Piazza 2.50 6.00
FAS8 Barry Bonds 4.00 10.00
FAS9 Vladimir Guerrero 1.50 4.00
FAS10 Ken Griffey Jr. 2.50 6.00

2001 Finest Autographs

Randomly inserted in packs at the rate of one in 22, this 29-card set features autographed color photos of players who made the moments. All of these cards are refractors and carry the Topps "Certified Autograph" stamp and the Topps "Genuine Issue" sticker.

FAAG Adrian Gonzalez 20.00 50.00
FAAH Adam Hyzdu 4.00 10.00
FAAK Adam Kennedy 6.00 15.00
FAAP Albert Pujols 300.00 500.00
FABD Ben Diggins 4.00 10.00
FABM Ben Molina 6.00 15.00
FABS Ben Sheets 10.00 25.00
FABZ Barry Zito 10.00 25.00
FABKC Brian Cole 4.00 10.00
FACD Chad Durham 4.00 10.00
FACP Carlos Pena 12.50 30.00
FADK Dave Krynzel 4.00 10.00
FADCP Corey Patterson 4.00 10.00
FAJC Joe Crede 10.00 25.00
FAJH Jason Hart 4.00 10.00
FAJM Justin Morneau 40.00 80.00
FAJO Jose Ortiz 4.00 10.00
FAJP Jay Payton 4.00 10.00
FAJHH Josh Hamilton 12.50 30.00
FAJRH J.R. House 4.00 10.00
FAKG Keith Ginter 4.00 10.00
FAKM Kevin Mench 6.00 15.00
FAMB Milton Bradley 6.00 15.00
FAMQ Mark Quinn 4.00 10.00
FAMR Mark Redman 4.00 10.00
FARF Rafael Furcal 6.00 15.00
FASB Sean Burnett 4.00 10.00
FATF Troy Farnsworth 4.00 10.00
FATL Terrence Long 4.00 10.00

2001 Finest Moments

Randomly inserted in packs at the rate of one in 12, this 25-card set features color photos of players involved in great moments from the 2000 season plus both active and retired 3000 Hit Club members. A refractive parallel version of this set was also produced with an insertion rate of 1:40.

COMPLETE SET (25) 60.00 120.00
*REF: .75X TO 2X BASIC MOMENTS
REFRACTOR ODDS 1:40 HOBBY, 1:20 HTA
FM1 Pat Burrell 1.00 2.50
FM2 Adam Kennedy 1.00 2.50
FM3 Mike Lamb 1.00 2.50
FM4 Rafael Furcal 1.00 2.50
FM5 Terrence Long 1.00 2.50
FM6 Jay Payton 1.00 2.50
FM7 Mark Quinn 1.00 2.50
FM8 Ben Molina 1.00 2.50
FM9 Kazuhiro Sasaki 1.00 2.50
FM10 Mark Redman 1.00 2.50
FM11 Barry Bonds 6.00 15.00
FM12 Alex Rodriguez 4.00 10.00
FM13 Roger Clemens 5.00 12.00
FM14 Jim Edmonds 1.00 2.50
FM15 Jason Giambi 1.00 2.50
FM16 Todd Helton 1.50 4.00
FM17 Troy Glaus 1.00 2.50
FM18 Carlos Delgado 1.00 2.50
FM19 Darin Erstad 1.00 2.50
FM20 Cal Ripken 8.00 20.00
FM21 Paul Molitor 1.00 2.50
FM22 Robin Yount 2.50 6.00
FM23 George Brett 5.00 12.00
FM24 Dave Winfield 1.00 2.50
FM25 Eddie Murray 2.50 6.00

2001 Finest Moments Refractors Autograph

Randomly inserted in packs at the rate of one in 250, this 10-card set features autographed player photos with the Topps "Certified Autograph" stamp and the Topps "Genuine Issue" sticker printed on these refractive cards. Exchange cards with a redemption deadline of April 30, 2003 were seeded into packs for Cal Ripken, Eddie Murray and Robin Yount.

FMABB Barry Bonds 100.00 175.00
FMACR Cal Ripken 75.00 150.00
FMADW Dave Winfield 15.00 40.00
FMAEM Eddie Murray 30.00 60.00
FMAGB George Brett 60.00 120.00
FMAJG Jason Giambi 15.00 40.00
FMAPM Paul Molitor 15.00 40.00
FMARY Robin Yount 30.00 60.00
FMATG Troy Glaus 15.00 40.00
FMATH Todd Helton 15.00 40.00

2001 Finest Origins

Randomly inserted in packs at the rate of one in seven, this 15-card set features some of today's best ballplayers who didn't make the 1993 Finest cut. These cards are printed in the 1993 classic Finest card design. A refractive parallel version of this set was also produced with an insertion rate of 1:40.

COMPLETE SET (15) 20.00 40.00
*REF: 1X TO 2.5X BASIC ORIGINS
REFRACTOR ODDS 1:40 HOBBY, 1:20 HTA
FO1 Derek Jeter 5.00 12.00
FO2 Jason Kendall .75 2.00
FO3 Jose Vidro .75 2.00
FO4 Preston Wilson .75 2.00
FO5 Jim Edmonds .75 2.00
FO6 Vladimir Guerrero 2.00 5.00
FO7 Andruw Jones 1.25 3.00
FO8 Scott Rolen 1.25 3.00
FO9 Edgardo Alfonzo .75 2.00
FO10 Mike Sweeney .75 2.00
FO11 Alex Rodriguez 3.00 8.00
FO12 Jermaine Dye .75 2.00
FO13 Charles Johnson .75 2.00
FO14 Darren Dreifort .75 2.00
FO15 Neifi Perez .75 2.00

2002 Finest

This 110 card set was issued in five card pack with an SRP of $6 per pack which were packed six per mini box with three mini boxes per full box and twelve boxes per case. Cards number 101 through 110 are Rookie Cards which were all autographed by the featured player. One of these autograph cards were inserted into each six pack mini box.

COMP.SET w/o SP's (100) 10.00 25.00
COMMON CARD (1-100) .20 .50
COMMON CARD (101-110) 4.00 10.00
1 Mike Mussina .30 .75
2 Steve Sparks .20 .50
3 Randy Johnson .50 1.25
4 Orlando Cabrera .20 .50
5 Jeff Kent .20 .50
6 Carlos Delgado .20 .50
7 Ivan Rodriguez .30 .75
8 Jose Cruz .20 .50
9 Jason Giambi .20 .50
10 Brad Penny .20 .50
11 Moises Alou .20 .50
12 Mike Piazza .75 2.00
13 Ben Grieve .20 .50
14 Derek Jeter 1.25 3.00
15 Roy Oswalt .20 .50
16 Pat Burrell .20 .50
17 Preston Wilson .20 .50
18 Kevin Brown .20 .50
19 Barry Bonds 1.25 3.00
20 Phil Nevin .20 .50
21 Aramis Ramirez .20 .50
22 Carlos Beltran .20 .50
23 Chipper Jones .50 1.25
24 Curt Schilling .20 .50
25 Jorge Posada .30 .75
26 Alfonso Soriano .20 .50
27 Cliff Floyd .20 .50
28 Rafael Palmeiro .30 .75
29 Terrence Long .20 .50
30 Ken Griffey Jr. .75 2.00
31 Jason Kendall .20 .50
32 Jose Vidro .20 .50
33 Jermaine Dye .20 .50
34 Bobby Higginson .20 .50
35 Albert Pujols 1.00 2.50
36 Miguel Tejada .20 .50
37 Jim Edmonds .20 .50
38 Barry Zito .20 .50
39 Jimmy Rollins .20 .50
40 Rafael Furcal .20 .50
41 Omar Vizquel .30 .75
42 Kazuhiro Sasaki .20 .50
43 Brian Giles .20 .50
44 Darin Erstad .20 .50
45 Mariano Rivera .50 1.25
46 Troy Percival .20 .50
47 Mike Sweeney .20 .50
48 Vladimir Guerrero .50 1.25
49 Troy Glaus .20 .50
50 So Taguchi RC 1.00 2.50
51 Edgardo Alfonzo .20 .50
52 Roger Clemens 1.00 2.50
53 Eric Chavez .20 .50
54 Alex Rodriguez .75 2.00
55 Cristian Guzman .20 .50
56 Jeff Bagwell .30 .75
57 Bernie Williams .30 .75
58 Kerry Wood .20 .50
59 Ryan Klesko .20 .50
60 Ichiro Suzuki 1.00 2.50
61 Larry Walker .20 .50
62 Nomar Garciaparra .75 2.00
63 Craig Biggio .30 .75
64 J.D. Drew .20 .50
65 Juan Pierre .20 .50
66 Roberto Alomar .30 .75
67 Luis Gonzalez .20 .50
68 Bud Smith .20 .50
69 Magglio Ordonez .20 .50
70 Scott Rolen .30 .75
71 Tsuyoshi Shinjo .20 .50
72 Paul Konerko .20 .50
73 Garret Anderson .20 .50
74 Tim Hudson .20 .50
75 Adam Dunn .20 .50
76 Gary Sheffield .20 .50
77 Johnny Damon Sox .30 .75
78 Todd Helton .30 .75
79 Geoff Jenkins .20 .50
80 Shawn Green .20 .50
81 C.C. Sabathia .20 .50
82 Kazuhisa Ishii RC UER 1.00 2.50
2001 ERA is incorrect
83 Rich Aurilia .20 .50
84 Mike Hampton .20 .50
85 Ben Sheets .20 .50
86 Andruw Jones .30 .75
87 Richie Sexson .20 .50
88 Jim Thome .30 .75
89 Sammy Sosa .50 1.25
90 Greg Maddux .75 2.00
91 Pedro Martinez .30 .75
92 Jeromy Burnitz .20 .50
93 Raul Mondesi .20 .50
94 Bret Boone .20 .50
95 Jerry Hairston .20 .50
96 Mike Rivera .20 .50
97 Juan Cruz .20 .50
98 Morgan Ensberg .20 .50
99 Nathan Haynes .20 .50
100 Xavier Nady .20 .50
101 Nic Jackson FY AU RC 4.00 10.00
102 Mauricio Lara FY AU RC 4.00 10.00
103 Freddy Sanchez FY AU RC 6.00 15.00
104 Clint Nageotte FY AU RC 4.00 10.00
105 Beltran Perez FY AU RC 4.00 10.00
106 Garrett Gentry FY AU RC 4.00 10.00
107 Chad Qualls FY AU RC 4.00 10.00
108 Jason Bay FY AU RC 10.00 25.00
109 Michael Hill FY AU RC 4.00 10.00
110 Brian Tallet FY AU RC 4.00 10.00

2002 Finest Refractors

Inserted in packs at stated odds of one in two mini boxes, these cards parallel the 2002 Finest set. These cards have the patented topps "refractor" sheen and have a stated print run of 499 serial numbered sets.

*REFRACTORS 1-100: 2.5X TO 6X BASIC
*REF.RC'S 1-100: 1.5X TO 4X BASIC
101 Nic Jackson FY 2.00 5.00
102 Mauricio Lara FY 2.00 5.00
103 Freddy Sanchez FY 5.00 12.00
104 Clint Nageotte FY 3.00 8.00
105 Beltran Perez FY 2.00 5.00
106 Garett Gentry FY 2.00 5.00
107 Chad Qualls FY 3.00 8.00
108 Jason Bay FY 6.00 15.00
109 Michael Hill FY 2.00 5.00
110 Brian Tallet FY 2.00 5.00

2002 Finest X-Fractors

Inserted at a rate of one in three mini boxes, these cards parallel the Finest set. These cards have a uniquely patterned finest design and are printed to a stated print run of 299 serial numbered sets.

*XF 1-100: 3X TO 8X BASIC
*XF RC'S 1-100: 2X TO 5X BASIC
*XF 101-110: .5X TO 1.2X REFRACTOR

2002 Finest X-Fractors Protectors

Inserted at a rate of one in seven mini boxes, these cards parallel the Finest set. These cards have a uniquely patterned finest design and were created with a "finest protector" and are printed to a stated print run of 99 serial numbered sets.

*XF PROT. 1-100: 6X TO 15X BASIC
*XF PROT.RC'S 1-100: 4X TO 10X BASIC
*XF PROT 101-110: .75X TO 2X REFRACTOR

2002 Finest Bat Relics

Inserted at a stated rate of one in 12 mini boxes these 15 cards feature a bat slice from the featured player.

FBRAJ Andruw Jones	6.00	15.00
FBRAP Albert Pujols	8.00	20.00
FBRAR Alex Rodriguez	6.00	15.00
FBRAS Alfonso Soriano	4.00	10.00
FBRBB Barry Bonds	10.00	25.00
FBRBO Bret Boone	4.00	10.00
FBRBW Bernie Williams	6.00	15.00
FBRCJ Chipper Jones	6.00	15.00
FBRIR Ivan Rodriguez	6.00	15.00
FBRLG Luis Gonzalez	4.00	10.00
FBRMP Mike Piazza	6.00	15.00
FBRNG Nomar Garciaparra	6.00	15.00
FBRTG Tony Gwynn	6.00	15.00
FBRTH Todd Helton	6.00	15.00
FBRTS Tsuyoshi Shinjo	4.00	10.00

2002 Finest Jersey Relics

Inserted at a stated rate of one in four mini boxes, these 24 cards feature the player photo along with a game-used jersey swatch.

FJRAJ Andruw Jones	6.00	15.00
FJRAR Alex Rodriguez	6.00	15.00
FJRBB Barry Bonds	10.00	25.00
FJRBO Bret Boone	4.00	10.00
FJRCD Carlos Delgado	4.00	10.00
FJRCJ Chipper Jones	6.00	15.00
FJRCS Curt Schilling	4.00	10.00
FJRFT Frank Thomas	6.00	15.00
FJRGM Greg Maddux	6.00	15.00
FJRHN Hideo Nomo	6.00	15.00
FJRIR Ivan Rodriguez	6.00	15.00
FJRJB Jeff Bagwell	6.00	15.00
FJRLG Luis Gonzalez	4.00	10.00
FJRLW Larry Walker	4.00	10.00
FJRMG Mark Grace	6.00	15.00
FJRMP Mike Piazza	6.00	15.00
FJRPM Pedro Martinez	6.00	15.00
FJRRA Roberto Alomar	6.00	15.00
FJRRH Rickey Henderson	6.00	15.00
FJRRP Rafael Palmeiro	6.00	15.00
FJRSG Shawn Green	4.00	10.00
FJRTG Tony Gwynn	6.00	15.00
FJRTH Todd Helton	6.00	15.00
FJRTS Tsuyoshi Shinjo	4.00	10.00

2002 Finest Moments Autographs

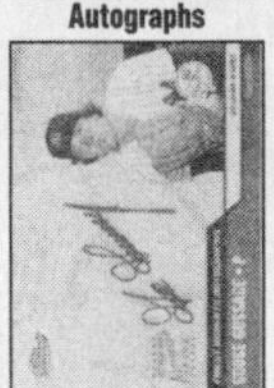

Inserted at a stated rate of one in three mini boxes, these cards feature leading retired players who signed cards honoring their greatest career moment.

FMABG Bob Gibson	12.50	30.00
FMABR Bobby Richardson	8.00	20.00
FMABT Bobby Thomson	10.00	25.00
FMADL Don Larsen	6.00	15.00
FMADM Don Mattingly	20.00	50.00
FMAFJ Fergie Jenkins	10.00	25.00
FMAGG Goose Gossage	10.00	25.00
FMAGP Gaylord Perry	6.00	15.00
FMAJB Jim Bunning	6.00	15.00
FMAJS Johnny Sain	10.00	25.00
FMALA Luis Aparicio	10.00	25.00
FMAMS Mike Schmidt	20.00	50.00
FMARS Red Schoendienst	6.00	15.00
FMAYB Yogi Berra	20.00	50.00
FMABRO Brooks Robinson	10.00	25.00

2003 Finest

This 110 card set was released in May, 2003. This product was issued in six pack mini-boxes with an SRP of $36. The first 100 cards are veterans while the final 10 cards featured autographed cards of leading rookies and prospects. Those cards (101-110) were issued at a stated rate of one in four mini boxes.

COMP.SET w/o SP's (100)	10.00	25.00
COMMON CARD (1-100)	.20	.50
COMMON CARD (101-110)	6.00	15.00
1 Sammy Sosa	.50	1.25
2 Paul Konerko	.20	.50
3 Todd Helton	.30	.75
4 Mike Lowell	.20	.50
5 Lance Berkman	.20	.50
6 Kazuhisa Ishii	.20	.50
7 A.J. Pierzynski	.20	.50
8 Jose Vidro	.20	.50
9 Roberto Alomar	.30	.75
10 Derek Jeter	1.25	3.00
11 Barry Zito	.20	.50
12 Jimmy Rollins	.20	.50
13 Brian Giles	.20	.50
14 Ryan Klesko	.20	.50
15 Rich Aurilia	.20	.50
16 Jim Edmonds	.20	.50
17 Aubrey Huff	.20	.50
18 Ivan Rodriguez	.30	.75
19 Eric Hinske	.20	.50
20 Barry Bonds	1.25	3.00
21 Darin Erstad	.20	.50
22 Curt Schilling	.20	.50
23 Andruw Jones	.30	.75
24 Jay Gibbons	.20	.50
25 Nomar Garciaparra	.75	2.00
26 Kerry Wood	.20	.50
27 Magglio Ordonez	.20	.50
28 Austin Kearns	.20	.50
29 Jason Jennings	.20	.50
30 Jason Giambi	.20	.50
31 Tim Hudson	.20	.50
32 Edgar Martinez	.30	.75
33 Carl Crawford	.20	.50
34 Hee Seop Choi	.20	.50
35 Vladimir Guerrero	.50	1.25
36 Jeff Kent	.20	.50
37 John Smoltz	.30	.75
38 Frank Thomas	.50	1.25
39 Cliff Floyd	.20	.50
40 Mike Piazza	.75	2.00
41 Mark Prior	.30	.75
42 Tim Salmon	.30	.75
43 Shawn Green	.20	.50
44 Bernie Williams	.30	.75
45 Jim Thome	.30	.75
46 John Olerud	.20	.50
47 Orlando Hudson	.20	.50
48 Mark Teixeira	.30	.75
49 Gary Sheffield	.20	.50
50 Ichiro Suzuki	1.00	2.50
51 Tom Glavine	.30	.75
52 Torii Hunter	.20	.50
53 Craig Biggio	.30	.75
54 Carlos Beltran	.20	.50
55 Bartolo Colon	.20	.50
56 Jorge Posada	.30	.75
57 Pat Burrell	.20	.50
58 Edgar Renteria	.20	.50
59 Rafael Palmeiro	.30	.75
60 Alfonso Soriano	.20	.50
61 Brandon Phillips	.20	.50
62 Luis Gonzalez	.20	.50
63 Manny Ramirez	.30	.75
64 Garret Anderson	.20	.50
65 Ken Griffey Jr.	.75	2.00
66 A.J. Burnett	.20	.50
67 Mike Sweeney	.20	.50
68 Doug Mientkiewicz	.20	.50
69 Eric Chavez	.20	.50
70 Adam Dunn	.20	.50
71 Shea Hillenbrand	.20	.50
72 Troy Glaus	.20	.50
73 Rodrigo Lopez	.20	.50
74 Moises Alou	.20	.50
75 Chipper Jones	.50	1.25
76 Bobby Abreu	.20	.50
77 Mark Mulder	.20	.50
78 Kevin Brown	.20	.50
79 Josh Beckett	.20	.50
80 Larry Walker	.20	.50
81 Randy Johnson	.50	1.25
82 Greg Maddux	.75	2.00
83 Johnny Damon	.30	.75
84 Omar Vizquel	.30	.75
85 Jeff Bagwell	.30	.75
86 Carlos Pena	.20	.50
87 Roy Oswalt	.20	.50
88 Richie Sexson	.20	.50
89 Roger Clemens	1.00	2.50
90 Miguel Tejada	.20	.50
91 Vicente Padilla	.20	.50
92 Phil Nevin	.20	.50
93 Edgardo Alfonzo	.20	.50
94 Bret Boone	.20	.50
95 Albert Pujols	1.00	2.50
96 Carlos Delgado	.20	.50
97 Jose Contreras RC	.75	2.00
98 Scott Rolen	.30	.75
99 Pedro Martinez	.30	.75
100 Alex Rodriguez	.75	2.00
101 Adam LaRoche AU	6.00	15.00
102 Andy Marte AU RC	25.00	50.00
103 Daryl Clark AU RC	4.00	10.00
104 J.D. Durbin AU RC	4.00	10.00
105 Craig Brazell AU RC	4.00	10.00
106 Brian Burgamy AU RC	4.00	10.00
107 Tyler Johnson AU RC	4.00	10.00
108 Joey Gomes AU RC	4.00	10.00
109 Bryan Bullington AU RC	6.00	15.00
110 Byron Gettis AU RC	4.00	10.00

2003 Finest Refractors

This is a complete parallel of the basic Finest set. Cards numbered 1-100 were issued at a stated rate of one per mini-box and cards numbered 101-110 were issued at a stated rate of one every 34 mini-boxes.

*REFRACTORS 1-100: 2X TO 5X BASIC
*REFRACTOR RC'S 1-100: 1.25X TO 3X BASIC
*REFRACTORS 101-110: .75X TO 2X BASIC

2003 Finest X-Fractors

Inserted at a stated rate of one in seven mini-boxes, this is a parallel to the Finest set. These cards were issued to a stated print run of 99 serial numbered sets.

*X-FRACTORS 1-100: 6X TO 15X BASIC
*X-FRACTOR RC'S 1-100: 4X TO 10X BASIC
*X-FRACTORS 101-110: 1X TO 2.5X BASIC

2003 Finest Uncirculated Gold X-Fractors

Issued as a box topper for the big box which contained all the mini-boxes, this is a parallel to the basic set. These cards are sealed in plastic holders and were issued to a stated print run of 199 serial numbered sets.

*GOLD X-F 1-100: 5X TO 12X BASIC
*GOLD X-F RC'S 1-100: 3X TO 8X BASIC
*GOLD X-F 101-110: .75X TO 2X BASIC

2003 Finest Bat Relics

These cards were inserted at different rates depending on what group the bat relic belonged to. We have notated what group the player belonged to next to their name in our checklist.

GROUP A STATED ODDS 1:104 MINI-BOXES
GROUP B STATED ODDS 1:32 MINI-BOXES
GROUP C STATED ODDS 1:29 MINI-BOXES
GROUP D STATED ODDS 1:42 MINI-BOXES
GROUP E STATED ODDS 1:40 MINI-BOXES
GROUP F STATED ODDS 1:23 MINI-BOXES
GROUP G STATED ODDS 1:18 MINI-BOXES
GROUP H STATED ODDS 1:24 MINI-BOXES
GROUP I STATED ODDS 1:12 MINI-BOXES
GROUP J STATED ODDS 1:22 MINI-BOXES
GROUP K STATED ODDS 1:21 MINI-BOXES

AD Adam Dunn H	3.00	8.00
AK Austin Kearns F	3.00	8.00
AP Albert Pujols I	6.00	15.00
AR Alex Rodriguez E	6.00	15.00
AS Alfonso Soriano H	3.00	8.00
BB Barry Bonds F	8.00	20.00
CJ Chipper Jones G	6.00	15.00
CR Cal Ripken B	15.00	40.00
DM Dale Murphy I	4.00	10.00
GM Greg Maddux F	6.00	15.00
IR Ivan Rodriguez G	4.00	10.00
JB Jeff Bagwell D	4.00	10.00
JT Jim Thome D	4.00	10.00
KP Kirby Puckett K	6.00	15.00
LB Lance Berkman C	3.00	8.00
MP Mike Piazza E	6.00	15.00
MR Manny Ramirez I	4.00	10.00
MS Mike Schmidt C	10.00	25.00
MT Miguel Tejada I	3.00	8.00
NG Nomar Garciaparra A	10.00	25.00
PM Paul Molitor C	3.00	8.00
RC Rod Carew K	4.00	10.00
RCL Roger Clemens J	6.00	15.00
RH Rickey Henderson B	6.00	15.00
RP Rafael Palmeiro J	4.00	10.00
TH Todd Helton B	4.00	10.00
WB Wade Boggs G	4.00	10.00

2003 Finest Moments Refractors Autographs

Inserted at different odds depening on whether the card was issued as part of group A or group B, this 12 card set features authentic signatures of baseball legends. Johnny Sain did not return his card in time for inclusion in this product and the exchange cards could be redeemed until April 30th, 2005.

GROUP A STATED ODDS 1:113 MINI-BOXES
GROUP B STATED ODDS 1:5 MINI-BOXES

DL Don Larsen B	8.00	20.00
EB Ernie Banks A	30.00	60.00
GC Gary Carter B	12.50	30.00
GF George Foster B	6.00	15.00
GG Goose Gossage B	6.00	15.00
GP Gaylord Perry B	6.00	15.00
JP Jim Palmer B	6.00	15.00
JS Johnny Sain B	6.00	15.00
KH Keith Hernandez B	10.00	25.00
LB Lou Brock B	10.00	25.00
OC Orlando Cepeda B	6.00	15.00
PB Paul Blair B	6.00	15.00
WMA Willie Mays A	100.00	200.00

2003 Finest Uniform Relics

These 22 cards were inserted in different odds depending on what group the player belonged to. We have notated what group the player belonged to next to their name in our checklist.

GROUP A STATED ODDS 1:28 MINI-BOXES
GROUP B STATED ODDS 1:11 MINI-BOXES
GROUP C STATED ODDS 1:11 MINI-BOXES
GROUP D STATED ODDS 1:10 MINI-BOXES
GROUP E STATED ODDS 1:19 MINI-BOXES
GROUP F STATED ODDS 1:12 MINI-BOXES
GROUP G STATED ODDS 1:34 MINI-BOXES
GROUP H STATED ODDS 1:17 MINI-BOXES

AD Adam Dunn B	3.00	8.00
AJ Andruw Jones H	4.00	10.00
AP Albert Pujols D	6.00	15.00
AR Alex Rodriguez F	6.00	15.00
AS Alfonso Soriano A	3.00	8.00
BB Barry Bonds D	8.00	20.00
CJ Chipper Jones B	6.00	15.00
CS Curt Schilling B	3.00	8.00
EC Eric Chavez B	3.00	8.00
GM Greg Maddux C	6.00	15.00
LG Luis Gonzalez D	3.00	8.00
LW Larry Walker C	3.00	8.00
MM Mark Mulder C	3.00	8.00
MP Mike Piazza C	6.00	15.00
MR Manny Ramirez E	4.00	10.00
MSW Mike Sweeney F	3.00	8.00
RJ Randy Johnson H	6.00	15.00
RO Roy Oswalt G	3.00	8.00
RP Rafael Palmeiro E	4.00	10.00
SS Sammy Sosa D	6.00	15.00
TH Todd Helton F	4.00	10.00
WM Willie Mays A	20.00	50.00

2004 Finest

This 122 card set was released in May, 2004. The set was issued in 30-card packs with a $40 SRP. Those packs were issued three to a box and 12 boxes to a case. The first 100 cards in this set feature veterans while cards 101-110 feature veteran players with a game-used jersey swatch on the card and cards 111-122 feature autograph rookie cards. Please note that David Murphy and Lastings Milledge did not sign their cards in time for pack out and those cards could be redeemed until April 30, 2006. In addition, troubled Marlins prospect Jeff Allison also had an exchange card with a 4/30/06 redemption deadline seeded into packs, but Topps was unable to fulfill the redemption and sent 2004 Topps World Series Highlights Autographs Bobby Thomson cards in their place.

COMP.SET w/o SP's (100)	10.00	25.00
COMMON CARD (1-100)	.20	.50
COMMON CARD (101-110)	3.00	8.00
101-110 STATED ODDS 1:7 MINI-BOXES		
COMMON CARD (111-122)	4.00	10.00
111-122 STATED ODDS 1:3 MINI-BOXES		
EXCHANGE DEADLINE 04/30/06		
CARD 112 EXCH UNABLE TO BE FULFILLED		
04 WS HL B.THOMSON AU SENT INSTEAD		
1 Juan Pierre	.20	.50
2 Derek Jeter	1.25	3.00
3 Garret Anderson	.20	.50
4 Javy Lopez	.20	.50
5 Corey Patterson	.20	.50
6 Todd Helton	.30	.75
7 Roy Oswalt	.30	.75
8 Shawn Green	.20	.50
9 Vladimir Guerrero	.50	1.25
10 Jorge Posada	.30	.75
11 Jason Kendall	.20	.50
12 Scott Rolen	.30	.75
13 Randy Johnson	.50	1.25
14 Bill Mueller	.20	.50
15 Magglio Ordonez	.30	.75
16 Larry Walker	.30	.75
17 Lance Berkman	.30	.75
18 Richie Sexson	.20	.50
19 Orlando Cabrera	.20	.50
20 Alfonso Soriano	.20	.50
21 Kevin Millwood	.20	.50
22 Edgar Martinez	.30	.75
23 Aubrey Huff	.20	.50
24 Carlos Delgado	.20	.50
25 Vernon Wells	.20	.50
26 Mark Teixeira	.50	1.25
27 Troy Glaus	.20	.50
28 Jeff Kent	.20	.50
29 Hideo Nomo	.50	1.25
30 Torii Hunter	.20	.50
31 Hank Blalock	.20	.50
32 Brandon Webb	.20	.50
33 Tony Batista	.20	.50
34 Bret Boone	.20	.50
35 Ryan Klesko	.20	.50
36 Barry Zito	.20	.50
37 Edgar Renteria	.20	.50
38 Geoff Jenkins	.20	.50
39 Jeff Bagwell	.30	.75
40 Dontrelle Willis	.20	.50
41 Adam Dunn	.30	.75
42 Mark Buehrle	.30	.75
43 Esteban Loaiza	.20	.50
44 Angel Berroa	.20	.50
45 Ivan Rodriguez	.30	.75
46 Jose Vidro	.20	.50
47 Mark Mulder	.20	.50
48 Roger Clemens	.60	1.50
49 Jim Edmonds	.30	.75
50 Eric Gagne	.20	.50
51 Marcus Giles	.20	.50
52 Curt Schilling	.30	.75
53 Ken Griffey Jr.	.75	2.00
54 Jason Schmidt	.20	.50
55 Miguel Tejada	.30	.75
56 Dmitri Young	.20	.50
57 Mike Lowell	.20	.50
58 Mike Sweeney	.20	.50
59 Scott Podsednik	.20	.50
60 Miguel Cabrera	.50	1.25
61 Johan Santana	.50	1.25
62 Bernie Williams	.30	.75
63 Eric Chavez	.20	.50
64 Bobby Abreu	.20	.50
65 Brian Giles	.20	.50
66 Michael Young	.20	.50
67 Paul Lo Duca	.20	.50
68 Austin Kearns	.20	.50
69 Jody Gerut	.20	.50
70 Kerry Wood	.20	.50
71 Luis Matos	.20	.50
72 Greg Maddux	.75	2.00
73 Alex Rodriguez Yanks	.75	2.00
74 Mike Lieberthal	.20	.50
75 Jim Thome	.30	.75
76 Javier Vazquez	.20	.50
77 Bartolo Colon	.20	.50
78 Manny Ramirez	.50	1.25
79 Jacque Jones	.20	.50
80 Johnny Damon	.30	.75
81 Carlos Beltran	.20	.50
82 C.C. Sabathia	.30	.75
83 Preston Wilson	.20	.50
84 Luis Castillo	.20	.50
85 Kevin Brown	.20	.50
86 Shannon Stewart	.20	.50
87 Cliff Floyd	.20	.50
88 Mike Mussina	.30	.75
89 Rafael Furcal	.20	.50
90 Roy Halladay	.50	1.25
91 Frank Thomas	.50	1.25
92 Melvin Mora	.20	.50
93 Andruw Jones	.20	.50
94 Luis Gonzalez	.20	.50
95 David Ortiz	.50	1.25
96 Gary Sheffield	.20	.50
97 Tim Hudson	.30	.75
98 Phil Nevin	.20	.50
99 Ichiro Suzuki	.75	2.00
100 Albert Pujols	1.25	3.00
101 Nomar Garciaparra SR Jsy	6.00	15.00
102 Sammy Sosa SR Jsy	4.00	10.00
103 Josh Beckett SR Jsy	3.00	8.00
104 Jason Giambi SR Jsy	3.00	8.00
105 Rocco Baldelli SR Jsy	3.00	8.00
106 Jose Reyes SR Jsy	3.00	8.00
107 Chipper Jones SR Jsy	4.00	10.00
108 Pedro Martinez SR Jsy	4.00	10.00
109 Mike Piazza SR Jsy	6.00	15.00
110 Mark Prior SR Jsy	4.00	10.00
111 Craig Ansman AU RC	4.00	10.00
113 David Murphy AU RC	5.00	12.00
114 Jason Hirsh AU RC	10.00	25.00
115 Matt Moses AU RC	6.00	15.00
116 Estee Harris AU RC	6.00	15.00
117 Logan Kensing AU RC	4.00	10.00
118 L.Milledge AU RC	10.00	25.00
119 Merkin Valdez AU RC	4.00	10.00
120 Travis Blackley AU RC	4.00	10.00
121 Vito Chiaravalloti AU RC	4.00	10.00
122 Dioner Navarro AU RC	4.00	10.00

2004 Finest Gold Refractors

*GOLD REF 1-100: 6X TO 15X BASIC
1-100 STATED ODDS 1:11
*GOLD REF 101-110: 1.25X TO 3X BASIC
101-110 STATED ODDS 1:102
*GOLD REF 111-122: 2X TO 4X BASIC
111-122 STATED ODDS 1:85
STATED PRINT RUN 50 SERIAL #'d SETS
EXCHANGE DEADLINE 04/30/06

2004 Finest Refractors

*REFRACTORS 1-100: 2X TO 5X BASIC
1-100 APPX.ODDS 3 IN EVERY 4 MINI-BOXES
*REFRACTORS 101-110: .5X TO 1.2X BASIC
101-110 STATED ODDS 1:26 MINI-BOXES
*REFRACTORS 111-122: .6X TO 1.5X BASIC
111-122 STATED ODDS 1:22 MINI-BOXES
EXCHANGE DEADLINE 04/30/06

2004 Finest Uncirculated Gold X-Fractors

*GOLD X-F 1-100: 4X TO 10X BASIC
*GOLD X-F 101-110: .75X TO 2X BASIC
*GOLD X-F 111-122: 1X TO 2.5X BASIC
ONE PER BASIC SEALED BOX
STATED PRINT RUN 139 SERIAL #'d SETS
EXCHANGE DEADLINE 04/30/06

2004 Finest Moments Autographs

GROUP A ODDS 1:86 MINI-BOXES
GROUP B ODDS 1:102 MINI-BOXES
GROUP C ODDS 1:5 MINI-BOXES

DS Duke Snider A	15.00	40.00
EK Ed Kranepool C	4.00	10.00
GS George Foster C	4.00	10.00
JA Jim Abbott A	10.00	25.00
JP Johnny Podres C	4.00	10.00
LD Lenny Dykstra C	4.00	10.00
OC Orlando Cepeda C	4.00	10.00
RY Robin Yount A	20.00	50.00
VB Vida Blue C	4.00	10.00
WM Willie Mays B	75.00	150.00

2004 Finest Relics

GROUP A ODDS 1:3 MINI-BOXES
GROUP B ODDS 1:4 MINI-BOXES

AB Angel Berroa Bat B	3.00	8.00
AD Adam Dunn Jsy A	3.00	8.00
AG Adrian Gonzalez Bat A	3.00	8.00
AJ Andruw Jones Bat A	4.00	10.00
AP Andy Pettitte Uni B	4.00	10.00
AP1 Albert Pujols Uni A	8.00	20.00
AP2 Albert Pujols Bat A	8.00	20.00
AR1 A.Rodriguez Rgr Jsy A	6.00	15.00
AR2 A.Rodriguez Yanks Jsy A	10.00	25.00
AS Alfonso Soriano Bat A	3.00	8.00
BM1 B.Myers Arm Down Jsy A	3.00	8.00
BM2 B.Myers Arm Up Jsy A	3.00	8.00
BW Bernie Williams Bat B	4.00	10.00
BZ Barry Zito Jsy A	3.00	8.00
CCS C.C. Sabathia Jsy A	3.00	8.00
CG Cristian Guzman Jsy A	3.00	8.00
CS Curt Schilling Jsy A	3.00	8.00
DE Darin Erstad Bat A	3.00	8.00
DL Derek Lowe Uni A	3.00	8.00
DW Dontrelle Willis Uni B	4.00	10.00
DY Delmon Young Bat B	4.00	10.00
EC Eric Chavez Uni B	3.00	8.00
FT Frank Thomas Jsy A	4.00	10.00
GM Greg Maddux Jsy A	6.00	15.00
GS Gary Sheffield Bat A	3.00	8.00
HB1 Hank Blalock Bat A	3.00	8.00
HB2 Hank Blalock Jsy B	3.00	8.00
IR1 I.Rodriguez Running Jsy A	4.00	10.00
IR2 I.Rodriguez w/Glove Jsy A	4.00	10.00
IR3 Ivan Rodriguez Bat B	4.00	10.00
JB Jeff Bagwell Jsy A	4.00	10.00
JL Javy Lopez Jsy A	3.00	8.00
JP Juan Pierre Bat A	3.00	8.00
JPB1 Josh Beckett Jsy A	3.00	8.00
JR1 Jose Reyes White Jsy A	3.00	8.00
JR2 Jose Reyes Bat A	3.00	8.00
JR3 Jose Reyes Black Jsy B	3.00	8.00
JS John Smoltz Uni A	4.00	10.00
JT Jim Thome Jsy A	4.00	10.00
KI Kazuhisa Ishii Jsy A	3.00	8.00
KM Kevin Millwood Jsy A	3.00	8.00
KS Kazuhiro Sasaki Jsy A	3.00	8.00
KW1 Kerry Wood Jsy A	3.00	8.00
KW2 Kerry Wood Bat A	3.00	8.00
LB1 Lance Berkman Bat A	3.00	8.00
LB2 Lance Berkman Jsy A	3.00	8.00
LG Luis Gonzalez Jsy A	3.00	8.00
LW Larry Walker Jsy A	3.00	8.00
MB Marlon Byrd Jsy A	3.00	8.00
MC Miguel Cabrera Bat B	4.00	10.00
ML1 Mike Lowell Grey Jsy A	3.00	8.00
ML2 Mike Lowell Black Jsy B	3.00	8.00
MM Mark Mulder Uni B	3.00	8.00
MO1 Magglio Ordonez Jsy A	3.00	8.00
MO2 Magglio Ordonez Bat A	3.00	8.00
MP Mark Prior Bat A	4.00	10.00
MR Mariano Rivera Uni A	4.00	10.00
MT1 Miguel Tejada Bat A	3.00	8.00
MT2 Miguel Tejada Uni A	3.00	8.00
NG Nomar Garciaparra Bat A	6.00	15.00
PB Pat Burrell Jsy A	3.00	8.00
PW Preston Wilson Bat A	3.00	8.00
RB1 R.Baldelli Bat Down Jsy B	3.00	8.00
RB3 R.Baldelli Bat on Ball Jsy B	3.00	8.00
RH Rich Harden Uni B	3.00	8.00
RJ Randy Johnson Jsy A	4.00	10.00
RP1 Rafael Palmeiro Bat A	4.00	10.00
RP2 Rafael Palmeiro Uni A	4.00	10.00
RP3 Rafael Palmeiro Jsy B	4.00	10.00
SB Sean Burroughs Bat A	3.00	8.00
SG Shawn Green Jsy A	3.00	8.00
SR Scott Rolen Bat A	4.00	10.00
SS Sammy Sosa Bat A	4.00	10.00
TG Troy Glaus Bat A	3.00	8.00
TH Tim Hudson Uni B	3.00	8.00
TH1 Todd Helton Bat A	4.00	10.00
TH2 Todd Helton Jsy A	4.00	10.00
TKH1 Torii Hunter Bat A	3.00	8.00
TKH2 Torii Hunter Jsy B	3.00	8.00
VG Vladimir Guerrero Jsy B	4.00	10.00
VW Vernon Wells Jsy A	3.00	8.00

2005 Finest

This 166-card set was released in May, 2005. The set was issued in three "mini-boxes" which contained 30 total cards (or 10 cards per mini-box). These "full boxes" came eight to a case. Cards numbered 1 through 140 featured active veterans while cards numbered 141 through 156 feature signed Rookie Cards which were issued to a varying print run amount and are noted in our checklist. Cards numbers 157 through 166 feature retired stars.

COMP.SET w/o SP's (150)	40.00	80.00
COMMON CARD (1-140)	.20	.50
COMMON CARD (157-166)	.30	.75
AU p/r 970 ODDS 1:3 MINI BOXES		
AU p/r 970 PRINT RUN 970 #'d SETS		
AU p/r 375 ODDS 1:41 MINI BOXES		
AU p/r 375 PRINT RUN 375 #'d SETS		
OVERALL PLATE ODDS 1:51 MINI BOX		
OVERALL AU PLATE ODDS 1:478 MINI BOX		
PLATE PRINT RUN 1 SET PER COLOR		
BLACK-CYAN-MAGENTA-YELLOW ISSUED		
NO PLATE PRICING DUE TO SCARCITY		
1 Alexis Rios	.30	.75
2 Hank Blalock	.20	.50
3 Bobby Abreu	.20	.50
4 Curt Schilling	.30	.75
5 Albert Pujols	1.25	3.00
6 Aaron Rowand	.20	.50
7 B.J. Upton	.30	.75
8 Andruw Jones	.20	.50
9 Jeff Francis	.20	.50
10 Sammy Sosa	.50	1.25
11 Aramis Ramirez	.20	.50
12 Carl Pavano	.20	.50
13 Bartolo Colon	.20	.50
14 Greg Maddux	.75	2.00
15 Scott Kazmir	.50	1.25
16 Melvin Mora	.20	.50
17 Brandon Backe	.20	.50
18 Bobby Crosby	.20	.50
19 Carlos Lee	.20	.50
20 Carl Crawford	.30	.75
21 Brian Giles	.20	.50
22 Jeff Bagwell	.30	.75
23 J.D. Drew	.20	.50
24 C.C. Sabathia	.30	.75
25 Alfonso Soriano	.30	.75
26 Chipper Jones	.50	1.25
27 Austin Kearns	.20	.50
28 Carlos Delgado	.20	.50
29 Jack Wilson	.20	.50
30 Dmitri Young	.20	.50
31 Carlos Guillen	.20	.50
32 Jim Thome	.30	.75
33 Eric Chavez	.20	.50
34 Jason Schmidt	.20	.50
35 Brad Radke	.20	.50
36 Frank Thomas	.50	1.25
37 Darin Erstad	.20	.50
38 Javier Vazquez	.20	.50
39 Garret Anderson	.20	.50
40 David Ortiz	.50	1.25
41 Javy Lopez	.20	.50
42 Geoff Jenkins	.20	.50
43 Jose Vidro	.20	.50
44 Aubrey Huff	.20	.50
45 Bernie Williams	.30	.75
46 Dontrelle Willis	.20	.50
47 Jim Edmonds	.30	.75
48 Ivan Rodriguez	.30	.75
49 Gary Sheffield	.20	.50
50 Alex Rodriguez	.75	2.00
51 John Buck	.20	.50
52 Andy Pettitte	.30	.75
53 Ichiro Suzuki	.75	2.00
54 Johnny Estrada	.20	.50
55 Jake Peavy	.20	.50
56 Carlos Zambrano	.30	.75
57 Jose Reyes	.30	.75
58 Bret Boone	.20	.50
59 Jason Bay	.20	.50
60 David Wright	.75	2.00
61 Jeromy Burnitz	.20	.50
62 Corey Patterson	.20	.50
63 Juan Pierre	.20	.50
64 Zack Greinke	.30	.75
65 Mike Lowell	.20	.50
66 Ken Griffey Jr.	.75	2.00
67 Marcus Giles	.20	.50
68 Edgar Renteria	.20	.50
69 Ken Harvey	.20	.50
70 Pedro Martinez	.30	.75
71 Johnny Damon	.30	.75
72 Lyle Overbay	.20	.50
73 Mike Maroth	.20	.50
74 Jorge Posada	.30	.75
75 Carlos Beltran	.20	.50
76 Mark Buehrle	.30	.75
77 Khalil Greene	.20	.50
78 Josh Beckett	.30	.75
79 Mark Loretta	.20	.50

80 Rafael Palmeiro .30 .75
81 Justin Morneau .50 1.25
82 Rocco Baldelli .20 .50
83 Ben Sheets .20 .50
84 Kerry Wood .20 .50
85 Miguel Tejada .30 .75
86 Magglio Ordonez .30 .75
87 Livan Hernandez .20 .50
88 Kazuo Matsui .20 .50
89 Manny Ramirez .50 1.25
90 Hideki Matsui .75 2.00
91 Jeff Kent .20 .50
92 Matt Lawton .20 .50
93 Richie Sexson .20 .50
94 Mike Mussina .30 .75
95 Adam Dunn .30 .75
96 Johan Santana .50 1.25
97 Nomar Garciaparra .50 1.25
98 Michael Young .30 .75
99 Victor Martinez .30 .75
100 Barry Bonds 1.00 2.50
101 Oliver Perez .20 .50
102 Randy Johnson .50 1.25
103 Mark Mulder .20 .50
104 Pat Burrell .20 .50
105 Mike Sweeney .20 .50
106 Mark Teixeira .50 1.25
107 Paul Lo Duca .20 .50
108 Jon Lieber .20 .50
109 Mike Piazza .50 1.25
110 Roger Clemens .60 1.50
111 Rafael Furcal .20 .50
112 Troy Glaus .20 .50
113 Miguel Cabrera .50 1.25
114 Randy Wolf .20 .50
115 Lance Berkman .30 .75
116 Mark Prior .30 .75
117 Rich Harden .20 .50
118 Preston Wilson .20 .50
119 Roy Oswalt .30 .75
120 Luis Gonzalez .20 .50
121 Ronnie Belliard .20 .50
122 Sean Casey .20 .50
123 Barry Zito .20 .50
124 Larry Walker .30 .75
125 Derek Jeter 1.25 3.00
126 Tim Hudson .30 .75
127 Tom Glavine .30 .75
128 Scott Rolen .30 .75
129 Torii Hunter .20 .50
130 Paul Konerko .30 .75
131 Shawn Green .20 .50
132 Travis Hafner .20 .50
133 Vernon Wells .20 .50
134 Sidney Ponson .20 .50
135 Vladimir Guerrero .50 1.25
136 Mark Kotsay .20 .50
137 Todd Helton .30 .75
138 Adrian Beltre .20 .50
139 Wily Mo Pena .20 .50
140 Joe Mauer .50 1.25
141 Brian Stavisky AU/970 RC 4.00 10.00
142 Nate McLouth AU/970 RC 6.00 15.00
143 Glen Perkins AU/375 RC 8.00 20.00
144 Chip Cannon AU/970 RC 8.00 20.00
145 Shane Costa AU/970 RC 4.00 10.00
146 W.Swackhamer AU/970 RC 4.00 10.00
147 Kevin Melillo AU/970 RC 6.00 15.00
148 Billy Butler AU/970 RC 10.00 25.00
149 Landon Powell AU/970 RC 6.00 15.00
150 Scott Mathieson AU/970 RC 4.00 10.00
151 Chris Roberson AU/970 4.00 10.00
152 Chad Orvella AU/375 RC 6.00 15.00
153 Eric Nielsen AU/970 RC 4.00 10.00
154 Matt Campbell AU/970 RC 4.00 10.00
155 Mike Rogers AU/970 RC 4.00 10.00
156 Melky Cabrera AU/970 RC 6.00 15.00
157 Nolan Ryan RET 2.00 5.00
158 Bo Jackson RET .75 2.00
159 Wade Boggs RET .50 1.25
160 Andre Dawson RET .50 1.25
161 Dave Winfield RET .30 .75
162 Reggie Jackson RET .75 2.00
163 David Justice RET .75 2.00
164 Dale Murphy RET .30 .75
165 Paul O'Neill RET .50 1.25
166 Tom Seaver RET .50 1.25

2005 Finest Refractors

*REF 1-140: 1.5X TO 4X BASIC
*REF 157-166: 1X TO 2.5X BASIC
1-140/157-166 ODDS ONE PER MINI BOX
COMMON AUTO (141-156) 4.00 10.00
*REF AU 141-156: .4X TO 1X p/r 970
*REF AU 141-156: .3X TO .8X p/r 375
AU 141-156 ODDS 1:5 MINI BOX
STATED PRINT RUN 399 SERIAL #'d SETS

2005 Finest Refractors Black

*REF BLACK 1-140: 4X TO 10X BASIC
*REF BLACK 157-166: 2.5X TO 6X BASIC
1-140/157-166 ODDS 1:2 MINI BOX
COMMON AUTO (141-156) 10.00 25.00
*REF BLK AU 141-156: .6X TO 1.5X p/r 970
*REF BLK AU 141-156: .5X TO 1.2X p/r 375
AU 141-156 ODDS 1:19 MINI BOX
STATED PRINT RUN 99 SERIAL #'d SETS

2005 Finest Refractors Blue

*REF BLUE 1-140: 1.5X TO 4X BASIC
*REF BLUE 157-166: 1X TO 2.5X BASIC
1-140/157-166 ODDS ONE PER MINI BOX
COMMON AUTO (141-156) 4.00 10.00
*REF BLUE AU 141-156: .4X TO 1X p/r 970
*REF BLUE AU 141-156: .3X TO .8X p/r 375
AU 141-156 ODDS 1:7 MINI BOX
STATED PRINT RUN 299 SERIAL #'d SETS

2005 Finest Refractors Gold

*REF GOLD 1-140: 5X TO 12X BASIC
*REF GOLD 157-166: 3X TO 8X BASIC
1-140/157-166 ODDS 1:5 MINI BOX
COMMON AUTO (141-156) 15.00 40.00
*REF GOLD AU 141-156: 1X TO 2.5X p/r 970
*REF GOLD AU 141-156: .75X TO 2X p/r 375
AU 141-156 ODDS 1:39 MINI BOX
STATED PRINT RUN 49 SERIAL #'d SETS
125 Derek Jeter 15.00 40.00

2005 Finest Refractors Green

*REF GREEN 1-140: 2X TO 5X BASIC
*REF GREEN 157-166: 1.25X TO 3X BASIC
1-140/157-166 ODDS ONE PER MINI BOX
COMMON AUTO (141-156) 5.00 12.00
*REF GRN AU 141-156: .4X TO 1X p/r 970
*REF GRN AU 141-156: .3X TO .8X p/r 375
AU 141-156 ODDS 1:10 MINI BOX
STATED PRINT RUN 199 SERIAL #'d SETS

2005 Finest Refractors White Framed

1-140/157-166 ODDS 1:202 MINI BOX
AU 141-165 ODDS 1:1914 MINI BOX
STATED PRINT RUN 1 SERIAL #'d SET
NO PRICING DUE TO SCARCITY

2005 Finest SuperFractors

1-140/157-166 ODDS 1:202 MINI BOX
AU 141-165 ODDS 1:1914 MINI BOX
STATED PRINT RUN 1 SERIAL #'d SET
NO PRICING DUE TO SCARCITY

2005 Finest X-Fractors

*XF 1-140: 2X TO 5X BASIC
*XF 157-166: 1.25X TO 3X BASIC
1-140/157-166 ODDS ONE PER MINI BOX
COMMON AUTO (141-156) 4.00 10.00
*XF AU 141-156: .4X TO 1X p/r 970
*XF AU 141-156: .3X TO 8X p/r 375
AU 141-156 ODDS 1:8 MINI BOX
STATED PRINT RUN 250 SERIAL #'d SETS

2005 Finest X-Fractors Black

*XF BLACK 1-140: 8X TO 20X BASIC
*XF BLACK 157-166: 5X TO 12X BASIC
1-140/157-166 ODDS 1:8 MINI BOX
AU 141-156 ODDS 1:76 MINI BOX
STATED PRINT RUN 25 SERIAL #'d SETS
AU 141-156 NO PRICING DUE TO SCARCITY
157 Nolan Ryan RET 25.00 60.00

2005 Finest X-Fractors Blue

*XF BLUE 1-140: 2.5X TO 6X BASIC
*XF BLUE 157-166: 1.5X TO 4X BASIC
1-140/157-166 ODDS 1:2 MINI BOX
COMMON AUTO (141-156) 6.00 15.00
*XF BLUE AU 141-156: .5X TO 1.2X p/r 970
*XF BLUE AU 141-156: .4X TO 1X p/r 375
AU 141-156 ODDS 1:13 MINI BOX
STATED PRINT RUN 150 SERIAL #'d SETS

2005 Finest X-Fractors Gold

1-140/157-166 ODDS 1:20 MINI BOX
AU 141-156 ODDS 1:190 MINI BOX
STATED PRINT RUN 10 SERIAL #'d SETS
NO PRICING DUE TO SCARCITY

2005 Finest X-Fractors Green

*XF GREEN 1-140: 5X TO 12X BASIC
*XF GREEN 157-166: 3X TO 8X BASIC
1-140/157-166 ODDS 1:2 MINI BOX
COMMON AUTO (141-156) 12.50 30.00
*XF GRN AU 141-156: .75X TO 2X p/r 970
*XF GRN AU 141-156: .6X TO 1.5X p/r 375
AU 141-156 ODDS 1:38 MINI BOX
STATED PRINT RUN 50 SERIAL #'d SETS

2005 Finest X-Fractors White Framed

1-140/157-166 ODDS 1:202 MINI BOX
AU 141-165 ODDS 1:1914 MINI BOX
STATED PRINT RUN 1 SERIAL #'d SET
NO PRICING DUE TO SCARCITY

2005 Finest A-Rod Moments

COMMON CARD (1-49) 3.00 8.00
ONE PER MASTER BOX
STATED PRINT RUN 190 SERIAL #'d SETS

2005 Finest A-Rod Moments Autographs

COMMON CARD (1-49) 90.00 180.00
APPROXIMATE ODDS 1:15 MASTER BOXES
STATED PRINT RUN 13 SERIAL #'d SETS

2005 Finest Autograph Refractors

GROUP A ODDS 1:435 MINI BOX
GROUP B ODDS 1:13 MINI BOX

GROUP C ODDS 1:32 MINI BOX
GROUP D ODDS 1:15 MINI BOX
GROUP A PRINT RUN 70 CARDS
GROUP A CARD IS NOT SERIAL-NUMBERED
GROUP A PRINT RUN PROVIDED BY TOPPS
OVERALL PLATE ODDS 1:513 MINI BOX
PLATE PRINT RUN 1 SET PER COLOR
BLACK-CYAN-MAGENTA-YELLOW ISSUED
NO PLATE PRICING DUE TO SCARCITY
SUPERFRACTOR ODDS 1:2051 MINI BOX
SUPERFRACTOR PRINT RUN 1 #'d SET
NO SUPERFRACTOR PRICING AVAILABLE
*X-FRACTOR: 1.25X TO 3X BASIC D
*X-FRACTOR: .75X TO 2X BASIC C
*X-FRACTOR: .6X TO 1.5X BASIC B
*X-FRACTOR: .6X TO 1.5X BASIC A
X-FRACTOR ODDS 1:81 MINI BOX
X-FRACTOR PRINT RUN 25 SERIAL #'d SETS
EXCHANGE DEADLINE 04/30/07
AS Alfonso Soriano B 10.00 25.00
BB Barry Bonds A/70 * 200.00 350.00
DO David Ortiz B 20.00 50.00
DW David Wright C 30.00 60.00
EC Eric Chavez B 10.00 25.00
EG Eric Gagne B 15.00 40.00
GS Gary Sheffield C 10.00 25.00
JB Jason Bay B 10.00 25.00
JE Johnny Estrada B 6.00 15.00
JS Johan Santana B 30.00 60.00
JST Jacob Stevens D 4.00 10.00
KM Kevin Millar B 15.00 40.00
MB Milton Bradley B 6.00 15.00
MR Mariano Rivera B 30.00 60.00

2005 Finest Moments Autograph Gold Refractors

STATED ODDS 1:305 MINI BOX
PEDRO PRINT RUN 50 SERIAL #'d CARDS
SCHILLING PRINT RUN 50 CARDS
SCHILLING IS NOT SERIAL-NUMBERED
SCHILLING QTY PROVIDED BY TOPPS
CS Curt Schilling/50 * 100.00 175.00
PM Pedro Martinez/50 50.00 100.00

2005 Finest Two of a Kind Autograph

STATED ODDS 1:9568 MINI BOX
STATED PRINT RUN 13 SERIAL #'d SETS
NO PRICING DUE TO SCARCITY
RB Alex Rodriguez
Ernie Banks

2006 Finest

This 155-card set was released in May, 2006. The set was issued in an "mini-box" form. There were three mini-boxes in a full box and each mini-box contained 30 cards. The SRP for an individual mini-box was $50 and there were eight full boxes in a case. Cards numbered 1-130 feature veterans while cards cards 131-155 feature 2006 rookies. Cards numbered 141 through 155 were all signed and all of those cards were issued to a stated print run of 963 signed copies.

COMP.SET w/o AU's (140) 30.00 60.00
COMMON CARD (1-131) .20 .50
COMMON ROOKIE (132-140) .30 .75
COMMON AUTO (141-155) 4.00 10.00
141-155 AU ODDS 1:4 MINI BOX
141-155 AU PRINT RUN 963 SETS
141-155 AU's NOT SERIAL NUMBERED
PRINT RUN INFO PROVIDED BY TOPPS
1-140 PLATES RANDOM INSERTS IN PACKS
AU 141-155 PLATE ODDS 1:792 MINI BOX
PLATE PRINT RUN 1 SET PER COLOR
BLACK-CYAN-MAGENTA-YELLOW ISSUED
NO PLATE PRICING DUE TO SCARCITY
1 Vladimir Guerrero .50 1.25
2 Troy Glaus .20 .50
3 Andruw Jones .20 .50
4 Miguel Tejada .30 .75
5 Manny Ramirez .50 1.25
6 Curt Schilling .30 .75
7 Mark Prior .30 .75
8 Kerry Wood .20 .50
9 Tadahito Iguchi .20 .50
10 Freddy Garcia .20 .50
11 Ryan Howard .75 2.00
12 Mark Buehrle .30 .75
13 Wily Mo Pena .20 .50
14 C.C. Sabathia .30 .75
15 Garret Anderson .20 .50
16 Shawn Green .20 .50
17 Rafael Furcal .20 .50
18 Jeff Francoeur .50 1.25
19 Ken Griffey Jr. .75 2.00
20 Derrek Lee .20 .50
21 Paul Konerko .30 .75
22 Rickie Weeks .30 .75
23 Magglio Ordonez .30 .75
24 Juan Pierre .20 .50
25 Felix Hernandez .50 1.25
26 Roger Clemens .60 1.50
27 Zack Greinke .30 .75
28 Johan Santana .50 1.25
29 Jose Reyes .30 .75
30 Bobby Crosby .20 .50
31 Jason Schmidt .20 .50
32 Khalil Greene .20 .50
33 Richie Sexson .20 .50
34 Mark Mulder .20 .50
35 Mark Teixeira .50 1.25
36 Nick Johnson .20 .50
37 Vernon Wells .20 .50
38 Scott Kazmir .30 .75
39 Jim Edmonds .30 .75
40 Adrian Beltre .20 .50
41 Dan Johnson .20 .50
42 Carlos Lee .20 .50
43 Lance Berkman .30 .75
44 Josh Beckett .30 .75
45 Morgan Ensberg .20 .50
46 Garrett Atkins .20 .50
47 Chase Utley .50 1.25
48 Joe Mauer .50 1.25
49 Travis Hafner .20 .50
50 Alex Rodriguez .75 2.00
51 Austin Kearns .20 .50
52 Scott Podsednik .20 .50
53 Jose Contreras .20 .50
54 Greg Maddux .75 2.00
55 Hideki Matsui .50 1.25
56 Matt Clement .20 .50
57 Javy Lopez .20 .50
58 Tim Hudson .30 .75
59 Luis Gonzalez .20 .50
60 Bartolo Colon .20 .50
61 Marcus Giles .20 .50
62 Justin Morneau .50 1.25
63 Nomar Garciaparra .50 1.25
64 Robinson Cano .50 1.25
65 Ervin Santana .20 .50
66 Brady Clark .20 .50
67 Edgar Renteria .20 .50
68 Jon Garland .20 .50
69 Felipe Lopez .20 .50
70 Ivan Rodriguez .30 .75
71 Dontrelle Willis .20 .50
72 Carlos Guillen .20 .50
73 J.D. Drew .20 .50
74 Rich Harden .20 .50
75 Albert Pujols 1.25 3.00
76 Livan Hernandez .20 .50
77 Roy Halladay .50 1.25
78 Hank Blalock .20 .50
79 David Wright .75 2.00
80 Jimmy Rollins .30 .75
81 John Smoltz .50 1.25
82 Miguel Cabrera .50 1.25
83 David DeJesus .20 .50
83 Zach Duke .20 .50
84 Torii Hunter .20 .50
85 Adam Dunn .30 .75
86 Randy Johnson .50 1.25
87 Roy Oswalt .30 .75
88 Bobby Abreu .20 .50
89 Rocco Baldelli .20 .50
90 Ichiro Suzuki .75 2.00
91 Jorge Cantu .20 .50
92 Jack Wilson .20 .50
93 Jose Vidro .20 .50
94 Kevin Millwood .20 .50
95 David Ortiz .30 .75
96 Victor Martinez .30 .75
97 Jeremy Bonderman .20 .50
98 Todd Helton .30 .75
99 Carlos Beltran .20 .50
100 Barry Bonds 1.00 2.50
101 Jeff Kent .20 .50
102 Mike Sweeney .20 .50
103 Ben Sheets .20 .50
104 Melvin Mora .20 .50
105 Gary Sheffield .20 .50
106 Craig Wilson .20 .50
107 Chris Carpenter .50 1.25
108 Michael Young .30 .75
109 Gustavo Chacin .20 .50
110 Chipper Jones .50 1.25
111 Mark Loretta .20 .50
112 Andy Pettitte .30 .75
113 Carlos Delgado .20 .50
114 Pat Burrell .20 .50
115 Jason Bay .20 .50
116 Brian Roberts .20 .50
117 Joe Crede .20 .50
118 Jake Peavy .20 .50
119 Aubrey Huff .20 .50
120 Pedro Martinez .30 .75
121 Jorge Posada .30 .75
122 Barry Zito .20 .50
123 Scott Rolen .30 .75
124 Brett Myers .20 .50
125 Derek Jeter 1.25 3.00
126 Eric Chavez .20 .50
127 Carl Crawford .30 .75
128 Jim Thome .30 .75
129 Johnny Damon .30 .75
130 Alfonso Soriano .30 .75
131 Clint Barmes .20 .50
132 Dustin Nippert (RC) .30 .75
133 Hanley Ramirez (RC) .75 2.00
134 Matt Capps (RC) .30 .75
135 Miguel Perez (RC) .30 .75
136 Tom Gorzelanny (RC) .30 .75
137 Charlton Jimerson (RC) .30 .75
138 Bryan Bullington (RC) .30 .75
139 Kenji Johjima RC .75 2.00
140 Craig Hansen RC .75 2.00
141 Craig Breslow AU/963 RC * 4.00 10.00
142 Adam Wainwright AU/963 (RC) * 12.50 30.00
143 Joey Devine AU/963 RC * 4.00 10.00
144 Hong-Chih Kuo AU/963 (RC) * 20.00 50.00
145 Jason Botts AU/963 (RC) * 4.00 10.00
146 Josh Johnson AU/963 (RC) * 12.50 30.00
147 Jason Bergmann AU/963 RC * 4.00 10.00
148 Scott Olsen AU/963 (RC) * 6.00 15.00
149 Darrell Rasner AU/963 (RC) * 4.00 10.00
150 Dan Ortmeier AU/963 (RC) * 4.00 10.00
151 Chuck James AU/963 (RC) * 6.00 15.00
152 Ryan Garko AU/963 (RC) * 4.00 10.00
153 Nelson Cruz AU/963 (RC) * 6.00 15.00
154 Anthony Lerew AU/963 (RC) * 4.00 10.00
155 Francisco Liriano AU/963 (RC) * 10.00 25.00

2006 Finest Refractors

*REF 1-131: 1.5X TO 4X BASIC
*REF 132-140: 1.5X TO 4X BASIC
1-140 ODDS ONE PER MINI BOX
*REF AU 141-155: .4X TO 1X BASIC AU
AU 141-155 ODDS 1:8 MINI BOX
STATED PRINT RUN 399 SERIAL #'d SETS

2006 Finest Refractors Black

*REF BLACK 1-131: 4X TO 10X BASIC
*REF BLACK 132-140: 4X TO 10X BASIC
1-140 ODDS 1:4 MINI BOX
*REF BLK AU 141-155: .6X TO 1.5X BASIC AU
AU 141-155 ODDS 1:32 MINI BOX
STATED PRINT RUN 99 SERIAL #'d SETS

2006 Finest Refractors Blue

*REF BLUE 1-131: 1.5X TO 4X BASIC
*REF BLUE 132-140: 1.5X TO 4X BASIC
1-140 ODDS 1:2 MINI BOX
*REF BLUE AU 141-155: .4X TO 1X BASIC AU
AU 141-155 ODDS 1:11 MINI BOX
STATED PRINT RUN 299 SERIAL #'d SETS

2006 Finest Refractors Gold

*REF GOLD 1-131: 5X TO 12X BASIC
*REF GOLD 132-140: 5X TO 12X BASIC
1-140 ODDS 1:7 MINI BOX
*REF GOLD AU 141-155: 1X TO 2.5X BASIC AU
AU 141-155 ODDS 1:64 MINI BOX
STATED PRINT RUN 49 SERIAL #'d SETS

2006 Finest Refractors Green

*REF GREEN 1-131: 2X TO 5X BASIC
*REF GREEN 132-140: 2X TO 5X BASIC
1-140 ODDS 1:2 MINI BOX
*REF GRN AU 141-155: .4X TO 1X BASIC AU
AU 141-155 ODDS 1:16 MINI BOX
STATED PRINT RUN 199 SERIAL #'d SETS

2006 Finest Refractors White Framed

1-140 ODDS 1:340 MINI BOX
AU 141-155 ODDS 1:3342 MINI BOX
STATED PRINT RUN 1 SERIAL #'d SET
NO PRICING DUE TO SCARCITY

2006 Finest SuperFractors

1-140 ODDS 1:340 MINI BOX
AU 141-155 ODDS 1:3342 MINI BOX
STATED PRINT RUN 1 SERIAL #'d SET
NO PRICING DUE TO SCARCITY

2006 Finest X-Fractors

*XF 1-131: 2X TO 5X BASIC
*XF 132-140: 2X TO 5X BASIC
1-140 ODDS 1:2 MINI BOX
*XF AU 141-155: .4X TO 1X BASIC AU
AU 141-155 ODDS 1:13 MINI BOX
STATED PRINT RUN 250 SERIAL #'d SETS

2006 Finest X-Fractors Black

*XF BLACK 1-131: 8X TO 20X BASIC
1-140 ODDS 1:14 MINI BOX
NO XF BLACK 132-140 PRICING
AU 141-155 ODDS 1:125 MINI BOX
STATED PRINT RUN 25 SERIAL #'d SETS
NO XF BLACK AU PRICING

2006 Finest X-Fractors Blue

*XF BLUE 1-131: 2.5X TO 6X BASIC
*XF BLUE 132-140: 2.5X TO 6X BASIC
1-140 ODDS 1:3 MINI BOX
*XF BLUE AU 141-155: .5X TO 1.2X BASIC AU
AU 141-155 ODDS 1:21 MINI BOX
STATED PRINT RUN 150 SERIAL #'d SETS

2006 Finest X-Fractors Gold

1-140 ODDS 1:34 MINI BOX
AU 141-155 ODDS 1:314 MINI BOX
STATED PRINT RUN 10 SERIAL #'d SETS
NO PRICING DUE TO SCARCITY

2006 Finest X-Fractors Green

*XF GREEN 1-131: 5X TO 12X BASIC
*XF GREEN 132-140: 5X TO 12X BASIC
1-140 ODDS 1:7 MINI BOX
*XF GREEN AU 141-155: .75X TO 2X BASIC AU
AU 141-155 ODDS 1:63 MINI BOX
STATED PRINT RUN 50 SERIAL #'d SETS

2006 Finest X-Fractors White Framed

1-140 ODDS 1:340 MINI BOX
AU 141-155 ODDS 1:3342 MINI BOX
STATED PRINT RUN 1 SERIAL #'d SET
NO PRICING DUE TO SCARCITY

2006 Finest Autograph Refractors

GROUP A ODDS 1:22 MINI BOX
GROUP B ODDS 1:8 MINI BOX
GROUP C ODDS 1:214 MINI BOX
GROUP A PRINT RUN 720 CARDS

GROUP B PRINT RUN 470 CARDS
GROUP C PRINT RUN 220 CARDS
CARDS ARE NOT SERIAL NUMBERED
PRINT RUN INFO PROVIDED BY TOPPS
OVERALL PLATE ODDS 1:654 MINI BOX
PLATE PRINT RUN 1 SET PER COLOR
BLACK-CYAN-MAGENTA-YELLOW ISSUED
NO PLATE PRICING DUE TO SCARCITY
SUPERFRACTOR ODDS 1:2751 MINI BOX
SUPERFRACTOR PRINT RUN 1 #'d SET
NO SUPERFRACTOR PRICING AVAILABLE
*GROUP A-B XF: .75X TO 2X BASIC
*GROUP C XF: 1X TO 2X BASIC
X-FRACTOR ODDS 1:104 MINI BOX
X-FRACTOR PRINT RUN 25 SERIAL #'d SETS
X-F JOHJIMA PRICING NOT AVAILABLE
APPROX. 10 PERCENT OF D.LEE ARE EXCH
EXCHANGE DEADLINE 04/30/08

AJ Andruw Jones B/470 *	15.00	40.00
AR Alex Rodriguez C/220 *	90.00	150.00
CJ Chipper Jones B/470 *	20.00	50.00
CW Craig Wilson B/470 *	4.00	10.00
DL Derrek Lee A/720 *	10.00	25.00
DW David Wright B/470 *	30.00	60.00
DWI Dontrelle Willis B/470 *	6.00	15.00
EC Eric Chavez A/720 *	6.00	15.00
GS Gary Sheffield B/470 *	5.00	12.00
JB Jason Bay B/470 *	6.00	15.00
JG Jose Guillen B/470 *	4.00	10.00
KJ Kenji Johjima B/470 *	50.00	100.00
MC Miguel Cabrera B/470 *	10.00	25.00
MG Marcus Giles B/470 *	6.00	15.00
RC Robinson Cano B/470 *	15.00	40.00
RH Rich Harden B/470 *	6.00	15.00
RO Roy Oswalt B/470 *	6.00	15.00
VG Vladimir Guerrero A/720 *	15.00	40.00

2006 Finest Bonds Moments Refractors

COMMON CARD (M1-M25)	3.00	8.00

STATED ODDS 1:2 MASTER BOX
STATED PRINT RUN 425 SERIAL #'d SETS
*REF GOLD: .5X TO 1.25X BASIC
REF.GOLD STATED ODDS 1:4 MASTER BOX
REF.GOLD PRINT RUN 199 SERIAL #'d SETS

2006 Finest Bonds Moments Refractors Gold Autographs

STATED ODDS 1:316 MASTER BOX
STATED PRINT RUN 2 SERIAL #'d SETS
NO PRICING DUE TO SCARCITY

2006 Finest Mantle Moments

COMMON CARD (M1-M20)	2.50	6.00

STATED ODDS 1:3 MINI BOX
STATED PRINT RUN 850 SERIAL #'d SETS
PRINTING PLATES RANDOM IN PACKS
PLATE PRINT RUN 1 SET PER COLOR
BLACK-CYAN-MAGENTA-YELLOW ISSUED
NO PLATE PRICING DUE TO SCARCITY
*REF: .5X TO 1.25X BASIC
REF ODDS 1:6 MINI BOX
REF PRINT RUN 399 SERIAL #'d SETS
*REF BLACK: 1.25X TO 3X BASIC
REF BLACK ODDS 1:24 MINI BOX
REF BLACK PRINT RUN 99 SERIAL #'d SETS
*REF BLUE: .6X TO 1.5X BASIC
REF BLUE ODDS 1:8 MINI BOX
REF BLUE PRINT RUN 299 SERIAL #'d SETS
*REF GOLD: 2.5X TO 6X BASIC
REF GOLD ODDS 1:49 MINI BOX
REF GOLD PRINT RUN 49 SERIAL #'d SETS
*REF GREEN: .75X TO 2X BASIC
REF GREEN ODDS 1:12 MINI BOX
REF GREEN PRINT RUN 199 SERIAL #'d SETS
REF WHITE FRAME ODDS 1:2482 MINI BOX
REF WHITE FRAME PRINT RUN 1 #'d SET
NO REF WF PRICING DUE TO SCARCITY
SUPERFRACTORS ODDS 1:2482 MINI BOX
SUPERFRACTORS PRINT RUN 1 #'d SET
NO SF PRICING DUE TO SCARCITY
*X-FRAC: .6X TO 1.5X BASIC
X-FRAC ODDS 1:10 MINI BOX
X-FRAC PRINT RUN 250 SERIAL #'d SETS
*X-FRAC BLACK: 3X TO 8X BASIC
X-FRAC BLACK ODDS 1:95 MINI BOX
X-FRAC BLACK PRINT RUN 25 #'d SETS
*X-FRAC BLUE: .75X TO 2X BASIC
X-FRAC BLUE ODDS 1:16 MINI BOX
X-FRAC BLUE PRINT RUN 150 #'d SETS
*X-FRAC GOLD: 8X TO 20X BASIC
X-FRAC GOLD ODDS 1:238 MINI BOX
X-FRAC GOLD PRINT RUN 10 SERIAL #'d SETS
X-FRAC GREEN: 2.5X TO 6X BASIC
X-FRAC GREEN ODDS 1:48 MINI BOX
X-FRAC GREEN PRINT RUN 50 #'d SETS
X-FRAC WF ODDS 1:2482 MINI BOX
X-FRAC WF PRINT RUN 1 SERIAL #'d SET
NO X-F WF PRICING DUE TO SCARCITY

2006 Finest Mantle Moments Cut Signatures

STATED ODDS 1:23,555 MINI BOX
STATED PRINT RUN 1 SERIAL #'d SET
NO PRICING DUE TO SCARCITY

2007 Finest

This 166-card set was released in March, 2007. The set was issued in five-card packs, which were issued six packs per mini box (which had an $50 SRP) and those mini-boxes were issued three per master box and eight master boxes per case. Cards numbered 1-135 feature veterans while cards numbered 135-150 were 2007 rookies and cards numbered 151-166 feature 2007 signed rookies. The signed rookie cards were issued at a stated rate of one in three mini-boxes.

COMP.SET w/o AU's (150)	30.00	60.00
COMMON CARD (1-135)	.15	.40
COMMON ROOKIE (136-150)	.40	1.00

151-166 AU ODDS 1:3 MINI BOX
1-150 PLATE ODDS 1:96 MINI BOX
AU 151-166 PLATE ODDS 1:909 MINI BOX
PLATE PRINT RUN 1 SET PER COLOR
BLACK-CYAN-MAGENTA-YELLOW ISSUED
NO PLATE PRICING DUE TO SCARCITY
EXCHANGE DEADLINE 02/28/09

1 David Wright	.60	1.50
2 Jered Weaver	.25	.60
3 Chipper Jones	.40	1.00
4 Magglio Ordonez	.25	.60
5 Ben Sheets	.15	.40
6 Nick Johnson	.15	.40
7 Melvin Mora	.15	.40
8 Chien-Ming Wang	.25	.60
9 Andre Ethier	.25	.60
10 Carlos Beltran	.15	.40
11 Ryan Zimmerman	.25	.60
12 Troy Glaus	.15	.40
13 Hanley Ramirez	.40	1.00
14 Mark Buehrle	.25	.60
15 Dan Uggla	.25	.60
16 Richie Sexson	.15	.40
17 Scott Kazmir	.25	.60
18 Garrett Atkins	.15	.40
19 Matt Cain	.25	.60
20 Jorge Posada	.25	.60
21 Brett Myers	.15	.40
22 Jeff Francoeur	.40	1.00
23 Scott Rolen	.25	.60
24 Derrek Lee	.15	.40
25 Manny Ramirez	.40	1.00
26 Johnny Damon	.25	.60
27 Mark Teixeira	.40	1.00
28 Mark Prior	.25	.60
29 Victor Martinez	.25	.60
30 Greg Maddux	.60	1.50
31 Prince Fielder	.25	.60
32 Jeremy Bonderman	.15	.40
33 Paul LoDuca	.15	.40
34 Brandon Webb	.25	.60
35 Robinson Cano	.40	1.00
36 Josh Beckett	.25	.60
37 David DeJesus	.15	.40
38 Kenny Rogers	.15	.40
39 Jim Thome	.25	.60
40 Brian McCann	.15	.40
41 Lance Berkman	.25	.60
42 Adam Dunn	.25	.60
43 Rocco Baldelli	.15	.40
44 Brian Roberts	.15	.40
45 Vladimir Guerrero	.40	1.00
46 Dontrelle Willis	.15	.40
47 Eric Chavez	.15	.40
48 Carlos Zambrano	.25	.60
49 Ivan Rodriguez	.25	.60
50 Alex Rodriguez	.60	1.50
51 Curt Schilling	.25	.60
52 Carlos Delgado	.15	.40
53 Matt Holliday	.40	1.00
54 Mark Teahen	.15	.40
55 Frank Thomas	.40	1.00
56 Grady Sizemore	.25	.60
57 Aramis Ramirez	.15	.40
58 Rafael Furcal	.15	.40
59 David Ortiz	.25	.60
60 Paul Konerko	.25	.60
61 Barry Zito	.15	.40
62 Travis Hafner	.15	.40
63 Nick Swisher	.40	1.00
64 Johan Santana	.40	1.00
65 Miguel Tejada	.25	.60
66 Carl Crawford	.25	.60
67 Kenji Johjima	.40	1.00
68 Derek Jeter	1.00	2.50
69 Francisco Liriano	.40	1.00
70 Ken Griffey Jr.	.60	1.50
71 Pat Burrell	.15	.40
72 Adrian Gonzalez	.25	.60
73 Miguel Cabrera	.40	1.00
74 Albert Pujols	1.00	2.50
75 Justin Verlander	.50	1.25
76 Carlos Lee	.15	.40
77 John Smoltz	.40	1.00
78 Orlando Hudson	.15	.40
79 Joe Mauer	.40	1.00
80 Freddy Sanchez	.15	.40
81 Bobby Abreu	.15	.40
82 Pedro Martinez	.25	.60
83 Vernon Wells	.15	.40
84 Justin Morneau	.40	1.00
85 Bill Hall	.15	.40
86 Jason Schmidt	.15	.40
87 Michael Young	.25	.60
88 Tadahito Iguchi	.15	.40
89 Kevin Millwood	.15	.40
90 Randy Johnson	.40	1.00
91 Roy Halladay	.40	1.00
92 Mike Lowell	.15	.40
93 Jake Peavy	.15	.40
94 Jason Varitek	.40	1.00
95 Todd Helton	.25	.60
96 Mark Loretta	.15	.40
97 Gary Matthews Jr.	.15	.40
98 Ryan Howard	.60	1.50
99 Jose Reyes	.25	.60
100 Chris Carpenter	.40	1.00
101 Hideki Matsui	.40	1.00
102 Brian Giles	.15	.40
103 Torii Hunter	.15	.40
104 Rich Harden	.15	.40
105 Ichiro Suzuki	.60	1.50
106 Chase Utley	.40	1.00
107 Nick Markakis	.40	1.00
108 Marcus Giles	.15	.40
109 Gary Sheffield	.15	.40
110 Jim Edmonds	.25	.60
111 Brandon Phillips	.15	.40
112 Roy Oswalt	.25	.60
113 Jeff Kent	.15	.40
114 Jason Bay	.25	.60
115 Raul Ibanez	.25	.60
116 Stephen Drew	.15	.40
117 Hank Blalock	.15	.40
118 Tom Glavine	.25	.60
119 Andruw Jones	.15	.40
120 Alfonso Soriano	.25	.60
121 Mariano Rivera	.40	1.00
122 Garret Anderson	.15	.40
123 Erik Bedard UER	.15	.40
Name misspelled Erick		
124 Huston Street	.15	.40
125 Austin Kearns	.15	.40
126 Jermaine Dye	.15	.40
127 C.C. Sabathia	.25	.60
128 Joe Nathan	.15	.40
129 Craig Monroe	.15	.40
130 Aubrey Huff	.15	.40
131 Billy Wagner	.15	.40
132 Jorge Cantu	.15	.40
133 Trevor Hoffman	.25	.60
134 Ronnie Belliard	.15	.40
135 B.J. Ryan	.15	.40
136 Adam Lind (RC)	.40	1.00
137 Hector Gimenez (RC)	.40	1.00
138 Shawn Riggans UER (RC)	.40	1.00
Name misspelled Riggins		
139 Joaquin Arias (RC)	.40	1.00
140 Drew Anderson RC	.40	1.00
141 Mike Rabelo RC	.40	1.00
142 Chris Narveson (RC)	.40	1.00
143 Ryan Feierabend (RC)	.40	1.00
144 Vinny Rottino (RC)	.40	1.00
145 Jon Knott (RC)	.40	1.00
146 Oswaldo Navarro RC	.40	1.00
147 Brian Stokes (RC)	.40	1.00
148 Glen Perkins (RC)	.40	1.00
149 Mitch Maier RC	.40	1.00
150 Delmon Young (RC) UER	.60	1.50
Listed as born in the wrong city		
151 Andrew Miller AU RC	15.00	40.00
152 Troy Tulowitzki AU (RC)	12.50	30.00
153 Philip Humber AU (RC)	6.00	15.00
154 Kevin Kouzmanoff AU (RC)	6.00	15.00
155 Michael Bourn AU (RC)	4.00	10.00
156 Miguel Montero AU (RC)	4.00	10.00
157 David Murphy AU (RC)	4.00	10.00
158 Ryan Sweeney AU (RC)	4.00	10.00
159 Jeff Baker AU (RC)	4.00	10.00
160 Jeff Salazar AU (RC)	4.00	10.00
161 Jose Garcia AU RC	4.00	10.00
162 Josh Fields AU (RC)	4.00	10.00
163 Delwyn Young AU (RC)	4.00	10.00
164 Fred Lewis AU (RC)	4.00	10.00
165 Scott Moore AU (RC)	4.00	10.00
166 Chris Stewart AU RC	4.00	10.00

2007 Finest Refractors

*REF 1-135: .5X TO 1.2X BASIC
*REF 136-150: .5X TO 1.2X BASIC
1-150 ODDS TWO PER MINI BOX
*REF AU 151-166: .4X TO 1X BASIC AU
AU 151-166 ODDS 1:10 MINI BOX
AU 151-166 PRINT RUN 399 SER.#'d SETS
EXCHANGE DEADLINE 02/28/09

2007 Finest Refractors Black

*REF BLACK 1-135: 4X TO 10X BASIC
*REF BLACK 136-150: 2.5X TO 6X BASIC
1-150 ODDS 1:4 MINI BOX
*REF BLK AU 151-166: 1X TO 2.5X BASIC AU
AU 151-166 ODDS 1:37 MINI BOX
STATED PRINT RUN 99 SERIAL #'d SETS
EXCHANGE DEADLINE 02/28/09

151 Andrew Miller AU	75.00	150.00
153 Philip Humber AU	10.00	25.00
159 Jeff Baker AU	5.00	12.00
160 Jeff Salazar AU	5.00	12.00
164 Fred Lewis AU	12.50	30.00

2007 Finest Refractors Blue

*REF BLUE 1-135: 1.5X TO 4X BASIC
*REF BLUE 136-150: 1X TO 2.5X BASIC
1-150 ODDS ONE PER MINI BOX
1-150 PRINT RUN 399 SER.#'d SETS
*REF BLUE AU 151-166: .5X TO 1.2X BASIC AU
AU 151-166 ODDS 1:13 MINI BOX
AU 151-166 PRINT RUN 299 SER.#'d SETS
EXCHANGE DEADLINE 02/28/09

2007 Finest Refractors Gold

*REF GOLD 1-135: 5X TO 12X BASIC
*REF GOLD 136-150: 4X TO 10X BASIC
1-150 ODDS 1:8 MINI BOX
1-150 PRINT RUN 50 SER.#'d SETS
*REF GOLD AU 151-166: 1.25X TO 3X BASIC AU
AU 151-166 ODDS 1:74 MINI BOX
AU 151-166 PRINT RUN 49 SER.#'d SETS
EXCHANGE DEADLINE 02/28/09

151 Andrew Miller AU	150.00	250.00
155 Michael Bourn AU	15.00	40.00
156 Miguel Montero AU	15.00	40.00
158 Ryan Sweeney AU	15.00	40.00
162 Josh Fields AU	15.00	40.00
164 Fred Lewis AU	15.00	40.00
165 Scott Moore AU	15.00	40.00

2007 Finest Refractors Green

*REF GREEN 1-135: 2X TO 5X BASIC
*REF GREEN 136-150: 1.25X TO 3X BASIC
1-150 ODDS 1:2 MINI BOX
*REF GRN AU 151-166: .6X TO 1.5X BASIC AU
AU 151-166 ODDS 1:19 MINI BOX
STATED PRINT RUN 199 SERIAL #'d SETS
EXCHANGE DEADLINE 02/28/09

2007 Finest SuperFractors

1-150 ODDS 1:385 MINI BOX
AU 151-166 ODDS 1:3582 MINI BOX
STATED PRINT RUN 1 SERIAL #'d SET
NO PRICING DUE TO SCARCITY
EXCHANGE DEADLINE 02/28/09

2007 Finest X-Fractors

*XF 1-135: 8X TO 20X BASIC
1-150 ODDS 1:16 MINI BOX
AU 151-166 ODDS 1:144 MINI BOX
STATED PRINT RUN 25 SER.#'d SETS
NO ROOKIE PRICING AVAILABLE
EXCHANGE DEADLINE 02/28/09

2007 Finest X-Fractors White Framed

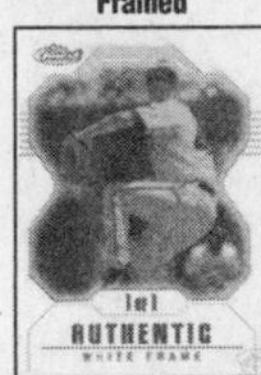

1-150 ODDS 1:385 MINI BOX
AU 151-166 ODDS 1:3582 MINI BOX
STATED PRINT RUN 1 SERIAL #'d SET
NO PRICING DUE TO SCARCITY
EXCHANGE DEADLINE 02/28/09

2007 Finest Mantle Cut Signature

STATED ODDS 1:11,400 MINI BOX
STATED PRINT RUN 1 SER.#'d SET
NO PRICING DUE TO SCARCITY
STATED PLATE ODDS 1:11,400 MINI BOX
PLATE PRINT RUN 1 SET PER COLOR
BLACK-CYAN-MAGENTA-YELLOW ISSUED
NO PLATE PRICING DUE TO SCARCITY

2007 Finest Rookie Finest Moments

STATED ODDS 2 PER MINI BOX
PRINTING PLATE ODDS 1:289 MINI BOX
PLATE PRINT RUN 1 SET PER COLOR
BLACK-CYAN-MAGENTA-YELLOW ISSUED
NO PLATE PRICING DUE TO SCARCITY
*REF: .6X TO 1.5X BASIC
REFRACTOR ODDS 1 PER MINI BOX
*REF BLACK: 2.5X TO 6X BASIC
REF BLACK ODDS 1:12 MINI BOX
REF BLACK PRINT RUN 99 SER.#'d SETS
*REF BLUE: 1X TO 2.5X BASIC
REF BLUE ODDS 1:4 MINI BOX
REF BLUE PRINT RUN 299 SER.#'d SETS
*REF GOLD: 5X TO 12X BASIC
REF GOLD ODDS 1:23 MINI BOX
REF GOLD PRINT RUN 50 SER.#'d SETS
*REF GREEN: 1.25X TO 3X BASIC
REF GREEN ODDS 1:6 MINI BOX
REF GREEN PRINT RUN 199 SER.#'d SETS
SUPERFRACTOR ODDS 1:1156 MINI BOX
SUPERFRACTOR PRINT RUN 1 SER.#'d SET
NO SUPERFRACTOR PRICING AVAILABLE
*X-FRACTOR: 8X TO 20X BASIC
X-FRACTOR ODDS 1:46 MINI BOX
X-FRACTOR PRINT RUN 25 SER.#'d SETS
X-F WHITE ODDS 1:1156 MINI BOX
X-F WHITE PRINT RUN 1 SER.#'d SET
NO X-F WHITE PRICING AVAILABLE

AD Adam Dunn	.40	1.00
AE Andre Ethier	.40	1.00
AJ Andruw Jones	.25	.60
AP Albert Pujols	1.50	4.00
AR Alex Rodriguez	1.00	2.50
AS Anibal Sanchez	.25	.60
AW Adam Wainwright	.40	1.00
CB Carlos Beltran	.25	.60
CC Carl Crawford	.40	1.00
CH Cole Hamels	.60	1.50
CJ Chipper Jones	.60	1.50
CQ Carlos Quentin	.25	.60
DJ Derek Jeter	1.50	4.00
DL Derrek Lee	.25	.60
DO David Ortiz	.40	1.00
DU Dan Uggla	.40	1.00
DW David Wright	1.00	2.50
FL Francisco Liriano	.60	1.50
HM Hideki Matsui	.60	1.50
HR Hanley Ramirez	.60	1.50
IK Ian Kinsler	.40	1.00
IS Ichiro Suzuki	1.00	2.50
JB Jason Bay	.40	1.00
JH Jason Hirsh	.25	.60
JM Joe Mauer	.60	1.50
JP Jonathan Papelbon	.60	1.50
JR Jose Reyes	.40	1.00
JS Jeremy Sowers	.25	.60
JV Justin Verlander	.75	2.00
JW Jered Weaver	.40	1.00
KG Ken Griffey Jr.	1.00	2.50
KJ Kenji Johjima	.60	1.50
MC Miguel Cabrera	.60	1.50
MK Matt Kemp	.40	1.00
MN Mike Napoli	.40	1.00
MP Mike Piazza	.60	1.50
MR Manny Ramirez	.60	1.50
MT Miguel Tejada	.40	1.00
NC Nelson Cruz	.40	1.00
NG Nomar Garciaparra	.60	1.50
NM Nick Markakis	.60	1.50
PF Prince Fielder	.40	1.00
RH Ryan Howard	1.00	2.50
RM Russ Martin	.25	.60
SD Stephen Drew	.25	.60
VG Vladimir Guerrero	.60	1.50
DWW Dontrelle Willis	.25	.60
JBA Josh Barfield	.25	.60
JST Brian Stokes	.25	.60
MCA Melky Cabrera	.25	.60

2007 Finest Rookie Finest Moments Autographs

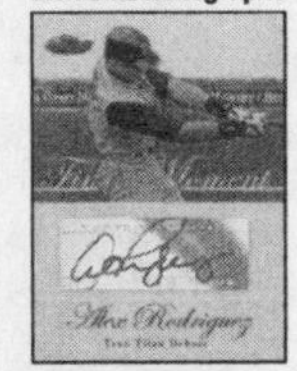

STATED ODDS 1:5 MINI BOX
PRINTING PLATE ODDS 1:482 MINI BOX
PLATE PRINT RUN 1 SET PER COLOR
BLACK-CYAN-MAGENTA-YELLOW ISSUED
NO PLATE PRICING DUE TO SCARCITY
REFRACTOR ODDS 1:77 MINI BOX
REFRACTOR PRINT RUN 25 #'d SETS
NO REFRACTOR PRICING AVAILABLE
SUPERFRACTOR ODDS 1:1975 MINI BOX
NO SUPERFRACTOR PRICING AVAILABLE
SUPERFRACTOR PRINT RUN 1 #'d SET

AR Alex Rodriguez	40.00	80.00
AS Anibal Sanchez	3.00	8.00
AW Adam Wainwright	10.00	25.00
BP Brandon Phillips	3.00	8.00
BW Brad Wilkerson	3.00	8.00
CH Cole Hamels	12.50	30.00
CJ Chuck James	4.00	10.00
CQ Carlos Quentin	6.00	15.00
DO David Ortiz	10.00	25.00
DU Dan Uggla	8.00	20.00
DW David Wright	30.00	60.00
DWW Dontrelle Willis	6.00	15.00
DY Delmon Young	10.00	25.00
ES Ervin Santana	3.00	8.00
FC Fausto Carmona	10.00	25.00
HR Hanley Ramirez	10.00	25.00
JM Justin Morneau	10.00	25.00
JN Joe Nathan	3.00	8.00
JP Jonathan Papelbon	12.50	30.00
LM Lastings Milledge	6.00	15.00
MC Melky Cabrera	15.00	40.00
MN Mike Napoli	8.00	20.00
MTC Matt Cain	8.00	20.00
RC Robinson Cano	15.00	40.00
RH Rich Hill	10.00	25.00
RH Ryan Howard	40.00	80.00
RM Russ Martin	6.00	15.00
RZ Ryan Zimmerman	12.50	30.00
TH Travis Hafner	6.00	15.00
YP Yusmeiro Petit	3.00	8.00

2007 Finest Rookie Finest Moments Autographs Dual

STATED ODDS 1:32 MINI BOX
STATED PRINT RUN 74 SER.#'d SETS
REFRACTOR ODDS 1:93 MINI BOX
REFRACTOR PRINT RUN 25 #'d SETS
NO REFRACTOR PRICING AVAILABLE
REF GOLD ODDS 1:2387 MINI BOX
REF GOLD PRINT RUN 1 #'d SET
NO REF GOLD PRICING AVAILABLE
EXCHANGE DEADLINE 02/28/09

BM Jason Bay	10.00	25.00
Justin Morneau		
CC Eric Chavez	20.00	50.00
Miguel Cabrera		
CK Nelson Cruz	30.00	60.00
Matt Kemp		
CR Matt Cain	15.00	40.00
Anthony Reyes		
CY Robinson Cano	40.00	80.00
Michael Young		
HJ Rich Hill	15.00	40.00
Josh Johnson		
HM Cole Hamels	20.00	50.00
Brett Myers		
HR Travis Hafner	20.00	50.00
Manny Ramirez		
JH Chuck James	8.00	20.00
Cole Hamels		
MC Lastings Milledge	15.00	40.00
Melky Cabrera		
MG Russ Martin	8.00	20.00
Ryan Garko		
MK Lastings Milledge	8.00	20.00
Matt Kemp		
MN Kendry Morales	12.50	30.00
Mike Napoli		
MNA Russ Martin	10.00	25.00
Mike Napoli		
OP Roy Oswalt	8.00	20.00
Mark Prior		
PO Yusmeiro Petit	8.00	20.00
Scott Olsen		
PP Jonathan Papelbon	20.00	50.00
Dustin Pedroia		
RP Mariano Rivera	75.00	150.00
Jorge Posada		
RU Hanley Ramirez	15.00	40.00
Dan Uggla		
UG Dan Uggla	8.00	20.00
Marcus Giles		
US Dan Uggla	10.00	25.00
Anibal Sanchez		
VE Justin Verlander	20.00	50.00
Hanley Ramirez		
WW Chien-Ming Wang	150.00	300.00
Brandon Webb		
ZC Joel Zumaya	8.00	20.00
Fausto Carmona		

2007 Finest Rookie Photo Variation

STATED ODDS 1:5 MINI BOX
STATED PRINT RUN 439 SER.#'d SETS
*REF: .75X TO 2X BASIC
REFRACTOR ODDS 1:13 MINI BOX
REFRACTOR PRINT RUN 149 #'d SETS
REF GOLD ODDS 1:1975 MINI BOX
REF GOLD PRINT RUN 1 SER.#'d SET
NO REF GOLD PRICING AVAILABLE
*X-FRACTOR: 2X TO 5X BASIC
X-FRACTOR ODDS 1:39 MINI BOX
X-FRACTOR PRINT RUN 50 SER.#'d SETS

136 Adam Lind Bat Up	.75	2.00
136 Adam Lind Bat Out	.75	2.00
137 Hector Gimenez Posed	.75	2.00
137 Hector Gimenez Batting	.75	2.00
138 Shawn Riggans w/Bat	.75	2.00
138 Shawn Riggans w/Glove	.75	2.00
139 Joaquin Arias w/Bat	.75	2.00
139 Joaquin Arias Throw	.75	2.00
140 Drew Anderson Run Away	.75	2.00
140 Drew Anderson w/Glove	.75	2.00
141 Mike Rabelo Bat Shoulder	.75	2.00
141 Mike Rabelo Bat Up	.75	2.00
142 Chris Narveson Portrait	.75	2.00
142 Chris Narveson w/Glove	.75	2.00
143 Ryan Feierabend Catch	.75	2.00
143 Ryan Feierabend Pitch	.75	2.00
144 Vinny Rottino Swing	.75	2.00
144 Vinny Rottino Field	.75	2.00
145 Jon Knott Run	.75	2.00
145 Jon Knott w/Bat	.75	2.00
146 Oswaldo Navarro Posed	.75	2.00
146 Oswaldo Navarro Swing	.75	2.00
147 Brian Stokes Windup	.75	2.00
147 Brian Stokes Throw	.75	2.00
148 Glen Perkins Windup	.75	2.00
148 Glen Perkins w/Jacket	.75	2.00
149 Mitch Maier In OF	.75	2.00
149 Mitch Maier On Deck	.75	2.00
150 Delmon Young Running	1.25	3.00
150 Delmon Young Portirat	1.25	3.00

2007 Finest Rookie Redemption

This 10-card set was announced during the year as new 2007 rookies made an impact in the majors. These cards, which were inserted at a stated rate of one in three mini-boxes, could be redeemed until December 31, 2007.

STATED ODDS 1:3 MINI BOX
REDEEMABLE FOR 07 RC LOGO PLAYER
EXCHANGE DEADLINE 12/30/07

1 Hideki Okajima	4.00	10.00
2 Elijah Dukes	1.25	3.00
3 Akinori Iwamura	2.00	5.00
4 Tim Lincecum	12.00	30.00
5 Daisuke Matsuzaka	3.00	8.00
6 Ryan Braun	4.00	10.00
7 Daisuke Matsuzaka	3.00	8.00
Hideki Okajima		
8 Justin Upton	6.00	15.00
9 Philip Hughes	4.00	10.00
10 Joba Chamberlain AU	10.00	25.00

2007 Finest Ryan Howard Finest Moments

COMMON CARD	1.50	4.00

STATED ODDS 2 PER HOWARD BOX LOADER
STATED PRINT RUN 459 SER.#'d SETS
*REF: .6X TO 1:5X BASIC
REFRACTOR ODDS 1:3 BOXES
REFRACTOR PRINT RUN 149 SER.#'d SETS
REF GOLD ODDS 1:329 BOXES
REF GOLD PRINT RUN 1 SER.#'d SET
NO REF GOLD PRICING AVAILABLE
*X-FRACTOR: .75X TO 2X BASIC
X-FRACTOR ODDS 1:7 BOXES
X-FRACTOR PRINT RUN 50 SER.#'d SETS

2008 Finest

COMP.SET w/o AUs (150)	40.00	80.00
COMMON CARD (1-125)	.15	.40
COMMON RC (126-150)	.75	2.00
COMMON AU RC (151-166)	4.00	10.00

151-166 AU ODDS 1:3 MINI BOX
1-150 PLATE ODDS 1:82 MINI BOX
AU 151-166 PLATE ODDS 1:775 MINI BOX
PLATE PRINT RUN 1 SET PER COLOR
BLACK-CYAN-MAGENTA-YELLOW ISSUED
NO PLATE PRICING DUE TO SCARCITY

1 Daisuke Matsuzaka	.40	1.00
2 Justin Upton	.25	.60
3 Andruw Jones	.15	.40
4 John Lackey	.15	.40
5 Brandon Phillips	.15	.40
6 Ryan Zimmerman	.25	.60
7 Tim Lincecum	.60	1.50
8 Johnny Damon	.25	.60
9 Garrett Atkins	.15	.40
10 Magglio Ordonez	.25	.60
11 Tom Gorzelanny	.15	.40
12 Eric Chavez	.15	.40
13 Troy Tulowitzki	.40	1.00
14 Mike Lowell	.15	.40
15 Brandon Webb	.25	.60
16 Chipper Jones	.40	1.00

17 Alex Gordon .25 .60
18 Ken Griffey Jr. .60 1.50
19 Roy Oswalt .25 .60
20 Miguel Cabrera .40 1.00
21 Chase Utley .40 1.00
22 Scott Kazmir .25 .60
23 Kenji Johjima .15 .40
24 Frank Thomas .40 1.00
25 Ryan Braun .50 1.25
26 Carlos Pena .25 .60
27 Robinson Cano .40 1.00
28 Ben Sheets .15 .40
29 Russell Martin .15 .40
30 Joe Mauer .40 1.00
31 Gary Sheffield .15 .40
32 Carlos Zambrano .25 .60
33 Jermaine Dye .15 .40
34 Dan Uggla .25 .60
35 Erik Bedard .15 .40
36 Tim Hudson .25 .60
37 David Ortiz .25 .60
38 Tom Glavine .25 .60
39 Adrian Gonzalez .25 .60
40 Jorge Posada .25 .60
41 Noah Lowry .15 .40
42 Vernon Wells .15 .40
43 Johan Santana .40 1.00
44 Dmitri Young .15 .40
45 Manny Ramirez .40 1.00
46 Jim Edmonds .25 .60
47 Roy Halladay .40 1.00
48 Delmon Young .25 .60
49 Nick Swisher .40 1.00
50 David Wright .50 1.25
51 Paul Konerko .25 .60
52 Curt Schilling .25 .60
53 Torii Hunter .15 .40
54 Gary Matthews .15 .40
55 Derrek Lee .15 .40
56 John Smoltz .40 1.00
57 Adam Dunn .25 .60
58 C.C Sabathia .25 .60
59 Chris Young .15 .40
60 Jake Peavy .15 .40
61 Joba Chamberlain .25 .60
62 Jason Bay .25 .60
63 Chris Carpenter .40 1.00
64 Jimmy Rollins .25 .60
65 Grady Sizemore .25 .60
66 Joe Blanton .15 .40
67 Justin Morneau .40 1.00
68 Lance Berkman .25 .60
69 Jeff Francis .15 .40
70 Nick Markakis .40 1.00
71 Orlando Cabrera .15 .40
72 Barry Zito .15 .40
73 Eric Byrnes .15 .40
74 Brian McCann .25 .60
75 Albert Pujols 1.00 2.50
76 Josh Beckett .25 .60
77 Jim Thome .25 .60
78 Fausto Carmona .15 .40
79 Brad Hawpe .15 .40
80 Prince Fielder .25 .60
81 Justin Verlander .50 1.25
82 Billy Butler .15 .40
83 J.J. Hardy .15 .40
84 Hideki Matsui .40 1.00
85 Matt Holliday .40 1.00
86 Bobby Crosby .15 .40
87 Orlando Hudson .15 .40
88 Ichiro Suzuki .60 1.50
89 Troy Glaus .25 .60
90 Hanley Ramirez .40 1.00
91 Carlos Beltran .15 .40
92 Mark Buehrle .25 .60
93 Andy Pettitte .25 .60
94 Mark Teixeira .40 1.00
95 Curtis Granderson .25 .60
96 Cole Hamels .40 1.00
97 Jarrod Saltalamacchia .15 .40
98 Carl Crawford .25 .60
99 Dontrelle Willis .15 .40
100 Alex Rodriguez .60 1.50
101 Brad Penny .15 .40
102 Michael Young .25 .60
103 Greg Maddux .50 1.25
104 Brian Roberts .15 .40
105 Hunter Pence .40 1.00
106 Aaron Harang .15 .40
107 Ivan Rodriguez .25 .60
108 Dan Haren .15 .40
109 Freddy Sanchez .15 .40
110 Alfonso Soriano .25 .60
111 Hank Blalock .15 .40
112 Chien- Ming Wang .25 .60
113 Carlos Delgado .15 .40
114 Aramis Ramirez .15 .40
115 Jose Reyes .25 .60
116 Victor Martinez .25 .60
117 Carlos Lee .15 .40
118 Jeff Kent .15 .40
119 Miguel Tejada .25 .60
120 Vladimir Guerrero .40 1.00
121 Travis Hafner .15 .40
122 Todd Helton .25 .60
123 Chris Young .15 .40
124 Derek Jeter 1.00 2.50
125 Ryan Howard .50 1.25
126 Alberto Gonzalez RC 1.25 3.00
127 Felipe Paulino RC 1.25 3.00
128 Donny Lucy (RC) .75 2.00
129 Nick Blackburn RC 1.25 3.00
130 Luke Hochevar RC 1.25 3.00
131 Bronson Sardinha (RC) .75 2.00
132 Heath Phillips RC 1.25 3.00
133 Bryan Bullington (RC) .75 2.00
134 Jeff Clement (RC) 1.25 3.00
135 Josh Banks (RC) .75 2.00
136 Emilio Bonifacio RC 2.00 5.00
137 Ryan Hanigan RC 1.25 3.00
138 Erick Threets (RC) .75 2.00
139 Seth Smith (RC) .75 2.00
140 Billy Buckner (RC) .75 2.00
141 Bill Murphy (RC) .75 2.00
142 Radhames Liz RC 1.25 3.00
143 Joey Votto (RC) 3.00 8.00
144 Mel Stocker RC .75 2.00
145 Dan Meyer (RC) .75 2.00
146 Rob Johnson (RC) .75 2.00
147 Josh Newman RC 1.25 3.00
148 Dan Giese (RC) .75 2.00
149 Luis Mendoza (RC) .75 2.00
150 Wladimir Balentien (RC) .75 2.00
151 Brandon Jones AU RC 4.00 10.00
152 Rich Thompson AU RC 4.00 10.00
153 Chin-Lung Hu AU (RC) 15.00 40.00
154 Chris Seddon AU (RC) 4.00 10.00
155 Steve Pearce AU RC 6.00 15.00
156 Lance Broadway AU (RC) 4.00 10.00
157 Nyjer Morgan AU (RC) 4.00 10.00
158 Jonathan Meloan AU RC 4.00 10.00
159 Josh Anderson AU (RC) 4.00 10.00
160 Clay Buchholz AU (RC) 12.50 30.00
161 Joe Koshansky AU (RC) 4.00 10.00
162 Clint Sammons AU (RC) 4.00 10.00
163 Daric Barton AU (RC) 5.00 12.00
164 Ross Detwiler AU RC 5.00 12.00
165 Sam Fuld AU RC 6.00 15.00
166 Justin Ruggiano AU RC 4.00 10.00

2008 Finest Refractors

*REF VET: 1X TO 2.5X BASIC
*REF RC: .5X TO 1.2X BASIC RC
1-150 REF.RANDOMLY INSERTED
*REF AU: .4X TO 1X BASIC AU
151-166 ODDS 1:7 MINI PACKS
151-166 PRINT RUN 499 SER.#'d SETS

2008 Finest Refractors Black

*BLACK VET: 4X TO 10X BASIC
*BLACK RC: 1X TO 2.5X BASIC RC
1-150 ODDS 1:4 MINI BOXES
1-150 PRINT RUN 99 SER.#'d SETS
*REF AU: .6X TO 1.5X BASIC AU
151-166 ODDS 1:32 MINI PACKS
151-166 PRINT RUN 99 SER.#'d SETS
153 Chin-Lung Hu AU 75.00 150.00
164 Ross Detwiler AU 10.00 25.00

2008 Finest Refractors Blue

*BLUE VET: 1.5X TO 4X BASIC
*BLUE RC: .6X TO 1.5X BASIC RC
1-150 ODDS 1:2 MINI BOXES
1-150 PRINT RUN 299 SER.#'d SETS
*REF AU: .5X TO 1.2X BASIC AU
151-166 ODDS 1:8 MINI PACKS
151-166 PRINT RUN 399 SER.#'d SETS
153 Chin-Lung Hu AU 30.00 60.00

2008 Finest Refractors Gold

*GOLD VET: 6X TO 15X BASIC
*GOLD RC: 2X TO 5X BASIC RC
1-150 ODDS 1:7 MINI BOXES
1-150 PRINT RUN 50 SER.#'d SETS
*REF AU: 1X TO 2.5X BASIC AU
151-166 ODDS 1:64 MINI PACKS
151-166 PRINT RUN 50 SER.#'d SETS
24 Frank Thomas 20.00 50.00
75 Albert Pujols 15.00 40.00
88 Ichiro Suzuki 15.00 40.00
100 Alex Rodriguez 15.00 40.00
103 Greg Maddux 20.00 50.00
124 Derek Jeter 30.00 60.00
126 Alberto Gonzalez 10.00 25.00
129 Nick Blackburn 20.00 50.00
132 Heath Phillips 6.00 15.00
134 Jeff Clement 15.00 40.00
147 Josh Newman 6.00 15.00
148 Dan Giese 6.00 15.00
150 Wladimir Balentien 6.00 15.00
153 Chin-Lung Hu AU 100.00 200.00
160 Clay Buchholz AU 30.00 60.00
163 Daric Barton AU 15.00 40.00
164 Ross Detwiler AU 15.00 40.00

2008 Finest Refractors Green

*GREEN VET: 2X TO 5X BASIC
*GREEN RC: .75X TO 2X BASIC RC
1-150 ODDS 1:2 MINI BOXES
1-150 PRINT RUN 199 SER.#'d SETS
*REF AU: .5X TO 1.2X BASIC AU
151-166 ODDS 1:16 MINI PACKS
151-166 PRINT RUN 199 SER.#'d SETS
153 Chin-Lung Hu AU 40.00 80.00

2008 Finest Refractors Red

1-150 ODDS 1:14 MINI BOXES
151-166 AU ODDS 1:128 MINI BOXES
STATED PRINT RUN 25 SER.#'d SETS
NO PRICING DUE TO SCARCITY

2008 Finest X-Fractors White Framed

1-150 ODDS 1:327 MINI BOXES
151-166 AU ODDS 1:2036 MINI BOXES
STATED PRINT RUN 1 SER.#'d SET
NO PRICING DUE TO SCARCITY

2008 Finest Finest Moments

*REF: .6X TO 1.5X BASIC
REF.RANDOMLY INSERTED
STATED ODDS XX PER MINI BOX
*BLACK REF: 1.5X TO 4X BASIC
BLACK ODDS 1:10 MINI BOXES
BLACK PRINT RUN 99 SER.#'d SETS
*BLUE REF: .75X TO 2X BASIC
BLUE ODDS 1:4 MINI BOXES
BLUE PRINT RUN 399 SER.#'d SETS
*GOLD REF: 2.5X TO 6X BASIC
GOLD ODDS 1:20 MINI BOXES
GOLD PRINT RUN 50 SER.#'d SETS
*GREEN REF: 1X TO 2.5X BASIC
GREEN ODDS 1:5 MINI BOXES
GREEN PRINT RUN 199 SER.#'d SETS
PRINTING PLATE ODDS 1:245 MINI BOXES
PLATE PRINT RUN 1 SET PER COLOR
BLACK-CYAN-MAGENTA-YELLOW ISSUED
NO PLATE PRICING DUE TO SCARCITY
AG Adrian Gonzalez .60 1.50
AP Andy Pettitte .60 1.50
APU Albert Pujols 2.50 6.00
AR Alex Rodriguez 1.50 4.00
AS Andy Sonnanstine .40 1.00
BP Brandon Phillips .40 1.00
BPB Brian Bannister .40 1.00
BW Brandon Webb .60 1.50
CB Clay Buchholz 1.00 2.50
CF Chone Figgins .40 1.00
CG Curtis Granderson .60 1.50
CH Cole Hamels 1.00 2.50
CP Carlos Pena .60 1.50
CS C.C. Sabathia .60 1.50
DH Dan Haren .40 1.00
DJ Derek Jeter 2.50 6.00
DL Derrek Lee .40 1.00
DO David Ortiz .60 1.50
DW David Wright 1.25 3.00
EB Eric Byrnes .40 1.00
FC Fausto Carmona .40 1.00
FH Felix Hernandez 1.00 2.50
FT Frank Thomas 1.00 2.50
HP Hunter Pence 1.00 2.50
HR Hanley Ramirez 1.00 2.50
IS Ichiro Suzuki 1.50 4.00
ISS Ichiro Suzuki 1.50 4.00
JAS Johan Santana 1.00 2.50
JMC Miguel Cabrera 1.00 2.50
JR Jose Reyes .60 1.50
JS John Smoltz 1.00 2.50
JSA Jarrod Saltalamacchia .40 1.00
JT Jim Thome .60 1.50
JV Justin Verlander 1.25 3.00
MB Mark Buehrle .60 1.50
ME Mark Ellis .40 1.00
MH Matt Holliday 1.00 2.50
MR Mark Reynolds .40 1.00
PF Prince Fielder .60 1.50
PM Pedro Martinez .60 1.50
RA Rick Ankiel .40 1.00
RB Ryan Braun 1.25 3.00
RH Ryan Howard 1.25 3.00
ROH Roy Halladay 1.00 2.50
SS Sammy Sosa 1.00 2.50
TG Tom Glavine .60 1.50
TH Trevor Hoffman .60 1.50
TOH Todd Helton .60 1.50
TT Troy Tulowitzki 1.00 2.50
VG Vladimir Guerrero 1.00 2.50

2008 Finest Finest Moments Refractors Red

STATED ODDS 1:39 MINI BOXES
STATED PRINT RUN 25 SER.#'d SETS
NO PRICING DUE TO SCARCITY

2008 Finest Finest Moments X-Fractors White Framed

STATED ODDS 1:982 MINI BOXES
STATED PRINT RUN 1 SER.#'d SET
NO PRICING DUE TO SCARCITY

2008 Finest Finest Moments Autographs

GROUP A ODDS 1:5 MINI BOXES
GROUP B ODDS 1:282 MINI BOXES
AR Alex Rios A 6.00 15.00
AS Andy Sonnanstine A 3.00 8.00
BP Brandon Phillips A 6.00 15.00
BPB Brian Bannister A 6.00 15.00
CG Curtis Granderson A 10.00 25.00
CH Cole Hamels A 6.00 15.00
CMW Chien-Ming Wang A 20.00 50.00
DW David Wright A 20.00 50.00
FC Fausto Carmona A 6.00 15.00
HR Hanley Ramirez A 10.00 25.00
JA Jeremy Accardo A 3.00 8.00
JC Jack Cust A 3.00 8.00
JD Justin Duchscherer A 6.00 15.00
JH Josh Hamilton A 10.00 25.00
JMC Miguel Cabrera A 10.00 25.00
JR Jose Reyes A 10.00 25.00
JS Jarrod Saltalamacchia A 3.00 8.00
ME Mark Ellis A 3.00 8.00
MR Mark Reynolds A 8.00 20.00
NM Nick Markakis A 10.00 25.00
PH Phil Hughes A 8.00 20.00
RB Ryan Braun A 12.50 30.00
RH Ryan Howard B 20.00 50.00
RZ Ryan Zimmerman A 10.00 25.00
VG Vladimir Guerrero A 12.50 30.00

2008 Finest Finest Moments Autographs Refractors Red

STATED ODDS 1:79 MINI BOXES
STATED PRINT RUN 25 SER.#'d SETS
NO PRICING DUE TO SCARCITY

2008 Finest Finest Moments Autographs X-Fractors White Framed

STATED ODDS 1:3260 MINI BOXES
STATED PRINT RUN 1 SER.#'d SET
NO PRICING DUE TO SCARCITY

2008 Finest Rookie Redemption

STATED ODDS 1:3 MINI BOXES
EXCHANGE DEADLINE 4/30/2009
1 Johnny Cueto EXCH 1.50 4.00
2 Jay Bruce AU 10.00 25.00
3 Kosuke Fukudome EXCH 3.00 8.00
4 Jeff Samardzija EXCH 3.00 8.00
5 Chris Davis EXCH 2.50 6.00
6 Justin Masterson EXCH 2.50 6.00
7 Clayton Kershaw EXCH 5.00 12.00
8 Daniel Murphy EXCH 5.00 12.00
9 Denard Span EXCH 1.50 4.00
10 Jed Lowrie AU EXCH 12.50 30.00

2008 Finest Topps Team Favorites

COMPLETE SET (8) 5.00 12.00
RANDOM INSERTS IN PACKS
*REF: .5X TO 1.2X BASIC
REF.ODDS 1:4 MINI BOXES
AS Alfonso Soriano 1.00 2.50
BC Bobby Crosby .60 1.50
DW David Wright 2.00 5.00
EC Eric Chavez .60 1.50
FP Felix Pie .60 1.50
JR Jose Reyes 1.00 2.50
MC Melky Cabrera .60 1.50
RC Robinson Cano 1.50 4.00

2008 Finest Topps Team Favorites Autographs

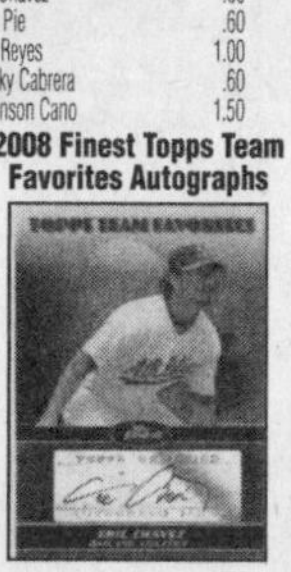

STATED PRINT RUN 100 SER.#'d SETS
AS Alfonso Soriano 20.00 50.00
BC Bobby Crosby 6.00 15.00
DW David Wright 40.00 80.00
EC Eric Chavez 6.00 15.00
FP Felix Pie 6.00 15.00
JR Jose Reyes 20.00 50.00
MC Melky Cabrera 10.00 25.00
RC Robinson Cano 15.00 40.00

2008 Finest Topps Team Favorites Autographs Refractors Red

STATED ODDS 1:164 MINI BOXES
STATED PRINT RUN 25 SER.#'d SETS
NO PRICING DUE TO SCARCITY

2008 Finest Topps Team Favorites Autographs X-Fractors White Framed

STATED ODDS 1:4092 MINI BOXES
STATED PRINT RUN 1 SER.#'d SET
NO PRICING DUE TO SCARCITY

2008 Finest Topps Team Favorites Dual

COMPLETE SET (4) 3.00 8.00
RANDOM INSERTS IN PACKS
*REF: .5X TO 1.2X BASIC
REF.RANDOMLY INSERTED
CC Melky Cabrera 1.50 4.00
 Robinson Cano
EB Eric Chavez .60 1.50
 Bobby Crosby
RW Jose Reyes 2.00 5.00
 David Wright
SP Alfonso Soriano 1.00 2.50
 Felix Pie

2008 Finest Topps Team Favorites Dual Autographs

STATED ODDS 1:166 MINI BOXES
STATED PRINT RUN 74 SER.#'d SETS
CC Melky Cabrera 12.50 30.00
 Robinson Cano
EB Eric Chavez 12.50 30.00
 Bobby Crosby
RW Jose Reyes 75.00 150.00
 David Wright
SP Alfonso Soriano 20.00 50.00
 Felix Pie

2008 Finest Topps Team Favorites Dual Autographs Refractors

STATED ODDS 1:164 MINI BOXES
STATED PRINT RUN 25 SER.#'d SETS
NO PRICING DUE TO SCARCITY

2008 Finest Topps Team Favorites Dual Autographs X-Fractors White Framed

STATED ODDS 1:4092 MINI BOXES
STATED PRINT RUN 1 SER.#'d SET
NO PRICING DUE TO SCARCITY

2008 Finest Topps Team Favorites Dual Autographs Cuts

STATED ODDS 1:9821 MINI BOXES
STATED PRINT RUN 1 SER.#'d SET
NO PRICING DUE TO SCARCITY

2008 Finest Topps TV Autographs

STATED ODDS 1:11 MINI BOXES
RM Alan 4.00 10.00
RGF Felicia 4.00 10.00
RGH Hollie 4.00 10.00
RGR Rachael 4.00 10.00
RGLS Lindsey/Stephanie 4.00 10.00

2008 Finest Topps TV Autographs Red Ink

RANDOM INSERTS IN PACKS
PRINT RUNS B/WN 5-10 COPIES PER
NO PRICING DUE TO SCARCITY

2008 Finest Topps TV Autographs Refractors

STATED ODDS 1:392 MINI BOXES
STATED PRINT RUN 1 SER.#'d SET
NO PRICING DUE TO SCARCITY

2009 Finest

COMP.SET w/o AU's (150) 40.00 80.00
COMMON CARD (1-125) .15 .40
COMMON RC (126-150) .75 2.00
COMMON AU RC (151-164) 5.00 12.00
AU RC ODDS 1:2 MINI BOX
LETTERS SER.#'d B/W 170-285 COPIES PER
TOTAL PRINT RUNS LISTED BELOW
EXCHANGE DEADLINE 4/30/2012
1-150 PLATE ODDS 1:45 MINI BOX
PLATE PRINT RUN 1 SET PER COLOR
BLACK-CYAN-MAGENTA-YELLOW ISSUED
NO PLATE PRICING DUE TO SCARCITY
1 Kosuke Fukudome .40 1.00
2 Derek Jeter 1.00 2.50
3 Evan Longoria .50 1.25
4 Alex Gordon .25 .60
5 David Wright .50 1.25
6 Ryan Howard .50 1.25
7 Jose Reyes .25 .60
8 Ryan Braun .50 1.25
9 Hunter Pence .25 .60
10 Chipper Jones .40 1.00
11 Jimmy Rollins .25 .60
12 Alfonso Soriano .25 .60
13 Alex Rodriguez .60 1.50
14 Paul Konerko .25 .60
15 Dustin Pedroia .50 1.25
16 Brian McCann .25 .60
17 Ken Griffey- .60 1.50
18 Daisuke Matsuzaka .40 1.00
19 Josh Beckett .25 .60
20 Jorge Posada .25 .60
21 Nick Markakis .40 1.00
22 Xavier Nady .15 .40
23 Carlos Pena .25 .60
24 Grady Sizemore .25 .60
25 Mark Teixeira .40 1.00
26 Chase Utley .40 1.00
27 Vladimir Guerrero .40 1.00
28 Prince Fielder .25 .60
29 Brian Roberts .15 .40
30 Magglio Ordonez .25 .60
31 Cliff Lee .25 .60
32 Josh Hamilton .40 1.00
33 Justin Morneau .40 1.00
34 David Ortiz .25 .60
35 Cole Hamels .40 1.00
36 Edinson Volquez .15 .40
37 Hanley Ramirez .40 1.00
38 Carlos Zambrano .25 .60
39 Brett Myers .15 .40
40 Chien-Ming Wang .25 .60
41 John Lackey .15 .40
42 B.J. Upton .25 .60
43 Gary Sheffield .15 .40
44 Jake Peavy .15 .40
45 Carlos Lee .15 :40
46 Jacoby Ellsbury .40 1.00
47 Francisco Liriano .15 .40
48 Torii Hunter .15 .40
49 Eric Chavez .15 .40
50 Jamie Moyer .15 .40
51 Ichiro Suzuki .60 1.50
52 CC Sabathia .25 .60
53 Matt Holliday .40 1.00
54 Ervin Santana .15 .40
55 Hideki Matsui .40 1.00
56 Mark Buehrle .25 .60
57 Johan Santana .40 1.00
58 Francisco Rodriguez .25 .60
59 Jorge Cantu .15 .40
60 Joe Mauer .40 1.00
61 Ian Kinsler .25 .60
62 Joba Chamberlain .25 .60
63 Stephen Drew .15 .40
64 J.D. Drew .15 .40
65 Justin Upton .25 .60
66 Troy Glaus .15 .40
67 Chone Figgins .15 .40
68 David DeJesus .15 .40
69 Joey Votto .40 1.00
70 Alex Rios .25 .60
71 Adam Jones .25 .60
72 Miguel Tejada .25 .60
73 Michael Young .25 .60
74 Vernon Wells .15 .40
75 Tim Lincecum .60 1.50
76 Ryan Zimmerman .25 .60
77 Nate McLouth .15 .40
78 Carl Crawford .25 .60
79 Dan Haren .15 .40
80 Brandon Webb .25 .60
81 Tim Hudson .25 .60
82 Rafael Furcal .15 .40
83 Ryan Dempster .15 .40
84 Carlos Beltran .15 .40
85 Lance Berkman .25 .60
86 Jhonny Peralta .15 .40
87 Aramis Ramirez .15 .40
88 Aubrey Huff .15 .40
89 Johnny Damon .25 .60
90 Carlos Quentin .25 .60
91 Yunel Escobar .15 .40
92 Scott Kazmir .15 .40
93 Delmon Young .25 .60
94 Jermaine Dye .15 .40
95 Miguel Cabrera .40 1.00
96 Zack Greinke .25 .60
97 Chris Young .15 .40
98 Derrek Lee .15 .40
99 Orlando Hudson .15 .40
100 Jay Bruce .25 .60
101 Garrett Atkins .15 .40
102 Curtis Granderson .25 .60
103 Adrian Gonzalez .25 .60
104 Raul Ibanez .25 .60
105 Roy Halladay .40 1.00
106 Jon Lester .40 1.00
107 Adam Dunn .25 .60
108 A.J. Burnett .25 .60
109 Gavin Floyd .15 .40
110 Russ Martin .15 .40
111 Dan Uggla .25 .60
112 Andre Ethier .25 .60
113 Casey Kotchman .15 .40
114 Matt Garza .15 .40
115 Kevin Youkilis .25 .60
116 Felix Hernandez .40 1.00
117 Rich Harden .15 .40
118 Roy Oswalt .25 .60
119 Jason Bay .25 .60
120 Geovany Soto .25 .60
121 Ryan Ludwick .25 .60
122 Joe Saunders .15 .40
123 Gil Meche .15 .40
124 Jim Thome .25 .60
125 Albert Pujols 1.00 2.50
126 Andrew Carpenter RC 1.25 3.00
127 Aaron Cunningham RC .75 2.00
128 Phil Coke RC 1.25 3.00
129 Alcides Escobar RC 2.00 5.00
130 Dexter Fowler (RC) 1.25 3.00
131 Michael Hinckley (RC) .75 2.00
132 Brad Nelson (RC) .75 2.00
133 Scott Lewis (RC) .75 2.00
134 Juan Miranda RC 1.25 3.00
135 Jason Motte (RC) 1.25 3.00
136 Travis Snider RC 1.25 3.00
137 Wade LeBlanc RC 1.25 3.00
138 Matt Tuiasosopo (RC) .75 2.00
139 Humberto Sanchez (RC) .75 2.00
140 Freddy Sandoval (RC) .75 2.00
141 Chris Lambert (RC) .75 2.00
142 John Jaso RC .75 2.00
143 James McDonald RC 2.00 5.00
144 Luis Valbuena RC 1.25 3.00
145 Rich Rundles (RC) .75 2.00
146 Josh Whitesell RC 1.25 3.00
147 Jeff Baisley RC .75 2.00
148 Ramon Ramirez (RC) .75 2.00
149 Jason Bourgeois (RC) .75 2.00
150 Jesus Delgado RC 1.25 3.00
151 Mat Gamel AU/1425 * RC 10.00 25.00
 Each letter numbered to 285
152 Travis Snider AU EXCH 10.00 25.00
153 Angel Salome AU/1308 * (RC) 5.00 12.00
 Each letter numbered to 218
154 Will Venable AU/1190 * RC 5.00 12.00
 Each letter numbered to 170
155 Michael Bowden AU/1308 * (RC) 5.00 12.00
 Each letter numbered to 218
156 Conor Gillaspie AU/963 * RC 6.00 15.00
 Each letter numbered to 107
157 Matt Antonelli AU/963 * RC 5.00 12.00
 Each letter numbered to 107
158 Greg Golson AU/1308 * (RC) 5.00 12.00
 Each letter numbered to 218
159 Kila Ka'aihue AU/1190 * (RC) 4.00 10.00
 Each letter numbered to 170
160 Bobby Parnell AU/1190 * RC 5.00 12.00
 Each letter numbered to 170
161 Gaby Sanchez AU/1190 * RC 6.00 15.00
 Each letter numbered to 170
162 Jonathon Niese AU/1425 * RC 5.00 12.00
 Each letter numbered to 285
163 Dexter Fowler AU EXCH 8.00 20.00
164 David Price AU/1425 * RC 15.00 40.00
 Each letter numbered to 285

2009 Finest Refractors

*REF VET: 1.2X TO 3X BASIC
*REF RC: .5X TO 1.2X BASIC RC
1-150 RANDOMLY INSERTED
*REF AU: .5X TO 1.2X BASIC AU
151-164 ODDS 1:4 MINI BOXES
EACH LETTER AU SER.#'d TO 75
TOTAL PRINT RUNS LISTED BELOW
EXCHANGE DEADLINE 4/30/2012

2009 Finest Refractors Blue

*BLUE REF VET: 1.5X TO 4X BASIC
*BLUE REF RC: .6X TO 1.5X BASIC RC
1-150 RANDOMLY INSERTED
1-150 PRINT RUN 399 SER.#'d SETS
*BLUE REF AU: .6X TO 1.5X BASIC AU.
151-164 ODDS 1:12 MINI BOXES
EACH LETTER AU SER.#'d TO 25
TOTAL PRINT RUNS LISTED BELOW
EXCHANGE DEADLINE 4/30/2012

2009 Finest Refractors Gold

*GOLD REF VET: 6X TO 15X BASIC
*GOLD REF RC: 1.5X TO 4X BASIC RC
1-150 STATED ODDS 1:4 MINI BOXES
1-150 PRINT RUN 50 SER.#'d SETS
*GOLD REF AU: .75X TO 2X BASIC AU
151-164 ODDS 1:30 MINI BOXES
EACH LETTER AU SER.#'d TO 10
TOTAL PRINT RUNS LISTED BELOW
EXCHANGE DEADLINE 4/30/2012
151 Mat Gamel AU/50 * 40.00 80.00
152 Travis Snider AU/60 * EXCH 40.00 80.00
163 Dexter Fowler AU/60 * EXCH 20.00 50.00
164 David Price AU/50 * 60.00 120.00

2009 Finest Refractors Green

*GREEN REF VET: 4X TO 10X BASIC
*GREEN REF RC: 1X TO 2.5X BASIC RC
1-150 STATED ODDS 1:2 MINI BOXES
STATED PRINT RUN 99 SER.#'d SETS

2009 Finest Refractors Red

*RED REF VET: 12X TO 30X BASIC
*RED REF RC: 2.5X TO 6X BASIC RC
1-150 STATED ODDS 1:8 MINI BOXES
1-150 PRINT RUN 25 SER.#'d SETS
*RED REF AU: 1.5X TO 4X BASIC AU
151-164 ODDS 1:60 MINI BOXES
EACH LETTER AU SER.#'d TO 5
TOTAL PRINT RUNS LISTED BELOW
EXCHANGE DEADLINE 4/30/2012

2009 Finest X-Fractors

1-150 ODDS 1:180 MINI BOX
151-164 AU ODDS 1:298 MINI BOX
STATED PRINT RUN 1 SER.#'d SET
NO PRICING DUE TO SCARCITY
EXCHANGE DEADLINE 4/30/2012

2009 Finest Finest Moments Autographs

GROUP A ODDS 1:10 MINI BOX
GROUP B ODDS 1:61 MINI BOX
REF.ODDS 1:68 MINI BOXES
REF.PRINT RUN 25 SER.#'d SETS
NO REF.PRICING DUE TO SCARCITY
X-F ODDS 1:1797 MINI BOX
X-F PRINT RUN 1 SER.#'d SET
NO X-F PRICING DUE TO SCARCITY
AC Asdrubal Cabrera A 10.00 25.00
AI Akinori Iwamura A 5.00 12.00
AR Alex Rodriguez B 100.00 175.00
DO David Ortiz B 15.00 40.00
DW David Wright A 12.50 30.00
EV Evan Longoria A 20.00 50.00
HP Hunter Pence A 8.00 20.00
JB Jay Bruce A 15.00 40.00
JC Joba Chamberlain A 12.50 30.00
JL Jon Lester A 10.00 25.00
JR Jose Reyes A 12.50 30.00
JT Jim Thome B 12.50 30.00
JV Joey Votto B 30.00 60.00
RC Robinson Cano A 20.00 50.00
RH Ryan Howard B 30.00 60.00
JBA Jason Bay B 15.00 40.00

2009 Finest Rookie Redemption

STATED ODDS 1:3 MINI BOXES
*REF: .5X TO 1.2X BASIC
REF.ODDS 1:14 MINI BOXES
*GOLD REF: 1.2X TO 3X BASIC
GOLD REF.ODDS 1:54 MINI BOXES
EXCHANGE DEADLINE 4/30/2010
1 Matt LaPorta 3.00 8.00
2 Tommy Hanson 4.00 10.00
3 Andrew Bailey 3.00 8.00
4 Julio Borbon 2.00 5.00
5 Colby Rasmus 3.00 8.00
6 Kyle Blanks 2.00 5.00
7 Neftali Feliz 4.00 10.00
8 Nolan Reimold 1.25 3.00
9 Rick Porcello 4.00 10.00
10 Tommy Hanson AU 10.00 25.00

2010 Finest

COMP.SET w/o AU's (150) 30.00 60.00
COMMON CARD (1-125) .15 .40
COMMON RC (126-150) .75 2.00
COMMON AU RC (151-164) 4.00 10.00
AU RC ODDS 1:2 MINI BOX
LETTERS SER.#'d B/W 106-284 COPIES PER
TOTAL PRINT RUNS LISTED BELOW
1-150 PLATE ODDS 1:50 MINI BOX
PLATE PRINT RUN 1 SET PER COLOR
BLACK-CYAN-MAGENTA-YELLOW ISSUED
NO PLATE PRICING DUE TO SCARCITY
1 Tim Lincecum .60 1.50
2 Evan Longoria .50 1.25
3 Alex Rodriguez .60 1.50
4 Ryan Braun .50 1.25
5 Grady Sizemore .25 .60
6 David Wright .50 1.25
7 Albert Pujols 1.00 2.50
8 Derrek Lee .15 .40
9 Ichiro Suzuki .60 1.50
10 Justin Morneau .40 1.00
11 Johan Santana .40 1.00
12 Matt Kemp .25 .60
13 Daisuke Matsuzaka .40 1.00
14 Derek Jeter 1.00 2.50
15 Mark Buehrle .25 .60
16 Chipper Jones .40 1.00
17 Prince Fielder .25 .60
18 Ryan Howard .50 1.25
19 Vladimir Guerrero .40 1.00
20 Alexei Ramirez .15 .40
21 Joba Chamberlain .25 .60
22 Russell Martin .15 .40
23 CC Sabathia .25 .60
24 Adam Dunn .25 .60
25 Jose Reyes .25 .60
26 Michael Young .25 .60
27 Joe Mauer .40 1.00
28 Mark Teixeira .40 1.00
29 Jason Bartlett .15 .40
30 Johnny Damon .25 .60
31 Miguel Cabrera .40 1.00
32 Adam Wainwright .25 .60
33 Brandon Webb .25 .60
34 Carlos Pena .25 .60
35 Jorge Posada .25 .60
36 Pablo Sandoval .25 .60
37 Manny Ramirez .40 1.00
38 Robinson Cano .40 1.00
39 Nick Markakis .40 1.00
40 Justin Upton .25 .60
41 Adrian Gonzalez .25 .60
42 Ian Kinsler .25 .60
43 Ryan Zimmerman .25 .60
44 Mark Reynolds .15 .40
45 Raul Ibanez .25 .60
46 Jason Bay .25 .60
47 Kendry Morales .15 .40
48 Todd Helton .25 .60
49 Dan Uggla .25 .60
50 Adam Lind .25 .60
51 Victor Martinez .25 .60
52 Mariano Rivera .40 1.00
53 Chase Utley .40 1.00
54 Kevin Youkilis .25 .60
55 Carlos Lee .15 .40
56 Josh Hamilton .40 1.00
57 Brad Hawpe .15 .40
58 Brandon Inge .25 .60
59 Bobby Abreu .15 .40
60 Nelson Cruz .25 .60
61 James Loney .25 .60

62 Jason Kubel .15 .40
63 Russell Branyan .15 .40
64 Curtis Granderson .25 .60
65 Ken Griffey Jr. .60 1.50
66 Troy Tulowitzki .40 1.00
67 Jermaine Dye .15 .40
68 Paul Konerko .25 .60
69 Josh Johnson .25 .60
70 David Ortiz .25 .60
71 Hideki Matsui .40 1.00
72 Dustin Pedroia .50 1.25
73 Jon Lester UER .40 1.00
Name spelled John
74 Joey Votto .40 1.00
75 Josh Beckett .25 .60
76 Billy Butler .15 .40
77 David DeJesus .15 .40
78 Nick Swisher .40 1.00
79 Brian Roberts .15 .40
80 Felix Hernandez .40 1.00
81 J.A. Happ .25 .60
82 Marco Scutaro .15 .40
83 Hanley Ramirez .40 1.00
84 Lance Berkman .25 .60
85 Dan Haren .15 .40
86 Yunel Escobar .15 .40
87 Justin Verlander .50 1.25
88 Carlos Beltran .15 .40
89 Shane Victorino .25 .60
90 Carl Crawford .25 .60
91 Adam Jones .25 .60
92 Jason Marquis .15 .40
93 Everth Cabrera .15 .40
94 B.J. Upton .25 .60
95 Ted Lilly .15 .40
96 Ubaldo Jimenez .25 .60
97 Aaron Hill .15 .40
98 Kosuke Fukudome .40 1.00
99 Jorge Cantu .15 .40
100 Jose Lopez .15 .40
101 Rick Porcello .15 .40
102 Matt Cain .25 .60
103 Chone Figgins .15 .40
104 Tommy Hanson .25 .60
105 Jacoby Ellsbury .40 1.00
106 Clayton Kershaw .40 1.00
107 Miguel Tejada .25 .60
108 Yovani Gallardo .15 .40
109 Andrew McCutchen .40 1.00
110 Felipe Lopez .15 .40
111 Asdrubal Cabrera .25 .60
112 Roy Halladay .40 1.00
113 Hunter Pence .25 .60
114 Gordon Beckham .25 .60
115 Cole Hamels .40 1.00
116 Brian McCann .25 .60
117 Michael Cuddyer .15 .40
118 Cliff Lee .25 .60
119 Roy Oswalt .25 .60
120 A.J. Pierzynski .15 .40
121 Jayson Werth .25 .60
122 Mike Lowell .15 .40
123 John Lannan .15 .40
124 Luis Castillo .15 .40
125 Andy Pettitte .25 .60
126 Neil Walker (RC) 1.25 3.00
127 Brad Kilby RC .75 2.00
128 Chris Johnson RC 2.00 5.00
129 Tommy Manzella (RC) .75 2.00
130 Sergio Escalona (RC) .75 2.00
131 Chris Pettit RC .75 2.00
132 Kevin Richardson (RC) .75 2.00
133 Armando Gabino RC .75 2.00
134 Reid Gorecki (RC) 1.25 3.00
135 Justin Turner RC .75 2.00
136 Adam Moore RC .75 2.00
137 Kyle Phillips RC .75 2.00
138 John Hester RC .75 2.00
139 Dusty Hughes RC .75 2.00
140 Waldis Joaquin RC .75 2.00
141 Jeff Manship RC .75 2.00
142 Dan Runzler RC 1.25 3.00
143 Pedro Viola RC .75 2.00
144 Craig Gentry RC .75 2.00
145 Brent Dlugach (RC) .75 2.00
146 Esmil Rogers RC .75 2.00
147 Josh Butler RC .75 2.00
148 Dustin Richardson RC .75 2.00
149 Matt Carson (RC) .75 2.00
150 Henry Rodriguez RC .75 2.00
151 Brandon Allen AU/1420 * (RC) 4.00 10.00
Each card serial #'d/284
152 Tyler Colvin AU/1302 * RC 15.00 40.00
Each card serial #'d/217
153 Daniel Hudson AU/1302 * RC 6.00 15.00
Each card serial #'d/217
154 Juan Francisco AU/954 * RC 6.00 15.00
Each card serial #'d/106
155 Drew Stubbs AU/1302 * RC 10.00 25.00
Each card serial #'d/217
156 Michael Brantley AU/1072 * RC 6.00 15.00
Each card serial #'d/134
157 Tobi Stoner AU/1302 * RC 6.00 15.00
Each card serial #'d/217
158 Josh Thole AU/1420 * RC 8.00 20.00
Each card serial #'d/284
159 Daniel McCutchen AU/954 * RC 5.00 12.00
Each card serial #'d/106
160 Eric Hacker AU/1302 * RC 4.00 10.00
Each card serial #'d/217
161 Madison Bumgarner AU/954 * RC 12.50 30.00
Each card serial #'d/106
162 Buster Posey AU/1420 * RC 50.00 100.00
Each card serial #'d/284
163 Dan Runzler AU/1190 * 4.00 10.00
Each card serial #'d/170
164 Ian Desmond AU/1190 * (RC) 4.00 10.00
Each card serial #'d/170
165 Dustin Richardson AU/2170 * 5.00 12.00
Each card serial #'d/217

2010 Finest Rookie Logo Patch

STATED ODDS 1:26 MINI BOX
STATED PRINT RUN 50 SER.#'d SETS
PURPLE ODDS 1:1197 MINI BOX
PURPLE PRINT RUN 1 SER.#'d SET
NO PURPLE PRICING DUE TO SCARCITY
126 Neil Walker 8.00 20.00
127 Brad Kilby 5.00 12.00
128 Chris Johnson 12.00 30.00
129 Tommy Manzella 5.00 12.00
130 Sergio Escalona 5.00 12.00
131 Chris Pettit 5.00 12.00
132 Kevin Richardson 5.00 12.00
133 Armando Gabino 5.00 12.00
134 Reid Gorecki 8.00 20.00
135 Justin Turner 5.00 12.00
136 Adam Moore 5.00 12.00
137 Kyle Phillips 5.00 12.00
138 John Hester 5.00 12.00
139 Dusty Hughes 5.00 12.00
140 Waldis Joaquin 5.00 12.00
141 Jeff Manship 5.00 12.00
142 Dan Runzler 8.00 20.00
143 Pedro Viola 5.00 12.00
144 Craig Gentry 5.00 12.00
145 Brent Dlugach 5.00 12.00
146 Esmil Rogers 5.00 12.00
147 Josh Butler 5.00 12.00
148 Dustin Richardson 5.00 12.00
149 Matt Carson 5.00 12.00
150 Henry Rodriguez 5.00 12.00

2010 Finest Refractors

*REF VET: 1.2X TO 3X BASIC
*REF RC: .5X TO 1.2X BASIC RC
1-150 RANDOMLY INSERTED
1-150 PRINT RUN 599 SER.#'d SETS
*REF AU: .5X TO 1.2X BASIC AU
151-165 ODDS 1:4 MINI BOX
EACH LETTER AU SER.#'d TO 75
TOTAL LETTER PRINT RUNS LISTED

2010 Finest Refractors Blue

*BLUE REF VET: 2.5X TO 6X BASIC
*BLUE REF RC: .6X TO 1.5X BASIC RC
1-150 STATED RANDOMLY INSERTED
1-150 PRINT RUN 299 SER.#'d SETS
*BLUE REF AU: .6X TO 1.5X BASIC AU
151-165 ODDS 1:13 MINI BOX
EACH LETTER AU SER.#'d TO 25
TOTAL LETTER PRINT RUNS LISTED

2010 Finest Refractors Gold

*GOLD REF VET: 15X TO 40X BASIC
*GOLD REF RC: 3X TO 8X BASIC RC
1-150 STATED ODDS 1:4 MINI BOX
1-150 PRINT RUN 50 SER.#'d SETS
*GOLD REF AU: 1X TO 2.5X BASIC AU
151-165 ODDS 1:32 MINI BOX
EACH LETTER AU SER.#'d TO 10
TOTAL LETTER PRINT RUNS LISTED
14 Derek Jeter 50.00 100.00

2010 Finest Refractors Green

*GREEN REF VET: 5X TO 12X BASIC
*GREEN REF RC: 1X TO 2.5X BASIC RC
STATED ODDS 1:3 MINI BOXES
STATED PRINT RUN 99 SER.#'d SETS

2010 Finest Refractors Purple

1-150 ODDS 1:200 MINI BOX
STATED PRINT RUN 1 SER.#'d SET
151-165 AU ODDS 1:302 MINI BOX
EACH LETTER #'d TO 1
TOTAL LETTER PRINT RUNS LISTED
NO PRICING DUE TO SCARCITY

2010 Finest Refractors Red

*RED REF VET: 20X TO 50X BASIC
*RED REF RC: 4X TO 10X BASIC RC
1-150 STATED ODDS 1:8 MINI BOX
1-150 PRINT RUN 25 SER.#'d SETS
*RED REF AU: 1.5X TO 4X BASIC AU
151-165 ODDS 1:60 MINI BOX
EACH LETTER AU SER.#'d TO 5
TOTAL LETTER PRINT RUNS LISTED
14 Derek Jeter 60.00 120.00

2010 Finest Finest Moments Autographs

GROUP A ODDS 1:10 MINI BOX
GROUP B ODDS 1:58 MINI BOX
PURPLE ODDS 1:1662 MINI BOX
PURPLE PRINT RUN 1 SER.#'d SET
NO PURPLE PRICING DUE TO SCARCITY
RED ODDS 1:67 MINI BOX
RED PRINT RUN 25 SER.#'d SETS
NO RED PRICING DUE TO SCARCITY
AE Andre Ethier A 10.00 25.00
AH Aaron Hill A 5.00 12.00
CF Chone Figgins A 4.00 10.00
CJ Chipper Jones B 40.00 80.00
CK Clayton Kershaw A 12.50 30.00
DP Dustin Pedroia A 12.50 30.00
DW David Wright B 15.00 40.00
JF Jeff Francoeur A 8.00 20.00
JM Justin Morneau B 12.50 30.00
JS Joe Saunders A 4.00 10.00
MS Max Scherzer A 4.00 10.00
PF Prince Fielder B 12.50 30.00
RC Robinson Cano A 12.50 30.00
RH Ryan Howard B 30.00 60.00
RP Rick Porcello B 15.00 40.00
UJ Ubaldo Jimenez A 8.00 20.00
YG Yovani Gallardo A 5.00 12.00
ZG Zack Greinke B 8.00 20.00

2010 Finest In the Name X-Fractor Autographs

STATED ODDS 1:2139 MINI BOX
STATED PRINT RUN 1 SER.#'d SET
NO PRICING DUE TO SCARCITY

2010 Finest Rookie Redemption

COMPLETE SET (11) 175.00 350.00
STATED ODDS 1:3 MINI BOX
*BLUE REF: .6X TO 1.5X BASIC
BLUE REF.ODDS 1:15 MINI BOX
*GOLD REF: 1.2X TO 3X BASIC
GOLD REF.ODDS 1:60 MINI BOX
EXCHANGE DEADLINE 4/30/2011
1a Jason Heyward 10.00 25.00
1b Jason Heyward AU 75.00 150.00
2 Ike Davis 4.00 10.00
3 Starlin Castro 6.00 15.00
4 Mike Leake 5.00 12.00
5 Mike Stanton 6.00 15.00
6 Stephen Strasburg 10.00 25.00
7 Andrew Cashner AU 8.00 20.00
8 Dayan Viciedo 2.50 6.00
9 Domonic Brown 6.00 15.00
10 Ryan Kalish 2.50 6.00

2011 Finest

COMPLETE SET (100) 20.00 50.00
COMMON CARD (1-60) .15 .40
COMMON RC (61-100) .40 1.00
1-100 PLATE ODDS 1:103 MINI BOX
PLATE PRINT RUN 1 SET PER COLOR
BLACK-CYAN-MAGENTA-YELLOW ISSUED
NO PLATE PRICING DUE TO SCARCITY
1 Hanley Ramirez .40 1.00
2 Jason Heyward .50 1.25
3 Buster Posey .50 1.25
4 Mark Teixeira .40 1.00
5 Evan Longoria .50 1.25
6 Chase Utley .40 1.00
7 Ryan Braun .50 1.25
8 Felix Hernandez .40 1.00
9 Hunter Pence .25 .60
10 Adrian Gonzalez .25 .60
11 Nick Markakis .40 1.00
12 Miguel Cabrera .40 1.00
13 Paul Konerko .25 .60
14 Ryan Zimmerman .25 .60
15 Troy Tulowitzki .40 1.00
16 Chipper Jones .40 1.00
17 Torii Hunter .15 .40
18 B.J. Upton .25 .60
19 Michael Young .25 .60
20 Ryan Howard .50 1.25
21 Andre Ethier .25 .60
22 Justin Verlander .50 1.25
23 Clay Buchholz .25 .60
24 Cole Hamels .40 1.00
25 Albert Pujols 1.00 2.50
26 Adrian Beltre .15 .40
27 Zack Greinke .25 .60
28 Derek Jeter 1.00 2.50
29 Jacoby Ellsbury .40 1.00
30 Dan Uggla .25 .60
31 Adam Dunn .25 .60
32 Matt Kemp .25 .60
33 Starlin Castro .40 1.00
34 Brian McCann .25 .60
35 David Wright .50 1.25
36 Tim Lincecum .40 1.00
37 David Price .40 1.00
38 Jayson Werth .25 .60
39 Roy Oswalt .25 .60
40 Ichiro Suzuki .60 1.50
41 Jose Bautista .25 .60
42 Robinson Cano .40 1.00
43 David Ortiz .25 .60
44 Mike Stanton .25 .60
45 Roy Halladay .40 1.00
46 Justin Upton .25 .60
47 Joey Votto .40 1.00
48 Andrew McCutchen .40 1.00
49 Matt Holliday .40 1.00
50 Alex Rodriguez .60 1.50
51 Jon Lester .40 1.00
52 Jered Weaver .15 .40
53 Kevin Youkilis .25 .60
54 Ike Davis .25 .60
55 Joe Mauer .40 1.00
56 Carl Crawford .40 1.00
57 Cliff Lee .40 1.00
58 Josh Hamilton .40 1.00
59 Stephen Strasburg .75 2.00
60 Prince Fielder .25 .60
61 Sergio Santos (RC) .40 1.00
62 Randall Delgado RC .60 1.50
63 Eric Hosmer RC 3.00 8.00
64 Julio Teheran RC 1.25 3.00
65 Danny Duffy RC .60 1.50
66 J.P. Arencibia (RC) .60 1.50
67 Domonic Brown (RC) 1.00 2.50
68 Mike Minor (RC) .40 1.00
69 Brett Wallace (RC) .40 1.00
70 Jerry Sands RC 1.50 4.00
71 Mark Trumbo (RC) .60 1.50
72 Freddie Freeman RC 1.50 4.00
73 Tsuyoshi Nishioka RC 1.25 3.00
74 Jeremy Hellickson RC 1.25 3.00
75 Kyle Drabek RC .60 1.50
76 Dustin Ackley RC 1.50 4.00
77 Brandon Beachy RC 1.00 2.50
78 Brent Morel RC .40 1.00
79 Dillon Gee RC .60 1.50
80 Chris Sale RC .60 1.50
81 Alex Cobb RC .40 1.00
82 Dee Gordon RC 1.00 2.50
83 Brandon Belt RC 1.50 4.00
84 Zach Britton RC 1.00 2.50
85 Craig Kimbrel RC 1.00 2.50
86 Michael Pineda RC 1.25 3.00
87 Andrew Cashner (RC) .40 1.00
88 Jordan Walden RC .40 1.00
89 Alexi Ogando RC 1.00 2.50
90 Jake McGee (RC) .40 1.00
91 Hector Noesi RC .60 1.50
92 Darwin Barney RC 1.25 3.00
93 Ben Revere RC .60 1.50
94 Mike Trout RC 2.50 6.00
95 Danny Espinosa RC .40 1.00
96 Aaron Crow RC .60 1.50
97 Anthony Rizzo RC .60 1.50
98 Mike Moustakas RC 1.00 2.50
99 Eduardo Sanchez RC .60 1.50
100 Daniel Descalso RC .40 1.00

2011 Finest Die Cuts

STATED ODDS 1:41 MINI BOX
STATED PRINT RUN 10 SER.#'d SETS
NO PRICING DUE TO SCARCITY

2011 Finest Refractors

*REF: 1.2X TO 3X BASIC
*REF RC: .5X TO 1.2X BASIC RC
STATED PRINT RUN 549 SER.#'d SETS

2011 Finest Gold Refractors

*GOLD: 6X TO 15X BASIC
*GOLD RC: 2.5X TO 6X BASIC RC
STATED ODDS 1:9 MINI BOX
STATED PRINT RUN 50 SER.#'d SETS
25 Albert Pujols 20.00 50.00
28 Derek Jeter 20.00 50.00
63 Eric Hosmer 30.00 60.00
76 Dustin Ackley 12.50 30.00

2011 Finest Gold Canary Diamond

STATED ODDS 1:414 MINI BOX
STATED PRINT RUN 1 SER.#'d SET
NO PRICING DUE TO SCARCITY

2011 Finest Green Refractors

*GREEN: 2.5X TO 6X BASIC
*GREEN RC: 1X TO 2.5X BASIC RC
STATED ODDS 1:3 MINI BOX
STATED PRINT RUN 199 SER.#'d SETS

2011 Finest Orange Refractors

*ORANGE: 3X TO 8X BASIC
*ORANGE RC: 1.2X TO 3X BASIC RC
STATED ODDS 1:5 MINI BOX
STATED PRINT RUN 99 SER.#'d SETS
28 Derek Jeter 15.00 40.00
29 Jacoby Ellsbury 10.00 25.00
40 Ichiro Suzuki 6.00 15.00

2011 Finest Purple Refractors

STATED ODDS 1:82 MINI BOX
STATED PRINT RUN 5 SER.#'d SETS
NO PRICING DUE TO SCARCITY

2011 Finest Red Refractors

STATED ODDS 1:18 MINI BOX
STATED PRINT RUN 25 SER.#'d SETS
NO PRICING DUE TO SCARCITY

2011 Finest Superfractors

STATED ODDS 1:410 MINI BOX
STATED PRINT RUN 1 SER.#'d SET
NO PRICING DUE TO SCARCITY

2011 Finest X-Fractors

*XF: 2.5X TO 6X BASIC
*XF RC: 1X TO 2.5X BASIC RC
STATED ODDS 1:2 MINI BOX
STATED PRINT RUN 299 SER.#'d SETS

2011 Finest Foundations

ORANGE ODDS 1:12 MINI BOX
PURPLE ODDS 1:96 MINI BOX
NO PURPLE PRICING DUE TO SCARCITY
FF1 Albert Pujols 2.50 6.00
FF2 Roy Halladay 1.00 2.50
FF3 Adrian Gonzalez .60 1.50
FF4 Ryan Howard 1.25 3.00
FF5 Alex Rodriguez 1.50 4.00
FF6 Evan Longoria 1.25 3.00
FF7 Buster Posey 1.25 3.00
FF8 Robinson Cano 1.00 2.50
FF9 Tim Lincecum 1.00 2.50
FF10 Jason Heyward 1.25 3.00
FF11 Troy Tulowitzki 1.00 2.50
FF12 Ichiro Suzuki 1.50 4.00
FF13 Stephen Strasburg 2.00 5.00
FF14 Hanley Ramirez 1.00 2.50
FF15 Derek Jeter 2.50 6.00

2011 Finest Foundations Orange Refractors

*ORANGE: .6X TO 1.5X BASIC
STATED ODDS 1:12 MINI BOX
FF12 Ichiro Suzuki 5.00 12.00
FF15 Derek Jeter 10.00 25.00

2011 Finest Freshmen

STATED ODDS 1:6 MINI BOX
*ORANGE: .6X TO 1.5X BASIC
ORANGE ODDS 1:12 MINI BOX
PURPLE ODDS 1:96 MINI BOX
NO PURPLE PRICING DUE TO SCARCITY
FFR1 Freddie Freeman 1.50 4.00
FFR2 Domonic Brown 1.00 2.50
FFR3 Jordan Walden .40 1.00
FFR4 Aroldis Chapman 1.25 3.00
FFR5 Zach Britton 1.00 2.50
FFR6 Mark Trumbo .60 1.50
FFR7 Brett Wallace .40 1.00
FFR8 Alexi Ogando 1.00 2.50
FFR9 Tsuyoshi Nishioka 1.25 3.00
FFR10 Jeremy Hellickson 1.25 3.00
FFR11 Brent Morel .40 1.00
FFR12 J.P. Arencibia .60 1.50
FFR13 Andrew Cashner .40 1.00
FFR14 Eric Hosmer 3.00 8.00
FFR15 Craig Kimbrel 1.00 2.50
FFR16 Kyle Drabek .60 1.50
FFR17 Michael Pineda 1.25 3.00

2011 Finest Jumbo Patch Orange Refractors

STATED ODDS 1:171 HOBBY
STATED PRINT RUN 10 SER.#'d SETS
NO PRICING DUE TO SCARCITY

2011 Finest Jumbo Patch Purple Refractors

STATED ODDS 1:341 HOBBY
STATED PRINT RUN 5 SER.#'d SETS
NO PRICING DUE TO SCARCITY

2011 Finest Jumbo Patch Superfractors

STATED ODDS 1:1709 HOBBY
STATED PRINT RUN 1 SER.#'d SET
NO PRICING DUE TO SCARCITY

2011 Finest Moments

STATED ODDS 1:6 MINI BOX
*ORANGE: .6X TO 1.5X BASIC
ORANGE ODDS 1:12 MINI BOX
PURPLE ODDS 1:96 MINI BOX
NO PURPLE PRICING DUE TO SCARCITY
FM1 Joe Mauer 1.00 2.50
FM2 Carl Crawford .60 1.50
FM3 Robinson Cano 1.00 2.50
FM4 Andrew McCutchen 1.00 2.50
FM5 Cliff Lee 1.00 2.50
FM6 Nick Markakis 1.00 2.50
FM7 Roy Halladay 1.00 2.50
FM8 Ryan Howard 1.25 3.00
FM9 David Wright 1.25 3.00
FM10 Buster Posey 1.25 3.00
FM11 Jason Heyward 1.25 3.00
FM12 Josh Hamilton 1.00 2.50
FM13 Alex Rodriguez 1.50 4.00
FM14 Chase Utley 1.00 2.50
FM15 David Ortiz .60 1.50
FM16 CC Sabathia .60 1.50
FM17 Stephen Strasburg 2.00 5.00
FM18 Ike Davis .60 1.50

2011 Finest Moments Relic Autographs

GROUP A ODDS 1:25 MINI BOX
GROUP B ODDS 1:93 MINI BOX
GROUP C ODDS 1:342 MINI BOX
GROUP A PRINT RUN 274 SER.#'d SETS
GROUP B PRINT RUN 74 SER.#'d SETS
GROUP C PRINT RUN 24 SER.#'d SETS
NO PRICING ON QTY 25 OR LESS
EXCHANGE DEADLINE 10/31/2014
FMA1 Joe Mauer/274 15.00 40.00
FMA2 Carl Crawford EXCH 8.00 20.00
FMA3 Robinson Cano/274 15.00 40.00
FMA5 Cliff Lee/274 20.00 50.00
FMA6 Nick Markakis/274 8.00 20.00
FMA7 Roy Halladay/74 40.00 80.00
FMA8 Ryan Howard/74 20.00 50.00
FMA9 David Wright/74 20.00 50.00
FMA10 Buster Posey EXCH
FMA11 Jason Heyward/74 15.00 40.00
FMA12 Josh Hamilton/74 15.00 40.00
FMA13 Alex Rodriguez/74 40.00 80.00
FMA14 Chase Utley/24
FMA15 David Ortiz/24
FMA16 CC Sabathia/24
FMA17 Stephen Strasburg/24
FMA18 Ike Davis/24
FMA22 Adrian Gonzalez/74 20.00 50.00

2011 Finest Moments Relic Autographs Orange Refractors

STATED ODDS 1:120 MINI BOX
STATED PRINT RUN 20 SER.#'d SETS
NO PRICING DUE TO SCARCITY
EXCHANGE DEADLINE 10/31/2014

2011 Finest Moments Relic Autographs Purple Refractors

STATED ODDS 1:482 MINI BOX
STATED PRINT RUN 5 SER.#'d SETS
NO PRICING DUE TO SCARCITY
EXCHANGE DEADLINE 10/31/2014

2011 Finest Moments Relic Autographs Superfractors

STATED ODDS 1:2413 MINI BOX
STATED PRINT RUN 1 SER.#'d SET
NO PRICING DUE TO SCARCITY
EXCHANGE DEADLINE 10/31/2014

2011 Finest Rookie Autographs Die Cut

STATED ODDS 1:241 MINI BOX
STATED PRINT RUN 10 SER.#'d SETS
NO PRICING DUE TO SCARCITY
EXCHANGE DEADLINE 10/31/2014

2011 Finest Rookie Autographs Refractors

STATED ODDS 1:5 MINI BOX
STATED PRINT RUN 499 SER.#'d SETS
PRINTING PLATE ODDS 1:603 MINI BOX
PLATE PRINT RUN 1 SET PER COLOR
BLACK-CYAN-MAGENTA-YELLOW ISSUED
NO PLATE PRICING DUE TO SCARCITY
EXCHANGE DEADLINE 10/31/2014
62 Randall Delgado 5.00 12.00
69 Brett Wallace 5.00 12.00
70 Jerry Sands 6.00 15.00
71 Mark Trumbo 8.00 20.00
72 Freddie Freeman 10.00 25.00
76 Dustin Ackley 15.00 40.00
78 Brent Morel 4.00 10.00
79 Dillon Gee 4.00 10.00
82 Dee Gordon 8.00 20.00
83 Brandon Belt 10.00 25.00
84 Zach Britton EXCH 5.00 12.00
86 Michael Pineda 8.00 20.00
88 Jordan Walden 4.00 10.00
93 Eric Sogard 4.00 10.00
94 Mike Trout 15.00 40.00
96 Aaron Crow 5.00 12.00
97 Anthony Rizzo 5.00 12.00
98 Mike Moustakas EXCH 8.00 20.00
99 Eduardo Sanchez 5.00 12.00
100 Daniel Descalso 4.00 10.00
105 Eduardo Nunez 5.00 12.00

2011 Finest Rookie Autographs Gold Refractors

*GOLD: .75X TO 2X BASIC
STATED ODDS 1:33 MINI BOX
STATED PRINT RUN 75 SER.#'d SETS
EXCHANGE DEADLINE 10/31/2014

2011 Finest Rookie Autographs Green Refractors

*GREEN: .5X TO 1.2X BASIC
STATED ODDS 1:13 MINI BOX
STATED PRINT RUN 199 SER.#'d SETS
EXCHANGE DEADLINE 10/31/2014

2011 Finest Rookie Autographs Orange Refractors

*ORANGE: .6X TO 1.5X BASIC
STATED ODDS 1:25 MINI BOX
STATED PRINT RUN 99 SER.#'d SETS
EXCHANGE DEADLINE 10/31/2014

2011 Finest Rookie Autographs Purple Refractors

STATED ODDS 1:482 MINI BOX
STATED PRINT RUN 5 SER.#'d SETS
NO PRICING DUE TO SCARCITY
EXCHANGE DEADLINE 10/31/2014

2011 Finest Rookie Autographs Red Refractors

STATED ODDS 1:101 MINI BOX
STATED PRINT RUN 25 SER.#'d SETS
NO PRICING DUE TO SCARCITY
EXCHANGE DEADLINE 10/31/2014

2011 Finest Rookie Autographs Superfractors

STATED ODDS 1:2413 MINI BOX
STATED PRINT RUN 1 SER.#'d SET
NO PRICING DUE TO SCARCITY
EXCHANGE DEADLINE 10/31/2014

2011 Finest Rookie Autographs X-Fractors

*XF: .5X TO 1.2X BASIC
STATED ODDS 1:9 MINI BOX
STATED PRINT RUN 299 SER.#'d SETS
EXCHANGE DEADLINE 10/31/2014

2011 Finest Rookie Dual Relic Autographs Refractors

STATED ODDS 1:4 MINI BOX
STATED PRINT RUN 499 SER.#'d SETS
PRINTING PLATE ODDS 1:427 MINI BOX
PLATE PRINT RUN 1 SET PER COLOR
BLACK-CYAN-MAGENTA-YELLOW ISSUED
NO PLATE PRICING DUE TO SCARCITY
EXCHANGE DEADLINE 10/31/2014
62 Eduardo Nunez 5.00 12.00
63 Eric Hosmer EXCH 40.00 80.00
64 Julio Teheran 10.00 25.00
68 Mike Minor 5.00 12.00
72 Freddie Freeman 12.50 30.00
77 Brandon Beachy 6.00 15.00
79 Dillon Gee 4.00 10.00
82 Dee Gordon 6.00 15.00
84 Zach Britton 5.00 12.00
85 Craig Kimbrel 12.50 30.00
86 Michael Pineda 10.00 25.00
87 Andrew Cashner 4.00 10.00
88 Jordan Walden 4.00 10.00
89 Alexi Ogando 6.00 15.00
91 Hector Noesi 6.00 15.00
92 Darwin Barney 6.00 15.00
96 Aaron Crow 5.00 12.00
100 Alex Cobb 4.00 10.00
98A Mike Moustakas 8.00 20.00
98B Ivan DeJesus Jr. 4.00 10.00

2011 Finest Rookie Dual Relic Autographs Die Cut

STATED ODDS 1:171 MINI BOX
STATED PRINT RUN 10 SER.#'d SETS
NO PRICING DUE TO SCARCITY
EXCHANGE DEADLINE 10/31/2014

2011 Finest Rookie Dual Relic Autographs Gold Refractors

*GOLD: .75X TO 2X BASIC
STATED ODDS 1:26 MINI BOX
STATED PRINT RUN 69 SER.#'d SETS
EXCHANGE DEADLINE 10/31/2014

2011 Finest Rookie Dual Relic Autographs Green Refractors

*GREEN: .4X TO 1X BASIC
STATED ODDS 1:12 MINI BOX
STATED PRINT RUN 149 SER.#'d SETS
EXCHANGE DEADLINE 10/31/2014

2011 Finest Rookie Dual Relic Autographs Orange Refractors

*ORANGE: .6X TO 1.5X BASIC
STATED ODDS 1:18 MINI BOX
STATED PRINT RUN 99 SER.#'d SETS
EXCHANGE DEADLINE 10/31/2014

2011 Finest Rookie Dual Relic Autographs Red Refractors

STATED ODDS 1:72 MINI BOX
STATED PRINT RUN 25 SER.#'d SETS
NO PRICING DUE TO SCARCITY
EXCHANGE DEADLINE 10/31/2014

2011 Finest Rookie Dual Relic Autographs Superfractors

STATED ODDS 1:1709 MINI BOX
STATED PRINT RUN 1 SER.#'d SET
NO PRICING DUE TO SCARCITY
EXCHANGE DEADLINE 10/31/2014

1993 Flair

This 300-card standard-size set represents Fleer's entrance into the super-premium category of trading cards. Cards were distributed exclusively in specially encased "hardpacks". The cards are made from heavy 24 point board card stock, with an additional three points of high-gloss laminate on each side, and feature full-bleed color fronts that sport two photos of each player, one superposed upon the other. The cards are numbered alphabetically within teams with National League preceding American league. There are no key Rookie Cards in this set.

COMPLETE SET (300) 20.00 50.00
1 Steve Avery .08 .25
2 Jeff Blauser .08 .25
3 Ron Gant .08 .25
4 Tom Glavine .30 .75
5 David Justice .20 .50
6 Mark Lemke .08 .25
7 Greg Maddux .75 2.00
8 Fred McGriff .30 .75
9 Terry Pendleton .20 .50
10 Deion Sanders .30 .75
11 John Smoltz .30 .75
12 Mike Stanton .08 .25
13 Steve Buechele .08 .25
14 Mark Grace .30 .75
15 Greg Hibbard .08 .25
16 Derrick May .08 .25
17 Chuck McElroy .08 .25
18 Mike Morgan .08 .25
19 Randy Myers .08 .25
20 Ryne Sandberg .75 2.00
21 Dwight Smith .08 .25
22 Sammy Sosa .50 1.25
23 Jose Vizcaino .08 .25
24 Tim Belcher .08 .25
25 Rob Dibble .20 .50
26 Roberto Kelly .08 .25
27 Barry Larkin .30 .75
28 Kevin Mitchell .08 .25
29 Hal Morris .08 .25
30 Joe Oliver .08 .25
31 Jose Rijo .08 .25
32 Bip Roberts .08 .25
33 Chris Sabo .08 .25
34 Reggie Sanders .20 .50
35 Dante Bichette .20 .50
36 Willie Blair .08 .25
37 Jerald Clark .08 .25
38 Alex Cole .08 .25
39 Andres Galarraga .20 .50
40 Joe Girardi .08 .25
41 Charlie Hayes .08 .25
42 Chris Jones .08 .25
43 David Nied .08 .25
44 Eric Young .08 .25
45 Alex Arias .08 .25
46 Jack Armstrong .08 .25
47 Bret Barberie .08 .25
48 Chuck Carr .08 .25
49 Jeff Conine .20 .50
50 Orestes Destrade .08 .25
51 Chris Hammond .08 .25
52 Bryan Harvey .08 .25
53 Benito Santiago .20 .50
54 Gary Sheffield .20 .50
55 Walt Weiss .08 .25
56 Eric Anthony .08 .25
57 Jeff Bagwell .30 .75
58 Craig Biggio .30 .75
59 Ken Caminiti .20 .50
60 Andujar Cedeno .08 .25
61 Doug Drabek .08 .25
62 Steve Finley .20 .50
63 Luis Gonzalez .20 .50
64 Pete Harnisch .08 .25
65 Doug Jones .08 .25
66 Darryl Kile .20 .50
67 Greg Swindell .08 .25
68 Brett Butler .20 .50
69 Jim Gott .08 .25
70 Orel Hershiser .20 .50
71 Eric Karros .20 .50
72 Pedro Martinez 1.00 2.50
73 Ramon Martinez .08 .25
74 Roger McDowell .08 .25
75 Mike Piazza 2.00 5.00
76 Jody Reed .08 .25
77 Tim Wallach .08 .25
78 Moises Alou .20 .50
79 Greg Colbrunn .08 .25
80 Wil Cordero .08 .25
81 Delino DeShields .08 .25
82 Jeff Fassero .08 .25
83 Marquis Grissom .20 .50
84 Ken Hill .08 .25
85 Mike Lansing RC .20 .50
86 Dennis Martinez .20 .50
87 Larry Walker .20 .50
88 John Wetteland .20 .50
89 Bobby Bonilla .20 .50
90 Vince Coleman .08 .25
91 Dwight Gooden .20 .50
92 Todd Hundley .08 .25
93 Howard Johnson .08 .25
94 Eddie Murray .50 1.25
95 Joe Orsulak .08 .25
96 Bret Saberhagen .20 .50
97 Darren Daulton .20 .50
98 Mariano Duncan .08 .25
99 Len Dykstra .20 .50
100 Jim Eisenreich .08 .25
101 Tommy Greene .08 .25
102 Dave Hollins .08 .25
103 Pete Incaviglia .08 .25
104 Danny Jackson .08 .25
105 John Kruk .20 .50
106 Terry Mulholland .08 .25
107 Curt Schilling .20 .50
108 Mitch Williams .08 .25
109 Stan Belinda .08 .25
110 Jay Bell .20 .50
111 Steve Cooke .08 .25
112 Carlos Garcia .08 .25
113 Jeff King .08 .25
114 Al Martin .08 .25
115 Orlando Merced .08 .25
116 Don Slaught .08 .25
117 Andy Van Slyke .30 .75
118 Tim Wakefield .50 1.25
119 Rene Arocha RC .20 .50
120 Bernard Gilkey .08 .25
121 Gregg Jefferies .08 .25
122 Ray Lankford .20 .50
123 Donovan Osborne .08 .25
124 Tom Pagnozzi .08 .25
125 Erik Pappas .08 .25
126 Geronimo Pena .08 .25
127 Lee Smith .20 .50
128 Ozzie Smith .75 2.00
129 Bob Tewksbury .08 .25
130 Mark Whiten .08 .25
131 Derek Bell .08 .25
132 Andy Benes .08 .25
133 Tony Gwynn .60 1.50
134 Gene Harris .08 .25
135 Trevor Hoffman .50 1.25
136 Phil Plantier .08 .25
137 Rod Beck .08 .25
138 Barry Bonds 1.25 3.00
139 John Burkett .08 .25
140 Will Clark .30 .75
141 Royce Clayton .08 .25
142 Mike Jackson .08 .25
143 Darren Lewis .08 .25
144 Kirt Manwaring .08 .25
145 Willie McGee .20 .50
146 Bill Swift .08 .25
147 Robby Thompson .08 .25
148 Matt Williams .20 .50
149 Brady Anderson .20 .50
150 Mike Devereaux .08 .25
151 Chris Hoiles .08 .25
152 Ben McDonald .08 .25
153 Mark McLemore .08 .25
154 Mike Mussina .30 .75
155 Gregg Olson .08 .25
156 Harold Reynolds .20 .50
157 Cal Ripken UER 1.50 4.00
(Back refers to his games streak going into 1992; should be 1993)
Also streak is spelled steak

158 Rick Sutcliffe .20 .50
159 Fernando Valenzuela .20 .50
160 Roger Clemens 1.00 2.50
161 Scott Cooper .08 .25
162 Andre Dawson .20 .50
163 Scott Fletcher .08 .25
164 Mike Greenwell .08 .25
165 Greg A. Harris .08 .25
166 Billy Hatcher .08 .25
167 Jeff Russell .08 .25
168 Mo Vaughn .20 .50
169 Frank Viola .20 .50
170 Chad Curtis .08 .25
171 Chili Davis .20 .50
172 Gary DiSarcina .08 .25
173 Damion Easley .08 .25
174 Chuck Finley .20 .50
175 Mark Langston .08 .25
176 Luis Polonia .08 .25
177 Tim Salmon .30 .75
178 Scott Sanderson .08 .25
179 J.T.Snow RC .30 .75
180 Wilson Alvarez .08 .25
181 Ellis Burks .20 .50
182 Joey Cora .08 .25
183 Alex Fernandez .08 .25
184 Ozzie Guillen .20 .50
185 Roberto Hernandez .08 .25
186 Bo Jackson .50 1.25
187 Lance Johnson .08 .25
188 Jack McDowell .08 .25
189 Frank Thomas .50 1.25
190 Robin Ventura .20 .50
191 Carlos Baerga .08 .25
192 Albert Belle .20 .50
193 Wayne Kirby .08 .25
194 Derek Lilliquist .08 .25
195 Kenny Lofton .20 .50
196 Carlos Martinez .08 .25
197 Jose Mesa .08 .25
198 Eric Plunk .08 .25
199 Paul Sorrento .08 .25
200 John Doherty .08 .25
201 Cecil Fielder .20 .50
202 Travis Fryman .20 .50
203 Kirk Gibson .20 .50
204 Mike Henneman .08 .25
205 Chad Kreuter .08 .25
206 Scott Livingstone .08 .25
207 Tony Phillips .08 .25
208 Mickey Tettleton .08 .25
209 Alan Trammell .20 .50
210 David Wells .20 .50
211 Lou Whitaker .20 .50
212 Kevin Appier .20 .50
213 George Brett 1.25 3.00
214 David Cone .20 .50
215 Tom Gordon .08 .25
216 Phil Hiatt .08 .25
217 Felix Jose .08 .25
218 Wally Joyner .20 .50
219 Jose Lind .08 .25
220 Mike Macfarlane .08 .25
221 Brian McRae .08 .25
222 Jeff Montgomery .08 .25
223 Cal Eldred .08 .25
224 Darryl Hamilton .08 .25
225 John Jaha .08 .25
226 Pat Listach .08 .25
227 Graeme Lloyd RC .20 .50
228 Kevin Reimer .08 .25
229 Bill Spiers .08 .25
230 B.J. Surhoff .20 .50
231 Greg Vaughn .08 .25
232 Robin Yount .75 2.00
233 Rick Aguilera .08 .25
234 Jim Deshaies .08 .25
235 Brian Harper .08 .25
236 Kent Hrbek .20 .50
237 Chuck Knoblauch .20 .50
238 Shane Mack .08 .25
239 David McCarty .08 .25
240 Pedro Munoz .08 .25
241 Mike Pagliarulo .08 .25
242 Kirby Puckett .50 1.25
243 Dave Winfield .20 .50
244 Jim Abbott .30 .75
245 Wade Boggs .30 .75
246 Pat Kelly .08 .25
247 Jimmy Key .20 .50
248 Jim Leyritz .08 .25
249 Don Mattingly 1.25 3.00
250 Matt Nokes .08 .25
251 Paul O'Neill .30 .75
252 Mike Stanley .08 .25
253 Danny Tartabull .08 .25
254 Bob Wickman .08 .25
255 Bernie Williams .30 .75
256 Mike Bordick .08 .25
257 Dennis Eckersley .20 .50
258 Brent Gates .08 .25
259 Rich Gossage .20 .50
260 Rickey Henderson .50 1.25
261 Mark McGwire 1.25 3.00
262 Ruben Sierra .20 .50
263 Terry Steinbach .08 .25
264 Bob Welch .08 .25
265 Bobby Witt .08 .25
266 Rich Amaral .08 .25
267 Chris Bosio .08 .25
268 Jay Buhner .20 .50
269 Norm Charlton .08 .25
270 Ken Griffey Jr. .75 2.00
271 Erik Hanson .08 .25
272 Randy Johnson .50 1.25
273 Edgar Martinez .30 .75
274 Tino Martinez .30 .75
275 Dave Valle .08 .25
276 Omar Vizquel .30 .75
277 Kevin Brown .20 .50
278 Jose Canseco .30 .75
279 Julio Franco .20 .50
280 Juan Gonzalez .20 .50
281 Tom Henke .08 .25
282 David Hulse RC .08 .25
283 Rafael Palmeiro .30 .75
284 Dean Palmer .20 .50
285 Ivan Rodriguez .30 .75
286 Nolan Ryan 2.00 5.00
287 Roberto Alomar .30 .75
288 Pat Borders .08 .25
289 Joe Carter .20 .50
290 Juan Guzman .08 .25
291 Pat Hentgen .08 .25
292 Paul Molitor .20 .50
293 John Olerud .20 .50
294 Ed Sprague .08 .25
295 Dave Stewart .20 .50
296 Duane Ward .08 .25
297 Devon White .20 .50
298 Checklist 1-100 .08 .25
299 Checklist 101-200 .08 .25
300 Checklist 201-300 .08 .25

1993 Flair Wave of the Future

This 20-card standard-size limited edition insert set features a selection of top prospects. Cards were randomly seeded into1993 Flair packs. Each card is made of the same thick card stock as the regular-issue set and features full-bleed color player action photos on the fronts, with the Flair logo, player's name, and the "Wave of the Future" name and logo in gold foil, all superimposed upon an ocean breaker. A Rookie Year Jim Edmonds card is a highlight of this set.

COMPLETE SET (20) 15.00 40.00
STATED ODDS 1:4
1 Jason Bere .40 1.00
2 Jeromy Burnitz .75 2.00
3 Russ Davis .75 2.00
4 Jim Edmonds 2.00 5.00
5 Cliff Floyd .75 2.00
6 Jeffrey Hammonds .40 1.00
7 Trevor Hoffman 1.50 4.00
8 Domingo Jean .40 1.00
9 David McCarty .40 1.00
10 Bobby Munoz .40 1.00
11 Brad Pennington .40 1.00
12 Mike Piazza 4.00 10.00
13 Manny Ramirez 1.50 4.00
14 John Roper .40 1.00
15 Tim Salmon 1.00 2.50
16 Aaron Sele .40 1.00
17 Allen Watson .40 1.00
18 Rondell White .75 2.00
19 Darrell Whitmore UER .40 1.00
(Nigel Wilson back)
20 Nigel Wilson UER .40 1.00
(Darrell Whitmore back)

1994 Flair

For the second consecutive year Fleer issued their premium-level Flair brand. These cards were issued in 10-card packs which were issued 24 packs to a box and 18 boxes to a case. The set consists of 450 full bleed cards in two series of 250 and 200. The card stock is thicker than the traditional standard card. Card fronts feature two photos with the player's name and team name at the bottom in gold foil. The cards are grouped alphabetically by team within each league with AL preceding NL. Notable Rookie Cards include Chan Ho Park and Alex Rodriguez. An Aaron Sele promo card was distributed to dealers and hobby media to preview the product.

COMPLETE SET (450) 35.00 80.00
COMP. SERIES 1 (250) 10.00 20.00
COMP. SERIES 2 (200) 25.00 60.00
1 Harold Baines .20 .50
2 Jeffrey Hammonds .08 .25
3 Chris Hoiles .08 .25
4 Ben McDonald .08 .25
5 Mark McLemore .08 .25
6 Jamie Moyer .20 .50
7 Jim Poole .08 .25
8 Cal Ripken Jr. 1.50 4.00
9 Chris Sabo .08 .25
10 Scott Bankhead .08 .25
11 Scott Cooper .08 .25
12 Danny Darwin .08 .25
13 Andre Dawson .20 .50
14 Billy Hatcher .08 .25
15 Aaron Sele .08 .25
16 John Valentin .08 .25
17 Dave Valle .08 .25
18 Mo Vaughn .20 .50
19 Brian Anderson RC .20 .50
20 Gary DiSarcina .08 .25
21 Jim Edmonds .50 1.25
22 Chuck Finley .20 .50
23 Bo Jackson .50 1.25
24 Mark Leiter .08 .25
25 Greg Myers .08 .25
26 Eduardo Perez .08 .25
27 Tim Salmon .30 .75
28 Wilson Alvarez .08 .25
29 Jason Bere .08 .25
30 Alex Fernandez .08 .25
31 Ozzie Guillen .20 .50
32 Joe Hall RC .08 .25
33 Darrin Jackson .08 .25
34 Kirk McCaskill .08 .25
35 Tim Raines .20 .50
36 Frank Thomas .50 1.25
37 Carlos Baerga .08 .25
38 Albert Belle .20 .50
39 Mark Clark .08 .25
40 Wayne Kirby .08 .25
41 Dennis Martinez .20 .50
42 Charles Nagy .08 .25
43 Manny Ramirez .50 1.25
44 Paul Sorrento .08 .25
45 Jim Thome .30 .75
46 Eric Davis .20 .50
47 John Doherty .08 .25
48 Junior Felix .08 .25
49 Cecil Fielder .20 .50
50 Kirk Gibson .20 .50
51 Mike Moore .08 .25
52 Tony Phillips .08 .25
53 Alan Trammell .20 .50
54 Kevin Appier .20 .50
55 Stan Belinda .08 .25
56 Vince Coleman .08 .25
57 Greg Gagne .08 .25
58 Bob Hamelin .08 .25
59 Dave Henderson .08 .25
60 Wally Joyner .20 .50
61 Mike Macfarlane .08 .25
62 Jeff Montgomery .08 .25
63 Ricky Bones .08 .25
64 Jeff Bronkey .08 .25
65 Alex Diaz RC .08 .25
66 Cal Eldred .08 .25
67 Darryl Hamilton .08 .25
68 John Jaha .08 .25
69 Mark Kiefer .08 .25
70 Kevin Seitzer .08 .25
71 Turner Ward .08 .25
72 Rich Becker .08 .25
73 Scott Erickson .08 .25
74 Keith Garagozzo RC .08 .25
75 Kent Hrbek .20 .50
76 Scott Leius .08 .25
77 Kirby Puckett .50 1.25
78 Matt Walbeck .08 .25
79 Dave Winfield .20 .50
80 Mike Gallego .08 .25
81 Xavier Hernandez .08 .25
82 Jimmy Key .20 .50
83 Jim Leyritz .08 .25
84 Don Mattingly 1.25 3.00
85 Matt Nokes .08 .25
86 Paul O'Neill .30 .75
87 Melido Perez .08 .25
88 Danny Tartabull .08 .25
89 Mike Bordick .08 .25
90 Ron Darling .08 .25
91 Dennis Eckersley .20 .50
92 Stan Javier .08 .25
93 Steve Karsay .08 .25
94 Mark McGwire 1.25 3.00
95 Troy Neel .08 .25
96 Terry Steinbach .08 .25
97 Bill Taylor RC .20 .50
98 Eric Anthony .08 .25
99 Chris Bosio .08 .25
100 Tim Davis .08 .25
101 Felix Fermin .08 .25
102 Dave Fleming .08 .25
103 Ken Griffey Jr. .75 2.00
104 Greg Hibbard .08 .25
105 Reggie Jefferson .08 .25
106 Tino Martinez .30 .75
107 Jack Armstrong .08 .25
108 Will Clark .30 .75
109 Juan Gonzalez .20 .50
110 Rick Helling .08 .25
111 Tom Henke .08 .25
112 David Hulse .08 .25
113 Manuel Lee .08 .25
114 Doug Strange .08 .25
115 Roberto Alomar .30 .75
116 Joe Carter .20 .50
117 Carlos Delgado .30 .75
118 Pat Hentgen .08 .25
119 Paul Molitor .20 .50
120 John Olerud .20 .50
121 Dave Stewart .20 .50
122 Todd Stottlemyre .08 .25
123 Mike Timlin .08 .25
124 Jeff Blauser .08 .25
125 Tom Glavine .30 .75
126 David Justice .20 .50
127 Mike Kelly .08 .25
128 Ryan Klesko .20 .50
129 Javier Lopez .20 .50
130 Greg Maddux .75 2.00
131 Fred McGriff .30 .75
132 Kent Mercker .08 .25
133 Mark Wohlers .08 .25
134 Willie Banks .08 .25
135 Steve Buechele .08 .25
136 Shawon Dunston .08 .25
137 Jose Guzman .08 .25
138 Glenallen Hill .08 .25
139 Randy Myers .08 .25
140 Karl Rhodes .08 .25
141 Ryne Sandberg .75 2.00
142 Steve Trachsel .08 .25
143 Bret Boone .20 .50
144 Tom Browning .08 .25
145 Hector Carrasco .08 .25
146 Barry Larkin .30 .75
147 Hal Morris .08 .25
148 Jose Rijo .08 .25
149 Reggie Sanders .20 .50
150 John Smiley .08 .25
151 Dante Bichette .20 .50
152 Ellis Burks .20 .50
153 Joe Girardi .08 .25
154 Mike Harkey .08 .25
155 Roberto Mejia .08 .25
156 Marcus Moore .08 .25
157 Armando Reynoso .08 .25
158 Bruce Ruffin .08 .25
159 Eric Young .08 .25
160 Kurt Abbott RC .20 .50
161 Jeff Conine .20 .50
162 Orestes Destrade .08 .25
163 Chris Hammond .08 .25
164 Bryan Harvey .08 .25
165 Dave Magadan .08 .25
166 Gary Sheffield .20 .50
167 David Weathers .08 .25
168 Andujar Cedeno .08 .25
169 Tom Edens .08 .25
170 Luis Gonzalez .20 .50
171 Pete Harnisch .08 .25
172 Todd Jones .08 .25
173 Darryl Kile .20 .50
174 James Mouton .08 .25
175 Scott Servais .08 .25
176 Mitch Williams .08 .25
177 Pedro Astacio .08 .25
178 Orel Hershiser .20 .50
179 Raul Mondesi .20 .50
180 Jose Offerman .08 .25
181 Chan Ho Park RC .30 .75
182 Mike Piazza 1.00 2.50
183 Cory Snyder .08 .25
184 Tim Wallach .08 .25
185 Todd Worrell .08 .25
186 Sean Berry .08 .25
187 Wil Cordero .08 .25
188 Darrin Fletcher .08 .25
189 Cliff Floyd .20 .50
190 Marquis Grissom .20 .50
191 Rod Henderson .08 .25
192 Ken Hill .08 .25
193 Pedro Martinez .50 1.25
194 Kirk Rueter .08 .25
195 Jeromy Burnitz .20 .50
196 John Franco .20 .50
197 Dwight Gooden .20 .50
198 Todd Hundley .08 .25
199 Bobby Jones .08 .25
200 Jeff Kent .30 .75
201 Mike Maddux .08 .25
202 Ryan Thompson .08 .25
203 Jose Vizcaino .08 .25
204 Darren Daulton .20 .50
205 Lenny Dykstra .20 .50
206 Jim Eisenreich .08 .25
207 Dave Hollins .08 .25
208 Danny Jackson .08 .25
209 Doug Jones .08 .25
210 Jeff Juden .08 .25
211 Ben Rivera .08 .25
212 Kevin Stocker .08 .25
213 Milt Thompson .08 .25
214 Jay Bell .20 .50
215 Steve Cooke .08 .25
216 Mark Dewey .08 .25
217 Al Martin .08 .25
218 Orlando Merced .08 .25
219 Don Slaught .08 .25
220 Zane Smith .08 .25
221 Rick White RC .08 .25
222 Kevin Young .08 .25
223 Rene Arocha .08 .25
224 Rheal Cormier .08 .25
225 Brian Jordan .20 .50
226 Ray Lankford .20 .50
227 Mike Perez .08 .25
228 Ozzie Smith .75 2.00
229 Mark Whiten .08 .25
230 Todd Zeile .08 .25
231 Derek Bell .08 .25
232 Archi Cianfrocco .08 .25
233 Ricky Gutierrez .08 .25
234 Trevor Hoffman .30 .75
235 Phil Plantier .08 .25
236 Dave Staton .08 .25
237 Wally Whitehurst .08 .25
238 Todd Benzinger .08 .25
239 Barry Bonds 1.25 3.00
240 John Burkett .08 .25
241 Royce Clayton .08 .25
242 Bryan Hickerson .08 .25
243 Mike Jackson .08 .25
244 Darren Lewis .08 .25
245 Kirt Manwaring .08 .25
246 Mark Portugal .08 .25
247 Salomon Torres .08 .25
248 Checklist .08 .25
249 Checklist .08 .25
250 Checklist .08 .25
251 Brady Anderson .20 .50
252 Mike Devereaux .08 .25
253 Sid Fernandez .08 .25
254 Leo Gomez .08 .25
255 Mike Mussina .30 .75
256 Mike Oquist .08 .25
257 Rafael Palmeiro .30 .75
258 Lee Smith .20 .50
259 Damon Berryhill .08 .25
260 Wes Chamberlain .08 .25
261 Roger Clemens 1.00 2.50
262 Gar Finnvold RC .08 .25
263 Mike Greenwell .08 .25
264 Tim Naehring .08 .25
265 Otis Nixon .08 .25
266 Ken Ryan .08 .25
267 Chad Curtis .08 .25
268 Chili Davis .20 .50
269 Damion Easley .08 .25
270 Jorge Fabregas .08 .25
271 Mark Langston .08 .25
272 Phil Leftwich RC .08 .25
273 Harold Reynolds .08 .25
274 J.T. Snow .20 .50
275 Joey Cora .08 .25
276 Julio Franco .20 .50
277 Roberto Hernandez .08 .25
278 Lance Johnson .08 .25
279 Ron Karkovice .08 .25
280 Jack McDowell .08 .25
281 Robin Ventura .20 .50
282 Sandy Alomar Jr. .08 .25
283 Kenny Lofton .20 .50
284 Jose Mesa .08 .25
285 Jack Morris .20 .50
286 Eddie Murray .50 1.25
287 Chad Ogea .08 .25
288 Eric Plunk .08 .25
289 Paul Shuey .08 .25
290 Omar Vizquel .30 .75
291 Danny Bautista .08 .25
292 Travis Fryman .20 .50
293 Greg Gohr .08 .25
294 Chris Gomez .08 .25
295 Mickey Tettleton .08 .25
296 Lou Whitaker .20 .50
297 David Cone .20 .50
298 Gary Gaetti .20 .50
299 Tom Gordon .08 .25
300 Felix Jose .08 .25
301 Jose Lind .08 .25
302 Brian McRae .08 .25
303 Mike Fetters .08 .25
304 Brian Harper .08 .25
305 Pat Listach .08 .25
306 Matt Mieske .08 .25
307 Dave Nilsson .08 .25
308 Jody Reed .08 .25
309 Greg Vaughn .08 .25
310 Bill Wegman .08 .25
311 Rick Aguilera .08 .25
312 Alex Cole .08 .25
313 Denny Hocking .08 .25
314 Chuck Knoblauch .20 .50
315 Shane Mack .08 .25
316 Pat Meares .08 .25
317 Kevin Tapani .08 .25
318 Jim Abbott .30 .75
319 Wade Boggs .30 .75
320 Sterling Hitchcock .08 .25
321 Pat Kelly .08 .25
322 Terry Mulholland .08 .25
323 Luis Polonia .08 .25
324 Mike Stanley .08 .25
325 Bob Wickman .08 .25
326 Bernie Williams .30 .75
327 Mark Acre RC .08 .25
328 Geronimo Berroa .08 .25
329 Scott Brosius .20 .50
330 Brent Gates .08 .25
331 Rickey Henderson .50 1.25
332 Carlos Reyes RC .08 .25
333 Ruben Sierra .20 .50
334 Bobby Witt .08 .25
335 Bobby Ayala .08 .25
336 Jay Buhner .20 .50
337 Randy Johnson .50 1.25
338 Edgar Martinez .30 .75
339 Bill Risley .08 .25
340 Alex Rodriguez RC 8.00 20.00
341 Roger Salkeld .08 .25
342 Dan Wilson .08 .25
343 Kevin Brown .20 .50
344 Jose Canseco .30 .75
345 Dean Palmer .20 .50
346 Ivan Rodriguez .30 .75
347 Kenny Rogers .20 .50
348 Pat Borders .08 .25
349 Juan Guzman .08 .25
350 Ed Sprague .08 .25
351 Devon White .20 .50
352 Steve Avery .08 .25
353 Roberto Kelly .08 .25
354 Mark Lemke .08 .25
355 Greg McMichael .08 .25
356 Terry Pendleton .20 .50
357 John Smoltz .30 .75
358 Mike Stanton .08 .25
359 Tony Tarasco .08 .25
360 Mark Grace .30 .75
361 Derrick May .08 .25
362 Rey Sanchez .08 .25
363 Sammy Sosa .50 1.25
364 Rick Wilkins .08 .25
365 Jeff Brantley .08 .25
366 Tony Fernandez .08 .25
367 Chuck McElroy .08 .25
368 Kevin Mitchell .08 .25
369 John Roper .08 .25
370 Johnny Ruffin .08 .25
371 Deion Sanders .30 .75
372 Marvin Freeman .08 .25
373 Andres Galarraga .20 .50
374 Charlie Hayes .08 .25
375 Nelson Liriano .08 .25
376 David Nied .08 .25
377 Walt Weiss .08 .25
378 Bret Barberie .08 .25
379 Jerry Browne .08 .25
380 Chuck Carr .08 .25
381 Greg Colbrunn .08 .25
382 Charlie Hough .20 .50
383 Kurt Miller .08 .25
384 Benito Santiago .20 .50
385 Jeff Bagwell .30 .75
386 Craig Biggio .30 .75
387 Ken Caminiti .20 .50
388 Doug Drabek .08 .25
389 Steve Finley .20 .50
390 John Hudek RC .08 .25
391 Orlando Miller .08 .25
392 Shane Reynolds .08 .25
393 Brett Butler .20 .50
394 Tom Candiotti .08 .25
395 Delino DeShields .08 .25
396 Kevin Gross .08 .25
397 Eric Karros .20 .50
398 Ramon Martinez .08 .25
399 Henry Rodriguez .08 .25
400 Moises Alou .20 .50
401 Jeff Fassero .08 .25
402 Mike Lansing .08 .25
403 Mel Rojas .08 .25
404 Larry Walker .20 .50
405 John Wetteland .20 .50
406 Gabe White .08 .25
407 Bobby Bonilla .20 .50
408 Josias Manzanillo .08 .25
409 Bret Saberhagen .20 .50
410 David Segui .08 .25
411 Mariano Duncan .08 .25
412 Tommy Greene .08 .25
413 Billy Hatcher .08 .25
414 Ricky Jordan .08 .25
415 John Kruk .20 .50
416 Bobby Munoz .08 .25
417 Curt Schilling .50 1.25
418 Fernando Valenzuela .20 .50
419 David West .08 .25
420 Carlos Garcia .08 .25
421 Brian Hunter .08 .25
422 Jeff King .08 .25
423 Jon Lieber .20 .50
424 Ravelo Manzanillo .08 .25
425 Denny Neagle .20 .50
426 Andy Van Slyke .30 .75
427 Bryan Eversgerd RC .08 .25
428 Bernard Gilkey .08 .25
429 Gregg Jefferies .08 .25
430 Tom Pagnozzi .08 .25
431 Bob Tewksbury .08 .25
432 Allen Watson .08 .25
433 Andy Ashby .08 .25
434 Andy Benes .08 .25
435 Donnie Elliott .08 .25
436 Tony Gwynn .60 1.50
437 Joey Hamilton .08 .25
438 Tim Hyers RC .08 .25
439 Luis Lopez .08 .25
440 Bip Roberts .08 .25
441 Scott Sanders .08 .25
442 Rod Beck .08 .25
443 Dave Burba .08 .25
444 Darryl Strawberry .20 .50
445 Bill Swift .08 .25
446 Robby Thompson .08 .25
447 B.VanLandingham RC .08 .25
448 Matt Williams .20 .50
449 Checklist .08 .25
450 Checklist .08 .25
P15 Aaron Sele Promo .40 1.00

1994 Flair Hot Gloves

Randomly inserted in second series packs at a rate of one in 24, this set highlights 10 of the game's top players that also have outstanding defensive ability. The cards feature a special die-cut "glove" design with the player appearing within the glove. The back has a short write-up and a photo.

COMPLETE SET (10) 50.00 120.00
RANDOM INSERTS IN SER.2 PACKS
1 Barry Bonds 10.00 25.00
2 Will Clark 2.50 6.00
3 Ken Griffey Jr. 6.00 15.00
4 Kenny Lofton 1.50 4.00
5 Greg Maddux 6.00 15.00
6 Don Mattingly 10.00 25.00
7 Kirby Puckett 4.00 10.00
8 Cal Ripken Jr. 12.50 30.00
9 Tim Salmon 2.50 6.00
10 Matt Williams 1.50 4.00

1994 Flair Hot Numbers

This 10-card set was randomly inserted in first series packs at a rate of one in 24. Metallic fronts feature a player photo with various numbers or statistics serving as background. The backs have a small photo centered in the middle surrounded by text highlighting achievements.

COMPLETE SET (10) 30.00 80.00
SER.1 STATED ODDS 1:24
1 Roberto Alomar 2.00 5.00
2 Carlos Baerga .60 1.50
3 Will Clark 2.00 5.00
4 Fred McGriff 2.00 5.00
5 Paul Molitor 1.25 3.00
6 John Olerud 1.25 3.00
7 Mike Piazza 6.00 15.00
8 Cal Ripken Jr. 10.00 25.00
9 Ryne Sandberg 5.00 12.00
10 Frank Thomas 3.00 8.00

1994 Flair Infield Power

Randomly inserted in second series packs at a rate of one in five, this 10-card standard-size set spotlights major league infielders who are power hitters. Card fronts feature a horizontal format with two photos of the player. The backs contain a short write-up with emphasis on power numbers and a small photo.

COMPLETE SET (10) 6.00 15.00
STATED ODDS 1:5
1 Jeff Bagwell .50 1.25
2 Will Clark .50 1.25
3 Darren Daulton .30 .75
4 Don Mattingly 2.00 5.00
5 Fred McGriff .50 1.25
6 Rafael Palmeiro .50 1.25
7 Mike Piazza 1.50 4.00
8 Cal Ripken Jr. 2.50 6.00
9 Frank Thomas .75 2.00
10 Matt Williams .30 .75

1994 Flair Outfield Power

This 10-card standard-size set was randomly inserted in both first and second series packs at a rate of one in five. Two photos on the front feature the player fielding and hitting. The back contains a small photo and text.

COMPLETE SET (10) 8.00 20.00
STATED ODDS 1:5
1 Albert Belle .40 1.00
2 Barry Bonds 2.50 6.00
3 Joe Carter .40 1.00
4 Lenny Dykstra .40 1.00
5 Juan Gonzalez .40 1.00
6 Ken Griffey Jr. 1.50 4.00
7 David Justice .40 1.00
8 Kirby Puckett 1.00 2.50
9 Tim Salmon .60 1.50
10 Dave Winfield .40 1.00

1994 Flair Wave of the Future

This 20-card standard-size set takes a look at potential big league stars. The cards were randomly inserted in packs at a rate of one in five -- the first 10 in series one, the second 10 in series two. The fronts and backs have the player superimposed over a wavy colored background. The front has the Wave of the Future logo and a paragraph or two about the player along with a photo on the back. This set is highlighted by an early Alex Rodriguez card.

COMPLETE SER.1 (10) 7.50 15.00
COMPLETE SER.2 (10) 15.00 40.00
A1-A10 SER.1 STATED ODDS 1:5
B1-B10 SER.2 STATED ODDS 1:5
A1 Kurt Abbott .40 1.00
A2 Carlos Delgado 1.00 2.50
A3 Steve Karsay .40 1.00
A4 Ryan Klesko .75 2.00
A5 Javier Lopez .75 2.00
A6 Raul Mondesi .75 2.00
A7 James Mouton .40 1.00
A8 Chan Ho Park 1.00 2.50
A9 Dave Staton .40 1.00
A10 Rick White .40 1.00
B1 Mark Acre .40 1.00
B2 Chris Gomez .40 1.00
B3 Joey Hamilton .40 1.00
B4 John Hudek .40 1.00
B5 Jon Lieber .75 2.00
B6 Matt Mieske .40 1.00
B7 Orlando Miller .40 1.00
B8 Alex Rodriguez 8.00 20.00
B9 Tony Tarasco .40 1.00
B10 W.VanLandingham .40 1.00

1995 Flair

This set (produced by Fleer) was issued in two series of 216 cards for a total of 432 standard-size cards. Horizontally designed fronts have a 100 percent etched foil surface containing two player photos. The backs feature a full-bleed photo with yearly statistics superimposed. The checklist is arranged alphabetically by league with AL preceding NL. Rookie Cards include Bobby Higginson and Hideo Nomo.

COMPLETE SET (432) 20.00 50.00
COMP. SERIES 1 (216) 12.00 30.00
COMP. SERIES 2 (216) 8.00 20.00
1 Brady Anderson .20 .50
2 Harold Baines .20 .50
3 Leo Gomez .08 .25
4 Alan Mills .08 .25
5 Jamie Moyer .20 .50
6 Mike Mussina .30 .75
7 Mike Oquist .08 .25
8 Arthur Rhodes .08 .25
9 Cal Ripken Jr. 1.50 4.00
10 Roger Clemens 1.00 2.50
11 Scott Cooper .08 .25
12 Mike Greenwell .08 .25
13 Aaron Sele .08 .25
14 John Valentin .08 .25
15 Mo Vaughn .20 .50
16 Chad Curtis .08 .25
17 Gary DiSarcina .08 .25
18 Chuck Finley .20 .50
19 Andrew Lorraine .08 .25
20 Spike Owen .08 .25
21 Tim Salmon .30 .75
22 J.T. Snow .20 .50
23 Wilson Alvarez .08 .25
24 Jason Bere .08 .25
25 Ozzie Guillen .20 .50
26 Mike LaValliere .08 .25
27 Frank Thomas .50 1.25
28 Robin Ventura .20 .50
29 Carlos Baerga .08 .25
30 Albert Belle .20 .50
31 Jason Grimsley .08 .25
32 Dennis Martinez .20 .50
33 Eddie Murray .50 1.25
34 Charles Nagy .08 .25
35 Manny Ramirez .30 .75
36 Paul Sorrento .08 .25
37 John Doherty .08 .25
38 Cecil Fielder .20 .50
39 Travis Fryman .20 .50
40 Chris Gomez .08 .25

41 Tony Phillips .08 .25
42 Lou Whitaker .20 .50
43 David Cone .20 .50
44 Gary Gaetti .20 .50
45 Mark Gubicza .08 .25
46 Bob Hamelin .08 .25
47 Wally Joyner .20 .50
48 Rusty Meacham .08 .25
49 Jeff Montgomery .08 .25
50 Ricky Bones .08 .25
51 Cal Eldred .08 .25
52 Pat Listach .08 .25
53 Matt Mieske .08 .25
54 Dave Nilsson .08 .25
55 Greg Vaughn .08 .25
56 Bill Wegman .08 .25
57 Chuck Knoblauch .20 .50
58 Scott Leius .08 .25
59 Pat Mahomes .08 .25
60 Pat Meares .08 .25
61 Pedro Munoz .08 .25
62 Kirby Puckett .50 1.25
63 Wade Boggs .30 .75
64 Jimmy Key .20 .50
65 Jim Leyritz .08 .25
66 Don Mattingly 1.25 3.00
67 Paul O'Neill .30 .75
68 Melido Perez .08 .25
69 Danny Tartabull .08 .25
70 John Briscoe .08 .25
71 Scott Brosius .20 .50
72 Ron Darling .08 .25
73 Brent Gates .08 .25
74 Rickey Henderson .50 1.25
75 Stan Javier .08 .25
76 Mark McGwire 1.25 3.00
77 Todd Van Poppel .08 .25
78 Bobby Ayala .08 .25
79 Mike Blowers .08 .25
80 Jay Buhner .20 .50
81 Ken Griffey Jr. .75 2.00
82 Randy Johnson .50 1.25
83 Tino Martinez .30 .75
84 Jeff Nelson .08 .25
85 Alex Rodriguez 1.25 3.00
86 Will Clark .30 .75
87 Jeff Frye .08 .25
88 Juan Gonzalez .20 .50
89 Rusty Greer .20 .50
90 Darren Oliver .08 .25
91 Dean Palmer .20 .50
92 Ivan Rodriguez .30 .75
93 Matt Whiteside .08 .25
94 Roberto Alomar .30 .75
95 Joe Carter .20 .50
96 Tony Castillo .08 .25
97 Juan Guzman .08 .25
98 Pat Hentgen .08 .25
99 Mike Huff .08 .25
100 John Olerud .20 .50
101 Woody Williams .08 .25
102 Roberto Kelly .08 .25
103 Ryan Klesko .20 .50
104 Javier Lopez .20 .50
105 Greg Maddux .75 2.00
106 Fred McGriff .30 .75
107 Jose Oliva .08 .25
108 John Smoltz .30 .75
109 Tony Tarasco .08 .25
110 Mark Wohlers .08 .25
111 Jim Bullinger .08 .25
112 Shawon Dunston .08 .25
113 Derrick May .08 .25
114 Randy Myers .08 .25
115 Karl Rhodes .08 .25
116 Rey Sanchez .08 .25
117 Steve Trachsel .08 .25
118 Eddie Zambrano .08 .25
119 Bret Boone .20 .50
120 Brian Dorsett .08 .25
121 Hal Morris .08 .25
122 Jose Rijo .08 .25
123 John Roper .08 .25
124 Reggie Sanders .20 .50
125 Pete Schourek .08 .25
126 John Smiley .08 .25
127 Ellis Burks .20 .50
128 Vinny Castilla .20 .50
129 Marvin Freeman .08 .25
130 Andres Galarraga .20 .50
131 Mike Munoz .08 .25
132 David Nied .08 .25
133 Bruce Ruffin .08 .25
134 Walt Weiss .08 .25
135 Eric Young .08 .25
136 Greg Colbrunn .08 .25
137 Jeff Conine .20 .50
138 Jeremy Hernandez .08 .25
139 Charles Johnson .20 .50
140 Robb Nen .20 .50
141 Gary Sheffield .20 .50
142 Dave Weathers .08 .25
143 Jeff Bagwell .30 .75
144 Craig Biggio .30 .75
145 Tony Eusebio .08 .25
146 Luis Gonzalez .20 .50
147 John Hudek .08 .25
148 Darryl Kile .20 .50
149 Dave Veres .08 .25
150 Billy Ashley .08 .25
151 Pedro Astacio .08 .25
152 Rafael Bournigal .08 .25
153 Delino DeShields .08 .25
154 Raul Mondesi .20 .50
155 Mike Piazza .75 2.00
156 Rudy Seanez .08 .25
157 Ismael Valdes .08 .25
158 Tim Wallach .08 .25
159 Todd Worrell .08 .25
160 Moises Alou .20 .50
161 Cliff Floyd .20 .50
162 Gil Heredia .08 .25
163 Mike Lansing .08 .25
164 Pedro Martinez .30 .75
165 Kirk Rueter .08 .25
166 Tim Scott .08 .25
167 Jeff Shaw .08 .25
168 Rondell White .20 .50
169 Bobby Bonilla .20 .50
170 Rico Brogna .08 .25
171 Todd Hundley .08 .25
172 Jeff Kent .20 .50
173 Jim Lindeman .08 .25
174 Joe Orsulak .08 .25
175 Bret Saberhagen .20 .50
176 Toby Borland .08 .25
177 Darren Daulton .20 .50
178 Lenny Dykstra .20 .50
179 Jim Eisenreich .08 .25
180 Tommy Greene .08 .25
181 Tony Longmire .08 .25
182 Bobby Munoz .08 .25
183 Kevin Stocker .08 .25
184 Jay Bell .20 .50
185 Steve Cooke .08 .25
186 Ravelo Manzanillo .08 .25
187 Al Martin .08 .25
188 Denny Neagle .20 .50
189 Don Slaught .08 .25
190 Paul Wagner .08 .25
191 Rene Arocha .08 .25
192 Bernard Gilkey .08 .25
193 Jose Oquendo .08 .25
194 Tom Pagnozzi .08 .25
195 Ozzie Smith .75 2.00
196 Allen Watson .08 .25
197 Mark Whiten .08 .25
198 Andy Ashby .08 .25
199 Donnie Elliott .08 .25
200 Bryce Florie .08 .25
201 Tony Gwynn .60 1.50
202 Trevor Hoffman .20 .50
203 Brian Johnson .08 .25
204 Tim Mauser .08 .25
205 Bip Roberts .08 .25
206 Rod Beck .08 .25
207 Barry Bonds 1.25 3.00
208 Royce Clayton .08 .25
209 Darren Lewis .08 .25
210 Mark Portugal .08 .25
211 Kevin Rogers .08 .25
212 W.VanLandingham .08 .25
213 Matt Williams .20 .50
214 Checklist .08 .25
215 Checklist .08 .25
216 Checklist .08 .25
217 Bret Barberie .08 .25
218 Armando Benitez .08 .25
219 Kevin Brown .20 .50
220 Sid Fernandez .08 .25
221 Chris Hoiles .08 .25
222 Doug Jones .08 .25
223 Ben McDonald .08 .25
224 Rafael Palmeiro .30 .75
225 Andy Van Slyke .30 .75
226 Jose Canseco .30 .75
227 Vaughn Eshelman .08 .25
228 Mike Macfarlane .08 .25
229 Tim Naehring .08 .25
230 Frank Rodriguez .08 .25
231 Lee Tinsley .08 .25
232 Mark Whiten .08 .25
233 Garret Anderson .20 .50
234 Chili Davis .20 .50
235 Jim Edmonds .30 .75
236 Mark Langston .08 .25
237 Troy Percival .20 .50
238 Tony Phillips .08 .25
239 Lee Smith .20 .50
240 Jim Abbott .30 .75
241 James Baldwin .08 .25
242 Mike Devereaux .08 .25
243 Ray Durham .20 .50
244 Alex Fernandez .08 .25
245 Roberto Hernandez .08 .25
246 Lance Johnson .08 .25
247 Ron Karkovice .08 .25
248 Tim Raines .20 .50
249 Sandy Alomar Jr. .08 .25
250 Orel Hershiser .20 .50
251 Julian Tavarez .08 .25
252 Jim Thome .30 .75
253 Omar Vizquel .30 .75
254 Dave Winfield .20 .50
255 Chad Curtis .08 .25
256 Kirk Gibson .20 .50
257 Mike Henneman .08 .25
258 Bob Higginson RC .40 1.00
259 Felipe Lira .08 .25
260 Rudy Pemberton .08 .25
261 Alan Trammell .20 .50
262 Kevin Appier .20 .50
263 Pat Borders .08 .25
264 Tom Gordon .08 .25
265 Jose Lind .08 .25
266 Jon Nunnally .08 .25
267 Dilson Torres RC .08 .25
268 Michael Tucker .08 .25
269 Jeff Cirillo .08 .25
270 Darryl Hamilton .08 .25
271 David Hulse .08 .25
272 Mark Kiefer .08 .25
273 Graeme Lloyd .08 .25
274 Joe Oliver .08 .25
275 Al Reyes RC .08 .25
276 Kevin Seitzer .08 .25
277 Rick Aguilera .08 .25
278 Marty Cordova .08 .25
279 Scott Erickson .08 .25
280 LaTroy Hawkins .08 .25
281 Brad Radke RC .40 1.00
282 Kevin Tapani .08 .25
283 Tony Fernandez .08 .25
284 Sterling Hitchcock .08 .25
285 Pat Kelly .08 .25
286 Jack McDowell .08 .25
287 Andy Pettitte .30 .75
288 Mike Stanley .08 .25
289 John Wetteland .20 .50
290 Bernie Williams .30 .75
291 Mark Acre .08 .25
292 Geronimo Berroa .08 .25
293 Dennis Eckersley .20 .50
294 Steve Ontiveros .08 .25
295 Ruben Sierra .20 .50
296 Terry Steinbach .08 .25
297 Dave Stewart .20 .50
298 Todd Stottlemyre .08 .25
299 Darren Bragg .08 .25
300 Joey Cora .08 .25
301 Edgar Martinez .30 .75
302 Bill Risley .08 .25
303 Ron Villone .08 .25
304 Dan Wilson .08 .25
305 Benji Gil .08 .25
306 Wilson Heredia .08 .25
307 Mark McLemore .08 .25
308 Otis Nixon .08 .25
309 Kenny Rogers .20 .50
310 Jeff Russell .08 .25
311 Mickey Tettleton .08 .25
312 Bob Tewksbury .08 .25
313 David Cone .20 .50
314 Carlos Delgado .20 .50
315 Alex Gonzalez .08 .25
316 Shawn Green .20 .50
317 Paul Molitor .20 .50
318 Ed Sprague .08 .25
319 Devon White .20 .50
320 Steve Avery .08 .25
321 Jeff Blauser .08 .25
322 Brad Clontz .08 .25
323 Tom Glavine .30 .75
324 Marquis Grissom .20 .50
325 Chipper Jones .50 1.25
326 David Justice .20 .50
327 Mark Lemke .08 .25
328 Kent Mercker .08 .25
329 Jason Schmidt .50 1.25
330 Steve Buechele .08 .25
331 Kevin Foster .08 .25
332 Mark Grace .30 .75
333 Brian McRae .08 .25
334 Sammy Sosa .50 1.25
335 Ozzie Timmons .08 .25
336 Rick Wilkins .08 .25
337 Hector Carrasco .08 .25
338 Ron Gant .20 .50
339 Barry Larkin .30 .75
340 Deion Sanders .30 .75
341 Benito Santiago .20 .50
342 Roger Bailey .08 .25
343 Jason Bates .08 .25
344 Dante Bichette .20 .50
345 Joe Girardi .08 .25
346 Bill Swift .08 .25
347 Mark Thompson .08 .25
348 Larry Walker .20 .50
349 Kurt Abbott .08 .25
350 John Burkett .08 .25
351 Chuck Carr .08 .25
352 Andre Dawson .20 .50
353 Chris Hammond .08 .25
354 Charles Johnson .20 .50
355 Terry Pendleton .20 .50
356 Quilvio Veras .08 .25
357 Derek Bell .08 .25
358 Jim Dougherty RC .08 .25
359 Doug Drabek .08 .25
360 Todd Jones .08 .25
361 Orlando Miller .08 .25
362 James Mouton .08 .25
363 Phil Plantier .08 .25
364 Shane Reynolds .08 .25
365 Todd Hollandsworth .08 .25
366 Eric Karros .20 .50
367 Ramon Martinez .08 .25
368 Hideo Nomo RC 1.50 4.00
369 Jose Offerman .08 .25
370 Antonio Osuna .08 .25
371 Todd Williams .08 .25
372 Shane Andrews .08 .25
373 Wil Cordero .08 .25
374 Jeff Fassero .08 .25
375 Darrin Fletcher .08 .25
376 Mark Grudzielanek RC .40 1.00
377 Carlos Perez RC .20 .50
378 Mel Rojas .08 .25
379 Tony Tarasco .08 .25
380 Edgardo Alfonzo .08 .25
381 Brett Butler .20 .50
382 Carl Everett .20 .50
383 John Franco .20 .50
384 Pete Harnisch .08 .25
385 Bobby Jones .08 .25
386 Dave Mlicki .08 .25
387 Jose Vizcaino .08 .25
388 Ricky Bottalico .08 .25
389 Tyler Green .08 .25
390 Charlie Hayes .08 .25
391 Dave Hollins .08 .25
392 Gregg Jefferies .08 .25
393 Michael Mimbs RC .08 .25
394 Mickey Morandini .08 .25
395 Curt Schilling .20 .50
396 Heathcliff Slocumb .08 .25
397 J.Christiansen RC .08 .25
398 Midre Cummings .08 .25
399 Carlos Garcia .08 .25
400 Mark Johnson RC .08 .25
401 Jeff King .08 .25
402 Jon Lieber .08 .25
403 Esteban Loaiza .08 .25
404 Orlando Merced .08 .25
405 Gary Wilson RC .08 .25
406 Scott Cooper .08 .25
407 Tom Henke .08 .25
408 Ken Hill .08 .25
409 Danny Jackson .08 .25
410 Brian Jordan .20 .50
411 Ray Lankford .20 .50
412 John Mabry .08 .25
413 Todd Zeile .08 .25
414 Andy Benes .08 .25
415 Andres Berumen .08 .25
416 Ken Caminiti .20 .50
417 Andujar Cedeno .08 .25
418 Steve Finley .20 .50
419 Joey Hamilton .08 .25
420 Dustin Hermanson .08 .25
421 Melvin Nieves .08 .25
422 Roberto Petagine .08 .25
423 Eddie Williams .08 .25
424 Glenallen Hill .08 .25
425 Kirt Manwaring .08 .25
426 Terry Mulholland .08 .25
427 J.R. Phillips .08 .25
428 Joe Rosselli .08 .25
429 Robby Thompson .08 .25
430 Checklist .08 .25
431 Checklist .08 .25
432 Checklist .08 .25
86P Will Clark PROMO

1995 Flair Hot Gloves

This 12-card standard-size set features players that are known for their defensive prowess. Randomly inserted in series two packs at a rate of one in 25, a player photo is superimposed over an embossed design of a bronze glove.

COMPLETE SET (12) 30.00 60.00
SER.2 STATED ODDS 1:25
1 Roberto Alomar 2.50 6.00
2 Barry Bonds 10.00 25.00
3 Ken Griffey Jr. 6.00 15.00
4 Marquis Grissom 1.50 4.00
5 Barry Larkin 2.50 6.00
6 Darren Lewis .75 2.00
7 Kenny Lofton 1.50 4.00
8 Don Mattingly 10.00 25.00
9 Cal Ripken 12.50 30.00
10 Ivan Rodriguez 2.50 6.00
11 Devon White 1.50 4.00
12 Matt Williams 1.50 4.00

1995 Flair Hot Numbers

Randomly inserted in series one packs at a rate of one in nine, this 10-card standard-size set showcases top players. A player photo on front is superimposed over a gold background that contains player stats from 1994.

COMPLETE SET (10) 20.00 50.00
SER.1 STATED ODDS 1:9
1 Jeff Bagwell 1.00 2.50
2 Albert Belle .60 1.50
3 Barry Bonds 4.00 10.00
4 Ken Griffey Jr. 2.50 6.00
5 Kenny Lofton 1.50 4.00
6 Greg Maddux 2.50 6.00
7 Mike Piazza 2.50 6.00
8 Cal Ripken 5.00 12.00
9 Frank Thomas 1.50 4.00
10 Matt Williams .60 1.50

1995 Flair Infield Power

Randomly inserted in second series packs at a rate of one in six, this 10-card standard-size set features sluggers that man the infield. A player photo on front is surrounded by multiple color schemes with a horizontal back offering a player photo and highlights.

COMPLETE SET (10) 5.00 12.00
SER.2 STATED ODDS 1:6
1 Jeff Bagwell .50 1.25
2 Darren Daulton .30 .75
3 Cecil Fielder .30 .75
4 Andres Galarraga .30 .75
5 Fred McGriff .50 1.25
6 Rafael Palmeiro .50 1.25
7 Mike Piazza 1.25 3.00
8 Frank Thomas .75 2.00
9 Mo Vaughn .30 .75
10 Matt Williams .30 .75

1995 Flair Outfield Power

Randomly inserted in first series packs at a rate of one in six, this 10-card standard-size set features sluggers that patrol the outfield. A player photo on front is surrounded by multiple color schemes with a horizontal back offering a player photo and highlights.

COMPLETE SET (10) 5.00 12.00
SER.1 STATED ODDS 1:6
1 Albert Belle .30 .75
2 Dante Bichette .30 .75
3 Barry Bonds 2.00 5.00
4 Jose Canseco .50 1.25
5 Joe Carter .30 .75
6 Juan Gonzalez .30 .75
7 Ken Griffey Jr. 1.25 3.00
8 Kirby Puckett .75 2.00
9 Gary Sheffield .30 .75
10 Ruben Sierra .30 .75

1995 Flair Ripken

Titled "Enduring", this 10-card standard-size set is a tribute to Cal Ripken's career through the '94 season. Cards were randomly inserted in second series packs at a rate of one in 12. Full-bleed fronts have the set title in silver foil toward the bottom. The backs have a photo and a write-up on a specific achievement as selected by Cal. A five-card mail-in wrapper offer completes the set. The expiration date on this offer was March 1, 1996.

COMPLETE SET (10) 30.00 80.00
COMMON CARD (1-10) 4.00 10.00
SER.2 STATED ODDS 1:12
COMMON MAIL (11-15) 2.00 5.00

1995 Flair Today's Spotlight

This 12-card die-cut set was randomly inserted in first series packs at a rate of one in 25 packs. The upper portion of the player photo on front has the spotlight effect as the remainder of the photo is darkened.

COMPLETE SET (12) 40.00 100.00
SER.1 STATED ODDS 1:25
1 Jeff Bagwell 3.00 8.00
2 Jason Bere 1.00 2.50
3 Cliff Floyd 2.00 5.00
4 Chuck Knoblauch 2.00 5.00
5 Kenny Lofton 5.00 12.00
6 Javier Lopez 2.00 5.00
7 Raul Mondesi 2.00 5.00
8 Mike Mussina 3.00 8.00
9 Mike Piazza 8.00 20.00
10 Manny Ramirez 3.00 8.00
11 Tim Salmon 3.00 8.00
12 Frank Thomas 5.00 12.00

1995 Flair Wave of the Future

Spotlighting 10 of the game's hottest young stars, cards were randomly inserted in second series packs at a rate of one in nine. An action photo is superimposed over primarily a solid background save for the player's name, team and same name which appear several times.

COMPLETE SET (10) 12.50 25.00
SER.2 STATED ODDS 1:9
1 Jason Bates .40 1.00
2 Armando Benitez .40 1.00
3 Marty Cordova .40 1.00
4 Ray Durham .60 1.50
5 Vaughn Eshelman .40 1.00
6 Carl Everett .60 1.50
7 Shawn Green .60 1.50
8 Dustin Hermanson .40 1.00
9 Chipper Jones 1.50 4.00
10 Hideo Nomo 2.00 5.00

1996 Flair

Released in July, 1996, this 400-card set (produced by Fleer) was issued in one series and sold in seven-card packs at a suggested retail price of $4.99. Gold and Silver etched foil front variations exist for all cards. These color variations were printed in similar quantities and are valued equally. This checklist is for the silver version. The fronts and backs each carry a color action player cut-out on a player portrait background with player statistics on the backs. The cards are grouped alphabetically within teams and checklisted below alphabetically according to teams for each league. Notable Rookie Cards include Tony Batista.

COMPLETE SET (400) 40.00 100.00
GOLD AND SILVER EQUAL VALUE
1 Roberto Alomar .60 1.50
2 Brady Anderson .40 1.00
3 Bobby Bonilla .40 1.00
4 Scott Erickson .40 1.00
5 Jeffrey Hammonds .40 1.00
6 Jimmy Haynes .40 1.00
7 Chris Hoiles .40 1.00
8 Kent Mercker .40 1.00
9 Mike Mussina .60 1.50
10 Randy Myers .40 1.00
11 Rafael Palmeiro .60 1.50
12 Cal Ripken 3.00 8.00
13 B.J. Surhoff .40 1.00
14 David Wells .40 1.00
15 Jose Canseco .60 1.50
16 Roger Clemens 2.00 5.00
17 Wil Cordero .40 1.00
18 Tom Gordon .40 1.00
19 Mike Greenwell .40 1.00
20 Dwayne Hosey .40 1.00
21 Jose Malave .40 1.00
22 Tim Naehring .40 1.00
23 Troy O'Leary .40 1.00
24 Aaron Sele .40 1.00
25 Heathcliff Slocumb .40 1.00
26 Mike Stanley .40 1.00
27 Jeff Suppan .40 1.00
28 John Valentin .40 1.00
29 Mo Vaughn .40 1.00
30 Tim Wakefield .40 1.00
31 Jim Abbott .60 1.50
32 Garret Anderson .40 1.00
33 George Arias .40 1.00
34 Chili Davis .40 1.00
35 Gary DiSarcina .40 1.00
36 Jim Edmonds .40 1.00
37 Chuck Finley .40 1.00
38 Todd Greene .40 1.00
39 Mark Langston .40 1.00
40 Troy Percival .40 1.00
41 Tim Salmon .60 1.50
42 Lee Smith .40 1.00
43 J.T. Snow .40 1.00
44 Randy Velarde .40 1.00
45 Tim Wallach .40 1.00
46 Wilson Alvarez .40 1.00
47 Harold Baines .40 1.00
48 Jason Bere .40 1.00
49 Ray Durham .40 1.00
50 Alex Fernandez .40 1.00
51 Ozzie Guillen .40 1.00
52 Roberto Hernandez .40 1.00
53 Ron Karkovice .40 1.00
54 Darren Lewis .40 1.00
55 Lyle Mouton .40 1.00
56 Tony Phillips .40 1.00
57 Chris Snopek .40 1.00
58 Kevin Tapani .40 1.00
59 Danny Tartabull .40 1.00
60 Frank Thomas 1.00 2.50
61 Robin Ventura .40 1.00
62 Sandy Alomar Jr. .40 1.00
63 Carlos Baerga .40 1.00
64 Albert Belle .40 1.00
65 Julio Franco .40 1.00
66 Orel Hershiser .40 1.00
67 Kenny Lofton .40 1.00
68 Dennis Martinez .40 1.00
69 Jack McDowell .40 1.00
70 Jose Mesa .40 1.00
71 Eddie Murray 1.00 2.50
72 Charles Nagy .40 1.00
73 Tony Pena .40 1.00
74 Manny Ramirez .60 1.50
75 Julian Tavarez .40 1.00
76 Jim Thome .60 1.50
77 Omar Vizquel .60 1.50
78 Chad Curtis .40 1.00
79 Cecil Fielder .40 1.00
80 Travis Fryman .40 1.00
81 Chris Gomez .40 1.00
82 Bob Higginson .40 1.00
83 Mark Lewis .40 1.00
84 Felipe Lira .40 1.00
85 Alan Trammell .40 1.00
86 Kevin Appier .40 1.00
87 Johnny Damon .60 1.50
88 Tom Goodwin .40 1.00
89 Mark Gubicza .40 1.00
90 Bob Hamelin .40 1.00
91 Keith Lockhart .40 1.00
92 Jeff Montgomery .40 1.00
93 Jon Nunnally .40 1.00
94 Bip Roberts .40 1.00
95 Michael Tucker .40 1.00
96 Joe Vitiello .40 1.00
97 Ricky Bones .40 1.00
98 Chuck Carr .40 1.00
99 Jeff Cirillo .40 1.00
100 Mike Fetters .40 1.00
101 John Jaha .40 1.00
102 Mike Matheny .40 1.00
103 Ben McDonald .40 1.00
104 Matt Mieske .40 1.00
105 Dave Nilsson .40 1.00
106 Kevin Seitzer .40 1.00
107 Steve Sparks .40 1.00
108 Jose Valentin .40 1.00
109 Greg Vaughn .40 1.00
110 Rick Aguilera .40 1.00
111 Rich Becker .40 1.00
112 Marty Cordova .40 1.00
113 LaTroy Hawkins .40 1.00
114 Dave Hollins .40 1.00
115 Roberto Kelly .40 1.00
116 Chuck Knoblauch .40 1.00
117 Matt Lawton RC .40 1.00
118 Pat Meares .40 1.00
119 Paul Molitor .40 1.00
120 Kirby Puckett 1.00 2.50
121 Brad Radke .40 1.00
122 Frank Rodriguez .40 1.00
123 Scott Stahoviak .40 1.00
124 Matt Walbeck .40 1.00
125 Wade Boggs .60 1.50
126 David Cone .40 1.00
127 Joe Girardi .40 1.00
128 Dwight Gooden .40 1.00
129 Derek Jeter 2.50 6.00
130 Jimmy Key .40 1.00
131 Jim Leyritz .40 1.00
132 Tino Martinez .60 1.50
133 Paul O'Neill .60 1.50
134 Andy Pettitte .60 1.50
135 Tim Raines .40 1.00
136 Ruben Rivera .40 1.00
137 Kenny Rogers .40 1.00
138 Ruben Sierra .40 1.00
139 John Wetteland .40 1.00
140 Bernie Williams .60 1.50
141 Tony Batista RC .60 1.50
142 Allen Battle .40 1.00
143 Geronimo Berroa .40 1.00
144 Mike Bordick .40 1.00
145 Scott Brosius .40 1.00
146 Steve Cox .40 1.00
147 Brent Gates .40 1.00
148 Jason Giambi .40 1.00
149 Doug Johns .40 1.00
150 Mark McGwire 2.50 6.00
151 Pedro Munoz .40 1.00
152 Ariel Prieto .40 1.00
153 Terry Steinbach .40 1.00
154 Todd Van Poppel .40 1.00
155 Bobby Ayala .40 1.00
156 Chris Bosio .40 1.00
157 Jay Buhner .40 1.00
158 Joey Cora .40 1.00
159 Russ Davis .40 1.00
160 Ken Griffey Jr. 1.50 4.00
161 Sterling Hitchcock .40 1.00
162 Randy Johnson 1.00 2.50
163 Edgar Martinez .60 1.50
164 Alex Rodriguez 2.00 5.00
165 Paul Sorrento .40 1.00
166 Dan Wilson .40 1.00
167 Will Clark .60 1.50
168 Benji Gil .40 1.00
169 Juan Gonzalez .40 1.00
170 Rusty Greer .40 1.00
171 Kevin Gross .40 1.00
172 Darryl Hamilton .40 1.00
173 Mike Henneman .40 1.00
174 Ken Hill .40 1.00
175 Mark McLemore .40 1.00
176 Dean Palmer .40 1.00
177 Roger Pavlik .40 1.00
178 Ivan Rodriguez .60 1.50
179 Mickey Tettleton .40 1.00
180 Bobby Witt .40 1.00
181 Joe Carter .40 1.00
182 Felipe Crespo .40 1.00
183 Alex Gonzalez .40 1.00
184 Shawn Green .40 1.00
185 Juan Guzman .40 1.00
186 Erik Hanson .40 1.00
187 Pat Hentgen .40 1.00
188 Sandy Martinez .40 1.00
189 Otis Nixon .40 1.00
190 John Olerud .40 1.00
191 Paul Quantrill .40 1.00
192 Bill Risley .40 1.00
193 Ed Sprague .40 1.00
194 Steve Avery .40 1.00
195 Jeff Blauser .40 1.00
196 Brad Clontz .40 1.00
197 Jermaine Dye .40 1.00
198 Tom Glavine .60 1.50
199 Marquis Grissom .40 1.00
200 Chipper Jones 1.00 2.50
201 David Justice .40 1.00
202 Ryan Klesko .40 1.00
203 Mark Lemke .40 1.00
204 Javier Lopez .40 1.00
205 Greg Maddux 1.50 4.00
206 Fred McGriff .60 1.50
207 Greg McMichael .40 1.00
208 Wonderful Monds RC .40 1.00
209 Jason Schmidt .60 1.50
210 John Smoltz .60 1.50
211 Mark Wohlers .40 1.00
212 Jim Bullinger .40 1.00
213 Frank Castillo .40 1.00
214 Kevin Foster .40 1.00
215 Luis Gonzalez .40 1.00
216 Mark Grace .60 1.50
217 Robin Jennings .40 1.00
218 Doug Jones .40 1.00
219 Dave Magadan .40 1.00
220 Brian McRae .40 1.00
221 Jaime Navarro .40 1.00
222 Rey Sanchez .40 1.00
223 Ryne Sandberg 1.50 4.00
224 Scott Servais .40 1.00
225 Sammy Sosa 1.00 2.50
226 Ozzie Timmons .40 1.00
227 Bret Boone .40 1.00
228 Jeff Branson .40 1.00
229 Jeff Brantley .40 1.00
230 Dave Burba .40 1.00
231 Vince Coleman .40 1.00
232 Steve Gibralter .40 1.00
233 Mike Kelly .40 1.00
234 Barry Larkin .60 1.50
235 Hal Morris .40 1.00
236 Mark Portugal .40 1.00
237 Jose Rijo .40 1.00
238 Reggie Sanders .40 1.00
239 Pete Schourek .40 1.00
240 John Smiley .40 1.00
241 Eddie Taubensee .40 1.00
242 Jason Bates .40 1.00
243 Dante Bichette .40 1.00
244 Ellis Burks .40 1.00
245 Vinny Castilla .40 1.00
246 Andres Galarraga .40 1.00
247 Darren Holmes .40 1.00
248 Curt Leskanic .40 1.00
249 Steve Reed .40 1.00
250 Kevin Ritz .40 1.00
251 Bret Saberhagen .40 1.00
252 Bill Swift .40 1.00
253 Larry Walker .40 1.00
254 Walt Weiss .40 1.00
255 Eric Young .40 1.00
256 Kurt Abbott .40 1.00
257 Kevin Brown .40 1.00
258 John Burkett .40 1.00
259 Greg Colbrunn .40 1.00
260 Jeff Conine .40 1.00
261 Andre Dawson .40 1.00
262 Chris Hammond .40 1.00
263 Charles Johnson .40 1.00
264 Al Leiter .40 1.00
265 Robb Nen .40 1.00
266 Terry Pendleton .40 1.00
267 Pat Rapp .40 1.00
268 Gary Sheffield .40 1.00
269 Quilvio Veras .40 1.00
270 Devon White .40 1.00

271 Bob Abreu	1.00	2.50
272 Jeff Bagwell	.60	1.50
273 Derek Bell	.40	1.00
274 Sean Berry	.40	1.00
275 Craig Biggio	.60	1.50
276 Doug Drabek	.40	1.00
277 Tony Eusebio	.40	1.00
278 Richard Hidalgo	.40	1.00
279 Brian L.Hunter	.40	1.00
280 Todd Jones	.40	1.00
281 Derrick May	.40	1.00
282 Orlando Miller	.40	1.00
283 James Mouton	.40	1.00
284 Shane Reynolds	.40	1.00
285 Greg Swindell	.40	1.00
286 Mike Blowers	.40	1.00
287 Brett Butler	.40	1.00
288 Tom Candiotti	.40	1.00
289 Roger Cedeno	.40	1.00
290 Delino DeShields	.40	1.00
291 Greg Gagne	.40	1.00
292 Karim Garcia	.40	1.00
293 Todd Hollandsworth	.40	1.00
294 Eric Karros	.40	1.00
295 Ramon Martinez	.40	1.00
296 Raul Mondesi	.40	1.00
297 Hideo Nomo	1.00	2.50
298 Mike Piazza	1.50	4.00
299 Ismael Valdes	.40	1.00
300 Todd Worrell	.40	1.00
301 Moises Alou	.40	1.00
302 Shane Andrews	.40	1.00
303 Yamil Benitez	.40	1.00
304 Jeff Fassero	.40	1.00
305 Darrin Fletcher	.40	1.00
306 Cliff Floyd	.40	1.00
307 Mark Grudzielanek	.40	1.00
308 Mike Lansing	.40	1.00
309 Pedro Martinez	.60	1.50
310 Ryan McGuire	.40	1.00
311 Carlos Perez	.40	1.00
312 Mel Rojas	.40	1.00
313 David Segui	.40	1.00
314 Rondell White	.40	1.00
315 Edgardo Alfonzo	.40	1.00
316 Rico Brogna	.40	1.00
317 Carl Everett	.40	1.00
318 John Franco	.40	1.00
319 Bernard Gilkey	.40	1.00
320 Todd Hundley	.40	1.00
321 Jason Isringhausen	.40	1.00
322 Lance Johnson	.40	1.00
323 Bobby Jones	.40	1.00
324 Jeff Kent	.40	1.00
325 Rey Ordonez	.40	1.00
326 Bill Pulsipher	.40	1.00
327 Jose Vizcaino	.40	1.00
328 Paul Wilson	.40	1.00
329 Ricky Bottalico	.40	1.00
330 Darren Daulton	.40	1.00
331 David Doster	.40	1.00
332 Lenny Dykstra	.40	1.00
333 Jim Eisenreich	.40	1.00
334 Sid Fernandez	.40	1.00
335 Gregg Jefferies	.40	1.00
336 Mickey Morandini	.40	1.00
337 Benito Santiago	.40	1.00
338 Curt Schilling	.40	1.00
339 Kevin Stocker	.40	1.00
340 David West	.40	1.00
341 Mark Whiten	.40	1.00
342 Todd Zeile	.40	1.00
343 Jay Bell	.40	1.00
344 John Ericks	.40	1.00
345 Carlos Garcia	.40	1.00
346 Charlie Hayes	.40	1.00
347 Jason Kendall	.40	1.00
348 Jeff King	.40	1.00
349 Mike Kingery	.40	1.00
350 Al Martin	.40	1.00
351 Orlando Merced	.40	1.00
352 Dan Miceli	.40	1.00
353 Denny Neagle	.40	1.00
354 Alan Benes	.40	1.00
355 Andy Benes	.40	1.00
356 Royce Clayton	.40	1.00
357 Dennis Eckersley	.40	1.00
358 Gary Gaetti	.40	1.00
359 Ron Gant	.40	1.00
360 Brian Jordan	.40	1.00
361 Ray Lankford	.40	1.00
362 John Mabry	.40	1.00
363 T.J. Mathews	.40	1.00
364 Mike Morgan	.40	1.00
365 Donovan Osborne	.40	1.00
366 Tom Pagnozzi	.40	1.00
367 Ozzie Smith	1.50	4.00
368 Todd Stottlemyre	.40	1.00
369 Andy Ashby	.40	1.00
370 Brad Ausmus	.40	1.00
371 Ken Caminiti	.40	1.00
372 Andujar Cedeno	.40	1.00
373 Steve Finley	.40	1.00
374 Tony Gwynn	1.25	3.00
375 Joey Hamilton	.40	1.00
376 Rickey Henderson	1.00	2.50
377 Trevor Hoffman	.40	1.00
378 Wally Joyner	.40	1.00
379 Marc Newfield	.40	1.00
380 Jody Reed	.40	1.00
381 Bob Tewksbury	.40	1.00
382 Fernando Valenzuela	.40	1.00
383 Rod Beck	.40	1.00
384 Barry Bonds	2.50	6.00
385 Mark Carreon	.40	1.00
386 Shawon Dunston	.40	1.00
387 O.Fernandez RC	.40	1.00
388 Glenallen Hill	.40	1.00
389 Stan Javier	.40	1.00
390 Mark Leiter	.40	1.00
391 Kirt Manwaring	.40	1.00
392 Robby Thompson	.40	1.00
393 W.VanLandingham	.40	1.00
394 Allen Watson	.40	1.00
395 Matt Williams	.40	1.00
396 Checklist 1-92	.40	1.00
397 Checklist 93-180	.40	1.00
398 Checklist 181-272	.40	1.00
399 Checklist 273-365	.40	1.00
400 CL 366-400/Inserts	.40	1.00
P12 Cal Ripken Jr PROMO		

1996 Flair Diamond Cuts

Randomly inserted in packs at a rate of one in 20, this 12-card set showcases the game's greatest stars with rainbow holofoil and glitter coating on the card.

COMPLETE SET (12)	40.00	100.00
STATED ODDS 1:20		
1 Jeff Bagwell	1.50	4.00
2 Albert Belle	1.00	2.50
3 Barry Bonds	6.00	15.00
4 Juan Gonzalez	1.00	2.50
5 Ken Griffey Jr.	4.00	10.00
6 Greg Maddux	4.00	10.00
7 Eddie Murray	2.50	6.00
8 Mike Piazza	4.00	10.00
9 Cal Ripken	8.00	20.00
10 Frank Thomas	2.50	6.00
11 Mo Vaughn	1.00	2.50
12 Matt Williams	1.00	2.50

1996 Flair Hot Gloves

Randomly inserted in hobby packs only at a rate of one in 90, this 10-card set is printed on special, thermo-embossed die-cut cards and spotlights the best defensive players.

COMPLETE SET (10)	50.00	120.00
STATED ODDS 1:90 HOBBY		
1 Roberto Alomar	4.00	10.00
2 Barry Bonds	15.00	40.00
3 Will Clark	4.00	10.00
4 Ken Griffey Jr.	10.00	25.00
5 Kenny Lofton	2.50	6.00
6 Greg Maddux	10.00	25.00
7 Mike Piazza	10.00	25.00
8 Cal Ripken	20.00	50.00
9 Ivan Rodriguez	4.00	10.00
10 Matt Williams	2.50	6.00

1996 Flair Powerline

Randomly inserted in packs at a rate of one in six, this 10-card set features baseball's leading power hitters. The fronts display a color action close-up player photo with a green overlay indicating his power. The backs carry a player portrait and a statement about the player's hitting power.

COMPLETE SET (10)	12.50	30.00
STATED ODDS 1:6		
1 Albert Belle	.40	1.00
2 Barry Bonds	2.50	6.00
3 Juan Gonzalez	.40	1.00
4 Ken Griffey Jr.	1.50	4.00
5 Mark McGwire	2.50	6.00
6 Mike Piazza	1.50	4.00
7 Manny Ramirez	.60	1.50
8 Sammy Sosa	1.00	2.50
9 Frank Thomas	1.00	2.50
10 Matt Williams	.40	1.00

1996 Flair Wave of the Future

Randomly inserted in packs at a rate of one in 72, this 20-card set highlights the top 1996 rookies and prospects on lenticular cards.

COMPLETE SET (20)	80.00	200.00
STATED ODDS 1:72		
1 Bob Abreu	6.00	15.00
2 George Arias	4.00	10.00
3 Tony Batista	6.00	15.00
4 Alan Benes	4.00	10.00
5 Yamil Benitez	4.00	10.00
6 Steve Cox	4.00	10.00
7 David Doster	4.00	10.00
8 Jermaine Dye	4.00	10.00
9 Osvaldo Fernandez	4.00	10.00
10 Karim Garcia	4.00	10.00
11 Steve Gibralter	4.00	10.00
12 Todd Greene	4.00	10.00
13 Richard Hidalgo	4.00	10.00
14 Robin Jennings	4.00	10.00
15 Jason Kendall	4.00	10.00
16 Jose Malave	4.00	10.00
17 Wonderful Monds	4.00	10.00
18 Rey Ordonez	4.00	10.00
19 Ruben Rivera	4.00	10.00
20 Paul Wilson	4.00	10.00

2002 Flair

This 138 card set was issued in April, 2002. These cards were issued in five card packs which came 20 boxes to a case with a cost of $7 per pack. Each unopened box also contained a "Sweet Swatch" box topper. The last 38 cards in the set are are future fame cards featuring leading prospects in the game. These cards have a stated print run of 1750 serial numbered sets.

COMP.SET w/o SP's (100)	10.00	25.00
COMMON CARD (1-100)	.20	.50
COMMON CARD (101-138)	2.00	5.00
1 Scott Rolen	.30	.75
2 Derek Jeter	1.25	3.00
3 Sean Casey	.20	.50
4 Hideo Nomo	.50	1.25
5 Craig Biggio	.30	.75
6 Randy Johnson	.50	1.25
7 J.D. Drew	.20	.50
8 Greg Maddux	.75	2.00
9 Paul LoDuca	.20	.50
10 John Olerud	.20	.50
11 Barry Larkin	.30	.75
12 Mark Grace	.30	.75
13 Jimmy Rollins	.20	.50
14 Todd Helton	.30	.75
15 Jim Edmonds	.20	.50
16 Roy Oswalt	.20	.50
17 Phil Nevin	.20	.50
18 Tim Salmon	.30	.75
19 Magglio Ordonez	.20	.50
20 Roger Clemens	1.00	2.50
21 Raul Mondesi	.20	.50
22 Edgar Martinez	.30	.75
23 Pedro Martinez	.30	.75
24 Edgardo Alfonzo	.20	.50
25 Bernie Williams	.30	.75
26 Gary Sheffield	.20	.50
27 D'Angelo Jimenez	.20	.50
28 Toby Hall	.20	.50
29 Joe Mays	.20	.50
30 Alfonso Soriano	.20	.50
31 Mike Piazza	.75	2.00
32 Lance Berkman	.20	.50
33 Jim Thome	.30	.75
34 Ben Sheets	.20	.50
35 Brandon Inge	.20	.50
36 Luis Gonzalez	.20	.50
37 Jeff Kent	.20	.50
38 Ben Grieve	.20	.50
39 Carlos Delgado	.20	.50
40 Pat Burrell	.20	.50
41 Mark Buehrle	.20	.50
42 Cristian Guzman	.20	.50
43 Shawn Green	.20	.50
44 Nomar Garciaparra	.75	2.00
45 Carlos Beltran	.20	.50
46 Troy Glaus	.20	.50
47 Paul Konerko	.20	.50
48 Moises Alou	.20	.50
49 Kerry Wood	.20	.50
50 Jose Vidro	.20	.50
51 Juan Encarnacion	.20	.50
52 Bobby Abreu	.20	.50
53 C.C. Sabathia	.20	.50
54 Alex Rodriguez	.75	2.00
55 Albert Pujols	1.00	2.50
56 Bret Boone	.20	.50
57 Orlando Hernandez	.20	.50
58 Jason Kendall	.20	.50
59 Tim Hudson	.20	.50
60 Darin Erstad	.20	.50
61 Mike Mussina	.30	.75
62 Ken Griffey Jr.	.75	2.00
63 Adrian Beltre	.20	.50
64 Jeff Bagwell	.30	.75
65 Vladimir Guerrero	.50	1.25
66 Mike Sweeney	.20	.50
67 Sammy Sosa	.50	1.25
68 Andruw Jones	.30	.75
69 Richie Sexson	.20	.50
70 Matt Morris	.20	.50
71 Ivan Rodriguez	.30	.75
72 Shannon Stewart	.20	.50
73 Barry Bonds	1.25	3.00
74 Matt Williams	.20	.50
75 Jason Giambi	.20	.50
76 Brian Giles	.20	.50
77 Cliff Floyd	.20	.50
78 Tino Martinez	.30	.75
79 Juan Gonzalez	.20	.50
80 Frank Thomas	.50	1.25
81 Ichiro Suzuki	1.00	2.50
82 Barry Zito	.20	.50
83 Chipper Jones	.50	1.25
84 Adam Dunn	.20	.50
85 Kazuhiro Sasaki	.20	.50
86 Mark Quinn	.20	.50
87 Rafael Palmeiro	.30	.75
88 Jeromy Burnitz	.20	.50
89 Curt Schilling	.20	.50
90 Chris Richard	.20	.50
91 Jon Lieber	.20	.50
92 Doug Mientkiewicz	.20	.50
93 Roberto Alomar	.30	.75
94 Rich Aurilia	.20	.50
95 Eric Chavez	.20	.50
96 Larry Walker	.20	.50
97 Manny Ramirez	.30	.75
98 Tony Clark	.20	.50
99 Tsuyoshi Shinjo	.20	.50
100 Josh Beckett	.20	.50
101 Dewon Brazelton FF	2.00	5.00
102 Jeremy Lambert FF RC	2.00	5.00
103 Andres Torres FF	2.00	5.00
104 Matt Childers FF RC	2.00	5.00
105 Wilson Betemit FF	2.00	5.00
106 Willie Harris FF	2.00	5.00
107 Drew Henson FF	2.00	5.00
108 Rafael Soriano FF	2.00	5.00
109 Carlos Valderrama FF	2.00	5.00
110 Victor Martinez FF	3.00	8.00
111 Juan Rivera FF	2.00	5.00
112 Felipe Lopez FF	2.00	5.00
113 Brandon Duckworth FF	2.00	5.00
114 Jeremy Owens FF	2.00	5.00
115 Aaron Cook FF RC	2.00	5.00
116 Derrick Lewis FF	2.00	5.00
117 Mark Teixeira FF	3.00	8.00
118 Ken Harvey FF	2.00	5.00
119 Tim Spooneybarger FF	2.00	5.00
120 Bill Hall FF	2.00	5.00
121 Adam Pettyjohn FF	2.00	5.00
122 Ramon Castro FF	2.00	5.00
123 Marlon Byrd FF	2.00	5.00
124 Matt White FF	2.00	5.00
125 Eric Cyr FF	2.00	5.00
126 Morgan Ensberg FF	2.00	5.00
127 Horacio Ramirez FF	2.00	5.00
128 Ron Calloway FF RC	2.00	5.00
129 Nick Punto FF	2.00	5.00
130 Joe Kennedy FF	2.00	5.00
131 So Taguchi FF RC	3.00	8.00
132 Austin Kearns FF	2.00	5.00
133 Mark Prior FF	3.00	8.00
134 Kazuhisa Ishii FF RC	3.00	8.00
135 Steve Torrealba FF	2.00	5.00
136 Adam Walker FF RC	2.00	5.00
137 Travis Hafner FF	2.00	5.00
138 Zach Day FF	2.00	5.00

2002 Flair Collection

Randomly inserted into packs, this is a parallel set to the basic Flair set. These cards are serial numbered to 175 for the lower number cards and to 50 for the future fame set.

*COLLECTION 1-100: 3X TO 8X BASIC
*COLLECTION 101-138: 1X TO 2.5X BASIC

2002 Flair Jersey Heights

This 25-card set features game-used jersey swatches from a selection of major league stars. The cards were seeded into packs at a rate of 1:18 hobby and 1:100 retail. Though the cards are not serial-numbered in any way, representatives at Fleer confirmed that the following players were produced in slightly lower quantities: Barry Bonds, Roger Clemens, J.D. Drew, Greg Maddux and Alex Rodriguez. In addition, based upon analysis of secondary market trading volume by our staff, the following cards are perceived to be in greater supply: Jeff Bagwell, Jim Edmonds, Randy Johnson, Chipper Jones, Ivan Rodriguez, Curt Schilling and Larry Walker.

1 Edgardo Alfonzo	3.00	8.00
2 Jeff Bagwell *	3.00	8.00
3 Craig Biggio	3.00	8.00
4 Barry Bonds SP	10.00	25.00
5 Sean Casey	3.00	8.00
6 Roger Clemens SP	10.00	25.00
7 Carlos Delgado	3.00	8.00
8 J.D. Drew SP	3.00	8.00
9 Jim Edmonds *	3.00	8.00
10 Nomar Garciaparra	8.00	20.00
11 Shawn Green	3.00	8.00
12 Todd Helton	3.00	8.00
13 Derek Jeter *	10.00	25.00
14 Randy Johnson *	4.00	10.00
15 Chipper Jones *	4.00	10.00
16 Barry Larkin	3.00	8.00
17 Greg Maddux SP	6.00	15.00
18 Pedro Martinez	3.00	8.00
19 Rafael Palmeiro	3.00	8.00
20 Mike Piazza	6.00	15.00
21 Manny Ramirez	3.00	8.00
22 Alex Rodriguez SP	6.00	15.00
23 Ivan Rodriguez *	3.00	8.00
24 Curt Schilling *	3.00	8.00
25 Larry Walker *	3.00	8.00

2002 Flair Jersey Heights Dual Swatch

Randomly inserted in packs, these 12 cards features not only two players (usually teammates) with something in common but also a jersey swatch from each player featured. These cards have a stated print run of 100 serial numbered sets.

1 Randy Johnson Curt Schilling	15.00	40.00
2 Pedro Martinez Nomar Garciaparra	40.00	80.00
3 Edgardo Alfonzo Mike Piazza	15.00	40.00
4 Derek Jeter Roger Clemens	40.00	80.00
5 Greg Maddux Chipper Jones	15.00	40.00
6 Jim Edmonds J.D. Drew	10.00	25.00
7 Jeff Bagwell Craig Biggio	15.00	40.00
8 Rafael Palmeiro Ivan Rodriguez	15.00	40.00
9 Carlos Delgado Shawn Green	10.00	25.00
10 Todd Helton Larry Walker	15.00	40.00
11 Sean Casey Barry Larkin	15.00	40.00
12 Alex Rodriguez Manny Ramirez	15.00	40.00

2002 Flair Jersey Heights Hot Numbers Patch

Randomly inserted into packs, these 24 cards feature a jersey patch from the featured player. These cards have a stated print run of 100 serial numbered sets.

1 Edgardo Alfonzo	10.00	25.00
2 Jeff Bagwell	15.00	40.00
3 Craig Biggio	15.00	40.00
4 Sean Casey	10.00	25.00
5 Roger Clemens		
6 Carlos Delgado	10.00	25.00
7 J.D. Drew	10.00	25.00
8 Jim Edmonds	10.00	25.00
9 Nomar Garciaparra	40.00	80.00
10 Shawn Green	10.00	25.00
11 Todd Helton	15.00	40.00
12 Derek Jeter	40.00	80.00
13 Randy Johnson	15.00	40.00
14 Chipper Jones	15.00	40.00
15 Barry Larkin	15.00	40.00
16 Greg Maddux	30.00	60.00
17 Pedro Martinez	15.00	40.00
18 Rafael Palmeiro	15.00	40.00
19 Mike Piazza	30.00	60.00
20 Manny Ramirez	15.00	40.00
21 Alex Rodriguez	30.00	60.00
22 Ivan Rodriguez	15.00	40.00
23 Curt Schilling	10.00	25.00
24 Larry Walker	10.00	25.00

2002 Flair Power Tools Bats

This 28-card set features game-used bat chips from a selection of major league stars. The cards were seeded into packs at a rate of 1:19 hobby and 1:123 retail. Though not serial-numbered, the following players were reported by Fleer as being short prints: Jeff Bagwell, Pat Burrell, J.D. Drew, Rafael Palmeiro, Scott Rolen, Reggie Sanders and Jim Thome. All of these cards are immeasurably tougher to pull from packs than others from this set. Please refer to our checklist for specific print run quantities on these short prints. In addition, based on market research by our staff, the following players appear to be in greater supply than other cards from this set: Bret Boone, Ivan Rodriguez and Tsuyoshi Shinjo.

1 Roberto Alomar	3.00	8.00
2 Jeff Bagwell SP/150	6.00	15.00
3 Craig Biggio	3.00	8.00
4 Barry Bonds	8.00	20.00
5 Bret Boone *	3.00	8.00
6 Pat Burrell SP/225	6.00	15.00
7 Eric Chavez	3.00	8.00
8 J.D. Drew SP/150	6.00	15.00
9 Jim Edmonds	3.00	8.00
10 Juan Gonzalez	3.00	8.00
11 Luis Gonzalez	3.00	8.00
12 Shawn Green	3.00	8.00
13 Derek Jeter	8.00	20.00
14 Doug Mientkiewicz	3.00	8.00
15 Magglio Ordonez	3.00	8.00
16 Rafael Palmeiro SP/100	6.00	15.00
17 Mike Piazza	6.00	15.00
18 Alex Rodriguez	6.00	15.00
19 Ivan Rodriguez *	3.00	8.00
20 Scott Rolen SP/42		
21 Reggie Sanders SP/120	6.00	15.00
22 Gary Sheffield	3.00	8.00
23 Tsuyoshi Shinjo *	3.00	8.00
24 Miguel Tejada	3.00	8.00
25 Frank Thomas	4.00	10.00
26 Jim Thome SP/225	6.00	15.00
27 Larry Walker	3.00	8.00
28 Bernie Williams	3.00	8.00

2002 Flair Power Tools Dual Bats

Randomly inserted into packs, these 15 cards feature not only two players but bat chips from each of the featured players. A few cards were issued in lesser quantity and we have notated those cards along with the stated print run in our checklist. Please note that these cards are not serial numbered.

*GOLD: 1X TO 2.5X BASIC DUAL BAT
GOLD PRINT RUN 50 SERIAL #'d SETS
GOLD CARDS 7 AND 13 DO NOT EXIST

1 Eric Chavez Miguel Tejada	6.00	15.00
2 Barry Bonds Tsuyoshi Shinjo	12.50	30.00
3 Jim Edmonds J.D. Drew	6.00	15.00
4 Jeff Bagwell Craig Biggio	10.00	25.00
5 Bernie Williams Derek Jeter	15.00	40.00
6 Roberto Alomar Mike Piazza	10.00	25.00
7 Sean Casey Jim Thome SP/40		
8 Pat Burrell Scott Rolen	6.00	15.00
9 Gary Sheffield Shawn Green	6.00	15.00
10 Ivan Rodriguez Alex Rodriguez	10.00	25.00
11 Juan Gonzalez Rafael Palmeiro	6.00	15.00
12 Magglio Ordonez Frank Thomas	8.00	20.00
13 Larry Walker Todd Helton SP/225	6.00	15.00
14 Luis Gonzalez Reggie Sanders	6.00	15.00
15 Doug Mientkiewicz Bret Boone	6.00	15.00

2002 Flair Sweet Swatch

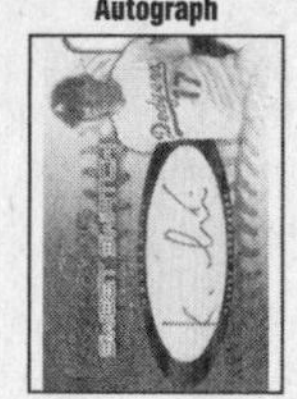

Issued one per hobby box as a "box-topper", these cards feature a larger jersey swatch from the featured players. Each player was issued to a different print run and we have notated the stated print run in our checklist.

1 Jeff Bagwell/490	6.00	15.00
2 Josh Beckett/500	6.00	15.00
3 Darin Erstad/525	6.00	15.00
4 Freddy Garcia/620	6.00	15.00
5 Brian Giles Pants/445	6.00	15.00
6 Juan Gonzalez/505	6.00	15.00
7 Mark Grace/795	6.00	15.00
8 Derek Jeter/525	15.00	40.00
9 Jason Kendall/990	6.00	15.00
10 Paul LoDuca/440	6.00	15.00
11 Greg Maddux/475	6.00	15.00
12 Magglio Ordonez/495	6.00	15.00
13 Rafael Palmeiro/535	6.00	15.00
14 Mike Piazza/1000	6.00	15.00
15 Alex Rodriguez/550	10.00	25.00
16 Ivan Rodriguez/475	6.00	15.00
17 Tim Salmon/465	6.00	15.00
18 Kazuhiro Sasaki/770	6.00	15.00
19 Alfonso Soriano/775	6.00	15.00
20 Larry Walker/430	6.00	15.00
21 Ted Williams/250	75.00	150.00

2002 Flair Sweet Swatch Bat Autograph

Randomly inserted as hobby box toppers, these cards feature not only a bat chip from the featured player but also an autograph. Each card was printed to a different amount and we have notated that stated print run information next to the player's name in our checklist. Some of the Drew Henson cards and all of the Derek Jeter cards were issued as exchange cards and those cards could be redeemed until April 30th, 2003.

GOLD PRINT RUN 15 SERIAL #'d SETS
GOLD NOT PRICED DUE TO SCARCITY

1 Barry Bonds/35	150.00	250.00
2 Dewon Brazelton/185	8.00	20.00
3 Marlon Byrd/185	8.00	20.00
4 Ron Cey/285	10.00	25.00
5 David Espinosa/485	8.00	20.00
6 Drew Henson/785	8.00	20.00
7 Kazuhisa Ishii/335	8.00	20.00
8 Derek Jeter/375	75.00	150.00
9 Al Kaline/285	30.00	60.00
10 Don Mattingly/85	100.00	200.00
11 Paul Molitor/85	20.00	50.00
12 Dale Murphy/285	40.00	80.00
13 Tony Perez/115	10.00	25.00
14 Mark Prior/285	10.00	25.00
15 Albert Pujols/50		
16 Brooks Robinson/185	15.00	40.00
17 Dane Sardinha/485	8.00	20.00
18 Ben Sheets/85	20.00	50.00
19 Ozzie Smith/185	50.00	100.00
20 So Taguchi/335	15.00	40.00
21 Mark Teixeira/185	20.00	50.00
22 Maury Wills/285	10.00	25.00

2002 Flair Sweet Swatch Patch

This 20-card over-sized set is a premium parallel version of the basic Sweet Swatch inserts. The cards were randomly seeded exclusively into hobby boxes as box-toppers. Unlike the basic cards, each of these parallels features a piece of jersey patch (often with very colorful pieces of the player's name or a team logo taken from their game used jersey). Each card was serial-numbered by hand. In general, between 50-80 copies of each card were produced, but please reference our checklist for specific quantities. Ted Williams (15 copies) and Derek Jeter (20 copies) are the scarcest cards in this set. Also, Pirates outfielder Brian Giles was the only player to have a basic Sweet Swatch card that was NOT featured in this Patch parallel because Fleer used a pair of his game-used pants for the basic card (thus no patch swatches were available).

*PREMIUM PATCHES: 2X LISTED PRICES
NO 1 OF 1 PRICING DUE TO SCARCITY

1 Jeff Bagwell/45	30.00	60.00
2 Josh Beckett/60	15.00	40.00
3 Darin Erstad/50	15.00	40.00
4 Freddy Garcia/50	15.00	40.00
5 Juan Gonzalez/55	15.00	40.00
6 Mark Grace/75	30.00	60.00
7 Derek Jeter/20		
8 Jason Kendall/120	6.00	15.00
9 Paul LoDuca/50	15.00	40.00
10 Greg Maddux/50	50.00	100.00
11 Magglio Ordonez/55	15.00	40.00
12 Rafael Palmeiro/60	30.00	60.00
13 Mike Piazza/95	40.00	80.00
14 Alex Rodriguez/50	50.00	100.00
15 Ivan Rodriguez/50	30.00	60.00
16 Tim Salmon/40	30.00	60.00
17 Kazuhiro Sasaki/80	15.00	40.00
18 Alfonso Soriano/35	15.00	40.00
19 Larry Walker/60	15.00	40.00
20 Ted Williams/15		

2003 Flair

This 135 card set was issued in two separate releases. The primary Flair product was released in June, 2003. These cards were issued in five card packs with an $6 SRP which came 20 packs to a box and 12 boxes to a case. Cards numbered 1-90 feature veterans while cards numbered 91-125 feature rookies. The cards 91 through 125 were issued to a stated print run of 500 serial numbered sets. Cards 126-135 were randomly seeded into packs of Fleer Rookies and Greats of which was distributed in December, 2003. Each of these update cards featured a top prospect and was serial numbered to 500 copies.

COMP.LO SET w/o SP's (90)	10.00	25.00
COMMON CARD (1-90)	.20	.50
COMMON CARD (91-135)	1.50	4.00
1 Hideo Nomo	.50	1.25
2 Derek Jeter	1.25	3.00
3 Junior Spivey	.20	.50
4 Rich Aurilia	.20	.50
5 Luis Gonzalez	.20	.50
6 Sean Burroughs	.20	.50
7 Pedro Martinez	.30	.75
8 Randy Winn	.20	.50
9 Carlos Delgado	.20	.50
10 Pat Burrell	.20	.50
11 Barry Larkin	.30	.75
12 Roberto Alomar	.30	.75
13 Tony Batista	.20	.50
14 Barry Bonds	1.25	3.00
15 Craig Biggio	.30	.75
16 Ivan Rodriguez	.30	.75
17 Javier Vazquez	.20	.50
18 Joe Borchard	.20	.50
19 Josh Phelps	.20	.50
20 Omar Vizquel	.30	.75
21 Tom Glavine	.30	.75
22 Darin Erstad	.20	.50
23 Hee Seop Choi	.20	.50
24 Roger Clemens	1.00	2.50
25 Michael Cuddyer	.20	.50
26 Mike Sweeney	.20	.50
27 Phil Nevin	.20	.50
28 Torii Hunter	.20	.50
29 Vladimir Guerrero	.50	1.25
30 Ellis Burks	.20	.50
31 Jimmy Rollins	.20	.50
32 Ken Griffey Jr.	.75	2.00
33 Magglio Ordonez	.20	.50
34 Mark Prior	.30	.75
35 Mike Lieberthal	.20	.50
36 Jorge Posada	.30	.75
37 Rodrigo Lopez	.20	.50
38 Todd Helton	.30	.75
39 Adam Kennedy	.20	.50
40 Curt Schilling	.30	.75
41 Jim Thome	.30	.75
42 Josh Beckett	.20	.50
43 Carlos Pena	.20	.50

44 Jason Kendall .20 .50
45 Sammy Sosa .50 1.25
46 Scott Rolen .30 .75
47 Alex Rodriguez .75 2.00
48 Aubrey Huff .20 .50
49 Bobby Abreu .20 .50
50 Jeff Kent .20 .50
51 Joe Randa .20 .50
52 Lance Berkman .20 .50
53 Orlando Cabrera .20 .50
54 Richie Sexson .20 .50
55 Albert Pujols .75 2.00
56 Alfonso Soriano .20 .50
57 Greg Maddux .75 2.00
58 Jason Giambi .20 .50
59 Jeff Bagwell .30 .75
60 Kerry Wood .20 .50
61 Manny Ramirez .30 .75
62 Eric Chavez .20 .50
63 Preston Wilson .20 .50
64 Shawn Green .20 .50
65 Shea Hillenbrand .20 .50
66 Austin Kearns .20 .50
67 Cliff Floyd .20 .50
68 Edgardo Alfonzo .20 .50
69 J.D. Drew .20 .50
70 Larry Walker .20 .50
71 Mike Piazza .75 2.00
72 Andruw Jones .30 .75
73 Ben Grieve .20 .50
74 Eric Hinske .20 .50
75 Geoff Jenkins .20 .50
76 Kazuhiro Sasaki .20 .50
77 Matt Morris .20 .50
78 Miguel Tejada .20 .50
79 Aramis Ramirez .20 .50
80 Troy Glaus .20 .50
81 Ichiro Suzuki .75 2.00
82 Mark Teixeira .30 .75
83 Nomar Garciaparra .75 2.00
84 Chipper Jones .50 1.25
85 Frank Thomas .50 1.25
86 Paul Lo Duca .20 .50
87 Bernie Williams .30 .75
88 Adam Dunn .20 .50
89 Randy Johnson .50 1.25
90 Barry Zito .20 .50
91 Lew Ford FF RC 2.50 6.00
92 Joe Valentine FF RC 1.50 4.00
93 Jhonny Peralta FF 2.50 6.00
94 Hideki Matsui FF RC 6.00 15.00
95 Francisco Rosario FF RC 1.50 4.00
96 Adam LaRoche FF 1.50 4.00
97 Josh Hall FF RC 1.50 4.00
98 Chien-Ming Wang FF RC 8.00 20.00
99 Josh Willingham FF RC 3.00 8.00
100 Guillermo Quiroz FF RC 1.50 4.00
101 Termel Sledge FF RC 1.50 4.00
102 Prentice Redman FF RC 1.50 4.00
103 Matt Bruback FF RC 1.50 4.00
104 Alejandro Machado FF RC 1.50 4.00
105 Shane Victorino FF RC 3.00 8.00
106 Chris Waters FF RC 1.50 4.00
107 Jose Contreras FF RC 2.50 6.00
108 Pete LaForest FF RC 1.50 4.00
109 Nook Logan FF RC 2.50 6.00
110 Hector Luna FF RC 1.50 4.00
111 Daniel Cabrera FF RC 2.50 6.00
112 Matt Kata FF RC 1.50 4.00
113 Rontrez Johnson FF RC 1.50 4.00
114 Josh Stewart FF RC 1.50 4.00
115 Michael Hessman FF RC 1.50 4.00
116 Felix Sanchez FF RC 1.50 4.00
117 Michel Hernandez FF RC 1.50 4.00
118 Arnaldo Munoz FF RC 1.50 4.00
119 Ian Ferguson FF RC 1.50 4.00
120 Clint Barmes FF RC 1.50 4.00
121 Brian Stokes FF RC 1.50 4.00
122 Craig Brazell FF RC 1.50 4.00
123 John Webb FF 1.50 4.00
124 Tim Olson FF RC 1.50 4.00
125 Jeremy Bonderman FF RC 5.00 12.00
126 Jeff Duncan RC 1.50 4.00
127 Rickie Weeks RC 3.00 8.00
128 Brandon Webb RC 4.00 10.00
129 Robby Hammock RC 1.50 4.00
130 Jon Leicester RC 1.50 4.00
131 Ryan Wagner RC 1.50 4.00
132 Bo Hart RC 1.50 4.00
133 Edwin Jackson RC 2.50 6.00
134 Sergio Mitre RC 2.50 6.00
135 Delmon Young RC 12.50 30.00

2003 Flair Collection Row 1

*ROW 1 1-90: 1.25X TO 3X BASIC
*ROW 1 91-125: .4X TO 1X BASIC
STATED PRINT RUN 150 SERIAL #'d SETS
98 Chien-Ming Wang FF 10.00 25.00

2003 Flair Collection Row 2

STATED PRINT RUN 25 SERIAL #'d SETS
NO PRICING DUE TO SCARCITY

2003 Flair Diamond Cuts Jersey

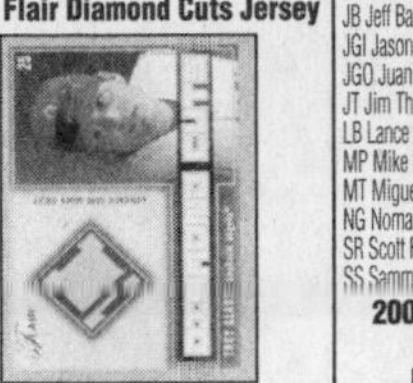

Issued at a stated rate of one in 10, these 15 cards feature jersey swatches from some of baseball's leading players.

STATED ODDS 1:10
*GOLD: 1X TO 2.5X BASIC
GOLD PRINT RUN 100 SERIAL #'d SETS
AR Alex Rodriguez 4.00 10.00
AS Alfonso Soriano 2.00 5.00
BZ Barry Zito 2.00 5.00
CJ Chipper Jones 3.00 8.00
DJ Derek Jeter 6.00 15.00
GM Greg Maddux 4.00 10.00
JD J.D. Drew 2.00 5.00
MP Mike Piazza 4.00 10.00
PB Pat Burrell 2.00 5.00
RA Roberto Alomar 3.00 8.00
RC Roger Clemens 4.00 10.00
RO Roy Oswalt 2.00 5.00
SR Scott Rolen 3.00 8.00
TG Troy Glaus 2.00 5.00
VG Vladimir Guerrero 3.00 8.00

2003 Flair Hot Numbers Patch

Randomly inserted into packs, these 15 cards feature game-used "patch pieces" from leading baseball players. Each of these cards were issued to a stated print run of 100 serial numbered sets.

AR Alex Rodriguez 15.00 40.00
AS Alfonso Soriano 10.00 25.00
BZ Barry Zito 10.00 25.00
CJ Chipper Jones 12.50 30.00
DJ Derek Jeter 25.00 60.00
GM Greg Maddux 15.00 40.00
JD J.D. Drew 10.00 25.00
MP Mike Piazza 15.00 40.00
PB Pat Burrell 10.00 25.00
RA Roberto Alomar 12.50 30.00
RC Roger Clemens
RO Roy Oswalt 10.00 25.00
SR Scott Rolen 12.50 30.00
TG Troy Glaus 10.00 25.00
VG Vladimir Guerrero 12.50 30.00

2003 Flair Hot Numbers Dual Patch

Randomly inserted into packs, these cards feature two "patch" swatches from leading baseball players. Each of these cards were issued to a stated print run of 25 serial numbered sets and no pricing is available due to market scarcity.

2003 Flair Power Tools Bats

Randomly inserted into packs, these 18 cards feature game-used bat chips from leading players. Each of these cards were issued to a stated print run of 500 serial numbered sets.

*GOLD: .6X TO 1.5X BASIC
GOLD PRINT RUN 100 SERIAL #'d SETS
AD Adam Dunn 3.00 8.00
AJ Andruw Jones 4.00 10.00
AK Austin Kearns 3.00 8.00
AR Alex Rodriguez 6.00 15.00
AS Alfonso Soriano 3.00 8.00
BW Bernie Williams 4.00 10.00
DJ Derek Jeter 8.00 20.00
HSC Hee-Seop Choi 3.00 8.00
JB Jeff Bagwell 4.00 10.00
JGI Jason Giambi 3.00 8.00
JGO Juan Gonzalez 3.00 8.00
JT Jim Thome 4.00 10.00
LB Lance Berkman 3.00 8.00
MP Mike Piazza 6.00 15.00
MT Miguel Tejada 3.00 8.00
NG Nomar Garciaparra 6.00 15.00
SR Scott Rolen 4.00 10.00
SS Sammy Sosa 4.00 10.00

2003 Flair Power Tools Dual Bats

Randomly inserted into packs, these cards feature two "game-used" bat chips of the featured players. Each of these cards were issued to a stated print run of 200 serial numbered sets.

ADAK Adam Dunn 6.00 15.00
Austin Kearns
ARNG Alex Rodriguez 12.50 30.00
Nomar Garciaparra
DJAS Derek Jeter 15.00 40.00
Alfonso Soriano
JGBW Jason Giambi 8.00 20.00
Bernie Williams
JGMP Jason Giambi 10.00 25.00
Mike Piazza
JTSS Jim Thome 8.00 20.00
Sammy Sosa
LBJB Lance Berkman 8.00 20.00
Jeff Bagwell
MTAR Miguel Tejada 8.00 20.00
Alex Rodriguez
NBDJ Nomar Garciaparra 15.00 40.00
Derek Jeter

2003 Flair Sweet Swatch Autos Jumbo

Randomly inserted into jumbo packs, these seven cards feature authentic autographs from leading players. There are three different varieties of Derek Jeter autographs. Please note that we have put the stated serial numbered print run next to the player's name in our checklist.

GOLD PRINT RUN 25 SERIAL #'d SETS
NO GOLD PRICING DUE TO SCARCITY
MASTERPIECE PRINT 1 SERIAL #'d SET
NO M'PIECE PRICING DUE TO SCARCITY
AD Adam Dunn/218 20.00 50.00
DJ Derek Jeter/312 60.00 120.00
DJA Derek Jeter/30
DJW Derek Jeter/50
JB Jeff Bagwell/218 20.00 50.00
RJ Randy Johnson/218 40.00 80.00
TG Troy Glaus/116 20.00 50.00

2003 Flair Sweet Swatch Jersey

Randomly inserted into packs, these 18 cards feature game-used jersey swatches from some of baseball's star players.

*JUMBO 50: 1X TO 2.5X BASIC
JUMBO 50 PRINT RUN 50 SERIAL #'d SETS
*JUMBO 150: .6X TO 1.5X BASIC
JUMBO 150 PRINT RUN 150 SERIAL #'d SETS
JUMBO MASTERPIECE 1 SERIAL #'d SET
NO JUMBO M'PIECE PRICING AVAILABLE
SSAD Adam Dunn 3.00 8.00
SSAR Alex Rodriguez 6.00 15.00
SSAS Alfonso Soriano 3.00 8.00
SSBW Bernie Williams 4.00 10.00
SSCJ Chipper Jones 4.00 10.00
SSDJ Derek Jeter 8.00 20.00
SSHN Hideo Nomo 6.00 15.00
SSJG Jason Giambi 3.00 8.00
SSKS Kazuhiro Sasaki 3.00 8.00
SSLB Lance Berkman 3.00 8.00
SSMP Mark Prior 4.00 10.00
SSMT Miguel Tejada 3.00 8.00
SSNG Nomar Garciaparra 6.00 15.00
SSPM Pedro Martinez 4.00 10.00
SSRC Roger Clemens 6.00 15.00
SSRJ Randy Johnson 4.00 10.00
SSSS Sammy Sosa 4.00 10.00
SSVG Vladimir Guerrero 4.00 10.00

2003 Flair Sweet Swatch Jersey Jumbo

Inserted at a stated rate of one per jumbo pack, these 18 cards feature jersey swatches from some of baseball's leading players.

ADSSJ Adam Dunn/1090 3.00 8.00

ARSSJ Alex Rodriguez/55 15.00 40.00
ASSSJ Alfonso Soriano/57
BWSSJ Bernie Williams/1420 4.00 10.00
CJSSJ Chipper Jones/80 10.00 25.00
DJSSJ Derek Jeter/47 20.00 50.00
HNSSJ Hideo Nomo/970 4.00 10.00
JGSSJ Jason Giambi/350 4.00 10.00
KSSSJ Kazuhiro Sasaki/505 4.00 10.00
LBSSJ Lance Berkman/1465 3.00 8.00
MPSSJ Mark Prior/1195 4.00 10.00
MTSSJ Miguel Tejada/518 4.00 10.00
NGSSJ Nomar Garciaparra/727 8.00 20.00
PMSSJ Pedro Martinez/1480 4.00 10.00
RCSSJ Roger Clemens/97 12.50 30.00
RJSSJ Randy Johnson/274 6.00 15.00
SSSSJ Sammy Sosa/279 6.00 15.00
VGSSJ Vladimir Guerrero/46 15.00 40.00

2003 Flair Sweet Swatch Jersey Dual Jumbo

Randomly inserted into jumbo packs, these eight cards feature two jersey swatches from some of baseball's leading players. Each of these cards were issued to a stated print run of 25 serial numbered sets and no pricing is available due to market scarcity.

2003 Flair Sweet Swatch Patch

Randomly inserted into packs, these 18 cards feature patches from some of baseball's superstars. Each of these cards were issued to a stated print run of 50 serial numbered sets.

SSPAD Adam Dunn
SSPAR Alex Rodriguez 20.00 50.00
SSPAS Alfonso Soriano 12.50 30.00
SSPBW Bernie Williams 15.00 40.00
SSPCJ Chipper Jones 15.00 40.00
SSPDJ Derek Jeter 30.00 80.00
SSPHN Hideo Nomo 15.00 40.00
SSPJG Jason Giambi 12.50 30.00
SSPKS Kazuhiro Sasaki 12.50 30.00
SSPLB Lance Berkman 12.50 30.00
SSPMP Mark Prior 15.00 40.00
SSPMT Miguel Tejada 12.50 30.00
SSPNG Nomar Garciaparra 20.00 50.00
SSPPM Pedro Martinez 15.00 40.00
SSPRC Roger Clemens 25.00 60.00
SSPRJ Randy Johnson 15.00 40.00
SSPSS Sammy Sosa 15.00 40.00
SSPVG Vladimir Guerrero 15.00 40.00

2003 Flair Sweet Swatch Patch Jumbo

Randomly inserted in jumbo packs, these 18 cards feature patch pieces of leading players. Each of these cards were produced to differing print runs and we have notated the print run next to the player's name in our checklist. If any card was issued to a stated print run of 25 or fewer cards, there is no pricing due to market scarcity.

ADSSPE Adam Dunn/130 12.50 30.00
ARSSPE Alex Rodriguez/298 20.00 50.00
ASSSPE Alfonso Soriano/28
BWSSPE Bernie Williams/123 15.00 40.00
CJSSPE Chipper Jones/284 12.50 30.00
DJSSPE Derek Jeter/35
HNSSPE Hideo Nomo/114 25.00 60.00
JGSSPE Jason Giambi/26
KSSSPE Kazuhiro Sasaki/90 12.50 30.00
LBSSPE Lance Berkman/287 10.00 25.00
MPSSPE Mark Prior/290 12.50 30.00
MTSSPE Miguel Tejada/183 10.00 25.00
NGSSPE Nomar Garciaparra/124 20.00 50.00
PMSSPE Pedro Martinez/185 12.50 30.00
RCSSPE Roger Clemens/1
RJSSPE Randy Johnson/46 20.00 50.00
SSSSPE Sammy Sosa/190 12.50 30.00
VGSSPE Vladimir Guerrero/290 12.50 30.00

2003 Flair Wave of the Future Memorabilia

Randomly inserted into packs, these six cards feature not only some of the up and coming young prospects but also an game-used memorabilia piece. Each of these cards were issued to a stated print run of 500 serial numbered sets.

*GOLD: .6X TO 1.5X BASIC
GOLD PRINT RUN 100 SERIAL #'d SETS
AH Aubrey Huff Bat 3.00 8.00
AK Austin Kearns Jsy 3.00 8.00
CC Carl Crawford Bat 3.00 8.00
HB Hank Blalock Bat 3.00 8.00
JP Josh Phelps Jsy 3.00 8.00
SB Sean Burroughs Jsy 3.00 8.00

2004 Flair

This 82 card set was released in April, 2004. It was issued in 12-card hobby packs with an $120 SRP packs (little boxes) which were packed 12 to a case. This set was also issued in four-card retail packs with an $3 SRP. The retail packs were issued 24 packs to a box and 20 boxes to a case. The first 60 cards in this set feature veterans while the final 22 cards feature leading rookies and prospects entering the 2004 season. The final 22 cards were issued at a stated rate of one per hobby pack and one in 200 retail packs and were issued to a stated print run of 799 serial numbered sets.

COMMON CARD (1-60) .40 1.00
COMMON CARD (61-82) .75 2.00
61-82 ODDS 1:1 HOBBY, 1:200 RETAIL
62-82 PRINT RUN 799 SERIAL #'d SETS
1 Brandon Webb .40 1.00
2 Todd Helton .60 1.50
3 Jeff Bagwell .60 1.50
4 Shawn Green .40 1.00
5 Vladimir Guerrero 1.00 2.50
6 Tom Glavine .60 1.50
7 Jason Giambi .40 1.00
8 Barry Zito .40 1.00
9 Jason Kendall .40 1.00
10 Carlos Delgado .40 1.00
11 Curt Schilling .60 1.50
12 Ken Griffey Jr. 1.50 4.00
13 Mike Piazza 1.00 2.50
14 Alfonso Soriano .40 1.00
15 Albert Pujols 2.50 6.00
16 Chipper Jones 1.00 2.50
17 Alex Rodriguez 1.50 4.00
18 Miguel Tejada .60 1.50
19 Pedro Martinez .60 1.50
20 Mark Prior .60 1.50
21 Magglio Ordonez .60 1.50
22 Scott Podsednik .40 1.00
23 Shannon Stewart .40 1.00
24 Rocco Baldelli .40 1.00
25 Darin Erstad .40 1.00
26 Omar Vizquel .60 1.50
27 Angel Berroa .40 1.00
28 Jose Vidro .40 1.00
29 Rich Harden .40 1.00
30 Andruw Jones .40 1.00
31 Troy Glaus .40 1.00
32 Sammy Sosa 1.00 2.50
33 Dontrelle Willis .40 1.00
34 Ivan Rodriguez .60 1.50
35 Nomar Garciaparra 1.00 2.50
36 Josh Beckett .60 1.50
37 Jose Reyes .60 1.50
38 Scott Rolen .60 1.50
39 Greg Maddux 1.50 4.00
40 Andy Pettitte .60 1.50
41 Jason Schmidt .40 1.00
42 Edgar Martinez .60 1.50
43 Manny Ramirez 1.00 2.50
44 Torii Hunter .40 1.00
45 Mark Teixeira 1.00 2.50
46 Hideo Nomo 1.00 2.50
47 Brian Giles .40 1.00
48 Adam Dunn .60 1.50
49 Fernando Vina .40 1.00
50 Hideki Matsui 1.50 4.00
51 Jim Thome .60 1.50
52 Hank Blalock .60 1.50
53 Miguel Cabrera 1.00 2.50
54 Randy Johnson 1.00 2.50
55 Javy Lopez .40 1.00
56 Frank Thomas 1.00 2.50
57 Roger Clemens 1.25 3.00
58 Marlon Byrd .40 1.00
59 Derek Jeter 2.50 6.00
60 Ichiro Suzuki 1.50 4.00
61 Kaz Matsui C04 RC 1.25 3.00
62 Chad Bentz C04 RC .75 2.00
63 Greg Dobbs C04 RC .75 2.00
64 John Gall C04 RC .75 2.00
65 Cory Sullivan C04 RC .75 2.00
66 Hector Gimenez C04 RC .75 2.00
67 Graham Koonce C04 .75 2.00
68 Jason Bartlett C04 RC 2.50 6.00
69 Angel Chavez C04 RC .75 2.00
70 Ronny Cedeno C04 RC .75 2.00
71 Don Kelly C04 RC 1.25 3.00
72 Ivan Ochoa C04 RC .75 2.00
73 Ruddy Yan C04 .75 2.00
74 Mike Gosling C04 RC .75 2.00
75 Alfredo Simon C04 RC .75 2.00
76 Jerome Gamble C04 RC .75 2.00
77 Chris Aguila C04 RC .75 2.00
78 Mike Rouse C04 RC .75 2.00
79 Justin Leone C04 RC .75 2.00
80 Merkin Valdez C04 RC .75 2.00
81 Aaron Baldiris C04 RC .75 2.00
82 Chris Shelton C04 RC .75 2.00

2004 Flair Collection Row 1

*ROW 1 1-60: 1.25X TO 3X BASIC
*ROW 1 61-82: .6X TO 1.5X BASIC
OVERALL PARALLEL ODDS 1:6 HOBBY
ROW 1 STATED ODDS 1:55 RETAIL
STATED PRINT RUN 100 SERIAL #'d SETS

2004 Flair Collection Row 2

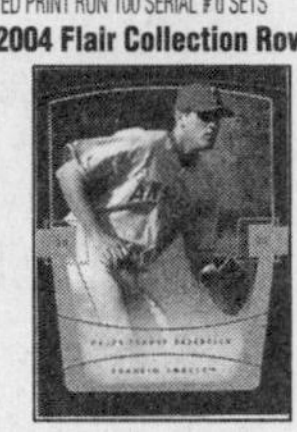

OVERALL PARALLEL ODDS 1:6 HOBBY
STATED PRINT RUN 1 SERIAL #'d SET
NO PRICING DUE TO SCARCITY

2004 Flair Autograph

PRINT RUNS B/WN 60-280 COPIES PER
*CROWN: .4X TO 1X p/r 122-280
*CROWN: .4X TO 1X p/r 60-96
CROWN PRINT RUN 100 SERIAL #'d SETS
MASTERPIECE PRINT RUN 1 SER.#'d SET
NO M'PIECE PRICING DUE TO SCARCITY
*PARCHMENT: .75X TO 2X p/r 122-280
*PARCHMENT: .6X TO 1.5X p/r 60-96
PARCHMENT PRINT RUN 25 SER.#'d SETS
NO RC YR PARCHMENT PRICING AVAIL.
PLATINUM PRINT RUN 10 SERIAL #'d SETS
NO PLATINUM PRICING DUE TO SCARCITY
OVERALL AU ODDS 1:1 HOBBY
OVERALL AU-GU ODDS 1:24 RETAIL
AB1 Aaron Baldiris/180 4.00 10.00
AB2 Angel Berroa/178 4.00 10.00
AJ Andruw Jones/163 10.00 25.00
ALR Adam LaRoche/280 4.00 10.00
AR Alexis Rios/185 6.00 15.00
BC Bobby Crosby/87 10.00 25.00
BN Bubba Nelson/185 4.00 10.00
BW Brandon Webb/122 4.00 10.00
CMW Chien-Ming Wang/178 75.00 150.00
CP Corey Patterson/172 4.00 10.00
CS Chris Shelton/170 8.00 20.00
DH Dan Haren/195 4.00 10.00
DW Dontrelle Willis/73 15.00 40.00
DY Delmon Young/177 10.00 25.00
EJ Edwin Jackson/193 4.00 10.00
GA Garrett Atkins/195 4.00 10.00
GK Graham Koonce/175 4.00 10.00
GS Grady Sizemore/197 15.00 40.00
JB1 Jason Bartlett/95 6.00 15.00
JB2 Josh Beckett/65 15.00 40.00
JE Jim Edmonds/73 15.00 40.00
JG John Gall/94 6.00 15.00
JL Josh Labandeira/166 4.00 10.00
JP Juan Pierre/94 6.00 15.00
JUL Justin Leone/180 4.00 10.00
JV Javier Vazquez/187 6.00 15.00
KG Khalil Greene/195 10.00 25.00
KWO Kerry Wood/73 15.00 40.00
MC Miguel Cabrera/172 10.00 25.00
MM Mike Mussina/69 15.00 40.00
MN Michael Nakamura/180 4.00 10.00
MP Mark Prior/60 12.50 30.00
MR Mike Rouse/195 4.00 10.00
MV Merkin Valdez/179 4.00 10.00
RB Rocco Baldelli/180 6.00 15.00
RH Ryan Howard/185 30.00 60.00
RM Ryan Meaux/180 4.00 10.00
RW1 Ryan Wagner/175 4.00 10.00
RW2 Rickie Weeks/169 4.00 10.00
SP Scott Podsednik/96 15.00 40.00

2004 Flair Autograph Die Cut

OVERALL AU ODDS 1:1 HOBBY
PRINT RUNS B/WN 10-113 COPIES PER
NO PRICING ON QTY OF 19 OR LESS
AB1 Aaron Baldiris/17
AB2 Angel Berroa/17
ALR Adam LaRoche/10
BC Bobby Crosby/102 10.00 25.00
BN Bubba Nelson/10
BW Brandon Webb/10
CMW Chien-Ming Wang/17
CP Corey Patterson/16
CS Chris Shelton/17
DH Dan Haren/10
DW Dontrelle Willis/10
EJ Edwin Jackson/16
GA Garrett Atkins/10
JB1 Jason Bartlett/113 6.00 15.00
JG John Gall/94 6.00 15.00
JL Josh Labandeira/19
JP Juan Pierre/80 10.00 25.00
KG Khalil Greene/10
MC Miguel Cabrera/14
MN Michael Nakamura/10
RH Ryan Howard/10
RM Ryan Meaux/10
RW1 Ryan Wagner/16
RW2 Rickie Weeks/16
SP Scott Podsednik/84 15.00 40.00

2004 Flair Cuts and Glory 100

STATED PRINT RUN 100 SERIAL #'d SETS
*CUTS/GLORY 50: .5X TO 1X BASIC
CUTS/GLORY 50 PRINT RUN 50 #'d SETS
CUTS/GLORY 15 PRINT RUN 15 #'d SETS
C/G 15 NO PRICING DUE TO SCARCITY
CUTS/GLORY 3 PRINT RUN 3 #'d SETS
C/G 3 NO PRICING DUE TO SCARCITY
CUTS/GLORY 1 PRINT RUN 1 #'d SET
C/G 1 NO PRICING DUE TO SCARCITY
OVERALL AU ODDS 1:1 HOBBY
OVERALL AU-GU ODDS 1:24 RETAIL
EXCHANGE DEADLINE INDEFINITE
AD Adam Dunn 15.00 40.00
AK Austin Kearns 6.00 15.00
AP Albert Pujols 150.00 250.00
CD Carlos Delgado 15.00 40.00
CJ Chipper Jones 30.00 60.00
EG Eric Gagne 15.00 40.00
EM Edgar Martinez 15.00 40.00
FT Frank Thomas 30.00 60.00
GA Garret Anderson 10.00 25.00
HB Hank Blalock 10.00 25.00
JR Jose Reyes 10.00 25.00
LG Luis Gonzalez 10.00 25.00
MB Marlon Byrd 6.00 15.00
MO Magglio Ordonez 10.00 25.00
MT Mark Teixeira 15.00 40.00
RH Ricky Henderson 40.00 80.00
RJ Randy Johnson 30.00 60.00
SR Scott Rolen 15.00 40.00
TH Torii Hunter 10.00 25.00
VG Vladimir Guerrero 20.00 50.00

2004 Flair Diamond Cuts Game Used Blue

STATED PRINT RUN 250 SERIAL #'d SETS
*BLUE DC: 1X TO 2.5X BLUE
BLUE DC PRINT RUN 25 SERIAL #'d SETS
*COPPER: .6X TO 1.5X BLUE
COPPER PRINT RUN 75 SERIAL #'d SETS
COPPER DC PRINT RUN 8 SERIAL #'d SETS
NO COPPER DC PRICING DUE TO SCARCITY
*GOLD p/r 38-55: 1.25X TO 3X BLUE
*GOLD p/r 21-35: 1.5X TO 4X BLUE
GOLD PRINT RUNS B/WN 2-55 COPIES PER
NO GOLD PRICING ON QTY OF 10 OR LESS
GOLD DC PRINT RUN 3 SERIAL #'d SETS
NO GOLD DC PRICING DUE TO SCARCITY
*PEWTER: .5X TO 1.2X BLUE
PEWTER PRINT RUN 125 SERIAL #'d SETS
PEWTER DC PRINT RUN 13 SER.#'d SETS
NO PEWTER DC PRICING DUE TO SCARCITY
*PLATINUM p/r 36-43: 1.25X TO 3X BLUE
*PLATINUM p/r 21-29: 1.5X TO 4X BLUE
*PLATINUM p/r 16-18: 2X TO 5X BLUE
PLAT.PRINT RUNS B/WN 5-43 COPIES PER
NO PLAT.PRICING ON QTY OF 14 OR LESS
PLATINUM DC PRINT RUN 1 SERIAL #'d SET
NO PLAT.DC PRICING DUE TO SCARCITY
PURPLE PRINT RUN 1 SERIAL #'d SET
NO PURPLE PRICING DUE TO SCARCITY
*RED: .4X TO 1X BLUE

RED PRINT RUN 175 SERIAL #'d SETS
RED DC: 1.25X TO 3X BLUE
RED DC PRINT RUN 18 SERIAL #'d SETS
*SILVER: 1.25X TO 3X BLUE
SILVER PRINT RUN 50 SERIAL #'d SETS
SILVER DC PRINT RUN 5 SERIAL #'d SETS
NO SILVER DC PRICING DUE TO SCARCITY
OVERALL GU ODDS 3 PER HOBBY PACK
ALL ARE JERSEY CARDS UNLESS NOTED
AJ Andruw Jones 3.00 8.00
ALP Albert Pujols 6.00 15.00
ANP Andy Pettitte 3.00 8.00
CJ Chipper Jones 3.00 8.00
CS Curt Schilling 3.00 8.00
DJ Derek Jeter 6.00 15.00
DW Dontrelle Willis 3.00 8.00
HB Hank Blalock 2.00 5.00
HM Hideki Matsui Base 6.00 15.00
IS Ichiro Suzuki Base 6.00 15.00
JB Josh Beckett 2.00 5.00
JR Jose Reyes 2.00 5.00
MAP Mark Prior 3.00 8.00
MIP Mike Piazza 5.00 12.00
MT Mark Teixeira 3.00 8.00
NG Nomar Garciaparra 5.00 12.00
PM Pedro Martinez 3.00 8.00
RC Roger Clemens 6.00 15.00
SR Scott Rolen 3.00 8.00
SS Sammy Sosa 3.00 8.00

2004 Flair Diamond Cuts Game Used Dual Gold

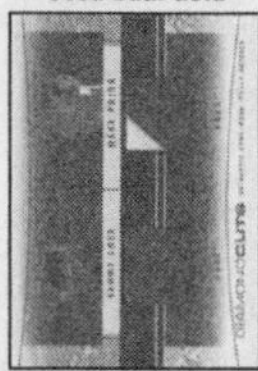

OVERALL GU ODDS 3 PER HOBBY PACK
STATED PRINT RUN 10 SERIAL #'d SETS
NO PRICING DUE TO SCARCITY
CJAJ Chipper Jones
Andruw Jones
CSPM Curt Schilling
Pedro Martinez
HBMT Hank Blalock
Mark Teixeira
ISHM Ichiro Suzuki
{Hideki Matsui
JBDW Josh Beckett
Dontrelle Willis
JRMP Jose Reyes
Mike Piazza
NGDJ Nomar Garciaparra
Derek Jeter
RCAP Roger Clemens
Andy Pettitte
SRAP Scott Rolen
Albert Pujols
SSMP Sammy Sosa
Mark Prior

2004 Flair Hot Numbers

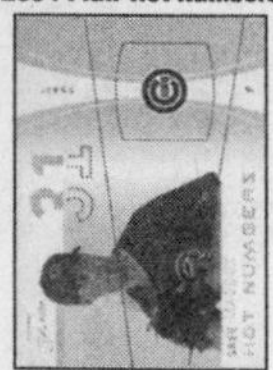

STATED ODDS 1:16 RETAIL
STATED PRINT RUN 500 SERIAL #'d SETS
*GOLD p/r 51-75: .75X TO 2X BASIC
*GOLD p/r 38-48: 1X TO 2.5X BASIC
*GOLD p/r 21-35: 1.25X TO 3X BASIC
*GOLD p/r 17: 1.5X TO 4X BASIC
GOLD ODDS 1:275 RETAIL
GOLD PRINT RUNS B/WN 2-75 COPIES PER
NO GOLD PRICING ON QTY OF 13 OR LESS
1 Chipper Jones 1.50 4.00
2 Derek Jeter 4.00 10.00
3 Alex Rodriguez 2.50 6.00
4 Torii Hunter .60 1.50
5 Nomar Garciaparra 1.50 4.00
6 Troy Glaus .60 1.50
7 Tom Glavine 1.00 2.50
8 Albert Pujols 4.00 10.00
9 Kerry Wood .60 1.50
10 Hideo Nomo 1.50 4.00
11 Rocco Baldelli .60 1.50
12 Mark Prior 1.00 2.50
13 Hank Blalock .60 1.50
14 Mark Teixeira 1.50 4.00
15 Curt Schilling 1.00 2.50
16 Randy Johnson 1.50 4.00
17 Barry Larkin 1.00 2.50
18 Vladimir Guerrero 1.50 4.00
19 Brandon Webb .60 1.50
20 Todd Helton 1.00 2.50
21 Jeff Bagwell 1.00 2.50
22 Barry Zito .60 1.50
23 Sammy Sosa 1.50 4.00
24 Pedro Martinez 1.00 2.50
25 Jim Thome 1.00 2.50
26 Frank Thomas 1.50 4.00
27 Greg Maddux 2.50 6.00
28 Jason Giambi .60 1.50
29 Manny Ramirez 1.50 4.00
30 Josh Beckett 1.00 2.50
31 Mike Piazza 1.50 4.00
32 Hideki Matsui 2.50 6.00
33 Ichiro Suzuki 2.50 6.00
34 Ken Griffey Jr. 2.50 6.00
35 Mike Mussina 1.00 2.50

2004 Flair Hot Numbers Game Used Blue

STATED PRINT RUN 250 SERIAL #'d SETS
*BLUE DC: 1X TO 2.5X BLUE

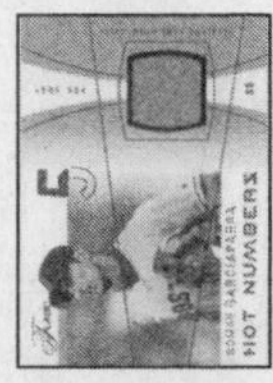

BLUE DC PRINT RUN 25 SERIAL #'d SETS
COPPER: .6X TO 1.5X BLUE
COPPER PRINT RUN 75 SERIAL #'d SETS
COPPER DC PRINT RUN 8 SERIAL #'d SETS
NO COPPER DC PRICING DUE TO SCARCITY
*GOLD p/r 38-55: 1.25X TO 3X BLUE
*GOLD p/r 21-35: 1.5X TO 4X BLUE
*GOLD p/r 17: 2X TO 5X BLUE
GOLD PRINT RUNS B/WN 2-55 COPIES PER
NO GOLD PRICING ON QTY OF 13 OR LESS
GOLD DC PRINT RUN 3 SERIAL #'d SETS
NO GOLD DC PRICING DUE TO SCARCITY
*PEWTER: .5X TO 1.2X BLUE
PEWTER PRINT RUN 125 SERIAL #'d SETS
PEWTER DC PRINT RUN 13 SER.#'d SETS
NO PEWTER DC PRICING DUE TO SCARCITY
*PLATINUM p/r 37-47: 1.25X TO 3X BLUE
*PLATINUM p/r 25-33: 1.5X TO 4X BLUE
*PLATINUM p/r 16-18: 2X TO 5X BLUE
PLAT.PRINT RUNS B/WN 2-47 COPIES PER
NO PLAT.PRICING ON QTY OF 14 OR LESS
PLATINUM DC PRINT RUN 1 SERIAL #'d SET
NO PLAT.DC PRICING DUE TO SCARCITY
PURPLE PRINT RUN 1 SERIAL #'d SET
NO PURPLE PRICING DUE TO SCARCITY
*RED: .4X TO 1X BLUE
RED PRINT RUN 175 SERIAL #'d SETS
*RED DC: 1.25X TO 3X BLUE
RED DC PRINT RUN 18 SERIAL #'d SETS
*SILVER: 1.25X TO 3X BLUE
SILVER PRINT RUN 50 SERIAL #'d SETS
SILVER DC PRINT RUN 5 SERIAL #'d SETS
NO SILVER DC PRICING DUE TO SCARCITY
OVERALL GU ODDS 3 PER HOBBY PACK
AP Albert Pujols 6.00 15.00
AR Alex Rodriguez 6.00 15.00
BL Barry Larkin 3.00 8.00
BW Brandon Webb 2.00 5.00
CJ Chipper Jones 3.00 8.00
CS Curt Schilling 3.00 8.00
DJ Derek Jeter 6.00 15.00
FT Frank Thomas 3.00 8.00
GM Greg Maddux 5.00 12.00
HB Hank Blalock 2.00 5.00
HN Hideo Nomo 3.00 8.00
JEB Jeff Bagwell 3.00 8.00
JG Jason Giambi 2.00 5.00
JOB Josh Beckett 2.00 5.00
JT Jim Thome 3.00 8.00
KW Kerry Wood 2.00 5.00
MAP Mark Prior 3.00 8.00
MIP Mike Piazza 5.00 12.00
MM Mike Mussina 3.00 8.00
MR Manny Ramirez 3.00 8.00
MT Mark Teixeira 3.00 8.00
NG Nomar Garciaparra 5.00 12.00
PM Pedro Martinez 3.00 8.00
RB Rocco Baldelli 2.00 5.00
RJ Randy Johnson 3.00 8.00
SS Sammy Sosa 3.00 8.00
TH Todd Helton 3.00 8.00
TOG Tom Glavine 3.00 8.00
TRG Troy Glaus 2.00 5.00
VG Vladimir Guerrero 3.00 8.00

2004 Flair Lettermen

OVERALL GU ODDS 3 PER HOBBY PACK
PRINT RUNS B/WN 4-11 COPIES PER

2004 Flair Power Tools Game Used Blue

STATED PRINT RUN 250 SERIAL #'d SETS
*BLUE DC: 1X TO 2.5X BLUE
BLUE DC PRINT RUN 25 SERIAL #'d SETS
*COPPER: .75X TO 2X BLUE
COPPER PRINT RUN 75 SERIAL #'d SETS
COPPER DC PRINT RUN 8 SERIAL #'d SETS
NO COPPER DC PRICING DUE TO SCARCITY
*GOLD p/r 44: 1.5X TO 4X BLUE
*GOLD p/r 20-31: 2X TO 5X BLUE
GOLD PRINT RUNS B/WN 2-44 COPIES PER
NO GOLD PRICING ON QTY OF 13 OR LESS
GOLD DC PRINT RUN 3 SERIAL #'d SETS
NO GOLD DC PRICING DUE TO SCARCITY
*PEWTER: .75X TO 2X BLUE
PEWTER PRINT RUN 125 SERIAL #'d SETS
PEWTER DC 13 SERIAL #'d SETS
NO PEWTER DC PRICING DUE TO SCARCITY
*PLATINUM p/r 37-47: 1.5X TO 4X BLUE
*PLATINUM p/r 25-30: 2X TO 5X BLUE
PLAT.PRINT RUN B/WN 10-47 COPIES PER
NO PLAT.PRICING ON QTY OF 11 OR LESS
PLATINUM DC PRINT RUN 1 SERIAL #'d SET
NO PLAT.DC PRICING DUE TO SCARCITY
PURPLE PRINT RUN 1 SERIAL #'d SET
NO PURPLE PRICING DUE TO SCARCITY
*RED: .4X TO 1X BLUE
RED PRINT RUN 175 SERIAL #'d SETS
*RED DC: 1.25X TO 3X BLUE
RED DC PRINT RUN 18 SERIAL #'d SETS
*SILVER: 1X TO 2.5X BLUE
SILVER PRINT RUN 50 SERIAL #'d SETS
SILVER DC PRINT RUN 5 SERIAL #'d SETS
NO SILVER DC PRICING DUE TO SCARCITY
OVERALL GU ODDS 3 PER HOBBY PACK
AD Adam Dunn 2.00 5.00
AP Albert Pujols 6.00 15.00
AR Alex Rodriguez 6.00 15.00
AS Alfonso Soriano 2.00 5.00
CJ Chipper Jones 3.00 8.00
DJ Derek Jeter 6.00 15.00
JG Jason Giambi 2.00 5.00
JP Jorge Posada 3.00 8.00
JT Jim Thome 3.00 8.00
MP Mike Piazza 5.00 12.00
MR Manny Ramirez 3.00 8.00
NG Nomar Garciaparra 5.00 12.00
RB Rocco Baldelli 2.00 5.00
SS Sammy Sosa 3.00 8.00
VG Vladimir Guerrero 3.00 8.00

2004 Flair Significant Cuts

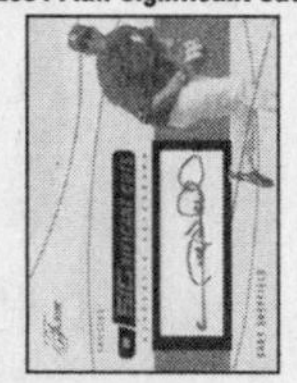

OVERALL AU ODDS 1:1 HOBBY
PRINT RUNS B/WN 1-200 COPIES PER
NO PRICING ON QTY OF 10 OR LESS
AP1 Andy Pettitte/50 30.00 60.00
AP2 Albert Pujols/20
BL Barry Larkin/75 15.00 40.00
BR Babe Ruth/1
BT Bill Terry/3
CG Charlie Gehringer/2
CJ Chipper Jones/22
CR Cal Ripken/25 150.00 250.00
DE Dennis Eckersley/75 15.00 40.00
DM Don Mattingly/25 60.00 120.00
ES Enos Slaughter/3
FF Frankie Frisch/1
GS Gary Sheffield/50 15.00 40.00
IR Ivan Rodriguez/50 20.00 50.00
JB1 Josh Beckett/10
JB2 Johnny Bench/25 30.00 60.00
JR Jose Reyes/25 12.50 30.00
JS John Smoltz/75 30.00 60.00
MR Mariano Rivera/50 40.00 80.00
MS Mike Schmidt/25 75.00 150.00
MT Miguel Tejada/25 20.00 50.00
NR Nolan Ryan/25 100.00 175.00
PM Paul Molitor/75 10.00 25.00
RA Roberto Alomar/50 15.00 40.00
RH Roy Halladay/50 40.00 80.00
RP Rafael Palmeiro/25 30.00 60.00
TC Ty Cobb/3
VC Vince Carter/200 20.00 40.00

2005 Flair

COMMON CARD (1-50) .40 1.00
COMMON CARD (51-80) .40 1.00
51-80 ODDS 1:1 HOBBY, 1:130 RETAIL
51-80 PRINT RUN 699 SERIAL #'d SETS
COMMON CARD (81-90) .40 1.00
81-90 ODDS 1:2 HOBBY, 1:240 RETAIL
81-90 PRINT RUN 699 SERIAL #'d SETS
1 Curt Schilling .60 1.50
2 Jim Thome .60 1.50
3 Miguel Cabrera 1.00 2.50
4 Randy Johnson 1.00 2.50
5 David Ortiz 1.00 2.50
6 Vladimir Guerrero 1.00 2.50
7 Nomar Garciaparra 1.00 2.50
8 Ivan Rodriguez .60 1.50
9 Jason Schmidt .40 1.00
10 Khalil Greene .40 1.00
11 Jose Vidro .40 1.00
12 Lyle Overbay .40 1.00
13 Todd Helton .60 1.50
14 Vernon Wells .40 1.00
15 B.J. Upton .60 1.50
16 Hideki Matsui 1.50 4.00
17 Pedro Martinez .60 1.50
18 Victor Martinez .60 1.50
19 Adam Dunn .60 1.50
20 Andruw Jones .40 1.00
21 Jeff Bagwell .60 1.50
22 Mike Sweeney .40 1.00
23 Mike Piazza 1.00 2.50
24 Ben Sheets .40 1.00
25 Adrian Beltre .40 1.00
26 Chipper Jones 1.00 2.50
27 Greg Maddux 1.50 4.00
28 Manny Ramirez 1.00 2.50
29 Roger Clemens 1.25 3.00
30 Johan Santana 1.00 2.50
31 Derek Jeter 2.50 6.00
32 Jason Bay .40 1.00
33 Ken Griffey Jr. 1.50 4.00
34 Miguel Tejada .60 1.50
35 Richie Sexson .40 1.00
36 Scott Rolen .60 1.50
37 Alfonso Soriano .60 1.50
38 Ichiro Suzuki 1.50 4.00
39 Sammy Sosa 1.00 2.50
40 Barry Zito .40 1.00
41 Kaz Matsui .40 1.00
42 Mark Teixeira 1.00 2.50
43 Carlos Beltran .40 1.00
44 Mark Prior .60 1.50
45 Travis Hafner .40 1.00
46 Alex Rodriguez 1.50 4.00
47 Lew Ford .40 1.00
48 Albert Pujols 2.50 6.00
49 Frank Thomas 1.00 2.50
50 Juan Pierre .40 1.00
51 David Aardsma C05 .40 1.00
52 J.D. Durbin C05 .40 1.00
53 Zack Greinke C05 .60 1.50
54 Dioner Navarro C05 .40 1.00
55 Edwin Encarnacion C05 .60 1.50
56 Luis Hernandez C05 RC .40 1.00
57 Jeff Baker C05 .40 1.00
58 Victor Diaz C05 .40 1.00
59 Joey Gathright C05 .40 1.00
60 Casey Kotchman C05 .40 1.00
61 David Wright C05 1.50 4.00
62 Jon Knott C05 .40 1.00
63 Charlton Jimerson C05 .40 1.00
64 Nick Swisher C05 1.00 2.50
65 Ryan Raburn C05 .40 1.00
66 Josh Kroeger C05 .40 1.00
67 Kelly Johnson C05 .40 1.00
68 Justin Verlander C05 RC 8.00 20.00
69 Taylor Buchholz C05 .40 1.00
70 Ubaldo Jimenez C05 RC 1.25 3.00
71 Russ Adams C05 .40 1.00
72 Ronny Cedeno C05 .40 1.00
73 Bobby Jenks C05 .40 1.00
74 Dan Meyer C05 .40 1.00
75 Jeff Francis C05 .40 1.00
76 Scott Kazmir C05 1.00 2.50
77 Sean Burnett C05 .40 1.00
78 Jose Lopez C05 .40 1.00
79 Andres Blanco C05 .40 1.00
80 Gavin Floyd C05 .40 1.00
81 Tom Seaver RET .60 1.50
82 Steve Carlton RET .40 1.00
83 Al Kaline RET 1.00 2.50
84 Cal Ripken RET 4.00 10.00
85 Willie McCovey RET .60 1.50
86 Johnny Bench RET 1.00 2.50
87 Nolan Ryan RET 2.50 6.00
88 Mike Schmidt RET 2.00 5.00
89 Carlton Fisk RET .60 1.50
90 Don Mattingly RET 2.00 5.00

2005 Flair Row 1

*ROW 1 1-50: 2X TO 5X BASIC
*ROW 1 51-80: 1X TO 2.5X BASIC
*ROW 1 81-90: 1.5X TO 4X BASIC
OVERALL PARALLEL ODDS 1:6 H, 1:55 R
STATED PRINT RUN 100 SERIAL #'d SETS

2005 Flair Row 2

OVERALL PARALLEL ODDS 1:6 HOBBY
STATED PRINT RUN 1 SERIAL #'d SET
NO PRICING DUE TO SCARCITY

2005 Flair Cuts and Glory Jersey

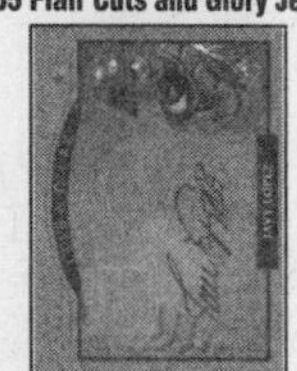

STATED PRINT RUN 100 SERIAL #'d SETS
LOGO PRINT RUN 1 SERIAL #'d SET
NO LOGO PRICING DUE TO SCARCITY
PATCH-JSY PRINT RUN 15 #'d SETS
NO PATCH-JSY PRICING DUE TO SCARCITY
OVERALL AU ODDS 1:1 H, AU-GU 1:24 R
BS Ben Sheets 10.00 25.00
CC Carl Crawford 10.00 25.00
HA Hank Aaron
JB Johnny Bench 30.00 60.00
JL Javy Lopez 10.00 25.00
JP Josh Phelps 6.00 15.00
SS Shannon Stewart 10.00 25.00

2005 Flair Cuts and Glory Patch

*PATCH: .6X TO 1.5X JSY
OVERALL AU ODDS 1:1 H, AU-GU 1:24 R
STATED PRINT RUN 50 SERIAL #'d SETS
HA Hank Aaron 175.00 300.00

2005 Flair Diamond Cuts Jersey

STATED PRINT RUN 150 SERIAL #'d SETS
*BLUE FOIL: .4X TO 1X BASIC
BLUE FOIL ODDS 1:48 RETAIL
BLUE FOIL CARDS ARE NOT SERIAL #'d
*DIE CUT: .5X TO 1.2X BASIC
DIE CUT PRINT RUN 75 SERIAL #'d SETS
*PATCH: 1X TO 2.5X BASIC
PATCH PRINT RUN 50 SERIAL #'d SETS
*PATCH DIE CUT: 1.5X TO 4X BASIC
PATCH DC PRINT RUN 25 SERIAL #'d SETS
PATCH MLB LOGO PRINT RUN 1 #'d SET
NO PATCH MLB LOGO PRICING AVAILABLE
PATCH SUPER PRINT RUN 20 #'d SETS
NO PATCH SUPER PRICING AVAILABLE
PATCH SUPER DC PRINT RUN 10 #'d SETS
NO PATCH SUPER DC PRICING AVAILABLE
OVERALL GU ODDS 2:1 HOBBY
AD Adam Dunn Jsy 3.00 8.00
Austin Kearns
AJ Andruw Jones Jsy 3.00 8.00
Chipper Jones
AK Austin Kearns Jsy 3.00 8.00
Adam Dunn
AP Albert Pujols Jsy 6.00 15.00
Scott Rolen
AS Alfonso Soriano Jsy 3.00 8.00
Hank Blalock
BU B.J. Upton Jsy 3.00 8.00
Hideo Nomo
CB Carlos Beltran Jsy 3.00 8.00
Pedro Martinez
CJ Chipper Jones Jsy 4.00 10.00
Andruw Jones
CS Curt Schilling Jsy 3.00 8.00
Randy Johnson
DO David Ortiz Jsy 3.00 8.00
Manny Ramirez
GS Gary Sheffield Jsy 3.00 8.00
Hideki Matsui
HB Hank Blalock Jsy 3.00 8.00
Alfonso Soriano
HM Hideki Matsui Jsy 10.00 25.00
Gary Sheffield
HN Hideo Nomo Jsy 4.00 10.00
B.J. Upton
JB Jeff Bagwell Jsy 3.00 8.00
Roger Clemens
JT Jim Thome Jsy 3.00 8.00
Mike Piazza
KW Kerry Wood Jsy 3.00 8.00
Mark Prior
MC Miguel Cabrera Jsy 3.00 8.00
Todd Helton
MP Mike Piazza Jsy 4.00 10.00
Jim Thome
MP2 Mark Prior Jsy 3.00 8.00
Kerry Wood
MR Manny Ramirez Jsy 3.00 8.00
David Ortiz
MT Mark Teixeira Jsy 3.00 8.00
Victor Martinez
PM Pedro Martinez Jsy 3.00 8.00
Carlos Beltran
RC Roger Clemens Jsy 4.00 10.00
Jeff Bagwell
RJ Randy Johnson Jsy 4.00 10.00
Curt Schilling
SR Scott Rolen Jsy 3.00 8.00
Albert Pujols
SS Sammy Sosa Jsy 4.00 10.00
Vladimir Guerrero
TH Todd Helton Jsy 3.00 8.00
Miguel Cabrera
VG Vladimir Guerrero Jsy 4.00 10.00
Sammy Sosa
VM Victor Martinez Jsy 3.00 8.00
Mark Teixeira

2005 Flair Diamond Cuts Dual Jersey

STATED PRINT RUN 99 SERIAL #'d SETS
*DIE CUT: .5X TO 1.2X BASIC
DIE CUT PRINT RUN 50 SERIAL #'d SETS
PATCH PRINT RUN 15 SERIAL #'d SETS
NO PATCH PRICING DUE TO SCARCITY
PATCH DIE CUT PRINT RUN 5 #'d SETS
NO PATCH DC PRICING DUE TO SCARCITY
OVERALL GU ODDS 2:1 HOBBY
BC Jeff Bagwell 6.00 15.00
Roger Clemens
BM Carlos Beltran 4.00 10.00
Pedro Martinez
BS Hank Blalock 4.00 10.00
Alfonso Soriano
CH Miguel Cabrera 4.00 10.00
Todd Helton
DK Adam Dunn 4.00 10.00
Austin Kearns
JJ Chipper Jones 6.00 15.00
Andruw Jones
JS Randy Johnson 6.00 15.00
Curt Schilling
MS Hideki Matsui 12.50 30.00
Gary Sheffield
MT Victor Martinez 4.00 10.00
Mark Teixeira
NU Hideo Nomo 6.00 15.00
B.J. Upton
OR David Ortiz 4.00 10.00
Manny Ramirez
PR Albert Pujols 10.00 25.00
Scott Rolen
PT Mike Piazza 6.00 15.00
Jim Thome
PW Mark Prior 4.00 10.00
Kerry Wood
SG Sammy Sosa 6.00 15.00
Vladimir Guerrero

2005 Flair Dynasty Cornerstones Signatures

OVERALL AU ODDS 1:1 HOBBY
PRINT RUNS B/WN 3-75 COPIES PER
NO PRICING ON QTY OF 16 OR LESS
AP Albert Pujols/3
DG Dwight Gooden/25 10.00 25.00
DO David Ortiz/75 20.00 50.00
DS Darryl Strawberry/16
JB Jeremy Bonderman/75 10.00 25.00
JV Jason Varitek/75 30.00 60.00
JV2 Justin Verlander/75 40.00 80.00
SM Stan Musial/3
TS Tom Seaver/3

2005 Flair Dynasty Cornerstones Dual Signatures

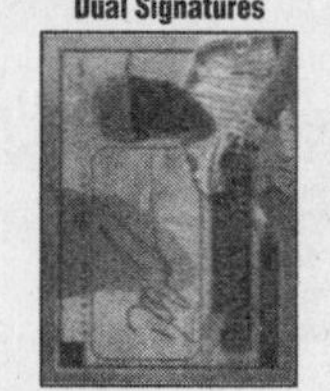

OVERALL AU ODDS 1:1 HOBBY
PRINT RUNS B/WN 2-30 COPIES PER
NO PRICING ON QTY OF 15 OR LESS
BV Jeremy Bonderman 50.00 100.00
Justin Verlander/30
GS Dwight Gooden
Darryl Strawberry/15
PM Albert Pujols
Stan Musial/2
PS Mike Piazza
Tom Seaver/3
VO Jason Varitek
David Ortiz/2

2005 Flair Dynasty Foundations

STATED PRINT RUN 500 SERIAL #'d SETS
*GOLD p/r 61-98: .75X TO 2X BASIC
GOLD PRINT RUNS B/WN 1-98 COPIES PER
NO GOLD PRICING ON QTY OF 1
OVERALL ODDS 1:25 RETAIL
1 Vladimir Guerrero 5.00 12.00
Garret Anderson
Darin Erstad
Rod Carew
Nolan Ryan
2 Cal Ripken 1.25 3.00
Miguel Tejada
Javy Lopez
Jim Palmer
Brooks Robinson
3 Manny Ramirez 2.00 5.00
Ted Williams
David Ortiz
Johnny Damon
Carl Yastrzemski
4 Sammy Sosa 4.00 10.00
Ernie Banks
Ryne Sandberg
Greg Maddux
Mark Prior
5 Adam Dunn 1.25 3.00
Austin Kearns
Joe Morgan
Johnny Bench
Tony Perez
6 Victor Martinez 1.25 3.00
Travis Hafner
C.C. Sabathia
Larry Doby
Bob Feller
7 Todd Helton 2.00 5.00
Garrett Atkins
Preston Wilson
Aaron Miles
Matt Holliday
8 Miguel Cabrera 2.00 5.00
Josh Beckett
Dontrelle Willis
Juan Pierre
Al Leiter
9 Jeff Bagwell 2.50 6.00
Lance Berkman
Craig Biggio
Roger Clemens
Roy Oswalt
10 Geoff Jenkins 2.00 5.00
Paul Molitor
Ben Sheets
Lyle Overbay
Robin Yount
11 Johan Santana 2.00 5.00
Harmon Killebrew
Torii Hunter
Shannon Stewart
Lew Ford
12 Mike Piazza 5.00 12.00
Tom Seaver
Nolan Ryan
Pedro Martinez
Tom Glavine
13 Barry Zito 2.00 5.00
Eric Chavez
Reggie Jackson
Bobby Crosby
Dennis Eckersley
14 Jim Thome 4.00 10.00
Bobby Abreu
Gavin Floyd
Robin Roberts
Mike Schmidt
15 Craig Wilson .75 2.00
Jack Wilson
Jason Bay
Willie Stargell
Bill Mazeroski
16 Jason Schmidt 1.25 3.00
Juan Marichal
Willie McCovey
Orlando Cepeda
Ray Durham
17 Scott Rolen 5.00 12.00
Albert Pujols
Jim Edmonds
Mark Mulder
Stan Musial
18 B.J. Upton 1.25 3.00
Carl Crawford
Scott Kazmir
Aubrey Huff
Rocco Baldelli
19 Alfonso Soriano 1.25 3.00
Mark Teixeira
Hank Blalock
Nolan Ryan
Michael Young
20 Orlando Hudson 2.00 5.00
Vernon Wells
Alexis Rios
Paul Molitor
Roy Halladay

2005 Flair Dynasty Foundations Level 1 Jersey

OVERALL AU-GU ODDS 1:24 RETAIL
STATED PRINT RUN 150 SERIAL #'d SETS
ACTUAL PRINT RUNS B/WN 140-150 PER
*PATCH: 1X TO 2.5X BASIC
PATCH ODDS OVERALL GU 2:1 HOBBY
PATCH PRINT RUN 99 SERIAL #'d SETS
ACTUAL PATCH PRINT B/WN 98-99 PER
BR David Ortiz Jsy 3.00 8.00
Manny Ramirez
Ted Williams
Johnny Damon
Carl Yastrzemski
CI Victor Martinez Jsy 3.00 8.00
Travis Hafner
C.C. Sabathia
Larry Doby
Bob Feller
CR1 Adam Dunn Jsy 3.00 8.00
Austin Kearns
Joe Morgan
Johnny Bench
Tony Perez/140 UER
CR2 Todd Helton Jsy 3.00 8.00
Garrett Atkins
Preston Wilson
Aaron Miles
Matt Holliday
FM Miguel Cabrera Jsy 3.00 8.00
Josh Beckett
Dontrelle Willis
Juan Pierre
Al Leiter/140 UER
HA Jeff Bagwell Jsy 3.00 8.00
Lance Berkman
Craig Biggio
Roger Clemens
Roy Oswalt/146 UER

LA Vladimir Guerrero Jsy 4.00 10.00
Garret Anderson
Darin Erstad
Rod Carew
Nolan Ryan
MB Lyle Overbay Jsy 3.00 8.00
Geoff Jenkins
Paul Molitor
Ben Sheets
Robin Yount
MT Johan Santana Jsy 4.00 10.00
Harmon Killebrew
Torii Hunter
Shannon Stewart
Lew Ford
NM Mike Piazza Jsy 4.00 10.00
Tom Seaver
Nolan Ryan
Pedro Martinez
Tom Glavine
OA Barry Zito Jsy 3.00 8.00
Eric Chavez
Reggie Jackson
Bobby Crosby
Dennis Eckersley
PP Jim Thome Jsy 3.00 8.00
Bobby Abreu
Gavin Floyd
Robin Roberts
Mike Schmidt
PT Jason Bay Jsy 3.00 8.00
Craig Wilson
Jack Wilson
Willie Stargell
Bill Mazeroski
SC Albert Pujols Jsy 6.00 15.00
Scott Rolen
Jim Edmonds
Mark Mulder
Stan Musial
SG Jason Schmidt Jsy 3.00 8.00
Juan Marichal
Willie McCovey
Orlando Cepeda
Ray Durham
TD B.J. Upton Jsy 3.00 8.00
Carl Crawford
Scott Kazmir
Aubrey Huff
Rocco Baldelli
TR Michael Young Jsy 3.00 8.00
Alfonso Soriano
Mark Teixeira
Hank Blalock
Nolan Ryan

2005 Flair Dynasty Foundations Level 2 Jersey

STATED PRINT RUN 150 SERIAL #'d SETS
*PATCH: 1X TO 2.5X BASIC
PATCH PRINT RUN 50 SERIAL #'d SETS
OVERALL GU ODDS 2:1 HOBBY
BR Manny Ramirez Jsy 4.00 10.00
David Ortiz Jsy
Ted Williams
Johnny Damon
Carl Yastrzemski
CI Victor Martinez Jsy 4.00 10.00
Travis Hafner Jsy
C.C. Sabathia
Larry Doby
Bob Feller
CR1 Adam Dunn Jsy 4.00 10.00
Austin Kearns Jsy
Joe Morgan
Johnny Bench
Tony Perez
CR2 Todd Helton Jsy 5.00 12.00
Preston Wilson Jsy
Garrett Atkins
Aaron Miles
Matt Holliday
FM Miguel Cabrera Jsy 4.00 10.00
Juan Pierre Jsy
Josh Beckett
Dontrelle Willis
Al Leiter
HA Jeff Bagwell Jsy 4.00 10.00
Lance Berkman Jsy
Craig Biggio
Roger Clemens
Roy Oswalt
LA Vladimir Guerrero Jsy 6.00 15.00
Garret Anderson Jsy
Darin Erstad
Rod Carew
Nolan Ryan
MT Johan Santana Jsy 6.00 15.00
Torii Hunter Jsy
Harmon Killebrew
Shannon Stewart
Lew Ford
NM Mike Piazza Jsy 6.00 15.00
Tom Glavine Jsy
Tom Seaver
Nolan Ryan
Pedro Martinez
OA Barry Zito Jsy 4.00 10.00
Eric Chavez Jsy
Reggie Jackson
Bobby Crosby
Dennis Eckersley
PP Jim Thome Jsy 4.00 10.00
Bobby Abreu Jsy
Gavin Floyd
Robin Roberts
Mike Schmidt
SC Scott Rolen Jsy 10.00 25.00
Albert Pujols Jsy
Jim Edmonds
Mark Mulder
Stan Musial
TD B.J. Upton Jsy 4.00 10.00
Scott Kazmir Jsy
Carl Crawford
Aubrey Huff
Rocco Baldelli
TR Mark Teixeira Jsy 4.00 10.00
Michael Young Jsy
Alfonso Soriano
Hank Blalock
Nolan Ryan

2005 Flair Dynasty Foundations Level 3 Jersey

OVERALL GU ODDS 2:1 HOBBY
STATED PRINT RUN 99 SERIAL #'d SETS
CR1 Adam Dunn Jsy 6.00 15.00
Austin Kearns Jsy
Joe Morgan Jsy
Johnny Bench
Tony Perez
FM Miguel Cabrera Jsy 6.00 15.00
Josh Beckett Jsy
Juan Pierre Jsy
Dontrelle Willis
Al Leiter
HA Jeff Bagwell Jsy 12.50 30.00
Lance Berkman Jsy
Roger Clemens Jsy
Craig Biggio
Roy Oswalt
LA Vladimir Guerrero Jsy 10.00 25.00
Garret Anderson Jsy
Darin Erstad Jsy
Rod Carew
Nolan Ryan
MT Johan Santana Jsy 10.00 25.00
Torii Hunter Jsy
Shannon Stewart Jsy
Harmon Killebrew
Lew Ford
NM Mike Piazza Jsy 10.00 25.00
Pedro Martinez Jsy
Tom Glavine Jsy
Tom Seaver
Nolan Ryan
SC Scott Rolen Jsy 20.00 50.00
Albert Pujols Jsy
Jim Edmonds Jsy
Mark Mulder
Stan Musial
TR Alfonso Soriano Jsy 6.00 15.00
Mark Teixeira Jsy
Michael Young Jsy
Hank Blalock
Nolan Ryan

2005 Flair Dynasty Foundations Level 3 Patch

*PATCH: 1X TO 2.5X L3 JSY
OVERALL GU ODDS 2:1 HOBBY
STATED PRINT RUN 25 SERIAL #'d SETS
TD B.J. Upton Patch
Scott Kazmir Patch
Aubrey Huff Patch
Carl Crawford
Rocco Baldelli

2005 Flair Dynasty Foundations Level 4 Jersey

STATED PRINT RUN 40 SERIAL #'d SETS
PATCH PRINT RUN 15 SERIAL #'d SETS
NO PATCH PRICING DUE TO SCARCITY
OVERALL GU ODDS 2:1 HOBBY
CR1 Adam Dunn Jsy 15.00 40.00
Austin Kearns Jsy
Joe Morgan Jsy
Johnny Bench Jsy
Tony Perez
FM Miguel Cabrera Jsy 10.00 25.00
Josh Beckett Jsy
Dontrelle Willis Jsy
Juan Pierre Jsy
Al Leiter
HA Jeff Bagwell Jsy 15.00 40.00
Lance Berkman Jsy
Roger Clemens Jsy
Roy Oswalt Jsy
Craig Biggio
LA Vladimir Guerrero Jsy
Garret Anderson Jsy
Darin Erstad Jsy
Nolan Ryan Jsy
Rod Carew
NM Mike Piazza Jsy 30.00 60.00
Nolan Ryan Jsy
Pedro Martinez Jsy
Tom Glavine Jsy
Tom Seaver
SC Scott Rolen Jsy 30.00 60.00
Albert Pujols Jsy
Jim Edmonds Jsy
Mark Mulder Jsy
Stan Musial
TD B.J. Upton Jsy
Scott Kazmir Jsy
Aubrey Huff Jsy
Rocco Baldelli Jsy
Carl Crawford
TR Alfonso Soriano Jsy 15.00 40.00
Mark Teixeira Jsy
Nolan Ryan Jsy
Michael Young Jsy
Hank Blalock

2005 Flair Dynasty Foundations Level 5 Jersey

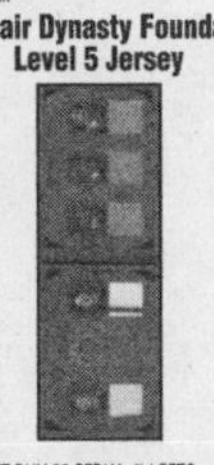

STATED PRINT RUN 25 SERIAL #'d SETS
MLB LOGO PRINT RUN 1 SERIAL #'d SET
NO MLB LOGO PRICING DUE TO SCARCITY
PATCH PRINT RUN 9 SERIAL #'d SETS
NO PATCH PRICING DUE TO SCARCITY
OVERALL GU ODDS 2:1 HOBBY
FM Miguel Cabrera Jsy 15.00 40.00
Josh Beckett Jsy
Dontrelle Willis Jsy
Juan Pierre Jsy
Al Leiter Jsy
HA Jeff Bagwell Jsy
Lance Berkman Jsy
Craig Biggio Jsy
Roger Clemens Jsy
Roy Oswalt Jsy
LA Vladimir Guerrero Jsy 40.00 80.00
Garret Anderson Jsy
Darin Erstad Jsy
Rod Carew Jsy
Nolan Ryan Jsy
NM Mike Piazza Jsy 75.00 150.00
Tom Seaver Jsy
Nolan Ryan Jsy
Pedro Martinez Jsy
Tom Glavine Jsy
TR Alfonso Soriano Jsy 40.00 80.00
Mark Teixeira Jsy
Hank Blalock Jsy
Nolan Ryan Jsy
Michael Young Jsy

2005 Flair Head of the Class Triple Jersey

PRINT RUNS B/WN 1-99 COPIES PER
NO PRICING ON QTY OF 3 OR LESS
LOGO PRINT RUN 1 SERIAL #'d SET
NO LOGO PRICING DUE TO SCARCITY
OVERALL GU ODDS 2:1 HOBBY
AGJ Bobby Abreu 6.00 15.00
Vladimir Guerrero
Andruw Jones/96
BGB Carlos Beltran 6.00 15.00
Troy Glaus
Adrian Beltre/98
BMK Hank Blalock
Victor Martinez
Austin Kearns/2
BSO Josh Beckett
Ben Sheets
Roy Oswalt/1
BTR Jeff Bagwell 6.00 15.00
Jim Thome
Ivan Rodriguez/91
CGB Miguel Cabrera
Khalil Greene
Jason Bay/3
GBH Eric Gagne 6.00 15.00
AJ Burnett
Tim Hudson/99
JDR Chipper Jones 6.00 15.00
Carlos Delgado
Manny Ramirez/93
OHS David Ortiz 6.00 15.00
Torii Hunter
Richie Sexson/97
SNP Jason Schmidt 10.00 25.00
Hideo Nomo
Andy Pettite/95
TMR Mark Teixeira
Hideki Matsui
Jose Reyes/3

2005 Flair Head of the Class Triple Patch

*PATCH: 1.25X TO 3X BASIC p/r 91-99
OVERALL GU ODDS 2:1 HOBBY
STATED PRINT RUN 33 SERIAL #'d SETS
BMK Hank Blalock 20.00 50.00

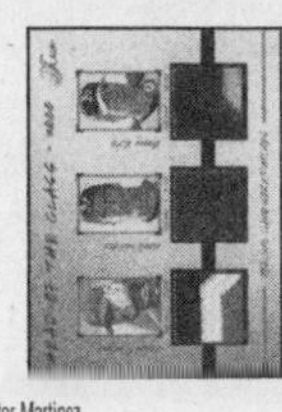

Victor Martinez
Austin Kearns
CGB Miguel Cabrera 20.00 50.00
Khalil Greene
Jason Bay
SMZ Johan Santana 20.00 50.00
Mark Mulder
Barry Zito

2005 Flair Letterman

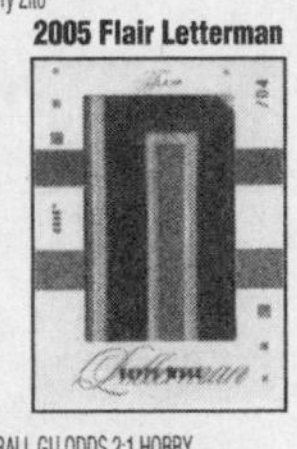

OVERALL GU ODDS 2:1 HOBBY
PRINT RUNS B/WN 4-8 COPIES PER
NO PRICING DUE TO SCARCITY
AP Albert Pujols/6
CJ Chipper Jones/6
CM Miguel Cabrera/7
CR Cal Ripken/6
GM Greg Maddux/6
HN Hideo Nomo/4
KW Kerry Wood/4
MP Mike Piazza/5
VG Vladimir Guerrero/8

2005 Flair Significant Signings Blue

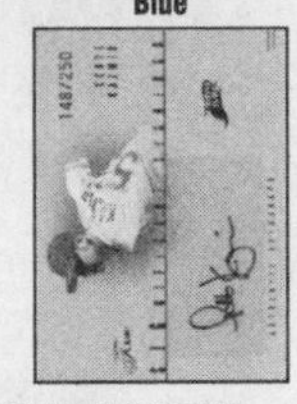

PRINT RUNS B/WN 4-250 COPIES PER
NO PRICING ON QTY OF 20 OR LESS
JSY TAG OVERALL AU ODDS 1:1 HOBBY
JSY TAG PRINT RUN 1 SERIAL #'d SET
NO JSY TAG PRICING DUE TO SCARCITY
PATCH PRINT RUN 15 SERIAL #'d SETS
ACTUAL HAFNER PATCH QTY 8 COPIES
NO PATCH PRICING DUE TO SCARCITY
OVERALL AU ODDS 1:1 H, AU-GU 1:24 R
AB Adrian Beltre/30 10.00 25.00
BC Bobby Crosby/93 6.00 15.00
BU B.J. Upton/250 6.00 15.00
CB Carlos Beltran/4
CK Casey Kotchman/250 6.00 15.00
CR Cal Ripken/16
DM Don Mattingly/103 30.00 60.00
DW David Wright/250 20.00 50.00
GF Gavin Floyd/221 4.00 10.00
JB Jason Bay/250 6.00 15.00
JM Justin Morneau/225 6.00 15.00
JP Jake Peavy UER 200/198 * 8.00 20.00
JR Jeremy Reed/250 4.00 10.00
KW Kerry Wood/200 10.00 25.00
LF Lew Ford/230 4.00 10.00
MC Miguel Cabrera/250 10.00 25.00
MS Mike Schmidt/20
MT Mark Teixeira/160 10.00 25.00
NR Nolan Ryan/92 50.00 100.00
PM Pedro Martinez/101 40.00 80.00
RC Roger Clemens UER 43/33 * 75.00 150.00
SC Steve Carlton/59 8.00 20.00
SK Scott Kazmir/250 8.00 20.00
TH T.Hafner UER 250/249 * 6.00 15.00
VM Victor Martinez/224 6.00 15.00
ZG Zack Greinke/250 6.00 15.00

2005 Flair Significant Signings Die Cut Silver

*DC SIL: .5X TO 1.2X BLUE p/r 160-250
*DC SIL: .5X TO 1.2X BLUE p/r 92-101
*DC SIL: .4X TO 1X BLUE p/r 43-59
*DC SIL: .3X TO .8X BLUE p/r 30
OVERALL AU ODDS 1:1 HOBBY
STATED PRINT RUN 50 SERIAL #'d SETS
CB Carlos Beltran 8.00 20.00
CR Cal Ripken 100.00 175.00
MS Mike Schmidt 40.00 80.00

2005 Flair Significant Signings Jersey Gold

*JSY GOLD: .75X TO 2X BLUE p/r 160-250
*JSY GOLD: .75X TO 2X BLUE p/r 92-103
OVERALL AU ODDS 1:1 H, AU-GU 1:24 R
STATED PRINT RUN 25 SERIAL #'d SETS
ACTUAL CLEMENS PRINT RUN 6 COPIES
NO PRICING ON CLEMENS

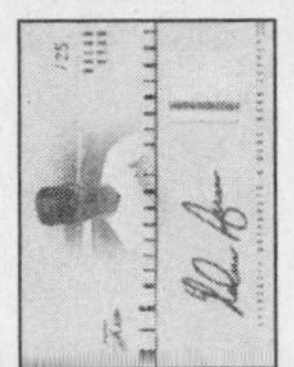

KG Khalil Greene 20.00 50.00
KW Kerry Wood 20.00 50.00
MS Mike Schmidt
NR Nolan Ryan 75.00 150.00
PM Pedro Martinez 60.00 120.00
RC Roger Clemens/6 UER *

2005 Flair Significant Signings Dual

STATED PRINT RUN 40 SERIAL #'d SETS
ACTUAL UPTON/KAZMIR QTY 33 COPIES
JSY PRINT RUN 15 SERIAL #'d SETS
NO JSY PRICING DUE TO SCARCITY
PATCH PRINT RUN 5 SERIAL #'d SETS
NO PATCH PRICING DUE TO SCARCITY
OVERALL AU ODDS 1:1 HOBBY
BR Adrian Beltre 20.00 50.00
Jeremy Reed
CF Steve Carlton 20.00 50.00
Gavin Floyd
FM Lew Ford 20.00 50.00
Justin Morneau
MH Victor Martinez 20.00 50.00
Travis Hafner
RC Nolan Ryan
Roger Clemens
SR Mike Schmidt 150.00 250.00
Cal Ripken
UK B.J. Upton 20.00 50.00
Scott Kazmir/33 UER

2003 Flair Greats

This 133 card set was released in December, 2002. These cards were issued in five card packs with an SRP of $6. These cards were issued in 20 pack boxes which came 12 boxes to a case. Cards numbered 96 through 133 were inserted four per special home team boxes which also had 20 packs in a box but only had 4 boxes to a case. A promo card of Al Kaline was also issued before the product was issued and we have placed that card at the end of our set listings.

COMP.SET w/o SP's (95) 15.00 40.00
COMMON CARD (1-95) .40 1.00
COMMON CARD (96-133) 2.00 5.00
1 Ozzie Smith 1.50 4.00
2 Red Schoendienst .40 1.00
3 Harmon Killebrew 1.00 2.50
4 Ralph Kiner .40 1.00
5 Johnny Bench 1.00 2.50
6 Al Kaline 1.00 2.50
7 Bobby Doerr .40 1.00
8 Cal Ripken 3.00 8.00
9 Enos Slaughter .40 1.00
10 Phil Rizzuto .60 1.50
11 Luis Aparicio .40 1.00
12 Pee Wee Reese .60 1.50
13 Richie Ashburn .60 1.50
14 Ernie Banks 1.00 2.50
15 Earl Weaver .40 1.00
16 Whitey Ford .60 1.50
17 Brooks Robinson .60 1.50
18 Lou Boudreau .40 1.00
19 Robin Yount 1.00 2.50
20 Mike Schmidt 2.00 5.00
21 Bob Lemon .40 1.00
22 Stan Musial 1.50 4.00
23 Joe Morgan .40 1.00
24 Early Wynn .40 1.00
25 Willie Stargell .60 1.50
26 Yogi Berra 1.00 2.50
27 Juan Marichal .40 1.00
28 Rick Ferrell .40 1.00
29 Rod Carew .60 1.50
30 Jim Bunning .40 1.00
31 Ferguson Jenkins .40 1.00
32 Steve Carlton .40 1.00
33 Larry Doby .40 1.00
34 Nolan Ryan 2.50 6.00
35 Phil Niekro UER .40 1.00
Career win total in blurb is wrong
36 Billy Williams .40 1.00
37 Hal Newhouser .40 1.00
38 Bob Feller .40 1.00
39 Lou Brock .60 1.50
40 Monte Irvin .40 1.00
41 Eddie Mathews 1.00 2.50
42 Rollie Fingers .40 1.00
43 Gaylord Perry .40 1.00
44 Reggie Jackson .60 1.50
45 Bob Gibson .60 1.50
46 Robin Roberts .60 1.50
47 Tom Seaver .60 1.50
48 Willie McCovey .40 1.00
49 Hoyt Wilhelm .40 1.00
50 George Kell .40 1.00
51 Warren Spahn .60 1.50
52 Catfish Hunter .60 1.50
53 Dom DiMaggio .40 1.00
54 Joe Medwick .40 1.00
55 Johnny Pesky .40 1.00
56 Steve Garvey .40 1.00
57 Harry Heilmann .40 1.00
58 Dave Winfield .40 1.00
59 Andre Dawson .40 1.00
60 Jimmie Foxx 1.00 2.50
61 Buddy Bell .40 1.00
62 Gabby Hartnett .40 1.00
63 Babe Ruth 3.00 8.00
64 Dizzy Dean .60 1.50
65 Hank Greenberg 1.00 2.50
66 Don Drysdale .60 1.50
67 Gary Carter .40 1.00
68 Wade Boggs .60 1.50
69 Tony Perez .40 1.00
70 Mickey Cochrane .60 1.50
71 Bill Dickey .60 1.50
72 George Brett 2.00 5.00
73 Honus Wagner 1.00 2.50
74 George Sisler .40 1.00
75 Walter Johnson 1.00 2.50
76 Ron Santo .60 1.50
77 Roy Campanella 1.00 2.50
78 Roger Maris 1.00 2.50
79 Kirby Puckett 1.00 2.50
80 Alan Trammell .40 1.00
81 Don Mattingly 2.00 5.00
82 Ty Cobb 1.25 3.00
83 Lou Gehrig 2.00 5.00
84 Jackie Robinson 1.00 2.50
85 Billy Martin .60 1.50
86 Paul Molitor .40 1.00
87 Duke Snider .60 1.50
88 Thurman Munson 1.00 2.50
89 Luke Appling .40 1.00
90 Ernie Lombardi .40 1.00
91 Rube Waddell .40 1.00
92 Travis Jackson .40 1.00
93 Joe Sewell .40 1.00
94 King Kelly .60 1.50
95 Heinie Manush .40 1.00
96 Bobby Doerr HT 2.00 5.00
97 Johnny Pesky HT 2.00 5.00
98 Wade Boggs HT 3.00 8.00
99 Tony Conigliaro HT 3.00 8.00
100 Carlton Fisk HT 3.00 8.00
101 Rico Petrocelli HT 2.00 5.00
102 Jim Rice HT 2.00 5.00
103 Al Lopez HT 2.00 5.00
104 Pee Wee Reese HT 3.00 8.00
105 Tommy Lasorda HT 2.00 5.00
106 Gil Hodges HT 3.00 8.00
107 Jackie Robinson HT 3.00 8.00
108 Duke Snider HT 3.00 8.00
109 Don Drysdale HT 3.00 8.00
110 Steve Garvey HT 2.00 5.00
111 Hoyt Wilhelm HT 2.00 5.00
112 Juan Marichal HT 2.00 5.00
113 Monte Irvin HT 2.00 5.00
114 Willie McCovey HT 2.00 5.00
115 Travis Jackson HT 2.00 5.00
116 Bobby Bonds HT 2.00 5.00
117 Orlando Cepeda HT 2.00 5.00
118 Whitey Ford HT 3.00 8.00
119 Phil Rizzuto HT 3.00 8.00
120 Reggie Jackson HT 3.00 8.00
121 Yogi Berra HT 3.00 8.00
122 Roger Maris HT 3.00 8.00
123 Don Mattingly HT 8.00 20.00
124 Babe Ruth HT 6.00 15.00
125 Dave Winfield HT 2.00 5.00
126 Bob Gibson HT 3.00 8.00
127 Enos Slaughter HT 2.00 5.00
128 Joe Medwick HT 2.00 5.00
129 Lou Brock HT 3.00 8.00
130 Ozzie Smith HT 4.00 10.00
131 Stan Musial HT 4.00 10.00
132 Steve Carlton HT 2.00 5.00
133 Dizzy Dean HT 3.00 8.00
P6 Al Kaline .75 2.00
Promotional Sample

2003 Flair Greats Ballpark Heroes

Issued at a stated rate of one in 10, these nine cards feature some of baseball's greatest players.

COMPLETE SET (9) 10.00 25.00
1 Nolan Ryan 2.50 6.00
2 Babe Ruth 3.00 8.00
3 Honus Wagner 1.00 2.50
4 Ty Cobb 1.50 4.00
5 Ernie Banks 1.00 2.50
6 Mike Schmidt 2.00 5.00
7 Duke Snider 1.00 2.50
8 Cal Ripken 3.00 8.00
9 Stan Musial 1.50 4.00

2003 Flair Greats Bat Rack Classics Quads

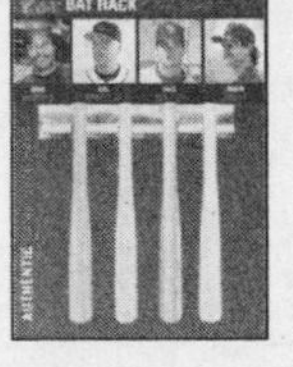

Randomly inserted into packs, these five cards feature game-used bat chips from four players all on the same card. These cards were issued to a stated print run of 150 serial numbered sets.

1 Don Mattingly 60.00 120.00
Joe Morgan
Cal Ripken
Brooks Robinson
2 Eddie Murray 20.00 50.00
Eddie Mathews
Reggie Jackson
Willie McCovey
3 Tony Perez 40.00 80.00
Don Mattingly
Hank Greenberg
Willie Stargell
4 Ryne Sandberg 30.00 60.00
Ron Santo
Billy Williams
Andre Dawson
5 Dave Winfield 40.00 80.00
Cal Ripken
Paul Molitor
Robin Yount

2003 Flair Greats Bat Rack Classics Trios

Randomly inserted into packs, these five cards feature game-used bat chips from three players all on the same card. These cards were issued to a stated print run of 300 serial numbered sets.

1 Tommy Agee 10.00 25.00
Jerry Grote
Bud Harrelson
2 Johnny Bench 15.00 40.00
Joe Morgan
Tony Perez
3 Hank Greenberg 20.00 50.00
Harry Heilman
George Kell
4 Reggie Jackson 20.00 50.00
Don Mattingly
Dave Winfield
5 Eddie Mathews 15.00 40.00
Paul Molitor
Robin Yount
6 Eddie Murray 40.00 80.00
Cal Ripken
Brooks Robinson
7 Dave Parker 10.00 25.00
Willie Stargell
8 Ryne Sandberg 20.00 50.00
Ron Santo
Billy Williams

2003 Flair Greats Classic Numbers

Inserted into packs at a stated rate of one in 20, these 13 cards feature some of the most famous uniform numbers ever.

1 Jackie Robinson 2.50 6.00
2 Willie McCovey 1.50 4.00
3 Brooks Robinson 1.50 4.00
4 Reggie Jackson 1.50 4.00
5 Ozzie Smith 4.00 10.00
6 Johnny Bench 2.50 6.00
7 Yogi Berra 2.50 6.00
8 Cal Ripken 8.00 20.00
9 George Brett 5.00 12.00
10 Thurman Munson 2.50 6.00
11 Joe Morgan 1.50 4.00
12 Nolan Ryan 6.00 15.00
13 Steve Carlton 1.50 4.00

2003 Flair Greats Classic Numbers Game Used

Inserted at stated odds of one in 24 hobby packs and one in 27 home team packs, these 11 cards feature game-worn material from 11 of the players from the Classic Numbers set. A few players were issued in shorter supply and we have notated that information along with their announced print run information next to the player's name in our checklist.

PATCH PRINT RUN 25 SERIAL #'d SETS
NO PATCH PRICING DUE TO SCARCITY
1 Johnny Bench Jsy 8.00 20.00
2 Yogi Berra Pants SP/75 10.00 25.00
3 George Brett Jsy 10.00 25.00
4 Steve Carlton Jsy 8.00 20.00
5 Willie McCovey Jsy SP/125 6.00 15.00
6 Joe Morgan Pants SP/200 6.00 15.00

7 Thurman Munson Pants 12.50 30.00
8 Cal Ripken Jsy 12.50 30.00
9 Nolan Ryan Jsy 20.00 50.00
10 Ryne Sandberg Jsy 10.00 25.00
11 Ozzie Smith Jsy 8.00 20.00

2003 Flair Greats Classic Numbers Game Used Dual

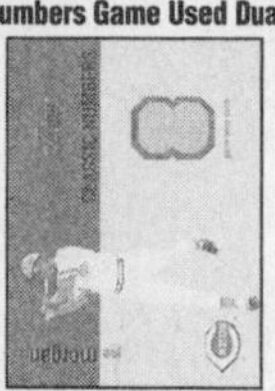

Randomly inserted into packs, these eight cards feature two players along with game-worn swatches of each of these players. Each of these cards was issued to a stated print run of 250 serial numbered sets.

1 Johnny Bench Jsy / Thurman Munson Pants 15.00 40.00
2 Yogi Berra Pants / Thurman Munson Pants 15.00 40.00
3 Yogi Berra Pants / Cal Ripken Jsy 30.00 60.00
4 George Brett Jsy / Nolan Ryan Jsy 30.00 60.00
5 Willie McCovey Jsy / Johnny Bench Jsy 10.00 25.00
6 Joe Morgan Pants / Ryne Sandberg Jsy 15.00 40.00
7 Cal Ripken Pants / Ozzie Smith Jsy 30.00 60.00
8 Nolan Ryan Jsy / Steve Carlton Jsy 30.00 60.00

2003 Flair Greats Cut of History Autographs

Randomly inserted into packs, these cards feature authentic autographs of the featured player. These cards were issued to different print runs and we have notated that information in our checklist.

1 Johnny Bench/161 30.00 60.00
2 Steve Carlton/506 10.00 25.00
3 Dom DiMaggio/402 50.00 100.00
4 Tony Kubek/161 20.00 50.00
5 Cal Ripken/155 100.00 175.00
6 Alan Trammell/211 10.00 25.00

2003 Flair Greats Cut of History Game Used

Issued at a stated rate of one in ten packs, these 27 cards feature game-used pieces of 27 of baseball's all time greats. A few players were issued in smaller quantity and we have notated that information along with their stated print run next to their name in our checklist.

1 Luis Aparicio Jsy 3.00 8.00
2 Frank Baker Bat SP/50 20.00 50.00
3 Buddy Bell Bat 3.00 8.00
4 Wade Boggs Jsy SP/250 8.00 20.00
5 Steve Carlton Pants 3.00 8.00
6 Gary Carter Jsy 3.00 8.00
7 Dennis Eckersley Jsy 3.00 8.00
8 Hank Greenberg Bat SP/100 20.00 50.00
9 Catfish Hunter Jsy SP/200 8.00 20.00
10 Reggie Jackson Bat 4.00 10.00
11 Ferguson Jenkins Pants 3.00 8.00
12 Roger Maris Jsy SP/250 30.00 60.00
13 Billy Martin Pants 4.00 10.00
14 Willie McCovey Pants 3.00 8.00
15 Joe Medwick Bat 8.00 20.00
16 Eddie Murray Jsy 4.00 10.00
17 Graig Nettles Bat 3.00 8.00
18 Phil Niekro Pants 3.00 8.00
19 Paul O'Neill Jsy 4.00 10.00
20 Jim Palmer Pants 3.00 8.00
21 Kirby Puckett Bat 4.00 10.00
22 Cal Ripken Pants 10.00 25.00
23 Tom Seaver Pants 4.00 10.00
24A Alan Trammell Bat 3.00 8.00
24B Alan Trammell Jsy 3.00 8.00
25 Hoyt Wilhelm Jsy 3.00 8.00
26 Early Wynn Jsy 3.00 8.00

2003 Flair Greats Cut of History Game Used Gold

This set parallels the Cut of History Game Used set. Each of these cards were issued to a stated print run of 100 serial numbered sets.

*GOLD: .75X TO 2X BASIC
*GOLD: .5X TO 1.2X BASIC SP'S
STATED PRINT RUN 100 SERIAL #'d SETS

2003 Flair Greats of the Grain

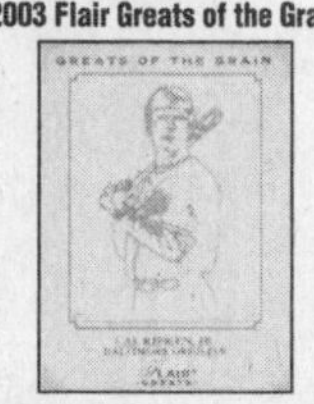

Randomly inserted into packs, these nine cards feature all-time greats laser etched on to a wood swatch. These cards were issued to a stated print run of 50 serial numbered sets. Please note that these cards do not contain game-used wood on them.

1 George Brett 40.00 80.00
2 Ty Cobb 40.00 80.00
3 Lou Gehrig 30.00 60.00
4 Eddie Mathews 30.00 60.00
5 Don Mattingly 40.00 80.00
6 Stan Musial 40.00 80.00
7 Cal Ripken 50.00 100.00
8 Babe Ruth 50.00 100.00
9 Mike Schmidt 40.00 80.00

2003 Flair Greats Hall of Fame Postmark

Randomly inserted into packs, these cards honor the day that Ozzie Smith was inducted into the Hall of Fame. Some of these cards were autographed and we have noted the print run for both of these cards in our checklist.

1 Ozzie Smith/2002 10.00 25.00
2 Ozzie Smith AU/202 50.00 100.00

2003 Flair Greats Home Team Cuts Game Used

These cards were issued at an overall rate of one in 20 for both single or dual game used cards in the home team boxes. A few cards were issued in smaller quantities than the others and we have notated that information in our checklist.

1 Wade Boggs Jsy SP/250 8.00 20.00
2 Bobby Bonds Bat 4.00 10.00
3 Carlton Fisk Jsy 6.00 15.00
4 Steve Garvey Jsy 4.00 10.00
5 Reggie Jackson Bat 6.00 15.00
6 Tom Lasorda Jsy SP/150 6.00 15.00
7 Juan Marichal Pants 4.00 10.00
8 Roger Maris Jsy SP/150 30.00 80.00
9 Billy Martin Pants 6.00 15.00
10 Willie McCovey Pants SP/200 6.00 15.00
11 Joe Medwick Bat SP/250 10.00 25.00
12 P.Reese Pants SP/75 8.00 20.00
13 Jim Rice Bat 4.00 10.00
14 R.Schoendienst Pants SP/200 6.00 15.00
15 Ozzie Smith Bat 8.00 20.00
16 Duke Snider Pants 6.00 15.00
17 Dave Winfield Bat 4.00 10.00

2003 Flair Greats Home Team Cuts Game Used Dual

These cards were issued at an overall rate of one in 20 for both single or dual game used cards in the home team boxes. A few cards were issued in smaller quantities than the others and we have notated that information in our checklist.

1 Bobby Bonds Bat / Willie McCovey Pants/100 15.00 40.00
2 Carlton Fisk Jsy / Jim Rice Bat/100 12.50 30.00
3 Billy Martin Pants / Reggie Jackson Bat/175 12.50 30.00
4 Pee Wee Reese Pants / Duke Snider Pants/100 12.50 30.00
5 Red Schoendienst Pants / Joe Medwick Bat/125 10.00 25.00

2003 Flair Greats Sweet Swatch Classic Bat

Randomly inserted into jumbo packs, these 12 cards feature game-used bat pieces of the featured players. Each player was issued to a different print run and we have notated that information in our checklist.

1 Johnny Bench/175 10.00 25.00
2 George Brett/320 15.00 40.00
3 Jose Canseco/175 10.00 25.00
4 Orlando Cepeda/165 8.00 20.00
5 Andre Dawson/310 6.00 15.00
6 Reggie Jackson/155 10.00 25.00
7 Eddie Mathews/185 10.00 25.00
8 Don Mattingly/340 15.00 40.00
9 Willie McCovey/155 8.00 20.00
10 Kirby Puckett/165 10.00 25.00
11 Pee Wee Reese/165 10.00 25.00
12 Cal Ripken/305 20.00 50.00

2003 Flair Greats Sweet Swatch Classic Bat Image

These four cards partially parallel the sweet swatch classic bat insert set. Each of these cards were issued to a stated print run of less than 50 copies.

1 Johnny Bench/36 40.00 80.00
2 Tony Kubek/35 30.00 60.00
3 Cal Ripken/42 75.00 150.00
4 Alan Trammell/44 30.00 60.00

2003 Flair Greats Sweet Swatch Classic Bat Image Autographs

These four cards partially parallel the sweet swatch classic bat insert image set along with the player's autograph. Each of these cards were issued to a stated print run of 40 serial numbered sets.

1 Johnny Bench 60.00 120.00
2 Tony Kubek 50.00 100.00
3 Cal Ripken 150.00 250.00
4 Alan Trammell 40.00 80.00

2003 Flair Greats Sweet Swatch Classic Jersey

Randomly inserted into jumbo packs, these 72 cards feature game-used jersey swatches of the featured players. Each player was issued to a different print run and we have notated that information in our checklist.

1 Johnny Bench Jsy/410 8.00 20.00
2 George Brett Jsy/384 15.00 40.00
3 Jose Canseco Jsy/1329 6.00 15.00
4 Jerry Coleman Jsy/528 8.00 20.00
5 Andre Dawson Jsy/335 8.00 20.00
6 Carlton Fisk Jsy/1200 6.00 15.00
7 Gil Hodges Jsy/545 8.00 20.00
8 Juan Marichal Jsy/385 8.00 20.00
9 Don Mattingly Jsy/880 10.00 25.00
10 Paul Molitor Jsy/592 8.00 20.00
11 Jim Palmer Jsy/335 8.00 20.00
12 Kirby Puckett Jsy/445 8.00 20.00
13 Cal Ripken Jsy/557 15.00 40.00
14 Nolan Ryan Jsy/590 10.00 25.00
15 Ryne Sandberg Jsy/374 12.50 30.00
17 Robin Yount Jsy/340 8.00 20.00
19 Tom Seaver Jsy/385 6.00 15.00

2003 Flair Greats Sweet Swatch Classic Patch

This 16 card set partially parallels the sweet swatch classic jersey set. Each of these cards feature a game-used patch piece and we have notated the stated print run in our checklist.

PATCH MASTERPIECE PRINT RUN 1 #'d SET
NO PATCH MP PRICING DUE TO SCARCITY
1 Johnny Bench/59 40.00 80.00
2 George Brett/53 75.00 150.00
3 Jose Canseco/177 30.00 60.00
4 Jerry Coleman/73 20.00 50.00
5 Andre Dawson/58 20.00 50.00
6 Carlton Fisk/51 40.00 80.00
7 Juan Marichal/48 20.00 50.00
8 Don Mattingly/106 60.00 120.00
9 Paul Molitor/96 30.00 60.00
10 Jim Palmer/63 30.00 60.00
11 Kirby Puckett/72 40.00 80.00
12 Cal Ripken/69 75.00 150.00
13 Nolan Ryan/60 75.00 150.00
14 Ryne Sandberg/40 75.00 150.00
15 Tom Seaver/66 30.00 60.00
16 Robin Yount/66 40.00 80.00

1997 Flair Showcase Rodriguez Sample Strip

This three-card unperforated strip was distributed to dealers and hobby media a few months prior to the release of 1997 Flair Showcase. The strip contains parallel versions of three different Alex Rodriguez cards later issued in packs. The cards on this promotional strip are identical to the standard Rodriguez Flair Showcase cards except for the text "PROMOTIONAL SAMPLE" written diagonally across the front and back.

NNO Alex Rodriguez Promo Strip
Row 2, Row 1, Row 0

1997 Flair Showcase Row 2

The 1997 Flair Showcase set (produced by Fleer) was issued in one series totalling 540 cards and was distributed in five-card packs with a suggested retail price of $4.99. Three groups of 60 cards were inserted at different rates: Cards numbered from one through 60 were inserted 1.5 cards per pack, cards numbered from 61 through 120 were inserted one every 1.5 packs and cards numbered from 121 through 180 were inserted at a rate of one per pack. This hobby exclusive set is divided into three 180-card sets (Row 2/Style, Row 1/Grace, and Row 0/Showcase) and features holographic foil fronts with an action photo of the player silhouetted over a larger black-and-white head-shot image in the background. The thick card stock is laminated with a shiny glossy coating for a super-premium "feel." Also inserted one in every pack was a Million Dollar Moments card. Rookie Cards include Brian Giles. Finally, 25 serial-numbered Alex Rodriguez Emerald Exchange cards (good for a signed Rodriguez glove) were randomly seeded into packs. The card fronts were very similar in design to the regular Row 2 Rodriguez, except for green foil accents. The card back, however, consisted entirely of text explaining prize guidelines. The deadline to exchange the card was 8/1/98.

COMPLETE SET (180) 40.00 80.00
COMMON CARD (1-60) .20 .50
ROW 2 1-60 ODDS 1.5:1
COMMON (61-120) .30 .75
ROW 2 61-120 ODDS 1:1.5
COMMON (121-180) .25 .60
ROW 2 121-180 STATED ODDS 1:1
A.ROD GLOVE EXCH RANDOM IN PACKS
A.ROD GLOVE EXCH.DEADLINE: 8/1/98
1 Andruw Jones .30 .75
2 Derek Jeter 1.25 3.00
3 Alex Rodriguez .75 2.00
4 Paul Molitor .20 .50
5 Jeff Bagwell .30 .75
6 Scott Rolen .30 .75
7 Kenny Lofton .20 .50
8 Cal Ripken 1.50 4.00
9 Brady Anderson .20 .50
10 Chipper Jones .50 1.25
11 Todd Greene .20 .50
12 Todd Walker .20 .50
13 Billy Wagner .20 .50
14 Craig Biggio .30 .75
15 Kevin Orie .20 .50
16 Hideo Nomo .50 1.25
17 Kevin Appier .20 .50
18 B.Trammell RC .20 .50
19 Juan Gonzalez .20 .50
20 Randy Johnson .50 1.25
21 Roger Clemens 1.00 2.50
22 Johnny Damon .30 .75
23 Ryne Sandberg .75 2.00
24 Ken Griffey Jr. .75 2.00
25 Barry Bonds 1.25 3.00
26 Nomar Garciaparra .75 2.00
27 Vladimir Guerrero .50 1.25
28 Ron Gant .20 .50
29 Joe Carter .20 .50
30 Tim Salmon .30 .75
31 Mike Piazza .75 2.00
32 Barry Larkin .30 .75
33 Manny Ramirez .30 .75
34 Sammy Sosa .50 1.25
35 Frank Thomas .50 1.25
36 Melvin Nieves .20 .50
37 Tony Gwynn .60 1.50
38 Gary Sheffield .20 .50
39 Darin Erstad .20 .50
40 Ken Caminiti .20 .50
41 Jermaine Dye .20 .50
42 Mo Vaughn .20 .50
43 Raul Mondesi .20 .50
44 Greg Maddux .75 2.00
45 Chuck Knoblauch .20 .50
46 Andy Pettitte .30 .75
47 Deion Sanders .30 .75
48 Albert Belle .20 .50
49 Jamey Wright .20 .50
50 Rey Ordonez .20 .50
51 Bernie Williams .30 .75
52 Mark McGwire 1.25 3.00
53 Mike Mussina .30 .75
54 Bob Abreu .30 .75
55 Reggie Sanders .20 .50
56 Brian Jordan .20 .50
57 Ivan Rodriguez .30 .75
58 Roberto Alomar .30 .75
59 Tim Naehring .20 .50
60 Edgar Renteria .20 .50
61 Dean Palmer .30 .75
62 Benito Santiago .30 .75
63 David Cone .30 .75
64 Carlos Delgado .30 .75
65 Brian Giles RC .75 2.00
66 Alex Ochoa .30 .75
67 Rondell White .30 .75
68 Robin Ventura .30 .75
69 Eric Karros .30 .75
70 Jose Valentin .30 .75
71 Rafael Palmeiro .50 1.25
72 Chris Snopek .30 .75
73 David Justice .30 .75
74 Tom Glavine .50 1.25
75 Rudy Pemberton .30 .75
76 Larry Walker .30 .75
77 Jim Thome .50 1.25
78 Charles Johnson .30 .75
79 Dante Powell .30 .75
80 Derrek Lee .50 1.25
81 Jason Kendall .30 .75
82 Todd Hollandsworth .30 .75
83 Bernard Gilkey .30 .75
84 Mel Rojas .30 .75
85 Dmitri Young .30 .75
86 Bret Boone .30 .75
87 Pat Hentgen .30 .75
88 Bobby Bonilla .30 .75
89 John Wetteland .30 .75
90 Todd Hundley .30 .75
91 Wilton Guerrero .30 .75
92 Geronimo Berroa .30 .75
93 Al Martin .30 .75
94 Danny Tartabull .30 .75
95 Brian McRae .30 .75
96 Steve Finley .30 .75
97 Todd Stottlemyre .30 .75
98 John Smoltz .50 1.25
99 Matt Williams .30 .75
100 Eddie Murray .75 2.00
101 Henry Rodriguez .30 .75
102 Marty Cordova .30 .75
103 Juan Guzman .30 .75
104 Chili Davis .30 .75
105 Eric Young .30 .75
106 Jeff Abbott .30 .75
107 Shannon Stewart .30 .75
108 Rocky Coppinger .30 .75
109 Jose Canseco .50 1.25
110 Dante Bichette .30 .75
111 Dwight Gooden .30 .75
112 Scott Brosius .30 .75
113 Steve Avery .30 .75
114 Andres Galarraga .30 .75
115 Sandy Alomar Jr. .30 .75
116 Ray Lankford .30 .75
117 Jorge Posada .50 1.25
118 Ryan Klesko .30 .75
119 Jay Buhner .30 .75
120 Jose Guillen .30 .75
121 Paul O'Neill .40 1.00
122 Jimmy Key .25 .60
123 Hal Morris .25 .60
124 Travis Fryman .25 .60
125 Jim Edmonds .25 .60
126 Jeff Cirillo .25 .60
127 Fred McGriff .40 1.00
128 Alan Benes .25 .60
129 Derek Bell .25 .60
130 Tony Graffanino .25 .60
131 Shawn Green .25 .60
132 Denny Neagle .25 .60
133 Alex Fernandez .25 .60
134 Mickey Morandini .25 .60
135 Royce Clayton .25 .60
136 Jose Mesa .25 .60
137 Edgar Martinez .40 1.00
138 Curt Schilling .25 .60
139 Lance Johnson .25 .60
140 Andy Benes .25 .60
141 Charles Nagy .25 .60
142 Mariano Rivera .60 1.50
143 Mark Wohlers .25 .60
144 Ken Hill .25 .60
145 Jay Bell .25 .60
146 Bob Higginson .25 .60
147 Mark Grudzielanek .25 .60
148 Ray Durham .25 .60
149 John Olerud .25 .60
150 Joey Hamilton .25 .60
151 Trevor Hoffman .25 .60
152 Dan Wilson .25 .60
153 J.T. Snow .25 .60
154 Marquis Grissom .25 .60
155 Yamil Benitez .25 .60
156 Rusty Greer .25 .60
157 Darryl Kile .25 .60
158 Ismael Valdes .25 .60
159 Jeff Conine .25 .60
160 Darren Daulton .25 .60
161 Chan Ho Park .25 .60
162 Troy Percival .25 .60
163 Wade Boggs .40 1.00
164 Dave Nilsson .25 .60
165 Vinny Castilla .25 .60
166 Kevin Brown .25 .60
167 Dennis Eckersley .25 .60
168 Wendell Magee Jr. .25 .60
169 John Jaha .25 .60
170 Garret Anderson .25 .60
171 Jason Giambi .25 .60
172 Mark Grace .40 1.00
173 Tony Clark .25 .60
174 Moises Alou .25 .60
175 Brett Butler .25 .60
176 Cecil Fielder .25 .60
177 Chris Widger .25 .60
178 Doug Drabek .25 .60
179 Ellis Burks .25 .60
180 S. Hasegawa RC .40 1.00
NNO A.Rod. Glove/25 .75 2.00

1997 Flair Showcase Row 1

Randomly inserted in packs at various rates: Cards number 1 through 60 at a rate of one in 2.5 packs, cards numbered 61 through 120 at one every two packs and cards numbered from 121 through 180 at a rate of one every three packs. This 180-card Grace set is parallel to the base Flair Showcase Row 2 (Style) set and features holographic foil fronts with an action photo of the player silhouetted over a larger color head-shot image in the background.

*STARS 1-60: .75X TO 2X ROW 2
ROW 1 1-60 ODDS 1:2.5
*STARS 61-120: .4X TO 1X ROW 2
*ROOKIES 61-120: .5X TO 1.25X ROW 2
ROW 1 61-120 ODDS 1:2
*ROOKIES 61-120: .5X TO 1.25X ROW 2
ROW 1 121-180 ODDS 1:3

1997 Flair Showcase Row 0

Randomly inserted in various rates depending on the card number: Cards numbered one through 60 were inserted one every 24 packs, cards numbered 61 through 120 at a rate of one per 12 and cards numbered 121 through 180 at a rate of one every five packs. This 180-card Showcase set is parallel to the base Flair Showcase Row 2 (Style) set and features holographic foil fronts with a head-shot image of the player silhouetted over a larger player action-shot in the background.

*STARS 1-60: 4X TO 10X ROW 2
ROW 0 1-60 ODDS 1:24
*STARS 61-120: 1.25X TO 3X ROW 2
*ROOKIES 61-120: 1.5X TO 4X ROW 2
ROW 0 61-120 ODDS 1:12
*STARS 121-180: 1X TO 2.5X ROW 2
ROW 0 121-180 ODDS 1:5

1997 Flair Showcase Legacy Collection Row 2

Randomly inserted in packs at a rate of one in 30 (cumulatively between all three rows of Legacy), this 180-card set is parallel to the regular set. Only 100 sequentially numbered sets were produced, each featuring an "alternate" player photo printed on a matte finish/foil stamped card.

*LC ROW 2 1-60: 25X TO 60X BASIC
*LC ROW 2 61-120: 15X TO 40X BASIC
*LC ROW 2 RC'S 61-120: 12.5X TO 30X BASIC
*LC ROW 2 121-180: 20X TO 50X BASIC
STATED ODDS 1:30

1997 Flair Showcase Legacy Collection Row 1

Randomly inserted in packs at a rate of one in 30 (cumulatively between all three rows of Legacy), this 180-card set is parallel to the regular set. Only 100 sequentially numbered sets were produced, each featuring an "alternate" player photo printed on a matte finish/foil stamped card.

*LC ROW 1 1-60: 25X TO 60X BASIC
*LC ROW 1 61-120: 15X TO 40X BASIC
*LC ROW 1 RC'S 61-120: 12.5X TO 30X BASIC
*LC ROW 1 121-180: 20X TO 50X BASIC
STATED ODDS 1:30

1997 Flair Showcase Legacy Collection Row 0

Randomly inserted in packs at a rate of one in 30 (cumulatively between all three rows of Legacy), this 180-card set is parallel to the regular set. Only 100 sequentially numbered sets were produced, each featuring an "alternate" player photo printed on a matte finish/foil stamped card.

*LC ROW 0 1-60: 25X TO 60X BASIC
*LC ROW 0 61-120: 15X TO 40X BASIC
*LC ROW 0 RC'S 61-120: 12.5X TO 30X BASIC
*LC ROW 0 121-180: 20X TO 50X BASIC
STATED ODDS 1:30

1997 Flair Showcase Diamond Cuts

Randomly inserted in packs at a rate of one in 20, this 20-card set features color images of baseball's brightest stars silhouetted on a holofoil-stamped die-cut diamond-design background.

COMPLETE SET (20) 60.00 150.00
STATED ODDS 1:20
1 Jeff Bagwell 1.50 4.00
2 Albert Belle 1.00 2.50
3 Ken Caminiti 1.00 2.50
4 Juan Gonzalez 1.00 2.50
5 Ken Griffey Jr. 4.00 10.00
6 Tony Gwynn 3.00 8.00
7 Todd Hundley 1.50 4.00
8 Andruw Jones 1.50 4.00
9 Chipper Jones 2.50 6.00
10 Greg Maddux 4.00 10.00
11 Mark McGwire 6.00 15.00
12 Mike Piazza 4.00 10.00
13 Derek Jeter 6.00 15.00
14 Manny Ramirez 1.50 4.00
15 Cal Ripken 8.00 20.00
16 Alex Rodriguez 4.00 10.00
17 Frank Thomas 2.50 6.00
18 Mo Vaughn 1.00 2.50
19 Bernie Williams 1.50 4.00
20 Matt Williams 1.50 4.00

1997 Flair Showcase Hot Gloves

Randomly inserted in packs at a rate of one in 90, this 15-card set features color images of baseball's top glovemen silhouetted against a die-cut flame and glove background with temperature-sensitive inks.

STATED ODDS 1:90
1 Roberto Alomar 5.00 12.00
2 Barry Bonds 20.00 50.00
3 Juan Gonzalez 3.00 8.00
4 Ken Griffey Jr. 12.50 30.00
5 Marquis Grissom 4.00 10.00
6 Derek Jeter 20.00 50.00
7 Chipper Jones 8.00 20.00
8 Barry Larkin 5.00 12.00
9 Kenny Lofton 3.00 8.00
10 Greg Maddux 12.50 30.00
11 Mike Piazza 12.50 30.00
12 Cal Ripken 25.00 60.00
13 Alex Rodriguez 12.50 30.00
14 Ivan Rodriguez 5.00 12.00
15 Frank Thomas 8.00 20.00

1997 Flair Showcase Wave of the Future

Randomly inserted in packs at a rate of one in four, this 27-card set features color images of top rookies silhouetted against a background of an embossed wave design with simulated sand.

COMPLETE SET (27) 15.00 40.00
COMMON RC YR .40 1.00
STATED ODDS 1:4
1 Todd Greene .40 1.00
2 Andruw Jones .75 2.00
3 Randall Simon .60 1.50
4 Wady Almonte .40 1.00
5 Pat Cline .40 1.00
6 Jeff Abbott .40 1.00
7 Justin Towle .40 1.00
8 Richie Sexson .60 1.50
9 Bubba Trammell .60 1.50
10 Bob Abreu .75 2.00
11 David Arias-Ortiz 5.00 12.00
12 Todd Walker .40 1.00
13 Orlando Cabrera 1.50 4.00

14 Vladimir Guerrero 1.25 3.00
15 Ricky Ledee .60 1.50
16 Jorge Posada .75 2.00
17 Ruben Rivera .40 1.00
18 Scott Spiezio .40 1.00
19 Scott Rolen .75 2.00
20 Emil Brown .40 1.00
21 Jose Guillen .60 1.50
22 T.J. Staton .40 1.00
23 Eli Marrero .40 1.00
24 Fernando Tatis .40 1.00
25 Ryan Jones .40 1.00
WF1 Hideki Irabu .60 1.50
WF2 Jose Cruz Jr. .60 1.50

1998 Flair Showcase Ripken Sample Strip

This four-card unperforated strip was distributed to dealers and hobby media a few months prior to the release of 1998 Flair Showcase. The strip contains parallel versions of four different Cal Ripken cards later issued in packs. The cards on this promotional strip are identical to the standard Ripken Flair Showcase cards except for the text "PROMOTIONAL SAMPLE" written diagonally across the front and back.

NNO Cal Ripken Promo Strip 1.25 3.00
Row 3 Cal Ripken Flair
Row 2 Cal Ripken Style
Row 1 Cal Ripken Grace
Row 0 Cal Ripken Showcase

1998 Flair Showcase Row 3

This set (produced by Fleer) was issued in five card packs which retailed for $4.99 per pack and were released in July, 1998. Each player was featured in four rows with Row 3 being the easiest to obtain from opening packs. This 120 card set features two photos of the player on the front. The Row 3 cards were inserted in different ratios depending on which numbers they are. The complete odds are listed below for each group of 30 cards. Cards numbered 1-30 were seeded one every 9/10th of a pack; cards numbered 31-60 were seeded one every 1.1 packs; cards numbered 61-90 were seeded one every 1.5 packs and cards 91-120 were seeded one every two packs. Rookie Cards include Magglio Ordonez.

COMPLETE SET (120) 30.00 60.00
COMMON CARD (1-30) .20 .50
COMMON CARD (31-60) .20 .50
COMMON CARD (61-90) .25 .60
COMMON CARD (91-120) .30 .75
1 Ken Griffey Jr. .75 2.00
2 Travis Lee .20 .50
3 Frank Thomas .50 1.25
4 Ben Grieve .20 .50
5 Nomar Garciaparra .75 2.00
6 Jose Cruz Jr. .20 .50
7 Alex Rodriguez .75 2.00
8 Cal Ripken 1.50 4.00
9 Mark McGwire 1.25 3.00
10 Chipper Jones .50 1.25
11 Paul Konerko .20 .50
12 Todd Helton .30 .75
13 Greg Maddux .75 2.00
14 Derek Jeter 1.25 3.00
15 Jaret Wright .20 .50
16 Livan Hernandez .20 .50
17 Mike Piazza .75 2.00
18 Juan Encarnacion .20 .50
19 Tony Gwynn .60 1.50
20 Scott Rolen .30 .75
21 Roger Clemens 1.00 2.50
22 Tony Clark .20 .50
23 Albert Belle .20 .50
24 Mo Vaughn .20 .50
25 Andruw Jones .30 .75
26 Jason Dickson .20 .50
27 Fernando Tatis .20 .50
28 Ivan Rodriguez .30 .75
29 Ricky Ledee .20 .50
30 Darin Erstad .20 .50
31 Brian Rose .20 .50
32 Magglio Ordonez RC 2.50 6.00
33 Larry Walker .20 .50
34 Bobby Higginson .20 .50
35 Chili Davis .20 .50
36 Barry Bonds 1.25 3.00
37 Vladimir Guerrero .50 1.25
38 Jeff Bagwell .30 .75
39 Kenny Lofton .20 .50
40 Ryan Klesko .20 .50
41 Mike Cameron .20 .50
42 Charles Johnson .20 .50
43 Andy Pettitte .30 .75
44 Juan Gonzalez .20 .50
45 Tim Salmon .30 .75
46 Hideki Irabu .20 .50
47 Paul Molitor .20 .50
48 Edgar Renteria .20 .50
49 Manny Ramirez .30 .75
50 Jim Edmonds .20 .50
51 Bernie Williams .30 .75
52 Roberto Alomar .30 .75
53 David Justice .20 .50
54 Rey Ordonez .20 .50
55 Ken Caminiti .20 .50
56 Jose Guillen .20 .50
57 Randy Johnson .50 1.25
58 Brady Anderson .20 .50
59 Hideo Nomo .50 1.25
60 Tino Martinez .30 .75
61 John Smoltz .40 1.00
62 Joe Carter .25 .60
63 Matt Williams .25 .60
64 Robin Ventura .25 .60
65 Barry Larkin .40 1.00
66 Dante Bichette .25 .60
67 Travis Fryman .25 .60
68 Gary Sheffield .25 .60
69 Eric Karros .25 .60
70 Matt Stairs .25 .60
71 Al Martin .25 .60
72 Jay Buhner .25 .60
73 Ray Lankford .25 .60
74 Carlos Delgado .25 .60
75 Edgardo Alfonzo .25 .60
76 Rondell White .25 .60
77 Chuck Knoblauch .25 .60
78 Raul Mondesi .25 .60
79 Johnny Damon .40 1.00
80 Matt Morris .25 .60
81 Tom Glavine .40 1.00
82 Kevin Brown .40 1.00
83 Garret Anderson .25 .60
84 Mike Mussina .40 1.00
85 Pedro Martinez .40 1.00
86 Craig Biggio .40 1.00
87 Darryl Kile .25 .60
88 Rafael Palmeiro .40 1.00
89 Jim Thome .40 1.00
90 Andres Galarraga .25 .60
91 Sammy Sosa .50 1.25
92 Willie Greene .30 .75
93 Vinny Castilla .30 .75
94 Justin Thompson .30 .75
95 Jeff King .30 .75
96 Jeff Cirillo .30 .75
97 Mark Grudzielanek .30 .75
98 Brad Radke .30 .75
99 John Olerud .30 .75
100 Curt Schilling .30 .75
101 Steve Finley .30 .75
102 J.T. Snow .30 .75
103 Edgar Martinez .50 1.25
104 Wilson Alvarez .30 .75
105 Rusty Greer .30 .75
106 Pat Hentgen .30 .75
107 David Cone .30 .75
108 Fred McGriff .50 1.25
109 Jason Giambi .30 .75
110 Tony Womack .30 .75
111 Bernard Gilkey .30 .75
112 Alan Benes .30 .75
113 Mark Grace .50 1.25
114 Reggie Sanders .30 .75
115 Moises Alou .30 .75
116 John Jaha .30 .75
117 Henry Rodriguez .30 .75
118 Dean Palmer .30 .75
119 Mike Lieberthal .30 .75
120 Shawn Estes .30 .75

1998 Flair Showcase Row 2

These Row 2 cards are parallel to regular base set. Similar to the other rows there is different pull ratios for each group of 30 cards as follows. Cards numbered 1 through 30 are seeded one every two packs; cards numbered from 31 through 60 are seeded one every 2.5 packs; cards numbered from 61 through 90 are seeded one every four packs and cards numbered from 91-120 are seeded one every 3.5 packs.

COMPLETE SET (120) 40.00 100.00
*STARS 1-30: .6X TO 1.5X ROW 3
ROW 2 1-30 STATED ODDS 1:3
*STARS 31-60: .5X TO 1.25X ROW 3
ROW 2 31-60 STATED ODDS 1:2.5
*STARS 61-90: .6X TO 1.5X ROW 3
ROW 2 61-90 STATED ODDS 1:4
*STARS 91-120: .5X TO 1.25X ROW 3
ROW 2 91-120 STATED ODDS 1:3.5

1998 Flair Showcase Row 1

These Row 1 cards are parallel to regular base set. Similar to the other rows there is different pull ratios for each group of 30 cards as follows. Cards numbered from 1 through 30 are inserted one every 16 packs; cards numbered from 31 through 60 are inserted one every 24 packs; cards numbered from 61 through 90 are inserted one every six packs and cards numbered from 91 through 120 are inserted one every 10 packs.

*STARS 1-30: 2X TO 5X ROW 3
ROW 1 1-30 STATED ODDS 1:16
*STARS 31-60: 2.5X TO 6X ROW 3
*ROOKIES 31-60: 2.5X TO 6X ROW 3
ROW 1 31-60 STATED ODDS 1:24
*STARS 61-90: .75X TO 2X ROW 3
ROW 1 61-90 STATED ODDS 1:6
*STARS 91-120: 1X TO 2.5X ROW 3
ROW 1 91-120 STATED ODDS 1:10

1998 Flair Showcase Row 0

These Row 0 cards are parallel to regular base set. These cards are serial numbered and get more plentiful as they are numbered higher in the set. Serial numbering is as follows: Cards numbered from 1 through 30 are serial numbered to 250, cards numbered from 31 through 60 are serial numbered to 500, cards numbered from 61 through 90 are serial numbered to 1000 and cards numbered 91 through 120 are serial numbered to 2000.

*STARS 1-30: 6X TO 15X ROW 3
*STARS 31-60: 5X TO 12X ROW 3
*ROOKIES 31-60: 5X TO 12X ROW 3
*STARS 61-90: 3X TO 8X ROW 3
*STARS 91-120: 1.5X TO 4X ROW 3

1998 Flair Showcase Legacy Collection Row 3

Yet another parallel version of the Flair Showcase set, these cards are serial numbered to 100 each.

*STARS 1-30: 12.5X TO 30X BASIC ROW 3
*STARS 31-60: 12.5X TO 30X BASIC ROW 3
*ROOKIES 31-60: 8X TO 20X BASIC ROW 3
*STARS 61-90: 8X TO 20X ROW 3
*STARS 91-120: 8X TO 20X BASIC ROW 3

1998 Flair Showcase Legacy Collection Row 2

Yet another parallel version of the Flair Showcase set, these cards are serial numbered to 100 each.

*STARS 1-30: 12.5X TO 30X BASIC ROW 3
*STARS 31-60: 12.5X TO 30X BASIC ROW 3
*ROOKIES 31-60: 8X TO 20X BASIC ROW 2
*STARS 61-90: 8X TO 20X ROW 3
*STARS 91-120: 8X TO 20X BASIC ROW 3

1998 Flair Showcase Legacy Collection Row 1

Yet another parallel version of the Flair Showcase set, these cards are serial numbered to 100 each.

*STARS 1-30: 12.5X TO 30X BASIC ROW 3
*STARS 31-60: 12.5X TO 30X BASIC ROW 3
*ROOKIES 31-60: 8X TO 20X BASIC ROW 1
*STARS 61-90: 8X TO 20X ROW 3
*STARS 91-120: 8X TO 20X BASIC ROW 3

1998 Flair Showcase Legacy Collection Row 0

Yet another parallel version of the Flair Showcase set, these cards are serial numbered to 100 each.

*STARS 1-30: 12.5X TO 30X BASIC ROW 3
*STARS 31-60: 12.5X TO 30X BASIC ROW 3
*ROOKIES 31-60: 8X TO 20X BASIC ROW 3
*STARS 61-90: 8X TO 20X ROW 3
*STARS 91-120: 8X TO 20X BASIC ROW 3

1998 Flair Showcase Perfect 10

Sequentially numbered to 10, this 10-card insert features color player photography using silk-screen technology. While no pricing is available due to scarcity, we provide a checklist for identification purposes.

1 Ken Griffey Jr.
2 Cal Ripken
3 Frank Thomas

4 Mike Piazza
5 Greg Maddux
6 Nomar Garciaparra
7 Mark McGwire
8 Scott Rolen
9 Alex Rodriguez
10 Roger Clemens

1998 Flair Showcase Wave of the Future

Randomly inserted in packs at a rate of one in 20, this 12-card insert feature color action photography on cards filled with vegetable oil and sparkles in an attempt to mimic ocean waters.

COMPLETE SET (12) 10.00 25.00
STATED ODDS 1:20
1 Travis Lee .75 2.00
2 Todd Helton 1.25 3.00
3 Ben Grieve .75 2.00
4 Juan Encarnacion .75 2.00
5 Brad Fullmer .75 2.00
6 Ruben Rivera .75 2.00
7 Paul Konerko .75 2.00
8 Derrek Lee 1.25 3.00
9 Mike Lowell 3.00 8.00
10 Magglio Ordonez 1.50 4.00
11 Rich Butler .75 2.00
12 Eli Marrero .75 2.00

1999 Flair Showcase Samples

These sample cards were distributed to dealers and hobby media as a complete set in a three-card clear cello-wrapped pack several weeks prior to the national release of 1999 Flair Showcase. Company spokesperson Scott Rolen was the only player featured. Each card is parallel to it's accompanying basic issue card except for the text "PROMOTIONAL SAMPLE" running diagonally across the front and back.

COMPLETE SET (3) 1.20 3.00
COMMON ROLEN (1-3) .40 1.00

1999 Flair Showcase Row 3

This 144-card set was distributed in five-card packs with a suggested retail price of $4.99 and features two color player photos on the front with full rainbow holofoil, silver foil and embossing. This set is considered the "Power" level. The set was broken into three separate tiers of 28 card subsets as follows: Cards numbered from 1 through 48 were seeded one every .9 packs; cards numbered 49 through 96 were seeded one every 1.1 packs and cards numbered 97 through 144 were seeded one every 1.2 packs. Rookie Cards include Pat Burrell.

COMPLETE SET (144) 25.00 60.00
COMMON CARD (1-48) .20 .50
COMMON CARD (49-96) .20 .50
COMMON CARD (97-144) .25 .60
1 Mark McGwire 1.25 3.00
2 Sammy Sosa .50 1.25
3 Ken Griffey Jr. .75 2.00
4 Chipper Jones .50 1.25
5 Ben Grieve .20 .50
6 J.D. Drew .20 .50
7 Jeff Bagwell .30 .75
8 Cal Ripken 1.50 4.00
9 Tony Gwynn .60 1.50
10 Nomar Garciaparra .75 2.00
11 Travis Lee .20 .50
12 Troy Glaus UER .30 .75
Spelled Tony on back
13 Mike Piazza .75 2.00
14 Alex Rodriguez .75 2.00
15 Kevin Brown .30 .75
16 Darin Erstad .20 .50
17 Scott Rolen .30 .75
18 Micah Bowie RC .20 .50
19 Juan Gonzalez .20 .50
20 Kerry Wood .20 .50
21 Roger Clemens 1.00 2.50
22 Derek Jeter 1.25 3.00
23 Pat Burrell RC 1.25 3.00
24 Tim Salmon .30 .75
25 Barry Bonds 1.25 3.00
26 Roosevelt Brown RC .20 .50
27 Vladimir Guerrero .50 1.25
28 Randy Johnson .50 1.25
29 Mo Vaughn .20 .50
30 Fernando Seguignol .20 .50
31 Greg Maddux .75 2.00
32 Tony Clark .20 .50
33 Eric Chavez .20 .50
34 Kris Benson .20 .50
35 Frank Thomas .50 1.25
36 Mario Encarnacion RC .20 .50
37 Gabe Kapler .20 .50
38 Jeremy Giambi .20 .50
39 Peter Tucci .20 .50
40 Manny Ramirez .30 .75
41 Albert Belle .20 .50
42 Warren Morris .20 .50
43 Michael Barrett .20 .50
44 Andruw Jones .30 .75
45 Carlos Delgado .20 .50
46 Jaret Wright .20 .50
47 Juan Encarnacion .20 .50
48 Scott Hunter RC .20 .50
49 Tino Martinez .30 .75
50 Craig Biggio .30 .75
51 Jim Thome .30 .75
52 Vinny Castilla .20 .50
53 Tom Glavine .30 .75
54 Bob Higginson .20 .50
55 Moises Alou .20 .50
56 Robin Ventura .20 .50
57 Bernie Williams .30 .75
58 Pedro Martinez .30 .75
59 Greg Vaughn .20 .50
60 Ray Lankford .20 .50
61 Jose Canseco .30 .75
62 Ivan Rodriguez .30 .75
63 Shawn Green .20 .50
64 Rafael Palmeiro .30 .75
65 Ellis Burks .20 .50
66 Jason Kendall .20 .50
67 David Wells .20 .50
68 Rondell White .20 .50
69 Gary Sheffield .20 .50
70 Ken Caminiti .20 .50
71 Cliff Floyd .20 .50
72 Larry Walker .20 .50
73 Bartolo Colon .20 .50
74 Barry Larkin .30 .75
75 Calvin Pickering .20 .50
76 Jim Edmonds .20 .50
77 Henry Rodriguez .20 .50
78 Roberto Alomar .30 .75
79 Andres Galarraga .20 .50
80 Richie Sexson .20 .50
81 Todd Helton .30 .75
82 Damion Easley .20 .50
83 Livan Hernandez .20 .50
84 Carlos Beltran .30 .75
85 Todd Hundley .20 .50
86 Todd Walker .20 .50
87 Scott Brosius .20 .50
88 Bob Abreu .20 .50
89 Corey Koskie .20 .50
90 Ruben Rivera .20 .50
91 Edgar Renteria .20 .50
92 Quinton McCracken .20 .50
93 Bernard Gilkey .20 .50
94 Shannon Stewart .20 .50
95 Dustin Hermanson .20 .50
96 Mike Caruso .20 .50
97 Alex Gonzalez .25 .60
98 Raul Mondesi .25 .60
99 David Cone .25 .60
100 Curt Schilling .25 .60
101 Brian Giles .25 .60
102 Edgar Martinez .40 1.00
103 Rolando Arrojo .25 .60
104 Derek Bell .25 .60
105 Denny Neagle .25 .60
106 Marquis Grissom .25 .60
107 Bret Boone .25 .60
108 Mike Mussina .40 1.00
109 John Smoltz .40 1.00
110 Brett Tomko .25 .60
111 David Justice .25 .60
112 Andy Pettitte .40 1.00
113 Eric Karros .25 .60
114 Dante Bichette .25 .60
115 Jeromy Burnitz .25 .60
116 Paul Konerko .25 .60
117 Steve Finley .25 .60
118 Ricky Ledee .25 .60
119 Edgardo Alfonzo .25 .60
120 Dean Palmer .25 .60
121 Rusty Greer .25 .60
122 Luis Gonzalez .25 .60
123 Randy Winn .25 .60
124 Jeff Kent .25 .60
125 Doug Glanville .25 .60
126 Justin Thompson .25 .60
127 Bret Saberhagen .25 .60
128 Wade Boggs .40 1.00
129 Al Leiter .25 .60
130 Paul O'Neill .40 1.00
131 Chan Ho Park .25 .60
132 Johnny Damon .40 1.00
133 Darryl Kile .25 .60
134 Reggie Sanders .25 .60
135 Kevin Millwood .25 .60
136 Charles Johnson .25 .60
137 Ray Durham .25 .60
138 Rico Brogna .25 .60
139 Matt Williams .25 .60
140 Sandy Alomar Jr. .25 .60
141 Jeff Cirillo .25 .60
142 Devon White .25 .60
143 Andy Benes .25 .60
144 Mike Stanley .25 .60

1999 Flair Showcase Row 2

This 144-card set is parallel to the Row 1 or base set and features two action player photos with embossed jersey-like background printed on full rainbow holofoil cards. This set is called the "Passion" level. Seeding rates are as follows, cards numbered one through 48 are seeded one every three packs; cards numbered 49 through 96 are seeded one every 1.33 packs and cards numbered 97-144 are seeded one every two packs.

*STARS 1-48: 1X TO 2.5X ROW 3
*ROOKIES 1-48: 1.25X TO 3X ROW 3
ROW 2 1-48 STATED ODDS 1:3
*STARS 49-96: .5X TO 1.25X ROW 3
ROW 2 49-96 STATED ODDS 1:1.33
*STARS 97-144: .5X TO 1.25X ROW 3
ROW 2 97-144 STATED ODDS 1:2

1999 Flair Showcase Row 1

This 144-card set is parallel to the base set and features three photos of the same player on a plastic laminate individual numbered card. Cards 1-48 are serially numbered to 1500; Cards 49-96 to 3000; Cards 97-144 to 6000. This set is the "Showcase" level.

*STARS 1-48: 4X TO 10X ROW 3
*ROOKIES 1-48: 4X TO 10X ROW 3
*STARS 49-96: 2.5X TO 6X ROW 3
*STARS 97-144: 1.25X TO 3X ROW 3

1999 Flair Showcase Legacy Collection

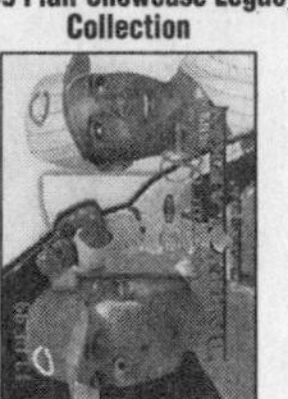

Randomly inserted in packs, this set is a blue foil parallel version of the regular Flair Showcase set. Only 99 sequentially numbered sets were produced for each Row. Similar to the regular Showcase set, each player has three different cards. Therefore, in actuality, 297 cards of each player were produced.

*STARS 1-48: 12.5X TO 30X ROW 3
*ROOKIES 1-48: 8X TO 20X ROW 3
*STARS 49-96: 12.5X TO 30X ROW 3
*STARS 97-144: 10X TO 25X ROW 3

1999 Flair Showcase Masterpiece

Randomly inserted into packs, three versions of this 144-card set were created as exclusive one of one parallels. Only one of each card was printed with purple foil stamping on the fronts and "The Only 1 of 1 Masterpiece" printed on the backs. No pricing is available due to scarcity.

PRINT RUN 1 SERIAL #'d SET FOR EACH ROW
NOT PRICED DUE TO SCARCITY

1999 Flair Showcase Measure of Greatness

Randomly inserted into packs, this 15-card set features color photos of superstars who are closing in on milestones of all-time great players. Only 500 serial-numbered cards were produced.

COMPLETE SET (15) 200.00 400.00
1 Roger Clemens 12.50 30.00
2 Nomar Garciaparra 10.00 25.00
3 Juan Gonzalez 2.50 6.00
4 Ken Griffey Jr. 10.00 25.00
5 Vladimir Guerrero 6.00 15.00
6 Tony Gwynn 8.00 20.00
7 Derek Jeter 15.00 40.00
8 Chipper Jones 6.00 15.00
9 Mark McGwire 15.00 40.00
10 Mike Piazza 10.00 25.00
11 Manny Ramirez 4.00 10.00
12 Cal Ripken 20.00 50.00
13 Alex Rodriguez 10.00 25.00
14 Sammy Sosa 6.00 15.00
15 Frank Thomas 6.00 15.00

1999 Flair Showcase Wave of the Future

Randomly inserted into packs, this 15-card set features color photos of young stars. Each card is serially numbered to 1000.

COMPLETE SET (15) 50.00 100.00
1 Kerry Wood 2.00 5.00
2 Ben Grieve 2.00 5.00
3 J.D. Drew 2.00 5.00
4 Juan Encarnacion 2.00 5.00
5 Travis Lee 2.00 5.00
6 Todd Helton 3.00 8.00
7 Troy Glaus 3.00 8.00
8 Ricky Ledee 2.00 5.00
9 Eric Chavez 2.00 5.00
10 Ben Davis 2.00 5.00
11 George Lombard 2.00 5.00
12 Jeremy Giambi 2.00 5.00
13 Roosevelt Brown 2.00 5.00
14 Pat Burrell 6.00 15.00
15 Preston Wilson 2.00 5.00

2006 Flair Showcase

This 200-card set was released in August, 2006. The set was issued in five-card hobby packs, which came 18 packs to a box and 16 boxes to a case, with an $4.99 SRP. Cards numbered 101-150, which were titled Field Box, were issued at a stated rate of one per four hobby and one per eight retail packs. Cards numbered 151-200, which were titled Suite Level, were issued at a stated rate of on per eight hobby packs and one per sixteen retail packs.

COMP.SET w/o SP's (100) 15.00 40.00
101-150 STATED ODDS 1:4 H, 1:8 R
151-200 STATED ODDS 1:8 H, 1:16 R
PLATE ODDS: 1-2 PER HOBBY CASE
PLATE PRINT RUN 1 SET PER COLOR
BLACK-CYAN-MAGENTA-YELLOW ISSUED
NO PLATE PRICING DUE TO SCARCITY
1 Jeremy Hermida UD (RC) .40 1.00
2 Albert Pujols UD 2.00 5.00
3 Ryan Shealy UD (RC) .40 1.00
4 Mark Prior UD .50 1.25
5 Chuck James UD (RC) .40 1.00
6 Shawn Green UD .30 .75
7 Rickie Weeks UD .50 1.25
8 Roy Halladay UD .75 2.00
9 Luis Gonzalez UD .30 .75
10 David Ortiz UD .50 1.25
11 Josh Beckett UD .50 1.25
12 Gary Sheffield UD .30 .75
13 Jose Reyes UD .50 1.25
14 Brandon Watson UD (RC) .40 1.00
15 Tadahito Iguchi UD .30 .75
16 Rich Harden UD .30 .75
17 Skip Schumaker UD (RC) .40 1.00
18 Vladimir Guerrero UD .75 2.00
19 Chris Carpenter UD .75 2.00
20 Brian Roberts UD .30 .75
21 Roy Oswalt UD .50 1.25
22 Ben Johnson UD (RC) .40 1.00
23 Todd Helton UD .50 1.25
24 Wil Nieves UD (RC) .40 1.00
25 Michael Young UD .50 1.25
26 A.J. Burnett UD .50 1.25
27 J.D. Drew UD .30 .75
28 Adrian Beltre UD .30 .75
29 Tim Hudson UD .50 1.25
30 Jake Peavy UD .30 .75
31 Magglio Ordonez UD .50 1.25
32 Brad Wilkerson UD .30 .75
33 Ryan Freel UD .30 .75
34 Javier Vazquez UD .30 .75
35 Tom Glavine UD .50 1.25
36 Jason Bergmann UD RC .40 1.00
37 Marcus Giles UD .30 .75
38 Jim Thome UD .50 1.25
39 Ichiro Suzuki UD 1.25 3.00
40 Jeff Harris UD RC .30 .75
41 Miguel Cabrera UD .75 2.00
42 Nomar Garciaparra UD .75 2.00
43 Brian Giles UD .30 .75
44 Jeremy Accardo UD RC .40 1.00
45 Taylor Buchholz UD (RC) .40 1.00
46 Mike Jacobs UD (RC) .40 1.00
47 Chris Denorfia UD (RC) .40 1.00
48 Ivan Rodriguez UD .50 1.25
49 Mike Piazza UD .75 2.00
50 Curt Schilling UD .50 1.25
51 Kelly Shoppach UD (RC) .40 1.00
52 Jason Kubel UD (RC) .40 1.00
53 Craig Biggio UD .50 1.25
54 Livan Hernandez UD .30 .75
55 Joe Mauer UD .75 2.00

56 Scott Feldman UD RC .40 1.00
57 Garret Anderson UD .30 .75
58 Steve Stemle UD RC .40 1.00
59 Boof Bonser UD (RC) .60 1.50
60 Jose Guillen UD .30 .75
61 Rafael Furcal UD .30 .75
62 John Van Benschoten UD (RC) .40 1.00
63 Dontrelle Willis UD .30 .75
64 Jose Vidro UD .30 .75
65 David Wright UD 1.25 3.00
66 Alfonso Soriano UD .50 1.25
67 Scott Podsednik UD .30 .75
68 Felix Hernandez UD .75 2.00
69 Richie Sexson UD .30 .75
70 Jeff Francoeur UD .75 2.00
71 Conor Jackson UD .50 1.25
72 Javy Lopez UD .30 .75
73 Jonathan Papelbon UD (RC) 2.00 5.00
74 Frank Thomas UD .75 2.00
75 Greg Maddux UD 1.25 3.00
76 Josh Rupe UD (RC) .40 1.00
77 Eric Chavez UD .30 .75
78 Ben Sheets UD .30 .75
79 Chase Utley UD .75 2.00
80 Derrek Lee UD .30 .75
81 Manny Ramirez UD .75 2.00
82 Pedro Martinez UD .50 1.25
83 Hideki Matsui UD .75 2.00
84 Jeremy Bonderman UD .30 .75
85 Ronny Cedeno UD .30 .75
86 Trevor Hoffman UD .50 1.25
87 Mark Buehrle UD .50 1.25
88 Jason Bay UD .30 .75
89 Reggie Sanders UD .30 .75
90 Brian Anderson UD (RC) .40 1.00
91 Travis Hafner UD .30 .75
92 Carlos Beltran UD .30 .75
93 Cody Ross UD (RC) 1.00 2.50
94 Melvin Mora UD .30 .75
95 Chris Duffy UD .30 .75
96 Vernon Wells UD .30 .75
97 Bartolo Colon UD .30 .75
98 Aubrey Huff UD .30 .75
99 Paul Konerko UD .50 1.25
100 Cesar Izturis UD .30 .75
101 Josh Willingham FB (RC) .75 2.00
102 Matt Cain FB (RC) 2.00 5.00
103 Macay McBride FB (RC) .75 2.00
104 Jeff Mathis FB .75 2.00
105 Alex Rodriguez FB 3.00 8.00
106 Justin Morneau FB 2.00 5.00
107 Felipe Lopez FB .75 2.00
108 Justin Verlander FB (RC) 6.00 15.00
109 Ryan Howard FB 3.00 8.00
110 Mike Sweeney FB .75 2.00
111 Scott Rolen FB 1.25 3.00
112 Hank Blalock FB .75 2.00
113 Kerry Wood FB .75 2.00
114 B.J. Ryan FB .75 2.00
115 Garrett Atkins FB .75 2.00
116 Carlos Delgado FB .75 2.00
117 Zack Greinke FB 1.25 3.00
118 Chad Cordero FB .75 2.00
119 Julio Lugo FB .75 2.00
120 Bobby Crosby FB .75 2.00
121 Barry Zito FB .75 2.00
122 Jhonny Peralta FB .75 2.00
123 Miguel Tejada FB 1.25 3.00
124 Grady Sizemore FB 1.25 3.00
125 Derek Jeter FB 5.00 12.00
126 Cliff Lee FB 1.25 3.00
127 Khalil Greene FB .75 2.00
128 Lance Berkman FB 1.25 3.00
129 Huston Street FB .75 2.00
130 Jermaine Dye FB .75 2.00
131 Chone Figgins FB .75 2.00
132 Torii Hunter FB .75 2.00
133 Jorge Cantu FB .75 2.00
134 Jason Giambi FB .75 2.00
135 Johan Santana FB 2.00 5.00
136 Chad Tracy FB .75 2.00
137 Troy Glaus FB .75 2.00
138 Moises Alou FB .75 2.00
139 Jason Schmidt FB .75 2.00
140 Ken Griffey Jr. FB 3.00 8.00
141 Jason Varitek FB 2.00 5.00
142 John Smoltz FB 2.00 5.00
143 Andy Pettitte FB 1.25 3.00
144 Jeff Kent FB .75 2.00
145 Coco Crisp FB .75 2.00
146 Jonny Gomes FB .75 2.00
147 Aaron Rowand FB .75 2.00
148 Mike Mussina FB 1.25 3.00
149 Johnny Damon FB 1.25 3.00
150 Edgar Renteria FB .75 2.00
151 Scott Kazmir SL 2.00 5.00
152 Lyle Overbay SL 1.25 3.00
153 Placido Polanco SL 1.25 3.00
154 Mariano Rivera SL 3.00 8.00
155 Hanley Ramirez SL (RC) 3.00 8.00
156 Morgan Ensberg SL 1.25 3.00
157 Kenny Rogers SL 1.25 3.00
158 Brad Lidge SL 1.25 3.00
159 A.J. Pierzynski SL 1.25 3.00
160 Aramis Ramirez SL 1.25 3.00
161 Mark Teixeira SL 3.00 8.00
162 Carl Crawford SL 2.00 5.00
163 Ryan Zimmerman SL (RC) 6.00 15.00
164 Adam Dunn SL 2.00 5.00
165 Joe Nathan SL 1.25 3.00
166 Juan Pierre SL 1.25 3.00
167 Pat Burrell SL 1.25 3.00
168 Carlos Lee SL 1.25 3.00
169 Billy Wagner SL 1.25 3.00
170 Prince Fielder SL (RC) 5.00 12.00
171 Randy Johnson SL 3.00 8.00
172 Andruw Jones SL 1.25 3.00
173 Francisco Rodriguez SL 2.00 5.00
174 Robinson Cano SL 3.00 8.00
175 Matt Holliday SL 3.00 8.00
176 Jim Edmonds SL 2.00 5.00
177 Josh Barfield SL (RC) 1.25 3.00
178 Chipper Jones SL 3.00 8.00
179 Bobby Jenks SL 1.25 3.00
180 Carlos Zambrano SL 2.00 5.00
181 Bobby Abreu SL 1.25 3.00
182 Brandon Webb SL 2.00 5.00
183 Kevin Millwood SL 1.25 3.00
184 Zach Duke SL 1.25 3.00
185 Randy Winn SL 1.25 3.00
186 Eric Gagne SL 1.25 3.00
187 Kenji Johjima SL RC 3.00 8.00
188 John Patterson SL 1.25 3.00
189 Mark Loretta SL 1.25 3.00
190 Anderson Hernandez SL (RC) 1.25 3.00
191 Chris Resop SL (RC) 1.25 3.00
192 Ian Kinsler SL (RC) 4.00 10.00
193 Francisco Liriano SL (RC) 3.00 8.00
194 Noah Lowry SL 1.25 3.00
195 Brett Myers SL 1.25 3.00
196 Rocco Baldelli SL 1.25 3.00
197 Cliff Floyd SL 1.25 3.00
198 Sean Casey SL 1.25 3.00
199 Geoff Jenkins SL 1.25 3.00
200 Clint Barmes SL 1.25 3.00

2006 Flair Showcase Legacy Blue

*BLUE 1-100: 1.5X TO 4X BASIC
*BLUE 1-100: 1.25X TO 3X BASIC RC's
*BLUE 101-150: .6X TO 1.5X BASIC
*BLUE 151-200: .4X TO 1X BASIC
STATED ODDS 1:18 HOBBY
STATED PRINT RUN 150 SERIAL #'d SETS

2006 Flair Showcase Legacy Emerald

*EMERALD 1-100: 1.5X TO 4X BASIC
*EMERALD 1-100: 1.25X TO 3X BASIC RC's
*EMERALD 101-150: .6X TO 1.5X BASIC
*EMERALD 151-200: .4X TO 1X BASIC
STATED ODDS 1:18 HOBBY
STATED PRINT RUN 150 SERIAL #'d SETS

2006 Flair Showcase Autographics

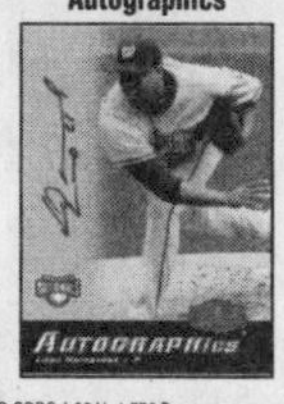

STATED ODDS 1:36 H, 1:576 R
SP PRINT RUNS PROVIDED BY UD
SP'S ARE NOT SERIAL-NUMBERED
NO SP PRICING ON QTY OF 46 OR LESS
PLATE ODDS: 1-2 PER HOBBY CASE
PLATE PRINT RUN 1 SET PER COLOR
BLACK-CYAN-MAGENTA-YELLOW-ISSUED
PLATES DO NOT FEATURE AUTOS
NO PLATE PRICING DUE TO SCARCITY
AH Aaron Harang 6.00 15.00
AR Aaron Rowand 6.00 15.00
BA Bronson Arroyo 10.00 25.00
BC Brandon Claussen 4.00 10.00
BO Jeremy Bonderman 6.00 15.00
CA Carl Crawford 8.00 20.00
CC Coco Crisp 8.00 20.00
CH Chad Cordero 4.00 10.00
CI Cesar Izturis 4.00 10.00
CL Cliff Lee 10.00 25.00
CO Craig Counsell 6.00 15.00
CU Chase Utley SP/100 * 20.00 50.00
DL Derrek Lee SP/43 *
GC Gustavo Chacin 4.00 10.00
HB Hank Blalock 6.00 15.00
JB Jason Bay 6.00 15.00
JG Jose Guillen 4.00 10.00
JH Jhonny Peralta 6.00 15.00
JK Jason Kendall SP/46 *
JM Justin Morneau 20.00 50.00
JP Joel Pineiro 4.00 10.00
JV Javier Vazquez 6.00 15.00
KG Ken Griffey Jr. 40.00 80.00
LH Livan Hernandez 4.00 10.00
MK Mark Kotsay 4.00 10.00
MT Mark Teixeira SP/25 *
OV Omar Vizquel 10.00 25.00
RA Aramis Ramirez 6.00 15.00
RO Roy Oswalt 6.00 15.00
RZ Ryan Zimmerman 15.00 40.00
SC Sean Casey 6.00 15.00
TH Travis Hafner 6.00 15.00
WP Wily Mo Pena 6.00 15.00
XN Xavier Nady 4.00 10.00

2006 Flair Showcase Fresh Ink

STATED ODDS 1:36 H, 1:576 R
SP PRINT RUNS PROVIDED BY UD
SP'S ARE NOT SERIAL-NUMBERED
NO SP PRICING ON QTY OF 43
PLATE ODDS: 1-2 PER HOBBY CASE
PLATE PRINT RUN 1 SET PER COLOR
BLACK-CYAN-MAGENTA-YELLOW ISSUED
PLATES DO NOT FEATURE AUTOS
NO PLATE PRICING DUE TO SCARCITY
BC Bobby Crosby 6.00 15.00
BM Brandon McCarthy 4.00 10.00
BR Brian Roberts 6.00 15.00
CB Clint Barmes 4.00 10.00
CC Chris Carpenter SP/43 *
CK Casey Kotchman 4.00 10.00
CS Chris Shelton 6.00 15.00
DD David DeJesus 4.00 10.00
DH Danny Haren 4.00 10.00
DW Dontrelle Willis 6.00 15.00
ES Ervin Santana 6.00 15.00
GA Garrett Atkins 4.00 10.00
GF Gavin Floyd 4.00 10.00
HA Rich Harden 6.00 15.00
HS Huston Street 6.00 15.00
JB Joe Blanton 4.00 10.00
JG Jonny Gomes 4.00 10.00
JM Joe Mauer SP/43 *
JR Jose Reyes SP/43 *
JS Johan Santana 15.00 40.00
KG Khalil Greene 10.00 25.00
KY Kevin Youkilis 6.00 15.00
MA Matt Cain 10.00 25.00
MC Miguel Cabrera 10.00 25.00
MT Mark Teahen 4.00 10.00
MY Michael Young SP/100 * 10.00 25.00
NL Noah Lowry 6.00 15.00
OP Odalis Perez 4.00 10.00
RE Jeremy Reed 4.00 10.00
RH Rich Hill 10.00 25.00
SK Scott Kazmir 8.00 20.00
TI Tadahito Iguchi 15.00 40.00
VM Victor Martinez 6.00 15.00
WR David Wright SP/100 * 30.00 60.00
ZG Zack Greinke 10.00 25.00

2006 Flair Showcase Hot Gloves

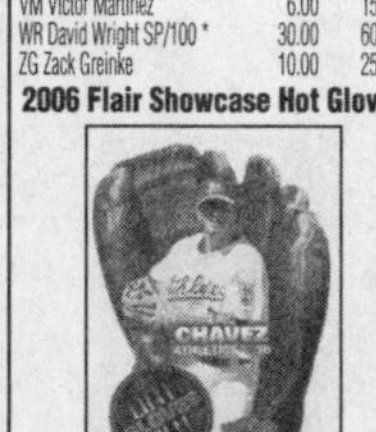

STATED ODDS 1:108 H, 1:576 R
ANNOUNCED PRINT RUN 125-150
UNPRICED PRINT.PLATE PRINT RUN 1
1 Derrek Lee 4.00 10.00
2 Andruw Jones 4.00 10.00
3 Bobby Abreu 4.00 10.00
4 Luis Castillo 4.00 10.00
5 Mike Matheny 4.00 10.00
6 Cesar Izturis 4.00 10.00
7 Craig Biggio 6.00 15.00
8 Darin Erstad 4.00 10.00
9 Derek Jeter 25.00 60.00
10 Eric Chavez 4.00 10.00
11 Greg Maddux 15.00 40.00
12 Ichiro Suzuki 15.00 40.00
13 Ivan Rodriguez 6.00 15.00
14 J.T. Snow 4.00 10.00
15 Jim Edmonds 6.00 15.00
16 Steve Finley 4.00 10.00
17 Kenny Rogers 4.00 10.00
18 Jason Varitek 10.00 25.00
19 Ken Griffey Jr. 15.00 40.00
20 Mark Teixeira 10.00 25.00
21 Orlando Hudson 4.00 10.00
22 Mike Hampton 4.00 10.00
23 Mike Mussina 6.00 15.00
24 Vernon Wells 4.00 10.00
25 Omar Vizquel 6.00 15.00
26 Alex Rodriguez 15.00 40.00
27 Mike Cameron 4.00 10.00
28 Scott Rolen 6.00 15.00
29 Todd Helton 6.00 15.00
30 Torii Hunter 4.00 10.00

2006 Flair Showcase Hot Numbers

STATED ODDS 1:6 H, 1:36 R
PLATE ODDS: 1-2 PER HOBBY CASE
PLATE PRINT RUN 1 SET PER COLOR
BLACK-CYAN-MAGENTA-YELLOW ISSUED
NO PLATE PRICING DUE TO SCARCITY
1 Albert Pujols 4.00 10.00
2 Alex Rodriguez 2.50 6.00
3 Andruw Jones .60 1.50
4 Bobby Abreu .60 1.50
5 Chipper Jones 1.50 4.00
6 Curt Schilling 1.00 2.50
7 David Ortiz 1.00 2.50
8 David Wright 2.50 6.00
9 Derek Jeter 4.00 10.00
10 Derrek Lee .60 1.50
11 Eric Gagne .60 1.50
12 Greg Maddux 2.50 6.00
13 Hideki Matsui 1.50 4.00
14 Ichiro Suzuki 2.50 6.00
15 Ivan Rodriguez 1.00 2.50
16 Johan Santana 1.50 4.00
17 Johnny Damon 1.00 2.50
18 Ken Griffey Jr. 2.50 6.00
19 Manny Ramirez 1.50 4.00
20 Mark Prior 1.00 2.50
21 Mark Teixeira 1.50 4.00
22 Miguel Cabrera 1.50 4.00
23 Miguel Tejada 1.00 2.50
24 Pedro Martinez 1.00 2.50
25 Randy Johnson 1.50 4.00
26 Rickie Weeks 1.00 2.50
27 Roger Clemens 2.00 5.00
28 Todd Helton 1.00 2.50
29 Torii Hunter .60 1.50
30 Vladimir Guerrero 1.50 4.00

2006 Flair Showcase Lettermen

RANDOM INSERTS IN HOBBY PACKS
PRINT RUNS B/WN 3-9 #'d COPIES PER
NO PRICING DUE TO SCARCITY

2006 Flair Showcase Signatures

RANDOM INSERTS IN HOBBY PACKS
STATED PRINT RUN 35 SERIAL #'d SETS
NO PRICING DUE TO SCARCITY
PLATE ODDS: 1-2 PER HOBBY CASE
PLATE PRINT RUN 1 SET PER COLOR
BLACK-CYAN-MAGENTA-YELLOW ISSUED
PLATES DO NOT FEATURE AUTOS
NO PLATE PRICING DUE TO SCARCITY

2006 Flair Showcase Stitches

OVERALL GU ODDS 1:9 H, 1:18 R
AB Adrian Beltre Jsy 3.00 8.00
AD Adam Dunn Jsy 3.00 8.00
AJ Andruw Jones Jsy 4.00 10.00
AN Andy Pettitte Jsy 4.00 10.00
AP Albert Pujols Pants 8.00 20.00
AR Aramis Ramirez Jsy 3.00 8.00
AS Alfonso Soriano Jsy 3.00 8.00
BA Bobby Abreu Jsy 3.00 8.00
BC Bobby Crosby Jsy 3.00 8.00
BG Brian Giles Jsy 3.00 8.00
BO Jeremy Bonderman Jsy 3.00 8.00
BR Brian Roberts Jsy 3.00 8.00
BS Ben Sheets Jsy 3.00 8.00
BZ Barry Zito Jsy 3.00 8.00
CA Carl Crawford Jsy 3.00 8.00
CB Carlos Beltran Jsy 3.00 8.00
CC C.C. Sabathia Jsy 3.00 8.00
CD Carlos Delgado Jsy 3.00 8.00
CJ Chipper Jones Jsy 4.00 10.00
CL Carlos Lee Jsy 3.00 8.00
CO Michael Collins Jsy 3.00 8.00
CS Curt Schilling Jsy 4.00 10.00
DJ Derek Jeter Pants 8.00 20.00
DL Derrek Lee Jsy 3.00 8.00
DM Daisuke Matsuzaka Jsy 12.50 30.00
DO David Ortiz Jsy 4.00 10.00
DR J.D. Drew Jsy 3.00 8.00
DW Dontrelle Willis Jsy 3.00 8.00
EC Eric Chavez Jsy 3.00 8.00
EG Eric Gagne Jsy 3.00 8.00
FG Freddy Garcia Jsy 3.00 8.00
FR Francisco Rodriguez Jsy 3.00 8.00
FT Frank Thomas Jsy 4.00 10.00
GM Greg Maddux Jsy 4.00 10.00
GR Khalil Greene Jsy 3.00 8.00
GS Gary Sheffield Jsy 3.00 8.00
HA J.J. Hardy Jsy 3.00 8.00
HB Hank Blalock Jsy 3.00 8.00
HO Trevor Hoffman Jsy 3.00 8.00
HU Tim Hudson Jsy 3.00 8.00
IR Ivan Rodriguez Jsy 4.00 10.00
JA Jason Schmidt Jsy 3.00 8.00
JC Jorge Cantu Jsy 3.00 8.00
JD Johnny Damon Jsy 4.00 10.00
JE Jim Edmonds Jsy 3.00 8.00
JG Jason Giambi Jsy 3.00 8.00
JJ Jacque Jones Jsy 3.00 8.00
JK Jeff Kent Jsy 3.00 8.00
JL Javy Lopez Jsy 3.00 8.00
JM Joe Mauer Jsy 4.00 10.00
JO Josh Beckett Jsy 3.00 8.00
JP Jake Peavy Jsy 3.00 8.00
JR Jose Reyes Jsy 3.00 8.00
JS Johan Santana Jsy 4.00 10.00
JT Jim Thome Jsy 4.00 10.00
JU Juan Uribe Jsy 3.00 8.00
JV Jason Varitek Jsy 4.00 10.00
KE Kevin Millwood Jsy 3.00 8.00
KG Ken Griffey Jr. Jsy 6.00 15.00
KM Kazuo Matsui Jsy 3.00 8.00
KW Kerry Wood Jsy 3.00 8.00
LB Lance Berkman Jsy 3.00 8.00
LG Luis Gonzalez Jsy 3.00 8.00
MA Moises Alou Jsy 3.00 8.00
MB Mark Buehrle Jsy 3.00 8.00
MC Miguel Cabrera Jsy 4.00 10.00
MH Matt Holliday Jsy 4.00 10.00
MI Mike Piazza Jsy 4.00 10.00
MM Mike Mussina Jsy 4.00 10.00
MP Mark Prior Jsy 3.00 8.00
MR Manny Ramirez Jsy 4.00 10.00
MT Mark Teixeira Jsy 3.00 8.00
MY Michael Young Jsy 3.00 8.00
OV Omar Vizquel Jsy 4.00 10.00
PL Paul Lo Duca Jsy 3.00 8.00
PM Pedro Martinez Jsy 4.00 10.00
PW Preston Wilson Jsy 3.00 8.00
RB Rocco Baldelli Jsy 3.00 8.00
RC Robinson Cano Jsy 6.00 15.00
RE Jeremy Reed Jsy 3.00 8.00
RF Rafael Furcal Jsy 3.00 8.00
RH Roy Halladay Jsy 3.00 8.00
RI Rich Harden Jsy 3.00 8.00
RJ Randy Johnson Jsy 4.00 10.00
RS Richie Sexson Jsy 3.00 8.00
RW Rickie Weeks Jsy 3.00 8.00
SK Scott Kazmir Jsy 3.00 8.00
SM John Smoltz Jsy 4.00 10.00
SR Scott Rolen Jsy 4.00 10.00
SW Mike Sweeney Jsy 3.00 8.00
TE Miguel Tejada Jsy 3.00 8.00
TG Tom Glavine Jsy 4.00 10.00
TH Todd Helton Jsy 4.00 10.00
TN Trot Nixon Jsy 3.00 8.00
TO Torii Hunter Jsy 3.00 8.00
TR Travis Hafner Jsy 3.00 8.00
VG Vladimir Guerrero Jsy 4.00 10.00
VW Vernon Wells Jsy 3.00 8.00
WR David Wright Jsy 4.00 10.00

2006 Flair Showcase Wave of the Future

STATED ODDS 1:3 H, 1:36 R
PLATE ODDS: 1-2 PER HOBBY CASE
PLATE PRINT RUN 1 SET PER COLOR
BLACK-CYAN-MAGENTA-YELLOW ISSUED
NO PLATE PRICING DUE TO SCARCITY
1 Jeremy Hermida .40 1.00
2 Kelly Shoppach .40 1.00
3 Adam Wainwright 1.00 2.50
4 Ryan Zimmerman 2.00 5.00
5 Josh Willingham .40 1.00
6 Brandon McCarthy .40 1.00
7 Conor Jackson .60 1.50
8 Grady Sizemore .60 1.50
9 Curtis Granderson .60 1.50
10 Jose Capellan .40 1.00
11 Mike Jacobs .40 1.00
12 Gavin Floyd .40 1.00
13 Hanley Ramirez 1.00 2.50
14 Jason Kubel .40 1.00
15 Nate McLouth .40 1.00
16 Felix Hernandez 1.00 2.50
17 Jeff Francoeur 1.00 2.50
18 Wil Nieves .40 1.00
19 Cody Ross 1.00 2.50
20 Justin Verlander 3.00 8.00
21 Ben Johnson .40 1.00
22 Guillermo Quiroz .40 1.00
23 Jonathan Papelbon 2.00 5.00
24 Prince Fielder 1.50 4.00
25 Rickie Weeks .60 1.50
26 Robinson Cano 1.00 2.50
27 Kenji Johjima 1.00 2.50
28 Anderson Hernandez .40 1.00
29 Yuniesky Betancourt .40 1.00
30 Zach Duke .40 1.00

2006 Flair Showcase World Baseball Classic

STATED ODDS 1:8 H, 1:36 R
PLATE ODDS: 1-2 PER HOBBY CASE
PLATE PRINT RUN 1 SET PER COLOR
BLACK-CYAN-MAGENTA-YELLOW ISSUED
NO PLATE PRICING DUE TO SCARCITY
1 Adam Stern .75 2.00
2 Jason Bay .75 2.00
3 Wei Wang .75 2.00
4 Yung Chi Chen 1.25 3.00
5 Pedro Lazo 1.25 3.00
6 Yoandy Garlobo .75 2.00
7 Ormari Romero .75 2.00
8 Frederich Cepeda .75 2.00
9 Yulieski Gourriel 2.00 5.00
10 Yadel Marti .75 2.00
11 David Ortiz 1.25 3.00
12 Albert Pujols 5.00 12.00
13 Adrian Beltre .75 2.00
14 Alberto Castillo .75 2.00
15 Odalis Perez .75 2.00
16 Jason Grilli .75 2.00
17 Daisuke Matsuzaka 2.50 6.00
18 Sadaharu Oh 5.00 12.00
19 Nobuhiko Matsunaka 1.25 3.00
20 Ichiro Suzuki 3.00 8.00
21 Akinori Otsuka .75 2.00
22 Koji Uehara 2.00 5.00
23 Kosuke Fukudome 2.00 5.00
24 Daisuke Matsuzaka 2.50 6.00
25 Ichiro Suzuki 3.00 8.00
26 Seung Yeop Lee 1.25 3.00
27 Seung Yeop Lee 1.25 3.00
28 Jong Beom Lee .75 2.00
29 Jae Seo .75 2.00
30 Chan Ho Park 1.25 3.00
31 Hee Seop Choi .75 2.00
32 Jorge Cantu .75 2.00
33 Oliver Perez .75 2.00
34 Vinny Castilla .75 2.00
35 Esteban Loaiza .75 2.00
36 Shairon Martis .75 2.00
37 Bernie Williams 1.25 3.00
38 Javier Vazquez .75 2.00
39 Carlos Beltran .75 2.00
40 Bernie Williams 1.25 3.00
41 Roger Clemens 2.50 6.00
42 Ken Griffey Jr. 3.00 8.00
43 Alex Rodriguez 3.00 8.00
44 Derrek Lee .75 2.00
45 Derek Jeter 5.00 12.00
46 Chipper Jones 2.00 5.00
47 Miguel Cabrera 2.00 5.00
48 Francisco Rodriguez 1.25 3.00
49 Victor Martinez 1.25 3.00
50 Freddy Garcia .75 2.00

1959 Fleer Ted Williams

The cards in this 80-card set measure 2 1/2" by 3 1/2". The 1959 Fleer set, with a catalog designation of R418-1, portrays the life of Ted Williams. The wording of the wrapper, "Baseball's Greatest Series," has led to speculation that Fleer contemplated similar sets honoring other baseball immortals, but chose to develop instead the format of the 1960 and 1961 issues. These packs contained either six or eight cards. The packs cost a nickel and were packed 24 to a box which were packed 24 to a case. Card number 68, which was withdrawn early in production, is considered scarce and has even been counterfeited; the fake has a rosy coloration and a cross-hatch pattern visible over the picture area. The card numbering is arranged essentially in chronological order.

COMPLETE SET (80) 900.00 1500.00
WRAPPER (6-CARD) 100.00 125.00
WRAPPER (8-CARD) 100.00 150.00
1 Ted Williams 60.00 100.00
The Early Years
Choosing up sides
on the sandlots
2 Ted Williams 60.00 100.00
Babe Ruth
Meeting boyhood idol
Babe Ruth
3 Ted Williams 7.50 15.00
Practice Makes Perfect
At place practicing on the sandlots
4 Ted Williams 7.50 15.00
Learns Fine Points
Sliding at Herbert Hoover High
5 Ted Williams 7.50 15.00
Ted's Fame Spreads
At plate at Herbert Hoover High
6 Ted Williams 12.50 25.00
Ted Turns Pro
Portrait
San Diego Padres
PCL League
uniform)
7 Ted Williams 7.50 15.00
From Mound to Plate
At plate
San Diego Padres, PCL
8 Ted Williams 7.50 15.00
1937 First Full Season
Making a leaping catch
9 Ted Williams 10.00 20.00
Eddie Collins
First Step to Majors
10 Ted Williams 7.50 15.00
Gunning as Pastime
Wearing hunting gear, taking aim
11 Ted Williams 20.00 40.00
Jimmie Foxx
First Spring Training
12 Ted Williams 10.00 20.00
Burning Up Minors
Pitching for Minneapolis
American Association
13 Ted Williams 7.50 15.00
1939 Shows Will Stay
Follow-through
14 Ted Williams 7.50 15.00
Outstanding Rookie '39
Follow-through
15 Ted Williams 10.00 20.00
Licks Sophomore Jinx
Sliding into third base
for a triple
16 Ted Williams 7.50 15.00
1941 Greatest Year
Follow-through at plate
17 Ted Williams 20.00 40.00
How Ted Hit .400
Youthful Williams
as he looked in '41
18 Ted Williams 10.00 20.00
1941 All Star Hero
Crossing plate
after home run
19 Ted Williams 7.50 15.00
Wins Triple Crown
Crossing plate at Fenway Park
20 Ted Williams 7.50 15.00
On to Naval Training
In training plane
at Amherst College
21 Ted Williams 7.50 15.00
Honors for Williams
Receiving 1942 Sporting News POY
22 Ted Williams 7.50 15.00
1944 Ted Solos
In cockpit at
Pensacola, FL Navy Air Station
23 Ted Williams 7.50 15.00
Williams Wins Wings
Wearing Naval
Aviation Cadet uniform
24 Ted Williams 7.50 15.00
1945 Sharpshooter
Taking Naval eye test
25 Ted Williams 7.50 15.00
1945 Ted Discharged
In cockpit, giving
the thumbs up
26 Ted Williams 7.50 15.00
Off to Flying Start
In batters box
spring training, 1946
27 Ted Williams 7.50 15.00
7/9/46 One Man Show
Riding blooper pitch out of park
28 Ted Williams 7.50 15.00
The Williams Shift
Diagram of Cleveland Indians
position shift to defense Williams
29 Ted Williams 10.00 20.00
Ted Hits for Cycle
Close-up of follow through
30 Ted Williams 7.50 15.00
Beating Williams Shift
Crossing plate after home run
31 Ted Williams 10.00 20.00
Sox Lose Series
Sliding across plate
Sept. 14, 1946
32 Ted Williams 7.50 15.00
Joseph Cashman
Most Valuable Player
Receiving MVP Award
33 Ted Williams 7.50 15.00
Another Triple Crown
Famous Williams' Grip
34 Ted Williams 7.50 15.00
Runs Scored Record
Sliding into 2nd base
in 1947 AS Game
35 Ted Williams 7.50 15.00
Sox Miss Pennant
Checking weight on
new 36 oz. hickory bat
36 Ted Williams 7.50 15.00
Banner Year for Ted
Bunting down the
3rd base line
37 Ted Williams 7.50 15.00
1949 Sox Miss Again
Two moods: grim and determined
smiling and happy
38 Ted Williams 7.50 15.00
1949 Power Rampage
Full shot of his
batting follow through
39 Ted Williams 12.50 25.00
Joe Cronin
Eddie Collins
1950 Great Start
Signing $125,000 contract
40 Ted Williams 7.50 15.00
Ted Crashes into Wall
Making catch in
1950 All Star game
and crashing into wall
41 Ted Williams 7.50 15.00
1950 Ted Recovers
Recuperating from elbow operation
in hospital
42 Ted Williams 7.50 15.00
Tom Yawkey
Slowed by Injury
43 Ted Williams 7.50 15.00
Double Play Lead
Leaping high to
make great catch
44 Ted Williams 7.50 15.00
Back to Marines
Hanging up number 9
prior to leaving for Marines
45 Ted Williams 7.50 15.00
Farewell to Baseball
Honored at Fenway Park
prior to return to service
46 Ted Williams 7.50 15.00
Ready for Combat
Drawing jet pilot equipment
in Willow Grove
47 Ted Williams 7.50 15.00
Ted Crash Lands Jet
In flying gear
and jet he crash landed in
48 Ted Williams 10.00 20.00
Ford Frick
1953 Ted Returns
Throwing out 1st ball
at All-Star Game in Cincinnati
49 Ted Williams 7.50 15.00
Smash Return
Giving his arm
whirlpool treatment
50 Ted Williams 12.50 25.00
1954 Spring Injury
Full batting pose at plate
51 Ted Williams 7.50 15.00
Ted is Patched Up
In first workout after
fractured collar bone
52 Ted Williams 10.00 20.00
1954 Ted's Comeback
Hitting a home run
against Detroit
53 Ted Williams 7.50 15.00
Comeback is Success
Beating catcher's
tag at home plate
54 Ted Williams 7.50 15.00
Ted Hooks Big One
With prize catch
1235 lb. black marlin
55 Ted Williams 10.00 20.00
Joe Cronin
Retirement 'No Go'

Returning from retirement		
56 Ted Williams	7.50	15.00
2,000th Hit		
8/11/55		
57 Ted Williams	10.00	20.00
400th Homer		
In locker room		
58 Ted Williams	7.50	15.00
Williams Hits .388		
Four-picture sequence		
of his batting swing		
59 Ted Williams	7.50	15.00
Hot September for Ted		
Full shot of follow through		
at plate		
60 Ted Williams	7.50	15.00
More Records for Ted		
Swinging and missing		
61 Ted Williams	10.00	20.00
1957 Outfielder		
Warming up prior		
to ball game		
62 Ted Williams	7.50	15.00
1958 Sixth Batting Title		
Slamming pitch into stands		
63 Ted Williams	50.00	80.00
Ted's All-Star Record		
Portrait and facsimile autograph		
64 Ted Williams	7.50	15.00
Barbara Williams		
Daughter and Daddy		
In uniform holding his daughter		
65 Ted Williams	10.00	20.00
1958 August 30		
Determination on face		
connecting with ball		
66 Ted Williams	7.50	15.00
1958 Powerhouse		
Stance and follow through		
in batters box		
67 Ted Williams	20.00	40.00
Sam Snead		
Two Famous Fishermen		
testing fishing equipment		
68 Ted Williams	400.00	700.00
Bucky Harris		
Ted Signs for 1959 SP		
signing contract		
69 Ted Williams	7.50	15.00
A Future Ted Williams		
With eager, young newcomer		
70 Ted Williams	20.00	40.00
Jim Thorpe		
at Sportsmen's Show		
71 Ted Williams	7.50	15.00
Hitting Fund. 1		
Proper gripping of		
a baseball bat		
72 Ted Williams	7.50	15.00
Hitting Fund. 2		
Checking his swing		
73 Ted Williams	7.50	15.00
Hitting Fund. 3		
Stance and follow-through		
74 Ted Williams	7.50	15.00
Here's How		
Demonstrating in locker room		
an aspect of hitting		
75 Ted Williams	30.00	50.00
Eddie Collins		
Babe Ruth		
Williams' Value to Sox		
76 Ted Williams	7.50	15.00
On Base Record		
Awaiting intentional walk		
to first base		
77 Ted Williams	7.50	15.00
Ted Relaxes		
Displaying bonefish		
which he caught		
78 Ted Williams	7.50	15.00
Rep. Joe Martin		
Justice Earl Warren		
Honors for Williams		
Clark Griffith Memorial Award		
79 Ted Williams	12.50	25.00
Where Ted Stands		
Wielding giant eight foot bat		
when honored as modern-day Paul Bunyan		
80 Ted Williams	20.00	40.00
Ted's Goals for 1959		
Admiring his portrait		

1960 Fleer

The cards in this 79-card set measure 2 1/2" by 3 1/2". The cards from the 1960 Fleer series of Baseball Greats are sometimes mistaken for 1930s cards by collectors not familiar with this set. The cards each contain a tinted photo of a baseball immortal, and were issued in one series. There are no known scarcities, although a number 80 card (Pepper Martin reverse with Eddie Collins, Joe Tinker or Lefty Grove obverse) exists (this is not considered part of the set). The catalog designation for 1960 Fleer is R418-2. The cards were printed on a 96-card sheet with 17 double prints. These are noted in the checklist below by DP. On the sheet the second Eddie Collins card is typically found in the number 80 position. According to correspondence sent from Fleers at the time -- no card 80 was issued because of contract problems. Some cards have been discovered with wrong backs. The cards were issued in nickel packs which were packed 24 to a box.

COMPLETE SET (79)	300.00	600.00
WRAPPER	50.00	100.00
1 Napoleon Lajoie DP	12.50	30.00
2 Christy Mathewson	6.00	15.00
3 Babe Ruth	50.00	100.00
4 Carl Hubbell	3.00	8.00
5 Grover C. Alexander	3.00	8.00
6 Walter Johnson DP	4.00	10.00
7 Chief Bender	1.50	4.00
8 Roger Bresnahan	1.50	4.00
9 Mordecai Brown	1.50	4.00
10 Tris Speaker	3.00	8.00
11 Arky Vaughan DP	1.50	4.00
12 Zach Wheat	1.50	4.00
13 George Sisler	1.50	4.00
14 Connie Mack	3.00	8.00
15 Clark Griffith	1.50	4.00
16 Lou Boudreau DP	3.00	8.00
17 Ernie Lombardi	1.50	4.00
18 Heinie Manush	1.50	4.00
19 Marty Marion	2.50	6.00
20 Eddie Collins DP	1.50	4.00
21 Rabbit Maranville DP	1.50	4.00
22 Joe Medwick	1.50	4.00
23 Ed Barrow	1.50	4.00
24 Mickey Cochrane	2.50	6.00
25 Jimmy Collins	1.50	4.00
26 Bob Feller DP	6.00	15.00
27 Luke Appling	2.50	6.00
28 Lou Gehrig	40.00	80.00
29 Gabby Hartnett	1.50	4.00
30 Chuck Klein	1.50	4.00
31 Tony Lazzeri DP	2.50	6.00
32 Al Simmons	1.50	4.00
33 Wilbert Robinson	1.50	4.00
34 Sam Rice	1.50	4.00
35 Herb Pennock	1.50	4.00
36 Mel Ott DP	3.00	8.00
37 Lefty O'Doul	1.50	4.00
38 Johnny Mize	3.00	8.00
39 Edmund (Bing) Miller	1.50	4.00
40 Joe Tinker	1.50	4.00
41 Frank Baker DP	1.50	4.00
42 Ty Cobb	30.00	60.00
43 Paul Derringer	1.50	4.00
44 Cap Anson	1.50	4.00
45 Jim Bottomley	1.50	4.00
46 Eddie Plank DP	1.50	4.00
47 Denton (Cy) Young	4.00	10.00
48 Hack Wilson	2.50	6.00
49 Ed Walsh UER	1.50	4.00
(Photo actually		
Ed Walsh Jr.)		
50 Frank Chance	1.50	4.00
51 Dazzy Vance DP	1.50	4.00
52 Bill Terry	2.50	6.00
53 Jimmie Foxx	4.00	10.00
54 Lefty Gomez	3.00	8.00
55 Branch Rickey	1.50	4.00
56 Ray Schalk DP	1.50	4.00
57 Johnny Evers	1.50	4.00
58 Charley Gehringer	2.50	6.00
59 Burleigh Grimes	1.50	4.00
60 Lefty Grove	3.00	8.00
61 Rube Waddell DP	1.50	4.00
62 John(Honus) Wagner	6.00	15.00
63 Red Ruffing	1.50	4.00
64 Kenesaw M. Landis	1.50	4.00
65 Harry Heilmann	1.50	4.00
66 John McGraw DP	1.50	4.00
67 Hughie Jennings	1.50	4.00
68 Hal Newhouser	2.50	6.00
69 Waite Hoyt	1.50	4.00
70 Bobo Newsom	1.50	4.00
71 Earl Averill DP	1.50	4.00
72 Ted Williams	40.00	80.00
73 Warren Giles	2.50	6.00
74 Ford Frick	2.50	6.00
75 Kiki Cuyler	1.50	4.00
76 Paul Waner DP	2.50	6.00
77 Pie Traynor	1.50	4.00
78 Lloyd Waner	1.50	4.00
79 Ralph Kiner	4.00	10.00
80A Pepper Martin SP	1250.00	2500.00
Eddie Collins		
pictured on obverse		
80B Pepper Martin SP	1000.00	2000.00
Lefty Grove		
pictured on obverse		
80C Pepper Martin SP	1000.00	2000.00
Joe Tinker on Front		

1961 Fleer

The cards in this 154-card set measure 2 1/2" by 3 1/2". In 1961, Fleer continued its Baseball Greats format by issuing this series of cards. The set was released in two distinct series, 1-88 and 89-154 (of which the latter is more difficult to obtain). The players within each series are conveniently numbered in alphabetical order. The catalog number for this set is F418-3. In each first series pack Fleer inserted a Major League team decal and a pennant sticker honoring past World Series winners. The cards were issued in nickel packs which were issued 24 to a box.

COMPLETE SET (154)	600.00	1200.00
COMMON CARD (1-88)	1.25	3.00
COMMON CARD (89-154)	3.00	8.00
WRAPPER (5-CENT)	50.00	100.00
1 Frank Baker CL	20.00	50.00
Ty Cobb		
Zack Wheat		
2 Grover C. Alexander	2.50	6.00
3 Nick Altrock	1.25	3.00
4 Cap Anson	1.50	4.00
5 Earl Averill	1.50	4.00
6 Frank Baker	1.50	4.00
7 Dave Bancroft	1.50	4.00
8 Chief Bender	1.50	4.00
9 Jim Bottomley	1.50	4.00
10 Roger Bresnahan	1.50	4.00
11 Mordecai Brown	1.50	4.00
12 Max Carey	1.50	4.00
13 Jack Chesbro	1.50	4.00
14 Ty Cobb	20.00	50.00
15 Mickey Cochrane	1.50	4.00
16 Eddie Collins	2.50	6.00
17 Earle Combs	1.50	4.00
18 Charles Comiskey	1.50	4.00
19 Kiki Cuyler	1.50	4.00
20 Paul Derringer	1.25	3.00
21 Howard Ehmke	1.25	3.00
22 Billy Evans UMP	1.50	4.00
23 Johnny Evers	1.50	4.00
24 Urban Faber	1.50	4.00
25 Bob Feller	5.00	12.00
26 Wes Ferrell	1.25	3.00
27 Lew Fonseca	1.25	3.00
28 Jimmie Foxx	2.50	6.00
29 Ford Frick	1.25	3.00
30 Frankie Frisch	1.50	4.00
31 Lou Gehrig	40.00	80.00
32 Charley Gehringer	1.50	4.00
33 Warren Giles	1.25	3.00
34 Lefty Gomez	1.50	4.00
35 Goose Goslin	1.50	4.00
36 Clark Griffith	1.50	4.00
37 Burleigh Grimes	1.50	4.00
38 Lefty Grove	2.50	6.00
39 Chick Hafey	1.50	4.00
40 Jesse Haines	1.50	4.00
41 Gabby Hartnett	1.50	4.00
42 Harry Heilmann	1.50	4.00
43 Rogers Hornsby	2.50	6.00
44 Waite Hoyt	1.50	4.00
45 Carl Hubbell	2.50	6.00
46 Miller Huggins	1.50	4.00
47 Hughie Jennings	1.50	4.00
48 Ban Johnson	1.50	4.00
49 Walter Johnson	5.00	12.00
50 Ralph Kiner	2.50	6.00
51 Chuck Klein	1.50	4.00
52 Johnny Kling	1.25	3.00
53 Kenesaw M. Landis	1.50	4.00
54 Tony Lazzeri	1.50	4.00
55 Ernie Lombardi	1.50	4.00
56 Dolf Luque	1.25	3.00
57 Heinie Manush	1.50	4.00
58 Marty Marion	1.25	3.00
59 Christy Mathewson	5.00	12.00
60 John McGraw	1.50	4.00
61 Joe Medwick	1.50	4.00
62 Edmund (Bing) Miller	1.25	3.00
63 Johnny Mize	1.50	4.00
64 John Mostil	1.25	3.00
65 Art Nehf	1.25	3.00
66 Hal Newhouser	1.50	4.00
67 Bobo Newsom	1.25	3.00
68 Mel Ott	2.50	6.00
69 Allie Reynolds	1.25	3.00
70 Sam Rice	1.50	4.00
71 Eppa Rixey	1.50	4.00
72 Edd Roush	1.50	4.00
73 Schoolboy Rowe	1.25	3.00
74 Red Ruffing	1.50	4.00
75 Babe Ruth	60.00	120.00
76 Joe Sewell	1.50	4.00
77 Al Simmons	1.50	4.00
78 George Sisler	1.50	4.00
79 Tris Speaker	1.50	4.00
80 Fred Toney	1.25	3.00
81 Dazzy Vance	1.50	4.00
82 Hippo Vaughn	1.25	3.00
83 Ed Walsh	1.50	4.00
84 Lloyd Waner	1.50	4.00
85 Paul Waner	1.50	4.00
86 Zack Wheat	1.50	4.00
87 Hack Wilson	1.50	4.00
88 Jimmy Wilson	1.25	3.00
89 George Sisler CL	30.00	60.00
Pie Traynor		
90 Babe Adams	3.00	8.00
91 Dale Alexander	3.00	8.00
92 Jim Bagby	3.00	8.00
93 Ossie Bluege	3.00	8.00
94 Lou Boudreau	4.00	10.00
95 Tommy Bridges	3.00	8.00
96 Donie Bush	3.00	8.00
97 Dolph Camilli	3.00	8.00
98 Frank Chance	4.00	10.00
99 Jimmy Collins	4.00	10.00
100 Stan Coveleskie	4.00	10.00
101 Hugh Critz	3.00	8.00
102 Alvin Crowder	3.00	8.00
103 Joe Dugan	3.00	8.00
104 Bibb Falk	3.00	8.00
105 Rick Ferrell	4.00	10.00
106 Art Fletcher	3.00	8.00
107 Dennis Galehouse	3.00	8.00
108 Chick Galloway	3.00	8.00
109 Mule Haas	3.00	8.00
110 Stan Hack	3.00	8.00
111 Bump Hadley	3.00	8.00
112 Billy Hamilton	4.00	10.00
113 Joe Hauser	3.00	8.00
114 Babe Herman	3.00	8.00
115 Travis Jackson	4.00	10.00
116 Eddie Joost	3.00	8.00
117 Addie Joss	4.00	10.00
118 Joe Judge	3.00	8.00
119 Joe Kuhel	3.00	8.00
120 Napoleon Lajoie	5.00	12.00
121 Dutch Leonard	3.00	8.00
122 Ted Lyons	4.00	10.00
123 Connie Mack	5.00	12.00
124 Rabbit Maranville	4.00	10.00
125 Fred Marberry	3.00	8.00
126 Joe McGinnity	4.00	10.00
127 Oscar Melillo	3.00	8.00
128 Ray Mueller	3.00	8.00
129 Kid Nichols	4.00	10.00
130 Lefty O'Doul	4.00	10.00
131 Bob O'Farrell	3.00	8.00
132 Roger Peckinpaugh	3.00	8.00
133 Herb Pennock	4.00	10.00
134 George Pipgras	3.00	8.00
135 Eddie Plank	4.00	10.00
136 Ray Schalk	4.00	10.00
137 Hal Schumacher	3.00	8.00
138 Luke Sewell	3.00	8.00
139 Bob Shawkey	3.00	8.00
140 Riggs Stephenson	3.00	8.00
141 Billy Sullivan	3.00	8.00
142 Bill Terry	5.00	12.00
143 Joe Tinker	4.00	10.00
144 Pie Traynor	4.00	10.00
145 Hal Trosky	3.00	8.00
146 George Uhle	3.00	8.00
147 Johnny VanderMeer	4.00	10.00
148 Arky Vaughan	4.00	10.00
149 Rube Waddell	4.00	10.00
150 Honus Wagner	20.00	50.00
151 Dixie Walker	3.00	8.00
152 Ted Williams	60.00	120.00
153 Cy Young	15.00	40.00
154 Ross Youngs	15.00	40.00

1963 Fleer

The Fleer set of current baseball players was marketed in 1963 in a gum card-style waxed wrapper package which contained a cherry cookie instead of gum. The five cent packs were packaged 24 to a box. The cards were printed in sheets of 66 with the scarce card of Joe Adcock (number 46) replaced by the unnumbered checklist card for the final press run. The complete set price includes the checklist card. The catalog designation for this set is R418-4. The key Rookie Card in this set is Maury Wills. The set is basically arranged numerically in alphabetical order by teams which are also in alphabetical order.

COMPLETE SET (67)	1000.00	2000.00
WRAPPER (5-CENT)	50.00	100.00
1 Steve Barber	10.00	25.00
2 Ron Hansen	6.00	15.00
3 Milt Pappas	8.00	20.00
4 Brooks Robinson	50.00	100.00
5 Willie Mays	100.00	200.00
6 Lou Clinton	6.00	15.00
7 Bill Monbouquette	6.00	15.00
8 Carl Yastrzemski	50.00	100.00
9 Ray Herbert	6.00	15.00
10 Jim Landis	6.00	15.00
11 Dick Donovan	6.00	15.00
12 Tito Francona	6.00	15.00
13 Jerry Kindall	6.00	15.00
14 Frank Lary	8.00	20.00
15 Dick Howser	8.00	20.00
16 Jerry Lumpe	6.00	15.00
17 Norm Siebern	6.00	15.00
18 Don Lee	6.00	15.00
19 Albie Pearson	8.00	20.00
20 Bob Rodgers	8.00	20.00
21 Leon Wagner	6.00	15.00
22 Jim Kaat	10.00	25.00
23 Vic Power	8.00	20.00
24 Rich Rollins	8.00	20.00
25 Bobby Richardson	10.00	25.00
26 Ralph Terry	8.00	20.00
27 Tom Cheney	6.00	15.00
28 Chuck Cottier	6.00	15.00
29 Jimmy Piersall	8.00	20.00
30 Dave Stenhouse	6.00	15.00
31 Glen Hobbie	6.00	15.00
32 Ron Santo	10.00	25.00
33 Gene Freese	6.00	15.00
34 Vada Pinson	10.00	25.00
35 Bob Purkey	6.00	15.00
36 Joe Amalfitano	6.00	15.00
37 Bob Aspromonte	6.00	15.00
38 Dick Farrell	6.00	15.00
39 Al Spangler	6.00	15.00
40 Tommy Davis	8.00	20.00
41 Don Drysdale	40.00	80.00
42 Sandy Koufax	100.00	200.00
43 Maury Wills RC	50.00	100.00
44 Frank Bolling	6.00	15.00
45 Warren Spahn	40.00	80.00
46 Joe Adcock SP	75.00	150.00
47 Roger Craig	8.00	20.00
48 Al Jackson	8.00	20.00
49 Rod Kanehl	8.00	20.00
50 Ruben Amaro	6.00	15.00
51 Johnny Callison	8.00	20.00
52 Clay Dalrymple	6.00	15.00
53 Don Demeter	6.00	15.00
54 Art Mahaffey	6.00	15.00
55 Smoky Burgess	8.00	20.00
56 Roberto Clemente	100.00	200.00
57 Roy Face	8.00	20.00
58 Vern Law	8.00	20.00
59 Bill Mazeroski	12.50	30.00
60 Ken Boyer	10.00	25.00
61 Bob Gibson	40.00	80.00
62 Gene Oliver	6.00	15.00
63 Bill White	8.00	20.00
64 Orlando Cepeda	12.50	30.00
65 Jim Davenport	6.00	15.00
66 Billy O'Dell	10.00	25.00
NNO Checklist card	250.00	500.00

1981 Fleer

This issue of cards marks Fleer's first modern era entry into the current player baseball card market since 1963. Unopened packs contained 17 cards as well as a piece of gum. Unopened boxes contained 38 packs. As a matter of fact, the boxes actually told the retailer there was extra profit as they were charged as if there were 36 packs in the box. These cards were packed 20 boxes to a case. Cards are grouped in team order and teams are ordered based upon their standings from the 1980 season with the World Series champion Philadelphia Phillies starting off the set. Cards 638-660 feature specials and checklists. The cards of pitchers in this set erroneously show a heading (on the card backs) of "Batting Record" over their career pitching statistics. There were three distinct printings: the two following the primary run were designed to correct numerous errors. The variations caused by these multiple printings are noted in the checklist below (P1, P2, or P3). The Craig Nettles variation was corrected before the end of the first printing and thus is not included in the complete set consideration due to scarcity. The key Rookie Cards in this set are Danny Ainge, Harold Baines, Kirk Gibson, Jeff Reardon, and Fernando Valenzuela, whose first name was erroneously spelled Fernand on the card front.

COMPLETE SET (660)	15.00	40.00
1 Pete Rose UER	1.25	3.00
270 hits in 63		
should be 170		
2 Larry Bowa	.08	.25
3 Manny Trillo	.02	.10
4 Bob Boone	.08	.25
5 Mike Schmidt	1.00	2.50
See also 640A		
6 Steve Carlton P1	.20	.50
Golden Arm		
Back 1066 Cardinals		
Number on back 6		
6B Steve Carlton P2	.60	1.50
Pitcher of Year		
Back 1066 Cardinals		
6C Steve Carlton P3	.75	2.00
1966 Cardinals		
7 Tug McGraw	.08	.25
See 657A		
8 Larry Christenson	.02	.10
9 Bake McBride	.08	.25
10 Greg Luzinski	.08	.25
11 Ron Reed	.02	.10
12 Dickie Noles	.02	.10
13 Keith Moreland RC	.02	.10
14 Bob Walk RC	.20	.50
15 Lonnie Smith	.08	.25
16 Dick Ruthven	.02	.10
17 Sparky Lyle	.08	.25
18 Greg Gross	.02	.10
19 Garry Maddox	.02	.10
20 Nino Espinosa	.02	.10
21 George Vukovich RC	.02	.10
22 John Vukovich	.02	.10
23 Ramon Aviles	.02	.10
24A Kevin Saucier P1	.02	.10
Name on back Ken		
24B Kevin Saucier P2	.02	.10
Name on back Ken		
24C Kevin Saucier P3	.20	.50
Name on back Kevin		
25 Randy Lerch	.02	.10
26 Del Unser	.02	.10
27 Tim McCarver	.08	.25
28 George Brett	1.00	2.50
See also 655A		
29 Willie Wilson	.08	.25
See also 653A		
30 Paul Splittorff	.02	.10
31 Dan Quisenberry	.02	.10
32A Amos Otis P1	.08	.25
(Batting Pose		
Outfield		
32 on back		
32B Amos Otis P2	.08	.25
Series Starter		
483 on back		
33 Steve Busby	.02	.10
34 U.L. Washington	.02	.10
35 Dave Chalk	.02	.10
36 Darrell Porter	.02	.10
37 Marty Pattin	.02	.10
38 Larry Gura	.02	.10
39 Renie Martin	.02	.10
40 Rich Gale	.02	.10
41A Hal McRae P1	.20	.50
(Royals on front		
in black letters		
41B Hal McRae P2	.08	.25
(Royals on front		
in blue letters		
42 Dennis Leonard	.02	.10
43 Willie Aikens	.02	.10
44 Frank White	.08	.25
45 Clint Hurdle	.02	.10
46 John Wathan	.02	.10
47 Pete LaCock	.02	.10
48 Rance Mulliniks	.02	.10
49 Jeff Twitty RC	.02	.10
50 Jamie Quirk	.02	.10
51 Art Howe	.02	.10
52 Ken Forsch	.02	.10
53 Vern Ruhle	.02	.10
54 Joe Niekro	.02	.10
55 Frank LaCorte	.02	.10
56 J.R. Richard	.08	.25
57 Nolan Ryan	2.00	5.00
58 Enos Cabell	.02	.10
59 Cesar Cedeno	.08	.25
60 Jose Cruz	.08	.25
61 Bill Virdon MG	.02	.10
62 Terry Puhl	.02	.10
63 Joaquin Andujar	.08	.25
64 Alan Ashby	.02	.10
65 Joe Sambito	.02	.10
66 Denny Walling	.02	.10
67 Jeff Leonard	.08	.25
68 Luis Pujols	.02	.10
69 Bruce Bochy	.02	.10
70 Rafael Landestoy	.02	.10
71 Dave Smith RC	.20	.50
72 Danny Heep RC	.02	.10
73 Julio Gonzalez	.02	.10
74 Craig Reynolds	.02	.10
75 Gary Woods	.02	.10
76 Dave Bergman	.02	.10
77 Randy Niemann	.02	.10
78 Joe Morgan	.20	.50
79 Reggie Jackson	.40	1.00
See also 650A		
80 Bucky Dent	.08	.25
81 Tommy John	.08	.25
82 Luis Tiant	.08	.25
83 Rick Cerone	.02	.10
84 Dick Howser MG	.02	.10
85 Lou Piniella	.08	.25
86 Ron Davis	.02	.10
87A Graig Nettles ERR	2.00	5.00
Name on back spelled Craig		
87B Graig Nettles COR	.08	.25
Graig		
88 Ron Guidry	.08	.25
89 Rich Gossage	.08	.25
90 Rudy May	.02	.10
91 Gaylord Perry	.08	.25
92 Eric Soderholm	.02	.10
93 Bob Watson	.02	.10
94 Bobby Murcer	.08	.25
95 Bobby Brown	.02	.10
96 Jim Spencer	.02	.10
97 Tom Underwood	.02	.10
98 Oscar Gamble	.02	.10
99 Johnny Oates	.08	.25
100 Fred Stanley	.02	.10
101 Ruppert Jones	.02	.10
102 Dennis Werth RC	.02	.10
103 Joe Lefebvre RC	.02	.10
104 Brian Doyle	.02	.10
105 Aurelio Rodriguez	.02	.10
106 Doug Bird	.02	.10
107 Mike Griffin RC	.05	.15
108 Tim Lollar RC	.02	.10
109 Willie Randolph	.08	.25
110 Steve Garvey	.20	.50
111 Reggie Smith	.08	.25
112 Don Sutton	.08	.25
113 Burt Hooton	.02	.10
114A Dave Lopes P1	.20	.50
Small hand on back		
114B Dave Lopes P2	.08	.25
No hand		
115 Dusty Baker	.08	.25
116 Tom Lasorda MG	.20	.50
117 Bill Russell	.08	.25
118 Jerry Reuss UER	.02	.10
Home omitted		
119 Terry Forster	.08	.25
120A Bob Welch P1	.08	.25
(Name on back is Bob		
120B Bob Welch P2	.08	.25
Name on back is Robert		
121 Don Stanhouse	.02	.10
122 Rick Monday	.08	.25
123 Derrel Thomas	.02	.10
124 Joe Ferguson	.02	.10
125 Rick Sutcliffe	.08	.25
126A Ron Cey P1	.08	.25
Small hand on back		
126B Ron Cey P2	.08	.25
No hand		
127 Dave Goltz	.02	.10
128 Jay Johnstone	.02	.10
129 Steve Yeager	.08	.25
130 Gary Weiss RC	.02	.10
131 Mike Scioscia RC	.60	1.50
132 Vic Davalillo	.02	.10
133 Doug Rau	.02	.10
134 Pepe Frias	.02	.10
135 Mickey Hatcher	.02	.10
136 Steve Howe RC	.20	.50
137 Robert Castillo RC	.02	.10
138 Gary Thomasson	.02	.10
139 Rudy Law	.02	.10
140 Fernando Valenzuela RC	2.00	5.00
UER Misspelled Fernand on card		
141 Manny Mota	.08	.25
142 Gary Carter	.20	.50
143 Steve Rogers	.08	.25
144 Warren Cromartie	.02	.10
145 Andre Dawson	.20	.50
146 Larry Parrish	.02	.10
147 Rowland Office	.02	.10
148 Ellis Valentine	.02	.10
149 Dick Williams MG	.02	.10
150 Bill Gullickson RC	.20	.50
151 Elias Sosa	.02	.10
152 John Tamargo	.02	.10
153 Chris Speier	.02	.10
154 Ron LeFlore	.08	.25
155 Rodney Scott	.02	.10
156 Stan Bahnsen	.02	.10
157 Bill Lee	.08	.25
158 Fred Norman	.02	.10
159 Woodie Fryman	.02	.10
160 David Palmer	.02	.10
161 Jerry White	.02	.10
162 Roberto Ramos RC	.02	.10
163 John D'Acquisto	.02	.10
164 Tommy Hutton	.02	.10
165 Charlie Lea RC	.02	.10
166 Scott Sanderson	.02	.10
167 Ken Macha	.02	.10
168 Tony Bernazard	.02	.10
169 Jim Palmer	.20	.50
170 Steve Stone	.02	.10
171 Mike Flanagan	.02	.10
172 Al Bumbry	.02	.10
173 Doug DeCinces	.02	.10
174 Scott McGregor	.02	.10
175 Mark Belanger	.02	.10
176 Tim Stoddard	.02	.10
177A Rick Dempsey P1	.08	.25
Small hand on front		
177B Rick Dempsey P2	.02	.10
No hand		
178 Earl Weaver MG	.08	.25
179 Tippy Martinez	.02	.10
180 Dennis Martinez	.08	.25
181 Sammy Stewart	.02	.10
182 Rich Dauer	.02	.10
183 Lee May	.02	.10
184 Eddie Murray	.60	1.50
185 Benny Ayala	.02	.10
186 John Lowenstein	.02	.10
187 Gary Roenicke	.02	.10
188 Ken Singleton	.08	.25
189 Dan Graham	.02	.10
190 Terry Crowley	.02	.10
191 Kiko Garcia	.02	.10
192 Dave Ford RC	.02	.10
193 Mark Corey	.02	.10
194 Lenn Sakata	.02	.10
195 Doug DeCinces	.02	.10
196 Johnny Bench	.40	1.00
197 Dave Concepcion	.08	.25
198 Ray Knight	.08	.25
199 Ken Griffey	.08	.25
200 Tom Seaver	.40	1.00
201 Dave Collins	.02	.10
202A George Foster P1	.20	.50
Slugger		
Number on back 216		
202B George Foster P2	.20	.50
Slugger		
Number on back 202		
203 Junior Kennedy	.02	.10
204 Frank Pastore	.02	.10
205 Dan Driessen	.02	.10
206 Hector Cruz	.02	.10
207 Paul Moskau	.02	.10
208 Charlie Leibrandt RC	.20	.50
209 Harry Spilman	.02	.10
210 Joe Price RC	.02	.10
211 Tom Hume	.02	.10
212 Joe Nolan RC	.02	.10
213 Doug Bair	.02	.10
214 Mario Soto	.08	.25
215A Bill Bonham P1	.20	.50
(Small hand on back)		
215B Bill Bonham P2	.02	.10
(No hand)		
216 George Foster SLG	.08	.25
(See 202)		
217 Paul Householder RC	.02	.10
218 Ron Oester	.02	.10
219 Sam Mejias	.02	.10
220 Sheldon Burnside RC	.02	.10
221 Carl Yastrzemski	.60	1.50
222 Jim Rice	.08	.25
223 Fred Lynn	.08	.25
224 Carlton Fisk	.20	.50
225 Rick Burleson	.02	.10
226 Dennis Eckersley	.20	.50
227 Butch Hobson	.02	.10
228 Tom Burgmeier	.02	.10
229 Garry Hancock	.02	.10
230 Don Zimmer MG	.08	.25
231 Steve Renko	.02	.10
232 Dwight Evans	.20	.50
233 Mike Torrez	.02	.10
234 Bob Stanley	.02	.10
235 Jim Dwyer	.02	.10
236 Dave Stapleton RC	.02	.10
237 Glenn Hoffman RC	.02	.10
238 Jerry Remy	.02	.10
239 Dick Drago	.02	.10
240 Bill Campbell	.02	.10
241 Tony Perez	.20	.50
242 Phil Niekro	.08	.25
243 Dale Murphy	.20	.50
244 Bob Horner	.08	.25
245 Jeff Burroughs	.08	.25
246 Rick Camp	.02	.10
247 Bobby Cox MG	.08	.25
248 Bruce Benedict	.02	.10
249 Gene Garber	.02	.10
250 Jerry Royster	.02	.10
251A Gary Matthews P1	.20	.50
Small hand on back		
251B Gary Matthews P2	.08	.25
No hand		
252 Chris Chambliss	.08	.25
253 Luis Gomez	.02	.10
254 Bill Nahorodny	.02	.10
255 Doyle Alexander	.02	.10
256 Brian Asselstine	.02	.10
257 Biff Pocoroba	.02	.10
258 Mike Lum	.02	.10
259 Charlie Spikes	.02	.10
260 Glenn Hubbard	.02	.10
261 Tommy Boggs	.02	.10
262 Al Hrabosky UER	.08	.25
Card lists him as 5' 1"		
263 Rick Matula	.02	.10
264 Preston Hanna	.02	.10
265 Larry Bradford	.02	.10
266 Rafael Ramirez RC	.02	.10
267 Larry McWilliams	.02	.10
268 Rod Carew	.20	.50
269 Bobby Grich	.08	.25
270 Carney Lansford	.08	.25
271 Don Baylor	.08	.25
272 Joe Rudi	.08	.25
273 Dan Ford	.02	.10
274 Jim Fregosi MG	.02	.10
275 Dave Frost	.02	.10
276 Frank Tanana	.08	.25
277 Dickie Thon	.02	.10
278 Jason Thompson	.02	.10
279 Rick Miller	.02	.10
280 Bert Campaneris	.08	.25
281 Tom Donohue	.02	.10
282 Brian Downing	.08	.25
283 Fred Patek	.02	.10
284 Bruce Kison	.02	.10
285 Dave LaRoche	.02	.10
286 Don Aase	.02	.10
287 Jim Barr	.02	.10
288 Alfredo Martinez RC	.02	.10
289 Larry Harlow	.02	.10
290 Andy Hassler	.02	.10
291 Dave Kingman	.08	.25
292 Bill Buckner	.08	.25
293 Rick Reuschel	.08	.25
294 Bruce Sutter	.20	.50
295 Jerry Martin	.02	.10
296 Scot Thompson	.02	.10
297 Ivan DeJesus	.02	.10
298 Steve Dillard	.02	.10
299 Dick Tidrow	.02	.10
300 Randy Martz RC	.02	.10
301 Lenny Randle	.02	.10
302 Lynn McGlothen	.02	.10
303 Cliff Johnson	.02	.10
304 Tim Blackwell	.02	.10
305 Dennis Lamp	.02	.10
306 Bill Caudill	.02	.10
307 Carlos Lezcano RC	.02	.10
308 Jim Tracy RC	.40	1.00
309 Doug Capilla UER	.02	.10
Cubs on front but		
Braves on back		
310 Willie Hernandez	.02	.10
311 Mike Vail	.02	.10
312 Mike Krukow RC	.02	.10
313 Barry Foote	.02	.10
314 Larry Biittner	.02	.10

315 Mike Tyson .02 .10
316 Lee Mazzilli .08 .25
317 John Stearns .02 .10
318 Alex Trevino .02 .10
319 Craig Swan .02 .10
320 Frank Taveras .02 .10
321 Steve Henderson .02 .10
322 Neil Allen .02 .10
323 Mark Bomback RC .02 .10
324 Mike Jorgensen .02 .10
325 Joe Torre MG .08 .25
326 Elliott Maddox .02 .10
327 Pete Falcone .02 .10
328 Ray Burris .02 .10
329 Claudell Washington .02 .10
330 Doug Flynn .02 .10
331 Joel Youngblood .02 .10
332 Bill Almon .02 .10
333 Tom Hausman .02 .10
334 Pat Zachry .02 .10
335 Jeff Reardon RC .40 1.00
336 Wally Backman RC .20 .50
337 Dan Norman .02 .10
338 Jerry Morales .02 .10
339 Ed Farmer .02 .10
340 Bob Molinaro .02 .10
341 Todd Cruz .02 .10
342A Britt Burns P1 .20 .50
Small hand on front
342B Britt Burns RC .08 .25
(P2 No hand)
343 Kevin Bell .02 .10
344 Tony LaRussa MG .08 .25
345 Steve Trout .02 .10
346 Harold Baines RC .75 2.00
347 Richard Wortham .02 .10
348 Wayne Nordhagen .02 .10
349 Mike Squires .02 .10
350 Lamar Johnson .02 .10
351 Rickey Henderson 1.25 3.00
Most Stolen Bases AL
352 Francisco Barrios .02 .10
353 Thad Bosley .02 .10
354 Chet Lemon .08 .25
355 Bruce Kimm .02 .10
356 Richard Dotson RC .02 .10
357 Jim Morrison .02 .10
358 Mike Proly .02 .10
359 Greg Pryor .02 .10
360 Dave Parker .08 .25
361 Omar Moreno .02 .10
362A Kent Tekulve P1 .02 .10
Back 1071 Waterbury
and 1078 Pirates
362B Kent Tekulve P2 .02 .10
1971 Waterbury and
1978 Pirates
363 Willie Stargell .20 .50
364 Phil Garner .08 .25
365 Ed Ott .02 .10
366 Don Robinson .02 .10
367 Chuck Tanner MG .02 .10
368 Jim Rooker .02 .10
369 Dale Berra .02 .10
370 Jim Bibby .02 .10
371 Steve Nicosia .02 .10
372 Mike Easler .02 .10
373 Bill Robinson .02 .10
374 Lee Lacy .02 .10
375 John Candelaria .08 .25
376 Manny Sanguillen .08 .25
377 Rick Rhoden .02 .10
378 Grant Jackson .02 .10
379 Tim Foli .02 .10
380 Rod Scurry RC .02 .10
381 Bill Madlock .08 .25
382A Kurt Bevacqua .08 .25
P1 ERR
P on cap backwards
382B Kurt Bevacqua P2 .02 .10
COR
383 Bert Blyleven .08 .25
384 Eddie Solomon .02 .10
385 Enrique Romo .02 .10
386 John Milner .02 .10
387 Mike Hargrove .02 .10
388 Jorge Orta .02 .10
389 Toby Harrah .08 .25
390 Tom Veryzer .02 .10
391 Miguel Dilone .02 .10
392 Dan Spillner .02 .10
393 Jack Brohamer .02 .10
394 Wayne Garland .02 .10
395 Sid Monge .02 .10
396 Rick Waits .02 .10
397 Joe Charboneau RC .40 1.00
398 Gary Alexander .02 .10
399 Jerry Dybzinski RC .02 .10
400 Mike Stanton RC .02 .10
401 Mike Paxton .02 .10
402 Gary Gray RC .02 .10
403 Rick Manning .02 .10
404 Bo Diaz .02 .10
405 Ron Hassey .02 .10
406 Ross Grimsley .02 .10
407 Victor,Cruz .02 .10
408 Len Barker .08 .25
409 Bob Bailor .02 .10
410 Otto Velez .02 .10
411 Ernie Whitt .02 .10
412 Jim Clancy .02 .10
413 Barry Bonnell .02 .10
414 Dave Stieb .08 .25
415 Damaso Garcia RC .02 .10
416 John Mayberry .02 .10
417 Roy Howell .02 .10
418 Danny Ainge RC 1.25 3.00
419A Jesse Jefferson P1 .02 .10
Back says Pirates
419B Jesse Jefferson P2 .02 .10
Back says Pirates
419C Jesse Jefferson P3 .20 .50
Back says Blue Jays
420 Joey McLaughlin .02 .10
421 Lloyd Moseby RC .20 .50
422 Alvis Woods .02 .10
423 Garth Iorg .02 .10
424 Doug Ault .02 .10
425 Ken Schrom RC .02 .10
426 Mike Willis .02 .10
427 Steve Braun .02 .10
428 Bob Davis .02 .10
429 Jerry Garvin .02 .10
430 Alfredo Griffin .02 .10
431 Bob Mattick MG RC .02 .10
432 Vida Blue .08 .25
433 Jack Clark .08 .25
434 Willie McCovey .20 .50
435 Mike Ivie .02 .10
436A Darrel Evans P1 ERR .20 .50
(Name on front Darrel
436B Darrell Evans P2 COR .20 .50
Name on front Darrell
437 Terry Whitfield .02 .10
438 Rennie Stennett .02 .10
439 John Montefusco .02 .10
440 Jim Wohlford .02 .10
441 Bill North .02 .10
442 Milt May .02 .10
443 Max Venable RC .02 .10
444 Ed Whitson .02 .10
445 Al Holland RC .02 .10
446 Randy Moffitt .02 .10
447 Bob Knepper .02 .10
448 Gary Lavelle .02 .10
449 Greg Minton .02 .10
450 Johnnie LeMaster .02 .10
451 Larry Herndon .02 .10
452 Rich Murray RC .02 .10
453 Joe Pettini RC .02 .10
454 Allen Ripley .02 .10
455 Dennis Littlejohn .02 .10
456 Tom Griffin .02 .10
457 Alan Hargesheimer RC .02 .10
458 Joe Strain .02 .10
459 Steve Kemp .02 .10
460 Sparky Anderson MG .08 .25
461 Alan Trammell .20 .50
462 Mark Fidrych .08 .25
463 Lou Whitaker .20 .50
464 Dave Rozema .02 .10
465 Milt Wilcox .02 .10
466 Champ Summers .02 .10
467 Lance Parrish .08 .25
468 Dan Petry .02 .10
469 Pat Underwood .02 .10
470 Rick Peters RC .02 .10
471 Al Cowens .02 .10
472 John Wockenfuss .02 .10
473 Tom Brookens .02 .10
474 Richie Hebner .02 .10
475 Jack Morris .20 .50
476 Jim Lentine RC .02 .10
477 Bruce Robbins .02 .10
478 Mark Wagner .02 .10
479 Tim Corcoran .02 .10
480A Stan Papi P1 .08 .25
Front as Pitcher
480B Stan Papi P2 .02 .10
Front as Shortstop
481 Kirk Gibson RC 2.00 5.00
482 Dan Schatzeder .02 .10
483A Amos Otis P1 .08 .25
See card 32
483B Amos Otis P2 .08 .25
See card 32
484 Dave Winfield .20 .50
485 Rollie Fingers .08 .25
486 Gene Richards .02 .10
487 Randy Jones .02 .10
488 Ozzie Smith 1.25 3.00
489 Gene Tenace .08 .25
490 Bill Fahey .02 .10
491 John Curtis .02 .10
492 Dave Cash .02 .10
493A Tim Flannery P1 .08 .25
Batting right
493B Tim Flannery P2 .02 .10
Batting left
494 Jerry Mumphrey .02 .10
495 Bob Shirley .02 .10
496 Steve Mura .02 .10
497 Eric Rasmussen .02 .10
498 Broderick Perkins .02 .10
499 Barry Evans RC .02 .10
500 Chuck Baker .02 .10
501 Luis Salazar RC .20 .50
502 Gary Lucas RC .02 .10
503 Mike Armstrong RC .02 .10
504 Jerry Turner .02 .10
505 Dennis Kinney RC .02 .10
506 Willie Montanez UER .02 .10
Spelled Willy on card front
507 Gorman Thomas .08 .25
508 Ben Oglivie .08 .25
509 Larry Hisle .02 .10
510 Sal Bando .08 .25
511 Robin Yount .60 1.50
512 Mike Caldwell .02 .10
513 Sixto Lezcano .02 .10
514A Bill Travers P1 ERR .08 .25
Jerry Augustine
with Augustine back
514B Bill Travers P2 COR .02 .10
515 Paul Molitor .40 1.00
516 Moose Haas .02 .10
517 Bill Castro .02 .10
518 Jim Slaton .02 .10
519 Lary Sorensen .02 .10
520 Bob McClure .02 .10
521 Charlie Moore .02 .10
522 Jim Gantner .02 .10
523 Reggie Cleveland .02 .10
524 Don Money .02 .10
525 Bill Travers .02 .10
526 Buck Martinez .02 .10
527 Dick Davis .02 .10
528 Ted Simmons .08 .25
529 Garry Templeton .08 .25
530 Ken Reitz .02 .10
531 Tony Scott .02 .10
532 Ken Oberkfell .02 .10
533 Bob Sykes .02 .10
534 Keith Smith .02 .10
535 John Littlefield RC .02 .10
536 Jim Kaat .08 .25
537 Bob Forsch .02 .10
538 Mike Phillips .02 .10
539 Terry Landrum RC .02 .10
540 Leon Durham RC .20 .50
541 Terry Kennedy .02 .10
542 George Hendrick .08 .25
543 Dane Iorg .02 .10
544 Mark Littell .02 .10
545 Keith Hernandez .08 .25
546 Silvio Martinez .02 .10
547A Don Hood P1 ERR .08 .25
Pete Vuckovich
with Vuckovich back
547B Don Hood P2 COR .02 .10
548 Bobby Bonds .08 .25
549 Mike Ramsey RC .05 .15
550 Tom Herr .02 .10
551 Roy Smalley .02 .10
552 Jerry Koosman .08 .25
553 Ken Landreaux .02 .10
554 John Castino .02 .10
555 Doug Corbett RC .02 .10
556 Bombo Rivera .02 .10
557 Ron Jackson .02 .10
558 Butch Wynegar .02 .10
559 Hosken Powell .02 .10
560 Pete Redfern .02 .10
561 Roger Erickson .02 .10
562 Glenn Adams .02 .10
563 Rick Sofield .02 .10
564 Geoff Zahn .02 .10
565 Pete Mackanin .02 .10
566 Mike Cubbage .02 .10
567 Darrell Jackson .02 .10
568 Dave Edwards .02 .10
569 Rob Wilfong .02 .10
570 Sal Butera RC .02 .10
571 Jose Morales .02 .10
572 Rick Langford .02 .10
573 Mike Norris .02 .10
574 Rickey Henderson 2.50 6.00
575 Tony Armas .08 .25
576 Dave Revering .02 .10
577 Jeff Newman .02 .10
578 Bob Lacey .02 .10
579 Brian Kingman .02 .10
580 Mitchell Page .02 .10
581 Billy Martin MG .20 .50
582 Rob Picciolo .02 .10
583 Mike Heath .02 .10
584 Mickey Klutts .02 .10
585 Orlando Gonzalez .02 .10
586 Mike Davis RC .20 .50
587 Wayne Gross .02 .10
588 Matt Keough .02 .10
589 Steve McCatty .02 .10
590 Dwayne Murphy .02 .10
591 Mario Guerrero .02 .10
592 Dave McKay RC .02 .10
593 Jim Essian .02 .10
594 Dave Heaverlo .02 .10
595 Maury Wills MG .08 .25
596 Juan Beniquez .02 .10
597 Rodney Craig .02 .10
598 Jim Anderson .02 .10
599 Floyd Bannister .02 .10
600 Bruce Bochte .02 .10
601 Julio Cruz .02 .10
602 Ted Cox .02 .10
603 Dan Meyer .02 .10
604 Larry Cox .02 .10
605 Bill Stein .02 .10
606 Steve Garvey .20 .50
Most Hits NL
607 Dave Roberts .02 .10
608 Leon Roberts .02 .10
609 Reggie Walton RC .02 .10
610 Dave Edler RC .02 .10
611 Larry Milbourne .02 .10
612 Kim Allen RC .02 .10
613 Mario Mendoza .02 .10
614 Tom Paciorek .02 .10
615 Glenn Abbott .02 .10
616 Joe Simpson .02 .10
617 Mickey Rivers .02 .10
618 Jim Kern .02 .10
619 Jim Sundberg .08 .25
620 Richie Zisk .02 .10
621 Jon Matlack .02 .10
622 Ferguson Jenkins .08 .25
623 Pat Corrales MG .02 .10
624 Ed Figueroa .02 .10
625 Buddy Bell .08 .25
626 Al Oliver .08 .25
627 Doc Medich .02 .10
628 Bump Wills .02 .10
629 Rusty Staub .08 .25
630 Pat Putnam .02 .10
631 John Grubb .02 .10
632 Danny Darwin .02 .10
633 Ken Clay .02 .10
634 Jim Norris .02 .10
635 John Butcher RC .02 .10
636 Dave Roberts .02 .10
637 Billy Sample .02 .10
638 Carl Yastrzemski .60 1.50
639 Cecil Cooper .08 .25
640 Mike Schmidt P1 1.00 2.50
Portrait
Third Base
number on back 5
640B Mike Schmidt P2 1.00 2.50
1980 Home Run King
640 on back
641A CL: Phils/Royals P1 .08 .25
41 is Hal McRae
641B CL: Phils/Royals P2 .08 .25
41 is Hal McRae
Double Threat
642 CL: Astros/Yankees .02 .10
643 CL: Expos/Dodgers .02 .10
644A CL: Reds/Orioles P1 .08 .25
202 is George Foster
Joe Nolan pitcher
should be catcher
644B CL: Reds/Orioles P2 .08 .25
202 is Foster Slugger
Joe Nolan pitcher
should be catcher
645 Pete Rose .60 1.50
Larry Bowa
Mike Schmidt
Triple Threat P1
No number on back
645B Pete Rose 1.00 2.50
Larry Bowa
Mike Schmidt
Triple Threat P2
Back numbered 645
646 CL: Braves/Red Sox .02 .10
647 CL: Cubs/Angels .02 .10
648 CL: Mets/White Sox .02 .10
649 CL: Indians/Pirates .02 .10
650 Reggie Jackson .40 1.00
Mr. Baseball P1
Number on back 79
650B Reggie Jackson .20 .50
Mr. Baseball P2
Number on back 650
651 CL: Giants/Blue Jays .02 .10
652A CL:Tigers/Padres P1 .08 .25
483 is listed
652B CL:Tigers/Padres P2 .08 .25
483 is deleted
653A Willie Wilson P1 .08 .25
Most Hits Most Runs
Number on back 29
653B Willie Wilson P2 .08 .25
Most Hits Most Runs
Number on back 653
654A Checklist Brewers .08 .25
Cards P1
514 Jerry Augustine
547 Pete Vuckovich
654B Checklist Brewers .08 .25
Cards P2
514 Billy Travers
547 Don Hood
655 George Brett P1 1.00 2.50
.390 Average
Number on back 28
655B George Brett P2 1.00 2.50
.390 Average
Number on back 655
656 CL:Twins/Oakland A's .08 .25
657A Tug McGraw P1 .08 .25
Game Saver
Number on back 7
657B Tug McGraw P2 .08 .25
Game Saver
Number on back 657
658 CL: Rangers/Mariners .02 .10
659A Checklist P1 .02 .10
of Special Cards
Last lines on front
Wilson Most Hits
659B Checklist P2 .02 .10
of Special Cards
Last lines on front
Otis Series Starter
660 Steve Carlton P1 .20 .50
Golden Arm
(Number on back 660
Back 1066 Cardinals
660B Steve Carlton P2 .75 2.00
Golden Arm
1966 Cardinals

1982 Fleer

The 1982 Fleer set contains 660-card standard-size cards, of which are grouped in team order based upon standings from the previous season. Cards numbered 628 through 646 are special cards highlighting some of the stars and leaders of the 1981 season. The last 14 cards in the set (647-660) are checklist cards. The backs feature player statistics and a full-color team logo in the upper right-hand corner of each card. The complete set price below does not include any of the more valuable variation cards listed. Fleer was not allowed to insert bubble gum or other confectionary products into these packs; therefore logo stickers were included in these 15-card packs. Those 15-card packs with an SRP of 30 cents were packed 36 packs to a box and 20 boxes to a case. Notable Rookie Cards in this set include Cal Ripken Jr., Lee Smith, and Dave Stewart.

COMPLETE SET (660) 20.00 50.00
1 Dusty Baker .07 .20
2 Robert Castillo .02 .10
3 Ron Cey .07 .20
4 Terry Forster .07 .20
5 Steve Garvey .07 .20
6 Dave Goltz .02 .10
7 Pedro Guerrero .07 .20
8 Burt Hooton .02 .10
9 Steve Howe .02 .10
10 Jay Johnstone .02 .10
11 Ken Landreaux .02 .10
12 Dave Lopes .07 .20
13 Mike A. Marshall RC .20 .50
14 Bobby Mitchell .02 .10
15 Rick Monday .07 .20
16 Tom Niedenfuer RC .20 .50
17 Ted Power RC .05 .15
18 Jerry Reuss UER .02 .10
19 Ron Roenicke .02 .10
20 Bill Russell .07 .20
21 Steve Sax RC .40 1.00
22 Mike Scioscia .07 .20
23 Reggie Smith .07 .20
24 Dave Stewart RC .60 1.50
25 Rick Sutcliffe .07 .20
26 Derrel Thomas .02 .10
27 Fernando Valenzuela .30 .75
28 Bob Welch .07 .20
29 Steve Yeager .07 .20
30 Bobby Brown .02 .10
31 Rick Cerone .02 .10
32 Ron Davis .02 .10
33 Bucky Dent .07 .20
34 Barry Foote .02 .10
35 George Frazier .02 .10
36 Oscar Gamble .02 .10
37 Rich Gossage .07 .20
38 Ron Guidry .07 .20
39 Reggie Jackson .15 .40
40 Tommy John .07 .20
41 Rudy May .02 .10
42 Larry Milbourne .02 .10
43 Jerry Mumphrey .02 .10
44 Bobby Murcer .07 .20
45 Gene Nelson .02 .10
46 Graig Nettles .07 .20
47 Johnny Oates .07 .20
48 Lou Piniella .07 .20
49 Willie Randolph .07 .20
50 Rick Reuschel .07 .20
51 Dave Revering .02 .10
52 Dave Righetti RC .60 1.50
53 Aurelio Rodriguez .02 .10
54 Bob Watson .02 .10
55 Dennis Werth .02 .10
56 Dave Winfield .07 .20
57 Johnny Bench .30 .75
58 Bruce Berenyi .02 .10
59 Larry Biittner .02 .10
60 Scott Brown .02 .10
61 Dave Collins .02 .10
62 Geoff Combe .02 .10
63 Dave Concepcion .07 .20
64 Dan Driessen .02 .10
65 Joe Edelen .02 .10
66 George Foster .07 .20
67 Ken Griffey .07 .20
68 Paul Householder .02 .10
69 Tom Hume .02 .10
70 Junior Kennedy .02 .10
71 Ray Knight .07 .20
72 Mike LaCoss .02 .10
73 Rafael Landestoy .02 .10
74 Charlie Leibrandt .02 .10
75 Sam Mejias .02 .10
76 Paul Moskau .02 .10
77 Joe Nolan .02 .10
78 Mike O'Berry .02 .10
79 Ron Oester .02 .10
80 Frank Pastore .02 .10
81 Joe Price .02 .10
82 Tom Seaver .30 .75
83 Mario Soto .07 .20
84 Mike Vail .02 .10
85 Tony Armas .07 .20
86 Shooty Babitt .02 .10
87 Dave Beard .02 .10
88 Rick Bosetti .02 .10
89 Keith Drumwright .02 .10
90 Wayne Gross .02 .10
91 Mike Heath .02 .10
92 Rickey Henderson 1.00 2.50
93 Cliff Johnson .02 .10
94 Jeff Jones .02 .10
95 Matt Keough .02 .10
96 Brian Kingman .02 .10
97 Mickey Klutts .02 .10
98 Rick Langford .02 .10
99 Steve McCatty .02 .10
100 Dave McKay .02 .10
101 Dwayne Murphy .02 .10
102 Jeff Newman .02 .10
103 Mike Norris .02 .10
104 Bob Owchinko .02 .10
105 Mitchell Page .02 .10
106 Rob Picciolo .02 .10
107 Jim Spencer .02 .10
108 Fred Stanley .02 .10
109 Tom Underwood .02 .10
110 Joaquin Andujar .07 .20
111 Steve Braun .02 .10
112 Bob Forsch .02 .10
113 George Hendrick .07 .20
114 Keith Hernandez .07 .20
115 Tom Herr .02 .10
116 Dane Iorg .02 .10
117 Jim Kaat .07 .20
118 Tito Landrum .02 .10
119 Sixto Lezcano .02 .10
120 Mark Littell .02 .10
121 John Martin RC .05 .15
122 Silvio Martinez .02 .10
123 Ken Oberkfell .02 .10
124 Darrell Porter .02 .10
125 Mike Ramsey .02 .10
126 Orlando Sanchez .02 .10
127 Bob Shirley .02 .10
128 Lary Sorensen .02 .10
129 Bruce Sutter .15 .40
130 Bob Sykes .02 .10
131 Garry Templeton .07 .20
132 Gene Tenace .07 .20
133 Jerry Augustine .02 .10
134 Sal Bando .07 .20
135 Mark Brouhard .02 .10
136 Mike Caldwell .02 .10
137 Reggie Cleveland .02 .10
138 Cecil Cooper .07 .20
139 Jamie Easterly .02 .10
140 Marshall Edwards .02 .10
141 Rollie Fingers .07 .20
142 Jim Gantner .02 .10
143 Moose Haas .02 .10
144 Larry Hisle .02 .10
145 Roy Howell .02 .10
146 Rickey Keeton .02 .10
147 Randy Lerch .02 .10
148 Paul Molitor .07 .20
149 Don Money .02 .10
150 Charlie Moore .02 .10
151 Ben Oglivie .07 .20
152 Ted Simmons .07 .20
153 Jim Slaton .02 .10
154 Gorman Thomas .07 .20
155 Robin Yount .50 1.25
156 Pete Vuckovich .02 .10
(Should precede Yount
in the team order)
157 Benny Ayala .02 .10
158 Mark Belanger .02 .10
159 Al Bumbry .02 .10
160 Terry Crowley .02 .10
161 Rich Dauer .02 .10
162 Doug DeCinces .02 .10
163 Rick Dempsey .02 .10
164 Jim Dwyer .02 .10
165 Mike Flanagan .02 .10
166 Dave Ford .02 .10
167 Dan Graham .02 .10
168 Wayne Krenchicki .02 .10
169 John Lowenstein .02 .10
170 Dennis Martinez .07 .20
171 Tippy Martinez .02 .10
172 Scott McGregor .02 .10
173 Jose Morales .02 .10
174 Eddie Murray .30 .75
175 Jim Palmer .07 .20
176 Cal Ripken RC 10.00 25.00
Fleer Ripken cards from 1982
through 1993 erroneously have 22
games played in 1981;not 23.
177 Gary Roenicke .02 .10
178 Lenn Sakata .02 .10
179 Ken Singleton .07 .20
180 Sammy Stewart .02 .10
181 Tim Stoddard .02 .10
182 Steve Stone .02 .10
183 Stan Bahnsen .02 .10
184 Ray Burris .02 .10
185 Gary Carter .07 .20
186 Warren Cromartie .02 .10
187 Andre Dawson .07 .20
188 Terry Francona RC 1.25 3.00
189 Woodie Fryman .02 .10
190 Bill Gullickson .02 .10
191 Grant Jackson .02 .10
192 Wallace Johnson .02 .10
193 Charlie Lea .02 .10
194 Bill Lee .07 .20
195 Jerry Manuel .02 .10
196 Brad Mills .02 .10
197 John Milner .02 .10
198 Rowland Office .02 .10
199 David Palmer .02 .10
200 Larry Parrish .02 .10
201 Mike Phillips .02 .10
202 Tim Raines .15 .40
203 Bobby Ramos .02 .10
204 Jeff Reardon .07 .20
205 Steve Rogers .07 .20
206 Scott Sanderson .02 .10
207 Rodney Scott UER .15 .40
(Photo actually
Tim Raines)
208 Elias Sosa .02 .10
209 Chris Speier .02 .10
210 Tim Wallach RC .40 1.00
211 Jerry White .02 .10
212 Alan Ashby .02 .10
213 Cesar Cedeno .07 .20
214 Jose Cruz .07 .20
215 Kiko Garcia .02 .10
216 Phil Garner .07 .20
217 Danny Heep .02 .10
218 Art Howe .02 .10
219 Bob Knepper .02 .10
220 Frank LaCorte .02 .10
221 Joe Niekro .02 .10
222 Joe Pittman .02 .10
223 Terry Puhl .02 .10
224 Luis Pujols .02 .10
225 Craig Reynolds .02 .10
226 J.R. Richard .07 .20
227 Dave Roberts .02 .10
228 Vern Ruhle .02 .10
229 Nolan Ryan 1.50 4.00
230 Joe Sambito .02 .10
231 Tony Scott .02 .10
232 Dave Smith .02 .10
233 Harry Spilman .02 .10
234 Don Sutton .07 .20
235 Dickie Thon .02 .10
236 Denny Walling .02 .10
237 Gary Woods .02 .10
238 Luis Aguayo .02 .10
239 Ramon Aviles .02 .10
240 Bob Boone .07 .20
241 Larry Bowa .07 .20
242 Warren Brusstar .02 .10
243 Steve Carlton .15 .40
244 Larry Christenson .02 .10
245 Dick Davis .02 .10
246 Greg Gross .02 .10
247 Sparky Lyle .07 .20
248 Garry Maddox .02 .10
249 Gary Matthews .07 .20
250 Bake McBride .07 .20
251 Tug McGraw .07 .20
252 Keith Moreland .02 .10
253 Dickie Noles .02 .10
254 Mike Proly .02 .10
255 Ron Reed .02 .10
256 Pete Rose 1.00 2.50
257 Dick Ruthven .02 .10
258 Mike Schmidt .75 2.00
259 Lonnie Smith .02 .10
260 Manny Trillo .02 .10
261 Del Unser .02 .10
262 George Vukovich .02 .10
263 Tom Brookens .02 .10
264 George Cappuzzello .02 .10
265 Marty Castillo .02 .10
266 Al Cowens .02 .10
267 Kirk Gibson .30 .75
268 Richie Hebner .02 .10
269 Ron Jackson .02 .10
270 Lynn Jones .02 .10
271 Steve Kemp .02 .10
272 Rick Leach .02 .10
273 Aurelio Lopez .02 .10
274 Jack Morris .07 .20
275 Kevin Saucier .02 .10
276 Lance Parrish .07 .20
277 Rick Peters .02 .10
278 Dan Petry .02 .10
279 Dave Rozema .02 .10
280 Stan Papi .02 .10
281 Dan Schatzeder .02 .10
282 Champ Summers .02 .10
283 Alan Trammell .07 .20
284 Lou Whitaker .07 .20
285 Milt Wilcox .02 .10
286 John Wockenfuss .02 .10
287 Gary Allenson .02 .10
288 Tom Burgmeier .02 .10
289 Bill Campbell .02 .10
290 Mark Clear .02 .10
291 Steve Crawford .02 .10
292 Dennis Eckersley .15 .40
293 Dwight Evans .15 .40
294 Rich Gedman .20 .50
295 Garry Hancock .02 .10
296 Glenn Hoffman .02 .10
297 Bruce Hurst .02 .10
298 Carney Lansford .07 .20
299 Rick Miller .02 .10
300 Reid Nichols .02 .10
301 Bob Ojeda RC .20 .50
302 Tony Perez .15 .40
303 Chuck Rainey .02 .10
304 Jerry Remy .02 .10
305 Jim Rice .07 .20
306 Joe Rudi .07 .20
307 Bob Stanley .02 .10
308 Dave Stapleton .02 .10
309 Frank Tanana .07 .20
310 Mike Torrez .02 .10
311 John Tudor .07 .20
312 Carl Yastrzemski .50 1.25
313 Buddy Bell .07 .20
314 Steve Comer .02 .10
315 Danny Darwin .02 .10
316 John Ellis .02 .10
317 John Grubb .02 .10
318 Rick Honeycutt .02 .10
319 Charlie Hough .07 .20
320 Ferguson Jenkins .07 .20
321 John Henry Johnson .02 .10
322 Jim Kern .02 .10
323 Jon Matlack .02 .10
324 Doc Medich .02 .10
325 Mario Mendoza .02 .10
326 Al Oliver .07 .20
327 Pat Putnam .02 .10
328 Mickey Rivers .02 .10
329 Leon Roberts .02 .10
330 Billy Sample .02 .10
331 Bill Stein .02 .10
332 Jim Sundberg .07 .20
333 Mark Wagner .02 .10
334 Bump Wills .02 .10
335 Bill Almon .02 .10
336 Harold Baines .07 .20
337 Ross Baumgarten .02 .10
338 Tony Bernazard .02 .10
339 Britt Burns .02 .10
340 Richard Dotson .02 .10
341 Jim Essian .02 .10
342 Ed Farmer .02 .10
343 Carlton Fisk .15 .40
344 Kevin Hickey RC .05 .15
345 LaMarr Hoyt .02 .10
346 Lamar Johnson .02 .10
347 Jerry Koosman .07 .20
348 Rusty Kuntz .02 .10
349 Dennis Lamp .02 .10
350 Ron LeFlore .07 .20
351 Chet Lemon .07 .20
352 Greg Luzinski .07 .20
353 Bob Molinaro .02 .10
354 Jim Morrison .02 .10
355 Wayne Nordhagen .02 .10
356 Greg Pryor .02 .10
357 Mike Squires .02 .10
358 Steve Trout .02 .10
359 Alan Bannister .02 .10
360 Len Barker .02 .10
361 Bert Blyleven .07 .20
362 Joe Charboneau .07 .20
363 John Denny .02 .10
364 Bo Diaz .02 .10
365 Miguel Dilone .02 .10
366 Jerry Dybzinski .02 .10
367 Wayne Garland .02 .10
368 Mike Hargrove .02 .10
369 Toby Harrah .07 .20
370 Ron Hassey .02 .10
371 Von Hayes RC .20 .50
372 Pat Kelly .02 .10
373 Duane Kuiper .02 .10
374 Rick Manning .02 .10
375 Sid Monge .02 .10
376 Jorge Orta .02 .10
377 Dave Rosello .02 .10
378 Dan Spillner .02 .10
379 Mike Stanton .02 .10
380 Andre Thornton .02 .10
381 Tom Veryzer .02 .10
382 Rick Waits .02 .10
383 Doyle Alexander .02 .10
384 Vida Blue .07 .20
385 Fred Breining .02 .10
386 Enos Cabell .02 .10
387 Jack Clark .07 .20
388 Darrell Evans .07 .20
389 Tom Griffin .02 .10
390 Larry Herndon .02 .10
391 Al Holland .02 .10
392 Gary Lavelle .02 .10
393 Johnnie LeMaster .02 .10
394 Jerry Martin .02 .10
395 Milt May .02 .10
396 Greg Minton .02 .10
397 Joe Morgan .07 .20
398 Joe Pettini .02 .10
399 Allen Ripley .02 .10
400 Billy Smith .02 .10
401 Rennie Stennett .02 .10
402 Ed Whitson .02 .10
403 Jim Wohlford .02 .10
404 Willie Aikens .02 .10
405 George Brett .75 2.00
406 Ken Brett .02 .10
407 Dave Chalk .02 .10
408 Rich Gale .02 .10
409 Cesar Geronimo .02 .10
410 Larry Gura .02 .10
411 Clint Hurdle .02 .10
412 Mike Jones .02 .10
413 Dennis Leonard .02 .10
414 Renie Martin .02 .10
415 Lee May .02 .10
416 Hal McRae .07 .20
417 Darryl Motley .02 .10
418 Rance Mulliniks .02 .10
419 Amos Otis .07 .20
420 Ken Phelps .02 .10
421 Jamie Quirk .02 .10
422 Dan Quisenberry .02 .10
423 Paul Splittorff .02 .10
424 U.L. Washington .02 .10

425 John Wathan	.02	.10
426 Frank White	.07	.20
427 Willie Wilson	.07	.20
428 Brian Asselstine	.02	.10
429 Bruce Benedict	.02	.10
430 Tommy Boggs	.02	.10
431 Larry Bradford	.02	.10
432 Rick Camp	.02	.10
433 Chris Chambliss	.07	.20
434 Gene Garber	.02	.10
435 Preston Hanna	.02	.10
436 Bob Horner	.07	.20
437 Glenn Hubbard	.02	.10
438A All Hrabosky ERR	3.00	8.00
(Height 5'1		
All on reverse)		
438B Al Hrabosky ERR	.15	.40
(Height 5'1)		
438C Al Hrabosky	.07	.20
(Height 5'10)		
439 Rufino Linares	.02	.10
440 Rick Mahler	.02	.10
441 Ed Miller	.02	.10
442 John Montefusco	.02	.10
443 Dale Murphy	.15	.40
444 Phil Niekro	.07	.20
445 Gaylord Perry	.07	.20
446 Biff Pocoroba	.02	.10
447 Rafael Ramirez	.02	.10
448 Jerry Royster	.02	.10
449 Claudell Washington	.02	.10
450 Don Aase	.02	.10
451 Don Baylor	.07	.20
452 Juan Beniquez	.02	.10
453 Rick Burleson	.02	.10
454 Bert Campaneris	.07	.20
455 Rod Carew	.15	.40
456 Bob Clark	.02	.10
457 Brian Downing	.07	.20
458 Dan Ford	.02	.10
459 Ken Forsch	.02	.10
460A Dave Frost (5 mm	.02	.10
space before ERA)		
460B Dave Frost	.02	.10
(1 mm space)		
461 Bobby Grich	.07	.20
462 Larry Harlow	.02	.10
463 John Harris	.02	.10
464 Andy Hassler	.02	.10
465 Butch Hobson	.02	.10
466 Jesse Jefferson	.02	.10
467 Bruce Kison	.02	.10
468 Fred Lynn	.07	.20
469 Angel Moreno	.02	.10
470 Ed Ott	.02	.10
471 Fred Patek	.02	.10
472 Steve Renko	.02	.10
473 Mike Witt	.20	.50
474 Geoff Zahn	.02	.10
475 Gary Alexander	.02	.10
476 Dale Berra	.02	.10
477 Kurt Bevacqua	.02	.10
478 Jim Bibby	.02	.10
479 John Candelaria	.02	.10
480 Victor Cruz	.02	.10
481 Mike Easler	.02	.10
482 Tim Foli	.02	.10
483 Lee Lacy	.02	.10
484 Vance Law	.02	.10
485 Bill Madlock	.07	.20
486 Willie Montanez	.02	.10
487 Omar Moreno	.02	.10
488 Steve Nicosia	.02	.10
489 Dave Parker	.07	.20
490 Tony Pena	.07	.20
491 Pascual Perez	.02	.10
492 Johnny Ray RC	.20	.50
493 Rick Rhoden	.02	.10
494 Bill Robinson	.02	.10
495 Don Robinson	.02	.10
496 Enrique Romo	.02	.10
497 Rod Scurry	.02	.10
498 Eddie Solomon	.02	.10
499 Willie Stargell	.15	.40
500 Kent Tekulve	.02	.10
501 Jason Thompson	.02	.10
502 Glenn Abbott	.02	.10
503 Jim Anderson	.02	.10
504 Floyd Bannister	.02	.10
505 Bruce Bochte	.02	.10
506 Jeff Burroughs	.02	.10
507 Bryan Clark RC	.05	.15
508 Ken Clay	.02	.10
509 Julio Cruz	.02	.10
510 Dick Drago	.02	.10
511 Gary Gray	.02	.10
512 Dan Meyer	.02	.10
513 Jerry Narron	.02	.10
514 Tom Paciorek	.02	.10
515 Casey Parsons	.02	.10
516 Lenny Randle	.02	.10
517 Shane Rawley	.02	.10
518 Joe Simpson	.02	.10
519 Richie Zisk	.02	.10
520 Neil Allen	.02	.10
521 Bob Bailor	.02	.10
522 Hubie Brooks	.02	.10
523 Mike Cubbage	.02	.10
524 Pete Falcone	.02	.10
525 Doug Flynn	.02	.10
526 Tom Hausman	.02	.10
527 Ron Hodges	.02	.10
528 Randy Jones	.02	.10
529 Mike Jorgensen	.02	.10
530 Dave Kingman	.07	.20
531 Ed Lynch	.02	.10
532 Mike G. Marshall	.02	.10
533 Lee Mazzilli	.07	.20
534 Dyar Miller	.02	.10
535 Mike Scott	.07	.20
536 Rusty Staub	.07	.20
537 John Stearns	.02	.10
538 Craig Swan	.02	.10
539 Frank Taveras	.02	.10
540 Alex Trevino	.02	.10
541 Ellis Valentine	.02	.10
542 Mookie Wilson	.07	.20
543 Joel Youngblood	.02	.10
544 Pat Zachry	.02	.10
545 Glenn Adams	.02	.10
546 Fernando Arroyo	.02	.10
547 John Verhoeven	.02	.10
548 Sal Butera	.02	.10
549 John Castino	.02	.10
550 Don Cooper	.02	.10
551 Doug Corbett	.02	.10
552 Dave Engle	.02	.10
553 Roger Erickson	.02	.10
554 Danny Goodwin	.02	.10
555A Darrell Jackson	.15	.40
(Black cap)		
555B Darrell Jackson	.07	.20
(Red cap with 1)		
555C Darrell Jackson	1.25	3.00
(Red cap, no emblem)		
556 Pete Mackanin	.02	.10
557 Jack O'Connor	.02	.10
558 Hosken Powell	.02	.10
559 Pete Redfern	.02	.10
560 Roy Smalley	.02	.10
561 Chuck Baker UER	.02	.10
(Shortshop on front)		
562 Gary Ward	.02	.10
563 Rob Wilfong	.02	.10
564 Al Williams	.02	.10
565 Butch Wynegar	.02	.10
566 Randy Bass	.20	.50
567 Juan Bonilla RC	.05	.15
568 Danny Boone	.02	.10
569 John Curtis	.02	.10
570 Juan Eichelberger	.02	.10
571 Barry Evans	.02	.10
572 Tim Flannery	.02	.10
573 Ruppert Jones	.02	.10
574 Terry Kennedy	.02	.10
575 Joe Lefebvre	.02	.10
576A John Littlefield ERR	30.00	60.00
(Left handed;		
reverse negative)		
576B John Littlefield COR	.07	.20
(Right handed)		
577 Gary Lucas	.02	.10
578 Steve Mura	.02	.10
579 Broderick Perkins	.02	.10
580 Gene Richards	.02	.10
581 Luis Salazar	.02	.10
582 Ozzie Smith	.60	1.50
583 John Urrea	.02	.10
584 Chris Welsh	.02	.10
585 Rick Wise	.02	.10
586 Doug Bird	.02	.10
587 Tim Blackwell	.02	.10
588 Bobby Bonds	.07	.20
589 Bill Buckner	.07	.20
590 Bill Caudill	.02	.10
591 Hector Cruz	.02	.10
592 Jody Davis	.02	.10
593 Ivan DeJesus	.02	.10
594 Steve Dillard	.02	.10
595 Leon Durham	.02	.10
596 Rawly Eastwick	.07	.20
597 Steve Henderson	.02	.10
598 Mike Krukow	.02	.10
599 Mike Lum	.02	.10
600 Randy Martz	.02	.10
601 Jerry Morales	.02	.10
602 Ken Reitz	.02	.10
603 Lee Smith RC ERR	.75	2.00
(Cubs logo reversed)		
603B Lee Smith COR	2.50	6.00
604 Dick Tidrow	.02	.10
605 Jim Tracy	.07	.20
606 Mike Tyson	.02	.10
607 Ty Waller	.02	.10
608 Danny Ainge	.07	.20
609 Jorge Bell RC	.40	1.00
610 Mark Bomback	.02	.10
611 Barry Bonnell	.02	.10
612 Jim Clancy	.02	.10
613 Damaso Garcia	.02	.10
614 Jerry Garvin	.02	.10
615 Alfredo Griffin	.02	.10
616 Garth Iorg	.02	.10
617 Luis Leal	.02	.10
618 Ken Macha	.02	.10
619 John Mayberry	.02	.10
620 Joey McLaughlin	.02	.10
621 Lloyd Moseby	.02	.10
622 Dave Stieb	.07	.20
623 Jackson Todd	.02	.10
624 Willie Upshaw	.20	.50
625 Otto Velez	.02	.10
626 Ernie Whitt	.02	.10
627 Alvis Woods	.02	.10
628 All Star Game	.07	.20
Cleveland, Ohio		
629 Frank White	.07	.20
Bucky Dent		
630 Dan Driessen	.07	.20
Dave Concepcion		
George Foster		
631 Bruce Sutter	.07	.20
Top NL Relief Pitcher		
632 Steve Carlton	.07	.20
Carlton Fisk		
633 Carl Yastrzemski	.30	.75
3000th Game		
634 Johnny Bench	.30	.75
Tom Seaver		
635 Fernando Valenzuela	.02	.10
Gary Carter		
636A Fernando Valenzuela:	.15	.40
NL SO King 'he' NL		
636B Fernando Valenzuela	.15	.40
NL SO King 'the' NL		
637 Mike Schmidt	.30	.75
Home Run King		
638 Gary Carter	.02	.10
Dave Parker		
639 Perfect Game UER	.07	.20
Len Barker		
Bo Diaz		
(Catcher actually		
Ron Hassey)		
640 Pete Rose	.30	.75
Pete Rose Jr.		
641 Lonnie Smith	.30	.75
Mike Schmidt		
Steve Carlton		
642 Fred Lynn	.15	.40
Dwight Evans		
643 Rickey Henderson	.50	1.25
Most Hits and Runs		
644 Rollie Fingers	.07	.20
Most Saves AL		
645 Tom Seaver	.07	.20
Most 1981 Wins		
646 Yankee Powerhouse	.07	.20
Reggie Jackson		
Dave Winfield		
(Comma on back		
after outfielder)		
646B Yankee Powerhouse	.07	.20
Reggie Jackson		
Dave Winfield		
(No comma)		
647 CL: Yankees/Dodgers	.02	.10
648 CL: A's/Reds	.02	.10
649 CL: Cards/Brewers	.02	.10
650 CL: Expos/Orioles	.02	.10
651 CL: Astros/Phillies	.02	.10
652 CL: Tigers/Red Sox	.02	.10
653 CL: Rangers/White Sox	.02	.10
654 CL: Giants/Indians	.02	.10
655 CL: Royals/Braves	.02	.10
656 CL: Angels/Pirates	.02	.10
657 CL: Mariners/Mets	.02	.10
658 CL: Padres/Twins	.02	.10
659 CL: Blue Jays/Cubs	.02	.10
660 Specials Checklist	.02	.10

1983 Fleer

In 1983, for the third straight year, Fleer produced a baseball series of 660 standard-size cards. Of these, 1-628 are player cards, 629-646 are special cards, and 647-660 are checklist cards. The player cards are again ordered alphabetically within team and teams seeded in descending order based upon the previous season's standings. The front of each card has a colorful team logo at bottom left and the player's name and position at lower right. The reverses are done in shades of brown on white. Wax packs consisted of 15 cards plus logo stickers in a 38-pack box. Notable Rookie Cards include Wade Boggs, Tony Gwynn and Ryne Sandberg.

COMPLETE SET (660)	30.00	60.00
1 Joaquin Andujar	.07	.20
2 Doug Bair	.02	.10
3 Steve Braun	.02	.10
4 Glenn Brummer	.02	.10
5 Bob Forsch	.02	.10
6 David Green RC	.20	.50
7 George Hendrick	.07	.20
8 Keith Hernandez	.07	.20
9 Tom Herr	.02	.10
10 Dane Iorg	.02	.10
11 Jim Kaat	.07	.20
12 Jeff Lahti	.02	.10
13 Tito Landrum	.02	.10
14 Dave LaPoint	.02	.10
15 Willie McGee RC	.60	1.50
16 Steve Mura	.02	.10
17 Ken Oberkfell	.02	.10
18 Darrell Porter	.02	.10
19 Mike Ramsey	.02	.10
20 Gene Roof	.02	.10
21 Lonnie Smith	.02	.10
22 Ozzie Smith	.50	1.25
23 John Stuper	.02	.10
24 Bruce Sutter	.15	.40
25 Gene Tenace	.07	.20
26 Jerry Augustine	.02	.10
27 Dwight Bernard	.02	.10
28 Mark Brouhard	.02	.10
29 Mike Caldwell	.02	.10
30 Cecil Cooper	.07	.20
31 Jamie Easterly	.02	.10
32 Marshall Edwards	.02	.10
33 Rollie Fingers	.07	.20
34 Jim Gantner	.02	.10
35 Moose Haas	.02	.10
36 Roy Howell	.02	.10
37 Pete Ladd	.02	.10
38 Bob McClure	.02	.10
39 Doc Medich	.02	.10
40 Paul Molitor	.07	.20
41 Don Money	.02	.10
42 Charlie Moore	.02	.10
43 Ben Oglivie	.07	.20
44 Ed Romero	.02	.10
45 Ted Simmons	.07	.20
46 Jim Slaton	.02	.10
47 Don Sutton	.07	.20
48 Gorman Thomas	.07	.20
49 Pete Vuckovich	.02	.10
50 Ned Yost	.02	.10
51 Robin Yount	.50	1.25
52 Benny Ayala	.02	.10
53 Bob Bonner	.02	.10
54 Al Bumbry	.02	.10
55 Terry Crowley	.02	.10
56 Storm Davis RC	.20	.50
57 Rich Dauer	.02	.10
58 Rick Dempsey UER	.02	.10
(Posing batting lefty)		
59 Jim Dwyer	.02	.10
60 Mike Flanagan	.02	.10
61 Dan Ford	.02	.10
62 Glenn Gulliver	.02	.10
63 John Lowenstein	.02	.10
64 Dennis Martinez	.07	.20
65 Tippy Martinez	.02	.10
66 Scott McGregor	.02	.10
67 Eddie Murray	.30	.75
68 Joe Nolan	.02	.10
69 Jim Palmer	.07	.20
70 Cal Ripken	2.50	6.00
71 Gary Roenicke	.02	.10
72 Lenn Sakata	.02	.10
73 Ken Singleton	.07	.20
74 Sammy Stewart	.02	.10
75 Tim Stoddard	.02	.10
76 Don Aase	.02	.10
77 Don Baylor	.07	.20
78 Juan Beniquez	.02	.10
79 Bob Boone	.07	.20
80 Rick Burleson	.02	.10
81 Rod Carew	.15	.40
82 Bobby Clark	.02	.10
83 Doug Corbett	.02	.10
84 John Curtis	.02	.10
85 Doug DeCinces	.02	.10
86 Brian Downing	.07	.20
87 Joe Ferguson	.02	.10
88 Tim Foli	.02	.10
89 Ken Forsch	.02	.10
90 Dave Goltz	.02	.10
91 Bobby Grich	.07	.20
92 Andy Hassler	.02	.10
93 Reggie Jackson	.15	.40
94 Ron Jackson	.02	.10
95 Tommy John	.07	.20
96 Bruce Kison	.02	.10
97 Fred Lynn	.07	.20
98 Ed Ott	.02	.10
99 Steve Renko	.02	.10
100 Luis Sanchez	.02	.10
101 Rob Wilfong	.02	.10
102 Mike Witt	.02	.10
103 Geoff Zahn	.02	.10
104 Willie Aikens	.02	.10
105 Mike Armstrong	.02	.10
106 Vida Blue	.07	.20
107 Bud Black RC	.20	.50
108 George Brett	.75	2.00
109 Bill Castro	.02	.10
110 Onix Concepcion	.02	.10
111 Dave Frost	.02	.10
112 Cesar Geronimo	.02	.10
113 Larry Gura	.02	.10
114 Steve Hammond	.02	.10
115 Don Hood	.02	.10
116 Dennis Leonard	.02	.10
117 Jerry Martin	.02	.10
118 Lee May	.02	.10
119 Hal McRae	.07	.20
120 Amos Otis	.07	.20
121 Greg Pryor	.02	.10
122 Dan Quisenberry	.02	.10
123 Don Slaught RC	.20	.50
124 Paul Splittorff	.02	.10
125 U.L. Washington	.02	.10
126 John Wathan	.02	.10
127 Frank White	.07	.20
128 Willie Wilson	.07	.20
129 Steve Bedrosian UER	.02	.10
(Height 6'33)		
130 Bruce Benedict	.02	.10
131 Tommy Boggs	.02	.10
132 Brett Butler	.07	.20
133 Rick Camp	.02	.10
134 Chris Chambliss	.07	.20
135 Ken Dayley	.02	.10
136 Gene Garber	.02	.10
137 Terry Harper	.02	.10
138 Bob Horner	.07	.20
139 Glenn Hubbard	.02	.10
140 Rufino Linares	.02	.10
141 Rick Mahler	.02	.10
142 Dale Murphy	.15	.40
143 Phil Niekro	.07	.20
144 Pascual Perez	.02	.10
145 Biff Pocoroba	.02	.10
146 Rafael Ramirez	.02	.10
147 Jerry Royster	.02	.10
148 Ken Smith	.02	.10
149 Bob Walk	.02	.10
150 Claudell Washington	.02	.10
151 Bob Watson	.02	.10
152 Larry Whisenton	.02	.10
153 Porfirio Altamirano	.02	.10
154 Marty Bystrom	.02	.10
155 Steve Carlton	.15	.40
156 Larry Christenson	.02	.10
157 Ivan DeJesus	.02	.10
158 John Denny	.02	.10
159 Bob Dernier	.02	.10
160 Bo Diaz	.02	.10
161 Ed Farmer	.02	.10
162 Greg Gross	.02	.10
163 Mike Krukow	.02	.10
164 Garry Maddox	.02	.10
165 Gary Matthews	.07	.20
166 Tug McGraw	.07	.20
167 Bob Molinaro	.02	.10
168 Sid Monge	.02	.10
169 Ron Reed	.02	.10
170 Bill Robinson	.02	.10
171 Pete Rose	1.00	2.50
172 Dick Ruthven	.02	.10
173 Mike Schmidt	.75	2.00
174 Manny Trillo	.02	.10
175 Ozzie Virgil	.02	.10
176 George Vukovich	.02	.10
177 Gary Allenson	.02	.10
178 Luis Aponte	.02	.10
179 Wade Boggs RC	4.00	10.00
180 Tom Burgmeier	.02	.10
181 Mark Clear	.02	.10
182 Dennis Eckersley	.15	.40
183 Dwight Evans	.15	.40
184 Rich Gedman	.02	.10
185 Glenn Hoffman	.02	.10
186 Bruce Hurst	.02	.10
187 Carney Lansford	.07	.20
188 Rick Miller	.02	.10
189 Reid Nichols	.02	.10
190 Bob Ojeda	.02	.10
191 Tony Perez	.15	.40
192 Chuck Rainey	.02	.10
193 Jerry Remy	.02	.10
194 Jim Rice	.07	.20
195 Bob Stanley	.02	.10
196 Dave Stapleton	.02	.10
197 Mike Torrez	.02	.10
198 John Tudor	.07	.20
199 Julio Valdez	.02	.10
200 Carl Yastrzemski	.50	1.25
201 Dusty Baker	.07	.20
202 Joe Beckwith	.02	.10
203 Greg Brock	.02	.10
204 Ron Cey	.07	.20
205 Terry Forster	.07	.20
206 Steve Garvey	.07	.20
207 Pedro Guerrero	.07	.20
208 Burt Hooton	.02	.10
209 Steve Howe	.02	.10
210 Ken Landreaux	.02	.10
211 Mike Marshall	.02	.10
212 Candy Maldonado RC	.20	.50
213 Rick Monday	.07	.20
214 Tom Niedenfuer	.02	.10
215 Jorge Orta	.02	.10
216 Jerry Reuss UER	.02	.10
217 Ron Roenicke	.02	.10
218 Vicente Romo	.02	.10
219 Bill Russell	.07	.20
220 Steve Sax	.07	.20
221 Mike Scioscia	.07	.20
222 Dave Stewart	.07	.20
223 Derrel Thomas	.02	.10
224 Fernando Valenzuela	.07	.20
225 Bob Welch	.07	.20
226 Ricky Wright	.02	.10
227 Steve Yeager	.07	.20
228 Bill Almon	.02	.10
229 Harold Baines	.07	.20
230 Salome Barojas	.02	.10
231 Tony Bernazard	.02	.10
232 Britt Burns	.02	.10
233 Richard Dotson	.02	.10
234 Ernesto Escarrega	.02	.10
235 Carlton Fisk	.15	.40
236 Jerry Hairston	.02	.10
237 Kevin Hickey	.02	.10
238 LaMarr Hoyt	.02	.10
239 Steve Kemp	.02	.10
240 Jim Kern	.02	.10
241 Ron Kittle RC	.40	1.00
242 Jerry Koosman	.07	.20
243 Dennis Lamp	.02	.10
244 Rudy Law	.02	.10
245 Vance Law	.02	.10
246 Ron LeFlore	.07	.20
247 Greg Luzinski	.07	.20
248 Tom Paciorek	.02	.10
249 Aurelio Rodriguez	.02	.10
250 Mike Squires	.02	.10
251 Steve Trout	.02	.10
252 Jim Barr	.02	.10
253 Dave Bergman	.02	.10
254 Fred Breining	.02	.10
255 Bob Brenly	.02	.10
256 Jack Clark	.07	.20
257 Chili Davis	.07	.20
258 Darrell Evans	.07	.20
259 Alan Fowlkes	.02	.10
260 Rich Gale	.02	.10
261 Atlee Hammaker	.02	.10
262 Al Holland	.02	.10
263 Duane Kuiper	.02	.10
264 Bill Laskey	.02	.10
265 Gary Lavelle	.02	.10
266 Johnnie LeMaster	.02	.10
267 Renie Martin	.02	.10
268 Milt May	.02	.10
269 Greg Minton	.02	.10
270 Joe Morgan	.07	.20
271 Tom O'Malley	.02	.10
272 Reggie Smith	.07	.20
273 Guy Sularz	.02	.10
274 Champ Summers	.02	.10
275 Max Venable	.02	.10
276 Jim Wohlford	.02	.10
277 Ray Burris	.02	.10
278 Gary Carter	.07	.20
279 Warren Cromartie	.02	.10
280 Andre Dawson	.07	.20
281 Terry Francona	.07	.20
282 Doug Flynn	.02	.10
283 Woodie Fryman	.02	.10
284 Bill Gullickson	.02	.10
285 Wallace Johnson	.02	.10
286 Charlie Lea	.02	.10
287 Randy Lerch	.02	.10
288 Brad Mills	.02	.10
289 Dan Norman	.02	.10
290 Al Oliver	.07	.20
291 David Palmer	.02	.10
292 Tim Raines	.07	.20
293 Jeff Reardon	.07	.20
294 Steve Rogers	.07	.20
295 Scott Sanderson	.02	.10
296 Dan Schatzeder	.02	.10
297 Bryn Smith	.02	.10
298 Chris Speier	.02	.10
299 Tim Wallach	.07	.20
300 Jerry White	.02	.10
301 Joel Youngblood	.02	.10
302 Ross Baumgarten	.02	.10
303 Dale Berra	.02	.10
304 John Candelaria	.02	.10
305 Dick Davis	.02	.10
306 Mike Easler	.02	.10
307 Richie Hebner	.02	.10
308 Lee Lacy	.02	.10
309 Bill Madlock	.07	.20
310 Larry McWilliams	.02	.10
311 John Milner	.02	.10
312 Omar Moreno	.02	.10
313 Jim Morrison	.02	.10
314 Steve Nicosia	.02	.10
315 Dave Parker	.07	.20
316 Tony Pena	.02	.10
317 Johnny Ray	.02	.10
318 Rick Rhoden	.02	.10
319 Don Robinson	.02	.10
320 Enrique Romo	.02	.10
321 Manny Sarmiento	.02	.10
322 Rod Scurry	.02	.10
323 Jimmy Smith	.02	.10
324 Willie Stargell	.15	.40
325 Jason Thompson	.02	.10
326 Kent Tekulve	.02	.10
327A Tom Brookens	.02	.10
(Short .375-inch brown box		
shaded in on card back)		
327B Tom Brookens	.02	.10
(Longer 1.25-inch brown box		
shaded in on card back)		
328 Enos Cabell	.02	.10
329 Kirk Gibson	.07	.20
330 Larry Herndon	.02	.10
331 Mike Ivie	.02	.10
332 Howard Johnson RC	.40	1.00
333 Lynn Jones	.02	.10
334 Rick Leach	.02	.10
335 Chet Lemon	.07	.20
336 Jack Morris	.07	.20
337 Lance Parrish	.07	.20
338 Larry Pashnick	.02	.10
339 Dan Petry	.02	.10
340 Dave Rozema	.02	.10
341 Dave Rucker	.02	.10
342 Elias Sosa	.02	.10
343 Dave Tobik	.02	.10
344 Alan Trammell	.07	.20
345 Jerry Turner	.02	.10
346 Jerry Ujdur	.02	.10
347 Pat Underwood	.02	.10
348 Lou Whitaker	.07	.20
349 Milt Wilcox	.02	.10
350 Glenn Wilson	.20	.50
351 John Wockenfuss	.02	.10
352 Kurt Bevacqua	.02	.10
353 Juan Bonilla	.02	.10
354 Floyd Chiffer	.02	.10
355 Luis DeLeon	.02	.10
356 Dave Dravecky RC	.40	1.00
357 Dave Edwards	.02	.10
358 Juan Eichelberger	.02	.10
359 Tim Flannery	.02	.10
360 Tony Gwynn RC	5.00	12.00
361 Ruppert Jones	.02	.10
362 Terry Kennedy	.02	.10
363 Joe Lefebvre	.02	.10
364 Sixto Lezcano	.02	.10
365 Tim Lollar	.02	.10
366 Gary Lucas	.02	.10
367 John Montefusco	.02	.10
368 Broderick Perkins	.02	.10
369 Joe Pittman	.02	.10
370 Gene Richards	.02	.10
371 Luis Salazar	.02	.10
372 Eric Show RC	.20	.50
373 Garry Templeton	.07	.20
374 Chris Welsh	.02	.10
375 Alan Wiggins	.02	.10
376 Rick Cerone	.02	.10
377 Dave Collins	.02	.10
378 Roger Erickson	.02	.10
379 George Frazier	.02	.10
380 Oscar Gamble	.02	.10
381 Rich Gossage	.07	.20
382 Ken Griffey	.07	.20
383 Ron Guidry	.07	.20
384 Dave LaRoche	.02	.10
385 Rudy May	.02	.10
386 John Mayberry	.02	.10
387 Lee Mazzilli	.07	.20
388 Mike Morgan	.02	.10
389 Jerry Mumphrey	.02	.10
390 Bobby Murcer	.07	.20
391 Graig Nettles	.07	.20
392 Lou Piniella	.07	.20
393 Willie Randolph	.07	.20
394 Shane Rawley	.02	.10
395 Dave Righetti	.07	.20
396 Andre Robertson	.02	.10
397 Roy Smalley	.02	.10
398 Dave Winfield	.07	.20
399 Butch Wynegar	.02	.10
400 Chris Bando	.02	.10
401 Alan Bannister	.02	.10
402 Len Barker	.02	.10
403 Tom Brennan	.02	.10
404 Carmelo Castillo	.02	.10
405 Miguel Dilone	.02	.10
406 Jerry Dybzinski	.02	.10
407 Mike Fischlin	.02	.10
408 Ed Glynn UER	.02	.10
(Photo actually		
Bud Anderson)		
409 Mike Hargrove	.02	.10
410 Toby Harrah	.07	.20
411 Ron Hassey	.02	.10
412 Von Hayes	.02	.10
413 Rick Manning	.02	.10
414 Bake McBride	.07	.20
415 Larry Milbourne	.02	.10
416 Bill Nahorodny	.02	.10
417 Jack Perconte	.02	.10
418 Lary Sorensen	.02	.10
419 Dan Spillner	.02	.10
420 Rick Sutcliffe	.07	.20
421 Andre Thornton	.02	.10
422 Rick Waits	.02	.10
423 Eddie Whitson	.02	.10
424 Jesse Barfield	.07	.20
425 Barry Bonnell	.02	.10
426 Jim Clancy	.02	.10
427 Damaso Garcia	.02	.10
428 Jerry Garvin	.02	.10
429 Alfredo Griffin	.02	.10
430 Garth Iorg	.02	.10
431 Roy Lee Jackson	.02	.10
432 Luis Leal	.02	.10
433 Buck Martinez	.02	.10
434 Joey McLaughlin	.02	.10
435 Lloyd Moseby	.02	.10
436 Rance Mulliniks	.02	.10
437 Dale Murray	.02	.10
438 Wayne Nordhagen	.02	.10
439 Geno Petralli	.20	.50
440 Hosken Powell	.02	.10
441 Dave Stieb	.07	.20
442 Willie Upshaw	.02	.10
443 Ernie Whitt	.02	.10
444 Alvis Woods	.02	.10
445 Alan Ashby	.02	.10
446 Jose Cruz	.07	.20
447 Kiko Garcia	.02	.10
448 Phil Garner	.07	.20
449 Danny Heep	.02	.10
450 Art Howe	.02	.10
451 Bob Knepper	.02	.10
452 Alan Knicely	.02	.10
453 Ray Knight	.07	.20
454 Frank LaCorte	.02	.10
455 Mike LaCoss	.02	.10
456 Randy Moffitt	.02	.10
457 Joe Niekro	.02	.10
458 Terry Puhl	.02	.10
459 Luis Pujols	.02	.10
460 Craig Reynolds	.02	.10
461 Bert Roberge	.02	.10
462 Vern Ruhle	.02	.10
463 Nolan Ryan	1.50	4.00
464 Joe Sambito	.02	.10
465 Tony Scott	.02	.10
466 Dave Smith	.02	.10
467 Harry Spilman	.02	.10
468 Dickie Thon	.02	.10
469 Denny Walling	.02	.10
470 Larry Andersen	.02	.10
471 Floyd Bannister	.02	.10
472 Jim Beattie	.02	.10
473 Bruce Bochte	.02	.10
474 Manny Castillo	.02	.10
475 Bill Caudill	.02	.10
476 Bryan Clark	.02	.10
477 Al Cowens	.02	.10
478 Julio Cruz	.02	.10
479 Todd Cruz	.02	.10
480 Gary Gray	.02	.10
481 Dave Henderson	.02	.10
482 Mike Moore RC	.20	.50
483 Gaylord Perry	.07	.20
484 Dave Revering	.02	.10
485 Joe Simpson	.02	.10
486 Mike Stanton	.02	.10
487 Rick Sweet	.02	.10
488 Ed VandeBerg	.02	.10
489 Richie Zisk	.02	.10
490 Doug Bird	.02	.10
491 Larry Bowa	.07	.20
492 Bill Buckner	.07	.20
493 Bill Campbell	.02	.10
494 Jody Davis	.02	.10
495 Leon Durham	.02	.10
496 Steve Henderson	.02	.10
497 Willie Hernandez	.02	.10
498 Ferguson Jenkins	.07	.20
499 Jay Johnstone	.02	.10
500 Junior Kennedy	.02	.10
501 Randy Martz	.02	.10
502 Jerry Morales	.02	.10
503 Keith Moreland	.02	.10
504 Dickie Noles	.02	.10
505 Mike Proly	.02	.10
506 Allen Ripley	.02	.10
507 R.Sandberg RC UER	4.00	10.00
Should say High School		
in Spokane, Washington		
508 Lee Smith	.15	.40
509 Pat Tabler	.02	.10
510 Dick Tidrow	.02	.10
511 Bump Wills	.02	.10
512 Gary Woods	.02	.10
513 Tony Armas	.07	.20
514 Dave Beard	.02	.10
515 Jeff Burroughs	.02	.10
516 John D'Acquisto	.02	.10
517 Wayne Gross	.02	.10
518 Mike Heath	.02	.10
519 R.Henderson UER	.60	1.50
Brock record listed		
as 120 steals		
520 Cliff Johnson	.02	.10
521 Matt Keough	.02	.10
522 Brian Kingman	.02	.10
523 Rick Langford	.02	.10
524 Dave Lopes	.07	.20
525 Steve McCatty	.02	.10
526 Dave McKay	.02	.10
527 Dan Meyer	.02	.10
528 Dwayne Murphy	.02	.10
529 Jeff Newman	.02	.10
530 Mike Norris	.02	.10
531 Bob Owchinko	.02	.10
532 Joe Rudi	.07	.20
533 Jimmy Sexton	.02	.10
534 Fred Stanley	.02	.10
535 Tom Underwood	.02	.10
536 Neil Allen	.02	.10
537 Wally Backman	.02	.10
538 Bob Bailor	.02	.10
539 Hubie Brooks	.02	.10
540 Carlos Diaz RC	.08	.25
541 Pete Falcone	.02	.10
542 George Foster	.07	.20
543 Ron Gardenhire	.02	.10
544 Brian Giles	.02	.10
545 Ron Hodges	.02	.10
546 Randy Jones	.02	.10
547 Mike Jorgensen	.02	.10
548 Dave Kingman	.07	.20
549 Ed Lynch	.02	.10
550 Jesse Orosco	.02	.10
551 Rick Ownbey	.02	.10
552 Charlie Puleo	.02	.10
553 Gary Rajsich	.02	.10
554 Mike Scott	.07	.20
555 Rusty Staub	.07	.20
556 John Stearns	.02	.10
557 Craig Swan	.02	.10
558 Ellis Valentine	.02	.10
559 Tom Veryzer	.02	.10
560 Mookie Wilson	.07	.20
561 Pat Zachry	.02	.10
562 Buddy Bell	.07	.20
563 John Butcher	.02	.10
564 Steve Comer	.02	.10
565 Danny Darwin	.02	.10
566 Bucky Dent	.07	.20
567 John Grubb	.02	.10
568 Rick Honeycutt	.02	.10
569 Dave Hostetler	.02	.10
570 Charlie Hough	.07	.20
571 Lamar Johnson	.02	.10
572 Jon Matlack	.02	.10
573 Paul Mirabella	.02	.10
574 Larry Parrish	.02	.10
575 Mike Richardt	.02	.10
576 Mickey Rivers	.02	.10
577 Billy Sample	.02	.10
578 Dave Schmidt	.02	.10
579 Bill Stein	.02	.10
580 Jim Sundberg	.07	.20
581 Frank Tanana	.07	.20
582 Mark Wagner	.02	.10
583 George Wright RC	.20	.50
584 Johnny Bench	.30	.75
585 Bruce Berenyi	.02	.10
586 Larry Biittner	.02	.10

587 Cesar Cedeno .07 .20
588 Dave Concepcion .07 .20
589 Dan Driessen .02 .10
590 Greg Harris .02 .10
591 Ben Hayes .02 .10
592 Paul Householder .02 .10
593 Tom Hume .02 .10
594 Wayne Krenchicki .02 .10
595 Rafael Landestoy .02 .10
596 Charlie Leibrandt .02 .10
597 Eddie Milner .02 .10
598 Ron Oester .02 .10
599 Frank Pastore .02 .10
600 Joe Price .02 .10
601 Tom Seaver .30 .75
602 Bob Shirley .02 .10
603 Mario Soto .07 .20
604 Alex Trevino .02 .10
605 Mike Vail .02 .10
606 Duane Walker .02 .10
607 Tom Brunansky .07 .20
608 Bobby Castillo .02 .10
609 John Castino .02 .10
610 Ron Davis .02 .10
611 Lenny Faedo .02 .10
612 Terry Felton .02 .10
613 Gary Gaetti RC .40 1.00
614 Mickey Hatcher .02 .10
615 Brad Havens .02 .10
616 Kent Hrbek .07 .20
617 Randy Johnson .02 .10
618 Tim Laudner .02 .10
619 Jeff Little .02 .10
620 Bobby Mitchell .02 .10
621 Jack O'Connor .02 .10
622 John Pacella .02 .10
623 Pete Redfern .02 .10
624 Jesus Vega .02 .10
625 Frank Viola RC .60 1.50
626 Ron Washington RC .10 .25
627 Gary Ward .02 .10
628 Al Williams .02 .10
629 Carl Yastrzemski .30 .75
Dennis Eckersley
Mark Clear
630 Gaylord Perry .02 .10
Terry Bulling 5/6/82
631 Dave Concepcion .07 .20
Manny Trillo
632 Robin Yount .30 .75
Buddy Bell
633 Dave Winfield .02 .10
Kent Hrbek
634 Willie Stargell .30 .75
Pete Rose
635 Toby Harrah .07 .20
Andre Thornton
636 Ozzie Smith .30 .75
Lonnie Smith
637 Bo Diaz .02 .10
Gary Carter
638 Carlton Fisk .07 .20
Gary Carter
639 Rickey Henderson IA .30 .75
640 Ben Oglivie .15 .40
Reggie Jackson
641 Joel Youngblood .02 .10
August 4, 1982
642 Ron Hassey .07 .20
Len Barker
643 Black and Blue .07 .20
Vida Blue
644 Black and Blue .02 .10
Bud Black
645 Reggie Jackson Power .07 .20
646 Rickey Henderson Speed .30 .75
647 CL: Cards/Brewers .02 .10
648 CL: Orioles/Angels .02 .10
649 CL: Royals/Braves .02 .10
650 CL: Phillies/Red Sox .02 .10
651 CL: Dodgers/White Sox .02 .10
652 CL: Giants/Expos .02 .10
653 CL: Pirates/Tigers .02 .10
654 CL: Padres/Yankees .02 .10
655 CL: Indians/Blue Jays .02 .10
656 CL: Astros/Mariners .02 .10
657 CL: Cubs/A's .02 .10
658 CL: Mets/Rangers .02 .10
659 CL: Reds/Twins .02 .10
660 CL: Specials/Teams .02 .10

1984 Fleer

The 1984 Fleer card 660-card standard-size set featured fronts with full-color team logos along with the player's name and position and the Fleer identification. Wax packs again consisted of 15 cards plus logo stickers. The set features many imaginative photos, several multi-player cards, and many more action shots than the 1983 card set. The backs are quite similar to the 1983 backs except that blue rather than brown ink is used. The player cards are alphabetized within team and the teams are ordered by their 1983 season finish and won-lost record. Specials (626-646) and checklist cards (647-660) make up the end of the set. The key Rookie Cards in this set are Don Mattingly, Darryl Strawberry and Andy Van Slyke.

COMPLETE SET (660) 25.00 50.00
1 Mike Boddicker .05 .15
2 Al Bumbry .05 .15
3 Todd Cruz .05 .15
4 Rich Dauer .05 .15
5 Storm Davis .05 .15
6 Rick Dempsey .05 .15
7 Jim Dwyer .05 .15
8 Mike Flanagan .05 .15
9 Dan Ford .05 .15
10 John Lowenstein .05 .15
11 Dennis Martinez .15 .40
12 Tippy Martinez .05 .15
13 Scott McGregor .05 .15
14 Eddie Murray .60 1.50
15 Joe Nolan .05 .15
16 Jim Palmer .15 .40
17 Cal Ripken 4.00 10.00
18 Gary Roenicke .05 .15
19 Lenn Sakata .05 .15
20 John Shelby .05 .15
21 Ken Singleton .15 .40
22 Sammy Stewart .05 .15
23 Tim Stoddard .05 .15
24 Marty Bystrom .05 .15
25 Steve Carlton .30 .75
26 Ivan DeJesus .05 .15
27 John Denny .05 .15
28 Bob Dernier .05 .15
29 Bo Diaz .05 .15
30 Kiko Garcia .05 .15
31 Greg Gross .05 .15
32 Kevin Gross RC .20 .50
33 Von Hayes .05 .15
34 Willie Hernandez .05 .15
35 Al Holland .05 .15
36 Charles Hudson .05 .15
37 Joe Lefebvre .05 .15
38 Sixto Lezcano .05 .15
39 Garry Maddox .05 .15
40 Gary Matthews .15 .40
41 Len Matuszek .05 .15
42 Tug McGraw .15 .40
43 Joe Morgan .15 .40
44 Tony Perez .30 .75
45 Ron Reed .05 .15
46 Pete Rose 2.00 5.00
47 Juan Samuel RC .40 1.00
48 Mike Schmidt 1.50 4.00
49 Ozzie Virgil .05 .15
50 Juan Agosto .05 .15
51 Harold Baines .15 .40
52 Floyd Bannister .05 .15
53 Salome Barojas .05 .15
54 Britt Burns .05 .15
55 Julio Cruz .05 .15
56 Richard Dotson .05 .15
57 Jerry Dybzinski .05 .15
58 Carlton Fisk .30 .75
59 Scott Fletcher .05 .15
60 Jerry Hairston .05 .15
61 Kevin Hickey .05 .15
62 Marc Hill .05 .15
63 LaMarr Hoyt .05 .15
64 Ron Kittle .05 .15
65 Jerry Koosman .15 .40
66 Dennis Lamp .05 .15
67 Rudy Law .05 .15
68 Vance Law .05 .15
69 Greg Luzinski .15 .40
70 Tom Paciorek .05 .15
71 Mike Squires .05 .15
72 Dick Tidrow .05 .15
73 Greg Walker .20 .50
74 Glenn Abbott .05 .15
75 Howard Bailey .05 .15
76 Doug Bair .05 .15
77 Juan Berenguer .05 .15
78 Tom Brookens .15 .40
79 Enos Cabell .05 .15
80 Kirk Gibson .60 1.50
81 John Grubb .05 .15
82 Larry Herndon .15 .40
83 Wayne Krenchicki .05 .15
84 Rick Leach .05 .15
85 Chet Lemon .15 .40
86 Aurelio Lopez .15 .40
87 Jack Morris .15 .40
88 Lance Parrish .30 .75
89 Dan Petry .15 .40
90 Dave Rozema .05 .15
91 Alan Trammell .15 .40
92 Lou Whitaker .15 .40
93 Milt Wilcox .05 .15
94 Glenn Wilson .15 .40
95 John Wockenfuss .05 .15
96 Dusty Baker .15 .40
97 Joe Beckwith .05 .15
98 Greg Brock .05 .15
99 Jack Fimple .05 .15
100 Pedro Guerrero .15 .40
101 Rick Honeycutt .05 .15
102 Burt Hooton .05 .15
103 Steve Howe .05 .15
104 Ken Landreaux .05 .15
105 Mike Marshall .05 .15
106 Rick Monday .15 .40
107 Jose Morales .05 .15
108 Tom Niedenfuer .05 .15
109 Alejandro Pena RC .40 1.00
110 Jerry Reuss UER .05 .15
111 Bill Russell .15 .40
112 Steve Sax .05 .15
113 Mike Scioscia .15 .40
114 Derrel Thomas .05 .15
115 Fernando Valenzuela .15 .40
116 Bob Welch .15 .40
117 Steve Yeager .15 .40
118 Pat Zachry .05 .15
119 Don Baylor .15 .40
120 Bert Campaneris .15 .40
121 Rick Cerone .05 .15
122 Ray Fontenot .05 .15
123 George Frazier .05 .15
124 Oscar Gamble .05 .15
125 Rich Gossage .15 .40
126 Ken Griffey .15 .40
127 Ron Guidry .15 .40
128 Jay Howell .05 .15
129 Steve Kemp .05 .15
130 Matt Keough .05 .15
131 Don Mattingly RC 8.00 20.00
132 John Montefusco .05 .15
133 Omar Moreno .05 .15
134 Dale Murray .05 .15
135 Graig Nettles .15 .40
136 Lou Piniella .15 .40
137 Willie Randolph .15 .40
138 Shane Rawley .05 .15
139 Dave Righetti .15 .40
140 Andre Robertson .05 .15
141 Bob Shirley .05 .15
142 Roy Smalley .05 .15
143 Dave Winfield .15 .40
144 Butch Wynegar .05 .15
145 Jim Acker .05 .15
146 Doyle Alexander .05 .15
147 Jesse Barfield .15 .40
148 Jorge Bell .15 .40
149 Barry Bonnell .05 .15
150 Jim Clancy .05 .15
151 Dave Collins .05 .15
152 Tony Fernandez RC .40 1.00
153 Damaso Garcia .05 .15
154 Dave Geisel .05 .15
155 Jim Gott .05 .15
156 Alfredo Griffin .05 .15
157 Garth Iorg .05 .15
158 Roy Lee Jackson .05 .15
159 Cliff Johnson .05 .15
160 Luis Leal .05 .15
161 Buck Martinez .05 .15
162 Joey McLaughlin .05 .15
163 Randy Moffitt .05 .15
164 Lloyd Moseby .05 .15
165 Rance Mulliniks .05 .15
166 Jorge Orta .05 .15
167 Dave Stieb .15 .40
168 Willie Upshaw .05 .15
169 Ernie Whitt .05 .15
170 Len Barker .05 .15
171 Steve Bedrosian .05 .15
172 Bruce Benedict .05 .15
173 Brett Butler .15 .40
174 Rick Camp .05 .15
175 Chris Chambliss .15 .40
176 Ken Dayley .05 .15
177 Pete Falcone .05 .15
178 Terry Forster .15 .40
179 Gene Garber .05 .15
180 Terry Harper .05 .15
181 Bob Horner .15 .40
182 Glenn Hubbard .05 .15
183 Randy Johnson .05 .15
184 Craig McMurtry .05 .15
185 Donnie Moore .05 .15
186 Dale Murphy .30 .75
187 Phil Niekro .15 .40
188 Pascual Perez .05 .15
189 Biff Pocoroba .05 .15
190 Rafael Ramirez .05 .15
191 Jerry Royster .05 .15
192 Claudell Washington .05 .15
193 Bob Watson .05 .15
194 Jerry Augustine .05 .15
195 Mark Brouhard .05 .15
196 Mike Caldwell .05 .15
197 Tom Candiotti RC .40 1.00
198 Cecil Cooper .15 .40
199 Rollie Fingers .15 .40
200 Jim Gantner .05 .15
201 Bob L. Gibson RC .08 .25
202 Moose Haas .05 .15
203 Roy Howell .05 .15
204 Pete Ladd .05 .15
205 Rick Manning .05 .15
206 Bob McClure .05 .15
207 Paul Molitor UER .15 .40
('83 stats should say
.270 BA and 608 AB)
208 Don Money .05 .15
209 Charlie Moore .05 .15
210 Ben Oglivie .15 .40
211 Chuck Porter .05 .15
212 Ed Romero .05 .15
213 Ted Simmons .15 .40
214 Jim Slaton .05 .15
215 Don Sutton .15 .40
216 Tom Tellmann .05 .15
217 Pete Vuckovich .05 .15
218 Ned Yost .05 .15
219 Robin Yount 1.00 2.50
220 Alan Ashby .05 .15
221 Kevin Bass .05 .15
222 Jose Cruz .15 .40
223 Bill Dawley .05 .15
224 Frank DiPino .05 .15
225 Bill Doran RC .20 .50
226 Phil Garner .15 .40
227 Art Howe .05 .15
228 Bob Knepper .05 .15
229 Ray Knight .15 .40
230 Frank LaCorte .05 .15
231 Mike LaCoss .05 .15
232 Mike Madden .05 .15
233 Jerry Mumphrey .05 .15
234 Joe Niekro .05 .15
235 Terry Puhl .05 .15
236 Luis Pujols .05 .15
237 Craig Reynolds .05 .15
238 Vern Ruhle .05 .15
239 Nolan Ryan 3.00 8.00
240 Mike Scott .15 .40
241 Tony Scott .05 .15
242 Dave Smith .05 .15
243 Dickie Thon .05 .15
244 Denny Walling .05 .15
245 Dale Berra .05 .15
246 Jim Bibby .05 .15
247 John Candelaria .05 .15
248 Jose DeLeon RC .20 .50
249 Mike Easler .05 .15
250 Cecilio Guante .05 .15
251 Richie Hebner .05 .15
252 Lee Lacy .05 .15
253 Bill Madlock .15 .40
254 Milt May .05 .15
255 Lee Mazzilli .15 .40
256 Larry McWilliams .05 .15
257 Jim Morrison .05 .15
258 Dave Parker .15 .40
259 Tony Pena .05 .15
260 Johnny Ray .05 .15
261 Rick Rhoden .05 .15
262 Don Robinson .05 .15
263 Manny Sarmiento .05 .15
264 Rod Scurry .05 .15
265 Kent Tekulve .05 .15
266 Gene Tenace .15 .40
267 Jason Thompson .05 .15
268 Lee Tunnell .05 .15
269 Marvell Wynne .20 .50
270 Ray Burris .05 .15
271 Gary Carter .15 .40
272 Warren Cromartie .05 .15
273 Andre Dawson .15 .40
274 Doug Flynn .05 .15
275 Terry Francona .15 .40
276 Bill Gullickson .05 .15
277 Bob James .05 .15
278 Charlie Lea .05 .15
279 Bryan Little .05 .15
280 Al Oliver .15 .40
281 Tim Raines .15 .40
282 Bobby Ramos .05 .15
283 Jeff Reardon .15 .40
284 Steve Rogers .15 .40
285 Scott Sanderson .05 .15
286 Dan Schatzeder .05 .15
287 Bryn Smith .05 .15
288 Chris Speier .05 .15
289 Manny Trillo .05 .15
290 Mike Vail .05 .15
291 Tim Wallach .05 .15
292 Chris Welsh .05 .15
293 Jim Wohlford .05 .15
294 Kurt Bevacqua .05 .15
295 Juan Bonilla .05 .15
296 Bobby Brown .05 .15
297 Luis DeLeon .05 .15
298 Dave Dravecky .05 .15
299 Tim Flannery .05 .15
300 Steve Garvey .15 .40
301 Tony Gwynn 2.50 6.00
302 Andy Hawkins .05 .15
303 Ruppert Jones .05 .15
304 Terry Kennedy .05 .15
305 Tim Lollar .05 .15
306 Gary Lucas .05 .15
307 Kevin McReynolds RC .40 1.00
308 Sid Monge .05 .15
309 Mario Ramirez .05 .15
310 Gene Richards .05 .15
311 Luis Salazar .05 .15
312 Eric Show .05 .15
313 Elias Sosa .05 .15
314 Garry Templeton .15 .40
315 Mark Thurmond .05 .15
316 Ed Whitson .05 .15
317 Alan Wiggins .05 .15
318 Neil Allen .05 .15
319 Joaquin Andujar .15 .40
320 Steve Braun .05 .15
321 Glenn Brummer .05 .15
322 Bob Forsch .05 .15
323 David Green .05 .15
324 George Hendrick .15 .40
325 Tom Herr .05 .15
326 Dane Iorg .05 .15
327 Jeff Lahti .05 .15
328 Dave LaPoint .05 .15
329 Willie McGee .15 .40
330 Ken Oberkfell .05 .15
331 Darrell Porter .05 .15
332 Jamie Quirk .05 .15
333 Mike Ramsey .05 .15
334 Floyd Rayford .05 .15
335 Lonnie Smith .05 .15
336 Ozzie Smith 1.00 2.50
337 John Stuper .05 .15
338 Bruce Sutter .30 .75
339 Andy Van Slyke RC 1.00 2.50
UER Batting and throwing
both wrong on card back
340 Dave Von Ohlen .05 .15
341 Willie Aikens .05 .15
342 Mike Armstrong .05 .15
343 Bud Black .05 .15
344 George Brett 1.50 4.00
345 Onix Concepcion .05 .15
346 Keith Creel .05 .15
347 Larry Gura .05 .15
348 Don Hood .05 .15
349 Dennis Leonard .05 .15
350 Hal McRae .15 .40
351 Amos Otis .15 .40
352 Gaylord Perry .15 .40
353 Greg Pryor .05 .15
354 Dan Quisenberry .05 .15
355 Steve Renko .05 .15
356 Leon Roberts .05 .15
357 Pat Sheridan .05 .15
358 Joe Simpson .05 .15
359 Don Slaught .15 .40
360 Paul Splittorff .05 .15
361 U.L. Washington .05 .15
362 John Wathan .05 .15
363 Frank White .15 .40
364 Willie Wilson .15 .40
365 Jim Barr .05 .15
366 Dave Bergman .05 .15
367 Fred Breining .05 .15
368 Bob Brenly .05 .15
369 Jack Clark .15 .40
370 Chili Davis .15 .40
371 Mark Davis .05 .15
372 Darrell Evans .15 .40
373 Atlee Hammaker .05 .15
374 Mike Krukow .05 .15
375 Duane Kuiper .05 .15
376 Bill Laskey .05 .15
377 Gary Lavelle .05 .15
378 Johnnie LeMaster .05 .15
379 Jeff Leonard .05 .15
380 Randy Lerch .05 .15
381 Renie Martin .05 .15
382 Andy McGaffigan .05 .15
383 Greg Minton .05 .15
384 Tom O'Malley .05 .15
385 Max Venable .05 .15
386 Brad Wellman .05 .15
387 Joel Youngblood .05 .15
388 Gary Allenson .05 .15
389 Luis Aponte .05 .15
390 Tony Armas .15 .40
391 Doug Bird .05 .15
392 Wade Boggs 1.50 4.00
393 Dennis Boyd .15 .40
394 Mike G. Brown UER .08 .25
(shown with record
of 31-104)
395 Mark Clear .05 .15
396 Dennis Eckersley .30 .75
397 Dwight Evans .30 .75
398 Rich Gedman .05 .15
399 Glenn Hoffman .05 .15
400 Bruce Hurst .05 .15
401 John Henry Johnson .05 .15
402 Ed Jurak .05 .15
403 Rick Miller .05 .15
404 Jeff Newman .05 .15
405 Reid Nichols .05 .15
406 Bob Ojeda .05 .15
407 Jerry Remy .05 .15
408 Jim Rice .15 .40
409 Bob Stanley .05 .15
410 Dave Stapleton .05 .15
411 John Tudor .15 .40
412 Carl Yastrzemski .60 1.50
413 Buddy Bell .15 .40
414 Larry Biittner .05 .15
415 John Butcher .05 .15
416 Danny Darwin .05 .15
417 Bucky Dent .15 .40
418 Dave Hostetler .05 .15
419 Charlie Hough .15 .40
420 Bobby Johnson .05 .15
421 Odell Jones .05 .15
422 Jon Matlack .05 .15
423 Pete O'Brien RC .20 .50
424 Larry Parrish .05 .15
425 Mickey Rivers .05 .15
426 Billy Sample .05 .15
427 Dave Schmidt .05 .15
428 Mike Smithson .05 .15
429 Bill Stein .05 .15
430 Dave Stewart .15 .40
431 Jim Sundberg .15 .40
432 Frank Tanana .15 .40
433 Dave Tobik .05 .15
434 Wayne Tolleson .05 .15
435 George Wright .05 .15
436 Bill Almon .05 .15
437 Keith Atherton .05 .15
438 Dave Beard .05 .15
439 Tom Burgmeier .05 .15
440 Jeff Burroughs .05 .15
441 Chris Codiroli .05 .15
442 Tim Conroy .05 .15
443 Mike Davis .05 .15
444 Wayne Gross .05 .15
445 Garry Hancock .05 .15
446 Mike Heath .05 .15
447 Rickey Henderson 1.00 2.50
448 Donnie Hill .05 .15
449 Bob Kearney .05 .15
450 Bill Krueger RC .08 .25
451 Rick Langford .05 .15
452 Carney Lansford .15 .40
453 Dave Lopes .15 .40
454 Steve McCatty .05 .15
455 Dan Meyer .05 .15
456 Dwayne Murphy .05 .15
457 Mike Norris .05 .15
458 Ricky Peters .05 .15
459 Tony Phillips RC .40 1.00
460 Tom Underwood .05 .15
461 Mike Warren .05 .15
462 Johnny Bench .60 1.50
463 Bruce Berenyi .05 .15
464 Dann Bilardello .05 .15
465 Cesar Cedeno .15 .40
466 Dave Concepcion .15 .40
467 Dan Driessen .05 .15
468 Nick Esasky .05 .15
469 Rich Gale .05 .15
470 Ben Hayes .05 .15
471 Paul Householder .05 .15
472 Tom Hume .05 .15
473 Alan Knicely .05 .15
474 Eddie Milner .05 .15
475 Ron Oester .05 .15
476 Kelly Paris .05 .15
477 Frank Pastore .05 .15
478 Ted Power .05 .15
479 Joe Price .05 .15
480 Charlie Puleo .05 .15
481 Gary Redus RC .20 .50
482 Bill Scherrer .05 .15
483 Mario Soto .15 .40
484 Alex Trevino .05 .15
485 Duane Walker .05 .15
486 Larry Bowa .15 .40
487 Warren Brusstar .05 .15
488 Bill Buckner .15 .40
489 Bill Campbell .05 .15
490 Ron Cey .15 .40
491 Jody Davis .05 .15
492 Leon Durham .05 .15
493 Mel Hall .15 .40
494 Ferguson Jenkins .15 .40
495 Jay Johnstone .05 .15
496 Craig Lefferts RC .08 .25
497 Carmelo Martinez .05 .15
498 Jerry Morales .05 .15
499 Keith Moreland .05 .15
500 Dickie Noles .05 .15
501 Mike Proly .05 .15
502 Chuck Rainey .05 .15
503 Dick Ruthven .05 .15
504 Ryne Sandberg 2.50 6.00
505 Lee Smith .15 .40
506 Steve Trout .05 .15
507 Gary Woods .05 .15
508 Juan Beniquez .05 .15
509 Bob Boone .15 .40
510 Rick Burleson .05 .15
511 Rod Carew .30 .75
512 Bobby Clark .05 .15
513 John Curtis .05 .15
514 Doug DeCinces .05 .15
515 Brian Downing .15 .40
516 Tim Foli .05 .15
517 Ken Forsch .05 .15
518 Bobby Grich .15 .40
519 Andy Hassler .05 .15
520 Reggie Jackson .30 .75
521 Ron Jackson .05 .15
522 Tommy John .15 .40
523 Bruce Kison .05 .15
524 Steve Lubratich .05 .15
525 Fred Lynn .15 .40
526 Gary Pettis .05 .15
527 Luis Sanchez .05 .15
528 Daryl Sconiers .05 .15
529 Ellis Valentine .05 .15
530 Rob Wilfong .05 .15
531 Mike Witt .05 .15
532 Geoff Zahn .05 .15
533 Bud Anderson .05 .15
534 Chris Bando .05 .15
535 Alan Bannister .05 .15
536 Bert Blyleven .15 .40
537 Tom Brennan .05 .15
538 Jamie Easterly .05 .15
539 Juan Eichelberger .05 .15
540 Jim Essian .05 .15
541 Mike Fischlin .05 .15
542 Julio Franco .15 .40
543 Mike Hargrove .05 .15
544 Toby Harrah .15 .40
545 Ron Hassey .05 .15
546 Neal Heaton .05 .15
547 Bake McBride .15 .40
548 Broderick Perkins .05 .15
549 Lary Sorensen .05 .15
550 Dan Spillner .05 .15
551 Rick Sutcliffe .15 .40
552 Pat Tabler .05 .15
553 Gorman Thomas .15 .40
554 Andre Thornton .05 .15
555 George Vukovich .05 .15
556 Darrell Brown .05 .15
557 Tom Brunansky .05 .15
558 Randy Bush .05 .15
559 Bobby Castillo .05 .15
560 John Castino .05 .15
561 Ron Davis .05 .15
562 Dave Engle .05 .15
563 Lenny Faedo .05 .15
564 Pete Filson .05 .15
565 Gary Gaetti .30 .75
566 Mickey Hatcher .05 .15
567 Kent Hrbek .15 .40
568 Rusty Kuntz .05 .15
569 Tim Laudner .05 .15
570 Rick Lysander .05 .15
571 Bobby Mitchell .05 .15
572 Ken Schrom .05 .15
573 Ray Smith .05 .15
574 Tim Teufel RC .20 .50
575 Frank Viola .30 .75
576 Gary Ward .05 .15
577 Ron Washington .05 .15
578 Len Whitehouse .05 .15
579 Al Williams .05 .15
580 Bob Bailor .05 .15
581 Mark Bradley .05 .15
582 Hubie Brooks .05 .15
583 Carlos Diaz .05 .15
584 George Foster .15 .40
585 Brian Giles .05 .15
586 Danny Heep .05 .15
587 Keith Hernandez .15 .40
588 Ron Hodges .05 .15
589 Scott Holman .05 .15
590 Dave Kingman .15 .40
591 Ed Lynch .05 .15
592 Jose Oquendo RC .20 .50
593 Jesse Orosco .05 .15
594 Junior Ortiz .05 .15
595 Tom Seaver .60 1.50
596 Doug Sisk .05 .15
597 Rusty Staub .15 .40
598 John Stearns .05 .15
599 Darryl Strawberry RC 2.00 5.00
600 Craig Swan .05 .15
601 Walt Terrell .05 .15
602 Mike Torrez .05 .15
603 Mookie Wilson .15 .40
604 Jamie Allen .05 .15
605 Jim Beattie .05 .15
606 Tony Bernazard .05 .15
607 Manny Castillo .05 .15
608 Bill Caudill .05 .15
609 Bryan Clark .05 .15
610 Al Cowens .05 .15
611 Dave Henderson .15 .40
612 Steve Henderson .05 .15
613 Orlando Mercado .05 .15
614 Mike Moore .05 .15
615 Ricky Nelson UER .05 .15
(Jamie Nelson's
stats on back)
616 Spike Owen RC .20 .50
617 Pat Putnam .05 .15
618 Ron Roenicke .05 .15
619 Mike Stanton .05 .15
620 Bob Stoddard .05 .15
621 Rick Sweet .05 .15
622 Roy Thomas .05 .15
623 Ed VandeBerg .05 .15
624 Matt Young RC .20 .50
625 Richie Zisk .05 .15
626 Fred Lynn IA .15 .40
627 Manny Trillo IA .05 .15
628 Steve Garvey IA .05 .15
629 Rod Carew IA .15 .40
630 Wade Boggs IA .60 1.50
631 Tim Raines IA .05 .15
632 Al Oliver IA .15 .40
633 Steve Sax IA .05 .15
634 Dickie Thon IA .05 .15
635 Dan Quisenberry .05 .15
Tippy Martinez
636 Joe Morgan .60 1.50
Pete Rose
Tony Perez
637 Lance Parrish .30 .75
Bob Boone
638 George Brett .75 2.00
Gaylord Perry
639 Dave Righetti .30 .75
Mike Warren
Bob Forsch
640 Johnny Bench .60 1.50
Carl Yastrzemski
641 Gaylord Perry IA .05 .15
642 Steve Carlton IA .15 .40
643 Joe Altobelli MG .05 .15
Paul Owens MG
644 Rick Dempsey WS .05 .15
645 Mike Boddicker WS .05 .15
646 Scott McGregor WS .05 .15
647 CL: Orioles/Royals .05 .15
Joe Altobelli MG
648 CL: Phillies/Giants .05 .15
Paul Owens MG
649 CL: White Sox/Red Sox .30 .75
Tony LaRussa MG
650 CL: Tigers/Rangers .30 .75
Sparky Anderson MG
651 CL: Dodgers/A's .30 .75
Tommy Lasorda MG
652 CL: Yankees/Reds .30 .75
Billy Martin MG
653 CL: Blue Jays/Cubs .15 .40
Bobby Cox MG
654 CL: Braves/Angels .30 .75
Joe Torre MG
655 CL: Brewers/Indians .05 .15
Rene Lachemann MG
656 CL: Astros/Twins .05 .15
Bob Lillis MG
657 CL: Pirates/Mets .05 .15
Chuck Tanner MG
658 CL: Expos/Mariners .05 .15
Bill Virdon MG
659 CL: Padres/Specials .15 .40
Dick Williams MG
660 CL: Cardinals/Teams .30 .75
Whitey Herzog MG

1984 Fleer Update

This set was Fleer's first update set and portrayed players with their proper team for the current year and rookies who were not in their regular issue. Like the Topps Traded sets of the time, the Fleer Update sets were distributed in factory set form through hobby dealers only. The set was quite popular with collectors, and, apparently, the print run was relatively short, as the set was quickly in short supply and exhibited a rapid and dramatic price increase in the mid to late 1980's. The cards are numbered on the back with a U prefix and placed in alphabetical order by player name. The key (extended) Rookie Cards in this set are Roger Clemens, John Franco, Dwight Gooden, Jimmy Key, Mark Langston, Kirby Puckett, and Bret Saberhagen. Collectors are urged to be careful if purchasing single cards of Clemens, Darling, Gooden, Puckett, Rose, or Saberhagen as these specific cards have been illegally reprinted. These fakes are blurry when compared to the real cards and have noticeably different printing dot patterns under 8X or greater magnification..

COMP.FACT.SET (132) 175.00 300.00
1 Willie Aikens .40 1.00
2 Luis Aponte .40 1.00
3 Mark Bailey .40 1.00
4 Bob Bailor .40 1.00
5 Dusty Baker .60 1.50
6 Steve Balboni .40 1.00
7 Alan Bannister .40 1.00
8 Marty Barrett XRC .75 2.00
9 Dave Beard .40 1.00
10 Joe Beckwith .40 1.00
11 Dave Bergman .40 1.00
12 Tony Bernazard .40 1.00
13 Bruce Bochte .40 1.00
14 Barry Bonnell .40 1.00
15 Phil Bradley .75 2.00
16 Fred Breining .40 1.00
17 Mike C. Brown .40 1.00
18 Bill Buckner .60 1.50
19 Ray Burris .40 1.00
20 John Butcher .40 1.00
21 Brett Butler .60 1.50
22 Enos Cabell .40 1.00
23 Bill Campbell .40 1.00
24 Bill Caudill .40 1.00
25 Bobby Clark .40 1.00
26 Bryan Clark .40 1.00
27 Roger Clemens XRC 60.00 120.00
28 Jaime Cocanower .40 1.00
29 Ron Darling XRC 2.00 5.00
30 Alvin Davis XRC .75 2.00
31 Bob Dernier .40 1.00
32 Carlos Diaz .40 1.00
33 Mike Easler .40 1.00
34 Dennis Eckersley 1.00 2.50
35 Jim Essian .40 1.00
36 Darrell Evans .60 1.50
37 Mike Fitzgerald .40 1.00
38 Tim Foli .40 1.00
39 John Franco XRC 2.00 5.00
40 George Frazier .40 1.00
41 Rich Gale .40 1.00
42 Barbaro Garbey .40 1.00
43 Dwight Gooden XRC 8.00 20.00
44 Rich Gossage .60 1.50
45 Wayne Gross .40 1.00
46 Mark Gubicza XRC .75 2.00
47 Jackie Gutierrez .40 1.00
48 Toby Harrah .60 1.50
49 Ron Hassey .40 1.00
50 Richie Hebner .40 1.00
51 Willie Hernandez .40 1.00
52 Ed Hodge .40 1.00
53 Ricky Horton .40 1.00
54 Art Howe .40 1.00
55 Dane Iorg .40 1.00
56 Brook Jacoby .75 2.00
57 Dion James XRC .40 1.00
58 Mike Jeffcoat XRC .40 1.00
59 Ruppert Jones .40 1.00
60 Bob Kearney .40 1.00
61 Jimmy Key XRC 2.00 5.00
62 Dave Kingman .60 1.50
63 Brad Komminsk XRC .40 1.00
64 Jerry Koosman .60 1.50
65 Wayne Krenchicki .40 1.00
66 Rusty Kuntz .40 1.00
67 Frank LaCorte .40 1.00
68 Dennis Lamp .40 1.00
69 Tito Landrum .40 1.00
70 Mark Langston XRC 2.00 5.00

Card	Low	High
71 Rick Leach	.40	1.00
72 Craig Lefferts	.40	1.00
73 Gary Lucas	.40	1.00
74 Jerry Martin	.40	1.00
75 Carmelo Martinez	.40	1.00
76 Mike Mason XRC	.40	1.00
77 Gary Matthews	.60	1.50
78 Andy McGaffigan	.40	1.00
79 Joey McLaughlin	.40	1.00
80 Joe Morgan	.60	1.50
81 Darryl Motley	.40	1.00
82 Graig Nettles	.60	1.50
83 Phil Niekro	.60	1.50
84 Ken Oberkfell	.40	1.00
85 Al Oliver	.60	1.50
86 Jorge Orta	.40	1.00
87 Amos Otis	.60	1.50
88 Bob Owchinko	.40	1.00
89 Dave Parker	.60	1.50
90 Jack Perconte	.40	1.00
91 Tony Perez	1.00	2.50
92 Gerald Perry	.75	2.00
93 Kirby Puckett XRC	40.00	80.00
94 Shane Rawley	.40	1.00
95 Floyd Rayford	.40	1.00
96 Ron Reed	.40	1.00
97 R.J. Reynolds	.40	1.00
98 Gene Richards	.40	1.00
99 Jose Rijo XRC	2.00	5.00
100 Jeff D. Robinson	.40	1.00
101 Ron Romanick	.40	1.00
102 Pete Rose	5.00	12.00
103 Bret Saberhagen XRC	4.00	10.00
104 Scott Sanderson	.40	1.00
105 Dick Schofield XRC	.75	2.00
106 Tom Seaver	1.50	4.00
107 Jim Slaton	.40	1.00
108 Mike Smithson	.40	1.00
109 Lary Sorensen	.40	1.00
110 Tim Stoddard	.40	1.00
111 Jeff Stone XRC	.40	1.00
112 Champ Summers	.40	1.00
113 Jim Sundberg	.60	1.50
114 Rick Sutcliffe	.60	1.50
115 Craig Swan	.40	1.00
116 Derrel Thomas	.40	1.00
117 Gorman Thomas	.60	1.50
118 Alex Trevino	.40	1.00
119 Manny Trillo	.40	1.00
120 John Tudor	.60	1.50
121 Tom Underwood	.40	1.00
122 Mike Vail	.40	1.00
123 Tom Waddell	.40	1.00
124 Gary Ward	.40	1.00
125 Terry Whitfield	.40	1.00
126 Curtis Wilkerson	.40	1.00
127 Frank Williams	.40	1.00
128 Glenn Wilson	.60	1.50
129 John Wockenfuss	.40	1.00
130 Ned Yost	.40	1.00
131 Mike Young XRC	.40	1.00
132 Checklist 1-132	.40	1.00

1985 Fleer

The 1985 Fleer set consists of 660 standard-size cards. Wax packs contained 15 cards plus logo stickers. Card fronts feature a full color photo, team logo along with the player's name and position. The borders enclosing the photo are color-coded to correspond to the player's team. The cards are ordered alphabetically within team. The teams are ordered based on their respective performance during the prior year. Subsets include Specials (626-643) and Major League Prospects (644-653). The black and white photo on the reverse is included for the third straight year. Rookie Cards include Roger Clemens, Eric Davis, Shawon Dunston, John Franco, Dwight Gooden, Orel Hershiser, Jimmy Key, Mark Langston, Terry Pendleton, Kirby Puckett and Bret Saberhagen

Card	Low	High
COMPLETE SET (660)	30.00	60.00
COMP.FACT.SET (660)	50.00	100.00
1 Doug Bair	.05	.15
2 Juan Berenguer	.05	.15
3 Dave Bergman	.05	.15
4 Tom Brookens	.05	.15
5 Marty Castillo	.05	.15
6 Darrell Evans	.15	.40
7 Barbaro Garbey	.05	.15
8 Kirk Gibson	.15	.40
9 John Grubb	.05	.15
10 Willie Hernandez	.05	.15
11 Larry Herndon	.05	.15
12 Howard Johnson	.15	.40
13 Ruppert Jones	.05	.15
14 Rusty Kuntz	.05	.15
15 Chet Lemon	.15	.40
16 Aurelio Lopez	.05	.15
17 Sid Monge	.05	.15
18 Jack Morris	.15	.40
19 Lance Parrish	.15	.40
20 Dan Petry	.05	.15
21 Dave Rozema	.05	.15
22 Bill Scherrer	.05	.15
23 Alan Trammell	.15	.40
24 Lou Whitaker	.15	.40
25 Milt Wilcox	.05	.15
26 Kurt Bevacqua	.05	.15
27 Greg Booker	.05	.15
28 Bobby Brown	.05	.15
29 Luis DeLeon	.05	.15
30 Dave Dravecky	.05	.15
31 Tim Flannery	.05	.15
32 Steve Garvey	.15	.40
33 Rich Gossage	.15	.40
34 Tony Gwynn	1.00	2.50
35 Greg Harris	.05	.15
36 Andy Hawkins	.05	.15
37 Terry Kennedy	.05	.15
38 Craig Lefferts	.05	.15
39 Tim Lollar	.05	.15
40 Carmelo Martinez	.05	.15
41 Kevin McReynolds	.15	.40
42 Graig Nettles	.15	.40
43 Luis Salazar	.05	.15
44 Eric Show	.05	.15
45 Garry Templeton	.15	.40
46 Mark Thurmond	.05	.15
47 Ed Whitson	.05	.15
48 Alan Wiggins	.05	.15
49 Rich Bordi	.05	.15
50 Larry Bowa	.15	.40
51 Warren Brusstar	.05	.15
52 Ron Cey	.15	.40
53 Henry Cotto RC	.08	.25
54 Jody Davis	.05	.15
55 Bob Dernier	.05	.15
56 Leon Durham	.05	.15
57 Dennis Eckersley	.30	.75
58 George Frazier	.05	.15
59 Richie Hebner	.05	.15
60 Dave Lopes	.15	.40
61 Gary Matthews	.15	.40
62 Keith Moreland	.05	.15
63 Rick Reuschel	.15	.40
64 Dick Ruthven	.05	.15
65 Ryne Sandberg	1.00	2.50
66 Scott Sanderson	.05	.15
67 Lee Smith	.15	.40
68 Tim Stoddard	.05	.15
69 Rick Sutcliffe	.15	.40
70 Steve Trout	.05	.15
71 Gary Woods	.05	.15
72 Wally Backman	.05	.15
73 Bruce Berenyi	.05	.15
74 Hubie Brooks UER	.05	.15
(Kelvin Chapman's		
stats on card back)		
75 Kelvin Chapman	.05	.15
76 Ron Darling	.15	.40
77 Sid Fernandez	.15	.40
78 Mike Fitzgerald	.05	.15
79 George Foster	.15	.40
80 Brent Gaff	.05	.15
81 Ron Gardenhire	.05	.15
82 Dwight Gooden RC	1.25	3.00
83 Tom Gorman	.05	.15
84 Danny Heep	.05	.15
85 Keith Hernandez	.15	.40
86 Ray Knight	.15	.40
87 Ed Lynch	.05	.15
88 Jose Oquendo	.05	.15
89 Jesse Orosco	.05	.15
90 Rafael Santana	.05	.15
91 Doug Sisk	.05	.15
92 Rusty Staub	.15	.40
93 Darryl Strawberry	.50	1.25
94 Walt Terrell	.05	.15
95 Mookie Wilson	.15	.40
96 Jim Acker	.05	.15
97 Willie Aikens	.05	.15
98 Doyle Alexander	.05	.15
99 Jesse Barfield	.15	.40
100 George Bell	.15	.40
101 Jim Clancy	.05	.15
102 Dave Collins	.05	.15
103 Tony Fernandez	.15	.40
104 Damaso Garcia	.05	.15
105 Jim Gott	.05	.15
106 Alfredo Griffin	.05	.15
107 Garth Iorg	.05	.15
108 Roy Lee Jackson	.05	.15
109 Cliff Johnson	.05	.15
110 Jimmy Key RC	.40	1.00
111 Dennis Lamp	.05	.15
112 Rick Leach	.05	.15
113 Luis Leal	.05	.15
114 Buck Martinez	.05	.15
115 Lloyd Moseby	.05	.15
116 Rance Mulliniks	.05	.15
117 Dave Stieb	.15	.40
118 Willie Upshaw	.05	.15
119 Ernie Whitt	.05	.15
120 Mike Armstrong	.05	.15
121 Don Baylor	.15	.40
122 Marty Bystrom	.05	.15
123 Rick Cerone	.05	.15
124 Joe Cowley	.05	.15
125 Brian Dayett	.05	.15
126 Tim Foli	.05	.15
127 Ray Fontenot	.05	.15
128 Ken Griffey	.15	.40
129 Ron Guidry	.15	.40
130 Toby Harrah	.15	.40
131 Jay Howell	.05	.15
132 Steve Kemp	.05	.15
133 Don Mattingly	2.00	5.00
134 Bobby Meacham	.05	.15
135 John Montefusco	.05	.15
136 Omar Moreno	.05	.15
137 Dale Murray	.05	.15
138 Phil Niekro	.15	.40
139 Mike Pagliarulo	.05	.15
140 Willie Randolph	.15	.40
141 Dennis Rasmussen	.05	.15
142 Dave Righetti	.15	.40
143 Jose Rijo RC	.40	1.00
144 Andre Robertson	.05	.15
145 Bob Shirley	.05	.15
146 Dave Winfield	.15	.40
147 Butch Wynegar	.05	.15
148 Gary Allenson	.05	.15
149 Tony Armas	.15	.40
150 Marty Barrett	.05	.15
151 Wade Boggs	.50	1.25
152 Dennis Boyd	.05	.15
153 Bill Buckner	.15	.40
154 Mark Clear	.05	.15
155 Roger Clemens RC	8.00	20.00
156 Steve Crawford	.05	.15
157 Mike Easler	.05	.15
158 Dwight Evans	.30	.75
159 Rich Gedman	.05	.15
160 Jackie Gutierrez	.15	.40
(Wade Boggs		
shown on deck)		
161 Bruce Hurst	.05	.15
162 John Henry Johnson	.05	.15
163 Rick Miller	.05	.15
164 Reid Nichols	.05	.15
165 Al Nipper	.05	.15
166 Bob Ojeda	.05	.15
167 Jerry Remy	.05	.15
168 Jim Rice	.15	.40
169 Bob Stanley	.05	.15
170 Mike Boddicker	.05	.15
171 Al Bumbry	.05	.15
172 Todd Cruz	.05	.15
173 Rich Dauer	.05	.15
174 Storm Davis	.05	.15
175 Rick Dempsey	.05	.15
176 Jim Dwyer	.05	.15
177 Mike Flanagan	.05	.15
178 Dan Ford	.05	.15
179 Wayne Gross	.05	.15
180 John Lowenstein	.05	.15
181 Dennis Martinez	.15	.40
182 Tippy Martinez	.05	.15
183 Scott McGregor	.05	.15
184 Eddie Murray	.50	1.25
185 Joe Nolan	.05	.15
186 Floyd Rayford	.05	.15
187 Cal Ripken	2.00	5.00
188 Gary Roenicke	.05	.15
189 Lenn Sakata	.05	.15
190 John Shelby	.05	.15
191 Ken Singleton	.15	.40
192 Sammy Stewart	.05	.15
193 Bill Swaggerty	.05	.15
194 Tom Underwood	.05	.15
195 Mike Young	.05	.15
196 Steve Balboni	.05	.15
197 Joe Beckwith	.05	.15
198 Bud Black	.05	.15
199 George Brett	1.25	3.00
200 Onix Concepcion	.05	.15
201 Mark Gubicza RC	.20	.50
202 Larry Gura	.05	.15
203 Mark Huismann	.05	.15
204 Dane Iorg	.05	.15
205 Danny Jackson	.05	.15
206 Charlie Leibrandt	.05	.15
207 Hal McRae	.15	.40
208 Darryl Motley	.05	.15
209 Jorge Orta	.05	.15
210 Greg Pryor	.05	.15
211 Dan Quisenberry	.05	.15
212 Bret Saberhagen RC	.60	1.50
213 Pat Sheridan	.05	.15
214 Don Slaught	.05	.15
215 U.L. Washington	.05	.15
216 John Wathan	.05	.15
217 Frank White	.15	.40
218 Willie Wilson	.15	.40
219 Neil Allen	.05	.15
220 Joaquin Andujar	.15	.40
221 Steve Braun	.05	.15
222 Danny Cox	.05	.15
223 Bob Forsch	.05	.15
224 David Green	.05	.15
225 George Hendrick	.15	.40
226 Tom Herr	.05	.15
227 Ricky Horton	.05	.15
228 Art Howe	.05	.15
229 Mike Jorgensen	.05	.15
230 Kurt Kepshire	.05	.15
231 Jeff Lahti	.05	.15
232 Tito Landrum	.05	.15
233 Dave LaPoint	.05	.15
234 Willie McGee	.15	.40
235 Tom Nieto	.05	.15
236 Terry Pendleton RC	.40	1.00
237 Darrell Porter	.05	.15
238 Dave Rucker	.05	.15
239 Lonnie Smith	.05	.15
240 Ozzie Smith	.75	2.00
241 Bruce Sutter	.15	.40
242 Andy Van Slyke UER	.30	.75
(Bats Right,		
Throws Left)		
243 Dave Von Ohlen	.05	.15
244 Larry Andersen	.05	.15
245 Bill Campbell	.05	.15
246 Steve Carlton	.15	.40
247 Tim Corcoran	.05	.15
248 Ivan DeJesus	.05	.15
249 John Denny	.05	.15
250 Bo Diaz	.05	.15
251 Greg Gross	.05	.15
252 Kevin Gross	.05	.15
253 Von Hayes	.05	.15
254 Al Holland	.05	.15
255 Charles Hudson	.05	.15
256 Jerry Koosman	.15	.40
257 Joe Lefebvre	.05	.15
258 Sixto Lezcano	.05	.15
259 Garry Maddox	.05	.15
260 Len Matuszek	.05	.15
261 Tug McGraw	.15	.40
262 Al Oliver	.15	.40
263 Shane Rawley	.05	.15
264 Juan Samuel	.05	.15
265 Mike Schmidt	1.25	3.00
266 Jeff Stone RC	.05	.15
267 Ozzie Virgil	.05	.15
268 Glenn Wilson	.05	.15
269 John Wockenfuss	.05	.15
270 Darrell Brown	.05	.15
271 Tom Brunansky	.05	.15
272 Randy Bush	.05	.15
273 John Butcher	.05	.15
274 Bobby Castillo	.05	.15
275 Ron Davis	.05	.15
276 Dave Engle	.05	.15
277 Pete Filson	.05	.15
278 Gary Gaetti	.15	.40
279 Mickey Hatcher	.05	.15
280 Ed Hodge	.05	.15
281 Kent Hrbek	.15	.40
282 Houston Jimenez	.05	.15
283 Tim Laudner	.05	.15
284 Rick Lysander	.05	.15
285 Dave Meier	.05	.15
286 Kirby Puckett RC	6.00	15.00
287 Pat Putnam	.05	.15
288 Ken Schrom	.05	.15
289 Mike Smithson	.05	.15
290 Tim Teufel	.05	.15
291 Frank Viola	.15	.40
292 Ron Washington	.05	.15
293 Don Aase	.05	.15
294 Juan Beniquez	.05	.15
295 Bob Boone	.15	.40
296 Mike C. Brown	.05	.15
297 Rod Carew	.30	.75
298 Doug Corbett	.05	.15
299 Doug DeCinces	.05	.15
300 Brian Downing	.15	.40
301 Ken Forsch	.05	.15
302 Bobby Grich	.15	.40
303 Reggie Jackson	.30	.75
304 Tommy John	.15	.40
305 Curt Kaufman	.05	.15
306 Bruce Kison	.05	.15
307 Fred Lynn	.15	.40
308 Gary Pettis	.05	.15
309 Ron Romanick	.05	.15
310 Luis Sanchez	.05	.15
311 Dick Schofield	.05	.15
312 Daryl Sconiers	.05	.15
313 Jim Slaton	.05	.15
314 Derrel Thomas	.05	.15
315 Rob Wilfong	.05	.15
316 Mike Witt	.05	.15
317 Geoff Zahn	.05	.15
318 Len Barker	.05	.15
319 Steve Bedrosian	.05	.15
320 Bruce Benedict	.05	.15
321 Rick Camp	.05	.15
322 Chris Chambliss	.15	.40
323 Jeff Dedmon	.05	.15
324 Terry Forster	.15	.40
325 Gene Garber	.05	.15
326 Albert Hall	.05	.15
327 Terry Harper	.05	.15
328 Bob Horner	.15	.40
329 Glenn Hubbard	.05	.15
330 Randy Johnson	.05	.15
331 Brad Komminsk	.05	.15
332 Rick Mahler	.05	.15
333 Craig McMurtry	.05	.15
334 Donnie Moore	.05	.15
335 Dale Murphy	.30	.75
336 Ken Oberkfell	.05	.15
337 Pascual Perez	.05	.15
338 Gerald Perry	.05	.15
339 Rafael Ramirez	.05	.15
340 Jerry Royster	.05	.15
341 Alex Trevino	.05	.15
342 Claudell Washington	.05	.15
343 Alan Ashby	.05	.15
344 Mark Bailey	.05	.15
345 Kevin Bass	.05	.15
346 Enos Cabell	.05	.15
347 Jose Cruz	.15	.40
348 Bill Dawley	.05	.15
349 Frank DiPino	.05	.15
350 Bill Doran	.05	.15
351 Phil Garner	.15	.40
352 Bob Knepper	.05	.15
353 Mike LaCoss	.05	.15
354 Jerry Mumphrey	.05	.15
355 Joe Niekro	.05	.15
356 Terry Puhl	.05	.15
357 Craig Reynolds	.05	.15
358 Vern Ruhle	.05	.15
359 Nolan Ryan	2.50	6.00
360 Joe Sambito	.05	.15
361 Mike Scott	.15	.40
362 Dave Smith	.05	.15
363 Julio Solano	.05	.15
364 Dickie Thon	.05	.15
365 Denny Walling	.05	.15
366 Dave Anderson	.05	.15
367 Bob Bailor	.05	.15
368 Greg Brock	.05	.15
369 Carlos Diaz	.05	.15
370 Pedro Guerrero	.15	.40
371 Orel Hershiser RC	1.25	3.00
372 Rick Honeycutt	.05	.15
373 Burt Hooton	.05	.15
374 Ken Howell	.05	.15
375 Ken Landreaux	.05	.15
376 Candy Maldonado	.05	.15
377 Mike Marshall	.05	.15
378 Tom Niedenfuer	.05	.15
379 Alejandro Pena	.05	.15
380 Jerry Reuss UER	.05	.15
381 R.J. Reynolds	.05	.15
382 German Rivera	.05	.15
383 Bill Russell	.15	.40
384 Steve Sax	.05	.15
385 Mike Scioscia	.15	.40
386 Franklin Stubbs	.05	.15
387 Fernando Valenzuela	.15	.40
388 Bob Welch	.15	.40
389 Terry Whitfield	.05	.15
390 Steve Yeager	.15	.40
391 Pat Zachry	.05	.15
392 Fred Breining	.05	.15
393 Gary Carter	.15	.40
394 Andre Dawson	.15	.40
395 Miguel Dilone	.05	.15
396 Dan Driessen	.05	.15
397 Doug Flynn	.05	.15
398 Terry Francona	.15	.40
399 Bill Gullickson	.05	.15
400 Bob James	.05	.15
401 Charlie Lea	.05	.15
402 Bryan Little	.05	.15
403 Gary Lucas	.05	.15
404 David Palmer	.05	.15
405 Tim Raines	.15	.40
406 Mike Ramsey	.05	.15
407 Jeff Reardon	.15	.40
408 Steve Rogers	.15	.40
409 Dan Schatzeder	.05	.15
410 Bryn Smith	.05	.15
411 Mike Stenhouse	.05	.15
412 Tim Wallach	.05	.15
413 Jim Wohlford	.05	.15
414 Bill Almon	.05	.15
415 Keith Atherton	.05	.15
416 Bruce Bochte	.05	.15
417 Tom Burgmeier	.05	.15
418 Ray Burris	.05	.15
419 Bill Caudill	.05	.15
420 Chris Codiroli	.05	.15
421 Tim Conroy	.05	.15
422 Mike Davis	.05	.15
423 Jim Essian	.05	.15
424 Mike Heath	.05	.15
425 Rickey Henderson	.60	1.50
426 Donnie Hill	.05	.15
427 Dave Kingman	.15	.40
428 Bill Krueger	.05	.15
429 Carney Lansford	.15	.40
430 Steve McCatty	.05	.15
431 Joe Morgan	.15	.40
432 Dwayne Murphy	.05	.15
433 Tony Phillips	.05	.15
434 Lary Sorensen	.05	.15
435 Mike Warren	.05	.15
436 Curt Young	.05	.15
437 Luis Aponte	.05	.15
438 Chris Bando	.05	.15
439 Tony Bernazard	.05	.15
440 Bert Blyleven	.15	.40
441 Brett Butler	.15	.40
442 Ernie Camacho	.05	.15
443 Joe Carter	.50	1.25
444 Carmelo Castillo	.05	.15
445 Jamie Easterly	.05	.15
446 Steve Farr RC	.20	.50
447 Mike Fischlin	.05	.15
448 Julio Franco	.15	.40
449 Mel Hall	.05	.15
450 Mike Hargrove	.05	.15
451 Neal Heaton	.05	.15
452 Brook Jacoby	.05	.15
453 Mike Jeffcoat	.05	.15
454 Don Schulze	.05	.15
455 Roy Smith	.05	.15
456 Pat Tabler	.05	.15
457 Andre Thornton	.05	.15
458 George Vukovich	.05	.15
459 Tom Waddell	.05	.15
460 Jerry Willard	.05	.15
461 Dale Berra	.05	.15
462 John Candelaria	.05	.15
463 Jose DeLeon	.05	.15
464 Doug Frobel	.05	.15
465 Cecilio Guante	.05	.15
466 Brian Harper	.05	.15
467 Lee Lacy	.05	.15
468 Bill Madlock	.15	.40
469 Lee Mazzilli	.15	.40
470 Larry McWilliams	.05	.15
471 Jim Morrison	.05	.15
472 Tony Pena	.05	.15
473 Johnny Ray	.05	.15
474 Rick Rhoden	.05	.15
475 Don Robinson	.05	.15
476 Rod Scurry	.05	.15
477 Kent Tekulve	.05	.15
478 Jason Thompson	.05	.15
479 John Tudor	.15	.40
480 Lee Tunnell	.05	.15
481 Marvell Wynne	.05	.15
482 Salome Barojas	.05	.15
483 Dave Beard	.05	.15
484 Jim Beattie	.05	.15
485 Barry Bonnell	.05	.15
486 Phil Bradley	.20	.50
487 Al Cowens	.05	.15
488 Alvin Davis RC	.20	.50
489 Dave Henderson	.05	.15
490 Steve Henderson	.05	.15
491 Bob Kearney	.05	.15
492 Mark Langston RC	.40	1.00
493 Larry Milbourne	.05	.15
494 Paul Mirabella	.05	.15
495 Mike Moore	.05	.15
496 Edwin Nunez	.05	.15
497 Spike Owen	.05	.15
498 Jack Perconte	.05	.15
499 Ken Phelps	.05	.15
500 Jim Presley	.20	.50
501 Mike Stanton	.05	.15
502 Bob Stoddard	.05	.15
503 Gorman Thomas	.15	.40
504 Ed VandeBerg	.05	.15
505 Matt Young	.05	.15
506 Juan Agosto	.05	.15
507 Harold Baines	.15	.40
508 Floyd Bannister	.05	.15
509 Britt Burns	.05	.15
510 Julio Cruz	.05	.15
511 Richard Dotson	.05	.15
512 Jerry Dybzinski	.05	.15
513 Carlton Fisk	.30	.75
514 Scott Fletcher	.05	.15
515 Jerry Hairston	.05	.15
516 Marc Hill	.05	.15
517 LaMarr Hoyt	.05	.15
518 Ron Kittle	.05	.15
519 Rudy Law	.05	.15
520 Vance Law	.05	.15
521 Greg Luzinski	.15	.40
522 Gene Nelson	.05	.15
523 Tom Paciorek	.05	.15
524 Ron Reed	.05	.15
525 Bert Roberge	.05	.15
526 Tom Seaver	.30	.75
527 Roy Smalley	.05	.15
528 Dan Spillner	.05	.15
529 Mike Squires	.05	.15
530 Greg Walker	.05	.15
531 Cesar Cedeno	.15	.40
532 Dave Concepcion	.15	.40
533 Eric Davis RC	1.25	3.00
534 Nick Esasky	.05	.15
535 Tom Foley	.05	.15
536 John Franco UER RC	.40	1.00
(Koufax misspelled		
as Kofax on back)		
537 Brad Gulden	.05	.15
538 Tom Hume	.05	.15
539 Wayne Krenchicki	.05	.15
540 Andy McGaffigan	.05	.15
541 Eddie Milner	.05	.15
542 Ron Oester	.05	.15
543 Bob Owchinko	.05	.15
544 Dave Parker	.15	.40
545 Frank Pastore	.05	.15
546 Tony Perez	.30	.75
547 Ted Power	.05	.15
548 Joe Price	.05	.15
549 Gary Redus	.05	.15
550 Pete Rose	1.50	4.00
551 Jeff Russell	.05	.15
552 Mario Soto	.15	.40
553 Jay Tibbs	.05	.15
554 Duane Walker	.05	.15
555 Alan Bannister	.05	.15
556 Buddy Bell	.15	.40
557 Danny Darwin	.05	.15
558 Charlie Hough	.15	.40
559 Bobby Jones	.05	.15
560 Odell Jones	.05	.15
561 Jeff Kunkel	.05	.15
562 Mike Mason RC	.08	.25
563 Pete O'Brien	.05	.15
564 Larry Parrish	.05	.15
565 Mickey Rivers	.05	.15
566 Billy Sample	.05	.15
567 Dave Schmidt	.05	.15
568 Donnie Scott	.05	.15
569 Dave Stewart	.15	.40
570 Frank Tanana	.15	.40
571 Wayne Tolleson	.05	.15
572 Gary Ward	.05	.15
573 Curtis Wilkerson	.05	.15
574 George Wright	.05	.15
575 Ned Yost	.05	.15
576 Mark Brouhard	.05	.15
577 Mike Caldwell	.05	.15
578 Bobby Clark	.05	.15
579 Jaime Cocanower	.05	.15
580 Cecil Cooper	.15	.40
581 Rollie Fingers	.15	.40
582 Jim Gantner	.05	.15
583 Moose Haas	.05	.15
584 Dion James	.05	.15
585 Pete Ladd	.05	.15
586 Rick Manning	.05	.15
587 Bob McClure	.05	.15
588 Paul Molitor	.15	.40
589 Charlie Moore	.05	.15
590 Ben Oglivie	.15	.40
591 Chuck Porter	.05	.15
592 Randy Ready RC	.08	.25
593 Ed Romero	.05	.15
594 Bill Schroeder	.05	.15
595 Ray Searage	.05	.15
596 Ted Simmons	.15	.40
597 Jim Sundberg	.15	.40
598 Don Sutton	.15	.40
599 Tom Tellmann	.05	.15
600 Rick Waits	.05	.15
601 Robin Yount	.75	2.00
602 Dusty Baker	.15	.40
603 Bob Brenly	.05	.15
604 Jack Clark	.15	.40
605 Chili Davis	.15	.40
606 Mark Davis	.05	.15
607 Dan Gladden RC	.20	.50
608 Atlee Hammaker	.05	.15
609 Mike Krukow	.05	.15
610 Duane Kuiper	.05	.15
611 Bob Lacey	.05	.15
612 Bill Laskey	.05	.15
613 Gary Lavelle	.05	.15
614 Johnnie LeMaster	.05	.15
615 Jeff Leonard	.05	.15
616 Randy Lerch	.05	.15
617 Greg Minton	.05	.15
618 Steve Nicosia	.05	.15
619 Gene Richards	.05	.15
620 Jeff D. Robinson	.05	.15
621 Scot Thompson	.05	.15
622 Manny Trillo	.05	.15
623 Brad Wellman	.05	.15
624 Frank Williams	.05	.15
625 Joel Youngblood	.05	.15
626 Cal Ripken IA	1.25	3.00
627 Mike Schmidt IA	.50	1.25
628 Sparky Anderson IA	.15	.40
629 Dave Winfield	.15	.40
Rickey Henderson		
630 Mike Schmidt	.75	2.00
Ryne Sandberg		
631 Darryl Strawberry	.50	1.25
Gary Carter		
Steve Garvey		
Ozzie Smith		
632 Gary Carter	.05	.15
Charlie Lea		
633 Steve Garvey	.15	.40
Rich Gossage		
634 Dwight Gooden	.50	1.25
Juan Samuel		
635 Willie Upshaw IA	.05	.15
636 Lloyd Moseby IA	.05	.15
637 HOLLAND	.05	.15
Al Holland		
638 TUNNELL	.05	.15
Lee Tunnell		
639 Reggie Jackson IA	.15	.40
640 Pete Rose	.50	1.25
4000th Hit IA		
641 Cal Ripken Jr.	1.25	3.00
Cal Ripken Sr.		
642 Cubs Division Champs	.15	.40
643 Two Perfect Games	.15	.40
and One No-Hitter:		
Mike Witt		
David Palmer		
Jack Morris		
644 Willie Lozado RC	.05	.15
Vic Mata RC		
645 Kelly Gruber RC	.20	.50
Randy O'Neal RC		
646 Jose Roman RC	.05	.15
Joel Skinner		
647 Steve Kiefer RC	.40	1.00
Danny Tartabull RC		
648 Rob Deer RC	.20	.50
Alejandro Sanchez RC		
649 Billy Hatcher RC	.40	1.00
Shawon Dunston RC		
650 Ron Robinson	.05	.15
Mike Bielecki RC		
651 Zane Smith RC	.20	.50
Paul Zuvella RC		
652 Joe Hesketh RC	.20	.50
Glenn Davis RC		
653 John Russell RC	.05	.15
Steve Jeltz RC		
654 CL: Tigers/Padres	.05	.15
and Cubs/Mets		
655 CL: Blue Jays/Yankees	.05	.15
and Red Sox/Orioles		
656 CL: Royals/Cardinals	.05	.15
and Phillies/Twins		
657 CL: Angels/Braves	.05	.15
and Astros/Dodgers		
658 CL: Expos/A's	.05	.15
and Indians/Pirates		
659 CL: Mariners/White Sox	.05	.15
and Reds/Rangers		
660 CL: Brewers/Giants	.05	.15
and Special Cards		

1985 Fleer Update

This 132-card standard-size update set was issued in factory set form exclusively through hobby dealers. Design is identical to the regular-issue 1985 Fleer cards except for the U prefixed card numbers on back. Cards are ordered alphabetically by the player's name. This set features the extended Rookie Cards of Vince Coleman, Darren Daulton, Ozzie Guillen and Mickey Tettleton.

Card	Low	High
COMP.FACT.SET (132)	3.00	8.00
1 Don Aase	.05	.15
2 Bill Almon	.05	.15
3 Dusty Baker	.15	.40
4 Dale Berra	.05	.15
5 Karl Best	.05	.15
6 Tim Birtsas	.05	.15
7 Vida Blue	.15	.40
8 Rich Bordi	.05	.15
9 Daryl Boston XRC	.08	.25
10 Hubie Brooks	.05	.15
11 Chris Brown XRC	.08	.25
12 Tom Browning XRC	.20	.50
13 Al Bumbry	.05	.15
14 Tim Burke	.05	.15
15 Ray Burris	.05	.15
16 Jeff Burroughs	.05	.15
17 Ivan Calderon XRC	.20	.50
18 Jeff Calhoun	.05	.15
19 Bill Campbell	.05	.15
20 Don Carman	.05	.15
21 Gary Carter	.15	.40
22 Bobby Castillo	.05	.15
23 Bill Caudill	.05	.15
24 Rick Cerone	.05	.15
25 Jack Clark	.15	.40
26 Pat Clements	.05	.15
27 Stu Cliburn	.05	.15
28 Vince Coleman XRC	.40	1.00
29 Dave Collins	.05	.15
30 Fritz Connally	.05	.15
31 Henry Cotto	.08	.25
32 Danny Darwin	.05	.15
33 Darren Daulton XRC	.40	1.00
34 Jerry Davis	.05	.15
35 Brian Dayett	.05	.15
36 Ken Dixon	.05	.15
37 Tommy Dunbar	.05	.15
38 Mariano Duncan XRC	.20	.50
39 Bob Fallon	.05	.15
40 Brian Fisher XRC	.08	.25
41 Mike Fitzgerald	.05	.15
42 Ray Fontenot	.05	.15
43 Greg Gagne XRC	.20	.50
44 Oscar Gamble	.05	.15
45 Jim Gott	.05	.15
46 David Green	.05	.15
47 Alfredo Griffin	.05	.15
48 Ozzie Guillen XRC	2.00	5.00
49 Toby Harrah	.15	.40
50 Ron Hassey	.05	.15
51 Rickey Henderson	1.00	2.50
52 Steve Henderson	.05	.15
53 George Hendrick	.15	.40
54 Teddy Higuera XRC	.20	.50
55 Al Holland	.05	.15
56 Burt Hooton	.05	.15
57 Jay Howell	.05	.15
58 LaMarr Hoyt	.05	.15
59 Tim Hulett XRC	.08	.25
60 Bob James	.05	.15
61 Cliff Johnson	.05	.15
62 Howard Johnson	.15	.40
63 Ruppert Jones	.05	.15
64 Steve Kemp	.05	.15
65 Bruce Kison	.05	.15
66 Mike LaCoss	.05	.15
67 Lee Lacy	.05	.15
68 Dave LaPoint	.05	.15
69 Gary Lavelle	.05	.15
70 Vance Law	.05	.15
71 Manny Lee XRC	.08	.25
72 Sixto Lezcano	.05	.15
73 Tim Lollar	.05	.15
74 Urbano Lugo	.05	.15
75 Fred Lynn	.15	.40
76 Steve Lyons XRC	.20	.50
77 Mickey Mahler	.05	.15
78 Ron Mathis	.05	.15
79 Len Matuszek	.05	.15
80 O.McDowell XRC UER	.20	.50
Part of bio		
actually Roger's		
81 R.McDowell XRC UER	.20	.50
Part of bio		
actually Oddibe's		
82 Donnie Moore	.05	.15
83 Ron Musselman	.05	.15
84 Al Oliver	.15	.40
85 Joe Orsulak XRC	.20	.50
86 Dan Pasqua XRC	.20	.50
87 Chris Pittaro	.05	.15
88 Rick Reuschel	.15	.40
89 Earnie Riles	.05	.15
90 Jerry Royster	.05	.15
91 Dave Rozema	.05	.15
92 Dave Rucker	.05	.15
93 Vern Ruhle	.05	.15
94 Mark Salas	.05	.15

95 Luis Salazar .05 .15
96 Joe Sambito .05 .15
97 Billy Sample .05 .15
98 Alejandro Sanchez XRC .08 .25
99 Calvin Schiraldi XRC .20 .50
100 Rick Schu .05 .15
101 Larry Sheets XRC .08 .25
102 Ron Shephard .05 .15
103 Nelson Simmons .05 .15
104 Don Slaught .05 .15
105 Roy Smalley .05 .15
106 Lonnie Smith .05 .15
107 Nate Snell .05 .15
108 Lary Sorensen .05 .15
109 Chris Speier .05 .15
110 Mike Stenhouse .05 .15
111 Tim Stoddard .05 .15
112 John Stuper .05 .15
113 Jim Sundberg .15 .40
114 Bruce Sutter .15 .40
115 Don Sutton .15 .40
116 Bruce Tanner .05 .15
117 Kent Tekulve .05 .15
118 Walt Terrell .05 .15
119 Mickey Tettleton XRC .20 .50
120 Rich Thompson .05 .15
121 Louis Thornton .05 .15
122 Alex Trevino .05 .15
123 John Tudor .15 .40
124 Jose Uribe .05 .15
125 Dave Valle XRC .20 .50
126 Dave Von Ohlen .05 .15
127 Curt Wardle .05 .15
128 U.L. Washington .05 .15
129 Ed Whitson .05 .15
130 Herm Winningham .05 .15
131 Rich Yett .05 .15
132 Checklist U1-U132 .05 .15

1986 Fleer

The 1986 Fleer set consists of 660-card standard-size cards. Wax packs included 15 cards plus logo stickers. Card fronts feature dark blue borders (resulting in extremely condition sensitive cards commonly found with chipped edges), a team logo along with the player's name and position. The player cards are alphabetized within team and the teams are ordered by their 1985 season finish and won-lost record. Subsets include Specials (626-643) and Major League Prospects (644-653). The Dennis and Tippy Martinez cards were apparently switched in the set numbering, as their adjacent numbers (279 and 280) were reversed on the Orioles checklist card. The set includes the Rookie Cards of Rick Aguilera, Jose Canseco, Darren Daulton, Len Dykstra, Cecil Fielder, Andres Galarraga and Paul O'Neill.

COMPLETE SET (660) 15.00 40.00
COMP.FACT.SET (660) 15.00 40.00
1 Steve Balboni .05 .15
2 Joe Beckwith .05 .15
3 Buddy Biancalana .05 .15
4 Bud Black .05 .15
5 George Brett .75 2.00
6 Onix Concepcion .05 .15
7 Steve Farr .05 .15
8 Mark Gubicza .05 .15
9 Dane Iorg .05 .15
10 Danny Jackson .05 .15
11 Lynn Jones .05 .15
12 Mike Jones .05 .15
13 Charlie Leibrandt .05 .15
14 Hal McRae .08 .25
15 Omar Moreno .05 .15
16 Darryl Motley .05 .15
17 Jorge Orta .05 .15
18 Dan Quisenberry .05 .15
19 Bret Saberhagen .08 .25
20 Pat Sheridan .05 .15
21 Lonnie Smith .05 .15
22 Jim Sundberg .08 .25
23 John Wathan .05 .15
24 Frank White .08 .25
25 Willie Wilson .08 .25
26 Joaquin Andujar .08 .25
27 Steve Braun .05 .15
28 Bill Campbell .05 .15
29 Cesar Cedeno .08 .25
30 Jack Clark .08 .25
31 Vince Coleman RC .40 1.00
32 Danny Cox .05 .15
33 Ken Dayley .05 .15
34 Ivan DeJesus .05 .15
35 Bob Forsch .05 .15
36 Brian Harper .05 .15
37 Tom Herr .05 .15
38 Ricky Horton .05 .15
39 Kurt Kepshire .05 .15
40 Jeff Lahti .05 .15
41 Tito Landrum .05 .15
42 Willie McGee .08 .25
43 Tom Nieto .05 .15
44 Terry Pendleton .08 .25
45 Darrell Porter .05 .15
46 Ozzie Smith .50 1.25
47 John Tudor .08 .25
48 Andy Van Slyke .20 .50
49 Todd Worrell RC .20 .50
50 Jim Acker .05 .15
51 Doyle Alexander .05 .15
52 Jesse Barfield .08 .25
53 George Bell .08 .25
54 Jeff Burroughs .05 .15
55 Bill Caudill .05 .15
56 Jim Clancy .05 .15
57 Tony Fernandez .05 .15
58 Tom Filer .05 .15
59 Damaso Garcia .05 .15
60 Tom Henke .08 .25
61 Garth Iorg .05 .15
62 Cliff Johnson .05 .15
63 Jimmy Key .08 .25
64 Dennis Lamp .05 .15
65 Gary Lavelle .05 .15
66 Buck Martinez .05 .15
67 Lloyd Moseby .05 .15
68 Rance Mulliniks .05 .15
69 Al Oliver .08 .25
70 Dave Stieb .08 .25
71 Louis Thornton .05 .15
72 Willie Upshaw .05 .15
73 Ernie Whitt .05 .15
74 Rick Aguilera RC .20 .50
75 Wally Backman .05 .15
76 Gary Carter .08 .25
77 Ron Darling .08 .25
78 Len Dykstra RC .60 1.50
79 Sid Fernandez .08 .25
80 George Foster .08 .25
81 Dwight Gooden .30 .75
82 Tom Gorman .05 .15
83 Danny Heep .05 .15
84 Keith Hernandez .08 .25
85 Howard Johnson .08 .25
86 Ray Knight .08 .25
87 Terry Leach .05 .15
88 Ed Lynch .05 .15
89 Roger McDowell RC .20 .50
90 Jesse Orosco .05 .15
91 Tom Paciorek .05 .15
92 Ronn Reynolds .05 .15
93 Rafael Santana .05 .15
94 Doug Sisk .05 .15
95 Rusty Staub .08 .25
96 Darryl Strawberry .20 .50
97 Mookie Wilson .08 .25
98 Neil Allen .05 .15
99 Don Baylor .08 .25
100 Dale Berra .05 .15
101 Rich Bordi .05 .15
102 Marty Bystrom .05 .15
103 Joe Cowley .05 .15
104 Brian Fisher RC .05 .15
105 Ken Griffey .08 .25
106 Ron Guidry .08 .25
107 Ron Hassey .05 .15
108 R.Henderson UER .30 .75
SB Record of 120, sic
109 Don Mattingly 1.00 2.50
110 Bobby Meacham .05 .15
111 John Montefusco .05 .15
112 Phil Niekro .08 .25
113 Mike Pagliarulo .05 .15
114 Dan Pasqua .05 .15
115 Willie Randolph .08 .25
116 Dave Righetti .08 .25
117 Andre Robertson .05 .15
118 Billy Sample .05 .15
119 Bob Shirley .05 .15
120 Ed Whitson .05 .15
121 Dave Winfield .08 .25
122 Butch Wynegar .05 .15
123 Dave Anderson .05 .15
124 Bob Bailor .05 .15
125 Greg Brock .05 .15
126 Enos Cabell .05 .15
127 Bobby Castillo .05 .15
128 Carlos Diaz .05 .15
129 Mariano Duncan RC .20 .50
130 Pedro Guerrero .08 .25
131 Orel Hershiser .30 .75
132 Rick Honeycutt .05 .15
133 Ken Howell .05 .15
134 Ken Landreaux .05 .15
135 Bill Madlock .08 .25
136 Candy Maldonado .05 .15
137 Mike Marshall .05 .15
138 Len Matuszek .05 .15
139 Tom Niedenfuer .05 .15
140 Alejandro Pena .05 .15
141 Jerry Reuss .05 .15
142 Bill Russell .08 .25
143 Steve Sax .05 .15
144 Mike Scioscia .08 .25
145 Fernando Valenzuela .08 .25
146 Bob Welch .08 .25
147 Terry Whitfield .05 .15
148 Juan Beniquez .05 .15
149 Bob Boone .08 .25
150 John Candelaria .05 .15
151 Rod Carew .20 .50
152 Stu Cliburn .05 .15
153 Doug DeCinces .05 .15
154 Brian Downing .08 .25
155 Ken Forsch .05 .15
156 Craig Gerber .05 .15
157 Bobby Grich .08 .25
158 George Hendrick .08 .25
159 Al Holland .05 .15
160 Reggie Jackson .20 .50
161 Ruppert Jones .05 .15
162 Urbano Lugo .05 .15
163 Kirk McCaskill RC .20 .50
164 Donnie Moore .05 .15
165 Gary Pettis .05 .15
166 Ron Romanick .05 .15
167 Dick Schofield .05 .15
168 Daryl Sconiers .05 .15
169 Jim Slaton .05 .15
170 Don Sutton .08 .25
171 Mike Witt .05 .15
172 Buddy Bell .08 .25
173 Tom Browning .05 .15
174 Dave Concepcion .08 .25
175 Eric Davis .30 .75
176 Bo Diaz .05 .15
177 Nick Esasky .05 .15
178 John Franco .08 .25
179 Tom Hume .05 .15
180 Wayne Krenchicki .05 .15
181 Andy McGaffigan .05 .15
182 Eddie Milner .05 .15
183 Ron Oester .05 .15
184 Dave Parker .08 .25
185 Frank Pastore .05 .15
186 Tony Perez .20 .50
187 Ted Power .05 .15
188 Joe Price .05 .15
189 Gary Redus .05 .15
190 Ron Robinson .05 .15
191 Pete Rose 1.00 2.50
192 Mario Soto .08 .25
193 John Stuper .05 .15
194 Jay Tibbs .05 .15
195 Dave Van Gorder .05 .15
196 Max Venable .05 .15
197 Juan Agosto .05 .15
198 Harold Baines .08 .25
199 Floyd Bannister .05 .15
200 Britt Burns .05 .15
201 Julio Cruz .05 .15
202 Joel Davis .05 .15
203 Richard Dotson .05 .15
204 Carlton Fisk .20 .50
205 Scott Fletcher .05 .15
206 Ozzie Guillen RC .75 2.00
207 Jerry Hairston .05 .15
208 Tim Hulett .05 .15
209 Bob James .05 .15
210 Ron Kittle .05 .15
211 Rudy Law .05 .15
212 Bryan Little .05 .15
213 Gene Nelson .05 .15
214 Reid Nichols .05 .15
215 Luis Salazar .05 .15
216 Tom Seaver .20 .50
217 Dan Spillner .05 .15
218 Bruce Tanner .05 .15
219 Greg Walker .05 .15
220 Dave Wehrmeister .05 .15
221 Juan Berenguer .05 .15
222 Dave Bergman .05 .15
223 Tom Brookens .05 .15
224 Darrell Evans .08 .25
225 Barbaro Garbey .05 .15
226 Kirk Gibson .08 .25
227 John Grubb .05 .15
228 Willie Hernandez .05 .15
229 Larry Herndon .05 .15
230 Chet Lemon .08 .25
231 Aurelio Lopez .05 .15
232 Jack Morris .08 .25
233 Randy O'Neal .05 .15
234 Lance Parrish .08 .25
235 Dan Petry .05 .15
236 Alejandro Sanchez .05 .15
237 Bill Scherrer .05 .15
238 Nelson Simmons .05 .15
239 Frank Tanana .08 .25
240 Walt Terrell .05 .15
241 Alan Trammell .08 .25
242 Lou Whitaker .08 .25
243 Milt Wilcox .05 .15
244 Hubie Brooks .05 .15
245 Tim Burke .05 .15
246 Andre Dawson .08 .25
247 Mike Fitzgerald .05 .15
248 Terry Francona .08 .25
249 Bill Gullickson .05 .15
250 Joe Hesketh .05 .15
251 Bill Laskey .05 .15
252 Vance Law .05 .15
253 Charlie Lea .05 .15
254 Gary Lucas .05 .15
255 David Palmer .05 .15
256 Tim Raines .08 .25
257 Jeff Reardon .08 .25
258 Bert Roberge .05 .15
259 Dan Schatzeder .05 .15
260 Bryn Smith .05 .15
261 Randy St.Claire .05 .15
262 Scot Thompson .05 .15
263 Tim Wallach .05 .15
264 U.L. Washington .05 .15
265 Mitch Webster .05 .15
266 Herm Winningham .05 .15
267 Floyd Youmans .05 .15
268 Don Aase .05 .15
269 Mike Boddicker .05 .15
270 Rich Dauer .05 .15
271 Storm Davis .05 .15
272 Rick Dempsey .05 .15
273 Ken Dixon .05 .15
274 Jim Dwyer .05 .15
275 Mike Flanagan .05 .15
276 Wayne Gross .05 .15
277 Lee Lacy .05 .15
278 Fred Lynn .08 .25
279 Tippy Martinez .05 .15
280 Dennis Martinez .08 .25
281 Scott McGregor .05 .15
282 Eddie Murray .30 .75
283 Floyd Rayford .05 .15
284 Cal Ripken 1.25 3.00
285 Gary Roenicke .05 .15
286 Larry Sheets .05 .15
287 John Shelby .05 .15
288 Nate Snell .05 .15
289 Sammy Stewart .05 .15
290 Alan Wiggins .05 .15
291 Mike Young .05 .15
292 Alan Ashby .05 .15
293 Mark Bailey .05 .15
294 Kevin Bass .05 .15
295 Jeff Calhoun .05 .15
296 Jose Cruz .08 .25
297 Glenn Davis .05 .15
298 Bill Dawley .05 .15
299 Frank DiPino .05 .15
300 Bill Doran .05 .15
301 Phil Garner .08 .25
302 Jeff Heathcock .05 .15
303 Charlie Kerfeld .05 .15
304 Bob Knepper .05 .15
305 Ron Mathis .05 .15
306 Jerry Mumphrey .05 .15
307 Jim Pankovits .05 .15
308 Terry Puhl .05 .15
309 Craig Reynolds .05 .15
310 Nolan Ryan 1.50 4.00
311 Mike Scott .08 .25
312 Dave Smith .05 .15
313 Dickie Thon .05 .15
314 Denny Walling .05 .15
315 Kurt Bevacqua .05 .15
316 Al Bumbry .05 .15
317 Jerry Davis .05 .15
318 Luis DeLeon .05 .15
319 Dave Dravecky .05 .15
320 Tim Flannery .05 .15
321 Steve Garvey .08 .25
322 Rich Gossage .08 .25
323 Tony Gwynn .50 1.25
324 Andy Hawkins .05 .15
325 LaMarr Hoyt .05 .15
326 Roy Lee Jackson .05 .15
327 Terry Kennedy .05 .15
328 Craig Lefferts .05 .15
329 Carmelo Martinez .05 .15
330 Lance McCullers .05 .15
331 Kevin McReynolds .05 .15
332 Graig Nettles .08 .25
333 Jerry Royster .05 .15
334 Eric Show .05 .15
335 Tim Stoddard .05 .15
336 Garry Templeton .08 .25
337 Mark Thurmond .05 .15
338 Ed Wojna .05 .15
339 Tony Armas .08 .25
340 Marty Barrett .05 .15
341 Wade Boggs .20 .50
342 Dennis Boyd .05 .15
343 Bill Buckner .08 .25
344 Mark Clear .05 .15
345 Roger Clemens 2.00 5.00
346 Steve Crawford .05 .15
347 Mike Easler .05 .15
348 Dwight Evans .20 .50
349 Rich Gedman .05 .15
350 Jackie Gutierrez .05 .15
351 Glenn Hoffman .05 .15
352 Bruce Hurst .05 .15
353 Bruce Kison .05 .15
354 Tim Lollar .05 .15
355 Steve Lyons .05 .15
356 Al Nipper .05 .15
357 Bob Ojeda .05 .15
358 Jim Rice .08 .25
359 Bob Stanley .05 .15
360 Mike Trujillo .05 .15
361 Thad Bosley .05 .15
362 Warren Brusstar .05 .15
363 Ron Cey .08 .25
364 Jody Davis .05 .15
365 Bob Dernier .05 .15
366 Shawon Dunston .08 .25
367 Leon Durham .05 .15
368 Dennis Eckersley .20 .50
369 Ray Fontenot .05 .15
370 George Frazier .05 .15
371 Billy Hatcher .05 .15
372 Dave Lopes .08 .25
373 Gary Matthews .08 .25
374 Ron Meridith .05 .15
375 Keith Moreland .05 .15
376 Reggie Patterson .05 .15
377 Dick Ruthven .05 .15
378 Ryne Sandberg .60 1.50
379 Scott Sanderson .05 .15
380 Lee Smith .08 .25
381 Lary Sorensen .05 .15
382 Chris Speier .05 .15
383 Rick Sutcliffe .08 .25
384 Steve Trout .05 .15
385 Gary Woods .05 .15
386 Bert Blyleven .08 .25
387 Tom Brunansky .05 .15
388 Randy Bush .05 .15
389 John Butcher .05 .15
390 Ron Davis .05 .15
391 Dave Engle .05 .15
392 Frank Eufemia .05 .15
393 Pete Filson .05 .15
394 Gary Gaetti .08 .25
395 Greg Gagne .05 .15
396 Mickey Hatcher .05 .15
397 Kent Hrbek .08 .25
398 Tim Laudner .05 .15
399 Rick Lysander .05 .15
400 Dave Meier .05 .15
401 Kirby Puckett UER .75 2.00
Card has him in NL,
should be AL
402 Mark Salas .05 .15
403 Ken Schrom .05 .15
404 Roy Smalley .05 .15
405 Mike Smithson .05 .15
406 Mike Stenhouse .05 .15
407 Tim Teufel .05 .15
408 Frank Viola .08 .25
409 Ron Washington .05 .15
410 Keith Atherton .05 .15
411 Dusty Baker .08 .25
412 Tim Birtsas .05 .15
413 Bruce Bochte .05 .15
414 Chris Codiroli .05 .15
415 Dave Collins .05 .15
416 Mike Davis .05 .15
417 Alfredo Griffin .05 .15
418 Mike Heath .05 .15
419 Steve Henderson .05 .15
420 Donnie Hill .05 .15
421 Jay Howell .05 .15
422 Tommy John .08 .25
423 Dave Kingman .08 .25
424 Bill Krueger .05 .15
425 Rick Langford .05 .15
426 Carney Lansford .08 .25
427 Steve McCatty .05 .15
428 Dwayne Murphy .05 .15
429 Steve Ontiveros RC .05 .15
430 Tony Phillips .05 .15
431 Jose Rijo .08 .25
432 Mickey Tettleton RC .20 .50
433 Luis Aguayo .05 .15
434 Larry Andersen .05 .15
435 Steve Carlton .08 .25
436 Don Carman .05 .15
437 Tim Corcoran .05 .15
438 Darren Daulton RC .40 1.00
439 John Denny .05 .15
440 Tom Foley .05 .15
441 Greg Gross .05 .15
442 Kevin Gross .05 .15
443 Von Hayes .05 .15
444 Charles Hudson .05 .15
445 Garry Maddox .05 .15
446 Shane Rawley .05 .15
447 Dave Rucker .05 .15
448 John Russell .05 .15
449 Juan Samuel .05 .15
450 Mike Schmidt .75 2.00
451 Rick Schu .05 .15
452 Dave Shipanoff .05 .15
453 Dave Stewart .08 .25
454 Jeff Stone .05 .15
455 Kent Tekulve .05 .15
456 Ozzie Virgil .05 .15
457 Glenn Wilson .05 .15
458 Jim Beattie .05 .15
459 Karl Best .05 .15
460 Barry Bonnell .05 .15
461 Phil Bradley .05 .15
462 Ivan Calderon RC .20 .50
463 Al Cowens .05 .15
464 Alvin Davis .05 .15
465 Dave Henderson .08 .25
466 Bob Kearney .05 .15
467 Mark Langston .08 .25
468 Bob Long .05 .15
469 Mike Moore .05 .15
470 Edwin Nunez .05 .15
471 Spike Owen .05 .15
472 Jack Perconte .05 .15
473 Jim Presley .05 .15
474 Donnie Scott .05 .15
475 Bill Swift .05 .15
476 Danny Tartabull .08 .25
477 Gorman Thomas .08 .25
478 Roy Thomas .05 .15
479 Ed VandeBerg .05 .15
480 Frank Wills .05 .15
481 Matt Young .05 .15
482 Ray Burris .05 .15
483 Jaime Cocanower .05 .15
484 Cecil Cooper .08 .25
485 Danny Darwin .05 .15
486 Rollie Fingers .08 .25
487 Jim Gantner .05 .15
488 Bob L. Gibson .05 .15
489 Moose Haas .05 .15
490 Teddy Higuera RC .20 .50
491 Paul Householder .05 .15
492 Pete Ladd .05 .15
493 Rick Manning .05 .15
494 Bob McClure .05 .15
495 Paul Molitor .08 .25
496 Charlie Moore .05 .15
497 Ben Oglivie .08 .25
498 Randy Ready .05 .15
499 Earnie Riles .05 .15
500 Ed Romero .05 .15
501 Bill Schroeder .05 .15
502 Ray Searage .05 .15
503 Ted Simmons .08 .25
504 Pete Vuckovich .05 .15
505 Rick Waits .05 .15
506 Robin Yount .50 1.25
507 Len Barker .05 .15
508 Steve Bedrosian .05 .15
509 Bruce Benedict .05 .15
510 Rick Camp .05 .15
511 Rick Cerone .05 .15
512 Chris Chambliss .08 .25
513 Jeff Dedmon .05 .15
514 Terry Forster .08 .25
515 Gene Garber .05 .15
516 Terry Harper .05 .15
517 Bob Horner .08 .25
518 Glenn Hubbard .05 .15
519 Joe Johnson .05 .15
520 Brad Komminsk .05 .15
521 Rick Mahler .05 .15
522 Dale Murphy .20 .50
523 Ken Oberkfell .05 .15
524 Pascual Perez .05 .15
525 Gerald Perry .05 .15
526 Rafael Ramirez .05 .15
527 Steve Shields .05 .15
528 Zane Smith .05 .15
529 Bruce Sutter .08 .25
530 Milt Thompson RC .20 .50
531 Claudell Washington .05 .15
532 Paul Zuvella .05 .15
533 Vida Blue .08 .25
534 Bob Brenly .05 .15
535 Chris Brown RC .05 .15
536 Chili Davis .08 .25
537 Mark Davis .05 .15
538 Rob Deer .05 .15
539 Dan Driessen .05 .15
540 Scott Garrelts .05 .15
541 Dan Gladden .05 .15
542 Jim Gott .05 .15
543 David Green .05 .15
544 Atlee Hammaker .05 .15
545 Mike Jeffcoat .05 .15
546 Mike Krukow .05 .15
547 Dave LaPoint .05 .15
548 Jeff Leonard .05 .15
549 Greg Minton .05 .15
550 Alex Trevino .05 .15
551 Manny Trillo .05 .15
552 Jose Uribe .05 .15
553 Brad Wellman .05 .15
554 Frank Williams .05 .15
555 Joel Youngblood .05 .15
556 Alan Bannister .05 .15
557 Glenn Brummer .05 .15
558 Steve Buechele RC .20 .50
559 Jose Guzman RC .05 .15
560 Toby Harrah .08 .25
561 Greg Harris .05 .15
562 Dwayne Henry .08 .25
563 Burt Hooton .05 .15
564 Charlie Hough .08 .25
565 Mike Mason .05 .15
566 Oddibe McDowell .08 .25
567 Dickie Noles .05 .15
568 Pete O'Brien .08 .25
569 Larry Parrish .05 .15
570 Dave Rozema .05 .15
571 Dave Schmidt .05 .15
572 Don Slaught .05 .15
573 Wayne Tolleson .05 .15
574 Duane Walker .05 .15
575 Gary Ward .05 .15
576 Chris Welsh .05 .15
577 Curtis Wilkerson .05 .15
578 George Wright .05 .15
579 Chris Bando .05 .15
580 Tony Bernazard .05 .15
581 Brett Butler .08 .25
582 Ernie Camacho .05 .15
583 Joe Carter .08 .25
584 Carmen Castillo .05 .15
585 Jamie Easterly .05 .15
586 Julio Franco .08 .25
587 Mel Hall .05 .15
588 Mike Hargrove .05 .15
589 Neal Heaton .05 .15
590 Brook Jacoby .05 .15
591 Otis Nixon RC .40 1.00
592 Jerry Reed .05 .15
593 Vern Ruhle .05 .15
594 Pat Tabler .05 .15
595 Rich Thompson .05 .15
596 Andre Thornton .05 .15
597 Dave Von Ohlen .05 .15
598 George Vukovich .08 .25
599 Tom Waddell .05 .15
600 Curt Wardle .05 .15
601 Jerry Willard .05 .15
602 Bill Almon .05 .15
603 Mike Bielecki .05 .15
604 Sid Bream .05 .15
605 Mike C. Brown .05 .15
606 Pat Clements .05 .15
607 Jose DeLeon .05 .15
608 Denny Gonzalez .05 .15
609 Cecilio Guante .05 .15
610 Steve Kemp .05 .15
611 Sammy Khalifa .05 .15
612 Lee Mazzilli .08 .25
613 Larry McWilliams .05 .15
614 Jim Morrison .05 .15
615 Joe Orsulak RC .20 .50
616 Tony Pena .05 .15
617 Johnny Ray .05 .15
618 Rick Reuschel .08 .25
619 R.J. Reynolds .05 .15
620 Rick Rhoden .05 .15
621 Don Robinson .05 .15
622 Jason Thompson .05 .15
623 Lee Tunnell .05 .15
624 Jim Winn .05 .15
625 Marvell Wynne .05 .15
626 Dwight Gooden IA .20 .50
627 Don Mattingly IA .50 1.25
628 Pete Rose 4192 .20 .50
629 Rod Carew 3000 Hits .08 .25
630 Tom Seaver .08 .25
Phil Niekro
631 Don Baylor Ouch .08 .25
632 Darryl Strawberry .08 .25
Tim Raines
633 Cal Ripken .60 1.50
Alan Trammell
634 Wade Boggs .40 1.00
George Brett
635 Bob Horner .20 .50
Dale Murphy
636 Willie McGee .08 .25
Vince Coleman
637 Vince Coleman IA .08 .25
638 Pete Rose .30 .75
Dwight Gooden
639 Wade Boggs .50 1.25
Don Mattingly
640 Dale Murphy .20 .50
Steve Garvey
Dave Parker
641 Fernando Valenzuela .20 .50
Dwight Gooden
642 Jimmy Key .08 .25
Dave Stieb
643 Carlton Fisk .08 .25
Rich Gedman
644 Gene Walter RC .75 2.00
Benito Santiago RC
645 Mike Woodard RC .05 .15
Colin Ward RC
646 Kal Daniels RC 1.50 4.00
Paul O'Neill RC
647 Andres Galarraga RC .60 1.50
Fred Toliver RC
648 Bob Kipper RC .05 .15
Curt Ford RC
649 Jose Canseco RC 3.00 8.00
Eric Plunk RC
650 Mark McLemore RC .40 1.00
Gus Polidor RC
651 Rob Woodward RC .05 .15
Mickey Brantley RC
652 Billy Joe Robidoux RC .05 .15
Mark Funderburk RC
653 Cecil Fielder RC .75 2.00
Cory Snyder
654 CL: Royals/Cardinals .05 .15
Blue Jays/Mets
655 CL: Yankees/Dodgers .05 .15
Angels/Reds UER
(168 Darly Sconiers)
656 CL: White Sox/Tigers .05 .15
Expos/Orioles
(279 Dennis&
280 Tippy)
657 CL: Astros/Padres .05 .15
Red Sox/Cubs
658 CL: Twins/A's .05 .15
Phillies/Mariners
659 CL: Brewers/Braves .05 .15
Giants/Rangers
660 CL: Indians/Pirates .05 .15
Special Cards

1986 Fleer All-Stars

Randomly inserted in wax and cello packs, this 12-card standard-size set features top stars. The cards feature red backgrounds (American Leaguers) and blue backgrounds (National Leaguers). The 12 selections cover each position, left and right-handed starting pitchers, a reliever, and a designated hitter.

COMPLETE SET (12) 12.50 25.00
RANDOM INSERTS IN PACKS 1.25 2.50
1 Don Mattingly 3.00 8.00
2 Tom Herr .20 .50
3 George Brett 2.50 6.00
4 Gary Carter .30 .75
5 Cal Ripken 4.00 10.00
6 Dave Parker .30 .75
7 Rickey Henderson UER 1.00 2.50
(Misspelled Ricky
on card back)
8 Pedro Guerrero .30 .75
9 Dan Quisenberry .20 .50
10 Dwight Gooden 1.00 2.50
11 Gorman Thomas .30 .75
12 John Tudor .30 .75

1986 Fleer Future Hall of Famers

These six standard-size cards were issued one per Fleer three-packs. This set features players that Fleer predicts will be "Future Hall of Famers." The card backs describe career highlights, records, and honors won by the player.

COMPLETE SET (6) 6.00 15.00
SEMISTARS .25 .60
ONE PER RACK PACK
1 Pete Rose 2.50 6.00
2 Steve Carlton .25 .60
3 Tom Seaver .50 1.25
4 Rod Carew .50 1.25
5 Nolan Ryan 4.00 10.00
6 Reggie Jackson .50 1.25

1986 Fleer Wax Box Cards

The cards in this eight-card set measure the standard size and were found on the bottom of the Fleer regular issue wax pack and cello pack boxes as four-card panel. Cards have essentially the same design as the 1986 Fleer regular issue set. These eight cards (C1 to C8) are considered a separate set in their own right and are not typically included in a complete set of the regular issue 1986 Fleer cards. The value of the panel uncut is slightly greater, perhaps by 25 percent greater, than the value of the individual cards cut up carefully.

COMPLETE SET (8) 2.40 6.00
C1 Royals Logo .08 .25
C2 George Brett 1.25 3.00
C3 Ozzie Guillen .30 .75
C4 Dale Murphy .30 .75
C5 Cardinals Logo .08 .25
C6 Tom Browning .08 .25
C7 Gary Carter .40 1.00
C8 Carlton Fisk .40 1.00

1986 Fleer Update

This 132-card standard-size set was distributed in factory set form through hobby dealers. These sets were distributed in 50-set cases. In addition to the complete set of 132 cards, the box also contains 25 Team Logo Stickers.The card fronts look very similar to the 1986 Fleer regular issue. These cards are just as condition sensitive with most cards having chipped edges straight out of the box. The cards are numbered (with a U prefix) alphabetically according to player's last name. The extended Rookie Cards in this set include Barry Bonds, Bobby Bonilla, Will Clark, Wally Joyner and John Kruk.

COMP.FACT.SET (132) 12.00 30.00
1 Mike Aldrete XRC .05 .15
2 Andy Allanson XRC .05 .15
3 Neil Allen .05 .15
4 Joaquin Andujar .08 .25
5 Paul Assenmacher XRC .20 .50
6 Scott Bailes XRC .05 .15
7 Jay Baller XRC .05 .15
8 Scott Bankhead .05 .15
9 Bill Bathe XRC .05 .15
10 Don Baylor .08 .25
11 Billy Beane XRC .40 1.00
12 Steve Bedrosian .05 .15
13 Juan Beniquez .05 .15
14 Barry Bonds XRC 5.00 12.00
15 Bobby Bonilla XRC .40 1.00
UER Wrong birthday
16 Rich Bordi .05 .15
17 Bill Campbell .05 .15
18 Tom Candiotti .05 .15
19 John Cangelosi XRC .20 .50

Card	Low	High
20 Jose Canseco UER (Headings on back for a pitcher)	1.50	4.00
21 Chuck Cary XRC	.05	.15
22 Juan Castillo XRC	.05	.15
23 Rick Cerone	.05	.15
24 John Cerutti XRC	.05	.15
25 Will Clark XRC	.75	2.00
26 Mark Clear	.05	.15
27 Darnell Coles	.05	.15
28 Dave Collins	.05	.15
29 Tim Conroy	.05	.15
30 Ed Correa XRC	.05	.15
31 Joe Cowley	.05	.15
32 Bill Dawley	.05	.15
33 Rob Deer	.05	.15
34 John Denny	.05	.15
35 Jim Deshaies XRC	.05	.15
36 Doug Drabek XRC	.40	1.00
37 Mike Easler	.05	.15
38 Mark Eichhorn XRC	.05	.15
39 Dave Engle	.05	.15
40 Mike Fischlin	.05	.15
41 Scott Fletcher	.05	.15
42 Terry Forster	.08	.25
43 Terry Francona	.08	.25
44 Andres Galarraga	.60	1.50
45 Lee Guetterman XRC	.05	.15
46 Bill Gullickson	.05	.15
47 Jackie Gutierrez	.05	.15
48 Moose Haas	.05	.15
49 Billy Hatcher	.05	.15
50 Mike Heath	.05	.15
51 Guy Hoffman	.05	.15
52 Tom Hume	.05	.15
53 Pete Incaviglia XRC	.20	.50
54 Dane Iorg	.05	.15
55 Chris James XRC	.05	.15
56 Stan Javier XRC	.20	.50
57 Tommy John	.08	.25
58 Tracy Jones XRC	.05	.15
59 Wally Joyner XRC	.40	1.00
60 Wayne Krenchicki	.05	.15
61 John Kruk XRC	.60	1.50
62 Mike LaCoss	.05	.15
63 Pete Ladd	.05	.15
64 Dave LaPoint	.05	.15
65 Mike LaValliere XRC	.20	.50
66 Rudy Law	.05	.15
67 Dennis Leonard	.05	.15
68 Steve Lombardozzi XRC	.05	.15
69 Aurelio Lopez	.05	.15
70 Mickey Mahler	.05	.15
71 Candy Maldonado	.05	.15
72 Roger Mason XRC	.05	.15
73 Greg Mathews XRC	.05	.15
74 Andy McGaffigan	.05	.15
75 Joel McKeon	.05	.15
76 Kevin Mitchell XRC	.40	1.00
77 Bill Mooneyham XRC	.05	.15
78 Omar Moreno	.05	.15
79 Jerry Mumphrey	.05	.15
80 Al Newman XRC	.08	.25
81 Phil Niekro	.08	.25
82 Randy Niemann	.05	.15
83 Juan Nieves XRC	.05	.15
84 Bob Ojeda	.05	.15
85 Rick Ownbey	.05	.15
86 Tom Paciorek	.05	.15
87 David Palmer	.05	.15
88 Jeff Parrett XRC	.05	.15
89 Pat Perry XRC	.05	.15
90 Dan Plesac XRC	.05	.15
91 Darrell Porter	.05	.15
92 Luis Quinones XRC	.05	.15
93 Rey Quinones XRC UER Misspelled Quinonez	.05	.15
94 Gary Redus	.05	.15
95 Jeff Reed	.05	.15
96 Bip Roberts XRC	.20	.50
97 Billy Joe Robidoux	.05	.15
98 Gary Roenicke	.05	.15
99 Ron Roenicke	.05	.15
100 Angel Salazar	.05	.15
101 Joe Sambito	.05	.15
102 Billy Sample	.05	.15
103 Dave Schmidt	.05	.15
104 Ken Schrom	.05	.15
105 Ruben Sierra XRC	.60	1.50
106 Ted Simmons	.08	.25
107 Sammy Stewart	.05	.15
108 Kurt Stillwell XRC	.05	.15
109 Dale Sveum XRC	.05	.15
110 Tim Teufel	.05	.15
111 Bob Tewksbury XRC	.20	.50
112 Andres Thomas XRC	.05	.15
113 Jason Thompson	.05	.15
114 Milt Thompson	.20	.50
115 Robby Thompson XRC	.20	.50
116 Jay Tibbs	.05	.15
117 Fred Toliver	.05	.15
118 Wayne Tolleson	.05	.15
119 Alex Trevino	.05	.15
120 Manny Trillo	.05	.15
121 Ed VandeBerg	.05	.15
122 Ozzie Virgil	.05	.15
123 Tony Walker XRC	.05	.15
124 Gene Walter	.05	.15
125 Duane Ward XRC	.20	.50
126 Jerry Willard	.05	.15
127 Mitch Williams XRC	.20	.50
128 Reggie Williams XRC	.05	.15
129 Bobby Witt XRC	.20	.50
130 Marvell Wynne	.05	.15
131 Steve Yeager	.08	.25
132 Checklist 1-132	.05	.15

1987 Fleer

This set consists of 660 standard-size cards. Cards were primarily issued in 17-card wax packs, rack packs and hobby and retail factory sets. The wax packs were packed 36 to a box and 20 boxes to a case. The rack packs were packed 24 to a box and 3 boxes to a case and had 51 regular cards and three sticker card per pack. Card fronts feature a distinctive light blue and white blended border encasing a color photo. Cards are again organized numerically by teams with team ordering based on the previous seasons record. The last 36 cards in the set consist of Specials (625-643), Rookie Pairs (644-653), and checklists (654-660). The key Rookie Cards in this set are Barry Bonds, Bobby Bonilla, Will Clark, Chuck Finley, Bo Jackson, Wally Joyner, John Kruk, Barry Larkin and Devon White.

Card	Low	High
COMPLETE SET (660)	20.00	40.00
COMP.FACT.SET (672)	25.00	50.00
1 Rick Aguilera	.05	.15
2 Richard Anderson	.05	.15
3 Wally Backman	.05	.15
4 Gary Carter	.08	.25
5 Ron Darling	.08	.25
6 Len Dykstra	.08	.25
7 Kevin Elster RC	.20	.50
8 Sid Fernandez	.05	.15
9 Dwight Gooden	.15	.40
10 Ed Hearn RC	.05	.15
11 Danny Heep	.05	.15
12 Keith Hernandez	.08	.25
13 Howard Johnson	.08	.25
14 Ray Knight	.08	.25
15 Lee Mazzilli	.08	.25
16 Roger McDowell	.05	.15
17 Kevin Mitchell RC	.50	1.25
18 Randy Niemann	.05	.15
19 Bob Ojeda	.05	.15
20 Jesse Orosco	.05	.15
21 Rafael Santana	.05	.15
22 Doug Sisk	.05	.15
23 Darryl Strawberry	.08	.25
24 Tim Teufel	.05	.15
25 Mookie Wilson	.08	.25
26 Tony Armas	.08	.25
27 Marty Barrett	.05	.15
28 Don Baylor	.08	.25
29 Wade Boggs	.15	.40
30 Oil Can Boyd	.05	.15
31 Bill Buckner	.08	.25
32 Roger Clemens	1.25	3.00
33 Steve Crawford	.05	.15
34 Dwight Evans	.15	.40
35 Rich Gedman	.05	.15
36 Dave Henderson	.05	.15
37 Bruce Hurst	.05	.15
38 Tim Lollar	.05	.15
39 Al Nipper	.05	.15
40 Spike Owen	.05	.15
41 Jim Rice	.08	.25
42 Ed Romero	.05	.15
43 Joe Sambito	.05	.15
44 Calvin Schiraldi	.05	.15
45 Tom Seaver UER Lifetime saves total 0, should be 1	.15	.40
46 Jeff Sellers	.05	.15
47 Bob Stanley	.05	.15
48 Sammy Stewart	.05	.15
49 Larry Andersen	.05	.15
50 Alan Ashby	.05	.15
51 Kevin Bass	.05	.15
52 Jeff Calhoun	.05	.15
53 Jose Cruz	.08	.25
54 Danny Darwin	.05	.15
55 Glenn Davis	.05	.15
56 Jim Deshaies RC	.08	.25
57 Bill Doran	.05	.15
58 Phil Garner	.08	.25
59 Billy Hatcher	.05	.15
60 Charlie Kerfeld	.05	.15
61 Bob Knepper	.05	.15
62 Dave Lopes	.08	.25
63 Aurelio Lopez	.05	.15
64 Jim Pankovits	.05	.15
65 Terry Puhl	.05	.15
66 Craig Reynolds	.05	.15
67 Nolan Ryan	1.25	3.00
68 Mike Scott	.08	.25
69 Dave Smith	.05	.15
70 Dickie Thon	.05	.15
71 Tony Walker	.05	.15
72 Denny Walling	.05	.15
73 Bob Boone	.08	.25
74 Rick Burleson	.05	.15
75 John Candelaria	.05	.15
76 Doug Corbett	.05	.15
77 Doug DeCinces	.05	.15
78 Brian Downing	.08	.25
79 Chuck Finley RC	.50	1.25
80 Terry Forster	.05	.15
81 Bob Grich	.08	.25
82 George Hendrick	.08	.25
83 Jack Howell	.05	.15
84 Reggie Jackson	.15	.40
85 Ruppert Jones	.05	.15
86 Wally Joyner RC	.50	1.25
87 Gary Lucas	.05	.15
88 Kirk McCaskill	.05	.15
89 Donnie Moore	.05	.15
90 Gary Pettis	.05	.15
91 Vern Ruhle	.05	.15
92 Dick Schofield	.05	.15
93 Don Sutton	.08	.25
94 Rob Wilfong	.05	.15
95 Mike Witt	.05	.15
96 Doug Drabek RC	.50	1.25
97 Mike Easler	.05	.15
98 Mike Fischlin	.05	.15
99 Brian Fisher	.05	.15
100 Ron Guidry	.08	.25
101 Rickey Henderson	.25	.60
102 Tommy John	.08	.25
103 Ron Kittle	.05	.15
104 Don Mattingly	.75	2.00
105 Bobby Meacham	.05	.15
106 Joe Niekro	.05	.15
107 Mike Pagliarulo	.05	.15
108 Dan Pasqua	.05	.15
109 Willie Randolph	.08	.25
110 Dennis Rasmussen	.05	.15
111 Dave Righetti	.08	.25
112 Gary Roenicke	.05	.15
113 Rod Scurry	.05	.15
114 Bob Shirley	.05	.15
115 Joel Skinner	.05	.15
116 Tim Stoddard	.05	.15
117 Bob Tewksbury RC	.20	.50
118 Wayne Tolleson	.05	.15
119 Claudell Washington	.05	.15
120 Dave Winfield	.08	.25
121 Steve Buechele	.05	.15
122 Ed Correa	.05	.15
123 Scott Fletcher	.05	.15
124 Jose Guzman	.05	.15
125 Toby Harrah	[illegible]	[illegible]
126 Greg Harris	.05	.15
127 Charlie Hough	.08	.25
128 Pete Incaviglia RC	.20	.50
129 Mike Mason	.05	.15
130 Oddibe McDowell	.05	.15
131 Dale Mohorcic	.05	.15
132 Pete O'Brien	.05	.15
133 Tom Paciorek	.05	.15
134 Larry Parrish	.05	.15
135 Geno Petralli	.05	.15
136 Darrell Porter	.05	.15
137 Jeff Russell	.05	.15
138 Ruben Sierra RC	.75	2.00
139 Don Slaught	.05	.15
140 Gary Ward	.05	.15
141 Curtis Wilkerson	.05	.15
142 Mitch Williams RC	.20	.50
143 Bobby Witt RC UER (Tulsa misspelled as Tusla; ERA should be 6.43, not .643)	.20	.50
144 Dave Bergman	.05	.15
145 Tom Brookens	.05	.15
146 Bill Campbell	.05	.15
147 Chuck Cary	.05	.15
148 Darnell Coles	.05	.15
149 Dave Collins	.05	.15
150 Darrell Evans	.08	.25
151 Kirk Gibson	.08	.25
152 John Grubb	.05	.15
153 Willie Hernandez	.05	.15
154 Larry Herndon	.05	.15
155 Eric King	.05	.15
156 Chet Lemon	.08	.25
157 Dwight Lowry	.05	.15
158 Jack Morris	.08	.25
159 Randy O'Neal	.05	.15
160 Lance Parrish	.08	.25
161 Dan Petry	.05	.15
162 Pat Sheridan	.05	.15
163 Jim Slaton	.05	.15
164 Frank Tanana	.08	.25
165 Walt Terrell	.05	.15
166 Mark Thurmond	.05	.15
167 Alan Trammell	.08	.25
168 Lou Whitaker	.08	.25
169 Luis Aguayo	.05	.15
170 Steve Bedrosian	.05	.15
171 Don Carman	.05	.15
172 Darren Daulton	.08	.25
173 Greg Gross	.05	.15
174 Kevin Gross	.05	.15
175 Von Hayes	.05	.15
176 Charles Hudson	.05	.15
177 Tom Hume	.05	.15
178 Steve Jeltz	.05	.15
179 Mike Maddux RC	.05	.15
180 Shane Rawley	.05	.15
181 Gary Redus	.05	.15
182 Ron Roenicke	.05	.15
183 Bruce Ruffin RC	.08	.25
184 John Russell	.05	.15
185 Juan Samuel	.05	.15
186 Dan Schatzeder	.05	.15
187 Mike Schmidt	.60	1.50
188 Rick Schu	.05	.15
189 Jeff Stone	.05	.15
190 Kent Tekulve	.05	.15
191 Milt Thompson	.05	.15
192 Glenn Wilson	.05	.15
193 Buddy Bell	.08	.25
194 Tom Browning	.05	.15
195 Sal Butera	.05	.15
196 Dave Concepcion	.08	.25
197 Kal Daniels	.05	.15
198 Eric Davis	.15	.40
199 John Denny	.05	.15
200 Bo Diaz	.05	.15
201 Nick Esasky	.05	.15
202 John Franco	.08	.25
203 Bill Gullickson	.05	.15
204 Barry Larkin RC	1.25	3.00
205 Eddie Milner	.05	.15
206 Rob Murphy	.05	.15
207 Ron Oester	.05	.15
208 Dave Parker	.08	.25
209 Tony Perez	.15	.40
210 Ted Power	.05	.15
211 Joe Price	.05	.15
212 Ron Robinson	.05	.15
213 Pete Rose	.75	2.00
214 Mario Soto	.08	.25
215 Kurt Stillwell	.05	.15
216 Max Venable	.05	.15
217 Chris Welsh	.05	.15
218 Carl Willis RC	.08	.25
219 Jesse Barfield	.08	.25
220 George Bell	.08	.25
221 Bill Caudill	.05	.15
222 John Cerutti	.05	.15
223 Jim Clancy	.05	.15
224 Mark Eichhorn	.08	.25
225 Tony Fernandez	.08	.25
226 Damaso Garcia	.05	.15
227 Kelly Gruber ERR (Wrong birth year)	.05	.15
228 Tom Henke	.05	.15
229 Garth Iorg	.05	.15
230 Joe Johnson	.05	.15
231 Cliff Johnson	.05	.15
232 Jimmy Key	.08	.25
233 Dennis Lamp	.05	.15
234 Rick Leach	.05	.15
235 Buddy Martinez	.05	.15
236 Lloyd Moseby	.05	.15
237 Rance Mulliniks	.05	.15
238 Dave Stieb	.08	.25
239 Willie Upshaw	.05	.15
240 Ernie Whitt	.05	.15
241 Andy Allanson RC	.05	.15
242 Scott Bailes	.05	.15
243 Chris Bando	.05	.15
244 Tony Bernazard	.05	.15
245 John Butcher	.05	.15
246 Brett Butler	.08	.25
247 Ernie Camacho	.05	.15
248 Tom Candiotti	.05	.15
249 Joe Carter	.08	.25
250 Carmen Castillo	.05	.15
251 Julio Franco	.08	.25
252 Mel Hall	.05	.15
253 Brook Jacoby	.05	.15
254 Phil Niekro	.08	.25
255 Otis Nixon	.05	.15
256 Dickie Noles	.05	.15
257 Bryan Oelkers	.05	.15
258 Ken Schrom	.05	.15
259 Don Schulze	.05	.15
260 Cory Snyder	.05	.15
261 Pat Tabler	.05	.15
262 Andre Thornton	.05	.15
263 Rich Yett	.05	.15
264 Mike Aldrete	.05	.15
265 Juan Berenguer	.05	.15
266 Vida Blue	.08	.25
267 Bob Brenly	.05	.15
268 Chris Brown	.05	.15
269 Will Clark RC	1.25	3.00
270 Chili Davis	.08	.25
271 Mark Davis	.05	.15
272 Kelly Downs RC	.08	.25
273 Scott Garrelts	.05	.15
274 Dan Gladden	.05	.15
275 Mike Krukow	.05	.15
276 Randy Kutcher	.05	.15
277 Mike LaCoss	.05	.15
278 Jeff Leonard	.05	.15
279 Candy Maldonado	.05	.15
280 Roger Mason	.05	.15
281 Bob Melvin	.05	.15
282 Greg Minton	.05	.15
283 Jeff D. Robinson	.05	.15
284 Harry Spilman	.05	.15
285 Robby Thompson RC	.20	.50
286 Jose Uribe	.05	.15
287 Frank Williams	.05	.15
288 Joel Youngblood	.05	.15
289 Jack Clark	.08	.25
290 Vince Coleman	.05	.15
291 Tim Conroy	.05	.15
292 Danny Cox	.05	.15
293 Ken Dayley	.05	.15
294 Curt Ford	.05	.15
295 Bob Forsch	.05	.15
296 Tom Herr	.05	.15
297 Ricky Horton	.05	.15
298 Clint Hurdle	.05	.15
299 Jeff Lahti	.05	.15
300 Steve Lake	.05	.15
301 Tito Landrum	.05	.15
302 Mike LaValliere RC	.20	.50
303 Greg Mathews	.05	.15
304 Willie McGee	.08	.25
305 Jose Oquendo	.05	.15
306 Terry Pendleton	.08	.25
307 Pat Perry	.05	.15
308 Ozzie Smith	.40	1.00
309 Ray Soff	.05	.15
310 John Tudor	.08	.25
311 Andy Van Slyke UER (Bats R, Throws L)	.15	.40
312 Todd Worrell	.05	.15
313 Dann Bilardello	.05	.15
314 Hubie Brooks	.05	.15
315 Tim Burke	.05	.15
316 Andre Dawson	.08	.25
317 Mike Fitzgerald	.05	.15
318 Tom Foley	.05	.15
319 Andres Galarraga	.08	.25
320 Joe Hesketh	.05	.15
321 Wallace Johnson	.05	.15
322 Wayne Krenchicki	.05	.15
323 Vance Law	.05	.15
324 Dennis Martinez	.08	.25
325 Bob McClure	.05	.15
326 Andy McGaffigan	.05	.15
327 Al Newman RC	.05	.15
328 Tim Raines	.08	.25
329 Jeff Reardon	.08	.25
330 Luis Rivera RC	.08	.25
331 Bob Sebra	.05	.15
332 Bryn Smith	.05	.15
333 Jay Tibbs	.05	.15
334 Tim Wallach	.05	.15
335 Mitch Webster	.05	.15
336 Jim Wohlford	.05	.15
337 Floyd Youmans	.05	.15
338 Chris Bosio RC	.20	.50
339 Glenn Braggs RC	.08	.25
340 Rick Cerone	.05	.15
341 Mark Clear	.05	.15
342 Bryan Clutterbuck	.05	.15
343 Cecil Cooper	.08	.25
344 Rob Deer	.05	.15
345 Jim Gantner	.05	.15
346 Ted Higuera	.05	.15
347 John Henry Johnson	.05	.15
348 Tim Leary	.05	.15
349 Rick Manning	.05	.15
350 Paul Molitor	.08	.25
351 Charlie Moore	.05	.15
352 Juan Nieves	.05	.15
353 Ben Oglivie	.08	.25
354 Dan Plesac	.05	.15
355 Ernest Riles	.05	.15
356 Billy Joe Robidoux	.05	.15
357 Bill Schroeder	.05	.15
358 Dale Sveum	.05	.15
359 Gorman Thomas	.08	.25
360 Bill Wegman	.05	.15
361 Robin Yount	.40	1.00
362 Steve Balboni	.05	.15
363 Scott Bankhead	.05	.15
364 Buddy Biancalana	.05	.15
365 Bud Black	.05	.15
366 George Brett	.60	1.50
367 Steve Farr	.05	.15
368 Mark Gubicza	.05	.15
369 Bo Jackson RC	3.00	8.00
370 Danny Jackson	.05	.15
371 Mike Kingery RC	.08	.25
372 Rudy Law	.05	.15
373 Charlie Leibrandt	.05	.15
374 Dennis Leonard	.05	.15
375 Hal McRae	.08	.25
376 Jorge Orta	.05	.15
377 Jamie Quirk	.05	.15
378 Dan Quisenberry	.05	.15
379 Bret Saberhagen	.08	.25
380 Angel Salazar	.05	.15
381 Lonnie Smith	.05	.15
382 Jim Sundberg	.08	.25
383 Frank White	.08	.25
384 Willie Wilson	.08	.25
385 Joaquin Andujar	.08	.25
386 Doug Bair	.05	.15
387 Dusty Baker	.08	.25
388 Bruce Bochte	.05	.15
389 Jose Canseco	.60	1.50
390 Chris Codiroli	.05	.15
391 Mike Davis	.05	.15
392 Alfredo Griffin	.05	.15
393 Moose Haas	.05	.15
394 Donnie Hill	.05	.15
395 Jay Howell	.05	.15
396 Dave Kingman	.08	.25
397 Carney Lansford	.08	.25
398 Dave Leiper	.05	.15
399 Bill Mooneyham	.05	.15
400 Dwayne Murphy	.05	.15
401 Steve Ontiveros	.05	.15
402 Tony Phillips	.05	.15
403 Eric Plunk	.05	.15
404 Jose Rijo	.08	.25
405 Terry Steinbach RC	.50	1.25
406 Dave Stewart	.08	.25
407 Mickey Tettleton	.05	.15
408 Dave Von Ohlen	.05	.15
409 Jerry Willard	.05	.15
410 Curt Young	.05	.15
411 Bruce Bochy	.05	.15
412 Dave Dravecky	.05	.15
413 Tim Flannery	.05	.15
414 Steve Garvey	.08	.25
415 Rich Gossage	.08	.25
416 Tony Gwynn	.40	1.00
417 Andy Hawkins	.05	.15
418 LaMarr Hoyt	.05	.15
419 Terry Kennedy	.05	.15
420 John Kruk RC	.75	2.00
421 Dave LaPoint	.05	.15
422 Craig Lefferts	.05	.15
423 Carmelo Martinez	.05	.15
424 Lance McCullers	.05	.15
425 Kevin McReynolds	.05	.15
426 Graig Nettles	.08	.25
427 Bip Roberts RC	.20	.50
428 Jerry Royster	.05	.15
429 Benito Santiago	.08	.25
430 Eric Show	.05	.15
431 Bob Stoddard	.05	.15
432 Garry Templeton	.08	.25
433 Gene Walter	.05	.15
434 Ed Whitson	.05	.15
435 Marvell Wynne	.05	.15
436 Dave Anderson	.05	.15
437 Greg Brock	.05	.15
438 Enos Cabell	.05	.15
439 Mariano Duncan	.05	.15
440 Pedro Guerrero	.08	.25
441 Orel Hershiser	.15	.40
442 Rick Honeycutt	.05	.15
443 Ken Howell	.05	.15
444 Ken Landreaux	.05	.15
445 Bill Madlock	.08	.25
446 Mike Marshall	.05	.15
447 Len Matuszek	.05	.15
448 Tom Niedenfuer	.05	.15
449 Alejandro Pena	.05	.15
450 Dennis Powell	.05	.15
451 Jerry Reuss	.05	.15
452 Bill Russell	.08	.25
453 Steve Sax	.05	.15
454 Mike Scioscia	.08	.25
455 Franklin Stubbs	.05	.15
456 Alex Trevino	.05	.15
457 Fernando Valenzuela	.08	.25
458 Ed VandeBerg	.05	.15
459 Bob Welch	.08	.25
460 Reggie Williams	.05	.15
461 Don Aase	.05	.15
462 Juan Beniquez	.05	.15
463 Mike Boddicker	.05	.15
464 Juan Bonilla	.05	.15
465 Rich Bordi	.05	.15
466 Storm Davis	.05	.15
467 Rick Dempsey	.05	.15
468 Ken Dixon	.05	.15
469 Jim Dwyer	.05	.15
470 Mike Flanagan	.05	.15
471 Jackie Gutierrez	.05	.15
472 Brad Havens	.05	.15
473 Lee Lacy	.05	.15
474 Fred Lynn	.08	.25
475 Scott McGregor	.05	.15
476 Eddie Murray	.25	.60
477 Tom O'Malley	.05	.15
478 Cal Ripken Jr.	1.00	2.50
479 Larry Sheets	.05	.15
480 John Shelby	.05	.15
481 Nate Snell	.05	.15
482 Jim Traber	.05	.15
483 Mike Young	.05	.15
484 Neil Allen	.05	.15
485 Harold Baines	.08	.25
486 Floyd Bannister	.05	.15
487 Daryl Boston	.05	.15
488 Ivan Calderon	.05	.15
489 John Cangelosi	.05	.15
490 Steve Carlton	.08	.25
491 Joe Cowley	.05	.15
492 Julio Cruz	.05	.15
493 Bill Dawley	.05	.15
494 Jose DeLeon	.05	.15
495 Richard Dotson	.05	.15
496 Carlton Fisk	.15	.40
497 Ozzie Guillen	.15	.40
498 Jerry Hairston	.05	.15
499 Ron Hassey	.05	.15
500 Tim Hulett	.05	.15
501 Bob James	.05	.15
502 Steve Lyons	.05	.15
503 Joel McKeon	.05	.15
504 Gene Nelson	.05	.15
505 Dave Schmidt	.05	.15
506 Ray Searage	.05	.15
507 Bobby Thigpen RC	.20	.50
508 Greg Walker	.05	.15
509 Jim Acker	.05	.15
510 Doyle Alexander	.05	.15
511 Paul Assenmacher	.20	.50
512 Bruce Benedict	.05	.15
513 Chris Chambliss	.08	.25
514 Jeff Dedmon	.05	.15
515 Gene Garber	.05	.15
516 Ken Griffey	.08	.25
517 Terry Harper	.05	.15
518 Bob Horner	.08	.25
519 Glenn Hubbard	.05	.15
520 Rick Mahler	.05	.15
521 Omar Moreno	.05	.15
522 Dale Murphy	.15	.40
523 Ken Oberkfell	.05	.15
524 Ed Olwine	.05	.15
525 David Palmer	.05	.15
526 Rafael Ramirez	.05	.15
527 Billy Sample	.05	.15
528 Ted Simmons	.08	.25
529 Zane Smith	.05	.15
530 Bruce Sutter	.08	.25
531 Andres Thomas	.05	.15
532 Ozzie Virgil	.05	.15
533 Allan Anderson RC	.05	.15
534 Keith Atherton	.05	.15
535 Billy Beane	.08	.25
536 Bert Blyleven	.08	.25
537 Tom Brunansky	.05	.15
538 Randy Bush	.05	.15
539 George Frazier	.05	.15
540 Gary Gaetti	.08	.25
541 Greg Gagne	.05	.15
542 Mickey Hatcher	.05	.15
543 Neal Heaton	.05	.15
544 Kent Hrbek	.08	.25
545 Roy Lee Jackson	.05	.15
546 Tim Laudner	.05	.15
547 Steve Lombardozzi	.05	.15
548 Mark Portugal RC	.20	.50
549 Kirby Puckett	.40	1.00
550 Jeff Reed	.05	.15
551 Mark Salas	.05	.15
552 Roy Smalley	.05	.15
553 Mike Smithson	.05	.15
554 Frank Viola	.08	.25
555 Thad Bosley	.05	.15
556 Ron Cey	.08	.25
557 Jody Davis	.05	.15
558 Ron Davis	.05	.15
559 Bob Dernier	.05	.15
560 Frank DiPino	.05	.15
561 Shawon Dunston UER (Wrong birth year listed on card back)	.05	.15
562 Leon Durham	.05	.15
563 Dennis Eckersley	.15	.40
564 Terry Francona	.08	.25
565 Dave Gumpert	.05	.15
566 Guy Hoffman	.05	.15
567 Ed Lynch	.05	.15
568 Gary Matthews	.08	.25
569 Keith Moreland	.05	.15
570 Jamie Moyer RC	.75	2.00
571 Jerry Mumphrey	.05	.15
572 Ryne Sandberg	.50	1.25
573 Scott Sanderson	.05	.15
574 Lee Smith	.08	.25
575 Chris Speier	.05	.15
576 Rick Sutcliffe	.08	.25
577 Manny Trillo	.05	.15
578 Steve Trout	.05	.15
579 Karl Best	.05	.15
580 Scott Bradley	.05	.15
581 Phil Bradley	.05	.15
582 Mickey Brantley	.05	.15
583 Mike G. Brown P	.05	.15
584 Alvin Davis	.05	.15
585 Lee Guetterman	.05	.15
586 Mark Huismann	.05	.15
587 Bob Kearney	.05	.15
588 Pete Ladd	.05	.15
589 Mark Langston	.05	.15
590 Mike Moore	.05	.15
591 Mike Morgan	.05	.15
592 John Moses	.05	.15
593 Ken Phelps	.05	.15
594 Jim Presley	.05	.15
595 Rey Quinones UER (Quinonez on front)	.05	.15
596 Harold Reynolds	.08	.25
597 Billy Swift	.05	.15
598 Danny Tartabull	.05	.15
599 Steve Yeager	.08	.25
600 Matt Young	.05	.15
601 Bill Almon	.05	.15
602 Rafael Belliard RC	.20	.50
603 Mike Bielecki	.05	.15
604 Barry Bonds RC	5.00	12.00
605 Bobby Bonilla RC	.50	1.25
606 Sid Bream	.05	.15
607 Mike C. Brown	.05	.15
608 Pat Clements	.05	.15
609 Mike Diaz	.05	.15
610 Cecilio Guante	.05	.15
611 Barry Jones	.05	.15
612 Bob Kipper	.05	.15
613 Larry McWilliams	.05	.15
614 Jim Morrison	.05	.15
615 Joe Orsulak	.05	.15
616 Junior Ortiz	.05	.15
617 Tony Pena	.05	.15
618 Johnny Ray	.08	.25
619 Rick Reuschel	.08	.25
620 R.J. Reynolds	.05	.15
621 Rick Rhoden	.05	.15
622 Don Robinson	.05	.15
623 Bob Walk	.05	.15
624 Jim Winn	.05	.15
625 Pete Incaviglia / Jose Canseco	.30	.75
626 Don Sutton / Phil Niekro	.08	.25
627 Dave Righetti / Don Aase	.05	.15
628 Wally Joyner / Jose Canseco	.30	.75
629 Gary Carter / Sid Fernandez / Dwight Gooden / Keith Hernandez / Darryl Strawberry	.15	.40
630 Mike Scott / Mike Krukow	.05	.15
631 Fernando Valenzuela / John Franco	.05	.15
632 Bob Horner 4 Homers	.05	.15
633 Jose Canseco / Jim Rice / Kirby Puckett	.30	.75
634 Gary Carter / Roger Clemens	.25	.60
635 Steve Carlton 4000K's	.08	.25
636 Glenn Davis / Eddie Murray	.25	.60
637 Wade Boggs / Keith Hernandez	.08	.25
638 Don Mattingly / Darryl Strawberry	.40	1.00
639 Dave Parker / Ryne Sandberg	.25	.60
640 Dwight Gooden / Roger Clemens	.25	.60
641 Mike Witt / Charlie Hough	.05	.15
642 Juan Samuel / Tim Raines	.08	.25
643 Harold Baines / Jesse Barfield	.08	.25
644 Dave Clark RC / Greg Swindell RC	.20	.50
645 Ron Karkovice RC / Russ Morman RC	.20	.50
646 Devon White RC / Willie Fraser RC	.50	1.25
647 Mike Stanley RC / Jerry Browne RC	.20	.50
648 Dave Magadan RC / Phil Lombardi RC	.20	.50
649 Jose Gonzalez RC / Ralph Bryant RC	.08	.25
650 Jimmy Jones RC / Randy Asadoor RC	.08	.25
651 Tracy Jones RC / Marvin Freeman RC	.08	.25
652 John Stefero / Kevin Seitzer RC	.20	.50
653 Rob Nelson RC / Steve Fireovid RC	.08	.25
654 CL: Mets/Red Sox Astros/Angels	.05	.15
655 CL: Yankees/Rangers Tigers/Phillies	.05	.15
656 CL: Reds/Blue Jays Indians/Giants ERR (230/231 wrong)	.05	.15
657 CL: Cardinals/Expos Brewers/Royals	.05	.15
658 CL: A's/Padres Dodgers/Orioles	.05	.15
659 CL: White Sox/Braves Twins/Cubs	.05	.15
660 CL: Mariners/Pirates Special Cards ER (580/581 wrong)	.05	.15

1987 Fleer Glossy

This set parallels the regular 1987 Fleer issue and signified a short-lived three year run of Glossy parallel cards likely produced in response to Topps' run of Tiffany parallel sets. The cards were issued in a special tin which also included a glossy version of the World Series set. These 672 standard-size are differentiated only by the gloss on the front. This set was produced in fairly large quantities, although still significantly less than regular issue cards. According to widely held beliefs in the hobby, somewhere between 75 and 100 thousand of these sets were produced.

Card	Low	High
COMP.FACT.SET (672)	40.00	80.00
*STARS: .5X TO 1.2X BASIC CARDS		
*ROOKIES: .5X TO 1.2X BASIC CARDS		
DISTRIBUTED ONLY IN FACTORY SET FORM		
FACTORY SET PRICE IS FOR SEALED SETS		
OPENED SETS SELL FOR 50-60% OF SEALED		
604 Barry Bonds	6.00	15.00

1987 Fleer All-Stars

This 12-card standard-size set was distributed as an insert in packs of the Fleer regular issue. The cards are designed with a color player photo superimposed on a gray or black background with yellow stars. The player's name, team, and position are printed in orange on black or gray at the bottom of the obverse. The card backs are done predominantly in gray, red, and black and are numbered on the back in the upper right hand corner.

Card	Low	High
COMPLETE SET (12)	10.00	20.00
RANDOM INSERTS IN PACKS		

1 Don Mattingly 2.50 6.00
2 Gary Carter .30 .75
3 Tony Fernandez .20 .50
4 Steve Sax .20 .50
5 Kirby Puckett 1.25 3.00
6 Mike Schmidt 2.00 5.00
7 Mike Easler .20 .50
8 Todd Worrell .20 .50
9 George Bell .30 .75
10 Fernando Valenzuela .30 .75
11 Roger Clemens 4.00 10.00
12 Tim Raines .30 .75

1987 Fleer Headliners

This six-card standard-size set was distributed one per rack pack as well as with three-pack wax pack rack packs. The obverse features the player photo against a beige background with irregular red stripes. The checklist below also lists each player's team affiliation. The set is sequenced in alphabetical order.

COMPLETE SET (6) 3.00 6.00
ONE PER RACK PACK
1 Wade Boggs .25 .60
2 Jose Canseco 1.00 2.50
3 Dwight Gooden .25 .60
4 Rickey Henderson .40 1.00
5 Keith Hernandez .15 .40
6 Jim Rice .15 .40

1987 Fleer Wax Box Cards

The cards in this 16-card set measure the standard, 2 1/2" by 3 1/2". Cards have essentially the same design as the 1987 Fleer regular issue set. The cards were printed on the bottoms of the regular issue wax pack boxes. These 16 cards (C1 to C16) are considered a separate set in their own right and are not typically included in a complete set of the regular issue 1987 Fleer cards. The value of the panel uncut is slightly greater, perhaps by 25 percent greater, than the value of the individual cards cut up carefully.

COMPLETE SET (16) 4.00 10.00
C1 Mets Logo .02 .10
C2 Jesse Barfield .02 .10
C3 George Brett 1.25 3.00
C4 Dwight Gooden .20 .50
C5 Boston Logo .02 .10
C6 Keith Hernandez .08 .25
C7 Wally Joyner .30 .75
C8 Dale Murphy .30 .75
C9 Astros Logo .02 .10
C10 Dave Parker .08 .25
C11 Kirby Puckett .80 1.00
C12 Dave Righetti .02 .10
C13 Angels Logo .02 .10
C14 Ryne Sandberg .75 2.00
C15 Mike Schmidt .60 1.50
C16 Robin Yount .30 .75

1987 Fleer World Series

This 12-card standard-size set of features highlights of the previous year's World Series between the Mets and the Red Sox. The sets were packaged as a complete set insert with the collated sets (of the 1987 Fleer regular issue) which were sold by Fleer directly to hobby card dealers; they were not available in the general retail candy store outlets.

COMPLETE SET (12) .75 2.00
ONE SET PER FACTORY SET
1 Bruce Hurst .05 .15
2 Keith Hernandez and Wade Boggs .08 .25
3 Roger Clemens 1.25 3.00
4 Gary Carter .08 .25
5 Ron Darling .08 .25
6 Marty Barrett .05 .15
7 Dwight Gooden .15 .40
8 Strategy at Work (Mets Conference) .08 .25
9 Dwight Evans Congratulated by Rich Gedman .15 .40
10 Dave Henderson .05 .15
11 Ray Knight Darryl Strawberry .08 .25
12 Ray Knight .08 .25

1987 Fleer World Series Glossy

*GLOSSY: .5X TO 1.2X BASIC WS
DISTRIBUTED ONLY IN FACTORY SET FORM

1987 Fleer Update

This 132-card standard-size set was distributed exclusively in factory set form through hobby dealers. In addition to the complete set of 132 cards, the box

also contained 25 Team Logo stickers. The cards look very similar to the 1987 Fleer regular issue except for the U-prefixed numbering on back. Cards are ordered alphabetically according to player's last name. The key extended Rookie Cards in this set are Ellis Burks, Greg Maddux, Fred McGriff and Matt Williams. In addition an early card of legendary slugger Mark McGwire highlights this set.

COMP.FACT.SET (132) 5.00 12.00
1 Scott Bankhead .02 .10
2 Eric Bell .05 .15
3 Juan Beniquez .02 .10
4 Juan Berenguer .02 .10
5 Mike Birkbeck .05 .15
6 Randy Bockus .02 .10
7 Rod Booker .02 .10
8 Thad Bosley .02 .10
9 Greg Brock .02 .10
10 Bob Brower .02 .10
11 Chris Brown .02 .10
12 Jerry Browne .05 .15
13 Ralph Bryant .02 .10
14 DeWayne Buice .02 .10
15 Ellis Burks XRC .30 .75
16 Casey Candaele .02 .10
17 Steve Carlton .05 .15
18 Juan Castillo .05 .15
19 Chuck Crim .02 .10
20 Mark Davidson .02 .10
21 Mark Davis .02 .10
22 Storm Davis .02 .10
23 Bill Dawley .02 .10
24 Andre Dawson .05 .15
25 Brian Dayett .02 .10
26 Rick Dempsey .02 .10
27 Ken Dowell .02 .10
28 Dave Dravecky .02 .10
29 Mike Dunne .02 .10
30 Dennis Eckersley .08 .25
31 Cecil Fielder .05 .15
32 Brian Fisher .02 .10
33 Willie Fraser .05 .15
34 Ken Gerhart .02 .10
35 Jim Gott .02 .10
36 Dan Gladden .02 .10
37 Mike Greenwell XRC .10 .30
38 Cecilio Guante .02 .10
39 Albert Hall .02 .10
40 Atlee Hammaker .02 .10
41 Mickey Hatcher .02 .10
42 Mike Heath .02 .10
43 Neal Heaton .02 .10
44 Mike Henneman XRC .10 .30
45 Guy Hoffman .02 .10
46 Charles Hudson .02 .10
47 Chuck Jackson .02 .10
48 Mike Jackson XRC .10 .30
49 Reggie Jackson .08 .25
50 Chris James .02 .10
51 Dion James .02 .10
52 Stan Javier .02 .10
53 Stan Jefferson .02 .10
54 Jimmy Jones .05 .15
55 Tracy Jones .05 .15
56 Terry Kennedy .02 .10
57 Mike Kingery .05 .15
58 Ray Knight .05 .15
59 Gene Larkin XRC .10 .30
60 Mike LaValliere .10 .30
61 Jack Lazorko .02 .10
62 Terry Leach .02 .10
63 Rick Leach .02 .10
64 Craig Lefferts .02 .10
65 Jim Lindeman .05 .15
66 Bill Long .02 .10
67 Mike Loynd XRC .05 .15
68 Greg Maddux XRC 3.00 8.00
69 Bill Madlock .05 .15
70 Dave Magadan .10 .30
71 Joe Magrane XRC .05 .15
72 Fred Manrique .02 .10
73 Mike Mason .02 .10
74 Lloyd McClendon XRC .10 .30
75 Fred McGriff .40 1.00
76 Mark McGwire 2.00 5.00
77 Mark McLemore .05 .15
78 Kevin McReynolds .02 .10
79 Dave Meads .02 .10
80 Greg Minton .02 .10
81 John Mitchell XRC .05 .15
82 Kevin Mitchell .08 .25
83 John Morris .02 .10
84 Jeff Musselman .02 .10
85 Randy Myers XRC .30 .75
86 Gene Nelson .02 .10
87 Joe Niekro .02 .10
88 Tom Nieto .02 .10
89 Reid Nichols .02 .10
90 Matt Nokes XRC .10 .30
91 Dickie Noles .02 .10
92 Edwin Nunez .02 .10
93 Jose Nunez XRC .02 .10
94 Paul O'Neill .15 .40
95 Jim Paciorek .02 .10
96 Lance Parrish .05 .15
97 Bill Pecota XRC .05 .15
98 Tony Pena .02 .10
99 Luis Polonia XRC .10 .30
100 Randy Ready .02 .10
101 Jeff Reardon .05 .15
102 Gary Redus .02 .10
103 Rick Rhoden .02 .10
104 Wally Ritchie .02 .10
105 Jeff M. Robinson UER (Wrong Jeff's stats on back) .02 .10
106 Mark Salas .02 .10
107 Dave Schmidt .02 .10
108 Kevin Seitzer UER (Wrong birth year) .10 .30
109 John Shelby .02 .10
110 John Smiley XRC .10 .30
111 Lary Sorensen .02 .10
112 Chris Speier .02 .10
113 Randy St.Claire .02 .10
114 Jim Sundberg .05 .15
115 B.J. Surhoff XRC .30 .75
116 Greg Swindell .10 .30
117 Danny Tartabull .02 .10
118 Dorn Taylor .02 .10
119 Lee Tunnell .02 .10
120 Ed VandeBerg .02 .10
121 Andy Van Slyke .08 .25
122 Gary Ward .02 .10
123 Devon White .30 .75
124 Alan Wiggins .02 .10
125 Bill Wilkinson .02 .10
126 Jim Winn .02 .10
127 Frank Williams .02 .10
128 Ken Williams XRC .02 .10
129 Matt Williams XRC .60 1.50
130 Herm Winningham .02 .10
131 Matt Young .02 .10
132 Checklist 1-132 .02 .10

1987 Fleer Update Glossy

This set parallels the regular Fleer Update issue. The cards were issued in a special tin. These 132 standard-size are differentiated only by the gloss on the front. This set was produced in fairly large quantities, although still significantly less than regular issue cards. Similar to the regular Glossy set -- it is believed that between 75 and 100 thousand of these sets were produced.

COMP.FACT.SET (132) 6.00 15.00
*STARS: .4X TO 1X BASIC CARDS
*ROOKIES: .4X TO 1X BASIC CARDS
DISTRIBUTED ONLY IN FACTORY SET FORM

1988 Fleer

This set consists of 660 standard-size cards. Cards were primarily issued in 15-card wax packs and hobby and retail factory sets. Each wax pack contained one of 26 different "Stadium Card" stickers. Card fronts feature a distinctive white background with red and blue diagonal stripes across the card. As in years past cards are organized numerically by teams and team order is based upon the previous season's record. Subsets include Specials (622-640), Rookie Pairs (641-653), and checklists (654-660). Rookie Cards in this set include Jay Bell, Ellis Burks, Ken Caminiti, Ron Gant, Tom Glavine, Mark Grace, Edgar Martinez, Jack McDowell and Matt Williams.

COMPLETE SET (660) 6.00 15.00
COMP.RETAIL SET (660) 6.00 15.00
COMP.HOBBY SET (672) 6.00 15.00
1 Keith Atherton .02 .10
2 Don Baylor .05 .15
3 Juan Berenguer .02 .10
4 Bert Blyleven .05 .15
5 Tom Brunansky .02 .10
6 Randy Bush .02 .10
7 Steve Carlton .05 .15
8 Mark Davidson .02 .10
9 George Frazier .02 .10
10 Gary Gaetti .05 .15
11 Greg Gagne .02 .10
12 Dan Gladden .02 .10
13 Kent Hrbek .05 .15
14 Gene Larkin RC .15 .40
15 Tim Laudner .02 .10
16 Steve Lombardozzi .02 .10
17 Al Newman .02 .10
18 Joe Niekro .02 .10
19 Kirby Puckett .10 .30
20 Jeff Reardon .05 .15
21A Dan Schatzeder ERR (Misspelled Schatzader on both sides of the card) .05 .15
21B Dan Schatzeder COR .02 .10
22 Roy Smalley .02 .10
23 Mike Smithson .02 .10
24 Les Straker .02 .10
25 Frank Viola .05 .15
26 Jack Clark .05 .15
27 Vince Coleman .02 .10
28 Danny Cox .02 .10
29 Bill Dawley .02 .10
30 Ken Dayley .02 .10
31 Doug DeCinces .02 .10
32 Curt Ford .02 .10
33 Bob Forsch .02 .10
34 David Green .02 .10
35 Tom Herr .02 .10
36 Ricky Horton .02 .10
37 Lance Johnson RC .15 .40
38 Steve Lake .02 .10
39 Jim Lindeman .02 .10
40 Joe Magrane RC .15 .40
41 Greg Mathews .02 .10
42 Willie McGee .05 .15
43 John Morris .02 .10
44 Jose Oquendo .02 .10
45 Tony Pena .02 .10
46 Terry Pendleton .05 .15
47 Ozzie Smith .20 .50
48 John Tudor .05 .15
49 Lee Tunnell .02 .10
50 Todd Worrell .02 .10
51 Doyle Alexander .02 .10
52 Dave Bergman .02 .10
53 Tom Brookens .02 .10
54 Darrell Evans .05 .15
55 Kirk Gibson .10 .30
56 Mike Heath .02 .10
57 Mike Henneman RC .15 .40
58 Willie Hernandez .02 .10
59 Larry Herndon .02 .10
60 Eric King .02 .10
61 Chet Lemon .05 .15
62 Scott Lusader .02 .10
63 Bill Madlock .05 .15
64 Jack Morris .05 .15
65 Jim Morrison .02 .10
66 Matt Nokes RC .15 .40
67 Dan Petry .02 .10
68A Jeff M. Robinson ERR, Stats for Jeff D. Robinson on card back Born 12-13-60 .07 .20
68B Jeff M. Robinson COR, Born 12-14-61 .02 .10
69 Pat Sheridan .02 .10
70 Nate Snell .02 .10
71 Frank Tanana .05 .15
72 Walt Terrell .02 .10
73 Mark Thurmond .02 .10
74 Alan Trammell .05 .15
75 Lou Whitaker .05 .15
76 Mike Aldrete .02 .10
77 Bob Brenly .02 .10
78 Will Clark .10 .30
79 Chili Davis .05 .15
80 Kelly Downs .02 .10
81 Dave Dravecky .02 .10
82 Scott Garrelts .02 .10
83 Atlee Hammaker .02 .10
84 Dave Henderson .02 .10
85 Mike Krukow .02 .10
86 Mike LaCoss .02 .10
87 Craig Lefferts .02 .10
88 Jeff Leonard .02 .10
89 Candy Maldonado .02 .10
90 Eddie Milner .02 .10
91 Bob Melvin .02 .10
92 Kevin Mitchell .05 .15
93 Jon Perlman .02 .10
94 Rick Reuschel .05 .15
95 Don Robinson .02 .10
96 Chris Speier .02 .10
97 Harry Spilman .02 .10
98 Robby Thompson .02 .10
99 Jose Uribe .02 .10
100 Mark Wasinger .02 .10
101 Matt Williams RC .60 1.50
102 Jesse Barfield .05 .15
103 George Bell .05 .15
104 Juan Beniquez .02 .10
105 John Cerutti .02 .10
106 Jim Clancy .02 .10
107 Rob Ducey .02 .10
108 Mark Eichhorn .02 .10
109 Tony Fernandez .02 .10
110 Cecil Fielder .05 .15
111 Kelly Gruber .02 .10
112 Tom Henke .02 .10
113A Garth Iorg ERR (Misspelled Iorg on card front) .07 .20
113B Garth Iorg COR .02 .10
114 Jimmy Key .05 .15
115 Rick Leach .02 .10
116 Manny Lee .02 .10
117 Nelson Liriano .02 .10
118 Fred McGriff .10 .30
119 Lloyd Moseby .02 .10
120 Rance Mulliniks .02 .10
121 Jeff Musselman .02 .10
122 Jose Nunez .02 .10
123 Dave Stieb .05 .15
124 Willie Upshaw .02 .10
125 Duane Ward .02 .10
126 Ernie Whitt .02 .10
127 Rick Aguilera .05 .15
128 Wally Backman .02 .10
129 Mark Carreon RC .05 .15
130 Gary Carter .05 .15
131 David Cone .05 .15
132 Ron Darling .05 .15
133 Len Dykstra .05 .15
134 Sid Fernandez .05 .15
135 Dwight Gooden .05 .15
136 Keith Hernandez .05 .15
137 Gregg Jefferies RC .15 .40
138 Howard Johnson .05 .15
139 Terry Leach .02 .10
140 Barry Lyons .02 .10
141 Dave Magadan .02 .10
142 Roger McDowell .02 .10
143 Kevin McReynolds .02 .10
144 Keith A. Miller RC .15 .40
145 John Mitchell RC .02 .10
146 Randy Myers .05 .15
147 Bob Ojeda .02 .10
148 Jesse Orosco .02 .10
149 Rafael Santana .02 .10
150 Doug Sisk .02 .10
151 Darryl Strawberry .05 .15
152 Tim Teufel .02 .10
153 Gene Walter .02 .10
154 Mookie Wilson .05 .15
155 Jay Aldrich .02 .10
156 Chris Bosio .02 .10
157 Glenn Braggs .02 .10
158 Greg Brock .02 .10
159 Juan Castillo .02 .10
160 Mark Clear .02 .10
161 Cecil Cooper .05 .15
162 Chuck Crim .02 .10
163 Rob Deer .02 .10
164 Mike Felder .02 .10
165 Jim Gantner .02 .10
166 Ted Higuera .02 .10
167 Steve Kiefer .02 .10
168 Rick Manning .02 .10
169 Paul Molitor .05 .15
170 Juan Nieves .02 .10
171 Dan Plesac .02 .10
172 Earnest Riles .02 .10
173 Bill Schroeder .02 .10
174 Steve Stanicek .02 .10
175 B.J. Surhoff .05 .15
176 Dale Sveum .02 .10
177 Bill Wegman .02 .10
178 Robin Yount .20 .50
179 Hubie Brooks .02 .10
180 Tim Burke .02 .10
181 Casey Candaele .02 .10
182 Mike Fitzgerald .02 .10
183 Tom Foley .02 .10
184 Andres Galarraga .05 .15
185 Neal Heaton .02 .10
186 Wallace Johnson .02 .10
187 Vance Law .02 .10
188 Dennis Martinez .05 .15
189 Bob McClure .02 .10
190 Andy McGaffigan .02 .10
191 Reid Nichols .02 .10
192 Pascual Perez .02 .10
193 Tim Raines .05 .15
194 Jeff Reed .02 .10
195 Bob Sebra .02 .10
196 Bryn Smith .02 .10
197 Randy St.Claire .02 .10
198 Tim Wallach .02 .10
199 Mitch Webster .02 .10
200 Herm Winningham .02 .10
201 Floyd Youmans .02 .10
202 Brad Arnsberg .02 .10
203 Rick Cerone .02 .10
204 Pat Clements .02 .10
205 Henry Cotto .02 .10
206 Mike Easler .02 .10
207 Ron Guidry .05 .15
208 Bill Gullickson .02 .10
209 Rickey Henderson .10 .30
210 Charles Hudson .02 .10
211 Tommy John .05 .15
212 Roberto Kelly RC .15 .40
213 Ron Kittle .02 .10
214 Don Mattingly .40 1.00
215 Bobby Meacham .02 .10
216 Mike Pagliarulo .02 .10
217 Dan Pasqua .02 .10
218 Willie Randolph .05 .15
219 Rick Rhoden .02 .10
220 Dave Righetti .05 .15
221 Jerry Royster .02 .10
222 Tim Stoddard .02 .10
223 Wayne Tolleson .02 .10
224 Gary Ward .02 .10
225 Claudell Washington .02 .10
226 Dave Winfield .05 .15
227 Buddy Bell .05 .15
228 Tom Browning .02 .10
229 Dave Concepcion .05 .15
230 Kal Daniels .02 .10
231 Eric Davis .05 .15
232 Bo Diaz .02 .10
233 Nick Esasky (Has a dollar sign before '87 SB totals) .02 .10
234 John Franco .05 .15
235 Guy Hoffman .02 .10
236 Tom Hume .02 .10
237 Tracy Jones .02 .10
238 Bill Landrum .02 .10
239 Barry Larkin .07 .20
240 Terry McGriff .02 .10
241 Rob Murphy .02 .10
242 Ron Oester .02 .10
243 Dave Parker .05 .15
244 Pat Perry .02 .10
245 Ted Power .02 .10
246 Dennis Rasmussen .02 .10
247 Ron Robinson .02 .10
248 Kurt Stillwell .02 .10
249 Jeff Treadway RC .15 .40
250 Frank Williams .02 .10
251 Steve Balboni .02 .10
252 Bud Black .02 .10
253 Thad Bosley .02 .10
254 George Brett .30 .75
255 John Davis .02 .10
256 Steve Farr .02 .10
257 Gene Garber .02 .10
258 Jerry Don Gleaton .02 .10
259 Mark Gubicza .02 .10
260 Bo Jackson .10 .30
261 Danny Jackson .02 .10
262 Ross Jones .02 .10
263 Charlie Leibrandt .02 .10
264 Bill Pecota RC .05 .15
265 Melido Perez RC .15 .40
266 Jamie Quirk .02 .10
267 Dan Quisenberry .02 .10
268 Bret Saberhagen .05 .15
269 Angel Salazar .02 .10
270 Kevin Seitzer UER (Wrong birth year) .05 .15
271 Danny Tartabull .02 .10
272 Gary Thurman .02 .10
273 Frank White .05 .15
274 Willie Wilson .05 .15
275 Tony Bernazard .02 .10
276 Jose Canseco .30 .75
277 Mike Davis .02 .10
278 Storm Davis .02 .10
279 Dennis Eckersley .07 .20
280 Alfredo Griffin .02 .10
281 Rick Honeycutt .02 .10
282 Jay Howell .02 .10
283 Reggie Jackson .07 .20
284 Dennis Lamp .02 .10
285 Carney Lansford .05 .15
286 Mark McGwire 1.00 2.50
287 Dwayne Murphy .02 .10
288 Gene Nelson .02 .10
289 Steve Ontiveros .02 .10
290 Tony Phillips .02 .10
291 Eric Plunk .02 .10
292 Luis Polonia RC .15 .40
293 Rick Rodriguez .02 .10
294 Terry Steinbach .05 .15
295 Dave Stewart .05 .15
296 Curt Young .02 .10
297 Luis Aguayo .02 .10
298 Steve Bedrosian .02 .10
299 Jeff Calhoun .02 .10
300 Don Carman .02 .10
301 Todd Frohwirth .02 .10
302 Greg Gross .02 .10
303 Kevin Gross .02 .10
304 Von Hayes .02 .10
305 Keith Hughes .02 .10
306 Mike Jackson RC .15 .40
307 Chris James .02 .10
308 Steve Jeltz .02 .10
309 Mike Maddux .02 .10
310 Lance Parrish .05 .15
311 Shane Rawley .02 .10
312 Wally Ritchie .02 .10
313 Bruce Ruffin .02 .10
314 Juan Samuel .02 .10
315 Mike Schmidt .30 .75
316 Rick Schu .02 .10
317 Jeff Stone .02 .10
318 Kent Tekulve .02 .10
319 Milt Thompson .02 .10
320 Glenn Wilson .02 .10
321 Rafael Belliard .02 .10
322 Barry Bonds 1.00 2.50
323 Bobby Bonilla UER (Wrong birth year) .05 .15
324 Sid Bream .02 .10
325 John Cangelosi .02 .10
326 Mike Diaz .02 .10
327 Doug Drabek .02 .10
328 Mike Dunne .02 .10
329 Brian Fisher .02 .10
330 Brett Gideon .02 .10
331 Terry Harper .02 .10
332 Bob Kipper .02 .10
333 Mike LaValliere .02 .10
334 Jose Lind RC .15 .40
335 Junior Ortiz .02 .10
336 Vicente Palacios .02 .10
337 Bob Patterson .02 .10
338 Al Pedrique .02 .10
339 R.J. Reynolds .02 .10
340 John Smiley RC .15 .40
341 Andy Van Slyke UER (Wrong batting and throwing listed) .07 .20
342 Bob Walk .02 .10
343 Marty Barrett .02 .10
344 Todd Benzinger RC .15 .40
345 Wade Boggs .07 .20
346 Tom Bolton .02 .10
347 Oil Can Boyd .02 .10
348 Ellis Burks RC .20 .50
349 Roger Clemens .60 1.50
350 Steve Crawford .02 .10
351 Dwight Evans .07 .20
352 Wes Gardner .02 .10
353 Rich Gedman .02 .10
354 Mike Greenwell .02 .10
355 Sam Horn RC .05 .15
356 Bruce Hurst .02 .10
357 John Marzano .02 .10
358 Al Nipper .02 .10
359 Spike Owen .02 .10
360 Jody Reed RC .15 .40
361 Jim Rice .05 .15
362 Ed Romero .02 .10
363 Kevin Romine .02 .10
364 Joe Sambito .02 .10
365 Calvin Schiraldi .02 .10
366 Jeff Sellers .02 .10
367 Bob Stanley .02 .10
368 Scott Bankhead .02 .10
369 Phil Bradley .02 .10
370 Scott Bradley .02 .10
371 Mickey Brantley .02 .10
372 Mike Campbell .02 .10
373 Alvin Davis .02 .10
374 Lee Guetterman .02 .10
375 Dave Hengel .02 .10
376 Mike Kingery .02 .10
377 Mark Langston .02 .10
378 Edgar Martinez RC 2.00 5.00
379 Mike Moore .02 .10
380 Mike Morgan .02 .10
381 John Moses .02 .10
382 Donell Nixon .02 .10
383 Edwin Nunez .02 .10
384 Ken Phelps .02 .10
385 Jim Presley .02 .10
386 Rey Quinones .02 .10
387 Jerry Reed .02 .10
388 Harold Reynolds .05 .15
389 Dave Valle .02 .10
390 Bill Wilkinson .02 .10
391 Harold Baines .05 .15
392 Floyd Bannister .02 .10
393 Daryl Boston .02 .10
394 Ivan Calderon .02 .10
395 Jose DeLeon .02 .10
396 Richard Dotson .02 .10
397 Carlton Fisk .07 .20
398 Ozzie Guillen .05 .15
399 Ron Hassey .02 .10
400 Donnie Hill .02 .10
401 Bob James .02 .10
402 Dave LaPoint .02 .10
403 Bill Lindsey .02 .10
404 Bill Long .02 .10
405 Steve Lyons .02 .10
406 Fred Manrique .02 .10
407 Jack McDowell RC .20 .50
408 Gary Redus .02 .10
409 Ray Searage .02 .10
410 Bobby Thigpen .02 .10
411 Greg Walker .02 .10
412 Ken Williams RC .02 .10
413 Jim Winn .02 .10
414 Jody Davis .02 .10
415 Andre Dawson .05 .15
416 Brian Dayett .02 .10
417 Bob Dernier .02 .10
418 Frank DiPino .02 .10
419 Shawon Dunston .02 .10
420 Leon Durham .02 .10
421 Les Lancaster .02 .10
422 Ed Lynch .02 .10
423 Greg Maddux .60 1.50
424 Dave Martinez .02 .10
425A Keith Moreland ERR (Photo actually Jody Davis) .60 1.50
425B Keith Moreland COR (Bat on shoulder) .05 .15
426 Jamie Moyer .05 .15
427 Jerry Mumphrey .02 .10
428 Paul Noce .02 .10
429 Rafael Palmeiro .25 .60
430 Wade Rowdon .02 .10
431 Ryne Sandberg .25 .60
432 Scott Sanderson .02 .10
433 Lee Smith .05 .15
434 Jim Sundberg .05 .15
435 Rick Sutcliffe .05 .15
436 Manny Trillo .02 .10
437 Juan Agosto .02 .10
438 Larry Andersen .02 .10
439 Alan Ashby .02 .10
440 Kevin Bass .02 .10
441 Ken Caminiti RC 1.25 3.00
442 Rocky Childress .02 .10
443 Jose Cruz .05 .15
444 Danny Darwin .02 .10
445 Glenn Davis .02 .10
446 Jim Deshaies .02 .10
447 Bill Doran .02 .10
448 Ty Gainey .02 .10
449 Billy Hatcher .02 .10
450 Jeff Heathcock .02 .10
451 Bob Knepper .02 .10
452 Rob Mallicoat .02 .10
453 Dave Meads .02 .10
454 Craig Reynolds .02 .10
455 Nolan Ryan .60 1.50
456 Mike Scott .05 .15
457 Dave Smith .02 .10
458 Denny Walling .02 .10
459 Robbie Wine .02 .10
460 Gerald Young .02 .10
461 Bob Brower .02 .10
462A Jerry Browne ERR (Photo actually Bob Brower, white player) .60 1.50
462B Jerry Browne COR (Black player) .05 .15
463 Steve Buechele .02 .10
464 Edwin Correa .02 .10
465 Cecil Espy RC .02 .10
466 Scott Fletcher .02 .10
467 Jose Guzman .02 .10
468 Greg Harris .02 .10
469 Charlie Hough .05 .15
470 Pete Incaviglia .02 .10
471 Paul Kilgus .02 .10
472 Mike Loynd .02 .10
473 Oddibe McDowell .02 .10
474 Dale Mohorcic .02 .10
475 Pete O'Brien .02 .10
476 Larry Parrish .02 .10
477 Geno Petralli .02 .10
478 Jeff Russell .02 .10
479 Ruben Sierra .05 .15
480 Mike Stanley .02 .10
481 Curtis Wilkerson .02 .10
482 Mitch Williams .02 .10
483 Bobby Witt .02 .10
484 Tony Armas .05 .15
485 Bob Boone .05 .15
486 Bill Buckner .05 .15
487 DeWayne Buice .02 .10
488 Brian Downing .05 .15
489 Chuck Finley .05 .15
490 Willie Fraser UER (Wrong bio stats, for George Hendrick) .02 .10
491 Jack Howell .02 .10
492 Ruppert Jones .02 .10
493 Wally Joyner .05 .15
494 Jack Lazorko .02 .10
495 Gary Lucas .02 .10
496 Kirk McCaskill .02 .10
497 Mark McLemore .02 .10
498 Darrell Miller .02 .10
499 Greg Minton .02 .10
500 Donnie Moore .02 .10
501 Gus Polidor .02 .10
502 Johnny Ray .02 .10
503 Mark Ryal .02 .10
504 Dick Schofield .02 .10
505 Don Sutton .05 .15
506 Devon White .05 .15
507 Mike Witt .02 .10
508 Dave Anderson .02 .10
509 Tim Belcher .02 .10
510 Ralph Bryant .02 .10
511 Tim Crews RC .15 .40
512 Mike Devereaux RC .15 .40
513 Mariano Duncan .02 .10
514 Pedro Guerrero .05 .15
515 Jeff Hamilton .02 .10
516 Mickey Hatcher .02 .10
517 Brad Havens .02 .10
518 Orel Hershiser .05 .15
519 Shawn Hillegas .02 .10
520 Ken Howell .02 .10
521 Tim Leary .02 .10
522 Mike Marshall .02 .10
523 Steve Sax .02 .10
524 Mike Scioscia .05 .15
525 Mike Sharperson .02 .10
526 John Shelby .02 .10
527 Franklin Stubbs .02 .10
528 Fernando Valenzuela .05 .15
529 Bob Welch .05 .15
530 Matt Young .02 .10
531 Jim Acker .02 .10
532 Paul Assenmacher .02 .10
533 Jeff Blauser RC .15 .40
534 Joe Boever .02 .10
535 Martin Clary .02 .10
536 Kevin Coffman .02 .10
537 Jeff Dedmon .02 .10
538 Ron Gant RC .20 .50
539 Tom Glavine RC 1.50 4.00
540 Ken Griffey .05 .15
541 Albert Hall .02 .10
542 Glenn Hubbard .02 .10

543 Dion James .02 .10
544 Dale Murphy .07 .20
545 Ken Oberkfell .02 .10
546 David Palmer .02 .10
547 Gerald Perry .02 .10
548 Charlie Puleo .02 .10
549 Ted Simmons .05 .15
550 Zane Smith .02 .10
551 Andres Thomas .02 .10
552 Ozzie Virgil .02 .10
553 Don Aase .02 .10
554 Jeff Ballard .02 .10
555 Eric Bell .02 .10
556 Mike Boddicker .02 .10
557 Ken Dixon .02 .10
558 Jim Dwyer .02 .10
559 Ken Gerhart .02 .10
560 Rene Gonzales RC .05 .15
561 Mike Griffin .02 .10
562 John Habyan UER .02 .10
(Misspelled Hayban on
both sides of card)
563 Terry Kennedy .02 .10
564 Ray Knight .05 .15
565 Lee Lacy .02 .10
566 Fred Lynn .05 .15
567 Eddie Murray .10 .30
568 Tom Niedenfuer .02 .10
569 Bill Ripken RC .15 .40
570 Cal Ripken .50 1.25
571 Dave Schmidt .02 .10
572 Larry Sheets .02 .10
573 Pete Stanicek .02 .10
574 Mark Williamson .02 .10
575 Mike Young .02 .10
576 Shawn Abner .02 .10
577 Greg Booker .02 .10
578 Chris Brown .02 .10
579 Keith Comstock .02 .10
580 Joey Cora RC .15 .40
581 Mark Davis .02 .10
582 Tim Flannery .07 .20
(With surfboard)
583 Goose Gossage .05 .15
584 Mark Grant .02 .10
585 Tony Gwynn .20 .50
586 Andy Hawkins .02 .10
587 Stan Jefferson .02 .10
588 Jimmy Jones .02 .10
589 John Kruk .05 .15
590 Shane Mack .02 .10
591 Carmelo Martinez .02 .10
592 Lance McCullers UER .02 .10
(6'11 tall)
593 Eric Nolte .02 .10
594 Randy Ready .02 .10
595 Luis Salazar .02 .10
596 Benito Santiago .05 .15
597 Eric Show .02 .10
598 Garry Templeton .05 .15
599 Ed Whitson .02 .10
600 Scott Bailes .02 .10
601 Chris Bando .02 .10
602 Jay Bell RC .20 .50
603 Brett Butler .05 .15
604 Tom Candiotti .02 .10
605 Joe Carter .05 .15
606 Carmen Castillo .02 .10
607 Brian Dorsett .02 .10
608 John Farrell RC .05 .15
609 Julio Franco .05 .15
610 Mel Hall .02 .10
611 Tommy Hinzo .02 .10
612 Brook Jacoby .02 .10
613 Doug Jones RC .15 .40
614 Ken Schrom .02 .10
615 Cory Snyder .02 .10
616 Sammy Stewart .02 .10
617 Greg Swindell .02 .10
618 Pat Tabler .02 .10
619 Ed VandeBerg .02 .10
620 Eddie Williams RC .05 .15
621 Rich Yett .02 .10
622 Wally Joyner .05 .15
Cory Snyder
623 George Bell .02 .10
Pedro Guerrero
624 Mark McGwire .60 1.50
Jose Canseco
625 Dave Righetti .02 .10
Dan Plesac
626 Bret Saberhagen .05 .15
Mike Witt
Jack Morris
627 John Franco .02 .10
Steve Bedrosian
628 Ozzie Smith .10 .30
Ryne Sandberg
629 Mark McGwire HL .50 1.25
630 Mike Greenwell .10 .30
Ellis Burks
Todd Benzinger
631 Tony Gwynn .07 .20
Tim Raines
632 Mike Scott .05 .15
Orel Hershiser
633 Pat Tabler .50 1.25
Mark McGwire
634 Tony Gwynn .07 .20
Vince Coleman
635 Tony Fernandez .20 .50
Cal Ripken
Alan Trammell
636 Mike Schmidt .10 .30
Gary Carter
637 Darryl Strawberry .05 .15
Eric Davis
638 Matt Nokes .07 .20
Kirby Puckett
639 Keith Hernandez .05 .15
Dale Murphy
640 Billy Ripken .30 .75
Cal Ripken
641 Mark Grace RC 1.25 3.00
Darrin Jackson
642 Damon Berryhill RC .15 .40
Jeff Montgomery RC
643 Felix Fermin .05 .15
Jesse Reid RC
644 Greg Myers .15 .40
Greg Tabor RC
645 Joey Meyer .05 .15
Jim Eppard RC
646 Adam Peterson RC .15 .40
Randy Velarde RC
647 Pete Smith RC .15 .40
Chris Gwynn RC
648 Tom Newell .05 .15
Greg Jelks RC
649 Mario Diaz .05 .15
Clay Parker RC
650 Jack Savage .05 .15
Todd Simmons RC
651 John Burkett .15 .40
Kirt Manwaring RC
652 Dave Otto .20 .50
Walt Weiss RC
653 Jeff King .15 .40
Randell Byers RC
654 CL: Twins/Cards .02 .10
Tigers/Giants UER
(90 Bob Melvin,
91 Eddie Milner)
655 CL: Blue Jays/Mets .02 .10
Brewers/Expos UER
(Mets listed before
Blue Jays on card)
656 CL: Yankees/Reds .02 .10
Royals/A's
657 CL: Phillies/Pirates .02 .10
Red Sox/Mariners
658 CL: White Sox/Cubs .02 .10
Astros/Rangers
659 CL: Angels/Dodgers .02 .10
Braves/Orioles
660 CL: Padres/Indians .02 .10
Rookies/Specials

1988 Fleer Glossy

This 660 card set is a parallel to the regular Fleer issue. The cards are the same as the regular issue except for the glossy sheen on the front. The cards (along with the 12-card World Series insert set) were issued in a factory tin distributed exclusively through hobby dealers. Since many dealers had problems selling their 1987 sets, production was reduced for the 1988 issues. It is believed that between 40 and 60 thousand of these sets were produced,

COMP.FACT.SET (672) 10.00 25.00
*STARS: .6X TO 1.5X BASIC CARDS
*ROOKIES: .75X TO 2X BASIC CARDS
DISTRIBUTED ONLY IN FACTORY SET FORM

1988 Fleer All-Stars

These 12 standard-size cards were inserted randomly in wax and cello packs of the 1988 Fleer set. The cards show the player silhouetted against a light green background with dark green stripes. The player's name, team, and position are printed in yellow at the bottom of the obverse. The card backs are done predominantly in green, white, and black. The players are the "best" at each position, three pitchers, eight position players, and a designated hitter.

COMPLETE SET (12) 3.00 6.00
RANDOM INSERTS IN PACKS .40 .75
1 Matt Nokes .60 1.50
2 Tom Henke .15 .40
3 Ted Higuera .15 .40
4 Roger Clemens 2.50 6.00
5 George Bell .25 .60
6 Andre Dawson .25 .60
7 Eric Davis .25 .60
8 Wade Boggs .30 .75
9 Alan Trammell .25 .60
10 Juan Samuel .15 .40
11 Jack Clark .25 .60
12 Paul Molitor .25 .60

1988 Fleer Headliners

This six-card standard-size set was distributed one per rack pack. The obverse features the player photo superimposed on a gray newsprint background. The cards are printed in red, black, and white on the back describing why that particular player made headlines the previous season. The set is sequenced in alphabetical order.

COMPLETE SET (6) 3.00 6.00
ONE PER RACK PACK .10 .20
1 Don Mattingly .50 1.25
2 Mark McGwire 1.50 4.00
3 Jack Morris .07 .20
4 Darryl Strawberry .07 .20
5 Dwight Gooden .10 .20
6 Tim Raines .07 .20

1988 Fleer Wax Box Cards

The cards in this 16-card set measure the standard size. Cards have essentially the same design as the 1988 Fleer regular issue set. The cards were printed on the bottoms of the regular issue wax pack boxes. These 16 cards (C1 to C16) are considered a separate set in their own right and are not typically included in a complete set of the regular issue 1988 Fleer cards. The value of the panel uncut is slightly greater, perhaps by 25 percent greater, than the value of the individual cards cut up carefully.

COMPLETE SET (16) 3.20 8.00
C1 Cardinals Logo .02 .10
C2 Dwight Evans .08 .25
C3 Andres Galarraga .40 1.00
C4 Wally Joyner .08 .25
C5 Twins Logo .02 .10
C6 Dale Murphy .40 1.00
C7 Kirby Puckett .50 1.25
C8 Shane Rawley .02 .10
C9 Giants Logo .02 .10
C10 Ryne Sandberg 1.00 2.50
C11 Mike Schmidt .50 1.25
C12 Kevin Seitzer .02 .10
C13 Tigers Logo .02 .10
C14 Dave Stewart .08 .25
C15 Tim Wallach .02 .10
C16 Todd Worrell .08 .25

1988 Fleer World Series

This 12-card standard-size set features highlights of the previous year's World Series between the Minnesota Twins and the St. Louis Cardinals. The sets were packaged as a complete set insert with the collated sets (of the 1988 Fleer regular issue) which were sold by Fleer directly to hobby card dealers; they were not available in the general retail candy store outlets. The set numbering is essentially in chronological order of the events from the immediate past World Series.

COMPLETE SET (12) .75 2.00
ONE SET PER FACTORY SET
1 Dan Gladden .02 .10
2 Randy Bush .02 .10
3 John Tudor .05 .15
4 Ozzie Smith .20 .50
5 Todd Worrell .02 .10
Tony Pena
6 Vince Coleman .02 .10
7 Tom Herr .02 .10
Dan Driessen
8 Kirby Puckett .10 .30
9 Kent Hrbek .05 .15
10 Tom Herr .02 .10
11 Don Baylor .05 .15
12 Frank Viola .05 .15

1988 Fleer World Series Glossy

*GLOSSY: .5X TO 1.2X BASIC WS
DISTRIBUTED ONLY IN FACTORY SET FORM

1988 Fleer Update

This 132-card standard-size set was distributed exclusively in factory set form in a red, white and blue, cellophane-wrapped box through hobby dealers. In addition to the complete set of 132 cards, the box also contained 25 Team Logo stickers. The cards look very similar to the 1988 Fleer regular issue except for the U-prefixed numbering on back. Cards are ordered alphabetically by player's last name. This was the first Fleer Update set to adopt the Fleer "alphabetical within team" numbering system. The key extended Rookie Cards in this set are Roberto Alomar, Craig Biggio Al Leiter, John Smoltz and David Wells.

COMP.FACT.SET (132) 4.00 10.00
1 Jose Bautista XRC .08 .25
2 Joe Orsulak .02 .10
3 Doug Sisk .02 .10
4 Craig Worthington .02 .10
5 Mike Boddicker .02 .10
6 Rick Cerone .02 .10
7 Larry Parrish .02 .10
8 Lee Smith .07 .20
9 Mike Smithson .02 .10
10 John Trautwein .02 .10
11 Sherman Corbett .02 .10
12 Chili Davis .07 .20
13 Jim Eppard .02 .10
14 Bryan Harvey XRC .20 .50
15 John Davis .02 .10
16 Dave Gallagher .02 .10
17 Ricky Horton .02 .10
18 Dan Pasqua .02 .10
19 Melido Perez .02 .10
20 Jose Segura .02 .10
21 Andy Allanson .02 .10
22 Jon Perlman .02 .10
23 Domingo Ramos .02 .10
24 Rick Rodriguez .02 .10
25 Willie Upshaw .02 .10
26 Paul Gibson .02 .10
27 Don Heinkel .02 .10
28 Ray Knight .07 .20
29 Gary Pettis .02 .10
30 Luis Salazar .02 .10
31 Mike Macfarlane XRC .20 .50
32 Jeff Montgomery .20 .50
33 Ted Power .02 .10
34 Israel Sanchez .02 .10
35 Kurt Stillwell .02 .10
36 Pat Tabler .02 .10
37 Don August .02 .10
38 Darryl Hamilton XRC .20 .50
39 Jeff Leonard .02 .10
40 Joey Meyer .02 .10
41 Allan Anderson .02 .10
42 Brian Harper .02 .10
43 Tom Herr .02 .10
44 Charlie Lea .02 .10
45 John Moses .02 .10
(Listed as Hohn on
checklist card)
46 John Candelaria .02 .10
47 Jack Clark .07 .20
48 Richard Dotson .02 .10
49 Al Leiter XRC .40 1.00
50 Rafael Santana .02 .10
51 Don Slaught .02 .10
52 Todd Burns .02 .10
53 Dave Henderson .02 .10
54 Doug Jennings .02 .10
55 Dave Parker .07 .20
56 Walt Weiss .30 .75
57 Bob Welch .07 .20
58 Henry Cotto .02 .10
59 Mario Diaz UER .02 .10
(Listed as Marion
on card front)
60 Mike Jackson .07 .20
61 Bill Swift .02 .10
62 Jose Cecena .02 .10
63 Ray Hayward .02 .10
64 Jim Steels UER .02 .10
(Listed as Jim Steele
on card back)
65 Pat Borders XRC .20 .50
66 Sil Campusano .02 .10
67 Mike Flanagan .02 .10
68 Todd Stottlemyre XRC .20 .50
69 David Wells XRC .60 1.50
70 Jose Alvarez XRC .08 .25
71 Paul Runge .02 .10
72 Cesar Jimenez .02 .10
(Card was intended
for German Jiminez&
it's his photo)
73 Pete Smith .02 .10
74 John Smoltz XRC 1.50 4.00
75 Damon Berryhill .08 .25
76 Goose Gossage .07 .20
77 Mark Grace .75 2.00
78 Darrin Jackson .08 .25
79 Vance Law .02 .10
80 Jeff Pico .02 .10
81 Gary Varsho .02 .10
82 Tim Birtsas .02 .10
83 Rob Dibble XRC .30 .75
84 Danny Jackson .02 .10
85 Paul O'Neill .10 .30
86 Jose Rijo .07 .20
87 Chris Sabo XRC .30 .75
88 John Fishel .02 .10
89 Craig Biggio XRC 2.00 5.00
90 Terry Puhl .02 .10
91 Rafael Ramirez .02 .10
92 Louie Meadows .02 .10
93 Kirk Gibson .20 .50
94 Alfredo Griffin .02 .10
95 Jay Howell .02 .10
96 Jesse Orosco .02 .10
97 Alejandro Pena .02 .10
98 Tracy Woodson XRC .08 .25
99 John Dopson .02 .10
100 Brian Holman XRC .08 .25
101 Rex Hudler .02 .10
102 Jeff Parrett .02 .10
103 Nelson Santovenia .02 .10
104 Kevin Elster .02 .10
105 Jeff Innis .02 .10
106 Mackey Sasser XRC .20 .50
107 Phil Bradley .02 .10
108 Danny Clay .02 .10
109 Greg A.Harris .02 .10
110 Ricky Jordan XRC .20 .50
111 David Palmer .02 .10
112 Jim Gott .02 .10
113 Tommy Gregg UER .02 .10
(Photo actually
Randy Milligan)
114 Barry Jones .02 .10
115 Randy Milligan XRC .08 .25
116 Luis Alicea XRC .20 .50
117 Tom Brunansky .02 .10
118 John Costello .02 .10
119 Jose DeLeon .02 .10
120 Bob Horner .07 .20
121 Scott Terry .02 .10
122 Roberto Alomar XRC .75 2.00
123 Dave Leiper .02 .10
124 Keith Moreland .02 .10
125 Mark Parent .02 .10
126 Dennis Rasmussen .02 .10
127 Randy Bockus .02 .10
128 Brett Butler .07 .20
129 Donell Nixon .02 .10
130 Earnest Riles .02 .10
131 Roger Samuels .02 .10
132 Checklist U1-U132 .02 .10

1988 Fleer Update Glossy

This 132 card set is a parallel to the regular Fleer Update issue. Except for a glossy sheen on the front, the cards are identical to the regular Fleer issue. The cards were issued through hobby dealers in a special tin box. The cards are not as plentiful as the regular Fleer update set. Similar to the regular Glossy set, it is believed that between 40 and 60 thousand of these sets were produced.

COMP.FACT.SET (132) 10.00 25.00
*STARS: .75X TO 2X BASIC CARDS
*ROOKIES: .75X TO 2X BASIC CARDS
DISTRIBUTED ONLY IN FACTORY SET FORM

1989 Fleer

This set consists of 660 standard-size cards. Cards were primarily issued in 15-card wax packs, rack packs and hobby and retail factory sets. Card fronts feature a distinctive gray border background with white and yellow trim. Cards are again organized alphabetically within teams and teams ordered by previous season record. The last 33 cards in the set consist of Specials (628-639), Rookie Pairs (640-653), and checklists (654-660). Approximately half of the California Angels players have white rather than yellow halos. Certain Oakland A's player cards have red instead of green lines for front photo borders. Checklist cards are available either with or without positions listed for each player. Rookie Cards in this set include Craig Biggio, Ken Griffey Jr., Randy Johnson, Gary Sheffield, and John Smoltz. An interesting variation was discovered in late 1999 by Beckett Grading Services on the Randy Johnson RC (card number 381). It seems the most common version features a crudely-blacked out image of an outfield billboard. A scarcer version clearly reveals the words "Marlboro" on the billboard. A value for this variation is not provided due to scarcity. One of the hobby's most notorious errors and variations hails from this product. Card number 616, Billy Ripken, was originally published with a four-letter word imprinted on the bat. Needless to say, this caused quite a stir in 1989 and the card was quickly reprinted. Because of this, several different variations were printed with the final solution (and the most common version of this card) being a black box covering the bat knob. The first variation is still actively sought after in the hobby and the other versions are still sought after by collectors seeking a "master" set.

COMPLETE SET (660) 6.00 15.00
COMP.FACT.SET (672) 6.00 15.00
1 Don Baylor .02 .10
2 Lance Blankenship RC .02 .10
3 Todd Burns UER .01 .05
(Wrong birthdate;
before/after All-Star
stats missing)
4 Greg Cadaret UER .01 .05
(All-Star Break stats
show 3 losses, should be 2
5 Jose Canseco .08 .25
6 Storm Davis .01 .05
7 Dennis Eckersley .05 .15
8 Mike Gallego .01 .05
9 Ron Hassey .01 .05
10 Dave Henderson .01 .05
11 Rick Honeycutt .01 .05
12 Glenn Hubbard .01 .05
13 Stan Javier .01 .05
14 Doug Jennings .01 .05
15 Felix Jose RC .02 .10
16 Carney Lansford .02 .10
17 Mark McGwire .40 1.00
18 Gene Nelson .01 .05
19 Dave Parker .02 .10
20 Eric Plunk .01 .05
21 Luis Polonia .01 .05
22 Terry Steinbach .02 .10
23 Dave Stewart .02 .10
24 Walt Weiss .01 .05
25 Bob Welch .02 .10
26 Curt Young .01 .05
27 Rick Aguilera .01 .05
28 Wally Backman .01 .05
29 Mark Carreon UER .01 .05
(After All-Star Break
batting 7.14)
30 Gary Carter .02 .10
31 David Cone .02 .10
32 Ron Darling .02 .10
33 Len Dykstra .02 .10
34 Kevin Elster .01 .05
35 Sid Fernandez .01 .05
36 Dwight Gooden .02 .10
37 Keith Hernandez .02 .10
38 Gregg Jefferies .01 .05
39 Howard Johnson .02 .10
40 Terry Leach .01 .05
41 Dave Magadan UER .01 .05
(Bio says 15 doubles,
should be 13)
42 Bob McClure .01 .05
43 Roger McDowell UER .01 .05
(Led Mets with 58,
should be 62)
44 Kevin McReynolds .01 .05
45 Keith A. Miller .01 .05
46 Randy Myers .02 .10
47 Bob Ojeda .01 .05
48 Mackey Sasser .01 .05
49 Darryl Strawberry .02 .10
50 Tim Teufel .01 .05
51 Dave West RC .02 .10
52 Mookie Wilson .02 .10
53 Dave Anderson .01 .05
54 Tim Belcher .01 .05
55 Mike Davis .01 .05
56 Mike Devereaux .01 .05
57 Kirk Gibson .02 .10
58 Alfredo Griffin .01 .05
59 Chris Gwynn .01 .05
60 Jeff Hamilton .01 .05
61A Danny Heep ERR .08 .25
Lake Hills
61B Danny Heep COR .01 .05
San Antonio
62 Orel Hershiser .02 .10
63 Brian Holton .01 .05
64 Jay Howell .01 .05
65 Tim Leary .01 .05
66 Mike Marshall .01 .05
67 Ramon Martinez RC .08 .25
68 Jesse Orosco .01 .05
69 Alejandro Pena .01 .05
70 Steve Sax .01 .05
71 Mike Scioscia .02 .10
72 Mike Sharperson .01 .05
73 John Shelby .01 .05
74 Franklin Stubbs .01 .05
75 John Tudor .02 .10
76 Fernando Valenzuela .02 .10
77 Tracy Woodson .01 .05
78 Marty Barrett .01 .05
79 Todd Benzinger .01 .05
80 Mike Boddicker UER .01 .05
(Rochester in '76,
should be '78)
81 Wade Boggs .05 .15
82 Oil Can Boyd .01 .05
83 Ellis Burks .02 .10
84 Rick Cerone .01 .05
85 Roger Clemens .40 1.00
86 Steve Curry .01 .05
87 Dwight Evans .05 .15
88 Wes Gardner .01 .05
89 Rich Gedman .01 .05
90 Mike Greenwell .01 .05
91 Bruce Hurst .01 .05
92 Dennis Lamp .01 .05
93 Spike Owen .01 .05
94 Larry Parrish UER .01 .05
(Before All-Star Break
batting 1.90)
95 Carlos Quintana RC .02 .10
96 Jody Reed .01 .05
97 Jim Rice .02 .10
98A Kevin Romine ERR .08 .25
(Photo actually
Randy Kutcher batting)
98B Kevin Romine COR .01 .05
(Arms folded)
99 Lee Smith .02 .10
100 Mike Smithson .01 .05
101 Bob Stanley .01 .05
102 Allan Anderson .01 .05
103 Keith Atherton .01 .05
104 Juan Berenguer .01 .05
105 Bert Blyleven .02 .10
106 Eric Bullock UER .01 .05
Bats/Throws Right,
should be Left
107 Randy Bush .01 .05
108 John Christensen .01 .05
109 Mark Davidson .01 .05
110 Gary Gaetti .02 .10
111 Greg Gagne .01 .05
112 Dan Gladden .01 .05
113 German Gonzalez .01 .05
114 Brian Harper .01 .05
115 Tom Herr .01 .05
116 Kent Hrbek .02 .10
117 Gene Larkin .01 .05
118 Tim Laudner .01 .05
119 Charlie Lea .01 .05
120 Steve Lombardozzi .01 .05
121A John Moses ERR .08 .25
Tempe
121B John Moses COR .01 .05
Phoenix
122 Al Newman .01 .05
123 Mark Portugal .01 .05
124 Kirby Puckett .08 .25
125 Jeff Reardon .02 .10
126 Fred Toliver .01 .05
127 Frank Viola .02 .10
128 Doyle Alexander .01 .05
129 Dave Bergman .01 .05
130A Tom Brookens ERR .30 .75
(Mike Heath back)
130B Tom Brookens COR .01 .05
131 Paul Gibson .01 .05
132A Mike Heath ERR .30 .75
(Tom Brookens back)
132B Mike Heath COR .01 .05
133 Don Heinkel .01 .05
134 Mike Henneman .01 .05
135 Guillermo Hernandez .01 .05
136 Eric King .01 .05
137 Chet Lemon .02 .10
138 Fred Lynn UER .02 .10
'74 and '75 stats missing
139 Jack Morris .02 .10
140 Matt Nokes .01 .05
141 Gary Pettis .01 .05
142 Ted Power .01 .05
143 Jeff M. Robinson .01 .05
144 Luis Salazar .01 .05
145 Steve Searcy .01 .05
146 Pat Sheridan .01 .05
147 Frank Tanana .02 .10
148 Alan Trammell .02 .10
149 Walt Terrell .01 .05
150 Jim Walewander .01 .05
151 Lou Whitaker .02 .10
152 Tim Birtsas .01 .05
153 Tom Browning .01 .05
154 Keith Brown .01 .05
155 Norm Charlton RC .08 .25
156 Dave Concepcion .02 .10
157 Kal Daniels .01 .05
158 Eric Davis .02 .10
159 Bo Diaz .01 .05
160 Rob Dibble RC .15 .40
161 Nick Esasky .01 .05
162 John Franco .02 .10
163 Danny Jackson .01 .05
164 Barry Larkin .05 .15
165 Rob Murphy .01 .05
166 Paul O'Neill .05 .15
167 Jeff Reed .01 .05
168 Jose Rijo .02 .10
169 Ron Robinson .01 .05
170 Chris Sabo RC .15 .40
171 Candy Sierra .01 .05
172 Van Snider .01 .05
173A Jeff Treadway 10.00 25.00
(Target registration
mark above head
on front in
light blue)
173B Jeff Treadway .01 .05
(No target on front)
174 Frank Williams UER .01 .05
(After All-Star Break
stats are jumbled)
175 Herm Winningham .01 .05
176 Jim Adduci .01 .05
177 Don August .01 .05
178 Mike Birkbeck .01 .05
179 Chris Bosio .01 .05
180 Glenn Braggs .01 .05
181 Greg Brock .01 .05
182 Mark Clear .01 .05
183 Chuck Crim .01 .05
184 Rob Deer .01 .05
185 Tom Filer .01 .05
186 Jim Gantner .01 .05
187 Darryl Hamilton RC .08 .25
188 Ted Higuera .01 .05
189 Odell Jones .01 .05
190 Jeffrey Leonard .01 .05
191 Joey Meyer .01 .05
192 Paul Mirabella .01 .05
193 Paul Molitor .02 .10
194 Charlie O'Brien .01 .05
195 Dan Plesac .01 .05
196 Gary Sheffield RC .60 1.50
197 B.J. Surhoff .02 .10
198 Dale Sveum .01 .05
199 Bill Wegman .01 .05
200 Robin Yount .15 .40
201 Rafael Belliard .01 .05
202 Barry Bonds .60 1.50
203 Bobby Bonilla .02 .10
204 Sid Bream .01 .05
205 Benny Distefano .01 .05
206 Doug Drabek .01 .05
207 Mike Dunne .01 .05
208 Felix Fermin .01 .05
209 Brian Fisher .01 .05
210 Jim Gott .01 .05
211 Bob Kipper .01 .05
212 Dave LaPoint .01 .05
213 Mike LaValliere .01 .05
214 Jose Lind .01 .05
215 Junior Ortiz .01 .05
216 Vicente Palacios .01 .05
217 Tom Prince .01 .05
218 Gary Redus .01 .05
219 R.J. Reynolds .01 .05
220 Jeff D. Robinson .01 .05
221 John Smiley .01 .05
222 Andy Van Slyke .05 .15
223 Bob Walk .01 .05
224 Glenn Wilson .01 .05
225 Jesse Barfield .02 .10
226 George Bell .02 .10
227 Pat Borders RC .08 .25
228 John Cerutti .01 .05
229 Jim Clancy .01 .05
230 Mark Eichhorn .01 .05
231 Tony Fernandez .01 .05
232 Cecil Fielder .02 .10
233 Mike Flanagan .01 .05
234 Kelly Gruber .01 .05
235 Tom Henke .01 .05
236 Jimmy Key .02 .10
237 Rick Leach .01 .05
238 Manny Lee UER .01 .05
(Bio says regular
shortstop, sic,
Tony Fernandez)
239 Nelson Liriano .01 .05
240 Fred McGriff .05 .15
241 Lloyd Moseby .01 .05
242 Rance Mulliniks .01 .05
243 Jeff Musselman .01 .05
244 Dave Stieb .02 .10
245 Todd Stottlemyre .01 .05
246 Duane Ward .01 .05
247 David Wells .02 .10
248 Ernie Whitt UER .01 .05
(HR total 21,
should be 121)
249 Luis Aguayo .01 .05
250A Neil Allen ERR .30 .75
Sarasota, FL
250B Neil Allen COR .01 .05
Syosset, NY
251 John Candelaria .01 .05
252 Jack Clark .02 .10
253 Richard Dotson .01 .05
254 Rickey Henderson .08 .25
255 Tommy John .02 .10
256 Roberto Kelly .01 .05
257 Al Leiter .08 .25
258 Don Mattingly .25 .60
259 Dale Mohorcic .01 .05
260 Hal Morris RC .08 .25
261 Scott Nielsen .01 .05
262 Mike Pagliarulo UER .01 .05
(Wrong birthdate)
263 Hipolito Pena .01 .05
264 Ken Phelps .01 .05
265 Willie Randolph .02 .10
266 Rick Rhoden .01 .05
267 Dave Righetti .02 .10

268 Rafael Santana .01 .05
269 Steve Shields .01 .05
270 Joel Skinner .01 .05
271 Don Slaught .01 .05
272 Claudell Washington .01 .05
273 Gary Ward .01 .05
274 Dave Winfield .02 .10
275 Luis Aquino .01 .05
276 Floyd Bannister .01 .05
277 George Brett .25 .60
278 Bill Buckner .02 .10
279 Nick Capra .01 .05
280 Jose DeJesus .01 .05
281 Steve Farr .01 .05
282 Jerry Don Gleaton .01 .05
283 Mark Gubicza .01 .05
284 Tom Gordon RC UER .20 .50
(16.2 innings in '88,
should be 15.2)
285 Bo Jackson .08 .25
286 Charlie Leibrandt .01 .05
287 Mike Macfarlane RC .08 .25
288 Jeff Montgomery .01 .05
289 Bill Pecota UER .01 .05
(Photo actually
Brad Wellman)
290 Jamie Quirk .01 .05
291 Bret Saberhagen .02 .10
292 Kevin Seitzer .01 .05
293 Kurt Stillwell .01 .05
294 Pat Tabler .01 .05
295 Danny Tartabull .01 .05
296 Gary Thurman .01 .05
297 Frank White .02 .10
298 Willie Wilson .02 .10
299 Roberto Alomar .08 .25
300 S.Alomar Jr. RC UER .15 .40
Wrong birthdate, says
6/16/66, should say
6/18/66
301 Chris Brown .01 .05
302 Mike Brumley UER .01 .05
(133 hits in '88,
should be 134)
303 Mark Davis .01 .05
304 Mark Grant .01 .05
305 Tony Gwynn .10 .30
306 Greg W. Harris RC .02 .10
307 Andy Hawkins .01 .05
308 Jimmy Jones .01 .05
309 John Kruk .02 .10
310 Dave Leiper .01 .05
311 Carmelo Martinez .01 .05
312 Lance McCullers .01 .05
313 Keith Moreland .01 .05
314 Dennis Rasmussen .01 .05
315 Randy Ready UER .01 .05
(1214 games in '88,
should be 114)
316 Benito Santiago .02 .10
317 Eric Show .01 .05
318 Todd Simmons .01 .05
319 Garry Templeton .02 .10
320 Dickie Thon .01 .05
321 Ed Whitson .01 .05
322 Marvell Wynne .01 .05
323 Mike Aldrete .01 .05
324 Brett Butler .02 .10
325 Will Clark UER .05 .15
(Three consecutive
100 RBI seasons)
326 Kelly Downs UER .01 .05
('88 stats missing)
327 Dave Dravecky .01 .05
328 Scott Garrelts .01 .05
329 Atlee Hammaker .01 .05
330 Charlie Hayes RC .08 .25
331 Mike Krukow .01 .05
332 Craig Lefferts .01 .05
333 Candy Maldonado .01 .05
334 Kirt Manwaring UER .01 .05
(Bats Rights)
335 Bob Melvin .01 .05
336 Kevin Mitchell .02 .10
337 Donell Nixon .01 .05
338 Tony Perezchica .01 .05
339 Joe Price .01 .05
340 Rick Reuschel .02 .10
341 Earnest Riles .01 .05
342 Don Robinson .01 .05
343 Chris Speier .01 .05
344 Robby Thompson UER .01 .05
(West Plam Beach)
345 Jose Uribe .01 .05
346 Matt Williams .08 .25
347 Trevor Wilson RC .02 .10
348 Juan Agosto .01 .05
349 Larry Andersen .01 .05
350A Alan Ashby ERR .75 2.00
(Throws Rig)
350B Alan Ashby COR .01 .05
351 Kevin Bass .01 .05
352 Buddy Bell .02 .10
353 Craig Biggio RC 1.00 2.50
354 Danny Darwin .01 .05
355 Glenn Davis .01 .05
356 Jim Deshaies .01 .05
357 Bill Doran .01 .05
358 John Fishel .01 .05
359 Billy Hatcher .01 .05
360 Bob Knepper .01 .05
361 L.Meadows UER .01 .05
Bio says 10 EBH's
and 6 SB's in '88,
should be 3 and 4
362 Dave Meads .01 .05
363 Jim Pankovits .01 .05
364 Terry Puhl .01 .05
365 Rafael Ramirez .01 .05
366 Craig Reynolds .01 .05
367 Mike Scott .02 .10
(Card number listed
as 368 on Astros CL)
368 Nolan Ryan .40 1.00
(Card number listed
as 367 on Astros CL)
369 Dave Smith .01 .05
370 Gerald Young .01 .05
371 Hubie Brooks .01 .05
372 Tim Burke .01 .05
373 John Dopson .01 .05
374 Mike R. Fitzgerald .01 .05
375 Tom Foley .01 .05
376 Andres Galarraga UER .02 .10
(Home: Caracus)
377 Neal Heaton .01 .05
378 Joe Hesketh .01 .05
379 Brian Holman RC .02 .10
380 Rex Hudler .01 .05
381 R.Johnson RC UER .75 2.00
Innings for '85 and
'86 shown as 27 and
120, should be 27.1
and 119.2
381B R.Johnson Marlboro ERR 10.00 25.00
382 Wallace Johnson .01 .05
383 Tracy Jones .01 .05
384 Dave Martinez .01 .05
385 Dennis Martinez .02 .10
386 Andy McGaffigan .01 .05
387 Otis Nixon .01 .05
388 Johnny Paredes .01 .05
389 Jeff Parrett .01 .05
390 Pascual Perez .01 .05
391 Tim Raines .02 .10
392 Luis Rivera .01 .05
393 Nelson Santovenia .01 .05
394 Bryn Smith .01 .05
395 Tim Wallach .01 .05
396 Andy Allanson UER .01 .05
1214 hits in '88,
should be 114
397 Rod Allen .01 .05
398 Scott Bailes .01 .05
399 Tom Candiotti .01 .05
400 Joe Carter .02 .10
401 Carmen Castillo UER .01 .05
(After All-Star Break
batting 2.50)
402 Dave Clark UER .01 .05
(Card front shows
position as Rookie;
after All-Star Break
batting 3.14)
403 John Farrell UER .01 .05
(Typo in runs
allowed in '88)
404 Julio Franco .02 .10
405 Don Gordon .01 .05
406 Mel Hall .01 .05
407 Brad Havens .01 .05
408 Brook Jacoby .01 .05
409 Doug Jones .01 .05
410 Jeff Kaiser .01 .05
411 Luis Medina .01 .05
412 Cory Snyder .01 .05
413 Greg Swindell .01 .05
414 Ron Tingley UER .01 .05
(Hit HR in first ML
at-bat, should be
first AL at-bat)
415 Willie Upshaw .01 .05
416 Ron Washington .01 .05
417 Rich Yett .01 .05
418 Damon Berryhill .01 .05
419 Mike Bielecki .01 .05
420 Doug Dascenzo .01 .05
421 Jody Davis UER .01 .05
(Braves stats for
'88 missing)
422 Andre Dawson .02 .10
423 Frank DiPino .01 .05
424 Shawon Dunston .01 .05
425 Rich Gossage .02 .10
426 Mark Grace UER .08 .25
(Minor League stats
for '88 missing)
427 Mike Harkey RC .02 .10
428 Darrin Jackson .02 .10
429 Les Lancaster .01 .05
430 Vance Law .01 .05
431 Greg Maddux .20 .50
432 Jamie Moyer .02 .10
433 Al Nipper .01 .05
434 Rafael Palmeiro UER .08 .25
170 hits in '88,
should be 178
435 Pat Perry .01 .05
436 Jeff Pico .01 .05
437 Ryne Sandberg .15 .40
438 Calvin Schiraldi .01 .05
439 Rick Sutcliffe .02 .10
440A Manny Trillo ERR .75 2.00
(Throws Rig)
440B Manny Trillo COR .01 .05
441 Gary Varsho UER .01 .05
(Wrong birthdate;
.303 should be .302;
11/28 should be 9/19)
442 Mitch Webster .01 .05
443 Luis Alicea RC .08 .25
444 Tom Brunansky .01 .05
445 Vince Coleman UER .01 .05
Third straight with 83
should be fourth straight with 81
446 John Costello UER .01 .05
(Home California,
should be New York)
447 Danny Cox .01 .05
448 Ken Dayley .01 .05
449 Jose DeLeon .01 .05
450 Curt Ford .01 .05
451 Pedro Guerrero .02 .10
452 Bob Horner .02 .10
453 Tim Jones .01 .05
454 Steve Lake .01 .05
455 Joe Magrane UER .01 .05
(Des Moines& IO)
456 Greg Mathews .01 .05
457 Willie McGee .02 .10
458 Larry McWilliams .01 .05
459 Jose Oquendo .01 .05
460 Tony Pena .01 .05
461 Terry Pendleton .02 .10
462 Steve Peters UER .01 .05
(Lives in Harrah,
not Harah)
463 Ozzie Smith .15 .40
464 Scott Terry .01 .05
465 Denny Walling .01 .05
466 Todd Worrell .01 .05
467 Tony Armas UER .02 .10
(Before All-Star Break
batting 2.39)
468 Dante Bichette RC .15 .40
469 Bob Boone .02 .10
470 Terry Clark .01 .05
471 Stu Cliburn .01 .05
472 Mike Cook UER .01 .05
(TM near Angels logo
missing from front)
473 Sherman Corbett .01 .05
474 Chili Davis .02 .10
475 Brian Downing .02 .10
476 Jim Eppard .01 .05
477 Chuck Finley .02 .10
478 Willie Fraser .01 .05
479 Bryan Harvey UER RC .08 .25
ML record shows 0-0,
should be 7-5
480 Jack Howell .01 .05
481 Wally Joyner UER .02 .10
(Yorba Linda, GA)
482 Jack Lazorko .01 .05
483 Kirk McCaskill .01 .05
484 Mark McLemore .01 .05
485 Greg Minton .01 .05
486 Dan Petry .01 .05
487 Johnny Ray .01 .05
488 Dick Schofield .01 .05
489 Devon White .02 .10
490 Mike Witt .01 .05
491 Harold Baines .02 .10
492 Daryl Boston .01 .05
493 Ivan Calderon UER .01 .05
('80 stats shifted)
494 Mike Diaz .01 .05
495 Carlton Fisk .05 .15
496 Dave Gallagher .01 .05
497 Ozzie Guillen .02 .10
498 Shawn Hillegas .01 .05
499 Lance Johnson .01 .05
500 Barry Jones .01 .05
501 Bill Long .01 .05
502 Steve Lyons .01 .05
503 Fred Manrique .01 .05
504 Jack McDowell .02 .10
505 Donn Pall .01 .05
506 Kelly Paris .01 .05
507 Dan Pasqua .01 .05
508 Ken Patterson .01 .05
509 Melido Perez .01 .05
510 Jerry Reuss .01 .05
511 Mark Salas .01 .05
512 Bobby Thigpen UER .01 .05
('86 ERA 4.69,
should be 4.68)
513 Mike Woodard .01 .05
514 Bob Brower .01 .05
515 Steve Buechele .01 .05
516 Jose Cecena .01 .05
517 Cecil Espy .01 .05
518 Scott Fletcher .01 .05
519 Cecilio Guante .01 .05
('87 Yankee stats
are off-centered)
520 Jose Guzman .01 .05
521 Ray Hayward .01 .05
522 Charlie Hough .02 .10
523 Pete Incaviglia .01 .05
524 Mike Jeffcoat .01 .05
525 Paul Kilgus .01 .05
526 Chad Kreuter RC .08 .25
527 Jeff Kunkel .01 .05
528 Oddibe McDowell .01 .05
529 Pete O'Brien .01 .05
530 Geno Petralli .01 .05
531 Jeff Russell .01 .05
532 Ruben Sierra .02 .10
533 Mike Stanley .01 .05
534A Ed VandeBerg ERR .75 2.00
(Throws Lef)
534B Ed VandeBerg COR .01 .05
535 Curtis Wilkerson ERR .01 .05
(Pitcher headings
at bottom)
536 Mitch Williams .01 .05
537 Bobby Witt UER .01 .05
('85 ERA .643,
should be 6.43)
538 Steve Balboni .01 .05
539 Scott Bankhead .01 .05
540 Scott Bradley .01 .05
541 Mickey Brantley .01 .05
542 Jay Buhner .02 .10
543 Mike Campbell .01 .05
544 Darnell Coles .01 .05
545 Henry Cotto .01 .05
546 Alvin Davis .01 .05
547 Mario Diaz .01 .05
548 Ken Griffey Jr. RC 4.00 10.00
549 Erik Hanson RC .08 .25
550 Mike Jackson UER .01 .05
(Lifetime ERA 3.345,
should be 3.45)
551 Mark Langston .01 .05
552 Edgar Martinez .08 .25
553 Bill McGuire .01 .05
554 Mike Moore .01 .05
555 Jim Presley .01 .05
556 Rey Quinones .01 .05
557 Jerry Reed .01 .05
558 Harold Reynolds .02 .10
559 Mike Schooler .01 .05
560 Bill Swift .01 .05
561 Dave Valle .01 .05
562 Steve Bedrosian .01 .05
563 Phil Bradley .01 .05
564 Don Carman .01 .05
565 Bob Dernier .01 .05
566 Marvin Freeman .01 .05
567 Todd Frohwirth .01 .05
568 Greg Gross .01 .05
569 Kevin Gross .01 .05
570 Greg A. Harris .01 .05
571 Von Hayes .01 .05
572 Chris James .01 .05
573 Steve Jeltz .01 .05
574 Ron Jones UER .02 .10
(Led IL in '88 with
85, should be 75)
575 Ricky Jordan RC .08 .25
576 Mike Maddux .01 .05
577 David Palmer .01 .05
578 Lance Parrish .02 .10
579 Shane Rawley .01 .05
580 Bruce Ruffin .01 .05
581 Juan Samuel .01 .05
582 Mike Schmidt .20 .50
583 Kent Tekulve .01 .05
584 Milt Thompson UER .01 .05
(19 hits in '88,
should be 109)
585 Jose Alvarez RC .02 .10
586 Paul Assenmacher .01 .05
587 Bruce Benedict .01 .05
588 Jeff Blauser .01 .05
589 Terry Blocker .01 .05
590 Ron Gant .02 .10
591 Tom Glavine .08 .25
592 Tommy Gregg .01 .05
593 Albert Hall .01 .05
594 Dion James .01 .05
595 Rick Mahler .01 .05
596 Dale Murphy .05 .15
597 Gerald Perry .01 .05
598 Charlie Puleo .01 .05
599 Ted Simmons .02 .10
600 Pete Smith .01 .05
601 Zane Smith .01 .05
602 John Smoltz RC .60 1.50
603 Bruce Sutter .02 .10
604 Andres Thomas .01 .05
605 Ozzie Virgil .01 .05
606 Brady Anderson RC .15 .40
607 Jeff Ballard .01 .05
608 Jose Bautista RC .02 .10
609 Ken Gerhart .01 .05
610 Terry Kennedy .01 .05
611 Eddie Murray .08 .25
612 Carl Nichols UER .01 .05
(Before All-Star Break
batting 1.88)
613 Tom Niedenfuer .01 .05
614 Joe Orsulak .01 .05
615 Oswald Peraza UER .01 .05
(Shown as Oswaldo)
616A Bill Ripken ERR 12.50 30.00
(Rick Face written
on knob of bat)
616B Bill Ripken 60.00 120.00
(Bat knob
whited out)
616C Bill Ripken 10.00 25.00
(Words on bat knob
scribbled out in White)
616D Bill Ripken 3.00 8.00
Words on Bat
covered by black scribble
616E Bill Ripken DP 2.50 6.00
(Black box covering
bat knob)
617 Cal Ripken .30 .75
618 Dave Schmidt .01 .05
619 Rick Schu .01 .05
620 Larry Sheets .01 .05
621 Doug Sisk .01 .05
622 Pete Stanicek .01 .05
623 Mickey Tettleton .01 .05
624 Jay Tibbs .01 .05
625 Jim Traber .01 .05
626 Mark Williamson .01 .05
627 Craig Worthington .01 .05
628 Jose Canseco 40/40 .08 .25
629 Tom Browning Perfect .01 .05
630 Roberto Alomar .08 .25
Sandy Alomar Jr. UER
(Names on card listed
in wrong order)
631 Will Clark .05 .15
Rafael Palmeiro UER
(Gallaraga, sic;
Clark 3 consecutive
100 RBI seasons;
third with 102 RBI's)
632 Darryl Strawberry .02 .10
Will Clark UER (Homeruns
should be two words)
633 Wade Boggs .02 .10
Carney Lansford UER
(Boggs hit .366 in
'86, should be '88)
634 Jose Canseco .30 .75
Terry Steinbach
Mark McGwire
635 Mark Davis .01 .05
Dwight Gooden
636 Danny Jackson .01 .05
David Cone UER
Hersheiser, sic
637 Chris Sabo .02 .10
Bobby Bonilla UER
Bobby Bonds, sic
638 Andres Galarraga UER .01 .05
(Misspelled Gallaraga
on card back)
Gerald Perry
639 Kirby Puckett .05 .15
Eric Davis
640 Steve Wilson .01 .05
Cameron Drew
641 Kevin Brown .08 .25
Kevin Reimer
642 Brad Pounders RC .02 .10
Jerald Clark
643 Mike Capel .01 .05
Drew Hall
644 Joe Girardi RC .15 .40
Rolando Roomes
645 Lenny Harris RC .08 .25
Marty Brown
646 Luis De Los Santos .01 .05
Jim Campbell
647 Randy Kramer .01 .05
Miguel Garcia
648 Torey Lovullo RC .02 .10
Robert Palacios
649 Jim Corsi .01 .05
Bob Milacki
650 Grady Hall .01 .05
Mike Rochford
651 Terry Taylor RC .02 .10
Vance Lovelace
652 Ken Hill RC .08 .25
Dennis Cook
653 Scott Service .01 .05
Shane Turner
654 CL: Oakland/Mets .01 .05
Dodgers/Red Sox
(10 Hendersor;
68 Jess Orosco)
655A CL: Twins/Tigers ERR .01 .05
Reds/Brewers
(179 Boslo and
Twins/Tigers positions
listed)
655B CL: Twins/Tigers COR .01 .05
Reds/Brewers
(179 Boslo but
Twins/Tigers positions
not listed)
656 CL: Pirates/Blue Jays .01 .05
Yankees/Royals
(225 Jess Barfield)
657 CL: Padres/Giants .01 .05
Astros/Expos
(367/368 wrong)
658 CL: Indians/Cubs .01 .05
Cardinals/Angels
(449 Deleon)
659 CL: White Sox/Rangers .01 .05
Mariners/Phillies
660 CL: Braves/Orioles .01 .05
Specials/Checklists
(632 hyphenated diff-
erently and 650 Hali;
595 Rich Mahler;
619 Rich Schu)

1989 Fleer Glossy

This 660 card set turned out to be the final parallel glossy issue for Fleer. These cards are identical to the regular Fleer cards except for the glossy sheen on the front. As many dealers did not order this product, this set is considerably scarcer than the regular 1989 Fleer set and the preceding years of Glossy parallels. Unlike the previous two seasons, the update set was not issued in Glossy form. It is estimated that Fleer made approximately 30,000 of these sets. The Ken Griffey Jr. card from this set is regarded as one of the most important early parallels in hobby history and is more often than not found with poor centering.

COMP.FACT.SET (672) 50.00 100.00
*STARS: 2X TO 5X BASIC CARDS
*ROOKIES: 2X TO 5X BASIC CARDS
DISTRIBUTED ONLY IN FACTORY SET FORM

1989 Fleer All-Stars

This twelve-card standard-size subset was randomly inserted in Fleer wax and cello packs. The players selected are the 1989 Fleer Major League All-Star team. One player has been selected for each position along with a DH and three pitchers. The cards feature a distinctive green background on the card fronts. The set is sequenced in alphabetical order.

COMPLETE SET (12) 2.50 5.00
RANDOM INSERTS IN PACKS 1.00 2.00
1 Bobby Bonilla .30 .75
2 Jose Canseco .75 2.00
3 Will Clark .50 1.25
4 Dennis Eckersley .50 1.25
5 Julio Franco .30 .75
6 Mike Greenwell .15 .40
7 Orel Hershiser .30 .75
8 Paul Molitor .30 .75
9 Mike Scioscia .30 .75
10 Darryl Strawberry .30 .75
11 Alan Trammell .30 .75
12 Frank Viola .30 .75

1989 Fleer For The Record

This six-card standard-size insert set was distributed one per rack pack. The set is subtitled "For The Record" and commemorates record-breaking events for those players from the previous season. The card backs are printed in red, black, and gray on white card stock. The set is sequenced in alphabetical order.

COMPLETE SET (6) 3.00 8.00
ONE PER RACK PACK .50 1.00
1 Wade Boggs .40 1.00
2 Roger Clemens 2.50 6.00
3 Andres Galarraga .25 .60
4 Kirk Gibson .25 .60
5 Greg Maddux 1.25 3.00
6 Don Mattingly UER 1.50 4.00
(Won batting title
'83& should say '84)

1989 Fleer Wax Box Cards

The cards in this 28-card set measure the standard 2 1/2" by 3 1/2". Cards have essentially the same design as the 1989 Fleer regular issue set. The cards were printed on the bottoms of the regular issue wax pack boxes. These 28 cards (C1 to C28) are considered a separate set in their own right and are not typically included in a complete set of the regular issue 1989 Fleer cards. The value of the panel uncut is slightly greater, perhaps by 25 percent greater, than the value of the individual cards cut up carefully. The wax box cards are further distinguished by the gray card stock used.

COMPLETE SET (28) 4.00 10.00
C1 Mets Logo .05 .15
C2 Wade Boggs .30 .75
C3 George Brett .60 1.50
C4 Jose Canseco UER .60 1.50
('88 strikeouts 121
and career strike-
outs 49, should
be 128 and 491)
C5 A's Logo .05 .15
C6 Will Clark .40 1.00
C7 David Cone .25 .60
C8 Andres Galarraga UER .25 .60
(Career average .289
should be .269)
C9 Dodgers Logo .05 .15
C10 Kirk Gibson .08 .25
C11 Mike Greenwell .05 .15
C12 Tony Gwynn 1.00 2.50
C13 Tigers Logo .05 .15
C14 Orel Hershiser .08 .25
C15 Danny Jackson .05 .15
C16 Wally Joyner .08 .25
C17 Red Sox Logo .05 .15
C18 Yankees Logo .05 .15
C19 Fred McGriff UER .40 1.00
(Career BA of .289
should be .269)
C20 Kirby Puckett .75 2.00
C21 Chris Sabo .05 .15
C22 Kevin Seitzer .05 .15
C23 Pirates Logo .05 .15
C24 Astros Logo .05 .15
C25 Darryl Strawberry .08 .25
C26 Alan Trammell .15 .40
C27 Andy Van Slyke .05 .15
C28 Frank Viola .05 .15

1989 Fleer World Series

This 12-card standard-size set features highlights of the previous year's World Series between the Dodgers and the Athletics. The sets were packaged as a complete set insert with the collated sets (of the 1989 Fleer regular issue) which were sold by Fleer directly to hobby card dealers; they were not available in the general retail candy store outlets. The Kirk Gibson card from this set highlights one of the most famous home runs in World Series history.

COMPLETE SET (12) .75 2.00
ONE SET PER FACTORY SET
1 Mickey Hatcher .01 .05
2 Tim Belcher .01 .05
3 Jose Canseco .08 .25
4 Mike Scioscia .02 .10
5 Kirk Gibson .02 .10
6 Orel Hershiser .02 .10
7 Mike Marshall .01 .05
8 Mark McGwire .40 1.00
9 Steve Sax UER .01 .05
actually 42 steals in '88
10 Walt Weiss .01 .05
11 Orel Hershiser .02 .10
12 Dodger Blue .02 .10
World Champs

1989 Fleer World Series Glossy

*GLOSSY: .5X TO 1.2X BASIC WS
DISTRIBUTED ONLY IN FACTORY SET FORM

1989 Fleer Update

The 1989 Fleer Update set contains 132 standard-size cards. The cards were distributed exclusively in factory set form in grey and white, cellophane wrapped boxes through hobby dealers. The cards are identical in design to regular issue 1989 Fleer cards except for the U-prefixed numbering on back. The set numbering is in team order with players within teams ordered alphabetically. The set includes special cards for Nolan Ryan's 5,000th strikeout and Mike Schmidt's retirement. Rookie Cards include Kevin Appier, Joey (Albert) Belle, Deion Sanders, Greg Vaughn, Robin Ventura and Todd Zeile.

COMP.FACT.SET (132) 2.00 5.00
1 Phil Bradley .01 .05
2 Mike Devereaux .01 .05
3 Steve Finley RC .30 .75
4 Kevin Hickey .01 .05
5 Brian Holton .01 .05
6 Bob Milacki .01 .05
7 Randy Milligan .01 .05
8 John Dopson .01 .05
9 Nick Esasky .01 .05
10 Rob Murphy .01 .05
11 Jim Abbott RC .40 1.00
12 Bert Blyleven .02 .10
13 Jeff Manto RC .02 .10
14 Bob McClure .01 .05
15 Lance Parrish .02 .10
16 Lee Stevens RC .08 .25
17 Claudell Washington .01 .05
18 Mark Davis RC .08 .25
19 Eric King .01 .05
20 Ron Kittle .01 .05
21 Matt Merullo .01 .05
22 Steve Rosenberg .01 .05
23 Robin Ventura RC .30 .75
24 Keith Atherton .01 .05
25 Joey Belle RC .40 1.00
26 Jerry Browne .01 .05
27 Felix Fermin .01 .05
28 Brad Komminsk .01 .05
29 Pete O'Brien .01 .05
30 Mike Brumley .01 .05
31 Tracy Jones .01 .05
32 Mike Schwabe .01 .05
33 Gary Ward .01 .05
34 Frank Williams .01 .05
35 Kevin Appier RC .20 .50
36 Bob Boone .02 .10
37 Luis DeLosSantos .01 .05
38 Jim Eisenreich .01 .05
39 Jaime Navarro RC .02 .10
40 Bill Spiers RC .08 .25
41 Greg Vaughn RC .15 .40
42 Randy Veres .01 .05
43 Wally Backman .01 .05
44 Shane Rawley .01 .05
45 Steve Balboni .01 .05
46 Jesse Barfield .02 .10
47 Alvaro Espinoza .01 .05
48 Bob Geren RC .01 .05
49 Mel Hall .01 .05
50 Andy Hawkins .01 .05
51 Hensley Meulens RC .02 .10
52 Steve Sax .01 .05
53 Deion Sanders RC .60 1.50
54 Rickey Henderson .08 .25
55 Mike Moore .01 .05
56 Tony Phillips .01 .05
57 Greg Briley .02 .10
58 Gene Harris RC .02 .10
59 Randy Johnson 1.00 2.50
60 Jeffrey Leonard .01 .05
61 Dennis Powell .01 .05
62 Omar Vizquel RC .40 1.00
63 Kevin Brown .08 .25
64 Julio Franco .02 .10
65 Jamie Moyer .02 .10
66 Rafael Palmeiro .08 .25
67 Nolan Ryan .60 1.50
68 Francisco Cabrera RC .02 .10
69 Junior Felix RC .02 .10
70 Al Leiter .08 .25
71 Alex Sanchez RC .01 .05
72 Geronimo Berroa .01 .05
73 Derek Lilliquist RC .02 .10
74 Lonnie Smith .01 .05
75 Jeff Treadway .01 .05
76 Paul Kilgus .01 .05
77 Lloyd McClendon .01 .05
78 Scott Sanderson .01 .05
79 Dwight Smith RC .08 .25
80 Jerome Walton RC .08 .25
81 Mitch Williams .01 .05
82 Steve Wilson .02 .10
83 Todd Benzinger .01 .05
84 Ken Griffey Sr. .02 .10
85 Rick Mahler .01 .05
86 Rolando Roomes .01 .05
87 Scott Scudder RC .02 .10
88 Jim Clancy .01 .05
89 Rick Rhoden .01 .05
90 Dan Schatzeder .01 .05
91 Mike Morgan .01 .05
92 Eddie Murray .08 .25
93 Willie Randolph .02 .10
94 Ray Searage .01 .05
95 Mike Aldrete .01 .05
96 Kevin Gross .01 .05
97 Mark Langston .01 .05
98 Spike Owen .01 .05
99 Zane Smith .01 .05
100 Don Aase .01 .05
101 Barry Lyons .01 .05
102 Juan Samuel .01 .05
103 Wally Whitehurst RC .02 .10
104 Dennis Cook .01 .05
105 Len Dykstra .02 .10
106 Charlie Hayes .08 .25
107 Tommy Herr .01 .05
108 Ken Howell .01 .05
109 John Kruk .02 .10
110 Roger McDowell .01 .05
111 Terry Mulholland .01 .05
112 Jeff Parrett .01 .05
113 Neal Heaton .01 .05
114 Jeff King .01 .05
115 Randy Kramer .01 .05
116 Bill Landrum .01 .05
117 Cris Carpenter RC .02 .10
118 Frank DiPino .01 .05
119 Ken Hill .08 .25
120 Dan Quisenberry .01 .05
121 Milt Thompson .01 .05
122 Todd Zeile RC .15 .40
123 Jack Clark .02 .10
124 Bruce Hurst .01 .05
125 Mark Parent .01 .05

126 Bip Roberts .01 .05
127 Jeff Brantley RC UER .08 .25
(Photo actually
Joe Kmak)
128 Terry Kennedy .01 .05
129 Mike LaCoss .01 .05
130 Greg Litton .01 .05
131 Mike Schmidt .30 .75
132 Checklist 1-132 .01 .05

1990 Fleer

The 1990 Fleer set contains 660 standard-size cards. Cards were primarily issued in wax packs, cello packs, rack packs and hobby and retail factory sets. Card fronts feature white outer borders with ribbon-like, colored inner borders. The set is again ordered numerically by teams based upon the previous season's record. Subsets include Decade Greats (621-630), Superstar Combinations (631-639), Rookie Prospects (640-653) and checklists (654-660). Rookie Cards of note include Moises Alou, Juan Gonzalez, David Justice, Sammy Sosa and Larry Walker.

COMPLETE SET (660) 6.00 15.00
COMP.RETAIL SET (660) 6.00 15.00
COMP.HOBBY SET (672) 6.00 15.00
1 Lance Blankenship .01 .05
2 Todd Burns .01 .05
3 Jose Canseco .05 .15
4 Jim Corsi .01 .05
5 Storm Davis .01 .05
6 Dennis Eckersley .02 .10
7 Mike Gallego .01 .05
8 Ron Hassey .01 .05
9 Dave Henderson .01 .05
10 Rickey Henderson .08 .25
11 Rick Honeycutt .01 .05
12 Stan Javier .01 .05
13 Felix Jose .01 .05
14 Carney Lansford .02 .10
15 Mark McGwire UER .40 1.00
(1989 runs listed as
4, should be 74)
16 Mike Moore .01 .05
17 Gene Nelson .01 .05
18 Dave Parker .02 .10
19 Tony Phillips .01 .05
20 Terry Steinbach .01 .05
21 Dave Stewart .02 .10
22 Walt Weiss .01 .05
23 Bob Welch .01 .05
24 Curt Young .01 .05
25 Paul Assenmacher .01 .05
26 Damon Berryhill .01 .05
27 Mike Bielecki .01 .05
28 Kevin Blankenship .01 .05
29 Andre Dawson .02 .10
30 Shawon Dunston .01 .05
31 Joe Girardi .05 .15
32 Mark Grace .05 .15
33 Mike Harkey .01 .05
34 Paul Kilgus .01 .05
35 Les Lancaster .01 .05
36 Vance Law .01 .05
37 Greg Maddux .15 .40
38 Lloyd McClendon .01 .05
39 Jeff Pico .01 .05
40 Ryne Sandberg .15 .40
41 Scott Sanderson .01 .05
42 Dwight Smith .01 .05
43 Rick Sutcliffe .02 .10
44 Jerome Walton .01 .05
45 Mitch Webster .01 .05
46 Curt Wilkerson .01 .05
47 Dean Wilkins RC .01 .05
48 Mitch Williams .01 .05
49 Steve Wilson .01 .05
50 Steve Bedrosian .01 .05
51 Mike Benjamin RC .02 .10
52 Jeff Brantley .01 .05
53 Brett Butler .02 .10
54 Will Clark UER .02 .10
(Did You Know says
first in runs, should
say tied for first)
55 Kelly Downs .01 .05
56 Scott Garrelts .01 .05
57 Atlee Hammaker .01 .05
58 Terry Kennedy .01 .05
59 Mike LaCoss .01 .05
60 Craig Lefferts .01 .05
61 Greg Litton .01 .05
62 Candy Maldonado .01 .05
63 Kirt Manwaring UER .01 .05
(No '88 Phoenix stats
as noted in box)
64 Randy McCament RC .01 .05
65 Kevin Mitchell .01 .05
66 Donell Nixon .01 .05
67 Ken Oberkfell .01 .05
68 Rick Reuschel .01 .05
69 Ernest Riles .01 .05
70 Don Robinson .01 .05
71 Pat Sheridan .01 .05
72 Chris Speier .01 .05
73 Robby Thompson .01 .05
74 Jose Uribe .01 .05
75 Matt Williams .02 .10
76 George Bell .01 .05
77 Pat Borders .01 .05
78 John Cerutti .01 .05
79 Junior Felix .01 .05
80 Tony Fernandez .01 .05
81 Mike Flanagan .01 .05
82 Mauro Gozzo RC .01 .05
83 Kelly Gruber .01 .05
84 Tom Henke .01 .05
85 Jimmy Key .02 .10
86 Manny Lee .01 .05
87 Nelson Liriano UER .01 .05
(Should say led the
IL instead of led
the TL)
88 Lee Mazzilli .01 .05
89 Fred McGriff .08 .25
90 Lloyd Moseby .01 .05
91 Rance Mulliniks .01 .05
92 Alex Sanchez .01 .05
93 Dave Stieb .02 .10
94 Todd Stottlemyre .02 .10
95 Duane Ward UER .01 .05
(Double line of '87
Syracuse stats)
96 David Wells .02 .10
97 Ernie Whitt .01 .05
98 Frank Wills .01 .05
99 Mookie Wilson .02 .10
100 Kevin Appier .02 .10
101 Luis Aquino .01 .05
102 Bob Boone .02 .10
103 George Brett .25 .60
104 Jose DeJesus .01 .05
105 Luis De Los Santos .01 .05
106 Jim Eisenreich .01 .05
107 Steve Farr .01 .05
108 Tom Gordon .02 .10
109 Mark Gubicza .01 .05
110 Bo Jackson .08 .25
111 Terry Leach .01 .05
112 Charlie Leibrandt .01 .05
113 Rick Luecken RC .01 .05
114 Mike Macfarlane .01 .05
115 Jeff Montgomery .02 .10
116 Bret Saberhagen .02 .10
117 Kevin Seitzer .01 .05
118 Kurt Stillwell .01 .05
119 Pat Tabler .01 .05
120 Danny Tartabull .01 .05
121 Gary Thurman .01 .05
122 Frank White .02 .10
123 Willie Wilson .01 .05
124 Matt Winters RC .01 .05
125 Jim Abbott .05 .15
126 Tony Armas .01 .05
127 Dante Bichette .02 .10
128 Bert Blyleven .02 .10
129 Chili Davis .02 .10
130 Brian Downing .01 .05
131 Mike Fetters RC .08 .25
132 Chuck Finley .02 .10
133 Willie Fraser .01 .05
134 Bryan Harvey .01 .05
135 Jack Howell .01 .05
136 Wally Joyner .02 .10
137 Jeff Manto .01 .05
138 Kirk McCaskill .01 .05
139 Bob McClure .01 .05
140 Greg Minton .01 .05
141 Lance Parrish .01 .05
142 Dan Petry .01 .05
143 Johnny Ray .01 .05
144 Dick Schofield .01 .05
145 Lee Stevens .02 .10
146 Claudell Washington .01 .05
147 Devon White .02 .10
148 Mike Witt .01 .05
149 Roberto Alomar .05 .15
150 Sandy Alomar Jr. .02 .10
151 Andy Benes .02 .10
152 Jack Clark .02 .10
153 Pat Clements .01 .05
154 Joey Cora .02 .10
155 Mark Davis .01 .05
156 Mark Grant .01 .05
157 Tony Gwynn .10 .30
158 Greg W. Harris .01 .05
159 Bruce Hurst .01 .05
160 Darrin Jackson .01 .05
161 Chris James .01 .05
162 Carmelo Martinez .01 .05
163 Mike Pagliarulo .01 .05
164 Mark Parent .01 .05
165 Dennis Rasmussen .01 .05
166 Bip Roberts .01 .05
167 Benito Santiago .02 .10
168 Calvin Schiraldi .01 .05
169 Eric Show .01 .05
170 Garry Templeton .01 .05
171 Ed Whitson .01 .05
172 Brady Anderson .02 .10
173 Jeff Ballard .01 .05
174 Phil Bradley .01 .05
175 Mike Devereaux .01 .05
176 Steve Finley .02 .10
177 Pete Harnisch .01 .05
178 Kevin Hickey .01 .05
179 Brian Holton .01 .05
180 Ben McDonald RC .08 .25
181 Bob Melvin .01 .05
182 Bob Milacki .01 .05
183 Randy Milligan UER .01 .05
(Double line of
'87 stats)
184 Gregg Olson .02 .10
185 Joe Orsulak .01 .05
186 Bill Ripken .01 .05
187 Cal Ripken .30 .75
188 Dave Schmidt .01 .05
189 Larry Sheets .01 .05
190 Mickey Tettleton .01 .05
191 Mark Thurmond .01 .05
192 Jay Tibbs .01 .05
193 Jim Traber .01 .05
194 Mark Williamson .01 .05
195 Craig Worthington .01 .05
196 Don Aase .01 .05
197 Blaine Beatty RC .01 .05
198 Mark Carreon .01 .05
199 Gary Carter .02 .10
200 David Cone .02 .10
201 Ron Darling .01 .05
202 Kevin Elster .01 .05
203 Sid Fernandez .01 .05
204 Dwight Gooden .02 .10
205 Keith Hernandez .02 .10
206 Jeff Innis RC .01 .05
207 Gregg Jefferies .02 .10
208 Howard Johnson .01 .05
209 Barry Lyons UER .01 .05
(Double line of
'87 stats)
210 Dave Magadan .01 .05
211 Kevin McReynolds .01 .05
212 Jeff Musselman .01 .05
213 Randy Myers .02 .10
214 Bob Ojeda .01 .05
215 Juan Samuel .01 .05
216 Mackey Sasser .01 .05
217 Darryl Strawberry .02 .10
218 Tim Teufel .01 .05
219 Frank Viola .01 .05
220 Juan Agosto .01 .05
221 Larry Andersen .01 .05
222 Eric Anthony RC .02 .10
223 Kevin Bass .01 .05
224 Craig Biggio .08 .25
225 Ken Caminiti .02 .10
226 Jim Clancy .01 .05
227 Danny Darwin .01 .05
228 Glenn Davis .01 .05
229 Jim Deshaies .01 .05
230 Bill Doran .01 .05
231 Bob Forsch .01 .05
232 Brian Meyer .01 .05
233 Terry Puhl .01 .05
234 Rafael Ramirez .01 .05
235 Rick Rhoden .01 .05
236 Dan Schatzeder .01 .05
237 Mike Scott .01 .05
238 Dave Smith .01 .05
239 Alex Trevino .01 .05
240 Glenn Wilson .01 .05
241 Gerald Young .01 .05
242 Tom Brunansky .01 .05
243 Cris Carpenter .01 .05
244 Alex Cole RC .02 .10
245 Vince Coleman .01 .05
246 John Costello .01 .05
247 Ken Dayley .01 .05
248 Jose DeLeon .01 .05
249 Frank DiPino .01 .05
250 Pedro Guerrero .01 .05
251 Ken Hill .02 .10
252 Joe Magrane .01 .05
253 Willie McGee UER .02 .10
(No decimal point
before 353)
254 John Morris .01 .05
255 Jose Oquendo .01 .05
256 Tony Pena .01 .05
257 Terry Pendleton .02 .10
258 Ted Power .01 .05
259 Dan Quisenberry .01 .05
260 Ozzie Smith .15 .40
261 Scott Terry .01 .05
262 Milt Thompson .01 .05
263 Denny Walling .01 .05
264 Todd Worrell .01 .05
265 Todd Zeile .02 .10
266 Marty Barrett .01 .05
267 Mike Boddicker .01 .05
268 Wade Boggs .05 .15
269 Ellis Burks .05 .15
270 Rick Cerone .01 .05
271 Roger Clemens .40 1.00
272 John Dopson .01 .05
273 Nick Esasky .01 .05
274 Dwight Evans .05 .15
275 Wes Gardner .01 .05
276 Rich Gedman .01 .05
277 Mike Greenwell .01 .05
278 Danny Heep .01 .05
279 Eric Hetzel .01 .05
280 Dennis Lamp .01 .05
281 Rob Murphy UER .01 .05
('89 stats say Reds,
should say Red Sox)
282 Joe Price .01 .05
283 Carlos Quintana .01 .05
284 Jody Reed .01 .05
285 Luis Rivera .01 .05
286 Kevin Romine .01 .05
287 Lee Smith .02 .10
288 Mike Smithson .01 .05
289 Bob Stanley .01 .05
290 Harold Baines .02 .10
291 Kevin Brown .02 .10
292 Steve Buechele .01 .05
293 Scott Coolbaugh RC .01 .05
294 Jack Daugherty RC .01 .05
295 Cecil Espy .01 .05
296 Julio Franco .02 .10
297 Juan Gonzalez RC .40 1.00
298 Cecilio Guante .01 .05
299 Drew Hall .01 .05
300 Charlie Hough .02 .10
301 Pete Incaviglia .01 .05
302 Mike Jeffcoat .01 .05
303 Chad Kreuter .01 .05
304 Jeff Kunkel .01 .05
305 Rick Leach .01 .05
306 Fred Manrique .01 .05
307 Jamie Moyer .02 .10
308 Rafael Palmeiro .05 .15
309 Geno Petralli .01 .05
310 Kevin Reimer .01 .05
311 Kenny Rogers .02 .10
312 Jeff Russell .01 .05
313 Nolan Ryan .40 1.00
314 Ruben Sierra .02 .10
315 Bobby Witt .01 .05
316 Chris Bosio .01 .05
317 Glenn Braggs UER .01 .05
(Stats say 111 K's,
but bio says 117 K's)
318 Greg Brock .01 .05
319 Chuck Crim .01 .05
320 Rob Deer .01 .05
321 Mike Felder .01 .05
322 Tom Filer .01 .05
323 Tony Fossas RC .01 .05
324 Jim Gantner .01 .05
325 Darryl Hamilton .01 .05
326 Teddy Higuera .01 .05
327 Mark Knudson .01 .05
328 Bill Krueger UER .01 .05
('86 stats missing)
329 Tim McIntosh RC .02 .10
330 Paul Molitor .02 .10
331 Jaime Navarro .01 .05
332 Charlie O'Brien .01 .05
333 Jeff Peterek RC .01 .05
334 Dan Plesac .01 .05
335 Jerry Reuss .01 .05
336 Gary Sheffield UER .08 .25
337 Bill Spiers .01 .05
338 B.J. Surhoff .02 .10
339 Greg Vaughn .01 .05
340 Robin Yount .15 .40
341 Hubie Brooks .01 .05
342 Tim Burke .01 .05
343 Mike Fitzgerald .01 .05
344 Tom Foley .01 .05
345 Andres Galarraga .02 .10
346 Damaso Garcia .01 .05
347 Marquis Grissom RC .15 .40
348 Kevin Gross .01 .05
349 Joe Hesketh .01 .05
350 Jeff Huson RC .01 .05
351 Wallace Johnson .01 .05
352 Mark Langston .01 .05
353A Dave Martinez .75 2.00
(Yellow on front)
353B Dave Martinez .01 .05
(Red on front)
354 Dennis Martinez UER .02 .10
('87 ERA is 616,
should be 6.16)
355 Andy McGaffigan .01 .05
356 Otis Nixon .01 .05
357 Spike Owen .01 .05
358 Pascual Perez .01 .05
359 Tim Raines .02 .10
360 Nelson Santovenia .01 .05
361 Bryn Smith .01 .05
362 Zane Smith .01 .05
363 Larry Walker RC .40 1.00
364 Tim Wallach .01 .05
365 Rick Aguilera .02 .10
366 Allan Anderson .01 .05
367 Wally Backman .01 .05
368 Doug Baker .01 .05
369 Juan Berenguer .01 .05
370 Randy Bush .01 .05
371 Carmelo Castillo .01 .05
372 Mike Dyer RC .01 .05
373 Gary Gaetti .02 .10
374 Greg Gagne .01 .05
375 Dan Gladden .01 .05
376 G.Gonzalez UER .01 .05
Bio says 31 saves in
'88, but stats say 30
377 Brian Harper .01 .05
378 Kent Hrbek .02 .10
379 Gene Larkin .01 .05
380 Tim Laudner UER .01 .05
(No decimal point
before '85 BA of 238)
381 John Moses .01 .05
382 Al Newman .01 .05
383 Kirby Puckett .08 .25
384 Shane Rawley .01 .05
385 Jeff Reardon .02 .10
386 Roy Smith .01 .05
387 Gary Wayne .01 .05
388 Dave West .01 .05
389 Tim Belcher .01 .05
390 Tim Crews UER .01 .05
(Stats say 163 IP for
'83, but bio says 136)
391 Mike Davis .01 .05
392 Rick Dempsey .01 .05
393 Kirk Gibson .02 .10
394 Jose Gonzalez .01 .05
395 Alfredo Griffin .01 .05
396 Jeff Hamilton .01 .05
397 Lenny Harris .01 .05
398 Mickey Hatcher .01 .05
399 Orel Hershiser .02 .10
400 Jay Howell .01 .05
401 Mike Marshall .01 .05
402 Ramon Martinez .01 .05
403 Mike Morgan .01 .05
404 Eddie Murray .08 .25
405 Alejandro Pena .01 .05
406 Willie Randolph .02 .10
407 Mike Scioscia .01 .05
408 Ray Searage .01 .05
409 Fernando Valenzuela .02 .10
410 Jose Vizcaino RC .08 .25
411 John Wetteland .08 .25
412 Jack Armstrong .01 .05
413 Todd Benzinger UER .01 .05
(Bio says .323 at
Pawtucket, but
stats say .321)
414 Tim Birtsas .01 .05
415 Tom Browning .01 .05
416 Norm Charlton .01 .05
417 Eric Davis .02 .10
418 Rob Dibble .02 .10
419 John Franco .02 .10
420 Ken Griffey Sr. .02 .10
421 Chris Hammond RC .02 .10
(No 1989 used for
Did Not Play stat,
actually did play for
Nashville in 1989)
422 Danny Jackson .01 .05
423 Barry Larkin .05 .15
424 Tim Leary .01 .05
425 Rick Mahler .01 .05
426 Joe Oliver .01 .05
427 Paul O'Neill .05 .15
428 Luis Quinones UER .01 .05
('86-'88 stats are
omitted from card but
included in totals)
429 Jeff Reed .01 .05
430 Jose Rijo .01 .05
431 Ron Robinson .01 .05
432 Rolando Roomes .01 .05
433 Chris Sabo .01 .05
434 Scott Scudder .01 .05
435 Herm Winningham .01 .05
436 Steve Balboni .01 .05
437 Jesse Barfield .01 .05
438 Mike Blowers RC .02 .10
439 Tom Brookens .01 .05
440 Greg Cadaret .01 .05
441 Alvaro Espinoza UER .01 .05
(Career games say
218, should be 219)
442 Bob Geren .01 .05
443 Lee Guetterman .01 .05
444 Mel Hall .01 .05
445 Andy Hawkins .01 .05
446 Roberto Kelly .01 .05
447 Don Mattingly .25 .60
448 Lance McCullers .01 .05
449 Hensley Meulens .01 .05
450 Dale Mohorcic .01 .05
451 Clay Parker .01 .05
452 Eric Plunk .01 .05
453 Dave Righetti .01 .05
454 Deion Sanders .08 .25
455 Steve Sax .01 .05
456 Don Slaught .01 .05
457 Walt Terrell .01 .05
458 Dave Winfield .02 .10
459 Jay Bell .02 .10
460 Rafael Belliard .01 .05
461 Barry Bonds .40 1.00
462 Bobby Bonilla .02 .10
463 Sid Bream .01 .05
464 Benny Distefano .01 .05
465 Doug Drabek .01 .05
466 Jim Gott .01 .05
467 Billy Hatcher UER .01 .05
(.1 hits for Cubs
in 1984)
468 Neal Heaton .01 .05
469 Jeff King .01 .05
470 Bob Kipper .01 .05
471 Randy Kramer .01 .05
472 Bill Landrum .01 .05
473 Mike LaValliere .01 .05
474 Jose Lind .01 .05
475 Junior Ortiz .01 .05
476 Gary Redus .01 .05
477 Rick Reed RC .08 .25
478 R.J. Reynolds .01 .05
479 Jeff D. Robinson .01 .05
480 John Smiley .01 .05
481 Andy Van Slyke .05 .15
482 Bob Walk .01 .05
483 Andy Allanson .01 .05
484 Scott Bailes .01 .05
485 Joey Belle UER .08 .25
(Has Jay Bell
Did You Know)
Later changed his name to Albert
486 Bud Black .01 .05
487 Jerry Browne .01 .05
488 Tom Candiotti .01 .05
489 Joe Carter .02 .10
490 Dave Clark .01 .05
(No '84 stats)
491 John Farrell .01 .05
492 Felix Fermin .01 .05
493 Brook Jacoby .01 .05
494 Dion James .01 .05
495 Doug Jones .01 .05
496 Brad Komminsk .01 .05
497 Rod Nichols .01 .05
498 Pete O'Brien .01 .05
499 Steve Olin RC .02 .10
500 Jesse Orosco .01 .05
501 Joel Skinner .01 .05
502 Cory Snyder .01 .05
503 Greg Swindell .01 .05
504 Rich Yett .01 .05
505 Scott Bankhead .01 .05
506 Scott Bradley .01 .05
507 Greg Briley UER .01 .05
(28 SB's in bio,
but 27 in stats)
508 Jay Buhner .02 .10
509 Darnell Coles .01 .05
510 Keith Comstock .01 .05
511 Henry Cotto .01 .05
512 Alvin Davis .01 .05
513 Ken Griffey Jr. .30 .75
514 Erik Hanson .01 .05
515 Gene Harris .01 .05
516 Brian Holman .01 .05
517 Mike Jackson .01 .05
518 Randy Johnson .20 .50
519 Jeffrey Leonard .01 .05
520 Edgar Martinez .05 .15
521 Dennis Powell .01 .05
522 Jim Presley .01 .05
523 Jerry Reed .01 .05
524 Harold Reynolds .02 .10
525 Mike Schooler .01 .05
526 Bill Swift .01 .05
527 Dave Valle .01 .05
528 Omar Vizquel .08 .25
529 Ivan Calderon .01 .05
530 Carlton Fisk UER .05 .15
(Bellow Falls, should
be Bellows Falls)
531 Scott Fletcher .01 .05
532 Dave Gallagher .01 .05
533 Ozzie Guillen .02 .10
534 Greg Hibbard RC .02 .10
535 Shawn Hillegas .01 .05
536 Lance Johnson .01 .05
537 Eric King .01 .05
538 Ron Kittle .01 .05
539 Steve Lyons .01 .05
540 Carlos Martinez .01 .05
541 Tom McCarthy .01 .05
542 Matt Merullo .01 .05
(Had 5 ML runs scored
entering '90, not 6)
543 Donn Pall UER .01 .05
(Stats say pro career
began in '85,
bio says '88)
544 Dan Pasqua .01 .05
545 Ken Patterson .01 .05
546 Melido Perez .01 .05
547 Steve Rosenberg .01 .05
548 Sammy Sosa RC 1.00 2.50
549 Bobby Thigpen .01 .05
550 Robin Ventura .08 .25
551 Greg Walker .01 .05
552 Don Carman .01 .05
553 Pat Combs .01 .05
(6 walks for Phillies
in '89 in stats,
brief bio says 4)
554 Dennis Cook .01 .05
555 Darren Daulton .02 .10
556 Len Dykstra .02 .10
557 Curt Ford .01 .05
558 Charlie Hayes .01 .05
559 Von Hayes .01 .05
560 Tommy Herr .01 .05
561 Ken Howell .01 .05
562 Steve Jeltz .01 .05
563 Ron Jones .01 .05
564 Ricky Jordan UER .01 .05
(Duplicate line of
statistics on back)
565 John Kruk .02 .10
566 Steve Lake .01 .05
567 Roger McDowell .01 .05
568 Terry Mulholland UER .01 .05
(Did You Know refers
to Dave Magadan)
569 Dwayne Murphy .01 .05
570 Jeff Parrett .01 .05
571 Randy Ready .01 .05
572 Bruce Ruffin .01 .05
573 Dickie Thon .01 .05
574 Jose Alvarez UER .01 .05
('78 and '79 stats
are reversed)
575 Geronimo Berroa .01 .05
576 Jeff Blauser .01 .05
577 Joe Boever .01 .05
578 Marty Clary UER .01 .05
(No comma between
city and state)
579 Jody Davis .01 .05
580 Mark Eichhorn .01 .05
581 Darrell Evans .02 .10
582 Ron Gant .02 .10
583 Tom Glavine .05 .15
584 Tommy Greene RC .02 .10
585 Tommy Gregg .01 .05
586 Dave Justice RC UER .20 .50
(Actually had 16 2B
in Sumter in '86)
587 Mark Lemke .01 .05
588 Derek Lilliquist .01 .05
589 Oddibe McDowell .01 .05
590 Kent Mercker UER RC .01 .05
(Bio says 2.75 ERA,
stats say 2.68 ERA)
591 Dale Murphy .05 .15
592 Gerald Perry .01 .05
593 Lonnie Smith .01 .05
594 Pete Smith .01 .05
595 John Smoltz .08 .25
596 Mike Stanton RC UER .08 .25
(No comma between
city and state)
597 Andres Thomas .01 .05
598 Jeff Treadway .01 .05
599 Doyle Alexander .01 .05
600 Dave Bergman .01 .05
601 Brian DuBois RC .01 .05
602 Paul Gibson .01 .05
603 Mike Heath .01 .05
604 Mike Henneman .01 .05
605 Guillermo Hernandez .01 .05
606 Shawn Holman RC .01 .05
607 Tracy Jones .01 .05
608 Chet Lemon .01 .05
609 Fred Lynn .01 .05
610 Jack Morris .02 .10
611 Matt Nokes .01 .05
612 Gary Pettis .01 .05
613 Kevin Ritz RC .01 .05
614 Jeff M. Robinson .01 .05
('88 stats are
not in line)
615 Steve Searcy .01 .05
616 Frank Tanana .01 .05
617 Alan Trammell .02 .10
618 Gary Ward .01 .05
619 Lou Whitaker .02 .10
620 Frank Williams .01 .05
621A George Brett '80 .75 2.00
ERR (Had 10 .390
hitting seasons)
621B George Brett '80 .10 .30
COR
622 Fern.Valenzuela '81 .01 .05
623 Dale Murphy '82 .05 .15
624A Cal Ripken '83 ERR 2.00 5.00
(Misspelled Ripkin
on card back)
624B Cal Ripken '83 COR .15 .40
625 Ryne Sandberg '84 .08 .25
626 Don Mattingly '85 .07 .20
627 Roger Clemens '86 .20 .50
628 George Bell '87 .01 .05
629 J.Canseco '88 UER .02 .10
Reggie won MVP in
'83, should say '73
630A Will Clark '89 ERR .40 1.00
(32 total bases
on card back)
630B Will Clark '89 COR .05 .15
(321 total bases;
technically still
an error, listing
only 24 runs)
631 Mark Davis .01 .05
Mitch Williams
632 Wade Boggs .02 .10
Mike Greenwell
633 Mark Gubicza .01 .05
Jeff Russell
634 Tony Fernandez .08 .25
Cal Ripken
635 Kirby Puckett .05 .15
Bo Jackson
636 Nolan Ryan .15 .40
Mike Scott
637 Will Clark .02 .10
Kevin Mitchell
638 Don Mattingly .10 .30
Mark McGwire
639 Howard Johnson .08 .25
Ryne Sandberg
640 Rudy Seanez RC .02 .10
Colin Charland RC
641 George Canale RC .08 .25
Kevin Maas RC
642 Kelly Mann RC .08 .25
Dave Hansen RC
643 Greg Smith RC .02 .10
Stu Tate RC
644 Tom Drees RC .02 .10
Dann Howitt RC
645 Mike Roesler RC .02 .10
Derrick May RC
646 Scott Hemond RC .02 .10
Mark Gardner RC
647 John Orton RC .02 .10
Scott Leius RC
648 Rich Monteleone RC .02 .10
Dana Williams RC
649 Mike Huff RC .02 .10
Steve Frey RC
650 Chuck McElroy .30 .75
Moises Alou RC
651 Bobby Rose RC .08 .25
Mike Hartley RC
652 Matt Kinzer RC .02 .10
Wayne Edwards RC
653 Delino DeShields RC .08 .25
Jason Grimsley RC
654 CL: A's/Cubs .01 .05
Giants/Blue Jays
655 CL: Royals/Angels .01 .05
Padres/Orioles
656 CL: Mets/Astros .01 .05
Cards/Red Sox
657 CL: Rangers/Brewers .01 .05
Expos/Twins
658 CL: Dodgers/Reds .01 .05
Yankees/Pirates
659 CL: Indians/Mariners .01 .05
White Sox/Phillies
660A CL: Braves/Tigers .01 .05
Specials/Checklists
(Checklist-660 in small-
er print on card front)
660B CL: Braves/Tigers .01 .05
Specials/Checklists
(Checklist-660 in nor-
mal print on card front)
NNO 10th Anniversary Pin .75 2.00

1990 Fleer Canadian

The 1990 Fleer Canadian set contains 660 standard-size cards. The cards were distributed in wax packs exclusively in Canada. The Canadian set differs from the U.S. version only in that it shows copyright "FLEER LTD./LTEE PTD. IN CANADA" on the card backs. Although these Canadian cards were undoubtedly produced in much lesser quantities compared to the U.S. issue, the fact that the versions are so similar has kept the demand down over the years.

*STARS: 2X to 5X BASIC CARDS
*YOUNG STARS: 3X to 6X BASIC CARDS
*ROOKIES: 4X to 10X BASIC CARDS

1990 Fleer All-Stars

The 1990 Fleer All-Star insert set includes 12 standard-size cards. The set was randomly inserted in 33-card cellos and wax packs. The set is sequenced in alphabetical order. The fronts are white with a light gray screen and bright red stripes. The player selection for the set is Fleer's opinion of the best Major Leaguer at each position.

COMPLETE SET (12) 1.50 3.00
RANDOM INSERTS IN PACKS
1 Harold Baines .08 .25
2 Will Clark .08 .25
3 Mark Davis .05 .15
4 Howard Johnson UER .05 .15
(In middle of 5th
line, the is
misspelled th)
5 Joe Magrane .05 .15
6 Kevin Mitchell .05 .15
7 Kirby Puckett .25 .60
8 Cal Ripken .75 2.00
9 Ryne Sandberg .40 1.00
10 Mike Scott UER .05 .15
Astros spelled Asatros on back
11 Ruben Sierra .08 .25
12 Mickey Tettleton .05 .15

1990 Fleer League Standouts

This six-card standard-size insert set was distributed one per 45-card rack pack. The set is subtitled "Standouts" and commemorates outstanding events for those players from the previous season.

Card	Low	High
COMPLETE SET (6)	3.00	6.00
1 Barry Larkin	.50	1.25
2 Don Mattingly	2.00	5.00
3 Darryl Strawberry	.30	.75
4 Jose Canseco	.50	1.25
5 Wade Boggs	.50	1.25
6 Mark Grace UER (Chris Sabo misspelled as Cris)	.50	1.25

1990 Fleer Soaring Stars

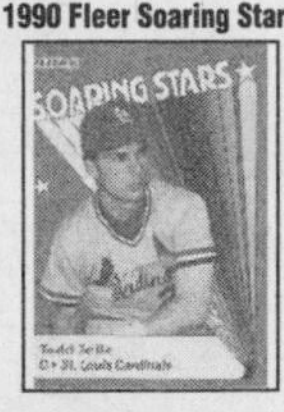

The 1990 Fleer Soaring Stars set was issued exclusively in jumbo cello packs. This 12-card, standard-size set features some of the most popular young players entering the 1990 season. The set gives the visual impression of rockets exploding in the air to honor these young players.

Card	Low	High
COMPLETE SET (12)	6.00	15.00
RANDOM INSERTS IN JUMBO PACKS		
1 Todd Zeile	.40	1.00
2 Mike Stanton	.20	.50
3 Larry Walker	.75	2.00
4 Robin Ventura	.75	2.00
5 Scott Coolbaugh	.20	.50
6 Ken Griffey Jr.	2.00	5.00
7 Tom Gordon	.40	1.00
8 Jerome Walton	.20	.50
9 Junior Felix	.20	.50
10 Jim Abbott	.60	1.50
11 Ricky Jordan	.20	.50
12 Dwight Smith	.20	.50

1990 Fleer Wax Box Cards

The 1990 Fleer wax box cards comprise seven different box bottoms with four cards each, for a total of 28 standard-size cards. The outer front borders are white; the inner, ribbon-like borders are different depending on the team. The vertically oriented backs are gray. The cards are numbered with a "C" prefix.

Card	Low	High
COMPLETE SET (28)	4.80	12.00
C1 Giants Logo	.02	.10
C2 Tim Belcher	.02	.10
C3 Roger Clemens	1.00	2.50
C4 Eric Davis	.08	.25
C5 Glenn Davis	.02	.10
C6 Cubs Logo	.02	.10
C7 John Franco	.08	.25
C8 Mike Greenwell	.02	.10
C9 A's Logo	.02	.10
C10 Ken Griffey Jr.	1.25	3.00
C11 Pedro Guerrero	.02	.10
C12 Tony Gwynn	1.00	2.50
C13 Blue Jays Logo	.02	.10
C14 Orel Hershiser	.08	.25
C15 Bo Jackson	.30	.75
C16 Howard Johnson	.02	.10
C17 Mets Logo	.02	.10
C18 Cardinals Logo	.02	.10
C19 Don Mattingly	1.00	2.50
C20 Mark McGwire	.75	2.00
C21 Kevin Mitchell	.02	.10
C22 Kirby Puckett	.40	1.00
C23 Royals Logo	.02	.10
C24 Orioles Logo	.02	.10
C25 Ruben Sierra	.08	.25
C26 Dave Stewart	.08	.25
C27 Jerome Walton	.02	.10
C28 Robin Yount	.50	1.25

1990 Fleer World Series

This 12-card standard-size set was issued as an insert in with the Fleer factory sets, celebrating the 1989 World Series. This set marked the fourth year that Fleer issued a special World Series set in their factory (or vend) set. The design of these cards are different from the regular Fleer issue as the photo is framed by a white border with red and blue World Series cards and the player description in black.

Card	Low	High
COMPLETE SET (12)	.40	1.00
1 Mike Moore	.01	.05
2 Kevin Mitchell	.01	.05
3 Terry Steinbach	.01	.05
4 Will Clark	.02	.10
5 Jose Canseco	.05	.15
6 Walt Weiss	.01	.05
7 Terry Steinbach	.01	.05
8 Dave Stewart	.02	.10
9 Dave Parker	.02	.10
10 Dave Parker / Jose Canseco / Will Clark	.02	.10
11 Rickey Henderson	.08	.25
12 Oakland A's Celebrate Baseball's Best in 89	.02	.10

1990 Fleer Update

The 1990 Fleer Update set contains 132 standard-size cards. This set marked the seventh consecutive year Fleer issued an end of season Update set. The set was issued exclusively as a boxed set through hobby dealers. The set is checklisted alphabetically by team for each league and then alphabetically within each team. The fronts are styled the same as the 1990 Fleer regular issue set. The backs are numbered with the prefix "U" for Update. Rookie Cards in this set include Travis Fryman, Todd Hundley, John Olerud and Frank Thomas.

Card	Low	High
COMP.FACT.SET (132)	1.50	4.00
1 Steve Avery	.01	.05
2 Francisco Cabrera	.01	.05
3 Nick Esasky	.01	.05
4 Jim Kremers RC	.01	.05
5 Greg Olson (C) RC	.02	.10
6 Jim Presley	.01	.05
7 Shawn Boskie RC	.02	.10
8 Joe Kraemer RC	.01	.05
9 Luis Salazar	.01	.05
10 Hector Villanueva RC	.01	.05
11 Glenn Braggs	.01	.05
12 Mariano Duncan	.01	.05
13 Billy Hatcher	.01	.05
14 Tim Layana RC	.01	.05
15 Hal Morris	.01	.05
16 Javier Ortiz RC	.01	.05
17 Dave Rohde RC	.01	.05
18 Eric Yelding RC	.01	.05
19 Hubie Brooks	.01	.05
20 Kal Daniels	.01	.05
21 Dave Hansen RC	.01	.05
22 Mike Hartley	.01	.05
23 Stan Javier	.01	.05
24 Jose Offerman RC	.08	.25
25 Juan Samuel	.01	.05
26 Dennis Boyd	.01	.05
27 Delino DeShields	.08	.25
28 Steve Frey	.01	.05
29 Mark Gardner	.01	.05
30 Chris Nabholz RC	.02	.10
31 Bill Sampen RC	.01	.05
32 Dave Schmidt	.01	.05
33 Daryl Boston	.01	.05
34 Chuck Carr RC	.02	.10
35 John Franco	.02	.10
36 Todd Hundley RC	.08	.25
37 Julio Machado RC	.01	.05
38 Alejandro Pena	.01	.05
39 Darren Reed RC	.01	.05
40 Kelvin Torve	.01	.05
41 Darrel Akerfelds	.01	.05
42 Jose DeJesus	.01	.05
43 Dave Hollins UER RC (Misspelled Dane on card back)	.08	.25
44 Carmelo Martinez	.01	.05
45 Brad Moore	.01	.05
46 Dale Murphy	.05	.15
47 Wally Backman	.01	.05
48 Stan Belinda RC	.02	.10
49 Bob Patterson	.01	.05
50 Ted Power	.01	.05
51 Don Slaught	.01	.05
52 Geronimo Pena RC	.02	.10
53 Lee Smith	.02	.10
54 John Tudor	.01	.05
55 Joe Carter	.02	.10
56 Thomas Howard	.01	.05
57 Craig Lefferts	.01	.05
58 Rafael Valdez RC	.01	.05
59 Dave Anderson	.01	.05
60 Kevin Bass	.01	.05
61 John Burkett	.01	.05
62 Gary Carter	.02	.10
63 Rick Parker RC	.01	.05
64 Trevor Wilson	.01	.05
65 Chris Hoiles RC	.08	.25
66 Tim Hulett	.01	.05
67 Dave Wayne Johnson RC	.01	.05
68 Curt Schilling	.40	1.00
69 David Segui RC	.15	.40
70 Tom Brunansky	.01	.05
71 Greg A. Harris	.01	.05
72 Dana Kiecker RC	.01	.05
73 Tim Naehring RC	.02	.10
74 Tony Pena	.01	.05
75 Jeff Reardon	.02	.10
76 Jerry Reed	.01	.05
77 Mark Eichhorn	.01	.05
78 Mark Langston	.01	.05
79 John Orton	.01	.05
80 Luis Polonia	.01	.05
81 Dave Winfield	.02	.10
82 Cliff Young RC	.01	.05
83 Wayne Edwards RC	.01	.05
84 Alex Fernandez RC	.08	.25
85 Craig Grebeck RC	.02	.10
86 Scott Radinsky RC	.02	.10
87 Frank Thomas RC	.75	2.00
88 Beau Allred RC	.01	.05
89 Sandy Alomar Jr.	.02	.10
90 Carlos Baerga RC	.08	.25
91 Kevin Bearse RC	.01	.05
92 Chris James	.01	.05
93 Candy Maldonado	.01	.05
94 Jeff Manto	.01	.05
95 Cecil Fielder	.02	.10
96 Travis Fryman RC	.15	.40
97 Lloyd Moseby	.01	.05
98 Edwin Nunez	.01	.05
99 Tony Phillips	.01	.05
100 Larry Sheets	.01	.05
101 Mark Davis	.01	.05
102 Storm Davis	.01	.05
103 Gerald Perry	.01	.05
104 Terry Shumpert RC	.01	.05
105 Edgar Diaz RC	.01	.05
106 Dave Parker	.02	.10
107 Tim Drummond RC	.01	.05
108 Junior Ortiz	.01	.05
109 Park Pittman RC	.01	.05
110 Kevin Tapani RC	.08	.25
111 Oscar Azocar RC	.01	.05
112 Jim Leyritz RC	.08	.25
113 Kevin Maas	.02	.10
114 Alan Mills RC	.02	.10
115 Matt Nokes	.01	.05
116 Pascual Perez	.01	.05
117 Ozzie Canseco	.01	.05
118 Scott Sanderson	.01	.05
119 Tino Martinez	.20	.50
120 Jeff Schaefer RC	.01	.05
121 Matt Young	.01	.05
122 Brian Bohanon RC	.02	.10
123 Jeff Huson	.01	.05
124 Ramon Manon RC	.01	.05
125 Gary Mielke UER RC (Shown as Blue Jay on front)	.01	.05
126 Willie Blair RC	.02	.10
127 Glenallen Hill	.01	.05
128 John Olerud RC UER (Listed as throwing right, should be left)	.20	.50
129 Luis Sojo RC	.01	.05
130 Mark Whiten RC	.08	.25
131 Nolan Ryan	.40	1.00
132 Checklist U1-U132	.01	.05

1991 Fleer

The 1991 Fleer set consists of 720 standard-size cards. Cards were primarily issued in wax packs, cello packs and factory sets. This set does not have what had been a Fleer tradition in prior years, the two-player Rookie Cards and there are less two-player special cards than in prior years. The design features bright yellow borders with the information in black indicating name, position, and team. The set is again ordered numerically by teams, followed by combination cards, rookie prospect pairs, and checklists. There are no notable Rookie Cards in this set. A number of the cards in the set can be found with photos cropped (very slightly) differently as Fleer used two separate printers in their attempt to maximize production.

Card	Low	High
COMPLETE SET (720)	3.00	8.00
COMP.RETAIL SET (732)	4.00	10.00
COMP.HOBBY SET (732)	4.00	10.00
1 Troy Afenir RC	.01	.05
2 Harold Baines	.02	.10
3 Lance Blankenship	.01	.05
4 Todd Burns	.01	.05
5 Jose Canseco	.05	.15
6 Dennis Eckersley	.02	.10
7 Mike Gallego	.01	.05
8 Ron Hassey	.01	.05
9 Dave Henderson	.01	.05
10 Rickey Henderson	.08	.25
11 Rick Honeycutt	.01	.05
12 Doug Jennings	.01	.05
13 Joe Klink	.01	.05
14 Carney Lansford	.02	.10
15 Darren Lewis	.01	.05
16 Willie McGee UER (Height 6'11)	.02	.10
17 Mark McGwire UER (183 extra base hits in 1987)	.30	.75
18 Mike Moore	.01	.05
19 Gene Nelson	.01	.05
20 Dave Otto	.01	.05
21 Jamie Quirk	.01	.05
22 Willie Randolph	.02	.10
23 Scott Sanderson	.01	.05
24 Terry Steinbach	.01	.05
25 Dave Stewart	.02	.10
26 Walt Weiss	.01	.05
27 Bob Welch	.01	.05
28 Curt Young	.01	.05
29 Wally Backman	.01	.05
30 Stan Belinda UER (Born in Huntington, should be State College)	.01	.05
31 Jay Bell	.02	.10
32 Rafael Belliard	.01	.05
33 Barry Bonds	.40	1.00
34 Bobby Bonilla	.02	.10
35 Sid Bream	.01	.05
36 Doug Drabek	.01	.05
37 Carlos Garcia RC	.02	.10
38 Neal Heaton	.01	.05
39 Jeff King	.01	.05
40 Bob Kipper	.01	.05
41 Bill Landrum	.01	.05
42 Mike LaValliere	.01	.05
43 Jose Lind	.01	.05
44 Carmelo Martinez	.01	.05
45 Bob Patterson	.01	.05
46 Ted Power	.01	.05
47 Gary Redus	.01	.05
48 R.J. Reynolds	.01	.05
49 Don Slaught	.01	.05
50 John Smiley	.01	.05
51 Zane Smith	.01	.05
52 Randy Tomlin RC	.02	.10
53 Andy Van Slyke	.05	.15
54 Bob Walk	.01	.05
55 Jack Armstrong	.01	.05
56 Todd Benzinger	.01	.05
57 Glenn Braggs	.01	.05
58 Keith Brown	.01	.05
59 Tom Browning	.01	.05
60 Norm Charlton	.01	.05
61 Eric Davis	.02	.10
62 Rob Dibble	.02	.10
63 Bill Doran	.01	.05
64 Mariano Duncan	.01	.05
65 Chris Hammond	.01	.05
66 Billy Hatcher	.01	.05
67 Danny Jackson	.01	.05
68 Barry Larkin	.05	.15
69 Tim Layana UER (Black line over made in first text line)	.01	.05
70 Terry Lee RC	.01	.05
71 Rick Mahler	.01	.05
72 Hal Morris	.01	.05
73 Randy Myers	.01	.05
74 Ron Oester	.01	.05
75 Joe Oliver	.01	.05
76 Paul O'Neill	.05	.15
77 Luis Quinones	.01	.05
78 Jeff Reed	.01	.05
79 Jose Rijo	.01	.05
80 Chris Sabo	.01	.05
81 Scott Scudder	.01	.05
82 Herm Winningham	.01	.05
83 Larry Andersen	.01	.05
84 Marty Barrett	.01	.05
85 Mike Boddicker	.01	.05
86 Wade Boggs	.05	.15
87 Tom Bolton	.01	.05
88 Tom Brunansky	.01	.05
89 Ellis Burks	.02	.10
90 Roger Clemens	.30	.75
91 Scott Cooper	.01	.05
92 John Dopson	.01	.05
93 Dwight Evans	.05	.15
94 Wes Gardner	.01	.05
95 Jeff Gray RC	.01	.05
96 Mike Greenwell	.01	.05
97 Greg A. Harris	.01	.05
98 Daryl Irvine RC	.01	.05
99 Dana Kiecker	.01	.05
100 Randy Kutcher	.01	.05
101 Dennis Lamp	.01	.05
102 Mike Marshall	.01	.05
103 John Marzano	.01	.05
104 Rob Murphy	.01	.05
105 Tim Naehring	.01	.05
106 Tony Pena	.01	.05
107 Phil Plantier RC	.08	.25
108 Carlos Quintana	.01	.05
109 Jeff Reardon	.02	.10
110 Jerry Reed	.01	.05
111 Jody Reed	.01	.05
112 Luis Rivera UER (Born 1/3/84)	.01	.05
113 Kevin Romine	.01	.05
114 Phil Bradley	.01	.05
115 Ivan Calderon	.01	.05
116 Wayne Edwards	.01	.05
117 Alex Fernandez	.01	.05
118 Carlton Fisk	.05	.15
119 Scott Fletcher	.01	.05
120 Craig Grebeck	.01	.05
121 Ozzie Guillen	.02	.10
122 Greg Hibbard	.01	.05
123 Lance Johnson UER (Born Cincinnati, should be Lincoln Heights)	.01	.05
124 Barry Jones	.01	.05
125 Ron Karkovice	.01	.05
126 Eric King	.01	.05
127 Steve Lyons	.01	.05
128 Carlos Martinez	.01	.05
129 Jack McDowell UER (Stanford misspelled as Standford on back)	.01	.05
130 Donn Pall (No dots over any i's in text)	.01	.05
131 Dan Pasqua	.01	.05
132 Ken Patterson	.01	.05
133 Melido Perez	.01	.05
134 Adam Peterson	.01	.05
135 Scott Radinsky	.01	.05
136 Sammy Sosa	.08	.25
137 Bobby Thigpen	.01	.05
138 Frank Thomas	.08	.25
139 Robin Ventura	.02	.10
140 Daryl Boston	.01	.05
141 Chuck Carr	.01	.05
142 Mark Carreon	.01	.05
143 David Cone	.02	.10
144 Ron Darling	.01	.05
145 Kevin Elster	.01	.05
146 Sid Fernandez	.01	.05
147 John Franco	.02	.10
148 Dwight Gooden	.02	.10
149 Tom Herr	.01	.05
150 Todd Hundley	.01	.05
151 Gregg Jefferies	.01	.05
152 Howard Johnson	.01	.05
153 Dave Magadan	.01	.05
154 Kevin McReynolds	.01	.05
155 Keith Miller UER (Text says Rochester in '87, stats say Tide-water, mixed up with other Keith Miller)	.01	.05
156 Bob Ojeda	.01	.05
157 Tom O'Malley	.01	.05
158 Alejandro Pena	.01	.05
159 Darren Reed	.01	.05
160 Mackey Sasser	.01	.05
161 Darryl Strawberry	.02	.10
162 Tim Teufel	.01	.05
163 Kelvin Torve	.01	.05
164 Julio Valera	.01	.05
165 Frank Viola	.02	.10
166 Wally Whitehurst	.01	.05
167 Jim Acker	.01	.05
168 Derek Bell	.02	.10
169 George Bell	.01	.05
170 Willie Blair	.01	.05
171 Pat Borders	.01	.05
172 John Cerutti	.01	.05
173 Junior Felix	.01	.05
174 Tony Fernandez	.01	.05
175 Kelly Gruber UER (Born in Houston, should be Bellaire)	.01	.05
176 Tom Henke	.01	.05
177 Glenallen Hill	.01	.05
178 Jimmy Key	.02	.10
179 Manny Lee	.01	.05
180 Fred McGriff	.05	.15
181 Rance Mulliniks	.01	.05
182 Greg Myers	.01	.05
183 John Olerud UER (Listed as throwing right, should be left)	.02	.10
184 Luis Sojo	.01	.05
185 Dave Stieb	.01	.05
186 Todd Stottlemyre	.01	.05
187 Duane Ward	.01	.05
188 David Wells	.02	.10
189 Mark Whiten	.01	.05
190 Ken Williams	.01	.05
191 Frank Wills	.01	.05
192 Mookie Wilson	.02	.10
193 Don Aase	.01	.05
194 Tim Belcher UER (Born Sparta, Ohio, should say Mt. Gilead)	.01	.05
195 Hubie Brooks	.01	.05
196 Dennis Cook	.01	.05
197 Tim Crews	.01	.05
198 Kal Daniels	.01	.05
199 Kirk Gibson	.02	.10
200 Jim Gott	.01	.05
201 Alfredo Griffin	.01	.05
202 Chris Gwynn	.01	.05
203 Dave Hansen	.01	.05
204 Lenny Harris	.01	.05
205 Mike Hartley	.01	.05
206 Mickey Hatcher	.01	.05
207 Carlos Hernandez	.01	.05
208 Orel Hershiser	.02	.10
209 Jay Howell UER (No 1982 Yankee stats)	.01	.05
210 Mike Huff	.01	.05
211 Stan Javier	.01	.05
212 Ramon Martinez	.01	.05
213 Mike Morgan	.01	.05
214 Eddie Murray	.08	.25
215 Jim Neidlinger RC	.01	.05
216 Jose Offerman	.01	.05
217 Jim Poole	.01	.05
218 Juan Samuel	.01	.05
219 Mike Scioscia	.01	.05
220 Ray Searage	.01	.05
221 Mike Sharperson	.01	.05
222 Fernando Valenzuela	.02	.10
223 Jose Vizcaino	.01	.05
224 Mike Aldrete	.01	.05
225 Scott Anderson RC	.01	.05
226 Dennis Boyd	.01	.05
227 Tim Burke	.01	.05
228 Delino DeShields	.02	.10
229 Mike Fitzgerald	.01	.05
230 Tom Foley	.01	.05
231 Steve Frey	.01	.05
232 Andres Galarraga	.02	.10
233 Mark Gardner	.01	.05
234 Marquis Grissom	.02	.10
235 Kevin Gross (No date given for first Expos win)	.01	.05
236 Drew Hall	.01	.05
237 Dave Martinez	.01	.05
238 Dennis Martinez	.02	.10
239 Dale Mohorcic	.01	.05
240 Chris Nabholz	.01	.05
241 Otis Nixon	.01	.05
242 Junior Noboa	.01	.05
243 Spike Owen	.01	.05
244 Tim Raines	.02	.10
245 Mel Rojas UER (Stats show 3.60 ERA, bio says 3.19 ERA)	.01	.05
246 Scott Ruskin	.01	.05
247 Bill Sampen	.01	.05
248 Nelson Santovenia	.01	.05
249 Dave Schmidt	.01	.05
250 Larry Walker	.08	.25
251 Tim Wallach	.01	.05
252 Dave Anderson	.01	.05
253 Kevin Bass	.01	.05
254 Steve Bedrosian	.01	.05
255 Jeff Brantley	.01	.05
256 John Burkett	.01	.05
257 Brett Butler	.02	.10
258 Gary Carter	.02	.10
259 Will Clark	.05	.15
260 Steve Decker RC	.02	.10
261 Kelly Downs	.01	.05
262 Scott Garrelts	.01	.05
263 Terry Kennedy	.01	.05
264 Mike LaCoss	.01	.05
265 Mark Leonard RC	.01	.05
266 Greg Litton	.01	.05
267 Kevin Mitchell	.01	.05
268 Randy O'Neal	.01	.05
269 Rick Parker	.01	.05
270 Rick Reuschel	.01	.05
271 Ernest Riles	.01	.05
272 Don Robinson	.01	.05
273 Robby Thompson	.01	.05
274 Mark Thurmond	.01	.05
275 Jose Uribe	.01	.05
276 Matt Williams	.02	.10
277 Trevor Wilson	.01	.05
278 Gerald Alexander RC	.01	.05
279 Brad Arnsberg	.01	.05
280 Kevin Belcher RC	.01	.05
281 Joe Bitker RC	.01	.05
282 Kevin Brown	.02	.10
283 Steve Buechele	.01	.05
284 Jack Daugherty	.01	.05
285 Julio Franco	.02	.10
286 Juan Gonzalez	.08	.25
287 Bill Haselman RC	.01	.05
288 Charlie Hough	.02	.10
289 Jeff Huson	.01	.05
290 Pete Incaviglia	.01	.05
291 Mike Jeffcoat	.01	.05
292 Jeff Kunkel	.01	.05
293 Gary Mielke	.01	.05
294 Jamie Moyer	.02	.10
295 Rafael Palmeiro	.05	.15
296 Geno Petralli	.01	.05
297 Gary Pettis	.01	.05
298 Kevin Reimer	.01	.05
299 Kenny Rogers	.02	.10
300 Jeff Russell	.01	.05
301 John Russell	.01	.05
302 Nolan Ryan	.40	1.00
303 Ruben Sierra	.02	.10
304 Bobby Witt	.01	.05
305 Jim Abbott UER (Text on back states he won Sullivan Award (outstanding amateur athlete) in 1989;should be '88)	.05	.15
306 Kent Anderson	.01	.05
307 Dante Bichette	.02	.10
308 Bert Blyleven	.02	.10
309 Chili Davis	.02	.10
310 Brian Downing	.01	.05
311 Mark Eichhorn	.01	.05
312 Mike Fetters	.01	.05
313 Chuck Finley	.02	.10
314 Willie Fraser	.01	.05
315 Bryan Harvey	.01	.05
316 Donnie Hill	.01	.05
317 Wally Joyner	.02	.10
318 Mark Langston	.01	.05
319 Kirk McCaskill	.01	.05
320 John Orton	.01	.05
321 Lance Parrish	.02	.10
322 Luis Polonia UER (1984 Madfison, should be Madison)	.01	.05
323 Johnny Ray	.01	.05
324 Bobby Rose	.01	.05
325 Dick Schofield	.01	.05
326 Rick Schu	.01	.05
327 Lee Stevens	.01	.05
328 Devon White	.02	.10
329 Dave Winfield	.02	.10
330 Cliff Young	.01	.05
331 Dave Bergman	.01	.05
332 Phil Clark RC	.02	.10
333 Darnell Coles	.01	.05
334 Milt Cuyler	.01	.05
335 Cecil Fielder	.02	.10
336 Travis Fryman	.02	.10
337 Paul Gibson	.01	.05
338 Jerry Don Gleaton	.01	.05
339 Mike Heath	.01	.05
340 Mike Henneman	.01	.05
341 Chet Lemon	.01	.05
342 Lance McCullers	.01	.05
343 Jack Morris	.02	.10
344 Lloyd Moseby	.01	.05
345 Edwin Nunez	.01	.05
346 Clay Parker	.01	.05
347 Dan Petry	.01	.05
348 Tony Phillips	.01	.05
349 Jeff M. Robinson	.01	.05
350 Mark Salas	.01	.05
351 Mike Schwabe	.01	.05
352 Larry Sheets	.01	.05
353 John Shelby	.01	.05
354 Frank Tanana	.01	.05
355 Alan Trammell	.02	.10
356 Gary Ward	.01	.05
357 Lou Whitaker	.02	.10
358 Beau Allred	.01	.05
359 Sandy Alomar Jr.	.01	.05
360 Carlos Baerga	.01	.05
361 Kevin Bearse	.01	.05
362 Tom Brookens	.01	.05
363 Jerry Browne UER (No dot over i in first text line)	.01	.05
364 Tom Candiotti	.01	.05
365 Alex Cole	.01	.05
366 John Farrell UER (Born in Neptune, should be Monmouth)	.01	.05
367 Felix Fermin	.01	.05
368 Keith Hernandez	.02	.10
369 Brook Jacoby	.01	.05
370 Chris James	.01	.05
371 Dion James	.01	.05
372 Doug Jones	.01	.05
373 Candy Maldonado	.01	.05
374 Steve Olin	.01	.05
375 Jesse Orosco	.01	.05
376 Rudy Seanez	.01	.05
377 Joel Skinner	.01	.05
378 Cory Snyder	.01	.05
379 Greg Swindell	.01	.05
380 Sergio Valdez	.01	.05
381 Mike Walker	.01	.05
382 Colby Ward RC	.01	.05
383 Turner Ward RC	.08	.25
384 Mitch Webster	.01	.05
385 Kevin Wickander	.01	.05
386 Darrel Akerfelds	.01	.05
387 Joe Boever	.01	.05
388 Rod Booker	.01	.05
389 Sil Campusano	.01	.05
390 Don Carman	.01	.05
391 Wes Chamberlain RC	.08	.25
392 Pat Combs	.01	.05
393 Darren Daulton	.02	.10
394 Jose DeJesus	.01	.05
395A Len Dykstra Name spelled Lenny on back	.02	.10
395B Len Dykstra Name spelled Len on back	.02	.10
396 Jason Grimsley	.01	.05
397 Charlie Hayes	.01	.05
398 Von Hayes	.01	.05
399 David Hollins UER (Atl-bats& should say at-bats)	.01	.05
400 Ken Howell	.01	.05
401 Ricky Jordan	.01	.05
402 John Kruk	.02	.10
403 Steve Lake	.01	.05
404 Chuck Malone	.01	.05
405 Roger McDowell UER (Says Phillies is saves, should say in)	.01	.05
406 Chuck McElroy	.01	.05
407 Mickey Morandini	.01	.05
408 Terry Mulholland	.01	.05
409 Dale Murphy	.05	.15
410A Randy Ready ERR (No Brewers stats listed for 1983)	.01	.05
410B Randy Ready COR	.01	.05
411 Bruce Ruffin	.01	.05
412 Dickie Thon	.01	.05
413 Paul Assenmacher	.01	.05
414 Damon Berryhill	.01	.05
415 Mike Bielecki	.01	.05
416 Shawn Boskie	.01	.05
417 Dave Clark	.01	.05
418 Doug Dascenzo	.01	.05
419A Andre Dawson ERR (No stats for 1976)	.02	.10
419B Andre Dawson COR	.02	.10
420 Shawon Dunston	.01	.05
421 Joe Girardi	.01	.05
422 Mark Grace	.05	.15
423 Mike Harkey	.01	.05
424 Les Lancaster	.01	.05
425 Bill Long	.01	.05
426 Greg Maddux	.15	.40
427 Derrick May	.01	.05
428 Jeff Pico	.01	.05
429 Domingo Ramos	.01	.05
430 Luis Salazar	.01	.05
431 Ryne Sandberg	.15	.40
432 Dwight Smith	.01	.05
433 Greg Smith	.01	.05
434 Rick Sutcliffe	.02	.10
435 Gary Varsho	.01	.05
436 Hector Villanueva	.01	.05
437 Jerome Walton	.01	.05
438 Curtis Wilkerson	.01	.05
439 Mitch Williams	.01	.05
440 Steve Wilson	.01	.05
441 Marvell Wynne	.01	.05
442 Scott Bankhead	.01	.05
443 Scott Bradley	.01	.05
444 Greg Briley	.01	.05
445 Mike Brumley UER (Text 40 SB's in 1988, stats say 41)	.01	.05
446 Jay Buhner	.02	.10
447 Dave Burba RC	.08	.25
448 Henry Cotto	.01	.05
449 Alvin Davis	.01	.05
450 Ken Griffey Jr. (Bat around .300)	.20	.50
450A Ken Griffey Jr. (Bat .300)	.40	1.00
451 Erik Hanson	.01	.05
452 Gene Harris UER (63 career runs, should be 73)	.01	.05
453 Brian Holman	.01	.05
454 Mike Jackson	.01	.05
455 Randy Johnson	.10	.30
456 Jeffrey Leonard	.01	.05
457 Edgar Martinez	.05	.15
458 Tino Martinez	.08	.25
459 Pete O'Brien UER (1987 BA .266, should be .286)	.01	.05
460 Harold Reynolds	.02	.10
461 Mike Schooler	.01	.05
462 Bill Swift	.01	.05
463 David Valle	.01	.05
464 Omar Vizquel	.05	.15
465 Matt Young	.01	.05
466 Brady Anderson	.02	.10
467 Jeff Ballard UER (Missing top of right parenthesis after Saberhagen in last text line)	.01	.05
468 Juan Bell	.01	.05
469A Mike Devereaux (First line of text ends with six)	.02	.10
469B Mike Devereaux (First line of text ends with runs)	.02	.10
470 Steve Finley	.02	.10
471 Dave Gallagher	.01	.05
472 Leo Gomez	.01	.05
473 Rene Gonzales	.01	.05
474 Pete Harnisch	.01	.05
475 Kevin Hickey	.01	.05
476 Chris Hoiles	.01	.05
477 Sam Horn	.01	.05
478 Tim Hulett (Photo shows National Leaguer sliding into second base)	.01	.05
479 Dave Johnson	.01	.05
480 Ron Kittle UER (Edmonton misspelled as Edmundton)	.01	.05
481 Ben McDonald	.01	.05
482 Bob Melvin	.01	.05
483 Bob Milacki	.01	.05
484 Randy Milligan	.01	.05
485 John Mitchell	.01	.05
486 Gregg Olson	.01	.05
487 Joe Orsulak	.01	.05
488 Joe Price	.01	.05
489 Bill Ripken	.01	.05
490 Cal Ripken	.30	.75
491 Curt Schilling	.08	.25
492 David Segui	.01	.05
493 Anthony Telford RC	.01	.05
494 Mickey Tettleton	.01	.05
495 Mark Williamson	.01	.05
496 Craig Worthington	.01	.05
497 Juan Agosto	.01	.05
498 Eric Anthony	.01	.05
499 Craig Biggio	.05	.15
500 Ken Caminiti UER (Born 4/4, should be 4/21)	.02	.10
501 Casey Candaele	.01	.05
502 Andujar Cedeno	.01	.05
503 Danny Darwin	.01	.05
504 Mark Davidson	.01	.05
505 Glenn Davis	.01	.05
506 Jim Deshaies	.01	.05
507 Luis Gonzalez RC	.20	.50
508 Bill Gullickson	.01	.05
509 Xavier Hernandez	.01	.05
510 Brian Meyer	.01	.05
511 Ken Oberkfell	.01	.05
512 Mark Portugal	.01	.05

513 Rafael Ramirez .01 .05
514 Karl Rhodes .01 .05
515 Mike Scott .01 .05
516 Mike Simms RC .01 .05
517 Dave Smith .01 .05
518 Franklin Stubbs .01 .05
519 Glenn Wilson .01 .05
520 Eric Yelding UER .01 .05
(Text has 63 steals,
stats have 64,
which is correct)
521 Gerald Young .01 .05
522 Shawn Abner .01 .05
523 Roberto Alomar .05 .15
524 Andy Benes .01 .05
525 Joe Carter .02 .10
526 Jack Clark .02 .10
527 Joey Cora .01 .05
528 Paul Faries RC .01 .05
529 Tony Gwynn .10 .30
530 Atlee Hammaker .01 .05
531 Greg W. Harris .01 .05
532 Thomas Howard .01 .05
533 Bruce Hurst .01 .05
534 Craig Lefferts .01 .05
535 Derek Lilliquist .01 .05
536 Fred Lynn .01 .05
537 Mike Pagliarulo .01 .05
538 Mark Parent .01 .05
539 Dennis Rasmussen .01 .05
540 Bip Roberts .01 .05
541 Richard Rodriguez RC .01 .05
542 Benito Santiago .02 .10
543 Calvin Schiraldi .01 .05
544 Eric Show .01 .05
545 Phil Stephenson .01 .05
546 Garry Templeton UER .01 .05
(Born 3/24/57,
should be 3/24/56)
547 Ed Whitson .01 .05
548 Eddie Williams .01 .05
549 Kevin Appier .02 .10
550 Luis Aquino .01 .05
551 Bob Boone .02 .10
552 George Brett .25 .60
553 Jeff Conine RC .15 .40
554 Steve Crawford .01 .05
555 Mark Davis .01 .05
556 Storm Davis .01 .05
557 Jim Eisenreich .01 .05
558 Steve Farr .01 .05
559 Tom Gordon .01 .05
560 Mark Gubicza .01 .05
561 Bo Jackson .08 .25
562 Mike Macfarlane .01 .05
563 Brian McRae RC .08 .25
564 Jeff Montgomery .01 .05
565 Bill Pecota .01 .05
566 Gerald Perry .01 .05
567 Bret Saberhagen .02 .10
568 Jeff Schulz RC .01 .05
569 Kevin Seitzer .01 .05
570 Terry Shumpert .01 .05
571 Kurt Stillwell .01 .05
572 Danny Tartabull .01 .05
573 Gary Thurman .01 .05
574 Frank White .02 .10
575 Willie Wilson .01 .05
576 Chris Bosio .01 .05
577 Greg Brock .01 .05
578 George Canale .01 .05
579 Chuck Crim .01 .05
580 Rob Deer .01 .05
581 Edgar Diaz .01 .05
582 Tom Edens RC .01 .05
583 Mike Felder .01 .05
584 Jim Gantner .01 .05
585 Darryl Hamilton .01 .05
586 Ted Higuera .01 .05
587 Mark Knudson .01 .05
588 Bill Krueger .01 .05
589 Tim McIntosh .01 .05
590 Paul Mirabella .01 .05
591 Paul Molitor .02 .10
592 Jaime Navarro .01 .05
593 Dave Parker .02 .10
594 Dan Plesac .01 .05
595 Ron Robinson .01 .05
596 Gary Sheffield .02 .10
597 Bill Spiers .01 .05
598 B.J. Surhoff .02 .10
599 Greg Vaughn .01 .05
600 Randy Veres .01 .05
601 Robin Yount .15 .40
602 Rick Aguilera .02 .10
603 Allan Anderson .01 .05
604 Juan Berenguer .01 .05
605 Randy Bush .01 .05
606 Carmelo Castillo .01 .05
607 Tim Drummond .01 .05
608 Scott Erickson .01 .05
609 Gary Gaetti .02 .10
610 Greg Gagne .01 .05
611 Dan Gladden .01 .05
612 Mark Guthrie .01 .05
613 Brian Harper .01 .05
614 Kent Hrbek .02 .10
615 Gene Larkin .01 .05
616 Terry Leach .01 .05
617 Nelson Liriano .01 .05
618 Shane Mack .01 .05
619 John Moses .01 .05
620 Pedro Munoz RC .02 .10
621 Al Newman .01 .05
622 Junior Ortiz .01 .05
623 Kirby Puckett .08 .25
624 Roy Smith .01 .05
625 Kevin Tapani .01 .05
626 Gary Wayne .01 .05
627 David West .01 .05
628 Cris Carpenter .01 .05
629 Vince Coleman .01 .05
630 Ken Dayley .01 .05
631A Jose DeLeon ERR .01 .05
(missing '79 Bradenton stats)
631B Jose DeLeon COR .01 .05
(with '79 Bradenton stats)
632 Frank DiPino .01 .05
633 Bernard Gilkey .01 .05
634A Pedro Guerrero ERR .02 .10
634B Pedro Guerrero COR .02 .10
635 Ken Hill .01 .05
636 Felix Jose .01 .05
637 Ray Lankford .02 .10
638 Joe Magrane .01 .05
639 Tom Niedenfuer .01 .05
640 Jose Oquendo .01 .05
641 Tom Pagnozzi .01 .05
642 Terry Pendleton .02 .10
643 Mike Perez RC .02 .10
644 Bryn Smith .01 .05
645 Lee Smith .02 .10
646 Ozzie Smith .15 .40
647 Scott Terry .01 .05
648 Bob Tewksbury .01 .05
649 Milt Thompson .01 .05
650 John Tudor .01 .05
651 Denny Walling .01 .05
652 Craig Wilson RC .01 .05
653 Todd Worrell .01 .05
654 Todd Zeile .01 .05
655 Oscar Azocar .01 .05
656 Steve Balboni UER .01 .05
(Born 1/5/57,
should be 1/16)
657 Jesse Barfield .01 .05
658 Greg Cadaret .01 .05
659 Chuck Cary .01 .05
660 Rick Cerone .01 .05
661 Dave Eiland .01 .05
662 Alvaro Espinoza .01 .05
663 Bob Geren .01 .05
664 Lee Guetterman .01 .05
665 Mel Hall .01 .05
666 Andy Hawkins .01 .05
667 Jimmy Jones .01 .05
668 Roberto Kelly .01 .05
669 Dave LaPoint UER .01 .05
(No '81 Brewers stats,
totals also are wrong)
670 Tim Leary .01 .05
671 Jim Leyritz .01 .05
672 Kevin Maas .01 .05
673 Don Mattingly .25 .60
674 Matt Nokes .01 .05
675 Pascual Perez .01 .05
676 Eric Plunk .01 .05
677 Dave Righetti .02 .10
678 Jeff D. Robinson .01 .05
679 Steve Sax .01 .05
680 Mike Witt .01 .05
681 Steve Avery UER .01 .05
(Born in New Jersey,
should say Michigan)
682 Mike Bell RC .01 .05
683 Jeff Blauser .01 .05
684 F.Cabrera UER .01 .05
Born 10/16,
should say 10/10
685 Tony Castillo .01 .05
686 Marty Clary UER .01 .05
(Shown pitching righty,
but bio has left)
687 Nick Esasky .01 .05
688 Ron Gant .02 .10
689 Tom Glavine .05 .15
690 Mark Grant .01 .05
691 Tommy Gregg .01 .05
692 Dwayne Henry .01 .05
693 Dave Justice .02 .10
694 Jimmy Kremers .01 .05
695 Charlie Leibrandt .01 .05
696 Mark Lemke .01 .05
697 Oddibe McDowell .01 .05
698 Greg Olson .01 .05
699 Jeff Parrett .01 .05
700 Jim Presley .01 .05
701 Victor Rosario RC .01 .05
702 Lonnie Smith .01 .05
703 Pete Smith .01 .05
704 John Smoltz .05 .15
705 Mike Stanton .01 .05
706 Andres Thomas .01 .05
707 Jeff Treadway .01 .05
708 Jim Vatcher RC .01 .05
709 Ryne Sandberg .08 .25
Cecil Fielder
710 Barry Bonds .40 1.00
Ken Griffey Jr.
711 Bobby Bonilla .02 .10
Barry Larkin
712 Bobby Thigpen .01 .05
John Franco
713 Andre Dawson .08 .25
Ryne Sandberg UER
(Ryno misspelled Rhino)
714 CL:A's/Pirates .01 .05
Reds/Red Sox
715 CL:White Sox/Mets .01 .05
Blue Jays/Dodgers
716 CL:Expos/Giants .01 .05
Rangers/Angels
717 CL:Tigers/Indians .01 .05
Phillies/Cubs
718 CL:Mariners/Orioles .01 .05
Astros/Padres
719 CL:Royals/Brewers .01 .05
Twins/Cardinals
720 CL:Yankees/Braves .01 .05
Superstars/Specials

1991 Fleer All-Stars

For the sixth consecutive year Fleer issued an All-Star insert set. This year the cards were only available as random inserts in Fleer cello packs. This ten-card standard-size set is reminiscent of the 1971 Topps Greatest Moments set with two pictures on the (black-bordered) front as well as a photo on the back.

COMPLETE SET (10) 7.50 15.00
RANDOM INSERTS IN CELLO PACKS
1 Ryne Sandberg 1.25 3.00
2 Barry Larkin .50 1.25
3 Matt Williams .30 .75
4 Cecil Fielder .30 .75
5 Barry Bonds 3.00 8.00
6 Rickey Henderson .75 2.00
7 Ken Griffey Jr. 1.50 4.00
8 Jose Canseco .50 1.25
9 Benito Santiago .30 .75
10 Roger Clemens 2.50 6.00

1991 Fleer Pro-Visions

This 12-card standard-size insert set features paintings by artist Terry Smith framed by distinctive black borders on each card front. The cards were randomly inserted in wax and rack packs. An additional four-card set was issued only in 1991 Fleer factory sets. Those cards are numbered F1-F4. Unlike the 12 cards inserted in packs, these factory set cards feature white borders on front.

COMPLETE REG.SET (12) 2.00 4.00
COMP.FACT.SET (4) 1.00 2.00
1-12: RANDOM INSERTS IN PACKS
F1-F4 IN FACTORY SETS
1 Kirby Puckett UER .30 .75
(.326 average,
should be .328)
2 Will Clark UER .20 .50
(On tenth line, pennant
misspelled pennent)
3 Ruben Sierra UER .10 .30
(No apostrophe
in hasn't)
4 Mark McGwire UER 1.00 2.50
(Fisk won ROY in
'72, not '82)
5 Bo Jackson .30 .75
(Bio says 6', others
have him at 6'1")
6 Jose Canseco UER .20 .50
(Bio 6'3", 230
text has 6'4", 240)
7 Dwight Gooden UER .10 .30
(2.80 ERA in Lynchburg,
should be 2.50)
8 Mike Greenwell UER .05 .15
(.328 BA and 87 RBI,
should be .325 and 95)
9 Roger Clemens 1.00 2.50
10 Eric Davis .10 .30
11 Don Mattingly .75 2.00
12 Darryl Strawberry .10 .30
F1 Barry Bonds 1.25 3.00
F2 Rickey Henderson .30 .75
F3 Ryne Sandberg .50 1.25
F4 Dave Stewart .10 .30

1991 Fleer Wax Box Cards

These cards were issued on the bottom of 1991 Fleer wax boxes. This set celebrated the spate of no-hitters in 1990 and were printed on three different boxes. These standard size cards, come four to a box, three about the no-hitters and one team logo card on each box. The cards are blank backed and are numbered on the front in a subtle way. They are ordered below as they are numbered, which is by chronological order of their no-hitters. Only the player cards are listed below since there was a different team logo card on each box.

COMPLETE SET (9) 1.60 4.00
1 Mark Langston .02 .10
and Mike Witt
2 Randy Johnson .40 1.00
3 Nolan Ryan 1.25 3.00
4 Dave Stewart .07 .20
5 Fernando Valenzuela .07 .20
6 Andy Hawkins .02 .10
7 Melido Perez .02 .10
8 Terry Mulholland .02 .10
9 Dave Stieb .07 .20

1991 Fleer World Series

This eight-card set captures highlights from the 1990 World Series between the Cincinnati Reds and the Oakland Athletics. The set was only available as an insert with the 1991 Fleer factory sets. The standard-size cards have on the fronts color action photos, bordered in blue on a white card face. The words "World Series '90" appears in red and blue lettering above the pictures. The backs have a similar design, only with a summary of an aspect of the Series on a yellow background.

COMPLETE SET (8) .30 .75
1 Eric Davis .02 .10
2 Billy Hatcher .01 .05
3 Jose Canseco .05 .15
4 Rickey Henderson .08 .25
5 Chris Sabo .01 .05
6 Dave Stewart .02 .10
7 Jose Rijo .01 .05
8 Reds Celebrate .01 .05

1991 Fleer Update

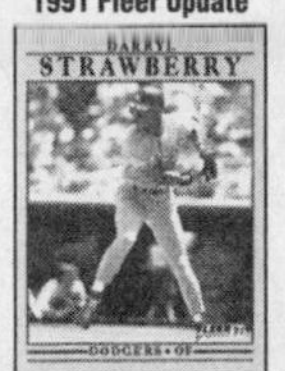

The 1991 Fleer Update set contains 132 standard-size cards. The cards were distributed exclusively in factory set form through hobby dealers. Card design is identical to regular issue 1991 Fleer cards with the notable bright yellow borders except for the U-prefixed numbering on back. The cards are ordered alphabetically by team. The key Rookie Cards in this set are Jeff Bagwell and Ivan Rodriguez.

COMP.FACT.SET (132) 2.00 5.00
1 Glenn Davis .01 .05
2 Dwight Evans .05 .15
3 Jose Mesa .01 .05
4 Jack Clark .02 .10
5 Danny Darwin .01 .05
6 Steve Lyons .01 .05
7 Mo Vaughn .02 .10
8 Floyd Bannister .01 .05
9 Gary Gaetti .02 .10
10 Dave Parker .02 .10
11 Joey Cora .01 .05
12 Charlie Hough .02 .10
13 Matt Merullo .01 .05
14 Warren Newson RC .01 .05
15 Tim Raines .02 .10
16 Albert Belle .02 .10
17 Glenallen Hill .01 .05
18 Shawn Hillegas .01 .05
19 Mark Lewis .01 .05
20 Charles Nagy .01 .05
21 Mark Whiten .01 .05
22 John Cerutti .01 .05
23 Rob Deer .01 .05
24 Mickey Tettleton .01 .05
25 Warren Cromartie .01 .05
26 Kirk Gibson .02 .10
27 David Howard RC .01 .05
28 Brent Mayne .01 .05
29 Dante Bichette .02 .10
30 Mark Lee RC .01 .05
31 Julio Machado .01 .05
32 Edwin Nunez .01 .05
33 Willie Randolph .02 .10
34 Franklin Stubbs .01 .05
35 Bill Wegman .01 .05
36 Chili Davis .02 .10
37 Chuck Knoblauch .02 .10
38 Scott Leius .01 .05
39 Jack Morris .02 .10
40 Mike Pagliarulo .01 .05
41 Lenny Webster .01 .05
42 John Habyan .01 .05
43 Steve Howe .01 .05
44 Jeff Johnson RC .01 .05
45 Scott Kamieniecki RC .01 .05
46 Pat Kelly RC .01 .05
47 Hensley Meulens .01 .05
48 Wade Taylor RC .01 .05
49 Bernie Williams .08 .25
50 Kirk Dressendorfer RC .01 .05
51 Ernest Riles .01 .05
52 Rich DeLucia RC .01 .05
53 Tracy Jones .01 .05
54 Bill Krueger .01 .05
55 Alonzo Powell RC .01 .05
56 Jeff Schaefer .01 .05
57 Russ Swan .01 .05
58 John Barfield .01 .05
59 Rich Gossage .02 .10
60 Jose Guzman .01 .05
61 Dean Palmer .02 .10
62 Ivan Rodriguez RC .75 2.00
63 Roberto Alomar .05 .15
64 Tom Candiotti .01 .05
65 Joe Carter .02 .10
66 Ed Sprague .01 .05
67 Pat Tabler .01 .05
68 Mike Timlin RC .02 .10
69 Devon White .02 .10
70 Rafael Belliard .01 .05
71 Juan Berenguer .01 .05
72 Sid Bream .01 .05
73 Marvin Freeman .01 .05
74 Kent Mercker .01 .05
75 Otis Nixon .01 .05
76 Terry Pendleton .02 .10
77 George Bell .01 .05
78 Danny Jackson .01 .05
79 Chuck McElroy .01 .05
80 Gary Scott RC .01 .05
81 Heathcliff Slocumb RC .02 .10
82 Dave Smith .01 .05
83 Rick Wilkins RC .01 .05
84 Freddie Benavides RC .01 .05
85 Ted Power .01 .05
86 Mo Sanford RC .01 .05
87 Jeff Bagwell RC .60 1.50
88 Steve Finley .02 .10
89 Pete Harnisch .01 .05
90 Darryl Kile .02 .10
91 Brett Butler .02 .10
92 John Candelaria .01 .05
93 Gary Carter .02 .10
94 Kevin Gross .01 .05
95 Bob Ojeda .01 .05
96 Darryl Strawberry .02 .10
97 Ivan Calderon .01 .05
98 Ron Hassey .01 .05
99 Gilberto Reyes .01 .05
100 Hubie Brooks .01 .05
101 Rick Cerone .01 .05
102 Vince Coleman .01 .05
103 Jeff Innis .01 .05
104 Pete Schourek RC .01 .05
105 Andy Ashby RC .08 .25
106 Wally Backman .01 .05
107 Darrin Fletcher .01 .05
108 Tommy Greene .01 .05
109 John Morris .01 .05
110 Mitch Williams .01 .05
111 Lloyd McClendon .01 .05
112 Orlando Merced RC .01 .05
113 Vicente Palacios .01 .05
114 Gary Varsho .01 .05
115 John Wehner RC .01 .05
116 Rex Hudler .01 .05
117 Tim Jones .01 .05
118 Geronimo Pena .01 .05
119 Gerald Perry .01 .05
120 Larry Andersen .01 .05
121 Jerald Clark .01 .05
122 Scott Coolbaugh .01 .05
123 Tony Fernandez .01 .05
124 Darrin Jackson .01 .05
125 Fred McGriff .05 .15
126 Jose Mota RC .01 .05
127 Tim Teufel .01 .05
128 Bud Black .01 .05
129 Mike Felder .01 .05
130 Willie McGee .02 .10
131 Dave Righetti .02 .10
132 Checklist U1-U132 .01 .05

1992 Fleer

The 1992 Fleer set contains 720 standard-size cards issued in one comprehensive series. The cards were distributed in plastic wrapped packs, 35-card cello packs, 42-card rack packs and factory sets. The card fronts shade from metallic pale green to white as one moves down the face. The team logo and player's name appear to the right of the picture, running the length of the card. The cards are ordered alphabetically within and according to teams for each league with AL preceding NL. Topical subsets feature Major League Prospects (652-680), Record Setters (681-687), League Leaders (688-697), Super Star Specials (698-707) and Pro Visions (708-713). Rookie Cards include Scott Brosius and Vinny Castilla.

COMPLETE SET (720) 4.00 10.00
COMP.HOBBY SET (732) 8.00 20.00
COMP.RETAIL SET (732) 8.00 20.00
1 Brady Anderson .02 .10
2 Jose Bautista .02 .10
3 Juan Bell .02 .10
4 Glenn Davis .02 .10
5 Mike Devereaux .02 .10
6 Dwight Evans .05 .15
7 Mike Flanagan .02 .10
8 Leo Gomez .02 .10
9 Chris Hoiles .02 .10
10 Sam Horn .02 .10
11 Tim Hulett .02 .10
12 Dave Johnson .02 .10
13 Chito Martinez .02 .10
14 Ben McDonald .02 .10
15 Bob Melvin .02 .10
16 Luis Mercedes .02 .10
17 Jose Mesa .02 .10
18 Bob Milacki .02 .10
19 Randy Milligan .02 .10
20 Mike Mussina UER .08 .25
(Card back refers
to him as Jeff)
21 Gregg Olson .02 .10
22 Joe Orsulak .02 .10
23 Jim Poole .02 .10
24 Arthur Rhodes .02 .10
25 Billy Ripken .02 .10
26 Cal Ripken .30 .75
27 David Segui .02 .10
28 Roy Smith .02 .10
29 Anthony Telford .02 .10
30 Mark Williamson .02 .10
31 Craig Worthington .02 .10
32 Wade Boggs .05 .15
33 Tom Bolton .02 .10
34 Tom Brunansky .02 .10
35 Ellis Burks .02 .10
36 Jack Clark .02 .10
37 Roger Clemens .20 .50
38 Danny Darwin .02 .10
39 Mike Greenwell .02 .10
40 Joe Hesketh .02 .10
41 Daryl Irvine .02 .10
42 Dennis Lamp .02 .10
43 Tony Pena .02 .10
44 Phil Plantier .02 .10
45 Carlos Quintana .02 .10
46 Jeff Reardon .02 .10
47 Jody Reed .02 .10
48 Luis Rivera .02 .10
49 Mo Vaughn .02 .10
50 Jim Abbott .05 .15
51 Kyle Abbott .02 .10
52 Ruben Amaro .02 .10
53 Scott Bailes .02 .10
54 Chris Beasley .02 .10
55 Mark Eichhorn .02 .10
56 Mike Fetters .02 .10
57 Chuck Finley .02 .10
58 Gary Gaetti .02 .10
59 Dave Gallagher .02 .10
60 Donnie Hill .02 .10
61 Bryan Harvey UER .02 .10
(Lee Smith led the
Majors with 47 saves)
62 Wally Joyner .02 .10
63 Mark Langston .02 .10
64 Kirk McCaskill .02 .10
65 John Orton .02 .10
66 Lance Parrish .02 .10
67 Luis Polonia .02 .10
68 Bobby Rose .02 .10
69 Dick Schofield .02 .10
70 Luis Sojo .02 .10
71 Lee Stevens .02 .10
72 Dave Winfield .02 .10
73 Cliff Young .02 .10
74 Wilson Alvarez .02 .10
75 Esteban Beltre .02 .10
76 Joey Cora .02 .10
77 Brian Drahman .02 .10
78 Alex Fernandez .02 .10
79 Carlton Fisk .05 .15
80 Scott Fletcher .02 .10
81 Craig Grebeck .02 .10
82 Ozzie Guillen .02 .10
83 Greg Hibbard .02 .10
84 Charlie Hough .02 .10
85 Mike Huff .02 .10
86 Bo Jackson .08 .25
87 Lance Johnson .02 .10
88 Ron Karkovice .02 .10
89 Jack McDowell .02 .10
90 Matt Merullo .02 .10
91 Warren Newson .02 .10
92 Donn Pall UER .02 .10
(Called Dunn on
card back)
93 Dan Pasqua .02 .10
94 Ken Patterson .02 .10
95 Melido Perez .02 .10
96 Scott Radinsky .02 .10
97 Tim Raines .02 .10
98 Sammy Sosa .08 .25
99 Bobby Thigpen .02 .10
100 Frank Thomas .08 .25
101 Robin Ventura .02 .10
102 Mike Aldrete .02 .10
103 Sandy Alomar Jr. .02 .10
104 Carlos Baerga .02 .10
105 Albert Belle .02 .10
106 Willie Blair .02 .10
107 Jerry Browne .02 .10
108 Alex Cole .02 .10
109 Felix Fermin .02 .10
110 Glenallen Hill .02 .10
111 Shawn Hillegas .02 .10
112 Chris James .02 .10
113 Reggie Jefferson .02 .10
114 Doug Jones .02 .10
115 Eric King .02 .10
116 Mark Lewis .02 .10
117 Carlos Martinez .02 .10
118 Charles Nagy UER .02 .10
(Throws right, but
card says left)
119 Rod Nichols .02 .10
120 Steve Olin .02 .10
121 Jesse Orosco .02 .10
122 Rudy Seanez .02 .10
123 Joel Skinner .02 .10
124 Greg Swindell .02 .10
125 Jim Thome .08 .25
126 Mark Whiten .02 .10
127 Scott Aldred .02 .10
128 Andy Allanson .02 .10
129 John Cerutti .02 .10
130 Milt Cuyler .02 .10
131 Mike Dalton .02 .10
132 Rob Deer .02 .10
133 Cecil Fielder .02 .10
134 Travis Fryman .02 .10
135 Dan Gakeler .02 .10
136 Paul Gibson .02 .10
137 Bill Gullickson .02 .10
138 Mike Henneman .02 .10
139 Pete Incaviglia .02 .10
140 Mark Leiter .02 .10
141 Scott Livingstone .02 .10
142 Lloyd Moseby .02 .10
143 Tony Phillips .02 .10
144 Mark Salas .02 .10
145 Frank Tanana .02 .10
146 Walt Terrell .02 .10
147 Mickey Tettleton .02 .10
148 Alan Trammell .02 .10
149 Lou Whitaker .02 .10
150 Kevin Appier .02 .10
151 Luis Aquino .02 .10
152 Todd Benzinger .02 .10
153 Mike Boddicker .02 .10
154 George Brett .25 .60
155 Storm Davis .02 .10
156 Jim Eisenreich .02 .10
157 Kirk Gibson .02 .10
158 Tom Gordon .02 .10
159 Mark Gubicza .02 .10
160 David Howard .02 .10
161 Mike Macfarlane .02 .10
162 Brent Mayne .02 .10
163 Brian McRae .02 .10
164 Jeff Montgomery .02 .10
165 Bill Pecota .02 .10
166 Harvey Pulliam .02 .10
167 Bret Saberhagen .02 .10
168 Kevin Seitzer .02 .10
169 Terry Shumpert .02 .10
170 Kurt Stillwell .02 .10
171 Danny Tartabull .02 .10
172 Gary Thurman .02 .10
173 Dante Bichette .02 .10
174 Kevin D. Brown .02 .10
175 Chuck Crim .02 .10
176 Jim Gantner .02 .10
177 Darryl Hamilton .02 .10
178 Ted Higuera .02 .10
179 Darren Holmes .02 .10
180 Mark Lee .02 .10
181 Julio Machado .02 .10
182 Paul Molitor .02 .10
183 Jaime Navarro .02 .10
184 Edwin Nunez .02 .10
185 Dan Plesac .02 .10
186 Willie Randolph .02 .10
187 Ron Robinson .02 .10
188 Gary Sheffield .02 .10
189 Bill Spiers .02 .10
190 B.J. Surhoff .02 .10
191 Dale Sveum .02 .10
192 Greg Vaughn .02 .10
193 Bill Wegman .02 .10
194 Robin Yount .15 .40
195 Rick Aguilera .02 .10
196 Allan Anderson .02 .10
197 Steve Bedrosian .02 .10
198 Randy Bush .02 .10
199 Larry Casian .02 .10
200 Chili Davis .02 .10
201 Scott Erickson .02 .10
202 Greg Gagne .02 .10
203 Dan Gladden .02 .10
204 Brian Harper .02 .10
205 Kent Hrbek .02 .10
206 C.Knoblauch UER .02 .10
Career hit total
of 59 is wrong
207 Gene Larkin .02 .10
208 Terry Leach .02 .10
209 Scott Leius .02 .10
210 Shane Mack .02 .10
211 Jack Morris .02 .10
212 Pedro Munoz .02 .10
213 Denny Neagle .02 .10
214 Al Newman .02 .10
215 Junior Ortiz .02 .10
216 Mike Pagliarulo .02 .10
217 Kirby Puckett .08 .25
218 Paul Sorrento .02 .10
219 Kevin Tapani .02 .10
220 Lenny Webster .02 .10
221 Jesse Barfield .02 .10
222 Greg Cadaret .02 .10
223 Dave Eiland .02 .10
224 Alvaro Espinoza .02 .10
225 Steve Farr .02 .10
226 Bob Geren .02 .10
227 Lee Guetterman .02 .10
228 John Habyan .02 .10
229 Mel Hall .02 .10
230 Steve Howe .02 .10
231 Mike Humphreys .02 .10
232 Scott Kamieniecki .02 .10
233 Pat Kelly .02 .10
234 Roberto Kelly .02 .10
235 Tim Leary .02 .10
236 Kevin Maas .02 .10
237 Don Mattingly .25 .60
238 Hensley Meulens .02 .10
239 Matt Nokes .02 .10
240 Pascual Perez .02 .10
241 Eric Plunk .02 .10
242 John Ramos .02 .10
243 Scott Sanderson .02 .10
244 Steve Sax .02 .10
245 Wade Taylor .02 .10
246 Randy Velarde .02 .10
247 Bernie Williams .05 .15
248 Troy Afenir .02 .10
249 Harold Baines .02 .10
250 Lance Blankenship .02 .10
251 Mike Bordick .02 .10
252 Jose Canseco .05 .15
253 Steve Chitren .02 .10
254 Ron Darling .02 .10
255 Dennis Eckersley .02 .10
256 Mike Gallego .02 .10
257 Dave Henderson .02 .10
258 R.Henderson UER .08 .25
Wearing 24 on front
and 22 on back
259 Rick Honeycutt .02 .10
260 Brook Jacoby .02 .10
261 Carney Lansford .02 .10
262 Mark McGwire .25 .60
263 Mike Moore .02 .10
264 Gene Nelson .02 .10
265 Jamie Quirk .02 .10
266 Joe Slusarski .02 .10
267 Terry Steinbach .02 .10
268 Dave Stewart .02 .10
269 Todd Van Poppel .02 .10
270 Walt Weiss .02 .10
271 Bob Welch .02 .10
272 Curt Young .02 .10
273 Scott Bradley .02 .10
274 Greg Briley .02 .10
275 Jay Buhner .02 .10
276 Henry Cotto .02 .10
277 Alvin Davis .02 .10
278 Rich DeLucia .02 .10
279 Ken Griffey Jr. .15 .40
280 Erik Hanson .02 .10
281 Brian Holman .02 .10
282 Mike Jackson .02 .10
283 Randy Johnson .08 .25
284 Tracy Jones .02 .10
285 Bill Krueger .02 .10
286 Edgar Martinez .05 .15
287 Tino Martinez .05 .15
288 Rob Murphy .02 .10
289 Pete O'Brien .02 .10
290 Alonzo Powell .02 .10
291 Harold Reynolds .02 .10
292 Mike Schooler .02 .10
293 Russ Swan .02 .10
294 Bill Swift .02 .10
295 Dave Valle .02 .10
296 Omar Vizquel .05 .15
297 Gerald Alexander .02 .10
298 Brad Arnsberg .02 .10
299 Kevin Brown .02 .10
300 Jack Daugherty .02 .10
301 Mario Diaz .02 .10
302 Brian Downing .02 .10
303 Julio Franco .02 .10
304 Juan Gonzalez .05 .15
305 Rich Gossage .02 .10
306 Jose Guzman .02 .10
307 Jose Hernandez RC .08 .25
308 Jeff Huson .02 .10
309 Mike Jeffcoat .02 .10
310 Terry Mathews .02 .10
311 Rafael Palmeiro .05 .15
312 Dean Palmer .02 .10
313 Geno Petralli .02 .10
314 Gary Pettis .02 .10
315 Kevin Reimer .02 .10

316 Ivan Rodriguez .08 .25
317 Kenny Rogers .02 .10
318 Wayne Rosenthal .02 .10
319 Jeff Russell .02 .10
320 Nolan Ryan .40 1.00
321 Ruben Sierra .02 .10
322 Jim Acker .02 .10
323 Roberto Alomar .05 .15
324 Derek Bell .02 .10
325 Pat Borders .02 .10
326 Tom Candiotti .02 .10
327 Joe Carter .02 .10
328 Rob Ducey .02 .10
329 Kelly Gruber .02 .10
330 Juan Guzman .02 .10
331 Tom Henke .02 .10
332 Jimmy Key .02 .10
333 Manny Lee .02 .10
334 Al Leiter .02 .10
335 Bob MacDonald .02 .10
336 Candy Maldonado .02 .10
337 Rance Mulliniks .02 .10
338 Greg Myers .02 .10
339 John Olerud UER .02 .10
(1991 BA has .256, but text says .258)
340 Ed Sprague .02 .10
341 Dave Stieb .02 .10
342 Todd Stottlemyre .02 .10
343 Mike Timlin .02 .10
344 Duane Ward .02 .10
345 David Wells .02 .10
346 Devon White .02 .10
347 Mookie Wilson .02 .10
348 Eddie Zosky .02 .10
349 Steve Avery .02 .10
350 Mike Bell .02 .10
351 Rafael Belliard .02 .10
352 Juan Berenguer .02 .10
353 Jeff Blauser .02 .10
354 Sid Bream .02 .10
355 Francisco Cabrera .02 .10
356 Marvin Freeman .02 .10
357 Ron Gant .02 .10
358 Tom Glavine .05 .15
359 Brian Hunter .02 .10
360 Dave Justice .02 .10
361 Charlie Leibrandt .02 .10
362 Mark Lemke .02 .10
363 Kent Mercker .02 .10
364 Keith Mitchell .02 .10
365 Greg Olson .02 .10
366 Terry Pendleton .02 .10
367 Armando Reynoso RC .08 .25
368 Deion Sanders .05 .15
369 Lonnie Smith .02 .10
370 Pete Smith .02 .10
371 John Smoltz .05 .15
372 Mike Stanton .02 .10
373 Jeff Treadway .02 .10
374 Mark Wohlers .02 .10
375 Paul Assenmacher .02 .10
376 George Bell .02 .10
377 Shawn Boskie .02 .10
378 Frank Castillo .02 .10
379 Andre Dawson .02 .10
380 Shawon Dunston .02 .10
381 Mark Grace .05 .15
382 Mike Harkey .02 .10
383 Danny Jackson .02 .10
384 Les Lancaster .02 .10
385 Ced Landrum .02 .10
386 Greg Maddux .15 .40
387 Derrick May .02 .10
388 Chuck McElroy .02 .10
389 Ryne Sandberg .15 .40
390 Heathcliff Slocumb .02 .10
391 Dave Smith .02 .10
392 Dwight Smith .02 .10
393 Rick Sutcliffe .02 .10
394 Hector Villanueva .02 .10
395 Chico Walker .02 .10
396 Jerome Walton .02 .10
397 Rick Wilkins .02 .10
398 Jack Armstrong .02 .10
399 Freddie Benavides .02 .10
400 Glenn Braggs .02 .10
401 Tom Browning .02 .10
402 Norm Charlton .02 .10
403 Eric Davis .02 .10
404 Rob Dibble .02 .10
405 Bill Doran .02 .10
406 Mariano Duncan .02 .10
407 Kip Gross .02 .10
408 Chris Hammond .02 .10
409 Billy Hatcher .02 .10
410 Chris Jones .02 .10
411 Barry Larkin .05 .15
412 Hal Morris .02 .10
413 Randy Myers .02 .10
414 Joe Oliver .02 .10
415 Paul O'Neill .05 .15
416 Ted Power .02 .10
417 Luis Quinones .02 .10
418 Jeff Reed .02 .10
419 Jose Rijo .02 .10
420 Chris Sabo .02 .10
421 Reggie Sanders .02 .10
422 Scott Scudder .02 .10
423 Glenn Sutko .02 .10
424 Eric Anthony .02 .10
425 Jeff Bagwell .08 .25
426 Craig Biggio .05 .15
427 Ken Caminiti .02 .10
428 Casey Candaele .02 .10
429 Mike Capel .02 .10
430 Andujar Cedeno .02 .10
431 Jim Corsi .02 .10
432 Mark Davidson .02 .10
433 Steve Finley .02 .10
434 Luis Gonzalez .02 .10
435 Pete Harnisch .02 .10
436 Dwayne Henry .02 .10
437 Xavier Hernandez .02 .10
438 Jimmy Jones .02 .10
439 Darryl Kile .02 .10
440 Rob Mallicoat .02 .10
441 Andy Mota .02 .10
442 Al Osuna .02 .10
443 Mark Portugal .02 .10
444 Scott Servais .02 .10
445 Mike Simms .02 .10
446 Gerald Young .02 .10
447 Tim Belcher .02 .10
448 Brett Butler .02 .10
449 John Candelaria .02 .10
450 Gary Carter .02 .10
451 Dennis Cook .02 .10
452 Tim Crews .02 .10
453 Kal Daniels .02 .10
454 Jim Gott .02 .10
455 Alfredo Griffin .02 .10
456 Kevin Gross .02 .10
457 Chris Gwynn .02 .10
458 Lenny Harris .02 .10
459 Orel Hershiser .02 .10
460 Jay Howell .02 .10
461 Stan Javier .02 .10
462 Eric Karros .02 .10
463 Ramon Martinez UER .02 .10
(Card says bats right, should be left)
464 Roger McDowell UER .02 .10
(Wins add up to 54, totals have 51)
465 Mike Morgan .02 .10
466 Eddie Murray .08 .25
467 Jose Offerman .02 .10
468 Bob Ojeda .02 .10
469 Juan Samuel .02 .10
470 Mike Scioscia .02 .10
471 Darryl Strawberry .02 .10
472 Bret Barberie .02 .10
473 Brian Barnes .02 .10
474 Eric Bullock .02 .10
475 Ivan Calderon .02 .10
476 Delino DeShields .02 .10
477 Jeff Fassero .02 .10
478 Mike Fitzgerald .02 .10
479 Steve Frey .02 .10
480 Andres Galarraga .02 .10
481 Mark Gardner .02 .10
482 Marquis Grissom .02 .10
483 Chris Haney .02 .10
484 Barry Jones .02 .10
485 Dave Martinez .02 .10
486 Dennis Martinez .02 .10
487 Chris Nabholz .02 .10
488 Spike Owen .02 .10
489 Gilberto Reyes .02 .10
490 Mel Rojas .02 .10
491 Scott Ruskin .02 .10
492 Bill Sampen .02 .10
493 Larry Walker .05 .15
494 Tim Wallach .02 .10
495 Daryl Boston .02 .10
496 Hubie Brooks .02 .10
497 Tim Burke .02 .10
498 Mark Carreon .02 .10
499 Tony Castillo .02 .10
500 Vince Coleman .02 .10
501 David Cone .02 .10
502 Kevin Elster .02 .10
503 Sid Fernandez .02 .10
504 John Franco .02 .10
505 Dwight Gooden .02 .10
506 Todd Hundley .02 .10
507 Jeff Innis .02 .10
508 Gregg Jefferies .02 .10
509 Howard Johnson .02 .10
510 Dave Magadan .02 .10
511 Terry McDaniel .02 .10
512 Kevin McReynolds .02 .10
513 Keith Miller .02 .10
514 Charlie O'Brien .02 .10
515 Mackey Sasser .02 .10
516 Pete Schourek .02 .10
517 Julio Valera .02 .10
518 Frank Viola .02 .10
519 Wally Whitehurst .02 .10
520 Anthony Young .02 .10
521 Andy Ashby .02 .10
522 Kim Batiste .02 .10
523 Joe Boever .02 .10
524 Wes Chamberlain .02 .10
525 Pat Combs .02 .10
526 Danny Cox .02 .10
527 Darren Daulton .02 .10
528 Jose DeJesus .02 .10
529 Len Dykstra .02 .10
530 Darrin Fletcher .02 .10
531 Tommy Greene .02 .10
532 Jason Grimsley .02 .10
533 Charlie Hayes .02 .10
534 Von Hayes .02 .10
535 Dave Hollins .02 .10
536 Ricky Jordan .02 .10
537 John Kruk .02 .10
538 Jim Lindeman .02 .10
539 Mickey Morandini .02 .10
540 Terry Mulholland .02 .10
541 Dale Murphy .05 .15
542 Randy Ready .02 .10
543 Wally Ritchie UER .02 .10
(Letters in data are cut off on card)
544 Bruce Ruffin .02 .10
545 Steve Searcy .02 .10
546 Dickie Thon .02 .10
547 Mitch Williams .02 .10
548 Stan Belinda .02 .10
549 Jay Bell .02 .10
550 Barry Bonds .40 1.00
551 Bobby Bonilla .02 .10
552 Steve Buechele .02 .10
553 Doug Drabek .02 .10
554 Neal Heaton .02 .10
555 Jeff King .02 .10
556 Bob Kipper .02 .10
557 Bill Landrum .02 .10
558 Mike LaValliere .02 .10
559 Jose Lind .02 .10
560 Lloyd McClendon .02 .10
561 Orlando Merced .02 .10
562 Bob Patterson .02 .10
563 Joe Redfield .02 .10
564 Gary Redus .02 .10
565 Rosario Rodriguez .02 .10
566 Don Slaught .02 .10
567 John Smiley .02 .10
568 Zane Smith .02 .10
569 Randy Tomlin .02 .10
570 Andy Van Slyke .05 .15
571 Gary Varsho .02 .10
572 Bob Walk .02 .10
573 John Wehner UER .02 .10
(Actually played for Carolina in 1991, not Cards)
574 Juan Agosto .02 .10
575 Cris Carpenter .02 .10
576 Jose DeLeon .02 .10
577 Rich Gedman .02 .10
578 Bernard Gilkey .02 .10
579 Pedro Guerrero .02 .10
580 Ken Hill .02 .10
581 Rex Hudler .02 .10
582 Felix Jose .02 .10
583 Ray Lankford .02 .10
584 Omar Olivares .02 .10
585 Jose Oquendo .02 .10
586 Tom Pagnozzi .02 .10
587 Geronimo Pena .02 .10
588 Mike Perez .02 .10
589 Gerald Perry .02 .10
590 Bryn Smith .02 .10
591 Lee Smith .02 .10
592 Ozzie Smith .15 .40
593 Scott Terry .02 .10
594 Bob Tewksbury .02 .10
595 Milt Thompson .02 .10
596 Todd Zeile .02 .10
597 Larry Andersen .02 .10
598 Oscar Azocar .02 .10
599 Andy Benes .02 .10
600 Ricky Bones .02 .10
601 Jerald Clark .02 .10
602 Pat Clements .02 .10
603 Paul Faries .02 .10
604 Tony Fernandez .02 .10
605 Tony Gwynn .10 .30
606 Greg W. Harris .02 .10
607 Thomas Howard .02 .10
608 Bruce Hurst .02 .10
609 Darrin Jackson .02 .10
610 Tom Lampkin .02 .10
611 Craig Lefferts .02 .10
612 Jim Lewis RC .02 .10
613 Mike Maddux .02 .10
614 Fred McGriff .05 .15
615 Jose Melendez .02 .10
616 Jose Mota .02 .10
617 Dennis Rasmussen .02 .10
618 Bip Roberts .02 .10
619 Rich Rodriguez .02 .10
620 Benito Santiago .02 .10
621 Craig Shipley .02 .10
622 Tim Teufel .02 .10
623 Kevin Ward .02 .10
624 Ed Whitson .02 .10
625 Dave Anderson .02 .10
626 Kevin Bass .02 .10
627 Rod Beck RC .15 .40
628 Bud Black .02 .10
629 Jeff Brantley .02 .10
630 John Burkett .02 .10
631 Will Clark .05 .15
632 Royce Clayton .02 .10
633 Steve Decker .02 .10
634 Kelly Downs .02 .10
635 Mike Felder .02 .10
636 Scott Garrelts .02 .10
637 Eric Gunderson .02 .10
638 Bryan Hickerson RC .02 .10
639 Darren Lewis .02 .10
640 Greg Litton .02 .10
641 Kirt Manwaring .02 .10
642 Paul McClellan .02 .10
643 Willie McGee .02 .10
644 Kevin Mitchell .02 .10
645 Francisco Oliveras .02 .10
646 Mike Remlinger .02 .10
647 Dave Righetti .02 .10
648 Robby Thompson .02 .10
649 Jose Uribe .02 .10
650 Matt Williams .02 .10
651 Trevor Wilson .02 .10
652 T.Goodwin MLP UER .02 .10
Timed in 3.5, should be be timed
653 Terry Bross MLP .02 .10
654 M.Christopher MLP .02 .10
655 Kenny Lofton MLP .05 .15
656 Chris Cron MLP .02 .10
657 Willie Banks MLP .02 .10
658 Pat Rice MLP .02 .10
659A R.Maurer MLP ERR .30 .75
Name misspelled as Mauer on card front
659B R.Maurer MLP COR .02 .10
660 Don Harris MLP .02 .10
661 Henry Rodriguez MLP .02 .10
662 Cliff Brantley MLP .02 .10
663 M.Linskey MLP UER .02 .10
220 pounds in data, 200 in text
664 Gary DiSarcina MLP .02 .10
665 Gil Heredia RC .08 .25
666 Vinny Castilla RC .40 1.00
667 Paul Abbott MLP .02 .10
668 M.Fariss MLP UER .02 .10
Called Paul on back
669 Jarvis Brown MLP .02 .10
670 Wayne Kirby RC .02 .10
671 Scott Brosius RC .15 .40
672 Bob Hamelin MLP .02 .10
673 Joel Johnston MLP .02 .10
674 Tim Spehr MLP .02 .10
675A J.Gardner MLP ERR .30 .75
P on front, should be SS
675B Jeff Gardner MLP COR .02 .10
676 Rico Rossy MLP .02 .10
677 R.Hernandez MLP RC .02 .10
678 Ted Wood MLP .02 .10
679 Cal Eldred MLP .02 .10
680 Sean Berry MLP .02 .10
681 Rickey Henderson RS .05 .15
682 Nolan Ryan RS .20 .50
683 Dennis Martinez RS .02 .10
684 Wilson Alvarez RS .02 .10
685 Joe Carter RS .02 .10
686 Dave Winfield RS .02 .10
687 David Cone RS .02 .10
688 Jose Canseco LL UER .02 .10
(Text on back has 42 stolen bases in 88; should be 40)
689 Howard Johnson LL .02 .10
690 Julio Franco LL .02 .10
691 Terry Pendleton LL .02 .10
692 Cecil Fielder LL .02 .10
693 Scott Erickson LL .02 .10
694 Tom Glavine LL .02 .10
695 Dennis Martinez LL .02 .10
696 Bryan Harvey LL .02 .10
697 Lee Smith LL .02 .10
698 Roberto Alomar .02 .10
Sandy Alomar Jr.
699 Bobby Bonilla .02 .10
Will Clark
700 Mark Wohlers .02 .10
Kent Mercker
Alejandro Pena
701 Stacy Jones .05 .15
Bo Jackson
Gregg Olson
Frank Thomas
702 Paul Molitor .02 .10
Brett Butler
703 Cal Ripken .15 .40
Joe Carter
704 Barry Larkin .05 .15
Kirby Puckett
705 Mo Vaughn .02 .10
Cecil Fielder
706 Ramon Martinez .02 .10
Ozzie Guillen
707 Harold Baines .02 .10
Wade Boggs
708 Robin Yount PV .08 .25
709 K.Griffey Jr. PV UER .08 .25
Missing quotations on back; BA has .322, but was actually .327
710 Nolan Ryan PV .20 .50
711 Cal Ripken PV .15 .40
712 Frank Thomas PV .05 .15
713 Dave Justice PV .02 .10
714 Checklist 1-101 .02 .10
715 Checklist 102-194 .02 .10
716 Checklist 195-296 .02 .10
717 Checklist 297-397 .02 .10
718 Checklist 398-494 .02 .10
719 Checklist 495-596 .02 .10
720A CL 597-720 ERR .02 .10
659 Rob Mauer
720B CL 597-720 COR .02 .10
659 Rob Maurer

1992 Fleer All-Stars

Cards from this 24-card standard-size set were randomly inserted in plastic wrap packs. Selected members of the American and National League 1991 All-Star squads comprise this set.

COMPLETE SET (24) 12.50 30.00
RANDOM INSERTS IN WAX PACKS
1 Felix Jose .30 .75
2 Tony Gwynn 1.00 2.50
3 Barry Bonds 3.00 8.00
4 Bobby Bonilla .30 .75
5 Mike LaValliere .30 .75
6 Tom Glavine .50 1.25
7 Ramon Martinez .30 .75
8 Lee Smith .30 .75
9 Mickey Tettleton .30 .75
10 Scott Erickson .30 .75
11 Frank Thomas .75 2.00
12 Danny Tartabull .30 .75
13 Will Clark .50 1.25
14 Ryne Sandberg 1.25 3.00
15 Terry Pendleton .30 .75
16 Barry Larkin .50 1.25
17 Rafael Palmeiro .50 1.25
18 Julio Franco .30 .75
19 Robin Ventura .30 .75
20 Cal Ripken UER 2.50 6.00
(Candidte; total bases misspelled as based)
21 Joe Carter .30 .75
22 Kirby Puckett .75 2.00
23 Ken Griffey Jr. 1.25 3.00
24 Jose Canseco .50 1.25

1992 Fleer Clemens

Roger Clemens served as a spokesperson for Fleer during 1992 and was the exclusive subject of this 15-card standard-size set. The first 12-card Clemens "Career Highlights" subseries was randomly inserted in 1992 Fleer packs. Two-thousand signed cards were randomly inserted in wax packs and could also be won by entering a drawing. However, these cards are uncertifiable as they do not have any distinguishable marks. Moreover, a three-card Clemens subset (13-15) was available through a special mail-in offer. The glossy color photos on the fronts are bordered in black and accented with gold stripes and lettering on the top of the card.

COMPLETE SET (12) 5.00 12.00
COMMON CARD (1-12) .40 1.00
RANDOM INSERTS IN PACKS
COMMON MAIL (13-15) .40 1.00
AU CARD RANDOM INSERT IN PACKS
AU Roger Clemens AU/2000 30.00 60.00
NNO Roger Clemens 2.50 6.00
Paul Mullan Promo

1992 Fleer Lumber Company

The 1992 Fleer Lumber Company standard-size set features nine outstanding hitters in Major League Baseball. This set was only available as a bonus in Fleer hobby factory sets.

COMPLETE SET (9) 4.00 10.00
L1 Cecil Fielder .30 .75
L2 Mickey Tettleton .30 .75
L3 Darryl Strawberry .30 .75
L4 Ryne Sandberg 1.25 3.00
L5 Jose Canseco .50 1.25
L6 Matt Williams UER .30 .75
In 17th line, cycle is spelled cyle
L7 Cal Ripken 2.50 6.00
L8 Barry Bonds 3.00 8.00
L9 Ron Gant .30 .75

1992 Fleer Rookie Sensations

Cards from the 20-card Fleer Rookie Sensations set were randomly inserted in 1992 Fleer 35-card cello packs. The cards were extremely popular upon release resulting in packs selling for levels far above suggested retail levels. The glossy color photos on the fronts have a white border on a royal blue card face. The words "Rookie Sensations" appear above the picture in gold foil lettering, while the player's name appears on a gold foil plaque beneath the picture. Through a mail-in offer for ten Fleer baseball card wrappers and 1.00 for postage and handling, Fleer offered an uncut 8 1/2" by 11" numbered promo sheet picturing ten of the 20-card set on each side in a reduced-size front-only format. The offer indicated an expiration date of July 31, 1992, or whenever the production quantity of 250,000 sheets was exhausted.

COMPLETE SET (20) 25.00 50.00
RANDOM INSERTS IN CELLO PACKS
1 Frank Thomas 2.00 5.00
2 Todd Van Poppel .60 1.50
3 Orlando Merced .60 1.50
4 Jeff Bagwell 2.00 5.00
5 Jeff Fassero .60 1.50
6 Darren Lewis .60 1.50
7 Milt Cuyler .60 1.50
8 Mike Timlin .60 1.50
9 Brian McRae .60 1.50
10 Chuck Knoblauch .75 2.00
11 Rich DeLucia .60 1.50
12 Ivan Rodriguez 2.00 5.00
13 Juan Guzman .60 1.50
14 Steve Chitren .60 1.50
15 Mark Wohlers .60 1.50
16 Wes Chamberlain .60 1.50
17 Ray Lankford .75 2.00
18 Chito Martinez .60 1.50
19 Phil Plantier .60 1.50
20 Scott Leius UER .60 1.50
(Misspelled Lieus on card front)

1992 Fleer Smoke 'n Heat

This 12-card standard-size set features outstanding major league pitchers, especially the premier fastball pitchers in both leagues. These cards were only available in Fleer's 1992 Christmas factory set.

COMPLETE SET (12) 4.00 10.00
S1 Lee Smith .30 .75
S2 Jack McDowell .30 .75
S3 David Cone .30 .75
S4 Roger Clemens 1.50 4.00
S5 Nolan Ryan 3.00 8.00
S6 Scott Erickson .30 .75
S7 Tom Glavine .50 1.25
S8 Dennis Martinez .30 .75
S9 Andy Benes .30 .75
S10 Steve Avery .30 .75
S11 Randy Johnson .75 2.00
S12 Jim Abbott .50 1.25

1992 Fleer Team Leaders

Cards from the 20-card Fleer Team Leaders set were randomly inserted in 1992 Fleer 42-card rack packs.

COMPLETE SET (20) 15.00 40.00
1 Don Mattingly 4.00 10.00
2 Howard Johnson .60 1.50
3 Chris Sabo UER .60 1.50
(Where he it, should be Where he hit)
4 Carlton Fisk 1.00 2.50
5 Kirby Puckett 1.50 4.00
6 Cecil Fielder .60 1.50
7 Tony Gwynn 2.00 5.00
8 Will Clark 1.00 2.50
9 Bobby Bonilla .60 1.50
10 Len Dykstra .60 1.50
11 Tom Glavine 1.00 2.50
12 Rafael Palmeiro 1.00 2.50
13 Wade Boggs 1.00 2.50
14 Joe Carter .60 1.50
15 Ken Griffey Jr. 2.50 6.00
16 Darryl Strawberry .60 1.50
17 Cal Ripken 5.00 12.00
18 Danny Tartabull .60 1.50
19 Jose Canseco 1.00 2.50
20 Andre Dawson .60 1.50

1992 Fleer Update

The 1992 Fleer Update set contains 132 standard-size cards. Cards were distributed exclusively in factory sets through hobby dealers. Factory sets included a four-card, black-bordered "92 Headliners" insert set for a total of 136 cards. Due to lackluster retail response for previous Fleer Update sets, wholesale orders for this product were low, resulting in a short print run. As word got out that the cards were in short supply, the secondary market prices soared soon after release. The basic card design is identical to the regular issue 1992 Fleer cards except for the U-prefixed numbering on back. The cards are checklisted alphabetically within and according to teams for each league with AL preceding NL. Rookie Cards in this set include Jeff Kent and Mike Piazza. The Piazza card is widely recognized as one of the more desirable singles issued in the 1990's.

COMP.FACT.SET (136) 30.00 60.00
COMPLETE SET (132) 30.00 60.00
1 Todd Frohwirth .20 .50
2 Alan Mills .20 .50
3 Rick Sutcliffe .40 1.00
4 John Valentin RC .60 1.50
5 Frank Viola .40 1.00
6 Bob Zupcic RC .20 .50
7 Mike Butcher .20 .50
8 Chad Curtis RC .60 1.50
9 Damion Easley RC .60 1.50
10 Tim Salmon .60 1.50
11 Julio Valera .20 .50
12 George Bell .20 .50
13 Roberto Hernandez .20 .50
14 Shawn Jeter RC .20 .50
15 Thomas Howard .20 .50
16 Jesse Levis .20 .50
17 Kenny Lofton .60 1.50
18 Paul Sorrento .20 .50
19 Rico Brogna .20 .50
20 John Doherty RC .20 .50
21 Dan Gladden .20 .50
22 Buddy Groom RC .20 .50
23 Shawn Hare RC .20 .50
24 John Kiely .20 .50
25 Kurt Knudsen .20 .50
26 Gregg Jefferies .20 .50
27 Wally Joyner .40 1.00
28 Kevin Koslofski .20 .50
29 Kevin McReynolds .20 .50
30 Rusty Meacham .20 .50
31 Keith Miller .20 .50
32 Hipolito Pichardo RC .20 .50
33 Jim Austin .20 .50
34 Scott Fletcher .20 .50
35 John Jaha RC .60 1.50
36 Pat Listach RC .60 1.50
37 Dave Nilsson .20 .50
38 Kevin Seitzer .20 .50
39 Tom Edens .20 .50
40 Pat Mahomes RC .60 1.50
41 John Smiley .20 .50
42 Charlie Hayes .20 .50
43 Sam Militello .20 .50
44 Andy Stankiewicz .20 .50
45 Danny Tartabull .20 .50
46 Bob Wickman 1.00 2.50
47 Jerry Browne .20 .50
48 Kevin Campbell .20 .50
49 Vince Horsman .20 .50
50 Troy Neel RC .20 .50
51 Ruben Sierra .40 1.00
52 Bruce Walton .20 .50
53 Willie Wilson .20 .50
54 Bret Boone .60 1.50
55 Dave Fleming .20 .50
56 Kevin Mitchell .20 .50
57 Jeff Nelson RC 1.00 2.50
58 Shane Turner .20 .50
59 Jose Canseco .60 1.50
60 Jeff Frye RC .20 .50
61 Danny Leon .20 .50
62 Roger Pavlik RC .20 .50
63 David Cone .40 1.00
64 Pat Hentgen .20 .50
65 Randy Knorr .20 .50
66 Jack Morris .40 1.00
67 Dave Winfield .40 1.00
68 David Nied RC .20 .50
69 Otis Nixon .20 .50
70 Alejandro Pena .20 .50
71 Jeff Reardon .40 1.00
72 Alex Arias RC .20 .50
73 Jim Bullinger .20 .50
74 Mike Morgan .20 .50
75 Rey Sanchez RC .60 1.50
76 Bob Scanlan .20 .50
77 Sammy Sosa 1.50 4.00
78 Scott Bankhead .20 .50
79 Tim Belcher .20 .50
80 Steve Foster .20 .50
81 Willie Greene .20 .50
82 Bip Roberts .20 .50
83 Scott Ruskin .20 .50
84 Greg Swindell .20 .50
85 Juan Guerrero .20 .50
86 Butch Henry .20 .50
87 Doug Jones .20 .50
88 Brian Williams RC .20 .50
89 Tom Candiotti .20 .50
90 Eric Davis .40 1.00
91 Carlos Hernandez .20 .50
92 Mike Piazza RC 12.50 30.00
93 Mike Sharperson .20 .50
94 Eric Young RC .60 1.50
95 Moises Alou .40 1.00
96 Greg Colbrunn .20 .50
97 Wil Cordero .20 .50
98 Ken Hill .20 .50
99 John Vander Wal RC .60 1.50
100 John Wetteland .40 1.00
101 Bobby Bonilla .40 1.00
102 Eric Hillman RC .20 .50
103 Pat Howell .20 .50
104 Jeff Kent RC 6.00 15.00
105 Dick Schofield .20 .50
106 Ryan Thompson RC .20 .50
107 Chico Walker .20 .50
108 Juan Bell .20 .50
109 Mariano Duncan .20 .50
110 Jeff Grotewold .20 .50
111 Ben Rivera .20 .50
112 Curt Schilling .60 1.50
113 Victor Cole RC .20 .50
114 Al Martin RC .60 1.50
115 Roger Mason .20 .50
116 Blas Minor .20 .50
117 Tim Wakefield RC 4.00 10.00
118 Mark Clark RC .20 .50
119 Rheal Cormier .20 .50
120 Donovan Osborne .20 .50
121 Todd Worrell .20 .50
122 Jeremy Hernandez RC .20 .50
123 Randy Myers .20 .50
124 Frank Seminara RC .20 .50
125 Gary Sheffield .40 1.00
126 Dan Walters .20 .50
127 Steve Hosey .20 .50
128 Mike Jackson .20 .50
129 Jim Pena .20 .50
130 Cory Snyder .20 .50
131 Bill Swift .20 .50
132 Checklist U1-U132 .20 .50

1992 Fleer Update Headliners

Each 1992 Fleer Update factory set included a four-card set of Headliner inserts. The cards are numbered separately and have a completely different design to the base cards. Each Headliner features UV coating and black borders. The set features a selection of stars that made headlines in the 1991 season. Cards are numbered on back X of 4.

COMPLETE SET (4) 3.00 8.00
1 Ken Griffey Jr. 1.25 3.00
2 Robin Yount 1.25 3.00
3 Jeff Reardon .30 .75
4 Cecil Fielder .30 .75

1993 Fleer

The 720-card 1993 Fleer baseball set contains two series of 360 standard-size cards. Cards were distributed in plastic wrapped packs, cello packs, jumbo packs and rack packs. For the first time in years, Fleer did not issue a factory set. In fact, Fleer discontinued issuing factory sets from 1993 through 1998. The cards are checklisted below alphabetically within and according to teams for each league with NL preceding AL. Topical subsets include League Leaders (344-348/704-708), Round Trippers (349-353/709-713), and Super Star Specials (354-357/714-717). Each series concludes with checklists (358-360/718-720). There are no key Rookie Cards in this set.

COMPLETE SET (720) 20.00 40.00

COMP.SERIES 1 (360) 10.00 20.00
COMP.SERIES 2 (360) 10.00 20.00
1 Steve Avery .02 .10
2 Sid Bream .02 .10
3 Ron Gant .07 .20
4 Tom Glavine .10 .30
5 Brian Hunter .02 .10
6 Ryan Klesko .07 .20
7 Charlie Leibrandt .02 .10
8 Kent Mercker .02 .10
9 David Nied .02 .10
10 Otis Nixon .02 .10
11 Greg Olson .02 .10
12 Terry Pendleton .07 .20
13 Deion Sanders .10 .30
14 John Smoltz .10 .30
15 Mike Stanton .02 .10
16 Mark Wohlers .02 .10
17 Paul Assenmacher .02 .10
18 Steve Buechele .02 .10
19 Shawon Dunston .02 .10
20 Mark Grace .10 .30
21 Derrick May .02 .10
22 Chuck McElroy .02 .10
23 Mike Morgan .02 .10
24 Rey Sanchez .02 .10
25 Ryne Sandberg .30 .75
26 Bob Scanlan .02 .10
27 Sammy Sosa .20 .50
28 Rick Wilkins .02 .10
29 Bobby Ayala RC .02 .10
30 Tim Belcher .02 .10
31 Jeff Branson .02 .10
32 Norm Charlton .02 .10
33 Steve Foster .02 .10
34 Willie Greene .02 .10
35 Chris Hammond .02 .10
36 Milt Hill .02 .10
37 Hal Morris .02 .10
38 Joe Oliver .02 .10
39 Paul O'Neill .10 .30
40 Tim Pugh RC .02 .10
41 Jose Rijo .02 .10
42 Bip Roberts .02 .10
43 Chris Sabo .02 .10
44 Reggie Sanders .07 .20
45 Eric Anthony .02 .10
46 Jeff Bagwell .10 .30
47 Craig Biggio .10 .30
48 Joe Boever .02 .10
49 Casey Candaele .02 .10
50 Steve Finley .07 .20
51 Luis Gonzalez .07 .20
52 Pete Harnisch .02 .10
53 Xavier Hernandez .02 .10
54 Doug Jones .02 .10
55 Eddie Taubensee .02 .10
56 Brian Williams .02 .10
57 Pedro Astacio .02 .10
58 Todd Benzinger .02 .10
59 Brett Butler .07 .20
60 Tom Candiotti .02 .10
61 Lenny Harris .02 .10
62 Carlos Hernandez .02 .10
63 Orel Hershiser .07 .20
64 Eric Karros .07 .20
65 Ramon Martinez .02 .10
66 Jose Offerman .02 .10
67 Mike Scioscia .02 .10
68 Mike Sharperson .02 .10
69 Eric Young .02 .10
70 Moises Alou .07 .20
71 Ivan Calderon .02 .10
72 Archi Cianfrocco .02 .10
73 Wil Cordero .02 .10
74 Delino DeShields .02 .10
75 Mark Gardner .02 .10
76 Ken Hill .02 .10
77 Tim Laker RC .02 .10
78 Chris Nabholz .02 .10
79 Mel Rojas .02 .10
80 John Vander Wal UER .02 .10
(Misspelled Vander Wall
in letters on back)
81 Larry Walker .07 .20
82 Tim Wallach .02 .10
83 John Wetteland .07 .20
84 Bobby Bonilla .07 .20
85 Daryl Boston .02 .10
86 Sid Fernandez .02 .10
87 Eric Hillman .02 .10
88 Todd Hundley .02 .10
89 Howard Johnson .02 .10
90 Jeff Kent .20 .50
91 Eddie Murray .20 .50
92 Bill Pecota .02 .10
93 Bret Saberhagen .07 .20
94 Dick Schofield .02 .10
95 Pete Schourek .02 .10
96 Anthony Young .02 .10
97 Ruben Amaro .02 .10
98 Juan Bell .02 .10
99 Wes Chamberlain .02 .10
100 Darren Daulton .07 .20
101 Mariano Duncan .02 .10
102 Mike Hartley .02 .10
103 Ricky Jordan .02 .10
104 John Kruk .07 .20
105 Mickey Morandini .02 .10
106 Terry Mulholland .02 .10
107 Ben Rivera .02 .10
108 Curt Schilling .07 .20
109 Keith Shepherd RC .02 .10
110 Stan Belinda .02 .10
111 Jay Bell .07 .20
112 Barry Bonds .60 1.50
113 Jeff King .02 .10
114 Mike LaValliere .02 .10
115 Jose Lind .02 .10
116 Roger Mason .02 .10
117 Orlando Merced .02 .10
118 Bob Patterson .02 .10
119 Don Slaught .02 .10
120 Zane Smith .02 .10
121 Randy Tomlin .02 .10
122 Andy Van Slyke .10 .30
123 Tim Wakefield .20 .50
124 Rheal Cormier .02 .10
125 Bernard Gilkey .02 .10
126 Felix Jose .02 .10
127 Ray Lankford .07 .20
128 Bob McClure .02 .10
129 Donovan Osborne .02 .10
130 Tom Pagnozzi .02 .10
131 Geronimo Pena .02 .10
132 Mike Perez .02 .10
133 Lee Smith .07 .20
134 Bob Tewksbury .02 .10
135 Todd Worrell .02 .10
136 Todd Zeile .02 .10
137 Jerald Clark .02 .10
138 Tony Gwynn .25 .60
139 Greg W. Harris .02 .10
140 Jeremy Hernandez .02 .10
141 Darrin Jackson .02 .10
142 Mike Maddux .02 .10
143 Fred McGriff .10 .30
144 Jose Melendez .02 .10
145 Rich Rodriguez .02 .10
146 Frank Seminara .02 .10
147 Gary Sheffield .07 .20
148 Kurt Stillwell .02 .10
149 Dan Walters .02 .10
150 Rod Beck .02 .10
151 Bud Black .02 .10
152 Jeff Brantley .02 .10
153 John Burkett .02 .10
154 Will Clark .10 .30
155 Royce Clayton .02 .10
156 Mike Jackson .02 .10
157 Darren Lewis .02 .10
158 Kirt Manwaring .02 .10
159 Willie McGee .07 .20
160 Cory Snyder .02 .10
161 Bill Swift .02 .10
162 Trevor Wilson .02 .10
163 Brady Anderson .07 .20
164 Glenn Davis .02 .10
165 Mike Devereaux .02 .10
166 Todd Frohwirth .02 .10
167 Leo Gomez .02 .10
168 Chris Hoiles .02 .10
169 Ben McDonald .02 .10
170 Randy Milligan .02 .10
171 Alan Mills .02 .10
172 Mike Mussina .10 .30
173 Gregg Olson .02 .10
174 Arthur Rhodes .02 .10
175 David Segui .02 .10
176 Ellis Burks .07 .20
177 Roger Clemens .40 1.00
178 Scott Cooper .02 .10
179 Danny Darwin .02 .10
180 Tony Fossas .02 .10
181 Paul Quantrill .02 .10
182 Jody Reed .02 .10
183 John Valentin .02 .10
184 Mo Vaughn .07 .20
185 Frank Viola .07 .20
186 Bob Zupcic .02 .10
187 Jim Abbott .10 .30
188 Gary DiSarcina .02 .10
189 Damion Easley .02 .10
190 Junior Felix .02 .10
191 Chuck Finley .07 .20
192 Joe Grahe .02 .10
193 Bryan Harvey .02 .10
194 Mark Langston .02 .10
195 John Orton .02 .10
196 Luis Polonia .02 .10
197 Tim Salmon .10 .30
198 Luis Sojo .02 .10
199 Wilson Alvarez .02 .10
200 George Bell .02 .10
201 Alex Fernandez .02 .10
202 Craig Grebeck .02 .10
203 Ozzie Guillen .07 .20
204 Lance Johnson .02 .10
205 Ron Karkovice .02 .10
206 Kirk McCaskill .02 .10
207 Jack McDowell .02 .10
208 Scott Radinsky .02 .10
209 Tim Raines .07 .20
210 Frank Thomas .20 .50
211 Robin Ventura .07 .20
212 Sandy Alomar Jr. .02 .10
213 Carlos Baerga .02 .10
214 Dennis Cook .02 .10
215 Thomas Howard .02 .10
216 Mark Lewis .02 .10
217 Derek Lilliquist .02 .10
218 Kenny Lofton .07 .20
219 Charles Nagy .02 .10
220 Steve Olin .02 .10
221 Paul Sorrento .02 .10
222 Jim Thome .10 .30
223 Mark Whiten .02 .10
224 Milt Cuyler .02 .10
225 Rob Deer .02 .10
226 John Doherty .02 .10
227 Cecil Fielder .07 .20
228 Travis Fryman .07 .20
229 Mike Henneman .02 .10
230 John Kiely UER .02 .10
(Card has batting
stats of Pat Kelly)
231 Kurt Knudsen .02 .10
232 Scott Livingstone .02 .10
233 Tony Phillips .02 .10
234 Mickey Tettleton .02 .10
235 Kevin Appier .07 .20
236 George Brett .50 1.25
237 Tom Gordon .02 .10
238 Gregg Jefferies .02 .10
239 Wally Joyner .07 .20
240 Kevin Koslofski .02 .10
241 Mike Macfarlane .02 .10
242 Brian McRae .02 .10
243 Rusty Meacham .02 .10
244 Keith Miller .02 .10
245 Jeff Montgomery .02 .10
246 Hipolito Pichardo .02 .10
247 Ricky Bones .02 .10
248 Cal Eldred .02 .10
249 Mike Fetters .02 .10
250 Darryl Hamilton .02 .10
251 Doug Henry .02 .10
252 John Jaha .02 .10
253 Pat Listach .02 .10
254 Paul Molitor .07 .20
255 Jaime Navarro .02 .10
256 Kevin Seitzer .02 .10
257 B.J. Surhoff .07 .20
258 Greg Vaughn .02 .10
259 Bill Wegman .02 .10
260 Robin Yount .30 .75
261 Rick Aguilera .02 .10
262 Chili Davis .07 .20
263 Scott Erickson .02 .10
264 Greg Gagne .02 .10
265 Mark Guthrie .02 .10
266 Brian Harper .02 .10
267 Kent Hrbek .07 .20
268 Terry Jorgensen .02 .10
269 Gene Larkin .02 .10
270 Scott Leius .02 .10
271 Pat Mahomes .02 .10
272 Pedro Munoz .02 .10
273 Kirby Puckett .20 .50
274 Kevin Tapani .02 .10
275 Carl Willis .02 .10
276 Steve Farr .02 .10
277 John Habyan .02 .10
278 Mel Hall .02 .10
279 Charlie Hayes .02 .10
280 Pat Kelly .02 .10
281 Don Mattingly .50 1.25
282 Sam Militello .02 .10
283 Matt Nokes .02 .10
284 Melido Perez .02 .10
285 Andy Stankiewicz .02 .10
286 Danny Tartabull .02 .10
287 Randy Velarde .02 .10
288 Bob Wickman .02 .10
289 Bernie Williams .10 .30
290 Lance Blankenship .02 .10
291 Mike Bordick .02 .10
292 Jerry Browne .02 .10
293 Dennis Eckersley .07 .20
294 Rickey Henderson .20 .50
295 Vince Horsman .02 .10
296 Mark McGwire .50 1.25
297 Jeff Parrett .02 .10
298 Ruben Sierra .07 .20
299 Terry Steinbach .02 .10
300 Walt Weiss .02 .10
301 Bob Welch .02 .10
302 Willie Wilson .02 .10
303 Bobby Witt .02 .10
304 Bret Boone .07 .20
305 Jay Buhner .07 .20
306 Dave Fleming .02 .10
307 Ken Griffey Jr. .30 .75
308 Erik Hanson .02 .10
309 Edgar Martinez .10 .30
310 Tino Martinez .10 .30
311 Jeff Nelson .02 .10
312 Dennis Powell .02 .10
313 Mike Schooler .02 .10
314 Russ Swan .02 .10
315 Dave Valle .02 .10
316 Omar Vizquel .10 .30
317 Kevin Brown .07 .20
318 Todd Burns .02 .10
319 Jose Canseco .10 .30
320 Julio Franco .07 .20
321 Jeff Frye .02 .10
322 Juan Gonzalez .07 .20
323 Jose Guzman .02 .10
324 Jeff Huson .02 .10
325 Dean Palmer .07 .20
326 Kevin Reimer .02 .10
327 Ivan Rodriguez .10 .30
328 Kenny Rogers .07 .20
329 Dan Smith .02 .10
330 Roberto Alomar .10 .30
331 Derek Bell .02 .10
332 Pat Borders .02 .10
333 Joe Carter .07 .20
334 Kelly Gruber .02 .10
335 Tom Henke .02 .10
336 Jimmy Key .07 .20
337 Manuel Lee .02 .10
338 Candy Maldonado .02 .10
339 John Olerud .07 .20
340 Todd Stottlemyre .02 .10
341 Duane Ward .02 .10
342 Devon White .07 .20
343 Dave Winfield .07 .20
344 Edgar Martinez LL .07 .20
345 Cecil Fielder LL .02 .10
346 Kenny Lofton LL .02 .10
347 Jack Morris LL .02 .10
348 Roger Clemens LL .20 .50
349 Fred McGriff RT .07 .20
350 Barry Bonds RT .30 .75
351 Gary Sheffield RT .02 .10
352 Darren Daulton RT .02 .10
353 Dave Hollins RT .02 .10
354 Pedro Martinez .20 .50
Ramon Martinez
355 Ivan Rodriguez .10 .30
Kirby Puckett
356 Ryne Sandberg .20 .50
Gary Sheffield
357 Roberto Alomar .07 .20
Chuck Knoblauch
Carlos Baerga
358 Checklist 1-120 .02 .10
359 Checklist 121-240 .02 .10
360 Checklist 241-360 .02 .10
361 Rafael Belliard .02 .10
362 Damon Berryhill .02 .10
363 Mike Bielecki .02 .10
364 Jeff Blauser .02 .10
365 Francisco Cabrera .02 .10
366 Marvin Freeman .02 .10
367 David Justice .07 .20
368 Mark Lemke .02 .10
369 Alejandro Pena .02 .10
370 Jeff Reardon .07 .20
371 Lonnie Smith .02 .10
372 Pete Smith .02 .10
373 Shawn Boskie .02 .10
374 Jim Bullinger .02 .10
375 Frank Castillo .02 .10
376 Doug Dascenzo .02 .10
377 Andre Dawson .07 .20
378 Mike Harkey .02 .10
379 Greg Hibbard .02 .10
380 Greg Maddux .30 .75
381 Ken Patterson .02 .10
382 Jeff D. Robinson .02 .10
383 Luis Salazar .02 .10
384 Dwight Smith .02 .10
385 Jose Vizcaino .02 .10
386 Scott Bankhead .02 .10
387 Tom Browning .02 .10
388 Darnell Coles .02 .10
389 Rob Dibble .07 .20
390 Bill Doran .02 .10
391 Dwayne Henry .02 .10
392 Cesar Hernandez .02 .10
393 Roberto Kelly .02 .10
394 Barry Larkin .10 .30
395 Dave Martinez .02 .10
396 Kevin Mitchell .02 .10
397 Jeff Reed .02 .10
398 Scott Ruskin .02 .10
399 Greg Swindell .02 .10
400 Dan Wilson .07 .20
401 Andy Ashby .02 .10
402 Freddie Benavides .02 .10
403 Dante Bichette .07 .20
404 Willie Blair .02 .10
405 Denis Boucher .02 .10
406 Vinny Castilla .20 .50
407 Braulio Castillo .02 .10
408 Alex Cole .02 .10
409 Andres Galarraga .07 .20
410 Joe Girardi .02 .10
411 Butch Henry .02 .10
412 Darren Holmes .02 .10
413 Calvin Jones .02 .10
414 Steve Reed RC .02 .10
415 Kevin Ritz .02 .10
416 Jim Tatum RC .02 .10
417 Jack Armstrong .02 .10
418 Bret Barberie .02 .10
419 Ryan Bowen .02 .10
420 Cris Carpenter .02 .10
421 Chuck Carr .02 .10
422 Scott Chiamparino .02 .10
423 Jeff Conine .07 .20
424 Jim Corsi .02 .10
425 Steve Decker .02 .10
426 Chris Donnels .02 .10
427 Monty Fariss .02 .10
428 Bob Natal .02 .10
429 Pat Rapp .02 .10
430 Dave Weathers .02 .10
431 Nigel Wilson .02 .10
432 Ken Caminiti .07 .20
433 Andujar Cedeno .02 .10
434 Tom Edens .02 .10
435 Juan Guerrero .02 .10
436 Pete Incaviglia .02 .10
437 Jimmy Jones .02 .10
438 Darryl Kile .07 .20
439 Rob Murphy .02 .10
440 Al Osuna .02 .10
441 Mark Portugal .02 .10
442 Scott Servais .02 .10
443 John Candelaria .02 .10
444 Tim Crews .02 .10
445 Eric Davis .07 .20
446 Tom Goodwin .02 .10
447 Jim Gott .02 .10
448 Kevin Gross .02 .10
449 Dave Hansen .02 .10
450 Jay Howell .02 .10
451 Roger McDowell .02 .10
452 Bob Ojeda .02 .10
453 Henry Rodriguez .02 .10
454 Darryl Strawberry .07 .20
455 Mitch Webster .02 .10
456 Steve Wilson .02 .10
457 Brian Barnes .02 .10
458 Sean Berry .02 .10
459 Jeff Fassero .02 .10
460 Darrin Fletcher .02 .10
461 Marquis Grissom .07 .20
462 Dennis Martinez .07 .20
463 Spike Owen .02 .10
464 Matt Stairs .02 .10
465 Sergio Valdez .02 .10
466 Kevin Bass .02 .10
467 Vince Coleman .02 .10
468 Mark Dewey .02 .10
469 Kevin Elster .02 .10
470 Tony Fernandez .02 .10
471 John Franco .07 .20
472 Dave Gallagher .02 .10
473 Paul Gibson .02 .10
474 Dwight Gooden .07 .20
475 Lee Guetterman .02 .10
476 Jeff Innis .02 .10
477 Dave Magadan .02 .10
478 Charlie O'Brien .02 .10
479 Willie Randolph .07 .20
480 Mackey Sasser .02 .10
481 Ryan Thompson .02 .10
482 Chico Walker .02 .10
483 Kyle Abbott .02 .10
484 Bob Ayrault .02 .10
485 Kim Batiste .02 .10
486 Cliff Brantley .02 .10
487 Jose DeLeon .02 .10
488 Len Dykstra .07 .20
489 Tommy Greene .02 .10
490 Jeff Grotewold .02 .10
491 Dave Hollins .02 .10
492 Danny Jackson .02 .10
493 Stan Javier .02 .10
494 Tom Marsh .02 .10
495 Greg Mathews .02 .10
496 Dale Murphy .10 .30
497 Todd Pratt RC .07 .20
498 Mitch Williams .02 .10
499 Danny Cox .02 .10
500 Doug Drabek .02 .10
501 Carlos Garcia .02 .10
502 Lloyd McClendon .02 .10
503 Denny Neagle .07 .20
504 Gary Redus .02 .10
505 Bob Walk .02 .10
506 John Wehner .02 .10
507 Luis Alicea .02 .10
508 Mark Clark .02 .10
509 Pedro Guerrero .07 .20
510 Rex Hudler .02 .10
511 Brian Jordan .07 .20
512 Omar Olivares .02 .10
513 Jose Oquendo .02 .10
514 Gerald Perry .02 .10
515 Bryn Smith .02 .10
516 Craig Wilson .02 .10
517 Tracy Woodson .02 .10
518 Larry Andersen .02 .10
519 Andy Benes .02 .10
520 Jim Deshaies .02 .10
521 Bruce Hurst .02 .10
522 Randy Myers .02 .10
523 Benito Santiago .07 .20
524 Tim Scott .02 .10
525 Tim Teufel .02 .10
526 Mike Benjamin .02 .10
527 Dave Burba .02 .10
528 Craig Colbert .02 .10
529 Mike Felder .02 .10
530 Bryan Hickerson .02 .10
531 Chris James .02 .10
532 Mark Leonard .02 .10
533 Greg Litton .02 .10
534 Francisco Oliveras .02 .10
535 John Patterson .02 .10
536 Jim Pena .02 .10
537 Dave Righetti .07 .20
538 Robby Thompson .02 .10
539 Jose Uribe .02 .10
540 Matt Williams .07 .20
541 Storm Davis .02 .10
542 Sam Horn .02 .10
543 Tim Hulett .02 .10
544 Craig Lefferts .02 .10
545 Chito Martinez .02 .10
546 Mark McLemore .02 .10
547 Luis Mercedes .02 .10
548 Bob Milacki .02 .10
549 Joe Orsulak .02 .10
550 Billy Ripken .02 .10
551 Cal Ripken Jr. .60 1.50
552 Rick Sutcliffe .07 .20
553 Jeff Tackett .02 .10
554 Wade Boggs .10 .30
555 Tom Brunansky .02 .10
556 Jack Clark .07 .20
557 John Dopson .02 .10
558 Mike Gardiner .02 .10
559 Mike Greenwell .02 .10
560 Greg A. Harris .02 .10
561 Billy Hatcher .02 .10
562 Joe Hesketh .02 .10
563 Tony Pena .02 .10
564 Phil Plantier .02 .10
565 Luis Rivera .02 .10
566 Herm Winningham .02 .10
567 Matt Young .02 .10
568 Bert Blyleven .07 .20
569 Mike Butcher .02 .10
570 Chuck Crim .02 .10
571 Chad Curtis .02 .10
572 Tim Fortugno .02 .10
573 Steve Frey .02 .10
574 Gary Gaetti .07 .20
575 Scott Lewis .02 .10
576 Lee Stevens .02 .10
577 Ron Tingley .02 .10
578 Julio Valera .02 .10
579 Shawn Abner .02 .10
580 Joey Cora .02 .10
581 Chris Cron .02 .10
582 Carlton Fisk .10 .30
583 Roberto Hernandez .02 .10
584 Charlie Hough .07 .20
585 Terry Leach .02 .10
586 Donn Pall .02 .10
587 Dan Pasqua .02 .10
588 Steve Sax .02 .10
589 Bobby Thigpen .02 .10
590 Albert Belle .07 .20
591 Felix Fermin .02 .10
592 Glenallen Hill .02 .10
593 Brook Jacoby .02 .10
594 Reggie Jefferson .02 .10
595 Carlos Martinez .02 .10
596 Jose Mesa .02 .10
597 Rod Nichols .02 .10
598 Junior Ortiz .02 .10
599 Eric Plunk .02 .10
600 Ted Power .02 .10
601 Scott Scudder .02 .10
602 Kevin Wickander .02 .10
603 Skeeter Barnes .02 .10
604 Mark Carreon .02 .10
605 Dan Gladden .02 .10
606 Bill Gullickson .02 .10
607 Chad Kreuter .02 .10
608 Mark Leiter .02 .10
609 Mike Munoz .02 .10
610 Rich Rowland .02 .10
611 Frank Tanana .02 .10
612 Walt Terrell .02 .10
613 Alan Trammell .07 .20
614 Lou Whitaker .07 .20
615 Luis Aquino .02 .10
616 Mike Boddicker .02 .10
617 Jim Eisenreich .02 .10
618 Mark Gubicza .02 .10
619 David Howard .02 .10
620 Mike Magnante .02 .10
621 Brent Mayne .02 .10
622 Kevin McReynolds .02 .10
623 Ed Pierce RC .02 .10
624 Bill Sampen .02 .10
625 Steve Shifflett .02 .10
626 Gary Thurman .02 .10
627 Curt Wilkerson .02 .10
628 Chris Bosio .02 .10
629 Scott Fletcher .02 .10
630 Jim Gantner .02 .10
631 Dave Nilsson .02 .10
632 Jesse Orosco .02 .10
633 Dan Plesac .02 .10
634 Ron Robinson .02 .10
635 Bill Spiers .02 .10
636 Franklin Stubbs .02 .10
637 Willie Banks .02 .10
638 Randy Bush .02 .10
639 Chuck Knoblauch .07 .20
640 Shane Mack .02 .10
641 Mike Pagliarulo .02 .10
642 Jeff Reboulet .02 .10
643 John Smiley .02 .10
644 Mike Trombley .02 .10
645 Gary Wayne .02 .10
646 Lenny Webster .02 .10
647 Tim Burke .02 .10
648 Mike Gallego .02 .10
649 Dion James .02 .10
650 Jeff Johnson .02 .10
651 Scott Kamieniecki .02 .10
652 Kevin Maas .02 .10
653 Rich Monteleone .02 .10
654 Jerry Nielsen .02 .10
655 Scott Sanderson .02 .10
656 Mike Stanley .02 .10
657 Gerald Williams .02 .10
658 Curt Young .02 .10
659 Harold Baines .07 .20
660 Kevin Campbell .02 .10
661 Ron Darling .02 .10
662 Kelly Downs .02 .10
663 Eric Fox .02 .10
664 Dave Henderson .02 .10
665 Rick Honeycutt .02 .10
666 Mike Moore .02 .10
667 Jamie Quirk .02 .10
668 Jeff Russell .02 .10
669 Dave Stewart .07 .20
670 Greg Briley .02 .10
671 Dave Cochrane .02 .10
672 Henry Cotto .02 .10
673 Rich DeLucia .02 .10
674 Brian Fisher .02 .10
675 Mark Grant .02 .10
676 Randy Johnson .20 .50
677 Tim Leary .02 .10
678 Pete O'Brien .02 .10
679 Lance Parrish .07 .20
680 Harold Reynolds .07 .20
681 Shane Turner .02 .10
682 Jack Daugherty .02 .10
683 David Hulse RC .02 .10
684 Terry Mathews .02 .10
685 Al Newman .02 .10
686 Edwin Nunez .02 .10
687 Rafael Palmeiro .10 .30
688 Roger Pavlik .02 .10
689 Geno Petralli .02 .10
690 Nolan Ryan .75 2.00
691 David Cone .07 .20
692 Alfredo Griffin .02 .10
693 Juan Guzman .02 .10
694 Pat Hentgen .02 .10
695 Randy Knorr .02 .10
696 Bob MacDonald .02 .10
697 Jack Morris .07 .20
698 Ed Sprague .02 .10
699 Dave Stieb .02 .10
700 Pat Tabler .02 .10
701 Mike Timlin .02 .10
702 David Wells .07 .20
703 Eddie Zosky .02 .10
704 Gary Sheffield LL .02 .10
705 Darren Daulton LL .02 .10
706 Marquis Grissom LL .02 .10
707 Greg Maddux LL .20 .50
708 Bill Swift LL .02 .10
709 Juan Gonzalez RT .02 .10
710 Mark McGwire RT .25 .60
711 Cecil Fielder RT .02 .10
712 Albert Belle RT .07 .20
713 Joe Carter RT .02 .10
714 Cecil Fielder SS .10 .30
Frank Thomas
715 Larry Walker SS .07 .20
Darren Daulton
716 Edgar Martinez SS .07 .20
Robin Ventura
717 Roger Clemens SS .20 .50
Dennis Eckersley
718 Checklist 361-480 .02 .10
719 Checklist 481-600 .02 .10
720 Checklist 601-720 .02 .10

1993 Fleer All-Stars

This 24-card standard-size set featuring members of the American and National league All-Star squads, was randomly inserted in wax packs. 12 American League players were seeded in series 1 packs and 12 National League players in series 2.

COMPLETE SET (24) 15.00 40.00
COMPLETE SER.1 (12) 10.00 25.00
COMPLETE SER.2 (12) 6.00 15.00
AL: RANDOM INSERTS IN SER.1 PACKS
NL: RANDOM INSERTS IN SER.2 PACKS
AL1 Frank Thomas 1.25 3.00
AL2 Roberto Alomar .75 2.00
AL3 Edgar Martinez .75 2.00
AL4 Pat Listach .25 .60
AL5 Cecil Fielder .50 1.25
AL6 Juan Gonzalez .50 1.25
AL7 Ken Griffey Jr. 2.00 5.00
AL8 Joe Carter .50 1.25
AL9 Kirby Puckett 1.25 3.00
AL10 Brian Harper .25 .60
AL11 Dave Fleming .25 .60
AL12 Jack McDowell .25 .60
NL1 Fred McGriff .75 2.00
NL2 Delino DeShields .25 .60
NL3 Gary Sheffield .50 1.25
NL4 Barry Larkin .75 2.00
NL5 Felix Jose .25 .60
NL6 Larry Walker .50 1.25
NL7 Barry Bonds 4.00 10.00
NL8 Andy Van Slyke .75 2.00
NL9 Darren Daulton .50 1.25
NL10 Greg Maddux 2.00 5.00
NL11 Tom Glavine .75 2.00
NL12 Lee Smith .50 1.25

1993 Fleer Glavine

As part of the Signature Series, this 12-card standard-size set spotlights Tom Glavine. An additional three cards (13-15) were available via a mail-in offer and are generally considered to be a separate set. The mail-in offer expired on September 30, 1993. Reportedly, a filmmaking problem during production resulted in eight variations in this 12-card insert set. Different backs appear on eight of the 12 cards. Cards 1-4 and 7-10 in wax packs feature card-back text variations from those included in the rack and jumbo magazine packs. The text differences occur in the first few words of text on the card back. No corrections were made in Series I. The correct Glavine cards appeared in Series II wax, rack, and jumbo magazine packs. In addition, Tom Glavine signed cards for this set. Unlike some of the previous autograph cards from Fleer, these cards were certified as authentic by the manufacturer.

COMPLETE SET (12) 1.50 4.00
COMMON CARD (1-12) .20 .50
RANDOM INSERTS IN ALL PACKS
COMMON MAIL (13-15) .75 2.00
AU Tom Glavine AU 30.00 60.00

1993 Fleer Golden Moments

Cards from this six-card standard-size set, featuring memorable moments from the previous season, were randomly inserted in 1993 Fleer wax packs, three each in series 1 and 2.

COMPLETE SET (6) 4.50 12.00
COMPLETE SER.1 (3) 1.50 4.00
COMPLETE SER.2 (3) 3.00 8.00
RANDOM INSERTS IN WAX PACKS
A1 George Brett 2.50 6.00
A2 Mickey Morandini .20 .50
A3 Dave Winfield .40 1.00
B1 Dennis Eckersley .40 1.00
B2 Bip Roberts .20 .50
B3 Frank Thomas 1.00 2.50
and Juan Gonzalez

1993 Fleer Major League Prospects

Cards from this 36-card standard-size set, featuring a selection of prospects, were randomly inserted in wax packs, 18 in each series. Early Cards of Pedro Martinez and Mike Piazza are featured within this set.

COMPLETE SET (36) 15.00 30.00
COMPLETE SERIES 1 (18) 10.00 20.00
COMPLETE SERIES 2 (18) 5.00 10.00
RANDOM INSERTS IN WAX PACKS
A1 Melvin Nieves .20 .50
A2 Sterling Hitchcock .30 .75
A3 Tim Costo .20 .50
A4 Manny Alexander .20 .50
A5 Alan Embree .20 .50
A6 Kevin Young .30 .75
A7 J.T. Snow .50 1.25
A8 Russ Springer .20 .50
A9 Billy Ashley .20 .50
A10 Kevin Rogers .20 .50
A11 Steve Hosey .20 .50
A12 Eric Wedge .20 .50
A13 Mike Piazza 3.00 8.00
A14 Jesse Levis .20 .50
A15 Rico Brogna .20 .50
A16 Alex Arias .20 .50
A17 Rod Brewer .20 .50
A18 Troy Neel .20 .50
B1 Scooter Tucker .20 .50
B2 Kerry Woodson .20 .50
B3 Greg Colbrunn .20 .50
B4 Pedro Martinez 2.50 6.00
B5 Dave Silvestri .20 .50
B6 Kent Bottenfield .20 .50
B7 Rafael Bournigal .20 .50
B8 J.T. Bruett .20 .50
B9 Dave Mlicki .20 .50
B10 Paul Wagner .20 .50
B11 Mike Williams .20 .50
B12 Henry Mercedes .20 .50
B13 Scott Taylor .20 .50
B14 Dennis Moeller .20 .50
B15 Javy Lopez .50 1.25
B16 Steve Cooke .20 .50
B17 Pete Young .20 .50
B18 Ken Ryan .20 .50

1993 Fleer Pro-Visions

Cards from this six-card standard-size set, featuring a selection of superstars in fantasy paintings, were randomly inserted in poly packs, three each in series one and series two.

COMPLETE SET (6) 2.00 5.00
COMPLETE SERIES 1 (3) 1.25 3.00
COMPLETE SERIES 2 (3) .75 2.00
RANDOM INSERTS IN WAX PACKS
A1 Roberto Alomar .75 2.00
A2 Dennis Eckersley .50 1.25
A3 Gary Sheffield .50 1.25
B1 Andy Van Slyke .75 2.00
B2 Tom Glavine .75 2.00
B3 Cecil Fielder .50 1.25

1993 Fleer Rookie Sensations

Cards from this 20-card standard-size set, featuring a selection of 1993's top rookies, were randomly inserted in cello packs, 10 in each series.

COMPLETE SET (20) 8.00 20.00
COMPLETE SERIES 1 (10) 4.00 10.00
COMPLETE SERIES 2 (10) 4.00 10.00
RANDOM INSERTS IN CELLO PACKS
RSA1 Kenny Lofton .75 2.00
RSA2 Cal Eldred .40 1.00
RSA3 Pat Listach .40 1.00
RSA4 Roberto Hernandez .40 1.00
RSA5 Dave Fleming .40 1.00
RSA6 Eric Karros .75 2.00
RSA7 Reggie Sanders .75 2.00
RSA8 Derrick May .40 1.00
RSA9 Mike Perez .40 1.00
RSA10 Donovan Osborne .40 1.00
RSB1 Moises Alou .75 2.00
RSB2 Pedro Astacio .40 1.00
RSB3 Jim Austin .40 1.00
RSB4 Chad Curtis .40 1.00
RSB5 Gary DiSarcina .40 1.00
RSB6 Scott Livingstone .40 1.00
RSB7 Sam Militello .40 1.00
RSB8 Arthur Rhodes .40 1.00
RSB9 Tim Wakefield 2.00 5.00
RSB10 Bob Zupcic .40 1.00

1993 Fleer Team Leaders

One Team Leader or Tom Glavine insert was seeded into each Fleer rack pack. Series 1 racks included 10 American League players, while series 2 racks included 10 National League players.

COMPLETE SET (20) 28.00 70.00
COMPLETE SERIES 1 (10) 20.00 50.00
COMPLETE SERIES 2 (10) 8.00 20.00
ONE TL OR GLAVINE PER RACK PACK
AL IN SERIES 1 NL IN SEARIES 2
NL: RANDOM INSERTS IN SER.2 PACKS
AL1 Kirby Puckett 2.00 5.00
AL2 Mark McGwire 5.00 12.00
AL3 Pat Listach .40 1.00
AL4 Roger Clemens 4.00 10.00
AL5 Frank Thomas 2.00 5.00
AL6 Carlos Baerga .40 1.00
AL7 Brady Anderson .75 2.00
AL8 Juan Gonzalez .75 2.00
AL9 Roberto Alomar 1.25 3.00
AL10 Ken Griffey Jr. 3.00 8.00
NL1 Will Clark 1.25 3.00
NL2 Terry Pendleton .75 2.00
NL3 Ray Lankford .75 2.00
NL4 Eric Karros .75 2.00
NL5 Gary Sheffield .75 2.00
NL6 Ryne Sandberg 3.00 8.00
NL7 Marquis Grissom .75 2.00
NL8 John Kruk .75 2.00
NL9 Jeff Bagwell 1.25 3.00
NL10 Andy Van Slyke 1.25 3.00

1993 Fleer Final Edition

This 300-card standard-size set was issued exclusively in factory set form (along with ten Diamond Tribute inserts) to update and feature rookies not in the regular 1993 Fleer set. The cards are identical in design to regular issue 1993 Fleer cards except for the F-prefixed numbering. Cards are ordered alphabetically within teams with NL preceding AL. The set closes with checklist cards (298-300). The only key Rookie Card in this set features Jim Edmonds.

COMP.FACT.SET (310) 4.00 10.00
COMPLETE SET (300) 3.00 8.00
1 Steve Bedrosian .02 .10
2 Jay Howell .02 .10
3 Greg Maddux .30 .75
4 Greg McMichael RC .05 .15
5 Tony Tarasco RC .05 .15
6 Jose Bautista .02 .10
7 Jose Guzman .02 .10
8 Greg Hibbard .02 .10
9 Candy Maldonado .02 .10
10 Randy Myers .02 .10
11 Matt Walbeck RC .15 .40
12 Turk Wendell .02 .10
13 Willie Wilson .02 .10
14 Greg Cadaret .02 .10
15 Roberto Kelly .02 .10
16 Randy Milligan .02 .10
17 Kevin Mitchell .02 .10
18 Jeff Reardon .07 .20
19 John Roper .02 .10
20 John Smiley .02 .10
21 Andy Ashby .02 .10
22 Dante Bichette .07 .20
23 Willie Blair .02 .10
24 Pedro Castellano .02 .10
25 Vinny Castilla .20 .50
26 Jerald Clark .02 .10
27 Alex Cole .02 .10
28 Scott Fredrickson RC .05 .15
29 Jay Gainer RC .05 .15
30 Andres Galarraga .07 .20
31 Joe Girardi .02 .10
32 Ryan Hawblitzel .02 .10
33 Charlie Hayes .02 .10
34 Darren Holmes .02 .10
35 Chris Jones .02 .10
36 David Nied .02 .10
37 J.Owens RC .05 .15
38 Lance Painter RC .15 .40
39 Jeff Parrett .02 .10
40 Steve Reed .02 .10
41 Armando Reynoso .02 .10
42 Bruce Ruffin .02 .10
43 Danny Sheaffer RC .05 .15
44 Keith Shepherd .02 .10
45 Jim Tatum .02 .10
46 Gary Wayne .02 .10
47 Eric Young .02 .10
48 Luis Aquino .02 .10
49 Alex Arias .02 .10
50 Jack Armstrong .02 .10
51 Bret Barberie .02 .10
52 Geronimo Berroa .02 .10
53 Ryan Bowen .02 .10
54 Greg Briley .02 .10
55 Cris Carpenter .02 .10
56 Chuck Carr .02 .10
57 Jeff Conine .07 .20
58 Jim Corsi .02 .10
59 Orestes Destrade .02 .10
60 Junior Felix .02 .10
61 Chris Hammond .02 .10
62 Bryan Harvey .02 .10
63 Charlie Hough .07 .20
64 Joe Klink .02 .10
65 Richie Lewis RC UER .05 .15
(Refers to place of birth and residence as Illinois instead of Indiana)
66 Mitch Lyden RC .05 .15
67 Bob Natal .02 .10
68 Scott Pose RC .05 .15
69 Rich Renteria .02 .10
70 Benito Santiago .07 .20
71 Gary Sheffield .07 .20
72 Matt Turner RC .05 .15
73 Walt Weiss .02 .10
74 Darrell Whitmore RC .05 .15
75 Nigel Wilson .02 .10
76 Kevin Bass .02 .10
77 Doug Drabek .02 .10
78 Tom Edens .02 .10
79 Chris James .02 .10
80 Greg Swindell .02 .10
81 Omar Daal RC .05 .15
82 Raul Mondesi .07 .20
83 Jody Reed .02 .10
84 Cory Snyder .02 .10
85 Rick Trlicek .02 .10
86 Tim Wallach .02 .10
87 Todd Worrell .02 .10
88 Tavo Alvarez .02 .10
89 Frank Bolick .02 .10
90 Kent Bottenfield .02 .10
91 Greg Colbrunn .02 .10
92 Cliff Floyd .07 .20
93 Lou Frazier RC .05 .15
94 Mike Gardiner .02 .10
95 Mike Lansing RC .15 .40
96 Bill Risley .02 .10
97 Jeff Shaw .02 .10
98 Kevin Baez .02 .10
99 Tim Bogar RC .05 .15
100 Jeromy Burnitz .07 .20
101 Mike Draper .02 .10
102 Darrin Jackson .02 .10
103 Mike Maddux .02 .10
104 Joe Orsulak .02 .10
105 Doug Saunders RC .05 .15
106 Frank Tanana .02 .10
107 Dave Telgheder RC .05 .15
108 Larry Andersen .02 .10
109 Jim Eisenreich .02 .10
110 Pete Incaviglia .02 .10
111 Danny Jackson .02 .10
112 David West .02 .10
113 Al Martin .02 .10
114 Blas Minor .02 .10
115 Dennis Moeller .02 .10
116 William Pennyfeather .02 .10
117 Rich Robertson RC .05 .15
118 Ben Shelton .02 .10
119 Lonnie Smith .02 .10
120 Freddie Toliver .02 .10
121 Paul Wagner .02 .10
122 Kevin Young .07 .20
123 Rene Arocha RC .15 .40
124 Gregg Jefferies .02 .10
125 Paul Kilgus .02 .10
126 Les Lancaster .02 .10
127 Joe Magrane .02 .10
128 Rob Murphy .02 .10
129 Erik Pappas .02 .10
130 Stan Royer .02 .10
131 Ozzie Smith .30 .75
132 Tom Urbani RC .05 .15
133 Mark Whiten .02 .10
134 Derek Bell .02 .10
135 Doug Brocail .02 .10
136 Phil Clark .02 .10
137 Mark Ettles RC .05 .15
138 Jeff Gardner .02 .10
139 Pat Gomez RC .05 .15
140 Ricky Gutierrez .02 .10
141 Gene Harris .02 .10
142 Kevin Higgins .02 .10
143 Trevor Hoffman .20 .50
144 Phil Plantier .02 .10
145 Kerry Taylor RC .05 .15
146 Guillermo Velasquez .02 .10
147 Wally Whitehurst .02 .10
148 Tim Worrell RC .15 .40
149 Todd Benzinger .02 .10
150 Barry Bonds .60 1.50
151 Greg Brummett RC .05 .15
152 Mark Carreon .02 .10
153 Dave Martinez .02 .10
154 Jeff Reed .02 .10
155 Kevin Rogers .02 .10
156 Harold Baines .07 .20
157 Damon Buford .02 .10
158 Paul Carey RC .05 .15
159 Jeffrey Hammonds .02 .10
160 Jamie Moyer .07 .20
161 Sherman Obando RC .05 .15
162 John O'Donoghue RC .05 .15
163 Brad Pennington .02 .10
164 Jim Poole .02 .10
165 Harold Reynolds .07 .20
166 Fernando Valenzuela .07 .20
167 Jack Voigt RC .05 .15
168 Mark Williamson .02 .10
169 Scott Bankhead .02 .10
170 Greg Blosser .02 .10
171 Jim Byrd RC .05 .15
172 Ivan Calderon .02 .10
173 Andre Dawson .07 .20
174 Scott Fletcher .02 .10
175 Jose Melendez .02 .10
176 Carlos Quintana .02 .10
177 Jeff Russell .02 .10
178 Aaron Sele .02 .10
179 Rod Correia RC .05 .15
180 Chili Davis .07 .20
181 Jim Edmonds RC 1.25 3.00
182 Rene Gonzales .02 .10
183 Hilly Hathaway RC .05 .15
184 Torey Lovullo .02 .10
185 Greg Myers .02 .10
186 Gene Nelson .02 .10
187 Troy Percival .10 .30
188 Scott Sanderson .02 .10
189 Darryl Scott RC .05 .15
190 J.T. Snow RC .25 .60
191 Russ Springer .02 .10
192 Jason Bere .02 .10
193 Rodney Bolton .02 .10
194 Ellis Burks .07 .20
195 Bo Jackson .20 .50
196 Mike LaValliere .02 .10
197 Scott Ruffcorn .02 .10
198 Jeff Schwarz .02 .10
199 Jerry DiPoto .02 .10
200 Alvaro Espinoza .02 .10
201 Wayne Kirby .02 .10
202 Tom Kramer RC .05 .15
203 Jesse Levis .02 .10
204 Manny Ramirez .30 .75
205 Jeff Treadway .02 .10
206 Bill Wertz RC .05 .15
207 Cliff Young .02 .10
208 Matt Young .02 .10
209 Kirk Gibson .07 .20
210 Greg Gohr .02 .10
211 Bill Krueger .02 .10
212 Bob MacDonald .02 .10
213 Mike Moore .02 .10
214 David Wells .07 .20
215 Billy Brewer .02 .10
216 David Cone .07 .20
217 Greg Gagne .02 .10
218 Mark Gardner .02 .10
219 Chris Haney .02 .10
220 Phil Hiatt .02 .10
221 Jose Lind .02 .10
222 Juan Bell .02 .10
223 Tom Brunansky .02 .10
224 Mike Ignasiak .02 .10
225 Joe Kmak .02 .10
226 Tom Lampkin .02 .10
227 Graeme Lloyd RC .15 .40
228 Carlos Maldonado .02 .10
229 Matt Mieske .02 .10
230 Angel Miranda .02 .10
231 Troy O'Leary RC .15 .40
232 Kevin Reimer .02 .10
233 Larry Casian .02 .10
234 Jim Deshaies .02 .10
235 Eddie Guardado RC .25 .60
236 Chip Hale .02 .10
237 Mike Maksudian RC .05 .15
238 David McCarty .02 .10
239 Pat Meares RC .15 .40
240 George Tsamis RC .05 .15
241 Dave Winfield .07 .20
242 Jim Abbott .10 .30
243 Wade Boggs .10 .30
244 Andy Cook RC .05 .15
245 Russ Davis RC .05 .15
246 Mike Humphreys .02 .10
247 Jimmy Key .07 .20
248 Jim Leyritz .02 .10
249 Bobby Munoz .02 .10
250 Paul O'Neill .10 .30
251 Spike Owen .02 .10
252 Dave Silvestri .02 .10
253 Marcos Armas RC .05 .15
254 Brent Gates .02 .10
255 Rich Gossage .07 .20
256 Scott Lydy RC .05 .15
257 Henry Mercedes .02 .10
258 Mike Mohler RC .15 .40
259 Troy Neel .02 .10
260 Edwin Nunez .02 .10
261 Craig Paquette .02 .10
262 Kevin Seitzer .02 .10
263 Rich Amaral .02 .10
264 Mike Blowers .02 .10
265 Chris Bosio .02 .10
266 Norm Charlton .02 .10
267 Jim Converse RC .05 .15
268 John Cummings RC .05 .15
269 Mike Felder .02 .10
270 Mike Hampton .07 .20
271 Bill Haselman .02 .10
272 Dwayne Henry .02 .10
273 Greg Litton .02 .10
274 Mackey Sasser .02 .10
275 Lee Tinsley .02 .10
276 David Wainhouse .02 .10
277 Jeff Bronkey .02 .10
278 Benji Gil .02 .10
279 Tom Henke .02 .10
280 Charlie Leibrandt .02 .10
281 Robb Nen .07 .20
282 Bill Ripken .02 .10
283 Jon Shave RC .05 .15
284 Doug Strange .02 .10
285 Matt Whiteside RC .05 .15
286 Scott Brow RC .05 .15
287 Willie Canate RC .05 .15
288 Tony Castillo .02 .10
289 Domingo Cedeno RC .05 .15
290 Darnell Coles .02 .10
291 Danny Cox .02 .10
292 Mark Eichhorn .02 .10
293 Tony Fernandez .02 .10
294 Al Leiter .07 .20
295 Paul Molitor .07 .20
296 Dave Stewart .07 .20
297 Woody Williams RC .25 .60
298 Checklist F1-F100 .02 .10
299 Checklist F101-F200 .02 .10
300 Checklist F201-F300 .02 .10

1993 Fleer Final Edition Diamond Tribute

Each Fleer Final Edition factory set contained a complete 10-card set of Diamond Tribute inserts. These cards are numbered separately and feature a totally different design from the base cards. Each card is numbered "X" of 10 on back.

COMPLETE SET (10) 2.00 4.00
ONE SET PER FINAL EDITION FACTORY SET
1 Wade Boggs .20 .50
2 George Brett .75 2.00
3 Andre Dawson .10 .30
4 Carlton Fisk .20 .50
5 Paul Molitor .10 .30
6 Nolan Ryan 1.25 3.00
7 Lee Smith .10 .30
8 Ozzie Smith .50 1.25
9 Dave Winfield .10 .30
10 Robin Yount .50 1.25

1994 Fleer

The 1994 Fleer baseball set consists of 720 standard-size cards. Cards were distributed in hobby, retail, and jumbo packs. The cards are numbered on the back, grouped alphabetically within teams, and checklisted below alphabetically according to teams for each league with AL preceding NL. The set closes with a Superstar Specials (706-713) subset. There are no key Rookie Cards in this set.

COMPLETE SET (720) 25.00 50.00
1 Brady Anderson .10 .30
2 Harold Baines .10 .30
3 Mike Devereaux .05 .15
4 Todd Frohwirth .05 .15
5 Jeffrey Hammonds .05 .15
6 Chris Hoiles .05 .15
7 Tim Hulett .05 .15
8 Ben McDonald .05 .15
9 Mark McLemore .05 .15
10 Alan Mills .05 .15
11 Jamie Moyer .10 .30
12 Mike Mussina .20 .50
13 Gregg Olson .05 .15
14 Mike Pagliarulo .05 .15
15 Brad Pennington .05 .15
16 Jim Poole .05 .15
17 Harold Reynolds .10 .30
18 Arthur Rhodes .05 .15
19 Cal Ripken Jr. 1.00 2.50
20 David Segui .05 .15
21 Rick Sutcliffe .10 .30
22 Fernando Valenzuela .10 .30
23 Jack Voigt .05 .15
24 Mark Williamson .05 .15
25 Scott Bankhead .05 .15
26 Roger Clemens .60 1.50
27 Scott Cooper .05 .15
28 Danny Darwin .05 .15
29 Andre Dawson .10 .30
30 Rob Deer .05 .15
31 John Dopson .05 .15
32 Scott Fletcher .05 .15
33 Mike Greenwell .05 .15
34 Greg A. Harris .05 .15
35 Billy Hatcher .05 .15
36 Bob Melvin .05 .15
37 Tony Pena .05 .15
38 Paul Quantrill .05 .15
39 Carlos Quintana .05 .15
40 Ernest Riles .05 .15
41 Jeff Russell .05 .15
42 Ken Ryan .05 .15
43 Aaron Sele .05 .15
44 John Valentin .05 .15
45 Mo Vaughn .10 .30
46 Frank Viola .10 .30
47 Bob Zupcic .05 .15
48 Mike Butcher .05 .15
49 Rod Correia .05 .15
50 Chad Curtis .05 .15
51 Chili Davis .10 .30
52 Gary DiSarcina .05 .15
53 Damion Easley .05 .15
54 Jim Edmonds .30 .75
55 Chuck Finley .10 .30
56 Steve Frey .05 .15
57 Rene Gonzales .05 .15
58 Joe Grahe .05 .15
59 Hilly Hathaway .05 .15
60 Stan Javier .05 .15
61 Mark Langston .05 .15
62 Phil Leftwich RC .05 .15
63 Torey Lovullo .05 .15
64 Joe Magrane .05 .15
65 Greg Myers .05 .15
66 Ken Patterson .05 .15
67 Eduardo Perez .05 .15
68 Luis Polonia .05 .15
69 Tim Salmon .20 .50
70 J.T. Snow .10 .30
71 Ron Tingley .05 .15
72 Julio Valera .05 .15
73 Wilson Alvarez .05 .15
74 Tim Belcher .05 .15
75 George Bell .05 .15
76 Jason Bere .05 .15
77 Rod Bolton .05 .15
78 Ellis Burks .10 .30
79 Joey Cora .05 .15
80 Alex Fernandez .05 .15
81 Craig Grebeck .05 .15
82 Ozzie Guillen .10 .30
83 Roberto Hernandez .05 .15
84 Bo Jackson .30 .75
85 Lance Johnson .05 .15
86 Ron Karkovice .05 .15
87 Mike LaValliere .05 .15
88 Kirk McCaskill .05 .15
89 Jack McDowell .05 .15
90 Warren Newson .05 .15
91 Dan Pasqua .05 .15
92 Scott Radinsky .05 .15
93 Tim Raines .10 .30
94 Steve Sax .05 .15
95 Jeff Schwarz .05 .15
96 Frank Thomas .30 .75
97 Robin Ventura .10 .30
98 Sandy Alomar Jr. .05 .15
99 Carlos Baerga .05 .15
100 Albert Belle .10 .30
101 Mark Clark .05 .15
102 Jerry DiPoto .05 .15
103 Alvaro Espinoza .05 .15
104 Felix Fermin .05 .15
105 Jeremy Hernandez .05 .15
106 Reggie Jefferson .05 .15
107 Wayne Kirby .05 .15
108 Tom Kramer .05 .15
109 Mark Lewis .05 .15
110 Derek Lilliquist .05 .15
111 Kenny Lofton .10 .30
112 Candy Maldonado .05 .15
113 Jose Mesa .05 .15
114 Jeff Mutis .05 .15
115 Charles Nagy .05 .15
116 Bob Ojeda .05 .15
117 Junior Ortiz .05 .15
118 Eric Plunk .05 .15
119 Manny Ramirez .30 .75
120 Paul Sorrento .05 .15
121 Jim Thome .20 .50
122 Jeff Treadway .05 .15
123 Bill Wertz .05 .15
124 Skeeter Barnes .05 .15
125 Milt Cuyler .05 .15
126 Eric Davis .10 .30
127 John Doherty .05 .15
128 Cecil Fielder .10 .30
129 Travis Fryman .10 .30
130 Kirk Gibson .10 .30
131 Dan Gladden .05 .15
132 Greg Gohr .05 .15
133 Chris Gomez .05 .15
134 Bill Gullickson .05 .15
135 Mike Henneman .05 .15
136 Kurt Knudsen .05 .15
137 Chad Kreuter .05 .15
138 Bill Krueger .05 .15
139 Scott Livingstone .05 .15
140 Bob MacDonald .05 .15
141 Mike Moore .05 .15
142 Tony Phillips .05 .15
143 Mickey Tettleton .05 .15
144 Alan Trammell .10 .30
145 David Wells .10 .30
146 Lou Whitaker .10 .30
147 Kevin Appier .10 .30
148 Stan Belinda .05 .15
149 George Brett .75 2.00
150 Billy Brewer .05 .15
151 Hubie Brooks .05 .15
152 David Cone .10 .30
153 Gary Gaetti .10 .30
154 Greg Gagne .05 .15
155 Tom Gordon .05 .15
156 Mark Gubicza .05 .15
157 Chris Gwynn .05 .15
158 John Habyan .05 .15
159 Chris Haney .05 .15
160 Phil Hiatt .05 .15
161 Felix Jose .05 .15
162 Wally Joyner .10 .30
163 Jose Lind .05 .15
164 Mike Macfarlane .05 .15
165 Mike Magnante .05 .15
166 Brent Mayne .05 .15
167 Brian McRae .05 .15
168 Kevin McReynolds .05 .15
169 Keith Miller .05 .15
170 Jeff Montgomery .05 .15
171 Hipolito Pichardo .05 .15
172 Rico Rossy .05 .15
173 Juan Bell .05 .15
174 Ricky Bones .05 .15
175 Cal Eldred .05 .15
176 Mike Fetters .05 .15
177 Darryl Hamilton .05 .15
178 Doug Henry .05 .15
179 Mike Ignasiak .05 .15
180 John Jaha .05 .15
181 Pat Listach .05 .15
182 Graeme Lloyd .05 .15
183 Matt Mieske .05 .15
184 Angel Miranda .05 .15
185 Jaime Navarro .05 .15
186 Dave Nilsson .05 .15
187 Troy O'Leary .05 .15
188 Jesse Orosco .05 .15
189 Kevin Reimer .05 .15
190 Kevin Seitzer .05 .15
191 Bill Spiers .05 .15
192 B.J. Surhoff .10 .30
193 Dickie Thon .05 .15
194 Jose Valentin .05 .15
195 Greg Vaughn .05 .15
196 Bill Wegman .05 .15
197 Robin Yount .50 1.25
198 Rick Aguilera .05 .15
199 Willie Banks .05 .15
200 Bernardo Brito .05 .15
201 Larry Casian .05 .15
202 Scott Erickson .05 .15
203 Eddie Guardado .10 .30
204 Mark Guthrie .05 .15
205 Chip Hale .05 .15
206 Brian Harper .05 .15
207 Mike Hartley .05 .15
208 Kent Hrbek .10 .30
209 Terry Jorgensen .05 .15
210 Chuck Knoblauch .10 .30
211 Gene Larkin .05 .15
212 Shane Mack .05 .15
213 David McCarty .05 .15
214 Pat Meares .05 .15
215 Pedro Munoz .05 .15
216 Derek Parks .05 .15
217 Kirby Puckett .30 .75
218 Jeff Reboulet .05 .15
219 Kevin Tapani .05 .15
220 Mike Trombley .05 .15
221 George Tsamis .05 .15
222 Carl Willis .05 .15
223 Dave Winfield .10 .30
224 Jim Abbott .20 .50
225 Paul Assenmacher .05 .15
226 Wade Boggs .20 .50
227 Russ Davis .05 .15
228 Steve Farr .05 .15
229 Mike Gallego .05 .15
230 Paul Gibson .05 .15
231 Steve Howe .05 .15
232 Dion James .05 .15
233 Domingo Jean .05 .15
234 Scott Kamieniecki .05 .15
235 Pat Kelly .05 .15
236 Jimmy Key .10 .30
237 Jim Leyritz .05 .15
238 Kevin Maas .05 .15
239 Don Mattingly .75 2.00
240 Rich Monteleone .05 .15
241 Bobby Munoz .05 .15
242 Matt Nokes .05 .15
243 Paul O'Neill .20 .50
244 Spike Owen .05 .15
245 Melido Perez .05 .15
246 Lee Smith .10 .30
247 Mike Stanley .05 .15
248 Danny Tartabull .05 .15
249 Randy Velarde .05 .15
250 Bob Wickman .05 .15
251 Bernie Williams .20 .50
252 Mike Aldrete .05 .15
253 Marcos Armas .05 .15
254 Lance Blankenship .05 .15
255 Mike Bordick .05 .15
256 Scott Brosius .10 .30
257 Jerry Browne .05 .15
258 Ron Darling .05 .15
259 Kelly Downs .05 .15
260 Dennis Eckersley .10 .30
261 Brent Gates .05 .15
262 Rich Gossage .10 .30
263 Scott Hemond .05 .15
264 Dave Henderson .05 .15
265 Rick Honeycutt .05 .15
266 Vince Horsman .05 .15
267 Scott Lydy .05 .15
268 Mark McGwire .75 2.00
269 Mike Mohler .05 .15
270 Troy Neel .05 .15
271 Edwin Nunez .05 .15
272 Craig Paquette .05 .15
273 Ruben Sierra .10 .30
274 Terry Steinbach .05 .15
275 Todd Van Poppel .05 .15
276 Bob Welch .05 .15
277 Bobby Witt .05 .15
278 Rich Amaral .05 .15
279 Mike Blowers .05 .15
280 Bret Boone UER .10 .30
(Name spelled Brett on front)
281 Chris Bosio .05 .15
282 Jay Buhner .10 .30
283 Norm Charlton .05 .15
284 Mike Felder .05 .15
285 Dave Fleming .05 .15
286 Ken Griffey Jr. .50 1.25
287 Erik Hanson .05 .15
288 Bill Haselman .05 .15
289 Brad Holman RC .05 .15
290 Randy Johnson .30 .75
291 Tim Leary .05 .15
292 Greg Litton .05 .15
293 Dave Magadan .05 .15
294 Edgar Martinez .20 .50
295 Tino Martinez .20 .50
296 Jeff Nelson .05 .15
297 Erik Plantenberg RC .05 .15
298 Mackey Sasser .05 .15
299 Brian Turang RC .05 .15
300 Dave Valle .05 .15
301 Omar Vizquel .20 .50
302 Brian Bohanon .05 .15
303 Kevin Brown .10 .30
304 Jose Canseco UER .20 .50
(Back mentions 1991 as his 40/40 MVP season; should be '88)
305 Mario Diaz .05 .15
306 Julio Franco .10 .30
307 Juan Gonzalez .10 .30
308 Tom Henke .05 .15
309 David Hulse .05 .15
310 Manuel Lee .05 .15
311 Craig Lefferts .05 .15
312 Charlie Leibrandt .05 .15
313 Rafael Palmeiro .20 .50
314 Dean Palmer .10 .30
315 Roger Pavlik .05 .15
316 Dan Peltier .05 .15
317 Gene Petralli .05 .15
318 Gary Redus .05 .15
319 Ivan Rodriguez .20 .50
320 Kenny Rogers .10 .30
321 Nolan Ryan 1.25 3.00
322 Doug Strange .05 .15
323 Matt Whiteside .05 .15
324 Roberto Alomar .20 .50
325 Pat Borders .05 .15
326 Joe Carter .10 .30
327 Tony Castillo .05 .15
328 Darnell Coles .05 .15
329 Danny Cox .05 .15
330 Mark Eichhorn .05 .15
331 Tony Fernandez .05 .15
332 Alfredo Griffin .05 .15
333 Juan Guzman .05 .15
334 Rickey Henderson .30 .75
335 Pat Hentgen .05 .15
336 Randy Knorr .05 .15
337 Al Leiter .10 .30
338 Paul Molitor .10 .30
339 Jack Morris .10 .30
340 John Olerud .10 .30
341 Dick Schofield .05 .15
342 Ed Sprague .05 .15
343 Dave Stewart .10 .30
344 Todd Stottlemyre .05 .15
345 Mike Timlin .05 .15
346 Duane Ward .05 .15
347 Turner Ward .05 .15
348 Devon White .10 .30
349 Woody Williams .10 .30
350 Steve Avery .05 .15
351 Steve Bedrosian .05 .15
352 Rafael Belliard .05 .15
353 Damon Berryhill .05 .15
354 Jeff Blauser .05 .15
355 Sid Bream .05 .15
356 Francisco Cabrera .05 .15
357 Marvin Freeman .05 .15
358 Ron Gant .10 .30
359 Tom Glavine .20 .50
360 Jay Howell .05 .15
361 David Justice .10 .30
362 Ryan Klesko .10 .30
363 Mark Lemke .05 .15
364 Javier Lopez .10 .30
365 Greg Maddux .50 1.25
366 Fred McGriff .20 .50
367 Greg McMichael .05 .15
368 Kent Mercker .05 .15
369 Otis Nixon .05 .15
370 Greg Olson .05 .15
371 Bill Pecota .05 .15
372 Terry Pendleton .10 .30
373 Deion Sanders .20 .50
374 Pete Smith .05 .15
375 John Smoltz .20 .50
376 Mike Stanton .05 .15
377 Tony Tarasco .05 .15
378 Mark Wohlers .05 .15
379 Jose Bautista .05 .15
380 Shawn Boskie .05 .15
381 Steve Buechele .05 .15
382 Frank Castillo .05 .15
383 Mark Grace .20 .50
384 Jose Guzman .05 .15
385 Mike Harkey .05 .15
386 Greg Hibbard .05 .15
387 Glenallen Hill .05 .15
388 Steve Lake .05 .15
389 Derrick May .05 .15
390 Chuck McElroy .05 .15
391 Mike Morgan .05 .15
392 Randy Myers .05 .15
393 Dan Plesac .05 .15
394 Kevin Roberson .05 .15
395 Rey Sanchez .05 .15
396 Ryne Sandberg .50 1.25
397 Bob Scanlan .05 .15
398 Dwight Smith .05 .15
399 Sammy Sosa .30 .75
400 Jose Vizcaino .05 .15
401 Rick Wilkins .05 .15
402 Willie Wilson .05 .15
403 Eric Yelding .05 .15
404 Bobby Ayala .05 .15
405 Jeff Branson .05 .15
406 Tom Browning .05 .15
407 Jacob Brumfield .05 .15
408 Tim Costo .05 .15
409 Rob Dibble .10 .30
410 Willie Greene .05 .15
411 Thomas Howard .05 .15
412 Roberto Kelly .05 .15

413 Bill Landrum .05 .15
414 Barry Larkin .20 .50
415 Larry Luebbers RC .05 .15
416 Kevin Mitchell .05 .15
417 Hal Morris .05 .15
418 Joe Oliver .05 .15
419 Tim Pugh .05 .15
420 Jeff Reardon .10 .30
421 Jose Rijo .05 .15
422 Bip Roberts .05 .15
423 John Roper .05 .15
424 Johnny Ruffin .05 .15
425 Chris Sabo .05 .15
426 Juan Samuel .05 .15
427 Reggie Sanders .10 .30
428 Scott Service .05 .15
429 John Smiley .05 .15
430 Jerry Spradlin RC .05 .15
431 Kevin Wickander .05 .15
432 Freddie Benavides .05 .15
433 Dante Bichette .10 .30
434 Willie Blair .05 .15
435 Daryl Boston .05 .15
436 Kent Bottenfield .05 .15
437 Vinny Castilla .10 .30
438 Jerald Clark .05 .15
439 Alex Cole .05 .15
440 Andres Galarraga .10 .30
441 Joe Girardi .05 .15
442 Greg W. Harris .05 .15
443 Charlie Hayes .05 .15
444 Darren Holmes .05 .15
445 Chris Jones .05 .15
446 Roberto Mejia .05 .15
447 David Nied .05 .15
448 Jayhawk Owens .05 .15
449 Jeff Parrett .05 .15
450 Steve Reed .05 .15
451 Armando Reynoso .05 .15
452 Bruce Ruffin .05 .15
453 Mo Sanford .05 .15
454 Danny Sheaffer .05 .15
455 Jim Tatum .05 .15
456 Gary Wayne .05 .15
457 Eric Young .05 .15
458 Luis Aquino .05 .15
459 Alex Arias .05 .15
460 Jack Armstrong .05 .15
461 Bret Barberie .05 .15
462 Ryan Bowen .05 .15
463 Chuck Carr .05 .15
464 Jeff Conine .10 .30
465 Henry Cotto .05 .15
466 Orestes Destrade .05 .15
467 Chris Hammond .05 .15
468 Bryan Harvey .05 .15
469 Charlie Hough .10 .30
470 Joe Klink .05 .15
471 Richie Lewis .05 .15
472 Bob Natal .05 .15
473 Pat Rapp .05 .15
474 Rich Renteria .05 .15
475 Rich Rodriguez .05 .15
476 Benito Santiago .10 .30
477 Gary Sheffield .10 .30
478 Matt Turner .05 .15
479 David Weathers .05 .15
480 Walt Weiss .05 .15
481 Darrell Whitmore .05 .15
482 Eric Anthony .05 .15
483 Jeff Bagwell .20 .50
484 Kevin Bass .05 .15
485 Craig Biggio .20 .50
486 Ken Caminiti .10 .30
487 Andujar Cedeno .05 .15
488 Chris Donnels .05 .15
489 Doug Drabek .05 .15
490 Steve Finley .10 .30
491 Luis Gonzalez .10 .30
492 Pete Harnisch .05 .15
493 Xavier Hernandez .05 .15
494 Doug Jones .05 .15
495 Todd Jones .05 .15
496 Darryl Kile .10 .30
497 Al Osuna .05 .15
498 Mark Portugal .05 .15
499 Scott Servais .05 .15
500 Greg Swindell .05 .15
501 Eddie Taubensee .05 .15
502 Jose Uribe .05 .15
503 Brian Williams .05 .15
504 Billy Ashley .05 .15
505 Pedro Astacio .05 .15
506 Brett Butler .10 .30
507 Tom Candiotti .05 .15
508 Omar Daal .05 .15
509 Jim Gott .05 .15
510 Kevin Gross .05 .15
511 Dave Hansen .05 .15
512 Carlos Hernandez .05 .15
513 Orel Hershiser .10 .30
514 Eric Karros .10 .30
515 Pedro Martinez .30 .75
516 Ramon Martinez .05 .15
517 Roger McDowell .05 .15
518 Raul Mondesi .10 .30
519 Jose Offerman .05 .15
520 Mike Piazza .60 1.50
521 Jody Reed .05 .15
522 Henry Rodriguez .05 .15
523 Mike Sharperson .05 .15
524 Cory Snyder .05 .15
525 Darryl Strawberry .10 .30
526 Rick Trlicek .05 .15
527 Tim Wallach .05 .15
528 Mitch Webster .05 .15
529 Steve Wilson .05 .15
530 Todd Worrell .05 .15
531 Moises Alou .10 .30
532 Brian Barnes .05 .15
533 Sean Berry .05 .15
534 Greg Colbrunn .05 .15
535 Delino DeShields .05 .15
536 Jeff Fassero .05 .15
537 Darrin Fletcher .05 .15
538 Cliff Floyd .10 .30
539 Lou Frazier .05 .15
540 Marquis Grissom .10 .30
541 Butch Henry .05 .15
542 Ken Hill .05 .15
543 Mike Lansing .05 .15
544 Brian Looney RC .05 .15
545 Dennis Martinez .10 .30
546 Chris Nabholz .05 .15
547 Randy Ready .05 .15
548 Mel Rojas .05 .15
549 Kirk Rueter .05 .15
550 Tim Scott .05 .15
551 Jeff Shaw .05 .15
552 Tim Spehr .05 .15
553 John Vander Wal .05 .15
554 Larry Walker .10 .30
555 John Wetteland .10 .30
556 Rondell White .10 .30
557 Tim Bogar .05 .15
558 Bobby Bonilla .10 .30
559 Jeromy Burnitz .10 .30
560 Sid Fernandez .05 .15
561 John Franco .10 .30
562 Dave Gallagher .05 .15
563 Dwight Gooden .10 .30
564 Eric Hillman .05 .15
565 Todd Hundley .05 .15
566 Jeff Innis .05 .15
567 Darrin Jackson .05 .15
568 Howard Johnson .05 .15
569 Bobby Jones .05 .15
570 Jeff Kent .20 .50
571 Mike Maddux .05 .15
572 Jeff McKnight .05 .15
573 Eddie Murray .30 .75
574 Charlie O'Brien .05 .15
575 Joe Orsulak .05 .15
576 Bret Saberhagen .10 .30
577 Pete Schourek .05 .15
578 Dave Telgheder .05 .15
579 Ryan Thompson .05 .15
580 Anthony Young .05 .15
581 Ruben Amaro .05 .15
582 Larry Andersen .05 .15
583 Kim Batiste .05 .15
584 Wes Chamberlain .05 .15
585 Darren Daulton .10 .30
586 Mariano Duncan .05 .15
587 Lenny Dykstra .10 .30
588 Jim Eisenreich .05 .15
589 Tommy Greene .05 .15
590 Dave Hollins .05 .15
591 Pete Incaviglia .05 .15
592 Danny Jackson .05 .15
593 Ricky Jordan .05 .15
594 John Kruk .10 .30
595 Roger Mason .05 .15
596 Mickey Morandini .05 .15
597 Terry Mulholland .05 .15
598 Todd Pratt .05 .15
599 Ben Rivera .05 .15
600 Curt Schilling .10 .30
601 Kevin Stocker .05 .15
602 Milt Thompson .05 .15
603 David West .05 .15
604 Mitch Williams .05 .15
605 Jay Bell .10 .30
606 Dave Clark .05 .15
607 Steve Cooke .05 .15
608 Tom Foley .05 .15
609 Carlos Garcia .05 .15
610 Joel Johnston .05 .15
611 Jeff King .05 .15
612 Al Martin .05 .15
613 Lloyd McClendon .05 .15
614 Orlando Merced .05 .15
615 Blas Minor .05 .15
616 Denny Neagle .10 .30
617 Mark Petkovsek RC .05 .15
618 Tom Prince .05 .15
619 Don Slaught .05 .15
620 Zane Smith .05 .15
621 Randy Tomlin .05 .15
622 Andy Van Slyke .20 .50
623 Paul Wagner .05 .15
624 Tim Wakefield .20 .50
625 Bob Walk .05 .15
626 Kevin Young .05 .15
627 Luis Alicea .05 .15
628 Rene Arocha .05 .15
629 Rod Brewer .05 .15
630 Rheal Cormier .05 .15
631 Bernard Gilkey .05 .15
632 Lee Guetterman .05 .15
633 Gregg Jefferies .05 .15
634 Brian Jordan .10 .30
635 Les Lancaster .05 .15
636 Ray Lankford .10 .30
637 Rob Murphy .05 .15
638 Omar Olivares .05 .15
639 Jose Oquendo .05 .15
640 Donovan Osborne .05 .15
641 Tom Pagnozzi .05 .15
642 Erik Pappas .05 .15
643 Geronimo Pena .05 .15
644 Mike Perez .05 .15
645 Gerald Perry .05 .15
646 Ozzie Smith .50 1.25
647 Bob Tewksbury .05 .15
648 Allen Watson .05 .15
649 Mark Whiten .05 .15
650 Tracy Woodson .05 .15
651 Todd Zeile .05 .15
652 Andy Ashby .05 .15
653 Brad Ausmus .20 .50
654 Billy Bean .05 .15
655 Derek Bell .05 .15
656 Andy Benes .05 .15
657 Doug Brocail .05 .15
658 Jarvis Brown .05 .15
659 Archi Cianfrocco .05 .15
660 Phil Clark .05 .15
661 Mark Davis .05 .15
662 Jeff Gardner .05 .15
663 Pat Gomez .05 .15
664 Ricky Gutierrez .05 .15
665 Tony Gwynn .40 1.00
666 Gene Harris .05 .15
667 Kevin Higgins .05 .15
668 Trevor Hoffman .20 .50
669 Pedro Martinez RC .05 .15
670 Tim Mauser .05 .15
671 Melvin Nieves .05 .15
672 Phil Plantier .05 .15
673 Frank Seminara .05 .15
674 Craig Shipley .05 .15
675 Kerry Taylor .05 .15
676 Tim Teufel .05 .15
677 Guillermo Velasquez .05 .15
678 Wally Whitehurst .05 .15
679 Tim Worrell .05 .15
680 Rod Beck .05 .15
681 Mike Benjamin .05 .15
682 Todd Benzinger .05 .15
683 Bud Black .05 .15
684 Barry Bonds .75 2.00
685 Jeff Brantley .05 .15
686 Dave Burba .05 .15
687 John Burkett .05 .15
688 Mark Carreon .05 .15
689 Will Clark .20 .50
690 Royce Clayton .05 .15
691 Bryan Hickerson .05 .15
692 Mike Jackson .05 .15
693 Darren Lewis .05 .15
694 Kirt Manwaring .05 .15
695 Dave Martinez .05 .15
696 Willie McGee .10 .30
697 John Patterson .05 .15
698 Jeff Reed .05 .15
699 Kevin Rogers .05 .15
700 Scott Sanderson .05 .15
701 Steve Scarsone .05 .15
702 Billy Swift .05 .15
703 Robby Thompson .05 .15
704 Matt Williams .10 .30
705 Trevor Wilson .05 .15
706 Fred McGriff .10 .30
Ron Gant
David Justice
707 John Olerud .10 .30
Paul Molitor
708 Mike Mussina .10 .30
Jack McDowell
709 Lou Whitaker .10 .30
Alan Trammell
710 Rafael Palmeiro .10 .30
Juan Gonzalez
711 Brett Butler .20 .50
Tony Gwynn
712 Kirby Puckett .20 .50
Chuck Knoblauch
713 Mike Piazza .30 .75
Eric Karros
714 Checklist 1 .05 .15
715 Checklist 2 .05 .15
716 Checklist 3 .05 .15
717 Checklist 4 .05 .15
718 Checklist 5 .05 .15
719 Checklist 6 .05 .15
720 Checklist 7 .05 .15
P69 Tim Salmon Promo .40 1.00

1994 Fleer All-Rookies

Collectors could redeem an All-Rookie Team Exchange card by mail for this nine-card set of top 1994 rookies at each position as chosen by Fleer. The expiration date to redeem this set was September 30, 1994. None of these players were in the basic 1994 Fleer set. The exchange card was randomly inserted into all 1994 Fleer packs.

COMPLETE SET (9) 4.00 8.00
M1 Kurt Abbott .20 .50
M2 Rich Becker .20 .50
M3 Carlos Delgado .60 1.50
M4 Jorge Fabregas .20 .50
M5 Bob Hamelin .20 .50
M6 John Hudek .20 .50
M7 Tim Hyers .20 .50
M8 Luis Lopez .20 .50
M9 James Mouton .20 .50
NNO Exp. All-Rookie Exch. .20 .50

1994 Fleer All-Stars

Fleer issued this 50-card standard-size set in 1994, to commemorate the All-Stars of the 1993 season. The cards were exclusively available in the Fleer wax packs at a rate of one in two. The set features 25 American League (1-25) and 25 National League (26-50) All-Stars. Each league's all-stars are sequenced in alphabetical order.

COMPLETE SET (50) 10.00 25.00
STATED ODDS 1:2
1 Roberto Alomar .25 .60
2 Carlos Baerga .07 .20
3 Albert Belle .15 .40
4 Wade Boggs .25 .60
5 Joe Carter .15 .40
6 Scott Cooper .07 .20
7 Cecil Fielder .15 .40
8 Travis Fryman .15 .40
9 Juan Gonzalez .15 .40
10 Ken Griffey Jr. .60 1.50
11 Pat Hentgen .07 .20
12 Randy Johnson .40 1.00
13 Jimmy Key .15 .40
14 Mark Langston .07 .20
15 Jack McDowell .07 .20
16 Paul Molitor .15 .40
17 Jeff Montgomery .07 .20
18 Mike Mussina .25 .60
19 John Olerud .15 .40
20 Kirby Puckett .40 1.00
21 Cal Ripken 1.25 3.00
22 Ivan Rodriguez .25 .60
23 Frank Thomas .40 1.00
24 Greg Vaughn .07 .20
25 Duane Ward .07 .20
26 Steve Avery .10 .20
27 Rod Beck .07 .20
28 Jay Bell .15 .40
29 Andy Benes .07 .20
30 Jeff Blauser .07 .20
31 Barry Bonds 1.00 2.50
32 Bobby Bonilla .15 .40
33 John Burkett .07 .20
34 Darren Daulton .15 .40
35 Andres Galarraga .15 .40
36 Tom Glavine .25 .60
37 Mark Grace .25 .60
38 Marquis Grissom .15 .40
39 Tony Gwynn .50 1.25
40 Bryan Harvey .07 .20
41 Dave Hollins .07 .20
42 David Justice .15 .40
43 Darryl Kile .15 .40
44 John Kruk .15 .40
45 Barry Larkin .25 .60
46 Terry Mulholland .07 .20
47 Mike Piazza .75 2.00
48 Ryne Sandberg .60 1.50
49 Gary Sheffield .15 .40
50 John Smoltz .25 .60

1994 Fleer Award Winners

Randomly inserted in foil packs at a rate of one in 37, this six-card standard-size set spotlights six outstanding players who received awards.

COMPLETE SET (6) 3.00 8.00
STATED ODDS 1:37
1 Frank Thomas .50 1.25
2 Barry Bonds 1.25 3.00
3 Jack McDowell .08 .25
4 Greg Maddux .75 2.00
5 Tim Salmon .30 .75
6 Mike Piazza 1.00 2.50

1994 Fleer Golden Moments

These standard-size cards were issued one per blue retail jumbo pack. The fronts feature borderless color player action photos. A shrink-wrapped package containing a jumbo set was issued one per Fleer hobby case. Jumbos were later issued for retail purposes with a production number of 10,000. The standard-size cards are not individually numbered.

COMPLETE SET (10) 12.50 30.00
*JUMBOS: 4X TO 1X BASIC GM
ONE JUMBO SET PER HOBBY CASE
JUMBOS ALSO REPACKAGED FOR RETAIL
1 Mark Whiten .25 .60
2 Carlos Baerga .25 .60
3 Dave Winfield .50 1.25
4 Ken Griffey Jr. 2.00 5.00
5 Bo Jackson 1.25 3.00
6 George Brett 3.00 8.00
7 Nolan Ryan 5.00 12.00
8 Fred McGriff .75 2.00
9 Frank Thomas 1.25 3.00
10 Chris Bosio .25 .60
Jim Abbott
Darryl Kile

1994 Fleer League Leaders

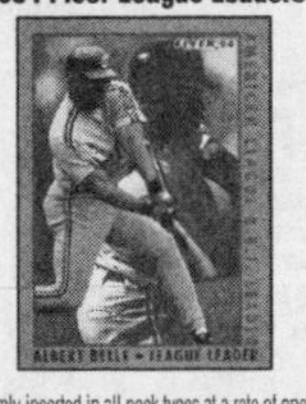

Randomly inserted in all pack types at a rate of one in 17, this 28-card set features six statistical leaders each for the American (1-6) and the National (7-12) Leagues.

COMPLETE SET (12) 2.00 5.00
STATED ODDS 1:17
1 John Olerud .15 .40
2 Albert Belle .15 .40
3 Rafael Palmeiro .20 .50
4 Kenny Lofton .15 .40
5 Jack McDowell .08 .25
6 Kevin Appier .15 .40
7 Andres Galarraga .15 .40
8 Barry Bonds .60 1.50
9 Lenny Dykstra .15 .40
10 Chuck Carr .08 .25
11 Tom Glavine UER .20 .50
No number on back of card
12 Greg Maddux 1.00 2.50

1994 Fleer Lumber Company

Randomly inserted in jumbo packs at a rate of one in five, this ten-card standard-size set features the best hitters in the game. The cards are numbered alphabetically.

COMPLETE SET (10) 4.00 10.00
STATED ODDS 1:5 JUMBO
1 Albert Belle .20 .50
2 Barry Bonds 1.25 3.00
3 Ron Gant .20 .50
4 Juan Gonzalez .20 .50
5 Ken Griffey Jr. .75 2.00
6 David Justice .20 .50
7 Fred McGriff .30 .75
8 Rafael Palmeiro .30 .75
9 Frank Thomas .50 1.25
10 Matt Williams .20 .50

1994 Fleer Major League Prospects

Randomly inserted in all pack types at a rate of one in six, this 35-card standard-size set showcases some of the outstanding young players in Major League Baseball. The cards are numbered on the back "X of 35" and are sequenced in alphabetical order.

COMPLETE SET (35) 6.00 15.00
STATED ODDS 1:6
1 Kurt Abbott .08 .25
2 Brian Anderson .30 .75
3 Rich Aude .08 .25
4 Cory Bailey .08 .25
5 Danny Bautista .08 .25
6 Marty Cordova .08 .25
7 Tripp Cromer .08 .25
8 Midre Cummings .08 .25
9 Carlos Delgado .50 1.25
10 Steve Dreyer .08 .25
11 Steve Dunn .08 .25
12 Jeff Granger .08 .25
13 Tyrone Hill .08 .25
14 Denny Hocking .08 .25
15 John Hope .08 .25
16 Butch Huskey .08 .25
17 Miguel Jimenez .08 .25
18 Chipper Jones .75 2.00
19 Steve Karsay .08 .25
20 Mike Kelly .08 .25
21 Mike Lieberthal .30 .75
22 Albie Lopez .08 .25
23 Jeff McNeely .08 .25
24 Danny Miceli .08 .25
25 Nate Minchey .08 .25
26 Marc Newfield .08 .25
27 Darren Oliver .30 .75
28 Luis Ortiz .08 .25
29 Curtis Pride .30 .75
30 Roger Salkeld .08 .25
31 Scott Sanders .08 .25
32 Dave Staton .08 .25
33 Salomon Torres .08 .25
34 Steve Trachsel .08 .25
35 Chris Turner .08 .25

1994 Fleer Pro-Visions

Randomly inserted in all pack types at a rate of one in 12, this nine-card standard-size set features on its fronts colorful artistic player caricatures with surrealistic backgrounds drawn by illustrator Wayne Still. When all nine cards are placed in order in a collector sheet, the backgrounds fit together to form a composite. The cards are numbered on the back "X of 9."

COMPLETE SET (9) 1.50 4.00
STATED ODDS 1:12
1 Darren Daulton .15 .40
2 John Olerud .15 .40
3 Matt Williams .15 .40
4 Carlos Baerga .07 .20
5 Ozzie Smith .60 1.50
6 Juan Gonzalez .15 .40
7 Jack McDowell .07 .20
8 Mike Piazza .75 2.00
9 Tony Gwynn .50 1.25

1994 Fleer Rookie Sensations

Randomly inserted in jumbo packs at a rate of one in four, this 20-card standard-size set features outstanding rookies. The fronts are "double exposed," with a player action cutout superimposed over a second photo. The cards are numbered on the back "X of 20" and are sequenced in alphabetical order.

COMPLETE SET (20) 8.00 20.00
STATED ODDS 1:4 JUMBO
1 Rene Arocha .40 1.00
2 Jason Bere .40 1.00
3 Jeromy Burnitz .75 2.00
4 Chuck Carr .40 1.00
5 Jeff Conine .75 2.00
6 Steve Cooke .40 1.00
7 Cliff Floyd .75 2.00
8 Jeffrey Hammonds .40 1.00
9 Wayne Kirby .40 1.00
10 Mike Lansing .40 1.00
11 Al Martin .40 1.00
12 Greg McMichael .40 1.00
13 Troy Neel .40 1.00
14 Mike Piazza 3.00 8.00
15 Armando Reynoso .40 1.00
16 Kirk Rueter .40 1.00
17 Tim Salmon 1.25 3.00
18 Aaron Sele .40 1.00
19 J.T. Snow .75 2.00
20 Kevin Stocker .40 1.00

1994 Fleer Salmon

Spotlighting American League Rookie of the Year Tim Salmon, this 15-card standard size set was issued in two forms. Cards 1-12 were randomly inserted in packs (one in eight) and 13-15 were available through a mail-in offer. Ten wrappers and 1.50 were necessary to acquire the mail-ins. The mail-in expiration date was September 30, 1994. Salmon autographed more than 2,000 of his cards.

COMPLETE SET (12) 6.00 15.00
COMMON CARD (1-12) .40 1.00
1-12 STATED ODDS 1:8
COMMON MAIL (13-15) .40 1.00
AU Tim Salmon AU/2000 6.00 15.00

1994 Fleer Smoke 'n Heat

Randomly inserted in wax packs at a rate of one in 36, this 12-card standard-size set showcases the best pitchers in the game. The cards are numbered on the back "X of 12." and are sequenced in alphabetical order.

COMPLETE SET (12) 25.00 60.00
STATED ODDS 1:36
1 Roger Clemens 4.00 10.00
2 David Cone .75 2.00
3 Juan Guzman .40 1.00
4 Pete Harnisch .40 1.00
5 Randy Johnson 2.00 5.00
6 Mark Langston .40 1.00
7 Greg Maddux 3.00 8.00
8 Mike Mussina 1.25 3.00
9 Jose Rijo .40 1.00
10 Nolan Ryan 8.00 20.00
11 Curt Schilling .75 2.00
12 John Smoltz 1.25 3.00

1994 Fleer Team Leaders

Randomly inserted in all pack types, this 28-card standard-size set features Fleer's selected top player from each of the 28 major league teams. The card numbering is arranged alphabetically by city according to the American (1-14) and the National (15-28) Leagues.

COMPLETE SET (28) 10.00 25.00
RANDOM INSERTS IN ALL PACKS
1 Cal Ripken 1.50 4.00
2 Mo Vaughn .20 .50
3 Tim Salmon .30 .75
4 Frank Thomas .50 1.25
5 Carlos Baerga .08 .25
6 Cecil Fielder .20 .50
7 Brian McRae .08 .25
8 Greg Vaughn .08 .25
9 Kirby Puckett .50 1.25
10 Don Mattingly 1.25 3.00
11 Mark McGwire 1.25 3.00
12 Ken Griffey Jr. .75 2.00
13 Juan Gonzalez .20 .50
14 Paul Molitor .20 .50
15 David Justice .20 .50
16 Ryne Sandberg .75 2.00
17 Barry Larkin .30 .75
18 Andres Galarraga .20 .50
19 Gary Sheffield .20 .50
20 Jeff Bagwell .30 .75
21 Mike Piazza 1.00 2.50
22 Marquis Grissom .20 .50
23 Bobby Bonilla .20 .50
24 Lenny Dykstra .20 .50
25 Jay Bell .20 .50
26 Gregg Jefferies .08 .25
27 Tony Gwynn .60 1.50
28 Will Clark .30 .75

1994 Fleer Update

This 200-card standard-size set highlights traded players in their new uniforms and promising young rookies. The Update set was exclusively distributed in factory set form through hobby dealers. Each hobby case contained 20 cases. A ten card Diamond Tribute set was included in each factory set for a total of 210 cards. The cards are numbered on the back, grouped alphabetically by team by league with AL preceding NL. Key Rookie Cards include Chan Ho Park and Alex Rodriguez.

COMP.FACT.SET (210) 25.00 50.00
1 Mark Eichhorn .08 .25
2 Sid Fernandez .08 .25
3 Leo Gomez .08 .25
4 Mike Oquist .08 .25
5 Rafael Palmeiro .30 .75
6 Chris Sabo .08 .25
7 Dwight Smith .08 .25
8 Lee Smith .20 .50
9 Damon Berryhill .08 .25
10 Wes Chamberlain .08 .25
11 Gar Finnvold .08 .25
12 Chris Howard .08 .25
13 Tim Naehring .08 .25
14 Otis Nixon .08 .25
15 Brian Anderson RC .20 .50
16 Jorge Fabregas .08 .25
17 Rex Hudler .08 .25
18 Bo Jackson .50 1.25
19 Mark Leiter .08 .25
20 Spike Owen .08 .25
21 Harold Reynolds .20 .50
22 Chris Turner .08 .25
23 Dennis Cook .08 .25
24 Jose DeLeon .08 .25
25 Julio Franco .20 .50
26 Joe Hall .08 .25
27 Darrin Jackson .08 .25
28 Dane Johnson .08 .25
29 Norberto Martin .08 .25
30 Scott Sanderson .08 .25
31 Jason Grimsley .08 .25
32 Dennis Martinez .20 .50
33 Jack Morris .20 .50
34 Eddie Murray .50 1.25
35 Chad Ogea .08 .25
36 Tony Pena .08 .25
37 Paul Shuey .08 .25
38 Omar Vizquel .30 .75
39 Danny Bautista .08 .25
40 Tim Belcher .08 .25
41 Joe Boever .08 .25
42 Storm Davis .08 .25
43 Junior Felix .08 .25
44 Mike Gardiner .08 .25
45 Buddy Groom .08 .25
46 Juan Samuel .08 .25
47 Vince Coleman .08 .25
48 Bob Hamelin .08 .25
49 Dave Henderson .08 .25
50 Rusty Meacham .08 .25
51 Terry Shumpert .08 .25
52 Jeff Bronkey .08 .25
53 Alex Diaz .08 .25
54 Brian Harper .08 .25
55 Jose Mercedes .08 .25
56 Jody Reed .08 .25
57 Bob Scanlan .08 .25
58 Turner Ward .08 .25
59 Rich Becker .08 .25
60 Alex Cole .08 .25
61 Denny Hocking .08 .25
62 Scott Leius .08 .25
63 Pat Mahomes .08 .25
64 Carlos Pulido .08 .25
65 Dave Stevens .08 .25
66 Matt Walbeck .08 .25
67 Xavier Hernandez .08 .25
68 Sterling Hitchcock .08 .25
69 Terry Mulholland .08 .25
70 Luis Polonia .08 .25
71 Gerald Williams .08 .25
72 Mark Acre RC .08 .25
73 Geronimo Berroa .08 .25
74 Rickey Henderson .50 1.25
75 Stan Javier .08 .25
76 Steve Karsay .08 .25
77 Carlos Reyes .08 .25
78 Bill Taylor RC .20 .50
79 Eric Anthony .08 .25
80 Bobby Ayala .08 .25

81 Tim Davis	.08	.25
82 Felix Fermin	.08	.25
83 Reggie Jefferson	.08	.25
84 Keith Mitchell	.08	.25
85 Bill Risley	.08	.25
86 Alex Rodriguez RC	8.00	20.00
87 Roger Salkeld	.08	.25
88 Dan Wilson	.08	.25
89 Cris Carpenter	.08	.25
90 Will Clark	.30	.75
91 Jeff Frye	.08	.25
92 Rick Helling	.08	.25
93 Chris James	.08	.25
94 Oddibe McDowell	.08	.25
95 Billy Ripken	.08	.25
96 Carlos Delgado	.30	.75
97 Alex Gonzalez	.08	.25
98 Shawn Green	.50	1.25
99 Darren Hall	.08	.25
100 Mike Huff	.08	.25
101 Mike Kelly	.08	.25
102 Roberto Kelly	.08	.25
103 Charlie O'Brien	.08	.25
104 Jose Oliva	.08	.25
105 Gregg Olson	.08	.25
106 Willie Banks	.08	.25
107 Jim Bullinger	.08	.25
108 Chuck Crim	.08	.25
109 Shawon Dunston	.08	.25
110 Karl Rhodes	.08	.25
111 Steve Trachsel	.08	.25
112 Anthony Young	.08	.25
113 Eddie Zambrano	.08	.25
114 Bret Boone	.20	.50
115 Jeff Brantley	.08	.25
116 Hector Carrasco	.08	.25
117 Tony Fernandez	.08	.25
118 Tim Fortugno	.08	.25
119 Erik Hanson	.08	.25
120 Chuck McElroy	.08	.25
121 Deion Sanders	.30	.75
122 Ellis Burks	.20	.50
123 Marvin Freeman	.08	.25
124 Mike Harkey	.08	.25
125 Howard Johnson	.08	.25
126 Mike Kingery	.08	.25
127 Nelson Liriano	.08	.25
128 Marcus Moore	.08	.25
129 Mike Munoz	.08	.25
130 Kevin Ritz	.08	.25
131 Walt Weiss	.08	.25
132 Kurt Abbott RC	.08	.25
133 Jerry Browne	.08	.25
134 Greg Colbrunn	.08	.25
135 Jeremy Hernandez	.08	.25
136 Dave Magadan	.08	.25
137 Kurt Miller	.08	.25
138 Robb Nen	.20	.50
139 Jesus Tavarez RC	.08	.25
140 Sid Bream	.08	.25
141 Tom Edens	.08	.25
142 Tony Eusebio	.08	.25
143 John Hudek RC	.08	.25
144 Brian L. Hunter	.08	.25
145 Orlando Miller	.08	.25
146 James Mouton	.08	.25
147 Shane Reynolds	.08	.25
148 Rafael Bournigal	.08	.25
149 Delino DeShields	.08	.25
150 Garey Ingram RC	.08	.25
151 Chan Ho Park RC	.30	.75
152 Wil Cordero	.08	.25
153 Pedro Martinez	.50	1.25
154 Randy Milligan	.08	.25
155 Lenny Webster	.08	.25
156 Rico Brogna	.08	.25
157 Josias Manzanillo	.08	.25
158 Kevin McReynolds	.08	.25
159 Mike Remlinger	.08	.25
160 David Segui	.08	.25
161 Pete Smith	.08	.25
162 Kelly Stinnett RC	.20	.50
163 Jose Vizcaino	.08	.25
164 Billy Hatcher	.08	.25
165 Doug Jones	.08	.25
166 Mike Lieberthal	.20	.50
167 Tony Longmire	.08	.25
168 Bobby Munoz	.08	.25
169 Paul Quantrill	.08	.25
170 Heathcliff Slocumb	.08	.25
171 Fernando Valenzuela	.20	.50
172 Mark Dewey	.08	.25
173 Brian R. Hunter	.08	.25
174 Jon Lieber	.20	.50
175 Ravelo Manzanillo	.08	.25
176 Dan Miceli	.08	.25
177 Rick White	.08	.25
178 Bryan Eversgerd	.08	.25
179 John Habyan	.08	.25
180 Terry McGriff	.08	.25
181 Vicente Palacios	.08	.25
182 Rich Rodriguez	.08	.25
183 Rick Sutcliffe	.20	.50
184 Donnie Elliott	.08	.25
185 Joey Hamilton	.08	.25
186 Tim Hyers RC	.08	.25
187 Luis Lopez	.08	.25
188 Ray McDavid	.08	.25
189 Bip Roberts	.08	.25
190 Scott Sanders	.08	.25
191 Eddie Williams	.08	.25
192 Steve Frey	.08	.25
193 Pat Gomez	.08	.25
194 Rich Monteleone	.08	.25
195 Mark Portugal	.08	.25
196 Darryl Strawberry	.20	.50
197 Salomon Torres	.08	.25
198 W.VanLandingham RC	.08	.25
199 Checklist	.08	.25
200 Checklist	.08	.25

1994 Fleer Update Diamond Tribute

Each 1994 Fleer Update factory set contained a complete 10-card set of Diamond Tribute inserts. This was the third and final year that Fleer included an insert set in their factory boxed update sets. The 1994 Diamond Tribute inserts feature a player action shot cut out against a backdrop of clouds and baseballs. The selection once again focuses on the game's top veterans. Cards are numbered "X" of 10 on the back.

COMPLETE SET (10)	1.00	2.00
1 Barry Bonds	.40	1.00
2 Joe Carter	.05	.15
3 Will Clark	.08	.25
4 Roger Clemens	.30	.75
5 Tony Gwynn	.20	.50
6 Don Mattingly	.40	1.00
7 Fred McGriff	.08	.25
8 Eddie Murray	.15	.40
9 Kirby Puckett	.15	.40
10 Cal Ripken	.50	1.25

1995 Fleer

The 1995 Fleer set consists of 600 standard-size cards issued as one series. Each pack contained at least one insert card with some "Hot Packs" containing nothing but insert cards. Full-bleed fronts have two player photos and, atypical of baseball cards fronts, biographical information such as height, weight, etc. The backgrounds are multi-colored. The backs are horizontal and contain year-by-year statistics along with a photo. There was a different design for each of baseball's six divisions. The checklist is arranged alphabetically by teams within each league with AL preceding NL. To preview the product prior to it's public release, Fleer printed up additional quantities of cards 26, 78, 155, 235, 285, 351, 509 and 514 and mailed them to dealers and hobby media.

COMPLETE SET (600)	20.00	50.00
1 Brady Anderson	.10	.30
2 Harold Baines	.10	.30
3 Damon Buford	.05	.15
4 Mike Devereaux	.05	.15
5 Mark Eichhorn	.05	.15
6 Sid Fernandez	.05	.15
7 Leo Gomez	.05	.15
8 Jeffrey Hammonds	.05	.15
9 Chris Hoiles	.05	.15
10 Rick Krivda	.05	.15
11 Ben McDonald	.05	.15
12 Mark McLemore	.05	.15
13 Alan Mills	.05	.15
14 Jamie Moyer	.10	.30
15 Mike Mussina	.20	.50
16 Mike Oquist	.05	.15
17 Rafael Palmeiro	.20	.50
18 Arthur Rhodes	.05	.15
19 Cal Ripken Jr.	1.00	2.50
20 Chris Sabo	.05	.15
21 Lee Smith	.10	.30
22 Jack Voigt	.05	.15
23 Damon Berryhill	.05	.15
24 Tom Brunansky	.05	.15
25 Wes Chamberlain	.05	.15
26 Roger Clemens	.60	1.50
27 Scott Cooper	.05	.15
28 Andre Dawson	.10	.30
29 Gar Finnvold	.05	.15
30 Tony Fossas	.05	.15
31 Mike Greenwell	.05	.15
32 Joe Hesketh	.05	.15
33 Chris Howard	.05	.15
34 Chris Nabholz	.05	.15
35 Tim Naehring	.05	.15
36 Otis Nixon	.05	.15
37 Carlos Rodriguez	.05	.15
38 Rich Rowland	.05	.15
39 Ken Ryan	.05	.15
40 Aaron Sele	.05	.15
41 John Valentin	.05	.15
42 Mo Vaughn	.10	.30
43 Frank Viola	.10	.30
44 Danny Bautista	.05	.15
45 Joe Boever	.05	.15
46 Milt Cuyler	.05	.15
47 Storm Davis	.05	.15
48 John Doherty	.05	.15
49 Junior Felix	.05	.15
50 Cecil Fielder	.10	.30
51 Travis Fryman	.10	.30
52 Mike Gardiner	.05	.15
53 Kirk Gibson	.10	.30
54 Chris Gomez	.05	.15
55 Buddy Groom	.05	.15
56 Mike Henneman	.05	.15
57 Chad Kreuter	.05	.15
58 Mike Moore	.05	.15
59 Tony Phillips	.05	.15
60 Juan Samuel	.05	.15
61 Mickey Tettleton	.05	.15
62 Alan Trammell	.10	.30
63 David Wells	.10	.30
64 Lou Whitaker	.10	.30
65 Jim Abbott	.20	.50
66 Joe Ausanio	.05	.15
67 Wade Boggs	.20	.50
68 Mike Gallego	.05	.15
69 Xavier Hernandez	.05	.15
70 Sterling Hitchcock	.05	.15
71 Steve Howe	.05	.15
72 Scott Kamieniecki	.05	.15
73 Pat Kelly	.05	.15
74 Jimmy Key	.10	.30
75 Jim Leyritz	.05	.15
76 Don Mattingly UER	.75	2.00
Photo is a reversed negative		
77 Terry Mulholland	.05	.15
78 Paul O'Neill	.20	.50
79 Melido Perez	.05	.15
80 Luis Polonia	.05	.15
81 Mike Stanley	.05	.15
82 Danny Tartabull	.05	.15
83 Randy Velarde	.05	.15
84 Bob Wickman	.05	.15
85 Bernie Williams	.20	.50
86 Gerald Williams	.05	.15
87 Roberto Alomar	.20	.50
88 Pat Borders	.05	.15
89 Joe Carter	.10	.30
90 Tony Castillo	.05	.15
91 Brad Cornett RC	.05	.15
92 Carlos Delgado	.10	.30
93 Alex Gonzalez	.05	.15
94 Shawn Green	.10	.30
95 Juan Guzman	.05	.15
96 Darren Hall	.05	.15
97 Pat Hentgen	.05	.15
98 Mike Huff	.05	.15
99 Randy Knorr	.05	.15
100 Al Leiter	.10	.30
101 Paul Molitor	.10	.30
102 John Olerud	.10	.30
103 Dick Schofield	.05	.15
104 Ed Sprague	.05	.15
105 Dave Stewart	.10	.30
106 Todd Stottlemyre	.05	.15
107 Devon White	.10	.30
108 Woody Williams	.05	.15
109 Wilson Alvarez	.05	.15
110 Paul Assenmacher	.05	.15
111 Jason Bere	.05	.15
112 Dennis Cook	.05	.15
113 Joey Cora	.05	.15
114 Jose DeLeon	.05	.15
115 Alex Fernandez	.05	.15
116 Julio Franco	.10	.30
117 Craig Grebeck	.05	.15
118 Ozzie Guillen	.10	.30
119 Roberto Hernandez	.05	.15
120 Darrin Jackson	.05	.15
121 Lance Johnson	.05	.15
122 Ron Karkovice	.05	.15
123 Mike LaValliere	.05	.15
124 Norberto Martin	.05	.15
125 Kirk McCaskill	.05	.15
126 Jack McDowell	.05	.15
127 Tim Raines	.10	.30
128 Frank Thomas	.30	.75
129 Robin Ventura	.10	.30
130 Sandy Alomar Jr.	.05	.15
131 Carlos Baerga	.05	.15
132 Albert Belle	.10	.30
133 Mark Clark	.05	.15
134 Alvaro Espinoza	.05	.15
135 Jason Grimsley	.05	.15
136 Wayne Kirby	.05	.15
137 Kenny Lofton	.10	.30
138 Albie Lopez	.05	.15
139 Dennis Martinez	.10	.30
140 Jose Mesa	.05	.15
141 Eddie Murray	.30	.75
142 Charles Nagy	.05	.15
143 Tony Pena	.05	.15
144 Eric Plunk	.05	.15
145 Manny Ramirez	.20	.50
146 Jeff Russell	.05	.15
147 Paul Shuey	.05	.15
148 Paul Sorrento	.05	.15
149 Jim Thome	.20	.50
150 Omar Vizquel	.20	.50
151 Dave Winfield	.10	.30
152 Kevin Appier	.10	.30
153 Billy Brewer	.05	.15
154 Vince Coleman	.05	.15
155 David Cone	.10	.30
156 Gary Gaetti	.10	.30
157 Greg Gagne	.05	.15
158 Tom Gordon	.05	.15
159 Mark Gubicza	.05	.15
160 Bob Hamelin	.05	.15
161 Dave Henderson	.05	.15
162 Felix Jose	.05	.15
163 Wally Joyner	.10	.30
164 Jose Lind	.05	.15
165 Mike Macfarlane	.05	.15
166 Mike Magnante	.05	.15
167 Brent Mayne	.05	.15
168 Brian McRae	.05	.15
169 Rusty Meacham	.05	.15
170 Jeff Montgomery	.05	.15
171 Hipolito Pichardo	.05	.15
172 Terry Shumpert	.05	.15
173 Michael Tucker	.05	.15
174 Ricky Bones	.05	.15
175 Jeff Cirillo	.05	.15
176 Alex Diaz	.05	.15
177 Cal Eldred	.05	.15
178 Mike Fetters	.05	.15
179 Darryl Hamilton	.05	.15
180 Brian Harper	.05	.15
181 John Jaha	.05	.15
182 Pat Listach	.05	.15
183 Graeme Lloyd	.05	.15
184 Jose Mercedes	.05	.15
185 Matt Mieske	.05	.15
186 Dave Nilsson	.05	.15
187 Jody Reed	.05	.15
188 Bob Scanlan	.05	.15
189 Kevin Seitzer	.05	.15
190 Bill Spiers	.05	.15
191 B.J. Surhoff	.10	.30
192 Jose Valentin	.05	.15
193 Greg Vaughn	.05	.15
194 Turner Ward	.05	.15
195 Bill Wegman	.05	.15
196 Rick Aguilera	.05	.15
197 Rich Becker	.05	.15
198 Alex Cole	.05	.15
199 Marty Cordova	.05	.15
200 Steve Dunn	.05	.15
201 Scott Erickson	.05	.15
202 Mark Guthrie	.05	.15
203 Chip Hale	.05	.15
204 LaTroy Hawkins	.05	.15
205 Denny Hocking	.05	.15
206 Chuck Knoblauch	.10	.30
207 Scott Leius	.05	.15
208 Shane Mack	.05	.15
209 Pat Mahomes	.05	.15
210 Pat Meares	.05	.15
211 Pedro Munoz	.05	.15
212 Kirby Puckett	.30	.75
213 Jeff Reboulet	.05	.15
214 Dave Stevens	.05	.15
215 Kevin Tapani	.05	.15
216 Matt Walbeck	.05	.15
217 Carl Willis	.05	.15
218 Brian Anderson	.05	.15
219 Chad Curtis	.05	.15
220 Chili Davis	.10	.30
221 Gary DiSarcina	.05	.15
222 Damion Easley	.05	.15
223 Jim Edmonds	.20	.50
224 Chuck Finley	.10	.30
225 Joe Grahe	.05	.15
226 Rex Hudler	.05	.15
227 Bo Jackson	.30	.75
228 Mark Langston	.05	.15
229 Phil Leftwich	.05	.15
230 Mark Leiter	.05	.15
231 Spike Owen	.05	.15
232 Bob Patterson	.05	.15
233 Troy Percival	.10	.30
234 Eduardo Perez	.05	.15
235 Tim Salmon	.20	.50
236 J.T. Snow	.10	.30
237 Chris Turner	.05	.15
238 Mark Acre	.05	.15
239 Geronimo Berroa	.05	.15
240 Mike Bordick	.05	.15
241 John Briscoe	.05	.15
242 Scott Brosius	.10	.30
243 Ron Darling	.05	.15
244 Dennis Eckersley	.10	.30
245 Brent Gates	.05	.15
246 Rickey Henderson	.30	.75
247 Stan Javier	.05	.15
248 Steve Karsay	.05	.15
249 Mark McGwire	.75	2.00
250 Troy Neel	.05	.15
251 Steve Ontiveros	.05	.15
252 Carlos Reyes	.05	.15
253 Ruben Sierra	.10	.30
254 Terry Steinbach	.05	.15
255 Bill Taylor	.05	.15
256 Todd Van Poppel	.05	.15
257 Bobby Witt	.05	.15
258 Rich Amaral	.05	.15
259 Eric Anthony	.05	.15
260 Bobby Ayala	.05	.15
261 Mike Blowers	.05	.15
262 Chris Bosio	.05	.15
263 Jay Buhner	.10	.30
264 John Cummings	.05	.15
265 Tim Davis	.05	.15
266 Felix Fermin	.05	.15
267 Dave Fleming	.05	.15
268 Goose Gossage	.10	.30
269 Ken Griffey Jr.	.50	1.25
270 Reggie Jefferson	.05	.15
271 Randy Johnson	.30	.75
272 Edgar Martinez	.20	.50
273 Tino Martinez	.20	.50
274 Greg Pirkl	.05	.15
275 Bill Risley	.05	.15
276 Roger Salkeld	.05	.15
277 Luis Sojo	.05	.15
278 Mac Suzuki	.05	.15
279 Dan Wilson	.05	.15
280 Kevin Brown	.10	.30
281 Jose Canseco	.20	.50
282 Cris Carpenter	.05	.15
283 Will Clark	.20	.50
284 Jeff Frye	.05	.15
285 Juan Gonzalez	.10	.30
286 Rick Helling	.05	.15
287 Tom Henke	.05	.15
288 David Hulse	.05	.15
289 Chris James	.05	.15
290 Manuel Lee	.05	.15
291 Oddibe McDowell	.05	.15
292 Dean Palmer	.10	.30
293 Roger Pavlik	.05	.15
294 Bill Ripken	.05	.15
295 Ivan Rodriguez	.20	.50
296 Kenny Rogers	.10	.30
297 Doug Strange	.05	.15
298 Matt Whiteside	.05	.15
299 Steve Avery	.05	.15
300 Steve Bedrosian	.05	.15
301 Rafael Belliard	.05	.15
302 Jeff Blauser	.05	.15
303 Dave Gallagher	.05	.15
304 Tom Glavine	.20	.50
305 David Justice	.10	.30
306 Mike Kelly	.05	.15
307 Roberto Kelly	.05	.15
308 Ryan Klesko	.10	.30
309 Mark Lemke	.05	.15
310 Javier Lopez	.10	.30
311 Greg Maddux	.50	1.25
312 Fred McGriff	.20	.50
313 Greg McMichael	.05	.15
314 Kent Mercker	.05	.15
315 Charlie O'Brien	.05	.15
316 Jose Oliva	.05	.15
317 Terry Pendleton	.10	.30
318 John Smoltz	.20	.50
319 Mike Stanton	.05	.15
320 Tony Tarasco	.05	.15
321 Terrell Wade	.05	.15
322 Mark Wohlers	.05	.15
323 Kurt Abbott	.05	.15
324 Luis Aquino	.05	.15
325 Bret Barberie	.05	.15
326 Ryan Bowen	.05	.15
327 Jerry Browne	.05	.15
328 Chuck Carr	.05	.15
329 Matias Carrillo	.05	.15
330 Greg Colbrunn	.05	.15
331 Jeff Conine	.10	.30
332 Mark Gardner	.05	.15
333 Chris Hammond	.05	.15
334 Bryan Harvey	.05	.15
335 Richie Lewis	.05	.15
336 Dave Magadan	.05	.15
337 Terry Mathews	.05	.15
338 Robb Nen	.10	.30
339 Yorkis Perez	.05	.15
340 Pat Rapp	.05	.15
341 Benito Santiago	.10	.30
342 Gary Sheffield	.10	.30
343 Dave Weathers	.05	.15
344 Moises Alou	.10	.30
345 Sean Berry	.05	.15
346 Wil Cordero	.05	.15
347 Joey Eischen	.05	.15
348 Jeff Fassero	.05	.15
349 Darrin Fletcher	.05	.15
350 Cliff Floyd	.10	.30
351 Marquis Grissom	.10	.30
352 Butch Henry	.05	.15
353 Gil Heredia	.05	.15
354 Ken Hill	.05	.15
355 Mike Lansing	.05	.15
356 Pedro Martinez	.20	.50
357 Mel Rojas	.05	.15
358 Kirk Rueter	.05	.15
359 Tim Scott	.05	.15
360 Jeff Shaw	.05	.15
361 Larry Walker	.10	.30
362 Lenny Webster	.05	.15
363 John Wetteland	.10	.30
364 Rondell White	.10	.30
365 Bobby Bonilla	.10	.30
366 Rico Brogna	.05	.15
367 Jeromy Burnitz	.10	.30
368 John Franco	.10	.30
369 Dwight Gooden	.10	.30
370 Todd Hundley	.05	.15
371 Jason Jacome	.05	.15
372 Bobby Jones	.05	.15
373 Jeff Kent	.10	.30
374 Jim Lindeman	.05	.15
375 Josias Manzanillo	.05	.15
376 Roger Mason	.05	.15
377 Kevin McReynolds	.05	.15
378 Joe Orsulak	.05	.15
379 Bill Pulsipher	.05	.15
380 Bret Saberhagen	.10	.30
381 David Segui	.05	.15
382 Pete Smith	.05	.15
383 Kelly Stinnett	.05	.15
384 Ryan Thompson	.05	.15
385 Jose Vizcaino	.05	.15
386 Toby Borland	.05	.15
387 Ricky Bottalico	.05	.15
388 Darren Daulton	.10	.30
389 Mariano Duncan	.05	.15
390 Lenny Dykstra	.10	.30
391 Jim Eisenreich	.05	.15
392 Tommy Greene	.05	.15
393 Dave Hollins	.05	.15
394 Pete Incaviglia	.05	.15
395 Danny Jackson	.05	.15
396 Doug Jones	.05	.15
397 Ricky Jordan	.05	.15
398 John Kruk	.10	.30
399 Mike Lieberthal	.10	.30
400 Tony Longmire	.05	.15
401 Mickey Morandini	.05	.15
402 Bobby Munoz	.05	.15
403 Curt Schilling	.10	.30
404 Heathcliff Slocumb	.05	.15
405 Kevin Stocker	.05	.15
406 Fernando Valenzuela	.10	.30
407 David West	.05	.15
408 Willie Banks	.05	.15
409 Jose Bautista	.05	.15
410 Steve Buechele	.05	.15
411 Jim Bullinger	.05	.15
412 Chuck Crim	.05	.15
413 Shawon Dunston	.05	.15
414 Kevin Foster	.05	.15
415 Mark Grace	.20	.50
416 Jose Hernandez	.05	.15
417 Glenallen Hill	.05	.15
418 Brooks Kieschnick	.05	.15
419 Derrick May	.05	.15
420 Randy Myers	.05	.15
421 Dan Plesac	.05	.15
422 Karl Rhodes	.05	.15
423 Rey Sanchez	.05	.15
424 Sammy Sosa	.30	.75
425 Steve Trachsel	.05	.15
426 Rick Wilkins	.05	.15
427 Anthony Young	.05	.15
428 Eddie Zambrano	.05	.15
429 Bret Boone	.10	.30
430 Jeff Branson	.05	.15
431 Jeff Brantley	.05	.15
432 Hector Carrasco	.05	.15
433 Brian Dorsett	.05	.15
434 Tony Fernandez	.05	.15
435 Tim Fortugno	.05	.15
436 Erik Hanson	.05	.15
437 Thomas Howard	.05	.15
438 Kevin Jarvis	.05	.15
439 Barry Larkin	.20	.50
440 Chuck McElroy	.05	.15
441 Kevin Mitchell	.05	.15
442 Hal Morris	.05	.15
443 Jose Rijo	.05	.15
444 John Roper	.05	.15
445 Johnny Ruffin	.05	.15
446 Deion Sanders	.20	.50
447 Reggie Sanders	.10	.30
448 Pete Schourek	.05	.15
449 John Smiley	.05	.15
450 Eddie Taubensee	.05	.15
451 Jeff Bagwell	.20	.50
452 Kevin Bass	.05	.15
453 Craig Biggio	.20	.50
454 Ken Caminiti	.10	.30
455 Andujar Cedeno	.05	.15
456 Doug Drabek	.05	.15
457 Tony Eusebio	.05	.15
458 Mike Felder	.05	.15
459 Steve Finley	.10	.30
460 Luis Gonzalez	.10	.30
461 Mike Hampton	.10	.30
462 Pete Harnisch	.05	.15
463 John Hudek	.05	.15
464 Todd Jones	.05	.15
465 Darryl Kile	.10	.30
466 James Mouton	.05	.15
467 Shane Reynolds	.05	.15
468 Scott Servais	.05	.15
469 Greg Swindell	.05	.15
470 Dave Veres RC	.15	.40
471 Brian Williams	.05	.15
472 Jay Bell	.10	.30
473 Jacob Brumfield	.05	.15
474 Dave Clark	.05	.15
475 Steve Cooke	.05	.15
476 Midre Cummings	.05	.15
477 Mark Dewey	.05	.15
478 Tom Foley	.05	.15
479 Carlos Garcia	.05	.15
480 Jeff King	.05	.15
481 Jon Lieber	.05	.15
482 Ravelo Manzanillo	.05	.15
483 Al Martin	.05	.15
484 Orlando Merced	.05	.15
485 Danny Miceli	.05	.15
486 Denny Neagle	.10	.30
487 Lance Parrish	.10	.30
488 Don Slaught	.05	.15
489 Zane Smith	.05	.15
490 Andy Van Slyke	.20	.50
491 Paul Wagner	.05	.15
492 Rick White	.05	.15
493 Luis Alicea	.05	.15
494 Rene Arocha	.05	.15
495 Rheal Cormier	.05	.15
496 Bryan Eversgerd	.05	.15
497 Bernard Gilkey	.05	.15
498 John Habyan	.05	.15
499 Gregg Jefferies	.05	.15
500 Brian Jordan	.10	.30
501 Ray Lankford	.10	.30
502 John Mabry	.05	.15
503 Terry McGriff	.05	.15
504 Tom Pagnozzi	.05	.15
505 Vicente Palacios	.05	.15
506 Geronimo Pena	.05	.15
507 Gerald Perry	.05	.15
508 Rich Rodriguez	.05	.15
509 Ozzie Smith	.50	1.25
510 Bob Tewksbury	.05	.15
511 Allen Watson	.05	.15
512 Mark Whiten	.05	.15
513 Todd Zeile	.05	.15
514 Dante Bichette	.10	.30
515 Willie Blair	.05	.15
516 Ellis Burks	.10	.30
517 Marvin Freeman	.05	.15
518 Andres Galarraga	.10	.30
519 Joe Girardi	.05	.15
520 Greg W. Harris	.05	.15
521 Charlie Hayes	.05	.15
522 Mike Kingery	.05	.15
523 Nelson Liriano	.05	.15
524 Mike Munoz	.05	.15
525 David Nied	.05	.15
526 Steve Reed	.05	.15
527 Kevin Ritz	.05	.15
528 Bruce Ruffin	.05	.15
529 John Vander Wal	.05	.15
530 Walt Weiss	.05	.15
531 Eric Young	.05	.15
532 Billy Ashley	.05	.15
533 Pedro Astacio	.05	.15
534 Rafael Bournigal	.05	.15
535 Brett Butler	.10	.30
536 Tom Candiotti	.05	.15
537 Omar Daal	.05	.15
538 Delino DeShields	.05	.15
539 Darren Dreifort	.05	.15
540 Kevin Gross	.05	.15
541 Orel Hershiser	.10	.30
542 Garey Ingram	.05	.15
543 Eric Karros	.10	.30
544 Ramon Martinez	.05	.15
545 Raul Mondesi	.10	.30
546 Chan Ho Park	.10	.30
547 Mike Piazza	.50	1.25
548 Henry Rodriguez	.05	.15
549 Rudy Seanez	.05	.15
550 Ismael Valdes	.05	.15
551 Tim Wallach	.05	.15
552 Todd Worrell	.05	.15
553 Andy Ashby	.05	.15
554 Brad Ausmus	.10	.30
555 Derek Bell	.05	.15
556 Andy Benes	.05	.15
557 Phil Clark	.05	.15
558 Donnie Elliott	.05	.15
559 Ricky Gutierrez	.05	.15
560 Tony Gwynn	.40	1.00
561 Joey Hamilton	.05	.15
562 Trevor Hoffman	.10	.30
563 Luis Lopez	.05	.15
564 Pedro A. Martinez	.05	.15
565 Tim Mauser	.05	.15
566 Phil Plantier	.05	.15
567 Bip Roberts	.05	.15
568 Scott Sanders	.05	.15
569 Craig Shipley	.05	.15
570 Jeff Tabaka	.05	.15
571 Eddie Williams	.05	.15
572 Rod Beck	.05	.15
573 Mike Benjamin	.05	.15
574 Barry Bonds	.75	2.00
575 Dave Burba	.05	.15
576 John Burkett	.05	.15
577 Mark Carreon	.05	.15
578 Royce Clayton	.05	.15
579 Steve Frey	.05	.15
580 Bryan Hickerson	.05	.15
581 Mike Jackson	.05	.15
582 Darren Lewis	.05	.15
583 Kirt Manwaring	.05	.15
584 Rich Monteleone	.05	.15
585 John Patterson	.05	.15
586 J.R. Phillips	.05	.15
587 Mark Portugal	.05	.15
588 Joe Rosselli	.05	.15
589 Darryl Strawberry	.10	.30
590 Bill Swift	.05	.15
591 Robby Thompson	.05	.15
592 W.VanLandingham	.05	.15
593 Matt Williams	.10	.30
594 Checklist	.05	.15
595 Checklist	.05	.15
596 Checklist	.05	.15
597 Checklist	.05	.15
598 Checklist	.05	.15
599 Checklist	.05	.15
600 Checklist	.05	.15

1995 Fleer All-Fleer

This nine-card standard-size set was available through a 1995 Fleer wrapper offer. Nine of the leading players for each position are featured in this set. The wrapper redemption offer expired on September 30, 1995. The fronts feature the player's photo covering most of the card with a small section on the right set off for the words "All Fleer 9" along with the player's name. The backs feature player information as to why they are among the best in the game.

COMPLETE SET (9)	4.00	10.00
1 Mike Piazza	.50	1.25
2 Frank Thomas	.30	.75
3 Roberto Alomar	.20	.50
4 Cal Ripken	1.00	2.50
5 Matt Williams	.10	.30
6 Barry Bonds	.75	2.00
7 Ken Griffey Jr.	.50	1.25
8 Tony Gwynn	.40	1.00
9 Greg Maddux	.50	1.25

1995 Fleer All-Rookies

This nine-card standard-size set was available through a Rookie Exchange redemption card randomly inserted in packs. The redemption deadline was 9/30/95. This set features players who made their major league debut in 1995. The fronts have an action photo with a grainy background. The player's name and team are in gold foil at the bottom. Horizontal backs have a player photo the left and minor league highlights to the right.

COMPLETE SET (9)	1.25	3.00
M1 Edgardo Alfonzo	.08	.25
M2 Jason Bates	.08	.25
M3 Brian Boehringer	.08	.25
M4 Darren Bragg	.08	.25
M5 Brad Clontz	.08	.25
M6 Jim Dougherty	.08	.25
M7 Todd Hollandsworth	.08	.25
M8 Rudy Pemberton	.08	.25
M9 Frank Rodriguez	.08	.25
NNO Exp. All-Rookie Exch.	.08	.25

1995 Fleer All-Stars

Randomly inserted in all pack types at a rate of one in three, this 25-card standard-size set showcases those that participated in the 1994 mid-season classic held in Pittsburgh. Horizontally designed, the fronts contain photos of American League stars with the back protraying the National League player from the same position. On each side, the 1994 All-Star Game logo appears in gold foil as does either the A.L. or N.L. logo in silver foil.

COMPLETE SET (25)	4.00	10.00
STATED ODDS 1:3		
1 Ivan Rodriguez / Mike Piazza	.60	1.50
2 Frank Thomas / Gregg Jefferies	.40	1.00
3 Robert Alomar / Mariano Duncan	.25	.60
4 Wade Boggs / Matt Williams	.25	.60
5 Cal Ripken Jr. / Ozzie Smith	1.25	3.00
6 Joe Carter / Barry Bonds	1.00	2.50
7 Ken Griffey Jr. / Tony Gwynn	.60	1.50
8 Kirby Puckett / David Justice	.40	1.00
9 Jimmy Key / Greg Maddux	.60	1.50
10 Chuck Knoblauch / Wil Cordero	.15	.40
11 Scott Cooper / Ken Caminiti	.15	.40
12 Will Clark / Carlos Garcia	.25	.60
13 Paul Molitor / Jeff Bagwell	.25	.60
14 Travis Fryman / Craig Biggio	.25	.60
15 Mickey Tettleton / Fred McGriff	.25	.60
16 Kenny Lofton / Moises Alou	.15	.40
17 Albert Belle / Marquis Grissom	.15	.40
18 Paul O'Neill	.25	.60

Card	Low	High
Dante Bichette		
19 David Cone	.15	.40
Ken Hill		
20 Mike Mussina	.25	.60
Doug Drabek		
21 Randy Johnson	.40	1.00
John Hudek		
22 Pat Hentgen	.07	.20
Danny Jackson		
23 Wilson Alvarez	.07	.20
Rod Beck		
24 Lee Smith	.15	.40
Randy Myers		
25 Jason Bere	.07	.20
Doug Jones		

1995 Fleer Award Winners

Randomly inserted in all pack types at a rate of one in 24, this six card standard-size set highlights the major award winners of 1994. Card fronts feature action photos that are full-bleed on the right border and have gold border on the left. Within the gold border are the player's name and Fleer Award Winner. The backs contain a photo with text that references 1994 accomplishments.

Card	Low	High
COMPLETE SET (6)	2.00	5.00
STATED ODDS 1:24		
1 Frank Thomas	.50	1.25
2 Jeff Bagwell	.30	.75
3 David Cone	.20	.50
4 Greg Maddux	.75	2.00
5 Bob Hamelin	.08	.25
6 Raul Mondesi	.20	.50

1995 Fleer League Leaders

Randomly inserted in all pack types at a rate of one in 12, this 10-card standard-size set features 1994 American and National League leaders in various categories. The horizontal cards have player photos on front and back. The back also has a brief write-up concerning the accomplishment.

Card	Low	High
COMPLETE SET (10)	3.00	8.00
STATED ODDS 1:12		
1 Paul O'Neill	.30	.75
2 Ken Griffey Jr.	.75	2.00
3 Kirby Puckett	.50	1.25
4 Jimmy Key	.20	.50
5 Randy Johnson	.50	1.25
6 Tony Gwynn	.60	1.50
7 Matt Williams	.20	.50
8 Jeff Bagwell	.30	.75
9 Greg Maddux	.75	2.00
Ken Hill		
10 Andy Benes	.08	.25

1995 Fleer Lumber Company

Randomly inserted in retail packs at a rate of one in 24, this standard-size set highlights 10 of the game's top sluggers. Full-bleed card fronts feature an action photo with the Lumber Company logo, which includes the player's name, toward the bottom of the photo. Card backs have a player photo and woodgrain background with a write-up that highlights individual achievements.

Card	Low	High
COMPLETE SET (10)	12.50	30.00
STATED ODDS 1:24 RETAIL		
1 Jeff Bagwell	1.00	2.50
2 Albert Belle	.60	1.50
3 Barry Bonds	4.00	10.00
4 Jose Canseco	1.00	2.50
5 Joe Carter	.60	1.50
6 Ken Griffey Jr.	2.50	6.00
7 Fred McGriff	1.00	2.50
8 Kevin Mitchell	.30	.75
9 Frank Thomas	1.50	4.00
10 Matt Williams	.60	1.50

1995 Fleer Major League Prospects

Randomly inserted in all pack types at a rate of one in six, this 10-card standard-size set spotlights major league hopefuls. Card fronts feature a player photo with the words "Major League Prospects" serving as part of the background. The player's name and team appear in silver foil at the bottom. The backs have a photo and a write-up on his minor league career.

Card	Low	High
COMPLETE SET (10)	4.00	10.00
STATED ODDS 1:6		
1 Garret Anderson	.20	.50
2 James Baldwin	.08	.25
3 Alan Benes	.08	.25
4 Armando Benitez	.08	.25
5 Ray Durham	.20	.50
6 Brian L. Hunter	.08	.25
7 Derek Jeter	1.50	4.00
8 Charles Johnson	.20	.50
9 Orlando Miller	.08	.25
10 Alex Rodriguez	1.50	4.00

1995 Fleer Pro-Visions

Randomly inserted in all pack types at a rate of one in nine, this six card standard-size set features top players illustrated by Wayne Anthony Still. The colorful artwork on front features the player in a surrealistic setting. The backs offer write-up on the player's previous season.

Card	Low	High
COMPLETE SET (6)	1.25	3.00
STATED ODDS 1:9		
1 Mike Mussina	.20	.50
2 Raul Mondesi	.10	.30
3 Jeff Bagwell	.20	.50
4 Greg Maddux	.50	1.25
5 Tim Salmon	.20	.50
6 Manny Ramirez	.20	.50

1995 Fleer Rookie Sensations

Randomly inserted in 18-card packs, this 20-card standard-size set features top rookies from the 1994 season. The fronts have full-bleed color photos with the team and player's name in gold foil along the right edge. The backs also have full-bleed color photos along with player information.

Card	Low	High
COMPLETE SET (20)	15.00	40.00
1 Kurt Abbott	.75	2.00
2 Rico Brogna	.75	2.00
3 Hector Carrasco	.75	2.00
4 Kevin Foster	.75	2.00
5 Chris Gomez	.75	2.00
6 Darren Hall	.75	2.00
7 Bob Hamelin	.75	2.00
8 Joey Hamilton	.75	2.00
9 John Hudek	.75	2.00
10 Ryan Klesko	1.50	4.00
11 Javier Lopez	1.50	4.00
12 Matt Mieske	.75	2.00
13 Raul Mondesi	1.50	4.00
14 Manny Ramirez	2.00	5.00
15 Shane Reynolds	.75	2.00
16 Bill Risley	.75	2.00
17 Johnny Ruffin	.75	2.00
18 Steve Trachsel	.75	2.00
19 W.VanLandingham	.75	2.00
20 Rondell White	1.50	4.00

1995 Fleer Team Leaders

Randomly inserted in 12-card hobby packs at a rate of one in 24, this 28-card standard-size set features top players from each team. Each team is represented with card the has the team's leading hitter on one side with the leading pitcher on the other side. The team logo, "Team Leaders" and the player's name are gold foil stamped on front and back.

Card	Low	High
COMPLETE SET (28)	50.00	100.00
STATED ODDS 1:24 HOBBY		
1 Cal Ripken Jr.	10.00	25.00
Mike Mussina		
2 Mo Vaughn	6.00	15.00
Roger Clemens		
3 Tim Salmon	2.00	5.00
Chuck Finley		
4 Frank Thomas	3.00	8.00
Jack McDowell		
5 Albert Belle	1.25	3.00
Dennis Martinez		
6 Cecil Fielder	1.25	3.00
Mike Moore		
7 Bob Hamelin	1.25	3.00
David Cone		
8 Greg Vaughn	.60	1.50
Ricky Bones		
9 Kirby Puckett	3.00	8.00
Rick Aguilera		
10 Don Mattingly	8.00	20.00
Jimmy Key		
11 Ruben Sierra	1.25	3.00
Dennis Eckersley		
12 Ken Griffey Jr.	5.00	12.00
Randy Johnson		
13 Jose Canseco	2.00	5.00
Kenny Rogers		
14 Joe Carter	1.25	3.00
Pat Hentgen		
15 David Justice	5.00	12.00
Greg Maddux		
16 Sammy Sosa	3.00	8.00
Steve Trachsel		
17 Kevin Mitchell	.60	1.50
Jose Rijo		
18 Dante Bichette	1.25	3.00
Bruce Ruffin		
19 Jeff Conine	1.25	3.00
Robb Nen		
20 Jeff Bagwell	2.00	5.00
Doug Drabek		
21 Mike Piazza	5.00	12.00
Ramon Martinez		
22 Moises Alou	1.25	3.00
Ken Hill		
23 Bobby Bonilla	1.25	3.00
Bret Saberhagen		
24 Darren Daulton	1.25	3.00
Danny Jackson		
25 Jay Bell	1.25	3.00
Zane Smith		
26 Gregg Jefferies	.60	1.50
Bob Tewksbury		
27 Tony Gwynn	4.00	10.00
Andy Benes		
28 Matt Williams	1.25	3.00
Rod Beck		

1995 Fleer Update

This 200-card standard-size set features many players who were either rookies in 1995 or played for new teams. These cards were issued in either 12-card packs with a suggested retail price of $1.49 or 18-card packs that had a suggested retail price of $2.29. Each Fleer Update pack included one card from several insert sets produced with this product. Hot packs featuring only these insert cards were included one every 72 packs. The full-bleed fronts have two player photos and, atypical of baseball card fronts, biographical information such as height, weight, etc. The backgrounds are multi-colored. The backs are horizontal, have yearly statistics, a photo, and are numbered with the prefix "U". The checklist is arranged alphabetically by team within each league's divisions. Key Rookie Cards in this set include Bobby Higginson and Hideo Nomo.

Card	Low	High
COMPLETE SET (200)	6.00	15.00
1 Manny Alexander	.02	.10
2 Bret Barberie	.02	.10
3 Armando Benitez	.02	.10
4 Kevin Brown	.07	.20
5 Doug Jones	.02	.10
6 Sherman Obando	.02	.10
7 Andy Van Slyke	.10	.30
8 Stan Belinda	.02	.10
9 Jose Canseco	.10	.30
10 Vaughn Eshelman	.02	.10
11 Mike Macfarlane	.02	.10
12 Troy O'Leary	.02	.10
13 Steve Rodriguez	.02	.10
14 Lee Tinsley	.02	.10
15 Tim Vanegmond	.02	.10
16 Mark Whiten	.02	.10
17 Sean Bergman	.02	.10
18 Chad Curtis	.02	.10
19 John Flaherty	.02	.10
20 Bob Higginson RC	.30	.75
21 Felipe Lira	.02	.10
22 Shannon Penn	.02	.10
23 Todd Steverson	.02	.10
24 Sean Whiteside	.02	.10
25 Tony Fernandez	.02	.10
26 Jack McDowell	.02	.10
27 Andy Pettitte	.10	.30
28 John Wetteland	.07	.20
29 David Cone	.07	.20
30 Mike Timlin	.02	.10
31 Duane Ward	.02	.10
32 Jim Abbott	.10	.30
33 James Baldwin	.02	.10
34 Mike Devereaux	.02	.10
35 Ray Durham	.07	.20
36 Tim Fortugno	.02	.10
37 Scott Ruffcorn	.02	.10
38 Chris Sabo	.02	.10
39 Paul Assenmacher	.02	.10
40 Bud Black	.02	.10
41 Orel Hershiser	.07	.20
42 Julian Tavarez	.02	.10
43 Dave Winfield	.07	.20
44 Pat Borders	.02	.10
45 Melvin Bunch RC	.02	.10
46 Tom Goodwin	.02	.10
47 Jon Nunnally	.02	.10
48 Joe Randa	.07	.20
49 Dilson Torres RC	.02	.10
50 Joe Vitiello	.02	.10
51 David Hulse	.02	.10
52 Scott Karl	.02	.10
53 Mark Kiefer	.02	.10
54 Derrick May	.02	.10
55 Joe Oliver	.02	.10
56 Al Reyes RC	.02	.10
57 Steve Sparks RC	.15	.40
58 Jerald Clark	.02	.10
59 Eddie Guardado	.02	.10
60 Kevin Maas	.02	.10
61 David McCarty	.02	.10
62 Brad Radke RC	.30	.75
63 Scott Stahoviak	.02	.10
64 Garret Anderson	.07	.20
65 Shawn Boskie	.02	.10
66 Mike James	.02	.10
67 Tony Phillips	.02	.10
68 Lee Smith	.07	.20
69 Mitch Williams	.02	.10
70 Jim Corsi	.02	.10
71 Mark Harkey	.02	.10
72 Dave Stewart	.07	.20
73 Todd Stottlemyre	.02	.10
74 Joey Cora	.02	.10
75 Chad Kreuter	.02	.10
76 Jeff Nelson	.02	.10
77 Alex Rodriguez	.50	1.25
78 Ron Villone	.02	.10
79 Bob Wells RC	.15	.40
80 Jose Alberro RC	.02	.10
81 Terry Burrows	.02	.10
82 Kevin Gross	.02	.10
83 Wilson Heredia	.02	.10
84 Mark McLemore	.02	.10
85 Otis Nixon	.02	.10
86 Jeff Russell	.02	.10
87 Mickey Tettleton	.02	.10
88 Bob Tewksbury	.02	.10
89 Pedro Borbon	.02	.10
90 Marquis Grissom	.07	.20
91 Chipper Jones	.20	.50
92 Mike Mordecai	.02	.10
93 Jason Schmidt	.20	.50
94 John Burkett	.02	.10
95 Andre Dawson	.07	.20
96 Matt Dunbar RC	.02	.10
97 Charles Johnson	.07	.20
98 Terry Pendleton	.07	.20
99 Rich Scheid	.02	.10
100 Quilvio Veras	.02	.10
101 Bobby Witt	.02	.10
102 Eddie Zosky	.02	.10
103 Shane Andrews	.02	.10
104 Reid Cornelius	.02	.10
105 Chad Fonville RC	.02	.10
106 Mark Grudzielanek RC	.30	.75
107 Roberto Kelly	.02	.10
108 Carlos Perez RC	.15	.40
109 Tony Tarasco	.02	.10
110 Brett Butler	.07	.20
111 Carl Everett	.07	.20
112 Pete Harnisch	.02	.10
113 Doug Henry	.02	.10
114 Kevin Lomon RC	.02	.10
115 Blas Minor	.02	.10
116 Dave Mlicki	.02	.10
117 Ricky Otero RC	.02	.10
118 Norm Charlton	.02	.10
119 Tyler Green	.02	.10
120 Gene Harris	.02	.10
121 Charlie Hayes	.02	.10
122 Gregg Jefferies	.02	.10
123 Michael Mimbs RC	.02	.10
124 Paul Quantrill	.02	.10
125 Frank Castillo	.02	.10
126 Brian McRae	.02	.10
127 Jaime Navarro	.02	.10
128 Mike Perez	.02	.10
129 Tanyon Sturtze	.02	.10
130 Ozzie Timmons	.02	.10
131 John Courtright	.02	.10
132 Ron Gant	.07	.20
133 Xavier Hernandez	.02	.10
134 Brian Hunter	.02	.10
135 Benito Santiago	.07	.20
136 Pete Smith	.02	.10
137 Scott Sullivan	.02	.10
138 Derek Bell	.02	.10
139 Doug Brocail	.02	.10
140 Ricky Gutierrez	.02	.10
141 Pedro A.Martinez	.02	.10
142 Orlando Miller	.02	.10
143 Phil Plantier	.02	.10
144 Craig Shipley	.02	.10
145 Rich Aude	.02	.10
146 J.Christiansen RC	.02	.10
147 Freddy Adrian Garcia RC	.02	.10
148 Jim Gott	.02	.10
149 Mark Johnson RC	.15	.40
150 Esteban Loaiza	.02	.10
151 Dan Plesac	.02	.10
152 Gary Wilson RC	.02	.10
153 Allen Battle	.02	.10
154 Terry Bradshaw	.02	.10
155 Scott Cooper	.02	.10
156 Tripp Cromer	.02	.10
157 John Frascatore RC	.02	.10
158 John Habyan	.02	.10
159 Tom Henke	.02	.10
160 Ken Hill	.02	.10
161 Danny Jackson	.02	.10
162 Donovan Osborne	.02	.10
163 Tom Urbani	.02	.10
164 Roger Bailey	.02	.10
165 Jorge Brito RC	.02	.10
166 Vinny Castilla	.07	.20
167 Darren Holmes	.02	.10
168 Roberto Mejia	.02	.10
169 Bill Swift	.02	.10
170 Mark Thompson	.02	.10
171 Larry Walker	.07	.20
172 Greg Hansell	.02	.10
173 Dave Hansen	.02	.10
174 Carlos Hernandez	.02	.10
175 Hideo Nomo RC	.75	2.00
176 Jose Offerman	.02	.10
177 Antonio Osuna	.02	.10
178 Reggie Williams	.02	.10
179 Todd Williams	.02	.10
180 Andres Berumen	.02	.10
181 Ken Caminiti	.07	.20
182 Andujar Cedeno	.02	.10
183 Steve Finley	.07	.20
184 Bryce Florie	.02	.10
185 Dustin Hermanson	.02	.10
186 Ray Holbert	.02	.10
187 Melvin Nieves	.02	.10
188 Roberto Petagine	.02	.10
189 Jody Reed	.02	.10
190 Fernando Valenzuela	.07	.20
191 Brian Williams	.02	.10
192 Mark Dewey	.02	.10
193 Glenallen Hill	.02	.10
194 Chris Hook RC	.02	.10
195 Terry Mulholland	.02	.10
196 Steve Scarsone	.02	.10
197 Trevor Wilson	.02	.10
198 Checklist	.02	.10
199 Checklist	.02	.10
200 Checklist	.02	.10

1995 Fleer Update Diamond Tribute

This 10-card standard-size set featuring some of baseball's leading stars were inserted at a stated rate of one in five packs. The cards are numbered in the lower right with an "X" of 10.

Card	Low	High
COMPLETE SET (10)	3.00	8.00
STATED ODDS 1:5 HOB/RET		
1 Jeff Bagwell	.20	.50
2 Albert Belle	.10	.30
3 Barry Bonds	.75	2.00
4 David Cone	.10	.30
5 Dennis Eckersley	.10	.30
6 Ken Griffey Jr.	.50	1.25
7 Rickey Henderson	.30	.75
8 Greg Maddux	.50	1.25
9 Frank Thomas	.30	.75
10 Matt Williams	.10	.30

1995 Fleer Update Headliners

Inserted one every three packs, this 20-card standard-size set features various major league stars. The cards are numbered in the lower left as "X" of 20.

Card	Low	High
COMPLETE SET (20)	5.00	12.00
STATED ODDS 1:3		
1 Jeff Bagwell	.20	.50
2 Albert Belle	.10	.30
3 Barry Bonds	.75	2.00
4 Jose Canseco	.20	.50
5 Joe Carter	.10	.30
6 Will Clark	.20	.50
7 Roger Clemens	.60	1.50
8 Lenny Dykstra	.10	.30
9 Cecil Fielder	.10	.30
10 Juan Gonzalez	.10	.30
11 Ken Griffey Jr.	.50	1.25
12 Kenny Lofton	.10	.30
13 Greg Maddux	.50	1.25
14 Fred McGriff	.20	.50
15 Mike Piazza	.50	1.25
16 Kirby Puckett	.30	.75
17 Tim Salmon	.20	.50
18 Frank Thomas	.30	.75
19 Mo Vaughn	.10	.30
20 Matt Williams	.10	.30

1995 Fleer Update Rookie Update

Inserted one in every four packs, this 10-card standard-size set features some of 1995's best rookies. The cards are numbered as "X of 10". Chipper Jones and Hideo Nomo are among the players included in this set.

Card	Low	High
COMPLETE SET (10)	5.00	10.00
STATED ODDS 1:4		
1 Shane Andrews	.08	.25
2 Ray Durham	.20	.50
3 Shawn Green	.20	.50
4 Charles Johnson	.20	.50
5 Chipper Jones	.60	1.50
6 Esteban Loaiza	.08	.25
7 Hideo Nomo	.75	2.00
8 Jon Nunnally	.08	.25
9 Alex Rodriguez	1.50	4.00
10 Julian Tavarez	.08	.25

1995 Fleer Update Smooth Leather

Inserted one every five jumbo packs, this 10-card standard-size set features many leading defensive wizards. The card fronts feature a player photo. Underneath the player photo, is his name along with the words "smooth leather" on the bottom. The right corner features a glove. All of this information as well as the "Fleer 95" logo is in gold print. All of this is on a card with a special leather-like coating. The back features a photo as well as fielding information. The cards are numbered in the lower left as "X of 10" and are sequenced in alphabetical order.

Card	Low	High
COMPLETE SET (10)	10.00	25.00
STATED ODDS 1:5 JUMBO		
1 Roberto Alomar	.60	1.50
2 Barry Bonds	2.50	6.00
3 Ken Griffey Jr.	1.50	4.00
4 Marquis Grissom	.40	1.00
5 Darren Lewis	.20	.50
6 Kenny Lofton	.40	1.00
7 Don Mattingly	2.50	6.00
8 Cal Ripken	3.00	8.00
9 Ivan Rodriguez	.60	1.50
10 Matt Williams	.40	1.00

1995 Fleer Update Soaring Stars

This nine-card standard-size set was inserted one every 36 packs. The fronts feature the player's photo set against a prismatic background of baseballs. The player's name, the "Soaring Stars" logo as well as a star are all printed in gold foil at the bottom. The back has a player photo, his name as well as some career information. The cards are numbered in the upper right "X of 9" and are sequenced in alphabetical order.

Card	Low	High
COMPLETE SET (9)	10.00	25.00
STATED ODDS 1:36		
1 Moises Alou UER	1.00	2.50
(says .399 BA in 1994)		
2 Jason Bere	.50	1.25
3 Jeff Conine	1.00	2.50
4 Cliff Floyd	1.00	2.50
5 Pat Hentgen	.50	1.25
6 Kenny Lofton	1.00	2.50
7 Raul Mondesi	1.00	2.50
8 Mike Piazza	4.00	10.00
9 Tim Salmon	1.50	4.00

1996 Fleer

The 1996 Fleer baseball set consists of 600 standard-size cards issued in one series. Cards were issued in 11-card packs with a suggested retail price of $1.49. Borderless fronts are matte-finished and have full-color action shots with the player's name, team and position stamped in gold foil. Backs contain a biography and career stats on the top and a full-color head shot with a 1995 synopsis on the bottom. The matte finish on the cards was designed so collectors could have an easier surface for cards to be autographed. Fleer included in each pack a "Thanks a Million" scratch-off game card redeemable for instant-win prizes and a chance to bat for a million-dollar prize in a Major League park. Rookie Cards in this set include Matt Lawton and Mike Sweeney. A Cal Ripken promo was distributed to dealers and hobby media to preview the set.

Card	Low	High
COMPLETE SET (600)	40.00	80.00
1 Manny Alexander	.10	.30
2 Brady Anderson	.10	.30
3 Harold Baines	.10	.30
4 Armando Benitez	.10	.30
5 Bobby Bonilla	.10	.30
6 Kevin Brown	.10	.30
7 Scott Erickson	.10	.30
8 Curtis Goodwin	.10	.30
9 Jeffrey Hammonds	.10	.30
10 Jimmy Haynes	.10	.30
11 Chris Hoiles	.10	.30
12 Doug Jones	.10	.30
13 Rick Krivda	.10	.30
14 Jeff Manto	.10	.30
15 Ben McDonald	.10	.30
16 Jamie Moyer	.10	.30
17 Mike Mussina	.20	.50
18 Jesse Orosco	.10	.30
19 Rafael Palmeiro	.20	.50
20 Cal Ripken	1.00	2.50
21 Rick Aguilera	.10	.30
22 Luis Alicea	.10	.30
23 Stan Belinda	.10	.30
24 Jose Canseco	.20	.50
25 Roger Clemens	.60	1.50
26 Vaughn Eshelman	.10	.30
27 Mike Greenwell	.10	.30
28 Erik Hanson	.10	.30
29 Dwayne Hosey	.10	.30
30 Mike Macfarlane UER	.10	.30
31 Tim Naehring	.10	.30
32 Troy O'Leary	.10	.30
33 Aaron Sele	.10	.30
34 Zane Smith	.10	.30
35 Jeff Suppan	.10	.30
36 Lee Tinsley	.10	.30
37 John Valentin	.10	.30
38 Mo Vaughn	.10	.30
39 Tim Wakefield	.10	.30
40 Jim Abbott	.20	.50
41 Brian Anderson	.10	.30
42 Garret Anderson	.10	.30
43 Chili Davis	.10	.30
44 Gary DiSarcina	.10	.30
45 Damion Easley	.10	.30
46 Jim Edmonds	.10	.30
47 Chuck Finley	.10	.30
48 Todd Greene	.10	.30
49 Mike Harkey	.10	.30
50 Mike James	.10	.30
51 Mark Langston	.10	.30
52 Greg Myers	.10	.30
53 Orlando Palmeiro	.10	.30
54 Bob Patterson	.10	.30
55 Troy Percival	.10	.30
56 Tony Phillips	.10	.30
57 Tim Salmon	.20	.50
58 Lee Smith	.10	.30
59 J.T. Snow	.10	.30
60 Randy Velarde	.10	.30
61 Wilson Alvarez	.10	.30
62 Luis Andujar	.10	.30
63 Jason Bere	.10	.30
64 Ray Durham	.10	.30
65 Alex Fernandez	.10	.30
66 Ozzie Guillen	.10	.30
67 Roberto Hernandez	.10	.30
68 Lance Johnson	.10	.30
69 Matt Karchner	.10	.30
70 Ron Karkovice	.10	.30
71 Norberto Martin	.10	.30
72 Dave Martinez	.10	.30
73 Kirk McCaskill	.10	.30
74 Lyle Mouton	.10	.30
75 Tim Raines	.10	.30
76 Mike Sirotka RC	.10	.30
77 Frank Thomas	.30	.75
78 Larry Thomas	.10	.30
79 Robin Ventura	.10	.30
80 Sandy Alomar Jr.	.10	.30
81 Paul Assenmacher	.10	.30
82 Carlos Baerga	.10	.30
83 Albert Belle	.10	.30
84 Mark Clark	.10	.30
85 Alan Embree	.10	.30
86 Alvaro Espinoza	.10	.30
87 Orel Hershiser	.10	.30
88 Ken Hill	.10	.30
89 Kenny Lofton	.10	.30
90 Dennis Martinez	.10	.30
91 Jose Mesa	.10	.30
92 Eddie Murray	.30	.75
93 Charles Nagy	.10	.30
94 Chad Ogea	.10	.30
95 Tony Pena	.10	.30
96 Herb Perry	.10	.30
97 Eric Plunk	.10	.30
98 Jim Poole	.10	.30
99 Manny Ramirez	.20	.50
100 Paul Sorrento	.10	.30
101 Julian Tavarez	.10	.30
102 Jim Thome	.20	.50
103 Omar Vizquel	.20	.50
104 Dave Winfield	.10	.30
105 Danny Bautista	.10	.30
106 Joe Boever	.10	.30
107 Chad Curtis	.10	.30
108 John Doherty	.10	.30
109 Cecil Fielder	.10	.30
110 John Flaherty	.10	.30
111 Travis Fryman	.10	.30
112 Chris Gomez	.10	.30
113 Bob Higginson	.10	.30
114 Mark Lewis	.10	.30
115 Jose Lima	.10	.30
116 Felipe Lira	.10	.30
117 Brian Maxcy	.10	.30
118 C.J. Nitkowski	.10	.30
119 Phil Plantier	.10	.30
120 Clint Sodowsky	.10	.30
121 Alan Trammell	.10	.30
122 Lou Whitaker	.10	.30
123 Kevin Appier	.10	.30
124 Johnny Damon	.20	.50
125 Gary Gaetti	.10	.30
126 Tom Goodwin	.10	.30
127 Tom Gordon	.10	.30
128 Mark Gubicza	.10	.30
129 Bob Hamelin	.10	.30
130 David Howard	.10	.30
131 Jason Jacome	.10	.30
132 Wally Joyner	.10	.30
133 Keith Lockhart	.10	.30
134 Brent Mayne	.10	.30
135 Jeff Montgomery	.10	.30
136 Jon Nunnally	.10	.30
137 Juan Samuel	.10	.30
138 Mike Sweeney RC	.40	1.00
139 Michael Tucker	.10	.30
140 Joe Vitiello	.10	.30
141 Ricky Bones	.10	.30
142 Chuck Carr	.10	.30
143 Jeff Cirillo	.10	.30
144 Mike Fetters	.10	.30
145 Darryl Hamilton	.10	.30
146 David Hulse	.10	.30
147 John Jaha	.10	.30
148 Scott Karl	.10	.30
149 Mark Kiefer	.10	.30
150 Pat Listach	.10	.30
151 Mark Loretta	.10	.30
152 Mike Matheny	.10	.30
153 Matt Mieske	.10	.30
154 Dave Nilsson	.10	.30
155 Joe Oliver	.10	.30
156 Al Reyes	.10	.30
157 Kevin Seitzer	.10	.30
158 Steve Sparks	.10	.30
159 B.J. Surhoff	.10	.30
160 Jose Valentin	.10	.30
161 Greg Vaughn	.10	.30
162 Fernando Vina	.10	.30
163 Rich Becker	.10	.30
164 Ron Coomer	.10	.30
165 Marty Cordova	.10	.30
166 Chuck Knoblauch	.10	.30
167 Matt Lawton RC	.20	.50
168 Pat Meares	.10	.30
169 Paul Molitor	.10	.30
170 Pedro Munoz	.10	.30
171 Jose Parra	.10	.30
172 Kirby Puckett	.30	.75
173 Brad Radke	.10	.30
174 Jeff Reboulet	.10	.30

175 Rich Robertson	.10	.30
176 Frank Rodriguez	.10	.30
177 Scott Stahoviak	.10	.30
178 Dave Stevens	.10	.30
179 Matt Walbeck	.10	.30
180 Wade Boggs	.20	.50
181 David Cone	.10	.30
182 Tony Fernandez	.10	.30
183 Joe Girardi	.10	.30
184 Derek Jeter	1.25	3.00
185 Scott Kamieniecki	.10	.30
186 Pat Kelly	.10	.30
187 Jim Leyritz	.10	.30
188 Tino Martinez	.20	.50
189 Don Mattingly	.75	2.00
190 Jack McDowell	.10	.30
191 Jeff Nelson	.10	.30
192 Paul O'Neill	.20	.50
193 Melido Perez	.10	.30
194 Andy Pettitte	.20	.50
195 Mariano Rivera	.60	1.50
196 Ruben Sierra	.10	.30
197 Mike Stanley	.10	.30
198 Darryl Strawberry	.10	.30
199 John Wetteland	.10	.30
200 Bob Wickman	.10	.30
201 Bernie Williams	.20	.50
202 Mark Acre	.10	.30
203 Geronimo Berroa	.10	.30
204 Mike Bordick	.10	.30
205 Scott Brosius	.10	.30
206 Dennis Eckersley	.10	.30
207 Brent Gates	.10	.30
208 Jason Giambi	.10	.30
209 Rickey Henderson	.30	.75
210 Jose Herrera	.10	.30
211 Stan Javier	.10	.30
212 Doug Johns	.10	.30
213 Mark McGwire	.75	2.00
214 Steve Ontiveros	.10	.30
215 Craig Paquette	.10	.30
216 Ariel Prieto	.10	.30
217 Carlos Reyes	.10	.30
218 Terry Steinbach	.10	.30
219 Todd Stottlemyre	.10	.30
220 Danny Tartabull	.10	.30
221 Todd Van Poppel	.10	.30
222 John Wasdin	.10	.30
223 George Williams	.10	.30
224 Steve Wojciechowski	.10	.30
225 Rich Amaral	.10	.30
226 Bobby Ayala	.10	.30
227 Tim Belcher	.10	.30
228 Andy Benes	.10	.30
229 Chris Bosio	.10	.30
230 Darren Bragg	.10	.30
231 Jay Buhner	.10	.30
232 Norm Charlton	.10	.30
233 Vince Coleman	.10	.30
234 Joey Cora	.10	.30
235 Russ Davis	.10	.30
236 Alex Diaz	.10	.30
237 Felix Fermin	.10	.30
238 Ken Griffey Jr.	.50	1.25
239 Sterling Hitchcock	.10	.30
240 Randy Johnson	.30	.75
241 Edgar Martinez	.20	.50
242 Bill Risley	.10	.30
243 Alex Rodriguez	.60	1.50
244 Luis Sojo	.10	.30
245 Dan Wilson	.10	.30
246 Bob Wolcott	.10	.30
247 Will Clark	.20	.50
248 Jeff Frye	.10	.30
249 Benji Gil	.10	.30
250 Juan Gonzalez	.10	.30
251 Rusty Greer	.10	.30
252 Kevin Gross	.10	.30
253 Roger McDowell	.10	.30
254 Mark McLemore	.10	.30
255 Otis Nixon	.10	.30
256 Luis Ortiz	.10	.30
257 Mike Pagliarulo	.10	.30
258 Dean Palmer	.10	.30
259 Roger Pavlik	.10	.30
260 Ivan Rodriguez	.20	.50
261 Kenny Rogers	.10	.30
262 Jeff Russell	.10	.30
263 Mickey Tettleton	.10	.30
264 Bob Tewksbury	.10	.30
265 Dave Valle	.10	.30
266 Matt Whiteside	.10	.30
267 Roberto Alomar	.20	.50
268 Joe Carter	.10	.30
269 Tony Castillo	.10	.30
270 Domingo Cedeno	.10	.30
271 Tim Crabtree UER	.10	.30
272 Carlos Delgado	.10	.30
273 Alex Gonzalez	.10	.30
274 Shawn Green	.10	.30
275 Juan Guzman	.10	.30
276 Pat Hentgen	.10	.30
277 Al Leiter	.10	.30
278 Sandy Martinez	.10	.30
279 Paul Menhart	.10	.30
280 John Olerud	.10	.30
281 Paul Quantrill	.10	.30
282 Ken Robinson	.10	.30
283 Ed Sprague	.10	.30
284 Mike Timlin	.10	.30
285 Steve Avery	.10	.30
286 Rafael Belliard	.10	.30
287 Jeff Blauser	.10	.30
288 Pedro Borbon	.10	.30
289 Brad Clontz	.10	.30
290 Mike Devereaux	.10	.30
291 Tom Glavine	.20	.50
292 Marquis Grissom	.10	.30
293 Chipper Jones	.30	.75
294 David Justice	.10	.30
295 Mike Kelly	.10	.30
296 Ryan Klesko	.10	.30
297 Mark Lemke	.10	.30
298 Javier Lopez	.10	.30
299 Greg Maddux	.50	1.25
300 Fred McGriff	.20	.50
301 Greg McMichael	.10	.30
302 Kent Mercker	.10	.30
303 Mike Mordecai	.10	.30
304 Charlie O'Brien	.10	.30
305 Eduardo Perez	.10	.30
306 Luis Polonia	.10	.30
307 Jason Schmidt	.20	.50
308 John Smoltz	.20	.50
309 Terrell Wade	.10	.30
310 Mark Wohlers	.10	.30
311 Scott Bullett	.10	.30
312 Jim Bullinger	.10	.30
313 Larry Casian	.10	.30
314 Frank Castillo	.10	.30
315 Shawon Dunston	.10	.30
316 Kevin Foster	.10	.30
317 Matt Franco	.10	.30
318 Luis Gonzalez	.10	.30
319 Mark Grace	.20	.50
320 Jose Hernandez	.10	.30
321 Mike Hubbard	.10	.30
322 Brian McRae	.10	.30
323 Randy Myers	.10	.30
324 Jaime Navarro	.10	.30
325 Mark Parent	.10	.30
326 Mike Perez	.10	.30
327 Rey Sanchez	.10	.30
328 Ryne Sandberg	.50	1.25
329 Scott Servais	.10	.30
330 Sammy Sosa	.30	.75
331 Ozzie Timmons	.10	.30
332 Steve Trachsel	.10	.30
333 Todd Zeile	.10	.30
334 Bret Boone	.10	.30
335 Jeff Branson	.10	.30
336 Jeff Brantley	.10	.30
337 Dave Burba	.10	.30
338 Hector Carrasco	.10	.30
339 Mariano Duncan	.10	.30
340 Ron Gant	.10	.30
341 Lenny Harris	.10	.30
342 Xavier Hernandez	.10	.30
343 Thomas Howard	.10	.30
344 Mike Jackson	.10	.30
345 Barry Larkin	.20	.50
346 Darren Lewis	.10	.30
347 Hal Morris	.10	.30
348 Eric Owens	.10	.30
349 Mark Portugal	.10	.30
350 Jose Rijo	.10	.30
351 Reggie Sanders	.10	.30
352 Benito Santiago	.10	.30
353 Pete Schourek	.10	.30
354 John Smiley	.10	.30
355 Eddie Taubensee	.10	.30
356 Jerome Walton	.10	.30
357 David Wells	.10	.30
358 Roger Bailey	.10	.30
359 Jason Bates	.10	.30
360 Dante Bichette	.10	.30
361 Ellis Burks	.10	.30
362 Vinny Castilla	.10	.30
363 Andres Galarraga	.10	.30
364 Darren Holmes	.10	.30
365 Mike Kingery	.10	.30
366 Curt Leskanic	.10	.30
367 Quinton McCracken	.10	.30
368 Mike Munoz	.10	.30
369 David Nied	.10	.30
370 Steve Reed	.10	.30
371 Bryan Rekar	.10	.30
372 Kevin Ritz	.10	.30
373 Bruce Ruffin	.10	.30
374 Bret Saberhagen	.10	.30
375 Bill Swift	.10	.30
376 John Vander Wal	.10	.30
377 Larry Walker	.10	.30
378 Walt Weiss	.10	.30
379 Eric Young	.10	.30
380 Kurt Abbott	.10	.30
381 Alex Arias	.10	.30
382 Jerry Browne	.10	.30
383 John Burkett	.10	.30
384 Greg Colbrunn	.10	.30
385 Jeff Conine	.10	.30
386 Andre Dawson	.10	.30
387 Chris Hammond	.10	.30
388 Charles Johnson	.10	.30
389 Terry Mathews	.10	.30
390 Robb Nen	.10	.30
391 Joe Orsulak	.10	.30
392 Terry Pendleton	.10	.30
393 Pat Rapp	.10	.30
394 Gary Sheffield	.10	.30
395 Jesus Tavarez	.10	.30
396 Marc Valdes	.10	.30
397 Quilvio Veras	.10	.30
398 Randy Veres	.10	.30
399 Devon White	.10	.30
400 Jeff Bagwell	.20	.50
401 Derek Bell	.10	.30
402 Craig Biggio	.20	.50
403 John Cangelosi	.10	.30
404 Jim Dougherty	.10	.30
405 Doug Drabek	.10	.30
406 Tony Eusebio	.10	.30
407 Ricky Gutierrez	.10	.30
408 Mike Hampton	.10	.30
409 Dean Hartgraves	.10	.30
410 John Hudek	.10	.30
411 Brian L. Hunter	.10	.30
412 Todd Jones	.10	.30
413 Darryl Kile	.10	.30
414 Dave Magadan	.10	.30
415 Derrick May	.10	.30
416 Orlando Miller	.10	.30
417 James Mouton	.10	.30
418 Shane Reynolds	.10	.30
419 Greg Swindell	.10	.30
420 Jeff Tabaka	.10	.30
421 Dave Veres	.10	.30
422 Billy Wagner	.10	.30
423 Donne Wall	.10	.30
424 Rick Wilkins	.10	.30
425 Billy Ashley	.10	.30
426 Mike Blowers	.10	.30
427 Brett Butler	.10	.30
428 Tom Candiotti	.10	.30
429 Juan Castro	.10	.30
430 John Cummings	.10	.30
431 Delino DeShields	.10	.30
432 Joey Eischen	.10	.30
433 Chad Fonville	.10	.30
434 Greg Gagne	.10	.30
435 Dave Hansen	.10	.30
436 Carlos Hernandez	.10	.30
437 Todd Hollandsworth	.10	.30
438 Eric Karros	.10	.30
439 Roberto Kelly	.10	.30
440 Ramon Martinez	.10	.30
441 Raul Mondesi	.10	.30
442 Hideo Nomo	.30	.75
443 Antonio Osuna	.10	.30
444 Chan Ho Park	.10	.30
445 Mike Piazza	.50	1.25
446 Felix Rodriguez	.10	.30
447 Kevin Tapani	.10	.30
448 Ismael Valdes	.10	.30
449 Todd Worrell	.10	.30
450 Moises Alou	.10	.30
451 Shane Andrews	.10	.30
452 Yamil Benitez	.10	.30
453 Sean Berry	.10	.30
454 Wil Cordero	.10	.30
455 Jeff Fassero	.10	.30
456 Darrin Fletcher	.10	.30
457 Cliff Floyd	.10	.30
458 Mark Grudzielanek	.10	.30
459 Gil Heredia	.10	.30
460 Tim Laker	.10	.30
461 Mike Lansing	.10	.30
462 Pedro J.Martinez	.20	.50
463 Carlos Perez	.10	.30
464 Curtis Pride	.10	.30
465 Mel Rojas	.10	.30
466 Kirk Rueter	.10	.30
467 F.P. Santangelo	.10	.30
468 Tim Scott	.10	.30
469 David Segui	.10	.30
470 Tony Tarasco	.10	.30
471 Rondell White	.10	.30
472 Edgardo Alfonzo	.10	.30
473 Tim Bogar	.10	.30
474 Rico Brogna	.10	.30
475 Damon Buford	.10	.30
476 Paul Byrd	.10	.30
477 Carl Everett	.10	.30
478 John Franco	.10	.30
479 Todd Hundley	.10	.30
480 Butch Huskey	.10	.30
481 Jason Isringhausen	.10	.30
482 Bobby Jones	.10	.30
483 Chris Jones	.10	.30
484 Jeff Kent	.10	.30
485 Dave Mlicki	.10	.30
486 Robert Person	.10	.30
487 Bill Pulsipher	.10	.30
488 Kelly Stinnett	.10	.30
489 Ryan Thompson	.10	.30
490 Jose Vizcaino	.10	.30
491 Howard Battle	.10	.30
492 Toby Borland	.10	.30
493 Ricky Bottalico	.10	.30
494 Darren Daulton	.10	.30
495 Lenny Dykstra	.10	.30
496 Jim Eisenreich	.10	.30
497 Sid Fernandez	.10	.30
498 Tyler Green	.10	.30
499 Charlie Hayes	.10	.30
500 Gregg Jefferies	.10	.30
501 Kevin Jordan	.10	.30
502 Tony Longmire	.10	.30
503 Tom Marsh	.10	.30
504 Michael Mimbs	.10	.30
505 Mickey Morandini	.10	.30
506 Gene Schall	.10	.30
507 Curt Schilling	.10	.30
508 Heathcliff Slocumb	.10	.30
509 Kevin Stocker	.10	.30
510 Andy Van Slyke	.20	.50
511 Lenny Webster	.10	.30
512 Mark Whiten	.10	.30
513 Mike Williams	.10	.30
514 Jay Bell	.10	.30
515 Jacob Brumfield	.10	.30
516 Jason Christiansen	.10	.30
517 Dave Clark	.10	.30
518 Midre Cummings	.10	.30
519 Angelo Encarnacion	.10	.30
520 John Ericks	.10	.30
521 Carlos Garcia	.10	.30
522 Mark Johnson	.10	.30
523 Jeff King	.10	.30
524 Nelson Liriano	.10	.30
525 Esteban Loaiza	.10	.30
526 Al Martin	.10	.30
527 Orlando Merced	.10	.30
528 Dan Miceli	.10	.30
529 Ramon Morel	.10	.30
530 Denny Neagle	.10	.30
531 Steve Parris	.10	.30
532 Dan Plesac	.10	.30
533 Don Slaught	.10	.30
534 Paul Wagner	.10	.30
535 John Wehner	.10	.30
536 Kevin Young	.10	.30
537 Allen Battle	.10	.30
538 David Bell	.10	.30
539 Alan Benes	.10	.30
540 Scott Cooper	.10	.30
541 Tripp Cromer	.10	.30
542 Tony Fossas	.10	.30
543 Bernard Gilkey	.10	.30
544 Tom Henke	.10	.30
545 Brian Jordan	.10	.30
546 Ray Lankford	.10	.30
547 John Mabry	.10	.30
548 T.J. Mathews	.10	.30
549 Mike Morgan	.10	.30
550 Jose Oliva	.10	.30
551 Jose Oquendo	.10	.30
552 Donovan Osborne	.10	.30
553 Tom Pagnozzi	.10	.30
554 Mark Petkovsek	.10	.30
555 Danny Sheaffer	.10	.30
556 Ozzie Smith	.50	1.25
557 Mark Sweeney	.10	.30
558 Allen Watson	.10	.30
559 Andy Ashby	.10	.30
560 Brad Ausmus	.10	.30
561 Willie Blair	.10	.30
562 Ken Caminiti	.10	.30
563 Andujar Cedeno	.10	.30
564 Glenn Dishman	.10	.30
565 Steve Finley	.10	.30
566 Bryce Florie	.10	.30
567 Tony Gwynn	.40	1.00
568 Joey Hamilton	.10	.30
569 Dustin Hermanson	.10	.30
570 Trevor Hoffman	.10	.30
571 Brian Johnson	.10	.30
572 Marc Kroon	.10	.30
573 Scott Livingstone	.10	.30
574 Marc Newfield	.10	.30
575 Melvin Nieves	.10	.30
576 Jody Reed	.10	.30
577 Bip Roberts	.10	.30
578 Scott Sanders	.10	.30
579 Fernando Valenzuela	.10	.30
580 Eddie Williams	.10	.30
581 Rod Beck	.10	.30
582 Marvin Benard RC	.10	.30
583 Barry Bonds	.75	2.00
584 Jamie Brewington RC	.10	.30
585 Mark Carreon	.10	.30
586 Royce Clayton	.10	.30
587 Shawn Estes	.10	.30
588 Glenallen Hill	.10	.30
589 Mark Leiter	.10	.30
590 Kirt Manwaring	.10	.30
591 David McCarty	.10	.30
592 Terry Mulholland	.10	.30
593 John Patterson	.10	.30
594 J.R. Phillips	.10	.30
595 Deion Sanders	.20	.50
596 Steve Scarsone	.10	.30
597 Robby Thompson	.10	.30
598 Sergio Valdez	.10	.30
599 W.Van Landingham	.10	.30
600 Matt Williams	.10	.30
P20 Cal Ripken Promo	1.25	3.00

1996 Fleer Tiffany

The Tiffany Collection is a 600-card parallel set that has a special UV coating that replaces the matte finish of the regular cards and silver holographic foil that takes the place of gold foil for lettering. These cards were inserted in regular packs at one card per pack.

*STARS: 2X TO 5X BASIC CARDS
*ROOKIES: 4X TO 10X BASIC CARDS

1996 Fleer Checklists

Checklist cards were seeded one per six regular packs and have glossy, borderless fronts with full-color shots of the Major League's best. "Checklist" and the player's name are stamped in gold foil. Backs list the entire rundown of '96 Fleer cards printed in black type on a white background.

COMPLETE SET (10)	1.50	4.00
STATED ODDS 1:6		
1 Barry Bonds	.40	1.00
2 Ken Griffey Jr.	.25	.60
3 Chipper Jones	.15	.40
4 Greg Maddux	.25	.60
5 Mike Piazza	.25	.60
6 Manny Ramirez	.08	.25
7 Cal Ripken	.50	1.25
8 Frank Thomas	.15	.40
9 Mo Vaughn	.05	.15
10 Matt Williams	.05	.15

1996 Fleer Golden Memories

Randomly inserted at a rate of one in 10 regular packs, this 10-card standard-size set features important highlights of the 1995 season. Fronts have two action shots, one serving as a background, the other a full-color cutout. "Golden Memories" and player's name are printed vertically in white type. Backs contain a biography, player close-up and career statistics.

COMPLETE SET (10)	3.00	8.00
STATED ODDS 1:10		
1 Albert Belle	.15	.40
2 Barry Bonds Sammy Sosa	.40	1.00
3 Greg Maddux	.60	1.50
4 Edgar Martinez	.25	.60
5 Ramon Martinez	.15	.40
6 Mark McGwire	1.00	2.50
7 Eddie Murray	.40	1.00
8 Cal Ripken	1.25	3.00
9 Frank Thomas	.40	1.00
10 Alan Trammell Lou Whitaker	.15	.40

1996 Fleer Lumber Company

This retail-exclusive 12-card set was inserted one in every nine packs and features RBI and HR power hitters. The fronts display a color action player cut-out on a wood background with embossed printing. The backs carry a player photo and information about the player.

COMPLETE SET (12)	10.00	25.00
STATED ODDS 1:9 RETAIL		
1 Albert Belle	.40	1.00
2 Dante Bichette	.40	1.00
3 Barry Bonds	2.50	6.00
4 Ken Griffey Jr.	1.50	4.00
5 Mark McGwire	2.50	6.00
6 Mike Piazza	1.50	4.00
7 Manny Ramirez	.60	1.50
8 Tim Salmon	.60	1.50
9 Sammy Sosa	1.00	2.50
10 Frank Thomas	1.00	2.50
11 Mo Vaughn	.40	1.00
12 Matt Williams	.40	1.00

1996 Fleer Postseason Glory

Randomly inserted in regular packs at a rate of one in five, this five-card standard-size set highlights great moments of the 1996 Divisional, League Championship and World Series games. Horizontal, white-bordered fronts feature a player in three full-color action cutouts with black strips on top and bottom. "Post-Season Glory" appears on top and the player's name is printed in silver hologram foil. White-bordered backs are split between a full-color player close-up and a description of his post-season play printed in white type on a black background.

COMPLETE SET (5)	.75	2.00
STATED ODDS 1:5		
1 Tom Glavine	.08	.25
2 Ken Griffey Jr.	.25	.60
3 Orel Hershiser	.05	.15
4 Randy Johnson	.15	.40
5 Jim Thome	.08	.25

1996 Fleer Prospects

Randomly inserted at a rate of one in six regular packs, this ten-card standard-size set focuses on players moving up through the farm system. Borderless fronts have full-color head shots on one-color backgrounds. "Prospect" and the player's name are stamped in silver hologram foil. Backs feature a full-color action shot with a synopsis of talent printed in a green box.

COMPLETE SET (10)	1.50	4.00
STATED ODDS 1:6		
1 Yamil Benitez	.20	.50
2 Roger Cedeno	.20	.50
3 Tony Clark	.20	.50
4 Micah Franklin	.20	.50
5 Karim Garcia	.20	.50
6 Todd Greene	.20	.50
7 Alex Ochoa	.20	.50
8 Ruben Rivera	.20	.50
9 Chris Snopek	.20	.50
10 Shannon Stewart	.40	1.00

1996 Fleer Road Warriors

Randomly inserted in regular packs at a rate of one in 13, this 10-card standard-size set focuses on players who thrive on the road. Fronts feature a full-color player cutout set against a winding rural highway background. "Road Warriors" is printed in reverse type with a hazy white border and the player's name is printed in white type underneath. Backs include the player's road stats, biography and a close-up shot.

COMPLETE SET (10)	5.00	12.00
STATED ODDS 1:13		
1 Derek Bell	.20	.50
2 Tony Gwynn	.60	1.50
3 Greg Maddux	.75	2.00
4 Mark McGwire	1.25	3.00
5 Mike Piazza	.75	2.00
6 Manny Ramirez	.30	.75
7 Tim Salmon	.30	.75
8 Frank Thomas	.50	1.25
9 Mo Vaughn	.20	.50
10 Matt Williams	.20	.50

1996 Fleer Rookie Sensations

Randomly inserted at a rate of one in 11 regular packs, this 15-card standard-size set highlights 1995's best rookies. Borderless, horizontal fronts have a full-color action shot and a silver hologram strip containing the player's name and team logo. Horizontal backs have full-color head shots with a player profile all printed on a white background.

COMPLETE SET (15)	6.00	15.00
STATED ODDS 1:11		
1 Garret Anderson	.50	1.25
2 Marty Cordova	.50	1.25
3 Johnny Damon	.75	2.00
4 Ray Durham	.50	1.25
5 Carl Everett	.50	1.25
6 Shawn Green	.50	1.25
7 Brian L.Hunter	.50	1.25
8 Jason Isringhausen	.50	1.25
9 Charles Johnson	.50	1.25
10 Chipper Jones	1.25	3.00
11 John Mabry	.50	1.25
12 Hideo Nomo	1.25	3.00
13 Troy Percival	.50	1.25
14 Andy Pettitte	.75	2.00
15 Quilvio Veras	.50	1.25

1996 Fleer Smoke 'n Heat

Randomly inserted at a rate of one in nine regular packs, this 10-card standard-size set celebrates the pitchers with rifle arms and a high strikeout count. Fronts feature a full-color player cutout set against a red flame background. "Smoke 'n Heat" and the player's name are printed in gold type. Backs feature the pitcher's 1995 numbers, a biography and career stats along with a full-color close-up.

COMPLETE SET (10)	2.50	6.00
STATED ODDS 1:9		
1 Kevin Appier	.20	.50
2 Roger Clemens	1.00	2.50
3 David Cone	.20	.50
4 Chuck Finley	.20	.50
5 Randy Johnson	.50	1.25
6 Greg Maddux	.75	2.00
7 Pedro Martinez	.30	.75
8 Hideo Nomo	.50	1.25
9 John Smoltz	.30	.75
10 Todd Stottlemyre	.20	.50

1996 Fleer Team Leaders

This hobby-exclusive 28-card set was randomly inserted one in every nine packs and features statistical and inspirational leaders. The fronts display color action player cut-out on a foil background of the team name and logo. The backs carry a player portrait and player information.

COMPLETE SET (28)	25.00	60.00
STATED ODDS 1:9 HOBBY		
1 Cal Ripken	4.00	10.00
2 Mo Vaughn	.50	1.25
3 Jim Edmonds	.50	1.25
4 Frank Thomas	1.25	3.00
5 Kenny Lofton	.50	1.25
6 Travis Fryman	.50	1.25
7 Gary Gaetti	.50	1.25
8 B.J. Surhoff	.50	1.25
9 Kirby Puckett	1.25	3.00
10 Don Mattingly	3.00	8.00
11 Mark McGwire	3.00	8.00
12 Ken Griffey Jr.	2.00	5.00
13 Juan Gonzalez	.50	1.25
14 Joe Carter	.50	1.25
15 Greg Maddux	2.00	5.00
16 Sammy Sosa	1.25	3.00
17 Barry Larkin	.75	2.00
18 Dante Bichette	.50	1.25
19 Jeff Conine	.50	1.25
20 Jeff Bagwell	.75	2.00
21 Mike Piazza	2.00	5.00
22 Rondell White	.50	1.25
23 Rico Brogna	.50	1.25
24 Darren Daulton	.50	1.25
25 Jeff King	.50	1.25
26 Ray Lankford	.50	1.25
27 Tony Gwynn	1.50	4.00
28 Barry Bonds	3.00	8.00

1996 Fleer Tomorrow's Legends

Randomly inserted in regular packs at a rate of one in 13, this 10-card set focuses on young talent with bright futures. Multicolored fronts have four panels of art that serve as a background and a full-color player cutout. "Tomorrow's Legends" and player's name are printed in white type at the bottom. Backs include the player's '95 stats, biography and a full-color close-up shot.

COMPLETE SET (10)	4.00	10.00
STATED ODDS 1:13		
1 Garret Anderson	.30	.75
2 Jim Edmonds	.30	.75
3 Brian L.Hunter	.30	.75
4 Jason Isringhausen	.30	.75
5 Charles Johnson	.30	.75
6 Chipper Jones	.75	2.00
7 Ryan Klesko	.30	.75
8 Hideo Nomo	.75	2.00
9 Manny Ramirez	.50	1.25
10 Rondell White	.30	.75

1996 Fleer Zone

This 12-card set was randomly inserted one in every 90 packs and features "unstoppable" hitters and "unhittable" pitchers. The fronts display a color action player cut-out printed on holographic foil. The backs carry a player portrait with information as to why they were selected for this set.

COMPLETE SET (12)	40.00	100.00
STATED ODDS 1:90		
1 Albert Belle	1.25	3.00
2 Barry Bonds	8.00	20.00
3 Ken Griffey Jr.	5.00	12.00
4 Tony Gwynn	4.00	10.00
5 Randy Johnson	3.00	8.00
6 Kenny Lofton	1.25	3.00
7 Greg Maddux	5.00	12.00
8 Edgar Martinez	2.00	5.00
9 Mike Piazza	5.00	12.00
10 Frank Thomas	3.00	8.00
11 Mo Vaughn	1.25	3.00
12 Matt Williams	1.25	3.00

1996 Fleer Update

The 1996 Fleer Update set was issued in one series totalling 250 cards. The 11-card packs retailed for $1.49 each. The fronts feature color action player photos. The backs carry complete player stats and a "Did you know?" fact. The cards are grouped alphabetically within teams and checklisted below alphabetically according to teams for each league with AL preceding NL. The set contains the subset: Encore (U211-U245). Notable Rookie Cards include Tony Batista, Mike Cameron, Matt Mantei and Chris Singleton.

COMPLETE SET (250)	12.50	30.00
U1 Roberto Alomar	.20	.50
U2 Mike Devereaux	.10	.30
U3 Scott McClain RC	.10	.30
U4 Roger McDowell	.10	.30
U5 Kent Mercker	.10	.30
U6 Jimmy Myers RC	.10	.30
U7 Randy Myers	.10	.30
U8 B.J. Surhoff	.10	.30
U9 Tony Tarasco	.10	.30
U10 David Wells	.10	.30
U11 Wil Cordero	.10	.30
U12 Tom Gordon	.10	.30
U13 Reggie Jefferson	.10	.30
U14 Jose Malave	.10	.30
U15 Kevin Mitchell	.10	.30
U16 Jamie Moyer	.10	.30
U17 Heathcliff Slocumb	.10	.30
U18 Mike Stanley	.10	.30
U19 George Arias	.10	.30
U20 Jorge Fabregas	.10	.30
U21 Don Slaught	.10	.30
U22 Randy Velarde	.10	.30
U23 Harold Baines	.10	.30
U24 Mike Cameron RC	.30	.75
U25 Darren Lewis	.10	.30
U26 Tony Phillips	.10	.30
U27 Bill Simas	.10	.30
U28 Chris Snopek	.10	.30
U29 Kevin Tapani	.10	.30
U30 Danny Tartabull	.10	.30
U31 Julio Franco	.10	.30
U32 Jack McDowell	.10	.30
U33 Kimera Bartee	.10	.30
U34 Mark Lewis	.10	.30
U35 Melvin Nieves	.10	.30

U36 Mark Parent .10 .30
U37 Eddie Williams .10 .30
U38 Tim Belcher .10 .30
U39 Sal Fasano .10 .30
U40 Chris Haney .10 .30
U41 Mike Macfarlane .10 .30
U42 Jose Offerman .10 .30
U43 Joe Randa .10 .30
U44 Bip Roberts .10 .30
U45 Chuck Carr .10 .30
U46 Bobby Hughes .10 .30
U47 Graeme Lloyd .10 .30
U48 Ben McDonald .10 .30
U49 Kevin Wickander .10 .30
U50 Rick Aguilera .10 .30
U51 Mike Durant .10 .30
U52 Chip Hale .10 .30
U53 LaTroy Hawkins .10 .30
U54 Dave Hollins .10 .30
U55 Roberto Kelly .10 .30
U56 Paul Molitor .10 .30
U57 Dan Naulty .10 .30
U58 Mariano Duncan .10 .30
U59 Andy Fox .10 .30
U60 Joe Girardi .10 .30
U61 Dwight Gooden .10 .30
U62 Jimmy Key .10 .30
U63 Matt Luke .10 .30
U64 Tino Martinez .20 .50
U65 Jeff Nelson .10 .30
U66 Tim Raines .10 .30
U67 Ruben Rivera .10 .30
U68 Kenny Rogers .10 .30
U69 Gerald Williams .10 .30
U70 Tony Batista RC .30 .75
U71 Allen Battle .10 .30
U72 Jim Corsi .10 .30
U73 Steve Cox .10 .30
U74 Pedro Munoz .10 .30
U75 Phil Plantier .10 .30
U76 Scott Spiezio .10 .30
U77 Ernie Young .10 .30
U78 Russ Davis .10 .30
U79 Sterling Hitchcock .10 .30
U80 Edwin Hurtado .10 .30
U81 Raul Ibanez RC 1.00 2.50
U82 Mike Jackson .10 .30
U83 Ricky Jordan .10 .30
U84 Paul Sorrento .10 .30
U85 Doug Strange .10 .30
U86 M.Brandenburg RC .10 .30
U87 Damon Buford .10 .30
U88 Kevin Elster .10 .30
U89 Darryl Hamilton .10 .30
U90 Ken Hill .10 .30
U91 Ed Vosberg .10 .30
U92 Craig Worthington .10 .30
U93 Tilson Brito RC .10 .30
U94 Giovanni Carrara RC .10 .30
U95 Felipe Crespo .10 .30
U96 Erik Hanson .10 .30
U97 Marty Janzen RC .10 .30
U98 Otis Nixon .10 .30
U99 Charlie O'Brien .10 .30
U100 Robert Perez .10 .30
U101 Paul Quantrill .10 .30
U102 Bill Risley .10 .30
U103 Juan Samuel .10 .30
U104 Jermaine Dye .10 .30
U105 W.Monds RC .10 .30
U106 Dwight Smith .10 .30
U107 Jerome Walton .10 .30
U108 Terry Adams .10 .30
U109 Leo Gomez .10 .30
U110 Robin Jennings .10 .30
U111 Doug Jones .10 .30
U112 Brooks Kieschnick .10 .30
U113 Dave Magadan .10 .30
U114 Jason Maxwell RC .10 .30
U115 Rodney Myers RC .10 .30
U116 Eric Anthony .10 .30
U117 Vince Coleman .10 .30
U118 Eric Davis .10 .30
U119 Steve Gibralter .10 .30
U120 Curtis Goodwin .10 .30
U121 Willie Greene .10 .30
U122 Mike Kelly .10 .30
U123 Marcus Moore .10 .30
U124 Chad Mottola .10 .30
U125 Chris Sabo .10 .30
U126 Roger Salkeld .10 .30
U127 Pedro Castellano .10 .30
U128 Trenidad Hubbard .10 .30
U129 Jayhawk Owens .10 .30
U130 Jeff Reed .10 .30
U131 Kevin Brown .10 .30
U132 Al Leiter .10 .30
U133 Matt Mantei RC .20 .50
U134 Dave Weathers .10 .30
U135 Devon White .10 .30
U136 Bob Abreu .30 .75
U137 Sean Berry .10 .30
U138 Doug Brocail .10 .30
U139 Richard Hidalgo .10 .30
U140 Alvin Morman .10 .30
U141 Mike Blowers .10 .30
U142 Roger Cedeno .10 .30
U143 Greg Gagne .10 .30
U144 Karim Garcia .10 .30
U145 Wilton Guerrero RC .10 .30
U146 Israel Alcantara RC .10 .30
U147 Omar Daal .10 .30
U148 Ryan McGuire .10 .30
U149 Sherman Obando .10 .30
U150 Jose Paniagua .10 .30
U151 Henry Rodriguez .10 .30
U152 Andy Stankiewicz .10 .30
U153 Dave Veres .10 .30
U154 Juan Acevedo .10 .30
U155 Mark Clark .10 .30
U156 Bernard Gilkey .10 .30
U157 Pete Harnisch .10 .30
U158 Lance Johnson .10 .30
U159 Brent Mayne .10 .30
U160 Rey Ordonez .10 .30
U161 Kevin Roberson .10 .30
U162 Paul Wilson .10 .30
U163 David Doster RC .10 .30
U164 Mike Grace RC .10 .30
U165 Rich Hunter RC .10 .30
U166 Pete Incaviglia .10 .30
U167 Mike Lieberthal .10 .30
U168 Terry Mulholland .10 .30
U169 Ken Ryan .10 .30
U170 Benito Santiago .10 .30
U171 Kevin Sefcik RC .10 .30
U172 Lee Tinsley .10 .30
U173 Todd Zeile .10 .30
U174 F.Cordova RC .20 .50
U175 Danny Darwin .10 .30
U176 Charlie Hayes .10 .30
U177 Jason Kendall .10 .30
U178 Mike Kingery .10 .30
U179 Jon Lieber .10 .30
U180 Zane Smith .10 .30
U181 Luis Alicea .10 .30
U182 Cory Bailey .10 .30
U183 Andy Benes .10 .30
U184 Pat Borders .10 .30
U185 Mike Busby RC .10 .30
U186 Royce Clayton .10 .30
U187 Dennis Eckersley .10 .30
U188 Gary Gaetti .10 .30
U189 Ron Gant .10 .30
U190 Aaron Holbert .10 .30
U191 Willie McGee .10 .30
U192 Miguel Mejia RC .10 .30
U193 Jeff Parrett .10 .30
U194 Todd Stottlemyre .10 .30
U195 Sean Bergman .10 .30
U196 Archi Cianfrocco .10 .30
U197 Rickey Henderson .30 .75
U198 Wally Joyner .10 .30
U199 Craig Shipley .10 .30
U200 Bob Tewksbury .10 .30
U201 Tim Worrell .10 .30
U202 Rich Aurilia RC .20 .50
U203 Doug Creek .10 .30
U204 Shawon Dunston .10 .30
U205 O.Fernandez RC .10 .30
U206 Mark Gardner .10 .30
U207 Stan Javier .10 .30
U208 Marcus Jensen .10 .30
U209 Chris Singleton RC .20 .50
U210 Allen Watson .10 .30
U211 Jeff Bagwell ENC .20 .50
U212 Derek Bell ENC .10 .30
U213 Albert Belle ENC .10 .30
U214 Wade Boggs ENC .20 .50
U215 Barry Bonds ENC .75 2.00
U216 Jose Canseco ENC .20 .50
U217 Marty Cordova ENC .10 .30
U218 Jim Edmonds ENC .10 .30
U219 Cecil Fielder ENC .10 .30
U220 A.Galarraga ENC .10 .30
U221 Juan Gonzalez ENC .10 .30
U222 Mark Grace ENC .20 .50
U223 Ken Griffey Jr. ENC .50 1.25
U224 Tony Gwynn ENC .40 1.00
U225 J. Isringhausen ENC .10 .30
U226 Derek Jeter ENC .75 2.00
U227 Randy Johnson ENC .30 .75
U228 Chipper Jones ENC .30 .75
U229 Ryan Klesko ENC .10 .30
U230 Barry Larkin ENC .20 .50
U231 Kenny Lofton ENC .10 .30
U232 Greg Maddux ENC .50 1.25
U233 Raul Mondesi ENC .10 .30
U234 Hideo Nomo ENC .30 .75
U235 Mike Piazza ENC .50 1.25
U236 Manny Ramirez ENC .20 .50
U237 Cal Ripken ENC .60 1.50
U238 Tim Salmon ENC .20 .50
U239 Ryne Sandberg ENC .50 1.25
U240 Reggie Sanders ENC .10 .30
U241 Gary Sheffield ENC .10 .30
U242 Sammy Sosa ENC .30 .75
U243 Frank Thomas ENC .30 .75
U244 Mo Vaughn ENC .10 .30
U245 Matt Williams ENC .10 .30
U246 Barry Bonds CL .40 1.00
U247 Ken Griffey Jr. CL .30 .75
U248 Rey Ordonez CL .10 .30
U249 Ryne Sandberg CL .30 .75
U250 Frank Thomas CL .20 .50

1996 Fleer Update Tiffany

Inserted one per pack, these 250 cards parallel the basic Fleer Update cards. Unlike the basic cards, Tiffany inserts feature a layer of UV coating and a special logo on each card front.

COMPLETE SET (250) 50.00 120.00
*STARS: 1.25X TO 3X BASIC CARDS
*ROOKIES: 2X TO 5X BASIC CARDS

1996 Fleer Update Diamond Tribute

Randomly inserted in packs at a rate of one in 100, this 10-card set spotlights future Hall of Famers with holographic foils in a diamond design.

COMPLETE SET (10) 60.00 150.00
STATED ODDS 1:100
1 Wade Boggs 2.50 6.00
2 Barry Bonds 10.00 25.00
3 Ken Griffey Jr. 6.00 15.00
4 Tony Gwynn 5.00 12.00
5 Rickey Henderson 4.00 10.00
6 Greg Maddux 6.00 15.00
7 Eddie Murray 4.00 10.00
8 Cal Ripken 12.50 30.00
9 Ozzie Smith 6.00 15.00
10 Frank Thomas 4.00 10.00

1996 Fleer Update Headliners

Randomly inserted exclusively in retail packs at a rate of one in 20, cards from this 20-card set feature raised textured printing. The fronts carry color action player photos with the word "headliner" running continuously across the background.

COMPLETE SET (20) 15.00 40.00
STATED ODDS 1:5 RETAIL
1 Roberto Alomar .50 1.25
2 Jeff Bagwell .50 1.25
3 Albert Belle .30 .75
4 Barry Bonds 2.00 5.00
5 Cecil Fielder .30 .75
6 Juan Gonzalez .30 .75
7 Ken Griffey Jr. 1.25 3.00
8 Tony Gwynn 1.00 2.50
9 Randy Johnson .75 2.00
10 Chipper Jones .75 2.00
11 Ryan Klesko .30 .75
12 Kenny Lofton .30 .75
13 Greg Maddux 1.25 3.00
14 Hideo Nomo .75 2.00
15 Mike Piazza 1.25 3.00
16 Manny Ramirez .50 1.25
17 Cal Ripken 2.50 6.00
18 Tim Salmon .50 1.25
19 Frank Thomas .75 2.00
20 Matt Williams .30 .75

1996 Fleer Update New Horizons

Randomly inserted in hobby packs only at a rate of one in five, this 20-card set features 1996 rookies and prospects. The fronts carry player action color photos printed on foil cards. The backs display a player portrait and information about the player.

COMPLETE SET (20) 6.00 15.00
STATED ODDS 1:5 HOBBY
1 Bob Abreu .60 1.50
2 George Arias .20 .50
3 Tony Batista .40 1.00
4 Steve Cox .20 .50
5 Jermaine Dye .20 .50
6 Andy Fox .20 .50
7 Mike Grace .20 .50
8 Todd Greene .20 .50
9 Wilton Guerrero .20 .50
10 Richard Hidalgo .20 .50
11 Raul Ibanez .50 1.25
12 Robin Jennings .20 .50
13 Marcus Jensen .20 .50
14 Jason Kendall .20 .50
15 Jason Maxwell .20 .50
16 Ryan McGuire .20 .50
17 Miguel Mejia .20 .50
18 Wonderful Monds .20 .50
19 Rey Ordonez .20 .50
20 Paul Wilson .20 .50

1996 Fleer Update Smooth Leather

Randomly inserted in packs at a rate of one in five, this 10-card set features defensive stars. The fronts display color player photos and gold foil printing. The backs carry a player portrait and information about why the player was selected for this set.

COMPLETE SET (10) 4.00 10.00
STATED ODDS 1:5
1 Roberto Alomar .25 .60
2 Barry Bonds 1.00 2.50
3 Will Clark .25 .60
4 Ken Griffey Jr. .60 1.50
5 Kenny Lofton .15 .40
6 Greg Maddux .60 1.50
7 Raul Mondesi .15 .40
8 Rey Ordonez .15 .40
9 Cal Ripken 1.25 3.00
10 Matt Williams .15 .40

1996 Fleer Update Soaring Stars

Randomly inserted in packs at a rate of one in 11, this 10-card set features 10 of the hottest young players. The fronts carry color player cut-outs on a background of soaring baseballs in etched foil. The backs display another player photo on the same background with player information.

COMPLETE SET (10) 10.00 25.00
STATED ODDS 1:11
1 Jeff Bagwell .50 1.25
2 Barry Bonds 2.00 5.00
3 Juan Gonzalez .30 .75
4 Ken Griffey Jr. 1.25 3.00
5 Chipper Jones .75 2.00
6 Greg Maddux 1.25 3.00
7 Mike Piazza 1.25 3.00
8 Manny Ramirez .50 1.25
9 Frank Thomas .75 2.00
10 Matt Williams .30 .75

1997 Fleer

The 1997 Fleer set was issued in two series totaling 761 cards and distributed in 10-card packs with a suggested retail price of $1.49. The fronts feature color action player photos with a matte finish and gold foil printing. The backs carry another player photo with player information and career statistics. Cards 491-500 are a Checklist subset of Series one and feature black-and-white or sepia tone photos of big-name players. Series two contains the following subsets: Encore (696-720) which are redesigned cards of the big-name players from Series one, and Checklists (721-748). Cards 749 and 750 are expansion team logo cards with the insert checklists on the backs. Many dealers believe that cards numbered 751-761 were shortprinted. An Andruw Jones autographed Circa card numbered to 200 was also randomly inserted into packs. Rookie Cards in this set include Jose Cruz Jr., Brian Giles and Fernando Tatis.

COMPLETE SET (761) 70.00 140.00
COMP. SERIES 1 (500) 30.00 60.00
COMP. SERIES 2 (261) 40.00 80.00
COMMON CARD (1-750) .10 .30
COMMON CARD (751-761) .20 .50
1 Roberto Alomar .20 .50
2 Brady Anderson .10 .30
3 Bobby Bonilla .10 .30
4 Rocky Coppinger .10 .30
5 Cesar Devarez .10 .30
6 Scott Erickson .10 .30
7 Jeffrey Hammonds .10 .30
8 Chris Hoiles .10 .30
9 Eddie Murray .30 .75
10 Mike Mussina .20 .50
11 Randy Myers .10 .30
12 Rafael Palmeiro .20 .50
13 Cal Ripken 1.00 2.50
14 B.J. Surhoff .10 .30
15 David Wells .10 .30
16 Todd Zeile .10 .30
17 Darren Bragg .10 .30
18 Jose Canseco .20 .50
19 Roger Clemens .60 1.50
20 Wil Cordero .10 .30
21 Jeff Frye .10 .30
22 Nomar Garciaparra .50 1.25
23 Tom Gordon .10 .30
24 Mike Greenwell .10 .30
25 Reggie Jefferson .10 .30
26 Jose Malave .10 .30
27 Tim Naehring .10 .30
28 Troy O'Leary .10 .30
29 Heathcliff Slocumb .10 .30
30 Mike Stanley .10 .30
31 John Valentin .10 .30
32 Mo Vaughn .10 .30
33 Tim Wakefield .10 .30
34 Garret Anderson .10 .30
35 George Arias .10 .30
36 Shawn Boskie .10 .30
37 Chili Davis .10 .30
38 Jason Dickson .10 .30
39 Gary DiSarcina .10 .30
40 Jim Edmonds .10 .30
41 Darin Erstad .10 .30
42 Jorge Fabregas .10 .30
43 Chuck Finley .10 .30
44 Todd Greene .10 .30
45 Mike Holtz .10 .30
46 Rex Hudler .10 .30
47 Mike James .10 .30
48 Mark Langston .10 .30
49 Troy Percival .10 .30
50 Tim Salmon .20 .50
51 Jeff Schmidt .10 .30
52 J.T. Snow .10 .30
53 Randy Velarde .10 .30
54 Wilson Alvarez .10 .30
55 Harold Baines .10 .30
56 James Baldwin .10 .30
57 Jason Bere .10 .30
58 Mike Cameron .10 .30
59 Ray Durham .10 .30
60 Alex Fernandez .10 .30
61 Ozzie Guillen .10 .30
62 Roberto Hernandez .10 .30
63 Ron Karkovice .10 .30
64 Darren Lewis .10 .30
65 Dave Martinez .10 .30
66 Lyle Mouton .10 .30
67 Greg Norton .10 .30
68 Tony Phillips .10 .30
69 Chris Snopek .10 .30
70 Kevin Tapani .10 .30
71 Danny Tartabull .10 .30
72 Frank Thomas .30 .75
73 Robin Ventura .10 .30
74 Sandy Alomar Jr. .10 .30
75 Albert Belle .10 .30
76 Mark Carreon .10 .30
77 Julio Franco .10 .30
78 Brian Giles RC .60 1.50
79 Orel Hershiser .10 .30
80 Kenny Lofton .10 .30
81 Dennis Martinez .10 .30
82 Jack McDowell .10 .30
83 Jose Mesa .10 .30
84 Charles Nagy .10 .30
85 Chad Ogea .10 .30
86 Eric Plunk .10 .30
87 Manny Ramirez .20 .50
88 Kevin Seitzer .10 .30
89 Julian Tavarez .10 .30
90 Jim Thome .20 .50
91 Jose Vizcaino .10 .30
92 Omar Vizquel .20 .50
93 Brad Ausmus .10 .30
94 Kimera Bartee .10 .30
95 Raul Casanova .10 .30
96 Tony Clark .10 .30
97 John Cummings .10 .30
98 Travis Fryman .10 .30
99 Bob Higginson .10 .30
100 Mark Lewis .10 .30
101 Felipe Lira .10 .30
102 Phil Nevin .10 .30
103 Melvin Nieves .10 .30
104 Curtis Pride .10 .30
105 A.J. Sager .10 .30
106 Ruben Sierra .10 .30
107 Justin Thompson .10 .30
108 Alan Trammell .10 .30
109 Kevin Appier .10 .30
110 Tim Belcher .10 .30
111 Jaime Bluma .10 .30
112 Johnny Damon .20 .50
113 Tom Goodwin .10 .30
114 Chris Haney .10 .30
115 Keith Lockhart .10 .30
116 Mike Macfarlane .10 .30
117 Jeff Montgomery .10 .30
118 Jose Offerman .10 .30
119 Craig Paquette .10 .30
120 Joe Randa .10 .30
121 Bip Roberts .10 .30
122 Jose Rosado .10 .30
123 Mike Sweeney .10 .30
124 Michael Tucker .10 .30
125 Jeromy Burnitz .10 .30
126 Jeff Cirillo .10 .30
127 Jeff D'Amico .10 .30
128 Mike Fetters .10 .30
129 John Jaha .10 .30
130 Scott Karl .10 .30
131 Jesse Levis .10 .30
132 Mark Loretta .10 .30
133 Mike Matheny .10 .30
134 Ben McDonald .10 .30
135 Matt Mieske .10 .30
136 Marc Newfield .10 .30
137 Dave Nilsson .10 .30
138 Jose Valentin .10 .30
139 Fernando Vina .10 .30
140 Bob Wickman .10 .30
141 Gerald Williams .10 .30
142 Rick Aguilera .10 .30
143 Rich Becker .10 .30
144 Ron Coomer .10 .30
145 Marty Cordova .10 .30
146 Roberto Kelly .10 .30
147 Chuck Knoblauch .10 .30
148 Matt Lawton .10 .30
149 Pat Meares .10 .30
150 Travis Miller .10 .30
151 Paul Molitor .10 .30
152 Greg Myers .10 .30
153 Dan Naulty .10 .30
154 Kirby Puckett .30 .75
155 Brad Radke .10 .30
156 Frank Rodriguez .10 .30
157 Scott Stahoviak .10 .30
158 Dave Stevens .10 .30
159 Matt Walbeck .10 .30
160 Todd Walker .10 .30
161 Wade Boggs .20 .50
162 David Cone .10 .30
163 Mariano Duncan .10 .30
164 Cecil Fielder .10 .30
165 Joe Girardi .10 .30
166 Dwight Gooden .10 .30
167 Charlie Hayes .10 .30
168 Derek Jeter .75 2.00
169 Jimmy Key .10 .30
170 Jim Leyritz .10 .30
171 Tino Martinez .20 .50
172 Ramiro Mendoza RC .10 .30
173 Jeff Nelson .10 .30
174 Paul O'Neill .20 .50
175 Andy Pettitte .20 .50
176 Mariano Rivera .30 .75
177 Ruben Rivera .10 .30
178 Kenny Rogers .10 .30
179 Darryl Strawberry .10 .30
180 John Wetteland .10 .30
181 Bernie Williams .20 .50
182 Willie Adams .10 .30
183 Tony Batista .10 .30
184 Geronimo Berroa .10 .30
185 Mike Bordick .10 .30
186 Scott Brosius .10 .30
187 Bobby Chouinard .10 .30
188 Jim Corsi .10 .30
189 Brent Gates .10 .30
190 Jason Giambi .10 .30
191 Jose Herrera .10 .30
192 Damon Mashore .10 .30
193 Mark McGwire .75 2.00
194 Mike Mohler .10 .30
195 Scott Spiezio .10 .30
196 Terry Steinbach .10 .30
197 Bill Taylor .10 .30
198 John Wasdin .10 .30
199 Steve Wojciechowski .10 .30
200 Ernie Young .10 .30
201 Rich Amaral .10 .30
202 Jay Buhner .10 .30
203 Norm Charlton .10 .30
204 Joey Cora .10 .30
205 Russ Davis .10 .30
206 Ken Griffey Jr. .50 1.25
207 Sterling Hitchcock .10 .30
208 Brian Hunter .10 .30
209 Raul Ibanez .10 .30
210 Randy Johnson .30 .75
211 Edgar Martinez .20 .50
212 Jamie Moyer .10 .30
213 Alex Rodriguez .50 1.25
214 Paul Sorrento .10 .30
215 Matt Wagner .10 .30
216 Bob Wells .10 .30
217 Dan Wilson .10 .30
218 Damon Buford .10 .30
219 Will Clark .20 .50
220 Kevin Elster .10 .30
221 Juan Gonzalez .10 .30
222 Rusty Greer .10 .30
223 Kevin Gross .10 .30
224 Darryl Hamilton .10 .30
225 Mike Henneman .10 .30
226 Ken Hill .10 .30
227 Mark McLemore .10 .30
228 Darren Oliver .10 .30
229 Dean Palmer .10 .30
230 Roger Pavlik .10 .30
231 Ivan Rodriguez .20 .50
232 Mickey Tettleton .10 .30
233 Bobby Witt .10 .30
234 Jacob Brumfield .10 .30
235 Joe Carter .10 .30
236 Tim Crabtree .10 .30
237 Carlos Delgado .10 .30
238 Huck Flener .10 .30
239 Alex Gonzalez .10 .30
240 Shawn Green .10 .30
241 Juan Guzman .10 .30
242 Pat Hentgen .10 .30
243 Marty Janzen .10 .30
244 Sandy Martinez .10 .30
245 Otis Nixon .10 .30
246 Charlie O'Brien .10 .30
247 John Olerud .10 .30
248 Robert Perez .10 .30
249 Ed Sprague .10 .30
250 Mike Timlin .10 .30
251 Steve Avery .10 .30
252 Jeff Blauser .10 .30
253 Brad Clontz .10 .30
254 Jermaine Dye .10 .30
255 Tom Glavine .20 .50
256 Marquis Grissom .10 .30
257 Andruw Jones .20 .50
258 Chipper Jones .30 .75
259 David Justice .10 .30
260 Ryan Klesko .10 .30
261 Mark Lemke .10 .30
262 Javier Lopez .10 .30
263 Greg Maddux .50 1.25
264 Fred McGriff .20 .50
265 Greg McMichael .10 .30
266 Denny Neagle .10 .30
267 Terry Pendleton .10 .30
268 Eddie Perez .10 .30
269 John Smoltz .20 .50
270 Terrell Wade .10 .30
271 Mark Wohlers .10 .30
272 Terry Adams .10 .30
273 Brant Brown .10 .30
274 Leo Gomez .10 .30
275 Luis Gonzalez .10 .30
276 Mark Grace .20 .50
277 Tyler Houston .10 .30
278 Robin Jennings .10 .30
279 Brooks Kieschnick .10 .30
280 Brian McRae .10 .30
281 Jaime Navarro .10 .30
282 Ryne Sandberg .50 1.25
283 Scott Servais .10 .30
284 Sammy Sosa .30 .75
285 Dave Swartzbaugh .10 .30
286 Amaury Telemaco .10 .30
287 Steve Trachsel .10 .30
288 Pedro Valdes .10 .30
289 Turk Wendell .10 .30
290 Bret Boone .10 .30
291 Jeff Branson .10 .30
292 Jeff Brantley .10 .30
293 Eric Davis .10 .30
294 Willie Greene .10 .30
295 Thomas Howard .10 .30
296 Barry Larkin .20 .50
297 Kevin Mitchell .10 .30
298 Hal Morris .10 .30
299 Chad Mottola .10 .30
300 Joe Oliver .10 .30
301 Mark Portugal .10 .30
302 Roger Salkeld .10 .30
303 Reggie Sanders .10 .30
304 Pete Schourek .10 .30
305 John Smiley .10 .30
306 Eddie Taubensee .10 .30
307 Dante Bichette .10 .30
308 Ellis Burks .10 .30
309 Vinny Castilla .10 .30
310 Andres Galarraga .10 .30
311 Curt Leskanic .10 .30
312 Quinton McCracken .10 .30
313 Neifi Perez .10 .30
314 Jeff Reed .10 .30
315 Steve Reed .10 .30
316 Armando Reynoso .10 .30
317 Kevin Ritz .10 .30
318 Bruce Ruffin .10 .30
319 Larry Walker .10 .30
320 Walt Weiss .10 .30
321 Jamey Wright .10 .30
322 Eric Young .10 .30
323 Kurt Abbott .10 .30
324 Alex Arias .10 .30
325 Kevin Brown .10 .30
326 Luis Castillo .10 .30
327 Greg Colbrunn .10 .30
328 Jeff Conine .10 .30
329 Andre Dawson .10 .30
330 Charles Johnson .10 .30
331 Al Leiter .10 .30
332 Ralph Milliard .10 .30
333 Robb Nen .10 .30
334 Pat Rapp .10 .30
335 Edgar Renteria .10 .30
336 Gary Sheffield .10 .30
337 Devon White .10 .30
338 Bob Abreu .20 .50
339 Jeff Bagwell .20 .50
340 Derek Bell .10 .30
341 Sean Berry .10 .30
342 Craig Biggio .20 .50
343 Doug Drabek .10 .30
344 Tony Eusebio .10 .30
345 Ricky Gutierrez .10 .30
346 Mike Hampton .10 .30
347 Brian Hunter .10 .30
348 Todd Jones .10 .30
349 Darryl Kile .10 .30
350 Derrick May .10 .30
351 Orlando Miller .10 .30
352 James Mouton .10 .30
353 Shane Reynolds .10 .30
354 Billy Wagner .10 .30
355 Donne Wall .10 .30
356 Mike Blowers .10 .30
357 Brett Butler .10 .30
358 Roger Cedeno .10 .30
359 Chad Curtis .10 .30
360 Delino DeShields .10 .30
361 Greg Gagne .10 .30
362 Karim Garcia .10 .30
363 Wilton Guerrero .10 .30
364 Todd Hollandsworth .10 .30
365 Eric Karros .10 .30
366 Ramon Martinez .10 .30
367 Raul Mondesi .10 .30
368 Hideo Nomo .30 .75
369 Antonio Osuna .10 .30
370 Chan Ho Park .10 .30
371 Mike Piazza .50 1.25
372 Ismael Valdes .10 .30
373 Todd Worrell .10 .30
374 Moises Alou .10 .30
375 Shane Andrews .10 .30
376 Yamil Benitez .10 .30
377 Jeff Fassero .10 .30
378 Darrin Fletcher .10 .30
379 Cliff Floyd .10 .30
380 Mark Grudzielanek .10 .30
381 Mike Lansing .10 .30
382 Barry Manuel .10 .30
383 Pedro Martinez .20 .50
384 Henry Rodriguez .10 .30
385 Mel Rojas .10 .30
386 F.P. Santangelo .10 .30
387 David Segui .10 .30
388 Ugueth Urbina .10 .30
389 Rondell White .10 .30
390 Edgardo Alfonzo .10 .30
391 Carlos Baerga .10 .30
392 Mark Clark .10 .30
393 Alvaro Espinoza .10 .30
394 John Franco .10 .30
395 Bernard Gilkey .10 .30
396 Pete Harnisch .10 .30
397 Todd Hundley .10 .30
398 Butch Huskey .10 .30
399 Jason Isringhausen .10 .30
400 Lance Johnson .10 .30
401 Bobby Jones .10 .30
402 Alex Ochoa .10 .30
403 Rey Ordonez .10 .30
404 Robert Person .10 .30
405 Paul Wilson .10 .30
406 Matt Beech .10 .30
407 Ron Blazier .10 .30
408 Ricky Bottalico .10 .30
409 Lenny Dykstra .10 .30
410 Jim Eisenreich .10 .30
411 Bobby Estalella .10 .30
412 Mike Grace .10 .30
413 Gregg Jefferies .10 .30
414 Mike Lieberthal .10 .30
415 Wendell Magee .10 .30
416 Mickey Morandini .10 .30
417 Ricky Otero .10 .30
418 Scott Rolen .20 .50
419 Ken Ryan .10 .30
420 Benito Santiago .10 .30
421 Curt Schilling .10 .30
422 Kevin Sefcik .10 .30
423 Jermaine Allensworth .10 .30
424 Trey Beamon .10 .30
425 Jay Bell .10 .30
426 Francisco Cordova .10 .30
427 Carlos Garcia .10 .30
428 Mark Johnson .10 .30
429 Jason Kendall .10 .30
430 Jeff King .10 .30
431 Jon Lieber .10 .30
432 Al Martin .10 .30
433 Orlando Merced .10 .30
434 Ramon Morel .10 .30
435 Matt Ruebel .10 .30
436 Jason Schmidt .10 .30
437 Marc Wilkins .10 .30
438 Alan Benes .10 .30
439 Andy Benes .10 .30
440 Royce Clayton .10 .30
441 Dennis Eckersley .10 .30
442 Gary Gaetti .10 .30
443 Ron Gant .10 .30
444 Aaron Holbert .10 .30
445 Brian Jordan .10 .30
446 Ray Lankford .10 .30
447 John Mabry .10 .30
448 T.J. Mathews .10 .30
449 Willie McGee .10 .30
450 Donovan Osborne .10 .30
451 Tom Pagnozzi .10 .30
452 Ozzie Smith .50 1.25
453 Todd Stottlemyre .10 .30
454 Mark Sweeney .10 .30
455 Dmitri Young .10 .30
456 Andy Ashby .10 .30
457 Ken Caminiti .10 .30
458 Archi Cianfrocco .10 .30
459 Steve Finley .10 .30
460 John Flaherty .10 .30
461 Chris Gomez .10 .30

462 Tony Gwynn .40 1.00
463 Joey Hamilton .10 .30
464 Rickey Henderson .30 .75
465 Trevor Hoffman .10 .30
466 Brian Johnson .10 .30
467 Wally Joyner .10 .30
468 Jody Reed .10 .30
469 Scott Sanders .10 .30
470 Bob Tewksbury .10 .30
471 Fernando Valenzuela .10 .30
472 Greg Vaughn .10 .30
473 Tim Worrell .10 .30
474 Rich Aurilia .10 .30
475 Rod Beck .10 .30
476 Marvin Benard .10 .30
477 Barry Bonds .75 2.00
478 Jay Canizaro .10 .30
479 Shawon Dunston .10 .30
480 Shawn Estes .10 .30
481 Mark Gardner .10 .30
482 Glenallen Hill .10 .30
483 Stan Javier .10 .30
484 Marcus Jensen .10 .30
485 Bill Mueller RC .50 1.25
486 Wm. VanLandingham .10 .30
487 Allen Watson .10 .30
488 Rick Wilkins .10 .30
489 Matt Williams .10 .30
490 Desi Wilson .10 .30
491 Albert Belle CL .10 .30
492 Ken Griffey Jr. CL .30 .75
493 Andruw Jones CL .10 .30
494 Chipper Jones CL .20 .50
495 Mark McGwire CL .40 1.00
496 Paul Molitor CL .10 .30
497 Mike Piazza CL .30 .75
498 Cal Ripken CL .50 1.25
499 Alex Rodriguez CL .30 .75
500 Frank Thomas CL .20 .50
501 Kenny Lofton .10 .30
502 Carlos Perez .10 .30
503 Tim Raines .10 .30
504 Danny Patterson .10 .30
505 Derrick May .10 .30
506 Dave Hollins .10 .30
507 Felipe Crespo .10 .30
508 Brian Banks .10 .30
509 Jeff Kent .10 .30
510 Bubba Trammell RC .15 .40
511 Robert Person .10 .30
512 David Arias-Ortiz RC 10.00 25.00
513 Ryan Jones .10 .30
514 David Justice .10 .30
515 Will Cunnane .10 .30
516 Russ Johnson .10 .30
517 John Burkett .10 .30
518 Robinson Checo RC .10 .30
519 Ricardo Rincon RC .10 .30
520 Woody Williams .10 .30
521 Rick Helling .10 .30
522 Jorge Posada .20 .50
523 Kevin Orie .10 .30
524 Fernando Tatis RC .10 .30
525 Jermaine Dye .10 .30
526 Brian Hunter .10 .30
527 Greg McMichael .10 .30
528 Matt Wagner .10 .30
529 Richie Sexson .10 .30
530 Scott Ruffcorn .10 .30
531 Luis Gonzalez .10 .30
532 Mike Johnson RC .10 .30
533 Mark Petkovsek .10 .30
534 Doug Drabek .10 .30
535 Jose Canseco .20 .50
536 Bobby Bonilla .10 .30
537 J.T. Snow .10 .30
538 Shawon Dunston .10 .30
539 John Ericks .10 .30
540 Terry Steinbach .10 .30
541 Jay Bell .10 .30
542 Joe Borowski RC .15 .40
543 David Wells .10 .30
544 Justin Towle RC .10 .30
545 Mike Blowers .10 .30
546 Shannon Stewart .10 .30
547 Rudy Pemberton .10 .30
548 Bill Swift .10 .30
549 Osvaldo Fernandez .10 .30
550 Eddie Murray .30 .75
551 Don Wengert .10 .30
552 Brad Ausmus .10 .30
553 Carlos Garcia .10 .30
554 Jose Guillen .10 .30
555 Rheal Cormier .10 .30
556 Doug Brocail .10 .30
557 Rex Hudler .10 .30
558 Armando Benitez .10 .30
559 Eli Marrero .10 .30
560 Ricky Ledee RC .15 .40
561 Bartolo Colon .10 .30
562 Quilvio Veras .10 .30
563 Alex Fernandez .10 .30
564 Darren Dreifort .10 .30
565 Benji Gil .10 .30
566 Kent Mercker .10 .30
567 Glendon Rusch .10 .30
568 Ramon Tatis RC .10 .30
569 Roger Clemens .60 1.50
570 Mark Lewis .10 .30
571 Emil Brown RC .10 .30
572 Jaime Navarro .10 .30
573 Sherman Obando .10 .30
574 John Wasdin .10 .30
575 Calvin Maduro .10 .30
576 Todd Jones .10 .30
577 Orlando Merced .10 .30
578 Cal Eldred .10 .30
579 Mark Gubicza .10 .30
580 Michael Tucker .10 .30
581 Tony Saunders RC .10 .30
582 Garvin Alston .10 .30
583 Joe Roa .10 .30
584 Brady Raggio RC .10 .30
585 Jimmy Key .10 .30
586 Marc Sagmoen RC .10 .30
587 Jim Bullinger .10 .30
588 Yorkis Perez .10 .30
589 Jose Cruz Jr. RC .15 .40
590 Mike Stanton .10 .30
591 Deivi Cruz RC .15 .40
592 Steve Karsay .10 .30
593 Mike Trombley .10 .30
594 Doug Glanville .10 .30
595 Scott Sanders .10 .30
596 Thomas Howard .10 .30
597 T.J. Staton RC .10 .30
598 Garrett Stephenson .10 .30
599 Rico Brogna .10 .30
600 Albert Belle .10 .30
601 Jose Vizcaino .10 .30
602 Chili Davis .10 .30
603 Shane Mack .10 .30
604 Jim Eisenreich .10 .30
605 Todd Zeile .10 .30
606 Brian Boehringer RC .10 .30
607 Paul Shuey .10 .30
608 Kevin Tapani .10 .30
609 John Wetteland .10 .30
610 Jim Leyritz .10 .30
611 Ray Montgomery RC .10 .30
612 Doug Bochtler .10 .30
613 Wady Almonte RC .10 .30
614 Danny Tartabull .10 .30
615 Orlando Miller .10 .30
616 Bobby Ayala .10 .30
617 Tony Graffanino .10 .30
618 Marc Valdes .10 .30
619 Ron Villone .10 .30
620 Derrek Lee .20 .50
621 Greg Colbrunn .10 .30
622 Felix Heredia RC .15 .40
623 Carl Everett .10 .30
624 Mark Thompson .10 .30
625 Jeff Granger .10 .30
626 Damian Jackson .10 .30
627 Mark Leiter .10 .30
628 Chris Holt .10 .30
629 Dario Veras RC .10 .30
630 Dave Burba .10 .30
631 Darryl Hamilton .10 .30
632 Mark Acre .10 .30
633 F.Hernandez RC .10 .30
634 Terry Mulholland .10 .30
635 Dustin Hermanson .10 .30
636 Delino DeShields .10 .30
637 Steve Avery .10 .30
638 Tony Womack RC .15 .40
639 Mark Whiten .10 .30
640 Marquis Grissom .10 .30
641 Xavier Hernandez .10 .30
642 Eric Davis .10 .30
643 Bob Tewksbury .10 .30
644 Dante Powell .10 .30
645 Carlos Castillo RC .10 .30
646 Chris Widger .10 .30
647 Moises Alou .10 .30
648 Pat Listach .10 .30
649 Edgar Ramos RC .10 .30
650 Deion Sanders .20 .50
651 John Olerud .10 .30
652 Todd Dunwoody .10 .30
653 Randall Simon RC .15 .40
654 Dan Carlson .10 .30
655 Matt Williams .10 .30
656 Jeff King .10 .30
657 Luis Alicea .10 .30
658 Brian Moehler RC .15 .40
659 Ariel Prieto .10 .30
660 Kevin Elster .10 .30
661 Mark Hutton .10 .30
662 Aaron Sele .10 .30
663 Graeme Lloyd .10 .30
664 John Burke .10 .30
665 Mel Rojas .10 .30
666 Sid Fernandez .10 .30
667 Pedro Astacio .10 .30
668 Jeff Abbott .10 .30
669 Darren Daulton .10 .30
670 Mike Bordick .10 .30
671 Sterling Hitchcock .10 .30
672 Damion Easley .10 .30
673 Armando Reynoso .10 .30
674 Pat Cline .10 .30
675 Orlando Cabrera RC .30 .75
676 Alan Embree .10 .30
677 Brian Bevil .10 .30
678 David Weathers .10 .30
679 Cliff Floyd .10 .30
680 Joe Randa .10 .30
681 Bill Haselman .10 .30
682 Jeff Fassero .10 .30
683 Matt Morris .10 .30
684 Mark Portugal .10 .30
685 Lee Smith .10 .30
686 Pokey Reese .10 .30
687 Benito Santiago .10 .30
688 Brian Johnson .10 .30
689 Brent Brede RC .10 .30
690 S.Hasegawa RC .20 .50
691 Julio Santana .10 .30
692 Steve Kline .10 .30
693 Julian Tavarez .10 .30
694 John Hudek .10 .30
695 Manny Alexander .10 .30
696 Roberto Alomar ENC .10 .30
697 Jeff Bagwell ENC .10 .30
698 Barry Bonds ENC .40 1.00
699 Ken Caminiti ENC .10 .30
700 Juan Gonzalez ENC .10 .30
701 Ken Griffey Jr. ENC .30 .75
702 Tony Gwynn ENC .20 .50
703 Derek Jeter ENC .40 1.00
704 Andruw Jones ENC .20 .50
705 Chipper Jones ENC .20 .50
706 Barry Larkin ENC .10 .30
707 Greg Maddux ENC .30 .75
708 Mark McGwire ENC .40 1.00
709 Paul Molitor ENC .10 .30
710 Hideo Nomo ENC .10 .30
711 Andy Pettitte ENC .10 .30
712 Mike Piazza ENC .30 .75
713 Manny Ramirez ENC .20 .50
714 Cal Ripken ENC .50 1.25
715 Alex Rodriguez ENC .30 .75
716 Ryne Sandberg ENC .30 .75
717 John Smoltz ENC .10 .30
718 Frank Thomas ENC .20 .50
719 Mo Vaughn ENC .10 .30
720 Bernie Williams ENC .10 .30
721 Tim Salmon CL .10 .30
722 Greg Maddux CL .30 .75
723 Cal Ripken CL .50 1.25
724 Mo Vaughn CL .10 .30
725 Ryne Sandberg CL .30 .75
726 Frank Thomas CL .20 .50
727 Barry Larkin CL .10 .30
728 Manny Ramirez CL .10 .30
729 Andres Galarraga CL .10 .30
730 Tony Clark CL .10 .30
731 Gary Sheffield CL .10 .30
732 Jeff Bagwell CL .10 .30
733 Kevin Appier CL .10 .30
734 Mike Piazza CL .30 .75
735 Jeff Cirillo CL .10 .30
736 Paul Molitor CL .10 .30
737 Henry Rodriguez CL .10 .30
738 Todd Hundley CL .10 .30
739 Derek Jeter CL .40 1.00
740 Mark McGwire CL .40 1.00
741 Curt Schilling CL .10 .30
742 Jason Kendall CL .10 .30
743 Tony Gwynn CL .20 .50
744 Barry Bonds CL .40 1.00
745 Ken Griffey Jr. CL .30 .75
746 Brian Jordan CL .10 .30
747 Juan Gonzalez CL .10 .30
748 Joe Carter CL .10 .30
749 Ariz. Diamondbacks CL Inserts .10 .30
750 Tampa Bay Devil Rays CL Inserts .10 .30
751 Hideki Irabu RC .30 .75
752 Jeremi Gonzalez RC .20 .50
753 Mario Valdez RC .20 .50
754 Aaron Boone .30 .75
755 Brett Tomko .20 .50
756 Jaret Wright RC .30 .75
757 Ryan McGuire .20 .50
758 Jason McDonald .20 .50
759 Adrian Brown RC .20 .50
760 Keith Foulke RC .75 2.00
761 Bonus Checklist .20 .50
P489 M.Williams Promo .40 1.00
NNO Andruw Jones Circa AU/200 10.00 25.00

1997 Fleer Tiffany

Randomly inserted in series one and two packs at a rate of one in 20, this 751-card set is a parallel version of the regular set featuring a glossy holographic design, foil stamping, and UV coating.

*TIFFANY 1-750: 10X TO 25X BASIC CARDS
*TIFFANY RC's 1-750: 6X TO 15X BASIC
*TIFFANY 751-761: 4X TO 10X BASIC
*TIFFANY 751-761: 3X TO 8X BASIC RC'S
STATED ODDS 1:20
512 David Arias-Ortiz 175.00 300.00
675 Orlando Cabrera 5.00 12.00
760 Keith Foulke 6.00 15.00

1997 Fleer Bleacher Blasters

Randomly inserted in Fleer series two retail packs only at a rate of one in 36, this 10-card set features color action photos of power hitters who reach the bleachers with great frequency.

COMPLETE SET (10) 40.00 80.00
SER.2 STATED ODDS 1:36 RETAIL
1 Albert Belle 1.00 2.50
2 Barry Bonds 6.00 15.00
3 Juan Gonzalez 1.00 2.50
4 Ken Griffey Jr. 4.00 10.00
5 Mark McGwire 6.00 15.00
6 Mike Piazza 4.00 10.00
7 Alex Rodriguez 4.00 10.00
8 Frank Thomas 2.50 6.00
9 Mo Vaughn 1.00 2.50
10 Matt Williams 1.00 2.50

1997 Fleer Decade of Excellence

Randomly inserted in Fleer Series two hobby packs only at a rate of one in 36, this 12-card set spotlights players who started their major league careers no later than 1987. The set features photos of these players from the 1987 season in the 1987 Fleer Baseball card design.

COMPLETE SET (12) 30.00 60.00
SER.2 STATED ODDS 1:36 HOBBY
*RARE TRAD: 2X TO 5X BASIC DECADE
RARE TRAD.STATED ODDS 1:360 HOBBY
1 Wade Boggs 1.25 3.00
2 Barry Bonds 5.00 12.00
3 Roger Clemens 4.00 10.00
4 Tony Gwynn 2.50 6.00
5 Rickey Henderson 2.00 5.00
6 Greg Maddux 3.00 8.00
7 Mark McGwire 5.00 12.00
8 Paul Molitor .75 2.00
9 Eddie Murray 2.00 5.00
10 Cal Ripken 6.00 15.00
11 Ryne Sandberg 3.00 8.00
12 Matt Williams .75 2.00

1997 Fleer Diamond Tribute

Randomly inserted in Fleer Series two packs at a rate of one in 288, this 12-card set features color action images of Baseball's top players on a dazzling foil background.

SER.2 STATED ODDS 1:288
1 Albert Belle 3.00 8.00
2 Barry Bonds 20.00 50.00
3 Juan Gonzalez 3.00 8.00
4 Ken Griffey Jr. 12.50 30.00
5 Tony Gwynn 10.00 25.00
6 Greg Maddux 12.50 30.00
7 Mark McGwire 20.00 50.00
8 Eddie Murray 8.00 20.00
9 Mike Piazza 12.50 30.00
10 Cal Ripken 25.00 60.00
11 Alex Rodriguez 12.50 30.00
12 Frank Thomas 8.00 20.00

1997 Fleer Golden Memories

Randomly inserted in first series packs at a rate of one in 16, this ten-card set commemorates major achievements by individual players from the 1996 season. The fronts feature color player images on a background of the top portion of the sun and its rays. The backs carry player information.

COMPLETE SET (10) 4.00 10.00
SER.1 STATED ODDS 1:16 HOBBY
1 Barry Bonds 1.25 3.00
2 Dwight Gooden .20 .50
3 Todd Hundley .20 .50
4 Mark McGwire 1.25 3.00
5 Paul Molitor .20 .50
6 Eddie Murray .50 1.25
7 Hideo Nomo .50 1.25
8 Mike Piazza .75 2.00
9 Cal Ripken 1.50 4.00
10 Ozzie Smith .75 2.00

1997 Fleer Goudey Greats

Randomly inserted in Fleer Series two packs at a rate of one in eight, this 15-card set features color player photos of today's stars on cards styled and sized to resemble the 1933 Goudey Baseball card set.

COMPLETE SET (15) 6.00 15.00
SER.2 STATED ODDS 1:8
*FOIL CARDS: 6X TO 15X BASIC GOUDEY
FOIL SER.2 STATED ODDS 1:800
1 Barry Bonds 1.25 3.00
2 Ken Griffey Jr. .75 2.00
3 Tony Gwynn .60 1.50
4 Derek Jeter 1.25 3.00
5 Chipper Jones .50 1.25
6 Kenny Lofton .20 .50
7 Greg Maddux .75 2.00
8 Mark McGwire 1.25 3.00
9 Eddie Murray .50 1.25
10 Mike Piazza .75 2.00
11 Cal Ripken 1.50 4.00
12 Alex Rodriguez .75 2.00
13 Ryne Sandberg .75 2.00
14 Frank Thomas .50 1.25
15 Mo Vaughn .20 .50

1997 Fleer Headliners

Randomly inserted in Fleer Series two packs at a rate of one in two, this 20-card set features color action photos of top players who make headlines for their teams. The backs carry player information.

COMPLETE SET (20) 4.00 10.00
SER.2 STATED ODDS 1:2
1 Jeff Bagwell .10 .30
2 Albert Belle .07 .20
3 Barry Bonds .50 1.25
4 Ken Caminiti .07 .20
5 Juan Gonzalez .07 .20
6 Ken Griffey Jr. .30 .75
7 Tony Gwynn .25 .60
8 Derek Jeter .50 1.25
9 Andruw Jones .10 .30
10 Chipper Jones .20 .50
11 Greg Maddux .30 .75
12 Mark McGwire .50 1.25
13 Paul Molitor .07 .20
14 Eddie Murray .20 .50
15 Mike Piazza .30 .75
16 Cal Ripken .60 1.50
17 Alex Rodriguez .30 .75
18 Ryne Sandberg .30 .75
19 John Smoltz .10 .30
20 Frank Thomas .20 .50

1997 Fleer Lumber Company

Randomly inserted exclusively in Fleer Series one retail packs, this 18-card set features a selection of the game's top sluggers. The innovative design displays pure die-cut circular borders, simulating the effect of a cut tree.

COMPLETE SET (18) 50.00 120.00
SER.1 STATED ODDS 1:48 RETAIL
1 Brady Anderson 1.25 3.00
2 Jeff Bagwell 2.00 5.00
3 Albert Belle 1.25 3.00
4 Barry Bonds 8.00 20.00
5 Jay Buhner 1.25 3.00
6 Ellis Burks 1.25 3.00
7 Andres Galarraga 1.25 3.00
8 Juan Gonzalez 1.25 3.00
9 Ken Griffey Jr. 5.00 12.00
10 Todd Hundley 1.25 3.00
11 Ryan Klesko 1.25 3.00
12 Mark McGwire 8.00 20.00
13 Mike Piazza 5.00 12.00
14 Alex Rodriguez 5.00 12.00
15 Gary Sheffield 1.25 3.00
16 Sammy Sosa 3.00 8.00
17 Frank Thomas 3.00 8.00
18 Mo Vaughn 1.25 3.00

1997 Fleer New Horizons

Randomly inserted in Fleer Series two packs at a rate of one in four, this 15-card set features borderless color action photos of Rookies and prospects. The backs carry player information.

COMPLETE SET (15) 3.00 8.00
SER.2 STATED ODDS 1:4
1 Bob Abreu .30 .75
2 Jose Cruz Jr. .25 .60
3 Darin Erstad .20 .50
4 Nomar Garciaparra .75 2.00
5 Vladimir Guerrero .50 1.25
6 Wilton Guerrero .20 .50
7 Jose Guillen .20 .50
8 Hideki Irabu .50 1.25
9 Andruw Jones .30 .75
10 Kevin Orie .20 .50
11 Scott Rolen .30 .75
12 Scott Spiezio .20 .50
13 Bubba Trammell .25 .60
14 Todd Walker .20 .50
15 Dmitri Young .20 .50

1997 Fleer Night and Day

Randomly inserted in Fleer Series one packs at a rate of one in 240, this ten-card set features color action player photos of superstars who excel in day games, night games, or both and are printed on lenticular 3D cards. The backs carry player information.

COMPLETE SET (10) 60.00 150.00
SER.1 STATED ODDS 1:240
1 Barry Bonds 12.50 30.00
2 Ellis Burks 2.00 5.00
3 Juan Gonzalez 2.00 5.00
4 Ken Griffey Jr. 8.00 20.00
5 Mark McGwire 12.50 30.00
6 Mike Piazza 8.00 20.00
7 Manny Ramirez 3.00 8.00
8 Alex Rodriguez 8.00 20.00
9 John Smoltz 3.00 8.00
10 Frank Thomas 5.00 12.00

1997 Fleer Rookie Sensations

Randomly inserted in Fleer Series one packs at a rate of one in six, this 20-card set honors the top rookies from the 1996 season and the 1997 season rookies/prospects. The fronts freature color action player images on a multi-color swirling background.

The backs carry a paragraph with information about the player.

COMPLETE SET (20) 8.00 20.00
SER.1 STATED ODDS 1:6
1 Jermaine Allensworth .30 .75
2 James Baldwin .30 .75
3 Alan Benes .30 .75
4 Jermaine Dye .30 .75
5 Darin Erstad .30 .75
6 Todd Hollandsworth .30 .75
7 Derek Jeter 2.00 5.00
8 Jason Kendall .30 .75
9 Alex Ochoa .30 .75
10 Rey Ordonez .30 .75
11 Edgar Renteria .30 .75
12 Bob Abreu .50 1.25
13 Nomar Garciaparra 1.25 3.00
14 Wilton Guerrero .30 .75
15 Andruw Jones .50 1.25
16 Wendell Magee .30 .75
17 Neifi Perez .30 .75
18 Scott Rolen .50 1.25
19 Scott Spiezio .30 .75
20 Todd Walker .30 .75

1997 Fleer Soaring Stars

Randomly inserted in Fleer Series two packs at a rate of one in 12, this 12-card set features color action photos of players who enjoyed a meteoric rise to stardom and have all the skills to stay there. The player's image is set on a background of twinkling stars.

COMPLETE SET (12) 12.50 30.00
SER.2 STATED ODDS 1:12
*GLOWING: 4X TO 10X BASIC SOARING
GLOWING: RANDOM INSERTS IN SER.2 PACKS
LAST 20% OF PRINT RUN WAS GLOWING
1 Albert Belle .25 .60
2 Barry Bonds 1.50 4.00
3 Juan Gonzalez .25 .60
4 Ken Griffey Jr. 1.00 2.50
5 Derek Jeter 1.50 4.00
6 Andruw Jones .40 1.00
7 Chipper Jones .60 1.50
8 Greg Maddux 1.00 2.50
9 Mark McGwire 1.50 4.00
10 Mike Piazza 1.00 2.50
11 Alex Rodriguez 1.00 2.50
12 Frank Thomas .60 1.50

1997 Fleer Team Leaders

Randomly inserted in Fleer Series one packs at a rate of one in 20, this 28-card set honors statistical or inspirational leaders from each team on a die-cut card. The fronts feature color action player images with the player's face in the background. The backs carry a paragraph with information about the player.

COMPLETE SET (28) 40.00 100.00
SER.1 STATED ODDS 1:20
1 Cal Ripken 6.00 15.00
2 Mo Vaughn .75 2.00
3 Jim Edmonds .75 2.00
4 Frank Thomas 2.00 5.00
5 Albert Belle .75 2.00
6 Bob Higginson .75 2.00
7 Kevin Appier .75 2.00
8 John Jaha .75 2.00
9 Paul Molitor .75 2.00
10 Andy Pettitte 1.25 3.00
11 Mark McGwire 5.00 12.00
12 Ken Griffey Jr. 3.00 8.00
13 Juan Gonzalez .75 2.00
14 Pat Hentgen .75 2.00
15 Chipper Jones 2.00 5.00
16 Mark Grace 1.25 3.00
17 Barry Larkin 1.25 3.00
18 Ellis Burks .75 2.00
19 Gary Sheffield .75 2.00
20 Jeff Bagwell 1.25 3.00
21 Mike Piazza 3.00 8.00
22 Henry Rodriguez .75 2.00
23 Todd Hundley .75 2.00
24 Curt Schilling .75 2.00
25 Jeff King .75 2.00
26 Brian Jordan .75 2.00
27 Tony Gwynn 2.50 6.00
28 Barry Bonds 5.00 12.00

1997 Fleer Zone

Randomly inserted in Fleer Series one hobby packs only at a rate of one in 80, this 20-card set features color player images of some of the 1996 season's unstoppable hitters and unhittable pitchers on a holographic card. The backs carry another color photo with a paragraph about the player.

COMPLETE SET (20) 80.00 200.00
SER.1 STATED ODDS 1:80 HOBBY
1 Jeff Bagwell 2.50 6.00
2 Albert Belle 1.50 4.00
3 Barry Bonds 10.00 25.00
4 Ken Caminiti 1.50 4.00
5 Andres Galarraga 1.50 4.00
6 Juan Gonzalez 1.50 4.00
7 Ken Griffey Jr. 6.00 15.00
8 Tony Gwynn 5.00 12.00
9 Chipper Jones 4.00 10.00
10 Greg Maddux 6.00 15.00
11 Mark McGwire 10.00 25.00
12 Dean Palmer 1.50 4.00
13 Andy Pettitte 2.50 6.00
14 Mike Piazza 6.00 15.00
15 Alex Rodriguez 6.00 15.00
16 Gary Sheffield 1.50 4.00
17 John Smoltz 2.50 6.00
18 Frank Thomas 4.00 10.00
19 Jim Thome 2.50 6.00
20 Matt Williams 1.50 4.00

2000 Fleer Club 3000

This set honors batters who have collected 3,000 hits and pitchers who have collected 3,000 strikeouts in their careers. The cards were seeded across all 2000 Fleer brands and each card in our checklist is marked with an abbreviation for the product it hails from. Pack odds are as follows - Fleer-distributed cards 1:36, Fleer Focus-distributed cards 1:36, Fleer Mystique-distributed cards 1:32, Fleer Showcase-distributed cards 1:24, and Ultra-distributed cards 1:24. These cards are unnumbered so we have sequenced them in alphabetical order by player initials.

COMP.FLEER SET (3) 5.00 10.00
COMP.FOCUS SET (3) 5.00 10.00
COMP.MYSTIQUE SET (3) 6.00 12.00
COMP.SHOWCASE SET (2) 5.00 10.00
COMP.ULTRA SET (3) 5.00 10.00
BG Bob Gibson MYST 1.25 3.00
CR Cal Ripken MYST 3.00 8.00
CY Carl Yastrzemski ULT 1.50 4.00
DW Dave Winfield MYST 1.25 3.00
GB George Brett FLE 3.00 8.00
LB Lou Brock SHOW 1.25 3.00
NR Nolan Ryan SHOW 2.50 6.00
PM Paul Molitor FOCUS 1.25 3.00
RC Rod Carew FLE 1.25 3.00
RY Robin Yount FLE 2.00 5.00
SC Steve Carlton FOCUS 1.25 3.00
SM Stan Musial FOCUS 1.50 4.00
TG Tony Gwynn ULT 1.25 3.00
WB Wade Boggs ULT 1.25 3.00

2000 Fleer Club 3000 Memorabilia

Randomly inserted into all 2000 Fleer products, these cards feature game used memorabilia from legends of the game that have either collected 3,000 hits or struck out 3,000 batters during their career. The cards (and patterns of distribution) parallel the more common Club 3000 cards that lack the memorabilia elements. Each player has five different cards: A bat, a hat, a jersey, a combo of bat and jersey and a combo of bat, hat and jersey. Each card is sequentially numbered and detailed within our checklist. Please see the Fleer Club 3000 listing for specific information on which Fleer product each card was distributed in.

BG1 Bob Gibson Bat/265 10.00 25.00
BG2 Bob Gibson Hat/55 30.00 60.00
BG3 Bob Gibson Jersey/825 6.00 15.00
BG4 Bob Gibson Bat-Jersey/100 30.00 60.00
BG5 Bob Gibson Bat-Hat-Jsy/25
CR1 Cal Ripken Bat/265 20.00 50.00
CR2 Cal Ripken Hat/55 75.00 150.00
CR3 Cal Ripken 15.00 40.00

Card	Low	High
Jersey/825		
CR4 Cal Ripken Bat-Jersey/100	75.00	150.00
CR5 Cal Ripken Bat-Hat-Jsy/25		
CY1 Carl Yastrzemski Bat/250	15.00	40.00
CY2 Carl Yastrzemski Hat/100	20.00	50.00
CY3 Carl Yastrzemski Jersey/440	10.00	25.00
CY4 Carl Yastrzemski Bat/Jersey/100	50.00	100.00
CY5 Carl Yastrzemski Bat/Hat/Jersey/25		
DW1 Dave Winfield Bat/270	6.00	15.00
DW2 Dave Winfield Hat/55	20.00	50.00
DW3 Dave Winfield Jersey/825	4.00	10.00
DW4 Dave Winfield Bat-Jersey/100	20.00	50.00
DW5 Dave Winfield Bat-Hat-Jsy/25		
GB1 George Brett Bat/240	15.00	40.00
GB2 George Brett Hat/105	60.00	120.00
GB3 George Brett Jersey/445	10.00	25.00
GB4 George Brett Bat-Jersey/100	60.00	120.00
GB5 George Brett Bat-Hat-Jersey/25		
LB1 Lou Brock Bat/270	10.00	25.00
LB2 Lou Brock Hat/60	30.00	60.00
LB3 Lou Brock Jersey/680	6.00	15.00
LB4 Lou Brock Bat-Jersey/100	30.00	60.00
LB5 Lou Brock Bat-Hat-Jsy/25		
NR1 Nolan Ryan Bat/265	15.00	40.00
NR2 Nolan Ryan Hat/65	60.00	120.00
NR3 Nolan Ryan Jersey/780	15.00	40.00
NR4 Nolan Ryan Bat-Jersey/100	60.00	120.00
NR5 Nolan Ryan Bat-Hat-Jsy/25		
PM1 Paul Molitor Bat/335	15.00	40.00
PM2 Paul Molitor Hat/65	20.00	50.00
PM3 Paul Molitor Jersey/975	4.00	10.00
PM4 Paul Molitor Bat-Jersey/100	20.00	50.00
PM5 Paul Molitor Bat-Hat-Jsy/25		
RC1 Rod Carew Bat/225	15.00	40.00
RC2 Rod Carew Hat/105	30.00	60.00
RC3 Rod Carew Jersey/395	6.00	15.00
RC4 Rod Carew Bat-Jersey/100	30.00	60.00
RC5 Rod Carew Bat-Hat-Jersey/25		
RY1 Robin Yount Bat/230	10.00	25.00
RY2 Robin Yount Hat/105	40.00	80.00
RY3 Robin Yount Jersey/445	6.00	15.00
RY4 Robin Yount Bat-Jersey/100	40.00	80.00
RY5 Robin Yount Bat-Hat-Jersey/25		
SC1 Steve Carlton Bat/325	6.00	15.00
SC2 Steve Carlton Hat/65	20.00	50.00
SC3 Steve Carlton Jersey/750	4.00	10.00
SC4 Steve Carlton Bat-Jersey/100	20.00	50.00
SC5 Steve Carlton Bat-Hat-Jsy/25		
SM1 Stan Musial Bat/325	15.00	40.00
SM2 Stan Musial Hat/65	60.00	120.00
SM3 Stan Musial Jersey/975	15.00	40.00
SM4 Stan Musial Bat-Jersey/100	60.00	120.00
SM5 Stan Musial Bat-Hat-Jsy/25		
TG1 Tony Gwynn Bat/260	10.00	25.00
TG2 Tony Gwynn Hat/115	40.00	80.00
TG3 Tony Gwynn Jersey/450	10.00	25.00
TG4 Tony Gwynn Bat-Jersey/100	40.00	80.00
TG5 Tony Gwynn Bat-Hat-Jersey/25		
WB1 Wade Boggs Bat/250	10.00	25.00
WB2 Wade Boggs Hat/100	30.00	60.00
WB3 Wade Boggs Jersey/440	6.00	15.00
WB4 Wade Boggs Bat-Jersey/100	30.00	60.00
WB5 Wade Boggs Bat-Hat-Jersey/25		

2001 Fleer Autographics

Randomly inserted into packs of Fleer Focus (1:72 w/memorabilia), Fleer Triple Crown (1:72 w/memorabilia cards), Ultra (1:48 w/memorabilia cards), 2002 Fleer Platinum Rack Packs (on average 1:6 racks contains an Autographics card) and 2002 Fleer Genuine (1:18 Hobby Direct box and 1:30 Hobby Distributor box), this insert set features authentic autographs from modern stars and prospects. The cards are designed horizontally with a full color player image at the side allowing plenty of room for the player's autograph. Card backs are unnumbered and feature Fleer's certificate of authenticity. Cards are checklisted alphabetically by player's last name and abbreviations indicating which brands each card was distributed in follows the player name. The brand legend is as follows: FC = Fleer Focus, TC = Fleer Triple Crown, UL = Ultra.

FC SUFFIX ON FOCUS DISTRIBUTION
FS SUFFIX ON SHOWCASE DISTRIBUTION
FP'02 SUFFIX ON ULTRA DISTRIBUTION
GN SUFFIX ON GENUINE DISTRIBUTION
PM SUFFIX ON PREMIUM DISTRIBUTION
TC SUFFIX ON TRIPLE CROWN DISTRIBUTION
UL SUFFIX ON ULTRA DISTRIBUTION

Card	Low	High
1 Roberto Alomar FC-FS-GN-PM-TC-UL	10.00	25.00
2 Jimmy Anderson TC-UL	4.00	10.00
3 Ryan Anderson TC	4.00	10.00
4 Rick Ankiel FC-FS-GN-PM-TC	10.00	25.00
5 Albert Belle FC-FS-GN	6.00	15.00
6 Carlos Beltran FS-GN	6.00	15.00
7 Adrian Beltre FC-FS-GN-PM-TC	8.00	20.00
8 Peter Bergeron GN-PM-TC	4.00	10.00
9 Lance Berkman FC-GN-TC-UL	6.00	15.00
10 Barry Bonds FC-GN-TC-UL	100.00	175.00
11 Milton Bradley FS-GN-TC	6.00	15.00
12 Ryan Bradley GN'02	4.00	10.00
13 Dee Brown FS-GN-PM-TC-FP'02	4.00	10.00
14 Roosevelt Brown TC-UL	4.00	10.00
15 Jeromy Burnitz FC-FS-GN-PM-UL	6.00	15.00
16 Pat Burrell FC-FS-GN-PM-TC-UL	6.00	15.00
17 Alex Cabrera UL	10.00	25.00
18 Sean Casey FC-FS-GN-PM-TC	6.00	15.00
19 Eric Chavez FC-GN-PM-TC-UL	6.00	15.00
20 Giuseppe Chiaramonte TC	4.00	10.00
21 Joe Crede FS-PM-TC-UL-FP'02	10.00	25.00
22 Jose Cruz Jr. FS-GN-PM-TC	4.00	10.00
23 Johnny Damon GN-PM-UL	15.00	40.00
24 Carlos Delgado FC-GN-TC-UL	6.00	15.00
25 Ryan Dempster FS-GN-TC-FP'02	4.00	10.00
26 J.D. Drew FC-FS-GN-PM	6.00	15.00
27 Adam Dunn FS-TC-UL-FP'02	10.00	25.00
28 Erubiel Durazo FS-GN	4.00	10.00
29 Jermaine Dye FC-FS-GN-PM	6.00	15.00
30 David Eckstein FS-TC	15.00	40.00
31 Jim Edmonds FC-GN-PM-TC-UL	10.00	25.00
32 Alex Escobar FS-GN-PM	4.00	10.00
33 Seth Etherton FS-GN	4.00	10.00
34 Adam Everett FS-GN	4.00	10.00
35 Carlos Febles FS-GN	4.00	10.00
36 Troy Glaus FC-FS-GN-PM-TC	10.00	25.00
37 Chad Green TC-UL	4.00	10.00
38 Ben Grieve FC-FS-GN	4.00	10.00
39 Wilton Guerrero GN'02	4.00	10.00
40 Tony Gwynn FC-GN-PM-TC	20.00	50.00
41 Toby Hall FS-GN	4.00	10.00
42 Todd Helton FS-GN-PM-TC	10.00	25.00
43 Chad Hermansen GN-PM-TC	4.00	10.00
44 Dustin Hermanson PM-UL	4.00	10.00
45 Shea Hillenbrand FS-GN-PM-TC	6.00	15.00
46 Aubrey Huff FS-GN-PM-TC	4.00	10.00
47 Derek Jeter GN-PM	75.00	150.00
48 D'Angelo Jimenez FS	4.00	10.00
49 Randy Johnson FC-GN-TC-UL	40.00	80.00
50 Chipper Jones FC-GN-PMTC	20.00	50.00
51 Cesar King GN	4.00	10.00
52 Paul Konerko FS-GN-PM-FP'02	10.00	25.00
53 Corey Koskie GN'02	6.00	15.00
54 Mike Lamb FC-FS-GN-TC	4.00	10.00
55 Matt Lawton FS-GN	4.00	10.00
56 Corey Lee GN-TC-UL	4.00	10.00
57 Derrek Lee FS-GN-PM-UL	10.00	25.00
58 Mike Lieberthal FC-FS-GN-PM	6.00	15.00
59 Cole Liniak		
60 Steve Lomasney TC	4.00	10.00
61 Terrence Long FC-GN-PM-TC-UL	4.00	10.00
62 Mike Lowell FS-GN	6.00	15.00
63 Julio Lugo FS-GN-PM-TC-UL	4.00	10.00
64 Greg Maddux FC-GN	40.00	80.00
65 Jason Marquis FS-GN-TC	6.00	15.00
66 Edgar Martinez FC-FS-GN-UL	10.00	25.00
67 Justin Miller GN-UL	4.00	10.00
68 Kevin Millwood FC-FS-GN-PM	6.00	15.00
69 Eric Milton FS-GN-PM	4.00	10.00
70 Bengie Molina FS-GN-TC	4.00	10.00
71 Mike Mussina FC-FS-GN-PM-TC	10.00	25.00
72 David Ortiz GN'02	12.50	30.00
73 Russ Ortiz FS-PM-UL	4.00	10.00
74 Pablo Ozuna GN-PM-TC-UL	4.00	10.00
75 Corey Patterson FC-FS-GN-PM-TC	4.00	10.00
76 Carl Pavano PM	6.00	15.00
77 Jay Payton FC-FS-GN-PM-TC	4.00	10.00
78 Wily Pena TC	6.00	15.00
79 Josh Phelps TC	4.00	10.00
80 Adam Piatt FS-GN-TC-UL-FP'02	4.00	10.00
81 Juan Pierre FC-FS-GN	6.00	15.00
82 Brad Radke FC-FS-GN-PM-FP'02	6.00	15.00
83 Mark Redman UL	4.00	10.00
84 Matt Riley GN-TC	4.00	10.00
85 Cal Ripken GN-PM	75.00	150.00
86 John Rocker FS-GN	10.00	25.00
87 Alex Rodriguez FS-GN-TC	50.00	100.00
88 Scott Rolen FC-FS-GN-PM	10.00	25.00
89 Alex Sanchez PM-TC	4.00	10.00
90 Fernando Seguignol GN'02	4.00	10.00
91 Richie Sexson FS-GN-PM-UL	6.00	15.00
92 Gary Sheffield FC-FS-GN-PM-TC-UL	10.00	25.00
93 Alfonso Soriano GN-PM-TC-UL	10.00	25.00
94 Dernell Stenson GN-PM	6.00	15.00
95 Garrett Stephenson PM	4.00	10.00
96 Shannon Stewart FS-GN-PM-TC	6.00	15.00
97 Fernando Tatis FC-GN-TC	4.00	10.00
98 Miguel Tejada FS-FP'02	10.00	25.00
99 Jorge Toca GN-PM	4.00	10.00
100 Robin Ventura FC-FS-GN-PM	6.00	15.00
101 Jose Vidro FS-GN-PM-TC-UL-FP'02	4.00	10.00
102 Billy Wagner FS-PM	10.00	25.00
103 Kip Wells FS-GN	4.00	10.00
104 Vernon Wells GN-PM-UL	6.00	15.00
105 Rondell White FS-GN	6.00	15.00
106 Bernie Williams FP'02	40.00	80.00
107 Scott Williamson GN	4.00	10.00
108 Preston Wilson FS-GN-TC-UL	6.00	15.00
109 Kerry Wood FC-FS-GN-PM-TC-FP'02	10.00	25.00
110 Jamey Wright GN-UL	4.00	10.00
111 Julio Zuleta FS-GN-PM-TC-UL	4.00	10.00

2001 Fleer Autographics Gold

Randomly inserted into a selection of Fleer products, this set is a complete parallel of the Autographics insert. These cards were produced with gold foil stamping on front and are individually serial numbered to 50. Corey Koskie was released exclusively in 2002 Fleer Platinum rack packs.

*GOLD: .75X TO 2X BASIC AUTOS

2001 Fleer Autographics Silver

Randomly inserted into a selection of Fleer products, this set is a complete parallel of the Autographics insert. These cards were produced with silver foil stamping on front and are individually serial numbered to 250. Corey Koskie was distributed exclusively in 2002 Fleer Platinum rack packs.

*SILVER: .6X TO 1.5X BASIC AUTOS

2001 Fleer Feel the Game

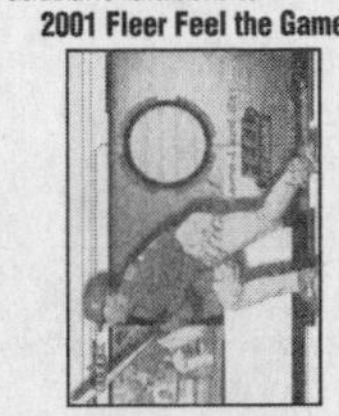

This insert set features game-used bat cards of major league stars. The cards were distributed across several different Fleer products issued in 2001. Please note that the cards are listed below in alphabetical order for convience. Cards with "FC" listed after the players name were inserted into Fleer Focus packs (one Autographic or Feel Game in every 72 packs), "TC" listed after the players name were inserted into packs of Fleer Triple Crown (one Feel Game, Autographic or Crown of Gold in every 72 packs), while cards with "UL" after their name were inserted into Ultra packs (one Autographic or Feel Game in every 48 packs).

*GOLD: 1.25X TO 2.5X BASIC FEEL GAME
GOLD PRINT RUN 50 SERIAL #'d SETS

Card	Low	High
1 Moises Alou Bat FC-UL	4.00	10.00
2 Brady Anderson Bat FC-UL	4.00	10.00
3 Adrian Beltre Bat TC-UL	4.00	10.00
4 Dante Bichette Bat FC-TC	4.00	10.00
5 Roger Cedeno BatTC	4.00	10.00
6 Ben Davis Bat TC	4.00	10.00
7 Carlos Delgado Bat TC-UL	4.00	10.00
8 J.D. Drew Bat Bat TC-UL	4.00	10.00
9 Jermaine Dye Bat FC-UL	4.00	10.00
10 Jason Giambi Bat TC-UL	4.00	10.00
11 Brian Giles Bat FC-TC	4.00	10.00
12 Juan Gonzalez Bat FC-TC	4.00	10.00
13 Rickey Henderson BatFC	6.00	15.00
14 Richard Hidalgo BatTC-UL	4.00	10.00
15 Chipper Jones Bat TC-UL	6.00	15.00
16 Eric Karros Bat TC-UL	4.00	10.00
17 Javy Lopez Bat FC-TC	4.00	10.00
18 Tino Martinez BatFC-TC	6.00	15.00
19 Raul Mondesi Bat TC-UL	4.00	10.00
20 Phil Nevin Bat FC-TC	4.00	10.00
21 Chan Ho Park Bat TC-UL	4.00	10.00
22 Ivan Rodriguez Bat TC-UL	6.00	15.00
23 Matt Stairs Bat FC-UL	4.00	10.00
24 Shannon Stewart BatFC-TC	4.00	10.00
25 Frank Thomas Bat TC-UL	6.00	15.00
26 Jose Vidro Bat FC-TC-UL	4.00	10.00
27 Matt Williams Bat TC-UL	4.00	10.00
28 Preston Wilson Bat TC-UL	4.00	10.00

2002 Fleer

This 540 card set was issued in May, 2002. These cards were issued in 10 card packs which came packed 24 packs to a box and 10 boxes to a case and had an SRP of $2 per pack. Cards number 432 through 491 featured players who switched teams in the off season while cards 492 through 531 featured leading prospects and cards numbered 532 through 540 feature photos of important ballparks along with checklists on the back.

Card	Low	High
COMPLETE SET (540)	30.00	80.00
COMMON CARD (1-540)	.08	.25
COMMON CARD (492-531)	.20	.50
1 Darin Erstad FP	.08	.25
2 Randy Johnson FP	.25	.60
3 Chipper Jones FP	.25	.60
4 Jay Gibbons FP	.08	.25
5 Nomar Garciaparra FP	.40	1.00
6 Sammy Sosa FP	.25	.60
7 Frank Thomas FP	.25	.60
8 Ken Griffey Jr. FP	.40	1.00
9 Jim Thome FP	.15	.40
10 Todd Helton FP	.15	.40
11 Jeff Weaver FP	.08	.25
12 Cliff Floyd FP	.08	.25
13 Jeff Bagwell FP	.15	.40
14 Mike Sweeney FP	.08	.25
15 Adrian Beltre FP	.08	.25
16 Richie Sexson FP	.08	.25
17 Brad Radke FP	.08	.25
18 Vladimir Guerrero FP	.25	.60
19 Mike Piazza FP	.40	1.00
20 Derek Jeter FP	.50	1.25
21 Eric Chavez FP	.08	.25
22 Pat Burrell FP	.08	.25
23 Brian Giles FP	.08	.25
24 Trevor Hoffman FP	.08	.25
25 Barry Bonds FP	.40	1.00
26 Ichiro Suzuki FP	.40	1.00
27 Albert Pujols FP	.40	1.00
28 Ben Grieve FP	.08	.25
29 Alex Rodriguez FP	.40	1.00
30 Carlos Delgado FP	.08	.25
31 Miguel Tejada	.15	.40
32 Todd Hollandsworth	.08	.25
33 Marlon Anderson	.08	.25
34 Kerry Robinson	.08	.25
35 Chris Richard	.08	.25
36 Jamey Wright	.08	.25
37 Ray Lankford	.15	.40
38 Mike Bordick	.15	.40
39 Danny Graves	.08	.25
40 A.J. Pierzynski	.15	.40
41 Shannon Stewart	.15	.40
42 Tony Armas Jr.	.08	.25
43 Brad Ausmus	.15	.40
44 Alfonso Soriano	.15	.40
45 Junior Spivey	.08	.25
46 Brent Mayne	.08	.25
47 Jim Thome	.25	.60
48 Dan Wilson	.08	.25
49 Geoff Jenkins	.08	.25
50 Kris Benson	.08	.25
51 Rafael Furcal	.15	.40
52 Wiki Gonzalez	.08	.25
53 Jeff Kent	.15	.40
54 Curt Schilling	.15	.40
55 Ken Harvey	.08	.25
56 Roosevelt Brown	.08	.25
57 David Segui	.08	.25
58 Mario Valdez	.08	.25
59 Adam Dunn	.15	.40
60 Bob Howry	.08	.25
61 Michael Barrett	.08	.25
62 Garret Anderson	.15	.40
63 Kelvim Escobar	.08	.25
64 Ben Grieve	.08	.25
65 Randy Johnson	.40	1.00
66 Jose Offerman	.08	.25
67 Jason Kendall	.15	.40
68 Joel Pineiro	.08	.25
69 Alex Escobar	.08	.25
70 Chris George	.08	.25
71 Bobby Higginson	.15	.40
72 Nomar Garciaparra	.60	1.50
73 Pat Burrell	.15	.40
74 Lee Stevens	.08	.25
75 Felipe Lopez	.08	.25
76 Al Leiter	.15	.40
77 Jim Edmonds	.15	.40
78 Al Levine	.08	.25
79 Raul Mondesi	.15	.40
80 Jose Valentin	.08	.25
81 Matt Clement	.15	.40
82 Richard Hidalgo	.08	.25
83 Jamie Moyer	.15	.40
84 Brian Schneider	.08	.25
85 John Franco	.15	.40
86 Brian Buchanan	.08	.25
87 Roy Oswalt	.15	.40
88 Johnny Estrada	.08	.25
89 Marcus Giles	.15	.40
90 Carlos Valderrama	.08	.25
91 Mark Mulder	.15	.40
92 Mark Grace	.25	.60
93 Andy Ashby	.08	.25
94 Woody Williams	.08	.25
95 Ben Petrick	.08	.25
96 Roy Halladay	.15	.40
97 Fred McGriff	.25	.60
98 Shawn Green	.15	.40
99 Todd Hundley	.08	.25
100 Carlos Febles	.08	.25
101 Jason Marquis	.08	.25
102 Mike Redmond	.08	.25
103 Shane Halter	.08	.25
104 Trot Nixon	.15	.40
105 Jeremy Giambi	.08	.25
106 Carlos Delgado	.15	.40
107 Richie Sexson	.15	.40
108 Russ Ortiz	.08	.25
109 David Ortiz	.40	1.00
110 Curtis Leskanic	.08	.25
111 Jay Payton	.08	.25
112 Travis Phelps	.08	.25
113 J.T. Snow	.15	.40
114 Edgar Renteria	.15	.40
115 Freddy Garcia	.15	.40
116 Cliff Floyd	.15	.40
117 Charles Nagy	.08	.25
118 Tony Batista	.08	.25
119 Rafael Palmeiro	.25	.60
120 Darren Dreifort	.08	.25
121 Warren Morris	.08	.25
122 Augie Ojeda	.08	.25
123 Rusty Greer	.15	.40
124 Esteban Yan	.08	.25
125 Corey Patterson	.08	.25
126 Matt Ginter	.08	.25
127 Matt Lawton	.08	.25
128 Miguel Batista	.08	.25
129 Randy Winn	.08	.25
130 Eric Milton	.08	.25
131 Jack Wilson	.08	.25
132 Sean Casey	.15	.40
133 Mike Sweeney	.15	.40
134 Jason Tyner	.08	.25
135 Carlos Hernandez	.08	.25
136 Shea Hillenbrand	.15	.40
137 Shawn Wooten	.08	.25
138 Peter Bergeron	.08	.25
139 Travis Lee	.08	.25
140 Craig Wilson	.08	.25
141 Carlos Guillen	.15	.40
142 Chipper Jones	.40	1.00
143 Gabe Kapler	.15	.40
144 Raul Ibanez	.08	.25
145 Eric Chavez	.15	.40
146 D'Angelo Jimenez	.08	.25
147 Chad Hermansen	.08	.25
148 Joe Kennedy	.08	.25
149 Mariano Rivera	.40	1.00
150 Jeff Bagwell	.25	.60
151 Joe McEwing	.08	.25
152 Ronnie Belliard	.08	.25
153 Desi Relaford	.08	.25
154 Vinny Castilla	.15	.40
155 Tim Hudson	.15	.40
156 Wilton Guerrero	.08	.25
157 Raul Casanova	.08	.25
158 Edgardo Alfonzo	.08	.25
159 Derrek Lee	.25	.60
160 Phil Nevin	.15	.40
161 Roger Clemens	.75	2.00
162 Jason LaRue	.08	.25
163 Brian Lawrence	.08	.25
164 Adrian Beltre	.15	.40
165 Troy Glaus	.15	.40
166 Jeff Weaver	.08	.25
167 B.J. Surhoff	.15	.40
168 Eric Byrnes	.08	.25
169 Mike Sirotka	.08	.25
170 Bill Haselman	.08	.25
171 Javier Vazquez	.15	.40
172 Sidney Ponson	.08	.25
173 Adam Everett	.08	.25
174 Bubba Trammell	.08	.25
175 Robb Nen	.15	.40
176 Barry Larkin	.25	.60
177 Tony Graffanino	.08	.25
178 Rich Garces	.08	.25
179 Juan Uribe	.08	.25
180 Tom Glavine	.25	.60
181 Eric Karros	.15	.40
182 Michael Cuddyer	.08	.25
183 Wade Miller	.08	.25
184 Matt Williams	.15	.40
185 Matt Morris	.15	.40
186 Rickey Henderson	.40	1.00
187 Trevor Hoffman	.15	.40
188 Wilson Betemit	.08	.25
189 Steve Karsay	.08	.25
190 Frank Catalanotto	.08	.25
191 Jason Schmidt	.15	.40
192 Roger Cedeno	.08	.25
193 Magglio Ordonez	.15	.40
194 Pat Hentgen	.08	.25
195 Mike Lieberthal	.15	.40
196 Andy Pettitte	.25	.60
197 Jay Gibbons	.08	.25
198 Rolando Arrojo	.08	.25
199 Joe Mays	.08	.25
200 Aubrey Huff	.15	.40
201 Nelson Figueroa	.08	.25
202 Paul Konerko	.15	.40
203 Ken Griffey Jr.	.60	1.50
204 Brandon Duckworth	.08	.25
205 Sammy Sosa	.40	1.00
206 Carl Everett	.15	.40
207 Scott Rolen	.25	.60
208 Orlando Hernandez	.15	.40
209 Todd Helton	.25	.60
210 Preston Wilson	.15	.40
211 Gil Meche	.08	.25
212 Bill Mueller	.15	.40
213 Craig Biggio	.25	.60
214 Dean Palmer	.15	.40
215 Randy Wolf	.08	.25
216 Jeff Suppan	.08	.25
217 Jimmy Rollins	.15	.40
218 Alexis Gomez	.08	.25
219 Ellis Burks	.15	.40
220 Ramon E. Martinez	.08	.25
221 Ramiro Mendoza	.08	.25
222 Einar Diaz	.08	.25
223 Brent Abernathy	.08	.25
224 Darin Erstad	.15	.40
225 Reggie Taylor	.08	.25
226 Jason Jennings	.08	.25
227 Ray Durham	.15	.40
228 John Parrish	.08	.25
229 Kevin Young	.08	.25
230 Xavier Nady	.08	.25
231 Juan Cruz	.08	.25
232 Greg Norton	.08	.25
233 Barry Bonds	1.00	2.50
234 Kip Wells	.08	.25
235 Paul LoDuca	.15	.40
236 Javy Lopez	.15	.40
237 Luis Castillo	.08	.25
238 Tom Gordon	.08	.25
239 Mike Mordecai	.08	.25
240 Damian Rolls	.08	.25
241 Julio Lugo	.08	.25
242 Ichiro Suzuki	.75	2.00
243 Tony Womack	.08	.25
244 Matt Anderson	.08	.25
245 Carlos Lee	.15	.40
246 Alex Rodriguez	.60	1.50
247 Bernie Williams	.25	.60
248 Scott Sullivan	.08	.25
249 Mike Hampton	.15	.40
250 Orlando Cabrera	.15	.40
251 Benito Santiago	.15	.40
252 Steve Finley	.15	.40
253 Dave Williams	.08	.25
254 Adam Kennedy	.08	.25
255 Omar Vizquel	.25	.60
256 Garrett Stephenson	.08	.25
257 Fernando Tatis	.08	.25
258 Mike Piazza	.60	1.50
259 Scott Spiezio	.08	.25
260 Jacque Jones	.15	.40
261 Russell Branyan	.08	.25
262 Mark McLemore	.08	.25
263 Mitch Meluskey	.08	.25
264 Marlon Byrd	.08	.25
265 Kyle Farnsworth	.08	.25
266 Billy Sylvester	.08	.25
267 C.C. Sabathia	.15	.40
268 Mark Buehrle	.15	.40
269 Geoff Blum	.08	.25
270 Bret Prinz	.08	.25
271 Placido Polanco	.08	.25
272 John Olerud	.15	.40
273 Pedro Martinez	.25	.60
274 Doug Mientkiewicz	.15	.40
275 Jason Bere	.08	.25
276 Bud Smith	.08	.25
277 Terrence Long	.08	.25
278 Troy Percival	.15	.40
279 Derek Jeter	1.00	2.50
280 Eric Owens	.08	.25
281 Jay Bell	.15	.40
282 Mike Cameron	.08	.25
283 Joe Randa	.15	.40
284 Brian Roberts	.15	.40
285 Ryan Klesko	.15	.40
286 Ryan Dempster	.08	.25
287 Cristian Guzman	.08	.25
288 Tim Salmon	.25	.60
289 Mark Johnson	.08	.25
290 Brian Giles	.15	.40
291 Jon Lieber	.08	.25
292 Fernando Vina	.08	.25
293 Mike Mussina	.25	.60
294 Juan Pierre	.15	.40
295 Carlos Beltran	.15	.40
296 Vladimir Guerrero	.40	1.00
297 Orlando Merced	.08	.25
298 Jose Hernandez	.08	.25
299 Mike Lamb	.08	.25
300 David Eckstein	.15	.40
301 Mark Loretta	.08	.25
302 Greg Vaughn	.08	.25
303 Jose Vidro	.08	.25
304 Jose Ortiz	.08	.25
305 Mark Grudzielanek	.08	.25
306 Rob Bell	.08	.25
307 Elmer Dessens	.08	.25
308 Tomas Perez	.08	.25
309 Jerry Hairston Jr.	.08	.25
310 Mike Stanton	.08	.25
311 Todd Walker	.08	.25
312 Jason Varitek	.40	1.00
313 Masato Yoshii	.08	.25
314 Ben Sheets	.15	.40
315 Roberto Hernandez	.08	.25
316 Eli Marrero	.08	.25
317 Josh Beckett	.15	.40
318 Robert Fick	.08	.25
319 Aramis Ramirez	.15	.40
320 Bartolo Colon	.15	.40
321 Kenny Kelly	.08	.25
322 Luis Gonzalez	.15	.40
323 John Smoltz	.25	.60
324 Homer Bush	.08	.25
325 Kevin Millwood	.15	.40
326 Manny Ramirez	.25	.60
327 Armando Benitez	.08	.25
328 Luis Alicea	.08	.25
329 Mark Kotsay	.15	.40
330 Felix Rodriguez	.08	.25
331 Eddie Taubensee	.08	.25
332 John Burkett	.08	.25
333 Ramon Ortiz	.08	.25
334 Daryle Ward	.08	.25
335 Jarrod Washburn	.08	.25
336 Benji Gil	.08	.25
337 Mike Lowell	.15	.40
338 Larry Walker	.15	.40
339 Andruw Jones	.25	.60
340 Scott Elarton	.08	.25
341 Tony McKnight	.08	.25
342 Frank Thomas	.40	1.00
343 Kevin Brown	.15	.40
344 Jermaine Dye	.15	.40
345 Luis Rivas	.08	.25
346 Jeff Conine	.15	.40
347 Bobby Kielty	.08	.25
348 Jeffrey Hammonds	.08	.25
349 Keith Foulke	.15	.40
350 Dave Martinez	.08	.25
351 Adam Eaton	.08	.25
352 Brandon Inge	.08	.25
353 Tyler Houston	.08	.25
354 Bobby Abreu	.15	.40
355 Ivan Rodriguez	.25	.60
356 Doug Glanville	.08	.25
357 Jorge Julio	.08	.25
358 Kerry Wood	.15	.40
359 Eric Munson	.08	.25
360 Joe Crede	.15	.40
361 Denny Neagle	.08	.25
362 Vance Wilson	.08	.25
363 Neifi Perez	.08	.25
364 Darryl Kile	.15	.40
365 Jose Macias	.08	.25
366 Michael Coleman	.08	.25
367 Erubiel Durazo	.08	.25
368 Darrin Fletcher	.08	.25
369 Matt White	.08	.25
370 Marvin Benard	.08	.25
371 Brad Penny	.08	.25
372 Chuck Finley	.15	.40
373 Delino DeShields	.08	.25
374 Adrian Brown	.08	.25
375 Corey Koskie	.08	.25
376 Kazuhiro Sasaki	.15	.40
377 Brent Butler	.08	.25
378 Paul Wilson	.08	.25
379 Scott Williamson	.08	.25
380 Mike Young	.40	1.00
381 Toby Hall	.08	.25
382 Shane Reynolds	.08	.25
383 Tom Goodwin	.08	.25
384 Seth Etherton	.08	.25
385 Billy Wagner	.15	.40
386 Josh Phelps	.08	.25
387 Kyle Lohse	.08	.25
388 Jeremy Fikac	.08	.25
389 Jorge Posada	.25	.60
390 Bret Boone	.15	.40
391 Angel Berroa	.08	.25
392 Matt Mantei	.08	.25
393 Alex Gonzalez	.08	.25
394 Scott Strickland	.08	.25
395 Charles Johnson	.15	.40
396 Ramon Hernandez	.08	.25
397 Damian Jackson	.08	.25
398 Albert Pujols	.75	2.00
399 Gary Bennett	.08	.25
400 Edgar Martinez	.25	.60
401 Carl Pavano	.15	.40
402 Chris Gomez	.08	.25

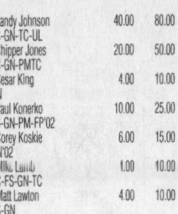

403 Jaret Wright .08 .25
404 Lance Berkman .15 .40
405 Robert Person .08 .25
406 Brook Fordyce .08 .25
407 Adam Pettyjohn .08 .25
408 Chris Carpenter .15 .40
409 Rey Ordonez .08 .25
410 Eric Gagne .15 .40
411 Damion Easley .08 .25
412 A.J. Burnett .15 .40
413 Aaron Boone .15 .40
414 J.D. Drew .15 .40
415 Kelly Stinnett .08 .25
416 Mark Quinn .08 .25
417 Brad Radke .15 .40
418 Jose Cruz Jr. .08 .25
419 Greg Maddux .60 1.50
420 Steve Cox .08 .25
421 Torii Hunter .15 .40
422 Sandy Alomar Jr. .08 .25
423 Barry Zito .15 .40
424 Bill Hall .15 .40
425 Marquis Grissom .15 .40
426 Rich Aurilia .08 .25
427 Royce Clayton .08 .25
428 Travis Fryman .15 .40
429 Pablo Ozuna .08 .25
430 David Dellucci .08 .25
431 Vernon Wells .15 .40
432 Gregg Zaun CP .08 .25
433 Alex Gonzalez CP .08 .25
434 Hideo Nomo CP .40 1.00
435 Jeromy Burnitz CP .15 .40
436 Gary Sheffield CP .15 .40
437 Tino Martinez CP .25 .60
438 Tsuyoshi Shinjo CP .15 .40
439 Chan Ho Park CP .15 .40
440 Tony Clark CP .08 .25
441 Brad Fullmer CP .08 .25
442 Jason Giambi CP .08 .25
443 Billy Koch CP .08 .25
444 Mo Vaughn CP .15 .40
445 Alex Ochoa CP .08 .25
446 Darren Lewis CP .08 .25
447 John Rocker CP .15 .40
448 Scott Hatteberg CP .08 .25
449 Brady Anderson CP .15 .40
450 Chuck Knoblauch CP .15 .40
451 Pokey Reese CP .08 .25
452 Brian Jordan CP .15 .40
453 Albie Lopez CP .08 .25
454 David Bell CP .08 .25
455 Juan Gonzalez CP .15 .40
456 Terry Adams CP .08 .25
457 Kenny Lofton CP .15 .40
458 Shawn Estes CP .08 .25
459 Josh Fogg CP .08 .25
460 Dmitri Young CP .15 .40
461 Johnny Damon Sox CP .25 .60
462 Chris Singleton CP .08 .25
463 Ricky Ledee CP .08 .25
464 Dustin Hermanson CP .08 .25
465 Aaron Sele CP .08 .25
466 Chris Stynes CP .08 .25
467 Matt Stairs CP .08 .25
468 Kevin Appier CP .15 .40
469 Omar Daal CP .08 .25
470 Moises Alou CP .15 .40
471 Juan Encarnacion CP .08 .25
472 Robin Ventura CP .15 .40
473 Eric Hinske CP .08 .25
474 Rondell White CP .15 .40
475 Carlos Pena CP .08 .25
476 Craig Paquette CP .08 .25
477 Marty Cordova CP .08 .25
478 Brett Tomko CP .08 .25
479 Reggie Sanders CP .08 .25
480 Roberto Alomar CP .25 .60
481 Jeff Cirillo CP .08 .25
482 Todd Zeile CP .15 .40
483 John Vander Wal CP .08 .25
484 Rick Helling CP .08 .25
485 Jeff D'Amico CP .08 .25
486 David Justice CP .15 .40
487 Jason Isringhausen CP .15 .40
488 Shigetoshi Hasegawa CP .15 .40
489 Eric Young CP .08 .25
490 David Wells CP .15 .40
491 Ruben Sierra CP .08 .25
492 Aaron Cook FF RC .30 .75
493 Takahito Nomura FF RC .30 .75
494 Austin Kearns FF .20 .50
495 Kazuhisa Ishii FF RC .50 1.25
496 Mark Teixeira FF .75 2.00
497 Rene Reyes FF RC .30 .75
498 Tim Spooneybarger FF .20 .50
499 Ben Broussard FF .20 .50
500 Eric Cyr FF .20 .50
501 Anastacio Martinez FF RC .30 .75
502 Morgan Ensberg FF .30 .75
503 Steve Kent FF RC .30 .75
504 Franklin Nunez FF RC .30 .75
505 Adam Walker FF RC .30 .75
506 Anderson Machado FF RC .30 .75
507 Ryan Drese FF .20 .50
508 Luis Ugueto FF RC .30 .75
509 Jorge Nunez FF RC .30 .75
510 Colby Lewis FF .20 .50
511 Ron Calloway FF RC .30 .75
512 Hansel Izquierdo FF RC .30 .75
513 Jason Lane FF .30 .75
514 Rafael Soriano FF .20 .50
515 Jackson Melian FF .20 .50
516 Edwin Almonte FF RC .30 .75
517 Satoru Komiyama FF RC .30 .75
518 Corey Thurman FF RC .30 .75
519 Jorge De La Rosa FF RC .30 .75
520 Victor Martinez FF .75 2.00
521 Dewon Brazelton FF .20 .50
522 Marlon Byrd FF .20 .50
523 Jae Seo FF .20 .50
524 Orlando Hudson FF .20 .50
525 Sean Burroughs FF .20 .50
526 Ryan Langerhans FF .30 .75
527 David Kelton FF .20 .50
528 So Taguchi FF RC .50 1.25
529 Tyler Walker FF .20 .50
530 Hank Blalock FF .50 1.25
531 Mark Prior FF .50 1.25
532 Yankee Stadium CL .15 .40
533 Fenway Park CL .15 .40
534 Wrigley Field CL .15 .40
535 Dodger Stadium CL .15 .40
536 Camden Yards CL .15 .40
537 PacBell Park CL .08 .25
538 Jacobs Field CL .08 .25
539 SAFECO Field CL .08 .25
540 Miller Field CL .08 .25
P279 Derek Jeter Promo

2002 Fleer Gold Backs

Randomly inserted in packs, this is a parallel to the 2002 Fleer set. These cards can be differentiated from the regular cards by either the "gold" stats or text used on the back of the cards. It was announced that 15 percent of the print run featured these gold backs.

*GOLD BACK: .75X TO 2X BASIC
*GOLD BACK 492-531: .75X TO 2X BASIC

2002 Fleer Mini

Randomly inserted in retail packs, these cards parallel the 2002 Fleer set. They are printed to a smaller size than the regular set and also were printed to a stated print run of 50 serial numbered sets.

*MINI: 10X TO 25X BASIC
*MINI 492-531: 5X TO 12X BASIC

2002 Fleer Tiffany

Randomly inserted in hobby packs, this is a parallel to the 2002 Fleer set and are printed to a stated print run of 200 serial numbered sets. These cards can be differentiated from the regular Fleer set by the glossy finish on the front.

*TIFFANY: 4X TO 10X BASIC
*TIFFANY 492-531: 2X TO 5X BASIC

2002 Fleer Barry Bonds Career Highlights

Issued at overall odds of one in 12 hobby packs and one in 36 retail packs, these 10 cards feature highlights from Barry Bonds career. These cards were issued in different rates depending on which card number it was.

COMPLETE SET (10) 15.00 40.00
COMMON CARD (1-3) 1.50 4.00
COMMON CARD (4-6) 2.00 5.00
COMMON CARD (7-9) 3.00 8.00
COMMON CARD (10) 2.00 5.00
1-3 ODDS 1:65 HOBBY, 1:225 RETAIL
4-6 ODDS 1:125 HOBBY, 1:400 RETAIL
7-9 ODDS 1:250 HOBBY, 1:500 RETAIL
10 ODDS 1:383 HOBBY, 1:800 RETAIL
OVERALL ODDS 1:12 HOBBY, 1:36 RETAIL

2002 Fleer Barry Bonds Career Highlights Autographs

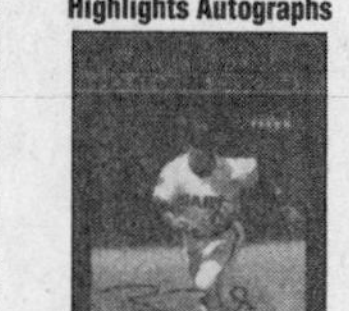

Randomly inserted in packs, these 10 cards not only parallel the Bonds Career Highlight set but also include an autograph from Barry Bonds on the card. Each card was issued to a stated print run of 25 serial numbered sets and due to market scarcity no pricing is provided.

COMMON CARD (1-10) 125.00 200.00

2002 Fleer Classic Cuts Autographs

Inserted in packs at a stated rate of one in 432 hobby packs, these nine cards feature autographs from a retired legend. A few cards were issued to a smaller quantity and we have notated that information along

with their stated print run next to their name in our checklist.

BRA Brooks Robinson SP/200 15.00 40.00
GPA Gaylord Perry SP/225 8.00 20.00
HKA Harmon Killebrew 30.00 60.00
JMA Juan Marichal 6.00 15.00
LAA Luis Aparicio 10.00 25.00
PRA Phil Rizzuto SP/125 30.00 60.00
RCA Ron Cey 6.00 15.00
RFA Rollie Fingers SP/35
TLA Tommy Lasorda SP/35

2002 Fleer Classic Cuts Game Used

Inserted at stated odds of one in 24, these 94 cards feature retired players along with an authentic game-used memorabilia piece of that player. Some cards were issued in shorter quantites and we have provided the stated print run next to the player's name in our checklist.

ADJ Andre Dawson Jsy 4.00 10.00
ATB Alan Trammell Bat 4.00 10.00
BBB Bobby Bonds Bat 4.00 10.00
BBJ Bobby Bonds Jsy 4.00 10.00
BDB Bill Dickey Bat/200 6.00 15.00
BJJ Bo Jackson Jsy 6.00 15.00
BMB Billy Martin Bat/65 10.00 25.00
BRB Brooks Robinson Bat/250 6.00 15.00
BTB Bill Terry Bat/85 20.00 50.00
CFB Carlton Fisk Bat 6.00 15.00
CFJ Carlton Fisk Jsy/150 6.00 15.00
CHJ Jim Hunter Jsy 6.00 15.00
CRBG Cal Ripken Btg Glv/100 20.00 50.00
CRFG Cal Ripken Fld Glv/60 20.00 50.00
CRJ Cal Ripken Jsy 12.50 30.00
CRP Cal Ripken Pants/200 15.00 40.00
DEB Dwight Evans Bat/250 6.00 15.00
DEJ Dwight Evans Jsy 6.00 15.00
DMB Don Mattingly Bat/200 10.00 25.00
DMJ Don Mattingly Jsy 10.00 25.00
DMP Don Mattingly Patch/50
DPB Dave Parker Bat 4.00 10.00
DRP Dave Righetti Patch
DWB Dave Winfield Bat 4.00 10.00
DWJ Dave Winfield Jsy/231 4.00 10.00
DWP Dave Winfield Pants 4.00 10.00
DWP Dave Winfield Patch/25
DZJ Don Zimmer Jsy/90 6.00 15.00
EMB Eddie Mathews Bat/200 6.00 15.00
EMB Eddie Murray Bat 6.00 15.00
EMJ Eddie Murray Jsy 6.00 15.00
EMP Eddie Murray Patch/45 15.00 40.00
EWJ Earl Weaver Jsy 4.00 10.00
FLB Fred Lynn Bat/25
GBB George Brett Bat/250 10.00 25.00
GBJ George Brett Jsy/250 10.00 25.00
GHB Gil Hodges Bat/200 6.00 15.00
GKB George Kell Bat/150 6.00 15.00
HBB Hank Bauer Bat 4.00 10.00
HGB Hank Greenberg Bat/13
HWB Hack Wilson Bat/8
HWP Hoyt Wilhelm Pants/150 4.00 10.00
JBB Johnny Bench Bat/100 10.00 25.00
JBJ Johnny Bench Jsy 6.00 15.00
JMB Joe Morgan Bat/250 4.00 10.00
JPJ Jim Palmer Jsy/273 4.00 10.00
JRB Jim Rice Bat/225 4.00 10.00
JRJ Jim Rice Jsy/90 6.00 15.00
JTJ Joe Torre Jsy/125 6.00 15.00
KGB Kirk Gibson Bat 4.00 10.00
KPB Kirby Puckett Bat/25
KPJ Kirby Puckett Jsy 6.00 15.00
LDB Larry Doby Bat/250 4.00 10.00
LPP Lou Piniella Pants 4.00 10.00
NFB Nellie Fox Bat/200 6.00 15.00
NRJ Nolan Ryan Jsy 15.00 40.00
NRP Nolan Ryan Pants/200 15.00 40.00
OCB Orlando Cepeda Bat/45 6.00 15.00
OCP Orlando Cepeda Pants 4.00 10.00
OSJ Ozzie Smith Jsy/250 10.00 25.00
PBB Paul Blair Bat 4.00 10.00
PMB Paul Molitor Bat/250 4.00 10.00
PMP Paul Molitor Patch/110 6.00 15.00
PRJ Preacher Roe Jsy/19
PWRJ Pee Wee Reese Jsy/20
RCB Roy Campanella Bat/7
RFJ Rollie Fingers Jsy 4.00 10.00
RJB Reggie Jackson Bat/50 10.00 25.00
RJP Reggie Jackson Pants 6.00 15.00
RKB Ralph Kiner Bat/47 6.00 15.00
RMP Roger Maris Pants/200 20.00 50.00
RSB Ryne Sandberg Bat 10.00 25.00
RYB Robin Yount Bat 6.00 15.00
SAP Sparky Anderson Pants 4.00 10.00
SCH Steve Carlton Hat/25
SCP Steve Carlton Pants 4.00 10.00
SGB Steve Garvey Bat 4.00 10.00
TJJ Tommy John Jsy/55 6.00 15.00
TJP Tommy John Patch/15
TKB Ted Kluszewski Bat/200 6.00 15.00
TKP Ted Kluszewski Pants 6.00 15.00
TLB Tony Lazzeri Bat/35
TMP Thurman Munson Pants/10
TPB Tony Perez Bat/250 4.00 10.00
TPJ Tony Perez Jsy 4.00 10.00
TWB Ted Williams Bat 40.00 80.00
TWP Ted Williams Pants 40.00 80.00
WBB Wade Boggs Bat/99 10.00 25.00
WBJ Wade Boggs Jsy 6.00 15.00
WBP Wade Boggs Patch/50 15.00 40.00
WMJ Willie McCovey Jsy/300 4.00 10.00
WRP Willie Randolph Patch/18
WSB Willie Stargell Bat/250 6.00 15.00
YBB Yogi Berra Bat/72 10.00 25.00

2002 Fleer Classic Cuts Game Used Autographs

Randomly inserted in packs, these three cards feature not only a game-used piece from a retired player but also an authentic autograph. The stated print run for each player is listed next to their name in our checklist.

BRB Brooks Robinson Bat/45 30.00 60.00
LAB Luis Aparicio Bat/45 15.00 40.00
RFJ Rollie Fingers Jsy/35 15.00 40.00

2002 Fleer Diamond Standouts

Randomly inserted in packs, these 10 cards have a stated print run of 1200 serial numbered sets. These cards feature players who most fans would consider the top 10 stars in Baseball.

COMPLETE SET (10) 30.00 80.00
1 Mike Piazza 3.00 8.00
2 Derek Jeter 5.00 12.00
3 Ken Griffey Jr. 3.00 8.00
4 Barry Bonds 5.00 12.00
5 Sammy Sosa 3.00 8.00
6 Alex Rodriguez 3.00 8.00
7 Ichiro Suzuki 4.00 10.00
8 Greg Maddux 3.00 8.00
9 Jason Giambi 3.00 8.00
10 Nomar Garciaparra 3.00 8.00

2002 Fleer Golden Memories

Issued in packs at a stated rate of one in 24 packs, these 15 cards feature players who have earned many honors during their playing career.

COMPLETE SET (15) 15.00 40.00
1 Frank Thomas 1.00 2.50
2 Derek Jeter 2.50 6.00
3 Albert Pujols 2.00 5.00
4 Barry Bonds 2.50 6.00
5 Alex Rodriguez 1.50 4.00
6 Randy Johnson 1.00 2.50
7 Jeff Bagwell .60 1.50
8 Greg Maddux 1.50 4.00
9 Ivan Rodriguez .60 1.50
10 Ichiro Suzuki 2.00 5.00
11 Mike Piazza 1.50 4.00
12 Pat Burrell .60 1.50
13 Rickey Henderson 1.00 2.50
14 Vladimir Guerrero 1.00 2.50
15 Sammy Sosa 1.00 2.50

2002 Fleer Headliners

Issued at a stated rate of one in eight hobby packs and one in 12 retail packs, these 20 cards feature players who achieved noteworthy feats during the 2001 season.

COMPLETE SET (20) 10.00 25.00
1 Randy Johnson .50 1.25
2 Alex Rodriguez .75 2.00
3 Todd Helton .40 1.00
4 Pedro Martinez .40 1.00
5 Ichiro Suzuki 1.00 2.50
6 Vladimir Guerrero .50 1.25
7 Derek Jeter 1.25 3.00
8 Adam Dunn .40 1.00
9 Luis Gonzalez .40 1.00
10 Kazuhiro Sasaki .40 1.00
11 Sammy Sosa .50 1.25
12 Jason Giambi .40 1.00
13 Ken Griffey Jr. .75 2.00
14 Roger Clemens 1.00 2.50
15 Brandon Duckworth .40 1.00
16 Nomar Garciaparra .75 2.00
17 Bud Smith .40 1.00
18 Juan Gonzalez .40 1.00
19 Chipper Jones .50 1.25
20 Barry Bonds 1.25 3.00

2002 Fleer Rookie Flashbacks

Issued at a stated rate of one in three retail packs, these 20 cards feature players who made their major league debut in 2001.

COMPLETE SET (20) 10.00 25.00
1 Bret Prinz .40 1.00
2 Albert Pujols 1.50 4.00
3 C.C. Sabathia .40 1.00
4 Ichiro Suzuki 1.50 4.00
5 Juan Cruz .40 1.00
6 Jay Gibbons .40 1.00
7 Bud Smith .40 1.00
8 Johnny Estrada .40 1.00
9 Roy Oswalt .40 1.00
10 Tsuyoshi Shinjo .40 1.00
11 Brandon Duckworth .40 1.00
12 Jackson Melian .40 1.00
13 Josh Beckett .40 1.00
14 Morgan Ensberg .40 1.00
15 Brian Lawrence .40 1.00
16 Eric Hinske .40 1.00
17 Juan Uribe .40 1.00
18 Matt White .40 1.00
19 Junior Spivey .40 1.00
20 Wilson Betemit .40 1.00

2002 Fleer Rookie Sensations

Randomly inserted in hobby packs and printed to a stated print run of 1500 serial numbered sets, these 20 cards feature players who made their major league debut in 2001.

COMPLETE SET (20) 20.00 50.00
1 Bret Prinz 2.00 5.00
2 Albert Pujols 6.00 15.00
3 C.C. Sabathia 2.00 5.00
4 Ichiro Suzuki 6.00 15.00
5 Juan Cruz 2.00 5.00
6 Jay Gibbons 2.00 5.00
7 Bud Smith 2.00 5.00
8 Johnny Estrada 2.00 5.00
9 Roy Oswalt 2.00 5.00
10 Tsuyoshi Shinjo 2.00 5.00
11 Brandon Duckworth 2.00 5.00
12 Jackson Melian 2.00 5.00
13 Josh Beckett 2.00 5.00
14 Morgan Ensberg 2.00 5.00
15 Brian Lawrence 2.00 5.00
16 Eric Hinske 2.00 5.00
17 Juan Uribe 2.00 5.00
18 Matt White 2.00 5.00
19 Junior Spivey 2.00 5.00
20 Wilson Betemit 2.00 5.00

2002 Fleer Then and Now

Randomly inserted in hobby packs, these 10 cards feature a player from the past who compares with one of today's stars. These cards are printed to a stated print run of 275 serial numbered sets.

COMPLETE SET (10) 60.00 150.00
1 Eddie Mathews / Chipper Jones 6.00 15.00
2 Willie McCovey / Barry Bonds 12.50 30.00
3 Johnny Bench / Mika Piazza 8.00 20.00
4 Ernie Banks / Alex Rodriguez 8.00 20.00
5 Rickey Henderson / Ichiro Suzuki 10.00 25.00
6 Tom Seaver / Roger Clemens 10.00 25.00
7 Juan Marichal / Pedro Martinez 6.00 15.00
8 Reggie Jackson / Derek Jeter 12.50 30.00
9 Nolan Ryan / Kerry Wood 20.00 50.00
10 Joe Morgan / Ken Griffey Jr. 8.00 20.00

2006 Fleer

This 400-card set was released in April, 2006. The set was issued in 10-card hobby or retail packs. Both the hobby and retail packs had an $1.59 SRP and came 36 packs to a box and 10 boxes to a case. Cards numbered 401-430 featured 2006 rookies and were only available in the Fleer factory sets.

Alay Soler RC
COMP.FACT.SET (430) 20.00 50.00
COMPLETE SET (400) 15.00 40.00
COMMON CARD (1-400) .15 .40
COMMON ROOKIE .20 .50
COMMON ROOKIE (401-430) .25 .60
401-430 AVAIL. IN FLEER FACT.SET
1 Adam Kennedy .15 .40
2 Bartolo Colon .15 .40
3 Bengie Molina .15 .40
4 Chone Figgins .15 .40
5 Dallas McPherson .15 .40
6 Darin Erstad .15 .40
7 Francisco Rodriguez .25 .60
8 Garret Anderson .15 .40
9 Jarrod Washburn .15 .40
10 John Lackey .15 .40
11 Orlando Cabrera .15 .40
12 Ryan Theriot RC .60 1.50
13 Steve Finley .15 .40
14 Vladimir Guerrero .40 1.00
15 Adam Everett .15 .40
16 Andy Pettitte .25 .60
17 Charlton Jimerson (RC) .20 .50
18 Brad Lidge .15 .40
19 Chris Burke .15 .40
20 Craig Biggio .25 .60
21 Jason Lane .15 .40
22 Jeff Bagwell .25 .60
23 Lance Berkman .25 .60
24 Morgan Ensberg .15 .40
25 Roger Clemens .50 1.25
26 Roy Oswalt .25 .60
27 Willy Taveras .15 .40
28 Barry Zito .15 .40
29 Bobby Crosby .15 .40
30 Bobby Kielty .15 .40
31 Dan Johnson .15 .40
32 Danny Haren .15 .40
33 Eric Chavez .15 .40
34 Huston Street .15 .40
35 Jason Kendall .15 .40
36 Jay Payton .15 .40
37 Joe Blanton .15 .40
38 Mark Kotsay .15 .40
39 Nick Swisher .40 1.00
40 Rich Harden .15 .40
41 Ron Flores RC .20 .50
42 Alex Rios .25 .60
43 John-Ford Griffin (RC) .20 .50
44 Dave Bush .15 .40
45 Eric Hinske .15 .40
46 Frank Catalanotto .15 .40
47 Gustavo Chacin .15 .40
48 Josh Towers .15 .40
49 Miguel Batista .15 .40
50 Orlando Hudson .15 .40
51 Roy Halladay .40 1.00
52 Shea Hillenbrand .15 .40
53 Shaun Marcum (RC) .20 .50
54 Vernon Wells .15 .40
55 Adam LaRoche .15 .40
56 Andruw Jones .15 .40
57 Chipper Jones .40 1.00
58 Anthony Lerew (RC) .20 .50
59 Jeff Francoeur .40 1.00
60 John Smoltz .40 1.00
61 Johnny Estrada .15 .40
62 Julio Franco .15 .40
63 Joey Devine RC .20 .50
64 Marcus Giles .15 .40
65 Mike Hampton .15 .40
66 Rafael Furcal .15 .40
67 Chuck James (RC) .20 .50
68 Tim Hudson .25 .60
69 Ben Sheets .15 .40
70 Bill Hall .15 .40
71 Brady Clark .15 .40
72 Carlos Lee .15 .40
73 Chris Capuano .15 .40
74 Nelson Cruz (RC) .30 .75
75 Derrick Turnbow .15 .40
76 Doug Davis .15 .40
77 Geoff Jenkins .15 .40
78 J.J. Hardy .15 .40
79 Lyle Overbay .15 .40
80 Prince Fielder .60 1.50
81 Rickie Weeks .25 .60
82 Albert Pujols 1.00 2.50
83 Chris Carpenter .40 1.00
84 David Eckstein .15 .40
85 Jason Isringhausen .15 .40
86 Tyler Johnson (RC) .20 .50
87 Adam Wainwright (RC) .50 1.25
88 Jim Edmonds .25 .60
89 Chris Duncan (RC) .30 .75
90 Mark Grudzielanek .15 .40
91 Mark Mulder .15 .40
92 Matt Morris .15 .40
93 Reggie Sanders .15 .40
94 Scott Rolen .25 .60
95 Yadier Molina .25 .60
96 Aramis Ramirez .15 .40
97 Carlos Zambrano .25 .60
98 Corey Patterson .15 .40
99 Derrek Lee .15 .40
100 Glendon Rusch .15 .40
101 Greg Maddux .60 1.50
102 Jeromy Burnitz .15 .40
103 Kerry Wood .15 .40
104 Mark Prior .25 .60
105 Michael Barrett .15 .40
106 Geovany Soto (RC) .50 1.25
107 Nomar Garciaparra .40 1.00
108 Ryan Dempster .15 .40
109 Todd Walker .15 .40
110 Alex S. Gonzalez .15 .40
111 Aubrey Huff .15 .40
112 Victor Diaz .15 .40
113 Carl Crawford .25 .60
114 Danys Baez .15 .40
115 Joey Gathright .15 .40
116 Jonny Gomes .15 .40
117 Jorge Cantu .15 .40
118 Julio Lugo .15 .40
119 Rocco Baldelli .15 .40
120 Scott Kazmir .25 .60
121 Toby Hall .15 .40
122 Tim Corcoran RC .20 .50
123 Alex Cintron .15 .40
124 Brandon Webb .25 .60
125 Chad Tracy .15 .40
126 Dustin Nippert (RC) .20 .50
127 Claudio Vargas .15 .40
128 Craig Counsell .15 .40
129 Javier Vazquez .15 .40
130 Jose Valverde .15 .40
131 Luis Gonzalez .15 .40
132 Royce Clayton .15 .40
133 Russ Ortiz .15 .40
134 Shawn Green .15 .40
135 Tony Clark .15 .40
136 Troy Glaus .15 .40
137 Brad Penny .15 .40
138 Cesar Izturis .15 .40
139 Derek Lowe .15 .40
140 Eric Gagne .15 .40
141 Hee Seop Choi .15 .40
142 J.D. Drew .15 .40
143 Jason Phillips .15 .40
144 Jayson Werth .25 .60
145 Jeff Kent .15 .40
146 Jeff Weaver .15 .40
147 Milton Bradley .15 .40
148 Odalis Perez .15 .40
149 Hong-Chih Kuo (RC) .50 1.25
150 Brian Myrow RC .20 .50
151 Armando Benitez .15 .40
152 Edgardo Alfonzo .15 .40
153 J.T. Snow .15 .40
154 Jason Schmidt .15 .40
155 Lance Niekro .15 .40
156 Doug Clark (RC) .20 .50
157 Dan Ortmeier (RC) .20 .50
158 Moises Alou .15 .40
159 Noah Lowry .15 .40
160 Omar Vizquel .25 .60
161 Pedro Feliz .15 .40
162 Randy Winn .15 .40
163 Jeremy Accardo RC .20 .50
164 Aaron Boone .15 .40
165 Ryan Garko (RC) .20 .50
166 C.C. Sabathia .25 .60
167 Casey Blake .15 .40
168 Cliff Lee .25 .60
169 Coco Crisp .15 .40
170 Grady Sizemore .25 .60
171 Jake Westbrook .15 .40
172 Jhonny Peralta .15 .40
173 Kevin Millwood .15 .40
174 Scott Elarton .15 .40
175 Travis Hafner .15 .40
176 Victor Martinez .25 .60
177 Adrian Beltre .15 .40
178 Eddie Guardado .15 .40
179 Felix Hernandez .40 1.00
180 Gil Meche .15 .40
181 Ichiro Suzuki .60 1.50
182 Jamie Moyer .15 .40
183 Jeremy Reed .15 .40
184 Jaime Bubela (RC) .20 .50
185 Raul Ibanez .25 .60
186 Richie Sexson .15 .40
187 Ryan Franklin .15 .40
188 Jeff Harris RC .15 .40
189 A.J. Burnett .25 .60
190 Josh Wilson (RC) .20 .50
191 Josh Johnson (RC) .50 1.25
192 Carlos Delgado .15 .40
193 Dontrelle Willis .15 .40
194 Bernie Castro (RC) .20 .50
195 Josh Beckett .25 .60
196 Juan Encarnacion .15 .40
197 Juan Pierre .15 .40
198 Robert Andino RC .20 .50
199 Miguel Cabrera .40 1.00
200 Ryan Jorgensen RC .20 .50
201 Paul Lo Duca .15 .40
202 Todd Jones .15 .40
203 Braden Looper .15 .40
204 Carlos Beltran .15 .40
205 Cliff Floyd .15 .40
206 David Wright .60 1.50
207 Doug Mientkiewicz .15 .40
208 Jae Seo .15 .40
209 Jose Reyes .25 .60
210 Anderson Hernandez (RC) .20 .50
211 Miguel Cairo .15 .40
212 Mike Cameron .15 .40
213 Mike Piazza .40 1.00
214 Pedro Martinez .25 .60
215 Tom Glavine .25 .60
216 Tim Hamulack (RC) .20 .50
217 Brad Wilkerson .15 .40
218 Darrell Rasner (RC) .20 .50
219 Chad Cordero .15 .40
220 Cristian Guzman .15 .40
221 Jason Bergmann RC .20 .50
222 John Patterson .15 .40
223 Jose Guillen .15 .40
224 Jose Vidro .15 .40
225 Livan Hernandez .15 .40
226 Nick Johnson .15 .40
227 Preston Wilson .15 .40
228 Ryan Zimmerman (RC) 1.00 2.50
229 Vinny Castilla .15 .40
230 B.J. Ryan .15 .40
231 B.J. Surhoff .15 .40
232 Brian Roberts .15 .40
233 Walter Young (RC) .20 .50
234 Daniel Cabrera .15 .40
235 Erik Bedard .15 .40
236 Javy Lopez .15 .40
237 Jay Gibbons .15 .40
238 Luis Matos .15 .40
239 Melvin Mora .15 .40
240 Miguel Tejada .25 .60
241 Rafael Palmeiro .25 .60
242 Alejandro Freire RC .20 .50

243 Sammy Sosa .40 1.00
244 Adam Eaton .15 .40
245 Brian Giles .15 .40
246 Brian Lawrence .15 .40
247 Dave Roberts .15 .40
248 Jake Peavy .15 .40
249 Khalil Greene .15 .40
250 Mark Loretta .15 .40
251 Ramon Hernandez .15 .40
252 Ryan Klesko .15 .40
253 Trevor Hoffman .25 .60
254 Woody Williams .15 .40
255 Craig Breslow RC .20 .50
256 Billy Wagner .15 .40
257 Bobby Abreu .15 .40
258 Brett Myers .15 .40
259 Chase Utley .40 1.00
260 David Bell .15 .40
261 Jim Thome .25 .60
262 Jimmy Rollins .25 .60
263 Jon Lieber .15 .40
264 Danny Sandoval RC .20 .50
265 Mike Lieberthal .15 .40
266 Pat Burrell .15 .40
267 Randy Wolf .15 .40
268 Ryan Howard .60 1.50
269 J.J. Furmaniak (RC) .20 .50
270 Ronny Paulino (RC) .20 .50
271 Craig Wilson .15 .40
272 Bryan Bullington (RC) .20 .50
273 Jack Wilson .15 .40
274 Jason Bay .15 .40
275 Matt Capps (RC) .20 .50
276 Oliver Perez .15 .40
277 Rob Mackowiak .15 .40
278 Tom Gorzelanny (RC) .20 .50
279 Zach Duke .15 .40
280 Alfonso Soriano .25 .60
281 Chris R. Young .15 .40
282 David Dellucci .15 .40
283 Francisco Cordero .15 .40
284 Jason Botts (RC) UER .20 .50
Michael Young pictured
285 Hank Blalock .15 .40
286 Josh Rupe (RC) .20 .50
287 Kevin Mench .15 .40
288 Laynce Nix .15 .40
289 Mark Teixeira .40 1.00
290 Michael Young .25 .60
291 Richard Hidalgo .15 .40
292 Scott Feldman RC .20 .50
293 Bill Mueller .15 .40
294 Hanley Ramirez (RC) .50 1.25
295 Curt Schilling .25 .60
296 David Ortiz .25 .60
297 Alejandro Machado (RC) .20 .50
298 Edgar Renteria .15 .40
299 Jason Varitek .40 1.00
300 Johnny Damon .25 .60
301 Keith Foulke .15 .40
302 Manny Ramirez .40 1.00
303 Matt Clement .15 .40
304 Craig Hansen RC .50 1.25
305 Tim Wakefield .15 .40
306 Trot Nixon .15 .40
307 Aaron Harang .15 .40
308 Adam Dunn .25 .60
309 Austin Kearns .15 .40
310 Brandon Claussen .15 .40
311 Chris Booker (RC) .20 .50
312 Edwin Encarnacion .15 .40
313 Chris Denorfia (RC) .20 .50
314 Felipe Lopez .15 .40
315 Miguel Perez (RC) .20 .50
316 Ken Griffey Jr. .60 1.50
317 Ryan Freel .15 .40
318 Sean Casey .15 .40
319 Wily Mo Pena .15 .40
320 Mike Esposito (RC) .20 .50
321 Aaron Miles .15 .40
322 Brad Hawpe .15 .40
323 Brian Fuentes .15 .40
324 Clint Barmes .15 .40
325 Cory Sullivan .15 .40
326 Garrett Atkins .15 .40
327 J.D. Closser .15 .40
328 Jeff Francis .15 .40
329 Luis Gonzalez .15 .40
330 Matt Holliday .40 1.00
331 Todd Helton .25 .60
332 Angel Berroa .15 .40
333 David DeJesus .15 .40
334 Emil Brown .15 .40
335 Jeremy Affeldt .15 .40
336 Chris Demaria RC .20 .50
337 Mark Teahen .15 .40
338 Matt Stairs .15 .40
339 Steve Stemle RC .20 .50
340 Mike Sweeney .15 .40
341 Runelvys Hernandez .15 .40
342 Jonah Bayliss RC .20 .50
343 Zack Greinke .25 .60
344 Brandon Inge .15 .40
345 Carlos Guillen .15 .40
346 Carlos Pena .25 .60
347 Chris Shelton .15 .40
348 Craig Monroe .15 .40
349 Dmitri Young .15 .40
350 Ivan Rodriguez .25 .60
351 Jeremy Bonderman .15 .40
352 Magglio Ordonez .25 .60
353 Mark Woodyard (RC) .20 .50
354 Omar Infante .15 .40
355 Placido Polanco .15 .40
356 Rondell White .15 .40
357 Brad Radke .15 .40
358 Carlos Silva .15 .40
359 Jacque Jones .15 .40
360 Joe Mauer .40 1.00
361 Chris Heintz RC .20 .50
362 Joe Nathan .15 .40
363 Johan Santana .40 1.00
364 Justin Morneau .40 1.00
365 Francisco Liriano (RC) .50 1.25
366 Travis Bowyer (RC) .20 .50
367 Michael Cuddyer .15 .40
368 Scott Baker .15 .40
369 Shannon Stewart .15 .40
370 Torii Hunter .15 .40
371 A.J. Pierzynski .15 .40
372 Aaron Rowand .15 .40
373 Carl Everett .15 .40
374 Dustin Hermanson .15 .40
375 Frank Thomas .40 1.00
376 Freddy Garcia .15 .40
377 Jermaine Dye .15 .40
378 Joe Crede .15 .40
379 Jon Garland .15 .40
380 Jose Contreras .15 .40
381 Juan Uribe .15 .40
382 Mark Buehrle .25 .60
383 Orlando Hernandez .15 .40
384 Paul Konerko .25 .60
385 Scott Podsednik .15 .40
386 Tadahito Iguchi .15 .40
387 Alex Rodriguez .60 1.50
388 Bernie Williams .25 .60
389 Chien-Ming Wang .25 .60
390 Derek Jeter 1.00 2.50
391 Gary Sheffield .15 .40
392 Hideki Matsui .40 1.00
393 Jason Giambi .15 .40
394 Jorge Posada .25 .60
395 Mike Vento (RC) .20 .50
396 Mariano Rivera .40 1.00
397 Mike Mussina .25 .60
398 Randy Johnson .40 1.00
399 Robinson Cano .40 1.00
400 Tino Martinez .15 .40
401 Alay Soler RC .25 .60
402 Boof Bonser (RC) .40 1.00
403 Cole Hamels (RC) 1.00 2.50
404 Ian Kinsler (RC) .75 2.00
405 Jason Kubel (RC) .25 .60
406 Joel Zumaya (RC) .60 1.50
407 Jonathan Papelbon (RC) 1.25 3.00
408 Jered Weaver (RC) .60 1.50
409 Kendry Morales (RC) .60 1.50
410 Lastings Milledge (RC) .25 .60
411 Matt Kemp (RC) 1.25 3.00
412 Taylor Buchholz (RC) .25 .60
413 Andre Ethier (RC) 1.00 2.50
414 Dan Uggla (RC) .60 1.50
415 Jeremy Sowers (RC) .25 .60
416 Chad Billingsley (RC) .40 1.00
417 Josh Barfield (RC) .25 .60
418 Matt Cain (RC) .60 1.50
419 Fausto Carmona (RC) .25 .60
420 Josh Willingham (RC) .25 .60
421 Jeremy Hermida (RC) .25 .60
422 Conor Jackson (RC) .40 1.00
423 Dave Gassner (RC) .25 .60
424 Brian Bannister (RC) .25 .60
425 Fernando Nieve (RC) .25 .60
426 Justin Verlander (RC) 2.00 5.00
427 Scott Olsen (RC) .25 .60
428 Takashi Saito RC .40 1.00
429 Willie Eyre (RC) .25 .60
430 Travis Ishikawa (RC) .25 .60

2006 Fleer Glossy Gold

STATED ODDS 1:144 HOBBY, 1:144 RETAIL
NO PRICING DUE TO SCARCITY

2006 Fleer Glossy Silver

*GLOSSY SILVER: 2X TO 5X BASIC
*GLOSSY SILVER: 1.5X TO 4X BASIC RC
STATED ODDS 1:12 HOBBY, 1:24 RETAIL

2006 Fleer Autographics

STATED ODDS 1:432 HOBBY, 1:432 RETAIL
SP PRINT RUNS PROVIDED BY UD
SP'S ARE NOT SERIAL-NUMBERED
NO SP PRICING ON QTY OF 25 OR LESS
AN Garret Anderson 6.00 15.00
CK Casey Kotchman SP/25 *
CS Chris Shelton 6.00 15.00
EC Eric Chavez 6.00 15.00
GA Garrett Atkins 6.00 15.00
GM Greg Maddux SP/15 *
JB Joe Blanton 6.00 15.00
JL Javy Lopez SP/25 *
JV Justin Verlander SP/25 *
KG Ken Griffey Jr.SP/150 * 40.00 80.00
KY Kevin Youkilis 10.00 25.00
MC Miguel Cabrera SP/25 *
MP Mark Prior SP/25 *
NS Nick Swisher 6.00 15.00
PM Pedro Martinez SP/15 *
TH Trevor Hoffman SP/25 *
TI Tadahito Iguchi 20.00 50.00

2006 Fleer Award Winners

COMPLETE SET (6) 6.00 15.00
OVERALL INSERT ODDS ONE PER PACK
AW1 Albert Pujols 2.50 6.00
AW2 Alex Rodriguez 1.50 4.00
AW3 Chris Carpenter 1.00 2.50
AW4 Bartolo Colon .40 1.00
AW5 Ryan Howard 1.50 4.00
AW6 Huston Street .40 1.00

2006 Fleer Fabrics

STATED ODDS 1:36 HOBBY, 1:72 RETAIL
SP INFO PROVIDED BY UPPER DECK
AJ Andruw Jones Jsy 3.00 8.00
AP Albert Pujols Jsy 6.00 15.00
AR Aramis Ramirez Jsy 3.00 8.00
AS Alfonso Soriano Jsy 3.00 8.00
BA Bobby Abreu Jsy 3.00 8.00
CB Carlos Beltran Jsy 3.00 8.00
CJ Chipper Jones Jsy 4.00 10.00
CS Curt Schilling Jsy 3.00 8.00
DJ Derek Jeter Jsy 10.00 25.00
DL Derrek Lee Jsy 3.00 8.00
DO David Ortiz Pants 4.00 10.00
DW Dontrelle Willis Jsy SP 4.00 10.00
EC Eric Chavez Jsy 3.00 8.00
EG Eric Gagne Jsy 3.00 8.00
GM Greg Maddux Jsy 4.00 10.00
GR Khalil Greene Jsy 4.00 10.00
GS Gary Sheffield Jsy SP 4.00 10.00
IR Ivan Rodriguez Jsy 3.00 8.00
JE Jim Edmonds Jsy 3.00 8.00
JM Joe Mauer Jsy 4.00 10.00
JP Jake Peavy Jsy 3.00 8.00
JS Johan Santana Jsy 4.00 10.00
JT Jim Thome Jsy 4.00 10.00
KG Ken Griffey Jr. Jsy 6.00 15.00
LG Luis Gonzalez Jsy 3.00 8.00
MC Miguel Cabrera Jsy 4.00 10.00
MP Mark Prior Jsy 4.00 10.00
MR Manny Ramirez Jsy 4.00 10.00
MT Mark Teixeira Jsy 4.00 10.00
MY Michael Young Jsy 3.00 8.00
PM Pedro Martinez Jsy 4.00 10.00
RC Roger Clemens Jsy 6.00 15.00
RH Roy Halladay Jsy 3.00 8.00
RJ Randy Johnson Jsy 4.00 10.00
RW Rickie Weeks Jsy 3.00 8.00
SM John Smoltz Jsy 4.00 10.00
TE Miguel Tejada Jsy 3.00 8.00
TH Todd Helton Jsy 4.00 10.00
VG Vladimir Guerrero Jsy 4.00 10.00
WR David Wright Jsy 4.00 10.00

2006 Fleer Lumber Company

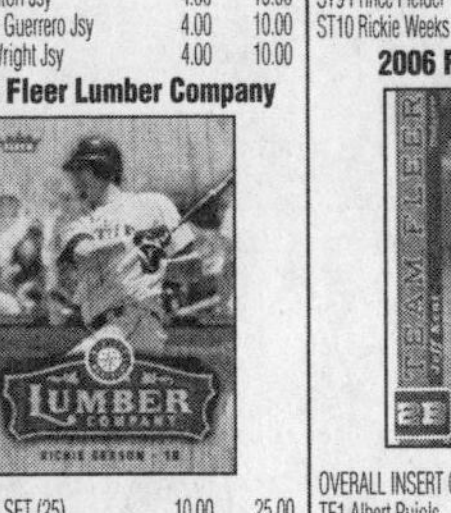

COMPLETE SET (25) 10.00 25.00
OVERALL INSERT ODDS ONE PER PACK
LC1 Adam Dunn .60 1.50
LC2 Albert Pujols 2.50 6.00
LC3 Alex Rodriguez 1.50 4.00
LC4 Alfonso Soriano .60 1.50
LC5 Andruw Jones .40 1.00
LC6 Aramis Ramirez .40 1.00
LC7 Bobby Abreu .40 1.00
LC8 Carlos Delgado .40 1.00
LC9 Carlos Lee .40 1.00
LC10 David Ortiz .60 1.50
LC11 David Wright 1.50 4.00
LC12 Derrek Lee .40 1.00
LC13 Eric Chavez .40 1.00
LC14 Gary Sheffield .40 1.00
LC15 Jeff Kent .40 1.00
LC16 Ken Griffey Jr. 1.50 4.00
LC17 Manny Ramirez 1.00 2.50
LC18 Mark Teixeira 1.00 2.50
LC19 Miguel Cabrera 1.00 2.50
LC20 Miguel Tejada .60 1.50
LC21 Paul Konerko .60 1.50
LC22 Richie Sexson .40 1.00
LC23 Todd Helton .60 1.50
LC24 Troy Glaus .40 1.00
LC25 Vladimir Guerrero 1.00 2.50

2006 Fleer Smoke 'n Heat

COMPLETE SET (15) 8.00 20.00
OVERALL INSERT ODDS ONE PER PACK
SH1 Carlos Zambrano .60 1.50
SH2 Chris Carpenter 1.00 2.50
SH3 Curt Schilling .60 1.50
SH4 Dontrelle Willis .40 1.00
SH5 Felix Hernandez 1.00 2.50
SH6 Jake Peavy .40 1.00
SH7 Johan Santana 1.00 2.50

SH8 John Smoltz 1.00 2.50
SH9 Mark Prior .60 1.50
SH10 Pedro Martinez .60 1.50
SH11 Randy Johnson 1.00 2.50
SH12 Roger Clemens 1.25 3.00
SH13 Roy Halladay 1.00 2.50
SH14 Roy Oswalt .60 1.50
SH15 Scott Kazmir .60 1.50

2006 Fleer Smooth Leather

COMPLETE SET (14) 10.00 25.00
OVERALL INSERT ODDS ONE PER PACK
SL1 Alex Rodriguez 1.50 4.00
SL2 Andruw Jones .40 1.00
SL3 Derek Jeter 2.50 6.00
SL4 Derrek Lee .40 1.00
SL5 Eric Chavez .40 1.00
SL6 Greg Maddux 1.50 4.00
SL7 Ichiro Suzuki 1.50 4.00
SL8 Ivan Rodriguez .60 1.50
SL9 Jim Edmonds .60 1.50
SL10 Mike Mussina .60 1.50
SL11 Omar Vizquel .60 1.50
SL12 Scott Rolen .60 1.50
SL13 Todd Helton .60 1.50
SL14 Torii Hunter .40 1.00

2006 Fleer Stars of Tomorrow

COMPLETE SET (10) 6.00 15.00
OVERALL INSERT ODDS ONE PER PACK
ST1 David Wright 1.50 4.00
ST2 Ryan Howard 1.50 4.00
ST3 Felix Hernandez 1.00 2.50
ST4 Jeff Francoeur 1.00 2.50
ST5 Joe Mauer 1.00 2.50
ST6 Mark Prior .60 1.50
ST7 Mark Teixeira 1.00 2.50
ST8 Miguel Cabrera 1.00 2.50
ST9 Prince Fielder 1.50 4.00
ST10 Rickie Weeks .60 1.50

2006 Fleer Team Fleer

OVERALL INSERT ODDS ONE PER PACK
TF1 Albert Pujols 12.00 30.00
TF2 Alex Rodriguez 8.00 20.00
TF3 Alfonso Soriano 3.00 8.00
TF4 Andruw Jones 2.00 5.00
TF5 Bobby Abreu 2.00 5.00
TF6 David Ortiz 3.00 8.00
TF7 David Wright 8.00 20.00
TF8 Eric Gagne 2.00 5.00
TF9 Ichiro Suzuki 8.00 20.00
TF10 Jason Varitek 5.00 12.00
TF11 Jeff Kent 2.00 5.00
TF12 Johan Santana 5.00 12.00
TF13 Jose Reyes 3.00 8.00
TF14 Manny Ramirez 5.00 12.00
TF15 Mariano Rivera 5.00 12.00
TF16 Miguel Cabrera 5.00 12.00
TF17 Miguel Tejada 3.00 8.00
TF18 Mike Piazza 5.00 12.00
TF19 Roger Clemens 6.00 15.00
TF20 Torii Hunter 2.00 5.00

2006 Fleer Team Leaders

COMPLETE SET (30) 15.00 40.00
OVERALL INSERT ODDS ONE PER PACK
TL1 Troy Glaus .60 1.50
Brandon Webb
TL2 Andruw Jones 1.00 2.50
John Smoltz
TL3 Miguel Tejada .60 1.50
Erik Bedard
TL4 David Ortiz .60 1.50
Curt Schilling
TL5 Derrek Lee .60 1.50
Mark Prior
TL6 Paul Konerko .60 1.50
Mark Buehrle
TL7 Ken Griffey Jr. 1.50 4.00
Aaron Harang
TL8 Travis Hafner .60 1.50
Cliff Lee
TL9 Todd Helton .60 1.50
Jeff Francis
TL10 Ivan Rodriguez .60 1.50
Jeremy Bonderman
TL11 Miguel Cabrera 1.00 2.50
Dontrelle Willis
TL12 Lance Berkman .60 1.50
Roger Clemens
TL13 Mike Sweeney .60 1.50
Zack Greinke
TL14 Jeff Kent .40 1.00
Derek Lowe
TL15 Carlos Lee .40 1.00
Ben Sheets
TL16 Torii Hunter 1.00 2.50
Johan Santana
TL17 David Wright 1.50 4.00
Pedro Martinez
TL18 Derek Jeter 2.50 6.00
Randy Johnson
TL19 Eric Chavez .40 1.00
Barry Zito
TL20 Bobby Abreu .40 1.00
Brett Myers
TL21 Jason Bay .40 1.00
Zach Duke
TL22 Brian Giles .40 1.00
Jake Peavy
TL23 Moises Alou .40 1.00
Jason Schmidt
TL24 Ichiro Suzuki 1.00 2.50
Felix Hernandez
TL25 Albert Pujols 2.50 6.00
Chris Carpenter
TL26 Carl Crawford .60 1.50
Scott Kazmir
TL27 Mark Teixeira 1.00 2.50
Kenny Rogers
TL28 Vernon Wells 1.00 2.50
Roy Halladay
TL29 Jose Guillen .40 1.00
Livan Hernandez
TL30 Vladimir Guerrero 1.00 2.50
Bartolo Colon

2006 Fleer Top 40

STATED ODDS 2:1 FAT PACKS
1 Ken Griffey Jr. 1.50 4.00
2 Derek Jeter 2.50 6.00
3 Albert Pujols 2.50 6.00
4 Alex Rodriguez 1.50 4.00
5 Vladimir Guerrero 1.00 2.50
6 Roger Clemens 1.25 3.00
7 Derrek Lee .40 1.00
8 David Ortiz .60 1.50
9 Miguel Cabrera 1.00 2.50
10 Bobby Abreu .40 1.00
11 Mark Teixeira 1.00 2.50
12 Johan Santana 1.00 2.50
13 Hideki Matsui 1.00 2.50
14 Ichiro Suzuki 1.50 4.00
15 Andruw Jones .40 1.00
16 Eric Chavez .40 1.00
17 Roy Oswalt .60 1.50
18 Curt Schilling .60 1.50
19 Randy Johnson 1.00 2.50
20 Ivan Rodriguez .60 1.50
21 Chipper Jones 1.00 2.50
22 Mark Prior .60 1.50
23 Jason Bay .40 1.00
24 Pedro Martinez .60 1.50
25 David Wright 1.50 4.00
26 Carlos Beltran .40 1.00
27 Jim Edmonds .60 1.50
28 Chris Carpenter 1.00 2.50
29 Roy Halladay 1.00 2.50
30 Jake Peavy .40 1.00
31 Paul Konerko .60 1.50
32 Travis Hafner .40 1.00
33 Barry Zito .40 1.00
34 Miguel Tejada .60 1.50
35 Josh Beckett .60 1.50
36 Todd Helton .60 1.50
37 Dontrelle Willis .40 1.00
38 Manny Ramirez 1.00 2.50
39 Mariano Rivera 1.00 2.50
40 Jeff Kent .40 1.00

2007 Fleer

COMPLETE SET (400) 30.00 60.00
COMP.FACT.SET (430) 30.00 60.00
COMMON CARD (1-430) .12 .30
COMMON RC .25 .60
401-430 ISSUED IN FACT.SET
OVERALL PRINTING PLATE ODDS 1:720
PLATE PRINT RUN 1 SET PER COLOR
BLACK-CYAN-MAGENTA-YELLOW ISSUED
NO PLATE PRICING DUE TO SCARCITY
1 Chad Cordero .12 .30
2 Alfonso Soriano .20 .50
3 Nick Johnson .12 .30
4 Austin Kearns .12 .30
5 Ramon Ortiz .12 .30
6 Brian Schneider .12 .30
7 Ryan Zimmerman .20 .50
8 Jose Vidro .12 .30
9 Felipe Lopez .12 .30
10 Cristian Guzman .12 .30
11 B.J. Ryan .12 .30
12 Alex Rios .20 .50
13 Vernon Wells .12 .30
14 Roy Halladay .30 .75
15 A.J. Burnett .12 .30
16 Lyle Overbay .12 .30
17 Troy Glaus .12 .30
18 Bengie Molina .12 .30
19 Gustavo Chacin .12 .30
20 Aaron Hill .12 .30
21 Vicente Padilla .12 .30
22 Kevin Millwood .12 .30
23 Akinori Otsuka .12 .30
24 Adam Eaton .12 .30
25 Hank Blalock .12 .30
26 Mark Teixeira .30 .75
27 Michael Young .20 .50
28 Mark DeRosa .12 .30
29 Gary Matthews .12 .30
30 Ian Kinsler .20 .50
31 Carlos Lee .12 .30
32 James Shields .12 .30
33 Scott Kazmir .20 .50
34 Carl Crawford .20 .50
35 Jonny Gomes .12 .30
36 Tim Corcoran .12 .30
37 B.J. Upton .12 .30
38 Rocco Baldelli .12 .30
39 Jae Seo .12 .30
40 Jorge Cantu .12 .30
41 Ty Wigginton .12 .30
42 Chris Carpenter .30 .75
43 Albert Pujols .75 2.00
44 Scott Rolen .20 .50
45 Jim Edmonds .20 .50
46 Jason Isringhausen .12 .30
47 Yadier Molina .20 .50
48 Adam Wainwright .20 .50
49 Mark Mulder .12 .30
50 Jason Marquis .12 .30
51 Juan Encarnacion .12 .30
52 Aaron Miles .12 .30
53 Ichiro Suzuki .50 1.25
54 Felix Hernandez .30 .75
55 Kenji Johjima .30 .75
56 Richie Sexson .12 .30
57 Yuniesky Betancourt .12 .30
58 J.J. Putz .12 .30
59 Jarrod Washburn .12 .30
60 Ben Broussard .12 .30
61 Adrian Beltre .12 .30
62 Raul Ibanez .20 .50
63 Jose Lopez .12 .30
64 Matt Cain .20 .50
65 Noah Lowry .12 .30
66 Jason Schmidt .12 .30
67 Pedro Feliz .12 .30
68 Matt Morris .12 .30
69 Ray Durham .12 .30
70 Steve Finley .12 .30
71 Randy Winn .12 .30
72 Moises Alou .12 .30
73 Eliezer Alfonzo .12 .30
74 Armando Benitez .12 .30
75 Omar Vizquel .20 .50
76 Chris R. Young .12 .30
77 Adrian Gonzalez .20 .50
78 Khalil Greene .12 .30
79 Mike Piazza .30 .75
80 Josh Barfield .12 .30
81 Brian Giles .12 .30
82 Jake Peavy .12 .30
83 Trevor Hoffman .20 .50
84 Mike Cameron .12 .30
85 Dave Roberts .12 .30
86 David Wells .12 .30
87 Zach Duke .12 .30
88 Ian Snell .12 .30
89 Jason Bay .20 .50
90 Freddy Sanchez .12 .30
91 Jack Wilson .12 .30
92 Tom Gorzelanny .12 .30
93 Chris Duffy .12 .30
94 Jose Castillo .12 .30
95 Matt Capps .12 .30
96 Mike Gonzalez .12 .30
97 Chase Utley .30 .75
98 Jimmy Rollins .20 .50
99 Aaron Rowand .12 .30
100 Ryan Howard .50 1.25
101 Cole Hamels .30 .75
102 Pat Burrell .12 .30
103 Shane Victorino .12 .30
104 Jamie Moyer .12 .30
105 Mike Lieberthal .12 .30
106 Tom Gordon .12 .30
107 Brett Myers .12 .30
108 Nick Swisher .30 .75
109 Barry Zito .12 .30
110 Jason Kendall .12 .30
111 Milton Bradley .12 .30
112 Bobby Crosby .12 .30
113 Huston Street .12 .30
114 Eric Chavez .12 .30
115 Frank Thomas .30 .75
116 Dan Haren .12 .30
117 Jay Payton .12 .30
118 Randy Johnson .30 .75
119 Mike Mussina .20 .50
120 Bobby Abreu .12 .30
121 Jason Giambi .12 .30
122 Derek Jeter .75 2.00
123 Alex Rodriguez .50 1.25
124 Jorge Posada .20 .50
125 Robinson Cano .30 .75
126 Mariano Rivera .30 .75
127 Chien-Ming Wang .20 .50
128 Hideki Matsui .30 .75
129 Gary Sheffield .12 .30
130 Lastings Milledge .20 .50
131 Tom Glavine .20 .50
132 Billy Wagner .12 .30
133 Pedro Martinez .20 .50
134 Paul LoDuca .12 .30
135 Carlos Delgado .12 .30
136 Carlos Beltran .12 .30
137 David Wright .50 1.25
138 Jose Reyes .20 .50
139 Julio Franco .12 .30
140 Michael Cuddyer .12 .30
141 Justin Morneau .30 .75
142 Johan Santana .30 .75
143 Francisco Liriano .30 .75
144 Joe Mauer .30 .75
145 Torii Hunter .12 .30
146 Luis Castillo .12 .30
147 Joe Nathan .12 .30
148 Carlos Silva .12 .30
149 Boof Bonser .12 .30
150 Ben Sheets .12 .30
151 Prince Fielder .20 .50
152 Bill Hall .12 .30
153 Rickie Weeks .20 .50
154 Geoff Jenkins .12 .30
155 Kevin Mench .12 .30
156 Francisco Cordero .12 .30
157 Chris Capuano .12 .30
158 Brady Clark .12 .30
159 Tony Gwynn Jr. .12 .30
160 Chad Billingsley .12 .30
161 Russell Martin .12 .30
162 Wilson Betemit .12 .30
163 Nomar Garciaparra .30 .75
164 Kenny Lofton .12 .30
165 Rafael Furcal .12 .30
166 Julio Lugo .12 .30
167 Brad Penny .12 .30
168 Jeff Kent .12 .30
169 Greg Maddux .50 1.25
170 Derek Lowe .12 .30
171 Andre Ethier .20 .50
172 Chone Figgins .12 .30
173 Francisco Rodriguez .20 .50
174 Garret Anderson .12 .30
175 Orlando Cabrera .12 .30
176 Adam Kennedy .12 .30
177 John Lackey .12 .30
178 Vladimir Guerrero .30 .75
179 Bartolo Colon .12 .30
180 Jered Weaver .20 .50
181 Juan Rivera .12 .30
182 Howie Kendrick .12 .30
183 Ervin Santana .12 .30
184 Mark Redman .12 .30
185 David DeJesus .12 .30
186 Joey Gathright .12 .30
187 Mike Sweeney .12 .30
188 Mark Teahen .12 .30
189 Angel Berroa .12 .30
190 Ambiorix Burgos .12 .30
191 Luke Hudson .12 .30
192 Mark Grudzielanek .12 .30
193 Roger Clemens .40 1.00
194 Willy Taveras .12 .30
195 Craig Biggio .20 .50
196 Andy Pettitte .20 .50
197 Roy Oswalt .20 .50
198 Lance Berkman .20 .50
199 Morgan Ensberg .12 .30
200 Brad Lidge .12 .30
201 Chris Burke .12 .30
202 Miguel Cabrera .30 .75
203 Dontrelle Willis .12 .30
204 Josh Johnson .30 .75
205 Ricky Nolasco .12 .30
206 Dan Uggla .20 .50
207 Jeremy Hermida .12 .30
208 Scott Olsen .12 .30
209 Josh Willingham .12 .30
210 Joe Borowski .12 .30
211 Hanley Ramirez .30 .75
212 Mike Jacobs .12 .30
213 Kenny Rogers .12 .30
214 Justin Verlander .40 1.00
215 Ivan Rodriguez .20 .50
216 Magglio Ordonez .20 .50
217 Todd Jones .12 .30
218 Joel Zumaya .20 .50
219 Jeremy Bonderman .12 .30
220 Nate Robertson .12 .30
221 Brandon Inge .12 .30
222 Craig Monroe .12 .30
223 Carlos Guillen .12 .30
224 Jeff Francis .12 .30
225 Brian Fuentes .12 .30
226 Todd Helton .20 .50
227 Matt Holliday .30 .75
228 Garrett Atkins .12 .30
229 Clint Barmes .12 .30
230 Jason Jennings .12 .30
231 Aaron Cook .12 .30
232 Brad Hawpe .12 .30
233 Cory Sullivan .12 .30
234 Aaron Boone .12 .30
235 C.C. Sabathia .20 .50
236 Grady Sizemore .20 .50
237 Travis Hafner .12 .30
238 Jhonny Peralta .12 .30
239 Jake Westbrook .12 .30
240 Jeremy Sowers .12 .30
241 Andy Marte .12 .30
242 Victor Martinez .20 .50
243 Jason Michaels .12 .30
244 Cliff Lee .20 .50
245 Bronson Arroyo .12 .30
246 Aaron Harang .12 .30
247 Ken Griffey Jr. .50 1.25
248 Adam Dunn .20 .50
249 Rich Aurilia .12 .30
250 Eric Milton .12 .30
251 David Ross .12 .30
252 Brandon Phillips .12 .30
253 Ryan Freel .12 .30
254 Eddie Guardado .12 .30
255 Jose Contreras .12 .30

256 Freddy Garcia	.12	.30
257 Jon Garland	.12	.30
258 Mark Buehrle	.20	.50
259 Bobby Jenks	.12	.30
260 Paul Konerko	.20	.50
261 Jermaine Dye	.12	.30
262 Joe Crede	.12	.30
263 Jim Thome	.20	.50
264 Javier Vazquez	.12	.30
265 A.J. Pierzynski	.12	.30
266 Tadahito Iguchi	.12	.30
267 Carlos Zambrano	.20	.50
268 Derrek Lee	.12	.30
269 Aramis Ramirez	.12	.30
270 Ryan Theriot	.12	.30
271 Juan Pierre	.12	.30
272 Rich Hill	.12	.30
273 Ryan Dempster	.12	.30
274 Jacque Jones	.12	.30
275 Mark Prior	.20	.50
276 Kerry Wood	.12	.30
277 Josh Beckett	.20	.50
278 David Ortiz	.20	.50
279 Kevin Youkilis	.12	.30
280 Jason Varitek	.30	.75
281 Manny Ramirez	.30	.75
282 Curt Schilling	.20	.50
283 Jon Lester	.30	.75
284 Jonathan Papelbon	.30	.75
285 Alex Gonzalez	.12	.30
286 Mike Lowell	.12	.30
287 Kyle Snyder	.12	.30
288 Miguel Tejada	.20	.50
289 Erik Bedard	.12	.30
290 Ramon Hernandez	.12	.30
291 Melvin Mora	.12	.30
292 Nick Markakis	.30	.75
293 Brian Roberts	.12	.30
294 Corey Patterson	.12	.30
295 Kris Benson	.12	.30
296 Jay Gibbons	.12	.30
297 Rodrigo Lopez	.12	.30
298 Chris Ray	.12	.30
299 Andruw Jones	.12	.30
300 Brian McCann	.12	.30
301 Jeff Francoeur	.30	.75
302 Chuck James	.12	.30
303 John Smoltz	.30	.75
304 Bob Wickman	.12	.30
305 Edgar Renteria	.12	.30
306 Adam LaRoche	.12	.30
307 Marcus Giles	.12	.30
308 Tim Hudson	.20	.50
309 Chipper Jones	.30	.75
310 Miguel Batista	.12	.30
311 Claudio Vargas	.12	.30
312 Brandon Webb	.20	.50
313 Luis Gonzalez	.12	.30
314 Livan Hernandez	.12	.30
315 Stephen Drew	.12	.30
316 Johnny Estrada	.12	.30
317 Orlando Hudson	.12	.30
318 Conor Jackson	.12	.30
319 Chad Tracy	.12	.30
320 Carlos Quentin	.12	.30
321 Alvin Colina RC	.60	1.50
322 Miguel Montero (RC)	.25	.60
323 Jeff Fiorentino (RC)	.25	.60
324 Jeff Baker (RC)	.25	.60
325 Brian Burres (RC)	.25	.60
326 David Murphy (RC)	.25	.60
327 Francisco Cruceta (RC)	.25	.60
328 Beltran Perez (RC)	.25	.60
329 Scott Moore (RC)	.25	.60
330 Sean Henn (RC)	.25	.60
331 Ryan Sweeney (RC)	.25	.60
332 Josh Fields (RC)	.25	.60
333 Jerry Owens (RC)	.25	.60
334 Vinny Rottino (RC)	.25	.60
335 Kevin Kouzmanoff (RC)	.25	.60
336 Alexi Casilla RC	.40	1.00
337 Justin Hampson (RC)	.25	.60
338 Troy Tulowitzki (RC)	1.50	4.00
339 Jose Garcia RC	.25	.60
340 Andrew Miller RC	.60	1.50
341 Glen Perkins (RC)	.25	.60
342 Ubaldo Jimenez (RC)	1.50	4.00
343 Doug Slaten RC	.25	.60
344 Angel Sanchez RC	.25	.60
345 Mitch Maier RC	.25	.60
346 Ryan Braun RC	.25	.60
347 Joselo Diaz (RC)	.25	.60
348 Delwyn Young (RC)	.25	.60
349 Kevin Hooper (RC)	.25	.60
350 Dennis Sarfate (RC)	.25	.60
351 Andy Cannizaro RC	.25	.60
352 Devern Hansack RC	.25	.60
353 Michael Bourn (RC)	.25	.60
354 Carlos Maldonado (RC)	.25	.60
355 Shane Youman RC	.25	.60
356 Philip Humber (RC)	.25	.60
357 Hector Gimenez (RC)	.25	.60
358 Fred Lewis (RC)	.40	1.00
359 Ryan Feierabend (RC)	.25	.60
360 Juan Morillo (RC)	.25	.60
361 Travis Chick (RC)	.25	.60
362 Oswaldo Navarro RC	.25	.60
363 Cesar Jimenez RC	.25	.60
364 Brian Stokes (RC)	.25	.60
365 Delmon Young (RC)	.40	1.00
366 Juan Salas (RC)	.25	.60
367 Shawn Riggans (RC)	.25	.60
368 Adam Lind (RC)	.25	.60
369 Joaquin Arias (RC)	.25	.60
370 Eric Stults RC	.25	.60
371 Brandon Webb CL	.20	.50
372 John Smoltz CL	.30	.75
373 Miguel Tejada CL	.20	.50
374 David Ortiz CL	.20	.50
375 Carlos Zambrano CL	.20	.50
376 Jermaine Dye CL	.12	.30
377 Ken Griffey Jr. CL	.50	1.25
378 Victor Martinez CL	.20	.50
379 Todd Helton CL	.20	.50
380 Ivan Rodriguez CL	.20	.50
381 Miguel Cabrera CL	.30	.75
382 Lance Berkman CL	.20	.50
383 Mike Sweeney CL	.12	.30
384 Vladimir Guerrero CL	.30	.75
385 Derek Lowe CL	.12	.30
386 Bill Hall CL	.12	.30
387 Johan Santana CL	.30	.75
388 Carlos Beltran CL	.12	.30
389 Derek Jeter CL	.75	2.00
390 Nick Swisher CL	.30	.75
391 Ryan Howard CL	.50	1.25
392 Jason Bay CL	.20	.50
393 Trevor Hoffman CL	.20	.50
394 Omar Vizquel CL	.20	.50
395 Ichiro Suzuki CL	.50	1.25
396 Albert Pujols CL	.75	2.00
397 Carl Crawford CL	.20	.50
398 Mark Teixeira CL	.30	.75
399 Roy Halladay CL	.30	.75
400 Ryan Zimmerman CL	.20	.50
401 Mark Reynolds RC	2.00	5.00
402 Micah Owings (RC)	.25	.60
403 Jarrod Saltalamacchia (RC)	.40	1.00
404 Daisuke Matsuzaka RC	1.00	2.50
405 Hideki Okajima RC	1.25	3.00
406 Felix Pie (RC)	.25	.60
407 Mike Fontenot (RC)	.25	.60
408 John Danks RC	.40	1.00
409 Josh Hamilton (RC)	1.00	2.50
410 Homer Bailey (RC)	.40	1.00
411 Alejandro De Aza RC	.40	1.00
412 Matt Lindstrom (RC)	.25	.60
413 Hunter Pence (RC)	1.25	3.00
414 Alex Gordon RC	.75	2.00
415 Billy Butler (RC)	.40	1.00
416 Brandon Wood (RC)	.25	.60
417 Andy LaRoche (RC)	.25	.60
418 Ryan Bruan (RC)	1.25	3.00
419 Joe Smith RC	.25	.60
420 Carlos Gomez RC	.40	1.00
421 Tyler Clippard (RC)	.40	1.00
422 Matt DeSalvo (RC)	.25	.60
423 Phil Hughes (RC)	1.25	3.00
424 Kei Igawa RC	.60	1.50
425 Chase Wright RC	.60	1.50
426 Travis Buck (RC)	.25	.60
427 Zack Segovia (RC)	.25	.60
428 Tim Lincecum RC	4.00	10.00
429 Elijah Dukes RC	.40	1.00
430 Akinori Iwamura RC	.60	1.50

2007 Fleer Mini Die Cuts

*MINI: 1.25X TO 3X BASIC
*MINI RC: .6X TO 1.5X BASIC RC
STATED ODDS 1:2 HOBBY, 1:2 RETAIL

2007 Fleer Mini Die Cuts Gold

STATED ODDS 1:576 HOBBY, 1:576 RETAIL
NO PRICING DUE TO SCARCITY

2007 Fleer Autographics

STATED ODDS 1:720
NO PRICING ON MOST DUE TO SCARCITY

BH Bill Hall	20.00	50.00
BK Bobby Keppel		
BU Chris Burke		
CA Dustin Pedroia		
CB Chris Booker	6.00	15.00
CI Cesar Izturis		
CJ Conor Jackson		
CK Casey Kotchman	6.00	15.00
DJ Dan Johnson	6.00	15.00
EJ Edwin Jackson		
FG Franklyn German		
FL Felipe Lopez SP		
GC Gustavo Chacin		
GO Jonny Gomes		
HR Hanley Ramirez SP		
JC Joe Crede SP		
JD Joey Devine		
JF Jeff Francis		
JG Jon Garland SP		
JJ Jorge Julio	6.00	15.00
JP Joel Peralta SP		
KG Ken Griffey Jr. SP		
KH Koyie Hill	6.00	15.00
LA Jason Lane		
NS Nick Swisher	6.00	15.00
SF Scott Feldman		

2007 Fleer Crowning Achievement

COMPLETE SET (20)	6.00	15.00

STATED ODDS 1:5
OVERALL PRINTING PLATE ODDS 1:720
PLATE PRINT RUN 1 SET PER COLOR
BLACK-CYAN-MAGENTA-YELLOW ISSUED
NO PLATE PRICING DUE TO SCARCITY

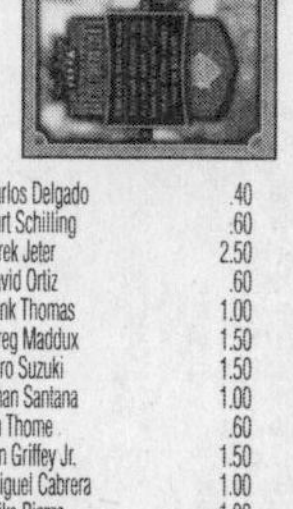

AP Albert Pujols	2.50	6.00
BZ Barry Zito	.40	1.00
CD Carlos Delgado	.40	1.00
CS Curt Schilling	.60	1.50
DJ Derek Jeter	2.50	6.00
DO David Ortiz	.60	1.50
FT Frank Thomas	1.00	2.50
GM Greg Maddux	1.50	4.00
IS Ichiro Suzuki	1.50	4.00
JS Johan Santana	1.00	2.50
JT Jim Thome	.60	1.50
KG Ken Griffey Jr.	1.50	4.00
MC Miguel Cabrera	1.00	2.50
MP Mike Piazza	1.00	2.50
MR Manny Ramirez	1.00	2.50
PM Pedro Martinez	.60	1.50
RC Roger Clemens	1.25	3.00
RH Ryan Howard	1.50	4.00
TG Tom Glavine	.60	1.50
TH Trevor Hoffman	.60	1.50

2007 Fleer Fresh Ink

STATED ODDS 1:720
NO PRICING ON MOST DUE TO SCARCITY

AC Aaron Cook		
BB Brandon Backe SP		
BW Brian Wilson		
CB Clint Barmes SP		
CC Craig Counsell	6.00	15.00
CR Coco Crisp SP		
DB Denny Bautista SP		
FG Franklyn German		
GQ Guillermo Quiroz	6.00	15.00
GR Ken Griffey Jr. SP		
JB Joe Blanton	6.00	15.00
JV John Van Benschoten		
KG Khalil Greene	10.00	25.00
LN Leo Nunez	6.00	15.00
MM Matt Murton	15.00	40.00
MR Mike Rouse		
RC Ryan Church		
RE Chris Resop		
RG Ryan Garko		
RM Russell Martin		
SC Sean Casey SP		
SD Scott Dunn	6.00	15.00
SR Saul Rivera	6.00	15.00
YB Yuniesky Betancourt		

2007 Fleer Genuine Coverage

STATED ODDS 1:720
MANY NOT PRICED DUE TO SCARCITY

AB Aaron Boone		
AP Albert Pujols	8.00	20.00
AR Aramis Ramirez	4.00	10.00
AS Alfonso Soriano		
BE Adrian Beltre	4.00	10.00
BR Brian Roberts	4.00	10.00
BS Ben Sheets	4.00	10.00
CB Carlos Beltran	6.00	15.00
CF Chone Figgins		
CS C.C. Sabathia	4.00	10.00
DJ Derek Jeter	10.00	25.00
DW Dontrelle Willis	4.00	10.00
ES Johnny Estrada		
FR Francisco Rodriguez		
GJ Geoff Jenkins	4.00	10.00
HA Rich Harden	4.00	10.00
IR Ivan Rodriguez		
IS Ian Snell	4.00	10.00
JB Josh Beckett		
JE Jim Edmonds		
JG Jason Giambi		
JJ Josh Johnson		
JM Justin Morneau	5.00	12.00
JN Joe Nathan		
JP Jake Peavy	4.00	10.00
JS Johan Santana		
JT Jim Thome		
KG Ken Griffey Jr.	8.00	20.00
LB Lance Berkman		
MR Manny Ramirez	6.00	15.00
PK Paul Konerko	4.00	10.00
PL Paul LoDuca		
RB Rocco Baldelli		
RC Robinson Cano		
RF Rafael Furcal		
RS Richie Sexson	4.00	10.00
SM John Smoltz		
TH Torii Hunter	4.00	10.00
VG Vladimir Guerrero		
VW Vernon Wells		

2007 Fleer In the Zone

COMPLETE SET (10)	5.00	12.00

STATED ODDS 1:10 HOBBY, 1:10 RETAIL

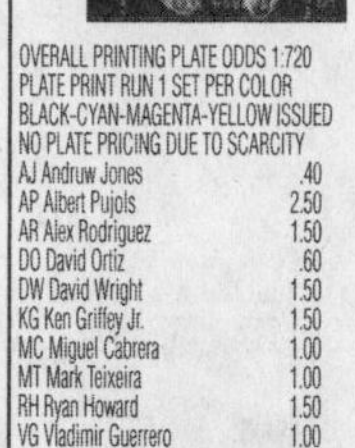

OVERALL PRINTING PLATE ODDS 1:720
PLATE PRINT RUN 1 SET PER COLOR
BLACK-CYAN-MAGENTA-YELLOW ISSUED
NO PLATE PRICING DUE TO SCARCITY

AJ Andruw Jones	.40	1.00
AP Albert Pujols	2.50	6.00
AR Alex Rodriguez	1.50	4.00
DO David Ortiz	.60	1.50
DW David Wright	1.50	4.00
KG Ken Griffey Jr.	1.50	4.00
MC Miguel Cabrera	1.00	2.50
MT Mark Teixeira	1.00	2.50
RH Ryan Howard	1.50	4.00
VG Vladimir Guerrero	1.00	2.50

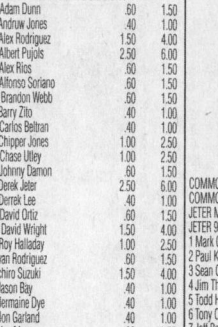

2007 Fleer Perfect 10

COMPLETE SET (20)	6.00	15.00

STATED ODDS 1:5
OVERALL PRINTING PLATE ODDS 1:720
PLATE PRINT RUN 1 SET PER COLOR
BLACK-CYAN-MAGENTA-YELLOW ISSUED
NO PLATE PRICING DUE TO SCARCITY

AP Albert Pujols	2.50	6.00
AS Alfonso Soriano	.60	1.50
BH Bill Hall	.40	1.00
CB Carlos Beltran	.40	1.00
CC Carl Crawford	.60	1.50
CJ Chipper Jones	1.00	2.50
CU Chase Utley	1.00	2.50
DJ Derek Jeter	2.50	6.00
DO David Ortiz	.60	1.50
IR Ivan Rodriguez	.60	1.50
JB Jason Bay	.60	1.50
JD Jermaine Dye	.40	1.00
JS Johan Santana	1.00	2.50
MC Miguel Cabrera	1.00	2.50
MM Mike Mussina	.60	1.50
MY Michael Young	.60	1.50
RC Roger Clemens	1.25	3.00
RH Roy Halladay	1.00	2.50
RH Ryan Howard	1.50	4.00
VG Vladimir Guerrero	1.00	2.50

2007 Fleer Rookie Sensations

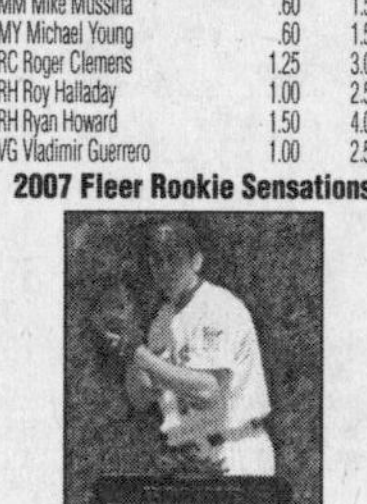

COMPLETE SET (25)	6.00	15.00

STATED ODDS APPX 1:1 HOBBY, 1:1 RETAIL
OVERALL PRINTING PLATE ODDS 1:720
PLATE PRINT RUN 1 SET PER COLOR
BLACK-CYAN-MAGENTA-YELLOW ISSUED
NO PLATE PRICING DUE TO SCARCITY

BB Boof Bonser	.40	1.00
CB Chad Billingsley	.40	1.00
CH Cole Hamels	1.00	2.50
CJ Conor Jackson	.40	1.00
DU Dan Uggla	.60	1.50
FL Francisco Liriano	1.00	2.50
HR Hanley Ramirez	1.00	2.50
IK Ian Kinsler	.60	1.50
JB Josh Barfield	.40	1.00
JH Jeremy Hermida	.40	1.00
JJ Josh Johnson	1.00	2.50
JL Jon Lester	1.00	2.50
JP Jonathan Papelbon	1.00	2.50
JS Jeremy Sowers	.40	1.00
JV Justin Verlander	1.25	3.00
JW Jered Weaver	.60	1.50
KJ Kenji Johjima	1.00	2.50
LO James Loney	.60	1.50
MK Matt Kemp	.60	1.50
NM Nick Markakis	1.00	2.50
PF Prince Fielder	.60	1.50
RG Matt Garza	.40	1.00
RN Ricky Nolasco	.40	1.00
RZ Ryan Zimmerman	.60	1.50
SO Scott Olsen	.40	1.00

2007 Fleer Soaring Stars

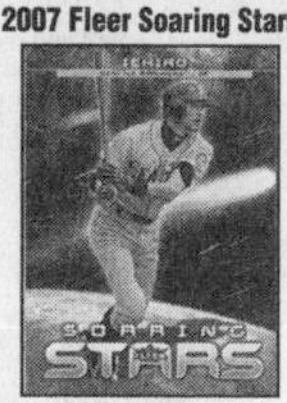

STATED ODDS 1:2 FAT PACKS
OVERALL PRINTING PLATE ODDS 1:720
PLATE PRINT RUN 1 SET PER COLOR
BLACK-CYAN-MAGENTA-YELLOW ISSUED
NO PLATE PRICING DUE TO SCARCITY

AD Adam Dunn	.60	1.50
AJ Andruw Jones	.40	1.00
AL Alex Rodriguez	1.50	4.00
AP Albert Pujols	2.50	6.00
AR Alex Rios	.60	1.50
AS Alfonso Soriano	.60	1.50
BW Brandon Webb	.60	1.50
BZ Barry Zito	.40	1.00
CB Carlos Beltran	.40	1.00
CJ Chipper Jones	1.00	2.50
CU Chase Utley	1.00	2.50
DA Johnny Damon	.60	1.50
DJ Derek Jeter	2.50	6.00
DL Derrek Lee	.40	1.00
DO David Ortiz	.60	1.50
DW David Wright	1.50	4.00
HA Roy Halladay	1.00	2.50
IR Ivan Rodriguez	.60	1.50
IS Ichiro Suzuki	1.50	4.00
JB Jason Bay	.40	1.00
JD Jermaine Dye	.40	1.00
JG Jon Garland	.40	1.00
JM Joe Mauer	.60	1.50
JS Johan Santana	1.00	2.50
JV Justin Verlander	1.25	3.00
KG Ken Griffey Jr.	1.50	4.00
LB Lance Berkman	.60	1.50
MC Miguel Cabrera	1.00	2.50
MP Mike Piazza	1.00	2.50
MR Manny Ramirez	1.00	2.50
MT Mark Teixeira	1.00	2.50
NG Nomar Garciaparra	1.00	2.50
PF Prince Fielder	.60	1.50
PM Pedro Martinez	.60	1.50
RH Ryan Howard	1.50	4.00
RI Mariano Rivera	1.00	2.50
RO Roy Oswalt	.60	1.50
TE Miguel Tejada	.60	1.50
TG Tom Glavine	.60	1.50
TH Travis Hafner	.40	1.00
VG Vladimir Guerrero	1.00	2.50
WI Dontrelle Willis	.40	1.00

2007 Fleer Year in Review

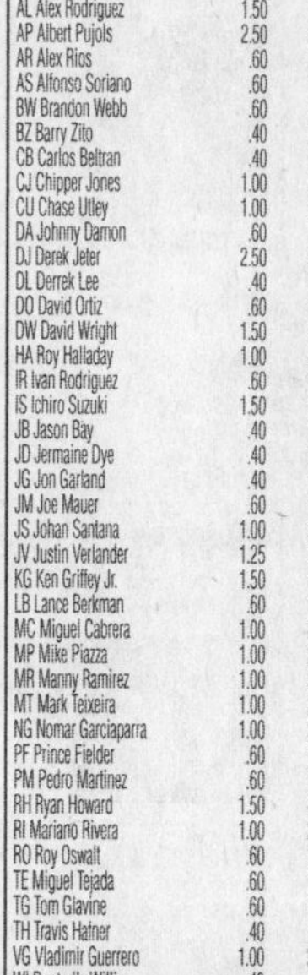

COMPLETE SET (20)	6.00	15.00

STATED ODDS 1:5
OVERALL PRINTING PLATE ODDS 1:720
PLATE PRINT RUN 1 SET PER COLOR
BLACK-CYAN-MAGENTA-YELLOW ISSUED
NO PLATE PRICING DUE TO SCARCITY

AP Albert Pujols	2.50	6.00
AR Alex Rodriguez	1.50	4.00
AS Alfonso Soriano	.60	1.50
BA Bobby Abreu	.40	1.00
CU Chase Utley	1.00	2.50
DJ Derek Jeter	2.50	6.00
DO David Ortiz	.60	1.50
FL Francisco Liriano	1.00	2.50
FS Freddy Sanchez	.40	1.00
HO Ryan Howard	1.50	4.00
JD Jermaine Dye	.40	1.00
JM Joe Mauer	1.00	2.50
JR Jose Reyes	.60	1.50
JV Justin Verlander	1.25	3.00
JW Jered Weaver	.60	1.50
KG Ken Griffey Jr.	1.50	4.00
MD Mark DeRosa	.40	1.00
MO Justin Morneau	1.00	2.50
RH Roy Halladay	1.00	2.50
TH Travis Hafner	.40	1.00

2004 Fleer Authentic Player Autographs

AVAIL.VIA MAIL REDEMPTION
STATED PRINT RUN 300 SERIAL #'d CARDS

RJ Randy Johnson/300	40.00	80.00
AJ Andruw Jones/50		

2005 Fleer Authentic Player Autographs

NO PRICING ON QTY OF 25 OR LESS

DW1 David Wright AU/300	10.00	25.00
DW2 David Wright Jsy AU/100	15.00	40.00
JF1 Jennie Finch AU/500	10.00	25.00
JF2 Jennie Finch AU/300	12.50	30.00
JF3 Jennie Finch AU/150	15.00	40.00
JF4 Jennie Finch AU/50	20.00	50.00
JV1 Justin Verlander AU/300	15.00	40.00
JV2 Justin Verlander AU/150	20.00	50.00
KS1 Kurt Suzuki AU/300	5.00	12.00
KW1 Kerry Wood Jsy AU/100	20.00	50.00
MC1 Miguel Cabrera AU/300	6.00	15.00
MC2 Miguel Cabrera AU/150	8.00	20.00
MC3 Miguel Cabrera AU/50	10.00	25.00
MC4 Miguel Cabrera Jsy AU/100	15.00	40.00
MC5 Miguel Cabrera Jsy AU/25		
RJ1 Randy Johnson AU/150	30.00	60.00
RJ2 Randy Johnson AU/50	40.00	80.00

2001 Fleer Authority

This product was released in late December 2001, and featured a 150-card base set that was broken into tiers as follows: 100 Base Veterans, and 50 Prospects (serial numbered to 2001). Each pack contained five cards.

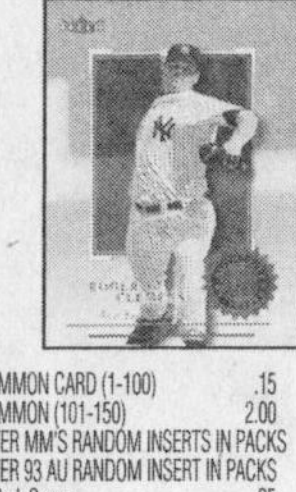

COMP.SET w/o SP's (100)	10.00	25.00
COMMON CARD (1-100)	.15	.40
COMMON (101-150)	2.00	5.00

JETER MM'S RANDOM INSERTS IN PACKS
JETER 93 AU RANDOM INSERT IN PACKS

1 Mark Grace	.25	.60
2 Paul Konerko	.15	.40
3 Sean Casey	.15	.40
4 Jim Thome	.25	.60
5 Todd Helton	.25	.60
6 Tony Clark	.15	.40
7 Jeff Bagwell	.25	.60
8 Mike Sweeney	.15	.40
9 Eric Karros	.15	.40
10 Richie Sexson	.15	.40
11 Doug Mientkiewicz	.15	.40
12 Ryan Klesko	.15	.40
13 John Olerud	.15	.40
14 Mark McGwire	1.00	2.50
15 Fred McGriff	.25	.60
16 Rafael Palmeiro	.25	.60
17 Carlos Delgado	.15	.40
18 Roberto Alomar	.25	.60
19 Craig Biggio	.25	.60
20 Jose Vidro	.15	.40
21 Edgardo Alfonzo	.15	.40
22 Jeff Kent	.15	.40
23 Bret Boone	.15	.40
24 Rafael Furcal	.15	.40
25 Nomar Garciaparra	.60	1.50
26 Barry Larkin	.25	.60
27 Cristian Guzman	.15	.40
28 Derek Jeter	1.00	2.50
29 Miguel Tejada	.15	.40
30 Jimmy Rollins	.15	.40
31 Rich Aurilia	.15	.40
32 Alex Rodriguez	.60	1.50
33 Cal Ripken	1.25	3.00
34 Troy Glaus	.15	.40
35 Matt Williams	.15	.40
36 Chipper Jones	.40	1.00
37 Jeff Cirillo	.15	.40
38 Robin Ventura	.15	.40
39 Eric Chavez	.15	.40
40 Scott Rolen	.25	.60
41 Phil Nevin	.15	.40
42 Mike Piazza	.60	1.50
43 Jorge Posada	.25	.60
44 Jason Kendall	.15	.40
45 Ivan Rodriguez	.25	.60
46 Frank Thomas	.40	1.00
47 Edgar Martinez	.25	.60
48 Darin Erstad	.15	.40
49 Tim Salmon	.25	.60
50 Luis Gonzalez	.15	.40
51 Andruw Jones	.25	.60
52 Carl Everett	.15	.40
53 Manny Ramirez Sox	.25	.60
54 Sammy Sosa	.40	1.00
55 Rondell White	.15	.40
56 Magglio Ordonez	.15	.40
57 Ken Griffey Jr.	.60	1.50
58 Juan Gonzalez	.15	.40
59 Larry Walker	.15	.40
60 Bobby Higginson	.15	.40
61 Cliff Floyd	.15	.40
62 Preston Wilson	.15	.40
63 Moises Alou	.15	.40
64 Lance Berkman	.15	.40
65 Richard Hidalgo	.15	.40
66 Jermaine Dye	.15	.40
67 Mark Quinn	.15	.40
68 Shawn Green	.15	.40
69 Gary Sheffield	.15	.40
70 Jeromy Burnitz	.15	.40
71 Geoff Jenkins	.15	.40
72 Vladimir Guerrero	.40	1.00
73 Bernie Williams	.25	.60
74 Johnny Damon	.25	.60
75 Jason Giambi	.15	.40
76 Bobby Abreu	.15	.40
77 Pat Burrell	.15	.40
78 Brian Giles	.15	.40
79 Tony Gwynn	.50	1.25
80 Barry Bonds	1.00	2.50
81 J.D. Drew	.15	.40
82 Jim Edmonds	.15	.40
83 Greg Vaughn	.15	.40
84 Raul Mondesi	.15	.40
85 Shannon Stewart	.15	.40
86 Randy Johnson	.40	1.00
87 Curt Schilling	.15	.40
88 Tom Glavine	.25	.60
89 Greg Maddux	.60	1.50
90 Pedro Martinez	.25	.60
91 Kerry Wood	.15	.40
92 David Wells	.15	.40
93 Bartolo Colon	.15	.40
94 Mike Hampton	.15	.40
95 Kevin Brown	.15	.40
96 Al Leiter	.15	.40
97 Roger Clemens	.75	2.00
98 Mike Mussina	.25	.60
99 Tim Hudson	.15	.40
100 Kazuhiro Sasaki	.15	.40
101 Ichiro Suzuki RC	12.50	30.00
102 Albert Pujols RC	40.00	80.00
103 Drew Henson RC	2.50	6.00
104 Adam Pettyjohn RC	2.00	5.00
105 Adrian Hernandez RC	2.00	5.00
106 Andy Morales RC	2.00	5.00
107 Tsuyoshi Shinjo RC	2.50	6.00
108 Juan Uribe RC	2.50	6.00
109 Jack Wilson RC	2.50	6.00
110 Jason Smith RC	2.00	5.00
111 Junior Spivey RC	2.50	6.00
112 Wilson Betemit RC	2.00	5.00
113 Elpidio Guzman RC	2.00	5.00
114 Esix Snead RC	2.00	5.00
115 Winston Abreu RC	2.00	5.00
116 Jeremy Owens RC	2.00	5.00
117 Jay Gibbons RC	2.50	6.00
118 Luis Lopez	2.00	5.00
119 Ryan Freel RC	2.00	5.00
120 Rafael Soriano RC	2.00	5.00
121 Johnny Estrada RC	2.50	6.00
122 Bud Smith RC	2.00	5.00
123 Jackson Melian RC	2.00	5.00
124 Matt White RC	2.00	5.00
125 Travis Hafner RC UER Card photo is an Reversed Negative	4.00	10.00
126 Morgan Ensberg RC	2.00	5.00
127 Endy Chavez RC	2.00	5.00
128 Brett Prinz RC	2.00	5.00
129 Juan Diaz RC	2.00	5.00
130 Erick Almonte RC	2.00	5.00
131 Rob Mackowiak RC	2.50	6.00
132 Carlos Valderrama RC	2.00	5.00
133 Wilkin Ruan RC	2.00	5.00
134 Angel Berroa RC	2.50	6.00
135 Henry Mateo RC	2.00	5.00
136 Bill Ortega RC	2.00	5.00
137 Billy Sylvester RC	2.00	5.00
138 Andres Torres RC	2.00	5.00
139 Nate Frese RC	2.00	5.00
140 Casey Fossum RC	2.00	5.00
141 Ricardo Rodriguez RC	2.00	5.00
142 Brian Roberts RC	2.00	5.00
143 Carlos Garcia RC	2.00	5.00
144 Brian Lawrence RC	2.00	5.00
145 Cory Aldridge RC	2.00	5.00
146 Mark Teixeira RC	8.00	20.00
147 Juan Cruz RC	2.00	5.00
148 B. Duckworth RC	2.00	5.00
149 Dewon Brazelton RC	2.00	5.00
150 Mark Prior RC	4.00	10.00
MM4 Derek Jeter MM/2000	6.00	15.00
MM4AU Derek Jeter MM AU/100	75.00	150.00

2001 Fleer Authority Prominence 125/75

This 150-card insert is actually a parallel of the 2001 Fleer Authority base set. The set is broken into tiers as follows: 100 Base Veterans (numbered to 125), and 50 Prospects (numbered to 75).

COMMON CARD (101-100)	1.50	4.00
*STARS 1-100: 5X TO 12X BASIC		
COMMON CARD (101-150)	3.00	8.00
*ROOKIES 101-150: 1.25X TO 3X BASIC		

2001 Fleer Authority Diamond Cuts Memorabilia

This 111-card insert set features various swatches of game-used memorabilia including shoes, hats, bats and jerseys. Overall odds on these cards were 1:10 packs. Please note that Manny Ramirez had 100 red Batting Glove cards and 100 blue Batting Glove cards. Announced print runs listed below.

1 Rick Ankiel Shoes/400	3.00	8.00
2 Jeff Bagwell Jsy/1000	4.00	10.00
3 Adrian Beltre Hat/240	4.00	10.00
4 Craig Biggio Bat/800	4.00	10.00
5 Barry Bonds Hat/240	15.00	40.00
6 Barry Bonds Jsy/1000	10.00	25.00
7 Barry Bonds Pants/800	10.00	25.00
8 Barry Bonds Shoes/400	10.00	25.00
9 B.Bonds Wristband/100	20.00	50.00
10 Kevin Brown Hat/240	4.00	10.00
11 Kevin Brown Pants/800	3.00	8.00
12 Eric Byrnes Bat/800	3.00	8.00
13 Sean Casey Jsy/1000	3.00	8.00
14 Eric Chavez Hat/240	4.00	10.00
15 Bartolo Colon Hat/240	4.00	10.00
16 Erubiel Durazo Bat/800	3.00	8.00
17 Ray Durham Bat/800	3.00	8.00
18 Jim Edmonds Hat/240	4.00	10.00
19 J.Edmonds Shoes/400	3.00	8.00
20 Darin Erstad Hat/240	4.00	10.00
21 Carlos Febles Bat/800	3.00	8.00
22 Carlos Febles Shoes/400	3.00	8.00
23 Rafael Furcal Hat/240	4.00	10.00
24 Brian Giles Pants/800	3.00	8.00
25 Juan Gonzalez Btg Glv/100	4.00	10.00
26 Juan Gonzalez Hat/240	4.00	10.00
27 Luis Gonzalez Hat/240	4.00	10.00
28 Shawn Green Bat/800	3.00	8.00
29 S.Green Btg Glv/100	4.00	10.00
30 V.Guerrero Bat/800	4.00	10.00
31 Tony Gwynn Bat/975	6.00	15.00
32 J.Hairston Jr. Hat/240	4.00	10.00
33 Mike Hampton Hat/240	4.00	10.00
34 M.Hampton Shoes/400	3.00	8.00
35 Jason Hart Bat/800	3.00	8.00
36 Todd Helton Jsy/1000	4.00	10.00
37 Todd Helton Pants/800	4.00	10.00
38 O.Hernandez Bat/800	3.00	8.00
39 R.Hidalgo Bat/800	3.00	8.00
40 R.Hidalgo Btg Glv/200	4.00	10.00
41 Derek Jeter Bat/800	15.00	40.00
42 D.Jeter Btg Glv/150	20.00	50.00
43 Derek Jeter Jsy/1000	15.00	40.00
44 Derek Jeter Pants/800	15.00	40.00

45 Derek Jeter Shoes/400 15.00 40.00
46 R.Johnson Hat/240 6.00 15.00
47 Chipper Jones Bat/800 4.00 10.00
48 C. Jones Jsy/1000 4.00 10.00
49 Andruw Jones Bat/800 4.00 10.00
50 Andruw Jones Hat/240 6.00 15.00
51 Jason Kendall Hat/240 4.00 10.00
52 Jason Kendall Base/250 4.00 10.00
53 Barry Larkin Base/250 6.00 15.00
54 Barry Larkin Jsy/1000 4.00 10.00
55 Matt Lawton Hat/240 4.00 10.00
56 M.Lieberthal Btg Glv/100 4.00 10.00
57 Mike Lieberthal Wristband/25
58 Kenny Lofton Bat/800 3.00 8.00
59 E.Martinez Btg Glv/200 6.00 15.00
60 P.Martinez Shoes/400 4.00 10.00
61 Raul Mondesi Bat/800 3.00 8.00
62 R.Mondesi Btg Glv/100 4.00 10.00
63 Hideo Nomo Bat/800 4.00 10.00
64 Hideo Nomo Hat/240 10.00 25.00
65 Magglio Ordonez Base/250 4.00 10.00
66 M.Ordonez Btg Glv/200 4.00 10.00
67 M.Ordonez Hat/240 4.00 10.00
68 David Ortiz Base/250 8.00 20.00
69 David Ortiz Bat/800 5.00 12.00
70 R.Palmeiro Bat/800 4.00 10.00
71 R.Palmeiro Hat/240 6.00 15.00
72 R.Palmeiro Hat/240 6.00 15.00
73 Chan Ho Park Hat/240 4.00 10.00
74 Mike Piazza Bat/600 6.00 15.00
75 Mike Piazza Jsy/1000 6.00 15.00
76 Mike Piazza Shoes/400 6.00 15.00
77 Albert Pujols Pants/800 20.00 50.00
78 M.Ramirez Sox Bat/800 4.00 10.00
79 M.Ramirez Sox Btg Glv/200 6.00 15.00
80 M.Ramirez Sox Hat/240 6.00 15.00
81 M.Ramirez Sox Hat/240 6.00 15.00
82 Cal Ripken Btg Glv/100 30.00 60.00
83 Cal Ripken Pants/800 15.00 40.00
84 Ivan Rodriguez Base/250 6.00 15.00
85 I.Rodriguez Btg Glv/100 6.00 15.00
86 Ivan Rodriguez Hat/240 6.00 15.00
87 I.Rodriguez Pants/800 4.00 10.00
88 I.Rodriguez Shoes/400 4.00 10.00
89 Ivan Rodriguez Wristband/50
90 Scott Rolen Base/250 6.00 15.00
91 Scott Rolen Hat/240 6.00 15.00
92 J.Sandberg Bat/800 3.00 8.00
93 D.Sanders Jsy/1000 4.00 10.00
94 Tsuy Shinjo Bat/800 4.00 10.00
95 T.Shinjo Wristband/150 6.00 15.00
96 J.T. Snow Bat/800 3.00 8.00
97 J.T. Snow Jsy/1000 3.00 8.00
98 A.Soriano Hat/240 6.00 15.00
99 Ichiro Suzuki Bat/350 15.00 40.00
100 Ichiro Suzuki Hat/240 15.00 40.00
101 M.Sweeney Hat/240 4.00 10.00
102 Mike Sweeney Wristband/25
103 M.Tejada Hat/240 4.00 10.00
104 Frank Thomas Base/250 6.00 15.00
105 F.Thomas Bat/800 4.00 10.00
106 F.Thomas Hat/240 6.00 15.00
107 Jim Thome Bat/800 4.00 10.00
108 Jim Thome Wristband/50
109 Larry Walker Bat/800 3.00 8.00
110 L.Walker Jsy/1000 3.00 8.00
111 B.Williams Bat/800 4.00 10.00

2001 Fleer Authority Figures

This 20-card insert pairs veteran players with comparable prospects. Each card is serial numbered to 1750.

COMPLETE SET (20) 75.00 150.00
1 Mark McGwire 6.00 15.00
Albert Pujols
2 Kazuhiro Sasaki 6.00 15.00
Ichiro Suzuki
3 Derek Jeter 5.00 12.00
Drew Henson
4 Ken Griffey Jr. 4.00 10.00
Jackson Melian
5 Chipper Jones 3.00 8.00
Wilson Betemit
6 Jeff Bagwell 3.00 8.00
Morgan Ensberg
7 Cal Ripken 12.50 30.00
Jay Gibbons
8 Mike Piazza 3.00 8.00
Tsuyoshi Shinjo
9 Luis Gonzalez 1.50 4.00
Junior Spivey
10 Barry Bonds 6.00 15.00
Carlos Valderrama
11 Todd Helton 1.50 4.00
Juan Uribe
12 Roger Clemens 5.00 12.00
Adrian Hernandez
13 Alex Rodriguez 5.00 12.00
Travis Hafner
14 Scott Rolen 1.50 4.00
Johnny Estrada
15 Brian Giles 1.50 4.00
Rob Mackowiak
16 Randy Johnson 2.50 6.00
Bret Prinz
17 Carlos Delgado 1.25 3.00
Luis Lopez
18 Manny Ramirez Sox 1.50 4.00
Juan Diaz
19 Mike Sweeney 1.25 3.00
Endy Chavez
20 Sammy Sosa 2.50 6.00
Jaisen Randolph

2001 Fleer Authority Seal of Approval

This 15-card insert features seasoned veterans that have received the "Seal of Approval" from fans across

America. These cards were inserted into packs at a rate of 1:20.

COMPLETE SET (15) 60.00 120.00
1 Derek Jeter 5.00 12.00
2 Alex Rodriguez 3.00 8.00
3 Nomar Garciaparra 3.00 8.00
4 Cal Ripken 6.00 15.00
5 Mike Piazza 3.00 8.00
6 Mark McGwire 5.00 12.00
7 Tony Gwynn 2.50 6.00
8 Barry Bonds 5.00 12.00
9 Greg Maddux 3.00 8.00
10 Chipper Jones 2.00 5.00
11 Roger Clemens 4.00 10.00
12 Ken Griffey Jr. 3.00 8.00
13 Vladimir Guerrero 2.00 5.00
14 Sammy Sosa 2.00 5.00
15 Todd Helton 2.00 5.00

2000 Fleer Focus

The 2000 Fleer Focus product was released in April, 2000 as a 250-card set. The set features 225-player cards (cards 1-225), and 25-prospect cards (cards 226-250). Cards numbered 226 through 250 were issued in two separate varieties. The first 999 of each of these cards feature a portrait shot on the front of the featured prospect. The next 3,000 cards issued have an action shot on the front of the featured prospect. Due to how this set was issued, collectors can consider the set complete minus short prints at 225 cards; complete with the more common pose of the prospect player at 250 cards; or complete as a master set with all 275 cards.

COMP.MASTER SET (275) 300.00 500.00
COMP.SET w/2999's (250) 60.00 150.00
COMP.SET w/o SP's (225) 10.00 25.00
COMMON CARD (1-225) .10 .30
COMMON (226-250) 2.00 5.00
COMMON (226P-250P) 4.00 10.00
1 Nomar Garciaparra .50 1.25
2 Adrian Beltre .10 .30
3 Miguel Tejada .10 .30
4 Joe Randa .10 .30
5 Larry Walker .10 .30
6 Jeff Weaver .10 .30
7 Jay Bell .10 .30
8 Ivan Rodriguez .20 .50
9 Edgar Martinez .20 .50
10 Desi Relaford .10 .30
11 Derek Jeter .75 2.00
12 Delino Deshields .10 .30
13 Craig Biggio .20 .50
14 Chuck Knoblauch .10 .30
15 Chuck Finley .10 .30
16 Brett Tomko .10 .30
17 Bobby Higginson .10 .30
18 Pedro Martinez .20 .50
19 Troy O'Leary .10 .30
20 Rickey Henderson .30 .75
21 Robb Nen .10 .30
22 Rolando Arrojo .10 .30
23 Rondell White .10 .30
24 Royce Clayton .10 .30
25 Rusty Greer .10 .30
26 Stan Spencer .10 .30
27 Steve Finley .10 .30
28 Tom Goodwin .10 .30
29 Troy Percival .10 .30
30 Wilton Guerrero .10 .30
31 Roberto Alomar .20 .50
32 Mike Hampton .10 .30
33 Michael Barrett .10 .30
34 Curt Schilling .10 .30
35 Bill Mueller .10 .30
36 Bernie Williams .20 .50
37 John Smoltz .20 .50
38 B.J. Surhoff .10 .30
39 Pete Harnisch .10 .30
40 Juan Encarnacion .10 .30
41 Derrek Lee .20 .50
42 Jeff Shaw .10 .30
43 David Cone .10 .30
44 Jason Christiansen .10 .30
45 Jeff Kent .10 .30
46 Randy Johnson .30 .75
47 Todd Walker .10 .30
48 Jose Lima .10 .30
49 Jason Giambi .10 .30
50 Ken Griffey Jr. Reds .50 1.25
51 Bartolo Colon .10 .30
52 Mike Lieberthal .10 .30
53 Shane Reynolds .10 .30
54 Travis Lee .10 .30
55 Travis Fryman .10 .30
56 John Valentin .10 .30
57 Joey Hamilton .10 .30
58 Jay Buhner .10 .30
59 Brad Radke .10 .30
60 A.J. Burnett .10 .30
61 Roy Halladay .10 .30
62 Raul Mondesi .10 .30
63 Matt Mantei .10 .30
64 Mark Grace .20 .50
65 David Justice .10 .30
66 Billy Wagner .10 .30
67 Eric Milton .10 .30
68 Eric Chavez .10 .30
69 Doug Glanville .10 .30
70 Ray Durham .10 .30
71 Mike Sirotka .10 .30
72 Greg Vaughn .10 .30
73 Brian Jordan .10 .30
74 Alex Gonzalez .10 .30
75 Alex Rodriguez .50 1.25
76 David Nilsson .10 .30
77 Robin Ventura .20 .50
78 Kevin Young .10 .30
79 Wilson Alvarez .10 .30
80 Matt Williams .10 .30
81 Ismael Valdes .10 .30
82 Kenny Lofton .10 .30
83 Carlos Beltran .10 .30
84 Doug Mientkiewicz .10 .30
85 Wally Joyner .10 .30
86 J.D. Drew .10 .30
87 Carlos Delgado .10 .30
88 Tony Womack .10 .30
89 Eric Young .10 .30
90 Manny Ramirez .20 .50
91 Johnny Damon .20 .50
92 Torii Hunter .10 .30
93 Kenny Rogers .10 .30
94 Trevor Hoffman .10 .30
95 John Wetteland .10 .30
96 Ray Lankford .10 .30
97 Tom Glavine .20 .50
98 Carlos Lee .10 .30
99 Richie Sexson .10 .30
100 Carlos Febles .10 .30
101 Chad Allen .10 .30
102 Sterling Hitchcock .10 .30
103 Joe McEwing .10 .30
104 Justin Thompson .10 .30
105 Jim Edmonds .10 .30
106 Kerry Wood .10 .30
107 Jim Thome .20 .50
108 Jeremy Giambi .10 .30
109 Mike Piazza .50 1.25
110 Darryl Kile .10 .30
111 Darin Erstad .10 .30
112 Kyle Farnsworth .10 .30
113 Omar Vizquel .20 .50
114 Orber Moreno .10 .30
115 Al Leiter .10 .30
116 John Olerud .10 .30
117 Aaron Sele .10 .30
118 Chipper Jones .30 .75
119 Paul Konerko .10 .30
120 Chris Singleton .10 .30
121 Fernando Vina .10 .30
122 Andy Ashby .10 .30
123 Eli Marrero .10 .30
124 Edgar Renteria .10 .30
125 Roberto Hernandez .10 .30
126 Andruw Jones .20 .50
127 Magglio Ordonez .10 .30
128 Bob Wickman .10 .30
129 Tony Gwynn .40 1.00
130 Mark McGwire .75 2.00
131 Albert Belle .10 .30
132 Pokey Reese .10 .30
133 Tony Clark .10 .30
134 Jeff Bagwell .20 .50
135 Mark Grudzielanek .10 .30
136 Dustin Hermanson .10 .30
137 Reggie Sanders .10 .30
138 Ryan Rupe .10 .30
139 Kevin Millwood .10 .30
140 Bret Saberhagen .10 .30
141 Juan Guzman .10 .30
142 Alex Gonzalez .10 .30
143 Gary Sheffield .10 .30
144 Roger Clemens .60 1.50
145 Ben Grieve .10 .30
146 Bobby Abreu .10 .30
147 Brian Giles .10 .30
148 Quinton McCracken .10 .30
149 Freddy Garcia .10 .30
150 Erubiel Durazo .10 .30
151 Sidney Ponson .10 .30
152 Scott Williamson .10 .30
153 Ken Caminiti .10 .30
154 Vladimir Guerrero .30 .75
155 Andy Pettitte .20 .50
156 Edwards Guzman .10 .30
157 Shannon Stewart .10 .30
158 Greg Maddux .50 1.25
159 Mike Stanley .10 .30
160 Sean Casey .10 .30
161 Cliff Floyd .10 .30
162 Devon White .10 .30
163 Scott Brosius .10 .30
164 Marlon Anderson .10 .30
165 Jason Kendall .10 .30
166 Ryan Klesko .10 .30
167 Sammy Sosa .30 .75
168 Frank Thomas .30 .75
169 Geoff Jenkins .10 .30
170 Jason Schmidt .10 .30
171 Dan Wilson .10 .30
172 Jose Canseco .20 .50
173 Troy Glaus .10 .30
174 Mariano Rivera .30 .75
175 Scott Rolen .20 .50
176 J.T. Snow .10 .30
177 Rafael Palmeiro .20 .50
178 A.J. Hinch .10 .30
179 Jose Offerman .10 .30
180 Jeff Cirillo .10 .30
181 Dean Palmer .10 .30
182 Jose Rosado .10 .30
183 Armando Benitez .10 .30
184 Brady Anderson .10 .30
185 Cal Ripken 1.00 2.50
186 Barry Larkin .20 .50
187 Damion Easley .10 .30
188 Moises Alou .10 .30
189 Todd Hundley .10 .30
190 Tim Hudson .10 .30
191 Livan Hernandez .10 .30
192 Fred McGriff .20 .50
193 Orlando Hernandez .10 .30
194 Tim Salmon .20 .50
195 Mike Mussina .20 .50
196 Todd Helton .20 .50
197 Juan Gonzalez .10 .30
198 Kevin Brown .20 .50
199 Ugueth Urbina .10 .30
200 Matt Stairs .10 .30
201 Shawn Estes .10 .30
202 Gabe Kapler .10 .30
203 Javy Lopez .10 .30
204 Henry Rodriguez .10 .30
205 Dante Bichette .10 .30
206 Jeromy Burnitz .10 .30
207 Todd Zeile .10 .30
208 Rico Brogna .10 .30
209 Warren Morris .10 .30
210 David Segui .10 .30
211 Vinny Castilla .10 .30
212 Mo Vaughn .10 .30
213 Charles Johnson .10 .30
214 Neifi Perez .10 .30
215 Shawn Green .10 .30
216 Carl Pavano .10 .30
217 Tino Martinez .20 .50
218 Barry Bonds .75 2.00
219 David Wells .10 .30
220 Paul O'Neill .20 .50
221 Masato Yoshii .10 .30
222 Kris Benson .10 .30
223 Fernando Tatis .10 .30
224 Lee Stevens .10 .30
225 Jose Cruz Jr. .10 .30
226 Rick Ankiel 2.00 5.00
226P Rick Ankiel PORT 4.00 10.00
227 Matt Riley 2.00 5.00
227P Matt Riley PORT 4.00 10.00
228 Norm Hutchins 2.00 5.00
228P N.Hutchins PORT 4.00 10.00
229 Ruben Mateo 2.00 5.00
229P Ruben Mateo PORT 4.00 10.00
230 Ben Petrick 2.00 5.00
230P Ben Petrick PORT 4.00 10.00
231 Mario Encarnacion 2.00 5.00
231P M.Encarnacion PORT 4.00 10.00
232 Nick Johnson 2.00 5.00
232P Nick Johnson PORT 4.00 10.00
233 Adam Piatt 2.00 5.00
233P Adam Piatt PORT 4.00 10.00
234 Mike Darr 2.00 5.00
234P Mike Darr PORT 4.00 10.00
235 Chad Hermansen 2.00 5.00
235P C.Hermansen PORT 4.00 10.00
236 Wily Pena 2.00 5.00
236P Wily Pena PORT 4.00 10.00
237 Octavio Dotel 2.00 5.00
237P Octavio Dotel PORT 4.00 10.00
238 Vernon Wells 2.00 5.00
238P Vernon Wells PORT 4.00 10.00
239 Daryle Ward 2.00 5.00
239P Daryle Ward PORT 4.00 10.00
240 Adam Kennedy 2.00 5.00
240P A.Kennedy PORT 4.00 10.00
241 Angel Pena 2.00 5.00
241P Angel Pena PORT 4.00 10.00
242 Lance Berkman 2.00 5.00
242P L.Berkman PORT 4.00 10.00
243 Gabe Molina 2.00 5.00
243P Gabe Molina PORT 4.00 10.00
244 Steve Lomasney 2.00 5.00
244P S.Lomasney PORT 4.00 10.00
245 Jacob Cruz 2.00 5.00
245P Jacob Cruz PORT 4.00 10.00
246 Mark Quinn 2.00 5.00
246P Mark Quinn PORT 4.00 10.00
247 Eric Munson 2.00 5.00
247P Eric Munson PORT 4.00 10.00
248 Alfonso Soriano 3.00 8.00
248P A.Soriano PORT 5.00 12.00
249 Kip Wells 2.00 5.00
249P Kip Wells PORT 4.00 10.00
250 Josh Beckett 3.00 8.00
250P Josh Beckett PORT 5.00 12.00

2000 Fleer Focus Masterpiece Errors

Randomly inserted into packs, this set features error cards of 25 of the Masterpiece edition parallels. The cards look just like the Masterpiece parallels, however, these cards lack the "One of One" stamp on the back of the card.

50 Ken Griffey Jr. Reds 6.00 15.00
202 Gabe Kapler 1.50 4.00
203 Javy Lopez 1.50 4.00
204 Henry Rodriguez 1.50 4.00
205 Dante Bichette 1.50 4.00
206 Jeromy Burnitz 1.50 4.00
207 Todd Zeile 1.50 4.00
208 Rico Brogna 1.50 4.00
209 Warren Morris 1.50 4.00
210 David Segui 1.50 4.00
211 Vinny Castilla 1.50 4.00
212 Mo Vaughn 1.50 4.00
213 Charles Johnson 1.50 4.00
214 Neifi Perez 1.50 4.00
215 Shawn Green 1.50 4.00
216 Carl Pavano 1.50 4.00
217 Tino Martinez 2.50 6.00
218 Barry Bonds 10.00 25.00
219 David Wells 1.50 4.00
220 Paul O'Neill 2.50 6.00
221 Masato Yoshii 1.50 4.00
222 Kris Benson 1.50 4.00
223 Fernando Tatis 1.50 4.00
224 Lee Stevens 1.50 4.00
225 Jose Cruz Jr. 1.50 4.00

2000 Fleer Focus Masterpiece Mania

Randomly inserted into packs, this 250-card set is a complete parallel of the Fleer Focus base set. There

were only 300 serial numbered sets of this insert produced.

*STARS 1-225: 6X TO 15X BASIC CARDS
*ROOKIES 226-250: .5X TO 1.2X BASIC

2000 Fleer Focus Feel the Game

Randomly inserted into packs at one in 288, this 10-card insert set features game-used jersey swatches of some of the best players in major league baseball.

1 Cal Ripken 15.00 40.00
2 Randy Johnson 6.00 15.00
3 Alex Rodriguez 6.00 15.00
4 Scott Rolen 6.00 15.00
5 Javy Lopez 4.00 10.00
6 Vladimir Guerrero 6.00 15.00
7 Tom Glavine 6.00 15.00
8 Tim Salmon 6.00 15.00
9 Adrian Beltre 4.00 10.00
10 Miguel Tejada 4.00 10.00

2000 Fleer Focus Focal Points

Randomly inserted into packs at one in six, this set features 15 players that play the game with style and grace. Card backs carry a "F" prefix.

COMPLETE SET (15) 10.00 25.00
*STRIKING: 8X TO 20X BASIC FOCAL
STRIKING PRINT RUN 50 SERIAL #'d SETS
F1 Mark McGwire 1.25 3.00
F2 Tony Gwynn .60 1.50
F3 Nomar Garciaparra .75 2.00
F4 Juan Gonzalez .20 .50
F5 Jeff Bagwell .30 .75
F6 Chipper Jones .50 1.25
F7 Cal Ripken 1.50 4.00
F8 Alex Rodriguez .75 2.00
F9 Scott Rolen .30 .75
F10 Vladimir Guerrero .50 1.25
F11 Mike Piazza .75 2.00
F12 Frank Thomas .50 1.25
F13 Ken Griffey Jr. .75 2.00
F14 Sammy Sosa .50 1.25
F15 Derek Jeter 1.25 3.00

2000 Fleer Focus Fresh Ink

Randomly inserted into packs at one in 96, this 48-card set features certified autographs of players such as J.D. Drew, Tony Gwynn, and Shawn Green. Exchange cards for Troy Glaus and Mike Lieberthal had an exchange deadline of 5/31/01. The Tony Gwynn and Derek Jeter cards were not on original checklists and were late additions seeded into packs just prior to shipping. According to Fleer, Jeter signed only 100 cards (though they are not serial numbered). The cards are unnumbered and checklisted in alphabetical order by player's last name.

1 Chad Allen 4.00 10.00
2 Michael Barrett 4.00 10.00
3 Josh Beckett 6.00 15.00
4 Rob Bell 4.00 10.00
5 Adrian Beltre 8.00 20.00
6 Milton Bradley 6.00 15.00
7 Rico Brogna 4.00 10.00
8 Mike Cameron 6.00 15.00
9 Eric Chavez 6.00 15.00
10 Bruce Chen 4.00 10.00
11 Johnny Damon 8.00 20.00
12 Ben Davis 4.00 10.00
13 J.D. Drew 6.00 15.00
14 Erubiel Durazo 4.00 10.00
15 Jeremy Giambi 4.00 10.00
16 Jason Giambi 6.00 15.00
17 Doug Glanville 6.00 15.00
18 Troy Glaus 10.00 25.00
19 Shawn Green 10.00 25.00
20 Tony Gwynn 20.00 50.00
21 Mike Hampton 6.00 15.00
22 Tim Hudson 10.00 25.00
23 John Jaha 4.00 10.00
24 Derek Jeter SP/100 * 75.00 150.00
25 D'Angelo Jimenez 4.00 10.00
26 Nick Johnson 6.00 15.00
27 Randy Johnson SP 50.00 100.00
28 Andruw Jones 10.00 25.00
29 Jason Kendall 6.00 15.00
30 Adam Kennedy 6.00 15.00
31 Mike Lieberthal 6.00 15.00
32 Edgar Martinez 15.00 40.00
33 Aaron McNeal 4.00 10.00
34 Kevin Millwood 6.00 15.00
35 Mike Mussina 10.00 25.00
36 Magglio Ordonez 6.00 15.00
37 Eric Owens 4.00 10.00
38 Rafael Palmeiro 20.00 50.00
39 Wily Pena 12.50 30.00
40 Adam Piatt 4.00 10.00
41 Cal Ripken 50.00 100.00
42 Alex Rodriguez 50.00 100.00
43 Tim Salmon 10.00 25.00
44 Chris Singleton 4.00 10.00
45 Mike Sweeney 6.00 15.00
46 Jose Vidro 4.00 10.00
47 Rondell Wells 6.00 15.00
48 Jaret Wright 4.00 10.00

2000 Fleer Focus Future Vision

Randomly inserted into packs at one in nine, this 15-card insert set features the year's top rookies with an innovative twist. Card backs carry a "FV" prefix.

COMPLETE SET (15) 6.00 15.00
FV1 Rick Ankiel .40 1.00
FV2 Matt Riley .40 1.00
FV3 Ruben Mateo .40 1.00
FV4 Ben Petrick .40 1.00
FV5 Mario Encarnacion .40 1.00
FV6 Octavio Dotel .40 1.00
FV7 Vernon Wells .40 1.00
FV8 Adam Kennedy .40 1.00
FV9 Lance Berkman .40 1.00
FV10 Chad Hermansen .40 1.00
FV11 Mark Quinn .40 1.00
FV12 Eric Munson .40 1.00
FV13 Alfonso Soriano .75 2.00
FV14 Kip Wells .40 1.00
FV15 Josh Beckett .75 2.00

2000 Fleer Focus Pocus

Randomly inserted into packs at one in 14, this set features 10 stars that display wizardry on the diamond. Card backs carry a "FP" prefix.

COMPLETE SET (10) 20.00 50.00
FP1 Cal Ripken 3.00 8.00
FP2 Tony Gwynn 1.25 3.00
FP3 Nomar Garciaparra 1.50 4.00
FP4 Juan Gonzalez .40 1.00
FP5 Mike Piazza 1.50 4.00
FP6 Mark McGwire 2.50 6.00
FP7 Chipper Jones 1.00 2.50
FP8 Ken Griffey Jr. 1.50 4.00
FP9 Derek Jeter 2.50 6.00
FP10 Alex Rodriguez 1.50 4.00

2001 Fleer Focus

The 2001 Fleer Focus product was released in late January, 2001. Each pack contained 10 cards, and carried a suggested retail price of $2.99. The 240-card base set is broken into tiers as follows: Base Veterans (1-200), and Prospects (201-240) - individually serial numbered by position). Breakdowns for the prospect cards are as follows: First Baseman (201-207) - 2,499 of each, Third Baseman (208-211) - 2,999 of each, Catcher (212) - 3,499 of each, Outfielders (213-224) - 1,999 of each, Pitchers (225-235) - 4,999 of each and Second Baseman/Shortstops (236-240) - 3,999 of each. Though not confirmed by the manufacturer, reports from dealers indicate that on average each 24-pack box of Focus contained three Prospect cards. An additional ten cards (241-250) featuring a selection of top prosects was distributed in late December, 2001 within Fleer Platinum RC packs. Each of these cards is serial numbered to 999 copies.

COMP.SET w/o SP's (200) 10.00 25.00
COMMON CARD (1-200) .10 .30
COMMON (201-240) 2.00 5.00
COMMON (241-250) 4.00 10.00
1 Derek Jeter .75 2.00
2 Manny Ramirez .20 .50
3 Ken Griffey Jr. .50 1.25
4 Ken Caminiti .10 .30
5 Joe Randa .10 .30
6 Jason Kendall .10 .30
7 Ron Coomer .10 .30
8 Rondell White .10 .30
9 Tino Martinez .20 .50
10 Nomar Garciaparra .50 1.25
11 Tony Batista .10 .30
12 Todd Stottlemyre .10 .30
13 Ryan Klesko .10 .30
14 Darin Erstad .10 .30
15 Todd Walker .10 .30
16 Al Leiter .10 .30
17 Carl Everett .10 .30
18 Bobby Abreu .10 .30
19 Raul Mondesi .10 .30
20 Vladimir Guerrero .30 .75
21 Mike Bordick .10 .30
22 Aaron Sele .10 .30
23 Ray Lankford .10 .30
24 Roger Clemens .60 1.50
25 Kevin Young .10 .30
26 Brad Radke .10 .30
27 Todd Hundley .10 .30
28 Ellis Burks .10 .30
29 Lee Stevens .10 .30
30 Eric Karros .10 .30
31 Darren Dreifort .10 .30
32 Ivan Rodriguez .20 .50
33 Pedro Martinez .20 .50
34 Travis Fryman .10 .30
35 Garret Anderson .10 .30
36 Rafael Palmeiro .20 .50
37 Jason Giambi .10 .30
38 Jeromy Burnitz .10 .30
39 Robin Ventura .10 .30
40 Derek Bell .10 .30
41 Carlos Guillen .10 .30
42 Albert Belle .10 .30
43 Henry Rodriguez .10 .30
44 Brian Jordan .10 .30
45 Mike Sweeney .10 .30
46 Ruben Rivera .10 .30
47 Greg Maddux .50 1.25
48 Corey Koskie .10 .30
49 Sandy Alomar Jr. .10 .30
50 Mike Mussina .20 .50
51 Tom Glavine .20 .50
52 Aaron Boone .10 .30
53 Frank Thomas .30 .75
54 Kenny Lofton .10 .30
55 Danny Graves .10 .30
56 Jose Valentin .10 .30
57 Travis Lee .10 .30
58 Jim Edmonds .10 .30
59 Jim Thome .20 .50
60 Steve Finley .10 .30
61 Shawn Green .10 .30
62 Lance Berkman .10 .30
63 Mark Quinn .10 .30
64 Randy Johnson .30 .75
65 Dmitri Young .10 .30
66 Andy Pettitte .20 .50
67 Paul O'Neill .20 .50
68 Gil Heredia .10 .30
69 Russell Branyan .10 .30
70 Alex Rodriguez .50 1.25
71 Geoff Jenkins .10 .30
72 Eric Chavez .10 .30
73 Cal Ripken 1.00 2.50
74 Mark Kotsay .10 .30
75 Jeff D'Amico .10 .30
76 Tony Womack .10 .30
77 Eric Milton .10 .30
78 Joe Girardi .10 .30
79 Peter Bergeron .10 .30
80 Miguel Tejada .10 .30
81 Luis Gonzalez .10 .30
82 Doug Glanville .10 .30
83 Gerald Williams .10 .30
84 Troy O'Leary .10 .30
85 Brian Giles .10 .30
86 Miguel Cairo .10 .30
87 Magglio Ordonez .10 .30
88 Rick Helling .10 .30
89 Bruce Chen .10 .30
90 Jason Varitek .30 .75
91 Mike Lieberthal .10 .30
92 Shawn Estes .10 .30
93 Rick Ankiel .10 .30
94 Tim Salmon .20 .50
95 Jacque Jones .10 .30
96 Johnny Damon .20 .50
97 Larry Walker .10 .30
98 Ruben Mateo .10 .30
99 Brad Fullmer .10 .30
100 Edgardo Alfonzo .10 .30
101 Mark Mulder .10 .30
102 Tony Gwynn .40 1.00
103 Mike Cameron .10 .30
104 Richie Sexson .10 .30
105 Barry Larkin .20 .50
106 Mike Piazza .50 1.25
107 Eric Young .10 .30
108 Edgar Renteria .10 .30
109 Todd Zeile .10 .30
110 Luis Castillo .10 .30
111 Sammy Sosa .30 .75
112 David Justice .10 .30
113 Delino DeShields .10 .30
114 Mariano Rivera .30 .75
115 Edgar Martinez .20 .50
116 Ray Durham .10 .30
117 Brady Anderson .10 .30
118 Eric Owens .10 .30
119 Alex Gonzalez .10 .30
120 Jay Buhner .10 .30
121 Greg Vaughn .10 .30
122 Mike Lowell .10 .30
123 Marquis Grissom .10 .30
124 Matt Williams .10 .30
125 Dean Palmer .10 .30
126 Troy Glaus .10 .30
127 Bret Boone .10 .30
128 David Ortiz .30 .75
129 Glenallen Hill .10 .30
130 Chipper Jones .30 .75
131 Tony Clark .10 .30
132 Terrence Long .10 .30
133 Chuck Finley .10 .30
134 Jeff Bagwell .20 .50
135 J.T. Snow .10 .30
136 Andruw Jones .20 .50
137 Carlos Delgado .10 .30
138 Mo Vaughn .10 .30
139 Derrek Lee .20 .50
140 Bobby Estalella .10 .30
141 Kerry Wood .10 .30
142 Jose Vidro .10 .30
143 Ben Grieve .10 .30
144 Barry Bonds .75 2.00
145 Javy Lopez .10 .30
146 Adam Kennedy .10 .30
147 Jeff Cirillo .10 .30
148 Cliff Floyd .10 .30
149 Carl Pavano .10 .30
150 Bobby Higginson .10 .30
151 Kevin Brown .10 .30

152 Fernando Tatis .10 .30
153 Matt Lawton .10 .30
154 Damion Easley .10 .30
155 Curt Schilling .10 .30
156 Mark McGwire .75 2.00
157 Mark Grace .20 .50
158 Adrian Beltre .10 .30
159 Jorge Posada .20 .50
160 Richard Hidalgo .10 .30
161 Vinny Castilla .10 .30
162 Bernie Williams .20 .50
163 John Olerud .10 .30
164 Todd Helton .20 .50
165 Craig Biggio .20 .50
166 David Wells .10 .30
167 Phil Nevin .10 .30
168 Andres Galarraga .10 .30
169 Moises Alou .10 .30
170 Denny Neagle .10 .30
171 Jeffrey Hammonds .10 .30
172 Sean Casey .10 .30
173 Gary Sheffield .10 .30
174 Carlos Lee .10 .30
175 Juan Encarnacion .10 .30
176 Roberto Alomar .20 .50
177 Kenny Rogers .10 .30
178 Charles Johnson .10 .30
179 Shannon Stewart .10 .30
180 B.J. Surhoff .10 .30
181 Paul Konerko .10 .30
182 Jermaine Dye .10 .30
183 Scott Rolen .20 .50
184 Fred McGriff .20 .50
185 Juan Gonzalez .10 .30
186 Carlos Beltran .10 .30
187 Jay Payton .10 .30
188 Chad Hermansen .10 .30
189 Pat Burrell .10 .30
190 Omar Vizquel .20 .50
191 Trot Nixon .10 .30
192 Mike Hampton .10 .30
193 Kris Benson .10 .30
194 Gabe Kapler .10 .30
195 Rickey Henderson .30 .75
196 J.D. Drew .10 .30
197 Pokey Reese .10 .30
198 Jeff Kent .10 .30
199 Jose Cruz Jr. .10 .30
200 Preston Wilson .10 .30
201 Eric Munson/2499 2.00 5.00
202 Alex Cabrera/2499 2.00 5.00
203 Nate Rolison/2499 2.00 5.00
204 Julio Zuleta/2499 2.00 5.00
205 Chris Richard/2499 2.00 5.00
206 Dernell Stenson/2499 2.00 5.00
207 Aaron McNeal/2499 2.00 5.00
208 Aubrey Huff/2999 2.00 5.00
209 Mike Lamb/2999 2.00 5.00
210 Xavier Nady/2999 2.00 5.00
211 Joe Crede/2999 3.00 8.00
212 Ben Petrick/3499 2.00 5.00
213 M.Burkhart/1999 2.00 5.00
214 Jason Tyner/1999 2.00 5.00
215 Juan Pierre/1999 2.00 5.00
216 Adam Dunn/1999 3.00 8.00
217 Adam Piatt/1999 2.00 5.00
218 Eric Byrnes/1999 2.00 5.00
219 Corey Patterson/1999 2.00 5.00
220 Kenny Kelly/1999 2.00 5.00
221 Tike Redman/1999 2.00 5.00
222 Luis Matos/1999 2.00 5.00
223 Timo Perez/1999 2.00 5.00
224 Vernon Wells/1999 2.00 5.00
225 Barry Zito/4999 3.00 8.00
226 Adam Bernero/4999 2.00 5.00
227 Kazuhiro Sasaki/4999 2.00 5.00
228 O.Mairena/4999 2.00 5.00
229 Mark Buehrle/4999 3.00 8.00
230 Ryan Dempster/4999 2.00 5.00
231 Tim Hudson/4999 2.00 5.00
232 Scott Downs/4999 2.00 5.00
233 A.J. Burnett/4999 2.00 5.00
234 Adam Eaton/4999 2.00 5.00
235 P.Crawford/4999 2.00 5.00
236 Jace Brewer/3999 2.00 5.00
237 Jose Ortiz/3999 2.00 5.00
238 Rafael Furcal/3999 2.00 5.00
239 Julio Lugo/3999 2.00 5.00
240 T. De la Rosa/3999 2.00 5.00
241 T. Shinjo/999 RC 4.00 10.00
242 W. Betemit/999 RC 4.00 10.00
243 J. Owens/999 RC 4.00 10.00
244 Drew Henson/999 RC 3.00 8.00
245 Albert Pujols/999 RC 60.00 120.00
246 Travis Hafner/999 RC 6.00 15.00
247 Ichiro Suzuki/999 RC 30.00 60.00
248 E. Guzman/999 RC 4.00 10.00
249 Matt White/999 RC 4.00 10.00
250 Junior Spivey/999 RC 4.00 10.00

2001 Fleer Focus Green

Randomly inserted into packs, this 240-card set is a complete parallel of the 2001 Fleer Focus base set. Each card is individually serial numbered to either the player's batting average or ERA. Please note that these cards were produced with green foil lettering on the card fronts, and are serial numbered on the back of each card.

*1-200 PRINT RUN b/wn 401-600: 3X TO 8X
*1-200 PRINT RUN b/wn 250-400: 4X TO 10X
*1-200 PRINT RUN b/wn 201-250: 5X TO 12X
*1-200 PRINT RUN b/wn 151-200: 6X TO 15X

2001 Fleer Focus Bat Company

Randomly inserted into packs at one in 24, this 10-card insert features players that crank out hits on a consistent basis. Card backs carry a "BC" prefix.

COMPLETE SET (10) 40.00 80.00

*VIP: 3X TO 6X BASIC BAT CO.
VIP PRINT RUN 50 SERIAL #'d SETS
BC1 Barry Bonds 5.00 12.00
BC2 Mark McGwire 5.00 12.00
BC3 Sammy Sosa 2.00 5.00
BC4 Ken Griffey Jr. 3.00 8.00
BC5 Mike Piazza 3.00 8.00
BC6 Derek Jeter 5.00 12.00
BC7 Gary Sheffield 1.50 4.00
BC8 Frank Thomas 2.00 5.00
BC9 Chipper Jones 2.00 5.00
BC10 Alex Rodriguez 3.00 8.00

2001 Fleer Focus Big Innings

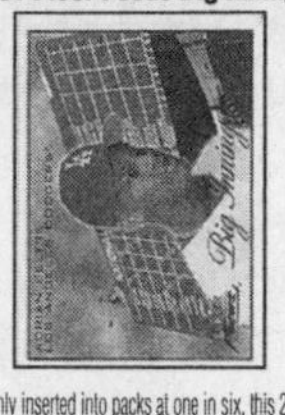

Randomly inserted into packs at one in six, this 25-card insert features players that are at the beginning of their promising careers. Card backs carry a "BI" prefix.

COMPLETE SET (25) 20.00 40.00
*VIP: 6X TO 12X BASIC BIG.INN.
VIP PRINT RUN 50 SERIAL #'d SETS
BI1 Rick Ankiel .60 1.50
BI2 Andruw Jones .60 1.50
BI3 Brian Giles .60 1.50
BI4 Derek Jeter 2.50 6.00
BI5 Rafael Furcal .60 1.50
BI6 Richie Sexson .60 1.50
BI7 Jay Payton .60 1.50
BI8 Carlos Delgado .60 1.50
BI9 Jermaine Dye .60 1.50
BI10 Darin Erstad .60 1.50
BI11 Pat Burrell .60 1.50
BI12 Richard Hidalgo .60 1.50
BI13 Adrian Beltre .60 1.50
BI14 Todd Helton .60 1.50
BI15 Vladimir Guerrero 1.00 2.50
BI16 Nomar Garciaparra 1.50 4.00
BI17 Gabe Kapler .60 1.50
BI18 Carlos Lee .60 1.50
BI19 J.D. Drew .60 1.50
BI20 Troy Glaus .60 1.50
BI21 Scott Rolen .60 1.50
BI22 Alex Rodriguez 1.50 4.00
BI23 Magglio Ordonez .60 1.50
BI24 Miguel Tejada .60 1.50
BI25 Ruben Mateo .60 1.50

2001 Fleer Focus Diamond Vision

Randomly inserted into packs at one in 12, this 15-card insert features players that keep the ballparks packed on a nightly basis. Card backs carry a "DV" prefix.

COMPLETE SET (15) 30.00 60.00
*VIP: 6X TO 12X BASIC DIAM.VIS.
VIP PRINT RUN 50 SERIAL #'d SETS
DV1 Derek Jeter 2.50 6.00
DV2 Nomar Garciaparra 1.50 4.00
DV3 Cal Ripken 3.00 8.00
DV4 Jeff Bagwell .75 2.00
DV5 Mark McGwire 2.50 6.00
DV6 Ken Griffey Jr. 1.50 4.00
DV7 Pedro Martinez .75 2.00
DV8 Carlos Delgado .75 2.00
DV9 Chipper Jones 1.00 2.50
DV10 Barry Bonds 2.50 6.00
DV11 Mike Piazza 1.50 4.00
DV12 Sammy Sosa 1.00 2.50
DV13 Alex Rodriguez 1.50 4.00
DV14 Frank Thomas 1.00 2.50
DV15 Randy Johnson 1.00 2.50

2001 Fleer Focus ROY Collection

Randomly inserted into packs at one in 24, this 25-card insert features players that have won the Rookie of the Year award. Card backs carry a "ROY" prefix. Please note that card number ROY23 (originally intended for 1981 Rookie of the Year Fernando Valenzuela) was switched at the last minute to 1998 Rookie of the Year Kerry Wood.

COMPLETE SET (25) 125.00 200.00
ROY1 Luis Aparicio 1.50 4.00
ROY2 Johnny Bench 3.00 8.00
ROY3 Joe Black 1.50 4.00
ROY4 Rod Carew 2.00 5.00
ROY5 Orlando Cepeda 1.50 4.00
ROY6 Carlton Fisk 2.00 5.00
ROY7 Ben Grieve 1.50 4.00
ROY8 Frank Howard 1.50 4.00
ROY9 Derek Jeter 6.00 15.00
ROY10 Fred Lynn 1.50 4.00
ROY11 Willie Mays 6.00 15.00
ROY12 Willie McCovey 1.50 4.00
ROY13 Mark McGwire 6.00 15.00
ROY14 Raul Mondesi 1.50 4.00
ROY15 Thurman Munson 3.00 8.00
ROY16 Eddie Murray 3.00 8.00
ROY17 Mike Piazza 4.00 10.00
ROY18 Cal Ripken 8.00 20.00
ROY19 Frank Robinson 2.00 5.00
ROY20 Jackie Robinson 3.00 8.00
ROY21 Scott Rolen 2.00 5.00
ROY22 Tom Seaver 2.00 5.00
ROY23 Kerry Wood 1.50 4.00
ROY24 David Justice 1.50 4.00
ROY25 Billy Williams 1.50 4.00

2001 Fleer Focus ROY Collection Memorabilia

Randomly inserted into packs at one in 288, this 21-card insert is a partial parallel of the ROY Collection insert. This parallel features swatches of game-used memorabilia from players that have won the Rookie of the Year award. Card backs carry a "ROY" prefix. Please note that card number ROY21 (intended for 1981 Rookie of the Year Fernando Valenzuela) does not exist.

ROY1 Luis Aparicio Bat 6.00 15.00
ROY2 Johnny Bench Jsy 10.00 25.00
ROY3 Orlando Cepeda Bat 6.00 15.00
ROY4 Carlton Fisk Jsy 10.00 25.00
ROY5 Ben Grieve Jsy 6.00 15.00
ROY6 Frank Howard Bat 6.00 15.00
ROY7 Derek Jeter Jsy 20.00 50.00
ROY8 Fred Lynn Bat 6.00 15.00
ROY9 Willie Mays Jsy 40.00 80.00
ROY10 W. McCovey Bat 6.00 15.00
ROY11 Mark McGwire Ball 10.00 25.00
ROY12 Raul Mondesi Bat 6.00 15.00
ROY13 T. Munson Bat 15.00 40.00
ROY14 Eddie Murray Jsy 10.00 25.00
ROY15 Mike Piazza Base 6.00 15.00
ROY16 Cal Ripken Jsy 20.00 50.00
ROY17 F. Robinson Bat 10.00 25.00
ROY18 J. Robinson Pants 30.00 60.00
ROY19 Scott Rolen Bat 10.00 25.00
ROY20 Tom Seaver Jsy 10.00 25.00
ROY22 David Justice Jsy 6.00 15.00

2001 Fleer Focus ROY Collection Memorabilia Autograph

Randomly inserted into packs, this 17-card insert is a partial parallel of the ROY Collection insert. This parallel features a swatch of game-used memorabilia and an authentic autograph of players that have won the Rookie of the Year award. Please note that these cards are serial numbered to the year in which each player won the ROY award (i.e. 1972=72). Card backs carry a "ROYSM" prefix. Please note that the Willie Mays, Carlton Fisk and Luis Aparicio cards packed out as exchange cards with a redemption deadline of February 1st, 2002. Also, card ROYSM17 (originally intended for Fernando Valenzuela) does not exist, thus the set is complete at 17 cards despite being numbered to 18.

1 Luis Aparicio Bat/56 20.00 50.00
2 Johnny Bench Jsy/68 50.00 100.00
3 Orlando Cepeda Bat/58 20.00 50.00
4 Carlton Fisk Jsy/72 40.00 80.00
5 Ben Grieve Jsy/98 20.00 50.00
6 Frank Howard Bat/60 20.00 50.00
7 Derek Jeter Jsy/96 200.00 300.00
8 Fred Lynn Bat/75 20.00 50.00
9 Willie Mays Jsy/51 250.00 500.00
10 Willie McCovey Bat/59 40.00 80.00
11 Raul Mondesi Bat/94 20.00 50.00
12 Eddie Murray Jsy/77 50.00 100.00
13 Cal Ripken Jsy/82 150.00 250.00
14 Frank Robinson Bat/56 40.00 80.00
15 Scott Rolen Bat/97 50.00 100.00
16 Tom Seaver Jsy/67 50.00 100.00
18 David Justice Jsy/90 20.00 50.00

2002 Fleer Focus JE

This 260 card standard-size set was issued in June, 2002. The product was issued in 10 card packs which were packaged 24 packs to a box and 16 boxes to a case with an SRP of $3 per pack. Cards numbered 225 through 260 feature rookies and prospects and were issued at a stated rate of one in four hobby packs and one in eight retail packs.

COMPLETE SET (260) 50.00 100.00
COMP.SET w/o SP's (225) 10.00 25.00
COMMON CARD (1-225) .10 .30
COMMON CARD (226-260) .75 2.00
1 Mike Piazza .50 1.25
2 Jason Giambi .10 .30
3 Jim Thome .20 .50
4 John Olerud .10 .30
5 J.D. Drew .10 .30
6 Richard Hidalgo .10 .30
7 Rusty Greer .10 .30
8 Tony Batista .10 .30
9 Omar Vizquel .20 .50
10 Randy Johnson .30 .75
11 Cristian Guzman .10 .30
12 Mark Grace .20 .50
13 Jeff Cirillo .10 .30
14 Mike Cameron .10 .30
15 Jeromy Burnitz .10 .30
16 Pokey Reese .10 .30
17 Richie Sexson .10 .30
18 Joe Randa .10 .30
19 Aramis Ramirez .10 .30
20 Pedro Martinez .20 .50
21 Todd Hollandsworth .10 .30
22 Rondell White .10 .30
23 Tsuyoshi Shinjo .10 .30
24 Melvin Mora .10 .30
25 Tim Hudson .10 .30
26 Darrin Fletcher .10 .30
27 Bill Mueller .10 .30
28 Jeff Weaver .10 .30
29 Tony Clark .10 .30
30 Tom Glavine .20 .50
31 Jarrod Washburn .10 .30
32 Greg Vaughn .10 .30
33 Lee Stevens .10 .30
34 Charles Johnson .10 .30
35 Lance Berkman .10 .30
36 Bud Smith .10 .30
37 Keith Foulke .10 .30
38 Ben Davis .10 .30
39 Daryle Ward .10 .30
40 Bernie Williams .20 .50
41 Dean Palmer .10 .30
42 Mark Mulder .10 .30
43 Jason LaRue .10 .30
44 Jay Gibbons .10 .30
45 Brandon Duckworth .10 .30
46 Carlos Delgado .10 .30
47 Barry Zito .10 .30
48 Matt Morris .10 .30
49 J.T. Snow .10 .30
50 Albert Pujols .60 1.50
51 Brad Fullmer .10 .30
52 Damion Easley .10 .30
53 Pat Burrell .10 .30
54 Kevin Brown .10 .30
55 Todd Walker .10 .30
56 Rich Garces .10 .30
57 Carlos Pena .10 .30
58 Paul LoDuca .10 .30
59 Mike Lieberthal .10 .30
60 Barry Larkin .20 .50
61 Jon Lieber .10 .30
62 Jose Cruz Jr. .10 .30
63 Mo Vaughn .10 .30
64 Ivan Rodriguez .20 .50
65 Jorge Posada .20 .50
66 Magglio Ordonez .10 .30
67 Juan Encarnacion .10 .30
68 Shawn Estes .10 .30
69 Kevin Appier .10 .30
70 Jeff Bagwell .20 .50
71 Tim Wakefield .10 .30
72 Shannon Stewart .10 .30
73 Scott Rolen .20 .50
74 Bobby Higginson .10 .30
75 Jim Edmonds .10 .30
76 Adam Dunn .10 .30
77 Eric Chavez .10 .30
78 Adrian Beltre .10 .30
79 Jason Varitek .30 .75
80 Barry Bonds .75 2.00
81 Edgar Renteria .10 .30
82 Raul Mondesi .10 .30
83 Eric Karros .10 .30
84 Ken Griffey Jr. .50 1.25
85 Jermaine Dye .10 .30
86 Carlos Beltran .10 .30
87 Mark Quinn .10 .30
88 Terrence Long .10 .30
89 Shawn Green .10 .30
90 Nomar Garciaparra .50 1.25
91 Sean Casey .10 .30
92 Homer Bush .10 .30
93 Bob Abreu .10 .30
94 Jamey Wright .10 .30
95 Tony Womack .10 .30
96 Larry Walker .10 .30
97 Doug Mientkiewicz .10 .30
98 Jimmy Rollins .10 .30
99 Brady Anderson .10 .30
100 Derek Jeter .75 2.00
101 Kevin Young .10 .30
102 Juan Pierre .10 .30
103 Edgar Martinez .20 .50
104 Corey Koskie .10 .30
105 Jeffrey Hammonds .10 .30
106 Luis Gonzalez .10 .30
107 Travis Fryman .10 .30
108 Kerry Wood .10 .30
109 Rafael Palmeiro .20 .50
110 Ichiro Suzuki .60 1.50
111 Russ Ortiz .10 .30
112 Jeff Kent .10 .30
113 Scott Erickson .10 .30
114 Bruce Chen .10 .30
115 Craig Biggio .20 .50
116 Robin Ventura .10 .30
117 Alex Rodriguez .50 1.25
118 Roy Oswalt .10 .30
119 Fred McGriff .20 .50
120 Juan Gonzalez .10 .30
121 David Justice .10 .30
122 Pat Hentgen .10 .30
123 Hideo Nomo .30 .75
124 Ramon Ortiz .10 .30
125 David Ortiz .30 .75
126 Phil Nevin .10 .30
127 Ryan Dempster .10 .30
128 Toby Hall .10 .30
129 Vladimir Guerrero .30 .75
130 Chipper Jones .30 .75
131 Russell Branyan .10 .30
132 Jose Vidro .10 .30
133 Bubba Trammell .10 .30
134 Tino Martinez .20 .50
135 Greg Maddux .50 1.25
136 Derrek Lee .20 .50
137 Troy Glaus .10 .30
138 Joe Crede .10 .30
139 Steve Cox .10 .30
140 Sammy Sosa .30 .75
141 Corey Patterson .10 .30
142 Vernon Wells .10 .30
143 Matt Lawton .10 .30
144 Gabe Kapler .10 .30
145 Johnny Damon Sox .20 .50
146 Marty Cordova .10 .30
147 Moises Alou .10 .30
148 Fernando Tatis .10 .30
149 Tanyon Sturtze .10 .30
150 Roger Clemens .60 1.50
151 Paul Konerko .10 .30
152 Chan Ho Park .10 .30
153 Marcus Giles .10 .30
154 David Eckstein .10 .30
155 Mike Lowell .10 .30
156 Preston Wilson .10 .30
157 John Vander Wal .10 .30
158 Tim Salmon .20 .50
159 Andy Pettitte .20 .50
160 Mike Mussina .20 .50
161 Doug Davis .10 .30
162 Peter Bergeron .10 .30
163 Rich Aurilia .10 .30
164 Eric Milton .10 .30
165 Geoff Jenkins .10 .30
166 Todd Helton .20 .50
167 Bret Boone .10 .30
168 Kris Benson .10 .30
169 Brian Anderson .10 .30
170 Roberto Alomar .20 .50
171 Javier Vazquez .10 .30
172 Scott Schoeneweis .10 .30
173 Ryan Klesko .10 .30
174 Jacque Jones .10 .30
175 Andruw Jones .20 .50
176 Aubrey Huff .10 .30
177 Mark Buehrle .10 .30
178 Josh Beckett .10 .30
179 Ben Sheets .10 .30
180 Curt Schilling .10 .30
181 C.C. Sabathia .10 .30
182 Denny Neagle .10 .30
183 Jamie Moyer .10 .30
184 Jason Kendall .10 .30
185 Dee Brown .10 .30
186 Frank Thomas .30 .75
187 Damian Rolls .10 .30
188 Carlos Lee .10 .30
189 Kevin Jarvis .10 .30
190 Manny Ramirez .20 .50
191 Cliff Floyd .10 .30
192 Freddy Garcia .10 .30
193 Orlando Cabrera .10 .30
194 Mike Sweeney .10 .30
195 Gary Sheffield .10 .30
196 Rafael Furcal .10 .30
197 Esteban Loaiza .10 .30
198 Mike Hampton .10 .30
199 Brian Giles .10 .30
200 Darin Erstad .10 .30
201 David Wells .10 .30
202 Kenny Lofton .10 .30
203 Aaron Sele .10 .30
204 Jason Schmidt .10 .30
205 Javy Lopez .10 .30
206 Dmitri Young .10 .30
207 Darryl Kile .10 .30
208 Matt Williams .10 .30
209 Joe Kennedy .10 .30
210 Chuck Knoblauch .10 .30
211 Brian Jordan .10 .30
212 Robert Person .10 .30
213 Alex Ochoa .10 .30
214 Steve Finley .10 .30
215 Ben Petrick .10 .30
216 Al Leiter .10 .30
217 Mark Kotsay .10 .30
218 Miguel Tejada .10 .30
219 David Segui .10 .30
220 A.J. Burnett .10 .30
221 Marlon Anderson .10 .30
222 Wiki Gonzalez .10 .30
223 Jeff Suppan .10 .30
224 Dave Roberts .10 .30
225 Jose Hernandez .10 .30
226 Angel Berroa ROO .75 2.00
227 Sean Burroughs ROO .75 2.00
228 Luis Martinez ROO RC .75 2.00
229 Adrian Burnside ROO RC .75 2.00
230 John Ennis ROO RC .75 2.00
231 An. Martinez ROO RC .75 2.00
232 Hank Blalock ROO 1.25 3.00
233 Eric Hinske ROO .75 2.00
234 Chris Booker ROO RC .75 2.00
235 Colin Young ROO RC .75 2.00
236 Mark Corey ROO RC .75 2.00
237 Satoru Komiyama ROO RC .75 2.00
238 So Taguchi ROO RC 1.25 3.00
239 Elio Serrano ROO RC .75 2.00
240 Reed Johnson ROO RC 1.25 3.00
241 Jeremy Lambert ROO RC .75 2.00
242 Chris Baker ROO RC .75 2.00
243 Orlando Hudson ROO .75 2.00
244 Travis Hughes ROO RC .75 2.00
245 Kevin Frederick ROO RC .75 2.00
246 Rodrigo Rosario ROO RC .75 2.00
247 Jeremy Ward ROO RC .75 2.00
248 Kazuhisa Ishii ROO RC 1.25 3.00
249 Austin Kearns ROO .75 2.00
250 Kyle Kane ROO RC .75 2.00
251 Cam Esslinger ROO RC .75 2.00
252 Jeff Austin ROO RC .75 2.00
253 Brian Mallette ROO RC .75 2.00
254 Mark Prior ROO 1.25 3.00
255 Mark Teixeira ROO 1.25 3.00
256 Carlos Valderrama ROO .75 2.00
257 Jason Hart ROO .75 2.00
258 Takahito Nomura ROO RC .75 2.00
259 Matt Thornton ROO RC .75 2.00
260 Marlon Byrd ROO .75 2.00

2002 Fleer Focus JE Century Parallel

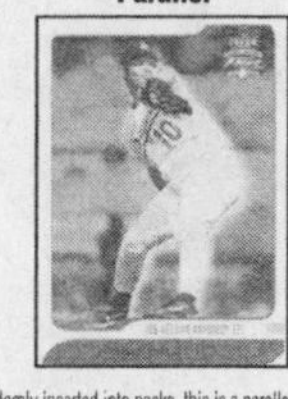

Randomly inserted into packs, this is a parallel to the basic set. Each card is serial numbered to the player's uniform number plus 100. Since each player has a different amount of cards printed we have put that information next to the player's name.

*CENTURY 1-225: 6X TO 15X BASIC
*CENTURY 226-260: 1X TO 2.5X BASIC
PRINT RUNS RANGE FROM 101-199 OF EACH
SEE BECKETT.COM FOR ALL PRINT RUNS

2002 Fleer Focus JE Jersey Parallel

Randomly inserted into packs, this is a parallel to the basic set. Each card is serial numbered to the player's uniform number. Since each player has a different amount of cards printed we have put that information next to the player's name. Players with a print run of 25 or less are not priced due to market scarcity.

*1-225 PRINT RUN b/wn 26-35 20X TO 50X
*1-225 PRINT RUN b/wn 36-50 15X TO 40X
*1-225 PRINT RUN b/wn 51-65 12.5X TO 30X
*1-225 PRINT RUN b/wn 66-80 10X TO 25X
COMMON (226-260) p/r 81-99 2.50 6.00
UNLISTED 226-260 p/r 81-99 6.00 15.00
COMMON (226-260) p/r 66-80 3.00 8.00
UNLISTED 226-260 p/r 66-80 8.00 20.00
COMMON (226-260) p/r 51-65 4.00 10.00
SEMIS 226-260 p/r 51-65 6.00 15.00
COMMON (226-260) p/r 36-50 5.00 12.00
UNLISTED 226-260 p/r 26-35 15.00 40.00
PRINT RUNS BASED ON UNIFORM NUMBER
SEE BECKETT.COM FOR PRINT RUNS
NO PRICING ON QUANTITIES OF 25 OR LESS

2002 Fleer Focus JE Blue Chips

Inserted at stated odds of one in six hobby and one in 12 retail, this 15 card set honors some of the best young talent in baseball.

COMPLETE SET (15) 6.00 15.00
1 Albert Pujols 2.00 5.00
2 Sean Burroughs .40 1.00
3 Vernon Wells .40 1.00
4 Adam Dunn .40 1.00
5 Pat Burrell .40 1.00
6 Juan Pierre .40 1.00
7 Russell Branyan .40 1.00
8 Carlos Pena .40 1.00
9 Toby Hall .40 1.00
10 Hank Blalock .60 1.50
11 Alfonso Soriano .40 1.00
12 Jimmy Rollins .40 1.00
13 Jose Ortiz .40 1.00
14 Eric Hinske .40 1.00
15 Nick Johnson .40 1.00

2002 Fleer Focus JE Blue Chips Game Used

Inserted at stated odds of one in 96 hobby and one in 180 retail, these two cards feature game-used memorabilia of two of the young stars in the Blue Chips insert set.

1 Russell Branyan Pants 4.00 10.00
2 Nick Johnson Jsy 4.00 10.00

2002 Fleer Focus JE Blue Chips Game Used Patch

Randomly inserted into packs, this card featured a game-used patch of the featured player from the Blue Chips set. This card has a stated print run of 100 serial numbered sets.

1 Nick Johnson 10.00 25.00

2002 Fleer Focus JE Intl Diamond Co.

Inserted into packs at a stated rate of one in eight hobby and one in 12 retail, this 25 card set features 25

players born outside the continental United States.

COMPLETE SET (25) 15.00 40.00
1 Bobby Abreu .75 2.00
2 Adrian Beltre .75 2.00
3 Jorge Posada .75 2.00
4 Vladimir Guerrero 1.25 3.00
5 Rafael Palmeiro .75 2.00
6 Sammy Sosa 1.25 3.00
7 Larry Walker .75 2.00
8 Manny Ramirez .75 2.00
9 Ichiro Suzuki 2.50 6.00
10 Jose Cruz Jr. .75 2.00
11 Juan Gonzalez .75 2.00
12 Bernie Williams .75 2.00
13 Ivan Rodriguez .75 2.00
14 Moises Alou .75 2.00
15 Cristian Guzman .75 2.00
16 Andruw Jones .75 2.00
17 Aramis Ramirez .75 2.00
18 Raul Mondesi .75 2.00
19 Edgar Martinez .75 2.00
20 Magglio Ordonez .75 2.00
21 Roberto Alomar .75 2.00
22 Chan Ho Park .75 2.00
23 Kazuhiro Sasaki .75 2.00
24 Tsuyoshi Shinjo .75 2.00
25 Hideo Nomo 1.25 3.00

2002 Fleer Focus JE Intl Diamond Co. Game Used

Inserted at stated odds of one in 144 hobby and one in 180 retail, these ten cards feature game-used memorabilia of ten of the players featured in in the International Diamond Company insert set.

1 Andruw Jones Jsy 6.00 15.00
2 Edgar Martinez Jsy 6.00 15.00
3 Raul Mondesi Jsy 4.00 10.00
4 Hideo Nomo Jsy 15.00 40.00
5 Rafael Palmeiro Jsy 6.00 15.00
6 Chan Ho Park Jsy 4.00 10.00
7 Aramis Ramirez Pants 4.00 10.00
8 Manny Ramirez Jsy 6.00 15.00
9 Ivan Rodriguez Jsy 6.00 15.00
10 Kazuhiro Sasaki Jsy SP/307 4.00 10.00

2002 Fleer Focus JE Intl Diamond Co. Game Used Patch

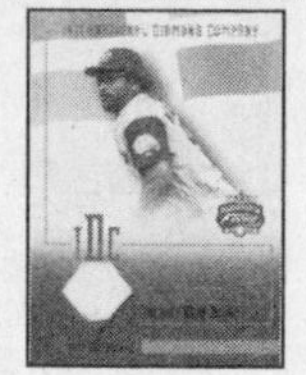

Randomly inserted into packs, these six cards feature game-used patches of the featured player from the International Diamond Company insert set. These cards have a stated print run of 100 serial numbered sets.

1 Edgar Martinez 12.50 30.00
2 Raul Mondesi 10.00 25.00
3 Hideo Nomo 75.00 150.00
4 Chan Ho Park 10.00 25.00
5 Manny Ramirez 12.50 30.00
6 Ivan Rodriguez 12.50 30.00

2002 Fleer Focus JE K Corps

Inserted in packs at a stated rate of one in 12, these 15 cards feature some of the top pitchers in baseball.

COMPLETE SET (15) 10.00 25.00
1 Roger Clemens 2.00 5.00
2 Randy Johnson 1.00 2.50
3 Tom Glavine .60 1.50
4 Josh Beckett .60 1.50
5 Matt Morris .60 1.50
6 Curt Schilling .60 1.50
7 Greg Maddux 1.50 4.00
8 Tim Hudson .60 1.50
9 Roy Oswalt .60 1.50
10 Kerry Wood .60 1.50
11 Barry Zito .60 1.50
12 Kevin Brown .60 1.50
13 Ryan Dempster .60 1.50
14 Ben Sheets .60 1.50
15 Pedro Martinez .60 1.50

2002 Fleer Focus JE K Corps Game Used

Inserted at stated odds of one in 96 hobby and one in 180 retail, these six cards feature game-used memorabilia of ten of the players featured in the K Corps insert set. A couple of the player were printed in shorter supply and we have printed the stated print run next to the player's name in our checklist.

1 Kevin Brown Jsy 4.00 10.00
2 Randy Johnson Jsy SP/316 6.00 15.00
3 Greg Maddux Jsy 6.00 15.00
4 Pedro Martinez Jsy 6.00 15.00
5 Curt Schilling Jsy 4.00 10.00
6 Barry Zito Jsy SP/220 4.00 10.00

2002 Fleer Focus JE K Corps Game Used Patch

Randomly inserted into packs, these three cards feature game-used patches of the featured player from the K Corps insert set. These cards have a stated print run of 100 serial numbered sets.

1 Kevin Brown 10.00 25.00
2 Pedro Martinez 12.50 30.00
3 Curt Schilling 10.00 25.00

2002 Fleer Focus JE Kings of Swing

Inserted at stated odds of one in 48, this 20 card insert set features some of baseball's heaviest hitters.

COMPLETE SET (20) 75.00 150.00
1 Barry Bonds 6.00 15.00
2 Mike Piazza 4.00 10.00
3 Albert Pujols 5.00 12.00
4 Todd Helton 2.00 5.00
5 Ken Griffey Jr. 4.00 10.00
6 Alex Rodriguez 4.00 10.00
7 Sammy Sosa 2.50 6.00
8 Troy Glaus 2.00 5.00
9 Derek Jeter 6.00 15.00
10 Ichiro Suzuki 5.00 12.00
11 Manny Ramirez 2.00 5.00
12 Roberto Alomar 2.00 5.00
13 Juan Gonzalez 2.00 5.00
14 Shawn Green 2.00 5.00
15 Vladimir Guerrero 2.50 6.00
16 Nomar Garciaparra 4.00 10.00
17 Adam Dunn 2.00 5.00
18 Jason Giambi 2.00 5.00
19 Edgar Martinez 2.00 5.00
20 Chipper Jones 2.50 6.00

2002 Fleer Focus JE Kings of Swing Game Used

Inserted at stated odds of one in 108 hobby and one in 180 retail, these six cards feature game-used memorabilia of ten of the players featured in in the Kings of Swing insert set.

1 Shawn Green Jsy 6.00 15.00
2 Todd Helton Jsy 6.00 15.00
3 Derek Jeter Jsy SP/348 15.00 40.00
4 Chipper Jones Jsy 6.00 15.00
5 Edgar Martinez Jsy 6.00 15.00
6 Mike Piazza Jsy 6.00 15.00
7 Manny Ramirez Jsy 6.00 15.00
8 Alex Rodriguez Jsy 6.00 15.00

2002 Fleer Focus JE Kings of Swing Game Used Patch

Randomly inserted into packs, these five cards feature game-used patches of the featured player from the Kings of Swing insert set. These cards have a stated print run of 100 serial numbered sets.

1 Shawn Green 12.50 30.00
2 Todd Helton 12.50 30.00
3 Edgar Martinez 12.50 30.00
4 Mike Piazza 20.00 50.00
5 Manny Ramirez 12.50 30.00

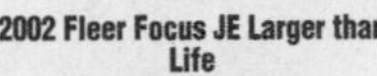

2002 Fleer Focus JE Larger than Life

Inserted in packs at a stated rate of one in 240, these 20 cards feature players who have achieved spectacular feats on the field.

1 Jason Giambi 4.00 10.00
2 Carlos Delgado 4.00 10.00
3 Alex Rodriguez 10.00 25.00
4 Preston Wilson 4.00 10.00
5 Frank Thomas 6.00 15.00
6 Nomar Garciaparra 10.00 25.00
7 Jim Edmonds 4.00 10.00
8 Jim Thome 6.00 15.00
9 Barry Bonds 15.00 40.00
10 Mo Vaughn 4.00 10.00
11 Ichiro Suzuki 12.50 30.00
12 Ivan Rodriguez 6.00 15.00
13 Gary Sheffield 4.00 10.00
14 Derek Jeter 15.00 40.00
15 Jeff Bagwell 6.00 15.00
16 Mike Piazza 10.00 25.00
17 J.D. Drew 4.00 10.00
18 Sammy Sosa 6.00 15.00
19 Albert Pujols 12.50 30.00
20 Luis Gonzalez 4.00 10.00

2002 Fleer Focus JE Larger than Life Game Used

Inserted at stated odds of one in 144 hobby and one in 180 retail, these ten cards feature game-used memorabilia of ten of the players featured in in the Larger than Life insert set. The Jeff Bagwell card was produced to a stated print run of 20 cards and therefore is not priced due to market scarcity.

1 Jeff Bagwell Jsy SP/20
2 Jim Edmonds Jsy 4.00 10.00
3 Luis Gonzalez Jsy 4.00 10.00
4 Derek Jeter Jsy 12.50 30.00
5 Mike Piazza Jsy 8.00 20.00
6 Alex Rodriguez Jsy 8.00 20.00
7 Ivan Rodriguez Jsy 6.00 15.00
8 Frank Thomas Jsy 6.00 15.00
9 Mo Vaughn Jsy 4.00 10.00
10 Preston Wilson Jsy 4.00 10.00

2002 Fleer Focus JE Larger than Life Game Used Patch

Randomly inserted into packs, these six cards feature game-used patches of the featured player from the Larger than Life insert set. These cards have a stated print run of 100 serial numbered sets.

1 Jim Edmonds 10.00 25.00
2 Luis Gonzalez 10.00 25.00
3 Mike Piazza 20.00 50.00
4 Ivan Rodriguez 12.50 30.00
5 Frank Thomas 15.00 40.00
6 Preston Wilson 10.00 25.00

2002 Fleer Focus JE Lettermen Jumbos

Randomly inserted as box toppers, these 106 cards feature one complete letter taken from a game-used jersey from a player's last name mounted to a card. Only one of each card was produced and no pricing is provided due to scarcity.

ONE CARD PER LETTER IN PLAYER'S NAME
NO PRICING DUE TO SCARCITY

2002 Fleer Focus JE Materialistic Away

Inserted in packs at a stated rate of one in 24, these 15 cards are printed on a jersey-like material and feature the game's best players on a simulation away jersey.

COMPLETE SET (15) 50.00 120.00
*HOME: 1.5X TO 4X BASIC
HOME PRINT RUN 50 SERIAL #'d SETS
*JUMBO AWAY: .5X TO 1.2X BASIC
JUMBO AWAY ONE PER HOBBY BOX

*JUMBO HOME: 1.5X TO 4X BASIC
JUMBO HOME PRINT RUN 50 #'d SETS
1 Derek Jeter 6.00 15.00
2 Alex Rodriguez 4.00 10.00
3 Mike Piazza 4.00 10.00
4 Ivan Rodriguez 1.50 4.00
5 Chipper Jones 2.50 6.00
6 Todd Helton 1.50 4.00
7 Nomar Garciaparra 4.00 10.00
8 Barry Bonds 6.00 15.00
9 Ichiro Suzuki 5.00 12.00
10 Ken Griffey Jr. 4.00 10.00
11 Jason Giambi 1.50 4.00
12 Sammy Sosa 2.50 6.00
13 Albert Pujols 5.00 12.00
14 Pedro Martinez 1.50 4.00
15 Vladimir Guerrero 2.50 6.00

2003 Fleer Focus JE

This 180 card set was released in May, 2003. The set was issued in seven card packs with an SRP of $3 which were issued 24 packs to a box and 16 boxes to a case. Cards number 161 through 180, which were issued at a stated rate of one in four featured leading prospects.

COMPLETE SET (180) 20.00 50.00
COMP.SET w/o SP's (160) 8.00 20.00
COMMON CARD (1-160) .10 .30
COMMON CARD (161-180) .75 2.00
1 Derek Jeter .75 2.00
2 Preston Wilson .10 .30
3 Trevor Hoffman .10 .30
4 Moises Alou .10 .30
5 Roberto Alomar .20 .50
6 Tim Salmon .20 .50
7 Mike Lowell .10 .30
8 Barry Bonds .75 2.00
9 Fred McGriff .20 .50
10 Mo Vaughn .10 .30
11 Junior Spivey .10 .30
12 Roy Oswalt .10 .30
13 Ichiro Suzuki .60 1.50
14 Magglio Ordonez .10 .30
15 Adam Kennedy .10 .30
16 Randy Johnson .30 .75
17 Carlos Beltran .10 .30
18 John Olerud .10 .30
19 Joe Borchard .10 .30
20 Alfonso Soriano .10 .30
21 Curt Schilling .10 .30
22 Mike Sweeney .10 .30
23 Tino Martinez .20 .50
24 Barry Larkin .20 .50
25 Miguel Tejada .10 .30
26 Chipper Jones .30 .75
27 Kevin Brown .10 .30
28 J.D. Drew .10 .30
29 Sean Casey .10 .30
30 Bernie Williams .20 .50
31 Troy Percival .10 .30
32 Jeff Bagwell .20 .50
33 Kenny Lofton .10 .30
34 Kerry Wood .10 .30
35 Armando Benitez .10 .30
36 David Eckstein .10 .30
37 Wade Miller .10 .30
38 Edgar Martinez .20 .50
39 Mark Prior .20 .50
40 Mike Piazza .50 1.25
41 Shea Hillenbrand .10 .30
42 Bartolo Colon .10 .30
43 Darin Erstad .10 .30
44 A.J. Burnett .10 .30
45 Jeff Kent .10 .30
46 Corey Patterson .10 .30
47 Ty Wigginton .10 .30
48 Troy Glaus .10 .30
49 Josh Beckett .10 .30
50 Brian Lawrence .10 .30
51 Frank Thomas .30 .75
52 Jason Giambi .10 .30
53 Luis Gonzalez .10 .30
54 Raul Ibanez .10 .30
55 Kazuhiro Sasaki .10 .30
56 Mark Buehrle .10 .30
57 Roger Clemens .60 1.50
58 Matt Williams .10 .30
59 Joe Randa .10 .30
60 Jamie Moyer .10 .30
61 Paul Konerko .10 .30
62 Mike Mussina .20 .50
63 Javy Lopez .10 .30
64 Brian Jordan .10 .30
65 Scott Rolen .20 .50
66 Aaron Boone .10 .30
67 Eric Chavez .10 .30
68 Mark Grace .20 .50
69 Shawn Green .10 .30
70 Albert Pujols .60 1.50
71 Sammy Sosa .30 .75
72 Edgardo Alfonzo .10 .30
73 Garret Anderson .10 .30
74 Lance Berkman .10 .30
75 Bret Boone .10 .30
76 Joe Crede .10 .30
77 Al Leiter .10 .30
78 Jarrod Washburn .10 .30
79 Craig Biggio .20 .50
80 Rich Aurilia .10 .30
81 Adam Dunn .10 .30
82 Jermaine Dye .10 .30
83 Tom Glavine .20 .50
84 Eric Gagne .10 .30
85 Jared Sandberg .10 .30
86 Jim Thome .20 .50
87 Barry Zito .10 .30
88 Gary Sheffield .10 .30
89 Paul Lo Duca .10 .30
90 Matt Morris .10 .30
91 Juan Pierre .10 .30
92 Randy Wolf .10 .30
93 Jay Gibbons .10 .30
94 Brad Radke .10 .30
95 Carlos Delgado .10 .30
96 Carlos Pena .10 .30
97 Brian Giles .10 .30
98 Rodrigo Lopez .10 .30
99 Jacque Jones .10 .30
100 Juan Gonzalez .10 .30
101 Randall Simon .10 .30
102 Mike Williams .10 .30
103 Derek Lowe .10 .30
104 Brad Wilkerson .10 .30
105 Eric Hinske .10 .30
106 Luis Castillo .10 .30
107 Phil Nevin .10 .30
108 Manny Ramirez .20 .50
109 Vladimir Guerrero .30 .75
110 Roy Halladay .10 .30
111 Ellis Burks .10 .30
112 Bobby Abreu .10 .30
113 Tony Batista .10 .30
114 Richie Sexson .10 .30
115 Rafael Palmeiro .20 .50
116 Todd Helton .20 .50
117 Pat Burrell .10 .30
118 John Smoltz .20 .50
119 Ben Sheets .10 .30
120 Aubrey Huff .10 .30
121 Andruw Jones .20 .50
122 Kazuhisa Ishii .10 .30
123 Jim Edmonds .10 .30
124 Austin Kearns .10 .30
125 Mark Mulder .10 .30
126 Greg Maddux .50 1.25
127 Jose Hernandez .10 .30
128 Ben Grieve .10 .30
129 Ken Griffey Jr. .50 1.25
130 Tim Hudson .10 .30
131 Jorge Julio .10 .30
132 Torii Hunter .10 .30
133 Ivan Rodriguez .20 .50
134 Jason Jennings .10 .30
135 Jason Kendall .10 .30
136 Nomar Garciaparra .50 1.25
137 Michael Cuddyer .10 .30
138 Shannon Stewart .10 .30
139 Larry Walker .10 .30
140 Aramis Ramirez .10 .30
141 Johnny Damon .20 .50
142 Orlando Cabrera .10 .30
143 Vernon Wells .10 .30
144 Bobby Higginson .10 .30
145 Sean Burroughs .10 .30
146 Pedro Martinez .20 .50
147 Jose Vidro .10 .30
148 Orlando Hudson .10 .30
149 Robert Fick .10 .30
150 Ryan Klesko .10 .30
151 Kevin Millwood .10 .30
152 Alex Sanchez .10 .30
153 Randy Winn .10 .30
154 Omar Vizquel .20 .50
155 Mike Lieberthal .10 .30
156 Marty Cordova .10 .30
157 Cristian Guzman .10 .30
158 Alex Rodriguez .50 1.25
159 C.C. Sabathia .10 .30
160 Jimmy Rollins .10 .30
161 Josh Willingham HP RC 1.50 4.00
162 Lance Niekro HP .75 2.00
163 Nook Logan HP RC 1.25 3.00
164 Chase Utley HP 1.25 3.00
165 Pete LaForest HP RC .75 2.00
166 Victor Martinez HP 1.25 3.00
167 Adam LaRoche HP .75 2.00
168 Ian Ferguson HP RC .75 2.00
169 Mark Teixeira HP 1.25 3.00
170 Chris Waters HP RC .75 2.00
171 Hideki Matsui HP RC 2.00 5.00
172 Alejandro Machado HP RC .75 2.00
173 Francisco Rosario HP RC .75 2.00
174 Termel Sledge HP RC .75 2.00
175 Guillermo Quiroz HP RC .75 2.00
176 Lew Ford HP RC 1.25 3.00
177 Hank Blalock HP .75 2.00
178 Lyle Overbay HP .75 2.00
179 Matt Bruback HP RC .75 2.00
180 Jose Contreras HP RC 1.25 3.00

2003 Fleer Focus JE Century Parallel

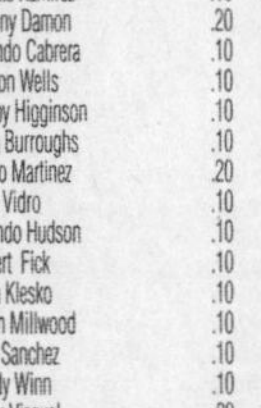

Randomly inserted into packs, this is a parallel to the basic Focus JE set. These cards were issued to a stated print run of the player's uniform number plus 100. Please note that we have put the stated print run next to the player's name in our checklist.

*CENTURY 1-160: 6X TO 15X BASIC
*CENTURY 161-180: 1X TO 2.5X BASIC
PRINT RUNS BASED ON JSY NUMBER +100

2003 Fleer Focus JE Franchise Focus

Inserted at a stated rate of one in four, this 20-card set features players who are among the keys to their franchise.

COMPLETE SET (20) 6.00 15.00
1 Troy Glaus .40 1.00
2 Randy Johnson .50 1.25
3 Chipper Jones .50 1.25
4 Nomar Garciaparra .75 2.00
5 Sammy Sosa .50 1.25
6 Ken Griffey Jr. .75 2.00
7 Jeff Bagwell .40 1.00
8 Mike Sweeney .40 1.00
9 Shawn Green .40 1.00
10 Torii Hunter .40 1.00
11 Vladimir Guerrero .50 1.25
12 Mike Piazza .75 2.00
13 Jason Giambi .40 1.00
14 Barry Zito .40 1.00
15 Pat Burrell .40 1.00
16 Barry Bonds 1.25 3.00
17 Ichiro Suzuki 1.00 2.50
18 Albert Pujols 1.00 2.50
19 Alex Rodriguez .75 2.00
20 Carlos Delgado .40 1.00

2003 Fleer Focus JE Home and Aways Game Jersey

Inserted at a stated rate of one in 288, this nine card set features a home jersey swatch on one side and a visiting jersey swatch on the other side of the card.

AR Alex Rodriguez 12.50 30.00
AS Alfonso Soriano 6.00 15.00
CJ Chipper Jones 6.00 15.00
DJ Derek Jeter 20.00 50.00
GM Greg Maddux 8.00 20.00
JD J.D. Drew 6.00 15.00
LB Lance Berkman 6.00 15.00
NG Nomar Garciaparra 12.50 30.00
RO Roy Oswalt 6.00 15.00

2003 Fleer Focus JE Materialistic Action Away

Inserted in packs at a stated rate of one in 192, this 15-card set features leading players as well as a swatch of their visiting uniform.

*HOME: .75X TO 2X BASIC AWAY
HOME PRINT RUN 50 SERIAL #'d SETS
I Ichiro Suzuki 6.00 15.00
AD Adam Dunn 4.00 10.00
AP Albert Pujols 6.00 15.00
AR Alex Rodriguez 6.00 15.00
AS Alfonso Soriano 4.00 10.00
CJ Chipper Jones 6.00 15.00
DJ Derek Jeter 10.00 25.00
GM Greg Maddux 6.00 15.00
JG Jason Giambi 4.00 10.00
KG Ken Griffey Jr. 6.00 15.00
MP Mike Piazza 6.00 15.00
NG Nomar Garciaparra 6.00 15.00
PB Pat Burrell 4.00 10.00
RC Roger Clemens 8.00 20.00
SS Sammy Sosa 6.00 15.00

2003 Fleer Focus JE Materialistic Oversized

Issued as a box topper, these "oversized" cards featured not only a larger card but also a larger jersey swatch piece. These cards were issued in special wrappers which differentiated these cards from the regular packs.

I Ichiro Suzuki 4.00 10.00
AD Adam Dunn 2.00 5.00
AP Albert Pujols 4.00 10.00
AR Alex Rodriguez 3.00 8.00
AS Alfonso Soriano 2.00 5.00
CJ Chipper Jones 2.00 5.00
DJ Derek Jeter 5.00 12.00
GM Greg Maddux 3.00 8.00
JG Jason Giambi 2.00 5.00
KG Ken Griffey Jr. 3.00 8.00
MP Mike Piazza 3.00 8.00
NG Nomar Garciaparra 3.00 8.00
PB Pat Burrell 2.00 5.00
RC Roger Clemens 4.00 10.00
RJ Reggie Jackson 2.00 5.00
SS Sammy Sosa 2.00 5.00

2003 Fleer Focus JE Materialistic Oversized Autographs

Randomly inserted in jumbo packs, these three cards feature not only the oversize cards but also authentic autographs of the featured player. The stated print runs for these players appears next to their name in our checklist.

CJ Chipper Jones/80 * 50.00 100.00
DJ Derek Jeter/360 * 75.00 150.00
RJ Reggie Jackson/360 * 30.00 60.00

2003 Fleer Focus JE Materialistic Plus Game Jersey

Randomly inserted in packs, these nine cards feature leading players along with a game-used jersey swatch of the featured player. These cards were issued to a stated print run of 250 serial numbered sets.

AD Adam Dunn 4.00 10.00
AR Alex Rodriguez 8.00 20.00
AS Alfonso Soriano 4.00 10.00
CJ Chipper Jones 6.00 15.00
DJ Derek Jeter 12.50 30.00
GM Greg Maddux 10.00 25.00
MP Mike Piazza 10.00 25.00
NG Nomar Garciaparra 10.00 25.00
RC Roger Clemens 10.00 25.00

2003 Fleer Focus JE Materialistic Portrait Away

Issued at a stated rate of one in 576, this 15 card set features portraits of leading players in their away uniforms.

HOME PRINT RUN 1 SERIAL #'d SET
NO HOME PRICING DUE TO SCARCITY
I Ichiro Suzuki 12.50 30.00
AD Adam Dunn 6.00 15.00
AP Albert Pujols 12.50 30.00
AR Alex Rodriguez 10.00 25.00
AS Alfonso Soriano 6.00 15.00
CJ Chipper Jones 8.00 20.00
DJ Derek Jeter 15.00 40.00
GM Greg Maddux 10.00 25.00
JG Jason Giambi 6.00 15.00
KG Ken Griffey Jr. 10.00 25.00
MP Mike Piazza 10.00 25.00
NG Nomar Garciaparra 10.00 25.00
PB Pat Burrell 6.00 15.00
RC Roger Clemens 12.50 30.00
SS Sammy Sosa 8.00 20.00

2003 Fleer Focus JE MLB Shirtified

Inserted at a stated rate of one in 24, this 15-card set features leading players along with various jersey designs.

1 Manny Ramirez 1.00 2.50
2 Jarrod Washburn 1.00 2.50
3 Greg Maddux 2.50 6.00
4 Austin Kearns 1.00 2.50
5 Jim Thome 1.00 2.50
6 Kazuhisa Ishii 1.00 2.50
7 Mike Piazza 2.50 6.00
8 Alfonso Soriano 1.00 2.50
9 Pat Burrell 1.00 2.50
10 Derek Jeter 4.00 10.00
11 Miguel Tejada 1.00 2.50
12 Roger Clemens 3.00 8.00
13 Alex Rodriguez 2.50 6.00
14 Roy Oswalt 1.00 2.50
15 Richie Sexson 1.00 2.50

2003 Fleer Focus JE MLB Shirtified Game Jersey

Issued at a stated rate of one in 35, this is a partial parallel to the MLB Shirtified set. These cards feature a game worn jersey swatch on them.

AR Alex Rodriguez 6.00 15.00
AS Alfonso Soriano 3.00 8.00
DJ Derek Jeter 10.00 25.00
GM Greg Maddux 4.00 10.00
MP Mike Piazza 4.00 10.00
MR Manny Ramirez 4.00 10.00
MT Miguel Tejada 3.00 8.00
RC Roger Clemens 6.00 15.00
RO Roy Oswalt 3.00 8.00
RS Richie Sexson 3.00 8.00

2003 Fleer Focus JE MLB Shirtified Patch

Randomly inserted into packs, this is a parallel to the MLB Shirtified Game Jersey set. These cards feature authentic patches and this set was issued to a stated print run of 200 serial numbered sets.

*PREMIUM LOGOS: 2X HI COLUMN
*4 OR MORE COLORS: 1.5X HI COLUMN
AR Alex Rodriguez 15.00 40.00
AS Alfonso Soriano 8.00 20.00
DJ Derek Jeter 30.00 60.00
GM Greg Maddux 15.00 40.00
MP Mike Piazza 15.00 40.00
MR Manny Ramirez 10.00 25.00
MT Miguel Tejada 8.00 20.00
RC Roger Clemens 15.00 40.00
RO Roy Oswalt 8.00 20.00
RS Richie Sexson 8.00 20.00

2003 Fleer Focus JE Team Colors

Inserted at a stated rate of one in 12, this 20 card set feature both an action and a portrait shot of the featured player.

1 Alex Rodriguez 1.50 4.00
2 Mark Prior .60 1.50
3 Derek Jeter 2.50 6.00
4 Curt Schilling .60 1.50
5 Pat Burrell .60 1.50
6 Josh Beckett .60 1.50
7 Sean Burroughs .60 1.50
8 Troy Glaus .60 1.50
9 Torii Hunter .60 1.50
10 Jeff Bagwell .60 1.50
11 Pedro Martinez .60 1.50
12 Mike Piazza 1.50 4.00
13 Lance Berkman .60 1.50
14 Nomar Garciaparra 1.50 4.00
15 Chipper Jones 1.00 2.50
16 Eric Chavez .60 1.50
17 Barry Zito .60 1.50
18 Barry Bonds 2.50 6.00
19 Adam Dunn .60 1.50
20 Randy Johnson 1.00 2.50

2003 Fleer Focus JE Team Colors Game Jersey

Inserted at a stated rate of one in 28, this is a partial parallel to the Team Colors set. These cards feature a game-used jersey swatch on them.

AD Adam Dunn 3.00 8.00
CJ Chipper Jones 4.00 10.00
CS Curt Schilling 3.00 8.00
DJ Derek Jeter 10.00 25.00
EC Eric Chavez 3.00 8.00
JBA Jeff Bagwell 4.00 10.00
JBE Josh Beckett 3.00 8.00
LB Lance Berkman 3.00 8.00
NG Nomar Garciaparra 6.00 15.00
PM Pedro Martinez 4.00 10.00

RJ Randy Johnson	4.00	10.00
TG Troy Glaus	3.00	8.00

2003 Fleer Focus JE Team Colors Game Jersey Multi Color

Randomly inserted in packs, this is a partial parallel to the Team Colors insert set. These cards feature multi-color pieces of the game-used jersery of the featured player. These cards were issued to a stated print run of 250 serial numbered sets.

*4 OR MORE COLORS: 1.5X HI COLUMN

AD Adam Dunn	8.00	20.00
AR Alex Rodriguez	15.00	40.00
CJ Chipper Jones	10.00	25.00
CS Curt Schilling	8.00	20.00
DJ Derek Jeter	20.00	50.00
EC Eric Chavez	8.00	20.00
JBA Jeff Bagwell	10.00	25.00
JBE Josh Beckett	8.00	20.00
LB Lance Berkman	8.00	20.00
MP Mike Piazza	15.00	40.00
NG Nomar Garciaparra	15.00	40.00
PM Pedro Martinez	10.00	25.00
RJ Randy Johnson	10.00	25.00
TG Troy Glaus	8.00	20.00

2001 Fleer Futures

The 2001 Fleer Futures product was released in late March, 2001 and features a 220-card base set that was broken into tiers as follows: Base Veterans (1-180), and Bright Futures Prospects (181-220). Each pack contained eight cards and carried a suggested retail price of $2.99. Please note that a three-card group of regular cards were inserted as a boxtopper on top of Futures Boxes so collectors could see what the cards looked like. An additional ten cards (221-230) featuring a selection of top prosects was distributed in late December, 2001 within Fleer Platinum RC packs. Each of these cards is serial numbered to 2499 copies.

COMPLETE SET (220)	10.00	25.00
COMMON CARD (1-220)	.10	.30
COMMON (221-230)	2.00	5.00
1 Darin Erstad	.10	.30
2 Manny Ramirez	.20	.50
3 Darryl Kile	.10	.30
4 Troy O'Leary	.10	.30
5 Mark Quinn	.10	.30
6 Brian Giles	.10	.30
7 Randy Johnson	.30	.75
8 Todd Walker	.10	.30
9 Mike Piazza	.30	.75
10 Fred McGriff	.20	.50
11 Sammy Sosa	.30	.75
12 Chan Ho Park	.10	.30
13 John Rocker	.10	.30
14 Luis Castillo	.10	.30
15 Eric Chavez	.10	.30
16 Carlos Delgado	.10	.30
17 Sean Casey	.10	.30
18 Corey Koskie	.10	.30
19 John Olerud	.10	.30
20 Nomar Garciaparra	.30	.75
21 Craig Biggio	.20	.50
22 Pat Burrell	.10	.30
23 Ben Molina	.10	.30
24 Jim Thome	.20	.50
25 Rey Ordonez	.10	.30
26 Fernando Tatis	.10	.30
27 Eric Young	.10	.30
28 Eric Karros	.10	.30
29 Adam Eaton	.10	.30
30 Brian Jordan	.10	.30
31 Jorge Posada	.20	.50
32 Gabe Kapler	.10	.30
33 Keith Foulke	.10	.30
34 Ron Coomer	.10	.30
35 Chipper Jones	.30	.75
36 Miguel Tejada	.10	.30
37 David Wells	.10	.30
38 Carlos Lee	.10	.30
39 Barry Bonds	.75	2.00
40 Derrek Lee	.20	.50
41 Tim Hudson	.10	.30
42 Billy Koch	.10	.30
43 Dmitri Young	.10	.30
44 Vladimir Guerrero	.30	.75
45 Rickey Henderson	.30	.75
46 Jeff Bagwell	.20	.50
47 Robert Person	.10	.30
48 Brady Anderson	.10	.30
49 Lance Berkman	.10	.30
50 Mike Lieberthal	.10	.30
51 Adam Kennedy	.10	.30
52 Russell Branyan	.10	.30
53 Robin Ventura	.10	.30
54 Mark McGwire	.75	2.00
55 Tony Gwynn	.40	1.00
56 Matt Williams	.10	.30
57 Jeff Cirillo	.10	.30
58 Roger Clemens	.60	1.50
59 Ivan Rodriguez	.20	.50
60 Brad Radke	.10	.30
61 Kazuhiro Sasaki	.10	.30
62 Cal Ripken	1.00	2.50
63 Ken Caminiti	.10	.30
64 Bob Abreu	.10	.30
65 Troy Glaus	.10	.30
66 Sandy Alomar Jr.	.10	.30
67 Jose Vidro	.10	.30
68 Pedro Martinez	.20	.50
69 Kevin Young	.10	.30
70 Jay Bell	.10	.30
71 Larry Walker	.10	.30
72 Derek Jeter	.75	2.00
73 Miguel Cairo	.10	.30
74 Magglio Ordonez	.10	.30
75 Jeromy Burnitz	.10	.30
76 J.T. Snow	.10	.30
77 Andres Galarraga	.10	.30
78 Ryan Dempster	.10	.30
79 Ken Griffey Jr.	.50	1.25
80 Aaron Sele	.10	.30
81 Tom Glavine	.20	.50
82 Hideo Nomo	.30	.75
83 Orlando Hernandez	.10	.30
84 Tony Batista	.10	.30
85 Aaron Boone	.10	.30
86 Jacque Jones	.10	.30
87 Delino DeShields	.10	.30
88 Garret Anderson	.10	.30
89 Fernando Seguignol	.10	.30
90 Jim Edmonds	.10	.30
91 Frank Thomas	.30	.75
92 Adrian Beltre	.10	.30
93 Ellis Burks	.10	.30
94 Andruw Jones	.20	.50
95 Tony Clark	.10	.30
96 Danny Graves	.10	.30
97 Alex Rodriguez	.50	1.25
98 Mike Mussina	.20	.50
99 Scott Elarton	.10	.30
100 Jason Giambi	.10	.30
101 Jay Payton	.10	.30
102 Gerald Williams	.10	.30
103 Kerry Wood	.10	.30
104 Shawn Green	.10	.30
105 Greg Maddux	.50	1.25
106 Juan Encarnacion	.10	.30
107 Bernie Williams	.20	.50
108 Mike Lamb	.10	.30
109 Charles Johnson	.10	.30
110 Richie Sexson	.10	.30
111 Jeff Kent	.10	.30
112 Albert Belle	.10	.30
113 Cliff Floyd	.10	.30
114 Ben Grieve	.10	.30
115 Tim Salmon	.20	.50
116 Carl Pavano	.10	.30
117 Rick Ankiel	.10	.30
118 Dante Bichette	.10	.30
119 Johnny Damon	.20	.50
120 Brian Anderson	.10	.30
121 Roberto Alomar	.20	.50
122 Mike Hampton	.10	.30
123 Greg Vaughn	.10	.30
124 Carl Everett	.10	.30
125 Moises Alou	.10	.30
126 Jason Kendall	.10	.30
127 Omar Vizquel	.20	.50
128 Mark Grace	.20	.50
129 Kevin Brown	.10	.30
130 Phil Nevin	.10	.30
131 Kevin Millwood	.10	.30
132 Bobby Higginson	.10	.30
133 Ruben Mateo	.10	.30
134 Luis Gonzalez	.10	.30
135 Dean Palmer	.10	.30
136 Mariano Rivera	.30	.75
137 Rick Helling	.10	.30
138 Paul Konerko	.10	.30
139 Marquis Grissom	.10	.30
140 Robb Nen	.10	.30
141 Javy Lopez	.10	.30
142 Preston Wilson	.10	.30
143 Terrence Long	.10	.30
144 Shannon Stewart	.10	.30
145 Barry Larkin	.20	.50
146 Cristian Guzman	.10	.30
147 Jay Buhner	.10	.30
148 Jermaine Dye	.10	.30
149 Kris Benson	.10	.30
150 Curt Schilling	.10	.30
151 Todd Helton	.20	.50
152 Paul O'Neill	.20	.50
153 Rafael Palmeiro	.20	.50
154 Ray Durham	.10	.30
155 Geoff Jenkins	.10	.30
156 Livan Hernandez	.10	.30
157 Rafael Furcal	.10	.30
158 Juan Gonzalez	.10	.30
159 Tino Martinez	.20	.50
160 Raul Mondesi	.10	.30
161 Matt Lawton	.10	.30
162 Edgar Martinez	.20	.50
163 Richard Hidalgo	.10	.30
164 Scott Rolen	.20	.50
165 Chuck Finley	.10	.30
166 Edgardo Alfonzo	.10	.30
167 J.D. Drew	.10	.30
168 Trot Nixon	.10	.30
169 Carlos Beltran	.10	.30
170 Ryan Klesko	.10	.30
171 Mo Vaughn	.10	.30
172 Kenny Lofton	.10	.30
173 Al Leiter	.10	.30
174 Rondell White	.10	.30
175 Mike Sweeney	.10	.30
176 Trevor Hoffman	.10	.30
177 Steve Finley	.10	.30
178 Jeffrey Hammonds	.10	.30
179 David Justice	.10	.30
180 Gary Sheffield	.10	.30
181 Eric Munson BF	.10	.30
182 Luis Matos BF	.10	.30
183 Alex Cabrera BF	.10	.30
184 Randy Keisler BF	.10	.30
185 Nate Rolison BF	.10	.30
186 Jason Hart BF	.10	.30
187 Timo Perez BF	.10	.30
188 Adam Bernero BF	.10	.30
189 Barry Zito BF	.20	.50
190 Ryan Kohlmeier BF	.10	.30
191 Joey Nation BF	.10	.30
192 Oswaldo Mairena BF	.10	.30
193 Aubrey Huff BF	.10	.30
194 Mark Buehrle BF	.20	.50
195 Jace Brewer BF	.10	.30
196 Julio Zuleta BF	.10	.30
197 Xavier Nady BF	.10	.30
198 Vernon Wells BF	.10	.30
199 Joe Crede BF	.30	.75
200 Scott Downs BF	.10	.30
201 Ben Petrick BF	.10	.30
202 A.J. Burnett BF	.10	.30
203 Esix Snead BF RC	.10	.30
204 Dernell Stenson BF	.10	.30
205 Jose Ortiz BF	.10	.30
206 Paxton Crawford BF	.10	.30
207 Jason Tyner BF	.10	.30
208 Jimmy Rollins BF	.10	.30
209 Juan Pierre BF	.10	.30
210 Keith Ginter BF	.10	.30
211 Adam Dunn BF	.20	.50
212 Larry Barnes BF	.10	.30
213 Adam Piatt BF	.10	.30
214 Rodney Lindsey BF	.10	.30
215 Eric Byrnes BF	.10	.30
216 Julio Lugo BF	.10	.30
217 Corey Patterson BF	.10	.30
218 Reggie Taylor BF	.10	.30
219 Kenny Kelly BF	.10	.30
220 Tike Redman BF	.10	.30
221 D.Henson/2499 RC	2.00	5.00
222 J.Estrada/2499 RC	2.00	5.00
223 E.Guzman/2499 RC	2.00	5.00
224 Albert Pujols/2499 RC	40.00	80.00
225 W.Betemit/2499 RC	2.00	5.00
226 M.Teixeira/2499 RC	6.00	15.00
227 T.Shinjo/2499 RC	2.00	5.00
228 Matt White/2499 RC	2.00	5.00
229 A.Hernandez/2499 RC	2.00	5.00
230 I.Suzuki/2499 RC	12.50	30.00

2001 Fleer Futures Black Gold

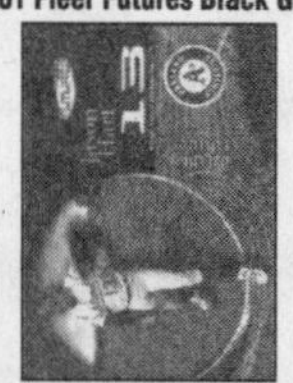

Randomly inserted into packs, this 220-card set is a complete parallel of the 2001 Fleer Futures base set. Each card in this set features a black foil background, and is individually serial numbered to 499.

*STARS 1-180: 3X TO 8X BASE HI
*BF 181-220: 3X TO 8X BASE HI
*BF RC'S 181-220: 3X TO 8X BASE HI

2001 Fleer Futures September Call-Ups Memorabilia

Randomly inserted into packs, this 15-card insert is a partial parallel of the Bright Future cards found in the 2001 Fleer Futures base set. This set features cards of young prospects with a swatch of game-used memorabilia that includes Caps, Bats, Gloves, and Cleats. Please note that there were only 200 of each card produced.

184 R. Keisler Cap/Cleat	3.00	8.00
185 Nate Rolison Bat	3.00	8.00
187 Timo Perez Bat	3.00	8.00
191 Joey Nation Glove	3.00	8.00
192 O. Mairena Glove	3.00	8.00
195 Jace Brewer Bat	3.00	8.00
197 Xavier Nady Glove	3.00	8.00
199 Joe Crede Bat	6.00	15.00
205 Jose Ortiz Bat	3.00	8.00
208 Jimmy Rollins Glove	3.00	8.00
210 Keith Ginter Bat	3.00	8.00
214 Rodney Lindsey Bat	3.00	8.00
217 Corey Patterson Bat	3.00	8.00
218 Reggie Taylor Bat	3.00	8.00
219 Kenny Kelly Bat	3.00	8.00

2001 Fleer Futures Bases Loaded

Randomly inserted into hobby packs at one in 134, this 15-card insert features a piece of game-used base from the player's home stadium. Card backs carry a "BL" prefix.

BL1 Ken Griffey Jr.	6.00	15.00
BL2 Mark McGwire	15.00	40.00
BL3 Carlos Delgado	3.00	8.00
BL4 Chipper Jones	4.00	10.00
BL5 Nomar Garciaparra	6.00	15.00
BL6 Cal Ripken	10.00	25.00
BL7 Sammy Sosa	4.00	10.00
BL8 Jeff Bagwell	4.00	10.00
BL9 Vladimir Guerrero	4.00	10.00
BL10 Tony Gwynn	4.00	10.00
BL11 Frank Thomas	4.00	10.00
BL12 Mike Piazza	4.00	10.00
BL13 Jason Giambi	3.00	8.00
BL14 Troy Glaus	3.00	8.00
BL15 Pat Burrell	3.00	8.00

2001 Fleer Futures Bats to the Future

Randomly inserted into packs at one in 28, this 25-card insert features the top Silver Slugger winners in baseball history. Card backs carry a "BF" prefix.

COMPLETE SET (25)	125.00	200.00
BF1 Mike Schmidt	6.00	15.00
BF2 Carlton Fisk	2.00	5.00
BF3 Paul Molitor	2.00	5.00
BF4 Vladimir Guerrero	2.50	6.00
BF5 Dave Parker	2.00	5.00
BF6 Chipper Jones	2.50	6.00
BF7 Carlos Delgado	2.00	5.00
BF8 Tony Gwynn	3.00	8.00
BF9 Reggie Jackson	2.00	5.00
BF10 Eddie Murray	2.50	6.00
BF11 Robin Yount	2.50	6.00
BF12 Alan Trammell	2.00	5.00
BF13 Frank Thomas	2.50	6.00
BF14 Cal Ripken	8.00	20.00
BF15 Don Mattingly	6.00	15.00
BF16 Jim Rice	2.00	5.00
BF17 Juan Gonzalez	2.00	5.00
BF18 Todd Helton	2.00	5.00
BF19 George Brett	6.00	15.00
BF20 Barry Bonds	6.00	15.00
BF21 Kirk Gibson	2.00	5.00
BF22 Matt Williams	2.00	5.00
BF23 Dave Winfield	2.00	5.00
BF24 Ryne Sandberg	6.00	15.00
BF25 Ivan Rodriguez	2.00	5.00

2001 Fleer Futures Bats to the Future Game Bat

Randomly inserted into packs at one in 114, this 25-card insert features pieces of actual game-used lumber. Cards are listed below in alphabetical order for convenience.

1 Barry Bonds	12.50	30.00
2 George Brett	15.00	40.00
3 Carlos Delgado	4.00	10.00
4 Carlton Fisk	10.00	25.00
5 Kirk Gibson	6.00	15.00
6 Juan Gonzalez	4.00	10.00
7 Vladimir Guerrero	6.00	15.00
8 Tony Gwynn	6.00	15.00
9 Todd Helton	6.00	15.00
10 Reggie Jackson	10.00	25.00
11 Chipper Jones	6.00	15.00
12 Don Mattingly	15.00	40.00
13 Paul Molitor	6.00	15.00
14 Eddie Murray	10.00	25.00
15 Dave Parker	6.00	15.00
16 Jim Rice	6.00	15.00
17 Cal Ripken	20.00	50.00
18 Ivan Rodriguez	6.00	15.00
19 Ryne Sandberg	15.00	40.00
20 Mike Schmidt	15.00	40.00
21 Frank Thomas	6.00	15.00
22 Alan Trammell	6.00	15.00
23 Matt Williams	4.00	10.00
24 Dave Winfield	6.00	15.00
25 Robin Yount	10.00	25.00

2001 Fleer Futures Bats to the Future Game Bat Autograph

Randomly inserted into packs, this 25-card insert features both an autograph and a piece of actual game-used lumber. Cards are listed below in alphabetical order for convenience. Please note that there were only 50 of each card produced. Also note that Jim Rice and Eddie Murray packed out as exchange cards with a redemption deadline of March 1st, 2002.

1 Barry Bonds	125.00	200.00
2 George Brett	75.00	150.00
3 Carlos Delgado	15.00	40.00
4 Carlton Fisk	30.00	60.00
5 Kirk Gibson	15.00	40.00
6 Juan Gonzalez	15.00	40.00
7 Vladimir Guerrero	20.00	50.00
8 Tony Gwynn	50.00	100.00
9 Todd Helton	20.00	50.00
10 Reggie Jackson	50.00	100.00
11 Chipper Jones	40.00	80.00
12 Don Mattingly	75.00	150.00
13 Paul Molitor	15.00	40.00
14 Eddie Murray	50.00	100.00
15 Dave Parker	15.00	40.00
16 Jim Rice	15.00	40.00
17 Cal Ripken	100.00	200.00
18 Ivan Rodriguez	40.00	80.00
19 Ryne Sandberg	75.00	150.00
20 Mike Schmidt	75.00	150.00
21 Frank Thomas	40.00	80.00
22 Alan Trammell	15.00	40.00
23 Matt Williams	20.00	50.00
24 Dave Winfield	30.00	60.00
25 Robin Yount	75.00	150.00

2001 Fleer Futures Characteristics

Randomly inserted into packs at one in nine, this 15-card insert pairs up players with the Japanese "Kanji" characters that describe their skills. Card backs carry a "C" prefix.

COMPLETE SET (15)	15.00	40.00
C1 Derek Jeter	2.00	5.00
C2 Mark McGwire	2.00	5.00
C3 Nomar Garciaparra	1.25	3.00
C4 Sammy Sosa	.75	2.00
C5 Pedro Martinez	.60	1.50
C6 Chipper Jones	.75	2.00
C7 Cal Ripken	2.50	6.00
C8 Todd Helton	.60	1.50
C9 Jim Edmonds	.60	1.50
C10 Ken Griffey Jr.	1.25	3.00
C11 Alex Rodriguez	1.25	3.00
C12 Mike Piazza	1.25	3.00
C13 Vladimir Guerrero	.75	2.00
C14 Frank Thomas	.75	2.00
C15 Carlos Delgado	.60	1.50

2001 Fleer Futures Hot Commodities

Randomly inserted into packs at one in 14, this 10-card insert set features players that every ballclub wishes they had on their team. Card backs carry a "HC" prefix.

COMPLETE SET (10)	15.00	40.00
HC1 Mark McGwire	2.00	5.00
HC2 Ken Griffey Jr.	1.25	3.00
HC3 Derek Jeter	2.00	5.00
HC4 Cal Ripken	2.50	6.00
HC5 Chipper Jones	.75	2.00
HC6 Barry Bonds	2.00	5.00
HC7 Mike Piazza	1.25	3.00
HC8 Sammy Sosa	.75	2.00
HC9 Alex Rodriguez	1.25	3.00
HC10 Frank Thomas	.75	2.00

2001 Fleer Game Time

The 2001 Fleer Game Time product was released in June, 2001 and featured a 121-card base set that was broken into tiers as follows: Base Veterans (1-90), and Next Game Rookies (91-121) serial numbered to 2000. Each pack contained five cards and carried a suggested retail price of $3.99.

COMP.SET w/o SP's (90)	10.00	25.00
COMMON CARD (1-90)	.15	.40
COMMON NG (91-121)	1.50	4.00
JETER MM'S RANDOMLY INSERTED IN PACKS		
1 Derek Jeter	1.00	2.50
2 Nomar Garciaparra	.60	1.50
3 Alex Rodriguez	.60	1.50
4 Jason Kendall	.15	.40
5 Barry Bonds	1.00	2.50
6 David Wells	.15	.40
7 Craig Biggio	.25	.60
8 Adrian Beltre	.15	.40
9 Pat Burrell	.15	.40
10 Rafael Palmeiro	.25	.60
11 Jim Thome	.25	.60
12 Mike Lowell	.15	.40
13 Trevor Hoffman	.15	.40
14 Pokey Reese	.15	.40
15 Juan Encarnacion	.15	.40
16 Shawn Green	.15	.40
17 Kerry Wood	.15	.40
18 Richard Hidalgo	.15	.40
19 Scott Rolen	.25	.60
20 Jeff Kent	.15	.40
21 Alex Gonzalez	.15	.40
22 Matt Williams	.15	.40
23 Mike Sweeney	.15	.40
24 Edgar Martinez	.25	.60
25 Sammy Sosa	.40	1.00
26 Bobby Higginson	.15	.40
27 Kevin Brown	.15	.40
28 Mike Lieberthal	.15	.40
29 Pedro Martinez	.25	.60
30 Jeff Weaver	.15	.40
31 Greg Maddux	.60	1.50
32 Mike Hampton	.15	.40
33 Vladimir Guerrero	.40	1.00
34 Greg Vaughn	.15	.40
35 Manny Ramirez Sox	.25	.60
36 Carlos Beltran	.15	.40
37 Eric Chavez	.15	.40
38 Troy Glaus	.15	.40
39 Todd Helton	.25	.60
40 Gary Sheffield	.15	.40
41 Brady Anderson	.15	.40
42 Juan Gonzalez	.15	.40
43 Tim Hudson	.15	.40
44 Kenny Lofton	.15	.40
45 Al Leiter	.15	.40
46 Eric Owens	.15	.40
47 Roberto Alomar	.25	.60
48 Preston Wilson	.15	.40
49 Tony Gwynn	.50	1.25
50 Cal Ripken	1.25	3.00
51 Ben Petrick	.15	.40
52 Jason Giambi	.15	.40
53 Ben Grieve	.15	.40
54 Albert Belle	.15	.40
55 Jose Vidro	.15	.40
56 Barry Zito	.25	.60
57 Ivan Rodriguez	.25	.60
58 Jeff Bagwell	.25	.60
59 Geoff Jenkins	.15	.40
60 Roger Clemens	.75	2.00
61 John Olerud	.15	.40
62 Randy Johnson	.40	1.00
63 Matt Lawton	.15	.40
64 Mark McGwire	1.00	2.50
65 Brad Radke	.15	.40
66 Frank Thomas	.40	1.00
67 Edgardo Alfonzo	.15	.40
68 Brian Giles	.15	.40
69 J.T. Snow	.15	.40
70 Carlos Delgado	.15	.40
71 Chipper Jones	.40	1.00
72 Mark Quinn	.15	.40
73 Mike Mussina	.25	.60
74 Rick Ankiel	.15	.40
75 Rafael Furcal	.15	.40
76 Jim Edmonds	.15	.40
77 Vinny Castilla	.15	.40
78 Sean Casey	.15	.40
79 Derrek Lee	.25	.60
80 Mike Piazza	.60	1.50
81 Warren Morris	.15	.40
82 Tim Salmon	.25	.60
83 Jeromy Burnitz	.15	.40
84 Freddy Garcia	.15	.40
85 Ken Griffey Jr.	.60	1.50
86 Andruw Jones	.25	.60
87 Darryl Kile	.15	.40
88 Magglio Ordonez	.15	.40
89 Bernie Williams	.25	.60
90 Timo Perez	.15	.40
91 Ichiro Suzuki NG RC	15.00	40.00
92 Larry Barnes Darin Erstad	1.50	4.00
93 J. Randolph NG RC	1.50	4.00
94 Paul Phillips NG RC	1.50	4.00
95 Esix Snead NG RC	1.50	4.00
96 Matt White NG RC	1.50	4.00
97 Ryan Freel NG RC	2.00	5.00
98 Winston Abreu NG RC	1.50	4.00
99 Junior Spivey NG RC	2.00	5.00
100 Randy Keisler Roger Clemens	3.00	8.00
101 Mike Piazza Brian Cole	2.50	6.00
102 Aubrey Huff Chipper Jones	2.00	5.00
103 Corey Patterson Sammy Sosa	2.00	5.00
104 Sun Woo Kim Pedro Martinez	2.00	5.00
105 Drew Henson NG RC	2.00	5.00
106 C. Vargas NG RC	1.50	4.00
107 Rafael Furcal Cesar Izturis	1.50	4.00
108 Paxton Crawford Pedro Martinez	2.00	5.00
109 A. Hernandez NG RC	1.50	4.00
110 Jace Brewer Derek Jeter	4.00	10.00
111 Andy Morales NG RC	1.50	4.00
112 W. Betemit NG RC	2.00	5.00
113 Juan Diaz NG RC	1.50	4.00
114 Erick Almonte NG RC	1.50	4.00
115 Nick Punto NG RC	1.50	4.00
116 T. Shinjo NG RC	2.00	5.00
117 Jay Gibbons NG RC	2.00	5.00
118 Andres Torres NG RC	1.50	4.00
119 Alexis Gomez NG RC	1.50	4.00
120 Wilkin Ruan NG RC	1.50	4.00
121 Albert Pujols NG RC	40.00	80.00
MM2 Derek Jeter/1996	5.00	12.00
MM2 Derek Jeter AU/96	60.00	120.00

2001 Fleer Game Time Next Game Extra

Randomly inserted into packs, this 31-card insert is actually a parallel of the Next game Rookies from the Fleer Game Time base set. Each card was produced with the words "Next Game Extra" on the card fronts. Please note that each card is serial numbered to 200 on the card back.

COMMON CARD (91-121)	6.00	15.00
*EXTRA: .75X TO 2X BASIC CARDS		
91 Ichiro Suzuki	30.00	60.00
121 Albert Pujols	100.00	175.00

2001 Fleer Game Time Famers Lumber

Randomly inserted into packs, this 29-card insert features actual pieces of game-used bats from Hall of Famers like Carlton Fisk and Roberto Clemente. Please note that each card is serial numbered to 100.

1 Luis Aparicio	6.00	15.00
2 Hank Bauer	6.00	15.00
3 Paul Blair	6.00	15.00
4 Bobby Bonds	6.00	15.00
5 Orlando Cepeda	6.00	15.00
6 Roberto Clemente	40.00	80.00
7 Rocky Colavito	10.00	25.00
8 Bucky Dent	6.00	15.00
9 Bill Dickey	10.00	25.00
10 Larry Doby	6.00	15.00
11 Dwight Evans		
12 Carlton Fisk	10.00	25.00
13 Hank Greenberg	30.00	60.00
14 Elston Howard	10.00	25.00
15 Frank Howard	6.00	15.00
16 Reggie Jackson	10.00	25.00
17 Harmon Killebrew	10.00	25.00
18 Tony Lazzeri	6.00	15.00
19 Roger Maris	20.00	50.00
20 Johnny Mize	6.00	15.00
21 Thurman Munson	15.00	40.00
22 Tony Perez	6.00	15.00
23 Jim Rice	6.00	15.00
24 Phil Rizzuto	10.00	25.00
25 Bill Skowron	10.00	25.00
26 Enos Slaughter	6.00	15.00
27 Duke Snider	10.00	25.00
28 Willie Stargell	10.00	25.00
29 Bill Terry	20.00	50.00
30 Ted Williams	40.00	80.00

2001 Fleer Game Time Let's Play Two

Randomly inserted into packs at one in 24, this 15-card insert set features cards of players that play the same position. Card backs carry a "LT" prefix.

COMPLETE SET (15)	50.00	120.00
LT1 Nomar Garciaparra Derek Jeter	4.00	10.00
LT2 Mark McGwire Sammy Sosa	5.00	12.00
LT3 Pedro Martinez Randy Johnson	2.00	5.00
LT4 Vladimir Guerrero Carlos Delgado	2.00	5.00
LT5 Mike Piazza Roger Clemens	5.00	12.00
LT6 Alex Rodriguez Miguel Tejada	3.00	8.00
LT7 Chipper Jones Troy Glaus	2.00	5.00
LT8 Alex Rodriguez Derek Jeter	5.00	12.00
LT9 Cal Ripken Derek Jeter	6.00	15.00
LT10 Jason Giambi Mark McGwire	5.00	12.00
LT11 Jeff Bagwell Craig Biggio	2.00	5.00
LT12 Tom Glavine Greg Maddux	3.00	8.00
LT13 Ken Griffey Jr. Barry Bonds	5.00	12.00
LT14 Manny Ramirez Sox Pedro Martinez	2.00	5.00
LT15 Ivan Rodriguez Alex Rodriguez	3.00	8.00

2001 Fleer Game Time Lumber

Randomly inserted into packs at one in 40, this 28-card insert features actual pieces of game-used bat from players like Barry Bonds and Nomar Garciaparra.

1 Roberto Alomar	6.00	15.00
2 Rick Ankiel	4.00	10.00
3 Adrian Beltre	4.00	10.00
4 Barry Bonds	10.00	25.00
5 Kevin Brown	4.00	10.00
6 Ken Caminiti	4.00	10.00
7 Eric Chavez	4.00	10.00
8 Carlos Delgado	4.00	10.00
9 J.D. Drew	4.00	10.00
10 Erubiel Durazo	4.00	10.00
11 Carl Everett	4.00	10.00
12 Rafael Furcal	4.00	10.00
13 Nomar Garciaparra	6.00	15.00

14 Brian Giles 4.00 10.00
15 Juan Gonzalez 4.00 10.00
16 Todd Helton 6.00 15.00
17 Randy Johnson 6.00 15.00
18 Chipper Jones 6.00 15.00
19 Pedro Martinez 6.00 15.00
20 Tino Martinez 6.00 15.00
21 Cal Ripken SP/275 15.00 40.00
22 Ivan Rodriguez 6.00 15.00
23 Frank Thomas 6.00 15.00
24 Jim Thome 6.00 15.00
25 Bernie Williams 6.00 15.00

2001 Fleer Game Time New Order

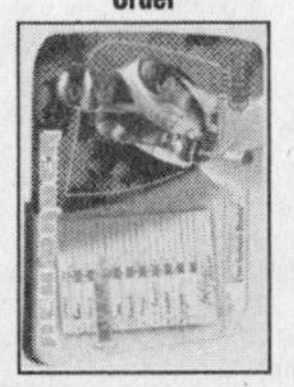

Randomly inserted into packs at one in 12, this 15-card insert set features players that are the future foundations of their ballclubs. Card backs carry a "NO" prefix.

COMPLETE SET (15) 15.00 40.00
NO1 Derek Jeter 2.50 6.00
NO2 Nomar Garciaparra 1.50 4.00
NO3 Alex Rodriguez 1.50 4.00
NO4 Mark McGwire 2.50 6.00
NO5 Sammy Sosa 1.00 2.50
NO6 Carlos Delgado .60 1.50
NO7 Troy Glaus .60 1.50
NO8 Jason Giambi .60 1.50
NO9 Mike Piazza 1.50 4.00
NO10 Todd Helton .60 1.50
NO11 Vladimir Guerrero 1.00 2.50
NO12 Manny Ramirez Sox .60 1.50
NO13 Frank Thomas 1.00 2.50
NO14 Ken Griffey Jr. 1.50 4.00
NO15 Chipper Jones 1.00 2.50

2001 Fleer Game Time Sticktoitness

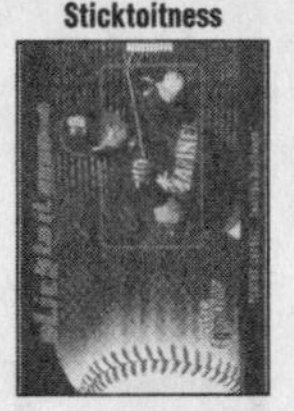

Randomly inserted into packs at one in 8, this 20-card insert set features players that stick to the game plan. Card backs carry a "S" prefix.

COMPLETE SET (20) 20.00 50.00
S1 Derek Jeter 2.50 6.00
S2 Nomar Garciaparra 1.50 4.00
S3 Alex Rodriguez 1.50 4.00
S4 Jeff Bagwell .60 1.50
S5 Bernie Williams .60 1.50
S6 Eric Chavez .60 1.50
S7 Richard Hidalgo .60 1.50
S8 Ichiro Suzuki 6.00 15.00
S9 Troy Glaus .60 1.50
S10 Magglio Ordonez .60 1.50
S11 Corey Patterson .60 1.50
S12 Todd Helton .60 1.50
S13 Jim Edmonds .60 1.50
S14 Rafael Furcal .60 1.50
S15 Mo Vaughn .60 1.50
S16 Pat Burrell .60 1.50
S17 Adrian Beltre .60 1.50
S18 Andruw Jones .60 1.50
S19 Manny Ramirez Sox .60 1.50
S20 Sean Casey .60 1.50

2001 Fleer Game Time Uniformity

Randomly inserted into packs at one in 25, this 23-card insert set features swatches of actual game-used jerseys. The cards have been listed below in alphabetical order for convenience.

1 Barry Bonds 10.00 25.00
2 Kevin Brown 4.00 10.00
3 Jay Buhner 4.00 10.00
4 Jeromy Burnitz 4.00 10.00
5 Andres Galarraga 4.00 10.00
6 Troy Glaus 4.00 10.00
7 Vladimir Guerrero 6.00 15.00
8 Carlos Guillen 4.00 10.00
9 Tony Gwynn 6.00 15.00
10 Brian Jordan 4.00 10.00
11 Greg Maddux 6.00 15.00
12 Fred McGriff 6.00 15.00
13 John Olerud 4.00 10.00
14 Magglio Ordonez 4.00 10.00
15 Ben Petrick 4.00 10.00
16 Brad Radke 4.00 10.00
17 Ivan Rodriguez 6.00 15.00
18 Fernando Seguignol 4.00 10.00
19 Gary Sheffield 4.00 10.00
20 Robin Ventura 4.00 10.00
21 Larry Walker 4.00 10.00
22 Rondell White 4.00 10.00
23 Matt Williams 4.00 10.00

2001 Fleer Genuine

The 2001 Fleer Genuine product was released in May, 2001 and featured a 130-card base set that was broken into tiers as follows: Base Veterans (1-100), and Rookies (100-130) featuring game-used materials and are serial numbered to 1500. Each pack contained five cards and carried a suggested retail price of $4.99. 500 exchange cards were seeded into packs for a Derek Jeter signed uncut sheet.

COMP.SET w/o SP's (90) 10.00 25.00
COMMON CARD (1-100) .20 .50
COMMON (101-130) 2.00 5.00
JETER AU SHEET AVAIL.VIA MAIL EXCH.
JETER SHEET EXCH. RANDOM IN PACKS
1 Derek Jeter 1.25 3.00
2 Nomar Garciaparra .75 2.00
3 Alex Rodriguez .75 2.00
4 Frank Thomas .50 1.25
5 Travis Fryman .20 .50
6 Gary Sheffield .20 .50
7 Jason Giambi .20 .50
8 Trevor Hoffman .20 .50
9 Todd Helton .30 .75
10 Ivan Rodriguez .30 .75
11 Roberto Alomar .30 .75
12 Barry Zito .30 .75
13 Kevin Brown .20 .50
14 Shawn Green .20 .50
15 Kenny Lofton .20 .50
16 Jeff Weaver .20 .50
17 Geoff Jenkins .20 .50
18 Carlos Delgado .20 .50
19 Mark Grace .30 .75
20 Ken Griffey Jr. .75 2.00
21 David Justice .20 .50
22 Brian Giles .20 .50
23 Scott Williamson .20 .50
24 Richie Sexson .20 .50
25 John Olerud .20 .50
26 Sammy Sosa .50 1.25
27 Bobby Higginson .20 .50
28 Matt Lawton .20 .50
29 Vinny Castilla .20 .50
30 Alex Gonzalez .20 .50
31 Manny Ramirez Sox .30 .75
32 Brad Radke .20 .50
33 Cal Ripken 1.50 4.00
34 Richard Hidalgo .20 .50
35 Al Leiter .20 .50
36 Freddy Garcia .20 .50
37 Juan Encarnacion .20 .50
38 Corey Koskie .20 .50
39 Greg Vaughn .20 .50
40 Rafael Palmeiro .30 .75
41 Vladimir Guerrero .50 1.25
42 Troy Glaus .20 .50
43 Mike Hampton .20 .50
44 Jose Vidro .20 .50
45 Ryan Rupe .20 .50
46 Troy O'Leary .20 .50
47 Ben Petrick .20 .50
48 Mike Lieberthal .20 .50
49 Mike Sweeney .20 .50
50 Scott Rolen .30 .75
51 Albert Belle .20 .50
52 Mark Quinn .20 .50
53 Mike Piazza .75 2.00
54 Mark McGwire 1.25 3.00
55 Brady Anderson .20 .50
56 Carlos Beltran .20 .50
57 Michael Barrett .20 .50
58 Jason Kendall .20 .50
59 Jim Edmonds .20 .50
60 Matt Williams .20 .50
61 Pokey Reese .20 .50
62 Bernie Williams .30 .75
63 Barry Bonds 1.25 3.00
64 David Wells .20 .50
65 Chipper Jones .50 1.25
66 Jim Parque .20 .50
67 Derrek Lee .30 .75
68 Darin Erstad .20 .50
69 Edgar Martinez .30 .75
70 Kerry Wood .20 .50
71 Omar Vizquel .30 .75
72 Jeromy Burnitz .20 .50
73 Warren Morris .20 .50
74 Rick Ankiel .20 .50
75 Andruw Jones .30 .75
76 Paul Konerko .20 .50
77 Mike Lowell .20 .50
78 Roger Clemens 1.00 2.50
79 Tim Hudson .20 .50
80 Rafael Furcal .20 .50
81 Craig Biggio .30 .75
82 Edgardo Alfonzo .20 .50
83 Pat Burrell .20 .50
84 Adrian Beltre .20 .50
85 Tony Gwynn .60 1.50
86 J.T. Snow .20 .50
87 Randy Johnson .50 1.25
88 Sean Casey .20 .50
89 Preston Wilson .20 .50
90 Mike Mussina .30 .75
91 Eric Chavez .20 .50
92 Tim Salmon .30 .75
93 Pedro Martinez .30 .75
94 Darryl Kile .20 .50
95 Greg Maddux .75 2.00
96 Magglio Ordonez .20 .50
97 Jeff Bagwell .30 .75
98 Timo Perez .20 .50
99 Jeff Kent .20 .50
100 Eric Owens .20 .50
101 Ichiro Suzuki GU RC 15.00 40.00
102 E. Guzman GU RC 2.00 5.00
103 T. Shinjo GU RC 2.50 6.00
104 Travis Hafner GU RC 6.00 15.00
105 Larry Barnes GU 2.00 5.00
106 J. Randolph GU RC 2.00 5.00
107 Paul Phillips GU RC 2.00 5.00
108 Erick Almonte GU RC 2.00 5.00
109 Nick Punto GU RC 2.00 5.00
110 Jack Wilson GU RC 2.50 6.00
111 Jeremy Owens GU RC 2.00 5.00
112 Esix Snead GU RC 2.00 5.00
113 Jay Gibbons GU RC 2.50 6.00
114 A. Hernandez GU RC 2.00 5.00
115 Matt White GU RC 2.00 5.00
116 Ryan Freel GU RC 2.00 5.00
117 Martin Vargas GU RC 2.00 5.00
118 Winston Abreu GU RC 2.00 5.00
119 Junior Spivey GU RC 2.50 6.00
120 Paxton Crawford GU 2.00 5.00
121 Randy Keisler GU 2.00 5.00
122 Juan Diaz GU RC 2.00 5.00
123 Aaron Rowand GU 2.00 5.00
124 Toby Hall GU 2.00 5.00
125 Brian Cole GU 2.00 5.00
126 Aubrey Huff GU 2.00 5.00
127 Corey Patterson GU 2.00 5.00
128 Sun Woo Kim GU 2.00 5.00
129 Jace Brewer GU 2.00 5.00
130 Cesar Izturis GU 2.00 5.00
NNO Derek Jeter 60.00 120.00
AU Sheet/500 EXCH

2001 Fleer Genuine At Large

Randomly inserted into packs at one in 23, this 15-card insert features major league talents "at large". Card backs carry an "ALG" prefix.

COMPLETE SET (15) 60.00 120.00
ALG1 Derek Jeter 5.00 12.00
ALG2 Nomar Garciaparra 3.00 8.00
ALG3 Mark McGwire 5.00 12.00
ALG4 Pedro Martinez 1.25 3.00
ALG5 Tony Gwynn 2.50 6.00
ALG6 Roger Clemens 4.00 10.00
ALG7 Ivan Rodriguez 1.25 3.00
ALG8 Sammy Sosa 2.00 5.00
ALG9 Magglio Ordonez 1.25 3.00
ALG10 Jason Giambi 1.25 3.00
ALG11 Carlos Delgado 1.25 3.00
ALG12 Chipper Jones 2.00 5.00
ALG13 Mike Piazza 3.00 8.00
ALG14 Cal Ripken 6.00 15.00
ALG15 Ken Griffey Jr. 3.00 8.00

2001 Fleer Genuine Coverage Plus

Randomly inserted into hobby packs, this 10-card insert features jersey swatches from players like Derek Jeter and Cal Ripken. Cards are listed below in alphabetical order for convenience. Please note that there were only 150 serial numbered sets produced.

1 Barry Bonds 20.00 50.00
2 Darin Erstad 6.00 15.00
3 Troy Glaus 6.00 15.00
4 Tony Gwynn 10.00 25.00
5 Derek Jeter 20.00 50.00
6 Randy Johnson 8.00 20.00
7 Andruw Jones 8.00 20.00
8 Chipper Jones 8.00 20.00
9 Cal Ripken 20.00 50.00
10 Frank Thomas 8.00 20.00

2001 Fleer Genuine Final Cut

Randomly inserted into packs at one in 30, this 28-card insert features jersey swatches from players like Derek Jeter and Cal Ripken. Cards are listed below in alphabetical order for convenience. Representatives at Fleer announced specific print runs on several short-printed cards within this set, though the cards lack actual serial-numbering. Don Larsen, Ron Guidry and Reggie Jackson were not intended for public release. It's rumored that Willie Randolph and Dave Righetti were also not intended for public release. The Guidry, Larsen, Randolph and Righetti cards are extremely scarce (estimated only a few copies of each exist) as Fleer attempted to pull all of the copies they could find from production prior to shipping.

*MULTI-COLOR PATCH: .75X TO 2X BASIC
1 Wade Boggs 6.00 15.00
2 Barry Bonds SP/330 30.00 60.00
3 George Brett 10.00 25.00
4 Sean Casey 4.00 10.00
5 J.D. Drew SP/75 10.00 25.00
6 Bob Gibson SP/200 15.00 40.00
7 Troy Glaus 4.00 10.00
8 Ron Guidry SP
9 Tony Gwynn 6.00 15.00
10 Reggie Jackson SP
11 Andruw Jones SP/135 15.00 40.00
12 Chipper Jones 6.00 15.00
13 Don Larsen SP
14 Greg Maddux 6.00 15.00
15 Edgar Martinez SP/130 UER 15.00 40.00
Card says it is part of a batting glove
but the pieces are game worn jersey swatches
15a Thurman Munson
16 Willie Randolph SP
17 Pokey Reese 4.00 10.00
18 Dave Righetti SP
19 Cal Ripken 15.00 40.00
20 Ivan Rodriguez SP/120 15.00 40.00
21 Scott Rolen 6.00 15.00
22 Tim Salmon 6.00 15.00
23 Miguel Tejada SP/170 10.00 25.00
24 Frank Thomas 6.00 15.00
25 Robin Ventura 4.00 10.00
26 Larry Walker 4.00 10.00
27 Matt Williams 4.00 10.00
28 Robin Yount 6.00 15.00

2001 Fleer Genuine High Interest

Randomly inserted into packs at one in 23, this 15-card insert features players that have earned the respect of the fans year in year out. Cards backs carry a "HI" prefix.

COMPLETE SET (15) 50.00 100.00
HI1 Derek Jeter 5.00 12.00
HI2 Nomar Garciaparra 3.00 8.00
HI3 Greg Maddux 3.00 8.00
HI4 Todd Helton 1.25 3.00
HI5 Sammy Sosa 2.00 5.00
HI6 Jeff Bagwell 1.25 3.00
HI7 Jason Giambi 1.25 3.00
HI8 Frank Thomas 2.00 5.00
HI9 Andruw Jones 1.25 3.00
HI10 Jim Edmonds 1.25 3.00
HI11 Bernie Williams 1.25 3.00
HI12 Randy Johnson 2.00 5.00
HI13 Ken Griffey Jr. 3.00 8.00
HI14 Pedro Martinez 1.25 3.00
HI15 Mark McGwire 5.00 12.00

2001 Fleer Genuine Material Issue

Randomly inserted into hobby packs at one in 30, this 21-card insert features game-used jersey swatches from players like Tony Gwynn and Pedro Martinez. Cards have been listed in alphabetical order for convenience. Representatives at Fleer announced that Pedro Martinez and Curt Schilling were both shortprints. Though the cards lack actual serial-numbering, it was announced that 60 copies of the Martinez card and 120 copies of the Schilling card were produced. A Mike Mussina card, hand-numbered in blue ink to 27 copies was releases within packs of 2005 National Pastime baseball as part of their "buyback" program. In addition, cards for Rod Carew and Tommy John were released in early 2006 as part of the ARA Fleer exchange card replacement program. This program was conducted after Fleer went bankrupt and their assets were purchased. A company named ARA was put in charge of sending out replacement cards to consumers that were waiting for redemption cards they had sent in when Fleer was still in business. These consumers did not receive the cards stated on the redemptions but instead got a random assortment of material - some of it of which was previously unreleased (such as the Carew and John cards). It's not known how many copies of these two cards were produced reports from dealers in the field indicate that the Carew is significantly easier to locate than the Tommy John. That's not to say the Carew is a common card by any means (given the fact it was only available through an obscure - and random - redemption process), but the Tommy John is legitimately scarce. Please note, none of these cards were printed with card numbers on back, thus we've checklisted them using the player's initials.

*MULTI-COLOR PATCH: 1X TO 2.5X BASIC
CJ Chipper Jones 6.00 15.00
CR Cal Ripken 15.00 40.00
CS Curt Schilling SP/120 * 10.00 25.00
DE Darin Erstad 4.00 10.00
EM Edgar Martinez SP * 12.50 30.00
FT Frank Thomas 6.00 15.00
GM Greg Maddux 6.00 15.00
JD J.D. Drew 4.00 10.00
KM Kevin Millwood 4.00 10.00
NR Nolan Ryan 20.00 50.00
PM1 Pedro Martinez SP/60 * 20.00 50.00
PM2 Paul Molitor SP * 10.00 25.00
RC Rod Carew SP
RJ Randy Johnson 6.00 15.00
RV Robin Ventura 4.00 10.00
SC Steve Carlton SP * 10.00 25.00
SR Scott Rolen 6.00 15.00
TG1 Troy Glaus 4.00 10.00
TG2 Tom Glavine 6.00 15.00
TG3 Tony Gwynn 6.00 15.00
TJ Tommy John SP
BM Billy Martin
EH Elston Howard

2001 Fleer Genuine Names Of The Game

Randomly inserted into packs, this 34-card insert features swatches of game-used memorabilia (either bat or jersey). Cards have been listed below in alphabetical order for convenience. Please note that there were only 50 serial numbered sets produced.

1 Yogi Berra Bat 15.00 40.00
2 Orlando Cepeda Bat 10.00 25.00
3 Rocky Colavito Bat 15.00 40.00
4 Andre Dawson Jsy 10.00 25.00
5 Bucky Dent Bat 10.00 25.00
6 Rollie Fingers Jsy 10.00 25.00
7 Carlton Fisk Bat 15.00 40.00
8 Whitey Ford Jsy 15.00 40.00
9 Jimmie Foxx Bat 40.00 80.00
10 Hank Greenberg Bat 40.00 80.00
11 Catfish Hunter Jsy 15.00 40.00
12 Reggie Jackson Jsy 15.00 40.00
13 Randy Johnson Jsy 15.00 40.00
14 Chipper Jones Bat 15.00 40.00
15 Harmon Killebrew Bat 15.00 40.00
16 Tony Lazzeri Bat 10.00 25.00
17 Don Mattingly Bat 15.00 40.00
18 Willie Mays Jsy
No Serial Number
19 Willie McCovey Bat 10.00 25.00
20 Johnny Mize Bat 10.00 25.00
21 Pee Wee Reese Jsy 15.00 40.00
22 Cal Ripken Bat 30.00 60.00
23 Phil Rizzuto Bat 30.00 60.00
24 Ivan Rodriguez Bat 15.00 40.00
25 Preacher Roe Jsy 15.00 40.00
26 Babe Ruth Bat 125.00 250.00
27 Nolan Ryan Jsy 30.00 60.00
28 Tom Seaver Jsy 15.00 40.00
29 Bill Skowron Bat 15.00 40.00
30 Enos Slaughter Bat 10.00 25.00
31 Duke Snider Bat 15.00 40.00
32 Willie Stargell Bat 15.00 40.00
33 Bill Terry Bat 20.00 50.00
34 Ted Williams Bat 50.00 100.00
35 Hack Wilson Bat 40.00 80.00

2001 Fleer Genuine Names Of The Game Autographs

Randomly inserted into packs, this 22-card insert features swatches of game-used memorabilia (either bat or jersey) and an authentic autograph from the depicted player. Cards have been listed below in alphabetical order for convenience. Please note that there were only 100 serial numbered sets produced. It is believed that the Phil Rizzuto card, which lacks serial numbering, was issued after Fleer ceased operations.

1 Yogi Berra Bat 40.00 80.00
2 Orlando Cepeda Bat 10.00 25.00
3 Rocky Colavito Bat 40.00 80.00
4 Andre Dawson Jsy 30.00 60.00
5 Bucky Dent Bat 10.00 25.00
6 Rollie Fingers Jsy 10.00 25.00
7 Carlton Fisk Bat 30.00 60.00
8 Whitey Ford Jsy 15.00 40.00
9 Reggie Jackson Jsy 30.00 60.00
10 Randy Johnson Jsy 30.00 60.00
11 Chipper Jones Bat 30.00 60.00
12 Harmon Killebrew Bat 40.00 80.00
13 Don Mattingly Bat 50.00 100.00
14 Willie McCovey Bat 15.00 40.00
15 Willie Mays Jsy
No Auto, No Serial Number
16 Cal Ripken Bat 75.00 150.00
17 Phil Rizzuto Bat
No Serial Number
18 Ivan Rodriguez Bat 15.00 40.00
19 Preacher Roe Jsy 10.00 25.00
20 Nolan Ryan Jsy 60.00 120.00
21 Tom Seaver Jsy 30.00 60.00
22 Bill Skowron Bat 10.00 25.00
23 Enos Slaughter Bat 15.00 40.00
24 Duke Snider Bat 15.00 40.00

2001 Fleer Genuine Pennant Aggression

Randomly inserted into packs at one in 23, this 10-card insert features players that play very aggressively down the stretch for the pennant. Card backs carry a "PA" prefix.

COMPLETE SET (10) 30.00 60.00
PA1 Derek Jeter 4.00 10.00
PA2 Alex Rodriguez 2.50 6.00
PA3 Nomar Garciaparra 2.50 6.00
PA4 Mark McGwire 4.00 10.00
PA5 Ken Griffey Jr. 2.50 6.00
PA6 Mike Piazza 2.50 6.00
PA7 Sammy Sosa 1.50 4.00
PA8 Barry Bonds 4.00 10.00
PA9 Chipper Jones 1.50 4.00
PA10 Pedro Martinez 1.50 4.00

2001 Fleer Genuine Tip Of The Cap

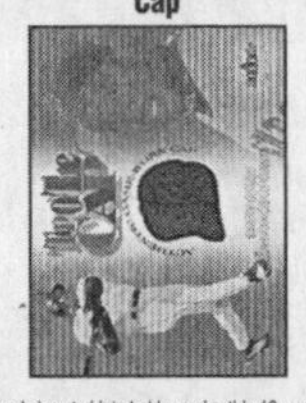

Randomly inserted into hobby packs, this 13-card insert features swatches of game-used hat. Cards have been listed below in alphabetical order for convenience. Please note that there were only 150 serial numbered sets produced. Card 4 was intended to be Troy Glaus but was pulled from production.

1 Roberto Alomar 10.00 25.00
2 Barry Bonds 30.00 60.00
3 Eric Chavez 6.00 15.00
5 Shawn Green 6.00 15.00
6 Vladimir Guerrero 10.00 25.00
7 Randy Johnson 10.00 25.00
8 Andruw Jones 10.00 25.00
9 Javy Lopez 6.00 15.00
10 Pedro Martinez 10.00 25.00
11 Rafael Palmeiro 10.00 25.00
12 Ivan Rodriguez 10.00 25.00
13 Miguel Tejada 6.00 15.00
4 Troy Glaus

2002 Fleer Genuine

This 140 card was released in May, 2002. These cards were issued in five card packs with an SRP of $4.99 per pack and they were issued 24 packs to a box and six boxes per case. The first 100 card feature veteran players and the final forty player feature prospect cards. Cards number 101 through 140 have a stated print run of 2002 serial numbered sets.

COMP.SET w/o SP's (100) 10.00 25.00
COMMON CARD (1-100) .20 .50
COMMON CARD (101-140) 2.00 5.00
1 Alex Rodriguez .75 2.00
2 Manny Ramirez .30 .75
3 Jim Thome .30 .75
4 Eric Milton .20 .50
5 Todd Helton .30 .75
6 Mike Mussina .30 .75
7 Ichiro Suzuki 1.00 2.50
8 Randy Johnson .50 1.25
9 Mark Mulder .20 .50
10 Johnny Damon Sox .30 .75
11 Sean Casey .20 .50
12 Albert Pujols 1.00 2.50
13 Mark Grace .30 .75
14 Moises Alou .20 .50
15 Raul Mondesi .20 .50
16 Cliff Floyd .20 .50
17 Vladimir Guerrero .50 1.25
18 Pat Burrell .20 .50
19 Ryan Klesko .20 .50
20 Mike Hampton .20 .50
21 Shawn Green .20 .50
22 Rich Aurilia .20 .50
23 Matt Morris .20 .50
24 Curt Schilling .20 .50
25 Kevin Brown .20 .50
26 Adrian Beltre .20 .50
27 Joe Mays .20 .50
28 Luis Gonzalez .20 .50
29 Barry Larkin .30 .75
30 A.J. Burnett .20 .50
31 Eric Munson .20 .50
32 Juan Gonzalez .20 .50
33 Lance Berkman .20 .50
34 Fred McGriff .30 .75
35 Paul Konerko .20 .50
36 Pedro Martinez .30 .75
37 Adam Dunn .20 .50
38 Jeromy Burnitz .20 .50
39 Mike Sweeney .20 .50
40 Bret Boone .20 .50
41 Ken Griffey Jr. .75 2.00
42 Eric Chavez .20 .50
43 Mark Quinn .20 .50
44 Roberto Alomar .30 .75
45 Bobby Abreu .20 .50
46 Bartolo Colon .20 .50
47 Jimmy Rollins .20 .50
48 Chipper Jones .50 1.25
49 Ben Sheets .20 .50
50 Freddy Garcia .20 .50
51 Sammy Sosa .50 1.25
52 Rafael Palmeiro .30 .75
53 Preston Wilson .20 .50
54 Troy Glaus .20 .50
55 Josh Beckett .20 .50
56 C.C. Sabathia .20 .50
57 Magglio Ordonez .20 .50
58 Brian Giles .20 .50
59 Darin Erstad .20 .50
60 Gary Sheffield .20 .50
61 Paul LoDuca .20 .50
62 Derek Jeter 1.25 3.00
63 Greg Maddux .75 2.00
64 Kerry Wood .20 .50
65 Toby Hall .20 .50
66 Barry Bonds 1.25 3.00
67 Jeff Bagwell .30 .75
68 Jason Kendall .20 .50
69 Richard Hidalgo .20 .50
70 J.D. Drew .20 .50
71 Tom Glavine .30 .75
72 Javier Vazquez .20 .50
73 Doug Mientkiewicz .20 .50
74 Jason Giambi .20 .50
75 Carlos Delgado .20 .50
76 Aramis Ramirez .20 .50
77 Torii Hunter .20 .50
78 Ivan Rodriguez .30 .75
79 Charles Johnson .20 .50
80 Jeff Kent .20 .50
81 Jacque Jones .20 .50
82 Larry Walker .20 .50
83 Cristian Guzman .20 .50
84 Jermaine Dye .20 .50
85 Roger Clemens 1.00 2.50
86 Mike Piazza .75 2.00
87 Craig Biggio .30 .75
88 Phil Nevin .20 .50
89 Jeff Cirillo .20 .50
90 Barry Zito .20 .50
91 Ryan Dempster .20 .50
92 Mark Buehrle .20 .50
93 Nomar Garciaparra .75 2.00
94 Frank Thomas .50 1.25
95 Jim Edmonds .20 .50
96 Geoff Jenkins .20 .50
97 Scott Rolen .30 .75
98 Tim Hudson .20 .50
99 Shannon Stewart .20 .50
100 Richie Sexson .20 .50
101 Orlando Hudson UP 2.00 5.00
102 Doug Devore UP RC 2.00 5.00
103 Rene Reyes UP RC 2.00 5.00
104 Steve Bechler UP RC 2.00 5.00
105 Jorge Nunez UP RC 2.00 5.00
106 Mitch Wylie UP RC 2.00 5.00
107 Jaime Cerda UP RC 2.00 5.00
108 Brandon Puffer UP RC 2.00 5.00
109 Tyler Yates UP RC 2.00 5.00
110 Bill Hall UP 2.00 5.00
111 Pete Zamora UP RC 2.00 5.00
112 Jeff Deardorff UP 2.00 5.00
113 J.J. Putz UP RC 2.00 5.00
114 Scotty Layfield UP RC 2.00 5.00
115 Brandon Backe UP RC 3.00 8.00
116 Andy Pratt UP RC 2.00 5.00
117 Mark Prior UP 3.00 8.00
118 Franklyn German UP RC 2.00 5.00
119 Todd Donovan UP RC 2.00 5.00
120 Franklin Nunez UP RC 2.00 5.00
121 Adam Walker UP RC 2.00 5.00
122 Ron Calloway UP RC 2.00 5.00
123 Tim Kalita UP RC 2.00 5.00
124 Kazuhisa Ishii UP RC 3.00 8.00
125 Mark Teixeira UP 3.00 8.00
126 Nate Field UP RC 2.00 5.00
127 Nelson Castro UP RC 2.00 5.00
128 So Taguchi UP RC 3.00 8.00
129 Marlon Byrd UP 2.00 5.00
130 Drew Henson UP 2.00 5.00
131 Kenny Kelly UP 2.00 5.00
132 John Ennis UP RC 2.00 5.00
133 Anastacio Martinez UP RC 2.00 5.00
134 Matt Guerrier UP 2.00 5.00
135 Tom Wilson UP RC 2.00 5.00
136 Ben Howard UP RC 2.00 5.00
137 Chris Baker UP RC 2.00 5.00
138 Kevin Frederick UP RC 2.00 5.00
139 Wilson Valdez UP RC 2.00 5.00
140 Austin Kearns UP 2.00 5.00

2002 Fleer Genuine Bats Incredible

Inserted in packs at a stated rate of one in 10 hobby and one in 20 retail, these 25 cards feature some of the leading hitters in baseball.

COMPLETE SET (25) 40.00 100.00
BI1 Todd Helton 1.00 2.50
BI2 Chipper Jones 1.50 4.00
BI3 Luis Gonzalez 1.00 2.50
BI4 Barry Bonds 4.00 10.00
BI5 Jason Giambi 1.00 2.50
BI6 Alex Rodriguez 2.50 6.00
BI7 Manny Ramirez 1.00 2.50
BI8 Jeff Bagwell 1.00 2.50
BI9 Shawn Green 1.00 2.50
BI10 Albert Pujols 3.00 8.00
BI11 Paul LoDuca 1.00 2.50
BI12 Mike Piazza 2.50 6.00
BI13 Derek Jeter 4.00 10.00
BI14 Edgar Martinez 1.00 2.50
BI15 Juan Gonzalez 1.00 2.50
BI16 Magglio Ordonez 1.00 2.50
BI17 Jermaine Dye 1.00 2.50
BI18 Larry Walker 1.00 2.50
BI19 Phil Nevin 1.00 2.50
BI20 Ivan Rodriguez 1.00 2.50
BI21 Ichiro Suzuki 3.00 8.00
BI22 J.D. Drew 1.00 2.50
BI23 Vladimir Guerrero 1.50 4.00
BI24 Sammy Sosa 1.50 4.00
BI25 Ken Griffey Jr. 2.50 6.00

2002 Fleer Genuine Bats Incredible Game Used

Inserted at a stated rate of one in 18 hobby and one in 90 retail packs, these 12 cards partially parallel the Bats Incredible insert set. These cards have a bat chip on them in addition to the player's photo.

1 Todd Helton 4.00 10.00
2 Chipper Jones 6.00 15.00
3 J.D. Drew 4.00 10.00
4 Alex Rodriguez 6.00 15.00
5 Manny Ramirez 4.00 10.00
6 Shawn Green 4.00 10.00
7 Derek Jeter 12.50 30.00
8 Edgar Martinez 4.00 10.00
9 Juan Gonzalez 4.00 10.00
10 Jermaine Dye 3.00 8.00
11 Phil Nevin 3.00 8.00
12 Ivan Rodriguez 4.00 10.00

2002 Fleer Genuine Ink

Randomly inserted in packs, these cards feature authentic autographs of the players featued. These cards all have diferent print runs and we have listed the stated print run next to the player's name. Paul Molitor did not sign his cards in time for inclusion in packs and those cards could be redeemed until June 1, 2003.

1 Barry Bonds/150 100.00 175.00
2 Ron Cey/975 6.00 15.00
3 Derek Jeter/150 75.00 150.00
4 Al Kaline/300 40.00 80.00
5 Don Mattingly/50 50.00 100.00
6 Paul Molitor/365 6.00 15.00
7 Dale Murphy/700 12.50 30.00
8 Phil Rizzuto/700 12.50 30.00
9 Brooks Robinson/140 20.00 50.00
10 Maury Wills/975 6.00 15.00

2002 Fleer Genuine Leaders

Inserted into packs at a stated rate of one in six hobby and one in eight retail, these 15 cards honor some of the leading players in the game.

COMPLETE SET (15) 15.00 40.00
1 Sammy Sosa 1.00 2.50
2 Todd Helton .60 1.50
3 Alex Rodriguez 1.50 4.00
4 Roger Clemens 2.00 5.00
5 Barry Bonds 2.50 6.00
6 Randy Johnson 1.00 2.50
7 Albert Pujols 2.00 5.00
8 Curt Schilling .60 1.50
9 Bernie Williams .60 1.50
10 Ken Griffey Jr. 1.50 4.00
11 Pedro Martinez .60 1.50
12 Juan Gonzalez .60 1.50
13 Hideo Nomo 1.00 2.50
14 Bret Boone .60 1.50
15 Ichiro Suzuki 2.00 5.00

2002 Fleer Genuine Leaders Game Jersey

Inserted into packs at stated odds of one in 11 hobby and one in 566 retail, these nine cards partially parallel the Leaders insert set. These cards feature a game jersey swatch on them in addition to the player's photo.

1 Todd Helton 6.00 15.00
2 Alex Rodriguez 6.00 15.00
3 Roger Clemens 8.00 20.00
4 Barry Bonds 10.00 25.00
5 Randy Johnson 6.00 15.00
6 Bernie Williams 6.00 15.00
7 Curt Schilling 6.00 15.00
8 Hideo Nomo 8.00 20.00
9 Pedro Martinez 6.00 15.00

2002 Fleer Genuine Names of the Game

Issued in packs at stated odds of one in 10 hobby and one in 20 retail, these 30 cards feature a good mix of the leading players in baseball.

COMPLETE SET (30) 50.00 120.00
1 Mike Piazza 3.00 8.00
2 Chipper Jones 2.00 5.00
3 Jim Edmonds 1.25 3.00
4 Barry Larkin 1.25 3.00
5 Frank Thomas 2.00 5.00
6 Manny Ramirez 1.25 3.00
7 Carlos Delgado 1.25 3.00
8 Brian Giles 1.25 3.00
9 Kerry Wood 1.25 3.00
10 Derek Jeter 5.00 12.00
11 Adam Dunn 1.25 3.00
12 Gary Sheffield 1.25 3.00
13 Luis Gonzalez 1.25 3.00
14 Mark Mulder 1.25 3.00
15 Roberto Alomar 1.25 3.00
16 Scott Rolen 1.25 3.00
17 Tom Glavine 1.25 3.00
18 Bobby Abreu 1.25 3.00
19 Nomar Garciaparra 3.00 8.00
20 Darin Erstad 1.25 3.00
21 Cliff Floyd 1.25 3.00
22 Tim Hudson 1.25 3.00
23 Jim Thome 1.25 3.00
24 Nolan Ryan 5.00 12.00
25 Reggie Jackson 1.25 3.00
26 Rafael Palmeiro 1.25 3.00
27 Ken Griffey Jr. 3.00 8.00
28 Sammy Sosa 2.00 5.00
29 Vladimir Guerrero 2.00 5.00
30 Ichiro Suzuki 4.00 10.00

2002 Fleer Genuine Names of the Game Memorabilia

Inserted in packs at stated odds of one in 24 hobby and one in 100 retail, these 19 cards are a partial parallel of the Names of the Game memorabilia set. These cards feature a memorabilia item to go with the player's photo. The Nomar Garciaparra card was issued in shorter supply and we have notated that information along with the stated print run for that card.

1 Roberto Alomar 6.00 15.00
2 Carlos Delgado 4.00 10.00
3 Jim Edmonds 4.00 10.00
4 Darin Erstad 4.00 10.00
5 Cliff Floyd 4.00 10.00
6 Nomar Garciaparra SP/90
7 Brian Giles 4.00 10.00
8 Luis Gonzalez 4.00 10.00
9 Tim Hudson 4.00 10.00
10 Derek Jeter 12.50 30.00
11 Chipper Jones 6.00 15.00
12 Barry Larkin 6.00 15.00
13 Mark Mulder 4.00 10.00
14 Rafael Palmeiro 6.00 15.00
15 Mike Piazza 6.00 15.00
16 Manny Ramirez 6.00 15.00
17 Scott Rolen 6.00 15.00
18 Nolan Ryan 40.00 80.00
19 Jim Thome 6.00 15.00

2002 Fleer Genuine Tip of the Cap

Inserted in packs at stated odds of one in six hobby and one in eight retail, this 25 cards feature a nice mix of active and retired players.

COMPLETE SET (25) 25.00 60.00
1 Alex Rodriguez 2.00 5.00
2 Derek Jeter 3.00 8.00
3 Kazuhiro Sasaki .75 2.00
4 Barry Bonds 3.00 8.00
5 J.D. Drew .75 2.00
6 Tsuyoshi Shinjo .75 2.00
7 Alfonso Soriano .75 2.00
8 Albert Pujols 2.50 6.00
9 Tom Seaver .75 2.00
10 Drew Henson .75 2.00
11 Dave Winfield .75 2.00
12 Carlos Delgado .75 2.00
13 Lou Boudreau .75 2.00
14 Shawn Green .75 2.00
15 Roger Clemens 2.50 6.00
16 Randy Johnson 1.25 3.00
17 Sammy Sosa 1.25 3.00
18 Rafael Palmeiro .75 2.00
19 Ken Griffey Jr. 2.00 5.00
20 Ichiro Suzuki 2.50 6.00
21 Eric Chavez .75 2.00
22 Andruw Jones .75 2.00
23 Miguel Tejada .75 2.00
24 Pedro Martinez .75 2.00
25 Tim Salmon .75 2.00

2002 Fleer Genuine Tip of the Cap Game Used

Randomly inserted into packs, these 26 cards feature pieces of memorabilia worn by the featured player. These cards all have different stated print runs and we have listed that information next to their names in our checklist.

1 Adrian Beltre/6
2 Barry Bonds/32
3 Lou Boudreau/303 10.00 25.00
4 Kevin Brown/6
5 Eric Chavez/14
6 Bartolo Colon/16
7 Carlos Delgado/219 8.00 20.00
8 J.D. Drew/8
9 Jim Edmonds/8
10 Darin Erstad/22
11 Rafael Furcal/12
12 Juan Gonzalez/6
13 Luis Gonzalez/12
14 Shawn Green/4
15 Drew Henson/361 8.00 20.00
16 Derek Jeter
17 Randy Johnson/74
18 Andruw Jones/19
19 Jason Kendall/41
20 Pedro Martinez/2
21 Rafael Palmeiro/300 10.00 25.00
22 Alex Rodriguez/670 10.00 25.00
23 Tim Salmon/6
24 Tom Seaver/224 10.00 25.00
25 Alfonso Soriano/4
26 Miguel Tejada/225 8.00 20.00
27 Dave Winfield/363 8.00 20.00

2002 Fleer Genuine Touch Em All

Inserted into packs at stated odds of one in 10 hobby and one in 20 retail, these 25 cards feature the leading sluggers in the game.

COMPLETE SET (25) 40.00 100.00
1 Derek Jeter 4.00 10.00
2 Sammy Sosa 1.50 4.00
3 Albert Pujols 3.00 8.00
4 Vladimir Guerrero 1.50 4.00
5 Ken Griffey Jr. 2.50 6.00
6 Nomar Garciaparra 2.50 6.00
7 Luis Gonzalez 1.00 2.50
8 Barry Bonds 4.00 10.00
9 Manny Ramirez 1.00 2.50
10 Jason Giambi 1.00 2.50
11 Chipper Jones 1.50 4.00
12 Ichiro Suzuki 3.00 8.00
13 Alex Rodriguez 2.50 6.00
14 Juan Gonzalez 1.00 2.50
15 Todd Helton 1.00 2.50
16 Roberto Alomar 1.00 2.50
17 Jeff Bagwell 1.00 2.50
18 Mike Piazza 2.50 6.00
19 Gary Sheffield 1.00 2.50
20 Ivan Rodriguez 1.00 2.50
21 Frank Thomas 1.50 4.00
22 Bobby Abreu 1.00 2.50
23 J.D. Drew 1.00 2.50
24 Scott Rolen 1.00 2.50
25 Darin Erstad 1.00 2.50

2002 Fleer Genuine Touch Em All Game Base

Randomly inserted into packs, these 25 cards parallel the Touch Em All insert set. These cards feature a piece of a game base used by the player in a game. These cards were issued to a stated print run of 350 serial numbered sets.

1 Derek Jeter 10.00 25.00
2 Sammy Sosa 6.00 15.00
3 Albert Pujols 8.00 20.00
4 Vladimir Guerrero 6.00 15.00
5 Ken Griffey Jr. 6.00 15.00
6 Nomar Garciaparra 6.00 15.00
7 Luis Gonzalez 4.00 10.00
8 Barry Bonds 10.00 25.00
9 Manny Ramirez 6.00 15.00
10 Jason Giambi 6.00 15.00
11 Chipper Jones 6.00 15.00
12 Ichiro Suzuki 10.00 25.00
13 Alex Rodriguez 6.00 15.00
14 Juan Gonzalez 4.00 10.00
15 Todd Helton 6.00 15.00
16 Roberto Alomar 6.00 15.00
17 Jeff Bagwell 6.00 15.00
18 Mike Piazza 6.00 15.00
19 Gary Sheffield 4.00 10.00
20 Ivan Rodriguez 6.00 15.00
21 Frank Thomas 6.00 15.00
22 Bobby Abreu 4.00 10.00
23 J.D. Drew 4.00 10.00
24 Scott Rolen 6.00 15.00
25 Darin Erstad 4.00 10.00

2003 Fleer Genuine

This 145-card set was distributed in two separate series. The primary Genuine product - of which contained the first 130 cards from the basic set - was released in July, 2003. This set was issued in five card packs with an $5 SRP which came 24 packs to a box and 12 boxes to a case. Cards numbered 1 through 100 feature veterans while cards numbered 101 through 130 feature a mix of rookies and prospects and those cards were issued to a stated print run of 799 serial numbered sets. Cards 131-145 were randomly seeded within packs of Fleer Rookies and Greats of which was distributed in December, 2003. These fifteen update cards continued the Genuine Upside prospect subset established with cards 101-130 from the primary "low series" set. Each update card was serial numbered to 1000 copies.

COMP.LO SET w/o SP's (100) 10.00 25.00
COMMON CARD (1-100) .20 .50
COMMON CARD (101-145) 1.50 4.00
1 Derek Jeter 1.25 3.00
2 Mo Vaughn .20 .50
3 Adam Dunn .20 .50
4 Aubrey Huff .20 .50
5 Jacque Jones .20 .50
6 Kerry Wood .20 .50
7 Barry Bonds 1.25 3.00
8 Kevin Brown .20 .50
9 Sammy Sosa .50 1.25
10 Ray Durham .20 .50
11 Carlos Beltran .20 .50
12 Tony Batista .20 .50
13 Bobby Abreu .20 .50
14 Craig Biggio .30 .75
15 Gary Sheffield .20 .50
16 Jermaine Dye .20 .50
17 Carlos Pena .20 .50
18 Tim Salmon .30 .75
19 Mike Piazza .75 2.00
20 Moises Alou .20 .50
21 Edgardo Alfonzo .20 .50
22 Mike Sweeney .20 .50
23 Jay Gibbons .20 .50
24 Kevin Millwood .20 .50
25 A.J. Burnett .20 .50
26 Austin Kearns .20 .50
27 Rafael Palmeiro .30 .75
28 Vladimir Guerrero .50 1.25
29 Paul Konerko .20 .50
30 Scott Rolen .30 .75
31 Fred McGriff .30 .75
32 Frank Thomas .50 1.25
33 John Olerud .20 .50
34 Eric Gagne .20 .50
35 Nomar Garciaparra .75 2.00
36 Ryan Klesko .20 .50
37 Lance Berkman .20 .50
38 Andruw Jones .30 .75
39 Pat Burrell .20 .50
40 Juan Encarnacion .20 .50
41 Curt Schilling .20 .50
42 Jason Giambi .20 .50
43 Barry Larkin .30 .75
44 Alex Rodriguez .75 2.00
45 Kazuhisa Ishii .20 .50
46 Pedro Martinez .30 .75
47 Sean Burroughs .20 .50
48 Roy Oswalt .20 .50
49 Chipper Jones .50 1.25
50 Barry Zito .20 .50
51 Jeff Kent .20 .50
52 Rodrigo Lopez .20 .50
53 Jim Thome .30 .75
54 Ivan Rodriguez .30 .75
55 Luis Gonzalez .20 .50
56 Alfonso Soriano .20 .50
57 Josh Beckett .20 .50
58 Junior Spivey .20 .50
59 Bernie Williams .30 .75
60 Omar Vizquel .30 .75
61 Eric Hinske .20 .50
62 Jose Vidro .20 .50
63 Bartolo Colon .20 .50
64 Jim Edmonds .20 .50
65 Ben Sheets .20 .50
66 Mark Prior .30 .75
67 Edgar Martinez .30 .75
68 Raul Ibanez .20 .50
69 Darin Erstad .20 .50
70 Roger Clemens 1.00 2.50
71 C.C. Sabathia .20 .50
72 Carlos Delgado .20 .50
73 Tom Glavine .30 .75
74 Magglio Ordonez .20 .50
75 Ichiro Suzuki 1.00 2.50
76 Johnny Damon .30 .75
77 Brian Giles .20 .50
78 Jeff Bagwell .30 .75
79 Greg Maddux .75 2.00
80 Eric Chavez .20 .50
81 Larry Walker .20 .50
82 Randy Johnson .50 1.25
83 Miguel Tejada .20 .50
84 Todd Helton .30 .75
85 Jarrod Washburn .20 .50
86 Troy Glaus .20 .50
87 Ken Griffey Jr. .75 2.00
88 Albert Pujols 1.00 2.50
89 Torii Hunter .20 .50
90 Joe Crede .20 .50
91 Matt Morris .20 .50
92 Shawn Green .20 .50
93 Manny Ramirez .30 .75
94 Jason Kendall .20 .50
95 Preston Wilson .20 .50
96 Garret Anderson .20 .50
97 Cliff Floyd .20 .50
98 Sean Casey .20 .50
99 Juan Gonzalez .20 .50
100 Richie Sexson .20 .50
101 Joe Borchard GU 1.50 4.00
102 Josh Stewart GU RC 1.50 4.00
103 Francisco Rodriguez GU 1.50 4.00
104 Jeremy Bonderman GU RC 4.00 10.00
105 Walter Young GU 1.50 4.00
106 Brandon Webb GU RC 3.00 8.00
107 Lyle Overbay GU 1.50 4.00
108 Jose Contreras GU RC 2.00 5.00
109 Victor Martinez GU 2.00 5.00
110 Hideki Matsui GU RC 4.00 10.00
111 Brian Stokes GU RC 1.50 4.00
112 Daniel Cabrera GU RC 2.00 5.00
113 Josh Willingham GU RC 2.50 6.00
114 Mark Teixeira GU 2.00 5.00
115 Pete LaForest GU RC 1.50 4.00
116 Chris Waters GU RC 1.50 4.00
117 Chien-Ming Wang GU RC 6.00 15.00
118 Ian Ferguson GU RC 1.50 4.00
119 Rocco Baldelli GU 1.50 4.00
120 Termel Sledge GU RC 1.50 4.00
121 Hank Blalock GU 1.50 4.00
122 Alejandro Machado GU RC 1.50 4.00
123 Hee Seop Choi GU 1.50 4.00
124 Guillermo Quiroz GU RC 1.50 4.00
125 Chase Utley GU 2.00 5.00
126 Nook Logan GU RC 2.00 5.00
127 Josh Hall GU RC 1.50 4.00
128 Ryan Church GU 1.50 4.00
129 Lew Ford GU RC 2.00 5.00
130 Francisco Rosario GU RC 1.50 4.00
131 Dan Haren GU RC 2.00 5.00
132 Rickie Weeks GU RC 2.50 6.00
133 Prentice Redman GU RC 1.50 4.00
134 Craig Brazell GU RC 1.50 4.00
135 Jon Leicester GU RC 1.50 4.00
136 Ryan Wagner GU RC 1.50 4.00
137 Matt Kata GU RC 1.50 4.00
138 Edwin Jackson GU RC 2.00 5.00
139 Mike Ryan GU RC 1.50 4.00
140 Delmon Young GU RC 4.00 10.00
141 Bo Hart GU RC 1.50 4.00
142 Jeff Duncan GU RC 1.50 4.00
143 Robby Hammock GU RC 1.50 4.00
144 Michael Hessman GU RC 1.50 4.00
145 Clint Barmes GU RC 1.25 3.00

2003 Fleer Genuine Reflection Ascending

*1-100 PRINT RUN b/wn 26-35: 8X TO 20X
*1-100 PRINT RUN b/wn 36-50: 6X TO 15X
*1-100 PRINT RUN b/wn 51-65: 5X TO 12X
*1-100 PRINT RUN b/wn 66-80: 4X TO 10X
*1-100 PRINT RUN b/wn 81-100: 3X TO 8X
*101-130 P/R b/wn 101-130: .6X TO 1.5X
*101-130 P/R b/wn 101-130: .6X TO 1.5X RC
PRINT RUNS B/WN 1-130 COPIES PER CARD
1-25 NOT PRICED DUE TO SCARCITY
117 Chien-Ming Wang GU/117 12.50 30.00

2003 Fleer Genuine Reflection Descending

*1-100 PRINT RUN b/wn 130-101: 2.5X TO 6X
*1-100 PRINT RUN b/wn 100-81: 3X TO 8X
*1-100 PRINT RUN b/wn 80-66: 4X TO 10X
*1-100 PRINT RUN b/wn 65-51: 5X TO 12X
*1-100 PRINT RUN b/wn 50-36: 6X TO 15X
*1-100 PRINT RUN b/wn 35-31: 8X TO 20X
*101-130 P/R b/wn 30-26: 1.25X TO 3X
PRINT RUNS B/WN 1-130 COPIES PER CARD
101-105 RC'S NOT PRICED DUE TO SCARCITY
106-130 NOT PRICED DUE TO SCARCITY

2003 Fleer Genuine Article Insider Game Jersey

Inserted into packs at a stated rate of one in 24, these 25 cards feature game-used swatches from some major league stars. Several of the cards in this set were produced in smaller quantities and we have noted the announced print run next to the player's name in our checklist.

AD Adam Dunn 3.00 8.00
AJ Andruw Jones SP/200 4.00 10.00
AR Alex Rodriguez SP/50
AS Alfonso Soriano SP/300 3.00 8.00
CJ Chipper Jones 4.00 10.00
CS Curt Schilling 3.00 8.00
DJ Derek Jeter SP/450 10.00 25.00
DM Don Mattingly Pants 10.00 25.00
JB Jeff Bagwell 4.00 10.00
JG Jason Giambi SP/50
LB Lance Berkman 3.00 8.00
MO Magglio Ordonez 3.00 8.00
MP Mike Piazza SP/100 8.00 20.00
MS Greg Maddux 4.00 10.00
MT Miguel Tejada SP/100 6.00 15.00
NG Nomar Garciaparra 6.00 15.00
PG Pat Burrell 3.00 8.00
PM Pedro Martinez 4.00 10.00
RJ Randy Johnson 4.00 10.00
SG Shawn Green 3.00 8.00
SS Sammy Sosa SP/300 4.00 10.00
TG Troy Glaus 3.00 8.00
TH Torii Hunter 3.00 8.00
TH2 Todd Helton 4.00 10.00
VG Vladimir Guerrero SP/100 8.00 20.00

2003 Fleer Genuine Article Insider Game Jersey Tag

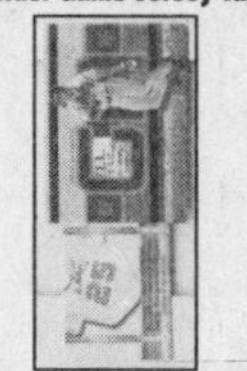

Randomly inserted into packs, these 19 cards feature pieces of the "tags" used on uniforms. Each of these cards were issued to a stated print run of 10 serial numbered sets and no pricing is available due to market scarcity.

2003 Fleer Genuine Article Insider Game Jersey Autographs

Randomly inserted into packs, these two cards parallel the Insider Game Jersey insert set but also have an autograph of the featured player.

PRINTS B/WN 165-170 COPIES PER CARD
GADM D.Mattingly Pants/170 50.00 100.00
GALB Lance Berkman/165 8.00 20.00

2003 Fleer Genuine Article Insider Game Jersey Autographs VIP Blue

STATED PRINT RUN 50 SERIAL #'d SETS
GADM Don Mattingly Pants 100.00 200.00
GALB Lance Berkman 15.00 40.00

2003 Fleer Genuine Article Insider Game Jersey Autographs VIP Red

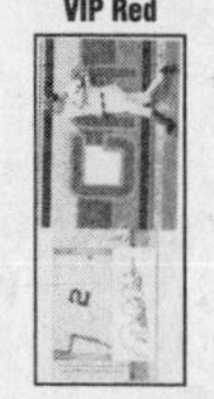

STATED PRINT RUN 100 SERIAL #'d SETS
GADJ Derek Jeter 75.00 150.00
GADM Don Mattingly Pants 75.00 150.00
GALB Lance Berkman 12.50 30.00

2003 Fleer Genuine Longball Threats

COMPLETE SET (15) 10.00 25.00
STATED ODDS 1:8
1 Derek Jeter / Nomar Garciaparra 2.50 6.00
2 Jim Thome / Pat Burrell .60 1.50
3 Alex Rodriguez / Rafael Palmeiro 1.50 4.00
4 Alfonso Soriano / Hideki Matsui 2.00 5.00
5 Torii Hunter / Vladimir Guerrero 1.00 2.50
6 Mike Sweeney / Phil Nevin .60 1.50
7 Mike Piazza / Sammy Sosa 1.00 2.50
8 Shawn Green / Jason Giambi .60 1.50
9 Magglio Ordonez / Andruw Jones .60 1.50
10 Eric Chavez / Carlos Delgado .60 1.50
11 Manny Ramirez / Jeff Bagwell .60 1.50
12 Scott Rolen / Troy Glaus .60 1.50
13 Barry Bonds / Miguel Tejada 2.50 6.00
14 Albert Pujols / Lance Berkman 2.00 5.00
15 Chipper Jones / Todd Helton 1.00 2.50

2003 Fleer Genuine Longball Threats Dual Patch

PRINT RUNS B/WN 36-100 COPIES PER CARD
1 Derek Jeter / Nomar Garciaparra/42 50.00 100.00
2 Jim Thome / Pat Burrell/89 10.00 25.00
3 Alex Rodriguez / Rafael Palmeiro/100 20.00 50.00
5 Torii Hunter / Vladimir Guerrero/68 15.00 40.00
6 Mike Sweeney / Phil Nevin/36 15.00 40.00
7 Mike Piazza / Sammy Sosa/82 10.00 25.00
8 Shawn Green / Jason Giambi/83 6.00 15.00
9 Magglio Ordonez / Andruw Jones/73 10.00 25.00
11 Manny Ramirez / Jeff Bagwell/64 15.00 40.00
12 Scott Rolen / Troy Glaus/61 15.00 40.00
15 Chipper Jones / Todd Helton/56 15.00 40.00

2003 Fleer Genuine Longball Threats Dual Swatch

STATED ODDS 1:72
1 Derek Jeter / Nomar Garciaparra 15.00 40.00
2 Jim Thome / Pat Burrell 6.00 15.00
3 Alex Rodriguez / Rafael Palmeiro 10.00 25.00
5 Torii Hunter / Vladimir Guerrero 6.00 15.00
6 Mike Sweeney / Phil Nevin 4.00 10.00
7 Mike Piazza / Sammy Sosa 6.00 15.00
8 Shawn Green / Jason Giambi 4.00 10.00
9 Magglio Ordonez / Andruw Jones 6.00 15.00
11 Manny Ramirez / Jeff Bagwell 6.00 15.00
12 Scott Rolen / Troy Glaus 6.00 15.00
15 Chipper Jones / Todd Helton 6.00 15.00

2003 Fleer Genuine Longball Threats Single Swatch

STATED ODDS 1:13
SP PRINT RUNS PROVIDED BY FLEER
SP'S ARE NOT SERIAL-NUMBERED
1A Derek Jeter Jsy 10.00 25.00
Nomar Garciaparra SP/300
1B Nomar Garciaparra Jsy 6.00 15.00
Derek Jeter
2A Jim Thome Jsy 4.00 10.00
Pat Burrell
2B Pat Burrell Jsy 3.00 8.00
Jim Thome
3B Rafael Palmeiro Jsy 4.00 10.00
Alex Rodriguez
4A Alfonso Soriano Jsy 10.00 25.00
Hideki Matsui SP/250
5A Torii Hunter Jsy 3.00 8.00
Vladimir Guerrero
5B Vladimir Guerrero Jsy 4.00 10.00
Torii Hunter
6A Mike Sweeney Jsy 3.00 8.00
Phil Nevin
6B Phil Nevin Jsy 3.00 8.00
Mike Sweeney SP/300
7A Mike Piazza Jsy 4.00 10.00
Sammy Sosa
7B Sammy Sosa Jsy 8.00 20.00
Mike Piazza SP/100
8A Shawn Green Jsy 3.00 8.00
Jason Giambi
8B Jason Giambi Jsy
Shawn Green SP/50
9A Magglio Ordonez Jsy 4.00 10.00
Andruw Jones
9B Andruw Jones Jsy 4.00 10.00
Magglio Ordonez SP/200
10B Carlos Delgado Jsy 3.00 8.00
Eric Chavez
11A Manny Ramirez Jsy 4.00 10.00
Jeff Bagwell
11B Jeff Bagwell Jsy 4.00 10.00
Manny Ramirez SP/450
12A Scott Rolen Jsy 4.00 10.00
Troy Glaus
12B Troy Glaus Jsy 3.00 8.00
Scott Rolen
13B Miguel Tejada Jsy 3.00 8.00
Barry Bonds
14B Lance Berkman Jsy 3.00 8.00
Albert Pujols
15A Chipper Jones Jsy 4.00 10.00
Todd Helton
15B Todd Helton Jsy 4.00 10.00
Chipper Jones

2003 Fleer Genuine Tools of the Game

STATED ODDS 1:20
1 Adam Dunn 1.25 3.00
2 Chipper Jones 2.00 5.00
3 Torii Hunter 1.25 3.00
4 Mike Piazza 3.00 8.00
5 Hideki Matsui 3.00 8.00
6 Nomar Garciaparra 3.00 8.00
7 Derek Jeter 5.00 12.00
8 Alex Rodriguez 3.00 8.00
9 Alfonso Soriano 1.25 3.00
10 Pat Burrell 1.25 3.00
11 Barry Bonds 5.00 12.00
12 Jason Giambi 1.25 3.00
13 Sammy Sosa 2.00 5.00
14 Vladimir Guerrero 2.00 5.00
15 Ichiro Suzuki 4.00 10.00

2003 Fleer Genuine Tools of the Game Bat

STATED ODDS 1:42
AD Adam Dunn 2.00 5.00
AR Alex Rodriguez 5.00 12.00
AS Alfonso Soriano 2.00 5.00
DJ Derek Jeter 8.00 20.00
JG Jason Giambi 2.00 5.00
MP Mike Piazza 5.00 12.00
SS Sammy Sosa 3.00 8.00
VG Vladimir Guerrero 3.00 8.00

2003 Fleer Genuine Tools of the Game Bat-Jersey

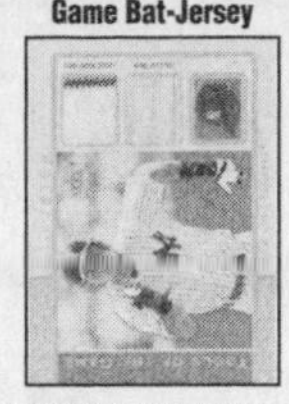

STATED PRINT RUN 250 SERIAL #'d SETS
AD Adam Dunn 4.00 10.00
AR Alex Rodriguez
AS Alfonso Soriano 4.00 10.00
DJ Derek Jeter 15.00 40.00
JG Jason Giambi 4.00 10.00
MP Mike Piazza 10.00 25.00
SS Sammy Sosa 6.00 15.00
VG Vladimir Guerrero 6.00 15.00

2003 Fleer Genuine Tools of the Game Bat-Jersey-Cap

STATED PRINT RUN 100 SERIAL #'d SETS
AD Adam Dunn 8.00 20.00
AR Alex Rodriguez 20.00 50.00
AS Alfonso Soriano 8.00 20.00
DJ Derek Jeter 30.00 80.00
JG Jason Giambi 8.00 20.00
MP Mike Piazza 20.00 50.00
SS Sammy Sosa 12.50 30.00
VG Vladimir Guerrero 12.50 30.00

2004 Fleer Genuine Insider

This 130-card set was released in June, 2004. The set was issued in five-card packs with an $5 SRP which came 18 packs to a box and 12 boxes to a case. Cards numbered 1-90 feature veterans while cards numbered 91-100 and 121-130 feature rookies and cards 101-120 feature prospects. Cards numbered 91-120 were issued at a stated rate of one in 14 hobby and one in 72 retail. Cards numbered 91-100 were issued to a stated print run of 499 serial numbered sets while cards 101-120 were issued to a stated print run of 799 serial numbered sets. Cards numbered 121-130 are "mini-cards" and those cards were issued to a stated print run of 350 serial numbered sets and those cards are "inside" those cards from 91-100.

COMP.SET w/o SP's (90) 10.00 25.00
COMMON CARD (1-90) .20 .50
COMMON CARD (91-100) 1.00 2.50
91-100 PRINT RUN 499 SERIAL #'d SETS
COMMON CARD (101-120) .75 2.00
101-120 PRINT RUN 799 SERIAL #'d SETS
91-120 STATED ODDS 1:14 HOB, 1:72 RET
COMMON CARD (121-130) 1.00 2.50
121-130 SEEDED WITHIN RI 91-100 CARDS
121-130 PRINT RUN 350 SERIAL #'d SETS
121-130 ARE MINI-SIZED CARDS
1 Troy Glaus .20 .50
2 Eric Chavez .20 .50
3 Lance Berkman .30 .75
4 Pedro Martinez .30 .75
5 Jim Edmonds .30 .75
6 Tom Glavine .30 .75
7 Ken Griffey Jr. .75 2.00
8 Vernon Wells .20 .50
9 Hideki Matsui .75 2.00
10 Jeff Bagwell .30 .75
11 Rafael Palmeiro .30 .75
12 Edgar Martinez .30 .75
13 Bernie Williams .30 .75
14 Josh Beckett .30 .75
15 Javy Lopez .20 .50
16 Ichiro Suzuki .75 2.00
17 Scott Podsednik .20 .50
18 Sammy Sosa .50 1.25
19 Mark Teixeira .50 1.25
20 Jorge Posada .30 .75
21 Miguel Cabrera .50 1.25
22 Chipper Jones .50 1.25
23 Sean Burroughs .20 .50
24 Dmitri Young .20 .50
25 Brandon Webb .20 .50
26 Bobby Abreu .20 .50
27 Hideo Nomo .50 1.25
28 Frank Thomas .50 1.25
29 Alex Rodriguez .75 2.00
30 Derek Jeter 1.25 3.00
31 Todd Helton .30 .75
32 Andruw Jones .20 .50
33 Jason Kendall .20 .50
34 Eric Gagne .30 .75
35 Omar Vizquel .30 .75
36 Vladimir Guerrero .50 1.25
37 Jim Thome .30 .75
38 Mike Sweeney .20 .50
39 Manny Ramirez .50 1.25
40 Scott Rolen .30 .75
41 Jose Vidro .20 .50
42 Adam Dunn .30 .75
43 Garret Anderson .20 .50
44 Mike Lieberthal .20 .50
45 Roy Oswalt .30 .75
46 Geoff Jenkins .20 .50
47 Magglio Ordonez .30 .75
48 Hank Blalock .20 .50
49 Barry Zito .20 .50
50 Dontrelle Willis .20 .50
51 Greg Maddux .75 2.00
52 Brian Giles .20 .50
53 Shawn Green .20 .50
54 Carlos Lee .20 .50
55 Carlos Delgado .20 .50
56 Alfonso Soriano .20 .50
57 Angel Berroa .20 .50
58 Kerry Wood .20 .50
59 Rocco Baldelli .20 .50
60 Gary Sheffield .20 .50
61 Ivan Rodriguez .30 .75
62 Richie Sexson .20 .50
63 Marlon Byrd .20 .50
64 Carlos Beltran .20 .50
65 Mark Prior .30 .75
66 Aubrey Huff .20 .50
67 Jason Giambi .20 .50
68 Curt Schilling .30 .75
69 Reggie Sanders .20 .50
70 Mike Piazza .50 1.25
71 Craig Monroe .20 .50
72 Randy Johnson .50 1.25
73 Pat Burrell .20 .50
74 Craig Biggio .30 .75
75 Nomar Garciaparra .50 1.25
76 Albert Pujols 1.25 3.00
77 Jose Reyes .20 .50
78 Preston Wilson .20 .50
79 Miguel Tejada .30 .75
80 Bret Boone .20 .50
81 Shannon Stewart .20 .50
82 Jody Gerut .20 .50
83 Tim Salmon .20 .50
84 Tim Hudson .30 .75
85 Juan Pierre .20 .50
86 Jay Gibbons .20 .50
87 Jason Schmidt .20 .50
88 Torii Hunter .20 .50
89 Austin Kearns .20 .50
90 Roy Halladay .50 1.25
91 John Gall RI RC 1.00 2.50
92 Kaz Matsui RI RC 1.50 4.00
93 Merkin Valdez RI RC 1.00 2.50
94 William Bergolla RI RC 1.00 2.50
95 Angel Chavez RI RC 1.00 2.50
96 Hector Gimenez RI RC 1.00 2.50
97 Aarom Baldiris RI RC 1.00 2.50
98 Justin Leone RI RC 1.00 2.50
99 Onil Joseph RI RC 1.00 2.50
100 Freddy Guzman RI RC 1.00 2.50
101 Rickie Weeks UP .75 2.00
102 Chad Bentz UP RC .75 2.00
103 Bobby Crosby UP .75 2.00
104 Dallas McPherson UP .75 2.00
105 Brandon Watson UP .75 2.00
106 Garrett Atkins UP .75 2.00
107 Graham Koonce UP .75 2.00
108 Chien-Ming Wang UP 4.00 10.00
109 Jonny Gomes UP .75 2.00
110 Edwin Jackson UP .75 2.00
111 Alfredo Simon UP RC .75 2.00
112 Delmon Young UP 1.25 3.00
113 Angel Guzman UP .75 2.00
114 Ryan Howard UP 2.50 6.00
115 Scott Hairston UP .75 2.00
116 Edwin Encarnacion UP 1.25 3.00
117 Byron Gettis UP .75 2.00
118 Kevin Youkilis UP 1.25 3.00
119 Grady Sizemore UP 1.25 3.00
120 Corey Hart UP .75 2.00
121 Greg Dobbs MRI RC 1.00 2.50
122 Jerry Gil MRI RC 1.00 2.50
123 Shawn Hill MRI RC 1.00 2.50
124 John Labandeira MRI RC 1.00 2.50
125 Jason Bartlett MRI RC 3.00 8.00
126 Ronny Cedeno MRI RC 1.00 2.50
127 Don Kelly MRI RC 1.50 4.00
128 Ivan Ochoa MRI RC 1.00 2.50
129 Mariano Gomez MRI RC 1.00 2.50
130 Ruddy Yan MRI 1.00 2.50

2004 Fleer Genuine Insider Mini Masterpiece

STATED PRINT RUN 1 SERIAL #'d SET
NO PRICING DUE TO SCARCITY

2004 Fleer Genuine Insider Mini Parallel 137

*PARA 137: .6X TO 1.5X BASIC
STATED PRINT RUN 137 SERIAL #'d SETS

2004 Fleer Genuine Insider Reflections

*REFL 1-90: 3X TO 8X BASIC
*REFL 101-120: .6X TO 1.5X BASIC
STATED ODDS 1:24 HOBBY, 1:200 RETAIL
STATED PRINT RUN 99 SERIAL #'d SETS

2004 Fleer Genuine Insider Article Jersey

STATED PRINT RUN 250 SERIAL #'d SETS
*ARTICLE BAT: .5X TO 1.2X BASIC
ARTICLE BAT PRINT RUN 100 #'d SETS
*ARTICLE BAT-JSY: 1X TO 2.5X BASIC
ARTICLE BAT-JSY PRINT RUN 50 #'d SETS
ARTICLE JSY TAG PRINT RUN 5 #'d SETS
NO ART.JSY TAG PRICE DUE TO SCARCITY
OVERALL ODDS GU 1:9 H, AU-GU 1:48 R
AD Adam Dunn 2.00 5.00
AP Albert Pujols 6.00 15.00
AR Alex Rodriguez 6.00 15.00
AS Alfonso Soriano 2.00 5.00
CD Carlos Delgado 2.00 5.00
CJ Chipper Jones 3.00 8.00
DJ Derek Jeter 8.00 20.00
GS Gary Sheffield 2.00 5.00
HB Hank Blalock 2.00 5.00
JG Jason Giambi 2.00 5.00
JR Jose Reyes 2.00 5.00
JT Jim Thome 3.00 8.00
LB Lance Berkman 2.00 5.00
MC Miguel Cabrera 3.00 8.00
MO Magglio Ordonez 2.00 5.00
MP Mike Piazza 5.00 12.00
MR Manny Ramirez 3.00 8.00
MT Mark Teixeira 3.00 8.00
NG Nomar Garciaparra 5.00 12.00
RB Rocco Baldelli 2.00 5.00
RP Rafael Palmeiro 3.00 8.00
SS Sammy Sosa 3.00 8.00
TG Troy Glaus 2.00 5.00
TH Todd Helton 3.00 8.00
VG Vladimir Guerrero 3.00 8.00

2004 Fleer Genuine Insider Autograph

OVERALL ODDS AU 1:18 H, AU-GU 1:48 R
PRINT RUNS B/WN 27-550 COPIES PER
AH Aubrey Huff/550 6.00 15.00
AK Austin Kearns/350 4.00 10.00
BW Brandon Webb/450 4.00 10.00
CJ Chipper Jones/50
DE David Eckstein/350 12.50 30.00
IR Ivan Rodriguez/150 15.00 40.00
JG Jody Gerut/550 4.00 10.00
JG2 Jay Gibbons/350 4.00 10.00
JR Jose Reyes/350 6.00 15.00
JR2 Jimmy Rollins/150 10.00 25.00
JS Jason Schmidt/300 6.00 15.00
JS2 John Smoltz/150 15.00 40.00
MB Marlon Byrd/550 4.00 10.00
MC Miguel Cabrera/250 10.00 25.00
MO Magglio Ordonez/250 6.00 15.00
MR Mariano Rivera/150 30.00 60.00
MT Mark Teixeira/350 10.00 25.00
OH Orlando Hudson/550 4.00 10.00
RA Roberto Alomar/150 10.00 25.00
RJ Randy Johnson/51 40.00 80.00
RP Rafael Palmeiro/150 15.00 40.00
SP Scott Podsednik/550 10.00 25.00
VG Vladimir Guerrero/27 30.00 60.00

2004 Fleer Genuine Insider Autograph Cuts

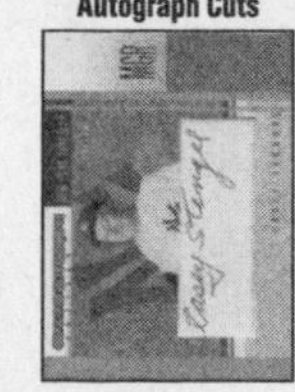

OVERALL ODDS AU 1:18 H, AU-GU 1:48 R
PRINT RUNS B/WN 1-10 COPIES PER
NO PRICING DUE TO SCARCITY
BT Bill Terry/10
CS Casey Stengel/3
PT Pie Traynor/1
RM Roger Maris/1
ZW Zack Wheat/1

2004 Fleer Genuine Insider Autograph-Jersey

STATED PRINT RUN 100 SERIAL #'d SETS
AUTO BALL PRINT RUN 10 #'d SETS
NO AUTO BALL PRICING DUE TO SCARCITY
*AUTO BAT: .5X TO 1.2X BASIC
AUTO BAT PRINT RUN 50 SERIAL #'d SETS
OVERALL ODDS AU 1:18 H, AU-GU 1:48 R
AH Aubrey Huff 6.00 15.00
AK Austin Kearns 6.00 15.00
AP Albert Pujols 125.00 200.00
BW Brandon Webb 6.00 15.00
DE David Eckstein 12.50 30.00
IR Ivan Rodriguez 20.00 50.00
JG Jody Gerut 6.00 15.00
JG2 Jay Gibbons 6.00 15.00
JR Jose Reyes 6.00 15.00
JR2 Jimmy Rollins 10.00 25.00
JS Jason Schmidt 6.00 15.00
JS2 John Smoltz 20.00 50.00
MB Marlon Byrd 6.00 15.00
MC Miguel Cabrera 10.00 25.00
MO Magglio Ordonez 6.00 15.00
MR Mariano Rivera 30.00 60.00
MT Mark Teixeira 10.00 25.00
OH Orlando Hudson 6.00 15.00
RA Roberto Alomar 10.00 25.00
RP Rafael Palmeiro 20.00 50.00
SP Scott Podsednik 10.00 25.00

2004 Fleer Genuine Insider Classic Confrontations

STATED ODDS 1:18 HOBBY, 1:24 RETAIL
1 Mike Piazza 1.25 3.00
Roger Clemens
2 Pedro Martinez 2.50 6.00
Derek Jeter
3 Randy Johnson 1.00 2.50
Jeff Bagwell
4 Mark Prior 2.50 6.00
Albert Pujols
5 Josh Beckett 1.00 2.50
Sammy Sosa
6 Eric Gagne .40 1.00
Hank Blalock
7 Mariano Rivera 1.00 2.50
Nomar Garciaparra
8 Curt Schilling 1.00 2.50
Chipper Jones
9 Kerry Wood .60 1.50
Jim Edmonds
10 Barry Zito .40 1.00
Alfonso Soriano
11 Randy Johnson 1.50 4.00
Ken Griffey Jr.
12 Derek Jeter 2.50 6.00
John Smoltz
13 Roy Oswalt 1.50 4.00
Ken Griffey Jr.
14 Dontrelle Willis .40 1.00
Hideki Matsui
15 Hideo Nomo 1.50 4.00
Ichiro Suzuki

2004 Fleer Genuine Insider Classic Confrontations Dual Swatch

STATED PRINT RUN 100 SERIAL #'d SETS
DUAL PATCH PRINT RUN 10 #'d SETS
NO DUAL PATCH PRICE DUE TO SCARCITY
OVERALL ODDS GU 1:9 H, AU-GU 1:48 R
BZAS Barry Zito 4.00 10.00
Alfonso Soriano
CSCJ Curt Schilling 6.00 15.00
Chipper Jones
EGHB Eric Gagne 4.00 10.00
Hank Blalock
JBSS Josh Beckett 6.00 15.00
Sammy Sosa
KWJE Kerry Wood 4.00 10.00
Jim Edmonds
MPAP Mark Prior 10.00 25.00
Albert Pujols
MPRC Mike Piazza
Roger Clemens
MRNG Mariano Rivera 6.00 15.00
Nomar Garciaparra
PMDJ Pedro Martinez 10.00 25.00
Derek Jeter
RJJB Randy Johnson 6.00 15.00
Jeff Bagwell

2004 Fleer Genuine Insider Classic Confrontations Swatch

OVERALL ODDS GU 1:9 H, AU-GU 1:48 R
STATED PRINT RUN 400 SERIAL #'d SETS
AP A.Pujols Jsy w/Prior 5.00 12.00
AS A.Soriano Jsy w/Zito 2.00 5.00
BZ B.Zito Jsy w/Soriano 2.00 5.00
CJ C.Jones Jsy w/Schilling 3.00 8.00
CS C.Schilling Jsy w/Chipper 3.00 8.00
DJ D.Jeter Jsy w/Pedro 6.00 15.00
DW D.Willis Jsy w/Matsui 3.00 8.00
EG E.Gagne Jsy w/Blalock 2.00 5.00
HB H.Blalock Jsy w/Gagne 2.00 5.00
HN H.Nomo Jsy w/Ichiro 3.00 8.00
JB J.Bagwell Jsy w/Randy 3.00 8.00
JB2 J.Beckett Jsy w/Sosa 2.00 5.00
JE J.Edmonds Jsy w/Wood 2.00 5.00
JS J.Smoltz Jsy w/Jeter 3.00 8.00
KW K.Wood Jsy w/Edmonds 2.00 5.00
MP M.Piazza Jsy w/Clemens 4.00 10.00
MP2 M.Prior Jsy w/Pujols 4.00 10.00
MR M.Rivera Jsy w/Nomar 3.00 8.00
NG N.Garciaparra Jsy w/Rivera 4.00 10.00
PM P.Martinez Jsy w/Jeter 3.00 8.00
RC R.Clemens Jsy w/Piazza 5.00 12.00
RJ1 R.Johnson Jsy w/Bagwell 3.00 8.00
RJ2 R.Johnson Jsy w/Griffey Jr. 3.00 8.00
RO R.Oswalt Jsy w/Griffey Jr. 2.00 5.00
SS S.Sosa Jsy w/Beckett 3.00 8.00

2004 Fleer Genuine Insider Tools of the Game

STATED ODDS 1:6 HOBBY, 1:12 RETAIL
1 Jason Giambi .40 1.00
2 Torii Hunter .40 1.00
3 Derek Jeter 2.50 6.00
4 Nomar Garciaparra 1.00 2.50
5 Albert Pujols 2.50 6.00
6 Jim Thome .60 1.50
7 Alex Rodriguez 1.50 4.00
8 Chipper Jones 1.00 2.50
9 Sammy Sosa 1.00 2.50
10 Jose Reyes .60 1.50
11 Pedro Martinez .60 1.50
12 Greg Maddux 1.50 4.00
13 Randy Johnson 1.00 2.50
14 Curt Schilling .60 1.50
15 Mark Prior .60 1.50
16 Ichiro Suzuki 1.50 4.00
17 Hideki Matsui 1.50 4.00
18 Kaz Matsui .60 1.50
19 Ken Griffey Jr. 1.50 4.00
20 Josh Beckett .60 1.50

2004 Fleer Genuine Insider Tools of the Game Jersey

STATED PRINT RUN 250 SERIAL #'d SETS
*TOOLS 2-PIECE: .75X TO 2X BASIC
TOOLS 2-PIECE PRINT RUN 125 #'d SETS
TOOLS 2-PIECE ARE BAT-JSY CARDS
*TOOLS 3-PIECE: 1.5X TO 4X BASIC
TOOLS 3-PIECE PRINT RUN 75 #'d SETS
TOOLS 3-PIECE ARE BAT-CAP-JSY CARDS
OVERALL ODDS GU 1:9 H, AU-GU 1:48 R
AP Albert Pujols Jsy 6.00 15.00
AR Alex Rodriguez Jsy 6.00 15.00
CJ Chipper Jones Jsy 3.00 8.00
CS Curt Schilling Jsy 3.00 8.00
DJ Derek Jeter Jsy 8.00 20.00
GM Greg Maddux Jsy 5.00 12.00
JG Jason Giambi Jsy 2.00 5.00
JR Jose Reyes Jsy 2.00 5.00
JT Jim Thome Jsy 3.00 8.00
MP Mark Prior Jsy 3.00 8.00
NG Nomar Garciaparra Jsy 5.00 12.00
PM Pedro Martinez Jsy 3.00 8.00
RJ Randy Johnson Jsy 3.00 8.00
SS Sammy Sosa Jsy 3.00 8.00
TH Torii Hunter Jsy 2.00 5.00

2004 Fleer InScribed

This 100 card set was released in September, 2004. The set was issued in five card hobby packs which came 12 packs to a box and six boxes to a case. The set consists of 75 veteran cards, 10 retired great cards (76-85) and 15 Rookie Cards (86-100). The retired greats cards were issued at stated odds of one in 20 hobby and one in 200 retail and were issued to a stated print run of 1000 serial numbered sets. The Rookie Cards were all serial numbered to 750 but the actual number of these cards issued are notated in our checklist. Please note that these cards were issued at a stated rate of one in 12 hobby and one in 100 retail packs. The reason that these cards all have different print runs in that many of these rookies signed cards for inclusion in this product.

COMP.SET w/o SP's (75) 10.00 25.00
COMMON CARD (1-75) .15 .40
COMMON CARD (76-85) .40 1.00
76-85 ODDS 1:20 HOBBY, 1:200 RETAIL
76-85 PRINT RUN 1000 SERIAL #'d SETS
COMMON CARD (86-100) .40 1.00
86-100 ODDS 1:12 HOBBY, 1:100 RETAIL
86-100 ARE ALL SERIAL #'d TO 750
86-100 ACTUAL PRINT RUNS B/WN 325-750
86-100 W/ASTERISK = ACTUAL PRINT RUN
ACTUAL PRINT RUNS PROVIDED BY FLEER
86-100: ON MANY, 1ST 75-425 #'d ARE AU'S
SEE AUTO PARALLEL SETS FOR AU PRICES
1 Vladimir Guerrero .40 1.00
2 Bartolo Colon .15 .40
3 Troy Glaus .15 .40
4 Richie Sexson .15 .40
5 Randy Johnson .40 1.00
6 Luis Gonzalez .15 .40
7 J.D. Drew .15 .40
8 Chipper Jones .40 1.00
9 Andruw Jones .15 .40
10 Melvin Mora .15 .40
11 Miguel Tejada .25 .60
12 Curt Schilling .25 .60
13 Pedro Martinez .25 .60
14 Nomar Garciaparra .40 1.00
15 Kerry Wood .15 .40
16 Mark Prior .25 .60
17 Sammy Sosa .40 1.00
18 Frank Thomas .40 1.00
19 Magglio Ordonez .25 .60
20 Sean Casey .15 .40
21 Ken Griffey Jr. .60 1.50
22 Adam Dunn .25 .60
23 Jody Gerut .15 .40
24 Omar Vizquel .25 .60
25 Todd Helton .25 .60
26 Vinny Castilla .15 .40
27 Alex Sanchez .15 .40
28 Ivan Rodriguez .25 .60
29 Dontrelle Willis .15 .40
30 Josh Beckett .25 .60
31 Miguel Cabrera .40 1.00
32 Roger Clemens .50 1.25
33 Andy Pettitte .25 .60
34 Jeff Bagwell .25 .60
35 Ken Harvey .15 .40
36 Carlos Beltran .15 .40
37 Shawn Green .15 .40
38 Hideo Nomo .40 1.00
39 Scott Podsednik .15 .40
40 Ben Sheets .15 .40
41 Torii Hunter .15 .40
42 Jacque Jones .15 .40
43 Jose Vidro .15 .40
44 Mike Piazza .40 1.00
45 Tom Glavine .25 .60
46 Derek Jeter 1.00 2.50
47 Alex Rodriguez .60 1.50
48 Jason Giambi .15 .40
49 Hideki Matsui .60 1.50
50 Eric Chavez .15 .40
51 Barry Zito .15 .40
52 Tim Hudson .25 .60
53 Mark Mulder .15 .40
54 Jim Thome .25 .60
55 Pat Burrell .15 .40
56 Chase Utley .40 1.00
57 Jason Kendall .15 .40
58 Jack Wilson .15 .40
59 Khalil Greene .25 .60
60 Brian Giles .15 .40
61 Jason Schmidt .15 .40
62 Marquis Grissom .15 .40
63 Ichiro Suzuki .60 1.50
64 Bret Boone .15 .40
65 Albert Pujols 1.00 2.50
66 Scott Rolen .25 .60
67 Jim Edmonds .25 .60
68 Tino Martinez .25 .60
69 Rocco Baldelli .15 .40
70 Alfonso Soriano .15 .40
71 Michael Young .15 .40
72 Hank Blalock .15 .40
73 Roy Halladay .40 1.00
74 Carlos Delgado .15 .40
75 Vernon Wells .15 .40
76 Johnny Bench RET 1.00 2.50
77 Reggie Jackson RET .60 1.50
78 Al Kaline RET 1.00 2.50
79 Nolan Ryan RET 3.00 8.00
80 Tom Seaver RET .60 1.50
81 Robin Yount RET 1.00 2.50
82 Mike Schmidt RET 1.50 4.00
83 Jim Palmer RET .40 1.00
84 Harmon Killebrew RET 1.00 2.50
85 Joe Morgan RET .40 1.00
86 Kaz Matsui ROO/675 RC * .60 1.50
87 L.Gonzalez ROO/435 RC * .40 1.00
88 Yadier Molina ROO/750 RC 2.50 6.00
89 Jon Knott ROO/675 RC * .40 1.00
90 Kevin Youkilis ROO/640 * .60 1.50
91 Chris Saenz ROO/325 RC * .40 1.00
92 A.Blanco ROO/675 RC * .40 1.00
93 D.Aardsma ROO/750 RC .40 1.00
94 Merkin Valdez ROO/500 RC * .40 1.00
95 Jason Bartlett ROO/675 RC * 1.25 3.00
96 John Gall ROO/325 RC * .40 1.00
97 Zack Greinke ROO/675 * .60 1.50
98 Scott Hairston ROO/675 * .40 1.00
99 Matt Holliday ROO/750 1.00 2.50
100 C.Kotchman ROO/375 * .40 1.00

2004 Fleer InScribed Gold

*GOLD 1-75: 3X TO 8X BASIC
*GOLD 76-85: .6X TO 1.5X BASIC
*GOLD 86-100: .6X TO 1.5X BASIC
OVERALL PARALLEL ODDS 1:18 H, 1:96 R
STATED PRINT RUN 199 SERIAL #'d SETS
BLACK BORDERED CARDS W/GOLD FOIL

2004 Fleer InScribed Red

OVERALL PARALLEL ODDS 1:18 H, 1:96 R
STATED PRINT RUN 5 SERIAL #'d SETS
BLACK BORDERED CARDS W/RED FOIL
NO PRICING DUE TO SCARCITY

2004 Fleer InScribed Autographs Purple

Randy Johnson's card is actually serial #'d to 51 copies, but according to representatives at Fleer only 40 copies were produced (skip-numbered across the print run).The card has been notated within our checklist as an uncorrected error with the erroneous and actual print runs detailed side-by-side.

*PUR p/r 38-52: .5X TO 1.2X SILV p/r 235-322
*PUR p/r 38-52: .5X TO 1.2X SILV p/r 134-195
*PUR p/r 38-52: .4X TO 1X SILV p/r 55-57
*PUR p/r 38-52: .3X TO .8X SILV 20-34
*PUR p/r 20-35: .6X TO 1.5X SILV p/r 235-322
*PUR p/r 20-35: .6X TO 1.5X SILV 134-195
*PUR p/r 20-35: .5X TO 1.2X SILV p/r 55-57
*PUR p/r 15-18: .75X TO 2X SILV p/r 235-322
OVERALL AU ODDS 1:12 H, AU-GU 1:48 R
PRINT RUNS B/WN 3-52 COPIES PER
NO PRICING ON QTY OF 11 OR LESS
CARDS W/UER = ERR #ING AND ACTUAL QTY
ACTUAL R.JOHNSON QTY FROM FLEER

2004 Fleer InScribed Autographs Red

The Albert Pujols and Randy Johnson cards within this set contain erroneous serial-numbering. The Pujols cards are serial #'d to 25 but according to Fleer only 10 copies (skip-numbered across the print run) were actually printed. Similarly, the Johnson cards are serial #'d to 25 but only 15 copies were produced. Each card has been notated within our checklist as an uncorrected error with the erroneous and actual print runs detailed side-by-side.

*RED: .6X TO 1.5X SILVER p/r 235-322
*RED: .6X TO 1.5X SILVER p/r 134-195
*RED: .5X TO 1.2X SILVER p/r 55-57
*RED: .4X TO 1X SILVER p/r 20-34
OVERALL AU ODDS 1:12 H, AU-GU 1:48 R
STATED PRINT RUN 25 SERIAL #'d SETS
UER'S ARE #'d OF 25 BUT 10-15 PER MADE
ACTUAL UER QTY PROVIDED BY FLEER
NO PUJOLS UER/10 PRICING AVAILABLE
AB Angel Berroa 6.00 15.00

2004 Fleer InScribed Autographs Silver

OVERALL AU ODDS 1:12 H, AU-GU 1:48 R
PRINT RUNS B/WN 5-322 COPIES PER
CARDS ARE NOT SERIAL-NUMBERED
PRINT RUN INFO PROVIDED BY FLEER
NO PRICING ON QTY OF 11 OR LESS
AB Angel Berroa/11 *
AP Albert Pujols/5 *
BG Brian Giles/134 * 4.00 10.00
BL Barry Larkin/140 * 10.00 25.00
BR Brad Radke/168 * 6.00 15.00
CB Carlos Beltran/296 * 6.00 15.00
DW Dontrelle Willis/290 * 10.00 25.00
EC Eric Chavez/322 * 6.00 15.00
EG Eric Gagne/57 * 12.50 30.00
JB Jeremy Bonderman/287 * 6.00 15.00
JL Javy Lopez/257 * 6.00 15.00
LG Luis Gonzalez/55 * 5.00 12.00
LO Lyle Overbay/240 * 4.00 10.00
RB Rocco Baldelli/34 * 10.00 25.00
RHL Roy Halladay/139 * 30.00 60.00
RHR Rich Harden/235 * 6.00 15.00
RJ Randy Johnson/20 * 40.00 80.00
SP Scott Podsednik/280 * 10.00 25.00
TH Trevor Hoffman/174 * 10.00 25.00
TN Trot Nixon/318 * 6.00 15.00
WM Wade Miller/195 * 4.00 10.00

2004 Fleer InScribed Rookie Autographs

OVERALL AU ODDS 1:12 H, AU-GU 1:48 R
CARDS ARE SERIAL #'d TO 750
ACTUAL PRINT RUNS B/WN 34-646 PER
ACTUAL PRINT RUNS PROVIDED BY FLEER
HENN/MCPHERSON AVAIL.ONLY AS AU'S
87 Luis A. Gonzalez/240 * 3.00 8.00
90 Kevin Youkilis/34 * 6.00 15.00
91 Chris Saenz/350 * 3.00 8.00
94 Merkin Valdez/175 * 4.00 10.00
96 John Gall/350 * 4.00 10.00
100 Casey Kotchman/300 * 5.00 12.00
DM Dallas McPherson/646 * 6.00 15.00
SH Sean Henn/526 * 3.00 8.00

2004 Fleer InScribed Rookie Autographs Notation

OVERALL AU ODDS 1:12 H, AU-GU 1:48 R
CARDS ARE SERIAL #'d TO 750
ACTUAL PRINT RUN 75 COPIES PER
J.GALL PRINT RUNS B/WN 25-50 PER
NOTATIONS ARE 1ST 75 #'d CARDS
NO GALL-STAR PRICING DUE TO SCARCITY
87 Luis A. Gonzalez 4/6/04 6.00 15.00
89 Jon Knott 5/30/04 6.00 15.00
90 Kevin Youkilis 5/15/04 6.00 15.00
91 Chris Saenz 4/24/04 6.00 15.00
92 Andres Blanco 4/17/04 6.00 15.00
94 Merkin Valdez Go Giants 8.00 20.00
95 Jason Bartlett Go Twins 8.00 20.00
96A John Gall Gall-Star/25 *
96B John Gall Go Cards/50 * 8.00 20.00
98 Scott Hairston 5/17/04 6.00 15.00
100 Casey Kotchman 5/9/04 6.00 15.00

2004 Fleer InScribed Award Winners

OVERALL INSERT ODDS 1:12 H, 1:12 R
STATED PRINT RUN 150 SERIAL #'d SETS
1 Alex Rodriguez 3.00 8.00
2 Eric Gagne .75 2.00
3 Miguel Tejada 1.25 3.00
4 Roy Halladay 2.00 5.00
5 Randy Johnson 2.00 5.00
6 Barry Zito .75 2.00
7 Chipper Jones 2.00 5.00
8 Ivan Rodriguez 1.25 3.00
9 Pedro Martinez 1.25 3.00
10 Barry Larkin 1.25 3.00
11 Dontrelle Willis .75 2.00
12 Angel Berroa .75 2.00
13 Kerry Wood .75 2.00
14 Albert Pujols 5.00 12.00
15 Hideo Nomo 2.00 5.00

2004 Fleer InScribed Award Winners Autographs

OVERALL AU ODDS 1:12 H, AU-GU 1:48 R
PRINT RUNS B/WN 15-103 COPIES PER
CARDS W/UER = ERR #ING AND ACTUAL QTY
ACTUAL UER QTY PROVIDED BY FLEER
EXCHANGE DEADLINE INDEFINITE
AB Angel Berroa/103 6.00 15.00
BL Barry Larkin UER 95/50 * 15.00 40.00
BZ Barry Zito UER 99/35 * 12.50 30.00
CJ Chipper Jones UER 99/35 * 30.00 60.00
DW Dontrelle Willis/103 15.00 40.00
IR Ivan Rodriguez UER 99/35 * 30.00 60.00
RH Roy Halladay/102 15.00 40.00

2004 Fleer InScribed Award Winners Jersey Silver

STATED PRINT RUN 175 SERIAL #'d SETS
*BLUE: 1.25X TO 3X SILVER
BLUE PRINT RUN 15 SERIAL #'d SETS
*COPPER: .4X TO 1X SILVER
COPPER PRINT RUN 99 SERIAL #'d SETS
*PURPLE PATCH: 1X TO 2.5X SILVER
PURPLE PATCH PRINT RUN 49 #'d SETS
OVERALL GU ODDS 1:6 H, AU-GU 1:48 R
AB Angel Berroa 2.50 6.00
AP Albert Pujols 8.00 20.00
BL Barry Larkin 4.00 10.00
BZ Barry Zito 2.50 6.00
CJ Chipper Jones 4.00 10.00
DW Dontrelle Willis 4.00 10.00
EG Eric Gagne 2.50 6.00
HN Hideo Nomo 4.00 10.00
IR Ivan Rodriguez 4.00 10.00
KW Kerry Wood 2.50 6.00
MT Miguel Tejada 2.50 6.00
PM Pedro Martinez 4.00 10.00
RH Roy Halladay 2.50 6.00
RJ Randy Johnson 4.00 10.00

2004 Fleer InScribed Induction Ceremony

OVERALL INSERT ODDS 1:12 H, 1:12 R
PRINT RUNS B/WN
1 Carlton Fisk/100 2.00 5.00
2 Tony Perez/100 1.25 3.00
3 Nolan Ryan/99 10.00 25.00
4 Robin Yount/99 3.00 8.00
5 Orlando Cepeda/99 1.25 3.00
6 Bill Mazeroski/101 2.00 5.00
7 Larry Doby/98 1.25 3.00
8 Phil Niekro/97 1.25 3.00
9 Jim Bunning/96 1.25 3.00
10 Sparky Anderson/100 1.25 3.00
11 Phil Rizzuto/94 2.00 5.00
12 Rollie Fingers/92 1.25 3.00
13 Hal Newhouser/92 1.25 3.00
14 Rod Carew/91 2.00 5.00
15 Reggie Jackson/93 2.00 5.00
16 Tom Seaver/92 2.00 5.00
17 Bob Gibson/81 2.00 5.00
18 Jim Palmer/90 2.00 5.00
19 Joe Morgan/90 1.25 3.00
20 Al Kaline/80 3.00 8.00

2004 Fleer InScribed Induction Ceremony Autographs Bronze

Though each card from this set is serial-numbered to 50, Nolan Ryan, Orlando Cepeda, Phil Niekro, Reggie Jackson, Robin Yount and Tom Seaver were all produced in smaller quantities ranging between 30-40 copies per. These cards have been tagged as UER's (uncorrected errors) in our checklist with the actual quantity listed as provided by Fleer.

OVERALL AU ODDS 1:12 H, AU-GU 1:48 R
STATED PRINT RUN 50 SERIAL #'d SETS
UER'S ARE #'d OF 50 BUT 30-40 PER MADE
ACTUAL UER QTY PROVIDED BY FLEER
EXCHANGE DEADLINE INDEFINITE
AK Al Kaline 30.00 60.00
BG Bob Gibson 15.00 40.00
CF Carlton Fisk 15.00 40.00
JB Jim Bunning 10.00 25.00
NR Nolan Ryan/35 UER * 60.00 120.00
OC Orlando Cepeda/40 UER * 10.00 25.00
PN Phil Niekro/35 UER * 20.00 50.00
RF Rollie Fingers 10.00 25.00
RJ Reggie Jackson/30 UER * 40.00 80.00
TP Tony Perez 15.00 40.00
TS Tom Seaver/30 UER * 30.00 60.00

2004 Fleer InScribed Induction Ceremony Autographs Gold

OVERALL AU ODDS 1:12 H, AU-GU 1:48 R
STATED PRINT RUN 5 SERIAL #'d SETS
EXCHANGE DEADLINE INDEFINITE
NO PRICING DUE TO SCARCITY

2004 Fleer InScribed Induction Ceremony Autographs Silver

Though each card from this set is serial-numbered to 15, Carlton Fisk, Nolan Ryan, Orlando Cepeda, Phil Niekro, Reggie Jackson, Robin Yount, Tony Perez and Tom Seaver were all produced in smaller quantities ranging between 10-12 copies per. These cards have been tagged as UER's (uncorrected errors) in our checklist with the actual quantity listed as provided by Fleer.

*SILVER: .6X TO 1.5X BRONZE
OVERALL AU ODDS 1:12 H, AU-GU 1:48 R
STATED PRINT RUN 15 SERIAL #'d SETS
UER'S ARE #'d OF 15 BUT 10-12 PER MADE
ACTUAL UER QTY PROVIDED BY FLEER
NO UER PRICING DUE TO SCARCITY
UER CL: CF/NR/OC/PN/RJ/RY/TP/TS
EXCHANGE DEADLINE INDEFINITE

2004 Fleer InScribed Induction Ceremony Material Silver

PRINT RUNS B/WN 80-101 COPIES PER
MASTERPIECE PRINT RUN 1 #'d SET
NO M'PIECE PRICING DUE TO SCARCITY
OVERALL GU ODDS 1:6 H, AU-GU 1:48 R
AK Al Kaline Pants/80 8.00 20.00
BM Bill Mazeroski Bat/101 6.00 15.00
CF Carlton Fisk Jsy/100 6.00 15.00
JM Joe Morgan Bat/90 4.00 10.00
JP Jim Palmer Jsy/90 4.00 10.00
LD Larry Doby Bat/98 4.00 10.00
NR Nolan Ryan Jsy/99 12.50 30.00
OC Orlando Cepeda Bat/99 4.00 10.00
PN Phil Niekro Jsy/97 4.00 10.00
PR Phil Rizzuto Bat/94 6.00 15.00
RC Rod Carew Jsy/91 6.00 15.00
RF Rollie Fingers Jsy/92 4.00 10.00
RJ Reggie Jackson Pants/93 6.00 15.00
RY Robin Yount Jsy/99 8.00 20.00
SA Sparky Anderson Jsy/100 4.00 10.00
TP Tony Perez Bat/100 4.00 10.00
TS Tom Seaver Jsy/92 6.00 15.00

2004 Fleer InScribed Names of the Game

OVERALL INSERT ODDS 1:12 H, 1:12 R
STATED PRINT RUN 299 SERIAL #'d SETS
1 Nomar Garciaparra 2.00 5.00
2 Randy Johnson 2.00 5.00
3 Hideki Matsui 3.00 8.00
4 Frank Thomas 2.00 5.00
5 Ivan Rodriguez 1.25 3.00
6 Roger Clemens 2.50 6.00
7 Chipper Jones 2.00 5.00
8 Dontrelle Willis .75 2.00
9 Luis Gonzalez .75 2.00
10 Alex Rodriguez 3.00 8.00
11 Eric Gagne .75 2.00
12 Juan Gonzalez .75 2.00
13 Hideo Nomo 2.00 5.00
14 Sean Casey .75 2.00
15 Greg Maddux 3.00 8.00
16 Cal Ripken 8.00 20.00
17 Carl Yastrzemski 2.00 5.00
18 Tony Perez .75 2.00
19 Joe Morgan .75 2.00
20 Carlton Fisk 1.25 3.00
21 Willie McCovey 1.25 3.00
22 Al Kaline 2.00 5.00
23 Dennis Eckersley .75 2.00
24 Ted Williams 5.00 12.00
25 Willie Stargell 1.25 3.00
26 Rollie Fingers .75 2.00
27 Yogi Berra 2.00 5.00
28 Reggie Jackson 1.25 3.00
29 Harmon Killebrew 2.00 5.00
30 Nolan Ryan 6.00 15.00

2004 Fleer InScribed Names of the Game Autographs Silver

OVERALL AU ODDS 1:12 H, AU-GU 1:48 R
CARDS ARE SERIAL #'d TO 99
UER'S ARE #'d OF 99 BUT 20-90 PER MADE
ACTUAL UER QTY PROVIDED BY FLEER
EXCHANGE DEADLINE INDEFINITE
AK Al Kaline/90 UER * 20.00 50.00
CF Carlton Fisk/50 UER * 15.00 40.00
CJ Chipper Jones/40 UER * 30.00 60.00
DE Dennis Eckersley/90 UER * 10.00 25.00
DW Dontrelle Willis 15.00 40.00
IR Ivan Rodriguez/40 UER * 30.00 60.00
LG Luis Gonzalez/75 UER * 6.00 15.00
NR Nolan Ryan/35 UER * 75.00 150.00
RF Rollie Fingers/90 UER * 10.00 25.00
RJ Reggie Jackson/35 UER * 40.00 80.00
SC Sean Casey 10.00 25.00
TP Tony Perez/40 UER *

2004 Fleer InScribed Names of the Game Autographs Gold

*GOLD p/r 25: .6X TO 1.5X SILVER p/r 75-99
*GOLD p/r 25: .5X TO 1.2X SILVER p/r 40-50
OVERALL AU ODDS 1:12 H, AU-GU 1:48 R
CARDS ARE SERIAL #'d TO 25
UER'S ARE #'d TO 25 BUT 1-22 PER MADE
ACTUAL UER QTY PROVIDED BY FLEER
UER p/r 15's ARE NOMO, REGGIE & RYAN
NO PRICING ON UER QTY B/WN 1-10 PER
EXCHANGE DEADLINE INDEFINITE
RC Roger Clemens/22 UER *
TW Ted Williams/1 UER *

2004 Fleer InScribed Names of the Game Material Copper

STATED PRINT RUN 250 SERIAL #'d SETS
*BLUE: 1.25X TO 3X COPPER
BLUE PRINT RUN 20 SERIAL #'d SETS
*GOLD: .4X TO 1X COPPER
GOLD PRINT RUN 150 SERIAL #'d SETS
*PURPLE BAT-PANTS: 1X TO 2.5X COPPER
*PURPLE PATCH: 1.5X TO 4X COPPER
PURPLE PRINT RUN 33 SERIAL #'d SETS
*RED: .5X TO 1.2X COPPER
RED PRINT RUN 79 SERIAL #'d SETS
*SILVER: .4X TO 1X COPPER
SILVER ODDS AU-GU 1:48 RETAIL
SILVER PRINT RUN 150 SETS
SILVER ARE NOT SERIAL-NUMBERED
SILVER PRINT RUN PROVIDED BY FLEER
OVERALL GU ODDS 1:6 H, AU-GU 1:48 R
AK Al Kaline Pants 6.00 15.00
CF Carlton Fisk Jsy 4.00 10.00
CJ Chipper Jones Jsy 3.00 8.00
CR Cal Ripken Jsy 10.00 25.00
CY Carl Yastrzemski Jsy 6.00 15.00
DE Dennis Eckersley Jsy 3.00 8.00
DW Dontrelle Willis Jsy 3.00 8.00
EG Eric Gagne Jsy 2.00 5.00
FT Frank Thomas Jsy 3.00 8.00
GM Greg Maddux Jsy 4.00 10.00
HK Harmon Killebrew Bat 6.00 15.00
HM Hideki Matsui Jsy 10.00 25.00
HN Hideo Nomo Jsy 3.00 8.00
IR Ivan Rodriguez Jsy 3.00 8.00
JG Juan Gonzalez Jsy 2.00 5.00
JM Joe Morgan Bat 3.00 8.00
LG Luis Gonzalez Jsy 2.00 5.00
NR Nolan Ryan Jsy 10.00 25.00
RC Roger Clemens Jsy 4.00 10.00
RF Rollie Fingers Jsy 3.00 8.00
RJA Reggie Jackson Pants 4.00 10.00
RJO Randy Johnson Jsy 3.00 8.00
SC Sean Casey Jsy 2.00 5.00
TP Tony Perez Bat 3.00 8.00
TW Ted Williams Bat 20.00 50.00
WM Willie McCovey Pants 4.00 10.00
WS Willie Stargell Jsy 4.00 10.00
YB Yogi Berra Bat 6.00 15.00

2001 Fleer Legacy

The 2001 Fleer Legacy product was released in mid-July, 2001 and featured a 105-card base set that was broken into tiers as follows: Base Veterans (1-90) and Prospects (91-105) that are individually serial numbered to 799. Please note that the first 300 serial-numbered cards of Albert Pujols packed out as exchange cards for a copy actually signed by Pujols. Card number 98 does not exist. Each box contained 15 packs with five cards per pack.

COMP.SET w/o SP's (90) 15.00 40.00
COMMON CARD (1-90) .40 1.00
COMMON AUTO (91-100) 4.00 10.00
COMMON CARD (101-105) 3.00 8.00
1 Pedro Martinez .60 1.50
2 Andruw Jones .60 1.50
3 Mike Hampton .40 1.00
4 Gary Sheffield .40 1.00
5 Barry Zito .60 1.50
6 J.D. Drew .40 1.00
7 Charles Johnson .40 1.00
8 David Wells .40 1.00
9 Kazuhiro Sasaki .40 1.00
10 Vladimir Guerrero 1.00 2.50
11 Pat Burrell .40 1.00
12 Ruben Mateo .40 1.00
13 Greg Maddux 1.50 4.00
14 Sean Casey .40 1.00
15 Craig Biggio .60 1.50
16 Bernie Williams .60 1.50
17 Jeff Kent .40 1.00
18 Nomar Garciaparra 1.50 4.00
19 Cal Ripken 3.00 8.00
20 Larry Walker .40 1.00
21 Adrian Beltre .40 1.00
22 Johnny Damon .60 1.50
23 Rick Ankiel .40 1.00
24 Matt Williams .40 1.00
25 Magglio Ordonez .40 1.00
26 Richard Hidalgo .40 1.00
27 Robin Ventura .40 1.00
28 Jason Kendall .40 1.00
29 Tony Batista .40 1.00
30 Chipper Jones 1.00 2.50
31 Jim Thome .60 1.50
32 Kevin Brown .40 1.00
33 Mike Mussina .60 1.50
34 Mark McGwire 2.50 6.00
35 Darin Erstad .40 1.00
36 Manny Ramirez Sox .60 1.50
37 Bobby Higginson .40 1.00
38 Richie Sexson .40 1.00
39 Jason Giambi .40 1.00
40 Alex Rodriguez 1.50 4.00
41 Mark Grace .60 1.50
42 Ken Griffey Jr. 1.50 4.00
43 Moises Alou .40 1.00
44 Edgardo Alfonzo .40 1.00
45 Phil Nevin .40 1.00
46 Rafael Palmeiro .60 1.50
47 Javy Lopez .40 1.00
48 Juan Gonzalez .40 1.00
49 Jermaine Dye .40 1.00
50 Roger Clemens 2.00 5.00
51 Barry Bonds 2.50 6.00
52 Carl Everett .40 1.00
53 Ben Sheets .60 1.50
54 Juan Encarnacion .40 1.00
55 Jeromy Burnitz .40 1.00
56 Miguel Tejada .40 1.00
57 Ben Grieve .40 1.00
58 Randy Johnson 1.00 2.50
59 Frank Thomas 1.00 2.50
60 Preston Wilson .40 1.00
61 Mike Piazza 1.50 4.00
62 Brian Giles .40 1.00
63 Carlos Delgado .40 1.00
64 Tom Glavine .60 1.50
65 Roberto Alomar .60 1.50
66 Mike Sweeney .40 1.00
67 Orlando Hernandez .40 1.00
68 Edgar Martinez .60 1.50
69 Tim Salmon .60 1.50
70 Kerry Wood .40 1.00
71 Jack Wilson RC .60 1.50
72 Matt Lawton .40 1.00
73 Scott Rolen .60 1.50
74 Ivan Rodriguez .60 1.50
75 Steve Finley .40 1.00
76 Barry Larkin .60 1.50
77 Jeff Bagwell .60 1.50
78 Derek Jeter 2.50 6.00
79 Tony Gwynn 1.25 3.00
80 Raul Mondesi .40 1.00
81 Rafael Furcal .40 1.00
82 Todd Helton .60 1.50
83 Shawn Green .40 1.00
84 Tim Hudson .40 1.00
85 Jim Edmonds .40 1.00
86 Troy Glaus .40 1.00
87 Sammy Sosa 1.00 2.50
88 Cliff Floyd .40 1.00
89 Jose Vidro .40 1.00
90 Bob Abreu .40 1.00
91 Drew Henson AU RC 6.00 15.00
92 Andy Morales AU RC 4.00 10.00
93 Wilson Betemit AU RC 10.00 25.00
94 Elpidio Guzman AU RC 4.00 10.00
95 Esix Snead AU RC 4.00 10.00
96 Winston Abreu AU RC 4.00 10.00
97 Jeremy Owens AU RC 4.00 10.00
98 Does Not Exist
99 Junior Spivey AU RC 6.00 15.00
100 J. Randolph AU RC 4.00 10.00
101 Ichiro Suzuki RC 30.00 60.00
102 Albert Pujols/499 RC 100.00 200.00
102AU Albert Pujols AU/300 200.00 350.00
103 Tsuyoshi Shinjo RC 4.00 10.00
104 Jay Gibbons RC 4.00 10.00
105 Juan Uribe RC 4.00 10.00

2001 Fleer Legacy Ultimate

Randomly inserted into packs, this 105-card set is actually a complete parallel of the 2001 Fleer Legacy base set. These cards have a gold backdrop, and are serial numbered to 250.

*STARS 1-90: 2.5X TO 6X BASIC CARDS
*ROOKIES 91-100: .2X TO .5X BASIC CARDS
*ROOKIES 101-105: .4X TO 1X BASIC CARDS

2001 Fleer Legacy Hit Kings

Randomly inserted into packs at one in 13, this 29-card insert features actual chips from game-used bats from the major leagues top hitters Cards have been listed in alphabetical order for convenience.

1 Rick Ankiel 4.00 10.00
2 Tony Batista 4.00 10.00
3 Carlos Beltran 4.00 10.00
4 Adrian Beltre 4.00 10.00
5 Barry Bonds 12.50 30.00
6 George Brett 10.00 25.00
7 Jose Canseco 6.00 15.00
8 Roger Cedeno 4.00 10.00
9 Johnny Damon 6.00 15.00
10 Erubiel Durazo 4.00 10.00
11 Juan Encarnacion 4.00 10.00
12 Troy Glaus 4.00 10.00
13 Shawn Green 4.00 10.00
14 Vladimir Guerrero 6.00 15.00
15 Reggie Jackson 6.00 15.00
16 Andruw Jones 6.00 15.00
17 Jason Kendall 4.00 10.00
18 Ralph Kiner 6.00 15.00
19 Billy Martin 6.00 15.00
20 Ruben Mateo 4.00 10.00
21 Stan Musial 10.00 25.00
22 Troy O'Leary 4.00 10.00
23 Magglio Ordonez 4.00 10.00
24 Corey Patterson 4.00 10.00
25 Juan Pierre 4.00 10.00
26 Ivan Rodriguez 6.00 15.00
27 Tim Salmon 6.00 15.00
28 Jim Thome 6.00 15.00
29 Jose Vidro 4.00 10.00

2001 Fleer Legacy Hit Kings Short Prints

Randomly inserted into packs, this 10-card insert features actual chips from game-used bats from the major leagues top hitters Cards have been listed in alphabetical order for convenience. Please note that there were only 100 serial numbered sets produced. These cards also have a special red-foil stamping on the card fronts.

1 Johnny Bench 15.00 40.00
2 Wade Boggs 15.00 40.00
3 Roger Clemens 40.00 80.00
4 Steve Garvey 10.00 25.00
5 Tony Gwynn 20.00 50.00
6 Eddie Mathews 15.00 40.00
7 Joe Morgan 10.00 25.00
8 Scott Rolen 15.00 40.00
9 Frank Thomas 15.00 40.00
10 Robin Yount 15.00 40.00

2001 Fleer Legacy Hot Gloves

Randomly inserted into packs at one in 180, this 15-card insert featured actual swatches of game-used gloves. Unfortunately, redemption cards had to be placed into packs for all fifteen cards. The exchange deadline was 07/01/02. Prices below refer to actual memorabilia cards. The redemption cards are valued at 25 percent of listed values.

*REDEMPTION CARDS: .25X VALUE
1 Andruw Jones 12.50 30.00
2 Mike Mussina 8.00 20.00

3 Roberto Alomar 12.50 30.00
4 Tony Gwynn 15.00 40.00
5 Bernie Williams 12.50 30.00
6 Ivan Rodriguez 12.50 30.00
7 Ken Griffey Jr. 25.00 60.00
8 Robin Ventura 8.00 20.00
9 Cal Ripken 30.00 80.00
10 Jeff Bagwell 8.00 20.00
11 Mark McGwire 50.00 120.00
12 Rafael Palmeiro 12.50 30.00
13 Scott Rolen 12.50 30.00
14 Barry Bonds 30.00 80.00
15 Greg Maddux 20.00 50.00

2001 Fleer Legacy Derek Jeter Collection

This set, which was issued as a redemption by Fleer over a period of about one year, features signed copies of some cards that never were of Derek Jeter.

ULTRA AU ISSUED VIA MAIL EXCH.IN 2004
FLEER PRINT RUN 500 CARDS
FLEER PRINT INFO PROVIDED BY FLEER
FLEER AU IS NOT SERIAL-NUMBERED
NNO D.Jeter 00 Grts AU 100.00 175.00
NNO D.Jeter 96 Autographics AU 100.00 175.00
NNO D.Jeter 93 Ultra AU 100.00 175.00
NNO Derek Jeter 100.00 175.00
93 Fleer AU/500

2001 Fleer Legacy MLB Autograph Fitted Caps

Inserted at one per box (chiptopper), this collection features actual autographed hats from both modern-day and classic players. Hats have been listed in alphabetical order for convenience. Specific quantities for caps in short supply were announced by Fleer shortly after the product went live. Those figures are detailed within our checklist. According to Fleer, no more than 500 of each cap was signed. Exchange cards, with a redemption deadline of July 1st, 2002, were seeded into packs for the following players: Pat Burrell, Darin Erstad, Nomar Garciaparra, Paul Molitor, Jim Thome and Robin Yount.

1 Edgardo Alfonzo 15.00 40.00
2 Roberto Alomar 20.00 50.00
3 Ernie Banks SP/100 75.00 150.00
4 Adrian Beltre 20.00 50.00
5 Johnny Bench SP/100 75.00 150.00
6 Lance Berkman 20.00 50.00
7 Yogi Berra SP/200 50.00 100.00
8 Craig Biggio 20.00 50.00
9 Barry Bonds 150.00 250.00
10 Jeromy Burnitz 15.00 40.00
11 Pat Burrell 15.00 40.00
12 Steve Carlton 15.00 40.00
13 Sean Casey 15.00 40.00
14 Orlando Cepeda 15.00 40.00
15 Eric Chavez 15.00 40.00
16 Tony Clark 10.00 25.00
17 Roger Clemens SP/100 175.00 300.00
18 Johnny Damon 40.00 80.00
19 Dom DiMaggio SP/200 50.00 100.00
20 J.D. Drew 15.00 40.00
21 Jermaine Dye 15.00 40.00
22 Darin Erstad 15.00 40.00
23 Carlton Fisk SP/150 40.00 80.00
24 Rafael Furcal 15.00 40.00
25 Nomar Garciaparra SP/150 75.00 150.00
26 Jason Giambi 15.00 40.00
27 Troy Glaus 20.00 50.00
28 Tom Glavine 40.00 80.00
29 Juan Gonzalez 15.00 40.00
30 Luis Gonzalez 15.00 40.00
31 Tony Gwynn 60.00 120.00
32 Drew Henson 10.00 25.00
33 Derek Jeter 250.00 350.00
34 Andruw Jones 20.00 50.00
35 David Justice 15.00 40.00
36 Paul Konerko 20.00 50.00
37 Don Mattingly 75.00 150.00
38 Willie McCovey 20.00 50.00
39 Paul Molitor 15.00 40.00
40 Stan Musial SP/200 75.00 150.00
41 Mike Mussina 20.00 50.00
42 Jim Palmer 15.00 40.00
43 Corey Patterson 10.00 25.00
44 Kirby Puckett SP/200 75.00 150.00
45 Cal Ripken SP/200 175.00 300.00
46 Brooks Robinson 20.00 50.00
47 Ivan Rodriguez 40.00 80.00
48 Scott Rolen 20.00 50.00
49 Nolan Ryan SP/150 150.00 250.00
50 Mike Schmidt SP/150 75.00 150.00
51 Tom Seaver SP/100 60.00 120.00
52 Ben Sheets 20.00 50.00
53 Ozzie Smith 60.00 120.00
54 Duke Snider 20.00 50.00
55 Miguel Tejada 20.00 50.00
56 Jim Thome 40.00 80.00
57 Matt Williams 20.00 50.00
58 Dave Winfield SP/150 40.00 80.00
59 C.Yastrzemski SP/150 60.00 120.00
60 Robin Yount 60.00 120.00
61 Barry Zito 20.00 50.00

2001 Fleer Legacy MLB Game Issue Base

Randomly inserted into packs at one in 52, this 15-card insert features actual swatches from game-used bases from top major league talents. Cards have been listed in alphabetical order for convenience.

1 Barry Bonds 12.50 30.00
2 Pat Burrell 4.00 10.00
3 Troy Glaus 4.00 10.00
4 Ken Griffey Jr. 6.00 15.00
5 Tony Gwynn 6.00 15.00
6 Todd Helton 4.00 10.00
7 Derek Jeter 12.50 30.00

8 Chipper Jones 4.00 10.00
9 Mark McGwire 20.00 50.00
10 Mike Piazza 8.00 20.00
11 Cal Ripken 15.00 40.00
12 Alex Rodriguez 10.00 25.00
13 Scott Rolen 4.00 10.00
14 Sammy Sosa 4.00 10.00
15 Frank Thomas 4.00 10.00

2001 Fleer Legacy MLB Game Issue Base-Ball

Randomly inserted into packs, this 15-card insert features actual swatches from both game-used bases and baseballs from top major league talents. Cards have been listed in alphabetical order for convenience. Please note that there were only 100 serial numbered sets produced.

1 Barry Bonds 30.00 80.00
2 Pat Burrell 10.00 25.00
3 Troy Glaus 10.00 25.00
4 Ken Griffey Jr. 20.00 50.00
5 Tony Gwynn 20.00 50.00
6 Todd Helton 10.00 25.00
7 Derek Jeter 30.00 80.00
8 Chipper Jones 15.00 40.00
9 Mark McGwire 60.00 150.00
10 Mike Piazza 30.00 80.00
11 Cal Ripken 40.00 100.00
12 Scott Rolen 10.00 25.00
13 Alex Rodriguez 30.00 80.00
14 Sammy Sosa 15.00 40.00
15 Frank Thomas 15.00 40.00

2001 Fleer Legacy MLB Game Issue Base-Ball-Jersey

Randomly inserted into packs, this 10-card insert features actual swatches from game-used bases, baseballs, and jerseys from top major league talents. Cards have been listed in alphabetical order for convenience. Please note that there were only 50 serial numbered sets produced. Exchange cards, with a redemption deadline of July 1st, 2002, were seeded into packs for the following players: Barry Bonds, Pat Burrell, Tony Gwynn, Cal Ripken and Scott Rolen.

1 Barry Bonds 60.00 150.00
2 Pat Burrell 20.00 50.00
3 Troy Glaus 20.00 50.00
4 Tony Gwynn 40.00 100.00
5 Todd Helton 20.00 50.00
6 Derek Jeter 60.00 150.00
7 Chipper Jones 30.00 80.00
8 Cal Ripken 80.00 200.00
9 Scott Rolen 20.00 50.00
10 Frank Thomas 30.00 80.00

2001 Fleer Legacy Tailor Made

Randomly inserted into packs at one in 15, this 23-card insert features actual swatches of game-used jersey from top major league talents like Barry Bonds and Reggie Jackson. Cards have been listed in alphabetical order for convenience. The Nomar Garciaparra card was released after Fleer's bankruptcy.

*MULTI-COLOR PATCH: .75X TO 2X BASIC
1 Edgardo Alfonzo 4.00 10.00
2 Rick Ankiel 4.00 10.00
3 Barry Bonds 12.50 30.00
4 Kevin Brown 4.00 10.00
5 Orlando Cepeda 4.00 10.00
6 Carlos Delgado 4.00 10.00
7 J.D. Drew 4.00 10.00
8 Nomar Garciaparra
9 Shawn Green 4.00 10.00
10 Todd Helton 6.00 15.00
11 Reggie Jackson 6.00 15.00
12 Jason Kendall 4.00 10.00
13 Greg Maddux 6.00 15.00
14 Don Mattingly 15.00 40.00
15 Willie McCovey 4.00 10.00
16 Rafael Palmeiro 6.00 15.00
17 Lou Piniella 4.00 10.00
18 Manny Ramirez Sox 6.00 15.00
19 Cal Ripken 20.00 50.00
20 Ivan Rodriguez 6.00 15.00
21 Nolan Ryan 20.00 50.00
22 Curt Schilling 4.00 10.00
23 Rondell White 4.00 10.00
24 Dave Winfield 4.00 10.00

2004 Fleer Legacy

This 75-card set was released in November, 2004. The set was issued in eight-card hobby packs which, although they had no SRP, were part of an $240 box which included a signed baseball. However, the autographed baseball, although it had a COA from Fleer had no stamping to indicate it was from the Legacy product. The retail packs had five cards with an $3 SRP and were issued 24 packs to a box and 20 boxes to a case. Cards numbered 1-60 feature veterans while cards 61-75 feature Rookie Cards which were issued to a stated print run of 599 serial numbered sets and were issued at a state rate of one per hobby pack and one in 96 retail packs.

COMP.SET w/o SP's (60) 30.00 60.00
COMMON CARD (1-60) .40 1.00
COMMON CARD (61-75) .75 2.00
61-75 ODDS 1:1 HOBBY, 1:96 RETAIL
61-75 PRINT RUN 599 SERIAL #'d SETS
1 Angel Berroa .40 1.00
2 Derek Jeter 2.50 6.00
3 Jody Gerut .40 1.00
4 Curt Schilling .60 1.50
5 Khalil Greene .60 1.50
6 Manny Ramirez 1.00 2.50
7 Rocco Baldelli .40 1.00
8 Sammy Sosa 1.00 2.50
9 Shawn Green .40 1.00
10 Austin Kearns .40 1.00
11 Frank Thomas 1.00 2.50
12 Alfonso Soriano .40 1.00
13 Alex Rodriguez 1.50 4.00
14 Carlos Delgado .40 1.00
15 Chipper Jones 1.00 2.50
16 Edgar Martinez .60 1.50
17 Ivan Rodriguez .60 1.50
18 Mark Prior .60 1.50
19 Mike Piazza 1.00 2.50
20 Orlando Cabrera .40 1.00
21 Adam Dunn .60 1.50
22 Andruw Jones .40 1.00
23 Eric Chavez .40 1.00
24 Mark Teixeira 1.00 2.50
25 Scott Podsednik .40 1.00
26 Torii Hunter .40 1.00
27 Miguel Cabrera 1.00 2.50
28 Hideki Matsui 1.50 4.00
29 Jose Reyes .60 1.50
30 Vladimir Guerrero 1.00 2.50
31 Albert Pujols 2.50 6.00
32 Greg Maddux 1.50 4.00
33 Jason Giambi .40 1.00
34 Randy Johnson 1.00 2.50
35 Roger Clemens 1.25 3.00
36 Casey Kotchman .40 1.00
37 Ken Griffey Jr. 1.50 4.00
38 Todd Helton .60 1.50
39 Javy Lopez .40 1.00
40 Jim Thome .60 1.50
41 Josh Beckett .60 1.50
42 Kerry Wood .40 1.00
43 Scott Rolen .60 1.50
44 Pat Burrell .40 1.00
45 Pedro Martinez .60 1.50
46 Barry Zito .40 1.00
47 Hank Blalock .40 1.00
48 Hideo Nomo 1.00 2.50
49 Jeff Bagwell .60 1.50
50 Magglio Ordonez .60 1.50
51 Ichiro Suzuki 1.50 4.00
52 Joe Mauer 1.00 2.50
53 Richie Sexson .40 1.00
54 Shannon Stewart .40 1.00
55 Craig Wilson .40 1.00
56 Miguel Tejada .60 1.50
57 Sean Casey .40 1.00
58 Tom Glavine .60 1.50
59 Jason Schmidt .40 1.00
60 Nomar Garciaparra 1.00 2.50
61 Kaz Matsui FL RC 1.25 3.00
62 Justin Leone FL RC .75 2.00
63 Merkin Valdez FL RC .75 2.00
64 Shingo Takatsu FL RC .75 2.00
65 Andres Blanco FL RC .75 2.00
66 Angel Chavez FL RC .75 2.00
67 Hector Gimenez FL RC .75 2.00
68 Akinori Otsuka FL RC .75 2.00
69 Jason Bartlett FL RC 2.50 6.00
70 Luis Gonzalez FL RC .75 2.00
71 Sean Henn FL RC .75 2.00
72 Mike Rouse FL RC .75 2.00
73 Chris Aguila FL RC .75 2.00
74 Aarom Baldiris FL RC .75 2.00
75 Jerry Gil FL RC .75 2.00

2004 Fleer Legacy Gold

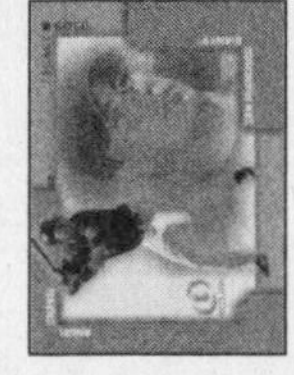

*GOLD 1-60: 1.5X TO 4X BASIC
*GOLD 61-75: .75X TO 2X BASIC
OVERALL PARALLEL ODDS 1:3 H, 1:240 R
STATED PRINT RUN 50 SERIAL #'d SETS

2004 Fleer Legacy Ultimate

OVERALL PARALLEL ODDS 1:3 HOBBY
STATED PRINT RUN 1 SERIAL #'d SET
NO PRICING DUE TO SCARCITY

2004 Fleer Legacy Franchise Patch 99

STATED PRINT RUN 99 SERIAL #'d SETS
PATCH 1 PRINT RUN 1 SERIAL #'d SET
NO PATCH 1 PRICING DUE TO SCARCITY
OVERALL PATCH ODDS 1:1 HOBBY
PRICES BELOW REFER TO NON LOGO/TAG
LOGO/TAG CARDS COMMAND 2X-3X HI
AP Albert Pujols 15.00 40.00
CJ Chipper Jones 6.00 15.00
CR Cal Ripken 20.00 50.00
DM Don Mattingly 10.00 25.00
GM Greg Maddux 10.00 25.00
HM Hideki Matsui 20.00 50.00
HN Hideo Nomo 10.00 25.00
IR Ivan Rodriguez 6.00 15.00
JBA Jeff Bagwell 6.00 15.00
JBE Josh Beckett 4.00 10.00
JL Javy Lopez 4.00 10.00
JT Jim Thome 6.00 15.00
KM Kaz Matsui 10.00 25.00
KW Kerry Wood 6.00 15.00
MP Mike Piazza 10.00 25.00
MPR Mark Prior 6.00 15.00
MT Miguel Tejada 4.00 10.00
NR Nolan Ryan 20.00 50.00
PM Pedro Martinez 6.00 15.00
RC Roger Clemens 10.00 25.00
RJ Randy Johnson 6.00 15.00
SS Sammy Sosa 6.00 15.00
VG Vladimir Guerrero 6.00 15.00

2004 Fleer Legacy Franchise Patch 50

*PATCH 50: .5X TO 1.2X BASIC
OVERALL PATCH ODDS 1:1 HOBBY
STATED PRINT RUN 50 SERIAL #'d SETS
PRICES BELOW REFER TO NON LOGO/TAG
LOGO/TAG CARDS COMMAND 2X-3X HI
JB Johnny Bench

2004 Fleer Legacy Franchise Patch 25

*PATCH 25: .75X TO 2X BASIC
OVERALL PATCH ODDS 1:1 HOBBY
STATED PRINT RUN 25 SERIAL #'d SETS
PRICES BELOW REFER TO NON LOGO/TAG
LOGO/TAG CARDS COMMAND 2X-3X HI
JB Johnny Bench

2004 Fleer Legacy Franchise Dual Patch

OVERALL PATCH ODDS 1:1 HOBBY
PRINT RUNS B/WN 5-31 COPIES PER
NO PRICING ON QTY OF 10 OR LESS
HNHM Hideo Nomo
Hideki Matsui/10
JBIR Johnny Bench
Ivan Rodriguez/5
JLMT Javy Lopez
Miguel Tejada/15
JTJB Jim Thome 20.00 50.00
Jeff Bagwell/27
KMMP Kaz Matsui
Mike Piazza/7
KWMP Kerry Wood 20.00 50.00
Mark Prior/30
PMRJ Pedro Martinez 20.00 50.00
Randy Johnson/15
RCNR Roger Clemens 60.00 120.00
Nolan Ryan/22
RCRJ Roger Clemens 40.00 80.00
Randy Johnson/29
SSAP Sammy Sosa 40.00 80.00
Albert Pujols/29
VGCJ Vladimir Guerrero 20.00 50.00
Chipper Jones/31

2004 Fleer Legacy Franchise Quad Patch

OVERALL PATCH ODDS 1:1 HOBBY
PRINT RUNS B/WN 2-22 COPIES PER
NO PRICING ON QTY OF 14 OR LESS
BLRP Johnny Bench
Javy Lopez
Ivan Rodriguez
Mike Piazza/2
BRCR Johnny Bench
Ivan Rodriguez
Roger Clemens
Nolan Ryan/9
CBTR Roger Clemens
Jeff Bagwell
Miguel Tejada
Cal Ripken/13
CRJM Roger Clemens
Nolan Ryan
Randy Johnson
Greg Maddux/11
GJSP Vladimir Guerrero 50.00 100.00
Chipper Jones
Sammy Sosa
Albert Pujols/22
MMMP Don Mattingly 125.00 200.00
Hideki Matsui
Kaz Matsui
Mike Piazza/16
MSPG Hideki Matsui
Sammy Sosa
Albert Pujols
Vladimir Guerrero/14
MSWP Greg Maddux 50.00 100.00
Sammy Sosa
Kerry Wood
Mark Prior/21
TBMP Jim Thome
Jeff Bagwell
Don Mattingly
Albert Pujols/6
WPNM Kerry Wood 40.00 80.00
Mark Prior
Pedro Martinez
Hideo Nomo/19

2004 Fleer Legacy Hit Kings

STATED ODDS 1:8 RETAIL
1 Sammy Sosa 1.00 2.50
2 Hideki Matsui 1.50 4.00
3 Vladimir Guerrero 1.00 2.50
4 Mike Piazza 1.00 2.50
5 Jeff Bagwell .60 1.50
6 Miguel Cabrera 1.00 2.50
7 Scott Rolen .60 1.50
8 Lance Berkman .60 1.50
9 Jason Giambi .40 1.00
10 Mark Teixeira 1.00 2.50
11 Jim Thome .60 1.50
12 Albert Pujols 2.50 6.00
13 Chipper Jones 1.00 2.50
14 Manny Ramirez 1.00 2.50
15 Adam Dunn .60 1.50

2004 Fleer Legacy Hit Kings Jersey Copper

STATED ODDS 1:24 RETAIL
AD Adam Dunn 2.00 5.00
AK Austin Kearns 2.00 5.00
AP Albert Pujols 6.00 15.00
CD Carlos Delgado 2.00 5.00
CJ Chipper Jones 3.00 8.00
FT Frank Thomas 3.00 8.00
GS Gary Sheffield 2.00 5.00
HB Hank Blalock 2.00 5.00
HM Hideki Matsui 8.00 20.00
JB Jeff Bagwell 3.00 8.00
JG Jason Giambi 2.00 5.00
JT Jim Thome 3.00 8.00
LB Lance Berkman 2.00 5.00
MC Miguel Cabrera 3.00 8.00
MP Mike Piazza 4.00 10.00
MR Manny Ramirez 3.00 8.00
MS Mike Schmidt 6.00 15.00
MT Mark Teixeira 3.00 8.00
RS Richie Sexson 2.00 5.00
SR Scott Rolen 3.00 8.00
SS Sammy Sosa 3.00 8.00
VG Vladimir Guerrero 3.00 8.00

2004 Fleer Legacy Hit Kings Dual Patch

OVERALL PATCH ODDS 1:1 HOBBY
PRINT RUNS B/WN 7-21 COPIES PER
NO PRICING ON QTY OF 13 OR LESS
AKAD Austin Kearns 15.00 40.00
Adam Dunn/20
CJMP Chipper Jones
Mike Piazza/7
HBMT Hank Blalock 20.00 50.00
Mark Teixeira/17
HMJG Hideki Matsui
Jason Giambi/15
JBLB Jeff Bagwell 20.00 50.00
Lance Berkman/21
JTCD Jim Thome
Carlos Delgado/8
JTMS Jim Thome
Mike Schmidt/10
MRGS Manny Ramirez 20.00 50.00
Gary Sheffield/19
SRAB Scott Rolen 50.00 100.00
Albert Pujols/16
SSAP Sammy Sosa
Albert Pujols/13
SSFT Sammy Sosa 20.00 50.00
Frank Thomas/20
VGMC Vladimir Guerrero
Miguel Cabrera/12
VGMR Vladimir Guerrero
Manny Ramirez/11

2004 Fleer Legacy Signed Baseballs

ONE PER HOBBY BOX
B/WN 1-99 ACTUAL SIGNED BALLS PER
MOST BALLS #'d B/WN 1-500 PER
SOME #ING DOESN'T MATCH ACTUAL QTY
SEE BECKETT.COM FOR ACTUAL QTY
NO PRICING AVAILABLE

2002 Fleer Maximum

This 270 card set was released in February, 2002. These cards were issued in 15 card packs which were packaged 16 packs to a box and 12 boxes to a case. The set has 200 base cards, 50 rookies and prospects (201-250) and 20 Impact cards (251-270). Cards numbered 201-250 were randomly inserted in packs are all serial numbered to 500. Cards numbered 251-270 were inserted one per hobby pack.

COMP.SET w/o SP's (200) 15.00 40.00
COMP.IMPACT SET (20) 10.00 25.00
COMMON CARD (1-200) .15 .40
COMMON CARD (201-250) 4.00 10.00
COMMON CARD (251-270) .30 .75
1 Barry Bonds 1.00 2.50
2 Alex Rodriguez .60 1.50
3 Jim Edmonds .15 .40
4 Manny Ramirez .25 .60
5 Jeff Bagwell .25 .60
6 Kazuhiro Sasaki .15 .40
7 Jason Giambi .15 .40
8 J.D. Drew .15 .40
9 Barry Larkin .25 .60
10 Chipper Jones .40 1.00
11 Rafael Palmeiro .25 .60
12 Roberto Alomar .25 .60
13 Randy Johnson .40 1.00
14 Juan Gonzalez .15 .40
15 Gary Sheffield .15 .40
16 Larry Walker .15 .40
17 Todd Helton .25 .60
18 Ivan Rodriguez .25 .60
19 Greg Maddux .60 1.50
20 Mike Piazza .60 1.50
21 Tsuyoshi Shinjo .15 .40
22 Luis Gonzalez .15 .40
23 Pedro Martinez .25 .60
24 Albert Pujols .75 2.00
25 Jose Canseco .25 .60
26 Edgar Martinez .25 .60
27 Moises Alou .15 .40
28 Vladimir Guerrero .40 1.00
29 Shawn Green .15 .40
30 Miguel Tejada .15 .40
31 Bernie Williams .25 .60
32 Frank Thomas .40 1.00
33 Jim Thome .25 .60
34 Derek Jeter 1.00 2.50
35 Julio Lugo .15 .40
36 Mo Vaughn .15 .40
37 Steve Cox .15 .40
38 Brad Radke .15 .40
39 Brian Jordan .15 .40
40 Garret Anderson .15 .40
41 Ichiro Suzuki .75 2.00
42 Mike Lieberthal .15 .40
43 Preston Wilson .15 .40
44 Bud Smith .15 .40
45 Curt Schilling .15 .40
46 Eric Chavez .15 .40
47 Javier Vazquez .15 .40
48 Jose Ortiz .15 .40
49 Mike Sweeney .15 .40
50 Travis Fryman .15 .40
51 Brady Anderson .15 .40
52 Chan Ho Park .15 .40
53 C.C. Sabathia .15 .40
54 Jack Wilson .15 .40
55 Joe Crede .15 .40
56 Mike Mussina .25 .60
57 Sean Casey .15 .40
58 Bobby Abreu .15 .40
59 Joe Randa .15 .40
60 Jose Vidro .15 .40
61 Juan Uribe .15 .40
62 Mark Grace .25 .60
63 Matt Morris .15 .40
64 Omar Vizquel .25 .60
65 Darryl Kile .15 .40
66 Dee Brown .15 .40
67 Fernando Tatis .15 .40
68 Jeff Cirillo .15 .40
69 Johnny Damon .25 .60
70 Milton Bradley .15 .40
71 Reggie Sanders .15 .40
72 Al Leiter .15 .40
73 Andres Galarraga .15 .40
74 Ellis Burks .15 .40
75 Jermaine Dye .15 .40
76 Juan Pierre .15 .40
77 Junior Spivey .15 .40
78 Mark Quinn .15 .40
79 Ben Sheets .15 .40
80 Brad Fullmer .15 .40
81 Bubba Trammell .15 .40
82 Dante Bichette .15 .40
83 Ken Griffey Jr. .60 1.50
84 Paul O'Neill .25 .60
85 Robert Fick .15 .40
86 Bret Boone .15 .40
87 Raul Mondesi .15 .40
88 Josh Beckett .15 .40
89 Geoff Jenkins .15 .40
90 Ramon Ortiz .15 .40
91 Robin Ventura .15 .40
92 Tom Glavine .25 .60
93 Jimmy Rollins .15 .40
94 Jamie Moyer .15 .40
95 Magglio Ordonez .15 .40
96 Mike Lowell .15 .40
97 Ryan Dempster .15 .40
98 Scott Schoeneweis .15 .40
99 Todd Zeile .15 .40
100 A.J. Burnett .15 .40
101 Aaron Sele .15 .40
102 Cal Ripken 1.25 3.00
103 Carlos Beltran .15 .40
104 David Eckstein .15 .40
105 Jason Marquis .15 .40
106 Matt Lawton .15 .40
107 Ben Grieve .15 .40
108 Brian Giles .15 .40
109 Josh Towers .15 .40
110 Lance Berkman .15 .40
111 Sammy Sosa .40 1.00
112 Torii Hunter .15 .40
113 Aubrey Huff .15 .40
114 Craig Biggio .25 .60
115 Doug Mientkiewicz .15 .40
116 Fred McGriff .25 .60
117 Jason Johnson .15 .40
118 Pat Burrell .15 .40
119 Aaron Boone .15 .40
120 Carlos Delgado .15 .40
121 Nomar Garciaparra .60 1.50
122 Richie Sexson .15 .40
123 Russ Ortiz .15 .40
124 Tim Hudson .15 .40
125 Tony Clark .15 .40
126 Jeromy Burnitz .15 .40
127 Jose Cruz .15 .40
128 Juan Encarnacion .15 .40
129 Mark Mulder .15 .40
130 Mike Hampton .15 .40
131 Rich Aurilia .15 .40
132 Trot Nixon .15 .40
133 Greg Vaughn .15 .40
134 Jacque Jones .15 .40
135 Jason Kendall .15 .40
136 Jay Gibbons .15 .40
137 Mark Buehrle .15 .40
138 Richard Hidalgo .15 .40
139 Rondell White .15 .40
140 Cristian Guzman .15 .40
141 Andy Pettitte .25 .60
142 Chris Richard .15 .40
143 Paul LoDuca .15 .40
144 Phil Nevin .15 .40
145 Ray Durham .15 .40
146 Todd Walker .15 .40
147 Bartolo Colon .15 .40
148 Ben Petrick .15 .40
149 Freddy Garcia .15 .40
150 Jon Lieber .15 .40
151 Jose Hernandez .15 .40
152 Matt Williams .15 .40
153 Shannon Stewart .15 .40
154 Adrian Beltre .15 .40

155 Carlos Lee .15 .40
156 Frank Catalanotto .15 .40
157 Jorge Posada .25 .60
158 Pokey Reese .15 .40
159 Ryan Klesko .15 .40
160 Ugueth Urbina .15 .40
161 Adam Dunn .15 .40
162 Alfonso Soriano .15 .40
163 Ben Davis .15 .40
164 Paul Konerko .15 .40
165 Eric Karros .15 .40
166 Jeff Weaver .15 .40
167 Ruben Sierra .15 .40
168 Bobby Higginson .15 .40
169 Eric Milton .15 .40
170 Kerry Wood .15 .40
171 Roy Oswalt .15 .40
172 Scott Rolen .25 .60
173 Tim Salmon .25 .60
174 Aramis Ramirez .15 .40
175 Jason Tyner .15 .40
176 Juan Cruz .15 .40
177 Keith Foulke .15 .40
178 Kevin Brown .15 .40
179 Roger Clemens .75 2.00
180 Tony Batista .15 .40
181 Andruw Jones .25 .60
182 Cliff Floyd .15 .40
183 Darin Erstad .15 .40
184 Joe Mays .15 .40
185 Mike Cameron .15 .40
186 Robert Person .15 .40
187 Jeff Kent .15 .40
188 Gabe Kapler .15 .40
189 Jason Jennings .15 .40
190 Jason Varitek .40 1.00
191 Barry Zito .15 .40
192 Rickey Henderson .40 1.00
193 Tino Martinez .25 .60
194 Brandon Duckworth .15 .40
195 Corey Koskie .15 .40
196 Derrek Lee .25 .60
197 Javy Lopez .15 .40
198 John Olerud .15 .40
199 Terrence Long .15 .40
200 Troy Glaus .15 .40
201 Scott MacRae RHW 4.00 10.00
202 Scott Chiasson RHW 4.00 10.00
203 Bart Miadich RHW 4.00 10.00
204 Brian Bowles RHW 4.00 10.00
205 David Williams RHW 4.00 10.00
206 Victor Zambrano RHW 4.00 10.00
207 Joe Beimel RHW 4.00 10.00
208 Scott Stewart RHW 4.00 10.00
209 Bob File RHW 4.00 10.00
210 Ryan Jensen RHW 4.00 10.00
211 Jason Karnuth RHW 4.00 10.00
212 Brandon Knight RHW 4.00 10.00
213 Andy Shibilo RHW RC 4.00 10.00
214 Chad Ricketts RHW RC 4.00 10.00
215 Mark Prior RHW 3.00 8.00
216 Chad Paronto RHW 4.00 10.00
217 Corky Miller RHW 4.00 10.00
218 Luis Pineda RHW 4.00 10.00
219 Ramon Vazquez RHW 4.00 10.00
220 Tony Cogan RHW 4.00 10.00
221 Roy Smith RHW 4.00 10.00
222 Mark Lukasiewicz RHW 4.00 10.00
223 Mike Rivera RHW 4.00 10.00
224 Brad Voyles RHW 4.00 10.00
225 Jamie Burke RHW RC 4.00 10.00
226 Justin Duchscherer RTC 4.00 10.00
227 Eric Cyr RTC 4.00 10.00
228 Mark Lukasiewicz RTC 4.00 10.00
229 Marlon Byrd RTC 4.00 10.00
230 Chris Piersoll RTC RC 4.00 10.00
231 Ramon Vazquez RTC 4.00 10.00
232 Tony Cogan RTC 4.00 10.00
233 Roy Smith RTC 4.00 10.00
234 Franklin Nunez RTC RC 4.00 10.00
235 Corky Miller RTC 4.00 10.00
236 Jorge Nunez RTC RC 4.00 10.00
237 Joe Beimel RTC 4.00 10.00
238 Eric Knott RTC 4.00 10.00
239 Victor Zambrano RTC 4.00 10.00
240 Jason Karnuth RTC 4.00 10.00
241 Jason Middlebrook RTC 4.00 10.00
242 Scott Stewart RTC 4.00 10.00
243 Tim Spooneybarger RTC 4.00 10.00
244 David Williams RTC 4.00 10.00
245 Bart Miadich RTC 4.00 10.00
246 Mike Koplove RTC 4.00 10.00
247 Ryan Jensen RTC 4.00 10.00
248 Jeremy Fikac RTC 4.00 10.00
249 Bob File RTC 4.00 10.00
250 Craig Monroe RTC 4.00 10.00
251 Albert Pujols MI 1.25 3.00
252 Ichiro Suzuki MI 1.25 3.00
253 Nomar Garciaparra MI 1.00 2.50
254 Barry Bonds MI 1.50 4.00
255 Jason Giambi MI .30 .75
256 Derek Jeter MI 1.50 4.00
257 Roberto Alomar MI .40 1.00
258 Roger Clemens MI 1.25 3.00
259 Mike Piazza MI 1.00 2.50
260 Vladimir Guerrero MI .60 1.50
261 Todd Helton MI .40 1.00
262 Shawn Green MI .30 .75
263 Chipper Jones MI .60 1.50
264 Pedro Martinez MI .40 1.00
265 Pat Burrell MI .30 .75
266 Sammy Sosa MI .60 1.50
267 Ken Griffey Jr. MI 1.00 2.50
268 Cal Ripken MI 2.00 5.00
269 Kerry Wood MI .30 .75
270 Alex Rodriguez MI 1.00 2.50
NNO Derek Jeter Promo 1.25 3.00

2002 Fleer Maximum To the Max

Randomly inserted into hobby packs, this set parallels the Fleer Maximum set. These cards all have different print runs which we have noted in our checklist.

* 1-200 PRINT RUN b/wn 201-417 4X TO 10X
* 1-200 PRINT RUN b/wn 151-200 5X TO 12X
* 1-200 PRINT RUN b/wn 121-150 6X TO 15X
* 1-200 PRINT RUN b/wn 81-120 8X TO 20X
* 1-200 PRINT RUN b/wn 66-80 10X TO 25X
* 1-200 PRINT RUN b/wn 51-65 12.5X TO 30X
* 1-200 PRINT RUN b/wn 36-50 15X TO 40X
* 1-200 PRINT RUN b/wn 26-35 20X TO 50X
* 1-200 PRINT RUN b/wn 21-25 25X TO 60X
1-200 PRINT RUN b/wn 24-417 OF EACH
* ROOKIES 151-200: .4X TO 1X BASIC
151-200 PRINT RUN 100 SERIAL #'d SETS
*IMPACT 251-270: 2.5X TO 6X BASIC
251-270 PRINT RUN b/wn 233-372 OF EACH
SEE BECKETT.COM FOR EXACT PRINT RUNS

2002 Fleer Maximum Americas Game

Inserted into retail packs at stated odds of one in 10, these 25 cards feature some of the fan favorites.

COMPLETE SET (25) 30.00 60.00
1 Pedro Martinez .75 2.00
2 Miguel Tejada .50 1.25
3 Randy Johnson 1.25 3.00
4 Barry Bonds 3.00 8.00
5 Rafael Palmeiro .75 2.00
6 Mike Piazza 2.00 5.00
7 Greg Maddux 2.00 5.00
8 Jeff Bagwell .75 2.00
9 Edgar Martinez .75 2.00
10 Albert Pujols 2.50 6.00
11 Todd Helton .75 2.00
12 Chipper Jones 1.25 3.00
13 Luis Gonzalez .50 1.25
14 Jason Giambi .50 1.25
15 Kazuhiro Sasaki .50 1.25
16 Dave Winfield .50 1.25
17 Reggie Jackson .75 2.00
18 Tom Glavine .75 2.00
19 Carlos Delgado .50 1.25
20 Bobby Abreu .50 1.25
21 Larry Walker .50 1.25
22 J.D. Drew .50 1.25
23 Alex Rodriguez 2.00 5.00
24 Frank Thomas 1.25 3.00
25 C.C. Sabathia .50 1.25

2002 Fleer Maximum Americas Game Jersey

These cards were Inserted into hobby packs at stated odds of one in 24 and retail packs at stated odds of one in 72. This is a partial parallel of the America's game insert set and features a star-shaped swatch of a game-used jersey on every card. Cards with asterisks next to them are perceived to be produced in shorter quantity.

*GOLD: .75X TO 2X BASIC AMERICA JERSEY
GOLD PRINT RUN 100 SERIAL #'d SETS
1 Jeff Bagwell 6.00 15.00
2 Craig Biggio * 6.00 15.00
3 Barry Bonds Pants 10.00 25.00
4 Carlos Delgado 4.00 10.00
5 J.D. Drew 4.00 10.00
6 Jason Giambi * 4.00 10.00
7 Tom Glavine * 6.00 15.00
8 Luis Gonzalez 4.00 10.00
9 Todd Helton 6.00 15.00
10 Reggie Jackson Pants* 6.00 15.00
11 Randy Johnson 6.00 15.00
12 Chipper Jones 6.00 15.00
13 Greg Maddux 6.00 15.00
14 Edgar Martinez 6.00 15.00
15 Pedro Martinez * 6.00 15.00
16 Rafael Palmeiro 6.00 15.00
17 Chan Ho Park 4.00 10.00
18 Mike Piazza 6.00 15.00
19 Albert Pujols 10.00 25.00
20 Kazuhiro Sasaki 4.00 10.00
21 Miguel Tejada * 4.00 10.00
22 Frank Thomas 6.00 15.00
23 Larry Walker 4.00 10.00
24 Dave Winfield * 4.00 10.00

2002 Fleer Maximum Americas Game Four Score

Randomly inserted into packs, these two cards feature four players on the card along with a memorabilia piece related to that player. These cards have a stated print run of 15 copies and due to market scarcity, no pricing is provided.

FS1 Mike Piazza Pants
Derek Jeter Jsy
Ichiro Suzuki Base
Albert Pujols Jsy
FS2 Todd Helton Jsy
Alex Rodriguez Bat
Ichiro Suzuki Base
Gary Sheffield Bat

2002 Fleer Maximum Coverage

Randomly inserted into packs these cards provide a large swatch of a game-used jersey or bat from the featured player. These cards have a stated print run of 100 copies. An exchange card with a deadline of March 1st, 2003 was seeded into packs for the Barry Bonds bat card.

1 Roberto Alomar Bat 6.00 15.00
2 Jeff Bagwell Jsy 6.00 15.00
3 Barry Bonds Bat 40.00 80.00
4 Jose Canseco Bat 6.00 15.00
5 J.D. Drew Bat
6 Jim Edmonds Bat 4.00 10.00
7 Jason Giambi Bat 4.00 10.00
8 Juan Gonzalez Bat 4.00 10.00
9 Luis Gonzalez Jsy 4.00 10.00
10 Todd Helton Jsy 6.00 15.00
11 Randy Johnson Jsy 6.00 15.00
12 Chipper Jones Bat 6.00 15.00
13 Greg Maddux Jsy 20.00 50.00
14 Pedro Martinez Jsy 6.00 15.00
15 Rafael Palmeiro Pants
16 Albert Pujols Jsy 40.00 80.00
17 Manny Ramirez Bat 6.00 15.00
18 Alex Rodriguez Bat
19 Ivan Rodriguez Bat 6.00 15.00
20 Kazuhiro Sasaki Jsy
21 Gary Sheffield Bat 4.00 10.00
22 Tsuyoshi Shinjo Bat 4.00 10.00

2002 Fleer Maximum Coverage Autographs

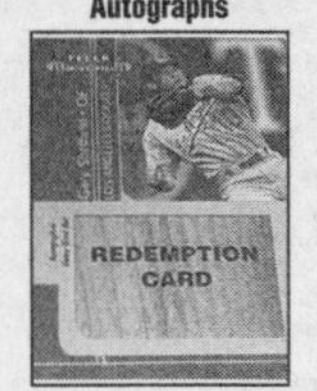

Exchange cards witrh a redemption deadline of March 1st, 2003 were andomly inserted into packs for upgraded parallels (whereby the player's signed the cards) of the Coverage insert set. Thes actual cards mailed out to collectors from Fleer are autographed and have varying stated print runs which we have noted in our checklist.

1 Barry Bonds Pants/50 150.00 250.00
2 J.D. Drew Bat/100 10.00 25.00
3 Jim Edmonds Bat/100 15.00 40.00
4 Drew Henson Bat/100 10.00 25.00
5 Chipper Jones Bat/50 40.00 80.00
6 Albert Pujols Jsy/100 175.00 300.00
7 Gary Sheffield Bat/100 15.00 40.00

2002 Fleer Maximum Derek Jeter Legacy Collection

These four card feature Derek Jeter memorabilia items. The memorabilia cards were inserted at stated odds of one in 236 while the auto cards were randomly inserted into packs.

1 D.Jeter Bronx Bat 20.00 50.00
2 D.Jeter Bronx Bat AU/222 150.00 250.00
3 D.Jeter Columbus Jsy 20.00 50.00
4 D.Jeter Columbus Jsy AU 175.00 300.00

2002 Fleer Maximum Power

Inserted into retail packs at stated odds of one in 20, these 25 cards feature heavy hitters who produce for their teams.

COMPLETE SET (25) 50.00 100.00
1 Luis Gonzalez .75 2.00
2 Jimmy Rollins .75 2.00
3 Larry Walker .75 2.00
4 Frank Thomas 2.00 5.00
5 Manny Ramirez 1.25 3.00
6 Barry Bonds 5.00 12.00
7 Jim Thome 1.25 3.00
8 Tsuyoshi Shinjo .75 2.00
9 Bernie Williams 1.25 3.00
10 Chipper Jones 2.00 5.00
11 Shawn Green .75 2.00
12 Drew Henson .75 2.00
13 Juan Gonzalez .75 2.00
14 Jim Edmonds .75 2.00
15 Moises Alou .75 2.00
16 Roberto Alomar 1.25 3.00
17 Jose Canseco 1.25 3.00
18 Ivan Rodriguez 1.25 3.00
19 Barry Larkin 1.25 3.00
20 Mike Piazza 3.00 8.00
21 Gary Sheffield .75 2.00
22 J.D. Drew .75 2.00
23 Alex Rodriguez 3.00 8.00
24 Jason Giambi .75 2.00
25 Todd Helton 1.25 3.00

2002 Fleer Maximum Power Bat

Inserted into packs at stated odds of one in 24 hobby and one in 72 retail, these 23 cards feature bat chips of these leading hitters. A few players were produced in lesser quantites and we have notated those quantities in our checklist. In addition, a few players had their distribution evenly split between retail and hobby packs and those players are noted in our checklist with asterisks.

GOLD PRINT RUN 25 SERIAL #'d SETS
GOLD NO PRICING DUE TO SCARCITY
1 Roberto Alomar 6.00 15.00
2 Moises Alou SP/150
3 Barry Bonds * 10.00 25.00
4 Jose Canseco 6.00 15.00
5 J.D. Drew SP/200 4.00 10.00
6 Jim Edmonds 4.00 10.00
7 Jason Giambi 4.00 10.00
8 Juan Gonzalez 4.00 10.00
9 Luis Gonzalez 4.00 10.00
10 Shawn Green 4.00 10.00
11 Todd Helton 6.00 15.00
12 Chipper Jones * 6.00 15.00
13 Barry Larkin SP/50
14 Mike Piazza * 6.00 15.00
15 Manny Ramirez 6.00 15.00
16 Alex Rodriguez * 6.00 15.00
17 Ivan Rodriguez 6.00 15.00
18 Gary Sheffield 4.00 10.00
19 Tsuyoshi Shinjo 4.00 10.00
20 Frank Thomas 6.00 15.00
21 Jim Thome 6.00 15.00
22 Larry Walker 4.00 10.00
23 Bernie Williams SP/175

1999 Fleer Mystique

This 160-card set features color action player photos with a palette name box and shadowed "Mystique" in the background. The cards were issued in four-card packs with an SRP of $4.99 per pack. The backs carry player statistics. The set included the following two subsets: Rookies (101-150) serially numbered to 2,999, and Stars (151-160) serially numbered to 2,500. The cards with "SP" following the player's name in our checklist were distributed only as peel offs. Peel off cards were seeded at a rate of one per pack. Collectors had to peel off the sparkling foil coating off the front and back of the card to reveal what it was (hence the name "Mystique"). Peel off cards were either short printed super stars from the basic set (1-100), a serial numbered Prospect or Star card (101-160) or an insert card. A promo card featuring J.D. Drew was distributed to dealers and hobby media several weeks prior to the product's release. This Drew card is easily identified by the text "PROMOTIONAL SAMPLE" running diagonally across the front and back of the card. This set contains Pat Burrell's "Best" Rookie Card. The Phillies player had 25 Rookie Cards issued in 1999 and the Fleer Mystique was the only one that was serial numbered. That, in large part, boosted this card to the top of many collectors wantlists after the product's release.

COMPLETE SET (160) 100.00 250.00
COMP.SHORT SET (100) 15.00 40.00
COMMON CARD (1-100) .15 .40
COMMON SP (1-100) .40 1.00
COMMON (101-150) 2.00 5.00
COMMON (151-160) 2.00 5.00
1 Ken Griffey Jr. SP 1.00 2.50
2 Livan Hernandez .15 .40
3 Jeff Kent .15 .40
4 Brian Jordan .15 .40
5 Kevin Young .15 .40
6 Vinny Castilla .15 .40
7 Orlando Hernandez SP .40 1.00
8 Bobby Abreu .15 .40
9 Vladimir Guerrero SP .60 1.50
10 Chuck Knoblauch .15 .40
11 Nomar Garciaparra SP 1.00 2.50
12 Jeff Bagwell .25 .60
13 Todd Walker .15 .40
14 Johnny Damon .25 .60
15 Mike Caruso .15 .40
16 Cliff Floyd .15 .40
17 Andy Pettitte .25 .60
18 Cal Ripken SP 2.00 5.00
19 Brian Giles .15 .40
20 Robin Ventura .15 .40
21 Alex Gonzalez .15 .40
22 Randy Johnson .40 1.00
23 Raul Mondesi .15 .40
24 Ken Caminiti .15 .40
25 Tom Glavine .25 .60
26 Derek Jeter SP 1.50 4.00
27 Carlos Delgado .15 .40
28 Adrian Beltre .15 .40
29 Tino Martinez .25 .60
30 Todd Helton .25 .60
31 Juan Gonzalez SP .40 1.00
32 Henry Rodriguez .15 .40
33 Jim Thome .25 .60
34 Paul O'Neill .25 .60
35 Scott Rolen SP .40 1.00
36 Rafael Palmeiro .25 .60
37 Will Clark .25 .60
38 Todd Hundley .15 .40
39 Andruw Jones SP .40 1.00
40 Rolando Arrojo .15 .40
41 Barry Larkin .25 .60
42 Tim Salmon .25 .60
43 Rondell White .15 .40
44 Curt Schilling .15 .40
45 Chipper Jones SP .60 1.50
46 Jeromy Burnitz .15 .40
47 Mo Vaughn .15 .40
48 Tony Clark .15 .40
49 Fernando Tatis .15 .40
50 Dmitri Young .15 .40
51 Wade Boggs .25 .60
52 Rickey Henderson .40 1.00
53 Manny Ramirez SP .40 1.00
54 Edgar Martinez .25 .60
55 Jason Giambi .15 .40
56 Jason Kendall .15 .40
57 Eric Karros .15 .40
58 Jose Canseco SP .40 1.00
59 Shawn Green .15 .40
60 Ellis Burks .15 .40
61 Derek Bell .15 .40
62 Shannon Stewart .15 .40
63 Roger Clemens SP 1.25 3.00
64 Sean Casey SP .40 1.00
65 Jose Offerman .15 .40
66 Sammy Sosa SP .60 1.50
67 Frank Thomas SP .60 1.50
68 Tony Gwynn SP .60 1.50
69 Roberto Alomar .25 .60
70 Mark McGwire SP 1.50 4.00
71 Troy Glaus .25 .60
72 Ray Durham .15 .40
73 Jeff Cirillo .15 .40
74 Alex Rodriguez SP 1.00 2.50
75 Jose Cruz Jr. .15 .40
76 Juan Encarnacion .15 .40
77 Mark Grace .25 .60
78 Barry Bonds SP 1.50 4.00
79 Ivan Rodriguez SP .40 1.00
80 Greg Vaughn .15 .40
81 Greg Maddux SP 1.00 2.50
82 Albert Belle .15 .40
83 John Olerud .15 .40
84 Kenny Lofton .15 .40
85 Bernie Williams .25 .60
86 Matt Williams .15 .40
87 Ray Lankford .15 .40
88 Darin Erstad .15 .40
89 Ben Grieve .15 .40
90 Craig Biggio .25 .60
91 Dean Palmer .15 .40
92 Reggie Sanders .15 .40
93 Dante Bichette .15 .40
94 Pedro Martinez SP .40 1.00
95 Larry Walker .15 .40
96 David Wells .15 .40
97 Travis Lee SP .40 1.00
98 Mike Piazza SP 1.00 2.50
99 Mike Mussina .25 .60
100 Kevin Brown .25 .60
101 Ruben Mateo PROS 2.00 5.00
102 Rob. Ramirez RC 2.00 5.00
103 Glen Barker PROS RC 2.00 5.00
104 C. Bellinger PROS RC 2.00 5.00
105 Carlos Guillen PROS 2.00 5.00
106 S.Schoeneweis PROS 2.00 5.00
107 C.Gubanich PROS RC 2.00 5.00
108 S.Williamson PROS 2.00 5.00
109 E.Guzman PROS RC 2.00 5.00
110 A.J. Burnett PROS RC 5.00 12.00
111 Jeremy Giambi PROS 2.00 5.00
112 Trot Nixon PROS 2.00 5.00
113 J.D. Drew PROS 2.00 5.00
114 Roy Halladay PROS 10.00 25.00
115 J.Macias PROS RC 2.00 5.00
116 Corey Koskie PROS 2.00 5.00
117 Ryan Rupe PROS RC 2.00 5.00
118 S.Hunter PROS RC 2.00 5.00
119 Rob Fick PROS 2.00 5.00
120 M.Christensen PROS 2.00 5.00
121 Carlos Febles PROS 2.00 5.00
122 Gabe Kapler PROS 2.00 5.00
123 Jeff Liefer PROS 2.00 5.00
124 Warren Morris PROS 2.00 5.00
125 Chris Pritchett PROS 2.00 5.00
126 Torii Hunter PROS 2.00 5.00
127 Armando Rios PROS 2.00 5.00
128 Ricky Ledee PROS 2.00 5.00
129 K.Dransfeldt RC 2.00 5.00
130 J.Zimmerman RC 2.00 5.00
131 Eric Chavez PROS 2.00 5.00
132 F.Garcia PROS RC 4.00 10.00
133 Jose Jimenez PROS 2.00 5.00
134 Pat Burrell PROS RC 12.50 30.00
135 J.McEwing PROS RC 2.00 5.00
136 Kris Benson PROS 2.00 5.00
137 Joe Mays PROS RC 2.00 5.00
138 R.Roque PROS RC 2.00 5.00
139 C.Guzman PROS 2.00 5.00
140 Michael Barrett PROS 2.00 5.00
141 D.Mientkiewicz RC 3.00 8.00
142 Jeff Weaver PROS RC 3.00 8.00
143 Mike Lowell PROS 2.00 5.00
144 J.Phillips PROS RC 2.00 5.00
145 M.Anderson PROS 2.00 5.00
146 B.Hinchliffe PROS RC 2.00 5.00
147 Matt Clement PROS 2.00 5.00
148 Terrence Long PROS 2.00 5.00
149 Carlos Beltran PROS 3.00 8.00
150 Preston Wilson PROS 2.00 5.00
151 Ken Griffey Jr. STAR 3.00 8.00
152 Mark McGwire STAR 5.00 12.00
153 Sammy Sosa STAR 2.00 5.00
154 Mike Piazza STAR 3.00 8.00
155 Alex Rodriguez STAR 3.00 8.00
156 N.Garciaparra STAR 3.00 8.00
157 Cal Ripken STAR 6.00 15.00
158 Greg Maddux STAR 3.00 8.00
159 Derek Jeter STAR 5.00 12.00
160 Juan Gonzalez STAR 2.00 5.00
P113 J.D. Drew Promo .40 1.00

1999 Fleer Mystique Gold

Randomly inserted into packs at the rate of one in eight, this 100-card set is a partial parallel gold version of the base set (cards 1-100).

*GOLD: 1.5X TO 4X BASIC CARDS
*GOLD: 1X TO 2.5X BASIC SP's
STATED ODDS 1:8

1999 Fleer Mystique Destiny

Randomly inserted into packs, this ten-card set features color photos of top young players printed on silver holofoil cards and sequentially numbered to 999.

COMPLETE SET (10) 60.00 120.00
1 Tony Gwynn 5.00 12.00
2 Juan Gonzalez 3.00 8.00
3 Scott Rolen 3.00 8.00
4 Nomar Garciaparra 8.00 20.00
5 Orlando Hernandez 3.00 8.00
6 Andruw Jones 3.00 8.00
7 Vladimir Guerrero 5.00 12.00
8 Darin Erstad 1.25 3.00
9 Manny Ramirez 3.00 8.00
10 Roger Clemens 10.00 25.00

1999 Fleer Mystique Established

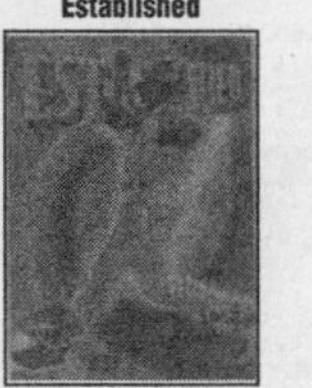

Randomly inserted into packs, this 10-card set features color action photos of veteran stars printed on plastic, highlighted with silver and red holofoil, and covered with opaque blue film. The cards are sequentially numbered on the back to 100.

1 Ken Griffey Jr. 30.00 60.00
2 Derek Jeter 30.00 60.00
3 Chipper Jones 10.00 25.00
4 Greg Maddux 15.00 40.00
5 Mark McGwire 30.00 60.00
6 Mike Piazza 15.00 40.00
7 Cal Ripken 40.00 80.00
8 Alex Rodriguez 15.00 40.00
9 Sammy Sosa 10.00 25.00
10 Frank Thomas 10.00 25.00

1999 Fleer Mystique Feel the Game

Randomly inserted into packs, this seven-card set features pieces of actual game-used equipment by top players. Each card is serial numbered by hand on the front. The print run for each card is listed after the player's name in the checklist below.

1 Adrian Beltre Shoe/430 6.00 15.00
2 J.D.Drew Jersey/450 6.00 15.00
3 Juan Gonzalez Batting Glove/415 6.00 15.00
4 Tony Gwynn Jersey/435 10.00 25.00
5 Kevin Millwood Jersey/435 6.00 15.00
6 Alex Rodriguez Batting Glove/345 20.00 50.00
7 Frank Thomas Jersey/450 10.00 25.00

1999 Fleer Mystique Fresh Ink

Randomly inserted into packs at the rate of one in 48, this 26-card set features autographed color action photos of top rookies and veterans. Each autograph is authenticated with the Fleer Seal of Authenticity and a certificate printed on the back of each card. The cards are unnumbered and checklisted in alphabetical order. The print run follows the player's name in our checklist.

STATED ODDS 1:48
1 Roberto Alomar/500 10.00 25.00
2 Michael Barrett/1000 4.00 10.00
3 Kris Benson/500 6.00 15.00
4 Micah Bowie/1000 4.00 10.00
5 A.J. Burnett/1000 10.00 25.00
6 Pat Burrell/500 10.00 25.00
7 Ken Caminiti/250 20.00 50.00
8 Jose Canseco/250 10.00 25.00
9 Sean Casey/1000 6.00 15.00
10 Edgard Clemente/1000 4.00 10.00
11 Bartolo Colon/500 6.00 15.00
12 J.D. Drew/400 6.00 15.00
13 Juan Encarnacion/1000 6.00 15.00
14 Troy Glaus/400 10.00 25.00
15 Juan Gonzalez/250 10.00 25.00
16 Shawn Green/250 15.00 40.00
17 Tony Gwynn/250 20.00 50.00
18 Chipper Jones/500 20.00 50.00
19 Gabe Kapler/750 6.00 15.00
20 Barry Larkin/250 15.00 40.00
21 Doug Mientkiewicz/500 6.00 15.00
22 Alex Rodriguez/200 50.00 100.00
23 Scott Rolen/140 15.00 40.00
24 Fernando Tatis/750 4.00 10.00
25 Robin Ventura/500 6.00 15.00
26 Todd Walker/1000 6.00 15.00

1999 Fleer Mystique Prophetic

Randomly inserted into packs, this 10-card set features color photos of top rookies and other young players printed with silver/blue holofoil highlights, gold foil stamping, and covered with opaque blue film. The cards are serially numbered on back to 1999. An early numbered card of Pat Burrell is in this set.

COMPLETE SET (10) 25.00 50.00
1 Eric Chavez 1.25 3.00
2 J.D. Drew 1.25 3.00
3 A.J. Burnett 1.50 4.00
4 Ben Grieve 1.25 3.00
5 Gabe Kapler 1.25 3.00
6 Todd Helton 2.00 5.00
7 Troy Glaus 2.00 5.00
8 Travis Lee 1.25 3.00
9 Pat Burrell 3.00 8.00
10 Kerry Wood 1.25 3.00

2003 Fleer Patchworks

This 115 card set was released in May, 2003. This set was issued in five-card packs which were issued in five card packs with a $4.99 SRP which came 24 packs to a box and 12 boxes to a case. The set consists of 90 veterans (1-90) and 25 rookies and leading prospects (91-115). The final 25 cards were randomly inserted in packs and issued to a stated print run of 1500 serial numbered sets.

COMP.SET w/o SP's (90) 6.00 15.00
COMMON CARD (1-90) .15 .40
COMMON CARD (91-115) 1.50 4.00
1 Luis Castillo .15 .40
2 Derek Jeter 1.00 2.50
3 Vladimir Guerrero .40 1.00
4 Bobby Higginson .15 .40
5 Pat Burrell .15 .40
6 Ivan Rodriguez .25 .60
7 Craig Biggio .25 .60
8 Troy Glaus .15 .40
9 Barry Bonds 1.00 2.50
10 Hideo Nomo .40 1.00
11 Barry Larkin .25 .60
12 Roberto Alomar .25 .60
13 Rodrigo Lopez .15 .40
14 Eric Chavez .15 .40
15 Shawn Green .15 .40
16 Joe Randa .15 .40
17 Mark Grace .25 .60
18 Jason Kendall .15 .40
19 Hee Seop Choi .15 .40
20 Luis Gonzalez .15 .40
21 Sammy Sosa .40 1.00
22 Larry Walker .15 .40
23 Phil Nevin .15 .40
24 Manny Ramirez .25 .60
25 Jim Thome .25 .60
26 Randy Johnson .40 1.00
27 Jose Vidro .15 .40
28 Austin Kearns .15 .40
29 Mike Sweeney .15 .40

30 Magglio Ordonez	.15	.40
31 Mike Piazza	.60	1.50
32 Eric Hinske	.15	.40
33 Alex Rodriguez	.60	1.50
34 Kerry Wood	.15	.40
35 Matt Morris	.15	.40
36 Lance Berkman	.15	.40
37 Michael Cuddyer	.15	.40
38 Curt Schilling	.15	.40
39 Sean Burroughs	.15	.40
40 Ken Griffey Jr.	.40	1.00
41 Edgardo Alfonzo	.15	.40
42 Carlos Pena	.15	.40
43 Adam Dunn	.15	.40
44 Pedro Martinez	.25	.60
45 Miguel Tejada	.15	.40
46 Tom Glavine	.25	.60
47 Torii Hunter	.15	.40
48 Jason Giambi	.15	.40
49 Tony Batista	.15	.40
50 Ben Grieve	.15	.40
51 Ichiro Suzuki	.75	2.00
52 Bobby Abreu	.15	.40
53 Todd Helton	.25	.60
54 Kazuhiro Sasaki	.15	.40
55 Nomar Garciaparra	.60	1.50
56 Francisco Rodriguez	.15	.40
57 Ellis Burks	.15	.40
58 Frank Thomas	.40	1.00
59 Greg Maddux	.60	1.50
60 Josh Beckett	.15	.40
61 Brad Wilkerson	.15	.40
62 Joe Borchard	.15	.40
63 Carlos Delgado	.15	.40
64 Alfonso Soriano	.15	.40
65 Chipper Jones	.40	1.00
66 J.D. Drew	.15	.40
67 Mark Prior	.25	.60
68 Rafael Palmeiro	.25	.60
69 Jeff Kent	.15	.40
70 Adrian Beltre	.15	.40
71 Marlon Byrd	.15	.40
72 Orlando Hudson	.15	.40
73 Junior Spivey	.15	.40
74 Jeff Bagwell	.25	.60
75 Barry Zito	.15	.40
76 Roger Clemens	.75	2.00
77 Aubrey Huff	.15	.40
78 Geoff Jenkins	.15	.40
79 Andruw Jones	.25	.60
80 Scott Rolen	.25	.60
81 Omar Vizquel	.25	.60
82 Darin Erstad	.15	.40
83 Bernie Williams	.25	.60
84 Freddy Garcia	.15	.40
85 Richie Sexson	.15	.40
86 Josh Phelps	.15	.40
87 Albert Pujols	.75	2.00
88 Aramis Ramirez	.15	.40
89 Shea Hillenbrand	.15	.40
90 Cristian Guzman	.15	.40
91 Adam LaRoche RR	1.50	4.00
92 David Pember RR RC	1.50	4.00
93 Termel Sledge RR RC	1.50	4.00
94 Hideki Matsui RR RC	4.00	10.00
95 Nook Logan RR RC	2.00	5.00
96 Jose Contreras RR RC	2.00	5.00
97 Pete LaForest RR RC	1.50	4.00
98 Rich Fischer RR RC	1.50	4.00
99 Francisco Rosario RR RC	1.50	4.00
100 Josh Willingham RR RC	2.50	6.00
101 Alejandro Machado RR RC	1.50	4.00
102 Lew Ford RR RC	2.00	5.00
103 Joe Valentine RR RC	1.50	4.00
104 Guillermo Quiroz RR RC	1.50	4.00
105 Chien-Ming Wang RR RC	3.00	8.00
106 Jhonny Peralta RR	2.00	5.00
107 Shane Victorino RR RC	2.50	6.00
108 Prentice Redman RR RC	1.50	4.00
109 Matt Bruback RR RC	1.50	4.00
110 Lance Niekro RR	1.50	4.00
111 Travis Hughes RR	1.50	4.00
112 Nic Jackson RR	1.50	4.00
113 Hector Luna RR RC	1.50	4.00
114 Cliff Lee RR	1.50	4.00
115 Tim Olson RR RC	1.50	4.00

2003 Fleer Patchworks Star Ruby

*RUBY 1-90: 4X TO 10X BASIC
*RUBY 91-115: .6X TO 1.5X BASIC
STATED PRINT RUN 100 SERIAL #'d SETS

105 Chien-Ming Wang RR	10.00	25.00

2003 Fleer Patchworks Diamond Ink

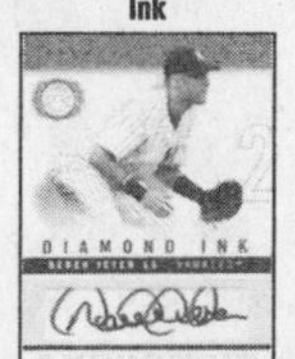

Randomly inserted into packs, these six cards feature authentic signed autographs from four different players. Derek Jeter signed his cards in a mix of Black, blue and red ink. We have printed the stated print run next to the player's name in our checklist.

DJ1 Derek Jeter Black/210	75.00	150.00
DJ2 Derek Jeter Blue/101	75.00	150.00
DJ3 Derek Jeter Red/50	75.00	150.00
MP Mark Prior/88	15.00	40.00
MS Mike Schmidt/194	40.00	80.00
TG Troy Glaus/351	10.00	25.00

2003 Fleer Patchworks Game-Worn Patch 100

ISSUED IN 04 AS QLTY CONTROL EXCH
STATED PRINT RUN 100 SERIAL #'d SETS

AB2 Adrian Beltre	6.00	15.00
AJ2 Andruw Jones	10.00	25.00
AK2 Austin Kearns	6.00	15.00
CB2 Carlos Beltran	6.00	15.00
KW2 Kerry Wood	10.00	25.00
RO2 Roy Oswalt	6.00	15.00
AR2 Alex Rodriguez		
GM2 Greg Maddux		

2003 Fleer Patchworks Game-Worn Patch 300

ISSUED IN 04 AS QLTY CONTROL EXCH
STATED PRINT RUN 300 SERIAL #'d SETS

AB2 Bob Abreu	4.00	10.00
AK2 Austin Kearns	4.00	10.00
CD2 Carlos Delgado	4.00	10.00
DE2 Darin Erstad	4.00	10.00
HC2 Hee Seop Choi	4.00	10.00
JB2 Josh Beckett		
RO2 Roy Oswalt		
TA2 Tony Armas Jr.		

2003 Fleer Patchworks Game-Worn Patch Level 1 Single

Randomly inserted into packs, these 17 cards feature a single color patch swatch. Please note that the second level cards feature dual-colored swatches and level 3 features multi-colored swatches. The level 1 patches were issued to a stated print run of 250 serial numbered sets.

AB Adrian Beltre	4.00	10.00
AJ Andruw Jones	6.00	15.00
AR Alex Rodriguez		
BA Bob Abreu	4.00	10.00
BW Bernie Williams	6.00	15.00
CD Carlos Delgado		
EC Eric Chavez	4.00	10.00
FT Frank Thomas	6.00	15.00
GM Greg Maddux	6.00	15.00
JB Josh Beckett	4.00	10.00
KS Kazuhiro Sasaki	4.00	10.00
KW Kerry Wood	4.00	10.00
LB Lance Berkman	4.00	10.00
MG Mark Grace	6.00	15.00
RA Roberto Alomar	6.00	15.00
RO Roy Oswalt	4.00	10.00
VG Vladimir Guerrero	6.00	15.00

2003 Fleer Patchworks Game-Worn Patch Level 2 Dual

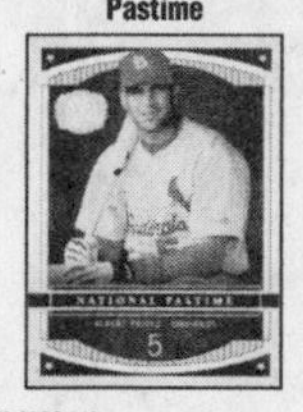

STATED PRINT RUN 100 SERIAL #'d SETS

AB Adrian Beltre	10.00	25.00
AJ Andruw Jones	12.50	30.00
AR Alex Rodriguez	20.00	50.00
BA Bob Abreu	10.00	25.00
BW Bernie Williams	12.50	30.00
CD Carlos Delgado	10.00	25.00
CS Curt Schilling	10.00	25.00
EC Eric Chavez	10.00	25.00
FT Frank Thomas	12.50	30.00
GM Greg Maddux	15.00	40.00
JB Josh Beckett	10.00	25.00
KS Kazuhiro Sasaki	10.00	25.00
KW Kerry Wood	10.00	25.00
LB Lance Berkman	10.00	25.00
MG Mark Grace	12.50	30.00
RA Roberto Alomar	12.50	30.00
RO Roy Oswalt	10.00	25.00
VG Vladimir Guerrero	12.50	30.00

2003 Fleer Patchworks Game-Worn Patch Level 3 Multi

STATED PRINT RUN 50 SERIAL #'d SETS

AB Adrian Beltre	12.50	30.00
AJ Andruw Jones	15.00	40.00
AR Alex Rodriguez	30.00	60.00
BA Bob Abreu	12.50	30.00
BW Bernie Williams	15.00	40.00
CD Carlos Delgado	12.50	30.00
CS Curt Schilling	12.50	30.00
EC Eric Chavez	12.50	30.00
FT Frank Thomas	15.00	40.00
GM Greg Maddux	20.00	50.00
JB Josh Beckett	12.50	30.00
KS Kazuhiro Sasaki	12.50	30.00
KW Kerry Wood	12.50	30.00
LB Lance Berkman	12.50	30.00
MG Mark Grace	15.00	40.00
RA Roberto Alomar	15.00	40.00
RO Roy Oswalt	12.50	30.00
VG Vladimir Guerrero	15.00	40.00

2003 Fleer Patchworks Licensed Apparel Jersey

STATED PRINT RUN 500 SERIAL #'d SETS
*ONE-COLOR PATCH: .75X TO 2X BASIC APP
*MULTI-COLOR PATCH: 1.25 TO 3X BASIC APP
PATCH PRINT RUN 300 SERIAL #'d SETS

AD Adam Dunn	3.00	8.00
CB Carlos Beltran	3.00	8.00
CJ Chipper Jones	4.00	10.00
DE Darin Erstad	3.00	8.00
DJ Derek Jeter	10.00	25.00
JD J.D. Drew	3.00	8.00
JR Jimmy Rollins	3.00	8.00
KB Kevin Brown	3.00	8.00
MM Mike Mussina	6.00	15.00
MO Magglio Ordonez	3.00	8.00
MP Mike Piazza	6.00	15.00
PK Paul Konerko	3.00	8.00
SG Shawn Green	3.00	8.00
SS Shannon Stewart	3.00	8.00
TH Todd Helton	4.00	10.00

2003 Fleer Patchworks Licensed Apparel Patch

STATED PRINT RUN 300 SERIAL #'d SETS

2003 Fleer Patchworks National Pastime

STATED ODDS 1:12

1 Barry Bonds	2.50	6.00
2 Kazuhiro Sasaki	.75	2.00
3 Mike Piazza	1.50	4.00
4 Barry Zito	.75	2.00
5 Sammy Sosa	1.00	2.50
6 Pedro Martinez	.75	2.00
7 Craig Biggio	.75	2.00
8 Rafael Palmeiro	.75	2.00
9 Greg Maddux	1.50	4.00
10 Manny Ramirez	.75	2.00
11 Adam Dunn	.75	2.00
12 Omar Vizquel	.75	2.00
13 Hideo Nomo	1.00	2.50
14 Alex Rodriguez	1.50	4.00
15 Pat Burrell	.75	2.00
16 Nomar Garciaparra	1.50	4.00
17 Randy Johnson	1.00	2.50
18 Juan Gonzalez	.75	2.00
19 Chipper Jones	1.00	2.50
20 Frank Thomas	1.00	2.50
21 Vladimir Guerrero	1.00	2.50
22 Troy Glaus	.75	2.00
23 Albert Pujols	2.00	5.00
24 Ichiro Suzuki	2.00	5.00
25 Ken Griffey Jr.	1.50	4.00

2003 Fleer Patchworks National Patchtime Commemorative

Randomly inserted into packs, these cards feature a commemorative patch piece from the featured uniform. These cards were issued to a stated print run of 25 serial numbered sets and no pricing is available due to market scarcity.

AR Alex Rodriguez
BZ Barry Zito
CB Craig Biggio
FT Frank Thomas
GM Greg Maddux
MP Mike Piazza
PM Pedro Martinez
RP Rafael Palmeiro
SS Sammy Sosa
TG Troy Glaus
VG Vladimir Guerrero

2003 Fleer Patchworks National Patchtime Nameplate

Randomly inserted into packs, these cards feature pieces from the player's uniform name. These cards were issued to a stated print run of 50 serial numbered sets.

AR Alex Rodriguez	20.00	50.00
BZ Barry Zito	12.50	30.00
CB Craig Biggio	15.00	40.00
CJ Chipper Jones	15.00	40.00
FT Frank Thomas	15.00	40.00
GM Greg Maddux	15.00	40.00
HN Hideo Nomo	40.00	80.00
MP Mike Piazza	15.00	40.00
NG Nomar Garciaparra	30.00	60.00
PB Pat Burrell	12.50	30.00
RJ Randy Johnson	15.00	40.00
RP Rafael Palmeiro	15.00	40.00
SS Sammy Sosa	15.00	40.00
TG Troy Glaus	12.50	30.00
VG Vladimir Guerrero	15.00	40.00

2003 Fleer Patchworks National Patchtime Number

Randomly inserted into packs, these cards feature swatches of the uniform number from the game-used jersey cut up for this insert set. These cards were issued to a stated print run of 75 serial numbered sets.

AR Alex Rodriguez	15.00	40.00
BZ Barry Zito	10.00	25.00
CB Craig Biggio	12.50	30.00
CJ Chipper Jones	12.50	30.00
FT Frank Thomas	12.50	30.00
GM Greg Maddux	12.50	30.00
HN Hideo Nomo	30.00	60.00
MP Mike Piazza	12.50	30.00
MR Manny Ramirez	12.50	30.00
NG Nomar Garciaparra	20.00	50.00
PB Pat Burrell	10.00	25.00
PM Pedro Martinez	12.50	30.00
RJ Randy Johnson	12.50	30.00
RP Rafael Palmeiro	12.50	30.00
SS Sammy Sosa	12.50	30.00
VG Vladimir Guerrero	12.50	30.00

2003 Fleer Patchworks National Patchtime Team Name

Randomly inserted into packs, these cards feature a swatch of the team name from the uniform used to create this game-used set. These cards were issued to a stated print run of 100 serial numbered sets.

AR Alex Rodriguez	15.00	40.00
BZ Barry Zito	10.00	25.00
CJ Chipper Jones	12.50	30.00
FT Frank Thomas	12.50	30.00
GM Greg Maddux	15.00	40.00
HN Hideo Nomo	30.00	60.00
MP Mike Piazza	15.00	40.00
NG Nomar Garciaparra	20.00	50.00
OV Omar Vizquel	12.50	30.00
PB Pat Burrell	10.00	25.00
RJ Randy Johnson	12.50	30.00
RP Rafael Palmeiro	12.50	30.00
SS Sammy Sosa	12.50	30.00
TG Troy Glaus	10.00	25.00
VG Vladimir Guerrero	12.50	30.00

2003 Fleer Patchworks National Patchtime Trim

Randomly inserted into packs, these cards feature pieces cut from the uniform "trim". These cards were issued to a stated print run of 200 serial numbered sets.

AR Alex Rodriguez	12.50	30.00
CJ Chipper Jones	10.00	25.00
FT Frank Thomas	10.00	25.00
GM Greg Maddux	12.50	30.00
HN Hideo Nomo	20.00	50.00
MP Mike Piazza	12.50	30.00
MR Manny Ramirez	10.00	25.00
NG Nomar Garciaparra	15.00	40.00
PM Pedro Martinez	10.00	25.00
RP Rafael Palmeiro	10.00	25.00
VG Vladimir Guerrero	10.00	25.00

2003 Fleer Patchworks National Patchtime 100

ISSUED IN 04 AS QLTY CONTROL EXCH
STATED PRINT RUN 100 SERIAL #'d SETS

JG2 Juan Gonzalez	10.00	25.00
KB2 Kris Benson	6.00	15.00
NG2 Nomar Garciaparra	15.00	40.00
CB2 Craig Biggio	6.00	15.00

2003 Fleer Patchworks National Patchtime 300

ISSUED IN 04 AS QLTY CONTROL EXCH
STATED PRINT RUN 300 SERIAL #'d SETS

AD2 Adam Dunn	4.00	10.00
BZ2 Barry Zito	4.00	10.00
MP2 Mike Piazza	10.00	25.00
NG2 Nomar Garciaparra	10.00	25.00
PB2 Pat Burrell	4.00	10.00
TH2 Tim Hudson	4.00	10.00
EH2 Eric Hinkse		
RJ2 Randy Johnson		
RP2 Rafael Palmeiro		

2003 Fleer Patchworks Numbers Game

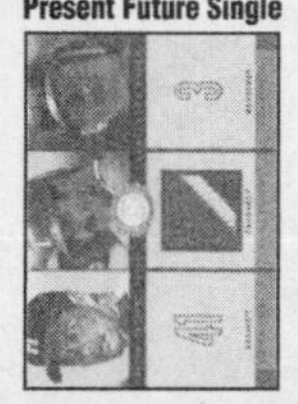

STATED ODDS 1:24

1 Ichiro Suzuki	2.50	6.00
2 Derek Jeter	3.00	8.00
3 Alex Rodriguez	2.00	5.00
4 Miguel Tejada	1.25	3.00
5 Nomar Garciaparra	2.00	5.00
6 Jason Giambi	1.25	3.00
7 J.D. Drew	1.25	3.00
8 Barry Bonds	3.00	8.00
9 Alfonso Soriano	1.25	3.00
10 Jeff Bagwell	1.25	3.00
11 Barry Larkin	1.25	3.00
12 Roberto Alomar	1.25	3.00
13 Larry Walker	1.25	3.00
14 Roger Clemens	2.50	6.00
15 Ken Griffey Jr.	2.00	5.00

2003 Fleer Patchworks Numbers Game Jersey

STATED ODDS 1:33

AR Alex Rodriguez	4.00	10.00
AS Alfonso Soriano	3.00	8.00
BL Barry Larkin	3.00	8.00
DJ Derek Jeter	6.00	15.00
JB Jeff Bagwell	3.00	8.00
JG Jason Giambi	3.00	8.00
LW Larry Walker	3.00	8.00
MT Miguel Tejada	3.00	8.00
RA Roberto Alomar	3.00	8.00
RC Roger Clemens	6.00	15.00

2003 Fleer Patchworks Numbers Game Patch

STATED PRINT RUN 300 SERIAL #'d SETS

AR Alex Rodriguez	15.00	40.00
AS Alfonso Soriano	6.00	15.00
BL Barry Larkin	10.00	25.00
DJ Derek Jeter	20.00	50.00
JB Jeff Bagwell	10.00	25.00
JG Jason Giambi	6.00	15.00
LW Larry Walker	6.00	15.00
MT Miguel Tejada	6.00	15.00
RA Roberto Alomar	10.00	25.00
RC Roger Clemens	15.00	40.00

2003 Fleer Patchworks Past Present Future

STATED ODDS 1:72

1 Eddie Mathews / Rafael Palmeiro / Alex Rodriguez	4.00	10.00
2 Phil Rizzuto / Derek Jeter / Alfonso Soriano	5.00	12.00
3 Reggie Jackson / Barry Bonds / Sammy Sosa	4.00	10.00
4 Billy Williams / Sammy Sosa / Hee Seop Choi	4.00	10.00
5 Joe Morgan / Roberto Alomar / Alfonso Soriano	4.00	10.00
6 Yogi Berra / Mike Piazza / Josh Phelps	4.00	10.00
7 Nolan Ryan / Roger Clemens / Kerry Wood	5.00	12.00
8 Mike Schmidt / Scott Rolen / Eric Hinske	4.00	10.00
9 Barry Bonds / Alex Rodriguez / Alfonso Soriano	4.00	10.00
10 Yogi Berra / Derek Jeter / Hideki Matsui	6.00	15.00

2003 Fleer Patchworks Patch Present Future Single

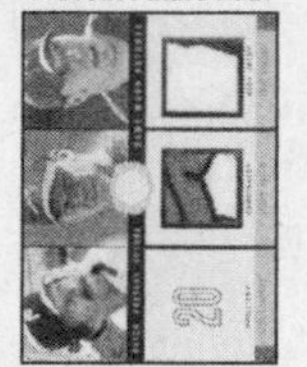

Randomly inserted into packs, these cards features three players on the card with one of the players having a game-worn swatch embedded on the card. These cards were issued to a stated print run of 200 serial numbered sets.

AR1 Eddie Mathews / Rafael Palmeiro / Alex Rodriguez Patch	15.00	40.00
AR2 Barry Bonds / Alex Rodriguez Patch / Alfonso Soriano		
AS1 Phil Rizzuto / Derek Jeter / Alfonso Soriano Patch	6.00	15.00
AS2 Joe Morgan / Roberto Alomar / Alfonso Soriano Patch	6.00	15.00
AS3 Barry Bonds / Alex Rodriguez / Alfonso Soriano Patch	6.00	15.00
BB Reggie Jackson / Barry Bonds Patch / Sammy Sosa	20.00	50.00
DJ1 Phil Rizzuto / Derek Jeter Patch / Alfonso Soriano	30.00	60.00
DJ2 Yogi Berra / Derek Jeter Patch / Hideki Matsui	30.00	60.00
EH Mike Schmidt / Scott Rolen / Eric Hinske Patch	6.00	15.00
KW Nolan Ryan / Roger Clemens / Kerry Wood Patch	15.00	40.00
MP Yogi Berra / Mike Piazza Patch / Josh Phelps	15.00	40.00
RA Joe Morgan / Roberto Alomar Patch / Alfonso Soriano	10.00	25.00
RC Nolan Ryan / Roger Clemens Patch / Kerry Wood	30.00	60.00
RP Eddie Mathews / Rafael Palmeiro Patch / Alex Rodriguez	10.00	25.00
SR Mike Schmidt / Scott Rolen Patch / Eric Hinske		
SS1 Reggie Jackson / Barry Bonds / Sammy Sosa Patch	15.00	40.00
SS2 Billy Williams / Sammy Sosa Patch / Hee Seop Choi	15.00	40.00

2003 Fleer Patchworks Patch Present Future Dual

Randomly inserted into packs, this partial parallel to the Patch Present Future Set features three players on the card with the two active players having a patch piece embedded on the card. These cards were issued to a stated print run of 100 serial numbered sets.

ARAS Barry Bonds / Alex Rodriguez Patch / Alfonso Soriano Patch	40.00	80.00
DJAS Phil Rizzuto / Derek Jeter Patch / Alfonso Soriano Patch	40.00	80.00
RAAS Joe Morgan / Roberto Alomar Patch / Alfonso Soriano Patch	15.00	40.00
RCKW Nolan Ryan / Roger Clemens Patch / Kerry Wood Patch	40.00	80.00
RPAR Eddie Mathews / Rafael Palmeiro Patch / Alex Rodriguez Patch	40.00	80.00
SREH Mike Schmidt / Scott Rolen Patch / Eric Hinske Patch	15.00	40.00

2004 Fleer Patchworks

This 110-card set was released in April, 2004. The set was issued in five-card packs with an $6 SRP which came 18 packs to a box and four boxes to a case. Cards numbered 1-90 feature veterans while cards numbered 91-110 feature leading rookies and prospects. Those cards were issued at a stated rate of one in 24 hobby and one in 48 retail packs and were issued to a stated print run of 799 serial numbered sets.

COMP.SET w/o SP's (90)	10.00	25.00
COMMON CARD (1-90)	.15	.40
COMMON CARD (91-110)	.60	1.50
91-110 ODDS 1:24 HOBBY, 1:48 RETAIL		
91-110 PRINT RUN 799 SERIAL #'d SETS		
1 Kerry Wood	.15	.40
2 Brian Giles	.15	.40
3 Tino Martinez	.25	.60
4 Mark Mulder	.15	.40
5 Andy Pettitte	.25	.60
6 Gary Sheffield	.15	.40
7 Mark Teixeira	.40	1.00
8 Garret Anderson	.15	.40
9 Craig Biggio	.25	.60
10 Alfonso Soriano	.15	.40
11 Bret Boone	.15	.40
12 Mike Piazza	.40	1.00
13 Todd Helton	.25	.60
14 Jay Gibbons	.15	.40
15 Eric Chavez	.15	.40
16 Andruw Jones	.15	.40
17 Adam Dunn	.25	.60
18 Corey Koskie	.15	.40
19 Rafael Palmeiro	.25	.60
20 Ivan Rodriguez	.25	.60
21 Tom Glavine	.25	.60
22 Luis Gonzalez	.15	.40
23 Miguel Tejada	.25	.60
24 Jose Vidro	.15	.40
25 Richie Sexson	.15	.40
26 Roy Halladay	.40	1.00
27 Vladimir Guerrero	.40	1.00
28 Randy Johnson	.40	1.00
29 Vernon Wells	.15	.40
30 Pat Burrell	.15	.40
31 Jason Schmidt	.15	.40
32 Casey Blake	.15	.40
33 Greg Maddux	.60	1.50
34 Mike Lowell	.15	.40
35 Hideo Nomo	.40	1.00
36 Carlos Delgado	.15	.40
37 Dontrelle Willis	.15	.40
38 Shawn Green	.15	.40
39 Pedro Martinez	.25	.60
40 Josh Beckett	.25	.60
41 Eric Gagne	.15	.40
42 Manny Ramirez	.40	1.00
43 Jim Edmonds	.25	.60
44 Curt Schilling	.25	.60
45 Mike Sweeney	.15	.40
46 Albert Pujols	1.00	2.50
47 Nomar Garciaparra	.40	1.00
48 Alex Rodriguez Yanks	.60	1.50
49 Angel Berroa	.15	.40
50 Jim Thome	.25	.60
51 Edgardo Alfonzo	.15	.40
52 Jeremy Bonderman	.15	.40
53 Miguel Cabrera	.40	1.00
54 Bobby Higginson	.15	.40
55 John Smoltz	.40	1.00
56 Jason Kendall	.15	.40
57 Torii Hunter	.15	.40
58 Troy Glaus	.15	.40
59 Rafael Furcal	.15	.40
60 Austin Kearns	.15	.40
61 Esteban Loaiza	.15	.40
62 Darin Erstad	.15	.40
63 Jose Reyes	.25	.60
64 Preston Wilson	.15	.40
65 Rocco Baldelli	.15	.40
66 Barry Zito	.15	.40
67 Ken Griffey Jr.	.60	1.50
68 Frank Thomas	.40	1.00
69 Roger Clemens	.50	1.25
70 Brett Myers	.15	.40
71 Billy Wagner	.15	.40
72 Scott Podsednik	.15	.40
73 Jody Gerut	.15	.40
74 Bartolo Colon	.15	.40
75 Jeff Bagwell	.25	.60
76 Jason Giambi	.15	.40
77 Edgar Martinez	.25	.60
78 Chipper Jones	.40	1.00
79 Jason Bay	.25	.60
80 Doug Mientkiewicz	.15	.40
81 Hank Blalock	.15	.40
82 Sammy Sosa	.40	1.00
83 Derek Jeter	1.00	2.50
84 Ichiro Suzuki	.60	1.50
85 Ben Sheets	.15	.40
86 Magglio Ordonez	.25	.60
87 Carlos Beltran	.15	.40
88 Mark Prior	.25	.60
89 Sean Burroughs	.15	.40
90 Tim Hudson	.25	.60
91 Hector Gimenez ROO RC	.60	1.50
92 Khalil Greene ROO	1.00	2.50
93 Rickie Weeks ROO	.60	1.50
94 Delmon Young ROO	1.00	2.50

95 Don Kelly ROO RC 1.00 2.50
96 Chad Bentz ROO RC .60 1.50
97 Greg Dobbs ROO RC .60 1.50
98 John Gall ROO RC .60 1.50
99 Cory Sullivan ROO RC .60 1.50
100 Kazuo Matsui ROO RC 1.00 2.50
101 Graham Koonce ROO .60 1.50
102 Jason Bartlett ROO RC 2.00 5.00
103 Angel Chavez ROO RC .60 1.50
104 Ronny Cedeno ROO RC .60 1.50
105 Jerry Gil ROO RC .60 1.50
106 Ivan Ochoa ROO RC .60 1.50
107 Ruddy Yan ROO .60 1.50
108 Mike Gosling ROO RC .60 1.50
109 Alfredo Simon ROO RC .60 1.50
110 Koyie Hill ROO .60 1.50

2004 Fleer Patchworks Star Ruby

*RUBY 1-90: 5X TO 12X BASIC
*RUBY 91-110: .75X TO 2X BASIC
STATED ODDS 1:48 HOBBY, 1:96 RETAIL
STATED PRINT RUN 50 SERIAL #'d SETS

2004 Fleer Patchworks Autoworks Black

PRINT RUNS B/WN 145-376 COPIES PER
*BLUE: .4X TO 1X BLACK p/r 263-376
*BLUE: .4X TO 1X BLACK p/r 145-193
RED PATCH PRINT RUN 10 SERIAL #'d SETS
NO RED PATCH PRICING DUE TO SCARCITY
ALL RED PATCH ARE EXCHANGE CARDS
RED PATCH EXCH.DEADLINE IS INDEFINITE
OVERALL AU ODDS 1:54 HOB, 1:120 RET
AB Angel Berroa/145 4.00 10.00
AP1 Andy Pettitte/148 15.00 40.00
AP2 Albert Pujols/193 125.00 200.00
EG Eric Gagne/193 10.00 25.00
GA Garret Anderson/145 6.00 15.00
GS Grady Sizemore/263 15.00 40.00
JB Josh Beckett/148 10.00 25.00
JG Jody Gerut/376 4.00 10.00
MM Mark Mulder/190 6.00 15.00
MT Miguel Tejada/164 10.00 25.00
RH Roy Halladay/286 15.00 40.00
SP Scott Podsednik/146 10.00 25.00

2004 Fleer Patchworks By the Numbers

STATED ODDS 1:24 HOBBY, 1:12 RETAIL
1 Albert Pujols 2.50 6.00
2 Derek Jeter 2.50 6.00
3 Mike Piazza 1.00 2.50
4 Nomar Garciaparra 1.00 2.50
5 Eric Gagne .40 1.00
6 Sammy Sosa 1.00 2.50
7 Josh Beckett .60 1.50
8 Vladimir Guerrero 1.00 2.50
9 Jose Reyes .60 1.50
10 Bret Boone .40 1.00
11 Alex Rodriguez Yanks 1.50 4.00
12 Randy Johnson 1.00 2.50
13 Chipper Jones 1.00 2.50
14 Tim Hudson .60 1.50
15 Rocco Baldelli .40 1.00

2004 Fleer Patchworks By the Numbers Patch

OVERALL GU ODDS 1:6 HOBBY, 1:36 RETAIL
STATED PRINT RUN 100 SERIAL #'d SETS
AP Albert Pujols 12.50 30.00
AR Alex Rodriguez 10.00 25.00
BB Bret Boone 6.00 15.00
CJ Chipper Jones 10.00 25.00
DJ Derek Jeter 10.00 25.00
EG Eric Gagne 6.00 15.00
JB Josh Beckett 6.00 15.00
JR Jose Reyes 6.00 15.00
MP Mike Piazza 10.00 25.00
NG Nomar Garciaparra 10.00 25.00
RB Rocco Baldelli 6.00 15.00
RJ Randy Johnson 10.00 25.00
SS Sammy Sosa 10.00 25.00
TH Tim Hudson 6.00 15.00
VG Vladimir Guerrero 10.00 25.00

2004 Fleer Patchworks Game Used Level 1

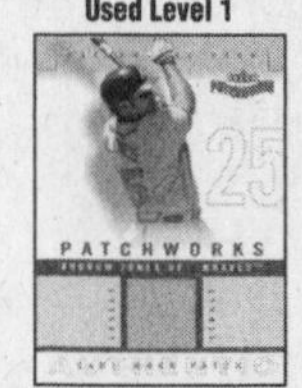

STATED PRINT RUN 200 SERIAL #'d SETS
*LEVEL 2: .5X TO 1.2X BASIC
LEVEL 2 PRINT RUN 100 SERIAL #'d SETS
*PATCH: 1.25X TO 3X BASIC
PATCH PRINT RUN 50 SERIAL #'d SETS
OVERALL GU ODDS 1:6 HOBBY, 1:36 RETAIL
AJ Andruw Jones 4.00 10.00
AP1 Andy Pettitte 4.00 10.00
AP2 Albert Pujols 6.00 15.00
AS Alfonso Soriano 3.00 8.00
BB Bret Boone 3.00 8.00
BW Bernie Williams 4.00 10.00
BZ Barry Zito 3.00 8.00
CD Carlos Delgado 3.00 8.00
DW Dontrelle Willis 4.00 10.00
GA Garret Anderson 3.00 8.00
HB Hank Blalock 3.00 8.00
JR Jose Reyes 3.00 8.00
LW Larry Walker 3.00 8.00
MP1 Mike Piazza 5.00 12.00
MP2 Mark Prior 4.00 10.00
RH Roy Halladay 3.00 8.00
SG Shawn Green 3.00 8.00
TG Troy Glaus 3.00 8.00
TH Torii Hunter 3.00 8.00

2004 Fleer Patchworks Licensed Apparel

STATED PRINT RUN 300 SERIAL #'d SETS
JSY TAG PRINT RUN 10 SERIAL #'d SETS
NO JSY TAG PRICING DUE TO SCARCITY
MLB LOGO PRINT RUN 1 SERIAL #'d SET
NO MLB LOGO PRICING DUE TO SCARCITY
*NAMEPLATE: 1.25X TO 3X BASIC
NAMEPLATE PRINT RUN 50 SERIAL #'d SETS
*NUMBER: .75X TO 2X BASIC
NUMBER PRINT RUN 100 SERIAL #'d SETS
*TEAM NAME: .75X TO 2X BASIC
TEAM NAME PRINT RUN 150 SER.#'d SETS
OVERALL GU ODDS 1:6 HOBBY, 1:36 RETAIL
AJ Andruw Jones 4.00 10.00
AK Austin Kearns 3.00 8.00
AP Albert Pujols 6.00 15.00
AR Alex Rodriguez 5.00 12.00
BB Bret Boone 3.00 8.00
DJ Derek Jeter 8.00 20.00
DW Dontrelle Willis 4.00 10.00
JB Jeff Bagwell 4.00 10.00
JT Jim Thome 4.00 10.00
MP1 Mike Piazza 5.00 12.00
MP2 Mark Prior 4.00 10.00
SS Sammy Sosa 4.00 10.00
TG Troy Glaus 3.00 8.00
TH1 Tim Hudson 3.00 8.00
TH2 Torii Hunter 3.00 8.00

2004 Fleer Patchworks National Pastime

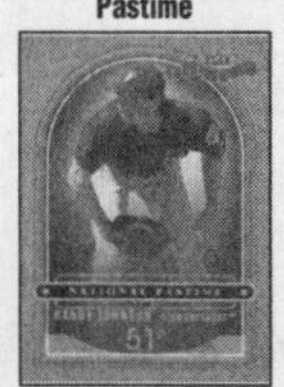

STATED ODDS 1:72 HOBBY, 1:144 RETAIL
STATED PRINT RUN 250 SERIAL #'d SETS
1 Albert Pujols 3.00 8.00
2 Alex Rodriguez Yanks 2.00 5.00
3 Derek Jeter 3.00 8.00
4 Nomar Garciaparra 1.25 3.00
5 Jim Thome .75 2.00
6 Chipper Jones 1.25 3.00
7 Mark Prior .75 2.00
8 Ichiro Suzuki 2.00 5.00
9 Jeff Bagwell .75 2.00
10 Troy Glaus .50 1.25
11 Randy Johnson 1.25 3.00
12 Sammy Sosa 1.25 3.00
13 Austin Kearns .50 1.25
14 Miguel Cabrera 1.25 3.00
15 Vladimir Guerrero 1.25 3.00

2004 Fleer Patchworks National Patchtime

STATED PRINT RUN 350 SERIAL #'d SETS
*GOLD: .4X TO 1X BASIC
GOLD PRINT RUN 200 SERIAL #'d SETS
*PATCH: .75X TO 2X BASIC
PATCH PRINT RUN 100 SERIAL #'d SETS
OVERALL GU ODDS 1:6 HOBBY, 1:36 RETAIL
AK Austin Kearns 3.00 8.00
AP Albert Pujols 6.00 15.00
AR Alex Rodriguez 5.00 12.00
CJ Chipper Jones 4.00 10.00
DJ Derek Jeter 8.00 20.00
JB Jeff Bagwell 4.00 10.00
JT Jim Thome 4.00 10.00
MC Miguel Cabrera 4.00 10.00
MP Mark Prior 4.00 10.00
NG Nomar Garciaparra 5.00 12.00
RJ Randy Johnson 4.00 10.00
SS Sammy Sosa 4.00 10.00
TG Troy Glaus 3.00 8.00
VG Vladimir Guerrero 4.00 10.00

2004 Fleer Patchworks Stitches In Time

STATED ODDS 1:12 HOBBY, 1:6 RETAIL
1 Albert Pujols 2.50 6.00
2 Alex Rodriguez Yanks 1.50 4.00
3 Derek Jeter 2.50 6.00
4 Nomar Garciaparra 1.00 2.50
5 Jim Thome .60 1.50
6 Chipper Jones 1.00 2.50
7 Mark Prior .60 1.50
8 Eric Gagne .40 1.00
9 Jeff Bagwell .60 1.50
10 Troy Glaus .40 1.00
11 Randy Johnson 1.00 2.50
12 Sammy Sosa 1.00 2.50
13 Austin Kearns .40 1.00
14 Miguel Cabrera 1.00 2.50
15 Vladimir Guerrero 1.00 2.50
16 Mike Piazza 1.00 2.50
17 Jason Giambi .40 1.00
18 Tim Hudson .60 1.50
19 Carlos Delgado .40 1.00
20 Rocco Baldelli .40 1.00
21 Ichiro Suzuki 1.50 4.00
22 Barry Zito .40 1.00
23 Pedro Martinez .60 1.50
24 Torii Hunter .40 1.00
25 Andruw Jones .40 1.00

2004 Fleer Patchworks Stitches in Time Jersey

STATED PRINT RUN 350 SERIAL #'d SETS
*PATCH: .75X TO 2X BASIC
PATCH PRINT RUN 150 SERIAL #'d SETS
OVERALL GU ODDS 1:6 HOBBY, 1:36 RETAIL
AJ Andruw Jones 4.00 10.00
AK Austin Kearns 3.00 8.00
AP Albert Pujols 6.00 15.00
AR Alex Rodriguez 5.00 12.00
BZ Barry Zito 3.00 8.00
CD Carlos Delgado 3.00 8.00
CJ Chipper Jones 4.00 10.00
DJ Derek Jeter 8.00 20.00
EG Eric Gagne 3.00 8.00
JB Jeff Bagwell 4.00 10.00
JG Jason Giambi 3.00 8.00
JT Jim Thome 4.00 10.00
MC Miguel Cabrera 4.00 10.00
MP Mike Piazza 5.00 12.00
MP Mark Prior 4.00 10.00
NG Nomar Garciaparra 5.00 12.00
PM Pedro Martinez 4.00 10.00
RB Rocco Baldelli 3.00 8.00
RJ Randy Johnson 4.00 10.00
SS Sammy Sosa 4.00 10.00
TG Troy Glaus 3.00 8.00
TH1 Tim Hudson 3.00 8.00
TH2 Torii Hunter 3.00 8.00
VG Vladimir Guerrero 4.00 10.00

2005 Fleer Patchworks

COMP.SET w/o SP's (70) 15.00 40.00
COMMON (1-70) .30 .75
COMMON (71-90) .40 1.00
71-90 PRINT RUN 499 SERIAL #'d SETS
COMMON (91-100) .40 1.00
91-100 PRINT RUN 999 SERIAL #'d SETS
71-100 ODDS 1:8 HOBBY
1 Bobby Abreu .30 .75
2 Miguel Cabrera .75 2.00
3 J.D. Drew .30 .75
4 Justin Morneau .75 2.00
5 David Ortiz .75 2.00
6 Ivan Rodriguez .50 1.25
7 Jason Schmidt .30 .75
8 Frank Thomas .75 2.00
9 Travis Hafner .30 .75
10 Curt Schilling .50 1.25
11 Jim Edmonds .50 1.25
12 Randy Johnson .75 2.00
13 Jose Vidro .30 .75
14 Vernon Wells .30 .75
15 Lance Berkman .50 1.25
16 Khalil Greene .30 .75
17 Andruw Jones .30 .75
18 Mark Prior .50 1.25
19 Mark Teixeira .75 2.00
20 Jack Wilson .30 .75
21 Adrian Beltre .30 .75
22 Lew Ford .30 .75
23 Shawn Green .30 .75
24 Juan Pierre .30 .75
25 Alfonso Soriano .50 1.25
26 Mike Sweeney .30 .75
27 Chipper Jones .75 2.00
28 Javy Lopez .30 .75
29 Victor Martinez .50 1.25
30 Kaz Matsui .30 .75
31 Bernie Williams .50 1.25
32 Kerry Wood .30 .75
33 Barry Zito .30 .75
34 Austin Kearns .30 .75
35 Todd Helton .50 1.25
36 B.J. Upton .50 1.25
37 Jeff Bagwell .50 1.25
38 Pedro Martinez .50 1.25
39 Lyle Overbay .30 .75
40 Ichiro Suzuki 1.25 3.00
41 Jason Bay .30 .75
42 Bobby Crosby .30 .75
43 Vladimir Guerrero .75 2.00
44 Richie Sexson .30 .75
45 Johan Santana .75 2.00
46 Magglio Ordonez .50 1.25
47 Derek Jeter 2.00 5.00
48 Eric Gagne .30 .75
49 Albert Pujols 2.00 5.00
50 Jim Thome .50 1.25
51 Hideki Matsui 1.25 3.00
52 Torii Hunter .30 .75
53 Greg Maddux 1.25 3.00
54 Michael Young .50 1.25
55 Carlos Beltran .30 .75
56 Carl Crawford .50 1.25
57 Adam Dunn .50 1.25
58 Nomar Garciaparra .75 2.00
59 Mike Piazza .75 2.00
60 Alex Rodriguez 1.25 3.00
61 Scott Rolen .50 1.25
62 Ben Sheets .30 .75
63 Sammy Sosa .75 2.00
64 Hank Blalock .30 .75
65 Carlos Delgado .30 .75
66 Ken Griffey Jr. 1.25 3.00
67 Manny Ramirez .75 2.00
68 Miguel Tejada .50 1.25
69 Roger Clemens 1.00 2.50
70 Gary Sheffield .30 .75
71 Jon Knott PO .40 1.00
72 Ryan Raburn PO .40 1.00
73 Zack Greinke PO .60 1.50
74 David Aardsma PO .40 1.00
75 Justin Verlander PO RC 8.00 20.00
76 Andres Blanco PO .40 1.00
77 David Wright PO 1.50 4.00
78 Jeff Baker PO .40 1.00
79 Charlton Jimerson PO .40 1.00
80 Sean Burnett PO .40 1.00
81 Joey Gathright PO .40 1.00
82 Victor Diaz PO .40 1.00
83 Scott Kazmir PO 1.00 2.50
84 Edwin Encarnacion PO .60 1.50
85 J.D. Durbin PO .40 1.00
86 Nick Swisher PO 1.00 2.50
87 Casey Kotchman PO .40 1.00
88 Gavin Floyd PO .40 1.00
89 Josh Kroeger PO .40 1.00
90 Taylor Buchholz PO .40 1.00
91 Reggie Jackson LS 1.00 2.50
92 Nolan Ryan LS 2.50 6.00
93 Eddie Murray LS 1.00 2.50
94 Carlton Fisk LS .60 1.50
95 Mike Schmidt LS 2.00 5.00
96 Joe Morgan LS .40 1.00
97 Rod Carew LS .60 1.50
98 Harmon Killebrew LS 1.00 2.50
99 Tom Seaver LS .60 1.50
100 Brooks Robinson LS .60 1.50

2005 Fleer Patchworks Gold

*GOLD 1-70: 1.5X TO 4X BASIC
*GOLD 71-90: .6X TO 1.5X BASIC
*GOLD 91-100: .6X TO 1.5X BASIC
OVERALL PARALLEL ODDS 1:16 H
STATED PRINT RUN 99 SERIAL #'d SETS

2005 Fleer Patchworks Masterpiece

OVERALL PARALLEL ODDS 1:16 H
STATED PRINT RUN 1 SERIAL #'d SET
NO PRICING DUE TO SCARCITY

2005 Fleer Patchworks Autoworks Copper

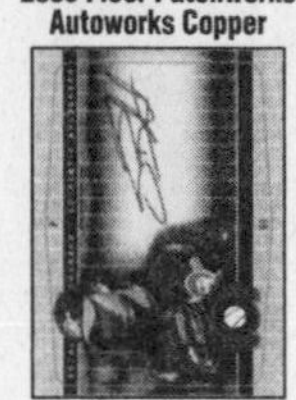

OVERALL AU ODDS 1:18 H
PRINT RUNS B/WN 75-250 COPIES PER
BL Brad Lidge/75 8.00 20.00
BU B.J. Upton/150 6.00 15.00
CC Carl Crawford/175 10.00 25.00
DW David Wright/250 20.00 50.00
JB Jason Bay/150 6.00 15.00
JBO Jeremy Bonderman/100 6.00 15.00
JD J.D. Durbin/100 4.00 10.00
JM Justin Morneau/175 6.00 15.00
JV Justin Verlander/100 20.00 50.00
MC Miguel Cabrera/75 8.00 10.00
RB Rocco Baldelli/100 6.00 15.00
SB Sean Burnett/100 4.00 10.00
TH Travis Hafner/150 6.00 15.00
VM Victor Martinez/100 6.00 15.00
ZG Zack Greinke/200 10.00 25.00

2005 Fleer Patchworks Autoworks Gold

*GOLD: .5X TO 1.2X COPPER p/r 150-250
OVERALL AU ODDS 1:18 H
STATED PRINT RUN 49 SERIAL #'d SETS
BS Ben Sheets 8.00 20.00
EB Ernie Banks 30.00 60.00
GF Gavin Floyd 5.00 12.00
HA Hank Aaron 150.00 250.00
JP Josh Phelps 5.00 12.00
LB Lance Berkman 12.50 30.00
LF Lew Ford 5.00 12.00
MCA Mike Cameron 5.00 12.00
MY Michael Young 8.00 20.00

2005 Fleer Patchworks Autoworks Masterpiece

OVERALL AU ODDS 1:18 H
STATED PRINT RUN 1 SERIAL #'d SET
NO PRICING DUE TO SCARCITY

2005 Fleer Patchworks Autoworks Silver

*SILVER: .4X TO 1X COPPER p/r 150-250
OVERALL AU ODDS 1:18 H
STATED PRINT RUN 99 SERIAL #'d SETS
BS Ben Sheets 6.00 15.00
JP Josh Phelps 4.00 10.00
LF Lew Ford 4.00 10.00
MCA Mike Cameron 4.00 10.00

2005 Fleer Patchworks Autoworks Dual

OVERALL AU ODDS 1:18 H
STATED PRINT RUN 25 SERIAL #'d SETS
NO PRICING DUE TO SCARCITY

2005 Fleer Patchworks Autoworks Quad

OVERALL AU ODDS 1:18 H
STATED PRINT RUN 10 SERIAL #'d SETS
NO PRICING DUE TO SCARCITY

2005 Fleer Patchworks By the Numbers

STATED ODDS 1:18 H, 1:24 R
1 Roy Oswalt .60 1.50
2 Hideki Matsui 1.50 4.00
3 Curt Schilling .60 1.50
4 Mike Piazza 1.00 2.50
5 Alex Rodriguez 1.50 4.00
6 Vladimir Guerrero 1.00 2.50
7 Victor Martinez .60 1.50
8 Adrian Beltre .40 1.00
9 Johnny Estrada .40 1.00
10 Ken Griffey Jr. 1.50 4.00
11 Sammy Sosa 1.00 2.50
12 Ichiro Suzuki 1.50 4.00
13 Roger Clemens 1.25 3.00
14 David Ortiz 1.00 2.50
15 Johan Santana 1.00 2.50
16 Pedro Martinez .60 1.50
17 Austin Kearns .40 1.00
18 Randy Johnson 1.00 2.50
19 Nomar Garciaparra 1.00 2.50
20 Albert Pujols 2.50 6.00

2005 Fleer Patchworks By the Numbers Jersey Die Cut

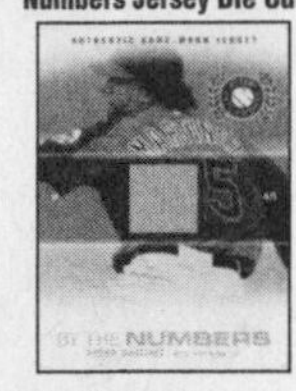
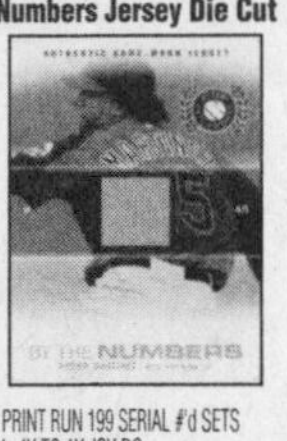

STATED PRINT RUN 199 SERIAL #'d SETS
*JERSEY: .4X TO 1X JSY DC
JERSEY RANDOM IN RETAIL PACKS
NO CLEMENS JSY PRICE DUE TO SCARCITY
JERSEY TAG PRINT RUN 1 #'d SET
NO JSY TAG PRICING DUE TO SCARCITY
OVERALL GAME-USED ODDS 1:9 H
AB Adrian Beltre 2.00 5.00
AP Albert Pujols 6.00 15.00
CS Curt Schilling 3.00 8.00
DO David Ortiz 3.00 8.00
HM Hideki Matsui 8.00 20.00
JE Johnny Estrada 2.00 5.00
JS Johan Santana 4.00 10.00
MP Mike Piazza/116 UER 4.00 10.00
PM Pedro Martinez 3.00 8.00
RC Roger Clemens 4.00 10.00
RJ Randy Johnson 4.00 10.00
RO Roy Oswalt 2.00 5.00
SS Sammy Sosa 4.00 10.00
VG Vladimir Guerrero 4.00 10.00

2005 Fleer Patchworks By the Numbers Patch

*PATCH: .75X TO 2X JSY DC
OVERALL GAME-USED ODDS 1:9 H
STATED PRINT RUN 99 SERIAL #'d SETS
AK Austin Kearns/78 UER 4.00 10.00

2005 Fleer Patchworks By the Numbers Patch Die Cut

*PATCH DC: 1.25X TO 3X JSY DC
OVERALL GAME-USED ODDS 1:9 H
STATED PRINT RUN 25 SERIAL #'d SETS
AK Austin Kearns 6.00 15.00

2005 Fleer Patchworks By the Numbers Patch Autograph

OVERALL AU ODDS 1:18 H
STATED PRINT RUN 25 SERIAL #'d SETS
NO PRICING DUE TO SCARCITY

2005 Fleer Patchworks Heart of the Team

STATED ODDS 1:108 H, 1:360 R
1 John Smoltz 1.25 3.00
Andruw Jones
Chipper Jones
Miguel Cabrera
Juan Pierre
Josh Beckett
2 David Ortiz 3.00 8.00
Manny Ramirez
Johnny Damon
Derek Jeter
Hideki Matsui
Alex Rodriguez
3 Jim Edmonds 3.00 8.00
Albert Pujols
Scott Rolen
Lance Berkman
Jeff Bagwell
Roger Clemens
4 Vladimir Guerrero 1.25 3.00
Tim Salmon
Darin Erstad
Barry Zito
Bobby Crosby
Eric Chavez
5 Bobby Abreu 1.25 3.00
Jim Thome
Pat Burrell
Kaz Matsui
Mike Piazza
Pedro Martinez
6 Lew Ford .75 2.00
Johan Santana
Torii Hunter
Frank Thomas
Paul Konerko
Aaron Rowand
7 Austin Kearns .75 2.00
Adam Dunn
Ken Griffey Jr.
Kerry Wood
Nomar Garciaparra
Mark Prior
8 Adrian Beltre 2.00 5.00
Ichiro Suzuki
Richie Sexson
Mark Teixeira
Alfonso Soriano
Hank Blalock
9 Rafael Palmeiro .75 2.00
Javy Lopez
Miguel Tejada
Jose Vidro
Brad Wilkerson
Vinny Castilla
10 Orlando Hudson .75 2.00
Vernon Wells
Alex Rios
Rocco Baldelli
B.J. Upton
Carl Crawford

2005 Fleer Patchworks Heart of the Team Jersey

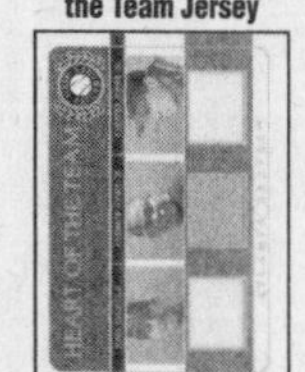

STATED PRINT RUN 199 SERIAL #'d SETS
PATCH PRINT RUN 15 SERIAL #'d SETS
NO PATCH PRICING DUE TO SCARCITY
OVERALL GAME-USED ODDS 1:9 H
ABFM John Smoltz 10.00 25.00
Andruw Jones
Chipper Jones
Miguel Cabrera
Juan Pierre
Josh Beckett/132 UER
PPNM Bobby Abreu 10.00 25.00
Jim Thome
Pat Burrell
Kaz Matsui
Mike Piazza
Pedro Martinez/132 UER
SCHA Jim Edmonds 15.00 40.00
Albert Pujols
Scott Rolen
Lance Berkman
Jeff Bagwell
Roger Clemens/132 UER

2005 Fleer Patchworks Jersey

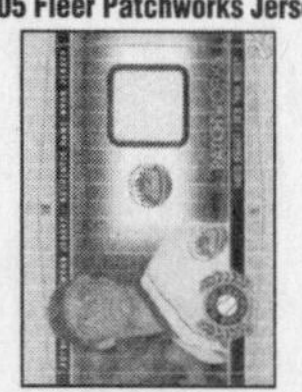

*JERSEY: .2X TO .5X PATCH
RANDOM INSERTS IN RETAIL PACKS
GS Gary Sheffield 2.00 5.00

2005 Fleer Patchworks Patch

STATED PRINT RUN 99 SERIAL #'d SETS
*PATCH DC: .6X TO 1.5X PATCH
PATCH DC PRINT RUN 49 SERIAL #'d SETS
OVERALL GAME-USED ODDS 1:9 H
AS Alfonso Soriano/73 UER 4.00 10.00
BW Bernie Williams 6.00 15.00
DO David Ortiz/51 UER 6.00 15.00
DW Dontrelle Willis 4.00 10.00
DWR David Wright 15.00 40.00
JB Josh Beckett 4.00 10.00
KW Kerry Wood 4.00 10.00
MARK Mark Prior 6.00 15.00

MIKE Mike Piazza 8.00 20.00
MR Manny Ramirez 6.00 15.00
MY Michael Young 4.00 10.00
SS Shannon Stewart 4.00 10.00
TH Torii Hunter 4.00 10.00

2005 Fleer Patchworks Dual Jersey Die Cut

STATED PRINT RUN 199 SERIAL #'d SETS
*DUAL JSY: .4X TO 1X DUAL JSY DC
DUAL JSY RANDOM IN RETAIL PACKS
GSBW JSY NOT PRICED DUE TO SCARCITY
DUAL MLB LOGO PRINT RUN 1 #'d SET
NO DUAL MLB LOGO PRICING AVAILABLE
DUAL PATCH PRINT RUN 25 #'d SETS
NO DUAL PATCH PRICING AVAILABLE
DUAL PATCH DC PRINT RUN 15 #'d SETS
NO DUAL PATCH DC PRICING AVAILABLE
DWJB Dontrelle Willis 3.00 8.00
Josh Beckett
DWMP David Wright 6.00 15.00
Mike Piazza
GSBW Gary Sheffield 4.00 10.00
Bernie Williams
KWMP Kerry Wood 4.00 10.00
Mark Prior
MRDO Manny Ramirez 6.00 15.00
David Ortiz
MYAS Michael Young 3.00 8.00
Alfonso Soriano
SSTH Shannon Stewart 3.00 8.00
Torii Hunter

2005 Fleer Patchworks Property of

STATED ODDS 1:6 H, 1:6 R
1 Vladimir Guerrero 1.00 2.50
2 Luis Gonzalez .40 1.00
3 Chipper Jones 1.00 2.50
4 Miguel Tejada .60 1.50
5 David Ortiz 1.00 2.50
6 Kerry Wood .40 1.00
7 Frank Thomas 1.00 2.50
8 Adam Dunn .60 1.50
9 Victor Martinez .60 1.50
10 Todd Helton .60 1.50
11 Ivan Rodriguez .60 1.50
12 Miguel Cabrera 1.00 2.50
13 Jeff Bagwell .60 1.50
14 Mike Sweeney .40 1.00
15 Eric Gagne .40 1.00
16 Lyle Overbay .40 1.00
17 Johan Santana 1.00 2.50
18 Mike Piazza 1.00 2.50
19 Derek Jeter 2.50 6.00
20 Bobby Crosby .40 1.00
21 Jim Thome .60 1.50
22 Jason Bay .40 1.00
23 Khalil Greene .40 1.00
24 Jason Schmidt .40 1.00
25 Ichiro Suzuki 1.50 4.00
26 Albert Pujols 2.50 6.00
27 B.J. Upton .60 1.50
28 Hank Blalock .40 1.00
29 Vernon Wells .40 1.00
30 Jose Vidro .40 1.00

2005 Fleer Patchworks Property of Jersey Die Cut

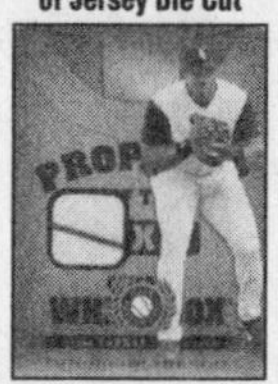

STATED PRINT RUN 199 SERIAL #'d SETS
*JERSEY: .4X TO 1X JSY DC
JERSEY RANDOM IN RETAIL PACKS
MLB LOGO PRINT RUN 1 SERIAL #'d SET
NO MLB LOGO PRICING AVAILABLE
OVERALL GAME-USED ODDS 1:9 H
AP Albert Pujols 6.00 15.00
BU B.J. Upton 2.00 5.00
CJ Chipper Jones 4.00 10.00
DO David Ortiz 4.00 10.00
EG Eric Gagne 2.00 5.00
FT Frank Thomas 4.00 10.00
HB Hank Blalock 2.00 5.00
IR Ivan Rodriguez 3.00 8.00
JB Jeff Bagwell 3.00 8.00
JBA Jason Bay 2.00 5.00
JS Johan Santana 4.00 10.00
JSC Jason Schmidt 2.00 5.00
JT Jim Thome 3.00 8.00
KG Khalil Greene 3.00 8.00
KW Kerry Wood 2.00 5.00
LG Luis Gonzalez 2.00 5.00
LO Lyle Overbay/86 UER 2.00 5.00
MC Miguel Cabrera 3.00 8.00
MP Mike Piazza 4.00 10.00
MT Miguel Tejada 2.00 5.00
VG Vladimir Guerrero 4.00 10.00
VW Vernon Wells 2.00 5.00

2005 Fleer Patchworks Property of Patch

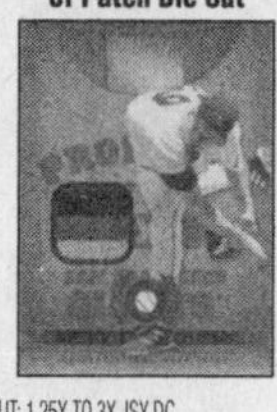

*PATCH: .75X TO 2X JSY DC
OVERALL GAME-USED ODDS 1:9 H
STATED PRINT RUN 99 SERIAL #'d SETS
AD Adam Dunn/42 UER 4.00 10.00
MS Mike Sweeney/77 UER 4.00 10.00

2005 Fleer Patchworks Property of Patch Die Cut

*DIE CUT: 1.25X TO 3X JSY DC
OVERALL GAME-USED ODDS 1:9 H
STATED PRINT RUN 25 SERIAL #'d SETS
NO PRICING DUE TO SCARCITY
AD Adam Dunn 6.00 15.00
MS Mike Sweeney 6.00 15.00

2005 Fleer Patchworks Property of Patch Nameplate

*PATCH NAMEPLATE: 1.25X TO 3X JSY DC
OVERALL GAME-USED ODDS 1:9 H
STATED PRINT RUN 49 SERIAL #'d SETS
MS Mike Sweeney 6.00 15.00

2001 Fleer Platinum

This 601-card set was distributed in two separate series. Series 1 was released in late May, 2001 with cards distributed in 10-card hobby packs with a suggested retail price of $2.99 and a 25-card jumbo pack for $9.99. Series 2 (entitled Platinum RC edition) was released in late December, 2001. The set features player photos printed in the original 1981 Fleer design. The first series contains 250 regular cards plus 31 dual short printed cards (251-280/301) and 20 All-Star cards (281-300) both with an insertion rate of 1:6 in the hobby packs and 1:2 in the jumbo packs. The second series set contains 300 cards composed of basic (302-401), Chart Toppers (402-431), Team Leaders (432-461), Franchise Futures (462-481), Postseason Glory (482-501) and Rookies (502-601), seeded at a rate of 1:3 packs). Notable Rookie Cards include Ichiro, Albert Pujols and Mark Teixeira. According to representatives at Fleer, card 529 (Mark Prior RC) and card 402 (Freddy Garcia CT) were mistakenly switched with each other on the printing forms - thereby making card 402 a short-print (available at the same ratio as cards 502-601) and card 529 a basic card (available at the same rate as cards 302-501).

COMP. SERIES 1 (301) 100.00 200.00
COMP. SERIES 2 (300) 100.00 200.00
COMP.SER.1 w/o SP's (250) 15.00 40.00
COMP.SER.2 w/o SP's (200) 15.00 40.00
COMMON (1-250/302-501) .10 .30
COMMON (251-280) .75 2.00
COMMON AS (281-300) .75 2.00
COMMON (502-601) .75 2.00
1 Bobby Abreu .10 .30
2 Brad Radke .10 .30
3 Bill Mueller .10 .30
4 Adam Eaton .10 .30
5 Antonio Alfonseca .10 .30
6 Manny Ramirez Sox .20 .50
7 Adam Kennedy .10 .30
8 Jose Valentin .10 .30
9 Jaret Wright .10 .30
10 Aramis Ramirez .10 .30
11 Jeff Kent .10 .30
12 Juan Encarnacion .10 .30
13 Sandy Alomar Jr. .10 .30
14 Joe Randa .10 .30
15 Darryl Kile .10 .30
16 Darren Dreifort .10 .30
17 Matt Kinney .10 .30
18 Pokey Reese .10 .30
19 Ryan Klesko .10 .30
20 Shawn Estes .10 .30
21 Moises Alou .10 .30
22 Edgar Renteria .10 .30
23 Chuck Knoblauch .10 .30
24 Carl Everett .10 .30
25 Garret Anderson .10 .30
26 Shane Reynolds .10 .30
27 Billy Koch .10 .30
28 Carlos Febles .10 .30
29 Brian Anderson .10 .30
30 Armando Rios .10 .30
31 Ryan Kohlmeier .10 .30
32 Steve Finley .10 .30
33 Brady Anderson .10 .30
34 Cal Ripken 1.00 2.50
35 Paul Konerko .10 .30
36 Chuck Finley .10 .30
37 Rick Ankiel .10 .30
38 Mariano Rivera .30 .75
39 Corey Koskie .10 .30
40 Cliff Floyd .10 .30
41 Kevin Appier .10 .30
42 Henry Rodriguez .10 .30
43 Mark Kotsay .10 .30
44 Brook Fordyce .10 .30
45 Brad Ausmus .10 .30
46 Alfonso Soriano .20 .50
47 Ray Lankford .10 .30
48 Keith Foulke .10 .30
49 Rich Aurilia .10 .30
50 Alex Rodriguez .60 1.50
51 Eric Byrnes .10 .30
52 Travis Fryman .10 .30
53 Jeff Bagwell .20 .50
54 Scott Rolen .20 .50
55 Matt Lawton .10 .30
56 Brad Fullmer .10 .30
57 Tony Batista .10 .30
58 Nate Rolison .10 .30
59 Carlos Lee .10 .30
60 Rafael Furcal .10 .30
61 Jay Bell .10 .30
62 Jimmy Rollins .10 .30
63 Derrek Lee .20 .50
64 Andres Galarraga .10 .30
65 Derek Bell .10 .30
66 Tim Salmon .20 .50
67 Travis Lee .10 .30
68 Kevin Millwood .10 .30
69 Albert Belle .10 .30
70 Kazuhiro Sasaki .10 .30
71 Al Leiter .10 .30
72 Britt Reames .10 .30
73 Carlos Beltran .10 .30
74 Curt Schilling .10 .30
75 Curtis Leskanic .10 .30
76 Jeremy Giambi .10 .30
77 Adrian Beltre .10 .30
78 David Segui .10 .30
79 Mike Lieberthal .10 .30
80 Brian Giles .10 .30
81 Marvin Benard .10 .30
82 Aaron Sele .10 .30
83 Kenny Lofton .10 .30
84 Doug Glanville .10 .30
85 Kris Benson .10 .30
86 Richie Sexson .10 .30
87 Javy Lopez .10 .30
88 Doug Mientkiewicz .10 .30
89 Peter Bergeron .10 .30
90 Gary Sheffield .10 .30
91 Derek Lowe .10 .30
92 Tom Glavine .20 .50
93 Lance Berkman .10 .30
94 Chris Singleton .10 .30
95 Mike Lowell .10 .30
96 Luis Gonzalez .10 .30
97 Dante Bichette .10 .30
98 Mike Sirotka .10 .30
99 Julio Lugo .10 .30
100 Juan Gonzalez .10 .30
101 Craig Biggio .20 .50
102 Armando Benitez .10 .30
103 Greg Maddux .50 1.25
104 Mark Grace .20 .50
105 John Smoltz .20 .50
106 J.T. Snow .10 .30
107 Al Martin .10 .30
108 Danny Graves .10 .30
109 Barry Bonds .75 2.00
110 Lee Stevens .10 .30
111 Pedro Martinez .20 .50
112 Shawn Green .10 .30
113 Bret Boone .10 .30
114 Matt Stairs .10 .30
115 Tino Martinez .20 .50
116 Rusty Greer .10 .30
117 Mike Bordick .10 .30
118 Garrett Stephenson .10 .30
119 Edgar Martinez .20 .50
120 Ben Grieve .10 .30
121 Milton Bradley .10 .30
122 Aaron Boone .10 .30
123 Ruben Mateo .10 .30
124 Ken Griffey Jr. .50 1.25
125 Russell Branyan .10 .30
126 Shannon Stewart .10 .30
127 Fred McGriff .20 .50
128 Ben Petrick .10 .30
129 Kevin Brown .10 .30
130 B.J. Surhoff .10 .30
131 Mark McGwire .75 2.00
132 Carlos Guillen .10 .30
133 Adrian Brown .10 .30
134 Mike Sweeney .10 .30
135 Eric Milton .10 .30
136 Cristian Guzman .10 .30
137 Ellis Burks .10 .30
138 Fernando Tatis .10 .30
139 Bengie Molina .10 .30
140 Tony Gwynn .40 1.00
141 Jeromy Burnitz .10 .30
142 Miguel Tejada .10 .30
143 Raul Mondesi .10 .30
144 Jeffrey Hammonds .10 .30
145 Pat Burrell .10 .30
146 Frank Thomas .30 .75
147 Eric Munson .10 .30
148 Mike Hampton .10 .30
149 Mike Cameron .10 .30
150 Jim Thome .20 .50
151 Mike Mussina .20 .50
152 Rick Helling .10 .30
153 Ken Caminiti .10 .30
154 John VanderWal .10 .30
155 Denny Neagle .10 .30
156 Robb Nen .10 .30
157 Jose Canseco .20 .50
158 Mo Vaughn .10 .30
159 Phil Nevin .10 .30
160 Pat Hentgen .10 .30
161 Sean Casey .10 .30
162 Greg Vaughn .10 .30
163 Trot Nixon .10 .30
164 Roberto Hernandez .10 .30
165 Vinny Castilla .10 .30
166 Robin Ventura .10 .30
167 Alex Ochoa .10 .30
168 Orlando Hernandez .10 .30
169 Luis Castillo .10 .30
170 Quilvio Veras .10 .30
171 Troy O'Leary .10 .30
172 Livan Hernandez .10 .30
173 Roger Cedeno .10 .30
174 Jose Vidro .10 .30
175 John Olerud .10 .30
176 Richard Hidalgo .10 .30
177 Eric Chavez .10 .30
178 Fernando Vina .10 .30
179 Chris Stynes .10 .30
180 Bobby Higginson .10 .30
181 Bruce Chen .10 .30
182 Omar Vizquel .20 .50
183 Rey Ordonez .10 .30
184 Trevor Hoffman .10 .30
185 Jeff Cirillo .10 .30
186 Billy Wagner .10 .30
187 David Ortiz .30 .75
188 Tim Hudson .10 .30
189 Tony Clark .10 .30
190 Larry Walker .10 .30
191 Eric Owens .10 .30
192 Aubrey Huff .10 .30
193 Royce Clayton .10 .30
194 Todd Walker .10 .30
195 Rafael Palmeiro .20 .50
196 Todd Hundley .10 .30
197 Roger Clemens .60 1.50
198 Jeff Weaver .10 .30
199 Dean Palmer .10 .30
200 Geoff Jenkins .10 .30
201 Matt Clement .10 .30
202 David Wells .10 .30
203 Chan Ho Park .10 .30
204 Hideo Nomo .30 .75
205 Bartolo Colon .10 .30
206 John Wetteland .10 .30
207 Corey Patterson .10 .30
208 Freddy Garcia .10 .30
209 David Cone .10 .30
210 Rondell White .10 .30
211 Carl Pavano .10 .30
212 Charles Johnson .10 .30
213 Ron Coomer .10 .30
214 Matt Williams .10 .30
215 Jay Payton .10 .30
216 Nick Johnson .10 .30
217 Deivi Cruz .10 .30
218 Scott Elarton .10 .30
219 Neifi Perez .10 .30
220 Jason Isringhausen .10 .30
221 Jose Cruz Jr. .10 .30
222 Gerald Williams .10 .30
223 Timo Perez .10 .30
224 Damion Easley .10 .30
225 Jeff D'Amico .10 .30
226 Preston Wilson .10 .30
227 Robert Person .10 .30
228 Jacque Jones .10 .30
229 Johnny Damon .20 .50
230 Tony Womack .10 .30
231 Adam Platt .10 .30
232 Brian Jordan .10 .30
233 Ben Davis .10 .30
234 Kerry Wood .10 .30
235 Mike Piazza .50 1.25
236 David Justice .10 .30
237 Dave Veres .10 .30
238 Eric Young .10 .30
239 Juan Pierre .10 .30
240 Gabe Kapler .10 .30
241 Ryan Dempster .10 .30
242 Dmitri Young .10 .30
243 Jorge Posada .20 .50
244 Eric Karros .10 .30
245 J.D. Drew .10 .30
246 Todd Zeile .10 .30
247 Mark Quinn .10 .30
248 Kenny Kelly UER .10 .30
Listed as a Mariner on the front
249 Jermaine Dye .10 .30
250 Barry Zito .20 .50
251 Jason Hart .75 2.00
Larry Barnes
252 Ichiro Suzuki RC 10.00 25.00
Elpidio Guzman RC
253 Tsuyoshi Shinjo RC 1.25 3.00
Brian Cole
254 John Barnes .75 2.00
Adrian Hernandez RC
255 Jason Tyner .75 2.00
Jace Brewer
256 Brian Buchanan .75 2.00
Luis Rivas
257 Brent Abernathy .75 2.00
Jose Ortiz
258 Marcus Giles .75 2.00
Keith Ginter
259 Tike Redman .75 2.00
Jaisen Randolph RC
260 Dane Sardinha .75 2.00
David Espinosa
261 Josh Beckett 1.25 3.00
Craig House
262 Jack Cust .75 2.00
Hiram Bocachica
263 Alex Escobar .75 2.00
Esix Snead RC
264 Chris Richard .75 2.00
Vernon Wells
265 Pedro Feliz .75 2.00
Xavier Nady
266 Brandon Inge 1.50 4.00
Joe Crede
267 Ben Sheets 1.50 4.00
Roy Oswalt
268 Drew Henson RC 1.25 3.00
Andy Morales RC
269 C.C. Sabathia .75 2.00
Justin Miller
270 David Eckstein .75 2.00
Jason Grabowski
271 Dee Brown .75 2.00
Chris Wakeland
272 Junior Spivey RC .75 2.00
Alex Cintron
273 Elvis Pena 1.25 3.00
Juan Uribe RC
274 Carlos Pena .75 2.00
Jason Romano
275 Winston Abreu 1.50 4.00
Wilson Betemit
276 Jose Mieses RC .75 2.00
Nick Neugebauer
277 Shea Hillenbrand .75 2.00
Dernell Stenson
278 Jared Sandberg .75 2.00
Toby Hall
279 Jay Gibbons RC 1.25 3.00
Ivanon Coffie
280 Pablo Ozuna .75 2.00
Santiago Perez
281 N.Garciaparra AS 3.00 8.00
282 Derek Jeter AS 5.00 12.00
283 Jason Giambi AS .75 2.00
284 Magglio Ordonez AS .75 2.00
285 Ivan Rodriguez AS 1.25 3.00
286 Troy Glaus AS .75 2.00
287 Carlos Delgado AS .75 2.00
288 Darin Erstad AS .75 2.00
289 Bernie Williams AS 1.25 3.00
290 Roberto Alomar AS 1.25 3.00
291 Barry Larkin AS 1.25 3.00
292 Chipper Jones AS 2.00 5.00
293 Vladimir Guerrero AS 2.00 5.00
294 Sammy Sosa AS 2.00 5.00
295 Todd Helton AS 1.25 3.00
296 Randy Johnson AS 2.00 5.00
297 Jason Kendall AS .75 2.00
298 Jim Edmonds AS .75 2.00
299 Andruw Jones AS 1.25 3.00
300 Edgardo Alfonzo AS .75 2.00
301 Albert Pujols RC 40.00 80.00
Donaldo Mendez RC/1500
302 Shawn Wooten .10 .30
303 Todd Walker .10 .30
304 Brian Buchanan .10 .30
305 Jim Edmonds .10 .30
306 Jarrod Washburn .10 .30
307 Jose Rijo .10 .30
308 Tim Raines .10 .30
309 Matt Morris .10 .30
310 Troy Glaus .10 .30
311 Barry Larkin .20 .50
312 Javier Vazquez .10 .30
313 Placido Polanco .10 .30
314 Darin Erstad .10 .30
315 Marty Cordova .10 .30
316 Vladimir Guerrero .30 .75
317 Kerry Robinson .10 .30
318 Byung-Hyun Kim .10 .30
319 C.C. Sabathia .10 .30
320 Edgardo Alfonzo .10 .30
321 Jason Tyner .10 .30
322 Reggie Sanders .10 .30
323 Roberto Alomar .20 .50
324 Matt Lawton .10 .30
325 Brent Abernathy .10 .30
326 Randy Johnson .30 .75
327 Todd Helton .20 .50
328 Andy Pettitte .20 .50
329 Josh Beckett .20 .50
330 Mark DeRosa .10 .30
331 Jose Ortiz .10 .30
332 Derek Jeter .75 2.00
333 Toby Hall .10 .30
334 Wes Helms .10 .30
335 Jose Macias .10 .30
336 Bernie Williams .20 .50
337 Ivan Rodriguez .20 .50
338 Chipper Jones .30 .75
339 Brandon Inge .10 .30
340 Jason Giambi .10 .30
341 Frank Catalanotto .10 .30
342 Andruw Jones .20 .50
343 Carlos Hernandez .10 .30
344 Jermaine Dye .10 .30
345 Mike Lamb .10 .30
346 Ken Caminiti .10 .30
347 A.J. Burnett .10 .30
348 Terrence Long .10 .30
349 Ruben Sierra .10 .30
350 Marcus Giles UER .10 .30
Listed as a pitcher on the back
351 Wade Miller .10 .30
352 Mark Mulder .10 .30
353 Carlos Delgado .10 .30
354 Chris Reitsma .10 .30
355 Daryle Ward .10 .30
356 Brad Penny .10 .30
357 Vernon Wells .10 .30
358 Jason Johnson .10 .30
359 Tim Redding .10 .30
360 Marlon Anderson .10 .30
361 Carlos Pena .10 .30
362 Nomar Garciaparra .50 1.25
363 Roy Oswalt .30 .75
364 Todd Ritchie .10 .30
365 Jose Mesa .10 .30
366 Shea Hillenbrand .10 .30
367 Dee Brown .10 .30
368 Jason Kendall .10 .30
369 Vinny Castilla .10 .30
370 Fred McGriff .20 .50
371 Neifi Perez .10 .30
372 Xavier Nady .10 .30
373 Abraham Nunez .10 .30
374 Jon Lieber .10 .30
375 Paul LoDuca .10 .30
376 Bubba Trammell .10 .30
377 Brady Clark .10 .30
378 Joel Pineiro .10 .30
379 Mark Grudzielanek .10 .30
380 D'Angelo Jimenez .10 .30
381 Junior Herndon .10 .30
382 Magglio Ordonez .10 .30
383 Ben Sheets .20 .50
384 John Vander Wal .10 .30
385 Pedro Astacio .10 .30
386 Jose Canseco .20 .50
387 Jose Hernandez .10 .30
388 Eric Davis .10 .30
389 Sammy Sosa .30 .75
390 Mark Buehrle .20 .50
391 Mark Loretta .10 .30
392 Andres Galarraga .10 .30
393 Scott Spiezio .10 .30
394 Joe Crede .30 .75
395 Luis Rivas .10 .30
396 David Bell .10 .30
397 Einar Diaz .10 .30
398 Adam Dunn .20 .50
399 A.J. Pierzynski .10 .30
400 Jamie Moyer .10 .30
401 Nick Johnson .10 .30
402 Freddy Garcia CT SP 4.00 10.00
403 Hideo Nomo CT .10 .30
404 Mark Mulder CT .10 .30
405 Steve Sparks CT .10 .30
406 Mariano Rivera CT .20 .50
407 Mark Buehrle .10 .30
Mike Mussina CT
408 Randy Johnson CT .20 .50
409 Randy Johnson CT .20 .50
410 Curt Schilling .10 .30
Matt Morris CT
411 Greg Maddux CT .30 .75
412 Robb Nen CT .10 .30
413 Randy Johnson CT .20 .50
414 Barry Bonds CT .40 1.00
415 Jason Giambi CT .10 .30
416 Ichiro Suzuki CT 2.00 5.00
417 Ichiro Suzuki CT 2.00 5.00
418 Alex Rodriguez CT .30 .75
419 Bret Boone CT .10 .30
420 Ichiro Suzuki CT 2.00 5.00
421 Alex Rodriguez CT .30 .75
422 Jason Giambi CT .10 .30
423 Alex Rodriguez CT .30 .75
424 Larry Walker CT .10 .30
425 Rich Aurilia CT .10 .30
426 Barry Bonds CT .40 1.00
427 Sammy Sosa CT .20 .50
428 Jimmy Rollins .10 .30
Juan Pierre CT
429 Sammy Sosa CT .20 .50
430 Lance Berkman CT .10 .30
431 Sammy Sosa CT .20 .50
432 Carlos Delgado TL .10 .30
433 Alex Rodriguez TL .30 .75
434 Greg Vaughn TL .10 .30
435 Albert Pujols TL 6.00 15.00
436 Ichiro Suzuki TL 2.00 5.00
437 Barry Bonds TL .40 1.00
438 Phil Nevin TL .10 .30
439 Brian Giles TL .10 .30
440 Bobby Abreu TL .10 .30
441 Jason Giambi TL .10 .30
442 Derek Jeter TL .40 1.00
443 Mike Piazza TL .30 .75
444 Vladimir Guerrero TL .20 .50
445 Corey Koskie TL .10 .30
446 Richie Sexson TL .10 .30
447 Shawn Green TL .10 .30
448 Mike Sweeney TL .10 .30
449 Jeff Bagwell TL .20 .50
450 Cliff Floyd TL .10 .30
451 Roger Cedeno TL .10 .30
452 Todd Helton TL .20 .50
453 Juan Gonzalez TL .10 .30
454 Sean Casey TL .10 .30
455 Magglio Ordonez TL .10 .30
456 Sammy Sosa TL .20 .50
457 Manny Ramirez Sox TL .20 .50
458 Jeff Conine TL .10 .30
459 Chipper Jones TL .20 .50
460 Luis Gonzalez TL .10 .30
461 Troy Glaus TL .10 .30
462 Ivan Rodriguez .20 .50
Jason Romano FF
463 Luis Gonzalez .10 .30
Jack Cust FF
464 Jim Thome .10 .30
C.C. Sabathia FF
465 Jason Giambi .10 .30
Jason Hart FF
466 Jeff Bagwell .30 .75
Roy Oswalt FF
467 Sammy Sosa .20 .50
Corey Patterson FF
468 Mike Piazza .30 .75
Alex Escobar FF
469 Ken Griffey Jr. .30 .75
Adam Dunn FF
470 Roger Clemens .30 .75
Nick Johnson FF
471 Cliff Floyd .10 .30
Josh Beckett FF
472 Cal Ripken Jr. .50 1.25
Jerry Hairston Jr. FF
473 Phil Nevin .10 .30
Xavier Nady FF
474 Scott Rolen .10 .30
Jimmy Rollins FF
475 Barry Larkin .10 .30
David Espinosa FF
476 Larry Walker .10 .30
Jose Ortiz FF
477 Chipper Jones .20 .50
Marcus Giles FF
478 Craig Biggio .10 .30
Keith Ginter FF
479 Magglio Ordonez .10 .30
Aaron Rowand FF
480 Alex Rodriguez .30 .75
Carlos Pena FF
481 Derek Jeter .40 1.00
Alfonso Soriano FF
482 Erubiel Durazo PG .10 .30
483 Bernie Williams PG .10 .30
484 Team Photo PG .10 .30
485 Team Photo PG .10 .30
486 Andy Pettitte PG .10 .30
487 Curt Schilling PG .10 .30
488 Randy Johnson PG .20 .50
489 Rudolph Giuliani PG .30 .75
Mayor of New York City
490 George W. Bush PG 2.00 5.00
President of United States
491 Roger Clemens PG .30 .75
492 Mariano Rivera PG .20 .50
493 Tino Martinez PG .10 .30
494 Derek Jeter PG .40 1.00
495 Scott Brosius PG .10 .30
496 Alfonso Soriano PG .10 .30
497 Matt Williams PG .10 .30
498 Tony Womack PG .10 .30
499 Luis Gonzalez PG .10 .30
500 Arizona Diamondbacks PG .30 .75
501 Randy Johnson .20 .50
Curt Schilling
Co-MVP's PG
502 Josh Fogg RC .75 2.00
503 Elpidio Guzman .75 2.00
504 Corky Miller RC .75 2.00
505 Cesar Crespo RC .75 2.00
506 Carlos Garcia RC .75 2.00
507 Carlos Valderrama RC .75 2.00
508 Joe Kennedy RC 1.25 3.00
509 Henry Mateo RC .75 2.00
510 B. Duckworth RC .75 2.00
511 Ichiro Suzuki 8.00 20.00
512 Zach Day RC .75 2.00
513 Ryan Freel RC 1.25 3.00
514 Brian Lawrence RC .75 2.00
515 Alexis Gomez RC .75 2.00
516 Will Ohman RC .75 2.00
517 Juan Diaz RC .75 2.00
518 Juan Moreno RC .75 2.00
519 Rob Mackowiak RC 1.25 3.00
520 Horacio Ramirez RC 1.25 3.00
521 Albert Pujols 40.00 80.00
522 Tsuyoshi Shinjo 1.25 3.00
523 Ryan Drese RC 1.25 3.00
524 Angel Berroa RC 1.25 3.00
525 Josh Towers RC 1.25 3.00
526 Junior Spivey 1.25 3.00
527 Greg Miller RC .75 2.00
528 Esix Snead .75 2.00
529 Mark Prior DP RC 3.00 8.00
530 Drew Henson 1.25 3.00
531 Brian Reith RC .75 2.00
532 Andres Torres RC .75 2.00
533 Casey Fossum RC .75 2.00
534 Wilmy Caceres RC .75 2.00
535 Matt White RC .75 2.00
536 Wilkin Ruan RC .75 2.00
537 Rick Bauer RC .75 2.00
538 Morgan Ensberg RC 1.50 4.00
539 Geronimo Gil RC .75 2.00
540 Dewon Brazelton RC .75 2.00
541 Johnny Estrada RC 1.25 3.00
542 Claudio Vargas RC .75 2.00
543 Donaldo Mendez .75 2.00
544 Kyle Lohse RC 1.25 3.00
545 Nate Frese RC .75 2.00
546 Christian Parker RC .75 2.00
547 Blaine Neal RC .75 2.00
548 Travis Hafner RC 4.00 10.00
549 Billy Sylvester RC .75 2.00
550 Adam Pettyjohn RC .75 2.00
551 Bill Ortega RC .75 2.00
552 Jose Acevedo RC .75 2.00
553 Steve Green RC .75 2.00
554 Jay Gibbons 1.25 3.00
555 Bert Snow RC .75 2.00
556 Erick Almonte RC .75 2.00
557 Jeremy Owens RC .75 2.00
558 Sean Douglass RC .75 2.00
559 Jason Smith RC .75 2.00
560 Ricardo Rodriguez RC .75 2.00
561 Mark Teixeira RC 5.00 12.00
562 Tyler Walker RC .75 2.00
563 Juan Uribe 1.25 3.00
564 Bud Smith RC .75 2.00
565 Angel Santos RC .75 2.00
566 Brandon Lyon RC .75 2.00
567 Eric Hinske RC UER 1.25 3.00
Front says he is a pitcher
568 Nick Punto RC .75 2.00
569 Winston Abreu .75 2.00
570 Jason Phillips RC .75 2.00
571 Rafael Soriano RC .75 2.00
572 Wilson Betemit 1.50 4.00
573 Endy Chavez RC .75 2.00
574 Juan Cruz RC .75 2.00
575 Cory Aldridge RC .75 2.00
576 Adrian Hernandez .75 2.00
577 Brandon Larson RC .75 2.00
578 Bret Prinz RC .75 2.00
579 Jackson Melian RC .75 2.00
580 Dave Maurer RC .75 2.00
581 Jason Michaels RC .75 2.00
582 Travis Phelps RC .75 2.00
583 Cody Ransom RC .75 2.00
584 Benito Baez RC .75 2.00
585 Brian Roberts RC 1.50 4.00
586 Nate Teut RC .75 2.00
587 Jack Wilson RC 1.25 3.00
588 Willie Harris RC .75 2.00
589 Martin Vargas RC .75 2.00
590 Steve Torrealba RC .75 2.00
591 Stubby Clapp RC .75 2.00
592 Dan Wright .75 2.00
593 Mike Rivera RC .75 2.00
594 Luis Pineda RC .75 2.00
595 Lance Davis RC .75 2.00
596 Ramon Vazquez RC .75 2.00
597 Dustan Mohr RC .75 2.00
598 Troy Mattes RC .75 2.00
599 Grant Balfour RC .75 2.00
600 Jared Fernandez RC .75 2.00
601 Jorge Julio RC .75 2.00

2001 Fleer Platinum Parallel

Randomly inserted in hobby packs, this 600-card set is a parallel version of the base set. Cards 1-250 and 302-501 are sequentially numbered to 201 and cards 251-300 and 502-601 to 21. Card number 300 was never produced as a Parallel.

*STARS 1-250/302-501: 2.5X TO 6X BASIC
*SUBSET RC'S 402-501: 2X TO 5X BASIC
435 Albert Pujols TL 75.00 150.00

2001 Fleer Platinum 20th Anniversary Reprints

Randomly inserted in hobby packs at the rate of one in eight and in jumbo packs at the rate of one in four, this 18-card set features reprints of Fleer's best rookie cards from the past 20 years of cards.

COMPLETE SET (18) 30.00 60.00
1 Cal Ripken 82F 5.00 12.00
2 Wade Boggs 83F 1.00 2.50
3 Ryne Sandberg 83F 2.50 6.00
4 Tony Gwynn 83F 2.00 5.00
5 Don Mattingly 84F 4.00 10.00
6 Roger Clemens 85F 3.00 8.00
7 Kirby Puckett 85F 1.50 4.00
8 Jose Canseco 86LL 1.00 2.50
9 Barry Bonds 87F 4.00 10.00
10 Ken Griffey Jr. 89F 2.50 6.00
11 Sammy Sosa 90F 1.50 4.00
12 Ivan Rodriguez 91UU 1.00 2.50
13 Jeff Bagwell 91UU 1.00 2.50
14 J.D. Drew 98UPD 1.00 2.50
15 Troy Glaus 98UPD 1.00 2.50
16 Rick Ankiel 99UPD 1.00 2.50
17 Xavier Nady 00GL 1.00 2.50
18 Jose Ortiz 00GL 1.00 2.50

2001 Fleer Platinum Classic Combinations

Randomly inserted in packs, this 40-card set features dual player cards which pair some of the greatest players in the game. Cards 1-10 are serially numbered to 250, 11-20 to 500, 21-30 to 1,000, and 31-40 to 2,000.

COMMON (CC1-CC10) 8.00 20.00
COMMON (CC11-CC20) 6.00 15.00
COMMON (CC21-CC30) 3.00 8.00
COMMON (CC31-CC40) 2.00 5.00
CC1 Derek Jeter Alex Rodriguez 8.00 20.00
CC2 Willie Mays Willie McCovey 10.00 25.00
CC3 Lou Gehrig Babe Ruth 15.00 40.00
CC4 Mark McGwire Ken Griffey Jr. 12.50 30.00
CC5 Johnny Bench Roy Campanella 8.00 20.00
CC6 Ted Williams Nomar Garciaparra 10.00 25.00
CC7 Yogi Berra Mike Piazza 8.00 20.00
CC8 Ernie Banks Sammy Sosa 8.00 20.00
CC9 Nolan Ryan Randy Johnson 12.50 30.00
CC10 Roberto Clemente Vladimir Guerrero 10.00 25.00
CC11 Stan Musial Lou Gehrig 12.50 30.00
CC12 Bill Mazeroski Roberto Clemente 8.00 20.00
CC13 Ernie Banks Alex Rodriguez 6.00 15.00
CC14 Phil Rizzuto Derek Jeter 10.00 25.00
CC15 Mike Piazza Johnny Bench 6.00 15.00
CC16 Mark McGwire Sammy Sosa 10.00 25.00
CC17 Ted Williams Tony Gwynn 8.00 20.00
CC18 Eddie Mathews Mike Schmidt 8.00 20.00
CC19 Barry Bonds Willie Mays 10.00 25.00
CC20 Nolan Ryan Pedro Martinez 12.50 30.00
CC21 Barry Bonds Ken Griffey Jr. 8.00 20.00
CC22 Willie McCovey Reggie Jackson 2.00 5.00
CC23 Roberto Clemente Sammy Sosa 6.00 15.00
CC24 Willie Mays Ernie Banks 6.00 15.00
CC25 Eddie Mathews Chipper Jones 3.00 8.00
CC26 Mike Schmidt Brooks Robinson 6.00 15.00
CC27 Stan Musial Mark McGwire 8.00 20.00
CC28 Ted Williams Roger Maris 6.00 15.00
CC29 Yogi Berra Roy Campanella 2.00 5.00
CC30 Johnny Bench Tony Perez 3.00 8.00
CC31 Bill Mazeroski Joe Carter 2.00 5.00
CC32 Mike Piazza Roy Campanella 3.00 8.00
CC33 Ernie Banks Craig Biggio 2.00 5.00
CC34 Frank Robinson Brooks Robinson 2.00 5.00
CC35 Mike Schmidt Scott Rolen 4.00 10.00
CC36 Roger Maris Mark McGwire 5.00 12.00
CC37 Stan Musial Tony Gwynn 3.00 8.00
CC38 Ted Williams Bill Terry 4.00 10.00
CC39 Derek Jeter Reggie Jackson 5.00 12.00
CC40 Yogi Berra Bill Dickey 2.00 5.00

2001 Fleer Platinum Classic Combinations Memorabilia

Randomly inserted in packs, this 11-card set features dual player cards which pair some of the greatest players in the game and contain pieces of game-used bats. Only 25 serially numbered sets were produced.

2001 Fleer Platinum Classic Combinations Retail

Randomly inserted into retail packs at the rate of one in 20, this 40-card set is a parallel version of the regular insert set.

COMPLETE SET (40) 150.00 300.00
CC1 Derek Jeter Alex Rodriguez 5.00 12.00
CC2 Willie Mays Willie McCovey 4.00 10.00
CC3 Lou Gehrig Babe Ruth 6.00 15.00
CC4 Mark McGwire Ken Griffey Jr. 5.00 12.00
CC5 Johnny Bench Roy Campanella
CC6 Ted Williams Nomar Garciaparra 4.00 10.00
CC7 Yogi Berra Mike Piazza 3.00 8.00
CC8 Ernie Banks Sammy Sosa 2.00 5.00
CC9 Nolan Ryan Randy Johnson 5.00 12.00
CC10 Roberto Clemente Vladimir Guerrero 4.00 10.00
CC11 Stan Musial Lou Gehrig 4.00 10.00
CC12 Bill Mazeroski Roberto Clemente 4.00 10.00
CC13 Ernie Banks Alex Rodriguez 3.00 8.00
CC14 Phil Rizzuto Derek Jeter 5.00 12.00
CC15 Mike Piazza Johnny Bench 3.00 8.00
CC16 Mark McGwire Sammy Sosa 5.00 12.00
CC17 Ted Williams Tony Gwynn 4.00 10.00
CC18 Eddie Mathews Mike Schmidt 4.00 10.00
CC19 Barry Bonds Willie Mays 5.00 12.00
CC20 Nolan Ryan Pedro Martinez 5.00 12.00
CC21 Barry Bonds Ken Griffey Jr. 5.00 12.00
CC22 Willie McCovey Reggie Jackson 1.50 4.00
CC23 Roberto Clemente Sammy Sosa 4.00 10.00
CC24 Willie Mays Ernie Banks 3.00 8.00
CC25 Eddie Mathews Chipper Jones 2.00 5.00
CC26 Mike Schmidt Brooks Robinson 4.00 10.00
CC27 Stan Musial Mark McGwire 5.00 12.00
CC28 Ted Williams Roger Maris 4.00 10.00
CC29 Yogi Berra Roy Campanella 2.00 5.00
CC30 Johnny Bench Tony Perez 2.00 5.00
CC31 Bill Mazeroski Joe Carter 1.50 4.00
CC32 Mike Piazza Roy Campanella 3.00 8.00
CC33 Ernie Banks Craig Biggio 2.00 5.00
CC34 Frank Robinson Brooks Robinson 1.50 4.00
CC35 Mike Schmidt Scott Rolen 4.00 10.00
CC36 Roger Maris Mark McGwire 5.00 12.00
CC37 Stan Musial Tony Gwynn 3.00 8.00
CC38 Ted Williams Bill Terry 4.00 10.00
CC39 Derek Jeter Reggie Jackson 5.00 12.00
CC40 Yogi Berra Bill Dickey 2.00 5.00

2001 Fleer Platinum Grandstand Greats

Randomly inserted in hobby packs at the rate of one in 12 and in jumbo packs at the rate of one in six, this 20-card set features color photos of the crowd-pleasers of the League.

COMPLETE SET (20) 40.00 80.00
GG1 Chipper Jones 1.25 3.00
GG2 Alex Rodriguez 2.00 5.00
GG3 Jeff Bagwell .75 2.00
GG4 Troy Glaus .75 2.00
GG5 Manny Ramirez Sox .75 2.00
GG6 Derek Jeter 3.00 8.00
GG7 Tony Gwynn 1.50 4.00
GG8 Greg Maddux 2.00 5.00
GG9 Nomar Garciaparra 2.00 5.00
GG10 Sammy Sosa 1.25 3.00
GG11 Mike Piazza 2.00 5.00
GG12 Barry Bonds 3.00 8.00
GG13 Mark McGwire 3.00 8.00
GG14 Vladimir Guerrero 1.25 3.00
GG15 Ivan Rodriguez .75 2.00
GG16 Ken Griffey Jr. 2.00 5.00
GG17 Todd Helton .75 2.00
GG18 Cal Ripken 4.00 10.00
GG19 Pedro Martinez .75 2.00
GG20 Frank Thomas 1.25 3.00

2001 Fleer Platinum Lumberjacks

This 27-card insert set features game-used bat chips from greats like Derek Jeter and Ivan Rodriguez. These cards were inserted at a stated rate of one per rack pack

1 Roberto Alomar 6.00 15.00
2 Moises Alou 4.00 10.00
3 Adrian Beltre 4.00 10.00
4 Lance Berkman 4.00 10.00
5 Barry Bonds 10.00 25.00
6 Bret Boone 4.00 10.00
7 J.D. Drew
8 Adam Dunn 6.00 15.00
9 Darin Erstad 4.00 10.00
10 Cliff Floyd 4.00 10.00
11 Brian Giles 4.00 10.00
12 Luis Gonzalez 4.00 10.00
13 Vladimir Guerrero 6.00 15.00
14 Cristian Guzman 4.00 10.00
15 Tony Gwynn 6.00 15.00
16 Todd Helton 6.00 15.00
17 Drew Henson 6.00 15.00
18 Derek Jeter 10.00 25.00
19 Chipper Jones 6.00 15.00
20 Mike Piazza 6.00 15.00
21 Albert Pujols 60.00 100.00
22 Manny Ramirez Sox 6.00 15.00
23 Cal Ripken
24 Ivan Rodriguez 6.00 15.00
25 Gary Sheffield 4.00 10.00
26 Mike Sweeney 4.00 10.00
27 Larry Walker 4.00 10.00

2001 Fleer Platinum Lumberjacks Autographs

This eight-card set is a partial parallel to the 2001 Fleer Platinum Lumberjacks insert. Each card is autographed and signed on actual game-used lumber. Though they lack serial-numbering, the manufacturer announced production at 100 copies per card. Not all the cards were signed in time for inclusion in packs and those exchange cards could be redeemed until November 30, 2002. The following players were seeded into packs as exchange cards: Barry Bonds, Derek Jeter, Albert Pujols and Cal Ripken.

6 Barry Bonds 125.00 200.00
7 J.D. Drew
8 Adam Dunn 40.00 80.00
12 Luis Gonzalez 20.00 50.00
18 Derek Jeter 175.00 350.00
21 Albert Pujols 500.00 800.00
23 Cal Ripken 125.00 200.00
26 Mike Sweeney

2001 Fleer Platinum Nameplates

Randomly inserted in jumbo packs only at the rate of one in 12, this 42-card set features color images of top players on a license plate design background and pieces of actual name plates from players' uniforms embedded in the cards.

1 Carlos Beltran/90 10.00 25.00
2 Adrian Beltre/55 * 10.00 25.00
3 Sean Casey/21
4 J.D. Drew/170 10.00 25.00
5 Darin Erstad/39 10.00 25.00
6 Troy Glaus/85 10.00 25.00
7 Tom Glavine/125 15.00 40.00
8 Vladimir Guerrero/80 15.00 40.00
9 Vladimir Guerrero/90 15.00 40.00
10 Tony Gwynn/35 40.00 80.00
11 Tony Gwynn/65 20.00 50.00
12 Tony Gwynn/70 20.00 50.00
13 Jeffrey Hammonds/135 10.00 25.00
14 Randy Johnson/99 15.00 40.00
15 Chipper Jones/95 15.00 40.00
16 Javy Lopez/49 * 10.00 25.00
17 Greg Maddux/180 20.00 50.00
18 Edgar Martinez/87 15.00 40.00
19 Pedro Martinez/120 15.00 40.00
20 Kevin Millwood/130 10.00 25.00
21 Stan Musial/30 60.00 120.00
22 Mike Mussina/91 15.00 40.00
23 Manny Ramirez Sox/75 15.00 40.00
24 Manny Ramirez Sox/105 15.00 40.00
25 Cal Ripken/19
26 Cal Ripken/21
27 Cal Ripken/23
28 Cal Ripken/110 50.00 100.00
29 Ivan Rodriguez/177 15.00 40.00
30 Scott Rolen/65 15.00 40.00
31 Scott Rolen/125 15.00 40.00
32 Nolan Ryan/40 75.00 150.00
33 Nolan Ryan/55 75.00 150.00
34 Curt Schilling/110 * 10.00 25.00
35 Frank Thomas/35 15.00 40.00
36 Frank Thomas/75 15.00 40.00
37 Frank Thomas/80 15.00 40.00
38 Robin Ventura/99 10.00 25.00
39 Larry Walker/79 10.00 25.00
40 Larry Walker/85 10.00 25.00
41 Matt Williams/175 10.00 25.00
42 Dave Winfield/80 10.00 25.00

2001 Fleer Platinum National Patch Time

Randomly inserted in first and second series hobby packs at the rate of one in 24 and first and second series retail packs at the rate of one in 36, this set features color images of superstars of baseball with authentic game-worn jersey and pants swatches embedded in the cards. Jersey cards featuring the following players: Mo Vaughn, Kazuhiro Sasaki, Aaron Sele, Todd Walker, Jorge Posada, Vida Blue, Jim Palmer, Mike Mussina, Jim Rice, and Carl Yastrzemski were produced. However, due to MLB regulations these cards were pulled at the last minute from series one packs. Vaughn and Sasaki were eventually seeded into second series packs and a lone Mike Mussina copy was verified as coming from a second series pack, but no Rice, Mussina's or Yastrzemski's were intended for release. In late 2004 copies of the Yastrzemski card were reportedly sent out to collectors as exchange premiums for other issues Fleer could not fulfill.

1 Edgardo Alfonzo S1 4.00 10.00
2 B.Anderson Pants S1 4.00 10.00
3 Jeff Bagwell S2 6.00 15.00
4 Adrian Beltre S2 4.00 10.00
5 Wade Boggs S1 6.00 15.00
6 Barry Bonds S2 10.00 25.00
7 George Brett S1 10.00 25.00
8 Eric Chavez S2 4.00 10.00
9 Jeff Cirillo S1 4.00 10.00
10 R.Clemens Gray S1 10.00 25.00
11 R.Clemens White S2 10.00 25.00
12 Pedro Martinez S1 6.00 15.00
12 J.D. Drew S2 4.00 10.00
13 Darin Erstad S2 4.00 10.00
14 Carl Everett S1 4.00 10.00
15 Rollie Fingers Pants S1 4.00 10.00
16 Freddy Garcia White S1 4.00 10.00
17 Freddy Garcia White S2 4.00 10.00
18 Jason Giambi SP S2 4.00 10.00
19 Juan Gonzalez SP S2 4.00 10.00
20 Mark Grace S2 6.00 15.00
21 Shawn Green S2 4.00 10.00
22 Ben Grieve S2 4.00 10.00
23 Vladimir Guerrero S2 6.00 15.00
24 Tony Gwynn White S1 6.00 15.00
25 Tony Gwynn White S2 6.00 15.00
26 Todd Helton S2 6.00 15.00
27 Randy Johnson S2 6.00 15.00
28 Chipper Jones S2 6.00 15.00
29 David Justice S2 4.00 10.00
30 Jason Kendall S1 4.00 10.00
31 Jeff Kent S2 4.00 10.00
32 Paul LoDuca S2 4.00 10.00
33 Greg Maddux White S1 6.00 15.00
34 G.Maddux Gray-White S2 6.00 15.00
36 Fred McGriff S1 6.00 15.00
37 Eddie Murray S1 6.00 15.00
38 Mike Mussina S2 SP
39 John Olerud S2 4.00 10.00
40 M.Ordonez Gray S1 4.00 10.00
41 M.Ordonez Gray SP S2 4.00 10.00
42 Adam Piatt S1 4.00 10.00
43 Jorge Posada S2 6.00 15.00
44 Manny Ramirez Sox S1 6.00 15.00
45 Cal Ripken Black S1 20.00 50.00
46 C.Ripken Gray-White S2 20.00 50.00
47 Mariano Rivera S2 6.00 15.00
48 Ivan Rodriguez Blue S1 6.00 15.00
49 I.Rodriguez Blue-WhiteS2 6.00 15.00
50 Scott Rolen S2 6.00 15.00
51 Nolan Ryan S1 15.00 40.00
52 Kazuhiro Sasaki S2 4.00 10.00
53 Mike Schmidt S1 10.00 25.00
54 Tom Seaver S1 6.00 15.00
55 Aaron Sele S2 4.00 10.00
56 Gary Sheffield S2 4.00 10.00
57 Ozzie Smith S1 6.00 15.00
58 John Smoltz S2 6.00 15.00
59 Frank Thomas S2 6.00 15.00
60 Mo Vaughn S2 4.00 10.00
61 Robin Ventura S2 4.00 10.00
62 Rondell White S1 4.00 10.00
63 Bernie Williams S2 6.00 15.00
64 Dave Winfield S1 4.00 10.00
65 Carl Yastrzemski Mail-In SP
NNO Jim Rice

2001 Fleer Platinum Prime Numbers

This 15-card insert set was issued in jumbo packs at 1:12, and features game-used jersey swatches from veteran players like Cal Ripken and Chipper Jones.

1 Jeff Bagwell 6.00 15.00
2 Cal Ripken 30.00 60.00
3 Barry Bonds 20.00 50.00
4 Todd Helton
5 Derek Jeter 20.00 50.00
6 Tony Gwynn 10.00 25.00
7 Kazuhiro Sasaki 4.00 10.00
8 Chan Ho Park 4.00 10.00
9 Sean Casey
10 Chipper Jones 6.00 15.00
11 Pedro Martinez 6.00 15.00
12 Mike Piazza 12.50 30.00
13 Carlos Delgado 4.00 10.00
14 Craig Biggio
15 Roger Clemens 15.00 40.00

2001 Fleer Platinum Rack Pack Autographs

Randomly inserted in rack packs only, this 21-card set features actual autographed player cards and autographics cards from the last 20 years. These cards were almost all originally inserted in Fleer packs and were bought back for signing for this product.

1 H.Aaron 1997 SI/90 125.00 200.00
2 L.Brock 1998 SITN/15
3 Roger Clemens 1998 SITN/125 50.00 100.00
4 Jose Cruz Jr. 1997 No Brand 2.00 5.00
5 J.Drew 1999 SI One's/10 *
6 S.Garvey 1987 Fleer/15 *
7 Bob Gibson 1998 SITN/300 10.00 25.00
8 B.Grieve No Brand/100 * 2.00 5.00
9 T.Gwynn 1998 SITN/125 20.00 50.00
10 Wes Helms 1997 No Brand 2.00 5.00
11 Harmon Killebrew 1998 SITN/300 20.00 50.00
12 Paul Konerko No Brand/135 * 10.00 25.00
13 W.Mays 1997 SI/115 75.00 150.00
14 Willie Mays 1998 SITN/120 75.00 150.00
15 K.Puckett 1997 SI/105 50.00 100.00
16 C.Ripken 1997 SI/5
17 Brooks Robinson 1998 SITN/40 30.00 60.00
18 Frank Robinson 1997 SI/115 10.00 25.00
19 Scott Rolen 1998 SITN/150 10.00 25.00
20 Alex Rodriguez 1997 SI/94 60.00 120.00
21 Alex Rodriguez 1998 Promo/150 40.00 80.00

2001 Fleer Platinum Tickets Autographs

3 Steve Carlton 300th Win 9/23/83 15.00 30.00

2001 Fleer Platinum Winning Combinations

This 40-card insert was issued in Series two hobby packs. The set pairs players that have similar abilities. Each card is serial numbered to either 2000, 1000, 500, or 250.

1 Derek Jeter Ozzie Smith/2000 5.00 12.00
2 Barry Bonds Mark McGwire/500 10.00 25.00
3 Ichiro Suzuki Albert Pujols/250 30.00 60.00
4 Ted Williams Manny Ramirez Sox/1000 6.00 15.00
5 Tony Gwynn Cal Ripken/250 15.00 40.00
6 Mike Piazza Derek Jeter/500 10.00 25.00
7 Dave Winfield Tony Gwynn/2000 2.50 6.00
8 Hideo Nomo Ichiro Suzuki/2000 8.00 20.00
9 Cal Ripken Ozzie Smith/1000 10.00 25.00
10 Mark McGwire Albert Pujols/2000 12.50 30.00
11 Jeff Bagwell Craig Biggio/1000 3.00 8.00
12 Bobby Bonds Barry Bonds/250 12.50 30.00
13 Ted Williams Stan Musial/250 10.00 25.00
14 Babe Ruth Reggie Jackson/500 12.50 30.00
15 Kazuhiro Sasaki Ichiro Suzuki/500 15.00 40.00
16 Nolan Ryan Roger Clemens/500 10.00 25.00
17 Roger Clemens Derek Jeter/250 12.50 30.00
18 Mike Piazza Ivan Rodriguez/1000 5.00 12.00
19 Vladimir Guerrero Sammy Sosa/2000 2.00 5.00
20 Barry Bonds Sammy Sosa/250 12.50 30.00
21 Roger Clemens Greg Maddux/1000 6.00 15.00
22 Juan Gonzalez Manny Ramirez Sox/2000 2.00 5.00
23 Todd Helton Jason Giambi/2000 2.00 5.00
24 Jeff Bagwell Lance Berkman/2000 2.00 5.00
25 Mike Sweeney George Brett/1000 5.00 12.00
26 Luis Gonzalez Babe Ruth/2000 6.00 15.00
27 Bill Skowron Don Mattingly/250 12.50 30.00
28 Yogi Berra Cal Ripken/2000 6.00 15.00
29 Pedro Martinez Nomar Garciaparra/500 6.00 15.00
30 Ted Kluszewski Frank Robinson/1000 3.00 8.00
31 Curt Schilling Randy Johnson/1000 3.00 8.00
32 Ken Griffey Jr. Cal Ripken/500 12.50 30.00
33 Mike Piazza Johnny Bench/1000 5.00 12.00
34 Stan Musial Albert Pujols 20.00 50.00
35 Jackie Robinson Nellie Fox/500 4.00 10.00
36 Lefty Grove Steve Carlton/250 6.00 15.00
37 Ty Cobb Tony Gwynn/250 8.00 20.00
38 Albert Pujols Frank Robinson/1000 8.00 20.00
39 Ryne Sandberg Sammy Sosa/500 10.00 25.00
40 Cal Ripken Lou Gehrig/250 15.00 40.00

2001 Fleer Platinum Winning Combinations Blue

This 40-card insert is a complete parallel of the 2001 Fleer Platinum Winning Combinations insert. Each blue bordered card can be found in jumbo packs at a rate of 1:12, rack packs at 1:6, and retail packs at 1:20.

COMPLETE SET (40) 150.00 300.00
1 Derek Jeter Ozzie Smith 5.00 12.00
2 Barry Bonds Mark McGwire 5.00 12.00
3 Ichiro Suzuki Albert Pujols 30.00 60.00
4 Ted Williams Manny Ramirez Sox 4.00 10.00
5 Tony Gwynn Cal Ripken 6.00 15.00
6 Mike Piazza Derek Jeter 5.00 12.00
7 Dave Winfield Tony Gwynn 2.50 6.00
8 Hideo Nomo Ichiro Suzuki 8.00 20.00
9 Cal Ripken Ozzie Smith 6.00 15.00
10 Mark McGwire Albert Pujols 12.50 30.00
11 Jeff Bagwell Craig Biggio 2.00 5.00
12 Bobby Bonds Barry Bonds 5.00 12.00
13 Ted Williams Stan Musial 4.00 10.00
14 Babe Ruth Reggie Jackson 6.00 15.00
15 Kazuhiro Sasaki Ichiro Suzuki 6.00 15.00
16 Nolan Ryan Roger Clemens 5.00 12.00
17 Roger Clemens Derek Jeter 5.00 12.00
18 Mike Piazza Ivan Rodriguez 3.00 8.00
19 Vladimir Guerrero Sammy Sosa 2.00 5.00
20 Barry Bonds Sammy Sosa 5.00 12.00
21 Roger Clemens Greg Maddux 4.00 10.00
22 Juan Gonzalez Manny Ramirez Sox 2.00 5.00
23 Todd Helton Jason Giambi 2.00 5.00
24 Jeff Bagwell Lance Berkman 2.00 5.00
25 Mike Sweeney George Brett 4.00 10.00
26 Luis Gonzalez Babe Ruth 6.00 15.00
27 Bill Skowron Don Mattingly 4.00 10.00
28 Yogi Berra Cal Ripken 6.00 15.00
29 Pedro Martinez Nomar Garciaparra 3.00 8.00
30 Ted Kluszewski Frank Robinson 2.00 5.00
31 Curt Schilling Randy Johnson 2.00 5.00
32 Ken Griffey Jr. Cal Ripken 6.00 15.00
33 Mike Piazza Johnny Bench 3.00 8.00
34 Stan Musial Albert Pujols 6.00 15.00
35 Jackie Robinson Nellie Fox 2.00 5.00
36 Lefty Grove Steve Carlton 2.00 5.00
37 Ty Cobb Tony Gwynn 3.00 8.00
38 Albert Pujols Frank Robinson 6.00 15.00
39 Ryne Sandberg Sammy Sosa 3.00 8.00
40 Cal Ripken Lou Gehrig 6.00 15.00

2002 Fleer Platinum

This 301 card set was issued in early Spring, 2002. These cards were issued in three different ways: 10 card hobby and retail packs. These packs were issued 24 packs to a box and six boxes to a case and had an SRP of $3. This product was also issued in 25 card jumbo packs which were packaged 12 to a box and eight boxes to a case. These cards had an SRP of $6. In addition, these cards were also issued in 45-card rack packs which were issued six packs to a box and two boxes to a case. These packs had an SRP of $10 per pack. The first 250 cards were basic cards while cards 251 through 260 are a Decade of Dominance subset, cards 261-270 feature the 10 players considered among the best young prospect and then 271-300 feature dual players prospects. Cards numbered 301 and 302 feature Japanese imports for 2002, So Taguchi and Kazuhisa Ishii. Card number 280 was not issued upon release of this set but was scheduled for release later in the 2002 season. At season's end, it was decided by the manufacturer to NOT release this card. A few copies of this card (with a large square box cut out from Satoru Komiyama's image) erroneously made their way into packs. Due to scarcity, a value has not been established. In addition, 73 redemption cards were seeded into packs whereby the holder of the card could exchange it for an actual vintage 1986 Fleer Update Bonds XRC signed and certified by Barry himself and hand-numbered "X/73". The deadline to send this card in was April 30th, 2003.

COMPLETE SET (301) 100.00 200.00
COMP.SET w/o SP's (250) 10.00 25.00
COMMON CARD (1-250) .10 .30
COMMON CARD (251-260) 1.25 3.00
COMMON CARD (261-270) 1.25 3.00
COMMON CARD (271-302) 1.25 3.00
1 Garret Anderson .10 .30
2 Randy Johnson .30 .75
3 Chipper Jones .30 .75
4 David Cone .10 .30
5 Corey Patterson .10 .30
6 Carlos Lee .10 .30
7 Barry Larkin .20 .50
8 Jim Thome .20 .50
9 Larry Walker .10 .30
10 Randall Simon .10 .30
11 Charles Johnson .10 .30
12 Richard Hidalgo .10 .30
13 Mark Quinn .10 .30
14 Paul LoDuca .10 .30
15 Cristian Guzman .10 .30
16 Orlando Cabrera .10 .30
17 Al Leiter .10 .30
18 Nick Johnson .10 .30
19 Eric Chavez .10 .30
20 Miguel Tejada .10 .30
21 Mike Lieberthal .10 .30
22 Rob Mackowiak .10 .30
23 Ryan Klesko .10 .30
24 Jeff Kent .10 .30
25 Edgar Martinez .20 .50
26 Steve Kline .10 .30
27 Toby Hall .10 .30
28 Rusty Greer .10 .30
29 Jose Cruz Jr. .10 .30
30 Darin Erstad .10 .30
31 Reggie Sanders .10 .30
32 Javy Lopez .10 .30
33 Carl Everett .10 .30
34 Sammy Sosa .30 .75
35 Magglio Ordonez .10 .30
36 Todd Walker .10 .30
37 Omar Vizquel .20 .50
38 Matt Anderson .10 .30
39 Jeff Weaver .10 .30
40 Derrek Lee .20 .50
41 Julio Lugo .10 .30
42 Joe Randa .10 .30
43 Chan Ho Park .10 .30
44 Torii Hunter .10 .30
45 Vladimir Guerrero .30 .75
46 Rey Ordonez .10 .30
47 Tino Martinez .20 .50
48 Johnny Damon Sox .20 .50
49 Barry Zito .10 .30
50 Robert Person .10 .30
51 Aramis Ramirez .10 .30
52 Mark Kotsay .10 .30
53 Jason Schmidt .10 .30
54 Jamie Moyer .10 .30
55 David Justice .10 .30
56 Aubrey Huff .10 .30
57 Rick Helling .10 .30
58 Carlos Delgado .10 .30
59 Troy Glaus .10 .30
60 Curt Schilling .10 .30
61 Greg Maddux .50 1.25
62 Nomar Garciaparra .50 1.25
63 Kerry Wood .10 .30
64 Frank Thomas .30 .75
65 Dmitri Young .10 .30
66 Alex Ochoa .10 .30
67 Jose Macias .10 .30
68 Antonio Alfonseca .10 .30
69 Mike Lowell .10 .30
70 Wade Miller .10 .30
71 Mike Sweeney .10 .30
72 Gary Sheffield .10 .30
73 Corey Koskie .10 .30
74 Lee Stevens .10 .30
75 Jay Payton .10 .30
76 Mike Mussina .20 .50
77 Jermaine Dye .10 .30
78 Bobby Abreu .10 .30
79 Scott Rolen .20 .50
80 Todd Ritchie .10 .30
81 D'Angelo Jimenez .10 .30
82 Robb Nen .10 .30
83 John Olerud .10 .30
84 Matt Morris .10 .30
85 Joe Kennedy .10 .30
86 Gabe Kapler .10 .30
87 Chris Carpenter .10 .30
88 David Eckstein .10 .30
89 Matt Williams .10 .30
90 John Smoltz .20 .50
91 Pedro Martinez .20 .50
92 Eric Young .10 .30
93 Jose Valentin .10 .30
94 Erubiel Durazo .10 .30
95 Jeff Cirillo .10 .30
96 Brandon Inge .10 .30
97 Josh Beckett .10 .30
98 Preston Wilson .10 .30
99 Damian Jackson .10 .30
100 Adrian Beltre .10 .30
101 Jeromy Burnitz .10 .30
102 Joe Mays .10 .30
103 Michael Barrett .10 .30
104 Mike Piazza .50 1.25
105 Brady Anderson .10 .30
106 Jason Giambi Yankees .10 .30
107 Marlon Anderson .10 .30
108 Jimmy Rollins .10 .30
109 Jack Wilson .10 .30
110 Brian Lawrence .10 .30
111 Russ Ortiz .10 .30
112 Kazuhiro Sasaki .10 .30
113 Placido Polanco .10 .30
114 Damian Rolls .10 .30
115 Rafael Palmeiro .20 .50
116 Brad Fullmer .10 .30
117 Tim Salmon .20 .50
118 Tony Womack .10 .30
119 Tony Batista .10 .30
120 Trot Nixon .10 .30
121 Mark Buehrle .10 .30
122 Derek Jeter .75 2.00
123 Ellis Burks .10 .30
124 Mike Hampton .10 .30
125 Roger Cedeno .10 .30
126 A.J. Burnett .10 .30
127 Moises Alou .10 .30
128 Billy Wagner .10 .30
129 Kevin Brown .10 .30
130 Jose Hernandez .10 .30
131 Doug Mientkiewicz .10 .30
132 Javier Vazquez .10 .30
133 Tsuyoshi Shinjo .10 .30
134 Andy Pettitte .20 .50
135 Tim Hudson .10 .30
136 Pat Burrell .10 .30
137 Brian Giles .10 .30
138 Kevin Young .10 .30
139 Xavier Nady .10 .30
140 J.T. Snow .10 .30
141 Aaron Sele .10 .30
142 Albert Pujols .60 1.50
143 Jason Tyner .10 .30
144 Ivan Rodriguez .20 .50
145 Raul Mondesi .10 .30
146 Matt Lawton .10 .30
147 Rafael Furcal .10 .30
148 Jeff Conine .10 .30
149 Hideo Nomo .30 .75
150 Jose Canseco .20 .50
151 Aaron Boone .10 .30
152 Bartolo Colon .10 .30
153 Todd Helton .20 .50
154 Tony Clark .10 .30
155 Pablo Ozuna .10 .30
156 Jeff Bagwell .20 .50
157 Carlos Beltran .10 .30
158 Shawn Green .10 .30
159 Geoff Jenkins .10 .30
160 Eric Milton .10 .30
161 Jose Vidro .10 .30
162 Robin Ventura .10 .30
163 Jorge Posada .20 .50
164 Terrence Long .10 .30
165 Brandon Duckworth .10 .30
166 Chad Hermansen .10 .30
167 Ben Davis .10 .30
168 Phil Nevin .10 .30
169 Bret Boone .10 .30
170 J.D. Drew .10 .30
171 Edgar Renteria .10 .30
172 Randy Winn .10 .30
173 Alex Rodriguez .50 1.25
174 Shannon Stewart .10 .30
175 Steve Finley .10 .30
176 Marcus Giles .10 .30
177 Jay Gibbons .10 .30
178 Manny Ramirez .20 .50
179 Ray Durham .10 .30
180 Sean Casey .10 .30
181 Travis Fryman .10 .30
182 Denny Neagle .10 .30
183 Deivi Cruz .10 .30
184 Luis Castillo .10 .30
185 Lance Berkman .10 .30
186 Dee Brown .10 .30
187 Jeff Shaw .10 .30
188 Mark Loretta .10 .30
189 David Ortiz .30 .75
190 Edgardo Alfonzo .10 .30
191 Roger Clemens .60 1.50
192 Mariano Rivera .30 .75
193 Jeremy Giambi .10 .30
194 Johnny Estrada .10 .30
195 Craig Wilson .10 .30
196 Adam Eaton .10 .30
197 Rich Aurilia .10 .30
198 Mike Cameron .10 .30
199 Jim Edmonds .10 .30
200 Fernando Vina .10 .30
201 Greg Vaughn .10 .30
202 Mike Young .30 .75
203 Vernon Wells .10 .30
204 Luis Gonzalez .10 .30
205 Tom Glavine .20 .50
206 Chris Richard .10 .30
207 Jon Lieber .10 .30
208 Keith Foulke .10 .30
209 Rondell White .10 .30
210 Bernie Williams .20 .50
211 Juan Pierre .10 .30
212 Juan Encarnacion .10 .30
213 Ryan Dempster .10 .30
214 Tim Redding .10 .30
215 Jeff Suppan .10 .30
216 Mark Grudzielanek .10 .30
217 Richie Sexson .10 .30
218 Brad Radke .10 .30
219 Armando Benitez .10 .30
220 Orlando Hernandez .10 .30
221 Alfonso Soriano .10 .30
222 Mark Mulder .10 .30
223 Travis Lee .10 .30
224 Jason Kendall .10 .30
225 Trevor Hoffman .10 .30
226 Barry Bonds .75 2.00
227 Freddy Garcia .10 .30
228 Darryl Kile .10 .30
229 Ben Grieve .10 .30
230 Frank Catalanotto .10 .30
231 Ruben Sierra .10 .30
232 Homer Bush .10 .30
233 Mark Grace .20 .50
234 Andruw Jones .20 .50
235 Brian Roberts .10 .30
236 Fred McGriff .20 .50
237 Paul Konerko .10 .30
238 Ken Griffey Jr. .50 1.25
239 John Burkett .10 .30
240 Juan Uribe .10 .30
241 Bobby Higginson .10 .30
242 Cliff Floyd .10 .30
243 Craig Biggio .20 .50
244 Neifi Perez .10 .30
245 Eric Karros .10 .30
246 [illegible] .10 [illegible]
247 Tony Armas Jr. .10 .30
248 Mo Vaughn .10 .30
249 David Wells .10 .30
250 Juan Gonzalez .10 .30
251 Barry Bonds DD 3.00 8.00
252 Sammy Sosa DD 1.25 3.00
253 Ken Griffey Jr. DD 2.00 5.00
254 Roger Clemens DD 2.50 6.00
255 Greg Maddux DD 2.00 5.00
256 Chipper Jones DD 1.25 3.00
257 Alex Rodriguez 2.50 6.00
Derek Jeter
Nomar Garciaparra DD
258 Roberto Alomar DD 1.25 3.00
259 Jeff Bagwell DD 1.25 3.00
260 Mike Piazza DD 2.00 5.00
261 Mark Teixeira BB 1.50 4.00
262 Mark Prior BB 1.50 4.00
263 Alex Escobar BB 1.25 3.00
264 C.C. Sabathia BB 1.25 3.00
265 Drew Henson BB 1.25 3.00
266 Wilson Betemit BB 1.25 3.00
267 Roy Oswalt BB 1.25 3.00
268 Adam Dunn BB 1.25 3.00
269 Bud Smith BB 1.25 3.00
270 Dewon Brazelton BB 1.25 3.00
271 Brandon Backe RC 1.25 3.00
Jason Standridge
272 Wilfredo Rodriguez 1.25 3.00
Carlos Hernandez
273 Geronimo Gil 1.25 3.00
Luis Rivera
274 Carlos Pena 1.25 3.00
Jovanny Cedeno
275 Austin Kearns 1.25 3.00
Ben Broussard
276 Jorge De La RosaRC 1.25 3.00
Kenny Kelly
277 Ryan Drese 1.50 4.00
Victor Martinez
278 Joel Pinero 1.25 3.00
Nate Cornejo
279 David Kelton 1.25 3.00
Carlos Zambrano
280 Bill Ortega
Satoru Komiyama ERR
Not intended for public release
Card features large cut out square over Komiyama image
281 Donnie Bridges 1.25 3.00
Wily Ruan
282 Wily Mo Pena 1.25 3.00
Brandon Claussen
283 Jason Jennings 1.25 3.00
Rene Reyes RC
284 Steve Green 1.25 3.00
Alfredo Amezaga
285 Eric Hinske 1.25 3.00
Felipe Lopez
286 Anderson Machado RC 1.25 3.00
Brad Baisley
287 Carlos Garcia 1.25 3.00
Sean Douglass
288 Pat Strange 1.25 3.00
Jae Weong Seo
289 Marcus Thames 1.25 3.00
Alex Graman
290 Matt Childers RC 1.25 3.00
Hansel Izquierdo RC
291 Ron Calloway RC 1.25 3.00
Adam Walker RC
292 J.R. House 1.25 3.00
J.J. Davis
293 Ryan Anderson 1.25 3.00
Rafael Soriano
294 Mike Bynum 1.25 3.00
Dennis Tankersley
295 Kurt Ainsworth 1.25 3.00
Carlos Valderrama
296 Billy Hall 1.25 3.00
Cristian Guerrero
297 Miguel Olivo 1.25 3.00
Danny Wright
298 Marlon Byrd 1.25 3.00
Jorge Padilla RC
299 Juan Cruz 1.25 3.00
Ben Christensen
300 Adam Johnson 1.25 3.00
Michael Restovich
301 So Taguchi SP RC 1.25 3.00
302 Kazuhisa Ishii SP RC 1.25 3.00
NNO B.Bonds 1986 AU/73 250.00 400.00

2002 Fleer Platinum Parallel

Randomly inserted into packs, this is a parallel set version of the 2002 Fleer Platinum set. These cards have a stated print run of 202 cards for cards numbered 1 through 250 and 22 for cards numbered 251-302. Please note that no pricing is provided for cards numbered 251-302 due to market scarcity.

*PARALLEL 1-250: 2.5X TO 6X BASIC

2002 Fleer Platinum Clubhouse Memorabilia

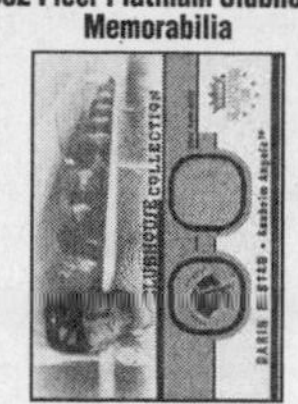

Inserted into packs at stated odds of one in 32 hobby and one in 44 retail packs, these 39 cards feature game-used memorabilia pieces. Though not actually serial-numbered, Fleer announced the print runs for each of these cards upon release of the product and we have included that information in our checklist.

1 Edgardo Alfonzo Jsy/1000 4.00 10.00
2 Rick Ankiel Jsy/500 4.00 10.00
3 Adrian Beltre Jsy/875 4.00 10.00
4 Craig Biggio Bat/600 6.00 15.00
5 Barry Bonds Jsy/1000 12.50 30.00
6 Sean Casey Jsy/800 4.00 10.00
7 Eric Chavez Jsy/1000 4.00 10.00
8 Roger Clemens Jsy/1000 10.00 25.00
9 J.Damon Sox Bat/700 6.00 15.00
10 Carlos Delgado Jsy/750 4.00 10.00
11 J.D. Drew Jsy/1000 4.00 10.00
12 Darin Erstad Jsy/850 4.00 10.00
13 N.Garciaparra Jsy/750 8.00 20.00
14 Juan Gonzalez Bat/1000 4.00 10.00
15 Todd Helton Jsy/925 6.00 15.00
16 Tim Hudson Jsy/825 4.00 10.00
17 D.Jeter Pants/1000 12.50 30.00
18 Randy Johnson Jsy/1000 6.00 15.00
19 A.Jones Jsy/1000 6.00 15.00
20 Jason Kendall Jsy/1000 4.00 10.00
21 Paul LoDuca Jsy/1000 4.00 10.00
22 Greg Maddux Jsy/875 6.00 15.00
23 Pedro Martinez Jsy/775 6.00 15.00
24 Raul Mondesi Bat/575 4.00 10.00
25 M.Ordonez Jsy/575 4.00 10.00
26 Mike Piazza Jsy/950 6.00 15.00
27 Mike Piazza Pants/1000 6.00 15.00
28 M.Ramirez Jsy/1000 6.00 15.00
29 Mariano Rivera Jsy/725 6.00 15.00
30 Alex Rodriguez Jsy/850 8.00 20.00
31 I.Rodriguez Jsy/1000 6.00 15.00
32 Scott Rolen Jsy/120 6.00 15.00
33 K.Sasaki Jsy/1000 4.00 10.00
34 Curt Schilling Jsy/1000 4.00 10.00
35 Gary Sheffield Bat/775 4.00 10.00
36 Gary Sheffield Jsy/800 4.00 10.00
37 Frank Thomas Jsy/850 6.00 15.00
38 Jim Thome Bat/750 6.00 15.00
39 Omar Vizquel Jsy/1000 6.00 15.00

2002 Fleer Platinum Clubhouse Memorabilia Combos

Inserted at a stated rate of one in 96 hobby packs and one in 192 retail packs, these 39 cards parallel the Clubhouse Memorabilia set. These cards can be differentiated by their having two distinct pieces of game-used memorabilia attached to the front. Since these cards have distinct press runs, we have notated that information in our checklist.

1 Edgardo Alfonzo Ball-Jsy/125 6.00 15.00
2 Rick Ankiel Bat-Jsy/200 6.00 15.00
3 Adrian Beltre Ball-Jsy/125 6.00 15.00
4 Craig Biggio Jsy-Bat/50
5 Barry Bonds Glove-Jsy/275 20.00 50.00
6 Sean Casey Ball-Jsy/125 6.00 15.00
7 Eric Chavez Base-Jsy/325 6.00 15.00
8 Roger Clemens Base-Jsy/325 15.00 40.00
9 J.Damon Sox Base-Bat/175 10.00 25.00
10 Carlos Delgado Bat-Jsy/325 6.00 15.00
11 J.D. Drew Ball-Jsy/125 6.00 15.00
12 Darin Erstad Bat-Jsy/125 6.00 15.00
13 N.Garciaparra Base-Jsy/275 15.00 40.00
14 Juan Gonzalez Jsy-Bat/75 6.00 15.00
15 Todd Helton Jsy-Bat/35
16 Tim Hudson Bat-Jsy/200 6.00 15.00
17 D.Jeter Btg Glv-Pants/200 20.00 50.00
18 Randy Johnson Bat-Jsy/125 10.00 25.00
19 And Jones Btg Glv-Jsy/100 10.00 25.00
20 Jason Kendall Bat-Jsy/50
21 Paul LoDuca Ball-Jsy/125 6.00 15.00
22 Greg Maddux Ball-Jsy/275 10.00 25.00
23 Pedro Martinez Base-Jsy/300 10.00 25.00
24 Raul Mondesi Bat-Btg Glv/75
25 M.Ordonez Bat-Jsy/325 6.00 15.00
26 Mike Piazza Ball-Jsy/125 15.00 40.00
27 Mike Piazza Ball-Pants/125 15.00 40.00
28 M.Ramirez Base-Jsy/350 10.00 25.00
29 Mariano Rivera Base-Jsy/175 10.00 25.00
30 Alex Rodriguez Base-Jsy/300 12.50 30.00
31 I.Rodriguez Btg Glv-Glv/100 10.00 25.00
32 Scott Rolen Ball-Jsy/125 10.00 25.00
33 K.Sasaki Base-Jsy/350 6.00 15.00
34 Curt Schilling Ball-Jsy/125 6.00 15.00
35 Gary Sheffield Ball-Jsy/125 6.00 15.00
36 Gary Sheffield Base-Jsy/125 6.00 15.00
37 Frank Thomas Base-Jsy/275 10.00 25.00
38 Jim Thome Base-Bat/275 10.00 25.00
39 Omar Vizquel Base-Jsy/300 10.00 25.00

2002 Fleer Platinum Cornerstones

These cards were distributed in jumbo packs (1:12), rack packs (1:6) and retail packs (1:20). Each card features two prominent active and retired ballplayers paired up in a horizontal design with an image of a base floating in front of them. The cards are identical in design to the hobby-only Cornerstones Numbered except these cards lack serial-numbering, feature the word "Cornerstones" in brown lettering on front (the hobby-only versions are serial-numbered on back and feature white lettering for the "Cornerstones" moniker on front and oddly enough are entirely devoid of any checklist card number on back. The cards have been checklisted in our database using the same order as the hobby Cornerstones set.

COMPLETE SET (40) 100.00 200.00
1 Bill Terry 1.25 3.00
Johnny Mize
2 Cal Ripken 6.00 15.00
Eddie Murray
3 Eddie Mathews 2.00 5.00
Chipper Jones
4 Albert Pujols 4.00 10.00
George Sisler
5 Sean Casey 1.25 3.00
Tony Perez
6 Jimmie Foxx 2.00 5.00
Scott Rolen
7 Wade Boggs 4.00 10.00
George Brett
8 Rod Carew 1.25 3.00
Troy Glaus
9 Jeff Bagwell 1.25 3.00
Rafael Palmeiro
10 Willie Stargell 1.25 3.00
Pie Traynor
11 Cal Ripken 6.00 15.00
Brooks Robinson
12 Tony Perez 1.25 3.00
Ted Kluszewski
13 Jason Giambi 3.00 8.00
Don Mattingly
14 Hank Greenberg 2.00 5.00
Jimmie Foxx
15 Ernie Banks 2.00 5.00
Willie McCovey
16 Jim Thome 1.25 3.00
Travis Fryman
17 Ted Kluszewski 1.25 3.00
Sean Casey
18 Gil Hodges 2.00 5.00
Johnny Mize
19 Brooks Robinson 1.25 3.00
Boog Powell
20 Bill Terry 1.25 3.00
George Sisler
21 Wade Boggs 4.00 10.00
Don Mattingly
22 Jason Giambi Yankees 1.25 3.00
Carlos Delgado
23 Willie Stargell 1.25 3.00
Bill Madlock
24 Mark Grace 1.25 3.00
Matt Williams
25 Paul Molitor 4.00 10.00
George Brett
26 Carlos Delgado 1.25 3.00
Mo Vaughn
27 Bill Terry 1.25 3.00
Willie McCovey
28 Mike Sweeney 4.00 10.00
George Brett
29 Eddie Mathews 2.00 5.00
Ernie Banks
30 Eric Karros 2.00 5.00
Gil Hodges
31 Paul Molitor 4.00 10.00
Don Mattingly
32 Brooks Robinson 1.25 3.00
Rod Carew
33 Chipper Jones 4.00 10.00
Albert Pujols
34 Harry Heilmann 2.00 5.00
Hank Greenberg
35 Frank Thomas 2.00 5.00
Carlos Delgado
36 Jeff Bagwell 1.25 3.00
Todd Helton
37 Rafael Palmeiro 1.25 3.00
Fred McGriff
38 Cal Ripken 6.00 15.00
Wade Boggs
39 Orlando Cepeda 1.25 3.00
Willie McCovey
40 John Olerud 1.25 3.00
Mark Grace

2002 Fleer Platinum Cornerstones Numbered

Randomly inserted into hobby packs, these 40 cards have different print runs depending on which group of cards they belong to. Cards numbered 1-10 were printed to a stated print run of 250 serial numbered sets while cards numbered 11-20 have a stated print run of 500 sets. Cards numbered 21-30 have a stated print run of 1000 sets and cards numbered 31-40 have a stated print run of 2000 sets. Other than Harry Heilmann, most of the players played a significant part of their career at either first or third base.

COMMON CARD (1-10) 6.00 15.00
COMMON CARD (11-20) 4.00 10.00
COMMON CARD (21-30) 3.00 8.00
COMMON CARD (31-40) 2.00 5.00
1 Bill Terry 6.00 15.00
Johnny Mize
2 Cal Ripken 15.00 40.00
Eddie Murray
3 Eddie Mathews 6.00 15.00
Chipper Jones
4 Albert Pujols 10.00 25.00
George Sisler
5 Sean Casey 6.00 15.00
Tony Perez
6 Jimmie Foxx 6.00 15.00
Scott Rolen
7 Wade Boggs 10.00 25.00
George Brett
8 Rod Carew 6.00 15.00
Troy Glaus
9 Jeff Bagwell 6.00 15.00
Rafael Palmeiro
10 Willie Stargell 6.00 15.00
Pie Traynor
11 Cal Ripken 12.50 30.00
Brooks Robinson
12 Tony Perez 4.00 10.00
Ted Kluszewski
13 Jason Giambi 10.00 25.00
Don Mattingly
14 Hank Greenberg 4.00 10.00
Jimmie Foxx
15 Ernie Banks 4.00 10.00
Willie McCovey
16 Jim Thome 4.00 10.00
Travis Fryman
17 Ted Kluszewski 4.00 10.00
Sean Casey
18 Gil Hodges 4.00 10.00
Johnny Mize
19 Brooks Robinson 4.00 10.00
Boog Powell
20 Bill Terry 4.00 10.00
George Sisler
21 Wade Boggs 6.00 15.00
Don Mattingly
22 Jason Giambi Yankees 3.00 8.00
Carlos Delgado
23 Willie Stargell 3.00 8.00
Bill Madlock
24 Mark Grace 3.00 8.00
Matt Williams
25 Paul Molitor 5.00 12.00
George Brett
26 Carlos Delgado 3.00 8.00
Mo Vaughn
27 Bill Terry 3.00 8.00
Willie McCovey
28 Mike Sweeney 5.00 12.00
George Brett
29 Eddie Mathews 3.00 8.00
Ernie Banks
30 Eric Karros 3.00 8.00
Gil Hodges
31 Paul Molitor 4.00 10.00
Don Mattingly
32 Brooks Robinson 2.00 5.00
Rod Carew
33 Chipper Jones 4.00 10.00
Albert Pujols
34 Harry Heilmann 2.00 5.00
Hank Greenberg
35 Frank Thomas 2.00 5.00
Carlos Delgado
36 Jeff Bagwell 2.00 5.00
Todd Helton
37 Rafael Palmeiro 2.00 5.00
Fred McGriff
38 Cal Ripken 6.00 15.00
Wade Boggs
39 Orlando Cepeda 2.00 5.00
Willie McCovey
40 John Olerud 2.00 5.00
Mark Grace

2002 Fleer Platinum Fence Busters

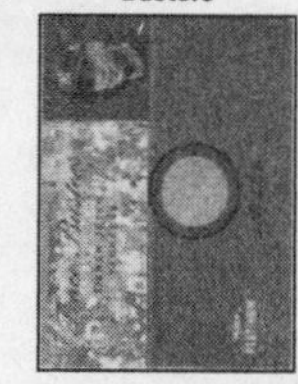

Randomly inserted into rack packs, these 22 cards feature some of the leading hitters in the game. We have provided the stated print runs for these cards in our checklist. The Jeff Bagwell card was not ready when Fleer went to press with this set and that card could be redeemed until April 30th, 2003.

1 Roberto Alomar/800 4.00 10.00
2 Moises Alou/800 3.00 8.00
3 Jeff Bagwell/400 4.00 10.00
4 Barry Bonds/700 10.00 25.00
5 J.D. Drew/800 3.00 8.00
6 Jim Edmonds/500 3.00 8.00
7 Brian Giles/700 3.00 8.00
8 Luis Gonzalez/625 3.00 8.00
9 Shawn Green/800 3.00 8.00
10 Todd Helton/675 4.00 10.00
11 Derek Jeter/400 10.00 25.00
12 Andruw Jones/800 4.00 10.00
13 Chipper Jones/800 4.00 10.00
14 Tino Martinez/800 4.00 10.00
15 Rafael Palmeiro/800 4.00 10.00
16 Mike Piazza/800 6.00 15.00
17 Manny Ramirez/800 4.00 10.00
18 Alex Rodriguez/675 6.00 15.00
19 Miguel Tejada/700 3.00 8.00
20 Frank Thomas/800 4.00 10.00
21 Jim Thome/800 4.00 10.00
22 Larry Walker/750 3.00 8.00

2002 Fleer Platinum Fence Busters Autographs

Randomly inserted into rack packs, these four cards feature signed copies of the Fence Busters insert set. These cards were all serial numbered to the selected player's 2001 home run total. All of these cards were issued as exchange cards and could be redeemed until April 30th, 2003.

1 Jeff Bagwell/39
2 Barry Bonds/73 125.00 200.00
3 Derek Jeter/21
4 Miguel Tejada/31

2002 Fleer Platinum National Patch Time

Inserted at stated odds at one in 12 jumbo packs, these 19 cards feature the selected player as well as game-worn jersey patch swatch of the featured player. The stated print runs for the players are listed next to their name in our checklist.

1 Barry Bonds/75 50.00 120.00
2 Pat Burrell/285 15.00 40.00
3 Jose Canseco/150 20.00 50.00
4 Carlos Delgado/70 20.00 50.00
5 J.D. Drew/210 15.00 40.00
6 Adam Dunn/75 20.00 50.00
7 Darin Erstad/315 15.00 40.00
8 Juan Gonzalez/50 25.00 60.00
9 Todd Helton/110 20.00 50.00
10 Derek Jeter/65 50.00 120.00
11 Greg Maddux/775 15.00 40.00
12 Pedro Martinez/45 25.00 60.00
13 Magglio Ordonez/85 20.00 50.00
14 Manny Ramirez/100 20.00 50.00
15 Cal Ripken/350 30.00 60.00
16 Alex Rodriguez/325 25.00 60.00
17 Ivan Rodriguez/125 15.00 40.00
18 Kazuhiro Sasaki/310 15.00 40.00
19 Miguel Tejada/55 20.00 50.00

2002 Fleer Platinum Wheelhouse

Inserted at stated odds of one in 12 hobby and one in 20 retail, these 20 cards feature some of the leading hitters in baseball.

COMPLETE SET (20) 40.00 80.00
1 Derek Jeter 3.00 8.00
2 Barry Bonds 3.00 8.00
3 Luis Gonzalez 1.25 3.00
4 Jason Giambi 1.25 3.00
5 Ivan Rodriguez 1.25 3.00
6 Mike Piazza 2.00 5.00
7 Troy Glaus 1.25 3.00
8 Nomar Garciaparra 2.00 5.00
9 Juan Gonzalez 1.25 3.00
10 Sammy Sosa 1.25 3.00
11 Albert Pujols 2.50 6.00
12 Ken Griffey Jr. 2.00 5.00
13 Scott Rolen 1.25 3.00
14 Jeff Bagwell 1.25 3.00
15 Ichiro Suzuki 2.50 6.00
16 Todd Helton 1.25 3.00
17 Chipper Jones 1.25 3.00
18 Alex Rodriguez 2.00 5.00
19 Vladimir Guerrero 1.25 3.00
20 Manny Ramirez 1.25 3.00

2003 Fleer Platinum

This 250 card set was release in February, 2003. These cards were issued in a variety of manners. Each box contained 14 wax packs as well as 4 jumbo packs and one rack pack. The wax packs had an SRP of $3, while the jumbos had an SRP of $5 and the rack packs had an SRP of $10. There are several subsets in the product. Cards numbered 201 through 220 feature Unsung Heroes. Cards numbered 221 through 250 are prospects but those cards were issued in different ratios throughout the set.

COMP.SET w/o SP's (220) 10.00 25.00
COMMON CARD (1-220) .10 .30
COMMON CARD (221-235) .75 2.00
221-235 ODDS 1:4 WAX, 1:2 JUM, 1:1 RACK
COMMON CARD (236-240) .75 2.00
236-240 ODDS 1:12 WAX
COMMON CARD (241-245) 1.25 3.00
241-245 ODDS 1:6 JUMBO
COMMON CARD (246-250) 1.25 3.00
246-250 ODDS 1:2 RACK
1 Barry Bonds .75 2.00
2 Sean Casey .10 .30
3 Todd Walker .10 .30
4 Tony Batista .10 .30
5 Todd Zeile .10 .30

6 Ruben Sierra	.10	.30
7 Jose Cruz Jr.	.10	.30
8 Ben Grieve	.10	.30
9 Rob Mackowiak	.10	.30
10 Gary Sheffield	.10	.30
11 Armando Benitez	.10	.30
12 Tim Hudson	.10	.30
13 Eric Milton	.10	.30
14 Andy Pettitte	.20	.50
15 Jeff Bagwell	.20	.50
16 Jeff Kent	.10	.30
17 Joe Randa	.10	.30
18 Benito Santiago	.10	.30
19 Russell Branyan	.10	.30
20 Cliff Floyd	.10	.30
21 Chris Richard	.10	.30
22 Randy Winn	.10	.30
23 Freddy Garcia	.10	.30
24 Derek Lowe	.10	.30
25 Ben Sheets	.10	.30
26 Fred McGriff	.20	.50
27 Bret Boone	.10	.30
28 Jose Hernandez	.10	.30
29 Phil Nevin	.10	.30
30 Mike Piazza	.50	1.25
31 Bobby Abreu	.10	.30
32 Darin Erstad	.10	.30
33 Andruw Jones	.20	.50
34 Brad Wilkerson	.10	.30
35 Brian Lawrence	.10	.30
36 Vladimir Nunez	.10	.30
37 Kazuhiro Sasaki	.10	.30
38 Carlos Delgado	.10	.30
39 Steve Cox	.10	.30
40 Adrian Beltre	.10	.30
41 Josh Bard	.10	.30
42 Randall Simon	.10	.30
43 Johnny Damon	.20	.50
44 Ken Griffey Jr.	.50	1.25
45 Sammy Sosa	.30	.75
46 Kevin Brown	.10	.30
47 Kazuhisa Ishii	.10	.30
48 Matt Morris	.10	.30
49 Mark Prior	.20	.50
50 Kip Wells	.10	.30
51 Hee Seop Choi	.10	.30
52 Craig Biggio	.20	.50
53 Derek Jeter	.75	2.00
54 Albert Pujols	.60	1.50
55 Joe Borchard	.10	.30
56 Robert Fick	.10	.30
57 Jacque Jones	.10	.30
58 Juan Pierre	.10	.30
59 Bernie Williams	.20	.50
60 Elmer Dessens	.10	.30
61 Al Leiter	.10	.30
62 Curt Schilling	.10	.30
63 Carlos Pena	.10	.30
64 Tino Martinez	.20	.50
65 Fernando Vina	.10	.30
66 Aaron Boone	.10	.30
67 Michael Barrett	.10	.30
68 Frank Thomas	.30	.75
69 J.D. Drew	.10	.30
70 Vladimir Guerrero	.30	.75
71 Shannon Stewart	.10	.30
72 Mark Buehrle	.10	.30
73 Jamie Moyer	.10	.30
74 Brad Radke	.10	.30
75 Mike Williams	.10	.30
76 Ryan Klesko	.10	.30
77 Roberto Alomar	.20	.50
78 Edgardo Alfonzo	.10	.30
79 Matt Williams	.10	.30
80 Edgar Martinez	.20	.50
81 Shawn Green	.10	.30
82 Kenny Lofton	.10	.30
83 Josh Beckett	.10	.30
84 Trevor Hoffman	.10	.30
85 Kevin Millwood	.10	.30
86 Odalis Perez	.10	.30
87 Jarrod Washburn	.10	.30
88 Jason Giambi	.10	.30
89 Eric Young	.10	.30
90 Barry Larkin	.20	.50
91 Aramis Ramirez	.10	.30
92 Ivan Rodriguez	.20	.50
93 Steve Finley	.10	.30
94 Brian Jordan	.10	.30
95 Manny Ramirez	.20	.50
96 Preston Wilson	.10	.30
97 Rodrigo Lopez	.10	.30
98 Ramon Ortiz	.10	.30
99 Jim Thome	.20	.50
100 Luis Castillo	.10	.30
101 Alex Rodriguez	.50	1.25
102 Jared Sandberg	.10	.30
103 Ellis Burks	.10	.30
104 Pat Burrell	.10	.30
105 Brian Giles	.10	.30
106 Mark Kotsay	.10	.30
107 Dave Roberts	.10	.30
108 Roy Halladay	.10	.30
109 Chan Ho Park	.10	.30
110 Erubiel Durazo	.10	.30
111 Bobby Hill	.10	.30
112 Cristian Guzman	.10	.30
113 Troy Glaus	.10	.30
114 Lance Berkman	.10	.30
115 Juan Encarnacion	.10	.30
116 Chipper Jones	.30	.75
117 Corey Patterson	.10	.30
118 Vernon Wells	.10	.30
119 Matt Clement	.10	.30
120 Billy Koch	.10	.30
121 Hideo Nomo	.30	.75
122 Derrek Lee	.20	.50
123 Todd Helton	.20	.50
124 Sean Burroughs	.10	.30
125 Jason Kendall	.10	.30
126 Dmitri Young	.10	.30
127 Adam Dunn	.10	.30
128 Bobby Higginson	.10	.30
129 Raul Mondesi	.10	.30
130 Bubba Trammell	.10	.30
131 A.J. Burnett	.10	.30
132 Randy Johnson	.30	.75
133 Mark Mulder	.10	.30
134 Mariano Rivera	.30	.75
135 Kerry Wood	.10	.30
136 Mo Vaughn	.10	.30
137 Jimmy Rollins	.10	.30
138 Jose Valentin	.10	.30
139 Brad Fullmer	.10	.30
140 Mike Cameron	.10	.30
141 Luis Gonzalez	.10	.30
142 Kevin Appier	.10	.30
143 Mike Hampton	.10	.30
144 Pedro Martinez	.20	.50
145 Javier Vazquez	.10	.30
146 Doug Mientkiewicz	.10	.30
147 Adam Kennedy	.10	.30
148 Rafael Furcal	.10	.30
149 Eric Chavez	.10	.30
150 Mike Lieberthal	.10	.30
151 Moises Alou	.10	.30
152 Jermaine Dye	.10	.30
153 Torii Hunter	.10	.30
154 Trot Nixon	.10	.30
155 Larry Walker	.10	.30
156 Jorge Julio	.10	.30
157 Mike Mussina	.20	.50
158 Kirk Rueter	.10	.30
159 Rafael Palmeiro	.20	.50
160 Pokey Reese	.10	.30
161 Miguel Tejada	.10	.30
162 Robin Ventura	.10	.30
163 Raul Ibanez	.10	.30
164 Roger Cedeno	.10	.30
165 Juan Gonzalez	.10	.30
166 Carlos Lee	.10	.30
167 Tim Salmon	.20	.50
168 Orlando Hernandez	.10	.30
169 Wade Miller	.10	.30
170 Troy Percival	.10	.30
171 Billy Wagner	.10	.30
172 Jeff Conine	.10	.30
173 Junior Spivey	.10	.30
174 Edgar Renteria	.10	.30
175 Scott Rolen	.20	.50
176 Jason Varitek	.30	.75
177 Ben Broussard	.10	.30
178 Jeremy Giambi	.10	.30
179 Gabe Kapler	.10	.30
180 Armando Rios	.10	.30
181 Ichiro Suzuki	.60	1.50
182 Tom Glavine	.20	.50
183 Greg Maddux	.50	1.25
184 Roy Oswalt	.10	.30
185 John Smoltz	.20	.50
186 Eric Karros	.10	.30
187 Alfonso Soriano	.10	.30
188 Nomar Garciaparra	.50	1.25
189 Joe Crede	.10	.30
190 Javy Lopez	.10	.30
191 Carlos Beltran	.10	.30
192 Jim Edmonds	.10	.30
193 Geoff Jenkins	.10	.30
194 Magglio Ordonez	.10	.30
195 Daryle Ward	.10	.30
196 Roger Clemens	.60	1.50
197 Byung-Hyun Kim	.10	.30
198 Robb Nen	.10	.30
199 C.C. Sabathia	.10	.30
200 Barry Zito	.10	.30
201 Mark Grace UH	.10	.30
202 Paul Konerko UH	.10	.30
203 Mike Sweeney UH	.10	.30
204 John Olerud UH	.10	.30
205 Jose Vidro UH	.10	.30
206 Ray Durham UH	.10	.30
207 Omar Vizquel UH	.10	.30
208 Shea Hillenbrand UH	.10	.30
209 Mike Lowell UH	.10	.30
210 Aubrey Huff UH	.10	.30
211 Eric Hinske UH	.10	.30
212 Paul Lo Duca UH	.10	.30
213 Jay Gibbons UH	.10	.30
214 Austin Kearns UH	.10	.30
215 Richie Sexson UH	.10	.30
216 Garret Anderson UH	.10	.30
217 Eric Gagne UH	.10	.30
218 Jason Jennings UH	.10	.30
219 Damian Moss UH	.10	.30
220 David Eckstein UH	.10	.30
221 Mark Teixeira PROS	1.25	3.00
222 Bill Hall PROS	.75	2.00
223 Bobby Jenks PROS	.75	2.00
224 Adam Morrissey PROS	.75	2.00
225 Rodrigo Rosario PROS	.75	2.00
226 Brett Myers PROS	.75	2.00
227 Tony Alvarez PROS	.75	2.00
228 Willie Bloomquist PROS	.75	2.00
229 Ben Howard PROS	.75	2.00
230 Nic Jackson PROS	.75	2.00
231 Carl Crawford PROS	.75	2.00
232 Omar Infante PROS	.75	2.00
233 Francisco Rodriguez PROS	.75	2.00
234 Andy Van Hekken PROS	.75	2.00
235 Kirk Saarloos PROS	.75	2.00
236 Dusty Wathan PROS RC	.75	2.00
237 Jamey Carroll PROS	.75	2.00
238 Jason Phillips PROS	.75	2.00
239 Jose Castillo PROS	.75	2.00
240 Arnaldo Munoz PROS RC	.75	2.00
241 Orlando Hudson PROS	1.25	3.00
242 Drew Henson PROS	1.25	3.00
243 Jason Lane PROS	1.25	3.00
244 Vinny Chulk PROS	1.25	3.00
245 Prentice Redman PROS RC	1.25	3.00
246 Marlon Byrd PROS	1.25	3.00
247 Chin-Feng Chen PROS,	1.25	3.00
248 Craig Brazell PROS RC	1.25	3.00
249 John Webb PROS	1.25	3.00
250 Adam LaRoche PROS	1.25	3.00

2003 Fleer Platinum Finish

Randomly inserted in packs, this is a parallel to the Fleer Platinum set. These cards with a "finished" type front were issued to a stated print run of 100 serial numbered sets.

*FINISH 1-220: 3X TO 8X BASIC
*FINISH 221-235: 1X TO 2.5X BASIC
*FINISH 236-240: 1X TO 2.5X BASIC
*FINISH 241-245: .6X TO 1.5X BASIC
*FINISH 2446-250: .6X TO 1.5X BASIC

2003 Fleer Platinum Barry Bonds Chasing History Game Used

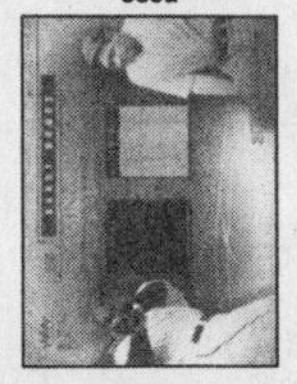

Randomly inserted in packs, these five cards feature game used swatches from both Barry Bonds and various retired players whose records he was chasing. The cards with two game-worn swatches were issued to a stated print run of 250 serial numbered sets while the five player card was issued to a stated print run of 25 serial numbered sets.

BB Barry Bonds Jsy	15.00	40.00
Bobby Bonds Bat		
BR Barry Bonds Jsy	125.00	200.00
Babe Ruth Bat		
RM Barry Bonds Jsy	30.00	60.00
Roger Maris Pants		
WM Barry Bonds Jsy	15.00	40.00
Willie McCovey Jsy		
CH Barry BondsJsy		
Bobby Bonds Bat		
Roger Maris Pants		
Willie McCovey Jsy		
Babe Ruth Bat		

2003 Fleer Platinum Guts and Glory

Inserted at a stated rate of one in four wax packs, one in two jumbo and one per rack pack, this 20 card set features some of the leading players in baseball.

COMPLETE SET (20)	10.00	25.00
1 Jason Giambi	.40	1.00
2 Alfonso Soriano	.40	1.00
3 Scott Rolen	.40	1.00
4 Ivan Rodriguez	.40	1.00
5 Barry Bonds	1.25	3.00
6 Jim Edmonds	.40	1.00
7 Darin Erstad	.40	1.00
8 Brian Giles	.40	1.00
9 Luis Gonzalez	.40	1.00
10 Adam Dunn	.40	1.00
11 Torii Hunter	.40	1.00
12 Andruw Jones	.40	1.00
13 Sammy Sosa	.50	1.25
14 Ichiro Suzuki	1.00	2.50
15 Miguel Tejada	.40	1.00
16 Roger Clemens	1.00	2.50
17 Curt Schilling	.40	1.00
18 Nomar Garciaparra	.75	2.00
19 Derek Jeter	1.25	3.00
20 Alex Rodriguez	.75	2.00

2003 Fleer Platinum Heart of the Order

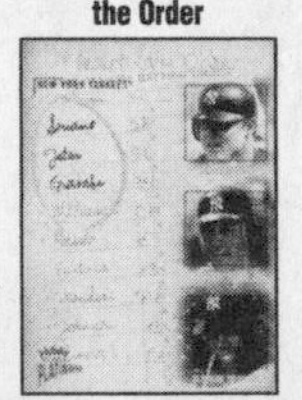

Inserted in packs at a rate of one in 12 wax, one in six jumbo and one in three rack, these cards feature three players who are the key offensive weapons for their teams.

1 Jason Giambi	1.50	4.00
Derek Jeter		
Alfonso Soriano		
2 Todd Helton	.75	2.00
Preston Wilson		
Larry Walker		
3 Rafael Palmeiro	1.25	3.00
Alex Rodriguez		
Ivan Rodriguez		
4 Adam Dunn	1.25	3.00
Ken Griffey Jr.		
Austin Kearns		
5 Jeff Bagwell	.75	2.00
Craig Biggio		
Lance Berkman		
6 Eric Chavez	.75	2.00
Miguel Tejada		
Jermaine Dye		
7 Troy Glaus	.75	2.00
Garrett Anderson		
Darin Erstad		
8 Mike Piazza	1.25	3.00
Mo Vaughn		
Roberto Alomar		
9 Torii Hunter	.75	2.00
Jacque Jones		
Corey Koskie		
10 Barry Bonds	2.00	5.00
Jeff Kent		
Rich Aurilia		
11 Pat Burrell	.75	2.00
Bobby Abreu		
Jimmy Rollins		
12 Shawn Green	.75	2.00
Adrian Beltre		
Paul Lo Duca		
13 Vladimir Guerrero	.75	2.00
Brad Wilkerson		
Jose Vidro		
14 Chipper Jones	.75	2.00
Andruw Jones		
Gary Sheffield		
15 Ichiro Suzuki	1.50	4.00
{Bret Boone		
Edgar Martinez		
16 Albert Pujols	1.50	4.00
Scott Rolen		
J.D. Drew		
17 Sammy Sosa	.75	2.00
Fred McGriff		
Moises Alou		
18 Nomar Garciaparra	1.25	3.00
Shea Hillenbrand		
Manny Ramirez		
19 Frank Thomas	.75	2.00
Magglio Ordonez		
Paul Konerko		
20 Jason Kendall	.75	2.00
Brian Giles		
Amaris Ramirez		

2003 Fleer Platinum Heart of the Order Game Used

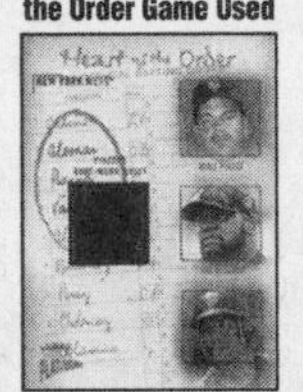

Inserted at a stated rate of one in two rack packs, this is a partial parallel to the Heart of the Order set. These cards feature a game-used memorabilia piece form one of the players on the card along with photos of the other two players. Each of these cards was issued to a stated print run of 400 serial numbered sets.

AB Adrian Beltre Jsy	3.00	8.00
Shawn Green		
Paul Lo Duca		
AK Austin Kearns Pants	3.00	8.00
Adam Dunn		
Ken Griffey Jr.		
AS Alfonso Soriano Bat	3.00	8.00
Jason Giambi		
Derek Jeter		
BB Bret Boone Jsy	3.00	8.00
Edgar Martinez		
Ichiro Suzuki		
BG Brian Giles Bat	3.00	8.00
Jason Kendall		
Aramis Ramirez		
CJ Chipper Jones Jsy	6.00	15.00
Andruw Jones		
Gary Sheffield		
DE Darin Erstad Jsy	3.00	8.00
Garret Anderson		
Troy Glaus		
FT Frank Thomas Jsy	6.00	15.00
Paul Konerko		
Magglio Ordonez		
JD J.D. Drew Jsy	3.00	8.00
Albert Pujols		
Scott Rolen		
JK Jeff Kent Jsy	3.00	8.00
Rich Aurilia		
Barry Bonds		
JR Jimmy Rollins Jsy	3.00	8.00
Bob Abreu		
Pat Burrell		
JV Jose Vidro Jsy	3.00	8.00
Vladimir Guerrero		
Brad Wilkerson		
LB Lance Berkman Bat	3.00	8.00
Jeff Bagwell		
Craig Biggio		
MP Mike Piazza Jsy	6.00	15.00
Roberto Alomar		
Mo Vaughn		
MR Manny Ramirez Jsy	4.00	10.00
Nomar Garciaparra		
Shea Hillenbrand		
RP Rafael Palmeiro Jsy	4.00	10.00
Alex Rodriguez		
Ivan Rodriguez		
SS Sammy Sosa Jsy	6.00	15.00
Moises Alou		
Fred McGriff		
TH Todd Helton Jsy	4.00	10.00
Larry Walker		
Preston Wilson		

2003 Fleer Platinum MLB Scouting Report

Randomly inserted in packs, this 32 card set features information about the noted player. Each card has some scouting type information to go with some hitting charts. These cards were issued to a stated print run of 400 serial numbered sets.

1 Jason Giambi	1.50	4.00
2 Paul Konerko	1.50	4.00
3 Jim Thome	1.50	4.00
4 Alfonso Soriano	1.50	4.00
5 Troy Glaus	1.50	4.00
6 Eric Hinske	1.50	4.00
7 Paul Lo Duca	1.50	4.00
8 Mike Piazza	2.50	6.00
9 Marlon Byrd	1.50	4.00
10 Garret Anderson	1.50	4.00
11 Barry Bonds	4.00	10.00
12 Pat Burrell	1.50	4.00
13 Joe Crede	1.50	4.00
14 J.D. Drew	1.50	4.00
15 Ken Griffey Jr.	2.50	6.00
16 Vladimir Guerrero	1.50	4.00
17 Torii Hunter	1.50	4.00
18 Chipper Jones	1.50	4.00
19 Austin Kearns	1.50	4.00
20 Albert Pujols	3.00	8.00
21 Manny Ramirez	1.50	4.00
22 Gary Sheffield	1.50	4.00
23 Sammy Sosa	1.50	4.00
24 Ichiro Suzuki	3.00	8.00
25 Bernie Williams	1.50	4.00
26 Randy Johnson	1.50	4.00
27 Greg Maddux	2.50	6.00
28 Hideo Nomo	1.50	4.00
29 Nomar Garciaparra	2.50	6.00
30 Derek Jeter	4.00	10.00
31 Alex Rodriguez	2.50	6.00
32 Miguel Tejada	1.50	4.00

2003 Fleer Platinum MLB Scouting Report Game Used

Randomly inserted in wax packs, this is a partial parallel to the Scouting Report insert set. These cards feature a game used piece to go with the scouting report information. These cards were issued to a stated print run of 250 serial numbered sets.

AK Austin Kearns Pants	4.00	10.00
AS Alfonso Soriano Bat	4.00	10.00
BB Barry Bonds Jsy	10.00	25.00
CJ Chipper Jones Jsy	6.00	15.00
DJ Derek Jeter Jsy	10.00	25.00
GM Greg Maddux Jsy	6.00	15.00
HN Hideo Nomo Jsy	12.50	30.00
JD J.D. Drew Jsy	4.00	10.00
JT Jim Thome Jsy	6.00	15.00
MP Mike Piazza Jsy	6.00	15.00
MR Manny Ramirez Jsy	6.00	15.00
RJ Randy Johnson Jsy	6.00	15.00
SS Sammy Sosa Jsy	6.00	15.00

2003 Fleer Platinum Nameplates

Inserted at a stated rate of one in eight jumbo packs, these 41 cards feature different amounts of the featured players. We have notated the print runs for the players in our checklist.

AD Adam Dunn/117	10.00	25.00
AJ Andruw Jones/170	10.00	25.00
AR Alex Rodriguez/248	20.00	50.00
BB Barry Bonds/251	30.00	60.00
BL Barry Larkin/97	15.00	40.00
BZ Barry Zito/248	10.00	25.00
CB Craig Biggio/152	10.00	25.00
CC Chin-Feng Chen/110	60.00	120.00
CJ Chipper Jones/251	12.50	30.00
CK Corey Koskie/130	10.00	25.00
EH Eric Hinske/173	10.00	25.00
EM Edgar Martinez/176	10.00	25.00
FT Frank Thomas/58	20.00	50.00
FT Frank Thomas/93	20.00	50.00
GM Greg Maddux/248	15.00	40.00
HN Hideo Nomo/150		
IR Ivan Rodriguez/189	10.00	25.00
JB Jeff Bagwell/121	10.00	25.00
JD Johnny Damon/35	30.00	60.00
JO John Olerud/180	10.00	25.00
JR Jimmy Rollins/74	10.00	25.00
JT Jim Thome/158	10.00	25.00
KI Kazuhisa Ishii/35	20.00	50.00
KS Kazuhiro Sasaki/82	10.00	25.00
KW Kerry Wood/49	20.00	50.00
LB Lance Berkman/176	10.00	25.00
LW Larry Walker/161	10.00	25.00
MP Mike Piazza/200	15.00	40.00
MP2 Mark Prior/123	10.00	25.00
MR Manny Ramirez/94	15.00	40.00
MS Mike Sweeney/175	10.00	25.00
MT Miguel Tejada/225	10.00	25.00
NG Nomar Garciaparra/258	15.00	40.00
PB Pat Burrell/176	10.00	25.00
PM Pedro Martinez/244	10.00	25.00
PN Phil Nevin/134		
RC Roger Clemens/141	30.00	60.00
RJ Randy Johnson/142		
RO Roy Oswalt/155	10.00	25.00
RP Rafael Palmeiro/245	10.00	25.00
RS Richie Sexson/160	10.00	25.00
VG Vladimir Guerrero/102	20.00	50.00

2003 Fleer Platinum Portraits

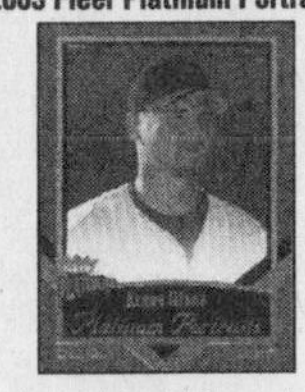

Inserted at a stated rate of one in 20 wax packs, one in 10 jumbo packs and one in five rack packs, these 20 cards feature painting like cards of the featured player.

1 Josh Beckett	1.25	3.00
2 Roberto Alomar	1.25	3.00
3 Alfonso Soriano	1.25	3.00
4 Mike Piazza	2.00	5.00
5 Ivan Rodriguez	1.25	3.00
6 Edgar Martinez	1.25	3.00
7 Barry Bonds	3.00	8.00
8 Adam Dunn	1.25	3.00
9 Juan Gonzalez	1.25	3.00
10 Chipper Jones	1.25	3.00
11 Albert Pujols	2.50	6.00
12 Magglio Ordonez	1.25	3.00
13 Shea Hillenbrand	1.25	3.00
14 Larry Walker	1.25	3.00
15 Pedro Martinez	1.25	3.00
16 Kerry Wood	1.25	3.00
17 Barry Zito	1.25	3.00
18 Nomar Garciaparra	2.00	5.00
19 Derek Jeter	3.00	8.00
20 Alex Rodriguez	2.00	5.00

2003 Fleer Platinum Portraits Game Jersey

Inserted at a stated rate of one in 86 wax packs, this is a partial parallel to the Portraits insert set. These cards feature a game-worn jersey swatch on the front. The Derek Jeter card was issued in smaller quantity and we have notated that information in our data base.

AD Adam Dunn	3.00	8.00
BB Barry Bonds	8.00	20.00
BZ Barry Zito	3.00	8.00
CJ Chipper Jones	4.00	10.00
DJ Derek Jeter SP/150	12.50	30.00
IR Ivan Rodriguez	4.00	10.00
JB Josh Beckett	3.00	8.00
KW Kerry Wood	3.00	8.00
MP Mike Piazza	6.00	15.00
NG Nomar Garciaparra	6.00	15.00
PM Pedro Martinez	4.00	10.00

2003 Fleer Platinum Portraits Game Patch

Inserted at a stated rate of one in 86 wax packs, this is a partial parallel to the Portraits insert set. These cards feature a game-worn jersey swatch on the front. These cards were issued to a stated print run of 100 serial numbered sets.

AD Adam Dunn	15.00	40.00
BB Barry Bonds	30.00	60.00
BZ Barry Zito	15.00	40.00
CJ Chipper Jones	15.00	40.00
DJ Derek Jeter		
IR Ivan Rodriguez	15.00	40.00
KW Kerry Wood	15.00	40.00
MP Mike Piazza	30.00	60.00
NG Nomar Garciaparra	30.00	60.00
PM Pedro Martinez	15.00	40.00

2004 Fleer Platinum

This 200-card set was released in February, 2004. The set was issued in seven-card packs with an $3 SRP which came 18 packs to a box and 16 boxes to a case. In addition, every hobby box had four jumbo packs included. Those jumbo packs had 20 cards in them. Plus rack packs were issued; those packs had 30 cards in each pack. Cards numbered 1-135 are major league veterans while cards numbered 136-143 were issued at a stated rate of one in three wax and one in 12 retail packs. Cards numbered 144-151 were issued at a stated rate of one per jumbo while cards 152 through 157 were issued exclusively in rack packs at a rate of one per and according to Fleer the stated print run of those cards was approximately 1000 cards. The set closes with the following subsets: UH (cards numbered 158 through 182 while cards numbered 183 through 200 feature multi-player prospect cards.

COMP.SET w/o SP's (178)	10.00	25.00
COMMON (1-135/158-182)	.10	.30
COMMON CARD (183-200)	.40	1.00
183-200 ARE NOT SHORT-PRINTS		
COMMON CARD (136-143)	.40	1.00
136-143 ODDS 1:3 WAX, 1:12 RETAIL		
COMMON CARD (144-151)	.40	1.00
144-151 ODDS ONE PER JUMBO		
COMMON CARD (152-157)	3.00	8.00
152-157 ODDS ONE PER RACK PACK		
152-157 STATED PRINT RUN APPX.1000 SETS		
152-157 PRINT RUN PROVIDED BY FLEER		
152-157 ARE NOT SERIAL-NUMBERED		
1 Luis Castillo	.12	.30
2 Preston Wilson	.12	.30
3 Johan Santana	.30	.75
4 Fred McGriff	.12	.30
5 Albert Pujols	.75	2.00
6 Reggie Sanders	.12	.30
7 Ivan Rodriguez	.20	.50
8 Roy Halladay	.30	.75
9 Brian Giles	.12	.30
10 Bernie Williams	.20	.50
11 Barry Larkin	.20	.50
12 Marlon Anderson	.12	.30
13 Ramon Ortiz	.12	.30
14 Luis Matos	.12	.30
15 Esteban Loaiza	.12	.30
16 Orlando Cabrera	.12	.30
17 Jamie Moyer	.12	.30
18 Tino Martinez	.20	.50
19 Josh Beckett	.20	.50
20 Derek Jeter	.75	2.00
21 Derek Lowe	.12	.30
22 Jack Wilson	.12	.30
23 Bret Boone	.12	.30
24 Matt Morris	.12	.30
25 Javier Vazquez	.12	.30
26 Joe Crede	.12	.30
27 Jose Vidro	.12	.30
28 Mike Piazza	.30	.75
29 Curt Schilling	.20	.50
30 Alex Rodriguez	.50	1.25
31 John Olerud	.12	.30
32 Dontrelle Willis	.12	.30
33 Larry Walker	.20	.50
34 Joe Randa	.12	.30
35 Paul Lo Duca	.12	.30
36 Marlon Byrd	.12	.30
37 Bo Hart	.12	.30
38 Rafael Palmeiro	.20	.50
39 Garret Anderson	.12	.30
40 Tom Glavine	.20	.50
41 Ichiro Suzuki	.50	1.25
42 Derrek Lee	.12	.30
43 Lance Berkman	.20	.50
44 Nomar Garciaparra	.30	.75
45 Mike Sweeney	.12	.30
46 A.J. Burnett	.20	.50
47 Sean Casey	.12	.30
48 Eric Gagne	.12	.30
49 Joel Pineiro	.12	.30
50 Russ Ortiz	.12	.30
51 Placido Polanco	.12	.30
52 Sammy Sosa	.30	.75
53 Mark Teixeira	.30	.75
54 Randy Wolf	.12	.30
55 Vladimir Guerrero	.30	.75
56 Tim Hudson	.20	.50
57 Lew Ford	.12	.30
58 Carlos Delgado	.12	.30
59 Darin Erstad	.12	.30
60 Mike Lieberthal	.12	.30
61 Craig Biggio	.20	.50
62 Ryan Klesko	.12	.30
63 C.C. Sabathia	.20	.50
64 Carlos Lee	.12	.30
65 Al Leiter	.12	.30
66 Brandon Webb	.12	.30
67 Jacque Jones	.12	.30
68 Kerry Wood	.12	.30
69 Omar Vizquel	.20	.50
70 Jeremy Bonderman	.12	.30
71 Kevin Brown	.12	.30
72 Richie Sexson	.12	.30
73 Zach Day	.12	.30
74 Mike Mussina	.20	.50
75 Sidney Ponson	.12	.30
76 Andruw Jones	.12	.30
77 Woody Williams	.12	.30
78 Kazuhiro Sasaki	.12	.30
79 Matt Clement	.12	.30
80 Shea Hillenbrand	.12	.30
81 Bartolo Colon	.12	.30
82 Ken Griffey Jr.	.50	1.25
83 Todd Helton	.20	.50
84 Dmitri Young	.12	.30
85 Richard Hidalgo	.12	.30
86 Carlos Beltran	.12	.30
87 Brad Wilkerson	.12	.30
88 Andy Pettitte	.20	.50
89 Miguel Tejada	.20	.50
90 Edgar Martinez	.20	.50
91 Vernon Wells	.12	.30
92 Magglio Ordonez	.20	.50
93 Tony Batista	.12	.30
94 Jose Reyes	.20	.50
95 Matt Stairs	.12	.30
96 Manny Ramirez	.30	.75
97 Carlos Pena	.20	.50
98 A.J. Pierzynski	.12	.30
99 Jim Thome	.20	.50
100 Aubrey Huff	.12	.30
101 Roberto Alomar	.20	.50
102 Luis Gonzalez	.12	.30
103 Chipper Jones	.30	.75
104 Jay Gibbons	.12	.30
105 Adam Dunn	.20	.50
106 Jay Payton	.12	.30
107 Scott Podsednik	.12	.30
108 Roy Oswalt	.20	.50
109 Milton Bradley	.12	.30
110 Shawn Green	.12	.30
111 Ryan Wagner	.12	.30
112 Eric Chavez	.12	.30
113 Pat Burrell	.12	.30
114 Frank Thomas	.30	.75
115 Jason Kendall	.12	.30
116 Jake Peavy	.12	.30

117 Mike Cameron .12 .30
118 Jim Edmonds .20 .50
119 Hank Blalock .12 .30
120 Troy Glaus .12 .30
121 Jeff Kent .12 .30
122 Jason Schmidt .12 .30
123 Corey Patterson .12 .30
124 Austin Kearns .12 .30
125 Edwin Jackson .12 .30
126 Alfonso Soriano .12 .30
127 Bobby Abreu .12 .30
128 Scott Rolen .20 .50
129 Jeff Bagwell .20 .50
130 Shannon Stewart .12 .30
131 Rich Aurilia .12 .30
132 Ty Wigginton .12 .30
133 Randy Johnson .30 .75
134 Rocco Baldelli .12 .30
135 Hideo Nomo .30 .75
136 Greg Maddux WE 1.50 4.00
137 Johnny Damon WE .60 1.50
138 Mark Prior WE .60 1.50
139 Corey Koskie WE .40 1.00
140 Miguel Cabrera WE 1.00 2.50
141 Hideki Matsui WE 1.50 4.00
142 Jose Cruz Jr. WE .40 1.00
143 Barry Zito WE .40 1.00
144 Javy Lopez JE .40 1.00
145 Jason Varitek JE 1.00 2.50
146 Moises Alou JE .40 1.00
147 Torii Hunter JE .40 1.00
148 Juan Encarnacion JE .40 1.00
149 Jorge Posada JE .60 1.50
150 Marquis Grissom JE .40 1.00
151 Rich Harden JE .40 1.00
152 Gary Sheffield RE .40 1.00
153 Pedro Martinez RE .60 1.50
154 Brad Radke RE .40 1.00
155 Mike Lowell RE .40 1.00
156 Jason Giambi RE .40 1.00
157 Mark Mulder RE .40 1.00
158 Ben Weber UH .12 .30
159 Mark DeRosa UH .12 .30
160 Melvin Mora UH .12 .30
161 Bill Mueller UH .12 .30
162 Jon Garland UH .12 .30
163 Jody Gerut UH .12 .30
164 Javier Lopez UH .12 .30
165 Craig Monroe UH .12 .30
166 Juan Pierre UH .12 .30
167 Morgan Ensberg UH .12 .30
168 Angel Berroa UH .12 .30
169 Geoff Jenkins UH .12 .30
170 Matt LeCroy UH .12 .30
171 Livan Hernandez UH .12 .30
172 Jason Phillips UH .12 .30
173 Mariano Rivera UH .30 .75
174 Erubiel Durazo UH .12 .30
175 Jason Michaels UH .12 .30
176 Kip Wells UH .12 .30
177 Ray Durham UH .12 .30
178 Randy Winn UH .12 .30
179 Edgar Renteria UH .12 .30
180 Carl Crawford UH .20 .50
181 Laynce Nix UH .12 .30
182 Greg Myers UH .12 .30
183 Delmon Young .60 1.50
Chad Gaudin
184 Humberto Quintero .40 1.00
Bernie Castro
185 Craig Brazell .40 1.00
Danny Garcia
186 Ryan Wing RC .40 1.00
Francisco Cruceta
187 William Bergolla RC .40 1.00
Josh Hall
188 Clint Barmes .60 1.50
Garrett Atkins
189 Chris Bootcheck .40 1.00
Richard Fischer
190 Edgar Gonzalez .40 1.00
Matt Kata
191 Andrew Brown .40 1.00
Koyie Hill
192 John Gall RC .40 1.00
Dan Haren
193 Chad Bentz RC .40 1.00
Luis Ayala
194 Hector Gimenez RC .40 1.00
Eric Bruntlett
195 Boof Bonser .40 1.00
Rob Bowen
196 Chris Snelling .40 1.00
Rett Johnson
197 Rickie Weeks .40 1.00
Adam Morrissey
198 Noah Lowry .40 1.00
Todd Linden
199 Chris Waters .40 1.00
Brett Evert
200 Jorge De Paula .40 1.00
Chien-Ming Wang

2004 Fleer Platinum Finish

*FINISH 1-135/158-182: 3X TO 8X BASIC
*FINISH 183-200: 1X TO 2.5X BASIC
*FINISH 136-143: 1.25X TO 3X BASIC
*FINISH 144-151: .75X TO 2X BASIC
*FINISH 152-157: .25X TO .6X BASIC
STATED ODDS 1:15 WAX
STATED PRINT RUN 100 SERIAL #'d SETS

2004 Fleer Platinum Big Signs

ODDS 1:9 WAX, 1:2 JUMBO, 1:8 RETAIL
1 Albert Pujols 2.50 6.00
2 Derek Jeter 2.50 6.00
3 Mike Piazza 1.00 2.50
4 Jason Giambi .40 1.00
5 Ichiro Suzuki 1.50 4.00
6 Nomar Garciaparra 1.00 2.50
7 Mark Prior .60 1.50
8 Randy Johnson 1.00 2.50
9 Greg Maddux 1.50 4.00
10 Sammy Sosa 1.00 2.50
11 Ken Griffey Jr. 1.50 4.00
12 Dontrelle Willis .40 1.00
13 Alex Rodriguez 1.50 4.00
14 Chipper Jones 1.00 2.50
15 Hank Blalock .40 1.00

2004 Fleer Platinum Big Signs Autographs

Albert Pujols and Chipper Jones did not return their cards in time for pack out. Please note there is no expiration date to return these cards by.

STATED PRINT RUN 100 SERIAL #'d SETS
EXCHANGE DEADLINE INDEFINITE
DW Dontrelle Willis 10.00 25.00
HB Hank Blalock 6.00 15.00

2004 Fleer Platinum Classic Combinations

STATED ODDS 1:108 WAX, 1:270 RETAIL
1 Ivan Rodriguez 2.50 6.00
Mike Piazza
2 Alex Rodriguez 4.00 10.00
Sammy Sosa
3 Dontrelle Willis 1.00 2.50
Angel Berroa
4 Nomar Garciaparra 6.00 15.00
Derek Jeter
5 Ichiro Suzuki 4.00 10.00
Hideo Nomo
6 Josh Beckett 1.50 4.00
Kerry Wood
7 Albert Pujols 6.00 15.00
Carlos Delgado
8 Alfonso Soriano 1.00 2.50
Joe Morgan
9 Jason Giambi 1.50 4.00
Reggie Jackson
10 Nolan Ryan 8.00 20.00
Tom Seaver

2004 Fleer Platinum Clubhouse Memorabilia

STATED ODDS 1:24 WAX, 1:96 RETAIL
SP INFO PROVIDED BY FLEER
*DUAL: 1X TO 2.5X BASIC
*DUAL: .75X TO 2X BASIC SP
DUAL RANDOM IN WAX AND RETAIL
DUAL PRINT RUN 50 SERIAL #'d SETS
DUAL FEATURE TWO JSY SWATCHES
AK Austin Kearns 3.00 8.00
AP Albert Pujols SP 8.00 20.00
AR Alex Rodriguez 4.00 10.00
AS Alfonso Soriano SP 3.00 8.00
CJ Chipper Jones SP 4.00 10.00
DJ Derek Jeter 8.00 20.00
DW Dontrelle Willis 4.00 10.00
GM Greg Maddux 4.00 10.00
HB Hank Blalock 3.00 8.00
HN Hideo Nomo 6.00 15.00
JB Josh Beckett 3.00 8.00
JG Jason Giambi 3.00 8.00
JT Jim Thome 4.00 10.00
MPI Mike Piazza 4.00 10.00
MPR Mark Prior SP 4.00 10.00
MT Miguel Tejada 3.00 8.00
NG Nomar Garciaparra 4.00 10.00
RB Rocco Baldelli 3.00 8.00
RS Richie Sexson 3.00 8.00
SS Sammy Sosa 4.00 10.00
THE Todd Helton 4.00 10.00
THU Torii Hunter 3.00 8.00
VG Vladimir Guerrero 4.00 10.00

2004 Fleer Platinum Inscribed

ONE PER RACK PACK
PRINT RUNS B/WN 20-315 COPIES PER
EXCH PRINT RUNS PROVIDED BY FLEER
EXCHANGE DEADLINE INDEFINITE
NO PRICING ON QTY OF 25 OR LESS
AB Angel Berroa/210 4.00 10.00
AP Albert Pujols/100 125.00 250.00
BWE Brandon Webb/150 6.00 15.00
CBE Chad Bentz/310 4.00 10.00
CBO Chris Bootcheck/210 4.00 10.00
CSN Chris Snelling/310 4.00 10.00
DH Dan Haren/200 4.00 10.00
DM Dallas McPherson/160 6.00 15.00
DW Dontrelle Willis/25
DY Delmon Young/210 10.00 25.00
EG Eric Gagne/130 15.00 40.00
EJ Edwin Jackson/200 4.00 10.00
JR1 Jose Reyes/20
JV Javier Vazquez/160 6.00 15.00
KG Khalil Greene/310 10.00 25.00
KH Koyie Hill/300 4.00 10.00
LN Laynce Nix/200 4.00 10.00
MB Marlon Byrd/255 4.00 10.00
MK Matt Kata/315 4.00 10.00
RB Rocco Baldelli/100 10.00 25.00
RHA Rich Harden/200 6.00 15.00
RHO Ryan Howard/160 30.00 60.00
RWE Rickie Weeks/200 6.00 15.00
SP Scott Podsednik/180 10.00 25.00
SR Scott Rolen/55
VW Vernon Wells/200 6.00 15.00

2004 Fleer Platinum MLB Scouting Report

ODDS 1:45 WAX, 1:96 JUMBO, 1:190 RETAIL
STATED PRINT RUN 400 SERIAL #'d SETS
1 Josh Beckett 1.25 3.00
2 Todd Helton 1.25 3.00
3 Rocco Baldelli .75 2.00
4 Pedro Martinez 1.25 3.00
5 Jeff Bagwell 1.25 3.00
6 Mark Prior 1.25 3.00
7 Ichiro Suzuki 3.00 8.00
8 Barry Zito .75 2.00
9 Manny Ramirez 2.00 5.00
10 Miguel Cabrera 2.00 5.00
11 Richie Sexson .75 2.00
12 Hideki Matsui 3.00 8.00
13 Magglio Ordonez 1.25 3.00
14 Brandon Webb .75 2.00
15 Kerry Wood .75 2.00

2004 Fleer Platinum MLB Scouting Report Game Jersey

STATED PRINT RUN 250 SERIAL #'d SETS
BW Brandon Webb 4.00 10.00
JB Josh Beckett 4.00 10.00
JBAG Jeff Bagwell 6.00 15.00
KW Kerry Wood 4.00 10.00
MP Mark Prior 4.00 10.00
MR Manny Ramirez 6.00 15.00
PM Pedro Martinez 6.00 15.00
RB Rocco Baldelli 4.00 10.00
TH Todd Helton 6.00 15.00

2004 Fleer Platinum Nameplates Player

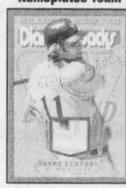

OVERALL NAMEPLATES ODDS 1:4 JUMBO
PRINT RUNS B/WN 25-320 COPIES PER
NO PRICING ON QTY OF 25 OR LESS
AK Austin Kearns/310 4.00 10.00
AP Albert Pujols/190 15.00 40.00
AR Alex Rodriguez/225 10.00 25.00
BZ Barry Zito/170 6.00 15.00
CJ Chipper Jones/150 10.00 25.00
CS Curt Schilling/260 8.00 20.00
GS Gary Sheffield/115 8.00 20.00
HB Hank Blalock/170 6.00 15.00
HN Hideo Nomo/85 20.00 50.00
HSC Hee Seop Choi/70 8.00 20.00
JB Josh Beckett/255 6.00 15.00
JP Juan Pierre/50 10.00 25.00
JR Jose Reyes/310 6.00 15.00
KB Kevin Brown/80 6.00 15.00
KW Kerry Wood/290 6.00 15.00
LC Luis Castillo/75 6.00 15.00
MB Marlon Byrd/75 6.00 15.00
MC Miguel Cabrera/75 10.00 25.00
MR Manny Ramirez/210 8.00 20.00
MT Mark Teixeira/75 8.00 20.00
NG Nomar Garciaparra/320 10.00 25.00
RJ Randy Johnson/200 8.00 20.00
RS Richie Sexson/165 6.00 15.00
SS Sammy Sosa/260 8.00 20.00
TG Tom Glavine/25

2004 Fleer Platinum Nameplates Team

OVERALL NAMEPLATES ODDS 1:4 JUMBO
PRINT RUNS B/WN 105-515 COPIES PER
AK Austin Kearns/515 4.00 10.00
AP Albert Pujols/470 12.50 30.00
AR Alex Rodriguez/510 8.00 20.00
BZ Barry Zito/515 4.00 10.00
CJ Chipper Jones/420 6.00 15.00
CS Curt Schilling/250 8.00 20.00
GS Gary Sheffield/500 4.00 10.00
HB Hank Blalock/515 4.00 10.00
HN Hideo Nomo/390 8.00 20.00
HSC Hee Seop Choi/220 6.00 15.00
JB Josh Beckett/390 4.00 10.00
JP Juan Pierre/110 8.00 20.00
JR Jose Reyes/510 4.00 10.00
KB Kevin Brown/220 4.00 10.00
KW Kerry Wood/510 4.00 10.00
LC Luis Castillo/225 4.00 10.00
MB Marlon Byrd/470 4.00 10.00
MC Miguel Cabrera/105 10.00 25.00
MR Manny Ramirez/480 6.00 15.00
MT Mark Teixeira/505 6.00 15.00
NG Nomar Garciaparra/250 10.00 25.00
RJ Randy Johnson/290 8.00 20.00
RS Richie Sexson/420 4.00 10.00
SS Sammy Sosa/490 6.00 15.00

2004 Fleer Platinum Portraits

ODDS 1:18 WAX, 1:4 JUMBO, 1:24 RETAIL
1 Jason Giambi .40 1.00
2 Nomar Garciaparra 1.00 2.50
3 Vladimir Guerrero 1.00 2.50
4 Mark Prior .60 1.50
5 Jim Thome .60 1.50
6 Derek Jeter 2.50 6.00
7 Sammy Sosa 1.00 2.50
8 Alex Rodriguez 1.50 4.00
9 Greg Maddux 1.50 4.00
10 Albert Pujols 2.50 6.00

2004 Fleer Platinum Portraits Game Jersey

STATED ODDS 1:48 WAX, 1:120 RETAIL
SP INFO PROVIDED BY FLEER
*PATCH: .75X TO 2X BASIC
*PATCH: .6X TO 1.5X BASIC SP
PATCH RANDOM IN WAX AND RETAIL
PATCH PRINT RUN 100 SERIAL #'d SETS
AP Albert Pujols 6.00 15.00
AR Alex Rodriguez 4.00 10.00
DJ Derek Jeter 8.00 20.00
GM Greg Maddux SP 6.00 15.00
JG Jason Giambi 3.00 8.00
JT Jim Thome 4.00 10.00
MP Mark Prior SP 6.00 15.00
NG Nomar Garciaparra 4.00 10.00
SS Sammy Sosa 4.00 10.00
VG Vladimir Guerrero 4.00 10.00

2005 Fleer Platinum

This 125 card set was released in April, 2005. The set was released in either five-card hobby packs which came 18 packs to a box and 16 boxes to a case or in five-card retail packs which came 24 packs to a box and 20 boxes to a case. The first 100 cards of the set feature active veterans while the final 25 cards feature leading prospects. Those final cards were issued at a stated rate of one in 18 hobby and one in 60 retail packs and were issued to a stated print run of 1000 serial numbered sets.

COMP.SET w/o SP's (100) 10.00 25.00
COMMON CARD (1-100) .10 .30
COMMON CARD (101-125) .60 1.50
101-125 ODDS 1:18 HOBBY, 1:60 RETAIL
101-125 PRINT RUN 1000 SERIAL #'d SETS
1 Nomar Garciaparra .30 .75
2 Matt Holliday .30 .75
3 Rickie Weeks .20 .50
4 Jim Thome .20 .50
5 Roy Halladay .30 .75
6 Paul Konerko .20 .50
7 Lance Berkman .20 .50
8 Ichiro Suzuki .50 1.25
9 Kerry Wood .12 .30
10 Lew Ford .12 .30
11 Omar Vizquel .20 .50
12 Manny Ramirez .30 .75
13 Carlos Beltran .12 .30
14 Lyle Overbay .12 .30
15 Billy Wagner .12 .30
16 Jose Vidro .12 .30
17 Vladimir Guerrero .30 .75
18 Miguel Tejada .20 .50
19 Alex Rodriguez .50 1.25
20 Rocco Baldelli .12 .30
21 David Ortiz .30 .75
22 Victor Martinez .20 .50
23 Shawn Green .12 .30
24 Jason Bay .12 .30
25 Pedro Martinez .20 .50
26 Travis Hafner .12 .30
27 Eric Gagne .12 .30
28 Jack Wilson .12 .30
29 Ivan Rodriguez .20 .50
30 Jody Gerut .12 .30
31 Adrian Beltre .12 .30
32 Craig Wilson .12 .30
33 J.D. Drew .12 .30
34 Craig Biggio .20 .50
35 Mark Mulder .12 .30
36 Mark Teixeira .30 .75
37 Melvin Mora .12 .30
38 Ken Griffey Jr. .50 1.25
39 Mike Sweeney .12 .30
40 Khalil Greene .12 .30
41 Rafael Palmeiro .20 .50
42 Austin Kearns .12 .30
43 Garret Anderson .12 .30
44 Trevor Hoffman .20 .50
45 Andruw Jones .12 .30
46 Adam Dunn .20 .50
47 Angel Berroa .12 .30
48 Ryan Klesko .12 .30
49 Sean Casey .12 .30
50 Kaz Matsui .12 .30
51 Jim Edmonds .20 .50
52 Magglio Ordonez .20 .50
53 Tom Glavine .20 .50
54 Larry Walker .20 .50
55 Johnny Estrada .12 .30
56 Brad Lidge .12 .30
57 Barry Zito .20 .50
58 Michael Young .20 .50
59 Chipper Jones .30 .75
60 Andy Pettitte .20 .50
61 Eric Chavez .12 .30
62 Carlos Delgado .20 .50
63 David Eckstein .12 .30
64 Dmitri Young .12 .30
65 Mike Piazza .30 .75
66 Albert Pujols .75 2.00
67 Luis Gonzalez .12 .30
68 Hideki Matsui .50 1.25
69 Gary Sheffield .12 .30
70 Carl Crawford .20 .50
71 Curt Schilling .20 .50
72 Todd Helton .20 .50
73 Ben Sheets .12 .30
74 Bobby Abreu .12 .30
75 Jose Guillen .12 .30
76 Richie Sexson .12 .30
77 Miguel Cabrera .30 .75
78 Bernie Williams .20 .50
79 Aubrey Huff .12 .30
80 John Smoltz .30 .75
81 Jeff Bagwell .20 .50
82 Tim Hudson .20 .50
83 Alfonso Soriano .20 .50
84 Freddy Garcia .12 .30
85 Johan Santana .30 .75
86 Bret Boone .12 .30
87 Troy Glaus .12 .30
88 Carlos Guillen .12 .30
89 Derek Jeter .75 2.00
90 Scott Rolen .20 .50
91 Sammy Sosa .30 .75
92 Jacque Jones .12 .30
93 Jason Schmidt .12 .30
94 Randy Johnson .30 .75
95 Dontrelle Willis .12 .30
96 Mariano Rivera .30 .75
97 Hank Blalock .12 .30
98 Mark Prior .20 .50
99 Torii Hunter .12 .30
100 Roger Clemens .40 1.00
101 David Wright ROO 2.50 6.00
102 Justin Morneau ROO 1.50 4.00
103 Scott Kazmir ROO 1.50 4.00
104 Gavin Floyd ROO .60 1.50
105 Justin Verlander ROO RC 12.00 30.00
106 Zack Greinke ROO 1.00 2.50
107 David Aardsma ROO .60 1.50
108 Ryan Raburn ROO .60 1.50
109 Joey Gathright ROO .60 1.50
110 J.D. Durbin ROO .60 1.50
111 Sean Burnett ROO .60 1.50
112 Jose Lopez ROO .60 1.50
113 Nick Swisher ROO 1.50 4.00
114 Bobby Jenks ROO .60 1.50
115 Kelly Johnson ROO .60 1.50
116 B.J. Upton ROO 1.00 2.50
117 Ronny Cedeno ROO .60 1.50
118 Edwin Encarnacion ROO 1.00 2.50
119 Jeff Baker ROO .60 1.50
120 Taylor Buchholz ROO .60 1.50
121 Luis Hernandez ROO RC .60 1.50
122 Dioner Navarro ROO .60 1.50
123 Victor Diaz ROO .60 1.50
124 Jon Knott ROO .60 1.50
125 Russ Adams ROO .60 1.50

2005 Fleer Platinum Extreme

OVERALL PARALLEL ODDS 1:9 H, 1:114 R
STATED PRINT RUN 20 SERIAL #'d SETS
NO PRICING DUE TO SCARCITY

2005 Fleer Platinum Finish

*FINISH 1-100: 2.5X TO 6X BASIC
*FINISH 101-125: .4X TO 1X BASIC
OVERALL PARALLEL ODDS 1:9 H, 1:114 R
STATED PRINT RUN 199 SERIAL #'d SETS

2005 Fleer Platinum Autograph Die Cuts

STATED ODDS 1:184 HOBBY
PRINT RUNS B/WN 10-99 COPIES PER
CARDS ARE NOT SERIAL-NUMBERED
PRINT RUN INFO PROVIDED BY FLEER
NO PRICING ON QTY OF 20 OR LESS
1 Lew Ford/99 * 4.00 10.00
3 Jason Bay/50 * 6.00 15.00
4 Travis Hafner/99 * 6.00 15.00
6 Brad Lidge/99 * 15.00 40.00
7 Michael Young/99 * 6.00 15.00
8 David Eckstein/99 * 12.50 30.00
9 Carl Crawford/50 * 6.00 15.00
10 Miguel Cabrera/50 * 10.00 25.00
11 David Wright ROO/50 * 20.00 50.00
12 Justin Morneau ROO/99 *
13 Scott Kazmir ROO/99 * 8.00 20.00
14 Gavin Floyd ROO/99 * 4.00 10.00
15 Justin Verlander ROO/99 * 20.00 50.00
16 David Aardsma ROO/10 *
18 Joey Gathright ROO/50 * 4.00 10.00
22 Russ Adams ROO/20 *

2005 Fleer Platinum Decade of Excellence

STATED ODDS 1:99 HOBBY, 1:125 RETAIL
1 Albert Pujols 2.50 6.00
2 Derek Jeter 2.50 6.00
3 Randy Johnson 1.00 2.50
4 Ichiro Suzuki 1.50 4.00
5 Alex Rodriguez 1.50 4.00
6 Mike Piazza 1.00 2.50
7 Greg Maddux 1.50 4.00
8 Curt Schilling .60 1.50
9 Frank Thomas 1.00 2.50
10 Torii Hunter .40 1.00
11 Al Kaline 1.00 2.50
12 Travis Hafner .40 1.00
13 Ivan Rodriguez .60 1.50
14 Rafael Palmeiro .60 1.50
15 Mike Schmidt 2.00 5.00
16 Johnny Bench 1.00 2.50
17 Jim Edmonds .60 1.50
18 Pedro Martinez .60 1.50
19 Robin Yount 1.00 2.50
20 Sammy Sosa 1.00 2.50

2005 Fleer Platinum Decade of Excellence Autograph Jersey Platinum

OVERALL AU ODDS 1:144 H, AU-GU 1:48 R
STATED PRINT RUN 5 SERIAL #'d SETS
NO PRICING DUE TO SCARCITY
AK Al Kaline
JB Johnny Bench
MS Mike Schmidt
TH Travis Hafner
TH Torii Hunter

2005 Fleer Platinum Decade of Excellence Jersey Silver

STATED ODDS 1:54 HOBBY
*GOLD: .5X TO 1.2X BASIC
GOLD PRINT RUN 99 SERIAL #'d SETS
PATCH PLATINUM PRINT 10 #'d SETS
NO PATCH PLT.PRICING DUE TO SCARCITY
OVERALL GU ODDS 1:9 H, AU-GU 1:48 R
AK Al Kaline 6.00 15.00
AP Albert Pujols 6.00 15.00
CS Curt Schilling 4.00 10.00
FT Frank Thomas 4.00 10.00
GM Greg Maddux 4.00 10.00
IR Ivan Rodriguez 4.00 10.00
JB Johnny Bench 6.00 15.00
JE Jim Edmonds 3.00 8.00
MP Mike Piazza 4.00 10.00
MS Mike Schmidt 6.00 15.00
PM Pedro Martinez 4.00 10.00
RJ Randy Johnson 4.00 10.00
RP Rafael Palmeiro 4.00 10.00
RY Robin Yount 6.00 15.00
SS Sammy Sosa 4.00 10.00
TF Travis Hafner 3.00 8.00
TH Torii Hunter 3.00 8.00

2005 Fleer Platinum Diamond Dominators

*DOM: .4X TO 1X METAL DOM
STATED ODDS 1:12 RETAIL

2005 Fleer Platinum Diamond Dominators Jersey Silver

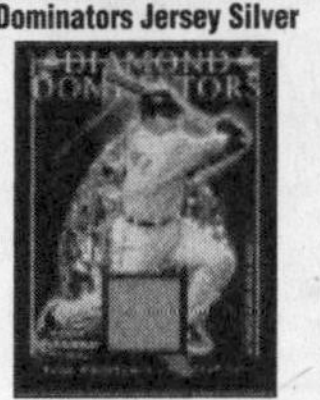

STATED ODDS 1:45 HOBBY
*GOLD: .4X TO 1X BASIC
OVERALL GU ODDS 1:9H, AU-GU 1:48 R
GOLD PRINT RUN 199 SERIAL #'d SETS
*RED: .4X TO 1X BASIC
RED STATED ODDS 1:50 RETAIL
AB Adrian Beltre 3.00 8.00
AP Albert Pujols 6.00 15.00
AS Alfonso Soriano 3.00 8.00
CJ Chipper Jones 4.00 10.00
CS Curt Schilling 4.00 10.00
DO David Ortiz 4.00 10.00
EG Eric Gagne 3.00 8.00
IR Ivan Rodriguez 4.00 10.00
JG Jason Giambi 3.00 8.00
KG Khalil Greene 4.00 10.00
KM Kaz Matsui 3.00 8.00
MC Miguel Cabrera 4.00 10.00
MP Mike Piazza 4.00 10.00
RB Rocco Baldelli 3.00 8.00
RJ Randy Johnson 4.00 10.00
SR Scott Rolen 4.00 10.00
SS Sammy Sosa 4.00 10.00
TH Tim Hudson 3.00 8.00
VG Vladimir Guerrero 4.00 10.00

2005 Fleer Platinum Diamond Dominators Metal

STATED ODDS 1:18 HOBBY
1 Albert Pujols 2.50 6.00
2 Curt Schilling .60 1.50
3 Adrian Beltre .40 1.00
4 Randy Johnson 1.00 2.50
5 Ivan Rodriguez .60 1.50
6 Mike Piazza 1.00 2.50
7 Chipper Jones 1.00 2.50
8 Sammy Sosa 1.00 2.50
9 Tim Hudson .60 1.50
10 Rocco Baldelli .40 1.00
11 Alfonso Soriano .60 1.50
12 David Ortiz 1.00 2.50
13 Kaz Matsui .40 1.00
14 Khalil Greene .40 1.00

15 Eric Gagne .40 1.00
16 Vladimir Guerrero 1.00 2.50
17 Jason Giambi .40 1.00
18 Scott Rolen .60 1.50
19 Miguel Cabrera 1.00 2.50

2005 Fleer Platinum Diamond Dominators Metal Autograph

OVERALL AU ODDS 1:144 H, AU-GU 1:48 R
STATED PRINT RUN 10 SERIAL #'d SETS
NO PRICING DUE TO SCARCITY

2005 Fleer Platinum Lumberjacks

STATED ODDS 1:6 HOBBY, 1:8 RETAIL
1 Albert Pujols 2.50 6.00
2 Jim Thome .60 1.50
3 Andruw Jones .40 1.00
4 Kaz Matsui .40 1.00
5 Adam Dunn .60 1.50
6 Bernie Williams .60 1.50
7 Hank Blalock .40 1.00
8 Bobby Abreu .40 1.00
9 Rocco Baldelli .40 1.00
10 Jacque Jones .40 1.00
11 Mark Teixeira 1.00 2.50
12 Ichiro Suzuki 1.50 4.00
13 Gary Sheffield .40 1.00
14 Sean Casey .40 1.00
15 Carl Crawford .60 1.50

2005 Fleer Platinum Lumberjacks Autograph Platinum

OVERALL AU ODDS 1:144 H, AU-GU 1:48 R
STATED PRINT RUN 20 SERIAL #'d SETS
NO PRICING DUE TO SCARCITY
CC Carl Crawford
HB Hank Blalock
JT Jim Thome
MT Mark Teixeira
RB Rocco Baldelli

2005 Fleer Platinum Lumberjacks Bat Silver

OVERALL GU ODDS 1:9 HOBBY
*GOLD: .4X TO 1X BASIC
GOLD PRINT RUN 250 SERIAL #'d SETS
BAT-PATCH PLATINUM PRINT 20 #'d SETS
NO BAT-PATCH PLT.PRICING AVAILABLE
AD Adam Dunn 3.00 8.00
AJ Andruw Jones 4.00 10.00
AP Albert Pujols 6.00 15.00
BA Bobby Abreu 3.00 8.00
BW Bernie Williams 4.00 10.00
CC Carl Crawford 3.00 8.00
GS Gary Sheffield 3.00 8.00
HB Hank Blalock 3.00 8.00
JJ Jacque Jones 3.00 8.00
JT Jim Thome 4.00 10.00
KM Kaz Matsui 3.00 8.00
MT Mark Teixeira 4.00 10.00
RB Rocco Baldelli 3.00 8.00
SC Sean Casey 3.00 8.00

2005 Fleer Platinum Nameplates Patch Platinum

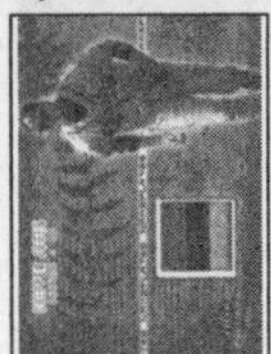

STATED PRINT RUN 25 SERIAL #'d SETS
MASTERPIECE PRINT RUN 1 #'d SET
OVERALL GU ODDS 1:9 H, AU-GU 1:48 R
NO PRICING DUE TO SCARCITY

2005 Fleer Platinum Nameplates Patch Autograph Platinum

OVERALL AU ODDS 1:144 H, AU-GU 1:48 R
STATED PRINT RUN 25 SERIAL #'d SETS
NO PRICING DUE TO SCARCITY
LB Lance Berkman
MB Marlon Byrd
SK Scott Kazmir
SR Scott Rolen

2005 Fleer Platinum Nameplates Dual Patch Platinum

STATED PRINT RUN 25 SERIAL #'d SETS
MASTERPIECE PRINT RUN 1 #'d SET
OVERALL GU ODDS 1:9 H, AU-GU 1:48 R
NO PRICING DUE TO SCARCITY

2005 Fleer Platinum Nameplates Dual Patch Autograph Platinum

OVERALL AU ODDS 1:144 H, AU-GU 1:48 R
STATED PRINT RUN 1 SERIAL #'d SET
NO PRICING DUE TO SCARCITY
SKJR Scott Kazmir
Jose Reyes
SRMB Scott Rolen
Marlon Byrd

2001 Fleer Premium

The 2001 Fleer Premium product was released in early April, 2001 and features a 235-card base set that was broken into tiers as follows: Base Veterans (1-200), and Prospects (201-235) which were individually serial numbered to 1999. Please note that cards 231-235 all packed out as exchange cards and needed to have been exchanged to Fleer by 5/01/02. Each pack contained eight cards and carried a suggested retail price of $3.99.

COMPSET w/o SP's (200) 12.50 30.00
COMMON CARD (1-200) .15 .40
COMMON (201-230) 2.00 5.00
COMMON (231-235) 3.00 8.00
1 Cal Ripken 1.25 3.00
2 Derek Jeter 1.00 2.50
3 Edgardo Alfonzo .15 .40
4 Luis Castillo .15 .40
5 Mike Lieberthal .15 .40
6 Kazuhiro Sasaki .15 .40
7 Jeff Kent .15 .40
8 Eric Karros .15 .40
9 Tom Glavine .25 .60
10 Jeromy Burnitz .15 .40
11 Travis Fryman .15 .40
12 Ron Coomer .15 .40
13 Jeff D'Amico .15 .40
14 Carlos Febles .15 .40
15 Kevin Brown .15 .40
16 Deivi Cruz .15 .40
17 Tino Martinez .25 .60
18 Bobby Abreu .15 .40
19 Roger Clemens .75 2.00
20 Jeffrey Hammonds .15 .40
21 Peter Bergeron .15 .40
22 Ray Lankford .15 .40
23 Scott Rolen .25 .60
24 Jermaine Dye .15 .40
25 Rusty Greer .15 .40
26 Frank Thomas .40 1.00
27 Jeff Bagwell .25 .60
28 Cliff Floyd .15 .40
29 Chris Singleton .15 .40
30 Steve Finley .15 .40
31 Orlando Hernandez .15 .40
32 Tom Goodwin .15 .40
33 Larry Walker .15 .40
34 Mike Sweeney .15 .40
35 Tim Hudson .15 .40
36 Kerry Wood .15 .40
37 Mike Lowell .15 .40
38 Andruw Jones .30 .75
39 Alex Gonzalez .15 .40
40 Juan Gonzalez .30 .75
41 J.D. Drew .15 .40
42 Mark McLemore .15 .40
43 Royce Clayton .15 .40
44 Paul O'Neill .25 .60
45 Carlos Beltran .15 .40
46 Phil Nevin .15 .40
47 Rondell White .15 .40
48 Gerald Williams .15 .40
49 Geoff Jenkins .15 .40
50 Marvin Benard .15 .40
51 Alex Rodriguez .60 1.50
52 Moises Alou .15 .40
53 Mike Lansing .15 .40
54 Omar Vizquel .25 .60
55 Eric Chavez .15 .40
56 Mark Quinn .15 .40
57 Mike Lamb .15 .40
58 Rick Ankiel .15 .40
59 Lance Berkman .15 .40
60 Jeff Conine .15 .40
61 B.J. Surhoff .15 .40
62 Todd Helton .25 .60
63 J.T. Snow .15 .40
64 John VanderWal .15 .40
65 Johnny Damon .25 .60
66 Bobby Higginson .15 .40
67 Carlos Delgado .30 .75
68 Shawn Green .15 .40
69 Mike Redmond .15 .40
70 Mike Piazza .60 1.50
71 Adrian Beltre .15 .40
72 Juan Encarnacion .15 .40
73 Chipper Jones .40 1.00
74 Garret Anderson .15 .40
75 Paul Konerko .15 .40
76 Barry Larkin .25 .60
77 Tony Gwynn .50 1.25
78 Rafael Palmeiro .25 .60
79 Randy Johnson .40 1.00
80 Mark Grace .30 .75
81 Javy Lopez .15 .40
82 Gabe Kapler .15 .40
83 Henry Rodriguez .15 .40
84 Raul Mondesi .15 .40
85 Adam Piatt .15 .40
86 Marquis Grissom .15 .40
87 Charles Johnson .15 .40
88 Sean Casey .15 .40
89 Manny Ramirez .25 .60
90 Curt Schilling .15 .40
91 Fernando Tatis .15 .40
92 Derek Bell .15 .40
93 Tony Clark .15 .40
94 Homer Bush .15 .40
95 Nomar Garciaparra .60 1.50
96 Vinny Castilla .15 .40
97 Ben Davis .15 .40
98 Carl Everett .15 .40
99 Damion Easley .15 .40
100 Craig Biggio .25 .60
101 Todd Hollandsworth .15 .40
102 Jay Payton .15 .40
103 Gary Sheffield .15 .40
104 Sandy Alomar Jr. .15 .40
105 Doug Glanville .15 .40
106 Barry Bonds 1.00 2.50
107 Tim Salmon .25 .60
108 Terrence Long .15 .40
109 Jorge Posada .25 .60
110 Jose Offerman .15 .40
111 Edgar Martinez .25 .60
112 Jeremy Giambi .15 .40
113 Dean Palmer .15 .40
114 Roberto Alomar .30 .75
115 Aaron Boone .15 .40
116 Adam Kennedy .15 .40
117 Joe Randa .15 .40
118 Jose Vidro .15 .40
119 Tony Batista .15 .40
120 Kevin Young .15 .40
121 Preston Wilson .15 .40
122 Jason Kendall .15 .40
123 Mark Kotsay .15 .40
124 Timo Perez .15 .40
125 Eric Young .15 .40
126 Greg Maddux .60 1.50
127 Richard Hidalgo .15 .40
128 Brian Giles .15 .40
129 Fred McGriff .25 .60
130 Troy Glaus .15 .40
131 Todd Walker .15 .40
132 Brady Anderson .15 .40
133 Jim Edmonds .15 .40
134 Ben Grieve .15 .40
135 Greg Vaughn .15 .40
136 Robin Ventura .15 .40
137 Sammy Sosa .40 1.00
138 Rich Aurilia .15 .40
139 Jose Valentin .15 .40
140 Trot Nixon .15 .40
141 Troy Percival .15 .40
142 Bernie Williams .25 .60
143 Warren Morris .15 .40
144 Jacque Jones .15 .40
145 Danny Bautista .15 .40
146 A.J. Pierzynski .15 .40
147 Mark McGwire 1.00 2.50
148 Rafael Furcal .15 .40
149 Ray Durham .15 .40
150 Mike Mussina .30 .75
151 Jay Bell .15 .40
152 David Wells .15 .40
153 Ken Caminiti .15 .40
154 Jim Thome .25 .60
155 Ivan Rodriguez .25 .60
156 Milton Bradley .15 .40
157 Ken Griffey Jr. .60 1.50
158 Al Leiter .15 .40
159 Corey Koskie .15 .40
160 Shannon Stewart .15 .40
161 Mo Vaughn .15 .40
162 Pedro Martinez .25 .60
163 Todd Hundley .15 .40
164 Darin Erstad .30 .75
165 Ruben Rivera .15 .40
166 Richie Sexson .15 .40
167 Andres Galarraga .15 .40
168 Darryl Kile .15 .40
169 Jose Cruz Jr. .15 .40
170 David Justice .15 .40
171 Vladimir Guerrero .40 1.00
172 Jeff Cirillo .15 .40
173 John Olerud .15 .40
174 Devon White .15 .40
175 Ron Belliard .15 .40
176 Pokey Reese .15 .40
177 Mike Hampton .15 .40
178 David Ortiz .40 1.00
179 Magglio Ordonez .15 .40
180 Ruben Mateo .15 .40
181 Carlos Lee .15 .40
182 Matt Williams .15 .40
183 Miguel Tejada .15 .40
184 Scott Elarton .15 .40
185 Bret Boone .15 .40
186 Pat Burrell .15 .40
187 Brad Radke .15 .40
188 Brian Jordan .15 .40
189 Matt Lawton .15 .40
190 Al Martin .15 .40
191 Albert Belle .15 .40
192 Tony Womack .15 .40
193 Roger Cedeno .15 .40
194 Travis Lee .15 .40
195 Dmitri Young .15 .40
196 Jay Buhner .15 .40
197 Jason Giambi .30 .75
198 Jason Tyner .15 .40
199 Ben Petrick .15 .40
200 Jose Canseco .30 .75
201 Nick Johnson 2.00 5.00
202 Jace Brewer 2.00 5.00
203 Ryan Freel RC 2.00 5.00
204 Jaisen Randolph RC 2.00 5.00
205 Marcus Giles 2.00 5.00
206 Claudio Vargas RC 2.00 5.00
207 Brian Cole 2.00 5.00
208 Scott Hodges 2.00 5.00
209 Winston Abreu RC 2.00 5.00
210 Shea Hillenbrand 2.00 5.00
211 Larry Barnes 2.00 5.00
212 Paul Phillips RC 2.00 5.00
213 Pedro Santana RC 2.00 5.00
214 Ivanon Coffie 2.00 5.00
215 Junior Spivey RC 3.00 8.00
216 Donzell McDonald 2.00 5.00
217 Vernon Wells 2.00 5.00
218 Corey Patterson 2.00 5.00
219 Sang-Hoon Lee 2.00 5.00
220 Jack Cust 2.00 5.00
221 Jason Romano 2.00 5.00
222 Jack Wilson RC 3.00 8.00
223 Adam Everett 2.00 5.00
224 Esix Snead RC 2.00 5.00
225 Jason Hart 2.00 5.00
226 Joe Lawrence 2.00 5.00
227 Brandon Inge 2.00 5.00
228 Alex Escobar 2.00 5.00
229 Abraham Nunez 2.00 5.00
230 Jared Sandberg 2.00 5.00
231 Ichiro Suzuki RC 15.00 40.00
232 Tsuyoshi Shinjo RC 4.00 10.00
233 Albert Pujols RC 60.00 120.00
234 Wilson Betemit RC 4.00 10.00
235 Drew Henson RC 4.00 10.00
MM1 D.Jeter MM/1995 5.00 12.00
NNO Derek Jeter MM AU/95 60.00 120.00

2001 Fleer Premium Star Ruby

Randomly inserted into packs, this set is a parallel of the first 230 cards of the 2001 Fleer Premium base set. Each card was produced with ruby-red foil stamping and are individually serial numbered to 125.

*RUBY 1-200: 5X TO 12X BASE HI
*RUBY 201-230: .3X TO .8X BASE HI

2001 Fleer Premium A Time for Heroes

Randomly inserted into packs at one in 20, this 20-card insert set pays homage to the heroes who have emerged in the modern game Card backs carry an "ATFH" prefix.

COMPLETE SET (20) 40.00 80.00
ATFH1 Darin Erstad .75 2.00
ATFH2 Alex Rodriguez 2.50 6.00
ATFH3 Shawn Green .75 2.00
ATFH4 Jeff Bagwell 1.00 2.50
ATFH5 Sammy Sosa 1.50 4.00
ATFH6 Derek Jeter 4.00 10.00
ATFH7 Nomar Garciaparra 2.50 6.00
ATFH8 Carlos Delgado .75 2.00
ATFH9 Pat Burrell .75 2.00
ATFH10 Tony Gwynn 2.00 5.00
ATFH11 Chipper Jones 1.50 4.00
ATFH12 Jason Giambi .75 2.00
ATFH13 Magglio Ordonez .75 2.00
ATFH14 Troy Glaus .75 2.00
ATFH15 Ivan Rodriguez 1.00 2.50
ATFH16 Andruw Jones 1.00 2.50
ATFH17 Vladimir Guerrero 1.50 4.00
ATFH18 Ken Griffey Jr. 2.50 6.00
ATFH19 J.D. Drew .75 2.00
ATFH20 Todd Helton 1.00 2.50

2001 Fleer Premium Brother Wood

Randomly inserted into packs at one in 108, this 9-card insert set features actual pieces of game-used bats. Card backs carry a "BW" prefix.

BW1 Vladimir Guerrero 6.00 15.00
BW2 Andruw Jones 6.00 15.00
BW3 Corey Patterson 4.00 10.00

BW4 Magglio Ordonez 4.00 10.00
BW5 Jason Giambi 4.00 10.00
BW6 Rafael Palmeiro 6.00 15.00
BW7 Eric Chavez 4.00 10.00
BW8 Pat Burrell 4.00 10.00
BW9 Adrian Beltre 4.00 10.00

2001 Fleer Premium Decades of Excellence

Randomly inserted into packs at one in 12, this 50-card insert spans 80 years of baseball, and pays homage to the best players from each decade. Card backs carry a "DE" prefix. The Willie Mays card was not supposed to exist but several copies have been found in packs and is tagged an SP without pricing in our checklist.

DE1 Lou Gehrig 8.00 20.00
Babe Ruth
DE2 Lloyd Waner 1.25 3.00
DE3 Jimmie Foxx 2.00 5.00
DE4 Hank Greenberg 2.00 5.00
DE5 Ted Williams UER 5.00 12.00
DE6 Johnny Mize 1.25 3.00
DE7 Enos Slaughter 1.25 3.00
DE8 Jackie Robinson 2.00 5.00
DE9 Stan Musial 3.00 8.00
DE10 Duke Snider 1.25 3.00
DE11 Eddie Mathews 2.00 5.00
DE12 Roy Campanella 2.00 5.00
DE13 Yogi Berra 2.00 5.00
DE14 Pee Wee Reese 2.00 5.00
DE15 Phil Rizzuto 2.00 5.00
DE16 Al Kaline 2.00 5.00
DE17 Willie Mays SP
DE18 Frank Howard 1.25 3.00
DE19 Roberto Clemente 6.00 15.00
DE20 Bob Gibson 1.25 3.00
DE21 Roger Maris 2.00 5.00
DE22 Don Drysdale 1.25 3.00
DE23 Maury Wills 1.25 3.00
DE24 Tom Seaver 1.25 3.00
DE25 Reggie Jackson 1.25 3.00
DE26 Johnny Bench 2.00 5.00
DE27 Carlton Fisk 1.25 3.00
DE28 Rod Carew 1.25 3.00
DE29 Steve Carlton 1.25 3.00
DE30 Mike Schmidt 5.00 12.00
DE31 Nolan Ryan 6.00 15.00
DE32 Rickey Henderson 2.00 5.00
DE33 Roger Clemens 4.00 10.00
DE34 Don Mattingly 5.00 12.00
DE35 George Brett 5.00 12.00
DE36 Greg Maddux 3.00 8.00
DE37 Cal Ripken 6.00 15.00
DE38 Chipper Jones 2.00 5.00
DE39 Barry Bonds 5.00 12.00
DE40 Ivan Rodriguez 1.25 3.00
DE41 Mark McGwire 6.00 15.00
Sammy Sosa
DE42 Ken Griffey Jr. 3.00 8.00
DE43 Tony Gwynn 2.50 6.00
DE44 Vladimir Guerrero 2.00 5.00
DE45 Shawn Green 1.25 3.00
DE46 Alex Rodriguez 5.00 12.00
Derek Jeter
Nomar Garciaparra
DE47 Pat Burrell 1.25 3.00
DE48 Rick Ankiel 1.25 3.00
DE49 Eric Chavez 1.25 3.00
DE50 Troy Glaus 1.25 3.00

2001 Fleer Premium Decades of Excellence Autograph

Randomly inserted into hobby packs, this 20-card insert set is a partial parallel of the 2001 Fleer Premium Decades of Excellence insert set. The set features authentic autographs from the player depicted on each card. Please note that each card is serial numbered to the year in which the player made his major league debut.

1 Rick Ankiel/99 20.00 50.00
2 Johnny Bench/67 40.00 80.00
3 Barry Bonds/86 100.00 175.00
4 George Brett/73 60.00 120.00
5 Rod Carew/67 30.00 60.00
6 Steve Carlton/65 15.00 40.00
7 Eric Chavez/98 15.00 40.00
8 Carlton Fisk/69 30.00 60.00
9 Bob Gibson/59 30.00 60.00
10 Tony Gwynn/82 30.00 60.00
11 Reggie Jackson/67 40.00 80.00
12 Chipper Jones/93 40.00 80.00
13 Al Kaline/53 40.00 80.00
14 Don Mattingly/82 60.00 120.00
15 Cal Ripken/81 75.00 150.00
16 Nolan Ryan/66 75.00 150.00
17 Mike Schmidt/72 60.00 120.00
18 Tom Seaver/67 30.00 60.00
19 Enos Slaughter/38 30.00 60.00
20 Maury Wills/59 15.00 40.00

2001 Fleer Premium Decades of Excellence Memorabilia

Randomly inserted into hobby packs at one in 217, this 21-card insert is a partial parallel of the 2001 Fleer Premium Decades of Excellence insert. Each of these cards features either a swatch of game-used jersey or a sliver of game-used bat. Please note that the Carlton Fisk and Roger Maris cards feature swatches of game-used uniform. The cards have been listed below in alphabetical order for convenience. Though the cards lack actual serial-numbering, representatives at Fleer publicly announced specific print runs on several short-printed cards within this set. That information is detailed within our checklist.

1 Rick Ankiel Jsy 4.00 10.00
2 Barry Bonds Jsy 30.00 60.00
3 Pat Burrell Jsy 6.00 15.00
4 Roy Campanella 20.00 50.00
Bat SP/50
5 Eric Chavez Bat 6.00 15.00
6 R.Clemente Bat SP/50 50.00 100.00
7 Carlton Fisk Uni 10.00 25.00
8 Jimmie Foxx Bat SP/50 50.00 100.00
9 Shawn Green Bat 6.00 15.00
10 Tony Gwynn Jsy 10.00 25.00
11 Reggie Jackson Jsy 10.00 25.00
12 Greg Maddux Jsy 10.00 25.00
13 Roger Maris Uni 30.00 60.00
14 Pee Wee Reese Jsy 10.00 25.00
15 Cal Ripken Jsy SP/50
16 Ivan Rodriguez Bat 10.00 25.00
17 Nolan Ryan Jsy
18 Mike Schmidt Jsy
19 Tom Seaver Jsy
20 Duke Snider Bat 10.00 25.00
21 Ted Williams 50.00 100.00
Jsy SP/50

2001 Fleer Premium Diamond Dominators Game Jersey

Randomly inserted into packs at one in 51, this 14-card insert features swatches of game-used jerseys of the players depicted below. Card backs carry a "DD" prefix.

DD1 Troy Glaus 4.00 10.00
DD2 Darin Erstad 4.00 10.00
DD3 J.D. Drew 4.00 10.00
DD4 Barry Bonds 15.00 40.00
DD5 Roger Clemens 12.50 30.00
DD6 Vladimir Guerrero 6.00 15.00
DD7 Tony Gwynn 8.00 20.00
DD8 Greg Maddux 10.00 25.00
DD9 Cal Ripken 20.00 50.00
DD10 Ivan Rodriguez 6.00 15.00
DD11 Frank Thomas 6.00 15.00
DD12 Bernie Williams 6.00 15.00
DD13 Jeromy Burnitz 4.00 10.00
DD14 Juan Gonzalez 4.00 10.00

2001 Fleer Premium Diamond Patches

Randomly inserted into packs, this 14-card insert features swatches of jersey patches of the players depicted below. Card backs carry a "DD" prefix. Please note that there were only 100 of each card produced.

DD1 Troy Glaus 20.00 50.00
DD2 Darin-Erstad 20.00 50.00
DD3 J.D. Drew 20.00 50.00
DD4 Barry Bonds 40.00 80.00
DD5 Roger Clemens 50.00 100.00
DD6 Vladimir Guerrero 40.00 80.00
DD7 Tony Gwynn 40.00 80.00
DD8 Greg Maddux 40.00 80.00
DD9 Cal Ripken 60.00 120.00
DD10 Ivan Rodriguez 40.00 80.00
DD11 Frank Thomas 40.00 80.00
DD12 Bernie Williams 40.00 80.00
DD13 Jeromy Burnitz 20.00 50.00
DD14 Juan Gonzalez 20.00 50.00

2001 Fleer Premium Grip It and Rip It

Randomly inserted into packs at one in 6, this 15-card insert pairs up teammates that get the job done with

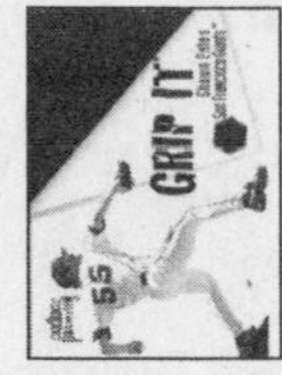

their ability to catch and hit . Card backs carry a "GRP" prefix.

COMPLETE SET (15) 8.00 20.00
GRP1 Roger Clemens 1.25 3.00
Derek Jeter
GRP2 Scott Rolen .40 1.00
Pat Burrell
GRP3 Greg Maddux .75 2.00
Andruw Jones
GRP4 Shannon Stewart .40 1.00
Carlos Delgado
GRP5 Shawn Estes 1.25 3.00
Barry Bonds
GRP6 Cal Eldred .50 1.25
Frank Thomas
GRP7 Mark McGwire 1.25 3.00
Jim Edmonds
GRP8 Jose Vidro .50 1.25
Vladimir Guerrero
GRP9 Pedro Martinez .75 2.00
Nomar Garciaparra
GRP10 Tom Glavine .50 1.25
Chipper Jones
GRP11 Ken Griffey Jr. .75 2.00
Sean Casey
GRP12 Jeff Bagwell .40 1.00
Moises Alou
GRP13 Troy Glaus .40 1.00
Darin Erstad
GRP14 Mike Piazza .75 2.00
Robin Ventura
GRP15 Eric Chavez .40 1.00
Jason Giambi

2001 Fleer Premium Grip It and Rip It Plus

Randomly inserted into hobby packs, this 15-card set is a complete parallel of the 2001 Fleer Premium Grip It and Rip It insert. Each of these cards feature either a swatch of game-used base and bat, or a swatch of game-used ball and bat. Please note that each Base/Bat card is serial numbered to 200, while each Ball/Bat card is serial numbered to 100.

GRP1 Roger Clemens Ball 60.00 120.00
Derek Jeter Bat
GRP2 Scott Rolen Base 10.00 25.00
Pat Burrell Bat/200
GRP3 Greg Maddux Ball 40.00 80.00
Andruw Jones Bat/100
GRP4 Shan. Stewart Base 6.00 15.00
Carlos Delgado Bat
GRP5 Shawn Estes 50.00 100.00
Barry Bonds
GRP6 Cal Eldred 10.00 25.00
Frank Thomas
GRP7 Mark McGwire Ball 40.00 80.00
Jim Edmonds Bat/100
GRP8 Jose Vidro Base 10.00 25.00
Vladimir Guerrero Bat/200
GRP9 Pedro Martinez 40.00 80.00
Nomar Garciaparra
GRP10 Tom Glavine 10.00 25.00
Chipper Jones
GRP11 K. Griffey Jr. Base 15.00 40.00
Sean Casey Bat/200
GRP12 Jeff Bagwell Base 10.00 25.00
Moises Alou Bat/200
GRP13 Troy Glaus Base 6.00 15.00
Darin Erstad Bat/200
GRP14 Mike Piazza Ball 40.00 80.00
Robin Ventura Bat
GRP15 Eric Chavez Base 6.00 15.00
Jason Giambi Bat/200

2001 Fleer Premium Heroes Game Jersey

Randomly inserted into hobby packs at one in 101, this 10-card insert is a partial parallel of the 2001 Fleer Premium A Time For Heroes insert. Each of these cards features a swatch of game-used jersey. The cards are listed below in alphabetical order for convenience.

1 Pat Burrell 4.00 10.00
2 J.D. Drew 4.00 10.00
3 Jason Giambi 4.00 10.00
4 Troy Glaus 4.00 10.00
5 Shawn Green 4.00 10.00
6 Todd Helton 6.00 15.00
7 Derek Jeter 20.00 50.00
8 Andruw Jones 6.00 15.00
9 Chipper Jones 6.00 15.00
10 Ivan Rodriguez 6.00 15.00

2001 Fleer Premium Home Field Advantage

Randomly inserted into packs at one in 72 Hobby, and 1:144 Retail this 15-card insert features players with their home field in the background. Card backs carry a "HFA" prefix.

COMPLETE SET (15)	100.00	200.00
HFA1 Mike Piazza	5.00	12.00
HFA2 Derek Jeter	8.00	20.00
HFA3 Ken Griffey Jr.	5.00	12.00
HFA4 Carlos Delgado	2.50	6.00
HFA5 Chipper Jones	3.00	8.00
HFA6 Alex Rodriguez	5.00	12.00
HFA7 Sammy Sosa	3.00	8.00
HFA8 Scott Rolen	2.50	6.00
HFA9 Nomar Garciaparra	5.00	12.00
HFA10 Todd Helton	2.50	6.00
HFA11 Vladimir Guerrero	3.00	8.00
HFA12 Jeff Bagwell	2.50	6.00
HFA13 Barry Bonds	8.00	20.00
HFA14 Cal Ripken	10.00	25.00
HFA15 Mark McGwire	8.00	20.00

2001 Fleer Premium Home Field Advantage Game Wall

Randomly inserted into packs, this 15-card insert is a complete parallel of the 2001 Fleer Premium Home Field Advantage insert. Each of these cards feature a swatch of actual game-used wall. Card backs carry a "HFA" prefix. 100 serial-numbered sets were produced.

HFA1 Mike Piazza	15.00	40.00
HFA2 Derek Jeter	25.00	60.00
HFA3 Ken Griffey Jr.	15.00	40.00
HFA4 Carlos Delgado	6.00	15.00
HFA5 Chipper Jones	10.00	25.00
HFA6 Alex Rodriguez	15.00	40.00
HFA7 Sammy Sosa	10.00	25.00
HFA8 Scott Rolen	10.00	25.00
HFA9 Nomar Garciaparra	15.00	40.00
HFA10 Todd Helton	10.00	25.00
HFA11 Vladimir Guerrero	10.00	25.00
HFA12 Jeff Bagwell	10.00	25.00
HFA13 Barry Bonds	25.00	60.00
HFA14 Cal Ripken	30.00	80.00
HFA15 Mark McGwire	30.00	80.00

2001 Fleer Premium Performers Game Base

Randomly inserted into hobby packs, this 15-card insert set is a complete parallel of the 2001 Fleer Premium Solid Performers insert. Each of these cards feature a swatch of game-used base. Card backs carry a "SP" prefix. Also note that there were only 150 of each card produced.

SP1 Mark McGwire	30.00	80.00
SP2 Alex Rodriguez	15.00	40.00
SP3 Nomar Garciaparra	12.50	30.00
SP4 Derek Jeter	20.00	50.00
SP5 Vladimir Guerrero	8.00	20.00
SP6 Todd Helton	8.00	20.00
SP7 Chipper Jones	8.00	20.00
SP8 Mike Piazza	12.50	30.00
SP9 Ivan Rodriguez	8.00	20.00
SP10 Tony Gwynn	12.50	30.00
SP11 Cal Ripken	25.00	60.00
SP12 Barry Bonds	20.00	50.00
SP13 Jeff Bagwell	8.00	20.00
SP14 Ken Griffey Jr.	12.50	30.00
SP15 Sammy Sosa	8.00	20.00

2001 Fleer Premium Solid Performers

Randomly inserted into packs at one in 20, this 15-card insert features players that ballclubs build their franchise around. Card backs carry a "SP" prefix.

COMPLETE SET (15)	40.00	80.00
SP1 Mark McGwire	3.00	8.00
SP2 Alex Rodriguez	2.00	5.00
SP3 Nomar Garciaparra	2.00	5.00
SP4 Derek Jeter	3.00	8.00
SP5 Vladimir Guerrero	1.25	3.00
SP6 Todd Helton	1.25	3.00
SP7 Chipper Jones	1.25	3.00
SP8 Mike Piazza	2.00	5.00
SP9 Ivan Rodriguez	1.25	3.00
SP10 Tony Gwynn	1.50	4.00
SP11 Cal Ripken	4.00	10.00
SP12 Barry Bonds	3.00	8.00
SP13 Jeff Bagwell	1.25	3.00
SP14 Ken Griffey Jr.	2.00	5.00
SP15 Sammy Sosa	1.25	3.00

2002 Fleer Premium

This 240 card set was released in early spring, 2002. This set was issued in 10 card packs which were issued 24 packs to a box. Cards numbered from 201 through 240 featured leading prospects entering the 2002 season and were seeded at stated odds of one in two packs. In late May, Fleer announced their "Player to be Named" program, whereby collectors could send in 10 copies of any of the short-printed prospect cards (201-240) and in turn receive ten new prospect cards (241-250) each serial numbered to 2002. The "Player to be Named" cards were actually released in October, 2002.

COMP.MASTER SET (250)	50.00	120.00
COMPLETE SET (240)	30.00	80.00
COMP.SET w/o SP'S (200)	12.50	30.00
COMP.UPDATE SET (10)	15.00	40.00
COMMON CARD (1-200)	.15	.40
COMMON CARD (201-240)	.75	2.00
COMMON CARD (241-250)	1.50	4.00
1 Garret Anderson	.15	.40
2 Derek Jeter	1.00	2.50
3 Ken Griffey Jr.	.60	1.50
4 Luis Castillo	.15	.40
5 Richie Sexson	.15	.40
6 Mike Mussina	.25	.60
7 Rickey Henderson	.40	1.00
8 Bud Smith	.15	.40
9 David Eckstein	.15	.40
10 Nomar Garciaparra	.60	1.50
11 Barry Larkin	.25	.60
12 Cliff Floyd	.15	.40
13 Ben Sheets	.15	.40
14 Jorge Posada	.25	.60
15 Phil Nevin	.15	.40
16 Fernando Vina	.15	.40
17 Darin Erstad	.15	.40
18 Shea Hillenbrand	.15	.40
19 Todd Walker	.15	.40
20 Charles Johnson	.15	.40
21 Cristian Guzman	.15	.40
22 Mariano Rivera	.40	1.00
23 Bubba Trammell	.15	.40
24 Brent Abernathy	.15	.40
25 Troy Glaus	.15	.40
26 Pedro Martinez	.25	.60
27 Dmitri Young	.15	.40
28 Derrek Lee	.25	.60
29 Torii Hunter	.15	.40
30 Alfonso Soriano	.15	.40
31 Rich Aurilia	.15	.40
32 Ben Grieve	.15	.40
33 Tim Salmon	.25	.60
34 Trot Nixon	.15	.40
35 Roberto Alomar	.25	.60
36 Mike Lowell	.15	.40
37 Jacque Jones	.15	.40
38 Bernie Williams	.25	.60
39 Barry Bonds	1.00	2.50
40 Toby Hall	.15	.40
41 Mo Vaughn	.15	.40
42 Hideo Nomo	.40	1.00
43 Travis Fryman	.15	.40
44 Preston Wilson	.15	.40
45 Corey Koskie	.15	.40
46 Eric Chavez	.15	.40
47 Andres Galarraga	.15	.40
48 Greg Vaughn	.15	.40
49 Shawn Wooten	.15	.40
50 Manny Ramirez	.25	.60
51 Juan Gonzalez	.15	.40
52 Moises Alou	.15	.40
53 Joe Mays	.15	.40
54 Johnny Damon	.25	.60
55 Jeff Kent	.15	.40
56 Frank Catalanotto	.15	.40
57 Steve Finley	.15	.40
58 Jason Varitek	.40	1.00
59 Kenny Lofton	.15	.40
60 Jeff Bagwell	.25	.60
61 Doug Mientkiewicz	.15	.40
62 Jermaine Dye	.15	.40
63 John Vander Wal	.15	.40
64 Gabe Kapler	.15	.40
65 Luis Gonzalez	.15	.40
66 Jon Lieber	.15	.40
67 C.C. Sabathia	.15	.40
68 Lance Berkman	.15	.40
69 Eric Milton	.15	.40
70 Jason Giambi Yankees	.15	.40
71 Ichiro Suzuki	.75	2.00
72 Rafael Palmeiro	.25	.60
73 Mark Grace	.25	.60
74 Fred McGriff	.25	.60
75 Jim Thome	.25	.60
76 Craig Biggio	.25	.60
77 A.J. Pierzynski	.15	.40
78 Ramon Hernandez	.15	.40
79 Paul Abbott	.15	.40
80 Alex Rodriguez	.60	1.50
81 Randy Johnson	.40	1.00
82 Corey Patterson	.15	.40
83 Omar Vizquel	.25	.60
84 Richard Hidalgo	.15	.40
85 Luis Rivas	.15	.40
86 Tim Hudson	.15	.40
87 Bret Boone	.15	.40
88 Ivan Rodriguez	.25	.60
89 Junior Spivey	.15	.40
90 Sammy Sosa	.40	1.00
91 Jeff Cirillo	.15	.40
92 Roy Oswalt	.15	.40
93 Orlando Cabrera	.15	.40
94 Terrence Long	.15	.40
95 Mike Cameron	.15	.40
96 Homer Bush	.15	.40
97 Reggie Sanders	.15	.40
98 Rondell White	.15	.40
99 Mike Hampton	.15	.40
100 Carlos Beltran	.15	.40
101 Vladimir Guerrero	.40	1.00
102 Miguel Tejada	.15	.40
103 Freddy Garcia	.15	.40
104 Jose Cruz Jr.	.15	.40
105 Curt Schilling	.15	.40
106 Kerry Wood	.15	.40
107 Todd Helton	.25	.60
108 Neifi Perez	.15	.40
109 Javier Vazquez	.15	.40
110 Barry Zito	.15	.40
111 Edgar Martinez	.25	.60
112 Carlos Delgado	.15	.40
113 Matt Williams	.15	.40
114 Eric Young	.15	.40
115 Alex Ochoa	.15	.40
116 Mark Quinn	.15	.40
117 Jose Vidro	.15	.40
118 Bobby Abreu	.15	.40
119 David Bell	.15	.40
120 Brad Fullmer	.15	.40
121 Rafael Furcal	.15	.40
122 Ray Durham	.15	.40
123 Jose Ortiz	.15	.40
124 Joe Randa	.15	.40
125 Edgardo Alfonzo	.15	.40
126 Marlon Anderson	.15	.40
127 Jamie Moyer	.15	.40
128 Alex Gonzalez	.15	.40
129 Marcus Giles	.15	.40
130 Keith Foulke	.15	.40
131 Juan Pierre	.15	.40
132 Mike Sweeney	.15	.40
133 Matt Lawton	.15	.40
134 Pat Burrell	.15	.40
135 John Olerud	.15	.40
136 Raul Mondesi	.15	.40
137 Tom Glavine	.25	.60
138 Paul Konerko	.15	.40
139 Larry Walker	.15	.40
140 Adrian Beltre	.15	.40
141 Al Leiter	.15	.40
142 Mike Lieberthal	.15	.40
143 Kazuhiro Sasaki	.15	.40
144 Shannon Stewart	.15	.40
145 Andruw Jones	.25	.60
146 Carlos Lee	.15	.40
147 Roger Cedeno	.15	.40
148 Kevin Brown	.15	.40
149 Jay Payton	.15	.40
150 Scott Rolen	.25	.60
151 J.D. Drew	.15	.40
152 Chipper Jones	.40	1.00
153 Magglio Ordonez	.15	.40
154 Tony Clark	.15	.40
155 Shawn Green	.15	.40
156 Mike Piazza	.60	1.50
157 Jimmy Rollins	.15	.40
158 Jim Edmonds	.15	.40
159 Javy Lopez	.15	.40
160 Chris Singleton	.15	.40
161 Juan Encarnacion	.15	.40
162 Eric Karros	.15	.40
163 Tsuyoshi Shinjo	.15	.40
164 Brian Giles	.15	.40
165 Darryl Kile	.15	.40
166 Greg Maddux	.60	1.50
167 Frank Thomas	.40	1.00
168 Shane Halter	.15	.40
169 Paul LoDuca	.15	.40
170 Robin Ventura	.15	.40
171 Jason Kendall	.15	.40
172 Jason Hart	.15	.40
173 Brady Anderson	.15	.40
174 Jose Valentin	.15	.40
175 Bobby Higginson	.15	.40
176 Gary Sheffield	.15	.40
177 Roger Clemens	.75	2.00
178 Aramis Ramirez	.15	.40
179 Matt Morris	.15	.40
180 Jeff Conine	.15	.40
181 Aaron Boone	.15	.40
182 Jose Macias	.15	.40
183 Jeromy Burnitz	.15	.40
184 Carl Everett	.15	.40
185 Trevor Hoffman	.15	.40
186 Placido Polanco	.15	.40
187 Jay Gibbons	.15	.40
188 Sean Casey	.15	.40
189 Josh Beckett	.15	.40
190 Jeffrey Hammonds	.15	.40
191 Chuck Knoblauch	.15	.40
192 Ryan Klesko	.15	.40
193 Albert Pujols	.75	2.00
194 Chris Richard	.15	.40
195 Adam Dunn	.15	.40
196 A.J. Burnett	.15	.40
197 Geoff Jenkins	.15	.40
198 Tino Martinez	.25	.60
199 Ray Lankford	.15	.40
200 Edgar Renteria	.15	.40
201 Eric Cyr PROS	.75	2.00
202 Travis Phelps PROS	.75	2.00
203 Rick Bauer PROS	.75	2.00
204 Mark Prior PROS	1.50	4.00
205 Wilson Betemit PROS	.75	2.00
206 Dewon Brazelton PROS	.75	2.00
207 Cody Ransom PROS	.75	2.00
208 Donnie Bridges PROS	.75	2.00
209 Justin Duchscherer PROS	.75	2.00
210 Nate Cornejo PROS	.75	2.00
211 Jason Romano PROS	.75	2.00
212 Juan Cruz PROS	.75	2.00
213 Pedro Santana PROS	.75	2.00
214 Ryan Drese PROS	.75	2.00
215 Bert Snow PROS	.75	2.00
216 Nate Frese PROS	.75	2.00
217 Rafael Soriano PROS	.75	2.00
218 Franklin Nunez PROS RC	.75	2.00
219 Tim Spooneybarger PROS	.75	2.00
220 Willie Harris PROS	.75	2.00
221 Billy Sylvester PROS	.75	2.00
222 Carlos Hernandez PROS	.75	2.00
223 Mark Teixeira PROS	1.50	4.00
224 Adrian Hernandez PROS	.75	2.00
225 Andres Torres PROS	.75	2.00
226 Marlon Byrd PROS	.75	2.00
227 Juan Rivera PROS	.75	2.00
228 Adam Johnson PROS	.75	2.00
229 Justin Kaye PROS	.75	2.00
230 Kyle Kessel PROS	.75	2.00
231 Horacio Ramirez PROS	.75	2.00
232 Brandon Larson PROS	.75	2.00
233 Luis Lopez PROS	.75	2.00
234 Rob Mackowiak PROS	.75	2.00
235 Henry Mateo PROS	.75	2.00
236 Corky Miller PROS	.75	2.00
237 Greg Miller PROS	.75	2.00
238 Dustan Mohr PROS	.75	2.00
239 Bill Ortega PROS	.75	2.00
240 Billy Hall PROS	.75	2.00
241 Kazuhisa Ishii UPD RC	2.00	5.00
242 So Taguchi UPD RC	2.00	5.00
243 Takahito Nomura UPD RC	1.50	4.00
244 Satoru Komiyama UPD RC	1.50	4.00
245 Jorge Padilla UPD RC	1.50	4.00
246 Anastacio Martinez UPD RC	1.50	4.00
247 Rodrigo Rosario UPD RC	1.50	4.00
248 Ben Howard UPD RC	1.50	4.00
249 Reed Johnson UPD RC	2.00	5.00
250 Mike Crudale UPD RC	1.50	4.00
P2 Derek Jeter Promo	1.00	2.50

2002 Fleer Premium Star Ruby

Randomly inserted into packs, this is a parallel of the 2002 Fleer Premium set. These cards were serial numbered to a stated print run of 125 sets. Cards 241-250 were available exclusively through the "Player to be Named" mail exchange program. The first 50 collectors that sent in cards for the "Player to be Named" program (of which was announced in May, 2002) received the Star Ruby parallel versions along with the basic update cards.

*STARS 1-200: 5X TO 12X BASIC
*PROSPECTS 201-240: 1X TO 2.5X BASIC

2002 Fleer Premium Diamond Stars

Issued at stated odds of one in 72, these 20 cards feature some of the leading players in baseball as the 2002 season began.

COMPLETE SET (20)	100.00	200.00
1 Pedro Martinez	2.00	5.00
2 Derek Jeter	8.00	20.00
3 Sammy Sosa	3.00	8.00
4 Ken Griffey Jr.	5.00	12.00
5 Chipper Jones	3.00	8.00
6 Roger Clemens	6.00	15.00
7 Ichiro Suzuki	6.00	15.00
8 Jeff Bagwell	2.00	5.00
9 Luis Gonzalez	2.00	5.00
10 Manny Ramirez	2.00	5.00
11 Alex Rodriguez	5.00	12.00
12 Kazuhiro Sasaki	2.00	5.00
13 Mike Piazza	5.00	12.00
14 Vladimir Guerrero	3.00	8.00
15 Randy Johnson	3.00	8.00
16 Ivan Rodriguez	2.00	5.00
17 Nomar Garciaparra	5.00	12.00
18 Barry Bonds	8.00	20.00
19 Todd Helton	2.00	5.00
20 Greg Maddux	5.00	12.00

2002 Fleer Premium Diamond Stars Autograph

Randomly inserted in packs, and with a stated (though not serial numbered) print run of 100 copies, this card features an autograph of Derek Jeter. As Jeter did not sign these cards in time for insertion into the product, the exchange cards seeded into packs could be redeemeed until April 1, 2003.

1 Derek Jeter/100 *	75.00	150.00

2002 Fleer Premium Diamond Stars Game Used

Issued at stated odds of one in 105, these 12 cards feature players from the Diamond Stars insert set along with a game-used memorabilia piece featuring that player.

1 Barry Bonds Jsy	10.00	25.00
2 Manny Ramirez Jsy	6.00	15.00
3 Ivan Rodriguez Jsy	6.00	15.00
4 Kazuhiro Sasaki Jsy	6.00	15.00
5 Roger Clemens Jsy	10.00	25.00
6 Alex Rodriguez Jsy	8.00	20.00
7 Derek Jeter Bat	15.00	40.00
8 Chipper Jones Jsy	6.00	15.00
9 Todd Helton Pants	6.00	15.00
10 Luis Gonzalez Jsy	6.00	15.00
11 Mike Piazza Jsy	6.00	15.00
12 N.Garciaparra Bat SP/150	15.00	40.00

2002 Fleer Premium Diamond Stars Game Used Premium

Randomly inserted into packs and with a stated print run of 75 serial numbered cards, these 10 cards feature players from the diamond star insert set along with a game-used patch piece.

1 Barry Bonds	40.00	100.00
2 Roger Clemens	40.00	100.00
3 Todd Helton	20.00	50.00
4 Chipper Jones	20.00	50.00
5 Manny Ramirez	20.00	50.00
6 Alex Rodriguez	30.00	80.00
7 Ivan Rodriguez	20.00	50.00
8 Luis Gonzalez	15.00	40.00
9 Mike Piazza	20.00	50.00
10 Kazuhiro Sasaki	15.00	40.00

2002 Fleer Premium Diamond Stars Dual Game Used

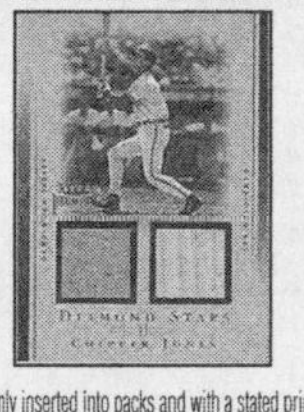

Randomly inserted into packs and with a stated print run of 100 serial numbered sets, these seven cards feature two game-used swatches of featured players from this set.

PREMIUM PRINT RUN 25 #'d SETS
NO PREMIUM PRICING DUE TO SCARCITY

1 Barry Bonds Jsy-Pants	40.00	100.00
2 Todd Helton Jsy-Bat	10.00	25.00
3 Derek Jeter Jsy-Bat	40.00	80.00
4 Chipper Jones Jsy-Bat	10.00	25.00
5 Mike Piazza Bat-Jsy	20.00	50.00
6 Manny Ramirez Jsy-Jsy	10.00	25.00
7 Alex Rodriguez Jsy-Hat	25.00	60.00

2002 Fleer Premium International Pride

Issued at stated odds of one in six, these 15 cards feature leading players born outside the continental United States.

COMPLETE SET (15)	10.00	25.00
1 Larry Walker	.75	2.00
2 Albert Pujols	1.50	4.00
3 Juan Gonzalez	.75	2.00
4 Ichiro Suzuki	1.50	4.00
5 Rafael Palmeiro	.75	2.00
6 Carlos Delgado	.75	2.00
7 Kazuhiro Sasaki	.75	2.00
8 Vladimir Guerrero	.75	2.00
9 Bobby Abreu	.75	2.00
10 Ivan Rodriguez	.75	2.00
11 Tsuyoshi Shinjo	.75	2.00
12 Pedro Martinez	.75	2.00
13 Andruw Jones	.75	2.00
14 Sammy Sosa	.75	2.00
15 Chan Ho Park	.75	2.00

2002 Fleer Premium International Pride Game Used

Issued at stated odds of one in 90, these 10 cards feature players from the International Pride insert set along with a game-used memorabilia piece.

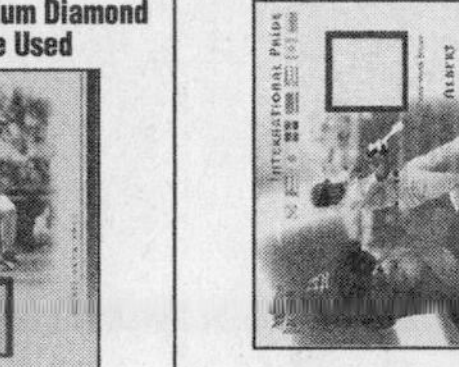

1 Carlos Delgado Jsy	6.00	15.00
2 Juan Gonzalez Jsy	6.00	15.00
3 Andruw Jones Bat	6.00	15.00
4 Pedro Martinez Jsy	6.00	15.00
5 Rafael Palmeiro Jsy	6.00	15.00
6 Chan Ho Park Jsy	6.00	15.00
7 Albert Pujols Jsy	10.00	25.00
8 Ivan Rodriguez Bat	6.00	15.00
9 Kazuhiro Sasaki Jsy	6.00	15.00
10 Tsuyoshi Shinjo Jsy	6.00	15.00

2002 Fleer Premium International Pride Game Used Premium

Randomly inserted into packs and with a stated print run of 75 serial numbered sets, these 10 cards feature players from the International Pride insert set along with a game-used jersey patch of said player.

1 Carlos Delgado	15.00	40.00
2 Juan Gonzalez	15.00	40.00
3 Andruw Jones	20.00	50.00
4 Pedro Martinez	20.00	50.00
5 Chan Ho Park	15.00	40.00
6 Ivan Rodriguez	20.00	50.00
7 Tsuyoshi Shinjo	15.00	40.00
8 Rafael Palmeiro	20.00	50.00
9 Albert Pujols	40.00	100.00
10 Kazuhiro Sasaki	15.00	40.00

2002 Fleer Premium Legendary Dynasties

Inserted at stated odds of one in 18, these 36 cards feature players from some of the greatest past and present teams in major league history.

*GOLD: .6X TO 1.5X BASIC DYNASTY
GOLD PRINT RUN 300 SERIAL #'d SETS

1 Honus Wagner	4.00	10.00
2 Christy Mathewson	4.00	10.00
3 Lou Gehrig	5.00	12.00
4 Babe Ruth	8.00	20.00
5 Jimmie Foxx	4.00	10.00
6 Lefty Grove	3.00	8.00
7 Al Simmons	2.00	5.00
8 Bill Dickey	3.00	8.00
9 Stan Musial	4.00	10.00
10 Enos Slaughter	2.00	5.00
11 Johnny Mize	2.00	5.00
12 Yogi Berra	4.00	10.00
13 Whitey Ford	3.00	8.00
14 Jackie Robinson	2.00	5.00
15 Duke Snider	3.00	8.00
16 Roger Maris	4.00	10.00
17 Jim Palmer	2.00	5.00
18 Don Drysdale	3.00	8.00
19 Brooks Robinson	3.00	8.00
20 Rollie Fingers	2.00	5.00
21 Reggie Jackson	3.00	8.00
22 Joe Morgan	2.00	5.00
23 Johnny Bench	4.00	10.00
24 Thurman Munson	2.00	5.00
25 Jose Canseco	2.00	5.00
26 Tom Glavine	2.00	5.00
27 Chipper Jones	2.00	5.00
28 Greg Maddux	3.00	8.00
29 Roberto Alomar	2.00	5.00
30 David Cone	2.00	5.00
31 Jim Thome	2.00	5.00
32 Manny Ramirez	2.00	5.00
33 Roger Clemens	4.00	10.00
34 Derek Jeter	5.00	12.00
35 Bernie Williams	2.00	5.00
36 Alfonso Soriano	2.00	5.00

2002 Fleer Premium Legendary Dynasties Autographs

Randomly inserted into packs, these nine cards feature autographs of selected players from the legendary dynasty set. These cards are all serial numbered to a year in which the player's team won the World Series - except for Brooks Robinson's card of which honors his 1964 MVP campaign. Since all cards have different print runs, we have notated that information in our checklist. In addition, all cards were issued as exchange cards and these cards could be redeemed until April 1, 2003.

1 Johnny Bench/76		
2 Yogi Berra/51		
3 Rollie Fingers/74		
4 Tom Glavine/95		
5 Reggie Jackson/73		
6 Derek Jeter/96	75.00	150.00
7 Greg Maddux/95		
8 Jim Palmer/70		
9 Brooks Robinson/64		

2002 Fleer Premium Legendary Dynasties Game Used

Issued at stated odds of one in 120, these 22 cards feature a game-worn memorabilia piece from 22 of the players featured in the Legendary Dynasty insert set. A few cards were issued in shorter supply, we have notated those cards with a SP in our checklist and their print run as well.

1 Roberto Alomar Jsy	8.00	20.00
2 Johnny Bench Jsy	8.00	20.00
3 Yogi Berra Bat SP/75		
4 Roger Clemens Jsy	10.00	25.00
5 Bill Dickey Bat SP/200	10.00	25.00
6 Rollie Fingers Jsy	6.00	15.00
7 Whitey Ford Jsy SP/25		
8 Reggie Jackson Bat SP/250	15.00	40.00
9 Derek Jeter Bat	15.00	40.00
10 Chipper Jones Jsy	8.00	20.00
11 Roger Maris Bat SP/225	20.00	50.00
12 Johnny Mize Bat SP/225	10.00	25.00
13 Joe Morgan Bat	6.00	15.00
14 T.Munson Bat SP/250	20.00	50.00
15 Jim Palmer Jsy	6.00	15.00
16 Manny Ramirez Jsy	8.00	20.00
17 Brooks Robinson Bat SP/200	15.00	40.00
18 J.Robinson Pants SP/150	30.00	60.00
19 Babe Ruth Bat SP/60	125.00	200.00
20 Duke Snider Bat SP/250	15.00	40.00
21 Alfonso Soriano Jsy	6.00	15.00
22 Bernie Williams Jsy	8.00	20.00

2002 Fleer Premium Legendary Dynasties Game Used Premium

Randomly inserted into packs, these 12 cards feature players from the set along with a game-worn jersey patch swatch. These cards are all serial numbered to the highest win total any of their teams accomplished and we have notated that information in our checklist.

1 Rollie Fingers/93	6.00	15.00
2 Roger Clemens/114	30.00	80.00
3 Roger Maris/109	40.00	100.00
4 Roberto Alomar/96	10.00	25.00
5 Reggie Jackson/93	10.00	25.00
6 Manny Ramirez/99	10.00	25.00
7 Johnny Bench/108	15.00	40.00
8 Jim Palmer/109	6.00	15.00
9 Derek Jeter/114	50.00	120.00
10 Alfonso Soriano/99	6.00	15.00
11 Chipper Jones/106	15.00	40.00
12 Bernie Williams/114	10.00	25.00

2002 Fleer Premium On Base!

Randomly inserted in packs, these 30 cards feature some of the leading offensive forces in baseball. These cards are all printed to stated print run of the player's 2002 on-base percentage. We have notated those print runs in our checklist.

COMPLETE SET (30)	100.00	250.00
1 Frank Thomas/316	3.00	8.00
2 Ivan Rodriguez/347	2.00	5.00
3 Nomar Garciaparra/352	5.00	12.00
4 Ken Griffey Jr./365	5.00	12.00
5 Juan Gonzalez/370	2.00	5.00
6 Shawn Green/372	2.00	5.00
7 Vladimir Guerrero/377	3.00	8.00
8 Derek Jeter/377	8.00	20.00
9 Scott Rolen/378	2.00	5.00
10 Ichiro Suzuki/381	6.00	15.00
11 Mike Piazza/384	5.00	12.00
12 Bernie Williams/395	2.00	5.00
13 Moises Alou/396	2.00	5.00
14 Jeff Bagwell/397	2.00	5.00
15 Alex Rodriguez/399	5.00	12.00
16 Albert Pujols/403	6.00	15.00

17 Manny Ramirez/405 2.00 5.00
18 Carlos Delgado/408 2.00 5.00
19 Jim Edmonds/410 2.00 5.00
20 Roberto Alomar/415 2.00 5.00
21 Jim Thome/416 2.00 5.00
22 Gary Sheffield/417 2.00 5.00
23 Chipper Jones/427 3.00 8.00
24 Luis Gonzalez/429 2.00 5.00
25 Lance Berkman/430 2.00 5.00
26 Todd Helton/432 2.00 5.00
27 Sammy Sosa/437 3.00 8.00
28 Larry Walker/449 2.00 5.00
29 Jason Giambi/477 2.00 5.00
30 Barry Bonds/515 8.00 20.00

2002 Fleer Premium On Base! Game Used

Randomly inserted into packs, this set parallels the On Base! Insert set and was issued in a quantity of 100 serial numbered sets. These cards all feature a game-used piece of the featured player.

1 Luis Gonzalez 4.00 10.00
2 Chipper Jones 6.00 15.00
3 Gary Sheffield 4.00 10.00
4 Nomar Garciaparra 10.00 25.00
5 Manny Ramirez 6.00 15.00
6 Moises Alou 4.00 10.00
7 Sammy Sosa 6.00 15.00
8 Frank Thomas 6.00 15.00
9 Ken Griffey Jr. 10.00 25.00
10 Jim Thome 6.00 15.00
11 Todd Helton 6.00 15.00
12 Larry Walker 4.00 10.00
13 Jeff Bagwell 6.00 15.00
14 Lance Berkman 4.00 10.00
15 Shawn Green 4.00 10.00
16 Vladimir Guerrero 6.00 15.00
17 Roberto Alomar 6.00 15.00
18 Mike Piazza 10.00 25.00
19 Jason Giambi 4.00 10.00
20 Derek Jeter 15.00 40.00
21 Bernie Williams 6.00 15.00
22 Scott Rolen 6.00 15.00
23 Barry Bonds 15.00 40.00
24 Ichiro Suzuki 15.00 40.00
25 Jim Edmonds 4.00 10.00
26 Albert Pujols 12.50 30.00
27 Juan Gonzalez 4.00 10.00
28 Alex Rodriguez 12.50 30.00
29 Ivan Rodriguez 6.00 15.00
30 Carlos Delgado 4.00 10.00

2001 Fleer Red Sox 100th

The 2001 Fleer Red Sox product released in late June, 2001 and featured a 100-card base set. The set was broken into three subsets: Red Sox Players (1-77), Beantown's Best (78-92), and Fenway Park cards (93-100). Each pack contained five cards, and carried a suggested retail price of $2.99. A Field the Game exchange card was randomly seeded into packs. Each of these cards was serial numbered of 7,150. Collectors received a special card that included an actual piece of Fenway Park. The deadline to exchange these cards was August 1st, 2002.

COMPLETE SET (100) 10.00 25.00
1 Carl Yastrzemski 1.25 3.00
2 Mel Parnell .20 .50
3 Birdie Tebbetts .20 .50
4 Tex Hughson .20 .50
5 Nomar Garciaparra 1.25 3.00
6 Fred Lynn .30 .75
7 John Valentin .20 .50
8 Rico Petrocelli .20 .50
9 Ted Williams 2.00 5.00
10 Roger Clemens 1.50 4.00
11 Luis Aparicio .30 .75
12 Cy Young .75 2.00
13 Carlton Fisk .50 1.25
14 Pedro Martinez .50 1.25
15 Joe Dobson .20 .50
16 Babe Ruth 2.50 6.00
17 Doc Cramer .20 .50
18 Pete Runnels .20 .50
19 Tony Conigliaro .50 1.25
20 Bill Monbouquette .20 .50
21 Boo Ferriss .20 .50
22 Harry Hooper .50 1.25
23 Tony Armas .20 .50
24 Joe Cronin .30 .75
25 Rick Ferrell .30 .75
26 Wade Boggs .50 1.25
27 Don Baylor .30 .75
28 Jeff Reardon .30 .75
29 Joe Wood .50 1.25
30 Mo Vaughn .30 .75
31 Walt Dropo .20 .50
32 Vern Stephens .20 .50
33 Bernie Carbo .20 .50
34 George Scott .20 .50
35 Lefty Grove .75 2.00
36 Dom DiMaggio .75 2.00
37 Dennis Eckersley .30 .75
38 Johnny Pesky .30 .75
39 Jim Lonborg .20 .50
40 Jimmy Piersall .30 .75
41 Tris Speaker .75 2.00
42 Frank Malzone .20 .50
43 Bobby Doerr .50 1.25
44 Jimmie Foxx .75 2.00
45 Tony Pena .20 .50
46 Billy Goodman .20 .50
47 Jim Rice .30 .75
48 Reggie Smith .30 .75
49 Bill Buckner .30 .75
50 Earl Wilson .20 .50
51 Rick Burleson .20 .50
52 George Kell .30 .75
53 Dick Radatz .20 .50
54 Dwight Evans .50 1.25
55 Luis Tiant .30 .75
56 Elijah Green .20 .50
57 Gene Conley .20 .50
58 Jackie Jensen .30 .75
59 Mike Fornieles .20 .50
60 Dutch Leonard .20 .50
61 Jake Stahl .20 .50
62 Don Schwall .20 .50
63 Jimmy Collins .30 .75
64 Herb Pennock .50 1.25
65 Red Ruffing .50 1.25
66 Carney Lansford .30 .75
67 Dick Stuart .20 .50
68 Dave Morehead .20 .50
69 Harry Agganis .30 .75
70 Lou Boudreau MGR .50 1.25
71 Joe Morgan MGR .20 .50
72 Don Zimmer MGR .30 .75
73 Tom Yawkey OWN .30 .75
74 Jean Yawkey OWN .20 .50
75 Boston Red Sox .30 .75
Origin of the Red Sox
76 Boston Red Sox .30 .75
The First Season - 1901
77 Boston Red Sox .30 .75
World Series Triumphs
78 Carl Yastrzemski BB .75 2.00
79 Carlton Fisk BB .30 .75
80 Dom DiMaggio BB .30 .75
81 Wade Boggs BB .30 .75
82 Nomar Garciaparra BB .75 2.00
83 Pedro Martinez BB .50 1.25
84 Ted Williams BB 1.00 2.50
85 Jim Rice BB .20 .50
86 Fred Lynn BB .20 .50
87 Mo Vaughn BB .20 .50
88 Bobby Doerr BB UER .30 .75
Card Pictures Lou Boudreau
89 Bernie Carbo BB .20 .50
90 Dennis Eckersley BB .30 .75
91 Jimmy Piersall BB .20 .50
92 Luis Tiant BB .20 .50
93 Fenway Park .20 .50
Jimmy Fund signage
94 Fenway Park .20 .50
Green Monster w/Ads
95 Fenway Park .20 .50
Green Monster w/All-Star logo
96 Fenway Park .20 .50
Ladder shot on Green Monster
97 Fenway Park .20 .50
Manual scoreboard
98 Fenway Park .20 .50
Panoramic of Fenway Park
99 Fenway Park .20 .50
Lansdowne Street
100 Fenway Park .20 .50
1999 All-Star Game
NNO Field the Game/7150 15.00 40.00

2001 Fleer Red Sox 100th BoSox Sigs

Randomly inserted into packs at one in 96, this 16-card insert set features authentic autographs from Red Sox greats like Roger Clemens and Nomar Garciaparra. Please note that Boggs, Clemens, Fisk, Garciaparra, Rice, Yastrzemski all packed out as exchange cards with a redemption deadline of 07/31/02.

1 Wade Boggs 40.00 80.00
2 Bill Buckner 20.00 50.00
3 Bernie Carbo 15.00 40.00
4 Roger Clemens 175.00 300.00
SP/100 EXCH
5 Dom DiMaggio 40.00 80.00
6 Bobby Doerr 20.00 50.00
7 Dennis Eckersley 40.00 80.00
8 Dwight Evans 40.00 80.00
9 Carlton Fisk 40.00 80.00
10 N.Garciaparra EXCH 60.00 120.00
11 Jim Lonborg 15.00 40.00
12 Fred Lynn 20.00 50.00
13 Rico Petrocelli 15.00 40.00
14 Jim Rice 20.00 50.00
15 Luis Tiant 20.00 50.00
16 C.Yastrzemski SP/200 175.00 300.00

2001 Fleer Red Sox 100th MLB Autographed Fitted Caps

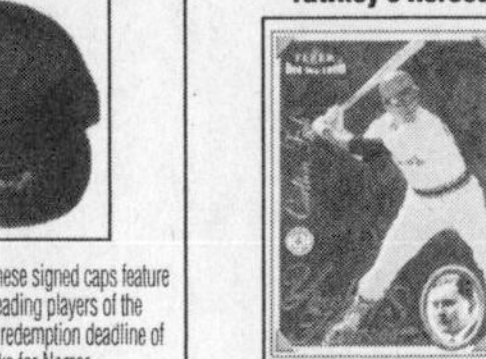

Inserted one per deluxe box, these signed caps feature some of the Boston Red Sox leading players of the past. An exchange card with a redemption deadline of 07/31/02 was seeded into packs for Nomar Garciaparra's cap.

1 Wade Boggs
2 Bill Buckner 15.00 40.00
3 Bernie Carbo 15.00 40.00
4 Roger Clemens
5 Bobby Doerr 20.00 50.00
6 Dennis Eckersley 30.00 60.00
7 Dwight Evans 20.00 50.00
8 Nomar Garciaparra 60.00 120.00
9 Jim Lonborg 15.00 40.00
10 Johnny Pesky 15.00 40.00
11 Rico Petrocelli 15.00 40.00
12 Jim Rice 15.00 40.00
13 Luis Tiant 15.00 40.00

2001 Fleer Red Sox 100th Splendid Splinters

Randomly inserted into packs at one in 10, this 15-card insert features some of the best hitters in Red Sox history. Card backs carry a "SS" prefix.

COMPLETE SET (15) 12.50 30.00
SS1 Babe Ruth 3.00 8.00
SS2 Dom DiMaggio 1.00 2.50
SS3 Carlton Fisk .60 1.50
SS4 Carl Yastrzemski 1.50 4.00
SS5 Nomar Garciaparra 2.00 5.00
SS6 Wade Boggs .60 1.50
SS7 Ted Williams 3.00 8.00
SS8 Jim Rice .40 1.00
SS9 Mo Vaughn .40 1.00
SS10 Tris Speaker 1.00 2.50
SS11 Dwight Evans .60 1.50
SS12 Jimmie Foxx 1.25 3.00
SS13 Bobby Doerr .60 1.50
SS14 Fred Lynn .40 1.00
SS15 Johnny Pesky .40 1.00

2001 Fleer Red Sox 100th Splendid Splinters Game Bat

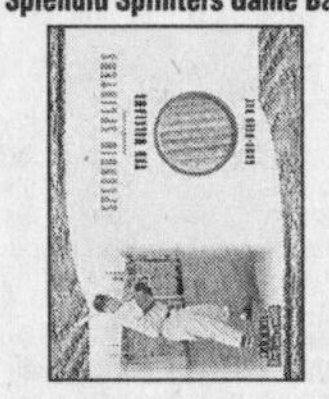

Randomly inserted into packs at one in 96, this eight-card insert set features game-used bat chips from Red Sox greats like Babe Ruth and Nomar Garciaparra. Card backs carry a "SS" prefix. Though they lack actual serial-numbering, the Jimmie Foxx, Babe Ruth and Ted Williams cards were announced by Fleer to be short-prints with 100 copies of each card produced.

1 Wade Boggs 15.00 40.00
2 Dwight Evans 15.00 40.00
3 Jimmie Foxx SP/100 125.00 200.00
4 Nomar Garciaparra 10.00 25.00
5 Jim Rice 10.00 25.00
6 Babe Ruth SP/100 300.00 500.00
7 Ted Williams SP/100 125.00 200.00
8 Carl Yastrzemski 40.00 80.00

2001 Fleer Red Sox 100th Threads

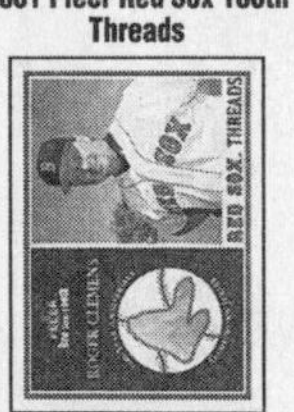

Randomly inserted into packs at one in 96, this nine card insert set features game-used jersey swatches from Red Sox greats like Wade Boggs and Ted Williams. Though they lack actual serial-numbering, the cards of Carlton Fisk, Pedro Martinez and Ted Williams were announced by Fleer to be short-prints. with 100 copies of each card produced.

1 Wade Boggs 15.00 40.00
2 Roger Clemens 15.00 40.00
3 Dwight Evans 15.00 40.00
4 Carlton Fisk SP/100 20.00 50.00
5 Pedro Martinez SP/100 20.00 50.00
6 Jim Rice 10.00 25.00
7 Ted Williams SP/100 125.00 200.00
8 Carl Yastrzemski 40.00 80.00
9 Don Zimmer 10.00 25.00

2001 Fleer Red Sox 100th Yawkey's Heroes

Randomly inserted into packs at one in four, this 20-card insert set features Red Sox greats like Babe Ruth, Ted Williams, and Nomar Garciaparra. Card backs carry a "YH" prefix.

COMPLETE SET (20) 6.00 15.00
YH1 Bobby Doerr .50 1.25
YH2 Dom DiMaggio .75 2.00
YH3 Jim Rice .30 .75
YH4 Wade Boggs .50 1.25
YH5 Carlton Fisk .50 1.25
YH6 Nomar Garciaparra 1.25 3.00
YH7 Dennis Eckersley .30 .75
YH8 Carl Yastrzemski 1.25 3.00
YH9 Ted Williams 2.00 5.00
YH10 Tony Conigliaro .50 1.25
YH11 Tony Armas .30 .75
YH12 Joe Cronin .75 2.00
YH13 Mo Vaughn .30 .75
YH14 Johnny Pesky .30 .75
YH15 Jim Lonborg .30 .75
YH16 Luis Tiant .30 .75
YH17 Tony Pena .30 .75
YH18 Dwight Evans .50 1.25
YH19 Fred Lynn .30 .75
YH20 Jimmy Piersall .30 .75

2003 Fleer Rookies and Greats

This 75-card standard-size set was released in December, 2003. The set was issued in five-card packs with an $6 SRP which came 20 packs to a box and six boxes to a case. Cards numbered 1-60 feature active stars while cards 61-75 feature a select group of retired greats. In additon, update cards for the following products: Flair, Fleer Authentix, Fleer Genuine, Fleer Hot Prospects, Fleer Showcase and Ultra were also inserted into these packs.

COMPLETE SET (75) 10.00 25.00
1 Troy Glaus .15 .40
2 Gary Sheffield .15 .40
3 Sammy Sosa .40 1.00
4 Mark Prior .25 .60
5 Dontrelle Willis .40 1.00
6 Shawn Green .15 .40
7 Vladimir Guerrero .40 1.00
8 Jose Reyes .15 .40
9 Miguel Tejada .15 .40
10 Bret Boone .15 .40
11 Rocco Baldelli .15 .40
12 Rafael Palmeiro .25 .60
13 Ichiro Suzuki .75 2.00
14 Carlos Delgado .15 .40
15 Garret Anderson .15 .40
16 Richie Sexson .15 .40
17 Roger Clemens .75 2.00
18 Barry Zito .15 .40
19 Jim Thome .25 .60
20 Alex Rodriguez .60 1.50
21 Randy Johnson .40 1.00
22 Chipper Jones .40 1.00
23 Kerry Wood .15 .40
24 Ken Griffey Jr. .60 1.50
25 Ivan Rodriguez .25 .60
26 Jeff Kent .15 .40
27 Todd Helton .25 .60
28 Jeff Bagwell .25 .60
29 Hideo Nomo .40 1.00
30 Torii Hunter .15 .40
31 Brian Giles .15 .40
32 Albert Pujols .75 2.00
33 Vernon Wells .15 .40
34 Nomar Garciaparra .60 1.50
35 Magglio Ordonez .15 .40
36 C.C. Sabathia .15 .40
37 Preston Wilson .15 .40
38 Mike Sweeney .15 .40
39 Jose Vidro .15 .40
40 Jason Giambi .15 .40
41 Derek Jeter 1.00 2.50
42 Mike Piazza .60 1.50
43 Rich Harden .25 .60
44 Jason Kendall .15 .40
45 Barry Bonds 1.00 2.50
46 Barry Larkin .25 .60
47 Dmitri Young .15 .40
48 Craig Biggio .25 .60
49 Angel Berroa .15 .40
50 Alfonso Soriano .15 .40
51 Kevin Millwood .15 .40
52 Edgar Martinez .25 .60
53 Jim Edmonds .15 .40
54 Curt Schilling .15 .40
55 Jay Gibbons .15 .40
56 Pedro Martinez .25 .60
57 Greg Maddux .60 1.50
58 Manny Ramirez .25 .60
59 Frank Thomas .40 1.00
60 Adam Dunn .15 .40
61 Babe Ruth GR 1.50 4.00
62 Bob Gibson GR .60 1.50
63 Willie Stargell GR .60 1.50
64 Mike Schmidt GR 1.25 3.00
65 Nolan Ryan GR 1.50 4.00
66 Tom Seaver GR .60 1.50
67 Brooks Robinson GR .60 1.50
68 Willie McCovey GR .40 1.00
69 Harmon Killebrew GR .60 1.50
70 Al Kaline GR .60 1.50
71 Reggie Jackson GR .60 1.50
72 Eddie Mathews GR .60 1.50
73 Ralph Kiner GR .40 1.00
74 Cal Ripken GR 2.00 5.00
75 Phil Rizzuto GR .60 1.50

2003 Fleer Rookies and Greats Blue

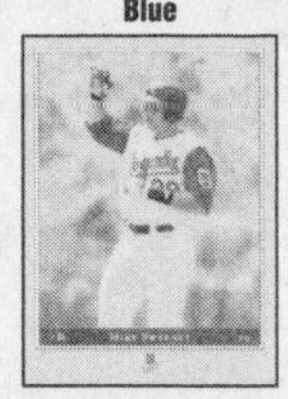

*BLUE 1-60: 2X TO 5X BASIC
*BLUE 61-75: 1.25X TO 3X BASIC
STATED ODDS 1:10
STATED PRINT RUN 250 SERIAL #'d SETS

2003 Fleer Rookies and Greats Boyhood Idols Game Used

OVERALL AU-GU ODDS 1:7
STATED PRINT RUN 615 SERIAL #'d SETS
BD Bucky Dent Jsy 4.00 10.00
BR Brooks Robinson Jsy 6.00 15.00
CF Carlton Fisk Jsy 6.00 15.00
CR Cal Ripken Jsy 12.50 30.00
DM Don Mattingly Jsy 8.00 20.00
FH Frank Howard Bat 4.00 10.00
HK Harmon Killebrew Pants 6.00 15.00
JC Joe Carter Bat 4.00 10.00
JM Joe Morgan Jsy 4.00 10.00
JP Jim Palmer Jsy 4.00 10.00
MS Mike Schmidt Jsy 8.00 20.00
MS2 Moose Skowron Pants 4.00 10.00
NR Nolan Ryan Jsy 10.00 25.00
RY Robin Yount Jsy 6.00 15.00

2003 Fleer Rookies and Greats Boyhood Idols Game Used Autograph

OVERALL AU-GU ODDS 1:7
PRINT RUNS B/WN 40-50 COPIES PER
BD Bucky Dent Jsy/50 12.50 30.00
BR Brooks Robinson Jsy/50 20.00 50.00
CF Carlton Fisk Jsy/50 20.00 50.00
FH Frank Howard Bat/50 12.50 30.00
HK Harmon Killebrew Pants/40 40.00 80.00
JC Joe Carter Bat/50 12.50 30.00
JP Jim Palmer Jsy/50 12.50 30.00
MS2 Moose Skowron Pants/50 12.50 30.00

2003 Fleer Rookies and Greats Dynamic Debuts

STATED ODDS 1:10
1 Rickie Weeks 1.50 4.00
2 Brandon Webb 1.50 4.00
3 Jose Reyes .75 2.00
4 Bo Hart .75 2.00
5 Dontrelle Willis 1.25 3.00
6 Rich Harden 1.25 3.00
7 Ryan Wagner .75 2.00
8 Rocco Baldelli .75 2.00
9 Mark Teixeira 1.25 3.00
10 Hideki Matsui 2.50 6.00

2003 Fleer Rookies and Greats Dynamic Debuts Autograph

OVERALL AU-GU ODDS 1:7
STATED PRINT RUN 100 SERIAL #'d SETS
BH Bo Hart 4.00 10.00
DW Dontrelle Willis 5.00 12.00
JR Jose Reyes 10.00 25.00
RW Rickie Weeks 15.00 40.00
RW2 Ryan Wagner 4.00 10.00

2003 Fleer Rookies and Greats Looming Large

STATED PRINT RUN 500 SERIAL #'d SETS
RARE PRINT RUN 15 SERIAL #'d SETS

NO RARE PRICING DUE TO SCARCITY
*UNCOMMON: .75X TO 2X BASIC
UNCOMMON PRINT RUN 150 SER. #'d SETS
BH Bo Hart .75 2.00
BW Brandon Webb 2.00 5.00
CB Clint Barmes .75 2.00
CW Chien-Ming Wang 4.00 10.00
DY Delmon Young 4.00 10.00
EJ Edwin Jackson 1.25 3.00
HM Hideki Matsui 3.00 8.00
JB Jeremy Bonderman 2.50 6.00
JC Jose Contreras 1.25 3.00
JD Jeff Duncan .75 2.00
MH Michael Hessman .75 2.00
MK Matt Kata .75 2.00
RH Robby Hammock .75 2.00
RW Rickie Weeks 2.00 5.00
RW2 Ryan Wagner .75 2.00

2003 Fleer Rookies and Greats Naturals

STATED ODDS 1:5
*UNCOMMON: 1.5X TO 4X BASIC
UNCOMMON PRINT RUN 75 SERIAL #'d SETS
TN1 Cal Ripken 4.00 10.00
TN2 Mike Schmidt 2.50 6.00
TN3 Derek Jeter 2.50 6.00
TN4 Joe Carter .75 2.00
TN5 Nomar Garciaparra 1.50 4.00
TN6 Frank Howard .75 2.00
TN7 Al Kaline 1.25 3.00
TN8 Albert Pujols 2.00 5.00
TN9 Nolan Ryan 3.00 8.00
TN10 Duke Snider 1.25 3.00
TN11 Alex Rodriguez 1.50 4.00
TN12 Brooks Robinson 1.25 3.00
TN13 Roger Clemens 2.00 5.00
TN14 Sammy Sosa 1.00 2.50
TN15 Jim Palmer .75 2.00
TN16 Alfonso Soriano .75 2.00
TN17 Don Mattingly 2.50 6.00
TN18 Harmon Killebrew 1.25 3.00
TN19 Bob Feller .75 2.00
TN20 Reggie Jackson 1.25 3.00
TN21 Ichiro Suzuki 2.00 5.00
TN22 Barry Bonds 2.50 6.00
TN23 Hideki Matsui 3.00 8.00
TN24 Willie Stargell 1.25 3.00
TN25 Pee Wee Reese 1.25 3.00

2003 Fleer Rookies and Greats Naturals Autograph

OVERALL AU-GU ODDS 1:7
STATED PRINT RUN 50 SERIAL #'d SETS
AK Al Kaline 20.00 50.00
BF Bob Feller 10.00 25.00
BR Brooks Robinson 15.00 40.00
CR Cal Ripken 75.00 150.00
DS Duke Snider 15.00 40.00
FH Frank Howard 15.00 40.00
HK Harmon Killebrew 30.00 60.00
JC Joe Carter 10.00 25.00
JP Jim Palmer 10.00 25.00
NR Nolan Ryan 60.00 120.00

2003 Fleer Rookies and Greats Naturals Game Used

PRINT RUNS B/WN 250-400 COPIES PER
PATCH PRINT RUN 25 SERIAL #'d SETS
NO PATCH PRICING DUE TO SCARCITY
OVERALL AU-GU ODDS 1:7
AK Al Kaline Bat/250 6.00 15.00
AP Albert Pujols Jsy/250 8.00 20.00
AR Alex Rodriguez Jsy/250 4.00 10.00
AS Alfonso Soriano Jsy/250 3.00 8.00
BR Brooks Robinson Jsy/400 6.00 15.00
CR Cal Ripken Jsy/250 12.50 30.00
DJ Derek Jeter Jsy/250 10.00 25.00
DM Don Mattingly Jsy/250 8.00 20.00
DS Duke Snider Jsy/250 6.00 15.00
FH Frank Howard Bat/400 4.00 10.00
HK Harmon Killebrew Pants/400 6.00 15.00
JC Joe Carter Bat/250 4.00 10.00
JP Jim Palmer Jsy/250 4.00 10.00
MS Mike Schmidt Jsy/250 8.00 20.00
NG Nomar Garciaparra Jsy/250 6.00 15.00
NR Nolan Ryan Jsy/400 10.00 25.00
RC Roger Clemens Jsy/400 6.00 15.00
RJ Reggie Jackson Jsy/400 6.00 15.00
SS Sammy Sosa Jsy/250 4.00 10.00

2003 Fleer Rookies and Greats Naturals Game Used Autograph

OVERALL AU-GU ODDS 1:7
STATED PRINT RUN 30 SERIAL #'d SETS
AU PATCH PRINT RUN 5 SERIAL #'d SETS
NO AU PATCH PRICING DUE TO SCARCITY
AK Al Kaline Bat 40.00 80.00
BR Brooks Robinson Jsy 30.00 60.00
CR Cal Ripken Jsy 125.00 200.00
DS Duke Snider Jsy 30.00 60.00
FH Frank Howard Bat 15.00 40.00
HK Harmon Killebrew Pants 50.00 100.00
JC Joe Carter Bat 15.00 40.00
JP Jim Palmer Jsy 15.00 40.00
NR Nolan Ryan Jsy 75.00 150.00

2003 Fleer Rookies and Greats Through the Years Game Used Dual

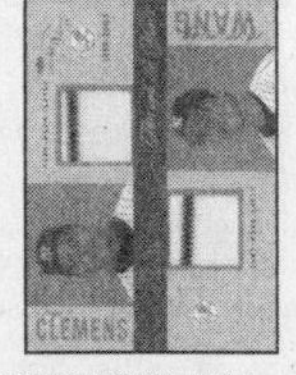

STATED PRINT RUN 360 SERIAL #'d SETS
PATCH PRINT RUN 25 SERIAL #'d SETS
NO PATCH PRICING DUE TO SCARCITY
OVERALL AU-GU ODDS 1:7
ALL ARE DUAL JSY UNLESS NOTED
ARMT Alex Rodriguez Jsy 6.00 15.00
Mark Teixeira Jsy
BHLB Bo Hart Pants 4.00 10.00
Lou Brock Jsy
BLJM Barry Larkin Jsy 6.00 15.00
Joe Morgan Jsy
DJPR Derek Jeter Jsy 15.00 40.00
Phil Rizzuto Pants
EMCJ Eddie Mathews Pants 8.00 20.00
Chipper Jones Jsy
HKTH Harmon Killebrew Pants 6.00 15.00
Torii Hunter Jsy
JCMM Jose Contreras Jsy 6.00 15.00
Mike Mussina Jsy
JGRJ Jason Giambi Jsy 6.00 15.00
Reggie Jackson Jsy
JTMS Jim Thome Jsy 12.50 30.00
Mike Schmidt Jsy
MHCJ Michael Hessman Pants 6.00 15.00
Chipper Jones Jsy
MPJR Mike Piazza Jsy 6.00 15.00
Jose Reyes Jsy
NGBD Nomar Garciaparra Jsy 10.00 25.00
Bobby Doerr Bat
NRHB Nolan Ryan Jsy 15.00 40.00
Hank Blalock Jsy
PRJR Phil Rizzuto Pants 8.00 20.00
Jose Reyes Jsy
RCCW Roger Clemens Jsy 15.00 40.00
Chien-Ming Wang Pants
RJBW Randy Johnson Jsy 6.00 15.00
Brandon Webb Jsy
RYSP Robin Yount Jsy 6.00 15.00
Scott Podsednik Bat
SCKM Steve Carlton Jsy 4.00 10.00
Kevin Millwood Jsy
SSMP Sammy Sosa Jsy 6.00 15.00
Mark Prior Jsy
WMBB Willie McCovey Pants 10.00 25.00
Barry Bonds Base

2000 Fleer Showcase

The 2000 Fleer Showcase product was released in October, 2000. The product featured a 140-card base set that was broken into tiers as follows: 100 Base Veterans (1-100), 40 Prospects (101-140): Please note that cards 101-115 were serial numbered to 1000, and cards 116-140 were serial numbered to 2000. Each pack contained five cards and carried a suggested retail price of $3.99.

COMP.SET w/o SP's (100) 10.00 25.00
COMMON CARD (1-100) .20 .50
COMMON (101-115) 3.00 8.00
COMMON (116-140) 2.00 5.00
1 Alex Rodriguez .75 2.00
2 Derek Jeter 1.25 3.00
3 Jeromy Burnitz .20 .50
4 John Olerud .20 .50
5 Paul Konerko .20 .50

6 Johnny Damon .30 .75
7 Curt Schilling .20 .50
8 Barry Larkin .30 .75
9 Adrian Beltre .20 .50
10 Scott Rolen .30 .75
11 Carlos Delgado .20 .50
12 Pedro Martinez .30 .75
13 Todd Helton .30 .75
14 Jacque Jones .20 .50
15 Jeff Kent .20 .50
16 Darin Erstad .20 .50
17 Juan Encarnacion .20 .50
18 Roger Clemens 1.00 2.50
19 Tony Gwynn .60 1.50
20 Nomar Garciaparra .75 2.00
21 Roberto Alomar .30 .75
22 Matt Lawton .20 .50
23 Rich Aurilia .20 .50
24 Charles Johnson .20 .50
25 Jim Thome .30 .75
26 Eric Milton .20 .50
27 Barry Bonds 1.25 3.00
28 Albert Belle .20 .50
29 Travis Fryman .20 .50
30 Ken Griffey Jr. .75 2.00
31 Phil Nevin .20 .50
32 Chipper Jones .50 1.25
33 Craig Biggio .30 .75
34 Mike Hampton .20 .50
35 Fred McGriff .30 .75
36 Cal Ripken 1.50 4.00
37 Manny Ramirez .30 .75
38 Jose Vidro .20 .50
39 Trevor Hoffman .20 .50
40 Tom Glavine .30 .75
41 Frank Thomas .50 1.25
42 Chris Widger .20 .50
43 J.D. Drew .20 .50
44 Andres Galarraga .20 .50
45 Pokey Reese .20 .50
46 Mike Piazza .75 2.00
47 Kevin Young .20 .50
48 Sean Casey .20 .50
49 Carlos Beltran .20 .50
50 Jason Kendall .20 .50
51 Vladimir Guerrero .50 1.25
52 Jermaine Dye .20 .50
53 Brian Giles .20 .50
54 Andruw Jones .30 .75
55 Richard Hidalgo .20 .50
56 Robin Ventura .20 .50
57 Ivan Rodriguez .30 .75
58 Greg Maddux .75 2.00
59 Billy Wagner .20 .50
60 Ruben Mateo .20 .50
61 Troy Glaus .20 .50
62 Dean Palmer .20 .50
63 Eric Chavez .20 .50
64 Edgar Martinez .30 .75
65 Randy Johnson .50 1.25
66 Preston Wilson .20 .50
67 Orlando Hernandez .20 .50
68 Jim Edmonds .20 .50
69 Carl Everett .20 .50
70 Larry Walker .20 .50
71 Ron Belliard .20 .50
72 Sammy Sosa .50 1.25
73 Matt Williams .20 .50
74 Cliff Floyd .20 .50
75 Bernie Williams .30 .75
76 Fernando Tatis .20 .50
77 Steve Finley .20 .50
78 Jeff Bagwell .30 .75
79 Edgardo Alfonzo .20 .50
80 Jose Canseco .30 .75
81 Magglio Ordonez .20 .50
82 Shawn Green .20 .50
83 Bobby Abreu .20 .50
84 Tony Batista .20 .50
85 Mo Vaughn .20 .50
86 Juan Gonzalez .20 .50
87 Paul O'Neill .30 .75
88 Mark McGwire 1.25 3.00
89 Mark Grace .30 .75
90 Kevin Brown .20 .50
91 Ben Grieve .20 .50
92 Shannon Stewart .20 .50
93 Erubiel Durazo .20 .50
94 Antonio Alfonseca .20 .50
95 Jeff Cirillo .20 .50
96 Greg Vaughn .20 .50
97 Kerry Wood .20 .50
98 Geoff Jenkins .20 .50
99 Jason Giambi .20 .50
100 Rafael Palmeiro .30 .75
101 Rafael Furcal PROS 3.00 8.00
102 Pablo Ozuna PROS 3.00 8.00
103 Brad Penny PROS 3.00 8.00
104 Mark Mulder PROS 3.00 8.00
105 Adam Piatt PROS 3.00 8.00
106 Mike Lamb PROS RC 4.00 10.00
107 K.Sasaki PROS RC 4.00 10.00
108 A.McNeal PROS RC 3.00 8.00
109 Pat Burrell PROS 3.00 8.00
110 Rick Ankiel PROS 3.00 8.00
111 Eric Munson PROS 3.00 8.00
112 Josh Beckett PROS 3.00 8.00
113 Adam Kennedy PROS 3.00 8.00
114 Alex Escobar PROS 3.00 8.00
115 C.Hermansen PROS 3.00 8.00
116 Kip Wells PROS 2.00 5.00
117 Matt LeCroy PROS 2.00 5.00
118 Julio Ramirez PROS 2.00 5.00
119 Ben Petrick PROS 2.00 5.00
120 Nick Johnson PROS 2.00 5.00
121 G.Dawkins PROS 2.00 5.00
122 Julio Zuleta PROS RC 2.00 5.00
123 A.Soriano PROS 3.00 8.00
124 K.McDonald RC 2.00 5.00
125 Kory DeHaan PROS 2.00 5.00
126 Vernon Wells PROS 2.00 5.00
127 D.Stenson PROS 2.00 5.00
128 David Eckstein PROS 2.00 5.00
129 Robert Fick PROS 2.00 5.00
130 Cole Liniak PROS 2.00 5.00
131 Mark Quinn PROS 2.00 5.00
132 Eric Gagne PROS 3.00 8.00
133 Wily Mo Pena PROS 2.00 5.00
134 A.Thompson RC 2.00 5.00
135 Steve Sisco PROS RC 2.00 5.00
136 P.Rigdon PROS RC 2.00 5.00
137 Rob Bell PROS 2.00 5.00
138 Carlos Guillen PROS 2.00 5.00
139 Jimmy Rollins PROS 2.00 5.00
140 Jason Conti PROS 2.00 5.00

2000 Fleer Showcase Legacy Collection

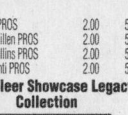

Randomly inserted into packs, this 140-card set is a complete parallel of the 2000 Fleer Showcase base set. Each card in the set is individually serial numbered to 20.

*STARS 1-100: 25X TO 60X BASIC

2000 Fleer Showcase Prospect Showcase First

Randomly inserted into packs, this 40-card set features MLB's top prospects. Each card is individually serial numbered to 500.

*PROSPECT 1-15: .4X TO 1X BASIC
*PROSPECT RC 1-15: .5X TO 1.2X BASIC
*PROSPECT 16-40: .6X TO 1.5X BASIC
*PROSPECT RC 16-40: .75X TO 2X BASIC

2000 Fleer Showcase Consummate Prose

Randomly inserted into packs at one in six, this 15-card die-cut set features players that perform at a higher level. Card backs carry a "CP" prefix.

COMPLETE SET (15) 12.50 30.00
CP1 Jeff Bagwell .40 1.00
CP2 Alex Rodriguez 1.00 2.50
CP3 Chipper Jones .60 1.50
CP4 Derek Jeter 1.50 4.00
CP5 Manny Ramirez .40 1.00
CP6 Tony Gwynn .75 2.00
CP7 Sammy Sosa .60 1.50
CP8 Ivan Rodriguez .40 1.00
CP9 Greg Maddux 1.00 2.50
CP10 Ken Griffey Jr. 1.00 2.50
CP11 Rick Ankiel .50 1.25
CP12 Cal Ripken 2.00 5.00
CP13 Pedro Martinez .40 1.00
CP14 Mike Piazza 1.00 2.50
CP15 Mark McGwire 1.50 4.00

2000 Fleer Showcase Feel the Game

Randomly inserted into packs at one in 72, this 10-card insert features game-used jersey cards of some of the biggest names in MLB. Card backs carry a "FG" prefix.

FG1 Barry Bonds 15.00 40.00
FG2 Gookie Dawkins 3.00 8.00
FG3 Darin Erstad 4.00 10.00
FG4 Troy Glaus 4.00 10.00
FG5 Scott Rolen 6.00 15.00
FG6 Alex Rodriguez 10.00 25.00
FG7 Andruw Jones 6.00 15.00
FG8 Robin Ventura 4.00 10.00
FG9 Sean Casey 4.00 10.00
FG10 Cal Ripken 20.00 50.00

2000 Fleer Showcase Final Answer

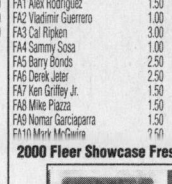

Randomly inserted into packs at one in 10, this 10-card set features hitters that get the job done in clutch situations. Card backs carry a "FA" prefix.

COMPLETE SET (10) 15.00 40.00
FA1 Alex Rodriguez 1.50 4.00
FA2 Vladimir Guerrero 1.00 2.50
FA3 Cal Ripken 3.00 8.00
FA4 Sammy Sosa 1.00 2.50
FA5 Barry Bonds 2.50 6.00
FA6 Derek Jeter 2.50 6.00
FA7 Ken Griffey Jr. 1.50 4.00
FA8 Mike Piazza 1.50 4.00
FA9 Nomar Garciaparra 1.50 4.00
FA10 Mark McGwire 2.50 6.00

2000 Fleer Showcase Fresh Ink

Randomly inserted into packs at one in 24, this 38-card insert set features autographs of many of MLB's top stars and prospects. Please note that Josh Beckett and Brad Penny packed out as exchange cards and must be submitted to Fleer by 07/01/01. These cards are not numbered and we have sequenced them in alphabetical order in our checklist.

1 Rick Ankiel 10.00 25.00
2 Josh Beckett 8.00 20.00
3 Barry Bonds 40.00 80.00
4 A.J. Burnett 5.00 12.00
5 Pat Burrell 6.00 15.00
6 Ken Caminiti 15.00 40.00
7 Sean Casey 6.00 15.00
8 Jose Cruz Jr. 4.00 10.00
9 Gookie Dawkins 4.00 10.00
10 Erubiel Durazo 4.00 10.00
11 Juan Encarnacion 6.00 15.00
12 Darin Erstad 6.00 15.00
13 Rafael Furcal 6.00 15.00
14 Nomar Garciaparra 50.00 100.00
15 Jason Giambi 10.00 25.00
16 Jeremy Giambi 4.00 10.00
17 Brian Giles 6.00 15.00
18 Troy Glaus 10.00 25.00
19 Vladimir Guerrero 15.00 40.00
20 Chad Hermansen 4.00 10.00
21 Randy Johnson 30.00 60.00
22 Andruw Jones 10.00 25.00
23 Jason Kendall 6.00 15.00
24 Paul Konerko 8.00 20.00
25 Mike Lowell 6.00 15.00
26 Aaron McNeal 4.00 10.00
27 Warren Morris 4.00 10.00
28 Paul O'Neill 10.00 25.00
29 Magglio Ordonez 6.00 15.00
30 Pablo Ozuna 4.00 10.00
31 Brad Penny 6.00 15.00
32 Ben Petrick 4.00 10.00
33 Pokey Reese 6.00 15.00
34 Cal Ripken 75.00 150.00
35 Alex Rodriguez 50.00 100.00
36 Scott Rolen 10.00 25.00
37 Jose Vidro 4.00 10.00
38 Kip Wells 4.00 10.00

2000 Fleer Showcase License to Skill

Randomly inserted into packs at one in 20, this 10-card set features highly skilled players. Card backs carry a "LS" prefix.

COMPLETE SET (10) 30.00 80.00
LS1 Vladimir Guerrero 2.00 5.00
LS2 Pedro Martinez 1.25 3.00
LS3 Nomar Garciaparra 3.00 8.00
LS4 Ivan Rodriguez 1.25 3.00
LS5 Mark McGwire 5.00 12.00
LS6 Derek Jeter 5.00 12.00
LS7 Ken Griffey Jr. 3.00 8.00
LS8 Randy Johnson 2.00 5.00
LS9 Sammy Sosa 2.00 5.00
LS10 Alex Rodriguez 3.00 8.00

2000 Fleer Showcase Long Gone

Randomly inserted into packs at one in 20, this 10-card set features hitters that are known for hitting the longball. Card backs carry a "LG" prefix.

COMPLETE SET (10) 10.00 25.00
LG1 Sammy Sosa .75 2.00
LG2 Derek Jeter 2.00 5.00
LG3 Nomar Garciaparra 1.25 3.00
LG4 Juan Gonzalez .30 .75
LG5 Vladimir Guerrero .75 2.00
LG6 Barry Bonds 2.00 5.00
LG7 Jeff Bagwell .50 1.25
LG8 Alex Rodriguez 1.25 3.00
LG9 Ken Griffey Jr. 1.25 3.00
LG10 Mark McGwire 2.00 5.00

2000 Fleer Showcase Noise of Summer

Randomly inserted into packs at one in 10, this 10-card set features players that make plenty of noise during the season. Card backs carry a "NS" prefix.

COMPLETE SET (10) 15.00 40.00
NS1 Chipper Jones 1.00 2.50
NS2 Jeff Bagwell .60 1.50
NS3 Manny Ramirez .60 1.50
NS4 Mark McGwire 2.50 6.00
NS5 Ken Griffey Jr. 1.50 4.00
NS6 Mike Piazza 1.50 4.00
NS7 Pedro Martinez .60 1.50
NS8 Alex Rodriguez 1.50 4.00
NS9 Derek Jeter 2.50 6.00
NS10 Randy Johnson 1.00 2.50

2000 Fleer Showcase Sweet Sigs

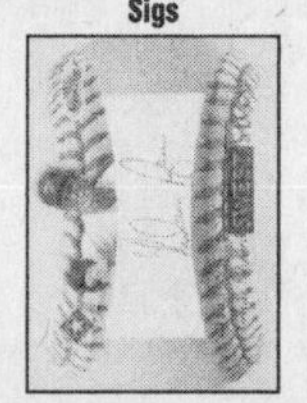

Randomly inserted into packs at one in 250, this 10-card set features autographs of MLB players like Alex Rodriguez and Nolan Ryan. Card backs carry a "SS" prefix. A month after the product went live, representatives at Fleer publicly released print run information on three short-printed cards (Clemens, Garciaparra and A.Rodriguez). Exact amounts are provided in our checklist.

SS1 N.Garciaparra SP/53 30.00 60.00
SS2 Alex Rodriguez SP/67 100.00 200.00
SS3 Tony Gwynn 20.00 50.00
SS4 Roger Clemens SP/79 100.00 200.00
SS5 Scott Rolen 15.00 40.00
SS6 Greg Maddux 50.00 100.00
SS7 Jose Cruz Jr. 6.00 15.00
SS8 Tony Womack 6.00 15.00
SS9 Jay Buhner 10.00 25.00
SS10 Nolan Ryan 75.00 150.00

2001 Fleer Showcase

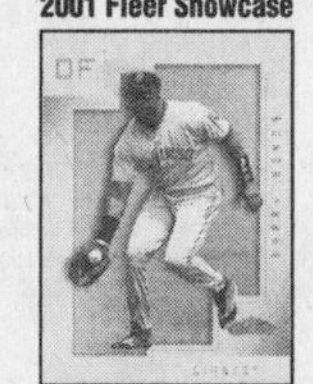

This 160-card set was distributed in five-card packs with a suggested retail price of $4.99. The set features color player images on Satin technology and contains the following subsets: Avant (101-115), Rookie Avant (116-125), and Rookie Showcase (126-160) with the first 20 sequentially numbered to 1,500 and the next 15 to 2,000)

COMP.SET w/o SP's (100) 12.50 30.00
COMMON CARD (1-100) .20 .50
COMMON (101-115) 2.00 5.00
COMMON (116-125) 3.00 8.00
COMMON (126-160) 2.00 5.00
1 Tony Gwynn .60 1.50
2 Barry Larkin .30 .75
3 Chan Ho Park .20 .50
4 Darin Erstad .20 .50
5 Rafael Furcal .20 .50
6 Roger Cedeno .20 .50
7 Timo Perez .20 .50
8 Rick Ankiel .20 .50
9 Pokey Reese .20 .50
10 Jeromy Burnitz .20 .50
11 Phil Nevin .20 .50
12 Matt Williams .20 .50
13 Mike Hampton .20 .50
14 Fernando Tatis .20 .50
15 Kazuhiro Sasaki .20 .50
16 Jim Thome .30 .75
17 Geoff Jenkins .20 .50
18 Jeff Kent .20 .50
19 Tom Glavine .30 .75
20 Dean Palmer .20 .50
21 Todd Zeile .20 .50
22 Edgar Renteria .20 .50
23 Andruw Jones .30 .75
24 Juan Encarnacion .20 .50
25 Robin Ventura .20 .50
26 J.D. Drew .20 .50
27 Ray Durham .20 .50
28 Richard Hidalgo .20 .50
29 Eric Chavez .20 .50
30 Rafael Palmeiro .30 .75
31 Steve Finley .20 .50
32 Jeff Weaver .20 .50
33 Al Leiter .20 .50
34 Jim Edmonds .20 .50
35 Garret Anderson .20 .50
36 Larry Walker .20 .50
37 Jose Vidro .20 .50
38 Mike Cameron .20 .50
39 Brady Anderson .20 .50
40 Mike Lowell .20 .50
41 Bernie Williams .30 .75
42 Gary Sheffield .20 .50
43 John Smoltz .30 .75
44 Mike Mussina .30 .75
45 Greg Vaughn .20 .50
46 Juan Gonzalez .20 .50
47 Matt Lawton .20 .50
48 Robb Nen .20 .50
49 Brad Radke .20 .50
50 Edgar Martinez .30 .75
51 Mike Bordick .20 .50
52 Shawn Green .20 .50
53 Carl Everett .20 .50
54 Adrian Beltre .20 .50
55 Kerry Wood .20 .50
56 Kevin Brown .20 .50
57 Brian Giles .20 .50
58 Greg Maddux .75 2.00
59 Preston Wilson .20 .50
60 Orlando Hernandez .20 .50
61 Ben Grieve .20 .50
62 Jermaine Dye .20 .50
63 Travis Lee .20 .50
64 Jose Cruz Jr. .20 .50
65 Rondell White .20 .50
66 Carlos Beltran .20 .50
67 Scott Rolen .30 .75
68 Brad Fullmer .20 .50
69 David Wells .20 .50
70 Mike Sweeney .20 .50
71 Barry Zito .30 .75
72 Tony Batista .20 .50
73 Curt Schilling .20 .50
74 Jeff Cirillo .20 .50
75 Edgardo Alfonzo .20 .50
76 John Olerud .20 .50
77 Carlos Lee .20 .50
78 Moises Alou .20 .50
79 Tim Hudson .20 .50
80 Andres Galarraga .20 .50
81 Roberto Alomar .30 .75
82 Richie Sexson .20 .50
83 Trevor Hoffman .20 .50
84 Omar Vizquel .30 .75
85 Jacque Jones .20 .50
86 J.T. Snow .20 .50
87 Sean Casey .20 .50
88 Craig Biggio .30 .75
89 Mariano Rivera .50 1.25
90 Rusty Greer .20 .50
91 Barry Bonds 1.25 3.00
92 Pedro Martinez .30 .75
93 Cal Ripken 1.50 4.00
94 Pat Burrell .20 .50
95 Chipper Jones .50 1.25
96 Magglio Ordonez .20 .50
97 Jeff Bagwell .30 .75
98 Randy Johnson .50 1.25
99 Frank Thomas .50 1.25
100 Jason Kendall .20 .50
101 N.Garciaparra AC 5.00 12.00
102 Mark McGwire AC 8.00 20.00
103 Troy Glaus AC 2.00 5.00
104 Ivan Rodriguez AC 2.00 5.00
105 Manny Ramirez Sox AC 2.00 5.00
106 Derek Jeter AC 8.00 20.00
107 Alex Rodriguez AC 5.00 12.00
108 Ken Griffey Jr. AC 5.00 12.00
109 Todd Helton AC 2.00 5.00
110 Sammy Sosa AC 3.00 8.00
111 Vladimir Guerrero AC 3.00 8.00
112 Mike Piazza AC 5.00 12.00
113 Roger Clemens AC 6.00 15.00
114 Jason Giambi AC 2.00 5.00
115 Carlos Delgado AC 2.00 5.00
116 Ichiro Suzuki AC RC 75.00 125.00
117 M.Ensberg AC RC 5.00 12.00
118 C. Valderrama AC RC 3.00 8.00
119 Erick Almonte AC RC 3.00 8.00
120 T.Shinjo AC RC 5.00 12.00
121 Albert Pujols AC RC 100.00 200.00
122 Wilson Betemit AC RC 5.00 12.00
123 A.Hernandez AC RC 3.00 8.00
124 J.Melian AC RC 3.00 8.00
125 Drew Henson AC RC 5.00 12.00
126 Paul Phillips RS RC 2.00 5.00
127 Esix Snead RS RC 2.00 5.00
128 Ryan Freel RS RC 2.00 5.00
129 Junior Spivey RS RC 3.00 8.00
130 E.Guzman RS RC 2.00 5.00
131 Juan Diaz RS RC 2.00 5.00
132 Andres Torres RS RC 2.00 5.00
133 Jay Gibbons RS RC 3.00 8.00
134 Bill Ortega RS RC 2.00 5.00
135 Alexis Gomez RS RC 2.00 5.00
136 Wilkin Ruan RS RC 2.00 5.00
137 Henry Mateo RS RC 2.00 5.00
138 Juan Uribe RS RC 3.00 8.00
139 J.Estrada RS RC 3.00 8.00
140 J.Randolph RS RC 2.00 5.00
141 Eric Hinske RS RC 3.00 8.00
142 Jack Wilson RS RC 3.00 8.00
143 Cody Ransom RS RC 2.00 5.00
144 Nate Frese RS RC 2.00 5.00
145 John Grabow RS RC 2.00 5.00
146 C.Parker RS RC 2.00 5.00
147 B.Lawrence RS RC 2.00 5.00
148 B. Duckworth RS RC 2.00 5.00
149 Winston Abreu RS RC 2.00 5.00
150 H.Ramirez RS RC 3.00 8.00
151 Nick Maness RS RC 2.00 5.00
152 Blaine Neal RS RC 2.00 5.00
153 Billy Sylvester RS RC 2.00 5.00
154 David Elder RS RC 2.00 5.00
155 Bert Snow RS RC 2.00 5.00
156 Claudio Vargas RS RC 2.00 5.00
157 Martin Vargas RS RC 2.00 5.00
158 Grant Balfour RS RC 2.00 5.00
159 Randy Keisler RS 2.00 5.00
160 Zach Day RS RC 2.00 5.00
P1 Tony Gwynn Promo .75 2.00
MM3 D.Jeter MM/2000 5.00 12.00
NNO D.Jeter MM AU/100 60.00 120.00

2001 Fleer Showcase Legacy

Randomly inserted in hobby packs only, this 160-card set is a parallel version of the base set. Only 50 serially numbered sets were produced.

*STARS 1-100: 8X TO 20X BASIC 1-100
*AVANT 101-115: 1.25X TO 3X BASIC 101-115
*AVANT 116-125: .75X TO 2X BASIC 116-125
*RS 126-145: 1.25X TO 3X BASIC 126-145
*RS 146-160: 1.5X TO 4X BASIC 146-160

2001 Fleer Showcase Awards Showcase

Randomly inserted in retail packs only at the rate of one in 20, this 20-card set features color photos of some of the big award winners from the 2000 season.

COMPLETE SET (20) 30.00 60.00
AS1 Derek Jeter 3.00 8.00
AS2 Derek Jeter 3.00 8.00
AS3 Jason Giambi .50 1.25
AS4 Jeff Kent .50 1.25
AS5 Pedro Martinez .75 2.00
AS6 Randy Johnson 1.25 3.00
AS7 Kazuhiro Sasaki .50 1.25
AS8 Rafael Furcal .50 1.25
AS9 Carlos Delgado .50 1.25
AS10 Todd Helton .75 2.00
AS11 Ivan Rodriguez .75 2.00
AS12 Darin Erstad .50 1.25
AS13 Bernie Williams .75 2.00
AS14 Greg Maddux 2.00 5.00
AS15 Jim Edmonds .50 1.25
AS16 Andruw Jones .75 2.00
AS17 Nomar Garciaparra 2.00 5.00
AS18 Todd Helton .75 2.00
AS19 Troy Glaus .50 1.25
AS20 Sammy Sosa 1.25 3.00

2001 Fleer Showcase Awards Showcase Memorabilia

Randomly inserted in hobby packs only, this 34-card set features color photos of players who were Cy Young and MVP winners with pieces of memorabilia embedded in the cards. Only 100 serially numbered sets were produced.

1 Johnny Bench Jsy 10.00 25.00
2 Yogi Berra Bat 10.00 25.00
3 George Brett Jsy 15.00 40.00
4 Lou Brock Bat 10.00 25.00
5 Roy Campanella Bat 15.00 40.00
6 Steve Carlton Jsy 6.00 15.00
7 Roger Clemens Jsy 15.00 40.00
9 Andre Dawson Jsy 6.00 15.00
10 Whitey Ford Jsy 10.00 25.00
12 Jimmie Foxx Bat 30.00 60.00
14 Kirk Gibson Bat 6.00 15.00
15 Tom Glavine Jsy 10.00 25.00
16 Juan Gonzalez Bat 6.00 15.00
17 Elston Howard Bat 10.00 25.00
18 Jim Hunter Jsy 10.00 25.00
19 Reggie Jackson Bat 10.00 25.00
20 Randy Johnson Jsy 10.00 25.00
21 Chipper Jones Bat 10.00 25.00
22 Harmon Killebrew Bat 10.00 25.00
23 Fred Lynn Bat 6.00 15.00
24 Greg Maddux Jsy 10.00 25.00
25 Don Mattingly Bat 15.00 40.00
27 Willie McCovey Jsy 6.00 15.00
28 Jim Palmer Jsy 6.00 15.00
29 Jim Rice Bat 6.00 15.00
30 Brooks Robinson Bat 10.00 25.00
31 Frank Robinson Bat 10.00 25.00
32 Jackie Robinson Pants 40.00 80.00
33 Ivan Rodriguez Jsy 10.00 25.00
34 Mike Schmidt Jsy 15.00 40.00
35 Tom Seaver Jsy 10.00 25.00
36 Willie Stargell Jsy 10.00 25.00
37 Ted Williams Jsy 50.00 100.00
38 Robin Yount Jsy 10.00 25.00

2001 Fleer Showcase Sticks

Randomly inserted into hobby packs at the rate of one in 24, this 36-card set color player photos with pieces of game-used bats embedded in the cards.

1 Roberto Alomar 6.00 15.00
2 Rick Ankiel 4.00 10.00
3 Adrian Beltre 4.00 10.00
4 Barry Bonds 10.00 25.00
5 Pat Burrell 4.00 10.00
6 Roger Cedeno 4.00 10.00
7 Tony Clark 4.00 10.00
8 Roger Clemens 6.00 15.00
9 Carlos Delgado 4.00 10.00
10 J.D. Drew 4.00 10.00
11 Steve Finley 4.00 10.00
12 Rafael Furcal 4.00 10.00
13 Alex Gonzalez 4.00 10.00
14 Juan Gonzalez 4.00 10.00
15 Shawn Green 4.00 10.00
16 Vladimir Guerrero 6.00 15.00
17 Richard Hidalgo 4.00 10.00
18 Reggie Jackson 6.00 15.00
19 Randy Johnson 6.00 15.00
20 Andruw Jones 6.00 15.00
21 Chipper Jones 6.00 15.00
22 Al Kaline 6.00 15.00
23 George Kell 4.00 10.00
24 Jason Kendall 4.00 10.00
25 Magglio Ordonez 4.00 10.00
26 Adam Piatt 4.00 10.00
27 Jorge Posada 6.00 15.00
28 Ivan Rodriguez 6.00 15.00
29 Scott Rolen 6.00 15.00
30 Tsuyoshi Shinjo 6.00 15.00
31 Shannon Stewart 4.00 10.00
32 Ichiro Suzuki 15.00 40.00
33 Frank Thomas 6.00 15.00
34 Jim Thome 6.00 15.00
35 Jose Vidro 4.00 10.00
36 Preston Wilson 4.00 10.00

2001 Fleer Showcase Sweet Sigs Leather

Randomly inserted in hobby packs at the rate of one in 24, this 23 card set features color player head shots with their autograph printed on a piece of simulated baseball leather. The following players cards were seeded into packs as exchange cards with a redemption deadline of 11/01/02: Bob Abreu, Wilson Betemit, Russell Branyan, Pat Burrell, Sean Casey, Eric Chavez, Rafael Furcal, Nomar Garciaparra, Juan Gonzalez, Elpidio Guzman, Brandon Inge, Willie Mays, Jackson Melian, Xavier Nady, Jose Ortiz, Ben Sheets and Mike Sweeney.

SP PRINT PRINT RUNS LISTED BELOW
1 Bob Abreu SP/100 15.00 40.00
2 Wilson Betemit 10.00 25.00
3 Russell Branyan 6.00 15.00
4 Pat Burrell SP/75 15.00 40.00
5 Sean Casey SP/75 15.00 40.00
6 E.Chavez SP/100 EXCH 15.00 40.00
7 Rafael Furcal 6.00 15.00
8 Nomar Garciaparra SP/75 50.00 100.00
9 Brian Giles SP/75 15.00 40.00
10 Juan Gonzalez SP/75 EXCH 15.00 40.00
11 Elpidio Guzman 6.00 15.00
12 Drew Henson SP/75 10.00 25.00
13 Brandon Inge 6.00 15.00
14 Derek Jeter SP/75 100.00 200.00
15 Andruw Jones SP/85 20.00 50.00
16 W.Mays SP/60 EXCH 125.00 200.00
17 Jackson Melian 6.00 15.00
18 Xavier Nady 6.00 15.00
19 Jose Ortiz 6.00 15.00
20 Albert Pujols SP/75 600.00 900.00
21 Ben Sheets 8.00 20.00
22 Mike Sweeney 6.00 15.00
23 Miguel Tejada SP/75 20.00 50.00

2001 Fleer Showcase Sweet Sigs Lumber

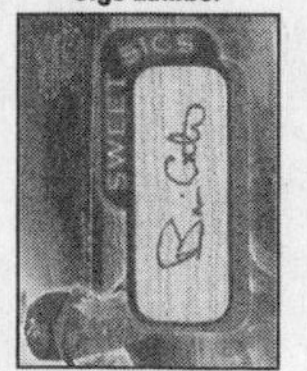

Randomly inserted in hobby packs at the rate of one in 24, this 23-card set features color player photos with their autograph printed on a piece of ash designed to look like a bat. The following players cards were seeded into packs as exchange cards with a redemption deadline of 11/01/02: Bob Abreu, Wilson Betemit, Russell Branyan, Pat Burrell, Sean Casey, Eric Chavez, Rafael Furcal, Nomar Garciaparra, Juan Gonzalez, Elpidio Guzman, Brandon Inge, Jackson Melian, Xavier Nady, Jose Ortiz, Ben Sheets and Mike Sweeney.

SP PRINT PRINT RUNS LISTED BELOW
1 Bob Abreu 6.00 15.00
2 Wilson Betemit 10.00 25.00
3 Russell Branyan 6.00 15.00
4 Pat Burrell SP/300 10.00 25.00
5 Sean Casey SP/300 10.00 25.00
6 Eric Chavez 6.00 15.00
7 Rafael Furcal 6.00 15.00
8 Nomar Garciaparra SP/155 EXCH 50.00 100.00
9 Brian Giles SP/155 10.00 25.00
10 Juan Gonzalez 10.00 25.00

SP/300 EXCH		
11 Elpidio Guzman	6.00	15.00
12 Drew Henson SP/145	10.00	25.00
13 Brandon Inge	6.00	15.00
14 Derek Jeter SP/300	100.00	175.00
15 Andruw Jones SP/300	12.50	30.00
16 Willie Mays SP/155	75.00	150.00
17 Jackson Melian	6.00	15.00
18 Xavier Nady	6.00	15.00
19 Jose Ortiz	6.00	15.00
20 Albert Pujols SP/150	400.00	700.00
21 Ben Sheets	8.00	20.00
22 Mike Sweeney	6.00	15.00
23 Miguel Tejada SP/300	12.50	30.00

2001 Fleer Showcase Sweet Sigs Wall

Randomly inserted in hobby packs at the rate of one in 24, this 23-card set features color player photos with their autograph printed on an actual piece of game-used outfield wall. The following players cards were seeded into packs as exchange cards with a redemption deadline of 11/01/02: Bob Abreu, Wilson Betemit, Russell Branyan, Pat Burrell, Eric Chavez, Rafael Furcal, Nomar Garciaparra, Juan Gonzalez, Elpidio Guzman, Brandon Inge, Willie Mays, Jackson Melian, Xavier Nady, Jose Ortiz and Ben Sheets.

SP PRINT PRINT RUNS LISTED BELOW

1 Bob Abreu	6.00	15.00
2 Wilson Betemit	10.00	25.00
3 Russell Branyan	6.00	15.00
4 Pat Burrell SP/93	12.50	30.00
5 Sean Casey SP/98	12.50	30.00
6 Eric Chavez	6.00	15.00
7 Rafael Furcal	6.00	15.00
8 Nomar Garciaparra SP/80 EXCH	20.00	50.00
9 Brian Giles SP/100	12.50	30.00
10 Juan Gonzalez SP/30 EXCH	15.00	40.00
11 Elpidio Guzman	6.00	15.00
12 Drew Henson SP/100	12.50	30.00
13 Brandon Inge	6.00	15.00
14 Derek Jeter SP/90	100.00	200.00
15 Andruw Jones SP/200	15.00	40.00
16 W.Mays SP/85 EXCH	125.00	200.00
17 Jackson Melian	6.00	15.00
18 Xavier Nady	6.00	15.00
19 Jose Ortiz	6.00	15.00
20 Albert Pujols SP/80	600.00	900.00
21 Ben Sheets	8.00	20.00
22 Mike Sweeney		
23 Miguel Tejada SP/120	15.00	40.00

2002 Fleer Showcase

This 166 card standard-size set was released in June, 2002. It was issued in five card packs which came 24 packs to a box and four boxes to a case. Each pack had an SRP of $5. Cards numbered 1-125 featured standard cards of veterans while cards 126-135 featured special veteran "avant" cards (seeded at a rate of 1:12 packs) and cards numbered 136-166 feature rookies/prospects (randomly seeded into packs at an undisclosed rate). Those rookie/prospect cards were issued in the following way: cards 136-141 have a stated print run of 500 serial numbered sets, cards numbered 142-156 have a stated print run of 1000 serial numbered sets and cards numbered 157-166 have a stated print run of 1500 serial numbered sets.

COMP.SET w/o SP's (125)	12.50	30.00
COMMON CARD (1-125)	.20	.50
COMMON CARD (126-135)	3.00	8.00
COMMON CARD (136-141)	4.00	10.00
COMMON CARD (142-166)	3.00	8.00
1 Albert Pujols	1.00	2.50
2 Pedro Martinez	.30	.75
3 Frank Thomas	.50	1.25
4 Gary Sheffield	.20	.50
5 Roberto Alomar	.30	.75
6 Luis Gonzalez	.20	.50
7 Bobby Abreu	.20	.50
8 Carlos Lee	.20	.50
9 Preston Wilson	.20	.50
10 Todd Helton	.30	.75
11 Juan Gonzalez	.20	.50
12 Chuck Knoblauch	.20	.50
13 Jason Kendall	.20	.50
14 Aaron Sele	.20	.50
15 Greg Vaughn	.20	.50
16 Fred McGriff	.30	.75
17 Doug Mientkiewicz	.20	.50
18 Richard Hidalgo	.20	.50
19 Alfonso Soriano	.20	.50
20 Matt Williams	.20	.50
21 Bobby Higginson	.20	.50
22 Mo Vaughn	.20	.50
23 Andruw Jones	.30	.75
24 Omar Vizquel	.30	.75
25 Bret Boone	.20	.50
26 Bernie Williams	.30	.75
27 Rafael Furcal	.20	.50
28 Jeff Bagwell	.30	.75
29 Marty Cordova	.20	.50
30 Lance Berkman	.20	.50
31 Vernon Wells	.20	.50
32 Garret Anderson	.20	.50
33 Larry Bigbie	.20	.50
34 Steve Finley	.20	.50
35 Barry Bonds	1.25	3.00
36 Eric Chavez	.20	.50
37 Tony Clark	.20	.50
38 Roger Clemens	1.00	2.50
39 Adam Dunn	.20	.50
40 Roger Cedeno	.20	.50
41 Carlos Delgado	.20	.50
42 Jermaine Dye	.20	.50
43 Brian Jordan	.20	.50
44 Darin Erstad	.20	.50
45 Paul LoDuca	.20	.50
46 Jim Edmonds	.20	.50
47 Tom Glavine	.30	.75
48 Cliff Floyd	.20	.50
49 Jon Lieber	.20	.50
50 Adrian Beltre	.20	.50
51 Joel Pineiro	.20	.50
52 Jim Thome	.30	.75
53 Jimmy Rollins	.20	.50
54 Pat Burrell	.20	.50
55 Jeromy Burnitz	.20	.50
56 Larry Walker	.20	.50
57 Damon Minor	.20	.50
58 John Olerud	.20	.50
59 Carlos Beltran	.20	.50
60 Vladimir Guerrero	.50	1.25
61 David Justice	.20	.50
62 Phil Nevin	.20	.50
63 Tino Martinez	.30	.75
64 Curt Schilling	.20	.50
65 Corey Patterson	.20	.50
66 Aubrey Huff	.20	.50
67 Mark Grace	.30	.75
68 Rafael Palmeiro	.30	.75
69 Jorge Posada	.30	.75
70 Craig Biggio	.30	.75
71 Manny Ramirez	.30	.75
72 Mark Quinn	.20	.50
73 Raul Mondesi	.20	.50
74 Shawn Green	.20	.50
75 Brian Giles	.20	.50
76 Paul Konerko	.20	.50
77 Troy Glaus	.20	.50
78 Mike Mussina	.30	.75
79 Greg Maddux	.75	2.00
80 Edgar Martinez	.30	.75
81 Jose Vidro	.20	.50
82 Scott Rolen	.30	.75
83 Ben Grieve	.20	.50
84 Jeff Kent	.20	.50
85 Magglio Ordonez	.20	.50
86 Freddy Garcia	.20	.50
87 Ivan Rodriguez	.30	.75
88 Pokey Reese	.20	.50
89 Shannon Stewart	.20	.50
90 Randy Johnson	.50	1.25
91 Cristian Guzman	.20	.50
92 Tsuyoshi Shinjo	.20	.50
93 Steve Cox	.20	.50
94 Mike Sweeney	.20	.50
95 Robert Fick	.20	.50
96 Sean Casey	.20	.50
97 Tim Hudson	.20	.50
98 Bud Smith	.20	.50
99 Corey Koskie	.20	.50
100 Richie Sexson	.20	.50
101 Aramis Ramirez	.20	.50
102 Barry Larkin	.30	.75
103 Rich Aurilia	.20	.50
104 Charles Johnson	.20	.50
105 Ryan Klesko	.20	.50
106 Ben Sheets	.20	.50
107 J.D. Drew	.20	.50
108 Jay Gibbons	.20	.50
109 Kerry Wood	.20	.50
110 C.C. Sabathia	.20	.50
111 Eric Munson	.20	.50
112 Josh Beckett	.20	.50
113 Javier Vazquez	.20	.50
114 Barry Zito	.20	.50
115 Kazuhiro Sasaki	.20	.50
116 Bubba Trammell	.20	.50
117 Russell Branyan	.20	.50
118 Todd Walker	.20	.50
119 Mike Hampton	.20	.50
120 Jeff Weaver	.20	.50
121 Geoff Jenkins	.20	.50
122 Edgardo Alfonzo	.20	.50
123 Mike Lieberthal	.20	.50
124 Mike Lowell	.20	.50
125 Kevin Brown	.20	.50
126 Derek Jeter AC	8.00	20.00
127 Ichiro Suzuki AC	6.00	15.00
128 Nomar Garciaparra AC	5.00	12.00
129 Ken Griffey Jr. AC	5.00	12.00
130 Jason Giambi AC	3.00	8.00
131 Alex Rodriguez AC	5.00	12.00
132 Chipper Jones AC	3.00	8.00
133 Mike Piazza AC	5.00	12.00
134 Sammy Sosa AC	3.00	8.00
135 Hideo Nomo AC	3.00	8.00
136 Kazuhisa Ishii AC RC	6.00	15.00
137 Satoru Komiyama AC RC	4.00	10.00
138 So Taguchi AC RC	6.00	15.00
139 Jorge Padilla AC RC	4.00	10.00
140 Rene Reyes AC RC	4.00	10.00
141 Jorge Nunez AC RC	4.00	10.00
142 Nelson Castro RS	3.00	8.00
143 Anderson Machado RS RC	3.00	8.00
144 Edwin Almonte RS RC	3.00	8.00
145 Luis Ugueto RS RC	3.00	8.00
146 Felix Escalona RS RC	3.00	8.00
147 Ron Calloway RS RC	3.00	8.00
148 Hansel Izquierdo RS RC	3.00	8.00
149 Mark Teixeira RS	4.00	10.00
150 Orlando Hudson RS	3.00	8.00
151 Aaron Cook RS RC	3.00	8.00
152 Aaron Taylor RS RC	3.00	8.00
153 Takahito Nomura RS RC	3.00	8.00
154 Matt Thornton RS RC	3.00	8.00
155 Mark Prior RS	4.00	10.00
156 Reed Johnson RS RC	4.00	10.00
157 Doug DeVore RS RC	3.00	8.00
158 Ben Howard RS RC	3.00	8.00
159 Francis Beltran RS RC	3.00	8.00
160 Brian Mallette RS RC	3.00	8.00
161 Sean Burroughs RS	3.00	8.00
162 Michael Restovich RS	3.00	8.00
163 Austin Kearns RS	3.00	8.00
164 Marlon Byrd RS	3.00	8.00
165 Hank Blalock RS	4.00	10.00
166 Mike Rivera RS	3.00	8.00

2002 Fleer Showcase Legacy

Issued at a stated rate of one per hobby box, this is a complete parallel of the Fleer Showcase set. Each of these cards have a stated print run of 175 serial numbered sets.

*LEGACY 1-125: 2.5X TO 6X BASIC
*LEGACY 126-135: .5X TO 1.2X BASIC
*LEGACY 136-141: .4X TO 1X BASIC
*LEGACY 142-166: .5X TO 1.2X BASIC

2002 Fleer Showcase Baseball's Best

Issued in hobby packs at a stated rate of one in eight and retail packs at a stated rate of one in 10, these 20 cards features the leading players in the game.

COMPLETE SET (20)	25.00	60.00
1 Derek Jeter	3.00	8.00
2 Barry Bonds	3.00	8.00
3 Mike Piazza	2.00	5.00
4 Alex Rodriguez	2.00	5.00
5 Pat Burrell	.75	2.00
6 Rafael Palmeiro	.75	2.00
7 Nomar Garciaparra	2.00	5.00
8 Todd Helton	.75	2.00
9 Roger Clemens	2.50	6.00
10 Shawn Green	.75	2.00
11 Chipper Jones	1.25	3.00
12 Pedro Martinez	.75	2.00
13 Luis Gonzalez	.75	2.00
14 Randy Johnson	1.25	3.00
15 Ichiro Suzuki	2.50	6.00
16 Ken Griffey Jr.	2.00	5.00
17 Vladimir Guerrero	1.25	3.00
18 Sammy Sosa	1.25	3.00
19 Jason Giambi	.75	2.00
20 Albert Pujols	2.50	6.00

2002 Fleer Showcase Baseball's Best Memorabilia

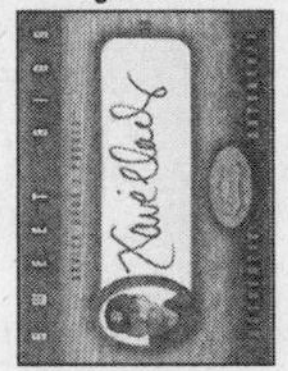

Inserted in packs at stated odds of one in 12 hobby and one in 36 retail, these 19 cards are a partial parallel of the Baseball's Best insert set. Each of these cards have a memorabilia piece attached to them.

*MULTI-COLOR PATCH: 1X TO 2.5X BASIC
*GOLD: 1X TO 2.5X BASIC
GOLD PRINT RUN 100 SERIAL #'d SETS

1 Derek Jeter Jsy	8.00	20.00
2 Barry Bonds Jsy	8.00	20.00
3 Mike Piazza Jsy	4.00	10.00
4 Alex Rodriguez Bat	6.00	15.00
6 Rafael Palmeiro Jsy	4.00	10.00
7 Nomar Garciaparra Jsy	6.00	15.00
8 Todd Helton Bat SP/350	4.00	10.00
9 Roger Clemens Jsy	6.00	15.00
10 Shawn Green Jsy	3.00	8.00
11 Chipper Jones Jsy	4.00	10.00
12 Pedro Martinez Jsy	4.00	10.00
13 Luis Gonzalez Jsy	3.00	8.00
14 Randy Johnson Jsy	4.00	10.00
15 Ichiro Suzuki Base	8.00	20.00
16 Ken Griffey Jr. Base	6.00	15.00
17 Vladimir Guerrero Base	3.00	8.00
18 Sammy Sosa Base	4.00	10.00
19 Jason Giambi Base	3.00	8.00
20 Albert Pujols Base	6.00	15.00

2002 Fleer Showcase Baseball's Best Memorabilia Autographs Silver

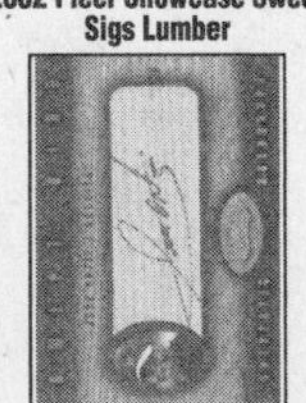

Randomly inserted in packs, these two cards are a parallel of the Baseball's Best Memorabilia insert set. Each of these cards have a stated print run of 400 serial numbered sets. Each of these cards feature not only the memorabilia swatch but also the player's autograph.

*GOLD: .6X TO 1.2X SILVER AU
GOLD PRINT RUN 100 SERIAL #'d SETS

1 Derek Jeter Jsy	75.00	150.00
2 Barry Bonds Jsy	100.00	175.00

2002 Fleer Showcase Derek Jeter Legacy Collection

Randomly inserted in packs, these 22 cards trace the entire career of Yankee superstar Derek Jeter who helped lead the Yankees to five pennants and four world championships in the first six years of his career.

COMPLETE SET (22)	40.00	100.00
COMMON CARD (1-22)	3.00	8.00

2002 Fleer Showcase Derek Jeter Legacy Collection Memorabilia

Randomly inserted in packs, these four cards feature various memorabilia which were part of Derek Jeter's career. Each card was printed to a different stated print run and we have notated that information in our checklist.

1 D.Jeter YC Jsy/300 *	125.00	200.00
2 Derek Jeter Combo Jsy/175 * Features white NY Yankees swatch and Blue Columbus Bombers swatch	150.00	250.00
3 D.Jeter WS Ball/50 *	125.00	200.00
4 D.Jeter Fldg Glv/425 *	50.00	100.00

2002 Fleer Showcase Sweet Sigs Leather

Randomly inserted in packs, these 13 cards feature player signatures on non game-used leather material. Since each player signed a different amount of cards we have put that stated information next to their name in our checklist. A few players signed less than 38 cards and those cards are not priced due to market scarcity.

1 Bobby Abreu/10		
2 Russell Branyan/90	6.00	15.00
3 Pat Burrell/35		
4 Sean Casey/35		
5 Eric Chavez/20		
6 Rafael Furcal/92	6.00	15.00
7 Nomar Garciaparra/5		
8 Brandon Inge/122	5.00	12.00
9 Jackson Melian/37		
10 Xavier Nady/301	6.00	15.00
11 Jose Ortiz/50	8.00	20.00
12 Ben Sheets/60	12.50	30.00
13 Mike Sweeney/103	8.00	20.00

2002 Fleer Showcase Sweet Sigs Lumber

Randomly inserted in packs, these 13 cards feature player signatures on non game-used wood material. Since each player signed a different amount of cards we have put that stated information next to their name in our checklist.

1 Bobby Abreu/231	6.00	15.00
2 Russell Branyan/425	4.00	10.00
3 Pat Burrell/115	8.00	20.00
4 Sean Casey/64	12.50	30.00
5 Eric Chavez/256	6.00	15.00
6 Rafael Furcal/530	4.00	10.00
7 Nomar Garciaparra/25		
8 Brandon Inge/528	4.00	10.00
9 Jackson Melian/636	4.00	10.00
10 Xavier Nady/589	4.00	10.00
11 Jose Ortiz/515	4.00	10.00
12 Ben Sheets/458	6.00	15.00
13 Mike Sweeney/495	6.00	15.00

2002 Fleer Showcase Sweet Sigs Wall

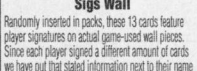

Randomly inserted in packs, these 13 cards feature player signatures on actual game-used wall pieces. Since each player signed a different amount of cards we have put that stated information next to their name in our checklist. Cards with a print run of 35 or fewer are not priced due to market scarcity.

1 Bobby Abreu/70	12.50	30.00
2 Russell Branyan/200	4.00	10.00
3 Pat Burrell/35		
4 Sean Casey/35		
5 Eric Chavez/108	8.00	20.00
6 Rafael Furcal/207	4.00	10.00
7 Nomar Garciaparra/25		
8 Brandon Inge/187	5.00	12.00
9 Jackson Melian/146	5.00	12.00
10 Xavier Nady/286	4.00	10.00
11 Jose Ortiz/116	5.00	12.00
12 Ben Sheets/150	8.00	20.00
13 Mike Sweeney/371	6.00	15.00

2003 Fleer Showcase

This 145-card set was issued in two separtate series. The primary Showcase product was released in March, 2003. Cards 1-95 are active ballplayers and 96- 105 feature retired players. Cards 106 through 135 are a subset entitled Showcasing Talent of which features a selection of top prospects. Three pack types were produced for this product (Jersey, Leather and Lumber) eight of each were placed into the 24-ct sealed boxes. Each pack type contained a selection of commonly available cards plus other inserts and subsets of which were exclusive to the theme. Cards 136-145 were randomly seeded within Fleer Rookies and Greats packs of which was distributed in December, 2003. Each of these 10 update cards features a top prospect and is serial numbered to 750 copies.

COMP.LO SET w/o SP's (105)	10.00	25.00
COMMON CARD (1-95)	.20	.50
COMMON CARD (96-105)	.40	1.00
COMMON CARD (106-135)	1.25	3.00
106-135 ODDS 1:3 HOBBY, 1:12 RETAIL		
106-115 DIST IN JERSEY AND RETAIL PACKS		
116-125 DIST IN LEATHER AND RETAIL PACKS		
126-135 DIST IN LUMBER AND RETAIL PACKS		
COMMON CARD (136-145)	1.50	4.00
1 David Eckstein	.20	.50
2 Curt Schilling	.20	.50
3 Jay Gibbons	.20	.50
4 Kerry Wood	.20	.50
5 Jeff Bagwell	.30	.75
6 Hideo Nomo	.50	1.25
7 Tim Hudson	.20	.50
8 J.D. Drew	.20	.50
9 Josh Phelps	.20	.50
10 Bartolo Colon	.20	.50
11 Bobby Abreu	.20	.50
12 Matt Morris	.20	.50
13 Kazuhiro Sasaki	.20	.50
14 Sean Burroughs	.20	.50
15 Vicente Padilla	.20	.50
16 Jorge Posada	.30	.75
17 Torii Hunter	.20	.50
18 Richie Sexson	.20	.50
19 Lance Berkman	.20	.50
20 Todd Helton	.30	.75
21 Paul Konerko	.20	.50
22 Pedro Martinez	.30	.75
23 Rodrigo Lopez	.20	.50
24 Gary Sheffield	.20	.50
25 Darin Erstad	.20	.50
26 Nomar Garciaparra	.75	2.00
27 Adam Dunn	.20	.50
28 Jason Giambi	.20	.50
29 Miguel Tejada	.20	.50
30 Chipper Jones	.50	1.25
31 Alex Rodriguez	.75	2.00
32 Barry Bonds	1.25	3.00
33 Roger Clemens	1.00	2.50
34 Sammy Sosa	.50	1.25
35 Randy Johnson	.50	1.25
36 Tim Salmon	.30	.75
37 Shea Hillenbrand	.20	.50
38 Larry Walker	.20	.50
39 A.J. Burnett	.20	.50
40 Shawn Green	.20	.50
41 Cristian Guzman	.20	.50
42 Bernie Williams	.30	.75
43 Mark Mulder	.20	.50
44 Brian Giles	.20	.50
45 Bret Boone	.20	.50
46 Juan Gonzalez	.20	.50
47 Roy Halladay	.20	.50
48 Wade Miller	.20	.50
49 Jeff Kent	.20	.50
50 Carlos Delgado	.20	.50
51 Mike Lowell	.20	.50
52 Jim Edmonds	.20	.50
53 Ivan Rodriguez	.30	.75
54 Aubrey Huff	.20	.50
55 Ryan Klesko	.20	.50
56 Paul Lo Duca	.20	.50
57 Roy Oswalt	.20	.50
58 Omar Vizquel	.30	.75
59 Manny Ramirez	.30	.75
60 Andruw Jones	.30	.75
61 Troy Glaus	.20	.50
62 Ichiro Suzuki	1.00	2.50
63 Albert Pujols	1.00	2.50
64 Derek Jeter	1.25	3.00
65 Mark Prior	.30	.75
66 Ken Griffey Jr.	.75	2.00
67 Vladimir Guerrero	.50	1.25
68 Mike Piazza	.75	2.00
69 Alfonso Soriano	.20	.50
70 Greg Maddux	.75	2.00
71 Adam Kennedy	.20	.50
72 Junior Spivey	.20	.50
73 Tom Glavine	.30	.75
74 Derek Lowe	.20	.50
75 Magglio Ordonez	.20	.50
76 Jim Thome	.30	.75
77 Robert Fick	.20	.50
78 Josh Beckett	.20	.50
79 Mike Sweeney	.20	.50
80 Kazuhisa Ishii	.20	.50
81 Roberto Alomar	.30	.75
82 Barry Zito	.20	.50
83 Pat Burrell	.20	.50
84 Scott Rolen	.30	.75
85 John Olerud	.20	.50
86 Eric Hinske	.20	.50
87 Rafael Palmeiro	.30	.75
88 Edgar Martinez	.30	.75
89 Eric Chavez	.20	.50
90 Jose Vidro	.20	.50
91 Craig Biggio	.30	.75
92 Rich Aurilia	.20	.50
93 Austin Kearns	.20	.50
94 Luis Gonzalez	.20	.50
95 Garret Anderson	.20	.50
96 Yogi Berra	.75	2.00
97 Al Kaline	.75	2.00
98 Robin Yount	.75	2.00
99 Reggie Jackson	.60	1.50
100 Harmon Killebrew	.75	2.00
101 Eddie Mathews	.75	2.00
102 Willie McCovey	.40	1.00
103 Nolan Ryan	1.50	4.00
104 Mike Schmidt	1.00	2.50
105 Tom Seaver	.60	1.50
106 Francisco Rodriguez ST	1.25	3.00
107 Carl Crawford ST	1.25	3.00
108 Ben Howard ST	1.25	3.00
109 Hank Blalock ST	1.25	3.00
110 Hee Seop Choi ST	1.25	3.00
111 Kirk Saarloos ST	1.25	3.00
112 Lew Ford ST RC	2.00	5.00
113 Andy Van Hekken ST	1.25	3.00
114 Drew Henson ST	1.25	3.00
115 Marlon Byrd ST	1.25	3.00
116 Jayson Werth ST	1.25	3.00
117 Willie Bloomquist ST	1.25	3.00
118 Joe Borchard ST	1.25	3.00
119 Mark Teixeira ST	2.00	5.00
120 Bobby Hill ST	1.25	3.00
121 Jason Lane ST	1.25	3.00
122 Omar Infante ST	1.25	3.00
123 Victor Martinez ST	2.00	5.00
124 Jorge Padilla ST	1.25	3.00
125 John Lackey ST	1.25	3.00
126 Anderson Machado ST	1.25	3.00
127 Rodrigo Rosario ST	1.25	3.00
128 Freddy Sanchez ST	1.25	3.00
129 Tony Alvarez ST	1.25	3.00
130 Matt Thornton ST	1.25	3.00
131 Joe Thurston ST	1.25	3.00
132 Brett Myers ST	1.25	3.00
133 Nook Logan ST RC	2.00	5.00
134 Chris Snelling ST	1.25	3.00
135 Termel Sledge ST RC	1.25	3.00
136 Chien-Ming Wang ST RC	6.00	15.00
137 Rickie Weeks ST RC	3.00	8.00
138 Brandon Webb ST RC	2.50	6.00
139 Hideki Matsui ST RC	6.00	15.00
140 Michael Hessman ST RC	1.50	4.00
141 Ryan Wagner ST RC	1.50	4.00
142 Bo Hart ST RC	1.50	4.00
143 Edwin Jackson ST RC	2.00	5.00
144 Jose Contreras ST RC	2.00	5.00
145 Delmon Young ST RC	6.00	15.00

2003 Fleer Showcase Legacy

This 135 card set was distributed exclusively in three separate forms of hobby packs. Cards 1-35 and 126-135 were available exclusively in hobby Lumber packs (signified by an orange-bar wrapper), 36-70 and 116-125 in hobby Leather packs (signified by brown-bar wrapper) and 71-105 and 106-115 in hobby Jersey packs (signified by a gray-bar wrapper). Only 150 serial numbered sets were produced. Each card is serial numbered on back in gold foil.

*LEGACY 1-95: 2.5X TO 6X BASIC
*LEGACY 96-105: 3X TO 8X BASIC
*LEGACY 106-135: .6X TO 1.5X BASIC

2003 Fleer Showcase Baseball's Best

Issued at a stated rate of one in eight leather packs and one in 24 retail packs, this 15-card insert set features the best players in baseball.

1 Curt Schilling	1.25	3.00
2 Barry Zito	1.25	3.00
3 Torii Hunter	1.25	3.00
4 Pedro Martinez	1.25	3.00
5 Bernie Williams	1.25	3.00
6 Magglio Ordonez	1.25	3.00
7 Alfonso Soriano	1.25	3.00
8 Hideo Nomo	1.25	3.00
9 Jason Giambi	1.25	3.00
10 Sammy Sosa	1.25	3.00
11 Vladimir Guerrero	1.25	3.00
12 Ken Griffey Jr.	2.00	5.00
13 Troy Glaus	1.25	3.00
14 Ichiro Suzuki	2.50	6.00
15 Albert Pujols	2.50	6.00

2003 Fleer Showcase Baseball's Best Game Jersey

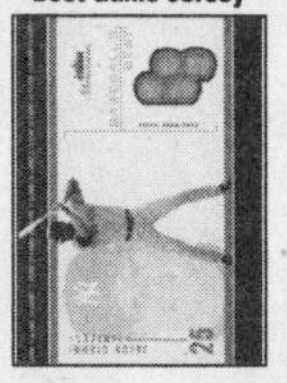

These cards parallel the Baseball's Best insert set. Although the wrappper stated odds list these cards as 1:27 Leather hobby packs - our analysis of the case breakdown, coupled with reports from dealers in the field indicates the cards were actually seeded at a rate of 1:9 Leather hobby packs.

AS Alfonso Soriano	3.00	8.00
BW Bernie Williams	4.00	10.00
BZ Barry Zito	3.00	8.00
CS Curt Schilling	3.00	8.00
HN Hideo Nomo Sox	4.00	10.00
JG Jason Giambi	3.00	8.00
MO Magglio Ordonez	3.00	8.00
PM Pedro Martinez	4.00	10.00
SS Sammy Sosa	4.00	10.00
TH Torii Hunter	3.00	8.00

2003 Fleer Showcase Hot Gloves

Inserted at a stated rate of one in 144 leather and one in 288 retail packs these 10 cards features some of the leading defensive players in baseball.

1 Greg Maddux	10.00	25.00
2 Ivan Rodriguez	6.00	15.00
3 Derek Jeter	15.00	40.00
4 Mike Piazza	10.00	25.00
5 Nomar Garciaparra	10.00	25.00
6 Andruw Jones	6.00	15.00
7 Scott Rolen	6.00	15.00
8 Barry Bonds	15.00	40.00
9 Roger Clemens	12.50	30.00
10 Alex Rodriguez	10.00	25.00

2003 Fleer Showcase Hot Gloves Game Jersey

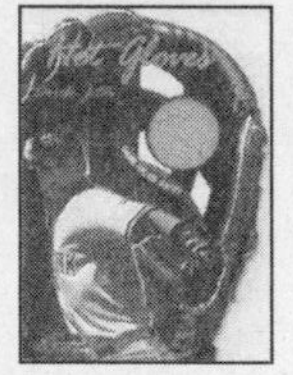

Randomly inserted in lumber packs, this is a parallel to the Hot Gloves insert set. These cards have a game-worn jersey card as well as the player's photo pictured.

AJ Andruw Jones	6.00	15.00
AR Alex Rodriguez	8.00	20.00
BB Barry Bonds	12.50	30.00
DJ Derek Jeter	12.50	30.00
GM Greg Maddux	8.00	20.00
IR Ivan Rodriguez	6.00	15.00
MP Mike Piazza	8.00	20.00
NG Nomar Garciaparra	8.00	20.00
RC Roger Clemens	10.00	25.00
SR Scott Rolen	6.00	15.00

2003 Fleer Showcase Sweet Sigs

Randomly inserted in both leather and retail packs, these cards feature authentic signatures of either Barry Bonds or Derek Jeter. As these cards are issued to various print runs, we have notated that information in our checklist.

BB1 Barry Bonds 90 MVP/150	100.00	175.00
BB2 Barry Bonds 92 MVP/100	100.00	175.00
BB3 Barry Bonds 93 MVP/75	125.00	200.00
BB4 Barry Bonds 01 MVP/50	150.00	250.00
BB5 Barry Bonds 02 MVP/25		
BB6 Barry Bonds 5X MVP/5		
DJ2 Derek Jeter Blue Ink/250	75.00	150.00
DJ3 Derek Jeter Red Ink/50	150.00	250.00

2003 Fleer Showcase Sweet Stitches

Issued at a stated rate of one in eight jersey packs and one in 24 retail packs, these 10 cards feature information about what various stars do in their off-field activities.

1 Derek Jeter 3.00 8.00
2 Randy Johnson 1.25 3.00
3 Jeff Bagwell 1.25 3.00
4 Nomar Garciaparra 2.00 5.00
5 Roger Clemens 2.50 6.00
6 Todd Helton 1.25 3.00
7 Barry Bonds 3.00 8.00
8 Alfonso Soriano 1.25 3.00
9 Miguel Tejada 1.25 3.00
10 Mark Prior 1.25 3.00

2003 Fleer Showcase Sweet Stitches Game Jersey

Randomly inserted in jersey packs, this is a parallel to the Sweet Stitches insert set. These cards feature game-used jersey pieces and were issued to assorted print runs and we have notated that information next to the player's name in our checklist.

AR Alex Rodriguez/899 6.00 15.00
AS Alfonso Soriano/599 3.00 8.00
BB Barry Bonds/899 8.00 20.00
DJ Derek Jeter/599 10.00 25.00
JB Jeff Bagwell/899 4.00 10.00
JD J.D. Drew/899 3.00 8.00
MP Mike Piazza/899 6.00 15.00
MP Mark Prior/899 4.00 10.00
MT Miguel Tejada/899 3.00 8.00
NG Nomar Garciaparra/899 6.00 15.00
RC Roger Clemens/599 8.00 20.00
RJ Randy Johnson/899 4.00 10.00
SS Sammy Sosa/899 4.00 10.00
TH Todd Helton/899 4.00 10.00

2003 Fleer Showcase Sweet Stitches Patch

Randomly inserted in jersey packs, this is a parallel to the sweet stitches insert set. These cards feature game-used jersey patch pieces and were issued to assorted print runs and we have notated that information next to the player's name in our checklist.

1 Derek Jeter/50
2 Randy Johnson/150 15.00 40.00
3 Jeff Bagwell/150 15.00 40.00
4 Nomar Garciaparra/150 30.00 60.00
5 Roger Clemens/50
6 Todd Helton/75 20.00 50.00
7 Barry Bonds/150 40.00 80.00
8 Alfonso Soriano/50 10.00 25.00
9 Miguel Tejada/150 10.00 25.00
10 Mark Prior/150 15.00 40.00
11 Sammy Sosa/150 15.00 40.00
12 J.D. Drew/150 10.00 25.00
13 Alex Rodriguez/150 30.00 60.00
14 Mike Piazza/150 30.00 60.00

2003 Fleer Showcase Thunder Sticks

Inserted in packs at a stated rate of one in eight lumber and one in 24 retail, these 10 cards feature some of the leading power hitters in baseball.

1 Adam Dunn 1.25 3.00
2 Alex Rodriguez 2.00 5.00
3 Barry Bonds 3.00 8.00
4 Jim Thome 1.25 3.00
5 Chipper Jones 1.25 3.00
6 Manny Ramirez 1.25 3.00
7 Carlos Delgado 1.25 3.00
8 Mike Piazza 2.00 5.00
9 Shawn Green 1.25 3.00
10 Pat Burrell 1.25 3.00

2003 Fleer Showcase Thunder Sticks Game Bat

Randomly inserted in lumber packs, these cards parallel the Thunder Sticks insert set. These cards feature a game bat piece and were issued to a varying amount of cards. We have notated the print run information next to the player's name in our checklist.

*GOLD: 1X TO 2.5X BASIC CARDS
GOLD PRINT RUN 99 SERIAL #'d SETS
AD Adam Dunn/799 3.00 8.00
AR Alex Rodriguez/799 6.00 15.00
BB Barry Bonds/899 8.00 20.00
CJ Chipper Jones/799 4.00 10.00
JT Jim Thome/799 4.00 10.00
MR Manny Ramirez/799 4.00 10.00
PB Pat Burrell/799 3.00 8.00
SG Shawn Green/799 3.00 8.00
TG Troy Glaus/799 3.00 8.00
VG Vladimir Guerrero/799 4.00 10.00

2004 Fleer Showcase

This 130-card set was released in March, 2004. The set was issued in five-card packs with an $5.50 SRP and came 24 packs to a box and 12 boxes to a case. Cards numbered 1-100 feature veterans while cards 101-130 feature veterans. Those final 30 cards were issued at a stated rate of one in six hobby and one in 12 retail packs.

COMP.SET w/o SP's (100) 10.00 25.00
COMMON CARD (1-100) .20 .50
COMMON CARD (101-130) .75 2.00
101-130 ODDS 1:6 HOBBY, 1:12 RETAIL
1 Corey Patterson .20 .50
2 Ken Griffey Jr. .75 2.00
3 Preston Wilson .20 .50
4 Juan Pierre .20 .50
5 Jose Reyes .30 .75
6 Jason Schmidt .20 .50
7 Rocco Baldelli .20 .50
8 Carlos Delgado .20 .50
9 Hideki Matsui .75 2.00
10 Nomar Garciaparra .50 1.25
11 Brian Giles .20 .50
12 Darin Erstad .20 .50
13 Larry Walker .30 .75
14 Bernie Williams .30 .75
15 Laynce Nix .20 .50
16 Manny Ramirez .50 1.25
17 Magglio Ordonez .30 .75
18 Khalil Greene .30 .75
19 Jim Edmonds .30 .75
20 Troy Glaus .20 .50
21 Curt Schilling .30 .75
22 Chipper Jones .50 1.25
23 Sammy Sosa .50 1.25
24 Frank Thomas .50 1.25
25 Todd Helton .30 .75
26 Craig Biggio .30 .75
27 Shannon Stewart .20 .50
28 Mark Mulder .20 .50
29 Mike Lieberthal .20 .50
30 Reggie Sanders .20 .50
31 Edgar Martinez .30 .75
32 Bo Hart .20 .50
33 Mark Teixeira .50 1.25
34 Jay Gibbons .20 .50
35 Roberto Alomar .30 .75
36 Kip Wells .20 .50
37 J.D. Drew .20 .50
38 Jason Varitek .50 1.25
39 Craig Monroe .20 .50
40 Roy Oswalt .30 .75
41 Edgardo Alfonzo .20 .50
42 Roy Halladay .50 1.25
43 Gary Sheffield .20 .50
44 Lance Berkman .30 .75
45 Torii Hunter .20 .50
46 Vladimir Guerrero .50 1.25
47 Marlon Byrd .20 .50
48 Austin Kearns .20 .50
49 Angel Berroa .20 .50
50 Geoff Jenkins .20 .50
51 Aubrey Huff .20 .50
52 Dontrelle Willis .20 .50
53 Tony Batista .20 .50
54 Shawn Green .20 .50
55 Jason Kendall .20 .50
56 Garret Anderson .20 .50
57 Andruw Jones .20 .50
58 Dmitri Young .20 .50
59 Richie Sexson .20 .50
60 Jorge Posada .30 .75
61 Bobby Abreu .20 .50
62 Vernon Wells .20 .50
63 Javy Lopez .30 .75
64 Josh Beckett .30 .75
65 Eric Chavez .20 .50
66 Tim Salmon .20 .50
67 Brandon Webb .20 .50
68 Pedro Martinez .30 .75
69 Kerry Wood .20 .50
70 Jose Vidro .20 .50
71 Alfonso Soriano .20 .50
72 Barry Zito .20 .50
73 Sean Burroughs .20 .50
74 Jamie Moyer .20 .50
75 Luis Gonzalez .20 .50
76 Adam Dunn .30 .75
77 Mike Piazza .50 1.25
78 Pat Burrell .20 .50
79 Scott Rolen .30 .75
80 Milton Bradley .20 .50
81 Mike Sweeney .20 .50
82 Hank Blalock .20 .50
83 Esteban Loaiza .20 .50
84 Hideo Nomo .50 1.25
85 Derek Jeter 1.25 3.00
86 Albert Pujols 1.25 3.00
87 Greg Maddux .75 2.00
88 Mark Prior .30 .75
89 Mike Lowell .20 .50
90 Jeff Bagwell .30 .75
91 Scott Podsednik .20 .50
92 Tom Glavine .30 .75
93 Jason Giambi .20 .50
94 Jim Thome .30 .75
95 Ichiro Suzuki .75 2.00
96 Randy Johnson .50 1.25
97 Omar Vizquel .30 .75
98 Ivan Rodriguez .30 .75
99 Miguel Tejada .30 .75
100 Alex Rodriguez .75 2.00
101 Rickie Weeks ST .40 1.00
102 Chad Gaudin ST .40 1.00
103 Rich Harden ST .40 1.00
104 Edwin Jackson ST .40 1.00
105 Chien-Ming Wang ST 2.00 5.00
106 Matt Kata ST .40 1.00
107 Delmon Young ST .60 1.50
108 Ryan Wagner ST .40 1.00
109 Jeff Duncan ST .40 1.00
110 Prentice Redman ST .40 1.00
111 Clint Barmes ST .60 1.50
112 Jeremy Guthrie ST .40 1.00
113 Brian Stokes ST .40 1.00
114 David DeJesus ST .40 1.00
115 Felix Sanchez ST .40 1.00
116 Josh Stewart ST .40 1.00
117 Daniel Garcia ST .40 1.00
118 Jon Leicester ST .40 1.00
119 Francisco Cruceta ST .40 1.00
120 Oscar Villarreal ST .40 1.00
121 Michael Hessman ST .40 1.00
122 Michel Hernandez ST .40 1.00
123 Richard Fischer ST .40 1.00
124 Robby Hammock ST .40 1.00
125 Guillermo Quiroz ST .40 1.00
126 Craig Brazell ST .40 1.00
127 Wilfredo Ledezma ST .40 1.00
128 Josh Willingham ST .40 1.00
129 Ramon Nivar ST .40 1.00
130 Matt Diaz ST .40 1.00

2004 Fleer Showcase Legacy

*LEGACY 1-100: 6X TO 15X BASIC
*LEGACY 101-130: 1.5X TO 4X BASIC
OVERALL PARALLEL ODDS 1:24
STATED PRINT RUN 99 SERIAL #'d SETS

2004 Fleer Showcase Masterpiece

OVERALL PARALLEL ODDS 1:24
STATED PRINT RUN 1 SERIAL #'d SET
NO PRICING DUE TO SCARCITY

2004 Fleer Showcase Baseballs Best

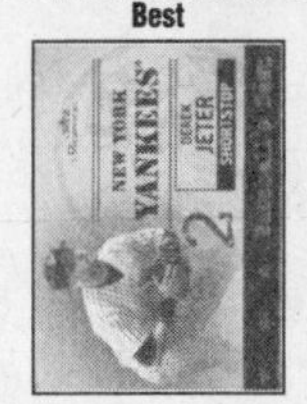

STATED ODDS 1:24 HOBBY, 1:12 RETAIL
1 Derek Jeter 2.50 6.00
2 Mark Prior .60 1.50
3 Mike Piazza 1.00 2.50
4 Jeff Bagwell .60 1.50
5 Kerry Wood .40 1.00
6 Ivan Rodriguez .60 1.50
7 Albert Pujols 2.50 6.00
8 Jim Thome .60 1.50
9 Sammy Sosa 1.00 2.50
10 Vladimir Guerrero 1.00 2.50
11 Eric Gagne .40 1.00
12 Randy Johnson 1.00 2.50
13 Todd Helton .60 1.50
14 Chipper Jones 1.00 2.50
15 Alex Rodriguez 1.50 4.00

2004 Fleer Showcase Baseballs Best Game Used

STATED ODDS 1:72 HOBBY, 1:48 RETAIL
*PATCH: 1.5X TO 4X BASIC

PATCH RANDOM INSERTS IN PACKS
PATCH PRINT RUN 50 SERIAL #'d SETS
*GOLD: .5X TO 1.2X BASIC
GOLD RANDOM INSERTS IN PACKS
GOLD PRINT RUN 150 SERIAL #'d SETS
*REWARD: 1X TO 2.5X BASIC
REWARD ISSUED ONLY IN DEALER PACKS
REWARD PRINTS B/WN 29-44 COPIES PER
AP Albert Pujols Jsy 6.00 15.00
AR Alex Rodriguez Jsy 4.00 10.00
CJ Chipper Jones Jsy 4.00 10.00
DJ Derek Jeter Bat 8.00 20.00
EG Eric Gagne Jsy 3.00 8.00
IR Ivan Rodriguez Jsy 4.00 10.00
JB Jeff Bagwell Jsy 4.00 10.00
JT Jim Thome Jsy 4.00 10.00
KW Kerry Wood Jsy 3.00 8.00
MPI Mike Piazza Jsy 4.00 10.00
MPR Mark Prior Jsy 4.00 10.00
RJ Randy Johnson Jsy 4.00 10.00
SS Sammy Sosa Jsy 4.00 10.00
TH Todd Helton Jsy 4.00 10.00
VG Vladimir Guerrero Jsy 4.00 10.00

2004 Fleer Showcase Grace

STATED ODDS 1:12 HOBBY/RETAIL
1 Kerry Wood .40 1.00
2 Derek Jeter 2.50 6.00
3 Nomar Garciaparra 1.00 2.50
4 Mike Piazza 1.00 2.50
5 Mark Prior .60 1.50
6 Jose Reyes .60 1.50
7 Dontrelle Willis .40 1.00
8 Pedro Martinez .60 1.50
9 Tim Hudson .60 1.50
10 Troy Glaus .40 1.00
11 Hank Blalock .40 1.00
12 Albert Pujols 2.50 6.00
13 Juan Pierre .40 1.00
14 Angel Berroa .40 1.00
15 Rocco Baldelli .40 1.00
16 Carlos Delgado .40 1.00
17 Manny Ramirez 1.00 2.50
18 Alex Rodriguez 1.50 4.00
19 Andruw Jones .40 1.00
20 Luis Gonzalez .40 1.00

2004 Fleer Showcase Grace Game Used

STATED ODDS 1:48 HOBBY/RETAIL
*PATCH: 1.5X TO 4X BASIC
PATCH RANDOM INSERTS IN PACKS
PATCH PRINT RUN 50 SERIAL #'d SETS
*GOLD: .5X TO 1.2X BASIC
GOLD RANDOM INSERTS IN PACKS
GOLD PRINT RUN 150 SERIAL #'d SETS
*REWARD p/r 44-55: 1X TO 2.5X BASIC
REWARD ISSUED ONLY IN DEALER PACKS
REWARD PRINTS B/WN 23-55 COPIES PER
NO REWARD PRICING ON QTY OF 23
AP Albert Pujols Jsy 6.00 15.00
AR Alex Rodriguez Jsy 4.00 10.00
DJ Derek Jeter Bat 8.00 20.00
DW Dontrelle Willis Jsy 4.00 10.00
MPI Mike Piazza Jsy 4.00 10.00
MPR Mark Prior Jsy 4.00 10.00
MR Manny Ramirez Jsy 4.00 10.00
NG Nomar Garciaparra Jsy 4.00 10.00
PM Pedro Martinez Jsy 4.00 10.00
RB Rocco Baldelli Jsy 3.00 8.00

2004 Fleer Showcase Hot Gloves

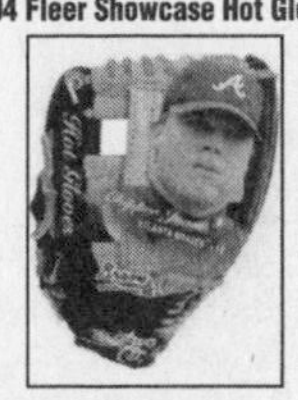

STATED ODDS 1:288 HOBBY, 1:576 RETAIL
NO MORE THAN 120 SETS PRODUCED
PRINT RUN INFO PROVIDED BY FLEER
CARDS ARE NOT SERIAL-NUMBERED
1 Derek Jeter 25.00 60.00
2 Nomar Garciaparra 10.00 25.00
3 Alex Rodriguez 15.00 40.00
4 Chipper Jones 10.00 25.00
5 Torii Hunter 4.00 10.00
6 Ichiro Suzuki 15.00 40.00
7 Mark Prior 6.00 15.00
8 Vladimir Guerrero 10.00 25.00
9 Albert Pujols 25.00 60.00
10 Ivan Rodriguez 6.00 15.00
11 Hideki Matsui 15.00 40.00
12 Sammy Sosa 10.00 25.00
13 Jim Thome 6.00 15.00
14 Rocco Baldelli 4.00 10.00
15 Jeff Bagwell 6.00 15.00

2004 Fleer Showcase Hot Gloves Game Used

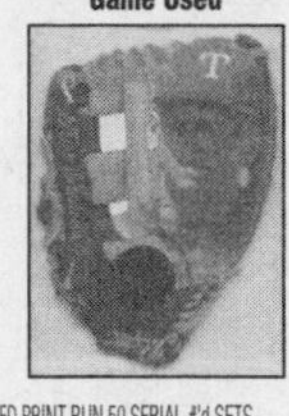

STATED PRINT RUN 50 SERIAL #'d SETS
AP Albert Pujols Jsy 30.00 60.00
AR Alex Rodriguez Jsy 20.00 50.00
CJ Chipper Jones Jsy 12.50 30.00
DJ Derek Jeter Jsy 40.00 80.00
HM Hideki Matsui Base 50.00 100.00
IR Ivan Rodriguez Jsy 12.50 30.00
IS Ichiro Suzuki Base 60.00 120.00
JB Jeff Bagwell Jsy 12.50 30.00
JT Jim Thome Jsy 12.50 30.00
MP Mark Prior Jsy 12.50 30.00
NG Nomar Garciaparra Jsy 20.00 50.00
RB Rocco Baldelli Jsy 12.50 30.00
SS Sammy Sosa Jsy 12.50 30.00
TH Torii Hunter Jsy 12.50 30.00
VG Vladimir Guerrero Jsy 12.50 30.00

2004 Fleer Showcase Pujols Legacy Collection

COMMON CARD (1-10) 3.00 8.00
STATED ODDS 1:24
STATED PRINT RUN 1000 SERIAL #'d SETS

2004 Fleer Showcase Pujols Legacy Collection Autograph

OVERALL AUTOGRAPH ODDS 1:24
PRINT RUNS B/WN 1-10 COPIES PER

2004 Fleer Showcase Pujols Legacy Collection Game Jersey

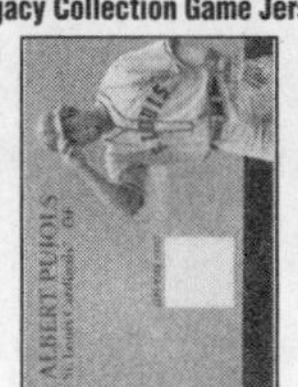

RANDOM INSERTS IN PACKS
PRINT RUNS B/WN 10-100 COPIES PER
NO PRICING ON QTY OF 40 OR LESS
1 Albert Pujols Draft 99/10
2 Albert Pujols 01 ROY/20
3 Albert Pujols 01 Slugger/30
4 Albert Pujols 4 Pos/40
5 Albert Pujols NL Records/50 12.50 30.00
6 Albert Pujols 2X AS/60 12.50 30.00
7 Albert Pujols HR Record/70 10.00 25.00
8 Albert Pujols 300-100-100/80 10.00 25.00
9 Albert Pujols 03 Btg Champ/90 10.00 25.00
10 Albert Pujols 03 POY/100 10.00 25.00

2004 Fleer Showcase Sweet Sigs

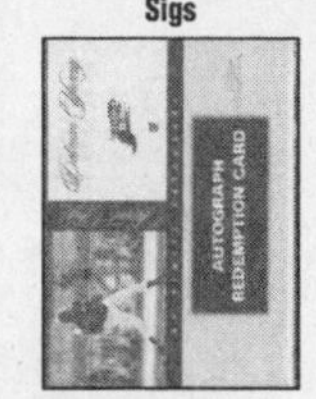

OVERALL AUTOGRAPH ODDS 1:24
PRINT RUNS B/WN 26-1000 COPIES PER
EXCH.PRINT RUNS PROVIDED BY FLEER
EXCHANGE DEADLINE INDEFINITE
AK Austin Kearns/224 4.00 10.00
AP1 Albert Pujols/199 150.00 250.00
BH Bo Hart/667 4.00 10.00
BW Brandon Webb/1000 4.00 10.00
BZ Barry Zito/248 10.00 25.00
CPA Corey Patterson/176 6.00 15.00
CPE Carlos Pena/48 8.00 20.00
CW Chien Mien-Wang/35 125.00 200.00
DW Dontrelle Willis/26 30.00 60.00
HB Hank Blalock/824 6.00 15.00
JR Jose Reyes/115 8.00 20.00
JW Josh Willingham/180 6.00 15.00
ML Mike Lowell/44 10.00 25.00
MR Michael Ryan/288 4.00 10.00
MT Miguel Tejada/52 15.00 40.00
RWE Rickie Weeks/416 6.00 15.00
SR Scott Rolen/200 10.00 25.00
TH Torii Hunter/294 6.00 15.00
WL Wilfredo Ledezma/376 4.00 10.00

2004 Fleer Showcase Sweet Sigs Game Jersey

OVERALL AUTOGRAPH ODDS 1:24
STATED PRINT RUN 5 SERIAL #'d CARDS
NO PRICING DUE TO SCARCITY
AP Albert Pujols/5

2005 Fleer Showcase

This 135-card set was released in January, 2005. The set was issued in either five card hobby or retail packs. These packs were issued 20 packs to a box and 12 boxes to a case for hobby accounts and 24 packs to a box and 20 boxes to a case for retail accounts. Cards numbered 1-100 feature veterans while cards 101-110 feature leading prospects and 111-135 feature retired greats. The cards 101-110 were issued at a stated rate of one in five hobby and one in 12 retail while cards 111-135 were issued at a stated rate of one in 20 hobby and one in 48 retail packs.

COMP.SET w/o SP's (100) 15.00 40.00
COMMON CARD (1-100) .30 .75
COMP.ST SUBSET (10) 6.00 15.00
COMMON CARD (101-110) .60 1.50
101-110 ODDS 1:5 HOBBY, 1:12 RETAIL
COMMON CARD (111-135) .60 1.50
111-135 ODDS 1:20 HOBBY, 1:48 RETAIL
1 Albert Pujols 2.00 5.00
2 Rocco Baldelli .30 .75
3 Bernie Williams .50 1.25
4 Shawn Green .30 .75
5 Garret Anderson .30 .75
6 Paul Konerko .50 1.25
7 Mike Sweeney .30 .75
8 Jim Thome .50 1.25
9 Mark Teixeira .75 2.00
10 Mark Prior .50 1.25
11 Angel Berroa .30 .75
12 Barry Zito .30 .75
13 Carlos Delgado .30 .75
14 Troy Glaus .30 .75
15 Travis Hafner .30 .75
16 Lyle Overbay .30 .75
17 David Ortiz .75 2.00
18 Ivan Rodriguez .50 1.25
19 Jack Wilson .30 .75
20 Jason Schmidt .30 .75
21 Mike Piazza .75 2.00
22 David Eckstein .30 .75
23 Ben Sheets .30 .75
24 Randy Johnson .75 2.00
25 Jacque Jones .30 .75
26 Jody Gerut .30 .75
27 Kris Benson .30 .75
28 Luis Gonzalez .30 .75
29 Victor Martinez .50 1.25
30 Torii Hunter .30 .75
31 Gary Sheffield .30 .75
32 Miguel Tejada .50 1.25
33 Dontrelle Willis .30 .75
34 Bret Boone .30 .75
35 Kaz Matsui .30 .75
36 Shea Hillenbrand .30 .75
37 Wily Mo Pena .30 .75
38 Johan Santana .75 2.00
39 Derek Jeter 2.00 5.00
40 Chipper Jones .75 2.00
41 Sean Casey .30 .75
42 Corey Koskie .30 .75
43 Alex Rodriguez 1.25 3.00
44 Andruw Jones .30 .75
45 Austin Kearns .30 .75
46 Jose Vidro .30 .75
47 Adam Dunn .50 1.25
48 Adrian Beltre .30 .75
49 Bobby Abreu .30 .75
50 Michael Young .30 .75
51 Freddy Garcia .30 .75
52 Eric Gagne .30 .75
53 Chase Utley .50 1.25
54 Alfonso Soriano .50 1.25
55 Nick Johnson .30 .75
56 Johnny Estrada .30 .75
57 Jeff Bagwell .50 1.25
58 Randy Wolf .30 .75
59 Roy Halladay .75 2.00
60 J.D. Drew .30 .75
61 Craig Biggio .50 1.25
62 Scott Rolen .50 1.25
63 Nomar Garciaparra .75 2.00
64 Matt Holliday .75 2.00
65 Billy Wagner .30 .75
66 Carl Crawford .50 1.25
67 Pedro Martinez .50 1.25
68 Jeremy Bonderman .30 .75
69 Jason Bay .30 .75
70 A.J. Pierzynski .30 .75
71 Vladimir Guerrero .75 2.00
72 Rickie Weeks .50 1.25
73 Mark Loretta .30 .75
74 Todd Helton .50 1.25
75 Manny Ramirez .75 2.00
76 Carlos Guillen .30 .75
77 Khalil Greene .30 .75
78 Javy Lopez .30 .75
79 Josh Beckett .50 1.25
80 Ichiro Suzuki 1.25 3.00
81 Magglio Ordonez .50 1.25
82 Ken Harvey .30 .75
83 Mark Mulder .30 .75
84 Hank Blalock .30 .75
85 Richard Hidalgo .30 .75
86 Curt Schilling .50 1.25
87 Jeromy Burnitz .30 .75
88 Craig Wilson .30 .75
89 Aubrey Huff .30 .75
90 Kerry Wood .30 .75
91 Andy Pettitte .50 1.25
92 Tim Hudson .50 1.25
93 Jim Edmonds .50 1.25
94 Melvin Mora .30 .75
95 Miguel Cabrera .75 2.00
96 Trevor Hoffman .50 1.25
97 J.T. Snow .30 .75
98 Sammy Sosa .75 2.00
99 Roger Clemens 1.00 2.50
100 Eric Chavez .30 .75
101 B.J. Upton ST 1.00 2.50
102 Gavin Floyd ST .60 1.50
103 Casey Kotchman ST .60 1.50
104 David Wright ST 2.50 6.00
105 Dioner Navarro ST .60 1.50
106 Scott Kazmir ST 1.50 4.00
107 Andres Blanco ST .60 1.50
108 Joey Gathright ST .60 1.50
109 Jon Knott ST .60 1.50
110 Charlton Jimerson ST .60 1.50
111 Larry Doby SH .60 1.50
112 Reggie Jackson SH 1.50 4.00
113 Enos Slaughter SH .60 1.50
114 Bill Skowron SH .60 1.50
115 Duke Snider SH 1.00 2.50
116 Harmon Killebrew SH 1.50 4.00
117 Willie McCovey SH 1.00 2.50
118 Rollie Fingers SH .60 1.50
119 Preacher Roe SH .60 1.50
120 Carlton Fisk SH 1.00 2.50
121 Andre Dawson SH 1.00 2.50
122 Orlando Cepeda SH .60 1.50
123 Bucky Dent SH .60 1.50
124 Cal Ripken SH 6.00 15.00
125 Nolan Ryan SH 4.00 10.00
126 Tony Perez SH .60 1.50
127 Mike Schmidt SH 3.00 8.00
128 Johnny Bench SH 1.50 4.00
129 Sparky Anderson SH .60 1.50
130 Ted Williams SH 3.00 8.00
131 Al Kaline SH 1.50 4.00
132 Carl Yastrzemski SH 2.00 5.00
133 Eddie Murray SH 1.50 4.00
134 Roberto Clemente SH 4.00 10.00
135 Yogi Berra SH 1.50 4.00

2005 Fleer Showcase Showdown

These cards parallel the basic 2005 Fleer Showcase, but the small action image in the foreground of the basic card has been pulled for the Showdown parallel, leaving only the larger posed image in the card's background.

BASIC PARALLEL ODDS 1:10 HOBBY
STATED PRINT RUN 15 SERIAL #'d SETS
NO PRICING DUE TO SCARCITY

2005 Fleer Showcase Showtime

These cards parallel the basic 2005 Fleer Showcase, but the posed player image in the background of the basic card has been pulled for the Showtime parallel, leaving only the smaller action image in the card's foreground.

*SHOWDOWN 1-100: 2.5X TO 6X BASIC
*SHOWDOWN 101-110: 1X TO 2.5X BASIC
*SHOWDOWN 111-135: .75X TO 2X BASIC
BASIC PARALLEL ODDS 1:10 HOBBY
STATED PRINT RUN 99 SERIAL #'d SETS

2005 Fleer Showcase Autographed Legacy

LEGACY PARALLEL ODDS 1:20 HOBBY
PRINT RUNS B/WN 7-460 COPIES PER
NO PRICING ON QTY OF 19 OR LESS
SKIP-NUMBERED 58-CARD SET
EXCHANGE DEADLINE 01/15/08
1 Albert Pujols/11
8 Jim Thome/34 30.00 60.00
10 Mark Prior/43 15.00 40.00
12 Barry Zito/45 15.00 40.00
18 Ivan Rodriguez/217 20.00 50.00
19 Jack Wilson/298 6.00 15.00
20 Jason Schmidt/127 6.00 15.00

21 Mike Piazza/26 60.00 120.00
22 David Eckstein/40 20.00 50.00
23 Ben Sheets/427 6.00 15.00
40 Chipper Jones/41 30.00 60.00
45 Austin Kearns/460 4.00 10.00
47 Adam Dunn/52 15.00 40.00
48 Adrian Beltre/180 6.00 15.00
50 Michael Young/80 8.00 20.00
52 Eric Gagne/310 10.00 25.00
59 Roy Halladay/99 15.00 40.00
60 J.D. Drew/14
65 Billy Wagner/12
68 Jeremy Bonderman/97 8.00 20.00
72 Rickie Weeks/453 6.00 15.00
75 Manny Ramirez/31 40.00 80.00
77 Khalil Greene/299 10.00 25.00
88 Craig Wilson/40 8.00 20.00
89 Aubrey Huff/453 6.00 15.00
90 Kerry Wood/28 15.00 40.00
92 Tim Hudson/183 10.00 25.00
95 Miguel Cabrera/32 15.00 40.00
99 Roger Clemens/64 60.00 120.00
100 Eric Chavez/204 10.00 25.00
103 Casey Kotchman ST/454 6.00 15.00
104 David Wright ST/298 20.00 50.00
106 Scott Kazmir ST/458 UER 8.00 20.00
Seattle Mariners on front
107 Andres Blanco ST/23 8.00 20.00
109 Jon Knott ST/402 4.00 10.00
111 Larry Doby SH/25
112 Reggie Jackson SH/17
114 Bill Skowron SH/64 10.00 25.00
119 Preacher Roe SH/304 10.00 25.00
120 Carlton Fisk SH/86 12.50 30.00
122 Orlando Cepeda SH/19
123 Bucky Dent SH/99 8.00 20.00
124 Cal Ripken SH/53
125 Nolan Ryan SH/13
131 Al Kaline SH/7
132 Carl Yastrzemski SH/14
135 Yogi Berra SH/25 40.00 80.00

2005 Fleer Showcase Legacy

*LEGACY 1-100: 2.5X TO 6X BASIC
*LEGACY 101-110: 1X TO 2.5X BASIC
*LEGACY 111-135: .75X TO 2X BASIC
LEGACY PARALLEL ODDS 1:20 HOBBY
STATED PRINT RUN 99 SERIAL #'d SETS
SKIP-NUMBERED 50-CARD SET

2005 Fleer Showcase Masterpiece Legacy

M'PIECE PARALLEL ODDS 1:240 HOBBY
STATED PRINT RUN 1 SERIAL #'d SET
NO PRICING DUE TO SCARCITY

2005 Fleer Showcase Masterpiece Showdown

M'PIECE PARALLEL ODDS 1:240 HOBBY
STATED PRINT RUN 1 SERIAL #'d SET
NO PRICING DUE TO SCARCITY

2005 Fleer Showcase Masterpiece Showtime

M'PIECE PARALLEL ODDS 1:240 HOBBY
STATED PRINT RUN 1 SERIAL #'d SET
NO PRICING DUE TO SCARCITY

2005 Fleer Showcase Masterpiece Showpiece Patch

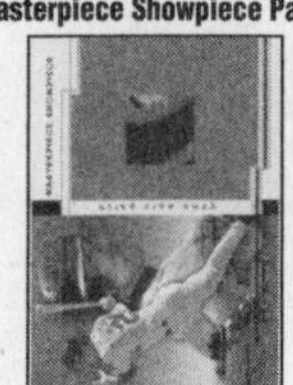

M'PIECE PARALLEL ODDS 1:240 HOBBY
STATED PRINT RUN 1 SERIAL #'d SET
NO PRICING DUE TO SCARCITY

2005 Fleer Showcase Masterpiece Showpiece Patch Showdown

M'PIECE PARALLEL ODDS 1:240 HOBBY
STATED PRINT RUN 1 SERIAL #'d SET
NO PRICING DUE TO SCARCITY

2005 Fleer Showcase Masterpiece Showpiece Patch Showtime

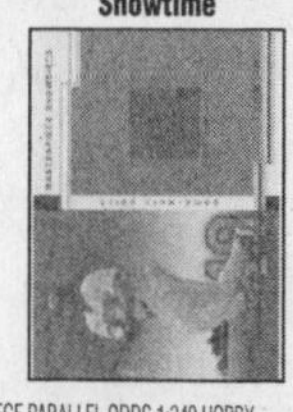

M'PIECE PARALLEL ODDS 1:240 HOBBY
STATED PRINT RUN 1 SERIAL #'d SET
NO PRICING DUE TO SCARCITY

2005 Fleer Showcase Masterpiece Showpiece Autograph Patch

M'PIECE PARALLEL ODDS 1:240 HOBBY
STATED PRINT RUN 1 SERIAL #'d SET
NO PRICING DUE TO SCARCITY

2005 Fleer Showcase Timepiece Extreme Autograph Barrel

OVERALL TIMEPIECE ODDS 1:510 HOBBY
OVERALL AU-GU ODDS 1:48 RETAIL
STATED PRINT RUN 1 SERIAL #'d SET
NO PRICING DUE TO SCARCITY

2005 Fleer Showcase Timepiece Ink Autograph Bat Knob

OVERALL TIMEPIECE ODDS 1:510 HOBBY
OVERALL AU-GU ODDS 1:48 RETAIL
STATED PRINT RUN 10 SERIAL #'d SETS
NO PRICING DUE TO SCARCITY
1 Albert Pujols
8 Jim Thome
9 Mark Teixeira
18 Ivan Rodriguez
40 Chipper Jones
45 Austin Kearns
47 Adam Dunn
66 Carl Crawford
72 Rickie Weeks
75 Manny Ramirez
95 Miguel Cabrera
112 Reggie Jackson
132 Carl Yastrzemski

2005 Fleer Showcase Timepiece Teammates Autograph Dual

OVERALL TIMEPIECE ODDS 1:510 HOBBY
OVERALL AU-GU ODDS 1:48 RETAIL
STATED PRINT RUN 1 SERIAL #'d SET
NO PRICING DUE TO SCARCITY

2005 Fleer Showcase Timepiece Unique Autograph Bat-Patch

OVERALL TIMEPIECE ODDS 1:510 HOBBY
OVERALL AU-GU ODDS 1:48 RETAIL
STATED PRINT RUN 5 SERIAL #'d SETS
NO PRICING DUE TO SCARCITY

2005 Fleer Showcase Measure of Greatness

STATED ODDS 1:5 HOBBY, 1:5 RETAIL
1 Albert Pujols 2.50 6.00
2 Mike Piazza 1.00 2.50
3 Vladimir Guerrero 1.00 2.50
4 Jim Thome .60 1.50
5 Pedro Martinez .60 1.50
6 Rafael Palmeiro .60 1.50
7 Adrian Beltre .40 1.00
8 Sammy Sosa 1.00 2.50
9 Todd Helton .60 1.50
10 Randy Johnson 1.00 2.50
11 Jeff Bagwell .60 1.50
12 Jason Giambi .40 1.00
13 Scott Rolen .60 1.50
14 Greg Maddux 1.50 4.00
15 Alfonso Soriano .60 1.50
16 Mariano Rivera 1.00 2.50
17 Curt Schilling .60 1.50
18 Derek Jeter 2.50 6.00
19 Chipper Jones 1.00 2.50
20 Roger Clemens 1.25 3.00

2005 Fleer Showcase Measure of Greatness Jersey Red

STATED PRINT RUN 340 SERIAL #'d SETS
*GREEN: .6X TO 1.5X BASIC
GREEN ODDS 1:144 RETAIL
PATCH PRINT RUN 10 SERIAL #'d SETS
NO PATCH PRICING DUE TO SCARCITY
PATCH MP PRINT RUN 1 SERIAL #'d SET
NO PATCH MP PRICING DUE TO SCARCITY
OVERALL GAME-USED ODDS 1:10 HOBBY
AB Adrian Beltre 3.00 8.00
AP Albert Pujols 8.00 20.00
AS Alfonso Soriano 3.00 8.00
CJ Chipper Jones 4.00 10.00
JT Jim Thome 4.00 10.00
MP Mike Piazza 4.00 10.00
MR Mariano Rivera 4.00 10.00
PM Pedro Martinez 4.00 10.00
RC Roger Clemens 6.00 15.00
RJ Randy Johnson 4.00 10.00
RP Rafael Palmeiro 4.00 10.00
SR Scott Rolen 4.00 10.00
SS Sammy Sosa 4.00 10.00
TH Todd Helton 4.00 10.00
VG Vladimir Guerrero 4.00 10.00

2005 Fleer Showcase Swing Time

STATED ODDS 1:45 HOBBY, 1:96 RETAIL
1 Ivan Rodriguez 1.00 2.50
2 Gary Sheffield .60 1.50
3 Bernie Williams 1.00 2.50
4 Vladimir Guerrero 1.50 4.00
5 Jim Edmonds 1.00 2.50
6 Manny Ramirez 1.50 4.00
7 Todd Helton 1.00 2.50
8 Hank Blalock .60 1.50
9 Hideki Matsui 2.50 6.00
10 David Ortiz 1.50 4.00
11 Albert Pujols 4.00 10.00
12 Miguel Tejada 1.00 2.50
13 Miguel Cabrera 1.50 4.00
14 Alex Rodriguez 2.50 6.00
15 Ichiro Suzuki 2.50 6.00

2005 Fleer Showcase Swing Time Jersey Red

STATED PRINT RUN 610 SERIAL #'d SETS
*GREEN: .75X TO 2X BASIC
GREEN ODDS 1:444 RETAIL
*PATCH: 1.25X TO 3X BASIC
PATCH PRINT RUN 50 SERIAL #'d SETS
PATCH MP PRINT RUN 1 SERIAL #'d SET
NO PATCH MP PRICING DUE TO SCARCITY
OVERALL GAME-USED ODDS 1:10 HOBBY
AP Albert Pujols 6.00 15.00
BW Bernie Williams 3.00 8.00
DO David Ortiz 3.00 8.00
HB Hank Blalock 2.00 5.00
HM Hideki Matsui 8.00 20.00
IR Ivan Rodriguez 3.00 8.00
JE Jim Edmonds 2.00 5.00
MC Miguel Cabrera 3.00 8.00
MR Manny Ramirez 3.00 8.00
TH Todd Helton 3.00 8.00

2005 Fleer Showcase Wave of the Future

STATED ODDS 1:15 HOBBY, 1:15 RETAIL
1 Kaz Matsui .40 1.00
2 Johan Santana 1.00 2.50
3 Khalil Greene .40 1.00
4 Dontrelle Willis .40 1.00
5 Mark Teixeira 1.00 2.50
6 Travis Hafner .40 1.00
7 Jason Bay .40 1.00
8 Angel Berroa .40 1.00
9 Miguel Cabrera 1.00 2.50
10 Joe Mauer 1.00 2.50
11 Adam Dunn .60 1.50
12 B.J. Upton .60 1.50
13 Victor Martinez .60 1.50
14 Michael Young .60 1.50
15 David Wright 1.50 4.00

2005 Fleer Showcase Wave of the Future Jersey Red

STATED PRINT RUN 610 SERIAL #'d SETS
*GREEN: .4X TO 1X BASIC
GREEN ODDS 1:48 RETAIL
*PATCH: 1.25X TO 3X BASIC
PATCH PRINT RUN 50 SERIAL #'d SETS
PATCH MP PRINT RUN 1 SERIAL #'d SET
NO PATCH MP PRICING DUE TO SCARCITY
OVERALL GAME-USED ODDS 1:10 HOBBY
AB Angel Berroa 2.00 5.00
AD Adam Dunn 2.00 5.00
BU B.J. Upton 3.00 8.00
DW David Wright 8.00 20.00
DW Dontrelle Willis 2.00 5.00
JB Jason Bay 2.00 5.00
JM Joe Mauer 3.00 8.00
JS Johan Santana 3.00 8.00
KG Khalil Greene 3.00 8.00
KM Kaz Matsui 2.00 5.00
MC Miguel Cabrera 3.00 8.00
MT Mark Teixeira 3.00 8.00
MY Michael Young 2.00 5.00
TH Travis Hafner 2.00 5.00
VM Victor Martinez 2.00 5.00

1998 Fleer Tradition

The 600-card 1998 Fleer set was issued in two series. Series one consists of 350 cards and Series two consists of 250 cards. The packs for either series consisted of 12 cards and had a SRP of $1.49. Card fronts feature borderless color action player photos with UV-coating and foil stamping. The backs display player information and career statistics. The set contains the following topical subsets: Smoke 'N Heat (301-310), Golden Memories (311-320), Tale of the Tape (321-340) and Unforgettable Moments (576-600). The Golden Memories (1:6 packs), Tale of the Tape (1:4 packs) and Unforgettable Moments (1:4 packs) cards are shortprinted. An Alex Rodriguez Promo card was distributed to dealers along with their 1998 Fleer series one order forms. The card can be readily distinguished by the "Promotional Sample" text running diagonally across both the front and back of the card. 50 Fleer Flashback Exchange cards were hand-numbered and randomly inserted into packs. Each of these cards could be exchanged for a framed, uncut press sheet from one of Fleer's baseball sets dating anywhere from 1981 to 1993.

COMPLETE SET (600) 60.00 150.00
COMP. SERIES 1 (350) 35.00 90.00
COMP. SERIES 2 (250) 25.00 60.00
COMMON CARD (1-600) .10 .30
COMMON GM (311-320) .20 .50
COMMON TT (321-340) .25 .60
COMMON UM (576-600) .30 .75
1 Ken Griffey Jr. .50 1.25
2 Derek Jeter .75 2.00
3 Gerald Williams .10 .30
4 Carlos Delgado .10 .30
5 Nomar Garciaparra .50 1.25
6 Gary Sheffield .10 .30
7 Jeff King .10 .30
8 Cal Ripken 1.00 2.50
9 Matt Williams .10 .30
10 Chipper Jones .30 .75
11 Chuck Knoblauch .10 .30
12 Mark Grudzielanek .10 .30
13 Edgardo Alfonzo .10 .30
14 Andres Galarraga .10 .30
15 Tim Salmon .20 .50
16 Reggie Sanders .10 .30
17 Tony Clark .10 .30
18 Jason Kendall .10 .30
19 Juan Gonzalez .10 .30
20 Ben Grieve .10 .30
21 Roger Clemens .60 1.50
22 Raul Mondesi .10 .30
23 Robin Ventura .10 .30
24 Derrek Lee .20 .50
25 Mark McGwire .75 2.00
26 Luis Gonzalez .10 .30
27 Kevin Brown .20 .50
28 Kirk Rueter .10 .30
29 Bobby Estalella .10 .30
30 Shawn Green .10 .30
31 Greg Maddux .50 1.25
32 Jorge Velandia .10 .30
33 Larry Walker .10 .30
34 Joey Cora .10 .30
35 Frank Thomas .30 .75
36 Curtis King RC .10 .30
37 Aaron Boone .10 .30
38 Curt Schilling .10 .30
39 Bruce Aven .10 .30
40 Ben McDonald .10 .30
41 Andy Ashby .10 .30
42 Jason McDonald .10 .30
43 Eric Davis .10 .30
44 Mark Grace .20 .50
45 Pedro Martinez .20 .50
46 Lou Collier .10 .30
47 Chan Ho Park .10 .30
48 Shane Halter .10 .30
49 Brian Hunter .10 .30
50 Jeff Bagwell .20 .50
51 Bernie Williams .20 .50
52 J.T. Snow .10 .30
53 Todd Greene .10 .30
54 Shannon Stewart .10 .30
55 Darren Bragg .10 .30
56 Fernando Tatis .10 .30
57 Darryl Kile .10 .30
58 Chris Stynes .10 .30
59 Javier Valentin .10 .30
60 Brian McRae .10 .30
61 Tom Evans .10 .30
62 Randall Simon .10 .30
63 Darrin Fletcher .10 .30
64 Jaret Wright .10 .30
65 Luis Ordaz .10 .30
66 Jose Canseco .20 .50
67 Edgar Renteria .10 .30
68 Jay Buhner .10 .30
69 Paul Konerko .10 .30
70 Adrian Brown .10 .30
71 Chris Carpenter .10 .30
72 Mike Lieberthal .10 .30
73 Dean Palmer .10 .30
74 Jorge Fabregas .10 .30
75 Stan Javier .10 .30
76 Damion Easley .10 .30
77 David Cone .10 .30
78 Aaron Sele .10 .30
79 Antonio Alfonseca .10 .30
80 Bobby Jones .10 .30
81 David Justice .10 .30
82 Jeffrey Hammonds .10 .30
83 Doug Glanville .10 .30
84 Jason Dickson .10 .30
85 Brad Radke .10 .30
86 David Segui .10 .30
87 Greg Vaughn .10 .30
88 Mike Cather RC .10 .30
89 Alex Fernandez .10 .30
90 Billy Taylor .10 .30
91 Jason Schmidt .10 .30
92 Mike DeJean RC .15 .40
93 Domingo Cedeno .10 .30
94 Jeff Cirillo .10 .30
95 Manny Aybar RC .15 .40
96 Jaime Navarro .10 .30
97 Dennis Reyes .10 .30
98 Barry Larkin .20 .50
99 Troy O'Leary .10 .30
100 Alex Rodriguez .50 1.25
101 Pat Hentgen .10 .30
102 Bubba Trammell .10 .30
103 Glendon Rusch .10 .30
104 Kenny Lofton .10 .30
105 Craig Biggio .20 .50
106 Kelvim Escobar .10 .30
107 Mark Kotsay .10 .30
108 Rondell White .10 .30
109 Darren Oliver .10 .30
110 Jim Thome .20 .50
111 Rich Becker .10 .30
112 Chad Curtis .10 .30
113 Dave Hollins .10 .30
114 Bill Mueller .10 .30
115 Antone Williamson .10 .30
116 Tony Womack .10 .30
117 Randy Myers .10 .30
118 Rico Brogna .10 .30
119 Pat Watkins .10 .30
120 Eli Marrero .10 .30
121 Jay Bell .10 .30
122 Kevin Tapani .10 .30
123 Todd Erdos RC .10 .30
124 Neifi Perez .10 .30
125 Todd Hundley .10 .30
126 Jeff Abbott .10 .30
127 Todd Zeile .10 .30
128 Travis Fryman .10 .30
129 Sandy Alomar Jr. .10 .30
130 Fred McGriff .20 .50
131 Richard Hidalgo .10 .30
132 Scott Spiezio .10 .30
133 John Valentin .10 .30
134 Quilvio Veras .10 .30
135 Mike Lansing .10 .30
136 Paul Molitor .10 .30
137 Randy Johnson .30 .75
138 Harold Baines .10 .30
139 Doug Jones .10 .30
140 Abraham Nunez .10 .30
141 Alan Benes .10 .30
142 Matt Perisho .10 .30
143 Chris Clemons .10 .30
144 Andy Pettitte .20 .50
145 Jason Giambi .10 .30
146 Moises Alou .10 .30
147 Chad Fox RC .10 .30
148 Felix Martinez .10 .30
149 Carlos Mendoza RC .10 .30
150 Scott Rolen .20 .50
151 Jose Cabrera RC .10 .30
152 Justin Thompson .10 .30
153 Ellis Burks .10 .30
154 Pokey Reese .10 .30
155 Bartolo Colon .10 .30
156 Ray Durham .10 .30
157 Ugueth Urbina .10 .30
158 Tom Goodwin .10 .30
159 Dave Dellucci RC .25 .60
160 Rod Beck .10 .30
161 Ramon Martinez .10 .30
162 Joe Carter .10 .30
163 Kevin Orie .10 .30
164 Trevor Hoffman .10 .30
165 Emil Brown .10 .30
166 Robb Nen .10 .30
167 Paul O'Neill .20 .50
168 Ryan Long .10 .30
169 Ray Lankford .10 .30
170 Ivan Rodriguez .20 .50
171 Rick Aguilera .10 .30
172 Deivi Cruz .10 .30
173 Ricky Bottalico .10 .30
174 Garret Anderson .10 .30
175 Jose Vizcaino .10 .30
176 Omar Vizquel .20 .50
177 Jeff Blauser .10 .30
178 Orlando Cabrera .10 .30
179 Russ Johnson .10 .30
180 Matt Stairs .10 .30
181 Will Cunnane .10 .30
182 Adam Riggs .10 .30
183 Matt Morris .10 .30
184 Mario Valdez .10 .30
185 Larry Sutton .10 .30
186 Marc Pisciotta RC .10 .30
187 Dan Wilson .10 .30
188 John Franco .10 .30
189 Darren Daulton .10 .30
190 Todd Helton .20 .50
191 Brady Anderson .10 .30
192 Ricardo Rincon .10 .30
193 Kevin Stocker .10 .30
194 Jose Valentin .10 .30
195 Ed Sprague .10 .30
196 Ryan McGuire .10 .30
197 Scott Eyre .10 .30
198 Steve Finley .10 .30
199 T.J. Mathews .10 .30
200 Mike Piazza .50 1.25
201 Mark Wohlers .10 .30
202 Brian Giles .10 .30
203 Eduardo Perez .10 .30
204 Shigetoshi Hasegawa .10 .30
205 Mariano Rivera .30 .75
206 Jose Rosado .10 .30
207 Michael Coleman .10 .30
208 James Baldwin .10 .30
209 Russ Davis .10 .30
210 Billy Wagner .10 .30
211 Sammy Sosa .30 .75
212 Frank Catalanotto RC .25 .60
213 Delino DeShields .10 .30
214 John Olerud .10 .30
215 Heath Murray .10 .30
216 Jose Vidro .10 .30
217 Jim Edmonds .10 .30
218 Shawon Dunston .10 .30
219 Homer Bush .10 .30
220 Midre Cummings .10 .30
221 Tony Saunders .10 .30
222 Jeromy Burnitz .10 .30
223 Enrique Wilson .10 .30
224 Chili Davis .10 .30
225 Jerry DiPoto .10 .30
226 Dante Powell .10 .30
227 Javier Lopez .10 .30
228 Kevin Polcovich .10 .30
229 Deion Sanders .20 .50
230 Jimmy Key .10 .30
231 Rusty Greer .10 .30
232 Reggie Jefferson .10 .30
233 Ron Coomer .10 .30
234 Bobby Higginson .10 .30
235 Magglio Ordonez RC 1.00 2.50
236 Miguel Tejada .30 .75
237 Rick Gorecki .10 .30
238 Charles Johnson .10 .30
239 Lance Johnson .10 .30
240 Derek Bell .10 .30
241 Will Clark .20 .50
242 Brady Raggio .10 .30
243 Orel Hershiser .10 .30
244 Vladimir Guerrero .30 .75
245 John LeRoy .10 .30
246 Shawn Estes .10 .30
247 Brett Tomko .10 .30
248 Dave Nilsson .10 .30
249 Edgar Martinez .20 .50
250 Tony Gwynn .40 1.00
251 Mark Bellhorn .10 .30
252 Jed Hansen .10 .30
253 Butch Huskey .10 .30
254 Eric Young .10 .30
255 Vinny Castilla .10 .30
256 Hideki Irabu .10 .30
257 Mike Cameron .10 .30
258 Juan Encarnacion .10 .30
259 Brian Rose .10 .30
260 Brad Ausmus .10 .30
261 Dan Serafini .10 .30
262 Willie Greene .10 .30
263 Troy Percival .10 .30
264 Jeff Wallace .10 .30
265 Richie Sexson .10 .30
266 Rafael Palmeiro .20 .50
267 Brad Fullmer .10 .30
268 Jeremi Gonzalez .10 .30
269 Rob Stanifer RC .10 .30
270 Mickey Morandini .10 .30
271 Andruw Jones .20 .50
272 Royce Clayton .10 .30
273 T.Kashiwada RC .15 .40
274 Steve Woodard .10 .30
275 Jose Cruz Jr. .10 .30
276 Keith Foulke .10 .30
277 Brad Rigby .10 .30
278 Tino Martinez .20 .50
279 Todd Jones .10 .30
280 John Wetteland .10 .30
281 Alex Gonzalez .10 .30
282 Ken Cloude .10 .30
283 Jose Guillen .10 .30
284 Danny Clyburn .10 .30
285 David Ortiz .40 1.00
286 John Thomson .10 .30
287 Kevin Appier .10 .30
288 Ismael Valdes .10 .30
289 Gary DiSarcina .10 .30
290 Todd Dunwoody .10 .30
291 Wally Joyner .10 .30
292 Charles Nagy .10 .30
293 Jeff Shaw .10 .30
294 Kevin Millwood RC .40 1.00
295 Rigo Beltran RC .10 .30
296 Jeff Frye .10 .30
297 Oscar Henriquez .10 .30
298 Mike Thurman .10 .30
299 Garrett Stephenson .10 .30
300 Barry Bonds .75 2.00
301 Roger Clemens SH .30 .75
302 David Cone SH .10 .30
303 Hideki Irabu SH .10 .30
304 Randy Johnson SH .20 .50
305 Greg Maddux SH .30 .75
306 Pedro Martinez SH .20 .50
307 Mike Mussina SH .10 .30
308 Andy Pettitte SH .10 .30
309 Curt Schilling SH .10 .30
310 John Smoltz SH .10 .30
311 Roger Clemens GM 1.00 2.50
312 Jose Cruz JR. GM .20 .50
313 N.Garciaparra GM .75 2.00
314 Ken Griffey Jr. GM .75 2.00
315 Tony Gwynn GM .60 1.50
316 Hideki Irabu GM .20 .50
317 Randy Johnson GM .50 1.25
318 Mark McGwire GM 1.25 3.00
319 Curt Schilling GM .20 .50
320 Larry Walker GM .20 .50
321 Jeff Bagwell TT .40 1.00
322 Albert Belle TT .25 .60
323 Barry Bonds TT 1.50 4.00
324 Jay Buhner TT .25 .60
325 Tony Clark TT .25 .60
326 Jose Cruz Jr. TT .25 .60
327 Andres Galarraga TT .25 .60
328 Juan Gonzalez TT .25 .60
329 Ken Griffey Jr. TT 1.00 2.50
330 Andruw Jones TT .40 1.00
331 Tino Martinez TT .40 1.00
332 Mark McGwire TT 1.50 4.00
333 Rafael Palmeiro TT .40 1.00
334 Mike Piazza TT 1.00 2.50
335 Manny Ramirez TT .40 1.00
336 Alex Rodriguez TT 1.00 2.50
337 Frank Thomas TT .60 1.50
338 Jim Thome TT .40 1.00
339 Mo Vaughn TT .25 .60
340 Larry Walker TT .25 .60
341 Jose Cruz Jr. CL .10 .30
342 Ken Griffey Jr. CL .30 .75
343 Derek Jeter CL .40 1.00
344 Andruw Jones CL .10 .30
345 Chipper Jones CL .20 .50
346 Greg Maddux CL .30 .75
347 Mike Piazza CL .30 .75
348 Cal Ripken CL .50 1.25
349 Alex Rodriguez CL .30 .75
350 Frank Thomas CL .20 .50
351 Mo Vaughn .10 .30
352 Andres Galarraga .10 .30
353 Roberto Alomar .20 .50
354 Darin Erstad .10 .30
355 Albert Belle .10 .30
356 Matt Williams .10 .30
357 Darryl Kile .10 .30
358 Kenny Lofton .10 .30
359 Orel Hershiser .10 .30
360 Bob Abreu .10 .30
361 Chris Widger .10 .30
362 Glenallen Hill .10 .30
363 Chili Davis .10 .30
364 Kevin Brown .20 .50
365 Marquis Grissom .10 .30
366 Livan Hernandez .10 .30
367 Moises Alou .10 .30
368 Matt Lawton .10 .30
369 Rey Ordonez .10 .30
370 Kenny Rogers .10 .30
371 Lee Stevens .10 .30
372 Wade Boggs .20 .50
373 Luis Gonzalez .10 .30
374 Jeff Conine .10 .30
375 Esteban Loaiza .10 .30
376 Jose Canseco .20 .50
377 Henry Rodriguez .10 .30
378 Dave Burba .10 .30
379 Todd Hollandsworth .10 .30
380 Ron Gant .10 .30
381 Pedro Martinez .20 .50
382 Ryan Klesko .10 .30
383 Derrek Lee .20 .50
384 Doug Glanville .10 .30
385 David Wells .10 .30
386 Ken Caminiti .10 .30
387 Damon Hollins .10 .30
388 Manny Ramirez .20 .50
389 Mike Mussina .20 .50
390 Jay Bell .10 .30
391 Mike Piazza .50 1.25
392 Mike Lansing .10 .30
393 Mike Hampton .10 .30
394 Geoff Jenkins .10 .30
395 Jimmy Haynes .10 .30
396 Scott Servais .10 .30
397 Kent Mercker .10 .30
398 Jeff Kent .10 .30
399 Kevin Elster .10 .30
400 Masato Yoshii RC .15 .40
401 Jose Vizcaino .10 .30
402 Javier Martinez RC .10 .30
403 David Segui .10 .30
404 Tony Saunders .10 .30
405 Karim Garcia .10 .30
406 Armando Benitez .10 .30
407 Joe Randa .10 .30
408 Vic Darensbourg .10 .30
409 Sean Casey .10 .30
410 Eric Milton .10 .30
411 Trey Moore .10 .30
412 Mike Stanley .10 .30
413 Tom Gordon .10 .30
414 Hal Morris .10 .30
415 Braden Looper .10 .30
416 Mike Kelly .10 .30
417 John Smoltz .20 .50
418 Roger Cedeno .10 .30
419 Al Leiter .10 .30
420 Chuck Knoblauch .10 .30
421 Felix Rodriguez .10 .30
422 Bip Roberts .10 .30
423 Ken Hill .10 .30
424 Jermaine Allensworth .10 .30
425 Esteban Yan RC .15 .40
426 Scott Karl .10 .30
427 Sean Berry .10 .30
428 Rafael Medina .10 .30

429 Javier Vazquez .10 .30
430 Rickey Henderson .30 .75
431 Adam Butler .10 .30
432 Todd Stottlemyre .10 .30
433 Yamil Benitez .10 .30
434 Sterling Hitchcock .10 .30
435 Paul Sorrento .10 .30
436 Bobby Ayala .10 .30
437 Tim Raines .10 .30
438 Chris Hoiles .10 .30
439 Rod Beck .10 .30
440 Donnie Sadler .10 .30
441 Charles Johnson .10 .30
442 Russ Ortiz .10 .30
443 Pedro Astacio .10 .30
444 Wilson Alvarez .10 .30
445 Mike Blowers .10 .30
446 Todd Zeile .10 .30
447 Mel Rojas .10 .30
448 F.P. Santangelo .10 .30
449 Dmitri Young .10 .30
450 Brian Anderson .10 .30
451 Cecil Fielder .10 .30
452 Roberto Hernandez .10 .30
453 Todd Walker .10 .30
454 Tyler Green .10 .30
455 Jorge Posada .20 .50
456 Geronimo Berroa .10 .30
457 Jose Silva .10 .30
458 Bobby Bonilla .10 .30
459 Walt Weiss .10 .30
460 Darren Dreifort .10 .30
461 B.J. Surhoff .10 .30
462 Quinton McCracken .10 .30
463 Derek Lowe .10 .30
464 Jorge Fabregas .10 .30
465 Joey Hamilton .10 .30
466 Brian Jordan .10 .30
467 Allen Watson .10 .30
468 John Jaha .10 .30
469 Heathcliff Slocumb .10 .30
470 Gregg Jefferies .10 .30
471 Scott Brosius .10 .30
472 Chad Ogea .10 .30
473 A.J. Hinch .10 .30
474 Bobby Smith .10 .30
475 Brian Moehler .10 .30
476 DaRond Stovall .10 .30
477 Kevin Young .10 .30
478 Jeff Suppan .10 .30
479 Marty Cordova .10 .30
480 John Halama RC .15 .40
481 Bubba Trammell .10 .30
482 Mike Caruso .10 .30
483 Eric Karros .10 .30
484 Jamey Wright .10 .30
485 Mike Sweeney .10 .30
486 Aaron Sele .10 .30
487 Cliff Floyd .10 .30
488 Jeff Brantley .10 .30
489 Jim Leyritz .10 .30
490 Denny Neagle .10 .30
491 Travis Fryman .10 .30
492 Carlos Baerga .10 .30
493 Eddie Taubensee .10 .30
494 Darryl Strawberry .10 .30
495 Brian Johnson .10 .30
496 Randy Myers .10 .30
497 Jeff Blauser .10 .30
498 Jason Wood .10 .30
499 Rolando Arrojo RC .15 .40
500 Johnny Damon .20 .50
501 Jose Mercedes .10 .30
502 Tony Batista .10 .30
503 Mike Piazza Mets .50 1.25
504 Hideo Nomo .30 .75
505 Chris Gomez .10 .30
506 Jesus Sanchez RC .10 .30
507 Al Martin .10 .30
508 Brian Edmondson .10 .30
509 Joe Girardi .10 .30
510 Shayne Bennett .10 .30
511 Joe Carter .10 .30
512 Dave Mlicki .10 .30
513 Rich Butler RC .10 .30
514 Dennis Eckersley .10 .30
515 Travis Lee .10 .30
516 John Mabry .10 .30
517 Jose Mesa .10 .30
518 Phil Nevin .10 .30
519 Raul Casanova .10 .30
520 Mike Fetters .10 .30
521 Gary Sheffield .10 .30
522 Terry Steinbach .10 .30
523 Steve Trachsel .10 .30
524 Josh Booty .10 .30
525 Darryl Hamilton .10 .30
526 Mark McLemore .10 .30
527 Kevin Stocker .10 .30
528 Bret Boone .10 .30
529 Shane Andrews .10 .30
530 Robb Nen .10 .30
531 Carl Everett .10 .30
532 LaTroy Hawkins .10 .30
533 Fernando Vina .10 .30
534 Michael Tucker .10 .30
535 Mark Langston .10 .30
536 Mickey Mantle 2.00 5.00
537 Bernard Gilkey .10 .30
538 Francisco Cordova .10 .30
539 Mike Bordick .10 .30
540 Fred McGriff .20 .50
541 Cliff Politte .10 .30
542 Jason Varitek .30 .75
543 Shawon Dunston .10 .30
544 Brian Meadows .10 .30
545 Pat Meares .10 .30
546 Carlos Perez .10 .30
547 Desi Relaford .10 .30
548 Antonio Osuna .10 .30
549 Devon White .10 .30
550 Sean Runyan .10 .30
551 Mickey Morandini .10 .30
552 Dave Martinez .10 .30
553 Jeff Fassero .10 .30
554 Ryan Jackson RC .10 .30
555 Stan Javier .10 .30
556 Jaime Navarro .10 .30
557 Jose Offerman .10 .30
558 Mike Lowell RC .60 1.50
559 Darrin Fletcher .10 .30
560 Mark Lewis .10 .30
561 Dante Bichette .10 .30
562 Chuck Finley .10 .30
563 Kerry Wood .15 .40
564 Andy Benes .10 .30
565 Freddy Garcia .10 .30
566 Tom Glavine .20 .50
567 Jon Nunnally .10 .30
568 Miguel Cairo .10 .30
569 Shane Reynolds .10 .30
570 Roberto Kelly .10 .30
571 Jose Cruz Jr. CL .10 .30
572 Ken Griffey Jr. CL .30 .75
573 Mark McGwire CL .40 1.00
574 Cal Ripken CL .50 1.25
575 Frank Thomas CL .20 .50
576 Jeff Bagwell UM .50 1.25
577 Barry Bonds UM 2.00 5.00
578 Tony Clark UM .30 .75
579 Roger Clemens UM 1.50 4.00
580 Jose Cruz Jr. UM .30 .75
581 N.Garciaparra UM 1.25 3.00
582 Juan Gonzalez UM .30 .75
583 Ben Grieve UM .30 .75
584 Ken Griffey Jr. UM 1.25 3.00
585 Tony Gwynn UM 1.00 2.50
586 Derek Jeter UM 2.00 5.00
587 Randy Johnson UM .75 2.00
588 Chipper Jones UM .75 2.00
589 Greg Maddux UM 1.25 3.00
590 Mark McGwire UM 2.00 5.00
591 Andy Pettitte UM .50 1.25
592 Paul Molitor UM .30 .75
593 Cal Ripken UM 2.50 6.00
594 Alex Rodriguez UM 1.25 3.00
595 Scott Rolen UM .50 1.25
596 Curt Schilling UM .30 .75
597 Frank Thomas UM .75 2.00
598 Jim Thome UM .50 1.25
599 Larry Walker UM .30 .75
600 Bernie Williams UM .50 1.25
P100 A.Rodriguez Promo .60 1.50

1998 Fleer Tradition Vintage '63

Randomly inserted one in every first and second series hobby pack, this 128-card set commemorates the 35th anniversary of the Fleer set and features color photos of top players printed in the 1963 Fleer Baseball card design.

STATED ODDS 1:1 HOBBY
*63 CLASSIC STARS: 30X TO 80X BASIC VINTAGE
63 CLASSIC RANDOM INS.IN HOBBY PACKS
63 CLASSIC PRINT RUN 63 SERIAL #'d SETS
1 Jason Dickson .15 .40
2 Tim Salmon .25 .60
3 Andruw Jones .25 .60
4 Chipper Jones .40 1.00
5 Kenny Lofton .15 .40
6 Greg Maddux .60 1.50
7 Rafael Palmeiro .25 .60
8 Cal Ripken 1.25 3.00
9 Nomar Garciaparra .60 1.50
10 Mark Grace .25 .60
11 Sammy Sosa .40 1.00
12 Frank Thomas .40 1.00
13 Deion Sanders .25 .60
14 Sandy Alomar Jr. .15 .40
15 David Justice .15 .40
16 Jim Thome .25 .60
17 Matt Williams .15 .40
18 Jaret Wright .15 .40
19 Vinny Castilla .15 .40
20 Andres Galarraga .15 .40
21 Todd Helton .25 .60
22 Larry Walker .15 .40
23 Tony Clark .15 .40
24 Moises Alou .15 .40
25 Kevin Brown .25 .60
26 Charles Johnson .15 .40
27 Edgar Renteria .15 .40
28 Gary Sheffield .15 .40
29 Jeff Bagwell .25 .60
30 Craig Biggio .25 .60
31 Raul Mondesi .15 .40
32 Mike Piazza .60 1.50
33 Chuck Knoblauch .15 .40
34 Paul Molitor .15 .40
35 Vladimir Guerrero .40 1.00
36 Pedro Martinez .25 .60
37 Todd Hundley .15 .40
38 Derek Jeter 1.00 2.50
39 Tino Martinez .25 .60
40 Paul O'Neill .25 .60
41 Andy Pettitte .25 .60
42 Mariano Rivera .40 1.00
43 Bernie Williams .25 .60
44 Ben Grieve .15 .40
45 Scott Rolen .25 .60
46 Curt Schilling .15 .40
47 Jason Kendall .15 .40
48 Tony Womack .15 .40
49 Ray Lankford .15 .40
50 Mark McGwire 1.00 2.50
51 Matt Morris .15 .40
52 Tony Gwynn .50 1.25
53 Barry Bonds 1.00 2.50
54 Jay Buhner .15 .40
55 Ken Griffey Jr. .60 1.50
56 Randy Johnson .40 1.00
57 Edgar Martinez .25 .60
58 Alex Rodriguez .60 1.50
59 Juan Gonzalez .15 .40
60 Rusty Greer .15 .40
61 Ivan Rodriguez .25 .60
62 Roger Clemens .75 2.00
63 Jose Cruz Jr. .15 .40
64 Darin Erstad .15 .40
65 Jay Bell .15 .40
66 Andy Benes .15 .40
67 Mickey Mantle 2.50 6.00
68 Karim Garcia .15 .40
69 Travis Lee .15 .40
70 Matt Williams .15 .40
71 Andres Galarraga .15 .40
72 Tom Glavine .25 .60
73 Ryan Klesko .15 .40
74 Denny Neagle .15 .40
75 John Smoltz .25 .60
76 Roberto Alomar .25 .60
77 Joe Carter .15 .40
78 Mike Mussina .25 .60
79 B.J. Surhoff .15 .40
80 Dennis Eckersley .15 .40
81 Pedro Martinez .25 .60
82 Mo Vaughn .15 .40
83 Henry Rodriguez .15 .40
84 Kerry Wood .20 .50
85 Albert Belle .15 .40
86 Sean Casey .15 .40
87 Travis Fryman .15 .40
88 Kenny Lofton .15 .40
89 Darryl Kile .15 .40
90 Mike Lansing .15 .40
91 Bobby Bonilla .15 .40
92 Cliff Floyd .15 .40
93 Livan Hernandez .15 .40
94 Derrek Lee .25 .60
95 Moises Alou .15 .40
96 Shane Reynolds .15 .40
97 Mike Piazza .60 1.50
98 Johnny Damon .25 .60
99 Eric Karros .15 .40
100 Hideo Nomo .40 1.00
101 Marquis Grissom .15 .40
102 Matt Lawton .15 .40
103 Todd Walker .15 .40
104 Gary Sheffield .15 .40
105 Bernard Gilkey .15 .40
106 Rey Ordonez .15 .40
107 Chili Davis .15 .40
108 Chuck Knoblauch .15 .40
109 Charles Johnson .15 .40
110 Rickey Henderson .40 1.00
111 Bob Abreu .15 .40
112 Doug Glanville .15 .40
113 Gregg Jefferies .15 .40
114 Al Martin .15 .40
115 Kevin Young .15 .40
116 Ron Gant .15 .40
117 Kevin Brown .25 .60
118 Ken Caminiti .15 .40
119 Joey Hamilton .15 .40
120 Jeff Kent .15 .40
121 Wade Boggs .25 .60
122 Quinton McCracken .15 .40
123 Fred McGriff .25 .60
124 Paul Sorrento .15 .40
125 Jose Canseco .25 .60
126 Randy Myers .15 .40
NNO Checklist 1 .15 .40
NNO Checklist 2 .15 .40

1998 Fleer Tradition Decade of Excellence

Randomly inserted in hobby packs only at the rate of one in 72, this 12-card set features 1988 season photos in Fleer's 1988 card design of current players who have been in playing major league baseball for ten years or more.

COMPLETE SET (12) 50.00 120.00
STATED ODDS 1:72 HOBBY
*RARE TRAD: 2X TO 5X BASIC DECADES
RARE TRAD. STATED ODDS 1:720 HOBBY
1 Roberto Alomar 1.50 4.00
2 Barry Bonds 6.00 15.00
3 Roger Clemens 5.00 12.00
4 David Cone 1.00 2.50
5 Andres Galarraga 1.00 2.50
6 Mark Grace 1.50 4.00
7 Tony Gwynn 3.00 8.00
8 Randy Johnson 2.50 6.00
9 Greg Maddux 4.00 10.00
10 Mark McGwire 6.00 15.00
11 Paul O'Neill 1.50 4.00
12 Cal Ripken 8.00 20.00

1998 Fleer Tradition Diamond Standouts

Randomly inserted in packs at the rate of one in 12, this 20-card set features color photos of great players on a diamond design silver foil background. The backs display detailed player information.

COMPLETE SET (20) 20.00 50.00
STATED ODDS 1:12
1 Jeff Bagwell .50 1.25
2 Barry Bonds 2.00 5.00
3 Roger Clemens 1.50 4.00
4 Jose Cruz Jr. .30 .75
5 Andres Galarraga .30 .75
6 Nomar Garciaparra 1.25 3.00
7 Juan Gonzalez .30 .75
8 Ken Griffey Jr. 1.25 3.00
9 Derek Jeter 2.00 5.00
10 Randy Johnson .75 2.00
11 Chipper Jones .75 2.00
12 Kenny Lofton .30 .75
13 Greg Maddux 1.25 3.00
14 Pedro Martinez .50 1.25
15 Mark McGwire 2.00 5.00
16 Mike Piazza 1.25 3.00
17 Alex Rodriguez 1.25 3.00
18 Curt Schilling .30 .75
19 Frank Thomas .75 2.00
20 Larry Walker .30 .75

1998 Fleer Tradition Diamond Tribute

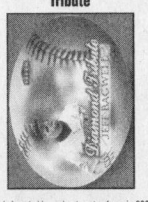

Randomly inserted in packs at a rate of one in 300, this 10-card insert set features color action photos printed on leatherette laminated stock with silver holofoil stamping.

COMPLETE SET (10) 75.00 200.00
SER.2 STATED ODDS 1:300
DT1 Jeff Bagwell 4.00 10.00
DT2 Roger Clemens 12.50 30.00
DT3 Nomar Garciaparra 10.00 25.00
DT4 Juan Gonzalez 2.50 6.00
DT5 Ken Griffey Jr. 10.00 25.00
DT6 Mark McGwire 15.00 40.00
DT7 Mike Piazza 10.00 25.00
DT8 Cal Ripken 20.00 50.00
DT9 Alex Rodriguez 10.00 25.00
DT10 Frank Thomas 6.00 15.00

1998 Fleer Tradition In The Clutch

Randomly inserted in packs at a rate of one in 20, this 15-card insert offers color action photos on a green holofoil background.

COMPLETE SET (15) 30.00 80.00
SER.2 STATED ODDS 1:20
IC1 Jeff Bagwell 1.00 2.50
IC2 Barry Bonds 4.00 10.00
IC3 Roger Clemens 3.00 8.00
IC4 Jose Cruz Jr. .60 1.50
IC5 Nomar Garciaparra 2.50 6.00
IC6 Juan Gonzalez .60 1.50
IC7 Ken Griffey Jr. 2.50 6.00
IC8 Tony Gwynn 2.00 5.00
IC9 Derek Jeter 4.00 10.00
IC10 Chipper Jones 1.50 4.00
IC11 Greg Maddux 2.50 6.00
IC12 Mark McGwire 4.00 10.00
IC13 Mike Piazza 2.50 6.00
IC14 Frank Thomas 1.50 4.00
IC15 Larry Walker .60 1.50

1998 Fleer Tradition Lumber Company

Randomly inserted in retail packs only at the rate of one in 36, this 15-card set features color photos of high-powered offensive players.

COMPLETE SET (15) 50.00 120.00
STATED ODDS 1:36 RETAIL
1 Jeff Bagwell 1.50 4.00
2 Barry Bonds 6.00 15.00
3 Jose Cruz Jr. 1.00 2.50
4 Nomar Garciaparra 4.00 10.00
5 Juan Gonzalez 1.00 2.50
6 Ken Griffey Jr. 4.00 10.00
7 Tony Gwynn 3.00 8.00
8 Chipper Jones 2.50 6.00
9 Tino Martinez 1.50 4.00
10 Mark McGwire 6.00 15.00
11 Mike Piazza 4.00 10.00
12 Cal Ripken 8.00 20.00
13 Alex Rodriguez 4.00 10.00
14 Frank Thomas 2.50 6.00
15 Larry Walker 1.00 2.50

1998 Fleer Tradition Mickey Mantle Monumental Moments

This 10 card set features highlights from Mickey Mantle's long and illustrious career with the New York Yankees. Mantle, who hit 536 Homers in his career and 18 more in the World Series is honored with these cards which were inserted one every 68 packs.

COMPLETE SET (10) 60.00 150.00
COMMON CARD (1-10) 10.00 25.00
SER.2 STATED ODDS 1:68
*GOLD: 1.5X TO 4X BASIC MANTLE
GOLD: RANDOM INSERTS IN SER.2 PACKS
GOLD PRINT RUN 61 SERIAL #'d SETS

1998 Fleer Tradition Power Game

Randomly inserted in packs at the rate of one in 36, this 20-card set features color action player photos of great pitchers and hitters highlighted with purple metallic foil and glossy UV coating. The backs display player statistics.

COMPLETE SET (20) 50.00 120.00
STATED ODDS 1:36
1 Jeff Bagwell 1.50 4.00
2 Albert Belle 1.00 2.50
3 Barry Bonds 6.00 15.00
4 Tony Clark 1.00 2.50
5 Roger Clemens 5.00 12.00
6 Jose Cruz Jr. 1.00 2.50
7 Andres Galarraga 1.00 2.50
8 Nomar Garciaparra 4.00 10.00
9 Juan Gonzalez 1.00 2.50
10 Ken Griffey Jr. 4.00 10.00
11 Randy Johnson 2.50 6.00
12 Greg Maddux 4.00 10.00
13 Pedro Martinez 1.50 4.00
14 Tino Martinez 1.50 4.00
15 Mark McGwire 6.00 15.00
16 Mike Piazza 4.00 10.00
17 Curt Schilling 1.00 2.50
18 Frank Thomas 2.50 6.00
19 Jim Thome 1.50 4.00
20 Larry Walker 1.00 2.50

1998 Fleer Tradition Promising Forecast

Randomly inserted in packs at a rate of one in 12, this 20-card insert features color action photos on cards with flood aqueous coating, silver foil stamping and a white glow around the player's UV coated image.

COMPLETE SET (20) 6.00 15.00
SER.2 STATED ODDS 1:12
PF1 Rolando Arrojo .50 1.25
PF2 Sean Casey .40 1.00
PF3 Brad Fullmer .40 1.00
PF4 Karim Garcia .40 1.00
PF5 Ben Grieve .40 1.00
PF6 Todd Helton .60 1.50
PF7 Richard Hidalgo .40 1.00
PF8 A.J. Hinch .40 1.00
PF9 Paul Konerko .40 1.00
PF10 Mark Kotsay .40 1.00
PF11 Derrek Lee .60 1.50
PF12 Travis Lee .40 1.00
PF13 Eric Milton .40 1.00
PF14 Magglio Ordonez 1.00 2.50
PF15 David Ortiz 1.25 3.00
PF16 Brian Rose .40 1.00
PF17 Miguel Tejada 1.00 2.50
PF18 Jason Varitek 1.00 2.50
PF19 Enrique Wilson .40 1.00
PF20 Kerry Wood .50 1.25

1998 Fleer Tradition Rookie Sensations

Randomly inserted in packs at the rate of one in 18, this 20-card set features gray-bordered action color images of the 1997 most promising players who were eligible for Rookie of the Year honors on multi-colored backgrounds.

COMPLETE SET (20) 15.00 40.00
STATED ODDS 1:18
1 Mike Cameron .60 1.50
2 Jose Cruz Jr. .60 1.50
3 Jason Dickson .60 1.50
4 Kelvim Escobar .60 1.50
5 Nomar Garciaparra 2.50 6.00
6 Ben Grieve .60 1.50
7 Vladimir Guerrero 1.50 4.00
8 Wilton Guerrero .60 1.50
9 Jose Guillen .60 1.50
10 Todd Helton 1.00 2.50
11 Livan Hernandez .60 1.50
12 Hideki Irabu .60 1.50
13 Andruw Jones 1.00 2.50
14 Matt Morris .60 1.50
15 Magglio Ordonez 3.00 8.00
16 Neifi Perez .60 1.50
17 Scott Rolen 1.00 2.50
18 Fernando Tatis .60 1.50
19 Brett Tomko .60 1.50
20 Jaret Wright .60 1.50

1998 Fleer Tradition Zone

Randomly inserted in packs at the rate of one in 288, this 15-card set features color photos of unstoppable players printed on cards with custom pattern rainbow foil and etching.

COMPLETE SET (15) 100.00 250.00
STATED ODDS 1:288
1 Jeff Bagwell 4.00 10.00
2 Barry Bonds 15.00 40.00
3 Roger Clemens 12.50 30.00
4 Jose Cruz Jr. 2.50 6.00
5 Nomar Garciaparra 10.00 25.00
6 Juan Gonzalez 2.50 6.00
7 Ken Griffey Jr. 10.00 25.00
8 Tony Gwynn 8.00 20.00
9 Chipper Jones 6.00 15.00
10 Greg Maddux 10.00 25.00
11 Mark McGwire 15.00 40.00
12 Mike Piazza 10.00 25.00
13 Alex Rodriguez 10.00 25.00
14 Frank Thomas 6.00 15.00
15 Larry Walker 2.50 6.00

1998 Fleer Tradition Update

The 1998 Fleer Update set was issued exclusively in factory set form. This set, issued in November, 1998, was created in large part to get the first J.D. Drew Rookie Card on the market. The set also took advantage of the "retro" themes that were popular in 1998 and represented the return of Fleer Update factory sets that had a rich history from 1984 through 1994. In addition to the aforementioned Drew, other notable RC's in this set include Troy Glaus, Orlando Hernandez and Gabe Kapler.

COMP.FACT.SET (100) 6.00 15.00
U1 Mark McGwire HL .50 1.25
U2 Sammy Sosa HL .10 .30
U3 Roger Clemens HL .40 1.00
U4 Barry Bonds HL .60 1.50
U5 Kerry Wood HL .08 .25
U6 Paul Molitor HL .07 .20
U7 Ken Griffey Jr. HL .30 .75
U8 Cal Ripken HL .60 1.50
U9 David Wells HL .07 .20
U10 Alex Rodriguez HL .30 .75
U11 Angel Pena RC .15 .40
U12 Bruce Chen .07 .20
U13 Craig Wilson .07 .20
U14 O.Hernandez RC .75 2.00
U15 Aramis Ramirez .07 .20
U16 Aaron Boone .07 .20
U17 Bob Henley .07 .20
U18 Juan Guzman .07 .20
U19 Darryl Hamilton .07 .20
U20 Jay Payton .07 .20
U21 Jeremy Powell .07 .20
U22 Ben Davis .07 .20
U23 Preston Wilson .07 .20
U24 Jim Parque RC .25 .60
U25 Odalis Perez RC .60 1.50
U26 Ronnie Belliard .07 .20
U27 Royce Clayton .07 .20
U28 George Lombard .07 .20
U29 Tony Phillips .07 .20
U30 F.Seguignol RC .15 .40
U31 Armando Rios RC .25 .60
U32 Jerry Hairston Jr. RC .25 .60
U33 Justin Baughman RC .15 .40
U34 Seth Greisinger .07 .20
U35 Alex Gonzalez .07 .20
U36 Michael Barrett .07 .20
U37 Carlos Beltran .40 1.00
U38 Ellis Burks .07 .20
U39 Jose Jimenez RC .40 1.00
U40 Carlos Guillen .07 .20
U41 Marlon Anderson .07 .20
U42 Scott Elarton .07 .20
U43 Glenallen Hill .07 .20
U44 Shane Monahan .07 .20
U45 Dennis Martinez .07 .20
U46 Carlos Febles RC .25 .60
U47 Carlos Perez .07 .20
U48 Wilton Guerrero .07 .20
U49 Randy Johnson .20 .50
U50 Brian Simmons RC .15 .40
U51 Carlton Loewer .07 .20
U52 Mark DeRosa RC .40 1.00
U53 Tim Young RC .15 .40
U54 Gary Gaetti .07 .20
U55 Eric Chavez .07 .20
U56 Carl Pavano .07 .20
U57 Mike Stanley .07 .20
U58 Todd Stottlemyre .07 .20
U59 Gabe Kapler RC .40 1.00
U60 Mike Jerzembeck RC .15 .40
U61 Mitch Meluskey RC .25 .60
U62 Bill Pulsipher .07 .20
U63 Derrick Gibson .07 .20
U64 John Rocker RC .40 1.00
U65 Calvin Pickering .07 .20
U66 Blake Stein .07 .20
U67 Fernando Tatis .07 .20
U68 Gabe Alvarez .07 .20
U69 Jeffrey Hammonds .07 .20
U70 Adrian Beltre .07 .20
U71 Ryan Bradley RC .15 .40
U72 Edgard Clemente .07 .20
U73 Rick Croushore RC .15 .40
U74 Matt Clement .07 .20
U75 Dermal Brown .07 .20
U76 Paul Bako .07 .20
U77 Placido Polanco RC .40 1.00
U78 Jay Tessmer .07 .20
U79 Jarrod Washburn .07 .20
U80 Kevin Witt .07 .20
U81 Mike Metcalfe .07 .20
U82 Daryle Ward .07 .20
U83 Benj Sampson RC .15 .40
U84 Mike Kinkade RC .15 .40
U85 Randy Winn .07 .20
U86 Jeff Shaw .07 .20
U87 Troy Glaus RC 1.25 3.00
U88 Hideo Nomo .20 .50
U89 Mark Grudzielanek .07 .20
U90 Mike Frank RC .15 .40
U91 Bobby Howry RC .15 .40
U92 Ryan Minor RC .15 .40
U93 Corey Koskie RC .40 1.00
U94 Matt Anderson RC .15 .40
U95 Joe Carter .07 .20
U96 Paul Konerko .07 .20
U97 Sidney Ponson .07 .20
U98 Jeremy Giambi RC .25 .60
U99 Jeff Kubenka RC .15 .40
U100 J.D. Drew RC 1.00 2.50

1999 Fleer Tradition

The 1999 Fleer set was issued in one series totalling 600 cards and was distributed in 10-card packs with a suggested retail price of $1.59. The fronts feature color action photos with gold foil player names. The backs carry another player photo with biographical information and career statistics. The set includes the following subsets: Franchise Futures (576-590) and Checklists (591-600).

COMPLETE SET (600) 30.00 60.00
1 Mark McGwire .75 2.00
2 Sammy Sosa .30 .75
3 Ken Griffey Jr. .50 1.25
4 Kerry Wood .10 .30
5 Derek Jeter .75 2.00
6 Stan Musial .60 1.50
7 J.D. Drew .10 .30
8 Cal Ripken 1.00 2.50
9 Alex Rodriguez .50 1.25
10 Travis Lee .07 .20
11 Andres Galarraga .10 .30
12 Nomar Garciaparra .50 1.25
13 Albert Belle .10 .30
14 Barry Larkin .20 .50
15 Dante Bichette .10 .30
16 Tony Clark .07 .20
17 Moises Alou .10 .30
18 Rafael Palmeiro .20 .50
19 Raul Mondesi .10 .30
20 Vladimir Guerrero .30 .75
21 John Olerud .10 .30
22 Bernie Williams .20 .50
23 Ben Grieve .07 .20
24 Scott Rolen .20 .50
25 Jeromy Burnitz .10 .30
26 Ken Caminiti .10 .30
27 Barry Bonds .75 2.00
28 Todd Helton .20 .50
29 Juan Gonzalez .10 .30
30 Roger Clemens .60 1.50
31 Andruw Jones .20 .50
32 Mo Vaughn .10 .30
33 Larry Walker .10 .30
34 Frank Thomas .30 .75
35 Manny Ramirez .20 .50
36 Randy Johnson .30 .75
37 Vinny Castilla .10 .30
38 Juan Encarnacion .07 .20
39 Jeff Bagwell .20 .50
40 Gary Sheffield .10 .30
41 Mike Piazza .50 1.25
42 Richie Sexson .10 .30
43 Tony Gwynn .40 1.00
44 Chipper Jones .30 .75
45 Jim Thome .20 .50
46 Craig Biggio .20 .50
47 Carlos Delgado .10 .30
48 Greg Vaughn .07 .20
49 Greg Maddux .50 1.25
50 Troy Glaus .20 .50
51 Roberto Alomar .20 .50
52 Dennis Eckersley .10 .30
53 Mike Caruso .07 .20
54 Bruce Chen .07 .20
55 Aaron Boone .10 .30
56 Bartolo Colon .10 .30
57 Derrick Gibson .07 .20
58 Brian Anderson .07 .20
59 Gabe Alvarez .07 .20
60 Todd Dunwoody .07 .20
61 Rod Beck .07 .20
62 Derek Bell .07 .20
63 Francisco Cordova .07 .20
64 Johnny Damon .20 .50
65 Adrian Beltre .10 .30
66 Garret Anderson .10 .30
67 Armando Benitez .07 .20

Card	Low	High
68 Edgardo Alfonzo	.07	.20
69 Ryan Bradley	.07	.20
70 Eric Chavez	.10	.30
71 Bobby Abreu	.10	.30
72 Andy Ashby	.07	.20
73 Ellis Burks	.10	.30
74 Jeff Cirillo	.07	.20
75 Jay Buhner	.10	.30
76 Ron Gant	.10	.30
77 Rolando Arrojo	.07	.20
78 Will Clark	.20	.50
79 Chris Carpenter	.10	.30
80 Jim Edmonds	.10	.30
81 Tony Batista	.07	.20
82 Shane Andrews	.07	.20
83 Mark DeRosa	.07	.20
84 Brady Anderson	.10	.30
85 Tom Gordon	.07	.20
86 Brant Brown	.07	.20
87 Ray Durham	.10	.30
88 Ron Coomer	.07	.20
89 Bret Boone	.10	.30
90 Travis Fryman	.10	.30
91 Darryl Kile	.10	.30
92 Paul Bako	.07	.20
93 Cliff Floyd	.10	.30
94 Scott Elarton	.07	.20
95 Jeremy Giambi	.07	.20
96 Darren Dreifort	.07	.20
97 Marquis Grissom	.10	.30
98 Marty Cordova	.07	.20
99 Fernando Seguignol	.07	.20
100 Orlando Hernandez	.10	.30
101 Jose Cruz Jr.	.07	.20
102 Jason Giambi	.10	.30
103 Damion Easley	.07	.20
104 Freddy Garcia	.07	.20
105 Marlon Anderson	.07	.20
106 Kevin Brown	.20	.50
107 Joe Carter	.10	.30
108 Russ Davis	.07	.20
109 Brian Jordan	.10	.30
110 Wade Boggs	.20	.50
111 Tom Goodwin	.07	.20
112 Scott Brosius	.10	.30
113 Darin Erstad	.10	.30
114 Jay Bell	.10	.30
115 Tom Glavine	.20	.50
116 Pedro Martinez	.20	.50
117 Mark Grace	.20	.50
118 Russ Ortiz	.07	.20
119 Magglio Ordonez	.10	.30
120 Sean Casey	.10	.30
121 Rafael Roque RC	.07	.20
122 Brian Giles	.10	.30
123 Mike Lansing	.07	.20
124 David Cone	.10	.30
125 Alex Gonzalez	.07	.20
126 Carl Everett	.10	.30
127 Jeff King	.07	.20
128 Charles Johnson	.10	.30
129 Geoff Jenkins	.07	.20
130 Corey Koskie	.07	.20
131 Brad Fullmer	.07	.20
132 Al Leiter	.10	.30
133 Rickey Henderson	.30	.75
134 Rico Brogna	.07	.20
135 Jose Guillen	.10	.30
136 Matt Clement	.10	.30
137 Carlos Guillen	.10	.30
138 Orel Hershiser	.10	.30
139 Ray Lankford	.10	.30
140 Miguel Cairo	.07	.20
141 Chuck Finley	.10	.30
142 Rusty Greer	.10	.30
143 Kelvim Escobar	.07	.20
144 Ryan Klesko	.10	.30
145 Andy Benes	.07	.20
146 Eric Davis	.10	.30
147 David Wells	.10	.30
148 Trot Nixon	.10	.30
149 Jose Hernandez	.07	.20
150 Mark Johnson	.07	.20
151 Mike Frank	.07	.20
152 Joey Hamilton	.07	.20
153 David Justice	.10	.30
154 Mike Mussina	.20	.50
155 Neifi Perez	.07	.20
156 Luis Gonzalez	.10	.30
157 Livan Hernandez	.10	.30
158 Dermal Brown	.07	.20
159 Jose Lima	.07	.20
160 Eric Karros	.10	.30
161 Ronnie Belliard	.07	.20
162 Matt Lawton	.07	.20
163 Dustin Hermanson	.07	.20
164 Brian McRae	.07	.20
165 Mike Kinkade	.07	.20
166 A.J. Hinch	.07	.20
167 Doug Glanville	.07	.20
168 Hideo Nomo	.30	.75
169 Jason Kendall	.10	.30
170 Steve Finley	.10	.30
171 Jeff Kent	.10	.30
172 Ben Davis	.07	.20
173 Edgar Martinez	.20	.50
174 Eli Marrero	.07	.20
175 Quinton McCracken	.07	.20
176 Rick Helling	.07	.20
177 Tom Evans	.07	.20
178 Carl Pavano	.10	.30
179 Todd Greene	.07	.20
180 Omar Daal	.07	.20
181 George Lombard	.07	.20
182 Ryan Minor	.07	.20
183 Troy O'Leary	.07	.20
184 Robb Nen	.10	.30
185 Mickey Morandini	.07	.20
186 Robin Ventura	.10	.30
187 Pete Harnisch	.07	.20
188 Kenny Lofton	.10	.30
189 Eric Milton	.07	.20
190 Bobby Higginson	.10	.30
191 Jamie Moyer	.10	.30
192 Mark Kotsay	.10	.30
193 Shane Reynolds	.07	.20
194 Carlos Febles	.07	.20
195 Jeff Kubenka	.07	.20
196 Chuck Knoblauch	.10	.30
197 Kenny Rogers	.10	.30
198 Bill Mueller	.10	.30
199 Shane Monahan	.07	.20
200 Matt Morris	.10	.30
201 Fred McGriff	.20	.50
202 Ivan Rodriguez	.20	.50
203 Kevin Witt	.07	.20
204 Troy Percival	.10	.30
205 David Dellucci	.07	.20
206 Kevin Millwood	.10	.30
207 Jerry Hairston Jr.	.07	.20
208 Mike Stanley	.07	.20
209 Henry Rodriguez	.07	.20
210 Trevor Hoffman	.10	.30
211 Craig Wilson	.07	.20
212 Reggie Sanders	.10	.30
213 Carlton Loewer	.07	.20
214 Omar Vizquel	.20	.50
215 Gabe Kapler	.10	.30
216 Derrek Lee	.20	.50
217 Billy Wagner	.10	.30
218 Dean Palmer	.10	.30
219 Chan Ho Park	.10	.30
220 Fernando Vina	.07	.20
221 Roy Halladay	.30	.75
222 Paul Molitor	.10	.30
223 Ugueth Urbina	.07	.20
224 Rey Ordonez	.07	.20
225 Ricky Ledee	.07	.20
226 Scott Spiezio	.07	.20
227 Wendell Magee	.07	.20
228 Aramis Ramirez	.10	.30
229 Brian Simmons	.07	.20
230 Fernando Tatis	.07	.20
231 Bobby Smith	.07	.20
232 Aaron Sele	.07	.20
233 Shawn Green	.10	.30
234 Mariano Rivera	.30	.75
235 Tim Salmon	.20	.50
236 Andy Fox	.07	.20
237 Denny Neagle	.07	.20
238 John Valentin	.07	.20
239 Kevin Tapani	.07	.20
240 Paul Konerko	.10	.30
241 Robert Fick	.07	.20
242 Edgar Renteria	.10	.30
243 Brett Tomko	.07	.20
244 Daryle Ward	.07	.20
245 Carlos Beltran	.20	.50
246 Angel Pena	.07	.20
247 Steve Woodard	.07	.20
248 David Ortiz	.30	.75
249 Justin Thompson	.07	.20
250 Rondell White	.10	.30
251 Jaret Wright	.07	.20
252 Ed Sprague	.07	.20
253 Jay Payton	.07	.20
254 Mike Lowell	.10	.30
255 Orlando Cabrera	.10	.30
256 Jason Schmidt	.10	.30
257 David Segui	.07	.20
258 Paul Sorrento	.07	.20
259 John Wetteland	.10	.30
260 Devon White	.10	.30
261 Odalis Perez	.07	.20
262 Calvin Pickering	.07	.20
263 Tyler Green	.07	.20
264 Preston Wilson	.10	.30
265 Brad Radke	.10	.30
266 Walt Weiss	.07	.20
267 Tim Young	.07	.20
268 Tino Martinez	.20	.50
269 Matt Stairs	.07	.20
270 Curt Schilling	.10	.30
271 Tony Womack	.07	.20
272 Ismael Valdes	.07	.20
273 Wally Joyner	.10	.30
274 Armando Rios	.07	.20
275 Andy Pettitte	.20	.50
276 Bubba Trammell	.07	.20
277 Todd Zeile	.10	.30
278 Shannon Stewart	.10	.30
279 Matt Williams	.10	.30
280 John Rocker	.10	.30
281 B.J. Surhoff	.10	.30
282 Eric Young	.07	.20
283 Dmitri Young	.10	.30
284 John Smoltz	.20	.50
285 Todd Walker	.07	.20
286 Paul O'Neill	.20	.50
287 Blake Stein	.07	.20
288 Kevin Young	.10	.30
289 Quilvio Veras	.07	.20
290 Kirk Rueter	.07	.20
291 Randy Winn	.07	.20
292 Miguel Tejada	.10	.30
293 J.T. Snow	.10	.30
294 Michael Tucker	.07	.20
295 Jay Tessmer	.07	.20
296 Scott Erickson	.07	.20
297 Tim Wakefield	.10	.30
298 Jeff Abbott	.07	.20
299 Eddie Taubensee	.07	.20
300 Darryl Hamilton	.07	.20
301 Kevin Orie	.07	.20
302 Jose Offerman	.07	.20
303 Scott Karl	.07	.20
304 Chris Widger	.07	.20
305 Todd Hundley	.07	.20
306 Desi Relaford	.07	.20
307 Sterling Hitchcock	.07	.20
308 Delino DeShields	.07	.20
309 Alex Gonzalez	.07	.20
310 Justin Baughman	.07	.20
311 Jamey Wright	.07	.20
312 Wes Helms	.07	.20
313 Dante Powell	.07	.20
314 Jim Abbott	.20	.50
315 Manny Alexander	.07	.20
316 Harold Baines	.10	.30
317 Danny Graves	.07	.20
318 Sandy Alomar Jr.	.07	.20
319 Pedro Astacio	.07	.20
320 Jermaine Allensworth	.07	.20
321 Matt Anderson	.07	.20
322 Chad Curtis	.07	.20
323 Antonio Osuna	.07	.20
324 Brad Ausmus	.10	.30
325 Steve Trachsel	.07	.20
326 Mike Blowers	.07	.20
327 Brian Bohanon	.07	.20
328 Chris Gomez	.07	.20
329 Valerio De Los Santos	.07	.20
330 Rich Aurilia	.07	.20
331 Michael Barrett	.07	.20
332 Rick Aguilera	.07	.20
333 Adrian Brown	.07	.20
334 Bill Spiers	.07	.20
335 Matt Beech	.07	.20
336 David Bell	.07	.20
337 Juan Acevedo	.07	.20
338 Jose Canseco	.20	.50
339 Wilson Alvarez	.07	.20
340 Luis Alicea	.07	.20
341 Jason Dickson	.07	.20
342 Mike Bordick	.07	.20
343 Ben Ford	.07	.20
344 Javy Lopez	.10	.30
345 Jason Christiansen	.07	.20
346 Darren Bragg	.07	.20
347 Doug Brocail	.07	.20
348 Jeff Blauser	.07	.20
349 James Baldwin	.07	.20
350 Jeffrey Hammonds	.07	.20
351 Ricky Bottalico	.07	.20
352 Russ Branyan	.07	.20
353 Mark Brownson RC	.07	.20
354 Dave Berg	.07	.20
355 Sean Bergman	.07	.20
356 Jeff Conine	.10	.30
357 Shayne Bennett	.07	.20
358 Bobby Bonilla	.10	.30
359 Bob Wickman	.07	.20
360 Carlos Baerga	.07	.20
361 Chris Fussell	.07	.20
362 Chili Davis	.10	.30
363 Jerry Spradlin	.07	.20
364 Carlos Hernandez	.07	.20
365 Roberto Hernandez	.07	.20
366 Marvin Benard	.07	.20
367 Ken Cloude	.07	.20
368 Tony Fernandez	.07	.20
369 John Burkett	.07	.20
370 Gary DiSarcina	.07	.20
371 Alan Benes	.07	.20
372 Karim Garcia	.07	.20
373 Carlos Perez	.07	.20
374 Damon Buford	.07	.20
375 Mark Clark	.07	.20
376 Edgard Clemente	.07	.20
377 Chad Bradford RC	.07	.20
378 Frank Catalanotto	.07	.20
379 Vic Darensbourg	.07	.20
380 Sean Berry	.07	.20
381 Dave Burba	.07	.20
382 Sal Fasano	.07	.20
383 Steve Parris	.07	.20
384 Roger Cedeno	.07	.20
385 Chad Fox	.07	.20
386 Wilton Guerrero	.07	.20
387 Dennis Cook	.07	.20
388 Joe Girardi	.07	.20
389 LaTroy Hawkins	.07	.20
390 Ryan Christenson	.07	.20
391 Paul Byrd	.07	.20
392 Lou Collier	.07	.20
393 Jeff Fassero	.07	.20
394 Jim Leyritz	.07	.20
395 Shawn Estes	.07	.20
396 Mike Kelly	.07	.20
397 Rich Croushore	.07	.20
398 Royce Clayton	.07	.20
399 Rudy Seanez	.07	.20
400 Darrin Fletcher	.07	.20
401 Shigetoshi Hasegawa	.10	.30
402 Bernard Gilkey	.07	.20
403 Juan Guzman	.07	.20
404 Jeff Frye	.07	.20
405 Donovan Osborne	.07	.20
406 Alex Fernandez	.07	.20
407 Gary Gaetti	.07	.20
408 Dan Miceli	.07	.20
409 Mike Cameron	.07	.20
410 Mike Remlinger	.07	.20
411 Joey Cora	.07	.20
412 Mark Gardner	.07	.20
413 Aaron Ledesma	.07	.20
414 Jerry Dipoto	.07	.20
415 Ricky Gutierrez	.07	.20
416 John Franco	.10	.30
417 Mendy Lopez	.07	.20
418 Hideki Irabu	.07	.20
419 Mark Grudzielanek	.07	.20
420 Bobby Hughes	.07	.20
421 Pat Meares	.07	.20
422 Jimmy Haynes	.07	.20
423 Bob Henley	.07	.20
424 Bobby Estalella	.07	.20
425 Jon Lieber	.07	.20
426 Giomar Guevara RC	.07	.20
427 Jose Jimenez	.07	.20
428 Deivi Cruz	.07	.20
429 Jonathan Johnson	.07	.20
430 Ken Hill	.07	.20
431 Craig Grebeck	.07	.20
432 Jose Rosado	.07	.20
433 Danny Klassen	.07	.20
434 Bobby Howry	.07	.20
435 Gerald Williams	.07	.20
436 Omar Olivares	.07	.20
437 Chris Hoiles	.07	.20
438 Seth Greisinger	.07	.20
439 Scott Hatteberg	.07	.20
440 Jeremi Gonzalez	.07	.20
441 Wil Cordero	.07	.20
442 Jeff Montgomery	.07	.20
443 Chris Stynes	.07	.20
444 Tony Saunders	.07	.20
445 Einar Diaz	.07	.20
446 Lariel Gonzalez	.07	.20
447 Ryan Jackson	.07	.20
448 Mike Hampton	.10	.30
449 Todd Hollandsworth	.07	.20
450 Gabe White	.07	.20
451 John Jaha	.07	.20
452 Bret Saberhagen	.10	.30
453 Otis Nixon	.07	.20
454 Steve Kline	.07	.20
455 Butch Huskey	.07	.20
456 Mike Jerzembeck	.07	.20
457 Wayne Gomes	.07	.20
458 Mike Macfarlane	.07	.20
459 Jesus Sanchez	.07	.20
460 Al Martin	.07	.20
461 Dwight Gooden	.10	.30
462 Ruben Rivera	.07	.20
463 Pat Hentgen	.07	.20
464 Jose Valentin	.07	.20
465 Vladimir Nunez	.07	.20
466 Charlie Hayes	.07	.20
467 Jay Powell	.07	.20
468 Raul Ibanez	.07	.20
469 Kent Mercker	.07	.20
470 John Mabry	.07	.20
471 Woody Williams	.07	.20
472 Roberto Kelly	.07	.20
473 Jim Mecir	.07	.20
474 Dave Hollins	.07	.20
475 Rafael Medina	.07	.20
476 Darren Lewis	.07	.20
477 Felix Heredia	.07	.20
478 Brian Hunter	.07	.20
479 Matt Mantei	.07	.20
480 Richard Hidalgo	.07	.20
481 Bobby Jones	.07	.20
482 Hal Morris	.07	.20
483 Ramiro Mendoza	.07	.20
484 Matt Luke	.07	.20
485 Esteban Loaiza	.07	.20
486 Mark Loretta	.07	.20
487 A.J. Pierzynski	.10	.30
488 Charles Nagy	.07	.20
489 Kevin Sefcik	.07	.20
490 Jason McDonald	.07	.20
491 Jeremy Powell	.07	.20
492 Scott Servais	.07	.20
493 Abraham Nunez	.07	.20
494 Stan Spencer	.07	.20
495 Stan Javier	.07	.20
496 Jose Paniagua	.07	.20
497 Gregg Jefferies	.07	.20
498 Gregg Olson	.07	.20
499 Derek Lowe	.10	.30
500 Willis Otanez	.07	.20
501 Brian Moehler	.07	.20
502 Glenallen Hill	.07	.20
503 Bobby M. Jones	.07	.20
504 Greg Norton	.07	.20
505 Mike Jackson	.07	.20
506 Kirt Manwaring	.07	.20
507 Eric Weaver RC	.07	.20
508 Mitch Meluskey	.07	.20
509 Todd Jones	.07	.20
510 Mike Matheny	.07	.20
511 Benj Sampson	.07	.20
512 Tony Phillips	.07	.20
513 Mike Thurman	.07	.20
514 Jorge Posada	.20	.50
515 Bill Taylor	.07	.20
516 Mike Sweeney	.10	.30
517 Jose Silva	.07	.20
518 Mark Lewis	.07	.20
519 Chris Peters	.07	.20
520 Brian Johnson	.07	.20
521 Mike Timlin	.07	.20
522 Mark McLemore	.07	.20
523 Dan Plesac	.07	.20
524 Kelly Stinnett	.07	.20
525 Sidney Ponson	.07	.20
526 Jim Parque	.07	.20
527 Tyler Houston	.07	.20
528 John Thomson	.07	.20
529 Reggie Jefferson	.07	.20
530 Robert Person	.07	.20
531 Marc Newfield	.07	.20
532 Javier Vazquez	.10	.30
533 Terry Steinbach	.07	.20
534 Turk Wendell	.07	.20
535 Tim Raines	.10	.30
536 Brian Meadows	.07	.20
537 Mike Lieberthal	.10	.30
538 Ricardo Rincon	.07	.20
539 Dan Wilson	.07	.20
540 John Johnstone	.07	.20
541 Todd Stottlemyre	.07	.20
542 Kevin Stocker	.07	.20
543 Ramon Martinez	.07	.20
544 Mike Simms	.07	.20
545 Paul Quantrill	.07	.20
546 Matt Walbeck	.07	.20
547 Turner Ward	.07	.20
548 Bill Pulsipher	.07	.20
549 Donnie Sadler	.07	.20
550 Lance Johnson	.07	.20
551 Bill Simas	.07	.20
552 Jeff Reed	.07	.20
553 Jeff Shaw	.07	.20
554 Joe Randa	.10	.30
555 Paul Shuey	.07	.20
556 Mike Redmond RC	.07	.20
557 Sean Runyan	.07	.20
558 Enrique Wilson	.07	.20
559 Scott Radinsky	.07	.20
560 Larry Sutton	.07	.20
561 Masato Yoshii	.07	.20
562 David Nilsson	.07	.20
563 Mike Trombley	.07	.20
564 Darryl Strawberry	.10	.30
565 Dave Mlicki	.07	.20
566 Placido Polanco	.07	.20
567 Yorkis Perez	.07	.20
568 Esteban Yan	.07	.20
569 Lee Stevens	.07	.20
570 Steve Sinclair	.07	.20
571 Jarrod Washburn	.07	.20
572 Lenny Webster	.07	.20
573 Mike Sirotka	.07	.20
574 Jason Varitek	.30	.75
575 Terry Mulholland	.07	.20
576 Adrian Beltre FF	.07	.20
577 Eric Chavez FF	.07	.20
578 J.D. Drew FF	.07	.20
579 Juan Encarnacion FF	.07	.20
580 Nomar Garciaparra FF	.30	.75
581 Troy Glaus FF	.10	.30
582 Ben Grieve FF	.07	.20
583 Vladimir Guerrero FF	.20	.50
584 Todd Helton FF	.10	.30
585 Derek Jeter FF	.40	1.00
586 Travis Lee FF	.07	.20
587 Alex Rodriguez FF	.30	.75
588 Scott Rolen FF	.10	.30
589 Richie Sexson FF	.07	.20
590 Kerry Wood FF	.07	.20
591 Ken Griffey Jr. CL	.30	.75
592 Chipper Jones CL	.20	.50
593 Alex Rodriguez CL	.30	.75
594 Sammy Sosa CL	.20	.50
595 Mark McGwire CL	.40	1.00
596 Cal Ripken CL	.50	1.25
597 Nomar Garciaparra CL	.30	.75
598 Derek Jeter CL	.40	1.00
599 Kerry Wood CL	.07	.20
600 J.D. Drew CL	.07	.20
P7 J.D. Drew Promo	.40	1.00

1999 Fleer Tradition Millenium

Fleer printed 5,000 Millenium factory sets, primarily intended for sale on Shop at Home at the end of the 1999 calendar year. Each set came shrink-wrapped in an attractive factory box, of which is sealed with a gold sticker serial numbered of 5,000. Each set contains 620 cards consisting of the 600-card basic issue set plus 20 cards from the Fleer Update set (rookies U1-U10 and highlights U141-U150). The cards hailing from the Update set have been renumbered. The Update rookies are numbered 601-610 and the Update highlights are numbered 611-620. All 620 cards contain a special gold foil "Year 2000" logo.

COMP.FACT.SET (620)	30.00	80.00
*STARS 1-600: 1X TO 2.5X BASIC CARDS		
*ROOKIES 1-600: 1X TO 2.5X BASIC CARDS		
601 Rick Ankiel	1.00	2.50
602 Peter Bergeron	.30	.75
603 Pat Burrell	3.00	8.00
604 Eric Munson	.60	1.50
605 Alfonso Soriano	6.00	15.00
606 Tim Hudson	3.00	8.00
607 Erubiel Durazo	.60	1.50
608 Chad Hermansen	.30	.75
609 Jeff Zimmerman	.60	1.50
610 Jesus Pena	.30	.75
611 Wade Boggs HL	.50	1.25
612 Jose Canseco HL	.50	1.25
613 Roger Clemens HL	1.50	4.00
614 David Cone HL	.30	.75
615 Tony Gwynn HL	1.00	2.50
616 Mark McGwire HL	2.00	5.00
617 Cal Ripken HL	2.50	6.00
618 Alex Rodriguez HL	1.25	3.00
619 Fernando Tatis HL	.20	.50
620 Robin Ventura HL	.30	.75

1999 Fleer Tradition Warning Track

Cards from this parallel set were seeded at a rate of one per retail pack. Warning Track cards can be easily identified by the red foil "Warning Track Collection" logo at the base of the card front and the W suffix numbering on the card backs.

*STARS: 2.5X TO 6X BASIC CARDS

1999 Fleer Tradition Vintage '61

Inserted one in every hobby pack only, this 50-card set features the first 50 cards of the 1999 Fleer Tradition set in cards designed similar to the 1961 Fleer Baseball Greats set.

COMPLETE SET (50)	12.50	25.00
*SINGLES: .4X TO 1X BASE CARD HI		

1999 Fleer Tradition Date With Destiny

These attractive bronze foil cards are designed to mimic the famous plaques on display at the Hall of Fame. Fleer selected ten of the games greatest active players, all of whom are well on their way to the Hall of Fame. Only 100 sets were printed (each card is serial numbered "X/100" on front) and the cards were randomly seeded into packs at an unannounced rate. Suffice to say, they're not easy to pull from packs.

1 Barry Bonds	25.00	60.00
2 Roger Clemens	20.00	50.00
3 Ken Griffey Jr.	15.00	40.00
4 Tony Gwynn	12.50	30.00
5 Greg Maddux	15.00	40.00
6 Mark McGwire	25.00	60.00
7 Mike Piazza	15.00	40.00
8 Cal Ripken	30.00	80.00
9 Alex Rodriguez	15.00	40.00
10 Frank Thomas	10.00	25.00

1999 Fleer Tradition Diamond Magic

Randomly inserted in packs at the rate of one in 96, this 15-card set features color action player images printed with a special die-cut treatment on a multi-layer card for a kaleidoscope effect behind the player image.

COMPLETE SET (15)	125.00	250.00
STATED ODDS 1:96		
1 Barry Bonds	10.00	25.00
2 Roger Clemens	8.00	20.00
3 Nomar Garciaparra	6.00	15.00
4 Ken Griffey Jr.	6.00	15.00
5 Tony Gwynn	5.00	12.00
6 Orlando Hernandez	1.50	4.00
7 Derek Jeter	10.00	25.00
8 Randy Johnson	4.00	10.00
9 Chipper Jones	4.00	10.00
10 Greg Maddux	6.00	15.00
11 Mark McGwire	10.00	25.00
12 Alex Rodriguez	6.00	15.00
13 Sammy Sosa	4.00	10.00
14 Bernie Williams	2.50	6.00
15 Kerry Wood	1.50	4.00

1999 Fleer Tradition Going Yard

Randomly inserted in packs at the rate of one in 18, this 15-card set features color action photos of players who hit the longest home runs printed on extra wide cards to illustrate the greatness of their feats.

COMPLETE SET (15)	15.00	40.00
STATED ODDS 1:18		
1 Moises Alou	.40	1.00
2 Albert Belle	.40	1.00
3 Jose Canseco	.60	1.50
4 Vinny Castilla	.40	1.00
5 Andres Galarraga	.40	1.00
6 Juan Gonzalez	.40	1.00
7 Ken Griffey Jr.	1.50	4.00
8 Chipper Jones	1.00	2.50
9 Mark McGwire	2.50	6.00
10 Rafael Palmeiro	.60	1.50
11 Mike Piazza	1.50	4.00
12 Alex Rodriguez	1.50	4.00
13 Sammy Sosa	1.00	2.50
14 Greg Vaughn	.25	.60
15 Mo Vaughn	.40	1.00

1999 Fleer Tradition Golden Memories

Randomly inserted in packs at the rate of one in 54, this 15-card set features color action player photos with an embossed frame design.

COMPLETE SET (15)	75.00	150.00
STATED ODDS 1:54		
1 Albert Belle	1.00	2.50
2 Barry Bonds	6.00	15.00
3 Roger Clemens	5.00	12.00
4 Nomar Garciaparra	4.00	10.00
5 Juan Gonzalez	1.00	2.50
6 Ken Griffey Jr.	4.00	10.00
7 Randy Johnson	2.50	6.00
8 Greg Maddux	4.00	10.00
9 Mark McGwire	6.00	15.00
10 Mike Piazza	4.00	10.00
11 Cal Ripken	8.00	20.00
12 Alex Rodriguez	4.00	10.00
13 Sammy Sosa	2.50	6.00
14 David Wells	1.00	2.50
15 Kerry Wood	1.00	2.50

1999 Fleer Tradition Stan Musial Monumental Moments

Randomly inserted in packs at the rate of one in 36, this 10-card set features photos of Stan Musial during his legendary career. As a bonus to collectors, Stan signed 50 of each of these cards in this set.

COMPLETE SET (10)	10.00	25.00
COMMON CARD (1-10)	1.00	2.50
STATED ODDS 1:36		

1999 Fleer Tradition Stan Musial Monumental Moments Autographs

Fleer got legendary star Stan Musial to sign fifty of each Monumental Moments cards. Musial signed each card in bold blue ink on front. The cards are also serial numbered by hand in blue ink just beneath Musial's signature. Finally, each card was embossed with a circular Fleer logo to certify authenticity.

COMMON CARD (1-10)	30.00	60.00

1999 Fleer Tradition Rookie Flashback

Randomly inserted in packs at the rate of one in six, this 15-card set features color action photos of players who were rookies during the 1998 season printed on sculpture embossed cards.

COMPLETE SET (15)	4.00	10.00
STATED ODDS 1:6		
1 Matt Anderson	.20	.50
2 Rolando Arrojo	.20	.50
3 Adrian Beltre	.30	.75
4 Mike Caruso	.20	.50
5 Eric Chavez	.30	.75
6 J.D. Drew	.30	.75
7 Juan Encarnacion	.20	.50
8 Brad Fullmer	.20	.50
9 Troy Glaus	.50	1.25
10 Ben Grieve	.20	.50
11 Todd Helton	.50	1.25
12 Orlando Hernandez	.30	.75
13 Travis Lee	.20	.50
14 Richie Sexson	.30	.75
15 Kerry Wood	.30	.75

1999 Fleer Tradition Update

The 1999 Fleer Update set was issued in one series totalling 150 cards and distributed only as a factory boxed set. The fronts feature color action player photos. The backs carry player information. The set features the Season Highlights subset (Cards 141-150). Over 100 Rookie Cards are featured in this set. Among these Rookie Cards are Rick Ankiel, Josh Beckett, Pat Burrell, Tim Hudson, Eric Munson, Wily Mo Pena and Alfonso Soriano.

COMP.FACT.SET (150)	10.00	25.00
U1 Rick Ankiel RC	3.00	8.00
U2 Peter Bergeron RC	.08	.25
U3 Pat Burrell RC	.75	2.00
U4 Eric Munson RC	.15	.40
U5 Alfonso Soriano RC	2.00	5.00
U6 Tim Hudson RC	.75	2.00
U7 Erubiel Durazo RC	.15	.40
U8 Chad Hermansen	.07	.20
U9 Jeff Zimmerman RC	.08	.25
U10 Jesus Pena RC	.08	.25
U11 Ramon Hernandez	.08	.25
U12 Trent Durrington RC	.08	.25
U13 Tony Armas Jr.	.07	.20
U14 Mike Fyhrie RC	.08	.25
U15 Danny Kolb RC	.30	.75
U16 Mike Porzio RC	.08	.25
U17 Will Brunson RC	.08	.25
U18 Mike Duvall RC	.08	.25
U19 D.Mientkiewicz RC	.30	.75
U20 Gabe Molina RC	.08	.25
U21 Luis Vizcaino RC	.08	.25
U22 Robinson Cancel RC	.08	.25
U23 Brett Laxton RC	.08	.25
U24 Joe McEwing RC	.08	.25
U25 Justin Speier RC	.08	.25
U26 Kip Wells RC	.15	.40
U27 Armando Almanza RC	.08	.25
U28 Joe Davenport RC	.08	.25
U29 Yamid Haad RC	.08	.25
U30 John Halama	.07	.20
U31 Adam Kennedy	.07	.20
U32 Micah Bowie RC	.08	.25
U33 Gookie Dawkins RC	.15	.40
U34 Ryan Rupe RC	.08	.25
U35 B.J. Ryan RC	.75	2.00
U36 Chance Sanford RC	.08	.25
U37 A.Shumaker RC	.08	.25

1999 Fleer Tradition Millenium

U38 Ryan Glynn RC .08 .25
U39 Roosevelt Brown RC .08 .25
U40 Ben Molina RC .60 1.50
U41 Scott Williamson .07 .20
U42 Eric Gagne RC 1.50 4.00
U43 John McDonald RC .08 .25
U44 Scott Sauerbeck RC .08 .25
U45 Mike Venafro RC .08 .25
U46 Edwards Guzman RC .08 .25
U47 Richard Barker RC .08 .25
U48 Braden Looper .07 .20
U49 Chad Meyers RC .08 .25
U50 Scott Strickland RC .08 .25
U51 Billy Koch .07 .20
U52 David Newhan RC .15 .40
U53 David Riske RC .08 .25
U54 Jose Santiago RC .08 .25
U55 Miguel Del Toro RC .08 .25
U56 Orber Moreno RC .08 .25
U57 Dave Roberts RC .30 .75
U58 Tim Byrdak RC .08 .25
U59 David Lee RC .08 .25
U60 Guillermo Mota RC .08 .25
U61 Wilton Veras RC .08 .25
U62 Joe Mays RC .15 .40
U63 Jose Fernandez RC .08 .25
U64 Ray King RC .08 .25
U65 Chris Petersen RC .08 .25
U66 Vernon Wells .07 .20
U67 Ruben Mateo .07 .20
U68 Ben Petrick .07 .20
U69 Chris Tremie RC .08 .25
U70 Lance Berkman .07 .20
U71 Dan Smith RC .08 .25
U72 Carlos E. Hernandez RC .15 .40
U73 Chad Harville RC .08 .25
U74 Damaso Marte RC .08 .25
U75 Aaron Myette RC .08 .25
U76 Willis Roberts RC .08 .25
U77 Erik Sabel RC .08 .25
U78 Hector Almonte RC .08 .25
U79 Kris Benson .07 .20
U80 Pat Daneker RC .08 .25
U81 Freddy Garcia RC .40 1.00
U82 Byung-Hyun Kim RC .40 1.00
U83 Wily Pena RC 1.25 3.00
U84 Dan Wheeler RC .15 .40
U85 Tim Harikkala RC .08 .25
U86 Derrin Ebert RC .08 .25
U87 Horacio Estrada RC .08 .25
U88 Liu Rodriguez RC .08 .25
U89 J.Zimmerman RC .08 .25
U90 A.J. Burnett RC .40 1.00
U91 Doug Davis RC .40 1.00
U92 Rob Ramsay RC .08 .25
U93 Clay Bellinger RC .08 .25
U94 Charlie Greene RC .08 .25
U95 Bo Porter RC .08 .25
U96 Jorge Toca RC .15 .40
U97 Casey Blake RC .50 1.25
U98 Amaury Garcia RC .08 .25
U99 Jose Molina RC .15 .40
U100 Melvin Mora RC 1.00 2.50
U101 Joe Nathan RC .50 1.25
U102 Juan Pena RC .08 .25
U103 Dave Borkowski RC .08 .25
U104 Eddie Gaillard RC .08 .25
U105 Glen Barker RC .08 .25
U106 Brett Hinchliffe RC .08 .25
U107 Carlos Lee .07 .20
U108 Rob Ryan RC .08 .25
U109 Jeff Weaver RC .30 .75
U110 Ed Yarnall .07 .20
U111 Nelson Cruz RC .08 .25
U112 C.Davidson RC .08 .25
U113 Tim Kubinski RC .08 .25
U114 Sean Spencer RC .08 .25
U115 Joe Winkelsas RC .08 .25
U116 Mike Colangelo RC .08 .25
U117 Tom Davey RC .08 .25
U118 Warren Morris .07 .20
U119 Dan Murray RC .08 .25
U120 Jose Nieves RC .08 .25
U121 Mark Quinn RC .08 .25
U122 Josh Beckett RC 4.00 10.00
U123 Chad Allen RC .08 .25
U124 Mike Figga .08 .25
U125 Beiker Graterol RC .08 .25
U126 Aaron Scheffer RC .08 .25
U127 Wiki Gonzalez RC .15 .40
U128 Ramon E.Martinez RC .08 .25
U129 Matt Riley RC .15 .40
U130 Chris Woodward RC .08 .25
U131 Albert Belle .07 .20
U132 Roger Cedeno .07 .20
U133 Roger Clemens .40 1.00
U134 Brian Giles .07 .20
U135 Rickey Henderson .20 .50
U136 Randy Johnson .20 .50
U137 Brian Jordan .07 .20
U138 Paul Konerko .07 .20
U139 Hideo Nomo .20 .50
U140 Kenny Rogers .07 .20
U141 Wade Boggs HL .10 .30
U142 Jose Canseco HL .07 .20
U143 Roger Clemens HL .40 1.00
U144 David Cone HL .07 .20
U145 Tony Gwynn HL .25 .60
U146 Mark McGwire HL .50 1.25
U147 Cal Ripken HL .60 1.50
U148 Alex Rodriguez HL .30 .75
U149 Fernando Tatis HL .07 .20
U150 Robin Ventura HL .07 .20

2000 Fleer Tradition

This 450-card single series set was released in February, 2000. Ten-card hobby and retail packs carried an SRP of $1.59. The basic cards are somewhat reminiscent of the 1954 Topps baseball set featuring a large headshot set against a flat color background and a small, cut-out action shot. Subsets are as follows: League Leaders (1-10), Award Winners (435-440), Division Playoffs-World Series Highlights (441-450). Dual-player prospect cards, team cards and six checklist cards (featuring a floating head image of several of the game's top stars) are also sprinkled throughout the set. In addition, a Cal Ripken promotional card was distributed to dealers and hobby media several weeks prior to the product's release. The card is easy to identify by the "PROMOTIONAL SAMPLE" text running diagonally across the front and back.

COMPLETE SET (450) 20.00 50.00
1 Ken Griffey Jr .30 .75
Rafael Palmeiro
Carlos Delgado LL
2 Mark McGwire .30 .75
Sammy Sosa
Chipper Jones LL
3 Manny Ramirez .10 .30
Rafael Palmeiro
Ken Griffey Jr. LL
4 Mark McGwire .30 .75
Matt Williams
Sammy Sosa LL
5 Nomar Garciaparra .30 .75
Derek Jeter
Bernie Williams LL
6 Larry Walker .10 .30
Luis Gonzalez
Bob Abreu LL
7 Pedro Martinez .10 .30
Bartolo Colon
Mike Mussina LL
8 Mike Hampton .10 .30
Jose Lima
Greg Maddux LL
9 Pedro Martinez .10 .30
David Cone
Mike Mussina LL
10 Randy Johnson .20 .50
Kevin Millwood
Mike Hampton LL
11 Matt Mantei .10 .30
12 John Rocker .10 .30
13 Kyle Farnsworth .10 .30
14 Juan Guzman .10 .30
15 Manny Ramirez .20 .50
16 Matt Riley .10 .30
Calvin Pickering
17 Tony Clark .10 .30
18 Brian Meadows .10 .30
19 Orber Moreno .10 .30
20 Eric Karros .10 .30
21 Steve Woodard .10 .30
22 Scott Brosius .10 .30
23 Gary Bennett .10 .30
24 Jason Wood .10 .30
Dave Borkowski
25 Joe McEwing .10 .30
26 Juan Gonzalez .10 .30
27 Roy Halladay .10 .30
28 Trevor Hoffman .10 .30
29 Arizona Diamondbacks .10 .30
30 Domingo Guzman RC .10 .30
Wiki Gonzalez
31 Bret Boone .10 .30
32 Nomar Garciaparra .50 1.25
33 Bo Porter .10 .30
34 Eddie Taubensee .10 .30
35 Pedro Astacio .10 .30
36 Derek Bell .10 .30
37 Jacque Jones .10 .30
38 Ricky Ledee .10 .30
39 Jeff Kent .10 .30
40 Matt Williams .10 .30
41 Alfonso Soriano .30 .75
D'Angelo Jimenez
42 B.J. Surhoff .10 .30
43 Denny Neagle .10 .30
44 Omar Vizquel .20 .50
45 Jeff Bagwell .20 .50
46 Mark Grudzielanek .10 .30
47 LaTroy Hawkins .10 .30
48 Orlando Hernandez .10 .30
49 Ken Griffey Jr. CL .30 .75
50 Fernando Tatis .10 .30
51 Quilvio Veras .10 .30
52 Wayne Gomes .10 .30
53 Rick Helling .10 .30
54 Shannon Stewart .10 .30
55 Dermal Brown .10 .30
Mark Quinn
56 Randy Johnson .30 .75
57 Greg Maddux .50 1.25
58 Mike Cameron .10 .30
59 Matt Anderson .10 .30
60 Milwaukee Brewers .10 .30
61 Derrek Lee .20 .50
62 Mike Sweeney .10 .30
63 Fernando Vina .10 .30
64 Orlando Cabrera .10 .30
65 Doug Glanville .10 .30
66 Stan Spencer .10 .30
67 Ray Lankford .10 .30
68 Kelly Dransfeldt .10 .30
69 Alex Gonzalez .10 .30
70 Russ Branyan .10 .30
Danny Peoples
71 Jim Edmonds .10 .30
72 Brady Anderson .10 .30
73 Mike Stanley .10 .30
74 Travis Fryman .10 .30
75 Carlos Febles .10 .30
76 Bobby Higginson .10 .30
77 Carlos Perez .10 .30
78 Steve Cox .10 .30
Alex Sanchez
79 Dustin Hermanson .10 .30
80 Kenny Rogers .10 .30
81 Miguel Tejada .10 .30
82 Ben Davis .10 .30
83 Reggie Sanders .10 .30
84 Eric Davis .10 .30
85 J.D. Drew .10 .30
86 Ryan Rupe .10 .30
87 Bobby Smith .10 .30
88 Jose Cruz Jr. .10 .30
89 Carlos Delgado .10 .30
90 Toronto Blue Jays .10 .30
91 Denny Stark RC .10 .30
Gil Meche
92 Randy Velarde .10 .30
93 Aaron Boone .10 .30
94 Javy Lopez .10 .30
95 Johnny Damon .20 .50
96 Jon Lieber .10 .30
97 Montreal Expos .10 .30
98 Mark Kotsay .10 .30
99 Luis Gonzalez .10 .30
100 Larry Walker .10 .30
101 Adrian Beltre .10 .30
102 Alex Ochoa .10 .30
103 Michael Barrett .10 .30
104 Tampa Bay Devil Rays .10 .30
105 Rey Ordonez .10 .30
106 Derek Jeter .60 1.50
107 Mike Lieberthal .10 .30
108 Ellis Burks .10 .30
109 Steve Finley .10 .30
110 Ryan Klesko .10 .30
111 Steve Avery .10 .30
112 Dave Veres .10 .30
113 Cliff Floyd .10 .30
114 Shane Reynolds .10 .30
115 Kevin Brown .20 .50
116 Dave Nilsson .10 .30
117 Mike Trombley .10 .30
118 Todd Walker .10 .30
119 John Olerud .10 .30
120 Chuck Knoblauch .10 .30
121 Nomar Garciaparra CL .30 .75
122 Trot Nixon .10 .30
123 Erubiel Durazo .10 .30
124 Edwards Guzman .10 .30
125 Curt Schilling .10 .30
126 Brian Jordan .10 .30
127 Cleveland Indians .10 .30
128 Benito Santiago .10 .30
129 Frank Thomas .30 .75
130 Neifi Perez .10 .30
131 Alex Fernandez .10 .30
132 Jose Lima .10 .30
133 Jorge Toca .10 .30
Melvin Mora
134 Scott Karl .10 .30
135 Brad Radke .10 .30
136 Paul O'Neill .20 .50
137 Kris Benson .10 .30
138 Colorado Rockies .10 .30
139 Jason Phillips .10 .30
140 Robb Nen .10 .30
141 Ken Hill .10 .30
142 Charles Johnson .10 .30
143 Paul Konerko .10 .30
144 Dmitri Young .10 .30
145 Justin Thompson .10 .30
146 Mark Loretta .10 .30
147 Edgardo Alfonzo .10 .30
148 Armando Benitez .10 .30
149 Octavio Dotel .10 .30
150 Wade Boggs .20 .50
151 Ramon Hernandez .10 .30
152 Freddy Garcia .10 .30
153 Edgar Martinez .20 .50
154 Ivan Rodriguez .20 .50
155 Kansas City Royals .10 .30
156 Cleatus Davidson .10 .30
Cristian Guzman
157 Andy Benes .10 .30
158 Todd Dunwoody .10 .30
159 Pedro Martinez .20 .50
160 Mike Caruso .10 .30
161 Mike Sirotka .10 .30
162 Houston Astros .10 .30
163 Darryl Kile .10 .30
164 Chipper Jones .30 .75
165 Carl Everett .10 .30
166 Geoff Jenkins .10 .30
167 Dan Perkins .10 .30
168 Andy Pettitte .20 .50
169 Francisco Cordova .10 .30
170 Jay Buhner .10 .30
171 Jay Bell .10 .30
172 Andruw Jones .20 .50
173 Bobby Howry .10 .30
174 Chris Singleton .10 .30
175 Todd Helton .20 .50
176 A.J. Burnett .10 .30
177 Marquis Grissom .10 .30
178 Eric Milton .10 .30
179 Los Angeles Dodgers .10 .30
180 Kevin Appier .10 .30
181 Brian Giles .10 .30
182 Tom Davey .10 .30
183 Mo Vaughn .10 .30
184 Jose Hernandez .10 .30
185 Jim Parque .10 .30
186 Derrick Gibson .10 .30
187 Bruce Aven .10 .30
188 Jeff Cirillo .10 .30
189 Doug Mientkiewicz .10 .30
190 Eric Chavez .10 .30
191 Al Martin .10 .30
192 Tom Glavine .20 .50
193 Butch Huskey .10 .30
194 Ray Durham .10 .30
195 Greg Vaughn .10 .30
196 Vinny Castilla .10 .30
197 Ken Caminiti .10 .30
198 Joe Mays .10 .30
199 Chicago White Sox .10 .30
200 Mariano Rivera .30 .75
201 Mark McGwire CL .40 1.00
202 Pat Meares .10 .30
203 Andres Galarraga .10 .30
204 Tom Gordon .10 .30
205 Henry Rodriguez .10 .30
206 Brett Tomko .10 .30
207 Dante Bichette .10 .30
208 Craig Biggio .20 .50
209 Matt Lawton .10 .30
210 Tino Martinez .20 .50
211 Aaron Myette .10 .30
Josh Paul
212 Warren Morris .10 .30
213 San Diego Padres .10 .30
214 Ramon E. Martinez .10 .30
215 Troy Percival .10 .30
216 Jason Johnson .10 .30
217 Carlos Lee .10 .30
218 Scott Williamson .10 .30
219 Jeff Weaver .10 .30
220 Ronnie Belliard .10 .30
221 Jason Giambi .10 .30
222 Ken Griffey Jr. .50 1.25
223 John Halama .10 .30
224 Brett Hinchliffe .10 .30
225 Wilson Alvarez .10 .30
226 Rolando Arrojo .10 .30
227 Ruben Mateo .10 .30
228 Rafael Palmeiro .20 .50
229 David Wells .10 .30
230 Eric Gagne RC .30 .75
Jeff Williams RC
231 Tim Salmon .20 .50
232 Mike Mussina .20 .50
233 Magglio Ordonez .10 .30
234 Ron Villone .10 .30
235 Antonio Alfonseca .10 .30
236 Jeromy Burnitz .10 .30
237 Ben Grieve .10 .30
238 Giomar Guevara .10 .30
239 Garret Anderson .10 .30
240 John Smoltz .20 .50
241 Mark Grace .20 .50
242 Cole Liniak .10 .30
Jose Molina
243 Damion Easley .10 .30
244 Jeff Montgomery .10 .30
245 Kenny Lofton .10 .30
246 Masato Yoshii .10 .30
247 Philadelphia Phillies .10 .30
248 Raul Mondesi .10 .30
249 Marlon Anderson .10 .30
250 Shawn Green .10 .30
251 Sterling Hitchcock .10 .30
252 Randy Wolf .10 .30
Anthony Shumaker
253 Jeff Fassero .10 .30
254 Eli Marrero .10 .30
255 Cincinnati Reds .10 .30
256 Rick Ankiel .10 .30
Adam Kennedy
257 Darin Erstad .10 .30
258 Albert Belle .10 .30
259 Bartolo Colon .10 .30
260 Bret Saberhagen .10 .30
261 Carlos Beltran .10 .30
262 Glenallen Hill .10 .30
263 Gregg Jefferies .10 .30
264 Matt Clement .10 .30
265 Miguel Del Toro .10 .30
266 Robinson Cancel .10 .30
Kevin Barker
267 San Francisco Giants .10 .30
268 Kent Bottenfield .10 .30
269 Fred McGriff .20 .50
270 Chris Carpenter .10 .30
271 Atlanta Braves .10 .30
272 Wilton Veras .15 .40
Tomo Ohka RC
273 Will Clark .20 .50
274 Troy O'Leary .10 .30
275 Sammy Sosa CL .20 .50
276 Travis Lee .10 .30
277 Sean Casey .10 .30
278 Ron Gant .10 .30
279 Roger Clemens .60 1.50
280 Phil Nevin .10 .30
281 Mike Piazza .50 1.25
282 Mike Lowell .10 .30
283 Kevin Millwood .10 .30
284 Joe Randa .10 .30
285 Jeff Shaw .10 .30
286 Jason Varitek .30 .75
287 Harold Baines .10 .30
288 Gabe Kapler .10 .30
289 Chuck Finley .10 .30
290 Carl Pavano .10 .30
291 Brad Ausmus .10 .30
292 Brad Fullmer .10 .30
293 Boston Red Sox .10 .30
294 Bob Wickman .10 .30
295 Billy Wagner .10 .30
296 Shawn Estes .10 .30
297 Gary Sheffield .10 .30
298 Fernando Seguignol .10 .30
299 Omar Olivares .10 .30
300 Baltimore Orioles .10 .30
301 Matt Stairs .10 .30
302 Andy Ashby .10 .30
303 Todd Greene .10 .30
304 Jesse Garcia .10 .30
305 Kerry Wood .10 .30
306 Roberto Alomar .20 .50
307 New York Mets .10 .30
308 Dean Palmer .10 .30
309 Mike Hampton .10 .30
310 Devon White .10 .30
311 Chad Hermansen .10 .30
Mike Garcia RC
312 Tim Hudson .10 .30
313 John Franco .10 .30
314 Jason Schmidt .10 .30
315 J.T. Snow .10 .30
316 Ed Sprague .10 .30
317 Chris Widger .10 .30
318 Ben Petrick .10 .30
Luther Hackman RC
319 Jose Mesa .10 .30
320 Jose Canseco .20 .50
321 John Wetteland .10 .30
322 Minnesota Twins .10 .30
323 Jeff DaVanon RC .15 .40
Brian Cooper
324 Tony Womack .10 .30
325 Rod Beck .10 .30
326 Mickey Morandini .10 .30
327 Pokey Reese .10 .30
328 Jaret Wright .10 .30
329 Glen Barker .10 .30
330 Darren Dreifort .10 .30
331 Torii Hunter .10 .30
332 Tony Armas .10 .30
Peter Bergeron
333 Hideki Irabu .10 .30
334 Desi Relaford .10 .30
335 Barry Bonds .75 2.00
336 Gary DiSarcina .10 .30
337 Gerald Williams .10 .30
338 John Valentin .10 .30
339 David Justice .10 .30
340 Juan Encarnacion .10 .30
341 Jeremy Giambi .10 .30
342 Chan Ho Park .10 .30
343 Vladimir Guerrero .30 .75
344 Robin Ventura .20 .50
345 Bob Abreu .10 .30
346 Tony Gwynn .40 1.00
347 Jose Jimenez .10 .30
348 Royce Clayton .10 .30
349 Kelvim Escobar .10 .30
350 Chicago Cubs .10 .30
351 Travis Dawkins .10 .30
Jason LaRue
352 Barry Larkin .20 .50
353 Cal Ripken 1.00 2.50
354 Alex Rodriguez CL .30 .75
355 Todd Stottlemyre .10 .30
356 Terry Adams .10 .30
357 Pittsburgh Pirates .10 .30
358 Jim Thome .20 .50
359 Corey Lee .10 .30
Doug Davis
360 Moises Alou .10 .30
361 Todd Hollandsworth .10 .30
362 Marty Cordova .10 .30
363 David Cone .10 .30
364 Joe Nathan .10 .30
Wilson Delgado
365 Paul Byrd .10 .30
366 Edgar Renteria .10 .30
367 Rusty Greer .10 .30
368 David Segui .10 .30
369 New York Yankees .20 .50
370 Daryle Ward .10 .30
Carlos Hernandez
371 Troy Glaus .10 .30
372 Delino DeShields .10 .30
373 Jose Offerman .10 .30
374 Sammy Sosa .30 .75
375 Sandy Alomar Jr. .10 .30
376 Masao Kida .10 .30
377 Richard Hidalgo .10 .30
378 Ismael Valdes .10 .30
379 Ugueth Urbina .10 .30
380 Darryl Hamilton .10 .30
381 John Jaha .10 .30
382 St. Louis Cardinals .10 .30
383 Scott Sauerbeck .10 .30
384 Russ Ortiz .10 .30
385 Jamie Moyer .10 .30
386 Dave Martinez .10 .30
387 Todd Zeile .10 .30
388 Anaheim Angels .10 .30
389 Rob Ryan .10 .30
Nick Bierbrodt
390 Rickey Henderson .30 .75
391 Alex Rodriguez .50 1.25
392 Texas Rangers .10 .30
393 Roberto Hernandez .10 .30
394 Tony Batista .10 .30
395 Oakland Athletics .10 .30
396 Randall Simon .10 .30
Dave Cortes RC
397 Gregg Olson .10 .30
398 Sidney Ponson .10 .30
399 Micah Bowie .10 .30
400 Mark McGwire .75 2.00
401 Florida Marlins .10 .30
402 Chad Allen .10 .30
403 Casey Blake .10 .30
Vernon Wells
404 Pete Harnisch .10 .30
405 Preston Wilson .10 .30
406 Richie Sexson .10 .30
407 Rico Brogna .10 .30
408 Todd Hundley .10 .30
409 Wally Joyner .10 .30
410 Tom Goodwin .10 .30
411 Joey Hamilton .10 .30
412 Detroit Tigers .10 .30
413 Michael Tejera RC .10 .30
Ramon Castro
414 Alex Gonzalez .10 .30
415 Jermaine Dye .10 .30
416 Jose Rosado .10 .30
417 Wilton Guerrero .10 .30
418 Rondell White .10 .30
419 Al Leiter .10 .30
420 Bernie Williams .20 .50
421 A.J. Hinch .10 .30
422 Pat Burrell .10 .30
423 Scott Rolen .20 .50
424 Jason Kendall .10 .30
425 Kevin Young .10 .30
426 Eric Owens .10 .30
427 Derek Jeter CL .30 .75
428 Livan Hernandez .10 .30
429 Russ Davis .10 .30
430 Dan Wilson .10 .30
431 Quinton McCracken .10 .30
432 Homer Bush .10 .30
433 Seattle Mariners .10 .30
434 Chad Harville .10 .30
Luis Vizcaino
435 Carlos Beltran AW .10 .30
436 Scott Williamson AW .10 .30
437 Pedro Martinez AW .20 .50
438 Randy Johnson AW .20 .50
439 Ivan Rodriguez AW .10 .30
440 Chipper Jones AW .20 .50
441 Bernie Williams DIV .10 .30
442 Pedro Martinez DIV .20 .50
443 Derek Jeter DIV .40 1.00
444 Brian Jordan DIV .10 .30
445 Todd Pratt DIV .10 .30
446 Kevin Millwood DIV .10 .30
447 Orl.Hernandez WS .10 .30
448 Derek Jeter WS .40 1.00
449 Chad Curtis WS .10 .30
450 Roger Clemens WS .30 .75
P353 Cal Ripken Promo 1.25 3.00

2000 Fleer Tradition Glossy

The 2000 Fleer Glossy set was released in early December, 2000 and features a 500-card base set. Please note that you only receive 455 of the 500 total cards that make up this set per sealed factory set. Card 451-500 are short-printed and are inserted into sets at five per factory sealed set. Cards 451-500 are serial numbered to 1000. It's assumed a total of 10,000 sets were issued based upon the insertion rate of the serial #'d "high series" cards.

COMP.FACT.SET (455) 30.00 60.00
*STARS 1-450: .75X TO 2X BASIC
*ROOKIES 1-450: .75X TO 2X BASIC
451 Carlos Casimiro RC 4.00 10.00
452 Adam Melhuse RC 4.00 10.00
453 Adam Bernero RC 4.00 10.00
454 Dusty Allen RC 4.00 10.00
455 Chan Perry RC 4.00 10.00
456 Damian Rolls RC 4.00 10.00
457 Josh Phelps RC 4.00 10.00
458 Barry Zito 12.50 30.00
459 Hector Ortiz RC 4.00 10.00
460 Juan Pierre RC 6.00 15.00
461 Jose Ortiz RC 4.00 10.00
462 Chad Zerbe RC 6.00 15.00
463 Julio Zuleta RC 4.00 10.00
464 Eric Byrnes 4.00 10.00
465 Wilf. Rodriguez RC 4.00 10.00
466 Wascar Serrano RC 4.00 10.00
467 Aaron McNeal RC 4.00 10.00
468 Paul Rigdon RC 4.00 10.00
469 John Snyder RC 4.00 10.00
470 J.C. Romero RC 4.00 10.00
471 Talmadge Nunnari RC 4.00 10.00
472 Mike Lamb 6.00 15.00
473 Ryan Kohlmeier RC 4.00 10.00
474 Rodney Lindsey RC 4.00 10.00
475 Elvis Pena RC 4.00 10.00
476 Alex Cabrera 4.00 10.00
477 Chris Richard 4.00 10.00
478 Pedro Feliz RC 2.50 6.00
479 Ross Gload RC 4.00 10.00
480 Timo Perez RC 4.00 10.00
481 Jason Woolf RC 4.00 10.00
482 Kenny Kelly RC 4.00 10.00
483 Sang-Hoon Lee 4.00 10.00
484 John Riedling RC 4.00 10.00
485 Chris Wakeland RC 4.00 10.00
486 Britt Reames RC 4.00 10.00
487 Greg LaRocca RC 4.00 10.00
488 Randy Keisler RC 4.00 10.00
489 Xavier Nady RC 6.00 15.00
490 Keith Ginter RC 4.00 10.00
491 Joey Nation RC 4.00 10.00
492 Kazuhiro Sasaki 6.00 15.00
493 Lesli Brea RC 4.00 10.00
494 Jace Brewer 4.00 10.00
495 Yohanny Valera RC 4.00 10.00
496 Adam Piatt 4.00 10.00
497 Nate Rolison 4.00 10.00
498 Aubrey Huff 4.00 10.00
499 Jason Tyner 4.00 10.00
500 Corey Patterson 4.00 10.00

2000 Fleer Tradition Glossy Hawaii

This is a parallel set to the regular Fleer Glossy set. Each paying participant to the Hawaii Trade Show received one of these cards at the Meet the Industry Event at the CTA booth. All of the cards in this set are given a special Hawaii Trade show logo where it says the card is a "1 of 1". Since these cards are extremely limited, no pricing information is provided.

STATED PRINT RUN 1 SERIAL #'d SET

2000 Fleer Tradition Dividends

Inserted at a rate of one in six packs, these 15 cards feature some of the best players in the game.

COMPLETE SET (15) 7.50 15.00
D1 Alex Rodriguez .50 1.25
D2 Ben Grieve .10 .30
D3 Cal Ripken 1.00 2.50
D4 Chipper Jones .30 .75
D5 Derek Jeter .60 1.50
D6 Frank Thomas .30 .75
D7 Jeff Bagwell .20 .50
D8 Sammy Sosa .30 .75
D9 Tony Gwynn .40 1.00
D10 Scott Rolen .20 .50
D11 Nomar Garciaparra .50 1.25
D12 Mike Piazza .50 1.25
D13 Mark McGwire .75 2.00
D14 Ken Griffey Jr. .50 1.25
D15 Juan Gonzalez .10 .30

2000 Fleer Tradition Fresh Ink

Randomly inserted into packs at one in 144 packs, this insert set features autographed cards of players such as Rick Ankiel, Sean Casey and J.D. Drew.

1 Rick Ankiel 10.00 25.00
2 Carlos Beltran 6.00 15.00
3 Pat Burrell 4.00 10.00
4 Miguel Cairo 4.00 10.00
5 Sean Casey 6.00 15.00
6 Will Clark 10.00 25.00
7 Mike Darr 6.00 15.00
8 J.D. Drew 6.00 15.00
9 Erubiel Durazo 4.00 10.00
10 Carlos Febles 4.00 10.00
11 Freddy Garcia 4.00 10.00
12 Jason Grilli 4.00 10.00
13 Vladimir Guerrero 15.00 40.00
14 Tony Gwynn 20.00 50.00
15 Jerry Hairston Jr. 4.00 10.00
16 Tim Hudson 10.00 25.00
17 John Jaha 4.00 10.00
18 D'Angelo Jimenez 4.00 10.00
19 Andruw Jones 10.00 25.00
20 Gabe Kapler 6.00 15.00
21 Cesar King 4.00 10.00
22 Jason LaRue 4.00 10.00
23 Mike Lieberthal 6.00 15.00
24 Greg Maddux 60.00 120.00
25 Pedro Martinez 40.00 80.00
26 Gary Matthews Jr. 4.00 10.00
27 Orber Moreno 4.00 10.00
28 Eric Munson 4.00 10.00
29 Rafael Palmeiro 20.00 50.00
30 Jim Parque 4.00 10.00
31 Wily Pena 12.50 30.00
32 Cal Ripken 75.00 150.00
33 Alex Rodriguez 50.00 100.00
34 Tim Salmon 10.00 25.00
35 Chris Singleton 4.00 10.00
36 Alfonso Soriano 8.00 20.00
37 Ed Yarnall 4.00 10.00

2000 Fleer Tradition Grasskickers

Inserted at a rate of one in 30 packs, these 15 cards printed on rainbow holofoil feature players who put fear into their opponents.

COMPLETE SET (15) 25.00 60.00
GK1 Tony Gwynn 2.00 5.00
GK2 Scott Rolen 1.00 2.50
GK3 Nomar Garciaparra 2.50 6.00
GK4 Mike Piazza 2.50 6.00
GK5 Mark McGwire 4.00 10.00
GK6 Frank Thomas 1.50 4.00
GK7 Cal Ripken 5.00 12.00
GK8 Chipper Jones 1.50 4.00
GK9 Greg Maddux 2.50 6.00
GK10 Ken Griffey Jr. 2.50 6.00
GK11 Juan Gonzalez .60 1.50
GK12 Derek Jeter 3.00 8.00
GK13 Sammy Sosa 1.50 4.00
GK14 Roger Clemens 3.00 8.00
GK15 Alex Rodriguez 2.50 6.00

2000 Fleer Tradition Hall's Well

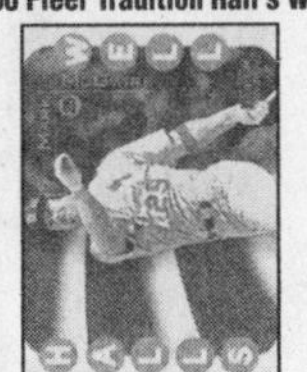

Inserted at a rate of one in 30 packs, these 15 cards feature players on their path to the Hall of Fame. The cards were printed on a combination of transparent plastic stock with overlays of silver foil stamping.

COMPLETE SET (15) 20.00 50.00
HW1 Mark McGwire 4.00 10.00
HW2 Alex Rodriguez 2.50 6.00
HW3 Cal Ripken 5.00 12.00
HW4 Chipper Jones 1.50 4.00
HW5 Derek Jeter 3.00 8.00
HW6 Frank Thomas 1.50 4.00
HW7 Greg Maddux 2.50 6.00
HW8 Juan Gonzalez .60 1.50
HW9 Ken Griffey Jr. 2.50 6.00
HW10 Mike Piazza 2.50 6.00
HW11 Nomar Garciaparra 2.50 6.00
HW12 Sammy Sosa 1.50 4.00
HW13 Roger Clemens 3.00 8.00
HW14 Ivan Rodriguez 1.00 2.50
HW15 Tony Gwynn 2.00 5.00

2000 Fleer Tradition Ripken Collection

Inserted at a rate of one in 30 packs, these 10 cards feature photos of Cal Ripken Jr. in the style of vintage Fleer cards. We have identified the style of the card and the sport next to Ripken's name.

COMPLETE SET (10) 40.00 80.00
COMMON CARD (1-10) 4.00 10.00

2000 Fleer Tradition Ten-4

Issued at a rate of one in 18 packs, these 10 cards feature the best home run hitters highlighted on a die-cut card with silver foil stamping.

COMPLETE SET (10) 10.00 25.00
TF1 Sammy Sosa .75 2.00
TF2 Nomar Garciaparra 1.25 3.00
TF3 Mike Piazza 1.25 3.00
TF4 Mark McGwire 2.00 5.00
TF5 Ken Griffey Jr. 1.25 3.00
TF6 Juan Gonzalez .30 .75
TF7 Derek Jeter 1.50 4.00
TF8 Chipper Jones .75 2.00
TF9 Cal Ripken 2.50 6.00
TF10 Alex Rodriguez 1.25 3.00

2000 Fleer Tradition Who To Watch

Inserted at a rate of one in three, these 15 cards feature leading prospects against a nostalgic die-cut background.

COMPLETE SET (15) 2.00 5.00
WW1 Rick Ankiel .20 .50
WW2 Matt Riley .20 .50
WW3 Wilton Veras .20 .50
WW4 Ben Petrick .20 .50
WW5 Chad Hermansen .20 .50
WW6 Peter Bergeron .20 .50
WW7 Mark Quinn .20 .50
WW8 Russell Branyan .20 .50
WW9 Alfonso Soriano .40 1.00
WW10 Randy Wolf .20 .50
WW11 Ben Davis .20 .50
WW12 Jeff DaVanon .20 .50
WW13 D'Angelo Jimenez .20 .50
WW14 Vernon Wells .20 .50
WW15 Adam Kennedy .20 .50

2000 Fleer Tradition Glossy Lumberjacks

Inserted into Fleer Glossy sets at one per set, this 45-card insert set features game-used bat pieces from some of the top players in baseball. Print runs are listed below.

1 Edgardo Alfonzo/145 5.00 12.00
2 Roberto Alomar/627 6.00 15.00
3 Moises Alou/529 4.00 10.00
4 Carlos Beltran/489 4.00 10.00
5 Adrian Beltre/127 5.00 12.00
6 Wade Boggs/30
7 Barry Bonds/305 15.00 40.00
8 Jeromy Burnitz/34
9 Pat Burrell/45
10 Sean Casey/50
11 Eric Chavez/259 4.00 10.00
12 Tony Clark/70 6.00 15.00
13 Carlos Delgado/70 6.00 15.00
14 J.D. Drew/135 5.00 12.00
15 Erubiel Durazo/70 6.00 15.00
16 Ray Durham/35
17 Carlos Febles/120 5.00 12.00
18 Jason Giambi/220 4.00 10.00
19 Shawn Green/429 4.00 10.00
20 Vladimir Guerrero/809 6.00 15.00
21 Derek Jeter/180 25.00 60.00
22 Chipper Jones/725 6.00 15.00
23 Gabe Kapler/160 5.00 12.00
24 Jason Kendall/34
25 Paul Konerko/70 6.00 15.00
26 Ray Lankford/35
27 Mike Lieberthal/45
28 Edgar Martinez/211 6.00 15.00
29 Raul Mondesi/458 4.00 10.00
30 Warren Morris/35
31 Magglio Ordonez/190 5.00 12.00
32 Rafael Palmeiro/49
33 Pokey Reese/110 5.00 12.00
34 Cal Ripken/235 30.00 80.00
35 Alex Rodriguez/292 15.00 40.00
36 Ivan Rodriguez/602 6.00 15.00
37 Scott Rolen/502 6.00 15.00
38 Chris Singleton/68 6.00 15.00
39 Alfonso Soriano/285 6.00 15.00
40 Frank Thomas/489 6.00 15.00
41 Jim Thome/479 6.00 15.00
42 Robin Ventura/114 5.00 12.00
43 Jose Vidro/60 6.00 15.00
44 Bernie Williams/215 6.00 15.00
45 Matt Williams/152 5.00 12.00

2000 Fleer Tradition Update

The 2000 Fleer Tradition Update set was released in October, 2000 as a 150-card factory set. The set includes 10 Season Highlight cards (1-10), and 140 cards of players that were either traded during the season or who made their major league debut (cards 11-150). Each set originally carried a suggested retail price of $29.99. Please note that card number 50 does not exist. All cards have a "U" prefix. Notable Rookie Cards include Johan Santana, Kazuhiro Sasaki and Barry Zito. Finally, one in every 80 sets contained a Mickey Mantle game-worn jersey memorabilia card. According to representatives at Fleer, the Mickey Mantle MP1 card features a pair of grey, away, game-used pants.

COMP.FACT.SET (149) 10.00 25.00
1 Ken Griffey Jr. SH .30 .75
2 Cal Ripken SH .40 1.00
3 Randy Velarde SH .10 .30
4 Fred McGriff SH .10 .30
5 Derek Jeter SH .30 .75
6 Tom Glavine SH .10 .30
7 Brent Mayne SH .10 .30
8 Alex Ochoa SH .10 .30
9 Scott Sheldon SH .10 .30
10 Randy Johnson SH .20 .50
11 Daniel Garibay RC .10 .30
12 Brad Fullmer .10 .30
13 Kazuhiro Sasaki RC .25 .60
14 Andy Tracy RC .10 .30
15 Bret Boone .10 .30
16 Chad Durbin RC .15 .40
17 Mark Buehrle RC 2.50 6.00
18 Julio Zuleta RC .10 .30
19 Jeremy Giambi .10 .30
20 Gene Stechschulte RC .10 .30
21 Lou Pote .10 .30
Bengie Molina
22 Darrell Einertson RC .10 .30
23 Ken Griffey Jr. .50 1.25
24 Jeff Sparks RC .10 .30
Dan Wheeler
25 Aaron Fultz RC .10 .30
26 Derek Bell .10 .30
27 Rob Bell .10 .30
D.T. Cromer
28 Robert Fick .10 .30
29 Darryl Kile .10 .30
30 Clayton Andrews .10 .30
John Bale RC
31 Dave Veres .10 .30
32 Hector Mercado RC .10 .30
33 Willie Morales RC .10 .30
34 Kelly Wunsch .10 .30
Kip Wells
35 Hideki Irabu .10 .30
36 Sean DePaula RC .10 .30
37 DeWayne Wise .10 .30
Chris Woodward
38 Curt Schilling .10 .30
39 Mark Johnson .10 .30
40 Mike Cameron .10 .30
41 Scott Sheldon .10 .30
Tom Evans
42 Brett Tomko .10 .30
43 Johan Santana RC 5.00 12.00
44 Andy Benes .10 .30
45 Matt LeCroy .10 .30
Mark Redman
46 Ryan Klesko .10 .30
47 Andy Ashby .10 .30
48 Octavio Dotel .10 .30
49 Eric Byrnes RC .15 .40
50 Does Not Exist
51 Kenny Rogers .10 .30
52 Ben Weber RC .10 .30
53 Matt Blank .10 .30
Scott Strickland
54 Tom Goodwin .10 .30
55 Jim Edmonds Cards .10 .30
56 Derrick Turnbow RC .60 1.50
57 Mark Mulder .10 .30
58 Tarrick Brock .10 .30
Ruben Quevedo
59 Danny Young RC .10 .30
60 Fernando Vina .10 .30
61 Justin Brunette RC .10 .30
62 Jimmy Anderson .10 .30
63 Reggie Sanders .10 .30
64 Adam Kennedy .10 .30
65 Jesse Garcia .10 .30
B.J. Ryan
66 Al Martin .10 .30
67 Kevin Walker RC .10 .30
68 Brad Penny .10 .30
69 B.J. Surhoff .10 .30
70 Geoff Blum .10 .30
Trace Coquillette RC
71 Jose Jimenez .10 .30
72 Chuck Finley .10 .30
73 Valerio De Los Santos .10 .30
Everett Stull
74 Terry Adams .10 .30
75 Rafael Furcal .10 .30
76 John Roskos .10 .30
Mike Darr
77 Quilvio Veras .10 .30
78 Armando Almanza .10 .30
Nate Rolison
79 Greg Vaughn .10 .30
80 Keith McDonald RC .10 .30
81 Eric Cammack RC .10 .30
82 Horacio Estrada .10 .30
Ray King
83 Kory DeHaan .10 .30
84 Kevin Hodges RC .10 .30
85 Mike Lamb RC .25 .60
86 Shawn Green .10 .30
87 Dan Reichert .10 .30
Jason Rakers
88 Adam Piatt .10 .30
89 Mike Garcia .10 .30
90 Rodrigo Lopez RC .25 .60
91 John Olerud .10 .30
92 Barry Zito RC 1.50 4.00
Terrence Long
93 Jimmy Rollins .10 .30
94 Denny Neagle .10 .30
95 Rickey Henderson .30 .75
96 Adam Eaton .10 .30
Buddy Carlyle
97 Brian O'Connor RC .10 .30
98 Andy Thompson RC .10 .30
99 Jason Boyd RC .10 .30
100 Joel Pineiro RC .40 1.00
Carlos Guillen
101 Raul Gonzalez RC .10 .30
102 Brandon Kolb RC .10 .30
103 Jason Maxwell .10 .30
Mike Lincoln
104 Luis Matos RC .15 .40
105 Morgan Burkhart RC .10 .30
106 Ismael Villegas RC .10 .30
Steve Sisco RC
107 David Justice Yankees .10 .30
108 Pablo Ozuna .10 .30
109 Jose Canseco .20 .50
110 Alex Cora .10 .30
Shawn Gilbert
111 Will Clark Cardinals .20 .50
112 Keith Luuloa .10 .30
Eric Weaver
113 Bruce Chen .10 .30
114 Adam Hyzdu .10 .30
115 Scott Forster RC .10 .30
Yovanny Lara RC
116 Allen McDill RC .10 .30
Jose Macias
117 Kevin Nicholson .10 .30
118 Israel Alcantara .10 .30
Tim Young
119 Juan Alvarez RC .10 .30
120 Julio Lugo .10 .30
Mitch Meluskey
121 B.J. Waszgis RC .10 .30
122 Jeff M. D'Amico RC .10 .30
Brett Laxton
123 Ricky Ledee .10 .30
124 Mark DeRosa .10 .30
Jason Marquis
125 Alex Cabrera RC .15 .40
126 Augie Ojeda RC .10 .30
Gary Matthews Jr.
127 Richie Sexson .10 .30
128 Santiago Perez RC .10 .30
Hector Ramirez RC
129 Rondell White .10 .30
130 Craig House RC .10 .30
131 Kevin Beirne .10 .30
Jon Garland
132 Wayne Franklin RC .10 .30
133 Henry Rodriguez .10 .30
134 Jay Payton .10 .30
Jim Mann
135 Ron Gant .10 .30
136 Paxton Crawford RC .10 .30
Sang-Hoon Lee RC
137 Kent Bottenfield .10 .30
138 Rocky Biddle RC .10 .30
139 Travis Lee .10 .30
140 Ryan Vogelsong RC 1.50 4.00
141 Jason Conti .10 .30
Geraldo Guzman RC
142 Tim Drew .10 .30
Mark Watson RC
143 John Parrish RC .10 .30
Chris Richard RC
144 Javier Cardona RC .10 .30
Brandon Villafuerte RC
145 Tike Redman RC .25 .60
Steve Sparks RC
146 Brian Schneider .10 .30
Matt Skrmetta RC
147 Pasqual Coco RC .10 .30
148 Lorenzo Barcelo RC .40 1.00
Joe Crede
149 Jace Brewer RC .10 .30
150 Milton Bradley .15 .40
Tomas De La Rosa RC
MP1 Mickey Mantle Pants 50.00 100.00

2001 Fleer Tradition

The 2001 Fleer Tradition product was released in early February, 2001 and initially featured a 450-card base set that was broken into tiers as follows: Base Veterans (1-350), Prospects (351-380), League Leaders (381-410), World Series Highlights (411-420), and Team Checklists (421-450). Each pack contained 10 cards and carried a suggested retail price of $1.99 per pack. In late October, 2001, a 485-card factory set carrying a $42.99 SRP was released. Each factory set contained the basic 450-card set plus 35 new cards (451-485) featuring a selection of rookies and prospects. Please note that there was also 100 exchange cards inserted into packs in which lucky collectors received an uncut sheet of 2001 Fleer.

COMP.FACT.SET (485) 50.00 100.00
COMPLETE SET (450) 20.00 50.00
COMMON CARD (1-450) .10 .30
COMMON (451-485) .20 .50
1 Andres Galarraga .10 .30
2 Armando Rios .10 .30
3 Julio Lugo .10 .30
4 Darryl Hamilton .10 .30
5 Dave Veres .10 .30
6 Edgardo Alfonzo .10 .30
7 Brook Fordyce .10 .30
8 Eric Karros .10 .30
9 Neifi Perez .10 .30
10 Jim Edmonds .10 .30
11 Barry Larkin .20 .50
12 Trot Nixon .10 .30
13 Andy Pettitte .20 .50
14 Jose Guillen .10 .30
15 David Wells .10 .30
16 Magglio Ordonez .10 .30
17 David Segui .10 .30
17A David Segui ERR .10 .30
Card has no number on the back
18 Juan Encarnacion .10 .30
19 Robert Person .10 .30
20 Quilvio Veras .10 .30
21 Mo Vaughn .10 .30
22 B.J. Surhoff .10 .30
23 Ken Caminiti .10 .30
24 Frank Catalanotto .10 .30
25 Luis Gonzalez .10 .30
26 Pete Harnisch .10 .30
27 Alex Gonzalez .10 .30
28 Mark Quinn .10 .30
29 Luis Castillo .10 .30
30 Rick Helling .10 .30
31 Barry Bonds .75 2.00
32 Warren Morris .10 .30
33 Aaron Boone .10 .30
34 Ricky Gutierrez .10 .30
35 Preston Wilson .10 .30
36 Erubiel Durazo .10 .30
37 Jermaine Dye .10 .30
38 John Rocker .10 .30
39 Mark Grudzielanek .10 .30
40 Pedro Martinez .20 .50
41 Phil Nevin .10 .30
42 Luis Matos .10 .30
43 Orlando Hernandez .10 .30
44 Steve Cox .10 .30
45 James Baldwin .10 .30
46 Rafael Furcal .10 .30
47 Todd Zeile .10 .30
48 Elmer Dessens .10 .30
49 Russell Branyan .10 .30
50 Juan Gonzalez .10 .30
51 Mac Suzuki .10 .30
52 Adam Kennedy .10 .30
53 Randy Velarde .10 .30
54 David Bell .10 .30
55 Royce Clayton .10 .30
56 Greg Colbrunn .10 .30
57 Rey Ordonez .10 .30
58 Kevin Millwood .10 .30
59 Fernando Vina .10 .30
60 Eddie Taubensee .10 .30
61 Enrique Wilson .10 .30
62 Jay Bell .10 .30
63 Brian Moehler .10 .30
64 Brad Fullmer .10 .30
65 Ben Petrick .10 .30
66 Orlando Cabrera .10 .30
67 Shane Reynolds .10 .30
68 Mitch Meluskey .10 .30
69 Jeff Shaw .10 .30
70 Chipper Jones .30 .75
71 Tomo Ohka .10 .30
72 Ruben Rivera .10 .30
73 Mike Sirotka .10 .30
74 Scott Rolen .20 .50
75 Glendon Rusch .10 .30
76 Miguel Tejada .10 .30
77 Brady Anderson .10 .30
78 Bartolo Colon .10 .30
79 Ron Coomer .10 .30
80 Gary DiSarcina .10 .30
81 Geoff Jenkins .10 .30
82 Billy Koch .10 .30
83 Mike Lamb .10 .30
84 Alex Rodriguez .50 1.25
85 Denny Neagle .10 .30
86 Michael Tucker .10 .30
87 Edgar Renteria .10 .30
88 Brian Anderson .10 .30
89 Glenallen Hill .10 .30
90 Aramis Ramirez .10 .30
91 Rondell White .10 .30
92 Tony Womack .10 .30
93 Jeffrey Hammonds .10 .30
94 Freddy Garcia .10 .30
95 Bill Mueller .10 .30
96 Mike Lieberthal .10 .30
97 Michael Barrett .10 .30
98 Derrek Lee .20 .50
99 Bill Spiers .10 .30
100 Derek Lowe .10 .30
101 Javy Lopez .10 .30
102 Adrian Beltre .10 .30
103 Jim Parque .10 .30
104 Marquis Grissom .10 .30
105 Eric Chavez .10 .30
106 Todd Jones .10 .30
107 Eric Owens .10 .30
108 Roger Clemens .60 1.50
109 Denny Hocking .10 .30
110 Roberto Hernandez .10 .30
111 Albert Belle .10 .30
112 Troy Glaus .10 .30
113 Ivan Rodriguez .20 .50
114 Carlos Guillen .10 .30
115 Chuck Finley .10 .30
116 Dmitri Young .10 .30
117 Paul Konerko .10 .30
118 Damon Buford .10 .30
119 Fernando Tatis .10 .30
120 Larry Walker .10 .30
121 Jason Kendall .10 .30
122 Matt Williams .10 .30
123 Henry Rodriguez .10 .30
124 Placido Polanco .10 .30
125 Bobby Estalella .10 .30
126 Pat Burrell .10 .30
127 Mark Loretta .10 .30
128 Moises Alou .10 .30
129 Tino Martinez .20 .50
130 Milton Bradley .10 .30
131 Todd Hundley .10 .30
132 Keith Foulke .10 .30
133 Robert Fick .10 .30
134 Cristian Guzman .10 .30
135 Rusty Greer .10 .30
136 John Olerud .10 .30
137 Mariano Rivera .30 .75
138 Jeromy Burnitz .10 .30
139 Dave Burba .10 .30
140 Ken Griffey Jr. .50 1.25
141 Tony Gwynn .40 1.00
142 Carlos Delgado .10 .30
143 Edgar Martinez .20 .50
144 Ramon Hernandez .10 .30
145 Pedro Astacio .10 .30
146 Ray Lankford .10 .30
147 Mike Mussina .20 .50
148 Ray Durham .10 .30
149 Lee Stevens .10 .30
150 Jay Canizaro .10 .30
151 Adrian Brown .10 .30
152 Mike Piazza .50 1.25
153 Cliff Floyd .10 .30
154 Jose Vidro .10 .30
155 Jason Giambi .10 .30
156 Andruw Jones .20 .50
157 Robin Ventura .10 .30
158 Gary Sheffield .10 .30
159 Jeff D'Amico .10 .30
160 Chuck Knoblauch .10 .30
161 Roger Cedeno .10 .30
162 Jim Thome .20 .50
163 Peter Bergeron .10 .30
164 Kerry Wood .10 .30
165 Gabe Kapler .10 .30
166 Corey Koskie .10 .30
167 Doug Glanville .10 .30
168 Brent Mayne .10 .30
169 Scott Spiezio .10 .30
170 Steve Karsay .10 .30
171 Al Martin .10 .30
172 Fred McGriff .20 .50
173 Gabe White .10 .30
174 Alex Gonzalez .10 .30
175 Mike Darr .10 .30
176 Bengie Molina .10 .30
177 Ben Grieve .10 .30
178 Marlon Anderson .10 .30
179 Brian Giles .10 .30
180 Jose Valentin .10 .30
181 Brian Jordan .10 .30
182 Randy Johnson .30 .75
183 Ricky Ledee .10 .30
184 Russ Ortiz .10 .30
185 Mike Lowell .10 .30
186 Curtis Leskanic .10 .30
187 Bob Abreu .10 .30
188 Derek Jeter .75 2.00
189 Lance Berkman .10 .30
190 Roberto Alomar .20 .50
191 Darin Erstad .10 .30
192 Richie Sexson .10 .30
193 Alex Ochoa .10 .30
194 Carlos Febles .10 .30
195 David Ortiz .30 .75
196 Shawn Green .10 .30
197 Mike Sweeney .10 .30
198 Vladimir Guerrero .30 .75
199 Jose Jimenez .10 .30
200 Travis Lee .10 .30
201 Rickey Henderson .30 .75
202 Bob Wickman .10 .30
203 Miguel Cairo .10 .30
204 Steve Finley .10 .30
205 Tony Batista .10 .30
206 Jamey Wright .10 .30
207 Terrence Long .10 .30
208 Trevor Hoffman .10 .30
209 John VanderWal .10 .30
210 Greg Maddux .50 1.25
211 Tim Salmon .20 .50
212 Herbert Perry .10 .30
213 Marvin Benard .10 .30
214 Jose Offerman .10 .30
215 Jay Payton .10 .30
216 Jon Lieber .10 .30
217 Mark Kotsay .10 .30
218 Scott Brosius .10 .30
219 Scott Williamson .10 .30
220 Omar Vizquel .20 .50
221 Mike Hampton .10 .30
222 Richard Hidalgo .10 .30
223 Rey Sanchez .10 .30
224 Matt Lawton .10 .30
225 Bruce Chen .10 .30
226 Ryan Klesko .10 .30
227 Garret Anderson .10 .30
228 Kevin Brown .10 .30
229 Mike Cameron .10 .30
230 Tony Clark .10 .30
231 Curt Schilling .10 .30
232 Vinny Castilla .10 .30
233 Carl Pavano .10 .30
234 Eric Davis .10 .30
235 Darrin Fletcher .10 .30
236 Matt Stairs .10 .30
237 Octavio Dotel .10 .30
238 Mark Grace .20 .50
239 John Smoltz .20 .50
240 Matt Clement .10 .30
241 Ellis Burks .10 .30
242 Charles Johnson .10 .30
243 Jeff Bagwell .20 .50
244 Derek Bell .10 .30
245 Nomar Garciaparra .50 1.25
246 Jorge Posada .20 .50
247 Ryan Dempster .10 .30
248 J.T. Snow .10 .30
249 Eric Young .10 .30
250 Daryle Ward .10 .30
251 Joe Randa .10 .30
252 Travis Fryman .10 .30
253 Mike Williams .10 .30
254 Jacque Jones .10 .30
255 Scott Elarton .10 .30
256 Mark McGwire .75 2.00
257 Jay Buhner .10 .30
258 Randy Wolf .10 .30
259 Sammy Sosa .30 .75
260 Chan Ho Park .10 .30
261 Damion Easley .10 .30
262 Rick Ankiel .10 .30
263 Frank Thomas .30 .75
264 Kris Benson .10 .30
265 Luis Alicea .10 .30
266 Jeromy Burnitz .10 .30
267 Geoff Blum .10 .30
268 Joe Girardi .10 .30
269 Livan Hernandez .10 .30
270 Jeff Conine .10 .30
271 Danny Graves .10 .30
272 Craig Biggio .20 .50
273 Jose Canseco .20 .50
274 Tom Glavine .20 .50
275 Ruben Mateo .10 .30
276 Jeff Kent .10 .30
277 Kevin Young .10 .30
278 A.J. Burnett .10 .30
279 Dante Bichette .10 .30
280 Sandy Alomar Jr. .10 .30
281 John Wetteland .10 .30
282 Torii Hunter .10 .30
283 Jarrod Washburn .10 .30
284 Rich Aurilia .10 .30
285 Jeff Cirillo .10 .30
286 Fernando Seguignol .10 .30
287 Darren Dreifort .10 .30
288 Deivi Cruz .10 .30
289 Pokey Reese .10 .30
290 Garrett Stephenson .10 .30
291 Bret Boone .10 .30
292 Tim Hudson .10 .30
293 John Flaherty .10 .30
294 Shannon Stewart .10 .30
295 Shawn Estes .10 .30
296 Wilton Guerrero .10 .30
297 Delino DeShields .10 .30
298 David Justice .10 .30
299 Harold Baines .10 .30
300 Al Leiter .10 .30
301 Wil Cordero .10 .30
302 Antonio Alfonseca .10 .30
303 Sean Casey .10 .30
304 Carlos Beltran .10 .30
305 Brad Radke .10 .30
306 Jason Varitek .30 .75
307 Shigetoshi Hasegawa .10 .30
308 Todd Stottlemyre .10 .30
309 Raul Mondesi .10 .30
310 Mike Bordick .10 .30
311 Darryl Kile .10 .30
312 Dean Palmer .10 .30
313 Johnny Damon .20 .50
314 Todd Helton .20 .50
315 Chad Hermansen .10 .30
316 Kevin Appier .10 .30
317 Greg Vaughn .10 .30
318 Robb Nen .10 .30
319 Jose Cruz Jr. .10 .30
320 Ron Belliard .10 .30
321 Bernie Williams .20 .50
322 Melvin Mora .10 .30
323 Kenny Lofton .10 .30
324 Armando Benitez .10 .30
325 Carlos Lee .10 .30
326 Damian Jackson .10 .30
327 Eric Milton .10 .30
328 J.D. Drew .10 .30
329 Byung-Hyun Kim .10 .30
330 Chris Stynes .10 .30
331 Kazuhiro Sasaki .10 .30
332 Troy O'Leary .10 .30
333 Pat Hentgen .10 .30
334 Brad Ausmus .10 .30
335 Todd Walker .10 .30
336 Jason Isringhausen .10 .30
337 Gerald Williams .10 .30
338 Aaron Sele .10 .30
339 Paul O'Neill .20 .50
340 Cal Ripken 1.00 2.50
341 Manny Ramirez .20 .50
342 Will Clark .20 .50
343 Mark Redman .10 .30
344 Bubba Trammell .10 .30
345 Troy Percival .10 .30
346 Chris Singleton .10 .30
347 Rafael Palmeiro .20 .50
348 Carl Everett .10 .30
349 Andy Benes .10 .30
350 Bobby Higginson .10 .30
351 Alex Cabrera .10 .30
352 Barry Zito .20 .50
353 Jace Brewer .10 .30
354 Paxton Crawford .10 .30
355 Oswaldo Mairena .10 .30
356 Joe Crede .30 .75
357 A.J. Pierzynski .10 .30
358 Daniel Garibay .10 .30
359 Jason Tyner .10 .30
360 Nate Rolison .10 .30
361 Scott Downs .10 .30
362 Keith Ginter .10 .30
363 Juan Pierre .10 .30
364 Adam Bernero .10 .30
365 Chris Richard .10 .30
366 Joey Nation .10 .30
367 Aubrey Huff .10 .30
368 Adam Eaton .10 .30
369 Jose Ortiz .20 .50
370 Eric Munson .10 .30
371 Matt Kinney .10 .30
372 Eric Byrnes .10 .30
373 Keith McDonald .10 .30
374 Matt Wise .10 .30
375 Timo Perez .10 .30
376 Julio Zuleta .10 .30
377 Jimmy Rollins .10 .30
378 Xavier Nady .10 .30
379 Ryan Kohlmeier .10 .30
380 Corey Patterson .10 .30
381 Todd Helton LL .10 .30
382 Moises Alou LL .10 .30
383 Vladimir Guerrero LL .20 .50
384 Luis Castillo LL .10 .30
385 Jeffrey Hammonds LL .10 .30
386 Nomar Garciaparra LL .30 .75
387 Carlos Delgado LL .10 .30
388 Darin Erstad LL .10 .30
389 Manny Ramirez LL .10 .30
390 Mike Sweeney LL .10 .30
391 Sammy Sosa LL .20 .50
392 Barry Bonds LL .40 1.00
393 Jeff Bagwell LL .10 .30
394 Richard Hidalgo LL .10 .30
395 Vladimir Guerrero LL .20 .50
396 Troy Glaus LL .10 .30
397 Frank Thomas LL .20 .50
398 Carlos Delgado LL .10 .30
399 David Justice LL .10 .30
400 Jason Giambi LL .10 .30
401 Randy Johnson LL .20 .50
402 Kevin Brown LL .10 .30
403 Greg Maddux LL .30 .75
404 Al Leiter LL .10 .30
405 Mike Hampton LL .10 .30
406 Pedro Martinez LL .20 .50
407 Roger Clemens LL .30 .75
408 Mike Sirotka LL .10 .30
409 Mike Mussina LL .10 .30
410 Bartolo Colon LL .10 .30
411 Subway Series WS .20 .50
412 Jose Vizcaino WS .20 .50
413 Jose Vizcaino WS .20 .50
414 Roger Clemens WS .30 .75
415 Armando Benitez .10 .30
Edgardo Alfonzo
Timo Perez WS
416 Al Leiter WS .20 .50
417 Luis Sojo WS .20 .50
418 Yankees 3-Peat WS .30 .75
419 Derek Jeter WS .40 1.00
420 Toast of the Town WS .20 .50
421 Rafael Furcal .10 .30
Chipper Jones
Greg Maddux
John Rocker
Tom Glavine CL
422 Armando Benitez .30 .75
Mike Piazza
Mike Hampton
Al Leiter CL
423 Ryan Dempster .10 .30
Luis Castillo
Antonio Alfonseca
Preston Wilson CL
424 Robert Person .10 .30
Scott Rolen
Randy Wolf
Bob Abreu
Doug Glanville CL
425 Vladimir Guerrero .10 .30
Peter Bergeron CL
426 Fernando Vina .10 .30
Dave Veres
Jim Edmonds
Rick Ankiel
Edgar Renteria
Darryl Kile CL
427 Danny Graves .10 .30
Ken Griffey Jr.
Sean Casey
Pokey Reese CL
428 Jon Lieber .20 .50
Sammy Sosa
Eric Young CL
429 Curtis Leskanic .10 .30
Geoff Jenkins
Jeff D'Amico
Jeromy Burnitz
Marquis Grissom CL
430 Scott Elarton .10 .30
Jeff Bagwell
Octavio Dotel
Moises Alou
Roger Cedeno CL
431 Mike Williams .20 .50
Jason Kendall
Kris Benson
Brian Giles CL
432 Livan Hernandez .10 .30
Jeff Kent
Robb Nen
Barry Bonds
Marvin Benard CL
433 Luis Gonzalez .10 .30
Steve Finley
Tony Womack
Randy Johnson CL
434 Jeff Shaw .10 .30
Gary Sheffield
Kevin Brown
Shawn Green
Chan Ho Park CL UER
B.Shaw should be J.Shaw
435 Jose Jimenez .10 .30
Todd Helton
Brian Bohanon
Tom Goodwin CL UER
C.Goodwin should be T.Goodwin
436 Trevor Hoffman .10 .30
Phil Nevin
Matt Clement
Eric Owens CL
437 Mariano Rivera .30 .75
Derek Jeter
Roger Clemens
Bernie Williams
Andy Pettitte CL
438 Pedro Martinez .20 .50
Nomar Garciaparra
Derek Lowe
Carl Everett CL
439 Ryan Kohlmeier .10 .30
Delino DeShields
Mike Mussina
Albert Belle CL

440 David Wells .10 .30
Carlos Delgado
Billy Koch
Raul Mondesi CL
441 Ramon Hernandez .10 .30
Fred McGriff
Miguel Cairo
Greg Vaughn CL
442 Mike Sirotka .20 .50
Frank Thomas
Keith Foulke
Ray Durham CL
443 Steve Karsay .10 .30
Manny Ramirez
Bartolo Colon
Roberto Alomar CL
444 Brian Moehler .10 .30
Deivi Cruz
Juan Encarnacion
Todd Jones
Bobby Higginson CL
445 Mac Suzuki .10 .30
Mike Sweeney
Johnny Damon
Jermaine Dye CL
446 Brad Radke .10 .30
Matt Lawton
Eric Milton
Jacque Jones
Cristian Guzman CL
447 Kazuhiro Sasaki .10 .30
Edgar Martinez
Aaron Sele
Rickey Henderson CL
448 Jason Isringhausen .10 .30
Jason Giambi
Tim Hudson
Randy Velarde CL
449 Shigetoshi Hasegawa .10 .30
Darin Erstad
Troy Percival
Troy Glaus CL
450 Rick Helling .10 .30
Rafael Palmeiro
John Wetteland
Luis Alicea CL
451 Albert Pujols RC 20.00 50.00
452 Ichiro Suzuki RC 8.00 20.00
453 Tsuyoshi Shinjo RC .30 .75
454 Johnny Estrada RC .30 .75
455 Elpidio Guzman RC .20 .50
456 Adrian Hernandez RC .20 .50
457 Rafael Soriano RC .20 .50
458 Drew Henson RC .30 .75
459 Juan Uribe RC .30 .75
460 Matt White RC .20 .50
461 Endy Chavez RC .20 .50
462 Bud Smith RC .20 .50
463 Morgan Ensberg RC 1.00 2.50
464 Jay Gibbons RC .30 .75
465 Jackson Melian RC .20 .50
466 Junior Spivey RC .30 .75
467 Juan Cruz RC .20 .50
468 Wilson Betemit RC 1.00 2.50
469 Alexis Gomez RC .20 .50
470 Mark Teixeira RC 5.00 12.00
471 Erick Almonte RC .20 .50
472 Travis Hafner RC 3.00 8.00
473 Carlos Valderrama RC .20 .50
474 Brandon Duckworth RC .20 .50
475 Ryan Freel RC .60 1.50
476 Wilkin Ruan RC .20 .50
477 Andres Torres RC .20 .50
478 Josh Towers RC .30 .75
479 Kyle Lohse RC .30 .75
480 Jason Michaels RC .20 .50
481 Alfonso Soriano .30 .75
482 C.C. Sabathia .20 .50
483 Roy Oswalt .50 1.25
484 Ben Sheets UER .30 .75
Wrong team logo on the front
485 Adam Dunn .30 .75

2001 Fleer Tradition Diamond Tributes

Randomly inserted into packs at one in seven, this 30-card insert is a tribute to some of the most classic players to ever step foot onto a playing field. Card backs carry a "DT" prefix.

COMPLETE SET (30) 30.00 60.00
DT1 Jackie Robinson .60 1.50
DT2 Mike Piazza 1.00 2.50
DT3 Alex Rodriguez 1.00 2.50
DT4 Barry Bonds 1.50 4.00
DT5 Nomar Garciaparra 1.00 2.50
DT6 Roger Clemens 1.25 3.00
DT7 Ivan Rodriguez .40 1.00
DT8 Cal Ripken 2.00 5.00
DT9 Manny Ramirez .40 1.00
DT10 Chipper Jones .60 1.50
DT11 Barry Larkin .40 1.00
DT12 Carlos Delgado .40 1.00
DT13 J.D. Drew .40 1.00
DT14 Carl Everett .40 1.00
DT15 Todd Helton .40 1.00
DT16 Greg Maddux 1.00 2.50
DT17 Scott Rolen .40 1.00
DT18 Troy Glaus .40 1.00
DT19 Brian Giles .40 1.00
DT20 Jeff Bagwell .40 1.00
DT21 Sammy Sosa .60 1.50
DT22 Randy Johnson .60 1.50
DT23 Andruw Jones .40 1.00
DT24 Ken Griffey Jr. 1.00 2.50
DT25 Mark McGwire 1.50 4.00
DT26 Derek Jeter 1.50 4.00
DT27 Vladimir Guerrero .60 1.50
DT28 Frank Thomas .60 1.50
DT29 Pedro Martinez .40 1.00
DT30 Bernie Williams .40 1.00

2001 Fleer Tradition Grass Roots

Inserted at a rate of one every 18 packs, this 15 card set describes some of the early moments of these star players careers.

COMPLETE SET (15) 30.00 60.00
GR1 Derek Jeter 2.50 6.00
GR2 Greg Maddux 1.50 4.00
GR3 Sammy Sosa 1.00 2.50
GR4 Alex Rodriguez 1.50 4.00
GR5 Vladimir Guerrero 1.00 2.50
GR6 Scott Rolen .60 1.50
GR7 Frank Thomas 1.00 2.50
GR8 Nomar Garciaparra 1.50 4.00
GR9 Cal Ripken 3.00 8.00
GR10 Mike Piazza 1.50 4.00
GR11 Ivan Rodriguez .60 1.50
GR12 Chipper Jones 1.00 2.50
GR13 Tony Gwynn 1.25 3.00
GR14 Ken Griffey Jr. 1.50 4.00
GR15 Mark McGwire 2.50 6.00

2001 Fleer Tradition Lumber Company

Randomly inserted into packs at one in 12, this 20-card insert set features players that are capable of breaking the game wide open with one swing of the bat. Card backs carry a "LC" prefix.

COMPLETE SET (20) 25.00 50.00
LC1 Vladimir Guerrero .75 2.00
LC2 Mo Vaughn .40 1.00
LC3 Ken Griffey Jr. 1.25 3.00
LC4 Juan Gonzalez .40 1.00
LC5 Tony Gwynn 1.00 2.50
LC6 Jim Edmonds .40 1.00
LC7 Jason Giambi .40 1.00
LC8 Alex Rodriguez 1.25 3.00
LC9 Derek Jeter 2.00 5.00
LC10 Darin Erstad .40 1.00
LC11 Andruw Jones .50 1.25
LC12 Cal Ripken 2.50 6.00
LC13 Magglio Ordonez .40 1.00
LC14 Nomar Garciaparra 1.25 3.00
LC15 Chipper Jones .75 2.00
LC16 Sean Casey .40 1.00
LC17 Shawn Green .40 1.00
LC18 Mike Piazza 1.25 3.00
LC19 Sammy Sosa .75 2.00
LC20 Barry Bonds 2.00 5.00

2001 Fleer Tradition Stitches in Time

Randomly inserted into packs at one in 18, this 24-card insert features Negro League greats like Josh Gibson and Satchel Paige. Card backs carry a "ST" prefix. It was originally believed that card ST3 did not exist. However, examples of the card have appeared on the secondary market. It is thought that the card possibly leaked to onto the secondary market after Fleer ceased operations. Please note that cards ST1 does not exist. The Henry Kimbro card is unnumbered.

COMPLETE SET (24) 50.00 100.00
ST1 Does Not Exist
ST2 Ernie Banks 2.00 5.00
ST3 Cool Papa Bell 2.00 5.00
ST4 Joe Black 1.25 3.00
ST5 Roy Campanella 2.50 6.00
ST6 Ray Dandridge 1.25 3.00
ST7 Leon Day 1.25 3.00
ST8 Larry Doby 1.25 3.00
ST9 Josh Gibson 2.00 5.00
ST10 Elston Howard 1.25 3.00
ST11 Monte Irvin 1.25 3.00
ST12 Buck Leonard 1.25 3.00
ST13 Max Manning 1.25 3.00
ST14 Willie Mays 4.00 10.00
ST15 Buck O'Neil 1.25 3.00
ST16 Satchel Paige 2.00 5.00
ST17 Ted Radcliffe 1.25 3.00
ST18 Jackie Robinson 2.00 5.00
ST19 Bill Perkins 1.25 3.00
ST20 Rube Foster 2.00 5.00
ST21 Judy Johnson 1.25 3.00
ST22 Oscar Charleston 1.25 3.00
ST23 Pop Lloyd 1.25 3.00
ST24 Artie Wilson 1.25 3.00
ST25 Sam Jethroe 1.25 3.00
NNO Henry Kimbro 1.25 3.00

2001 Fleer Tradition Stitches in Time Autographs

Randomly inserted at one in four boxes, this seven-card insert set features authentic autographs from players like Willie Mays and Ernie Banks. Please note that these cards are not numbered and are listed below in alphabetical order. Also note that Willie Mays and Artie Wilson packed out as exchange cards with a redemption deadline of 02/01/02.

1 Ernie Banks 40.00 80.00
2 Joe Black 15.00 40.00
3 Monte Irvin 20.00 50.00
4 Willie Mays 100.00 200.00
5 Buck O'Neil 30.00 60.00
6 Ted Radcliffe 30.00 60.00
7 Artie Wilson 10.00 25.00

2001 Fleer Tradition Stitches in Time Memorabilia

Randomly inserted at one in four boxes, this five-card insert set features actual swatches from game-used Bats or Pants from players like Willie Mays and Jackie Robinson. Please note that these cards are not numbered and are listed below in alphabetical order.

1 Roy Campanella Bat 40.00 80.00
2 Larry Doby Bat 30.00 60.00
3 Elston Howard Bat 20.00 50.00
4 Willie Mays Pants 75.00 150.00
5 Jackie Robinson Pants 60.00 120.00

2001 Fleer Tradition Turn Back the Clock Game Jersey

Randomly inserted at one in four boxes, this 21-card insert set features swatches from actual game-used jerseys from players like Cal Ripken and Chipper Jones. Card backs carry a "TBC" prefix.

TBC1 Tom Glavine 6.00 15.00
TBC2 Greg Maddux 15.00 40.00
TBC3 Sean Casey 4.00 10.00
TBC4 Pokey Reese 4.00 10.00
TBC5 Jason Giambi 4.00 10.00
TBC6 Tim Hudson 4.00 10.00
TBC7 Larry Walker 4.00 10.00
TBC8 Jeffrey Hammonds 4.00 10.00
TBC9 Scott Rolen 6.00 15.00
TBC10 Pat Burrell 4.00 10.00
TBC11 Chipper Jones 6.00 15.00
TBC12 Greg Maddux 15.00 40.00
TBC13 Troy Glaus 4.00 10.00
TBC14 Tony Gwynn 10.00 25.00
TBC15 Cal Ripken 10.00 25.00
TBC16 Tom Glavine 40.00 80.00
Greg Maddux
TBC17 Sean Casey 15.00 40.00
Pokey Reese
TBC18 Chipper Jones 50.00 100.00
Greg Maddux
TBC19 Larry Walker 15.00 40.00
Jeffrey Hammonds
TBC20 Scott Rolen 15.00 40.00
Pat Burrell
TBC21 Jason Giambi 10.00 25.00
Tim Hudson

2001 Fleer Tradition Warning Track

Randomly inserted into packs at one in 72, this 23-card insert takes a look at how today's power hitters stack up to yesterdays greats. Card backs carry a "WT" prefix. Please note, cards 2 and 5 (originally intended for Hank Aaron and Ernie Banks) were never produced, thus though numbered 1-25, the set is complete at 23 cards.

COMPLETE SET (23) 150.00 250.00
WT1 Josh Gibson 4.00 10.00
WT2 Does Not Exist
WT3 Willie Mays 6.00 15.00
WT4 Mark McGwire 8.00 20.00
WT5 Does Not Exist
WT6 Barry Bonds 8.00 20.00
WT7 Jose Canseco 2.00 5.00
WT8 Ken Griffey Jr. 5.00 12.00
WT9 Cal Ripken 10.00 25.00
WT10 Rafael Palmeiro 2.00 5.00
WT11 Sammy Sosa 3.00 8.00
WT12 Juan Gonzalez 2.00 5.00
WT13 Frank Thomas 3.00 8.00
WT14 Jeff Bagwell 2.00 5.00
WT15 Gary Sheffield 2.00 5.00
WT16 Larry Walker 2.00 5.00
WT17 Mike Piazza 5.00 12.00
WT18 Larry Doby 2.00 5.00
WT19 Roy Campanella 4.00 10.00
WT20 Manny Ramirez 2.00 5.00
WT21 Chipper Jones 3.00 8.00
WT22 Alex Rodriguez 5.00 12.00
WT23 Ivan Rodriguez 2.00 5.00
WT24 Vladimir Guerrero 3.00 8.00
WT25 Nomar Garciaparra 5.00 12.00

2002 Fleer Tradition

This 500 card set was issued early in 2002. This set was issued in 10 card packs and 36 packs to a box with a SRP of $1.49 per pack. The first 100 cards in this set were issued at an overall rate of one in two. In addition, cards numbered 436 through 470 featured leading prospects and cards numbered 471 through 500 featured players who had noteworthy seasons in 2001. These cards feature the 1934 Goudey-style design.

COMPLETE SET (500) 125.00 200.00
COMP.SET w/o SP's (400) 20.00 50.00
COMMON CARD (101-500) .10 .30
COMMON SP (1-100) 1.25 3.00
COMMON CARD (436-470) .20 .50
1 Barry Bonds SP 5.00 12.00
2 Cal Ripken SP 6.00 15.00
3 Tony Gwynn SP 2.50 6.00
4 Brad Radke SP 1.25 3.00
5 Jose Ortiz SP 1.25 3.00
6 Mark Mulder SP 1.25 3.00
7 Jon Lieber SP 1.25 3.00
8 John Olerud SP 1.25 3.00
9 Phil Nevin SP 1.25 3.00
10 Craig Biggio SP 1.25 3.00
11 Pedro Martinez SP 1.25 3.00
12 Fred McGriff SP 1.25 3.00
13 Vladimir Guerrero SP 2.00 5.00
14 Jason Giambi SP 1.25 3.00
15 Mark Kotsay SP 1.25 3.00
16 Bud Smith SP 1.25 3.00
17 Kevin Brown SP 1.25 3.00
18 Darin Erstad SP 1.25 3.00
19 Julio Franco SP 1.25 3.00
20 C.C. Sabathia SP 1.25 3.00
21 Larry Walker SP 1.25 3.00
22 Doug Mientkiewicz SP 1.25 3.00
23 Luis Gonzalez SP 1.25 3.00
24 Albert Pujols SP 4.00 10.00
25 Brian Lawrence SP 1.25 3.00
26 Al Leiter SP 1.25 3.00
27 Mike Sweeney SP 1.25 3.00
28 Jeff Weaver SP 1.25 3.00
29 Matt Morris SP 1.25 3.00
30 Hideo Nomo SP 2.00 5.00
31 Tom Glavine SP 1.25 3.00
32 Magglio Ordonez SP 1.25 3.00
33 Roberto Alomar SP 1.25 3.00
34 Roger Cedeno SP 1.25 3.00
35 Greg Vaughn SP 1.25 3.00
36 Chan Ho Park SP 1.25 3.00
37 Rich Aurilia SP 1.25 3.00
38 Tsuyoshi Shinjo SP 1.25 3.00
39 Eric Young SP 1.25 3.00
40 Bobby Higginson SP 1.25 3.00
41 Marlon Anderson SP 1.25 3.00
42 Mark Grace SP 1.25 3.00
43 Steve Cox SP 1.25 3.00
44 Cliff Floyd SP 1.25 3.00
45 Brian Roberts SP 1.25 3.00
46 Paul Konerko SP 1.25 3.00
47 Brandon Duckworth SP 1.25 3.00
48 Josh Beckett SP 1.25 3.00
49 David Ortiz SP 2.00 5.00
50 Geoff Jenkins SP 1.25 3.00
51 Ruben Sierra SP 1.25 3.00
52 John Franco SP 1.25 3.00
53 Einar Diaz SP 1.25 3.00
54 Luis Castillo SP 1.25 3.00
55 Mark Quinn SP 1.25 3.00
56 Shea Hillenbrand SP 1.25 3.00
57 Rafael Palmeiro SP 1.25 3.00
58 Paul O'Neill SP 1.25 3.00
59 Andruw Jones SP 1.25 3.00
60 Lance Berkman SP 1.25 3.00
61 Jimmy Rollins SP 1.25 3.00
62 Jose Hernandez SP 1.25 3.00
63 Rusty Greer SP 1.25 3.00
64 Wade Miller SP 1.25 3.00
65 David Eckstein SP 1.25 3.00
66 Jose Valentin SP 1.25 3.00
67 Javier Vazquez SP 1.25 3.00
68 Roger Clemens SP 4.00 10.00
69 Omar Vizquel SP 1.25 3.00
70 Roy Oswalt SP 1.25 3.00
71 Shannon Stewart SP 1.25 3.00
72 Byung-Hyun Kim SP 1.25 3.00
73 Jay Gibbons SP 1.25 3.00
74 Barry Larkin SP 1.25 3.00
75 Brian Giles SP 1.25 3.00
76 Andres Galarraga SP 1.25 3.00
77 Sammy Sosa SP 2.00 5.00
78 Manny Ramirez SP 1.25 3.00
79 Carlos Delgado SP 1.25 3.00
80 Jorge Posada SP 1.25 3.00
81 Todd Ritchie SP 1.25 3.00
82 Russ Ortiz SP 1.25 3.00
83 Brent Mayne SP 1.25 3.00
84 Mike Mussina SP 1.25 3.00
85 Raul Mondesi SP 1.25 3.00
86 Mark Loretta SP 1.25 3.00
87 Tim Raines SP 1.25 3.00
88 Ichiro Suzuki SP 4.00 10.00
89 Juan Pierre SP 1.25 3.00
90 Adam Dunn SP 1.25 3.00
91 Jason Tyner SP 1.25 3.00
92 Miguel Tejada SP 1.25 3.00
93 Elpidio Guzman SP 1.25 3.00
94 Freddy Garcia SP 1.25 3.00
95 Marcus Giles SP 1.25 3.00
96 Junior Spivey SP 1.25 3.00
97 Aramis Ramirez SP 1.25 3.00
98 Jose Rijo SP 1.25 3.00
99 Paul LoDuca SP 1.25 3.00
100 Mike Cameron SP 1.25 3.00
101 Alex Hernandez .10 .30
102 Benji Gil .10 .30
103 Benito Santiago .10 .30
104 Bobby Abreu .10 .30
105 Brad Penny .10 .30
106 Calvin Murray .10 .30
107 Chad Durbin .10 .30
108 Chris Singleton .10 .30
109 Chris Carpenter .10 .30
110 David Justice .10 .30
111 Eric Chavez .10 .30
112 Fernando Tatis .10 .30
113 Frank Castillo .10 .30
114 Jason LaRue .10 .30
115 Jim Edmonds .10 .30
116 Joe Kennedy .10 .30
117 Jose Jimenez .10 .30
118 Josh Towers .10 .30
119 Junior Herndon .10 .30
120 Luke Prokopec .10 .30
121 Mac Suzuki .10 .30
122 Mark DeRosa .10 .30
123 Marty Cordova .10 .30
124 Michael Tucker .10 .30
125 Michael Young .30 .75
126 Robin Ventura .10 .30
127 Shane Halter .10 .30
128 Shane Reynolds .10 .30
129 Tony Womack .10 .30
130 A.J. Pierzynski .10 .30
131 Aaron Rowand .10 .30
132 Antonio Alfonseca .10 .30
133 Arthur Rhodes .10 .30
134 Bob Wickman .10 .30
135 Brady Clark .10 .30
136 Chad Hermansen .10 .30
137 Marlon Byrd .10 .30
138 Dan Wilson .10 .30
139 David Cone .10 .30
140 Dean Palmer .10 .30
141 Denny Neagle .10 .30
142 Derek Jeter .75 2.00
143 Erubiel Durazo .10 .30
144 Felix Rodriguez .10 .30
145 Jason Hart .10 .30
146 Jay Bell .10 .30
147 Jeff Suppan .10 .30
148 Jeff Zimmerman .10 .30
149 Kerry Wood .10 .30
150 Kerry Robinson .10 .30
151 Kevin Appier .10 .30
152 Michael Barrett .10 .30
153 Mo Vaughn .10 .30
154 Rafael Furcal .10 .30
155 Sidney Ponson .10 .30
156 Terry Adams .10 .30
157 Tim Redding .10 .30
158 Toby Hall .10 .30
159 Aaron Sele .10 .30
160 Bartolo Colon .10 .30
161 Brad Ausmus .10 .30
162 Carlos Pena .10 .30
163 Jace Brewer .10 .30
164 David Wells .10 .30
165 David Segui .10 .30
166 Derek Lowe .10 .30
167 Derek Bell .10 .30
168 Jason Grabowski .10 .30
169 Johnny Damon .20 .50
170 Jose Mesa .10 .30
171 Juan Encarnacion .10 .30
172 Ken Caminiti .10 .30
173 Ken Griffey Jr. .50 1.25
174 Luis Rivas .10 .30
175 Mariano Rivera .30 .75
176 Mark Grudzielanek .10 .30
177 Mark McGwire .75 2.00
178 Mike Bordick .10 .30
179 Mike Hampton .10 .30
180 Nick Bierbrodt .10 .30
181 Paul Byrd .10 .30
182 Robb Nen .10 .30
183 Ryan Dempster .10 .30
184 Ryan Klesko .10 .30
185 Scott Spiezio .10 .30
186 Scott Strickland .10 .30
187 Todd Zeile .10 .30
188 Tom Gordon .10 .30
189 Troy Glaus .10 .30
190 Matt Williams .10 .30
191 Wes Helms .10 .30
192 Jerry Hairston Jr. .10 .30
193 Brook Fordyce .10 .30
194 Nomar Garciaparra .50 1.25
195 Kevin Tapani .10 .30
196 Mark Buehrle .10 .30
197 Dmitri Young .10 .30
198 John Rocker .10 .30
199 Juan Uribe .10 .30
200 Matt Anderson .10 .30
201 Alex Gonzalez .10 .30
202 Julio Lugo .10 .30
203 Roberto Hernandez .10 .30
204 Richie Sexson .10 .30
205 Corey Koskie .10 .30
206 Tony Armas Jr. .10 .30
207 Rey Ordonez .10 .30
208 Orlando Hernandez .10 .30
209 Pokey Reese .10 .30
210 Mike Lieberthal .10 .30
211 Kris Benson .10 .30
212 Jermaine Dye .10 .30
213 Livan Hernandez .10 .30
214 Bret Boone .10 .30
215 Dustin Hermanson .10 .30
216 Placido Polanco .10 .30
217 Jesus Colome .10 .30
218 Alex Gonzalez .10 .30
219 Adam Everett .10 .30
220 Adam Piatt .10 .30
221 Brad Fullmer .10 .30
222 Brian Buchanan .10 .30
223 Chipper Jones .30 .75
224 Chuck Finley .10 .30
225 David Bell .10 .30
226 Jack Wilson .10 .30
227 Jason Bere .10 .30
228 Jeff Conine .10 .30
229 Jeff Bagwell .20 .50
230 Joe McEwing .10 .30
231 Kip Wells .10 .30
232 Mike Lansing .10 .30
233 Neifi Perez .10 .30
234 Omar Daal .10 .30
235 Reggie Sanders .10 .30
236 Shawn Wooten .10 .30
237 Shawn Chacon .10 .30
238 Shawn Estes .10 .30
239 Steve Sparks .10 .30
240 Steve Kline .10 .30
241 Tino Martinez .20 .50
242 Tyler Houston .10 .30
243 Xavier Nady .10 .30
244 Bengie Molina .10 .30
245 Ben Davis .10 .30
246 Casey Fossum .10 .30
247 Chris Stynes .10 .30
248 Danny Graves .10 .30
249 Pedro Feliz .10 .30
250 Darren Oliver .10 .30
251 Dave Veres .10 .30
252 Deivi Cruz .10 .30
253 Desi Relaford .10 .30
254 Devon White .10 .30
255 Edgar Martinez .20 .50
256 Eric Munson .10 .30
257 Eric Karros .10 .30
258 Homer Bush .10 .30
259 Jason Kendall .10 .30
260 Javy Lopez .10 .30
261 Keith Foulke .10 .30
262 Keith Ginter .10 .30
263 Nick Johnson .10 .30
264 Pat Burrell .10 .30
265 Ricky Gutierrez .10 .30
266 Russ Johnson .10 .30
267 Steve Finley .10 .30
268 Terrence Long .10 .30
269 Tony Batista .10 .30
270 Torii Hunter .10 .30
271 Vinny Castilla .10 .30
272 A.J. Burnett .10 .30
273 Adrian Beltre .10 .30
274 Alex Rodriguez .50 1.25
275 Armando Benitez .10 .30
276 Billy Koch .10 .30
277 Brady Anderson .10 .30
278 Brian Jordan .10 .30
279 Carlos Febles .10 .30
280 Daryle Ward .10 .30
281 Eli Marrero .10 .30
282 Garret Anderson .10 .30
283 Jack Cust .10 .30
284 Jacque Jones .10 .30
285 Jamie Moyer .10 .30
286 Jeffrey Hammonds .10 .30
287 Jim Thome .20 .50
288 Jon Garland .10 .30
289 Jose Offerman .10 .30
290 Matt Stairs .10 .30
291 Orlando Cabrera .10 .30
292 Ramiro Mendoza .10 .30
293 Ray Durham .10 .30
294 Rickey Henderson .30 .75
295 Rob Mackowiak .10 .30
296 Scott Rolen .20 .50
297 Tim Hudson .10 .30
298 Todd Helton .20 .50
299 Tony Clark .10 .30
300 B.J. Surhoff .10 .30
301 Bernie Williams .20 .50
302 Bill Mueller .10 .30
303 Chris Richard .10 .30
304 Craig Paquette .10 .30
305 Curt Schilling .10 .30
306 Damian Jackson .10 .30
307 Derrek Lee .20 .50
308 Eric Milton .10 .30
309 Frank Catalanotto .10 .30
310 J.T. Snow .10 .30
311 Jared Sandberg .10 .30
312 Jason Varitek .30 .75
313 Jeff Cirillo .10 .30
314 Jeromy Burnitz .10 .30
315 Joe Crede .10 .30
316 Joel Pineiro .10 .30
317 Jose Cruz Jr. .10 .30
318 Kevin Young .10 .30
319 Marquis Grissom .10 .30
320 Moises Alou .10 .30
321 Randall Simon .10 .30
322 Royce Clayton .10 .30
323 Tim Salmon .20 .50
324 Travis Fryman .10 .30
325 Travis Lee .10 .30
326 Vance Wilson .10 .30
327 Jarrod Washburn .10 .30
328 Ben Petrick .10 .30
329 Ben Grieve .10 .30
330 Carl Everett .10 .30
331 Eric Byrnes .10 .30
332 Doug Glanville .10 .30
333 Edgardo Alfonzo .10 .30
334 Ellis Burks .10 .30
335 Gabe Kapler .10 .30
336 Gary Sheffield .10 .30
337 Greg Maddux .50 1.25
338 J.D. Drew .10 .30
339 Jamey Wright .10 .30
340 Jeff Kent .10 .30
341 Jeremy Giambi .10 .30
342 Joe Randa .10 .30
343 Joe Mays .10 .30
344 Jose Macias .10 .30
345 Kazuhiro Sasaki .10 .30
346 Mike Kinkade .10 .30
347 Mike Lowell .10 .30
348 Randy Johnson .30 .75
349 Randy Wolf .10 .30
350 Richard Hidalgo .10 .30
351 Ron Coomer .10 .30
352 Sandy Alomar Jr. .10 .30
353 Sean Casey .10 .30
354 Trevor Hoffman .10 .30
355 Adam Eaton .10 .30
356 Alfonso Soriano .10 .30
357 Barry Zito .10 .30
358 Billy Wagner .10 .30
359 Brent Abernathy .10 .30
360 Bret Prinz .10 .30
361 Carlos Beltran .10 .30
362 Carlos Guillen .10 .30
363 Charles Johnson .10 .30
364 Cristian Guzman .10 .30
365 Damion Easley .10 .30
366 Darryl Kile .10 .30
367 Delino DeShields .10 .30
368 Eric Davis .10 .30
369 Frank Thomas .30 .75
370 Ivan Rodriguez .20 .50
371 Jay Payton .10 .30
372 Jeff D'Amico .10 .30
373 John Burkett .10 .30
374 Melvin Mora .10 .30
375 Ramon Ortiz .10 .30
376 Robert Person .10 .30
377 Russell Branyan .10 .30
378 Shawn Green .10 .30
379 Todd Hollandsworth .10 .30
380 Tony McKnight .10 .30
381 Trot Nixon .10 .30
382 Vernon Wells .10 .30
383 Troy Percival .10 .30
384 Albie Lopez .10 .30
385 Alex Ochoa .10 .30
386 Andy Pettitte .20 .50
387 Brandon Inge .10 .30
388 Bubba Trammell .10 .30
389 Corey Patterson .10 .30
390 Damian Rolls .10 .30
391 Dee Brown .10 .30
392 Edgar Renteria .10 .30
393 Eric Gagne .10 .30
394 Jason Johnson .10 .30
395 Jeff Nelson .10 .30
396 John Vander Wal .10 .30
397 Johnny Estrada .10 .30
398 Jose Canseco .20 .50
399 Juan Gonzalez .10 .30
400 Kevin Millwood .10 .30
401 Lee Stevens .10 .30
402 Matt Lawton .10 .30
403 Mike Lamb .10 .30
404 Octavio Dotel .10 .30
405 Ramon Hernandez .10 .30
406 Ruben Quevedo .10 .30
407 Todd Walker .10 .30
408 Troy O'Leary .10 .30
409 Wascar Serrano .10 .30
410 Aaron Boone .10 .30
411 Aubrey Huff .10 .30
412 Ben Sheets .10 .30
413 Carlos Lee .10 .30
414 Chuck Knoblauch .10 .30
415 Steve Karsay .10 .30
416 Dante Bichette .10 .30
417 David Dellucci .10 .30
418 Esteban Loaiza .10 .30
419 Fernando Vina .10 .30
420 Ismael Valdes .10 .30
421 Jason Isringhausen .10 .30
422 Jeff Shaw .10 .30
423 John Smoltz .20 .50
424 Jose Vidro .10 .30
425 Kenny Lofton .10 .30
426 Mark Little .10 .30
427 Mark McLemore .10 .30
428 Marvin Benard .10 .30
429 Mike Piazza .50 1.25
430 Pat Hentgen .10 .30
431 Preston Wilson .10 .30
432 Rick Helling .10 .30
433 Robert Fick .10 .30
434 Rondell White .10 .30
435 Adam Kennedy .10 .30
436 David Espinosa PROS .20 .50
437 Dewon Brazelton PROS .20 .50
438 Drew Henson PROS .20 .50
439 Juan Cruz PROS .20 .50
440 Jason Jennings PROS .20 .50
441 Carlos Garcia PROS .20 .50
442 Carlos Hernandez PROS .20 .50
443 Wilkin Ruan PROS .20 .50
444 Wilson Betemit PROS .20 .50
445 Horacio Ramirez PROS .20 .50
446 Danys Baez PROS .20 .50
447 Abraham Nunez PROS .20 .50
448 Josh Hamilton PROS .40 1.00
449 Chris George PROS .20 .50
450 Rick Bauer PROS .20 .50
451 Donnie Bridges PROS .20 .50
452 Erick Almonte PROS .20 .50
453 Cory Aldridge PROS .20 .50
454 Ryan Drese PROS .20 .50
455 Jason Romano PROS .20 .50
456 Corky Miller PROS .20 .50
457 Rafael Soriano PROS .20 .50
458 Mark Prior PROS .50 1.25
459 Mark Teixeira PROS .50 1.25
460 Adrian Hernandez PROS .20 .50
461 Tim Spooneybarger PROS .20 .50
462 Bill Ortega PROS .20 .50
463 D'Angelo Jimenez PROS .20 .50
464 Andres Torres PROS .20 .50
465 Alexis Gomez PROS .20 .50
466 Angel Berroa PROS .20 .50
467 Henry Mateo PROS .20 .50
468 Endy Chavez PROS .20 .50
469 Billy Sylvester PROS .20 .50
470 Nate Frese PROS .20 .50
471 Luis Gonzalez BNR .10 .30
472 Barry Bonds BNR .75 2.00
473 Rich Aurilia BNR .10 .30
474 Albert Pujols BNR .60 1.50
475 Todd Helton BNR .20 .50

476 Moises Alou BNR .10 .30
477 Lance Berkman BNR .10 .30
478 Brian Giles BNR .10 .30
479 Cliff Floyd BNR .10 .30
480 Sammy Sosa BNR .30 .75
481 Shawn Green BNR .10 .30
482 Jon Lieber BNR .10 .30
483 Matt Morris BNR .10 .30
484 Curt Schilling BNR .10 .30
485 Randy Johnson BNR .20 .50
486 Manny Ramirez BNR .20 .50
487 Ichiro Suzuki BNR .60 1.50
488 Juan Gonzalez BNR .10 .30
489 Derek Jeter BNR .75 2.00
490 Alex Rodriguez BNR .50 1.25
491 Bret Boone BNR .10 .30
492 Roberto Alomar BNR .20 .50
493 Jason Giambi BNR .10 .30
494 Rafael Palmeiro BNR .20 .50
495 Doug Mientkiewicz BNR .10 .30
496 Jim Thome BNR .10 .30
497 Freddy Garcia BNR .10 .30
498 Mark Buehrle BNR .10 .30
499 Mark Mulder BNR .10 .30
500 Roger Clemens BNR .60 1.50

2002 Fleer Tradition Glossy

Randomly inserted into Fleer Tradition Update packs, this is a parallel of the basic Fleer Tradition set. These cards can be differentiated from the regular Fleer cards by their "glossy" sheen and have a stated print run of 200 serial numbered sets.

*GLOSSY 1-100: .5X TO 1.2X BASIC
*GLOSSY 101-435/471-500: 3X TO 8X BASIC
*GLOSSY 436-470: 2X TO 5X BASIC

2002 Fleer Tradition Diamond Tributes

Inserted into hobby packs at stated odds of one in six and retail packs at stated odds of one in 10, these 15 cards feature players who have performed on the field of play but have also had a positive impact on the community.

COMPLETE SET (15) 8.00 20.00
1 Cal Ripken 1.50 4.00
2 Tony Gwynn .60 1.50
3 Derek Jeter 1.25 3.00
4 Pedro Martinez .50 1.25
5 Mark McGwire 1.25 3.00
6 Sammy Sosa .50 1.25
7 Barry Bonds 1.25 3.00
8 Roger Clemens 1.00 2.50
9 Mike Piazza .75 2.00
10 Alex Rodriguez .75 2.00
11 Randy Johnson .50 1.25
12 Chipper Jones .50 1.25
13 Nomar Garciaparra .75 2.00
14 Ichiro Suzuki 1.00 2.50
15 Jason Giambi .50 1.25

2002 Fleer Tradition Grass Patch

This 10 card set is a parallel to the Grass Roots insert set. Each card in this set features not only the defensive whiz pictured but also a special game-worn jersey swatch. According to representatives at Fleer, each cards has a stated print run of 50 copies (though the cards lack any form of serial-numbering).

1 Jeff Bagwell 15.00 40.00
2 Barry Bonds 40.00 80.00
3 Derek Jeter
4 Greg Maddux 30.00 60.00
5 Cal Ripken 75.00 150.00
6 Alex Rodriguez 30.00 60.00
7 Ivan Rodriguez 15.00 40.00
8 Scott Rolen 15.00 40.00
9 Larry Walker 15.00 40.00
10 Bernie Williams 15.00 40.00

2002 Fleer Tradition Grass Roots

Inserted into hobby packs at stated odds of one in 18 and retail packs at stated odds of one in 20, these 10 cards feature leading defensive players.

COMPLETE SET (10) 12.50 30.00
1 Barry Bonds 2.50 6.00
2 Alex Rodriguez 1.50 4.00
3 Derek Jeter 2.50 6.00
4 Greg Maddux 1.50 4.00
5 Ivan Rodriguez .60 1.50
6 Cal Ripken 3.00 8.00
7 Bernie Williams .60 1.50
8 Jeff Bagwell .60 1.50
9 Scott Rolen .60 1.50
10 Larry Walker .60 1.50

2002 Fleer Tradition Heads Up

Inserted into hobby packs at stated odds of one in 36 and retail packs at stated odds of one in 40, these 10 cards feature leading players as they would look as bobbleheads.

COMPLETE SET (10) 30.00 80.00
1 Derek Jeter 4.00 10.00
2 Ichiro Suzuki 3.00 8.00
3 Sammy Sosa 2.50 6.00
4 Mike Piazza 2.50 6.00
5 Ken Griffey Jr. 2.50 6.00
6 Alex Rodriguez 2.50 6.00
7 Barry Bonds 4.00 10.00
8 Nomar Garciaparra 2.50 6.00
9 Mark McGwire 4.00 10.00
10 Cal Ripken 5.00 12.00

2002 Fleer Tradition Lumber Company

Inserted into packs at stated odds of one in 12 hobby and one in 20 retail, these 30 cards feature superstars who can hit the ball with above average skills.

COMPLETE SET (30) 25.00 60.00
1 Moises Alou .60 1.50
2 Luis Gonzalez .60 1.50
3 Todd Helton .60 1.50
4 Mike Piazza 1.50 4.00
5 J.D. Drew .60 1.50
6 Albert Pujols 2.00 5.00
7 Chipper Jones 1.00 2.50
8 Manny Ramirez .60 1.50
9 Miguel Tejada .60 1.50
10 Curt Schilling .60 1.50
11 Alex Rodriguez 1.50 4.00
12 Barry Larkin .60 1.50
13 Nomar Garciaparra 1.50 4.00
14 Cliff Floyd .60 1.50
15 Alfonso Soriano .60 1.50
16 Sean Casey .60 1.50
17 Scott Rolen .60 1.50
18 Jose Ortiz .60 1.50
19 Corey Patterson .60 1.50
20 Joe Crede .60 1.50
21 Jace Brewer .60 1.50
22 Derek Jeter 2.50 6.00
23 Jim Thome .60 1.50
24 Frank Thomas 1.00 2.50
25 Shawn Green .60 1.50
26 Drew Henson .60 1.50
27 Jimmy Rollins .60 1.50
28 David Justice .60 1.50
29 Roberto Alomar .60 1.50
30 Bernie Williams .60 1.50

2002 Fleer Tradition Lumber Company Game Bat

This parallel to the Lumber Company insert set was inserted in packs at a rate of one in 72 packs. These cards feature not only the player pictured but a bat piece swatch related to that player. Jace Brewer, Sean Casey, Joe Crede, Derek Jeter, Corey Patterson and Scott Rolen were all short-prints according to representatives at Fleer.

1 Roberto Alomar 6.00 15.00
2 Moises Alou 4.00 10.00
3 Jace Brewer SP/250 4.00 10.00
4 Sean Casey SP/250 4.00 10.00
5 Joe Crede SP/250 4.00 10.00
6 J.D. Drew 4.00 10.00
7 Cliff Floyd 4.00 10.00
8 Nomar Garciaparra 8.00 20.00
9 Luis Gonzalez 4.00 10.00
10 Shawn Green 4.00 10.00
11 Todd Helton 6.00 15.00
12 Drew Henson 4.00 10.00
13 Derek Jeter SP/250 15.00 40.00
14 Chipper Jones 6.00 15.00
15 David Justice 4.00 10.00
16 Barry Larkin 6.00 15.00
17 Jose Ortiz SP/250 4.00 10.00
18 Corey Patterson SP/250 4.00 10.00
19 Mike Piazza 6.00 15.00
20 Albert Pujols 10.00 25.00
21 Manny Ramirez 6.00 15.00
22 Alex Rodriguez 8.00 20.00
23 Scott Rolen SP/250 6.00 15.00
24 Jimmy Rollins 4.00 10.00
25 Curt Schilling 4.00 10.00
26 Alfonso Soriano 4.00 10.00
27 Miguel Tejada 4.00 10.00
28 Frank Thomas 6.00 15.00
29 Jim Thome 6.00 15.00
30 Bernie Williams 6.00 15.00

2002 Fleer Tradition This Day in History

Inserted into hobby packs at stated odds of one in 18 and retail packs at stated odds of one in 24, these 29 cards feature highlights of some of the greatest days in baseball history. Please note that card number 24 (originally intended to feature Orel Hershiser) was pulled from production, thus the set is complete at 29 cards.

COMPLETE SET (29) 60.00 150.00
1 Cal Ripken 6.00 15.00
2 Barry Bonds 5.00 12.00
3 George Brett 4.00 10.00
4 Tony Gwynn 2.50 6.00
5 Nolan Ryan 5.00 12.00
6 Reggie Jackson 1.25 3.00
7 Paul Molitor 1.25 3.00
8 Ichiro Suzuki 4.00 10.00
9 Alex Rodriguez 3.00 8.00
10 Don Mattingly 4.00 10.00
11 Sammy Sosa 2.00 5.00
12 Mark McGwire 5.00 12.00
13 Derek Jeter 5.00 12.00
14 Roger Clemens 4.00 10.00
15 Jim Hunter 1.25 3.00
16 Greg Maddux 3.00 8.00
17 Ken Griffey Jr. 3.00 8.00
18 Gil Hodges 2.00 5.00
19 Edgar Martinez 1.25 3.00
20 Mike Piazza 3.00 8.00
21 Jimmie Foxx 2.00 5.00
22 Albert Pujols 4.00 10.00
23 Chipper Jones 2.00 5.00
24 Does Not Exist
25 Jeff Bagwell 1.25 3.00
26 Nomar Garciaparra 3.00 8.00
27 Randy Johnson 2.00 5.00
28 Todd Helton 1.25 3.00
29 Ted Kluszewski 1.25 3.00
30 Ivan Rodriguez 1.25 3.00

2002 Fleer Tradition This Day in History Autographs

Randomly inserted into packs, these eight cards feature autographs of the player notated. Most of the players did not sign their cards in time for inclusion in this product so they were available as exchange cards. Please note that Fleer provided print run information for these cards but they are not serial numbered. Exchange cards with a redemption deadline of 01/31/03 were seeded into packs for the following players: Gwynn, R.Jackson, R.Johnson, Mattingly, Molitor and Ripken.

1 Tony Gwynn/50
2 Reggie Jackson/50
3 Derek Jeter/100 75.00 150.00
4 Randy Johnson/75 40.00 80.00
5 Don Mattingly/50 50.00 100.00
6 Paul Molitor/50
7 Albert Pujols/50 150.00 250.00
8 Cal Ripken/50 75.00 150.00

2002 Fleer Tradition This Day in History Game Used

Randomly inserted into packs, these 22 cards feature memorabilia pieces from the noted player. As these cards are printed to different amounts, we have notated that information in our checklist.

1 Jeff Bagwell Bat/100 10.00 25.00
2 Barry Bonds Jsy/250 20.00 50.00
3 George Brett Jsy/50
4 Roger Clemens Jsy/150 15.00 40.00
5 Jimmie Foxx Bat/250 20.00 50.00
6 Todd Helton Bat/150 10.00 25.00
7 Gil Hodges Bat/50
8 Jim Hunter Jsy/250 10.00 25.00
10 Reggie Jackson Bat/50
11 Derek Jeter Jsy/250 25.00 60.00
12 Randy Johnson Jsy/50
13 Chipper Jones Bat/50
14 Ted Kluszewski Jsy/50
15 Greg Maddux Jsy/100 12.50 30.00
16 Don Mattingly Jsy/50
17 Paul Molitor Bat/50
18 Mike Piazza Bat/150 10.00 25.00
19 Albert Pujols Jsy/50
20 Cal Ripken Jsy/50
21 Alex Rodriguez Hat/250 15.00 40.00
22 Ivan Rodriguez Jsy/50
23 Nolan Ryan Pants/50

2002 Fleer Tradition Update

This 400 card set was released in October, 2003. This set was issued in 10 card packs which came 28 packs to a box and six boxes to a case with the packs having an SRP of $2. Cards numbered U1 through U100, which feature a mix of rookies and prospects, were issued at a stated rate of one per pack and are in shorter supply than the rest of the set. Other subsets include Diamond Standouts (U276-U297), All-Stars (U298-U360), Curtain Call (U361-U385) and Tale of the Tape (U386-U400).

COMPLETE SET (400) 60.00 120.00
COMP.SET w/o SP's (300) 15.00 40.00
COMMON CARD (U101-U400) .10 .30
COMMON CARD (U1-U100) .40 1.00
U1 P.J. Bevis SP RC .40 1.00
U2 Mike Crudale SP RC .40 1.00
U3 Ben Howard SP RC .40 1.00
U4 Travis Driskill SP RC .40 1.00
U5 Reed Johnson SP RC .60 1.50
U6 Kyle Kane SP RC .40 1.00
U7 Deivis Santos SP .40 1.00
U8 Tim Kalita SP RC .40 1.00
U9 Brandon Puffer SP RC .40 1.00
U10 Chris Snelling SP RC .60 1.50
U11 Juan Brito SP RC .40 1.00
U12 Tyler Yates SP RC .40 1.00
U13 Victor Alvarez SP RC .40 1.00
U14 Takahito Nomura SP RC .40 1.00
U15 Ron Calloway SP RC .40 1.00
U16 Satoru Komiyama SP RC .40 1.00
U17 Julius Matos SP RC .40 1.00
U18 Jorge Nunez SP RC .40 1.00
U19 Anderson Machado SP RC .40 1.00
U20 Scott Layfield SP RC .40 1.00
U21 Aaron Cook SP RC .40 1.00
U22 Alex Pelaez SP RC .40 1.00
U23 Corey Thurman SP RC .40 1.00
U24 Nelson Castro SP RC .40 1.00
U25 Jeff Austin SP RC .40 1.00
U26 Felix Escalona SP RC .40 1.00
U27 Luis Ugueto SP RC .40 1.00
U28 Jaime Cerda SP RC .40 1.00
U29 J.J. Trujillo SP RC .40 1.00
U30 Rodrigo Rosario SP RC .40 1.00
U31 Jorge Padilla SP RC .40 1.00
U32 Shawn Sedlacek SP RC .40 1.00
U33 Nate Field SP RC .40 1.00
U34 Earl Snyder SP RC .40 1.00
U35 Miguel Asencio SP RC .40 1.00
U36 Ken Huckaby SP RC .40 1.00
U37 Valentino Pascucci SP .40 1.00
U38 So Taguchi SP RC .50 1.25
U39 Brian Mallette SP RC .40 1.00
U40 Kazuhisa Ishii SP RC .50 1.25
U41 Matt Thornton SP RC .40 1.00
U42 Mark Corey SP RC .40 1.00
U43 Kirk Saarloos SP RC .40 1.00
U44 Josh Bard SP RC .40 1.00
U45 Hansel Izquierdo SP RC .40 1.00
U46 Rene Reyes SP RC .40 1.00
U47 Luis Garcia SP .40 1.00
U48 Jason Simontacchi SP RC .40 1.00
U49 John Ennis SP RC .40 1.00
U50 Franklyn German SP RC .40 1.00
U51 Aaron Guiel SP RC .40 1.00
U52 Howie Clark SP RC .40 1.00
U53 David Ross SP RC .50 1.25
U54 Jason Davis SP RC .40 1.00
U55 Francis Beltran SP RC .40 1.00
U56 Barry Wesson SP RC .40 1.00
U57 Run. Hernandez SP RC .40 1.00
U58 Oliver Perez SP RC .60 1.50
U59 Ryan Bukvich SP RC .40 1.00
U60 Steve Kent SP RC .40 1.00
U61 Julio Mateo SP RC .40 1.00
U62 Jason Jimenez SP RC .40 1.00
U63 Jayson Durocher SP RC .40 1.00
U64 Kevin Frederick SP RC .40 1.00
U65 Kevin Gryboski SP RC .40 1.00
U66 Edwin Almonte SP RC .40 1.00
U67 John Foster SP RC .40 1.00
U68 Doug Devore SP RC .40 1.00
U69 Tom Shearn SP RC .40 1.00
U70 Colin Young SP RC .40 1.00
U71 Jon Adkins SP RC .40 1.00
U72 Wilbert Nieves SP RC .40 1.00
U73 Matt Duff SP RC .40 1.00
U74 Carl Sadler SP RC .40 1.00
U75 Jason Kershner SP RC .40 1.00
U76 Brandon Backe SP RC .50 1.25
U77 Josh Hancock SP RC .50 1.25
U78 Chris Baker SP RC .40 1.00
U79 Travis Hughes SP RC .40 1.00
U80 Steve Bechler SP RC .40 1.00
U81 Allan Simpson SP RC .40 1.00
U82 Aaron Taylor SP RC .40 1.00
U83 Kevin Cash SP RC .40 1.00
U84 Chone Figgins SP RC .75 2.00
U85 Clay Condrey SP RC .40 1.00
U86 Shane Nance SP RC .40 1.00
U87 Freddy Sanchez SP RC 1.25 3.00
U88 Jim Rushford SP RC .40 1.00
U89 Jeriome Robertson SP RC .40 1.00
U90 Trey Lunsford SP RC .40 1.00
U91 Cody McKay SP RC .40 1.00
U92 Trey Hodges SP RC .40 1.00
U93 Hee Seop Choi SP .40 1.00
U94 Joe Borchard SP .40 1.00
U95 Orlando Hudson SP .40 1.00
U96 Carl Crawford SP .40 1.00
U97 Mark Prior SP .75 2.00
U98 Brett Myers SP .40 1.00
U99 Kenny Lofton SP .40 1.00
U100 Cliff Floyd SP .40 1.00
U101 Randy Winn .10 .30
U102 Ryan Dempster .10 .30
U103 Josh Phelps .10 .30
U104 Marcus Giles .10 .30
U105 Rickey Henderson .30 .75
U106 Jose Leon .10 .30
U107 Tino Martinez .20 .50
U108 Greg Norton .10 .30
U109 Odalis Perez .10 .30
U110 J.C. Romero .10 .30
U111 Gary Sheffield .10 .30
U112 Ismael Valdes .10 .30
U113 Juan Acevedo .10 .30
U114 Ben Broussard .10 .30
U115 Deivi Cruz .10 .30
U116 Geronimo Gil .10 .30
U117 Eric Hinske .10 .30
U118 Ted Lilly .10 .30
U119 Quinton McCracken .10 .30
U120 Antonio Alfonseca .10 .30
U121 Brent Abernathy .10 .30
U122 Johnny Damon Sox .20 .50
U123 Francisco Cordero .10 .30
U124 Sterling Hitchcock .10 .30
U125 Vladimir Nunez .10 .30
U126 Andres Galarraga .10 .30
U127 Timo Perez .10 .30
U128 Tsuyoshi Shinjo .10 .30
U129 Joe Girardi .10 .30
U130 Roberto Alomar .20 .50
U131 Ellis Burks .10 .30
U132 Mike DeJean .10 .30
U133 Alex Gonzalez .10 .30
U134 Johan Santana .50 1.25
U135 Kenny Lofton .10 .30
U136 Juan Encarnacion .10 .30
U137 Dewon Brazelton .10 .30
U138 Jeromy Burnitz .10 .30
U139 Elmer Dessens .10 .30
U140 Juan Gonzalez .10 .30
U141 Todd Hundley .10 .30
U142 Tomo Ohka .10 .30
U143 Robin Ventura .10 .30
U144 Rodrigo Lopez .10 .30
U145 Ruben Sierra .10 .30
U146 Jason Phillips .10 .30
U147 Ryan Rupe .10 .30
U148 Kevin Appier .10 .30
U149 Sean Burroughs .10 .30
U150 Masato Yoshii .10 .30
U151 Juan Diaz .10 .30
U152 Tony Graffanino .10 .30
U153 Raul Ibanez .10 .30
U154 Kevin Mench .10 .30
U155 Pedro Astacio .10 .30
U156 Brent Butler .10 .30
U157 Kirk Rueter .10 .30
U158 Eddie Guardado .10 .30
U159 Hideki Irabu .10 .30
U160 Wendell Magee .10 .30
U161 Antonio Osuna .10 .30
U162 Jose Vizcaino .10 .30
U163 Danny Bautista .10 .30
U164 Vinny Castilla .10 .30
U165 Chris Singleton .10 .30
U166 Mark Redman .10 .30
U167 Olmedo Saenz .10 .30
U168 Scott Erickson .10 .30
U169 Ty Wigginton .10 .30
U170 Jason Isringhausen .10 .30
U171 Andy Van Hekken .10 .30
U172 Chris Magruder .10 .30
U173 Brandon Berger .10 .30
U174 Roger Cedeno .10 .30
U175 Kelvim Escobar .10 .30
U176 Jose Guillen .10 .30
U177 Damian Jackson .10 .30
U178 Eric Owens .10 .30
U179 Angel Berroa .10 .30
U180 Alex Cintron .10 .30
U181 Jeff Weaver .10 .30
U182 Damon Minor .10 .30
U183 Bobby Estalella .10 .30
U184 David Justice .10 .30
U185 Roy Halladay .10 .30
U186 Brian Jordan .10 .30
U187 Mike Maroth .10 .30
U188 Pokey Reese .10 .30
U189 Rey Sanchez .10 .30
U190 Hank Blalock .20 .50
U191 Jeff Cirillo .10 .30
U192 Dmitri Young .10 .30
U193 Carl Everett .10 .30
U194 Joey Hamilton .10 .30
U195 Jorge Julio .10 .30
U196 Pablo Ozuna .10 .30
U197 Jason Marquis .10 .30
U198 Dustan Mohr .10 .30
U199 Joe Borowski .10 .30
U200 Tony Clark .10 .30
U201 David Wells .10 .30
U202 Josh Fogg .10 .30
U203 Aaron Harang .10 .30
U204 John McDonald .10 .30
U205 John Stephens .10 .30
U206 Chris Reitsma .10 .30
U207 Alex Sanchez .10 .30
U208 Milton Bradley .10 .30
U209 Matt Clement .10 .30
U210 Brad Fullmer .10 .30
U211 Shigetoshi Hasegawa .10 .30
U212 Austin Kearns .10 .30
U213 Damaso Marte .10 .30
U214 Vicente Padilla .10 .30
U215 Raul Mondesi .10 .30
U216 Russell Branyan .10 .30
U217 Bartolo Colon .10 .30
U218 Moises Alou .10 .30
U219 Scott Hatteberg .10 .30
U220 Bobby Kielty .10 .30
U221 Kip Wells .10 .30
U222 Scott Stewart .10 .30
U223 Victor Martinez .30 .75
U224 Marty Cordova .10 .30
U225 Desi Relaford .10 .30
U226 Reggie Sanders .10 .30
U227 Jason Giambi .10 .30
U228 Jimmy Haynes .10 .30
U229 Billy Koch .10 .30
U230 Damian Moss .10 .30
U231 Chan Ho Park .10 .30
U232 Cliff Floyd .10 .30
U233 Todd Zeile .10 .30
U234 Jeremy Giambi .10 .30
U235 Rick Helling .10 .30
U236 Matt Lawton .10 .30
U237 Ramon Martinez .10 .30
U238 Rondell White .10 .30
U239 Scott Sullivan .10 .30
U240 Hideo Nomo .30 .75
U241 Todd Ritchie .10 .30
U242 Ramon Santiago .10 .30
U243 Jake Peavy .20 .50
U244 Brad Wilkerson .10 .30
U245 Reggie Taylor .10 .30
U246 Carlos Pena .10 .30
U247 Willis Roberts UER .10 .30
No U in front of card number
U248 Jason Schmidt .10 .30
U249 Mike Williams .10 .30
U250 Alan Zinter .10 .30
U251 Michael Tejera .10 .30
U252 Dave Roberts .10 .30
U253 Scott Schoeneweis .10 .30
U254 Woody Williams .10 .30
U255 John Thomson .10 .30
U256 Ricardo Rodriguez .10 .30
U257 Aaron Sele .10 .30
U258 Paul Wilson .10 .30
U259 Brett Tomko .10 .30
U260 Kenny Rogers .10 .30
U261 Mo Vaughn .10 .30
U262 John Burkett .10 .30
U263 Dennis Stark .10 .30
U264 Ray Durham .10 .30
U265 Scott Rolen .20 .50
U266 Gabe Kapler .10 .30
U267 Todd Hollandsworth .10 .30
U268 Bud Smith .10 .30
U269 Jay Payton .10 .30
U270 Tyler Houston .10 .30
U271 Brian Moehler .10 .30
U272 David Espinosa .10 .30
U273 Placido Polanco .10 .30
U274 John Patterson .10 .30
U275 Adam Hyzdu .10 .30
U276 Albert Pujols DS .30 .75
U277 Larry Walker DS .10 .30
U278 Magglio Ordonez DS .10 .30
U279 Ryan Klesko DS .10 .30
U280 Darin Erstad DS .10 .30
U281 Jeff Kent DS .10 .30
U282 Paul Lo Duca DS .10 .30
U283 Jim Edmonds DS .10 .30
U284 Chipper Jones DS .20 .50
U285 Bernie Williams DS .10 .30
U286 Pat Burrell DS .10 .30
U287 Cliff Floyd DS .10 .30
U288 Troy Glaus DS .10 .30
U289 Brian Giles DS .10 .30
U290 Jim Thome DS .10 .30
U291 Greg Maddux DS .30 .75
U292 Roberto Alomar DS .10 .30
U293 Jeff Bagwell DS .10 .30
U294 Rafael Furcal DS .10 .30
U295 Josh Beckett DS .10 .30
U296 Carlos Delgado DS .10 .30
U297 Ken Griffey Jr. DS .30 .75
U298 Jason Giambi AS .10 .30
U299 Paul Konerko AS .10 .30
U300 Mike Sweeney AS .10 .30
U301 Alfonso Soriano AS .10 .30
U302 Shea Hillenbrand AS .10 .30
U303 Tony Batista AS .10 .30
U304 Robin Ventura AS .10 .30
U305 Alex Rodriguez AS .30 .75
U306 Nomar Garciaparra AS .30 .75
U307 Derek Jeter AS .40 1.00
U308 Miguel Tejada AS .10 .30
U309 Omar Vizquel AS .10 .30
U310 Jorge Posada AS .10 .30
U311 A.J. Pierzynski AS .10 .30
U312 Ichiro Suzuki AS .30 .75
U313 Manny Ramirez AS .20 .50
U314 Torii Hunter AS .10 .30
U315 Garret Anderson AS .10 .30
U316 Robert Fick AS .10 .30
U317 Randy Winn AS .10 .30
U318 Mark Buehrle AS .10 .30
U319 Freddy Garcia AS .10 .30
U320 Eddie Guardado AS .10 .30
U321 Roy Halladay AS .10 .30
U322 Derek Lowe AS .10 .30
U323 Pedro Martinez AS .20 .50
U324 Mariano Rivera AS .20 .50
U325 Kazuhiro Sasaki AS .10 .30
U326 Barry Zito AS .10 .30
U327 Johnny Damon Sox AS .20 .50
U328 Ugueth Urbina AS .10 .30
U329 Todd Helton AS .10 .30
U330 Richie Sexson AS .10 .30
U331 Jose Vidro AS .10 .30
U332 Luis Castillo AS .10 .30
U333 Junior Spivey AS .10 .30
U334 Scott Rolen AS .10 .30
U335 Mike Lowell AS .10 .30
U336 Jimmy Rollins AS .10 .30
U337 Jose Hernandez AS .10 .30
U338 Mike Piazza AS .30 .75
U339 Benito Santiago AS .10 .30
U340 Sammy Sosa AS .20 .50
U341 Barry Bonds AS .40 1.00
U342 Vladimir Guerrero AS .20 .50
U343 Lance Berkman AS .10 .30
U344 Adam Dunn AS .10 .30
U345 Shawn Green AS .10 .30
U346 Luis Gonzalez AS .10 .30
U347 Eric Gagne AS .10 .30
U348 Tom Glavine AS .10 .30
U349 Trevor Hoffman AS .10 .30
U350 Randy Johnson AS .20 .50
U351 Byung-Hyun Kim AS .10 .30
U352 Matt Morris AS .10 .30
U353 Odalis Perez AS .10 .30
U354 Curt Schilling AS .10 .30
U355 John Smoltz AS .10 .30
U356 Mike Williams AS .10 .30
U357 Andruw Jones AS .10 .30
U358 Vicente Padilla AS .10 .30
U359 Mike Remlinger AS .10 .30
U360 Robb Nen AS .10 .30
U361 Shawn Green CC .10 .30
U362 Derek Jeter CC .40 1.00
U363 Troy Glaus CC .10 .30
U364 Ken Griffey Jr. CC .30 .75
U365 Mike Piazza CC .30 .75
U366 Jason Giambi CC .10 .30
U367 Greg Maddux CC .30 .75
U368 Albert Pujols CC .30 .75
U369 Pedro Martinez CC .20 .50
U370 Barry Zito CC .10 .30
U371 Ichiro Suzuki CC .30 .75
U372 Nomar Garciaparra CC .30 .75
U373 Vladimir Guerrero CC .20 .50
U374 Randy Johnson CC .20 .50
U375 Barry Bonds CC .40 1.00
U376 Sammy Sosa CC .20 .50
U377 Hideo Nomo CC .20 .50
U378 Jeff Bagwell CC .10 .30
U379 Curt Schilling CC .10 .30
U380 Jim Thome CC .10 .30
U381 Todd Helton CC .10 .30
U382 Roger Clemens CC .30 .75
U383 Chipper Jones CC .20 .50
U384 Alex Rodriguez CC .30 .75
U385 Manny Ramirez CC .20 .50
U386 Barry Bonds TT .40 1.00
U387 Jim Thome TT .10 .30
U388 Adam Dunn TT .10 .30
U389 Alex Rodriguez TT .30 .75
U390 Shawn Green TT .10 .30
U391 Jason Giambi TT .10 .30
U392 Lance Berkman TT .10 .30
U393 Pat Burrell TT .10 .30
U394 Eric Chavez TT .10 .30
U395 Mike Piazza TT .30 .75
U396 Vladimir Guerrero TT .20 .50
U397 Paul Konerko TT .10 .30
U398 Sammy Sosa TT .20 .50
U399 Richie Sexson TT .10 .30
U400 Torii Hunter TT .10 .30

2002 Fleer Tradition Update Glossy

Randomly inserted into packs, this is a parallel to the basic Fleer Tradition Update set. These cards can be differentiated from the regular cards by their "glossy" sheen on the front and each card has a stated print run of 200 serial numbered sets.

*GLOSSY 1-100: 1X TO 2.5X BASIC
*GLOSSY 101-275: 3X TO 8X BASIC
*GLOSSY 276-400: 6X TO 15X BASIC

2002 Fleer Tradition Update Diamond Debuts

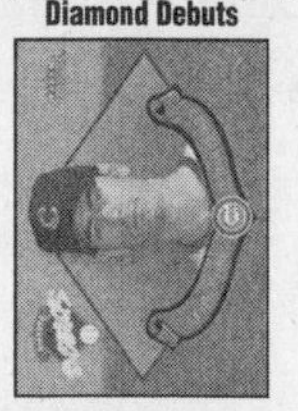

Inserted into packs at a stated rate of one in six, these 15 cards feature players who made their major league debut during the 2002 season.

COMPLETE SET (15) 6.00 15.00
U1 Mark Prior .50 1.25
U2 Eric Hinske .40 1.00
U3 Kazuhisa Ishii .50 1.25
U4 Ben Broussard .40 1.00
U5 Sean Burroughs .40 1.00
U6 Austin Kearns .40 1.00
U7 Hee Seop Choi .40 1.00
U8 Kirk Saarloos .40 1.00
U9 Orlando Hudson .40 1.00
U10 So Taguchi .50 1.25
U11 Kevin Mench .40 1.00
U12 Carl Crawford .40 1.00
U13 Marlon Byrd .40 1.00
U14 Hank Blalock .50 1.25
U15 Brett Myers .40 1.00

2002 Fleer Tradition Update Grass Patch

Randomly inserted into packs, these seven cards feature some of the leading fielders in the game. Each card not only has a game-used memorabilia swatch on it but also has a stated print run of 50 serial numbered sets.

1 Roberto Alomar 15.00 40.00
2 Jim Edmonds 10.00 25.00
3 Nomar Garciaparra 40.00 80.00
4 Shawn Green 10.00 25.00
5 Torii Hunter 10.00 25.00
6 Andruw Jones 15.00 40.00
7 Alfonso Soriano 10.00 25.00

2002 Fleer Tradition Update Grass Roots

Inserted into packs at a stated rate of one in 18, this 10 card set honors some of the most exciting fielders in baseball.

COMPLETE SET (10) 6.00 15.00
U1 Alfonso Soriano .75 2.00
U2 Torii Hunter .75 2.00
U3 Andruw Jones .75 2.00
U4 Jim Edmonds .75 2.00
U5 Shawn Green .75 2.00
U6 Todd Helton .75 2.00
U7 Nomar Garciaparra 1.50 4.00
U8 Roberto Alomar .75 2.00
U9 Vladimir Guerrero 1.00 2.50
U10 Ichiro Suzuki 2.00 5.00

2002 Fleer Tradition Update Heads Up

Inserted at a stated rate of one in 36, this 10 card set is designed in the style of the old Heads Up set of the 1930's.

U1 Roger Clemens 3.00 8.00
U2 Adam Dunn 1.25 3.00
U3 Kazuhisa Ishii 1.25 3.00
U4 Barry Zito 1.25 3.00
U5 Pedro Martinez 1.25 3.00
U6 Alfonso Soriano 1.25 3.00
U7 Mark Prior 1.50 4.00
U8 Chipper Jones 1.50 4.00
U9 Randy Johnson 1.50 4.00
U10 Lance Berkman 1.25 3.00

2002 Fleer Tradition Update Heads Up Game Used Caps

Randomly inserted in packs, these cards are designed in the style of the old Heads Up cards from the 1930's. However, they are different from the regular insert set as a piece of a game-used cap is also part of the card. Each card is also printed to a stated print run of 150.

1 Lance Berkman 8.00 20.00
2 Barry Bonds 25.00 60.00
3 Roger Clemens 20.00 50.00
4 Adam Dunn 8.00 20.00
5 Kazuhisa Ishii 6.00 15.00
6 Randy Johnson 10.00 25.00
7 Chipper Jones 10.00 25.00
8 Mike Piazza 12.50 30.00
9 Mark Prior 10.00 25.00
10 Alfonso Soriano 8.00 20.00
11 Barry Zito 8.00 20.00

2002 Fleer Tradition Update New York's Finest

Inserted into packs at stated odds of one in 83, these 15 cards honor some of the best players for either the New York Yankees or the New York Mets.

1 Edgardo Alfonzo 3.00 8.00
2 Roberto Alomar 3.00 8.00
3 Jeromy Burnitz 3.00 8.00
4 Satoru Komiyama 3.00 8.00
5 Rey Ordonez 3.00 8.00
6 Mike Piazza 5.00 12.00
7 Mo Vaughn 3.00 8.00
8 Roger Clemens 6.00 15.00
9 Jason Giambi 3.00 8.00
10 Derek Jeter 8.00 20.00
11 Mike Mussina 3.00 8.00
12 Jorge Posada 3.00 8.00
13 Alfonso Soriano 3.00 8.00
14 Robin Ventura 3.00 8.00
15 Bernie Williams 3.00 8.00

2002 Fleer Tradition Update New York's Finest Dual Swatch

Randomly inserted into packs, these six cards feature two leading players from New York along with a game-used memorabilia piece for both players.

1 Derek Jeter Jsy 40.00 80.00
Rey Ordonez Jsy
2 Alfonso Soriano Jsy 15.00 40.00
Roberto Alomar Jsy
3 Roger Clemens Jsy 60.00 120.00
Mike Piazza Jsy
4 Mike Mussina Jsy 15.00 40.00
Mo Vaughn Jsy
5 Bernie Williams Jsy 15.00 40.00
Jeromy Burnitz Jsy
6 Robin Ventura Jsy 10.00 25.00
Edgardo Alfonzo Jsy

2002 Fleer Tradition Update New York's Finest Single Swatch

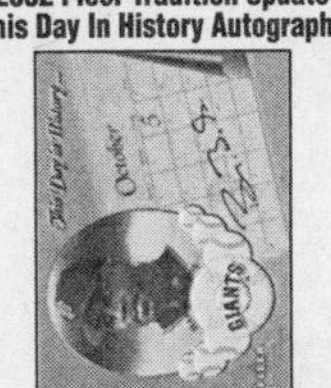

Inserted into packs at stated odds of one in 112, these cards feature two star players from New York but only one memorabilia piece on each card. The player who has a memorabilia piece is listed first in our checklist along with what type of memorabilia piece is used.

1 Derek Jeter Jsy 12.50 30.00
Rey Ordonez
2 Alfonso Soriano Jsy 6.00 15.00
Roberto Alomar
3 Roger Clemens Jsy 8.00 20.00
Mike Piazza
4 Mike Mussina Jsy 6.00 15.00
Mo Vaughn
5 Bernie Williams Jsy 6.00 15.00
Jeromy Burnitz
6 Derek Jeter Jsy 12.50 30.00
Satoru Komiyama
7 Robin Ventura Jsy 4.00 10.00
Edgardo Alfonzo
8 Jorge Posada Jsy 6.00 15.00
Mike Piazza
9 Jason Giambi Base SP 4.00 10.00
Mo Vaughn
10 Alfonso Soriano Jsy 4.00 10.00
Edgardo Alfonzo
11 Rey Ordonez Jsy 4.00 10.00
Derek Jeter
12 Roberto Alomar Jsy 6.00 15.00
Alfonso Soriano
13 Mike Piazza Jsy 6.00 15.00
Roger Clemens
14 Mo Vaughn Jsy 4.00 10.00
Mike Mussina
15 Jeromy Burnitz Jsy 4.00 10.00
Bernie Williams
16 Satoru Komiyama Bat 6.00 15.00
Derek Jeter
17 Edgardo Alfonzo Jsy 4.00 10.00
Robin Ventura
18 Mike Piazza Jsy 6.00 15.00
Jorge Posada
19 Mo Vaughn Jsy 4.00 10.00
Jason Giambi
20 Edgardo Alfonzo Jsy 4.00 10.00
Alfonso Soriano

2002 Fleer Tradition Update Plays of the Week

Inserted at stated odds of one in 12, these 30 cards feature some of the leading players of the 2002 season along with their highlight play of the season.

1 Troy Glaus .60 1.50
2 Andruw Jones .60 1.50
3 Curt Schilling .60 1.50
4 Manny Ramirez .60 1.50
5 Sammy Sosa 1.00 2.50
6 Magglio Ordonez .60 1.50
7 Ken Griffey Jr. 1.50 4.00
8 Jim Thome .60 1.50
9 Larry Walker .60 1.50
10 Robert Fick .60 1.50
11 Josh Beckett .60 1.50
12 Roy Oswalt .60 1.50
13 Mike Sweeney .60 1.50
14 Shawn Green .60 1.50
15 Torii Hunter .60 1.50
16 Vladimir Guerrero 1.00 2.50
17 Mike Piazza 1.50 4.00
18 Jason Giambi .60 1.50
19 Eric Chavez .60 1.50
20 Pat Burrell .60 1.50
21 Brian Giles .60 1.50
22 Ryan Klesko .60 1.50
23 Barry Bonds 2.50 6.00
24 Mike Cameron .60 1.50
25 Albert Pujols 2.00 5.00
26 Alex Rodriguez 1.50 4.00
27 Carlos Delgado .60 1.50
28 Richie Sexson .60 1.50
29 Jay Gibbons .60 1.50
30 Randy Winn .60 1.50

2002 Fleer Tradition Update This Day In History

Inserted into packs at stated odds of one in 12, this 25 card set feature a mix of active and retired players along with an historical highlight that the player was involved with.

U1 Shawn Green .60 1.50
U2 Ozzie Smith 1.25 3.00
U3 Derek Lowe .60 1.50
U4 Ken Griffey Jr. 1.50 4.00
U5 Barry Bonds 2.50 6.00
U6 Juan Gonzalez .60 1.50
U7 Wade Boggs .75 2.00
U8 Mark Prior 1.00 2.50
U9 Thurman Munson 1.25 3.00
U10 Curt Schilling .60 1.50
U11 Jason Giambi .60 1.50
U12 Cal Ripken 4.00 10.00
U13 Craig Biggio .60 1.50
U14 Drew Henson .60 1.50
U15 Steve Carlton .75 2.00
U16 Greg Maddux 1.50 4.00
U17 Adam Dunn .60 1.50
U18 Vladimir Guerrero 1.00 2.50
U19 Alex Rodriguez 1.50 4.00
U20 Carlton Fisk .75 2.00
U21 Ichiro Suzuki 2.00 5.00
U22 Johnny Bench 1.25 3.00
U23 Kazuhisa Ishii .60 1.50
U24 Derek Jeter 2.50 6.00
U25 Jim Thome .60 1.50

2002 Fleer Tradition Update This Day In History Autographs

Inserted into packs at a stated rate of one in 582, this is a partial parallel to the This Day in History insert set. A few players signed an amount of cards in much shorter supply than others. Fortunately, Fleer provided the specific quantities signed for the short prints and the information is detailed in full within our checklist. In addition, an exchange card with a redemption deadline of October 31st, 2003 was seeded into packs for the Greg Maddux card.

1 Barry Bonds SP/150 100.00 175.00
2 Mark Prior SP/64 10.00 25.00
3 Cal Ripken SP/35
4 Drew Henson 8.00 20.00
5 Greg Maddux SP/99 125.00 200.00
6 Derek Jeter 60.00 120.00

2002 Fleer Tradition Update This Day In History Game Used

Inserted into packs at a stated rate of one in 28, these 20 cards form a partial parallel to the This Day in History insert set. These cards feature a game-used memorabilia piece of the featured player. A couple players are featured on more than one memorabilia card and we have notated that information in our checklist as well as the stated print run for the cards which were issued in notably shorter supply.

1 Craig Biggio Bat SP/60
2 Craig Biggio Jsy 6.00 15.00
3 Wade Boggs Jsy 6.00 15.00
4 Wade Boggs Pants 6.00 15.00
5 Barry Bonds Bat 8.00 20.00
6 Barry Bonds Jsy 8.00 20.00
7 Adam Dunn Jsy 4.00 10.00
8 Carlton Fisk Bat 6.00 15.00
9 Juan Gonzalez Bat 4.00 10.00
10 Shawn Green Jsy 4.00 10.00
11 Kazuhisa Ishii Bat 4.00 10.00
12 Derek Jeter Pants 10.00 25.00
13 Greg Maddux Jsy 6.00 15.00
14 Thurman Munson Jsy SP/40
15 Alex Rodriguez Bat 6.00 15.00
16 Alex Rodriguez Jsy 6.00 15.00
17 Curt Schilling Jsy 4.00 10.00
18 Ozzie Smith Jsy 8.00 20.00
19 Jim Thome Bat SP/120
20 Jim Thome Jsy 6.00 15.00

2003 Fleer Tradition

This 485 card set, deisgned in the style of 1963 Fleer, was released in January, 2003. These cards were issued in 10 card packs which were packed 40 packs to a box and 20 boxes to a case with an SRP of $1.49 per pack. The following subsets are part of the set: Cards numbered 1 through 30 are Team Leader cards, cards number 67 through 85 are Missing Link (featuring players active but not on Fleer cards in 1963) cards, cards number 417 through 425 are Award Winner cards, cards number 426 through 460 are Prospect cards and cards numbered 461 through 485 are Banner Season cards. All cards numbered 1 through 100 were short printed and inserted at an rate of one per hobby pack and one per 12 retail pack. In addition, retail boxes had a special Barry Bonds pin as a box topper and a Derek Jeter promo card was issued a few weeks before this product became live so media and dealers could see what this set look like.

COMPLETE SET (485) 75.00 150.00
COMP.SET w/o SP's (385) 15.00 40.00
COMMON CARD (1-30) .40 1.00
COMM.SP (31-66/86-100) .40 1.00
COMMON ML (67-85) .60 1.50
COMMON CARD (.10 .30
COMMON PR (426-460) .10 .30
1 Jarrod Washburn .40 1.00
Troy Glaus
Garret Anderson
Ramon Ortiz TL SP
2 Luis Gonzalez .60 1.50
Randy Johnson TL SP
3 Andruw Jones .60 1.50
Chipper Jones
Tom Glavine
Kevin Millwood TL SP
4 Tony Batista .40 1.00
Rodrigo Lopez TL SP
5 Manny Ramirez .60 1.50
Nomar Garciaparra
Derek Lowe
Pedro Martinez TL SP
6 Sammy Sosa 1.00 2.50
Matt Clement
Kerry Wood TL SP
7 Matt Buehrle .40 1.00
Magglio Ordonez
Danny Wright TL SP
8 Adam Dunn .40 1.00
Aaron Boone
Jimmy Haynes TL SP
9 C.C. Sabathia .40 1.00
Jim Thome TL SP
10 Todd Helton .40 1.00
Jason Jennings TL SP
11 Randall Simon .40 1.00
Steve Sparks
Mark Redman TL SP
12 Derrek Lee .60 1.50
Mike Lowell
A.J. Burnett TL SP
13 Lance Berkman .40 1.00
Roy Oswalt TL SP
14 Paul Byrd .40 1.00
Carlos Beltran TL SP
15 Shawn Green .60 1.50
Hideo Nomo TL SP
16 Richie Sexson .40 1.00
Ben Sheets TL SP
17 Torii Hunter .60 1.50
Kyle Lohse
Johan Santana TL SP
18 Vladimir Guerrero .60 1.50
Tomo Ohka
Javier Vazquez TL SP
19 Mike Piazza 1.00 2.50
Al Leiter TL SP
20 Jason Giambi 1.00 2.50
David Wells
Roger Clemens TL SP
21 Eric Chavez .40 1.00
Miguel Tejada
Barry Zito TL SP
22 Pat Burrell .40 1.00
Vicente Padilla
Randy Wolf TL SP
23 Brian Giles .40 1.00
Josh Fogg
Kip Wells TL SP
24 Ryan Klesko .40 1.00
Brian Lawrence TL SP
25 Barry Bonds 1.00 2.50
Russ Ortiz
Jason Schmidt TL SP
26 Mike Cameron .40 1.00
Bret Boone
Freddy Garcia TL SP
27 Albert Pujols 1.00 2.50
Matt Morris TL SP
28 Aubrey Huff .40 1.00
Randy Winn
Joe Kennedy
Tanyon Sturtze TL SP
29 Alex Rodriguez 1.00 2.50
Kenny Rogers
Chan Ho Park TL SP
30 Carlos Delgado .40 1.00
Roy Halladay TL SP
31 Greg Maddux SP 1.50 4.00
32 Nick Neugebauer SP .40 1.00
33 Larry Walker SP .40 1.00
34 Freddy Garcia SP .40 1.00
35 Rich Aurilia SP .40 1.00
36 Craig Wilson SP .40 1.00
37 Jeff Suppan SP .40 1.00
38 Joel Pineiro SP .40 1.00
39 Pedro Feliz SP .40 1.00
40 Bartolo Colon SP .40 1.00
41 Pete Walker SP .40 1.00
42 Mo Vaughn SP .40 1.00
43 Sidney Ponson SP .40 1.00
44 Jason Isringhausen SP .40 1.00
45 Hideki Irabu SP .40 1.00
46 Pedro Martinez SP .60 1.50
47 Tom Glavine SP .60 1.50
48 Matt Lawton SP .40 1.00
49 Kyle Lohse SP .40 1.00
50 Corey Patterson SP .40 1.00
51 Ichiro Suzuki SP UER 2.00 5.00
RBI total for 2002 incorrect
52 Wade Miller SP .40 1.00
53 Ben Diggins SP .40 1.00
54 Jayson Werth SP .40 1.00
55 Masato Yoshii SP .40 1.00
56 Mark Buehrle SP .40 1.00
57 Drew Henson SP .40 1.00
58 Dave Williams SP .40 1.00
59 Juan Rivera SP .40 1.00
60 Scott Schoeneweis SP .40 1.00
61 Josh Beckett SP .40 1.00
62 Vinny Castilla SP .40 1.00
63 Barry Zito SP .40 1.00
64 Jose Valentin SP .40 1.00
65 Jon Lieber SP .40 1.00
66 Jorge Padilla SP .40 1.00
67 Luis Aparicio ML SP .60 1.50
68 Boog Powell ML SP 1.00 2.50
69 Dick Radatz ML SP .60 1.50
70 Frank Malzone ML SP .60 1.50
71 Lou Brock ML SP 1.00 2.50
72 Billy Williams ML SP .60 1.50
73 Early Wynn ML SP .60 1.50
74 Jim Bunning ML SP 1.00 2.50
75 Al Kaline ML SP 1.50 4.00
76 Eddie Mathews ML SP 1.50 4.00
77 Harmon Killebrew ML SP 1.50 4.00
78 Gil Hodges ML SP 1.00 2.50
79 Duke Snider ML SP 1.00 2.50
80 Yogi Berra ML SP 1.50 4.00
81 Whitey Ford ML SP 1.00 2.50
82 Willie Stargell ML SP 1.00 2.50
83 Willie McCovey ML SP .60 1.50
84 Gaylord Perry ML SP .60 1.50
85 Red Schoendienst ML SP .60 1.50
86 Luis Castillo SP .40 1.00
87 Derek Jeter SP 2.50 6.00
88 Orlando Hudson SP .40 1.00
89 Bobby Higginson SP .40 1.00
90 Brent Butler SP .40 1.00
91 Brad Wilkerson SP .40 1.00
92 Craig Biggio SP .60 1.50
93 Marlon Anderson SP .40 1.00
94 Ty Wigginton SP .40 1.00
95 Hideo Nomo SP 1.00 2.50
96 Barry Larkin SP .60 1.50
97 Roberto Alomar SP .60 1.50
98 Omar Vizquel SP .60 1.50
99 Andres Galarraga SP .40 1.00
100 Shawn Green SP .40 1.00
101 Rafael Furcal .10 .30
102 Bill Selby .10 .30
103 Brent Abernathy .10 .30
104 Nomar Garciaparra .50 1.25
105 Michael Barrett .10 .30
106 Travis Hafner .10 .30
107 Carl Crawford .10 .30
108 Jeff Cirillo .10 .30
109 Mike Hampton .10 .30
110 Kip Wells .10 .30
111 Luis Alicea .10 .30
112 Ellis Burks .10 .30
113 Matt Anderson .10 .30
114 Carlos Beltran .10 .30
115 Paul Lo Duca .10 .30
116 Lance Berkman .10 .30
117 Moises Alou .10 .30
118 Roger Cedeno .10 .30
119 Brad Fullmer .10 .30
120 Sean Burroughs .10 .30
121 Eric Byrnes .10 .30
122 Milton Bradley .10 .30
123 Jason Giambi .10 .30
124 Brook Fordyce .10 .30
125 Kevin Appier .10 .30
126 Steve Cox .10 .30
127 Danny Bautista .10 .30
128 Edgardo Alfonzo .10 .30
129 Matt Clement .10 .30
130 Robb Nen .10 .30
131 Roy Halladay .10 .30
132 Brian Jordan .10 .30
133 A.J. Burnett .10 .30
134 Aaron Cook .10 .30
135 Paul Byrd .10 .30
136 Ramon Ortiz .10 .30
137 Adam Hyzdu .10 .30
138 Rafael Soriano .10 .30
139 Marty Cordova .10 .30
140 Nelson Cruz .10 .30
141 Jamie Moyer .10 .30
142 Raul Mondesi .10 .30
143 Josh Bard .10 .30
144 Elmer Dessens .10 .30
145 Rickey Henderson .30 .75
146 Joe McEwing .10 .30
147 Luis Rivas .10 .30
148 Armando Benitez .10 .30
149 Keith Foulke .10 .30
150 Zach Day .10 .30
151 Trey Lunsford .10 .30
152 Bobby Abreu .10 .30
153 Juan Cruz .10 .30
154 Ramón Hernandez .10 .30
155 Brandon Duckworth .10 .30
156 Matt Ginter .10 .30
157 Rob Mackowiak .10 .30
158 Josh Pearce .10 .30
159 Marlon Byrd .10 .30
160 Todd Walker .10 .30
161 Chad Hermansen .10 .30
162 Felix Escalona .10 .30
163 Ruben Mateo .10 .30
164 Mark Johnson .10 .30
165 Juan Pierre .10 .30
166 Gary Sheffield .10 .30
167 Edgar Martinez .20 .50
168 Randy Winn .10 .30
169 Pokey Reese .10 .30
170 Kevin Mench .10 .30
171 Albert Pujols .60 1.50
172 J.T. Snow .10 .30
173 Dean Palmer .10 .30
174 Jay Payton .10 .30
175 Abraham Nunez .10 .30
176 Richie Sexson .10 .30
177 Jose Vidro .10 .30
178 Geoff Jenkins .10 .30
179 Dan Wilson .10 .30
180 John Olerud .10 .30
181 Javy Lopez .10 .30
182 Carl Everett .10 .30
183 Vernon Wells .10 .30
184 Juan Gonzalez .10 .30
185 Jorge Posada .20 .50
186 Mike Sweeney .10 .30
187 Cesar Izturis .10 .30
188 Jason Schmidt .10 .30
189 Chris Richard .10 .30
190 Jason Phillips .10 .30
191 Fred McGriff .20 .50
192 Shea Hillenbrand .10 .30
193 Ivan Rodriguez .20 .50
194 Mike Lowell .10 .30
195 Neifi Perez .10 .30
196 Kenny Lofton .10 .30
197 A.J. Pierzynski .10 .30
198 Larry Bigbie .10 .30
199 Juan Uribe .10 .30
200 Jeff Bagwell .20 .50
201 Timo Perez .10 .30
202 Jeremy Giambi .10 .30
203 Deivi Cruz .10 .30
204 Marquis Grissom .10 .30
205 Chipper Jones .30 .75
206 Alex Gonzalez .10 .30
207 Steve Finley .10 .30
208 Ben Davis .10 .30
209 Mike Bordick .10 .30
210 Casey Fossum .10 .30
211 Aramis Ramirez .10 .30
212 Aaron Boone .10 .30
213 Orlando Cabrera .10 .30
214 Hee Seop Choi .10 .30
215 Jeromy Burnitz .10 .30
216 Todd Hollandsworth .10 .30
217 Rey Sanchez .10 .30
218 Jose Cruz .10 .30
219 Roosevelt Brown .10 .30
220 Odalis Perez .10 .30
221 Carlos Delgado .10 .30
222 Orlando Hernandez .10 .30
223 Adam Everett .10 .30
224 Adrian Beltre .10 .30
225 Ken Griffey Jr. .50 1.25
226 Brad Penny .10 .30
227 Carlos Lee .10 .30
228 J.C. Romero .10 .30
229 Ramon Martinez .10 .30
230 Matt Morris .10 .30
231 Ben Howard .10 .30
232 Damon Minor .10 .30
233 Jason Marquis .10 .30
234 Paul Wilson .10 .30
235 Ryan Dempster .10 .30
236 Jeffrey Hammonds .10 .30
237 Jaret Wright .10 .30
238 Carlos Pena .10 .30
239 Toby Hall .10 .30
240 Rick Helling .10 .30
241 Alex Escobar .10 .30
242 Trevor Hoffman .10 .30
243 Bernie Williams .20 .50
244 Jorge Julio .10 .30
245 Byung-Hyun Kim .10 .30
246 Mike Redmond .10 .30
247 Tony Armas .10 .30
248 Aaron Rowand .10 .30
249 Rusty Greer .10 .30
250 Aaron Harang .10 .30
251 Jeremy Fikac .10 .30
252 Jay Gibbons .10 .30
253 Brandon Puffer .10 .30
254 Dewayne Wise .10 .30
255 Chan Ho Park .10 .30
256 David Bell .10 .30
257 Kenny Rogers .10 .30
258 Mark Quinn .10 .30
259 Greg LaRocca .10 .30
260 Reggie Taylor .10 .30
261 Brett Tomko .10 .30
262 Jack Wilson .10 .30
263 Billy Wagner .10 .30
264 Greg Norton .10 .30
265 Tim Salmon .20 .50
266 Joe Randa .10 .30
267 Geronimo Gil .10 .30
268 Johnny Damon 1.00 2.50
269 Robin Ventura .10 .30
270 Frank Thomas .30 .75
271 Terrence Long .10 .30
272 Mark Redman .10 .30
273 Mark Kotsay .10 .30
274 Ben Sheets .10 .30
275 Reggie Sanders .10 .30
276 Mark Grace .20 .50
277 Eddie Guardado .10 .30
278 Julio Mateo .10 .30
279 Bengie Molina .10 .30
280 Bill Hall .10 .30
281 Eric Chavez .10 .30
282 Joe Kennedy .10 .30
283 John Valentin .10 .30
284 Ray Durham .10 .30
285 Trot Nixon .10 .30
286 Rondell White .10 .30
287 Alex Gonzalez .10 .30
288 Tomas Perez .10 .30
289 Jared Sandberg .10 .30
290 Jacque Jones .10 .30
291 Cliff Floyd .10 .30
292 Ryan Klesko .10 .30
293 Morgan Ensberg .10 .30
294 Jerry Hairston .10 .30
295 Doug Mientkiewicz .10 .30
296 Darin Erstad .10 .30
297 Jeff Conine .10 .30
298 Johnny Estrada .10 .30
299 Mark Mulder .10 .30
300 Jeff Kent .10 .30
301 Roger Clemens .60 1.50
302 Endy Chavez .10 .30
303 Joe Crede .10 .30
304 J.D. Drew .10 .30
305 David Dellucci .10 .30
306 Eli Marrero .10 .30
307 Josh Fogg .10 .30
308 Mike Crudale .10 .30
309 Bret Boone .10 .30
310 Mariano Rivera .30 .75
311 Mike Piazza .50 1.25
312 Jason Jennings .10 .30
313 Jason Varitek .30 .75
314 Vicente Padilla .10 .30
315 Kevin Millwood .10 .30
316 Nick Johnson .10 .30
317 Shane Reynolds .10 .30
318 Joe Thurston .10 .30
319 Mike Lamb .10 .30
320 Aaron Sele .10 .30
321 Fernando Tatis .10 .30
322 Randy Wolf .10 .30
323 David Justice .10 .30
324 Andy Pettitte .20 .50
325 Freddy Sanchez .10 .30
326 Scott Spiezio .10 .30
327 Randy Johnson .30 .75
328 Karim Garcia .10 .30
329 Eric Milton .10 .30
330 Jermaine Dye .10 .30
331 Kevin Brown .10 .30
332 Adam Pettyjohn .10 .30
333 Jason Lane .10 .30
334 Mark Prior .20 .50
335 Mike Lieberthal .10 .30
336 Matt White .10 .30
337 John Patterson .10 .30
338 Marcus Giles .10 .30
339 Kazuhisa Ishii .10 .30
340 Willie Harris .10 .30
341 Travis Phelps .10 .30
342 Randall Simon .10 .30
343 Manny Ramirez .20 .50
344 Kerry Wood .10 .30
345 Shannon Stewart .10 .30
346 Mike Mussina .20 .50
347 Joe Borchard .10 .30
348 Tyler Walker .10 .30
349 Preston Wilson .10 .30
350 Damian Moss .10 .30
351 Eric Karros .10 .30
352 Bobby Kielty .10 .30
353 Jason LaRue .10 .30
354 Phil Nevin .10 .30
355 Tony Graffanino .10 .30
356 Antonio Alfonseca .10 .30
357 Eddie Taubensee .10 .30
358 Luis Ugueto .10 .30
359 Greg Vaughn .10 .30
360 Corey Thurman .10 .30
361 Omar Infante .10 .30
362 Alex Cintron .10 .30
363 Esteban Loaiza .10 .30
364 Tino Martinez .20 .50
365 David Eckstein .10 .30
366 Dave Pember RC .10 .30
367 Damian Rolls .10 .30
368 Richard Hidalgo .10 .30
369 Brad Radke .10 .30
370 Alex Sanchez .10 .30
371 Ben Grieve .10 .30
372 Brandon Inge .10 .30
373 Adam Piatt .10 .30
374 Charles Johnson .10 .30
375 Rafael Palmeiro .20 .50
376 Joe Mays .10 .30
377 Derrek Lee .20 .50
378 Fernando Vina .10 .30
379 Andruw Jones .20 .50
380 Troy Glaus .10 .30
381 Bobby Hill .10 .30
382 C.C. Sabathia .10 .30
383 Jose Hernandez .10 .30
384 Al Leiter .10 .30
385 Jarrod Washburn .10 .30
386 Cody Ransom .10 .30
387 Matt Stairs .10 .30
388 Edgar Renteria .10 .30
389 Tsuyoshi Shinjo .10 .30
390 Matt Williams .10 .30
391 Bubba Trammell .10 .30
392 Jason Kendall .10 .30
393 Scott Rolen .20 .50
394 Chuck Knoblauch .10 .30
395 Jimmy Rollins .10 .30
396 Gary Bennett .10 .30
397 David Wells .10 .30
398 Ronnie Belliard .10 .30
399 Austin Kearns .10 .30
400 Tim Hudson .10 .30
401 Andy Van Hekken .10 .30
402 Ray Lankford .10 .30
403 Todd Helton .20 .50
404 Jeff Weaver .10 .30
405 Gabe Kapler .10 .30
406 Luis Gonzalez .10 .30
407 Sean Casey .10 .30
408 Kazuhiro Sasaki .10 .30
409 Mark Teixeira .20 .50
410 Brian Giles .10 .30
411 Robert Fick .10 .30
412 Wilkin Ruan .10 .30
413 Jose Rijo .10 .30
414 Ben Broussard .10 .30
415 Aubrey Huff .10 .30
416 Magglio Ordonez .10 .30
417 Barry Bonds AW .40 1.00
418 Miguel Tejada AW .10 .30
419 Randy Johnson AW .20 .50
420 Barry Zito AW .10 .30
421 Jason Jennings AW .10 .30
422 Eric Hinske AW .10 .30
423 Benito Santiago AW .10 .30
424 Adam Kennedy AW .10 .30
425 Troy Glaus AW .10 .30
426 Brandon Phillips PR .10 .30

427 Jake Peavy PR .10 .30
428 Jason Romano PR .10 .30
429 Jeriome Robertson PR .10 .30
430 Aaron Guiel PR .10 .30
431 Hank Blalock PR .10 .30
432 Brad Lidge PR .10 .30
433 Francisco Rodriguez PR .10 .30
434 Jaime Cerda PR .10 .30
435 Jung Bong PR .10 .30
436 Reed Johnson PR .10 .30
437 Rene Reyes PR .10 .30
438 Chris Snelling PR .10 .30
439 Miguel Olivo PR .10 .30
440 Brian Banks PR .10 .30
441 Eric Junge PR .10 .30
442 Kirk Saarloos PR .10 .30
443 Jamey Carroll PR .10 .30
444 Josh Hancock PR .10 .30
445 Michael Restovich PR .10 .30
446 Willie Bloomquist PR .10 .30
447 John Lackey PR .10 .30
448 Marcus Thames PR .10 .30
449 Victor Martinez PR .20 .50
450 Brett Myers PR .10 .30
451 Wes Obermueller PR .10 .30
452 Hansel Izquierdo PR .10 .30
453 Brian Tallet PR .10 .30
454 Craig Monroe PR .10 .30
455 Doug Devore PR .10 .30
456 John Buck PR .10 .30
457 Tony Alvarez PR .10 .30
458 Wily Mo Pena PR .10 .30
459 John Stephens PR .10 .30
460 Tony Torcato PR .10 .30
461 Adam Kennedy BNR .10 .30
462 Alex Rodriguez BNR .30 .75
463 Derek Lowe BNR .10 .30
464 Garret Anderson BNR .10 .30
465 Pat Burrell BNR .10 .30
466 Eric Gagne BNR .10 .30
467 Tomo Ohka BNR .10 .30
468 Josh Phelps BNR .10 .30
469 Sammy Sosa BNR .30 .75
470 Jim Thome BNR .10 .30
471 Vladimir Guerrero BNR .20 .50
472 Jason Simontacchi BNR .10 .30
473 Adam Dunn BNR .10 .30
474 Jim Edmonds BNR .10 .30
475 Barry Bonds BNR .40 1.00
476 Paul Konerko BNR .10 .30
477 Alfonso Soriano BNR .10 .30
478 Curt Schilling BNR .10 .30
479 John Smoltz BNR .10 .30
480 Torii Hunter BNR .10 .30
481 Rodrigo Lopez BNR .10 .30
482 Miguel Tejada BNR .10 .30
483 Eric Hinske BNR .10 .30
484 Roy Oswalt BNR .10 .30
485 Junior Spivey BNR .10 .30
P1 Barry Bonds Pin 3.00 8.00
P87 Derek Jeter Promo .75 2.00

2003 Fleer Tradition Glossy

*GLOSSY 1-100: 1.5X TO 4X BASIC
*GLOSSY 101-485: 5X TO 12X BASIC
STATED ODDS 1:24 RETAIL
STATED PRINT RUN 100 SERIAL #'d SETS

2003 Fleer Tradition Game Used

Inserted in packs at a stated rate of one in 35 hobby and one in 90 retail; these cards partially parallel the regular Fleer Tradition set. Some of these cards were issued to a shorter print run and we have notated that information next to the player's name in our checklist.

*GOLD: .75X TO 2X BASIC GU
*GOLD: .6X TO 1.5X GU p/r 150-200
*GOLD ML: .6X TO 1.5X GU p/r 150-200
*GOLD: .4X TO 1X GU p/r 50-60
GOLD PRINT RUN 100 SERIAL #'d SETS
2 Adrian Beltre Jsy 3.00 8.00
7 Andruw Jones Bat SP/150 UER 6.00 15.00
Card has a piece of jersey
10 Barry Bonds AW Jsy SP/50 20.00 50.00
11 Barry Larkin Jsy SP/200 6.00 15.00
22 Barry Zito Jsy 3.00 8.00
31 Craig Biggio Bat 4.00 10.00
42 Chipper Jones Jsy 6.00 15.00
46 Darin Erstad Jsy 3.00 8.00
63 Derek Jeter Jsy SP/150 12.50 30.00
67 Edg Alfonzo Jsy SP/200 4.00 10.00
97 Eric Karros Jsy 3.00 8.00
104 Frank Thomas Jsy 6.00 15.00
128 Greg Maddux Jsy 6.00 15.00
180 Hideo Nomo Jsy SP/200 10.00 25.00
184 Ivan Rodriguez Jsy 4.00 10.00
185 Jeromy Burnitz Jsy SP/200 4.00 10.00
192 Jeff Bagwell Jsy SP/200 6.00 15.00
193 J.D. Drew Jsy 3.00 8.00
194 Juan Gonzalez Bat SP/200 4.00 10.00
200 Jason Jennings AW Pants 3.00 8.00
205 Jason Kendall Pants 3.00 8.00
215 John Olerud Jsy 3.00 8.00
224 Jorge Posada Bat 4.00 10.00
269 Jimmy Rollins Jsy 3.00 8.00
270 Kazuhisa Ishii Jsy 3.00 8.00
276 Kazuhiro Sasaki Jsy SP/200 4.00 10.00
296 Kerry Wood Jsy SP/200 4.00 10.00
301 Luis Aparicio ML Jsy SP/150 6.00 15.00
304 Mark Grace Jsy 4.00 10.00
311 Mike Lowell Bat 3.00 8.00
327 Mike Mussina Jsy 4.00 10.00
334 Mike Piazza Jsy SP/150 10.00 25.00
339 Mark Prior Jsy SP/200 6.00 15.00
343 Manny Ramirez Jsy SP/150 6.00 15.00
344 M.Tejada AW Bat SP/150 4.00 10.00
346 Mo Vaughn Jsy SP/60 6.00 15.00
351 N.Garciaparra Jsy SP/200 10.00 25.00
375 Pedro Martinez Jsy SP/200 6.00 15.00
379 Roger Clemens Jsy SP/150 10.00 25.00
392 Randy Johnson Jsy SP/150 6.00 15.00
395 Rafael Palmeiro Jsy 4.00 10.00
402 Robin Ventura Jsy 3.00 8.00
403 Shea Hillenbrand Bat 3.00 8.00
406 W.Stargell ML Pants SP/150 6.00 15.00

2003 Fleer Tradition Black-White Goudey

Inserted randomly into hobby packs, these cards were issued in the design of the 1936 Goudey Black and White set. To honor the 1936 set further each of these cards were issued to a stated print run of 1936 serial numbered sets.

*GOLD: 2.5X TO 6X BASIC B/W GOUDEY
GOLD PRINT RUN 36 SERIAL #'d SETS
*RED: X TO X BASIC B/W GOUDEY
RED PRINT RUN 500 SERIAL #'d SETS
1 Jim Thome 1.50 4.00
2 Derek Jeter 4.00 10.00
3 Alex Rodriguez 2.50 6.00
4 Mark Prior 1.50 4.00
5 Nomar Garciaparra 2.50 6.00
6 Curt Schilling 1.50 4.00
7 Pat Burrell 1.50 4.00
8 Frank Thomas 1.50 4.00
9 Roger Clemens 3.00 8.00
10 Chipper Jones 1.50 4.00
11 Barry Larkin 1.50 4.00
12 Hideo Nomo 1.50 4.00
13 Pedro Martinez 1.50 4.00
14 Jeff Bagwell 1.50 4.00
15 Greg Maddux 2.50 6.00
16 Vladimir Guerrero 1.50 4.00
17 Ichiro Suzuki 3.00 8.00
18 Mike Piazza 2.50 6.00
19 Drew Henson 1.50 4.00
20 Albert Pujols 3.00 8.00
21 Sammy Sosa 1.50 4.00
22 Jason Giambi 1.50 4.00
23 Randy Johnson 1.50 4.00
24 Ken Griffey Jr. 2.50 6.00
25 Barry Bonds 4.00 10.00

2003 Fleer Tradition Checklists

Inserted in packs at a stated rate of one in four, these 18 cards feature either Derek Jeter or Barry Bonds. These cards when matched together make up a puzzle of the featured players

COMP.JETER PUZZLE (9) 3.00 8.00
COMMON JETER .40 1.00
COMP.BONDS PUZZLE (9) 3.00 8.00
COMMON BONDS .40 1.00

2003 Fleer Tradition Hardball Preview

Inserted into packs at a stated rate of one in 400 hobby and one in 480 retail, this 10 card set was issued to preview what the new Hardball set that Fleer would be releasing slightly later in 2003.

1 Miguel Tejada 8.00 20.00
2 Derek Jeter 15.00 40.00
3 Mike Piazza 10.00 25.00
4 Barry Bonds 15.00 40.00
5 Mark Prior 8.00 20.00
6 Ichiro Suzuki 10.00 25.00
7 Alex Rodriguez 10.00 25.00
8 Nomar Garciaparra 10.00 25.00
9 Alfonso Soriano 8.00 20.00
10 Ken Griffey Jr. 10.00 25.00

2003 Fleer Tradition Lumber Company

Issued at a stated rate of one in 10 hobby and one in 12 retail, these 30 cards focus on players known for the prowess with the bat.

COMPLETE SET (30) 25.00 60.00
1 Mike Piazza 1.50 4.00
2 Derek Jeter 2.50 6.00
3 Alex Rodriguez 1.50 4.00

4 Miguel Tejada .60 1.50
5 Nomar Garciaparra 1.50 4.00
6 Andruw Jones .60 1.50
7 Pat Burrell .60 1.50
8 Albert Pujols 2.00 5.00
9 Jeff Bagwell .60 1.50
10 Chipper Jones 1.00 2.50
11 Ichiro Suzuki 2.00 5.00
12 Alfonso Soriano .60 1.50
13 Eric Chavez .60 1.50
14 Brian Giles .60 1.50
15 Shawn Green .60 1.50
16 Jim Thome .60 1.50
17 Lance Berkman .60 1.50
18 Bernie Williams .60 1.50
19 Manny Ramirez .60 1.50
20 Vladimir Guerrero 1.00 2.50
21 Carlos Delgado .60 1.50
22 Scott Rolen .60 1.50
23 Sammy Sosa 1.00 2.50
24 Ken Griffey Jr. 1.50 4.00
25 Barry Bonds 2.50 6.00
26 Todd Helton .60 1.50
27 Jason Giambi .60 1.50
28 Austin Kearns .60 1.50
29 Jeff Kent .60 1.50
30 Magglio Ordonez .60 1.50

2003 Fleer Tradition Lumber Company Game Used

Inserted at a stated rate of one in 108 hobby and one in 195 retail, this is a partial parallel to the Lumber Company insert set. A few cards were issued in shorter supply and we have notated the print run information in our checklist.

AJ Andruw Jones 4.00 10.00
AK Austin Kearns SP/75 6.00 15.00
AS Alfonso Soriano SP/200 4.00 10.00
BB Barry Bonds SP/150 12.50 30.00
BG Brian Giles SP/200 4.00 10.00
BW Bernie Williams 4.00 10.00
CD Carlos Delgado SP/200 4.00 10.00
CJ Chipper Jones 6.00 15.00
DJ Derek Jeter SP/96 15.00 40.00
EC Eric Chavez SP/125 4.00 10.00
JB Jeff Bagwell SP/200 6.00 15.00
JK Jeff Kent SP/200 4.00 10.00
JT Jim Thome SP/200 6.00 15.00
LB Lance Berkman SP/200 4.00 10.00
MO Magglio Ordonez 3.00 8.00
MP Mike Piazza SP/200 10.00 25.00
MR Manny Ramirez 4.00 10.00
MT Miguel Tejada 3.00 8.00
NG Nomar Garciaparra SP/200 8.00 20.00
PB Pat Burrell SP/75 6.00 15.00
RA Alex Rodriguez 6.00 15.00
SG Shawn Green SP/200 4.00 10.00
SR Scott Rolen SP/80 10.00 25.00
TH Todd Helton 4.00 10.00

2003 Fleer Tradition Lumber Company Game Used Gold

Randomly inserted in packs, this is a parallel to the Lumber Company Game Used insert set. These cards were printed to a stated print run matching the number of homers the featured player hit in 2002. If the card was issued to a stated print run of 25 or fewer, no pricing is provided due to market scarcity.

AJ Andruw Jones/35 15.00 40.00
AK Austin Kearns/13
AR Alex Rodriguez/57 20.00 50.00
AS Alfonso Soriano/39 10.00 25.00
BB Barry Bonds/46 30.00 80.00
BG Brian Giles/38 10.00 25.00
BW Bernie Williams/19
CD Carlos Delgado/33 10.00 25.00
CJ Chipper Jones/26 15.00 40.00
DJ Derek Jeter/18
EC Eric Chavez/34 10.00 25.00
JB Jeff Bagwell/31
JK Jeff Kent/37 10.00 25.00
JT Jim Thome/52 15.00 40.00
LB Lance Berkman/42 10.00 25.00
MO Magglio Ordonez/38 10.00 25.00
MP Mike Piazza/33 30.00 80.00
MR Manny Ramirez/33 15.00 40.00
MT Miguel Tejada/34 10.00 25.00
NG Nomar Garciaparra/24
PB Pat Burrell/37 10.00 25.00
SG Shawn Green/42 10.00 25.00
SR Scott Rolen/31 15.00 40.00
TH Todd Helton/30 15.00 40.00

2003 Fleer Tradition Milestones

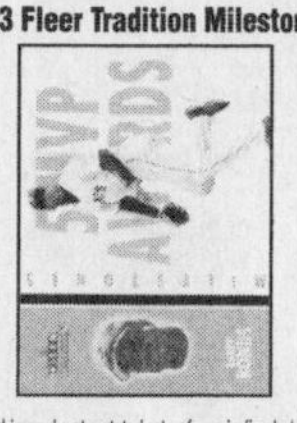

Inserted in packs at a stated rate of one in five hobby and one in four retail, these 25 cards feature either milestones passed by active players in the 2002 season or by retired players in past seasons.

COMPLETE SET (25) 12.50 30.00
1 Eddie Mathews .75 2.00
2 Rickey Henderson .50 1.25
3 Harmon Killebrew .75 2.00
4 Al Kaline .75 2.00
5 Willie McCovey .75 2.00
6 Tom Seaver .75 2.00
7 Reggie Jackson .75 2.00
8 Mike Schmidt 1.25 3.00
9 Nolan Ryan 1.50 4.00
10 Mike Piazza .75 2.00
11 Randy Johnson .50 1.25
12 Bernie Williams .40 1.00
13 Rafael Palmeiro .40 1.00
14 Juan Gonzalez .40 1.00
15 Ken Griffey Jr. .75 2.00
16 Derek Jeter 1.25 3.00
17 Roger Clemens 1.00 2.50
18 Roberto Alomar .40 1.00
19 Manny Ramirez .40 1.00
20 Luis Gonzalez .40 1.00
21 Barry Bonds 1.25 3.00
22 Nomar Garciaparra .75 2.00
23 Fred McGriff .40 1.00
24 Greg Maddux .75 2.00
25 Barry Bonds 1.25 3.00

2003 Fleer Tradition Milestones Game Used

Inserted at a stated rate of one in 143 hobby and one in 270 retail these 14 cards feature memorabilia cards from the some of the featured players in the Milestone set. A few of these cards were issued to a smaller print run and we have notated that information along with the print run information provided in our checklist.

*GOLD: .75X TO 2X BASIC MILE
*GOLD: .6X TO 1.5X MILE SP/150-200
*GOLD: .5X TO 1.2X MILE SP/100
GOLD PRINT RUN 100 SERIAL #'d SETS
BB1 B.Bonds 5 MVP Jsy SP/200 12.50 30.00
BB2 B.Bonds 600 HR Bat SP/100 15.00 40.00
BW Bernie Williams Jsy SP/200 6.00 15.00
DJ Derek Jeter Jsy SP/150 12.50 30.00
FM Fred McGriff Bat 4.00 10.00
GM Greg Maddux Jsy 6.00 15.00
JG Juan Gonzalez Bat SP/250 4.00 10.00
MP Mike Piazza Jsy SP/100 10.00 25.00
MR Manny Ramirez Jsy SP/150 6.00 15.00
NG N.Garciaparra Jsy SP/200 8.00 20.00
RA Roberto Alomar Bat SP/200 6.00 15.00
RC Roger Clemens Jsy SP/150 10.00 25.00
RJ Randy Johnson Jsy SP/100 6.00 15.00
RP Rafael Palmeiro Jsy SP/200 6.00 15.00

2003 Fleer Tradition Standouts

Inserted in packs at a stated rate of one in 40 hobby and one in 72 retail, these 15 cards become mini-standees when the player's photo is "popped-out" of the card.

1 Barry Bonds 4.00 10.00
2 Pat Burrell 2.00 5.00
3 Roger Clemens 3.00 8.00
4 Adam Dunn 2.00 5.00
5 Nomar Garciaparra 2.50 6.00
6 Ken Griffey Jr. 2.50 6.00
7 Vladimir Guerrero 2.00 5.00
8 Derek Jeter 4.00 10.00
9 Greg Maddux 2.50 6.00
10 Mike Piazza 2.50 6.00
11 Alex Rodriguez 2.50 6.00
12 Alfonso Soriano 2.00 5.00
13 Sammy Sosa 2.00 5.00
14 Ichiro Suzuki 3.00 8.00
15 Miguel Tejada 2.00 5.00

2003 Fleer Tradition Update

This 398 card set was released in October, 2003. The set was issued in 10-card packs with an $2 SRP which came 32 packs to a box and 20 boxes to a case. In addition, each sealed box contained a 25 card "mini-box". Cards numbered 1-200 featured veterans, cards numbered 201 through 259 featured all stars, cards 260 through 275 feature interleague match-up cards while cards numbered 276 through 285 is a Tale of the Tape subset. Cards numbered 286 through 299 feature 2003 rookies and those cards were inserted at a stated rate of one in four. Cards numbered 300 through 398

feature 2003 rookies and those cards were issued as part of the 25 card mini-boxes.

COMP.SET w/o SP's (285) 15.00 40.00
COMMON CARD (1-285) .10 .30
COMMON CARD (286-299) .40 1.00
COMMON RC (286-299) .40 1.00
286-299 STATED ODDS 1:4 HOB/RET
COMMON CARD (300-398) .40 1.00
COMMON RC (300-398) .40 1.00
300-398 ISSUED IN MINI-BOXES
ONE MINI-BOX PER UPDATE BOX
25 CARDS PER MINI-BOX
1 Aaron Boone .10 .30
2 Carl Everett .10 .30
3 Eduardo Perez .10 .30
4 Jason Michaels .10 .30
5 Karim Garcia .10 .30
6 Rainer Olmedo .10 .30
7 Scott Williamson .10 .30
8 Adam Kennedy .10 .30
9 Carl Pavano .10 .30
10 Eli Marrero .10 .30
11 Jason Simontacchi .10 .30
12 Keith Foulke .10 .30
13 Preston Wilson .10 .30
14 Scott Hatteberg .10 .30
15 Adam Dunn .10 .30
16 Carlos Baerga .10 .30
17 Elmer Dessens .10 .30
18 Javier Vazquez .10 .30
19 Kenny Rogers .10 .30
20 Quinton McCracken .10 .30
21 Shane Reynolds .10 .30
22 Adam Eaton .10 .30
23 Carlos Zambrano .10 .30
24 Enrique Wilson .10 .30
25 Jeff DaVanon .10 .30
26 Kenny Lofton .10 .30
27 Ramon Castro .10 .30
28 Shannon Stewart .10 .30
29 Al Martin .10 .30
30 Carlos Guillen .10 .30
31 Eric Karros .10 .30
32 Tim Worrell .10 .30
33 Kevin Millwood .10 .30
34 Randall Simon .10 .30
35 Shawn Chacon .10 .30
36 Alex Rodriguez .50 1.25
37 Casey Blake .10 .30
38 Eric Munson .10 .30
39 Jeff Kent .10 .30
40 Kris Benson .10 .30
41 Randy Winn .10 .30
42 Shea Hillenbrand .10 .30
43 Alfonso Soriano .10 .30
44 Chris George .10 .30
45 Eric Bruntlett .10 .30
46 Jeromy Burnitz .10 .30
47 Kyle Farnsworth .10 .30
48 Torii Hunter .10 .30
49 Sidney Ponson .10 .30
50 Andres Galarraga .10 .30
51 Chris Singleton .10 .30
52 Eric Gagne .10 .30
53 Jesse Foppert .10 .30
54 Lance Carter .10 .30
55 Ray Durham .10 .30
56 Tanyon Sturtze .10 .30
57 Andy Ashby .10 .30
58 Cliff Floyd .10 .30
59 Eric Young .10 .30
60 Jhonny Peralta .50 1.25
61 Livan Hernandez .10 .30
62 Reggie Sanders .10 .30
63 Tim Spooneybarger .10 .30
64 Angel Berroa .10 .30
65 Coco Crisp .20 .50
66 Eric Hinske .10 .30
67 Jim Edmonds .10 .30
68 Luis Matos .10 .30
69 Rickey Henderson .30 .75
70 Todd Walker .10 .30
71 Antonio Alfonseca .10 .30
72 Corey Koskie .10 .30
73 Erubiel Durazo .10 .30
74 Jim Thome .20 .50
75 Lyle Overbay .10 .30
76 Robert Fick .10 .30
77 Todd Hollandsworth .10 .30
78 Aramis Ramirez .10 .30
79 Cristian Guzman .10 .30
80 Esteban Loaiza .10 .30
81 Jody Gerut .10 .30
82 Mark Grudzielanek .10 .30
83 Roberto Alomar .20 .50
84 Todd Hundley .10 .30
85 Mike Hampton .10 .30
86 Curt Schilling .10 .30
87 Francisco Rodriguez .10 .30
88 John Lackey .10 .30
89 Mark Redman .10 .30
90 Robin Ventura .10 .30
91 Todd Zeile .10 .30
92 B.J. Surhoff .10 .30
93 Raul Mondesi .10 .30
94 Frank Catalanotto .10 .30
95 John Smoltz .20 .50
96 Mark Ellis .10 .30
97 Rocco Baldelli .10 .30
98 Todd Pratt .10 .30
99 Barry Bonds .75 2.00
100 Danny Graves .10 .30
101 Fred McGriff .20 .50
102 John Burkett .10 .30
103 Marquis Grissom .10 .30
104 Rocky Biddle .10 .30
105 Tom Glavine .20 .50
106 Bartolo Colon .10 .30
107 Darren Bragg .10 .30
108 Gabe Kapler .10 .30
109 John Franco .10 .30
110 Matt Mantei .10 .30
111 Rod Beck .10 .30
112 Tomo Ohka .10 .30
113 Ben Petrick .10 .30
114 Darren Dreifort .10 .30
115 Garret Anderson .10 .30
116 John Vander Wal .10 .30
117 Melvin Mora .10 .30
118 Rodrigo Lopez .10 .30
119 Raul Ibanez .10 .30
120 Benito Santiago .10 .30
121 David Ortiz Sox .30 .75
122 Gary Bennett .10 .30
123 Jon Garland .10 .30
124 Michael Young .20 .50
125 Rodrigo Rosario .10 .30
126 Travis Lee .10 .30
127 Bill Mueller .10 .30
128 Derek Lowe .10 .30
129 Gil Meche .10 .30
130 Jose Guillen .10 .30
131 Miguel Cabrera .30 .75
132 Ron Calloway .10 .30
133 Troy Percival .10 .30
134 Billy Koch .10 .30
135 Dmitri Young .10 .30
136 Glendon Rusch .10 .30
137 Jose Jimenez .10 .30
138 Miguel Tejada .10 .30
139 John Thomson .10 .30
140 Troy O'Leary .10 .30
141 Bobby Kielty .10 .30
142 Dontrelle Willis .30 .75
143 Greg Myers .10 .30
144 Jose Vizcaino .10 .30
145 Mike MacDougal .10 .30
146 Ronnie Belliard .10 .30
147 Tyler Houston .10 .30
148 Brady Clark .10 .30
149 Edgardo Alfonzo .10 .30
150 Guillermo Mota .10 .30
151 Jose Lima .10 .30
152 Mike Williams .10 .30
153 Roy Oswalt .10 .30
154 Scott Podsednik 2.00 5.00
155 Brandon Lyon .10 .30
156 Henry Mateo .10 .30
157 Jose Macias .10 .30
158 Mike Bordick .10 .30
159 Royce Clayton .10 .30
160 Vance Wilson .10 .30
161 Brent Abernathy .10 .30
162 Horacio Ramirez .10 .30
163 Jose Reyes .10 .30
164 Nick Punto .10 .30
165 Ruben Sierra .10 .30
166 Victor Zambrano .10 .30
167 Brett Tomko .10 .30
168 Ivan Rodriguez .20 .50
169 Jose Mesa .10 .30
170 Octavio Dotel .10 .30
171 Russ Ortiz .10 .30
172 Vladimir Guerrero .30 .75
173 Brian Lawrence .10 .30
174 Jae Weong Seo .10 .30
175 Jose Cruz Jr. .10 .30
176 Pat Burrell .10 .30
177 Russell Branyan .10 .30
178 Warren Morris .10 .30
179 Brian Boehringer .10 .30
180 Jason Johnson .10 .30
181 Josh Phelps .10 .30
182 Paul Konerko .10 .30
183 Ryan Franklin .10 .30
184 Wes Helms .10 .30
185 Brooks Kieschnick .10 .30
186 Jason Davis .10 .30
187 Juan Pierre .10 .30
188 Paul Wilson .10 .30
189 Sammy Sosa .30 .75
190 Wil Cordero .10 .30
191 Byung-Hyun Kim .10 .30
192 Juan Encarnacion .10 .30
193 Placido Polanco .10 .30
194 Sandy Alomar Jr. .10 .30
195 Julio Lugo .10 .30
196 Junior Spivey .10 .30
197 Woody Williams .10 .30
198 Xavier Nady .10 .30
199 Mark Loretta .10 .30
200 Deivi Cruz .10 .30
201 Jorge Posada AS .10 .30
202 Carlos Delgado AS .10 .30
203 Alfonso Soriano AS .10 .30
204 Alex Rodriguez AS .30 .75
205 Troy Glaus AS .10 .30
206 Garret Anderson AS .10 .30
207 Hideki Matsui AS .75 2.00
208 Ichiro Suzuki AS .30 .75
209 Esteban Loaiza AS .10 .30
210 Manny Ramirez AS .20 .50
211 Roger Clemens AS .30 .75
212 Roy Halladay AS .10 .30
213 Jason Giambi AS .10 .30
214 Edgar Martinez AS .10 .30
215 Bret Boone AS .10 .30
216 Hank Blalock AS .10 .30
217 Nomar Garciaparra AS .30 .75
218 Vernon Wells AS .10 .30
219 Melvin Mora AS .10 .30
220 Magglio Ordonez AS .10 .30
221 Mike Sweeney AS .10 .30
222 Barry Zito AS .10 .30
223 Carl Everett AS .10 .30
224 Shigetoshi Hasegawa AS .10 .30
225 Jamie Moyer AS .10 .30
226 Mark Mulder AS .10 .30
227 Eddie Guardado AS .10 .30
228 Ramon Hernandez AS .10 .30
229 Keith Foulke AS .10 .30
230 Javy Lopez AS .10 .30
231 Todd Helton AS .10 .30
232 Marcus Giles AS .10 .30
233 Edgar Renteria AS .10 .30
234 Scott Rolen AS .10 .30
235 Barry Bonds AS .40 1.00
236 Albert Pujols AS .30 .75
237 Gary Sheffield AS .10 .30
238 Jim Edmonds AS .10 .30
239 Jason Schmidt AS .10 .30
240 Mark Prior AS .10 .30
241 Dontrelle Willis AS .20 .50
242 Kerry Wood AS .10 .30
243 Kevin Brown AS .10 .30
244 Woody Williams AS .10 .30
245 Paul Lo Duca AS .10 .30
246 Richie Sexson AS .10 .30
247 Jose Vidro AS .10 .30
248 Luis Castillo AS .10 .30
249 Aaron Boone AS .10 .30
250 Mike Lowell AS .10 .30
251 Rafael Furcal AS .10 .30
252 Andruw Jones AS .10 .30
253 Preston Wilson AS .10 .30
254 John Smoltz AS .10 .30
255 Eric Gagne AS .10 .30
256 Randy Wolf AS .10 .30
257 Billy Wagner AS .10 .30
258 Luis Gonzalez AS .10 .30
259 Russ Ortiz AS .10 .30
260 Jim Thome .20 .50
Pedro Martinez IL
261 Alfonso Soriano .20 .50
Jeff Bagwell IL
262 Dontrelle Willis .20 .50
Rocco Baldelli IL
263 Carlos Delgado .20 .50
Vladimir Guerrero IL
264 Sammy Sosa .30 .75
Magglio Ordonez IL
265 Jason Giambi .10 .30
Adam Dunn IL
266 Mike Sweeney .30 .75
Albert Pujols IL
267 Barry Bonds .40 1.00
Torii Hunter IL
268 Ichiro Suzuki .30 .75
Andruw Jones IL
269 Chipper Jones .20 .50
Hank Blalock IL
270 Mark Prior .10 .30
Vernon Wells IL
271 Nomar Garciaparra .30 .75
Scott Rolen IL
272 Alex Rodriguez .30 .75
Lance Berkman IL
273 Roger Clemens .30 .75
Kerry Wood IL
274 Derek Jeter .40 1.00
Jose Reyes IL
275 Greg Maddux .30 .75
Barry Zito IL
276 Carlos Delgado TT .10 .30
277 J.D. Drew TT .10 .30
278 Barry Bonds TT .40 1.00
279 Albert Pujols TT .30 .75
280 Jim Thome TT .10 .30
281 Sammy Sosa TT .20 .50
282 Alfonso Soriano TT .10 .30
283 Hideki Matsui TT .75 2.00
284 Mike Piazza TT .30 .75
285 Vladimir Guerrero TT .20 .50
286 Rich Harden ROO .60 1.50
287 Chin-Hui Tsao ROO .40 1.00
288 Edwin Jackson ROO RC .60 1.50
289 Chien-Ming Wang ROO RC 2.00 5.00
290 Josh Willingham ROO RC 1.00 2.50
291 Matt Kata ROO RC .40 1.00
292 Jose Contreras ROO RC .75 2.00
293 Chris Bootcheck ROO .40 1.00
294 Javier A. Lopez ROO RC .40 1.00
295 Delmon Young ROO RC 3.00 8.00
296 Pedro Liriano ROO .40 1.00
297 Noah Lowry ROO .60 1.50
298 Khalil Greene ROO UER 1.00 2.50
First Name misspelled
299 Rob Bowen ROO .40 1.00
300 Bo Hart ROO RC .40 1.00
301 Beau Kemp ROO RC .40 1.00
302 Gerald Laird ROO .40 1.00
303 Miguel Ojeda ROO RC .40 1.00
304 Todd Wellemeyer ROO RC .40 1.00
305 Ryan Wagner ROO RC .40 1.00
306 Jeff Duncan ROO RC .40 1.00
307 Wilfredo Ledezma ROO RC .40 1.00
308 Wes Obermueller ROO .40 1.00
309 Bernie Castro ROO RC .40 1.00
310 Tim Olson ROO RC .40 1.00
311 Colin Porter ROO RC .40 1.00
312 Francisco Cruceta ROO RC .40 1.00
313 Guillermo Quiroz ROO RC .40 1.00
314 Brian Stokes ROO RC .40 1.00
315 Robby Hammock ROO RC .40 1.00
316 Lew Ford ROO RC .60 1.50
317 Todd Linden ROO .40 1.00
318 Mike Gallo ROO RC .40 1.00
319 Francisco Rosario ROO RC .40 1.00
320 Rosman Garcia ROO RC .40 1.00
321 Felix Sanchez ROO RC .40 1.00
322 Chad Gaudin ROO RC .40 1.00
323 Phil Seibel ROO RC .40 1.00
324 Jason Gilfillan ROO RC .40 1.00
325 Termel Sledge ROO RC .40 1.00
326 Alfredo Gonzalez ROO RC .40 1.00
327 Josh Stewart ROO RC .40 1.00
328 Jeremy Griffiths ROO RC .40 1.00
329 Cory Stewart ROO RC .40 1.00
330 Josh Hall ROO RC .40 1.00
331 Arnie Munoz ROO RC .40 1.00
332 Garrett Atkins ROO .40 1.00
333 Neal Cotts ROO .40 1.00
334 Dan Haren ROO RC .75 2.00
335 Shane Victorino ROO RC 1.00 2.50
336 David Sanders ROO RC .40 1.00
337 Oscar Villarreal ROO RC .40 1.00
338 Michael Hessman ROO RC .40 1.00
339 Andrew Brown ROO RC .60 1.50
340 Kevin Hooper ROO .40 1.00
341 Prentice Redman ROO RC .40 1.00
342 Brandon Webb ROO RC 2.00 5.00
343 Jimmy Gobble ROO .40 1.00
344 Pete LaForest ROO RC .40 1.00
345 Chris Waters ROO RC .40 1.00
346 Hideki Matsui ROO RC 3.00 8.00
347 Chris Capuano ROO RC .75 2.00
348 Jon Leicester ROO RC .40 1.00
349 Mike Nicolas ROO RC .40 1.00
350 Nook Logan ROO RC .60 1.50

351 Craig Brazell ROO RC .40 1.00
352 Aaron Looper ROO RC .40 1.00
353 D.J. Carrasco ROO RC .40 1.00
354 Clint Barmes ROO RC .75 2.00
355 Doug Waechter ROO RC .60 1.50
356 Julio Manon ROO RC .40 1.00
357 Jer. Bonderman ROO RC 2.50 6.00
358 D. Markwell ROO RC .40 1.00
359 Dave Matranga ROO RC .40 1.00
360 Luis Ayala ROO RC .40 1.00
361 Jason Stanford ROO .40 1.00
362 Roger Deago ROO RC .40 1.00
363 Geoff Geary ROO RC .40 1.00
364 Edgar Gonzalez ROO RC .40 1.00
365 Michel Hernandez ROO RC .40 1.00
366 Aquilino Lopez ROO RC .40 1.00
367 David Manning ROO .40 1.00
368 Carlos Mendez ROO RC .40 1.00
369 Matt Miller ROO RC .40 1.00
370 Mi. Nakamura ROO RC .40 1.00
371 Mike Neu ROO RC .40 1.00
372 Ramon Nivar ROO RC .40 1.00
373 Kevin Ohme ROO RC .40 1.00
374 Alex Prieto ROO RC .40 1.00
375 Stephen Randolph ROO RC .40 1.00
376 Brian Sweeney ROO RC .40 1.00
377 Matt Diaz ROO RC .75 2.00
378 Mike Gonzalez ROO .40 1.00
379 Daniel Cabrera ROO RC .75 2.00
380 Fernando Cabrera ROO RC .40 1.00
381 David DeJesus ROO RC .75 2.00
382 Mike Ryan ROO RC .40 1.00
383 Rick Roberts ROO RC .40 1.00
384 Seung Song ROO .40 1.00
385 Rickie Weeks ROO RC 2.00 5.00
386 Hum. Quintero ROO RC .40 1.00
387 Alexis Rios ROO .40 1.00
388 Aaron Miles ROO RC .60 1.50
389 Tom Gregorio ROO RC .40 1.00
390 Anthony Ferrari ROO RC .40 1.00
391 Kevin Correia ROO RC .40 1.00
392 Rafael Betancourt ROO RC .60 1.50
393 Rett Johnson ROO RC .40 1.00
394 Richard Fischer ROO RC .40 1.00
395 Greg Aquino ROO RC .40 1.00
396 Daniel Garcia ROO RC .40 1.00
397 Sergio Mitre ROO RC .60 1.50
398 Edwin Almonte ROO RC .40 1.00

2003 Fleer Tradition Update Glossy

*GLOSSY 1-285: 5X TO 12X BASIC
*GLOSSY 1-285: 3X TO 8X BASIC RC's
*GLOSSY MATSUI 207/283: 2.5X TO 6X BASIC
*GLOSSY 286-299: 1.5X TO 4X BASIC
*GLOSSY 286-299: 1.5X TO 4X BASIC RC's
*GLOSSY 300-398: 1.5X TO 4X BASIC
*GLOSSY 300-398: 1.5X TO 4X BASIC RC's
STATED ODDS 1:24 RETAIL
STATED PRINT RUN 100 SERIAL #'d SETS
289 Chien-Ming Wang ROO 12.50 30.00

2003 Fleer Tradition Update Diamond Debuts

STATED ODDS 1:10 HOBBY, 1:8 RETAIL
1 Dontrelle Willis 1.00 2.50
2 Bo Hart .40 1.00
3 Jose Reyes .40 1.00
4 Chin-Hui Tsao .40 1.00
5 Brandon Webb 1.50 4.00
6 Rich Harden .60 1.50
7 Jesse Foppert .40 1.00
8 Rocco Baldelli .40 1.00
9 Hideki Matsui 3.00 8.00
10 Ron Calloway .40 1.00
11 Jeremy Bonderman 2.00 5.00
12 Mark Teixeira .60 1.50
13 Ryan Wagner .40 1.00
14 Jose Contreras 1.00 2.50
15 Miguel Cabrera 1.00 2.50
16 Lew Ford .60 1.50
17 Jeff Duncan .40 1.00
18 Matt Kata .40 1.00
19 Jeremy Griffiths .40 1.00
20 Todd Wellemeyer .40 1.00
21 Robby Hammock .40 1.00
22 Dave Matranga .40 1.00
23 Laynce Nix .40 1.00
24 Jhonny Peralta 1.00 2.50
25 Oscar Villarreal .40 1.00

2003 Fleer Tradition Update Long Gone!

STATED ODDS 1:72 RETAIL
1 Barry Bonds/475 5.00 12.00
2 Jason Giambi/440 2.00 5.00
3 Albert Pujols/452 4.00 10.00
4 Chipper Jones/420 2.00 5.00
5 Manny Ramirez/430 2.00 5.00
6 Sammy Sosa/536 2.00 5.00
7 Alfonso Soriano/440 2.00 5.00
8 Alex Rodriguez/430 3.00 8.00
9 Jim Thome/445 2.00 5.00
10 Vladimir Guerrero/502 2.00 5.00
11 Austin Kearns/430 2.00 5.00
12 Jeff Bagwell/420 2.00 5.00
13 Andruw Jones/430 2.00 5.00
14 Carlos Delgado/451 2.00 5.00
15 Nomar Garciaparra/440 3.00 8.00
16 Adam Dunn/464 2.00 5.00
17 Mike Piazza/450 3.00 8.00
18 Derek Jeter/410 5.00 12.00
19 Ken Griffey Jr./430 3.00 8.00
20 Hank Blalock/424 2.00 5.00

2003 Fleer Tradition Update Milestones

STATED ODDS 1:8 HOBBY, 1:6 RETAIL
1 Roger Clemens 1.50 4.00
2 Rafael Palmeiro .50 1.25
3 Jeff Bagwell .50 1.25
4 Barry Bonds 2.00 5.00
5 Sammy Sosa .75 2.00
6 Albert Pujols 1.50 4.00
7 Ichiro Suzuki 1.50 4.00
8 Alfonso Soriano .30 .75
9 Alex Rodriguez 1.25 3.00
10 Randy Johnson .75 2.00
11 Manny Ramirez .50 1.25
12 Chipper Jones .75 2.00
13 Todd Helton .50 1.25
14 Ken Griffey Jr. 1.25 3.00
15 Jim Thome .50 1.25
16 Frank Thomas .75 2.00
17 Pedro Martinez .50 1.25
18 Hideo Nomo .75 2.00
19 Jason Schmidt .30 .75
20 Carlos Delgado .30 .75

2003 Fleer Tradition Update Milestones Game Jersey

STATED ODDS 1:20 HOBBY, 1:96 RETAIL
*GOLD: .75X TO 2X BASIC
GOLD PRINT RUN 100 SERIAL #'d SETS
AR Alex Rodriguez 4.00 10.00
AS Alfonso Soriano 3.00 8.00
CD Carlos Delgado 3.00 8.00
CJ Chipper Jones 4.00 10.00
FT Frank Thomas 4.00 10.00
HN Hideo Nomo 4.00 10.00
JB Jeff Bagwell 4.00 10.00
JS Jason Schmidt 3.00 8.00
JT Jim Thome 4.00 10.00
MR Manny Ramirez 4.00 10.00
PM Pedro Martinez 4.00 10.00
RC Roger Clemens 6.00 15.00
RJ Randy Johnson 4.00 10.00
RP Rafael Palmeiro 4.00 10.00
SS Sammy Sosa 4.00 10.00
TH Todd Helton 4.00 10.00

2003 Fleer Tradition Update Throwback Threads

STATED ODDS 1:64 HOBBY, 1:288 RETAIL
*PATCH: 1X TO 2.5X BASIC
PATCH PRINT RUN 100 SERIAL #'d SETS
AL Al Leiter 3.00 8.00
KM Kevin Millwood 3.00 8.00
MP Mike Piazza 6.00 15.00
TG Troy Glaus 3.00 8.00
VG Vladimir Guerrero 4.00 10.00

2003 Fleer Tradition Update Throwback Threads Dual

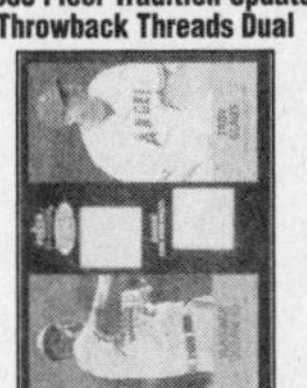

STATED PRINT RUN 100 SERIAL #'d SETS
MPAL Mike Piazza 10.00 25.00
Al Leiter
VGTG Vladimir Guerrero 8.00 20.00
Troy Glaus

2003 Fleer Tradition Update Turn Back the Clock

STATED ODDS 1:160 HOBBY, 1:288 RETAIL
1 Yogi Berra 6.00 15.00
2 Mike Schmidt 8.00 20.00
3 Tom Seaver 4.00 10.00
4 Reggie Jackson 4.00 10.00
5 Pee Wee Reese 4.00 10.00
6 Phil Rizzuto 4.00 10.00
7 Jim Palmer 4.00 10.00
8 Robin Yount 6.00 15.00
9 Nolan Ryan 8.00 20.00
10 Al Kaline 6.00 15.00

2004 Fleer Tradition

This 500-card standard-size set was released in January, 2004. The set was issued in 10 card packs which came 36 packs to a box and six boxes to a case. Cards numbered 401 through 500 were printed in lesser quantity than the first 400 cards in this set. This set has these topical subsets: Cards 1 through 10 feature World Series highlights, Cards 11-40 feature Team Leaders. In the higher numbers cards 446 through 462 feature young players in an "Standout" subset which cards 462 through 471 feature players who won major awards in 2003. The set concludes with a 30-card three player prospect set which features leading prospects for each of the major league teams.

COMPLETE SET (500) 75.00 150.00
COMP.SET w/o SP's (400) 15.00 40.00
COMMON CARD (1-400) .10 .30
COMMON CARD (401-470) .40 1.00
COMMON CARD (471-500) .40 1.00
401-445 STATED ODDS 1:2
446-461 STATED ODDS 1:6
462-470 STATED ODDS 1:9
471-500 STATED ODDS 1:3
1 Juan Pierre WS .12 .30
2 Josh Beckett WS .20 .50
3 Ivan Rodriguez WS .20 .50
4 Miguel Cabrera WS .30 .75
5 Dontrelle Willis WS .12 .30
6 Derek Jeter WS .75 2.00
7 Jason Giambi WS .12 .30
8 Bernie Williams WS .20 .50
9 Alfonso Soriano WS .12 .30
10 Hideki Matsui WS .50 1.25
11 Garret Anderson .12 .30
Garret Anderson
Ramon Ortiz
John Lackey TL
12 Luis Gonzalez .20 .50
Luis Gonzalez
Brandon Webb
Curt Schilling TL
13 Javy Lopez .12 .30
Gary Sheffield
Russ Ortiz
Russ Ortiz TL
14 Tony Batista .12 .30
Jay Gibbons
Sidney Ponson
Jason Johnson TL
15 Manny Ramirez .30 .75
Nomar Garciaparra
Derek Lowe
Pedro Martinez TL
16 Sammy Sosa .30 .75
Sammy Sosa
Mark Prior
Kerry Wood TL
17 Frank Thomas .30 .75
Carlos Lee
Esteban Loaiza
Esteban Loaiza TL
18 Adam Dunn .20 .50
Sean Casey
Chris Reitsma
Paul Wilson TL
19 Jody Gerut .20 .50
Jody Gerut
C.C. Sabathia
C.C. Sabathia TL
20 Preston Wilson .12 .30
Preston Wilson
Darren Oliver
Jason Jennings TL
21 Dmitri Young .12 .30
Dmitri Young
Mike Maroth
Jeremy Bonderman TL
22 Mike Lowell .12 .30
Mike Lowell
Dontrelle Willis
Josh Beckett TL
23 Jeff Bagwell .20 .50
Jeff Bagwell
Jeriome Robertson
Wade Miller TL
24 Carlos Beltran .12 .30
Carlos Beltran
Darrell May
Darrell May TL
25 Adrian Beltre .30 .75
Shawn Green
Hideo Nomo
Kevin Brown TL
26 Richie Sexson .12 .30
Richie Sexson
Ben Sheets
Dan Choate TL
27 Torii Hunter .30 .75
Torii Hunter
Brad Radke
Johan Santana TL
28 Vladimir Guerrero .30 .75
Orlando Cabrera
Livan Hernandez
Javier Vazquez TL
29 Cliff Floyd .12 .30
Ty Wigginton
Steve Trachsel
Al Leiter TL
30 Jason Giambi .20 .50
Jason Giambi
Andy Pettitte
Mike Mussina TL
31 Eric Chavez .20 .50
Miguel Tejada
Tim Hudson
Tim Hudson TL
32 Jim Thome .20 .50
Jim Thome
Randy Wolf
Randy Wolf TL
33 Reggie Sanders .12 .30
Reggie Sanders
Josh Fogg
Kip Wells TL
34 Ryan Klesko .12 .30
Mark Loretta
Jake Peavy
Jake Peavy TL
35 Jose Cruz Jr. .12 .30
Edgardo Alfonzo
Jason Schmidt
Jason Schmidt TL
36 Bret Boone .12 .30
Bret Boone
Jamie Moyer
Joel Pineiro TL
37 Albert Pujols .75 2.00
Albert Pujols
Woody Williams
Woody Williams TL
38 Aubrey Huff .12 .30
Aubrey Huff
Victor Zambrano
Victor Zambrano TL
39 Alex Rodriguez .50 1.25
Alex Rodriguez
John Thomson
John Thomson TL
40 Carlos Delgado .30 .75
Carlos Delgado
Roy Halladay
Roy Halladay TL
41 Greg Maddux .50 1.25
42 Ben Grieve .12 .30
43 Darin Erstad .12 .30
44 Ruben Sierra .12 .30
45 Byung-Hyung Kim .12 .30
46 Freddy Garcia .12 .30
47 Richard Hidalgo .12 .30
48 Tike Redman .12 .30
49 Kevin Millwood .12 .30
50 Marquis Grissom .12 .30
51 Jae Weong Seo .12 .30
52 Wil Cordero .12 .30
53 LaTroy Hawkins .12 .30
54 Jolbert Cabrera .12 .30
55 Kevin Appier .12 .30
56 John Lackey .12 .30
57 Garret Anderson .12 .30
58 R.A. Dickey .12 .30
59 David Segui .12 .30
60 Erubiel Durazo .12 .30
61 Bobby Abreu .12 .30
62 Travis Hafner .12 .30
63 Victor Zambrano .12 .30
64 Randy Johnson .30 .75
65 Bernie Williams .20 .50
66 J.T. Snow .12 .30
67 Sammy Sosa .30 .75
68 Al Leiter .12 .30
69 Jason Jennings .12 .30
70 Matt Morris .12 .30
71 Mike Hampton .12 .30
72 Juan Encarnacion .12 .30
73 Alex Gonzalez .12 .30
74 Bartolo Colon .12 .30
75 Brett Myers .12 .30
76 Michael Young .12 .30
77 Ichiro Suzuki .50 1.25
78 Jason Johnson .12 .30
79 Brad Ausmus .12 .30
80 Ted Lilly .12 .30
81 Ken Griffey Jr. .50 1.25
82 Chone Figgins .12 .30
83 Edgar Martinez .20 .50
84 Adam Eaton .12 .30
85 Ken Harvey .12 .30
86 Francisco Rodriguez .20 .50
87 Bill Mueller .12 .30
88 Mike Maroth .12 .30
89 Charles Johnson .12 .30
90 Jhonny Peralta .12 .30
91 Kip Wells .12 .30
92 Cesar Izturis .12 .30
93 Matt Clement .12 .30
94 Lyle Overbay .12 .30
95 Kirk Rueter .12 .30
96 Cristian Guzman .12 .30
97 Garrett Stephenson .12 .30
98 Lance Berkman .20 .50
99 Brett Tomko .12 .30
100 Chris Stynes .12 .30
101 Nate Cornejo .12 .30
102 Aaron Rowand .12 .30
103 Javier Vazquez .12 .30
104 Jason Kendall .12 .30
105 Mark Redman .12 .30
106 Benito Santiago .12 .30
107 C.C. Sabathia .20 .50
108 David Wells .12 .30
109 Mark Ellis .12 .30
110 Casey Blake .12 .30
111 Sean Burroughs .12 .30
112 Carlos Beltran .12 .30
113 Ramon Hernandez .12 .30
114 Eric Hinske .12 .30
115 Luis Gonzalez .12 .30
116 Jarrod Washburn .12 .30
117 Ronnie Belliard .12 .30
118 Troy Percival .12 .30
119 Jose Valentin .12 .30
120 Chase Utley .30 .75
121 Odalis Perez .12 .30
122 Steve Finley .12 .30
123 Bret Boone .12 .30
124 Jeff Conine .12 .30
125 Josh Fogg .12 .30
126 Neifi Perez .12 .30
127 Ben Sheets .12 .30
128 Randy Winn .12 .30
129 Matt Stairs .12 .30
130 Carlos Delgado .12 .30
131 Morgan Ensberg .12 .30
132 Vinny Castilla .12 .30
133 Matt Mantei .12 .30
134 Alex Rodriguez .50 1.25
135 Matthew LeCroy .12 .30
136 Woody Williams .12 .30
137 Frank Catalanotto .12 .30
138 Rondell White .12 .30
139 Scott Rolen .20 .50
140 Cliff Floyd .12 .30
141 Chipper Jones .30 .75
142 Robin Ventura .12 .30
143 Mariano Rivera .30 .75
144 Brady Clark .12 .30
145 Ramon Ortiz .12 .30
146 Omar Infante .12 .30
147 Mike Matheny .12 .30
148 Pedro Martinez .20 .50
149 Carlos Baerga .12 .30
150 Shannon Stewart .12 .30
151 Travis Lee .12 .30
152 Eric Byrnes .12 .30
153 Rafael Furcal .12 .30
154 B.J. Surhoff .12 .30
155 Zach Day .12 .30
156 Marlon Anderson .12 .30
157 Mark Hendrickson .12 .30
158 Mike Mussina .20 .50
159 Randall Simon .12 .30
160 Jeff DaVanon .12 .30
161 Joel Pineiro .12 .30
162 Vernon Wells .12 .30
163 Adam Kennedy .12 .30
164 Trot Nixon .12 .30
165 Rodrigo Lopez .12 .30
166 Curt Schilling .20 .50
167 Horacio Ramirez .12 .30
168 Jason Marquis .12 .30
169 Magglio Ordonez .20 .50
170 Scott Schoeneweis .12 .30
171 Andruw Jones .12 .30
172 Tino Martinez .20 .50
173 Moises Alou .12 .30
174 Kelvim Escobar .12 .30
175 Xavier Nady .12 .30
176 Ramon Martinez .12 .30
177 Pat Hentgen .12 .30
178 Austin Kearns .12 .30
179 D'Angelo Jimenez .12 .30
180 Deivi Cruz .12 .30
181 John Smoltz .30 .75
182 Toby Hall .12 .30
183 Mark Buehrle .20 .50
184 Howie Clark .12 .30
185 David Ortiz .30 .75
186 Raul Mondesi .12 .30
187 Milton Bradley .12 .30
188 Jorge Julio .12 .30
189 Victor Martinez .20 .50
190 Gabe Kapler .12 .30
191 Julio Franco .12 .30
192 Ryan Freel .12 .30
193 Brad Fullmer .12 .30
194 Joe Borowski .12 .30
195 Darren Oliver .12 .30
196 Jason Varitek .30 .75
197 Greg Myers .12 .30
198 Eric Munson .12 .30
199 Tim Wakefield .12 .30
200 Kyle Farnsworth .12 .30
201 Johnny Vander Wal .12 .30
202 Alex Escobar .12 .30
203 Sean Casey .12 .30
204 John Thomson .12 .30
205 Carlos Zambrano .20 .50
206 Kenny Lofton .12 .30
207 Marcus Giles .12 .30
208 Wade Miller .12 .30
209 Geoff Blum .12 .30
210 Jason LaRue .12 .30
211 Omar Vizquel .20 .50
212 Carlos Pena .20 .50
213 Adam Dunn .20 .50
214 Oscar Villarreal .12 .30
215 Paul Konerko .20 .50
216 Hideo Nomo .30 .75
217 Mike Sweeney .12 .30
218 Coco Crisp .12 .30
219 Shawn Chacon .12 .30
220 Brook Fordyce .12 .30
221 Josh Beckett .20 .50
222 Paul Wilson .12 .30
223 Josh Towers .12 .30
224 Geoff Jenkins .12 .30
225 Shawn Green .12 .30
226 Derrek Lee .12 .30
227 Karim Garcia .12 .30
228 Preston Wilson .12 .30
229 Dane Sardinha .12 .30
230 Aramis Ramirez .12 .30
231 Doug Mientkiewicz .12 .30
232 Jay Gibbons .12 .30
233 Adam Everett .12 .30
234 Brooks Kieschnick .12 .30
235 Dmitri Young .12 .30
236 Brad Penny .12 .30
237 Todd Zeile .12 .30
238 Eric Gagne .12 .30
239 Esteban Loaiza .12 .30
240 Billy Wagner .12 .30
241 Nomar Garciaparra .30 .75
242 Desi Relaford .12 .30
243 Luis Rivas .12 .30
244 Andy Pettitte .20 .50
245 Ty Wigginton .12 .30
246 Edgar Gonzalez .12 .30
247 Brian Anderson .12 .30
248 Richie Sexson .12 .30
249 Russell Branyan .12 .30
250 Jose Guillen .12 .30
251 Chin-Hui Tsao .12 .30
252 Jose Hernandez .12 .30
253 Kevin Brown .12 .30
254 Pete LaForest .12 .30
255 Adrian Beltre .12 .30
256 Jacque Jones .12 .30
257 Jimmy Rollins .20 .50
258 Brandon Phillips .12 .30
259 Derek Jeter .75 2.00
260 Carl Everett .12 .30
261 Wes Helms .12 .30
262 Kyle Lohse .12 .30
263 Jason Phillips .12 .30
264 Jake Peavy .12 .30
265 Orlando Hernandez .12 .30
266 Keith Foulke .12 .30
267 Brad Wilkerson .12 .30
268 Corey Koskie .12 .30
269 Josh Hall .12 .30
270 Bobby Higginson .12 .30
271 Andres Galarraga .12 .30
272 Alfonso Soriano .12 .30
273 Carlos Rivera .12 .30
274 Steve Trachsel .12 .30
275 David Bell .12 .30
276 Endy Chavez .12 .30
277 Jay Payton .12 .30
278 Mark Mulder .12 .30
279 Terrence Long .12 .30
280 A.J. Burnett .20 .50
281 Pokey Reese .12 .30
282 Phil Nevin .12 .30
283 Jose Contreras .12 .30
284 Jim Thome .20 .50
285 Pat Burrell .12 .30
286 Luis Castillo .12 .30
287 Juan Uribe .12 .30
288 Raul Ibanez .12 .30
289 Sidney Ponson .12 .30
290 Scott Hatteberg .12 .30
291 Jack Wilson .12 .30
292 Reggie Sanders .12 .30
293 Brian Giles .12 .30
294 Craig Biggio .20 .50
295 Kazuhisa Ishii .12 .30
296 Jim Edmonds .20 .50
297 Trevor Hoffman .20 .50
298 Ray Durham .12 .30
299 Mike Lieberthal .12 .30
300 Tim Worrell .12 .30
301 Chris George .12 .30
302 Jamie Moyer .12 .30
303 Mike Cameron .12 .30
304 Matt Kinney .12 .30
305 Aubrey Huff .12 .30
306 Brian Lawrence .12 .30
307 Carlos Guillen .12 .30
308 J.D. Drew .12 .30
309 Paul Lo Duca .12 .30
310 Tim Salmon .12 .30
311 Jason Schmidt .12 .30
312 A.J. Pierzynski .12 .30
313 Lance Carter .12 .30
314 Julio Lugo .12 .30
315 Johan Santana .30 .75
316 Laynce Nix .12 .30
317 John Olerud .12 .30
318 Robb Quinlan .12 .30
319 Scott Spiezio .12 .30
320 Tony Clark .12 .30
321 Jose Vidro .12 .30
322 Shea Hillenbrand .12 .30
323 Doug Glanville .12 .30
324 Orlando Palmeiro .12 .30
325 Juan Gonzalez .12 .30
326 Jason Giambi .12 .30
327 Junior Spivey .12 .30
328 Tom Glavine .20 .50
329 Reed Johnson .12 .30
330 David Eckstein .12 .30
331 Damian Jackson .12 .30
332 Orlando Hudson .12 .30
333 Barry Zito .12 .30
334 Robert Fick .12 .30
335 Aaron Boone .12 .30
336 Rafael Palmeiro .20 .50
337 Bobby Kielty .12 .30
338 Tony Batista .12 .30
339 Ryan Dempster .12 .30
340 Derek Lowe .12 .30
341 Alex Cintron .12 .30
342 Jermaine Dye .12 .30
343 John Burkett .12 .30
344 Javy Lopez .12 .30
345 Eric Karros .12 .30
346 Corey Patterson .12 .30
347 Josh Phelps .12 .30
348 Ryan Klesko .12 .30
349 Craig Wilson .12 .30
350 Brian Roberts .12 .30
351 Roberto Alomar .20 .50
352 Frank Thomas .30 .75
353 Gary Sheffield .12 .30
354 Alex Gonzalez .12 .30
355 Jose Cruz Jr. .12 .30
356 Jerome Williams .12 .30
357 Mark Kotsay .12 .30
358 Chris Reitsma .12 .30
359 Carlos Lee .12 .30
360 Todd Helton .20 .50
361 Gil Meche .12 .30
362 Ryan Franklin .12 .30
363 Josh Bard .12 .30
364 Juan Pierre .12 .30
365 Barry Larkin .20 .50
366 Edgar Renteria .12 .30
367 Alex Sanchez .12 .30
368 Jeff Bagwell .20 .50
369 Ben Broussard .12 .30
370 Chan-Ho Park .20 .50
371 Darrell May .12 .30
372 Roy Oswalt .20 .50
373 Craig Monroe .12 .30
374 Fred McGriff .12 .30
375 Bengie Molina .12 .30
376 Aaron Guiel .12 .30
377 Jeriome Robertson .12 .30
378 Kenny Rogers .12 .30
379 Colby Lewis .12 .30
380 Jeromy Burnitz .12 .30
381 Orlando Cabrera .12 .30
382 Joe Randa .12 .30
383 Miguel Batista .12 .30
384 Brad Radke .12 .30
385 Jeremy Giambi .12 .30
386 Vladimir Guerrero .30 .75
387 Melvin Mora .12 .30
388 Royce Clayton .12 .30
389 Danny Garcia .12 .30
390 Manny Ramirez .30 .75
391 Dave McCarty .12 .30
392 Mark Grudzielanek .12 .30
393 Mike Piazza .30 .75
394 Jorge Posada .20 .50
395 Tim Hudson .20 .50
396 Placido Polanco .12 .30
397 Mark Loretta .12 .30
398 Jesse Foppert .12 .30
399 Albert Pujols .75 2.00
400 Jeremi Gonzalez .12 .30
401 Paul Bako SP .40 1.00
402 Luis Matos SP .40 1.00
403 Johnny Damon SP .60 1.50
404 Kerry Wood SP .40 1.00
405 Joe Crede SP .40 1.00
406 Jason Davis SP .40 1.00
407 Larry Walker SP .60 1.50
408 Ivan Rodriguez SP .60 1.50
409 Nick Johnson SP .40 1.00
410 Jose Lima SP .40 1.00
411 Brian Jordan SP .40 1.00
412 Eddie Guardado SP .40 1.00
413 Ron Calloway SP .40 1.00
414 Aaron Heilman SP .40 1.00
415 Eric Chavez SP .40 1.00
416 Randy Wolf SP .40 1.00
417 Jason Bay SP .60 1.50
418 Edgardo Alfonzo SP .40 1.00
419 Kazuhiro Sasaki SP .40 1.00
420 Eduardo Perez SP .40 1.00
421 Carl Crawford SP .60 1.50
422 Troy Glaus SP .40 1.00
423 Joaquin Benoit SP .40 1.00
424 Russ Ortiz SP .40 1.00
425 Larry Bigbie SP .40 1.00
426 Todd Walker SP .40 1.00
427 Kris Benson SP .40 1.00
428 Sandy Alomar Jr. SP .40 1.00
429 Jody Gerut SP .40 1.00
430 Rene Reyes SP .40 1.00
431 Mike Lowell SP .40 1.00
432 Jeff Kent SP .40 1.00
433 Mike MacDougal SP .40 1.00
434 Dave Roberts SP .40 1.00
435 Torii Hunter SP .40 1.00
436 Tomo Ohka SP .40 1.00
437 Jeremy Griffiths SP .40 1.00
438 Miguel Tejada SP .60 1.50
439 Vicente Padilla SP .40 1.00
440 Bobby Hill SP .40 1.00
441 Rich Aurilia SP .40 1.00
442 Shigetoshi Hasegawa SP .40 1.00
443 So Taguchi SP .40 1.00
444 Damian Rolls SP .40 1.00
445 Roy Halladay SP 1.00 2.50
446 Rocco Baldelli SO SP .40 1.00
447 Dontrelle Willis SO SP .40 1.00
448 Mark Prior SO SP .60 1.50
449 Jason Lane SO SP .40 1.00
450 Angel Berroa SO SP .40 1.00
451 Jose Reyes SO SP .60 1.50
452 Ryan Wagner SO SP .40 1.00
453 Marlon Byrd SO SP .40 1.00
454 Hee Seop Choi SO SP .40 1.00
455 Brandon Webb SO SP .40 1.00
456 Bo Hart SO SP .40 1.00
457 Hank Blalock SO SP .40 1.00
458 Mark Teixeira SO SP 1.00 2.50
459 Hideki Matsui SO SP 1.50 4.00
460 Scott Podsednik SO SP .40 1.00
461 Miguel Cabrera SO SP 1.00 2.50
462 Josh Beckett AW SP .60 1.50
463 Mariano Rivera AW SP 1.00 2.50
464 Ivan Rodriguez AW SP .60 1.50
465 Alex Rodriguez AW SP 1.50 4.00
466 Albert Pujols AW SP 2.50 6.00
467 Roy Halladay AW SP 1.00 2.50
468 Eric Gagne AW SP .40 1.00
469 Angel Berroa AW SP .40 1.00
470 Dontrelle Willis AW SP .40 1.00
471 Chris Bootcheck .40 1.00
Tom Gregorio
Richard Fischer SP
472 Matt Kata .40 1.00
Tim Olson
Robby Hammock SP
473 Michael Hessman .40 1.00
Chris Waters
Greg Aquino SP
474 Carlos Mendez .40 1.00
Daniel Cabrera
Jeremy Guthrie SP
475 Edwin Almonte .40 1.00
Phil Seibel
Felix Sanchez SP
476 Todd Wellemeyer .40 1.00
Jon Leicester
Sergio Mitre SP
477 Josh Stewart .40 1.00
Neal Cotts
Aaron Miles SP
478 Termel Sledge .40 1.00
Josh Hall
Brandon Claussen SP
479 Francisco Cruceta .40 1.00
Jason Stanford

Rafael Betancourt SP
480 Javier A.Lopez .60 1.50
Garrett Atkins
Clint Barmes SP
481 Wilfredo Ledezma .40 1.00
Nook Logan
Jeremy Bonderman SP
482 Josh Willingham .40 1.00
Kevin Hooper
Rick Roberts SP
483 Colin Porter .40 1.00
Mike Gallo
Dave Matranga SP
484 David DeJesus .40 1.00
Jason Gilfillan
Jimmy Gobble SP
485 Koyie Hill .40 1.00
Alfredo Gonzalez
Andrew Brown SP
486 Rickie Weeks .40 1.00
Pedro Liriano
Wes Obermueller SP
487 Alex Prieto .40 1.00
Mike Ryan
Lew Ford SP
488 Julio Manon .40 1.00
Luis Ayala
Seung Song SP
489 Jeff Duncan .40 1.00
Prentice Redman
Craig Brazell SP
490 Chien-Ming Wang 2.00 5.00
Michel Hernandez
Mike Gonzalez SP
491 Rich Harden .40 1.00
Mike Neu
Geoff Geary SP
492 Diegomar Markwell .40 1.00
Chad Gaudin
David Sanders SP
493 Beau Kemp .40 1.00
Micheal Nakamura
D.J. Carrasco SP
494 Khalil Greene .60 1.50
Miguel Ojeda
Bernie Castro SP
495 Noah Lowry .40 1.00
Todd Linden
Kevin Correia SP
496 Aaron Looper .40 1.00
Brian Sweeney
Rett Johnson SP
497 John Gall RC .40 1.00
Dan Haren
Kevin Ohme SP
498 Delmon Young .60 1.50
Doug Waechter
Matt Diaz SP
499 Gerald Laird .40 1.00
Rosman Garcia
Ramon Nivar SP
500 Alexis Rios .60 1.50
Guillermo Quiroz
Francisco Rosario SP

2004 Fleer Tradition Career Tributes

PRINT RUNS B/WN 1956-1993 COPIES PER
*DIE CUT: 1.25X TO 3X BASIC
DIE CUT PRINTS B/WN 56-93 COPIES PER
OVERALL CAREER TRIBUTE ODDS 1:36
1 Mike Schmidt/1989 2.50 6.00
2 Nolan Ryan/1993 5.00 12.00
3 Tom Seaver/1986 1.00 2.50
4 Reggie Jackson/1987 1.00 2.50
5 Bob Gibson/1975 1.00 2.50
6 Harmon Killebrew/1975 1.50 4.00
7 Phil Rizzuto/1956 1.00 2.50
8 Lou Brock/1979 1.00 2.50
9 Eddie Mathews/1968 1.50 4.00
10 Al Kaline/1974 1.50 4.00

2004 Fleer Tradition Diamond Tributes

COMPLETE SET (20) 8.00 20.00
STATED ODDS 1:6
1 Derek Jeter 2.50 6.00
2 Chipper Jones 1.00 2.50
3 Vladimir Guerrero 1.00 2.50
4 Kerry Wood .40 1.00
5 Jim Thome .60 1.50
6 Nomar Garciaparra 1.00 2.50
7 Alex Rodriguez 1.50 4.00
8 Mike Piazza 1.00 2.50
9 Jason Giambi .40 1.00
10 Barry Zito .40 1.00
11 Dontrelle Willis .40 1.00
12 Albert Pujols 2.50 6.00
13 Todd Helton .60 1.50
14 Richie Sexson .40 1.00
15 Randy Johnson 1.00 2.50
16 Pedro Martinez .60 1.50
17 Josh Beckett .60 1.50
18 Manny Ramirez 1.00 2.50
19 Roy Halladay 1.00 2.50
20 Mark Prior .60 1.50

2004 Fleer Tradition Diamond Tributes Game Jersey

STATED ODDS 1:36
*PATCH: 1X TO 2.5X BASIC
PATCH RANDOM INSERTS IN PACKS
PATCH PRINT RUN 50 SERIAL #'d SETS
AP Albert Pujols 6.00 15.00
AR Alex Rodriguez 4.00 10.00
BZ Barry Zito 3.00 8.00
CJ Chipper Jones 4.00 10.00
DJ Derek Jeter 8.00 20.00
DW Dontrelle Willis 4.00 10.00
JB Josh Beckett 3.00 8.00
JG Jason Giambi 3.00 8.00
JT Jim Thome 4.00 10.00
KW Kerry Wood 3.00 8.00
MP Mike Piazza 4.00 10.00
MP2 Mark Prior 4.00 10.00
MR Manny Ramirez 4.00 10.00
NG Nomar Garciaparra 4.00 10.00
PM Pedro Martinez 4.00 10.00
RH Roy Halladay 3.00 8.00
RJ Randy Johnson 4.00 10.00
RS Richie Sexson 3.00 8.00
TH Todd Helton 4.00 10.00
VG Vladimir Guerrero 4.00 10.00

2004 Fleer Tradition Retrospection

STATED ODDS 1:360
1 Rickie Weeks 2.00 5.00
2 Delmon Young 3.00 8.00
3 Torii Hunter 2.00 5.00
4 Aubrey Huff 2.00 5.00
5 Rocco Baldelli 2.00 5.00
6 Mike Lowell 2.00 5.00
7 Dontrelle Willis 2.00 5.00
8 Albert Pujols 12.00 30.00
9 Bo Hart 2.00 5.00
10 Brandon Webb 2.00 5.00

2004 Fleer Tradition Retrospection Autographs

Please note that a few players did not return their autographs in time for inclusion in this product and no expiration date was set for redeeming those cards.

OVERALL AUTO ODDS 1:720
STATED PRINT RUN 60 SERIAL #'d SETS
AH Aubrey Huff 10.00 25.00
AK Austin Kearns 10.00 25.00
BO Bo Hart 10.00 25.00
BW Brandon Webb 10.00 25.00
CP Corey Patterson 10.00 25.00
DW Dontrelle Willis 15.00 40.00
HB Hank Blalock 10.00 25.00
JR Jose Reyes 10.00 25.00
JW Josh Willingham 10.00 25.00
MR Mike Ryan 10.00 25.00
RW Rickie Weeks 10.00 25.00
SR Scott Rolen 15.00 40.00
TH Torii Hunter 10.00 25.00

2004 Fleer Tradition Retrospection Autographs Dual

OVERALL AUTO ODDS 1:720
STATED PRINT RUN 19 SERIAL #'d SETS
NO PRICING DUE TO SCARCITY
EXCHANGE DEADLINE INDEFINITE
AHAK Aubrey Huff
Austin Kearns
CPJR Corey Patterson
Jose Reyes
HBSR Hank Blalock
Scott Rolen
JWDW Josh Willingham
Dontrelle Willis
THMR Torii Hunter
Mike Ryan

2004 Fleer Tradition Stand Outs Game Used

STATED ODDS 1:41
GOLD RANDOM INSERTS IN PACKS
GOLD PRINTS B/WN 20-27 COPIES PER
NO GOLD PRICING DUE TO SCARCITY
AB Angel Berroa Pants 3.00 8.00
BH Bo Hart Jsy 3.00 8.00
BW Brandon Webb Pants 3.00 8.00
DW Dontrelle Willis Jsy 4.00 10.00
HB Hank Blalock Jsy 3.00 8.00
HC Hee Seop Choi Jsy 3.00 8.00
JR Jose Reyes Jsy 3.00 8.00
MB Marlon Byrd Jsy 3.00 8.00
MC Miguel Cabrera Jsy 4.00 10.00
MT Mark Teixeira Jsy 4.00 10.00
RB Rocco Baldelli Jsy 3.00 8.00

2004 Fleer Tradition This Day in History

STATED ODDS 1:18
1 Josh Beckett .60 1.50
2 Carlos Delgado .40 1.00
3 Javy Lopez .40 1.00
4 Greg Maddux 1.50 4.00
5 Rafael Palmeiro .60 1.50
6 Sammy Sosa 1.00 2.50
7 Jeff Bagwell .60 1.50
8 Frank Thomas 1.00 2.50
9 Kevin Millwood .40 1.00
10 Jose Reyes .60 1.50
11 Rafael Furcal .40 1.00
12 Alfonso Soriano .40 1.00
13 Eric Gagne .40 1.00
14 Hideki Matsui 1.50 4.00
15 Hank Blalock .40 1.00

2004 Fleer Tradition This Day in History Game Used

STATED ODDS 1:288
AS Alfonso Soriano Jsy 4.00 10.00
CD Carlos Delgado Jsy 4.00 10.00
FT Frank Thomas Jsy 6.00 15.00
GM Greg Maddux Jsy 6.00 15.00
JB Josh Beckett Jsy 4.00 10.00
JB Jeff Bagwell Jsy 6.00 15.00
JL Javy Lopez Jsy 4.00 10.00
JR Jose Reyes Jsy 4.00 10.00
RP Rafael Palmeiro Jsy 6.00 15.00
SS Sammy Sosa Bat 6.00 15.00

2004 Fleer Tradition This Day in History Game Used Dual

STATED PRINT RUN 25 SERIAL #'d SETS
NO PRICING DUE TO SCARCITY
CDJR Carlos Delgado Jsy
Jose Reyes Jsy
FTJB Frank Thomas Jsy
Jeff Bagwell Jsy
JBGM Josh Beckett Jsy
Greg Maddux Jsy
JLAS Javy Lopez Jsy
Alfonso Soriano Jsy
RPSS Rafael Palmeiro Jsy
Sammy Sosa Bat

2005 Fleer Tradition

This 350-card set was released in February, 2005. The set was issued in 10-card hobby or retail packs. The hobby packs came 36 packs to a box and 20 boxes to a case while the retail packs came 24 packs to a box and 20 boxes to a case. The first 300 cards were all printed to the same quantity and there is a season leader subset in the first 12 cards. Cards 301-330 feature a grouping of prospects while 331-340 feature Award Winners and cards 341-350 feature Post-Season heroes. These cards were issued at an overall stated rate of one in two hobby packs and one in four retail packs. Many dealers believe that cards 301-330 were significantly tougher to pull than cards 331-350.

COMPLETE SET (350) 75.00 150.00
COMP.SET w/o SP's (300) 15.00 40.00
COMMON CARD (1-300) .10 .30
COMMON CARD (301-330) .40 1.00
COMMON CARD (331-350) .40 1.00
301-350 STATED ODDS 1:2 H, 1:4 R
1 Johan Santana .30 .75
Curt Schilling
Jake Westbrook SL
2 Ben Sheets .12 .30
Jake Peavy
Randy Johnson SL
3 Johan Santana .30 .75
Bartolo Colon
Curt Schilling SL
4 Carl Pavano .20 .50
Roy Oswalt
Roger Clemens SL
5 Johan Santana .30 .75
Pedro Martinez
Curt Schilling SL
6 Jason Schmidt .30 .75
Randy Johnson
Ben Sheets SL
7 Melvin Mora .50 1.25
Vladimir Guerrero
Ichiro Suzuki SL
8 Adrian Beltre .20 .50
Todd Helton
Mark Loretta SL
9 Manny Ramirez .20 .50
Paul Konerko
David Ortiz SL
10 Albert Pujols .20 .50
Adrian Beltre
Adam Dunn SL
11 David Ortiz .20 .50
Manny Ramirez
Miguel Tejada SL
12 Albert Pujols .75 2.00
Vinny Castilla
Scott Rolen SL
13 Jason Bay .12 .30
14 Greg Maddux .50 1.25
15 Melvin Mora .12 .30
16 Matt Stairs .12 .30
17 Scott Podsednik .12 .30
18 Bartolo Colon .12 .30
19 Roger Clemens .40 1.00
20 Eric Hinske .12 .30
21 Johnny Estrada .12 .30
22 Brett Tomko .12 .30
23 John Buck .12 .30
24 Nomar Garciaparra .30 .75
25 Milton Bradley .12 .30
26 Craig Biggio .20 .50
27 Kyle Denney .12 .30
28 Brad Penny .12 .30
29 Todd Helton .20 .50
30 Luis Gonzalez .12 .30
31 Bill Hall .12 .30
32 Ruben Sierra .12 .30
33 Zack Greinke .20 .50
34 Sandy Alomar Jr. .12 .30
35 Jason Giambi .12 .30
36 Ben Sheets .12 .30
37 Edgardo Alfonzo .12 .30
38 Kenny Rogers .12 .30
39 Coco Crisp .12 .30
40 Randy Choate .12 .30
41 Braden Looper .12 .30
42 Adam Dunn .20 .50
43 Adam Eaton .12 .30
44 Luis Castillo .12 .30
45 Casey Fossum .12 .30
46 Mike Piazza .30 .75
47 Juan Pierre .12 .30
48 Doug Davis .12 .30
49 Manny Ramirez .30 .75
50 Travis Hafner .12 .30
51 Jack Wilson .12 .30
52 Mike Maroth .12 .30
53 Ken Harvey .12 .30
54 Brooks Kieschnick .12 .30
55 Brad Fullmer .12 .30
56 Octavio Dotel .12 .30
57 Mike Matheny .12 .30
58 Andruw Jones .12 .30
59 Alfonso Soriano .20 .50
60 Royce Clayton .12 .30
61 Jon Garland .12 .30
62 John Mabry .12 .30
63 Rafael Palmeiro .20 .50
64 Garett Atkins .12 .30
65 Brian Meadows .12 .30
66 Tony Armas Jr. .12 .30
67 Toby Hall .12 .30
68 Carlos Baerga .12 .30
69 Barry Larkin .20 .50
70 Jody Gerut .12 .30
71 Brent Mayne .12 .30
72 Shigetoshi Hasegawa .12 .30
73 Jose Cruz Jr. .12 .30
74 Dan Wilson .12 .30
75 Sidney Ponson .12 .30
76 Jason Jennings .12 .30
77 A.J. Burnett .20 .50
78 Tony Batista .12 .30
79 Kris Benson .12 .30
80 Sean Burroughs .12 .30
81 Eric Young .12 .30
82 Casey Kotchman .12 .30
83 Derrek Lee .12 .30
84 Mariano Rivera .30 .75
85 Julio Franco .12 .30
86 Corey Patterson .12 .30
87 Carlos Beltran .12 .30
88 Trevor Hoffman .20 .50
89 Danny Garcia .12 .30
90 Marcos Scutaro .12 .30
91 Marquis Grissom .12 .30
92 Aubrey Huff .12 .30
93 Tony Womack .12 .30
94 Placido Polanco .12 .30
95 Bengie Molina .12 .30
96 Roger Cedeno .12 .30
97 Geoff Jenkins .12 .30
98 Kip Wells .12 .30
99 Derek Jeter .75 2.00
100 Omar Infante .12 .30
101 Phil Nevin .12 .30
102 Edgar Renteria .12 .30
103 B.J. Surhoff .12 .30
104 David DeJesus .12 .30
105 Raul Ibanez .12 .30
106 Hank Blalock .12 .30
107 Shawn Estes .12 .30
108 Wily Mo Pena .12 .30
109 Shawn Green .12 .30
110 David Wright .50 1.25
111 Kenny Lofton .12 .30
112 Matt Clement .12 .30
113 Cesar Izturis .12 .30
114 John Lackey .12 .30
115 Torii Hunter .12 .30
116 Charles Johnson .12 .30
117 Ray Durham .12 .30
118 Luke Hudson .12 .30
119 Jeremy Bonderman .12 .30
120 Sean Casey .12 .30
121 Johnny Damon .20 .50
122 Eric Milton .12 .30
123 Shea Hillenbrand .12 .30
124 Johan Santana .30 .75
125 Jim Edmonds .20 .50
126 Javier Vazquez .12 .30
127 Jon Adkins .12 .30
128 Mike Lowell .12 .30
129 Khalil Greene .12 .30
130 Quinton McCracken .12 .30
131 Edgar Martinez .20 .50
132 Matt Lawton .12 .30
133 Jeff Weaver .12 .30
134 Marlon Byrd .12 .30
135 John Smoltz .30 .75
136 Grady Sizemore .20 .50
137 Brian Roberts .12 .30
138 Dee Brown .12 .30
139 Joel Pineiro .12 .30
140 David Dellucci .12 .30
141 Bobby Higginson .12 .30
142 Ryan Madson .12 .30
143 Scott Hatteberg .12 .30
144 Greg Zaun .12 .30
145 Brian Jordan .12 .30
146 Jason Isringhausen .12 .30
147 Vinnie Chulk .12 .30
148 Al Leiter .12 .30
149 Pedro Martinez .20 .50
150 Carlos Guillen .12 .30
151 Randy Wolf .12 .30
152 Vernon Wells .12 .30
153 Barry Zito .12 .30
154 Pedro Feliz .12 .30
155 Omar Vizquel .20 .50
156 Chone Figgins .12 .30
157 David Ortiz .30 .75
158 Sunny Kim .12 .30
159 Adam Kennedy .12 .30
160 Carlos Lee .12 .30
161 Rick Ankiel .12 .30
162 Roy Oswalt .20 .50
163 Armando Benitez .12 .30
164 Erubiel Durazo .12 .30
165 Adam Hyzdu .12 .30
166 Esteban Yan .12 .30
167 Victor Santos .12 .30
168 Kevin Millwood .12 .30
169 Andy Pettitte .20 .50
170 Mike Cameron .12 .30
171 Scott Rolen .20 .50
172 Trot Nixon .12 .30
173 Eric Munson .12 .30
174 Roy Halladay .30 .75
175 Juan Encarnacion .12 .30
176 Eric Chavez .12 .30
177 Termel Sledge .12 .30
178 Jason Schmidt .12 .30
179 Endy Chavez .12 .30
180 Carlos Zambrano .20 .50
181 Carlos Delgado .12 .30
182 Dewon Brazelton .12 .30
183 J.D. Drew .12 .30
184 Orlando Cabrera .12 .30
185 Craig Wilson .12 .30
186 Chin-Hui Tsao .12 .30
187 Jolbert Cabrera .12 .30
188 Rod Barajas .12 .30
189 Craig Monroe .12 .30
190 Dave Berg .12 .30
191 Carlos Silva .12 .30
192 Eric Gagne .12 .30
193 Marcus Giles .12 .30
194 Nick Johnson .12 .30
195 Kelvim Escobar .12 .30
196 Wade Miller .12 .30
197 David Bell .12 .30
198 Rondell White .12 .30
199 Brian Giles .12 .30
200 Jeromy Burnitz .12 .30
201 Carl Pavano .12 .30
202 Alex Rios .20 .50
203 Ryan Freel .12 .30
204 R.A. Dickey .12 .30
205 Miguel Cairo .12 .30
206 Kerry Wood .12 .30
207 C.C. Sabathia .20 .50
208 Jaime Cerda .12 .30
209 Jerome Williams .12 .30
210 Ryan Wagner .12 .30
211 Javy Lopez .12 .30
212 Tike Redman .12 .30
213 Richie Sexson .12 .30
214 Shannon Stewart .12 .30
215 Ben Davis .12 .30
216 Jeff Bagwell .20 .50
217 David Wells .12 .30
218 Justin Leone .12 .30
219 Brad Radke .12 .30
220 Ramon Santiago .12 .30
221 Richard Hidalgo .12 .30
222 Aaron Miles .12 .30
223 Mark Loretta .12 .30
224 Aaron Boone .12 .30
225 Steve Trachsel .12 .30
226 Geoff Blum .12 .30
227 Shingo Takatsu .12 .30
228 Kevin Youkilis .12 .30
229 Laynce Nix .12 .30
230 Daniel Cabrera .12 .30
231 Kyle Lohse .12 .30
232 Todd Pratt .12 .30
233 Reed Johnson .12 .30
234 Lance Berkman .20 .50
235 Hideki Matsui .50 1.25
236 Randy Winn .12 .30
237 Joe Randa .12 .30
238 Bob Howry .12 .30
239 Jason LaRue .12 .30
240 Jose Valentin .12 .30
241 Livan Hernandez .12 .30
242 Jamie Moyer .12 .30
243 Garret Anderson .12 .30
244 Brad Ausmus .12 .30
245 Russell Branyan .12 .30
246 Paul Wilson .12 .30
247 Tim Wakefield .12 .30
248 Roberto Alomar .20 .50
249 Kazuhisa Ishii .12 .30
250 Tino Martinez .20 .50
251 Tomo Ohka .12 .30
252 Mark Redman .12 .30
253 Paul Byrd .12 .30
254 Greg Aquino .12 .30
255 Adrian Beltre .12 .30
256 Ricky Ledee .12 .30
257 Josh Fogg .12 .30
258 Derek Lowe .12 .30
259 Lew Ford .12 .30
260 Bobby Crosby .12 .30
261 Jim Thome .20 .50
262 Jaret Wright .12 .30
263 Chin-Feng Chen .12 .30
264 Troy Glaus .12 .30
265 Jorge Sosa .12 .30
266 Mike Lamb .12 .30
267 Russ Ortiz .12 .30
268 Reggie Sanders .12 .30
269 Orlando Hudson .12 .30
270 Rodrigo Lopez .12 .30
271 Jose Vidro .12 .30
272 Akinori Otsuka .12 .30
273 Victor Martinez .20 .50
274 Carl Crawford .20 .50
275 Roberto Novoa .12 .30
276 Brian Lawrence .12 .30
277 Angel Berroa .12 .30
278 Josh Beckett .20 .50
279 Lyle Overbay .12 .30
280 Dustin Hermanson .12 .30
281 Jeff Conine .12 .30
282 Mark Prior .20 .50
283 Kevin Brown .12 .30
284 Magglio Ordonez .20 .50
285 Dontrelle Willis .12 .30
286 Dallas McPherson .12 .30
287 Rafael Furcal .12 .30
288 Ty Wigginton .12 .30
289 Moises Alou .12 .30
290 A.J. Pierzynski .12 .30
291 Todd Walker .12 .30
292 Hideo Nomo .30 .75
293 Larry Walker .20 .50
294 Choo Freeman .12 .30
295 Eduardo Perez .12 .30
296 Miguel Tejada .20 .50
297 Corey Koskie .12 .30
298 Jermaine Dye .12 .30
299 John Riedling .12 .30
300 John Olerud .12 .30
301 Tim Bittner .40 1.00
Jake Woods
Bobby Jenks TP
302 Josh Kroeger .40 1.00
Casey Daigle
Brandon Medders TP
303 Kelly Johnson .40 1.00
Charles Thomas
Dan Meyer TP
304 Eddy Rodriguez .40 1.00
Ryan Hannaman
John Maine TP
305 Anastacio Martinez
Jerome Gamble
Lenny Dinardo TP
306 Ronny Cedeno .40 1.00
Carlos Vasquez
Renyel Pinto TP
307 Arnie Munoz .40 1.00
Ryan Wing
Felix Diaz TP
308 William Bergolla .60 1.50
Ray Olmedo
Edwin Encarnacion TP
309 Mariano Gomez .40 1.00
Ivan Ochoa
Kazuhito Tadano TP
310 Tony Miller 1.00 2.50
Jeff Baker
Matt Holliday TP
311 Preston Larrison .60 1.50
Curtis Granderson
Ryan Raburn TP
312 Josh Wilson .40 1.00
Logan Kensing
Kevin Cave TP
313 Hector Gimenez .40 1.00
Willy Taveras
Taylor Buchholz TP
314 Ruben Gotay .40 1.00
Brian Bass
Andres Blanco TP
315 Joel Hanrahan .60 1.50
Willy Aybar
Yhency Brazoban TP
316 Dave Krynzel .40 1.00
Ben Hendrickson
Corey Hart TP
317 Colby Miller .40 1.00
Jason Kubel
J.D. Durbin TP
318 Maicer Izturis .40 1.00
Chad Cordero
Brandon Watson TP
319 Victor Diaz .40 1.00
Aarom Baldiris
Wayne Lydon TP
320 Edwardo Sierra .40 1.00
Dioner Navarro
Sean Henn TP
321 Nick Swisher 1.00 2.50
Joe Blanton
Dan Johnson TP
322 Ryan Howard 2.00 5.00
Gavin Floyd
Keith Bucktrot TP
323 Ryan Doumit .40 1.00
Sean Burnett
Bobby Bradley TP
324 Justin Germano .40 1.00
Rusty Tucker
Freddy Guzman TP
325 David Aardsma .40 1.00
Justin Knoedler
Alfredo Simon TP
326 Jose Lopez .40 1.00
Rene Rivera
Cha Seung Baek TP
327 Yadier Molina 1.00 2.50
Evan Rust
Adam Wainwright TP
328 Jorge Cantu 1.00 2.50
Scott Kazmir
B.J. Upton TP
329 Adrian Gonzalez .60 1.50
Ramon Nivar
Jason Bourgeois TP
330 Russ Adams .40 1.00
Dustin McGowan
Gustavo Chacin TP
331 Alfonso Soriano AW .60 1.50
332 Albert Pujols AW 2.50 6.00
333 David Ortiz AW 1.00 2.50
334 Manny Ramirez AW 1.00 2.50
335 Jason Bay AW .40 1.00
336 Bobby Crosby AW .40 1.00
337 Roger Clemens AW 1.25 3.00
338 Johan Santana AW 1.00 2.50
339 Jim Thome AW .60 1.50
340 Vladimir Guerrero AW 1.00 2.50
341 David Ortiz PS 1.00 2.50
342 Alex Rodriguez PS 1.50 4.00
343 Albert Pujols PS 2.50 6.00
344 Carlos Beltran PS .40 1.00
345 Johnny Damon PS .60 1.50
346 Scott Rolen PS .60 1.50
347 Larry Walker PS .60 1.50
348 Curt Schilling PS .60 1.50
349 Pedro Martinez PS .60 1.50
350 David Ortiz PS 1.00 2.50

2005 Fleer Tradition Gray Backs

*GRAY BACK 1-300: 1.25X TO 3X BASIC
*GRAY BACK 301-330: .5X TO 1.2X BASIC
*GRAY BACK 331-350: .6X TO 1.5X BASIC
STATED ODDS 1:2 HOBBY, 1:2 RETAIL

2005 Fleer Tradition Gray Backs Gold Letter

*GOLD LTR: 6X TO 15X BASIC
STATED ODDS 1:96 HOBBY, 1:288 RETAIL
STATED APPROX. PRINT RUN 185 SETS
PRINT RUN INFO PROVIDED BY FLEER
CARDS ARE NOT SERIAL-NUMBERED

2005 Fleer Tradition Club 3000/500/300

STATED ODDS 1:360 HOBBY, 1:480 RETAIL
STATED APPROX. PRINT RUN 175 SETS
PRINT RUN INFO PROVIDED BY FLEER
1 Ernie Banks 500 6.00 15.00
2 Stan Musial 3000 10.00 25.00
3 Steve Carlton 3000 2.50 6.00
4 Greg Maddux 300 10.00 25.00
5 Dave Winfield 3000 2.50 6.00
6 Rafael Palmeiro 500 4.00 10.00
7 Rickey Henderson 3000 4.00 10.00
8 Roger Clemens 3000 8.00 20.00
9 Don Sutton 300 2.50 6.00
10 George Brett 3000 12.00 30.00
11 Reggie Jackson 500 6.00 15.00
12 Wade Boggs 3000 4.00 10.00
13 Bob Gibson 3000 4.00 10.00
14 Eddie Murray 3000 6.00 15.00
15 Tom Seaver 3000 4.00 10.00
16 Willie McCovey 500 4.00 10.00
17 Rod Carew 3000 4.00 10.00
18 Fergie Jenkins 300 2.50 6.00
19 Phil Niekro 300 2.50 6.00
20 Frank Robinson 500 4.00 10.00

2005 Fleer Tradition Cooperstown Tribute

STATED ODDS 1:72 HOBBY
RANDOM INSERTS IN RETAIL PACKS
*GOLD: .4X TO 1X BASIC
GOLD ODDS 1:24 RETAIL

1 Mike Schmidt/1995 3.00 8.00
2 Al Kaline/1980 1.50 4.00
3 Yogi Berra/1972 1.50 4.00
4 Robin Yount/1999 1.50 4.00
5 Joe Morgan/1990 .60 1.50
6 Willie Stargell/1988 1.00 2.50
7 Harmon Killebrew/1984 1.50 4.00
8 Nolan Ryan/1999 4.00 10.00
9 Carlton Fisk/2000 1.00 2.50
10 Johnny Bench/1989 1.50 4.00

2005 Fleer Tradition Cooperstown Tribute Jersey

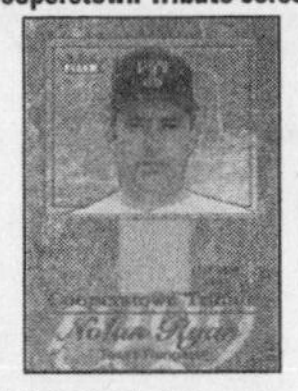

STATED ODDS 1:200 H, 1:1250 R
STATED APPROX. PRINT RUN 400 SETS
STATED SP PRINT RUN 20 COPIES PER
PRINT RUN INFO PROVIDED BY FLEER
NO SP PRICING DUE TO SCARCITY
PATCH RANDOM IN HOB/RET PACKS
PATCH PRINT RUN 10 SERIAL #'d SETS
NO PATCH PRICING DUE TO SCARCITY
AK Al Kaline 10.00 25.00
CF Carlton Fisk 6.00 15.00
HK Harmon Killebrew 6.00 15.00
JB Johnny Bench 6.00 15.00
JM Joe Morgan SP/20 *
MS Mike Schmidt 8.00 20.00
NR Nolan Ryan 12.50 30.00
RY Robin Yount 6.00 15.00
WS Willie Stargell 6.00 15.00
YB Yogi Berra SP/20 *

2005 Fleer Tradition Diamond Tributes

COMPLETE SET (25) 10.00 25.00
STATED ODDS 1:6 H, 1:8 R
1 Albert Pujols 2.50 6.00
2 Alex Rodriguez 1.50 4.00
3 Ken Griffey Jr. 1.50 4.00
4 Sammy Sosa 1.00 2.50
5 Chipper Jones 1.00 2.50
6 Johan Santana 1.00 2.50
7 Roger Clemens 1.25 3.00
8 Pedro Martinez .60 1.50
9 Jim Thome .60 1.50
10 Greg Maddux 1.50 4.00
11 Alfonso Soriano .60 1.50
12 Derek Jeter 2.50 6.00
13 Randy Johnson 1.00 2.50
14 Miguel Cabrera 1.00 2.50
15 Adrian Beltre .40 1.00
16 Ivan Rodriguez .60 1.50
17 Manny Ramirez 1.00 2.50
18 Mark Teixeira 1.00 2.50
19 Adam Dunn .60 1.50
20 Scott Rolen .60 1.50
21 Mike Piazza 1.00 2.50
22 J.D. Drew .40 1.00
23 Hideki Matsui 1.50 4.00
24 Nomar Garciaparra 1.00 2.50
25 Kaz Matsui .40 1.00

2005 Fleer Tradition Diamond Tributes Game Used

STATED ODDS 1:30 H, 1:625 R
SP PRINT RUNS PROVIDED BY FLEER
SP'S ARE NOT SERIAL-NUMBERED
NO SP PRICING DUE TO SCARCITY
AB Adrian Beltre Bat 3.00 8.00
AP Albert Pujols Bat 6.00 15.00
AS Alfonso Soriano Bat 3.00 8.00
CJ Chipper Jones Bat 4.00 10.00
GM Greg Maddux Jsy 4.00 10.00
HM Hideki Matsui Bat 6.00 15.00
JD J.D. Drew Bat 3.00 8.00
JS Johan Santana Jsy 4.00 10.00
JT Jim Thome Bat 4.00 10.00
KM Kaz Matsui Bat 3.00 8.00
MC Miguel Cabrera Bat SP/30 *
MP Mike Piazza Bat 4.00 10.00
MR Manny Ramirez Bat 4.00 10.00

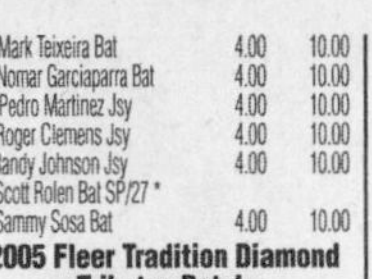

MT Mark Teixeira Bat 4.00 10.00
NG Nomar Garciaparra Bat 4.00 10.00
PM Pedro Martinez Jsy 4.00 10.00
RC Roger Clemens Jsy 4.00 10.00
RJ Randy Johnson Jsy 4.00 10.00
SR Scott Rolen Bat SP/27 *
SS Sammy Sosa Bat 4.00 10.00

2005 Fleer Tradition Diamond Tributes Patch

*PATCH: 1X TO 2.5X BASIC DT JSY
STATED PRINT RUN 50 SERIAL #'d SETS
IR Ivan Rodriguez 10.00 25.00
MC Miguel Cabrera 10.00 25.00
SR Scott Rolen 10.00 25.00

2005 Fleer Tradition Diamond Tributes Dual Patch

STATED PRINT RUN 25 SERIAL #'d SETS
NO PRICING DUE TO SCARCITY
APSR Albert Pujols
Scott Rolen
ASMT Alfonso Soriano
Mark Teixeira
CJJD Chipper Jones
J.D. Drew
HMKM Hideki Matsui
Kaz Matsui
JTAB Jim Thome
Adrian Beltre
MPIR Mike Piazza
Ivan Rodriguez
PMMR Pedro Martinez
Manny Ramirez
RCJS Roger Clemens
Johan Santana
RJGM Randy Johnson
Greg Maddux
SSMC Miguel Cabrera
Sammy Sosa

2005 Fleer Tradition Standouts

COMPLETE SET (15) 15.00 40.00
STATED ODDS 1:18 H, 1:24 R
1 Albert Pujols 2.50 6.00
2 Ichiro Suzuki 1.50 4.00
3 Derek Jeter 2.50 6.00
4 Randy Johnson 1.00 2.50
5 Greg Maddux 1.50 4.00
6 Hideki Matsui 1.50 4.00
7 Mike Piazza 1.00 2.50
8 Vladimir Guerrero 1.00 2.50
9 Sammy Sosa 1.00 2.50
10 Jim Thome .60 1.50
11 Chipper Jones 1.00 2.50
12 Alex Rodriguez 1.50 4.00
13 Roger Clemens 1.25 3.00
14 Nomar Garciaparra 1.00 2.50
15 Lance Berkman .60 1.50

2005 Fleer Tradition Standouts Jersey

STATED ODDS 1:65 H, 1:950 R
*PATCH: 1X TO 2.5X BASIC
PATCH RANDOM IN HOB/RET PACKS
PATCH PRINT RUN 50 SERIAL #'d SETS
AP Albert Pujols 6.00 15.00
CJ Chipper Jones 4.00 10.00
GM Greg Maddux 4.00 10.00
HM Hideki Matsui 8.00 20.00
JT Jim Thome 4.00 10.00
LB Lance Berkman 3.00 8.00
MP Mike Piazza 4.00 10.00
RC Roger Clemens 4.00 10.00
RJ Randy Johnson 4.00 10.00
SS Sammy Sosa 4.00 10.00
VG Vladimir Guerrero 4.00 10.00

2006 Fleer Tradition

This 200-card set was released in August, 2006. The set was issued in 10-card hobby packs, with an $1.99 SRP which came 36 packs per box and 12 boxes per

case. This product was also issued in a retail pack format. The major difference between the retail and hobby packs was that the hobby boxes had stated information that there was either a memorabilia or a printing plate card in every box.

COMPLETE SET (200) 12.50 30.00

2006 Fleer Tradition

COMMON CARD (1-200) .12 .30
COMMON RC (1-200) .20 .50
OVERALL PLATE ODDS 1:288 HOBBY
PLATE PRINT RUN 1 SET PER COLOR
BLACK-CYAN-MAGENTA-YELLOW ISSUED
NO PLATE PRICING DUE TO SCARCITY
EXQUISITE EXCH ODDS 1:864 HOBBY
EXQUISITE EXCH DEADLINE 07/27/07
1 Andruw Jones .12 .30
2 Chipper Jones .30 .75
3 John Smoltz .30 .75
4 Tim Hudson .20 .50
5 Joey Devine RC .20 .50
6 Chuck James (RC) .20 .50
7 Alay Soler RC .20 .50
8 Conor Jackson (RC) .30 .75
9 Luis Gonzalez .12 .30
10 Brandon Webb .20 .50
11 Chad Tracy .12 .30
12 Orlando Hudson .12 .30
13 Shawn Green .12 .30
14 Vladimir Guerrero .30 .75
15 Bartolo Colon .12 .30
16 Chone Figgins .12 .30
17 Garret Anderson .12 .30
18 Francisco Rodriguez .20 .50
19 Casey Kotchman .12 .30
20 Lance Berkman .20 .50
21 Craig Biggio .20 .50
22 Andy Pettitte .20 .50
23 Morgan Ensberg .12 .30
24 Brad Lidge .12 .30
25 Jered Weaver (RC) .50 1.25
26 Roy Oswalt .20 .50
27 Eric Chavez .12 .30
28 Rich Harden .12 .30
29 Cole Hamels (RC) .75 2.00
30 Huston Street .12 .30
31 Bobby Crosby .12 .30
32 Nick Swisher .30 .75
33 Vernon Wells .12 .30
34 Roy Halladay .30 .75
35 A.J. Burnett .12 .30
36 Troy Glaus .12 .30
37 B.J. Ryan .12 .30
38 Bengie Molina .12 .30
39 Alex Rios .20 .50
40 Prince Fielder (RC) .75 2.00
41 Jose Capellan (RC) .20 .50
42 Rickie Weeks .20 .50
43 Ben Sheets .12 .30
44 Carlos Lee .12 .30
45 J.J. Hardy .12 .30
46 Albert Pujols .75 2.00
47 Skip Schumaker (RC) .20 .50
48 Adam Wainwright (RC) .50 1.25
49 Jim Edmonds .20 .50
50 Scott Rolen .20 .50
51 Chris Carpenter .30 .75
52 David Eckstein .12 .30
53 Derrek Lee .12 .30
54 Jon Lester RC .75 2.00
55 Mark Prior .20 .50
56 Aramis Ramirez .12 .30
57 Juan Pierre .12 .30
58 Greg Maddux .50 1.25
59 Michael Barrett .12 .30
60 Carl Crawford .20 .50
61 Scott Kazmir .20 .50
62 Jorge Cantu .12 .30
63 Jonny Gomes .12 .30
64 Julio Lugo .12 .30
65 Aubrey Huff .12 .30
66 Jeff Kent .12 .30
67 Nomar Garciaparra .30 .75
68 Rafael Furcal .12 .30
69 Tim Hamulack (RC) .20 .50
70 Chad Billingsley (RC) .30 .75
71 Hong-Chih Kuo (RC) .50 1.25
72 J.D. Drew .12 .30
73 Moises Alou .12 .30
74 Randy Winn .12 .30
75 Jason Schmidt .12 .30
76 Jeremy Accardo RC .20 .50
77 Matt Cain (RC) .50 1.25
78 Joel Zumaya (RC) .50 1.25
79 Travis Hafner .12 .30
80 Victor Martinez .20 .50
81 Grady Sizemore .20 .50
82 C.C. Sabathia .20 .50
83 Jhonny Peralta .12 .30
84 Jason Michaels .12 .30
85 Jeremy Sowers (RC) .20 .50
86 Ichiro Suzuki .50 1.25
87 Richie Sexson .12 .30
88 Adrian Beltre .12 .30
89 Felix Hernandez .30 .75
90 Kenji Johjima RC .50 1.25
91 Jeff Harris RC .20 .50
92 Taylor Buchholz (RC) .20 .50
93 Miguel Cabrera .30 .75
94 Dontrelle Willis .12 .30
95 Jeremy Hermida (RC) .20 .50
96 Mike Jacobs (RC) .20 .50
97 Josh Johnson (RC) .50 1.25
98 Hanley Ramirez (RC) .50 1.25
99 Josh Willingham (RC) .20 .50
100 Dan Uggla (RC) .50 1.25
101 David Wright .50 1.25
102 Jose Reyes .20 .50
103 Pedro Martinez .20 .50
104 Carlos Beltran .12 .30
105 Carlos Delgado .12 .30
106 Billy Wagner .12 .30
107 Lastings Milledge (RC) .20 .50
108 Alfonso Soriano .20 .50
109 Jose Vidro .12 .30
110 Livan Hernandez .12 .30
111 Matt Kemp (RC) 1.00 2.50
112 Brandon Watson (RC) .20 .50
113 Ryan Zimmerman (RC) 1.00 2.50
114 Miguel Tejada .20 .50
115 Ramon Hernandez .12 .30
116 Brian Roberts .12 .30
117 Melvin Mora .12 .30
118 Erik Bedard .12 .30
119 Jay Gibbons .12 .30
120 Aaron Rakers (RC) .20 .50
121 Jake Peavy .12 .30
122 Brian Giles .12 .30
123 Khalil Greene .12 .30
124 Trevor Hoffman .20 .50
125 Josh Barfield (RC) .20 .50
126 Ben Johnson (RC) .20 .50
127 Ryan Howard .50 1.25
128 Bobby Abreu .12 .30
129 Chase Utley .30 .75
130 Pat Burrell .12 .30
131 Jimmy Rollins .20 .50
132 Brett Myers .12 .30
133 Mike Thompson RC .20 .50
134 Jason Bay .20 .50
135 Oliver Perez .12 .30
136 Matt Capps (RC) .20 .50
137 Paul Maholm (RC) .20 .50
138 Nate McLouth (RC) .20 .50
139 John Van Benschoten (RC) .20 .50
140 Mark Teixeira .30 .75
141 Michael Young .20 .50
142 Hank Blalock .12 .30
143 Kevin Millwood .12 .30
144 Laynce Nix .12 .30
145 Francisco Cordero .12 .30
146 Ian Kinsler (RC) .60 1.50
147 David Ortiz .30 .75
148 Manny Ramirez .30 .75
149 Jason Varitek .30 .75
150 Curt Schilling .20 .50
151 Josh Beckett .20 .50
152 Coco Crisp .12 .30
153 Jonathan Papelbon (RC) 1.00 2.50
154 Ken Griffey Jr. .50 1.25
155 Adam Dunn .20 .50
156 Felipe Lopez .12 .30
157 Bronson Arroyo .20 .50
158 Ryan Freel .12 .30
159 Chris Denorfia (RC) .20 .50
160 Todd Helton .20 .50
161 Garrett Atkins .12 .30
162 Matt Holliday .30 .75
163 Clint Barmes .12 .30
164 Kendry Morales (RC) .50 1.25
165 Ryan Shealy (RC) .20 .50
166 Josh Wilson (RC) .20 .50
167 Reggie Sanders .12 .30
168 Angel Berroa .12 .30
169 Mike Sweeney .12 .30
170 Mark Grudzielanek .12 .30
171 Jeremy Affeldt .12 .30
172 Steve Stemle RC .12 .30
173 Justin Verlander (RC) 1.50 4.00
174 Ivan Rodriguez .20 .50
175 Chris Shelton .12 .30
176 Jeremy Bonderman .12 .30
177 Magglio Ordonez .20 .50
178 Carlos Guillen .12 .30
179 Placido Polanco .12 .30
180 Johan Santana .30 .75
181 Torii Hunter .12 .30
182 Joe Nathan .12 .30
183 Joe Mauer .30 .75
184 Dave Gassner (RC) .20 .50
185 Jason Kubel (RC) .20 .50
186 Francisco Liriano (RC) .50 1.25
187 Jim Thome .20 .50
188 Paul Konerko .20 .50
189 Scott Podsednik .12 .30
190 Tadahito Iguchi .12 .30
191 A.J. Pierzynski .12 .30
192 Jose Contreras .12 .30
193 Brian Anderson (RC) .20 .50
194 Hideki Matsui .30 .75
195 Wil Nieves (RC) .20 .50
196 Alex Rodriguez .50 1.25
197 Gary Sheffield .12 .30
198 Randy Johnson .30 .75
199 Johnny Damon .20 .50
200 Derek Jeter .75 2.00
NNO Exquisite Redemption

2006 Fleer Tradition Black and White

*B/W 1-200: 2.5X TO 6X BASIC
*B/W 1-200: 1.25X TO 3X BASIC RC
STATED ODDS 1:9 HOBBY, 1:36 RETAIL

2006 Fleer Tradition Sepia

*SEPIA 1-200: 1X TO 2.5X BASIC
*SEPIA 1-200: .5X TO 1.2X BASIC RC
STATED ODDS 1:3 HOBBY, 1:18 RETAIL

2006 Fleer Tradition 1934 Goudey Greats

STATED ODDS 1:36 HOBBY
OVERALL PLATE ODDS 1:288 HOBBY
PLATE PRINT RUN 1 SET PER COLOR
BLACK-CYAN-MAGENTA-YELLOW ISSUED
NO PLATE PRICING DUE TO SCARCITY
GG1 Andruw Jones 2.00 5.00
GG2 Chipper Jones 5.00 12.00
GG3 John Smoltz 5.00 12.00
GG4 Tim Hudson 3.00 8.00
GG5 Conor Jackson 3.00 8.00
GG6 Luis Gonzalez 2.00 5.00
GG7 Brandon Webb 3.00 8.00
GG8 Vladimir Guerrero 5.00 12.00
GG9 Bartolo Colon 2.00 5.00
GG10 Lance Berkman 3.00 8.00
GG11 Craig Biggio 3.00 8.00
GG12 Andy Pettitte 3.00 8.00
GG13 Morgan Ensberg 2.00 5.00
GG14 Roy Oswalt 3.00 8.00
GG15 Eric Chavez 2.00 5.00
GG16 Rich Harden 2.00 5.00
GG17 Huston Street 2.00 5.00
GG18 Vernon Wells 2.00 5.00
GG19 Roy Halladay 5.00 12.00
GG20 Troy Glaus 2.00 5.00
GG21 Prince Fielder 8.00 20.00
GG22 Rickie Weeks 3.00 8.00
GG23 Ben Sheets 2.00 5.00
GG24 Carlos Lee 2.00 5.00
GG25 Albert Pujols 12.00 30.00
GG26 Jim Edmonds 3.00 8.00
GG27 Scott Rolen 3.00 8.00
GG28 Chris Carpenter 5.00 12.00
GG29 Derrek Lee 2.00 5.00
GG30 Mark Prior 3.00 8.00
GG31 Greg Maddux 8.00 20.00
GG32 Carl Crawford 3.00 8.00
GG33 Scott Kazmir 3.00 8.00
GG34 Jorge Cantu 2.00 5.00
GG35 Jeff Kent 2.00 5.00
GG36 Nomar Garciaparra 5.00 12.00
GG37 J.D. Drew 2.00 5.00
GG38 Randy Winn 2.00 5.00
GG39 Jason Schmidt 2.00 5.00
GG40 Travis Hafner 2.00 5.00
GG41 Victor Martinez 3.00 8.00
GG42 Grady Sizemore 3.00 8.00
GG43 Jhonny Peralta 2.00 5.00
GG44 Ichiro Suzuki 8.00 20.00
GG45 Richie Sexson 2.00 5.00
GG46 Felix Hernandez 5.00 12.00
GG47 Kenji Johjima 5.00 12.00
GG48 Miguel Cabrera 5.00 12.00
GG49 Dontrelle Willis 2.00 5.00
GG50 Josh Willingham 2.00 5.00
GG51 David Wright 8.00 20.00
GG52 Jose Reyes 3.00 8.00
GG53 Pedro Martinez 3.00 8.00
GG54 Carlos Beltran 2.00 5.00
GG55 Alfonso Soriano 3.00 8.00
GG56 Ryan Zimmerman 10.00 25.00
GG57 Miguel Tejada 3.00 8.00
GG58 Brian Roberts 2.00 5.00
GG59 Jake Peavy 2.00 5.00
GG60 Brian Giles 2.00 5.00
GG61 Khalil Greene 2.00 5.00
GG62 Ryan Howard 8.00 20.00
GG63 Bobby Abreu 2.00 5.00
GG64 Chase Utley 5.00 12.00
GG65 Jimmy Rollins 3.00 8.00
GG66 Jason Bay 3.00 8.00
GG67 Mark Teixeira 5.00 12.00
GG68 Michael Young 3.00 8.00
GG69 Hank Blalock 2.00 5.00
GG70 David Ortiz 3.00 8.00
GG71 Manny Ramirez 5.00 12.00
GG72 Curt Schilling 3.00 8.00
GG73 Josh Beckett 3.00 8.00
GG74 Jonathan Papelbon 10.00 25.00
GG75 Ken Griffey Jr. 8.00 20.00
GG76 Adam Dunn 3.00 8.00
GG77 Todd Helton 3.00 8.00
GG78 Garrett Atkins 2.00 5.00
GG79 Matt Holliday 5.00 12.00
GG80 Reggie Sanders 2.00 5.00
GG81 Justin Verlander 15.00 40.00
GG82 Ivan Rodriguez 3.00 8.00
GG83 Chris Shelton 2.00 5.00
GG84 Jeremy Bonderman 2.00 5.00
GG85 Magglio Ordonez 3.00 8.00
GG86 Johan Santana 5.00 12.00
GG87 Torii Hunter 2.00 5.00
GG88 Joe Nathan 2.00 5.00
GG89 Joe Mauer 5.00 12.00
GG90 Francisco Liriano 5.00 12.00
GG91 Jim Thome 3.00 8.00
GG92 Paul Konerko 3.00 8.00
GG93 Scott Podsednik 2.00 5.00
GG94 Tadahito Iguchi 2.00 5.00
GG95 A.J. Pierzynski 2.00 5.00
GG96 Hideki Matsui 5.00 12.00
GG97 Alex Rodriguez 8.00 20.00
GG98 Gary Sheffield 2.00 5.00
GG99 Derek Jeter 12.00 30.00
GG100 Jason Giambi 2.00 5.00

2006 Fleer Tradition Blue Chip Prospects

COMPLETE SET (25) 12.50 30.00
STATED ODDS 1:6 HOBBY, 1:18 RETAIL
OVERALL PLATE ODDS 1:288 HOBBY
PLATE PRINT RUN 1 SET PER COLOR
BLACK-CYAN-MAGENTA-YELLOW ISSUED
NO PLATE PRICING DUE TO SCARCITY
BC1 Ryan Zimmerman 2.00 5.00
BC2 Conor Jackson .60 1.50
BC3 Jonathan Papelbon 2.00 5.00
BC4 Justin Verlander 3.00 8.00
BC5 Jeremy Hermida .40 1.00
BC6 Josh Willingham .40 1.00
BC7 Hanley Ramirez 1.00 2.50
BC8 Prince Fielder 1.50 4.00
BC9 Francisco Liriano 1.00 2.50
BC10 Lastings Milledge .40 1.00
BC11 Jon Lester 1.50 4.00
BC12 Matt Cain 1.00 2.50
BC13 Adam Wainwright 1.00 2.50
BC14 Chuck James .40 1.00
BC15 Kenji Johjima 1.00 2.50
BC16 Josh Johnson 1.00 2.50
BC17 Jason Kubel .40 1.00
BC18 Brian Anderson .40 1.00
BC19 Cole Hamels 1.50 4.00
BC20 Mike Jacobs .40 1.00
BC21 Jered Weaver 1.00 2.50
BC22 Kendry Morales 1.00 2.50
BC23 Alay Soler .40 1.00
BC24 Chris Denorfia .40 1.00
BC25 Chad Billingsley .60 1.50

2006 Fleer Tradition Diamond Tribute

COMPLETE SET (25) 12.50 30.00
STATED ODDS 1:9 HOBBY, 1:36 RETAIL
OVERALL PLATE ODDS 1:288 HOBBY
PLATE PRINT RUN 1 SET PER COLOR
BLACK-CYAN-MAGENTA-YELLOW ISSUED
NO PLATE PRICING DUE TO SCARCITY
DT1 Derek Jeter 2.50 6.00
DT2 Ken Griffey Jr. 1.50 4.00
DT3 Vladimir Guerrero 1.00 2.50
DT4 Albert Pujols 2.50 6.00
DT5 Derrek Lee .40 1.00
DT6 David Ortiz .60 1.50
DT7 Miguel Tejada .60 1.50
DT8 Jim Thome .60 1.50
DT9 Travis Hafner .40 1.00
DT10 Grady Sizemore .60 1.50
DT11 Chris Shelton .40 1.00
DT12 Dontrelle Willis .40 1.00
DT13 Craig Biggio .60 1.50
DT14 Roy Oswalt .60 1.50
DT15 Prince Fielder 1.50 4.00
DT16 David Wright 1.50 4.00
DT17 Jose Reyes .60 1.50
DT18 Hideki Matsui 1.00 2.50
DT19 Rich Harden .40 1.00
DT20 Bobby Abreu .40 1.00
DT21 Jason Bay .40 1.00
DT22 Jake Peavy .40 1.00
DT23 Felix Hernandez 1.00 2.50
DT24 Carl Crawford .60 1.50
DT25 Vernon Wells .40 1.00

2006 Fleer Tradition Grass Roots

COMPLETE SET (25) 12.50 30.00
STATED ODDS 1:6 HOBBY, 1:36 RETAIL
OVERALL PLATE ODDS 1:288 HOBBY
PLATE PRINT RUN 1 SET PER COLOR
BLACK-CYAN-MAGENTA-YELLOW ISSUED
NO PLATE PRICING DUE TO SCARCITY
GR1 Ken Griffey Jr. 1.50 4.00
GR2 Albert Pujols 2.50 6.00
GR3 Derek Jeter 2.50 6.00
GR4 Derrek Lee .40 1.00
GR5 Vladimir Guerrero 1.00 2.50
GR6 Andruw Jones .40 1.00
GR7 Manny Ramirez 1.00 2.50
GR8 Johan Santana 1.00 2.50
GR9 Victor Martinez .60 1.50
GR10 Todd Helton .60 1.50
GR11 Ivan Rodriguez .60 1.50
GR12 Miguel Cabrera 1.00 2.50
GR13 Lance Berkman .60 1.50
GR14 Bartolo Colon .40 1.00
GR15 Jeff Kent .40 1.00
GR16 Carlos Lee .40 1.00
GR17 Torii Hunter .40 1.00
GR18 Carlos Beltran .40 1.00
GR19 Alex Rodriguez 1.50 4.00
GR20 Randy Johnson 1.00 2.50
GR21 Eric Chavez .40 1.00
GR22 Ryan Howard 1.50 4.00
GR23 Ichiro Suzuki 1.50 4.00
GR24 Chris Carpenter 1.00 2.50
GR25 Mark Teixeira 1.00 2.50

2006 Fleer Tradition Ken Griffey Jr. 1989 Autograph Buyback

RANDOM INSERT IN HOBBY PACKS
STATED PRINT RUN 99 CARDS
CARD IS NOT SERIAL-NUMBERED
PRINT RUN PROVIDED BY UPPER DECK
NO PRICING DUE TO SCARCITY
548 Ken Griffey Jr./99 *

2006 Fleer Tradition Signature Tradition

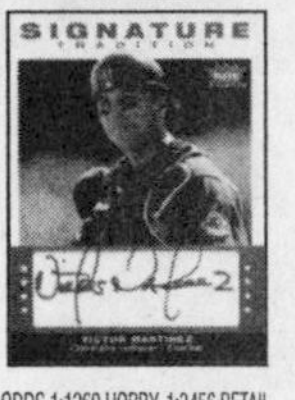

STATED ODDS 1:1269 HOBBY, 1:3456 RETAIL
SP INFO PROVIDED BY UPPER DECK
NO PRICING DUE TO SCARCITY
OVERALL PLATE ODDS: 1:288 HOBBY
PLATE PRINT RUN 1 SET PER COLOR
BLACK-CYAN-MAGENTA-YELLOW-ISSUED
PLATES DO NOT FEATURE AUTOS
NO PLATE PRICING DUE TO SCARCITY

2006 Fleer Tradition Traditional Threads

STATED ODDS 1:41 HOBBY, 1:108 RETAIL
SP INFO PROVIDED BY UPPER DECK
OVERALL PLATE ODDS: 1:288 HOBBY
PLATE PRINT RUN 1 SET PER COLOR
BLACK-CYAN-MAGENTA-YELLOW-ISSUED
PLATES DO NOT FEATURE MATERIAL
NO PLATE PRICING DUE TO SCARCITY
AP Albert Pujols Jsy 8.00 20.00
AR Aramis Ramirez Jsy 3.00 8.00
AS Alfonso Soriano Jsy 3.00 8.00
BA Jason Bay Jsy 3.00 8.00
BG Brian Giles Jsy 3.00 8.00
BR Brian Roberts Jsy 3.00 8.00
BS Ben Sheets Jsy 3.00 8.00
CF Chone Figgins Jsy 3.00 8.00
CK Casey Kotchman Jsy SP 4.00 10.00
CL Carlos Lee Jsy 3.00 8.00
CZ Carlos Zambrano Jsy SP 4.00 10.00
DJ Derek Jeter Pants 8.00 20.00
DL Derrek Lee Jsy 3.00 8.00
DO David Ortiz Jsy 4.00 10.00
EB Erik Bedard Jsy 3.00 8.00
FH Felix Hernandez Jsy 4.00 10.00
GJ Geoff Jenkins Jsy 3.00 8.00
GM Greg Maddux Jsy 4.00 10.00
GR Khalil Greene Jsy 4.00 10.00
HB Hank Blalock Jsy 3.00 8.00
JB Josh Barfield Jsy 3.00 8.00
JD Johnny Damon Jsy 4.00 10.00
JH Jeremy Hermida Jsy 4.00 10.00
JL Javy Lopez Jsy 3.00 8.00
JP Jake Peavy Jsy 3.00 8.00
JV Jose Vidro Jsy 3.00 8.00
KG Ken Griffey Jr. Jsy 6.00 15.00
LH Livan Hernandez Jsy 3.00 8.00
MG Marcus Giles Jsy 3.00 8.00
MM Melvin Mora Jsy 3.00 8.00
MT Miguel Tejada Pants 3.00 8.00
MY Michael Young Jsy 3.00 8.00

OV Omar Vizquel Jsy SP 4.00 10.00
PF Prince Fielder Jsy 4.00 10.00
RO Roy Oswalt Jsy 3.00 8.00
RW Rickie Weeks Jsy 3.00 8.00
RZ Ryan Zimmerman Jsy 6.00 15.00
SC Sean Casey Jsy 3.00 8.00
TE Mark Teixeira Jsy 4.00 10.00
VG Vladimir Guerrero Jsy 4.00 10.00
ZD Zach Duke Jsy 3.00 8.00

2006 Fleer Tradition Triple Crown Contenders

COMPLETE SET (15) 10.00 25.00
STATED ODDS 1:9 HOBBY, 1:36 RETAIL
OVERALL PLATE ODDS 1:288 HOBBY
PLATE PRINT RUN 1 SET PER COLOR
BLACK-CYAN-MAGENTA-YELLOW ISSUED
NO PLATE PRICING DUE TO SCARCITY
TC1 Albert Pujols 2.50 6.00
TC2 Derrek Lee .40 1.00
TC3 Manny Ramirez 1.00 2.50
TC4 David Ortiz .60 1.50
TC5 Mark Teixeira 1.00 2.50
TC6 Alex Rodriguez 1.50 4.00
TC7 Andruw Jones .40 1.00
TC8 Todd Helton .60 1.50
TC9 Vladimir Guerrero 1.00 2.50
TC10 Miguel Cabrera 1.00 2.50
TC11 Hideki Matsui 1.00 2.50
TC12 Travis Hafner .40 1.00
TC13 David Wright 1.50 4.00
TC14 Ken Griffey Jr. 1.50 4.00
TC15 Jason Bay .40 1.00

2001 Fleer Triple Crown

The 2001 Fleer Triple Crown product was released in January, 2001 and featured a 300-card base set. The set is broken into two subset: Base Veterans (1-250), and Prospects (251-300). Please note that Fleer created three parallels of the first 100 cards (Red, Blue, and Green). Each pack contained 10 cards and carried a suggested retail price of $1.99.

COMPLETE SET (300) 12.50 30.00
COMMON CARD (1-300) .10 .30
COMMON (301-310) 1.50 4.00
1 Derek Jeter .75 2.00
2 Vladimir Guerrero .30 .75
3 Henry Rodriguez .10 .30
4 Jason Giambi .10 .30
5 Nomar Garciaparra .50 1.25
6 Jeff Kent .10 .30
7 Garret Anderson .10 .30
8 Todd Helton .20 .50
9 Barry Bonds .75 2.00
10 Preston Wilson .10 .30
11 Troy Glaus .10 .30
12 Geoff Jenkins .10 .30
13 Jim Edmonds .10 .30
14 Bobby Higginson .10 .30
15 Mark Quinn .10 .30
16 Barry Larkin .20 .50
17 Richie Sexson .10 .30
18 Fernando Tatis .10 .30
19 John VanderWal .10 .30
20 Darin Erstad .10 .30
21 Shawn Green .10 .30
22 Scott Rolen .20 .50
23 Tony Batista .10 .30
24 Phil Nevin .10 .30
25 Tim Salmon .20 .50
26 Gary Sheffield .10 .30
27 Ben Grieve .10 .30
28 Jermaine Dye .10 .30
29 Andres Galarraga .10 .30
30 Adrian Beltre .10 .30
31 Rafael Palmeiro .20 .50
32 J.T. Snow .10 .30
33 Edgardo Alfonzo .10 .30
34 Paul Konerko .10 .30
35 Jim Thome .20 .50
36 Andruw Jones .20 .50
37 Mike Sweeney .10 .30
38 Jose Cruz Jr. .10 .30
39 David Ortiz .30 .75
40 Pat Burrell .10 .30
41 Chipper Jones .30 .75
42 Jeff Bagwell .20 .50
43 Raul Mondesi .10 .30
44 Rondell White .10 .30
45 Edgar Martinez .20 .50
46 Cal Ripken 1.00 2.50
47 Moises Alou .10 .30
48 Shannon Stewart .10 .30
49 Tino Martinez .20 .50
50 Jason Kendall .10 .30
51 Richard Hidalgo .10 .30
52 Albert Belle .10 .30
53 Jay Payton .10 .30
54 Cliff Floyd .10 .30
55 Rusty Greer .10 .30
56 Matt Williams .10 .30
57 Sammy Sosa .30 .75
58 Carl Everett .10 .30
59 Carlos Delgado .10 .30
60 Jeremy Giambi .10 .30
61 Jose Canseco .20 .50
62 David Segui .10 .30
63 Jose Vidro .10 .30
64 Matt Stairs .10 .30
65 Travis Fryman .10 .30
66 Ken Griffey Jr. .50 1.25
67 Mike Piazza .50 1.25
68 Mark McGwire .75 2.00
69 Craig Biggio .20 .50
70 Eric Chavez .10 .30
71 Mo Vaughn .10 .30
72 Matt Lawton .10 .30
73 Miguel Tejada .10 .30
74 Brian Giles .10 .30
75 Sean Casey .10 .30
76 Robin Ventura .10 .30
77 Ivan Rodriguez .20 .50
78 Dean Palmer .10 .30
79 Frank Thomas .30 .75
80 Bernie Williams .20 .50
81 Juan Encarnacion .10 .30
82 John Olerud .10 .30
83 Rich Aurilia .10 .30
84 Juan Gonzalez .10 .30
85 Ray Durham .10 .30
86 Steve Finley .10 .30
87 Ken Caminiti .10 .30
88 Roberto Alomar .20 .50
89 Jeromy Burnitz .10 .30
90 J.D. Drew .10 .30
91 Lance Berkman .10 .30
92 Gabe Kapler .10 .30
93 Larry Walker .10 .30
94 Alex Rodriguez .50 1.25
95 Jeffrey Hammonds .10 .30
96 Magglio Ordonez .10 .30
97 David Justice .10 .30
98 Eric Karros .10 .30
99 Manny Ramirez .20 .50
100 Paul O'Neill .20 .50
101 Ron Gant .10 .30
102 Erubiel Durazo .10 .30
103 Jason Varitek .30 .75
104 Chan Ho Park .10 .30
105 Corey Koskie .10 .30
106 Jeff Conine .10 .30
107 Kevin Tapani .10 .30
108 Mike Lowell .10 .30
109 Tim Hudson .10 .30
110 Bobby Abreu .10 .30
111 Bret Boone .10 .30
112 David Wells .10 .30
113 Brian Jordan .10 .30
114 Mitch Meluskey .10 .30
115 Terrence Long .10 .30
116 Matt Clement .10 .30
117 Fernando Vina .10 .30
118 Luis Alicea .10 .30
119 Jay Bell .10 .30
120 Mark Grace .20 .50
121 Carlos Febles .10 .30
122 Mark Redman .10 .30
123 Kevin Jordan .10 .30
124 Pat Meares .10 .30
125 Mark McLemore .10 .30
126 Chris Singleton .10 .30
127 Trot Nixon .10 .30
128 Carlos Beltran .10 .30
129 Lee Stevens .10 .30
130 Kris Benson .10 .30
131 Jay Buhner .10 .30
132 Greg Vaughn .10 .30
133 Eric Young .10 .30
134 Tony Womack .10 .30
135 Roger Cedeno .10 .30
136 Travis Lee .10 .30
137 Marvin Benard .10 .30
138 Aaron Sele .10 .30
139 Rick Ankiel .10 .30
140 Ruben Mateo .10 .30
141 Randy Johnson .30 .75
142 Jason Tyner .10 .30
143 Mike Redmond .10 .30
144 Ron Coomer .10 .30
145 Scott Elarton .10 .30
146 Javy Lopez .10 .30
147 Carlos Lee .10 .30
148 Tony Clark .10 .30
149 Roger Clemens .60 1.50
150 Mike Lieberthal .10 .30
151 Shawn Estes .10 .30
152 Vinny Castilla .10 .30
153 Alex Gonzalez .10 .30
154 Troy Percival .10 .30
155 Pokey Reese .10 .30
156 Todd Hollandsworth .10 .30
157 Marquis Grissom .10 .30
158 Greg Maddux .50 1.25
159 Dante Bichette .10 .30
160 Hideo Nomo .30 .75
161 Jacque Jones .10 .30
162 Kevin Young .10 .30
163 B.J. Surhoff .10 .30
164 Eddie Taubensee .10 .30
165 Neifi Perez .10 .30
166 Orlando Hernandez .10 .30
167 Francisco Cordova .10 .30
168 Miguel Cairo .10 .30
169 Rafael Furcal .10 .30
170 Sandy Alomar Jr. .10 .30
171 Jeff Cirillo .10 .30
172 A.J. Pierzynski .10 .30
173 Fred McGriff .20 .50
174 Mike Mussina .20 .50
175 Aaron Boone .10 .30
176 Nick Johnson .10 .30
177 Kent Bottenfield .10 .30
178 Felipe Crespo .10 .30
179 Ryan Minor .10 .30
180 Charles Johnson .10 .30
181 Damion Easley .10 .30
182 Michael Barrett .10 .30
183 Doug Glanville .10 .30
184 Ben Davis .10 .30
185 Rickey Henderson .30 .75
186 Edgard Clemente .10 .30
187 Dmitri Young .10 .30
188 Tom Goodwin .10 .30
189 Mike Hampton .10 .30
190 Gerald Williams .10 .30
191 Omar Vizquel .20 .50
192 Ben Petrick .10 .30
193 Brad Radke .10 .30
194 Russ Davis .10 .30
195 Milton Bradley .10 .30
196 John Parrish .10 .30
197 Todd Hundley .10 .30
198 Carl Pavano .10 .30
199 Bruce Chen .10 .30
200 Royce Clayton .10 .30
201 Homer Bush .10 .30
202 Mark Grudzielanek .10 .30
203 Mike Lansing .10 .30
204 Daryle Ward .10 .30
205 Jeff D'Amico .10 .30
206 Ray Lankford .10 .30
207 Curt Schilling .10 .30
208 Pedro Martinez .20 .50
209 Johnny Damon .20 .50
210 Al Leiter .10 .30
211 Ruben Rivera .10 .30
212 Kazuhiro Sasaki .10 .30
213 Will Clark .20 .50
214 Rick Helling .10 .30
215 Adam Piatt .10 .30
216 Joe Girardi .10 .30
217 A.J. Burnett .10 .30
218 Mike Bordick .10 .30
219 Mike Cameron .10 .30
220 Tony Gwynn .40 1.00
221 Deivi Cruz .10 .30
222 Bubba Trammell .10 .30
223 Scott Erickson .10 .30
224 Kerry Wood .10 .30
225 Derrek Lee .20 .50
226 Peter Bergeron .10 .30
227 Chris Gomez .10 .30
228 Al Martin .10 .30
229 Brady Anderson .10 .30
230 Ramon Martinez .10 .30
231 Darryl Kile .10 .30
232 Devon White .10 .30
233 Charlie Hayes .10 .30
234 Aramis Ramirez .10 .30
235 Mike Lamb .10 .30
236 Tom Glavine .20 .50
237 Troy O'Leary .10 .30
238 Joe Randa .10 .30
239 Dustin Hermanson .10 .30
240 Adam Kennedy .10 .30
241 Jose Valentin .10 .30
242 Derek Bell .10 .30
243 Mark Kotsay .10 .30
244 Ron Belliard .10 .30
245 Warren Morris .10 .30
246 Ozzie Guillen .10 .30
247 Andy Ashby .10 .30
248 Jose Offerman .10 .30
249 Kevin Brown .10 .30
250 Jorge Posada .20 .50
251 Alex Cabrera .10 .30
252 Chan Perry .10 .30
253 Augie Ojeda .10 .30
254 Santiago Perez .10 .30
255 Grant Roberts .10 .30
256 Dusty Allen .10 .30
257 Elvis Pena .10 .30
258 Matt Kinney .10 .30
259 Timo Perez .10 .30
260 Adam Eaton .10 .30
261 Geraldo Guzman .10 .30
262 Damian Rolls .10 .30
263 Alfonso Soriano .20 .50
264 Corey Patterson .10 .30
265 Juan Alvarez .10 .30
266 Shawn Gilbert .10 .30
267 Adam Bernero .10 .30
268 Ben Weber .10 .30
269 Tike Redman .10 .30
270 Willie Morales .10 .30
271 Tomas De la Rosa .10 .30
272 Rodney Lindsey .10 .30
273 Carlos Casimiro .10 .30
274 Jim Mann .10 .30
275 Pasqual Coco .10 .30
276 Julio Zuleta .10 .30
277 Damon Minor .10 .30
278 Jose Ortiz .10 .30
279 Eric Munson .10 .30
280 Andy Thompson .10 .30
281 Aubrey Huff .10 .30
282 Chris Richard .10 .30
283 Ross Gload .10 .30
284 Travis Dawkins .10 .30
285 Tim Drew .10 .30
286 Barry Zito .20 .50
287 Andy Tracy .10 .30
288 Julio Lugo .10 .30
289 Greg LaRocca .10 .30
290 Keith McDonald .10 .30
291 J.C. Romero .10 .30
292 Adam Melhuse .10 .30
293 Ryan Kohlmeier .10 .30
294 John Bale .10 .30
295 Eric Cammack .10 .30
296 Morgan Burkhart .10 .30
297 Kory DeHaan .10 .30
298 Mike Mahoney .10 .30
299 Hector Ortiz .10 .30
300 Talmadge Nunnari .10 .30
301 E.Guzman/2999 RC 1.50 4.00
302 D.Henson/2999 RC 2.00 5.00
303 Bud Smith/2999 RC 1.50 4.00
304 C.Valderrama/2999 RC 1.50 4.00
305 T.Shinjo/2999 RC 2.00 5.00
306 I.Suzuki/2999 RC 12.50 30.00
307 J.Melian/2999 RC 1.50 4.00
308 M.Ensberg/2999 RC 2.00 5.00
309 Albert Pujols/2999 RC 50.00 100.00
310 J.Estrada/2999 RC 2.00 5.00

2001 Fleer Triple Crown Blue

Randomly inserted exclusively into hobby packs, this 100-card set is a complete parallel of the first 100 cards in the 2001 Fleer Triple Crown base set. Please note that these cards have blue-foil lettering on the card fronts, and are individually serial numbered to each player's 2000 home run total. Cards with a print run of 15 or less are not priced.

*PRINT RUN b/wn 36-50: 15X TO 40X BASIC
*PRINT RUN b/wn 26-35: 20X TO 50X BASIC

*PRINT RUN b/wn 21-25: 25X TO 60X BASIC
*PRINT RUN b/wn 16-20: 30X TO 80X BASIC

2001 Fleer Triple Crown Green

Randomly inserted exclusively into hobby packs, this 100-card set is a complete parallel of the first 100 cards in the 2001 Fleer Triple Crown base set. Please note that these cards have green-foil lettering on the card fronts, and are individually serial numbered to each player's 2000 RBI total.

*PRINT RUN b/wn 121-150: 6X TO 15X BASIC
*PRINT RUN b/wn 81-120: 8X TO 20X BASIC
*PRINT RUN b/wn 66-80: 10X TO 25X BASIC
*PRINT RUN b/wn 51-65: 12.5X TO 30X BASIC
*PRINT RUN b/wn 36-50: 15X TO 40X BASIC

2001 Fleer Triple Crown Purple

Randomly inserted into retail packs, this 100-card set is a complete parallel of the first 100 cards in the 2001 Fleer Triple Crown base set. Please note that these cards have purple-foil lettering on the card fronts, and were only available in retail packs at the rate of approximately one per box.

*STARS: 2.5X TO 6X BASIC CARDS

2001 Fleer Triple Crown Red

Randomly inserted exclusively into hobby packs, this 100-card set is a complete parallel of the first 100 cards in the 2001 Fleer Triple Crown base set. Please note that these cards have red-foil lettering on the card fronts, and are individually serial numbered to each player's 2000 batting average.

*STARS: 4X TO 10X BASIC CARDS

2001 Fleer Triple Crown Crowning Achievements

Randomly inserted into hobby packs at one in nine and retail packs at a rate of one in 12, this 15-card insert features players that have had significant achievements in their career or will reach one in 2001. Card backs carry a "CA" prefix.

COMPLETE SET (15) 20.00 40.00
CA1 Troy Glaus .50 1.25
CA2 Mark McGwire 2.00 5.00
CA3 Barry Larkin .50 1.25
Andres Galarraga
Craig Biggio
CA4 Ken Griffey Jr. 1.25 3.00
CA5 Rafael Palmeiro .50 1.25
CA6 Alex Rodriguez 1.25 3.00
CA7 Roger Clemens 1.50 4.00
CA8 Mike Piazza 1.25 3.00
CA9 Cal Ripken 2.50 6.00
CA10 Randy Johnson .75 2.00
CA11 Jeff Bagwell .50 1.25
CA12 Sammy Sosa .75 2.00
CA13 Greg Maddux 1.25 3.00
CA14 Barry Bonds 2.00 5.00
CA15 Fred McGriff .50 1.25

2001 Fleer Triple Crown Crowns of Gold Memorabilia

Randomly inserted exclusively into hobby packs, this 12-card insert features swatches of game-used memorabilia from players that have either won the Triple Crown award, or that will be in the running to win it. Card are listed below in alphabetical order for

convenience. Out of one in every 72 packs, collectors received either a Crowns of Gold, Crowns of Gold Autograph, Feel the Game or Autographics card.

1 Rick Ankiel Jsy 4.00 10.00
2 Steve Carlton Jsy 4.00 10.00
3 Roger Clemens Jsy 10.00 25.00
4 Carlos Delgado Bat 4.00 10.00
5 Darin Erstad Bat 4.00 10.00
6 Jimmie Foxx Bat 40.00 80.00
7 Todd Helton Bat 6.00 15.00
8 Randy Johnson Jsy 6.00 15.00
9 Frank Robinson Bat 6.00 15.00
10 Gary Sheffield Jsy 4.00 10.00
11 Frank Thomas Bat 6.00 15.00
12 Ted Williams Bat 50.00 100.00

2001 Fleer Triple Crown Crowns of Gold Memorabilia Autographs

Randomly inserted into packs, this four-card insert features both game-used memorabilia swatches and autographs from some of the best players in the history of baseball. This set includes Frank Robinson, Steve Carlton, Roger Clemens, and Ted Williams. Cards are listed below in alphabetical order. The Williams card was an exchange and the deadline to exchange this card was February 1, 2002. Sadly, Williams was never able to sign his card and all collectors who redeemed that card were reimbursed with a significant amount of signed and memorabilia cards of their choice in it's place.

1 Steve Carlton Jsy/72 20.00 50.00
2 Roger Clemens Jsy/98 40.00 80.00
3 Frank Robinson Bat/66 40.00 80.00
4 Ted Williams Bat/9
. Williams never signed this card

2001 Fleer Triple Crown Future Threats

Randomly inserted into hobby packs at one in seven and retail packs at a rate of one in 10, this 15-card insert features players that look to dominate starting pitching for years to come. Card backs carry a "FT" prefix.

COMPLETE SET (15) 15.00 30.00
FT1 Derek Jeter 1.50 4.00
FT2 Alex Rodriguez 1.00 2.50
FT3 Magglio Ordonez .40 1.00
Shawn Green
Andruw Jones
FT4 Larry Walker .40 1.00
FT5 Vladimir Guerrero .60 1.50
FT6 Nomar Garciaparra 1.00 2.50
FT7 Ken Griffey Jr. 1.00 2.50
FT8 Barry Bonds 1.50 4.00
FT9 Chipper Jones .60 1.50
FT10 Todd Helton .40 1.00
FT11 Ivan Rodriguez .40 1.00
FT12 Jeff Bagwell .40 1.00
FT13 Frank Thomas .60 1.50
FT14 Carlos Delgado .40 1.00
FT15 Mike Piazza 1.00 2.50

2001 Fleer Triple Crown Glamour Boys

Randomly inserted into hobby packs at one in 24 and retail packs at a rate of one in 20, this 15-card insert features players that give maximum effort every game. Card backs carry a "GB" prefix.

COMPLETE SET (15) 50.00 100.00
GB1 Derek Jeter 4.00 10.00
GB2 Vladimir Guerrero 1.50 4.00
GB3 Scott Rolen 1.50 4.00
Jeff Bagwell
Bernie Williams
GB4 Sammy Sosa 1.50 4.00
GB5 Ken Griffey Jr. 2.50 6.00
GB6 Mark McGwire 4.00 10.00
GB7 Ivan Rodriguez 1.50 4.00
GB8 Mike Piazza 2.50 6.00
GB9 Nomar Garciaparra 2.50 6.00
GB10 Cal Ripken 5.00 12.00
GB11 Tony Gwynn 2.00 5.00
GB12 Barry Bonds 4.00 10.00
GB13 Randy Johnson 1.50 4.00
GB14 Alex Rodriguez 2.50 6.00
GB15 Pedro Martinez 1.50 4.00

2002 Fleer Triple Crown

This set was issued in March, 2002. These cards were issued in ten-card packs with an SRP of $2.50 and had 24 packs to a box and either 6 or 16 boxes to a case. The following subsets were included in this set: Cards

numbered 201-230 featured leading rookie prospects while 231-240 featured a scrapbook and cards 241-260 featured pace setters. An unnumbered Derek Jeter promo card was issued a few weeks before this product was released and is noted at the end of our listings.

COMPLETE SET (270) 15.00 40.00
1 Mo Vaughn .10 .30
2 Derek Jeter .75 2.00
3 Ken Griffey Jr. .50 1.25
4 Charles Johnson .10 .30
5 Geoff Jenkins .10 .30
6 Chuck Knoblauch .10 .30
7 Jason Kendall .10 .30
8 Jim Edmonds .10 .30
9 David Eckstein .10 .30
10 Carl Everett .10 .30
11 Barry Larkin .20 .50
12 Cliff Floyd .10 .30
13 Ben Sheets .10 .30
14 Jeff Conine .10 .30
15 Brian Giles .10 .30
16 Darryl Kile .10 .30
17 Troy Glaus .10 .30
18 Trot Nixon .10 .30
19 Jim Thome .20 .50
20 Preston Wilson .10 .30
21 Roger Clemens .60 1.50
22 Chad Hermansen .10 .30
23 Matt Morris .10 .30
24 Shawn Wooten .10 .30
25 Manny Ramirez .20 .50
26 Roberto Alomar .20 .50
27 Josh Beckett .10 .30
28 Jose Hernandez .10 .30
29 Mike Mussina .20 .50
30 Jack Wilson .10 .30
31 Bud Smith .10 .30
32 Garret Anderson .10 .30
33 Pedro Martinez .20 .50
34 Travis Fryman .10 .30
35 Jeff Bagwell .20 .50
36 Doug Mientkiewicz .10 .30
37 Andy Pettitte .20 .50
38 Ryan Klesko .10 .30
39 Edgar Renteria .10 .30
40 Mariano Rivera .30 .75
41 Darin Erstad .10 .30
42 Hideo Nomo .30 .75
43 Ellis Burks .10 .30
44 Craig Biggio .20 .50
45 Corey Koskie .10 .30
46 Jason Varitek .30 .75
47 Xavier Nady .10 .30
48 Aubrey Huff .10 .30
49 Tim Salmon .20 .50
50 Nomar Garciaparra .50 1.25
51 Juan Gonzalez .10 .30
52 Moises Alou .10 .30
53 A.J. Pierzynski .10 .30
54 Bernie Williams .20 .50
55 Phil Nevin .10 .30
56 Ben Grieve .10 .30
57 Mark Grace .20 .50
58 Mike Lansing .10 .30
59 Kenny Lofton .10 .30
60 Lance Berkman .10 .30
61 David Ortiz .30 .75
62 Jason Giambi .10 .30
63 Mark Kotsay .10 .30
64 Greg Vaughn .10 .30
65 Junior Spivey .10 .30
66 Fred McGriff .20 .50
67 C.C. Sabathia .10 .30
68 Richard Hidalgo .10 .30
69 Torii Hunter .10 .30
70 Jason Hart .10 .30
71 Bubba Trammell .10 .30
72 Jace Brewer .10 .30
73 Matt Williams .10 .30
74 Matt Stairs .10 .30
75 Omar Vizquel .20 .50
76 Daryle Ward .10 .30
77 Joe Mays .10 .30
78 Eric Chavez .10 .30
79 Andres Galarraga .10 .30
80 Rafael Palmeiro .20 .50
81 Steve Finley .10 .30
82 Eric Young .10 .30
83 Todd Helton .20 .50
84 Roy Oswalt .10 .30
85 Eric Milton .10 .30
86 Ramon Hernandez .10 .30
87 Jeff Kent .10 .30
88 Ivan Rodriguez .20 .50
89 Luis Gonzalez .10 .30
90 Corey Patterson .10 .30
91 Jose Ortiz .10 .30
92 Mike Sweeney .10 .30
93 Cristian Guzman .10 .30
94 Johnny Damon .20 .50
95 Barry Bonds .75 2.00
96 Rusty Greer .10 .30
97 Reggie Sanders .10 .30
98 Sammy Sosa .30 .75
99 Jeff Cirillo .10 .30
100 Carlos Febles .10 .30
101 Jose Vidro .10 .30
102 Jermaine Dye .10 .30
103 Rich Aurilia .10 .30
104 Gabe Kapler .10 .30
105 Randy Johnson .30 .75
106 Rondell White .10 .30
107 Ben Petrick .10 .30
108 Joe Randa .10 .30
109 Fernando Tatis .10 .30
110 Tim Hudson .10 .30
111 John Olerud .10 .30
112 Alex Rodriguez .50 1.25
113 Curt Schilling .10 .30
114 Kerry Wood .10 .30
115 Alex Ochoa .10 .30
116 Carlos Beltran .10 .30
117 Vladimir Guerrero .30 .75
118 Mark Mulder .10 .30
119 Bret Boone .10 .30
120 Carlos Delgado .10 .30
121 Marcus Giles .10 .30
122 Paul Konerko .10 .30
123 Juan Pierre .10 .30
124 Mark Quinn .10 .30
125 Edgardo Alfonzo .10 .30
126 Barry Zito .10 .30
127 Dan Wilson .10 .30
128 Jose Cruz Jr. .10 .30
129 Chipper Jones .30 .75
130 Ray Durham .10 .30
131 Larry Walker .10 .30
132 Neifi Perez .10 .30
133 Robin Ventura .10 .30
134 Miguel Tejada .10 .30
135 Edgar Martinez .20 .50
136 Raul Mondesi .10 .30
137 Javy Lopez .10 .30
138 Jose Canseco .20 .50
139 Mike Hampton .10 .30
140 Eric Karros .10 .30
141 Mike Piazza .50 1.25
142 Travis Lee .10 .30
143 Ichiro Suzuki .60 1.50
144 Shannon Stewart .10 .30
145 Andruw Jones .20 .50
146 Frank Thomas .30 .75
147 Tony Clark .10 .30
148 Adrian Beltre .10 .30
149 Matt Lawton .10 .30
150 Marlon Anderson .10 .30
151 Freddy Garcia .10 .30
152 Brian Jordan .10 .30
153 Carlos Lee .10 .30
154 Eric Munson .10 .30
155 Paul LoDuca .10 .30
156 Jay Payton .10 .30
157 Scott Rolen .20 .50
158 Jamie Moyer .10 .30
159 Tom Glavine .20 .50
160 Magglio Ordonez .10 .30
161 Brandon Inge .10 .30
162 Shawn Green .10 .30
163 Tsuyoshi Shinjo .10 .30
164 Mike Lieberthal .10 .30
165 Kazuhiro Sasaki .10 .30
166 Greg Maddux .50 1.25
167 Chris Singleton .10 .30
168 Juan Encarnacion .10 .30
169 Gary Sheffield .10 .30
170 Nick Johnson .10 .30
171 Bob Abreu .10 .30
172 Aaron Boone .10 .30
173 Rafael Furcal .10 .30
174 Mark Buehrle .10 .30
175 Bobby Higginson .10 .30
176 Kevin Brown .10 .30
177 Tino Martinez .20 .50
178 Pat Burrell .10 .30
179 Fernando Vina .10 .30
180 Jay Gibbons .10 .30
181 Jose Valentin .10 .30
182 Derrek Lee .20 .50
183 Richie Sexson .10 .30
184 Alfonso Soriano .10 .30
185 Jimmy Rollins .10 .30
186 Albert Pujols .60 1.50
187 Brady Anderson .10 .30
188 Sean Casey .10 .30
189 Luis Castillo .10 .30
190 Jeromy Burnitz .10 .30
191 Jorge Posada .20 .50
192 Kevin Young .10 .30
193 Eli Marrero .10 .30
194 Shea Hillenbrand .10 .30
195 Adam Dunn .10 .30
196 Mike Lowell .10 .30
197 Jeffrey Hammonds .10 .30
198 David Justice .10 .30
199 Aramis Ramirez .10 .30
200 J.D. Drew .10 .30
201 Pedro Santana FS .08 .25
202 Endy Chavez FS .08 .25
203 Donnie Bridges FS .08 .25
204 Travis Phelps FS .08 .25
205 Drew Henson FS .08 .25
206 Angel Berroa FS .08 .25
207 George Perez FS .08 .25
208 Billy Sylvester FS .08 .25
209 Juan Cruz FS .08 .25
210 Horacio Ramirez FS .08 .25
211 J.J. Davis FS .08 .25
212 Cody Ransom FS .08 .25
213 Mark Teixeira FS .60 1.50
214 Nate Frese FS .08 .25
215 Brian Rogers FS .08 .25
216 Dewon Brazelton FS .08 .25
217 Carlos Hernandez FS .08 .25
218 Juan Rivera FS .08 .25
219 Luis Lopez FS .08 .25
220 Benito Baez FS .08 .25
221 Bill Ortega FS .08 .25
222 Dustan Mohr FS .08 .25
223 Corky Miller FS .08 .25
224 Tyler Walker FS .08 .25
225 Rick Bauer FS .08 .25
226 Mark Prior FS .60 1.50
227 Rafael Soriano FS .08 .25
228 Greg Miller FS .08 .25
229 Dave Williams FS .08 .25
230 Bert Snow FS .08 .25
231 Barry Bonds SB .40 1.00
232 Rickey Henderson SB .30 .75
233 Alex Rodriguez SB .30 .75
234 Luis Gonzalez SB .10 .30
235 Derek Jeter SB .40 1.00
236 Bud Smith SB .10 .30
237 Sammy Sosa SB .20 .50
238 Jeff Bagwell SB .10 .30
239 Jim Thome SB .10 .30
240 Hideo Nomo SB .20 .50
241 Greg Maddux SB .30 .75
242 Ken Griffey Jr. SB .30 .75

243 Curt Schilling	.30	.75
Randy Johnson SB		
244 Arizona Diamondbacks SB	.30	.75
245 Ichiro Suzuki SB	.30	.75
246 Albert Pujols SB	.30	.75
247 Ichiro Suzuki SB	.30	.75
248 Barry Bonds SB	.40	1.00
249 Roger Clemens SB	.30	.75
250 Randy Johnson SB	.20	.50
251 Todd Helton PS	.10	.30
252 Rafael Palmeiro PS	.10	.30
253 Mike Piazza PS	.30	.75
254 Alex Rodriguez PS	.30	.75
255 Manny Ramirez PS	.20	.50
256 Ken Griffey Jr. PS	.30	.75
257 Jason Giambi PS	.10	.30
258 Chipper Jones PS	.20	.50
259 Larry Walker PS	.10	.30
260 Sammy Sosa PS	.20	.50
261 Vladimir Guerrero PS	.20	.50
262 Nomar Garciaparra PS	.30	.75
263 Randy Johnson PS	.20	.50
264 Roger Clemens PS	.30	.75
265 Ichiro Suzuki PS	.30	.75
266 Barry Bonds PS	.40	1.00
267 Paul LoDuca PS	.10	.30
268 Albert Pujols PS	.30	.75
269 Derek Jeter PS	.40	1.00
270 Adam Dunn PS	.10	.30
NNO Derek Jeter Promo	1.25	3.00

2002 Fleer Triple Crown Batting Average Parallel

Randomly inserted in packs and featuring green foil, this is a partial parallel to the Triple Crown insert set. Only the first 150 cards are featured in this and these have stated print runs to the players 2001 batting average. Since each card has a different print run we have notated that information in our checklist.

*BATTING AVG: 4X TO 10X BASIC CARDS
PRINT RUNS: 221-350 OF EACH CARD
SEE BECKETT.COM FOR EXACT PRINT RUNS
150-CARD SKIP-NUMBERED SET

2002 Fleer Triple Crown Home Run Parallel

Randomly inserted in packs and featuring red foil, this is a partial parallel to the Triple Crown insert set. Only the first 150 cards are featured in this and these have stated print runs to the players 2001 home run total. Since each card has a different print run we have notated that information in our checklist. Please note that if the card had a stated print run of 15 or less no pricing is provided due to market scarcity.

*PRINT RUN b/wn 66-80: 10X TO 25X
*PRINT RUN b/wn 51-65: 12.5X TO 30X
*PRINT RUN b/wn 36-50: 15X TO 40X
*PRINT RUN b/wn 26-35: 20X TO 50X
*PRINT RUN b/wn 21-25: 25X TO 60X
*PRINT RUN b/wn 16-20: 30X TO 80X
SEE BECKETT.COM FOR EXACT PRINT RUNS
150-CARD SKIP-NUMBERED SET

2002 Fleer Triple Crown RBI Parallel

Randomly inserted in packs and featuring blue foil, this is a partial parallel to the Triple Crown insert set. Only the first 150 cards are featured in this and these have stated print runs to the players 2001 RBI total. Since each card has a different print run we have notated that information in our checklist.

*PRINT RUN b/wn 151-200: 5X TO 12X
*PRINT RUN b/wn 121-150: 6X TO 15X
*PRINT RUN b/wn 81-120: 8X TO 20X
*PRINT RUN b/wn 66-80: 10X TO 25X
*PRINT RUN b/wn 51-65: 12.5X TO 30X
*PRINT RUN b/wn 36-50: 15X TO 40X
*PRINT RUN b/wn 26-35: 20X TO 50X
*PRINT RUN b/wn 21-25: 25X TO 60X
*PRINT RUN b/wn 16-20: 30X TO 80X
SEE BECKETT.COM FOR EXACT PRINT RUNS
150-CARD SKIP-NUMBERED SET

2002 Fleer Triple Crown Diamond Immortality

Inserted in packs at stated odds of one in 12 hobby and one in 20 retail, these 10 cards feature players who are on their way to becoming members of the Baseball Hall of Fame.

COMPLETE SET (10)	15.00	40.00
1 Derek Jeter	2.50	6.00
2 Barry Bonds	2.50	6.00
3 Rickey Henderson	1.50	4.00
4 Roger Clemens	2.00	5.00
5 Alex Rodriguez	1.50	4.00
6 Albert Pujols	2.00	5.00
7 Nomar Garciaparra	1.50	4.00
8 Ichiro Suzuki	2.00	5.00
9 Chipper Jones	1.50	4.00
10 Ken Griffey Jr.	1.50	4.00

2002 Fleer Triple Crown Diamond Immortality Game Used

Inserted in packs at stated odds of one in 129, these eight cards are a partial parallel to the Diamond Immortality insert set. A couple of players were printed to a shorter print run and we have notated that information in our checklist with stated print run information.

SP PRINT RUN INFO PROVIDED BY FLEER
*MULTI-COLOR PATCH: .75X TO 2X BASIC

1 Barry Bonds Pants	10.00	25.00
2 Roger Clemens Jsy	12.50	30.00
3 N.Garciaparra Jsy SP/150	15.00	40.00
4 Rickey Henderson Bat	6.00	15.00
5 Derek Jeter Bat	12.50	30.00
6 Chipper Jones Bat	6.00	15.00
7 Albert Pujols Jsy	12.50	30.00
8 Alex Rodriguez Jsy SP/400	10.00	25.00

2002 Fleer Triple Crown Home Run Kings

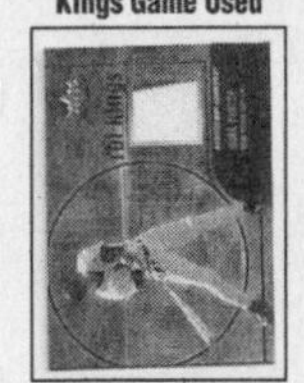

Inserted at stated odds of one in 24 hobby and one in 36 retail packs, these 25 cards feature a mix of active and retired sluggers.

COMPLETE SET (25)	75.00	150.00
1 Ted Williams	5.00	12.00
2 Todd Helton	2.00	5.00
3 Eddie Murray	3.00	8.00
4 Jeff Bagwell	2.00	5.00
5 Babe Ruth	8.00	20.00
6 Eddie Mathews	3.00	8.00
7 Alex Rodriguez	4.00	10.00
8 Juan Gonzalez	2.00	5.00
9 Chipper Jones	2.50	6.00
10 Luis Gonzalez	2.00	5.00
11 Johnny Bench	3.00	8.00
12 Frank Thomas	2.50	6.00
13 Ernie Banks	3.00	8.00
14 Jimmie Foxx	3.00	8.00
15 Ken Griffey Jr.	4.00	10.00
16 Rafael Palmeiro	2.00	5.00
17 Sammy Sosa	2.50	6.00
18 Reggie Jackson	2.00	5.00
19 Barry Bonds	6.00	15.00
20 Willie McCovey	2.00	5.00
21 Manny Ramirez	2.00	5.00
22 Larry Walker	2.00	5.00
23 Jason Giambi	2.00	5.00
24 Mike Piazza	4.00	10.00
25 Jose Canseco	2.00	5.00

2002 Fleer Triple Crown Home Run Kings Autographs

Randomly inserted in packs, these cards are a partial parallel to the Home Run Kings insert set. Each player signed cards which matched their leading homer total for a season and we have notated that information in our checklist. All cards were exchange cards and they could be redeemed until January 31, 2003.

1 Johnny Bench/45		
2 Barry Bonds/73	125.00	200.00
3 Alex Rodriguez/52 UER	60.00	120.00
Alex spelled as Aleh and Texas spelled as Tehas		

2002 Fleer Triple Crown Home Run Kings Game Used

Inserted in packs at stated odds of one in 155, these 16 cards are a partial parallel to the Home Run Kings insert set. A couple of players were printed to a shorter print run and we have notated that information in our checklist with stated print run information.

*JERSEYS w/PATCH: .75X TO 2X HI COLUMN

1 Jeff Bagwell Jsy	6.00	15.00
2 Johnny Bench Bat SP/90		
3 Barry Bonds Jsy	10.00	25.00
4 Jimmie Foxx Bat	20.00	50.00
5 Jason Giambi Jsy	6.00	15.00
6 Reggie Jackson Bat	6.00	15.00
7 Eddie Mathews Bat	6.00	15.00
8 Eddie Murray Bat	6.00	15.00
9 Rafael Palmeiro Bat	6.00	15.00
10 Mike Piazza Jsy	6.00	15.00
11 Manny Ramirez Bat SP/40		
12 Todd Helton Bat	6.00	15.00
13 Alex Rodriguez Bat	6.00	15.00
14 Babe Ruth Bat SP/27		
15 Larry Walker Bat	6.00	15.00
16 Ted Williams Jsy	50.00	100.00

2002 Fleer Triple Crown RBI Kings

Inserted at stated odds of one in 144 hobby and one in 288 retail, these 15 cards feature the leading run producers in the game today.

COMPLETE SET (15)	100.00	200.00
1 Sammy Sosa	5.00	12.00
2 Todd Helton	4.00	10.00
3 Albert Pujols	10.00	25.00
4 Manny Ramirez	4.00	10.00
5 Luis Gonzalez	4.00	10.00
6 Shawn Green	4.00	10.00
7 Barry Bonds	12.50	30.00
8 Ken Griffey Jr.	8.00	20.00
9 Alex Rodriguez	10.00	25.00
10 Jason Giambi	4.00	10.00
11 Jeff Bagwell	4.00	10.00
12 Vladimir Guerrero	5.00	12.00
13 Juan Gonzalez	4.00	10.00
14 Chipper Jones	5.00	12.00
15 Mike Piazza	8.00	20.00

2002 Fleer Triple Crown RBI Kings Game Used

Inserted in packs at stated odds of one in 70, these 11 cards are a partial parallel to the RBI Kings insert set. A couple of players were printed to a shorter print run and we have notated that information in our checklist with stated print run information.

1 Jeff Bagwell Jsy	6.00	15.00
2 Barry Bonds Pants	10.00	25.00
3 Jason Giambi Jsy	4.00	10.00
4 Luis Gonzalez Bat	4.00	10.00
5 Juan Gonzalez Bat	4.00	10.00
6 Shawn Green Jsy	4.00	10.00
7 Todd Helton Jsy	6.00	15.00
8 Mike Piazza Jsy	10.00	25.00
9 Albert Pujols Bat SP/80		
10 Manny Ramirez Bat	6.00	15.00
11 Alex Rodriguez Shoe SP/500	10.00	25.00

2002 Fleer Triple Crown Season Crowns

Inserted at stated odds of one in 12 hobby and one in 20 retail, these 10 cards feature three players who are among the best at any specific category.

COMPLETE SET (10)	15.00	40.00
1 Barry Bonds	2.50	6.00
Sammy Sosa		
Luis Gonzalez		
2 Larry Walker	1.00	2.50
Nomar Garciaparra		
Todd Helton		
3 Sammy Sosa	1.00	2.50
Todd Helton		
Manny Ramirez		
4 Pedro Martinez	3.00	8.00
Derek Jeter		
Cal Ripken		
5 Jose Canseco	2.50	6.00
Barry Bonds		
Alex Rodriguez		
6 Barry Bonds	2.00	5.00
Jeff Kent		
Chipper Jones		
7 Ichiro Suzuki	2.00	5.00
Jason Giambi		
Ivan Rodriguez		
8 Curt Schilling	1.00	2.50
Tom Glavine		
Pedro Martinez		
9 Randy Johnson	1.50	4.00
Pedro Martinez		
Greg Maddux		
10 Radny Johnson	1.00	2.50
Curt Schilling		
John Smoltz		

2002 Fleer Triple Crown Season Crowns Autographs

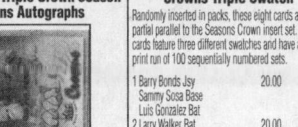

Randomly inserted in packs, these two cards are a partial parallel to the Season Crowns insert set. Each player signed a different number of cards Both cards were exchange cards and they could be redeemed until February 25, 2003.

SCBB Barry Bonds/77	100.00	175.00
SCDJ Derek Jeter/160	100.00	200.00

2002 Fleer Triple Crown Season Crowns Game Used

Inserted in packs at stated odds of one in 90, these 30 cards are a parallel plus to the Season Crowns insert set. Each player on each card had one piece of memorabilia attached to the card. A couple of cards were printed to a shorter print run and we have notated that information in our checklist with stated print run information.

1A Barry Bonds HR Jsy	12.50	30.00
Sammy Sosa		
Luis Gonzalez		
1B Sammy Sosa HR Base	6.00	15.00
Barry Bonds		
Luis Gonzalez		
2A Larry Walker BA Bat	4.00	10.00
Nomar Garciaparra		
Todd Helton		
2B Nomar Garciaparra BA Jsy	10.00	25.00
Larry Walker		
Todd Helton		
2C Todd Helton BA Jsy	6.00	15.00
Larry Walker		
Nomar Garciaparra		
3A Sammy Sosa RBI Base	6.00	15.00
Todd Helton		
Manny Ramirez		
3B Todd Helton RBI Jsy	6.00	15.00
Sammy Sosa		
Manny Ramirez		
3C Manny Ramirez RBI Jsy	6.00	15.00
Sammy Sosa		
Todd Helton		
4A Pedro Martinez AS Jsy	6.00	15.00
Derek Jeter		
Cal Ripken		
4B Derek Jeter AS Pants	12.50	30.00
Pedro Martinez		
Cal Ripken		
4C Cal Ripken AS Bat SP/75	40.00	80.00
Pedro Martinez		
Derek Jeter		
5A Jose Canseco 40/40 Jsy	6.00	15.00
Barry Bonds		
Alex Rodriguez		
5B Barry Bonds 40/40 Jsy	12.50	30.00
Jose Canseco		
Alex Rodriguez		
5C Alex Rodriguez 40/40 Jsy	10.00	25.00
Jose Canseco		
Barry Bonds		
6A Barry Bonds MVP Jsy	12.50	30.00
Jeff Kent		
Chipper Jones		
6B Jeff Kent MVP Jsy	4.00	10.00
Barry Bonds		
Chipper Jones		
7A Ichiro Suzuki MVP Base	12.50	30.00
Jason Giambi		
Ivan Rodriguez		
7B Jason Giambi MVP Jsy	4.00	10.00
Ichiro Suzuki		
Ivan Rodriguez		
7C Ivan Rodriguez MVP Jsy	6.00	15.00
Ichiro Suzuki		
Jason Giambi		
8A Curt Schilling Wins Jsy	4.00	10.00
Tom Glavine		
Pedro Martinez		
8B Tom Glavine Wins Jsy	6.00	15.00
Curt Schilling		
Pedro Martinez		
8C Pedro Martinez Wins Jsy	6.00	15.00
Curt Schilling		
Tom Glavine		
9A Randy Johnson ERA Jsy	6.00	15.00
Pedro Martinez		
Greg Maddux		
9B Pedro Martinez ERA Jsy	6.00	15.00
Randy Johnson		
Greg Maddux		
9C Greg Maddux Jsy	6.00	15.00
Randy Johnson		
Pedro Martinez		
10A Randy Johnson K's Jsy	6.00	15.00
Curt Schilling		
John Smoltz		
10B Curt Schilling K's Jsy	4.00	10.00
Randy Johnson		
John Smoltz		
10C John Smoltz K's Jsy	6.00	15.00
Randy Johnson		
Curt Schilling		

2002 Fleer Triple Crown Season Crowns Triple Swatch

Randomly inserted in packs, these eight cards are a partial parallel to the Seasons Crown insert set. These cards feature three different swatches and have a stated print run of 100 sequentially numbered sets.

1 Barry Bonds Jsy	20.00	50.00
Sammy Sosa Base		
Luis Gonzalez Bat		
2 Larry Walker Bat	20.00	50.00
Nomar Garciaparra Jsy		
Todd Helton Jsy		
3 Sammy Sosa Base	20.00	50.00
Todd Helton Jsy		
Manny Ramirez Jsy		
6 Barry Bonds Jsy	20.00	50.00
Jeff Kent Jsy		
Chipper Jones Bat		
7 Ichiro Suzuki Base	50.00	100.00
Jason Giambi Jsy		
Ivan Rodriguez Jsy		
8 Curt Schilling Jsy	20.00	50.00
Tom Glavine Jsy		
Pedro Martinez Jsy		
9 Randy Johnson Jsy	20.00	50.00
Pedro Martinez Jsy		
Greg Maddux Jsy		
10 Randy Johnson Jsy	20.00	50.00
Curt Schilling Jsy		
John Smoltz Jsy		

1888 Goodwin Champions N162

This 50-card set issued by Goodwin was one of the major competitors to the N28 and N29 sets marketed by Allen and Ginter. It contains individuals representing 18 sports, with eight baseball players pictured. Each color card is backlisted and bears advertising for "Old Judge" and "Gypsy Queen" cigarettes on the front. The set was released to the public in 1888 and an album (catalog: A36) is associated with it as a premium issue.

1 Ed Andrews (Baseball)	350.00	700.00
2 Cap Anson (Baseball)	1750.00	3500.00
3 Dan Brouthers (Baseball)	700.00	1400.00
4 Bob Caruthers (Baseball)	400.00	750.00
5 Fred Dunlap (Baseball)	350.00	700.00
6 Jack Glasscock (Baseball)	400.00	750.00
7 Tim Keefe (Baseball)	700.00	1400.00
8 King Kelly (Baseball)	1250.00	2500.00

1933 Goudey

The cards in this 240-card set measure approximately 2 3/8" by 2 7/8". The 1933 Goudey set, was that company's first baseball issue. The four Babe Ruth and two Lou Gehrig cards in the set are extremely popular with collectors. Card number 106, Napoleon Lajoie, was not printed in 1933, and was circulated to a limited number of collectors in 1934 upon request (it was printed along with the 1934 Goudey cards). An album was offered to house the 1933 set. Several minor leaguers are depicted. Card number 1 (Bengough) is very rarely found in mint condition; in fact, as a general rule all the first series cards are more difficult to find in Mint condition. Players with more than one card are also sometimes differentiated below by their pose: BAT (Batting), FIELD (Fielding), PIT (Pitching), THROW (Throwing). One of the Babe Ruth cards was double printed (DP) apparently in place of the Lajoie and hence is easier to obtain than the others. Due to the scarcity of the Lajoie card, the set is considered complete at 239 cards and is priced as such below. One copy of card number 106 as Leo Durocher is known to exist. The card was apparently cut from a proof sheet and is the only known copy to exist. A large window display poster which measured 5 3/8" by 11 1/4" was sent to stores and used the same Babe Ruth photo as in the Goudey Premium set. The gum used was approximately the same dimension as the actual card. At the factory each piece was scored twice so it could be snapped into three pieces. The gum had a spearmint flavor and according to collectors who remember chewing said gum, the flavor did not last very long.

COMPLETE SET (239)	25000.00	40000.00
COMMON CARD (1-52)	45.00	75.00
COMMON (41/43/53-240)	35.00	60.00
WRAP.(1-CENT, BATTER)	75.00	100.00
WRAP.(1-CENT, AD FRONT)	150.00	175.00
1 Benny Bengough RC	900.00	1500.00
2 Dazzy Vance RC	125.00	200.00
3 Hugh Critz BAT RC	40.00	75.00
4 Heinie Schuble RC	45.00	75.00
5 Babe Herman RC	40.00	75.00
6 Jimmy Dykes RC	40.00	75.00
7 Ted Lyons RC	90.00	150.00
8 Roy Johnson RC	45.00	75.00
9 Dave Harris RC	45.00	75.00
10 Glenn Myatt RC	45.00	75.00
11 Billy Rogell RC	45.00	75.00
12 George Pipgras RC	45.00	75.00
13 Fresco Thompson RC	45.00	75.00
14 Henry Johnson RC	45.00	75.00
15 Victor Sorrell RC	45.00	75.00
16 George Blaeholder RC	45.00	75.00
17 Watson Clark RC	45.00	75.00
18 Muddy Ruel RC	45.00	75.00
19 Bill Dickey RC	200.00	350.00
20 Bill Terry THROW RC	150.00	250.00
21 Phil Collins RC	45.00	75.00
22 Pie Traynor RC	150.00	250.00
23 Kiki Cuyler RC	125.00	200.00
24 Horace Ford RC	45.00	75.00
25 Paul Waner RC	125.00	200.00
26 Bill Cissell RC	45.00	75.00
27 George Connally RC	45.00	75.00
28 Dick Bartell RC	40.00	75.00
29 Jimmie Foxx RC	350.00	600.00
30 Frank Hogan RC	45.00	75.00
31 Tony Lazzeri RC	250.00	400.00
32 Bud Clancy RC	40.00	75.00
33 Ralph Kress RC	45.00	75.00
34 Bob O'Farrell RC	45.00	75.00
35 Al Simmons RC	200.00	350.00
36 Tommy Thevenow RC	45.00	75.00
37 Jimmy Wilson RC	45.00	75.00
38 Fred Brickell RC	45.00	75.00
39 Mark Koenig RC	40.00	75.00
40 Taylor Douthit RC	45.00	75.00
41 Gus Mancuso CATCH	35.00	60.00
42 Eddie Collins RC	90.00	150.00
43 Lew Fonseca RC	35.00	60.00
44 Jim Bottomley RC	90.00	150.00
45 Larry Benton RC	45.00	75.00
46 Ethan Allen RC	40.00	75.00
47 Heinie Manush BAT RC	100.00	175.00
48 Marty McManus RC	45.00	75.00
49 Frankie Frisch RC	175.00	300.00
50 Ed Brandt RC	45.00	75.00
51 Charlie Grimm RC	40.00	75.00
52 Andy Cohen RC	45.00	75.00
53 Babe Ruth RC	5000.00	8000.00
54 Ray Kremer RC	35.00	60.00
55 Pat Malone RC	35.00	60.00
56 Red Ruffing RC	100.00	175.00
57 Earl Clark RC	35.00	60.00
58 Lefty O'Doul RC	75.00	125.00
59 Bing Miller RC	35.00	60.00
60 Waite Hoyt RC	75.00	125.00
61 Max Bishop RC	35.00	60.00
62 Pepper Martin RC	75.00	125.00
63 Joe Cronin BAT RC	90.00	150.00
64 Burleigh Grimes RC	150.00	250.00
65 Milt Gaston RC	35.00	60.00
66 George Grantham RC	35.00	60.00
67 Guy Bush RC	35.00	60.00
68 Horace Lisenbee RC	35.00	60.00
69 Randy Moore RC	35.00	60.00
70 Floyd (Pete) Scott RC	35.00	60.00
71 Robert J. Burke RC	35.00	60.00
72 Owen Carroll RC	35.00	60.00
73 Jesse Haines RC	75.00	125.00
74 Eppa Rixey RC	90.00	150.00
75 Willie Kamm RC	35.00	60.00
76 Mickey Cochrane RC	300.00	500.00
77 Adam Comorosky RC	35.00	60.00
78 Jack Quinn RC	35.00	60.00
79 Red Faber RC	75.00	125.00
80 Clyde Manion RC	35.00	60.00
81 Sam Jones RC	35.00	60.00
82 Dib Williams RC	35.00	60.00
83 Pete Jablonowski RC	35.00	60.00
84 Glenn Spencer RC	35.00	60.00
85 Heinie Sand RC	35.00	60.00
86 Phil Todt RC	35.00	60.00
87 Frank O'Rourke RC	35.00	60.00
88 Russell Rollings RC	35.00	60.00
89 Tris Speaker RET	175.00	300.00
90 Jess Petty RC	35.00	60.00
91 Tom Zachary RC	35.00	60.00
92 Lou Gehrig RC	1500.00	2500.00
93 John Welch RC	35.00	60.00
94 Bill Walker RC	35.00	60.00
95 Alvin Crowder RC	35.00	60.00
96 Willis Hudlin RC	35.00	60.00
97 Joe Morrissey RC	35.00	60.00
98 Wally Berger RC	45.00	75.00
99 Tony Cuccinello RC	45.00	75.00
100 George Uhle RC	35.00	60.00
101 Richard Coffman RC	35.00	60.00
102 Travis Jackson RC	90.00	150.00
103 Earle Combs RC	75.00	125.00
104 Fred Marberry RC	35.00	60.00
105 Bernie Friberg RC	35.00	60.00
106 Napoleon Lajoie SP	15000.00	25000.00
(Not issued		
until 1934)		
107 Heinie Manush RC	75.00	125.00
108 Joe Kuhel RC	35.00	60.00
109 Joe Cronin RC	175.00	300.00
110 Goose Goslin RC	150.00	250.00
111 Monte Weaver RC	35.00	60.00
112 Fred Schulte RC	35.00	60.00
113 Oswald Bluege POR RC	35.00	60.00
114 Luke Sewell FIELD RC	45.00	75.00
115 Cliff Heathcote RC	35.00	60.00
116 Eddie Morgan RC	35.00	60.00
117 Rabbit Maranville RC	75.00	125.00
118 Val Picinich RC	35.00	60.00
119 Rogers Hornsby Field RC	350.00	600.00
120 Carl Reynolds RC	35.00	60.00
121 Walter Stewart RC	35.00	60.00
122 Alvin Crowder RC	35.00	60.00
123 Jack Russell RC	35.00	60.00
124 Earl Whitehill RC	35.00	60.00
125 Bill Terry RC	150.00	250.00
126 Joe Moore BAT RC	35.00	60.00
127 Mel Ott RC	250.00	400.00
128 Chuck Klein RC	100.00	175.00
129 Hal Schumacher PIT RC	35.00	60.00
130 Fred Fitzsimmons POR RC	35.00	60.00
131 Fred Frankhouse RC	35.00	60.00
132 Jim Elliott RC	35.00	60.00
133 Fred Lindstrom RC	75.00	125.00
134 Sam Rice RC	125.00	200.00
135 Woody English RC	35.00	60.00
136 Flint Rhem RC	35.00	60.00
137 Red Lucas RC	35.00	60.00
138 Herb Pennock RC	100.00	175.00
139 Ben Cantwell RC	35.00	60.00
140 Bump Hadley RC	35.00	60.00
141 Ray Benge RC	35.00	60.00
142 Paul Richards RC	45.00	75.00
143 Glenn Wright RC	35.00	60.00
144 Babe Ruth Bat DP RC	2500.00	4000.00
145 Rube Walberg RC	35.00	60.00
146 Walter Stewart PIT RC	35.00	60.00
147 Leo Durocher RC	125.00	200.00
148 Eddie Farrell RC	35.00	60.00
149 Babe Ruth RC	3000.00	5000.00
150 Ray Kolp RC	35.00	60.00
151 Jake Flowers RC	35.00	60.00
152 Zack Taylor RC	35.00	60.00
153 Buddy Myer RC	35.00	60.00
154 Jimmie Foxx RC	350.00	600.00
155 Joe Judge RC	35.00	60.00
156 Danny MacFayden RC	35.00	60.00
157 Sam Byrd RC UER	35.00	60.00
Yankees on back is spelled Yankess		
158 Moe Berg RC	250.00	400.00
159 Oswald Bluege FIELD RC	35.00	60.00
160 Lou Gehrig RC	1800.00	3000.00
161 Al Spohrer RC	35.00	60.00
162 Leo Mangum RC	35.00	60.00
163 Luke Sewell POR RC	45.00	75.00
164 Lloyd Waner RC	150.00	250.00
165 Joe Sewell RC	75.00	125.00
166 Sam West RC	35.00	60.00
167 Jack Russell RC	35.00	60.00
168 Goose Goslin RC	125.00	200.00
169 Al Thomas RC	35.00	60.00
170 Harry McCurdy RC	35.00	60.00
171 Charlie Jamieson RC	35.00	60.00
172 Billy Hargrave RC	35.00	60.00
173 Roscoe Holm RC	35.00	60.00
174 Warren (Curly) Ogden RC	35.00	60.00
175 Dan Howley MG RC	35.00	60.00
176 John Ogden RC	35.00	60.00
177 Walter French RC	35.00	60.00
178 Jackie Warner RC	35.00	60.00
179 Fred Leach RC	35.00	60.00
180 Eddie Moore RC	35.00	60.00
181 Babe Ruth RC	3500.00	5000.00
182 Andy High RC	35.00	60.00
183 Rube Walberg RC	35.00	60.00
184 Charley Berry RC	35.00	60.00
185 Bob Smith RC	35.00	60.00
186 John Schulte RC	35.00	60.00
187 Heinie Manush RC	90.00	150.00
188 Rogers Hornsby RC	350.00	600.00
189 Joe Cronin RC	125.00	200.00
190 Fred Schulte RC	35.00	60.00
191 Ben Chapman RC	45.00	75.00
192 Walter Brown RC	35.00	60.00
193 Lynford Lary RC	35.00	60.00
194 Earl Averill RC	125.00	200.00
195 Evar Swanson RC	35.00	60.00
196 Leroy Mahaffey RC	35.00	60.00
197 Rick Ferrell RC	75.00	125.00
198 Jack Burns RC	35.00	60.00
199 Tom Bridges RC	35.00	60.00
200 Bill Hallahan RC	35.00	60.00
201 Ernie Orsatti RC	35.00	60.00
202 Gabby Hartnett RC	150.00	250.00
203 Lon Warneke RC	35.00	60.00
204 Riggs Stephenson RC	35.00	60.00
205 Heinie Meine RC	35.00	60.00
206 Gus Suhr RC	35.00	60.00
207 Mel Ott Bat RC	250.00	400.00
208 Bernie James RC	35.00	60.00
209 Adolfo Luque RC	45.00	75.00
210 Spud Davis RC	35.00	60.00
211 Hack Wilson RC	250.00	400.00
212 Billy Urbanski RC	35.00	60.00
213 Earl Adams RC	35.00	60.00
214 John Kerr RC	35.00	60.00
215 Russ Van Atta RC	35.00	60.00
216 Lefty Gomez RC	175.00	300.00
217 Frank Crosetti RC	90.00	150.00
218 Wes Ferrell RC	45.00	75.00
219 Mule Haas UER RC	35.00	60.00
Name spelled Hass on front		
220 Lefty Grove RC	300.00	500.00
221 Dale Alexander RC	35.00	60.00
222 Charley Gehringer RC	250.00	400.00
223 Dizzy Dean RC	500.00	800.00
224 Frank Demaree RC	35.00	60.00
225 Bill Jurges RC	35.00	60.00
226 Charley Root RC	35.00	60.00
227 Billy Herman RC	90.00	150.00
228 Tony Piet RC	35.00	60.00
229 Arky Vaughan RC	90.00	150.00
230 Carl Hubbell PIT RC	250.00	400.00
231 Joe Moore FIELD RC	35.00	60.00
232 Lefty O'Doul RC	75.00	125.00
233 Johnny Vergez RC	35.00	60.00
234 Carl Hubbell RC	250.00	400.00
235 Fred Fitzsimmons PIT RC	35.00	60.00
236 George Davis RC	35.00	60.00
237 Gus Mancuso FIELD RC	35.00	60.00
238 Hugh Critz FIELD RC	35.00	60.00
239 Leroy Parmelee RC	35.00	60.00
240 Hal Schumacher RC	75.00	125.00

1934 Goudey

The cards in this 96-card color set measure approximately 2 3/8" by 2 7/8". Cards 1-48 are considered to be the easiest to find (although card number 1, Foxx, is very scarce in mint condition) while 73-96 are much more difficult to find. Cards of this 1934 Goudey series are slightly less abundant than cards of the 1933 Goudey set. Of the 96 cards, 84 contain a "Lou Gehrig Says" line on the front in a blue design, while 12 of the high series (80-91) contain a "Chuck Klein Says" line in a red design. These Chuck Klein cards are indicated in the checklist below by CK and are in fact the 12 National Leaguers in the high series.

COMPLETE SET (96)	9000.00	16000.00
COMMON CARD (1-48)	30.00	50.00
COMMON CARD (49-72)	40.00	75.00
COMMON CARD (73-96)	100.00	175.00
WRAP.(1-CENT, WHITE)	75.00	100.00
WRAP.(1-CENT, CLEAR)	75.00	100.00
1 Jimmie Foxx	450.00	750.00
2 Mickey Cochrane	100.00	175.00
3 Charlie Grimm	35.00	60.00
4 Woody English	30.00	50.00
5 Ed Brandt	30.00	50.00
6 Dizzy Dean	400.00	700.00
7 Leo Durocher	100.00	175.00
8 Tony Piet	30.00	50.00
9 Ben Chapman	35.00	60.00
10 Chuck Klein	90.00	150.00

11 Paul Waner 90.00 150.00
12 Carl Hubbell 100.00 175.00
13 Frankie Frisch 100.00 175.00
14 Willie Kamm 30.00 50.00
15 Alvin Crowder 30.00 50.00
16 Joe Kuhel 30.00 50.00
17 Hugh Critz 30.00 50.00
18 Heinie Manush 75.00 125.00
19 Lefty Grove 175.00 300.00
20 Frank Hogan 30.00 50.00
21 Bill Terry 125.00 200.00
22 Arky Vaughan 75.00 125.00
23 Charley Gehringer 125.00 200.00
24 Ray Benge 30.00 50.00
25 Roger Cramer RC 35.00 60.00
26 Gerald Walker RC 30.00 50.00
27 Luke Appling RC 90.00 150.00
28 Ed Coleman RC 30.00 50.00
29 Larry French RC 30.00 50.00
30 Julius Solters RC 30.00 50.00
31 Buck Jordan RC 30.00 50.00
32 Blondy Ryan RC 30.00 50.00
33 Don Hurst RC 30.00 50.00
34 Chick Hafey RC 75.00 125.00
35 Ernie Lombardi RC 90.00 150.00
36 Walter Betts RC 30.00 50.00
37 Lou Gehrig 2000.00 3000.00
38 Oral Hildebrand RC 30.00 50.00
39 Fred Walker RC 30.00 50.00
40 John Stone 30.00 50.00
41 George Earnshaw RC 30.00 50.00
42 John Allen RC 30.00 50.00
43 Dick Porter RC 30.00 50.00
44 Tom Bridges 35.00 60.00
45 Oscar Melillo RC 30.00 50.00
46 Joe Stripp RC 30.00 50.00
47 John Frederick RC 30.00 50.00
48 Tex Carleton RC 30.00 50.00
49 Sam Leslie RC 40.00 75.00
50 Walter Beck RC 40.00 75.00
51 Rip Collins RC 40.00 75.00
52 Herman Bell RC 40.00 75.00
53 George Watkins RC 40.00 75.00
54 Wesley Schulmerich RC 40.00 75.00
55 Ed Holley RC 40.00 75.00
56 Mark Koenig 60.00 100.00
57 Bill Swift RC 40.00 75.00
58 Earl Grace RC 40.00 75.00
59 Joe Mowry RC 40.00 75.00
60 Lynn Nelson RC 40.00 75.00
61 Lou Gehrig 2000.00 3000.00
62 Hank Greenberg RC 400.00 700.00
63 Minter Hayes RC 40.00 75.00
64 Frank Grube RC 40.00 75.00
65 Cliff Bolton RC 40.00 75.00
66 Mel Harder RC 60.00 100.00
67 Bob Weiland RC 40.00 75.00
68 Bob Johnson RC 60.00 100.00
69 John Marcum RC 40.00 75.00
70 Pete Fox RC 40.00 75.00
71 Lyle Tinning RC 40.00 75.00
72 Arndt Jorgens RC 40.00 75.00
73 Ed Wells RC 100.00 175.00
74 Bob Boken RC 100.00 175.00
75 Bill Werber RC 100.00 175.00
76 Hal Trosky RC 125.00 200.00
77 Joe Vosmik RC 100.00 175.00
78 Pinky Higgins RC 125.00 200.00
79 Eddie Durham RC 100.00 175.00
80 Marty McManus CK 100.00 175.00
81 Bob Brown CK RC 100.00 175.00
82 Bill Hallahan CK 100.00 175.00
83 Jim Mooney CK RC 100.00 175.00
84 Paul Derringer CK RC 125.00 225.00
85 Adam Comorosky CK 100.00 175.00
86 Lloyd Johnson CK RC 100.00 175.00
87 George Darrow CK RC 100.00 175.00
88 Homer Peel CK RC 100.00 175.00
89 Linus Frey CK RC 100.00 175.00
90 KiKi Cuyler CK 200.00 350.00
91 Dolph Camilli CK RC 125.00 200.00
92 Steve Larkin RC 100.00 175.00
93 Fred Ostermueller RC 100.00 175.00
94 Red Rolfe RC 125.00 200.00
95 Myril Hoag RC 100.00 175.00
96 James DeShong RC 300.00 500.00

1935 Goudey 4-in-1

The cards in this confusing 36-card set (the number of different front pictures) measure approximately 2 3/8" by 2 7/8". The 1935 Goudey set is sometimes called the Goudey Puzzle set, or the Goudey 4-in-1n set. There are 36 different card fronts but 114 different front/back combinations. Our checklist details all 114 cards, grouped together by the 36 different card front combinations. The player combinations are listed alphabetically by reading the player names in clockwise order starting from the top left corner. The card backs can be arranged to form one of nine different puzzles picturing either a player or a team and each back specifically details both the puzzle (or "picture" as it states on the actual card backs) it belongs too using numbers 1-9 and the specific piece it is within the puzzle (using letters A-M). The following is the list of the puzzle back pictures: 1) Detroit Tigers; 2) Chuck Klein; 3) Frankie Frisch; 4) Mickey Cochrane; 5) Joe Cronin; 6) Jimmy Foxx; 7) Al Simmons; 8) Cleveland Indians; and 9) Washington Senators. The first seven puzzles were actually created in two separate combinations of card fronts; thus the Chuck Klein puzzle (catalogued as "Picture 2" on the card backs) is actually available in two different groups of six card fronts - one group of which has been verified as a short print. The SP cards have all been tagged in our checklist. Finally, a limited number of cards feature blue borders (rather than the standard red borders). Though they're not short-printed, we've tagged the cards for referential purposes.

COMPLETE SET (114) 8000.00 13500.00
COMMON CARDS (1-9) 30.00 50.00
COMMON CARDS (11-17) 45.00 80.00
WRAP.(1-CENT, WHITE) 150.00 200.00
1-2 Charlie Berry 60.00 100.00
Bobby Burke
Red Kress
Dazzy Vance
2C SP (Chuck Klein Puzzle)
Blue Border
1-4 Charlie Berry 35.00 60.00
Bobby Burke
Red Kress
Dazzy Vance
4C {4A Mickey Cochrane Puzzle)
Blue Border
1-7 Charlie Berry 35.00 60.00
Bobby Burke
Red Kress
Dazzy Vance
7C (Al Simmons Puzzle)
Blue Border
2-8 Jack Burns 30.00 50.00
Rollie Hemsley
Frank Grube
Bob Weiland
8C (Cleveland Indians Puzzle)
2-9 Jack Burns 30.00 50.00
Rollie Hemsley
Frank Grube
Bob Weiland
9C (Washington Senators Puzzle)
3-8 Bruce Campbell 30.00 50.00
Billy Meyers
Ival Goodman
Alex Kampouris XRC
8D (Cleveland Indians Puzzle)
3-9 Bruce Campbell 30.00 50.00
Billy Meyers
Ival Goodman
Alex Kampouris XRC
9D (Washington Senators Puzzle)
4-1 Mickey Cochrane 60.00 120.00
Charlie Gehringer
Tommy Bridges
Billy Rogell#1D (Detroit Tigers Puzzle)
4-2 Mickey Cochrane 70.00 120.00
Charlie Gehringer
Tommy Bridges
Billy Rogell
2D (Chuck Klein Puzzle)
4-6 Mickey Cochrane 90.00 150.00
Charlie Gehringer
Tom Bridges
Billy Rogell#6D SP (Jimmie Foxx Puzzle)
4-7 Mickey Cochrane 90.00 150.00
Charlie Gehringer
Tom Bridges
Billy Rogell
7D SP (Al Simmons Puzzle)
5-2 Hugh Critz 90.00 150.00
Dick Bartell
Mel Ott
Gus Mancuso
2A SP (Chuck Klein Puzzle)
Blue Border
5-4 Hugh Critz 60.00 100.00
Dick Bartell
Mel Ott
Gus Mancuso
4A (Mickey Cochrane Puzzle)
Blue Border
5-7 Hugh Critz 60.00 100.00
Dick Bartell
Mel Ott
Gus Mancuso
7A (Al Simmons Puzzle)
Blue Border
6-1 Joe Cronin 60.00 100.00
Carl Reynolds
Max Bishop
Chalmer Cissell
1G SP (Detroit Tigers Puzzle)
6-3 Joe Cronin 60.00 100.00
Carl Reynolds
Max Bishop
Chalmer Cissell
3E SP (Frankie Frisch Puzzle)
6-5 Joe Cronin 60.00 100.00
Carl Reynolds
Max Bishop
Chalmer Cissell
5E SP (Joe Cronin Puzzle)
6-6 Joe Cronin 35.00 60.00
Carl Reynolds
Max Bishop
Chalmer Cissell
6E (Jimmie Foxx Puzzle)
7-8 Jimmy DeShong 30.00 50.00
Johnny Allen
Red Rolfe
Dixie Walker
8E (Cleveland Indians Puzzle)
7-9 Jimmy DeShong 30.00 50.00
Johnny Allen
Red Rolfe
Fred Walker
9E (Washington Senators Puzzle)
8-1 George Earnshaw 35.00 60.00
Jimmie Dykes
Luke Sewell
Luke Appling
1I (Detroit Tigers Puzzle)
8-2 George Earnshaw 35.00 60.00
Jimmie Dykes
Luke Sewell
Luke Appling
2F (Chuck Klein Puzzle)
8-6 George Earnshaw 60.00 100.00
Jimmie Dykes
Luke Sewell
Luke Appling
6F SP (Jimmie Foxx Puzzle)
8-7 George Earnshaw 60.00 100.00
Jimmie Dykes
Luke Sewell
Luke Appling
7F SP (Al Simmons Puzzle)
9-8 Pete Fox 60.00 100.00
Hank Greenberg
Gee Walker
Schoolboy Rowe
8F (Cleveland Indians Puzzle)
9-9 Pete Fox 60.00 100.00
Hank Greenberg
Gee Walker
Schoolboy Rowe
9F (Washington Senators Puzzle)
10-1 Frank Frisch 90.00 150.00
Dizzy Dean
Ernie Orsatti
Tex Carleton
1A (Detroit Tigers Puzzle)
10-2 Frank Frisch 90.00 150.00
Dizzy Dean
Ernie Orsatti
Tex Carleton
2A (Chuck Klein Puzzle)
10-6 Frank Frisch 150.00 250.00
Dizzy Dean
Ernie Orsatti
Tex Carleton
6A SP (Jimmie Foxx Puzzle)
10-7 Frank Frisch 150.00 250.00
Dizzy Dean
Ernie Orsatti
Tex Carleton
7A SP (Al Simmons Puzzle)
11-1 Burleigh Grimes 60.00 100.00
Chuck Klein
Kiki Cuyler
Woody English
1F (Detroit Tigers Puzzle)
11-3 Burleigh Grimes 60.00 100.00
Chuck Klein
Kiki Cuyler
Woody English
3D (Frankie Frisch Puzzle)
11-4 Burleigh Grimes 90.00 150.00
Chuck Klein
Kiki Cuyler
Woody English
4D SP (Mickey Cochrane Puzzle)
11-5 Burleigh Grimes 90.00 150.00
Chuck Klein
Kiki Cuyler
Woody English
5D SP (Joe Cronin Puzzle)
12-8 Minter Hayes 35.00 60.00
Ted Lyons
Mule Haas
Zeke Bonura
8B (Cleveland Indians Puzzle)
12-9 Minter Hayes 35.00 60.00
Ted Lyons
Mule Haas
Zeke Bonura
9B (Washington Senators Puzzle)
13-8 Babe Herman 35.00 60.00
Gus Suhr
Tom Padden XRC
Cy Blanton
8K (Cleveland Indians Puzzle)
13-9 Babe Herman 35.00 60.00
Gus Suhr
Tom Padden XRC
Cy Blanton
9K (Washington Senators Puzzle)
14-1 Willis Hudlin 60.00 100.00
George Myatt XRC
Adam Comorosky
Jim Bottomley
1K SP (Detroit Tigers Puzzle)
14-3 Willis Hudlin 60.00 100.00
George Myatt XRC
Adam Comorosky
Jim Bottomley
3B SP (Frankie Frisch Puzzle)
14-5 Willis Hudlin 35.00 60.00
George Myatt XRC
Adam Comorosky
Jim Bottomley
5B (Joe Cronin Puzzle)
14-6 Willis Hudlin 35.00 60.00
George Myatt XRC
Adam Comorosky
Jim Bottomley
6B (Jimmie Foxx Puzzle)
15-8 Bob Johnson 30.00 50.00
Ed Coleman
Johnny Marcum
Doc Cramer
8J (Cleveland Indians Puzzle)
15-9 Bob Johnson 30.00 50.00
Ed Coleman
Johnny Marcum
Doc Cramer
9J (Washington Senators Puzzle)
16-1 Willie Kamm 35.00 60.00
Oral Hildebrand
Earl Averill
Hal Trosky
1L (Detroit Tigers Puzzle)
16-2 Willie Kamm 35.00 60.00
Oral Hildebrand
Earl Averill
Hal Trosky
2E (Chuck Klein Puzzle)
16-6 Willie Kamm 60.00 100.00
Oral Hildebrand
Earl Averill
Hal Trosky
6E SP (Jimmie Foxx Puzzle)
16-7 Willie Kamm 60.00 100.00
Oral Hildebrand
Earl Averill
Hal Trosky
7E SP (Al Simmons Puzzle)
17-8 Mark Koenig 30.00 50.00
Fred Fitzsimmons
Ray Benge
Tom Zachary
8A (Cleveland Indians Puzzle)
17-8 Mark Koenig 30.00 50.00
Fred Fitzsimmons
Ray Benge
Tom Zachary
8M (Cleveland Indians Puzzle)
18-8 Joe Kuhel 30.00 50.00
Earl Whitehill
Buddy Myer
John Stone
8H (Cleveland Indians Puzzle)
18-9 Joe Kuhel 30.00 50.00
Earl Whitehill
Buddy Myer
John Stone
9H (Washington Senators Puzzle)
19-1 Sam Leslie 30.00 50.00
Lonnie Frey
Joe Stripp
Watson Clark
1G (Detroit Tigers Puzzle)
19-3 Sam Leslie 30.00 50.00
Lonnie Frey
Joe Stripp
Watson Clark
3E (Frankie Frisch Puzzle)
19-4 Sam Leslie 45.00 80.00
Lonnie Frey
Joe Stripp
Watson Clark
4E SP (Mickey Cochrane Puzzle)
19-5 Sam Leslie 30.00 50.00
Lonnie Frey
Joe Stripp
Watson Clark
5E (Joe Cronin Puzzle)
20-1 Roy Mahaffey 70.00 120.00
Jimmie Foxx
Dib Williams
Pinky Higgins
1B (Detroit Tigers Puzzle)
20-2 Roy Mahaffey 70.00 120.00
Jimmie Foxx
Dib Williams
Pinky Higgins
2B (Chuck Klein Puzzle)
20-6 Roy Mahaffey 90.00 150.00
Jimmie Foxx
Dib Williams
Pinky Higgins
6B SP (Jimmie Foxx Puzzle)
20-7 Roy Mahaffey 125.00 200.00
Jimmie Foxx
Dib Williams
Pinky Higgins
7B SP (Al Simmons Puzzle)
21-1 Heinie Manush 35.00 60.00
Lyn Lary
Monte Weaver
Bump Hadley
1C (Detroit Tigers Puzzle)
21-2 Heinie Manush 35.00 60.00
Lyn Lary
Monte Weaver
Bump Hadley
2C (Chuck Klein Puzzle)
21-6 Heinie Manush 60.00 100.00
Lyn Lary
Monte Weaver
Bump Hadley
6C SP (Jimmie Foxx Puzzle)
21-7 Heinie Manush 60.00 100.00
Lyn Lary
Monte Weaver
Bump Hadley
7C SP (Al Simmons Puzzle)
22-2 Pepper Martin BLUE 45.00 80.00
Bob O'Farrell
Sam Byrd
Danny MacFayden
2F SP (Chuck Klein Puzzle)
22-4 Pepper Martin BLUE 30.00 50.00
Bob O'Farrell
Sam Byrd
Danny MacFayden
4F (Mickey Cochrane Puzzle)
22-7 Pepper Martin BLUE 30.00 50.00
Bob O'Farrell
Sam Byrd
Danny MacFayden
7F (Al Simmons Puzzle)
23-2 Randy Moore BLUE 45.00 80.00
Shanty Hogan
Fred Frankhouse
Eddie Brandt
2E SP (Chuck Klein Puzzle)
23-4 Randy Moore BLUE 30.00 50.00
Shanty Hogan
Fred Frankhouse
Eddie Brandt
4E (Mickey Cochrane Puzzle)
23-7 Randy Moore BLUE 30.00 50.00
Shanty Hogan
Fred Frankhouse
Eddie Brandt
7E (Al Simmons Puzzle)
24-1 Tony Piet 35.00 60.00
Adam Comorosky
Jim Bottomley
Sparky Adams
1H (Detroit Tigers Puzzle)
24-3 Tony Piet 35.00 60.00
Adam Comorosky
Jim Bottomley
Sparky Adams
3F (Frankie Frisch Puzzle)
24-4 Tony Piet 60.00 100.00
Adam Comorosky
Jim Bottomley
Sparky Adams
4F SP (Mickey Cochrane Puzzle)
24-5 Tony Piet 60.00 100.00
Adam Comorosky
Jim Bottomley
Sparky Adams
5F SP (Joe Cronin Puzzle)
25-1 Muddy Ruel 90.00 150.00
Al Simmons
Willie Kamm
Mickey Cochrane
1J SP (Detroit Tigers Puzzle)
25-3 Muddy Ruel 90.00 150.00
Al Simmons
Willie Kamm
Mickey Cochrane
3A SP (Frankie Frisch Puzzle)
25-5 Muddy Ruel 60.00 100.00
Al Simmons
Willie Kamm
Mickey Cochrane
5A (Joe Cronin Puzzle)
25-6 Muddy Ruel 60.00 100.00
Al Simmons
Willie Kamm
Mickey Cochrane
6A (Jimmie Foxx Puzzle)
26-2 Red Ruffing 150.00 250.00
Pat Malone
Tony Lazzeri
Bill Dickey
2D SP (Chuck Klein Puzzle)
Blue Border
26-4 Red Ruffing 90.00 150.00
Pat Malone
Tony Lazzeri
Bill Dickey
4D (Mickey Cochrane Puzzle)
Blue Border
26-7 Red Ruffing 90.00 150.00
Pat Malone
Tony Lazzeri
Bill Dickey
7D (Al Simmons Puzzle)
Blue Border
27-1 Babe Ruth 600.00 1000.00
Marty McManus
Eddie Brandt
Rabbit Maranville
1J (Detroit Tigers Puzzle)
27-3 Babe Ruth 600.00 1000.00
Marty McManus
Eddie Brandt
Rabbit Maranville
3A (Frankie Frisch Puzzle)
27-4 Babe Ruth 1000.00 1500.00
Marty McManus
Eddie Brandt
Rabbit Maranville
4A SP (Mickey Cochrane Puzzle)
27-5 Babe Ruth 1000.00 1500.00
Marty McManus
Eddie Brandt
Rabbit Maranville
5A SP (Joe Cronin Puzzle)
28-1 Heine Schuble 60.00 100.00
Fred Marberry
Goose Goslin
General Crowder
1H SP (Detroit Tigers Puzzle)
28-3 Heine Schuble 60.00 100.00
Fred Marberry
Goose Goslin
General Crowder
3F SP (Frankie Frisch Puzzle)
28-5 Heine Schuble 35.00 60.00
Fred Marberry
Goose Goslin
General Crowder
5F (Joe Cronin Puzzle)
28-6 Heine Schuble 35.00 60.00
Fred Marberry
Goose Goslin
General Crowder
6F (Jimmie Foxx Puzzle)
29-8 Al Spohrer 30.00 50.00
Flint Rhem
Ben Cantwell
Larry Benton
8L (Cleveland Indians Puzzle)
29-9 Al Spohrer 30.00 50.00
Flint Rhem
Ben Cantwell
Larry Benton
9L (Washington Senators Puzzle)
30-1 Bill Terry 60.00 100.00
Hal Schumacher
Gus Mancuso
Travis Jackson
1K (Detroit Tigers Puzzle)
30-3 Bill Terry 60.00 100.00
Hal Schumacher
Gus Mancuso
Travis Jackson
3B (Frankie Frisch Puzzle)
30-4 Bill Terry 90.00 150.00
Hal Schumacher
Gus Mancuso
Travis Jackson
4B SP (Mickey Cochrane Puzzle)
30-5 Bill Terry 90.00 150.00
Hal Schumacher
Gus Mancuso
Travis Jackson
5B SP (Joe Cronin Puzzle)
31-2 Pie Traynor 60.00 100.00
Red Lucas
Tommy Thevenow
Glenn Wright
2B SP (Chuck Klein Puzzle)
Blue Border
31-4 Pie Traynor 35.00 60.00
Red Lucas
Tommy Thevenow
Glenn Wright
4B (Mickey Cochrane Puzzle)
Blue Border
31-7 Pie Traynor 35.00 60.00
Red Lucas
Tommy Thevenow
Glenn Wright
7B (Al Simmons Puzzle)
Blue Border
32-8 Joe Vosmik 30.00 50.00
Bill Knickerbocker
Mel Harder
Lefty Stewart
8I (Cleveland Indians Puzzle)
32-9 Joe Vosmik 30.00 50.00
Bill Knickerbocker
Mel Harder
Lefty Stewart
9I (Washington Senators Puzzle)
33-1 Paul Waner 60.00 100.00
Guy Bush
Waite Hoyt
Lloyd Waner
1E (Detroit Tigers Puzzle)
33-3 Paul Waner 60.00 100.00
Guy Bush
Waite Hoyt
Lloyd Waner
3C (Frankie Frisch Puzzle)
33-4 Paul Waner 90.00 150.00
Guy Bush
Waite Hoyt
Lloyd Waner
4C SP (Mickey Cochrane Puzzle)
33-5 Paul Waner 60.00 100.00
Guy Bush
Waite Hoyt
Lloyd Waner
5C (Joe Cronin Puzzle)
34-8 Billy Werber 35.00 60.00
Rick Ferrell
Wes Ferrell
Fritz Ostermueller
8G (Cleveland Indians Puzzle)
34-9 Billy Werber 35.00 60.00
Rick Ferrell
Wes Ferrell
Fritz Ostermueller
9G (Washington Senators Puzzle)
35-1 Sam West 45.00 80.00
Oscar Melillo
George Blaeholder
Dick Coffman
1F SP (Detroit Tigers Puzzle)
35-3 Sam West 45.00 80.00
Oscar Melillo
George Blaeholder
Dick Coffman
3D SP (Frankie Frisch Puzzle)
35-5 Sam West 30.00 50.00
Oscar Melillo
George Blaeholder
Dick Coffman
5D (Joe Cronin Puzzle)
35-6 Sam West 30.00 50.00
Oscar Melillo
George Blaeholder
Dick Coffman
6D (Jimmie Foxx Puzzle)
36-1 Jimmy Wilson 45.00 80.00
Ethan Allen
Bubba Jonnard XRC
Fred Brickell
1E SP (Detroit Tigers Puzzle)
36-3 Jimmy Wilson 45.00 80.00
Ethan Allen
Bubba Jonnard XRC
Fred Brickell
3C SP (Frankie Frisch Puzzle)
36-5 Jimmy Wilson 45.00 80.00
Ethan Allen
Bubba Jonnard XRC
Fred Brickell
5C SP (Joe Cronin Puzzle)
36-6 Jimmy Wilson 30.00 50.00
Ethan Allen
Bubba Jonnard XRC
Fred Brickell
6C (Jimmie Foxx Puzzle)

1938 Goudey Heads-Up

The cards in this 48-card set measure approximately 2 3/8" by 2 7/8". The 1938 Goudey set is commonly referred to as the Heads-Up set. These very popular but difficult to obtain cards came in two series of the same 24 players. The first series, numbers 241-264, is distinguished from the second series, numbers 265-288, in that the second contains etched cartoons and comments surrounding the player picture. Although the set starts with number 241, it is not a continuation of the 1933 Goudey set, but a separate set in its own right.

COMPLETE SET (48) 9000.00 15000.00
COMMON (241-264) 60.00 100.00
COMMON (265-288) 60.00 100.00
WRAP.(1-CENT, 6-FIGURE) 700.00 800.00
241 Charley Gehringer 175.00 300.00
242 Pete Fox 60.00 100.00
243 Joe Kuhel 60.00 100.00
244 Frank Demaree 60.00 100.00
245 Frank Pytlak XRC 60.00 100.00
246 Ernie Lombardi 100.00 175.00
247 Joe Vosmik 60.00 100.00
248 Dick Bartell 60.00 100.00
249 Jimmie Foxx 250.00 400.00
250 Joe DiMaggio XRC 2000.00 3500.00
251 Bump Hadley 60.00 100.00
252 Zeke Bonura 60.00 100.00
253 Hank Greenberg 250.00 400.00
254 Van Lingle Mungo 75.00 125.00
255 Moose Solters 60.00 100.00
256 Vernon Kennedy XRC 60.00 100.00
257 Al Lopez 125.00 200.00
258 Bobby Doerr XRC 150.00 250.00
259 Billy Werber 60.00 100.00
260 Rudy York XRC 75.00 125.00
261 Rip Radcliff XRC 60.00 100.00
262 Joe Medwick 150.00 250.00
263 Marvin Owen 60.00 100.00
264 Bob Feller XRC 350.00 600.00
265 Charley Gehringer 175.00 300.00
266 Pete Fox 60.00 100.00
267 Joe Kuhel 60.00 100.00
268 Frank Demaree 60.00 100.00
269 Frank Pytlak XRC 60.00 100.00
270 Ernie Lombardi 125.00 200.00
271 Joe Vosmik 60.00 100.00
272 Dick Bartell 60.00 100.00
273 Jimmie Foxx 250.00 400.00
274 Joe DiMaggio XRC 2000.00 3500.00
275 Bump Hadley 60.00 100.00
276 Zeke Bonura 60.00 100.00
277 Hank Greenberg 250.00 400.00
278 Van Lingle Mungo 75.00 125.00
279 Moose Solters 60.00 100.00
280 Vernon Kennedy XRC 60.00 100.00
281 Al Lopez 150.00 250.00
282 Bobby Doerr XRC 150.00 250.00
283 Billy Werber 60.00 100.00
284 Rudy York XRC 75.00 125.00
285 Rip Radcliff XRC 60.00 100.00
286 Joe Medwick 150.00 250.00
287 Marvin Owen 60.00 100.00
288 Bob Feller XRC 450.00 750.00

1941 Goudey

The cards in this 33-card set measure 2 3/8" by 2 7/8". The 1941 Series of blank backed baseball cards was the last baseball issue marketed by Goudey before the war closed the door on that company for good. Each black and white player photo comes with four color backgrounds (blue, green, red, or yellow). Cards without numbers are probably miscut. Cards 21-25 are especially scarce in relation to the rest of the set. In fact the eight hardest to find cards in the set are, in order, 22, 24, 23, 25, 21, 27, 29 and 32.

COMPLETE SET (33) 1200.00 2000.00
COMMON CARD (1-33) 15.00 30.00
COMMON SP
WRAPPER (1-CENT) 150.00 200.00
1 Hugh Mulcahy 15.00 30.00
2 Harland Clift XRC 15.00 30.00
3 Louis Chiozza 15.00 30.00
4 Buddy Rosar XRC 15.00 30.00
5 George McQuinn 15.00 30.00
6 George Dickman 15.00 30.00
7 Wayne Ambler 15.00 30.00
8 Bob Muncrief XRC 15.00 30.00
9 Bill Dietrich XRC 15.00 30.00
10 Taft Wright 15.00 30.00
11 Don Heffner 15.00 30.00
12 Fritz Ostermueller 15.00 30.00
13 Frank Hayes 15.00 30.00
14 John Kramer XRC 15.00 30.00
15 Dario Lodigiani XRC 15.00 30.00
16 George Case 15.00 30.00
17 Vito Tamulis 15.00 30.00
18 Whitlow Wyatt 20.00 40.00
19 Bill Posedel 15.00 30.00
20 Carl Hubbell 50.00 80.00
21 Harold Warstler SP 60.00 120.00
22 Joe Sullivan SP XRC 175.00 300.00
23 Norman Young SP 100.00 200.00
24 Stanley Andrews SP XRC 125.00 250.00
25 Morris Arnovich SP 60.00 120.00
26 Elbert Fletcher 15.00 30.00
27 Bill Crouch XRC 40.00 60.00
28 Al Todd XRC 15.00 30.00
29 Debs Garms 30.00 50.00
30 Jim Tobin 15.00 30.00
31 Chester Ross XRC 15.00 30.00
32 George Coffman 20.00 40.00
33 Mel Ott 75.00 125.00

2000 Greats of the Game

The 2000 Fleer Greats of the Game set was released in late March, 2000 as a 107-card set that features some of the greatest players to ever play the game. There was only one series offered. Each pack contained six cards and carried a suggested retail price of 4.99. A promotional sample card featuring Nolan Ryan was distributed to dealers and hobby media several weeks before the product went live. Card fronts featured an attractive burgundy frame with (in most cases) a full color player image. Fueled by a great selection of autographs, the popular Yankee Clippings game-used jersey inserts and the aforementioned superior design of the base set, the product turned out to be one of the most popular releases of the 2000 calendar.

COMPLETE SET (107) 15.00 40.00
1 Mickey Mantle 4.00 10.00
2 Gil Hodges .60 1.50
3 Monte Irvin .40 1.00
4 Satchel Paige .60 1.50
5 Roy Campanella .60 1.50
6 Richie Ashburn .40 1.00
7 Roger Maris .60 1.50
8 Ozzie Smith 1.00 2.50
9 Reggie Jackson .40 1.00
10 Eddie Mathews .60 1.50
11 Dave Righetti .25 .60
12 Dave Winfield .25 .60
13 Lou Whitaker .25 .60
14 Phil Garner .25 .60
15 Ron Cey .25 .60
16 Brooks Robinson .40 1.00
17 Bruce Sutter .25 .60
18 Dave Parker .25 .60
19 Johnny Bench .60 1.50
20 Fernando Valenzuela .25 .60
21 George Brett 1.50 4.00
22 Paul Molitor .25 .60
23 Hoyt Wilhelm .25 .60
24 Luis Aparicio .25 .60
25 Frank White .25 .60
26 Herb Score .25 .60
27 Kirk Gibson .25 .60
28 Mike Schmidt 1.25 3.00
29 Don Baylor .25 .60
30 Joe Pepitone .25 .60
31 Hal McRae .25 .60
32 Lee Smith .25 .60
33 Nolan Ryan 1.50 4.00
34 Bill Mazeroski .40 1.00

35 Bobby Doerr	.40	1.00
36 Duke Snider	.40	1.00
37 Dick Groat	.25	.60
38 Larry Doby	.25	.60
39 Kirby Puckett	.60	1.50
40 Steve Carlton	.25	.60
41 Dennis Eckersley	.25	.60
42 Jim Bunning	.40	1.00
43 Ron Guidry	.25	.60
44 Alan Trammell	.25	.60
45 Bob Feller	.25	.60
46 Dave Concepcion	.25	.60
47 Dwight Evans	.40	1.00
48 Enos Slaughter	.25	.60
49 Tom Seaver	.40	1.00
50 Tony Oliva	.25	.60
51 Mel Stottlemyre	.25	.60
52 Tommy John	.25	.60
53 Willie McCovey	.25	.60
54 Red Schoendienst	.25	.60
55 Gorman Thomas	.25	.60
56 Ralph Kiner	.25	.60
57 Robin Yount	1.00	2.50
58 Andre Dawson	.25	.60
59 Al Kaline	.60	1.50
60 Dom DiMaggio	.40	1.00
61 Juan Marichal	.25	.60
62 Jack Morris	.25	.60
63 Warren Spahn	.40	1.00
64 Preacher Roe	.25	.60
65 Darrell Evans	.25	.60
66 Jim Bouton	.25	.60
67 Rocky Colavito	.40	1.00
68 Bob Gibson	.40	1.00
69 Whitey Ford	.40	1.00
70 Moose Skowron	.25	.60
71 Boog Powell	.25	.60
72 Al Lopez	.40	1.00
73 Lou Brock	.40	1.00
74 Mickey Lolich	.25	.60
75 Rod Carew	.40	1.00
76 Bob Lemon	.40	1.00
77 Frank Howard	.25	.60
78 Phil Rizzuto	.60	1.50
79 Carl Yastrzemski	1.00	2.50
80 Rico Carty	.25	.60
81 Jim Kaat	.25	.60
82 Bert Blyleven	.25	.60
83 George Kell	.25	.60
84 Jim Palmer	.25	.60
85 Maury Wills	.25	.60
86 Jim Rice	.25	.60
87 Joe Carter	.25	.60
88 Clete Boyer	.25	.60
89 Yogi Berra	.60	1.50
90 Cecil Cooper	.25	.60
91 Davey Johnson	.25	.60
92 Lou Boudreau	.40	1.00
93 Orlando Cepeda	.25	.60
94 Tommy Henrich	.25	.60
95 Hank Bauer	.25	.60
96 Don Larsen	.25	.60
97 Vida Blue	.25	.60
98 Ben Oglivie	.25	.60
99 Don Mattingly	1.50	4.00
100 Dale Murphy	.40	1.00
101 Ferguson Jenkins	.25	.60
102 Bobby Bonds	.25	.60
103 Dick Allen	.25	.60
104 Stan Musial	1.00	2.50
105 Gaylord Perry	.25	.60
106 Willie Randolph	.25	.60
107 Willie Stargell	.40	1.00
P33 Nolan Ryan Promo	.60	1.50

2000 Greats of the Game Autographs

Randomly inserted in packs at one in six, this 93-card insert features autographed cards of some of the greatest players in major league history. The card design closely parallels the attractive basic issue cards, except of course for the player's singature. Representatives at Fleer eventually released cryptic details on a few cards confirming widespread belief on suspected shortprints within the set. It's known that the scarcest cards are Johnny Bench and Mike Schmidt. Several other cards from this set experienced amazing surges iin value throughout the course of the year 2000 as collectors scrambled to complete their sets in the midst of heavy demand and rumours of additional short prints. Also, Herb Score mistakenly signed several of his basic autographs with an "ROY 55" notation. Score was supposed so sign only 55 purple-bordered Memorable Moments variations. Finally, a Derek Jeter card was released in early 2004. It's believed that the card was only made available as a redemption to collectors for autograph exchange cards of other players that they could not fulfill. Please note that these cards are unnumbered and we have sequenced them in alphabetical order.

JETER EXCH PRINT RUN 150 CARDS
JETER EXCH IS NOT SERIAL #'d
JETER PRINT RUN PROVIDED BY FLEER

1 Luis Aparicio	15.00	40.00
2 Hank Bauer	6.00	15.00
3 Don Baylor	10.00	25.00
4 Johnny Bench SP	150.00	250.00
5 Yogi Berra SP	125.00	200.00
6 Vida Blue	6.00	15.00
7 Bert Blyleven	10.00	25.00
8 Bobby Bonds	30.00	60.00
9 Lou Boudreau	90.00	150.00
10 Jim Bouton	6.00	15.00
11 Clete Boyer	10.00	25.00
12 George Brett SP	250.00	400.00
13 Lou Brock	15.00	40.00
14 Jim Bunning	15.00	40.00
15 Rod Carew	30.00	60.00
16 Steve Carlton	10.00	25.00
17 Joe Carter SP	90.00	150.00
18 Orlando Cepeda	6.00	15.00
19 Ron Cey	6.00	15.00
20 Rocky Colavito	20.00	50.00
21 Dave Concepcion	15.00	40.00
21A Dave Concepcion	20.00	50.00
Signed in Red Ink		
22 Cecil Cooper	6.00	15.00
23 Andre Dawson	10.00	25.00
24 Dom DiMaggio	50.00	100.00
25 Bobby Doerr	10.00	25.00
26 Darrell Evans	6.00	15.00
27 Bob Feller	15.00	40.00
28 Whitey Ford SP	100.00	175.00
29 Phil Garner	6.00	15.00
30 Bob Gibson	15.00	40.00
31 Kirk Gibson	15.00	40.00
32 Dick Groat	6.00	15.00
33 Ron Guidry	6.00	15.00
34 Tommy Henrich SP	150.00	250.00
35 Frank Howard	6.00	15.00
36 Reggie Jackson SP	125.00	200.00
37 Ferguson Jenkins	10.00	25.00
38 Derek Jeter Mail-In/150	300.00	450.00
39 Tommy John	10.00	25.00
40 Davey Johnson	6.00	15.00
41 Jim Kaat	10.00	25.00
42 Al Kaline	12.50	30.00
43 George Kell	10.00	25.00
44 Ralph Kiner	15.00	40.00
45 Don Larsen	10.00	25.00
46 Mickey Lolich	6.00	15.00
47 Juan Marichal	30.00	60.00
48 Eddie Mathews	125.00	200.00
49 Don Mattingly SP	125.00	250.00
50 Bill Mazeroski	20.00	50.00
51 Willie McCovey SP	125.00	200.00
52 Hal McRae	6.00	15.00
53 Paul Molitor	20.00	50.00
54 Jack Morris	6.00	15.00
55 Dale Murphy	10.00	25.00
56 Stan Musial SP	100.00	175.00
57 Ben Oglivie	10.00	25.00
58 Tony Oliva	10.00	25.00
59 Jim Palmer SP	100.00	175.00
60 Dave Parker	10.00	25.00
61 Joe Pepitone	6.00	15.00
62 Gaylord Perry	10.00	25.00
63 Boog Powell	10.00	25.00
64 Kirby Puckett SP	300.00	450.00
65 Willie Randolph	10.00	25.00
66 Jim Rice	15.00	40.00
67 Dave Righetti	10.00	25.00
68 Phil Rizzuto SP	150.00	250.00
69 Brooks Robinson	15.00	40.00
70 Preacher Roe	6.00	15.00
71 Nolan Ryan	125.00	200.00
72 Mike Schmidt SP	450.00	700.00
73 Red Schoendienst	10.00	25.00
74 Herb Score	10.00	25.00
Card has no ROY 55 on signature		
75 Herb Score	30.00	60.00
ROY 55 in signature		
76 Tom Seaver	60.00	120.00
77 Moose Skowron	10.00	25.00
78 Enos Slaughter	15.00	40.00
79 Lee Smith	10.00	25.00
80 Ozzie Smith SP	175.00	300.00
81 Duke Snider SP	150.00	250.00
82 Warren Spahn SP	200.00	350.00
83 Willie Stargell	60.00	120.00
84 Bruce Sutter	10.00	25.00
85 Gorman Thomas	6.00	15.00
86 Alan Trammell	10.00	25.00
87 Frank White	6.00	15.00
88 Hoyt Wilhelm	15.00	40.00
89 Maury Wills	10.00	25.00
90 Dave Winfield SP	200.00	400.00
91 Carl Yastrzemski	40.00	80.00
92 Robin Yount SP	200.00	350.00

2000 Greats of the Game Autographs Memorable Moments

Randomly inserted in packs, this insert features autographs of Ron Guidry, Nolan Ryan, Herb Score and Tom Seaver. Each card is autographed and contains a notion by the player related to a career achievement. Each card is serial-numbered to the year of that achievement. The fronts of these cards are purple-bordered instead of burgandy-bordered. Please note that Herb Score signed some of his regular burgandy-bordered autograph cards with the "HOF 55" notation. Please refer to the basic autograph set for price listings on that card.

1 Ron Guidry/CY 78	125.00	200.00
2 Nolan Ryan/HOF 99	350.00	500.00
3 Herb Score/ROY 55	125.00	200.00
4 Tom Seaver/CY 69	200.00	400.00

2000 Greats of the Game Retrospection

Randomly inserted in packs at one in six, this insert set pays tribute to 15 truly legendary players. Card backs carry a "R" prefix.

COMPLETE SET (15)	40.00	100.00
R1 Rod Carew	1.25	3.00
R2 Stan Musial	3.00	8.00
R3 Nolan Ryan	5.00	12.00
R4 Tom Seaver	1.25	3.00
R5 Brooks Robinson	1.25	3.00
R6 Al Kaline	2.00	5.00
R7 Mike Schmidt	4.00	10.00
R8 Thurman Munson	2.00	5.00
R9 Steve Carlton	.75	2.00
R10 Roger Maris	2.00	5.00
R11 Duke Snider	1.25	3.00
R12 Yogi Berra	2.00	5.00
R13 Carl Yastrzemski	3.00	8.00
R14 Reggie Jackson	1.25	3.00
R15 Johnny Bench	2.00	5.00

2000 Greats of the Game Yankees Clippings

Randomly inserted in packs at one in 48, this insert set features 15 cards that contain pieces of game-used jerseys of legendary New York Yankee players. Card backs carry a "YC" prefix. This set represents one of the earliest attempts by manufacturers to incorporate a theme into a memorabilia-based insert. According to representatives at Fleer, the Mantle card features a pair of home, pin-striped game-used pants.

YC1 Mickey Mantle Pants	100.00	200.00
YC2 Ron Guidry	12.50	30.00
YC3 Don Larsen	15.00	40.00
YC4 Elston Howard	40.00	80.00
YC5 Mel Stottlemyre	12.50	30.00
YC6 Don Mattingly	40.00	80.00
YC7 Reggie Jackson	15.00	40.00
YC8 Tommy John	6.00	15.00
YC9 Dave Winfield	15.00	40.00
YC10 Willie Randolph	15.00	40.00
Uniform is home pinstripes		
YC10A Willie Randolph	6.00	15.00
Grey Uniform		
YC11 Tommy Henrich	6.00	15.00
YC12 Billy Martin	30.00	60.00
YC13 Dave Righetti	12.50	30.00
YC14 Joe Pepitone	10.00	25.00
YC15 Thurman Munson	75.00	150.00

2001 Greats of the Game Promo Sheets

These six promo sheets were inserted into Sports Cards Magazine starting in February, 2001. Each uncut sheet features six Greats of the Game trading cards. Please note that Fleer released these one month at a time.

COMPLETE SET (6)	9.00	18.00
1 Rick Ankiel	1.50	3.00
Jeff Bagwell		
Barry Bonds		
Pat Burrell		
Roger Clemens		
Carlos Delgado		
2 J.D. Drew	1.50	3.00
Jim Edmonds		
Darin Erstad		
Andres Galarraga		
Nomar Garciaparra		
Jason Giambi		
3 Troy Glaus	1.50	3.00
Roberto Alomar		
Ken Griffey Jr.		
Vladimir Guerrero		
Tony Gwynn		
Todd Helton		
4 Derek Jeter	1.50	3.00
Randy Johnson		
Chipper Jones		
Andruw Jones		
Greg Maddux		
Pedro Martinez		
5 Mark McGwire	1.50	3.00
Magglio Ordonez		
Mike Piazza		
Manny Ramirez		
Cal Ripken		
Alex Rodriguez		
6 Ivan Rodriguez	1.50	3.00
Jeff Kent		
Gary Sheffield		
Sammy Sosa		
Frank Thomas		
Bernie Williams		

2001 Greats of the Game

The 2001 Fleer Greats of the Game product was released in March, 2001 and features a 137-card base set that includes many players that are in the Major League Hall of Fame. Each pack contains five cards and carried a suggested retail price of $4.99.

COMPLETE SET (137)	20.00	50.00
1 Roberto Clemente	2.50	6.00
2 George Anderson	.40	1.00
3 Babe Ruth	3.00	8.00
4 Paul Molitor	.40	1.00
5 Don Larsen	.40	1.00
6 Cy Young	1.00	2.50
7 Billy Martin	.60	1.50
8 Lou Brock	.60	1.50
9 Fred Lynn	.40	1.00
10 Johnny VanderMeer	.40	1.00
11 Harmon Killebrew	1.00	2.50
12 Dave Winfield	.40	1.00
13 Orlando Cepeda	.40	1.00
14 Johnny Mize	.60	1.50
15 Walter Johnson	1.00	2.50
16 Roy Campanella	1.00	2.50
17 Monte Irvin	.60	1.50
18 Mookie Wilson	.40	1.00
19 Elston Howard	.60	1.50
20 Walter Alston	.40	1.00
21 Rollie Fingers	.40	1.00
22 Brooks Robinson	.60	1.50
23 Hank Greenberg	1.00	2.50
24 Maury Wills	.40	1.00
25 Rich Gossage	.40	1.00
26 Leon Day	.40	1.00
27 Jimmie Foxx	1.00	2.50
28 Alan Trammell	.40	1.00
29 Dennis Martinez	.40	1.00
30 Don Drysdale	.60	1.50
31 Bob Feller	.40	1.00
32 Jackie Robinson	1.00	2.50
33 Whitey Ford	.60	1.50
34 Enos Slaughter	.40	1.00
35 Rod Carew	.60	1.50
36 Eddie Mathews	1.00	2.50
37 Ron Cey	.40	1.00
38 Thurman Munson	1.00	2.50
39 Henry Kimbro	.40	1.00
40 Ty Cobb	1.50	4.00
41 Rocky Colavito	1.00	2.50
42 Satchel Paige	1.00	2.50
43 Andre Dawson	.40	1.00
44 Phil Rizzuto	1.00	2.50
45 Roger Maris	1.00	2.50
46 Bobby Bonds	.40	1.00
47 Joe Carter	.40	1.00
48 Christy Mathewson	1.00	2.50
49 Tony Lazzeri	.40	1.00
50 Gil Hodges	1.00	2.50
51 Ray Dandridge	.40	1.00
52 Gaylord Perry	.40	1.00
53 Ernie Banks	1.00	2.50
54 Lou Gehrig	2.00	5.00
55 George Kell	.40	1.00
56 Wes Parker	.40	1.00
57 Sam Jethroe	.40	1.00
58 Joe Morgan	.40	1.00
59 Steve Garvey	.40	1.00
60 Joe Torre	.60	1.50
61 Roger Craig	.40	1.00
62 Warren Spahn	.60	1.50
63 Willie McCovey	.40	1.00
64 Cool Papa Bell	.40	1.00
65 Frank Robinson	.60	1.50
66 Richie Allen	.40	1.00
67 Bucky Dent	.40	1.00
68 George Foster	.40	1.00
69 Hoyt Wilhelm	.40	1.00
70 Phil Niekro	.40	1.00
71 Buck Leonard	.40	1.00
72 Preacher Roe	.40	1.00
73 Yogi Berra	1.00	2.50
74 Joe Black	.40	1.00
75 Nolan Ryan	2.50	6.00
76 Pop Lloyd	.40	1.00
77 Lester Lockett	.40	1.00
78 Paul Blair	.40	1.00
79 Ryne Sandberg	1.50	4.00
80 Bill Perkins	.40	1.00
81 Frank Howard	.40	1.00
82 Hack Wilson	.60	1.50
83 Robin Yount	1.00	2.50
84 Harry Heilmann	.40	1.00
85 Mike Schmidt	2.00	5.00
86 Vida Blue	.40	1.00
87 George Brett	2.00	5.00
88 Juan Marichal	.40	1.00
89 Tom Seaver	.60	1.50
90 Bill Skowron	.40	1.00
91 Don Mattingly	2.00	5.00
92 Jim Bunning	.60	1.50
93 Eddie Murray	1.00	2.50
94 Tommy Lasorda	.40	1.00
95 Pee Wee Reese	1.00	2.50
96 Bill Dickey	.60	1.50
97 Ozzie Smith	1.50	4.00
98 Dale Murphy	.60	1.50
99 Artie Wilson	.40	1.00
100 Bill Terry	.40	1.00
101 Jim Hunter	.60	1.50
102 Don Sutton	.40	1.00
103 Luis Aparicio	.40	1.00
104 Reggie Jackson	.60	1.50
105 Ted Radcliffe	.40	1.00
106 Carl Erskine	.40	1.00
107 Johnny Bench	1.00	2.50
108 Carl Furillo	.40	1.00
109 Stan Musial	1.50	4.00
110 Carlton Fisk	.60	1.50
111 Rube Foster	.40	1.00
112 Tony Oliva	.40	1.00
113 Hank Bauer	.40	1.00
114 Jim Rice	.40	1.00
115 Willie Mays	2.00	5.00
116 Ralph Kiner	.40	1.00
117 Al Kaline	1.00	2.50
118 Billy Williams	.40	1.00
119 Buck O'Neil	.40	1.00
120 Tony Perez	.40	1.00
121 Dave Parker	.40	1.00
122 Kirk Gibson	.40	1.00
123 Lou Piniella	.40	1.00
124 Ted Williams	2.00	5.00
125 Steve Carlton	.40	1.00
126 Dizzy Dean	1.00	2.50
127 Willie Stargell	.60	1.50
128 Joe Niekro	.40	1.00
129 Lloyd Waner	.60	1.50
130 Wade Boggs	.60	1.50
131 Wilmer Fields	.40	1.00
132 Bill Mazeroski	.60	1.50
133 Duke Snider	.60	1.50
134 Joe Williams	.40	1.00
135 Bob Gibson	.60	1.50
136 Jim Palmer	.40	1.00
137 Oscar Charleston	.40	1.00

2001 Greats of the Game Autographs

Randomly inserted into packs at one in eight Hobby, and one in 20 Retail, this 93-card insert set features authentic autographs from legendary players such as Nolan Ryan, Mike Schmidt, and recently inducted Hall of Famer Dave Winfield. Please note, the following players packed out as exchange cards with a redemption deadline of March 1st, 2002: Luis Aparicio, Sam Jethroe, Tommy Lasorda, Juan Marichal, Willie Mays, Phil Rizzuto and Willie Stargell. In addition, the following players had about 50 percent actual signed cards and 50 percent exchange cards seeded into packs: Jim Bunning, Ron Cey, Rollie Fingers, Carlton Fisk, Harmon Killebrew, Gaylord Perry and Brooks Robinson. Also, representatives at Fleer announced specific print runs for several short-printed cards within this set. Though the cards lack actual serial-numbering, the announced quantities for these SP's have been added to our checklist. Willie Stargell passed on before he could sign his card and Fleer used various redemption cards to send to those collectors who had pulled one of those cards from packs.

1 Richie Allen	12.50	30.00
2 Sparky Anderson	20.00	50.00
3 Luis Aparicio	6.00	15.00
4 Ernie Banks SP/250	75.00	150.00
5 Hank Bauer	6.00	15.00
6 Johnny Bench SP/400	50.00	100.00
7 Yogi Berra SP/500	40.00	80.00
8 Joe Black	12.50	30.00
9 Paul Blair	6.00	15.00
9A Paul Blair	6.00	15.00
Double-Signed		
10 Vida Blue	6.00	15.00
11 Wade Boggs	15.00	40.00
12 Bobby Bonds	10.00	25.00
13 George Brett SP/247	60.00	120.00
14 Lou Brock SP/500	30.00	60.00
15 Jim Bunning	15.00	40.00
16 Rod Carew	20.00	50.00
17 Steve Carlton	12.50	30.00
18 Joe Carter	6.00	15.00
19 Orlando Cepeda	6.00	15.00
20 Ron Cey	6.00	15.00
21 Rocky Colavito	15.00	40.00
22 Roger Craig	10.00	25.00
23 Andre Dawson	6.00	15.00
24 Bucky Dent	6.00	15.00
25 Carl Erskine	6.00	15.00
26 Bob Feller	10.00	25.00
27 Wilmer Fields	10.00	25.00
28 Rollie Fingers	6.00	15.00
29 Carlton Fisk	10.00	25.00
30 Whitey Ford	15.00	40.00
31 George Foster	6.00	15.00
32 Steve Garvey SP/400	15.00	40.00
33 Bob Gibson	15.00	40.00
34 Kirk Gibson	6.00	15.00
35 Rich Gossage	10.00	25.00
36 Frank Howard	6.00	15.00
37 Monte Irvin	10.00	25.00
38 Reg. Jackson SP/400	50.00	100.00
39 Sam Jethroe	20.00	50.00
40 Al Kaline	10.00	25.00
41 George Kell	10.00	25.00
42 H. Killebrew EXCH*	30.00	60.00
43 Ralph Kiner	10.00	25.00
44 Don Larsen	10.00	25.00
45 Tommy Lasorda SP/400	75.00	150.00
46 Lester Lockett	12.50	30.00
47 Fred Lynn	6.00	15.00
48 Juan Marichal	12.50	30.00
49 Dennis Martinez	6.00	15.00
50 Don Mattingly	40.00	80.00
51 Willie Mays SP/100	500.00	800.00
52 Bill Mazeroski UER	10.00	25.00
Baltimore Elite Giants logo on card back		
53 Willie McCovey	20.00	50.00
54 Paul Molitor	12.50	30.00
55 Joe Morgan	20.00	50.00
56 Dale Murphy	10.00	25.00
57 Eddie Murray SP/140	200.00	350.00
58 Stan Musial SP/525	50.00	100.00
59 Joe Niekro	6.00	15.00
60 Phil Niekro	6.00	15.00
61 Tony Oliva	6.00	15.00
62 Buck O'Neil	30.00	60.00
63 Jim Palmer SP/600	15.00	40.00
64 Dave Parker	6.00	15.00
65 Tony Perez	10.00	25.00
66 Gaylord Perry	6.00	15.00
67 Lou Piniella	10.00	25.00
68 Ted Radcliffe	10.00	25.00
69 Jim Rice	10.00	25.00
70 Phil Rizzuto	30.00	60.00
EXCH SP/425		
71 Brooks Robinson	10.00	25.00
72 Frank Robinson	12.50	30.00
73 Preacher Roe	10.00	25.00
74 Nolan Ryan SP/650	60.00	120.00
75 Ryne Sandberg	30.00	60.00
76 Mike Schmidt SP/213	125.00	200.00
77 Tom Seaver	30.00	60.00
78 Bill Skowron	6.00	15.00
79 Enos Slaughter	10.00	25.00
80 Ozzie Smith	20.00	50.00
81 Duke Snider SP/600	30.00	60.00
82 Warren Spahn	12.50	30.00
83 Willie Stargell NO AU	10.00	25.00
Stargell passed away before he had a chance to sign for this set		
84 Don Sutton	10.00	25.00
85 Joe Torre SP/500	50.00	100.00
86 Alan Trammell	6.00	15.00
87 Hoyt Wilhelm	15.00	40.00
88 Billy Williams	6.00	15.00
89 Maury Wills	6.00	15.00
90 Artie Wilson	12.50	30.00
91 Mookie Wilson	6.00	15.00
92 Dave Winfield SP/370	30.00	60.00
93 Robin Yount SP/400	50.00	100.00

2001 Greats of the Game Dodger Blues

Randomly inserted into packs at one in 36 Hobby, this 15-card insert set features swatches from actual game used Jerseys, Uniforms, and Bats from legendary Dodger players. The cards have been listed below in alphabetical order for convenience. Please note, according to representatives at Fleer less than 200 of each SP was produced.

1 Walter Alston Jsy	10.00	25.00
2 Walter Alston Uni	10.00	25.00
3 Roy Campanella Bat SP	100.00	200.00
4 Roger Craig Jsy	10.00	25.00
5 Don Drysdale Jsy	15.00	40.00
6 Carl Furillo Jsy	10.00	25.00
7 Steve Garvey Jsy	10.00	25.00
8 Gil Hodges Uni	15.00	40.00
9 Wes Parker Bat	10.00	25.00
10 Wes Parker Jsy	10.00	25.00
11 Pee Wee Reese Jsy	15.00	40.00
12 Jackie Robinson	125.00	250.00
Uni SP		
13 Preacher Roe Jsy	10.00	25.00
14 Duke Snider Bat SP	75.00	150.00
15 Don Sutton Jsy	10.00	25.00

2001 Greats of the Game Feel the Game Classics

Randomly inserted into packs at one in 72 Hobby, and one in 400 Retail, this 24-card insert features swatches of actual game-used Bats or Jerseys from legendary players like Babe Ruth and Roger Maris. Please note that the cards are listed below in alphabetical order. Though the cards lack actual serial-numbering, specific print runs for several short-printed cards was publicly announced by representatives at Fleer. These figures are detailed in our checklist.

1 L. Aparicio Bat SP/200	10.00	25.00
2 George Brett Jsy SP/300	20.00	50.00
3 Lou Brock Jsy	6.00	15.00
4 O. Cepeda Bat SP/300	10.00	25.00
5 Whitey Ford Jsy	10.00	25.00
6 Hank Greenberg Bat SP/300	40.00	80.00
7 Elston Howard Bat SP/300	10.00	25.00
8 Jim Hunter Jsy	6.00	15.00
9 Harmon Killebrew Bat	10.00	25.00
10 Roger Maris Bat	20.00	50.00
11 Eddie Mathews Bat	6.00	15.00
12 Willie McCovey	10.00	25.00
Bat SP/200		
13 Johnny Mize Bat	6.00	15.00
14 Paul Molitor Jsy	4.00	10.00
15 Jim Palmer Jsy	4.00	10.00
16 Tony Perez Bat	4.00	10.00
17 B.Robinson Bat SP/144	15.00	40.00
18 Babe Ruth Bat SP/250	125.00	200.00
19 Mike Schmidt Jsy	15.00	40.00
20 Tom Seaver Jsy	6.00	15.00
21 Enos Slaughter	10.00	25.00
Bat SP/200		
22 Willie Stargell Jsy	6.00	15.00
23 Hack Wilson Bat	40.00	80.00
24 Harry Heilmann Bat	4.00	10.00

2001 Greats of the Game Retrospection

Randomly inserted into hobby and retail packs at one in six, this 10-card insert set takes a look at the careers of some of the best players to have ever played the game. Card backs carry a "RC" prefix.

COMPLETE SET (10)	15.00	30.00
RC1 Babe Ruth	6.00	15.00
RC2 Stan Musial	2.50	6.00
RC3 Jimmie Foxx	2.00	5.00
RC4 Roberto Clemente	5.00	12.00
RC5 Ted Williams	4.00	10.00
RC6 Mike Schmidt	3.00	8.00
RC7 Cy Young	2.00	5.00
RC8 Satchel Paige	2.00	5.00
RC9 Hank Greenberg	2.00	5.00
RC10 Jim Bunning	1.25	3.00

2002 Greats of the Game

This product was released in mid-December 2001, and featured a 100-card base set of Hall of Famers like Cy Young and Ted Williams. Each pack contained five-cards and carried a suggested retail price of $4.99.

COMPLETE SET (100)	20.00	50.00
1 Cal Ripken	3.00	8.00
2 Paul Molitor	.40	1.00
3 Roberto Clemente	2.50	6.00
4 Cy Young	1.00	2.50
5 Tris Speaker	1.00	2.50
6 Lou Brock	.60	1.50
7 Fred Lynn	.40	1.00
8 Harmon Killebrew	1.00	2.50
9 Ted Williams	2.00	5.00
10 Dave Winfield	.40	1.00
11 Orlando Cepeda	.40	1.00
12 Johnny Mize	.60	1.50
13 Walter Johnson	1.00	2.50
14 Roy Campanella	1.00	2.50
15 George Sisler	.40	1.00
16 Bo Jackson	1.00	2.50
17 Rollie Fingers	.40	1.00
18 Brooks Robinson	.60	1.50
19 Billy Williams	.40	1.00
20 Maury Wills	.40	1.00
21 Jimmie Foxx	1.00	2.50
22 Alan Trammell	.40	1.00
23 Rogers Hornsby	1.00	2.50
24 Don Drysdale	.60	1.50
25 Bob Feller	.40	1.00
26 Jackie Robinson	1.00	2.50
27 Whitey Ford	.60	1.50
28 Enos Slaughter	.40	1.00
29 Rod Carew	.60	1.50
30 Eddie Mathews	1.00	2.50
31 Ron Cey	.40	1.00
32 Thurman Munson	1.00	2.50
33 Ty Cobb	1.50	4.00
34 Rocky Colavito	1.00	2.50
35 Satchel Paige	1.00	2.50
36 Andre Dawson	.40	1.00
37 Phil Rizzuto	1.00	2.50
38 Roger Maris	1.00	2.50
39 Earl Weaver	.40	1.00
40 Joe Carter	.40	1.00
41 Christy Mathewson	1.00	2.50
42 Tony Lazzeri	.40	1.00
43 Gil Hodges	1.00	2.50
44 Gaylord Perry	.40	1.00
45 Steve Carlton	.40	1.00
46 George Kell	.40	1.00
47 Mickey Cochrane	.60	1.50
48 Joe Morgan	.40	1.00
49 Steve Garvey	.40	1.00
50 Bob Gibson	.60	1.50
51 Lefty Grove	.60	1.50
52 Warren Spahn	.60	1.50
53 Willie McCovey	.40	1.00
54 Frank Robinson	.60	1.50
55 Rich Gossage	.40	1.00
56 Hank Bauer	.40	1.00
57 Hoyt Wilhelm	.40	1.00
58 Mel Ott	1.00	2.50
59 Preacher Roe	.40	1.00
60 Yogi Berra	1.00	2.50
61 Nolan Ryan	2.50	6.00
62 Dizzy Dean	1.00	2.50
63 Ryne Sandberg	1.50	4.00
64 Frank Howard	.40	1.00
65 Hack Wilson	.60	1.50
66 Robin Yount	1.00	2.50
67 Al Kaline	1.00	2.50
68 Mike Schmidt	2.00	5.00
69 Vida Blue	.40	1.00
70 George Brett	2.00	5.00
71 Sparky Anderson	.40	1.00
72 Tom Seaver	.60	1.50
73 Bill Skowron	.40	1.00
74 Don Mattingly	2.00	5.00
75 Carl Yastrzemski	1.50	4.00
76 Eddie Murray	1.00	2.50
77 Jim Palmer	.40	1.00
78 Bill Dickey	.60	1.50
79 Ozzie Smith	1.50	4.00
80 Dale Murphy	.60	1.50
81 Nap Lajoie	1.00	2.50
82 Jim Hunter	.60	1.50
83 Duke Snider	.60	1.50
84 Luis Aparicio	.40	1.00
85 Reggie Jackson	.60	1.50
86 Honus Wagner	1.25	3.00
87 Johnny Bench	1.00	2.50
88 Stan Musial	1.50	4.00
89 Carlton Fisk	.60	1.50
90 Tony Oliva	.40	1.00
91 Wade Boggs	.60	1.50
92 Jim Rice	.40	1.00
93 Bill Mazeroski	.60	1.50
94 Ralph Kiner	.40	1.00
95 Tony Perez	.40	1.00
96 Kirby Puckett	1.00	2.50
97 Bobby Bonds	.40	1.00
98 Bill Terry	.40	1.00
99 Juan Marichal	.40	1.00
100 Hank Greenberg	1.00	2.50

2002 Greats of the Game Autographs

Randomly inserted into packs at one in 24, this insert set features authentic autographs from legendary players such as Nolan Ryan, Bob Gibson, and recently inducted Hall of Famer Ozzie Smith. Please note that a few of the players were short-printed and are listed below with an "SP" after their name. A number of exchange cards with a redemption deadline of 12/01/02 were seeded into packs. The following players were available via redemption: Al Kaline, Alan Trammell, Bobby Bonds, Bob Feller, Carlton Fisk, Rocky Colavito, Cal Ripken, Dave Winfield, Eddie Murray, Enos Slaughter, Harmon Killebrew, Juan Marichal, Kirby Puckett, Luis Aparicio, Lou Brock, Mike Schmidt, Dale Murphy, Maury Wills, Nolan Ryan, Ozzie Smith, Phil Rizzuto, Rod Carew, Rollie Fingers, Rich Gossage, Ralph Kiner, Robin Yount, Steve Garvey, Whitey Ford, Willie McCovey and Yogi Berra.

AD Andre Dawson	6.00	15.00
AK Al Kaline	15.00	40.00
AT Alan Trammell	6.00	15.00
BB Bobby Bonds	15.00	40.00
BF Bob Feller	12.50	30.00
BG Bob Gibson SP/200	12.50	30.00
BM Bill Mazeroski SP/200	12.50	30.00

Card	Low	High
BR Brooks Robinson	10.00	25.00
BS Bill Skowron	6.00	15.00
BW Billy Williams	6.00	15.00
CE Ron Cey	4.00	10.00
CF Carlton Fisk SP/100	40.00	80.00
CO Rocky Colavito	15.00	40.00
CR Cal Ripken SP/100	125.00	200.00
CY C.Yastrzemski SP/200	40.00	80.00
DM Don Mattingly SP/300	40.00	80.00
DP Dave Parker	10.00	25.00
DS Duke Snider	10.00	25.00
DW Dave Winfield SP/250	12.50	30.00
EM Eddie Murray SP/250	40.00	80.00
ES Enos Slaughter	10.00	25.00
FH Frank Howard	6.00	15.00
FL Fred Lynn	6.00	15.00
FR Frank Robinson SP/250	12.50	30.00
GB George Brett SP/150	75.00	150.00
GK George Kell	6.00	15.00
GP Gaylord Perry	6.00	15.00
HB Hank Bauer	6.00	15.00
HK Harmon Killebrew	15.00	40.00
HW Hoyt Wilhelm	6.00	15.00
JB Johnny Bench	30.00	60.00
JC Joe Carter	6.00	15.00
JM Juan Marichal	10.00	25.00
JM Joe Morgan	10.00	25.00
JP Jim Palmer	10.00	25.00
JR Jim Rice	6.00	15.00
KP Kirby Puckett SP/250	50.00	100.00
LA Luis Aparicio	6.00	15.00
LB Lou Brock SP/250	12.50	30.00
MS Mike Schmidt SP/150	30.00	60.00
MU Dale Murphy	10.00	25.00
MW Maury Wills	6.00	15.00
NR Nolan Ryan SP/150	60.00	120.00
OC Orlando Cepeda	4.00	10.00
OS Ozzie Smith SP/300	40.00	80.00
PB Paul Blair	4.00	10.00
PM Paul Molitor	6.00	15.00
PR Phil Rizzuto SP/300	30.00	60.00
PR Preacher Roe	6.00	15.00
RC Rod Carew SP/250	20.00	50.00
RF Rollie Fingers	6.00	15.00
RG Rich Gossage	6.00	15.00
RJ R.Jackson SP/150	40.00	80.00
RK Ralph Kiner SP/250	10.00	25.00
RS R.Sandberg SP/200	40.00	80.00
RY Robin Yount SP/250	40.00	80.00
SA Sparky Anderson	10.00	25.00
SC Steve Carlton	10.00	25.00
SG Steve Garvey	6.00	15.00
SM Stan Musial SP/200	60.00	120.00
TO Tony Oliva	6.00	15.00
TP Tony Perez	6.00	15.00
TS Tom Seaver SP/150	30.00	60.00
VB Vida Blue	6.00	15.00
WB Wade Boggs	10.00	25.00
WF Whitey Ford	15.00	40.00
WM Willie McCovey	10.00	25.00
WS Warren Spahn	15.00	40.00
YB Yogi Berra	20.00	50.00

2002 Greats of the Game Dueling Duos

This 29-card insert pairs contemporaries that competed against each other in their respective eras. These cards were inserted into packs at one in six.

Card	Low	High
COMPLETE SET (29)	75.00	150.00
1 Johnny Bench	1.50	4.00
Carlton Fisk		
2 Roy Campanella	2.00	5.00
Yogi Berra		
3 Stan Musial	2.50	6.00
Ted Williams		
4 Carl Yastrzemski	2.00	5.00
Reggie Jackson		
5 Babe Ruth	4.00	10.00
Jimmie Foxx		
6 Kirby Puckett	2.50	6.00
Don Mattingly		
7 Steve Carlton	3.00	8.00
Nolan Ryan		
8 Wade Boggs	3.00	8.00
Don Mattingly		
9 Brooks Robinson	1.50	4.00
Roger Maris		
10 Paul Molitor	3.00	8.00
Don Mattingly		
11 Sparky Anderson	1.25	3.00
Earl Weaver		
12 Bob Gibson	1.25	3.00
Duke Snider		
13 Yogi Berra	2.00	5.00
Gil Hodges		
14 Joe Morgan	2.50	6.00
Ryne Sandberg		
15 Tony Perez	2.00	5.00
Carl Yastrzemski		
16 Jimmie Foxx	1.50	4.00
Bill Dickey		
17 Ralph Kiner	1.25	3.00
Duke Snider		
18 Nellie Fox	1.25	3.00
Rocky Colavito		
19 Willie McCovey	1.50	4.00
Johnny Bench		
20 Duke Snider	1.25	3.00
Eddie Mathews		
21 Reggie Jackson	1.25	3.00
Jim Rice		
22 Eddie Murray	1.50	4.00
Jim Rice		
23 Paul Molitor	1.25	3.00
Dave Winfield		
24 Robin Yount	1.50	4.00
Dave Winfield		
25 Enos Slaughter	1.25	3.00
Ted Kluszewski		
26 Wade Boggs	3.00	8.00
George Brett		
27 George Brett	3.00	8.00
Mike Schmidt		
28 George Brett	3.00	8.00
Eddie Murray		
29 George Brett	5.00	12.00
Cal Ripken		

2002 Greats of the Game Dueling Duos Autographs

This six-card insert set is a partial parallel of the 2002 Fleer Greats of the Game Dueling Duos insert, and features dual autographs from greats like Bench/Fisk. Each card has an announced print run of 25 copies. Due to market scarcity, no pricing is provided. The following cards were distributed in packs as exchange cards with a redemption deadline of 12/01/02: Bench/Fisk, Boggs/Mattingly, Brett/Schmidt and Puckett/Mattingly.

2002 Greats of the Game Dueling Duos Game Used Double

This 27-card insert is a partial parallel of the 2002 Fleer Greats of the Game Dueling Duos insert. Each card features dual jersey swatches from greats like Boggs/Brett, and is individually serial numbered to 25. Due to market scarcity, no pricing is provided.

2002 Greats of the Game Dueling Duos Game Used Single

This 54-card insert features a single swatch of game-used jersey, and was inserted into packs at 1:24. Please note that a few of the players were short-printed and are notated as such in our checklist.

Card	Low	High
BD1 Jimmie Foxx	8.00	20.00
Bill Dickey Bat		
BG1 Bob Gibson Jsy	8.00	20.00
Duke Snider SP/200		
BR1 Brooks Robinson Bat	8.00	20.00
Roger Maris		
BR1 Babe Ruth Bat		
Jimmie Foxx SP/75		
CF1 Johnny Bench	8.00	20.00
Carlton Fisk Bat		
CR1 George Brett	15.00	40.00
Cal Ripken Bat		
CY1 Carl Yastrzemski Bat	12.50	30.00
Reggie Jackson		
CY2 Tony Perez	12.50	30.00
Carl Yastrzemski Bat		
DM1 Kirby Puckett	8.00	20.00
Don Mattingly Bat		
DM2 Wade Boggs	8.00	20.00
Don Mattingly Bat		
DM3 Paul Molitor	8.00	20.00
Don Mattingly Bat		
DS1 Bob Gibson	8.00	20.00
Duke Snider Bat SP/200		
DS2 Ralph Kiner	8.00	20.00
Duke Snider Bat		
DS3 Duke Snider Bat	8.00	20.00
Eddie Mathews		
DW1 Paul Molitor	6.00	15.00
Dave Winfield Bat		
DW2 Robin Yount	6.00	15.00
Dave Winfield Bat		
EM1 Duke Snider	8.00	20.00
Eddie Mathews Bat		
EM1 Eddie Murray Bat	8.00	20.00
Jim Rice		
EM2 George Brett	8.00	20.00
Eddie Murray Bat		
ES1 Enos Slaughter Bat	6.00	15.00
Ted Kluszewski		
EW1 Sparky Anderson	6.00	15.00
Earl Weaver Pants SP/400		
GB1 Wade Boggs	8.00	20.00
George Brett Bat		
GB2 George Brett Bat	8.00	20.00
Eddie Murray		
GB3 George Brett Bat	10.00	25.00
Cal Ripken		
GH1 Yogi Berra	8.00	20.00
Gil Hodges Bat		
JB1 Johnny Bench Bat	8.00	20.00
Carlton Fisk		
JB2 Willie McCovey	8.00	20.00
Johnny Bench Bat		
JF1 Babe Ruth		
Jimmie Foxx Bat SP/75		
JF2 Jimmie Foxx Bat	12.50	30.00
Bill Dickey SP/400		
JM1 Joe Morgan Bat	6.00	15.00
Ryne Sandberg		
JR1 Reggie Jackson	6.00	15.00
Jim Rice Bat		
JR2 Eddie Murray	8.00	20.00
Jim Rice Bat		
KP1 Kirby Puckett Bat	8.00	20.00
Don Mattingly		
NF1 Nellie Fox Bat	8.00	20.00
Rocky Colavito		
NR1 Steve Carlton		
Nolan Ryan Jsy SP/100		
PM1 Paul Molitor Bat	6.00	15.00
Don Mattingly		
PM2 Paul Molitor Bat	6.00	15.00
Dave Winfield		
RC1 Nellie Fox	8.00	20.00
Rocky Colavito Bat		
RJ1 Carl Yastrzemski	8.00	20.00
Reggie Jackson Bat		
RJ2 Reggie Jackson Bat	8.00	20.00
Jim Rice		
RK1 Ralph Kiner Bat	8.00	20.00
Duke Snider		
RM1 Brooks Robinson	20.00	50.00
Roger Maris Pants		
RS1 Joe Morgan	10.00	25.00
Ryne Sandberg Bat		
RY1 Robin Yount Bat	8.00	20.00
Dave Winfield		
SA1 Sparky Anderson Pants SP/400	6.00	15.00
Earl Weaver		
SC1 Steve Carlton Jersey		
Nolan Ryan SP/100		
TK1 Enos Slaughter	8.00	20.00
Ted Kluszewski Bat		
TP1 Tony Perez Bat	6.00	15.00
Carl Yastrzemski		
WB1 Wade Boggs Bat	8.00	20.00
Don Mattingly		
WB2 Wade Boggs Bat	8.00	20.00
George Brett		
WM1 Willie McCovey Bat	8.00	20.00
Johnny Bench		
YB1 Roy Campanella	8.00	20.00
Yogi Berra Bat		
YB2 Yogi Berra Bat	8.00	20.00
Gil Hodges		
YB3 Roy Campanella	12.50	30.00
Yogi Berra Glove		

2002 Greats of the Game Through the Years Level 1

This 31-card insert features swatches of authentic game-used jersey on a silver-foil based card. These cards were inserted into packs at a rate of 1:24.

Card	Low	High
1 Johnny Bench Pants	8.00	20.00
2 Vida Blue	6.00	15.00
3 Wade Boggs	6.00	15.00
4 George Brett	10.00	25.00
5 Carlton Fisk Hitting	6.00	15.00
6 Carlton Fisk Fielding	6.00	15.00
7 Bo Jackson Royals	8.00	20.00
8 Bo Jackson White Sox	8.00	20.00
9 Reggie Jackson A's	6.00	15.00
10 Reggie Jackson Angels	6.00	15.00
11 Ted Kluszewski	6.00	15.00
12 Don Mattingly	10.00	25.00
13 Willie McCovey	6.00	15.00
14 Paul Molitor Blue Jays	6.00	15.00
15 Paul Molitor Brewers	6.00	15.00
16 Eddie Murray	8.00	20.00
17 Jim Palmer	6.00	15.00
18 Tony Perez	6.00	15.00
19 J.Rice Red Sox Home	6.00	15.00
20 Jim Rice Red Sox Road	6.00	15.00
21 C.Ripken Orioles Hitting	15.00	40.00
22 Cal Ripken Orioles Fielding	15.00	40.00
23 Brooks Robinson Bat	6.00	15.00
24 Frank Robinson	6.00	15.00
25 J.Robinson Pants SP/200	30.00	60.00
26 Nolan Ryan	15.00	40.00
27 Hoyt Wilhelm	6.00	15.00
28 Ted Williams SP/350	30.00	60.00
29 Dave Winfield	6.00	15.00
30 Carl Yastrzemski	10.00	25.00
31 Robin Yount	8.00	20.00

2002 Greats of the Game Through the Years Level 1 Patch

This 27-card insert features swatches of authentic jersey patch on a gold-foil based card. Each card is also individually serial numbered to 100.

Card	Low	High
1 Johnny Bench	20.00	50.00
2 Wade Boggs	15.00	40.00
3 George Brett	40.00	80.00
4 Carlton Fisk Hitting	15.00	40.00
5 Carlton Fisk Fielding	15.00	40.00
6 Bo Jackson Royals	20.00	50.00
7 Bo Jackson White Sox	20.00	50.00
8 Reggie Jackson A's	15.00	40.00
9 Reggie Jackson Angels	15.00	40.00
10 Ted Kluszewski	15.00	40.00
11 Don Mattingly	40.00	80.00
12 Willie McCovey	15.00	40.00
13 Paul Molitor Blue Jays	15.00	40.00
14 Paul Molitor Brewers	15.00	40.00
15 Eddie Murray	20.00	50.00
16 Jim Palmer	15.00	40.00
17 Tony Perez	15.00	40.00
18 Jim Rice Red Sox	15.00	40.00
19 Jim Rice Red Sox	15.00	40.00
20 Cal Ripken Hitting	50.00	100.00
21 Cal Ripken Fielding	50.00	100.00
22 Frank Robinson	15.00	40.00
23 Nolan Ryan	40.00	80.00
24 Ted Williams	60.00	120.00
25 Dave Winfield	15.00	40.00
26 Carl Yastrzemski	40.00	80.00
27 Robin Yount	20.00	50.00

2002 Greats of the Game Through the Years Level 2

This 22-card insert features swatches of authentic game-used jersey on a silver-foil based card. These cards were individually serial numbered to 100.

Card	Low	High
1 Johnny Bench	20.00	50.00
2 Wade Boggs	15.00	40.00
3 George Brett	40.00	80.00
4 Carlton Fisk White Sox	15.00	40.00
5 Bo Jackson Royals	20.00	50.00
6 Bo Jackson White Sox	20.00	50.00
7 Reggie Jackson A's	15.00	40.00
8 Ted Kluszewski	15.00	40.00
9 Don Mattingly	40.00	80.00
10 Willie McCovey	15.00	40.00
11 Paul Molitor Brewers	15.00	40.00
12 Eddie Murray	20.00	50.00
13 Jim Palmer	15.00	40.00
14 Jim Rice Home	15.00	40.00
15 Jim Rice Road	15.00	40.00
16 Cal Ripken Hitting	50.00	100.00
17 Cal Ripken Fielding	50.00	100.00
18 Nolan Ryan	20.00	50.00
19 Ted Williams	60.00	120.00
20 Dave Winfield	15.00	40.00
21 Carl Yastrzemski	40.00	80.00
22 Robin Yount	20.00	50.00

2002 Greats of the Game Through the Years Level 3

This 19-card insert features swatches of authentic game-used jersey on a silver-foil based card. These cards were individually serial numbered to 25. Due to market scarcity, no pricing is provided for these cards.

1 Johnny Bench
2 Wade Boggs
3 George Brett
4 Carlton Fisk White Sox
5 Reggie Jackson A's
6 Ted Kluszewski
7 Don Mattingly
8 Willie McCovey
9 Paul Molitor Brewers
10 Eddie Murray
11 Jim Rice Home
12 Jim Rice Road
13 Cal Ripken Hitting
14 Cal Ripken Batting
15 Nolan Ryan
16 Ted Williams
17 Dave Winfield
18 Carl Yastrzemski
19 Robin Yount

2004 Greats of the Game

This 80-card set was initially released in June, 2004. The set was issued in five card packs with an $10 SRP which came packed 15 packs to a box and 12 boxes to a case. An update entitled Cut Signature Edition was released in December, 2004 containing cards 81-145.

Card	Low	High
COMPLETE SERIES 1 (80)	15.00	40.00
COMPLETE SERIES 2 (65)	10.00	25.00
COMMON CARD (1-145)	.20	.50
1 Lou Gehrig	1.00	2.50
2 Ty Cobb	.75	2.00
3 Dizzy Dean	.30	.75
4 Jimmie Foxx	.50	1.25
5 Hank Greenberg	.50	1.25
6 Babe Ruth	1.25	3.00
7 Honus Wagner	.50	1.25
8 Mickey Cochrane	.20	.50
9 Pepper Martin	.20	.50
10 Charlie Gehringer	.20	.50
11 Carl Hubbell	.20	.50
12 Bill Terry	.20	.50
13 Mel Ott	.50	1.25
14 Bill Dickey	.20	.50
15 Ted Williams	1.25	3.00
16 Roger Maris Yanks	.50	1.25
17 Thurman Munson	.50	1.25
18 Phil Rizzuto	.30	.75
19 Stan Musial	.75	2.00
20 Duke Snider Brooklyn	.30	.75
21 Reggie Jackson Yanks	.30	.75
22 Don Mattingly	1.00	2.50
23 Vida Blue	.20	.50
24 Harmon Killebrew	.50	1.25
25 Lou Brock	.30	.75
26 Al Kaline	.50	1.25
27 Dave Parker	.20	.50
28 Nolan Ryan Astros	1.50	4.00
29 Jim Rice	.30	.75
30 Paul Molitor Brewers	.50	1.25
31 Dwight Evans	.20	.50
32 Brooks Robinson	.30	.75
33 Jose Canseco	.30	.75
34 Alan Trammell	.20	.50
35 Johnny Bench	.50	1.25
36 Carlton Fisk R.Sox	.30	.75
37 Jim Palmer	.20	.50
38 George Brett	1.00	2.50
39 Mike Schmidt	.75	2.00
40 Tony Perez	.20	.50
41 Paul Blair	.20	.50
42 Fred Lynn	.20	.50
43 Carl Yastrzemski	.50	1.25
44 Steve Carlton Phils	.20	.50
45 Dennis Eckersley	.20	.50
46 Tom Seaver Mets	.30	.75
47 Juan Marichal	.20	.50
48 Tony Gwynn	.50	1.25
49 Moose Skowron	.20	.50
50 Bob Gibson	.30	.75
51 Luis Tiant	.20	.50
52 Eddie Murray O's	.50	1.25
53 Frank Robinson Reds	.30	.75
54 Rocky Colavito	.30	.75
55 Bobby Shantz	.20	.50
56 Ernie Banks	.50	1.25
57 Rod Carew Angels	.30	.75
58 Gorman Thomas	.20	.50
59 Bernie Carbo	.20	.50
60 Joe Rudi	.20	.50
61 Graig Nettles	.20	.50
62 Ron Guidry	.20	.50
63 Whitey Ford	.30	.75
64 George Kell	.20	.50
65 Cal Ripken	2.00	5.00
66 Willie McCovey	.30	.75
67 Bo Jackson	.50	1.25
68 Kirby Puckett	.50	1.25
69 Ted Kluszewski	.30	.75
70 Johnny Podres	.20	.50
71 Davey Lopes	.20	.50
72 Chris Short	.20	.50
73 Jeff Torborg	.20	.50
74 Bill Freehan	.20	.50
75 Frank Tanana	.20	.50
76 Jack Morris	.20	.50
77 Rick Dempsey	.20	.50
78 Yogi Berra	.50	1.25
79 Tim McCarver	.20	.50
80 Rusty Staub	.20	.50
81 Tony Lazzeri	.20	.50
82 Al Rosen	.20	.50
83 Willie McGee	.20	.50
84 Preacher Roe	.20	.50
85 Dave Kingman	.20	.50
86 Luis Aparicio	.20	.50
87 John Kruk	.20	.50
88 Bing Miller	.20	.50
89 Joe Charboneau	.20	.50
90 Mark Fidrych	.20	.50
91 Catfish Hunter	.20	.50
92 Nap Lajoie	.30	.75
93 Eddie Murray Indians	.50	1.25
94 Johnny Pesky	.20	.50
95 Tom Seaver Reds	.30	.75
96 Frank Robinson O's	.30	.75
97 Enos Slaughter	.20	.50
98 Cecil Travis	.20	.50
99 Robin Yount	.50	1.25
100 Don Zimmer	.20	.50
101 Babe Herman	.20	.50
102 Ron Santo	.30	.75
103 Willie Stargell	.30	.75
104 Paul Molitor Jays	.50	1.25
105 Jimmy Piersall	.20	.50
106 Johnny Sain	.20	.50
107 Joe Pepitone	.20	.50
108 Ryne Sandberg	1.00	2.50
109 Jim Thorpe	.50	1.25
110 Steve Garvey	.20	.50
111 Ray Knight	.20	.50
112 Fernando Valenzuela	.20	.50
113 Will Clark	.30	.75
114 Tony Kubek	.20	.50
115 Jim Bouton	.20	.50
116 Jerry Koosman	.20	.50
117 Steve Carlton Cards	.20	.50
118 Richie Ashburn	.30	.75
119 Roberto Clemente	1.25	3.00
120 Paul O'Neill	.30	.75
121 Reggie Jackson Angels	.30	.75
122 Andre Dawson	.30	.75
123 Hoyt Wilhelm	.20	.50
124 Dale Murphy	.30	.75
125 Dwight Gooden	.20	.50
126 Roger Maris Cards	.50	1.25
127 Bill Mazeroski	.30	.75
128 Don Newcombe	.20	.50
129 Robin Roberts	.20	.50
130 Duke Snider LA	.30	.75
131 Eddie Mathews	.50	1.25
132 Wade Boggs	.30	.75
133 Rollie Fingers	.20	.50
134 Frankie Frisch	.30	.75
135 Billy Williams	.20	.50
136 Rod Carew Twins	.30	.75
137 Dom DiMaggio	.20	.50
138 Orel Hershiser	.20	.50
139 Gary Carter	.20	.50
140 Keith Hernandez	.20	.50
141 Bob Lemon	.20	.50
142 Nolan Ryan Angels	1.50	4.00
143 Ozzie Smith	.75	2.00
144 Rick Sutcliffe	.20	.50
145 Carlton Fisk W.Sox	.30	.75

2004 Greats of the Game Blue

*1-80 POST-WAR: 1.25X TO 3X
*1-80 PRE-WAR: 1X TO 2.5X
*81-145 POST-WAR p/r 81-96: 4X TO 10X
*81-145 POST-WAR p/r 51-80: 4X TO 10X
*81-145 POST-WAR p/r 36-50: 5X TO 12X
*81-145 PRE-WAR p/r 36-50: 4X TO 10X
*81-145 PRE-WAR p/r 26-35: 5X TO 12X
*81-145 PRE-WAR p/r 18-25: 6X TO 15X
1-80 SER.1 ODDS 1:7.5 H, 1:24 R
81-145 SER.2 ODDS 1:60 H, 1:110 R
1-80 PRINT RUN 500 SERIAL #'d SETS
81-145 PRINT RUN B/WN 1-96 COPIES PER
81-145 NO PRICING ON QTY OF 1

2004 Greats of the Game Autographs

OVERALL SER.1 AU ODDS 1:5 H, 1:960 R
OVERALL SER.2 AU ODDS 1:7.5 H, 1:960 R
GROUP A PRINT RUN 125-150 SETS
GROUP B PRINT RUN 175-250 SETS
GROUP C1 PRINT RUN 275-300 SETS
A-C CARDS ARE NOT SERIAL-NUMBERED
PRINT RUN INFO PROVIDED BY FLEER
EXCHANGE DEADLINE INDEFINITE

Card	Low	High
AD Andre Dawson C2	10.00	25.00
AK Al Kaline D1	15.00	40.00
AR Al Rosen E2	6.00	15.00
AT Alan Trammell F1	10.00	25.00
BC Bernie Carbo G1	6.00	15.00
BF Bill Freehan G1	6.00	15.00
BG Bob Gibson F1	10.00	25.00
BJ Bo Jackson C1	20.00	50.00
BM Bill Mazeroski C2	15.00	40.00
BR Brooks Robinson F1	10.00	25.00
BS Bobby Shantz G1	6.00	15.00
BW Billy Williams C2	10.00	25.00
CF1 Carlton Fisk R.Sox D1	15.00	40.00
CF2 Carlton Fisk W.Sox D2	15.00	40.00
CR Cal Ripken A1	75.00	150.00
CY Carl Yastrzemski D1	30.00	60.00
DD Dom DiMaggio B2	50.00	100.00
DE Dennis Eckersley B1	15.00	40.00
DEV Dwight Evans F1	10.00	25.00
DG Dwight Gooden B2	10.00	25.00
DK Dave Kingman E2	6.00	15.00
DL Davey Lopes G1	4.00	10.00
DM Don Mattingly A1	50.00	100.00
DMU Dale Murphy C2	15.00	40.00
DP Dave Parker G1	6.00	15.00
DS1 D.Snider Brooklyn D1	15.00	40.00
DS2 Duke Snider LA B2	15.00	40.00
DZ Don Zimmer C2	10.00	25.00
EB Ernie Banks A1	30.00	60.00
EM Eddie Murray B1	40.00	80.00
FL Fred Lynn F1	6.00	15.00
FR1 Frank Robinson Reds E1	10.00	25.00
FR2 Frank Robinson O's C2	15.00	40.00
FT Frank Tanana G1	6.00	15.00
GB George Brett A1	40.00	80.00
GK George Kell F1	10.00	25.00
GN Graig Nettles G1	6.00	15.00
GT Gorman Thomas G1	4.00	10.00
HK Harmon Killebrew F1	20.00	50.00
JB Johnny Bench D1	30.00	60.00
JBO Jim Bouton D2	6.00	15.00
JC Jose Canseco D1	10.00	25.00
JCH Joe Charboneau E2	6.00	15.00
JK Jerry Koosman E2	10.00	25.00
JKR John Kruk B2	10.00	25.00
JM Juan Marichal F1	10.00	25.00
JMO Jack Morris F1	6.00	15.00
JP Jim Palmer F1	6.00	15.00
JPI Jimmy Piersall D2	6.00	15.00
JPO Johnny Podres G1	4.00	10.00
JPP Joe Pepitone E2	6.00	15.00
JPS Johnny Pesky E2	6.00	15.00
JR Jim Rice F1	6.00	15.00
JRU Joe Rudi G1	4.00	10.00
JT Jeff Torborg G1	4.00	10.00
KH Keith Hernandez D2	6.00	15.00
LA Luis Aparicio E2	6.00	15.00
LB Lou Brock F1	10.00	25.00
LT Luis Tiant G1	6.00	15.00
MM Marty Marion G1	6.00	15.00
MS Mike Schmidt B1	30.00	60.00
MSK Moose Skowron G1	6.00	15.00
NR1 Nolan Ryan Astros A1	60.00	120.00
NR2 Nolan Ryan Angels B2	60.00	120.00
OH Orel Hershiser A2	15.00	40.00
OS Ozzie Smith B2	20.00	50.00
PB Paul Blair G1	4.00	10.00
PM1 Paul Molitor Brewers B1	10.00	25.00
PO Paul O'Neill B2	15.00	40.00
PRO Preacher Roe B2	10.00	25.00
RCO Rocky Colavito D1	40.00	80.00
RC1 Rod Carew Angels D1	10.00	25.00
RD Rick Dempsey A1	10.00	25.00
RF Rollie Fingers D2	6.00	15.00
RG Ron Guidry F1	6.00	15.00
RJ1 R.Jackson Yanks A1	30.00	60.00
RJ2 R.Jackson Angels B2	15.00	40.00
RK Ray Knight E2	6.00	15.00
RR Robin Roberts E2	15.00	40.00
RS Ryne Sandberg B2	30.00	60.00
RST Rusty Staub G1	6.00	15.00
RST Ron Santo D2	12.50	30.00
SC1 Steve Carlton Phils D1	6.00	15.00
SC2 Steve Carlton Cards D2	6.00	15.00
SG Steve Garvey D2	6.00	15.00
SM Stan Musial A1	60.00	120.00
TG Tony Gwynn E1	15.00	40.00
TK Tony Kubek C2	15.00	40.00
TM Tim McCarver F1	6.00	15.00
TP Tony Perez F1	10.00	25.00
TS1 Tom Seaver Mets A1	40.00	80.00
VB Vida Blue G1	4.00	10.00
WF Whitey Ford D1	15.00	40.00
WM Willie McCovey E1	10.00	25.00
WMG Willie McGee D2	10.00	25.00
YB Yogi Berra B1	40.00	80.00

2004 Greats of the Game Announcing Greats

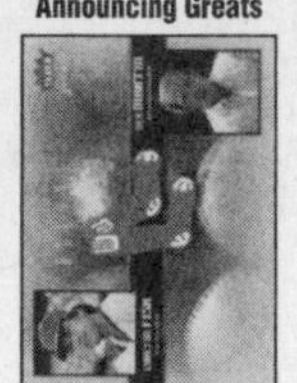

SER.2 STATED ODDS 1:12 RETAIL

Card	Low	High
1 Harry Kalas	1.50	4.00
Mike Schmidt		
2 Vin Scully	.40	1.00
Steve Garvey		
3 Harry Caray	.60	1.50
Ryne Sandberg		
4 Ned Martin	.60	1.50
Carlton Fisk		
5 Ernie Harwell	.60	1.50
Kirk Gibson		
6 Ken Harrelson	1.00	2.50
Carl Yastrzemski		
7 Phil Rizzuto	2.00	5.00
Don Mattingly		
8 Mel Allen	.40	1.00
Yogi Berra		
9 Jon Miller	4.00	10.00
Cal Ripken		
10 Marty Brennaman	1.00	2.50
Johnny Bench		

2004 Greats of the Game Announcing Greats Autograph Dual

OVERALL SER.2 AU ODDS 1:7.5 HOBBY
OVERALL SER.2 AU-GU ODDS 1:24 RETAIL
PRINT RUNS B/WN 1-50 COPIES PER
NO PRICING ON QTY OF 8 OR LESS
EXCHANGE DEADLINE INDEFINITE
HCRS Harry Caray

Ryne Sandberg/2
HKMS Harry Kalas 100.00 200.00
Mike Schmidt/25
MAYB Mel Allen
Yogi Berra/1

2004 Greats of the Game Battery Mates

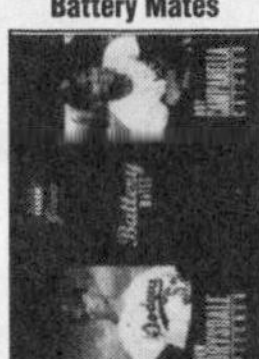

PRINT RUNS B/WN 1934-1979 COPIES PER
1 Steve Carlton .40 1.00
Tim McCarver/1972
2 Don Drysdale 1.00 2.50
Roy Campanella/1957
3 Tom Seaver 1.00 2.50
Johnny Bench/1979
4 Whitey Ford 1.00 2.50
Yogi Berra/1956
5 Ron Guidry 1.00 2.50
Thurman Munson/1978
6 Nolan Ryan 3.00 8.00
Jeff Torborg/1973
7 Denny McLain .40 1.00
Bill Freehan/1968
8 Lefty Gomez .40 1.00
Bill Dickey/1934
9 Jim Palmer .40 1.00
Rick Dempsey/1977
10 Luis Tiant .60 1.50
Carlton Fisk/1973

2004 Greats of the Game Battery Mates Autograph

OVERALL SER.1 AU ODDS 1:5 H, 1:960 R
PRINT RUNS B/WN 56-79 COPIES PER
AUTO IS ONLY FOR 1ST PLAYER LISTED
DMBF Denny McLain w/Freehan/68
JPRD Jim Palmer w/Dempsey/77 8.00 20.00
NRJT Jeff Torborg w/Ryan/73 6.00 15.00
RGTM Ron Guidry w/Munson/78 10.00 25.00
SCTM Steve Carlton w/McCarver/72 8.00 20.00
TSJB Johnny Bench w/Seaver/79 20.00 50.00
WFYB Whitey Ford w/Berra/56 15.00 40.00

2004 Greats of the Game Battery Mates Autograph Dual

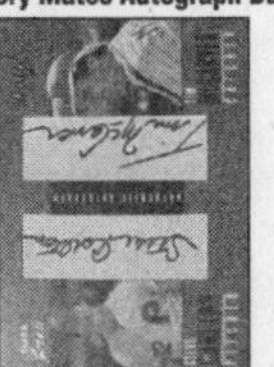

OVERALL SER.1 AU ODDS 1:5 H, 1:960 R
STATED PRINT RUN 10 SERIAL #'d SETS
NO PRICING DUE TO SCARCITY

2004 Greats of the Game Comparison Cuts

An innovative pairing of Wally Pipp and the guy who replaced him at 1st for the Yankees; Lou Gehrig, was a highlight of this set.

OVERALL SER.1 AU ODDS 1:5 H, 1:960 R
STATED PRINT RUN 1 SERIAL #'d SET
NO PRICING DUE TO SCARCITY
BRRM Babe Ruth
Roger Maris
JRLD Jackie Robinson
Larry Doby
LGCR Lou Gehrig
Cal Ripken
LGWP Lou Gehrig
Wally Pipp
LWPW Lloyd Waner
Paul Waner
TWCY Ted Williams
Carl Yastrzemski

2004 Greats of the Game Etched in Time Cuts

OVERALL SER.1 AU ODDS 1:5 H, 1:960 R
OVERALL SER.2 AU ODDS 1:7.5 HOBBY
OVERALL SER.2 AU-GU ODDS 1:24 RETAIL
PRINT RUNS B/WN 1-95 COPIES PER
NO PRICING ON QTY OF 10 OR LESS
BD Bill Dickey S1/1
BG Bob Grim S2/5
BGR Burleigh Grimes S2/5
BH Babe Herman S2/35 75.00 150.00

BL Bob Lemon S2/10
BT Bill Terry S1/3
BUD Buddy Myer S2/3
CAT Catfish Hunter S2/5
CG Charlie Gehringer S1/1
CH Carl Hubbell S1/3
CR Chico Ruiz S2/5
CS Chris Short S2/30 100.00 200.00
DC Dolph Camilli S2/40 100.00 200.00
DD Dizzy Dean S1/1
EA Elhan Allen S2/75 75.00 150.00
EAV Earl Averill S2/50 40.00 80.00
EC Earle Combs S2/1
ER Edd Roush S2/95 50.00 100.00
EW Early Wynn S2/5
FL Freddie Lindstrom S2/5
GB George H. Burns S2/4
GH Gabby Hartnett S2/5
GIL Gil Hodges S2/2
GK George Kelly S2/3
HG Hank Greenberg S1/1
HK Harvey Kuenn S2/32 60.00 120.00
HW Honus Wagner S1/1
HWI Hoyt Wilhelm S2/10
JC Joe Cronin S2/5
JF Jimmie Foxx S1/1
JM Joe Medwick S2/8
JT Jim Thorpe S2/1
LA Luke Appling S2/23 60.00 120.00
LOD Lefty O'Doul S2/3
MC Max Carey S2/1
MCO Mickey Cochrane S1/1
MO Mel Ott S1/1
NF Nellie Fox S2/2
NL Nap Lajoie S2/1
PR Pete Runnels S2/35 60.00 120.00
PT Pie Traynor S2/1
RA Richie Ashburn S2/2
RC Roy Campanella S1/1
RCL Roberto Clemente S1/1
RF Rick Ferrell S2/50 60.00 120.00
RR Red Ruffing S2/5
SM Sal Maglie S2/40 60.00 120.00
TC Ty Cobb S1/1
TCN Tony Conigliaro S2/1
TM Thurman Munson S1/1
TW1 Ted Williams S1/1
TW2 Ted Williams S2/1
WC Walker Cooper S2/20 60.00 120.00
WS Willie Stargell S2/16
ZW Zack Wheat S2/4

2004 Greats of the Game Forever

OVERALL SER.2 ODDS 1:5 HOB, 1:12 RET
PRINT RUNS B/WN 1909-1984 COPIES PER
1 Fernando Valenzuela/1980 .60 1.50
2 Steve Garvey/1969 .60 1.50
3 Zach Wheat/1909 .60 1.50
4 Orel Hershiser/1983 .60 1.50
5 Duke Snider/1947 1.00 2.50
6 Jim Rice/1974 1.00 2.50
7 Carlton Fisk/1969 1.00 2.50
8 Wade Boggs/1982 1.00 2.50
9 Ted Williams/1939 4.00 10.00
10 Carl Yastrzemski/1961 1.50 4.00
11 Dom DiMaggio/1940 .60 1.50
12 Ron Santo/1960 1.00 2.50
13 Billy Williams/1959 .60 1.50
14 Ryne Sandberg/1981 3.00 8.00
15 Ernie Banks/1953 1.50 4.00
16 Gabby Hartnett/1922 .60 1.50
17 Hack Wilson/1923 1.00 2.50
18 Dwight Gooden/1984 .60 1.50
19 Ray Knight/1974 .60 1.50
20 Tom Seaver/1967 1.00 2.50
21 Nolan Ryan/1966 5.00 12.00
22 Keith Hernandez/1974 .60 1.50
23 Darryl Strawberry/1983 .60 1.50
24 Bob Gibson/1959 1.00 2.50
25 Pepper Martin/1928 .60 1.50
26 Stan Musial/1941 2.50 6.00
27 Frankie Frisch/1919 1.00 2.50
28 Steve Carlton/1965 .60 1.50
29 Ozzie Smith/1978 2.50 6.00

2004 Greats of the Game Forever Game Jersey

SER.2 STATED ODDS 1:24 RETAIL
SP INFO PROVIDED BY FLEER
NO SP PRICING DUE TO SCARCITY
EXCHANGE DEADLINE INDEFINITE
BG Bob Gibson 6.00 15.00
BW Billy Williams 4.00 10.00
CF Carlton Fisk 6.00 15.00
DD Dom DiMaggio 10.00 25.00
DG Dwight Gooden 4.00 10.00
DS Darryl Strawberry 4.00 10.00
OH Orel Hershiser 4.00 10.00
OS Ozzie Smith 6.00 15.00
SC Steve Carlton 4.00 10.00
SM Stan Musial 10.00 25.00
TW Ted Williams 30.00 60.00
WB Wade Boggs 6.00 15.00

2004 Greats of the Game Forever Game Jersey Logo

STATED PRINT RUN 149 SERIAL #'d SETS
*JSY NBR: .5X TO 1.2X JSY LOGO
JSY NBR PRINT RUN 99 SERIAL #'d SETS
SER.2 GU ODDS 1:15 HOBBY
EXCHANGE DEADLINE INDEFINITE
BG Bob Gibson 6.00 15.00
BW Billy Williams 4.00 10.00
CF Carlton Fisk 6.00 15.00
CY Carl Yastrzemski 8.00 20.00
DD Dom DiMaggio 10.00 25.00
DG Dwight Gooden 4.00 10.00
DS Darryl Strawberry 4.00 10.00
EB Ernie Banks 10.00 25.00
JR Jim Rice 4.00 10.00
NR Nolan Ryan 30.00 60.00
OH Orel Hershiser 4.00 10.00
OS Ozzie Smith 6.00 15.00
RK Ray Knight 4.00 10.00
RS Ryne Sandberg 6.00 15.00
SM Stan Musial 10.00 25.00
TW Ted Williams 30.00 60.00
WB Wade Boggs 6.00 15.00

2004 Greats of the Game Forever Game Patch Logo

STATED PRINT RUN 49 SERIAL #'d SETS
NUMBER PRINT RUN 25 SERIAL #'d SETS
NO NUMBER PRICING DUE TO SCARCITY
SER.2 GU ODDS 1:15 HOBBY
EXCHANGE DEADLINE INDEFINITE
BG Bob Gibson 10.00 25.00
BW Billy Williams
CF Carlton Fisk 10.00 25.00
CY Carl Yastrzemski 20.00 50.00
DD Dom DiMaggio
DG Dwight Gooden 6.00 15.00
DS Darryl Strawberry 6.00 15.00
EB Ernie Banks 40.00 80.00
JR Jim Rice 10.00 25.00
NR Nolan Ryan
OH Orel Hershiser
OS Ozzie Smith 20.00 50.00
RK Ray Knight
RS Ryne Sandberg 20.00 50.00
SM Stan Musial
TW Ted Williams 60.00 120.00
WB Wade Boggs 10.00 25.00

2004 Greats of the Game Forever Game Patch Dual Logo

STATED PRINT RUN 19 SERIAL #'d SETS
DUAL NBR PRINT RUN 5 SERIAL #'d SETS
OVERALL SER.2 GU ODDS 1:15 HOBBY
EXCHANGE DEADLINE INDEFINITE
NO PRICING DUE TO SCARCITY
DGDS Dwight Gooden
Darryl Strawberry
JRCF Jim Rice
Carlton Fisk
SMOS Stan Musial
Ozzie Smith
TWCY Ted Williams
Carl Yastrzemski
TWDD Ted Williams
Dom DiMaggio
WBCY Wade Boggs
Carl Yastrzemski

2004 Greats of the Game Glory of Their Time

PRINT RUNS B/WN
1 Harmon Killebrew/1961 1.25 3.00
2 Johnny Bench/1974 1.25 3.00
3 George Brett/1980 2.50 6.00
4 Tony Gwynn/1987 1.25 3.00
5 Paul Molitor/1987 1.25 3.00
6 Don Mattingly/1986 2.50 6.00
7 Reggie Jackson/1980 .75 2.00
8 Carlton Fisk/1985 .75 2.00
9 Cal Ripken/1983 5.00 12.00
10 Brooks Robinson/1964 .75 2.00
11 Eddie Murray/1980 1.25 3.00
12 Moose Skowron/1960 .50 1.25
13 Lou Brock/1974 .75 2.00
14 Don Drysdale/1962 .75 2.00
15 Tony Gwynn/1997 1.25 3.00
16 Mike Schmidt/1980 2.00 5.00
17 Carl Yastrzemski/1967 1.25 3.00
18 Babe Ruth/1927 3.00 8.00
19 Nolan Ryan/1989 4.00 10.00
20 Yogi Berra/1950 1.25 3.00
21 Al Kaline/1955 1.25 3.00
22 Ty Cobb/1911 2.00 5.00
23 Duke Snider/1955 .75 2.00
24 Stan Musial/1948 2.00 5.00
25 Jose Canseco/1988 .75 2.00
26 Rocky Colavito/1958 .75 2.00
27 Dave Winfield/1979 .50 1.25
28 Nolan Ryan/1982 4.00 10.00
29 Thurman Munson/1977 1.25 3.00
30 Jackie Robinson/1949 1.25 3.00
31 Kirby Puckett/1988 1.25 3.00
32 Ted Kluszewski/1954 .75 2.00
33 Warren Spahn/1953 .75 2.00
34 Willie McCovey/1969 .75 2.00
35 Phil Rizzuto/1950 .75 2.00

2004 Greats of the Game Glory of Their Time Game Used

STATED PRINT RUN 250 SERIAL #'d SETS
*GOLD: .4X TO 1X BASIC
GOLD STATED ODDS 1:24 RETAIL
OVERALL SER.1 GU ODDS 1:30 H, 1:24 R
AK Al Kaline Pants 6.00 15.00
BR Brooks Robinson Jsy 6.00 15.00
CF1 Carlton Fisk Jsy 6.00 15.00
CF2 Carlton Fisk Bat 6.00 15.00
CR Cal Ripken Jsy 10.00 25.00
CY Carl Yastrzemski Jsy 8.00 20.00
DD Don Drysdale Jsy 6.00 15.00
DM Don Mattingly Pants 8.00 20.00
DW Dave Winfield Jsy 4.00 10.00
EM Eddie Murray Jsy 6.00 15.00
GB George Brett Jsy 8.00 20.00
HK Harmon Killebrew Bat 6.00 15.00
JB Johnny Bench Jsy 6.00 15.00
JC1 Jose Canseco Jsy 6.00 15.00
JC2 Jose Canseco Bat 6.00 15.00
KP Kirby Puckett Bat 6.00 15.00
LB Lou Brock Jsy 6.00 15.00
MS Mike Schmidt Jsy 8.00 20.00
MS Moose Skowron Pants 4.00 10.00
NR1 Nolan Ryan Jsy 10.00 25.00
NR2 Nolan Ryan Bat 10.00 25.00
PM Paul Molitor Jsy 4.00 10.00
PR Phil Rizzuto Pants 6.00 15.00
RC Rocky Colavito Bat 12.50 30.00
RJ Reggie Jackson Pants 6.00 15.00
TG1 Tony Gwynn White Jsy 6.00 15.00
TG2 Tony Gwynn Grey Jsy 6.00 15.00
TK Ted Kluszewski Pants 6.00 15.00
TM Thurman Munson Pants 10.00 25.00
WM Willie McCovey Pants 6.00 15.00
WS Warren Spahn Jsy 6.00 15.00
YB Yogi Berra Pants 6.00 15.00

2004 Greats of the Game Personality Cuts

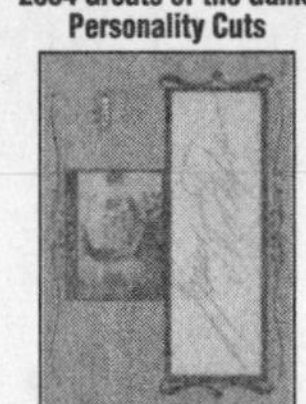

OVERALL SER.1 AU ODDS 1:5 H, 1:960 R
OVERALL SER.2 AU ODDS 1:7.5 HOBBY
OVERALL SER.2 AU-GU ODDS 1:24 RETAIL
PRINT RUNS B/WN 1-2 COPIES PER
NO PRICING DUE TO SCARCITY
AD Abner Doubleday S2/1
BC Bing Crosby S2/1
CF Charles O. Finley S2/2
CM Connie Mack S1/1
EG August Busch Jr. S2/1
HC Happy Chandler S1/1
RK Ray Kroc S2/1
RR Ronald Reagan S2/1
TY Tom Yawkey S2/1
WT William Taft S1/1

2004 Greats of the Game Yankees Clippings

SER.2 STATED ODDS 1:45 HOBBY
SP PRINT RUNS PROVIDED BY FLEER
SP'S ARE NOT SERIAL-NUMBERED
EXCHANGE DEADLINE INDEFINITE
BS Bill Skowron 20.00 50.00
DM Don Mattingly 40.00 80.00
PO Paul O'Neill 30.00 60.00
RJ Reggie Jackson 30.00 60.00
WB Wade Boggs 20.00 50.00
YB Yogi Berra 40.00 80.00

2004 Greats of the Game Yankees Clippings Autograph

OVERALL SER.2 AU ODDS 1:7.5 HOBBY
PRINT RUNS B/WN 3-26 COPIES PER
NO PRICING DUE TO SCARCITY
EXCHANGE DEADLINE INDEFINITE
BS Bill Skowron/26
PO Paul O'Neill/26
RJ Reggie Jackson/15
YB Yogi Berra/15

2006 Greats of the Game

This 100-card set, featuring all retired players, was released in April, 2006. The set was issued in 10-card hobby or retail packs which came 15 packs to a box and 12 boxes to a case. The set is sequenced in alphabetical order by the player's first name.

COMPLETE SET (100) 20.00 50.00
COMMON CARD (1-100) .30 .75
ONE PLATE PER FOIL PLATE PACK
PLATE PACKS ISSUED TO DEALERS
PLATE PRINT RUN 1 SET PER COLOR
BLACK-CYAN-MAGENTA-YELLOW ISSUED
NO PLATE PRICING DUE TO SCARCITY
1 Al Kaline .75 2.00
2 Alan Trammell .30 .75
3 Andre Dawson .50 1.25
4 Barry Larkin .50 1.25
5 Bill Buckner .30 .75
6 Bill Freehan .30 .75
7 Bill Madlock .30 .75
8 Bill Mazeroski .50 1.25
9 Billy Williams .30 .75
10 Bo Jackson .75 2.00
11 Bob Feller .30 .75
12 Bob Gibson .50 1.25
13 Bobby Doerr .30 .75
14 Bobby Murcer .30 .75
15 Boog Powell .30 .75
16 Brooks Robinson .50 1.25
17 Bruce Sutter .30 .75
18 Bucky Dent .30 .75
19 Cal Ripken 3.00 8.00
20 Rico Petrocelli .30 .75
21 Carlton Fisk .50 1.25
22 Chris Chambliss .30 .75
23 Dave Concepcion .30 .75
24 Dave Parker .30 .75
25 Dave Winfield .30 .75
26 David Cone .30 .75
27 Denny McLain .30 .75
28 Don Mattingly 1.50 4.00
29 Don Newcombe .30 .75
30 Don Sutton .30 .75
31 Dusty Baker .30 .75
32 Dwight Evans .30 .75
33 Eric Davis .30 .75
34 Ernie Banks .75 2.00
35 Fergie Jenkins .30 .75
36 Frank Robinson .30 .75
37 Fred Lynn .30 .75
38 Fred McGriff .50 1.25
39 Andre Thornton .30 .75
40 Garry Maddox .30 .75
41 Gary Matthews .30 .75
42 Gaylord Perry .30 .75
43 George Foster .30 .75
44 George Kell .30 .75
45 Graig Nettles .30 .75
46 Greg Luzinski .30 .75
47 Harmon Killebrew .75 2.00
48 Jack Clark .30 .75
49 Jack Morris .30 .75
50 Jim Palmer .30 .75
51 Jim Rice .30 .75
52 Joe Morgan .30 .75
53 John Kruk .30 .75
54 Johnny Bench .75 2.00
55 Jose Canseco .50 1.25
56 Kirby Puckett .75 2.00
57 Kirk Gibson .30 .75
58 Lee Mazzilli .30 .75
59 Lou Brock .50 1.25
60 Lou Piniella .30 .75
61 Luis Aparicio .30 .75
62 Luis Tiant .30 .75
63 Mark Fidrych .30 .75
64 Mark Grace .50 1.25
65 Maury Wills .30 .75
66 Mike Schmidt 1.25 3.00
67 Nolan Ryan 2.00 5.00
68 Ozzie Smith 1.25 3.00
69 Paul Molitor .75 2.00
70 Paul O'Neill .50 1.25
71 Phil Niekro .30 .75
72 Ralph Kiner .50 1.25
73 Randy Hundley .30 .75
74 Red Schoendienst .30 .75
75 Reggie Jackson .50 1.25
76 Robin Yount .75 2.00
77 Rod Carew .50 1.25
78 Rollie Fingers .30 .75
79 Ron Cey .30 .75
80 Ron Guidry .30 .75
81 Ron Santo .50 1.25
82 Rusty Staub .30 .75
83 Ryne Sandberg 1.50 4.00
84 Sparky Lyle .30 .75
85 Stan Musial 1.25 3.00
86 Steve Carlton .30 .75
87 Steve Garvey .30 .75
88 Steve Sax .30 .75
89 Tommy Herr .30 .75
90 Tim McCarver .30 .75
91 Tim Raines .30 .75
92 Tom Seaver .50 1.25
93 Tony Gwynn .75 2.00
94 Tony Perez .30 .75
95 Wade Boggs .50 1.25
96 Whitey Ford .50 1.25
97 Will Clark .50 1.25
98 Willie Horton .30 .75
99 Willie McCovey .50 1.25
100 Yogi Berra .75 2.00

2006 Greats of the Game Copper

*COPPER: 1.5X TO 4X BASIC
STATED ODDS 1:15 H
STATED PRINT RUN 299 SERIAL #'d SETS

2006 Greats of the Game Pewter

*PEWTER: 1X TO 2.5X BASIC
STATED ODDS 1:15 H, 1:15 R

2006 Greats of the Game Autographs

Originally intended as a 99-card premium signed version of the basic 2006 Greats of the Game 100-card issue, this set actually contains 106 cards due to unintentional variations on several cards. The variations were the cause of problems with the dissemination of the clear stickers that each athlete signed. This set was intended to feature standard signatures, bereft of any inscriptions or nicknames. Due to problems at the production stage, however, several cards had signed stickers with inscribed nicknames (of which were earmarked for a separate signature insert for this product entitled Nickname Greats) placed on them. Our staff has researched the varying quantities seen on the secondary market for these variations and that information is detailed in our checklist within parentheses at the end of the card descriptions. The players with signature variations are as follows: Jack Clark (50% standard, 50% w/Jack the Ripper inscription), Will Clark (60% standard, 40% w/Will the Thrill inscription), Dwight Evans (90% standard, 10% w/Dewey inscription), Ron Guidry (50% standard, 50% with Gator inscription), Tommy Herr (100% w/T-Bird inscription), Bill Madlock (35% standard, 65% w/Maddog inscription), Gary Matthews (100% w/Sarge inscription), Tim Raines (50% standard, 50% w/Rock inscription), Rusty Staub (20% standard, 80% w/Le Grand Orange inscription), Andre Thornton (100% w/Thunder inscription). In addition, though all of these cards lack serial-numbering, representatives at Upper Deck provided print run information by breaking the set into four tiers of scarcity. Tier 4 cards (tagged with a "T4" notation in our checklist) have announced print runs between 301-600 copies per, Tier 3 between 151-300 copies per, Tier 2 between 100-150 per and Tier 1 between 50-90 per. Furthermore, specific quantities for each Tier 1 card were announced and that information is also provided in our checklist. These signed inserts were seeded at a rate of 1:15 hobby and retail packs.

Al Kaline T3
STATED ODDS 1:15 H, 1:15 R
TIER 1 QTY B/WN 50-90 COPIES PER
TIER 2 QTY B/WN 100-150 COPIES PER
TIER 3 QTY B/WN 151-300 COPIES PER
TIER 4 QTY B/WN 301-600 COPIES PER
CARDS ARE NOT SERIAL-NUMBERED
PRINT RUN INFO PROVIDED BY UD
SOME CARDS CARRY AU INSCRIPTIONS
AU INSCRIPTIONS NOT INTENDED FOR SET
AU INSCRIPTIONS DETAILED BELOW
PARENTHESES PERCENTAGE OF PRINT RUN
1 Al Kaline T3 8.00 20.00
2 Alan Trammell T3 4.00 10.00
3 Andre Dawson T3 8.00 20.00
4 Barry Larkin T3 10.00 25.00
5 Bill Buckner T3 6.00 15.00
6 Bill Freehan T4 4.00 10.00
7a Bill Madlock T4 (35) 4.00 10.00
7b Bill Madlock T4 (65) 5.00 12.00
Maddog
8 Bill Mazeroski T2 12.50 30.00
9 Billy Williams T3 6.00 15.00
10 Bo Jackson T2 30.00 60.00
11 Bob Feller T2 10.00 25.00
12 Bob Gibson T2 12.50 30.00
13 Bobby Doerr T3 6.00 15.00
14 Bobby Murcer T3 20.00 50.00
15 Boog Powell T4 4.00 10.00
16 Brooks Robinson T3 12.50 30.00
17 Bruce Sutter T3 10.00 25.00
18 Bucky Dent T3 5.00 12.00
19 Cal Ripken T1/50 * 40.00 80.00
20 Rico Petrocelli T4 4.00 10.00
21 Carlton Fisk T2 10.00 25.00
22 Chris Chambliss T3 8.00 20.00
23 Dave Concepcion T3 6.00 15.00
24 Dave Parker T2 6.00 15.00
25 Dave Winfield T2 12.50 30.00
26 David Cone T3 4.00 10.00
27 Denny McLain T3 6.00 15.00
28 Don Mattingly T2 40.00 80.00
29 Don Newcombe T4 6.00 15.00
30 Don Sutton T3 4.00 10.00
31 Dusty Baker T1/75 * 8.00 20.00
32a Dwight Evans T3 (90) 6.00 15.00
32b Dwight Evans T3 (10)
Dewey
33 Eric Davis T4 8.00 20.00
34 Ernie Banks T2 30.00 60.00
35 Fergie Jenkins T2 5.00 12.00
36 Frank Robinson T2 12.50 30.00
37 Fred Lynn T3 6.00 15.00
38 Fred McGriff T3 12.50 30.00
39 Andre Thornton T4 4.00 10.00
Thunder
40 Garry Maddox T2 6.00 15.00
41 Gary Matthews T4 12.50 30.00
Sarge
42 Gaylord Perry T3 5.00 12.00
43 George Foster T3 4.00 10.00
44 George Kell T3 8.00 20.00
45 Graig Nettles T3 6.00 15.00
46 Greg Luzinski T3 6.00 15.00
47 Harmon Killebrew T2 15.00 40.00
48a Jack Clark T4 (50) 8.00 20.00
48b Jack Clark T4 (50) 8.00 20.00
Jack the Ripper
49 Jack Morris T3 4.00 10.00
50 Jim Palmer T3 5.00 12.00
51 Jim Rice T3 6.00 15.00
52 Joe Morgan T2 10.00 25.00
53 John Kruk T3 6.00 15.00
54 Johnny Bench T2 15.00 40.00
56 Kirby Puckett T2 40.00 80.00
57 Kirk Gibson T2 8.00 20.00
58 Lee Mazzilli T3 4.00 10.00
59 Lou Brock T2 12.50 30.00
60 Lou Piniella T3 8.00 20.00
61 Luis Aparicio T3 6.00 15.00
62 Luis Tiant T3 4.00 10.00
63 Mark Fidrych T2 15.00 40.00
64 Mark Grace T3 10.00 25.00
65 Maury Wills T3 6.00 15.00
66 Mike Schmidt T2 12.50 30.00
67 Nolan Ryan T1/50 * 60.00 120.00
68 Ozzie Smith T2 15.00 40.00
69 Paul Molitor T3 8.00 20.00
70 Paul O'Neill T3 12.50 30.00
71 Phil Niekro T3 5.00 12.00
72 Ralph Kiner T2 12.50 30.00
73 Randy Hundley T4 4.00 10.00
74 Red Schoendienst T3 6.00 15.00
75 Reggie Jackson T2 15.00 40.00
76 Robin Yount T2 12.50 30.00
77 Rod Carew T3 10.00 25.00
78 Rollie Fingers T3 4.00 10.00
79 Ron Cey T3 4.00 10.00
80a Ron Guidry T3 (50) 12.50 30.00
80b Ron Guidry T3 (50) 15.00 40.00
Gator
81 Ron Santo T3 12.50 30.00
82a Rusty Staub T3 (20) 20.00 50.00
82b Rusty Staub T3 (80) 30.00 60.00
Le Grand Orange
83 Ryne Sandberg T1/90 * 20.00 50.00
84 Sparky Lyle T4 4.00 10.00
85 Stan Musial T2 20.00 50.00
86 Steve Carlton T3 6.00 15.00
87 Steve Garvey T2 5.00 12.00
88 Steve Sax T4 4.00 10.00
89 Tommy Herr T4 4.00 10.00
T-Bird
90 Tim McCarver T3 5.00 12.00
91a Tim Raines T3 (50) 10.00 25.00
91b Tim Raines T3 (50) 12.50 30.00
Rock
92 Tom Seaver T2 12.50 30.00
93 Tony Gwynn T2 12.50 30.00
94 Tony Perez T3 8.00 20.00
95 Wade Boggs T2 12.50 30.00
96 Whitey Ford T2 20.00 50.00
97a Will Clark T2 (60) 10.00 25.00
97b Will Clark T2 (40) 12.50 30.00
The Thrill
98 Willie Horton T4 5.00 12.00
99 Willie McCovey T1/75 * 12.50 30.00
100 Yogi Berra T2 15.00 40.00

2006 Greats of the Game Autographics

STATED ODDS 1:180 H, 1:960 R
PRINT RUNS B/WN 10-99 COPIES PER
CARDS ARE NOT SERIAL-NUMBERED
PRINT RUN INFO PROVIDED BY UD
NO PRICING ON QTY OF 25 OR LESS
ONE PLATE PER FOIL PLATE PACK

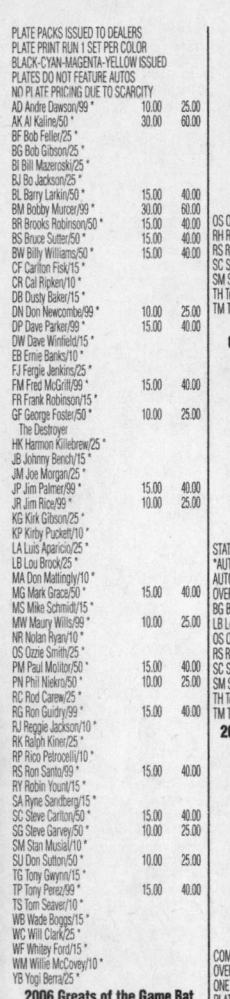

PLATE PACKS ISSUED TO DEALERS
PLATE PRINT RUN 1 SET PER COLOR
BLACK-CYAN-MAGENTA-YELLOW ISSUED
PLATES DO NOT FEATURE AUTOS
NO PLATE PRICING DUE TO SCARCITY
AD Andre Dawson/99 * 10.00 25.00
AK Al Kaline/50 * 30.00 60.00
BF Bob Feller/25 *
BG Bob Gibson/25 *
BI Bill Mazeroski/25 *
BJ Bo Jackson/25 *
BL Barry Larkin/50 * 15.00 40.00
BM Bobby Murcer/99 * 30.00 60.00
BR Brooks Robinson/50 * 15.00 40.00
BS Bruce Sutter/50 * 15.00 40.00
BW Billy Williams/50 * 15.00 40.00
CF Carlton Fisk/15 *
CR Cal Ripken/10 *
DB Dusty Baker/15 *
DN Don Newcombe/99 * 10.00 25.00
DP Dave Parker/99 * 15.00 40.00
DW Dave Winfield/15 *
EB Ernie Banks/10 *
FJ Fergie Jenkins/25 *
FM Fred McGriff/99 * 15.00 40.00
FR Frank Robinson/15 *
GF George Foster/50 * 10.00 25.00
The Destroyer
HK Harmon Killebrew/25 *
JB Johnny Bench/15 *
JM Joe Morgan/25 *
JP Jim Palmer/99 * 15.00 40.00
JR Jim Rice/99 * 10.00 25.00
KG Kirk Gibson/25 *
KP Kirby Puckett/10 *
LA Luis Aparicio/25 *
LB Lou Brock/25 *
MA Don Mattingly/10 *
MG Mark Grace/50 * 15.00 40.00
MS Mike Schmidt/15 *
MW Maury Wills/99 * 10.00 25.00
NR Nolan Ryan/10 *
OS Ozzie Smith/25 *
PM Paul Molitor/50 * 15.00 40.00
PN Phil Niekro/50 * 10.00 25.00
RC Rod Carew/25 *
RG Ron Guidry/99 * 15.00 40.00
RJ Reggie Jackson/10 *
RK Ralph Kiner/25 *
RP Rico Petrocelli/10 *
RS Ron Santo/99 * 15.00 40.00
RY Robin Yount/15 *
SA Ryne Sandberg/15 *
SC Steve Carlton/50 * 15.00 40.00
SG Steve Garvey/50 * 10.00 25.00
SM Stan Musial/10 *
SU Don Sutton/50 * 10.00 25.00
TG Tony Gwynn/15 *
TP Tony Perez/99 * 15.00 40.00
TS Tom Seaver/10 *
WB Wade Boggs/15 *
WC Will Clark/25 *
WF Whitey Ford/15 *
WM Willie McCovey/10 *
YB Yogi Berra/25 *

2006 Greats of the Game Bat Barrel Auto Greats

OVERALL AUTO ODDS 2:15 H, 2:15 R
PRINT RUNS B/WN 1-5 COPIES PER
NO PRICING DUE TO SCARCITY
ONE PLATE PER FOIL PLATE PACK
PLATE PACKS ISSUED TO DEALERS
PLATE PRINT RUN 1 SET PER COLOR
BLACK-CYAN-MAGENTA-YELLOW ISSUED
PLATES DO NOT FEATURE AUTOS OR GU
NO PLATE PRICING DUE TO SCARCITY

2006 Greats of the Game Cardinals Greats

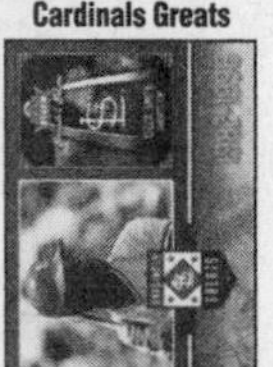

COMPLETE SET (10) 10.00 25.00
OVERALL INSERTS ONE PER PACK
ONE PLATE PER FOIL PLATE PACK
PLATE PACKS ISSUED TO DEALERS
PLATE PRINT RUN 1 SET PER COLOR
BLACK-CYAN-MAGENTA-YELLOW ISSUED
NO PLATE PRICING DUE TO SCARCITY
BG Bob Gibson 1.25 3.00
DD Dizzy Dean 1.25 3.00
LB Lou Brock 1.25 3.00
OS Ozzie Smith 3.00 8.00
RH Rogers Hornsby 1.25 3.00
RS Red Schoendienst .75 2.00
SC Steve Carlton .75 2.00
SM Stan Musial 3.00 8.00
TH Tommy Herr .75 2.00
TM Tim McCarver .75 2.00

2006 Greats of the Game Cardinals Greats Memorabilia

OVERALL GAME-USED ODDS 2:15 H, 1:15 R
SP PRINT RUN INFO PROVIDED BY UD
SP's ARE NOT SERIAL-NUMBERED
BG Bob Gibson Pants 4.00 10.00
DD Dizzy Dean Jsy SP/99 * 20.00 50.00
LB Lou Brock Pants 4.00 10.00

OS Ozzie Smith Bat 6.00 15.00
RH Rogers Hornsby Bat 12.50 30.00
RS Red Schoendienst Bat 3.00 8.00
SC Steve Carlton Bat 3.00 8.00
SM Stan Musial Bat 6.00 15.00
TH Tommy Herr Bat 3.00 8.00
TM Tim McCarver Pants 3.00 8.00

2006 Greats of the Game Cardinals Greats Autograph

STATED PRINT RUN 30 SERIAL #'d SETS
*AUTO MEM: .4X TO 1X AUTO
AUTO MEM PRINT RUN 30 SERIAL #'d SETS
OVERALL AUTO ODDS 2:15 H, 2:15 R
BG Bob Gibson 20.00 50.00
LB Lou Brock 20.00 50.00
OS Ozzie Smith 30.00 60.00
RS Red Schoendienst 15.00 40.00
SC Steve Carlton 15.00 40.00
SM Stan Musial 50.00 100.00
TH Tommy Herr 10.00 25.00
TM Tim McCarver 10.00 25.00

2006 Greats of the Game Cubs Greats

COMPLETE SET (10) 10.00 25.00
OVERALL INSERTS ONE PER PACK
ONE PLATE PER FOIL PLATE PACK
PLATE PACKS ISSUED TO DEALERS
PLATE PRINT RUN 1 SET PER COLOR
BLACK-CYAN-MAGENTA-YELLOW ISSUED
NO PLATE PRICING DUE TO SCARCITY
AD Andre Dawson 1.25 3.00
BS Bruce Sutter .75 2.00
BW Billy Williams .75 2.00
EB Ernie Banks 2.00 5.00
FJ Fergie Jenkins .75 2.00
GM Gary Matthews .75 2.00
MG Mark Grace 1.25 3.00
RH Randy Hundley .75 2.00
RS Ron Santo 1.25 3.00
SA Ryne Sandberg 4.00 10.00

2006 Greats of the Game Cubs Greats Memorabilia

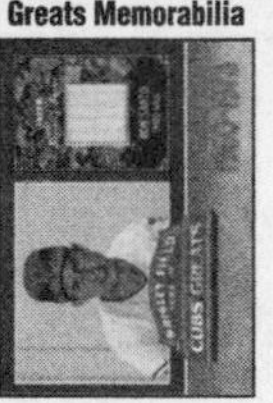

OVERALL GAME-USED ODDS 2:15 H, 1:15 R
AD Andre Dawson Bat 3.00 8.00
BS Bruce Sutter Pants 3.00 8.00
BW Billy Williams Jsy 3.00 8.00
EB Ernie Banks Pants 6.00 15.00
FJ Fergie Jenkins Jsy 3.00 8.00
GM Gary Matthews Bat 3.00 8.00
MG Mark Grace Bat 4.00 10.00
RS Ron Santo Bat 8.00 20.00
SA Ryne Sandberg Bat 6.00 15.00

2006 Greats of the Game Cubs Greats Autograph

STATED PRINT RUN 30 SERIAL #'d SETS
*AUTO MEM: .4X TO 1X AUTO
AUTO MEM PRINT RUN 30 SERIAL #'d SETS
OVERALL AUTO ODDS 2:15 H, 2:15 R
AD Andre Dawson 15.00 40.00
BS Bruce Sutter 15.00 40.00
BW Billy Williams 15.00 40.00
EB Ernie Banks 50.00 100.00
FJ Fergie Jenkins 10.00 25.00
GM Gary Matthews 10.00 25.00
MG Mark Grace 20.00 50.00
RA Randy Hundley
RS Ron Santo 30.00 60.00
SA Ryne Sandberg 30.00 60.00

2006 Greats of the Game Decade Greats

COMPLETE SET (30) 30.00 60.00
OVERALL INSERTS ONE PER PACK
ONE PLATE PER FOIL PLATE PACK
PLATE PACKS ISSUED TO DEALERS
PLATE PRINT RUN 1 SET PER COLOR
BLACK-CYAN-MAGENTA-YELLOW ISSUED
NO PLATE PRICING DUE TO SCARCITY
BF Bob Feller .75 2.00
BI Bill Madlock .75 2.00
BJ Bo Jackson 2.00 5.00
BM Bill Mazeroski 1.25 3.00
BR Brooks Robinson 1.25 3.00
CC Chris Chambliss .75 2.00
CR Cal Ripken 8.00 20.00
DP Dave Parker .75 2.00
EA Earl Averill .75 2.00
EM Eddie Mathews 2.00 5.00
JC Jack Clark .75 2.00
JK John Kruk .75 2.00
JM Johnny Mize .75 2.00
KP Kirby Puckett 2.00 5.00
MC Mickey Cochrane .75 2.00
MO Mel Ott .75 2.00
MS Mike Schmidt 3.00 8.00
NR Nolan Ryan 5.00 12.00
PM Paul Molitor 2.00 5.00
PT Pie Traynor .75 2.00
RC Roberto Clemente 6.00 15.00
RO Rod Carew 1.25 3.00
RY Robin Yount 2.00 5.00
SC Steve Carlton .75 2.00
TG Tony Gwynn 2.00 5.00
TR Tim Raines .75 2.00
TS Tom Seaver 1.25 3.00
WC Will Clark 1.25 3.00
WM Willie McCovey 1.25 3.00
WS Willie Stargell 1.25 3.00

2006 Greats of the Game Decade Greats Memorabilia

OVERALL GAME-USED ODDS 2:15 H, 1:15 R
SP PRINT RUNS B/WN 50-99 COPIES PER
SP PRINT RUN INFO PROVIDED BY UD
SP's ARE NOT SERIAL-NUMBERED
BF Bob Feller Pants 4.00 10.00
BI Bill Madlock Bat 3.00 8.00
BJ Bo Jackson Bat 6.00 15.00
BM Bill Mazeroski Bat 4.00 10.00
BR Brooks Robinson Bat 4.00 10.00
CC Chris Chambliss Bat 3.00 8.00
CR Cal Ripken Pants 8.00 20.00
DP Dave Parker Pants 3.00 8.00
EA Earl Averill Bat 8.00 20.00
EM Eddie Mathews Pants 6.00 15.00
JC Jack Clark Bat 3.00 8.00
JK John Kruk Bat 3.00 8.00
JM Johnny Mize Pants 4.00 10.00
KP Kirby Puckett Bat 6.00 15.00
MC M.Cochrane Bat SP/50 * 40.00 80.00
MO Mel Ott Bat SP/99 * 20.00 50.00
MS Mike Schmidt Bat 4.00 10.00
NR Nolan Ryan Jsy 6.00 15.00
PM Paul Molitor Bat 3.00 8.00
RC Roberto Clemente Jsy 20.00 50.00
RO Rod Carew Pants 4.00 10.00
RY Robin Yount Bat 4.00 10.00
SC Steve Carlton Bat 3.00 8.00
TG Tony Gwynn Pants 4.00 10.00
TR Tim Raines Jsy 3.00 8.00
TS Tom Seaver Jsy 4.00 10.00
WC Will Clark Jsy 4.00 10.00
WM Willie McCovey Bat 4.00 10.00
WS Willie Stargell Bat 4.00 10.00

2006 Greats of the Game Decade Greats Autograph

STATED PRINT RUN 30 SERIAL #'d SETS
*AUTO MEM: .4X TO 1X AUTO
AUTO MEM PRINT RUN 30 SERIAL #'d SETS
OVERALL AUTO ODDS 2:15 H, 2:15 R
BF Bob Feller 20.00 50.00
BI Bill Madlock 15.00 40.00
BJ Bo Jackson 40.00 80.00
BM Bill Mazeroski 30.00 60.00
BR Brooks Robinson 20.00 50.00
CC Chris Chambliss 10.00 25.00
CR Cal Ripken 90.00 150.00
DP Dave Parker 15.00 40.00
JC Jack Clark 10.00 25.00
JK John Kruk 15.00 40.00
KP Kirby Puckett 50.00 100.00
MS Mike Schmidt 40.00 80.00
NR Nolan Ryan 60.00 120.00
PM Paul Molitor 20.00 50.00
RO Rod Carew 20.00 50.00
RY Robin Yount 30.00 60.00
SC Steve Carlton 15.00 40.00
TG Tony Gwynn 30.00 60.00
TR Tim Raines 10.00 25.00
TS Tom Seaver 30.00 60.00
WC Will Clark 20.00 50.00
WM Willie McCovey 20.00 50.00

2006 Greats of the Game Dodger Greats

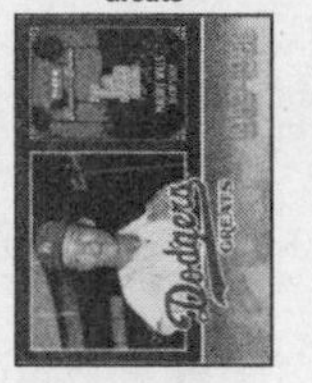

COMPLETE SET (10) 10.00 25.00
OVERALL INSERTS ONE PER PACK
ONE PLATE PER FOIL PLATE PACK
PLATE PACKS ISSUED TO DEALERS
PLATE PRINT RUN 1 SET PER COLOR
BLACK-CYAN-MAGENTA-YELLOW ISSUED
NO PLATE PRICING DUE TO SCARCITY
CA Roy Campanella 2.00 5.00
DB Dusty Baker .75 2.00
DD Don Drysdale 1.25 3.00
DS Don Sutton .75 2.00
JR Jackie Robinson 2.00 5.00
MW Maury Wills .75 2.00
PR Pee Wee Reese 1.25 3.00
RC Ron Cey .75 2.00
SG Steve Garvey .75 2.00
SS Steve Sax .75 2.00

2006 Greats of the Game Dodger Greats Memorabilia

OVERALL GAME-USED ODDS 2:15 H, 1:15 R
SP PRINT RUNS B/WN 25-199 COPIES PER
SP PRINT RUN INFO PROVIDED BY UD
SP's ARE NOT SERIAL-NUMBERED
NO PRICING ON QTY OF 30 OR LESS
CA Roy Campanella Jsy SP/25 *
DB Dusty Baker Jsy 3.00 8.00
DD Don Drysdale Jsy SP/69 * 8.00 20.00
DS Don Sutton Jsy SP/30 *
JR Jackie Robinson Bat SP/199 * 20.00 50.00
MW Maury Wills Bat 3.00 8.00
PR Pee Wee Reese Jsy 4.00 10.00
RC Ron Cey Jsy 3.00 8.00
SG Steve Garvey Jsy 3.00 8.00
SS Steve Sax Jsy 3.00 8.00

2006 Greats of the Game Dodger Greats Autograph

STATED PRINT RUN 30 SERIAL #'d SETS
*AUTO MEM: .4X TO 1X AUTO
AUTO MEM PRINT RUN 30 SERIAL #'d SETS
OVERALL AUTO ODDS 2:15 H, 2:15 R
DB Dusty Baker 20.00 50.00
DS Don Sutton 10.00 25.00
MW Maury Wills 10.00 25.00
RC Ron Cey 10.00 25.00
SG Steve Garvey 15.00 40.00
SS Steve Sax 10.00 25.00

2006 Greats of the Game Nickname Greats

OVERALL INSERTS ONE PER PACK
ONE PLATE PER FOIL PLATE PACK
PLATE PACKS ISSUED TO DEALERS
PLATE PRINT RUN 1 SET PER COLOR
BLACK-CYAN-MAGENTA-YELLOW ISSUED
NO PLATE PRICING DUE TO SCARCITY
AG Andres Galarraga 1.25 3.00
Big Cat
AH Al Hrabosky 1.25 3.00
The Mad Hungarian
AT Andre Thornton 1.25 3.00
Thunder
BE Steve Bedrosian 1.25 3.00
Bedrock
BF Bob Feller 1.25 3.00
Rapid Robert
BH Burt Hooton 1.25 3.00
Happy
BL Bill Lee 1.25 3.00
Spaceman
BM Bill Madlock 1.25 3.00
Mad Dog
CF Carlton Fisk 2.00 5.00
Pudge
CH Joe Charboneau 1.25 3.00
Super Joe
DB Don Baylor 1.25 3.00
Groove
DD Darren Daulton 1.25 3.00
Dutch
DE Dwight Evans 1.25 3.00
Dewey
DF Dan Ford 1.25 3.00
Disco Dan
DM Don Mattingly 6.00 15.00
Donny Baseball
DP Dave Parker 1.25 3.00
The Cobra
DR Dave Righetti 1.25 3.00
Rags
EV Ellis Valentine 1.25 3.00
Bubba
FR Frank Robinson 1.25 3.00
The Judge
FS Fred Stanley 1.25 3.00
Chicken
GF George Foster 1.25 3.00
The Destroyer
GH Glenn Hubbard 1.25 3.00
Bam Bam
GM Garry Maddox 1.25 3.00
The Secretary of Defense
GS George Scott 1.25 3.00
Boomer
HE Tommy Herr 1.25 3.00
T-Bird
HJ Howard Johnson 1.25 3.00
Hojo
JB Jim Bouton 1.25 3.00
Bulldog or Ball Four
JC Jack Clark 1.25 3.00
Jack the Ripper
JJ Jay Johnstone 1.25 3.00
Moon Man
JM John Montefusco 1.25 3.00
The Count
JP Joe Pepitone 1.25 3.00
Pepi
JS John Shelby 1.25 3.00
T-Bone
JW Jimmy Wynn 1.25 3.00
The Toy Cannon
KH Ken Harrelson 1.25 3.00
The Hawk
LA Luis Aparicio 1.25 3.00
Little Louie
LM Lee Mazzilli 1.25 3.00
The Italian Stallion
LP Lou Piniella 1.25 3.00
Sweet Lou
MA Gary Matthews 1.25 3.00
Sarge
MF Mark Fidrych 1.25 3.00
The Bird
MH Mike Hargrove 1.25 3.00
The Human Rain Delay
ML Mike Lavalliere 1.25 3.00
Spanky
MR Mickey Rivers 1.25 3.00
Mick the Quick
MW Mitch Williams 1.25 3.00
Wild Thing
MZ Dennis Martinez 1.25 3.00
El Presidente
RA Doug Rader 1.25 3.00
The Red Rooster
RB Rick Burleson 1.25 3.00
Rooster
RC Ron Cey 1.25 3.00
The Penguin
RG Ron Guidry 1.25 3.00
Louisiana Lightning (or Gator)
RR Rick Reuschel 1.25 3.00
Big Daddy
RS Rusty Staub 1.25 3.00
Le Grand Orange
SB Steve Balboni 1.25 3.00
Bye Bye
SF Sid Fernandez 1.25 3.00
El Sid
SL Sparky Lyle 1.25 3.00
The Count
SM Sam McDowell 1.25 3.00
Sudden Sam
ST Steve Trout 1.25 3.00
Rainbow
TB Tom Brunansky 1.25 3.00
Bruno
TH Tom Henke 1.25 3.00
The Terminator
TR Tim Raines 1.25 3.00
Rock
WC Will Clark 2.00 5.00
Will the Thrill
WM Willie McCovey 2.00 5.00
Stretch

2006 Greats of the Game Nickname Greats Autographs

Originally intended as a 54-card collection, this set actually contains 57 cards due to variations produced by unintentional mistakes at the production stage. It was the manufacturers intent for each of these Nickname Greats inserts to feature a signed sticker that would also include the featured athletes nickname. Unfortunately, some athletes didn't sign their stickers in the intended fashion and some nicknamed stickers were erroneously placed on other signed cards within the 2006 Greats of the Game product. Please note, our checklist has been carefully constructed to indicate which cards were correctly signed and which weren't. For cards that were correctly produced with nicknamed signature stickers the actual inscription will be listed after the player's name (for example, Al Hrabosky correctly signed all of his stickers as "Al 'The Mad Hungarian' Hrabosky" and all of those stickers were correctly placed on the cards - thus our description is listed as A.Hrabosky Hungarian). Other cards feature no cinknamed stickers whatsoever, such as Bill Madlock. Madlock did sign a good amount of his stickers as Bill "Maddog" Madlock, but those stickers were erroneously placed on other cards in this product and standard Madlock signed stickers were used for this set. Thus, Madlock's card in this set is simply listed as "Bill Madlock". Finally, variations for nicknamed and non-nicknamed stickers have been found for three cards as follows . . . George Foster (50% feature Destroyer inscription and 50% are standard), Andre Thornton (10% feature Thunder inscription and 90% are standard) and Steve Trout (80% feature Rainbow inscription and 20% are standard). Also, an exchange card with a redemption deadline of April 10th, 2009 was seeded into packs for the Dennis Martinez card. On average 1:15 hobby and retail packs contained a Nicknames Greats signed insert.

OVERALL AUTO ODDS 2:15 H, 2:15 R
TIER 1 QTY B/WN 29-50 COPIES PER
TIER 2 QTY 100 COPIES PER
TIER 3 QTY B/WN 175-250 COPIES PER
TIER 4 QTY B/WN 251-400 COPIES PER
TIER 5 QTY B/WN 401-650 COPIES PER
CARDS ARE NOT SERIAL-NUMBERED
PRINT RUN INFO PROVIDED BY UD
AU INSCRIPTIONS INTENDED FOR ALL CARDS
NOT ALL CARDS CARRY AU INSCRIPTIONS
AU INSCRIPTIONS ARE DETAILED BELOW
PARENTHESES PERCENTAGE OF PRINT RUN
NO MCCOVEY PRICING DUE TO SCARCITY
EXCHANGE DEADLINE 04/10/09
AH Al Hrabosky T5 6.00 15.00
The Mad Hungarian
AT1 Andre Thornton T5 (90) 4.00 10.00
AT2 Andre Thornton T5 (10) 6.00 15.00
Thunder
BE Steve Bedrosian T5 6.00 15.00
Bedrock
BF Bob Feller T2/100 * 20.00 50.00
Rapid Robert
BH Burt Hooton T5 4.00 10.00
Happy
BL Bill Lee T5 8.00 20.00
Spaceman
BM Bill Madlock T4 4.00 10.00
CF Carlton Fisk T1/50 * 20.00 50.00
CH Joe Charboneau T5 6.00 15.00
Super Joe
DD Darren Daulton T5 6.00 15.00
Dutch
DE Dwight Evans T2/100 * 10.00 25.00
DF Dan Ford T5 4.00 10.00
Disco Dan
DP Dave Parker T2/100 * 20.00 50.00
The Cobra
DR Dave Righetti T5 8.00 20.00
Rags
EV Ellis Valentine T5 4.00 10.00
Bubba
FR Frank Robinson T1/50 * 30.00 60.00
FS Fred Stanley T5 6.00 15.00
Chicken
GF1 George Foster T3 (50) 4.00 10.00
GF2 George Foster T3 (50) 6.00 15.00
The Destroyer
GH Glenn Hubbard T5 4.00 10.00
Bam Bam
GM Garry Maddox T5 6.00 15.00
The Secretary of Defense
GS George Scott T5 6.00 15.00
Boomer
HE Tommy Herr T5 8.00 20.00
HJ Howard Johnson T3 10.00 25.00
Hojo
JB Jim Bouton T3 6.00 15.00
Bulldog
JC Jack Clark T4 6.00 15.00
JJ Jay Johnstone T5 6.00 15.00
Moon Man
JM John Montefusco T5 6.00 15.00
The Count
JP Joe Pepitone T5 6.00 15.00
Pepi
JS John Shelby T5 4.00 10.00
T-Bone
JW Jimmy Wynn T5 6.00 15.00
The Toy Cannon
LM Lee Mazzilli T5 6.00 15.00
The Italian Stallion
LP Lou Piniella T2/100 * 20.00 50.00
Sweet Lou
MA Gary Matthews T5 4.00 10.00
Sarge
MF Mark Fidrych T4 20.00 50.00
The Bird
MH Mike Hargrove T5 8.00 20.00
The Human Rain Delay
ML Mike Lavalliere T5 4.00 10.00
Spanky
MR Mickey Rivers T3 8.00 20.00
Mick the Quick
MW Mitch Williams T5 6.00 15.00
Wild Thing
RA Doug Rader T5 6.00 15.00
The Red Rooster
RB Rick Burleson T5 4.00 10.00
Rooster
RG Ron Guidry T3 15.00 40.00
RR Rick Reuschel T5 8.00 20.00
Big Daddy
RS Rusty Staub T3 15.00 40.00
SB Steve Balboni T5 8.00 20.00
Bye Bye
SF Sid Fernandez T5 6.00 15.00
El Sid
SL Sparky Lyle T4 6.00 15.00
The Count
SM Sam McDowell T5 6.00 15.00
Sudden Sam
ST1 Steve Trout T5 (20) 6.00 15.00
ST2 Steve Trout T5 (80) 8.00 20.00
Rainbow
TB Tom Brunansky T5 4.00 10.00
Bruno
TH Tom Henke T5 6.00 15.00
The Terminator
TR Tim Raines T3 6.00 15.00
WC Will Clark T2/100 * 12.50 30.00
WM Willie McCovey T1/29 *

2006 Greats of the Game Red Sox Greats

COMPLETE SET (10) 10.00 25.00
OVERALL INSERTS ONE PER PACK
ONE PLATE PER FOIL PLATE PACK
PLATE PACKS ISSUED TO DEALERS
PLATE PRINT RUN 1 SET PER COLOR
BLACK-CYAN-MAGENTA-YELLOW ISSUED
NO PLATE PRICING DUE TO SCARCITY
BD Bobby Doerr .75 2.00
CF Carlton Fisk 1.25 3.00
DE Dwight Evans .75 2.00
FL Fred Lynn .75 2.00
JF Jimmie Foxx 2.00 5.00
JR Jim Rice .75 2.00
LT Luis Tiant .75 2.00
RP Rico Petrocelli .75 2.00
TW Ted Williams 5.00 12.00
WB Wade Boggs 1.25 3.00

2006 Greats of the Game Red Sox Greats Memorabilia

OVERALL GAME-USED ODDS 2:15 H, 1:15 R
SP PRINT RUNS B/WN 25-199 COPIES PER
SP PRINT RUN INFO PROVIDED BY UD
SP's ARE NOT SERIAL-NUMBERED
BD Bobby Doerr Bat 3.00 8.00
CF Carlton Fisk Pants 4.00 10.00
DE Dwight Evans Jsy 4.00 10.00
FL Fred Lynn Pants 3.00 8.00
JF Jimmie Foxx Bat SP/99 * 15.00 40.00
JR Jim Rice Bat 3.00 8.00
LT Luis Tiant Jsy 3.00 8.00
RP Rico Petrocelli Pants 3.00 8.00
TW Ted Williams Jsy SP/199 * 20.00 50.00
WB Wade Boggs Pants 4.00 10.00

2006 Greats of the Game Red Sox Greats Autograph

STATED PRINT RUN 30 SERIAL #'d SETS
*AUTO MEM: .4X TO 1X AUTO
AUTO MEM PRINT RUN 30 SERIAL #'d SETS
OVERALL AUTO ODDS 2:15 H, 2:15 R
BD Bobby Doerr 10.00 25.00
CF Carlton Fisk 20.00 50.00
DE Dwight Evans 30.00 60.00
FL Fred Lynn 10.00 25.00
JR Jim Rice 10.00 25.00
LT Luis Tiant 10.00 25.00
RP Rico Petrocelli 10.00 25.00
WB Wade Boggs 20.00 50.00

2006 Greats of the Game Reds Greats

COMPLETE SET (10) 10.00 25.00
OVERALL INSERTS ONE PER PACK
ONE PLATE PER FOIL PLATE PACK
PLATE PACKS ISSUED TO DEALERS
PLATE PRINT RUN 1 SET PER COLOR
BLACK-CYAN-MAGENTA-YELLOW ISSUED
NO PLATE PRICING DUE TO SCARCITY
BL Barry Larkin 1.25 3.00
DC Dave Concepcion .75 2.00
ED Eric Davis .75 2.00
FR Frank Robinson .75 2.00
GF George Foster .75 2.00
JB Johnny Bench 2.00 5.00
JM Joe Morgan .75 2.00
KG Ken Griffey Sr. .75 2.00
TP Tony Perez .75 2.00
TS Tom Seaver 1.25 3.00

2006 Greats of the Game Reds Greats Memorabilia

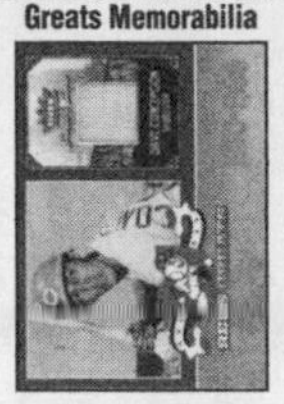

OVERALL GAME-USED ODDS 2:15 H, 1:15 R

BL Barry Larkin Pants	4.00	10.00
DC Dave Concepcion Bat	3.00	8.00
ED Eric Davis Jsy	3.00	8.00
FR Frank Robinson Bat	4.00	10.00
GF George Foster Bat	3.00	8.00
JB Johnny Bench Bat	6.00	15.00
JM Joe Morgan Bat	3.00	8.00
KG Ken Griffey Sr. Pants	3.00	8.00
TP Tony Perez Bat	3.00	8.00
TS Tom Seaver Bat	4.00	10.00

2006 Greats of the Game Reds Greats Autograph

STATED PRINT RUN 30 SERIAL #'d SETS
*AUTO MEM: .4X TO 1X AUTO
AUTO MEM PRINT RUN 30 SERIAL #'d SETS
OVERALL AUTO ODDS 2:15 H, 2:15 R

BL Barry Larkin	20.00	50.00
DC Dave Concepcion	15.00	40.00
ED Eric Davis	20.00	50.00
FR Frank Robinson	30.00	60.00
GF George Foster	15.00	40.00
The Destroyer		
JB Johnny Bench	30.00	60.00
JM Joe Morgan	15.00	40.00
KG Ken Griffey Sr.	15.00	40.00
TP Tony Perez	15.00	40.00
TS Tom Seaver	30.00	60.00

2006 Greats of the Game Tigers Greats

COMPLETE SET (10)	10.00	25.00

OVERALL INSERTS ONE PER PACK
ONE PLATE PER FOIL PLATE PACK
PLATE PACKS ISSUED TO DEALERS
PLATE PRINT RUN 1 SET PER COLOR
BLACK-CYAN-MAGENTA-YELLOW ISSUED
NO PLATE PRICING DUE TO SCARCITY

AK Al Kaline	2.00	5.00
AT Alan Trammell	.75	2.00
BF Bill Freehan	.75	2.00
DM Denny McLain	.75	2.00
GK George Kell	.75	2.00
JM Jack Morris	.75	2.00
KG Kirk Gibson	.75	2.00
MF Mark Fidrych	.75	2.00
TC Ty Cobb	3.00	8.00
WH Willie Horton	.75	2.00

2006 Greats of the Game Tigers Greats Memorabilia

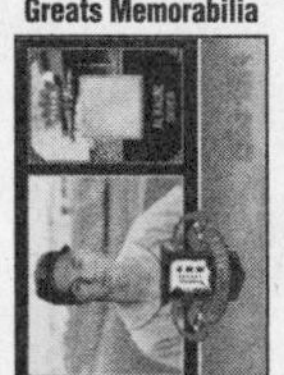

OVERALL GAME-USED ODDS 2:15 H, 1:15 R
SP PRINT RUNS 99 COPIES PER
SP PRINT RUN INFO PROVIDED BY UD
SP's ARE NOT SERIAL NUMBERED

AK Al Kaline Bat	4.00	10.00
AT Alan Trammell Bat	3.00	8.00
BF Bill Freehan Bat	3.00	8.00
GK George Kell Bat	4.00	10.00
JM Jack Morris Jsy	3.00	8.00
KG Kirk Gibson Jsy	4.00	10.00
MF Mark Fidrych Jsy	3.00	8.00
TC Ty Cobb Bat SP/99 *	60.00	120.00
WH Willie Horton Bat SP/99 *	4.00	10.00

2006 Greats of the Game Tigers Greats Autograph

STATED PRINT RUN 30 SERIAL #'d SETS
*AUTO MEM: .4X TO 1X AUTO
AUTO MEM PRINT RUN 30 SERIAL #'d SETS
OVERALL AUTO ODDS 2:15 H, 2:15 R

AK Al Kaline	30.00	60.00
AT Alan Trammell	15.00	40.00
BF Bill Freehan	15.00	40.00
DM Denny McLain	10.00	25.00
GK George Kell	30.00	60.00
JM Jack Morris	10.00	25.00
KG Kirk Gibson	15.00	40.00
MF Mark Fidrych	20.00	50.00
WH Willie Horton	10.00	25.00

2006 Greats of the Game Yankee Clippings

COMPLETE SET (10)	12.50	30.00

OVERALL INSERTS ONE PER PACK
ONE PLATE PER FOIL PLATE PACK
PLATE PACKS ISSUED TO DEALERS
PLATE PRINT RUN 1 SET PER COLOR
BLACK-CYAN-MAGENTA-YELLOW ISSUED
NO PLATE PRICING DUE TO SCARCITY

BM Bobby Murcer	.75	2.00
BR Babe Ruth	5.00	12.00
DM Don Mattingly	4.00	10.00
GN Graig Nettles	.75	2.00
JD Joe DiMaggio	5.00	12.00
RG Ron Guidry	.75	2.00
RJ Reggie Jackson	1.25	3.00
TM Thurman Munson	2.00	5.00
WF Whitey Ford	1.25	3.00
YB Yogi Berra	2.00	5.00

2006 Greats of the Game Yankee Clippings Memorabilia

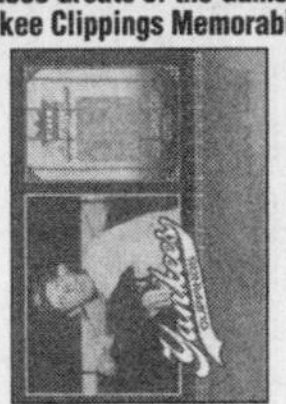

OVERALL GAME-USED ODDS 2:15 H, 1:15 R
SP PRINT RUNS B/WN 25-199 COPIES PER
SP PRINT RUN INFO PROVIDED BY UD
SP's ARE NOT SERIAL-NUMBERED
NO SP PRICING ON QTY OF 30 OR LESS

BM Bobby Murcer Bat	4.00	10.00
BR Babe Ruth Bat SP/25 *		
DM Don Mattingly Bat	6.00	15.00
GN Graig Nettles Bat	3.00	8.00
JD Joe DiMaggio Pants SP/99 *	40.00	80.00
RG Ron Guidry Jsy	4.00	10.00
RJ Reggie Jackson Jsy	4.00	10.00
TM Thurman Munson Pants	8.00	20.00
WF Whitey Ford Pants	6.00	15.00
YB Yogi Berra Bat SP/199 *	8.00	20.00

2006 Greats of the Game Yankee Clippings Autograph

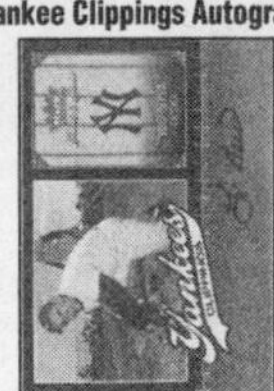

STATED PRINT RUN 30 SERIAL #'d SETS
*AUTO MEM: .4X TO 1X AUTO
AUTO MEM PRINT RUN 30 SERIAL #'d SETS
OVERALL AUTO ODDS 2:15 H, 2:15 R

BM Bobby Murcer	20.00	50.00
DM Don Mattingly	50.00	100.00
GN Graig Nettles	15.00	40.00
RG Ron Guidry	30.00	60.00
RJ Reggie Jackson	30.00	60.00
WF Whitey Ford	40.00	80.00
YB Yogi Berra	40.00	80.00

1912 Hassan Triple Folders T202

The cards in this 132-card set measure approximately 2 1/4" by 5 1/4". The 1912 T202 Hassan Triple Folder issue is perhaps the most ingenious baseball card ever issued. The two end cards of each panel are full color, T205-like individual cards whereas the black and white center panel pictures an action photo or portrait. The end cards can be folded across the center panel and stored in this manner. Seventy-six different center panels are known to exist; however, many of the center panels contain more than one combination of end cards. The center panel titles are listed below in alphabetical order while the different combinations of end cards are listed below each center panel as they appear left to right on the front of the card. A total of 132 different card fronts exist. The set price below includes all panel and player combinations listed in the checklist. Back color variations (red or black) also exist. The Birmingham's Home Run card is difficult to obtain as are other cards whose center panel exists with but one combination of end cards. The Devlin with Mathewson end panels on numbers 29A and 74C picture Devlin as a Giant. Devlin is pictured as a Rustler on 29B and 74D. Listed pricing references cards in raw "EX" condition.

COMPLETE SET (132)	20000.00	35000.00
1 A Close Play at Home Plate	150.00	250.00
Bobby Wallace		
Frank LaPorte		
2 A Close Play at Home Plate	150.00	250.00
Bobby Wallace		
Barney Pelty		
3 A Desperate Slide for Third	900.00	1500.00
Charley O'Leary		
Ty Cobb		
4 A Great Batsman	125.00	200.00
Cy Barger		
Bill Bergen		
5 A Great Batsman	125.00	200.00
Nap Rucker		
Bill Bergen		
6 A Wide Throw Saves Crawford	125.00	200.00
George Mullin		
Oscar Stanage		
7 Ambrose McConnell at Bat	125.00	200.00
Walter Blair		
Jack Quinn		
8 Baker Gets His Man	250.00	400.00
Eddie Collins		
Frank Baker		
9 Birmingham Gets to Third	350.00	600.00
Walter Johnson		
Gabby Street		
10 Birmingham's Home Run	150.00	250.00
Doc Birmingham		
Terry Turner		
11 Bush Just Misses Austin	125.00	200.00
Pat Moran		
Sherry Magee		
12 Carrigan Blocks His Man	125.00	200.00
Harry Gaspar		
Larry McLean		
13 Carrigan Blocks His Man	125.00	200.00
Heinie Wagner		
Bill Carrigan		
14 Catching Him Napping	150.00	250.00
Rebel Oakes		
Roger Bresnahan		
15 Caught Asleep Off First	150.00	250.00
Roger Bresnahan		
Robert Harmon		
16 Chance Beats Out a Hit	150.00	250.00
Frank Chance		
Bill Foxen		
17 Chance Beats Out a Hit	125.00	200.00
Harry McIntire		
Jimmy Archer		
18 Chance Beats Out a Hit	125.00	200.00
Orval Overall		
Jimmy Archer		
19 Chance Beats Out a Hit	125.00	200.00
John Rowan		
Jimmy Archer		
20 Chance Beats Out a Hit	150.00	250.00
David Shean		
Frank Chance		
21 Chase Dives into Third	125.00	200.00
Hal Chase		
Harry Wolter		
22 Chase Dives into Third	150.00	250.00
George Gibson		
Fred Clarke		
23 Chase Dives into Third	125.00	200.00
Deacon Phillippe		
George Gibson		
24 Chase Gets Ball Too Late	125.00	200.00
Dick Egan		
Mike Mitchell		
25 Chase Gets Ball Too Late	125.00	200.00
Harry Wolter		
Hal Chase		
26 Chase Guarding First	125.00	200.00
Hal Chase		
Harry Wolter		
27 Chase Guarding First	125.00	200.00
George Gibson		
Fred Clarke		
28 Chase Guarding First	125.00	200.00
Lefty Leifield		
George Gibson		
29 Chase Ready for Squeeze Play	125.00	200.00
Dode Paskert		
Sherry Magee		
30 Chase Safe at Third	300.00	500.00
Jack Barry		
Frank Baker		
31 Chief Bender Waiting For a Good One 150.00250.00		
Chief Bender		
Ira Thomas		
32 Clarke Hikes for Home	125.00	200.00
Al Bridwell		
Johnny Kling		
33 Close at First	125.00	200.00
Neal Ball		
George Stovall		
34 Close at the Plate	125.00	200.00
Fred Payne		
Doc White		
35 Close at the Plate	150.00	250.00
Ed Walsh		
Fred Payne		
36 Close at Third	125.00	200.00
Bill Carrigan		
Heinie Wagner		
37 Close at Third	300.00	500.00
Joe Wood		
Tris Speaker		
38 Collins Easily Safe	150.00	250.00
Bobby Byrne		
Fred Clarke		
39 Collins Easily Safe	250.00	400.00
Eddie Collins		
Frank Baker		
40 Collins Easily Safe	150.00	250.00
Eddie Collins		
Danny Murphy		
41 Crawford About to Smash One	125.00	200.00
Oscar Stanage		
Ed Summers		
42 Cree Rolls Home	125.00	200.00
Jake Daubert		
John Hummell		
43 Davy Jones Great Slide	125.00	200.00
Jim Delahanty		
Tom Jones		
44 Devlin Gets His Man	500.00	800.00
Art Devlin (Giants)		
Christy Mathewson		
45 Devlin Gets His Man	500.00	800.00
Art Devlin (Rustlers)		
Christy Mathewson		
46 Devlin Gets His Man	350.00	600.00
Art Fletcher		
Christy Mathewson		
47 Devlin Gets His Man	300.00	500.00
Chief Meyers		
Christy Mathewson		
48 Donlin Out at First	125.00	200.00
Howie Camnitz		
George Gibson		
49 Donlin Out at First	125.00	200.00
Red Dooin		
Sherry Magee		
50 Donlin Out at First	125.00	200.00
Larry Doyle		
Fred Merkle		
51 Donlin Out at First	125.00	200.00
George Gibson		
Deacon Phillippe		
52 Donlin Out at First	125.00	200.00
Tommy Leach		
Chief Wilson		
53 Dooin Gets His Man	125.00	200.00
Red Dooin		
Mickey Doolan		
54 Dooin Gets His Man	125.00	200.00
Red Dooin		
Hans Lobert		
55 Dooin Gets His Man	125.00	200.00
Red Dooin		
John Titus		
56 Easy for Larry	125.00	200.00
Larry Doyle		
Fred Merkle		
57 Elberfeld Beats the Throw	125.00	200.00
Clyde Milan		
Kid Elberfeld		
58 Elberfeld Gets His Man	125.00	200.00
Clyde Milan		
Kid Elberfeld		
59 Engle in a Close Play	175.00	300.00
Tris Speaker		
Hack Engle		
60 Evers Makes a Safe Slide	150.00	250.00
Jimmy Archer		
Johnny Evers		
61 Evers Makes a Safe Slide	125.00	200.00
Jimmy Archer		
Orval Overall		
62 Evers Makes a Safe Slide	125.00	200.00
Jimmy Archer		
Ed Reulbach		
63 Evers Makes a Safe Slide	250.00	400.00
Frank Chance		
Johnny Evers		
64 Evers Makes a Safe Slide	500.00	800.00
Joe Tinker		
Frank Chance		
65 Fast Work at Third	900.00	1500.00
Charley O'Leary		
Ty Cobb		
66 Ford Putting Over a Spitter	125.00	200.00
Russ Ford		
Jeff Sweeney		
67 Ford Putting Over a Spitter	125.00	200.00
Russ Ford		
Hippo Vaughn		
68 Good Play at Third	900.00	1500.00
George Moriarty		
Ty Cobb		
69 Grant Gets His Man	125.00	200.00
Eddie Grant		
Doc Hoblitzel		
70 Hal Chase Too Late	125.00	200.00
Ambrose McConnell		
Matty McIntyre		
71 Hal Chase Too Late	125.00	200.00
Larry McLean		
George Suggs		
72 Harry Lord at Third:	150.00	250.00
Ed Lennox		
Joe Tinker		
73 Hartsel Strikes Out	125.00	200.00
Dolly Gray		
Bob Groom		
74 Hartzell Covering Third	125.00	200.00
Bill Dahlen		
Doc Scanlon		
75 Held at Third	125.00	200.00
Harry Lord		
Jesse Tannehill		
76 Jake Stahl Guarding First	125.00	200.00
Eddie Cicotte		
Jake Stahl		
77 Jim Delahanty at Bat	125.00	200.00
Jim Delahanty		
Davy Jones		
78 Just Before the Battle	125.00	200.00
Red Ames		
Chief Meyers		
79 Just Before the Battle	125.00	200.00
Josh Devore		
Beals Becker		
80 Just Before the Battle	250.00	400.00
Roger Bresnahan		
John McGraw MG		
81 Just Before the Battle	125.00	200.00
Doc Crandall		
Chief Meyers		
82 Just Before the Battle	350.00	600.00
Art Fletcher		
Christy Mathewson		
83 Just Before the Battle	150.00	250.00
Rube Marquard		
Chief Meyers		
84 Just Before the Battle	250.00	400.00
John McGraw MG		
Hugh Jennings		
85 Just Before the Battle	300.00	500.00
Chief Meyers		
Christy Mathewson		
86 Just Before the Battle	125.00	200.00
Chief Meyers		
Hook Wiltse		
87 Just Before the Battle	125.00	200.00
Fred Snodgrass		
Red Murray		
88 Knight Catches a Runner	350.00	600.00
Jack Knight		
Walter Johnson		
89 Lobert Almost Caught	125.00	200.00
Al Bridwell		
Johnny Kling		
90 Lobert Almost Caught	125.00	200.00
Johnny Kling		
Harry Steinfeldt		
91 Lobert Almost Caught	350.00	600.00
Johnny Kling		
Cy Young		
92 Lobert Almost Caught	125.00	200.00
Al Mattern		
Johnny Kling		
93 Lobert Gets Tenney	125.00	200.00
Red Dooin		
Hans Lobert		
94 Lord Catches His Man	125.00	200.00
Harry Lord		
Lee Tannehill		
95 McConnell Caught	125.00	200.00
Tom Needham		
Lew Richie		
96 McIntyre at Bat	125.00	200.00
Ambrose McConnell		
Matty McIntyre		
97 Moriarty Spiked	125.00	200.00
Oscar Stanage		
Ed Willett		
98 Nearly Caught	125.00	200.00
Johnny Bates		
Bob Bescher		
99 Oldring Almost Home	125.00	200.00
Harry Lord		
Rube Oldring		
100 Schaefer on First	125.00	200.00
George McBride		
Clyde Milan		
101 Schaefer Steals Second	125.00	200.00
George McBride		
Clark Griffith		
102 Scoring from Second	125.00	200.00
Harry Lord		
Rube Oldring		
103 Scrambling Back to First	125.00	200.00
Cy Barger		
Bill Bergen		
104 Scrambling Back to First	125.00	200.00
Harry Wolter		
Hal Chase		
105 Speaker Almost Caught	150.00	250.00
Dots Miller		
Fred Clarke		
106 Speaker Rounding Third	350.00	600.00
Joe Wood		
Tris Speaker		
107 Speaker Scores	300.00	500.00
Tris Speaker		
Hack Engle		
108 Stahl Safe	125.00	200.00
Jimmy Austin		
George Stovall		
109 Stone About to Swing	125.00	200.00
Wildfire Schulte		
Jimmy Sheckard		
110 Sullivan Puts Up a High One	150.00	250.00
Steve Evans		
Miller Huggins		
111 Sullivan Puts up a High One	125.00	200.00
Dolly Gray		
Bob Groom		
112 Sweeney Gets Stahl	125.00	200.00
Russ FordJeff Sweeney		
113 Sweeney Gets Stahl	125.00	200.00
Russ Ford		
Hippo Vaughn		
114 Tenney Lands Safely	125.00	200.00
Arlie Latham		
Bugs Raymond		
115 The Athletic Infield	175.00	300.00
Jack Barry		
Frank Baker		
116 The Athletic Infield	150.00	250.00
Mordecai Brown		
Peaches Graham		
117 The Athletic Infield	125.00	200.00
Arnold Hauser		
Ed Konetchy		
118 The Athletic Infield	125.00	200.00
Harry Krause		
Ira Thomas		
119 The Pinch Hitter	125.00	200.00
Dick Egan		
Doc Hoblitzel		
120 The Scissors Slide	125.00	200.00
Doc Birmingham		
Terry Turner		
121 Tom Jones at Bat	125.00	200.00
Art Fromme		
Larry McLean		
122 Tom Jones at Bat	125.00	200.00
Harry Gaspar		
Larry McLean		
123 Too Late For Devlin	125.00	200.00
Red Ames		
Chief Meyers		
124 Too Late For Devlin	125.00	200.00
Doc Crandall		
Chief Meyers		
125 Too Late For Devlin	700.00	1200.00
Art Devlin (Giants)		
Christy Mathewson		
126 Too Late For Devlin	900.00	1500.00
Art Devlin (Rustlers)		
Christy Mathewson		
127 Too Late For Devlin	250.00	400.00
Rube Marquard		
Chief Meyers		
128 Too Late For Devlin	125.00	200.00
Chief Meyers		
Hooks Wiltse		
129 Ty Cobb Steals Third	1200.00	2000.00
Hughie Jennings		
Ty Cobb		
130 Ty Cobb Steals Third	1200.00	2000.00
George Moriarty		
Ty Cobb		
131 Ty Cobb Steals Third	600.00	1000.00
George Stovall		
Jimmy Austin		
132 Wheat Strikes Out	150.00	250.00
Bill Dahlen		
Zach Wheat		

2002 Hot Prospects

This 125 standard-size set was released in August, 2002. It was issued in five card packs with an $3 SRP which were issued 15 packs to a box and 6 boxes to a case. Cards numbered 81-105 feature not only a rookie/prospect card but also has a game-used memorabilia piece attached to the card while cards numbered 106 through 125 just features rookies. Cards 81-105 have a stated print run of 1000 serial numbered sets and cards 106-125 have a stated print run of 1500 sets.

COMP.SET w/o SP's (80)	12.50	30.00
COMMON CARD (1-80)	.20	.50
COMMON CARD (81-105)	3.00	8.00
COMMON CARD (106-125)	2.00	5.00
1 Derek Jeter	1.25	3.00
2 Garret Anderson	.20	.50
3 Scott Rolen	.30	.75
4 Bret Boone	.20	.50
5 Lance Berkman	.20	.50
6 Andruw Jones	.30	.75
7 Ivan Rodriguez	.30	.75
8 Bernie Williams	.30	.75
9 Cristian Guzman	.20	.50
10 Mo Vaughn	.20	.50
11 Troy Glaus	.20	.50
12 Tim Salmon	.30	.75
13 Jason Giambi	.20	.50
14 Cliff Floyd	.20	.50
15 Tim Hudson	.20	.50
16 Curt Schilling	.20	.50
17 Sammy Sosa	.50	1.25
18 Alex Rodriguez	.75	2.00
19 Chuck Knoblauch	.20	.50
20 Jason Kendall	.20	.50
21 Ben Sheets	.20	.50
22 Nomar Garciaparra	.75	2.00
23 Ryan Klesko	.20	.50
24 Greg Vaughn	.20	.50
25 Rafael Palmeiro	.30	.75
26 Miguel Tejada	.20	.50
27 Shea Hillenbrand	.20	.50
28 Jim Thome	.30	.75
29 Randy Johnson	.50	1.25
30 Barry Larkin	.30	.75
31 Paul LoDuca	.20	.50
32 Pedro Martinez	.30	.75
33 Luis Gonzalez	.20	.50
34 Carlos Delgado	.20	.50
35 Richie Sexson	.20	.50
36 Albert Pujols	1.00	2.50
37 Bobby Abreu	.20	.50
38 Gary Sheffield	.20	.50
39 Magglio Ordonez	.20	.50
40 Eric Chavez	.20	.50
41 Jeff Bagwell	.30	.75
42 Doug Mientkiewicz	.20	.50
43 Moises Alou	.20	.50
44 Todd Helton	.30	.75
45 Ichiro Suzuki	1.00	2.50
46 Jose Cruz Jr.	.20	.50
47 Freddy Garcia	.20	.50
48 Tino Martinez	.30	.75
49 Roger Clemens	1.00	2.50
50 Greg Maddux	.75	2.00
51 Mike Piazza	.75	2.00
52 Roberto Alomar	.30	.75
53 Adam Dunn	.20	.50
54 Kerry Wood	.20	.50
55 Edgar Martinez	.30	.75
56 Ken Griffey Jr.	.75	2.00
57 Juan Gonzalez	.20	.50
58 Pat Burrell	.20	.50
59 Corey Koskie	.20	.50
60 Jose Vidro	.20	.50
61 Ben Grieve	.20	.50
62 Barry Bonds	1.25	3.00
63 Raul Mondesi	.20	.50
64 Jimmy Rollins	.20	.50
65 Mike Sweeney	.20	.50
66 Josh Beckett	.20	.50
67 Chipper Jones	.50	1.25
68 Jeff Kent	.20	.50
69 Tony Batista	.20	.50
70 Phil Nevin	.20	.50
71 Brian Jordan	.20	.50
72 Rich Aurilia	.20	.50
73 Brian Giles	.20	.50
74 Frank Thomas	.50	1.25
75 Larry Walker	.20	.50
76 Shawn Green	.20	.50
77 Manny Ramirez	.30	.75
78 Craig Biggio	.30	.75
79 Vladimir Guerrero	.50	1.25
80 Jeromy Burnitz	.20	.50
81 Mark Teixeira FS Pants	4.00	10.00
82 Corey Thurman FS Pants RC	3.00	8.00
83 Mark Prior FS Bat	4.00	10.00
84 Marlon Byrd FS Pants	3.00	8.00
85 Austin Kearns FS Pants	3.00	8.00
86 Satoru Komiyama FS Jsy RC	3.00	8.00
87 So Taguchi FS Bat RC	4.00	10.00
88 Jorge Padilla FS Pants RC	3.00	8.00
89 Rene Reyes FS Pants RC	3.00	8.00
90 Jorge Nunez FS Pants RC	3.00	8.00
91 Ron Calloway FS Pants RC	3.00	8.00
92 Kazuhisa Ishii FS Jsy RC	4.00	10.00
93 Dewon Brazelton FS Pants	3.00	8.00
94 Angel Berroa FS Pants	3.00	8.00
95 Felix Escalona FS Pants RC	3.00	8.00
96 Sean Burroughs FS Bat	3.00	8.00
97 Br. Duckworth FS Pants	3.00	8.00
98 Hank Blalock FS Pants	4.00	10.00
99 Eric Hinske FS Pants	3.00	8.00
100 Carlos Pena FS Jsy	3.00	8.00
101 Morgan Ensberg FS Pants	3.00	8.00
102 Ryan Ludwick FS Pants	3.00	8.00
103 C.Snelling FS Pants RC	3.00	8.00
104 Jason Lane FS Pants	3.00	8.00
105 Drew Henson FS Bat	3.00	8.00
106 Bobby Kielty HP	2.00	5.00
107 Earl Snyder HP RC	2.00	5.00
108 Nate Field HP RC	2.00	5.00
109 Juan Diaz HP	2.00	5.00
110 Ryan Anderson HP	2.00	5.00
111 Esteban German HP	2.00	5.00
112 Takahito Nomura HP RC	2.00	5.00
113 David Kelton HP	2.00	5.00
114 Steve Kent HP RC	2.00	5.00
115 Colby Lewis HP	2.00	5.00
116 Jason Simontacchi HP RC	2.00	5.00
117 Rodrigo Rosario HP RC	2.00	5.00
118 Ben Howard HP RC	2.00	5.00
119 Hansel Izquierdo HP RC	2.00	5.00
120 John Ennis HP RC	2.00	5.00
121 Anderson Machado HP RC	2.00	5.00
122 Luis Ugueto HP RC	2.00	5.00
123 Anastacio Martinez HP RC	2.00	5.00
124 Reed Johnson HP RC	3.00	8.00
125 Juan Cruz HP	2.00	5.00

2002 Hot Prospects Future Swatch Autographs

Randomly inserted into packs, these four cards feature autographs of the noted rookie player. Each card has a stated print run of 100 serial numbered sets. All four of these cards were issued as redemptions within packs - each with an exchange deadline of July 31, 2003.

83 Mark Prior FS Bat	10.00	25.00
87 So Taguchi FS Bat	10.00	25.00
89 Rene Reyes FS Pants	6.00	15.00
105 Drew Henson FS Bat	6.00	15.00

2002 Hot Prospects Co-Stars

Inserted in hobby packs at a stated rate of one in six, these 15 cards feature two players with something in common who are either stars or upcoming prospects.

COMPLETE SET (15)	20.00	50.00
1 Barry Bonds	3.00	8.00
Alex Rodriguez		
2 Derek Jeter	2.50	6.00
Nomar Garciaparra		
3 Andruw Jones	1.25	3.00
Chipper Jones		
4 Juan Gonzalez	.75	2.00
Jim Thome		
5 Pedro Martinez	1.25	3.00
Randy Johnson		
6 Adam Dunn	.75	2.00
Pat Burrell		
7 Frank Thomas	1.25	3.00
Manny Ramirez		
8 Jeff Bagwell	.75	2.00
Lance Berkman		
9 So Taguchi	.75	2.00
Kazuhisa Ishii		
10 Jimmy Rollins	.75	2.00
Miguel Tejada		
11 Morgan Ensberg	.75	2.00
Carlos Pena		
12 Adam Dunn	.75	2.00
Austin Kearns		
13 Vladimir Guerrero	1.25	3.00
Scott Rolen		
14 Drew Henson	.75	2.00
Xavier Nady		
15 Mike Piazza	2.00	5.00
Ivan Rodriguez		

2002 Hot Prospects Inside Barry Bonds Memorabilia

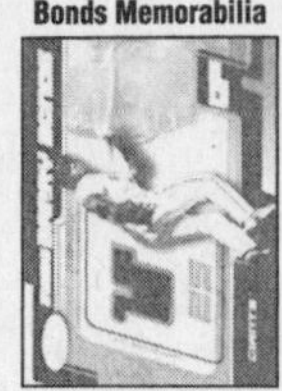

Randomly inserted into packs, these eight cards feature different Barry Bonds memorabilia. Since each card has a different stated print run, we have put that information next to the player's name in our checklist along with the specific item cut up for use on the card.

Card		
1 B.Bonds Home Pants/1000	10.00	25.00
2 B.Bonds Away Pants/900	10.00	25.00
3 B.Bonds Away Jsy/800	10.00	25.00
4 B.Bonds Bat/700	10.00	25.00
5 B.Bonds Base/600	8.00	20.00
6 B.Bonds Cleats/500	12.50	30.00
7 B.Bonds Btg Glv/400	12.50	30.00
8 B.Bonds Cap/300	15.00	40.00

2002 Hot Prospects Jerseygraphs

Inserted in hobby packs at stated odds of one in 186, these nine cards feature the player's signature on actual MLB jersey material. A few players were produced in shorter quantities and we have put that stated information next to their name in our checklist.

Card		
JAB Adrian Beltre SP/169	10.00	25.00
JBB Barry Bonds SP/65	150.00	250.00
JCJ Chipper Jones SP/100	50.00	100.00
JDE David Espinosa	6.00	15.00
JDH Drew Henson	10.00	25.00
JDJ Derek Jeter SP/108	125.00	250.00
JDS Dane Sardinha	6.00	15.00
JGM Kazuhisa Ishii SP/40	20.00	50.00
JST So Taguchi SP/100	15.00	40.00

2002 Hot Prospects MLB Hot Materials

Inserted at a stated rate of one in nine, these 44 cards feature material worn and used by a variety of stars and rookies. A few players were printed in shorter quantities and we have provided the stated print run information next to their name in our checklist.

Card		
AD2 Adam Dunn Jsy	3.00	8.00
AR Alex Rodriguez Jsy	6.00	15.00
BB Bret Boone Bat	3.00	8.00
BB2 Barry Bonds Pants	12.50	30.00
BD Brandon Duckworth Pants	3.00	8.00
BG Brian Giles Pants	3.00	8.00
BW Bernie Williams Jsy	4.00	10.00
CD Carlos Delgado Jsy	3.00	8.00
CG Cristian Guzman Bat SP/261	4.00	10.00
CP Carlos Pena Jsy SP/120	4.00	10.00
CP2 Corey Patterson Jsy	3.00	8.00
CS Curt Schilling Jsy	3.00	8.00
FG Freddy Garcia Jsy	3.00	8.00
FT Frank Thomas Jsy	4.00	10.00
GK Gabe Kapler Jsy	3.00	8.00
GM Greg Maddux Jsy	6.00	15.00
GS Gary Sheffield Bat	3.00	8.00
IR Ivan Rodriguez Jsy	4.00	10.00
JB Josh Beckett Jsy	3.00	8.00
JB2 Jeff Bagwell Jsy SP/108	6.00	15.00
JG Juan Gonzalez Jsy	3.00	8.00
JT Jim Thome Bat	4.00	10.00
JU Juan Uribe Bat	3.00	8.00
KI Kazuhisa Ishii Jsy SP/70	6.00	15.00
LB Lance Berkman Jsy	3.00	8.00
MM Mark Mulder Jsy	3.00	8.00
MO Moises Alou Bat	3.00	8.00
MO Magglio Ordonez Jsy	3.00	8.00
MP Mike Piazza Jsy	6.00	15.00
MS Mike Sweeney Jsy	3.00	8.00
NJ Nick Johnson Jsy	3.00	8.00
PL Paul LoDuca Jsy	3.00	8.00
PM Pedro Martinez Jsy	4.00	10.00
RF Rafael Furcal Jsy	3.00	8.00
RO Roy Oswalt Jsy	3.00	8.00
RP Rafael Palmeiro Jsy	4.00	10.00
SB Sean Burroughs Bat SP/350	4.00	10.00
SG Shawn Green Jsy	3.00	8.00
ST So Taguchi Bat	3.00	8.00
TA Tony Armas Jr. Jsy	3.00	8.00
TH Todd Helton Jsy	4.00	10.00
TH Torii Hunter Bat	3.00	8.00
TM Tino Martinez Bat	4.00	10.00
VW Vernon Wells Bat	3.00	8.00

2002 Hot Prospects MLB Hot Tandems

Randomly inserted in packs, these 45 cards feature dual memorabilia cards of two players who have something in common.

Card		
ADCP Adam Dunn Jsy	6.00	15.00
Corey Patterson Jsy		
ADLB Adam Dunn Jsy	6.00	15.00
Lance Berkman Jsy		
ARIR Alex Rodriguez Jsy	15.00	40.00
Ivan Rodriguez Jsy		
BBDJ Barry Bonds Pants	30.00	80.00
Derek Jeter Jsy		
BBFG Bret Boone Bat	6.00	15.00
Freddy Garcia Jsy		
BBKI Barry Bonds Pants	15.00	40.00
Kazuhisa Ishii Jsy		
BBTH Bret Boone Bat	12.50	30.00
Torii Hunter Bat		
BDJB Brandon Duckworth Pants	6.00	15.00
Josh Beckett Jsy		
BDRO Brandon Duckworth Pants	6.00	15.00
Roy Oswalt Jsy		
BWJP Bernie Williams Jsy	8.00	20.00
Jorge Posada Bat		
BWNJ Bernie Williams Jsy	8.00	20.00
Nick Johnson Jsy		
CDVW Carlos Delgado Jsy	6.00	15.00
Vernon Wells Bat		
CGTH Cristian Guzman Bat	6.00	15.00
Torii Hunter Bat		
CPCP Carlos Pena Jsy	6.00	15.00
Corey Patterson Jsy		
CPNJ Carlos Pena Jsy	6.00	15.00
Nick Johnson Jsy		
CSGM Curt Schilling Jsy	12.50	30.00
Greg Maddux Jsy		
CSPM Curt Schilling Jsy	10.00	25.00
Pedro Martinez Jsy		
FTMO Frank Thomas Jsy	10.00	25.00
Magglio Ordonez Jsy		
GKJG Gabe Kapler Jsy	6.00	15.00
Juan Gonzalez Jsy		
GKRP Gabe Kapler Jsy	8.00	20.00
Rafael Palmeiro Jsy		
GMPM Greg Maddux Jsy	12.50	30.00
Pedro Martinez Jsy		
GSRF Gary Sheffield Bat	6.00	15.00
Rafael Furcal Jsy		
HBAK Hank Blalock Pants	6.00	15.00
Austin Kearns Pants		
HBMT Hank Blalock Pants	6.00	15.00
Mark Teixeira Pants		
JBLB Jeff Bagwell Jsy	8.00	20.00
Lance Berkman Jsy		
JBMP Jeff Bagwell Jsy	12.50	30.00
Mike Piazza Jsy		
JBRO Josh Beckett Jsy	6.00	15.00
Roy Oswalt Jsy		
JGRP Juan Gonzalez Jsy	8.00	20.00
Rafael Palmeiro Jsy		
JPMP Jorge Posada Bat	12.50	30.00
Mike Piazza Jsy		
JTSG Jim Thome Bat	8.00	20.00
Shawn Green Jsy		
JUCG Juan Uribe Bat	6.00	15.00
Cristian Guzman Bat		
JUMT Juan Uribe Bat	6.00	15.00
Miguel Tejada Jsy		
KIDJ Kazuhisa Ishii Jsy	15.00	40.00
Derek Jeter Jsy		
KIMP Kazuhisa Ishii Jsy	6.00	15.00
Mark Prior Bat		
KISK Kazuhisa Ishii Jsy	8.00	20.00
Satoru Komiyama Jsy		
KIST Kazuhisa Ishii Jsy	8.00	20.00
So Taguchi Bat		
MAMO Moises Alou Bat	6.00	15.00
Magglio Ordonez Jsy		
MBAK Marlon Byrd Pants	6.00	15.00
Austin Kearns Pants		
MBJP Marlon Byrd Pants	6.00	15.00
Jorge Padilla Pants		
MMMT Mark Mulder Jsy	6.00	15.00
Miguel Tejada Jsy		
MSTH Mike Sweeney Jsy	8.00	20.00
Todd Helton Jsy		
PLSG Paul LoDuca Jsy	6.00	15.00
Shawn Green Jsy		
SBDH Sean Burroughs Bat	6.00	15.00
Drew Henson Bat		
TAFG Tony Armas Jr. Jsy	6.00	15.00
Freddy Garcia Jsy		
TMTH Tino Martinez Bat	8.00	20.00
Todd Helton Jsy		

2002 Hot Prospects We're Number One

Inserted in packs at a stated rate of one in 15, these 10 cards feature players who had been drafted in the first round of the amateur draft.

Card		
COMPLETE SET (10)	20.00	50.00
AR Alex Rodriguez	3.00	8.00
BB Barry Bonds	5.00	12.00
CJ Chipper Jones	1.50	4.00
DJ Derek Jeter	5.00	12.00
JD J.D. Drew	1.00	2.50
KG Ken Griffey Jr.	3.00	8.00
MR Manny Ramirez	1.00	2.50
NG Nomar Garciaparra	3.00	8.00
RC Roger Clemens	4.00	10.00
TH Todd Helton	1.00	2.50

2002 Hot Prospects We're Number One Autographs

These two cards form a partial parallel to the We're Number One insert set. The two player, Bonds and Jeter each signed the number of cards numbered to the last two digits of their draft year.

Card		
BB Barry Bonds/85	100.00	175.00
DJ Derek Jeter/92	75.00	150.00

2002 Hot Prospects We're Number One Memorabilia

Inserted in hobby packs at stated odds, these nine cards form a partial parallel to the We're Number One insert set. With the exception of Ken Griffey Jr, each player has a game-used jersery swatch attached to it. Griffey's memorabilia piece comes from a game-used base.

Card		
AR Alex Rodriguez Jsy	6.00	15.00
BB Barry Bonds Jsy	10.00	25.00
CJ Chipper Jones Jsy	6.00	15.00
DJ Derek Jeter Jsy	10.00	25.00
JD J.D. Drew Jsy	6.00	15.00
KG Ken Griffey Jr. Base SP	8.00	20.00
MR Manny Ramirez Jsy	6.00	15.00
NG Nomar Garciaparra Jsy	8.00	20.00
TH Todd Helton Jsy	6.00	15.00

2003 Hot Prospects

This 127-card set was distributed in two separate releases. The primary Hot Porspects product - containing the first 119 cards from the basic set - was released in August, 2003. This set was issued in five card packs with a $12 SRP which came 15 packs to a box and 12 boxes to a case. Cards numbered 1 through 80 feature veterans. Cards 81-119 feature a selection of prospects and rookies with many cards including a certified autograph or game used element (and in some cases both). One card from this run was guaranteed within each sealed box. In addition, all of these prospect cards are serial numbered to quantities ranging between 400-1250 copies per. Please note that cards 88, 96, 106 and 108 were never produced. Cards 120-127 were randomly seeded within packs of Fleer Rookies and Greats of which was distributed in December, 2003. These eight update cards (featuring a selection of top prospects) were all serial numbered to a mere 250 copies per and all included a game used element.

Card		
COMP.LO SET w/o SP's (80)	12.50	30.00
COMMON CARD (1-80)	.20	.50
FS BAT/JSY PRINT RUN 1250 #'d SETS		
CUT AU PRINT RUN 500 SERIAL #'d SETS		
GG AU PRINT RUN 400 SERIAL #'d SETS		
COMMON CARD (120-127)	3.00	8.00
1 Derek Jeter	1.25	3.00
2 Ryan Klesko	.20	.50
3 Troy Glaus	.20	.50
4 Jeff Kent	.20	.50
5 Frank Thomas	.50	1.25
6 Gary Sheffield	.20	.50
7 Jim Edmonds	.20	.50
8 Pat Burrell	.20	.50
9 Jacque Jones	.20	.50
10 Jason Jennings	.20	.50
11 Pedro Martinez	.30	.75
12 Rafael Palmeiro	.30	.75
13 Jason Kendall	.20	.50
14 Tom Glavine	.30	.75
15 Josh Beckett	.20	.50
16 Luis Gonzalez	.20	.50
17 Edgar Martinez	.30	.75
18 Miguel Tejada	.20	.50
19 Fred McGriff	.30	.75
20 Adam Dunn	.20	.50
21 Lance Berkman	.20	.50
22 Magglio Ordonez	.20	.50
23 Darin Erstad	.20	.50
24 Rich Aurilia	.20	.50
25 Mike Piazza	.75	2.00
26 Shawn Green	.20	.50
27 Larry Walker	.20	.50
28 Manny Ramirez	.30	.75
29 Juan Gonzalez	.20	.50
30 Eric Chavez	.20	.50
31 Torii Hunter	.20	.50
32 A.J. Burnett	.20	.50
33 Sammy Sosa	.50	1.25
34 Eric Hinske	.20	.50
35 Brian Giles	.20	.50
36 Mike Sweeney	.20	.50
37 Sean Casey	.20	.50
38 Chipper Jones	.50	1.25
39 Scott Rolen	.30	.75
40 Jason Giambi	.20	.50
41 Mo Vaughn	.20	.50
42 Roy Oswalt	.20	.50
43 Paul Konerko	.20	.50
44 Tim Salmon	.30	.75
45 Edgardo Alfonzo	.20	.50
46 Jermaine Dye	.20	.50
47 Ben Sheets	.20	.50
48 Todd Helton	.30	.75
49 Greg Maddux	.75	2.00
50 Albert Pujols	1.00	2.50
51 Jim Thome	.30	.75
52 Vladimir Guerrero	.50	1.25
53 Ivan Rodriguez	.30	.75
54 Nomar Garciaparra	.75	2.00
55 Alex Rodriguez	.75	2.00
56 Alfonso Soriano	.20	.50
57 Kazuhisa Ishii	.20	.50
58 Austin Kearns	.20	.50
59 Curt Schilling	.20	.50
60 Bret Boone	.20	.50
61 Mark Prior	.30	.75
62 Garret Anderson	.20	.50
63 Barry Bonds	1.25	3.00
64 Roger Clemens	1.00	2.50
65 Jeff Bagwell	.30	.75
66 Omar Vizquel	.30	.75
67 Jay Gibbons	.20	.50
68 Aubrey Huff	.20	.50
69 Bobby Abreu	.20	.50
70 Richie Sexson	.20	.50
71 Bobby Higginson	.20	.50
72 Kerry Wood	.20	.50
73 Carlos Delgado	.20	.50
74 Sean Burroughs	.20	.50
75 Jose Vidro	.20	.50
76 Ken Griffey Jr.	.75	2.00
77 Randy Johnson	.50	1.25
78 Ichiro Suzuki	1.00	2.50
79 Barry Zito	.20	.50
80 Carlos Beltran	.20	.50
81 Joe Borchard FS Jsy	2.00	5.00
82 Mark Teixeira FS Bat	3.00	8.00
83 Brandon Webb FS Jsy RC	6.00	15.00
84 S.Victorino Pants AU RC	10.00	25.00
85 Hee Seop Choi FS Jsy	2.00	5.00
86 Hank Blalock FS Bat	2.00	5.00
87 Brett Myers FS Jsy	2.00	5.00
89 Jesse Foppert FS Jsy	2.00	5.00
90 Lyle Overbay FS Jsy	2.00	5.00
91 Brian Stokes Pants AU RC	4.00	10.00
92 Josh Hall Bat AU RC	4.00	10.00
93 Chris Waters Pants AU RC	3.00	8.00
94 Lew Ford Pants AU RC	3.00	8.00
95 Ian Ferguson AU RC	3.00	8.00
97 Josh Stewart AU RC	3.00	8.00
98 Pete LaForest AU RC	3.00	8.00
99 Jose Contreras Jsy AU/300 RC	12.50	30.00
100 Termel Sledge AU RC	3.00	8.00
101 Guillermo Quiroz AU RC	3.00	8.00
102 Alejandro Machado AU RC	3.00	8.00
103 Nook Logan Pants AU RC	6.00	15.00
104 R.Hammock Pants AU RC	4.00	10.00
105 Hideki Matsui FS Base RC	5.00	12.00
107 Rocco Baldelli FS Jsy	2.00	5.00
109 T.Wellemeyer Pants AU RC	4.00	10.00
110 Mi. Hessman Pants AU RC	4.00	10.00
111 J.Bonderman Pants AU RC	20.00	50.00
112 Craig Brazell Pants AU RC	4.00	10.00
113 Franc Rosario Pants AU RC	4.00	10.00
114 Jeff Duncan Pants AU RC	4.00	10.00
115 Dan Cabrera Pants AU RC	10.00	25.00
116 Dontrelle Willis Pants AU	6.00	15.00
117 Cory Stewart AU RC	3.00	8.00
118 Tim Olson Pants AU RC	4.00	10.00
119 C.Wang Pants AU/500 RC	125.00	250.00
120 Josh Willingham Pants RC	5.00	12.00
121 Rickie Weeks Bat RC	5.00	12.00
122 Prentice Redman Pants RC	3.00	8.00
123 Mike Ryan Pants RC	3.00	8.00
124 Oscar Villarreal Pants RC	3.00	8.00
125 Ryan Wagner Pants RC	2.00	5.00
126 Bo Hart Pants RC	2.00	5.00
127 Edwin Jackson Pants RC	3.00	8.00

2003 Hot Prospects Class Of

COMPLETE SET (10)	12.50	30.00
STATED ODDS 1:15		
1 Barry Zito	1.00	2.50
Josh Beckett		
2 Pat Burrell	1.00	2.50
J.D. Drew		
3 Mark Prior	1.00	2.50
Mark Teixeira		
4 Austin Kearns	1.00	2.50
Sean Burroughs		
5 Troy Glaus	1.00	2.50
Lance Berkman		
6 Darin Erstad	1.00	2.50
Todd Helton		
7 Manny Ramirez	1.00	2.50
Shawn Green		
8 Matt Morris	1.00	2.50
Kerry Wood		
9 Nomar Garciaparra	1.50	4.00
Paul Konerko		
10 Alex Rodriguez	2.50	6.00
Torii Hunter		

2003 Hot Prospects Class Of Game Used

STATED PRINT RUN 375 SERIAL #'d SETS

AKSB Austin Kearns Jsy	4.00	10.00
Sean Burroughs Jsy		
ARTH Alex Rodriguez Jsy	8.00	20.00
Torii Hunter Jsy		
BZJB Barry Zito Jsy	4.00	10.00
Josh Beckett Jsy		
DETH Darin Erstad Jsy	6.00	15.00
Todd Helton Jsy		
MMKW Matt Morris Jsy	4.00	10.00
Kerry Wood Jsy		
MPMT Mark Prior Jsy	6.00	15.00
Mark Teixeira Bat		
MRSG Manny Ramirez Jsy	6.00	15.00
Shawn Green Jsy		
NGPK Nomar Garciaparra Jsy	6.00	15.00
Paul Konerko Jsy		
PBJD Pat Burrell Jsy	4.00	10.00
J.D. Drew Jsy		
TGLB Troy Glaus Jsy	4.00	10.00
Lance Berkman Jsy		

2003 Hot Prospects Cream of the Crop

COMPLETE SET (15)	20.00	50.00
STATED ODDS 1:5		
1 Barry Bonds	2.50	6.00
2 Derek Jeter	2.50	6.00
3 Ichiro Suzuki	2.00	5.00
4 Nomar Garciaparra	1.50	4.00
5 Roger Clemens	2.00	5.00
6 Alex Rodriguez	1.50	4.00
7 Greg Maddux	1.50	4.00
8 Mike Piazza	1.50	4.00
9 Sammy Sosa	1.00	2.50
10 Jason Giambi	1.00	2.50
11 Hideki Matsui	3.00	8.00
12 Albert Pujols	2.00	5.00
13 Vladimir Guerrero	1.00	2.50
14 Jim Thome	1.00	2.50
15 Pedro Martinez	1.00	2.50

2003 Hot Prospects MLB Hot Materials

STATED PRINT RUN 499 SERIAL #'d SETS		
*RED HOT: .75X TO 2X BASIC		
RED HOT PRINT RUN 50 SERIAL #'d SETS		
AD Adam Dunn Jsy	3.00	8.00
AR Alex Rodriguez Jsy	6.00	15.00
AS Alfonso Soriano Jsy	3.00	8.00
BA Tom Glavine Jsy	4.00	10.00
CD Carlos Delgado Jsy	3.00	8.00
CJ Chipper Jones Jsy	4.00	10.00
DJ Derek Jeter Jsy	10.00	25.00
GM Greg Maddux Jsy	4.00	10.00
HC Hee Seop Choi Jsy	3.00	8.00
JB Josh Beckett Jsy	3.00	8.00
JG Jason Giambi Jsy	3.00	8.00
JT Jim Thome Jsy	4.00	10.00
LB Lance Berkman Bat	3.00	8.00
LO Lyle Overbay Jsy	3.00	8.00
MPI Mike Piazza Jsy	4.00	10.00
MPR Mark Prior Jsy	4.00	10.00
MR Manny Ramirez Jsy	4.00	10.00
MS Mike Sweeney Jsy	3.00	8.00
MTJ Miguel Tejada Jsy	3.00	8.00
MTX Mark Teixeira Bat	4.00	10.00
NG Nomar Garciaparra Jsy	6.00	15.00
PB Pat Burrell Jsy	3.00	8.00
RJ Randy Johnson Jsy	4.00	10.00
RP Rafael Palmeiro Jsy	4.00	10.00
SG Shawn Green Jsy	3.00	8.00
SS Sammy Sosa Jsy	4.00	10.00
TG Troy Glaus Jsy	3.00	8.00
THE Todd Helton Jsy	4.00	10.00
THU Torii Hunter Jsy	3.00	8.00
VG Vladimir Guerrero Jsy	4.00	10.00

2003 Hot Prospects MLB Hot Tandems

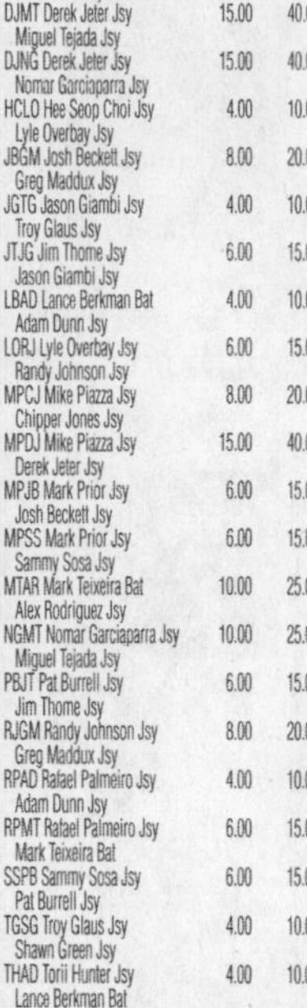

STATED PRINT RUN 100 SERIAL #'d SETS		
RED HOT PRINT RUN 10 SERIAL #'d SETS		
NO RED HOT PRICING DUE TO SCARCITY		
ARMT Alex Rodriguez Jsy	10.00	25.00
Miguel Tejada Jsy		
CJDJ Chipper Jones Jsy	15.00	40.00
Derek Jeter Jsy		
DJMT Derek Jeter Jsy	15.00	40.00
Miguel Tejada Jsy		
DJNG Derek Jeter Jsy	15.00	40.00
Nomar Garciaparra Jsy		
HCLO Hee Seop Choi Jsy	4.00	10.00
Lyle Overbay Jsy		
JBGM Josh Beckett Jsy	8.00	20.00
Greg Maddux Jsy		
JGTG Jason Giambi Jsy	4.00	10.00
Troy Glaus Jsy		
JTJG Jim Thome Jsy	6.00	15.00
Jason Giambi Jsy		
LBAD Lance Berkman Bat	4.00	10.00
Adam Dunn Jsy		
LORJ Lyle Overbay Jsy	6.00	15.00
Randy Johnson Jsy		
MPCJ Mike Piazza Jsy	8.00	20.00
Chipper Jones Jsy		
MPDJ Mike Piazza Jsy	15.00	40.00
Derek Jeter Jsy		
MPJB Mark Prior Jsy	6.00	15.00
Josh Beckett Jsy		
MPSS Mark Prior Jsy	6.00	15.00
Sammy Sosa Jsy		
MTAR Mark Teixeira Bat	10.00	25.00
Alex Rodriguez Jsy		
NGMT Nomar Garciaparra Jsy	10.00	25.00
Miguel Tejada Jsy		
PBJT Pat Burrell Jsy	6.00	15.00
Jim Thome Jsy		
RJGM Randy Johnson Jsy	8.00	20.00
Greg Maddux Jsy		
RPAD Rafael Palmeiro Jsy	4.00	10.00
Adam Dunn Jsy		
RPMT Rafael Palmeiro Jsy	6.00	15.00
Mark Teixeira Bat		
SSPB Sammy Sosa Jsy	6.00	15.00
Pat Burrell Jsy		
TGSG Troy Glaus Jsy	4.00	10.00
Shawn Green Jsy		
THAD Torii Hunter Jsy	4.00	10.00
Lance Berkman Bat		
THVG Torii Hunter Jsy	6.00	15.00
Vladimir Guerrero Jsy		
VGSG Vladimir Guerrero Jsy	6.00	15.00
Shawn Green Jsy		

2003 Hot Prospects MLB Hot Triple Patch

STATED PRINT RUN 50 SERIAL #'d SETS		
BGJ Lance Berkman	30.00	60.00
Troy Glaus		
Chipper Jones		
BTB Pat Burrell	20.00	50.00
Jim Thome		
Lance Berkman		
DJB Adam Dunn	15.00	40.00
Randy Johnson		
Josh Beckett		
GGJ Vladimir Guerrero	30.00	60.00
Troy Glaus		
Chipper Jones		
GRT Jason Giambi	30.00	60.00
Alex Rodriguez		
Miguel Tejada		
GSP Nomar Garciaparra	30.00	60.00
Sammy Sosa		
Mike Piazza		
GTD Jason Giambi	15.00	40.00
Miguel Tejada		
Adam Dunn		
HSG Torii Hunter	30.00	60.00
Sammy Sosa		
Vladimir Guerrero		
JGR Derek Jeter	60.00	120.00
Nomar Garciaparra		
Alex Rodriguez		
JHP Derek Jeter	50.00	100.00
Torii Hunter		
Mark Prior		
JSG Randy Johnson	30.00	60.00
Alfonso Soriano		
Shawn Green		
PBM Mark Prior	50.00	100.00
Josh Beckett		
Greg Maddux		
PBT Mike Piazza	30.00	60.00
Pat Burrell		
Jim Thome		
PCT Rafael Palmeiro	20.00	50.00
Hee Seop Choi		
Mark Teixeira		
SMG Alfonso Soriano	40.00	80.00
Greg Maddux		
Shawn Green		

2003 Hot Prospects PlayerGraphs

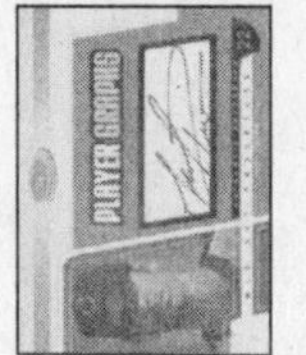

Randomly inserted in packs, these 11 cards feature authentic autographs from the featured player. Each of these cards were issued to a stated print run of 400 serial numbered sets.

Card		
*RED HOT: .6X TO 1.5X BASIC		
RED HOT PRINT RUN 100 SERIAL #'d SETS		
AH Aubrey Huff	6.00	15.00
BM Brett Myers	6.00	15.00
CZ Carlos Zambrano	10.00	25.00
FR Francisco Rodriguez	10.00	25.00
HB Hank Blalock	6.00	15.00
JR Jose Reyes	6.00	15.00
MP Mark Prior	6.00	15.00
MT Mark Teixiera	10.00	25.00
RO Roy Oswalt	6.00	15.00
VW Vernon Wells	6.00	15.00
XN Xavier Nady	6.00	15.00

2004 Hot Prospects Draft

This 120-card set was released in November, 2004. The set was issued in five-card hobby packs and though packs lacked an official SRP, estimates placed the average price at $8.50 per. Packs were issued 15 to a box and 12 boxes to a case. This set was also issued in six-card retail packs with an SRP of $3 per. Retail boxes featured 24 packs and retail cases contained 20 boxes. Cards numbered 1-60 feature veterans while cards 61-70 and 112-113 feature unsigned Rookie Cards issued to a stated print run of 1000 serial numbered copies per and seeded at a stated rate of one in 15 hobby packs and one in 120 retail packs. Cards numbered 71-111 and 114-120 are signed Rookie Cards featuring players from the 2004 MLB Draft. These cards were issued to a stated print run of 299 serial numbered copies per and seeded at a rate of one in nine hobby and one in 990 retail packs. Please note, the following cards packed out as exchange cards: 74, 84, 91, 112, 113, 114 and 118.

Card		
COMP.SET w/o RC's (60)	6.00	15.00
COMMON CARD (1-60)	.20	.50
COMMON (61-70/112-113)	.75	2.00
61-70/112-113 ODDS 1:15 H, 1:120 R		
61-70/112-113 PRINT RUN 1000 #'d SETS		
COMMON (71-110/114-120)	3.00	8.00
71-111/114-120 ODDS 1:9 H, 1:990 R		
71-111/114-120 PRINT RUN 299 #'d SETS		
EXCHANGE DEADLINE INDEFINITE		
1 Miguel Tejada	.30	.75
2 Jose Vidro	.20	.50
3 Hideki Matsui	.75	2.00
4 Roger Clemens	.60	1.50
5 Craig Wilson	.20	.50
6 Bobby Crosby	.20	.50
7 Pat Burrell	.20	.50
8 Mike Sweeney	.20	.50
9 Craig Biggio	.30	.75
10 Scott Rolen	.30	.75
11 Roy Halladay	.50	1.25
12 Lyle Overbay	.20	.50
13 Rocco Baldelli	.20	.50
14 Mike Piazza	.50	1.25
15 Rafael Palmeiro	.30	.75
16 Hank Blalock	.20	.50
17 Sammy Sosa	.50	1.25
18 Dontrelle Willis	.20	.50
19 Alfonso Soriano	.20	.50
20 Gary Sheffield	.20	.50
21 Jim Thome	.30	.75
22 Ivan Rodriguez	.30	.75
23 Adam Dunn	.30	.75
24 Kerry Wood	.20	.50
25 Khalil Greene	.30	.75
26 Richie Sexson	.20	.50
27 Nomar Garciaparra	.50	1.25
28 Andruw Jones	.20	.50
29 Tom Glavine	.30	.75
30 Carlos Beltran	.20	.50
31 Chipper Jones	.50	1.25
32 Jeff Bagwell	.30	.75
33 Tim Hudson	.30	.75
34 Alex Rodriguez	.75	2.00
35 Omar Vizquel	.30	.75
36 Albert Pujols	1.25	3.00
37 Frank Thomas	.50	1.25
38 Ben Sheets	.20	.50
39 Jason Schmidt	.20	.50
40 Miguel Cabrera	.50	1.25
41 Carlos Delgado	.20	.50
42 Ichiro Suzuki	.75	2.00
43 Curt Schilling	.30	.75
44 Todd Helton	.30	.75
45 Ken Griffey Jr.	.75	2.00
46 Mark Prior	.30	.75
47 Vladimir Guerrero	.50	1.25
48 Pedro Martinez	.30	.75
49 Manny Ramirez	.50	1.25
50 Joe Mauer	.50	1.25
51 Jorge Posada	.30	.75
52 Troy Glaus	.20	.50
53 Randy Johnson	.50	1.25
54 Adrian Beltre	.20	.50
55 Eric Gagne	.20	.50
56 Josh Beckett	.30	.75
57 Jason Giambi	.20	.50
58 Barry Zito	.20	.50
59 Lance Berkman	.30	.75
60 Derek Jeter	1.25	3.00
61 Kaz Matsui HP RC	1.25	3.00
62 Jason Bartlett HP RC	2.50	6.00
63 John Gall HP RC	.75	2.00
64 Chris Saenz HP RC	.75	2.00
65 Merkin Valdez HP RC	.75	2.00
66 Akinori Otsuka HP RC	.75	2.00
67 Joey Gathright HP RC	.75	2.00
68 Brad Halsey HP RC	.75	2.00
69 David Aardsma HP RC	.75	2.00
70 Scott Kazmir HP RC	4.00	10.00
71 Matt Bush AU RC	20.00	40.00
72 John Bowker AU RC	12.50	30.00
73 Mike Ferris AU RC	3.00	8.00
75 Scott Elbert AU RC	6.00	15.00
76 Josh Fields AU RC	3.00	8.00
77 Bill Bray AU RC	3.00	8.00

78 Greg Golson AU RC 12.50 30.00
79 Neil Walker AU RC 6.00 15.00
80 Philip Hughes AU RC 40.00 80.00
81 Chris Nelson AU RC 20.00 40.00
82 Mark Rogers AU RC 10.00 25.00
83 Trevor Plouffe AU RC 10.00 25.00
85 Thomas Diamond AU RC 20.00 40.00
86 B.J. Szymanski AU RC 10.00 25.00
87 Richie Robnett AU RC 10.00 25.00
88 Seth Smith AU RC 3.00 8.00
89 Kyle Waldrop AU RC 10.00 25.00
90 Curtis Thigpen AU RC 3.00 8.00
92 Blake DeWitt AU RC 12.50 30.00
93 Taylor Tankersley AU RC 3.00 8.00
94 Zach Jackson AU RC 3.00 8.00
95 Justin Orenduff AU RC 3.00 8.00
96 Tyler Lumsden AU RC 3.00 8.00
97 Danny Putnam AU RC 3.00 8.00
98 Jon Poterson AU RC 3.00 8.00
99 Matt Fox AU RC 1.25 3.00
100 Gio Gonzalez AU RC 3.00 8.00
101 Huston Street AU RC 3.00 8.00
102 Jay Rainville AU RC 15.00 30.00
103 Matt Durkin AU RC 3.00 8.00
104 Brett Smith AU RC 10.00 25.00
105 Justin Hoyman AU RC 3.00 8.00
106 Erick San Pedro AU RC 3.00 8.00
107 Jeff Marquez AU RC 10.00 25.00
108 Hunter Pence AU RC 20.00 50.00
109 Dustin Pedroia AU RC 75.00 150.00
110 Kurt Suzuki AU RC 5.00 12.00
111 Billy Buckner AU RC 3.00 8.00
115 Homer Bailey AU RC 4.00 10.00
116 David Purcey AU RC 3.00 8.00
117 Jeremy Sowers AU RC 3.00 8.00
119 Eric Hurley AU RC 3.00 8.00
120 Grant Johnson AU RC 3.00 8.00

2004 Hot Prospects Draft Die Cuts

Forty-three of the 48 total Draft Pick autograph cards from the basic Hot Prospects product were featured in this Die Cut parallel. The cards were issued exclusively in 1-card red foil bonus packs. The red foil wrappers did not feature any print design indicating they contained Hot Prospect Draft autographs - they were simply blank red foil wrappers. Just shy of 2,000 red foil bonus packs were produced and sent in in early January, 2005 exclusively to Fleer's network of hobby distributors as an incentive to help move boxes of Hot Prospects Draft to their own network of hobby dealers and shop owners. Though the cards lack serial-numbering, representatives at Fleer publicly released print runs for all 43 cards to Beckett Media LP about eight weeks after the cards were issued. Print runs range from as few as 15 to as many as 92 copies of each card.

*DIE CUT p/r 47-64: .5X TO 1.2X BASIC
*DIE CUT p/r 92: .4X TO 1X BASIC
ONE PER RED FOIL BONUS PACK
RED PACKS ISSUED TO DISTRIBUTORS
PRINT RUNS B/WN 15-92 COPIES PER
NO PRICING ON QTY OFF 3 OR LESS
CARDS ARE NOT SERIAL-NUMBERED
PRINT RUN INFO PROVIDED BY FLEER
SEE BECKETT.COM FOR ALL PRINT RUNS
71 Matt Bush AU/59 * 20.00 50.00
72 John Bowker AU/26 *
73 Mike Ferris AU/28 *
75 Scott Elbert AU/51 * 10.00 25.00
76 Josh Fields AU/50 * 6.00 15.00
77 Bill Bray AU/29 *
78 Greg Golson AU/50 * 15.00 40.00
79 Neil Walker AU/15 *
80 Philip Hughes AU/47 * 75.00 150.00
81 Chris Nelson AU/62 * 20.00 50.00
82 Mark Rogers AU/59 * 15.00 40.00
83 Trevor Plouffe AU/58 * 12.50 30.00
85 Thomas Diamond AU/58 * 20.00 50.00
86 B.J. Szymanski AU/26 *
87 Richie Robnett AU/61 * 12.50 30.00
88 Seth Smith AU/25 *
89 Kyle Waldrop AU/62 * 12.50 30.00
90 Curtis Thigpen AU/29 *
92 Blake DeWitt AU/64 * 40.00 80.00
93 Taylor Tankersley AU/63 * 8.00 20.00
94 Zach Jackson AU/61 * 8.00 20.00
95 Justin Orenduff AU/26 *
96 Tyler Lumsden AU/59 * 8.00 20.00
97 Danny Putnam AU/61 * 8.00 20.00
98 Jon Poterson AU/58 * 8.00 20.00
99 Matt Fox AU/61 * 1.50 4.00
100 Gio Gonzalez AU/60 * 15.00 40.00
101 Huston Street AU/27 * 6.00 15.00
102 Jay Rainville AU/28 *
103 Matt Durkin AU/18 *
104 Brett Smith AU/30 *
105 Justin Hoyman AU/62 * 8.00 20.00
106 Erick San Pedro AU/33 *
107 Jeff Marquez AU/27 *
108 Hunter Pence AU/30 *
109 Dustin Pedroia AU/17 *
110 Kurt Suzuki AU/92 * 10.00 25.00
111 Billy Buckner AU/29 *
115 Homer Bailey AU/48 * 5.00 12.00
116 David Purcey AU/61 * 6.00 15.00
117 Jeremy Sowers AU/61 * 30.00 60.00
119 Eric Hurley AU/61 * 12.50 30.00
120 Grant Johnson AU/29 *

2004 Hot Prospects Draft Red Hot

*RED 1-60: 2.5X TO 6X BASIC
*RED 61-70: 1X TO 2.5X BASIC
1-70 PRINT RUN 150 SERIAL #'d SETS
71-120 PRINT RUN 25 SERIAL #'d SETS
71-120 NO PRICING DUE TO SCARCITY
OVERALL PARALLEL ODDS 1:15 H, 1:120 R

CARDS 112 AND 113 DO NOT EXIST
EXCHANGE DEADLINE INDEFINITE

2004 Hot Prospects Draft White Hot

OVERALL PARALLEL ODDS 1:15 H, 1:120 R
STATED PRINT RUN 1 SERIAL #'d SET
NO PRICING DUE TO SCARCITY
CARDS 112 AND 113 DO NOT EXIST
EXCHANGE DEADLINE INDEFINITE

2004 Hot Prospects Draft Alumni Ink

STATED PRINT RUN 15 SERIAL #'d SETS
RED HOT PRINT RUN 5 SERIAL #'d SETS
WHITE HOT PRINT RUN 1 SERIAL #'d SET
OVERALL AU-GU ODDS 1:12 H, 1:24 R
NO PRICING DUE TO SCARCITY
EXCHANGE DEADLINE INDEFINITE
PJ Mark Prior
Randy Johnson
TG Mark Teixeira
Nomar Garciaparra

2004 Hot Prospects Draft Double Team Jersey

STATED PRINT RUN 100 SERIAL #'d SETS
*RED HOT: .6X TO 1.5X BASIC
RED HOT PRINT RUN 25 SERIAL #'d SETS
WHITE HOT PRINT RUN 1 SERIAL #'d SET
NO WHITE HOT PRICING DUE TO SCARCITY
*PATCH: 1X TO 2.5X BASIC
PATCH PRINT RUN 50 SERIAL #'d SETS
PATCH RED HOT PRINT RUN 10 #'d SETS
NO PATCH RED HOT PRICING AVAILABLE
PATCH WHITE HOT PRINT RUN 1 #'d SET
NO PATCH WHITE HOT PRICING AVAILABLE
OVERALL AU-GU ODDS 1:12 H, 1:24 R
AS Alfonso Soriano Rgr-Yanks 4.00 10.00
CB Carlos Beltran Astros-Royals 4.00 10.00
EM Eddie Murray Mets-O's 10.00 25.00
GM Greg Maddux Braves-Cubs 8.00 20.00
HN Hideo Nomo Dgr-Sox 6.00 15.00
IR I.Rodriguez Marlins-Tigers 6.00 15.00
JG Jason Giambi A's-Yanks 4.00 10.00
MP Mike Piazza Dgr-Mets 8.00 20.00
MR Manny Ramirez Indians-Sox 6.00 15.00
MT Miguel Tejada A's-O's 4.00 10.00
NR Nolan Ryan Astros-Rgr 15.00 40.00
PM Pedro Martinez Expos-Sox 6.00 15.00
RCA Rod Carew Angels-Twins 10.00 25.00
RCL Roger Clemens Astros-Sox 8.00 20.00
RH R.Henderson A's-Padres 10.00 25.00
RJ Reggie Jackson A's-Yanks 10.00 25.00
SR Scott Rolen Cards-Phils 6.00 15.00
TG Tom Glavine Braves-Mets 6.00 15.00
VG Vlad Guerrero Angels-Expos 6.00 15.00

2004 Hot Prospects Draft Double Team Autograph Patch Red Hot

STATED PRINT RUN 22 SERIAL #'d SETS
WHITE HOT PRINT RUN 1 SERIAL #'d SET
NO WHITE HOT PRICING DUE TO SCARCITY
OVERALL AU-GU ODDS 1:12 H, 1:24 R
HN Hideo Nomo Dgr-Sox
IR I.Rodriguez Marlins-Tigers 50.00 100.00
MP Mike Piazza Dgr-Mets 100.00 200.00

MR Manny Ramirez Indians-Sox 60.00 120.00
RJ Reggie Jackson A's-Yanks 50.00 100.00
SR Scott Rolen Cards-Phils 40.00 80.00
VG Vlad Guerrero Angels-Expos 50.00 100.00

2004 Hot Prospects Draft MLB Hot Materials

STATED PRINT RUN 325 SERIAL #'d SETS
*RED HOT: .75X TO 2X BASIC
RED HOT PRINT RUN 50 SERIAL #'d SETS
WHITE HOT PRINT RUN 1 SERIAL #'d SET
NO WHITE HOT PRICING DUE TO SCARCITY
OVERALL AU-GU ODDS 1:12 H, 1:24 R
AD Adam Dunn Jsy 2.00 5.00
AJ Andruw Jones Jsy 3.00 8.00
APE Andy Pettitte Jsy 3.00 8.00
APU Albert Pujols Jsy 6.00 15.00
AS Alfonso Soriano Jsy 2.00 5.00
CD Carlos Delgado Jsy 2.00 5.00
CJ Chipper Jones Jsy 3.00 8.00
CS Curt Schilling Jsy 3.00 8.00
DW Dontrelle Willis Jsy 3.00 8.00
EG Eric Gagne Jsy 2.00 5.00
FT Frank Thomas Jsy 3.00 8.00
HB Hank Blalock Jsy 2.00 5.00
HM Hideki Matsui Jsy 8.00 20.00
HN Hideo Nomo Jsy 3.00 8.00
IR Ivan Rodriguez Jsy 3.00 8.00
JB Jeff Bagwell Jsy 3.00 8.00
JD J.D. Drew Jsy 2.00 5.00
JE Jim Edmonds Jsy 2.00 5.00
JM Joe Mauer Jsy 3.00 8.00
JP Jorge Posada Jsy 3.00 8.00
JS Jason Schmidt Jsy 2.00 5.00
JT Jim Thome Jsy 3.00 8.00
KM Kaz Matsui Jsy 3.00 8.00
KW Kerry Wood Jsy 2.00 5.00
LB Lance Berkman Jsy 2.00 5.00
LO Lyle Overbay Jsy 2.00 5.00
MC Miguel Cabrera Jsy 3.00 8.00
MM Mike Mussina Jsy 3.00 8.00
MPI Mike Piazza Jsy 4.00 10.00
MPR Mark Prior Jsy 3.00 8.00
MR Manny Ramirez Jsy 3.00 8.00
MTJ Miguel Tejada Jsy 2.00 5.00
MTX Mark Teixeira Jsy 3.00 8.00
RC Roger Clemens Jsy 4.00 10.00
RJ Randy Johnson Jsy 3.00 8.00
SS Sammy Sosa Jsy 3.00 8.00
THE Todd Helton Jsy 3.00 8.00
THN Torii Hunter Jsy 2.00 5.00
THU Tim Hudson Jsy 2.00 5.00
VG Vladimir Guerrero Jsy 3.00 8.00

2004 Hot Prospects Draft Past Present Future Autograph

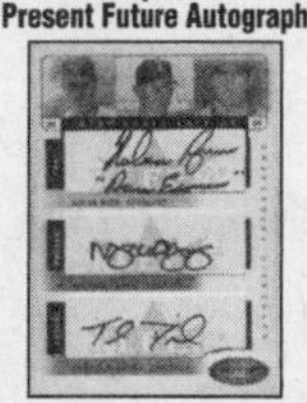

STATED PRINT RUN 33 SERIAL #'d SETS
RED HOT PRINT RUN 3 SERIAL #'d SETS
NO RED HOT PRICING DUE TO SCARCITY
WHITE HOT PRINT RUN 1 SERIAL #'d SET
NO WHITE HOT PRICING DUE TO SCARCITY
OVERALL AU-GU ODDS 1:12 H, 1:24 R
EXCHANGE DEADLINE INDEFINITE
BDB Johnny Bench 75.00 150.00
Adam Dunn
Homer Bailey
BMH Yogi Berra 75.00 150.00
Mike Mussina
Philip Hughes
BRP Bill Buckner 50.00 100.00
Manny Ramirez
Dustin Pedroia
CTG Steve Carlton 50.00 100.00
Jim Thome
Greg Golson
FMF Carlton Fisk 10.00 25.00
Ryan Meaux
Josh Fields
GNE Kirk Gibson 200.00 350.00
Hideo Nomo
Scott Elbert
KWW Ralph Kiner 40.00 80.00
Jack Wilson
Neil Walker
RYD Nolan Ryan 125.00 200.00
Michael Young
Thomas Diamond
SCT Gary Sheffield
Miguel Cabrera
Taylor Tankersley
WPD Mookie Wilson 75.00 150.00
Mike Piazza
Matt Durkin

2004 Hot Prospects Draft Rewind

STATED ODDS 1:5
1 Joe Mauer 1.00 2.50
2 Derek Jeter 2.50 6.00
3 Chipper Jones 1.00 2.50
4 Greg Maddux 1.50 4.00
5 Alex Rodriguez 1.50 4.00
6 Nomar Garciaparra 1.00 2.50
7 Curt Schilling .60 1.50
8 Kerry Wood .60 1.50
9 Troy Glaus .40 1.00

10 Pat Burrell .40 1.00
11 Mark Mulder .40 1.00
12 Josh Beckett .60 1.50
13 Barry Zito .40 1.00
14 Mark Prior .60 1.50
15 Rickie Weeks .40 1.00
16 Khalil Greene .60 1.50
17 Ken Griffey Jr. 1.50 4.00
18 Gary Sheffield .40 1.00
19 Todd Helton .60 1.50
20 Barry Larkin .60 1.50
21 Kevin Brown .40 1.00
22 Frank Thomas 1.00 2.50
23 Manny Ramirez 1.00 2.50
24 Roger Clemens 1.25 3.00
25 Lance Berkman .60 1.50
26 Randy Johnson 1.00 2.50
27 Jason Giambi .40 1.00
28 Ben Sheets .40 1.00
29 Scott Rolen .60 1.50
30 Tom Glavine .60 1.50

2004 Hot Prospects Draft Rewind Jersey

PRINT RUNS B/WN 101-158 COPIES PER
RED HOT PRINT RUN 10 SERIAL #'d SETS
NO RED HOT PRICING DUE TO SCARCITY
WHITE HOT PRINT RUN 1 SERIAL #'d SET
NO WHITE HOT PRICING DUE TO SCARCITY
*PATCH p/r 68: .6X TO 1.5X BASIC
*PATCH p/r 41-57: .6X TO 1.5X BASIC
*PATCH p/r 20-29: .75X TO 2X BASIC
*PATCH p/r 16-19: 1X TO 2.5X BASIC
PATCH PRINT RUNS B/WN 10-68 PER
NO PATCH PRICING ON QTY OF 14 OR LESS
PATCH RED HOT PRINT RUN 5 #'d SETS
NO PATCH RED HOT PRICING AVAILABLE
PATCH WHITE HOT PRINT RUN 1 #'d SET
NO PATCH WHITE HOT PRICING AVAILABLE
OVERALL AU-GU ODDS 1:12 H, 1:24 R
BL Barry Larkin/104 4.00 10.00
BS Ben Sheets/110 3.00 8.00
BZ Barry Zito/109 3.00 8.00
CJ Chipper Jones/101 4.00 10.00
CK Casey Kotchman/113 6.00 15.00
CS Curt Schilling/139 4.00 10.00
EC Eric Chavez/110 3.00 8.00
FT Frank Thomas/107 4.00 10.00
GM Greg Maddux/131 6.00 15.00
GS Gary Sheffield/106 3.00 8.00
JB Josh Beckett/102 3.00 8.00
JG Jason Giambi/158 3.00 8.00
JM Joe Mauer/101 4.00 10.00
KB Kevin Brown/104 3.00 8.00
KG Khalil Greene/113 4.00 10.00
KW Kerry Wood/104 3.00 8.00
LB Lance Berkman/116 3.00 8.00
MM Mark Mulder/102 3.00 8.00
MP Mark Prior/102 4.00 10.00
MR Manny Ramirez/113 4.00 10.00
PB Pat Burrell/101 3.00 8.00
RB Rocco Baldelli/119 3.00 8.00
RC Roger Clemens/119 6.00 15.00
RJ Randy Johnson/136 4.00 10.00
RW Rickie Weeks/102 3.00 8.00
SR Scott Rolen/146 4.00 10.00
TG Troy Glaus/103 3.00 8.00
TG Tom Glavine/147 4.00 10.00
TH Todd Helton/108 4.00 10.00
ZG Zack Greinke/106 3.00 8.00

2004 Hot Prospects Draft Tandems

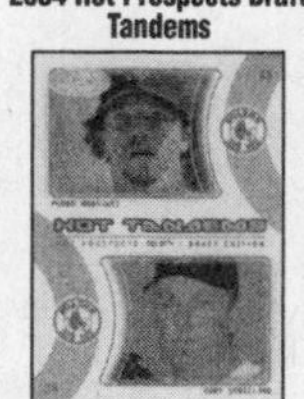

STATED ODDS 1:15 H/R
1 Mark Prior 1.50 4.00
Greg Maddux
2 Jim Thome .60 1.50
Pat Burrell
3 Ken Griffey Jr. .60 1.50
Adam Dunn
4 Mike Piazza 1.00 2.50
Tom Glavine
5 Alex Rodriguez 2.50 6.00
Derek Jeter
6 Roger Clemens 1.25 3.00
Andy Pettitte
7 Jason Giambi 1.50 4.00
Hideki Matsui
8 Alfonso Soriano .40 1.00
Hank Blalock
9 Manny Ramirez 1.00 2.50
David Ortiz
10 Miguel Cabrera .40 1.00

Dontrelle Willis
11 Hideki Matsui 1.50 4.00
Ichiro Suzuki
12 Albert Pujols 2.50 6.00
Scott Rolen
13 Pedro Martinez .60 1.50
Curt Schilling
14 Sammy Sosa 1.00 2.50
Nomar Garciaparra
15 Kaz Matsui 2.50 6.00
Derek Jeter

1949 Leaf

The cards in this 98-card set measure 2 3/8" by 2 7/8". The 1949 Leaf set was the first post-war baseball series issued in color. This effort was not entirely successful due to a lack of refinement which resulted in many color variations and cards out of register. In addition, the set was skip numbered from 1-168, with 49 of the 98 cards printed in limited quantities (marked with SP in the checklist). Cards 102 and 136 have variations, and cards are sometimes found with overprinted, incorrect or blank backs. Some cards were produced with a 1948 copyright date but overwhelming evidence seemed to indicate that this set was not actually released until early in 1949. An album to hold these cards was available as a premium. The album could only be obtained by sending in five wrappers and 25 cents. Since so few albums appear on the secondary market, no value is attached to them. Notable Rookie Cards in this set include Stan Musial, Satchel Paige, and Jackie Robinson. A proof card of Hal Newhouser; with a different photo and back biography recently surfaced. So far, there is only one known copy of this card.

COMPLETE SET (98) 25000.00 40000.00
COMMON CARD (1-168) 15.00 25.00
COMMON SP's 200.00 300.00
WRAPPER (1-CENT) 120.00 160.00
1 Joe DiMaggio 1800.00 3000.00
3 Babe Ruth 1500.00 2500.00
4 Stan Musial 600.00 1000.00
5 Virgil Trucks SP RC 250.00 400.00
8 Satchel Paige SP RC 9000.00 15000.00
10 Dizzy Trout 25.00 40.00
11 Phil Rizzuto 200.00 350.00
13 Cass Michaels SP RC 200.00 300.00
14 Billy Johnson 25.00 40.00
17 Frank Overmire RC 15.00 25.00
19 Johnny Wyrostek SP 200.00 300.00
20 Hank Sauer SP 250.00 400.00
22 Al Evans RC 15.00 25.00
26 Sam Chapman 25.00 40.00
27 Mickey Harris RC 15.00 25.00
28 Jim Hegan RC 25.00 40.00
29 Elmer Valo RC 25.00 40.00
30 Billy Goodman SP RC 250.00 400.00
31 Lou Brissie RC 15.00 25.00
32 Warren Spahn 200.00 350.00
33 Peanuts Lowrey SP RC 200.00 300.00
36 Al Zarilla SP 200.00 300.00
38 Ted Kluszewski RC 125.00 200.00
39 Ewell Blackwell 35.00 60.00
43 Ed Stevens SP RC 200.00 300.00
45 Ken Keltner SP RC 200.00 300.00
46 Johnny Mize 60.00 100.00
47 George Vico RC 15.00 25.00
48 Johnny Schmitz SP RC 200.00 300.00
49 Del Ennis RC 35.00 60.00
50 Dick Wakefield RC 15.00 25.00
51 Al Dark SP RC 300.00 500.00
53 Johnny VanderMeer 60.00 100.00
54 Bobby Adams SP RC 200.00 300.00
55 Tommy Henrich SP 300.00 500.00
56 Larry Jansen 25.00 40.00
57 Bob McCall RC 15.00 25.00
59 Luke Appling 60.00 100.00
61 Jake Early RC 15.00 25.00
62 Eddie Joost SP 200.00 300.00
63 Barney McCosky SP 200.00 300.00
65 Bob Elliott UER 60.00 100.00
66 Orval Grove SP RC 200.00 300.00
68 Eddie Miller SP 200.00 300.00
70 Honus Wagner 200.00 350.00
72 Hank Edwards RC 15.00 25.00
73 Pat Seerey RC 15.00 25.00
75 Dom DiMaggio SP 350.00 600.00
76 Ted Williams 700.00 1200.00
77 Roy Smalley RC 15.00 25.00
78 Hoot Evers SP RC 200.00 300.00
79 Jackie Robinson RC 1200.00 2000.00
81 Whitey Kurowski SP RC 200.00 300.00
82 Johnny Lindell 25.00 40.00
83 Bobby Doerr 60.00 100.00
84 Sid Hudson 15.00 25.00
85 Dave Philley SP RC 250.00 400.00
86 Ralph Weigel RC 15.00 25.00
88 Frank Gustine SP RC 200.00 300.00
91 Ralph Kiner 125.00 200.00
93 Bob Feller SP 1400.00 2000.00
95 Snuffy Stirnweiss 25.00 40.00
97 Marty Marion 35.00 60.00
98 Hal Newhouser SP RC 350.00 600.00
102 Eddie Stewart SP RC 200.00 300.00
104 Eddie Stewart SP RC 200.00 300.00
106 Lou Boudreau MG RC 60.00 100.00
108 Matt Batts SP RC 200.00 300.00
111 Jerry Priddy RC 15.00 25.00
113 Dutch Leonard SP 200.00 300.00
117 Joe Gordon RC 25.00 40.00
120 George Kell SP RC 350.00 600.00
121 Johnny Pesky SP RC 250.00 400.00
123 Cliff Fannin SP RC 200.00 300.00
125 Andy Pafko RC 15.00 25.00
127 Enos Slaughter SP 500.00 800.00
128 Buddy Rosar 15.00 25.00
129 Kirby Higbe SP 200.00 300.00
131 Sid Gordon SP 200.00 300.00
133 Tommy Holmes SP RC 300.00 500.00
137 Harry Walker SP RC 250.00 400.00
138 Larry Doby SP RC 400.00 700.00
139 Johnny Hopp RC 15.00 25.00
142 D.Murtaugh SP RC 250.00 400.00
143 Dick Sisler SP RC 200.00 300.00
144 Bob Dillinger SP RC 200.00 300.00
146 Pete Reiser SP 300.00 500.00
149 Hank Majeski SP RC 200.00 300.00
153 Floyd Baker SP RC 200.00 300.00
158 H.Brecheen SP RC 250.00 400.00
159 Mizell Platt RC 15.00 25.00
160 Bob Scheffing SP RC 200.00 300.00
161 Vern Stephens SP RC 250.00 400.00
163 F.Hutchinson SP RC 250.00 400.00
165 Dale Mitchell SP RC 250.00 400.00
168 Phil Cavarretta SP RC 300.00 500.00
42A Kent Peterson RC 15.00 25.00
42B Kent Peterson Red Cap
98A Hal Newhouser Proof
Photo and Biography is different from card later released in packs
NNO Album
102A G.Hermanski ERR 150.00 250.00
102B Gene Hermanski COR RC 25.00 40.00
136A Cliff Aberson 15.00 25.00
Full sleeve] RC
136B Cliff Aberson 150.00 250.00
Short Sleeve

1960 Leaf

The cards in this 144-card set measure the standard size. The 1960 Leaf set was issued in a regular gum package style but with a marble instead of gum. This set was issued in five card nickel packs which came 24 to a box. The series was a joint production by Sports Novelties, Inc., and Leaf, two Chicago-based companies. Cards 73-144 are more difficult to find than the lower numbers. Photo variations exist (probably proof cards) for the eight cards listed with an asterisk and there is a well-known error card, number 25 showing Brooks Lawrence (in a Reds uniform) with Jim Grant's name on front, and Grant's biography and record on back. The corrected version with Grant's photo is the more difficult variety. The only notable Rookie Card in this set is Dallas Green. The complete set price below includes both versions of Jim Grant.

COMPLETE SET (144) 1000.00 2000.00
COMMON CARD (1-72) 1.25 3.00
COMMON CARD (73-144) 12.50 30.00
WRAPPER 20.00 50.00
1 Luis Aparicio * 10.00 25.00
2 Woody Held 1.25 3.00
3 Frank Lary 1.50 4.00
4 Camilo Pascual 2.00 5.00
5 Pancho Herrera 1.25 3.00
6 Felipe Alou 3.00 8.00
7 Benjamin Daniels 1.25 3.00
8 Roger Craig 2.00 5.00
9 Eddie Kasko 1.25 3.00
10 Bob Grim 1.50 4.00
11 Jim Busby 1.50 4.00
12 Ken Boyer * 3.00 8.00
13 Bob Boyd 1.25 3.00
14 Sam Jones 1.50 4.00
15 Larry Jackson 1.50 4.00
16 Elroy Face 1.50 4.00
17 Walt Moryn * 1.25 3.00
18 Jim Gilliam 2.00 5.00
19 Don Newcombe 2.00 5.00
20 Glen Hobbie 1.25 3.00
21 Pedro Ramos 1.50 4.00
22 Ryne Duren 1.25 3.00
23 Joey Jay * 1.50 4.00
24 Lou Berberet 1.25 3.00
25A Jim Grant ERR 6.00 15.00
(Photo actually Brooks Lawrence)
25B Jim Grant COR 10.00 25.00
26 Tom Borland RC 1.25 3.00
27 Brooks Robinson 15.00 40.00
28 Jerry Adair RC 1.25 3.00
29 Ron Jackson 1.25 3.00
30 George Strickland 1.25 3.00
31 Rocky Bridges 1.25 3.00
32 Bill Tuttle 1.50 4.00
33 Ken Hunt RC 1.25 3.00
34 Hal Griggs 1.25 3.00
35 Jim Coates * 1.25 3.00
36 Brooks Lawrence 1.25 3.00
37 Duke Snider 15.00 40.00
38 Al Spangler RC 1.25 3.00
39 Jim Owens 1.25 3.00
40 Bill Virdon 2.00 5.00
41 Ernie Broglio 1.25 3.00
42 Andre Rodgers 1.25 3.00
43 Julio Becquer 1.50 4.00
44 Tony Taylor 1.50 4.00
45 Jerry Lynch 1.50 4.00
46 Cletis Boyer 3.00 8.00
47 Jerry Lumpe 1.25 3.00
48 Charlie Maxwell 1.50 4.00
49 Jim Perry 1.50 4.00
50 Danny McDevitt 1.25 3.00
51 Juan Pizarro 1.25 3.00
52 Dallas Green RC 3.00 8.00
53 Bob Friend 1.50 4.00
54 Jack Sanford 1.50 4.00
55 Jim Rivera 1.25 3.00
56 Ted Wills RC 1.25 3.00
57 Milt Pappas 1.50 4.00
58 Hal Smith * 1.25 3.00
59 Bobby Avila 1.25 3.00
60 Clem Labine 2.00 5.00
61 Norman Rehm RC * 1.25 3.00
62 John Gabler RC 1.50 4.00
63 John Tsitouris RC 1.25 3.00
64 Dave Sisler 1.25 3.00
65 Vic Power 1.50 4.00
66 Earl Battey 1.25 3.00
67 Bob Purkey 1.25 3.00
68 Moe Drabowsky 1.50 4.00
69 Hoyt Wilhelm 6.00 15.00
70 Humberto Robinson 1.25 3.00
71 Whitey Herzog 3.00 8.00
72 Dick Donovan * 1.25 3.00
73 Gordon Jones 12.50 30.00
74 Joe Hicks RC 12.50 30.00
75 Ray Culp RC 15.00 40.00
76 Dick Drott 12.50 30.00
77 Bob Duliba RC 12.50 30.00
78 Art Ditmar 12.50 30.00
79 Steve Korcheck 12.50 30.00
80 Henry Mason RC 12.50 30.00
81 Harry Simpson 12.50 30.00
82 Gene Green 12.50 30.00
83 Bob Shaw 12.50 30.00
84 Howard Reed 12.50 30.00
85 Dick Stigman 12.50 30.00
86 Rip Repulski 12.50 30.00
87 Seth Morehead 12.50 30.00
88 Camilo Carreon RC 12.50 30.00
89 John Blanchard 15.00 40.00
90 Billy Hoeft 12.50 30.00
91 Fred Hopke RC 12.50 30.00
92 Joe Martin RC 12.50 30.00
93 Wally Shannon RC 12.50 30.00
94 Hal R. Smith 15.00 40.00
Hal W. Smith
95 Al Schroll 12.50 30.00
96 John Kucks 12.50 30.00
97 Tom Morgan 12.50 30.00
98 Willie Jones 12.50 30.00
99 Marshall Renfroe RC 12.50 30.00
100 Willie Tasby 12.50 30.00
101 Irv Noren 12.50 30.00
102 Russ Snyder RC 12.50 30.00
103 Bob Turley 15.00 40.00
104 Jim Woods RC 12.50 30.00
105 Ronnie Kline 12.50 30.00
106 Steve Bilko 12.50 30.00
107 Elmer Valo 12.50 30.00
108 Tom McAvoy RC 12.50 30.00
109 Stan Williams 12.50 30.00
110 Earl Averill Jr. 12.50 30.00
111 Lee Walls 12.50 30.00
112 Paul Richards MG 12.50 30.00
113 Ed Sadowski 12.50 30.00
114 Stover McIlwain RC 12.50 30.00
115 Chuck Tanner UER 15.00 40.00
(Photo actually Ken Kuhn)
116 Lou Klimchock RC 12.50 30.00
117 Neil Chrisley 12.50 30.00
118 John Callison 20.00 50.00
119 Hal Smith 12.50 30.00
120 Carl Sawatski 12.50 30.00
121 Frank Leja 12.50 30.00
122 Earl Torgeson 12.50 30.00
123 Art Schult 12.50 30.00
124 Jim Brosnan 12.50 30.00
125 Sparky Anderson 30.00 60.00
126 Joe Pignatano 12.50 30.00
127 Rocky Nelson 12.50 30.00
128 Orlando Cepeda 40.00 80.00
129 Daryl Spencer 12.50 30.00
130 Ralph Lumenti 12.50 30.00
131 Sam Taylor 12.50 30.00
132 Harry Brecheen CO 15.00 40.00
133 Johnny Groth 12.50 30.00
134 Wayne Terwilliger 12.50 30.00
135 Kent Hadley 12.50 30.00
136 Faye Throneberry 12.50 30.00
137 Jack Meyer 12.50 30.00
138 Chuck Cottier RC 12.50 30.00
139 Joe DeMaestri 12.50 30.00
140 Gene Freese 12.50 30.00
141 Curt Flood 20.00 50.00
142 Gino Cimoli 12.50 30.00
143 Clay Dalrymple RC 12.50 30.00
144 Jim Bunning 40.00 80.00

1990 Leaf

The 1990 Leaf set was the first premium set introduced by Donruss and represents one of the more significant products issued in the 1990's. The cards were issued in 15-card foil wrapped packs and were not available in factory sets. Each pack also contained one three-piece puzzle panel of a 63-piece Yogi Berra "Donruss Hall of Fame Diamond King" puzzle. This set, which was produced on high quality paper stock, was issued in two separate series of 264 standard-size cards each. The second series was issued approximately six weeks after the release of the first series. The cards feature full-color photos on both the front and back. Rookie Cards in the set include David Justice, John Olerud, Sammy Sosa, Frank Thomas and Larry Walker.

COMPLETE SET (528) 30.00 60.00
COMPLETE SERIES 1 (264) 20.00 40.00
COMPLETE SERIES 2 (264) 10.00 20.00
COMP. BERRA PUZZLE .40 1.00
1 Introductory Card .15 .40
2 Mike Henneman .15 .40
3 Steve Bedrosian .15 .40
4 Mike Scott .15 .40
5 Allan Anderson .15 .40
6 Rick Sutcliffe .25 .60
7 Gregg Olson .25 .60
8 Kevin Elster .15 .40
9 Pete O'Brien .15 .40
10 Carlton Fisk .40 1.00
11 Joe Magrane .15 .40
12 Roger Clemens 1.50 4.00
13 Tom Glavine .40 1.00
14 Tom Gordon .25 .60
15 Todd Benzinger .15 .40
16 Hubie Brooks .15 .40
17 Roberto Kelly .15 .40

18 Barry Larkin .40 1.00
19 Mike Boddicker .15 .40
20 Roger McDowell .15 .40
21 Nolan Ryan 2.00 5.00
22 John Farrell .15 .40
23 Bruce Hurst .15 .40
24 Wally Joyner .25 .60
25 Greg Maddux 2.00 5.00
26 Chris Bosio .15 .40
27 John Cerutti .15 .40
28 Tim Burke .15 .40
29 Dennis Eckersley .25 .60
30 Glenn Davis .15 .40
31 Jim Abbott .40 1.00
32 Mike LaValliere .15 .40
33 Andres Thomas .15 .40
34 Lou Whitaker .25 .60
35 Alvin Davis .15 .40
36 Melido Perez .15 .40
37 Craig Biggio .60 1.50
38 Rick Aguilera .25 .60
39 Pete Harnisch .15 .40
40 David Cone .25 .60
41 Scott Garrelts .15 .40
42 Jay Howell .15 .40
43 Eric King .15 .40
44 Pedro Guerrero .15 .40
45 Mike Bielecki .15 .40
46 Bob Boone .25 .60
47 Kevin Brown .25 .60
48 Jerry Browne .15 .40
49 Mike Scioscia .15 .40
50 Chuck Cary .15 .40
51 Wade Boggs .40 1.00
52 Von Hayes .15 .40
53 Tony Fernandez .15 .40
54 Dennis Martinez .25 .60
55 Tom Candiotti .15 .40
56 Andy Benes .25 .60
57 Rob Dibble .25 .60
58 Chuck Crim .15 .40
59 John Smoltz .60 1.50
60 Mike Heath .15 .40
61 Kevin Gross .15 .40
62 Mark McGwire 1.50 4.00
63 Bert Blyleven .25 .60
64 Bob Walk .15 .40
65 Mickey Tettleton .15 .40
66 Sid Fernandez .15 .40
67 Terry Kennedy .15 .40
68 Fernando Valenzuela .25 .60
69 Don Mattingly 1.50 4.00
70 Paul O'Neill .40 1.00
71 Robin Yount 1.00 2.50
72 Bret Saberhagen .25 .60
73 Geno Petralli .15 .40
74 Brook Jacoby .15 .40
75 Roberto Alomar .40 1.00
76 Devon White .25 .60
77 Jose Lind .15 .40
78 Pat Combs .15 .40
79 Dave Stieb .25 .60
80 Tim Wallach .15 .40
81 Dave Stewart .25 .60
82 Eric Anthony RC .15 .40
83 Randy Bush .15 .40
84 Rickey Henderson CL .25 .60
85 Jaime Navarro .15 .40
86 Tommy Gregg .15 .40
87 Frank Tanana .15 .40
88 Omar Vizquel .60 1.50
89 Ivan Calderon .15 .40
90 Vince Coleman .15 .40
91 Barry Bonds 2.00 5.00
92 Randy Milligan .15 .40
93 Frank Viola .15 .40
94 Matt Williams .25 .60
95 Alfredo Griffin .15 .40
96 Steve Sax .15 .40
97 Gary Gaetti .25 .60
98 Ryne Sandberg 1.25 3.00
99 Danny Tartabull .15 .40
100 Rafael Palmeiro .40 1.00
101 Jesse Orosco .15 .40
102 Garry Templeton .15 .40
103 Frank DiPino .15 .40
104 Tony Pena .15 .40
105 Dickie Thon .15 .40
106 Kelly Gruber .15 .40
107 Marquis Grissom RC .75 2.00
108 Jose Canseco .40 1.00
109 Mike Blowers RC .15 .40
110 Tom Browning .15 .40
111 Greg Vaughn .15 .40
112 Oddibe McDowell .15 .40
113 Gary Ward .15 .40
114 Jay Buhner .25 .60
115 Eric Show .15 .40
116 Bryan Harvey .15 .40
117 Andy Van Slyke .40 1.00
118 Jeff Ballard .15 .40
119 Barry Lyons .15 .40
120 Kevin Mitchell .15 .40
121 Mike Gallego .15 .40
122 Dave Smith .15 .40
123 Kirby Puckett .60 1.50
124 Jerome Walton .15 .40
125 Bo Jackson .60 1.50
126 Harold Baines .25 .60
127 Scott Bankhead .15 .40
128 Ozzie Guillen .25 .60
129 Jose Oquendo UER .15 .40
(League misspelled
as Legue)
130 John Dopson .15 .40
131 Charlie Hayes .15 .40
132 Fred McGriff .60 1.50
133 Chet Lemon .15 .40
134 Gary Carter .25 .60
135 Rafael Ramirez .15 .40
136 Shane Mack .15 .40
137 Mark Grace UER .40 1.00
(Card back has OB:L,
should be B:L)
138 Phil Bradley .15 .40
139 Dwight Gooden .25 .60
140 Harold Reynolds .25 .60
141 Scott Fletcher .15 .40
142 Ozzie Smith 1.00 2.50
143 Mike Greenwell .15 .40
144 Pete Smith .15 .40
145 Mark Gubicza .15 .40
146 Chris Sabo .15 .40
147 Ramon Martinez .15 .40
148 Tim Leary .15 .40
149 Randy Myers .25 .60
150 Jody Reed .15 .40
151 Bruce Ruffin .15 .40
152 Jeff Russell .15 .40
153 Doug Jones .15 .40
154 Tony Gwynn .75 2.00
155 Mark Langston .15 .40
156 Mitch Williams .15 .40
157 Gary Sheffield .60 1.50
158 Tom Henke .15 .40
159 Oil Can Boyd .15 .40
160 Rickey Henderson .60 1.50
161 Bill Doran .15 .40
162 Chuck Finley .25 .60
163 Jeff King .15 .40
164 Nick Esasky .15 .40
165 Cecil Fielder .25 .60
166 Dave Valle .15 .40
167 Robin Ventura .60 1.50
168 Jim Deshaies .15 .40
169 Juan Berenguer .15 .40
170 Craig Worthington .15 .40
171 Gregg Jefferies .25 .60
172 Will Clark .40 1.00
173 Kirk Gibson .25 .60
174 Carlton Fisk CL .25 .60
175 Bobby Thigpen .15 .40
176 John Tudor .15 .40
177 Andre Dawson .25 .60
178 George Brett 1.50 4.00
179 Steve Buechele .15 .40
180 Joey Belle .60 1.50
181 Eddie Murray .60 1.50
182 Bob Geren .15 .40
183 Rob Murphy .15 .40
184 Tom Herr .15 .40
185 George Bell .15 .40
186 Spike Owen .15 .40
187 Cory Snyder .15 .40
188 Fred Lynn .15 .40
189 Eric Davis .25 .60
190 Dave Parker .25 .60
191 Jeff Blauser .15 .40
192 Matt Nokes .15 .40
193 Delino DeShields RC .40 1.00
194 Scott Sanderson .15 .40
195 Lance Parrish .15 .40
196 Bobby Bonilla .25 .60
197 Cal Ripken UER 2.00 5.00
(Reistertown, should
be Reisterstown)
198 Kevin McReynolds .15 .40
199 Robby Thompson .15 .40
200 Tim Belcher .15 .40
201 Jesse Barfield .15 .40
202 Mariano Duncan .15 .40
203 Bill Spiers .15 .40
204 Frank White .25 .60
205 Julio Franco .25 .60
206 Greg Swindell .15 .40
207 Benito Santiago .25 .60
208 Johnny Ray .15 .40
209 Gary Redus .15 .40
210 Jeff Parrett .15 .40
211 Jimmy Key .25 .60
212 Tim Raines .25 .60
213 Carney Lansford .25 .60
214 Gerald Young .15 .40
215 Gene Larkin .15 .40
216 Dan Plesac .15 .40
217 Lonnie Smith .15 .40
218 Alan Trammell .25 .60
219 Jeffrey Leonard .15 .40
220 Sammy Sosa RC 5.00 12.00
221 Todd Zeile .25 .60
222 Bill Landrum .15 .40
223 Mike Devereaux .15 .40
224 Mike Marshall .15 .40
225 Jose Uribe .15 .40
226 Juan Samuel .15 .40
227 Mel Hall .15 .40
228 Kent Hrbek .25 .60
229 Shawon Dunston .15 .40
230 Kevin Seitzer .15 .40
231 Pete Incaviglia .15 .40
232 Sandy Alomar Jr. .25 .60
233 Bip Roberts .15 .40
234 Scott Terry .15 .40
235 Dwight Evans .40 1.00
236 Ricky Jordan .15 .40
237 John Olerud RC 1.25 3.00
238 Zane Smith .15 .40
239 Walt Weiss .15 .40
240 Alvaro Espinoza .15 .40
241 Billy Hatcher .15 .40
242 Paul Molitor .25 .60
243 Dale Murphy .40 1.00
244 Dave Bergman .15 .40
245 Ken Griffey Jr. 2.00 5.00
246 Ed Whitson .15 .40
247 Kirk McCaskill .15 .40
248 Jay Bell .25 .60
249 Ben McDonald RC .40 1.00
250 Darryl Strawberry .25 .60
251 Brett Butler .25 .60
252 Terry Steinbach .15 .40
253 Ken Caminiti .25 .60
254 Dan Gladden .15 .40
255 Dwight Smith .15 .40
256 Kurt Stillwell .15 .40
257 Ruben Sierra .25 .60
258 Mike Schooler .15 .40
259 Lance Johnson .15 .40
260 Terry Pendleton .25 .60
261 Ellis Burks .40 1.00
262 Len Dykstra .25 .60
263 Mookie Wilson .25 .60
264 Nolan Ryan CL UER .60 1.50
No TM after Ranger logo
265 Nolan Ryan 1.00 2.50
No Hit King
266 Brian DuBois RC .15 .40
267 Don Robinson .15 .40
268 Glenn Wilson .15 .40
269 Kevin Tapani RC .40 1.00
270 Marvell Wynne .15 .40
271 Bill Ripken .15 .40
272 Howard Johnson .15 .40
273 Brian Holman .15 .40
274 Dan Pasqua .15 .40
275 Ken Dayley .15 .40
276 Jeff Reardon .25 .60
277 Jim Presley .15 .40
278 Jim Eisenreich .15 .40
279 Danny Jackson .15 .40
280 Orel Hershiser .25 .60
281 Andy Hawkins .15 .40
282 Jose Rijo .15 .40
283 Luis Rivera .15 .40
284 John Kruk .25 .60
285 Jeff Huson RC .15 .40
286 Joel Skinner .15 .40
287 Jack Clark .25 .60
288 Chili Davis .25 .60
289 Joe Girardi .40 1.00
290 B.J. Surhoff .25 .60
291 Luis Sojo RC .15 .40
292 Tom Foley .15 .40
293 Mike Moore .15 .40
294 Ken Oberkfell .15 .40
295 Luis Polonia .15 .40
296 Doug Drabek .15 .40
297 Dave Justice RC 1.25 3.00
298 Paul Gibson .15 .40
299 Edgar Martinez .40 1.00
300 Frank Thomas RC UER 5.00 12.00
No B in front
of birthdate
301 Eric Yelding RC .15 .40
302 Greg Gagne .15 .40
303 Brad Komminsk .15 .40
304 Ron Darling .15 .40
305 Kevin Bass .15 .40
306 Jeff Hamilton .15 .40
307 Ron Karkovice .15 .40
308 Milt Thompson UER .40 1.00
(Ray Lankford pictured
on card back)
309 Mike Harkey .15 .40
310 Mel Stottlemyre Jr. .15 .40
311 Kenny Rogers .25 .60
312 Mitch Webster .15 .40
313 Kal Daniels .15 .40
314 Matt Nokes .15 .40
315 Dennis Lamp .15 .40
316 Ken Howell .15 .40
317 Glenallen Hill .15 .40
318 Dave Martinez .15 .40
319 Chris James .15 .40
320 Mike Pagliarulo .15 .40
321 Hal Morris .15 .40
322 Rob Deer .15 .40
323 Greg Olson (C) RC .15 .40
324 Tony Phillips .15 .40
325 Larry Walker RC 3.00 8.00
326 Ron Hassey .15 .40
327 Jack Howell .15 .40
328 John Smiley .15 .40
329 Steve Finley .25 .60
330 Dave Magadan .15 .40
331 Greg Litton .15 .40
332 Mickey Hatcher .15 .40
333 Lee Guetterman .15 .40
334 Norm Charlton .15 .40
335 Edgar Diaz RC .15 .40
336 Willie Wilson .15 .40
337 Bobby Witt .15 .40
338 Candy Maldonado .15 .40
339 Craig Lefferts .15 .40
340 Dante Bichette .25 .60
341 Wally Backman .15 .40
342 Dennis Cook .15 .40
343 Pat Borders .15 .40
344 Wallace Johnson .15 .40
345 Willie Randolph .25 .60
346 Danny Darwin .15 .40
347 Al Newman .15 .40
348 Mark Knudson .15 .40
349 Joe Boever .15 .40
350 Larry Sheets .15 .40
351 Mike Jackson .15 .40
352 Wayne Edwards RC .15 .40
353 Bernard Gilkey RC .40 1.00
354 Don Slaught .15 .40
355 Joe Orsulak .15 .40
356 John Franco .25 .60
357 Jeff Brantley .15 .40
358 Mike Morgan .15 .40
359 Deion Sanders .60 1.50
360 Terry Leach .15 .40
361 Les Lancaster .15 .40
362 Storm Davis .15 .40
363 Scott Coolbaugh RC .15 .40
364 Ozzie Smith CL .40 1.00
365 Cecilio Guante .15 .40
366 Joey Cora .25 .60
367 Willie McGee .25 .60
368 Jerry Reed .15 .40
369 Darren Daulton .25 .60
370 Manny Lee .15 .40
371 Mark Gardner RC .15 .40
372 Rick Honeycutt .15 .40
373 Steve Balboni .15 .40
374 Jack Armstrong .15 .40
375 Charlie O'Brien .15 .40
376 Ron Gant .25 .60
377 Lloyd Moseby .15 .40
378 Gene Harris .15 .40
379 Joe Carter .25 .60
380 Scott Bailes .15 .40
381 R.J. Reynolds .15 .40
382 Bob Melvin .15 .40
383 Tim Teufel .15 .40
384 John Burkett .15 .40
385 Felix Jose .15 .40
386 Larry Andersen .15 .40
387 David West .15 .40
388 Luis Salazar .15 .40
389 Mike Macfarlane .15 .40
390 Charlie Hough .25 .60
391 Greg Briley .15 .40
392 Donn Pall .15 .40
393 Bryn Smith .15 .40
394 Carlos Quintana .15 .40
395 Steve Lake .15 .40
396 Mark Whiten RC .40 1.00
397 Edwin Nunez .15 .40
398 Rick Parker RC .15 .40
399 Mark Portugal .15 .40
400 Roy Smith .15 .40
401 Hector Villanueva RC .15 .40
402 Bob Milacki .15 .40
403 Alejandro Pena .15 .40
404 Scott Bradley .15 .40
405 Ron Kittle .15 .40
406 Bob Tewksbury .15 .40
407 Wes Gardner .15 .40
408 Ernie Whitt .15 .40
409 Terry Shumpert RC .15 .40
410 Tim Layana RC .15 .40
411 Chris Gwynn .15 .40
412 Jeff D. Robinson .15 .40
413 Scott Scudder .15 .40
414 Kevin Romine .15 .40
415 Jose DeJesus .15 .40
416 Mike Jeffcoat .15 .40
417 Rudy Seanez RC .15 .40
418 Mike Dunne .15 .40
419 Dick Schofield .15 .40
420 Steve Wilson .15 .40
421 Bill Krueger .15 .40
422 Junior Felix .15 .40
423 Drew Hall .15 .40
424 Curt Young .15 .40
425 Franklin Stubbs .15 .40
426 Dave Winfield .25 .60
427 Rick Reed RC .40 1.00
428 Charlie Leibrandt .15 .40
429 Jeff M. Robinson .15 .40
430 Erik Hanson .15 .40
431 Barry Jones .15 .40
432 Alex Trevino .15 .40
433 John Moses .15 .40
434 Dave Wayne Johnson RC .15 .40
435 Mackey Sasser .15 .40
436 Rick Leach .15 .40
437 Lenny Harris .15 .40
438 Carlos Martinez .15 .40
439 Rex Hudler .15 .40
440 Domingo Ramos .15 .40
441 Gerald Perry .15 .40
442 Jeff Russell .15 .40
443 Carlos Baerga RC .40 1.00
444 Will Clark CL .25 .60
445 Stan Javier .15 .40
446 Kevin Maas RC .40 1.00
447 Tom Brunansky .15 .40
448 Carmelo Martinez .15 .40
449 Willie Blair RC .15 .40
450 Andres Galarraga .25 .60
451 Bud Black .15 .40
452 Greg W. Harris .15 .40
453 Joe Oliver .15 .40
454 Greg Brock .15 .40
455 Jeff Treadway .15 .40
456 Lance McCullers .15 .40
457 Dave Schmidt .15 .40
458 Todd Burns .15 .40
459 Max Venable .15 .40
460 Neal Heaton .15 .40
461 Mark Williamson .15 .40
462 Keith Miller .15 .40
463 Mike LaCoss .15 .40
464 Jose Offerman RC .40 1.00
465 Jim Leyritz RC .75 2.00
466 Glenn Braggs .15 .40
467 Ron Robinson .15 .40
468 Mark Davis .15 .40
469 Gary Pettis .15 .40
470 Keith Hernandez .25 .60
471 Dennis Rasmussen .15 .40
472 Mark Eichhorn .15 .40
473 Ted Power .15 .40
474 Terry Mulholland .15 .40
475 Todd Stottlemyre .25 .60
476 Jerry Goff RC .15 .40
477 Gene Nelson .15 .40
478 Rich Gedman .15 .40
479 Brian Harper .15 .40
480 Mike Felder .15 .40
481 Steve Avery .15 .40
482 Jack Morris .25 .60
483 Randy Johnson 1.25 3.00
484 Scott Radinsky RC .15 .40
485 Jose DeLeon .15 .40
486 Stan Belinda RC .15 .40
487 Brian Holton .15 .40
488 Mark Carreon .15 .40
489 Trevor Wilson .15 .40
490 Mike Sharperson .15 .40
491 Alan Mills RC .15 .40
492 John Candelaria .15 .40
493 Paul Assenmacher .15 .40
494 Steve Crawford .15 .40
495 Brad Arnsberg .15 .40
496 Sergio Valdez RC .15 .40
497 Mark Parent .15 .40
498 Tom Pagnozzi .15 .40
499 Greg A. Harris .15 .40
500 Randy Ready .15 .40
501 Duane Ward .15 .40
502 Nelson Santovenia .15 .40
503 Joe Klink RC .15 .40
504 Eric Plunk .15 .40
505 Jeff Reed .15 .40
506 Ted Higuera .15 .40
507 Joe Hesketh .15 .40
508 Dan Petry .15 .40
509 Matt Young .15 .40
510 Jerald Clark .15 .40
511 John Orton RC .15 .40
512 Scott Ruskin RC .15 .40
513 Chris Hoiles RC .40 1.00
514 Daryl Boston .15 .40
515 Francisco Oliveras .15 .40
516 Ozzie Canseco .15 .40
517 Xavier Hernandez RC .15 .40
518 Fred Manrique .15 .40
519 Shawn Boskie RC .15 .40
520 Jeff Montgomery .25 .60
521 Jack Daugherty RC .15 .40
522 Keith Comstock .15 .40
523 Greg Hibbard RC .15 .40
524 Lee Smith .25 .60
525 Dana Kiecker RC .15 .40
526 Darrel Akerfelds .15 .40
527 Greg Myers .15 .40
528 Ryne Sandberg CL .60 1.50

1991 Leaf

This 528-card standard size set was issued by Donruss in two separate series of 264 cards. Cards were exclusively issued in foil packs. The front design has color action player photos, with white and silver borders. A thicker stock was used for these (then) premium level cards. Production for the 1991 set was greatly increased due to the huge demand for the benchmark 1990 Leaf set. However, the 1991 cards were met with modest enthusiasm due to a weak selection of Rookie Cards and superior competition from brands like 1991 Stadium Club.

COMPLETE SET (528) 6.00 15.00
COMP. SERIES 1 (264) 2.00 5.00
COMP. SERIES 2 (264) 4.00 10.00
COMP. KILLEBREW PUZZLE .50 1.00
1 The Leaf Card .02 .10
2 Kurt Stillwell .02 .10
3 Bobby Witt .02 .10
4 Tony Phillips .02 .10
5 Scott Garrelts .02 .10
6 Greg Swindell .02 .10
7 Billy Ripken .02 .10
8 Dave Martinez .02 .10
9 Kelly Gruber .02 .10
10 Juan Samuel .02 .10
11 Brian Holman .02 .10
12 Craig Biggio .10 .30
13 Lonnie Smith .02 .10
14 Ron Robinson .02 .10
15 Mike LaValliere .02 .10
16 Mark Davis .02 .10
17 Jack Daugherty .02 .10
18 Mike Henneman .02 .10
19 Mike Greenwell .02 .10
20 Dave Magadan .02 .10
21 Mark Williamson .02 .10
22 Marquis Grissom .07 .20
23 Pat Borders .02 .10
24 Mike Scioscia .02 .10
25 Shawon Dunston .02 .10
26 Randy Bush .02 .10
27 John Smoltz .10 .30
28 Chuck Crim .02 .10
29 Don Slaught .02 .10
30 Mike Macfarlane .02 .10
31 Wally Joyner .07 .20
32 Pat Combs .02 .10
33 Tony Pena .02 .10
34 Howard Johnson .02 .10
35 Leo Gomez .02 .10
36 Spike Owen .02 .10
37 Eric Davis .07 .20
38 Roberto Kelly .02 .10
39 Jerome Walton .02 .10
40 Shane Mack .02 .10
41 Kent Mercker .02 .10
42 B.J. Surhoff .07 .20
43 Jerry Browne .02 .10
44 Lee Smith .07 .20
45 Chuck Finley .07 .20
46 Terry Mulholland .02 .10
47 Tom Bolton .02 .10
48 Tom Herr .02 .10
49 Jim Deshaies .02 .10
50 Walt Weiss .02 .10
51 Hal Morris .02 .10
52 Lee Guetterman .02 .10
53 Paul Assenmacher .02 .10
54 Brian Harper .02 .10
55 Paul Gibson .02 .10
56 John Burkett .02 .10
57 Doug Jones .02 .10
58 Jose Oquendo .02 .10
59 Dick Schofield .02 .10
60 Dickie Thon .02 .10
61 Ramon Martinez .02 .10
62 Jay Buhner .07 .20
63 Mark Portugal .02 .10
64 Bob Welch .02 .10
65 Chris Sabo .02 .10
66 Chuck Cary .02 .10
67 Mark Langston .02 .10
68 Joe Boever .02 .10
69 Jody Reed .02 .10
70 Alejandro Pena .02 .10
71 Jeff King .02 .10
72 Tom Pagnozzi .02 .10
73 Joe Oliver .02 .10
74 Mike Witt .02 .10
75 Hector Villanueva .02 .10
76 Dan Gladden .02 .10
77 Dave Justice .07 .20
78 Mike Gallego .02 .10
79 Tom Candiotti .02 .10
80 Ozzie Smith .30 .75
81 Luis Polonia .02 .10
82 Randy Ready .02 .10
83 Greg A. Harris .02 .10
84 David Justice CL .02 .10
85 Kevin Mitchell .02 .10
86 Mark McLemore .02 .10
87 Terry Steinbach .02 .10
88 Tom Browning .02 .10
89 Matt Nokes .02 .10
90 Mike Harkey .02 .10
91 Omar Vizquel .10 .30
92 Dave Bergman .02 .10
93 Matt Williams .07 .20
94 Steve Olin .02 .10
95 Craig Wilson RC .02 .10
96 Dave Stieb .02 .10
97 Ruben Sierra .07 .20
98 Jay Howell .02 .10
99 Scott Bradley .02 .10
100 Eric Yelding .02 .10
101 Rickey Henderson .20 .50
102 Jeff Reed .02 .10
103 Jimmy Key .07 .20
104 Terry Shumpert .02 .10
105 Kenny Rogers .07 .20
106 Cecil Fielder .07 .20
107 Robby Thompson .02 .10
108 Alex Cole .02 .10
109 Randy Milligan .02 .10
110 Andres Galarraga .07 .20
111 Bill Spiers .02 .10
112 Kal Daniels .02 .10
113 Henry Cotto .02 .10
114 Casey Candaele .02 .10
115 Jeff Blauser .02 .10
116 Robin Yount .30 .75
117 Ben McDonald .02 .10
118 Bret Saberhagen .07 .20
119 Juan Gonzalez .20 .50
120 Lou Whitaker .07 .20
121 Ellis Burks .07 .20
122 Charlie O'Brien .02 .10
123 John Smiley .02 .10
124 Tim Burke .02 .10
125 John Olerud .07 .20
126 Eddie Murray .20 .50
127 Greg Maddux .30 .75
128 Kevin Tapani .02 .10
129 Ron Gant .07 .20
130 Jay Bell .07 .20
131 Chris Hoiles .02 .10
132 Tom Gordon .02 .10
133 Kevin Seitzer .02 .10
134 Jeff Huson .02 .10
135 Jerry Don Gleaton .02 .10
136 Jeff Brantley UER .02 .10
(Photo actually Rick
Leach on back)
137 Felix Fermin .02 .10
138 Mike Devereaux .02 .10
139 Delino DeShields .07 .20
140 David Wells .07 .20
141 Tim Crews .02 .10
142 Erik Hanson .02 .10
143 Mark Davidson .02 .10
144 Tommy Gregg .02 .10
145 Jim Gantner .02 .10
146 Jose Lind .02 .10
147 Danny Tartabull .02 .10
148 Geno Petralli .02 .10
149 Travis Fryman .07 .20
150 Tim Naehring .02 .10
151 Kevin McReynolds .02 .10
152 Joe Orsulak .02 .10
153 Steve Frey .02 .10
154 Duane Ward .02 .10
155 Stan Javier .02 .10
156 Damon Berryhill .02 .10
157 Gene Larkin .02 .10
158 Greg Olson .02 .10
159 Mark Knudson .02 .10
160 Carmelo Martinez .02 .10
161 Storm Davis .02 .10
162 Jim Abbott .10 .30
163 Len Dykstra .07 .20
164 Tom Brunansky .02 .10
165 Dwight Gooden .07 .20
166 Jose Mesa .02 .10
167 Oil Can Boyd .02 .10
168 Barry Larkin .10 .30
169 Scott Sanderson .02 .10
170 Mark Grace .10 .30
171 Mark Guthrie .02 .10
172 Tom Glavine .10 .30
173 Gary Sheffield .07 .20
174 Roger Clemens CL .30 .75
175 Chris James .02 .10
176 Milt Thompson .02 .10
177 Donnie Hill .02 .10
178 Wes Chamberlain RC .02 .10
179 John Marzano .02 .10
180 Frank Viola .07 .20
181 Eric Anthony .02 .10
182 Jose Canseco .10 .30
183 Scott Scudder .02 .10
184 Dave Eiland .02 .10
185 Luis Salazar .02 .10
186 Pedro Munoz RC .02 .10
187 Steve Searcy .02 .10
188 Don Robinson .02 .10
189 Sandy Alomar Jr. .02 .10
190 Jose DeLeon .02 .10
191 John Orton .02 .10
192 Darren Daulton .07 .20
193 Mike Morgan .02 .10
194 Greg Briley .02 .10
195 Karl Rhodes .02 .10
196 Harold Baines .07 .20
197 Bill Doran .02 .10
198 Alvaro Espinoza .02 .10
199 Kirk McCaskill .02 .10
200 Jose DeJesus .02 .10
201 Jack Clark .07 .20
202 Daryl Boston .02 .10
203 Randy Tomlin RC .02 .10
204 Pedro Guerrero .07 .20
205 Billy Hatcher .02 .10
206 Tim Leary .02 .10
207 Ryne Sandberg .30 .75
208 Kirby Puckett .20 .50
209 Charlie Leibrandt .02 .10
210 Rick Honeycutt .02 .10
211 Joel Skinner .02 .10
212 Rex Hudler .02 .10
213 Bryan Harvey .02 .10
214 Charlie Hayes .02 .10
215 Matt Young .02 .10
216 Terry Kennedy .02 .10
217 Carl Nichols .02 .10
218 Mike Moore .02 .10
219 Paul O'Neill .10 .30
220 Steve Sax .02 .10
221 Shawn Boskie .02 .10
222 Rich DeLucia RC .02 .10
223 Lloyd Moseby .02 .10
224 Mike Kingery .02 .10
225 Carlos Baerga .02 .10
226 Bryn Smith .02 .10
227 Todd Stottlemyre .02 .10
228 Julio Franco .07 .20
229 Jim Gott .02 .10
230 Mike Schooler .02 .10
231 Steve Finley .07 .20
232 Dave Henderson .02 .10
233 Luis Quinones .02 .10
234 Mark Whiten .02 .10
235 Brian McRae RC .07 .20
236 Rich Gossage .07 .20
237 Rob Deer .02 .10
238 Will Clark .10 .30
239 Albert Belle .07 .20
240 Bob Melvin .02 .10
241 Larry Walker .20 .50
242 Dante Bichette .07 .20
243 Orel Hershiser .07 .20
244 Pete O'Brien .02 .10
245 Pete Harnisch .02 .10
246 Jeff Treadway .02 .10
247 Julio Machado .02 .10
248 Dave Johnson .02 .10
249 Kirk Gibson .07 .20
250 Kevin Brown .07 .20
251 Milt Cuyler .02 .10
252 Jeff Reardon .07 .20
253 David Cone .07 .20
254 Gary Redus .02 .10
255 Junior Noboa .02 .10
256 Greg Myers .02 .10
257 Dennis Cook .02 .10
258 Joe Girardi .02 .10
259 Allan Anderson .02 .10
260 Paul Marak RC .02 .10
261 Barry Bonds .60 1.50
262 Juan Bell .02 .10
263 Russ Morman .02 .10
264 George Brett CL .20 .50
265 Jerald Clark .02 .10
266 Dwight Evans .10 .30
267 Roberto Alomar .10 .30
268 Danny Jackson .02 .10
269 Brian Downing .02 .10
270 John Cerutti .02 .10
271 Robin Ventura .07 .20
272 Gerald Perry .02 .10
273 Wade Boggs .10 .30
274 Dennis Martinez .07 .20
275 Andy Benes .02 .10
276 Tony Fossas .02 .10
277 Franklin Stubbs .02 .10
278 John Kruk .07 .20
279 Kevin Gross .02 .10
280 Von Hayes .02 .10
281 Frank Thomas .20 .50
282 Rob Dibble .07 .20
283 Mel Hall .02 .10
284 Rick Mahler .02 .10
285 Dennis Eckersley .07 .20
286 Bernard Gilkey .02 .10
287 Dan Plesac .02 .10
288 Jason Grimsley .02 .10
289 Mark Lewis .02 .10
290 Tony Gwynn .25 .60
291 Jeff Russell .02 .10
292 Curt Schilling .20 .50
293 Pascual Perez .02 .10
294 Jack Morris .07 .20
295 Hubie Brooks .02 .10
296 Alex Fernandez .02 .10
297 Harold Reynolds .07 .20
298 Craig Worthington .02 .10
299 Willie Wilson .02 .10
300 Mike Maddux .02 .10
301 Dave Righetti .07 .20
302 Paul Molitor .07 .20
303 Gary Gaetti .07 .20
304 Terry Pendleton .07 .20
305 Kevin Elster .02 .10
306 Scott Fletcher .02 .10
307 Jeff Robinson .02 .10
308 Jesse Barfield .02 .10
309 Mike LaCoss .02 .10
310 Andy Van Slyke .10 .30
311 Glenallen Hill .02 .10
312 Bud Black .02 .10
313 Kent Hrbek .07 .20
314 Tim Teufel .02 .10
315 Tony Fernandez .02 .10
316 Beau Allred .02 .10
317 Curtis Wilkerson .02 .10
318 Bill Sampen .02 .10
319 Randy Johnson .25 .60
320 Mike Heath .02 .10
321 Sammy Sosa .20 .50
322 Mickey Tettleton .02 .10
323 Jose Vizcaino .02 .10
324 John Candelaria .02 .10
325 Dave Howard RC .02 .10
326 Jose Rijo .02 .10
327 Todd Zeile .02 .10
328 Gene Nelson .02 .10
329 Dwayne Henry .02 .10
330 Mike Boddicker .02 .10
331 Ozzie Guillen .07 .20
332 Sam Horn .02 .10
333 Wally Whitehurst .02 .10
334 Dave Parker .07 .20
335 George Brett .50 1.25
336 Bobby Thigpen .02 .10
337 Ed Whitson .02 .10
338 Ivan Calderon .02 .10
339 Mike Pagliarulo .02 .10
340 Jack McDowell .02 .10
341 Dana Kiecker .02 .10
342 Fred McGriff .10 .30
343 Mark Lee RC .02 .10
344 Alfredo Griffin .02 .10
345 Scott Bankhead .02 .10
346 Darrin Jackson .02 .10
347 Rafael Palmeiro .10 .30
348 Steve Farr .02 .10
349 Hensley Meulens .02 .10
350 Danny Cox .02 .10
351 Alan Trammell .07 .20
352 Edwin Nunez .02 .10
353 Joe Carter .07 .20
354 Eric Show .02 .10
355 Vance Law .02 .10
356 Jeff Gray RC .02 .10
357 Bobby Bonilla .07 .20
358 Ernest Riles .02 .10
359 Ron Hassey .02 .10
360 Willie McGee .07 .20
361 Mackey Sasser .02 .10

362 Glenn Braggs .02 .10
363 Mario Diaz .02 .10
364 Barry Bonds CL .40 1.00
365 Kevin Bass .02 .10
366 Pete Incaviglia .02 .10
367 Luis Sojo UER .02 .10
(1989 stats inter-
spersed with 1990's)
368 Lance Parrish .07 .20
369 Mark Leonard RC .02 .10
370 Heath. Slocumb RC .07 .20
371 Jimmy Jones .02 .10
372 Ken Griffey Jr. .40 1.00
373 Chris Hammond .02 .10
374 Chili Davis .07 .20
375 Joey Cora .02 .10
376 Ken Hill .02 .10
377 Darryl Strawberry .07 .20
378 Ron Darling .02 .10
379 Sid Bream .02 .10
380 Bill Swift .02 .10
381 Shawn Abner .02 .10
382 Eric King .02 .10
383 Mickey Morandini .02 .10
384 Carlton Fisk .10 .30
385 Steve Lake .02 .10
386 Mike Jeffcoat .02 .10
387 Darren Holmes RC .07 .20
388 Tim Wallach .02 .10
389 George Bell .02 .10
390 Craig Lefferts .02 .10
391 Ernie Whitt .02 .10
392 Felix Jose .02 .10
393 Kevin Maas .02 .10
394 Devon White .07 .20
395 Otis Nixon .02 .10
396 Chuck Knoblauch .07 .20
397 Scott Coolbaugh .02 .10
398 Glenn Davis .02 .10
399 Manny Lee .02 .10
400 Andre Dawson .07 .20
401 Scott Chiamparino .02 .10
402 Bill Gullickson .02 .10
403 Lance Johnson .02 .10
404 Juan Agosto .02 .10
405 Danny Darwin .02 .10
406 Barry Jones .02 .10
407 Larry Andersen .02 .10
408 Luis Rivera .02 .10
409 Jaime Navarro .02 .10
410 Roger McDowell .02 .10
411 Brett Butler .07 .20
412 Dale Murphy .10 .30
413 Tim Raines UER .07 .20
(Listed as hitting .500
in 1980, should be .050)
414 Norm Charlton .02 .10
415 Greg Cadaret .02 .10
416 Chris Nabholz .02 .10
417 Dave Stewart .07 .20
418 Rich Gedman .02 .10
419 Willie Randolph .07 .20
420 Mitch Williams .02 .10
421 Brook Jacoby .02 .10
422 Greg W. Harris .02 .10
423 Nolan Ryan .75 2.00
424 Dave Rohde .02 .10
425 Don Mattingly .50 1.25
426 Greg Gagne .02 .10
427 Vince Coleman .02 .10
428 Dan Pasqua .02 .10
429 Alvin Davis .02 .10
430 Cal Ripken .60 1.50
431 Jamie Quirk .02 .10
432 Benito Santiago .07 .20
433 Jose Uribe .02 .10
434 Candy Maldonado .02 .10
435 Junior Felix .02 .10
436 Deion Sanders .10 .30
437 John Franco .07 .20
438 Greg Hibbard .02 .10
439 Floyd Bannister .02 .10
440 Steve Howe .02 .10
441 Steve Decker RC .02 .10
442 Vicente Palacios .02 .10
443 Pat Tabler .02 .10
444 Darryl Strawberry CL .02 .10
445 Mike Felder .02 .10
446 Al Newman .02 .10
447 Chris Donnels RC .02 .10
448 Rich Rodriguez RC .02 .10
449 Turner Ward RC .07 .20
450 Bob Walk .02 .10
451 Gilberto Reyes .02 .10
452 Mike Jackson .02 .10
453 Rafael Belliard .02 .10
454 Wayne Edwards .02 .10
455 Andy Allanson .02 .10
456 Dave Smith .02 .10
457 Gary Carter .07 .20
458 Warren Cromartie .02 .10
459 Jack Armstrong .02 .10
460 Bob Tewksbury .02 .10
461 Joe Klink .02 .10
462 Xavier Hernandez .02 .10
463 Scott Radinsky .02 .10
464 Jeff Robinson .02 .10
465 Gregg Jefferies .02 .10
466 Denny Neagle RC .20 .50
467 Carmelo Martinez .02 .10
468 Donn Pall .02 .10
469 Bruce Hurst .02 .10
470 Eric Bullock .02 .10
471 Rick Aguilera .07 .20
472 Charlie Hough .07 .20
473 Carlos Quintana .02 .10
474 Marty Barrett .02 .10
475 Kevin D. Brown .02 .10
476 Bobby Ojeda .02 .10
477 Edgar Martinez .10 .30
478 Bip Roberts .02 .10
479 Mike Flanagan .02 .10
480 John Habyan .02 .10
481 Larry Casian RC .02 .10
482 Wally Backman .02 .10
483 Doug Dascenzo .02 .10
484 Rick Dempsey .02 .10
485 Ed Sprague .02 .10
486 Steve Chitren RC .02 .10
487 Mark McGwire .60 1.50
488 Roger Clemens .60 1.50
489 Orlando Merced RC .02 .10
490 Rene Gonzales .02 .10
491 Mike Stanton .02 .10
492 Al Osuna RC .02 .10
493 Rick Cerone .02 .10
494 Mariano Duncan .02 .10
495 Zane Smith .02 .10
496 John Morris .02 .10
497 Frank Tanana .02 .10
498 Junior Ortiz .02 .10
499 Dave Winfield .07 .20
500 Gary Varsho .02 .10
501 Chico Walker .02 .10
502 Ken Caminiti .07 .20
503 Ken Griffey Sr. .07 .20
504 Randy Myers .02 .10
505 Steve Bedrosian .02 .10
506 Cory Snyder .02 .10
507 Cris Carpenter .02 .10
508 Tim Belcher .02 .10
509 Jeff Hamilton .02 .10
510 Steve Avery .02 .10
511 Dave Valle .02 .10
512 Tom Lampkin .02 .10
513 Shawn Hillegas .02 .10
514 Reggie Jefferson .02 .10
515 Ron Karkovice .02 .10
516 Doug Drabek .02 .10
517 Tom Henke .02 .10
518 Chris Bosio .02 .10
519 Greg Olson .02 .10
520 Bob Scanlan RC .02 .10
521 Alonzo Powell RC .02 .10
522 Jeff Ballard .02 .10
523 Ray Lankford .07 .20
524 Tommy Greene .02 .10
525 Mike Timlin RC .07 .20
526 Juan Berenguer .02 .10
527 Scott Erickson .02 .10
528 Sandy Alomar Jr. CL .02 .10

1992 Leaf

The 1992 Leaf set consists of 528 cards, issued in two separate 264-card series. Cards were distributed in first and second series 15-card foil packs. Each pack contained a selection of basic cards and one black gold parallel card. The basic card fronts feature color action player photos on a silver card face. The player's name appears in a black bar edged at the bottom by a thin red stripe. The team logo overlaps the bar at the right corner. Rookie Cards in this set include Brian Jordan and Jeff Kent.

COMPLETE SET (528) 6.00 15.00
COMP. SERIES 1 (264) 2.00 5.00
COMP. SERIES 2 (264) 4.00 10.00
1 Jim Abbott .08 .25
2 Cal Eldred .01 .05
3 Bud Black .01 .05
4 Dave Howard .01 .05
5 Luis Sojo .01 .05
6 Gary Scott .01 .05
7 Joe Oliver .01 .05
8 Chris Gardner .01 .05
9 Sandy Alomar Jr. .01 .05
10 Greg W. Harris .01 .05
11 Doug Drabek .01 .05
12 Darryl Hamilton .01 .05
13 Mike Mussina .15 .40
14 Kevin Tapani .01 .05
15 Ron Gant .05 .15
16 Mark McGwire .40 1.00
17 Robin Ventura .05 .15
18 Pedro Guerrero .05 .15
19 Roger Clemens .30 .75
20 Steve Farr .01 .05
21 Frank Tanana .01 .05
22 Joe Hesketh .01 .05
23 Erik Hanson .01 .05
24 Greg Cadaret .01 .05
25 Rex Hudler .01 .05
26 Mark Grace .08 .25
27 Kelly Gruber .01 .05
28 Jeff Bagwell .15 .40
29 Darryl Strawberry .05 .15
30 Dave Smith .01 .05
31 Kevin Appier .05 .15
32 Steve Chitren .01 .05
33 Kevin Gross .01 .05
34 Rick Aguilera .05 .15
35 Juan Guzman .01 .05
36 Joe Orsulak .01 .05
37 Tim Raines .05 .15
38 Harold Reynolds .05 .15
39 Charlie Hough .05 .15
40 Tony Phillips .01 .05
41 Nolan Ryan .60 1.50
42 Vince Coleman .01 .05
43 Andy Van Slyke .08 .25
44 Tim Burke .01 .05
45 Luis Polonia .01 .05
46 Tom Browning .01 .05
47 Willie McGee .05 .15
48 Gary DiSarcina .01 .05
49 Mark Lewis .01 .05
50 Phil Plantier .01 .05
51 Doug Dascenzo .01 .05
52 Cal Ripken .50 1.25
53 Pedro Munoz .01 .05
54 Carlos Hernandez .01 .05
55 Jerald Clark .01 .05
56 Jeff Brantley .01 .05
57 Don Mattingly .40 1.00
58 Roger McDowell .01 .05
59 Steve Avery .01 .05
60 John Olerud .05 .15
61 Bill Gullickson .01 .05
62 Juan Gonzalez .08 .25
63 Felix Jose .01 .05
64 Robin Yount .25 .60
65 Greg Briley .01 .05
66 Steve Finley .05 .15
67 Frank Thomas CL .08 .25
68 Tom Gordon .01 .05
69 Rob Dibble .05 .15
70 Glenallen Hill .01 .05
71 Calvin Jones .01 .05
72 Joe Girardi .01 .05
73 Barry Larkin .08 .25
74 Andy Benes .01 .05
75 Milt Cuyler .01 .05
76 Kevin Bass .01 .05
77 Pete Harnisch .01 .05
78 Wilson Alvarez .01 .05
79 Mike Devereaux .01 .05
80 Doug Henry RC .02 .10
81 Orel Hershiser .05 .15
82 Shane Mack .01 .05
83 Mike Macfarlane .01 .05
84 Thomas Howard .01 .05
85 Alex Fernandez .01 .05
86 Reggie Jefferson .01 .05
87 Leo Gomez .01 .05
88 Mel Hall .01 .05
89 Mike Greenwell .01 .05
90 Jeff Russell .01 .05
91 Steve Buechele .01 .05
92 David Cone .05 .15
93 Kevin Reimer .01 .05
94 Mark Lemke .01 .05
95 Bob Tewksbury .01 .05
96 Zane Smith .01 .05
97 Mark Eichhorn .01 .05
98 Kirby Puckett .15 .40
99 Paul O'Neill .08 .25
100 Dennis Eckersley .05 .15
101 Duane Ward .01 .05
102 Matt Nokes .01 .05
103 Mo Vaughn .05 .15
104 Pat Kelly .01 .05
105 Ron Karkovice .01 .05
106 Bill Spiers .01 .05
107 Gary Gaetti .05 .15
108 Mackey Sasser .01 .05
109 Robby Thompson .01 .05
110 Marvin Freeman .01 .05
111 Jimmy Key .05 .15
112 Dwight Gooden .05 .15
113 Charlie Leibrandt .01 .05
114 Devon White .05 .15
115 Charles Nagy .01 .05
116 Rickey Henderson .15 .40
117 Paul Assenmacher .01 .05
118 Junior Felix .01 .05
119 Julio Franco .05 .15
120 Norm Charlton .01 .05
121 Scott Servais .01 .05
122 Gerald Perry .01 .05
123 Brian McRae .01 .05
124 Don Slaught .01 .05
125 Juan Samuel .01 .05
126 Harold Baines .05 .15
127 Scott Livingstone .01 .05
128 Jay Buhner .05 .15
129 Darrin Jackson .01 .05
130 Luis Mercedes .01 .05
131 Brian Harper .01 .05
132 Howard Johnson .01 .05
133 Nolan Ryan CL .15 .40
134 Dante Bichette .05 .15
135 Dave Righetti .05 .15
136 Jeff Montgomery .05 .15
137 Joe Grahe .01 .05
138 Delino DeShields .01 .05
139 Jose Rijo .01 .05
140 Ken Caminiti .05 .15
141 Steve Olin .01 .05
142 Kurt Stillwell .01 .05
143 Jay Bell .05 .15
144 Jaime Navarro .01 .05
145 Ben McDonald .01 .05
146 Greg Gagne .01 .05
147 Jeff Blauser .01 .05
148 Carney Lansford .05 .15
149 Ozzie Guillen .05 .15
150 Milt Thompson .01 .05
151 Jeff Reardon .05 .15
152 Scott Sanderson .01 .05
153 Cecil Fielder .05 .15
154 Greg A. Harris .01 .05
155 Rich DeLucia .01 .05
156 Roberto Kelly .01 .05
157 Bryn Smith .01 .05
158 Chuck McElroy .01 .05
159 Tom Henke .01 .05
160 Luis Gonzalez .05 .15
161 Steve Wilson .01 .05
162 Shawn Boskie .01 .05
163 Mark Davis .01 .05
164 Mike Moore .01 .05
165 Mike Scioscia .01 .05
166 Scott Erickson .01 .05
167 Todd Stottlemyre .01 .05
168 Alvin Davis .01 .05
169 Greg Hibbard .01 .05
170 David Valle .01 .05
171 Dave Winfield .05 .15
172 Alan Trammell .05 .15
173 Kenny Rogers .05 .15
174 John Franco .05 .15
175 Jose Lind .01 .05
176 Pete Schourek .01 .05
177 Von Hayes .01 .05
178 Chris Hammond .01 .05
179 John Burkett .01 .05
180 Dickie Thon .01 .05
181 Joel Skinner .01 .05
182 Scott Cooper .01 .05
183 Andre Dawson .05 .15
184 Billy Ripken .01 .05
185 Kevin Mitchell .01 .05
186 Brett Butler .05 .15
187 Tony Fernandez .01 .05
188 Cory Snyder .01 .05
189 John Habyan .01 .05
190 Dennis Martinez .05 .15
191 John Smoltz .08 .25
192 Greg Myers .01 .05
193 Rob Deer .01 .05
194 Ivan Rodriguez .15 .40
195 Ray Lankford .05 .15
196 Bill Wegman .01 .05
197 Edgar Martinez .08 .25
198 Darryl Kile .05 .15
199 Cal Ripken CL .15 .40
200 Brent Mayne .01 .05
201 Larry Walker .08 .25
202 Carlos Baerga .01 .05
203 Russ Swan .01 .05
204 Mike Morgan .01 .05
205 Hal Morris .01 .05
206 Tony Gwynn .20 .50
207 Mark Leiter .01 .05
208 Kirt Manwaring .01 .05
209 Al Osuna .01 .05
210 Bobby Thigpen .01 .05
211 Chris Hoiles .01 .05
212 B.J. Surhoff .05 .15
213 Lenny Harris .01 .05
214 Scott Leius .01 .05
215 Gregg Jefferies .01 .05
216 Bruce Hurst .01 .05
217 Steve Sax .01 .05
218 Dave Otto .01 .05
219 Sam Horn .01 .05
220 Charlie Hayes .01 .05
221 Frank Viola .05 .15
222 Jose Guzman .01 .05
223 Gary Redus .01 .05
224 Dave Gallagher .01 .05
225 Dean Palmer .05 .15
226 Greg Olson .01 .05
227 Jose DeLeon .01 .05
228 Mike LaValliere .01 .05
229 Mark Langston .01 .05
230 Chuck Knoblauch .05 .15
231 Bill Doran .01 .05
232 Dave Henderson .01 .05
233 Roberto Alomar .08 .25
234 Scott Fletcher .01 .05
235 Tim Naehring .01 .05
236 Mike Gallego .01 .05
237 Lance Johnson .01 .05
238 Paul Molitor .05 .15
239 Dan Gladden .01 .05
240 Willie Randolph .05 .15
241 Will Clark .08 .25
242 Sid Bream .01 .05
243 Derek Bell .05 .15
244 Bill Pecota .01 .05
245 Terry Pendleton .05 .15
246 Randy Ready .01 .05
247 Jack Armstrong .01 .05
248 Todd Van Poppel .01 .05
249 Shawon Dunston .01 .05
250 Bobby Rose .01 .05
251 Jeff Huson .01 .05
252 Bip Roberts .01 .05
253 Doug Jones .01 .05
254 Lee Smith .05 .15
255 George Brett .40 1.00
256 Randy Tomlin .01 .05
257 Todd Benzinger .01 .05
258 Dave Stewart .05 .15
259 Mark Carreon .01 .05
260 Pete O'Brien .01 .05
261 Tim Teufel .01 .05
262 Bob Milacki .01 .05
263 Mark Guthrie .01 .05
264 Darrin Fletcher .01 .05
265 Omar Vizquel .08 .25
266 Chris Bosio .01 .05
267 Jose Canseco .08 .25
268 Mike Boddicker .01 .05
269 Lance Parrish .05 .15
270 Jose Vizcaino .01 .05
271 Chris Sabo .01 .05
272 Royce Clayton .01 .05
273 Marquis Grissom .05 .15
274 Fred McGriff .08 .25
275 Barry Bonds .60 1.50
276 Greg Vaughn .01 .05
277 Gregg Olson .01 .05
278 Dave Hollins .01 .05
279 Tom Glavine .08 .25
280 Bryan Hickerson UER .01 .05
Name spelled Brian on front
281 Scott Radinsky .01 .05
282 Omar Olivares .01 .05
283 Ivan Calderon .01 .05
284 Kevin Maas .01 .05
285 Mickey Tettleton .01 .05
286 Wade Boggs .08 .25
287 Stan Belinda .01 .05
288 Bret Barberie .01 .05
289 Jose Oquendo .01 .05
290 Frank Castillo .01 .05
291 Dave Stieb .01 .05
292 Tommy Greene .01 .05
293 Eric Karros .05 .15
294 Greg Maddux .25 .60
295 Jim Eisenreich .01 .05
296 Rafael Palmeiro .08 .25
297 Ramon Martinez .01 .05
298 Tim Wallach .01 .05
299 Jim Thome .15 .40
300 Chito Martinez .01 .05
301 Mitch Williams .01 .05
302 Randy Johnson .15 .40
303 Carlton Fisk .08 .25
304 Travis Fryman .05 .15
305 Bobby Witt .01 .05
306 Dave Magadan .01 .05
307 Alex Cole .01 .05
308 Bobby Bonilla .05 .15
309 Bryan Harvey .01 .05
310 Rafael Belliard .01 .05
311 Mariano Duncan .01 .05
312 Chuck Crim .01 .05
313 John Kruk .05 .15
314 Ellis Burks .05 .15
315 Craig Biggio .08 .25
316 Glenn Davis .01 .05
317 Ryne Sandberg .25 .60
318 Mike Sharperson .01 .05
319 Rich Rodriguez .01 .05
320 Lee Guetterman .01 .05
321 Benito Santiago .05 .15
322 Jose Offerman .01 .05
323 Tony Pena .01 .05
324 Pat Borders .01 .05
325 Mike Henneman .01 .05
326 Kevin Brown .05 .15
327 Chris Nabholz .01 .05
328 Franklin Stubbs .01 .05
329 Tino Martinez .08 .25
330 Mickey Morandini .01 .05
331 Ryne Sandberg CL .15 .40
332 Mark Gubicza .01 .05
333 Bill Landrum .01 .05
334 Mark Whiten .01 .05
335 Darren Daulton .05 .15
336 Rick Wilkins .01 .05
337 Brian Jordan RC .20 .50
338 Kevin Ward .01 .05
339 Ruben Amaro .01 .05
340 Trevor Wilson .01 .05
341 Andujar Cedeno .01 .05
342 Michael Huff .01 .05
343 Brady Anderson .05 .15
344 Craig Grebeck .01 .05
345 Bob Ojeda .01 .05
346 Mike Pagliarulo .01 .05
347 Terry Shumpert .01 .05
348 Dann Bilardello .01 .05
349 Frank Thomas .15 .40
350 Albert Belle .05 .15
351 Jose Mesa .01 .05
352 Rich Monteleone .01 .05
353 Bob Walk .01 .05
354 Monty Fariss .01 .05
355 Luis Rivera .01 .05
356 Anthony Young .01 .05
357 Geno Petralli .01 .05
358 Otis Nixon .01 .05
359 Tom Pagnozzi .01 .05
360 Reggie Sanders .05 .15
361 Lee Stevens .01 .05
362 Kent Hrbek .05 .15
363 Orlando Merced .01 .05
364 Mike Bordick .01 .05
365 Dion James UER .01 .05
(Blue Jays logo
on card back)
366 Jack Clark .05 .15
367 Mike Stanley .01 .05
368 Randy Velarde .01 .05
369 Dan Pasqua .01 .05
370 Pat Listach RC .08 .25
371 Mike Fitzgerald .01 .05
372 Tom Foley .01 .05
373 Matt Williams .05 .15
374 Brian Hunter .01 .05
375 Joe Carter .05 .15
376 Bret Saberhagen .05 .15
377 Mike Stanton .01 .05
378 Hubie Brooks .01 .05
379 Eric Bell .01 .05
380 Walt Weiss .01 .05
381 Danny Jackson .01 .05
382 Manuel Lee .01 .05
383 Ruben Sierra .05 .15
384 Greg Swindell .01 .05
385 Ryan Bowen .01 .05
386 Kevin Ritz .01 .05
387 Curtis Wilkerson .01 .05
388 Gary Varsho .01 .05
389 Dave Hansen .01 .05
390 Bob Welch .01 .05
391 Lou Whitaker .05 .15
392 Ken Griffey Jr. .25 .60
393 Mike Maddux .01 .05
394 Arthur Rhodes .01 .05
395 Chili Davis .05 .15
396 Eddie Murray .15 .40
397 Robin Yount CL .08 .25
398 Dave Cochrane .01 .05
399 Kevin Seitzer .01 .05
400 Ozzie Smith .25 .60
401 Paul Sorrento .01 .05
402 Les Lancaster .01 .05
403 Junior Noboa .01 .05
404 David Justice .05 .15
405 Andy Ashby .01 .05
406 Danny Tartabull .01 .05
407 Bill Swift .01 .05
408 Craig Lefferts .01 .05
409 Tom Candiotti .01 .05
410 Lance Blankenship .01 .05
411 Jeff Tackett .01 .05
412 Sammy Sosa .15 .40
413 Jody Reed .01 .05
414 Bruce Ruffin .01 .05
415 Gene Larkin .01 .05
416 John Vander Wal RC .08 .25
417 Tim Belcher .01 .05
418 Steve Frey .01 .05
419 Dick Schofield .01 .05
420 Jeff King .01 .05
421 Kim Batiste .01 .05
422 Jack McDowell .01 .05
423 Damon Berryhill .01 .05
424 Gary Wayne .01 .05
425 Jack Morris .05 .15
426 Moises Alou .05 .15
427 Mark McLemore .01 .05
428 Juan Guerrero .01 .05
429 Scott Scudder .01 .05
430 Eric Davis .05 .15
431 Joe Slusarski .01 .05
432 Todd Zeile .01 .05
433 Dwayne Henry .01 .05
434 Cliff Brantley .01 .05
435 Butch Henry RC .02 .10
436 Todd Worrell .01 .05
437 Bob Scanlan .01 .05
438 Wally Joyner .05 .15
439 John Flaherty .01 .05
440 Brian Downing .01 .05
441 Darren Lewis .01 .05
442 Gary Carter .05 .15
443 Wally Ritchie .01 .05
444 Chris Jones .01 .05
445 Jeff Kent RC 1.00 2.50
446 Gary Sheffield .05 .15
447 Ron Darling .01 .05
448 Deion Sanders .08 .25
449 Andres Galarraga .05 .15
450 Chuck Finley .05 .15
451 Derek Lilliquist .01 .05
452 Carl Willis .01 .05
453 Wes Chamberlain .01 .05
454 Roger Mason .01 .05
455 Spike Owen .01 .05
456 Thomas Howard .01 .05
457 Dave Martinez .01 .05
458 Pete Incaviglia .01 .05
459 Keith A. Miller .01 .05
460 Mike Fetters .01 .05
461 Paul Gibson .01 .05
462 George Bell .01 .05
463 Bobby Bonilla CL .01 .05
464 Terry Mulholland .01 .05
465 Storm Davis .01 .05
466 Gary Pettis .01 .05
467 Randy Bush .01 .05
468 Ken Hill .01 .05
469 Rheal Cormier .01 .05
470 Andy Stankiewicz .01 .05
471 Dave Burba .01 .05
472 Henry Cotto .01 .05
473 Dale Sveum .01 .05
474 Rich Gossage .05 .15
475 William Suero .01 .05
476 Doug Strange .01 .05
477 Bill Krueger .01 .05
478 John Wetteland .05 .15
479 Melido Perez .01 .05
480 Lonnie Smith .01 .05
481 Mike Jackson .01 .05
482 Mike Gardiner .01 .05
483 David Wells .05 .15
484 Barry Jones .01 .05
485 Scott Bankhead .01 .05
486 Terry Leach .01 .05
487 Vince Horsman .01 .05
488 Dave Eiland .01 .05
489 Alejandro Pena .01 .05
490 Julio Valera .01 .05
491 Joe Boever .01 .05
492 Paul Miller RC .01 .05
493 Archi Cianfrocco RC .02 .10
494 Dave Fleming .01 .05
495 Kyle Abbott .01 .05
496 Chad Kreuter .01 .05
497 Chris James .01 .05
498 Donnie Hill .01 .05
499 Jacob Brumfield .01 .05
500 Ricky Bones .01 .05
501 Terry Steinbach .01 .05
502 Bernard Gilkey .01 .05
503 Dennis Cook .01 .05
504 Len Dykstra .05 .15
505 Mike Bielecki .01 .05
506 Bob Kipper .01 .05
507 Jose Melendez .01 .05
508 Rick Sutcliffe .05 .15
509 Ken Patterson .01 .05
510 Andy Allanson .01 .05
511 Al Newman .01 .05
512 Mark Gardner .01 .05
513 Jeff Schaefer .01 .05
514 Jim McNamara .01 .05
515 Peter Hoy .01 .05
516 Curt Schilling .08 .25
517 Kirk McCaskill .01 .05
518 Chris Gwynn .01 .05
519 Sid Fernandez .01 .05
520 Jeff Parrett .01 .05
521 Scott Ruskin .01 .05
522 Kevin McReynolds .01 .05
523 Rick Cerone .01 .05
524 Jesse Orosco .01 .05
525 Troy Afenir .01 .05
526 John Smiley .01 .05
527 Dale Murphy .08 .25
528 Leaf Set Card .01 .05

1993 Leaf

The 1993 Leaf baseball set consists of three series of 220, 220, and 110 standard-size cards, respectively. Cards were distributed in 14-card foil packs, jumbo packs and magazine packs. Rookie Cards in this set include J.T. Snow. White Sox slugger (and at that time, Leaf Representative) Frank Thomas signed 3,500 cards, which were randomly seeded into packs. In addition, a special card commemorating Dave Winfield's 3,000 hit was also seeded into packs. Both cards are listed at the end of our checklist but are not.considered part of the 550-card basic set.

COMPLETE SET (550) 14.00 35.00
COMP. SERIES 1 (220) 6.00 15.00
COMP. SERIES 2 (220) 6.00 15.00
COMPLETE UPDATE (110) 2.00 5.00
COMMON RC .05 .15
1 Ben McDonald .05 .15
2 Sid Fernandez .05 .15
3 Juan Guzman .05 .15
4 Curt Schilling .10 .30
5 Ivan Rodriguez .20 .50
6 Don Slaught .05 .15
7 Terry Steinbach .05 .15
8 Todd Zeile .05 .15
9 Andy Stankiewicz .05 .15
10 Tim Teufel .05 .15
11 Marvin Freeman .05 .15
12 Jim Austin .05 .15
13 Bob Scanlan .05 .15
14 Rusty Meacham .05 .15
15 Casey Candaele .05 .15
16 Travis Fryman .10 .30
17 Jose Offerman .05 .15
18 Albert Belle .10 .30
19 John Vander Wal .05 .15
20 Dan Pasqua .05 .15
21 Frank Viola .10 .30
22 Terry Mulholland .05 .15
23 Gregg Olson .05 .15
24 Randy Tomlin .05 .15
25 Todd Stottlemyre .05 .15
26 Jose Oquendo .05 .15
27 Julio Franco .10 .30
28 Tony Gwynn .40 1.00
29 Ruben Sierra .10 .30
30 Robby Thompson .05 .15
31 Jim Bullinger .05 .15
32 Rick Aguilera .05 .15
33 Scott Servais .05 .15
34 Cal Eldred .05 .15
35 Mike Piazza 1.25 3.00
36 Brent Mayne .05 .15
37 Wil Cordero .05 .15
38 Milt Cuyler .05 .15
39 Howard Johnson .05 .15
40 Kenny Lofton .10 .30
41 Alex Fernandez .05 .15
42 Denny Neagle .10 .30
43 Tony Pena .05 .15
44 Bob Tewksbury .05 .15
45 Glenn Davis .05 .15
46 Fred McGriff .20 .50
47 John Olerud .10 .30
48 Steve Hosey .05 .15
49 Rafael Palmeiro .20 .50
50 David Justice .10 .30
51 Pete Harnisch .05 .15
52 Sam Militello .05 .15
53 Orel Hershiser .10 .30
54 Pat Mahomes .05 .15
55 Greg Colbrunn .05 .15
56 Greg Vaughn .05 .15
57 Vince Coleman .05 .15
58 Brian McRae .05 .15
59 Len Dykstra .10 .30
60 Dan Gladden .05 .15
61 Ted Power .05 .15
62 Donovan Osborne .05 .15
63 Ron Karkovice .05 .15
64 Frank Seminara .05 .15
65 Bob Zupcic .05 .15
66 Kirt Manwaring .05 .15
67 Mike Devereaux .05 .15
68 Mark Lemke .05 .15
69 Devon White .10 .30
70 Sammy Sosa .30 .75
71 Pedro Astacio .05 .15
72 Dennis Eckersley .10 .30
73 Chris Nabholz .05 .15
74 Melido Perez .05 .15
75 Todd Hundley .05 .15
76 Kent Hrbek .10 .30
77 Mickey Morandini .05 .15
78 Tim McIntosh .05 .15
79 Andy Van Slyke .20 .50
80 Kevin McReynolds .05 .15
81 Mike Henneman .05 .15
82 Greg W. Harris .05 .15
83 Sandy Alomar Jr. .05 .15
84 Mike Jackson .05 .15
85 Ozzie Guillen .10 .30
86 Jeff Blauser .05 .15
87 John Valentin .05 .15
88 Rey Sanchez .05 .15
89 Rick Sutcliffe .10 .30
90 Luis Gonzalez .10 .30
91 Jeff Fassero .05 .15
92 Kenny Rogers .10 .30
93 Bret Saberhagen .10 .30
94 Bob Welch .05 .15
95 Darren Daulton .10 .30
96 Mike Gallego .05 .15
97 Orlando Merced .05 .15
98 Chuck Knoblauch .10 .30
99 Bernard Gilkey .05 .15
100 Billy Ashley .05 .15
101 Kevin Appier .10 .30
102 Jeff Brantley .05 .15
103 Bill Gullickson .05 .15
104 John Smoltz .20 .50
105 Paul Sorrento .05 .15
106 Steve Buechele .05 .15
107 Steve Sax .05 .15
108 Andujar Cedeno .05 .15
109 Billy Hatcher .05 .15
110 Checklist .05 .15
111 Alan Mills .05 .15
112 John Franco .10 .30
113 Jack Morris .10 .30
114 Mitch Williams .05 .15
115 Nolan Ryan 1.25 3.00
116 Jay Bell .10 .30
117 Mike Bordick .05 .15
118 Geronimo Pena .05 .15
119 Danny Tartabull .05 .15
120 Checklist .05 .15
121 Steve Avery .05 .15
122 Ricky Bones .05 .15
123 Mike Morgan .05 .15
124 Jeff Montgomery .05 .15
125 Jeff Bagwell .20 .50
126 Tony Phillips .05 .15
127 Lenny Harris .05 .15
128 Glenallen Hill .05 .15
129 Marquis Grissom .10 .30
130 Gerald Williams UER .05 .15
(Bernie Williams
picture and stats)
131 Greg A. Harris .05 .15
132 Tommy Greene .05 .15
133 Chris Hoiles .05 .15
134 Bob Walk .05 .15
135 Duane Ward .05 .15
136 Tom Pagnozzi .05 .15
137 Jeff Huson .05 .15
138 Kurt Stillwell .05 .15
139 Dave Henderson .05 .15
140 Darrin Jackson .05 .15
141 Frank Castillo .05 .15
142 Scott Erickson .05 .15
143 Darryl Kile .10 .30
144 Bill Wegman .05 .15
145 Steve Wilson .05 .15
146 George Brett .75 2.00
147 Moises Alou .10 .30
148 Lou Whitaker .10 .30
149 Chico Walker .05 .15
150 Jerry Browne .05 .15
151 Kirk McCaskill .05 .15
152 Zane Smith .05 .15
153 Matt Young .05 .15
154 Lee Smith .10 .30

155 Leo Gomez .05 .15
156 Dan Walters .05 .15
157 Pat Borders .05 .15
158 Matt Williams .10 .30
159 Dean Palmer .10 .30
160 John Patterson .05 .15
161 Doug Jones .05 .15
162 John Habyan .05 .15
163 Pedro Martinez .60 1.50
164 Carl Willis .05 .15
165 Darrin Fletcher .05 .15
166 B.J. Surhoff .10 .30
167 Eddie Murray .30 .75
168 Keith Miller .05 .15
169 Ricky Jordan .05 .15
170 Juan Gonzalez .10 .30
171 Charles Nagy .05 .15
172 Mark Clark .05 .15
173 Bobby Thigpen .05 .15
174 Tim Scott .05 .15
175 Scott Cooper .05 .15
176 Royce Clayton .05 .15
177 Brady Anderson .10 .30
178 Sid Bream .05 .15
179 Derek Bell .05 .15
180 Otis Nixon .05 .15
181 Kevin Gross .05 .15
182 Ron Darling .05 .15
183 John Wetteland .10 .30
184 Mike Stanley .05 .15
185 Jeff Kent .30 .75
186 Brian Harper .05 .15
187 Mariano Duncan .05 .15
188 Robin Yount .50 1.25
189 Al Martin .05 .15
190 Eddie Zosky .05 .15
191 Mike Munoz .05 .15
192 Andy Benes .05 .15
193 Dennis Cook .05 .15
194 Bill Swift .05 .15
195 Frank Thomas .30 .75
195A Frank Thomas .50 1.25
Franklin visible on batting glove
196 Damon Berryhill .05 .15
197 Mike Greenwell .05 .15
198 Mark Grace .20 .50
199 Darryl Hamilton .05 .15
200 Derrick May .05 .15
201 Ken Hill .05 .15
202 Kevin Brown .10 .30
203 Dwight Gooden .10 .30
204 Bobby Witt .05 .15
205 Juan Bell .05 .15
206 Kevin Maas .05 .15
207 Jeff King .05 .15
208 Scott Leius .05 .15
209 Rheal Cormier .05 .15
210 Darryl Strawberry .10 .30
211 Tom Gordon .05 .15
212 Bud Black .05 .15
213 Mickey Tettleton .05 .15
214 Pete Smith .05 .15
215 Felix Fermin .05 .15
216 Rick Wilkins .05 .15
217 George Bell .05 .15
218 Eric Anthony .05 .15
219 Pedro Munoz .05 .15
220 Albert Bell CL .10 .30
221 Lance Blankenship .05 .15
222 Deion Sanders .20 .50
223 Craig Biggio .20 .50
224 Ryne Sandberg .50 1.25
225 Ron Gant .10 .30
226 Tom Brunansky .05 .15
227 Chad Curtis .05 .15
228 Joe Carter .10 .30
229 Brian Jordan .10 .30
230 Brett Butler .10 .30
231 Frank Bolick .05 .15
232 Rod Beck .05 .15
233 Carlos Baerga .05 .15
234 Eric Karros .10 .30
235 Jack Armstrong .05 .15
236 Bobby Bonilla .10 .30
237 Don Mattingly .75 2.00
238 Jeff Gardner .05 .15
239 Dave Hollins .05 .15
240 Steve Cooke .05 .15
241 Jose Canseco .20 .50
242 Ivan Calderon .05 .15
243 Tim Belcher .05 .15
244 Freddie Benavides .05 .15
245 Roberto Alomar .20 .50
246 Rob Deer .05 .15
247 Will Clark .20 .50
248 Mike Felder .05 .15
249 Harold Baines .10 .30
250 David Cone .10 .30
251 Mark Guthrie .05 .15
252 Ellis Burks .10 .30
253 Jim Abbott .20 .50
254 Chili Davis .10 .30
255 Chris Bosio .05 .15
256 Bret Barberie .05 .15
257 Hal Morris .05 .15
258 Dante Bichette .10 .30
259 Storm Davis .05 .15
260 Gary DiSarcina .05 .15
261 Ken Caminiti .10 .30
262 Paul Molitor .10 .30
263 Joe Oliver .05 .15
264 Pat Listach .05 .15
265 Gregg Jefferies .05 .15
266 Jose Guzman .05 .15
267 Eric Davis .10 .30
268 Delino DeShields .05 .15
269 Barry Bonds .75 2.00
270 Mike Bielecki .05 .15
271 Jay Buhner .10 .30
272 Scott Pose RC .05 .15
273 Tony Fernandez .05 .15
274 Chito Martinez .05 .15
275 Phil Plantier .05 .15
276 Pete Incaviglia .05 .15
277 Carlos Garcia .05 .15
278 Tom Henke .05 .15
279 Roger Clemens .60 1.50
280 Rob Dibble .05 .15
281 Daryl Boston .05 .15
282 Greg Gagne .05 .15
283 Cecil Fielder .10 .30
284 Carlton Fisk .20 .50
285 Wade Boggs .20 .50
286 Damion Easley .05 .15
287 Norm Charlton .05 .15
288 Jeff Conine .10 .30
289 Roberto Kelly .05 .15
290 Jerald Clark .05 .15
291 Rickey Henderson .30 .75
292 Chuck Finley .10 .30
293 Doug Drabek .05 .15
294 Dave Stewart .10 .30
295 Tom Glavine .20 .50
296 Jaime Navarro .05 .15
297 Ray Lankford .10 .30
298 Greg Hibbard .05 .15
299 Jody Reed .05 .15
300 Dennis Martinez .10 .30
301 Dave Martinez .05 .15
302 Reggie Jefferson .05 .15
303 John Cummings RC .05 .15
304 Orestes Destrade .05 .15
305 Mike Maddux .05 .15
306 David Segui .05 .15
307 Gary Sheffield .10 .30
308 Danny Jackson .05 .15
309 Craig Lefferts .05 .15
310 Andre Dawson .10 .30
311 Barry Larkin .20 .50
312 Alex Cole .05 .15
313 Mark Gardner .05 .15
314 Kirk Gibson .10 .30
315 Shane Mack .05 .15
316 Bo Jackson .30 .75
317 Jimmy Key .10 .30
318 Greg Myers .05 .15
319 Ken Griffey Jr. .50 1.25
320 Monty Fariss .05 .15
321 Kevin Mitchell .05 .15
322 Andres Galarraga .10 .30
323 Mark McGwire .75 2.00
324 Mark Langston .05 .15
325 Steve Finley .10 .30
326 Greg Maddux .50 1.25
327 Dave Nilsson .05 .15
328 Ozzie Smith .50 1.25
329 Candy Maldonado .05 .15
330 Checklist .05 .15
331 Tim Pugh RC .05 .15
332 Joe Girardi .05 .15
333 Junior Felix .05 .15
334 Greg Swindell .05 .15
335 Ramon Martinez .05 .15
336 Sean Berry .05 .15
337 Joe Orsulak .05 .15
338 Wes Chamberlain .05 .15
339 Stan Belinda .05 .15
340 Checklist UER .05 .15
(306 Luis Mercedes)
341 Bruce Hurst .05 .15
342 John Burkett .05 .15
343 Mike Mussina .20 .50
344 Scott Fletcher .05 .15
345 Rene Gonzales .05 .15
346 Roberto Hernandez .05 .15
347 Carlos Martinez .05 .15
348 Bill Krueger .05 .15
349 Felix Jose .05 .15
350 John Jaha .05 .15
351 Willie Banks .05 .15
352 Matt Nokes .05 .15
353 Kevin Seitzer .05 .15
354 Erik Hanson .05 .15
355 David Hulse RC .05 .15
356 Domingo Martinez RC .05 .15
357 Greg Olson .05 .15
358 Randy Myers .05 .15
359 Tom Browning .05 .15
360 Charlie Hayes .05 .15
361 Bryan Harvey .05 .15
362 Eddie Taubensee .05 .15
363 Tim Wallach .05 .15
364 Mel Rojas .05 .15
365 Frank Tanana .05 .15
366 John Kruk .10 .30
367 Tim Laker RC .05 .15
368 Rich Rodriguez .05 .15
369 Darren Lewis .05 .15
370 Harold Reynolds .10 .30
371 Jose Melendez .05 .15
372 Joe Grahe .05 .15
373 Lance Johnson .05 .15
374 Jose Mesa .05 .15
375 Scott Livingstone .05 .15
376 Wally Joyner .10 .30
377 Kevin Reimer .05 .15
378 Kirby Puckett .30 .75
379 Paul O'Neill .20 .50
380 Randy Johnson .30 .75
381 Manuel Lee .05 .15
382 Dick Schofield .05 .15
383 Darren Holmes .05 .15
384 Charlie Hough .10 .30
385 John Orton .05 .15
386 Edgar Martinez .20 .50
387 Terry Pendleton .10 .30
388 Dan Plesac .05 .15
389 Jeff Reardon .10 .30
390 David Nied .05 .15
391 Dave Magadan .05 .15
392 Larry Walker .10 .30
393 Ben Rivera .05 .15
394 Lonnie Smith .05 .15
395 Craig Shipley .05 .15
396 Willie McGee .10 .30
397 Arthur Rhodes .05 .15
398 Mike Stanton .05 .15
399 Luis Polonia .05 .15
400 Jack McDowell .05 .15
401 Mike Moore .05 .15
402 Jose Lind .05 .15
403 Bill Spiers .05 .15
404 Kevin Tapani .05 .15
405 Spike Owen .05 .15
406 Tino Martinez .20 .50
407 Charlie Leibrandt .05 .15
408 Ed Sprague .05 .15
409 Bryn Smith .05 .15
410 Benito Santiago .10 .30
411 Jose Rijo .05 .15
412 Pete O'Brien .05 .15
413 Willie Wilson .05 .15
414 Bip Roberts .05 .15
415 Eric Young .05 .15
416 Walt Weiss .05 .15
417 Milt Thompson .05 .15
418 Chris Sabo .05 .15
419 Scott Sanderson .05 .15
420 Tim Raines .10 .30
421 Alan Trammell .10 .30
422 Mike Macfarlane .05 .15
423 Dave Winfield .10 .30
424 Bob Wickman .05 .15
425 David Valle .05 .15
426 Gary Redus .05 .15
427 Turner Ward .05 .15
428 Reggie Sanders .10 .30
429 Todd Worrell .05 .15
430 Julio Valera .05 .15
431 Cal Ripken Jr. 1.00 2.50
432 Mo Vaughn .10 .30
433 John Smiley .05 .15
434 Omar Vizquel .20 .50
435 Billy Ripken .05 .15
436 Cory Snyder .05 .15
437 Carlos Quintana .05 .15
438 Omar Olivares .05 .15
439 Robin Ventura .10 .30
440 Checklist .05 .15
441 Kevin Higgins .05 .15
442 Carlos Hernandez .05 .15
443 Dan Peltier .05 .15
444 Derek Lilliquist .05 .15
445 Tim Salmon .20 .50
446 Sherman Obando RC .05 .15
447 Pat Kelly .05 .15
448 Todd Van Poppel .05 .15
449 Mark Whiten .05 .15
450 Checklist .05 .15
451 Pat Meares RC .15 .40
452 Tony Tarasco RC .05 .15
453 Chris Gwynn .05 .15
454 Armando Reynoso .05 .15
455 Danny Darwin .05 .15
456 Willie Greene .05 .15
457 Mike Blowers .05 .15
458 Kevin Roberson RC .05 .15
459 Graeme Lloyd RC .15 .40
460 David West .05 .15
461 Joey Cora .05 .15
462 Alex Arias .05 .15
463 Chad Kreuter .05 .15
464 Mike Lansing RC .15 .40
465 Mike Timlin .05 .15
466 Paul Wagner .05 .15
467 Mark Portugal .05 .15
468 Jim Leyritz .05 .15
469 Ryan Klesko .10 .30
470 Mario Diaz .05 .15
471 Guillermo Velasquez .05 .15
472 Fernando Valenzuela .10 .30
473 Raul Mondesi .10 .30
474 Mike Pagliarulo .05 .15
475 Chris Hammond .05 .15
476 Torey Lovullo .05 .15
477 Trevor Wilson .05 .15
478 Marcos Armas RC .05 .15
479 Dave Gallagher .05 .15
480 Jeff Treadway .05 .15
481 Jeff Branson .05 .15
482 Dickie Thon .05 .15
483 Eduardo Perez .05 .15
484 David Wells .10 .30
485 Brian Williams .05 .15
486 Domingo Cedeno RC .05 .15
487 Tom Candiotti .05 .15
488 Steve Frey .05 .15
489 Greg McMichael RC .05 .15
490 Marc Newfield .05 .15
491 Larry Andersen .05 .15
492 Damon Buford .05 .15
493 Ricky Gutierrez .05 .15
494 Jeff Russell .05 .15
495 Vinny Castilla .30 .75
496 Wilson Alvarez .05 .15
497 Scott Bullett .05 .15
498 Larry Casian .05 .15
499 Jose Vizcaino .05 .15
500 J.T. Snow RC .25 .60
501 Bryan Hickerson .05 .15
502 Jeremy Hernandez .05 .15
503 Jeromy Burnitz .10 .30
504 Steve Farr .05 .15
505 J. Owens RC .05 .15
506 Craig Paquette .05 .15
507 Jim Eisenreich .05 .15
508 Matt Whiteside RC .05 .15
509 Luis Aquino .05 .15
510 Mike LaValliere .05 .15
511 Jim Gott .05 .15
512 Mark McLemore .05 .15
513 Randy Milligan .05 .15
514 Gary Gaetti .10 .30
515 Lou Frazier RC .05 .15
516 Rich Amaral .05 .15
517 Gene Harris .05 .15
518 Aaron Sele .05 .15
519 Mark Wohlers .05 .15
520 Scott Kamieniecki .05 .15
521 Kent Mercker .05 .15
522 Jim Deshaies .05 .15
523 Kevin Stocker .05 .15
524 Jason Bere .05 .15
525 Tim Bogar RC .05 .15
526 Brad Pennington .05 .15
527 Curt Leskanic RC .15 .40
528 Wayne Kirby .05 .15
529 Tim Costo .05 .15
530 Doug Henry .05 .15
531 Trevor Hoffman .30 .75
532 Kelly Gruber .05 .15
533 Mike Harkey .05 .15
534 John Doherty .05 .15
535 Erik Pappas .05 .15
536 Brent Gates .05 .15
537 Roger McDowell .05 .15
538 Chris Haney .05 .15
539 Blas Minor .05 .15
540 Pat Hentgen .05 .15
541 Chuck Carr .05 .15
542 Doug Strange .05 .15
543 Xavier Hernandez .05 .15
544 Paul Quantrill .05 .15
545 Anthony Young .05 .15
546 Bret Boone .10 .30
547 Dwight Smith .05 .15
548 Bobby Munoz .05 .15
549 Russ Springer .05 .15
550 Roger Pavlik .05 .15
DW Dave Winfield .40 1.00
3000 Hits
FT Frank Thomas AU/3500 40.00 80.00

1994 Leaf

The 1994 Leaf baseball set consists of two series of 220 standard-size cards for a total of 440. Randomly seeded "Super Packs" contained complete insert sets. Cards featuring players from the Texas Rangers, Cleveland Indians, Milwaukee Brewers and Houston Astros were held out of the first series in order to have up-to-date photography in each team's new uniforms. A limited number of players from the San Francisco Giants are featured in the first series because of minor modifications to the team's uniforms. Randomly inserted in hobby packs at a rate of one in 36 was a stamped version of Frank Thomas' 1990 Leaf rookie card.

COMPLETE SET (440) 10.00 24.00
COMP. SERIES 1 (220) 5.00 12.00
COMP. SERIES 2 (220) 5.00 12.00
1 Cal Ripken Jr. 1.00 2.50
2 Tony Tarasco .05 .15
3 Joe Girardi .05 .15
4 Bernie Williams .20 .50
5 Chad Kreuter .05 .15
6 Troy Neel .05 .15
7 Tom Pagnozzi .05 .15
8 Kirk Rueter .05 .15
9 Chris Bosio .05 .15
10 Dwight Gooden .10 .30
11 Mariano Duncan .05 .15
12 Jay Bell .10 .30
13 Lance Johnson .05 .15
14 Richie Lewis .05 .15
15 Dave Martinez .05 .15
16 Orel Hershiser .10 .30
17 Rob Butler .05 .15
18 Glenallen Hill .05 .15
19 Chad Curtis .05 .15
20 Mike Stanton .05 .15
21 Tim Wallach .05 .15
22 Milt Thompson .05 .15
23 Kevin Young .05 .15
24 John Smiley .05 .15
25 Jeff Montgomery .05 .15
26 Robin Ventura .10 .30
27 Scott Lydy .05 .15
28 Todd Stottlemyre .05 .15
29 Mark Whiten .05 .15
30 Robby Thompson .05 .15
31 Bobby Bonilla .10 .30
32 Andy Ashby .05 .15
33 Greg Myers .05 .15
34 Billy Hatcher .05 .15
35 Brad Holman .05 .15
36 Mark McLemore .05 .15
37 Scott Sanders .05 .15
38 Jim Abbott .20 .50
39 David Wells .10 .30
40 Roberto Kelly .05 .15
41 Jeff Conine .10 .30
42 Sean Berry .05 .15
43 Mark Grace .20 .50
44 Eric Young .05 .15
45 Rick Aguilera .05 .15
46 Chipper Jones .30 .75
47 Mel Rojas .05 .15
48 Ryan Thompson .05 .15
49 Al Martin .05 .15
50 Cecil Fielder .10 .30
51 Pat Kelly .05 .15
52 Kevin Tapani .05 .15
53 Tim Costo .05 .15
54 Dave Hollins .05 .15
55 Kirt Manwaring .05 .15
56 Gregg Jefferies .05 .15
57 Ron Darling .05 .15
58 Bill Haselman .05 .15
59 Phil Plantier .05 .15
60 Frank Viola .10 .30
61 Todd Zeile .05 .15
62 Bret Barberie .05 .15
63 Roberto Mejia .05 .15
64 Chuck Knoblauch .10 .30
65 Jose Lind .05 .15
66 Brady Anderson .10 .30
67 Ruben Sierra .10 .30
68 Jose Vizcaino .05 .15
69 Joe Grahe .05 .15
70 Kevin Appier .10 .30
71 Wilson Alvarez .05 .15
72 Tom Candiotti .05 .15
73 John Burkett .05 .15
74 Anthony Young .05 .15
75 Scott Cooper .05 .15
76 Nigel Wilson .05 .15
77 John Valentin .05 .15
78 David McCarty .05 .15
79 Archi Cianfrocco .05 .15
80 Lou Whitaker .10 .30
81 Dante Bichette .10 .30
82 Mark Dewey .05 .15
83 Danny Jackson .05 .15
84 Harold Baines .10 .30
85 Todd Benzinger .05 .15
86 Damion Easley .05 .15
87 Danny Cox .05 .15
88 Jose Bautista .05 .15
89 Mike Lansing .05 .15
90 Phil Hiatt .05 .15
91 Tim Pugh .05 .15
92 Tino Martinez .20 .50
93 Raul Mondesi .10 .30
94 Greg Maddux .50 1.25
95 Al Leiter .10 .30
96 Benito Santiago .10 .30
97 Lenny Dykstra .10 .30
98 Sammy Sosa .30 .75
99 Tim Bogar .05 .15
100 Checklist .05 .15
101 Deion Sanders .20 .50
102 Bobby Witt .05 .15
103 Wil Cordero .05 .15
104 Rich Amaral .05 .15
105 Mike Mussina .20 .50
106 Reggie Sanders .10 .30
107 Ozzie Guillen .10 .30
108 Paul O'Neill .20 .50
109 Tim Salmon .20 .50
110 Rheal Cormier .05 .15
111 Billy Ashley .05 .15
112 Jeff Kent .20 .50
113 Derek Bell .05 .15
114 Danny Darwin .05 .15
115 Chip Hale .05 .15
116 Tim Raines .10 .30
117 Ed Sprague .05 .15
118 Darrin Fletcher .05 .15
119 Darren Holmes .05 .15
120 Alan Trammell .10 .30
121 Don Mattingly .75 2.00
122 Greg Gagne .05 .15
123 Jose Offerman .05 .15
124 Joe Orsulak .05 .15
125 Jack McDowell .05 .15
126 Barry Larkin .20 .50
127 Ben McDonald .05 .15
128 Mike Bordick .05 .15
129 Devon White .10 .30
130 Mike Perez .05 .15
131 Jay Buhner .10 .30
132 Phil Leftwich RC .05 .15
133 Tommy Greene .05 .15
134 Charlie Hayes .05 .15
135 Don Slaught .05 .15
136 Mike Gallego .05 .15
137 Dave Winfield .10 .30
138 Steve Avery .05 .15
139 Derrick May .05 .15
140 Bryan Harvey .05 .15
141 Wally Joyner .10 .30
142 Andre Dawson .10 .30
143 Andy Benes .05 .15
144 John Franco .10 .30
145 Jeff King .05 .15
146 Joe Oliver .05 .15
147 Bill Gullickson .05 .15
148 Armando Reynoso .05 .15
149 Dave Fleming .05 .15
150 Checklist .05 .15
151 Todd Van Poppel .05 .15
152 Bernard Gilkey .05 .15
153 Kevin Gross .05 .15
154 Mike Devereaux .05 .15
155 Tim Wakefield .20 .50
156 Andres Galarraga .10 .30
157 Pat Meares .05 .15
158 Jim Leyritz .05 .15
159 Mike Macfarlane .05 .15
160 Tony Phillips .05 .15
161 Brent Gates .05 .15
162 Mark Langston .05 .15
163 Allen Watson .05 .15
164 Randy Johnson .30 .75
165 Doug Brocail .05 .15
166 Rob Dibble .10 .30
167 Roberto Hernandez .05 .15
168 Felix Jose .05 .15
169 Steve Cooke .05 .15
170 Darren Daulton .10 .30
171 Eric Karros .10 .30
172 Geronimo Pena .05 .15
173 Gary DiSarcina .05 .15
174 Marquis Grissom .10 .30
175 Joey Cora .05 .15
176 Jim Eisenreich .05 .15
177 Brad Pennington .05 .15
178 Terry Steinbach .05 .15
179 Pat Borders .05 .15
180 Steve Buechele .05 .15
181 Jeff Fassero .05 .15
182 Mike Greenwell .05 .15
183 Mike Henneman .05 .15
184 Ron Karkovice .05 .15
185 Pat Hentgen .05 .15
186 Jose Guzman .05 .15
187 Brett Butler .10 .30
188 Charlie Hough .10 .30
189 Terry Pendleton .10 .30
190 Melido Perez .05 .15
191 Orestes Destrade .05 .15
192 Mike Morgan .05 .15
193 Joe Carter .10 .30
194 Jeff Blauser .05 .15
195 Chris Hoiles .05 .15
196 Ricky Gutierrez .05 .15
197 Mike Moore .05 .15
198 Carl Willis .05 .15
199 Aaron Sele .05 .15
200 Checklist .05 .15
201 Tim Naehring .05 .15
202 Scott Livingstone .05 .15
203 Luis Alicea .05 .15
204 Torey Lovullo .05 .15
205 Jim Gott .05 .15
206 Bob Wickman .05 .15
207 Greg McMichael .05 .15
208 Scott Brosius .10 .30
209 Chris Gwynn .05 .15
210 Steve Sax .05 .15
211 Dick Schofield .05 .15
212 Robb Nen .10 .30
213 Ben Rivera .05 .15
214 Vinny Castilla .10 .30
215 Jamie Moyer .10 .30
216 Wally Whitehurst .05 .15
217 Frank Castillo .05 .15
218 Mike Blowers .05 .15
219 Tim Scott .05 .15
220 Paul Wagner .05 .15
221 Jeff Bagwell .20 .50
222 Ricky Bones .05 .15
223 Sandy Alomar Jr. .05 .15
224 Rod Beck .05 .15
225 Roberto Alomar .20 .50
226 Jack Armstrong .05 .15
227 Scott Erickson .05 .15
228 Rene Arocha .05 .15
229 Eric Anthony .05 .15
230 Jeromy Burnitz .10 .30
231 Kevin Brown .10 .30
232 Tim Belcher .05 .15
233 Bret Boone .10 .30
234 Dennis Eckersley .10 .30
235 Tom Glavine .20 .50
236 Craig Biggio .20 .50
237 Pedro Astacio .05 .15
238 Ryan Bowen .05 .15
239 Brad Ausmus .20 .50
240 Vince Coleman .05 .15
241 Jason Bere .05 .15
242 Ellis Burks .10 .30
243 Wes Chamberlain .05 .15
244 Ken Caminiti .10 .30
245 Willie Banks .05 .15
246 Sid Fernandez .05 .15
247 Carlos Baerga .05 .15
248 Carlos Garcia .05 .15
249 Jose Canseco .20 .50
250 Alex Diaz .05 .15
251 Albert Belle .10 .30
252 Moises Alou .10 .30
253 Bobby Ayala .05 .15
254 Tony Gwynn .40 1.00
255 Roger Clemens .60 1.50
256 Eric Davis .10 .30
257 Wade Boggs .20 .50
258 Chili Davis .10 .30
259 Rickey Henderson .30 .75
260 Andujar Cedeno .05 .15
261 Cris Carpenter .05 .15
262 Juan Guzman .05 .15
263 David Justice .10 .30
264 Barry Bonds .75 2.00
265 Pete Incaviglia .05 .15
266 Tony Fernandez .05 .15
267 Cal Eldred .05 .15
268 Alex Fernandez .05 .15
269 Kent Hrbek .10 .30
270 Steve Farr .05 .15
271 Doug Drabek .05 .15
272 Brian Jordan .10 .30
273 Xavier Hernandez .05 .15
274 David Cone .10 .30
275 Brian Hunter .05 .15
276 Mike Harkey .05 .15
277 Delino DeShields .05 .15
278 David Hulse .05 .15
279 Mickey Tettleton .05 .15
280 Kevin McReynolds .05 .15
281 Darryl Hamilton .05 .15
282 Ken Hill .05 .15
283 Wayne Kirby .05 .15
284 Chris Hammond .05 .15
285 Mo Vaughn .10 .30
286 Ryan Klesko .10 .30
287 Rick Wilkins .05 .15
288 Bill Swift .05 .15
289 Rafael Palmeiro .20 .50
290 Brian Harper .05 .15
291 Chris Turner .05 .15
292 Luis Gonzalez .10 .30
293 Kenny Rogers .10 .30
294 Kirby Puckett .30 .75
295 Mike Stanley .05 .15
296 Carlos Reyes RC .05 .15
297 Charles Nagy .05 .15
298 Reggie Jefferson .05 .15
299 Bip Roberts .05 .15
300 Darrin Jackson .05 .15
301 Mike Jackson .05 .15
302 Dave Nilsson .05 .15
303 Ramon Martinez .05 .15
304 Bobby Jones .05 .15
305 Johnny Ruffin .05 .15
306 Brian McRae .05 .15
307 Bo Jackson .30 .75
308 Dave Stewart .10 .30
309 John Smoltz .20 .50
310 Dennis Martinez .10 .30
311 Dean Palmer .10 .30
312 David Nied .05 .15
313 Eddie Murray .30 .75
314 Darryl Kile .10 .30
315 Rick Sutcliffe .10 .30
316 Shawon Dunston .05 .15
317 John Jaha .05 .15
318 Salomon Torres .05 .15
319 Gary Sheffield .10 .30
320 Curt Schilling .10 .30
321 Greg Vaughn .05 .15
322 Jay Howell .05 .15
323 Todd Hundley .05 .15
324 Chris Sabo .05 .15
325 Stan Javier .05 .15
326 Willie Greene .05 .15
327 Hipolito Pichardo .05 .15
328 Doug Strange .05 .15
329 Dan Wilson .05 .15
330 Checklist .05 .15
331 Omar Vizquel .20 .50
332 Scott Servais .05 .15
333 Bob Tewksbury .05 .15
334 Matt Williams .10 .30
335 Tom Foley .05 .15
336 Jeff Russell .05 .15
337 Scott Leius .05 .15
338 Ivan Rodriguez .20 .50
339 Kevin Seitzer .05 .15
340 Jose Rijo .05 .15
341 Eduardo Perez .05 .15
342 Kirk Gibson .10 .30
343 Randy Milligan .05 .15
344 Edgar Martinez .20 .50
345 Fred McGriff .20 .50
346 Kurt Abbott RC .05 .15
347 John Kruk .10 .30
348 Mike Felder .05 .15
349 Dave Staton .05 .15
350 Kenny Lofton .10 .30
351 Graeme Lloyd .05 .15
352 David Segui .05 .15
353 Danny Tartabull .05 .15
354 Bob Welch .05 .15
355 Duane Ward .05 .15
356 Karl Rhodes .05 .15
357 Lee Smith .10 .30
358 Chris James .05 .15
359 Walt Weiss .05 .15
360 Pedro Munoz .05 .15
361 Paul Sorrento .05 .15
362 Todd Worrell .05 .15
363 Bob Hamelin .05 .15
364 Julio Franco .10 .30
365 Roberto Petagine .05 .15
366 Willie McGee .10 .30
367 Pedro Martinez .30 .75
368 Ken Griffey Jr. .50 1.25
369 B.J. Surhoff .10 .30
370 Kevin Mitchell .05 .15
371 John Doherty .05 .15
372 Manuel Lee .05 .15
373 Terry Mulholland .05 .15
374 Zane Smith .05 .15
375 Otis Nixon .05 .15
376 Jody Reed .05 .15
377 Doug Jones .05 .15
378 John Olerud .10 .30
379 Greg Swindell .05 .15
380 Checklist .05 .15
381 Royce Clayton .05 .15
382 Jim Thome .20 .50
383 Steve Finley .10 .30
384 Ray Lankford .10 .30
385 Henry Rodriguez .05 .15
386 Dave Magadan .05 .15
387 Gary Redus .05 .15
388 Orlando Merced .05 .15
389 Tom Gordon .05 .15
390 Luis Polonia .05 .15
391 Mark McGwire .75 2.00
392 Mark Lemke .05 .15
393 Doug Henry .05 .15
394 Chuck Finley .10 .30
395 Paul Molitor .10 .30
396 Randy Myers .05 .15
397 Larry Walker .10 .30
398 Pete Harnisch .05 .15
399 Darren Lewis .05 .15
400 Frank Thomas .30 .75
401 Jack Morris .10 .30
402 Greg Hibbard .05 .15
403 Jeffrey Hammonds .05 .15
404 Will Clark .20 .50
405 Travis Fryman .10 .30
406 Scott Sanderson .05 .15
407 Gene Harris .05 .15
408 Chuck Carr .05 .15
409 Ozzie Smith .50 1.25
410 Kent Mercker .05 .15
411 Andy Van Slyke .20 .50
412 Jimmy Key .10 .30
413 Pat Mahomes .05 .15
414 John Wetteland .10 .30
415 Todd Jones .05 .15
416 Greg Harris .05 .15
417 Kevin Stocker .05 .15
418 Juan Gonzalez .10 .30
419 Pete Smith .05 .15
420 Pat Listach .05 .15
421 Trevor Hoffman .20 .50
422 Scott Fletcher .05 .15
423 Mark Lewis .05 .15
424 Mickey Morandini .05 .15
425 Ryne Sandberg .50 1.25
426 Erik Hanson .05 .15
427 Gary Gaetti .10 .30
428 Harold Reynolds .10 .30
429 Mark Portugal .05 .15
430 David Valle .05 .15
431 Mitch Williams .05 .15
432 Howard Johnson .05 .15
433 Hal Morris .05 .15
434 Tom Henke .05 .15
435 Shane Mack .05 .15
436 Mike Piazza .60 1.50
437 Bret Saberhagen .10 .30
438 Jose Mesa .05 .15
439 Jaime Navarro .05 .15
440 Checklist .05 .15
A300 Frank Thomas .75 2.00
Leaf 5th Anniversary

1995 Leaf

The 1995 Leaf set was issued in two series of 200 standard-size cards for a total of 400. Full-bleed fronts contain diamond-shaped player hologram in the upper left. The team name is done in silver foil up the left side. Peculiar backs contain two photos, the card number within a stamp or seal like emblem in the upper right and '94 and career stats graph toward bottom left. Hideo Nomo is the only key Rookie Card in this set.

COMPLETE SET (400) 16.00 40.00
COMP. SERIES 1 (200) 6.00 15.00
COMP. SERIES 2 (200) 10.00 25.00
1 Frank Thomas .30 .75
2 Carlos Garcia .05 .15
3 Todd Hundley .05 .15
4 Damion Easley .05 .15
5 Roberto Mejia .05 .15
6 John Mabry .05 .15
7 Aaron Sele .05 .15
8 Kenny Lofton .10 .30
9 John Doherty .05 .15
10 Joe Carter .10 .30
11 Mike Lansing .05 .15
12 John Valentin .05 .15
13 Ismael Valdes .05 .15
14 Dave McCarty .05 .15
15 Melvin Nieves .05 .15

16 Bobby Jones .05 .15
17 Trevor Hoffman .10 .30
18 John Smoltz .20 .50
19 Leo Gomez .05 .15
20 Roger Pavlik .05 .15
21 Dean Palmer .10 .30
22 Rickey Henderson .30 .75
23 Eddie Taubensee .05 .15
24 Damon Buford .05 .15
25 Mark Wohlers .05 .15
26 Jim Edmonds .20 .50
27 Wilson Alvarez .05 .15
28 Matt Williams .10 .30
29 Jeff Montgomery .05 .15
30 Shawon Dunston .05 .15
31 Tom Pagnozzi .05 .15
32 Jose Lind .05 .15
33 Royce Clayton .05 .15
34 Cal Eldred .05 .15
35 Chris Gomez .05 .15
36 Henry Rodriguez .05 .15
37 Dave Fleming .05 .15
38 Jon Lieber .05 .15
39 Scott Servais .05 .15
40 Wade Boggs .20 .50
41 John Olerud .10 .30
42 Eddie Williams .05 .15
43 Paul Sorrento .05 .15
44 Ron Karkovice .05 .15
45 Kevin Foster .05 .15
46 Miguel Jimenez .05 .15
47 Reggie Sanders .10 .30
48 Rondell White .10 .30
49 Scott Leius .05 .15
50 Jose Valentin .05 .15
51 Wm. VanLandingham .05 .15
52 Denny Hocking .05 .15
53 Jeff Fassero .05 .15
54 Chris Hoiles .05 .15
55 Walt Weiss .05 .15
56 Geronimo Berroa .05 .15
57 Rich Rowland .05 .15
58 Dave Weathers .05 .15
59 Sterling Hitchcock .05 .15
60 Raul Mondesi .10 .30
61 Rusty Greer .10 .30
62 David Justice .10 .30
63 Cecil Fielder .10 .30
64 Brian Jordan .10 .30
65 Mike Lieberthal .10 .30
66 Rick Aguilera .05 .15
67 Chuck Finley .10 .30
68 Andy Ashby .05 .15
69 Alex Fernandez .05 .15
70 Ed Sprague .05 .15
71 Steve Buechele .05 .15
72 Willie Greene .05 .15
73 Dave Nilsson .05 .15
74 Bret Saberhagen .10 .30
75 Jimmy Key .10 .30
76 Darren Lewis .05 .15
77 Steve Cooke .05 .15
78 Kirk Gibson .10 .30
79 Ray Lankford .10 .30
80 Paul O'Neill .20 .50
81 Mike Bordick .05 .15
82 Wes Chamberlain .05 .15
83 Rico Brogna .05 .15
84 Kevin Appier .10 .30
85 Juan Guzman .05 .15
86 Kevin Seitzer .05 .15
87 Mickey Morandini .05 .15
88 Pedro Martinez .20 .50
89 Matt Mieske .05 .15
90 Tino Martinez .20 .50
91 Paul Shuey .05 .15
92 Bip Roberts .05 .15
93 Chili Davis .10 .30
94 Deion Sanders .20 .50
95 Darrell Whitmore .05 .15
96 Joe Orsulak .05 .15
97 Bret Boone .10 .30
98 Kent Mercker .05 .15
99 Scott Livingstone .05 .15
100 Brady Anderson .10 .30
101 James Mouton .05 .15
102 Jose Rijo .05 .15
103 Bobby Munoz .05 .15
104 Ramon Martinez .05 .15
105 Bernie Williams .20 .50
106 Troy Neel .05 .15
107 Ivan Rodriguez .20 .50
108 Salomon Torres .05 .15
109 Johnny Ruffin .05 .15
110 Darryl Kile .10 .30
111 Bobby Ayala .05 .15
112 Ron Darling .05 .15
113 Jose Lima .05 .15
114 Joey Hamilton .05 .15
115 Greg Maddux .50 1.25
116 Greg Colbrunn .05 .15
117 Ozzie Guillen .10 .30
118 Brian Anderson .05 .15
119 Jeff Bagwell .20 .50
120 Pat Listach .05 .15
121 Sandy Alomar Jr. .05 .15
122 Jose Vizcaino .05 .15
123 Rick Helling .05 .15
124 Allen Watson .05 .15
125 Pedro Munoz .05 .15
126 Craig Biggio .20 .50
127 Kevin Stocker .05 .15
128 Wil Cordero .05 .15
129 Rafael Palmeiro .20 .50
130 Gar Finnvold .05 .15
131 Darren Hall .05 .15
132 Heathcliff Slocumb .05 .15
133 Darrin Fletcher .05 .15
134 Cal Ripken 1.00 2.50
135 Dante Bichette .10 .30
136 Don Slaught .05 .15
137 Pedro Astacio .05 .15
138 Ryan Thompson .05 .15
139 Greg Gohr .05 .15
140 Javier Lopez .10 .30
141 Lenny Dykstra .10 .30
142 Pat Rapp .05 .15
143 Mark Kiefer .05 .15
144 Greg Gagne .05 .15
145 Eduardo Perez .05 .15
146 Felix Fermin .05 .15
147 Jeff Frye .05 .15
148 Terry Steinbach .05 .15
149 Jim Eisenreich .05 .15
150 Brad Ausmus .10 .30
151 Randy Myers .05 .15
152 Rick White .05 .15
153 Mark Portugal .05 .15
154 Delino DeShields .05 .15
155 Scott Cooper .05 .15
156 Pat Hentgen .05 .15
157 Mark Gubicza .05 .15
158 Carlos Baerga .05 .15
159 Joe Girardi .05 .15
160 Rey Sanchez .05 .15
161 Todd Jones .05 .15
162 Luis Polonia .05 .15
163 Steve Trachsel .05 .15
164 Roberto Hernandez .05 .15
165 John Patterson .05 .15
166 Rene Arocha .05 .15
167 Will Clark .20 .50
168 Jim Leyritz .05 .15
169 Todd Van Poppel .05 .15
170 Robb Nen .10 .30
171 Midre Cummings .05 .15
172 Jay Buhner .10 .30
173 Kevin Tapani .05 .15
174 Mark Lemke .05 .15
175 Marcus Moore .05 .15
176 Wayne Kirby .05 .15
177 Rich Amaral .05 .15
178 Lou Whitaker .10 .30
179 Jay Bell .10 .30
180 Rick Wilkins .05 .15
181 Paul Molitor .10 .30
182 Gary Sheffield .10 .30
183 Kirby Puckett .30 .75
184 Cliff Floyd .10 .30
185 Darren Oliver .05 .15
186 Tim Naehring .05 .15
187 John Hudek .05 .15
188 Eric Young .05 .15
189 Roger Salkeld .05 .15
190 Kirt Manwaring .05 .15
191 Kurt Abbott .05 .15
192 David Nied .05 .15
193 Todd Zeile .05 .15
194 Wally Joyner .10 .30
195 Dennis Martinez .10 .30
196 Billy Ashley .05 .15
197 Ben McDonald .05 .15
198 Bob Hamelin .05 .15
199 Chris Turner .05 .15
200 Lance Johnson .05 .15
201 Willie Banks .05 .15
202 Juan Gonzalez .10 .30
203 Scott Sanders .05 .15
204 Scott Brosius .10 .30
205 Curt Schilling .10 .30
206 Alex Gonzalez .05 .15
207 Travis Fryman .10 .30
208 Tim Raines .10 .30
209 Steve Avery .05 .15
210 Hal Morris .05 .15
211 Ken Griffey Jr. .50 1.25
212 Ozzie Smith .50 1.25
213 Chuck Carr .05 .15
214 Ryan Klesko .10 .30
215 Robin Ventura .10 .30
216 Luis Gonzalez .10 .30
217 Ken Ryan .05 .15
218 Mike Piazza .50 1.25
219 Matt Walbeck .05 .15
220 Jeff Kent .10 .30
221 Orlando Miller .05 .15
222 Kenny Rogers .10 .30
223 J.T. Snow .10 .30
224 Alan Trammell .10 .30
225 John Franco .10 .30
226 Gerald Williams .05 .15
227 Andy Benes .05 .15
228 Dan Wilson .05 .15
229 Dave Hollins .05 .15
230 Vinny Castilla .10 .30
231 Devon White .10 .30
232 Fred McGriff .20 .50
233 Quilvio Veras .05 .15
234 Tom Candiotti .05 .15
235 Jason Bere .05 .15
236 Mark Langston .05 .15
237 Mel Rojas .05 .15
238 Chuck Knoblauch .10 .30
239 Bernard Gilkey .05 .15
240 Mark McGwire .75 2.00
241 Kirk Rueter .05 .15
242 Pat Kelly .05 .15
243 Ruben Sierra .10 .30
244 Randy Johnson .30 .75
245 Shane Reynolds .05 .15
246 Danny Tartabull .05 .15
247 Darryl Hamilton .05 .15
248 Danny Bautista .05 .15
249 Tom Gordon .05 .15
250 Tom Glavine .20 .50
251 Orlando Merced .05 .15
252 Eric Karros .10 .30
253 Benji Gil .05 .15
254 Sean Bergman .05 .15
255 Roger Clemens .60 1.50
256 Roberto Alomar .20 .50
257 Benito Santiago .10 .30
258 Robby Thompson .05 .15
259 Marvin Freeman .05 .15
260 Jose Offerman .05 .15
261 Greg Vaughn .05 .15
262 David Segui .05 .15
263 Geronimo Pena .05 .15
264 Tim Salmon .20 .50
265 Eddie Murray .30 .75
266 Mariano Duncan .05 .15
267 Hideo Nomo RC .75 2.00
268 Derek Bell .05 .15
269 Mo Vaughn .10 .30
270 Jeff King .05 .15
271 Edgar Martinez .20 .50
272 Sammy Sosa .30 .75
273 Scott Ruffcorn .05 .15
274 Darren Daulton .10 .30
275 John Jaha .05 .15
276 Andres Galarraga .10 .30
277 Mark Grace .20 .50
278 Mike Moore .05 .15
279 Barry Bonds .75 2.00
280 Manny Ramirez .20 .50
281 Ellis Burks .10 .30
282 Greg Swindell .05 .15
283 Barry Larkin .20 .50
284 Albert Belle .10 .30
285 Shawn Green .10 .30
286 John Roper .05 .15
287 Scott Erickson .05 .15
288 Moises Alou .10 .30
289 Mike Blowers .05 .15
290 Brent Gates .05 .15
291 Sean Berry .05 .15
292 Mike Stanley .05 .15
293 Jeff Conine .10 .30
294 Tim Wallach .05 .15
295 Bobby Bonilla .10 .30
296 Bruce Ruffin .05 .15
297 Chad Curtis .05 .15
298 Mike Greenwell .05 .15
299 Tony Gwynn .40 1.00
300 Russ Davis .05 .15
301 Danny Jackson .05 .15
302 Pete Harnisch .05 .15
303 Don Mattingly .75 2.00
304 Rheal Cormier .05 .15
305 Larry Walker .10 .30
306 Hector Carrasco .05 .15
307 Jason Jacome .05 .15
308 Phil Plantier .05 .15
309 Harold Baines .10 .30
310 Mitch Williams .05 .15
311 Charles Nagy .05 .15
312 Ken Caminiti .10 .30
313 Alex Rodriguez .75 2.00
314 Chris Sabo .05 .15
315 Gary Gaetti .10 .30
316 Andre Dawson .10 .30
317 Mark Clark .05 .15
318 Vince Coleman .05 .15
319 Brad Clontz .05 .15
320 Steve Finley .10 .30
321 Doug Drabek .05 .15
322 Mark McLemore .05 .15
323 Stan Javier .05 .15
324 Ron Gant .10 .30
325 Charlie Hayes .05 .15
326 Carlos Delgado .10 .30
327 Ricky Bottalico .05 .15
328 Rod Beck .05 .15
329 Mark Acre .05 .15
330 Chris Bosio .05 .15
331 Tony Phillips .05 .15
332 Garret Anderson .10 .30
333 Pat Meares .05 .15
334 Todd Worrell .05 .15
335 Marquis Grissom .10 .30
336 Brent Mayne .05 .15
337 Lee Tinsley .05 .15
338 Terry Pendleton .10 .30
339 David Cone .10 .30
340 Tony Fernandez .05 .15
341 Jim Bullinger .05 .15
342 Armando Benitez .05 .15
343 John Smiley .05 .15
344 Dan Miceli .05 .15
345 Charles Johnson .10 .30
346 Lee Smith .10 .30
347 Brian McRae .05 .15
348 Jim Thome .20 .50
349 Jose Oliva .05 .15
350 Terry Mulholland .05 .15
351 Tom Henke .05 .15
352 Dennis Eckersley .10 .30
353 Sid Fernandez .05 .15
354 Paul Wagner .05 .15
355 John Dettmer .05 .15
356 John Wetteland .10 .30
357 John Burkett .05 .15
358 Marty Cordova .05 .15
359 Norm Charlton .05 .15
360 Mike Devereaux .05 .15
361 Alex Cole .05 .15
362 Brett Butler .10 .30
363 Mickey Tettleton .05 .15
364 Al Martin .05 .15
365 Tony Tarasco .05 .15
366 Pat Mahomes .05 .15
367 Gary DiSarcina .05 .15
368 Bill Swift .05 .15
369 Chipper Jones .30 .75
370 Orel Hershiser .10 .30
371 Kevin Gross .05 .15
372 Dave Winfield .10 .30
373 Andujar Cedeno .05 .15
374 Jim Abbott .20 .50
375 Glenallen Hill .05 .15
376 Otis Nixon .05 .15
377 Roberto Kelly .05 .15
378 Chris Hammond .05 .15
379 Mike Macfarlane .05 .15
380 J.R. Phillips .05 .15
381 Luis Alicea .05 .15
382 Bret Barberie .05 .15
383 Tom Goodwin .05 .15
384 Mark Whiten .05 .15
385 Jeffrey Hammonds .05 .15
386 Omar Vizquel .20 .50
387 Mike Mussina .20 .50
388 Ricky Bones .05 .15
389 Steve Ontiveros .05 .15
390 Jeff Blauser .05 .15
391 Jose Canseco .20 .50
392 Bob Tewksbury .05 .15
393 Jacob Brumfield .05 .15
394 Doug Jones .05 .15
395 Ken Hill .05 .15
396 Pat Borders .05 .15
397 Carl Everett .10 .30
398 Gregg Jefferies .05 .15
399 Jack McDowell .05 .15
400 Denny Neagle .10 .30
NNO Frank Thomas
Jumbo/10,000
NNO Barry Bonds
Jumbo/10,000

1996 Leaf

The 1996 Leaf set was issued in one series totalling 220 cards. The fronts feature color action player photos

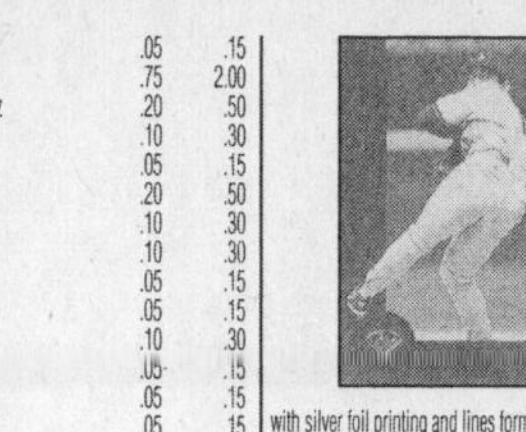

with silver foil printing and lines forming a border on the left and bottom. The backs display another player photo with 1995 season and career statistics. Card number 210 is a checklist for the insert sets and cards number 211-220 feature rookies. The fronts of these 10 cards are different in design from the first 200 with a color action player cut-out over a green-shadow background of the same picture and gold lettering.

COMPLETE SET (220) 8.00 20.00
1 John Smoltz .20 .50
2 Dennis Eckersley .10 .30
3 Delino DeShields .10 .30
4 Cliff Floyd .10 .30
5 Chuck Finley .10 .30
6 Cecil Fielder .10 .30
7 Tim Naehring .10 .30
8 Carlos Perez .10 .30
9 Brad Ausmus .10 .30
10 Matt Lawton RC .15 .40
11 Alan Trammell .10 .30
12 Steve Finley .10 .30
13 Paul O'Neill .20 .50
14 Gary Sheffield .10 .30
15 Mark McGwire .75 2.00
16 Bernie Williams .20 .50
17 Jeff Montgomery .10 .30
18 Chan Ho Park .10 .30
19 Greg Vaughn .10 .30
20 Jeff Kent .10 .30
21 Cal Ripken 1.00 2.50
22 Charles Johnson .10 .30
23 Eric Karros .10 .30
24 Alex Rodriguez .60 1.50
25 Chris Snopek .10 .30
26 Jason Isringhausen .10 .30
27 Chili Davis .10 .30
28 Chipper Jones .30 .75
29 Bret Saberhagen .10 .30
30 Tony Clark .10 .30
31 Marty Cordova .10 .30
32 Dwayne Hosey .10 .30
33 Fred McGriff .20 .50
34 Deion Sanders .20 .50
35 Orlando Merced .10 .30
36 Brady Anderson .10 .30
37 Ray Lankford .10 .30
38 Manny Ramirez .20 .50
39 Alex Fernandez .10 .30
40 Greg Colbrunn .10 .30
41 Ken Griffey, Jr. .50 1.25
42 Mickey Morandini .10 .30
43 Chuck Knoblauch .10 .30
44 Quinton McCracken .10 .30
45 Tim Salmon .20 .50
46 Jose Mesa .10 .30
47 Marquis Grissom .10 .30
48 Greg Maddux .10 .30
Randy Johnson CL
49 Raul Mondesi .10 .30
50 Mark Grudzielanek .10 .30
51 Ray Durham .10 .30
52 Matt Williams .10 .30
53 Bob Hamelin .10 .30
54 Lenny Dykstra .10 .30
55 Jeff King .10 .30
56 LaTroy Hawkins .10 .30
57 Terry Pendleton .10 .30
58 Kevin Stocker .10 .30
59 Ozzie Timmons .10 .30
60 David Justice .10 .30
61 Ricky Bottalico .10 .30
62 Andy Ashby .10 .30
63 Larry Walker .10 .30
64 Jose Canseco .20 .50
65 Bret Boone .10 .30
66 Shawn Green .10 .30
67 Chad Curtis .10 .30
68 Travis Fryman .10 .30
69 Roger Clemens .60 1.50
70 David Bell .10 .30
71 Rusty Greer .10 .30
72 Bob Higginson .10 .30
73 Joey Hamilton .10 .30
74 Kevin Seitzer .10 .30
75 Julian Tavarez .10 .30
76 Troy Percival .10 .30
77 Kirby Puckett .30 .75
78 Barry Bonds .75 2.00
79 Michael Tucker .10 .30
80 Paul Molitor .10 .30
81 Carlos Garcia .10 .30
82 Johnny Damon .20 .50
83 Mike Hampton .10 .30
84 Ariel Prieto .10 .30
85 Tony Tarasco .10 .30
86 Pete Schourek .10 .30
87 Tom Glavine .20 .50
88 Rondell White .10 .30
89 Jim Edmonds .10 .30
90 Robby Thompson .10 .30
91 Wade Boggs .20 .50
92 Pedro Martinez .20 .50
93 Gregg Jefferies .10 .30
94 Albert Belle .10 .30
95 Benji Gil .10 .30
96 Denny Neagle .10 .30
97 Mark Langston .10 .30
98 Sandy Alomar Jr. .10 .30
99 Tony Gwynn .40 1.00
100 Todd Hundley .10 .30
101 Dante Bichette .10 .30
102 Eddie Murray .30 .75
103 Lyle Mouton .10 .30
104 John Jaha .10 .30
105 Barry Larkin .10 .30
Mo Vaughn CL
106 Jon Nunnally .10 .30
107 Juan Gonzalez .10 .30
108 Kevin Appier .10 .30
109 Brian McRae .10 .30
110 Lee Smith .10 .30
111 Tim Wakefield .10 .30
112 Sammy Sosa .30 .75
113 Jay Buhner .10 .30
114 Garret Anderson .10 .30
115 Edgar Martinez .20 .50
116 Edgardo Alfonzo .10 .30
117 Billy Ashley .10 .30
118 Joe Carter .10 .30
119 Javy Lopez .10 .30
120 Bobby Bonilla .10 .30
121 Ken Caminiti .10 .30
122 Barry Larkin .20 .50
123 Shannon Stewart .10 .30
124 Orel Hershiser .10 .30
125 Jeff Conine .10 .30
126 Mark Grace .20 .50
127 Kenny Lofton .10 .30
128 Luis Gonzalez .10 .30
129 Rico Brogna .10 .30
130 Mo Vaughn .10 .30
131 Brad Radke .10 .30
132 Jose Herrera .10 .30
133 Rick Aguilera .10 .30
134 Gary DiSarcina .10 .30
135 Andres Galarraga .10 .30
136 Carl Everett .10 .30
137 Steve Avery .10 .30
138 Vinny Castilla .10 .30
139 Dennis Martinez .10 .30
140 John Wetteland .10 .30
141 Alex Gonzalez .10 .30
142 Brian Jordan .10 .30
143 Todd Hollandsworth .10 .30
144 Terrell Wade .10 .30
145 Wilson Alvarez .10 .30
146 Reggie Sanders .10 .30
147 Will Clark .20 .50
148 Hideo Nomo .30 .75
149 J.T.Snow .10 .30
150 Frank Thomas .30 .75
151 Ivan Rodriguez .20 .50
152 Jay Bell .10 .30
153 Hideo Nomo CL .10 .30
Marty Cordova
154 David Cone .10 .30
155 Roberto Alomar .20 .50
156 Carlos Delgado .10 .30
157 Carlos Baerga .10 .30
158 Geronimo Berroa .10 .30
159 Joe Vitiello .10 .30
160 Terry Steinbach .10 .30
161 Doug Drabek .10 .30
162 David Segui .10 .30
163 Ozzie Smith .50 1.25
164 Kurt Abbott .10 .30
165 Randy Johnson .30 .75
166 John Valentin .10 .30
167 Mickey Tettleton .10 .30
168 Ruben Sierra .10 .30
169 Jim Thome .20 .50
170 Mike Greenwell .10 .30
171 Quilvio Veras .10 .30
172 Robin Ventura .10 .30
173 Bill Pulsipher .10 .30
174 Rafael Palmeiro .20 .50
175 Hal Morris .10 .30
176 Ryan Klesko .10 .30
177 Eric Young .10 .30
178 Shane Andrews .10 .30
179 Brian L.Hunter .10 .30
180 Brett Butler .10 .30
181 John Olerud .10 .30
182 Moises Alou .10 .30
183 Glenallen Hill .10 .30
184 Ismael Valdes .10 .30
185 Andy Pettitte .20 .50
186 Yamil Benitez .10 .30
187 Jason Bere .10 .30
188 Dean Palmer .10 .30
189 Jimmy Haynes .10 .30
190 Trevor Hoffman .10 .30
191 Mike Mussina .20 .50
192 Greg Maddux .50 1.25
193 Ozzie Guillen .10 .30
194 Pat Listach .10 .30
195 Derek Bell .10 .30
196 Darren Daulton .10 .30
197 John Mabry .10 .30
198 Ramon Martinez .10 .30
199 Jeff Bagwell .20 .50
200 Mike Piazza .50 1.25
201 Al Martin .10 .30
202 Aaron Sele .10 .30
203 Ed Sprague .10 .30
204 Rod Beck .10 .30
205 Tony Gwynn .10 .30
Edgar Martinez CL
206 Mike Lansing .10 .30
207 Craig Biggio .20 .50
208 Jeffrey Hammonds .10 .30
209 Dave Nilsson .10 .30
210 Dante Bichette .10 .30
Albert Belle CL
211 Derek Jeter .75 2.00
212 Alan Benes .10 .30
213 Jason Schmidt .20 .50
214 Alex Ochoa .10 .30
215 Ruben Rivera .10 .30
216 Roger Cedeno .10 .30
217 Jeff Suppan .10 .30
218 Billy Wagner .10 .30
219 Mark Loretta .10 .30
220 Karim Garcia .10 .30

1997 Leaf

The 400-card Leaf set was issued in two separate 200-card series. 10-card packs carried a suggested retail of $2.99. Each card features color action player photos with foil enhancement. The backs carry another player photo and season and career statistics. The set contains the following subsets: Legacy (188-197/348-367), Checklists (198-200/398-400) and Gamers (368-397). Rookie Cards in this set include Jose Cruz Jr., Brian Giles and Hideki Irabu. In a tie in with the 50th anniversary of Jackie Robinson's major league debut, Donruss/Leaf also issued some collectible items. They made 42 all-leather jackets (issued to match Robinson's uniform number). There were also 311 leather jackets produced (to match Robinson's career batting average). 1,500 lithographs were also produced of which Rachel Robinson (Jackie's widow) signed 500 of them.

COMPLETE SET (400) 16.00 40.00
COMP. SERIES 1 (200) 8.00 20.00
COMP. SERIES 2 (200) 8.00 20.00
1 Wade Boggs .20 .50
2 Brian McRae .10 .30
3 Jeff D'Amico .10 .30
4 George Arias .10 .30
5 Billy Wagner .10 .30
6 Ray Lankford .10 .30
7 Will Clark .20 .50
8 Edgar Renteria .10 .30
9 Alex Ochoa .10 .30
10 Roberto Hernandez .10 .30
11 Joe Carter .10 .30
12 Gregg Jefferies .10 .30
13 Mark Grace .20 .50
14 Roberto Alomar .20 .50
15 Joe Randa .10 .30
16 Alex Rodriguez .50 1.25
17 Tony Gwynn .40 1.00
18 Steve Gibralter .10 .30
19 Scott Stahoviak .10 .30
20 Matt Williams .10 .30
21 Quinton McCracken .10 .30
22 Ugueth Urbina .10 .30
23 Jermaine Allensworth .10 .30
24 Paul Molitor .10 .30
25 Carlos Delgado .10 .30
26 Bob Abreu .20 .50
27 John Jaha .10 .30
28 Rusty Greer .10 .30
29 Kimera Bartee .10 .30
30 Ruben Rivera .10 .30
31 Jason Kendall .10 .30
32 Lance Johnson .10 .30
33 Robin Ventura .10 .30
34 Kevin Appier .10 .30
35 John Mabry .10 .30
36 Ricky Otero .10 .30
37 Mike Lansing .10 .30
38 Mark McGwire .75 2.00
39 Tim Naehring .10 .30
40 Tom Glavine .20 .50
41 Rey Ordonez .10 .30
42 Tony Clark .10 .30
43 Rafael Palmeiro .20 .50
44 Pedro Martinez .20 .50
45 Keith Lockhart .10 .30
46 Dan Wilson .10 .30
47 John Wetteland .10 .30
48 Chan Ho Park .10 .30
49 Gary Sheffield .10 .30
50 Shawn Estes .10 .30
51 Royce Clayton .10 .30
52 Jaime Navarro .10 .30
53 Raul Casanova .10 .30
54 Jeff Bagwell .20 .50
55 Barry Larkin .20 .50
56 Charles Nagy .10 .30
57 Ken Caminiti .10 .30
58 Todd Hollandsworth .10 .30
59 Pat Hentgen .10 .30
60 Jose Valentin .10 .30
61 Frank Rodriguez .10 .30
62 Mickey Tettleton .10 .30
63 Marty Cordova .10 .30
64 Cecil Fielder .10 .30
65 Barry Bonds .75 2.00
66 Scott Servais .10 .30
67 Ernie Young .10 .30
68 Wilson Alvarez .10 .30
69 Mike Grace .10 .30
70 Shane Reynolds .10 .30
71 Henry Rodriguez .10 .30
72 Eric Karros .10 .30
73 Mark Langston .10 .30
74 Scott Karl .10 .30
75 Trevor Hoffman .10 .30
76 Orel Hershiser .10 .30
77 John Smoltz .20 .50
78 Raul Mondesi .10 .30
79 Jeff Brantley .10 .30
80 Donne Wall .10 .30
81 Joey Cora .10 .30
82 Mel Rojas .10 .30
83 Chad Mottola .10 .30
84 Omar Vizquel .20 .50
85 Greg Maddux .50 1.25
86 Jamey Wright .10 .30
87 Chuck Finley .10 .30
88 Brady Anderson .10 .30
89 Alex Gonzalez .10 .30
90 Andy Benes .10 .30
91 Reggie Jefferson .10 .30
92 Paul O'Neill .20 .50
93 Javier Lopez .10 .30
94 Mark Grudzielanek .10 .30
95 Marc Newfield .10 .30
96 Kevin Ritz .10 .30
97 Fred McGriff .20 .50
98 Dwight Gooden .10 .30
99 Hideo Nomo .30 .75
100 Steve Finley .10 .30
101 Juan Gonzalez .10 .30
102 Jay Buhner .10 .30
103 Paul Wilson .10 .30
104 Alan Benes .10 .30
105 Manny Ramirez .20 .50
106 Kevin Elster .10 .30
107 Frank Thomas .30 .75
108 Orlando Miller .10 .30
109 Ramon Martinez .10 .30
110 Kenny Lofton .10 .30
111 Bernie Williams .20 .50
112 Robby Thompson .10 .30
113 Bernard Gilkey .10 .30
114 Ray Durham .10 .30
115 Jeff Cirillo .10 .30
116 Brian Jordan .10 .30
117 Rich Becker .10 .30
118 Al Leiter .10 .30
119 Mark Johnson .10 .30
120 Ellis Burks .10 .30
121 Sammy Sosa .30 .75
122 Willie Greene .10 .30
123 Michael Tucker .10 .30
124 Eddie Murray .30 .75
125 Joey Hamilton .10 .30
126 Antonio Osuna .10 .30
127 Bobby Higginson .10 .30
128 Tomas Perez .10 .30
129 Tim Salmon .20 .50
130 Mark Wohlers .10 .30
131 Charles Johnson .10 .30
132 Randy Johnson .30 .75
133 Brooks Kieschnick .10 .30
134 Al Martin .10 .30
135 Dante Bichette .10 .30
136 Andy Pettitte .20 .50
137 Jason Giambi .10 .30
138 James Baldwin .10 .30
139 Ben McDonald .10 .30
140 Shawn Green .10 .30
141 Geronimo Berroa .10 .30
142 Jose Offerman .10 .30
143 Curtis Pride .10 .30
144 Terrell Wade .10 .30
145 Ismael Valdes .10 .30
146 Mike Mussina .20 .50
147 Mariano Rivera .30 .75
148 Ken Hill .10 .30
149 Darin Erstad .10 .30
150 Jay Bell .10 .30
151 Mo Vaughn .10 .30
152 Ozzie Smith .50 1.25
153 Jose Mesa .10 .30
154 Osvaldo Fernandez .10 .30
155 Vinny Castilla .10 .30
156 Jason Isringhausen .10 .30
157 B.J. Surhoff .10 .30
158 Robert Perez .10 .30
159 Ron Coomer .10 .30
160 Darren Oliver .10 .30
161 Mike Mohler .10 .30
162 Russ Davis .10 .30
163 Bret Boone .10 .30
164 Ricky Bottalico .10 .30
165 Derek Jeter .75 2.00
166 Orlando Merced .10 .30
167 John Valentin .10 .30
168 Andruw Jones .20 .50
169 Angel Echevarria .10 .30
170 Todd Walker .10 .30
171 Desi Relaford .10 .30
172 Trey Beamon .10 .30
173 Brian Giles RC .60 1.50
174 Scott Rolen .20 .50
175 Shannon Stewart .10 .30
176 Dmitri Young .10 .30
177 Justin Thompson .10 .30
178 Trot Nixon .10 .30
179 Josh Booty .10 .30
180 Robin Jennings .10 .30
181 Marvin Benard .10 .30
182 Luis Castillo .10 .30
183 Wendell Magee .10 .30
184 Vladimir Guerrero .30 .75
185 Nomar Garciaparra .50 1.25
186 Ryan Hancock .10 .30
187 Mike Cameron .10 .30
188 Cal Ripken LG .50 1.25
189 Chipper Jones LG .20 .50
190 Albert Belle LG .10 .30
191 Mike Piazza LG .30 .75
192 Chuck Knoblauch LG .10 .30
193 Ken Griffey Jr. LG .30 .75
194 Ivan Rodriguez LG .10 .30
195 Jose Canseco LG .10 .30
196 Ryne Sandberg LG .30 .75
197 Jim Thome LG .10 .30
198 Andy Pettitte CL .10 .30
199 Andruw Jones CL .10 .30
200 Derek Jeter CL .40 1.00
201 Chipper Jones .30 .75
202 Albert Belle .10 .30
203 Mike Piazza .50 1.25
204 Ken Griffey Jr. .50 1.25
205 Ryne Sandberg .50 1.25
206 Jose Canseco .20 .50
207 Chili Davis .10 .30
208 Roger Clemens .60 1.50
209 Deion Sanders .20 .50
210 Darryl Hamilton .10 .30
211 Jermaine Dye .10 .30
212 Matt Williams .10 .30
213 Kevin Elster .10 .30
214 John Wetteland .10 .30
215 Garret Anderson .10 .30
216 Kevin Brown .10 .30
217 Matt Lawton .10 .30
218 Cal Ripken 1.00 2.50
219 Moises Alou .10 .30
220 Chuck Knoblauch .10 .30
221 Ivan Rodriguez .20 .50
222 Travis Fryman .10 .30
223 Jim Thome .20 .50
224 Eddie Murray .30 .75
225 Eric Young .10 .30
226 Ron Gant .10 .30
227 Tony Phillips .10 .30
228 Reggie Sanders .10 .30
229 Johnny Damon .20 .50
230 Bill Pulsipher .10 .30
231 Jim Edmonds .10 .30
232 Melvin Nieves .10 .30
233 Ryan Klesko .10 .30
234 David Cone .10 .30
235 Derek Bell .10 .30
236 Julio Franco .10 .30
237 Juan Guzman .10 .30
238 Larry Walker .10 .30
239 Delino DeShields .10 .30
240 Troy Percival .10 .30
241 Andres Galarraga .10 .30

242 Rondell White	.10	.30
243 John Burkett	.10	.30
244 J.T. Snow	.10	.30
245 Alex Fernandez	.10	.30
246 Edgar Martinez	.20	.50
247 Craig Biggio	.20	.50
248 Todd Hundley	.10	.30
249 Jimmy Key	.10	.30
250 Cliff Floyd	.10	.30
251 Jeff Conine	.10	.30
252 Curt Schilling	.10	.30
253 Jeff King	.10	.30
254 Tino Martinez	.20	.50
255 Carlos Baerga	.10	.30
256 Jeff Fassero	.10	.30
257 Dean Palmer	.10	.30
258 Robb Nen	.10	.30
259 Sandy Alomar Jr.	.10	.30
260 Carlos Perez	.10	.30
261 Rickey Henderson	.30	.75
262 Bobby Bonilla	.10	.30
263 Darren Daulton	.10	.30
264 Jim Leyritz	.10	.30
265 Dennis Martinez	.10	.30
266 Butch Huskey	.10	.30
267 Joe Vitiello	.10	.30
268 Steve Trachsel	.10	.30
269 Glenallen Hill	.10	.30
270 Terry Steinbach	.10	.30
271 Mark McLemore	.10	.30
272 Devon White	.10	.30
273 Jeff Kent	.10	.30
274 Tim Raines	.10	.30
275 Carlos Garcia	.10	.30
276 Hal Morris	.10	.30
277 Gary Gaetti	.10	.30
278 John Olerud	.10	.30
279 Wally Joyner	.10	.30
280 Brian Hunter	.10	.30
281 Steve Karsay	.10	.30
282 Denny Neagle	.10	.30
283 Jose Herrera	.10	.30
284 Todd Stottlemyre	.10	.30
285 Bip Roberts	.10	.30
286 Kevin Seitzer	.10	.30
287 Benji Gil	.10	.30
288 Dennis Eckersley	.10	.30
289 Brad Ausmus	.10	.30
290 Otis Nixon	.10	.30
291 Darryl Strawberry	.10	.30
292 Marquis Grissom	.10	.30
293 Darryl Kile	.10	.30
294 Quilvio Veras	.10	.30
295 Tom Goodwin	.10	.30
296 Benito Santiago	.10	.30
297 Mike Bordick	.10	.30
298 Roberto Kelly	.10	.30
299 David Justice	.10	.30
300 Carl Everett	.10	.30
301 Mark Whiten	.10	.30
302 Aaron Sele	.10	.30
303 Darren Dreifort	.10	.30
304 Bobby Jones	.10	.30
305 Fernando Vina	.10	.30
306 Ed Sprague	.10	.30
307 Andy Ashby	.10	.30
308 Tony Fernandez	.10	.30
309 Roger Pavlik	.10	.30
310 Mark Clark	.10	.30
311 Mariano Duncan	.10	.30
312 Tyler Houston	.10	.30
313 Eric Davis	.10	.30
314 Greg Vaughn	.10	.30
315 David Segui	.10	.30
316 Dave Nilsson	.10	.30
317 F.P. Santangelo	.10	.30
318 Wilton Guerrero	.10	.30
319 Jose Guillen	.10	.30
320 Kevin Orie	.10	.30
321 Derrek Lee	.20	.50
322 Bubba Trammell RC	.15	.40
323 Pokey Reese	.10	.30
324 Hideki Irabu RC	.15	.40
325 Scott Spiezio	.10	.30
326 Bartolo Colon	.10	.30
327 Damon Mashore	.10	.30
328 Ryan McGuire	.10	.30
329 Chris Carpenter	.10	.30
330 Jose Cruz Jr. RC	.15	.40
331 Todd Greene	.10	.30
332 Brian Moehler RC	.10	.30
333 Mike Sweeney	.10	.30
334 Neifi Perez	.10	.30
335 Matt Morris	.10	.30
336 Marvin Benard	.10	.30
337 Karim Garcia	.10	.30
338 Jason Dickson	.10	.30
339 Brant Brown	.10	.30
340 Jeff Suppan	.10	.30
341 Deivi Cruz RC	.15	.40
342 Antone Williamson	.10	.30
343 Curtis Goodwin	.10	.30
344 Brooks Kieschnick	.10	.30
345 Tony Womack RC	.15	.40
346 Rudy Pemberton	.10	.30
347 Todd Dunwoody	.10	.30
348 Frank Thomas LG	.20	.50
349 Andruw Jones LG	.10	.30
350 Alex Rodriguez LG	.30	.75
351 Greg Maddux LG	.30	.75
352 Jeff Bagwell LG	.10	.30
353 Juan Gonzalez LG	.10	.30
354 Barry Bonds LG	.40	1.00
355 Mark McGwire LG	.40	1.00
356 Tony Gwynn LG	.20	.50
357 Gary Sheffield LG	.10	.30
358 Derek Jeter LG	.40	1.00
359 Manny Ramirez LG	.10	.30
360 Hideo Nomo LG	.10	.30
361 Sammy Sosa LG	.20	.50
362 Paul Molitor LG	.10	.30
363 Kenny Lofton LG	.10	.30
364 Eddie Murray LG	.20	.50
365 Barry Larkin LG	.10	.30
366 Roger Clemens LG	.30	.75
367 John Smoltz LG	.10	.30
368 Alex Rodriguez GM	.30	.75
369 Frank Thomas GM	.20	.50
370 Cal Ripken GM	.50	1.25
371 Ken Griffey Jr. GM	.30	.75
372 Greg Maddux GM	.30	.75
373 Mike Piazza GM	.30	.75
374 Chipper Jones GM	.20	.50
375 Albert Belle GM	.10	.30
376 Chuck Knoblauch GM	.10	.30
377 Brady Anderson GM	.10	.30
378 David Justice GM	.10	.30
379 Randy Johnson GM	.20	.50
380 Wade Boggs GM	.10	.30
381 Kevin Brown GM	.10	.30
382 Tom Glavine GM	.10	.30
383 Raul Mondesi GM	.10	.30
384 Ivan Rodriguez GM	.10	.30
385 Larry Walker GM	.10	.30
386 Bernie Williams GM	.10	.30
387 Rusty Greer GM	.10	.30
388 Rafael Palmeiro GM	.10	.30
389 Matt Williams GM	.10	.30
390 Eric Young GM	.10	.30
391 Fred McGriff GM	.10	.30
392 Ken Caminiti GM	.10	.30
393 Roberto Alomar GM	.10	.30
394 Brian Jordan GM	.10	.30
395 Mark Grace GM	.10	.30
396 Jim Edmonds GM	.10	.30
397 Deion Sanders GM	.10	.30
398 Vladimir Guerrero CL	.20	.50
399 Darin Erstad CL	.10	.30
400 N. Garciaparra CL	.30	.75
NNO J.Robinson Reprint	10.00	25.00

1997 Leaf Fractal Matrix

Randomly inserted in packs, this 400-card set is parallel to the regular Leaf issue and features color player photos with either a bronze, silver or gold finish. Only 200 cards are bronze, 120 cards are silver, and 80 cards are gold. No card is available in more than one of the colors. In a convoluted effort, the fractal matrix parallel concept split the 400 card set into nine different tiered levels of parallels, each with print runs that varied from as many of several thousand of some cards (mostly the Bronze cards) to less than a few hundred of other cards (In the Gold X subset). Cards were split into colors (Bronze, Gold and Silver) and axis (X, Y and Z). Cards are listed in our checklist with color and axis designation. Unfortunately, the designers at Leaf failed to create any notable markings to differentiate the X, Y and Z axis for all the cards in this set. Leaf did issue an axis schematic on the back of the 1997 boxes and we've carefully incorporated that information into our checklist for accurate reference.

*BRONZE: 1.5X TO 4X BASIC CARDS
*SILVER: 2X TO 5X BASIC CARDS
*SILVER ROOKIES: .6X TO 1.5X BASIC
*GOLD Y/Z: 3X TO 8X BASIC CARDS
*GOLD X: 6X TO 15X BASIC CARDS
*GOLD X RC's: 2X TO 5X BASIC CARDS
RANDOM INSERTS IN PACKS
SEE WEBSITE FOR AXIS SCHEMATIC

1997 Leaf Fractal Matrix Die Cuts

This 400-card set is parallel to the regular set and features three different die-cut versions in three different finishes. 200 of the 400-card set are produced in the X-Axis cut with 150 of those bronze, 40 of those silver, and 10 of those gold. 120 of the 400-card set are available in type Y-Axis cut with 40 of those bronze, 60 silver, and 20 gold. Eighty of the 200-card set are produced in the Z-Axis cut with 10 of those bronze, 20 of those silver and 50 of those gold. No card was available in more than one color nor in more than one die-cut version. Unlike the non die-cut Fractal Matrix cards, these Die Cut parallels have distinguishable axis groupings based on the shape of the die cut edges.

*X-AXIS: 2X TO 5X BASIC CARDS
*X-AXIS ROOKIES: 1.25X TO 3X BASIC
*Y-AXIS: 3X TO 8X BASIC CARDS
*Y-AXIS ROOKIES: .75X TO 2X BASIC
*Z-AXIS: 2.5X TO 6X BASIC CARDS
RANDOM INSERTS IN PACKS
SEE WEBSITE FOR AXIS SCHEMATIC

1997 Leaf Banner Season

Randomly inserted in series one magazine packs, this 15-card set features color action player photos on die-cut cards and is printed on canvas card stock. Only 2500 of each card was produced and are sequentially numbered.

COMPLETE SET (15)	50.00	120.00
1 Jeff Bagwell	3.00	8.00
2 Ken Griffey Jr.	8.00	20.00
3 Juan Gonzalez	2.00	5.00
4 Frank Thomas	5.00	12.00
5 Alex Rodriguez	8.00	20.00
6 Kenny Lofton	2.00	5.00
7 Chuck Knoblauch	2.00	5.00
8 Mo Vaughn	2.00	5.00
9 Chipper Jones	5.00	12.00
10 Ken Caminiti	2.00	5.00
11 Craig Biggio	3.00	8.00
12 John Smoltz	3.00	8.00
13 Pat Hentgen	2.00	5.00
14 Derek Jeter	12.50	30.00
15 Todd Hollandsworth	2.00	5.00

1997 Leaf Dress for Success

Randomly inserted in series one retail packs, this 18-card retail only set features color player photos prined on a jersey-simulated, nylon card stock and is accented with flocking on the team logo and gold-foil stamping. Only 3,500 of each card were produced and are sequentially numbered.

COMPLETE SET (18)	15.00	40.00
1 Greg Maddux	1.25	3.00
2 Cal Ripken	2.50	6.00
3 Albert Belle	.30	.75
4 Frank Thomas	.75	2.00
5 Dante Bichette	.30	.75
6 Gary Sheffield	.30	.75
7 Jeff Bagwell	.50	1.25
8 Mike Piazza	1.25	3.00
9 Mark McGwire	2.00	5.00
10 Ken Caminiti	.30	.75
11 Alex Rodriguez	1.25	3.00
12 Ken Griffey Jr.	1.25	3.00
13 Juan Gonzalez	.30	.75
14 Brian Jordan	.30	.75
15 Mo Vaughn	.30	.75
16 Ivan Rodriguez	.50	1.25
17 Andruw Jones	.50	1.25
18 Chipper Jones	.75	2.00

1997 Leaf Get-A-Grip

Randomly inserted in series one hobby packs, this 16-card double player insert set features color player photos of some of the current top pitchers matched against some of the league's current power hitters. The set is printed on full-silver, ploy-laminated card stock with gold-foil stamping. Only 3,500 of each card was produced and are sequentially numbered.

COMPLETE SET (16)	60.00	150.00
1 Ken Griffey Jr.	5.00	12.00
Greg Maddux		
2 John Smoltz	3.00	8.00
Frank Thomas		
3 Mike Piazza	5.00	12.00
Andy Pettitte		
4 Randy Johnson	3.00	8.00
Chipper Jones		
5 Tom Glavine	5.00	12.00
Alex Rodriguez		
6 Pat Hentgen	2.00	5.00
Jeff Bagwell		
7 Kevin Brown	1.25	3.00
Juan Gonzalez		
8 Barry Bonds	8.00	20.00
Mike Mussina		
9 Hideo Nomo	3.00	8.00
Albert Belle		
10 Troy Percival	2.00	5.00
Andruw Jones		
11 Roger Clemens	6.00	15.00
Brian Jordan		
12 Paul Wilson	2.00	5.00
Ivan Rodriguez		
13 Andy Benes	1.25	3.00
Mo Vaughn		
14 Al Leiter	8.00	20.00
Derek Jeter		
15 Bill Pulsipher	10.00	25.00
Cal Ripken		
16 Mariano Rivera	3.00	8.00
Ken Caminiti		

1997 Leaf Gold Stars

Randomly inserted in all series two packs, this 36-card set features color action images of some of Baseball's hottest names with actual 24kt. gold foil stamping. Only 2,500 of each card were produced and are sequentially numbered.

1 Frank Thomas	3.00	8.00
2 Alex Rodriguez	5.00	12.00
3 Ken Griffey Jr.	5.00	12.00
4 Andruw Jones	2.00	5.00
5 Chipper Jones	3.00	8.00
6 Jeff Bagwell	2.00	5.00
7 Derek Jeter	8.00	20.00
8 Deion Sanders	2.00	5.00
9 Ivan Rodriguez	2.00	5.00
10 Juan Gonzalez	1.25	3.00
11 Greg Maddux	5.00	12.00
12 Andy Pettitte	2.00	5.00
13 Roger Clemens	6.00	15.00
14 Hideo Nomo	3.00	8.00
15 Tony Gwynn	4.00	10.00
16 Barry Bonds	8.00	20.00
17 Kenny Lofton	1.25	3.00
18 Paul Molitor	1.25	3.00
19 Jim Thome	2.00	5.00
20 Albert Belle	1.25	3.00
21 Cal Ripken	10.00	25.00
22 Mark McGwire	8.00	20.00
23 Barry Larkin	2.00	5.00
24 Mike Piazza	5.00	12.00
25 Darin Erstad	1.25	3.00
26 Chuck Knoblauch	1.25	3.00
27 Vladimir Guerrero	3.00	8.00
28 Tony Clark	1.25	3.00
29 Scott Rolen	2.00	5.00
30 Nomar Garciaparra	5.00	12.00
31 Eric Young	1.25	3.00
32 Ryne Sandberg	5.00	12.00
33 Roberto Alomar	2.00	5.00
34 Eddie Murray	3.00	8.00
35 Rafael Palmeiro	2.00	5.00
36 Jose Guillen	1.25	3.00

1997 Leaf Knot-Hole Gang Samples

One of twelve different sample cards was distributed to dealers and hobby media prior to the release of 1997 Leaf to preview the set. The cards are marked "PROMO/5000" on back and are straight parallels to the basic Knot-Hole Gang insert cards.

COMPLETE SET (12)	16.00	40.00
1 Chuck Knoblauch	.40	1.00
2 Ken Griffey Jr.	1.50	4.00
3 Frank Thomas	.75	2.00
4 Tony Gwynn	1.50	4.00
5 Mike Piazza	2.50	6.00
6 Jeff Bagwell	.75	2.00
7 Rusty Greer	.40	1.00
8 Cal Ripken	3.00	8.00
9 Chipper Jones	1.50	4.00
10 Ryan Klesko	.30	.75
11 Barry Larkin	.60	1.50
12 Paul Molitor	1.00	2.50

1997 Leaf Knot-Hole Gang

This 12-card insert set, randomly seeded into first series hobby packs, features color action player photos printed on wooden card stock. The die-cut card resembles a wooden fence with the player being seen in action through a knot hole. Only 5,000 of this set was produced and is sequentially numbered.

COMPLETE SET (12)	20.00	50.00
1 Chuck Knoblauch	.60	1.50
2 Ken Griffey Jr.	2.50	6.00
3 Frank Thomas	1.50	4.00
4 Tony Gwynn	2.00	5.00
5 Mike Piazza	2.50	6.00
6 Jeff Bagwell	1.00	2.50
7 Rusty Greer	.60	1.50
8 Cal Ripken	5.00	12.00
9 Chipper Jones	1.50	4.00
10 Ryan Klesko	.60	1.50
11 Barry Larkin	1.00	2.50
12 Paul Molitor	.60	1.50

1997 Leaf Leagues of the Nation

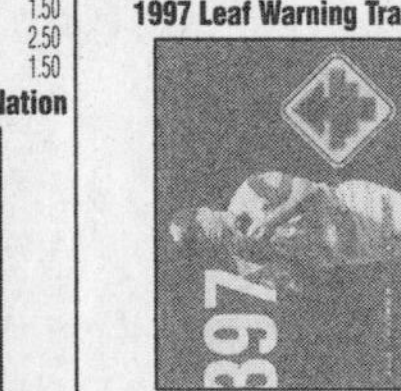

Randomly inserted in all series two packs, this 15-card set celebrates the first season of interleague play with double-sided, die-cut cards that highlight some of the best interleague match-ups. Using flocking technology, the cards display color action player photos with the place and date of the game where the match-up between the pictured players took place. Only 2,500 of each card were produced and are sequentially numbered.

1 Juan Gonzalez	12.50	30.00
Barry Bonds		
2 Cal Ripken	15.00	40.00
Chipper Jones		
3 Mark McGwire	12.50	30.00
Ken Caminiti		
4 Derek Jeter	12.50	30.00
Kenny Lofton		
5 Ivan Rodriguez	8.00	20.00
Mike Piazza		
6 Ken Griffey Jr.	8.00	20.00
Larry Walker		
7 Frank Thomas	5.00	12.00
Sammy Sosa		
8 Paul Molitor	2.00	5.00
Barry Larkin		
9 Albert Belle	2.00	5.00
Deion Sanders		
10 Matt Williams	3.00	8.00
Jeff Bagwell		
11 Mo Vaughn	2.00	5.00
Gary Sheffield		
12 Alex Rodriguez	8.00	20.00
Tony Gwynn		
13 Tino Martinez	3.00	8.00
Scott Rolen		
14 Darin Erstad	2.00	5.00
Wilton Guerrero		
15 Tony Clark	5.00	12.00
Vladimir Guerrero		

1997 Leaf Statistical Standouts

This 15-card insert set, randomly seeded into all first series packs, showcases some of the league's statistical leaders and is printed on full-leather, die-cut, foil-stamped card stock. The player's statistics are displayed beside a color player photo. Only 1,000 of this set were produced and are sequentially numbered.

1 Albert Belle	3.00	8.00
2 Juan Gonzalez	3.00	8.00
3 Ken Griffey Jr.	12.50	30.00
4 Alex Rodriguez	12.50	30.00
5 Frank Thomas	8.00	20.00
6 Chipper Jones	8.00	20.00
7 Greg Maddux	12.50	30.00
8 Mike Piazza	12.50	30.00
9 Cal Ripken	25.00	60.00
10 Mark McGwire	20.00	50.00
11 Barry Bonds	20.00	50.00
12 Derek Jeter	20.00	50.00
13 Ken Caminiti	3.00	8.00
14 John Smoltz	5.00	12.00
15 Paul Molitor	3.00	8.00

1997 Leaf Thomas Collection

Randomly inserted in all series two packs, this six-card set commemorates the multi-faceted talents of first baseman and at the time, Leaf Company spokesman, Frank Thomas with actual pieces of his game-used hats, jerseys (home and away), sweatbands, batting gloves or bats embedded in the cards. Only 100 of each card were produced and are sequentially numbered. This set, along with the 1997 Upper Deck Game Jersey inserts, represents one of the earliest forays by an mlb-licensed manufactuer into game-used memorabilia inserts.

1 Frank Thomas	125.00	250.00
Game Hat/Blue Text		
2 Frank Thomas	125.00	250.00
Home Jersey/Orange Text		
3 Frank Thomas	125.00	250.00
Batting Glove/Yellow Text		
4 Frank Thomas	125.00	250.00
Bat/Green Text		
5 Frank Thomas	125.00	250.00
Sweatband/Purple Text		
6 Frank Thomas	125.00	250.00
Away Jersey/Red Text		

1997 Leaf Warning Track

Randomly inserted in all series two packs, this 18-card set features color action photos of outstanding outfielders printed on embossed canvas card stock. Only 3,500 of each card were produced and are sequentially numbered.

COMPLETE SET (18)	40.00	100.00
1 Ken Griffey Jr.	5.00	12.00
2 Albert Belle	1.25	3.00
3 Barry Bonds	8.00	20.00
4 Andruw Jones	2.00	5.00
5 Kenny Lofton	1.25	3.00
6 Tony Gwynn	4.00	10.00
7 Manny Ramirez	2.00	5.00
8 Rusty Greer	1.25	3.00
9 Bernie Williams	2.00	5.00
10 Gary Sheffield	1.25	3.00
11 Juan Gonzalez	1.25	3.00
12 Raul Mondesi	1.25	3.00
13 Brady Anderson	1.25	3.00
14 Rondell White	1.25	3.00
15 Sammy Sosa	3.00	8.00
16 Deion Sanders	2.00	5.00
17 Dave Justice	1.25	3.00
18 Jim Edmonds	1.25	3.00

1998 Leaf

The 1998 Leaf set was issued in one series totalling 200 cards. The 10-card packs carried a suggested retail price of $2.99. The set contains the topical subsets: Curtain Calls (148-157), Gold Leaf Stars (158-177), and Gold Leaf Rookies (178-197). All three subsets are short-printed in relation to cards from 1-147 and 201. Those short prints represent one of the early efforts by a manufacturer to incorportate short-print subsets cards into a basic issue set. The product went live in mid-March, 1998. Card number 42 does not exist as Leaf retired the number in honor of Jackie Robinson.

COMPLETE SET (200)	25.00	60.00
COMP.SET w/o SP's (147)	6.00	15.00
COMMON CARD (1-201)	.10	.30
COMMON SP (148-197)	.60	1.50
1 Rusty Greer	.10	.30
2 Tino Martinez	.20	.50
3 Bobby Bonilla	.10	.30
4 Jason Giambi	.10	.30
5 Matt Morris	.10	.30
6 Craig Counsell	.10	.30
7 Reggie Jefferson	.10	.30
8 Brian Rose	.10	.30
9 Ruben Rivera	.10	.30
10 Shawn Estes	.10	.30
11 Tony Gwynn	.40	1.00
12 Jeff Abbott	.10	.30
13 Jose Cruz Jr.	.10	.30
14 Francisco Cordova	.10	.30
15 Ryan Klesko	.10	.30
16 Tim Salmon	.20	.50
17 Brett Tomko	.10	.30
18 Matt Williams	.10	.30
19 Joe Carter	.10	.30
20 Harold Baines	.10	.30
21 Gary Sheffield	.10	.30
22 Charles Johnson	.10	.30
23 Aaron Boone	.10	.30
24 Eddie Murray	.30	.75
25 Matt Stairs	.10	.30
26 David Cone	.10	.30
27 Jon Nunnally	.10	.30
28 Chris Stynes	.10	.30
29 Enrique Wilson	.10	.30
30 Randy Johnson	.30	.75
31 Garret Anderson	.10	.30
32 Manny Ramirez	.20	.50
33 Jeff Suppan	.10	.30
34 Rickey Henderson	.30	.75
35 Scott Spiezio	.10	.30
36 Rondell White	.10	.30
37 Todd Greene	.10	.30
38 Delino DeShields	.10	.30
39 Kevin Brown	.20	.50
40 Chili Davis	.10	.30
41 Jimmy Key	.10	.30
43 Mike Mussina	.20	.50
44 Joe Randa	.10	.30
45 Chan Ho Park	.10	.30
46 Brad Radke	.10	.30
47 Geronimo Berroa	.10	.30
48 Wade Boggs	.20	.50
49 Kevin Appier	.10	.30
50 Moises Alou	.10	.30
51 David Justice	.10	.30
52 Ivan Rodriguez	.20	.50
53 J.T. Snow	.10	.30
54 Brian Giles	.10	.30
55 Will Clark	.20	.50
56 Justin Thompson	.10	.30
57 Javier Lopez	.10	.30
58 Hideki Irabu	.10	.30
59 Mark Grudzielanek	.10	.30
60 Abraham Nunez	.10	.30
61 Todd Hollandsworth	.10	.30
62 Jay Bell	.10	.30
63 Nomar Garciaparra	.50	1.25
64 Vinny Castilla	.10	.30
65 Lou Collier	.10	.30
66 Kevin Orie	.10	.30
67 John Valentin	.10	.30
68 Robin Ventura	.10	.30
69 Denny Neagle	.10	.30
70 Tony Womack	.10	.30
71 Dennis Reyes	.10	.30
72 Wally Joyner	.10	.30
73 Kevin Brown	.20	.50
74 Ray Durham	.10	.30
75 Mike Cameron	.10	.30
76 Dante Bichette	.10	.30
77 Jose Guillen	.10	.30
78 Carlos Delgado	.10	.30
79 Paul Molitor	.10	.30
80 Jason Kendall	.10	.30
81 Mark Bellhorn	.10	.30
82 Damian Jackson	.10	.30
83 Bill Mueller	.10	.30
84 Kevin Young	.10	.30
85 Curt Schilling	.10	.30
86 Jeffrey Hammonds	.10	.30
87 Sandy Alomar Jr.	.10	.30
88 Bartolo Colon	.10	.30
89 Wilton Guerrero	.10	.30
90 Bernie Williams	.20	.50
91 Deion Sanders	.20	.50
92 Mike Piazza	.50	1.25
93 Butch Huskey	.10	.30
94 Edgardo Alfonzo	.10	.30
95 Alan Benes	.10	.30
96 Craig Biggio	.20	.50
97 Mark Grace	.20	.50
98 Shawn Green	.10	.30
99 Derrek Lee	.20	.50
100 Ken Griffey Jr.	.50	1.25
101 Tim Raines	.10	.30
102 Pokey Reese	.10	.30
103 Lee Stevens	.10	.30
104 Shannon Stewart	.10	.30
105 John Smoltz	.20	.50
106 Frank Thomas	.30	.75
107 Jeff Fassero	.10	.30
108 Jay Buhner	.10	.30
109 Jose Canseco	.20	.50
110 Omar Vizquel	.20	.50
111 Travis Fryman	.10	.30
112 Dave Nilsson	.10	.30
113 John Olerud	.10	.30
114 Larry Walker	.10	.30
115 Jim Edmonds	.10	.30
116 Bobby Higginson	.10	.30
117 Todd Hundley	.10	.30
118 Paul O'Neill	.20	.50
119 Bip Roberts	.10	.30
120 Ismael Valdes	.10	.30
121 Pedro Martinez	.20	.50
122 Jeff Cirillo	.10	.30
123 Andy Benes	.10	.30
124 Bobby Jones	.10	.30
125 Brian Hunter	.10	.30
126 Darryl Kile	.10	.30
127 Pat Hentgen	.10	.30
128 Marquis Grissom	.10	.30
129 Eric Davis	.10	.30
130 Chipper Jones	.30	.75
131 Edgar Martinez	.20	.50
132 Andy Pettitte	.20	.50
133 Cal Ripken	1.00	2.50
134 Scott Rolen	.20	.50
135 Ron Coomer	.10	.30
136 Luis Castillo	.10	.30
137 Fred McGriff	.20	.50
138 Neifi Perez	.10	.30
139 Eric Karros	.10	.30
140 Alex Fernandez	.10	.30
141 Jason Dickson	.10	.30
142 Lance Johnson	.10	.30
143 Ray Lankford	.10	.30
144 Sammy Sosa	.30	.75
145 Eric Young	.10	.30
146 Bubba Trammell	.10	.30
147 Todd Walker	.10	.30
148 Mo Vaughn CC	.60	1.50
149 Jeff Bagwell CC	1.00	2.50
150 Kenny Lofton CC	.60	1.50
151 Raul Mondesi CC	.60	1.50
152 Mike Piazza CC	2.50	6.00
153 Chipper Jones CC	1.50	4.00
154 Larry Walker CC	.60	1.50
155 Greg Maddux CC	2.50	6.00
156 Ken Griffey Jr. CC	2.50	6.00
157 Frank Thomas CC	1.50	4.00
158 Darin Erstad GLS	.60	1.50
159 Roberto Alomar GLS	1.00	2.50
160 Albert Belle GLS	.60	1.50
161 Jim Thome GLS	1.00	2.50
162 Tony Clark GLS	.60	1.50
163 Chuck Knoblauch GLS	.60	1.50
164 Derek Jeter GLS	4.00	10.00
165 Alex Rodriguez GLS	2.50	6.00
166 Tony Gwynn GLS	2.00	5.00
167 Roger Clemens GLS	3.00	8.00
168 Barry Larkin GLS	1.00	2.50
169 Andres Galarraga GLS	.60	1.50
170 Vlad. Guerrero GLS	1.50	4.00
171 Mark McGwire GLS	4.00	10.00
172 Barry Bonds GLS	4.00	10.00
173 Juan Gonzalez GLS	.60	1.50
174 Andruw Jones GLS	1.00	2.50
175 Paul Molitor GLS	.60	1.50
176 Hideo Nomo GLS	1.50	4.00
177 Cal Ripken GLS	5.00	12.00
178 Brad Fullmer GLR	.60	1.50
179 Jaret Wright GLR	.60	1.50
180 Bobby Estalella GLR	.60	1.50
181 Ben Grieve GLR	.60	1.50
182 Paul Konerko GLR	.60	1.50
183 David Ortiz GLR	2.00	5.00
184 Todd Helton GLR	1.00	2.50
185 J.Encarnacion GLR	.60	1.50
186 Miguel Tejada GLR	1.50	4.00
187 Jacob Cruz GLR	.60	1.50
188 Mark Kotsay GLR	.60	1.50
189 Fernando Tatis GLR	.60	1.50
190 Ricky Ledee GLR	.60	1.50
191 Richard Hidalgo GLR	.60	1.50
192 Richie Sexson GLR	.60	1.50
193 Luis Ordaz GLR	.60	1.50
194 Eli Marrero GLR	.60	1.50
195 Livan Hernandez GLR	.60	1.50
196 Homer Bush GLR	.60	1.50
197 Raul Ibanez GLR	.60	1.50
198 Nomar Garciaparra CL	.30	.75
199 Scott Rolen CL	.10	.30
200 Jose Cruz Jr. CL	.10	.30
201 Al Martin	.10	.30

1998 Leaf Fractal Diamond Axis

Randomly inserted in packs, this 200-card set is parallel to the Leaf base set. Each card features die cut edges and blue foil fronts. Only 50 serially numbered sets were produced. Card number 42 does not exist.

*STARS 1-147/198-201: 15X TO 40X BASIC
*SP STARS 148-197: 3X TO 8X BASIC SP'S

1998 Leaf Fractal Matrix

Randomly inserted in packs, this 200-card set is parallel to the Leaf base set and features color player photos with either a bronze, silver or gold finish. Only 100 cards are bronze, 60 are silver, and 40 are gold. No

card is available in more than one of the colors. The set is broken into nine tiers based on three colors (Bronze, Gold and Silver) and three axis (X, Y and Z). Unlike the previous year, the 1998 cards carry an axis-logo on the card front, allowing collectors to identify the specific tier. It's estimated that print runs range from as few as 50 to as many of 2000 of each card.

*BRONZE 1-147/198-201: 1.5X TO 4X BASIC
*BRONZE 148-197: .3X TO .8X BASIC
BRONZE X STATED PRINT RUN 1600 SETS
BRONZE Y STATED PRINT RUN 1800 SETS
BRONZE Z STATED PRINT RUN 1900 SETS
*SILVER 1-147/198-201: 3X TO 8X BASIC
*SILVER: 148-197: .6X TO 1.5X BASIC
SILVER X STATED PRINT RUN 600 SETS
SILVER Y STATED PRINT RUN 800 SETS
SILVER Z STATED PRINT RUN 900 SETS
*GOLD 1-147/198-201: 5X TO 12X BASIC
*GOLD: 148-197: 1X TO 2.5X BASIC
GOLD X STATED PRINT RUN 100 SETS
GOLD Y STATED PRINT RUN 300 SETS
GOLD Z STATED PRINT RUN 400 SETS
RANDOM INSERTS IN PACKS
CARD NUMBER 42 DOES NOT EXIST

1998 Leaf Fractal Matrix Die Cuts

Randomly inserted in packs, this 200-card set is parallel to the regular set and features three different die-cut versions in three different finishes. Only 100 of the set are produced in the x-axis cut with 75 of those bronze, 20 silver, and five gold. Only 60 are available in the type y-axis cut with 20 of those bronze, 30 silver, and 10 gold. Only 40 are produced in the z-axis cut with five bronze, 10 silver and 25 gold. No card is available in more than one color nor in more than one die-cut version. Card number 42 does not exist.

*X-AXIS 1-147/198-201: 5X TO 12X BASIC
*X-AXIS 148-197: 1X TO 2.5X BASIC
X-AXIS STATED PRINT RUN 400 SETS
*Y-AXIS 1-147/198-201: 8X TO 20X BASIC
*Y-AXIS 148-197: 1.5X TO 4X BASIC
Y-AXIS STATED PRINT RUN 200 SETS
*Z-AXIS 1-147/198-201: 12.5X TO 30X BASIC
*Z-AXIS 148-197: 2.5X TO 6X BASIC
Z-AXIS STATED PRINT RUN 100 SETS
RANDOM INSERTS IN PACKS
CARD NUMBER 42 DOES NOT EXIST
SEE WEBSITE FOR AXIS SCHEMATIC

1998 Leaf Crusade Green

As part of the 1998 Donruss/Leaf Crusade insert program, 30 cards were exclusively issued in 1998 Leaf Packs. Please refer to 1998 Donruss Crusade for further information.

PLEASE SEE 1998 DONRUSS CRUSADE

1998 Leaf Heading for the Hall Samples

To preview the 1998 Leaf product, all dealer wholesale order forms contained one of these twenty different samples. The cards differ from the basic Heading for the Hall inserts in two ways: the large "SAMPLE" text printed diagonally across the card back and the lack of serial numbering on back.

COMPLETE SET (20)	32.00	80.00
1 Roberto Alomar	.60	1.50
2 Jeff Bagwell	.75	2.00
3 Albert Belle	.30	.75
4 Wade Boggs	1.50	4.00
5 Barry Bonds	2.00	5.00
6 Roger Clemens	2.00	5.00
7 Juan Gonzalez	.60	1.50
8 Ken Griffey Jr.	2.00	5.00
9 Tony Gwynn	2.00	5.00
10 Barry Larkin	.60	1.50
11 Kenny Lofton	.40	1.00
12 Greg Maddux	2.50	6.00
13 Mark McGwire	2.50	6.00
14 Paul Molitor	1.00	2.50
15 Eddie Murray	.60	1.50
16 Mike Piazza	3.00	8.00
17 Cal Ripken	4.00	10.00
18 Ivan Rodriguez	1.25	3.00
19 Ryne Sandberg	1.50	4.00
20 Frank Thomas	1.00	2.50

1998 Leaf Heading for the Hall

This 20 card set was randomly inserted into 1998 Leaf packs. The fronts have a design similar to the Hall of Fame packs. The player's name and team is at top. The back has another photo along with a brief blurb. The

cards are numbered "X of 3500" on the back as well.

COMPLETE SET (20)	40.00	100.00
1 Roberto Alomar	2.00	5.00
2 Jeff Bagwell	2.00	5.00
3 Albert Belle	1.25	3.00
4 Wade Boggs	2.00	5.00
5 Barry Bonds	8.00	20.00
6 Roger Clemens	6.00	15.00
7 Juan Gonzalez	1.25	3.00
8 Ken Griffey Jr.	5.00	12.00
9 Tony Gwynn	4.00	10.00
10 Barry Larkin	2.00	5.00
11 Kenny Lofton	1.25	3.00
12 Greg Maddux	5.00	12.00
13 Mark McGwire	8.00	20.00
14 Paul Molitor	1.25	3.00
15 Eddie Murray	3.00	8.00
16 Mike Piazza	5.00	12.00
17 Cal Ripken	10.00	25.00
18 Ivan Rodriguez	2.00	5.00
19 Ryne Sandberg	5.00	12.00
20 Frank Thomas	3.00	8.00

1998 Leaf State Representatives

This 30 card set was randomly inserted into packs. The fronts have the words 'State Representatives" on the top with the player's name and team on the bottom. The player's photo has a metallic sheen to it as he is pictured against a state outline. The back has a small player portrait along with some information about the player. The cards are serial numbered "X of 5,000" on the back.

COMPLETE SET (30)	60.00	150.00
1 Ken Griffey Jr.	4.00	10.00
2 Frank Thomas	2.50	6.00
3 Alex Rodriguez	4.00	10.00
4 Cal Ripken	8.00	20.00
5 Chipper Jones	2.50	6.00
6 Andruw Jones	1.50	4.00
7 Scott Rolen	1.50	4.00
8 Nomar Garciaparra	4.00	10.00
9 Tim Salmon	1.50	4.00
10 Manny Ramirez	1.50	4.00
11 Jose Cruz Jr.	1.00	2.50
12 Vladimir Guorroro	2.50	6.00
13 Tino Martinez	1.50	4.00
14 Larry Walker	1.00	2.50
15 Mo Vaughn	1.00	2.50
16 Jim Thome	1.50	4.00
17 Tony Clark	1.00	2.50
18 Derek Jeter	6.00	15.00
19 Juan Gonzalez	1.00	2.50
20 Jeff Bagwell	1.50	4.00
21 Ivan Rodriguez	1.50	4.00
22 Mark McGwire	6.00	15.00
23 David Justice	1.00	2.50
24 Chuck Knoblauch	1.00	2.50
25 Andy Pettitte	1.50	4.00
26 Raul Mondesi	1.00	2.50
27 Randy Johnson	2.50	6.00
28 Greg Maddux	4.00	10.00
29 Bernie Williams	1.50	4.00
30 Rusty Greer	1.00	2.50

1998 Leaf Statistical Standouts

These 24 horizontal cards feature leading players. The front of the card has the players photo against a background of a glove and ball. The ball has been signed by that player. The card's front feels like leather and the words "Statistical Standouts" is printed on the side. The backs have year and career stats on the back along with another player photo. The cards are serial numbered "X of 2500" on the back, though only 2,250 of each card were produced due to the fact that the first 250 #'D sets were devoted to the Statistical Standouts Die Cut parallel..

COMPLETE SET (24) 100.00 250.00
*DIE CUTS: .75X TO 2X BASIC STAT.STAND.
DIE CUT PRINT RUN 250 SERIAL #'d SETS
RANDOM INSERTS IN PACKS

1 Frank Thomas	4.00	10.00
2 Ken Griffey Jr.	6.00	15.00
3 Alex Rodriguez	6.00	15.00
4 Mike Piazza	6.00	15.00
5 Greg Maddux	6.00	15.00
6 Cal Ripken	12.50	30.00
7 Chipper Jones	4.00	10.00
8 Juan Gonzalez	1.50	4.00
9 Jeff Bagwell	2.50	6.00
10 Mark McGwire	10.00	25.00
11 Tony Gwynn	5.00	12.00
12 Mo Vaughn	1.50	4.00
13 Nomar Garciaparra	6.00	15.00
14 Jose Cruz Jr.	1.50	4.00
15 Vladimir Guerrero	4.00	10.00
16 Scott Rolen	2.50	6.00
17 Andy Pettitte	2.50	6.00
18 Randy Johnson	4.00	10.00
19 Larry Walker	1.50	4.00
20 Kenny Lofton	1.50	4.00
21 Tony Clark	1.50	4.00
22 David Justice	1.50	4.00
23 Derek Jeter	10.00	25.00
24 Barry Bonds	10.00	25.00

2002 Leaf

This 200 card set was issued in late winter, 2002. This set was distributed in four card packs with an SRP of $3 which were sent in 24 packs to a box with 20 boxes to a case. Cards numbered from 151-200, which were inserted at a stated rate of one in six, featured 50 of the leading rookie prospects entering the 2002 season. Card number 42, which Leaf had previously retired in honor of Jackie Robinson, was originally intended to feature a short-print card honoring the sensational rookie season of Ichiro Suzuki. However, Leaf decided to continue honoring Robinson and never went through with printing card 42. Cards numbered 201 and 202 feature Japanese imports So Taguchi and Kazuhisa Ishii, both of which were short-printed in relation to the other prospect cards 151-200. The cards production runs were announced by the manufacturer as 250 copies for Ishii and 500 for Taguchi.

COMP.SET w/o SP's (149)	10.00	25.00
COMMON (1-41/43-150)	.10	.30
COMMON CARD (151-200)	1.50	4.00
1 Tim Salmon	.20	.50
2 Troy Glaus	.10	.30
3 Curt Schilling	.10	.30
4 Luis Gonzalez	.10	.30
5 Mark Grace	.20	.50
6 Matt Williams	.10	.30
7 Randy Johnson	.30	.75
8 Tom Glavine	.20	.50
9 Brady Anderson	.10	.30
10 Hideo Nomo	.30	.75
11 Pedro Martinez	.20	.50
12 Corey Patterson	.10	.30
13 Paul Konerko	.10	.30
14 Jon Lieber	.10	.30
15 Carlos Lee	.10	.30
16 Magglio Ordonez	.10	.30
17 Adam Dunn	.10	.30
18 Ken Griffey Jr.	.50	1.25
19 C.C. Sabathia	.10	.30
20 Jim Thome	.20	.50
21 Juan Gonzalez	.10	.30
22 Kenny Lofton	.10	.30
23 Juan Encarnacion	.10	.30
24 Tony Clark	.10	.30
25 A.J. Burnett	.10	.30
26 Josh Beckett	.10	.30
27 Lance Berkman	.10	.30
28 Eric Karros	.10	.30
29 Shawn Green	.10	.30
30 Brad Radke	.10	.30
31 Joe Mays	.10	.30
32 Javier Vazquez	.10	.30
33 Alfonso Soriano	.10	.30
34 Jorge Posada	.20	.50
35 Eric Chavez	.10	.30
36 Mark Mulder	.10	.30
37 Miguel Tejada	.10	.30
38 Tim Hudson	.10	.30
39 Bob Abreu	.10	.30
40 Pat Burrell	.10	.30
41 Ryan Klesko	.10	.30
43 John Olerud	.10	.30
44 Ellis Burks	.10	.30
45 Mike Cameron	.10	.30
46 Jim Edmonds	.10	.30
47 Ben Grieve	.10	.30
48 Carlos Pena	.10	.30
49 Alex Rodriguez	.50	1.25
50 Raul Mondesi	.10	.30
51 Billy Koch	.10	.30
52 Manny Ramirez	.20	.50
53 Darin Erstad	.10	.30
54 Troy Percival	.10	.30
55 Andruw Jones	.20	.50
56 Chipper Jones	.30	.75
57 David Segui	.10	.30
58 Chris Stynes	.10	.30
59 Trot Nixon	.10	.30
60 Sammy Sosa	.30	.75
61 Kerry Wood	.10	.30
62 Frank Thomas	.30	.75
63 Barry Larkin	.20	.50
64 Bartolo Colon	.10	.30
65 Kazuhiro Sasaki	.10	.30
66 Roberto Alomar	.20	.50
67 Mike Hampton	.10	.30
68 Roger Cedeno	.10	.30
69 Cliff Floyd	.10	.30
70 Mike Lowell	.10	.30
71 Billy Wagner	.10	.30
72 Craig Biggio	.20	.50
73 Jeff Bagwell	.20	.50
74 Carlos Beltran	.10	.30
75 Mark Quinn	.10	.30
76 Mike Sweeney	.10	.30
77 Gary Sheffield	.10	.30
78 Kevin Brown	.10	.30
79 Paul LoDuca	.10	.30
80 Ben Sheets	.10	.30
81 Jeromy Burnitz	.10	.30
82 Richie Sexson	.10	.30
83 Corey Koskie	.10	.30
84 Eric Milton	.10	.30
85 Jose Vidro	.10	.30
86 Mike Piazza	.50	1.25
87 Robin Ventura	.10	.30
88 Andy Pettitte	.20	.50
89 Mike Mussina	.20	.50
90 Orlando Hernandez	.10	.30
91 Roger Clemens	.60	1.50
92 Barry Zito	.10	.30
93 Jermaine Dye	.10	.30
94 Jimmy Rollins	.10	.30
95 Jason Kendall	.10	.30
96 Rickey Henderson	.30	.75
97 Andres Galarraga	.10	.30
98 Bret Boone	.10	.30
99 Freddy Garcia	.10	.30
100 J.D. Drew	.10	.30
101 Jose Cruz Jr.	.10	.30
102 Greg Maddux	.50	1.25
103 Javy Lopez	.10	.30
104 Nomar Garciaparra	.50	1.25
105 Fred McGriff	.20	.50
106 Keith Foulke	.10	.30
107 Ray Durham	.10	.30
108 Sean Casey	.10	.30
109 Todd Walker	.10	.30
110 Omar Vizquel	.20	.50
111 Travis Fryman	.10	.30
112 Larry Walker	.10	.30
113 Todd Helton	.20	.50
114 Bobby Higginson	.10	.30
115 Charles Johnson	.10	.30
116 Moises Alou	.10	.30
117 Richard Hidalgo	.10	.30
118 Roy Oswalt	.10	.30
119 Neifi Perez	.10	.30
120 Adrian Beltre	.10	.30
121 Chan Ho Park	.10	.30
122 Geoff Jenkins	.10	.30
123 Doug Mientkiewicz	.10	.30
124 Torii Hunter	.10	.30
125 Vladimir Guerrero	.30	.75
126 Matt Lawton	.10	.30
127 Tsuyoshi Shinjo	.10	.30
128 Bernie Williams	.20	.50
129 Derek Jeter	.75	2.00
130 Mariano Rivera	.30	.75
131 Tino Martinez	.20	.50
132 Jason Giambi	.10	.30
133 Scott Rolen	.20	.50
134 Brian Giles	.10	.30
135 Phil Nevin	.10	.30
136 Trevor Hoffman	.10	.30
137 Barry Bonds	.75	2.00
138 Jeff Kent	.10	.30
139 Shannon Stewart	.10	.30
140 Shawn Estes	.10	.30
141 Edgar Martinez	.20	.50
142 Ichiro Suzuki	.60	1.50
143 Albert Pujols	.60	1.50
144 Bud Smith	.10	.30
145 Matt Morris	.10	.30
146 Frank Catalanotto	.10	.30
147 Gabe Kapler	.10	.30
148 Ivan Rodriguez	.20	.50
149 Rafael Palmeiro	.20	.50
150 Carlos Delgado	.10	.30
151 Marlon Byrd ROO	1.50	4.00
152 Alex Herrera ROO	1.50	4.00
153 Brandon Backe ROO RC	2.00	5.00
154 Jorge De La Rosa ROO RC	1.50	4.00
155 Corky Miller ROO	1.50	4.00
156 Dennis Tankersley ROO	1.50	4.00
157 Kyle Kane ROO RC	1.50	4.00
158 Justin Duchscherer ROO	1.50	4.00
159 Brian Mallette ROO RC	1.50	4.00
160 Eric Hinske ROO	1.50	4.00
161 Jason Lane ROO	1.50	4.00
162 Hee Seop Choi ROO	1.50	4.00
163 Juan Cruz ROO	1.50	4.00
164 Rodrigo Rosario ROO RC	1.50	4.00
165 Matt Guerrier ROO	1.50	4.00
166 And. Machado ROO RC	1.50	4.00
167 Geronimo Gil ROO	1.50	4.00
168 Dewon Brazelton ROO	1.50	4.00
169 Mark Prior ROO	2.00	5.00
170 Bill Hall ROO	1.50	4.00
171 Jorge Padilla ROO RC	1.50	4.00
172 Josh Pearce ROO	1.50	4.00
173 Allan Simpson ROO RC	1.50	4.00
174 Doug Devore ROO RC	1.50	4.00
175 Luis Garcia ROO	1.50	4.00
176 Angel Berroa ROO	1.50	4.00
177 Steve Bechler ROO RC	1.50	4.00
178 Antonio Perez ROO	1.50	4.00
179 Mark Teixeira ROO	3.00	8.00
180 Mark Ellis ROO	1.50	4.00
181 Michael Cuddyer ROO	1.50	4.00
182 Michael Rivera ROO	1.50	4.00
183 Raul Chavez ROO RC	1.50	4.00
184 Juan Pena ROO	1.50	4.00
185 Austin Kearns ROO	1.50	4.00
186 Ryan Ludwick ROO	1.50	4.00
187 Ed Rogers ROO	1.50	4.00
188 Wilson Betemit ROO	1.50	4.00
189 Nick Neugebauer ROO	1.50	4.00
190 Tom Shearn ROO RC	1.50	4.00
191 Eric Cyr ROO	1.50	4.00
192 Victor Martinez ROO	3.00	8.00
193 Brandon Berger ROO	1.50	4.00
194 Erik Bedard ROO	1.50	4.00
195 Franklyn German ROO RC	1.50	4.00
196 Joe Thurston ROO	1.50	4.00
197 John Buck ROO	1.50	4.00
198 Jeff Deardorff ROO	1.50	4.00
199 Ryan Jamison ROO	1.50	4.00
200 Alfredo Amezaga ROO	1.50	4.00
201 So Taguchi ROO/500 RC *	6.00	15.00
202 Kazuhisa Ishii ROO/250 RC *	10.00	25.00

2002 Leaf Autographs

Taguchi signed 50 serial numbered cards and Ishii signed 25 serial numbered cards. The Taguchi autographs were distributed in packs but an exchange card with a deadline of October 1st, 2003 was seeded into packs for the Ishii autographs. Each card is a straight parallel of the basic RC's except for a signed silver foil sticker placed over the front and foil serial-numbering on back.

Card		
201 So Taguchi/50	20.00	50.00
202 Kazuhisa Ishii/25		

2002 Leaf Lineage

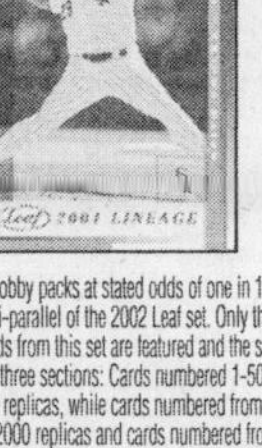

Inserted in hobby packs at stated odds of one in 12, this is a mini-parallel of the 2002 Leaf set. Only the first 150 cards from this set are featured and the set is split up into three sections: Cards numbered 1-50 feature 1999 replicas, while cards numbered from 51-100 feature 2000 replicas and cards numbered from 101-150 feature 2001 replicas.

*LINEAGE: 3X TO 8X BASIC CARDS

2002 Leaf Lineage Century

Randomly iserted in hobby packs, this is a mini-parallel of the 2002 Leaf set. Only the first 150 cards from this set are featured and the set is split up into three sections: Cards numbered 1-50 feature 1999 replicas, while cards numbered from 51-100 feature 2000 replicas and cards numbered from 101-150 feature 2001 replicas. These cards are serial numbered to 100.

*CENTURY: 8X TO 20X BASIC CARDS

2002 Leaf Press Proofs Blue

Inserted at stated odds of one in 24 retail packs, this is a partial parallel of the 2002 Leaf set and featured the first 150 cards from that set.

*BLUE: 6X TO 15X BASIC CARDS

2002 Leaf Press Proofs Platinum

Randomly inserted in hobby packs, this is a mini-parallel of the 2002 Leaf set. Only the first 150 cards from the basic Leaf set and cards 201 and 202 are featured in this parallel. All cards except for card 202 are serial numbered to 25. Only ten serial-numbered copies of card number 202 (featuring Japanese pitcher Kazuhisa Ishii) were produced.

*PLATINUM: 30X TO 80X BASIC CARDS
201-202 NOT PRICED DUE TO SCARCITY

2002 Leaf Press Proofs Red

Issued at stated odds of one in 12 retail packs, this set parallels the first 150 cards of the 2002 Leaf set. In addition, the two cards of Japanese imports So Taguchi and Kazuhisa Ishii are printed to stated print runs of 500 and 250 respectively.

*RED 1-150: 3X TO 8X BASIC CARDS

Card		
201 So Taguchi/500	6.00	15.00
202 Kazuhisa Ishii/250	10.00	25.00

2002 Leaf Burn and Turn

Issued at stated odds of one in 96 hobby and one in 120 retail packs, these 10 cards feature most of the leading double play duos in major league baseball.

COMPLETE SET (10)	40.00	100.00
1 Fernando Vina	3.00	8.00
Edgar Renteria		
2 Alex Rodriguez	6.00	15.00
Mike Young		
3 Derek Jeter	10.00	25.00
Alfonso Soriano		
4 Carlos Guillen	3.00	8.00
Bret Boone		
5 Jose Vidro	3.00	8.00
Orlando Cabrera		
6 Barry Larkin	3.00	8.00
Todd Walker		
7 Carlos Febles	3.00	8.00
Neifi Perez		
8 Jeff Kent	3.00	8.00
Rich Aurilia		
9 Craig Biggio	3.00	8.00
Julio Lugo		
10 Miguel Tejada	3.00	8.00
Mark Ellis		

2002 Leaf Clean Up Crew

Issued at stated odds of one in 192 hobby and one in 240 retail packs, these 15 cards feature leading sluggers of the game. The cards are set on

conventional cardboard with silver foil stamping.

COMPLETE SET (15)	100.00	200.00
1 Barry Bonds	12.50	30.00
2 Sammy Sosa	5.00	12.00
3 Luis Gonzalez	4.00	10.00
4 Richie Sexson	4.00	10.00
5 Jim Thome	4.00	10.00
6 Chipper Jones	5.00	12.00
7 Alex Rodriguez	8.00	20.00
8 Troy Glaus	4.00	10.00
9 Rafael Palmeiro	4.00	10.00
10 Lance Berkman	4.00	10.00
11 Mike Piazza	8.00	20.00
12 Jason Giambi	4.00	10.00
13 Todd Helton	4.00	10.00
14 Shawn Green	4.00	10.00
15 Carlos Delgado	4.00	10.00

2002 Leaf Clubhouse Signatures Bronze

Randomly inserted in packs, these 33 cards feature a mix of signed cards of retired legends, superstar veterans and future stars. Each of these cards is serial numbered and we have listed the print run in our checklist. Cards with a print run of 100 or fewer are not priced due to market scarcity.

Card		
1 Adam Dunn/200	10.00	25.00
2 Alan Trammell/75	6.00	15.00
3 Alfonso Soriano/75		
4 Andre Dawson/100		
5 Aramis Ramirez/250	6.00	15.00
6 Austin Kearns/300	4.00	10.00
7 Barry Zito/100	12.50	30.00
8 Billy Williams/150	6.00	15.00
9 Bob Feller/250	6.00	15.00
10 Bud Smith/200	4.00	10.00
11 Don Mattingly/25		
12 Edgar Martinez/50		
13 J.D. Drew/25		
14 Jason Lane/250	6.00	15.00
15 Jermaine Dye/125	8.00	20.00
16 Joe Crede/200	6.00	15.00
17 Joe Mays/200	4.00	10.00
18 Johnny Estrada/250	4.00	10.00
19 Mark Ellis/300	4.00	10.00
20 Mark Mulder/50		
21 Marlon Byrd/200	4.00	10.00
22 Ozzie Smith/25		
23 Paul LoDuca/300	6.00	15.00
24 Phil Rizzuto/25		
25 Robert Fick/300	4.00	10.00
26 Ron Santo/300	12.50	30.00
27 Roy Oswalt/300	6.00	15.00
28 Ryne Sandberg/25		
29 Steve Garvey/200	6.00	15.00
30 Terrence Long/250	4.00	10.00
31 Tim Redding/300	4.00	10.00
32 Wilson Betemit/150	4.00	10.00
33 Xavier Nady/200	4.00	10.00

2002 Leaf Clubhouse Signatures Silver

Randomly inserted in packs, these 37 cards feature a mix of signed cards of retired legends, superstar veterans and future stars. Each of these cards is serial numbered and we have listed the print run in our checklist. Cards with a stated print run of 25 or fewer are not priced due to market scarcity.

Card		
1 Adam Dunn/75	12.50	30.00
2 Andre Dawson/100		
3 Aramis Ramirez/100	8.00	20.00
4 Austin Kearns/100	6.00	15.00
5 Barry Zito/100	12.50	30.00
6 Billy Williams/100	8.00	20.00
7 Bob Feller/100	15.00	40.00
8 Bud Smith/100	6.00	15.00
9 Cal Ripken/25		
10 Edgar Martinez/100	15.00	40.00
11 Eric Chavez/100	8.00	20.00
12 Jason Lane/100	8.00	20.00
13 Jermaine Dye/100	8.00	20.00
14 Joe Crede/50	8.00	20.00
15 Joe Mays/50	6.00	15.00
16 Johnny Estrada/100	6.00	15.00
17 Javier Vazquez/100	8.00	20.00
18 Mark Ellis/100	6.00	15.00
19 Mark Mulder/100	8.00	20.00
20 Marlon Byrd/100	6.00	15.00
21 Miguel Tejada/100	12.50	30.00
22 Mike Schmidt/75		
23 Paul LoDuca/100		
24 Phil Rizzuto/25		
25 Rich Aurilia/100	6.00	15.00
26 Robert Fick/100	6.00	15.00
27 Roger Clemens/25		
28 Ron Santo/100	15.00	40.00
29 Roy Oswalt/100	8.00	20.00
30 Sean Casey/50		
31 Steve Garvey/100	8.00	20.00
32 Terrence Long/100	6.00	15.00
33 Tim Redding/100	6.00	15.00
34 Todd Helton/25		
35 Vladimir Guerrero/25		
36 Wilson Betemit/100	6.00	15.00
37 Xavier Nady/100	6.00	15.00

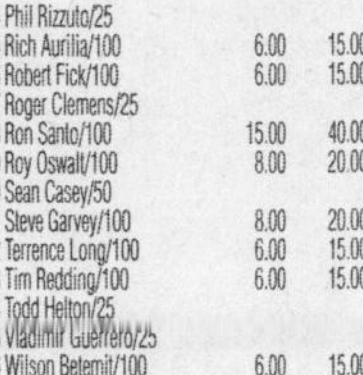

2002 Leaf Cornerstones

Randomly inserted in packs, these 10 cards feature some of the elite perfomers with dual-player game-worn jersey swatches. These cards are serial numbered to 50. Due to market scarcity, no pricing is provided for these cards.

1 Andruw Jones
Chipper Jones
2 Craig Biggio
Jeff Bagwell
3 Ivan Rodriguez
Rafael Palmeiro
4 Curt Schilling
Randy Johnson
5 Gary Sheffield
Shawn Green
6 Larry Walker
Todd Helton
7 Carlos Delgado
Shannon Stewart
8 Omar Vizquel
Jim Thome
9 Vladimir Guerrero
Jose Vidro
10 Bernie Williams
Roger Clemens

2002 Leaf Future 500 Club

Inserted at stated odds of one in 64 hobby and one in 103 retail, these 10 cards honor players who appear to have good chances of reaching the 500 career homer mark. These cards have holo-foil stamping as well as the year that the player is projected to arrive at the 500 homer club.

COMPLETE SET (10)	40.00	80.00
1 Sammy Sosa	2.50	6.00
2 Mike Piazza	4.00	10.00
3 Alex Rodriguez	4.00	10.00
4 Chipper Jones	2.50	6.00
5 Jeff Bagwell	2.00	5.00
6 Carlos Delgado	2.00	5.00
7 Shawn Green	2.00	5.00
8 Ken Griffey Jr.	4.00	10.00
9 Rafael Palmeiro	2.00	5.00
10 Vladimir Guerrero	2.50	6.00

2002 Leaf Game Collection

Inserted into retail packs at stated odds of one in 62, these 46 cards feature game-used memorabilia from the featured player. Some cards were printed in shorter quantities and we have provided those stated print runs in our checklist. For cards with a stated print run of 25 or fewer, no pricing is provided due to market scarcity.

Card		
ABB Adrian Beltre Bat	4.00	10.00
ADBG Adam Dunn Btg Glv SP/25		
AGB Andres Galarraga Bat	4.00	10.00
AJB Andruw Jones Bat SP/300	10.00	25.00
BGB Brian Giles Bat	4.00	10.00
BHB Bobby Higginson Bat	4.00	10.00
BSH Ben Sheets Hat SP/25		
BWS Bernie Williams Shoes SP/25		
BZFG Barry Zito Fld Glv SP/25		
CBB Carlos Beltran Bat	4.00	10.00
CBIB Craig Biggio Bat	6.00	15.00
CFB Carlton Fisk Bat	6.00	15.00
CKB Chuck Knoblauch Bat	4.00	10.00
CPS Corey Patterson Shoes SP/25		
EMB Eddie Murray Bat SP/250	10.00	25.00
GJP Geoff Jenkins Pants	4.00	10.00
IRBG Ivan Rodriguez Btg Glv SP/25		
JBB Jeff Bagwell Bat SP/100		
JDH Johnny Damon Hat SP/25		
JEB Juan Encarnacion Bat	4.00	10.00
JGB Juan Gonzalez Bat	4.00	10.00
KLB Kenny Lofton Bat	4.00	10.00
KWS Kerry Wood Shoes SP/25		
LBBG Lance Berkman Btg Glv SP/25		

LWB Larry Walker Bat SP/50
MBBG Marlon Byrd Btg Glv SP/25
MGB Mark Grace Bat SP/200 10.00 25.00
MMFG Mike Mussina Fld Glv SP/25
MOB Magglio Ordonez Bat SP/150 6.00 15.00
MPB Mike Piazza Bat SP/100
PBB Pat Burrell Bat SP/100
RAB Roberto Alomar Bat 6.00 15.00
RDB Ray Durham Bat 4.00 10.00
RGB Rusty Greer Bat 4.00 10.00
RJFG Randy Johnson Fld Glv SP/25
RPB Rafael Palmeiro Bat 6.00 15.00
RPBG Rafael Palmeiro Btg Glv SP/25
RVB Robin Ventura Bat 4.00 10.00
SCB Sean Casey Bat 4.00 10.00
SRB Scott Rolen Bat SP/250 10.00 25.00
SSH Shannon Stewart Hat SP/25
TCB Tony Clark Bat 4.00 10.00
TGBG Tony Gwynn Btg Glv SP/25
THB Todd Helton Bat 6.00 15.00
TNB Trot Nixon Bat 4.00 10.00
WBB Wade Boggs Bat 6.00 15.00

2002 Leaf Gold Rookies

Inserted at stated rate of one in 24 hobby or retail packs, these 10 cards feature the leading prospects entering the 2002 season. These cards are spotlighted on mirror board with gold foil.

COMPLETE SET (10) 25.00 50.00
1 Josh Beckett 1.50 4.00
2 Marlon Byrd 1.50 4.00
3 Dennis Tankersley 1.50 4.00
4 Jason Lane 1.50 4.00
5 Dewon Brazelton 1.50 4.00
6 Mark Prior 1.50 4.00
7 Bill Hall 1.50 4.00
8 Angel Berroa 1.50 4.00
9 Mark Teixeira 2.50 6.00
10 John Buck 1.50 4.00

2002 Leaf Heading for the Hall

Inserted at stated odds of one in 64 hobby and one in 240 retail, these 10 cards feature active or retired players who are virtually insured enshirement in the Baseball Hall of Fame.

COMPLETE SET (10) 40.00 80.00
1 Greg Maddux 4.00 10.00
2 Ozzie Smith 4.00 10.00
3 Andre Dawson 2.00 5.00
4 Dennis Eckersley 2.00 5.00
5 Roberto Alomar 2.00 5.00
6 Cal Ripken 8.00 20.00
7 Roger Clemens 5.00 12.00
8 Tony Gwynn 3.00 8.00
9 Alex Rodriguez 4.00 10.00
10 Jeff Bagwell 2.00 5.00

2002 Leaf Heading for the Hall Autographs

Randomly inserted in hobby packs, these cards parallel the Leaf Heading to the Hall insert set. Each player signed 50 cards for this product. These cards can also be differentiated from the regular cards as these cards are also die cut. No pricing is provided due to market scarcity.

1 Greg Maddux
2 Ozzie Smith
3 Andre Dawson
4 Dennis Eckersley
5 Roberto Alomar
6 Cal Ripken
7 Roger Clemens
8 Tony Gwynn
9 Alex Rodriguez
10 Jeff Bagwell

2002 Leaf League of Nations

Inserted at stated odds of one in 60, these 10 cards feature players from foreign countries. These cards are highlighted with holo-foil and color tint relating to their homeland colors.

COMPLETE SET (10) 30.00 60.00
1 Ichiro Suzuki 5.00 12.00
2 Tsuyoshi Shinjo 2.00 5.00
3 Chan Ho Park 2.00 5.00
4 Larry Walker 2.00 5.00
5 Andruw Jones 2.00 5.00
6 Hideo Nomo 5.00 12.00
7 Byung-Hyun Kim 2.00 5.00
8 Sun-Woo Kim 2.00 5.00
9 Orlando Hernandez 2.00 5.00
10 Luke Prokopec 2.00 5.00

2002 Leaf Chicago Collection

ISSUED AT '02 NATIONAL CONVENTION
STATED PRINT RUN 5 SERIAL #'d SETS
NO PRICING DUE TO SCARCITY

2002 Leaf Retired Number Jerseys

Randomly inserted in packs, these five cards feature jersey swatches from players who have had their uniform numbers retired. This insert set is sequentially numbered to the player's jersey number. We have listed each print run in our checklist below. Please note that these cards are not priced due to market scarcity.

RN1 Mike Schmidt/20
RN2 Tom Seaver/41
RN3 Rod Carew/29
RN4 Ted Williams/9
RN5 Johnny Bench/5

2002 Leaf Rookie Reprints

Randomly inserted in packs, these six cards feature reprints sequentially numbered to the card's original year of issue. We have listed those print runs in our checklist.

COMPLETE SET (6) 25.00 50.00
1 Roger Clemens/1985 6.00 15.00
2 Kirby Puckett/1985 3.00 8.00
3 Andres Galarraga/1986 2.00 5.00
4 Fred McGriff/1986 2.00 5.00
5 Sammy Sosa/1990 3.00 8.00
6 Frank Thomas/1990 3.00 8.00

2002 Leaf Shirt Off My Back

Inserted at stated odds of one in 29 hobby packs, these 60 cards feature a game-worn jersey swatch from either an active or retired star. Some cards were printed in shorter quantity than others, we have noted those cards with their stated print runs in our checklist. Cards with a stated print run of 50 or fewer are not priced due to market scarcity.

*MULTI-COLOR PATCH 1.25X TO 3X HI
AB A.J. Burnett 4.00 10.00
AK Al Kaline SP/100 15.00 40.00
AP Andy Pettitte SP/50 20.00 50.00
AR Alex Rodriguez SP/150 15.00 40.00
BJA Bo Jackson SP/25
BL Barry Larkin 6.00 15.00
BR Brad Radke 4.00 10.00
CB Carlos Beltran 4.00 10.00
CD Carlos Delgado 4.00 10.00
CF Cliff Floyd 4.00 10.00
CHP Chan Ho Park SP/100 10.00 25.00
CJ Chipper Jones SP/100 15.00 40.00
CL Carlos Lee 4.00 10.00
CR Cal Ripken SP/50 75.00 150.00
CS Curt Schilling SP/150 10.00 25.00
DE Darin Erstad SP/100 10.00 25.00
DM Don Mattingly SP/100 30.00 60.00
DW Dave Winfield SP/150 10.00 25.00
EK Eric Karros 12.50 30.00
EM Edgar Martinez SP/150 15.00 40.00
FG Freddy Garcia SP/100 10.00 25.00
GB George Brett SP/100 30.00 60.00
GM Greg Maddux SP/100 15.00 40.00
HN Hideo Nomo SP/100 15.00 40.00
JB Jeff Bagwell SP/100 15.00 40.00
JBU Jeromy Burnitz 15.00 40.00
JL Javy Lopez 4.00 10.00
JO John Olerud 4.00 10.00
JS John Smoltz 6.00 15.00
KB Kevin Brown SP/100 10.00 25.00
KM Kevin Millwood 4.00 10.00
KP Kirby Puckett SP/100 15.00 40.00
KS Kazuhiro Sasaki SP/100 10.00 25.00
LB Lance Berkman SP/300 10.00 25.00
LG Luis Gonzalez 4.00 10.00
LW Larry Walker SP/50 12.50 30.00
MB Michael Barrett 4.00 10.00
MBU Mark Buehrle 4.00 10.00
MH Mike Hampton 4.00 10.00
MO Magglio Ordonez 4.00 10.00
MP Mike Piazza SP/150 15.00 40.00
MR Manny Ramirez SP/100 15.00 40.00
MS Mike Sweeney 4.00 10.00
MT Miguel Tejada 4.00 10.00
MW Matt Williams 4.00 10.00
NG Nomar Garciaparra SP/25
PM Pedro Martinez SP/100 15.00 40.00
RA Roberto Alomar SP/250 6.00 15.00
RD Ryan Dempster 4.00 10.00
RJ Randy Johnson SP/100 15.00 40.00
RP Rafael Palmeiro 6.00 15.00
RS Richie Sexson 4.00 10.00
SR Scott Rolen SP/250 15.00 40.00
TG Tony Gwynn SP/100 15.00 40.00
TG Tom Glavine 6.00 15.00
TGL Troy Glaus SP/275 10.00 25.00
TH Todd Helton 6.00 15.00
TH Tim Hudson 4.00 10.00
TP Troy Percival 4.00 10.00
TS Tsuyoshi Shinjo SP/100 10.00 25.00

2003 Leaf

This 329-card set was issued in two separate releases. The primary Leaf product - containing cards 1-320 from the basic set - was released in February, 2003. This product was issued in 10-card packs with an SRP of $3 per pack. These packs were issued in 24 pack boxes which came 20 boxes to a case. This set includes the following subsets: Passing the Torch (251 to 270) and a Rookies subset (271-320). Jose Contreras, the cuban refugee signed to a large free-agent contract, had his very first card in this set. Cards 321-329 were issued within packs of DLP Rookies and Traded in December, 2003. There is no card number 42 as both Bobby Higginson and Carlos Pena share card number 41.

COMP.LO SET (320) 15.00 40.00
COMP.UPDATE SET (9) 3.00 8.00
COMMON CARD (1-270) .10 .30
COMMON CARD (271-320) .15 .40
COMMON CARD (321-329) .20 .50
1 Brad Fullmer .10 .30
2 Darin Erstad .10 .30
3 David Eckstein .10 .30
4 Garret Anderson .10 .30
5 Jarrod Washburn .10 .30
6 Kevin Appier .10 .30
7 Tim Salmon .20 .50
8 Troy Glaus .10 .30
9 Troy Percival .10 .30
10 Buddy Groom .10 .30
11 Jay Gibbons .10 .30
12 Jeff Conine .10 .30
13 Marty Cordova .10 .30
14 Melvin Mora .10 .30
15 Rodrigo Lopez .10 .30
16 Tony Batista .10 .30
17 Jorge Julio .10 .30
18 Cliff Floyd .10 .30
19 Derek Lowe .10 .30
20 Jason Varitek .30 .75
21 Johnny Damon .20 .50
22 Manny Ramirez .20 .50
23 Nomar Garciaparra .50 1.25
24 Pedro Martinez .20 .50
25 Rickey Henderson .30 .75
26 Shea Hillenbrand .10 .30
27 Trot Nixon .10 .30
28 Carlos Lee .10 .30
29 Frank Thomas .30 .75
30 Jose Valentin .10 .30
31 Magglio Ordonez .10 .30
32 Mark Buehrle .10 .30
33 Paul Konerko .10 .30
34 C.C. Sabathia .10 .30
35 Danys Baez .10 .30
36 Ellis Burks .10 .30
37 Jim Thome .20 .50
38 Omar Vizquel .20 .50
39 Ricky Gutierrez .10 .30
40 Travis Fryman .10 .30
41A Bobby Higginson .10 .30
41B Carlos Pena .10 .30
43 Juan Acevedo .10 .30
44 Mark Redman .10 .30
45 Randall Simon .10 .30
46 Robert Fick .10 .30
47 Steve Sparks .10 .30
48 Carlos Beltran .10 .30
49 Joe Randa .10 .30
50 Michael Tucker .10 .30
51 Mike Sweeney .10 .30
52 Paul Byrd .10 .30
53 Raul Ibanez .10 .30
54 Runelvys Hernandez .10 .30
55 A.J. Pierzynski .10 .30
56 Brad Radke .10 .30
57 Corey Koskie .10 .30
58 Cristian Guzman .10 .30
59 David Ortiz .30 .75
60 Doug Mientkiewicz .10 .30
61 Dustan Mohr .10 .30
62 Eddie Guardado .10 .30
63 Jacque Jones .10 .30
64 Torii Hunter .10 .30
65 Alfonso Soriano .10 .30
66 Andy Pettitte .20 .50
67 Bernie Williams .20 .50
68 David Wells .10 .30
69 Derek Jeter .75 2.00
70 Jason Giambi .10 .30
71 Jeff Weaver .10 .30
72 Jorge Posada .20 .50
73 Mike Mussina .20 .50
74 Nick Johnson .10 .30
75 Raul Mondesi .10 .30
76 Robin Ventura .10 .30
77 Roger Clemens .60 1.50
78 Barry Zito .10 .30
79 Billy Koch .10 .30
80 David Justice .10 .30
81 Eric Chavez .10 .30
82 Jermaine Dye .10 .30
83 Mark Mulder .10 .30
84 Miguel Tejada .10 .30
85 Ray Durham .10 .30
86 Scott Hatteberg .10 .30
87 Ted Lilly .10 .30
88 Tim Hudson .10 .30
89 Bret Boone .10 .30
90 Carlos Guillen .10 .30
91 Chris Snelling .10 .30
92 Dan Wilson .10 .30
93 Edgar Martinez .20 .50
94 Freddy Garcia .10 .30
95 Ichiro Suzuki .60 1.50
96 Jamie Moyer .10 .30
97 Joel Pineiro .10 .30
98 John Olerud .10 .30
99 Mark McLemore .10 .30
100 Mike Cameron .10 .30
101 Kazuhiro Sasaki .10 .30
102 Aubrey Huff .10 .30
103 Ben Grieve .10 .30
104 Joe Kennedy .10 .30
105 Paul Wilson .10 .30
106 Randy Winn .10 .30
107 Steve Cox .10 .30
108 Alex Rodriguez .50 1.25
109 Chan Ho Park .10 .30
110 Hank Blalock .10 .30
111 Herbert Perry .10 .30
112 Ivan Rodriguez .20 .50
113 Juan Gonzalez .10 .30
114 Kenny Rogers .10 .30
115 Kevin Mench .10 .30
116 Rafael Palmeiro .20 .50
117 Carlos Delgado .10 .30
118 Eric Hinske .10 .30
119 Jose Cruz .10 .30
120 Josh Phelps .10 .30
121 Roy Halladay .10 .30
122 Shannon Stewart .10 .30
123 Vernon Wells .10 .30
124 Curt Schilling .10 .30
125 Junior Spivey .10 .30
126 Luis Gonzalez .10 .30
127 Mark Grace .20 .50
128 Randy Johnson .30 .75
129 Steve Finley .10 .30
130 Tony Womack .10 .30
131 Andruw Jones .20 .50
132 Chipper Jones .30 .75
133 Gary Sheffield .10 .30
134 Greg Maddux .50 1.25
135 John Smoltz .20 .50
136 Kevin Millwood .10 .30
137 Rafael Furcal .10 .30
138 Tom Glavine .20 .50
139 Alex Gonzalez .10 .30
140 Corey Patterson .10 .30
141 Fred McGriff .20 .50
142 Jon Lieber .10 .30
143 Kerry Wood .10 .30
144 Mark Prior .20 .50
145 Matt Clement .10 .30
146 Moises Alou .10 .30
147 Sammy Sosa .30 .75
148 Aaron Boone .10 .30
149 Adam Dunn .10 .30
150 Austin Kearns .10 .30
151 Barry Larkin .20 .50
152 Danny Graves .10 .30
153 Elmer Dessens .10 .30
154 Ken Griffey Jr. .50 1.25
155 Sean Casey .10 .30
156 Todd Walker .10 .30
157 Gabe Kapler .10 .30
158 Jason Jennings .10 .30
159 Jay Payton .10 .30
160 Larry Walker .10 .30
161 Mike Hampton .10 .30
162 Todd Helton .20 .50
163 Todd Zeile .10 .30
164 A.J. Burnett .10 .30
165 Derrek Lee .20 .50
166 Josh Beckett .10 .30
167 Juan Encarnacion .10 .30
168 Luis Castillo .10 .30
169 Mike Lowell .10 .30
170 Preston Wilson .10 .30
171 Billy Wagner .10 .30
172 Craig Biggio .20 .50
173 Daryle Ward .10 .30
174 Jeff Bagwell .20 .50
175 Lance Berkman .10 .30
176 Octavio Dotel .10 .30
177 Richard Hidalgo .10 .30
178 Roy Oswalt .10 .30
179 Adrian Beltre .10 .30
180 Eric Gagne .10 .30
181 Eric Karros .10 .30
182 Hideo Nomo .30 .75
183 Kazuhisa Ishii .10 .30
184 Kevin Brown .10 .30
185 Mark Grudzielanek .10 .30
186 Odalis Perez .10 .30
187 Paul Lo Duca .10 .30
188 Shawn Green .10 .30
189 Alex Sanchez .10 .30
190 Ben Sheets .10 .30
191 Jeffrey Hammonds .10 .30
192 Jose Hernandez .10 .30
193 Takahito Nomura .10 .30
194 Richie Sexson .10 .30
195 Andres Galarraga .10 .30
196 Bartolo Colon .10 .30
197 Brad Wilkerson .10 .30
198 Javier Vazquez .10 .30
199 Jose Vidro .10 .30
200 Michael Barrett .10 .30
201 Tomo Ohka .10 .30
202 Vladimir Guerrero .30 .75
203 Al Leiter .10 .30
204 Armando Benitez .10 .30
205 Edgardo Alfonzo .10 .30
206 Mike Piazza .50 1.25
207 Mo Vaughn .10 .30
208 Pedro Astacio .10 .30
209 Roberto Alomar .20 .50
210 Roger Cedeno .10 .30
211 Timo Perez .10 .30
212 Bobby Abreu .10 .30
213 Jimmy Rollins .10 .30
214 Mike Lieberthal .10 .30
215 Pat Burrell .10 .30
216 Randy Wolf .10 .30
217 Travis Lee .10 .30
218 Vicente Padilla .10 .30
219 Aramis Ramirez .10 .30
220 Brian Giles .10 .30
221 Craig Wilson .10 .30
222 Jason Kendall .10 .30
223 Josh Fogg .10 .30
224 Kevin Young .10 .30
225 Kip Wells .10 .30
226 Mike Williams .10 .30
227 Brett Tomko .10 .30
228 Brian Lawrence .10 .30
229 Mark Kotsay .10 .30
230 Oliver Perez .10 .30
231 Phil Nevin .10 .30
232 Ryan Klesko .10 .30
233 Sean Burroughs .10 .30
234 Trevor Hoffman .10 .30
235 Barry Bonds .75 2.00
236 Benito Santiago .10 .30
237 Jeff Kent .10 .30
238 Kirk Rueter .10 .30
239 Livan Hernandez .10 .30
240 Kenny Lofton .10 .30
241 Rich Aurilia .10 .30
242 Russ Ortiz .10 .30
243 Albert Pujols .60 1.50
244 Edgar Renteria .10 .30
245 J.D. Drew .10 .30
246 Jason Isringhausen .10 .30
247 Jim Edmonds .10 .30
248 Matt Morris .10 .30
249 Tino Martinez .20 .50
250 Scott Rolen .20 .50
251 Curt Schilling PT .10 .30
252 Ivan Rodriguez PT .10 .30
253 Mike Piazza PT .30 .75
254 Sammy Sosa PT .20 .50
255 Matt Williams PT .10 .30
256 Frank Thomas PT .20 .50
257 Barry Bonds PT .40 1.00
258 Roger Clemens PT .30 .75
259 Rickey Henderson PT .30 .75
260 Ken Griffey Jr. PT .30 .75
261 Greg Maddux PT .30 .75
262 Randy Johnson PT .20 .50
263 Jeff Bagwell PT .10 .30
264 Roberto Alomar PT .10 .30
265 Tom Glavine PT .10 .30
266 Juan Gonzalez PT .10 .30
267 Mark Grace PT .10 .30
268 Mike Mussina PT .10 .30
269 Ryan Klesko PT .10 .30
270 Fred McGriff PT .10 .30
271 Joe Borchard ROO .15 .40
272 Chris Snelling ROO .15 .40
273 Brian Tallet ROO .15 .40
274 Cliff Lee ROO 1.50 4.00
275 Freddy Sanchez ROO .15 .40
276 Chone Figgins ROO .15 .40
277 Kevin Cash ROO .15 .40
278 Josh Bard ROO .15 .40
279 Jeriome Robertson ROO .15 .40
280 Jeremy Hill ROO .15 .40
281 Shane Nance ROO .15 .40
282 Jeff Baker ROO .15 .40
283 Trey Hodges ROO .15 .40
284 Eric Eckenstahler ROO .15 .40
285 Jim Rushford ROO .15 .40
286 Carlos Rivera ROO .15 .40
287 Josh Bonifay ROO .15 .40
288 Garrett Atkins ROO .15 .40
289 Nic Jackson ROO .15 .40
290 Corwin Malone ROO .15 .40
291 Jimmy Gobble ROO .15 .40
292 Josh Wilson ROO .15 .40
293 Clint Barmes ROO RC .40 1.00
294 Jon Adkins ROO .15 .40
295 Tim Kalita ROO .15 .40
296 Nelson Castro ROO .15 .40
297 Colin Young ROO .15 .40
298 Adrian Burnside ROO .15 .40
299 Luis Martinez ROO .15 .40
300 Termel Sledge ROO RC .15 .40
301 Todd Donovan ROO .15 .40
302 Jeremy Ward ROO .15 .40
303 Wilson Valdez ROO .15 .40
304 Jose Contreras ROO RC .30 .75
305 Marshall McDougall ROO .15 .40
306 Mitch Wylie ROO .15 .40
307 Ron Calloway ROO .15 .40
308 Jose Valverde ROO .15 .40
309 Jason Davis ROO .15 .40
310 Scotty Layfield ROO .15 .40
311 Matt Thornton ROO .15 .40
312 Adam Walker ROO .15 .40
313 Gustavo Chacin ROO .15 .40
314 Ron Chiavacci ROO .15 .40
315 Wilbert Nieves ROO .15 .40
316 Cliff Bartosh ROO .15 .40
317 Mike Gonzalez ROO .15 .40
318 Jeremy Guthrie ROO .15 .40
319 Eric Junge ROO .15 .40
320 Ben Kozlowski ROO .15 .40
321 Hideki Matsui ROO RC .75 2.00
322 Ramon Nivar ROO RC .20 .50
323 Adam Loewen ROO RC .20 .50
324 Brandon Webb ROO RC 1.00 2.50
325 Chien-Ming Wang ROO RC .75 2.00
326 Delmon Young ROO RC 1.25 3.00
327 Ryan Wagner ROO RC .20 .50
328 Dan Haren ROO RC .20 .50
329 Rickie Weeks ROO RC .60 1.50

2003 Leaf Autographs

This nine card set was issued in two separate series. Card 304 features Yankees rookie Jose Contreras and was distrbuted within standard 2003 Leaf packs. The remaining eight cards from this set were randomly seeded into packs of 2003 DLP Rookies and Traded.

Print runs range from 10-100 copies per and all cards are serial numbered.

304 Jose Contreras ROO/100 12.50 30.00
322 Ramon Nivar ROO/100 4.00 10.00
323 Adam Loewen ROO/100 6.00 15.00
324 Brandon Webb ROO/100 10.00 25.00
325 Chien-Ming Wang ROO/50 75.00 150.00
326 Delmon Young ROO/25
327 Ryan Wagner ROO/100 4.00 10.00
328 Dan Haren ROO/100 10.00 25.00
329 Rickie Weeks ROO/10

2003 Leaf Chicago Collection

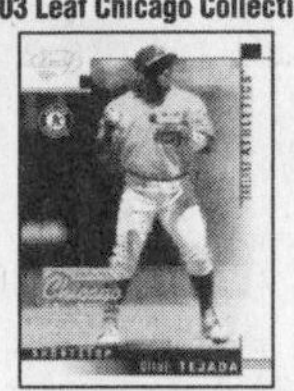

This set, which parallels the 2003 Leaf set was issued at the March, 2003 Chicago Sun Times show as part of a show special. Any collector who opened three packs of a Playoff/Donruss product at the Donruss booth received one of these cards as a redemption for the wrappers. These cards were issued to a stated print run of five serial numbered sets and no pricing is available due to market scarcity.

DISTRIBUTED AT CHICAGO SPORTSFEST
STATED PRINT RUN 5 SERIAL #'d SETS
NO PRICING DUE TO SCARCITY

2003 Leaf Orange County

DISTRIBUTED AT '03 ORANGE CTY SHOW
STATED PRINT RUN 5 SERIAL #'d SETS
CARD FRONTS HAVE EMBOSSED STAMP
NO PRICING DUE TO SCARCITY

2003 Leaf Press Proofs Blue

Randomly inserted into packs, this is a parallel to the Leaf Set. Cards 321-329 were randomly seeded into packs of DLP Rookies and Traded. These cards feature a blue foil logo and were issued to a stated print run of 50 serial numbered sets.

*BLUE 1-250: 6X TO 15X BASIC
*BLUE 251-270: 10X TO 25X BASIC
*BLUE 271-320: 4X TO 10X BASIC
*BLUE 271-320: 4X TO 10X BASIC RC's
*BLUE 321-329: 5X TO 12X BASIC
325 Chien-Ming Wang ROO 15.00 40.00

2003 Leaf Press Proofs Red

Inserted in packs at a stated rate of one in 12, this is a complete parallel to the Leaf Set. Cards 321-329 were randomly seeded into packs of DLP Rookies and Traded - and unlike the first 320 cards - are serial numbered to 100 copies per. These cards feature the words Press Proof printed in red foil on each card front.

*RED 1-250: 2.5X TO 6X BASIC
*RED 251-270: 4X TO 10X BASIC
*RED 271-320: 2.5X TO 6X BASIC
*RED 271-320: 2X TO 5X BASIC RC's
*RED 321-329: 3X TO 8X BASIC RC's
325 Chien-Ming Wang ROO 10.00 25.00

2003 Leaf 60

This 50 card insert set was issued at a stated rate of one in eight packs. These cards were designed in the style of the 1960 Leaf set and feature black and white photos.

*FOIL: 2X TO 5X BASIC CARDS
FOIL PRINT RUN 60 SERIAL #'d SETS
1 Troy Glaus 1.25 3.00
2 Curt Schilling 1.25 3.00
3 Randy Johnson 1.50 4.00
4 Andruw Jones 1.25 3.00
5 Chipper Jones 1.50 4.00
6 Greg Maddux 2.50 6.00
7 Tom Glavine 1.25 3.00
8 Manny Ramirez 1.25 3.00
9 Nomar Garciaparra 2.50 6.00
10 Pedro Martinez 1.25 3.00
11 Rickey Henderson 1.50 4.00
12 Sammy Sosa 1.50 4.00
13 Frank Thomas 1.50 4.00
14 Magglio Ordonez 1.25 3.00
15 Mark Buehrle 1.25 3.00
16 Adam Dunn 1.25 3.00
17 Ken Griffey Jr. 2.50 6.00
18 Jim Thome 1.25 3.00
19 Omar Vizquel 1.25 3.00
20 Larry Walker 1.25 3.00
21 Todd Helton 1.25 3.00
22 Lance Berkman 1.25 3.00
23 Roy Oswalt 1.25 3.00
24 Mike Sweeney 1.25 3.00
25 Hideo Nomo 1.50 4.00
26 Kazuhisa Ishii 1.25 3.00
27 Shawn Green 1.25 3.00
28 Torii Hunter 1.25 3.00
29 Vladimir Guerrero 1.50 4.00
30 Mike Piazza 2.50 6.00
31 Alfonso Soriano 1.25 3.00
32 Bernie Williams 1.25 3.00
33 Derek Jeter 4.00 10.00
34 Jason Giambi 1.25 3.00
35 Roger Clemens 3.00 8.00
36 Barry Zito 1.25 3.00
37 Miguel Tejada 1.25 3.00
38 Pat Burrell 1.25 3.00
39 Ryan Klesko 1.25 3.00
40 Barry Bonds 4.00 10.00
41 Jeff Kent 1.25 3.00
42 Ichiro Suzuki 3.00 8.00
43 John Olerud 1.25 3.00
44 Albert Pujols 3.00 8.00
45 Jim Edmonds 1.25 3.00
46 Scott Rolen 1.25 3.00
47 Alex Rodriguez 2.50 6.00
48 Ivan Rodriguez 1.25 3.00
49 Rafael Palmeiro 1.25 3.00
50 Roy Halladay 1.25 3.00

2003 Leaf Certified Samples

Inserted in packs at a stated rate of one in 23, this 15-card insert set previews the upcoming Leaf Certified set. These cards were printed on metalized film board.

*MIRROR RED: 1.5X TO 4X BASIC
MIRROR RED PRINT RUN 150 #'d SETS
*MIRROR BLUE: 1X TO 2.5X BASIC
MIRROR BLUE PRINT RUN 75 #'d SETS
MIRROR GOLD PRINT RUN 25 #'d SETS
MIRROR GOLD TOO SCARCE TO PRICE
1 Derek Jeter 4.00 10.00
2 Greg Maddux 2.50 6.00
3 Mike Piazza 2.50 6.00
4 Barry Bonds 4.00 10.00
5 Lance Berkman 1.25 3.00
6 Alex Rodriguez 2.50 6.00
7 Alfonso Soriano 1.25 3.00
8 Ichiro Suzuki 3.00 8.00
9 Sammy Sosa 1.50 4.00
10 Vladimir Guerrero 1.50 4.00
11 Albert Pujols 3.00 8.00
12 Pedro Martinez 1.25 3.00
13 Randy Johnson 1.50 4.00
14 Nomar Garciaparra 2.50 6.00
15 Barry Zito 1.25 3.00

2003 Leaf Clean Up Crew

Inserted in packs at a stated rate of one in 49, these ten cards feature the middle of the lineup for ten different major league teams.

1 Alex Rodriguez 2.50 6.00
Rafael Palmeiro
Ivan Rodriguez
2 Nomar Garciaparra 2.50 6.00
Manny Ramirez
Cliff Floyd
3 Jason Giambi 1.50 4.00
Bernie Williams
Jorge Posada
4 Rich Aurilla 4.00 10.00
Jeff Kent
Barry Bonds
5 Larry Walker 1.50 4.00
Todd Helton
Jay Payton
6 Lance Berkman 1.50 4.00
Jeff Bagwell
Darryl Ward
7 Scott Rolen 3.00 8.00
Albert Pujols
Jim Edmonds
8 Gary Sheffield 1.50 4.00
Chipper Jones
Andruw Jones

9 Miguel Tejada 1.50 4.00
Eric Chavez
Jermaine Dye
10 Sammy Sosa 1.50 4.00
Moises Alou
Fred McGriff

2003 Leaf Clean Up Crew Materials

Randomly inserted into packs, this is a parallel to the Clean Up Crew set. These cards feature a memorabilia piece from each of the three players featured and these cards were issued to a stated print run of 25 serial numbered sets.

1 Alex Rodriguez Jsy 15.00 40.00
Rafael Palmeiro Jsy
Ivan Rodriguez Jsy
2 Nomar Garciaparra Jsy 15.00 40.00
Manny Ramirez Jsy
Cliff Floyd Bat
3 Jason Giambi Ball 15.00 40.00
Bernie Williams Ball
Jorge Posada Ball
4 Rich Aurilia Ball 30.00 60.00
Jeff Kent Ball
Barry Bonds Ball
5 Larry Walker Jsy 15.00 40.00
Todd Helton Jsy
Jay Payton Jsy
6 Lance Berkman Jsy 15.00 40.00
Jeff Bagwell Jsy
Daryle Ward Bat
7 Scott Rolen Ball 30.00 60.00
Albert Pujols Ball
Jim Edmonds Base
8 Gary Sheffield Bat 15.00 40.00
Chipper Jones Jsy
Andruw Jones Jsy
9 Miguel Tejada Jsy 10.00 25.00
Eric Chavez Jsy
Jermaine Dye Bat
10 Sammy Sosa Ball 15.00 40.00
Moises Alou Ball
Fred McGriff Ball

2003 Leaf Clubhouse Signatures Bronze

Randomly inserted into packs, these 24 cards feature authentic signatures of the players. Some of these cards were issued to a smaller quantity and we have notated that information and the stated print run information next to the player's name in our checklist. Please note that for cards with a print run of 25 or fewer, no pricing is provided due to market scarcity..

1 Edwin Almonte 3.00 8.00
2 Franklin Nunez 3.00 8.00
3 Josh Bard 3.00 8.00
4 J.C. Romero 3.00 8.00
5 Omar Infante 3.00 8.00
6 Adam Dunn SP/10
7 Andre Dawson SP/50 10.00 25.00
8 Brian Tallet SP/100 4.00 10.00
9 Bobby Doerr SP/100 6.00 15.00
10 Chris Snelling SP/100 4.00 10.00
11 Corey Patterson SP/100 4.00 10.00
12 Doc Gooden SP/100 6.00 15.00
13 Eric Hinske 3.00 8.00
14 Jeff Baker SP/100 4.00 10.00
15 Jack Morris SP/100 6.00 15.00
16 Joe Crede SP/25
17 Torii Hunter SP/75 10.00 25.00
18 Kevin Mench 4.00 10.00
20 Alfonso Soriano SP/25
21 Angel Berroa SP/100 4.00 10.00
22 Brian Lawrence 3.00 8.00
23 Drew Henson SP/50 6.00 15.00
24 Jhonny Peralta 6.00 15.00
25 Magglio Ordonez SP/50 10.00 25.00

2003 Leaf Clubhouse Signatures Silver

Randomly inserted into packs, this is a parallel to the Leaf Clubhouse Signatures set. These cards were issued to a stated print run of 100 serial numbered sets except for Andre Dawson who was issued to a stated print run of 25 serial numbered sets.

1 Edwin Almonte 3.00 8.00
2 Franklin Nunez 3.00 8.00
3 Josh Bard 3.00 8.00
4 J.C. Romero 3.00 8.00
5 Omar Infante 3.00 8.00
7 Andre Dawson SP/25
8 Brian Tallet 3.00 8.00
9 Bobby Doerr 6.00 15.00
10 Chris Snelling 3.00 8.00
12 Doc Gooden 6.00 15.00
13 Eric Hinske 3.00 8.00
14 Jeff Baker 3.00 8.00
15 Jack Morris 6.00 15.00
17 Torii Hunter 4.00 10.00
18 Kevin Mench 4.00 10.00
21 Angel Berroa 3.00 8.00
22 Brian Lawrence 3.00 8.00
23 Drew Henson 3.00 8.00
24 Jhonny Peralta 6.00 15.00
25 Magglio Ordonez 6.00 15.00

2003 Leaf Game Collection

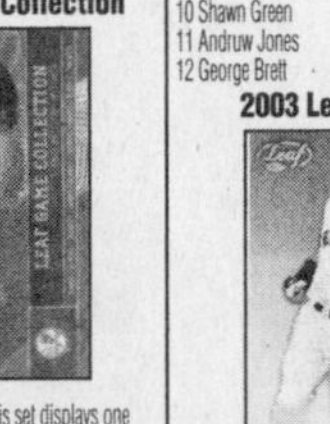

Randomly inserted into packs, this set displays one swatch of game-used materials. These cards were issued to a stated print run of 150 serial numbered sets.

1 Miguel Tejada Hat 4.00 10.00
2 Shannon Stewart Hat 4.00 10.00
3 Mike Schmidt Jacket 20.00 50.00
4 Nolan Ryan Jacket 40.00 80.00
5 Rafael Palmeiro Fld Glv 10.00 25.00
6 Andruw Jones Shoe 6.00 15.00
7 Bernie Williams Shoe 6.00 15.00
8 Ivan Rodriguez Shoe 6.00 15.00
9 Lance Berkman Shoe 4.00 10.00
10 Magglio Ordonez Shoe 4.00 10.00
11 Roy Oswalt Fld Glv 6.00 15.00
12 Andy Pettitte Shoe 6.00 15.00
13 Vladimir Guerrero Fld Glv 15.00 40.00
14 Jason Jennings Fld Glv 6.00 15.00
15 Mike Sweeney Shoe 4.00 10.00
16 Joe Borchard Shoe 4.00 10.00
17 Mark Prior Shoe 6.00 15.00
18 Gary Carter Jacket 4.00 10.00
19 Austin Kearns Fld Glv 6.00 15.00
20 Ryan Klesko Fld Glv 6.00 15.00

2003 Leaf Gold Rookies

Issued at a stated rate of one in 24, this 10 card set features some of the leading candidates for Rookie of the Year. These cards were issued on a special foil board.

MIRROR GOLD PRINT RUN 25 #'d SETS
MIRROR GOLD TOO SCARCE TO PRICE
1 Joe Borchard 1.25 3.00
2 Chone Figgins 1.25 3.00
3 Alexis Gomez 1.25 3.00
4 Chris Snelling 1.25 3.00
5 Cliff Lee 1.25 3.00
6 Victor Martinez 2.00 5.00
7 Hee Seop Choi 1.25 3.00
8 Michael Restovich 1.25 3.00
9 Anderson Machado 1.25 3.00
10 Drew Henson 1.25 3.00

2003 Leaf Hard Hats

Issued at a stated rate of one in 13, these 12 cards feature the 1997 Studio design set against a rainbow board.

COMPLETE SET (12) 10.00 25.00
1 Alex Rodriguez 1.50 4.00
2 Bernie Williams .75 2.00
3 Ivan Rodriguez .75 2.00
4 Jeff Bagwell .75 2.00
5 Rafael Furcal .75 2.00
6 Rafael Palmeiro .75 2.00
7 Tony Gwynn 1.25 3.00
8 Vladimir Guerrero 1.00 2.50
9 Adrian Beltre .75 2.00
10 Shawn Green .75 2.00
11 Andruw Jones .75 2.00
12 George Brett 2.00 5.00

2003 Leaf Hard Hats Batting Helmets

Randomly inserted into packs, this is a parallel to the Hard Hats insert set. These cards feature a swatch of a game-worn batting helmet embedded on the card and these cards were issued to a stated print run of 100 serial numbered sets.

1 Alex Rodriguez 30.00 60.00
2 Bernie Williams 15.00 40.00
3 Ivan Rodriguez 15.00 40.00
4 Jeff Bagwell 15.00 40.00
5 Rafael Furcal 10.00 25.00
6 Rafael Palmeiro 15.00 40.00
7 Tony Gwynn 20.00 50.00
8 Vladimir Guerrero 15.00 40.00
9 Adrian Beltre 10.00 25.00
10 Shawn Green 10.00 25.00
11 Andruw Jones 15.00 40.00
12 George Brett 60.00 120.00

2003 Leaf Home/Away

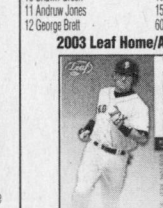

Issued at a stated rate of one in 34, these 20 cards feature either home or away stats for these 10 featured players. The last three year of stats are featured on the cards.

1A Andruw Jones A 1.50 4.00
1H Andruw Jones H 1.50 4.00
2A Cal Ripken A 6.00 15.00
2H Cal Ripken H 6.00 15.00
3A Edgar Martinez A 1.50 4.00
3H Edgar Martinez H 1.50 4.00
4A Jim Thome A 1.50 4.00
4H Jim Thome H 1.50 4.00
5A Larry Walker A 1.50 4.00
5H Larry Walker H 1.50 4.00
6A Nomar Garciaparra A 3.00 8.00
6H Nomar Garciaparra H 3.00 8.00
7A Mark Prior A 1.50 4.00
7H Mark Prior H 1.50 4.00
8A Mike Piazza A 3.00 8.00
8H Mike Piazza H 3.00 8.00
9A Vladimir Guerrero A 2.00 5.00
9H Vladimir Guerrero H 2.00 5.00
10A Chipper Jones A 2.00 5.00
10H Chipper Jones H 2.00 5.00

2003 Leaf Home/Away Materials

Randomly inserted into packs, this is a parallel to the Home/Away set. These cards feature jersey swatches displayed on the front and these cards were issued to a stated print run of 250 serial numbered sets.

1A Andruw Jones A 6.00 15.00
1H Andruw Jones H 6.00 15.00
2A Cal Ripken A 15.00 40.00
2H Cal Ripken H 15.00 40.00
3A Edgar Martinez A 6.00 15.00
3H Edgar Martinez H 6.00 15.00
4A Jim Thome A 6.00 15.00
4H Jim Thome H 6.00 15.00
5A Larry Walker A 4.00 10.00
5H Larry Walker H 4.00 10.00
6A Nomar Garciaparra A 8.00 20.00
6H Nomar Garciaparra H 8.00 20.00
7A Mark Prior A 6.00 15.00
7H Mark Prior H 6.00 15.00
8A Mike Piazza A 8.00 20.00
8H Mike Piazza H 8.00 20.00
9A Vladimir Guerrero A 6.00 15.00
9H Vladimir Guerrero H 6.00 15.00
10A Chipper Jones A 6.00 15.00
10H Chipper Jones H 6.00 15.00

2003 Leaf Maple and Ash

Randomly inserted into packs, these cards feature faux wood grain and also have a game-used bat piece. These cards were issued to a stated print run of 400 serial numbered sets.

1 Jorge Posada 6.00 15.00
2 Mike Piazza 8.00 20.00
3 Alex Rodriguez 8.00 20.00
4 Jeff Bagwell 6.00 15.00
5 Joe Borchard 4.00 10.00
6 Miguel Tejada 4.00 10.00
7 Adam Dunn 4.00 10.00
8 Jim Thome 6.00 15.00
9 Lance Berkman 4.00 10.00
10 Torii Hunter 4.00 10.00
11 Carlos Delgado 4.00 10.00
12 Reggie Jackson 6.00 15.00
13 Juan Gonzalez 4.00 10.00
14 Vladimir Guerrero 6.00 15.00
15 Richie Sexson 4.00 10.00

2003 Leaf Number Off My Back

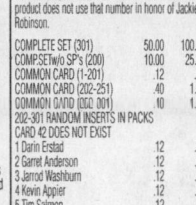

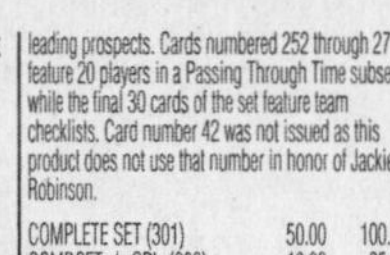

Randomly inserted in packs, these cards feature a swatch from a game-worn jersey number. These cards were issued to a stated print run of 50 serial numbered sets.

1 Carlos Delgado 10.00 25.00
2 Don Mattingly 60.00 120.00
3 Todd Helton 15.00 40.00
4 Vernon Wells 10.00 25.00
5 Bernie Williams 15.00 40.00
6 Luis Gonzalez 10.00 25.00
7 Kerry Wood 10.00 25.00
8 Eric Chavez 10.00 25.00
9 Shawn Green 10.00 25.00
10 Roy Oswalt 10.00 25.00
11 Nomar Garciaparra 30.00 60.00
12 Robin Yount 50.00 100.00
13 Troy Glaus 10.00 25.00
14 C.C. Sabathia 10.00 25.00
15 Alex Rodriguez 30.00 60.00
16 Mark Mulder 10.00 25.00
17 Will Clark 50.00 100.00
18 Alfonso Soriano 10.00 25.00
19 Andy Pettitte 15.00 40.00
20 Curt Schilling 10.00 25.00

2003 Leaf Shirt Off My Back

Randomly inserted into packs, this 20-card insert set features one swatch of game-worn jersey of the featured player. These cards were issued to a stated print run of 500 serial numbered sets.

1 Carlos Delgado 3.00 8.00
2 Don Mattingly 10.00 25.00
3 Todd Helton 4.00 10.00
4 Vernon Wells 3.00 8.00
5 Bernie Williams 4.00 10.00
6 Luis Gonzalez 3.00 8.00
7 Kerry Wood 3.00 8.00
8 Eric Chavez 3.00 8.00
9 Shawn Green 3.00 8.00
10 Roy Oswalt 3.00 8.00
11 Nomar Garciaparra 6.00 15.00
12 Robin Yount 6.00 15.00
13 Troy Glaus 3.00 8.00
14 C.C. Sabathia 3.00 8.00
15 Alex Rodriguez 4.00 10.00
16 Mark Mulder 3.00 8.00
17 Will Clark 6.00 15.00
18 Alfonso Soriano 3.00 8.00
19 Andy Pettitte 4.00 10.00
20 Curt Schilling 3.00 8.00

2003 Leaf Slick Leather

Issued at a stated rate of one in 21, this 15-card insert set features the most skilled fielders on cards featuring faux leather grain.

1 Omar Vizquel 1.25 3.00
2 Roberto Alomar 1.25 3.00
3 Ivan Rodriguez 1.25 3.00
4 Greg Maddux 2.50 6.00
5 Scott Rolen 1.25 3.00
6 Todd Helton 1.25 3.00
7 Andruw Jones 1.25 3.00
8 Jim Edmonds 1.25 3.00
9 Barry Bonds 4.00 10.00
10 Eric Chavez 1.25 3.00
11 Ichiro Suzuki 3.00 8.00
12 Mike Mussina 1.25 3.00
13 John Olerud 1.25 3.00
14 Torii Hunter 1.25 3.00
15 Larry Walker 1.25 3.00

2004 Leaf

This 301-card standard-size set was released in January, 2004. The set was issued in six-card packs with an $3 SRP which came 24 packs to a box and six boxes to a case. The first 200 cards were printed in higher quantities than the last 101 cards in this set. Cards numbered 201 through 251 feature 50 of the leading prospects. Cards numbered 252 through 271 feature 20 players in a Passing Through Time subset while the final 30 cards of the set feature team checklists. Card number 42 was not issued as this product does not use that number in honor of Jackie Robinson.

COMPLETE SET (301) 50.00 100.00
COMP.SETw/o SP's (200) 10.00 25.00
COMMON CARD (1-201) .12 .30
COMMON CARD (202-251) .40 1.00
COMMON CARD (252-301) .40 1.00
202-301 RANDOM INSERTS IN PACKS
CARD 42 DOES NOT EXIST
1 Darin Erstad .12 .30
2 Garret Anderson .12 .30
3 Jarrod Washburn .12 .30
4 Kevin Appier .12 .30
5 Tim Salmon .12 .30
6 Troy Glaus .12 .30
7 Troy Percival .12 .30
8 Jason Johnson .12 .30
9 Jay Gibbons .12 .30
10 Melvin Mora .12 .30
11 Sidney Ponson .12 .30
12 Tony Batista .12 .30
13 Derek Lowe .12 .30
14 Robert Person .12 .30
15 Manny Ramirez .30 .75
16 Nomar Garciaparra .30 .75
17 Pedro Martinez .20 .50
18 Jorge De La Rosa .12 .30
19 Bartolo Colon .12 .30
20 Carlos Lee .12 .30
21 Esteban Loaiza .12 .30
22 Frank Thomas .30 .75
23 Joe Crede .12 .30
24 Magglio Ordonez .20 .50
25 Ryan Ludwick .12 .30
26 Luis Garcia .12 .30
27 Brandon Phillips .12 .30
28 C.C Sabathia .20 .50
29 Jhonny Peralta .12 .30
30 Josh Bard .12 .30
31 Omar Vizquel .20 .50
32 Fernando Rodney .12 .30
33 Mike Maroth .12 .30
34 Bobby Higginson .12 .30
35 Omar Infante .12 .30
36 Dmitri Young .12 .30
37 Eric Munson .12 .30
38 Jeremy Bonderman .12 .30
39 Carlos Beltran .12 .30
40 Jeremy Affeldt .12 .30
41 Dee Brown .12 .30
43 Mike Sweeney .12 .30
44 Brent Abernathy .12 .30
45 Runelvys Hernandez .12 .30
46 A.J. Pierzynski .12 .30
47 Corey Koskie .12 .30
48 Cristian Guzman .12 .30
49 Jacque Jones .12 .30
50 Kenny Rogers .12 .30
51 J.C. Romero .12 .30
52 Torii Hunter .12 .30
53 Alfonso Soriano .12 .30
54 Bernie Williams .20 .50
55 David Wells .12 .30
56 Derek Jeter .75 2.00
57 Hideki Matsui .50 1.25
58 Jason Giambi .12 .30
59 Jorge Posada .20 .50
60 Jose Contreras .12 .30
61 Mike Mussina .20 .50
62 Nick Johnson .12 .30
63 Roger Clemens .40 1.00
64 Barry Zito .12 .30
65 Justin Duchscherer .12 .30
66 Eric Chavez .12 .30
67 Erubial Durazo .12 .30
68 Miguel Tejada .20 .50
69 Mark Mulder .12 .30
70 Terrence Long .12 .30
71 Tim Hudson .20 .50
72 Bret Boone .12 .30
73 Dan Wilson .12 .30
74 Edgar Martinez .20 .50
75 Freddy Garcia .12 .30
76 Rafael Soriano .12 .30
77 Ichiro Suzuki .50 1.25
78 Jamie Moyer .12 .30
79 John Olerud .12 .30
80 Kazuhiro Sasaki .12 .30
81 Aubrey Huff .12 .30
82 Carl Crawford .20 .50
83 Joe Kennedy .12 .30
84 Rocco Baldelli .12 .30
85 Toby Hall .12 .30
86 Alex Rodriguez .50 1.25
87 Kevin Mench .12 .30
88 Hank Blalock .12 .30
89 Juan Gonzalez .12 .30
90 Mark Teixeira .30 .75
91 Rafael Palmeiro .20 .50
92 Carlos Delgado .12 .30
93 Eric Hinske .12 .30
94 Josh Phelps .12 .30
95 Brian Bowles .12 .30
96 Roy Halladay .30 .75
97 Shannon Stewart .12 .30
98 Vernon Wells .12 .30
99 Curt Schilling .20 .50
100 Junior Spivey .12 .30
101 Luis Gonzalez .12 .30
102 Lyle Overbay .12 .30
103 Mark Grace .20 .50
104 Randy Johnson .30 .75
105 Shea Hillenbrand .12 .30
106 Andruw Jones .12 .30
107 Chipper Jones .30 .75
108 Gary Sheffield .12 .30
109 Greg Maddux .50 1.25
110 Javy Lopez .12 .30
111 John Smoltz .30 .75
112 Marcus Giles .12 .30
113 Rafael Furcal .12 .30
114 Corey Patterson .12 .30
115 Juan Cruz .12 .30
116 Kerry Wood .12 .30
117 Mark Prior .20 .50
118 Moises Alou .12 .30
119 Sammy Sosa .30 .75
120 Aaron Boone .12 .30
121 Adam Dunn .20 .50
122 Austin Kearns .12 .30
123 Barry Larkin .20 .50
124 Ken Griffey Jr. .50 1.25
125 Brian Reith .12 .30
126 Wily Mo Pena .12 .30
127 Jason Jennings .12 .30
128 Jay Payton .12 .30
129 Larry Walker .20 .50
130 Preston Wilson .12 .30
131 Todd Helton .20 .50
132 Dontrelle Willis .12 .30
133 Ivan Rodriguez .20 .50
134 Josh Beckett .20 .50
135 Juan Encarnacion .12 .30
136 Mike Lowell .12 .30
137 Craig Biggio .20 .50
138 Jeff Bagwell .20 .50
139 Jeff Kent .12 .30
140 Lance Berkman .20 .50
141 Richard Hidalgo .12 .30
142 Roy Oswalt .20 .50
143 Eric Gagne .12 .30
144 Fred McGriff .12 .30
145 Hideo Nomo .30 .75
146 Kazuhisa Ishii .12 .30
147 Kevin Brown .12 .30
148 Paul Lo Duca .12 .30
149 Shawn Green .12 .30
150 Ben Sheets .12 .30
151 Geoff Jenkins .12 .30
152 Rey Sanchez .12 .30
153 Richie Sexson .12 .30
154 Wes Helms .12 .30
155 Shane Nance .12 .30
156 Fernando Tatis .12 .30
157 Javier Vazquez .12 .30
158 Jose Vidro .12 .30
159 Orlando Cabrera .12 .30
160 Henry Mateo .12 .30
161 Vladimir Guerrero .30 .75
162 Zach Day .12 .30
163 Edwin Almonte .12 .30
164 Al Leiter .12 .30
165 Cliff Floyd .12 .30
166 Jae Weong Seo .12 .30
167 Mike Piazza .30 .75
168 Roberto Alomar .20 .50
169 Tom Glavine .20 .50
170 Bobby Abreu .12 .30
171 Brandon Duckworth .12 .30
172 Jim Thome .20 .50
173 Kevin Millwood .12 .30
174 Pat Burrell .12 .30
175 Aramis Ramirez .12 .30
176 Jack Wilson .12 .30
177 Brian Giles .12 .30
178 Jason Kendall .12 .30
179 Kenny Lofton .12 .30
180 Kip Wells .12 .30
181 Kris Benson .12 .30
182 Albert Pujols .75 2.00
183 J.D. Drew .12 .30
184 Jim Edmonds .20 .50
185 Matt Morris .12 .30
186 Scott Rolen .20 .50
187 Woody Williams .12 .30
188 Cliff Bartosh .12 .30
189 Brian Lawrence .12 .30
190 Ryan Klesko .12 .30
191 Sean Burroughs .12 .30
192 Xavier Nady .12 .30
193 Dennis Tankersley .12 .30
194 Donaldo Mendez .12 .30
195 Barry Bonds .60 1.50
196 Benito Santiago .12 .30
197 Edgardo Alfonzo .12 .30
198 Cody Ransom .12 .30
199 Jason Schmidt .12 .30
200 Rich Aurilia .12 .30
201 Ken Harvey .12 .30
202 Adam Loewen ROO .40 1.00
203 Alfredo Gonzalez ROO .40 1.00
204 Arnie Munoz ROO .40 1.00
205 Andrew Brown ROO .40 1.00
206 Josh Hall ROO .40 1.00
207 Josh Stewart PROS .40 1.00
208 Clint Barmes PROS .60 1.50
209 Brandon Webb PROS .40 1.00
210 Chien-Ming Wang PROS 2.00 5.00
211 Edgar Gonzalez PROS .40 1.00
212 Alejandro Machado PROS .40 1.00
213 Jeremy Griffiths PROS .40 1.00
214 Craig Brazell PROS .40 1.00
215 Daniel Cabrera PROS .40 1.00
216 Fernando Cabrera PROS .40 1.00
217 Termel Sledge PROS .40 1.00
218 Rob Hammock PROS .40 1.00
219 Francisco Rosario PROS .40 1.00
220 Francisco Cruceta PROS .40 1.00
221 Rett Johnson PROS .40 1.00
222 Guillermo Quiroz PROS .40 1.00
223 Hong-Chih Kuo PROS .40 1.00
224 Ian Ferguson PROS .40 1.00
225 Tim Olson PROS .40 1.00
226 Todd Wellemeyer PROS .40 1.00
227 Rich Fischer PROS .40 1.00
228 Phil Seibel PROS .40 1.00
229 Joe Valentine PROS .40 1.00
230 Matt Kata PROS .40 1.00
231 Michael Hessman PROS .40 1.00
232 Michel Hernandez PROS .40 1.00
233 Doug Waechter PROS .40 1.00
234 Prentice Redman PROS .40 1.00
235 Nook Logan PROS .40 1.00
236 Oscar Villarreal PROS .40 1.00
237 Pete LaForest PROS .40 1.00
238 Matt Bruback PROS .40 1.00
239 Josh Willingham PROS .40 1.00
240 Greg Aquino PROS .40 1.00
241 Lew Ford PROS .40 1.00
242 Jeff Duncan PROS .40 1.00
243 Chris Waters PROS .40 1.00
244 Miguel Ojeda PROS .40 1.00
245 Rosman Garcia PROS .40 1.00
246 Felix Sanchez PROS .40 1.00
247 Jon Leicester PROS .40 1.00
248 Roger Deago PROS .40 1.00
249 Mike Ryan PROS .40 1.00
250 Chris Capuano PROS .40 1.00
251 Matt White PROS .40 1.00
252 Bernie Williams PTT .60 1.50
253 Mark Grace PTT .60 1.50
254 Chipper Jones PTT 1.00 2.50
255 Greg Maddux PTT 1.50 4.00
256 Sammy Sosa PTT 1.00 2.50
257 Mike Mussina PTT .60 1.50
258 Tim Salmon PTT .40 1.00
259 Barry Larkin PTT .60 1.50
260 Randy Johnson PTT 1.00 2.50
261 Jeff Bagwell PTT .60 1.50
262 Roberto Alomar PTT .60 1.50
263 Tom Glavine PTT .60 1.50
264 Roger Clemens PTT 1.25 3.00
265 Barry Bonds PTT 2.00 5.00
266 Ivan Rodriguez PTT .60 1.50
267 Pedro Martinez PTT .60 1.50
268 Ken Griffey Jr. PTT 1.50 4.00
269 Jim Thome PTT .60 1.50
270 Frank Thomas PTT 1.00 2.50
271 Mike Piazza PTT 1.00 2.50
272 Troy Glaus TC .40 1.00
273 Melvin Mora TC .40 1.00
274 Nomar Garciaparra TC 1.00 2.50
275 Magglio Ordonez TC .60 1.50
276 Omar Vizquel TC .60 1.50
277 Dmitri Young TC .40 1.00
278 Mike Sweeney TC .40 1.00
279 Torii Hunter TC .40 1.00
280 Derek Jeter TC 2.50 6.00
281 Barry Zito TC .40 1.00
282 Ichiro Suzuki TC 1.50 4.00
283 Rocco Baldelli TC .40 1.00
284 Alex Rodriguez TC 1.50 4.00
285 Carlos Delgado TC .40 1.00
286 Randy Johnson TC 1.00 2.50
287 Greg Maddux TC 1.50 4.00
288 Sammy Sosa TC 1.00 2.50
289 Ken Griffey Jr. TC 1.50 4.00
290 Todd Helton TC .60 1.50
291 Ivan Rodriguez TC .60 1.50
292 Jeff Bagwell TC .60 1.50
293 Hideo Nomo TC 1.00 2.50
294 Richie Sexson TC .40 1.00
295 Vladimir Guerrero TC 1.00 2.50
296 Mike Piazza TC 1.00 2.50
297 Jim Thome TC .60 1.50
298 Jason Kendall TC .40 1.00
299 Albert Pujols TC 2.50 6.00
300 Ryan Klesko TC .40 1.00
301 Barry Bonds TC 2.00 5.00

2004 Leaf Second Edition

*2ND ED 1-201: .4X TO 1X BASIC
*2ND ED 202-301: .4X TO 1X BASIC
ISSUED IN SECOND EDITION PACKS

2004 Leaf Autographs

RANDOM INSERTS IN PACKS
SP INFO PROVIDED BY DONRUSS
SP'S ARE NOT SERIAL-NUMBERED
14 Robert Person 4.00 10.00
18 Jorge De La Rosa 4.00 10.00
25 Ryan Ludwick 12.50 30.00
26 Luis Garcia 4.00 10.00
29 Jhonny Peralta 6.00 15.00
30 Josh Bard 4.00 10.00
32 Fernando Rodney 4.00 10.00
33 Mike Maroth 4.00 10.00
35 Omar Infante 4.00 10.00
37 Eric Munson SP/9
41 Dee Brown 4.00 10.00
44 Brent Abernathy SP 6.00 15.00
51 J.C. Romero 4.00 10.00
65 Justin Duchscherer 6.00 15.00
70 Terrence Long SP 6.00 15.00
76 Rafael Soriano 6.00 15.00
85 Toby Hall SP 6.00 15.00
87 Kevin Mench 6.00 15.00
95 Brian Bowles 4.00 10.00
115 Juan Cruz 4.00 10.00
125 Brian Reith 4.00 10.00
126 Wily Mo Pena 6.00 15.00
127 Jason Jennings 4.00 10.00
150 Ben Sheets SP/17
155 Shane Nance 4.00 10.00
160 Henry Mateo SP 6.00 15.00
163 Edwin Almonte 4.00 10.00
171 Brandon Duckworth 4.00 10.00
176 Jack Wilson 6.00 15.00
180 Kip Wells 4.00 10.00
188 Cliff Bartosh 4.00 10.00
189 Brian Lawrence 4.00 10.00
193 Dennis Tankersley 4.00 10.00
194 Donaldo Mendez 4.00 10.00
198 Cody Ransom SP 6.00 15.00
247 Jon Leicester PROS SP 6.00 15.00

2004 Leaf Autographs Second Edition

*2ND ED: .4X TO 1X BASIC
*2ND ED: .4X TO 1X BASIC SP
25 Ryan Ludwick 10.00 25.00
37 Eric Munson 4.00 10.00
150 Ben Sheets 10.00 25.00

2004 Leaf Press Proofs Blue

*BLUE 1-201: 4X TO 10X BASIC
*BLUE 202-251: 1.25X TO 3X BASIC
*BLUE 252-301: 1.25X TO 3X BASIC
STATED PRINT RUN 100 SERIAL #'d SETS

2004 Leaf Press Proofs Gold

STATED PRINT RUN 25 SERIAL #'d SETS
NO PRICING DUE TO SCARCITY

2004 Leaf Press Proofs Red

*RED 1-201: 2X TO 5X BASIC
*RED 202-251: .6X TO 1.5X BASIC
*RED 252-301: .6X TO 1.5X BASIC
STATED ODDS 1:8

2004 Leaf Press Proofs Silver

*SILVER 1-201: 6X TO 15X BASIC
*SILVER 202-251: 2X TO 5X BASIC
*SILVER 252-301: 2X TO 5X BASIC
STATED PRINT RUN 50 SERIAL #'d SETS

2004 Leaf Clean Up Crew

STATED ODDS 1:49
*2ND ED: .4X TO 1X BASIC
2ND ED.ODDS 1:72 2ND ED.PACKS
1 Sammy Sosa 1.00 2.50
Moises Alou
Hee Seop Choi
2 Jason Giambi 1.50 4.00
Alfonso Soriano
Hideki Matsui
3 Vernon Wells .40 1.00
Carlos Delgado
Josh Phelps
4 Alex Rodriguez 1.50 4.00
Juan Gonzalez
Hank Blalock
5 Gary Sheffield .40 1.00
Chipper Jones
Andruw Jones
6 Ken Griffey Jr. 1.50 4.00
Austin Kearns
Aaron Boone
7 Albert Pujols 2.50 6.00
Jim Edmonds
Scott Rolen
8 Jeff Bagwell .60 1.50
Lance Berkman
Jeff Kent
9 Todd Helton .60 1.50
Preston Wilson
Larry Walker
10 Miguel Tejada .60 1.50
Erubial Durazo
Eric Chavez

2004 Leaf Clean Up Crew Materials

STATED PRINT RUN 50 SERIAL #'d SETS
2ND ED.RANDOM IN 2ND ED.PACKS
2ND ED.PRINT RUNS 5 SERIAL #'d SETS
NO 2ND ED.PRICING DUE TO SCARCITY
1 Sammy Sosa Bat 15.00 40.00
Moises Alou Bat
Hee Seop Choi Jsy
2 Alfonso Soriano Base 30.00 60.00
Jason Giambi Base
Hideki Matsui Base
3 Vernon Wells Jsy 10.00 25.00
Carlos Delgado Jsy
Josh Phelps Jsy
4 Alex Rodriguez Bat 15.00 40.00
Juan Gonzalez Bat
Hank Blalock Bat
5 Gary Sheffield Jsy 15.00 40.00
Chipper Jones Jsy
Andruw Jones Bat
6 Ken Griffey Jr. Base 15.00 40.00
Austin Kearns Base
Aaron Boone Base
7 Albert Pujols Bat 20.00 50.00
Jim Edmonds Jsy
Scott Rolen Bat
8 Jeff Bagwell Bat 15.00 40.00
Lance Berkman Bat
Jeff Kent Jsy
9 Todd Helton Bat 15.00 40.00
Preston Wilson Bat
Larry Walker Jsy
10 Miguel Tejada Jsy 10.00 25.00
Erubial Durazo Bat
Eric Chavez Jsy

2004 Leaf Cornerstones

STATED ODDS 1:78
*2ND ED: .4X TO 1X BASIC
2ND ED.ODDS 1:90 2ND ED.PACKS
1 Alex Rodriguez 2.50 6.00
Hank Blalock
2 Kerry Wood 1.00 2.50
Mark Prior
3 Roger Clemens 2.00 5.00
Alfonso Soriano
4 Nomar Garciaparra 1.50 4.00
Manny Ramirez
5 Austin Kearns 1.00 2.50
Adam Dunn
6 Tom Glavine 1.50 4.00
Mike Piazza
7 Andruw Jones .60 1.50
Chipper Jones
8 Albert Pujols 4.00 10.00
Scott Rolen
9 Curt Schilling 1.50 4.00
Randy Johnson
10 Hideo Nomo 1.50 4.00
Kazuhisa Ishii

2004 Leaf Cornerstones Materials

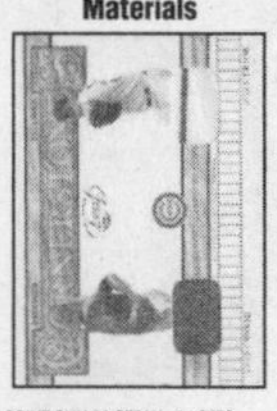

STATED PRINT RUN 50 SERIAL #'d SETS
2ND ED.RANDOM IN 2ND ED.PACKS
2ND ED.PRINT RUN 10 SERIAL #'d SETS
NO 2ND ED.PRICING DUE TO SCARCITY
1 Alex Rodriguez Bat 10.00 25.00
Hank Blalock Bat
2 Kerry Wood Jsy 6.00 15.00
Mark Prior Jsy
3 Roger Clemens Jsy 12.50 30.00
Alfonso Soriano Bat
4 Nomar Garicaparra Bat 10.00 25.00
Manny Ramirez Jsy
5 Austin Kearns Bat 6.00 15.00
Adam Dunn Jsy
6 Tom Glavine Jsy 10.00 25.00
Mike Piazza Bat
7 Andruw Jones Bat 10.00 25.00
Chipper Jones Jsy
8 Albert Pujols Bat 20.00 50.00
Scott Rolen Bat
9 Curt Schilling Jsy 10.00 25.00
Randy Johnson Jsy
10 Hideo Nomo Jsy 10.00 25.00
Kazuhisa Ishii Jsy

2004 Leaf Exhibits 1947-66 Made by Donruss-Playoff Print

This 51-card set features players in the design of the old exhibit company cards issued from 1921 through 1964. Please note that there were more than 40 varieties for each of these cards issued and we have notated what the multipier is for each card.

STATED PRINT RUN 66 SERIAL #'d SETS
*1921 ACTIVE: .75X TO 2X
*1921 RETIRED: .75X TO 2X
1921 PRINT RUN 21 #'d SETS
*1921 AML ACTIVE: .75X TO 2X
*1921 AML RETIRED: .75X TO 2X
1921 AL P.RUN 21 #'d SETS
*1925 L ACTIVE: .75X TO 2X
*1925 L RETIRED: .75X TO 2X
1925 L PRINT RUN 25 #'d SETS
*1925 R ACTIVE: .75X TO 2X
*1925 R RETIRED: .75X TO 2X
1925 R PRINT RUN25 #'d SETS
*1926 B ACTIVE: .75X TO 2X
*1926 B RETIRED: .75X TO 2X
1926 B PRINT RUN 26 #'d SETS
*1926 BDP ACTIVE: .75X TO 2X
*1926 BDP RETIRED: .75X TO 2X
1926 BDP PRINT RUN 26 #'d SETS
*1926 U ACTIVE: .75X TO 2X
*1926 U RETIRED: .75X TO 2X
1926 U PRINT RUN 26 #'d SETS
*1926 UDP ACTIVE: .75X TO 2X
*1926 UDP RETIRED: .75X TO 2X
1926 UDP PRINT RUN 26 #'d SETS
*1927 ACTIVE: .75X TO 2X
*1927 RETIRED: .75X TO 2X
1927 PRINT RUN 27 #'d SETS
*1927 DP ACTIVE: .75X TO 2X
*1927 DP RETIRED: .75X TO 2X
1927 DP PRINT RUN 27 #'d SETS
*1939-46 BOLL: .5X TO 1.2X
1939-46 BOLL PRINT RUN 46 #'d SETS
*1939-46 BOLR: .5X TO 1.2X
1939-46 BOLR PRINT RUN 46 #'d SETS
*1939-46 BWL: .5X TO 1.2X
1939-46 BWL PRINT RUN 46 #'d SETS
*1939-46 BWR: .5X TO 1.2X
1939-46 BWR PRINT RUN 46 #'d SETS
*1939-46 CL: .5X TO 1.2X
1939-46 CL PRINT RUN 46 #'d SETS
*1939-46 CR: .5X TO 1.2X
1939-46 CR PRINT RUN 46 #'d SETS
*1939-46 CYL: .5X TO 1.2X
1939-46 CYL PRINT RUN 46 #'d SETS
*1939-46 CYR: .5X TO 1.2X
1939-46 CYR PRINT RUN 46 #'d SETS
*1939-46 SL: .5X TO 1.2X
1939-46 SL PRINT RUN 46 #'d SETS
*1939-46 SR: .5X TO 1.2X
1939-46 SR PRINT RUN 46 #'d SETS
*1939-46 SYL: .5X TO 1.2X
1939-46 SYL PRINT RUN 46 #'d SETS
*1939-46 SYR: .5X TO 1.2X
1939-46 SYR PRINT RUN 46 #'d SETS
*1939-46 TYL: .5X TO 1.2X
1939-46 TYL PRINT RUN 46 #'d SETS
*1939-46 TYR: .5X TO 1.2X
1939-46 TYR PRINT RUN 46 #'d SETS
*1939-46 VBWL: .5X TO 1.2X
1939-46 VBWL PRINT RUN 46 #'d SETS
*1939-46 VBWR: .5X TO 1.2X
1939-46 VBWR PRINT RUN 46 #'d SETS
*1939-46 VTYL: .5X TO 1.2X
1939-46 VTYL PRINT RUN 46 #'d SETS
*1939-46 VTYR: .5X TO 1.2X
1939-46 VTYR PRINT RUN 46 #'d SETS
*1939-46 YTL: .5X TO 1.2X
1939-46 YTL PRINT RUN 46 #'d SETS
*1939-46 YTR: .5X TO 1.2X
1939-46 YTR PRINT RUN 46 #'d SETS
*1947-66 DP SIG: .4X TO 1X
1947-66 DP SIG PRINT RUN 66 #'d SETS
*1947-66 MPRI: .4X TO 1X
1947-66 MPRI PRINT RUN 66 #'d SETS
*1947-66 MSIG: .4X TO 1X
1947-66 MSIG PRINT RUN 66 #'d SETS
*1947-66 PDPPRI: .4X TO 1X
1947-66 PDPPRI PRINT RUN 66 #'d SETS
*1947-66 PDPSIG: .4X TO 1X
1947-66 PDPSIG PRINT RUN 66 #'d SETS
*1947-66 PPRI: .4X TO 1X
1947-66 PPRI PRINT RUN 66 #'d SETS
*1947-66 PSIG: .4X TO 1X
1947-66 PSIG PRINT RUN 66 #'d SETS
*1962-63 NSNL: .4X TO 1X
1962-63 NSNL PRINT RUN 63 #'d SETS
*1962-63 NSNR: .4X TO 1X
1962-63 NSNR PRINT RUN 63 #'d SETS
*1962-63 SBNL: .4X TO 1X
1962-63 SBNL PRINT RUN 63 #'d SETS
*1962-63 SBNR: .4X TO 1X
1962-63 SBNR PRINT RUN 63 #'d SETS
*1962-63 SRNL: .4X TO 1X
1962-63 SRNL PRINT RUN 63 #'d SETS
*1962-63 SRNR: .4X TO 1X
1962-63 SRNR PRINT RUN 63 #'d SETS
*ALL 2ND ED: .4X TO 1X
SEE CARD BACKS FOR ABBREV.LEGEND
1 Adam Dunn 1.00 2.50
2 Albert Pujols 4.00 10.00
3 Alex Rodriguez 2.50 6.00
4 Alfonso Soriano .60 1.50
5 Andruw Jones .60 1.50
6 Barry Bonds 3.00 8.00
7 Barry Larkin 1.00 2.50
8 Barry Zito .60 1.50
9 Cal Ripken 6.00 15.00
10 Chipper Jones 1.50 4.00
11 Dale Murphy 1.00 2.50
12 Derek Jeter 4.00 10.00
13 Don Mattingly 3.00 8.00
14 Ernie Banks 1.50 4.00
15 Frank Thomas 1.50 4.00
16 George Brett 3.00 8.00
17 Greg Maddux 2.50 6.00
18 Hank Blalock .60 1.50
19 Hideo Nomo 1.50 4.00
20 Ichiro Suzuki 2.50 6.00
21 Jason Giambi .60 1.50
22 Jim Thome 1.00 2.50
23 Juan Gonzalez .60 1.50
24 Ken Griffey Jr. 2.50 6.00
25 Kirby Puckett 1.50 4.00
26 Mark Prior 1.00 2.50
27 Mike Mussina 1.00 2.50
28 Mike Piazza 1.50 4.00
29 Mike Schmidt 2.50 6.00
30 Nolan Ryan Angels 5.00 12.00
31 Nolan Ryan Astros 5.00 12.00
32 Nolan Ryan Rangers 5.00 12.00
33 Nomar Garciaparra 1.50 4.00
34 Ozzie Smith 2.50 6.00
35 Pedro Martinez 1.00 2.50
36 Randy Johnson 1.50 4.00
37 Reggie Jackson Yanks 1.00 2.50
38 Reggie Jackson A's 1.00 2.50
39 Rickey Henderson 1.50 4.00
40 Roberto Alomar 1.00 2.50
41 Roberto Clemente 4.00 10.00
42 Rod Carew 1.00 2.50
43 Roger Clemens 2.00 5.00
44 Sammy Sosa 1.50 4.00
45 Stan Musial 2.50 6.00
46 Tom Glavine 1.00 2.50
47 Tom Seaver 1.00 2.50
48 Tony Gwynn 1.50 4.00
49 Vladimir Guerrero 1.50 4.00
50 Yogi Berra 1.50 4.00

2004 Leaf Gamers

STATED ODDS 1:19
*QUANTUM: 1X TO 2.5X BASIC
QUANTUM RANDOM INSERTS IN PACKS
QUANTUM PRINT RUN 100 #'d SETS
*2ND ED: .4X TO 1X BASIC
2ND ED.ODDS 1:22 2ND ED.PACKS
2ND ED.QUAN.RANDOM IN 2ND.ED PACKS
2ND ED.QUANTUM PRINT RUN 10 #'d SETS
NO 2ND ED.QUAN.PRICE DUE TO SCARCITY
1 Albert Pujols 2.50 6.00
2 Alex Rodriguez 1.50 4.00
3 Alfonso Soriano .40 1.00
4 Barry Bonds 2.00 5.00
5 Barry Zito .40 1.00
6 Chipper Jones 1.00 2.50
7 Derek Jeter 2.50 6.00
8 Greg Maddux 1.50 4.00
9 Ichiro Suzuki 1.50 4.00
10 Jason Giambi .40 1.00
11 Jeff Bagwell .60 1.50
12 Ken Griffey Jr. 1.50 4.00
13 Manny Ramirez 1.00 2.50
14 Mark Prior .60 1.50
15 Mike Piazza 1.00 2.50
16 Nomar Garciaparra 1.00 2.50
17 Pedro Martinez .60 1.50
18 Randy Johnson 1.00 2.50
19 Roger Clemens 1.25 3.00
20 Sammy Sosa 1.00 2.50

2004 Leaf Gold Rookies

STATED ODDS 1:23
MIRROR RANDOM INSERTS IN PACKS
MIRROR PRINT RUN 25 SERIAL #'d SETS
NO MIRROR PRICING DUE TO SCARCITY
*2ND ED: .4X TO 1X BASIC
2ND ED.ODDS 1:24 2ND ED.PACKS
2ND ED.MIRROR PRINT RUN 5 #'d SETS
NO 2ND ED.MIRR.PRICE DUE TO SCARCITY
1 Adam Loewen .40 1.00
2 Rickie Weeks .40 1.00
3 Khalil Greene .60 1.50
4 Chad Tracy .40 1.00
5 Alexis Rios .60 1.50
6 Craig Brazell .40 1.00
7 Clint Barmes .60 1.50
8 Pete LaForest .40 1.00
9 Alfredo Gonzalez .40 1.00
10 Arnie Munoz .40 1.00

2004 Leaf Home/Away

STATED ODDS 1:35
*2ND ED: .4X TO 1X BASIC
2ND ED.ODDS 1:35 2ND ED.PACKS
1A Greg Maddux A 2.50 6.00
1H Greg Maddux H 2.50 6.00
2A Sammy Sosa A 1.50 4.00
2H Sammy Sosa H 1.50 4.00
3A Alex Rodriguez A 2.50 6.00
3H Alex Rodriguez H 2.50 6.00
4A Albert Pujols A 4.00 10.00
4H Albert Pujols H 4.00 10.00
5A Jason Giambi A .60 1.50
5H Jason Giambi H .60 1.50
6A Chipper Jones A 1.50 4.00
6H Chipper Jones H 1.50 4.00
7A Vladimir Guerrero A 1.50 4.00
7H Vladimir Guerrero H 1.50 4.00
8A Mike Piazza A 1.50 4.00
8H Mike Piazza H 1.50 4.00
9A Nomar Garciaparra A 1.50 4.00
9H Nomar Garciaparra H 1.50 4.00
10A Austin Kearns A .60 1.50
10H Austin Kearns H .60 1.50

2004 Leaf Home/Away Jerseys

STATED ODDS 1:119
*PRIME: 1.25X TO 3X BASIC
PRIME RANDOM INSERTS IN PACKS
PRIME PRINT RUN 50 #'d SETS
*2ND ED: .4X TO 1X BASIC
2ND ED.RANDOM IN 2ND.ED PACKS
2ND ED.PRIME PRINT RUN 5 #'d SETS
NO 2ND ED.PRIME PRICE DUE SCARCITY
1A Greg Maddux A 4.00 10.00
1H Greg Maddux H 4.00 10.00
2A Sammy Sosa A 3.00 8.00
2H Sammy Sosa H 3.00 8.00
3A Alex Rodriguez A 4.00 10.00
3H Alex Rodriguez H 4.00 10.00
4A Albert Pujols A 6.00 15.00
4H Albert Pujols H 6.00 15.00
5A Jason Giambi A 2.00 5.00
5H Jason Giambi H 2.00 5.00
6A Chipper Jones A 3.00 8.00
6H Chipper Jones H 3.00 8.00
7A Vladimir Guerrero A 3.00 8.00
7H Vladimir Guerrero H 3.00 8.00
8A Mike Piazza A 4.00 10.00
8H Mike Piazza H 4.00 10.00
9A Nomar Garciaparra A 4.00 10.00
9H Nomar Garciaparra H 4.00 10.00
10A Austin Kearns A 2.00 5.00
10H Austin Kearns H 2.00 5.00

2004 Leaf Limited Previews

STATED PRINT RUN 999 SERIAL #'d SETS
*GOLD: 1.25X TO 3X BASIC
GOLD PRINT RUN 50 SERIAL #'d SETS
*SILVER: .75X TO 2X BASIC
SILVER PRINT RUN 100 SERIAL #'d SETS
RANDOM INSERTS IN PACKS
1 Derek Jeter 3.00 8.00
2 Barry Zito .50 1.25
3 Ichiro Suzuki 2.00 5.00
4 Pedro Martinez .75 2.00
5 Alfonso Soriano .50 1.25
6 Alex Rodriguez 2.00 5.00
7 Greg Maddux 2.00 5.00
Back of card talks about Tom Glavine
8 Mike Piazza 1.25 3.00
9 Mark Prior .75 2.00
10 Albert Pujols 3.00 8.00
11 Sammy Sosa 1.25 3.00
12 Ken Griffey Jr. 1.25 3.00
13 Nomar Garciaparra 1.25 3.00
14 Randy Johnson 1.25 3.00
15 Jason Giambi .50 1.25
16 Barry Bonds 2.50 6.00
17 Manny Ramirez 1.25 3.00
18 Chipper Jones 1.25 3.00
19 Jeff Bagwell .75 2.00
20 Roger Clemens 1.50 4.00

2004 Leaf MVP Winners

STATED ODDS 1:11
*GOLD: .6X TO 1.5X BASIC
GOLD RANDOM INSERTS IN PACKS
GOLD PRINT RUN 500 SERIAL #'d SETS
*2ND ED: .4X TO 1X BASIC
2ND ED.ODDS 1:12 2ND ED.PACKS
2ND ED.GOLD PRINT RUN 25 #'d SETS
NO 2ND ED.GOLD PRICE DUE TO SCARCITY
1 Stan Musial 1.50 4.00
2 Ernie Banks 1.00 2.50
3 Roberto Clemente 2.50 6.00
4 George Brett 2.00 5.00
5 Mike Schmidt 1.50 4.00
6 Cal Ripken 83 4.00 10.00
7 Dale Murphy .60 1.50
8 Ryne Sandberg 2.00 5.00
9 Don Mattingly 2.00 5.00
10 Roger Clemens 1.25 3.00
11 Rickey Henderson 1.00 2.50
12 Cal Ripken 91 4.00 10.00
13 Barry Bonds 92 2.00 5.00
14 Barry Bonds 93 2.00 5.00
15 Frank Thomas 1.00 2.50
16 Ken Griffey Jr. 1.50 4.00
17 Sammy Sosa 1.00 2.50
18 Chipper Jones 1.00 2.50
19 Jason Giambi .40 1.00
20 Ichiro Suzuki 1.50 4.00

2004 Leaf Picture Perfect

STATED ODDS 1:37
*2ND ED: .4X TO 1X BASIC
2ND ED.ODDS 1:45 2ND ED.PACKS
1 Albert Pujols 4.00 10.00
2 Alex Rodriguez 2.50 6.00
3 Alfonso Soriano .60 1.50
4 Austin Kearns .60 1.50
5 Carlos Delgado .60 1.50
6 Chipper Jones 1.50 4.00
7 Hank Blalock .60 1.50
8 Jason Giambi .60 1.50
9 Jeff Bagwell 1.00 2.50
10 Jim Thome 1.00 2.50
11 Manny Ramirez 1.50 4.00
12 Mike Piazza 1.50 4.00
13 Nomar Garciaparra 1.50 4.00
14 Sammy Sosa 1.50 4.00
15 Todd Helton 1.00 2.50

2004 Leaf Picture Perfect Bats

STATED ODDS 1:437
*2ND ED: .4X TO 1X BASIC
2ND ED.RANDOM IN 2ND ED.PACKS
1 Albert Pujols 6.00 15.00
2 Alex Rodriguez 4.00 10.00
3 Alfonso Soriano 2.00 5.00
4 Austin Kearns 2.00 5.00
5 Carlos Delgado 2.00 5.00
6 Chipper Jones 3.00 8.00
7 Hank Blalock 2.00 5.00
8 Jason Giambi 2.00 5.00
9 Jeff Bagwell 3.00 8.00
10 Jim Thome 3.00 8.00
11 Manny Ramirez 3.00 8.00
12 Mike Piazza 4.00 10.00
13 Nomar Garciaparra 4.00 10.00
14 Sammy Sosa 3.00 8.00
15 Todd Helton 3.00 8.00

2004 Leaf Players Collection Jersey Green

*LEAF GREEN: .4X TO 1X PRESTIGE
*LEAF PLAT: 1X TO 2.5X PRESTIGE
PLATINUM PRINT RUN 25 SERIAL #'d SETS
RANDOM INSERTS IN PACKS

2004 Leaf Recollection Autographs

PRINT RUNS B/WN 1-31 COPIES PER
NO PRICING ON QTY OF 25 OR LESS
ALL CARDS ARE 1990 LEAF BUYBACKS
3 Jesse Barfield 90/29 12.50 30.00
15 Charlie Hough 90/31 8.00 20.00

2004 Leaf Shirt Off My Back

STATED ODDS 1:47
*2ND ED: .4X TO 1X BASIC
2ND ED.RANDOM IN 2ND ED.PACKS
1 Shawn Green 2.00 5.00
2 Andruw Jones 3.00 8.00
3 Ivan Rodriguez 3.00 8.00
4 Hideo Nomo 3.00 8.00
5 Don Mattingly 6.00 15.00
6 Mark Prior 3.00 8.00
7 Alfonso Soriano 2.00 5.00
8 Richie Sexson 2.00 5.00
9 Vernon Wells 2.00 5.00
10 Nomar Garciaparra 4.00 10.00
11 Jason Giambi 2.00 5.00
12 Austin Kearns 2.00 5.00
13 Chipper Jones 3.00 8.00
14 Rickey Henderson 3.00 8.00
15 Alex Rodriguez 4.00 10.00
16 Garret Anderson 2.00 5.00
17 Vladimir Guerrero 3.00 8.00
18 Sammy Sosa 3.00 8.00
19 Mike Piazza 4.00 10.00
20 David Wells 2.00 5.00
21 Scott Rolen 3.00 8.00
22 Adam Dunn 2.00 5.00
23 Carlos Delgado 2.00 5.00
24 Greg Maddux 4.00 10.00
25 Hank Blalock 2.00 5.00

2004 Leaf Shirt Off My Back Autographs Second Edition

STATED PRINT RUN 1 SERIAL #'d SET
NO PRICING DUE TO SCARCITY

2004 Leaf Shirt Off My Back Jersey Number Patch

STATED PRINT RUN 50 SERIAL #'d SETS
BLALOCK PRINT RUN 32 SERIAL #'d CARDS
SOSA PRINT RUN 42 SERIAL #'d CARDS
2ND ED.RANDOM IN 2ND ED.PACKS
2ND ED.PRINT RUN SERIAL 5 #'d SETS
NO 2ND ED.PRICING DUE TO SCARCITY
1 Shawn Green 6.00 15.00
2 Andruw Jones 10.00 25.00
3 Ivan Rodriguez 10.00 25.00
4 Hideo Nomo 10.00 25.00
5 Don Mattingly 15.00 40.00
6 Mark Prior 10.00 25.00
7 Alfonso Soriano 6.00 15.00
8 Richie Sexson 6.00 15.00
9 Vernon Wells 6.00 15.00
10 Nomar Garciaparra 12.50 30.00
11 Jason Giambi 6.00 15.00
12 Austin Kearns 6.00 15.00
13 Chipper Jones 10.00 25.00
14 Rickey Henderson 10.00 25.00
15 Alex Rodriguez 12.50 30.00
16 Garret Anderson 6.00 15.00
17 Vladimir Guerrero 10.00 25.00
18 Sammy Sosa/42 10.00 25.00
19 Mike Piazza 12.50 30.00
20 David Wells 6.00 15.00
21 Scott Rolen 10.00 25.00
22 Adam Dunn 6.00 15.00
23 Carlos Delgado 6.00 15.00
24 Greg Maddux 12.50 30.00
25 Hank Blalock/32 6.00 15.00

2004 Leaf Shirt Off My Back Jersey Number Patch Autographs

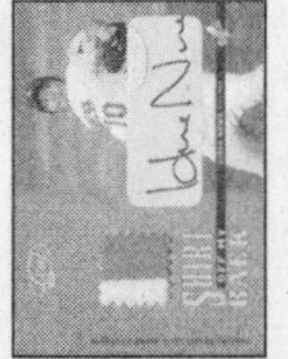

STATED PRINT RUN 5 SERIAL #'d SETS
2ND ED.RANDOM IN 2ND ED.PACKS
2ND ED.PRINT RUN 5 SERIAL #'d SETS
NO PRICING DUE TO SCARCITY

2004 Leaf Shirt Off My Back Team Logo Patch

RANDOM INSERTS IN PACKS
PRINT RUNS B/WN 7-75 COPIES PER
NO PRICING ON QTY OF 25 OR LESS
2ND ED.PRINT RUN 5 SERIAL #'d SETS
NO 2ND ED.PRICING DUE TO SCARCITY
1 Shawn Green/41 6.00 15.00
2 Andruw Jones/75 10.00 25.00
3 Ivan Rodriguez/75 10.00 25.00
4 Hideo Nomo/74 12.50 30.00
5 Don Mattingly/7
6 Mark Prior/46 10.00 25.00
7 Alfonso Soriano/28 8.00 20.00
8 Richie Sexson/38 6.00 15.00
9 Vernon Wells/74 6.00 15.00
10 Nomar Garciaparra/75 12.50 30.00
11 Jason Giambi/26 8.00 20.00
12 Austin Kearns/32 8.00 20.00
13 Chipper Jones/75 10.00 25.00
14 Rickey Henderson/40 10.00 25.00
15 Alex Rodriguez/75 12.50 30.00
16 Garret Anderson/71 6.00 15.00
17 Vladimir Guerrero/55 10.00 25.00
18 Sammy Sosa/39 10.00 25.00
19 Mike Piazza/75 12.50 30.00
20 David Wells/74 6.00 15.00
21 Scott Rolen/29 12.50 30.00
22 Adam Dunn/32 8.00 20.00
23 Carlos Delgado/56 6.00 15.00
24 Greg Maddux/75 12.50 30.00
25 Hank Blalock/62 6.00 15.00

2004 Leaf Shirt Off My Back Team Logo Patch Autographs

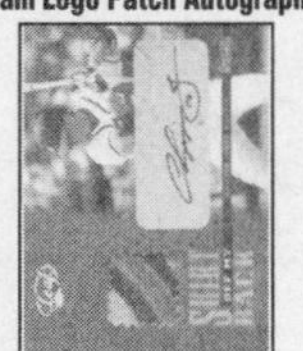

STATED PRINT RUN 5 SERIAL #'d SETS
2ND ED.RANDOM IN 2ND ED.PACKS
2ND ED.PRINT RUN 5 SERIAL #'d SETS
NO PRICING DUE TO SCARCITY

2004 Leaf Sunday Dress

STATED ODDS 1:17
*2ND ED: .4X TO 1X BASIC
2ND ED.ODDS 1:20 2ND ED.PACKS

1 Frank Thomas 1.00 2.50
2 Barry Zito .40 1.00
3 Mike Piazza 1.00 2.50
4 Mark Prior .60 1.50
5 Jeff Bagwell .60 1.50
6 Roy Oswalt .60 1.50
7 Todd Helton .60 1.50
8 Magglio Ordonez .60 1.50
9 Alex Rodriguez 1.50 4.00
10 Manny Ramirez 1.00 2.50

2004 Leaf Sunday Dress Jerseys

STATED ODDS 1:119
*PRIME: .75X TO 2X BASIC
PRIME RANDOM INSERTS IN PACKS
PRIME PRINT RUN 100 SERIAL #'d SETS
*2ND ED: .4X TO 1X BASIC
2ND ED.RANDOM IN 2ND ED.PACKS
2ND ED.PRIME PRINT RUN 15 #'d SETS
NO 2ND ED.PRIME PRICE DUE SCARCITY
1 Frank Thomas 3.00 8.00
2 Barry Zito 2.00 5.00
3 Mike Piazza 4.00 10.00
4 Mark Prior 3.00 8.00
5 Jeff Bagwell 3.00 8.00
6 Roy Oswalt 2.00 5.00
7 Todd Helton 3.00 8.00
8 Magglio Ordonez 2.00 5.00
9 Alex Rodriguez 4.00 10.00
10 Manny Ramirez 3.00 8.00

2005 Leaf

This 300-card set was released in January, 2005. The set was issued in eight-card packs with an $3 SRP which came 24 packs to a box and 12 boxes to a case. Cards numbered 1-200 feature veterans while cards 201 through 250 feature players who were prospects during the 2004 season. Cards 251 through 270 feature the traditional passing through time subset while cards 271 through 300 are team checklist cards. All cards numbered above 200 were inserted at rates between one in three and one in six.

COMPLETE SET (300) 75.00 150.00
COMP.SET w/o SP's (200) 10.00 25.00
COMMON CARD (1-200) .10 .30
COMMON CARD (201-250) .60 1.50
201-250 STATED ODDS 1:3
COMMON CARD (251-300) .30 .75
251-270 STATED ODDS 1:6
271-300 STATED ODDS 1:4
1 Bartolo Colon .12 .30
2 Casey Kotchman .12 .30
3 Chone Figgins .12 .30
4 Darin Erstad .12 .30
5 Francisco Rodriguez .20 .50
6 Garret Anderson .12 .30
7 Jarrod Washburn .12 .30
8 Troy Glaus .12 .30
9 Vladimir Guerrero .30 .75
10 Brandon Webb .20 .50
11 Casey Fossum .12 .30
12 Luis Gonzalez .12 .30
13 Randy Johnson .30 .75
14 Richie Sexson .12 .30
15 Andruw Jones .12 .30
16 Chipper Jones .30 .75
17 J.D. Drew .12 .30
18 John Smoltz .30 .75
19 Johnny Estrada .12 .30
20 Marcus Giles .12 .30
21 Rafael Furcal .12 .30
22 Russ Ortiz .12 .30
23 Javy Lopez .12 .30
24 Jay Gibbons .12 .30
25 Melvin Mora .12 .30
26 Miguel Tejada .20 .50
27 Rafael Palmeiro .20 .50
28 Sidney Ponson .12 .30
29 Bill Mueller .12 .30
30 Curt Schilling .20 .50
31 David Ortiz .30 .75
32 Doug Mientkiewicz .12 .30
33 Jason Varitek .30 .75
34 Johnny Damon .20 .50
35 Manny Ramirez .30 .75
36 Pedro Martinez .20 .50
37 Trot Nixon .12 .30
38 Aramis Ramirez .12 .30
39 Corey Patterson .12 .30
40 Derrek Lee .12 .30
41 Greg Maddux .50 1.25
42 Kerry Wood .12 .30
43 Mark Prior .20 .50
44 Moises Alou .12 .30
45 Nomar Garciaparra .30 .75
46 Sammy Sosa .30 .75
47 Carlos Lee .12 .30
48 Kip Wells .12 .30
49 Magglio Ordonez .20 .50
50 Mark Buehrle .20 .50
51 Paul Konerko .20 .50
52 Roberto Alomar .20 .50
53 Adam Dunn .20 .50
54 Austin Kearns .12 .30
55 Barry Larkin .20 .50
56 Danny Graves .12 .30
57 Ken Griffey Jr. .50 1.25
58 Sean Casey .12 .30
59 C.C. Sabathia .20 .50
60 Cliff Lee .20 .50
61 Jody Gerut .12 .30
62 Omar Vizquel .20 .50
63 Travis Hafner .12 .30
64 Victor Martinez .20 .50
65 Charles Johnson .12 .30
66 Jason Jennings .12 .30
67 Jeromy Burnitz .12 .30
68 Preston Wilson .12 .30
69 Todd Helton .20 .50
70 Bobby Higginson .12 .30
71 Dmitri Young .12 .30
72 Eric Munson .12 .30
73 Ivan Rodriguez .20 .50
74 Jeremy Bonderman .12 .30
75 Rondell White .12 .30
76 A.J. Burnett .20 .50
77 Carl Pavano .12 .30
78 Dontrelle Willis .12 .30
79 Hee Seop Choi .12 .30
80 Josh Beckett .20 .50
81 Juan Pierre .12 .30
82 Miguel Cabrera .30 .75
83 Mike Lowell .12 .30
84 Paul Lo Duca .12 .30
85 Andy Pettitte .20 .50
86 Carlos Beltran .12 .30
87 Craig Biggio .20 .50
88 Jeff Bagwell .20 .50
89 Jeff Kent .12 .30
90 Lance Berkman .20 .50
91 Roger Clemens .40 1.00
92 Roy Oswalt .20 .50
93 Andres Blanco .12 .30
94 Jeremy Affeldt .12 .30
95 Juan Gonzalez .12 .30
96 Ken Harvey .12 .30
97 Mike Sweeney .12 .30
98 Zack Greinke .20 .50
99 Adrian Beltre .12 .30
100 Brad Penny .12 .30
101 Eric Gagne .12 .30
102 Kazuhisa Ishii .12 .30
103 Milton Bradley .12 .30
104 Shawn Green .12 .30
105 Steve Finley .12 .30
106 Ben Sheets .12 .30
107 Bill Hall .12 .30
108 Danny Kolb .12 .30
109 Geoff Jenkins .12 .30
110 Junior Spivey .12 .30
111 Lyle Overbay .12 .30
112 Scott Podsednik .12 .30
113 A.J. Pierzynski .12 .30
114 Brad Radke .12 .30
115 Corey Koskie .12 .30
116 Jacque Jones .12 .30
117 Joe Mauer .30 .75
118 Joe Nathan .12 .30
119 Shannon Stewart .12 .30
120 Torii Hunter .12 .30
121 Brad Wilkerson .12 .30
122 Jeff Fassero .12 .30
123 Jose Vidro .12 .30
124 Livan Hernandez .12 .30
125 Nick Johnson .12 .30
126 Al Leiter .12 .30
127 Jose Reyes .20 .50
128 Kazuo Matsui .12 .30
129 Mike Cameron .12 .30
130 Mike Piazza .30 .75
131 Richard Hidalgo .12 .30
132 Tom Glavine .20 .50
133 Alex Rodriguez .50 1.25
134 Bernie Williams .20 .50
135 Derek Jeter .75 2.00
136 Gary Sheffield .12 .30
137 Jason Giambi .12 .30
138 Javier Vazquez .12 .30
139 Jorge Posada .20 .50
140 Kevin Brown .12 .30
141 Mariano Rivera .30 .75
142 Mike Mussina .20 .50
143 Barry Zito .12 .30
144 Bobby Crosby .12 .30
145 Eric Chavez .12 .30
146 Erubiel Durazo .12 .30
147 Jermaine Dye .12 .30
148 Mark Mulder .12 .30
149 Tim Hudson .20 .50
150 Bobby Abreu .12 .30
151 Eric Milton .12 .30
152 Jim Thome .20 .50
153 Kevin Millwood .12 .30
154 Mike Lieberthal .12 .30
155 Pat Burrell .12 .30
156 Randy Wolf .12 .30
157 Craig Wilson .12 .30
158 Jack Wilson .12 .30
159 Jason Bay .12 .30
160 Jason Kendall .12 .30
161 Kris Benson .12 .30
162 Brian Giles .12 .30
163 Jake Peavy .12 .30
164 Jay Payton .12 .30
165 Khalil Greene .12 .30
166 Mark Loretta .12 .30
167 Ryan Klesko .12 .30
168 Sean Burroughs .12 .30
169 David Aardsma .12 .30
170 Edgardo Alfonzo .12 .30
171 Jason Schmidt .12 .30
172 Merkin Valdez .12 .30
173 Ray Durham .12 .30
174 Bret Boone .12 .30
175 Dan Wilson .12 .30
176 Ichiro Suzuki .50 1.25
177 Jamie Moyer .12 .30
178 Rich Aurilia .12 .30
179 Albert Pujols .75 2.00
180 Edgar Renteria .12 .30
181 Jason Isringhausen .12 .30
182 Jeff Suppan .12 .30
183 Jim Edmonds .20 .50
184 Scott Rolen .20 .50
185 Woody Williams .12 .30
186 Aubrey Huff .12 .30
187 Carl Crawford .20 .50
188 Dewon Brazelton .12 .30
189 Jose Cruz Jr. .12 .30
190 Rocco Baldelli .12 .30
191 Alfonso Soriano .20 .50
192 Hank Blalock .12 .30
193 Kenny Rogers .12 .30
194 Laynce Nix .12 .30
195 Mark Teixeira .30 .75
196 Michael Young .20 .50
197 Alexis Rios .20 .50
198 Carlos Delgado .12 .30
199 Roy Halladay .30 .75
200 Vernon Wells .12 .30
201 Josh Kroeger PROS .60 1.50
202 Angel Guzman PROS .60 1.50
203 Brad Halsey PROS .60 1.50
204 Bucky Jacobsen PROS .60 1.50
205 Carlos Hines PROS .60 1.50
206 Carlos Vasquez PROS .60 1.50
207 Billy Traber PROS .60 1.50
208 Bubba Crosby PROS .60 1.50
209 Chris Oxspring PROS .60 1.50
210 Chris Shelton PROS .60 1.50
211 Colby Miller PROS .60 1.50
212 Dave Crouthers PROS .60 1.50
213 Dennis Sarfate PROS .60 1.50
214 Don Kelly PROS .60 1.50
215 Edwardo Sierra PROS .60 1.50
216 Edwin Moreno PROS .60 1.50
217 Fernando Nieve PROS .60 1.50
218 Freddy Guzman PROS .60 1.50
219 Greg Dobbs PROS .60 1.50
220 Hector Gimenez PROS .60 1.50
221 Andy Green PROS .60 1.50
222 Jason Bartlett PROS .60 1.50
223 Jerry Gil PROS .60 1.50
224 Jesse Crain PROS .60 1.50
225 Joey Gathright PROS .60 1.50
226 John Gall PROS .60 1.50
227 Jorge Sequea PROS .60 1.50
228 Jorge Vasquez PROS .60 1.50
229 Josh Labandeira PROS .60 1.50
230 Justin Leone PROS .60 1.50
231 Lance Cormier PROS .60 1.50
232 Lincoln Holdzkom PROS .60 1.50
233 Miguel Olivo PROS .60 1.50
234 Mike Rouse PROS .60 1.50
235 Onil Joseph PROS .60 1.50
236 Phil Stockman PROS .60 1.50
237 Ramon Ramirez PROS .60 1.50
238 Robb Quinlan PROS .60 1.50
239 Roberto Novoa PROS .60 1.50
240 Ronald Belisario PROS .60 1.50
241 Ronny Cedeno PROS .60 1.50
242 Ruddy Yan PROS .60 1.50
243 Ryan Meaux PROS .60 1.50
244 Ryan Wing PROS .60 1.50
245 Scott Proctor PROS .60 1.50
246 Sean Henn PROS .60 1.50
247 Tim Bausher PROS .60 1.50
248 Tim Bittner PROS .60 1.50
249 William Bergolla PROS .60 1.50
250 Yadier Molina PROS 1.00 2.50
251 Bernie Williams PTT .50 1.25
252 Craig Biggio PTT .50 1.25
253 Chipper Jones PTT .75 2.00
254 Greg Maddux PTT 1.25 3.00
255 Sammy Sosa PTT .75 2.00
256 Mike Mussina PTT .50 1.25
257 Tim Salmon PTT .30 .75
258 Barry Larkin PTT .50 1.25
259 Randy Johnson PTT .75 2.00
260 Jeff Bagwell PTT .50 1.25
261 Roberto Alomar PTT .50 1.25
262 Tom Glavine PTT .50 1.25
263 Roger Clemens PTT 1.00 2.50
264 Alex Rodriguez PTT 1.25 3.00
265 Ivan Rodriguez PTT .50 1.25
266 Pedro Martinez PTT .50 1.25
267 Ken Griffey Jr. PTT 1.25 3.00
268 Jim Thome PTT .50 1.25
269 Frank Thomas PTT .75 2.00
270 Mike Piazza PTT .75 2.00
271 Garret Anderson TC .30 .75
272 Luis Gonzalez TC .30 .75
273 John Smoltz TC .75 2.00
274 Rafael Palmeiro TC .50 1.25
275 Curt Schilling TC .50 1.25
276 Mark Prior TC .50 1.25
277 Magglio Ordonez TC .50 1.25
278 Adam Dunn TC .50 1.25
279 Travis Hafner TC .30 .75
280 Jeromy Burnitz TC .30 .75
281 Carlos Guillen TC .30 .75
282 Dontrelle Willis TC .30 .75
283 Carlos Beltran TC .30 .75
284 Zack Greinke TC .50 1.25
285 Adrian Beltre TC .30 .75
286 Ben Sheets TC .30 .75
287 Johan Santana TC .75 2.00
288 Livan Hernandez TC .30 .75
289 Kazuo Matsui TC .30 .75
290 Derek Jeter TC 2.00 5.00
291 Tim Hudson TC .50 1.25
292 Eric Milton TC .30 .75
293 Jason Kendall TC .30 .75
294 Jake Peavy TC .30 .75
295 Ray Durham TC .30 .75
296 Ichiro Suzuki TC 1.25 3.00
297 Scott Rolen TC .50 1.25
298 Carl Crawford TC .50 1.25
299 Hank Blalock TC .30 .75
300 Roy Halladay TC .75 2.00

2005 Leaf Black

*BLACK 1-200: 1X TO 2.5X BASIC
*BLACK 201-250: .4X TO 1X BASIC
*BLACK 251-300: .5X TO 1.2X BASIC
ONE PER RETAIL PACK

2005 Leaf Green

*GREEN 1-200: 1.5X TO 4X BASIC
*GREEN 201-250: .4X TO 1X BASIC
*GREEN 251-300: .6X TO 1.5X BASIC
ONE PER RETAIL BLASTER PACK

2005 Leaf Orange

*ORANGE 1-200: 1.5X TO 4X BASIC
*ORANGE 201-250: .4X TO 1X BASIC
*ORANGE 251-300: .6X TO 1.5X BASIC
ONE PER RETAIL BLISTER PACK

2005 Leaf Press Proofs Blue

*BLUE 1-200: 5X TO 12X BASIC
*BLUE 201-250: .75X TO 2X BASIC
*BLUE 251-300: 2X TO 5X BASIC
STATED PRINT RUN 75 SERIAL #'d SETS

2005 Leaf Press Proofs Gold

*GOLD 1-200: 5X TO 12X BASIC
*GOLD 201-250: 1.5X TO 4X BASIC
*GOLD 251-300: 4X TO 10X BASIC
STATED PRINT RUN 25 SERIAL #'d SETS

2005 Leaf Press Proofs Red

*RED 1-200: 2X TO 5X BASIC
*RED 201-250: .4X TO 1X BASIC
*RED 251-300: .75X TO 2X BASIC
STATED ODDS 1:8

2005 Leaf Autographs

SP INFO BASED ON BECKETT RESEARCH
201 Josh Kroeger PROS 4.00 10.00
202 Angel Guzman PROS 4.00 10.00
203 Brad Halsey PROS 4.00 10.00
204 Bucky Jacobsen PROS 4.00 10.00
205 Carlos Hines PROS 4.00 10.00
206 Carlos Vasquez PROS 4.00 10.00
207 Billy Traber PROS 4.00 10.00
208 Bubba Crosby PROS 4.00 10.00
210 Chris Shelton PROS 6.00 15.00
211 Colby Miller PROS 4.00 10.00
212 Dave Crouthers PROS 4.00 10.00
216 Edwin Moreno PROS SP
217 Fernando Nieve PROS 4.00 10.00
220 Hector Gimenez PROS 4.00 10.00
221 Andy Green PROS 4.00 10.00
222 Jason Bartlett PROS 4.00 10.00
223 Jerry Gil PROS SP
225 Joey Gathright PROS SP
226 John Gall PROS SP
227 Jorge Sequea PROS SP
228 Jorge Vasquez PROS 4.00 10.00
232 Lincoln Holdzkom PROS 4.00 10.00
233 Miguel Olivo PROS 4.00 10.00
234 Mike Rouse PROS 4.00 10.00
235 Onil Joseph PROS SP
236 Phil Stockman PROS 4.00 10.00
237 Ramon Ramirez PROS 4.00 10.00
242 Ruddy Yan PROS 4.00 10.00
245 Scott Proctor PROS 4.00 10.00
246 Sean Henn PROS SP
247 Tim Bausher PROS 4.00 10.00
248 Tim Bittner PROS SP
249 William Bergolla PROS 4.00 10.00

2005 Leaf Autographs Red

PRINT RUNS B/WN 50-100 COPIES PER
BLUE PRINT RUNS B/WN 15-25 PER
NO BLUE PRICING DUE TO SCARCITY
GOLD PRINT RUNS B/WN 9-10 PER
NO GOLD PRICING DUE TO SCARCITY
RANDOM INSERTS IN PACKS
3 Chone Figgins/100 4.00 10.00
19 Johnny Estrada/100 4.00 10.00
24 Jay Gibbons/100 4.00 10.00
47 Carlos Lee/100 6.00 15.00
56 Danny Graves/100 4.00 10.00
60 Cliff Lee/100 12.50 30.00
63 Travis Hafner/50 8.00 20.00
74 Jeremy Bonderman/100 6.00 15.00
94 Jeremy Affeldt/100 4.00 10.00
96 Ken Harvey/100 4.00 10.00
103 Milton Bradley/100 6.00 15.00
111 Lyle Overbay/50 5.00 12.00
118 Joe Nathan/100 10.00 25.00
144 Bobby Crosby/100 6.00 15.00
154 Mike Lieberthal/50 8.00 20.00
157 Craig Wilson/50 5.00 12.00
158 Jack Wilson/100 6.00 15.00
163 Jake Peavy/50 12.50 30.00
172 Merkin Valdez/100 4.00 10.00
182 Jeff Suppan/100 6.00 15.00
187 Carl Crawford/50 8.00 20.00
188 Dewon Brazelton/50 5.00 12.00
194 Laynce Nix/100 4.00 10.00
201 Josh Kroeger PROS/100 4.00 10.00
202 Angel Guzman PROS/100 4.00 10.00
203 Brad Halsey PROS/100 4.00 10.00
204 Bucky Jacobsen PROS/100 4.00 10.00
205 Carlos Hines PROS/100 4.00 10.00
207 Billy Traber PROS/100 4.00 10.00
208 Bubba Crosby PROS/100 4.00 10.00
210 Chris Shelton PROS/100 10.00 25.00
211 Colby Miller PROS/100 4.00 10.00
212 Dave Crouthers PROS/100 4.00 10.00
217 Fernando Nieve PROS/100 4.00 10.00
218 Freddy Guzman PROS/100 4.00 10.00
220 Hector Gimenez PROS/100 4.00 10.00
221 Andy Green PROS/100 4.00 10.00
222 Jason Bartlett PROS/100 4.00 10.00
224 Jesse Crain PROS/100 6.00 15.00
227 Jorge Sequea PROS/84 4.00 10.00
228 Jorge Vasquez PROS/100 4.00 10.00
233 Miguel Olivo PROS/100 4.00 10.00
234 Mike Rouse PROS/100 4.00 10.00
236 Phil Stockman PROS/100 4.00 10.00
237 Ramon Ramirez PROS/100 4.00 10.00
238 Robb Quinlan PROS/100 4.00 10.00
241 Ronny Cedeno PROS/65 10.00 25.00
242 Ruddy Yan PROS/100 4.00 10.00
243 Ryan Meaux PROS/93 4.00 10.00
247 Tim Bausher PROS/100 4.00 10.00
249 William Bergolla PROS/100 4.00 10.00
250 Yadier Molina PROS/100 6.00 15.00

2005 Leaf 4 Star Staffs

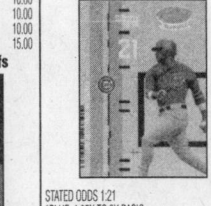

STATED ODDS 1:48
*DIE CUT: .6X TO 1.5X BASIC
DIE CUT RANDOM INSERTS IN PACKS
DIE CUT PRINT RUN 250 SERIAL #'d SETS
1 Tom Glavine 1.50 4.00
Greg Maddux
John Smoltz
Kevin Millwood
2 Josh Beckett 1.00 2.50
A.J. Burnett
Dontrelle Willis
Carl Pavano
3 Roger Clemens 2.00 5.00
Mike Mussina
David Wells
Andy Pettitte
4 Mark Prior 1.00 2.50
Greg Maddux
Kerry Wood
Carlos Zambrano
5 Roger Clemens 2.00 5.00
Andy Pettitte
Mike Mussina
Mariano Rivera
6 Pedro Martinez 1.00 2.50
Curt Schilling
Derek Lowe
Tim Wakefield
7 Mark Mulder 1.00 2.50
Barry Zito
Tim Hudson
Rich Harden
8 Randy Johnson 1.00 2.50
Curt Schilling
Brandon Webb
Byung-Hyun Kim
9 Nolan Ryan 4.00 10.00
Kevin Brown
Jamie Moyer
Kenny Rogers
10 Woody Williams 1.50 4.00
Roger Clemens
Roy Halladay
Kelvim Escobar
11 Roger Clemens 1.00 2.50
Andy Pettitte
Roy Oswalt
Wade Miller
12 Barry Zito 1.00 2.50
Mark Mulder
Tim Hudson
Billy Koch
13 Hideo Nomo 1.50 4.00
Kevin Brown
Kazuhisa Ishii
Eric Gagne
14 Tom Glavine 1.50 4.00
John Smoltz
Greg Maddux
Jason Schmidt
15 Hideo Nomo 1.50 4.00
Pedro Martinez
Derek Lowe
Tim Wakefield

2005 Leaf Alternate Threads

STATED ODDS 1:18
*HOLO: .75X TO 2X BASIC
HOLO RANDOM INSERTS IN PACKS
HOLO PRINT RUN 150 SERIAL #'d SETS
*HOLO DC: 1.5X TO 4X BASIC
HOLO DC RANDOM INSERTS IN PACKS
HOLO DC PRINT RUN 50 SERIAL #'d SETS
1 Adam Dunn .60 1.50
2 C.C. Sabathia .60 1.50
3 Curt Schilling .60 1.50
4 Dontrelle Willis .40 1.00
5 Greg Maddux 1.50 4.00
6 Hank Blalock .40 1.00
7 Ichiro Suzuki 1.50 4.00
8 Jeff Bagwell .60 1.50
9 Ken Griffey Jr. 1.50 4.00
10 Ken Harvey .40 1.00
11 Magglio Ordonez .60 1.50
12 Mark Mulder .40 1.00
13 Mark Teixeira 1.00 2.50
14 Michael Young .60 1.50
15 Miguel Tejada .60 1.50
16 Mike Piazza 1.00 2.50
17 Pedro Martinez .60 1.50
18 Randy Johnson 1.00 2.50
19 Roger Clemens 1.25 3.00
20 Sammy Sosa 1.00 2.50
21 Tim Hudson .60 1.50
22 Todd Helton .60 1.50
23 Torii Hunter .40 1.00
24 Travis Hafner .40 1.00
25 Vernon Wells .40 1.00

2005 Leaf Certified Materials Preview

STATED ODDS 1:21
*BLUE: 1.25X TO 3X BASIC
BLUE RANDOM INSERTS IN PACKS
BLUE PRINT RUN 100 SERIAL #'d SETS
*GOLD: 3X TO 8X BASIC
GOLD RANDOM INSERTS IN PACKS
GOLD PRINT RUN 25 SERIAL #'d SETS
*RED: 1X TO 2.5X BASIC
RED RANDOM INSERTS IN PACKS
RED PRINT RUN 200 SERIAL #'d SETS
1 Albert Pujols 2.50 6.00
2 Alex Rodriguez 1.50 4.00
3 Alfonso Soriano .60 1.50
4 Curt Schilling .60 1.50
5 Derek Jeter 2.50 6.00
6 Greg Maddux 1.50 4.00
7 Ichiro Suzuki 1.50 4.00
8 Jim Thome .60 1.50
9 Ken Griffey Jr. 1.50 4.00
10 Manny Ramirez 1.00 2.50
11 Mark Prior .60 1.50
12 Randy Johnson 1.00 2.50
13 Roger Clemens 1.25 3.00
14 Sammy Sosa 1.00 2.50
15 Vladimir Guerrero 1.00 2.50

2005 Leaf Clean Up Crew

STATED ODDS 1:49
*DIE CUT: .6X TO 1.5X BASIC
DIE CUT RANDOM INSERTS IN PACKS
DIE CUT PRINT RUN 250 SERIAL #'d SETS
1 Albert Pujols 2.50 6.00
Jim Edmonds
Scott Rolen
2 Melvin Mora .60 1.50
Miguel Tejada
Rafael Palmeiro
3 Alfonso Soriano .60 1.50
Michael Young
Hank Blalock
4 Gary Sheffield 1.50 4.00
Alex Rodriguez
Hideki Matsui
5 Moises Alou 1.00 2.50
Sammy Sosa
Nomar Garciaparra
6 Paul Lo Duca 1.00 2.50
Mike Lowell
Miguel Cabrera
7 Carlos Beltran .60 1.50
Lance Berkman
Jeff Bagwell
8 Paul Konerko .60 1.50
Magglio Ordonez
Frank Thomas
9 Sean Casey .60 1.50
Ken Griffey Jr.
Adam Dunn
10 Vladimir Guerrero 1.00 2.50
Garret Anderson
Troy Glaus
11 Joe Morgan 1.00 2.50
Johnny Bench
Tony Perez
12 Keith Hernandez .40 1.00
Darryl Strawberry
Gary Carter
13 Jim Rice 1.25 3.00
Carl Yastrzemski
Dwight Evans
14 Ryne Sandberg 2.00 5.00
Andre Dawson
Mark Grace
15 Cal Ripken 4.00 10.00
Eddie Murray
Rafael Palmeiro

2005 Leaf Cornerstones

STATED ODDS 1:37
1 Albert Pujols 2.50 6.00
Scott Rolen
2 Hideki Matsui 1.50 4.00
Jorge Posada
3 Sammy Sosa 1.00 2.50
Nomar Garciaparra
4 Manny Ramirez 1.00 2.50
David Ortiz
5 Miguel Cabrera 1.00 2.50
Mike Lowell
6 Hank Blalock 1.00 2.50
Mark Teixeira
7 Chipper Jones 1.00 2.50
J.D. Drew
8 Craig Biggio .60 1.50
Jeff Bagwell
9 Mike Piazza 1.00 2.50
Kazuo Matsui
10 Shawn Green .40 1.00
Adrian Beltre
11 Jim Thome .60 1.50
Bobby Abreu
12 Mike Schmidt 2.00 5.00
Steve Carlton
13 Cal Ripken 4.00 10.00
Eddie Murray
14 Carl Yastrzemski 1.25 3.00
Dwight Evans
15 Johnny Bench 1.00 2.50
Joe Morgan
16 Dale Murphy .40 1.00
Phil Niekro
17 Alan Trammell .40 1.00
Kirk Gibson
18 Jose Canseco .60 1.50
Rickey Henderson
19 Paul Molitor 1.00 2.50
Robin Yount
20 George Brett 2.00 5.00
Bo Jackson

2005 Leaf Cornerstones Bats

1 Albert Pujols 10.00 25.00
Scott Rolen
2 Hideki Matsui 15.00 40.00
Jorge Posada
3 Sammy Sosa 6.00 15.00
Nomar Garciaparra
4 Manny Ramirez 10.00 25.00
David Ortiz
5 Miguel Cabrera 6.00 15.00
Mike Lowell
6 Hank Blalock 6.00 15.00
Mark Teixeira
7 Chipper Jones 6.00 15.00
J.D. Drew
8 Craig Biggio 6.00 15.00
Jeff Bagwell
9 Mike Piazza 6.00 15.00
Kazuo Matsui
10 Shawn Green 4.00 10.00
Adrian Beltre

2005 Leaf Cornerstones Jerseys

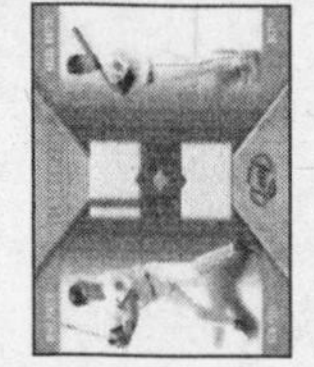

STATED PRINT RUN 250 SERIAL #'d SETS
*PRIME p/r 50: 1X TO 2.5X BASIC
*PRIME p/r 25: 1.2X TO 3X BASIC
PRIME PRINT RUN B/WN 25-50 PER
RANDOM INSERTS IN PACKS
1 Albert Pujols 10.00 25.00
Scott Rolen
2 Hideki Matsui 15.00 40.00
Jorge Posada
4 Manny Ramirez 10.00 25.00
David Ortiz
5 Miguel Cabrera 6.00 15.00
Mike Lowell
6 Hank Blalock 6.00 15.00
Mark Teixeira
8 Craig Biggio 6.00 15.00

Jeff Bagwell
9 Mike Piazza 6.00 15.00
Kazuo Matsui
10 Shawn Green 4.00 10.00
Adrian Beltre

2005 Leaf Cy Young Winners

STATED ODDS 1:31
*GOLD: .6X TO 1.5X BASIC
GOLD RANDOM INSERTS IN PACKS
GOLD PRINT RUN 350 SERIAL #'d SETS
*GOLD DC: 1X TO 2.5X BASIC
GOLD DC RANDOM INSERTS IN PACKS
GOLD DC PRINT RUN 100 SERIAL #'d SETS
1 Warren Spahn .60 1.50
2 Whitey Ford .60 1.50
3 Bob Gibson .60 1.50
4 Tom Seaver .60 1.50
5 Steve Carlton .40 1.00
6 Jim Palmer .40 1.00
7 Rollie Fingers .40 1.00
8 Dwight Gooden .40 1.00
9 Roger Clemens 1.25 3.00
10 Orel Hershiser .40 1.00
11 Greg Maddux 1.50 4.00
12 Dennis Eckersley .40 1.00
13 Randy Johnson 1.00 2.50
14 Pedro Martinez .60 1.50
15 Eric Gagne .40 1.00

2005 Leaf Fans of the Game

STATED ODDS 1:24
1 Sean Astin .75 2.00
2 Tony Danza .75 2.00
3 Taye Diggs .75 2.00

2005 Leaf Fans of the Game Autographs

RANDOM INSERTS IN PACKS
SP PRINT RUNS PROVIDED BY DONRUSS
SP'S ARE NOT SERIAL-NUMBERED
1 Sean Astin 12.50 30.00
2 Tony Danza SP/50 150.00 250.00
3 Taye Diggs 10.00 25.00

2005 Leaf Game Collection

STATED ODDS 1:118
SP INFO BASED ON BECKETT RESEARCH
1 Cal Ripken Bat 15.00 40.00
2 Carl Crawford Jsy 3.00 8.00
3 Dale Murphy Bat SP 8.00 20.00
4 Don Mattingly Bat SP 10.00 25.00
5 George Brett Jsy SP 10.00 25.00
6 Victor Martinez Bat SP 4.00 10.00
7 Sean Casey Bat 3.00 8.00
8 Torii Hunter Bat 3.00 8.00
9 Magglio Ordonez Bat 3.00 8.00
10 Lance Berkman Bat 3.00 8.00
11 Mike Schmidt Bat SP 10.00 25.00
12 Nolan Ryan Jkt SP 15.00 40.00
13 Paul Lo Duca Bat 3.00 8.00
14 Preston Wilson Bat 3.00 8.00
15 Rod Carew Jkt SP 8.00 20.00
16 Reggie Jackson Bat SP 8.00 20.00
17 Ivan Rodriguez Bat 4.00 10.00
18 L.Walker Cards Bat 4.00 10.00
19 Miguel Tejada Bat SP 4.00 10.00
20 Vladimir Guerrero Bat SP 6.00 15.00

2005 Leaf Game Collection Autograph

RANDOM INSERTS IN PACKS
PRINT RUNS B/WN 5-200 COPIES PER
NO PRICING ON QTY OF 25 OR LESS
1 Cal Ripken Jkt/5
2 Carl Crawford Jsy/200 10.00 25.00
3 Dale Murphy Bat/25
4 Don Mattingly Bat/5
5 George Brett Jsy/5
6 Victor Martinez Bat/200 10.00 25.00
7 Sean Casey Bat/200 10.00 25.00
8 Torii Hunter Bat/50 12.50 30.00

9 Magglio Ordonez Bat/25
10 Lance Berkman Bat/5
11 Mike Schmidt Bat/5
12 Nolan Ryan Jkt/10
13 Paul Lo Duca Bat/100 10.00 25.00
15 Rod Carew Jkt/5

2005 Leaf Gamers

STATED ODDS 1:13
*QUANTUM: 1.25X TO 3X BASIC
QUANTUM RANDOM INSERTS IN PACKS
QUANTUM PRINT RUN 175 SER.#'d SETS
*QUANTUM DC: 2.5X TO 6X BASIC
QUANTUM DC RANDOM INSERTS IN PACKS
QUANTUM DC PRINT RUN 50 SER.#'d SETS
1 Albert Pujols 2.50 6.00
2 Alex Rodriguez 1.50 4.00
3 Alfonso Soriano .60 1.50
4 Chipper Jones 1.00 2.50
5 Derek Jeter 2.50 6.00
6 Greg Maddux 1.50 4.00
7 Ichiro Suzuki 1.50 4.00
8 Jim Thome .60 1.50
9 Ken Griffey Jr. 1.50 4.00
10 Lance Berkman .60 1.50
11 Miguel Tejada .60 1.50
12 Mike Piazza 1.00 2.50
13 Roger Clemens 1.25 3.00
14 Scott Rolen .60 1.50
15 Vladimir Guerrero 1.00 2.50

2005 Leaf Gold Rookies

STATED ODDS 1:24
*MIRROR: 2X TO 5X BASIC
MIRROR RANDOM INSERTS IN PACKS
MIRROR PRINT RUN 25 SERIAL #'d SETS
1 Dennis Sarfate .40 1.00
2 Don Kelly .40 1.00
3 Eddy Rodriguez .40 1.00
4 Edwin Moreno .40 1.00
5 Greg Dobbs .40 1.00
6 Josh Labandeira .40 1.00
7 Kevin Cave .40 1.00
8 Mariano Gomez .40 1.00
9 Ronald Belisario .40 1.00
10 Ruddy Yan .40 1.00

2005 Leaf Gold Rookies Autograph

SP INFO BASED ON BECKETT RESEARCH
MIRROR PRINT RUN 25 SERIAL #'d SETS
NO MIRROR PRICING DUE TO SCARCITY
RANDOM INSERTS IN PACKS
1 Dennis Sarfate SP
2 Don Kelly 4.00 10.00
3 Eddy Rodriguez SP
4 Edwin Moreno SP
5 Greg Dobbs 4.00 10.00
6 Josh Labandeira SP
7 Kevin Cave SP
8 Mariano Gomez SP
9 Ronald Belisario 4.00 10.00
10 Ruddy Yan 4.00 10.00

2005 Leaf Gold Stars

STATED ODDS 1:27
*MIRROR: 2.5X TO 6X BASIC
MIRROR RANDOM INSERTS IN PACKS
MIRROR PRINT RUN 25 SERIAL #'d SETS
1 Albert Pujols 2.50 6.00
2 Ichiro Suzuki 1.50 4.00
3 Derek Jeter 2.50 6.00
4 Alex Rodriguez 1.50 4.00
5 Scott Rolen .60 1.50
6 Randy Johnson 1.00 2.50
7 Roger Clemens 1.25 3.00
8 Greg Maddux 1.50 4.00
9 Alfonso Soriano .60 1.50
10 Mark Mulder .40 1.00
11 Sammy Sosa 1.00 2.50
12 Mike Piazza 1.00 2.50
13 Rafael Palmeiro .60 1.50
14 Ivan Rodriguez .60 1.50
15 Miguel Cabrera 1.00 2.50
16 Stan Musial 1.50 4.00
17 Nolan Ryan 2.50 6.00
18 Don Mattingly 2.00 5.00
19 George Brett 2.00 5.00
20 Cal Ripken 4.00 10.00

2005 Leaf Home/Road

STATED ODDS 1:22
HOME AND ROAD VALUED EQUALLY
1H Albert Pujols H 2.50 6.00
1R Albert Pujols R 2.50 6.00
2H Alfonso Soriano H .60 1.50
2R Alfonso Soriano R .60 1.50
3H Carlos Beltran H .40 1.00
3R Carlos Beltran R .40 1.00
4H Chipper Jones H 1.00 2.50
4R Chipper Jones R 1.00 2.50
5H Frank Thomas H 1.00 2.50
5R Frank Thomas R 1.00 2.50
6H Hank Blalock H .40 1.00
6R Hank Blalock R .40 1.00
7H Ivan Rodriguez H .60 1.50
7R Ivan Rodriguez R .60 1.50
8H Manny Ramirez H 1.00 2.50
8R Manny Ramirez R 1.00 2.50
9H Mark Prior H .60 1.50
9R Mark Prior R .60 1.50
10H Miguel Cabrera H 1.00 2.50
10R Miguel Cabrera R 1.00 2.50
11H Miguel Tejada H .60 1.50
11R Miguel Tejada R .60 1.50
12H Mike Piazza H 1.00 2.50
12R Mike Piazza R 1.00 2.50
13H Roger Clemens H 1.25 3.00
13R Roger Clemens R 1.25 3.00
14H Todd Helton H .60 1.50
14R Todd Helton R .60 1.50
15H Vladimir Guerrero H 1.00 2.50
15R Vladimir Guerrero R 1.00 2.50

2005 Leaf Home/Road Jersey

RANDOM INSERTS IN PACKS
SP INFO BASED ON BECKETT RESEARCH
1H Albert Pujols H 8.00 20.00
1R Albert Pujols R 8.00 20.00
2H Alfonso Soriano H 3.00 8.00
3H Carlos Beltran H 3.00 8.00
3R Carlos Beltran R 3.00 8.00
4R Chipper Jones R 4.00 10.00
5H Frank Thomas H 4.00 10.00
5R Frank Thomas R 4.00 10.00
6H Hank Blalock H 3.00 8.00
7H Ivan Rodriguez H 4.00 10.00
7R Ivan Rodriguez R 4.00 10.00
8R Manny Ramirez R 4.00 10.00
9H Mark Prior H 4.00 10.00
10H Miguel Cabrera H SP
10R Miguel Cabrera R SP
11H Miguel Tejada H 3.00 8.00
11R Miguel Tejada R 3.00 8.00
12H Mike Piazza H 4.00 10.00
13H Roger Clemens H 6.00 15.00
13R Roger Clemens R 6.00 15.00
14H Todd Helton H 4.00 10.00
14R Todd Helton R 4.00 10.00
15H Vladimir Guerrero H 4.00 10.00

2005 Leaf Home/Road Jersey Prime

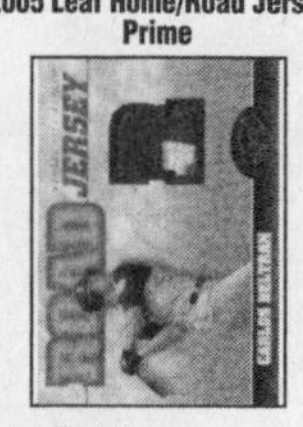

*PRIME: 1X TO 2.5X BASIC
STATED PRINT RUN 50 SERIAL #'d SETS
4H Chipper Jones H 10.00 25.00
6R Hank Blalock R 8.00 20.00
8H Manny Ramirez H 10.00 25.00
9R Mark Prior R 10.00 25.00
10H Miguel Cabrera H 10.00 25.00
10R Miguel Cabrera R 10.00 25.00
12R Mike Piazza R 10.00 25.00
15R Vladimir Guerrero R 10.00 25.00

2005 Leaf Patch Off My Back

*PATCH: 1X TO 2.5X SHIRT OFF BACK
*PATCH: .6X TO 1.5X SHIRT OFF BACK SP
STATED PRINT RUN 50 SERIAL #'d SETS
2 Aubrey Huff 6.00 15.00
3 Austin Kearns 6.00 15.00
24 Mariano Rivera 10.00 25.00

2005 Leaf Patch Off My Back Autograph

RANDOM INSERTS IN PACKS
PRINT RUNS B/WN 10-75 COPIES PER
NO PRICING ON QTY OF 25 OR LESS
1 Adam Dunn/10
2 Aubrey Huff/50 15.00 40.00
4 Bobby Crosby/75 15.00 40.00
5 C.C. Sabathia/75 15.00 40.00
7 David Ortiz/50 40.00 80.00
8 Dewon Brazelton/75 10.00 25.00
11 Garret Anderson/25
14 Jack Wilson/75 15.00 40.00
16 Jay Gibbons/50 10.00 25.00
18 Jody Gerut/75 10.00 25.00
20 Johan Santana/50 30.00 60.00
22 Jose Vidro/75 10.00 25.00
25 Mark Teixeira/10
26 Michael Young/75 15.00 40.00
29 Omar Vizquel/10
33 Sean Burroughs/25
34 Sean Casey/10
36 Torii Hunter/10
39 Vernon Wells/10
40 Victor Martinez/75

2005 Leaf Picture Perfect

STATED ODDS 1:20
*DIE CUT: 1.25X TO 3X BASIC
DIE CUT RANDOM INSERTS IN PACKS
DIE CUT PRINT RUN 100 SERIAL #'d SETS
1 Albert Pujols 2.50 6.00
2 Alex Rodriguez 1.50 4.00
3 Alfonso Soriano .60 1.50
4 Derek Jeter 2.50 6.00
5 Greg Maddux 1.50 4.00
6 Hideki Matsui 1.50 4.00
7 Ichiro Suzuki 1.50 4.00
8 Ivan Rodriguez .60 1.50
9 Jim Thome .60 1.50
10 Mark Mulder .40 1.00
11 Mark Prior .60 1.50
12 Miguel Tejada .60 1.50
13 Mike Mussina .60 1.50
14 Mike Piazza 1.00 2.50
15 Nomar Garciaparra 1.00 2.50
16 Randy Johnson 1.00 2.50
17 Roger Clemens 1.25 3.00
18 Sammy Sosa 1.00 2.50
19 Scott Rolen .60 1.50
20 Vladimir Guerrero 1.00 2.50

2005 Leaf Recollection Autographs

RANDOM INSERTS IN PACKS
PRINT RUNS B/WN 1-29 COPIES PER
NO PRICING DUE TO SCARCITY

2005 Leaf Shirt Off My Back

STATED ODDS 1:48
SP INFO BASED ON BECKETT RESEARCH
1 Adam Dunn SP 4.00 10.00
4 Bobby Crosby SP 4.00 10.00
5 C.C. Sabathia SP 4.00 10.00
7 David Ortiz SP 6.00 15.00
8 Dewon Brazelton 3.00 8.00
9 Edgar Martinez 4.00 10.00
10 Frankie Francisco 3.00 8.00
11 Garret Anderson 3.00 8.00
12 Hideki Matsui SP 10.00 25.00
13 Hideo Nomo 4.00 10.00
14 Jack Wilson 3.00 8.00
15 Javy Lopez SP 4.00 10.00
16 Jay Gibbons SP 4.00 10.00
17 Jim Edmonds SP
18 Jody Gerut SP 4.00 10.00
19 Joey Gathright 3.00 8.00
20 Johan Santana 4.00 10.00
21 Jose Reyes 3.00 8.00
22 Jose Vidro 3.00 8.00
23 Lance Berkman SP 4.00 10.00
25 Mark Teixeira 4.00 10.00
26 Michael Young SP 4.00 10.00
27 Mike Cameron 3.00 8.00
28 Mike Sweeney 3.00 8.00
29 Omar Vizquel SP 6.00 15.00
30 Preston Wilson SP 4.00 10.00
31 Rocco Baldelli SP 4.00 10.00
32 Scott Rolen SP 6.00 15.00
33 Sean Burroughs SP 4.00 10.00
34 Sean Casey 3.00 8.00
35 Tim Hudson 3.00 8.00
36 Torii Hunter 3.00 8.00
37 Trevor Hoffman 3.00 8.00
38 Troy Glaus 3.00 8.00
39 Vernon Wells 3.00 8.00
40 Victor Martinez SP 4.00 10.00

2005 Leaf Sportscasters 70 Green Batting-Ball

STATED PRINT RUN 70 SERIAL #'d SETS
*PARALLEL #'d OF 50-65: .4X TO 1X
*PARALLEL #'d OF 40-45: .5X TO 1.2X
*PARALLEL #'d OF 30-35: .6X TO 1.5X
*PARALLEL #'d OF 20-25: .75X TO 2X
*PARALLEL #'d OF 15: 1X TO 2.5X
PARALLELS #'d FROM 5-65 COPIES PER
NO PRICING ON QTY OF 10 OR LESS
OVERALL SPORTSCASTER ODDS 1:4
1 Adam Dunn 1.00 2.50
2 Al Kaline 1.50 4.00
3 Albert Pujols 4.00 10.00
4 Alex Rodriguez 2.50 6.00
5 Alfonso Soriano 1.00 2.50
6 Bob Gibson 1.00 2.50
7 Cal Ripken 6.00 15.00
8 Carl Yastrzemski 2.00 5.00
9 Dale Murphy .60 1.50
10 Derek Jeter 4.00 10.00
11 Don Mattingly 3.00 8.00
12 Duke Snider 1.00 2.50
13 Eric Gagne .60 1.50
14 Ernie Banks 1.50 4.00
15 Frank Robinson 1.00 2.50
16 George Brett 3.00 8.00
17 Greg Maddux 2.50 6.00
18 Harmon Killebrew 1.50 4.00
19 Ichiro Suzuki 2.50 6.00
20 Ivan Rodriguez 1.00 2.50
21 Jim Edmonds 1.00 2.50
22 Jim Palmer .60 1.50
23 Jim Thome 1.00 2.50
24 Johnny Bench 1.50 4.00
25 Ken Griffey Jr. 2.50 6.00
26 Larry Walker 1.00 2.50
27 Mark Mulder .60 1.50
28 Mark Prior 1.00 2.50
29 Miguel Tejada 1.00 2.50
30 Mike Mussina 1.00 2.50
31 Mike Piazza 1.50 4.00
32 Mike Schmidt 3.00 8.00
33 Nolan Ryan 4.00 10.00
34 Nomar Garciaparra 1.50 4.00
35 Pedro Martinez 1.00 2.50
36 Rafael Palmeiro 1.00 2.50
37 Randy Johnson 1.50 4.00
38 Reggie Jackson 1.50 4.00
39 Rickey Henderson 1.00 2.50
40 Roberto Clemente 4.00 10.00
41 Rod Carew 1.00 2.50
42 Roger Clemens 2.00 5.00
43 Ryne Sandberg 3.00 8.00
44 Sammy Sosa 1.50 4.00
45 Stan Musial 2.50 6.00
46 Steve Carlton .60 1.50
47 Tony Gwynn UER 2.00 5.00
Name spelled as Green in text on back
48 Vladimir Guerrero 1.50 4.00
49 Warren Spahn 1.00 2.50
50 Willie McCovey 1.00 2.50

2005 Leaf Century

This 200-card set was released in January, 2005. The set was issued in five card packs with an $10 SRP which came 10 packs to a box and 24 boxes to a case. An innovation with this set was the usage of real U.S. Stamps on various insert sets.

COMPLETE SET (200) 30.00 60.00
COMMON ACTIVE .20 .50
COMMON RET .20 .50
1 Brian Roberts .20 .50
2 Derek Jeter 1.25 3.00
3 Harmon Killebrew .50 1.25
4 Angel Berroa .20 .50
5 George Brett 1.00 2.50
6 Stan Musial .75 2.00
7 Ivan Rodriguez .30 .75
8 Cal Ripken 2.00 5.00
9 Hank Blalock .20 .50
10 Miguel Tejada .30 .75
11 Barry Larkin .30 .75
12 Alfonso Soriano .30 .75
13 Alex Rodriguez .75 2.00
14 Paul Konerko .30 .75
15 Jim Edmonds .30 .75
16 Garret Anderson .20 .50
17 Todd Helton .30 .75
18 Moises Alou .20 .50
19 Tony Gwynn .60 1.50
20 Mike Schmidt 1.00 2.50
21 Sammy Sosa .50 1.25
22 Roger Clemens .60 1.50
23 Tony Perez .20 .50
24 Manny Ramirez .50 1.25
25 Jim Thome .30 .75
26 Chase Utley .30 .75
27 Scott Rolen .30 .75
28 Austin Kearns .20 .50
29 John Smoltz .50 1.25
30 Ken Griffey Jr. .75 2.00
31 Mike Piazza .50 1.25
32 Steve Carlton .20 .50
33 Larry Walker .30 .75
34 Nolan Ryan 1.25 3.00
35 Mike Mussina .30 .75
36 Joe Nathan .20 .50
37 Kenny Rogers .20 .50
38 Eric Gagne .20 .50
39 Brett Myers .20 .50
40 Rich Harden .20 .50
41 Victor Martinez .30 .75
42 Mariano Rivera .50 1.25
43 Dennis Eckersley .20 .50
44 Roy Oswalt .30 .75
45 Pedro Martinez .30 .75
46 Jason Bay .20 .50
47 Tom Glavine .30 .75
48 Torii Hunter .20 .50
49 Larry Bigbie .20 .50
50 Nomar Garciaparra .50 1.25
51 Ichiro Suzuki .75 2.00
52 C.C. Sabathia .30 .75
53 Bobby Abreu .20 .50
54 Doug Mientkiewicz .20 .50
55 Hideki Matsui .75 2.00
56 Mark Buehrle .30 .75
57 Johan Santana .50 1.25
58 Johnny Damon .30 .75
59 Edgar Martinez .30 .75
60 Preston Wilson .20 .50
61 Livan Hernandez .20 .50
62 Eric Chavez .20 .50
63 Lyle Overbay .20 .50
64 Jason Schmidt .20 .50
65 Cliff Lee .30 .75
66 Shingo Takatsu .20 .50
67 Jeff Bagwell .30 .75
68 Danny Graves .20 .50
69 Kip Wells .20 .50
70 Steve Finley .20 .50
71 Lew Ford .20 .50
72 Chone Figgins .20 .50
73 Delmon Young .50 1.25
74 Esteban Loaiza .20 .50
75 Barry Zito .20 .50
76 Carlos Delgado .20 .50
77 Joe Mauer .50 1.25
78 Ryan Wagner .20 .50
79 John Lackey .20 .50
80 Adrian Beltre .20 .50
81 Vernon Wells .20 .50
82 Sean Burroughs .20 .50
83 Francisco Cordero .20 .50
84 Carlos Guillen .20 .50
85 Eric Byrnes .20 .50
86 Jose Reyes .30 .75
87 Rocco Baldelli .20 .50
88 Josh Beckett .30 .75
89 Casey Kotchman .20 .50
90 Scott Podsednik .20 .50
91 Mike Sweeney .20 .50
92 Khalil Greene .20 .50
93 Trot Nixon .20 .50
94 Chad Cordero .20 .50
95 Derek Lowe .20 .50
96 Jason Giambi .20 .50
97 Jose Guillen .20 .50
98 Craig Biggio .30 .75
99 Pat Burrell .20 .50
100 Kazuo Matsui .20 .50
101 Rafael Furcal .20 .50
102 Jack Wilson .20 .50
103 Edgar Renteria .20 .50
104 Carlos Beltran .20 .50
105 Albert Pujols 1.25 3.00
106 Melvin Mora .20 .50
107 J.D. Drew .20 .50
108 Andre Dawson .30 .75
109 Jody Gerut .20 .50
110 Michael Young .30 .75
111 Gary Sheffield .20 .50
112 Wade Boggs .30 .75
113 Carl Crawford .30 .75
114 Paul Lo Duca .20 .50
115 Tim Hudson .30 .75
116 Aramis Ramirez .20 .50
117 Lance Berkman .30 .75
118 Javy Lopez .20 .50
119 Robin Yount .50 1.25
120 Mark Mulder .20 .50
121 Sean Casey .20 .50
122 Will Clark .30 .75
123 Don Mattingly 1.00 2.50
124 Miguel Cabrera .50 1.25
125 Rafael Palmeiro .30 .75
126 David Ortiz .50 1.25
127 Vladimir Guerrero .50 1.25
128 Ken Harvey .20 .50
129 Rod Carew .30 .75
130 Magglio Ordonez .30 .75
131 Greg Maddux .75 2.00
132 Roy Halladay .50 1.25
133 Javier Vazquez .20 .50
134 Kerry Wood .20 .50
135 Frank Thomas .50 1.25
136 Tom Gordon .20 .50
137 Jake Peavy .20 .50
138 Curt Schilling .30 .75
139 Dewon Brazelton .20 .50
140 Jae Weong Seo .20 .50
141 Danny Kolb .20 .50
142 Jeff Kent .20 .50
143 Juan Encarnacion .20 .50
144 Adam Dunn .30 .75
145 Carlos Lee .20 .50
146 Matt Clement .20 .50
147 Guillermo Mota .20 .50
148 Travis Hafner .20 .50
149 Brad Wilkerson .20 .50
150 Eric Milton .20 .50
151 Randy Johnson .50 1.25
152 Joe Crede .20 .50
153 Mark Kotsay .20 .50
154 Jason Varitek .50 1.25
155 David Wright .75 2.00
156 Brad Penny .20 .50
157 Francisco Rodriguez .30 .75
158 Gary Carter .20 .50
159 Adrian Gonzalez .30 .75
160 Derrek Lee .20 .50
161 Mark Prior .30 .75
162 Carlos Zambrano .30 .75
163 Bobby Crosby .20 .50
164 Jermaine Dye .20 .50
165 Kris Benson .20 .50
166 Dontrelle Willis .20 .50
167 Dallas McPherson .20 .50
168 Johnny Estrada .20 .50
169 Milton Bradley .20 .50
170 Shannon Stewart .20 .50
171 Ben Sheets .20 .50
172 Richard Hidalgo .20 .50
173 Laynce Nix .20 .50
174 B.J. Upton .30 .75
175 Craig Wilson .20 .50
176 Hideo Nomo .50 1.25
177 Troy Glaus .20 .50
178 Akinori Otsuka .20 .50
179 Rickie Weeks .30 .75
180 Mike Lowell .20 .50
181 Marcus Giles .20 .50
182 Randy Wolf .20 .50
183 A.J. Burnett .30 .75
184 Aubrey Huff .20 .50
185 Billy Ripken .20 .50
186 Octavio Dotel .20 .50
187 Kazuhisa Ishii .20 .50
188 Mark Teixeira .50 1.25
189 Todd Walker .20 .50
190 Dale Murphy .20 .50
191 Alexis Rios .30 .75
192 Reggie Sanders .20 .50
193 Orlando Cabrera .20 .50
194 Shawn Green .20 .50
195 Andy Pettitte .30 .75
196 Chipper Jones .50 1.25
197 Jose Vidro .20 .50
198 Jacque Jones .20 .50
199 Brian Giles .20 .50
200 Andruw Jones .20 .50

2005 Leaf Century Post Marks Gold

*GOLD ACTIVE: 3X TO 8X BASIC
*GOLD RETIRED: 2.5X TO 6X BASIC
OVERALL INSERT ODDS 1:3
STATED PRINT RUN 50 SERIAL #'d SETS

2005 Leaf Century Post Marks Platinum

OVERALL INSERT ODDS 1:3
STATED PRINT RUN 1 SERIAL #'d SET
NO PRICING DUE TO SCARCITY

2005 Leaf Century Post Marks Silver

*SILVER ACTIVE: 2.5X TO 6X BASIC
*SILVER RETIRED: 2X TO 5X BASIC
OVERALL INSERT ODDS 1:3
STATED PRINT RUN 100 SERIAL #'d SETS

2005 Leaf Century Material Bat

*BAT p/r 250: .4X TO 1X POS p/r 250
*BAT p/r 250: .3X TO .8X POS p/r 100
*BAT p/r 100: .5X TO 1.2X POS p/r 250
*BAT p/r 100: .4X TO 1X POS p/r 100
*BAT p/r 50: .75X TO 2X POS p/r 250
*BAT p/r 50: .6X TO 1.5X POS p/r 100
*BAT p/r 25: 1.25X TO 3X POS p/r 250
OVERALL INSERT ODDS 1:3
PRINT RUNS B/WN 5-250 COPIES PER
NO PRICING ON QTY OF 5
18 Moises Alou/50 3.00 8.00

50 Nomar Garciaparra/100 4.00 10.00
54 Doug Mientkiewicz/50 3.00 8.00
58 Johnny Damon/100 3.00 8.00
73 Delmon Young/100 3.00 8.00
107 J.D. Drew/100 2.00 5.00
114 Paul Lo Duca/100 2.00 5.00
143 Juan Encarnacion/50 3.00 8.00
149 Brad Wilkerson/100 2.00 5.00
152 Joe Crede/50 2.00 5.00
156 Brad Penny/50 3.00 8.00
160 Derrek Lee/25 3.00 8.00
172 Richard Hidalgo/50 3.00 8.00
174 B.J. Upton/50 5.00 12.00
179 Rickie Weeks/25 3.00 8.00
191 Alexis Rios/50 3.00 8.00
193 Orlando Cabrera/50 3.00 8.00
199 Brian Giles/250 2.00 5.00

2005 Leaf Century Material Fabric Number

*NBR p/r 75: .5X TO 1.2X POS p/r 250
*NBR p/r 36-65: .75X TO 2X POS p/r 250
*NBR p/r 36-65: .6X TO 1.5X POS p/r 100
*NBR p/r 20-35: 1.25X TO 3X POS p/r 250
*NBR p/r 20-35: 1X TO 2.5X POS p/r 100
*NBR p/r 20-35: .4X TO 1X POS p/r 25
*NBR p/r 15-19: 1.5X TO 4X POS p/r 250
*NBR p/r 15-19: 1.25X TO 3X POS p/r 100
OVERALL INSERT ODDS 1:3
PRINT RUNS B/WN 1-75 COPIES PER
NO PRICING ON QTY OF 14 OR LESS

2005 Leaf Century Material Fabric Position

PRINT RUNS B/WN 1-250 COPIES PER
NO PRICING ON QTY OF 5 OR LESS
PRIME PRINT RUN 1 SERIAL #'d SET
NO PRIME PRICING DUE TO SCARCITY
OVERALL INSERT ODDS 1:3
1 Brian Roberts Jsy/250 2.00 5.00
3 Harmon Killebrew Jsy/250 6.00 15.00
4 Angel Berroa Jsy/250 2.00 5.00
5 George Brett Jsy/250 8.00 20.00
6 Stan Musial Pants/100 8.00 20.00
7 Ivan Rodriguez Jsy/250 3.00 8.00
8 Cal Ripken Jkt/250 10.00 25.00
9 Hank Blalock Jsy/250 2.00 5.00
10 Miguel Tejada Jsy/250 2.00 5.00
11 Barry Larkin Jsy/100 3.00 8.00
12 Alfonso Soriano Jsy/250 2.00 5.00
14 Paul Konerko Jsy/250 2.00 5.00
15 Jim Edmonds Jsy/250 2.00 5.00
16 Garret Anderson Jsy/250 2.00 5.00
17 Todd Helton Jsy/250 3.00 8.00
19 Tony Gwynn Jsy/250 6.00 15.00
20 Mike Schmidt Jsy/250 8.00 20.00
21 Sammy Sosa Jsy/250 3.00 8.00
22 Roger Clemens Jsy/250 5.00 12.00
23 Tony Perez Jsy/250 3.00 8.00
24 Manny Ramirez Jsy/250 3.00 8.00
25 Jim Thome Jsy/250 3.00 8.00
27 Scott Rolen Jsy/250 3.00 8.00
28 Austin Kearns Jsy/250 2.00 5.00
29 John Smoltz Jsy/250 3.00 8.00
31 Mike Piazza Jsy/250 3.00 8.00
32 Steve Carlton Pants/250 3.00 8.00
34 Nolan Ryan Jsy/250 10.00 25.00
35 Mike Mussina Jsy/250 3.00 8.00
39 Brett Myers Jsy/250 2.00 5.00
40 Rich Harden Jsy/1
41 Victor Martinez Jsy/250 2.00 5.00
42 Mariano Rivera Jsy/250 3.00 8.00
43 Dennis Eckersley Jsy/250 2.00 5.00
44 Roy Oswalt Jsy/250 2.00 5.00
45 Pedro Martinez Jsy/250 3.00 8.00
46 Jason Bay Jsy/250 2.00 5.00
47 Tom Glavine Jsy/250 3.00 8.00
48 Torii Hunter Jsy/250 2.00 5.00
49 Larry Bigbie Jsy/250 2.00 5.00
52 C.C. Sabathia Jsy/250 2.00 5.00
53 Bobby Abreu Jsy/250 2.00 5.00
55 Hideki Matsui Jsy/250 8.00 20.00
56 Mark Buehrle Jsy/250 2.00 5.00
57 Johan Santana Jsy/250 3.00 8.00
59 Edgar Martinez Jsy/250 3.00 8.00
60 Preston Wilson Jsy/250 2.00 5.00
61 Livan Hernandez Jsy/250 2.00 5.00
62 Eric Chavez Jsy/250 2.00 5.00
63 Lyle Overbay Jsy/250 2.00 5.00
65 Cliff Lee Jsy/250 2.00 5.00
67 Jeff Bagwell Jsy/250 3.00 8.00
71 Lew Ford Jsy/250 2.00 5.00
72 Chone Figgins Jsy/250 2.00 5.00
75 Barry Zito Jsy/250 2.00 5.00
76 Carlos Delgado Jsy/250 2.00 5.00
78 Ryan Wagner Jsy/250 2.00 5.00
80 Adrian Beltre Jsy/250 2.00 5.00
81 Vernon Wells Jsy/250 2.00 5.00
82 Sean Burroughs Jsy/250 2.00 5.00
83 Francisco Cordero Jsy/250 2.00 5.00
85 Eric Byrnes Jsy/25 5.00 12.00
86 Jose Reyes Jsy/250 2.00 5.00
87 Rocco Baldelli Jsy/250 2.00 5.00
88 Josh Beckett Jsy/250 2.00 5.00
90 Scott Podsednik Jsy/250 2.00 5.00
91 Mike Sweeney Jsy/250 2.00 5.00
93 Trot Nixon Jsy/250 2.00 5.00
96 Jason Giambi Jsy/250 2.00 5.00
98 Craig Biggio Jsy/250 3.00 8.00
99 Pat Burrell Jsy/250 2.00 5.00
100 Kazuo Matsui Jsy/250 2.00 5.00
101 Rafael Furcal Jsy/250 2.00 5.00
102 Jack Wilson Jsy/250 2.00 5.00
103 Edgar Renteria Jsy/250 2.00 5.00
104 Carlos Beltran Jsy/250 2.00 5.00
105 Albert Pujols Jsy/250 6.00 15.00
106 Melvin Mora Jsy/100 2.00 5.00
108 Andre Dawson Jsy/250 3.00 8.00
109 Jody Gerut Jsy/250 2.00 5.00
110 Michael Young Jsy/250 2.00 5.00
111 Gary Sheffield Jsy/250 2.00 5.00
112 Wade Boggs Jsy/100 5.00 12.00
113 Carl Crawford Jsy/250 2.00 5.00
115 Tim Hudson Jsy/250 2.00 5.00
116 Aramis Ramirez Jsy/250 2.00 5.00
117 Lance Berkman Jsy/250 2.00 5.00
118 Javy Lopez Jsy/250 2.00 5.00
119 Robin Yount Jsy/250 4.00 10.00
120 Mark Mulder Jsy/250 2.00 5.00
121 Sean Casey Jsy/250 2.00 5.00
122 Will Clark Jsy/250 4.00 10.00
123 Don Mattingly Pants/250 8.00 20.00
124 Miguel Cabrera Jsy/250 3.00 8.00
125 Rafael Palmeiro Jsy/250 3.00 8.00
126 David Ortiz Jsy/250 3.00 8.00
127 Vladimir Guerrero Jsy/250 3.00 8.00
128 Ken Harvey Jsy/250 2.00 5.00
129 Rod Carew Jsy/250 4.00 10.00
130 Magglio Ordonez Jsy/250 2.00 5.00
131 Greg Maddux Jsy/250 5.00 12.00
132 Roy Halladay Jsy/250 2.00 5.00
134 Kerry Wood Jsy/250 2.00 5.00
135 Frank Thomas Jsy/250 3.00 8.00
136 Curt Schilling Jsy/250 3.00 8.00
139 Dewon Brazelton Jsy/100 2.00 5.00
140 Jae Weong Seo Jsy/100 2.00 5.00
141 Danny Kolb Jsy/250 2.00 5.00
142 Jeff Kent Jsy/100 2.00 5.00
144 Adam Dunn Jsy/250 2.00 5.00
145 Carlos Lee Jsy/250 2.00 5.00
146 Matt Clement Jsy/250 2.00 5.00
148 Travis Hafner Jsy/250 2.00 5.00
151 Randy Johnson Pants/250 3.00 8.00
154 Jason Varitek Jsy/100 4.00 10.00
157 Fran Rodriguez Jsy/100 2.00 5.00
158 Gary Carter Jsy/100 3.00 8.00
161 Mark Prior Jsy/250 3.00 8.00
162 Carlos Zambrano Jsy/100 3.00 8.00
163 Bobby Crosby Jsy/250 2.00 5.00
164 Jermaine Dye Jsy/100 2.00 5.00
166 Dontrelle Willis Jsy/250 2.00 5.00
168 Johnny Estrada Jsy/250 2.00 5.00
170 Shannon Stewart Jsy/100 2.00 5.00
171 Ben Sheets Jsy/250 2.00 5.00
173 Laynce Nix Jsy/250 2.00 5.00
175 Craig Wilson Jsy/100 2.00 5.00
176 Hideo Nomo Jsy/250 3.00 8.00
177 Troy Glaus Jsy/250 2.00 5.00
180 Mike Lowell Jsy/250 2.00 5.00
181 Marcus Giles Jsy/5
183 A.J. Burnett Jsy/100 2.00 5.00
184 Aubrey Huff Jsy/100 2.00 5.00
187 Kazuhisa Ishii Jsy/250 2.00 5.00
188 Mark Teixeira Jsy/250 3.00 8.00
190 Dale Murphy Jsy/250 4.00 10.00
194 Shawn Green Jsy/250 2.00 5.00
195 Andy Pettitte Jsy/250 3.00 8.00
196 Chipper Jones Jsy/250 3.00 8.00
197 Jose Vidro Jsy/100 2.00 5.00
198 Jacque Jones Jsy/250 2.00 5.00
199 Brian Giles Jsy/5
200 Andruw Jones Jsy/250 3.00 8.00

2005 Leaf Century Signature Post Marks Gold

*GOLD p/r 50: .6X TO 1.5X SILV p/r 250
*GOLD p/r 50: .5X TO 1.2X SILV p/r 100
*GOLD p/r 25: .75X TO 2X SILV p/r 250
*GOLD p/r 25: .6X TO 1.5X SILV p/r 100
*GOLD p/r 25: .5X TO 1.2X SILV p/r 50
OVERALL INSERT ODDS 1:3
PRINT RUNS B/WN 1-50 COPIES PER
NO PRICING ON QTY OF 10 OR LESS

2005 Leaf Century Signature Post Marks Platinum

OVERALL INSERT ODDS 1:3
STATED PRINT RUN 1 SERIAL #'d SET
NO PRICING DUE TO SCARCITY

2005 Leaf Century Signature Post Marks Silver

OVERALL INSERT ODDS 1:3
PRINT RUNS B/WN 1-250 COPIES PER
NO PRICING ON QTY OF 10 OR LESS
1 Brian Roberts/250 6.00 15.00
3 Harmon Killebrew/1
4 Angel Berroa/25 6.00 15.00
5 George Brett/1
6 Stan Musial/1
8 Cal Ripken/1
9 Hank Blalock/5
12 Alfonso Soriano/5
14 Paul Konerko/10
15 Jim Edmonds/1
16 Garret Anderson/5
17 Todd Helton/1
19 Tony Gwynn/1
20 Mike Schmidt/1
21 Sammy Sosa/1
22 Roger Clemens/1
23 Tony Perez/5
24 Manny Ramirez/1
27 Scott Rolen/1
28 Austin Kearns/1
31 Mike Piazza/1
32 Steve Carlton/1
34 Nolan Ryan/1
35 Mike Mussina/1
36 Joe Nathan/250 10.00 25.00
39 Brett Myers/250 6.00 15.00
40 Rich Harden/100 6.00 15.00
41 Victor Martinez/5
43 Dennis Eckersley/1
44 Roy Oswalt/5
45 Pedro Martinez/1
46 Jason Bay/5
47 Tom Glavine/1
48 Torii Hunter/1
49 Larry Bigbie/250 6.00 15.00
52 C.C. Sabathia/25 10.00 25.00
56 Mark Buehrle/50 15.00 40.00
57 Johan Santana/5
59 Edgar Martinez/1
61 Livan Hernandez/250 8.00 20.00
62 Eric Chavez/1
63 Lyle Overbay/100 4.00 10.00
65 Cliff Lee/250 10.00 25.00
66 Shingo Takatsu/5
67 Jeff Bagwell/1
68 Danny Graves/100 4.00 10.00
70 Steve Finley/5
71 Lew Ford/100 4.00 10.00
72 Chone Figgins/250 6.00 15.00
73 Delmon Young/1
74 Esteban Loaiza/250 6.00 15.00
75 Barry Zito/1
78 Ryan Wagner/250 4.00 10.00
79 John Lackey/250 6.00 15.00
80 Adrian Beltre/1
81 Vernon Wells/1
82 Sean Burroughs/25 6.00 15.00
83 Francisco Cordero/100 6.00 15.00
85 Eric Byrnes/100 4.00 10.00
86 Jose Reyes/1
88 Josh Beckett/1
89 Casey Kotchman/250 6.00 15.00
90 Scott Podsednik/100 10.00 25.00
93 Trot Nixon/25 10.00 25.00
94 Chad Cordero/250 6.00 15.00
97 Jose Guillen/100 6.00 15.00
98 Craig Biggio/1
101 Rafael Furcal/1
102 Jack Wilson/100 6.00 15.00
103 Edgar Renteria/1
104 Carlos Beltran/1
105 Albert Pujols/1
106 Melvin Mora/100 6.00 15.00
108 Andre Dawson/25 10.00 25.00
109 Jody Gerut/250 4.00 10.00
110 Michael Young/5
111 Gary Sheffield/1
112 Wade Boggs/1
113 Carl Crawford/5
114 Paul Lo Duca/1
115 Tim Hudson/1
116 Aramis Ramirez/25 10.00 25.00
117 Lance Berkman/1
119 Robin Yount/1
120 Mark Mulder/1
121 Sean Casey/1
122 Will Clark/1
123 Don Mattingly/1
124 Miguel Cabrera/5
125 Rafael Palmeiro/1
126 David Ortiz/5
128 Ken Harvey/250 4.00 10.00
129 Rod Carew/1
130 Magglio Ordonez/1
131 Greg Maddux/1
132 Roy Halladay/1
134 Kerry Wood/1
135 Frank Thomas/1
136 Tom Gordon/250 6.00 15.00
137 Jake Peavy/100 10.00 25.00
138 Curt Schilling/1
139 Dewon Brazelton/250 4.00 10.00
140 Jae Weong Seo/100 6.00 15.00
141 Danny Kolb/250 4.00 10.00
144 Adam Dunn/1
145 Carlos Lee/100 6.00 15.00
146 Matt Clement/1
147 Guillermo Mota/250 4.00 10.00
148 Travis Hafner/100 6.00 15.00
151 Randy Johnson/1
152 Joe Crede/6
154 Jason Varitek/5
155 David Wright/25 40.00 80.00
156 Brad Penny/250 4.00 10.00
157 Francisco Rodriguez/100 10.00 25.00
158 Gary Carter/1
159 Adrian Gonzalez/250 10.00 25.00
160 Derrek Lee/25 15.00 40.00
161 Mark Prior/1
162 Carlos Zambrano/25 10.00 25.00
163 Bobby Crosby/100 6.00 15.00
164 Jermaine Dye/100 6.00 15.00
166 Dontrelle Willis/1
168 Johnny Estrada/200 4.00 10.00
169 Milton Bradley/100 6.00 15.00
170 Shannon Stewart/50 8.00 20.00
171 Ben Sheets/1
173 Laynce Nix/250 4.00 10.00
174 B.J. Upton/10
175 Craig Wilson/100 4.00 10.00
176 Hideo Nomo/1
178 Akinori Otsuka/5
179 Rickie Weeks/1
180 Mike Lowell/1
181 Marcus Giles/25 10.00 25.00
182 Randy Wolf/250 4.00 10.00
184 Aubrey Huff/100 6.00 15.00
185 Billy Ripken/250 4.00 10.00
186 Octavio Dotel/250 6.00 15.00
187 Kazuhisa Ishii/1
188 Mark Teixeira/1
189 Todd Walker/100 6.00 15.00
190 Dale Murphy/5
191 Alexis Rios/200 6.00 15.00
193 Orlando Cabrera/25 10.00 25.00
194 Shawn Green/1
195 Andy Pettitte/1
196 Chipper Jones/1
197 Jose Vidro/25 10.00 25.00
198 Jacque Jones/100 6.00 15.00
200 Andruw Jones/1

2005 Leaf Century Air Mail Bat

OVERALL INSERT ODDS 1:3
PRINT RUNS B/WN 50-250 COPIES PER
1 Babe Ruth/50 100.00 200.00
2 Frank Robinson/250 3.00 8.00
3 Harmon Killebrew/100 8.00 20.00
4 Sammy Sosa/100 4.00 10.00
5 Reggie Jackson/250 4.00 10.00
6 Mike Schmidt/100 10.00 25.00
7 Rafael Palmeiro/100 3.00 8.00
8 Ted Williams/50 60.00 120.00
9 Willie McCovey/250 4.00 10.00
10 Ernie Banks/100 6.00 15.00

2005 Leaf Century Air Mail Bat Signature

OVERALL INSERT ODDS 1:3
PRINT RUNS B/WN 1-25 COPIES PER
NO PRICING ON QTY OF 5 OR LESS
2 Frank Robinson/25 20.00 50.00
3 Harmon Killebrew/25 50.00 100.00
4 Sammy Sosa/1
5 Reggie Jackson/1
6 Mike Schmidt/5
7 Rafael Palmeiro/1
9 Willie McCovey/25 20.00 50.00
10 Ernie Banks/5

2005 Leaf Century Pennant Patches

OVERALL INSERT ODDS 1:3
PRINT RUNS B/WN 5-25 COPIES PER
NO PRICING ON QTY OF 10 OR LESS
1 Ozzie Smith/25 20.00 50.00
2 Keith Hernandez/25 10.00 25.00
3 Rickey Henderson/25 15.00 40.00
4 Paul Molitor/25 10.00 25.00
5 George Brett/25 30.00 60.00
6 Steve Garvey/25 10.00 25.00
7 Randy Johnson/25 12.50 30.00
8 Cal Ripken/25 60.00 120.00
9 Darryl Strawberry/25 10.00 25.00
10 Chipper Jones/25 15.00 40.00
11 Steve Carlton/25 10.00 25.00
12 Orel Hershiser/25 10.00 25.00
13 Carlton Fisk/25 12.50 30.00
14 Dave Parker/25 10.00 25.00
15 Rollie Fingers/25 10.00 25.00
16 Dwight Gooden/25 10.00 25.00
17 Mark Grace/10
18 Dontrelle Willis/25 6.00 15.00
19 Dave Righetti/25 10.00 25.00
20 Brooks Robinson/5

2005 Leaf Century Pennant Patches Signature

OVERALL INSERT ODDS 1:3
PRINT RUNS B/WN 5-25 COPIES PER
NO PRICING ON QTY OF 10 OR LESS
1 Ozzie Smith/5
2 Keith Hernandez/25 20.00 50.00
3 Rickey Henderson/5
4 Paul Molitor/10
5 George Brett/5
6 Steve Garvey/25 20.00 50.00
7 Randy Johnson/5
8 Cal Ripken/5
9 Darryl Strawberry/25 20.00 50.00
10 Chipper Jones/5
11 Steve Carlton/25 20.00 50.00
12 Orel Hershiser/5
13 Carlton Fisk/5
14 Dave Parker/10
15 Rollie Fingers/25 20.00 50.00
16 Dwight Gooden/25 20.00 50.00
17 Mark Grace/5
18 Dontrelle Willis/5
19 Dave Righetti/10
20 Brooks Robinson/5

2005 Leaf Century Shirts

OVERALL INSERT ODDS 1:3
PRINT RUNS B/WN 25-100 COPIES PER
1 Rod Carew/100 5.00 12.00
2 Red Schoendienst/50 4.00 10.00
3 Harmon Killebrew/50 10.00 25.00
4 Joe Cronin/50 20.00 50.00
5 Early Wynn/50 4.00 10.00
6 Gaylord Perry/100 3.00 8.00
7 Willie McCovey/100 5.00 12.00
8 Carl Yastrzemski/100 10.00 25.00
9 Reggie Jackson/100 5.00 12.00
10 Duke Snider/50 6.00 15.00
11 Luis Aparicio/100 3.00 8.00
12 Bob Gibson/50 6.00 15.00
13 Maury Wills/50 4.00 10.00
14 Ernie Banks/50 8.00 20.00
15 Enos Slaughter/100 8.00 20.00
16 Whitey Ford/100 6.00 15.00
17 Warren Spahn/100 8.00 20.00
18 Roger Maris/100 20.00 50.00
19 Hal Newhouser/100 6.00 15.00
20 Marty Marion/25 6.00 15.00

2005 Leaf Century Shirts Signature

PRINT RUNS B/WN 1-50 COPIES PER
NO PRICING ON QTY OF 10 OR LESS
PRIME PRINT RUN 1 SERIAL #'d SET
NO PRIME PRICING DUE TO SCARCITY
OVERALL INSERT ODDS 1:3
1 Rod Carew/5
2 Red Schoendienst/25 12.50 30.00
3 Harmon Killebrew/10
6 Gaylord Perry/50 10.00 25.00
7 Willie McCovey/50 15.00 40.00
8 Carl Yastrzemski/5
9 Reggie Jackson/5
10 Duke Snider/5
11 Luis Aparicio/50 10.00 25.00
12 Bob Gibson/5
13 Maury Wills/50 10.00 25.00
14 Ernie Banks/5
16 Whitey Ford/5
17 Warren Spahn/1
20 Marty Marion/5

2005 Leaf Century Stamps Material Centennial

*CTL p/r 39: .5X TO 1.2X USA p/r 72-100
*CTL p/r 39: .4X TO 1X USA p/r 44-48
*CTL p/r 39: .3X TO .8X USA p/r 20-28
*CTL p/r 21: .4X TO 1X USA p/r 20-28
*CTL p/r 16: .4X TO 1X USA p/r 16
OVERALL INSERT ODDS 1:3
PRINT RUNS B/WN 1-39 COPIES PER
NO PRICING ON QTY OF 11 OR LESS
COOP.STAMP ON 1ST #'d COPY PER CARD
3 Babe Ruth Jsy/39 250.00 400.00
8 Ted Williams Jsy/39 125.00 200.00
12 Dave Concepcion Jsy/39 8.00 20.00
23 Roger Maris Jsy/39 40.00 80.00
60 Lou Boudreau Jsy/39 12.50 30.00
61 Alan Trammell Bat/39 8.00 20.00
69 Michael Young Jsy/39 8.00 20.00

2005 Leaf Century Stamps Material Legendary Fields

*LGD FLD p/r 34: .6X TO 1.5X USA p/r 72-100
*LGD FLD p/r 34: .5X TO 1.2X USA p/r 44-48
*LGD FLD p/r 34: .4X TO 1X USA p/r 20-28
*LGD FLD p/r 34: .3X TO .8X USA p/r 16
*LGD FLD p/r 21: .4X TO 1X USA p/r 20-28
OVERALL INSERT ODDS 1:3
PRINT RUNS B/WN 1-34 COPIES PER
NO PRICING ON QTY OF 11 OR LESS
COOP.STAMP ON 1ST #'d COPY PER CARD
12 Dave Concepcion Jsy/34 10.00 25.00
23 Roger Maris Jsy/34 40.00 80.00
61 Alan Trammell Bat/34 10.00 25.00
74 Kirk Gibson Jsy/34 30.00 60.00

2005 Leaf Century Stamps Material Legendary Players 20

*LGD PLY p/r 21: .4X TO 1X USA p/r 21
OVERALL INSERT ODDS 1:3
PRINT RUNS B/WN 19-21 COPIES PER
20-CENT STAMP FEATURED
COOP.STAMP ON 1ST #'d COPY PER CARD
3 Babe Ruth Jsy/19 300.00 500.00

2005 Leaf Century Stamps Material Legendary Players 33

*LGD PLY p/r 21: .4X TO 1X USA p/r 21
OVERALL INSERT ODDS 1:3
PRINT RUNS B/WN 19-21 COPIES PER
33-CENT STAMP FEATURED
COOP.STAMP ON 1ST #'d COPY PER CARD
3 Babe Ruth Jsy/19 300.00 500.00

2005 Leaf Century Stamps Material Olympic

*OLY p/r 92: .4X TO 1X USA p/r 72-100
*OLY p/r 92: .3X TO .8X USA p/r 44-48
*OLY p/r 92: .25X TO .6X USA p/r 20-28
*OLY p/r 44-48: .5X TO 1.2X USA p/r 72-100
*OLY p/r 44-48: .4X TO 1X USA p/r 44-48
*OLY p/r 20-30: .6X TO 1.5X USA p/r 72-100
*OLY p/r 20-30: .4X TO 1X USA p/r 20-28
*OLY p/r 16: .4X TO 1X USA p/r 16
OVERALL INSERT ODDS 1:3
PRINT RUNS B/WN 1-92 COPIES PER
NO PRICING ON QTY OF 13 OR LESS
COOP.STAMP ON 1ST #'d COPY PER CARD
60 Lou Boudreau Jsy/92 10.00 25.00
61 Alan Trammell Bat/92 6.00 15.00

2005 Leaf Century Stamps Material Pro Ball

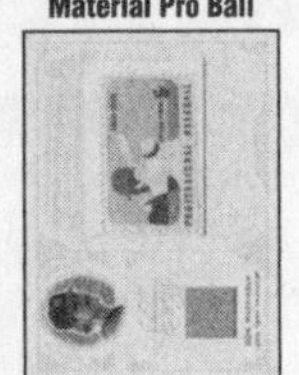

*PRO p/r 69: .4X TO 1X USA p/r 72-100
*PRO p/r 69: .3X TO .8X USA p/r 44-48
*PRO p/r 69: .25X TO .6X USA p/r 20-28
*PRO p/r 45-48: .5X TO 1.2X USA p/r 72-100
*PRO p/r 45-48: .4X TO 1X USA p/r 44-48
*PRO p/r 20-27: .6X TO 1.5X USA p/r 72-100
*PRO p/r 20-27: .4X TO 1X USA p/r 20-28
*PRO p/r 16: .4X TO 1X USA p/r 16
OVERALL INSERT ODDS 1:3
COOP.STAMP ON 1ST #'d COPY PER CARD
60 Lou Boudreau Jsy/69 10.00 25.00
61 Alan Trammell Bat/69 6.00 15.00

2005 Leaf Century Stamps Material USA Flag

OVERALL INSERT ODDS 1:3
PRINT RUNS B/WN 1-100 COPIES PER
NO PRICING ON QTY OF 13 OR LESS
COOP.STAMP ON 1ST #'d COPY PER CARD
1 Pee Wee Reese Bat/100 8.00 20.00
2 Red Schoendienst Jsy/2
3 Babe Ruth Jsy/3
4 George Brett Jsy/100 15.00 40.00
5 Stan Musial Bat/100 12.50 30.00
6 Bob Feller Pants/100 8.00 20.00
7 Cal Ripken Pants/100 40.00 80.00
8 Ted Williams Jsy/9
9 Phil Rizzuto Jsy/1
10 Luis Aparicio Pants/11
11 Dwight Evans Jsy/24 12.50 30.00
12 Dave Concepcion Jsy/13
13 Ernie Banks Jsy/100 10.00 25.00
14 Pedro Martinez Jsy/45 10.00 25.00
15 Whitey Ford Jsy/16 15.00 40.00
16 Scott Rolen Jsy/27 12.50 30.00
17 Tony Gwynn Jsy/100 12.50 30.00
18 Mike Schmidt Jsy/100 20.00 50.00
19 Roberto Clemente Hat/21 75.00 150.00
20 Roger Clemens Jsy/100 10.00 25.00
21 Don Mattingly Jsy/100 15.00 40.00
22 Tony Perez Bat/100 6.00 15.00
23 Roger Maris Jsy/9
24 Billy Williams Jsy/100 6.00 15.00
25 Juan Marichal Pants/100 6.00 15.00
26 Hank Blalock Jsy/100 6.00 15.00
27 Maury Wills Jsy/100 6.00 15.00
28 Fergie Jenkins Pants/100 6.00 15.00
29 Steve Carlton Jsy/100 6.00 15.00
30 Dale Murphy Jsy/100 8.00 20.00
31 Kerry Wood Jsy/100 6.00 15.00
32 Gaylord Perry Jsy/100 6.00 15.00
33 Fred Lynn Jsy/100 6.00 15.00
34 Tom Seaver Bat/100 8.00 20.00
36 Reggie Jackson Pants/44 10.00 25.00
37 Bob Gibson Jsy/100 8.00 20.00
38 Jack Morris Jsy/100 6.00 15.00
39 Torii Hunter Jsy/48 8.00 20.00
40 Andre Dawson Jsy/100 6.00 15.00
41 Dave Righetti Jsy/100 6.00 15.00
42 Hideki Matsui Pants/100 20.00 50.00
43 Lou Brock Jkt/100 8.00 20.00
44 Yogi Berra Bat/100 10.00 25.00
45 Frankie Frisch Jkt/100 10.00 25.00
46 Sean Casey Jsy/100 6.00 15.00
47 Sammy Sosa Jsy/100 10.00 25.00
48 Ralph Kiner Bat/100 6.00 15.00
49 Hoyt Wilhelm Jsy/100 6.00 15.00
50 Jim Rice Jsy/100 6.00 15.00
51 Duke Snider Pants/100 10.00 25.00
52 Harold Baines Jsy/100 6.00 15.00
53 Willie Stargell Jsy/100 8.00 20.00
54 Johnny Bench Pants/100 10.00 25.00
55 Carlton Fisk Jsy/72 8.00 20.00
56 Jim Palmer Jsy/100 6.00 15.00
57 Bobby Doerr Jsy/100 6.00 15.00
58 Mark Prior Jsy/100 8.00 20.00
60 Lou Boudreau Jsy/5
61 Alan Trammell Bat/3
62 Al Kaline Bat/100 10.00 25.00
63 Warren Spahn Pants/100 10.00 25.00
64 Bert Blyleven Jsy/28 10.00 25.00
65 Miguel Cabrera Jsy/24 12.50 30.00
66 Luis Tiant Jsy/23 10.00 25.00
67 Harmon Killebrew Jsy/100 15.00 40.00
68 Richie Ashburn Pants/100 10.00 25.00
69 Michael Young Jsy/10
70 Tony Oliva Jsy/100 6.00 15.00
71 Mark Mulder Jsy/20 10.00 25.00
72 Nolan Ryan Jsy/100 30.00 60.00
73 Willie McCovey Jsy/44 10.00 25.00
74 Kirk Gibson Jsy/100 6.00 15.00
75 Carl Yastrzemski Pants/100 12.50 30.00

2005 Leaf Century Stamps Signature Centennial

*CTL p/r 39-59: .5X TO 1.2X USA p/r 100
*CTL p/r 39-59: .4X TO 1X USA p/r 48-49
*CTL p/r 39-59: .3X TO .8X USA p/r 20-27
*CTL p/r 39-59: .25X TO .6X USA p/r 19
*CTL p/r 20-27: .4X TO 1X USA p/r 20-27
OVERALL INSERT ODDS 1:3
PRINT RUNS B/WN 1-59 COPIES PER
NO PRICING ON QTY OF 10 OR LESS
COOP.STAMP ON 1ST #'d COPY PER CARD

2005 Leaf Century Stamps Signature Legendary Fields

*LGD FLD p/r 23-34: .6X TO 1.5X USA p/r 100
*LGD FLDp/r23-34: .5X TO 1.2X USA p/r 48-49
*LGD FLD p/r 23-34: .4X TO 1X USA p/r 20-27

*LGD FLD p/r 23-34: .3X TO .8X USA p/r 19
OVERALL INSERT ODDS 1:3
PRINT RUNS B/WN 1-34 COPIES PER
NO PRICING ON QTY OF 10 OR LESS
COOP.STAMP ON 1ST #'d COPY PER CARD
50 Jim Rice/34 15.00 40.00

2005 Leaf Century Stamps Signature Olympic

*OLY p/r 91-92: .4X TO 1X USA p/r 100
*OLY p/r 91-92: .25X TO .6X USA p/r 20-27
*OLY p/r 48: .4X TO 1X USA p/r 48-49
*OLY p/r 20-27: .4X TO 1X USA p/r 20-27
*OLY p/r 19: .4X TO 1X USA p/r 19
OVERALL INSERT ODDS 1:3
PRINT RUNS B/WN 1-34 COPIES PER
NO PRICING ON QTY OF 10 OR LESS
COOP.STAMP ON 1ST #'d COPY PER CARD
50 Jim Rice/92 10.00 25.00

2005 Leaf Century Stamps Signature Pro Ball

*PRO p/r 69: .4X TO 1X USA p/r 100
*PRO p/r 69: .25X TO .6X USA p/r 20-27
*PRO p/r 47-49: .5X TO 1.2X USA p/r 100
*PRO p/r 47-49: .4X TO 1X USA p/r 48-49
*PRO p/r 20-28: .6X TO 1.5X USA p/r 100
*PRO p/r 20-28: .4X TO 1X USA p/r 20-27
*PRO p/r 19: .4X TO 1X USA p/r 19
OVERALL INSERT ODDS 1:3
PRINT RUNS B/WN 1-69 COPIES PER
NO PRICING ON QTY OF 14 OR LESS
COOP.STAMP ON 1ST #'d COPY PER CARD

2005 Leaf Century Stamps Signature USA Flag

OVERALL INSERT ODDS 1:3
PRINT RUNS B/WN 1-100 COPIES PER
NO PRICING ON QTY OF 14 OR LESS
COOP.STAMP ON 1ST #'d COPY PER CARD
2 Red Schoendienst/100 10.00 25.00
4 George Brett/1
5 Stan Musial/1
6 Bob Feller/100 12.50 30.00
7 Cal Ripken/1
9 Phil Rizzuto/10
11 Dwight Evans/24 20.00 50.00
15 Whitey Ford/1
17 Tony Gwynn/1
18 Mike Schmidt/1
21 Don Mattingly/1
22 Tony Perez/24 20.00 50.00
24 Billy Williams/26 15.00 40.00
25 Juan Marichal/27 15.00 40.00
27 Maury Wills/100 10.00 25.00
28 Fergie Jenkins/100 10.00 25.00
29 Steve Carlton/100 10.00 25.00
30 Dale Murphy/100 12.50 30.00
31 Kerry Wood/1
32 Gaylord Perry/100 10.00 25.00
33 Fred Lynn/100 10.00 25.00
35 Ron Guidry/49 15.00 40.00
36 Reggie Jackson/1
37 Bob Gibson/10
38 Jack Morris/100 8.00 20.00
39 Torii Hunter/48 10.00 25.00
40 Andre Dawson/100 10.00 25.00
41 Dave Righetti/19 15.00 40.00
43 Lou Brock/20 20.00 50.00
44 Yogi Berra/1
46 Sean Casey/21 15.00 40.00
48 Ralph Kiner/100 15.00 40.00
50 Jim Rice/14
51 Duke Snider/25 20.00 50.00
52 Harold Baines/100 10.00 25.00
54 Johnny Bench/1
56 Jim Palmer/22 20.00 50.00
57 Bobby Doerr/100 10.00 25.00
58 Mark Prior/1
59 Monte Irvin/100 10.00 25.00
61 Alan Trammell/100 10.00 25.00
62 Al Kaline/100 15.00 40.00
64 Bert Blyleven/100 10.00 25.00
65 Miguel Cabrera/24 20.00 50.00
66 Luis Tiant/100 8.00 20.00
67 Harmon Killebrew/3
69 Michael Young/10
70 Tony Oliva/100 10.00 25.00
71 Mark Mulder/20 15.00 40.00
72 Nolan Ryan/1
74 Kirk Gibson/3
75 Carl Yastrzemski/1

2005 Leaf Century Stamps Signature Material Centennial

*M.CTL p/r 39: .6X TO 1.5X USA p/r 100
*M.CTL p/r 39: .4X TO 1X USA p/r 20-27
*M.CTL p/r 20-24: .5X TO 1.2X USA p/r 20-27
*M.CTL p/r 19: .5X TO 1.2X USA p/r 19
OVERALL INSERT ODDS 1:3
COOP.STAMP ON 1ST #'d COPY PER CARD
37 Bob Gibson Jsy/39 20.00 50.00
50 Jim Rice Jsy/39 15.00 40.00
67 Harmon Killebrew Jsy/39 40.00 80.00
74 Kirk Gibson Jsy/39 15.00 40.00

2005 Leaf Century Stamps Signature Material Legendary Fields

*M.LGD FLDp/r23-34: .75X TO 2X USA p/r100
*M.LGD FLDp/r23-34: .5X TO 1.2XUSAp/r20-27
*M.LGD FLD p/r 23-34: .4X TO 1X USA p/r 19
OVERALL INSERT ODDS 1:3
PRINT RUNS B/WN 1-34 COPIES PER
NO PRICING ON QTY OF 6 OR LESS
COOP.STAMP ON 1ST #'d COPY PER CARD
50 Jim Rice Jsy/33 20.00 50.00
74 Kirk Gibson Jsy/23 20.00 50.00

2005 Leaf Century Stamps Signature Material Olympic

*M.OLY p/r 20-29: .75X TO 2X USA p/r 100
*M.OLY p/r 20-29: .5X TO 1.2X USA p/r 20-27
*M.OLY p/r 19: .5X TO 1.2X USA p/r 19
OVERALL INSERT ODDS 1:3
PRINT RUNS B/WN 1-29 COPIES PER
NO PRICING ON QTY OF 14 OR LESS
COOP.STAMP ON 1ST #'d COPY PER CARD
15 Whitey Ford Jsy/16 40.00 80.00
37 Bob Gibson Jsy/29 30.00 60.00
74 Kirk Gibson Jsy/23 20.00 50.00

2005 Leaf Century Stamps Signature Material Pro Ball

*M.PRO p/r 69: .5X TO 1.2X USA p/r 100
*M.PRO p/r 45-48: .6X TO 1.5X USA p/r 100
*M.PRO p/r 20-27: .75X TO 2X USA p/r 100
*M.PRO p/r 20-27: .5X TO 1.2X USA p/r 20-27
*M.PRO p/r 19: .5X TO 1.2X USA p/r 19
OVERALL INSERT ODDS 1:3
PRINT RUNS B/WN 1-69 COPIES PER
NO PRICING ON QTY OF 14 OR LESS
COOP.STAMP ON 1ST #'d COPY PER CARD
37 Bob Gibson Jsy/45 20.00 50.00
74 Kirk Gibson Jsy/23 20.00 50.00

2005 Leaf Century Stamps Signature Material USA Flag

*M.USA p/r 37: .6X TO 1.5X USA p/r 100
*M.USA p/r 37: .4X TO 1X USA p/r 20-27
*M.USA p/r 37: .3X TO .8X USA p/r 19
OVERALL INSERT ODDS 1:3
PRINT RUNS B/WN 1-37 COPIES PER
NO PRICING ON QTY OF 10 OR LESS
COOP.STAMP ON 1ST #'d COPY PER CARD
74 Kirk Gibson Jsy/23 20.00 50.00

2005 Leaf Century Stamps Signature Material Prime Centennial

OVERALL INSERT ODDS 1:3
PRINT RUNS B/WN 1-3 COPIES PER
NO PRICING DUE TO SCARCITY
COOP.STAMP ON 1ST #'d COPY PER CARD

2005 Leaf Century Stamps Signature Material Prime Legendary Fields

OVERALL INSERT ODDS 1:3
STATED PRINT RUN 1 SERIAL #'d SET
NO PRICING DUE TO SCARCITY
COOP.STAMP ON 1ST #'d COPY PER CARD

2005 Leaf Century Stamps Signature Material Prime Olympic

OVERALL INSERT ODDS 1:3
PRINT RUNS B/WN 1-10 COPIES PER
NO PRICING DUE TO SCARCITY
COOP.STAMP ON 1ST #'d COPY PER CARD

2005 Leaf Century Stamps Signature Material Prime Pro Ball

OVERALL INSERT ODDS 1:3
PRINT RUNS B/WN 1-6 COPIES PER
NO PRICING DUE TO SCARCITY
COOP.STAMP ON 1ST #'d COPY PER CARD

2005 Leaf Century Stamps Signature Material Prime USA Flag

OVERALL INSERT ODDS 1:3
PRINT RUNS B/WN 1-10 COPIES PER
NO PRICING DUE TO SCARCITY
COOP.STAMP ON 1ST #'d COPY PER CARD

2005 Leaf Century Stamps Masterpiece Signature Centennial

OVERALL INSERT ODDS 1:3
PRINT RUNS B/WN 1-3 COPIES PER
NO PRICING DUE TO SCARCITY

2005 Leaf Century Timeline Threads Jersey Number

*NBR p/r 36-65: .6X TO 1.5X POS p/r 66-125
*NBR p/r 20-35: 1X TO 2.5X POS p/r 66-125
*NBR p/r 20-35: .6X TO 1.5X POS p/r 36-65
*NBR p/r 15-19: 1.25X TO 3X POS p/r 66-125
*NBR p/r 15-19: .75X TO 2X POS p/r 36-65
OVERALL INSERT ODDS 1:3
PRINT RUNS B/WN 1-51 COPIES PER
NO PRICING ON QTY OF 14 OR LESS
40 Sandy Koufax Jsy/32 75.00 150.00

2005 Leaf Century Timeline Threads Position

PRINT RUNS B/WN 26-103 COPIES PER
PRIME PRINT RUN 1 SERIAL #'d SET
NO PRIME PRICING DUE TO SCARCITY
OVERALL INSERT ODDS 1:3
1 Bobby Doerr Jsy/39 4.00 10.00
2 Burleigh Grimes Pants/26 30.00 60.00
3 Babe Ruth Pants/30 150.00 250.00
4 Joe Cronin Pants/38 10.00 25.00
5 Johnny Bench Pants/71 6.00 15.00
6 Orlando Cepeda Pants/62 4.00 10.00
7 Ivan Rodriguez Jsy/103 3.00 8.00
8 Cal Ripken Jsy/98 30.00 60.00
9 Tony Perez Jsy/78 3.00 8.00
10 Andre Dawson Jsy/86 3.00 8.00
11 Tommy John Jsy/86 3.00 8.00
12 Alfonso Soriano Jsy/102 2.00 5.00
13 Ozzie Smith Jsy/78 10.00 25.00
14 Ernie Banks Jsy/70 6.00 15.00
15 Carlton Fisk Jsy/80 5.00 12.00
16 Bo Jackson Jsy/89 6.00 15.00
17 Bert Blyleven Jsy/83 3.00 8.00
18 Darryl Strawberry Jsy/88 3.00 8.00
19 Bob Feller Pants/36 6.00 15.00
20 Lou Brock Jsy/74 5.00 12.00
21 Sammy Sosa Jsy/103 4.00 10.00
22 Roger Clemens Jsy/101 6.00 15.00
23 Don Mattingly Jsy/94 10.00 25.00
24 Rickey Henderson Jsy/83 6.00 15.00
25 Albert Pujols Jsy/103 8.00 20.00
26 Wade Boggs Jsy/87 5.00 12.00
27 Joe Morgan Jsy/82 3.00 8.00
28 Gary Carter Jsy/86 3.00 8.00
29 Catfish Hunter Jsy/78 5.00 12.00
30 Maury Wills Jsy/65 4.00 10.00
31 Hoyt Wilhelm Jsy/68 3.00 8.00
32 Matt Williams Jsy/95 3.00 8.00
33 Eddie Murray Pants/88 8.00 20.00
34 Nolan Ryan Pants/90 12.50 30.00
35 Phil Niekro Jsy/80 3.00 8.00
36 Paul Molitor Jsy/96 3.00 8.00
37 Dale Murphy Jsy/83 5.00 12.00
38 Curt Schilling Jsy/99 3.00 8.00
39 Fred Lynn Jsy/75 3.00 8.00
40 Sandy Koufax Jsy/64 75.00 150.00
41 Don Sutton Jsy/76 3.00 8.00
42 Randy Johnson Jsy/98 4.00 10.00
43 Dennis Eckersley Jsy/97 3.00 8.00
44 Frank Thomas Jsy/94 4.00 10.00
45 Mike Mussina Jsy/100 3.00 8.00
46 Greg Maddux Jsy/96 6.00 15.00
47 Jim Palmer Pants/76 3.00 8.00
48 Harmon Killebrew Jsy/62 10.00 25.00
49 Mike Piazza Jsy/99 4.00 10.00
50 Billy Martin Jsy/83 5.00 12.00

2005 Leaf Century Timeline Threads Signature Position

*SIG NBR: .4X TO 1X SIG POS
PRINT RUNS B/WN 1-19 COPIES PER
NO PRICING ON QTY OF 14 OR LESS
PRIME PRINT RUN 1 SERIAL #'d SET
NO PRIME PRICING DUE TO SCARCITY
OVERALL INSERT ODDS 1:3
1 Bobby Doerr Jsy/19 15.00 40.00
5 Johnny Bench Pants/5
6 Orlando Cepeda Pants/19 15.00 40.00
8 Cal Ripken Jsy/8
9 Tony Perez Jsy/19 30.00 60.00
10 Andre Dawson Jsy/10
11 Tommy John Jsy/19 15.00 40.00
12 Alfonso Soriano Jsy/12
13 Ozzie Smith Jsy/19 40.00 80.00
14 Ernie Banks Jsy/14
15 Carlton Fisk Jsy/1
16 Bo Jackson Jsy/16 60.00 120.00
17 Bert Blyleven Jsy/19 15.00 40.00
18 Darryl Strawberry Jsy/18 15.00 40.00
19 Bob Feller Pants/19 30.00 60.00
20 Lou Brock Jsy/19 30.00 60.00
21 Sammy Sosa Jsy/1
22 Roger Clemens Jsy/1
23 Don Mattingly Jsy/19 60.00 120.00
24 Rickey Henderson Jsy/1
25 Albert Pujols Jsy/5
26 Wade Boggs Jsy/1
27 Joe Morgan Jsy/8
28 Gary Carter Jsy/8
30 Maury Wills Jsy/19 15.00 40.00
31 Hoyt Wilhelm Jsy/19 30.00 60.00
32 Matt Williams Jsy/1
33 Eddie Murray Pants/1
34 Nolan Ryan Pants/19 75.00 150.00
35 Phil Niekro Jsy/19 15.00 40.00
36 Paul Molitor Jsy/4
37 Dale Murphy Jsy/3
38 Curt Schilling Jsy/1
39 Fred Lynn Jsy/19 15.00 40.00
41 Don Sutton Jsy/19 15.00 40.00
42 Randy Johnson Jsy/1
43 Dennis Eckersley Jsy/19 15.00 40.00
44 Frank Thomas Jsy/1
45 Mike Mussina Jsy/1
46 Greg Maddux Jsy/1
47 Jim Palmer Pants/19 30.00 60.00
48 Harmon Killebrew Jsy/3
49 Mike Piazza Jsy/1

2004 Leaf Certified Cuts

This 300-card set was released in September, 2004. The first 200 cards in this set consist of veteran players. Cards 201-221 conists of players who switched teams in the off-season while cards 221-250 are retired legends of baseball and cards 251-300 all feature Rookie Cards. Cards numbered 201 through 250 were randomly inserted into packs and were issued to a stated print run of 599 serial numbered sets. Most cards from 251 through 300 were issued to a stated print run of 499 serial numbered sets and those cards were all autographed by the featured player except to Kazuo Matsui.

COMP.SET w/o SP's (200) 20.00 50.00
COMMON CARD (1-200) .30 .75
COMMON CARD (201-221) .60 1.50
COMMON CARD (222-250) .60 1.50
201-250 RANDOM INSERTS IN PACKS
201-250 PRNT RUN 599 SERIAL #'d SETS
COMMON CARD (251-300) .75 2.00
251-300 RANDOM INSERTS IN PACKS
251-300 PRINT RUN 499 SERIAL #'d SETS
COMMON AU p/r 299-499 3.00 8.00
COMMON AU p/r 199 4.00 10.00
OVERALL AU ODDS THREE PER BOX
AUTO PRINT RUNS B/WN 99-499 #'d PER
*OTSUKA JAPANESE SIG: .75X TO 2X HI
1 Vladimir Guerrero .75 2.00
2 Garret Anderson .30 .75
3 John Lackey .30 .75
4 Bartolo Colon .30 .75
5 Troy Glaus .30 .75
6 Tim Salmon .30 .75
7 Shea Hillenbrand .30 .75
8 Brandon Webb .30 .75
9 Roberto Alomar .50 1.25
10 Randy Johnson .75 2.00
11 Alex Cintron .30 .75
12 Richie Sexson .30 .75
13 Luis Gonzalez .30 .75
14 Adam LaRoche .30 .75
15 Rafael Furcal .30 .75
16 Chipper Jones .75 2.00
17 Marcus Giles .30 .75
18 Andruw Jones .30 .75
19 Russ Ortiz .30 .75
20 Rafael Palmeiro .50 1.25
21 Melvin Mora .30 .75
22 Luis Matos .30 .75
23 Jay Gibbons .30 .75
24 Adam Loewen .30 .75
25 Larry Bigbie .30 .75
26 Rodrigo Lopez .30 .75
27 Javy Lopez .30 .75
28 Miguel Tejada .50 1.25
29 Trot Nixon .30 .75
30 Curt Schilling .50 1.25
31 Jason Varitek .75 2.00
32 Manny Ramirez .75 2.00
33 Keith Foulke Sox .30 .75
34 Derek Lowe .30 .75
35 Pedro Martinez .50 1.25
36 Nomar Garciaparra .75 2.00
37 Bill Mueller .30 .75
38 Johnny Damon .50 1.25
39 David Ortiz .75 2.00
40 Mark Prior .50 1.25
41 Kerry Wood .30 .75
42 Sammy Sosa .75 2.00
43 Derrek Lee .30 .75
44 Greg Maddux 1.25 3.00
45 Aramis Ramirez .30 .75
46 Matt Clement .30 .75
47 Carlos Zambrano .50 1.25
48 Todd Walker .30 .75
49 Moises Alou .30 .75
50 Corey Patterson .30 .75
51 Frank Thomas .75 2.00
52 Magglio Ordonez .50 1.25
53 Carlos Lee .30 .75
54 Mark Buehrle .50 1.25
55 Esteban Loaiza .30 .75
56 Joe Crede .30 .75
57 Paul Konerko .50 1.25
58 Adam Dunn .50 1.25
59 Austin Kearns .30 .75
60 Barry Larkin .50 1.25
61 Ryan Wagner .30 .75
62 Danny Graves .30 .75
63 Sean Casey .30 .75
64 Ken Griffey Jr. 1.25 3.00
65 Jody Gerut .30 .75
66 Cliff Lee .50 1.25
67 Victor Martinez .50 1.25
68 C.C. Sabathia .50 1.25
69 Omar Vizquel .50 1.25
70 Travis Hafner .30 .75
71 Todd Helton .50 1.25
72 Preston Wilson .30 .75
73 Jeromy Burnitz .30 .75
74 Larry Walker .50 1.25
75 Ivan Rodriguez .50 1.25
76 Rondell White .30 .75
77 Miguel Cabrera .75 2.00
78 Luis Castillo .30 .75
79 Josh Beckett .50 1.25
80 Mike Lowell .30 .75
81 Dontrelle Willis .30 .75
82 Brad Penny .30 .75
83 Hee Seop Choi .30 .75
84 Juan Pierre .30 .75
85 Andy Pettitte .50 1.25
86 Jeff Bagwell .50 1.25
87 Roy Oswalt .50 1.25
88 Lance Berkman .50 1.25
89 Morgan Ensberg .30 .75
90 Craig Biggio .50 1.25
91 Octavio Dotel .30 .75
92 Wade Miller .30 .75
93 Jeff Kent .30 .75
94 Richard Hidalgo .30 .75
95 Roger Clemens 1.00 2.50
96 Carlos Beltran .30 .75
97 Angel Berroa .30 .75
98 Jeremy Affeldt .30 .75
99 Juan Gonzalez .30 .75
100 Mike Sweeney .30 .75
101 Kazuhisa Ishii .30 .75
102 Shawn Green .30 .75
103 Milton Bradley .30 .75
104 Paul Lo Duca .30 .75
105 Hideo Nomo .75 2.00
106 Eric Gagne .30 .75
107 Adrian Beltre .30 .75
108 Scott Podsednik .30 .75
109 Rickie Weeks .30 .75
110 Ben Sheets .30 .75
111 Geoff Jenkins .30 .75
112 Jacque Jones .30 .75
113 Johan Santana .75 2.00
114 Shannon Stewart .30 .75
115 Corey Koskie .30 .75
116 Lew Ford .30 .75
117 Torii Hunter .30 .75
118 Chad Cordero .30 .75
119 Orlando Cabrera .30 .75
120 Jose Vidro .30 .75
121 Nick Johnson .30 .75
122 Brad Wilkerson .30 .75
123 Mike Piazza .75 2.00
124 Jae Weong Seo .30 .75
125 Jose Reyes .50 1.25
126 Tom Glavine .50 1.25
127 Jorge Posada .50 1.25
128 Gary Sheffield .30 .75
129 Bernie Williams .50 1.25
130 Mike Mussina .50 1.25
131 Mariano Rivera .75 2.00
132 Bubba Crosby .30 .75
133 Kevin Brown .30 .75
134 Javier Vazquez .30 .75
135 Jason Giambi .30 .75
136 Derek Jeter 2.00 5.00
137 Alex Rodriguez 1.25 3.00
138 Hideki Matsui 1.25 3.00
139 Mark Mulder .30 .75
140 Jermaine Dye .30 .75
141 Tim Hudson .50 1.25
142 Barry Zito .30 .75
143 Eric Chavez .30 .75
144 Bobby Crosby .30 .75
145 Eric Byrnes .30 .75
146 Marlon Byrd .30 .75
147 Billy Wagner .30 .75
148 Mike Lieberthal .30 .75
149 Jimmy Rollins .50 1.25
150 Jim Thome .50 1.25
151 Bobby Abreu .30 .75
152 Pat Burrell .30 .75
153 Jose Castillo .30 .75
154 Craig Wilson .30 .75
155 Jason Bay .50 1.25
156 Jason Kendall .30 .75
157 Raul Mondesi .30 .75
158 Jay Payton .30 .75
159 Trevor Hoffman .50 1.25
160 Jake Peavy .30 .75
161 Sean Burroughs .30 .75
162 Phil Nevin .30 .75
163 Brian Giles .30 .75
164 Ryan Klesko .30 .75
165 Todd Linden .30 .75
166 Jerome Williams .30 .75
167 Jason Schmidt .30 .75
168 Ray Durham .30 .75
169 Marquis Grissom .30 .75
170 Shigetoshi Hasegawa .30 .75
171 Edgar Martinez .50 1.25
172 Freddy Garcia .30 .75
173 Bret Boone .30 .75
174 Raul Ibanez .30 .75
175 Ichiro Suzuki 1.25 3.00
176 Randy Winn .30 .75
177 Scott Rolen .50 1.25
178 Jim Edmonds .50 1.25
179 Albert Pujols 2.00 5.00
180 Matt Morris .30 .75
181 Edgar Renteria .30 .75
182 Aubrey Huff .30 .75
183 Delmon Young .50 1.25
184 Dewon Brazelton .30 .75
185 Rocco Baldelli .30 .75
186 Carl Crawford .50 1.25
187 Mark Teixeira .75 2.00
188 Hank Blalock .30 .75
189 Michael Young .30 .75
190 Laynce Nix .30 .75
191 Alfonso Soriano .30 .75
192 Kevin Mench .30 .75
193 Adrian Gonzalez .50 1.25
194 Alexis Rios .50 1.25
195 Roy Halladay .75 2.00
196 Vernon Wells .30 .75
197 Carlos Delgado .30 .75
198 Bill Hall .30 .75
199 Jose Guillen .30 .75
200 Jeremy Bonderman .30 .75
201 Roger Clemens Yanks SP 2.00 5.00
202 Alex Rodriguez Rgr SP 2.50 6.00
203 Greg Maddux Braves SP 2.50 6.00
204 Miguel Tejada A's SP 1.00 2.50
205 Alfonso Soriano Yanks SP .60 1.50
206 Andy Pettitte Yanks SP 1.00 2.50
207 Curt Schilling D'backs SP 1.00 2.50
208 Gary Sheffield Braves SP .60 1.50
209 Ivan Rodriguez Marlins SP 1.00 2.50
210 Jim Thome Indians SP 1.00 2.50
211 Mike Mussina O's SP 1.00 2.50
212 Mike Piazza Dodgers SP 1.50 4.00
213 Randy Johnson M's SP 1.50 4.00
214 Roger Clemens Sox SP 2.00 5.00
215 Sammy Sosa Sox SP 1.50 4.00
216 Alex Rodriguez M's SP 2.50 6.00
217 Randy Johnson Astros SP 1.50 4.00
218 Vladimir Guerrero Expos SP 1.50 4.00
219 Rafael Palmeiro Rgr SP 1.00 2.50
220 Manny Ramirez Indians SP 1.50 4.00
221 Mike Piazza Marlins SP 1.50 4.00
222 Cal Ripken LGD 6.00 15.00
223 Ted Williams LGD 4.00 10.00
224 Duke Snider LGD 1.00 2.50
225 Ernie Banks LGD 1.50 4.00
226 Ryne Sandberg LGD 3.00 8.00
227 Mark Grace LGD 1.00 2.50
228 Andre Dawson LGD 1.00 2.50
229 Bob Feller LGD .60 1.50
230 Ty Cobb LGD 2.50 6.00
231 George Brett LGD 3.00 8.00
232 Bo Jackson LGD 1.50 4.00
233 Robin Yount LGD 1.50 4.00
234 Harmon Killebrew LGD 1.50 4.00
235 Gary Carter LGD .60 1.50
236 Don Mattingly LGD 3.00 8.00
237 Phil Rizzuto LGD 1.00 2.50
238 Babe Ruth LGD 4.00 10.00
239 Lou Gehrig LGD 3.00 8.00
240 Reggie Jackson LGD 1.00 2.50
241 Rickey Henderson LGD 1.50 4.00
242 Mike Schmidt LGD 2.50 6.00
243 Roberto Clemente LGD 4.00 10.00
244 Tony Gwynn LGD 1.50 4.00
245 Will Clark LGD 1.00 2.50
246 Lou Brock LGD 1.00 2.50
247 Bob Gibson LGD 1.00 2.50
248 Stan Musial LGD 2.50 6.00
249 Nolan Ryan LGD 5.00 12.00
250 Dale Murphy LGD 1.00 2.50
251 A.Baldiris ROO AU/499 RC 3.00 8.00
252 A.Otsuka ROO AU/99 RC 12.50 30.00
253 A.Blanco ROO AU/499 RC 3.00 8.00
254 A.Chavez ROO AU/499 RC 3.00 8.00
255 C.Hines ROO AU/199 RC 4.00 10.00
256 C.Vasquez ROO AU/499 RC 4.00 10.00
257 Casey Daigle ROO/499 RC .75 2.00
258 C.Oxspring ROO AU/499 RC 3.00 8.00
259 C.Miller ROO AU/499 RC 3.00 8.00
260 D.Crouthers ROO AU/199 RC 4.00 10.00
261 D.Kelly ROO AU/499 RC 3.00 8.00
262 E.Rodriguez ROO AU/499 RC 4.00 10.00
263 E.Sierra ROO AU/299 RC 4.00 10.00
264 E.Moreno ROO AU/499 RC 4.00 10.00
265 F.Nieve ROO AU/499 RC 3.00 8.00
266 F.Guzman ROO AU/499 RC 3.00 8.00
267 G.Dobbs ROO AU/499 RC 3.00 8.00
268 B.Halsey ROO AU/499 RC 4.00 10.00
269 H.Gimenez ROO AU/499 RC 3.00 8.00
270 I.Ochoa ROO AU/499 RC 3.00 8.00
271 J.Woods ROO AU/499 RC 3.00 8.00
272 J.Brown ROO AU/499 RC 3.00 8.00
273 J.Bartlett ROO AU/499 RC 4.00 10.00
274 J.Szuminski ROO AU/499 RC 3.00 8.00
275 John Gall ROO/499 RC .75 2.00
276 J.Vasquez ROO AU/499 RC 3.00 8.00
277 J.Labandeira ROO AU/499 RC 3.00 8.00

278 J.Hampson ROO AU/499 RC 3.00 8.00
279 Kazuo Matsui ROO/499 RC 1.25 3.00
280 K.Cave ROO AU/499 RC 3.00 8.00
281 L.Cormier ROO AU/499 RC 3.00 8.00
282 L.Holdzkom ROO AU/199 RC 4.00 10.00
283 M.Valdez ROO AU/199 RC 4.00 10.00
284 M.Wuertz ROO AU/499 RC 4.00 10.00
285 M.Johnston ROO AU/499 RC 3.00 8.00
286 M.Rouse ROO AU/329 RC 3.00 8.00
287 O.Joseph ROO AU/499 RC 3.00 8.00
288 P.Stockman ROO AU/499 RC 3.00 8.00
289 R.Novoa ROO AU/499 RC 3.00 8.00
290 R.Belisario ROO AU/499 RC 3.00 8.00
291 R.Cedeno ROO AU/499 RC 6.00 15.00
292 R.Meaux ROO AU/499 RC 3.00 8.00
293 Scott Proctor ROO/499 RC .75 2.00
294 S.Henn ROO AU/199 RC 4.00 10.00
295 S.Camp ROO AU/499 RC 3.00 8.00
296 S.Hill ROO AU/499 RC 3.00 8.00
297 S.Takatsu ROO AU/99 RC 10.00 25.00
298 T.Bittner ROO AU/199 RC 4.00 10.00
299 William Bergolla ROO/499 RC .75 2.00
300 Y.Molina ROO AU/499 RC 10.00 25.00

2004 Leaf Certified Cuts Marble Black

STATED PRINT RUN 1 SERIAL #'d SET
NO PRICING DUE TO SCARCITY

2004 Leaf Certified Cuts Marble Blue

*BLUE 1-200: 2.5X TO 6X BASIC
*BLUE 201-221: 1.25X TO 3X BASIC
*BLUE 222-250: 1.25X TO 3X BASIC
*BLUE 251-300: .6X TO 1.5X BASIC
COMMON CARD (251-300) 2.00 5.00
SEMISTARS 3.00 8.00
UNLISTED STARS 5.00 12.00
RANDOM INSERTS IN PACKS
STATED PRINT RUN 50 SERIAL #'d SETS
251 Aarom Baldiris ROO 2.00 5.00
252 Akinori Otsuka ROO 2.00 5.00
253 Andres Blanco ROO 2.00 5.00
254 Angel Chavez ROO 2.00 5.00
255 Carlos Hines ROO 2.00 5.00
256 Carlos Vasquez ROO 2.00 5.00
257 Casey Daigle ROO 2.00 5.00
258 Chris Oxspring ROO 2.00 5.00
259 Colby Miller ROO 2.00 5.00
260 Dave Crouthers ROO 2.00 5.00
261 Don Kelly ROO 3.00 8.00
262 Eddy Rodriguez ROO 2.00 5.00
263 Edwardo Sierra ROO 2.00 5.00
264 Edwin Moreno ROO 2.00 5.00
265 Fernando Nieve ROO 2.00 5.00
266 Freddy Guzman ROO 2.00 5.00
267 Greg Dobbs ROO 2.00 5.00
268 Brad Halsey ROO 2.00 5.00
269 Hector Gimenez ROO 2.00 5.00
270 Ivan Ochoa ROO 2.00 5.00
271 Jake Woods ROO 2.00 5.00
272 Jamie Brown ROO 2.00 5.00
273 Jason Bartlett ROO 6.00 15.00
274 Jason Szuminski ROO 2.00 5.00
275 John Gall ROO 2.00 5.00
276 Jorge Vasquez ROO 2.00 5.00
277 Josh Labandeira ROO 2.00 5.00
278 Justin Hampson ROO 2.00 5.00
279 Kazuo Matsui ROO 3.00 8.00
280 Kevin Cave ROO 2.00 5.00
281 Lance Cormier ROO 2.00 5.00
282 Lincoln Holdzkom ROO 2.00 5.00
283 Merkin Valdez ROO 2.00 5.00
284 Michael Wuertz ROO 2.00 5.00
285 Mike Johnston ROO 2.00 5.00
286 Mike Rouse ROO 2.00 5.00
287 Onil Joseph ROO 2.00 5.00
288 Phil Stockman ROO 2.00 5.00
289 Roberto Novoa ROO 2.00 5.00
290 Ronald Belisario ROO 2.00 5.00
291 Ronny Cedeno ROO 2.00 5.00
292 Ryan Meaux ROO 2.00 5.00
293 Scott Proctor ROO 2.00 5.00
294 Sean Henn ROO 2.00 5.00
295 Shawn Camp ROO 2.00 5.00
296 Shawn Hill ROO 2.00 5.00
297 Shingo Takatsu ROO 2.00 5.00
298 Tim Bittner ROO 2.00 5.00
299 William Bergolla ROO 2.00 5.00
300 Yadier Molina ROO 12.00 30.00

2004 Leaf Certified Cuts Marble Emerald

STATED PRINT RUN 5 SERIAL #'d SETS
NO PRICING DUE TO SCARCITY

2004 Leaf Certified Cuts Marble Gold

*GOLD 1-200: 4X TO 10X BASIC
*GOLD 201-221: 2X TO 5X BASIC
*GOLD 222-250: 2X TO 5X BASIC
STATED PRINT RUN 25 SERIAL #'d SETS
251-300 NO PRICING DUE TO SCARCITY

2004 Leaf Certified Cuts Marble Red

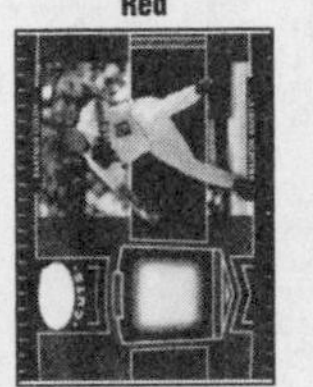

*RED 1-200: 1.5X TO 4X BASIC
*RED 201-221: .75X TO 2X BASIC
*RED 222-250: .75X TO 2X BASIC
*RED 251-300: .4X TO 1X BASIC
COMMON CARD (250-300) 1.25 3.00
SEMISTARS 2.00 5.00
UNLISTED STARS 3.00 8.00
RANDOM INSERTS IN PACKS
STATED PRINT RUN 100 SERIAL #'d SETS
251 Aarom Baldiris ROO 1.25 3.00
252 Akinori Otsuka ROO 1.25 3.00
253 Andres Blanco ROO 1.25 3.00
254 Angel Chavez ROO 1.25 3.00
255 Carlos Hines ROO 1.25 3.00
256 Carlos Vasquez ROO 1.25 3.00
257 Casey Daigle ROO 1.25 3.00
258 Chris Oxspring ROO 1.25 3.00
259 Colby Miller ROO 1.25 3.00
260 Dave Crouthers ROO 1.25 3.00
261 Don Kelly ROO 2.00 5.00
262 Eddy Rodriguez ROO 1.25 3.00
263 Edwardo Sierra ROO 1.25 3.00
264 Edwin Moreno ROO 1.25 3.00
265 Fernando Nieve ROO 1.25 3.00
266 Freddy Guzman ROO 1.25 3.00
267 Greg Dobbs ROO 1.25 3.00
268 Brad Halsey ROO 1.25 3.00
269 Hector Gimenez ROO 1.25 3.00
270 Ivan Ochoa ROO 1.25 3.00
271 Jake Woods ROO 1.25 3.00
272 Jamie Brown ROO 1.25 3.00
273 Jason Bartlett ROO 4.00 10.00
274 Jason Szuminski ROO 1.25 3.00
275 John Gall ROO 1.25 3.00
276 Jorge Vasquez ROO 1.25 3.00
277 Josh Labandeira ROO 1.25 3.00
278 Justin Hampson ROO 1.25 3.00
279 Kazuo Matsui ROO 2.00 5.00
280 Kevin Cave ROO 1.25 3.00
281 Lance Cormier ROO 1.25 3.00
282 Lincoln Holdzkom ROO 1.25 3.00
283 Merkin Valdez ROO 1.25 3.00
284 Michael Wuertz ROO 1.25 3.00
285 Mike Johnston ROO 1.25 3.00
286 Mike Rouse ROO 1.25 3.00
287 Onil Joseph ROO 1.25 3.00
288 Phil Stockman ROO 1.25 3.00
289 Roberto Novoa ROO 1.25 3.00
290 Ronald Belisario ROO 1.25 3.00
291 Ronny Cedeno ROO 1.25 3.00
292 Ryan Meaux ROO 1.25 3.00
293 Scott Proctor ROO 1.25 3.00
294 Sean Henn ROO 1.25 3.00
295 Shawn Camp ROO 1.25 3.00
296 Shawn Hill ROO 1.25 3.00
297 Shingo Takatsu ROO 1.25 3.00
298 Tim Bittner ROO 1.25 3.00
299 William Bergolla ROO 1.25 3.00
300 Yadier Molina ROO 8.00 20.00

2004 Leaf Certified Cuts Marble Material Black Number

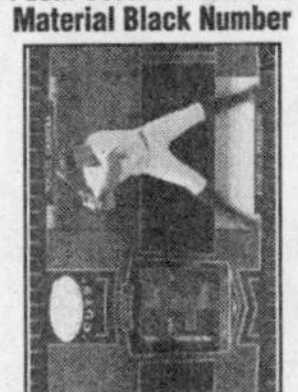

OVERALL GU ODDS ONE PER BOX
STATED PRINT RUN 1 SERIAL #'d SET
NO PRICING DUE TO SCARCITY

2004 Leaf Certified Cuts Marble Material Black Position

OVERALL GU ODDS ONE PER BOX
STATED PRINT RUN 1 SERIAL #'d SET
NO PRICING DUE TO SCARCITY

2004 Leaf Certified Cuts Marble Material Black Prime

OVERALL GU ODDS ONE PER BOX
STATED PRINT RUN 1 SERIAL #'d SET
NO PRICING DUE TO SCARCITY

2004 Leaf Certified Cuts Marble Material Blue Number

*BLUE p/r 66-100: .4X TO 1X RED p/r 66-100
*BLUE p/r 36-65: .6X TO 1.5X RED p/r 66-100
*BLUE p/r 36-65: .25X TO .6X RED p/r 20-35
*BLUE p/r 36-65: .2X TO .5X RED p/r 15-19
*BLUE p/r 20-35: 1X TO 2.5X RED p/r 66-100
*BLUE p/r 20-35: .6X TO 1.5X RED p/r 36-65
*BLUE p/r 20-35: .4X TO 1X RED p/r 20-35
*BLUE p/r 20-35: .3X TO .8X RED p/r 15-19
*BLUE p/r 15-19: 1.25X TO 3X RED p/r 66-100
*BLUE p/r 15-19: .75X TO 2X RED p/r 36-65
*BLUE p/r 15-19: .5X TO 1.2X RED p/r 20-35
*BLUE p/r 15-19: .4X TO 1X RED p/r 15-19
OVERALL GU ODDS ONE PER BOX
PRINT RUNS B/WN 1-75 COPIES PER
NO PRICING ON QTY OF 14 OR LESS

2004 Leaf Certified Cuts Marble Material Emerald Prime

OVERALL GU ODDS ONE PER BOX
STATED PRINT RUN 5 SERIAL #'d SETS
NO PRICING DUE TO SCARCITY

2004 Leaf Certified Cuts Marble Material Red Position

OVERALL GU ODDS ONE PER BOX
PRINT RUNS B/WN 1-100 COPIES PER
NO PRICING ON QTY OF 10 OR LESS
1 Vladimir Guerrero Jsy/100 4.00 10.00
2 Garret Anderson Jsy/100 2.00 5.00
5 Troy Glaus Jsy/75 2.00 5.00
6 Tim Salmon Jsy/75 3.00 8.00
8 Brandon Webb Jsy/10
10 Randy Johnson Jsy/100 4.00 10.00
12 Richie Sexson Jsy/10
13 Luis Gonzalez Jsy/100 2.00 5.00
15 Rafael Furcal Jsy/100 2.00 5.00
16 Chipper Jones Jsy/100 4.00 10.00
17 Marcus Giles Jsy/100 2.00 5.00
18 Andruw Jones Jsy/100 3.00 8.00
20 Rafael Palmeiro Jsy/100 3.00 8.00
21 Melvin Mora Jsy/50 3.00 8.00
22 Luis Matos Jsy/50 3.00 8.00
23 Jay Gibbons Jsy/100 2.00 5.00
25 Larry Bigbie Jsy/50 3.00 8.00
26 Rodrigo Lopez Jsy/50 3.00 8.00
27 Javy Lopez Jsy/25 5.00 12.00
28 Miguel Tejada Jsy/100 2.00 5.00
30 Curt Schilling Jsy/50 5.00 12.00
31 Jason Varitek Jsy/100 4.00 10.00
32 Manny Ramirez Jsy/100 3.00 8.00
35 Pedro Martinez Jsy/100 3.00 8.00
39 David Ortiz Jsy/100 4.00 10.00
40 Mark Prior Jsy/100 3.00 8.00
41 Kerry Wood Pants/100 2.00 5.00
42 Sammy Sosa Jsy/100 4.00 10.00
44 Greg Maddux Jsy/50 8.00 20.00
45 Aramis Ramirez Jsy/100 2.00 5.00
49 Moises Alou Jsy/10
51 Frank Thomas Jsy/100 4.00 10.00
52 Magglio Ordonez Jsy/100 2.00 5.00
53 Carlos Lee Jsy/100 2.00 5.00
54 Mark Buehrle Jsy/100 2.00 5.00
57 Paul Konerko Jsy/50 3.00 8.00
58 Adam Dunn Jsy/100 2.00 5.00
59 Austin Kearns Jsy/100 2.00 5.00
60 Barry Larkin Jsy/100 2.00 5.00
63 Sean Casey Jsy/10
65 Jody Gerut Jsy/100 2.00 5.00
66 Cliff Lee Jsy/100 2.00 5.00
67 Victor Martinez Jsy/100 2.00 5.00
68 C.C. Sabathia Jsy/100 2.00 5.00
69 Omar Vizquel Jsy/100 3.00 8.00
70 Travis Hafner Jsy/100 2.00 5.00
71 Todd Helton Jsy/100 3.00 8.00
72 Preston Wilson Jsy/100 2.00 5.00
73 Jeromy Burnitz Jsy/10
74 Larry Walker Jsy/10
75 Ivan Rodriguez Jsy/50 5.00 12.00
77 Miguel Cabrera Jsy/100 3.00 8.00
79 Josh Beckett Jsy/100 2.00 5.00
81 Dontrelle Willis Jsy/100 3.00 8.00
82 Brad Penny Jsy/100 2.00 5.00
85 Andy Pettitte Jsy/10
86 Jeff Bagwell Jsy/100 3.00 8.00
87 Roy Oswalt Jsy/100 2.00 5.00
88 Lance Berkman Jsy/100 2.00 5.00
89 Morgan Ensberg Jsy/100 2.00 5.00
90 Craig Biggio Jsy/100 3.00 8.00
93 Jeff Kent Jsy/100 2.00 5.00
94 Richard Hidalgo Pants/100 2.00 5.00
95 Roger Clemens Jsy/25 12.50 30.00
96 Carlos Beltran Jsy/100 2.00 5.00
97 Angel Berroa Pants/100 2.00 5.00
100 Mike Sweeney Jsy/100 2.00 5.00
101 Kazuhisa Ishii Jsy/100 2.00 5.00
102 Shawn Green Jsy/100 2.00 5.00
104 Paul Lo Duca Jsy/100 2.00 5.00
105 Hideo Nomo Jsy/100 4.00 10.00
107 Adrian Beltre Jsy/100 2.00 5.00
110 Ben Sheets Jsy/100 2.00 5.00
111 Geoff Jenkins Jsy/100 2.00 5.00
112 Jacque Jones Jsy/100 2.00 5.00
113 Johan Santana Jsy/100 3.00 8.00
114 Shannon Stewart Jsy/100 2.00 5.00
117 Torii Hunter Jsy/75 2.00 5.00
119 Orlando Cabrera Jsy/10
120 Jose Vidro Jsy/10
123 Mike Piazza Jsy/100 5.00 12.00
124 Jae Weong Seo Jsy/10
125 Jose Reyes Jsy/75 2.00 5.00
126 Tom Glavine Jsy/75 3.00 8.00
127 Jorge Posada Jsy/100 3.00 8.00
129 Bernie Williams Jsy/100 3.00 8.00
130 Mike Mussina Jsy/25 8.00 20.00
131 Mariano Rivera Jsy/100 4.00 10.00
135 Jason Giambi Jsy/10
138 Hideki Matsui Jsy/100 12.50 30.00
139 Mark Mulder Jsy/100 2.00 5.00
141 Tim Hudson Jsy/10
142 Barry Zito Jsy/100 2.00 5.00
143 Eric Chavez Jsy/100 2.00 5.00
146 Marlon Byrd Jsy/100 2.00 5.00
150 Jim Thome Jsy/100 3.00 8.00
151 Bobby Abreu Jsy/100 2.00 5.00
152 Pat Burrell Jsy/100 2.00 5.00
154 Craig Wilson Jsy/100 2.00 5.00
156 Jason Kendall Jsy/100 2.00 5.00
161 Sean Burroughs Jsy/100 2.00 5.00
163 Brian Giles Jsy/10
164 Ryan Klesko Jsy/100 2.00 5.00
166 Jerome Williams Jsy/25 5.00 12.00
171 Edgar Martinez Jsy/100 3.00 8.00
172 Freddy Garcia Jsy/100 2.00 5.00
177 Scott Rolen Jsy/100 3.00 8.00
178 Jim Edmonds Jsy/100 2.00 5.00
179 Albert Pujols Jsy/100 10.00 25.00
180 Matt Morris Jsy/75 2.00 5.00
181 Edgar Renteria Jsy/25 5.00 12.00
182 Aubrey Huff Jsy/100 2.00 5.00
184 Dewon Brazelton Jsy/100 2.00 5.00
185 Rocco Baldelli Jsy/100 2.00 5.00
186 Carl Crawford Jsy/100 2.00 5.00
187 Mark Teixeira Jsy/25 8.00 20.00
188 Hank Blalock Jsy/100 2.00 5.00
191 Alfonso Soriano Jsy/100 2.00 5.00
192 Kevin Mench Jsy/100 2.00 5.00
195 Roy Halladay Jsy/100 2.00 5.00
196 Vernon Wells Jsy/100 2.00 5.00
197 Carlos Delgado Jsy/100 2.00 5.00
200 Jeremy Bonderman Jsy/100 2.00 5.00
201 R.Clemens Yanks Jsy/100 5.00 12.00
202 Alex Rodriguez Rgr Jsy/100 5.00 12.00
203 G.Maddux Braves Jsy/100 5.00 12.00
204 Miguel Tejada A's Jsy/100 2.00 5.00
205 Alf Soriano Yanks Jsy/100 2.00 5.00
206 A.Pettitte Yanks Jsy/100 3.00 8.00
207 C.Schilling D'backs Jsy/100 2.00 5.00
208 G.Sheffield Braves Jsy/50 3.00 8.00
209 I.Rodriguez Marlins Jsy/100 3.00 8.00
210 Jim Thome Indians Jsy/25 8.00 20.00
211 Mike Mussina O's Jsy/50 5.00 12.00
212 M.Piazza Dodgers Jsy/100 5.00 12.00
213 R.Johnson M's Jsy/100 4.00 10.00
214 R.Clemens Sox Jsy/100 5.00 12.00
215 Sammy Sosa Sox Jsy/50 6.00 15.00
216 A.Rodriguez M's Jsy/100 5.00 12.00
217 R.Johnson Astros Jsy/100 4.00 10.00
218 V.Guerrero Expos Jsy/100 4.00 10.00
219 R.Palmeiro Rgr Jsy/100 3.00 8.00
221 M.Piazza Marlins Jsy/100 5.00 12.00
222 Cal Ripken LGD Jsy/50 30.00 60.00
223 Ted Williams LGD Jsy/25 60.00 120.00
225 Ernie Banks LGD Jsy/50 8.00 20.00
226 R.Sandberg LGD Jsy/100 8.00 20.00
227 Mark Grace LGD Jsy/25 10.00 25.00
228 Andre Dawson LGD Jsy/100 3.00 8.00
229 Bob Feller LGD Jsy/25 10.00 25.00
230 Ty Cobb LGD Pants/1
231 George Brett LGD Jsy/100 8.00 20.00
232 Bo Jackson LGD Jsy/100 6.00 15.00
233 Robin Yount LGD Jsy/100 6.00 15.00
234 H.Killebrew LGD Jsy/25 12.50 30.00
235 Gary Carter LGD Jkt/100 3.00 8.00
236 Don Mattingly LGD Jsy/50 12.50 30.00
237 Phil Rizzuto LGD Pants/25 10.00 25.00
238 Babe Ruth LGD Pants/50 125.00 200.00
239 Lou Gehrig LGD Pants/50 75.00 150.00
240 R.Jackson LGD Jsy/100 5.00 12.00
241 R.Henderson LGD Jsy/100 6.00 15.00
242 Mike Schmidt LGD Jsy/50 12.50 30.00
243 R.Clemente LGD Jsy/50 50.00 100.00
244 Tony Gwynn LGD Jsy/100 6.00 15.00
245 Will Clark LGD Jsy/100 5.00 12.00
246 Lou Brock LGD Jsy/25 10.00 25.00
247 Bob Gibson LGD Jsy/25 10.00 25.00
248 Stan Musial LGD Jsy/25 20.00 50.00
249 Nolan Ryan LGD Jsy/50 15.00 40.00
250 Dale Murphy LGD Jsy/100 5.00 12.00

2004 Leaf Certified Cuts Marble Signature Black

OVERALL AU ODDS THREE PER BOX
STATED PRINT RUN 1 SERIAL #'d SET
NO PRICING DUE TO SCARCITY

2004 Leaf Certified Cuts Marble Signature Blue

*1-250 p/r 75: .4X TO 1X RED p/r 66-100
*1-250 p/r 50: .5X TO 1.2X RED p/r 66-100
*1-250 p/r 50: .4X TO 1X RED p/r 36-65
*1-250 p/r 50: .3X TO .8X RED p/r 20-35
*1-250 p/r 50: .25X TO .6X RED p/r 15-19
*1-250 p/r 25: .6X TO 1.5X RED p/r 66-100
*1-250 p/r 25: .5X TO 1.2X RED p/r 36-65
*1-250 p/r 25: .4X TO 1X RED p/r 20-35
*251-300 p/r 65-75: .4X TO 1X RED p/r 66-100
OVERALL AU ODDS THREE PER BOX
PRINT RUNS B/WN 1-75 COPIES PER
1-250 NO PRICING ON QTY OF 10 OR LESS
251-300 NO PRICING ON QTY 25 OR LESS
66 Cliff Lee/75 12.50 30.00
265 Fernando Nieve ROO/75 5.00 12.00

2004 Leaf Certified Cuts Marble Signature Emerald

OVERALL AU ODDS THREE PER BOX
PRINT RUNS B/WN 1-5 COPIES PER
NO PRICING DUE TO SCARCITY

2004 Leaf Certified Cuts Marble Signature Gold

*1-250 p/r 25: .6X TO 1.5X RED p/r 66-100
*1-250 p/r 25: .5X TO 1.2X RED p/r 36-65
*1-250 p/r 25: .4X TO 1X RED p/r 20-35
*1-250 p/r 25: .3X TO .8X RED p/r 15-19
OVERALL AU ODDS THREE PER BOX
PRINT RUNS B/WN 1-25 COPIES PER
1-250 NO PRICING ON QTY OF 10 OR LESS
251-300 NO PRICING DUE TO SCARCITY
33 Keith Foulke Sox/25 15.00 40.00
66 Cliff Lee/25 30.00 60.00

2004 Leaf Certified Cuts Marble Signature Red

OVERALL AU ODDS THREE PER BOX
PRINT RUNS B/WN 1-100 COPIES PER
1-250 NO PRICING ON QTY OF 10 OR LESS
251-300 NO PRICING ON QTY 25 OR LESS
2 Garret Anderson/50 8.00 20.00
3 John Lackey/100 6.00 15.00
7 Shea Hillenbrand/100 6.00 15.00
8 Brandon Webb/100 8.00 20.00
9 Roberto Alomar/1
11 Alex Cintron/100 4.00 10.00
14 Adam LaRoche/100 4.00 10.00
15 Rafael Furcal/50 8.00 20.00
16 Chipper Jones/1
17 Marcus Giles/50 8.00 20.00
18 Andruw Jones/1
19 Russ Ortiz/100 4.00 10.00
20 Rafael Palmeiro/1
21 Melvin Mora/100 6.00 15.00
22 Luis Matos/100 4.00 10.00
23 Jay Gibbons/100 4.00 10.00
24 Adam Loewen/17 8.00 20.00
25 Larry Bigbie/100 6.00 15.00
26 Rodrigo Lopez/100 4.00 10.00
29 Trot Nixon/50 8.00 20.00
32 Manny Ramirez/1
33 Keith Foulke Sox/100 10.00 25.00
39 David Ortiz/50 20.00 50.00
40 Mark Prior/25 12.50 30.00
41 Kerry Wood/10
42 Sammy Sosa/10
43 Derrek Lee/50 12.50 30.00
44 Greg Maddux/1
45 Aramis Ramirez/100 6.00 15.00
46 Matt Clement/25 10.00 25.00
47 Carlos Zambrano/100 10.00 25.00
48 Todd Walker/100 4.00 10.00
51 Frank Thomas/5
53 Carlos Lee/100 6.00 15.00
54 Mark Buehrle/50 15.00 40.00
55 Esteban Loaiza/100 4.00 10.00
58 Adam Dunn/25 15.00 40.00
59 Austin Kearns/25 6.00 15.00
60 Barry Larkin/5
63 Sean Casey/25 10.00 25.00
65 Jody Gerut/100 4.00 10.00
66 Cliff Lee/100 12.50 30.00
67 Victor Martinez/100 6.00 15.00
68 C.C. Sabathia/100 10.00 25.00
70 Travis Hafner/100 6.00 15.00
71 Todd Helton/1
72 Preston Wilson/100 6.00 15.00
77 Miguel Cabrera/50 12.50 30.00
80 Mike Lowell/25 10.00 25.00
81 Dontrelle Willis/5
82 Brad Penny/100 4.00 10.00
85 Andy Pettitte/1
86 Jeff Bagwell/10
88 Lance Berkman/5
89 Morgan Ensberg/100 6.00 15.00
90 Craig Biggio/25 15.00 40.00
91 Octavio Dotel/100 4.00 10.00
92 Wade Miller/100 4.00 10.00
95 Roger Clemens/1
96 Carlos Beltran/50 8.00 20.00
97 Angel Berroa/50 5.00 12.00
98 Jeremy Affeldt/100 4.00 10.00
99 Juan Gonzalez/5
101 Kazuhisa Ishii/1
102 Shawn Green/1
103 Milton Bradley/100 6.00 15.00
104 Paul Lo Duca/50 8.00 20.00
105 Hideo Nomo/1
108 Scott Podsednik/100 10.00 25.00
109 Rickie Weeks/25 10.00 25.00
112 Jacque Jones/100 6.00 15.00
113 Johan Santana/50 12.50 30.00
114 Shannon Stewart/50 8.00 20.00
116 Lew Ford/100 4.00 10.00
117 Torii Hunter/25 10.00 25.00
118 Chad Cordero/100 6.00 15.00
119 Orlando Cabrera/100 6.00 15.00
120 Jose Vidro/50 5.00 12.00
123 Mike Piazza/5
124 Jae Weong Seo/5
127 Jorge Posada/5
128 Gary Sheffield/10
129 Bernie Williams/1
130 Mike Mussina/5
131 Mariano Rivera/1
132 Bubba Crosby/100 4.00 10.00
139 Mark Mulder/25 10.00 25.00
140 Jermaine Dye/100 6.00 15.00
141 Tim Hudson/1
142 Barry Zito/1
144 Bobby Crosby/100 6.00 15.00
145 Eric Byrnes/100 4.00 10.00
146 Marlon Byrd/100 4.00 10.00
148 Mike Lieberthal/100 6.00 15.00
153 Jose Castillo/100 4.00 10.00
154 Craig Wilson/100 4.00 10.00
155 Jason Bay/100 6.00 15.00
158 Jay Payton/100 4.00 10.00
161 Sean Burroughs/25 6.00 15.00
165 Todd Linden/100 4.00 10.00
170 Shigetoshi Hasegawa/50 20.00 50.00
171 Edgar Martinez/25 20.00 50.00
174 Raul Ibanez/100 8.00 20.00
177 Scott Rolen/50 12.50 30.00
178 Jim Edmonds/5
179 Albert Pujols/10
182 Aubrey Huff/100 6.00 15.00
183 Delmon Young/25 15.00 40.00
184 Dewon Brazelton/100 4.00 10.00
186 Carl Crawford/100 6.00 15.00
187 Mark Teixeira/25 15.00 40.00
188 Hank Blalock/50 8.00 20.00
189 Michael Young/100 6.00 15.00
190 Laynce Nix/100 4.00 10.00
191 Alfonso Soriano/25 15.00 40.00
193 Adrian Gonzalez/100 8.00 20.00
194 Alexis Rios/100 6.00 15.00
195 Roy Halladay/5
196 Vernon Wells/50 8.00 20.00
198 Bill Hall/100 4.00 10.00
199 Jose Guillen/100 6.00 15.00
200 Jeremy Bonderman/100 6.00 15.00
201 Roger Clemens Yanks/1
203 Greg Maddux Braves/1
205 Alfonso Soriano Yanks/25 15.00 40.00
206 Andy Pettitte Yanks/1
208 Gary Sheffield Braves/10
211 Mike Mussina O's/1
212 Mike Piazza Dodgers/5
215 Sammy Sosa Sox/5
220 Manny Ramirez Indians/1
221 Mike Piazza Marlins/5
222 Cal Ripken LGD/25 100.00 200.00
224 Duke Snider LGD/25 15.00 40.00
226 Ryne Sandberg LGD/5
227 Mark Grace LGD/5
228 Andre Dawson LGD/100 6.00 15.00
229 Bob Feller LGD/100 10.00 25.00
231 George Brett LGD/10
232 Bo Jackson LGD/5
234 Harmon Killebrew LGD/10
235 Gary Carter LGD/25 10.00 25.00
236 Don Mattingly LGD/5
237 Phil Rizzuto LGD/25 15.00 40.00
240 Reggie Jackson LGD/10
241 Rickey Henderson LGD/1
242 Mike Schmidt LGD/1
244 Tony Gwynn LGD/5
245 Will Clark LGD/25 12.50 30.00
246 Lou Brock LGD/10
247 Bob Gibson LGD/25 15.00 40.00
248 Stan Musial LGD/25 40.00 80.00
249 Nolan Ryan LGD/25 75.00 150.00
250 Dale Murphy LGD/50 12.50 30.00
251 Aarom Baldiris ROO/100 4.00 10.00
252 Akinori Otsuka ROO/25
253 Andres Blanco ROO/100 3.00 8.00
254 Angel Chavez ROO/100 3.00 8.00
255 Carlos Hines ROO/100 3.00 8.00
256 Carlos Vasquez ROO/100 5.00 12.00
258 Chris Oxspring ROO/100 3.00 8.00
259 Colby Miller ROO/100 3.00 8.00
260 Dave Crouthers ROO/50 4.00 10.00
261 Don Kelly ROO/100 3.00 8.00
262 Eddy Rodriguez ROO/100 5.00 12.00
263 Edwardo Sierra ROO/100 5.00 12.00
264 Edwin Moreno ROO/100 5.00 12.00
266 Freddy Guzman ROO/100 3.00 8.00
267 Greg Dobbs ROO/100 3.00 8.00
268 Brad Halsey ROO/100 5.00 12.00
269 Hector Gimenez ROO/100 3.00 8.00
270 Ivan Ochoa ROO/100 3.00 8.00
271 Jake Woods ROO/100 3.00 8.00
272 Jamie Brown ROO/100 3.00 8.00
273 Jason Bartlett ROO/100 5.00 12.00
274 Jason Szuminski ROO/100 3.00 8.00
275 John Gall ROO/100 5.00 12.00
276 Jorge Vasquez ROO/100 3.00 8.00
277 Josh Labandeira ROO/100 3.00 8.00
280 Kevin Cave ROO/100 3.00 8.00
281 Lance Cormier ROO/100 3.00 8.00
283 Merkin Valdez ROO/100 5.00 12.00
284 Michael Wuertz ROO/100 5.00 12.00
285 Mike Johnston ROO/100 3.00 8.00
287 Onil Joseph ROO/100 3.00 8.00
288 Phil Stockman ROO/100 3.00 8.00
289 Roberto Novoa ROO/100 4.00 10.00
291 Ronny Cedeno ROO/100 8.00 20.00
292 Ryan Meaux ROO/100 3.00 8.00
293 Scott Proctor ROO/100 5.00 12.00
295 Shawn Camp ROO/100 3.00 8.00
297 Shingo Takatsu ROO/25
299 William Bergolla ROO/100 3.00 8.00
300 Yadier Molina ROO/100 12.50 30.00

2004 Leaf Certified Cuts Marble Signature Material Black Number

OVERALL AU ODDS THREE PER BOX
STATED PRINT RUN 1 SERIAL #'d SET
NO PRICING DUE TO SCARCITY

2004 Leaf Certified Cuts Marble Signature Material Black Position

OVERALL AU ODDS THREE PER BOX
STATED PRINT RUN 1 SERIAL #'d SET
NO PRICING DUE TO SCARCITY

2004 Leaf Certified Cuts Marble Signature Material Black Prime

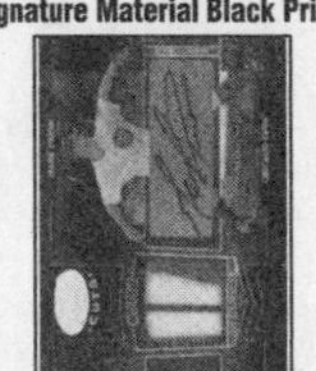

OVERALL AU ODDS THREE PER BOX
STATED PRINT RUN 1 SERIAL #'d SET
NO PRICING DUE TO SCARCITY

2004 Leaf Certified Cuts Marble Signature Material Emerald Prime

OVERALL AU ODDS THREE PER BOX
STATED PRINT RUN 5 SERIAL #'d SETS
CARD 233 PRINT RUN 2 #'d CARDS
NO PRICING DUE TO SCARCITY

2004 Leaf Certified Cuts Marble Signature Material Gold Number

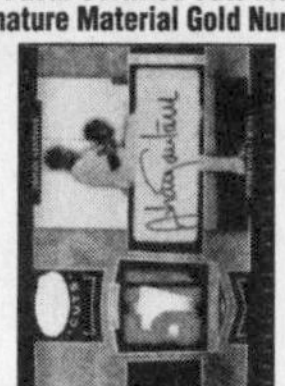

*1-221 p/r 35-65: .6X TO 1.5X RED p/r 66-100
*1-221 p/r 35-65: .5X TO 1.2X RED p/r 36-65
*1-221 p/r 35-65: .4X TO 1X RED p/r 20-35
*1-221 p/r 20-35: .75X TO 2X RED p/r 66-100
*1-221 p/r 20-35: .6X TO 1.5X RED p/r 36-65
*1-221 p/r 20-35: .5X TO 1.2X RED p/r 20-35
*1-221 p/r 15-19: 1X TO 2.5X RED p/r 66-100
*1-221 p/r 15-19: .75X TO 2X RED p/r 36-65
*222-250 p/r 36-65: .4X TO 1X RED p/r 20-35
*222-250p/r20-35: .5X TO 1.2X REDp/r20-35
*222-250p/r15-19: 1X TO 2.5X REDp/r66-100
OVERALL AU ODDS THREE PER BOX
PRINT RUNS B/WN 1-57 COPIES PER
NO PRICING ON QTY OF 13 OR LESS
18 Andruw Jones Jsy/25 20.00 50.00
32 Manny Ramirez Jsy/24 40.00 80.00
41 Kerry Wood Pants/34 20.00 50.00
42 Sammy Sosa Jsy/21 50.00 100.00
44 Greg Maddux Jsy/31 60.00 120.00
51 Frank Thomas Jsy/35 30.00 60.00
52 Magglio Ordonez Jsy/30 12.50 30.00
66 Cliff Lee Jsy/34 10.00 25.00
71 Todd Helton Jsy/17 30.00 60.00
81 Dontrelle Willis Jsy/35 20.00 50.00
85 Andy Pettitte Jsy/21 30.00 60.00
88 Lance Berkman Jsy/17 30.00 60.00
101 Kazuhisa Ishii Jsy/17 15.00 40.00
102 Shawn Green Jsy/15 30.00 60.00
123 Mike Piazza Jsy/31 75.00 150.00
124 Jae Weong Seo Jsy/26 12.50 30.00
127 Jorge Posada Jsy/20 30.00 60.00
130 Mike Mussina Jsy/35 20.00 50.00
141 Tim Hudson Jsy/15 30.00 60.00
178 Jim Edmonds Jsy/15 30.00 60.00
195 Roy Halladay Jsy/32 20.00 50.00
227 Mark Grace LGD Jsy/17 30.00 60.00
232 Bo Jackson LGD Jsy/16 75.00 150.00
236 D.Mattingly LGD Jsy/23 50.00 100.00
240 R.Jackson LGD Jsy/44 30.00 60.00
241 R.Henderson LGD Jsy/35 40.00 80.00
242 M.Schmidt LGD Pants/20 50.00 100.00
244 Tony Gwynn LGD Jsy/19 50.00 100.00
246 Lou Brock LGD Jsy/20 20.00 50.00

2004 Leaf Certified Cuts Marble Signature Material Gold Position

*1-221 p/r 50: .6X TO 1.5X RED p/r 66-100
*1-221 p/r 50: .5X TO 1.2X RED p/r 36-65
*1-221 p/r 50: .4X TO 1X RED p/r 20-35
*1-221 p/r 25: .6X TO 1.5X RED p/r 36-65
*1-221 p/r 25: .5X TO 1.2X RED p/r 20-35
*222-250 p/r 50: .6X TO 1.5X RED p/r 66-100
*222-250 p/r 25: .6X TO 1.5X RED p/r 36-65
OVERALL AU ODDS THREE PER BOX
PRINT RUNS B/WN 1-50 COPIES PER
NO PRICING ON QTY OF 10 OR LESS
66 Cliff Lee Jsy/50 10.00 25.00
234 H.Killebrew LGD Jsy/25 50.00 100.00

2004 Leaf Certified Cuts Check Signature Blue

OVERALL AU ODDS THREE PER BOX
PRINT RUNS B/WN 2-60 COPIES PER
NO PRICING ON QTY OF 10 OR LESS
ALL CARDS FEATURE BLUE CHECKS
1 Al Kaline/22 40.00 80.00
2 Andre Dawson/22 12.50 30.00
22 Duke Snider/20 20.00 50.00
31 George Kell/60 10.00 25.00
77 Whitey Ford/16 30.00 60.00

2004 Leaf Certified Cuts Check Signature Green

*GREEN p/r 15-18: .6X TO 1.5X BLUE p/r 60
*GREEN p/r 15-18: .4X TO 1X BLUE p/r 16
OVERALL AU ODDS THREE PER BOX
PRINT RUNS B/WN 1-18 COPIES PER
NO PRICING ON QTY OF 5 OR LESS
ALL BUT RYAN FEATURE GREEN CHECKS
RYAN IS BLUE CHECK W/GREEN HOF LOGO

2004 Leaf Certified Cuts Check Signature Red

*RED p/r 36: .4X TO 1X BLUE p/r 60
*RED p/r 16-17: .5X TO 1.2X BLUE p/r 20
*RED p/r 16-17: .4X TO 1X BLUE p/r 16
OVERALL AU ODDS THREE PER BOX
PRINT RUNS B/WN 3-36 COPIES PER
NO PRICING ON QTY OF 11 OR LESS
ALL BUT RYAN FEATURE RED CHECKS
RYAN IS BLUE CHECK W/RED 34 LOGO

2004 Leaf Certified Cuts Check Signature Material Blue

OVERALL AU ODDS THREE PER BOX
PRINT RUNS B/WN 1-100 COPIES PER
NO PRICING ON QTY OF 6 OR LESS
1 Al Kaline Bat/50 30.00 60.00
2 Andre Dawson Jsy/50 10.00 25.00
3 Babe Ruth Jsy/2
4 Bob Gibson Hat/50 15.00 40.00
5 Bobby Doerr Jsy/50 10.00 25.00
6 Brooks Robinson Bat/50 15.00 40.00
7 Cal Ripken White Jsy/25 125.00 250.00
8 Cal Ripken Orange Jsy/25 125.00 250.00
9 Cal Ripken Bat/25 125.00 250.00
10 Cal Ripken Jkt/25 125.00 250.00
11 Carl Yastrzemski Jsy/6
12 Carl Yastrzemski Bat/6
13 Carlton Fisk Jkt/35 20.00 50.00
14 Carlton Fisk Jsy/35 20.00 50.00
15 Catfish Hunter Jsy/2
16 Dale Murphy White Jsy/50 15.00 40.00
17 Dale Murphy Gray Jsy/50 15.00 40.00
18 Don Mattingly White Jsy/25 50.00 100.00
19 Don Mattingly Gray Jsy/25 50.00 100.00
20 Don Mattingly Bat/25 50.00 100.00
21 Don Mattingly Jkt/25 50.00 100.00
22 Duke Snider Pants/100 15.00 40.00
23 Ozzie Smith Padres Jsy/40 40.00 80.00
24 Ozzie Smith Cards Jsy/40 40.00 80.00
25 Ozzie Smith Bat/40 40.00 80.00
26 Frank Robinson Bat/50 15.00 40.00
27 George Brett White Jsy/30 50.00 100.00
28 George Brett Blue Jsy/30 50.00 100.00
29 George Brett Bat/30 50.00 100.00
30 Hack Wilson Bat/2
32 Hal Newhouser Jsy/15 20.00 50.00
33 Harmon Killebrew Shoe/35 50.00 100.00
34 Harmon Killebrew Bat/35 50.00 100.00
36 Jackie Robinson Jkt/1
37 Jimmie Foxx Bat/3
38 Kirby Puckett Fld Glv/25 50.00 100.00
39 Kirby Puckett Bat/25 50.00 100.00
40 Lou Boudreau Jsy/15 60.00 120.00
41 Lou Brock Jsy/50 15.00 40.00
42 Lou Gehrig Pants/2
43 Luis Aparicio Pants/50 10.00 25.00
44 Mark Grace Fld Glv/50 15.00 40.00
45 Mel Ott Bat/1
46 Mike Schmidt Fld Glv/25 50.00 100.00
47 Mike Schmidt Jsy/25 50.00 100.00
48 Mike Schmidt Jkt/25 50.00 100.00
49 Mike Schmidt Bat/25 50.00 100.00
50 Nolan Ryan Astros Jkt/30 75.00 150.00
51 Nolan Ryan Rgr Pants/30 75.00 150.00
52 Nolan Ryan Angels Jkt/30 75.00 150.00
53 Paul Molitor Bat/50 10.00 25.00
54 Pee Wee Reese Bat/5
57 Red Schoendienst Bat/50 10.00 25.00
58 Roberto Clemente Bat/2
61 Roger Maris Pants/1
62 Rogers Hornsby Bat/2
63 Ron Santo Bat/25 20.00 50.00
64 Roy Campanella Pants/1
65 Ryne Sandberg Jsy/50 40.00 80.00
66 Satchel Paige CO Jsy/1
67 Stan Musial White Jsy/30 50.00 100.00
68 Stan Musial Gray Jsy/30 50.00 100.00
69 Stan Musial Bat/30 50.00 100.00
70 Steve Carlton Pants/25 12.50 30.00
71 Steve Carlton Jsy/25 12.50 30.00
72 Ted Williams Jsy/2
73 Tony Gwynn White Jsy/50 30.00 60.00
74 Tony Gwynn Navy Jsy/50 30.00 60.00
75 Ty Cobb Pants/2
77 Whitey Ford Pants/50 15.00 40.00
78 Will Clark Jsy/50 15.00 40.00
79 Will Clark Bat/50 15.00 40.00
80 Willie Stargell Jsy/2

2004 Leaf Certified Cuts Check Signature Material Green

*GREEN p/r 25-33: .6X TO 1.5X BLUE p/r 100
*GREEN p/r 25-33: .5X TO 1.2X BLUE p/r 50
*GREEN p/r 15: .6X TO 1.5X BLUE p/r 50
OVERALL AU ODDS THREE PER BOX
PRINT RUNS B/WN 5-33 COPIES PER
NO PRICING ON QTY OF 10 OR LESS

2004 Leaf Certified Cuts Check Signature Material Red

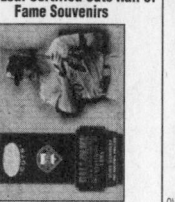

*RED p/r 50: .5X TO 1.2X BLUE p/r 100
*RED p/r 25: .5X TO 1.2X BLUE p/r 36-65
*RED p/r 25: .4X TO 1X BLUE p/r 20-35
*RED p/r 15: .5X TO 1.2X BLUE p/r 20-35
OVERALL AU ODDS THREE PER BOX
PRINT RUNS B/WN 6-50 COPIES PER
NO PRICING ON QTY OF 14 OR LESS

2004 Leaf Certified Cuts Hall of Fame Souvenirs

PRINT RUNS B/WN 75-100 COPIES PER
1 Ernie Banks/84 2.50 6.00
2 Stan Musial/93 4.00 10.00
3 Nolan Ryan/99 8.00 20.00
4 Duke Snider/87 1.50 4.00
5 Bob Feller/94 1.00 2.50
6 George Brett/98 5.00 12.00
7 Robin Yount/78 2.50 6.00
8 Harmon Killebrew/83 2.50 6.00
9 Gary Carter/78 1.00 2.50
10 Phil Rizzuto/75 1.50 4.00
11 Reggie Jackson/94 1.50 4.00
12 Mike Schmidt/97 4.00 10.00
13 Lou Brock/80 1.50 4.00
14 Bob Gibson/84 1.50 4.00
15 Bobby Doerr/75 1.00 2.50
16 Tony Perez/77 1.00 2.50
17 Whitey Ford/78 1.50 4.00
18 Juan Marichal/84 1.00 2.50
19 Monte Irvin/75 1.00 2.50
20 Fergie Jenkins/75 1.00 2.50
21 Ralph Kiner/75 1.50 4.00
22 Eddie Murray/85 2.50 6.00
23 George Kell/75 1.00 2.50
24 Hoyt Wilhelm/84 1.00 2.50
25 Carlton Fisk/80 1.50 4.00
26 Rod Carew/91 1.50 4.00
27 Frank Robinson/89 1.50 4.00
28 Gaylord Perry/77 1.00 2.50
29 Red Schoendienst/75 1.00 2.50
30 Brooks Robinson/92 1.50 4.00
31 Al Kaline/88 2.50 6.00
32 Orlando Cepeda/75 1.00 2.50
33 Steve Carlton/96 1.00 2.50
34 Luis Aparicio/85 1.00 2.50
35 Warren Spahn/83 1.50 4.00
36 Kirby Puckett/82 2.50 6.00
37 Phil Niekro/80 1.00 2.50
38 Jim Bunning/75 1.00 2.50
39 Tom Seaver/99 1.50 4.00
40 Paul Molitor/85 2.50 6.00
41 Johnny Bench/96 2.50 6.00
42 Don Sutton/82 1.00 2.50
43 Robin Roberts/87 1.00 2.50
44 Jim Palmer/93 1.00 2.50
45 Joe Morgan/82 1.00 2.50
46 Roberto Clemente/93 6.00 15.00
47 Lou Gehrig/100 5.00 12.00
48 Babe Ruth/95 6.00 15.00
49 Ty Cobb/98 4.00 10.00
50 Ted Williams/94 6.00 15.00

2004 Leaf Certified Cuts Hall of Fame Souvenirs Material

OVERALL GU ODDS ONE PER BOX
STATED PRINT RUN 25 SERIAL #'d SETS
1 Ernie Banks Jsy 12.50 30.00
2 Stan Musial Jsy 20.00 50.00
3 Nolan Ryan Jsy 30.00 60.00
4 Duke Snider Pants 10.00 25.00
5 Bob Feller Jsy 10.00 25.00
6 George Brett Jsy 20.00 50.00
7 Robin Yount Jsy 12.50 30.00
8 Harmon Killebrew Jsy 12.50 30.00
9 Gary Carter Jkt 6.00 15.00
10 Phil Rizzuto Pants 10.00 25.00
11 Reggie Jackson Jsy 10.00 25.00
12 Mike Schmidt Jsy 20.00 50.00
13 Lou Brock Jsy 10.00 25.00
14 Bob Gibson Jsy 10.00 25.00
15 Bobby Doerr Jsy 6.00 15.00
16 Tony Perez Bat 6.00 15.00
17 Whitey Ford Pants 10.00 25.00
18 Juan Marichal Jsy 6.00 15.00
20 Fergie Jenkins Pants 6.00 15.00
21 Ralph Kiner Bat 10.00 25.00
22 Eddie Murray Jsy 12.50 30.00
24 Hoyt Wilhelm Jsy 6.00 15.00
25 Carlton Fisk Jsy 10.00 25.00
26 Rod Carew Jsy 10.00 25.00
27 Frank Robinson Jsy 6.00 15.00
29 Red Schoendienst Jsy 6.00 15.00
30 Brooks Robinson Bat 10.00 25.00
31 Al Kaline Pants 12.50 30.00
32 Orlando Cepeda Bat 6.00 15.00
33 Steve Carlton Pants 6.00 15.00
34 Luis Aparicio Pants 6.00 15.00
35 Warren Spahn Pants 12.50 30.00
36 Kirby Puckett Jsy 12.50 30.00
37 Phil Niekro Jsy 6.00 15.00
39 Tom Seaver Jsy 10.00 25.00
40 Paul Molitor Bat 6.00 15.00
41 Johnny Bench Jsy 12.50 30.00
42 Don Sutton Jsy 6.00 15.00
43 Robin Roberts Hat 6.00 15.00
44 Jim Palmer Jsy 6.00 15.00
45 Joe Morgan Jsy 6.00 15.00
46 Roberto Clemente Jsy 50.00 100.00
47 Lou Gehrig Pants 75.00 150.00
48 Babe Ruth Pants 150.00 250.00
49 Ty Cobb Pants 60.00 120.00
50 Ted Williams Jsy 60.00 120.00

2004 Leaf Certified Cuts Hall of Fame Souvenirs Signature

OVERALL AU ODDS THREE PER BOX
PRINT RUNS B/WN 5-50 COPIES PER
NO PRICING ON QTY OF 10 OR LESS
2 Stan Musial/10
3 Nolan Ryan/34 50.00 100.00
4 Duke Snider/50 12.50 30.00
5 Bob Feller/50 12.50 30.00
6 George Brett/5
8 Harmon Killebrew/25 40.00 80.00
9 Gary Carter/50 8.00 20.00
10 Phil Rizzuto/50 12.50 30.00
11 Reggie Jackson/9
12 Mike Schmidt/20 40.00 80.00
13 Lou Brock/50 12.50 30.00
14 Bob Gibson/45 12.50 30.00
15 Bobby Doerr/50 8.00 20.00
16 Tony Perez/50 8.00 20.00
17 Whitey Ford/16 20.00 50.00
18 Juan Marichal/50 8.00 20.00
19 Monte Irvin/50 12.50 30.00
20 Fergie Jenkins/50 8.00 20.00
21 Ralph Kiner/50 12.50 30.00
22 Eddie Murray/33 40.00 80.00
23 George Kell/50 12.50 30.00
24 Hoyt Wilhelm/49 12.50 30.00
25 Carlton Fisk/27 15.00 40.00
26 Rod Carew/29 15.00 40.00
28 Gaylord Perry/50 8.00 20.00
29 Red Schoendienst/50 8.00 20.00
30 Brooks Robinson/50 12.50 30.00
31 Al Kaline/50 20.00 50.00
32 Orlando Cepeda/50 8.00 20.00
33 Steve Carlton/50 8.00 20.00
34 Luis Aparicio/50 8.00 20.00
35 Warren Spahn/21 30.00 60.00
36 Kirby Puckett/34 50.00 100.00
37 Phil Niekro/50 8.00 20.00
38 Jim Bunning/50 8.00 20.00
40 Paul Molitor/25 10.00 25.00
41 Johnny Bench/5
42 Don Sutton/50 8.00 20.00
43 Robin Roberts/50 12.50 30.00
44 Jim Palmer/22 10.00 25.00
45 Joe Morgan/25 10.00 25.00

2004 Leaf Certified Cuts Hall of Fame Souvenirs Signature Material

*MTL AU p/r 36-45: .5X TO 1.2X AU p/r 36-50
*MTL AU p/r 20-35: .6X TO 1.5X AU p/r 36-50
*MTL AU p/r 20-35: .5X TO 1.2X AU p/r 20-35
*MTL AU p/r 16-19: .75X TO 2X AU p/r 36-50
*MTL AU p/r 16-19: .6X TO 1.5X AU p/r 20-35
*MTL AU p/r 16-19: .5X TO 1.2X AU p/r 15-19
OVERALL AU ODDS THREE PER BOX
PRINT RUNS B/WN 1-45 COPIES PER
NO PRICING ON QTY OF 11 OR LESS

2004 Leaf Certified Cuts K-Force

1-44 PRINT RUNS B/WN 17-500 #'d PER
45-50 PRINT RUNS B/WN 20-500 #'d PER
1 Nolan Ryan Rgr/500 4.00 10.00
2 Steve Carlton/500 .50 1.25
3 Roger Clemens Astros/500 1.50 4.00
4 Randy Johnson D'backs/500 1.25 3.00
5 Bert Blyleven/500 .50 1.25
6 Tom Seaver Reds/500 .75 2.00
7 Don Sutton/500 .50 1.25
8 Gaylord Perry/500 .50 1.25
9 Phil Niekro/500 .50 1.25
10 Fergie Jenkins/500 .50 1.25
11 Bob Gibson/500 .75 2.00
12 Nolan Ryan Angels/383 4.00 10.00
13 Randy Johnson M's/308 1.25 3.00
14 Bob Feller/348 .50 1.25
15 Curt Schilling Phils/319 .75 2.00
16 Pedro Martinez Sox/313 .75 2.00
17 Dwight Gooden/276 .50 1.25
18 John Smoltz/276 1.25 3.00
19 Curt Schilling D'backs/316 .75 2.00
20 Randy Johnson Astros/329 1.25 3.00
21 Pedro Martinez Expos/305 .75 2.00
22 Roger Clemens Sox/291 1.50 4.00
23 Roger Clemens Jays/292 1.50 4.00
24 Tom Seaver Mets/289 .75 2.00
25 Hal Newhouser/275 .50 1.25
26 Jim Bunning/201 .60 1.50
27 Robin Roberts/198 .60 1.50
28 Warren Spahn/191 1.00 2.50
29 Jack Morris/232 .60 1.50
30 Nolan Ryan Astros/270 4.00 10.00
31 Hideo Nomo/236 1.50 4.00
32 Barry Zito/205 .60 1.50
33 Mike Mussina/214 1.00 2.50
34 Roy Oswalt/208 1.00 2.50
35 Mark Prior/245 1.00 2.50
36 Kerry Wood/266 .50 1.25
37 Roy Halladay/204 1.50 4.00
38 Esteban Loaiza/207 .60 1.50
39 Whitey Ford/94 1.25 3.00
40 Bob Gibson/17 2.50 6.00
41 Ben Sheets/18 1.50 4.00
42 Hoyt Wilhelm/139 .60 1.50
43 Satchel Paige/91 2.00 5.00
44 Burleigh Grimes/136 .60 1.50
45 Mark Prior .75 2.00
Kerry Wood/500
46 Nolan Ryan 4.00 10.00
Roger Clemens/500
47 Steve Carlton 1.25 3.00
Randy Johnson/500
48 Nolan Ryan 4.00 10.00
Roger Clemens/500
49 Nolan Ryan 4.00 10.00
Steve Carlton/500
50 Kerry Wood 5.00 12.00
Roger Clemens/20

2004 Leaf Certified Cuts K-Force Material

1-44 PRINT RUNS B/WN 2-100 #'d PER
1-44 NO PRICING ON QTY OF 5 OR LESS
45-50 PRINT RUN 50 SERIAL #'d SETS
OVERALL GU ODDS ONE PER BOX
1 Nolan Ryan Rgr Jsy/100 10.00 25.00
2 Steve Carlton Jsy/32 6.00 15.00
3 R.Clemens Astros Jsy/25 12.50 30.00
4 R.Johnson D'backs Jsy/51 6.00 15.00
5 Bert Blyleven Jsy/28 6.00 15.00
6 Tom Seaver Reds Jsy/25 10.00 25.00
7 Don Sutton Jsy/2
8 Gaylord Perry Jsy/36 4.00 10.00
9 Phil Niekro Jsy/35 6.00 15.00
10 Fergie Jenkins Pants/31 6.00 15.00
11 Bob Gibson Jsy/45 6.00 15.00
12 Nolan Ryan Angels Jkt/100 15.00 40.00
13 Randy Johnson M's Jsy/51 6.00 15.00
14 Bob Feller Jsy/25 10.00 25.00
15 Curt Schilling Phils Jsy/25 5.00 12.00
16 Pedro Martinez Sox Jsy/45 5.00 12.00
17 Dwight Gooden Jsy/25 6.00 15.00
18 John Smoltz Jsy/25 8.00 20.00
19 C.Schilling D'backs Jsy/25 5.00 12.00
20 R.Johnson Astros Jsy/51 6.00 15.00
21 P.Martinez Expos Jsy/45 5.00 12.00
22 R.Clemens Sox Jsy/100 5.00 12.00
25 Hal Newhouser Jsy/25 10.00 25.00
28 Warren Spahn Jsy/50 8.00 20.00
29 Jack Morris Jsy/47 4.00 10.00
30 N.Ryan Astros Jkt/100 10.00 25.00
31 Hideo Nomo Jsy/25 10.00 25.00
32 Barry Zito Jsy/25 5.00 12.00
33 Mike Mussina Jsy/25 8.00 20.00
34 Roy Oswalt Jsy/44 3.00 8.00
35 Mark Prior Jsy/50 5.00 12.00
36 Kerry Wood Jsy/34 5.00 12.00
37 Roy Halladay Jsy/5
39 Whitey Ford Jsy/50 6.00 15.00
40 Bob Gibson Jsy/50 6.00 15.00
41 Ben Sheets Jsy/25 5.00 12.00
43 Satchel Paige CO Jsy/100 30.00 60.00
44 Burleigh Grimes Pants/100 20.00 50.00
45 Mark Prior Jsy 10.00 25.00
Kerry Wood Pants/50
46 Nolan Ryan Jsy 20.00 50.00
Roger Clemens Astros Jsy/50
47 Steve Carlton Jsy 10.00 25.00
Randy Johnson Jsy/50
48 Nolan Ryan Pants 20.00 50.00
Roger Clemens Yanks Jsy/50
49 Nolan Ryan Jsy 15.00 40.00
Steve Carlton Pants/50
50 Kerry Wood Jsy 10.00 25.00
Roger Clemens Jsy/50

2004 Leaf Certified Cuts K-Force Signature

OVERALL AU ODDS THREE PER BOX
PRINT RUNS B/WN 1-50 COPIES PER
NO PRICING ON QTY OF 10 OR LESS
1 Nolan Ryan Rgr/10
2 Steve Carlton/50 8.00 20.00
3 Roger Clemens Astros/1
5 Bert Blyleven/50 8.00 20.00
6 Tom Seaver Reds/5
7 Don Sutton/50 8.00 20.00
8 Gaylord Perry/50 8.00 20.00

9 Phil Niekro/50 12.50 30.00
10 Fergie Jenkins/50 8.00 20.00
11 Bob Gibson/10
12 Nolan Ryan Angels/10
14 Bob Feller/50 12.50 30.00
15 Curt Schilling Phils/1
16 Pedro Martinez Sox/1
17 Dwight Gooden/50 8.00 20.00
19 Curt Schilling D'backs/1
21 Pedro Martinez Expos/1
22 Roger Clemens Sox/1
23 Roger Clemens Jays/1
24 Tom Seaver Mets/5
26 Jim Bunning/50 12.50 30.00
27 Robin Roberts/50 8.00 20.00
28 Warren Spahn/10
29 Jack Morris/50 8.00 20.00
30 Nolan Ryan Astros/10
31 Hideo Nomo/1
32 Barry Zito/1
33 Mike Mussina/1
34 Roy Oswalt/50 8.00 20.00
35 Mark Prior/10
36 Kerry Wood/5
37 Roy Halladay/10
38 Esteban Loaiza/50 5.00 12.00
39 Whitey Ford/5
40 Bob Gibson/10
45 Mark Prior
Kerry Wood/10
46 Nolan Ryan
Roger Clemens Astros/1
48 Nolan Ryan
Roger Clemens Yanks/1
49 Nolan Ryan
Steve Carlton/5
50 Kerry Wood
Roger Clemens/1

2004 Leaf Certified Cuts K-Force Signature Material

*A.MTL AU p/r 36-50: .5X TO 1.2X AU p/r 50
*R.MTL AU p/r 36-50: .5X TO 1.2X AU p/r 50
*R.MTL AU p/r 20-35: .6X TO 1.5X AU p/r 50
*R.MTL AU p/r 15-19: .75X TO 2X AU p/r 50
PRINT RUNS B/WN 1-47 COPIES PER
NO PRICING ON QTY OF 5 OR LESS
PRIME PRINT RUN 1 SERIAL #'d SET
NO PRIME PRICING DUE TO SCARCITY
OVERALL AU ODDS THREE PER BOX
1 Nolan Ryan Rgr Jsy/34 75.00 150.00
11 Bob Gibson Jsy/45 15.00 40.00
12 Nolan Ryan Angels Jkt/34 75.00 150.00
28 Warren Spahn Jsy/21 40.00 80.00
30 Nolan Ryan Astros Jkt/34 75.00 150.00
36 Kerry Wood Jsy/34 20.00 50.00
37 Roy Halladay Jsy/32 20.00 50.00
39 Whitey Ford Jsy/16 30.00 60.00
40 Bob Gibson Jsy/45 15.00 40.00

2004 Leaf Certified Cuts Stars

RANDOM INSERTS IN PACKS
STATED PRINT RUN 599 SERIAL #'d SETS
1 Ryne Sandberg 3.00 8.00
2 Mark Prior 1.00 2.50
3 Andre Dawson 1.00 2.50
4 Don Mattingly 3.00 8.00
5 Vladimir Guerrero 1.50 4.00
6 Garret Anderson .60 1.50
7 Dale Murphy 1.00 2.50
8 Cal Ripken 6.00 15.00
9 Mark Grace 1.00 2.50
10 Kerry Wood .60 1.50
11 Frank Thomas 1.50 4.00
12 Magglio Ordonez 1.00 2.50
13 Adam Dunn 1.00 2.50
14 Preston Wilson .60 1.50
15 Bo Jackson 1.50 4.00
16 Carlos Beltran .60 1.50
17 Tony Gwynn 1.50 4.00
18 Will Clark 1.00 2.50
19 Edgar Martinez 1.00 2.50
20 Scott Rolen 1.00 2.50
21 Alfonso Soriano .60 1.50
22 Randy Johnson 1.50 4.00
23 Chipper Jones 1.50 4.00
24 Andruw Jones .60 1.50
25 Javy Lopez .60 1.50
26 Curt Schilling 1.00 2.50
27 Manny Ramirez 1.50 4.00
28 Sammy Sosa 1.50 4.00
29 Greg Maddux 2.50 6.00
30 Todd Helton 1.00 2.50
31 Jeff Bagwell 1.00 2.50
32 Shawn Green .60 1.50
33 Mike Piazza 1.50 4.00
34 Jorge Posada 1.00 2.50
35 Gary Sheffield .60 1.50
36 Mike Mussina 1.00 2.50
37 Miguel Cabrera 1.50 4.00
38 Rickey Henderson 1.50 4.00
39 Albert Pujols 4.00 10.00
40 Vernon Wells .60 1.50
41 Fred Lynn .60 1.50
42 Alan Trammell .60 1.50
43 Lenny Dykstra .60 1.50
44 Dwight Gooden .60 1.50
45 Keith Hernandez .60 1.50
46 Luis Tiant .60 1.50
47 Orel Hershiser .60 1.50
48 George Foster .60 1.50
49 Darryl Strawberry .60 1.50
50 Marty Marion .60 1.50

2004 Leaf Certified Cuts Stars Signature

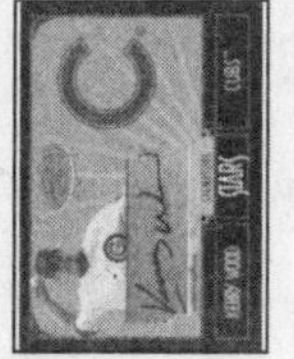

OVERALL AU ODDS THREE PER BOX
PRINT RUNS B/WN 1-50 COPIES PER
NO PRICING ON QTY OF 10 OR LESS
1 Ryne Sandberg/5
2 Mark Prior/5
3 Andre Dawson/50 8.00 20.00
4 Don Mattingly/25 40.00 80.00
5 Vladimir Guerrero/5
6 Garret Anderson/50 8.00 20.00
7 Dale Murphy/50 12.50 30.00
8 Cal Ripken/5
9 Mark Grace/5
10 Kerry Wood/5
11 Frank Thomas/10
12 Magglio Ordonez/25 10.00 25.00
13 Adam Dunn/25 15.00 40.00
14 Preston Wilson/50 8.00 20.00
15 Bo Jackson/5
16 Carlos Beltran/50 8.00 20.00
17 Tony Gwynn/5
18 Will Clark/25 15.00 40.00
19 Edgar Martinez/25 20.00 50.00
20 Scott Rolen/25 15.00 40.00
21 Alfonso Soriano/5
23 Chipper Jones/5
24 Andruw Jones/5
26 Curt Schilling/5
27 Manny Ramirez/5
28 Sammy Sosa/5
29 Greg Maddux/5
30 Todd Helton/5
31 Jeff Bagwell/5
32 Shawn Green/5
33 Mike Piazza/5
34 Jorge Posada/10
35 Gary Sheffield/10
36 Mike Mussina/5
37 Miguel Cabrera/50 12.50 30.00
38 Rickey Henderson/5
39 Albert Pujols/5
40 Vernon Wells/25 10.00 25.00
41 Fred Lynn/50 5.00 12.00
42 Alan Trammell/50 8.00 20.00
43 Lenny Dykstra/50 8.00 20.00
44 Dwight Gooden/50 8.00 20.00
45 Keith Hernandez/50 8.00 20.00
46 Luis Tiant/50 8.00 20.00
47 Orel Hershiser/50 12.50 30.00
48 George Foster/50 5.00 12.00
49 Darryl Strawberry/50 8.00 20.00

2004 Leaf Certified Cuts Stars Signature Jersey

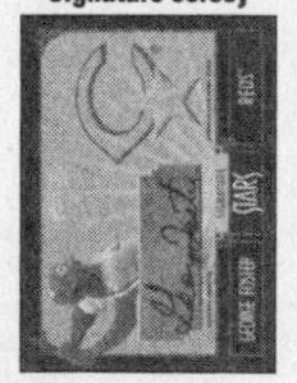

*JSY AU p/r 36-50: .5X TO 1.2X AU p/r 36-50
*JSY AU p/r 36-50: .6X TO 1.5X AU p/r 36-50
*JSY AU p/r 20-35: .6X TO 1.5X AU p/r 36-50
*JSY AU p/r 20-35: .5X TO 1.2X AU p/r 20-35
*JSY AU p/r 15-19: .75X TO 2X AU p/r 36-50
PRINT RUNS B/WN 1-44 COPIES PER
NO PRICING ON QTY OF 12 OR LESS
PRIME PRINT RUN 1 SERIAL #'d SET
NO PRIME PRICING DUE TO SCARCITY
OVERALL AU ODDS THREE PER BOX
1 Ryne Sandberg/23 50.00 100.00
2 Mark Prior/22 15.00 40.00
5 Vladimir Guerrero/27 30.00 60.00
9 Mark Grace/17 30.00 60.00
10 Kerry Wood/34 20.00 50.00
11 Frank Thomas/35 30.00 60.00
15 Bo Jackson/16 75.00 150.00
17 Tony Gwynn/19 50.00 100.00
24 Andruw Jones/25 20.00 50.00
28 Sammy Sosa/21 50.00 100.00
29 Greg Maddux/31 60.00 120.00
30 Todd Helton/17 30.00 60.00
32 Shawn Green/15 30.00 60.00
34 Jorge Posada/20 30.00 60.00
50 Marty Marion/25 12.50 30.00

2001 Leaf Certified Materials

This 160 card set was issued in five card packs. Cards numbered 111-160 feature young players along with a piece of game-used memorabilia. These cards are

serial numbered to 200.

COMP.SET w/o SP's (110) 15.00 40.00
COMMON CARD (1-110) .40 1.00
COMMON (111-160) 4.00 10.00
1 Alex Rodriguez 1.50 4.00
2 Barry Bonds 2.50 6.00
3 Cal Ripken 3.00 8.00
4 Chipper Jones 1.00 2.50
5 Derek Jeter 2.50 6.00
6 Troy Glaus .40 1.00
7 Frank Thomas 1.00 2.50
8 Greg Maddux 1.50 4.00
9 Ivan Rodriguez .60 1.50
10 Jeff Bagwell .60 1.50
11 Eric Karros .40 1.00
12 Todd Helton .60 1.50
13 Ken Griffey Jr. 1.50 4.00
14 Manny Ramirez Sox .60 1.50
15 Mark McGwire 2.50 6.00
16 Mike Piazza 1.50 4.00
17 Nomar Garciaparra 1.50 4.00
18 Pedro Martinez .60 1.50
19 Randy Johnson 1.00 2.50
20 Rick Ankiel .40 1.00
21 Rickey Henderson 1.00 2.50
22 Roger Clemens 2.00 5.00
23 Sammy Sosa 1.00 2.50
24 Tony Gwynn 1.25 3.00
25 Vladimir Guerrero 1.00 2.50
26 Kazuhiro Sasaki .40 1.00
27 Roberto Alomar .60 1.50
28 Barry Zito .60 1.50
29 Pat Burrell .40 1.00
30 Harold Baines .40 1.00
31 Carlos Delgado .40 1.00
32 J.D. Drew .40 1.00
33 Jim Edmonds .40 1.00
34 Darin Erstad .40 1.00
35 Jason Giambi .40 1.00
36 Tom Glavine .60 1.50
37 Juan Gonzalez .40 1.00
38 Mark Grace .60 1.50
39 Shawn Green .40 1.00
40 Tim Hudson .40 1.00
41 Andruw Jones .60 1.50
42 Jeff Kent .40 1.00
43 Barry Larkin .60 1.50
44 Rafael Furcal .40 1.00
45 Mike Mussina .60 1.50
46 Hideo Nomo 1.00 2.50
47 Rafael Palmeiro .60 1.50
48 Scott Rolen .60 1.50
49 Gary Sheffield .40 1.00
50 Bernie Williams .60 1.50
51 Bob Abreu .40 1.00
52 Edgardo Alfonzo .40 1.00
53 Edgar Martinez .60 1.50
54 Magglio Ordonez .40 1.00
55 Kerry Wood .40 1.00
56 Adrian Beltre .40 1.00
57 Lance Berkman .40 1.00
58 Kevin Brown .40 1.00
59 Sean Casey .40 1.00
60 Eric Chavez .40 1.00
61 Bartolo Colon .40 1.00
62 Johnny Damon .60 1.50
63 Jermaine Dye .40 1.00
64 Juan Encarnacion UER .40 1.00
Card has him playing for Detroit Lions
65 Carl Everett .40 1.00
66 Brian Giles .40 1.00
67 Mike Hampton .40 1.00
68 Richard Hidalgo .40 1.00
69 Geoff Jenkins .40 1.00
70 Jacque Jones .40 1.00
71 Jason Kendall .40 1.00
72 Ryan Klesko .40 1.00
73 Chan Ho Park .40 1.00
74 Richie Sexson .40 1.00
75 Mike Sweeney .40 1.00
76 Fernando Tatis .40 1.00
77 Miguel Tejada .40 1.00
78 Jose Vidro .40 1.00
79 Larry Walker .40 1.00
80 Preston Wilson .40 1.00
81 Craig Biggio .60 1.50
82 Fred McGriff .60 1.50
83 Jim Thome .60 1.50
84 Garret Anderson .40 1.00
85 Russell Branyan .40 1.00
86 Tony Batista .40 1.00
87 Terrence Long .40 1.00
88 Deion Sanders .60 1.50
89 Rusty Greer .40 1.00
90 Orlando Hernandez .40 1.00
91 Gabe Kapler .40 1.00
92 Paul Konerko .40 1.00
93 Carlos Lee .40 1.00
94 Kenny Lofton .40 1.00
95 Raul Mondesi .40 1.00
96 Jorge Posada .60 1.50
97 Tim Salmon .60 1.50
98 Greg Vaughn .40 1.00
99 Mo Vaughn .40 1.00
100 Omar Vizquel .60 1.50
101 Ray Durham .40 1.00
102 Jeff Cirillo .40 1.00
103 Dean Palmer .40 1.00
104 Ryan Dempster .40 1.00
105 Carlos Beltran .40 1.00
106 Timo Perez .40 1.00
107 Robin Ventura .40 1.00
108 Andy Pettitte .60 1.50
109 Aramis Ramirez .40 1.00
110 Phil Nevin .40 1.00
111 Alex Escobar FF Fld Glv 4.00 10.00
112 Johnny Estrada FF Fld Glv RC 6.00 15.00
113 Pedro Feliz FF Fld Glv 4.00 10.00
114 Nate Frese FF Fld Glv RC 4.00 10.00
115 Joe Kennedy FF Fld Glv RC 6.00 15.00
116 Brandon Larson FF Fld Glv RC 4.00 10.00
117 Alexis Gomez FF Fld Glv RC 4.00 10.00
118 Jason Hart FF 4.00 10.00
119 Jason Michaels FF Fld Glv RC 4.00 10.00
120 Marcus Giles FF Fld Glv 4.00 10.00
121 Christian Parker FF RC 4.00 10.00
122 Jackson Melian FF RC 4.00 10.00
123 Donaldo Mendez FF Spikes RC 4.00 10.00
124 Adrian Hernandez FF RC 4.00 10.00
125 Bud Smith FF RC 4.00 10.00
126 Jose Mieses FF Fld Glv RC 4.00 10.00
127 Roy Oswalt FF Spikes 10.00 25.00
128 Eric Munson FF 4.00 10.00
129 Xavier Nady FF Fld Glv 4.00 10.00
130 Horacio Ramirez FF Fld Glv RC 6.00 15.00
131 Abraham Nunez FF Spikes 4.00 10.00
132 Jose Ortiz FF 4.00 10.00
133 Jeremy Owens FF RC 4.00 10.00
134 Claudio Vargas FF RC 4.00 10.00
135 R.Rodriguez FF Fld Glv RC 4.00 10.00
136 Aubrey Huff FF Jsy 4.00 10.00
137 Ben Sheets FF 6.00 15.00
138 Adam Dunn FF Fld Glv 6.00 15.00
139 Andres Torres FF Fld Glv RC 4.00 10.00
140 Elpidio Guzman FF Fld Glv RC 4.00 10.00
141 Jay Gibbons FF Fld Glv RC 6.00 15.00
142 Wilkin Ruan FF RC 4.00 10.00
143 Tsuyoshi Shinjo FF Base RC 6.00 15.00
144 Alfonso Soriano FF 6.00 15.00
145 Josh Towers FF Fld Glv RC 6.00 15.00
146 Ichiro Suzuki FF Base RC 100.00 200.00
147 Juan Uribe FF RC 6.00 15.00
148 Joe Crede FF Fld Glv 10.00 25.00
149 Carlos Valderrama FF RC 4.00 10.00
150 Matt White FF Fld Glv RC 4.00 10.00
151 Dee Brown FF Jsy 4.00 10.00
152 Juan Cruz FF Spikes RC 4.00 10.00
153 Cory Aldridge FF RC 4.00 10.00
154 Wilmy Caceres FF RC 4.00 10.00
155 Josh Beckett FF 6.00 15.00
156 Wilson Betemit FF Spikes RC 8.00 20.00
157 Corey Patterson FF Pants 4.00 10.00
158 Albert Pujols FF Hat RC 200.00 350.00
159 Rafael Soriano FF Fld Glv RC 4.00 10.00
160 Jack Wilson FF RC 6.00 15.00

2001 Leaf Certified Materials Mirror Gold

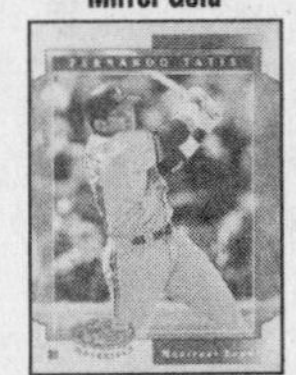

Randomly inserted into packs, these 160 cards parallel the basic Leaf Certified Material set. Each card is serial numbered to 25.

*STARS 1-110: 10X TO 25X BASIC CARDS

2001 Leaf Certified Materials Mirror Red

Randomly inserted into packs, these 160 cards parallel the basic Leaf Certified Material set. Each card is serial numbered to 75. An exchange card with a redemption deadline of November 1st, 2003 was seeded into packs for card 125 Bud Smith.

*STARS 1-110: 4X TO 10X BASIC CARDS
111 Alex Escobar FF Fld Glv AU 6.00 15.00
112 Johnny Estrada FF Fld Glv AU 10.00 25.00
113 Pedro Feliz FF Fld Glv AU 6.00 15.00
114 Nate Frese FF Fld Glv AU 6.00 15.00
115 Joe Kennedy FF Fld Glv 6.00 15.00
116 Brandon Larson FF Fld Glv AU 4.00 10.00
117 Alexis Gomez FF Fld Glv AU 4.00 10.00
118 Jason Hart FF AU 6.00 15.00
119 Jason Michaels FF Fld Glv AU 6.00 15.00
120 Marcus Giles FF Fld Glv AU 10.00 25.00
121 Christian Parker FF AU 4.00 10.00
122 Jackson Melian FF 4.00 10.00
123 Donaldo Mendez FF Spikes AU 4.00 10.00
124 Adrian Hernandez FF AU 4.00 10.00
125 Bud Smith FF AU 4.00 10.00
126 Jose Mieses FF Fld Glv AU 6.00 15.00
127 Roy Oswalt FF Spikes AU 20.00 50.00
128 Eric Munson FF 4.00 10.00
129 Xavier Nady FF Fld Glv AU 10.00 25.00
130 Horacio Ramirez FF Fld Glv AU 10.00 25.00
131 Abraham Nunez FF Spikes AU 6.00 15.00
132 Jose Ortiz FF AU 6.00 15.00
133 Jeremy Owens FF AU 6.00 15.00
134 Claudio Vargas FF AU 4.00 10.00
135 Ricardo Rodriguez FF Fld Glv AU 6.00 15.00
136 Aubrey Huff FF Jsy AU 10.00 25.00
137 Ben Sheets FF AU 15.00 40.00
138 Adam Dunn FF Fld Glv AU 15.00 40.00
139 Andres Torres FF Fld Glv AU 4.00 10.00
140 Elpidio Guzman FF Fld Glv AU 4.00 10.00
141 Jay Gibbons FF Fld Glv AU 10.00 25.00
142 Wilkin Ruan FF AU 6.00 15.00
143 Tsuyoshi Shinjo FF Base 6.00 15.00
144 Alfonso Soriano FF AU 10.00 25.00
145 Josh Towers FF Fld Glv AU 10.00 25.00
146 Ichiro Suzuki FF Base 150.00 250.00
147 Juan Uribe FF AU 10.00 25.00
148 Joe Crede FF Fld Glv AU 15.00 40.00
149 Carlos Valderrama FF AU 4.00 10.00
150 Matt White FF Fld Glv AU 6.00 15.00
151 Dee Brown FF Jsy AU 6.00 15.00
152 Juan Cruz FF Spikes AU 6.00 15.00
153 Cory Aldridge FF AU 4.00 10.00
154 Wilmy Caceres FF AU 6.00 15.00
155 Josh Beckett FF AU 15.00 40.00
156 Wilson Betemit FF Spikes AU 12.50 30.00
157 Corey Patterson FF Pants AU 6.00 15.00
158 Albert Pujols FF Hat AU 700.00 1000.00
159 Rafael Soriano FF Fld Glv AU 6.00 15.00
160 Jack Wilson FF AU 10.00 25.00

2001 Leaf Certified Materials Fabric of the Game

Randomly inserted into packs, 118 players are featured in this set. Each player has a base card as well as cards serial numbered to a key career stat, jersey number, a key seasonal stat or a Century card. All the Century cards are serial numbered to 21. Certain players had less basic cards issued, these cards are notated with an SP and according to the manufacturer less than 100 of these cards were produced. In addition, exchange cards with a redemption deadline of November 1st, 2003 were seeded into packs for the following: Jeff Bagwell CE AU, Ernie Banks JN AU, Roger Clemens JN AU, Vladimir Guerrero JN AU, Tony Gwynn CE AU, Don Mattingly CE AU, Kirby Puckett JN AU, Nolan Ryan CE AU, Ryne Sandberg CE AU and Mike Schmidt JN AU. Card 32 was originally intended to feature Jackie Robinson but was pulled from production. We've since verified a basic (non-serial-numbered) copy of the Robinson card in circulation in the secondary market but it's likely less than a handful of copies exist given only one copy has been seen since the product was released in 2001.

1BA Lou Gehrig SP
1CE Lou Gehrig/21
1CR Lou Gehrig/23
1JN Lou Gehrig/4
1SN Lou Gehrig/184 150.00 250.00
2BA Babe Ruth SP
2CE Babe Ruth/21
2CR Babe Ruth/136 175.00 300.00
2JN Babe Ruth/3
2SN Babe Ruth/60 250.00 400.00
3BA Stan Musial SP 40.00 80.00
3CE Stan Musial/21
3CR Stan Musial/177 20.00 50.00
3JN Stan Musial/6
3SN Stan Musial/39 50.00 100.00
4BA Nolan Ryan 20.00 50.00
4CE Nolan Ryan AU/21
4CR Nolan Ryan/61 50.00 100.00
4JN Nolan Ryan/34 60.00 120.00
4SN Nolan Ryan/22
5BA Roberto Clemente SP
5CE Roberto Clemente/21
5CR R. Clemente/166 60.00 120.00
5JN Roberto Clemente/21
5SN Roberto Clemente/29 150.00 250.00
6BA Al Kaline SP 15.00 40.00
6CE Al Kaline/21
6CR Al Kaline/137 15.00 40.00
6JN Al Kaline/6
6SN Al Kaline/29 40.00 80.00
7BA Brooks Robinson 10.00 25.00
7CE Brooks Robinson/21
7CR Brooks Robinson/68 15.00 40.00
7JN Brooks Robinson/5
7SN Brooks Robinson/28 40.00 80.00
8BA Mel Ott 20.00 50.00
8CE Mel Ott/21
8CR Mel Ott/72 30.00 60.00
8JN Mel Ott/4
8SN Mel Ott/42 40.00 80.00
9BA Dave Winfield SP 10.00 25.00
9CE Dave Winfield/21
9CR Dave Winfield/88 10.00 25.00
9JN Dave Winfield/31 15.00 40.00
9SN Dave Winfield/37 15.00 40.00
10BA Eddie Mathews SP 15.00 40.00
10CE Eddie Mathews/21
10CR Eddie Mathews/72 8.00 20.00
10JN Eddie Mathews/41 12.50 30.00
10SN Eddie Mathews/47 12.50 30.00
11BA Ernie Banks 10.00 25.00
11CE Ernie Banks/21
11CR Ernie Banks/50 15.00 40.00
11JN Ernie Banks AU/14
11SN Ernie Banks/47 25.00 60.00
12BA Frank Robinson SP 15.00 40.00
12CE Frank Robinson/21
12CR Frank Robinson/72 15.00 40.00
12JN Frank Robinson/20
12SN Frank Robinson/49 25.00 60.00
13BA George Brett SP 20.00 50.00
13CE George Brett/21
13CR George Brett/137 20.00 50.00
13JN George Brett/5
13SN George Brett/30 50.00 100.00
14BA Hank Aaron SP 60.00 120.00
14CE Hank Aaron/21
14CR Hank Aaron/98 40.00 80.00
14JN Hank Aaron/44 125.00 200.00
14SN Hank Aaron/47 75.00 150.00
15BA Harmon Killebrew 10.00 25.00
15CE Harmon Killebrew/21
15CR Harmon Killebrew/24
15JN Harmon Killebrew/3
15SN H. Killebrew/49 25.00 60.00
16BA Joe Morgan SP 12.50 30.00
16CE Joe Morgan/21
16CR Joe Morgan/96 12.50 30.00
16JN Joe Morgan/8
16SN Joe Morgan/27 25.00 60.00
17BA Johnny Bench 10.00 25.00
17CE Johnny Bench/21
17CR Johnny Bench/68 15.00 40.00
17JN Johnny Bench/5
17SN Johnny Bench/45 25.00 60.00
18BA Kirby Puckett SP 15.00 40.00
18CE Kirby Puckett/21
18CR Kirby Puckett/134 15.00 40.00
18JN Kirby Puckett AU/34 125.00 200.00
18SN Kirby Puckett/31 40.00 80.00
19BA Mike Schmidt SP 20.00 50.00
19CE Mike Schmidt/21
19CR Mike Schmidt/59 30.00 60.00
19JN Mike Schmidt AU/20
19SN Mike Schmidt/48 40.00 80.00
20BA Phil Rizzuto SP 15.00 40.00
20CE Phil Rizzuto/21
20CR Phil Rizzuto/149 15.00 40.00
20JN Phil Rizzuto/10
20SN Phil Rizzuto/7
21BA Reggie Jackson SP 15.00 40.00
21CE Reggie Jackson/21
21CR Reggie Jackson/49 25.00 60.00
21JN Reggie Jackson/44 25.00 60.00
21SN Reggie Jackson/47 25.00 60.00
22BA Jim Hunter 10.00 25.00
22CE Jim Hunter/21
22CR Jim Hunter/42 15.00 40.00
22JN Jim Hunter/27 20.00 50.00
22SN Jim Hunter/25
23BA Rod Carew SP 15.00 40.00
23CE Rod Carew/21
23CR Rod Carew/92 15.00 40.00
23JN Rod Carew/29 40.00 80.00
23SN Rod Carew/100 15.00 40.00
24BA Bob Feller 6.00 15.00
24CE Bob Feller/21
24CR Bob Feller/44 15.00 40.00
24JN Bob Feller/19
24SN Bob Feller/36 15.00 40.00
25BA Lou Brock SP 15.00 40.00
25CE Lou Brock/21
25CR Lou Brock/141 15.00 40.00
25JN Lou Brock/20
25SN Lou Brock/21
26BA Tom Seaver SP 15.00 40.00
26CE Tom Seaver/21
26CR Tom Seaver/61 15.00 40.00
26JN Tom Seaver/41 25.00 60.00
26SN Tom Seaver/25
27BA Paul Molitor SP 10.00 25.00
27CE Paul Molitor/21
27CR Paul Molitor/114 10.00 25.00
27JN Paul Molitor/4
27SN Paul Molitor/41 15.00 40.00
28BA Willie McCovey SP 10.00 25.00
28CE Willie McCovey/21
28CR Willie McCovey/18
28JN Willie McCovey/44 15.00 40.00
28SN Willie McCovey/126 10.00 25.00
29BA Yogi Berra 10.00 25.00
29CE Yogi Berra/21
29CR Yogi Berra/49 25.00 60.00
29JN Yogi Berra/35 40.00 80.00
29SN Yogi Berra/30 40.00 80.00
30BA Don Drysdale SP 15.00 40.00
30CE Don Drysdale/21
30CR Don Drysdale/49 25.00 60.00
30JN Don Drysdale/53 15.00 40.00
30SN Don Drysdale/25
31BA Duke Snider SP 15.00 40.00
31CE Duke Snider/21
31CR Duke Snider/99 15.00 40.00
31JN Duke Snider/4
31SN Duke Snider/43 25.00 60.00
32BA Jackie Robinson SP *
33BA Orlando Cepeda 6.00 15.00
33CE Orlando Cepeda/21
33CR Orlando Cepeda/27 20.00 50.00
33JN Orlando Cepeda/30 20.00 50.00
33SN Orlando Cepeda/46 15.00 40.00
34BA Casey Stengel SP 15.00 40.00
34CE Casey Stengel/21
34CR Casey Stengel/10
34JN Casey Stengel/37 25.00 60.00
34SN Casey Stengel/103 15.00 40.00
35BA Robin Yount SP 15.00 40.00
35CE Robin Yount/21
35CR Robin Yount/126 15.00 40.00
35JN Robin Yount/19
35SN Robin Yount/29 40.00 80.00
36BA Eddie Murray 10.00 25.00
36CE Eddie Murray/21
36CR Eddie Murray/35 40.00 80.00
36JN Eddie Murray/22
36SN Eddie Murray/33 40.00 80.00
37BA Jim Palmer 6.00 15.00
37CE Jim Palmer/21
37CR Jim Palmer/53 10.00 25.00
37JN Jim Palmer/22
37SN Jim Palmer/23
38BA Juan Marichal 6.00 15.00
38CE Juan Marichal/21
38CR Juan Marichal/52 10.00 25.00
38JN Juan Marichal/27 20.00 50.00
38SN Juan Marichal/26 20.00 50.00
39BA Willie Stargell 10.00 25.00
39CE Willie Stargell/21
39CR Willie Stargell/55 15.00 40.00
39JN Willie Stargell/8
39SN Willie Stargell/48 25.00 60.00
40BA Ted Williams SP 50.00 100.00
40CE Ted Williams/21
40CR Ted Williams/71 50.00 100.00
40JN Ted Williams/9
40SN Ted Williams/43 75.00 150.00
41BA Cal Ripken 15.00 40.00
41CE Cal Ripken/21
41CR Cal Ripken/277 20.00 50.00
41JN Cal Ripken/8
41SN Cal Ripken/114 50.00 100.00
42BA V. Guerrero SP 10.00 25.00
42CE Vladimir Guerrero/21
42CR V. Guerrero/322 6.00 15.00
42JN Vladimir Guerrero AU/27
42SN V. Guerrero/44 20.00 50.00
43BA Greg Maddux 10.00 25.00
43CE Greg Maddux/21
43CR Greg Maddux/240 10.00 25.00
43JN Greg Maddux/31 40.00 80.00
43SN Greg Maddux/20
44BA Barry Bonds 12.50 30.00
44CE Barry Bonds/21
44CR Barry Bonds/289 15.00 40.00
44JN Barry Bonds/25
44SN Barry Bonds/49 50.00 100.00
45BA Pedro Martinez 6.00 15.00
45CE Pedro Martinez/21
45CR Pedro Martinez/268 6.00 15.00
45JN Pedro Martinez/45 20.00 50.00
45SN Pedro Martinez/23
46BA Ivan Rodriguez 6.00 15.00
46CE Ivan Rodriguez/21
46CR Ivan Rodriguez/304 6.00 15.00
46JN Ivan Rodriguez/7
46SN Ivan Rodriguez/35 25.00 60.00
47BA Roger Maris 20.00 50.00
47CE Roger Maris/21
47CR Roger Maris/275 20.00 50.00
47JN Roger Maris/3
47SN Roger Maris/61 50.00 100.00
48BA Randy Johnson 6.00 15.00
48CE Randy Johnson/21
48CR Randy Johnson/179 6.00 15.00
48JN Randy Johnson/51 15.00 40.00
48SN Randy Johnson/20
49BA Roger Clemens 10.00 25.00
49CE Roger Clemens/21
49CR Roger Clemens/260 12.50 30.00
49JN Roger Clemens AU/22
49SN Roger Clemens/24
50BA Todd Helton 6.00 15.00
50CE Todd Helton/21
50CR Todd Helton/334 6.00 15.00
50JN Todd Helton/17
50SN Todd Helton/42 20.00 50.00
51BA Tony Gwynn 6.00 15.00
51CE Tony Gwynn AU/21
51CR Tony Gwynn/134 15.00 40.00
51JN Tony Gwynn/19
51SN Tony Gwynn/119 15.00 40.00
52BA Troy Glaus 4.00 10.00
52CE Troy Glaus/21
52CR Troy Glaus/256 4.00 10.00
52JN Troy Glaus/25
52SN Troy Glaus/47 12.50 30.00
53BA Phil Niekro 6.00 15.00
53CE Phil Niekro/21
53CR Phil Niekro/245 6.00 15.00
53JN Phil Niekro/35 20.00 50.00
53SN Phil Niekro/23
54BA Don Sutton 6.00 15.00
54CE Don Sutton/21
54CR Don Sutton/178 6.00 15.00
54JN Don Sutton/20
54SN Don Sutton/21
55BA Frank Thomas 6.00 15.00
55CE Frank Thomas/21
55CR Frank Thomas/321 6.00 15.00
55JN Frank Thomas/35 25.00 60.00
55SN Frank Thomas/43 20.00 50.00
56BA Jeff Bagwell 6.00 15.00
56CE Jeff Bagwell AU/21
56CR Jeff Bagwell/305 6.00 15.00
56JN Jeff Bagwell/5
56SN Jeff Bagwell/135 10.00 25.00
57BA Rickey Henderson 6.00 15.00
57CE Rickey Henderson/21
57CR R. Henderson/282 6.00 15.00
57JN R. Henderson/35 25.00 60.00
57SN R. Henderson/28 25.00 60.00
58BA Darin Erstad SP 6.00 15.00
58CE Darin Erstad/21
58CR Darin Erstad/301 4.00 10.00
58JN Darin Erstad/17
58SN Darin Erstad/100 6.00 15.00
59BA Andruw Jones 6.00 15.00
59CE Andruw Jones/21
59CR Andruw Jones/272 6.00 15.00
59JN Andruw Jones/25
59SN Andruw Jones/36 20.00 50.00
60BA Roberto Alomar 6.00 15.00
60CE Roberto Alomar/21
60CR Roberto Alomar/170 6.00 15.00
60JN Roberto Alomar/12
60SN Roberto Alomar/120 10.00 25.00
61BA Mike Piazza SP 15.00 40.00
61CE Mike Piazza/21
61CR Mike Piazza/328 10.00 25.00
61JN Mike Piazza/31 40.00 80.00
61SN Mike Piazza/40 40.00 80.00
62BA Chipper Jones 6.00 15.00
62CE Chipper Jones/21
62CR Chipper Jones/189 6.00 15.00
62JN Chipper Jones/10
62SN Chipper Jones/45 20.00 50.00
63BA Shawn Green 4.00 10.00
63CE Shawn Green/21
63CR Shawn Green/143 6.00 15.00
63JN Shawn Green/15
63SN Shawn Green/123 6.00 15.00
64BA Don Mattingly SP 20.00 50.00
64CE Don Mattingly AU/21
64CR Don Mattingly/222 15.00 40.00
64JN Don Mattingly/23
64SN Don Mattingly/145 20.00 50.00
65BA Rafael Palmeiro 6.00 15.00
65CE Rafael Palmeiro/21
65CR Rafael Palmeiro/296 6.00 15.00
65JN Rafael Palmeiro/25
65SN Rafael Palmeiro/47 20.00 50.00
66BA Wade Boggs 10.00 25.00
66CE Wade Boggs/21
66CR Wade Boggs/116 15.00 40.00
66JN Wade Boggs/26 40.00 80.00
66SN Wade Boggs/89 15.00 40.00
67BA Hoyt Wilhelm 6.00 15.00
67CE Hoyt Wilhelm/21
67CR Hoyt Wilhelm/143 10.00 25.00
67JN Hoyt Wilhelm/31 20.00 50.00
67SN Hoyt Wilhelm/27 20.00 50.00
68BA Andre Dawson 6.00 15.00
68CE Andre Dawson/21
68CR Andre Dawson/314 6.00 15.00
68JN Andre Dawson/8
68SN Andre Dawson/49 15.00 40.00
69BA Ryne Sandberg 15.00 40.00
69CE Ryne Sandberg AU/21
69CR Ryne Sandberg/282 10.00 25.00
69JN Ryne Sandberg/23
69SN Ryne Sandberg/40 40.00 80.00
70BA N.Garciaparra SP 15.00 40.00
70CE Nomar Garciaparra/21
70CR N.Garciaparra/333 10.00 25.00
70JN Nomar Garciaparra/5
70SN N.Garciaparra/35 50.00 100.00
71BA Tom Glavine 6.00 15.00
71CE Tom Glavine/21
71CR Tom Glavine/208 6.00 15.00
71JN Tom Glavine/47 20.00 50.00
71SN Tom Glavine/247 6.00 15.00
72BA Magglio Ordonez 4.00 10.00
72CE Magglio Ordonez/21
72CR M.Ordonez/301 4.00 10.00
72JN Magglio Ordonez/30 15.00 40.00
72SN Magglio Ordonez/126 6.00 15.00
73BA Bernie Williams 6.00 15.00
73CE Bernie Williams/21
73CR Bernie Williams/304 6.00 15.00
73JN Bernie Williams/51 15.00 40.00
73SN Bernie Williams/30 25.00 60.00
74BA Jim Edmonds 4.00 10.00
74CE Jim Edmonds/21
74CR Jim Edmonds/291 6.00 15.00
74JN Jim Edmonds/15
74SN Jim Edmonds/108 6.00 15.00
75BA Hideo Nomo 20.00 50.00
75CE Hideo Nomo/21
75CR Hideo Nomo/69 50.00 100.00
75JN Hideo Nomo/11
75SN Hideo Nomo/16
76BA Barry Larkin 6.00 15.00
76CE Barry Larkin/21
76CR Barry Larkin/300 6.00 15.00
76JN Barry Larkin/11
76SN Barry Larkin/33 25.00 60.00
77BA Scott Rolen 6.00 15.00
77CE Scott Rolen/21
77CR Scott Rolen/284 6.00 15.00
77JN Scott Rolen/17
77SN Scott Rolen/31 25.00 60.00
78BA Miguel Tejada 4.00 10.00
78CE Miguel Tejada/21
78CR Miguel Tejada/253 4.00 10.00
78JN Miguel Tejada/4
78SN Miguel Tejada/30 15.00 40.00
79BA Freddy Garcia 4.00 10.00
79CE Freddy Garcia/21
79CR Freddy Garcia/249 4.00 10.00
79JN Freddy Garcia/34 15.00 40.00
79SN Freddy Garcia/170 4.00 10.00
80BA Edgar Martinez 6.00 15.00
80CE Edgar Martinez/21
80CR Edgar Martinez/320 6.00 15.00
80JN Edgar Martinez/11
80SN Edgar Martinez/37 20.00 50.00
81BA Edgardo Alfonzo 4.00 10.00
81CE Edgardo Alfonzo/21
81CR E. Alfonzo/296 4.00 10.00
81JN Edgardo Alfonzo/13
81SN E. Alfonzo/108 6.00 15.00
82BA Steve Garvey 6.00 15.00
82CE Steve Garvey/21
82CR Steve Garvey/272 6.00 15.00
82JN Steve Garvey/6
82SN Steve Garvey/33 20.00 50.00
83BA Larry Walker 4.00 10.00
83CE Larry Walker/21
83CR Larry Walker/311 4.00 10.00
83JN Larry Walker/12
83SN Larry Walker/49 12.50 30.00
84BA A.J. Burnett 4.00 10.00
84CE A.J. Burnett/21
84CR A.J. Burnett/90 6.00 15.00
84JN A.J. Burnett/43 12.50 30.00
84SN A.J. Burnett/57 10.00 25.00
85BA Richie Sexson 4.00 10.00
85CE Richie Sexson/21
85CR Richie Sexson/242 4.00 10.00
85JN Richie Sexson/11
85SN Richie Sexson/116 6.00 15.00
86BA Mark Mulder 4.00 10.00
86CE Mark Mulder/21
86CR Mark Mulder/88 6.00 15.00
86JN Mark Mulder/20
86SN Mark Mulder/9
87BA Kerry Wood 4.00 10.00
87CE Kerry Wood/21
87CR Kerry Wood/21
87JN Kerry Wood/34 15.00 40.00
87SN Kerry Wood/233 4.00 10.00
88BA Sean Casey 4.00 10.00
88CE Sean Casey/21
88CR Sean Casey/312 4.00 10.00
88JN Sean Casey/21
88SN Sean Casey/25
89BA Jermaine Dye SP 6.00 15.00
89CE Jermaine Dye/21
89CR Jermaine Dye/286 4.00 10.00
89JN Jermaine Dye/24
89SN Jermaine Dye/118 6.00 15.00
90BA Kevin Brown SP 6.00 15.00
90CE Kevin Brown/21
90CR Kevin Brown/170 4.00 10.00
90JN Kevin Brown/27 15.00 40.00
90SN Kevin Brown/257 4.00 10.00
91BA Craig Biggio 6.00 15.00
91CE Craig Biggio/21
91CR Craig Biggio/291 6.00 15.00
91JN Craig Biggio/7
91SN Craig Biggio/88 10.00 25.00
92BA Mike Sweeney SP 6.00 15.00
92CE Mike Sweeney/21
92CR Mike Sweeney/302 4.00 10.00
92JN Mike Sweeney/29 15.00 40.00
92SN Mike Sweeney/144 6.00 15.00
93BA Jim Thome 6.00 15.00
93CE Jim Thome/21
93CR Jim Thome/233 6.00 15.00
93JN Jim Thome/25
93SN Jim Thome/40 20.00 50.00
94BA Al Leiter 4.00 10.00
94CE Al Leiter/21
94CR Al Leiter/106 6.00 15.00
94JN Al Leiter/22
94SN Al Leiter/247 4.00 10.00
95BA Barry Zito 6.00 15.00
95CE Barry Zito/21
95CR Barry Zito/272 6.00 15.00
95JN Barry Zito/75 10.00 25.00
95SN Barry Zito/78 10.00 25.00
96BA Rafael Furcal 4.00 10.00
96CE Rafael Furcal/21
96CR Rafael Furcal/295 4.00 10.00
96JN Rafael Furcal/1
96SN Rafael Furcal/37 12.50 30.00
97BA J.D. Drew 4.00 10.00
97CE J.D. Drew/21
97CR J.D. Drew/276 4.00 10.00
97JN J.D. Drew/7
97SN J.D. Drew/18
98BA Andres Galarraga 4.00 10.00
98CE Andres Galarraga/21
98CR A. Galarraga/291 4.00 10.00
98JN Andres Galarraga/14
98SN A. Galarraga/150 4.00 10.00
99BA Kazuhiro Sasaki 4.00 10.00
99CE Kazuhiro Sasaki/21
99CR Kazuhiro Sasaki/266 4.00 10.00
99JN Kazuhiro Sasaki/22
99SN Kazuhiro Sasaki/45 12.50 30.00
100BA Chan Ho Park 4.00 10.00
100CE Chan Ho Park/21
100CR Chan Ho Park/65 10.00 25.00
100JN Chan Ho Park/61 10.00 25.00
100SN Chan Ho Park/217 4.00 10.00
101BA Eric Milton 4.00 10.00
101CE Eric Milton/21
101CR Eric Milton/28 15.00 40.00
101JN Eric Milton/21
101SN Eric Milton/163 4.00 10.00
102BA Carlos Lee 4.00 10.00
102CE Carlos Lee/21
102CR Carlos Lee/297 4.00 10.00
102JN Carlos Lee/45 12.50 30.00
102SN Carlos Lee/24
103BA Preston Wilson 4.00 10.00
103CE Preston Wilson/21
103CR P. Wilson/266 4.00 10.00
103JN Preston Wilson/44 12.50 30.00
103SN Preston Wilson/31 15.00 40.00
104BA Adrian Beltre 4.00 10.00
104CE Adrian Beltre/21
104CR Adrian Beltre/272 4.00 10.00
104JN Adrian Beltre/29 15.00 40.00
104SN Adrian Beltre/85 6.00 15.00
105BA Luis Gonzalez 4.00 10.00
105CE Luis Gonzalez/21
105CR Luis Gonzalez/281 4.00 10.00
105JN Luis Gonzalez/20
105SN Luis Gonzalez/114 6.00 15.00
106BA Kenny Lofton 4.00 10.00
106CE Kenny Lofton/21
106CR Kenny Lofton/306 4.00 10.00
106JN Kenny Lofton/7
106SN Kenny Lofton/15
107BA Shannon Stewart 4.00 10.00
107CE Shannon Stewart/21
107CR S. Stewart/297 4.00 10.00
107JN Shannon Stewart/24
107SN Shannon Stewart/21
108BA Javy Lopez 4.00 10.00
108CE Javy Lopez/21
108CR Javy Lopez/290 4.00 10.00
108JN Javy Lopez/8
108SN Javy Lopez/106 6.00 15.00
109BA Raul Mondesi 4.00 10.00
109CE Raul Mondesi/21
109CR Raul Mondesi/286 4.00 10.00
109JN Raul Mondesi/43 12.50 30.00
109SN Raul Mondesi/33 15.00 40.00
110BA Mark Grace 6.00 15.00
110CE Mark Grace/21
110CR Mark Grace/308 6.00 15.00
110JN Mark Grace/17
110SN Mark Grace/51 15.00 40.00
111BA Curt Schilling 4.00 10.00
111CE Curt Schilling/21
111CR Curt Schilling/110 6.00 15.00
111JN Curt Schilling/38 12.50 30.00
111SN Curt Schilling/235 4.00 10.00
112BA Cliff Floyd 4.00 10.00
112CE Cliff Floyd/21
112CR Cliff Floyd/275 4.00 10.00
112JN Cliff Floyd/30 15.00 40.00
112SN Cliff Floyd/22
113BA Moises Alou 4.00 10.00
113CE Moises Alou/21
113CR Moises Alou/303 4.00 10.00
113JN Moises Alou/18
113SN Moises Alou/124 6.00 15.00
114BA Aaron Sele 4.00 10.00
114CE Aaron Sele/21
114CR Aaron Sele/92 6.00 15.00
114JN Aaron Sele/30 15.00 40.00
114SN Aaron Sele/19
115BA Jose Cruz Jr. 4.00 10.00
115CE Jose Cruz Jr./21
115CR Jose Cruz Jr./245 4.00 10.00
115JN Jose Cruz Jr./23
115SN Jose Cruz Jr./31 15.00 40.00
116BA John Olerud 4.00 10.00
116CE John Olerud/21
116CR John Olerud/186 4.00 10.00
116JN John Olerud/5
116SN John Olerud/107 6.00 15.00
117BA Jose Vidro 4.00 10.00
117CE Jose Vidro/21
117CR Jose Vidro/296 4.00 10.00
117JN Jose Vidro/3
117SN Jose Vidro/24
118BA John Smoltz 6.00 15.00
118CE John Smoltz/21
118CR John Smoltz/335 6.00 15.00
118JN John Smoltz/29 25.00 60.00
118SN John Smoltz/24

2002 Leaf Certified

This 200-card set was released in early September, 2002. It was issued in five card packs which came 12 packs to a box and six boxes to a case. The first 150 card featured veteran stars while the final 50 cards features rookies and prospects along with a game-used memorabilia piece for each of them. Those final fifty cards have a stated print run of 500 serial numbered sets.

COMP.SET w/o SP's (150) 30.00 80.00
COMMON CARD (1-150) .40 1.00
COMMON CARD (151-200) 3.00 8.00
1 Alex Rodriguez 1.50 4.00
2 Luis Gonzalez .40 1.00
3 Javier Vazquez .40 1.00
4 Juan Uribe .40 1.00
5 Ben Sheets .40 1.00
6 George Brett 2.00 5.00
7 Magglio Ordonez .40 1.00
8 Randy Johnson 1.00 2.50
9 Joe Kennedy .40 1.00
10 Richie Sexson .40 1.00
11 Larry Walker .40 1.00
12 Lance Berkman .40 1.00
13 Jose Cruz Jr. .40 1.00
14 Doug Davis .40 1.00
15 Cliff Floyd .40 1.00
16 Ryan Klesko .40 1.00
17 Troy Glaus .40 1.00
18 Robert Person .40 1.00
19 Bartolo Colon .40 1.00
20 Adam Dunn .40 1.00
21 Kevin Brown .40 1.00
22 John Smoltz .60 1.50
23 Edgar Martinez .60 1.50
24 Eric Karros .40 1.00
25 Tony Gwynn 1.25 3.00
26 Mark Mulder .40 1.00
27 Don Mattingly 2.00 5.00
28 Brandon Duckworth .40 1.00
29 C.C. Sabathia .40 1.00
30 Nomar Garciaparra 1.50 4.00
31 Adam Johnson .40 1.00
32 Miquel Tejada .40 1.00
33 Ryne Sandberg 2.00 5.00
34 Roger Clemens 2.00 5.00
35 Edgardo Alfonzo .40 1.00
36 Jason Jennings .40 1.00
37 Todd Helton .60 1.50
38 Nolan Ryan 2.50 6.00
39 Paul LoDuca .40 1.00
40 Cal Ripken 3.00 8.00
41 Terrence Long .40 1.00
42 Mike Sweeney .40 1.00
43 Carlos Lee .40 1.00
44 Ben Grieve .40 1.00
45 Tony Armas Jr. .40 1.00
46 Joe Mays .40 1.00
47 Jeff Kent .40 1.00
48 Andy Pettitte .60 1.50
49 Kirby Puckett 1.00 2.50
50 Aramis Ramirez .40 1.00
51 Tim Redding .40 1.00
52 Freddy Garcia .40 1.00
53 Javy Lopez .40 1.00
54 Mike Schmidt 2.00 5.00
55 Wade Miller .40 1.00
56 Ramon Ortiz .40 1.00
57 Ray Durham .40 1.00
58 J.D. Drew .40 1.00
59 Bret Boone .40 1.00
60 Mark Buehrle .40 1.00
61 Geoff Jenkins .40 1.00
62 Greg Maddux 1.50 4.00
63 Mark Grace .60 1.50
64 Toby Hall .40 1.00
65 A.J. Burnett .40 1.00
66 Bernie Williams .60 1.50
67 Roy Oswalt .40 1.00
68 Shannon Stewart .40 1.00
69 Barry Zito .40 1.00
70 Juan Pierre .40 1.00
71 Preston Wilson .40 1.00
72 Rafael Furcal .40 1.00
73 Sean Casey .40 1.00
74 John Olerud .40 1.00
75 Paul Konerko .40 1.00
76 Vernon Wells .40 1.00
77 Juan Gonzalez .40 1.00
78 Ellis Burks .40 1.00
79 Jim Edmonds .40 1.00
80 Robert Fick .40 1.00
81 Michael Cuddyer .40 1.00
82 Tim Hudson .40 1.00
83 Phil Nevin .40 1.00
84 Curt Schilling .40 1.00
85 Juan Cruz .40 1.00
86 Jeff Bagwell .60 1.50
87 Raul Mondesi .40 1.00
88 Bud Smith .40 1.00
89 Omar Vizquel .60 1.50
90 Vladimir Guerrero 1.00 2.50
91 Garret Anderson .40 1.00
92 Mike Piazza 1.50 4.00
93 Josh Beckett .40 1.00
94 Carlos Delgado .40 1.00
95 Kazuhiro Sasaki .40 1.00
96 Chipper Jones 1.00 2.50
97 Jacque Jones .40 1.00
98 Pedro Martinez .60 1.50
99 Marcus Giles .40 1.00
100 Craig Biggio .60 1.50
101 Orlando Cabrera .40 1.00
102 Al Leiter .40 1.00
103 Michael Barrett .40 1.00
104 Hideo Nomo 1.00 2.50
105 Mike Mussina .60 1.50
106 Jeremy Giambi .40 1.00
107 Cristian Guzman .40 1.00
108 Frank Thomas 1.00 2.50
109 Carlos Beltran .40 1.00
110 Jorge Posada .60 1.50
111 Roberto Alomar .60 1.50
112 Bob Abreu .40 1.00
113 Robin Ventura .40 1.00
114 Pat Burrell .40 1.00
115 Kenny Lofton .40 1.00
116 Adrian Beltre .40 1.00
117 Gary Sheffield .40 1.00
118 Jermaine Dye .40 1.00
119 Manny Ramirez .60 1.50
120 Brian Giles .40 1.00
121 Tsuyoshi Shinjo .40 1.00
122 Rafael Palmeiro .60 1.50
123 Mo Vaughn UER .40 1.00
Yankee Logo on back
124 Kerry Wood .40 1.00
125 Moises Alou .40 1.00
126 Rickey Henderson 1.00 2.50
127 Corey Patterson .40 1.00
128 Jim Thome .60 1.50
129 Richard Hidalgo .40 1.00
130 Darin Erstad .40 1.00
131 Johnny Damon Sox .60 1.50
132 Juan Encarnacion .40 1.00
133 Scott Rolen .60 1.50
134 Tom Glavine .60 1.50
135 Ivan Rodriguez .60 1.50
136 Jay Gibbons .40 1.00
137 Trot Nixon .40 1.00
138 Nick Neugebauer .40 1.00
139 Barry Larkin .60 1.50
140 Andruw Jones .60 1.50
141 Shawn Green .40 1.00
142 Jose Vidro .40 1.00
143 Derek Jeter 2.50 6.00
144 Ichiro Suzuki 2.00 5.00
145 Ken Griffey Jr. 1.50 4.00
146 Barry Bonds 2.50 6.00
147 Albert Pujols 2.00 5.00
148 Sammy Sosa 1.00 2.50
149 Jason Giambi .40 1.00
150 Alfonso Soriano .40 1.00
151 Drew Henson NG Bat 3.00 8.00
152 Luis Garcia NG Bat 3.00 8.00
153 Geronimo Gil NG Jsy 3.00 8.00
154 Corky Miller NG Jsy 3.00 8.00
155 Mike Rivera NG Bat 3.00 8.00
156 Mark Ellis NG Jsy 3.00 8.00
157 Josh Pearce NG Bat 3.00 8.00
158 Ryan Ludwick NG Bat 3.00 8.00
159 So Taguchi NG Bat RC 4.00 10.00
160 Cody Ransom NG Jsy 3.00 8.00
161 Jeff Deardorff NG Bat 3.00 8.00
162 Fr. German NG Bat RC 3.00 8.00
163 Ed Rogers NG Jsy 3.00 8.00
164 Eric Cyr NG Jsy 3.00 8.00
165 Victor Alvarez NG Jsy RC 3.00 8.00
166 Victor Martinez NG Jsy 4.00 10.00
167 Brandon Berger NG Jsy 3.00 8.00
168 Juan Diaz NG Jsy 3.00 8.00
169 Kevin Frederick NG Jsy RC 3.00 8.00
170 Earl Snyder NG Bat RC 3.00 8.00
171 Morgan Ensberg NG Bat 3.00 8.00
172 Ryan Jamison NG Jsy 3.00 8.00
173 Rod. Rosario NG Jsy RC 3.00 8.00
174 Willie Harris NG Bat 3.00 8.00
175 Ramon Vazquez NG Bat 3.00 8.00
176 Kazuhisa Ishii NG Bat RC 4.00 10.00
177 Hank Blalock NG Jsy 4.00 10.00
178 Mark Prior NG Bat 4.00 10.00
179 Dewon Brazelton NG Jsy 3.00 8.00
180 Doug Devore NG Jsy RC 3.00 8.00
181 Jorge Padilla NG Bat RC 3.00 8.00
182 Mark Teixeira NG Jsy 4.00 10.00
183 Orlando Hudson NG Bat 3.00 8.00
184 John Buck NG Jsy 3.00 8.00
185 Erik Bedard NG Jsy 3.00 8.00
186 Allan Simpson NG Jsy RC 3.00 8.00
187 Travis Hafner NG Jsy 3.00 8.00
188 Jason Lane NG Jsy 3.00 8.00
189 Marlon Byrd NG Jsy 3.00 8.00
190 Joe Thurston NG Jsy 3.00 8.00
191 Brandon Backe NG Jsy RC 4.00 10.00
192 Josh Phelps NG Jsy 3.00 8.00
193 Bill Hall NG Bat 3.00 8.00
194 Chris Snelling NG Bat RC 3.00 8.00
195 Austin Kearns NG Jsy 3.00 8.00
196 Antonio Perez NG Bat 3.00 8.00
197 Angel Berroa NG Bat 3.00 8.00
198 Andy Machado NG Jsy RC 3.00 8.00
199 Alfredo Amezaga NG Jsy 3.00 8.00
200 Eric Hinske NG Bat 3.00 8.00

2002 Leaf Certified Mirror Blue

Randomly inserted in packs, this is a parallel to the Leaf Certified set. These cards used blue tint and foil and are printed to a stated print run of 75 serial numbered set.

*MIRROR BLUE 1-150: .6X TO 1.5X MIR.RED
*MIRROR BLUE 151-200: .6X TO 1.5X MIR.RED

2002 Leaf Certified Mirror Red

Randomly inserted in packs, this is a parallel to the Leaf Certified set. These cards used red tint and foil and are printed to a stated print run of 150 serial numbered sets.

1 Alex Rodriguez Jsy 10.00 25.00
2 Luis Gonzalez Jsy 4.00 10.00
3 Javier Vazquez Jsy 4.00 10.00
4 Juan Uribe Jsy 4.00 10.00
5 Ben Sheets Jsy 4.00 10.00
6 George Brett Jsy 20.00 50.00
7 Magglio Ordonez Jsy 4.00 10.00
8 Randy Johnson Jsy 8.00 20.00
9 Joe Kennedy Jsy 4.00 10.00
10 Richie Sexson Jsy 4.00 10.00
11 Larry Walker Jsy 4.00 10.00
12 Lance Berkman Jsy 4.00 10.00
13 Jose Cruz Jr. Jsy 4.00 10.00
14 Doug Davis Jsy 4.00 10.00
15 Cliff Floyd Jsy 4.00 10.00
16 Ryan Klesko Bat SP/100 4.00 10.00
17 Troy Glaus Jsy 4.00 10.00
18 Robert Person Jsy 4.00 10.00
19 Bartolo Colon Jsy 4.00 10.00
20 Adam Dunn Jsy 4.00 10.00
21 Kevin Brown Jsy 4.00 10.00
22 John Smoltz Jsy 6.00 15.00
23 Edgar Martinez Jsy 6.00 15.00
24 Eric Karros Jsy 4.00 10.00
25 Tony Gwynn Jsy 10.00 25.00
26 Mark Mulder Jsy 4.00 10.00
27 Don Mattingly Jsy 20.00 50.00
28 Brandon Duckworth Jsy 4.00 10.00
29 C.C. Sabathia Jsy 4.00 10.00
30 Nomar Garciaparra Jsy 10.00 25.00
31 Adam Johnson Jsy 4.00 10.00
32 Miguel Tejada Jsy 4.00 10.00
33 Ryne Sandberg Jsy 20.00 50.00
34 Roger Clemens Jsy 15.00 40.00
35 Edgardo Alfonzo Jsy 4.00 10.00
36 Jason Jennings Jsy 4.00 10.00
37 Todd Helton Jsy 6.00 15.00
38 Nolan Ryan Jsy 40.00 80.00
39 Paul LoDuca Jsy 4.00 10.00
40 Cal Ripken Jsy 40.00 80.00
41 Terrence Long Jsy 4.00 10.00
42 Mike Sweeney Jsy 4.00 10.00
43 Carlos Lee Jsy 4.00 10.00
44 Ben Grieve Jsy 4.00 10.00
45 Tony Armas Jr. Jsy 4.00 10.00
46 Joe Mays Jsy 4.00 10.00
47 Jeff Kent Jsy 4.00 10.00
48 Andy Pettitte Jsy 6.00 15.00
49 Kirby Puckett Jsy 8.00 20.00
50 Aramis Ramirez Jsy 4.00 10.00
51 Tim Redding Jsy 4.00 10.00
52 Freddy Garcia Jsy 4.00 10.00
53 Javy Lopez Jsy 4.00 10.00
54 Mike Schmidt Jsy 20.00 50.00
55 Wade Miller Jsy 4.00 10.00
56 Ramon Ortiz Jsy 4.00 10.00
57 Ray Durham Jsy 4.00 10.00
58 J.D. Drew Jsy 4.00 10.00
59 Bret Boone Jsy 4.00 10.00
60 Mark Buehrle Jsy 4.00 10.00
61 Geoff Jenkins Jsy 4.00 10.00
62 Greg Maddux Jsy 10.00 25.00
63 Mark Grace Jsy 6.00 15.00
64 Toby Hall Jsy 4.00 10.00
65 A.J. Burnett Jsy 4.00 10.00
66 Bernie Williams Jsy 6.00 15.00
67 Roy Oswalt Jsy 4.00 10.00
68 Shannon Stewart Jsy 4.00 10.00
69 Barry Zito Jsy 4.00 10.00
70 Juan Pierre Jsy 4.00 10.00
71 Preston Wilson Jsy 4.00 10.00
72 Rafael Furcal Jsy 4.00 10.00
73 Sean Casey Jsy 4.00 10.00
74 John Olerud Jsy 4.00 10.00
75 Paul Konerko Jsy 4.00 10.00
76 Vernon Wells Jsy 4.00 10.00
77 Juan Gonzalez Jsy 4.00 10.00
78 Ellis Burks Jsy 4.00 10.00
79 Jim Edmonds Jsy 4.00 10.00
80 Robert Fick Jsy 4.00 10.00
81 Michael Cuddyer Jsy 4.00 10.00
82 Tim Hudson Jsy 4.00 10.00
83 Phil Nevin Jsy 4.00 10.00
84 Curt Schilling Jsy 4.00 10.00
85 Juan Cruz Jsy 4.00 10.00
86 Jeff Bagwell Jsy 6.00 15.00
87 Raul Mondesi Jsy 4.00 10.00
88 Bud Smith Jsy 4.00 10.00
89 Omar Vizquel Jsy 6.00 15.00
90 Vladimir Guerrero Jsy 8.00 20.00
91 Garret Anderson Jsy 4.00 10.00
92 Mike Piazza Jsy 10.00 25.00
93 Josh Beckett Jsy 4.00 10.00
94 Carlos Delgado Jsy 4.00 10.00
95 Kazuhiro Sasaki Jsy 4.00 10.00
96 Chipper Jones Jsy 8.00 20.00
97 Jacque Jones Jsy 4.00 10.00
98 Pedro Martinez Jsy 6.00 15.00
99 Marcus Giles Jsy 4.00 10.00
100 Craig Biggio Jsy 6.00 15.00
101 Orlando Cabrera Jsy 4.00 10.00
102 Al Leiter Jsy 4.00 10.00
103 Michael Barrett Jsy 4.00 10.00
104 Hideo Nomo Jsy 8.00 20.00
105 Mike Mussina Jsy 6.00 15.00
106 Jeremy Giambi Jsy 4.00 10.00
107 Cristian Guzman Jsy 4.00 10.00
108 Frank Thomas Jsy 8.00 20.00
109 Carlos Beltran Bat 4.00 10.00
110 Jorge Posada Bat 6.00 15.00
111 Roberto Alomar Bat 6.00 15.00
112 Bob Abreu Bat 4.00 10.00
113 Robin Ventura Bat 4.00 10.00
114 Pat Burrell Bat 4.00 10.00
115 Kenny Lofton Bat 4.00 10.00
116 Adrian Beltre Bat 4.00 10.00
117 Gary Sheffield Bat 4.00 10.00
118 Jermaine Dye Bat 4.00 10.00
119 Manny Ramirez Bat 6.00 15.00
120 Brian Giles Bat 4.00 10.00
121 Tsuyoshi Shinjo Bat 4.00 10.00
122 Rafael Palmeiro Bat 6.00 15.00
123 Mo Vaughn Bat 4.00 10.00
124 Kerry Wood Bat 4.00 10.00
125 Moises Alou Bat 4.00 10.00
126 Rickey Henderson Bat 8.00 20.00
127 Corey Patterson Bat 4.00 10.00
128 Jim Thome Bat 6.00 15.00
129 Richard Hidalgo Bat 4.00 10.00
130 Darin Erstad Bat 4.00 10.00
131 Johnny Damon Sox Bat 6.00 15.00
132 Juan Encarnacion Bat 4.00 10.00
133 Scott Rolen Bat 6.00 15.00
134 Tom Glavine Bat 6.00 15.00
135 Ivan Rodriguez Bat 6.00 15.00
136 Jay Gibbons Bat 4.00 10.00
137 Trot Nixon Bat 4.00 10.00
138 Nick Neugebauer Bat 4.00 10.00
139 Barry Larkin Bat 6.00 15.00
140 Andruw Jones Bat 6.00 15.00
141 Shawn Green Bat 4.00 10.00
142 Jose Vidro Jsy 4.00 10.00
143 Derek Jeter Base 12.50 30.00
144 Ichiro Suzuki Base 10.00 25.00
145 Ken Griffey Jr. Base 8.00 20.00
146 Barry Bonds Base 12.50 30.00
147 Albert Pujols Base 8.00 20.00
148 Sammy Sosa Base 8.00 20.00
149 Jason Giambi Base 4.00 10.00
150 Alfonso Soriano Jsy 4.00 10.00
151 Drew Henson NG Bat 3.00 8.00
152 Luis Garcia NG Bat 3.00 8.00
153 Geronimo Gil NG Jsy 3.00 8.00
154 Corky Miller NG Jsy 3.00 8.00
155 Mike Rivera NG Bat 3.00 8.00
156 Mark Ellis NG Jsy 3.00 8.00
157 Josh Pearce NG Bat 3.00 8.00
158 Ryan Ludwick NG Bat 3.00 8.00
159 So Taguchi NG Bat 4.00 10.00
160 Cody Ransom NG Jsy 3.00 8.00
161 Jeff Deardorff NG Bat 3.00 8.00
162 Franklyn German NG Bat 3.00 8.00
163 Ed Rogers NG Jsy 3.00 8.00
164 Eric Cyr NG Jsy 3.00 8.00
165 Victor Alvarez NG Jsy 3.00 8.00
166 Victor Martinez NG Jsy 4.00 10.00
167 Brandon Berger NG Jsy 3.00 8.00
168 Juan Diaz NG Jsy 3.00 8.00
169 Kevin Frederick NG Jsy 3.00 8.00
170 Earl Snyder NG Bat 3.00 8.00
171 Morgan Ensberg NG Bat 3.00 8.00
172 Ryan Jamison NG Jsy 3.00 8.00
173 Rodrigo Rosario NG Jsy 3.00 8.00
174 Willie Harris NG Bat 3.00 8.00
175 Ramon Vazquez NG Bat 3.00 8.00
176 Kazuhisa Ishii NG Bat 4.00 10.00
177 Hank Blalock NG Jsy 4.00 10.00
178 Mark Prior NG Bat 4.00 10.00
179 Dewon Brazelton NG Jsy 3.00 8.00
180 Doug Devore NG Jsy 3.00 8.00
181 Jorge Padilla NG Bat 3.00 8.00
182 Mark Teixeira NG Jsy 4.00 10.00
183 Orlando Hudson NG Bat 3.00 8.00
184 John Buck NG Jsy 3.00 8.00
185 Erik Bedard NG Jsy 3.00 8.00
186 Allan Simpson NG Jsy 3.00 8.00
187 Travis Hafner NG Jsy 3.00 8.00
188 Jason Lane NG Jsy 3.00 8.00
189 Marlon Byrd NG Jsy 3.00 8.00
190 Joe Thurston NG Jsy 3.00 8.00
191 Brandon Backe NG Jsy 4.00 10.00
192 Josh Phelps NG Jsy 3.00 8.00
193 Bill Hall NG Bat 3.00 8.00
194 Chris Snelling NG Bat 3.00 8.00
195 Austin Kearns NG Jsy 3.00 8.00
196 Antonio Perez NG Bat 3.00 8.00
197 Angel Berroa NG Bat 3.00 8.00
198 Anderson Machado NG Jsy 3.00 8.00
199 Alfredo Amezaga NG Jsy 3.00 8.00
200 Eric Hinske NG Bat 3.00 8.00

2002 Leaf Certified All-Certified Team

Inserted at stated odds of one in 17, these 25 card feature major stars using mirror board and gold foil stamping.

COMPLETE SET (25) 40.00 100.00
*BLUE: 2X TO 5X BASIC ALL-CERT.TEAM
BLUE PRINT RUN 50 SERIAL #'d SETS
GOLD PRINT RUN 25 SERIAL #'d SETS
NO GOLD PRICING DUE TO SCARCITY
*RED: 1.25X TO 3X BASIC ALL-CERT.TEAM
RED PRINT RUN 75 SERIAL #'d SETS
1 Ichiro Suzuki 3.00 8.00
2 Alex Rodriguez 2.50 6.00
3 Sammy Sosa 1.50 4.00
4 Jeff Bagwell 1.25 3.00
5 Greg Maddux 2.50 6.00
6 Todd Helton 1.25 3.00
7 Nomar Garciaparra 2.50 6.00
8 Ken Griffey Jr. 2.50 6.00
9 Roger Clemens 3.00 8.00
10 Adam Dunn 1.25 3.00
11 Chipper Jones 1.50 4.00
12 Hideo Nomo 1.50 4.00
13 Lance Berkman 1.25 3.00
14 Barry Bonds 4.00 10.00
15 Manny Ramirez 1.25 3.00
16 Jason Giambi 1.25 3.00
17 Rickey Henderson 1.50 4.00
18 Randy Johnson 1.50 4.00
19 Derek Jeter 4.00 10.00
20 Kazuhisa Ishii 1.25 3.00
21 Frank Thomas 1.50 4.00
22 Mike Piazza 2.50 6.00
23 Albert Pujols 3.00 8.00
24 Pedro Martinez 1.25 3.00
25 Vladimir Guerrero 1.50 4.00

2002 Leaf Certified Fabric of the Game

Randomly inserted in packs, these 703 cards feature a game-used swatch and are broken up into the following categories. There is a base card which has a stated print run of anywhere from five to 100 copies and cut into a design of a base. There is also pattern which have a stated print run of five to 50 copies with the swatch cut into the shape of the player's position. There is also a jersey subset which is cut into the shape of the player's uniform number. These cards range anywhere from a stated print run to anywhere from one to 75 serial numbered cards. There is also the debut year subset which has a stated print run of anywhere from 14 to 101 serial numbered cards. In addition, an unannouced subset featured either information about the player's induction into the Hall of Fame or their nickname. These cards mostly have stated print runs of 25 or less and therefore are not priced due to market scarcity.

1BA Bobby Doerr/10
1DY Bobby Doerr/37 12.50 30.00
1IN Bobby Doerr HOF 86/4
1JN Bobby Doerr/1
1PS Bobby Doerr/25
1INA Bobby Doerr HOF 86 AU/1
2BA Ozzie Smith/15
2DY Ozzie Smith/78 15.00 40.00
2JN Ozzie Smith/1
2PS Ozzie Smith/15
2INA Ozzie Smith HOF 02 AU/5
3BA Pee Wee Reese/5
3DY Pee Wee Reese/40 20.00 50.00
3IN Pee Wee Reese HOF 84/5
3JN Pee Wee Reese/1
3PS Pee Wee Reese/10
4BA Tommy Lasorda/80 6.00 15.00
4DY Tommy Lasorda/54 10.00 25.00
4IN Tommy Lasorda HOF 97/20
4JN Tommy Lasorda/2
4PS Tommy Lasorda/50 10.00 25.00
5BA Red Schoendienst/5
5DY Red Schoendienst/45 12.50 30.00
5IN Red Schoendienst HOF 89/5
5JN Red Schoendienst/2
5PS Red Schoendienst/10
6BA Lou Gehrig/5
6DY Lou Gehrig/23
6IN Lou Gehrig HOF 39/5
6JN Lou Gehrig/4
6PS Lou Gehrig/10
7BA Harmon Killebrew/10
7DY Harmon Killebrew/54 15.00 40.00
7JN Harmon Killebrew/3
7PS Harmon Killebrew/20
7INA Harmon Killebrew HOF 84 AU/5
8BA Roger Maris A's/10
8DY Roger Maris A's/57 60.00 120.00
8JN Roger Maris A's/3
8PS Roger Maris A's/10
9BA Babe Ruth/5
9DY Babe Ruth/14
9IN Babe Ruth HOF 36/5
9JN Babe Ruth/3
9PS Babe Ruth/10
10BA Mel Ott/5
10DY Mel Ott/26 50.00 100.00
10IN Mel Ott HOF 51/5
10JN Mel Ott/4
10PS Mel Ott/10
11BA Paul Molitor/100 6.00 15.00
11DY Paul Molitor/78 6.00 15.00
11JN Paul Molitor/4
11PS Paul Molitor/50 10.00 25.00
12BA Duke Snider/5
12DY Duke Snider/47 20.00 50.00
12JN Duke Snider/4
12PS Duke Snider/10
12INA Duke Snider HOF 80 AU/5
13BA Brooks Robinson/5
13DY Brooks Robinson/55 15.00 40.00
13JN Brooks Robinson/5
13PS Brooks Robinson/10
13INA Brooks Robinson HOF 83 AU/5
14BA George Brett/40 40.00 80.00
14DY George Brett/73 30.00 60.00
14IN George Brett HOF 99/5
14JN George Brett/5
14PS George Brett/25
14INA George Brett HOF 99 AU/5
15BA Johnny Bench/80 10.00 25.00
15DY Johnny Bench/67 15.00 40.00
15IN Johnny Bench HOF 89/15
15JN Johnny Bench/5
15PS Johnny Bench/50 15.00 40.00
15INA Johnny Bench HOF 89 AU/5
16BA Lou Boudreau/5
16DY Lou Boudreau/38 12.50 30.00
16IN Lou Boudreau HOF 70/5
16JN Lou Boudreau/5
16PS Lou Boudreau/10
17BA Stan Musial/5
17DY Stan Musial/41 40.00 80.00
17JN Stan Musial/6
17PS Stan Musial/10
17INA Stan Musial HOF 69 AU/5
18BA Al Kaline/5
18DY Al Kaline/53 15.00 40.00
18JN Al Kaline/6
18PS Al Kaline/10
18INA Al Kaline HOF 80 AU/5
19BA Steve Garvey/100 6.00 15.00
19DY Steve Garvey/69 10.00 25.00
19JN Steve Garvey/6
19PS Steve Garvey/45 12.50 30.00
20BA Nomar Garciaparra/100 12.50 30.00
20DY Nomar Garciaparra/96 12.50 30.00
20PS Nomar Garciaparra/50 15.00 40.00
20JNA Nomar Garciaparra AU /5
21BA Joe Morgan/80 6.00 15.00
21DY Joe Morgan/63 10.00 25.00
21IN Joe Morgan HOF 90/15
21JN Joe Morgan/8
21PS Joe Morgan/50 10.00 25.00
21INA Joe Morgan HOF 90 AU/5
22BA Willie Stargell/5
22DY Willie Stargell/62 15.00 40.00
22IN Willie Stargell HOF 88/5
22JN Willie Stargell/8
22PS Willie Stargell/10
23BA Andre Dawson/80 6.00 15.00
23DY Andre Dawson/76 6.00 15.00
23IN Andre Dawson Hawk/15
23JN Andre Dawson/8
23PS Andre Dawson/50 10.00 25.00
23INA Andre Dawson Hawk AU/5
24BA Gary Carter/100 6.00 15.00
24DY Gary Carter/74 10.00 25.00
24JN Gary Carter/8
24PS Gary Carter/50 10.00 25.00
25BA Reggie Jackson A's/10
25DY Reggie Jackson A's/67 15.00 40.00
25JN Reggie Jackson A's/9
25PS Reggie Jackson A's/25
25INA Reggie Jackson A's HOF 93 AU/5
26BA Ted Williams/5
26DY Ted Williams/39
26IN Ted Williams HOF 66/5
26JN Ted Williams/9
26PS Ted Williams/10
27BA Phil Rizzuto/5
27DY Phil Rizzuto/41 20.00 50.00
27JN Phil Rizzuto/10
27PS Phil Rizzuto/10
27INA Phil Rizzuto HOF 94 AU/5
28BA Luis Aparicio/5
28DY Luis Aparicio/56 10.00 25.00
28JN Luis Aparicio/11
28PS Luis Aparicio/10
28INA Luis Aparicio HOF 84 AU/5
29BA Robin Yount/80 10.00 25.00
29DY Robin Yount/74 15.00 40.00
29IN Robin Yount HOF 99/15
29JN Robin Yount/19
29PS Robin Yount/50 15.00 40.00
29INA Robin Yount HOF 99 AU/5
30BA Tony Gwynn/100 10.00 25.00
30DY Tony Gwynn/82 10.00 25.00
30JN Tony Gwynn/14
30PS Tony Gwynn/50 15.00 40.00
30JNA Tony Gwynn AU/5
31BA Ernie Banks/5
31DY Ernie Banks/53 15.00 40.00
31JN Ernie Banks/14
31PS Ernie Banks/10
31INA Ernie Banks HOF 77 AU/5
32BA Joe Torre/50 15.00 40.00
32DY Joe Torre/60 15.00 40.00
32JN Joe Torre/15
32PS Joe Torre/25
33BA Bo Jackson/100 10.00 25.00
33DY Bo Jackson/86 10.00 25.00
33JN Bo Jackson/16
33PS Bo Jackson/35 30.00 60.00
34BA Alfonso Soriano/80 6.00 15.00
34DY Alfonso Soriano/99 6.00 15.00
34JN Alfonso Soriano/12
34PS Alfonso Soriano/50 10.00 25.00
35BA Cal Ripken/80 40.00 80.00
35DY Cal Ripken/81 40.00 80.00
35IN Cal Ripken Iron Man/15
35JN Cal Ripken/8
35PS Cal Ripken/50 50.00 100.00
35INA Cal Ripken Iron Man AU/5
36BA Miguel Tejada/100 6.00 15.00
36DY Miguel Tejada/97 6.00 15.00
36JN Miguel Tejada/4
36PS Miguel Tejada/50 10.00 25.00
37BA Alex Rodriguez M's/100 10.00 25.00
37DY Alex Rodriguez M's/94 10.00 25.00
37JN Alex Rodriguez M's/3
37PS Alex Rodriguez M's/50 15.00 40.00
38BA Mike Schmidt/80 20.00 50.00
38DY Mike Schmidt/72 20.00 50.00
38IN Mike Schmidt HOF 95/15
38JN Mike Schmidt/20
38PS Mike Schmidt/50 30.00 60.00
38INA Mike Schmidt HOF 95 AU/5
39BA Lou Brock/5
39DY Lou Brock/61 15.00 40.00
39JN Lou Brock/20
39PS Lou Brock/10
39INA Lou Brock HOF 85 AU/5
40BA Don Sutton/80 6.00 15.00
40DY Don Sutton/66 10.00 25.00
40IN Don Sutton HOF 98/15
40JN Don Sutton/20
40PS Don Sutton/50 10.00 25.00
40INA Don Sutton HOF 98 AU/5
41BA Roberto Clemente/5
41DY Roberto Clemente/55 75.00 150.00
41IN Roberto Clemente HOF 73/5
41JN Roberto Clemente/21
41PS Roberto Clemente/10
42BA Jim Palmer/20
42DY Jim Palmer/65 10.00 25.00
42JN Jim Palmer/22
42PS Jim Palmer/15
42INA Jim Palmer HOF 90 AU/5
43BA Don Mattingly/40 40.00 80.00
43DY Don Mattingly/82 20.00 50.00
43IN Don Mattingly Donnie BB/5
43JN Don Mattingly/23
43PS Don Mattingly/25
43INA Don Mattingly Donnie BB AU/5
44BA Ryne Sandberg 40 40.00 80.00
44DY Ryne Sandberg/81 30.00 60.00
44IN Ryne Sandberg Ryno/5
44JN Ryne Sandberg/23
44PS Ryne Sandberg/25
44INA Ryne Sandberg Ryno AU/5
45BA Early Wynn/5
45DY Early Wynn/39 12.50 30.00
45IN Early Wynn HOF 72/5
45JN Early Wynn/24
45PS Early Wynn/10
46BA Mike Piazza Dodgers/100 10.00 25.00
46DY Mike Piazza Dodgers/92 10.00 25.00
46JN Mike Piazza Dodgers/31 20.00 50.00
46PS Mike Piazza Dodgers/50 12.50 30.00
47BA Wade Boggs/100 10.00 25.00
47DY Wade Boggs/82 10.00 25.00
47JN Wade Boggs/26 30.00 60.00
47PS Wade Boggs/45 20.00 50.00
48BA Catfish Hunter/10
48DY Catfish Hunter/65 15.00 40.00
48IN Catfish Hunter HOF 87/5
48JN Catfish Hunter/27 30.00 60.00
48PS Catfish Hunter/25
49BA Juan Marichal/20
49DY Juan Marichal/60 10.00 25.00
49JN Juan Marichal/27 15.00 40.00
49PS Juan Marichal/15
49INA Juan Marichal HOF 83 AU/5
50BA Carlton Fisk Red Sox/80 10.00 25.00
50DY Carlton Fisk Red Sox/69 15.00 40.00
50IN Carlton Fisk Red Sox HOF 00/15
50JN Carlton Fisk Red Sox/27 30.00 60.00
50PS Carlton Fisk Red Sox/50 15.00 40.00
50INA Carlton Fisk Red Sox HOF 00 AU/5
51BA Curt Schilling/100 6.00 15.00
51DY Curt Schilling/88 6.00 15.00
51JN Curt Schilling/38 12.50 30.00
51PS Curt Schilling/50 10.00 25.00
52BA Rod Carew Angels/80 10.00 25.00
52DY Rod Carew Angels/67 15.00 40.00
52IN Rod Carew Angels HOF 91/15
52JN Rod Carew Angels/29
52PS Rod Carew Angels/50 15.00 40.00
52INA Rod Carew Angels HOF 91 AU/5
53BA Rod Carew Twins/10
53DY Rod Carew Twins/67 15.00 40.00
53JN Rod Carew Twins/29
53PS Rod Carew Twins/25
53INA Rod Carew Twins HOF 91 AU/5
54BA Joe Carter/100 6.00 15.00
54DY Joe Carter/83 6.00 15.00
54JN Joe Carter/29 15.00 40.00
54PS Joe Carter/50 10.00 25.00
55BA Nolan Ryan Angels/5
55DY Nolan Ryan Angels/66 40.00 80.00
55IN Nolan Ryan Angels HOF 99/5
55JN Nolan Ryan Angels/30
55PS Nolan Ryan Angels/10
55INA Nolan Ryan Angels HOF 99 AU/5
56BA Orlando Cepeda/80 6.00 15.00
56DY Orlando Cepeda/58 10.00 25.00
56IN Orlando Cepeda HOF 99/15
56JN Orlando Cepeda/30 15.00 40.00
56PS Orlando Cepeda/50 10.00 25.00
56INA Orlando Cepeda HOF 99 AU/5
57BA Dave Winfield/80 6.00 15.00
57DY Dave Winfield/73 10.00 25.00
57IN Dave Winfield HOF 01/15
57JN Dave Winfield/31 15.00 40.00
57PS Dave Winfield/50 10.00 25.00
57INA Dave Winfield HOF 01 AU/5
58BA Hoyt Wilhelm/80 6.00 15.00
58DY Hoyt Wilhelm/52 10.00 25.00
58IN Hoyt Wilhelm HOF 85/15
58JN Hoyt Wilhelm/31 15.00 40.00
58PS Hoyt Wilhelm/50 10.00 25.00
58INA Hoyt Wilhelm HOF 85 AU/5
59BA Steve Carlton/80 6.00 15.00
59DY Steve Carlton/65 10.00 25.00
59IN Steve Carlton HOF 94/15
59JN Steve Carlton/32 15.00 40.00
59PS Steve Carlton/50 10.00 25.00
59INA Steve Carlton HOF 94 AU/5
60BA Eddie Murray/100 10.00 25.00
60DY Eddie Murray/77 10.00 25.00
60JN Eddie Murray/33 30.00 60.00
60PS Eddie Murray/50 15.00 40.00
61BA Nolan Ryan Rangers/40 50.00 100.00
61DY Nolan Ryan Rangers/66 40.00 80.00
61IN Nolan Ryan Rangers HOF 99/5
61JN Nolan Ryan Rangers/34 50.00 100.00
61PS Nolan Ryan Rangers/25
61INA Nolan Ryan Rangers HOF 99 AU/5
62BA Nolan Ryan Astros/40 30.00 60.00
62DY Nolan Ryan Astros/66 40.00 80.00
62IN Nolan Ryan Astros HOF 99/5
62JN Nolan Ryan Astros/34 30.00 60.00
62PS Nolan Ryan Astros/25
62INA Nolan Ryan Astros HOF 99 AU/5
63BA Kirby Puckett/40 20.00 50.00
63DY Kirby Puckett/84 10.00 25.00
63IN Kirby Puckett HOF 01/5
63JN Kirby Puckett/34 30.00 60.00
63PS Kirby Puckett/25
63INA Kirby Puckett HOF 01 AU/5
64BA Yogi Berra/5
64DY Yogi Berra/46 20.00 50.00
64JN Yogi Berra/35 30.00 60.00
64PS Yogi Berra/10
64INA Yogi Berra HOF 72 AU/5
65BA Phil Niekro/80 6.00 15.00
65DY Phil Niekro/64 10.00 25.00
65IN Phil Niekro HOF 97/15
65JN Phil Niekro/35 15.00 40.00
65PS Phil Niekro/50 10.00 25.00
65INA Phil Niekro HOF 97 AU/5
66BA Gaylord Perry/80 6.00 15.00
66DY Gaylord Perry/62 10.00 25.00
66IN Gaylord Perry HOF 91/20
66JN Gaylord Perry/36 12.50 30.00
66PS Gaylord Perry/50 10.00 25.00
67BA Pedro Martinez Expos/100 10.00 25.00
67DY Pedro Martinez Expos/92 10.00 25.00
67JN Pedro Martinez Expos/45 20.00 50.00
67PS Pedro Martinez Expos/50 15.00 40.00
68BA Alex Rodriguez Rgr/100 10.00 25.00
68DY Alex Rodriguez Rgr/94 10.00 25.00
68PS Alex Rodriguez Rgr/50 15.00 40.00
68JNA Alex Rodriguez Rgr AU/3
69BA Dave Parker/100 6.00 15.00
69DY Dave Parker/73 10.00 25.00
69JN Dave Parker/39 12.50 30.00
69PS Dave Parker/50 10.00 25.00
70BA Darin Erstad/100 6.00 15.00
70DY Darin Erstad/96 6.00 15.00
70JN Darin Erstad 17
70PS Darin Erstad/50 10.00 25.00
71BA Eddie Mathews/5
71DY Eddie Mathews/52 15.00 40.00
71IN Eddie Mathews HOF 78/5
71JN Eddie Mathews/41 20.00 50.00
71PS Eddie Mathews/10
72BA Tom Seaver Mets/5
72DY Tom Seaver Mets/67 15.00 40.00
72JN Tom Seaver Mets/41 20.00 50.00
72PS Tom Seaver Mets/10
72INA Tom Seaver Mets HOF 92 AU/5
73BA Tom Seaver Reds/10
73DY Tom Seaver Reds/67 15.00 40.00
73JN Tom Seaver Reds/41 20.00 50.00
73PS Tom Seaver Reds/25
73INA Tom Seaver Reds HOF 92 AU/5
74BA Jackie Robinson/5
74DY Jackie Robinson/47 50.00 100.00
74IN Jackie Robinson HOF 62/5
74JN Jackie Robinson/42 50.00 100.00
74PS Jackie Robinson/10
75BA Randy Johnson M's/80 10.00 25.00
75DY Randy Johnson M's/88 10.00 25.00
75IN Randy Johnson M's Big Unit/20
75JN Randy Johnson M's/51 15.00 40.00
75PS Randy Johnson M's/50 15.00 40.00
76BA Reggie Jackson Yanks/10
76DY Reggie Jackson Yanks/67 15.00 40.00
76JN Reggie Jackson Yanks/44 20.00 50.00
76PS Reggie Jackson Yanks/25
76INA Reggie Jackson Yanks HOF 93 AU/5
77BA Reggie Jackson Angels/80 10.00 25.00
77DY Reggie Jackson Angels/67 15.00 40.00
77IN Reggie Jackson Angels HOF 93/15
77JN Reggie Jackson Angels/44 20.00 50.00

77PS Reggie Jackson Angels/50 15.00 40.00
77INA Reggie Jackson Angels HOF 93 AU/5
78BA Willie McCovey/80 6.00 15.00
78DY Willie McCovey/59 10.00 25.00
78IN Willie McCovey HOF 86/15
78JN Willie McCovey/44 12.50 30.00
78PS Willie McCovey/50 10.00 25.00
78INA Willie McCovey HOF 86 AU/5
79BA Eric Davis/100 6.00 15.00
79DY Eric Davis/84 6.00 15.00
79JN Eric Davis/34 15.00 40.00
79PS Eric Davis/50 10.00 25.00
79JNA Eric Davis AU/10
80BA Carlos Delgado/95 6.00 15.00
80DY Carlos Delgado/93 6.00 15.00
80JN Carlos Delgado/25
80PS Carlos Delgado/25
81BA Dale Murphy/100 10.00 25.00
81DY Dale Murphy/76 10.00 25.00
81PS Dale Murphy/50 15.00 40.00
81JNA Dale Murphy AU/3
82BA Brian Giles/100 6.00 15.00
82DY Brian Giles/95 6.00 15.00
82JN Brian Giles/24
82PS Brian Giles/50 10.00 25.00
83BA Kazuhiro Sasaki/100 6.00 15.00
83DY Kazuhiro Sasaki/100 6.00 15.00
83JN Kazuhiro Sasaki/22
83PS Kazuhiro Sasaki 50 10.00 25.00
84BA Phil Nevin/100 6.00 15.00
84DY Phil Nevin/95 6.00 15.00
84JN Phil Nevin/23
84PS Phil Nevin/50 10.00 25.00
85BA Frank Thomas/80 20.00 50.00
85DY Frank Thomas/90 20.00 50.00
85IN Frank Thomas Big Hurt/15
85JN Frank Thomas/35 30.00 60.00
85PS Frank Thomas/50 20.00 50.00
85INA Frank Thomas Big Hurt AU/5
86BA Raul Mondesi/100 6.00 15.00
86DY Raul Mondesi/93 6.00 15.00
86JN Raul Mondesi/43 12.50 30.00
86PS Raul Mondesi/50 10.00 25.00
87BA Don Drysdale/5
87DY Don Drysdale/56 15.00 40.00
87IN Don Drysdale HOF 84/5
87JN Don Drysdale/53 15.00 40.00
87PS Don Drysdale/10
88BA Gary Sheffield/100 6.00 15.00
88DY Gary Sheffield/88 6.00 15.00
88JN Gary Sheffield/10
88PS Gary Sheffield/50 10.00 25.00
89BA Andy Pettitte/100 10.00 25.00
89DY Andy Pettitte/95 10.00 25.00
89JN Andy Pettitte/46 20.00 50.00
89PS Andy Pettitte/50 15.00 40.00
90BA Lance Berkman/45 12.50 30.00
90DY Lance Berkman/99 6.00 15.00
90JN Lance Berkman/12
90PS Lance Berkman/25
90JNA Lance Berkman AU/5
91BA Paul Lo Duca/100 6.00 15.00
91DY Paul Lo Duca/98 6.00 15.00
91JN Paul Lo Duca/16
91PS Paul Lo Duca/50 10.00 25.00
92BA Kevin Brown/25
92DY Kevin Brown/86 6.00 15.00
92JN Kevin Brown/27 15.00 40.00
92PS Kevin Brown/25
93BA Jim Thome/100 10.00 25.00
93DY Jim Thome/91 10.00 25.00
93JN Jim Thome/20
93PS Jim Thome/50 15.00 40.00
93JNA Jim Thome AU/5
94BA Mike Sweeney/100 6.00 15.00
94DY Mike Sweeney/95 6.00 15.00
94JN Mike Sweeney/29 15.00 40.00
94PS Mike Sweeney/50 10.00 25.00
95BA Pedro Martinez Red Sox/100 10.00 25.00
95DY Pedro Martinez Red Sox/92 10.00 25.00
95JN Pedro Martinez Red Sox/45 20.00 50.00
95PS Pedro Martinez Red Sox/45 20.00 50.00
96BA Cliff Floyd/100 6.00 15.00
96DY Cliff Floyd/93 6.00 15.00
96JN Cliff Floyd/30 15.00 40.00
96PS Cliff Floyd/50 10.00 25.00
97BA Larry Walker/100 6.00 15.00
97DY Larry Walker/89 6.00 15.00
97JN Larry Walker/33 15.00 40.00
97PS Larry Walker/50 10.00 25.00
98BA Ivan Rodriguez/80 10.00 25.00
98DY Ivan Rodriguez/91 10.00 25.00
98IN Ivan Rodriguez Pudge/15
98JN Ivan Rodriguez/7
98PS Ivan Rodriguez/50 15.00 40.00
98INA Ivan Rodriguez Pudge AU/5
99BA Aramis Ramirez/100 6.00 15.00
99DY Aramis Ramirez/98 6.00 15.00
99JN Aramis Ramirez/16
99PS Aramis Ramirez/50 10.00 25.00
100BA Roberto Alomar/100 10.00 25.00
100DY Roberto Alomar/88 10.00 25.00
100JN Roberto Alomar/12
100PS Roberto Alomar/50 15.00 40.00
101BA Ben Sheets/100 6.00 15.00
101DY Ben Sheets/101 6.00 15.00
101JN Ben Sheets/15
101PS Ben Sheets/50 10.00 25.00
102BA Adam Dunn/5
102DY Adam Dunn/101 6.00 15.00
102JN Adam Dunn/39 12.50 30.00
102PS Adam Dunn/5
102JNA Adam Dunn AU/5
103BA Hideo Nomo/15
103DY Hideo Nomo/95 15.00 40.00
103JN Hideo Nomo/11
103PS Hideo Nomo/20
104BA C.C. Sabathia/50 10.00 25.00
104DY C.C. Sabathia/101 6.00 15.00
104JN C.C. Sabathia/52 10.00 25.00
104PS C.C. Sabathia/50 10.00 25.00
105BA R.Henderson A's/100 10.00 25.00
105DY Rickey Henderson A's/79 10.00 25.00
105JN R.Henderson A's/30 30.00 60.00
105PS Rickey Henderson A's/50 15.00 40.00
105JNA Rickey Henderson A's AU/5
106BA Carlton Fisk W.Sox/80 10.00 25.00
106DY Carlton Fisk W.Sox/69 15.00 40.00
106IN Carlton Fisk W.Sox HOF 00/15
106JN Carlton Fisk W.Sox/72 15.00 40.00
106PS Carlton Fisk W.Sox/50 15.00 40.00
106INA Carlton Fisk W.Sox HOF 00 AU/5
107BA Chan Ho Park/100 6.00 15.00
107DY Chan Ho Park/94 6.00 15.00
107JN Chan Ho Park/61 10.00 25.00
107PS Chan Ho Park/50 10.00 25.00
108BA Mike Mussina/100 10.00 25.00
108DY Mike Mussina/91 10.00 25.00
108JN Mike Mussina 35 30.00 60.00
108PS Mike Mussina/50 15.00 40.00
109BA Mark Mulder/100 6.00 15.00
109DY Mark Mulder/100 6.00 15.00
109JN Mark Mulder/20
109PS Mark Mulder/35 15.00 40.00
110BA Tsuyoshi Shinjo/100 6.00 15.00
110DY Tsuyoshi Shinjo/101 6.00 15.00
110JN Tsuyoshi Shinjo/5
110PS Tsuyoshi Shinjo/30 15.00 40.00
111BA Pat Burrell/100 6.00 15.00
111DY Pat Burrell/100 6.00 15.00
111JN Pat Burrell/5
111PS Pat Burrell/50 10.00 25.00
112BA Edgar Martinez/100 10.00 25.00
112DY Edgar Martinez/87 10.00 25.00
112JN Edgar Martinez/11
112PS Edgar Martinez/50 15.00 40.00
113BA Barry Larkin/100 10.00 25.00
113DY Barry Larkin/86 10.00 25.00
113JN Barry Larkin/11
113PS Barry Larkin/50 15.00 40.00
114BA Jeff Kent/100 6.00 15.00
114DY Jeff Kent/92 6.00 15.00
114JN Jeff Kent/21
114PS Jeff Kent/50 10.00 25.00
115BA Chipper Jones/100 10.00 25.00
115DY Chipper Jones/93 10.00 25.00
115JN Chipper Jones/10
115PS Chipper Jones/50 15.00 40.00
116BA Magglio Ordonez/100 6.00 15.00
116DY Magglio Ordonez/97 6.00 15.00
116JN Magglio Ordonez/30 15.00 40.00
116PS Magglio Ordonez/50 10.00 25.00
117BA Jim Edmonds/100 6.00 15.00
117DY Jim Edmonds/93 6.00 15.00
117JN Jim Edmonds/15
117PS Jim Edmonds/50 10.00 25.00
118BA Andruw Jones/100 10.00 25.00
118DY Andruw Jones/96 10.00 25.00
118JN Andruw Jones/25
118PS Andruw Jones/45 20.00 50.00
119BA Jose Canseco/100 10.00 25.00
119DY Jose Canseco/85 10.00 25.00
119JN Jose Canseco/23
119PS Jose Canseco/50 15.00 40.00
119JNA Jose Canseco AU/10
120BA Manny Ramirez/100 10.00 25.00
120DY Manny Ramirez/93 10.00 25.00
120JN Manny Ramirez/24
120PS Manny Ramirez/50 15.00 40.00
121BA Sean Casey/100 6.00 15.00
121DY Sean Casey/97 6.00 15.00
121JN Sean Casey/21
121PS Sean Casey/50 10.00 25.00
122BA Bret Boone/100 6.00 15.00
122DY Bret Boone/92 6.00 15.00
122JN Bret Boone/29 15.00 40.00
122PS Bret Boone/50 10.00 25.00
123BA Tim Hudson/100 6.00 15.00
123DY Tim Hudson/99 6.00 15.00
123JN Tim Hudson/15
123PS Tim Hudson/50 10.00 25.00
124BA Craig Biggio/100 10.00 25.00
124DY Craig Biggio/88 10.00 25.00
124JN Craig Biggio/7
124PS Craig Biggio/50 15.00 40.00
125BA Mike Piazza Mets/100 10.00 25.00
125DY Mike Piazza Mets/92 10.00 25.00
125JN Mike Piazza Mets/31 20.00 50.00
125PS Mike Piazza Mets/50 12.50 30.00
126BA Jack Morris/100 6.00 15.00
126DY Jack Morris/77 6.00 15.00
126JN Jack Morris/47 12.50 30.00
126PS Jack Morris/25
127BA Roy Oswalt/100 6.00 15.00
127DY Roy Oswalt/101 6.00 15.00
127JN Roy Oswalt/39 12.50 30.00
127PS Roy Oswalt/50 10.00 25.00
127JNA Roy Oswalt AU/5
128BA Shawn Green/100 6.00 15.00
128DY Shawn Green/93 6.00 15.00
128JN Shawn Green/15
128PS Shawn Green/50 10.00 25.00
129BA Carlos Beltran/100 6.00 15.00
129DY Carlos Beltran/98 6.00 15.00
129JN Carlos Beltran/15
129PS Carlos Beltran/50 10.00 25.00
130BA Todd Helton/100 10.00 25.00
130DY Todd Helton/97 10.00 25.00
130JN Todd Helton/17
130PS Todd Helton/50 15.00 40.00
131BA Barry Zito/75 6.00 15.00
131DY Barry Zito/100 6.00 15.00
131JN Barry Zito/75 6.00 15.00
131PS Barry Zito/30 15.00 40.00
132BA J.D. Drew/100 6.00 15.00
132DY J.D. Drew/98 6.00 15.00
132JN J.D. Drew/7
132PS J.D. Drew/50 10.00 25.00
133BA Mark Grace/100 10.00 25.00
133DY Mark Grace 88 10.00 25.00
133JN Mark Grace/17
133PS Mark Grace/50 15.00 40.00
134BA R.Henderson Mets/100 10.00 25.00
134DY R.Henderson Mets/79 10.00 25.00
134JN Rickey Henderson Mets/24
134PS R.Henderson Mets/50 15.00 40.00
135BA Greg Maddux/100 10.00 25.00
135DY Greg Maddux/86 10.00 25.00
135JN Greg Maddux/31
135PS Greg Maddux/50 12.50 30.00
136BA Garret Anderson/100 6.00 15.00
136DY Garret Anderson/94 6.00 15.00
136JN Garret Anderson/16
136PS Garret Anderson/50 10.00 25.00
137BA Rafael Palmeiro/100 10.00 25.00
137DY Rafael Palmeiro/86 10.00 25.00
137JN Rafael Palmeiro/20
137PS Rafael Palmeiro/50 15.00 40.00
137JNA Rafael Palmeiro AU/5
138BA Luis Gonzalez/50 10.00 25.00
138DY Luis Gonzalez/90 6.00 15.00
138JN Luis Gonzalez/20
138PS Luis Gonzalez/45 12.50 30.00
139BA Nick Johnson/100 6.00 15.00
139DY Nick Johnson/101 6.00 15.00
139JN Nick Johnson/26 15.00 40.00
139PS Nick Johnson/50 10.00 25.00
139JNA Nick Johnson AU/10
140BA Vladimir Guerrero/80 10.00 25.00
140DY Vladimir Guerrero/96 10.00 25.00
140JN Vladimir Guerrero/22
140PS Vladimir Guerrero/50 15.00 40.00
140JNA Vladimir Guerrero AU/5
141BA Mark Buehrle/20
141DY Mark Buehrle/100 6.00 15.00
141JN Mark Buehrle/56 10.00 25.00
141PS Mark Buehrle/20
142BA Troy Glaus/100 6.00 15.00
142DY Troy Glaus/98 6.00 15.00
142JN Troy Glaus/25
142PS Troy Glaus/50 10.00 25.00
143BA Juan Gonzalez/100 6.00 15.00
143DY Juan Gonzalez/89 6.00 15.00
143JN Juan Gonzalez/22
143PS Juan Gonzalez/50 10.00 25.00
144BA Kerry Wood/100 6.00 15.00
144DY Kerry Wood/98 6.00 15.00
144JN Kerry Wood/34 15.00 40.00
144PS Kerry Wood/50 10.00 25.00
145BA Roger Clemens/80 15.00 40.00
145DY Roger Clemens/84 15.00 40.00
145IN Roger Clemens Rocket/16
145JN Roger Clemens/20
145PS Roger Clemens/50 30.00 60.00
145INA Roger Clemens Rocket AU/5
146BA Bob Abreu/100 6.00 15.00
146DY Bob Abreu/96 6.00 15.00
146JN Bob Abreu/53 10.00 25.00
146PS Bob Abreu/50 10.00 25.00
147BA Bernie Williams/95 10.00 25.00
147DY Bernie Williams/91 10.00 25.00
147JN Bernie Williams/51 15.00 40.00
147PS Bernie Williams/25
148BA Tom Glavine/100 10.00 25.00
148DY Tom Glavine/87 10.00 25.00
148JN Tom Glavine/47 20.00 50.00
148PS Tom Glavine/50 15.00 40.00
149BA Jorge Posada/100 10.00 25.00
149DY Jorge Posada/95 10.00 25.00
149JN Jorge Posada/20
149PS Jorge Posada/50 15.00 40.00
150BA R.Johnson D'Backs/80 10.00 25.00
150DY R.Johnson D'Backs/88 10.00 25.00
150IN Randy Johnson D'Backs Big Unit/20
150JN R.Johnson D'Backs/51 15.00 40.00
150PS R.Johnson D'Backs/50 15.00 40.00

2002 Leaf Certified Skills

Inserted at stated odds of one in 17, these 20 cards feature players who have have already established excellent stats be it for a game, season or career. These cards are produced on mirror board with silver foil stamping.

COMPLETE SET (20) 50.00 120.00
*BLUE: 1.25X TO 3X BASIC SKILLS
BLUE PRINT RUN 75 SERIAL #'d SETS
GOLD PRINT RUN 25 SERIAL #'d SETS
NO GOLD PRICING DUE TO SCARCITY
*RED: .75X TO 2X BASIC SKILLS
RED PRINT RUN 150 SERIAL #'d SETS
1 Barry Bonds 4.00 10.00
2 Greg Maddux 2.50 6.00
3 Rickey Henderson 1.50 4.00
4 Ichiro Suzuki 3.00 8.00
5 Pedro Martinez 1.25 3.00
6 Kazuhisa Ishii 1.25 3.00
7 Alex Rodriguez 2.50 6.00
8 Mike Piazza 2.50 6.00
9 Sammy Sosa 1.50 4.00
10 Derek Jeter 4.00 10.00
11 Albert Pujols 3.00 8.00
12 Roger Clemens 3.00 8.00
13 Mark Prior 1.00 2.50
14 Chipper Jones 1.50 4.00
15 Ken Griffey Jr. 2.50 6.00
16 Frank Thomas 1.50 4.00
17 Randy Johnson 1.50 4.00
18 Vladimir Guerrero 1.50 4.00
19 Nomar Garciaparra 2.50 6.00
20 Jeff Bagwell 1.25 3.00

2003 Leaf Certified Materials

This 259-card set was issued in two separate series. The primary Leaf Certified Materials brand - containing cards 1-250 from the basic set - was released in August, 2003. The set was issued in seven card packs with an $10 SRP which were packaged 10 to a box and 20 boxes to a case. Cards numbered 1 through 200 feature veterans. Cards numbered 201 through 205 featured some baseball legends while cards numbered 206 through 250 are entitled New Generation and feature top prospects and rookies. Those cards, with the exception of card 220 were issued to a stated print run of 400 serial numbered sets. Card 220, featuring Jose Contreras, was issued to a stated print run of 100 serial numbered sets. Cards 251-259 were randomly seeded into packs of DLP Rookies and Traded of which was distributed in December, 2003. The nine update cards carry on the New Generation subset featuring top prospects, and like the earlier cards feature certified autographs. Serial numbered print runs for these update cards range from 100-250 copies per.

COMP.LO SET w/o SP's (200) 20.00 50.00
COMMON CARD (1-200) .40 1.00
COMMON CARD (201-205) 4.00 10.00
COM (201-219/221-250) 4.00 10.00
201-219/221-250 RANDOM IN LCM PACKS
COMMON (251-259) p/r 250 4.00 10.00
1 Troy Glaus .40 1.00
2 Alfredo Amezaga .40 1.00
3 Garret Anderson .40 1.00
4 Nolan Ryan Angels 2.50 6.00
5 Darin Erstad .40 1.00
6 Junior Spivey .40 1.00
7 Randy Johnson 1.00 2.50
8 Curt Schilling .40 1.00
9 Luis Gonzalez .40 1.00
10 Steve Finley .40 1.00
11 Matt Williams .40 1.00
12 Greg Maddux 1.50 4.00
13 Chipper Jones 1.00 2.50
14 Gary Sheffield .40 1.00
15 Adam LaRoche .40 1.00
16 Andruw Jones .60 1.50
17 Robert Fick .40 1.00
18 John Smoltz .60 1.50
19 Javy Lopez .40 1.00
20 Jay Gibbons .40 1.00
21 Geronimo Gil .40 1.00
22 Cal Ripken 3.00 8.00
23 Nomar Garciaparra 1.50 4.00
24 Pedro Martinez .60 1.50
25 Freddy Sanchez .40 1.00
26 Rickey Henderson 1.00 2.50
27 Manny Ramirez .60 1.50
28 Casey Fossum .40 1.00
29 Sammy Sosa 1.00 2.50
30 Kerry Wood .40 1.00
31 Corey Patterson .40 1.00
32 Nic Jackson .40 1.00
33 Mark Prior .60 1.50
34 Juan Cruz .40 1.00
35 Steve Smyth .40 1.00
36 Magglio Ordonez .40 1.00
37 Joe Borchard .40 1.00
38 Frank Thomas 1.00 2.50
39 Mark Buehrle .40 1.00
40 Joe Crede .40 1.00
41 Carlos Lee .40 1.00
42 Paul Konerko .40 1.00
43 Adam Dunn .40 1.00
44 Corky Miller .40 1.00
45 Brandon Larson .40 1.00
46 Ken Griffey Jr. 1.50 4.00
47 Barry Larkin .60 1.50
48 Sean Casey .40 1.00
49 Wily Mo Pena .40 1.00
50 Austin Kearns .40 1.00
51 Victor Martinez .60 1.50
52 Brian Tallet .40 1.00
53 Cliff Lee .40 1.00
54 Jeremy Guthrie .40 1.00
55 C.C. Sabathia .40 1.00
56 Ricardo Rodriguez .40 1.00
57 Omar Vizquel .60 1.50
58 Travis Hafner .40 1.00
59 Todd Helton .60 1.50
60 Jason Jennings .40 1.00
61 Jeff Baker .40 1.00
62 Larry Walker .40 1.00
63 Travis Chapman .40 1.00
64 Mike Maroth .40 1.00
65 Josh Beckett .40 1.00
66 Ivan Rodriguez .60 1.50
67 Brad Penny .40 1.00
68 A.J. Burnett .40 1.00
69 Craig Biggio .60 1.50
70 Roy Oswalt .40 1.00
71 Jason Lane .40 1.00
72 Nolan Ryan Astros 2.50 6.00
73 Wade Miller .40 1.00
74 Richard Hidalgo .40 1.00
75 Jeff Bagwell .60 1.50
76 Lance Berkman .40 1.00
77 Rodrigo Rosario .40 1.00
78 Jeff Kent .40 1.00
79 John Buck .40 1.00
80 Angel Berroa .40 1.00
81 Mike Sweeney .40 1.00
82 Mac Suzuki .40 1.00
83 Alexis Gomez .40 1.00
84 Carlos Beltran .40 1.00
85 Runelvys Hernandez .40 1.00
86 Hideo Nomo 1.00 2.50
87 Paul Lo Duca .40 1.00
88 Cesar Izturis .40 1.00
89 Kazuhisa Ishii .40 1.00
90 Shawn Green .40 1.00
91 Joe Thurston .40 1.00
92 Adrian Beltre .40 1.00
93 Kevin Brown .40 1.00
94 Richie Sexson .40 1.00
95 Ben Sheets .40 1.00
96 Takahito Nomura .40 1.00
97 Geoff Jenkins .40 1.00
98 Bill Hall .40 1.00
99 Torii Hunter .40 1.00
100 A.J. Pierzynski .40 1.00
101 Michael Cuddyer .40 1.00
102 Jose Morban .40 1.00
103 Brad Radke .40 1.00
104 Jacque Jones .40 1.00
105 Eric Milton .40 1.00
106 Joe Mays .40 1.00
107 Adam Johnson .40 1.00
108 Javier Vazquez .40 1.00
109 Vladimir Guerrero 1.00 2.50
110 Jose Vidro .40 1.00
111 Michael Barrett .40 1.00
112 Orlando Cabrera .40 1.00
113 Tom Glavine .60 1.50
114 Roberto Alomar .60 1.50
115 Tsuyoshi Shinjo .40 1.00
116 Cliff Floyd .40 1.00
117 Mike Piazza 1.50 4.00
118 Al Leiter .40 1.00
119 Don Mattingly 2.00 5.00
120 Roger Clemens 2.00 5.00
121 Derek Jeter 2.50 6.00
122 Alfonso Soriano .40 1.00
123 Drew Henson .40 1.00
124 Brandon Claussen .40 1.00
125 Christian Parker .40 1.00
126 Jason Giambi .40 1.00
127 Mike Mussina .60 1.50
128 Bernie Williams .60 1.50
129 Jason Anderson .40 1.00
130 Nick Johnson .40 1.00
131 Jorge Posada .60 1.50
132 Andy Pettitte .60 1.50
133 Barry Zito .40 1.00
134 Miguel Tejada .40 1.00
135 Eric Chavez .40 1.00
136 Tim Hudson .40 1.00
137 Mark Mulder .40 1.00
138 Terrence Long .40 1.00
139 Mark Ellis .40 1.00
140 Jim Thome .60 1.50
141 Pat Burrell .40 1.00
142 Marlon Byrd .40 1.00
143 Bobby Abreu .40 1.00
144 Brandon Duckworth .40 1.00
145 Robert Person .40 1.00
146 Anderson Machado .40 1.00
147 Aramis Ramirez .40 1.00
148 Jack Wilson .40 1.00
149 Carlos Rivera .40 1.00
150 Jose Castillo .40 1.00
151 Walter Young .40 1.00
152 Brian Giles .40 1.00
153 Jason Kendall .40 1.00
154 Ryan Klesko .40 1.00
155 Mike Rivera .40 1.00
156 Sean Burroughs .40 1.00
157 Brian Lawrence .40 1.00
158 Xavier Nady .40 1.00
159 Dennis Tankersley .40 1.00
160 Phil Nevin .40 1.00
161 Barry Bonds 2.50 6.00
162 Kenny Lofton .40 1.00
163 Rich Aurilia .40 1.00
164 Ichiro Suzuki 2.00 5.00
165 Edgar Martinez .60 1.50
166 Chris Snelling .40 1.00
167 Rafael Soriano .40 1.00
168 John Olerud .40 1.00
169 Bret Boone .40 1.00
170 Freddy Garcia .40 1.00
171 Aaron Sele .40 1.00
172 Kazuhiro Sasaki .40 1.00
173 Albert Pujols 2.00 5.00
174 Scott Rolen .60 1.50
175 So Taguchi .40 1.00
176 Jim Edmonds .40 1.00
177 Edgar Renteria .40 1.00
178 J.D. Drew .40 1.00
179 Antonio Perez .40 1.00
180 Dewon Brazelton .40 1.00
181 Aubrey Huff .40 1.00
182 Toby Hall .40 1.00
183 Ben Grieve .40 1.00
184 Joe Kennedy .40 1.00
185 Alex Rodriguez 1.50 4.00
186 Rafael Palmeiro .60 1.50
187 Hank Blalock .40 1.00
188 Mark Teixeira .60 1.50
189 Juan Gonzalez .40 1.00
190 Kevin Mench .40 1.00
191 Nolan Ryan Rgr 2.50 6.00
192 Doug Davis .40 1.00
193 Eric Hinske .40 1.00
194 Vinny Chulk .40 1.00
195 Alexis Rios .40 1.00
196 Carlos Delgado .40 1.00
197 Shannon Stewart .40 1.00
198 Josh Phelps .40 1.00
199 Vernon Wells .40 1.00
200 Roy Halladay .40 1.00
201 Babe Ruth RET 8.00 20.00
202 Lou Gehrig RET 5.00 12.00
203 Jackie Robinson RET 4.00 10.00
204 Ty Cobb RET 6.00 15.00
205 Thurman Munson RET 4.00 10.00
206 Pr. Redman NG AU RC 4.00 10.00
207 Craig Brazell NG AU RC 4.00 10.00
208 Nook Logan NG AU RC 6.00 15.00
209 Hong-Chih Kuo NG AU RC 60.00 120.00
210 Matt Kata NG AU RC 4.00 10.00
211 C.Wang NG AU RC 50.00 100.00
212 Alej Machado NG AU RC 4.00 10.00
213 Mike Hessman NG AU RC 4.00 10.00
214 Franc Rosario NG AU RC 4.00 10.00
215 Pedro Liriano NG AU 4.00 10.00
216 J.Bonderman NG AU RC 15.00 40.00
217 Oscar Villarreal NG AU RC 4.00 10.00
218 Arnie Munoz NG AU RC 4.00 10.00
219 Tim Olson NG AU RC 4.00 10.00
220 J.Contreras NG AU/100 RC 15.00 40.00
221 Franc Cruceta NG AU RC 4.00 10.00
222 John Webb NG AU 4.00 10.00
223 Phil Seibel NG AU RC 4.00 10.00
224 Aaron Looper NG AU RC 4.00 10.00
225 Brian Stokes NG AU RC 4.00 10.00
226 G.Quiroz NG AU RC 4.00 10.00
227 Fern Cabrera NG AU RC 4.00 10.00
228 Josh Hall NG AU RC 4.00 10.00
229 Diego Markwell NG AU RC 4.00 10.00
230 Andrew Brown NG AU RC 6.00 15.00
231 Doug Waechter NG AU RC 6.00 15.00
232 Felix Sanchez NG AU RC 4.00 10.00
233 Gerardo Garcia NG AU 4.00 10.00
234 Matt Bruback NG AU RC 4.00 10.00
235 Mi. Hernandez NG AU RC 4.00 10.00
236 Rett Johnson NG AU RC 4.00 10.00
237 Ryan Cameron NG AU RC 4.00 10.00
238 Rob Hammock NG AU RC 4.00 10.00
239 Clint Barmes NG AU RC 6.00 15.00
240 Brandon Webb NG AU RC 10.00 25.00
241 Jon Leicester NG AU RC 4.00 10.00
242 Shane Bazzell NG AU RC 4.00 10.00
243 Joe Valentine NG AU RC 4.00 10.00
244 Josh Stewart NG AU RC 4.00 10.00
245 Pete LaForest NG AU RC 4.00 10.00
246 Shane Victorino NG AU RC 15.00 40.00
247 Termel Sledge NG AU RC 4.00 10.00
248 Lew Ford NG AU RC 6.00 15.00
249 T.Wellemeyer NG AU RC 4.00 10.00
250 Hideki Matsui NG RC 6.00 15.00
251 A.Loewen NG AU/250 RC 6.00 15.00
252 Dan Haren NG AU/250 RC 8.00 20.00
253 D.Willis NG AU/150 6.00 15.00
254 Ramon Nivar NG AU/250 RC 4.00 10.00
255 Chad Gaudin NG AU/250 RC 4.00 10.00
256 Kevin Correia NG AU/150 RC 4.00 10.00
257 R.Weeks NG AU/100 RC 40.00 80.00
258 R.Wagner NG AU/250 RC 4.00 10.00
259 Del.Young NG AU/100 RC 125.00 175.00

2003 Leaf Certified Materials Mirror Black

STATED PRINT RUN 1 SERIAL #'d SET
NO PRICING DUE TO SCARCITY

2003 Leaf Certified Materials Mirror Black Autographs

STATED PRINT RUN 1 SERIAL #'d SET
NO PRICING DUE TO SCARCITY

2003 Leaf Certified Materials Mirror Black Materials

STATED PRINT RUN 1 SERIAL #'d SET
NO PRICING DUE TO SCARCITY

2003 Leaf Certified Materials Mirror Blue

*BLUE 1-200: 3X TO 8X BASIC
*BLUE 201-205: 1X TO 2.5X BASIC
*BLUE 206-219/221-249: .3X TO .8X BASIC
*BLUE 220: .2X TO .5X BASIC 220
*BLUE 250: .75X TO 2X BASIC 250
*BLUE 251-259: .3X TO .8X BASIC p/r 250
*BLUE 251-259: .2X TO .5X BASIC p/r 100-150
STATED PRINT RUN 50 SERIAL #'d SETS
209 Hong-Chih Kuo NG 30.00 60.00
211 Chien-Ming Wang NG 20.00 50.00

2003 Leaf Certified Materials Mirror Blue Autographs

PRINT RUNS B/WN 5-50 COPIES PER
NO PRICING ON QTY OF 25 OR LESS
2 Alfredo Amezaga/50 6.00 15.00
3 Garret Anderson/10
4 Nolan Ryan Angels/5
6 Junior Spivey/50 6.00 15.00
15 Adam LaRoche/50 6.00 15.00
17 Robert Fick/10
20 Jay Gibbons/50 6.00 15.00
21 Geronimo Gil/50 6.00 15.00
22 Cal Ripken/5
25 Freddy Sanchez/17
28 Casey Fossum/50 6.00 15.00
31 Corey Patterson/5
32 Nic Jackson/50 6.00 15.00
33 Mark Prior/50 12.50 30.00
34 Juan Cruz/50 6.00 15.00
35 Steve Smyth/50 6.00 15.00
37 Joe Borchard/50 6.00 15.00
39 Mark Buehrle/50 20.00 50.00
40 Joe Crede/30 10.00 25.00
41 Carlos Lee/5
45 Brandon Larson/50 6.00 15.00
49 Wily Mo Pena/50 10.00 25.00
51 Victor Martinez/50 15.00 40.00
52 Brian Tallet/50 6.00 15.00
53 Cliff Lee/50 30.00 60.00
54 Jeremy Guthrie/50 6.00 15.00
55 C.C. Sabathia/4
56 Ricardo Rodriguez/50 6.00 15.00
60 Jason Jennings/50 6.00 15.00
61 Jeff Baker/50 6.00 15.00
63 Travis Chapman/50 6.00 15.00
64 Mike Maroth/50 6.00 15.00
70 Roy Oswalt/50 10.00 25.00
71 Jason Lane/50 10.00 25.00
72 Nolan Ryan Astros/10
73 Wade Miller/50 6.00 15.00
74 Richard Hidalgo/5
77 Rodrigo Rosario/50 6.00 15.00
79 John Buck/10
80 Angel Berroa/50 6.00 15.00
81 Mike Sweeney/5
82 Mac Suzuki/50 10.00 25.00
83 Alexis Gomez/10
85 Runelvys Hernandez/50 6.00 15.00
86 Hideo Nomo/15
87 Paul Lo Duca/10
88 Cesar Izturis/50 6.00 15.00
89 Kazuhisa Ishii/5
91 Joe Thurston/50 6.00 15.00
94 Richie Sexson/5
95 Ben Sheets/5
96 Takahito Nomura/10
98 Bill Hall/30 6.00 15.00
100 A.J. Pierzynski/5
102 Jose Morban/50 6.00 15.00
107 Adam Johnson/50 6.00 15.00
108 Javier Vazquez/10
110 Jose Vidro/10
116 Cliff Floyd/5
117 Mike Piazza/15
119 Don Mattingly/5
122 Alfonso Soriano/10
123 Drew Henson/5
124 Brandon Claussen/50 6.00 15.00
125 Christian Parker/50 6.00 15.00
129 Jason Anderson/50 6.00 15.00
130 Nick Johnson/10
133 Barry Zito/5
134 Miguel Tejada/5
135 Eric Chavez/5
136 Tim Hudson/5
138 Terrence Long/50 6.00 15.00
142 Marlon Byrd/50 6.00 15.00
143 Bobby Abreu/5
144 Brandon Duckworth/50 6.00 15.00
145 Robert Person/50 6.00 15.00
146 Anderson Machado/50 6.00 15.00
147 Aramis Ramirez/8
148 Jack Wilson/50 10.00 25.00
149 Carlos Rivera/50 6.00 15.00
150 Jose Castillo/50 6.00 15.00
151 Walter Young/50 6.00 15.00
154 Ryan Klesko/5
155 Mike Rivera/50 6.00 15.00
157 Brian Lawrence/50 6.00 15.00
158 Xavier Nady/50 6.00 15.00
159 Dennis Tankersley/50 6.00 15.00
165 Edgar Martinez/5
166 Chris Snelling/50 6.00 15.00
167 Rafael Soriano/50 6.00 15.00
170 Freddy Garcia/5
173 Albert Pujols/5
176 Jim Edmonds/10
179 Antonio Perez/50 6.00 15.00
180 Dewon Brazelton/50 6.00 15.00
181 Aubrey Huff/50 10.00 25.00
182 Toby Hall/50 6.00 15.00
184 Joe Kennedy/50 6.00 15.00
187 Hank Blalock/50 10.00 25.00
188 Mark Teixeira/50 15.00 40.00
189 Juan Gonzalez/10
190 Kevin Mench/50 10.00 25.00
191 Nolan Ryan Rgr/5
193 Eric Hinske/50 6.00 15.00
194 Vinny Chulk/50 6.00 15.00
195 Alexis Rios/50 10.00 25.00
197 Shannon Stewart/10
206 Prentice Redman NG/50 6.00 15.00
207 Craig Brazell NG/50 6.00 15.00
208 Nook Logan NG/50 10.00 25.00
209 Hong-Chih Kuo NG/40 75.00 150.00
210 Matt Kata NG/50 6.00 15.00
211 Chien-Ming Wang NG/40 75.00 150.00
212 Alejandro Machado NG/50 6.00 15.00
213 Michael Hessman NG/50 6.00 15.00
214 Francisco Rosario NG/50 6.00 15.00
215 Pedro Liriano NG/50 6.00 15.00
216 Jeremy Bonderman NG/50 30.00 60.00
217 Oscar Villarreal NG/50 6.00 15.00
218 Arnie Munoz NG/50 6.00 15.00
219 Tim Olson NG/50 6.00 15.00
220 Jose Contreras NG/15
221 Francisco Cruceta NG/50 6.00 15.00
222 John Webb NG/50 6.00 15.00
223 Phil Seibel NG/50 6.00 15.00
224 Aaron Looper NG/50 6.00 15.00
225 Brian Stokes NG/50 6.00 15.00
226 Guillermo Quiroz NG/50 6.00 15.00
227 Fernando Cabrera NG/50 6.00 15.00
228 Josh Hall NG/50 6.00 15.00
229 Diegomar Markwell NG/50 6.00 15.00
230 Andrew Brown NG/50 10.00 25.00
231 Doug Waechter NG/50 10.00 25.00
232 Felix Sanchez NG/50 6.00 15.00
233 Gerardo Garcia NG/50 6.00 15.00
234 Matt Bruback NG/50 6.00 15.00
235 Michel Hernandez NG/50 6.00 15.00
236 Rett Johnson NG/50 6.00 15.00
237 Ryan Cameron NG/50 6.00 15.00
238 Rob Hammock NG/50 6.00 15.00
239 Clint Barmes NG/50 12.50 30.00
240 Brandon Webb NG/50 20.00 50.00
241 Jon Leicester NG/50 6.00 15.00
242 Shane Bazzell NG/50 6.00 15.00
243 Joe Valentine NG/50 6.00 15.00
244 Josh Stewart NG/50 6.00 15.00
245 Pete LaForest NG/50 6.00 15.00
246 Shane Victorino NG/50 20.00 50.00
247 Termel Sledge NG/50 6.00 15.00
248 Lew Ford NG/50 10.00 25.00
249 Todd Wellemeyer NG/50 6.00 15.00
251 Adam Loewen NG/50 15.00 40.00
252 Dan Haren NG/50 15.00 40.00
253 Dontrelle Willis NG/25
254 Ramon Nivar NG/50 6.00 15.00
255 Chad Gaudin NG/50 6.00 15.00
256 Kevin Correia NG/25
257 Rickie Weeks NG/15
258 Ryan Wagner NG/50 6.00 15.00
259 Delmon Young NG/25

2003 Leaf Certified Materials Mirror Blue Materials

PRINT RUNS B/WN 10-100 COPIES PER
NO PRICING ON QTY OF 25 OR FEWER
1 Troy Glaus Jsy/100 4.00 10.00
2 Alfredo Amezaga Jsy/100 4.00 10.00
3 Garret Anderson Bat/100 4.00 10.00
4 Nolan Ryan Angels Jsy/15
5 Darin Erstad Bat/100 4.00 10.00
6 Junior Spivey Bat/100 4.00 10.00
7 Randy Johnson Jsy/100 6.00 15.00
8 Curt Schilling Jsy/100 4.00 10.00
9 Luis Gonzalez Jsy/100 4.00 10.00
10 Steve Finley Jsy/100 4.00 10.00
11 Matt Williams Jsy/100 4.00 10.00
12 Greg Maddux Jsy/100 10.00 25.00
13 Chipper Jones Jsy/50 10.00 25.00
14 Gary Sheffield Bat/100 4.00 10.00
15 Adam LaRoche Bat/100 4.00 10.00
16 Andruw Jones Jsy/100 6.00 15.00
17 Robert Fick Bat/100 4.00 10.00
18 John Smoltz Jsy/100 6.00 15.00
19 Javy Lopez Jsy/100 4.00 10.00
20 Jay Gibbons Jsy/100 4.00 10.00
21 Geronimo Gil Jsy/100 4.00 10.00
22 Cal Ripken Jsy/15
23 Nomar Garciaparra Jsy/100 12.50 30.00
24 Pedro Martinez Jsy/100 6.00 15.00
25 Freddy Sanchez Bat/100 4.00 10.00
26 Rickey Henderson Bat/100 6.00 15.00
27 Manny Ramirez Jsy/100 6.00 15.00
28 Casey Fossum Jsy/100 4.00 10.00
29 Sammy Sosa Jsy/100 6.00 15.00
30 Kerry Wood Jsy/100 4.00 10.00
31 Corey Patterson Bat/100 4.00 10.00
32 Nic Jackson Bat/100 4.00 10.00
33 Mark Prior Jsy/100 6.00 15.00
34 Juan Cruz Jsy/100 4.00 10.00
35 Steve Smyth Jsy/100 4.00 10.00
36 Magglio Ordonez Jsy/100 4.00 10.00
37 Joe Borchard Jsy/100 4.00 10.00
38 Frank Thomas Jsy/100 6.00 15.00
39 Mark Buehrle Jsy/100 4.00 10.00
40 Joe Crede Hat/100 4.00 10.00
41 Carlos Lee Jsy/100 4.00 10.00
42 Paul Konerko Jsy/100 4.00 10.00
43 Adam Dunn Jsy/100 4.00 10.00
45 Brandon Larson Spikes/40 6.00 15.00
46 Ken Griffey Jr. Base/100 10.00 25.00
47 Barry Larkin Jsy/100 6.00 15.00
48 Sean Casey Bat/100 4.00 10.00
49 Wily Mo Pena Bat/100 4.00 10.00
50 Austin Kearns Jsy/100 4.00 10.00
51 Victor Martinez Jsy/100 6.00 15.00
55 C.C. Sabathia Jsy/100 4.00 10.00
56 Ricardo Rodriguez Bat/100 4.00 10.00
57 Omar Vizquel Jsy/100 6.00 15.00
58 Travis Hafner Bat/100 4.00 10.00
59 Todd Helton Jsy/100 6.00 15.00
60 Jason Jennings Jsy/100 4.00 10.00
62 Larry Walker Jsy/100 4.00 10.00
63 Travis Chapman Bat/100 4.00 10.00
64 Mike Maroth Jsy/100 4.00 10.00
65 Josh Beckett Jsy/100 4.00 10.00
66 Ivan Rodriguez Bat/100 6.00 15.00
67 Brad Penny Jsy/100 4.00 10.00
68 A.J. Burnett Jsy/100 4.00 10.00
69 Craig Biggio Jsy/100 6.00 15.00
70 Roy Oswalt Jsy/100 4.00 10.00
71 Jason Lane Jsy/100 4.00 10.00
72 Nolan Ryan Astros Jsy/15
73 Wade Miller Jsy/100 4.00 10.00
74 Richard Hidalgo Pants/100 4.00 10.00
75 Jeff Bagwell Jsy/100 6.00 15.00
76 Lance Berkman Jsy/100 4.00 10.00
77 Rodrigo Rosario Jsy/100 4.00 10.00
78 Jeff Kent Bat/100 4.00 10.00
79 John Buck Jsy/100 4.00 10.00
80 Angel Berroa Bat/100 4.00 10.00
81 Mike Sweeney Jsy/100 4.00 10.00
84 Carlos Beltran Jsy/100 4.00 10.00
86 Hideo Nomo Jsy/100 15.00 40.00
87 Paul Lo Duca Jsy/100 4.00 10.00
88 Cesar Izturis Pants/100 4.00 10.00
89 Kazuhisa Ishii Jsy/100 4.00 10.00
90 Shawn Green Jsy/100 4.00 10.00
91 Joe Thurston Jsy/100 4.00 10.00
92 Adrian Beltre Bat/100 4.00 10.00
93 Kevin Brown Jsy/100 4.00 10.00
94 Richie Sexson Jsy/100 4.00 10.00
95 Ben Sheets Jsy/100 4.00 10.00
97 Geoff Jenkins Jsy/100 4.00 10.00
98 Bill Hall Bat/100 4.00 10.00
99 Torii Hunter Jsy/100 4.00 10.00
101 Michael Cuddyer Jsy/100 4.00 10.00
102 Jose Morban Bat/100 4.00 10.00
103 Brad Radke Jsy/100 4.00 10.00
104 Jacque Jones Jsy/100 4.00 10.00
105 Eric Milton Jsy/100 4.00 10.00
106 Joe Mays Jsy/100 4.00 10.00
107 Adam Johnson Jsy/100 4.00 10.00
108 Javier Vazquez Jsy/100 4.00 10.00
109 Vladimir Guerrero Jsy/100 6.00 15.00
110 Jose Vidro Jsy/100 4.00 10.00
111 Michael Barrett Jsy/40 6.00 15.00
112 Orlando Cabrera Jsy/100 4.00 10.00
113 Tom Glavine Bat/100 6.00 15.00
114 Roberto Alomar Bat/100 6.00 15.00
115 Tsuyoshi Shinjo Jsy/100 4.00 10.00
116 Cliff Floyd Bat/100 4.00 10.00
117 Mike Piazza Jsy/100 10.00 25.00
118 Al Leiter Jsy/100 4.00 10.00
119 Don Mattingly Jsy/15
120 Roger Clemens Jsy/100 12.50 30.00
121 Derek Jeter Base/100 15.00 40.00
122 Alfonso Soriano Jsy/100 4.00 10.00
123 Drew Henson Bat/100 4.00 10.00
124 Brandon Claussen Hat/40 6.00 15.00
125 Christian Parker Pants/100 4.00 10.00
126 Jason Giambi Jsy/100 4.00 10.00
127 Mike Mussina Jsy/40 10.00 25.00
128 Bernie Williams Jsy/100 6.00 15.00
130 Nick Johnson Jsy/100 4.00 10.00
131 Jorge Posada Jsy/100 6.00 15.00
132 Andy Pettitte Jsy/100 6.00 15.00
133 Barry Zito Jsy/100 4.00 10.00
134 Miguel Tejada Jsy/100 4.00 10.00
135 Eric Chavez Jsy/100 4.00 10.00
136 Tim Hudson Jsy/100 4.00 10.00
137 Mark Mulder Jsy/100 4.00 10.00
138 Terrence Long Jsy/100 4.00 10.00
139 Mark Ellis Jsy/100 4.00 10.00
140 Jim Thome Bat/100 6.00 15.00
141 Pat Burrell Bat/100 4.00 10.00
142 Marlon Byrd Jsy/100 4.00 10.00
143 Bobby Abreu Jsy/100 4.00 10.00
144 Brandon Duckworth Jsy/100 4.00 10.00
145 Robert Person Jsy/100 4.00 10.00
146 Anderson Machado Jsy/100 4.00 10.00
147 Aramis Ramirez Jsy/100 4.00 10.00
148 Jack Wilson Bat/100 4.00 10.00
150 Jose Castillo Bat/100 4.00 10.00
151 Walter Young Bat/100 4.00 10.00
152 Brian Giles Bat/100 4.00 10.00
153 Jason Kendall Jsy/100 4.00 10.00
154 Ryan Klesko Jsy/50 6.00 15.00
155 Mike Rivera Bat/100 4.00 10.00
157 Brian Lawrence Bat/100 4.00 10.00
158 Xavier Nady Hat/40 6.00 15.00
159 Dennis Tankersley Jsy/100 4.00 10.00
160 Phil Nevin Jsy/100 4.00 10.00
161 Barry Bonds Base/100 12.50 30.00
162 Kenny Lofton Bat/100 4.00 10.00
163 Rich Aurilia Jsy/100 4.00 10.00
164 Ichiro Suzuki Base/100 15.00 40.00
165 Edgar Martinez Jsy/100 6.00 15.00
166 Chris Snelling Bat/100 4.00 10.00
167 Rafael Soriano Jsy/100 4.00 10.00
168 John Olerud Jsy/100 4.00 10.00
169 Bret Boone Jsy/100 4.00 10.00
170 Freddy Garcia Jsy/100 4.00 10.00
171 Aaron Sele Jsy/100 4.00 10.00
172 Kazuhiro Sasaki Jsy/100 4.00 10.00
173 Albert Pujols Jsy/100 15.00 40.00
174 Scott Rolen Bat/100 6.00 15.00
175 So Taguchi Jsy/100 4.00 10.00
176 Jim Edmonds Jsy/100 4.00 10.00
177 Edgar Renteria Jsy/100 4.00 10.00
178 J.D. Drew Jsy/100 4.00 10.00
179 Antonio Perez Bat/100 4.00 10.00
180 Dewon Brazelton Jsy/100 4.00 10.00
181 Aubrey Huff Jsy/50 6.00 15.00
182 Toby Hall Jsy/100 4.00 10.00
183 Ben Grieve Jsy/100 4.00 10.00
184 Joe Kennedy Jsy/100 4.00 10.00
185 Alex Rodriguez Jsy/100 12.50 30.00
186 Rafael Palmeiro Jsy/100 6.00 15.00
187 Hank Blalock Jsy/100 4.00 10.00
188 Mark Teixeira Jsy/100 6.00 15.00
189 Juan Gonzalez Bat/100 4.00 10.00
190 Kevin Mench Jsy/100 4.00 10.00
191 Nolan Ryan Rgr Jsy/15
192 Doug Davis Jsy/100 4.00 10.00
193 Eric Hinske Jsy/100 4.00 10.00
196 Carlos Delgado Jsy/100 4.00 10.00
197 Shannon Stewart Jsy/100 4.00 10.00
198 Josh Phelps Jsy/100 4.00 10.00
199 Vernon Wells Jsy/100 4.00 10.00
200 Roy Halladay Jsy/100 4.00 10.00
201 Babe Ruth RET Pants/10
202 Lou Gehrig RET Pants/10
203 Jackie Robinson RET Jsy/10
204 Ty Cobb RET Pants/10
205 Thurman Munson RET Jsy/10

2003 Leaf Certified Materials Mirror Emerald

STATED PRINT RUN 5 SERIAL #'d SETS
NO PRICING DUE TO SCARCITY

2003 Leaf Certified Materials Mirror Emerald Autographs

STATED PRINT RUN 5 SERIAL #'d SETS
NO PRICING DUE TO SCARCITY

2003 Leaf Certified Materials Mirror Emerald Materials

STATED PRINT RUN 5 SERIAL #'d SETS
NO PRICING DUE TO SCARCITY

2003 Leaf Certified Materials Mirror Gold

STATED PRINT RUN 25 SERIAL #'d SETS
NO PRICING DUE TO SCARCITY

2003 Leaf Certified Materials Mirror Gold Autographs

PRINT RUNS B/WN 5-25 COPIES PER
NO PRICING DUE TO SCARCITY

2003 Leaf Certified Materials Mirror Gold Materials

PRINT RUNS B/WN 5-25 COPIES PER
NO PRICING DUE TO SCARCITY

2003 Leaf Certified Materials Mirror Red

*ACTIVE RED 1-200: 2X TO 5X BASIC
*RETIRED RED 1-200: 2.5X TO 6X BASIC
*RED 201-205: .75X TO 2X BASIC
*RED 206-219/221-250: .2X TO .5X BASIC
*RED 220: .12X TO .3X BASIC 220
*RED 250: .5X TO 1.2X BASIC 250
*RED 251-259: .2X TO .5X BASIC p/r 250
*RED 251-259: .15X TO .4X BASIC p/r 100-150
STATED PRINT RUN 100 SERIAL #'d SETS
209 Hong-Chih Kuo NG 20.00 50.00
211 Chien-Ming Wang NG 12.50 30.00

2003 Leaf Certified Materials Mirror Red Autographs

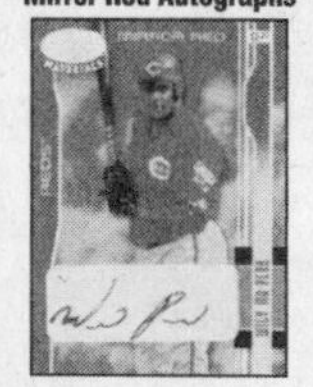

PRINT RUNS B/WN 5-100 COPIES PER
NO PRICING ON QTY OF 25 OR LESS
2 Alfredo Amezaga/100 6.00 15.00
3 Garret Anderson/10
4 Nolan Ryan Angels/5
6 Junior Spivey/15
15 Adam LaRoche/100 6.00 15.00
17 Robert Fick/15
20 Jay Gibbons/100 6.00 15.00
21 Geronimo Gil/15
22 Cal Ripken/5
25 Freddy Sanchez/100 6.00 15.00
28 Casey Fossum/50 6.00 15.00
31 Corey Patterson/6
32 Nic Jackson/100 6.00 15.00
33 Mark Prior/15
34 Juan Cruz/15
35 Steve Smyth/94 6.00 15.00
37 Joe Borchard/15
39 Mark Buehrle/15
40 Joe Crede/15
45 Brandon Larson/100 6.00 15.00
49 Wily Mo Pena/100 10.00 25.00
51 Victor Martinez/15
52 Brian Tallet/15
53 Cliff Lee/15
54 Jeremy Guthrie/15
56 Ricardo Rodriguez/100 6.00 15.00
60 Jason Jennings/15
61 Jeff Baker/15
63 Travis Chapman/100 6.00 15.00
64 Mike Maroth/100 6.00 15.00
70 Roy Oswalt/15
71 Jason Lane/100 10.00 25.00
72 Nolan Ryan Astros/5
73 Wade Miller/15
74 Richard Hidalgo/10
77 Rodrigo Rosario/100 6.00 15.00
79 John Buck/15
80 Angel Berroa/15
81 Mike Sweeney/10
82 Mac Suzuki/15
83 Alexis Gomez/15
85 Runelvys Hernandez/100 6.00 15.00
86 Hideo Nomo/16
87 Paul Lo Duca/15
88 Cesar Izturis/100 6.00 15.00
89 Kazuhisa Ishii/5
91 Joe Thurston/100 6.00 15.00
94 Richie Sexson/10
95 Ben Sheets/10
96 Takahito Nomura/15
98 Bill Hall/100 6.00 15.00
100 A.J. Pierzynski/10
102 Jose Morban/100 6.00 15.00
124 Brandon Claussen/60 6.00 15.00
125 Christian Parker/15
129 Jason Anderson/100 6.00 15.00
142 Marlon Byrd/100 6.00 15.00
143 Bobby Abreu/10
144 Brandon Duckworth/15
145 Robert Person/15
146 Anderson Machado/100 6.00 15.00
148 Jack Wilson/15
149 Carlos Rivera/100 6.00 15.00
150 Jose Castillo/100 6.00 15.00
151 Walter Young/100 6.00 15.00
152 Brian Giles/15
154 Ryan Klesko/10
155 Mike Rivera/100 6.00 15.00
157 Brian Lawrence/100 6.00 15.00
158 Xavier Nady Hat/15
159 Dennis Tankersley/15
165 Edgar Martinez/10
166 Chris Snelling/100 6.00 15.00
190 Kevin Mench/100 10.00 25.00
191 Nolan Ryan Rgr/5
193 Eric Hinske/100 6.00 15.00
194 Vinny Chulk/100 6.00 15.00
195 Alexis Rios/100 8.00 20.00
197 Shannon Stewart/15
206 Prentice Redman NG/100 4.00 10.00
207 Craig Brazell NG/100 4.00 10.00
208 Nook Logan NG/100 6.00 15.00
209 Hong-Chih Kuo NG/50 60.00 120.00
210 Matt Kata NG/100 4.00 10.00
211 Chien-Ming Wang NG/50 75.00 150.00
212 Alejandro Machado NG/100 4.00 10.00
213 Michael Hessman NG/100 4.00 10.00
214 Francisco Rosario NG/100 4.00 10.00
215 Pedro Liriano NG/100 4.00 10.00
216 Jeremy Bonderman NG/100 20.00 50.00
217 Oscar Villarreal NG/100 4.00 10.00
218 Arnie Munoz NG/100 4.00 10.00
219 Tim Olson NG/100 4.00 10.00
220 Jose Contreras NG/5
221 Francisco Cruceta NG/100 4.00 10.00
222 John Webb NG/100 4.00 10.00
223 Phil Seibel NG/100 4.00 10.00
224 Aaron Looper NG/100 4.00 10.00
225 Brian Stokes NG/100 4.00 10.00
226 Guillermo Quiroz NG/100 4.00 10.00
227 Fernando Cabrera NG/100 4.00 10.00
228 Josh Hall NG/100 4.00 10.00
229 Diegomar Markwell NG/100 4.00 10.00
230 Andrew Brown NG/100 6.00 15.00
231 Doug Waechter NG/100 6.00 15.00
232 Felix Sanchez NG/100 4.00 10.00
233 Gerardo Garcia NG/100 4.00 10.00
234 Matt Bruback NG/100 4.00 10.00
235 Michel Hernandez NG/100 4.00 10.00
236 Rett Johnson NG/100 4.00 10.00
237 Ryan Cameron NG/100 4.00 10.00
238 Rob Hammock NG/100 4.00 10.00
239 Clint Barmes NG/100 10.00 25.00
240 Brandon Webb NG/100 10.00 25.00
241 Jon Leicester NG/100 4.00 10.00
242 Shane Bazzell NG/100 4.00 10.00
243 Joe Valentine NG/100 4.00 10.00
244 Josh Stewart NG/100 4.00 10.00
245 Pete LaForest NG/100 4.00 10.00
246 Shane Victorino NG/100 15.00 40.00
247 Termel Sledge NG/100 4.00 10.00
248 Lew Ford NG/100 6.00 15.00
249 Todd Wellemeyer NG/100 4.00 10.00
251 Adam Loewen NG/100 10.00 25.00
252 Dan Haren NG/100 10.00 25.00
253 Dontrelle Willis NG/50 10.00 25.00
254 Ramon Nivar NG/100 4.00 10.00
255 Chad Gaudin NG/100 4.00 10.00
256 Kevin Correia NG/100 4.00 10.00
257 Rickie Weeks NG/25
258 Ryan Wagner NG/100 4.00 10.00
259 Delmon Young NG/50 100.00 200.00

2003 Leaf Certified Materials Mirror Red Materials

PRINT RUNS B/WN 15-250 COPIES PER
NO PRICING ON QTY OF 25 OR LESS
1 Troy Glaus Jsy/250 3.00 8.00
2 Alfredo Amezaga Jsy/100 4.00 10.00
3 Garret Anderson Bat/250 3.00 8.00
4 Nolan Ryan Angels Jsy/35 40.00 80.00
5 Darin Erstad Bat/250 3.00 8.00
6 Junior Spivey Bat/250 3.00 8.00
7 Randy Johnson Jsy/250 4.00 10.00
8 Curt Schilling Jsy/250 3.00 8.00
9 Luis Gonzalez Jsy/250 3.00 8.00
10 Steve Finley Jsy/250 3.00 8.00
11 Matt Williams Jsy/100 4.00 10.00
12 Greg Maddux Jsy/250 8.00 20.00
13 Chipper Jones Jsy/250 4.00 10.00
14 Gary Sheffield Bat/125 4.00 10.00
15 Adam LaRoche Bat/250 3.00 8.00
16 Andruw Jones Jsy/250 4.00 10.00
17 Robert Fick Bat/250 3.00 8.00
18 John Smoltz Jsy/250 4.00 10.00
19 Javy Lopez Jsy/250 3.00 8.00
20 Jay Gibbons Jsy/250 3.00 8.00
21 Geronimo Gil Jsy/250 3.00 8.00
22 Cal Ripken Jsy/35 60.00 120.00
23 Nomar Garciaparra Jsy/250 10.00 25.00
24 Pedro Martinez Jsy/250 4.00 10.00
25 Freddy Sanchez Bat/250 3.00 8.00
26 Rickey Henderson Bat/250 4.00 10.00
27 Manny Ramirez Jsy/250 4.00 10.00
28 Casey Fossum Jsy/250 3.00 8.00
29 Sammy Sosa Jsy/250 4.00 10.00
30 Kerry Wood Jsy/250 3.00 8.00
31 Corey Patterson Bat/250 3.00 8.00
32 Nic Jackson Bat/250 3.00 8.00
33 Mark Prior Jsy/250 4.00 10.00
34 Juan Cruz Jsy/250 3.00 8.00
35 Steve Smyth Jsy/250 3.00 8.00
36 Magglio Ordonez Jsy/250 3.00 8.00
37 Joe Borchard Jsy/250 3.00 8.00
38 Frank Thomas Jsy/250 4.00 10.00
39 Mark Buehrle Jsy/250 3.00 8.00
40 Joe Crede Hat/100 4.00 10.00
41 Carlos Lee Jsy/250 3.00 8.00
42 Paul Konerko Jsy/250 3.00 8.00
43 Adam Dunn Jsy/250 3.00 8.00
45 Brandon Larson Spikes/150 3.00 8.00
46 Ken Griffey Jr. Base/250 8.00 20.00
47 Barry Larkin Jsy/250 4.00 10.00
48 Sean Casey Bat/250 3.00 8.00
49 Wily Mo Pena Bat/250 3.00 8.00
50 Austin Kearns Jsy/250 3.00 8.00
51 Victor Martinez Jsy/100 6.00 15.00
55 C.C. Sabathia Jsy/250 3.00 8.00
56 Ricardo Rodriguez Bat/250 3.00 8.00
57 Omar Vizquel Jsy/250 4.00 10.00
58 Travis Hafner Bat/250 3.00 8.00
59 Todd Helton Jsy/250 4.00 10.00
60 Jason Jennings Jsy/250 3.00 8.00
62 Larry Walker Jsy/250 3.00 8.00
63 Travis Chapman Bat/250 3.00 8.00
64 Mike Maroth Jsy/250 3.00 8.00
65 Josh Beckett Jsy/250 3.00 8.00
66 Ivan Rodriguez Bat/250 4.00 10.00
67 Brad Penny Jsy/250 3.00 8.00
68 A.J. Burnett Jsy/250 3.00 8.00
69 Craig Biggio Jsy/250 4.00 10.00
70 Roy Oswalt Jsy/250 3.00 8.00
71 Jason Lane Jsy/250 3.00 8.00
72 Nolan Ryan Astros Jsy/35 40.00 80.00
73 Wade Miller Jsy/250 3.00 8.00
74 Richard Hidalgo Pants/250 3.00 8.00
75 Jeff Bagwell Jsy/250 4.00 10.00
76 Lance Berkman Jsy/250 3.00 8.00
77 Rodrigo Rosario Jsy/250 3.00 8.00
78 Jeff Kent Bat/250 3.00 8.00
79 John Buck Jsy/250 3.00 8.00
80 Angel Berroa Bat/250 4.00 10.00
81 Mike Sweeney Jsy/250 3.00 8.00
84 Carlos Beltran Jsy/250 3.00 8.00
86 Hideo Nomo Jsy/250 12.50 30.00
87 Paul Lo Duca Jsy/250 3.00 8.00
88 Cesar Izturis Pants/250 3.00 8.00
89 Kazuhisa Ishii Jsy/250 3.00 8.00
90 Shawn Green Jsy/250 3.00 8.00
91 Joe Thurston Jsy/250 3.00 8.00
92 Adrian Beltre Bat/250 3.00 8.00
93 Kevin Brown Jsy/250 3.00 8.00
94 Richie Sexson Jsy/250 3.00 8.00
95 Ben Sheets Jsy/250 3.00 8.00
97 Geoff Jenkins Jsy/250 3.00 8.00
98 Bill Hall Bat/250 3.00 8.00
99 Torii Hunter Jsy/250 3.00 8.00
101 Michael Cuddyer Jsy/250 3.00 8.00
102 Jose Morban Bat/250 3.00 8.00
103 Brad Radke Jsy/250 3.00 8.00
104 Jacque Jones Jsy/250 3.00 8.00
105 Eric Milton Jsy/250 3.00 8.00
106 Joe Mays Jsy/250 3.00 8.00
107 Adam Johnson Jsy/250 3.00 8.00
108 Javier Vazquez Jsy/250 3.00 8.00
109 Vladimir Guerrero Jsy/250 4.00 10.00
110 Jose Vidro Jsy/250 3.00 8.00
111 Michael Barrett Jsy/50 6.00 15.00
112 Orlando Cabrera Jsy/250 3.00 8.00
113 Tom Glavine Bat/250 4.00 10.00
114 Roberto Alomar Bat/250 4.00 10.00
115 Tsuyoshi Shinjo Jsy/250 3.00 8.00
116 Cliff Floyd Bat/250 3.00 8.00
117 Mike Piazza Jsy/250 8.00 20.00
118 Al Leiter Jsy/250 3.00 8.00
119 Don Mattingly Jsy/35 40.00 80.00
120 Roger Clemens Jsy/250 10.00 25.00
121 Derek Jeter Base/250 12.50 30.00
122 Alfonso Soriano Jsy/250 3.00 8.00
123 Drew Henson Bat/250 3.00 8.00
124 Brandon Claussen Hat/50 6.00 15.00
125 Christian Parker Pants/250 3.00 8.00
126 Jason Giambi Jsy/250 3.00 8.00
127 Mike Mussina Jsy/250 4.00 10.00
128 Bernie Williams Jsy/250 4.00 10.00
130 Nick Johnson Jsy/250 3.00 8.00
131 Jorge Posada Jsy/250 4.00 10.00
132 Andy Pettitte Jsy/250 4.00 10.00
133 Barry Zito Jsy/250 3.00 8.00
134 Miguel Tejada Jsy/250 3.00 8.00
135 Eric Chavez Jsy/250 3.00 8.00
136 Tim Hudson Jsy/250 3.00 8.00
137 Mark Mulder Jsy/250 3.00 8.00
138 Terrence Long Jsy/250 3.00 8.00
139 Mark Ellis Jsy/250 3.00 8.00
140 Jim Thome Bat/250 4.00 10.00
141 Pat Burrell Bat/250 3.00 8.00
142 Marlon Byrd Jsy/250 3.00 8.00
143 Bobby Abreu Jsy/250 3.00 8.00
144 Brandon Duckworth Jsy/250 3.00 8.00
145 Robert Person Jsy/250 3.00 8.00
146 Anderson Machado Jsy/250 3.00 8.00
147 Aramis Ramirez Jsy/250 3.00 8.00
148 Jack Wilson Bat/250 3.00 8.00
150 Jose Castillo Bat/250 3.00 8.00
151 Walter Young Bat/250 3.00 8.00
152 Brian Giles Bat/250 3.00 8.00
153 Jason Kendall Jsy/250 3.00 8.00
154 Ryan Klesko Jsy/25
155 Mike Rivera Bat/250 3.00 8.00
157 Brian Lawrence Bat/250 3.00 8.00
158 Xavier Nady Hat/60 6.00 15.00
159 Dennis Tankersley Jsy/250 3.00 8.00
160 Phil Nevin Jsy/250 3.00 8.00
161 Barry Bonds Base/250 10.00 25.00
162 Kenny Lofton Bat/250 3.00 8.00
163 Rich Aurilia Jsy/250 3.00 8.00
164 Ichiro Suzuki Base/250 12.50 30.00
165 Edgar Martinez Jsy/100 6.00 15.00
166 Chris Snelling Bat/250 3.00 8.00
167 Rafael Soriano Jsy/250 3.00 8.00
168 John Olerud Jsy/250 3.00 8.00
169 Bret Boone Jsy/250 3.00 8.00
170 Freddy Garcia Jsy/250 3.00 8.00
171 Aaron Sele Jsy/250 3.00 8.00
172 Kazuhiro Sasaki Jsy/250 3.00 8.00
173 Albert Pujols Jsy/250 12.50 30.00
174 Scott Rolen Bat/250 4.00 10.00
175 So Taguchi Jsy/250 3.00 8.00
176 Jim Edmonds Jsy/250 3.00 8.00
177 Edgar Renteria Jsy/250 3.00 8.00
178 J.D. Drew Jsy/250 3.00 8.00
179 Antonio Perez Bat/250 3.00 8.00
180 Dewon Brazelton Jsy/250 3.00 8.00
181 Aubrey Huff Jsy/50 6.00 15.00
182 Toby Hall Jsy/250 3.00 8.00
183 Ben Grieve Jsy/100 4.00 10.00
184 Joe Kennedy Jsy/250 3.00 8.00
185 Alex Rodriguez Jsy/250 10.00 25.00
186 Rafael Palmeiro Jsy/250 4.00 10.00
187 Hank Blalock Jsy/250 3.00 8.00
188 Mark Teixeira Jsy/250 4.00 10.00
189 Juan Gonzalez Bat/250 3.00 8.00
190 Kevin Mench Jsy/250 3.00 8.00
191 Nolan Ryan Rgr Jsy/35 40.00 80.00
192 Doug Davis Jsy/250 3.00 8.00
193 Eric Hinske Jsy/250 3.00 8.00
196 Carlos Delgado Jsy/250 3.00 8.00
197 Shannon Stewart Jsy/250 3.00 8.00
198 Josh Phelps Jsy/250 3.00 8.00
199 Vernon Wells Jsy/250 3.00 8.00
200 Roy Halladay Jsy/250 3.00 8.00
201 Babe Ruth RET Pants/15
202 Lou Gehrig RET Pants/15
203 Jackie Robinson RET Jsy/15
204 Ty Cobb RET Pants/15
205 Thurman Munson RET Jsy/15

2003 Leaf Certified Materials Fabric of the Game

Randomly inserted into packs, these 900 cards feature six versions of 150 different cards. The set is broken down into BA (designed like a Base); DY (indicating the year the team was 1st known by their current nomenclature); IN (inscription; JN (Jersey Number); JY (Jersey Year that this jersey was used in) and PS (Position). We have put the stated print run next to the player's name in our checklist.

PRINT RUNS BETWEEN 1-102 COPIES PER
NO PRICING ON QTY OF 25 OR LESS
1BA Bobby Doerr BA/50 4.00 10.00
1DY Bobby Doerr DY/7
1IN Bobby Doerr IN/25
1JN Bobby Doerr JN/1
1JY Bobby Doerr JY/39 6.00 15.00
1PS Bobby Doerr PS/50 4.00 10.00
2BA Ozzie Smith BA/100 10.00 25.00
2DY Ozzie Smith DY/1
2IN Ozzie Smith IN/50 12.50 30.00
2JN Ozzie Smith JN/1
2JY Ozzie Smith JY/88 10.00 25.00
2PS Ozzie Smith PS/50 12.50 30.00
3BA Pee Wee Reese BA/20
3DY Pee Wee Reese DY/32 12.50 30.00
3IN Pee Wee Reese IN/15
3JN Pee Wee Reese JN/1
3JY Pee Wee Reese JY/58 6.00 15.00
3PS Pee Wee Reese PS/20
4BA Jeff Bagwell Pants BA/100 4.00 10.00
4DY Jeff Bagwell Pants DY/65 6.00 15.00
4IN Jeff Bagwell Pants IN/50 6.00 15.00
4JN Jeff Bagwell Pants JN/5
4JY Jeff Bagwell Pants JY/98 4.00 10.00
4PS Jeff Bagwell Pants PS/50 6.00 15.00
5BA Tommy Lasorda BA/100 4.00 10.00
5DY Tommy Lasorda DY/58 4.00 10.00
5IN Tommy Lasorda IN/25
5JN Tommy Lasorda JN/2
5JY Tommy Lasorda JY/84 4.00 10.00
5PS Tommy Lasorda PS/50 4.00 10.00
6BA Red Schoendienst BA/25
6DY Red Schoendienst DY/1
6IN Red Schoendienst IN/15
6JN Red Schoendienst JN/2
6JY Red Schoendienst JY/55 4.00 10.00
6PS Red Schoendienst PS/50 4.00 10.00
7BA Harmon Killebrew BA/50 6.00 15.00
7DY Harmon Killebrew DY/61 6.00 15.00
7IN Harmon Killebrew IN/50 6.00 15.00
7JN Harmon Killebrew JN/3
7JY Harmon Killebrew JY/71 6.00 15.00
7PS Harmon Killebrew PS/50 6.00 15.00
8BA Roger Maris BA/25
8DY Roger Maris DY/55 15.00 40.00
8IN Roger Maris IN/20
8JN Roger Maris JN/3
8JY Roger Maris JY/58 15.00 40.00
8PS Roger Maris PS/50 15.00 40.00
9BA Alex Rodriguez M's BA/100 6.00 15.00
9DY Alex Rodriguez M's DY/77 6.00 15.00
9IN Alex Rodriguez M's IN/50 10.00 25.00
9JN Alex Rodriguez M's JN/3
9JY Alex Rodriguez M's JY/99 6.00 15.00
9PS Alex Rodriguez M's PS/50 10.00 25.00
10BA Alex Rodriguez Rgr BA/100 6.00 15.00
10DY Alex Rodriguez Rgr DY/72 10.00 25.00
10IN Alex Rodriguez Rgr IN/50 10.00 25.00
10JN Alex Rodriguez Rgr JN/3
10JY Alex Rodriguez Rgr JY/101 6.00 15.00
10PS Alex Rodriguez Rgr PS/50 10.00 25.00
11BA Dale Murphy BA/50 6.00 15.00
11DY Dale Murphy DY/66 6.00 15.00
11IN Dale Murphy IN/50 6.00 15.00
11JN Dale Murphy JN/3
11JY Dale Murphy JY/85 6.00 15.00
11PS Dale Murphy PS/50 6.00 15.00
12BA Alan Trammell BA/100 4.00 10.00
12DY Alan Trammell DY/1
12IN Alan Trammell IN/50 4.00 10.00
12JN Alan Trammell JN/3
12JY Alan Trammell JY/90 4.00 10.00
12PS Alan Trammell PS/50 4.00 10.00
13BA Babe Ruth Pants BA/10
13DY Babe Ruth Pants DY/13
13IN Babe Ruth Pants IN/10
13JN Babe Ruth Pants JN/3
13JY Babe Ruth Pants JY/30 200.00 350.00
13PS Babe Ruth Pants PS/10
14BA Lou Gehrig BA/10
14DY Lou Gehrig DY/13
14IN Lou Gehrig IN/10
14JN Lou Gehrig JN/4
14JY Lou Gehrig JY/38 175.00 300.00
14PS Lou Gehrig PS/10
15BA Babe Ruth BA/10
15DY Babe Ruth DY/13
15IN Babe Ruth IN/10
15JN Babe Ruth JN/3
15JY Babe Ruth JY/30 250.00 400.00
15PS Babe Ruth PS/10
16BA Mel Ott BA/10
16DY Mel Ott DY/1
16IN Mel Ott IN/10
16JN Mel Ott JN/4
16JY Mel Ott JY/46 15.00 40.00
16PS Mel Ott PS/10
17BA Paul Molitor BA/100 4.00 10.00
17DY Paul Molitor DY/70 4.00 10.00
17IN Paul Molitor IN/50 4.00 10.00
17JN Paul Molitor JN/4
17JY Paul Molitor JY/84 4.00 10.00
17PS Paul Molitor PS/50 4.00 10.00
18BA Duke Snider BA/15
18DY Duke Snider DY/58 6.00 15.00
18IN Duke Snider IN/15
18JN Duke Snider JN/4
18JY Duke Snider JY/62 6.00 15.00
18PS Duke Snider PS/15
19BA Miguel Tejada BA/50 4.00 10.00
19DY Miguel Tejada DY/68 4.00 10.00
19IN Miguel Tejada IN/50 4.00 10.00
19JN Miguel Tejada JN/4
19JY Miguel Tejada JY/99 3.00 8.00
19PS Miguel Tejada PS/50 4.00 10.00
20BA Lou Gehrig Pants BA/10
20DY Lou Gehrig Pants DY/13
20IN Lou Gehrig Pants IN/10
20JN Lou Gehrig Pants JN/4
20JY Lou Gehrig Pants JY/38 150.00 250.00
20PS Lou Gehrig Pants PS/10
21BA Brooks Robinson BA/15
21DY Brooks Robinson DY/54 6.00 15.00
21IN Brooks Robinson IN/15
21JN Brooks Robinson JN/5
21JY Brooks Robinson JY/66 6.00 15.00
21PS Brooks Robinson PS/15
22BA George Brett BA/50 15.00 40.00
22DY George Brett DY/69 15.00 40.00
22IN George Brett IN/50 15.00 40.00
22JN George Brett JN/5
22JY George Brett JY/91 12.50 30.00
22PS George Brett PS/50 15.00 40.00
23BA Johnny Bench BA/50 6.00 15.00
23DY Johnny Bench DY/59 6.00 15.00
23IN Johnny Bench IN/50 6.00 15.00
23JN Johnny Bench JN/5
23JY Johnny Bench JY/81 6.00 15.00
23PS Johnny Bench PS/50 6.00 15.00
24BA Lou Boudreau BA/15
24DY Lou Boudreau DY/15
24IN Lou Boudreau IN/15
24JN Lou Boudreau JN/5
24JY Lou Boudreau JY/48 6.00 15.00
24PS Lou Boudreau PS/15
25BA Nomar Garciaparra BA/100 10.00 25.00
25DY Nomar Garciaparra DY/7
25IN Nomar Garciaparra IN/50 10.00 25.00
25JN Nomar Garciaparra JN/5
25JY Nomar Garciaparra JY/100 10.00 25.00
25PS Nomar Garciaparra PS/50 10.00 25.00
26BA Tsuyoshi Shinjo BA/50 4.00 10.00
26DY Tsuyoshi Shinjo DY/62 4.00 10.00
26IN Tsuyoshi Shinjo IN/25
26JN Tsuyoshi Shinjo JN/5
26JY Tsuyoshi Shinjo JY/101 3.00 8.00
26PS Tsuyoshi Shinjo PS/25
27BA Pat Burrell BA/100 3.00 8.00
27DY Pat Burrell DY/46 5.00 12.00
27IN Pat Burrell IN/25
27JN Pat Burrell JN/5
27JY Pat Burrell JY/101 3.00 8.00
27PS Pat Burrell PS/25
28BA Albert Pujols BA/100 10.00 25.00
28DY Albert Pujols DY/1
28IN Albert Pujols IN/50 12.50 30.00
28JN Albert Pujols JN/5
28JY Albert Pujols JY/101 10.00 25.00
28PS Albert Pujols PS/50 12.50 30.00
29BA Stan Musial BA/10
29DY Stan Musial DY/1
29IN Stan Musial IN/10
29JN Stan Musial JN/6
29JY Stan Musial JY/43 15.00 40.00
29PS Stan Musial PS/10
30BA Al Kaline BA/20
30DY Al Kaline DY/1
30IN Al Kaline IN/15
30JN Al Kaline JN/6
30JY Al Kaline JY/64 6.00 15.00
30PS Al Kaline PS/15
31BA Ivan Rodriguez BA/100 4.00 10.00
31DY Ivan Rodriguez DY/72 6.00 15.00
31IN Ivan Rodriguez IN/50 6.00 15.00
31JN Ivan Rodriguez JN/7
31JY Ivan Rodriguez JY/101 4.00 10.00
31PS Ivan Rodriguez PS/50 6.00 15.00
32BA Craig Biggio BA/100 4.00 10.00
32DY Craig Biggio DY/65 6.00 15.00
32IN Craig Biggio IN/25
32JN Craig Biggio JN/7
32JY Craig Biggio JY/101 4.00 10.00
32PS Craig Biggio PS/50 6.00 15.00
33BA Joe Morgan BA/10

33DY Joe Morgan DY/59 4.00 10.00
33IN Joe Morgan IN/10
33JN Joe Morgan JN/8
33JY Joe Morgan JY/74 4.00 10.00
33PS Joe Morgan PS/10
34BA Willie Stargell BA/50 6.00 15.00
34DY Willie Stargell DY/1
34IN Willie Stargell IN/15
34JN Willie Stargell JN/8
34JY Willie Stargell JY/68 6.00 15.00
34PS Willie Stargell PS/50 6.00 15.00
35BA Andre Dawson BA/100 4.00 10.00
35DY Andre Dawson DY/7
35IN Andre Dawson IN/50 4.00 10.00
35JN Andre Dawson JN/8
35JY Andre Dawson JY/87 4.00 10.00
35PS Andre Dawson PS/50 4.00 10.00
36BA Gary Carter BA/100 4.00 10.00
36DY Gary Carter DY/62 4.00 10.00
36IN Gary Carter IN/50 4.00 10.00
36JN Gary Carter JN/8
36JY Gary Carter JY/85 4.00 10.00
36PS Gary Carter PS/50 4.00 10.00
37BA Cal Ripken BA/50 30.00 60.00
37DY Cal Ripken DY/54 30.00 60.00
37IN Cal Ripken IN/50 30.00 60.00
37JN Cal Ripken JN/8
37JY Cal Ripken JY/101 20.00 50.00
37PS Cal Ripken PS/50 30.00 60.00
38BA Enos Slaughter BA/15
38DY Enos Slaughter DY/1
38IN Enos Slaughter IN/15
38JN Enos Slaughter JN/9
38JY Enos Slaughter JY/53 6.00 15.00
38PS Enos Slaughter PS/25
39BA Reggie Jackson A's BA/50 6.00 15.00
39DY Reggie Jackson A's DY/68 6.00 15.00
39IN Reggie Jackson A's IN/25
39JN Reggie Jackson A's JN/9
39JY Reggie Jackson A's JY/75 6.00 15.00
39PS Reggie Jackson A's PS/50 6.00 15.00
40BA Phil Rizzuto BA/20
40DY Phil Rizzuto DY/13
40IN Phil Rizzuto IN/15
40JN Phil Rizzuto JN/10
40JY Phil Rizzuto JY/47 10.00 25.00
40PS Phil Rizzuto PS/15
41BA Chipper Jones BA/100 4.00 10.00
41DY Chipper Jones DY/66 6.00 15.00
41IN Chipper Jones IN/50 6.00 15.00
41JN Chipper Jones JN/10
41JY Chipper Jones JY/101 4.00 10.00
41PS Chipper Jones PS/50 6.00 15.00
42BA H.Nomo Dodgers BA/100 4.00 10.00
42DY H.Nomo Dodgers DY/56 6.00 15.00
42IN H.Nomo Dodgers IN/50 6.00 15.00
42JN H.Nomo Dodgers JN/10
42JY H.Nomo Dodgers JY/95 4.00 10.00
42PS H.Nomo Dodgers PS/50 6.00 15.00
43BA Luis Aparicio BA/25
43DY Luis Aparicio DY/4
43IN Luis Aparicio IN/15
43JN Luis Aparicio JN/11
43JY Luis Aparicio JY/69 4.00 10.00
43PS Luis Aparicio PS/20
44BA H.Nomo R.Sox BA/100 4.00 10.00
44DY H.Nomo R.Sox DY/7
44IN H.Nomo R.Sox IN/50 6.00 15.00
44JN H.Nomo R.Sox JN/11
44JY H.Nomo R.Sox JY/101 4.00 10.00
44PS H.Nomo R.Sox PS/50 6.00 15.00
45BA Edgar Martinez BA/100 4.00 10.00
45DY Edgar Martinez DY/77 4.00 10.00
45IN Edgar Martinez IN/25
45JN Edgar Martinez JN/11
45JY Edgar Martinez JY/100 4.00 10.00
45PS Edgar Martinez PS/50 6.00 15.00
46BA Barry Larkin BA/100 4.00 10.00
46DY Barry Larkin DY/59 6.00 15.00
46IN Barry Larkin IN/25
46JN Barry Larkin JN/11
46JY Barry Larkin JY/100 4.00 10.00
46PS Barry Larkin PS/50 6.00 15.00
47BA Alfonso Soriano BA/100 3.00 8.00
47DY Alfonso Soriano DY/2
47IN Alfonso Soriano IN/50 4.00 10.00
47JN Alfonso Soriano JN/12
47JY Alfonso Soriano JY/102 3.00 8.00
47PS Alfonso Soriano PS/50 4.00 10.00
48BA Wade Boggs Rays BA/100 6.00 15.00
48DY Wade Boggs Rays DY/98 6.00 15.00
48IN Wade Boggs Rays IN/50 6.00 15.00
48JN Wade Boggs Rays JN/12
48JY Wade Boggs Rays JY/99 6.00 15.00
48PS Wade Boggs Rays PS/50 6.00 15.00
49BA Wade Boggs Yanks BA/50 6.00 15.00
49DY Wade Boggs Yanks DY/13
49IN Wade Boggs Yanks IN/50 6.00 15.00
49JN Wade Boggs Yanks JN/12
49JY Wade Boggs Yanks JY/94 6.00 15.00
49PS Wade Boggs Yanks PS/50 6.00 15.00
50BA Ernie Banks BA/15
50DY Ernie Banks DY/7
50IN Ernie Banks IN/15
50JN Ernie Banks JN/14
50JY Ernie Banks JY/68 6.00 15.00
50PS Ernie Banks PS/15
51BA Joe Torre BA/50 4.00 10.00
51DY Joe Torre DY/66 4.00 10.00
51IN Joe Torre IN/50 4.00 10.00
51JN Joe Torre JN/15
51JY Joe Torre JY/66 4.00 10.00
51PS Joe Torre PS/50 4.00 10.00
52BA Tim Hudson BA/100 3.00 8.00
52DY Tim Hudson DY/68 4.00 10.00
52IN Tim Hudson IN/25
52JN Tim Hudson JN/15
52JY Tim Hudson JY/101 3.00 8.00
52PS Tim Hudson PS/50 4.00 10.00
53BA Shawn Green BA/100 3.00 8.00
53DY Shawn Green DY/58 4.00 10.00
53IN Shawn Green IN/25
53JN Shawn Green JN/15
53JY Shawn Green JY/102 3.00 8.00
53PS Shawn Green PS/50 4.00 10.00
54BA Carlos Beltran BA/100 3.00 8.00
54DY Carlos Beltran DY/69 4.00 10.00
54IN Carlos Beltran IN/25
54JN Carlos Beltran JN/15
54JY Carlos Beltran JY/101 3.00 8.00
54PS Carlos Beltran PS/50 4.00 10.00
55BA Bo Jackson BA/50 6.00 15.00
55DY Bo Jackson DY/69 6.00 15.00
55IN Bo Jackson IN/25
55JN Bo Jackson JN/16
55JY Bo Jackson JY/90 6.00 15.00
55PS Bo Jackson PS/50 6.00 15.00
56BA Hal Newhouser BA/50 4.00 10.00
56DY Hal Newhouser DY/15
56IN Hal Newhouser IN/25
56JN Hal Newhouser JN/16
56JY Hal Newhouser JY/55 4.00 10.00
56PS Hal Newhouser PS/30 4.00 10.00
57BA Jason Giambi A's BA/100 3.00 8.00
57DY Jason Giambi A's DY/68 4.00 10.00
57IN Jason Giambi A's IN/50 4.00 10.00
57JN Jason Giambi A's JN/16
57JY Jason Giambi A's JY/101 3.00 8.00
57PS Jason Giambi A's PS/50 4.00 10.00
58BA Lance Berkman BA/100 3.00 8.00
58DY Lance Berkman DY/65 4.00 10.00
58IN Lance Berkman IN/50 4.00 10.00
58JN Lance Berkman JN/17
58JY Lance Berkman JY/102 3.00 8.00
58PS Lance Berkman PS/50 4.00 10.00
59BA Todd Helton BA/100 4.00 10.00
59DY Todd Helton DY/93 4.00 10.00
59IN Todd Helton IN/25
59JN Todd Helton JN/17
59JY Todd Helton JY/100 4.00 10.00
59PS Todd Helton PS/50 6.00 15.00
60BA Mark Grace BA/100 4.00 10.00
60DY Mark Grace DY/7
60IN Mark Grace IN/25
60JN Mark Grace JN/17
60JY Mark Grace JY/95 4.00 10.00
60PS Mark Grace PS/50 6.00 15.00
61BA Fred Lynn BA/100 4.00 10.00
61DY Fred Lynn DY/7
61IN Fred Lynn IN/25
61JN Fred Lynn JN/19
61JY Fred Lynn JY/75 4.00 10.00
61PS Fred Lynn PS/50 4.00 10.00
62BA Bob Feller BA/10
62DY Bob Feller DY/15
62IN Bob Feller IN/25
62JN Bob Feller JN/19
62JY Bob Feller JY/52 6.00 15.00
62PS Bob Feller PS/10
63BA Robin Yount BA/100 6.00 15.00
63DY Robin Yount DY/70 6.00 15.00
63IN Robin Yount IN/50 6.00 15.00
63JN Robin Yount JN/19
63JY Robin Yount JY/88 6.00 15.00
63PS Robin Yount PS/50 6.00 15.00
64BA Tony Gwynn BA/100 8.00 20.00
64DY Tony Gwynn DY/69 10.00 25.00
64IN Tony Gwynn IN/50 10.00 25.00
64JN Tony Gwynn JN/19
64JY Tony Gwynn JY/99 10.00 25.00
64PS Tony Gwynn PS/50 8.00 20.00
65BA Tony Gwynn Pants BA/100 8.00 20.00
65DY Tony Gwynn Pants DY/69 10.00 25.00
65IN Tony Gwynn Pants IN/50 10.00 25.00
65JN Tony Gwynn Pants JN/19
65JY Tony Gwynn Pants JY/99 8.00 20.00
65PS Tony Gwynn Pants PS/50 10.00 25.00
66BA Frank Robinson BA/10
66DY Frank Robinson DY/54 6.00 15.00
66IN Frank Robinson IN/25
66JN Frank Robinson JN/20
66JY Frank Robinson JY/70 6.00 15.00
66PS Frank Robinson PS/10
67BA Mike Schmidt BA/50 15.00 40.00
67DY Mike Schmidt DY/46 15.00 40.00
67IN Mike Schmidt IN/50 15.00 40.00
67JN Mike Schmidt JN/20
67JY Mike Schmidt JY/81 12.50 30.00
67PS Mike Schmidt PS/50 15.00 40.00
68BA Lou Brock BA/20
68DY Lou Brock DY/1
68IN Lou Brock IN/15
68JN Lou Brock JN/20
68JY Lou Brock JY/66 6.00 15.00
68PS Lou Brock PS/15
69BA Don Sutton BA/50 4.00 10.00
69DY Don Sutton DY/58 4.00 10.00
69IN Don Sutton IN/25
69JN Don Sutton JN/20
69JY Don Sutton JY/72 4.00 10.00
69PS Don Sutton PS/25
70BA Mark Mulder BA/100 3.00 8.00
70DY Mark Mulder DY/68 4.00 10.00
70IN Mark Mulder IN/25
70JN Mark Mulder JN/20
70JY Mark Mulder JY/101 3.00 8.00
70PS Mark Mulder PS/50 4.00 10.00
71BA Luis Gonzalez BA/100 3.00 8.00
71DY Luis Gonzalez DY/98 3.00 8.00
71IN Luis Gonzalez IN/25
71JN Luis Gonzalez JN/20
71JY Luis Gonzalez JY/101 3.00 8.00
71PS Luis Gonzalez PS/50 4.00 10.00
72BA Jorge Posada BA/100 4.00 10.00
72DY Jorge Posada DY/13
72IN Jorge Posada IN/25
72JN Jorge Posada JN/20
72JY Jorge Posada JY/101 4.00 10.00
72PS Jorge Posada PS/50 6.00 15.00
73BA Sammy Sosa BA/100 4.00 10.00
73DY Sammy Sosa DY/7
73IN Sammy Sosa IN/50 6.00 15.00
73JN Sammy Sosa JN/21
73JY Sammy Sosa JY/101 4.00 10.00
73PS Sammy Sosa PS/50 6.00 15.00
74BA Roberto Alomar BA/100 4.00 10.00
74DY Roberto Alomar DY/62 6.00 15.00
74IN Roberto Alomar IN/25
74JN Roberto Alomar JN/12
74JY Roberto Alomar JY/102 4.00 10.00
74PS Roberto Alomar PS/50 6.00 15.00
75BA Roberto Clemente BA/10
75DY Roberto Clemente DY/1
75IN Roberto Clemente IN/10
75JN Roberto Clemente JN/21
75JY Roberto Clemente JY/69 60.00 120.00
75PS Roberto Clemente PS/10
76BA Jeff Kent BA/100 3.00 8.00
76DY Jeff Kent DY/58 4.00 10.00
76IN Jeff Kent IN/25
76JN Jeff Kent JN/21
76JY Jeff Kent JY/101 3.00 8.00
76PS Jeff Kent PS/50 4.00 10.00
77BA Sean Casey BA/20
77DY Sean Casey DY/59 4.00 10.00
77IN Sean Casey IN/25
77JN Sean Casey JN/21
77JY Sean Casey JY/100 3.00 8.00
77PS Sean Casey PS/25
78BA R.Clemens R.Sox BA/50 10.00 25.00
78DY R.Clemens R.Sox DY/7
78IN R.Clemens R.Sox IN/50 10.00 25.00
78JN R.Clemens R.Sox JN/21
78JY R.Clemens R.Sox JY/83 10.00 25.00
78PS R.Clemens R.Sox PS/50 10.00 25.00
79BA Warren Spahn BA/20
79DY Warren Spahn DY/53 6.00 15.00
79IN Warren Spahn IN/15
79JN Warren Spahn JN/21
79JY Warren Spahn JY/58 6.00 15.00
79PS Warren Spahn PS/15
80BA R.Clemens Yanks BA/100 10.00 25.00
80DY R.Clemens Yanks DY/13
80IN R.Clemens Yanks IN/50 10.00 25.00
80JN R.Clemens Yanks JN/22
80JY R.Clemens Yanks JY/102 10.00 25.00
80PS R.Clemens Yanks PS/50 10.00 25.00
81BA Jim Palmer BA/50 6.00 15.00
81DY Jim Palmer DY/54 6.00 15.00
81IN Jim Palmer IN/25
81JN Jim Palmer JN/22
81JY Jim Palmer JY/69 6.00 15.00
81PS Jim Palmer PS/50 6.00 15.00
82BA Juan Gonzalez BA/50 4.00 10.00
82DY Juan Gonzalez DY/15
82IN Juan Gonzalez IN/25
82JN Juan Gonzalez JN/22
82JY Juan Gonzalez JY/101 3.00 8.00
82PS Juan Gonzalez PS/50 4.00 10.00
83BA Will Clark BA/100 6.00 15.00
83DY Will Clark DY/58 6.00 15.00
83IN Will Clark IN/25
83JN Will Clark JN/22
83JY Will Clark JY/88 6.00 15.00
83PS Will Clark PS/50 6.00 15.00
84BA Don Mattingly BA/50 12.50 30.00
84DY Don Mattingly DY/13
84IN Don Mattingly IN/50 12.50 30.00
84JN Don Mattingly JN/23
84JY Don Mattingly JY/93 12.50 30.00
84PS Don Mattingly PS/50 12.50 30.00
85BA Ryne Sandberg BA/40 15.00 40.00
85DY Ryne Sandberg DY/7
85IN Ryne Sandberg IN/50 15.00 40.00
85JN Ryne Sandberg JN/23
85JY Ryne Sandberg JY/85 12.50 30.00
85PS Ryne Sandberg PS/50 15.00 40.00
86BA Early Wynn BA/20
86DY Early Wynn DY/15
86IN Early Wynn IN/15
86JN Early Wynn JN/24
86JY Early Wynn JY/55 4.00 10.00
86PS Early Wynn PS/20
87BA Manny Ramirez BA/50 6.00 15.00
87DY Manny Ramirez DY/7
87IN Manny Ramirez IN/25
87JN Manny Ramirez JN/24
87JY Manny Ramirez JY/102 4.00 10.00
87PS Manny Ramirez PS/50 4.00 10.00
88BA R.Henderson Mets BA/100 4.00 10.00
88DY R.Henderson Mets DY/62 6.00 15.00
88IN R.Henderson Mets IN/50 6.00 15.00
88JN R.Henderson Mets JN/24
88JY R.Henderson Mets JY/99 4.00 10.00
88PS R.Henderson Mets PS/50 6.00 15.00
89BA R.Henderson Padres BA/100 6.00 15.00
89DY R.Henderson Padres DY/69 6.00 15.00
89IN R.Henderson Padres IN/25
89JN R.Henderson Padres JN/24
89JY R.Henderson Padres JY/102 4.00 10.00
89PS R.Henderson Padres PS/50 6.00 15.00
90BA Jason Giambi Yanks BA/100 3.00 8.00
90DY Jason Giambi Yanks DY/13
90IN Jason Giambi Yanks IN/50 4.00 10.00
90JN Jason Giambi Yanks JN/25
90JY Jason Giambi Yanks JY/102 3.00 8.00
90PS Jason Giambi Yanks PS/50 4.00 10.00
91BA Carlos Delgado BA/100 3.00 8.00
91DY Carlos Delgado DY/77 3.00 8.00
91IN Carlos Delgado IN/25
91JN Carlos Delgado JN/25
91JY Carlos Delgado JY/100 3.00 8.00
91PS Carlos Delgado PS/50 4.00 10.00
92BA Jim Thome BA/100 4.00 10.00
92DY Jim Thome DY/15
92IN Jim Thome IN/25
92JN Jim Thome JN/25
92JY Jim Thome JY/102 4.00 10.00
92PS Jim Thome PS/50 6.00 15.00
93BA Andruw Jones BA/100 4.00 10.00
93DY Andruw Jones DY/66 6.00 15.00
93IN Andruw Jones IN/25
93JN Andruw Jones JN/25
93JY Andruw Jones JY/101 4.00 10.00
93PS Andruw Jones PS/50 6.00 15.00
94BA Rafael Palmeiro BA/100 6.00 15.00
94DY Rafael Palmeiro DY/72 6.00 15.00
94IN Rafael Palmeiro IN/25
94JN Rafael Palmeiro JN/25
94JY Rafael Palmeiro JY/102 4.00 10.00
94PS Rafael Palmeiro PS/50 6.00 15.00
95BA Troy Glaus BA/100 3.00 8.00
95DY Troy Glaus DY/97 3.00 8.00
95IN Troy Glaus IN/50 4.00 10.00
95JN Troy Glaus JN/25
95JY Troy Glaus JY/100 3.00 8.00
95PS Troy Glaus PS/50 4.00 10.00
96BA Wade Boggs R.Sox BA/100 6.00 15.00
96DY Wade Boggs R.Sox DY/7
96IN Wade Boggs R.Sox IN/50 6.00 15.00
96JN Wade Boggs R.Sox JN/26 12.50 30.00
96JY Wade Boggs R.Sox JY/86 6.00 15.00
96PS Wade Boggs R.Sox PS/50 6.00 15.00
97BA Catfish Hunter BA/50 6.00 15.00
97DY Catfish Hunter DY/68 6.00 15.00
97IN Catfish Hunter IN/25
97JN Catfish Hunter JN/27 12.50 30.00
97JY Catfish Hunter JY/68 6.00 15.00
97PS Catfish Hunter PS/50 6.00 15.00
98BA Juan Marichal BA/50 4.00 10.00
98DY Juan Marichal DY/53 4.00 10.00
98IN Juan Marichal IN/25
98JN Juan Marichal JN/27 8.00 20.00
98JY Juan Marichal JY/67 4.00 10.00
98PS Juan Marichal PS/50 4.00 10.00
99BA Carlton Fisk R.Sox BA/50 6.00 15.00
99DY Carlton Fisk R.Sox DY/7
99IN Carlton Fisk R.Sox IN/25
99JN Carlton Fisk R.Sox JN/27 12.50 30.00
99JY Carlton Fisk R.Sox JY/80 6.00 15.00
99PS Carlton Fisk R.Sox PS/50 6.00 15.00
100BA Vladimir Guerrero BA/100 4.00 10.00
100DY Vladimir Guerrero DY/69 6.00 15.00
100IN Vladimir Guerrero IN/25
100JN Vladimir Guerrero JN/27 10.00 25.00
100JY Vladimir Guerrero JY/101 4.00 10.00
100PS Vladimir Guerrero PS/50 6.00 15.00
101BA Rod Carew Angels BA/50 6.00 15.00
101DY Rod Carew Angels DY/65 6.00 15.00
101IN Rod Carew Angels IN/25
101JN Rod Carew Angels JN/29 12.50 30.00
101JY Rod Carew Angels JY/85 6.00 15.00
101PS Rod Carew Angels PS/50 6.00 15.00
102BA Rod Carew Twins BA/50 6.00 15.00
102DY Rod Carew Twins DY/61 6.00 15.00
102IN Rod Carew Twins IN/25
102JN Rod Carew Twins JN/29 12.50 30.00
102JY Rod Carew Twins JY/71 6.00 15.00
102PS Rod Carew Twins PS/50 6.00 15.00
103BA Joe Carter BA/50 4.00 10.00
103DY Joe Carter DY/77 4.00 10.00
103IN Joe Carter IN/25
103JN Joe Carter JN/29 8.00 20.00
103JY Joe Carter JY/94 4.00 10.00
103PS Joe Carter PS/25
104BA Mike Sweeney BA/100 3.00 8.00
104DY Mike Sweeney DY/69 4.00 10.00
104IN Mike Sweeney IN/25
104JN Mike Sweeney JN/29 6.00 15.00
104JY Mike Sweeney JY/101 3.00 8.00
104PS Mike Sweeney PS/50 4.00 10.00
105BA Nolan Ryan Angels BA/25
105DY Nolan Ryan Angels DY/65 15.00 40.00
105IN Nolan Ryan Angels IN/25
105JN Nolan Ryan Angels JN/30 20.00 50.00
105JY N.Ryan Angels JY/70 UER 15.00 40.00
Jersey year is credited to 1970; Ryan did not arrive in California till 1972
105PS Nolan Ryan Angels PS/50 15.00 40.00
106BA Orlando Cepeda BA/50 4.00 10.00
106DY Orlando Cepeda DY/58 4.00 10.00
106IN Orlando Cepeda IN/25
106JN Orlando Cepeda JN/30 8.00 20.00
106JY Orlando Cepeda JY/65 4.00 10.00
106PS Orlando Cepeda PS/50 4.00 10.00
107BA Magglio Ordonez BA/100 3.00 8.00
107DY Magglio Ordonez DY/4
107IN Magglio Ordonez IN/25
107JN Magglio Ordonez JN/30 6.00 15.00
107JY Magglio Ordonez JY/102 3.00 8.00
107PS Magglio Ordonez PS/50 4.00 10.00
108BA Hoyt Wilhelm BA/50 4.00 10.00
108DY Hoyt Wilhelm DY/4
108IN Hoyt Wilhelm IN/25
108JN Hoyt Wilhelm JN/31 8.00 20.00
108JY Hoyt Wilhelm JY/68 4.00 10.00
108PS Hoyt Wilhelm PS/50 4.00 10.00
109BA Mike Piazza BA/100 6.00 15.00
109DY Mike Piazza DY/62 10.00 25.00
109IN Mike Piazza IN/50 10.00 25.00
109JN Mike Piazza JN/31 15.00 40.00
109JY Mike Piazza JY/100 6.00 15.00
109PS Mike Piazza PS/50 10.00 25.00
110BA Greg Maddux BA/100 6.00 15.00
110DY Greg Maddux DY/66 10.00 25.00
110IN Greg Maddux IN/50 10.00 25.00
110JN Greg Maddux JN/31 15.00 40.00
110JY Greg Maddux JY/102 6.00 15.00
110PS Greg Maddux PS/50 10.00 25.00
111BA Mark Prior BA/100 4.00 10.00
111DY Mark Prior DY/7
111IN Mark Prior IN/50 6.00 15.00
111JN Mark Prior JN/22
111JY Mark Prior JY/102 4.00 10.00
111PS Mark Prior PS/50 6.00 15.00
112BA Torii Hunter BA/100 3.00 8.00
112DY Torii Hunter DY/61 4.00 10.00
112IN Torii Hunter IN/50 4.00 10.00
112JN Torii Hunter JN/48 5.00 12.00
112JY Torii Hunter JY/101 3.00 8.00
112PS Torii Hunter PS/50 4.00 10.00
113BA Steve Carlton BA/100 4.00 10.00
113DY Steve Carlton DY/46 6.00 15.00
113IN Steve Carlton IN/50 4.00 10.00
113JN Steve Carlton JN/32 8.00 20.00
113JY Steve Carlton JY/81 4.00 10.00
113PS Steve Carlton PS/50 4.00 10.00
114BA Jose Canseco BA/100 6.00 15.00
114DY Jose Canseco DY/68 6.00 15.00
114IN Jose Canseco IN/25
114JN Jose Canseco JN/33 10.00 25.00
114JY Jose Canseco JY/69 6.00 15.00
114PS Jose Canseco PS/50 6.00 15.00
115BA Nolan Ryan Rgr BA/50 15.00 40.00
115DY Nolan Ryan Rgr DY/72 15.00 40.00
115IN Nolan Ryan Rgr IN/50 15.00 40.00
115JN Nolan Ryan Rgr JN/34 20.00 50.00
115JY Nolan Ryan Rgr JY/90 15.00 40.00
115PS Nolan Ryan Rgr PS/50 15.00 40.00
116BA Nolan Ryan Astros BA/50 15.00 40.00
116DY Nolan Ryan Astros DY/65 15.00 40.00
116IN Nolan Ryan Astros IN/25
116JN Nolan Ryan Astros JN/34 20.00 50.00
116JY Nolan Ryan Astros JY/84 15.00 40.00
116PS Nolan Ryan Astros PS/50 15.00 40.00
117BA Ty Cobb Pants BA/25
117DY Ty Cobb Pants DY/1
117IN Ty Cobb Pants IN/25
117JN Ty Cobb Pants JN/1
117JY Ty Cobb Pants JY/27 75.00 150.00
117PS Ty Cobb Pants PS/10
118BA Kerry Wood BA/100 3.00 8.00
118DY Kerry Wood DY/50
118IN Kerry Wood IN/25
118JN Kerry Wood JN/34 6.00 15.00
118JY Kerry Wood JY/101 3.00 8.00
118PS Kerry Wood PS/50 4.00 10.00
119BA M.Mussina Yanks BA/50 6.00 15.00
119DY M.Mussina Yanks DY/13
119IN M.Mussina Yanks IN/25
119JN M.Mussina Yanks JN/35 10.00 25.00
119JY M.Mussina Yanks JY/101 4.00 10.00
119PS M.Mussina Yanks PS/50 6.00 15.00
120BA Yogi Berra BA/10
120DY Yogi Berra DY/13
120IN Yogi Berra IN/10
120JN Yogi Berra JN/35 12.50 30.00
120JY Yogi Berra JY/47 10.00 25.00
120PS Yogi Berra PS/10
121BA Thurman Munson BA/25
121DY Thurman Munson DY/13
121IN Thurman Munson IN/25
121JN Thurman Munson IN/15
121JY Thurman Munson JY/79 15.00 40.00
121PS Thurman Munson PS/5
122BA Frank Thomas BA/100 4.00 10.00
122DY Frank Thomas DY/4
122IN Frank Thomas IN/25
122JN Frank Thomas JN/35 10.00 25.00
122JY Frank Thomas JY/94 4.00 10.00
122PS Frank Thomas PS/50 6.00 15.00
123BA R.Henderson A's BA/50 6.00 15.00
123DY R.Henderson A's DY/68 6.00 15.00
123IN R.Henderson A's IN/25
123JN R.Henderson A's JN/35 10.00 25.00
123JY R.Henderson A's JY/80 6.00 15.00
123PS R.Henderson A's PS/50 6.00 15.00
124BA M.Muss O's Pants BA/100 4.00 10.00
124DY M.Muss O's Pants DY/54 6.00 15.00
124IN M.Muss O's Pants IN/25
124JN M.Muss O's Pants JN/35 10.00 25.00
124JY M.Muss O's Pants JY/97 4.00 10.00
124PS M.Muss O's Pants PS/50 6.00 15.00
125BA Gaylord Perry BA/100 4.00 10.00
125DY Gaylord Perry DY/77 4.00 10.00
125IN Gaylord Perry IN/25
125JN Gaylord Perry JN/36 6.00 15.00
125JY Gaylord Perry JY/82 4.00 10.00
125PS Gaylord Perry PS/50 4.00 10.00
126BA Nick Johnson BA/100 3.00 8.00
126DY Nick Johnson DY/13
126IN Nick Johnson IN/25
126JN Nick Johnson JN/36 5.00 12.00
126JY Nick Johnson JY/102 3.00 8.00
126PS Nick Johnson PS/50 4.00 10.00
127BA Curt Schilling BA/100 3.00 8.00
127DY Curt Schilling DY/98 3.00 8.00
127IN Curt Schilling IN/25
127JN Curt Schilling JN/38 5.00 12.00
127JY Curt Schilling JY/102 3.00 8.00
127PS Curt Schilling PS/50 4.00 10.00
128BA Dave Parker BA/100 4.00 10.00
128DY Dave Parker DY/1
128IN Dave Parker IN/25
128JN Dave Parker JN/39 6.00 15.00
128JY Dave Parker JY/80 4.00 10.00
128PS Dave Parker PS/50 4.00 10.00
129BA Eddie Mathews BA/15
129DY Eddie Mathews DY/53 6.00 15.00
129IN Eddie Mathews IN/15
129JN Eddie Mathews JN/41 10.00 25.00
129JY Eddie Mathews JY/59 6.00 15.00
129PS Eddie Mathews PS/15
130BA Tom Seaver Mets BA/10
130DY Tom Seaver Mets DY/62 6.00 15.00
130IN Tom Seaver Mets IN/10
130JN Tom Seaver Mets JN/41 10.00 25.00
130JY Tom Seaver Mets JY/69 6.00 15.00
130PS Tom Seaver Mets PS/10
131BA Tom Seaver Reds BA/10
131DY Tom Seaver Reds DY/59 6.00 15.00
131IN Tom Seaver Reds IN/10
131JN Tom Seaver Reds JN/41 10.00 25.00
131JY Tom Seaver Reds JY/78 6.00 15.00
131PS Tom Seaver Reds PS/22
132BA Jackie Robinson BA/10
132DY Jackie Robinson DY/32
132IN Jackie Robinson IN/10
132JN Jackie Robinson JN/42 40.00 80.00
132JY Jackie Robinson JY/52 40.00 80.00
132PS Jackie Robinson PS/10
133BA R.Jackson Angels BA/100 6.00 15.00
133DY R.Jackson Angels DY/65 6.00 15.00
133IN R.Jackson Angels IN/50 6.00 15.00
133JN R.Jackson Angels JN/44 10.00 25.00
133JY R.Jackson Angels JY/80 6.00 15.00
133PS R.Jackson Angels PS/50 6.00 15.00
134BA Willie McCovey BA/50 4.00 10.00
134DY Willie McCovey DY/58 4.00 10.00
134IN Willie McCovey IN/25
134JN Willie McCovey JN/44 6.00 15.00
134JY Willie McCovey JY/77 4.00 10.00
134PS Willie McCovey PS/50 4.00 10.00
135BA Eric Davis BA/100 4.00 10.00
135DY Eric Davis DY/59 4.00 10.00
135IN Eric Davis IN/25
135JN Eric Davis JN/44 6.00 15.00
135JY Eric Davis JY/89 4.00 10.00
135PS Eric Davis PS/50 4.00 10.00
136BA Adam Dunn BA/100 3.00 8.00
136DY Adam Dunn DY/59 4.00 10.00
136IN Adam Dunn IN/25
136JN Adam Dunn JN/44 5.00 12.00
136JY Adam Dunn JY/102 3.00 8.00
136PS Adam Dunn PS/50 4.00 10.00
137BA Roy Oswalt BA/100 3.00 8.00
137DY Roy Oswalt DY/65 4.00 10.00
137IN Roy Oswalt IN/50 4.00 10.00
137JN Roy Oswalt JN/44 5.00 12.00
137JY Roy Oswalt JY/102 3.00 8.00
137PS Roy Oswalt PS/50 4.00 10.00
138BA P.Martinez Expos BA/50 6.00 15.00
138DY P.Martinez Expos DY/69 6.00 15.00
138IN P.Martinez Expos IN/25
138JN P.Martinez Expos JN/45 8.00 20.00
138JY P.Martinez Expos JY/95 4.00 10.00
138PS P.Martinez Expos PS/50 6.00 15.00
139BA P.Martinez R.Sox BA/100 4.00 10.00
139DY P.Martinez R.Sox DY/7
139IN P.Martinez R.Sox IN/50 6.00 15.00
139JN P.Martinez R.Sox JN/45 8.00 20.00
139JY P.Martinez R.Sox JY/102 4.00 10.00
139PS P.Martinez R.Sox PS/50 6.00 15.00
140BA Andy Pettitte BA/100 4.00 10.00
140DY Andy Pettitte DY/13
140IN Andy Pettitte IN/25
140JN Andy Pettitte JN/46 8.00 20.00
140JY Andy Pettitte JY/97 4.00 10.00
140PS Andy Pettitte PS/50 6.00 15.00
141BA Jack Morris BA/100 4.00 10.00
141DY Jack Morris DY/1
141IN Jack Morris IN/50 4.00 10.00
141JN Jack Morris JN/47 6.00 15.00
141JY Jack Morris JY/85 4.00 10.00
141PS Jack Morris PS/50 4.00 10.00
142BA Tom Glavine BA/100 4.00 10.00
142DY Tom Glavine DY/66 6.00 15.00
142IN Tom Glavine IN/25
142JN Tom Glavine JN/47 8.00 20.00
142JY Tom Glavine JY/100 4.00 10.00
142PS Tom Glavine PS/50 6.00 15.00
143BA R.Johnson M's BA/100 4.00 10.00
143DY R.Johnson M's DY/77 4.00 10.00
143IN R.Johnson M's IN/50 6.00 15.00
143JN R.Johnson M's JN/51 6.00 15.00
143JY R.Johnson M's JY/98 4.00 10.00
143PS R.Johnson M's PS/50 6.00 15.00
144BA Bernie Williams BA/100 4.00 10.00
144DY Bernie Williams DY/13
144IN Bernie Williams IN/50 6.00 15.00
144JN Bernie Williams JN/51 6.00 15.00
144JY Bernie Williams JY/100 4.00 10.00
144PS Bernie Williams PS/50 6.00 15.00
145BA R.Johnson D'backs BA/50 6.00 15.00
145DY R.Johnson D'backs DY/98 4.00 10.00
145IN R.Johnson D'backs IN/50 6.00 15.00
145JN R.Johnson D'backs JN/51 6.00 15.00
145JY R.Johnson D'backs JY/102 4.00 10.00
145PS R.Johnson D'backs PS/50 6.00 15.00
146BA Don Drysdale BA/15
146DY Don Drysdale DY/58 6.00 15.00
146IN Don Drysdale IN/25
146JN Don Drysdale JN/53 6.00 15.00
146JY Don Drysdale JY/64 6.00 15.00
146PS Don Drysdale PS/25
147BA Mark Buehrle BA/100 3.00 8.00
147DY Mark Buehrle DY/4
147IN Mark Buehrle IN/25
147JN Mark Buehrle JN/56 4.00 10.00
147JY Mark Buehrle JY/101 3.00 8.00
147PS Mark Buehrle PS/50 4.00 10.00
148BA Chan Ho Park BA/100 4.00 10.00
148DY Chan Ho Park DY/58 6.00 15.00
148IN Chan Ho Park IN/25
148JN Chan Ho Park JN/61 6.00 15.00
148JY Chan Ho Park JY/101 4.00 10.00
148PS Chan Ho Park PS/50 6.00 15.00
149BA Carlton Fisk W.Sox BA/100 6.00 15.00
149DY Carlton Fisk W.Sox DY/4
149IN Carlton Fisk W.Sox IN/50 6.00 15.00
149JN Carlton Fisk W.Sox JN/72 6.00 15.00
149JY Carlton Fisk W.Sox JY/92 6.00 15.00
149PS Carlton Fisk W.Sox PS/50 6.00 15.00
150BA Barry Zito BA/100 3.00 8.00
150DY Barry Zito DY/68 4.00 10.00
150IN Barry Zito IN/25
150JN Barry Zito JN/75 4.00 10.00
150JY Barry Zito JY/101 3.00 8.00
150PS Barry Zito PS/50 4.00 10.00

2003 Leaf Certified Materials Fabric of the Game Autographs

This is a partial parallel to the Fabric of the Game insert set. Each of these cards were signed, using Donruss/Playoff "band-aid" autographs to a stated print run of five or fewer cards. We have put the announced print run next to the player's name in our checklist and please note there is no pricing due to market scarcity. In addition, because of the use of stickered autographs, please note that autographs of deceased players such as Enos Slaughter and Hoyt Wilhelm are included in this set.

CARDS DISPLAY CUMULATIVE PRINT RUNS
ACTUAL PRINT RUNS B/WN 1-5 COPIES PER
SKIP-NUMBERED 302-CARD SET
NO PRICING DUE TO SCARCITY

2004 Leaf Certified Materials

This 300-card set was released in July, 2004. The set was issued in five-card packs with an $10 SRP which were issued 10 packs per box and 24 boxes per case. The first 200 cards featured active players while cards numbered 201-211 feature players who moved teams in the off-season in their old uniform. Cards numbered 201-211 were inserted at a stated rate of one in 120. Cards 212 through 240 featured retired legends while cards 241-300 featured signed Rookie Cards (except for Kaz Matsui). Cards 212-240 were issued to a stated print run of 500 serial numbered sets and cards numbered 241-300 were issued to a stated print run of 1000 serial numbered sets unless noted in our checklist.

COMP.SET w/o SP's (200) 15.00 40.00
COMMON CARD (1-200) .25 .60
COMMON CARD (201-211) .60 1.50
201-211 STATED ODDS 1:120
COMMON CARD (212 .60 1.50
212-240 PRINT RUN 500 SERIAL #'d SETS
COMMON NO AU (241-300) .60 1.50
241-300 NO AU PRINT RUN 500 #'d PER
COMMON AU p/r 1000 3.00 8.00
COMMON AU p/r 300-500 3.00 8.00
AU MINORS p/r 200-250 4.00 10.00
COMMON AU p/r 100 5.00 12.00
OVERALL AU ODDS 1:10
AU PRINT RUNS B/WN 100-1000 PER
AU PRINT RUN 500 #'d PER UNLESS NOTED
1 A.J. Burnett .40 1.00
2 Adam Dunn .40 1.00
3 Adam LaRoche .25 .60
4 Adam Loewen .25 .60
5 Adrian Beltre .25 .60
6 Al Leiter .25 .60
7 Albert Pujols 1.50 4.00
8 Alex Rodriguez Yanks 1.00 2.50
9 Alexis Rios .40 1.00
10 Alfonso Soriano Rgr .25 .60
11 Andruw Jones .25 .60
12 Andy Pettitte .40 1.00
13 Angel Berroa .25 .60
14 Aramis Ramirez .25 .60
15 Aubrey Huff .25 .60
16 Austin Kearns .25 .60
17 Barry Larkin .40 1.00
18 Barry Zito .25 .60
19 Ben Sheets .25 .60
20 Bernie Williams .40 1.00
21 Bobby Abreu .25 .60
22 Brad Penny .25 .60
23 Brad Wilkerson .25 .60
24 Brandon Webb .25 .60
25 Brendan Harris .25 .60
26 Bret Boone .25 .60
27 Brett Myers .25 .60
28 Bubba Crosby .25 .60
29 Brian Giles .25 .60
30 Chad Cordero .25 .60
31 Bubba Nelson .25 .60
32 Byron Gettis .25 .60
33 C.C. Sabathia .40 1.00
34 Carl Crawford .40 1.00
35 Carl Everett .25 .60
36 Carlos Beltran .25 .60
37 Carlos Delgado .25 .60
38 Carlos Lee .25 .60
39 Chad Gaudin .25 .60
40 Cliff Lee .40 1.00
41 Chipper Jones .60 1.50
42 Cliff Floyd .25 .60
43 Clint Barmes .40 1.00
44 Corey Patterson .25 .60
45 Craig Biggio .40 1.00
46 Curt Schilling Sox .40 1.00
47 Dan Haren .25 .60
48 Darin Erstad .25 .60
49 David Ortiz .60 1.50
50 Delmon Young .40 1.00
51 Derek Jeter 1.50 4.00
52 Dewon Brazelton .25 .60
53 Dontrelle Willis .25 .60
54 Edgar Martinez .40 1.00
55 Edgar Renteria .25 .60
56 Edwin Almonte .25 .60
57 Edwin Jackson .25 .60
58 Eric Chavez .25 .60
59 Eric Hinske .25 .60
60 Eric Munson .25 .60
61 Erubiel Durazo .25 .60
62 Frank Thomas .60 1.50
63 Fred McGriff .25 .60
64 Freddy Garcia .25 .60
65 Garret Anderson .25 .60
66 Garrett Atkins .25 .60
67 Gary Sheffield .25 .60
68 Geoff Jenkins .25 .60
69 Greg Maddux Cubs 1.00 2.50
70 Hank Blalock .25 .60
71 Hee Seop Choi .25 .60
72 Hideki Matsui 1.00 2.50
73 Hideo Nomo .60 1.50
74 Craig Wilson .25 .60
75 Ichiro Suzuki 1.00 2.50
76 Ivan Rodriguez Tigers .40 1.00
77 J.D. Drew .25 .60
78 John Lackey .25 .60
79 Jacque Jones .25 .60
80 Jae Weong Seo .25 .60
81 Jamie Moyer .25 .60
82 Jason Giambi Yanks .25 .60
83 Jason Jennings .25 .60
84 Jason Kendall .25 .60
85 Melvin Mora .25 .60
86 Jason Varitek .60 1.50
87 Javier Vazquez .25 .60
88 Javy Lopez .25 .60
89 Jay Gibbons .25 .60
90 Jay Payton .25 .60
91 Jeff Bagwell .40 1.00
92 Jeff Baker .25 .60
93 Jeff Kent .25 .60
94 Jeremy Bonderman .25 .60
95 Milton Bradley .25 .60
96 Jerome Williams .25 .60
97 Jim Edmonds .40 1.00
98 Jim Thome .40 1.00
99 Jody Gerut .25 .60
100 Joe Borchard .25 .60
101 Joe Crede .25 .60
102 Johan Santana .60 1.50
103 John Olerud .25 .60
104 John Smoltz .60 1.50
105 Johnny Damon .40 1.00
106 Jorge Posada .40 1.00
107 Jose Castillo .25 .60
108 Jose Reyes .40 1.00
109 Jose Vidro .25 .60
110 Josh Beckett .40 1.00
111 Josh Phelps .25 .60
112 Juan Encarnacion .25 .60
113 Juan Gonzalez .25 .60
114 Junior Spivey .25 .60
115 Kazuhisa Ishii .25 .60
116 Kenny Lofton .25 .60
117 Kerry Wood .25 .60
118 Kevin Millwood .25 .60
119 Kevin Youkilis .40 1.00
120 Lance Berkman .40 1.00
121 Larry Bigbie .25 .60
122 Larry Walker .40 1.00
123 Luis Castillo .25 .60
124 Luis Gonzalez .25 .60
125 Luis Matos .25 .60
126 Lyle Overbay .25 .60
127 Magglio Ordonez .40 1.00
128 Manny Ramirez .60 1.50
129 Marcus Giles .25 .60
130 Mariano Rivera .60 1.50
131 Mark Buehrle .40 1.00
132 Mark Mulder .25 .60
133 Mark Prior .40 1.00
134 Mark Teixeira .60 1.50

135 Marlon Byrd .25 .60
136 Matt Morris .25 .60
137 Miguel Cabrera .60 1.50
138 Mike Lowell .25 .60
139 Mike Mussina .40 1.00
140 Mike Piazza .60 1.50
141 Mike Sweeney .25 .60
142 Morgan Ensberg .25 .60
143 Nick Johnson .25 .60
144 Nomar Garciaparra .60 1.50
145 Omar Vizquel .40 1.00
146 Orlando Cabrera .25 .60
147 Orlando Hudson .25 .60
148 Pat Burrell .25 .60
149 Paul Konerko .40 1.00
150 Paul Lo Duca .25 .60
151 Pedro Martinez .40 1.00
152 Jermaine Dye .25 .60
153 Preston Wilson .25 .60
154 Rafael Furcal .25 .60
155 Rafael Palmeiro O's .40 1.00
156 Randy Johnson .60 1.50
157 Rich Aurilia .25 .60
158 Rich Harden .25 .60
159 Richard Hidalgo .25 .60
160 Richie Sexson .25 .60
161 Rickie Weeks .25 .60
162 Roberto Alomar .40 1.00
163 Rocco Baldelli .25 .60
164 Roger Clemens Astros .75 2.00
165 Roy Halladay .60 1.50
166 Roy Oswalt .40 1.00
167 Ryan Howard .75 2.00
168 Ryan Klesko .25 .60
169 Rodrigo Lopez .25 .60
170 Sammy Sosa .60 1.50
171 Scott Podsednik .25 .60
172 Scott Rolen .40 1.00
173 Sean Burroughs .25 .60
174 Sean Casey .25 .60
175 Shannon Stewart .25 .60
176 Shawn Green .25 .60
177 Shea Hillenbrand .25 .60
178 Shigetoshi Hasegawa .25 .60
179 Steve Finley .25 .60
180 Tim Hudson .40 1.00
181 Todd Helton .40 1.00
182 Tom Glavine .40 1.00
183 Torii Hunter .25 .60
184 Trot Nixon .25 .60
185 Troy Glaus .25 .60
186 Vernon Wells .25 .60
187 Victor Martinez .40 1.00
188 Vladimir Guerrero Angels .60 1.50
189 Wade Miller .25 .60
190 Brandon Larson .25 .60
191 Travis Hafner .25 .60
192 Tim Salmon .25 .60
193 Tim Redding .25 .60
194 Runelvys Hernandez .25 .60
195 Ramon Nivar .25 .60
196 Moises Alou .25 .60
197 Michael Young .25 .60
198 Laynce Nix .25 .60
199 Tino Martinez .40 1.00
200 Randall Simon .25 .60
201 Roger Clemens Yanks SP 2.00 5.00
202 Greg Maddux Braves SP 2.50 6.00
203 Vladimir Guerrero Expos SP 1.50 4.00
204 Miguel Tejada SP 1.00 2.50
205 Kevin Brown SP .60 1.50
206 Jason Giambi A's SP .60 1.50
207 Curt Schilling D'backs SP 1.00 2.50
208 Alex Rodriguez Rgr SP 2.50 6.00
209 Alfonso Soriano Yanks SP .60 1.50
210 Ivan Rodriguez Marlins SP 1.00 2.50
211 Rafael Palmeiro Rgr SP 1.00 2.50
212 Gary Carter LGD .60 1.50
213 Duke Snider LGD 1.00 2.50
214 Whitey Ford LGD 1.00 2.50
215 Bob Feller LGD .60 1.50
216 Reggie Jackson LGD 1.00 2.50
217 Ryne Sandberg LGD 3.00 8.00
218 Dale Murphy LGD 1.00 2.50
219 Tony Gwynn LGD 1.50 4.00
220 Don Mattingly LGD 3.00 8.00
221 Mike Schmidt LGD 2.50 6.00
222 Rickey Henderson LGD 1.50 4.00
223 Cal Ripken LGD 6.00 15.00
224 Nolan Ryan LGD 5.00 12.00
225 George Brett LGD 3.00 8.00
226 Bob Gibson LGD 1.00 2.50
227 Lou Brock LGD 1.00 2.50
228 Andre Dawson LGD 1.00 2.50
229 Rod Carew LGD 1.00 2.50
230 Wade Boggs LGD 1.00 2.50
231 Roberto Clemente LGD 4.00 10.00
232 Roy Campanella LGD 1.50 4.00
233 Babe Ruth LGD 4.00 10.00
234 Lou Gehrig LGD 3.00 8.00
235 Ty Cobb LGD 2.50 6.00
236 Roger Maris LGD 1.50 4.00
237 Satchel Paige LGD 1.50 4.00
238 Ernie Banks LGD 1.50 4.00
239 Ted Williams LGD 4.00 10.00
240 Stan Musial LGD 2.50 6.00
241 Hector Gimenez NG AU RC 3.00 8.00
242 Justin Germano NG AU RC 4.00 10.00
243 Ian Snell NG AU RC 6.00 15.00
244 Graham Koonce NG AU 3.00 8.00
245 Jose Capellan NG AU RC 3.00 8.00
246 Onil Joseph NG AU RC 3.00 8.00
247 S.Takatsu NG AU/200 RC 6.00 15.00
248 Carlos Hines NG AU RC 3.00 8.00
249 Linc Holdzkom NG AU RC 3.00 8.00
250 Mike Gosling NG AU RC 3.00 8.00
251 Eduardo Sierra NG AU RC 4.00 10.00
252 Renyel Pinto NG AU RC 3.00 8.00
253 Merkin Valdez NG AU RC 3.00 8.00
254 Angel Chavez NG AU RC 3.00 8.00
255 I.Ochoa NG AU/1000 RC 3.00 8.00
256 G.Dobbs NG AU/300 RC 3.00 8.00
257 William Bergolla NG AU RC 3.00 8.00
258 Aarom Baldiris NG AU RC 3.00 8.00
259 Kazuo Matsui NG RC 1.00 2.50
260 Carlos Vasquez NG AU RC 4.00 10.00
261 Freddy Guzman NG AU RC 3.00 8.00
262 Aki Otsuka NG AU/200 RC 12.50 30.00
263 M.Gomez NG AU/200 RC 4.00 10.00
264 Nick Regilio NG AU RC 3.00 8.00
265 Jamie Brown NG AU RC 3.00 8.00
266 Shawn Hill NG AU RC 3.00 8.00
267 Roberto Novoa NG AU RC 3.00 8.00
268 Sean Henn NG AU RC 3.00 8.00
269 Ramon Ramirez NG AU RC 3.00 8.00
270 R.Cedeno NG AU/1000 RC 6.00 15.00
271 Ryan Wing NG AU/400 RC 3.00 8.00
272 Ruddy Yan NG AU 3.00 8.00
273 Fernando Nieve NG AU RC 3.00 8.00
274 Rusty Tucker NG AU RC 4.00 10.00
275 Jason Bartlett NG AU RC 4.00 10.00
276 Mike Rouse NG AU RC 3.00 8.00
277 Dennis Sarfate NG AU RC 3.00 8.00
278 Cory Sullivan NG AU RC 3.00 8.00
279 C.Daigle NG AU/250 RC 4.00 10.00
280 C.Shelton NG AU/400 RC 10.00 25.00
281 J.Harper NG AU/400 RC 3.00 8.00
282 Michael Wuertz NG AU RC 4.00 10.00
283 T.Bausher NG AU/400 RC 3.00 8.00
284 Jorge Sequea NG AU RC 3.00 8.00
285 J.Labandeira NG AU/100 RC 5.00 12.00
286 Justin Leone NG AU RC 4.00 10.00
287 Tim Bittner NG AU RC 3.00 8.00
288 Andres Blanco NG AU RC 3.00 8.00
289 K.Cave NG AU/1000 RC 3.00 8.00
290 M.Johnston NG AU/1000 RC 3.00 8.00
291 J.Szuminski NG AU RC 3.00 8.00
292 Shawn Camp NG RC .60 1.50
293 Colby Miller NG AU RC 3.00 8.00
294 Jake Woods NG AU RC 3.00 8.00
295 Ryan Meaux NG AU RC 3.00 8.00
296 Don Kelly NG AU RC 3.00 8.00
297 Edwin Moreno NG AU RC 3.00 8.00
298 Phil Stockman NG AU RC 3.00 8.00
299 Jorge Vasquez NG RC .60 1.50
300 Kaz Tadano NG AU RC 6.00 15.00

2004 Leaf Certified Materials Mirror Black

STATED PRINT RUN 1 SERIAL #'d SET
NO PRICING DUE TO SCARCITY

2004 Leaf Certified Materials Mirror Blue

*1-200: 2.5X TO 6X BASIC
*BLUE 201-211: 1.25X TO 3X BASIC
*BLUE 212-240: 1.25X TO 3X BASIC
RANDOM INSERTS IN PACKS
STATED PRINT RUN 50 SERIAL #'d SETS
COMMON CARD (241-300) 1.50 4.00
241 Hector Gimenez NG 1.50 4.00
242 Justin Germano NG 1.50 4.00
243 Ian Snell NG 1.50 4.00
244 Graham Koonce NG 1.50 4.00
245 Jose Capellan NG 1.50 4.00
246 Onil Joseph NG 1.50 4.00
247 Shingo Takatsu NG 1.50 4.00
248 Carlos Hines NG 1.50 4.00
249 Lincoln Holdzkom NG 1.50 4.00
250 Mike Gosling NG 1.50 4.00
251 Eduardo Sierra NG 1.50 4.00
252 Renyel Pinto NG 1.50 4.00
253 Merkin Valdez NG 1.50 4.00
254 Angel Chavez NG 1.50 4.00
255 Ivan Ochoa NG 1.50 4.00
256 Greg Dobbs NG 1.50 4.00
257 William Bergolla NG 1.50 4.00
258 Aarom Baldiris NG 1.50 4.00
259 Kazuo Matsui NG 2.50 6.00
260 Carlos Vasquez NG 1.50 4.00
261 Freddy Guzman NG 1.50 4.00
262 Akinori Otsuka NG 1.50 4.00
263 Mariano Gomez NG 1.50 4.00
264 Nick Regilio NG 1.50 4.00
265 Jamie Brown NG 1.50 4.00
266 Shawn Hill NG 1.50 4.00
267 Roberto Novoa NG 1.50 4.00
268 Sean Henn NG 1.50 4.00
269 Ramon Ramirez NG 1.50 4.00
270 Ronny Cedeno NG 1.50 4.00
271 Ryan Wing NG 1.50 4.00
272 Ruddy Yan NG 1.50 4.00
273 Fernando Nieve NG 1.50 4.00
274 Rusty Tucker NG 1.50 4.00
275 Jason Bartlett NG 5.00 12.00
276 Mike Rouse NG 1.50 4.00
277 Dennis Sarfate NG 1.50 4.00
278 Cory Sullivan NG 1.50 4.00
279 Casey Daigle NG 1.50 4.00
280 Chris Shelton NG 1.50 4.00
281 Jesse Harper NG 1.50 4.00
282 Michael Wuertz NG 1.50 4.00
283 Tim Bausher NG 1.50 4.00
284 Jorge Sequea NG 1.50 4.00
285 Josh Labandeira NG 1.50 4.00
286 Justin Leone NG 1.50 4.00
287 Tim Bittner NG 1.50 4.00
288 Andres Blanco NG 1.50 4.00
289 Kevin Cave NG 1.50 4.00
290 Mike Johnston NG 1.50 4.00
291 Jason Szuminski NG 1.50 4.00
292 Shawn Camp NG 1.50 4.00
293 Colby Miller NG 1.50 4.00
294 Jake Woods NG 1.50 4.00
295 Ryan Meaux NG 1.50 4.00
296 Don Kelly NG 2.50 6.00
297 Edwin Moreno NG 1.50 4.00
298 Phil Stockman NG 1.50 4.00
299 Jorge Vasquez NG 1.50 4.00
300 Kazuhito Tadano NG 1.50 4.00

2004 Leaf Certified Materials Mirror Emerald

STATED PRINT RUN 5 SERIAL #'d SETS
NO PRICING DUE TO SCARCITY

2004 Leaf Certified Materials Mirror Gold

*GOLD 1-200: 4X TO 10X BASIC
*GOLD 201-211: 1.5X TO 4X BASIC
*GOLD 212-240: 1.5X TO 4X BASIC
RANDOM INSERTS IN PACKS
STATED PRINT RUN 25 SERIAL #'d SETS
241-300 NO PRICING DUE TO SCARCITY

2004 Leaf Certified Materials Mirror Red

*RED 1-200: 1.5X TO 4X BASIC
*RED 201-211: .75X TO 2X BASIC
*RED 212-240: .75X TO 2X BASIC
RANDOM INSERTS IN PACKS
STATED PRINT RUN 100 SERIAL #'d SETS
COMMON CARD (241-300) 1.00 2.50
241 Hector Gimenez NG 1.00 2.50
242 Justin Germano NG 1.00 2.50
243 Ian Snell NG 1.00 2.50
244 Graham Koonce NG 1.00 2.50
245 Jose Capellan NG 1.00 2.50
246 Onil Joseph NG 1.00 2.50
247 Shingo Takatsu NG 1.00 2.50
248 Carlos Hines NG 1.00 2.50
249 Lincoln Holdzkom NG 1.00 2.50
250 Mike Gosling NG 1.00 2.50
251 Eduardo Sierra NG 1.00 2.50
252 Renyel Pinto NG 1.00 2.50
253 Merkin Valdez NG 1.00 2.50
254 Angel Chavez NG 1.00 2.50
255 Ivan Ochoa NG 1.00 2.50
256 Greg Dobbs NG 1.00 2.50
257 William Bergolla NG 1.00 2.50
258 Aarom Baldiris NG 1.00 2.50
259 Kazuo Matsui NG 1.50 4.00
260 Carlos Vasquez NG 1.00 2.50
261 Freddy Guzman NG 1.00 2.50
262 Akinori Otsuka NG 1.00 2.50
263 Mariano Gomez NG 1.00 2.50
264 Nick Regilio NG 1.00 2.50
265 Jamie Brown NG 1.00 2.50
266 Shawn Hill NG 1.00 2.50
267 Roberto Novoa NG 1.00 2.50
268 Sean Henn NG 1.00 2.50
269 Ramon Ramirez NG 1.00 2.50
270 Ronny Cedeno NG 1.00 2.50
271 Ryan Wing NG 1.00 2.50
272 Ruddy Yan NG 1.00 2.50
273 Fernando Nieve NG 1.00 2.50
274 Rusty Tucker NG 1.00 2.50
275 Jason Bartlett NG 3.00 8.00
276 Mike Rouse NG 1.00 2.50
277 Dennis Sarfate NG 1.00 2.50
278 Cory Sullivan NG 1.00 2.50
279 Casey Daigle NG 1.00 2.50
280 Chris Shelton NG 1.00 2.50
281 Jesse Harper NG 1.00 2.50
282 Michael Wuertz NG 1.00 2.50
283 Tim Bausher NG 1.00 2.50
284 Jorge Sequea NG 1.00 2.50
285 Josh Labandeira NG 1.00 2.50
286 Justin Leone NG 1.00 2.50
287 Tim Bittner NG 1.00 2.50
288 Andres Blanco NG 1.00 2.50
289 Kevin Cave NG 1.00 2.50
290 Mike Johnston NG 1.00 2.50
291 Jason Szuminski NG 1.00 2.50
292 Shawn Camp NG 1.00 2.50
293 Colby Miller NG 1.00 2.50
294 Jake Woods NG 1.00 2.50
295 Ryan Meaux NG 1.00 2.50
296 Don Kelly NG 1.50 4.00
297 Edwin Moreno NG 1.00 2.50
298 Phil Stockman NG 1.00 2.50
299 Jorge Vasquez NG 1.00 2.50
300 Kazuhito Tadano NG 1.00 2.50

2004 Leaf Certified Materials Mirror White

*WHITE 1-200: 1.5X TO 4X BASIC
*WHITE 201-211: .75X TO 2X BASIC
*WHITE 212-240: .75X TO 2X BASIC
RANDOM INSERTS IN PACKS
PRINT RUN 100 SERIAL #'d SETS

COMMON CARD (241-300) 1.00 2.50
241 Hector Gimenez NG 1.00 2.50
242 Justin Germano NG 1.00 2.50
243 Ian Snell NG 1.00 2.50
244 Graham Koonce NG 1.00 2.50
245 Jose Capellan NG 1.00 2.50
246 Onil Joseph NG 1.00 2.50
247 Shingo Takatsu NG 1.00 2.50
248 Carlos Hines NG 1.00 2.50
249 Lincoln Holdzkom NG 1.00 2.50
250 Mike Gosling NG 1.00 2.50
251 Eduardo Sierra NG 1.00 2.50
252 Renyel Pinto NG 1.00 2.50
253 Merkin Valdez NG 1.00 2.50
254 Angel Chavez NG 1.00 2.50
255 Ivan Ochoa NG 1.00 2.50
256 Greg Dobbs NG 1.00 2.50
257 William Bergolla NG 1.00 2.50
258 Aarom Baldiris NG 1.00 2.50
259 Kazuo Matsui NG 1.50 4.00
260 Carlos Vasquez NG 1.00 2.50
261 Freddy Guzman NG 1.00 2.50
262 Akinori Otsuka NG 1.00 2.50
263 Mariano Gomez NG 1.00 2.50
264 Nick Regilio NG 1.00 2.50
265 Jamie Brown NG 1.00 2.50
266 Shawn Hill NG 1.00 2.50
267 Roberto Novoa NG 1.00 2.50
268 Sean Henn NG 1.00 2.50
269 Ramon Ramirez NG 1.00 2.50
270 Ronny Cedeno NG 1.00 2.50
271 Ryan Wing NG 1.00 2.50
272 Ruddy Yan NG 1.00 2.50
273 Fernando Nieve NG 1.00 2.50
274 Rusty Tucker NG 1.00 2.50
275 Jason Bartlett NG 3.00 8.00
276 Mike Rouse NG 1.00 2.50
277 Dennis Sarfate NG 1.00 2.50
278 Cory Sullivan NG 1.00 2.50
279 Casey Daigle NG 1.00 2.50
280 Chris Shelton NG 1.00 2.50
281 Jesse Harper NG 1.00 2.50
282 Michael Wuertz NG 1.00 2.50
283 Tim Bausher NG 1.00 2.50
284 Jorge Sequea NG 1.00 2.50
285 Josh Labandeira NG 1.00 2.50
286 Justin Leone NG 1.00 2.50
287 Tim Bittner NG 1.00 2.50
288 Andres Blanco NG 1.00 2.50
289 Kevin Cave NG 1.00 2.50
290 Mike Johnston NG 1.00 2.50
291 Jason Szuminski NG 1.00 2.50
292 Shawn Camp NG 1.00 2.50
293 Colby Miller NG 1.00 2.50
294 Jake Woods NG 1.00 2.50
295 Ryan Meaux NG 1.00 2.50
296 Don Kelly NG 1.50 4.00
297 Edwin Moreno NG 1.00 2.50
298 Phil Stockman NG 1.00 2.50
299 Jorge Vasquez NG 1.00 2.50
300 Kazuhito Tadano NG 1.00 2.50

2004 Leaf Certified Materials Mirror Autograph Black

OVERALL AU ODDS 1:10
STATED PRINT RUN 1 SERIAL #'d SET
NO PRICING DUE TO SCARCITY

2004 Leaf Certified Materials Mirror Autograph Blue

*1-240 p/r 100: .5X TO 1.2X RED p/r 200-250
*1-240 p/r 100: .4X TO 1X RED p/r 100
*1-240 p/r 50: .6X TO 1.5X RED p/r 200-250
*1-240 p/r 50: .5X TO 1.2X RED p/r 100
*1-240 p/r 50: .4X TO 1X RED p/r 50
*1-240 p/r 25: 1X TO 2.5X RED p/r 200-250
*1-240 p/r 25: .6X TO 1.5X RED p/r 50
*1-240 p/r 25: .4X TO 1X RED p/r 25
*241-300 p/r 100: .5X TO 1.2X RED p/r 200-250
*241-300 p/r 100: .4X TO 1X RED p/r 100
*241-300 p/r 50: .4X TO 1X RED p/r 50
OVERALL AU ODDS 1:10
PRINT RUNS B/WN 1-100 COPIES PER
NO PRICING ON QTY OF 10 OR LESS
2 Adam Dunn/47 12.50 30.00
167 Ryan Howard/100 40.00 80.00

2004 Leaf Certified Materials Mirror Autograph Emerald

OVERALL AU ODDS 1:10
PRINT RUNS B/WN 1-5 COPIES PER
NO PRICING DUE TO SCARCITY

2004 Leaf Certified Materials Mirror Autograph Gold

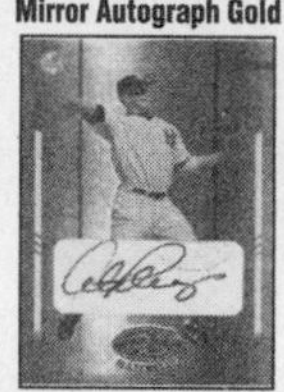

*1-240 p/r 25: 1X TO 2.5X RED p/r 200-250
*1-240 p/r 25: .75X TO 2X RED p/r 100
*1-240 p/r 25: .6X TO 1.5X RED p/r 50
*1-240 p/r 25: .4X TO 1X RED p/r 25
OVERALL AU ODDS 1:10
PRINT RUNS B/WN 1-25 COPIES PER
1-240 NO PRICING ON QTY OF 10 OR LESS
241-300 NO PRICING ON QTY OF 25 OR LESS
167 Ryan Howard/25 75.00 150.00

2004 Leaf Certified Materials Mirror Autograph Red

OVERALL AU ODDS 1:10
PRINT RUNS B/WN 1-250 COPIES PER
NO PRICING ON QTY OF 10 OR LESS
3 Adam LaRoche/250 3.00 8.00
4 Adam Loewen/250 3.00 8.00
7 Albert Pujols/25 150.00 250.00
8 Alex Rodriguez Yanks/1
9 Alexis Rios/250 5.00 12.00
10 Alfonso Soriano Rgr/25 20.00 50.00
11 Andruw Jones/25 20.00 50.00
12 Andy Pettitte/25 20.00 50.00
13 Angel Berroa/100 4.00 10.00
14 Aramis Ramirez/100 6.00 15.00
15 Aubrey Huff/250 5.00 12.00
16 Austin Kearns/200 3.00 8.00
17 Barry Larkin/25 20.00 50.00
18 Barry Zito/10
20 Bernie Williams/5
22 Brad Penny/25 8.00 20.00
24 Brandon Webb/250 3.00 8.00
25 Brendan Harris/50 5.00 12.00
27 Brett Myers/100 6.00 15.00
28 Bubba Crosby/250 3.00 8.00
30 Chad Cordero/250 5.00 12.00
31 Bubba Nelson/250 3.00 8.00
32 Byron Gettis/250 3.00 8.00
36 Carlos Beltran/100 6.00 15.00
38 Carlos Lee/250 5.00 12.00
39 Chad Gaudin/100 4.00 10.00
40 Cliff Lee/250 8.00 20.00
41 Chipper Jones/5
43 Clint Barmes/100 6.00 15.00
45 Craig Biggio/1
46 Curt Schilling Sox/5
47 Dan Haren/250 3.00 8.00
49 David Ortiz/250 15.00 40.00
50 Delmon Young/50 12.50 30.00
52 Dewon Brazelton/250 3.00 8.00
53 Dontrelle Willis/100 10.00 25.00
56 Edwin Almonte/250 3.00 8.00
57 Edwin Jackson/250 5.00 12.00
58 Eric Chavez/25 12.50 30.00
59 Eric Hinske/5
62 Frank Thomas/50 20.00 50.00
63 Fred McGriff/10
65 Garret Anderson/250 5.00 12.00
67 Gary Sheffield/50 12.50 30.00
70 Hank Blalock/100 6.00 15.00
73 Hideo Nomo/1
74 Craig Wilson/250 3.00 8.00
77 J.D. Drew/1
78 John Lackey/250 5.00 12.00
79 Jacque Jones/250 5.00 12.00
80 Jae Weong Seo/100 6.00 15.00
85 Melvin Mora/250 5.00 12.00
86 Jason Varitek/100 15.00 40.00
87 Javier Vazquez/5
89 Jay Gibbons/250 3.00 8.00
90 Jay Payton/250 3.00 8.00
91 Jeff Bagwell/50 20.00 50.00
92 Jeff Baker/25 8.00 20.00
96 Jerome Williams/100 4.00 10.00
97 Jim Edmonds/25 20.00 50.00
99 Jody Gerut/250 3.00 8.00
100 Joe Borchard/250 3.00 8.00
101 Joe Crede/50 8.00 20.00
102 Johan Santana/250 10.00 25.00
106 Jorge Posada/25 20.00 50.00
107 Jose Castillo/250 3.00 8.00
108 Jose Reyes/10
109 Jose Vidro/250 3.00 8.00
110 Josh Beckett/25 20.00 50.00
111 Josh Phelps/10
113 Juan Gonzalez/25 12.50 30.00
114 Junior Spivey/25 8.00 20.00
115 Kazuhisa Ishii/10
117 Kerry Wood/50 12.50 30.00
119 Kevin Youkilis/250 3.00 8.00
120 Lance Berkman/25 12.50 30.00
121 Larry Bigbie/250 5.00 12.00
123 Luis Castillo/25 8.00 20.00
125 Luis Matos/250 3.00 8.00
127 Magglio Ordonez/250 5.00 12.00
128 Manny Ramirez/1
129 Marcus Giles/250 5.00 12.00
130 Mariano Rivera/1
131 Mark Buehrle/250 10.00 25.00
132 Mark Mulder/250 5.00 12.00
133 Mark Prior/100 10.00 25.00
134 Mark Teixeira/100 10.00 25.00
135 Marlon Byrd/250 3.00 8.00
137 Miguel Cabrera/250 8.00 20.00
138 Mike Lowell/5
139 Mike Mussina/1
140 Mike Piazza/25 75.00 150.00
142 Morgan Ensberg/250 5.00 12.00
143 Nick Johnson/1
146 Orlando Cabrera/25 12.50 30.00
147 Orlando Hudson/10
150 Paul Lo Duca/25 12.50 30.00
151 Pedro Martinez/1
152 Jermaine Dye/250 5.00 12.00
153 Preston Wilson/250 5.00 12.00
154 Rafael Furcal/100 6.00 15.00
155 Rafael Palmeiro O's/5
156 Randy Johnson/5
157 Rich Aurilia/25 8.00 20.00
158 Rich Harden/203 5.00 12.00
160 Richie Sexson/1
161 Rickie Weeks/4
162 Roberto Alomar/10
163 Rocco Baldelli/5
165 Roy Halladay/50 8.00 20.00
166 Roy Oswalt/50 8.00 20.00
167 Ryan Howard/100 40.00 80.00
169 Rodrigo Lopez/250 3.00 8.00
170 Sammy Sosa/50 50.00 100.00
171 Scott Podsednik/250 8.00 20.00
172 Scott Rolen/100 10.00 25.00
175 Shannon Stewart/100 6.00 15.00
176 Shawn Green/25 20.00 50.00
177 Shea Hillenbrand/250 5.00 12.00
178 Shigetoshi Hasegawa/250 15.00 40.00
179 Steve Finley/100 6.00 15.00
180 Tim Hudson/10
181 Todd Helton/10
182 Tom Glavine/5
183 Torii Hunter/250 5.00 12.00
184 Trot Nixon/250 5.00 12.00
185 Troy Glaus/1
186 Vernon Wells/5
187 Victor Martinez/250 5.00 12.00
188 Vlad Guerrero Angels/50 20.00 50.00
189 Wade Miller/5
190 Brandon Larson/200 3.00 8.00
191 Travis Hafner/250 5.00 12.00
195 Ramon Nivar/10
197 Michael Young/250 8.00 20.00
203 Vladimir Guerrero Expos/5
204 Miguel Tejada/1
207 Curt Schilling D'backs/1
208 Alex Rodriguez Rgr/1
209 Alfonso Soriano Yanks/5
211 Rafael Palmeiro Rgr/1
212 Gary Carter LGD/250 5.00 12.00
213 Duke Snider LGD/250 8.00 20.00
214 Whitey Ford LGD/50 20.00 50.00
215 Bob Feller LGD/250 8.00 20.00
216 Reggie Jackson LGD/50 20.00 50.00
217 Ryne Sandberg LGD/50 40.00 80.00
218 Dale Murphy LGD/50 12.50 30.00
219 Tony Gwynn LGD/50 30.00 60.00
220 Don Mattingly LGD/50 40.00 80.00
221 Mike Schmidt LGD/50 40.00 80.00
222 Rickey Henderson LGD/50 40.00 80.00
223 Cal Ripken LGD/50 125.00 200.00
224 Nolan Ryan LGD/50 40.00 80.00
225 George Brett LGD/50 40.00 80.00
226 Bob Gibson LGD/100 10.00 25.00
227 Lou Brock LGD/100 10.00 25.00
228 Andre Dawson LGD/250 5.00 12.00
229 Rod Carew LGD/50 12.50 30.00
230 Wade Boggs LGD/50 12.50 30.00
238 Ernie Banks LGD/50 30.00 60.00
240 Stan Musial LGD/100 20.00 50.00
241 Hector Gimenez NG/200 3.00 8.00
242 Justin Germano NG/100 5.00 12.00
243 Ian Snell NG/100 6.00 15.00
244 Graham Koonce NG/200 3.00 8.00
245 Jose Capellan NG/100 4.00 10.00
246 Onil Joseph NG/200 3.00 8.00
247 Shingo Takatsu NG/50 10.00 25.00
248 Carlos Hines NG/200 3.00 8.00
249 Lincoln Holdzkom NG/100 4.00 10.00
250 Mike Gosling NG/100 4.00 10.00
251 Eduardo Sierra NG/200 4.00 10.00
252 Renyel Pinto NG/100 4.00 10.00
253 Merkin Valdez NG/200 3.00 8.00
254 Angel Chavez NG/200 3.00 8.00
255 Ivan Ochoa NG/200 3.00 8.00
257 William Bergolla NG/200 3.00 8.00
258 Aarom Baldiris NG/200 3.00 8.00
260 Carlos Vasquez NG/200 4.00 10.00
261 Freddy Guzman NG/200 3.00 8.00
262 Akinori Otsuka NG/50 15.00 40.00
264 Nick Regilio NG/200 3.00 8.00
266 Shawn Hill NG/200 3.00 8.00
268 Sean Henn NG/200 3.00 8.00
269 Ramon Ramirez NG/200 3.00 8.00
270 Ronny Cedeno NG/100 6.00 15.00
273 Fernando Nieve NG/200 3.00 8.00
274 Rusty Tucker NG/200 4.00 10.00
275 Jason Bartlett NG/200 4.00 10.00
276 Mike Rouse NG/200 3.00 8.00
277 Dennis Sarfate NG/200 3.00 8.00
278 Cory Sullivan NG/200 3.00 8.00
282 Michael Wuertz NG/200 4.00 10.00
284 Jorge Sequea NG/100 4.00 10.00
287 Tim Bittner NG/250 3.00 8.00
288 Andres Blanco NG/100 4.00 10.00
289 Kevin Cave NG/100 4.00 10.00
290 Mike Johnston NG/100 4.00 10.00
293 Colby Miller NG/100 4.00 10.00
294 Jake Woods NG/100 4.00 10.00
295 Ryan Meaux NG/200 3.00 8.00
296 Don Kelly NG/100 4.00 10.00
297 Edwin Moreno NG/100 4.00 10.00
298 Phil Stockman NG/100 4.00 10.00

2004 Leaf Certified Materials Mirror Autograph White

*1-240 p/r 100: .5X TO 1.2X RED p/r 250
*1-240 p/r 100: .4X TO 1X RED p/r 100
*1-240 p/r 50: .6X TO 1.5X RED p/r 200-250
*1-240 p/r 50: .5X TO 1.2X RED p/r 100
*1-240 p/r 50: .4X TO 1X RED p/r 50
*1-240 p/r 25: 1X TO 2.5X RED p/r 203
*1-240 p/r 25: .75X TO 2X RED p/r 100
*1-240 p/r 25: .6X TO 1.5X RED p/r 50
*1-240 p/r 25: .4X TO 1X RED p/r 25
*241-300 p/r 100: .5X TO 1.2X RED p/r 200
*241-300 p/r 100: .4X TO 1X RED p/r 100
*241-300 p/r 50: .6X TO 1.5X RED p/r 200-250
*241-300 p/r 50: .5X TO 1.2X RED p/r 100
OVERALL AU ODDS 1:10
PRINT RUNS B/WN 1-100 COPIES PER
NO PRICING ON QTY OF 10 OR LESS
2 Adam Dunn/24 20.00 50.00
167 Ryan Howard/25 75.00 150.00

2004 Leaf Certified Materials Mirror Bat Blue

*BLUE p/r 100: .5X TO 1.2X RED p/r 175-250
*BLUE p/r 50: .75X TO 2X RED p/r 150-250
*BLUE p/r 25: 1X TO 2.5X RED p/r 100
RANDOM INSERTS IN PACKS
PRINT RUNS B/WN 25-100 COPIES PER
23 Brad Wilkerson/100 2.00 5.00
58 Eric Chavez/50 3.00 8.00
142 Morgan Ensberg/50 3.00 8.00
151 Pedro Martinez/50 5.00 12.00
156 Randy Johnson/50 6.00 15.00
166 Roy Oswalt/50 3.00 8.00
172 Scott Rolen/50 5.00 12.00
180 Tim Hudson/50 3.00 8.00
182 Tom Glavine/50 5.00 12.00
207 Curt Schilling D'backs/50 3.00 8.00
217 Ryne Sandberg LGD/50 12.50 30.00
218 Dale Murphy LGD/50 6.00 15.00
219 Tony Gwynn LGD/50 10.00 25.00
221 Mike Schmidt LGD/50 12.50 30.00
223 Cal Ripken LGD/50 25.00 60.00
224 Nolan Ryan LGD/50 15.00 40.00
225 George Brett LGD/50 12.50 30.00

2004 Leaf Certified Materials Mirror Bat Gold

*GOLD p/r 25: 1.25X TO 3X RED p/r 150-250
*GOLD p/r 25: 1X TO 2.5X RED p/r 100
RANDOM INSERTS IN PACKS
207 SCHILLING PRINT RUN 20 COPIES
18 Barry Zito 5.00 12.00
19 Ben Sheets 5.00 12.00
22 Brad Penny 5.00 12.00
23 Brad Wilkerson 5.00 12.00
46 Curt Schilling Sox 8.00 20.00
58 Eric Chavez 5.00 12.00
69 Greg Maddux Cubs 12.50 30.00
142 Morgan Ensberg 5.00 12.00
151 Pedro Martinez 8.00 20.00
156 Randy Johnson 10.00 25.00
166 Roy Oswalt 5.00 12.00
172 Scott Rolen 8.00 20.00
180 Tim Hudson 5.00 12.00
182 Tom Glavine 8.00 20.00
207 Curt Schilling D'backs/20 5.00 12.00
213 Duke Snider LGD 10.00 25.00
217 Ryne Sandberg LGD 20.00 50.00
218 Dale Murphy LGD 8.00 20.00
219 Tony Gwynn LGD 15.00 40.00
221 Mike Schmidt LGD 20.00 50.00
223 Cal Ripken LGD 40.00 100.00
224 Nolan Ryan LGD 25.00 60.00
225 George Brett LGD 20.00 50.00
231 Roberto Clemente LGD 40.00 100.00
232 Roy Campanella LGD 12.50 30.00
233 Babe Ruth LGD 150.00 250.00
234 Lou Gehrig LGD 75.00 150.00
235 Ty Cobb LGD 60.00 120.00
236 Roger Maris LGD 20.00 50.00
238 Ernie Banks LGD 12.50 30.00
239 Ted Williams LGD 40.00 100.00

2004 Leaf Certified Materials Mirror Bat Red

PRINT RUNS B/WN 100-250 COPIES PER
BLACK PRINT RUN 1 SERIAL #'d SET
NO BLACK PRICING DUE TO SCARCITY

EMERALD PRINT RUN 5 SERIAL #'d SETS
NO EMERALD PRICING DUE TO SCARCITY
2 Adam Dunn/150 2.00 5.00
3 Adam LaRoche/250 2.00 5.00
5 Adrian Beltre/150 2.00 5.00
7 Albert Pujols/150 6.00 15.00
8 Alex Rodriguez Yanks/250 4.00 10.00
9 Alexis Rios/250 2.00 5.00
10 Alfonso Soriano Rgr/150 2.00 5.00
11 Andruw Jones/150 3.00 8.00
12 Andy Pettitte/250 3.00 8.00
13 Angel Berroa/150 2.00 5.00
15 Aubrey Huff/150 2.00 5.00
16 Austin Kearns/150 2.00 5.00
17 Barry Larkin/150 3.00 8.00
20 Bernie Williams/150 3.00 8.00
21 Bobby Abreu/150 2.00 5.00
24 Brandon Webb/150 2.00 5.00
25 Brendan Harris/250 2.00 5.00
26 Bret Boone/150 2.00 5.00
29 Brian Giles/250 2.00 5.00
35 Carl Everett/250 2.00 5.00
36 Carlos Beltran/150 2.00 5.00
37 Carlos Delgado/150 2.00 5.00
38 Carlos Lee/150 2.00 5.00
41 Chipper Jones/150 3.00 8.00
42 Cliff Floyd/250 2.00 5.00
43 Clint Barmes/250 2.00 5.00
44 Corey Patterson/250 2.00 5.00
45 Craig Biggio/150 3.00 8.00
47 Dan Haren/150 2.00 5.00
48 Darin Erstad/150 2.00 5.00
49 David Ortiz/250 3.00 8.00
50 Delmon Young/250 3.00 8.00
51 Derek Jeter/150 8.00 20.00
54 Edgar Martinez/150 3.00 8.00
55 Edgar Renteria/150 2.00 5.00
59 Eric Hinske/150 2.00 5.00
60 Eric Munson/250 2.00 5.00
61 Erubial Durazo/250 2.00 5.00
62 Frank Thomas/150 3.00 8.00
63 Fred McGriff/150 3.00 8.00
65 Garret Anderson/150 2.00 5.00
67 Gary Sheffield/250 2.00 5.00
68 Geoff Jenkins/150 2.00 5.00
70 Hank Blalock/150 2.00 5.00
71 Hee Seop Choi/250 2.00 5.00
73 Hideo Nomo/150 3.00 8.00
76 Ivan Rodriguez Tigers/250 3.00 8.00
77 J.D. Drew/250 2.00 5.00
79 Jacque Jones/150 2.00 5.00
82 Jason Giambi Yanks/150 2.00 5.00
83 Jason Jennings/150 2.00 5.00
86 Jason Varitek/150 3.00 8.00
88 Javy Lopez/250 2.00 5.00
89 Jay Gibbons/150 2.00 5.00
91 Jeff Bagwell/150 3.00 8.00
92 Jeff Baker/250 2.00 5.00
93 Jeff Kent/150 2.00 5.00
97 Jim Edmonds/150 2.00 5.00
98 Jim Thome/150 3.00 8.00
100 Joe Borchard/150 2.00 5.00
101 Joe Crede/250 2.00 5.00
103 John Olerud/150 2.00 5.00
105 Johnny Damon/250 3.00 8.00
106 Jorge Posada/150 3.00 8.00
107 Jose Castillo/250 2.00 5.00
108 Jose Reyes/150 2.00 5.00
109 Jose Vidro/150 2.00 5.00
110 Josh Beckett/150 2.00 5.00
111 Josh Phelps/150 2.00 5.00
112 Juan Encarnacion/250 2.00 5.00
113 Juan Gonzalez/250 2.00 5.00
114 Junior Spivey/250 2.00 5.00
115 Kazuhisa Ishii/150 2.00 5.00
116 Kenny Lofton/250 2.00 5.00
117 Kerry Wood/150 2.00 5.00
119 Kevin Youkilis/250 2.00 5.00
120 Lance Berkman/150 2.00 5.00
122 Larry Walker/150 2.00 5.00
123 Luis Castillo/150 2.00 5.00
124 Luis Gonzalez/150 2.00 5.00
126 Lyle Overbay/250 2.00 5.00
127 Magglio Ordonez/150 2.00 5.00
128 Manny Ramirez/150 3.00 8.00
129 Marcus Giles/250 2.00 5.00
131 Mark Buehrle/150 2.00 5.00
132 Mark Mulder/150 2.00 5.00
133 Mark Prior/150 3.00 8.00
134 Mark Teixeira/150 3.00 8.00
135 Marlon Byrd/150 2.00 5.00
137 Miguel Cabrera/250 3.00 8.00
138 Mike Lowell/150 2.00 5.00
140 Mike Piazza/150 4.00 10.00
141 Mike Sweeney/150 2.00 5.00
143 Nick Johnson/250 2.00 5.00
144 Nomar Garciaparra/150 5.00 12.00
145 Omar Vizquel/150 3.00 8.00
146 Orlando Cabrera/250 2.00 5.00
147 Orlando Hudson/150 2.00 5.00
148 Pat Burrell/150 2.00 5.00
149 Paul Konerko/150 2.00 5.00
150 Paul Lo Duca/150 2.00 5.00
152 Jermaine Dye/250 2.00 5.00
153 Preston Wilson/150 2.00 5.00
154 Rafael Furcal/150 2.00 5.00
155 Rafael Palmeiro O's/150 3.00 8.00
157 Rich Aurilia/250 2.00 5.00
159 Richard Hidalgo/150 2.00 5.00
160 Richie Sexson/250 2.00 5.00
161 Rickie Weeks/250 2.00 5.00
162 Roberto Alomar/250 3.00 8.00
163 Rocco Baldelli/150 2.00 5.00
164 Roger Clemens Astros/250 4.00 10.00
168 Ryan Klesko/150 2.00 5.00
170 Sammy Sosa/150 3.00 8.00
174 Sean Casey/250 2.00 5.00
175 Shannon Stewart/150 2.00 5.00
176 Shawn Green/150 2.00 5.00
181 Todd Helton/150 3.00 8.00
183 Torii Hunter/150 2.00 5.00
184 Trot Nixon/150 2.00 5.00
185 Troy Glaus/150 2.00 5.00
186 Vernon Wells/150 2.00 5.00
187 Victor Martinez/250 2.00 5.00
188 Vladimir Guerrero Angels/250 3.00 8.00
189 Wade Miller/250 2.00 5.00
190 Brandon Larson/175 2.00 5.00
191 Travis Hafner/150 2.00 5.00
192 Tim Salmon/150 3.00 8.00
195 Ramon Nivar/150 2.00 5.00
196 Moises Alou/250 2.00 5.00
197 Michael Young/250 2.00 5.00
198 Laynce Nix/150 2.00 5.00
199 Tino Martinez/250 3.00 8.00
200 Randall Simon/250 2.00 5.00
201 Roger Clemens Yanks/150 4.00 10.00
203 Vladimir Guerrero Expos/150 3.00 8.00
204 Miguel Tejada/150 2.00 5.00
206 Jason Giambi A's/150 2.00 5.00
208 Alex Rodriguez Rgr/150 4.00 10.00
209 Alfonso Soriano Yanks/150 2.00 5.00
210 Ivan Rodriguez Marlins/150 3.00 8.00
211 Rafael Palmeiro Rgr/150 3.00 8.00
212 Gary Carter LGD/150 3.00 8.00
216 Reggie Jackson LGD/150 4.00 10.00
220 Don Mattingly LGD/150 6.00 15.00
222 Rickey Henderson LGD/150 4.00 10.00
227 Lou Brock LGD/150 4.00 10.00
228 Andre Dawson LGD/150 3.00 8.00
229 Rod Carew LGD/150 4.00 10.00
230 Wade Boggs LGD/150 4.00 10.00
240 Stan Musial LGD/100 10.00 25.00

2004 Leaf Certified Materials Mirror Bat White

*WHITE p/r 200: .4X TO 1X RED p/r 250
*WHITE p/r 100: .5X TO 1.2X RED p/r 150
*WHITE p/r 50: .6X TO 1.5X RED p/r 100
RANDOM INSERTS IN PACKS
PRINT RUNS B/WN 25-200 COPIES PER
14 Aramis Ramirez/100 2.00 5.00
23 Brad Wilkerson/200 2.00 5.00
156 Randy Johnson/100 4.00 10.00
166 Roy Oswalt/100 2.00 5.00
180 Tim Hudson/100 2.00 5.00
182 Tom Glavine/100 3.00 8.00
205 Kevin Brown/100 2.00 5.00
218 Dale Murphy LGD/100 5.00 12.00
219 Tony Gwynn LGD/100 6.00 15.00
221 Mike Schmidt LGD/100 8.00 20.00
223 Cal Ripken LGD/100 15.00 40.00
224 Nolan Ryan LGD/100 10.00 25.00
225 George Brett LGD/100 8.00 20.00
231 Roberto Clemente LGD/50 30.00 80.00
232 Roy Campanella LGD/50 8.00 20.00
233 Babe Ruth LGD/25 150.00 250.00
234 Lou Gehrig LGD/25 75.00 150.00
235 Ty Cobb LGD/25 60.00 120.00
236 Roger Maris LGD/25 20.00 50.00
238 Ernie Banks LGD/50 8.00 20.00
239 Ted Williams LGD/25 40.00 100.00

2004 Leaf Certified Materials Mirror Combo Red

2-211 PRINT RUN 250 SERIAL #'d SETS
212-239 PRINT RUNS B/WN 50-250 PER
BLACK PRIME PRINT RUN 1 SERIAL #'d SET
NO BLACK PRIME PRICING AVAILABLE
RANDOM INSERTS IN PACKS
2 Adam Dunn Bat-Jsy 3.00 8.00
5 Adrian Beltre Bat-Jsy 3.00 8.00
7 Albert Pujols Bat-Jsy 10.00 25.00
11 Andruw Jones Bat-Jsy 5.00 12.00
13 Angel Berroa Bat-Pants 3.00 8.00
15 Aubrey Huff Bat-Jsy 3.00 8.00
16 Austin Kearns Bat-Jsy 3.00 8.00
17 Barry Larkin Bat-Jsy 5.00 12.00
18 Barry Zito Bat-Jsy 3.00 8.00
19 Ben Sheets Bat-Jsy 3.00 8.00
20 Bernie Williams Bat-Jsy 5.00 12.00
21 Bobby Abreu Bat-Jsy 3.00 8.00
22 Brad Penny Bat-Jsy 3.00 8.00
24 Brandon Webb Bat-Jsy 3.00 8.00
26 Bret Boone Bat-Jsy 3.00 8.00
36 Carlos Beltran Bat-Jsy 3.00 8.00
37 Carlos Delgado Bat-Jsy 3.00 8.00
38 Carlos Lee Bat-Jsy 3.00 8.00
41 Chipper Jones Bat-Jsy 5.00 12.00
45 Craig Biggio Bat-Pants 5.00 12.00
47 Dan Haren Bat-Jsy 3.00 8.00
51 Derek Jeter Bat-Jsy 12.50 30.00
52 Dewon Brazelton Fld Glv-Jsy 3.00 8.00
54 Edgar Martinez Bat-Jsy 5.00 12.00
55 Edgar Renteria Bat-Jsy 3.00 8.00
58 Eric Chavez Bat-Jsy 3.00 8.00
59 Eric Hinske Bat-Jsy 3.00 8.00
62 Frank Thomas Bat-Jsy 5.00 12.00
63 Fred McGriff Bat-Jsy 5.00 12.00
65 Garret Anderson Bat-Jsy 3.00 8.00
68 Geoff Jenkins Bat-Jsy 3.00 8.00
70 Hank Blalock Bat-Jsy 3.00 8.00
73 Hideo Nomo Bat-Jsy 5.00 12.00
79 Jacque Jones Bat-Jsy 3.00 8.00
82 Jason Giambi Yanks Bat-Jsy 3.00 8.00
83 Jason Jennings Bat-Jsy 3.00 8.00
86 Jason Varitek Bat-Jsy 5.00 12.00
89 Jay Gibbons Bat-Jsy 3.00 8.00
91 Jeff Bagwell Bat-Jsy 5.00 12.00
93 Jeff Kent Bat-Jsy 3.00 8.00
97 Jim Edmonds Bat-Jsy 3.00 8.00
98 Jim Thome Bat-Jsy 5.00 12.00
100 Joe Borchard Bat-Jsy 3.00 8.00
103 John Olerud Bat-Jsy 3.00 8.00
106 Jorge Posada Bat-Jsy 5.00 12.00
108 Jose Reyes Bat-Jsy 3.00 8.00
109 Jose Vidro Bat-Jsy 3.00 8.00
110 Josh Beckett Bat-Jsy 3.00 8.00
111 Josh Phelps Bat-Jsy 3.00 8.00
115 Kazuhisa Ishii Bat-Jsy 3.00 8.00
117 Kerry Wood Bat-Jsy 3.00 8.00
120 Lance Berkman Bat-Jsy 3.00 8.00
122 Larry Walker Bat-Jsy 3.00 8.00
123 Luis Castillo Bat-Jsy 3.00 8.00
124 Luis Gonzalez Bat-Jsy 3.00 8.00
127 Magglio Ordonez Bat-Jsy 3.00 8.00
128 Manny Ramirez Bat-Jsy 5.00 12.00
131 Mark Buehrle Bat-Jsy 3.00 8.00
132 Mark Mulder Bat-Jsy 3.00 8.00
133 Mark Prior Bat-Jsy 5.00 12.00
134 Mark Teixeira Bat-Jsy 5.00 12.00
135 Marlon Byrd Bat-Jsy 3.00 8.00
138 Mike Lowell Bat-Jsy 3.00 8.00
140 Mike Piazza Bat-Jsy 6.00 15.00
141 Mike Sweeney Bat-Jsy 3.00 8.00
142 Morgan Ensberg Bat-Jsy 3.00 8.00
144 Nomar Garciaparra Bat-Jsy 6.00 15.00
145 Omar Vizquel Bat-Jsy 5.00 12.00
147 Orlando Hudson Bat-Jsy 3.00 8.00
148 Pat Burrell Bat-Jsy 3.00 8.00
149 Paul Konerko Bat-Jsy 3.00 8.00
150 Paul Lo Duca Bat-Jsy 3.00 8.00
151 Pedro Martinez Bat-Jsy 5.00 12.00
153 Preston Wilson Bat-Jsy 3.00 8.00
154 Rafael Furcal Bat-Jsy 3.00 8.00
155 Rafael Palmeiro O's Bat-Jsy 5.00 12.00
156 Randy Johnson Bat-Jsy 5.00 12.00
159 Richard Hidalgo Bat-Pants 3.00 8.00
163 Rocco Baldelli Bat-Jsy 3.00 8.00
166 Roy Oswalt Bat-Jsy 3.00 8.00
168 Ryan Klesko Bat-Jsy 3.00 8.00
170 Sammy Sosa Bat-Jsy 5.00 12.00
172 Scott Rolen Bat-Jsy 5.00 12.00
175 Shannon Stewart Bat-Jsy 3.00 8.00
176 Shawn Green Bat-Jsy 3.00 8.00
180 Tim Hudson Bat-Jsy 3.00 8.00
181 Todd Helton Bat-Jsy 5.00 12.00
182 Tom Glavine Bat-Jsy 5.00 12.00
183 Torii Hunter Bat-Jsy 3.00 8.00
184 Trot Nixon Bat-Jsy 3.00 8.00
185 Troy Glaus Bat-Jsy 3.00 8.00
186 Vernon Wells Bat-Jsy 3.00 8.00
191 Travis Hafner Bat-Jsy 3.00 8.00
192 Tim Salmon Bat-Jsy 5.00 12.00
195 Ramon Nivar Bat-Jsy 3.00 8.00
201 R.Clemens Yanks Bat-Jsy 6.00 15.00
203 Vlad Guerrero Expos Bat-Jsy 5.00 12.00
204 Miguel Tejada Bat-Jsy 3.00 8.00
206 Jason Giambi A's Bat-Jsy 3.00 8.00
207 Curt Schilling D'backs Bat-Jsy 3.00 8.00
208 Alex Rodriguez Rgr Bat-Jsy 6.00 15.00
209 Alf Soriano Yanks Bat-Jsy 3.00 8.00
210 Ivan Rod Marlins Bat-Jsy 5.00 12.00
211 Rafael Palmeiro Rgr Bat-Jsy 5.00 12.00
212 G.Carter LGD Bat-Pants/250 4.00 10.00
216 R.Jackson LGD Bat-Jsy/250 6.00 15.00
217 R.Sandberg LGD Bat-Jsy/250 10.00 25.00
218 D.Murphy LGD Bat-Jsy/250 6.00 15.00
219 T.Gwynn LGD Bat-Jsy/250 6.00 15.00
220 D.Mattingly LGD Bat-Jsy/250 10.00 25.00
221 M.Schm LGD Bat-Pants/250 10.00 25.00
222 R.Hend LGD Bat-Jsy/250 6.00 15.00
223 C.Ripken LGD Bat-Jsy/250 15.00 40.00
224 N.Ryan LGD Bat-Jsy/250 15.00 40.00
225 G.Brett LGD Bat-Jsy/250 10.00 25.00
227 L.Brock LGD Bat-Jsy/250 6.00 15.00
228 A.Dawson LGD Bat-Jsy/250 4.00 10.00
229 R.Carew LGD Bat-Jkt/250 6.00 15.00
230 W.Boggs LGD Bat-Jsy/250 6.00 15.00
231 R.Clemente LGD Bat-Jsy/100 60.00 120.00
232 R.Campy LGD Bat-Pants/100 8.00 20.00
233 B.Ruth LGD Bat-Pants/50 200.00 350.00
234 L.Gehrig LGD Bat-Pants/50 100.00 200.00
235 T.Cobb LGD Bat-Pants/50 100.00 200.00
236 R.Maris LGD Bat-Pants/100 20.00 50.00
238 E.Banks LGD Bat-Pants/100 8.00 20.00
239 T.Williams LGD Bat-Jkt/100 50.00 100.00

2004 Leaf Certified Materials Mirror Fabric Blue Position

*1-211 p/r 100: .5X TO 1.2X RED p/r 150-250
1-211 PRINT RUN 100 SERIAL #'d SETS
*212-239 p/r 100: .5X TO 1.2X REDp/r150-250
*212-239 p/r 25: 1X TO 2.5X RED p/r 100
212-239 PRINT RUN 25-100 #'d COPIES PER
24 Brandon Webb Jsy 2.00 5.00
26 Bret Boone Jsy 2.00 5.00
37 Carlos Delgado Jsy 2.00 5.00
52 Dewon Brazelton Jsy 2.00 5.00
65 Garret Anderson Jsy 2.00 5.00
80 Jae Weong Seo Jsy 2.00 5.00
100 Joe Borchard Jsy 2.00 5.00
106 Jorge Posada Jsy 3.00 8.00
127 Magglio Ordonez Jsy 2.00 5.00
128 Manny Ramirez Jsy 3.00 8.00
132 Mark Mulder Jsy 2.00 5.00
134 Mark Teixeira Jsy 3.00 8.00
138 Mike Lowell Jsy 2.00 5.00
149 Paul Konerko Jsy 2.00 5.00
150 Paul Lo Duca Jsy 2.00 5.00
155 Rafael Palmeiro O's Jsy 3.00 8.00
166 Roy Oswalt Jsy 2.00 5.00
183 Torii Hunter Jsy 2.00 5.00
184 Trot Nixon Jsy 2.00 5.00
211 Rafael Palmeiro Rgr Jsy 3.00 8.00
214 W.Ford LGD Jsy/100 5.00 12.00
216 R.Jackson LGD Jsy/100 5.00 12.00
217 R.Sandberg LGD Jsy/100 8.00 20.00
218 D.Murphy LGD Jsy/100 5.00 12.00
219 T.Gwynn LGD Jsy/100 6.00 15.00
220 Don Mattingly LGD Jsy/100 8.00 20.00
221 M.Schmidt LGD Pants/100 8.00 20.00
222 R.Henderson LGD Jsy/100 6.00 15.00
223 Cal Ripken LGD Jsy/100 15.00 40.00
224 Nolan Ryan LGD Jsy/100 10.00 25.00
225 George Brett LGD Jsy/100 8.00 20.00
227 L.Brock LGD Jsy/100 5.00 12.00
228 A.Dawson LGD Jsy/100 3.00 8.00
229 R.Carew LGD Jkt/100 5.00 12.00
230 W.Boggs LGD Jsy/100 5.00 12.00
231 R.Clemente LGD Jsy/25 40.00 100.00
232 R.Campy LGD Pants/25 12.50 30.00
233 Babe Ruth LGD Pants/25 150.00 250.00
234 Lou Gehrig LGD Pants/25 75.00 150.00
235 Ty Cobb LGD Pants/25 60.00 120.00
236 Roger Maris LGD Pants/25 20.00 50.00
238 E.Banks LGD Pants/25 12.50 30.00
239 Ted Williams LGD Jkt/25 40.00 100.00

2004 Leaf Certified Materials Mirror Fabric Gold Number

*1-211 p/r 25: 1.25X TO 3X RED p/r 150-250
1-211 PRINT RUN 25 SERIAL #'d SETS
*212-239 p/r 25: 1.25X TO 3X RED p/r 150-250
212-239 PRINT RUNS B/WN 10-25 #'d PER
212-239 NO PRICING ON QTY OF 10 OR LESS
RANDOM INSERTS IN PACKS
24 Brandon Webb Jsy 5.00 12.00
26 Bret Boone Jsy 5.00 12.00
37 Carlos Delgado Jsy 5.00 12.00
52 Dewon Brazelton Jsy 5.00 12.00
63 Fred McGriff Jsy 8.00 20.00
65 Garret Anderson Jsy 5.00 12.00
80 Jae Weong Seo Jsy 5.00 12.00
100 Joe Borchard Jsy 5.00 12.00
106 Jorge Posada Jsy 8.00 20.00
127 Magglio Ordonez Jsy 5.00 12.00
128 Manny Ramirez Jsy 8.00 20.00
132 Mark Mulder Jsy 5.00 12.00
134 Mark Teixeira Jsy 8.00 20.00
138 Mike Lowell Jsy 5.00 12.00
149 Paul Konerko Jsy 5.00 12.00
150 Paul Lo Duca Jsy 5.00 12.00
155 Rafael Palmeiro O's Jsy 8.00 20.00
166 Roy Oswalt Jsy 5.00 12.00
183 Torii Hunter Jsy 5.00 12.00
184 Trot Nixon Jsy 5.00 12.00
211 Rafael Palmeiro Rgr Jsy 8.00 20.00
214 Whitey Ford LGD Jsy/25 10.00 25.00
215 B.Feller LGD Jsy/25 6.00 15.00
216 R.Jackson LGD Jsy/25 10.00 25.00
217 Ryne Sandberg LGD Jsy/25 20.00 50.00
218 D.Murphy LGD Jsy/25 10.00 25.00
219 Tony Gwynn LGD Jsy/25 15.00 40.00
220 Don Mattingly LGD Jsy/25 20.00 50.00
221 Mike Schmidt LGD Pants/25 20.00 50.00
222 R.Henderson LGD Jsy/25 12.50 30.00
223 Cal Ripken LGD Jsy/25 40.00 100.00
224 Nolan Ryan LGD Jsy/25 25.00 60.00
225 George Brett LGD Jsy/25 20.00 50.00
227 L.Brock LGD Jsy/25 10.00 25.00
228 A.Dawson LGD Jsy/25 6.00 15.00
229 R.Carew LGD Jkt/25 10.00 25.00
230 W.Boggs LGD Jsy/25 10.00 25.00
231 R.Clemente LGD Jsy/10
232 R.Campy LGD Pants/10
233 B.Ruth LGD Pants/10
234 L.Gehrig LGD Pants/10
235 T.Cobb LGD Pants/10
236 R.Maris LGD Pants/10
238 E.Banks LGD Pants/10
239 Ted Williams LGD Jkt/10

2004 Leaf Certified Materials Mirror Fabric Red

PRINT RUNS B/WN 100-250 COPIES PER
BLACK AL/NL PRINT RUN 1 SERIAL #'d SET
NO BLK AL/NL PRICING DUE TO SCARCITY
BLACK NUMBER PRINT RUN 1 #'d SET
NO BLACK NBR.PRICING DUE TO SCARCITY
BLACK POSITION PRINT RUN 1 #'d SET
NO BLACK POS.PRICING DUE TO SCARCITY
BLACK PRIME PRINT RUN 1 SERIAL #'d SET
NO BLK PRIME PRICING DUE TO SCARCITY
EMERALD PRINT RUN 1-5 COPIES PER
NO EMERALD PRICING DUE TO SCARCITY
1 A.J. Burnett Jsy/250 2.00 5.00
2 Adam Dunn Jsy/150 2.00 5.00
5 Adrian Beltre Jsy/150 2.00 5.00
6 Al Leiter Jsy/250 2.00 5.00
7 Albert Pujols Jsy/150 6.00 15.00
11 Andruw Jones Jsy/150 3.00 8.00
13 Angel Berroa Pants/150 2.00 5.00
15 Aubrey Huff Jsy/150 2.00 5.00
16 Austin Kearns Jsy/150 2.00 5.00
17 Barry Larkin Jsy/150 3.00 8.00
18 Barry Zito Jsy/150 2.00 5.00
19 Ben Sheets Jsy/150 2.00 5.00
20 Bernie Williams Jsy/150 3.00 8.00
21 Bobby Abreu Jsy/150 2.00 5.00
22 Brad Penny Jsy/150 2.00 5.00
27 Brett Myers Jsy/250 2.00 5.00
33 C.C. Sabathia Jsy/250 2.00 5.00
34 Carl Crawford Jsy/250 2.00 5.00
36 Carlos Beltran Jsy/150 2.00 5.00
38 Carlos Lee Jsy/150 2.00 5.00
39 Chad Gaudin Jsy/250 2.00 5.00
41 Chipper Jones Jsy/150 3.00 8.00
45 Craig Biggio Pants/150 3.00 8.00
47 Dan Haren Jsy/150 2.00 5.00
48 Darin Erstad Jsy/250 2.00 5.00
51 Derek Jeter Jsy/150 8.00 20.00
53 Dontrelle Willis Jsy/250 3.00 8.00
54 Edgar Martinez Jsy/150 3.00 8.00
55 Edgar Renteria Jsy/150 2.00 5.00
58 Eric Chavez Jsy/150 2.00 5.00
59 Eric Hinske Jsy/150 2.00 5.00
62 Frank Thomas Jsy/150 3.00 8.00
64 Freddy Garcia Jsy/250 2.00 5.00
66 Garrett Atkins Jsy/250 2.00 5.00
68 Geoff Jenkins Jsy/150 2.00 5.00
70 Hank Blalock Jsy/150 2.00 5.00
72 Hideki Matsui Base/250 6.00 15.00
73 Hideo Nomo Jsy/150 3.00 8.00
75 Ichiro Suzuki Base/250 6.00 15.00
79 Jacque Jones Jsy/150 2.00 5.00
81 Jamie Moyer Jsy/250 2.00 5.00
82 Jason Giambi Yanks Jsy/150 2.00 5.00
83 Jason Jennings Jsy/150 2.00 5.00
84 Jason Kendall Jsy/250 2.00 5.00
86 Jason Varitek Jsy/150 3.00 8.00
89 Jay Gibbons Jsy/150 2.00 5.00
91 Jeff Bagwell Jsy/150 3.00 8.00
93 Jeff Kent Jsy/150 2.00 5.00
96 Jerome Williams Jsy/250 2.00 5.00
97 Jim Edmonds Jsy/150 2.00 5.00
98 Jim Thome Jsy/150 3.00 8.00
102 Johan Santana Jsy/250 3.00 8.00
103 John Olerud Jsy/150 2.00 5.00
104 John Smoltz Jsy/250 3.00 8.00
108 Jose Reyes Jsy/150 2.00 5.00
109 Jose Vidro Jsy/150 2.00 5.00
110 Josh Beckett Jsy/150 2.00 5.00
111 Josh Phelps Jsy/150 2.00 5.00
115 Kazuhisa Ishii Jsy/150 2.00 5.00
117 Kerry Wood Jsy/150 2.00 5.00
118 Kevin Millwood Jsy/250 2.00 5.00
120 Lance Berkman Jsy/150 2.00 5.00
121 Larry Bigbie Jsy/250 2.00 5.00
122 Larry Walker Jsy/150 2.00 5.00
123 Luis Castillo Jsy/150 2.00 5.00
124 Luis Gonzalez Jsy/150 2.00 5.00
130 Mariano Rivera Jsy/250 3.00 8.00
131 Mark Buehrle Jsy/150 2.00 5.00
133 Mark Prior Jsy/150 3.00 8.00
135 Marlon Byrd Jsy/150 2.00 5.00
136 Matt Morris Jsy/250 2.00 5.00
139 Mike Mussina Jsy/250 3.00 8.00
140 Mike Piazza Jsy/150 4.00 10.00
141 Mike Sweeney Jsy/150 2.00 5.00
142 Morgan Ensberg Jsy/150 2.00 5.00
144 Nomar Garciaparra Jsy/150 5.00 12.00
145 Omar Vizquel Jsy/150 3.00 8.00
147 Orlando Hudson Jsy/150 2.00 5.00
148 Pat Burrell Jsy/150 2.00 5.00
151 Pedro Martinez Jsy/150 3.00 8.00
153 Preston Wilson Jsy/150 2.00 5.00
154 Rafael Furcal Jsy/150 2.00 5.00
156 Randy Johnson Jsy/150 3.00 8.00
158 Rich Harden Jsy/250 2.00 5.00
159 Richard Hidalgo Pants/150 2.00 5.00
163 Rocco Baldelli Jsy/150 2.00 5.00
165 Roy Halladay Jsy/250 2.00 5.00
168 Ryan Klesko Jsy/150 2.00 5.00
170 Sammy Sosa Jsy/150 3.00 8.00
172 Scott Rolen Jsy/150 3.00 8.00
173 Sean Burroughs Jsy/250 2.00 5.00
175 Shannon Stewart Jsy/150 2.00 5.00
176 Shawn Green Jsy/150 2.00 5.00
179 Steve Finley Jsy/250 2.00 5.00
180 Tim Hudson Jsy/150 2.00 5.00
181 Todd Helton Jsy/150 3.00 8.00
182 Tom Glavine Jsy/150 3.00 8.00
185 Troy Glaus Jsy/150 2.00 5.00
186 Vernon Wells Jsy/150 2.00 5.00
191 Travis Hafner Jsy/150 2.00 5.00
192 Tim Salmon Jsy/150 3.00 8.00
193 Tim Redding Jsy/250 2.00 5.00
194 Runelvys Hernandez Jsy/250 2.00 5.00
195 Ramon Nivar Jsy/150 2.00 5.00
201 R.Clemens Yanks Jsy/150 4.00 10.00
202 G.Maddux Braves Jsy/250 5.00 12.00
203 V.Guerrero Expos Jsy/150 3.00 8.00
204 Miguel Tejada Jsy/150 2.00 5.00
205 Kevin Brown Jsy/250 2.00 5.00
206 Jason Giambi A's Jsy/150 2.00 5.00
207 C.Schilling D'backs Jsy/150 2.00 5.00
208 Alex Rodriguez Rgr Jsy/150 4.00 10.00
209 Alf Soriano Yanks Jsy/150 2.00 5.00
210 Ivan Rod Marlins Jsy/150 3.00 8.00
212 Gary Carter LGD Pants/150 3.00 8.00
226 Bob Gibson LGD Jsy/250 4.00 10.00
237 S.Paige LGD CO Jsy/100 25.00 60.00

2004 Leaf Certified Materials Mirror Fabric White

*1-211 p/r 200-215: .4X TO 1X REDp/r150-250
*1-211 p/r 100: .5X TO 1.2X RED p/r 150-250
*1-211 p/r 50: .75X TO 2X RED p/r 250
*212-239 p/r 200: .4X TO 1X RED p/r 150
*212-239 p/r 25: 1.25X TO 3X RED p/r 250
*212-239 p/r 25: 1X TO 2.5X RED p/r 100
212-239 PRINT RUNS B/WN 25-200 #'d PER
RANDOM INSERTS IN PACKS
24 Brandon Webb Pants/200 2.00 5.00
37 Carlos Delgado Jsy/200 2.00 5.00
52 Dewon Brazelton Jsy/200 2.00 5.00
65 Garret Anderson Jsy/200 2.00 5.00
106 Jorge Posada Jsy/200 3.00 8.00
127 Magglio Ordonez Jsy/200 2.00 5.00
128 Manny Ramirez Jsy/200 3.00 8.00
132 Mark Mulder Jsy/200 2.00 5.00
134 Mark Teixeira Jsy/200 3.00 8.00
138 Mike Lowell Jsy/75 2.00 5.00
149 Paul Konerko Jsy/100 2.00 5.00
150 Paul Lo Duca Jsy/200 2.00 5.00
155 Rafael Palmeiro O's Jsy/50 5.00 12.00
166 Roy Oswalt Jsy/100 2.00 5.00
183 Torii Hunter Jsy/200 2.00 5.00
184 Trot Nixon Jsy/50 3.00 8.00
211 Rafael Palmeiro Rgr Jsy/200 3.00 8.00
216 Reggie Jackson LGD Jsy/25 10.00 25.00
217 Ryne Sandberg LGD Jsy/25 20.00 50.00
219 Tony Gwynn LGD Jsy/25 15.00 40.00
220 Don Mattingly LGD Jsy/25 20.00 50.00
221 Mike Schmidt LGD Pants/25 20.00 50.00
222 R.Henderson LGD Jsy/25 12.50 30.00
223 Cal Ripken LGD Jsy/25 40.00 100.00
224 Nolan Ryan LGD Jsy/25 25.00 60.00
225 George Brett LGD Jsy/25 20.00 50.00
227 Lou Brock LGD Jsy/25 10.00 25.00
228 Andre Dawson LGD Jsy/25 6.00 15.00
229 Rod Carew LGD Jkt/25 10.00 25.00
230 Wade Boggs LGD Jsy/25 10.00 25.00
231 R.Clemente LGD Jsy/25 40.00 100.00
232 R.Campy LGD Pants/25 12.50 30.00
233 Babe Ruth LGD Pants/25 150.00 250.00
234 Lou Gehrig LGD Pants/25 75.00 150.00
235 Ty Cobb LGD Pants/25 60.00 120.00
236 Roger Maris LGD Pants/25 20.00 50.00
238 Ernie Banks LGD Pants/25 12.50 30.00
239 Ted Williams LGD Jkt/25 40.00 100.00

2004 Leaf Certified Materials Fabric of the Game

This set was highlighted by the debut of swatches cut from a 1968 Atlanta Braves jersey of Negro League legend Satchel Paige who was serving as a coach for the Braves at that time so he could qualify for a baseball pension.

RANDOM INSERTS IN PACKS
PRINT RUNS B/WN 1-100 COPIES PER
NO PRICING ON QTY OF 10 OR LESS
1 Ozzie Smith Padres Jsy/100 6.00 15.00
2 Al Kaline Pants/100 6.00 15.00
3 Alan Trammell Jsy/100 3.00 8.00
4 Albert Pujols Grey Jsy/100 10.00 25.00
5 Alex Rodriguez M's Jsy/100 5.00 12.00
6 Alex Rodriguez Rgr Jsy/100 5.00 12.00
7 A.Dawson Cubs Jsy/100 3.00 8.00
8 A.Dawson Cubs Pants/100 3.00 8.00
9 Babe Ruth Jsy/10
10 Babe Ruth Pants/10
11 Billy Williams Jsy/100 3.00 8.00
12 Bo Jackson Royals Jsy/100 6.00 15.00
13 Bob Feller Jsy/50 6.00 15.00
14 Bob Gibson Jsy/50 6.00 15.00
15 Bobby Doerr Jsy/100 3.00 8.00
16 Brooks Robinson Jsy/25 10.00 25.00
17 Cal Ripken Jsy/100 15.00 40.00
18 Carl Yastrzemski Jsy/100 8.00 20.00
19 Carlton Fisk R.Sox Jsy/100 5.00 12.00
20 Dale Murphy Jsy/100 5.00 12.00
21 D.Strawberry Mets Pants/100 3.00 8.00
22 D.Strawberry Dgr Jsy/100 3.00 8.00
23 Dave Parker Reds Jsy/100 3.00 8.00
24 Dave Parker Pirates Jsy/100 3.00 8.00
25 D.Winfield Yanks Jsy/50 4.00 10.00
26 D.Winfield Padres Jsy/100 3.00 8.00
27 Deion Sanders Jsy/25 10.00 25.00
28 Derek Jeter Jsy/100 10.00 25.00
29 Don Drysdale Jsy/100 6.00 15.00
30 Don Mattingly Jsy/100 8.00 20.00
31 Don Mattingly Jkt/100 8.00 20.00
32 Don Sutton Jsy/100 3.00 8.00
33 Duke Snider Jsy/100 5.00 12.00
34 Dwight Gooden Jsy/100 3.00 8.00
35 Early Wynn Jsy/100 3.00 8.00
36 Eddie Mathews Jsy/50 8.00 20.00
37 Eddie Murray Dgr Jsy/100 5.00 12.00
38 Eddie Murray O's Jsy/100 5.00 12.00
39 Enos Slaughter Jsy/100 6.00 15.00
40 Eric Davis Jsy/50 4.00 10.00
41 Ernie Banks Jsy/100 6.00 15.00
42 Fergie Jenkins Pants/100 3.00 8.00
43 Frank Robinson Jsy/100 3.00 8.00
44 Fred Lynn Jsy/10
45 Gary Carter Jsy/100 3.00 8.00
46 Gaylord Perry Jsy/25 6.00 15.00
47 George Brett White Jsy/100 8.00 20.00
48 George Foster Jsy/100 3.00 8.00
49 Hal Newhouser Jsy/100 3.00 8.00
50 Harmon Killebrew Jsy/25 12.50 30.00
51 Harmon Killebrew Pants/25 12.50 30.00
52 Harold Baines Jsy/100 3.00 8.00
53 Hoyt Wilhelm Jsy/50 4.00 10.00
54 Jack Morris Jsy/100 3.00 8.00
55 Jackie Robinson Jsy/10
56 Catfish Hunter Jsy/100 5.00 12.00
57 Jim Palmer Jsy/100 3.00 8.00
58 Jim Rice Jsy/100 3.00 8.00
59 Joe Carter Jsy/100 3.00 8.00
60 Joe Morgan Reds Jsy/100 3.00 8.00
61 Tommy Lasorda Jsy/100 3.00 8.00
62 Johnny Mize Pants/100 5.00 12.00
63 Johnny Bench Jsy/100 6.00 15.00
64 Jose Canseco Grey Jsy/100 5.00 12.00
65 Juan Marichal Jsy/100 3.00 8.00
66 Kirby Puckett Jsy/100 6.00 15.00
67 Lou Boudreau Jsy/100 3.00 8.00
68 Lou Brock Jsy/100 5.00 12.00
69 Lou Gehrig Jsy/10
70 Lou Gehrig Pants/10
71 Luis Aparicio Jsy/100 3.00 8.00
72 Luis Aparicio Pants/100 3.00 8.00
73 Mariano Rivera Jsy/100 4.00 10.00
74 Mark Grace Cubs Jsy/100 5.00 12.00
75 Mark Prior Jsy/100 3.00 8.00
76 Mel Ott Jsy/25 20.00 50.00
77 Mel Ott Pants/25 20.00 50.00
78 Mike Schmidt Jsy/100 8.00 20.00
79 Mike Schmidt Pants/100 8.00 20.00
80 Mike Schmidt Jkt/100 8.00 20.00
81 Nolan Ryan Angels Jsy/100 10.00 25.00
82 Nolan Ryan Angels Jkt/100 10.00 25.00
83 Nolan Ryan Astros Jsy/100 10.00 25.00
84 Nolan Ryan Astros Jkt/100 10.00 25.00
85 Nolan Ryan Rgr Jsy/100 10.00 25.00
86 Nolan Ryan Rgr Pants/100 20.00 50.00
87 Ty Cobb Pants/10
88 Ozzie Smith Cards Jsy/100 6.00 15.00
89 Paul Molitor Jsy/100 3.00 8.00
90 Pee Wee Reese Jsy/100 5.00 12.00
91 Phil Niekro Jsy/100 3.00 8.00
92 Phil Rizzuto Jsy/100 5.00 12.00
93 Phil Rizzuto Pants/100 5.00 12.00
94 Red Schoendienst Jsy/100 3.00 8.00
95 R.Jackson A's Jkt/100 5.00 12.00
96 R.Jackson Angels Jsy/100 5.00 12.00
97 Richie Ashburn Jsy/100 10.00 25.00
98 R.Henderson Yanks Jsy/50 6.00 15.00
99 Roberto Clemente Jsy/50 30.00 80.00
100 Robin Yount Jsy/100 6.00 15.00
101 R.Carew Angels Jsy/100 5.00 12.00
102 R.Carew Angels Pants/100 5.00 12.00
103 R.Carew Angels Jkt/100 5.00 12.00
104 R.Carew Twins Jsy/100 5.00 12.00
105 R.Clemens Sox Jsy/100 5.00 12.00
106 R.Clemens Yanks Jsy/100 5.00 12.00
107 Roger Maris A's Jsy/100 15.00 40.00
108 Roger Maris A's Pants/100 12.50 30.00
109 Roger Maris Yanks Jsy/100 15.00 40.00
110 Roy Campanella Pants/100 6.00 15.00
111 Ryne Sandberg Jsy/100 8.00 20.00
112 Stan Musial White Jsy/50 12.50 30.00
113 Steve Carlton Phils Jsy/100 3.00 8.00
114 Ted Williams Jsy/100 30.00 80.00
115 Ted Williams Jkt/100 25.00 60.00
116 Thurman Munson Jsy/100 10.00 25.00
117 T.Munson Pants/100 10.00 25.00
118 Tony Gwynn Jsy/100 6.00 15.00
119 Wade Boggs Yanks Jsy/100 5.00 12.00
120 Wade Boggs Sox Jsy/100 5.00 12.00
121 Warren Spahn Jsy/100 6.00 15.00
122 Warren Spahn Pants/100 6.00 15.00
123 Whitey Ford Jsy/100 5.00 12.00
124 Whitey Ford Pants/100 5.00 12.00
125 Will Clark Jsy/100 5.00 12.00
126 Willie McCovey Jsy/100 5.00 12.00
127 W.Stargell Black Jsy/100 5.00 12.00
128 Yogi Berra Jsy/25 12.50 30.00
129 Frankie Frisch Jkt/100 8.00 20.00
130 Marty Marion Jsy/100 3.00 8.00
131 Tommy John Pants/100 3.00 8.00
132 Chipper Jones Jsy/100 4.00 10.00
133 S.Sosa White Jsy/100 4.00 10.00
134 R.Henderson Dgr Jsy/100 4.00 10.00
135 Mike Piazza Dgr Jsy/100 5.00 12.00
136 Mike Piazza Mets Jsy/100 5.00 12.00
137 N.Garciaparra Grey Jsy/100 5.00 12.00
138 Hideo Nomo Dgr Jsy/100 4.00 10.00
139 Hideo Nomo Mets Jsy/50 6.00 15.00
140 R.Johnson M's Jsy/100 4.00 10.00
141 R.Johnson D'backs Jsy/100 4.00 10.00
142 R.Johnson Astros Jsy/100 4.00 10.00
143 J.Giambi Yanks Jsy/100 2.00 5.00
144 Jason Giambi A's Jsy/100 2.00 5.00
145 C.Schilling Phils Jsy/100 2.00 5.00
146 Dennis Eckersley Jsy/100 5.00 12.00
147 Carlton Fisk W.Sox Jkt/100 5.00 12.00
148 Tom Seaver Mets Jsy/25 10.00 25.00
149 Joe Torre Jsy/100 5.00 12.00
150 P.Martinez Sox Jsy/100 3.00 8.00
151 A.Pujols White Jsy/100 10.00 25.00
152 Andre Dawson Sox Jsy/50 4.00 10.00
153 Bert Blyleven Jsy/100 3.00 8.00
154 Bo Jackson Sox Jsy/100 6.00 15.00
155 Cal Ripken Pants/100 15.00 40.00
156 C.Fisk W.Sox Jsy/100 5.00 12.00
157 C.Schill D'backs Jsy/100 2.00 5.00
158 D.Strawberry Yanks Jsy/100 3.00 8.00
159 Dave Concepcion Jsy/100 3.00 8.00
160 Dwight Evans Jsy/100 5.00 12.00
161 Ernie Banks Pants/100 6.00 15.00
162 Fred McGriff Jsy/1
163 Gary Carter Pants/100 3.00 8.00
164 Gary Sheffield Jsy/100 2.00 5.00
165 George Brett Blue Jsy/100 8.00 20.00
166 Greg Maddux Jsy/100 5.00 12.00
167 Ivan Rodriguez Jsy/100 3.00 8.00
168 Joe Morgan Giants Jsy/100 3.00 8.00
169 J.Canseco White Jsy/100 5.00 12.00
170 J.Gonzalez Rgr Jsy/100 2.00 5.00
171 J.Gonzalez Indians Jsy/100 2.00 5.00
172 Keith Hernandez Jsy/100 3.00 8.00
173 Ken Boyer Jsy/100 8.00 20.00
174 Kerry Wood Jsy/100 2.00 5.00
175 Lee Smith Jsy/100 3.00 8.00
176 Luis Tiant Jsy/100 3.00 8.00
177 Manny Ramirez Jsy/100 3.00 8.00
178 M.Grace D'backs Jsy/100 5.00 12.00
179 Matt Williams Jsy/100 3.00 8.00
180 Miguel Tejada Jsy/100 2.00 5.00
181 Mike Mussina Jsy/100 3.00 8.00
182 M.Piazza Marlins Jsy/100 5.00 12.00
183 N.Garc White Jsy/100 5.00 12.00
184 P.Martinez Dgr Jsy/100 3.00 8.00
185 Rafael Palmeiro Jsy/100 3.00 8.00
186 R.Jackson Yanks Pants/100 5.00 12.00
187 R.Henderson M's Jsy/100 4.00 10.00
188 R.Hend Mets Pants/100 4.00 10.00
189 R.Henderson A's Jsy/100 4.00 10.00
190 Sammy Sosa Blue Jsy/100 4.00 10.00
191 Satchel Paige CO Jsy/100 25.00 60.00
192 Shawn Green Jsy/100 2.00 5.00
193 Stan Musial Grey Jsy/50 12.50 30.00
194 Steve Carlton Sox Jsy/100 3.00 8.00
195 Steve Garvey Jsy/100 3.00 8.00
196 Tom Seaver Reds Jsy/100 5.00 12.00
197 Tony Gwynn Pants/100 6.00 15.00
198 Vladimir Guerrero Jsy/100 4.00 10.00
199 Wade Boggs Rays Jsy/100 5.00 12.00
200 W.Stargell Grey Jsy/100 5.00 12.00

2004 Leaf Certified Materials Fabric of the Game AL/NL

*AL/NL p/r 100: .4X TO 1X FOTG p/r 100
*AL/NL p/r 50: .6X TO 1.5X FOTG p/r 100
*AL/NL p/r 50: .4X TO 1X FOTG p/r 50
*AL/NL p/r 25: 1X TO 2.5X FOTG p/r 100
*AL/NL p/r 25: .6X TO 1.5X FOTG p/r 50
*AL/NL p/r 25: .4X TO 1X FOTG p/r 25
PRINT RUNS B/WN 1-100 #'d COPIES PER
NO PRICING ON QTY OF 10 OR LESS

2004 Leaf Certified Materials Fabric of the Game Jersey Number

*JSY # p/r 72: .4X TO 1X FOTG p/r 100
*JSY # p/r 36-53: .6X TO 1.5X FOTG p/r 100
*JSY # p/r 36-53: .4X TO 1X FOTG p/r 50
*JSY # p/r 36-53: .25X TO .6X FOTG p/r 25
*JSY # p/r 20-35: 1X TO 2.5X FOTG p/r 100
*JSY # p/r 20-35: .6X TO 1.5X FOTG p/r 50
*JSY # p/r 20-35: .4X TO 1X FOTG p/r 25
*JSY # p/r 15-19: 1.25X TO 3X FOTG p/r 100
*JSY # p/r 15-19: .75X TO 2X FOTG p/r 50
PRINT RUNS B/WN 1-72 #'d COPIES PER
NO PRICING ON QTY OF 14 OR LESS
44 Fred Lynn Jsy/19 8.00 20.00
55 Jackie Robinson Jsy/42 25.00 60.00

2004 Leaf Certified Materials Fabric of the Game Jersey Year

*JSY YR p/r 66-99: .4X TO 1X FOTG p/r 100
*JSY YR p/r 66-99: .25X TO .6X FOTG p/r 50
*JSY YR p/r 66-99: .15X TO .4X FOTG p/r 25
*JSY YR p/r 38-65: .6X TO 1.5X FOTG p/r 100
*JSY YR p/r 38-65: .4X TO 1X FOTG p/r 50
*JSY YR p/r 38-65: .25X TO .6X FOTG p/r 25
*JSY YR p/r 20-34: 1X TO 2.5X FOTG p/r 100
*JSY YR p/r 19: 1.25X TO 3X FOTG p/r 100
*JSY YR p/r 19: .75X TO 2X FOTG p/r 50
*JSY YR p/r 19: .5X TO 1.2X FOTG p/r 25
PRINT RUNS B/WN 1-99 COPIES PER
NO PRICING ON QTY OF 1 CARD
9 Babe Ruth Jsy/25 300.00 500.00
10 Babe Ruth Pants/30 150.00 250.00
44 Fred Lynn Jsy/19 8.00 20.00
55 Jackie Robinson Jsy/19 40.00 100.00
69 Lou Gehrig Jsy/19 175.00 300.00
70 Lou Gehrig Pants/38 100.00 200.00
87 Ty Cobb Pants/25 60.00 120.00

2004 Leaf Certified Materials Fabric of the Game Position

*POS p/r 100: .4X TO 1X FOTG p/r 100
*POS p/r 50: .6X TO 1.5X FOTG p/r 100
*POS p/r 50: .4X TO 1X FOTG p/r 50
*POS p/r 25: 1X TO 2.5X FOTG p/r 100
*POS p/r 25: .6X TO 1.5X FOTG p/r 50
*POS p/r 25: .4X TO 1X FOTG p/r 25
PRINT RUNS B/WN 1-100 COPIES PER
NO PRICING ON QTY OF 10 OR LESS

2004 Leaf Certified Materials Fabric of the Game Prime

STATED PRINT RUN 1 SERIAL #'d SET
NO PRICING DUE TO SCARCITY

2004 Leaf Certified Materials Fabric of the Game Reward

*RWD p/r 50: .6X TO 1.5X FOTG p/r 100
*RWD p/r 50: .4X TO 1X FOTG p/r 50
*RWD p/r 25: 1X TO 2.5X FOTG p/r 100
*RWD p/r 25: .6X TO 1.5X FOTG p/r 50
*RWD p/r 25: .4X TO 1X FOTG p/r 25
PRINT RUNS B/WN 1-50 #'d COPIES PER
NO PRICING ON QTY OF 10 OR LESS
87 Ty Cobb Pants/50 50.00 100.00

2004 Leaf Certified Materials Fabric of the Game Stats

*STAT p/r 66: .4X TO 1X FOTG p/r 100
*STAT p/r 36-57: .6X TO 1.5X FOTG p/r 100
*STAT p/r 36-57: .4X TO 1X FOTG p/r 50
*STAT p/r 36-57: .25X TO .6X FOTG p/r 25
*STAT p/r 20-35: 1X TO 2.5X FOTG p/r 100
*STAT p/r 20-35: .6X TO 1.5X FOTG p/r 50
*STAT p/r 20-35: .4X TO 1X FOTG p/r 25
*STAT p/r 15-19: 1.25X TO 3X FOTG p/r 100
*STAT p/r 15-19: .75X TO 2X FOTG p/r 50
PRINT RUNS B/WN 1-66 #'d COPIES PER
NO PRICING ON QTY OF 14 OR LESS
55 Jackie Robinson Jsy/19 40.00 100.00

2004 Leaf Certified Materials Fabric of the Game Autograph

PRINT RUNS B/WN 1-10 COPIES PER
NO PRICING DUE TO SCARCITY

2004 Leaf Certified Materials Fabric of the Game Autograph AL/NL

PRINT RUNS B/WN 1-25 COPIES PER
NO PRICING ON QTY OF 10 OR LESS
15 Bobby Doerr Jsy/25 15.00 40.00

2004 Leaf Certified Materials Fabric of the Game Autograph Jersey Number

PRINT RUNS B/WN 1-8 COPIES PER
NO PRICING DUE TO SCARCITY

2004 Leaf Certified Materials Fabric of the Game Autograph Jersey Year

PRINT RUNS B/WN 1-8 COPIES PER
NO PRICING DUE TO SCARCITY

2004 Leaf Certified Materials Fabric of the Game Autograph Position

PRINT RUNS B/WN 1-8 COPIES PER
NO PRICING DUE TO SCARCITY

2004 Leaf Certified Materials Fabric of the Game Autograph Reward

PRINT RUNS B/WN 1-8 COPIES PER
NO PRICING DUE TO SCARCITY

2004 Leaf Certified Materials Fabric of the Game Autograph Stats

PRINT RUNS B/WN 1-8 COPIES PER
NO PRICING DUE TO SCARCITY

2005 Leaf Certified Materials

This 250-card set was released in July, 2005. The set was issued in five-card packs with an $10 SRP which came 10 packs to a box and 24 boxes to a case. Cards numbered 1-190 feature active veterans while cards 191-200 feature retired legends and cards 201-250 feature rookies. Cards 201-243 and 249-250 were all signed by the player. Most of the cards 201-250 had a stated print run of 499 serial numbered sets except for those cards noted as T2 which had a print run of 299 serial numbered sets and card number 211 was printed to a stated print run of 115 sets. All cards 201-250 were randomly inserted into packs.

COMP.SET w/o SP's (200) 15.00 40.00
COMMON CARD (1-190) .25 .60
COMMON CARD (191-200) .25 .60
COMMON (201-250) p/r 499 1.25 3.00
COMMON AU (201-250) p/r 499 3.00 8.00
COMMON AU (201-250) p/r 299 4.00 10.00
COMMON AU (211) p/r 115 6.00 15.00
201-250 RANDOM INSERTS IN PACKS
201-250 PRINT RUN 499 SERIAL #'d SETS
201-250 T2 PRINT RUN 299 #'d COPIES PER
CARD 211 T3 PRINT RUN 115 #'d COPIES
1 A.J. Burnett .40 1.00
2 Adam Dunn .40 1.00
3 Adrian Beltre .25 .60
4 Bret Boone .25 .60
5 Albert Pujols 1.50 4.00
6 Alex Rodriguez 1.00 2.50
7 Alfonso Soriano .40 1.00
8 Andruw Jones .25 .60
9 Andy Pettitte .40 1.00
10 Aramis Ramirez .25 .60
11 Aubrey Huff .25 .60
12 Austin Kearns .25 .60
13 B.J. Upton .40 1.00
14 Brandon Webb .40 1.00
15 Barry Zito .25 .60
16 Tim Salmon .25 .60
17 Bobby Abreu .25 .60
18 Bobby Crosby .25 .60
19 Brad Penny .25 .60
20 Preston Wilson .25 .60
21 C.C. Sabathia .40 1.00
22 Carl Crawford .40 1.00
23 Keith Foulke .25 .60
24 Carlos Beltran .25 .60
25 Casey Kotchman .25 .60
26 Chipper Jones .60 1.50
27 Chone Figgins .25 .60
28 Craig Biggio .40 1.00
29 Craig Wilson .25 .60
30 Curt Schilling Sox .40 1.00
31 Danny Kolb .25 .60
32 David Ortiz Sox .60 1.50
33 Orlando Hudson .25 .60
34 David Wright 1.00 2.50
35 Derek Jeter 1.50 4.00
36 Jake Peavy .25 .60
37 Derrek Lee .25 .60
38 Dontrelle Willis .25 .60
39 Edgar Renteria .25 .60
40 Angel Berroa .25 .60
41 Eric Chavez .25 .60
42 Akinori Otsuka .25 .60
43 Francisco Rodriguez .40 1.00
44 Garret Anderson .25 .60
45 Gary Sheffield .25 .60
46 Greg Maddux Cubs 1.00 2.50
47 Hideki Matsui 1.00 2.50
48 Hideo Nomo .60 1.50
49 Ichiro Suzuki 1.00 2.50
50 Ivan Rodriguez Tigers .40 1.00
51 J.D. Drew .25 .60
52 J.T. Snow .25 .60
53 Jack Wilson .25 .60
54 Jamie Moyer .25 .60
55 Jason Bay .25 .60
56 Jason Giambi .25 .60
57 Trot Nixon .25 .60
58 Jason Schmidt .25 .60
59 Jason Varitek .60 1.50
60 Roy Oswalt .40 1.00
61 Javy Lopez .25 .60
62 Eric Byrnes .25 .60
63 Jeff Bagwell .40 1.00
64 Jeff Kent Dgr .25 .60
65 Jeff Suppan .25 .60
66 Jeremy Bonderman .25 .60
67 Jermaine Dye .25 .60
68 Kazuhito Tadano .25 .60
69 Jim Edmonds .40 1.00
70 Jim Thome .40 1.00
71 Johan Santana .60 1.50
72 John Smoltz .60 1.50
73 Johnny Damon .40 1.00
74 Johnny Estrada .25 .60
75 Brett Myers .25 .60
76 Jose Guillen .25 .60
77 Jose Vidro .25 .60
78 Josh Beckett .40 1.00
79 Edwin Jackson .25 .60
80 Raul Ibanez .25 .60
81 Rich Harden .25 .60
82 Justin Morneau .60 1.50
83 Kazuhisa Ishii .25 .60
84 Kazuo Matsui .25 .60
85 Ken Griffey Jr. 1.00 2.50
86 Ken Harvey .25 .60
87 Frank Thomas .60 1.50
88 Kerry Wood .25 .60
89 Wade Miller .25 .60
90 Kevin Millwood .25 .60
91 Jeremy Affeldt .25 .60
92 Francisco Cordero .25 .60
93 Lance Berkman .40 1.00
94 Larry Walker Cards .40 1.00
95 Laynce Nix .25 .60
96 Luis Gonzalez .25 .60
97 Lyle Overbay .25 .60
98 Carlos Zambrano .40 1.00
99 Manny Ramirez .60 1.50
100 Marcus Giles .25 .60
101 Mark Buehrle .40 1.00
102 Mark Loretta .25 .60
103 Mark Mulder .25 .60
104 Mark Prior .40 1.00
105 Mark Teixeira .60 1.50
106 Marlon Byrd .25 .60
107 Rafael Furcal .25 .60
108 Melvin Mora .25 .60
109 Michael Young .40 1.00
110 Miguel Cabrera .60 1.50
111 Miguel Tejada O's .40 1.00
112 Mike Lowell .25 .60
113 Mike Mussina .40 1.00
114 Mike Piazza .60 1.50
115 Moises Alou .25 .60
116 Livan Hernandez .25 .60
117 Nomar Garciaparra .60 1.50
118 Omar Vizquel .40 1.00
119 Orlando Cabrera .25 .60
120 Pat Burrell .25 .60
121 Paul Konerko .40 1.00
122 Paul Lo Duca .25 .60
123 Pedro Martinez Mets .40 1.00
124 Rafael Palmeiro O's .40 1.00
125 Randy Johnson .60 1.50
126 Richard Hidalgo .25 .60
127 Richie Sexson .25 .60
128 Magglio Ordonez .40 1.00
129 Roger Clemens Astros .75 2.00
130 Russ Ortiz .25 .60
131 Sammy Sosa Cubs .60 1.50
132 Scott Podsednik .25 .60
133 Scott Rolen .40 1.00
134 Sean Burroughs .25 .60
135 Sean Casey .25 .60
136 Shawn Green D'backs .25 .60
137 Jorge Posada .40 1.00
138 Roy Halladay .60 1.50
139 Steve Finley .25 .60
140 Tim Hudson Braves .40 1.00
141 Todd Helton .40 1.00
142 Tom Glavine Mets .40 1.00
143 Torii Hunter .25 .60
144 Travis Hafner .25 .60
145 Trevor Hoffman .40 1.00
146 Troy Glaus D'backs .25 .60
147 Vernon Wells .25 .60
148 Victor Martinez .40 1.00
149 Vladimir Guerrero Angels .60 1.50
150 Sammy Sosa O's .60 1.50
151 Hank Blalock .25 .60
152 Danny Graves .25 .60
153 Rocco Baldelli .25 .60
154 Carlos Delgado Marlins .25 .60
155 Bubba Nelson .25 .60
156 Kevin Youkilis .25 .60
157 Jacque Jones .25 .60
158 Mike Lieberthal .25 .60
159 Ben Sheets .25 .60
160 Lew Ford .25 .60
161 Ervin Santana .25 .60
162 Jody Gerut .25 .60
163 Nick Johnson .25 .60
164 Brian Roberts .25 .60
165 Joe Nathan .25 .60
166 Mike Sweeney .25 .60
167 Ryan Wagner .25 .60
168 David Dellucci .25 .60
169 Jae Weong Seo .25 .60
170 Tom Gordon .25 .60
171 Carlos Lee .25 .60
172 Octavio Dotel .25 .60
173 Jose Castillo .25 .60
174 Troy Percival .25 .60
175 Carlos Delgado Jays .25 .60
176 Curt Schilling D'backs .40 1.00
177 David Ortiz Twins .60 1.50
178 Greg Maddux Braves 1.00 2.50
179 Ivan Rodriguez Rgr .40 1.00
180 Jeff Kent Giants .25 .60
181 Larry Walker Rockies .40 1.00
182 Miguel Tejada A's .40 1.00
183 Pedro Martinez Sox .40 1.00
184 Rafael Palmeiro Rgr .40 1.00
185 Roger Clemens Yanks .75 2.00
186 Shawn Green Dgr .25 .60
187 Tim Hudson A's .40 1.00
188 Tom Glavine Braves .40 1.00
189 Troy Glaus Angels .25 .60
190 Vladimir Guerrero Expos .60 1.50
191 Cal Ripken LGD 2.50 6.00
192 Don Mattingly LGD 1.25 3.00
193 George Brett LGD 1.25 3.00
194 Harmon Killebrew LGD .60 1.50
195 Mike Schmidt LGD 1.25 3.00
196 Nolan Ryan LGD 1.50 4.00
197 Stan Musial LGD 1.00 2.50
198 Tony Gwynn LGD .75 2.00
199 Wade Boggs LGD .40 1.00
200 Willie Mays LGD 1.25 3.00
201 A.Concepcion NG AU RC 3.00 8.00
202 Agustin Montero NG AU RC 3.00 8.00
203 Carlos Ruiz NG AU RC 10.00 25.00
204 C.Rogowski NG AU RC 4.00 10.00
205 Chris Resop NG AU RC 4.00 10.00
206 Chris Roberson NG AU RC 3.00 8.00
207 Colter Bean NG RC 1.25 3.00
208 Danny Rueckel NG AU RC 3.00 8.00
209 Dave Gassner NG AU RC 3.00 8.00
210 Devon Lowery NG AU RC 3.00 8.00
211 N.Nakamura NG AU T3 RC 15.00 40.00
212 E.Threets NG AU T2 RC 4.00 10.00
213 Garrett Jones NG AU T2 RC 10.00 25.00
214 Geovany Soto NG AU RC 8.00 20.00
215 J.Gothreaux NG AU T2 RC 4.00 10.00
216 J.Hammel NG AU T2 RC 4.00 10.00
217 Jeff Miller NG AU T2 RC 4.00 10.00
218 Jeff Niemann NG AU T2 RC 6.00 15.00
219 Huston Street NG 1.50 4.00
220 John Hattig NG AU RC 3.00 8.00
221 J.Verlander NG AU T2 RC 30.00 60.00
222 Justin Wechsler NG AU RC 3.00 8.00
223 Luke Scott NG AU RC 10.00 25.00
224 Mark McLemore NG AU RC 3.00 8.00
225 M.Woodyard NG AU T2 RC 4.00 10.00
226 M.Lindstrom NG AU T2 RC 4.00 10.00
227 Miguel Negron NG AU RC 4.00 10.00
228 Mike Morse NG AU RC 4.00 10.00
229 Nate McLouth NG AU RC 6.00 15.00
230 P.Reynoso NG AU T2 RC 4.00 10.00
231 Phil Humber NG AU T2 RC 8.00 20.00
232 Tony Pena NG AU RC 3.00 8.00
233 R.Messenger NG AU RC 3.00 8.00
234 Raul Tablado NG AU RC 3.00 8.00
235 Russ Rohlicek NG AU RC 3.00 8.00
236 Ryan Speier NG AU RC 3.00 8.00
237 Scott Munter NG AU RC 3.00 8.00
238 Sean Thompson NG AU RC 3.00 8.00
239 Sean Tracey NG AU T2 RC 4.00 10.00
240 Marcos Carvajal NG RC 1.25 3.00
241 Travis Bowyer NG AU RC 3.00 8.00
242 Ubaldo Jimenez NG AU RC 10.00 25.00
243 W.Balentien NG AU RC 4.00 10.00
244 Eude Brito NG RC 1.25 3.00
245 Ambiorix Burgos NG RC 1.25 3.00
246 Tadahito Iguchi NG RC 3.00 8.00
247 Dae-Sung Koo NG RC 1.25 3.00
248 Chris Seddon NG RC 1.25 3.00
249 Keiichi Yabu NG AU RC 6.00 15.00
250 Y.Betancourt NG AU RC 12.50 30.00

2005 Leaf Certified Materials Mirror Black

RANDOM INSERTS IN PACKS
STATED PRINT RUN 1 SERIAL #'d SET
NO PRICING DUE TO SCARCITY

2005 Leaf Certified Materials Mirror Blue

*1-190: 2.5X TO 6X BASIC
*BLUE 212-240: 1.25X TO 3X BASIC
COMMON (201-250) 2.50 6.00
SEMIS 201-250 4.00 10.00
UNLISTED 201-250 6.00 15.00
RANDOM INSERTS IN PACKS
STATED PRINT RUN 50 SERIAL #'d SETS
201 Ambiorix Concepcion NG 2.50 6.00
202 Agustin Montero NG 2.50 6.00
203 Carlos Ruiz NG 2.50 6.00
204 Casey Rogowski NG 4.00 10.00
205 Chris Resop NG 2.50 6.00
206 Chris Roberson NG 2.50 6.00
207 Colter Bean NG 2.50 6.00
208 Danny Rueckel NG 2.50 6.00
209 Dave Gassner NG 2.50 6.00
210 Devon Lowery NG 2.50 6.00
211 Norihiro Nakamura NG 2.50 6.00
212 Erick Threets NG 2.50 6.00
213 Garrett Jones NG 4.00 10.00
214 Geovany Soto NG 12.00 30.00
215 Jared Gothreaux NG 2.50 6.00
216 Jason Hammel NG 2.50 6.00
217 Jeff Miller NG 2.50 6.00
218 Jeff Niemann NG 6.00 15.00
219 Huston Street NG 2.50 6.00
220 John Hattig NG 2.50 6.00
222 Justin Wechsler NG 2.50 6.00
223 Luke Scott NG 6.00 15.00
224 Mark McLemore NG 2.50 6.00
225 Mark Woodyard NG 2.50 6.00
226 Matt Lindstrom NG 2.50 6.00
227 Miguel Negron NG 4.00 10.00
228 Mike Morse NG 6.00 15.00
229 Nate McLouth NG 4.00 10.00
230 Paulino Reynoso NG 2.50 6.00
231 Phil Humber NG 6.00 15.00
232 Tony Pena NG 2.50 6.00
233 Randy Messenger NG 2.50 6.00
234 Raul Tablado NG 2.50 6.00
235 Russ Rohlicek NG 2.50 6.00
236 Ryan Speier NG 2.50 6.00
237 Scott Munter NG 2.50 6.00
238 Sean Thompson NG 2.50 6.00
239 Sean Tracey NG 2.50 6.00
240 Marcos Carvajal NG 2.50 6.00
241 Travis Bowyer NG 2.50 6.00
243 Wladimir Balentien NG 4.00 10.00
244 Eude Brito NG 2.50 6.00
245 Ambiorix Burgos NG 2.50 6.00
246 Tadahito Iguchi NG 4.00 10.00
247 Dae-Sung Koo NG 2.50 6.00
248 Chris Seddon NG 2.50 6.00
249 Keiichi Yabu NG 2.50 6.00
250 Yuniesky Betancourt NG 10.00 25.00

2005 Leaf Certified Materials Mirror Emerald

STATED PRINT RUN 5 SERIAL #'d SETS
NO PRICING DUE TO SCARCITY

2005 Leaf Certified Materials Mirror Gold

*GOLD 1-190: 4X TO 10X BASIC
*GOLD 191-200: 4X TO 10X BASIC
STATED PRINT RUN 25 SERIAL #'d SETS
201-250 NO PRICING DUE TO SCARCITY

2005 Leaf Certified Materials Mirror Red

*1-190: 1.5X TO 4X BASIC
*191-200: 1.5X TO 4X BASIC
COMMON (201-250) 1.50 4.00
SEMIS 201-250 2.50 6.00
UNLISTED 201-250 4.00 10.00
RANDOM INSERTS IN PACKS
STATED PRINT RUN 100 SERIAL #'d SETS
201 Ambiorix Concepcion NG 1.50 4.00
202 Agustin Montero NG 1.50 4.00
203 Carlos Ruiz NG 1.50 4.00
204 Casey Rogowski NG 2.50 6.00
205 Chris Resop NG 1.50 4.00
206 Chris Roberson NG 1.50 4.00
207 Colter Bean NG 1.50 4.00
208 Danny Rueckel NG 1.50 4.00
209 Dave Gassner NG 1.50 4.00
210 Devon Lowery NG 1.50 4.00
211 Norihiro Nakamura NG 1.50 4.00
212 Erick Threets NG 1.50 4.00
213 Garrett Jones NG 2.50 6.00
214 Geovany Soto NG 8.00 20.00
215 Jared Gothreaux NG 1.50 4.00
216 Jason Hammel NG 1.50 4.00
217 Jeff Miller NG 1.50 4.00
218 Jeff Niemann NG 4.00 10.00
219 Huston Street NG 1.50 4.00
220 John Hattig NG 1.50 4.00
221 Justin Verlander NG 30.00 80.00
222 Justin Wechsler NG 1.50 4.00
223 Luke Scott NG 4.00 10.00
224 Mark McLemore NG 1.50 4.00
225 Mark Woodyard NG 1.50 4.00
226 Matt Lindstrom NG 1.50 4.00
227 Miguel Negron NG 2.50 6.00
228 Mike Morse NG 4.00 10.00
229 Nate McLouth NG 2.50 6.00
230 Paulino Reynoso NG 1.50 4.00
231 Phil Humber NG 4.00 10.00
232 Tony Pena NG 1.50 4.00
233 Randy Messenger NG 1.50 4.00
234 Raul Tablado NG 1.50 4.00
235 Russ Rohlicek NG 1.50 4.00
236 Ryan Speier NG 1.50 4.00
237 Scott Munter NG 1.50 4.00
238 Sean Thompson NG 1.50 4.00
239 Sean Tracey NG 1.50 4.00
240 Marcos Carvajal NG 1.50 4.00
241 Travis Bowyer NG 1.50 4.00
243 Wladimir Balentien NG 2.50 6.00
244 Eude Brito NG 1.50 4.00
245 Ambiorix Burgos NG 1.50 4.00
246 Tadahito Iguchi NG 2.50 6.00
247 Dae-Sung Koo NG 1.50 4.00
248 Chris Seddon NG 1.50 4.00
249 Keiichi Yabu NG 1.50 4.00
250 Yuniesky Betancourt NG 6.00 15.00

2005 Leaf Certified Materials Mirror White

*1-190: 1.5X TO 4X BASIC
*191-200: 1.5X TO 4X BASIC
COMMON (201-250) 1.50 4.00
SEMIS 201-250 2.50 6.00
UNLISTED 201-250 4.00 10.00
RANDOM INSERTS IN PACKS
201 Ambiorix Concepcion NG 1.50 4.00
202 Agustin Montero NG 1.50 4.00
203 Carlos Ruiz NG 1.50 4.00
204 Casey Rogowski NG 2.50 6.00
205 Chris Resop NG 1.50 4.00
206 Chris Roberson NG 1.50 4.00
207 Colter Bean NG 1.50 4.00
208 Danny Rueckel NG 1.50 4.00
209 Dave Gassner NG 1.50 4.00
210 Devon Lowery NG 1.50 4.00
211 Norihiro Nakamura NG 1.50 4.00
212 Erick Threets NG 1.50 4.00
213 Garrett Jones NG 2.50 6.00
214 Geovany Soto NG 8.00 20.00
215 Jared Gothreaux NG 1.50 4.00
216 Jason Hammel NG 1.50 4.00
217 Jeff Miller NG 1.50 4.00
218 Jeff Niemann NG 4.00 10.00
219 Huston Street NG 1.50 4.00
220 John Hattig NG 1.50 4.00
221 Justin Verlander NG 30.00 80.00
222 Justin Wechsler NG 1.50 4.00
223 Luke Scott NG 4.00 10.00
224 Mark McLemore NG 1.50 4.00
225 Mark Woodyard NG 1.50 4.00
226 Matt Lindstrom NG 1.50 4.00
227 Miguel Negron NG 2.50 6.00
228 Mike Morse NG 4.00 10.00
229 Nate McLouth NG 2.50 6.00
230 Paulino Reynoso NG 1.50 4.00
231 Phil Humber NG 4.00 10.00
232 Tony Pena NG 1.50 4.00
233 Randy Messenger NG 1.50 4.00
234 Raul Tablado NG 1.50 4.00
235 Russ Rohlicek NG 1.50 4.00
236 Ryan Speier NG 1.50 4.00
237 Scott Munter NG 1.50 4.00
238 Sean Thompson NG 1.50 4.00
239 Sean Tracey NG 1.50 4.00
240 Marcos Carvajal NG 1.50 4.00
241 Travis Bowyer NG 1.50 4.00
243 Wladimir Balentien NG 2.50 6.00
244 Eude Brito NG 1.50 4.00
245 Ambiorix Burgos NG 1.50 4.00
246 Tadahito Iguchi NG 2.50 6.00
247 Dae-Sung Koo NG 1.50 4.00
248 Chris Seddon NG 1.50 4.00
249 Keiichi Yabu NG 1.50 4.00
250 Yuniesky Betancourt NG 6.00 15.00

2005 Leaf Certified Materials Mirror Autograph Black

OVERALL AU-GU ODDS 4 PER BOX
STATED PRINT RUN 1 SERIAL #'d SET
NO PRICING DUE TO SCARCITY

2005 Leaf Certified Materials Mirror Autograph Blue

*1-190 p/r 100: .5X TO 1.2X RED p/r 250
*1-190 p/r 50: .5X TO 1.2X RED p/r 100
*1-190 p/r 25: .5X TO 1.2X RED p/r 50
*1-190 p/r 25: .4X TO 1X RED p/r 25
*201-250 p/r 49: .5X TO 1.2X RED p/r 99
OVERALL AU-GU ODDS 4 PER BOX
PRINT RUNS B/WN 1-100 COPIES PER
1-200 NO PRICING ON 10 OR LESS
201-250 NO PRICING ON 25 OR LESS

2005 Leaf Certified Materials Mirror Autograph Emerald

OVERALL AU-GU ODDS 4 PER BOX
PRINT RUNS B/WN 1-5 COPIES PER
NO PRICING DUE TO SCARCITY

2005 Leaf Certified Materials Mirror Autograph Gold

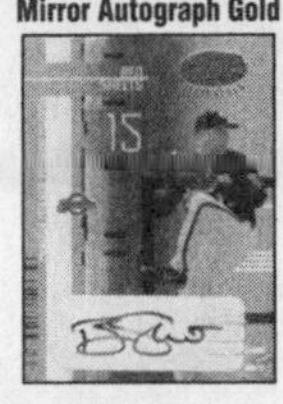

*1-190 p/r 25: .75X TO 2X RED p/r 250
*1-190 p/r 25: .6X TO 1.5X RED p/r 100
*1-190 p/r 25: .5X TO 1.2X RED p/r 50
*1-190 p/r 25: .4X TO 1X RED p/r 25
OVERALL AU-GU ODDS 4 PER BOX
PRINT RUNS B/WN 1-25 COPIES PER
1-200 NO PRICING ON QTY OF 5 OR LESS
201-250 NO PRICING DUE TO SCARCITY
2 Adam Dunn/25 15.00 40.00
11 Aubrey Huff/25 10.00 25.00
12 Austin Kearns/25 6.00 15.00
13 B.J. Upton/25 10.00 25.00
14 Brandon Webb/25 6.00 15.00
19 Brad Penny/25 6.00 15.00
21 C.C. Sabathia/25 10.00 25.00
23 Keith Foulke/25 15.00 40.00
27 Chone Figgins/25 6.00 15.00
29 Craig Wilson/25 6.00 15.00
31 Danny Kolb/25 6.00 15.00
34 David Wright/25 30.00 60.00
36 Jake Peavy/25 15.00 40.00
37 Derrek Lee/25 20.00 50.00
39 Edgar Renteria/25 10.00 25.00
40 Angel Berroa/25 6.00 15.00
41 Eric Chavez/25 10.00 25.00
42 Akinori Otsuka/25 10.00 25.00
43 Francisco Rodriguez/25 15.00 40.00
44 Garret Anderson/25 10.00 25.00
54 Jamie Moyer/25 10.00 25.00
55 Jason Bay/25 10.00 25.00
57 Trot Nixon/25 10.00 25.00
60 Roy Oswalt/25 10.00 25.00
63 Jeff Bagwell/25 30.00 60.00
65 Jeff Suppan/25 10.00 25.00
75 Brett Myers/25 10.00 25.00
76 Jose Guillen/25 10.00 25.00
77 Jose Vidro/25 10.00 25.00
81 Rich Harden/25 10.00 25.00
97 Lyle Overbay/25 10.00 25.00
98 Carlos Zambrano/25 15.00 40.00
101 Mark Buehrle/25 20.00 50.00
102 Mark Loretta/25 6.00 15.00
107 Rafael Furcal/25 10.00 25.00
109 Michael Young/25 10.00 25.00
110 Miguel Cabrera/25 15.00 40.00
116 Livan Hernandez/25 10.00 25.00
118 Omar Vizquel/25 15.00 40.00
119 Orlando Cabrera/25 10.00 25.00
121 Paul Konerko/25 15.00 40.00
128 Magglio Ordonez/25 10.00 25.00
130 Russ Ortiz/25 6.00 15.00
134 Sean Burroughs/25 6.00 15.00
135 Sean Casey/25 10.00 25.00
139 Steve Finley/25 10.00 25.00
143 Torii Hunter/25 10.00 25.00
144 Travis Hafner/25 10.00 25.00
147 Vernon Wells/25 10.00 25.00
152 Danny Graves/25 6.00 15.00
157 Jacque Jones/25 10.00 25.00
158 Mike Lieberthal/25 10.00 25.00
163 Nick Johnson/25 10.00 25.00
170 Tom Gordon/25 6.00 15.00
171 Carlos Lee/25 10.00 25.00
172 Octavio Dotel/25 6.00 15.00
174 Troy Percival/25 10.00 25.00
194 Harmon Killebrew LGD/25 30.00 60.00

2005 Leaf Certified Materials Mirror Autograph Red

OVERALL AU-GU ODDS 4 PER BOX
PRINT RUNS B/WN 1-250 COPIES PER
1-200 NO PRICING ON QTY OF 10 OR LESS
201-250 NO PRICING ON QTY OF 19 OR LESS
16 Tim Salmon/25 15.00 40.00
18 Bobby Crosby/50 8.00 20.00
25 Casey Kotchman/50 8.00 20.00
33 Orlando Hudson/250 3.00 8.00
53 Jack Wilson/50 8.00 20.00
62 Eric Byrnes/50 5.00 12.00
66 Jeremy Bonderman/50 8.00 20.00
67 Jermaine Dye/50 8.00 20.00
68 Kazuhito Tadano/100 6.00 15.00
79 Edwin Jackson/250 6.00 15.00
80 Raul Ibanez/50 10.00 25.00
86 Ken Harvey/250 3.00 8.00
89 Wade Miller/250 3.00 8.00
91 Jeremy Affeldt/250 3.00 8.00
92 Francisco Cordero/25 10.00 25.00
95 Laynce Nix/100 4.00 10.00
106 Marlon Byrd/250 3.00 8.00
155 Bubba Nelson/250 3.00 8.00
156 Kevin Youkilis/50 5.00 12.00
160 Lew Ford/50 5.00 12.00
161 Ervin Santana/250 3.00 8.00
162 Jody Gerut/50 5.00 12.00
164 Brian Roberts/25 10.00 25.00
165 Joe Nathan/50 8.00 20.00
167 Ryan Wagner/50 5.00 12.00
168 David Dellucci/50 12.50 30.00
169 Jae Weong Seo/25 6.00 15.00
173 Jose Castillo/250 3.00 8.00
202 Agustin Montero NG/99 3.00 8.00
211 Norihiro Nakamura NG/99 20.00 50.00
218 Jeff Niemann NG/49 10.00 25.00
221 Justin Verlander NG/50 60.00 120.00
223 Luke Scott NG/99 12.50 30.00
229 Nate McLouth NG/99 8.00 20.00
230 Paulino Reynoso NG/49 4.00 10.00
231 Phil Humber NG/49 12.50 30.00
234 Raul Tablado NG/99 3.00 8.00
239 Sean Tracey NG/49 4.00 10.00
243 Wladimir Balentien NG/99 8.00 20.00

2005 Leaf Certified Materials Mirror Autograph White

*1-190 p/r 50: .6X TO 1.5X RED p/r 250
*1-190 p/r 50: .5X TO 1.2X RED p/r 100
*1-190 p/r 25: .75X TO 2X RED p/r 250
*1-190 p/r 25: .5X TO 1.2X RED p/r 50
*201-250 p/r 49: .5X TO 1.2X RED p/r 99
*201-250 p/r 49: .4X TO 1X RED p/r 49
OVERALL AU-GU ODDS 4 PER BOX
PRINT RUNS B/WN 1-50 COPIES PER
1-200 NO PRICING ON QTY OF 10 OR LESS
201-250 NO PRICING ON QTY OF 15 OR LESS
19 Brad Penny/25 6.00 15.00
81 Rich Harden/50 8.00 20.00
211 Norihiro Nakamura NG/49 30.00 60.00

2005 Leaf Certified Materials Mirror Bat Black

OVERALL AU-GU ODDS 4 PER BOX
STATED PRINT RUN 1 SERIAL #'d SET
NO PRICING DUE TO SCARCITY

2005 Leaf Certified Materials Mirror Bat Blue

*BLUEp/r75-100: .5X TO 1.2X REDp/r200-250
*BLUE p/r 75-100: .4X TO 1X RED p/r 100
OVERALL AU-GU ODDS 4 PER BOX
PRINT RUNS B/WN 75-100 COPIES PER
32 David Ortiz Sox/100 3.00 8.00
37 Derrek Lee/100 3.00 8.00
117 Nomar Garciaparra/100 4.00 10.00
144 Travis Hafner/100 2.50 6.00

2005 Leaf Certified Materials Mirror Bat Emerald

OVERALL AU-GU ODDS 4 PER BOX
STATED PRINT RUN 5 SERIAL #'d SETS
NO PRICING DUE TO SCARCITY

2005 Leaf Certified Materials Mirror Bat Gold

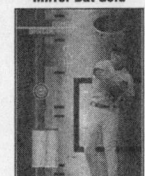

*GOLD: .75X TO 2X RED p/r 200-250
*GOLD: .6X TO 1.5X RED p/r 100
*GOLD: .5X TO 1.2X RED p/r 50
OVERALL AU-GU ODDS 4 PER BOX
STATED PRINT RUN 25 SERIAL #'d SETS
7 Alfonso Soriano 4.00 10.00
24 Carlos Beltran 4.00 10.00
30 Curt Schilling Sox 5.00 12.00
32 David Ortiz Sox 5.00 12.00
37 Derrek Lee 5.00 12.00
39 Edgar Renteria 4.00 10.00
78 Josh Beckett 4.00 10.00
84 Kazuo Matsui 4.00 10.00
88 Kerry Wood 4.00 10.00
97 Lyle Overbay 4.00 10.00
117 Nomar Garciaparra 6.00 15.00
140 Tim Hudson Braves 4.00 10.00
144 Travis Hafner 4.00 10.00

2005 Leaf Certified Materials Mirror Bat Red

OVERALL AU-GU ODDS 4 PER BOX
PRINT RUNS B/WN 50-250 COPIES PER
2 Adam Dunn/250 2.00 5.00
5 Albert Pujols/250 6.00 15.00
8 Andruw Jones/250 2.50 6.00
11 Aubrey Huff/250 2.00 5.00
13 B.J. Upton/250 2.00 5.00
14 Brandon Webb/100 2.50 6.00
16 Tim Salmon/250 2.50 6.00
25 Casey Kotchman/250 2.00 5.00
26 Chipper Jones/250 3.00 8.00
28 Craig Biggio/50 4.00 10.00
29 Craig Wilson/250 2.00 5.00
34 David Wright/250 4.00 10.00
38 Dontrelle Willis/250 2.00 5.00
44 Garret Anderson/250 2.00 5.00
45 Gary Sheffield/250 2.00 5.00
59 Jason Varitek/250 3.00 8.00
61 Javy Lopez/250 2.00 5.00
63 Jeff Bagwell/250 2.50 6.00
77 Jose Vidro/250 2.00 5.00
93 Lance Berkman/250 2.00 5.00
99 Manny Ramirez/250 2.50 6.00
105 Mark Teixeira/250 2.50 6.00
109 Michael Young/250 2.00 5.00
110 Miguel Cabrera/250 2.50 6.00
111 Miguel Tejada O's/250 2.00 5.00
121 Paul Konerko/250 2.00 5.00
124 Rafael Palmeiro O's/250 2.50 6.00
128 Magglio Ordonez/250 2.00 5.00
136 Shawn Green D'backs/250 2.00 5.00
141 Todd Helton/250 2.50 6.00
142 Tom Glavine Mets/250 2.50 6.00
143 Torii Hunter/200 2.00 5.00
148 Victor Martinez/250 2.00 5.00
149 Vladimir Guerrero Angels/250 3.00 8.00
150 Sammy Sosa O's/250 3.00 8.00
153 Rocco Baldelli/250 2.00 5.00
160 Lew Ford/250 2.00 5.00
166 Mike Sweeney/100 2.50 6.00
184 Rafael Palmeiro Rgr/100 3.00 8.00
188 Tom Glavine Braves/250 2.50 6.00
190 Vladimir Guerrero Expos/250 3.00 8.00

2005 Leaf Certified Materials Mirror Bat White

*WHITE p/r 250: .4X TO 1X RED p/r 200-250
*WHITE p/r 250: .3X TO .8X RED p/r 100
*WHITEp/r75-100: .5XTO1.2X REDp/r200-250
*WHITE p/r 75-100: .3X TO .8X RED p/r 50
*WHITE p/r 50: .5X TO 1.2X RED p/r 100
OVERALL AU-GU ODDS 4 PER BOX
PRINT RUNS B/WN 50-250 COPIES PER

2005 Leaf Certified Materials Mirror Fabric Black HR

OVERALL AU-GU ODDS 4 PER BOX
STATED PRINT RUN 1 SERIAL #'d SET
NO PRICING DUE TO SCARCITY

2005 Leaf Certified Materials Mirror Fabric Black MLB Logo

OVERALL AU-GU ODDS 4 PER BOX
STATED PRINT RUN 1 SERIAL #'d SET
NO PRICING DUE TO SCARCITY

2005 Leaf Certified Materials Mirror Fabric Black Number

OVERALL AU-GU ODDS 4 PER BOX
STATED PRINT RUN 1 SERIAL #'d SET
NO PRICING DUE TO SCARCITY

2005 Leaf Certified Materials Mirror Fabric Black Position

OVERALL AU-GU ODDS 4 PER BOX
STATED PRINT RUN 1 SERIAL #'d SET
NO PRICING DUE TO SCARCITY

2005 Leaf Certified Materials Mirror Fabric Black Prime

OVERALL AU-GU ODDS 4 PER BOX
STATED PRINT RUN 1 SERIAL #'d SET
NO PRICING DUE TO SCARCITY

2005 Leaf Certified Materials Mirror Fabric Blue

*BLUE p/r 100: .5X TO 1.2X RED p/r 225-250
*BLUE p/r 100: .4X TO 1X RED p/r 100
*BLUE p/r 50: .6X TO 1.5X RED p/r 225-250
OVERALL AU-GU ODDS 4 PER BOX
PRINT RUNS B/WN 50-100 COPIES PER
18 Bobby Crosby/50 3.00 8.00
73 Johnny Damon Jsy/100 3.00 8.00
78 Josh Beckett Jsy/100 2.50 6.00
113 Mike Mussina Jsy/100 4.00 10.00
151 Hank Blalock Jsy/100 2.50 6.00

2005 Leaf Certified Materials Mirror Fabric Emerald

OVERALL AU-GU ODDS 4 PER BOX
STATED PRINT RUN 5 SERIAL #'d SETS
NO PRICING DUE TO SCARCITY

2005 Leaf Certified Materials Mirror Fabric Gold

*GOLD: .75X TO 2X RED p/r 225-250
*GOLD: .6X TO 1.5X RED p/r 100
OVERALL AU-GU ODDS 4 PER BOX
STATED PRINT RUN 25 SERIAL #'d SETS
18 Bobby Crosby Jsy 4.00 10.00
55 Jason Bay Jsy 4.00 10.00
77 Jose Vidro Jsy 4.00 10.00
78 Josh Beckett Jsy 4.00 10.00
105 Mark Teixeira Jsy 5.00 12.00
108 Melvin Mora Jsy 4.00 10.00
151 Hank Blalock Jsy 4.00 10.00

2005 Leaf Certified Materials Mirror Fabric Red

OVERALL AU-GU ODDS 4 PER BOX
PRINT RUNS B/WN 100-250 COPIES PER
2 Adam Dunn Jsy/250 2.00 5.00
5 Albert Pujols Jsy/250 6.00 15.00
7 Alfonso Soriano Jsy/250 2.00 5.00
8 Andruw Jones Jsy/250 2.50 6.00
10 Aramis Ramirez Jsy/250 2.00 5.00
11 Aubrey Huff Jsy/250 2.00 5.00
13 B.J. Upton Jsy/250 2.00 5.00
14 Brandon Webb Pants/100 2.50 6.00
15 Barry Zito Jsy/250 2.00 5.00
17 Bobby Abreu Jsy/250 2.00 5.00
20 Preston Wilson Jsy/250 2.00 5.00
25 Casey Kotchman Jsy/250 2.00 5.00
26 Chipper Jones Jsy/250 3.00 8.00
28 Craig Biggio Jsy/250 2.50 6.00
30 Curt Schilling Sox Jsy/250 2.50 6.00
32 David Ortiz Sox Jsy/250 3.00 8.00
37 Derrek Lee Jsy/250 2.50 6.00
38 Dontrelle Willis Jsy/225 2.00 5.00
41 Eric Chavez Jsy/250 2.00 5.00
43 Francisco Rodriguez Jsy/250 2.00 5.00
44 Garret Anderson Jsy/250 2.00 5.00
45 Gary Sheffield Jsy/250 2.00 5.00
46 Greg Maddux Cubs Jsy/250 4.00 10.00
47 Hideki Matsui Jsy/250 6.00 15.00
48 Hideo Nomo Jsy/250 3.00 8.00
50 Ivan Rodriguez Tigers Jsy/250 2.50 6.00
57 Trot Nixon Jsy/250 2.00 5.00
60 Roy Oswalt Jsy/250 2.00 5.00
61 Javy Lopez Jsy/250 2.00 5.00
63 Jeff Bagwell Jsy/250 2.50 6.00
69 Jim Edmonds Jsy/250 2.00 5.00
70 Jim Thome Jsy/250 2.50 6.00
71 Johan Santana Jsy/250 3.00 8.00
82 Justin Morneau Jsy/250 2.00 5.00
84 Kazuo Matsui Jsy/250 2.00 5.00
87 Frank Thomas Jsy/250 3.00 8.00
88 Kerry Wood Jsy/250 2.00 5.00
92 Francisco Cordero Jsy/250 2.00 5.00
93 Lance Berkman Jsy/250 2.00 5.00
94 Larry Walker Cards Jsy/250 2.50 6.00
96 Luis Gonzalez Jsy/250 2.00 5.00
97 Lyle Overbay Jsy/250 2.00 5.00
98 Carlos Zambrano Jsy/250 2.00 5.00
99 Manny Ramirez Jsy/250 2.50 6.00
104 Mark Prior Jsy/250 2.50 6.00
109 Michael Young Jsy/250 2.00 5.00
110 Miguel Cabrera Jsy/250 2.50 6.00
111 Miguel Tejada O's Jsy/250 2.00 5.00
114 Mike Piazza Jsy/250 3.00 8.00
121 Paul Konerko Jsy/250 2.00 5.00
124 Rafael Palmeiro O's Jsy/250 2.50 6.00
129 Roger Clemens Astros Jsy/250 4.00 10.00
131 Sammy Sosa Cubs Jsy/250 3.00 8.00
133 Scott Rolen Jsy/250 2.50 6.00
135 Sean Casey Jsy/250 2.00 5.00
138 Roy Halladay Jsy/250 2.00 5.00
141 Todd Helton Jsy/250 2.50 6.00
144 Travis Hafner Jsy/250 2.00 5.00
147 Vernon Wells Jsy/250 2.00 5.00
148 Victor Martinez Jsy/250 2.00 5.00
149 Vladimir Guerrero Angels Jsy/250 3.00 8.00
153 Rocco Baldelli Jsy/250 2.00 5.00
159 Ben Sheets Jsy/250 2.00 5.00
160 Lew Ford Jsy/250 2.00 5.00
166 Mike Sweeney Jsy/250 2.00 5.00
178 G.Maddux Braves Jsy/250 10.00 25.00
179 I.Rodriguez Rgr Jsy/250 2.50 6.00
183 P.Martinez Sox Jsy/250 2.50 6.00
184 Rafael Palmeiro Rgr Jsy/250 2.50 6.00
185 Roger Clemens Yanks Jsy/250 4.00 10.00
188 T.Glav Braves Jsy/250 2.50 6.00
190 V.Guer Expos Jsy/100 4.00 10.00

2005 Leaf Certified Materials Mirror Fabric White

*WHITEp/r150-250: .4XTO1X REDp/r225-250
*WHITEp/r100: .5X TO 1.2X REDp/r 225-250
*WHITE p/r 50: .6X TO 1.5X RED p/r 225-250
*WHITE p/r 25: .75X TO 2X RED p/r 225-250
OVERALL AU-GU ODDS 4 PER BOX
PRINT RUNS B/WN 25-250 COPIES PER
34 David Wright Jsy/100 5.00 12.00
78 Josh Beckett Jsy/250 2.00 5.00
95 Laynce Nix Jsy/100 2.50 6.00
113 Mike Mussina Jsy/100 3.00 8.00
151 Hank Blalock Jsy/100 2.50 6.00

2005 Leaf Certified Materials Cuts Blue

OVERALL AU-GU ODDS 4 PER BOX
PRINT RUNS B/WN 1-80 COPIES PER
NO PRICING ON QTY OF 10 OR LESS
3 Willie Mays/26 90.00 150.00
7 Jim Palmer/50 8.00 20.00
12 Steve Carlton/50 8.00 20.00
15 Maury Wills/80 6.00 15.00
20 Dale Murphy/50 12.50 30.00

2005 Leaf Certified Materials Cuts Green

*GREEN p/r 80: .4X TO 1X BLUE p/r 80
*GREEN p/r 50: .4X TO 1X BLUE p/r 50
OVERALL AU-GU ODDS 4 PER BOX
PRINT RUNS B/WN 3-80 COPIES PER
NO PRICING ON QTY OF 11 OR LESS

2005 Leaf Certified Materials Cuts Red

*RED p/r 60: .5X TO 1.2X BLUE p/r 80
*RED p/r 50: .4X TO 1X BLUE p/r 50
OVERALL AU-GU ODDS 4 PER BOX
PRINT RUNS B/WN 1-60 COPIES PER
NO PRICING ON QTY OF 10 OR LESS

2005 Leaf Certified Materials Cuts Material Blue

OVERALL AU-GU ODDS 4 PER BOX
PRINT RUNS B/WN 4-43 COPIES PER
NO PRICING ON QTY OF 8 OR LESS
2 Hank Aaron Bat/43 200.00 300.00
3 Willie Mays Pants/24 125.00 200.00
4 Sandy Koufax Jsy/32 175.00 300.00
5 Cal Ripken Pants/8
6 Nolan Ryan Jsy/34 60.00 120.00
7 Jim Palmer Hat/22 15.00 40.00
8 Tony Gwynn Pants/19 30.00 60.00
9 Rod Carew Jsy/29 15.00 40.00
10 Ryne Sandberg Jsy/23 60.00 120.00
12 Steve Carlton Pants/32 10.00 25.00
14 Mike Schmidt Jsy/20 40.00 80.00
16 Harmon Killebrew Jsy/5
18 Duke Snider Pants/4
19 Don Mattingly Jsy/23 50.00 100.00
20 Dale Murphy Jsy/7

2005 Leaf Certified Materials Cuts Material Green

*GRN p/r 20-32: .4X TO 1X BLUE p/r 20-34
*GRN p/r 19: .4X TO 1X BLUE p/r 19
OVERALL AU-GU ODDS 4 PER BOX
PRINT RUNS B/WN 4-32 COPIES PER
NO PRICING ON QTY OF 10 OR LESS
3 Willie Mays Pants/24 125.00 200.00

2005 Leaf Certified Materials Cuts Material Red

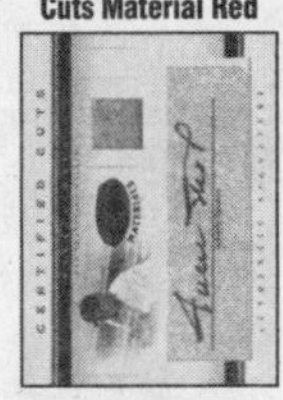

*RED p/r 20-32: .4X TO 1X BLUE p/r 20-34
*RED p/r 19: .4X TO 1X BLUE p/r 19
OVERALL AU-GU ODDS 4 PER BOX
PRINT RUNS B/WN 4-32 COPIES PER
NO PRICING ON QTY OF 10 OR LESS
3 Willie Mays Pants/24 125.00 200.00

2005 Leaf Certified Materials Fabric of the Game

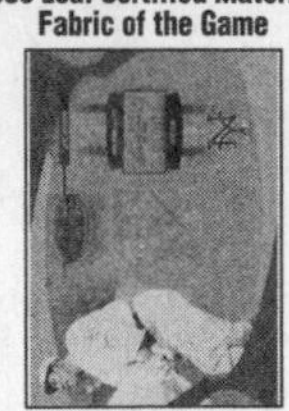

1-160 PRINT RUNS B/WN 5-100 COPIES PER
161-180 PRINTS B/WN 10-100 COPIES PER
OVERALL AU-GU ODDS 4 PER BOX
NO PRICING ON QTY OF 10 OR LESS
1 Al Oliver Jsy/50 4.00 10.00
2 Alan Trammell Jsy/100 3.00 8.00
3 Andres Galarraga Braves Jsy/100 3.00 8.00
4 Andres Galarraga Giants Jsy/100 3.00 8.00
5 Babe Ruth Jsy/10
6 Babe Ruth Pants/25 175.00 300.00
7 Billy Martin Pants/100 4.00 10.00
8 Billy Williams Jsy/50 4.00 10.00
9 Bo Jackson Sox Jsy/100 5.00 12.00
10 B.Jackson Royals Jsy/100 5.00 12.00
11 Bob Feller Pants/5
12 Bob Gibson Jsy/25 6.00 15.00
13 Bobby Doerr Pants/50 4.00 10.00
14 Burleigh Grimes Pants/25 30.00 60.00
15 Cal Ripken Jsy/50 15.00 40.00
16 Cal Ripken Jsy/50 15.00 40.00
17 Carl Yastrzemski Pants/50 6.00 15.00
18 Carlton Fisk Jkt/50 5.00 12.00
19 Catfish Hunter Pants/50 4.00 10.00
20 Darryl Strawberry Yanks Jsy/25 5.00 12.00
21 Darryl Strawberry Dgr Jsy/100 3.00 8.00
22 Dave Concepcion Jsy/50 4.00 10.00
23 Dave Righetti Jsy/50 4.00 10.00
24 Dave Winfield Pants/100 3.00 8.00
25 David Cone Jsy/100 3.00 8.00
26 David Justice Jsy/100 4.00 10.00
27 D.Sanders Yanks Jsy/50 5.00 12.00
28 D.Sanders Reds Jsy/50 5.00 12.00
29 Dennis Eckersley Cards Jsy/50 4.00 10.00
30 Dennis Eckersley A's Pants/50 4.00 10.00
31 Don Mattingly Jsy/100 6.00 15.00
32 Don Sutton Astros Jsy/25 5.00 12.00
33 Don Sutton Dgr Jsy/50 4.00 10.00
34 Duke Snider Dgr Jsy/10
35 Duke Snider Mets Jsy/10
36 Dwight Evans Jsy/5
37 Dwight Gooden Jsy/100 3.00 8.00
38 Eddie Murray Dgr Jsy/25 8.00 20.00
39 Eddie Murray O's Pants/50 6.00 15.00
40 Edgar Martinez Jsy/100 3.00 8.00
41 Ernie Banks Jsy/25 8.00 20.00
42 Fergie Jenkins Jsy/50 4.00 10.00
43 Frankie Frisch Jkt/50 6.00 15.00
44 Fred Lynn Jsy/50 4.00 10.00
45 Fred McGriff Jsy/100 4.00 10.00
46 Gary Carter Mets Jsy/50 4.00 10.00
47 Gary Carter Expos Jsy/50 4.00 10.00
48 Gaylord Perry M's Jsy/50 4.00 10.00
49 Gaylord Perry Giants Jsy/50 4.00 10.00
50 George Brett Jsy/25 10.00 25.00
51 Hal Newhouser Jsy/50 5.00 12.00
52 Hank Aaron Atl Jsy/5
53 Hank Aaron Mil Jsy/5
54 Harmon Killebrew Twins Jsy/25 8.00 20.00
55 Harmon Killebrew Senators Jsy/50 6.00 15.00
56 Harold Baines Jsy/50 4.00 10.00
57 Hoyt Wilhelm Jsy/100 3.00 8.00
58 Jack Morris Jsy/100 3.00 8.00
59 Jim Thorpe Jsy/25 125.00 200.00
60 Jose Cruz Jsy/100 3.00 8.00
61 Jim Rice Jsy/50 4.00 10.00
62 Joe Cronin Jsy/50 6.00 15.00
63 Joe Cronin Pants/100 5.00 12.00
64 Joe Morgan Jsy/50 4.00 10.00
65 Joe Torre Jsy/50 5.00 12.00
66 John Kruk Jsy/100 4.00 10.00
67 Johnny Bench Jsy/50 6.00 15.00
68 Juan Marichal Pants/100 3.00 8.00
69 Keith Hernandez Jsy/10
70 Kirby Puckett Jsy/10
71 Kirk Gibson Jsy/100 3.00 8.00
72 Lee Smith Jsy/100 3.00 8.00
73 Lenny Dykstra Jsy/100 3.00 8.00
74 Lou Boudreau Jsy/25 6.00 15.00
75 Luis Aparicio Jsy/50 4.00 10.00
76 Luis Tiant Pants/100 3.00 8.00
77 Mark Grace Jsy/50 5.00 12.00
78 Hoyt Wilhelm Jsy/100 3.00 8.00
79 Matt Williams Giants Jsy/100 4.00 10.00
80 Matt Williams D'acks Jsy/50 5.00 12.00
81 Mike Schmidt Jkt/5
82 Nolan Ryan Astros Jsy/50 10.00 25.00
83 Nolan Ryan Rgr Jsy/15 15.00 40.00
84 Nolan Ryan Mets Jsy/25 12.50 30.00
85 Nolan Ryan Angels Jsy/25 12.50 30.00
86 Orlando Cepeda Pants/50 4.00 10.00
87 Ozzie Smith Pants/25 8.00 20.00
88 Paul Molitor Brewers Jsy/50 4.00 10.00
89 Paul Molitor Twins Jsy/50 4.00 10.00
90 Paul Molitor Brewers Pants/50 4.00 10.00
91 Phil Niekro Jsy/50 4.00 10.00
92 Reggie Jack Yanks Pants/100 4.00 10.00
93 R.Jackson A's Jkt/100 4.00 10.00
94 Reggie Jackson Angels Jsy/50 5.00 12.00
95 Reggie Jackson A's Jsy/50 5.00 12.00
96 Rickey Henderson Mets Jkt/100 5.00 12.00
97 Rickey Henderson Dgr Jsy/50 6.00 15.00
98 Rickey Henderson A's Jsy/50 6.00 15.00
99 Rickey Henderson M's Jsy/50 6.00 15.00
100 Rickey Henderson Yanks Jsy/50 6.00 15.00
101 Rickey Henderson Padres Pants/50 6.00 15.00
102 Robin Ventura Yanks Jsy/100 3.00 8.00
103 R.Ventura Mets Jsy/100 3.00 8.00
104 Robin Yount Jsy/50 6.00 15.00
105 Rod Carew Angels Jsy/100 4.00 10.00
106 Rod Carew Twins Jsy/100 4.00 10.00
107 Roger Maris Pants/50 12.50 30.00
108 Ron Cey Jsy/50 4.00 10.00
109 Ron Guidry Pants/100 3.00 8.00
110 Ryne Sandberg Jsy/50 15.00 40.00
111 Sandy Koufax Jsy/25 75.00 150.00
112 Stan Musial Jsy/25 10.00 25.00
113 Stan Musial Pants/25 10.00 25.00
114 Steve Garvey Jsy/100 3.00 8.00
115 Ted Williams Jkt/50 20.00 50.00
116 Ted Williams Jsy/25 30.00 60.00
117 Tom Seaver Jsy/50 5.00 12.00
118 Tom Seaver Pants/50 5.00 12.00
119 Tommy John Jsy/100 3.00 8.00
120 Tommy John Pants/100 3.00 8.00
121 Tommy Lasorda Jsy/100 4.00 10.00
122 Tony Gwynn Jsy/100 5.00 12.00
123 Tony Gwynn Pants/100 5.00 12.00
124 Tony Perez Jsy/50 4.00 10.00
125 Wade Boggs Jsy/100 4.00 10.00
126 Warren Spahn Jsy/25 6.00 15.00
127 Whitey Ford Jsy/25 6.00 15.00
128 Will Clark Jsy/50 5.00 12.00
129 Willie Mays Pants/50 15.00 40.00
130 Willie McCovey Pants/100 4.00 10.00
131 Roger Clemens Astros Jsy/50 6.00 15.00
132 R.Clemens Yanks Jsy/50 6.00 15.00
133 Roger Clemens Sox Jsy/50 6.00 15.00
134 Randy Johnson M's Jsy/50 5.00 12.00
135 R.Johnson Expos Jsy/50 5.00 12.00
136 Cal Ripken Jsy/50 15.00 40.00
137 Don Mattingly Jsy/100 6.00 15.00
138 George Brett Jsy/25 10.00 25.00
139 Harmon Killebrew Twins Jsy/25 8.00 20.00
140 Mike Schmidt Jsy/50 8.00 20.00
141 Nolan Ryan Angels Jkt/25 12.50 30.00
142 Stan Musial Jsy/5
143 Tony Gwynn Jsy/100 5.00 12.00
144 Wade Boggs Jsy/50 5.00 12.00
145 Willie Mays Jsy/25 20.00 50.00
146 Hideo Nomo Jsy/100 4.00 10.00
147 D.Murphy Braves Jsy/100 4.00 10.00
148 D.Murphy Phils Jsy/100 4.00 10.00
149 Bo Jackson Royals Jsy/50 6.00 15.00
150 Darryl Strawberry Dgr Jsy/50 4.00 10.00
151 D.Sanders Yanks Jsy/50 5.00 12.00
152 Deion Sanders Yanks Pants/50 5.00 12.00
153 Dennis Eckersley A's Jsy/50 4.00 10.00
154 Dwight Gooden Jsy/100 3.00 8.00
155 Edgar Martinez Jsy/100 4.00 10.00
156 Lou Brock Jsy/50 5.00 12.00
157 Steve Carlton Pants/50 4.00 10.00
158 Albert Pujols Jsy/50 10.00 25.00
159 Tom Glavine Jsy/100 4.00 10.00
160 Hideki Matsui Pants/50 10.00 25.00
161 Babe Ruth Pants Jim Thorpe Jsy/25 300.00 500.00
162 Ted Will Jkt Stan Musial Jsy/50 30.00 60.00

163 Willie Mays Jsy
Bob Gibson Jsy/10
164 Whitey Ford Jsy 75.00 150.00
Sandy Koufax Jsy/25
165 Roger Maris Pants 40.00 80.00
Don Matt Jsy/25
166 Nolan Ryan Jsy 15.00 40.00
Tom Seaver Jsy/50
167 Cal Ripken Jsy 20.00 50.00
George Brett Jsy/100
168 Ryne Sandberg Jsy 15.00 40.00
Mike Schmidt Jsy/50
169 Tony Gwynn Jsy 8.00 20.00
Wade Boggs Jsy/50
170 Carlton Fisk Jsy 8.00 20.00
Johnny Bench Pants/50
171 Duke Snider Pants
Harmon Killebrew Jsy/10
172 Reggie Jackson Pants 6.00 15.00
Darryl Strawberry Jsy/50
173 Robin Yount Jsy 8.00 20.00
Paul Molitor Jsy/50
174 Warren Spahn Pants 6.00 15.00
Juan Marichal Jsy/50
175 Bo Jackson Jsy 6.00 15.00
Deion Sanders Pants/100
176 Tony Gwynn Jsy 10.00 25.00
Rickey Henderson Jsy/100
177 Hideki Matsui Jsy 10.00 25.00
Jim Edmonds Jsy/100
178 Rickey Henderson Pants 6.00 15.00
Lou Brock Jsy/100
179 Roger Clemens Jsy 10.00 25.00
Albert Pujols Jsy/100
180 Hideo Nomo Jsy 6.00 15.00
Kazuhisa Ishii Jsy/100

2005 Leaf Certified Materials Fabric of the Game Jersey Number

*1-160 p/r 72: .3X TO .8X FOTG p/r 50
*1-160 p/r 36-55: .5X TO 1.2X FOTG p/r 100
*1-160 p/r 36-55: .4X TO 1X FOTG p/r 50
*1-160 p/r 36-55: .3X TO .8X FOTG p/r 25
*1-160 p/r 20-35: .6X TO 1.5X FOTG p/r 100
*1-160 p/r 20-35: .5X TO 1.2X FOTG p/r 50
*1-160 p/r 20-35: .4X TO 1X FOTG p/r 25
*1-160 p/r 20-35: .3X TO .8X FOTG p/r 15
*1-160 p/r 15-19: .75X TO 2X FOTG p/r 100
*1-160 p/r 15-19: .6X TO 1.5X FOTG p/r 50
*1-160 p/r 15-19: .5X TO 1.2X FOTG p/r 25
1-160 PRINT RUNS B/WN 1-72 COPIES PER
*161-180 p/r 50: .5X TO 1.2X FOTG p/r 100
*161-180 p/r 50: .4X TO 1X FOTG p/r 50
*161-180 p/r 25: .6X TO 1.5X FOTG p/r 100
*161-180 p/r 25: .5X TO 1.2X FOTG p/r 50
161-180 PRINTS B/WN 3-50 COPIES PER
OVERALL AU-GU ODDS 4 PER BOX
NO PRICING ON QTY OF 14 OR LESS
36 Dwight Evans Jsy/24 6.00 15.00
52 Hank Aaron Atl Jsy/44 20.00 50.00
53 Hank Aaron Mil Jsy/44 20.00 50.00
111 Sandy Koufax Jsy/32 75.00 150.00

2005 Leaf Certified Materials Fabric of the Game Position

*1-160 p/r 100: .4X TO 1X FOTG p/r 100
*1-160 p/r 100: .3X TO .8X FOTG p/r 50
*1-160 p/r 50: .5X TO 1.2X FOTG p/r 100
*1-160 p/r 50: .4X TO 1X FOTG p/r 50
*1-160 p/r 25: .6X TO 1.5X FOTG p/r 100
*1-160 p/r 25: .5X TO 1.2X FOTG p/r 50
*1-160 p/r 25: .4X TO 1X FOTG p/r 25
1-160 PRINT RUNS B/WN 3-100 COPIES PER
*161-180 p/r 100: .4X TO 1X FOTG p/r 100
*161-180 p/r 100: .3X TO .8X FOTG p/r 50
*161-180 p/r 50: .5X TO 1.2X FOTG p/r 100
*161-180 p/r 50: .4X TO 1X FOTG p/r 50
*161-180 p/r 25: .5X TO 1.2X FOTG p/r 50
*161-180 p/r 25: .4X TO 1X FOTG p/r 25
161-180 PRINTS B/WN 5-100 COPIES PER
OVERALL AU-GU ODDS 4 PER BOX
NO PRICING ON QTY OF 10 OR LESS
111 Sandy Koufax Jsy/25 75.00 150.00
161 Babe Ruth Pants 300.00 500.00
Jim Thorpe Jsy/25
164 Whitey Ford Jsy 75.00 150.00
Sandy Koufax Jsy/25

2005 Leaf Certified Materials Fabric of the Game Reward

*1-160 p/r 50: .5X TO 1.2X FOTG p/r 100
*1-160 p/r 50: .4X TO 1X FOTG p/r 50
*1-160 p/r 50: .3X TO .8X FOTG p/r 25
*1-160 p/r 25: .6X TO 1.5X FOTG p/r 100
*1-160 p/r 25: .5X TO 1.2X FOTG p/r 50
*1-160 p/r 25: .4X TO 1X FOTG p/r 25
1-160 PRINT RUNS B/WN 3-100 COPIES PER
*161-180 p/r 50: .5X TO 1.2X FOTG p/r 100
*161-180 p/r 50: .4X TO 1X FOTG p/r 50
*161-180 p/r 25: .5X TO 1.2X FOTG p/r 50
*161-180 p/r 25: .4X TO 1X FOTG p/r 25
161-180 PRINTS B/WN 10-50 COPIES PER
OVERALL AU-GU ODDS 4 PER BOX
NO PRICING ON QTY OF 10 OR LESS
111 Sandy Koufax Jsy/25 75.00 150.00
161 Babe Ruth Pants 300.00 500.00
Jim Thorpe Jsy/25
163 Willie Mays Pants 20.00 50.00
Bob Gibson Jsy/25
164 Whitey Ford Jsy 75.00 150.00
Sandy Koufax Jsy/25

2005 Leaf Certified Materials Fabric of the Game Stats

*1-160 p/r 75: .4X TO 1X FOTG p/r 100
*1-160 p/r 75: .3X TO .8X FOTG p/r 50
*1-160 p/r 75: .25X TO .6X FOTG p/r 25
*1-160 p/r 50: .5X TO 1.2X FOTG p/r 100
*1-160 p/r 50: .4X TO 1X FOTG p/r 50
*1-160 p/r 25: .6X TO 1.5X FOTG p/r 100
*1-160 p/r 25: .5X TO 1.2X FOTG p/r 50
*1-160 p/r 25: .4X TO 1X FOTG p/r 25
1-160 PRINT RUNS B/WN 3-75 COPIES PER
*161-180 p/r 50: .5X TO 1.2X FOTG p/r 100
*161-180 p/r 50: .4X TO 1X FOTG p/r 50
*161-180 p/r 25: .5X TO 1.2X FOTG p/r 50
*161-180 p/r 25: .4X TO 1X FOTG p/r 25
161-180 PRINTS B/WN 10-50 COPIES PER
OVERALL AU-GU ODDS 4 PER BOX
NO PRICING ON QTY OF 10 OR LESS
111 Sandy Koufax Jsy/25 75.00 150.00
142 Stan Musial Jsy/25 10.00 25.00
161 Babe Ruth Pants 300.00 500.00
Jim Thorpe Jsy/25
163 Willie Mays Pants 20.00 50.00
Bob Gibson Jsy/25
164 Whitey Ford Jsy 75.00 150.00
Sandy Koufax Jsy/25

2005 Leaf Certified Materials Fabric of the Game Prime

*1-160 p/r 25: 1X TO 2.5X FOTG p/r 100
*1-160 p/r 25: .75X TO 2X FOTG p/r 50
*1-160 p/r 25: .6X TO 1.5X FOTG p/r 25
*1-160 p/r 25: .5X TO 1.2X FOTG p/r 15
*1-160 p/r 17-18: .75X TO 2X FOTG p/r 50
*1-160 p/r 17-18: .6X TO 1.5X FOTG p/r 25
1-160 PRINT RUNS B/WN 5-25 COPIES PER
161-180 PRINTS B/WN 3-5 COPIES PER
OVERALL AU-GU ODDS 4 PER BOX
NO PRICING ON QTY OF 13 OR LESS
36 Dwight Evans Jsy/25 10.00 25.00
69 Keith Hernandez Jsy/25 8.00 20.00
81 Mike Schmidt Jsy/25

2005 Leaf Certified Materials Fabric of the Game Autograph

OVERALL AU-GU ODDS 4 PER BOX
STATED PRINT RUN 1 SERIAL #'d SET
NO PRICING DUE TO SCARCITY

2005 Leaf Certified Materials Fabric of the Game Autograph Jersey Number

OVERALL AU-GU ODDS 4 PER BOX
STATED PRINT RUN 1 SERIAL #'d SET
NO PRICING DUE TO SCARCITY

2005 Leaf Certified Materials Fabric of the Game Autograph Position

OVERALL AU-GU ODDS 4 PER BOX
STATED PRINT RUN 1 SERIAL #'d SET
NO PRICING DUE TO SCARCITY

2005 Leaf Certified Materials Fabric of the Game Autograph Reward

OVERALL AU-GU ODDS 4 PER BOX
STATED PRINT RUN 1 SERIAL #'d SET
NO PRICING DUE TO SCARCITY

2005 Leaf Certified Materials Fabric of the Game Autograph Stats

OVERALL AU-GU ODDS 4 PER BOX
STATED PRINT RUN 1 SERIAL #'d SET
NO PRICING DUE TO SCARCITY

2005 Leaf Certified Materials Fabric of the Game Autograph Prime

OVERALL AU-GU ODDS 4 PER BOX
STATED PRINT RUN 1 SERIAL #'d SET
NO PRICING DUE TO SCARCITY

2005 Leaf Certified Materials Gold Team

STATED ODDS 1:7
*MIRROR: 1.25X TO 3X BASIC
MIRROR RANDOM INSERTS IN PACKS
1 Albert Pujols 2.50 6.00
2 Alex Rodriguez 1.50 4.00
3 Carlos Beltran Astros .40 1.00
4 Chipper Jones 1.00 2.50
5 Curt Schilling .60 1.50
6 Derek Jeter 2.50 6.00
7 Greg Maddux 1.50 4.00
8 Hank Blalock .40 1.00
9 Ichiro Suzuki 1.50 4.00
10 Ivan Rodriguez .60 1.50
11 Jim Thome .60 1.50
12 Ken Griffey Jr. 1.50 4.00
13 Lyle Overbay .40 1.00
14 Manny Ramirez 1.00 2.50
15 Mark Mulder A's .40 1.00
16 Mark Prior .60 1.50
17 Michael Young .60 1.50
18 Miguel Cabrera 1.00 2.50
19 Mike Piazza 1.00 2.50
20 Pedro Martinez .60 1.50
21 Randy Johnson M's 1.00 2.50
22 Roger Clemens 1.25 3.00
23 Sammy Sosa Cubs 1.00 2.50
24 Tim Hudson A's .60 1.50
25 Todd Helton .60 1.50

2005 Leaf Certified Materials Gold Team Autograph

OVERALL AU-GU ODDS 4 PER BOX
PRINT RUNS B/WN 5-10 COPIES PER
NO PRICING DUE TO SCARCITY

2005 Leaf Certified Materials Gold Team Jersey Number

OVERALL AU-GU ODDS 4 PER BOX
PRINT RUNS B/WN 100-250 COPIES PER
1 Albert Pujols/100 8.00 20.00
3 Carlos Beltran Astros/200 2.00 5.00
4 Chipper Jones/100 4.00 10.00
5 Curt Schilling/250 2.50 6.00
7 Greg Maddux/100 5.00 12.00
8 Hank Blalock/250 2.00 5.00
10 Ivan Rodriguez/120 3.00 8.00
11 Jim Thome/250 2.50 6.00
13 Lyle Overbay/250 2.00 5.00
14 Manny Ramirez/250 2.50 6.00
15 Mark Mulder A's/250 2.00 5.00
16 Mark Prior/100 3.00 8.00
17 Michael Young/250 2.00 5.00
18 Miguel Cabrera/100 3.00 8.00
19 Mike Piazza/250 3.00 8.00
20 Pedro Martinez/100 3.00 8.00
21 Randy Johnson M's/250 3.00 8.00
22 Roger Clemens/250 4.00 10.00
23 Sammy Sosa Cubs/250 3.00 8.00
24 Tim Hudson A's/100 2.50 6.00
25 Todd Helton/100 3.00 8.00

2005 Leaf Certified Materials Gold Team Jersey Number Prime

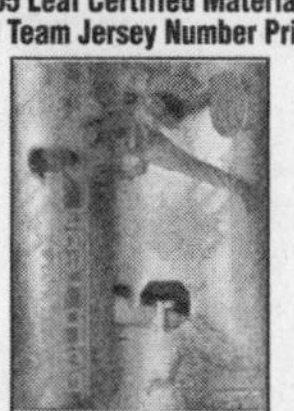

*PRIME p/r 25: 1.25X TO 3X JSY p/r 200-250
*PRIME p/r 25: 1X TO 2.5X JSY p/r 100-120
OVERALL AU-GU ODDS 4 PER BOX
PRINT RUNS B/WN 5-25 COPIES PER
NO PRICING ON QTY OF 10 OR LESS

2005 Leaf Certified Materials Skills

STATED ODDS 1:7
*MIRROR: 1.25X TO 3X BASIC
MIRROR RANDOM INSERTS IN PACKS
1 Andy Pettitte .60 1.50
2 Barry Zito .40 1.00
3 Bobby Crosby .40 1.00
4 Brandon Webb .60 1.50
5 Craig Biggio .60 1.50
6 David Ortiz 1.00 2.50
7 Dontrelle Willis .40 1.00
8 Francisco Rodriguez .60 1.50
9 Gary Sheffield .40 1.00
10 Jack Wilson .40 1.00
11 Jason Bay .40 1.00
12 Jeff Bagwell .60 1.50
13 Jim Edmonds .60 1.50
14 Josh Beckett .60 1.50
15 Kerry Wood .40 1.00
16 Lance Berkman .60 1.50
17 Mark Buehrle .60 1.50
18 Mark Teixeira 1.00 2.50
19 Miguel Tejada .60 1.50
20 Paul Konerko .60 1.50
21 Scott Rolen .60 1.50
22 Sean Burroughs .40 1.00
23 Vernon Wells .40 1.00
24 Victor Martinez .60 1.50
25 Vladimir Guerrero 1.00 2.50

2005 Leaf Certified Materials Skills Autograph

OVERALL AU-GU ODDS 4 PER BOX
PRINT RUNS B/WN 5-25 COPIES PER
NO PRICING ON QTY OF 10 OR LESS
3 Bobby Crosby/25 10.00 25.00
11 Jason Bay/25 10.00 25.00

2005 Leaf Certified Materials Skills Jersey Position

OVERALL AU-GU ODDS 4 PER BOX
PRINT RUNS B/WN 100-250 COPIES PER
1 Andy Pettitte/250 2.50 6.00
2 Barry Zito/250 2.00 5.00
3 Bobby Crosby/100 2.50 6.00
4 Brandon Webb Pants/100 2.50 6.00
5 Craig Biggio/250 2.50 6.00
6 David Ortiz/250 2.50 6.00
7 Dontrelle Willis/100 2.50 6.00
8 Francisco Rodriguez/250 2.00 5.00
9 Gary Sheffield/50 3.00 8.00
10 Jack Wilson/50 3.00 8.00
11 Jason Bay/100 2.50 6.00
12 Jeff Bagwell/250 2.50 6.00
13 Jim Edmonds/250 2.00 5.00
14 Josh Beckett/250 2.00 5.00
15 Kerry Wood/50 3.00 8.00
16 Lance Berkman/250 2.00 5.00
17 Mark Buehrle/150 2.00 5.00
19 Miguel Tejada/250 2.00 5.00
20 Paul Konerko/100 2.50 6.00
21 Scott Rolen/100 3.00 8.00
22 Sean Burroughs/100 2.50 6.00
23 Vernon Wells/250 2.00 5.00
24 Victor Martinez/250 2.00 5.00
25 Vladimir Guerrero/250 3.00 8.00

2005 Leaf Certified Materials Skills Jersey Position Prime

*PRIME p/r 25: 1.25X TO 3X JSY p/r 150-250
*PRIME p/r 25: 1X TO 2.5X JSY p/r 100
*PRIME p/r 25: .75X TO 2X JSY p/r 50
OVERALL AU-GU ODDS 4 PER BOX
PRINT RUNS B/WN 5-25 COPIES PER
NO PRICING ON QTY OF 5
18 Mark Teixeira/25 8.00 20.00

2010 Leaf Joe Jackson

This 15-card set was issued in the 2010 Leaf Sports Icons Cut Signature Edition Update product. Each box of the product included one Joe Jackson card.

COMPLETE SET (15) 20.00 50.00
COMMON JACKSON (1-15) 2.50 6.00

1994 Leaf Limited

This 160-card standard-size set was issued exclusively to hobby dealers. The set is organized alphabetically within teams with AL preceding NL.

COMPLETE SET (160) 30.00 80.00
1 Jeffrey Hammonds .20 .50
2 Ben McDonald .20 .50
3 Mike Mussina .60 1.50
4 Rafael Palmeiro .60 1.50
5 Cal Ripken Jr. 3.00 8.00
6 Lee Smith .40 1.00
7 Roger Clemens 2.00 5.00
8 Scott Cooper .20 .50
9 Andre Dawson .40 1.00
10 Mike Greenwell .20 .50
11 Aaron Sele .20 .50
12 Mo Vaughn .40 1.00
13 Brian Anderson RC .40 1.00
14 Chad Curtis .20 .50
15 Chili Davis .40 1.00
16 Gary DiSarcina .20 .50
17 Mark Langston .20 .50
18 Tim Salmon .60 1.50
19 Wilson Alvarez .20 .50
20 Jason Bere .20 .50
21 Julio Franco .40 1.00
22 Jack McDowell .20 .50
23 Tim Raines .40 1.00
24 Frank Thomas 1.00 2.50
25 Robin Ventura .40 1.00
26 Carlos Baerga .20 .50
27 Albert Belle .40 1.00
28 Kenny Lofton .40 1.00
29 Eddie Murray 1.00 2.50
30 Manny Ramirez 1.00 2.50
31 Cecil Fielder .40 1.00
32 Travis Fryman .40 1.00
33 Mickey Tettleton .20 .50
34 Alan Trammell .40 1.00
35 Lou Whitaker .40 1.00
36 David Cone .40 1.00
37 Gary Gaetti .40 1.00
38 Greg Gagne .20 .50
39 Bob Hamelin .20 .50
40 Wally Joyner .40 1.00
41 Brian McRae .20 .50
42 Ricky Bones .20 .50
43 Brian Harper .20 .50
44 John Jaha .20 .50
45 Pat Listach .20 .50
46 Dave Nilsson .20 .50
47 Greg Vaughn .20 .50
48 Kent Hrbek .40 1.00
49 Chuck Knoblauch .40 1.00
50 Shane Mack .20 .50
51 Kirby Puckett 1.00 2.50
52 Dave Winfield .40 1.00
53 Jim Abbott .60 1.50
54 Wade Boggs .60 1.50
55 Jimmy Key .40 1.00
56 Don Mattingly 2.50 6.00
57 Paul O'Neill .60 1.50
58 Danny Tartabull .20 .50
59 Dennis Eckersley .40 1.00
60 Rickey Henderson 1.00 2.50
61 Mark McGwire 2.50 6.00
62 Troy Neel .20 .50
63 Ruben Sierra .40 1.00
64 Eric Anthony .20 .50
65 Jay Buhner .40 1.00
66 Ken Griffey Jr. 1.50 4.00
67 Randy Johnson 1.00 2.50
68 Edgar Martinez .60 1.50
69 Tino Martinez .60 1.50
70 Jose Canseco .60 1.50
71 Will Clark .60 1.50
72 Juan Gonzalez .40 1.00
73 Dean Palmer .40 1.00
74 Ivan Rodriguez .60 1.50
75 Roberto Alomar .60 1.50
76 Joe Carter .40 1.00
77 Carlos Delgado .60 1.50
78 Paul Molitor .40 1.00
79 John Olerud .40 1.00
80 Devon White .40 1.00
81 Steve Avery .20 .50
82 Tom Glavine .60 1.50
83 David Justice .40 1.00
84 Roberto Kelly .20 .50
85 Ryan Klesko .40 1.00
86 Javier Lopez .40 1.00
87 Greg Maddux 1.50 4.00
88 Fred McGriff .60 1.50
89 Shawon Dunston .20 .50
90 Mark Grace .60 1.50
91 Derrick May .20 .50
92 Sammy Sosa 1.00 2.50
93 Rick Wilkins .20 .50
94 Bret Boone .40 1.00
95 Barry Larkin .60 1.50
96 Kevin Mitchell .20 .50
97 Hal Morris .20 .50
98 Deion Sanders .60 1.50
99 Reggie Sanders .40 1.00
100 Dante Bichette .40 1.00
101 Ellis Burks .40 1.00
102 Andres Galarraga .40 1.00
103 Joe Girardi .20 .50
104 Charlie Hayes .20 .50
105 Chuck Carr .20 .50
106 Jeff Conine .40 1.00
107 Bryan Harvey .20 .50
108 Benito Santiago .40 1.00
109 Gary Sheffield .40 1.00
110 Jeff Bagwell .60 1.50
111 Craig Biggio .60 1.50
112 Ken Caminiti .40 1.00
113 Andujar Cedeno .20 .50
114 Doug Drabek .20 .50
115 Luis Gonzalez .40 1.00
116 Brett Butler .40 1.00
117 Delino DeShields .20 .50
118 Eric Karros .40 1.00
119 Raul Mondesi .40 1.00
120 Mike Piazza 2.00 5.00
121 Henry Rodriguez .20 .50
122 Tim Wallach .20 .50
123 Moises Alou .40 1.00
124 Cliff Floyd .40 1.00
125 Marquis Grissom .40 1.00
126 Ken Hill .20 .50
127 Larry Walker .40 1.00
128 John Wetteland .40 1.00
129 Bobby Bonilla .40 1.00
130 John Franco .40 1.00
131 Jeff Kent .60 1.50
132 Bret Saberhagen .40 1.00
133 Ryan Thompson .20 .50
134 Darren Daulton .40 1.00
135 Mariano Duncan .20 .50
136 Lenny Dykstra .40 1.00
137 Danny Jackson .20 .50
138 John Kruk .40 1.00
139 Jay Bell .40 1.00
140 Jeff King .20 .50
141 Al Martin .20 .50
142 Orlando Merced .20 .50
143 Andy Van Slyke .60 1.50
144 Bernard Gilkey .20 .50
145 Gregg Jefferies .20 .50
146 Ray Lankford .40 1.00
147 Ozzie Smith 1.50 4.00
148 Mark Whiten .20 .50
149 Todd Zeile .20 .50
150 Derek Bell .20 .50
151 Andy Benes .20 .50
152 Tony Gwynn 1.25 3.00
153 Phil Plantier .20 .50
154 Bip Roberts .20 .50
155 Rod Beck .20 .50
156 Barry Bonds 2.50 6.00
157 John Burkett .20 .50
158 Royce Clayton .20 .50
159 Bill Swift .20 .50
160 Matt Williams .40 1.00

1994 Leaf Limited Gold All-Stars

Randomly inserted in packs at a rate of one in seven, this 18-card standard-size set features the starting players at each position in both the National and American leagues for the 1994 All-Star Game. They are identical in design to the basic Limited product except for being gold and individually numbered out of 10,000.

COMPLETE SET (18) 15.00 40.00
STATED ODDS 1:7
1 Frank Thomas .75 2.00
2 Gregg Jefferies .15 .40
3 Roberto Alomar .50 1.25
4 Mariano Duncan .15 .40
5 Wade Boggs .50 1.25
6 Matt Williams .30 .75
7 Cal Ripken Jr. 2.50 6.00
8 Ozzie Smith 1.25 3.00
9 Kirby Puckett .75 2.00
10 Barry Bonds 2.00 5.00
11 Ken Griffey Jr. 1.25 3.00
12 Tony Gwynn 1.00 2.50
13 Joe Carter .30 .75
14 David Justice .30 .75
15 Ivan Rodriguez .50 1.25
16 Mike Piazza 1.50 4.00
17 Jimmy Key .30 .75
18 Greg Maddux 1.25 3.00

1994 Leaf Limited Rookies

This 80-card standard-size premium set was issued by Donruss exclusively to hobby dealers. The set showcases top rookies and prospects of 1994. Rookie Cards in this set include Armando Benitez, Rusty Greer and Chan Ho Park.

COMPLETE SET (80) 10.00 25.00
1 Charles Johnson .30 .75
2 Rico Brogna .15 .40
3 Melvin Nieves .15 .40
4 Rich Becker .15 .40
5 Russ Davis .15 .40
6 Matt Mieske .15 .40
7 Paul Shuey .15 .40
8 Hector Carrasco .15 .40
9 J.R. Phillips .15 .40
10 Scott Ruffcorn .15 .40
11 Kurt Abbott RC .15 .40
12 Danny Bautista .15 .40
13 Rick White .15 .40
14 Steve Dunn .15 .40
15 Joe Ausanio .15 .40
16 Salomon Torres .15 .40
17 Ricky Bottalico RC .15 .40
18 Johnny Ruffin .15 .40
19 Kevin Foster RC .15 .40
20 W.VanLandingham RC .15 .40
21 Troy O'Leary .15 .40
22 Mark Acre RC .15 .40
23 Norberto Martin .15 .40
24 Jason Jacome RC .15 .40
25 Steve Trachsel .15 .40
26 Denny Hocking .15 .40
27 Mike Lieberthal .30 .75
28 Gerald Williams .15 .40
29 John Mabry RC .30 .75
30 Greg Blosser .15 .40
31 Carl Everett .30 .75
32 Steve Karsay .15 .40
33 Jose Valentin .15 .40
34 Jon Lieber .30 .75
35 Chris Gomez .15 .40
36 Jesus Tavarez RC .15 .40
37 Tony Longmire .15 .40
38 Luis Lopez .15 .40
39 Matt Walbeck .15 .40
40 Rikkert Faneyte RC .15 .40
41 Shane Reynolds .15 .40
42 Joey Hamilton .15 .40
43 Ismael Valdes RC .30 .75
44 Danny Miceli .15 .40
45 Darren Bragg RC .15 .40
46 Alex Gonzalez .15 .40
47 Rick Helling .15 .40
48 Jose Oliva .15 .40
49 Jim Edmonds .75 2.00
50 Miguel Jimenez .15 .40
51 Tony Eusebio .15 .40
52 Shawn Green .75 2.00
53 Billy Ashley .15 .40
54 Rondell White .30 .75
55 Cory Bailey RC .15 .40
56 Tim Davis .15 .40
57 John Hudek RC .15 .40
58 Darren Hall .15 .40
59 Darren Dreifort .15 .40
60 Mike Kelly .15 .40
61 Marcus Moore .15 .40
62 Garret Anderson .75 2.00
63 Brian L. Hunter .15 .40
64 Mark Smith .15 .40
65 Garey Ingram RC .15 .40
66 Rusty Greer RC .50 1.25
67 Marc Newfield .15 .40
68 Gar Finnvold .15 .40
69 Paul Spoljaric .15 .40
70 Ray McDavid .15 .40
71 Orlando Miller .15 .40
72 Jorge Fabregas .15 .40
73 Ray Holbert .15 .40
74 Armando Benitez RC .30 .75
75 Ernie Young RC .30 .75
76 James Mouton .15 .40
77 Robert Perez RC .15 .40
78 Chan Ho Park RC .50 1.25
79 Roger Salkeld .15 .40
80 Tony Tarasco .15 .40

1994 Leaf Limited Rookies Phenoms

This 10-card standard-size set was randomly inserted in Leaf Limited Rookies packs at a rate of approximately of one in twelve. This set showcases top 1994 rookies especially Alex Rodriguez. The fronts are designed much like the Limited Rookies basic set cards except the card is comprised of gold foil instead of silver on the front. Gold backs are also virtually identical to the Limited Rookies in terms of content and layout. The cards are individually numbered on back out of 5,000. The Rodriguez card, primarily because of it's status as one of A-Rod's earliest serial-numbered MLB-liscensed issues (coupled with high-end production qualities and a known print run) has become one of the more desirable cards issued in the 1990's. Collectors should take caution of trimmed copies when purchasing this card in "raw" form.

COMPLETE SET (10) 175.00 300.00
STATED ODDS 1:12
1 Raul Mondesi 3.00 8.00
2 Bob Hamelin 2.00 5.00
3 Midre Cummings 2.00 5.00
4 Carlos Delgado 4.00 10.00
5 Cliff Floyd 3.00 8.00
6 Jeffrey Hammonds 2.00 5.00
7 Ryan Klesko 3.00 8.00
8 Javier Lopez 3.00 8.00

9 Manny Ramirez 8.00 20.00
10 Alex Rodriguez 150.00 300.00

1995 Leaf Limited

This 192 standard-size card set was issued in two series. Each series contained 96 cards. These cards were issued in six-box cases with 20 packs per box and five cards per pack. Forty-five thousand boxes of each series was produced. Rookie Cards in this set include Bob Higginson and Hideo Nomo.

COMPLETE SET (192) 15.00 40.00
COMPLETE SERIES 1 (96) 8.00 20.00
COMPLETE SERIES 2 (96) 8.00 20.00
1 Frank Thomas .50 1.25
2 Geronimo Berroa .08 .25
3 Tony Phillips .08 .25
4 Roberto Alomar .30 .75
5 Steve Avery .08 .25
6 Darryl Hamilton .08 .25
7 Scott Cooper .08 .25
8 Mark Grace .30 .75
9 Billy Ashley .08 .25
10 Wil Cordero .08 .25
11 Barry Bonds 1.25 3.00
12 Kenny Lofton .20 .50
13 Jay Buhner .20 .50
14 Alex Rodriguez 1.25 3.00
15 Bobby Bonilla .20 .50
16 Brady Anderson .20 .50
17 Ken Caminiti .20 .50
18 Charlie Hayes .08 .25
19 Jay Bell .20 .50
20 Will Clark .30 .75
21 Jose Canseco .30 .75
22 Bret Boone .20 .50
23 Dante Bichette .20 .50
24 Kevin Appier .20 .50
25 Chad Curtis .08 .25
26 Marty Cordova .08 .25
27 Jason Bere .08 .25
28 Jimmy Key .20 .50
29 Rickey Henderson .50 1.25
30 Tim Salmon .30 .75
31 Joe Carter .20 .50
32 Tom Glavine .30 .75
33 Pat Listach .08 .25
34 Brian Jordan .20 .50
35 Brian McRae .08 .25
36 Eric Karros .20 .50
37 Pedro Martinez .30 .75
38 Royce Clayton .08 .25
39 Eddie Murray .50 1.25
40 Randy Johnson .50 1.25
41 Jeff Conine .20 .50
42 Brett Butler .20 .50
43 Jeffrey Hammonds .08 .25
44 Andujar Cedeno .08 .25
45 Dave Hollins .08 .25
46 Jeff King .08 .25
47 Benji Gil .08 .25
48 Roger Clemens 1.00 2.50
49 Barry Larkin .30 .75
50 Joe Girardi .08 .25
51 Bob Hamelin .08 .25
52 Travis Fryman .20 .50
53 Chuck Knoblauch .20 .50
54 Ray Durham .20 .50
55 Don Mattingly 1.25 3.00
56 Ruben Sierra .20 .50
57 J.T. Snow .20 .50
58 Derek Bell .08 .25
59 David Cone .20 .50
60 Marquis Grissom .20 .50
61 Kevin Seitzer .08 .25
62 Ozzie Smith .75 2.00
63 Rick Wilkins .08 .25
64 Hideo Nomo RC 1.25 3.00
65 Tony Tarasco .08 .25
66 Manny Ramirez .30 .75
67 Charles Johnson .20 .50
68 Craig Biggio .30 .75
69 Bobby Jones .08 .25
70 Mike Mussina .30 .75
71 Alex Gonzalez .08 .25
72 Gregg Jefferies .08 .25
73 Rusty Greer .20 .50
74 Mike Greenwell .08 .25
75 Hal Morris .08 .25
76 Paul O'Neill .30 .75
77 Luis Gonzalez .20 .50
78 Chipper Jones .50 1.25
79 Mike Piazza .75 2.00
80 Rondell White .20 .50
81 Glenallen Hill .08 .25
82 Shawn Green .20 .50
83 Bernie Williams .30 .75
84 Jim Thome .30 .75
85 Terry Pendleton .20 .50
86 Rafael Palmeiro .30 .75
87 Tony Gwynn .60 1.50
88 Mickey Tettleton .08 .25
89 John Valentin .08 .25
90 Deion Sanders .30 .75
91 Larry Walker .20 .50
92 Michael Tucker .08 .25
93 Alan Trammell .20 .50
94 Tim Raines .20 .50
95 David Justice .20 .50
96 Tino Martinez .30 .75
97 Cal Ripken Jr. 1.50 4.00
98 Deion Sanders .30 .75
99 Darren Daulton .20 .50
100 Paul Molitor .20 .50
101 Randy Myers .08 .25
102 Wally Joyner .20 .50
103 Carlos Perez RC .20 .50
104 Brian Hunter .08 .25
105 Wade Boggs .30 .75
106 Bob Higginson RC .30 .75
107 Jeff Kent .20 .50
108 Jose Offerman .08 .25
109 Dennis Eckersley .20 .50
110 Dave Nilsson .08 .25
111 Chuck Finley .20 .50
112 Devon White .20 .50
113 Bip Roberts .08 .25
114 Ramon Martinez .08 .25
115 Greg Maddux .75 2.00
116 Curtis Goodwin .08 .25
117 John Jaha .08 .25
118 Ken Griffey Jr. .75 2.00
119 Geronimo Pena .08 .25
120 Shawon Dunston .08 .25
121 Ariel Prieto RC .08 .25
122 Kirby Puckett .50 1.25
123 Carlos Baerga .08 .25
124 Todd Hundley .08 .25
125 Tim Naehring .08 .25
126 Gary Sheffield .20 .50
127 Dean Palmer .20 .50
128 Rondell White .20 .50
129 Greg Gagne .08 .25
130 Jose Rijo .08 .25
131 Ivan Rodriguez .30 .75
132 Jeff Bagwell .30 .75
133 Greg Vaughn .08 .25
134 Chili Davis .20 .50
135 Al Martin .08 .25
136 Kenny Rogers .20 .50
137 Aaron Sele .08 .25
138 Raul Mondesi .20 .50
139 Cecil Fielder .20 .50
140 Tim Wallach .08 .25
141 Andres Galarraga .20 .50
142 Lou Whitaker .20 .50
143 Jack McDowell .08 .25
144 Matt Williams .20 .50
145 Ryan Klesko .20 .50
146 Carlos Garcia .08 .25
147 Albert Belle .20 .50
148 Ryan Thompson .08 .25
149 Roberto Kelly .08 .25
150 Edgar Martinez .30 .75
151 Robby Thompson .08 .25
152 Mo Vaughn .20 .50
153 Todd Zeile .08 .25
154 Harold Baines .20 .50
155 Phil Plantier .08 .25
156 Mike Stanley .08 .25
157 Ed Sprague .08 .25
158 Moises Alou .20 .50
159 Quilvio Veras .08 .25
160 Reggie Sanders .20 .50
161 Delino DeShields .08 .25
162 Rico Brogna .08 .25
163 Greg Colbrunn .08 .25
164 Steve Finley .20 .50
165 Orlando Merced .08 .25
166 Mark McGwire 1.25 3.00
167 Garret Anderson .20 .50
168 Paul Sorrento .08 .25
169 Mark Langston .08 .25
170 Danny Tartabull .08 .25
171 Vinny Castilla .20 .50
172 Javier Lopez .20 .50
173 Bret Saberhagen .20 .50
174 Eddie Williams .08 .25
175 Scott Leius .08 .25
176 Juan Gonzalez .20 .50
177 Gary Gaetti .20 .50
178 Jim Edmonds .30 .75
179 John Olerud .20 .50
180 Lenny Dykstra .20 .50
181 Ray Lankford .20 .50
182 Ron Gant .20 .50
183 Doug Drabek .08 .25
184 Fred McGriff .30 .75
185 Andy Benes .08 .25
186 Kurt Abbott .08 .25
187 Bernard Gilkey .08 .25
188 Sammy Sosa .50 1.25
189 Lee Smith .20 .50
190 Dennis Martinez .20 .50
191 Ozzie Guillen .20 .50
192 Robin Ventura .20 .50

1995 Leaf Limited Gold

These 24 standard-size quasi-parallel cards were inserted one per series one pack. Players from both series were included in this set. While using the same design as the regular issue, they are distinguished by different photos, different numbers and gold holographic foil.

1 Frank Thomas .50 1.25
2 Jeff Bagwell .30 .75
3 Raul Mondesi .20 .50
4 Barry Bonds 1.25 3.00
5 Albert Belle .20 .50
6 Ken Griffey Jr. .75 2.00
7 Cal Ripken UER 1.50 4.00
Name spelled Ripkin on card
8 Will Clark .30 .75
9 Jose Canseco .30 .75
10 Larry Walker .20 .50
11 Kirby Puckett .50 1.25
12 Don Mattingly 1.25 3.00
13 Tim Salmon .30 .75
14 Roberto Alomar .30 .75
15 Greg Maddux .75 2.00
16 Mike Piazza .75 2.00
17 Matt Williams .20 .50
18 Kenny Lofton .20 .50
19 Alex Rodriguez UER 1.25 3.00
Name spelled Rodriquez on card
20 Tony Gwynn .60 1.50
21 Mo Vaughn .20 .50
22 Chipper Jones .50 1.25
23 Manny Ramirez .30 .75
24 Deion Sanders .30 .75

1995 Leaf Limited Bat Patrol

These 24 standard-size cards were inserted one per series two pack. The cards are numbered in the upper right corner as "X" of 24.

COMPLETE SET (24) 10.00 25.00
1 Frank Thomas .50 1.25
2 Tony Gwynn .60 1.50
3 Wade Boggs .30 .75
4 Larry Walker .20 .50
5 Ken Griffey, Jr. .75 2.00
6 Jeff Bagwell .30 .75
7 Manny Ramirez .30 .75
8 Mark Grace .30 .75
9 Kenny Lofton .20 .50
10 Mike Piazza .75 2.00
11 Will Clark .30 .75
12 Mo Vaughn .20 .50
13 Carlos Baerga .08 .25
14 Rafael Palmeiro .30 .75
15 Barry Bonds 1.25 3.00
16 Kirby Puckett .50 1.25
17 Roberto Alomar .30 .75
18 Barry Larkin .30 .75
19 Eddie Murray .50 1.25
20 Tim Salmon .30 .75
21 Don Mattingly 1.25 3.00
22 Fred McGriff .30 .75
23 Albert Belle .20 .50
24 Dante Bichette .20 .50

1995 Leaf Limited Lumberjacks

These eight standard-size cards were randomly inserted into second series packs. The cards are individually numbered out of 5,000. The fronts feature a player photo surrounded by his name, the word "Lumberjacks" and "Handcrafted" in a semi-circular pattern on a simulated wood grain stock. Please note, these cards do not feature elements of game-used material.

COMPLETE SET (16) 80.00 200.00
COMPLETE SERIES 1 (8) 40.00 100.00
COMPLETE SERIES 2 (8) 40.00 100.00
STATED ODDS 1:23
1 Albert Belle 1.50 4.00
2 Barry Bonds 10.00 25.00
3 Juan Gonzalez 1.50 4.00
4 Ken Griffey Jr. 6.00 15.00
5 Fred McGriff 2.50 6.00
6 Mike Piazza 6.00 15.00
7 Kirby Puckett 4.00 10.00
8 Mo Vaughn 1.50 4.00
9 Frank Thomas 4.00 10.00
10 Jeff Bagwell 2.50 6.00
11 Matt Williams 1.50 4.00
12 Jose Canseco 2.50 6.00
13 Raul Mondesi 1.50 4.00
14 Manny Ramirez 2.50 6.00
15 Cecil Fielder 1.50 4.00
16 Cal Ripken 12.50 30.00

1996 Leaf Limited

The 1996 Leaf Limited set was issued exclusively to hobby outlets with a maximum production run of 45,000 boxes. Each box contained two smaller mini-boxes, enabling the dealer to use his imagination in the marketing of this product. The five-card packs carried a suggested retail price of $3.24. Each Master Box was sequentially- numbered via a box topper. If this number matched the 1996 year-ending stats, the collector and the dealer both had a chance to win prizes such as a Frank Thomas game-used bat, autographed batting glove, or a "Two Biggest Weapons" poster. The collector would return the winning box number to the hobby shop, and the dealer would mail it to Donruss with both receiving the same prize. The card fronts displayed color player photos with another photo and player information on the backs.

COMPLETE SET (90) 20.00 50.00
1 Ivan Rodriguez .40 1.00
2 Roger Clemens 1.25 3.00
3 Gary Sheffield .25 .60
4 Tino Martinez .40 1.00
5 Sammy Sosa .60 1.50
6 Reggie Sanders .25 .60
7 Ray Lankford .25 .60
8 Manny Ramirez .40 1.00
9 Jeff Bagwell .40 1.00
10 Greg Maddux 1.00 2.50
11 Ken Griffey Jr. 1.00 2.50
12 Rondell White .25 .60
13 Mike Piazza 1.00 2.50
14 Marc Newfield .25 .60
15 Cal Ripken 2.00 5.00
16 Carlos Delgado .25 .60
17 Tim Salmon .40 1.00
18 Andres Galarraga .25 .60
19 Chuck Knoblauch .25 .60
20 Matt Williams .25 .60
21 Mark McGwire 1.50 4.00
22 Ben McDonald .25 .60
23 Frank Thomas .60 1.50
24 Johnny Damon .40 1.00
25 Gregg Jefferies .25 .60
26 Travis Fryman .25 .60
27 Chipper Jones .60 1.50
28 David Cone .25 .60
29 Kenny Lofton .25 .60
30 Mike Mussina .40 1.00
31 Alex Rodriguez 1.25 3.00
32 Carlos Baerga .25 .60
33 Brian Hunter .25 .60
34 Juan Gonzalez .25 .60
35 Bernie Williams .40 1.00
36 Wally Joyner .25 .60
37 Fred McGriff .40 1.00
38 Randy Johnson .60 1.50
39 Marty Cordova .25 .60
40 Garret Anderson .25 .60
41 Albert Belle .25 .60
42 Edgar Martinez .40 1.00
43 Barry Larkin .40 1.00
44 Paul O'Neill .40 1.00
45 Cecil Fielder .25 .60
46 Rusty Greer .25 .60
47 Mo Vaughn .25 .60
48 Dante Bichette .25 .60
49 Ryan Klesko .25 .60
50 Roberto Alomar .40 1.00
51 Raul Mondesi .25 .60
52 Robin Ventura .25 .60
53 Tony Gwynn .75 2.00
54 Mark Grace .40 1.00
55 Jim Thome .40 1.00
56 Jason Giambi .25 .60
57 Tom Glavine .40 1.00
58 Jim Edmonds .25 .60
59 Pedro Martinez .40 1.00
60 Charles Johnson .25 .60
61 Wade Boggs .40 1.00
62 Orlando Merced .25 .60
63 Craig Biggio .40 1.00
64 Brady Anderson .25 .60
65 Hideo Nomo .60 1.50
66 Ozzie Smith 1.00 2.50
67 Eddie Murray .60 1.50
68 Will Clark .40 1.00
69 Jay Buhner .25 .60
70 Kirby Puckett .60 1.50
71 Barry Bonds 1.50 4.00
72 Ray Durham .25 .60
73 Sterling Hitchcock .25 .60
74 John Smoltz .40 1.00
75 Andre Dawson .25 .60
76 Joe Carter .25 .60
77 Ryne Sandberg 1.00 2.50
78 Rickey Henderson .60 1.50
79 Brian Jordan .25 .60
80 Greg Vaughn .25 .60
81 Andy Pettitte .40 1.00
82 Dean Palmer .25 .60
83 Paul Molitor .25 .60
84 Rafael Palmeiro .40 1.00
85 Henry Rodriguez .25 .60
86 Larry Walker .25 .60
87 Ismael Valdes .25 .60
88 Derek Bell .25 .60
89 J.T. Snow .25 .60
90 Jack McDowell .25 .60

1996 Leaf Limited Gold

Randomly inserted into one in every 11 packs, cards from this 90-card insert set parallel the regular Leaf Limited issue. Similar in design, it differs from the regular set with its gold holographic foil treatment.

*STARS: 2.5X TO 6X BASIC CARDS
STATED ODDS 1:11

1996 Leaf Limited Lumberjacks Samples

One of ten different Leaf Limited Lumberjacks Samples cards was inserted into 1996 Leaf Limited dealer order forms and hobby media press releases. The cards parallel the standard Lumberjacks inserts except for the text "sample card" running diagonally across the front and back of the card and "PROMO/5000" text on back.

COMPLETE SET (10) 32.00 80.00
1 Ken Griffey Jr. 3.00 8.00
2 Sammy Sosa 2.00 5.00
3 Cal Ripken 6.00 15.00
4 Frank Thomas 1.25 3.00
5 Alex Rodriguez 4.00 10.00
6 Mo Vaughn .60 1.50
7 Chipper Jones 3.00 8.00
8 Mike Piazza 4.00 10.00
9 Jeff Bagwell 1.50 4.00
10 Mark McGwire 4.00 10.00

1996 Leaf Limited Lumberjacks

Printed with maple stock that puts wood grains on both sides (but does not incorporate game-used bat chips), this 10-card insert set features the league's top sluggers. The fronts carry color player photos with player information and statistics on the backs. Only 5,000 sets were produced and each card is individually numbered.

COMPLETE SET (10) 50.00 120.00
*BLACK: 1.5X TO 4X BASIC LUMBERJACK
BLACK PRINT RUN 500 SERIAL #'d SETS
1 Ken Griffey Jr. 5.00 12.00
2 Sammy Sosa 3.00 8.00
3 Cal Ripken 10.00 25.00
4 Frank Thomas 3.00 8.00
5 Alex Rodriguez 6.00 15.00
6 Mo Vaughn 1.25 3.00
7 Chipper Jones 3.00 8.00
8 Mike Piazza 5.00 12.00
9 Jeff Bagwell 2.00 5.00
10 Mark McGwire 8.00 20.00

1996 Leaf Limited Pennant Craze Promos

Issued to promote the Leaf Limited Pennant Craze insert set, these cards are differentiated from the regular Leaf Limited insert cards as they are numbered 0000/2500 on the back.

COMPLETE SET (10) 16.00 40.00
1 Juan Gonzalez .75 2.00
2 Cal Ripken 4.00 10.00
3 Frank Thomas .75 2.00
4 Ken Griffey Jr. 2.00 5.00
5 Albert Belle .30 .75
6 Greg Maddux 2.50 6.00
7 Paul Molitor 1.00 2.50
8 Alex Rodriguez 2.00 5.00
9 Barry Bonds 2.00 5.00
10 Chipper Jones 2.00 5.00

1996 Leaf Limited Pennant Craze

This 10-card insert set features 10 superstars who have a thirst for the pennant. A special flocking technique puts the felt feel of a pennant on a die cut card. Only 2,500 sets were produced and are individually numbered.

COMPLETE SET (10) 80.00 200.00
1 Juan Gonzalez 2.50 6.00
2 Cal Ripken 20.00 50.00
3 Frank Thomas 6.00 15.00
4 Ken Griffey Jr. 10.00 25.00
5 Albert Belle 2.50 6.00
6 Greg Maddux 10.00 25.00
7 Paul Molitor 2.50 6.00
8 Alex Rodriguez 12.50 30.00
9 Barry Bonds 15.00 40.00
10 Chipper Jones 6.00 15.00

1996 Leaf Limited Rookies

Randomly inserted in packs at a rate of one in seven, this 10-card set printed in silver holographic foil features some of the hottest rookies of the year. A first year card of Darin Erstad is in this set.

COMPLETE SET (10) 20.00 40.00
STATED ODDS 1:7
*GOLD: 1X TO 2.5X BASIC ROOKIES
GOLD: RANDOM INSERTS IN PACKS
1 Alex Ochoa .40 1.00
2 Darin Erstad 1.50 4.00
3 Ruben Rivera .40 1.00
4 Derek Jeter 8.00 20.00
5 Jermaine Dye .75 2.00
6 Jason Kendall .75 2.00
7 Mike Grace .40 1.00
8 Andruw Jones 1.25 3.00
9 Rey Ordonez .40 1.00
10 George Arias .40 1.00

2001 Leaf Limited

This hobby-exclusive product was released in mid-December 2001, and featured a 375-card base set that was broken into tiers as follows: 150 Base Veterans, 50 Lumberjacks (numbered to either 500, 250, or 100), 100 Rookies (numbered to either 1500 or 1000), 25 Autographed Rookies (numbered to 1000, 750, or 500), and 50 Memorabilia Rookies (see print runs below). Each pack contained three cards, and carried a $6.99 S.R.P.

COMP.SET w/o SP'S (150) 40.00 100.00
COMMON CARD (1-150) .40 1.00
COMMON HAT (326-375) 10.00 25.00
COMMON LUM/500 (151-200) 3.00 8.00
COMMON LUM/250 (151-200) 4.00 10.00
COMMON LUM/100 (151-200) 6.00 15.00
COMMON (201-250) 2.00 5.00
COMMON (251-300) 2.00 5.00
COMMON (301-325) 4.00 10.00
COMMON BASE (326-375) 6.00 15.00
COMMON BAT (326-375) 3.00 8.00
COMMON JSY (326-375) 3.00 8.00
COMMON PANTS (326-375) 3.00 8.00
COMMON SPIKES (326-375) 10.00 25.00
1 Curt Schilling .40 1.00
2 Craig Biggio .60 1.50
3 Brian Giles .40 1.00
4 Scott Brosius .40 1.00
5 Barry Larkin .60 1.50
6 Bartolo Colon .40 1.00
7 John Olerud .40 1.00
8 Cal Ripken 3.00 8.00
9 Moises Alou .40 1.00
10 Barry Zito .60 1.50
11 Ken Griffey Jr. 1.50 4.00
12 Garret Anderson .40 1.00
13 Andy Pettitte .60 1.50
14 Jim Edmonds .40 1.00
15 Tom Glavine .60 1.50
16 Jose Canseco .60 1.50
17 Fred McGriff .60 1.50
18 Robin Ventura .40 1.00
19 Tony Gwynn 1.25 3.00
20 Jeff Cirillo .40 1.00
21 Brad Radke .40 1.00
22 Ellis Burks .40 1.00
23 Scott Rolen .60 1.50
24 Rickey Henderson 1.00 2.50
25 Edgar Martinez .60 1.50
26 Kerry Wood .40 1.00
27 Al Leiter .40 1.00
28 Jose Cruz Jr. .40 1.00
29 Sean Casey .40 1.00
30 Eric Chavez .40 1.00
31 Jarrod Washburn .40 1.00
32 Gary Sheffield .40 1.00
33 Jermaine Dye .40 1.00
34 Bernie Williams .60 1.50
35 Tony Armas Jr. .40 1.00
36 Carlos Beltran .40 1.00
37 Geoff Jenkins .40 1.00
38 Shawn Green .40 1.00
39 Ryan Klesko .40 1.00
40 Richie Sexson .40 1.00
41 Pat Burrell .40 1.00
42 J.D. Drew .40 1.00
43 Larry Walker .40 1.00
44 Andres Galarraga .40 1.00
45 Tino Martinez .60 1.50
46 Rafael Furcal .40 1.00
47 Cristian Guzman .40 1.00
48 Omar Vizquel .60 1.50
49 Bret Boone .40 1.00
50 Wade Miller .40 1.00
51 Eric Milton .40 1.00
52 Gabe Kapler .40 1.00
53 Johnny Damon .60 1.50
54 Shannon Stewart .40 1.00
55 Kenny Lofton .40 1.00
56 Raul Mondesi .40 1.00
57 Jorge Posada .60 1.50
58 Mark Grace .60 1.50
59 Robert Fick .40 1.00
60 Phil Nevin .40 1.00
61 Mike Mussina .60 1.50
62 Joe Mays .40 1.00
63 Todd Helton .60 1.50
64 Tim Hudson .40 1.00
65 Manny Ramirez Sox .60 1.50
66 Sammy Sosa 1.00 2.50
67 Darin Erstad .40 1.00
68 Roberto Alomar .60 1.50
69 Jeff Bagwell .60 1.50
70 Mark McGwire 2.50 6.00
71 Jason Giambi .40 1.00
72 Cliff Floyd .40 1.00
73 Barry Bonds 2.50 6.00
74 Juan Gonzalez .40 1.00
75 Jeremy Giambi .40 1.00
76 Carlos Lee .40 1.00
77 Randy Johnson 1.00 2.50
78 Frank Thomas 1.00 2.50
79 Carlos Delgado .40 1.00
80 Pedro Martinez .60 1.50
81 Rusty Greer .40 1.00
82 Brian Jordan .40 1.00
83 Vladimir Guerrero 1.00 2.50
84 Mike Sweeney .40 1.00
85 Jose Vidro .40 1.00
86 Paul LoDuca .40 1.00
87 Matt Morris .40 1.00
88 Adrian Beltre .40 1.00
89 Aramis Ramirez .40 1.00
90 Derek Jeter 2.50 6.00
91 Rich Aurilia .40 1.00
92 Freddy Garcia .40 1.00
93 Preston Wilson .40 1.00
94 Greg Maddux 1.50 4.00
95 Miguel Tejada .40 1.00
96 Luis Gonzalez .40 1.00
97 Torii Hunter .40 1.00
98 Nomar Garciaparra 1.50 4.00
99 Jamie Moyer .40 1.00
100 Javier Vazquez .40 1.00
101 Ben Grieve .40 1.00
102 Mike Piazza 1.50 4.00
103 Paul O'Neill .60 1.50
104 Terrence Long .40 1.00
105 Charles Johnson .40 1.00
106 Rafael Palmeiro .60 1.50
107 David Cone .40 1.00
108 Alex Rodriguez 1.50 4.00
109 John Burkett .40 1.00
110 Chipper Jones 1.00 2.50
111 Ryan Dempster .40 1.00
112 Bobby Abreu .40 1.00
113 Brad Fullmer .40 1.00
114 Kazuhiro Sasaki .40 1.00
115 Mariano Rivera 1.00 2.50
116 Edgardo Alfonzo .40 1.00
117 Ray Durham .40 1.00
118 Richard Hidalgo .40 1.00
119 Jeff Weaver .40 1.00
120 Paul Konerko .40 1.00
121 Jon Lieber .40 1.00
122 Mike Hampton .40 1.00
123 Mike Cameron .40 1.00
124 Kevin Brown .40 1.00
125 Doug Mientkiewicz .40 1.00
126 Jim Thome .60 1.50
127 Corey Koskie .40 1.00
128 Trot Nixon .40 1.00
129 Darryl Kile .40 1.00
130 Ivan Rodriguez .60 1.50
131 Carl Everett .40 1.00
132 Jeff Kent .40 1.00
133 Rondell White .40 1.00
134 Chan Ho Park .40 1.00
135 Robert Person .40 1.00
136 Troy Glaus .40 1.00
137 Aaron Sele .40 1.00
138 Roger Clemens 2.00 5.00
139 Tony Clark .40 1.00
140 Mark Buehrle .60 1.50
141 David Justice .40 1.00
142 Magglio Ordonez .40 1.00
143 Bobby Higginson .40 1.00
144 Hideo Nomo 1.00 2.50
145 Tim Salmon .60 1.50
146 Mark Mulder .40 1.00
147 Troy Percival .40 1.00
148 Lance Berkman .40 1.00
149 Russ Ortiz .40 1.00
150 Andruw Jones .40 1.00
151 Mike Piazza LUM/500 6.00 15.00
152 M.Ramirez Sox LUM/500 4.00 10.00
153 B.Williams LUM/500 4.00 10.00
154 N.Garciaparra LUM/500 6.00 15.00
155 A.Galarraga LUM/500 3.00 8.00
156 K.Lofton LUM/500 3.00 8.00
157 Scott Rolen LUM/250 6.00 15.00
158 Jim Thome LUM/500 4.00 10.00
159 Darin Erstad LUM/500 3.00 8.00
160 G.Anderson LUM/500 3.00 8.00
161 A.Jones LUM/500 4.00 10.00
162 J.Gonzalez LUM/500 3.00 8.00
163 R.Palmeiro LUM/500 4.00 10.00
164 M.Ordonez LUM/500 3.00 8.00
165 Jeff Bagwell LUM/250 6.00 15.00
166 Eric Chavez LUM/500 3.00 8.00
167 Brian Giles LUM/500 3.00 8.00
168 A.Beltre LUM/500 3.00 8.00
169 T.Gwynn LUM/500 6.00 15.00
170 S.Green LUM/500 3.00 8.00
171 Todd Helton LUM/500 4.00 10.00
172 Troy Glaus LUM/100 6.00 15.00
173 L.Berkman LUM/500 3.00 8.00
174 I.Rodriguez LUM/500 4.00 10.00
175 Sean Casey LUM/500 3.00 8.00
176 A.Ramirez LUM/100 6.00 15.00
177 J.D. Drew LUM/500 3.00 8.00
178 Barry Bonds LUM/250 12.50 30.00
179 Barry Larkin LUM/500 4.00 10.00
180 Cal Ripken LUM/500 15.00 40.00
181 F.Thomas LUM/500 4.00 10.00
182 Craig Biggio LUM/250 6.00 15.00
183 Carlos Lee LUM/500 3.00 8.00
184 C. Jones LUM/500 4.00 10.00
185 Miguel Tejada LUM/250 4.00 10.00
186 Jose Vidro LUM/500 3.00 8.00
187 T.Long LUM/500 3.00 8.00
188 Moises Alou LUM/500 3.00 8.00
189 Trot Nixon LUM/500 3.00 8.00
190 S.Stewart LUM/500 3.00 8.00
191 Ryan Klesko LUM/500 3.00 8.00
192 C.Beltran LUM/500 3.00 8.00
193 V.Guerrero LUM/500 4.00 10.00
194 E.Martinez LUM/500 4.00 10.00
195 L.Gonzalez LUM/500 3.00 8.00
196 R.Hidalgo LUM/500 3.00 8.00
197 R.Alomar LUM/500 4.00 10.00
198 M.Sweeney LUM/100 6.00 15.00
199 B.Abreu LUM/250 4.00 10.00
200 Cliff Floyd LUM/500 3.00 8.00
201 Jackson Melian RC 2.00 5.00
202 Jason Jennings 2.00 5.00
203 Toby Hall 2.00 5.00
204 Jason Karnuth RC 2.00 5.00
205 Jason Smith RC 2.00 5.00
206 Mike Maroth RC 3.00 8.00
207 Sean Douglass RC 2.00 5.00
208 Adam Johnson 2.00 5.00
209 Luke Hudson RC 2.00 5.00
210 Nick Maness RC 2.00 5.00
211 Les Walrond RC 2.00 5.00
212 Travis Phelps RC 2.00 5.00
213 Carlos Garcia RC 2.00 5.00
214 Bill Ortega RC 2.00 5.00
215 Gene Altman RC 2.00 5.00
216 Nate Frese RC 2.00 5.00
217 Bob File RC 2.00 5.00
218 Steve Green RC 2.00 5.00
219 Kris Keller RC 2.00 5.00
220 Matt White RC 2.00 5.00
221 Nate Teut RC 2.00 5.00
222 Nick Johnson 2.00 5.00
223 Jeremy Fikac RC 2.00 5.00
224 Abraham Nunez 2.00 5.00
225 Mike Penney RC 2.00 5.00
226 Roy Smith RC 2.00 5.00
227 Tim Christman RC 2.00 5.00
228 Carlos Pena 2.00 5.00
229 Joe Beimel RC 2.00 5.00
230 Mike Koplove RC 2.00 5.00
231 Scott MacRae RC 2.00 5.00
232 Kyle Lohse RC 3.00 8.00
233 Jerrod Riggan RC 2.00 5.00
234 Scott Podsednik RC 6.00 15.00
235 Winston Abreu RC 2.00 5.00
236 Ryan Freel RC 3.00 8.00
237 Ken Vining RC 2.00 5.00
238 Bret Prinz RC 2.00 5.00
239 Paul Phillips RC 2.00 5.00
240 Josh Fogg RC 2.00 5.00
241 Saul Rivera RC 2.00 5.00
242 Esix Snead RC 2.00 5.00
243 John Grabow RC 2.00 5.00
244 Tony Cogan RC 2.00 5.00
245 Pedro Santana RC 2.00 5.00
246 Jack Cust 2.00 5.00
247 Joe Crede 3.00 8.00
248 Juan Moreno RC 2.00 5.00
249 Kevin Joseph RC 2.00 5.00
250 Scott Stewart RC 2.00 5.00
251 Rob Mackowiak RC 3.00 8.00
252 Luis Pineda RC 2.00 5.00
253 Bert Snow RC 2.00 5.00
254 Dustan Mohr RC 2.00 5.00
255 Justin Kaye RC 2.00 5.00
256 Chad Paronto RC 2.00 5.00
257 Nick Punto RC 2.00 5.00
258 Brian Roberts RC 3.00 8.00
259 Eric Hinske RC 3.00 8.00
260 Victor Zambrano RC 3.00 8.00
261 Juan Pena RC 2.00 5.00
262 Rick Bauer RC 2.00 5.00
263 Jorge Julio RC 2.00 5.00
264 Craig Monroe RC 3.00 8.00
265 Stubby Clapp RC 2.00 5.00
266 Martin Vargas RC 2.00 5.00
267 Josue Perez RC 2.00 5.00
268 Cody Ransom RC 2.00 5.00
269 Will Ohman RC 2.00 5.00
270 Juan Diaz RC 2.00 5.00
271 Ramon Vazquez RC 2.00 5.00
272 Grant Balfour RC 2.00 5.00
273 Ryan Jensen RC 2.00 5.00
274 Benito Baez RC 2.00 5.00
275 Angel Santos RC 2.00 5.00
276 Brian Reith RC 2.00 5.00
277 Brandon Lyon RC 2.00 5.00
278 Erik Hiljus RC 2.00 5.00
279 Brandon Knight RC 2.00 5.00
280 Jose Acevedo RC 2.00 5.00
281 Cesar Crespo RC 2.00 5.00
282 Kevin Olsen RC 2.00 5.00
283 Duaner Sanchez RC 2.00 5.00
284 Endy Chavez RC 2.00 5.00
285 Blaine Neal RC 2.00 5.00
286 Brett Jodie RC 2.00 5.00
287 Brad Voyles RC 2.00 5.00
288 Doug Nickle RC 2.00 5.00
289 Junior Spivey RC 3.00 8.00
290 Henry Mateo RC 2.00 5.00
291 Xavier Nady 2.00 5.00
292 Lance Davis RC 2.00 5.00
293 Willie Harris RC 2.00 5.00
294 Mark Lukasiewicz RC 2.00 5.00
295 Ryan Drese RC 2.00 5.00
296 Morgan Ensberg RC 3.00 8.00
297 Jose Mieses RC 2.00 5.00
298 Jason Michaels RC 2.00 5.00

299 Kris Foster RC	2.00	5.00
300 J.Duchscherer RC	2.00	5.00
301 Elpidio Guzman AU RC	4.00	10.00
302 Cory Aldridge AU RC	4.00	10.00
303 A.Berroa AU/500 RC	6.00	15.00
304 Travis Hafner AU RC	10.00	25.00
305 H.Ramirez AU RC	6.00	15.00
306 Juan Uribe AU RC	10.00	25.00
307 M.Prior AU/500 RC	10.00	25.00
308 B.Larson AU RC	4.00	10.00
309 N.Neugebauer AU/750	4.00	10.00
310 Zach Day AU/750 RC	4.00	10.00
311 Jeremy Owens AU RC	4.00	10.00
312 D.Brazelton AU/500 RC	4.00	10.00
313 B.Duckworth AU/750 RC	4.00	10.00
314 A.Hernandez AU RC	4.00	10.00
315 M.Teixeira AU/500 RC	60.00	120.00
316 Brian Rogers AU RC	4.00	10.00
317 D.Brous AU/750 RC	4.00	10.00
318 Geronimo Gil AU RC	4.00	10.00
319 Erick Almonte AU RC	4.00	10.00
320 Claudio Vargas AU RC	4.00	10.00
321 Wilkin Ruan AU RC	4.00	10.00
322 David Williams AU RC	4.00	10.00
323 Alexis Gomez AU RC	4.00	10.00
324 Mike Rivera AU RC	4.00	10.00
325 B.Berger AU RC	4.00	10.00
326 Keith Ginter Bat/125	10.00	25.00
327 Brandon Inge Bat/700	3.00	8.00
328 B.Abernathy Bat/700	3.00	8.00
329 B.Sylvester Bat/700 RC	3.00	8.00
330 B.Miadich Jsy/500 RC	3.00	8.00
331 T.Shinjo Jsy/500 RC	4.00	10.00
332 E.Valent Spikes/125	10.00	25.00
333 Dee Brown Jsy/500	3.00	8.00
334 A.Torres Spikes/125 RC	10.00	25.00
335 Timo Perez Bat/700	3.00	8.00
336 C.Izturis Pants/650	3.00	8.00
337 P.Feliz Spikes/125	10.00	25.00
338 Jason Hart Bat/200	4.00	10.00
339 G.Miller Bat/700 RC	3.00	8.00
340 Eric Munson Bat/700	3.00	8.00
341 Aubrey Huff Jsy/450	3.00	8.00
342 W.Caceres Bat/700 RC	3.00	8.00
343 A.Escobar Pants/650	3.00	8.00
344 B.Lawrence Bat/700 RC	3.00	8.00
345 Adam Pettyjohn Pants/650 RC	3.00	8.00
346 D.Mendez Bat/700 RC	3.00	8.00
347 Carlos Valderrama Jsy/250 RC	4.00	10.00
348 C.Parker Pants/650 RC	3.00	8.00
349 C.Miller Jsy/500 RC	3.00	8.00
350 M.Cuddyer Jsy/500	3.00	8.00
351 Adam Dunn Bat/500	4.00	10.00
352 J.Beckett Pants/650	4.00	10.00
353 Juan Cruz Jsy/500 RC	3.00	8.00
354 Ben Sheets Jsy/400	4.00	10.00
355 Roy Oswalt Bat/100	15.00	40.00
356 R.Soriano Pants/650 RC	3.00	8.00
357 R.Rodriguez Pants/650 RC	3.00	8.00
358 J.Rollins Base/300	6.00	15.00
359 C.C. Sabathia Jsy/500	3.00	8.00
360 B.Smith Jsy/500 RC	3.00	8.00
361 Jose Ortiz Hat/100	10.00	25.00
362 Marcus Giles Jsy/400	3.00	8.00
363 J.Wilson Hat/100 RC	10.00	25.00
364 W.Betemit Hat/100 RC	10.00	25.00
365 C.Patterson Pants/650	3.00	8.00
366 J.Gibbons Spikes/125 RC	15.00	40.00
367 A.Pujols Jsy/250 RC	150.00	300.00
368 J.Kennedy Hat/100 RC	10.00	25.00
369 A.Soriano Hat/100	15.00	40.00
370 D.James Pants/650 RC	3.00	8.00
371 J.Towers Pants/650 RC	4.00	10.00
372 J.Affeldt Pants/650 RC	3.00	8.00
373 Tim Redding Jsy/500	3.00	8.00
374 I.Suzuki Base/100 RC	400.00	600.00
375 J.Estrada Bat/100 RC	10.00	25.00

2003 Leaf Limited

This 204 card set was issued in two separate series. The primary Leaf Limited product - containing cards 1-200 from the basic set - was released in September, 2003. The set was issued in four card packs with an $70 SRP which came four packs to a box and 10 boxes to a case. The first 150 cards feature active veteran players and were issued to a stated print run of 999 serial numbered sets. Cards numbered 151 through 170 feature retired greats and were randomly inserted into packs and issued to a stated print run of 399 serial numbered sets. Cards numbered 171 through 200 are entitled Phenoms and feature rookie players, most of whom signed their cards and most of those cards were issued to a stated print run of 99 serial numbered sets. Cards number 174 and 199 are not autographed and those cards just feature game-used pieces of memorabilia. Cards 201-204 were randomly seeded within packs of DLP Rookies and Traded released in December, 2003. Each of these Update cards was signed by the featured athltete, serial-numbered to 99 copies and continued the Phenoms subset established in cards 171-200.

COMMON CARD (1-151) 1.25 3.00
1-151 PRINT RUN 999 SERIAL #'d SETS
COMMON CARD (151-170) 1.50 4.00
151-170 RANDOM INSERTS IN PACKS
151-170 PRINT RUN 399 SERIAL #'d SETS
COMMON AU GU (171-200) 6.00 15.00
AU GU 171-200 PRINT 99 SERIAL #'d SETS
GU 174/199 PRINT RUN 99 SERIAL #'d SETS
COMMON AU (171-204) p/r 99 6.00 15.00
AU 171-204 PRINT B/WN 49-99 COPIES PER
171-200 RANDOM INSERTS IN PACKS
201-204 RANDOM IN DLP R/T PACKS
A EQUALS AWAY UNIFORM IMAGE
H EQUALS HOME UNIFORM IMAGE

1 Derek Jeter Btg	3.00	8.00
2 Eric Chavez	1.25	3.00
3 Alex Rodriguez Rgr A	2.50	6.00
4 Miguel Tejada Fldg	1.25	3.00
5 Nomar Garciaparra H	1.50	4.00
6 Jeff Bagwell H	1.25	3.00
7 Jim Thome Phils A	1.25	3.00
8 Pat Burrell w/Bat	1.25	3.00
9 Albert Pujols H	3.00	8.00
10 Juan Gonzalez Rgr Btg	1.25	3.00
11 Shawn Green Jays	1.25	3.00
12 Craig Biggio H	1.25	3.00
13 Chipper Jones H	1.50	4.00
14 H.Nomo Dodgers	1.50	4.00
15 Vernon Wells	1.25	3.00
16 Gary Sheffield	1.25	3.00
17 Barry Larkin	1.25	3.00
18 Josh Beckett White	1.25	3.00
19 Edgar Martinez A	1.25	3.00
20 I.Rodriguez Marlins	1.25	3.00
21 Jeff Kent Astros	1.25	3.00
22 Roberto Alomar Mets A	1.25	3.00
23 Alfonso Soriano A	1.25	3.00
24 Jim Thome Indians H	1.25	3.00
25 J.Gonzalez Indians Btg	1.25	3.00
26 Carlos Beltran	1.25	3.00
27 S.Green Dodgers H	1.25	3.00
28 Tim Hudson H	1.25	3.00
29 Deion Sanders	1.25	3.00
30 Rafael Palmeiro O's	1.25	3.00
31 Todd Helton H	1.25	3.00
32 L.Berkman No Socks	1.25	3.00
33 M.Mussina Yanks H	1.25	3.00
34 Kazuhisa Ishii H	1.25	3.00
35 Pat Burrell Run	1.25	3.00
36 Miguel Tejada Btg	1.25	3.00
37 J.Gonzalez Rgr Stand	1.25	3.00
38 Roberto Alomar Mets H	1.25	3.00
39 R.Alom Indians Bunt	1.25	3.00
40 Luis Gonzalez	1.25	3.00
41 Jorge Posada	1.25	3.00
42 Mark Mulder Leg	1.25	3.00
43 Sammy Sosa H	1.50	4.00
44 Mark Prior H	1.25	3.00
45 R.Clemens Yanks H	3.00	8.00
46 Tom Glavine Mets H	1.25	3.00
47 Mark Teixeira A	1.25	3.00
48 Manny Ramirez H	1.25	3.00
49 Frank Thomas Swing	1.50	4.00
50 Troy Glaus White	1.25	3.00
51 Andruw Jones H	1.25	3.00
52 J.Giambi Yanks H	1.25	3.00
53 Jim Thome Phils H	1.25	3.00
54 Barry Bonds H	4.00	10.00
55 R.Palmeiro Rgr A	1.25	3.00
56 Edgar Martinez H	1.25	3.00
57 Vladimir Guerrero H	1.50	4.00
58 Roberto Alomar O's	1.25	3.00
59 Mike Sweeney	1.25	3.00
60 Magglio Ordonez A	1.25	3.00
61 Ken Griffey Jr. Btg	2.50	6.00
62 Craig Biggio A	1.25	3.00
63 Greg Maddux H	2.50	6.00
64 Mike Piazza Mets H	2.50	6.00
65 T.Glavine Braves A	1.25	3.00
66 Kerry Wood H	1.25	3.00
67 Frank Thomas Arms	1.50	4.00
68 M.Mussina Yanks A	1.25	3.00
69 Nick Johnson H	1.25	3.00
70 Bernie Williams H	1.25	3.00
71 Scott Rolen	1.25	3.00
72 C.Schill D'backs Leg	1.25	3.00
73 Adam Dunn A	1.25	3.00
74 Roy Oswalt A	1.25	3.00
75 P.Martinez Sox H	1.25	3.00
76 Tom Glavine Mets A	1.25	3.00
77 Torii Hunter Swing	1.25	3.00
78 Austin Kearns	1.25	3.00
79 R.Johnson D'backs A	1.50	4.00
80 Bernie Williams A	1.25	3.00
81 Ichiro Suzuki Btg	3.00	8.00
82 Kerry Wood A	1.25	3.00
83 Kazuhisa Ishii A	1.25	3.00
84 R.Johnson Astros	1.50	4.00
85 Nick Johnson A	1.25	3.00
86 J.Beckett Pinstripe	1.25	3.00
87 Curt Schilling Phils	1.25	3.00
88 Mike Mussina O's	1.25	3.00
89 P.Martinez Dodgers	1.25	3.00
90 Barry Zito A	1.25	3.00
91 Jim Edmonds	1.25	3.00
92 R.Henderson Sox	1.50	4.00
93 R.Henderson Padres	1.50	4.00
94 R.Henderson M's	1.50	4.00
95 R.Henderson Mets	1.50	4.00
96 R.Henderson Jays	1.50	4.00
97 R.Johnson M's Arm Up	1.50	4.00
98 Mark Grace	1.25	3.00
99 P.Martinez Expos	1.25	3.00
100 Hee Seop Choi	1.25	3.00
101 Ivan Rodriguez Rgr	1.25	3.00
102 Jeff Kent Giants	1.25	3.00
103 Hideo Nomo Sox	1.50	4.00
104 Hideo Nomo Mets	1.50	4.00
105 Mike Piazza Dodgers	2.50	6.00
106 T.Glavine Braves H	1.25	3.00
107 R.Alom Indians Swing	1.25	3.00
108 Roger Clemens Sox	3.00	8.00
109 Jason Giambi A's H	1.25	3.00
110 Jim Thome Indians A	1.25	3.00
111 Alex Rodriguez M's H	2.50	6.00
112 J.Gonz Indians Hands	1.25	3.00
113 Torii Hunter Crouch	1.25	3.00
114 Roy Oswalt H	1.25	3.00
115 C.Schill D'backs Throw	1.25	3.00
116 Magglio Ordonez H	1.25	3.00
117 R.Palmeiro Rgr H	1.25	3.00
118 Andruw Jones A	1.25	3.00
119 Manny Ramirez A	1.25	3.00
120 Mark Teixeira H	1.25	3.00
121 Mark Mulder Stance	1.25	3.00
122 Garret Anderson	1.25	3.00
123 Tim Hudson A	1.25	3.00
124 Todd Helton A	1.25	3.00
125 Troy Glaus Pinstripe	1.25	3.00
126 Derek Jeter Run	3.00	8.00
127 Barry Bonds A	4.00	10.00
128 Greg Maddux A	2.50	6.00
129 R.Clemens Yanks A	3.00	8.00
130 Nomar Garciaparra A	1.50	4.00
131 Mike Piazza Mets A	2.50	6.00
132 Alex Rodriguez Rgr H	2.50	6.00
133 Ichiro Suzuki Run	3.00	8.00
134 R.Johnson D'backs H	1.50	4.00
135 Sammy Sosa A	1.50	4.00
136 Ken Griffey Jr. Fldg	2.50	6.00
137 Alfonso Soriano H	1.25	3.00
138 J.Giambi Yanks A	1.25	3.00
139 Albert Pujols A	3.00	8.00
140 Chipper Jones A	1.50	4.00
141 Adam Dunn H	1.25	3.00
142 P.Martinez Sox A	1.25	3.00
143 Vladimir Guerrero A	1.50	4.00
144 Mark Prior A	1.25	3.00
145 Barry Zito H	1.25	3.00
146 Jeff Bagwell A	1.25	3.00
147 Lance Berkman Socks	1.25	3.00
148 S.Green Dodgers A	1.25	3.00
149 Jason Giambi A's A	1.25	3.00
150 R.Johnson M's Arm Out	1.50	4.00
151 Alex Rodriguez M's A	2.50	6.00
152 Babe Ruth	4.00	10.00
153 Ty Cobb	2.50	6.00
154 Jackie Robinson	2.00	5.00
155 Lou Gehrig	3.00	8.00
156 Thurman Munson	2.00	5.00
157 Roberto Clemente	4.00	10.00
158 Nolan Ryan Rgr	4.00	10.00
159 Nolan Ryan Angels	4.00	10.00
160 Nolan Ryan Astros	4.00	10.00
161 Cal Ripken	6.00	15.00
162 Don Mattingly	3.00	8.00
163 Stan Musial	3.00	8.00
164 Tony Gwynn	3.00	8.00
165 Yogi Berra	2.00	5.00
166 Johnny Bench	2.00	5.00
167 Mike Schmidt	3.00	8.00
168 George Brett	3.00	8.00
169 Ryne Sandberg	3.00	8.00
170 Ernie Banks	2.00	5.00
171 J.Bonder A PH AU Jsy RC	30.00	60.00
172 J.Contreras A PH AU RC	15.00	40.00
173 C.Wang PH AU RC	100.00	200.00
174 H.Matsui H PH Base RC	10.00	25.00
175 H.Kuo PH AU Bat RC	100.00	175.00
176 B.Webb A PH AU Bat RC	12.50	30.00
177 Rich Fischer PH AU RC	6.00	15.00
178 R.Hammock PH AU Bat RC	6.00	15.00
179 T.Welle Stance PH AU/49 RC	10.00	25.00
180 P.Redman PH AU Bat RC	6.00	15.00
181 Nook Logan PH AU RC	10.00	25.00
182 Craig Brazell PH AU RC	6.00	15.00
183 Tim Olson PH AU Bat RC	6.00	15.00
184 Matt Kata PH AU Bat RC	6.00	15.00
185 Alej Machado PH AU RC	6.00	15.00
186 Mike Hessman PH AU RC	6.00	15.00
187 Oscar Villarreal PH AU RC	6.00	15.00
188 G.Quiroz PH AU Bat RC	6.00	15.00
189 M.Hernandez PH AU RC	6.00	15.00
190 C.Barmes H PH AU Bat RC	10.00	25.00
191 P.LaForest PH AU Bat RC	6.00	15.00
192 Adam Loewen PH AU RC	15.00	40.00
193 T.Sledge PH AU Bat RC	6.00	15.00
194 Lew Ford PH AU Bat RC	10.00	25.00
195 T.Welle Throw PH AU/49 RC	10.00	25.00
196 C.Barmes A PH AU Bat RC	10.00	25.00
197 J.Bonder H PH AU Jsy RC	30.00	60.00
198 B.Webb H PH AU Jsy RC	12.50	30.00
199 H.Matsui A PH Base RC	10.00	25.00
200 J.Contreras H PH AU RC	15.00	40.00
201 Delmon Young PH AU RC	150.00	250.00
202 Rickie Weeks PH AU RC	50.00	100.00
203 Edwin Jackson PH AU RC	6.00	15.00
204 Dan Haren PH AU RC	15.00	40.00
NNO Roger Clemens Jeremy Bonderman Jumbo/900		

2003 Leaf Limited Gold Spotlight

*GOLD 1-151: 1.25X TO 3X BASIC
*GOLD 152-170: 1.25X TO 3X BASIC
1-170 PRINT RUN 50 SERIAL #'d SETS
171-204 PRINT RUN 25 SERIAL #'d SETS
179/195/202 PRINT RUN 10 SERIAL #'d PER
171-204 NO PRICING DUE TO SCARCITY

2003 Leaf Limited Silver Spotlight

*SILVER 1-151: .75X TO 2X BASIC
*SILVER 152-170: .75X TO 2X BASIC
1-170 PRINT RUN 100 SERIAL #'d SETS
*SILVER AU GU 171-200: .5X TO 1.2X
*SILVER GU 174/199: .6X TO 1.5X
*SILVER AU 171-204 p/r 50: .5X TO 1.2X
171-204 PRINT RUN 50 SERIAL #'d SETS
179/195 PRINT 29 SERIAL #'d COPIES PER
CARD 202 PRINT RUN 25 SERIAL #'d COPIES
NO PRICING ON QTY OF 29 OR LESS

171 J.Bonderman A PH AU Jsy	40.00	80.00
173 Chien-Ming Wang PH AU	125.00	250.00
174 Hideki Matsui H PH Base	15.00	40.00
175 Hong-Chih Kuo PH AU Bat	200.00	400.00
190 C.Barmes H PH AU Bat	20.00	40.00
196 C.Barmes A PH AU Bat	20.00	40.00
197 J.Bonderman H PH AU Jsy	40.00	80.00
199 Hideki Matsui A PH Base	15.00	40.00
201 Delmon Young PH AU	175.00	300.00

2003 Leaf Limited Moniker

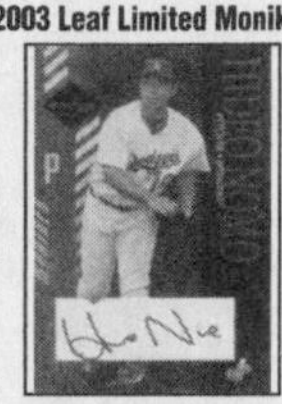

PRINT RUNS B/WN 1-10 COPIES PER
NO PRICING DUE TO SCARCITY

2003 Leaf Limited Moniker Bat

PRINT RUNS B/WN 1-25 COPIES PER
NO PRICING ON QTY OF 10 OR LESS

2003 Leaf Limited Moniker Jersey

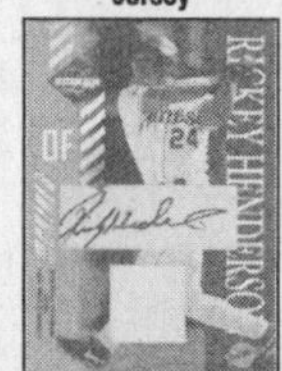

PRINT RUNS B/WN 1-25 COPIES PER
NO PRICING ON QTY OF 10 OR LESS

2003 Leaf Limited Moniker Jersey Number

PRINT RUNS B/WN 1-25 COPIES PER
NO PRICING ON QTY OF 10 OR LESS

2003 Leaf Limited Moniker Jersey Position

PRINT RUNS B/WN 1-25 COPIES PER
NO PRICING ON QTY OF 10 OR LESS

2003 Leaf Limited Threads

PRINT RUNS B/WN 5-100 COPIES PER
NO PRICING ON QTY OF 10 OR LESS

1 Derek Jeter Btg Base/50	15.00	40.00
2 Eric Chavez/25	6.00	15.00
3 Alex Rodriguez Rgr A/100	6.00	15.00
4 Miguel Tejada Fldg/50	4.00	10.00
5 Nomar Garciaparra H/100	6.00	15.00
6 Jeff Bagwell H/50	6.00	15.00
7 Jim Thome Phils A/50	6.00	15.00
8 Pat Burrell w/Bat/25	6.00	15.00
9 Albert Pujols H/100	10.00	25.00
10 Juan Gonzalez Rgr Btg/25	6.00	15.00
11 Shawn Green Jays/25	6.00	15.00
12 Craig Biggio H/25	10.00	25.00
13 Chipper Jones H/50	6.00	15.00
14 H.Nomo Dodgers/100	8.00	20.00
15 Vernon Wells/25	6.00	15.00
16 Gary Sheffield/25	6.00	15.00
17 Barry Larkin/25	10.00	25.00
18 Josh Beckett White/25	6.00	15.00
19 Edgar Martinez A/25	10.00	25.00
20 I.Rodriguez Marlins/25	10.00	25.00
21 Jeff Kent Astros/25	6.00	15.00
22 Roberto Alomar Mets A/25	10.00	25.00
23 Alfonso Soriano A/100	3.00	8.00
24 Jim Thome Indians H/25	10.00	25.00
25 J.Gonzalez Indians Btg/25	6.00	15.00
26 Carlos Beltran/25	6.00	15.00
27 S.Green Dodgers H/50	4.00	10.00
28 Tim Hudson H/25	6.00	15.00
29 Deion Sanders/25	10.00	25.00
30 Rafael Palmeiro O's/25	10.00	25.00
31 Todd Helton H/50	6.00	15.00
32 L.Berkman No Socks/25	6.00	15.00
33 M.Mussina Yanks H/50	6.00	15.00
34 Kazuhisa Ishii H/50	4.00	10.00
35 Pat Burrell Run/25	6.00	15.00
36 Miguel Tejada Btg/50	4.00	10.00
37 J.Gonzalez Rgr Stand/25	6.00	15.00
38 Roberto Alomar Mets H/25	10.00	25.00
39 R.Alom Indians Bunt/25	10.00	25.00
40 Luis Gonzalez/25	6.00	15.00
41 Jorge Posada/50	6.00	15.00
42 Mark Mulder Leg/25	6.00	15.00
43 Sammy Sosa H/100	4.00	10.00
44 Mark Prior H/50	6.00	15.00
45 R.Clemens Yanks H/100	6.00	15.00
46 Tom Glavine Mets H/25	10.00	25.00
47 Mark Teixeira A/25	10.00	25.00
48 Manny Ramirez H/50	6.00	15.00
49 Frank Thomas Swing/25	10.00	25.00
50 Troy Glaus White/50	4.00	10.00
51 Andruw Jones H/50	6.00	15.00
52 J.Giambi Yanks H/100	3.00	8.00
53 Jim Thome Phils H/50	6.00	15.00
54 Barry Bonds H Base/50	15.00	40.00
55 R.Palmeiro Rgr A/25	10.00	25.00
56 Edgar Martinez H/25	10.00	25.00
57 Vladimir Guerrero H/50	6.00	15.00
58 Roberto Alomar O's/25	10.00	25.00
59 Mike Sweeney/25	6.00	15.00
60 Magglio Ordonez A/25	6.00	15.00
62 Craig Biggio A/25	10.00	25.00
63 Greg Maddux H/100	6.00	15.00
64 Mike Piazza Mets H/100	6.00	15.00
65 T.Glavine Braves A/25	10.00	25.00
66 Kerry Wood H/25	6.00	15.00
67 Frank Thomas Arms/25	10.00	25.00
68 M.Mussina Yanks A/50	6.00	15.00
69 Nick Johnson H/25	6.00	15.00
70 Bernie Williams H/50	6.00	15.00
71 Scott Rolen/25	10.00	25.00
72 C.Schill D'backs Leg/25	6.00	15.00
73 Adam Dunn A/50	4.00	10.00
74 Roy Oswalt A/25	6.00	15.00
75 P.Martinez Sox H/50	6.00	15.00
76 Tom Glavine Mets A/25	10.00	25.00
77 Torii Hunter Swing/25	6.00	15.00
78 Austin Kearns/25	6.00	15.00
79 R.Johnson D'backs A/100	4.00	10.00
80 Bernie Williams A/50	6.00	15.00
81 Ichiro Suzuki Btg Base/50	15.00	40.00
82 Kerry Wood A/25	6.00	15.00
83 Kazuhisa Ishii A/50	4.00	10.00
84 R.Johnson Astros/50	6.00	15.00
85 Nick Johnson A/25	6.00	15.00
86 J.Beckett Pinstripe/25	6.00	15.00
87 Curt Schilling Phils/25	6.00	15.00
88 Mike Mussina O's/50	6.00	15.00
89 P.Martinez Dodgers/25	10.00	25.00
90 Barry Zito A/50	4.00	10.00
91 Jim Edmonds/100	3.00	8.00
92 R.Henderson Sox/100	4.00	10.00
93 R.Henderson Padres/50	6.00	15.00
94 R.Henderson M's/50	6.00	15.00
95 R.Henderson Mets/50	6.00	15.00
96 R.Henderson Jays/50	6.00	15.00
97 R.Johnson M's Arm Up/50	6.00	15.00
98 Mark Grace/50	6.00	15.00
99 P.Martinez Expos/25	10.00	25.00
100 Hee Seop Choi/25	6.00	15.00
101 Ivan Rodriguez Rgr/25	10.00	25.00
102 Jeff Kent Giants/25	6.00	15.00
103 Hideo Nomo Sox/5		
104 Hideo Nomo Mets/50	8.00	20.00
105 Mike Piazza Dodgers/100	6.00	15.00
106 T.Glavine Braves H/25	10.00	25.00
107 R.Alom Indians Swing/25	10.00	25.00
108 Roger Clemens Sox/100	6.00	15.00
109 Jason Giambi A's H/25	6.00	15.00
110 Jim Thome Indians A/25	10.00	25.00
111 Alex Rodriguez M's H/100	6.00	15.00
112 J.Gonz Indians Hands/25	6.00	15.00
113 Torii Hunter Crouch/25	6.00	15.00
114 Roy Oswalt H/25	6.00	15.00
115 C.Schill D'backs Throw/25	6.00	15.00
116 Magglio Ordonez H/25	6.00	15.00
117 R.Palmeiro Rgr H/25	10.00	25.00
118 Andruw Jones A/50	6.00	15.00
119 Manny Ramirez A/50	6.00	15.00
120 Mark Teixeira H/25	10.00	25.00
121 Mark Mulder Stance/25	6.00	15.00
123 Tim Hudson A/25	6.00	15.00
124 Todd Helton A/50	6.00	15.00
125 Troy Glaus Pinstripe/50	4.00	10.00
126 Derek Jeter Run Base/50	15.00	40.00
127 Barry Bonds A Base/50	15.00	40.00
128 Greg Maddux A/100	6.00	15.00
129 R.Clemens Yanks A/100	6.00	15.00
130 Nomar Garciaparra A/100	6.00	15.00
131 Mike Piazza Mets A/100	6.00	15.00
132 Alex Rodriguez Rgr H/100	6.00	15.00
133 Ichiro Suzuki Run Base/50	15.00	40.00
134 R.Johnson D'backs H/100	4.00	10.00
135 Sammy Sosa A/100	4.00	10.00
137 Alfonso Soriano H/100	3.00	8.00
138 J.Giambi Yanks A/100	3.00	8.00
139 Albert Pujols A/100	10.00	25.00
140 Chipper Jones A/25	10.00	25.00
141 Adam Dunn H/50	4.00	10.00
142 P.Martinez Sox A/50	6.00	15.00
143 Vladimir Guerrero A/50	6.00	15.00
144 Mark Prior A/50	6.00	15.00
145 Barry Zito H/50	4.00	10.00
146 Jeff Bagwell A/50	6.00	15.00
147 Lance Berkman Socks/25	6.00	15.00
148 S.Green Dodgers A/25	6.00	15.00
149 Jason Giambi A's A/25	6.00	15.00
150 R.Johnson M's Arm Out/25	10.00	25.00
151 Alex Rodriguez M's A/100	6.00	15.00
152 Babe Ruth/5		
153 Ty Cobb Pants/100	100.00	200.00
154 Jackie Robinson/50	30.00	60.00
155 Lou Gehrig/5		
156 Thurman Munson/100	10.00	25.00
157 Roberto Clemente/10		
158 Nolan Ryan Rgr/100	20.00	50.00
159 Nolan Ryan Angels/100	20.00	50.00
160 Nolan Ryan Astros/100	20.00	50.00
161 Cal Ripken/100	25.00	60.00
162 Don Mattingly/100	15.00	40.00
163 Stan Musial/100	15.00	40.00
164 Tony Gwynn/100	8.00	20.00
165 Yogi Berra/100	8.00	20.00
166 Johnny Bench/100	8.00	20.00
167 Mike Schmidt/100	15.00	40.00
168 George Brett/100	15.00	40.00
169 Ryne Sandberg/100	15.00	40.00
170 Ernie Banks/50	20.00	50.00

2003 Leaf Limited Threads Button

STATED PRINT RUN 6 SERIAL #'d SETS
CARD 74 OSWALT PRINT RUN 2 CARDS
CARD 100 CHOI PRINT RUN 5 CARDS
NO PRICING DUE TO SCARCITY

2003 Leaf Limited Threads Double

PRINT RUNS B/WN 5-25 COPIES PER
NO PRICING ON QTY 15 OR LESS

3 A.Rod Rgr A Hat-Jsy/25	25.00	60.00
4 M.Tejada Fldg Hat-Jsy/25	10.00	25.00
9 Albert Pujols H Hat-Jsy/15		
10 J.Gonz Rgr Btg Hat-Jsy/25	10.00	25.00
12 Craig Biggio H Hat-Jsy/25	15.00	40.00
14 H.Nomo Dgr Jsy-Pants/25	30.00	80.00
15 Vernon Wells Hat-Jsy/25	10.00	25.00
26 Carlos Beltran Hat-Jsy/25	10.00	25.00
28 Tim Hudson H Hat-Jsy/25	10.00	25.00
31 Todd Helton H Hat-Jsy/25	15.00	40.00
32 L.Berk No Socks Hat-Jsy/25	10.00	25.00
34 Kazuhisa Ishii H Hat-Jsy/25	10.00	25.00
37 J.Gonz Rgr Stand Hat-Jsy/25	10.00	25.00
43 Sammy Sosa H Hat-Jsy/25	15.00	40.00
44 Mark Prior H Hat-Jsy/25	15.00	40.00
47 Mark Teixeira A Hat-Jsy/25	15.00	40.00
51 Andruw Jones H Hat-Jsy/25	15.00	40.00
54 Barry Bonds H Ball-Base/25	30.00	80.00
55 R.Palmeiro Rgr A Hat-Jsy/25	15.00	40.00
60 M.Ordonez A Hat-Jsy/25	10.00	25.00
66 Kerry Wood H Hat-Jsy/5		
73 Adam Dunn A Hat-Jsy/25	10.00	25.00
75 P.Martinez Sox H Hat-Jsy/25	15.00	40.00
78 Austin Kearns Hat-Jsy/25	10.00	25.00
81 I.Suzuki Btg Ball-Base/25	30.00	80.00
90 Barry Zito A Hat-Jsy/25	10.00	25.00
94 R.Hend M's Hat-Jsy/25	15.00	40.00
101 I.Rodriguez Rgr Hat-Jsy/25	15.00	40.00
109 J.Giambi A's H Hat-Jsy/25	10.00	25.00
116 M.Ordonez H Hat-Jsy/25	10.00	25.00
117 R.Palmeiro Rgr H Hat-Jsy/25	15.00	40.00
118 Andruw Jones A Hat-Jsy/25	15.00	40.00
120 Mark Teixeira H Hat-Jsy/25	15.00	40.00
123 Tim Hudson A Hat-Jsy/25	10.00	25.00
124 Todd Helton A Hat-Jsy/25	15.00	40.00
127 Barry Bonds A Ball-Base/25	30.00	80.00
132 A.Rod Rgr H Hat-Jsy/25	25.00	60.00
133 I.Suzuki Run Ball-Base/25	30.00	80.00
135 Sammy Sosa A Hat-Jsy/25	15.00	40.00
141 Adam Dunn H Hat-Jsy/25	10.00	25.00
142 P.Martinez Sox A Hat-Jsy/25	15.00	40.00
144 Mark Prior A Hat-Jsy/25	15.00	40.00
145 Barry Zito H Hat-Jsy/25	10.00	25.00
146 Jeff Bagwell A Jsy-Pants/25	15.00	40.00
147 L.Berkman Socks Hat-Jsy/25	10.00	25.00
149 J.Giambi A's A Hat-Jsy/25	10.00	25.00
152 Babe Ruth Jsy-Pants/5		
155 Lou Gehrig Jsy-Pants/5		
157 Roberto Clemente Hat-Jsy/5		
158 N.Ryan Rgr Jsy-Pants/25	50.00	120.00
162 D.Mattingly Btg Glv-Jsy/25	40.00	100.00
164 Tony Gwynn Btg Glv-Jsy/25	25.00	60.00
167 Mike Schmidt Hat-Jsy/25	40.00	100.00
168 George Brett Hat-Jsy/25	40.00	100.00
169 Ryne Sandberg Hat-Jsy/25	50.00	120.00

2003 Leaf Limited Threads Double Prime

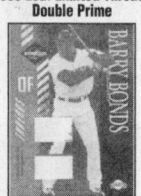

PRINT RUNS B/WN 1-10 COPIES PER
NO PRICING DUE TO SCARCITY

2003 Leaf Limited Threads Number

PRINT RUNS B/WN 1-75 COPIES PER
NO PRICING ON QTY OF 19 OR LESS

7 Jim Thome Phils A/25	10.00	25.00
18 Josh Beckett White/61	4.00	10.00
24 Jim Thome Indians H/25	10.00	25.00
25 J.Gonzalez Indians Btg/22	10.00	25.00
29 Deion Sanders/21	15.00	40.00
30 Rafael Palmeiro O's/25	10.00	25.00
33 M.Mussina Yanks H/35	10.00	25.00
40 Luis Gonzalez/20	10.00	25.00
41 Jorge Posada/20	15.00	40.00
42 Mark Mulder Leg/20	10.00	25.00
43 Sammy Sosa H/21	15.00	40.00
44 Mark Prior H/22	15.00	40.00
45 R.Clemens Yanks H/22	25.00	60.00
46 Tom Glavine Mets H/47	6.00	15.00
47 Mark Teixeira A/23	15.00	40.00
48 Manny Ramirez H/24	15.00	40.00
49 Frank Thomas Swing/35	10.00	25.00
50 Troy Glaus White/25	6.00	15.00
51 Andruw Jones H/25	10.00	25.00
52 J.Giambi Yanks H/25	6.00	15.00
53 Jim Thome Phils H/25	10.00	25.00
55 R.Palmeiro Rgr A/25	10.00	25.00
57 Vladimir Guerrero H/27	10.00	25.00
59 Mike Sweeney/29	6.00	15.00
60 Magglio Ordonez A/30	6.00	15.00
63 Greg Maddux H/31	15.00	40.00
64 Mike Piazza Mets H/31	15.00	40.00
65 T.Glavine Braves A/47	6.00	15.00
66 Kerry Wood H/52	4.00	10.00
67 Frank Thomas Arms/35	10.00	25.00
68 M.Mussina Yanks A/35	10.00	25.00
69 Nick Johnson H/36	4.00	10.00
70 Bernie Williams H/51	6.00	15.00
71 Scott Rolen/27	10.00	25.00
72 C.Schill D'backs Leg/38	4.00	10.00
73 Adam Dunn A/44	4.00	10.00
74 Roy Oswalt A/44	4.00	10.00
75 P.Martinez Sox H/45	6.00	15.00
76 Tom Glavine Mets A/47	6.00	15.00
77 Torii Hunter Swing/48	4.00	10.00
78 Austin Kearns/28	6.00	15.00
79 R.Johnson D'backs A/51	6.00	15.00
80 Bernie Williams A/51	6.00	15.00
82 Kerry Wood A/34	6.00	15.00
84 R.Johnson Astros/51	6.00	15.00
85 Nick Johnson A/36	4.00	10.00
86 J.Beckett Pinstripe/61	4.00	10.00
87 Curt Schilling Phils/38	4.00	10.00
88 Mike Mussina O's/35	10.00	25.00
89 P.Martinez Dodgers/45	6.00	15.00
90 Barry Zito A/75	4.00	10.00
92 R.Henderson Sox/35	10.00	25.00
93 R.Henderson Padres/24	15.00	40.00
94 R.Henderson M's/35	10.00	25.00
95 R.Henderson Mets/24	15.00	40.00
96 R.Henderson Jays/24	15.00	40.00
97 R.Johnson M's Arm Up/51	6.00	15.00
99 P.Martinez Expos/45	6.00	15.00
102 Jeff Kent Giants/21	10.00	25.00
105 Mike Piazza Dodgers/31	15.00	40.00
106 T.Glavine Braves H/47	6.00	15.00
108 Roger Clemens Sox/21	25.00	60.00
110 Jim Thome Indians A/25	10.00	25.00
112 J.Gonz Indians Hands/22	10.00	25.00
113 Torii Hunter Crouch/48	4.00	10.00
114 Roy Oswalt H/44	4.00	10.00
115 C.Schill D'backs Throw/38	4.00	10.00
116 Magglio Ordonez H/30	6.00	15.00
117 R.Palmeiro Rgr H/25	10.00	25.00
118 Andruw Jones A/25	10.00	25.00
119 Manny Ramirez A/24	15.00	40.00
120 Mark Teixeira H/23	15.00	40.00
121 Mark Mulder Stance/20	10.00	25.00
125 Troy Glaus Pinstripe/25	6.00	15.00
128 Greg Maddux A/31	15.00	40.00
129 R.Clemens Yanks A/22	25.00	60.00
131 Mike Piazza Mets A/31	15.00	40.00
134 R.Johnson D'backs H/51	6.00	15.00
135 Sammy Sosa A/21	15.00	40.00
138 J.Giambi Yanks A/25	6.00	15.00
141 Adam Dunn H/44	4.00	10.00
142 P.Martinez Sox A/45	6.00	15.00
143 Vladimir Guerrero A/27	10.00	25.00
145 Barry Zito H/75	4.00	10.00
150 R.Johnson M's Arm Out/51	6.00	15.00
154 Jackie Robinson/42	30.00	60.00
157 Roberto Clemente/21	60.00	120.00
158 Nolan Ryan Rgr/34	30.00	80.00
159 Nolan Ryan Angels/30	30.00	80.00
160 Nolan Ryan Astros/34	30.00	80.00
162 Don Mattingly/23	25.00	60.00
165 Yogi Berra/42	10.00	25.00
167 Mike Schmidt/20	25.00	60.00
169 Ryne Sandberg/23	30.00	80.00

2003 Leaf Limited Threads Position

2-151 PRINT RUNS 25 SERIAL #'d SETS
152-170 PRINTS B/WN 5-25 COPIES PER
NO PRICING ON QTY OF 10 OR LESS

2 Eric Chavez	6.00	15.00
3 Alex Rodriguez Rgr A	15.00	40.00
4 Miguel Tejada Fldg	6.00	15.00
5 Nomar Garciaparra H	15.00	40.00
6 Jeff Bagwell H	10.00	25.00
7 Jim Thome Phils A	10.00	25.00
8 Pat Burrell w/Bat	6.00	15.00
9 Albert Pujols H	25.00	60.00
10 Juan Gonzalez Rgr Btg	6.00	15.00
11 Shawn Green Jays	6.00	15.00
12 Craig Biggio H	10.00	25.00
13 Chipper Jones H	10.00	25.00
14 Hideo Nomo Dodgers	20.00	50.00
15 Vernon Wells	6.00	15.00
16 Gary Sheffield	6.00	15.00
17 Barry Larkin	10.00	25.00

18 Josh Beckett White 6.00 15.00
19 Edgar Martinez A 10.00 25.00
20 Ivan Rodriguez Marlins 10.00 25.00
21 Jeff Kent Astros 6.00 15.00
22 Roberto Alomar Mets A 10.00 25.00
23 Alfonso Soriano A 6.00 15.00
24 Jim Thome Indians H 10.00 25.00
25 J.Gonzalez Indians Btg 6.00 15.00
26 Carlos Beltran 6.00 15.00
27 S.Green Dodgers H 6.00 15.00
28 Tim Hudson H 6.00 15.00
29 Deion Sanders 10.00 25.00
30 Rafael Palmeiro O's 10.00 25.00
31 Todd Helton H 10.00 25.00
32 L.Berkman No Socks 6.00 15.00
33 Mike Mussina Yanks H 10.00 25.00
34 Kazuhisa Ishii H 6.00 15.00
35 Pat Burrell Run 6.00 15.00
36 Miguel Tejada Btg 6.00 15.00
37 J.Gonzalez Rgr Stand 6.00 15.00
38 Roberto Alomar Mets H 10.00 25.00
39 R.Alomar Indians Bunt 10.00 25.00
40 Luis Gonzalez 6.00 15.00
41 Jorge Posada 10.00 25.00
42 Mark Mulder Leg 6.00 15.00
43 Sammy Sosa H 10.00 25.00
44 Mark Prior H 10.00 25.00
45 R.Clemens Yanks H 15.00 40.00
46 Tom Glavine Mets H 10.00 25.00
47 Mark Teixeira A 10.00 25.00
48 Manny Ramirez H 10.00 25.00
49 Frank Thomas Swing 10.00 25.00
50 Troy Glaus White 6.00 15.00
51 Andruw Jones H 10.00 25.00
52 Jason Giambi Yanks H 10.00 25.00
53 Jim Thome Phils H 10.00 25.00
55 Rafael Palmeiro Rgr A 10.00 25.00
56 Edgar Martinez H 10.00 25.00
57 Vladimir Guerrero H 10.00 25.00
58 Roberto Alomar O's 10.00 25.00
59 Mike Sweeney 6.00 15.00
60 Magglio Ordonez A 6.00 15.00
62 Craig Biggio A 10.00 25.00
63 Greg Maddux H 15.00 40.00
64 Mike Piazza Mets H 15.00 40.00
65 T.Glavine Braves A 10.00 25.00
66 Kerry Wood H 6.00 15.00
67 Frank Thomas Arms 10.00 25.00
68 Mike Mussina Yanks A 10.00 25.00
69 Nick Johnson H 6.00 15.00
70 Bernie Williams H 10.00 25.00
71 Scott Rolen 10.00 25.00
72 C.Schilling D'backs Leg 6.00 15.00
73 Adam Dunn A 6.00 15.00
74 Roy Oswalt A 6.00 15.00
75 Pedro Martinez Sox H 10.00 25.00
76 Tom Glavine Mets A 10.00 25.00
77 Torii Hunter Swing 6.00 15.00
78 Austin Kearns 6.00 15.00
79 R.Johnson D'backs A 10.00 25.00
80 Bernie Williams A 10.00 25.00
82 Kerry Wood A 6.00 15.00
83 Kazuhisa Ishii A 6.00 15.00
84 Randy Johnson Astros 10.00 25.00
85 Nick Johnson A 6.00 15.00
86 J.Beckett Pinstripe 6.00 15.00
87 Curt Schilling Phils 6.00 15.00
88 Mike Mussina O's 10.00 25.00
89 P.Martinez Dodgers 10.00 25.00
90 Barry Zito A 6.00 15.00
91 Jim Edmonds 6.00 15.00
92 R.Henderson Sox 10.00 25.00
93 R.Henderson Padres 10.00 25.00
94 R.Henderson M's 10.00 25.00
95 R.Henderson Mets 10.00 25.00
96 R.Henderson Jays 10.00 25.00
97 R.Johnson M's Arm Up 10.00 25.00
98 Mark Grace 10.00 25.00
99 Pedro Martinez Expos 10.00 25.00
100 Hee Seop Choi 6.00 15.00
101 Ivan Rodriguez Rgr 10.00 25.00
102 Jeff Kent Giants 6.00 15.00
103 Hideo Nomo Sox 20.00 50.00
104 Hideo Nomo Mets 20.00 50.00
105 Mike Piazza Dodgers 15.00 40.00
106 Tom Glavine Braves H 10.00 25.00
107 R.Alomar Indians Swing 10.00 25.00
108 Roger Clemens Sox 15.00 40.00
109 Jason Giambi A's H 6.00 15.00
110 Jim Thome Indians A 10.00 25.00
111 Alex Rodriguez M's H 15.00 40.00
112 J.Gonz Indians Hands 6.00 15.00
113 Torii Hunter Crouch 6.00 15.00
114 Roy Oswalt H 6.00 15.00
115 C.Schilling D'backs Throw 6.00 15.00
116 Magglio Ordonez H 6.00 15.00
117 Rafael Palmeiro Rgr H 10.00 25.00
118 Andruw Jones A 10.00 25.00
119 Manny Ramirez A 10.00 25.00
120 Mark Teixeira H 10.00 25.00
121 Mark Mulder Stance 6.00 15.00
123 Tim Hudson A 6.00 15.00
124 Todd Helton A 10.00 25.00
125 Troy Glaus Pinstripe 6.00 15.00
128 Greg Maddux A 15.00 40.00
129 Roger Clemens Yanks A 15.00 40.00
130 Nomar Garciaparra A 15.00 40.00
131 Mike Piazza Mets A 15.00 40.00
132 Alex Rodriguez Rgr H 15.00 40.00
134 R.Johnson D'backs H 10.00 25.00
135 Sammy Sosa A 10.00 25.00
137 Alfonso Soriano H 6.00 15.00
138 J.Giambi Yanks A 10.00 25.00
139 Albert Pujols A 25.00 60.00
140 Chipper Jones A 10.00 25.00
141 Adam Dunn H 6.00 15.00
142 Pedro Martinez Sox A 10.00 25.00
143 Vladimir Guerrero A 10.00 25.00
144 Mark Prior A 10.00 25.00
145 Barry Zito H 6.00 15.00
146 Jeff Bagwell A 10.00 25.00
147 Lance Berkman Socks 6.00 15.00
148 S.Green Dodgers A 6.00 15.00
149 Jason Giambi A's A 6.00 15.00
150 R.Johnson M's Arm Out 10.00 25.00
151 Alex Rodriguez M's A 15.00 40.00
152 Babe Ruth/5
153 Ty Cobb Pants 75.00 150.00
154 Jackie Robinson/10
155 Lou Gehrig/5
156 Thurman Munson 20.00 50.00
157 Roberto Clemente/5
158 Nolan Ryan Rgr 30.00 80.00
159 Nolan Ryan Angels 30.00 80.00
160 Nolan Ryan Astros 30.00 80.00
161 Cal Ripken 50.00 120.00
162 Don Mattingly 25.00 60.00
163 Stan Musial 30.00 80.00
164 Tony Gwynn 15.00 40.00
165 Yogi Berra 12.50 30.00
166 Johnny Bench 12.50 30.00
167 Mike Schmidt 25.00 60.00
168 George Brett 25.00 60.00
169 Ryne Sandberg 30.00 80.00
170 Ernie Banks/5

2003 Leaf Limited Threads Prime

2-151 PRINTS 25 #'d PER UNLESS NOTED
152-170 PRINTS B/WN 3-25 COPIES PER
NO PRICING ON QTY OF 10 OR LESS

2 Eric Chavez 10.00 25.00
3 Alex Rodriguez Rgr A 25.00 60.00
4 Miguel Tejada Fldg 10.00 25.00
5 Nomar Garciaparra H 25.00 60.00
6 Jeff Bagwell H 15.00 40.00
7 Jim Thome Phils A/20 20.00 50.00
8 Pat Burrell w/Bat 10.00 25.00
9 Albert Pujols H 40.00 100.00
10 Juan Gonzalez Rgr Btg 10.00 25.00
11 Shawn Green Jays 10.00 25.00
12 Craig Biggio H 15.00 40.00
13 Chipper Jones H 15.00 40.00
14 Hideo Nomo Dodgers 30.00 80.00
15 Vernon Wells 10.00 25.00
16 Gary Sheffield 10.00 25.00
17 Barry Larkin 15.00 40.00
18 Josh Beckett White 10.00 25.00
19 Edgar Martinez A 15.00 40.00
20 Ivan Rodriguez Marlins 15.00 40.00
21 Jeff Kent Astros 10.00 25.00
22 Roberto Alomar Mets A 15.00 40.00
23 Alfonso Soriano A 10.00 25.00
24 Jim Thome Indians H 15.00 40.00
25 J.Gonzalez Indians Btg 10.00 25.00
26 Carlos Beltran 10.00 25.00
27 S.Green Dodgers H 10.00 25.00
28 Tim Hudson H 10.00 25.00
29 Deion Sanders 15.00 40.00
30 Rafael Palmeiro O's 15.00 40.00
31 Todd Helton H 15.00 40.00
32 L.Berkman No Socks 10.00 25.00
33 Mike Mussina Yanks H 15.00 40.00
34 Kazuhisa Ishii H 10.00 25.00
35 Pat Burrell Run 10.00 25.00
36 Miguel Tejada Btg 10.00 25.00
37 J.Gonzalez Rgr Stand 10.00 25.00
38 Roberto Alomar Mets H 15.00 40.00
39 R.Alomar Indians Bunt 15.00 40.00
40 Luis Gonzalez 10.00 25.00
41 Jorge Posada 15.00 40.00
42 Mark Mulder Leg 10.00 25.00
43 Sammy Sosa H 15.00 40.00
44 Mark Prior H 15.00 40.00
45 Roger Clemens Yanks H 25.00 60.00
46 Tom Glavine Mets H 15.00 40.00
47 Mark Teixeira A 15.00 40.00
48 Manny Ramirez H 15.00 40.00
49 Frank Thomas Swing 15.00 40.00
50 Troy Glaus White 10.00 25.00
51 Andruw Jones H 15.00 40.00
52 Jason Giambi Yanks H 10.00 25.00
53 Jim Thome Phils H 15.00 40.00
55 Rafael Palmeiro Rgr A 15.00 40.00
56 Edgar Martinez H 15.00 40.00
57 Vladimir Guerrero H 15.00 40.00
58 Roberto Alomar O's 15.00 40.00
59 Mike Sweeney 10.00 25.00
60 Magglio Ordonez A 10.00 25.00
62 Craig Biggio A 15.00 40.00
63 Greg Maddux H 25.00 60.00
64 Mike Piazza Mets H 25.00 60.00
65 Tom Glavine Braves A 15.00 40.00
66 Kerry Wood H 10.00 25.00
67 Frank Thomas Arms 15.00 40.00
68 Mike Mussina Yanks A 15.00 40.00
69 Nick Johnson H 10.00 25.00
70 Bernie Williams H 15.00 40.00
71 Scott Rolen 15.00 40.00
72 C.Schilling D'backs Leg 10.00 25.00
73 Adam Dunn A 10.00 25.00
74 Roy Oswalt A 10.00 25.00
75 Pedro Martinez Sox H 15.00 40.00
76 Tom Glavine Mets A 15.00 40.00
77 Torii Hunter Swing 10.00 25.00
78 Austin Kearns 10.00 25.00
79 R.Johnson D'backs A 15.00 40.00
80 Bernie Williams A 15.00 40.00
82 Kerry Wood A 10.00 25.00
83 Kazuhisa Ishii A 10.00 25.00
84 Randy Johnson Astros 15.00 40.00
85 Nick Johnson A 10.00 25.00
86 J.Beckett Pinstripe 10.00 25.00
87 Curt Schilling Phils 10.00 25.00
88 Mike Mussina O's 15.00 40.00
89 P.Martinez Dodgers 15.00 40.00
90 Barry Zito A 10.00 25.00
91 Jim Edmonds 10.00 25.00
92 R.Henderson Sox 15.00 40.00
93 R.Henderson Padres 15.00 40.00
94 R.Henderson M's 15.00 40.00
95 R.Henderson Mets 15.00 40.00
96 R.Henderson Jays 15.00 40.00
97 R.Johnson M's Arm Up 15.00 40.00
98 Mark Grace 15.00 40.00
99 Pedro Martinez Expos 15.00 40.00
100 Hee Seop Choi 10.00 25.00
101 Ivan Rodriguez Rgr 15.00 40.00
102 Jeff Kent Giants 10.00 25.00
104 Hideo Nomo Mets 30.00 80.00
105 Mike Piazza Dodgers 25.00 60.00
106 Tom Glavine Braves H 15.00 40.00
107 R.Alomar Indians Swing 15.00 40.00
108 Roger Clemens Sox 25.00 60.00
109 Jason Giambi A's H 10.00 25.00
110 Jim Thome Indians A 15.00 40.00
111 Alex Rodriguez M's H 25.00 60.00
112 J.Gonz Indians Hands 10.00 25.00
113 Torii Hunter Crouch 10.00 25.00
114 Roy Oswalt H 10.00 25.00
115 C.Schilling D'backs Throw 10.00 25.00
116 Magglio Ordonez H 10.00 25.00
117 Rafael Palmeiro Rgr H 15.00 40.00
118 Andruw Jones A 15.00 40.00
119 Manny Ramirez A 15.00 40.00
120 Mark Teixeira H 15.00 40.00
121 Mark Mulder Stance 10.00 25.00
123 Tim Hudson A 10.00 25.00
124 Todd Helton A 15.00 40.00
125 Troy Glaus Pinstripe 10.00 25.00
128 Greg Maddux A 25.00 60.00
129 Roger Clemens Yanks A 25.00 60.00
130 Nomar Garciaparra A 25.00 60.00
131 Mike Piazza Mets A 25.00 60.00
132 Alex Rodriguez Rgr H 25.00 60.00
134 R.Johnson D'backs H 15.00 40.00
135 Sammy Sosa A 15.00 40.00
137 Alfonso Soriano H 10.00 25.00
138 J.Giambi Yanks A 10.00 25.00
139 Albert Pujols A 40.00 100.00
140 Chipper Jones A 15.00 40.00
141 Adam Dunn H 10.00 25.00
142 P.Martinez Sox A 15.00 40.00
143 Vladimir Guerrero A 15.00 40.00
144 Mark Prior A 15.00 40.00
145 Barry Zito H 10.00 25.00
146 Jeff Bagwell A 15.00 40.00
147 Lance Berkman Socks 10.00 25.00
148 S.Green Dodgers A 10.00 25.00
149 Jason Giambi A's A 10.00 25.00
150 R.Johnson M's Arm Out 15.00 40.00
151 Alex Rodriguez M's A 25.00 60.00
152 Babe Ruth/3
153 Ty Cobb Pants 100.00 200.00
154 Jackie Robinson/10
155 Lou Gehrig/5
156 Thurman Munson 30.00 80.00
157 Roberto Clemente/5
158 Nolan Ryan Rgr 50.00 120.00
159 Nolan Ryan Angels 50.00 120.00
160 Nolan Ryan Astros 50.00 120.00
161 Cal Ripken 60.00 150.00
162 Don Mattingly 40.00 100.00
163 Stan Musial 60.00 150.00
164 Tony Gwynn 25.00 60.00
165 Yogi Berra 20.00 50.00
166 Johnny Bench 20.00 50.00
167 Mike Schmidt 40.00 100.00
168 George Brett 40.00 100.00
169 Ryne Sandberg 50.00 120.00
170 Ernie Banks/10

2003 Leaf Limited Timber

STATED PRINT RUN 25 SERIAL #'d SETS
CARD 170 PRINT RUN 1 SERIAL #'d CARD
NO 170 PRICING DUE TO SCARCITY

2 Eric Chavez 6.00 15.00
3 Alex Rodriguez Rgr A 15.00 40.00
4 Miguel Tejada Fldg 6.00 15.00
5 Nomar Garciaparra H 15.00 40.00
6 Jeff Bagwell H 10.00 25.00
7 Jim Thome Phils A 10.00 25.00
8 Pat Burrell w/Bat 6.00 15.00
9 Albert Pujols H 25.00 60.00
10 Juan Gonzalez Rgr Btg 6.00 15.00
11 Shawn Green Jays 6.00 15.00
12 Craig Biggio H 10.00 25.00
13 Chipper Jones H 10.00 25.00
14 Hideo Nomo Dodgers 20.00 50.00
15 Vernon Wells 6.00 15.00
16 Gary Sheffield 6.00 15.00
17 Barry Larkin 10.00 25.00
18 Josh Beckett White 6.00 15.00
19 Edgar Martinez A 10.00 25.00
20 Ivan Rodriguez Marlins 10.00 25.00
21 Jeff Kent Astros 6.00 15.00
22 Roberto Alomar Mets A 10.00 25.00
23 Alfonso Soriano A 6.00 15.00
24 Jim Thome Indians H 10.00 25.00
25 J.Gonzalez Indians Btg 6.00 15.00
26 Carlos Beltran 6.00 15.00
27 S.Green Dodgers H 6.00 15.00
28 Tim Hudson H 6.00 15.00
30 Rafael Palmeiro O's 10.00 25.00
31 Todd Helton H 10.00 25.00
32 L.Berkman No Socks 6.00 15.00
33 Mike Mussina Yanks H 10.00 25.00
34 Kazuhisa Ishii H 6.00 15.00
35 Pat Burrell Run 6.00 15.00
36 Miguel Tejada Btg 6.00 15.00
37 J.Gonzalez Rgr Stand 6.00 15.00
38 Roberto Alomar Mets H 10.00 25.00
39 R.Alomar Indians Bunt 10.00 25.00
40 Luis Gonzalez 6.00 15.00
41 Jorge Posada 10.00 25.00
42 Mark Mulder Leg 6.00 15.00
43 Sammy Sosa H 10.00 25.00
44 Mark Prior H 10.00 25.00
45 R.Clemens Yanks H 15.00 40.00
46 Tom Glavine Mets H 10.00 25.00
47 Mark Teixeira A 10.00 25.00
48 Manny Ramirez H 10.00 25.00
49 Frank Thomas Swing 10.00 25.00
50 Troy Glaus White 6.00 15.00
51 Andruw Jones H 10.00 25.00
52 Jason Giambi Yanks H 6.00 15.00
53 Jim Thome Phils H 10.00 25.00
55 Rafael Palmeiro Rgr A 10.00 25.00
56 Edgar Martinez H 10.00 25.00
57 Vladimir Guerrero H 10.00 25.00
58 Roberto Alomar O's 10.00 25.00
59 Mike Sweeney 6.00 15.00
60 Magglio Ordonez A 6.00 15.00
62 Craig Biggio A 10.00 25.00
63 Greg Maddux H 15.00 40.00
64 Mike Piazza Mets H 15.00 40.00
65 T.Glavine Braves A 10.00 25.00
66 Kerry Wood H 6.00 15.00
67 Frank Thomas Arms 10.00 25.00
68 Mike Mussina Yanks A 10.00 25.00
69 Nick Johnson H 6.00 15.00
70 Bernie Williams H 10.00 25.00
71 Scott Rolen 10.00 25.00
72 C.Schilling D'backs Leg 6.00 15.00
73 Adam Dunn A 6.00 15.00
74 Roy Oswalt A 6.00 15.00
75 Pedro Martinez Sox H 10.00 25.00
76 Tom Glavine Mets A 10.00 25.00
77 Torii Hunter Swing 6.00 15.00
78 Austin Kearns 6.00 15.00
79 R.Johnson D'backs A 10.00 25.00
80 Bernie Williams A 10.00 25.00
82 Kerry Wood A 6.00 15.00
83 Kazuhisa Ishii A 6.00 15.00
84 Randy Johnson Astros 10.00 25.00
85 Nick Johnson A 6.00 15.00
86 J.Beckett Pinstripe 6.00 15.00
87 Curt Schilling Phils 6.00 15.00
88 Mike Mussina O's 10.00 25.00
89 P.Martinez Dodgers 10.00 25.00
90 Barry Zito A 6.00 15.00
91 Jim Edmonds 6.00 15.00
92 R.Henderson Sox 10.00 25.00
93 R.Henderson Padres 10.00 25.00
94 R.Henderson M's 10.00 25.00
95 R.Henderson Mets 10.00 25.00
96 R.Henderson Jays 10.00 25.00
97 R.Johnson M's Arm Up 10.00 25.00
98 Mark Grace 10.00 25.00
99 Pedro Martinez Expos 10.00 25.00
101 Ivan Rodriguez Rgr 10.00 25.00
102 Jeff Kent Giants 6.00 15.00
103 Hideo Nomo Sox 20.00 50.00
104 Hideo Nomo Mets 20.00 50.00
105 Mike Piazza Dodgers 15.00 40.00
106 Tom Glavine Braves H 10.00 25.00
107 R.Alomar Indians Swing 10.00 25.00
108 Roger Clemens Sox 15.00 40.00
109 Jason Giambi A's H 6.00 15.00
110 Jim Thome Indians A 10.00 25.00
111 Alex Rodriguez M's H 15.00 40.00
112 J.Gonz Indians Hands 6.00 15.00
113 Torii Hunter Crouch 6.00 15.00
114 Roy Oswalt H 6.00 15.00
115 C.Schilling D'backs Throw 6.00 15.00
116 Magglio Ordonez H 6.00 15.00
117 Rafael Palmeiro Rgr H 10.00 25.00
118 Andruw Jones A 10.00 25.00
119 Manny Ramirez A 10.00 25.00
120 Mark Teixeira H 10.00 25.00
121 Mark Mulder Stance 6.00 15.00
122 Garret Anderson 6.00 15.00
123 Tim Hudson A 6.00 15.00
124 Todd Helton A 10.00 25.00
125 Troy Glaus Pinstripe 6.00 15.00
128 Greg Maddux A 15.00 40.00
129 Roger Clemens Yanks A 15.00 40.00
130 Nomar Garciaparra A 15.00 40.00
131 Mike Piazza Mets A 15.00 40.00
132 Alex Rodriguez Rgr H 15.00 40.00
134 R.Johnson D'backs H 10.00 25.00
135 Sammy Sosa A 10.00 25.00
137 Alfonso Soriano H 6.00 15.00
138 J.Giambi Yanks A 6.00 15.00
139 Albert Pujols A 25.00 60.00
140 Chipper Jones A 10.00 25.00
141 Adam Dunn H 6.00 15.00
142 Pedro Martinez Sox A 10.00 25.00
143 Vladimir Guerrero A 10.00 25.00
144 Mark Prior A 10.00 25.00
145 Barry Zito H 6.00 15.00
146 Jeff Bagwell A 10.00 25.00
147 Lance Berkman Socks 6.00 15.00
148 S.Green Dodgers A 6.00 15.00
149 Jason Giambi A's A 6.00 15.00
150 R.Johnson M's Arm Out 10.00 25.00
151 Alex Rodriguez M's A 15.00 40.00
152 Babe Ruth 125.00 250.00
153 Ty Cobb 60.00 120.00
155 Lou Gehrig 75.00 150.00
156 Thurman Munson 20.00 50.00
157 Roberto Clemente 60.00 120.00
158 Nolan Ryan Rgr 30.00 80.00
159 Nolan Ryan Angels 30.00 80.00
160 Nolan Ryan Astros 30.00 80.00
161 Cal Ripken 50.00 120.00
162 Don Mattingly 25.00 60.00
163 Stan Musial 25.00 60.00
164 Tony Gwynn 15.00 40.00
165 Yogi Berra 12.50 30.00
166 Johnny Bench 12.50 30.00
167 Mike Schmidt 25.00 60.00
168 George Brett 25.00 60.00
169 Ryne Sandberg 30.00 80.00
170 Ernie Banks/1

2003 Leaf Limited TNT

PRINT RUNS B/WN 1-25 COPIES PER
NO PRICING ON QTY OF 10 OR LESS

2 Eric Chavez Bat-Jsy 10.00 25.00
3 A.Rod Rgr A Bat-Jsy 20.00 50.00
4 M.Tejada Fldg Bat-Jsy/10
5 N.Garciaparra H Bat-Jsy 20.00 50.00
6 Jeff Bagwell H Bat-Jsy 15.00 40.00
7 J.Thome Phils A Bat-Jsy 15.00 40.00
8 P.Burrell w/Bat Bat-Jsy 10.00 25.00
9 Albert Pujols H Bat-Jsy 25.00 60.00
10 J.Gonz Rgr Btg Bat-Jsy 10.00 25.00
11 S.Green Jays Bat-Jsy 10.00 25.00
12 Craig Biggio H Bat-Jsy 15.00 40.00
13 C.Jones H Bat-Jsy 15.00 40.00
14 H.Nomo Dodgers Bat-Jsy 20.00 50.00
15 Vernon Wells Bat-Jsy 10.00 25.00
16 G.Sheffield Bat-Jsy 10.00 25.00
17 Barry Larkin Bat-Jsy 15.00 40.00
18 J.Beckett White Bat-Jsy 10.00 25.00
19 E.Martinez A Bat-Jsy 15.00 40.00
20 I.Rodriguez Marlins Bat-Jsy 15.00 40.00
21 Jeff Kent Astros Bat-Jsy 10.00 25.00
22 R.Alomar Mets A Bat-Jsy 15.00 40.00
23 A.Soriano A Bat-Jsy 10.00 25.00
24 J.Thome Indians H Bat-Jsy 15.00 40.00
25 J.Gonz Indians Btg Bat-Jsy 10.00 25.00
26 Carlos Beltran Bat-Jsy 10.00 25.00
27 S.Green Dodgers H Bat-Jsy 10.00 25.00
28 Tim Hudson H Bat-Jsy 10.00 25.00
30 R.Palmeiro O's Bat-Jsy 15.00 40.00
31 Todd Helton H Bat-Jsy 15.00 40.00
32 L.Berk No Socks Bat-Jsy 10.00 25.00
33 M.Mussina Yanks H Bat-Jsy 15.00 40.00
34 Kazuhisa Ishii H Bat-Jsy 10.00 25.00
35 Pat Burrell Run Bat-Jsy 10.00 25.00
36 M.Tejada Btg Bat-Jsy/10
37 J.Gonz Rgr Stand Bat-Jsy 10.00 25.00
38 R.Alomar Mets H Bat-Jsy 15.00 40.00
39 R.Alom Indians Bunt Bat-Jsy 15.00 40.00
40 Luis Gonzalez Bat-Jsy 10.00 25.00
41 Jorge Posada Bat-Jsy 15.00 40.00
42 M.Mulder Leg Bat-Jsy 10.00 25.00
43 Sammy Sosa H Bat-Jsy 15.00 40.00
44 Mark Prior H Bat-Jsy 15.00 40.00
45 R.Clemens Yanks H Bat-Jsy 20.00 50.00
46 T.Glavine Mets H Bat-Jsy 15.00 40.00
47 Mark Teixeira A Bat-Jsy 15.00 40.00
48 Manny Ramirez H Bat-Jsy 15.00 40.00
49 F.Thomas Swing Bat-Jsy 15.00 40.00
50 Troy Glaus White Bat-Jsy 10.00 25.00
51 Andruw Jones H Bat-Jsy 15.00 40.00
52 J.Giambi Yanks H Bat-Jsy 10.00 25.00
53 J.Thome Phils H Bat-Jsy 15.00 40.00
55 R.Palmeiro Rgr A Bat-Jsy 15.00 40.00
56 E.Martinez H Bat-Jsy 15.00 40.00
57 V.Guerrero H Bat-Jsy 15.00 40.00
59 Mike Sweeney Bat-Jsy 10.00 25.00
60 M.Ordonez A Bat-Jsy 10.00 25.00
62 Craig Biggio A Bat-Jsy 15.00 40.00
63 Greg Maddux H Bat-Jsy 20.00 50.00
64 M.Piazza Mets H Bat-Jsy 20.00 50.00
65 T.Glavine Braves A Bat-Jsy 15.00 40.00
66 Kerry Wood H Bat-Jsy 10.00 25.00
67 F.Thomas Arms Bat-Jsy 15.00 40.00
68 M.Mussina Yanks A Bat-Jsy 15.00 40.00
69 Nick Johnson H Bat-Jsy 10.00 25.00
70 Bernie Williams H Bat-Jsy 15.00 40.00
71 Scott Rolen Bat-Jsy 15.00 40.00
72 C.Schill D'backs Leg Bat-Jsy 10.00 25.00
73 Adam Dunn A Bat-Jsy 10.00 25.00
74 Roy Oswalt A Bat-Jsy 10.00 25.00
75 P.Martinez Sox H Bat-Jsy 15.00 40.00
76 T.Glavine Mets A Bat-Jsy 15.00 40.00
77 T.Hunter Swing Bat-Jsy 10.00 25.00
78 Austin Kearns Bat-Jsy 10.00 25.00
79 R.John D'backs A Bat-Jsy 15.00 40.00
80 Bernie Williams A Bat-Jsy 15.00 40.00
82 Kerry Wood A Bat-Jsy 10.00 25.00
83 Kazuhisa Ishii A Bat-Jsy 10.00 25.00
84 R.Johnson Astros Bat-Jsy 15.00 40.00
85 Nick Johnson A Bat-Jsy 10.00 25.00
86 J.Beckett Pinstripe Bat-Jsy 10.00 25.00
87 C.Schilling Phils Bat-Jsy 10.00 25.00
88 Mike Mussina O's Bat-Jsy 15.00 40.00
89 P.Martinez Dgr Bat-Jsy 15.00 40.00
90 Barry Zito A Bat-Jsy 10.00 25.00
91 Jim Edmonds Bat-Jsy 10.00 25.00
92 R.Henderson Sox Bat-Jsy 15.00 40.00
93 R.Hend Padres Bat-Jsy 15.00 40.00
94 R.Henderson M's Bat-Jsy 15.00 40.00
95 R.Hend Mets Bat-Jsy 15.00 40.00
96 R.Hend Jays Bat-Jsy 15.00 40.00
97 R.John M's Arm Up Bat-Jsy 15.00 40.00
98 Mark Grace Bat-Jsy 15.00 40.00
99 P.Martinez Expos Bat-Jsy 15.00 40.00
101 I.Rodriguez Rgr Bat-Jsy 15.00 40.00
102 Jeff Kent Giants Bat-Jsy 10.00 25.00
103 Hideo Nomo Sox Bat-Jsy 20.00 50.00
104 Hideo Nomo Mets Bat-Jsy 20.00 50.00
105 M.Piazza Dodgers Bat-Jsy 20.00 50.00
106 T.Glav Braves H Bat-Jsy 15.00 40.00
107 R.Alom Ind Swing Bat-Jsy 15.00 40.00
108 R.Clemens Sox Bat-Jsy 20.00 50.00
109 J.Giambi A's H Bat-Jsy 10.00 25.00
110 J.Thome Indians A Bat-Jsy 15.00 40.00
111 A.Rod M's H Bat-Jsy 20.00 50.00
112 J.Gonz Ind Hands Bat-Jsy 10.00 25.00
113 T.Hunter Crouch Bat-Jsy 10.00 25.00
114 Roy Oswalt H Bat-Jsy 10.00 25.00
115 C.Schill D'b Throw Bat-Jsy 10.00 25.00
116 M.Ordonez H Bat-Jsy 10.00 25.00
117 R.Palmeiro Rgr H Bat-Jsy 15.00 40.00
118 Andruw Jones A Bat-Jsy 15.00 40.00
119 Manny Ramirez A Bat-Jsy 15.00 40.00
120 Mark Teixeira H Bat-Jsy 15.00 40.00
121 M.Mulder Stance Bat-Jsy 10.00 25.00
123 Tim Hudson A Bat-Jsy 10.00 25.00
124 Todd Helton A Bat-Jsy 15.00 40.00
125 T.Glaus Pinstripe Bat-Jsy 10.00 25.00
128 Greg Maddux A Bat-Jsy 20.00 50.00
129 R.Clemens Yanks A Bat-Jsy 20.00 50.00
130 N.Garciaparra A Bat-Jsy 20.00 50.00
131 M.Piazza Mets A Bat-Jsy 20.00 50.00
132 A.Rod Rgr H Bat-Jsy 20.00 50.00
134 R.John D'backs H Bat-Jsy 15.00 40.00
135 Sammy Sosa A Bat-Jsy 15.00 40.00
137 A.Soriano H Bat-Jsy 10.00 25.00
138 J.Giambi Yanks A Bat-Jsy 10.00 25.00
139 Albert Pujols A Bat-Jsy 25.00 60.00
140 Chipper Jones A Bat-Jsy 15.00 40.00
141 Adam Dunn H Bat-Jsy 10.00 25.00
142 P.Martinez Sox A Bat-Jsy 15.00 40.00
143 V.Guerrero A Bat-Jsy 15.00 40.00
144 Mark Prior A Bat-Jsy 15.00 40.00
145 Barry Zito H Bat-Jsy 10.00 25.00
146 Jeff Bagwell A Bat-Jsy 15.00 40.00
147 L.Berkman Socks Bat-Jsy 10.00 25.00
148 S.Green Dgr A Bat-Jsy 10.00 25.00
149 J.Giambi A's A Bat-Jsy 10.00 25.00
150 R.John M's Arm Out Bat-Jsy 15.00 40.00
151 A.Rod M's A Bat-Jsy 20.00 50.00
152 Babe Ruth Bat-Jsy/5
153 Ty Cobb Bat-Pants/10
155 Lou Gehrig Bat-Jsy/5
156 Thurman Munson Bat-Jsy 30.00 80.00
157 Roberto Clemente Bat-Jsy/5
158 Nolan Ryan Rgr Bat-Jsy 40.00 100.00
159 N.Ryan Angels Bat-Jsy 40.00 100.00
160 N.Ryan Astros Bat-Jsy 40.00 100.00
161 Cal Ripken Bat-Jsy 50.00 120.00
162 Don Mattingly Bat-Jsy 30.00 80.00
163 Stan Musial Bat-Jsy 40.00 100.00
164 Tony Gwynn Bat-Jsy 20.00 50.00
165 Yogi Berra Bat-Jsy 25.00 60.00
166 Johnny Bench Bat-Jsy 25.00 60.00
167 Mike Schmidt Bat-Jsy 30.00 80.00
168 George Brett Bat-Jsy 30.00 80.00
169 Ryne Sandberg Bat-Jsy 40.00 100.00
170 Ernie Banks Bat-Jsy/1

2003 Leaf Limited TNT Prime

*TNT PRIME: .5X TO 1.2X BASIC TNT
PRINT RUNS B/WN 1-25 COPIES PER
NO PRICING ON QTY OF 10 OR LESS

2003 Leaf Limited 7th Inning Stretch Jersey

PRINT RUNS B/WN 40-50 COPIES PER

1 Alex Rodriguez 10.00 25.00
3 Sammy Sosa 6.00 15.00
4 Juan Gonzalez 6.00 15.00
5 Albert Pujols 15.00 40.00
6 Chipper Jones 6.00 15.00
7 Alfonso Soriano/40 6.00 15.00
8 Jim Thome 6.00 15.00
9 Mike Piazza 10.00 25.00
10 Rafael Palmeiro 6.00 15.00

2003 Leaf Limited Jersey Numbers

1-54 PRINT RUNS B/WN 5-100 COPIES PER
55-100 PRINT RUNS B/WN 5-25 COPIES PER
NO PRICING ON QTY OF 10 OR LESS

1 Rod Carew Angels/50 10.00 25.00
2 Nolan Ryan Angels/50 25.00 60.00
3 Reggie Jackson Angels/50 10.00 25.00
4 Brooks Robinson/50 10.00 25.00
5 Frank Robinson/25 10.00 25.00
6 Cal Ripken/100 25.00 60.00
7 Carlton Fisk W.Sox/50 10.00 25.00
8 Roger Clemens/100 8.00 20.00
9 Carlton Fisk R.Sox/5
10 Lou Boudreau/50 6.00 15.00
11 Bob Feller/25 10.00 25.00
12 Al Kaline/10
13 Alan Trammell/50 6.00 15.00
14 Harmon Killebrew/50 15.00 40.00
15 Rod Carew Twins/50 10.00 25.00
16 Kirby Puckett/50 15.00 40.00
17 Babe Ruth/5
18 Lou Gehrig/5
19 Yogi Berra/50 15.00 40.00
20 Thurman Munson/50 15.00 40.00
21 Don Mattingly/100 15.00 40.00
22 Roger Maris Pants/10
23 Rickey Henderson/5
24 Reggie Jackson A's/5
25 Alex Rodriguez/100 8.00 20.00
26 Randy Johnson M's/50 6.00 15.00
27 Nolan Ryan Rgr/100 20.00 50.00
28 Dale Murphy/50 10.00 25.00
29 Warren Spahn/50 15.00 40.00
30 Eddie Mathews/50 15.00 40.00
31 Ernie Banks/5
32 Ryne Sandberg/100 15.00 40.00
33 Johnny Bench/50 15.00 40.00
34 Joe Morgan/50 6.00 15.00
35 Randy Johnson Astros/50 6.00 15.00
36 Nolan Ryan Astros/100 20.00 50.00
37 Pee Wee Reese/50 10.00 25.00
38 Duke Snider/50 10.00 25.00
39 Jackie Robinson/25 40.00 100.00
40 Robin Yount/50 15.00 40.00
41 Paul Molitor/50 6.00 15.00
42 Pedro Martinez/50 6.00 15.00
43 Randy Johnson Expos/50 6.00 15.00
44 Tom Seaver/25 15.00 40.00
45 Gary Carter/50 6.00 15.00
46 Mike Schmidt/50 20.00 50.00
47 Steve Carlton/50 6.00 15.00
48 Willie Stargell/50 10.00 25.00
49 Roberto Clemente/5
50 Ozzie Smith/50 20.00 50.00
51 Stan Musial/100 15.00 40.00
52 Enos Slaughter/50 15.00 40.00
53 Orlando Cepeda/50 6.00 15.00
54 Willie McCovey/50 6.00 15.00
55 Brooks Robinson
Frank Robinson/10
56 Lou Boudreau
Bob Feller/10
57 Harmon Killebrew 40.00 100.00
Rod Carew/25
58 Harmon Killebrew 40.00 100.00
Kirby Puckett/25
59 Babe Ruth
Lou Gehrig/5
60 Babe Ruth
Yogi Berra/5
61 Babe Ruth
Thurman Munson/5
62 Babe Ruth
Don Mattingly/5
63 Babe Ruth
Roger Maris Pants/5
64 Lou Gehrig
Yogi Berra/5
65 Lou Gehrig
Thurman Munson/5
66 Lou Gehrig
Don Mattingly/5
67 Lou Gehrig
Roger Maris Pants/5
68 Yogi Berra 30.00 80.00
Thurman Munson/25
69 Yogi Berra 40.00 100.00
Don Mattingly/25
70 Yogi Berra
Roger Maris/5
71 Dale Murphy 30.00 80.00
Warren Spahn/25
72 Dale Murphy 30.00 80.00
Eddie Mathews/25
73 Warren Spahn 30.00 80.00
Eddie Mathews/25
74 Johnny Bench 25.00 60.00
Joe Morgan/25
75 Pee Wee Reese 25.00 60.00
Duke Snider/25
76 Pee Wee Reese
Jackie Robinson/10
77 Duke Snider
Jackie Robinson/10
78 Robin Yount 30.00 80.00
Paul Molitor/25
79 Mike Schmidt
Steve Carlton/25
80 Willie Stargell
Roberto Clemente/5
81 Ozzie Smith 40.00 100.00
Stan Musial/25
82 Stan Musial 40.00 100.00
Enos Slaughter/25
83 Orlando Cepeda 25.00 60.00
Willie McCovey/25
84 Nolan Ryan 40.00 100.00
Reggie Jackson/25
85 Brooks Robinson
Cal Ripken/25
86 Frank Robinson
Cal Ripken/10
87 Carlton Fisk
Roger Clemens/5
88 Al Kaline
Alan Trammell/10
89 Rickey Henderson
Reggie Jackson/5
90 Alex Rodriguez 20.00 50.00
Randy Johnson/25
91 Pedro Martinez 20.00 50.00
Randy Johnson/25
92 Tom Seaver
Gary Carter/10
93 Ernie Banks
Ryne Sandberg/10
94 Reggie Jackson A's 25.00 60.00
Reggie Jackson Angels/25
95 Nolan Ryan Angels 40.00 100.00
Nolan Ryan Rgr/25
96 Nolan Ryan Rgr 40.00 100.00
Nolan Ryan Astros/25
97 Nolan Ryan Astros 40.00 100.00
Nolan Ryan Angels/25
98 Nolan Ryan 40.00 100.00
Randy Johnson/25
99 Cal Ripken 60.00 120.00
Rafael Palmeiro/25
100 Dale Murphy 30.00 80.00
Deion Sanders/25

2003 Leaf Limited Jersey Numbers Retired

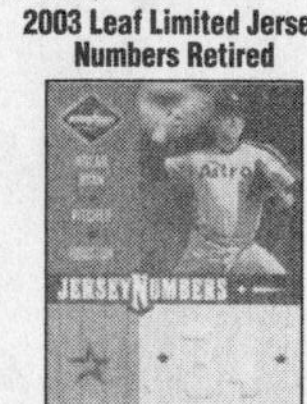

PRINT RUNS B/WN 1-72 COPIES PER
NO PRICING ON QTY OF 19 OR LESS

1 Rod Carew Angels/29 15.00 40.00
2 Nolan Ryan Angels/30 30.00 80.00
4 Brooks Robinson/5
5 Frank Robinson/20 12.50 30.00
7 Carlton Fisk R.Sox/27 15.00 40.00
9 Carlton Fisk W.Sox/72 10.00 25.00
10 Lou Boudreau/5
11 Bob Feller/19
12 Al Kaline/6
14 Harmon Killebrew/3
15 Rod Carew Twins/29 15.00 40.00
16 Kirby Puckett/34 20.00 50.00
17 Babe Ruth/3
18 Lou Gehrig/4
19 Yogi Berra/8
20 Thurman Munson/15
21 Don Mattingly/23 25.00 60.00

22 R.Maris Pants/9
27 Nolan Ryan Rgr/34 30.00 80.00
28 Dale Murphy/3
29 Warren Spahn/21 25.00 60.00
30 Eddie Mathews/41 10.00 25.00
31 Ernie Banks/14
33 Johnny Bench/5
34 Joe Morgan/8
36 Nolan Ryan Astros/34 30.00 80.00
37 Pee Wee Reese/1
38 Duke Snider/4
39 Jackie Robinson/42 30.00 80.00
40 Robin Yount/19
41 Paul Molitor/4
44 Tom Seaver/41 10.00 25.00
46 Mike Schmidt/20 25.00 60.00
47 Steve Carlton/32 10.00 25.00
48 Willie Stargell/8
49 Roberto Clemente/21 60.00 120.00
50 Ozzie Smith/1
51 Stan Musial/6
52 Enos Slaughter/9
53 Orlando Cepeda/30 10.00 25.00
54 Willie McCovey/44 6.00 15.00

2003 Leaf Limited Leather

PRINT RUNS B/WN 10-25 COPIES PER
NO PRICNG ON QTY OF 10 OR LESS
1 Alex Rodriguez/25 25.00 60.00
2 Chipper Jones/25 15.00 40.00
3 Jimmie Foxx/25 50.00 100.00
4 Kirby Puckett/25 15.00 40.00
5 Mike Schmidt/25 40.00 100.00
6 Roger Clemens/25 25.00 60.00
7 Steve Carlton/25 15.00 40.00
8 Tony Gwynn/25 25.00 60.00
9 Nolan Ryan/10
10 Vladimir Guerrero/25 15.00 40.00
11 Adam Dunn/25 15.00 40.00
12 Andruw Jones/25 15.00 40.00
13 Curt Schilling/25 15.00 40.00
14 Randy Johnson/25 15.00 40.00
15 Mark Prior/25 15.00 40.00

2003 Leaf Limited Leather Gold

STATED PRINT RUN 10 SERIAL #'d SETS
RYAN PRINT RUN 5 SERIAL #'d CARDS
NO PRICING DUE TO SCARCITY

2003 Leaf Limited Leather and Lace

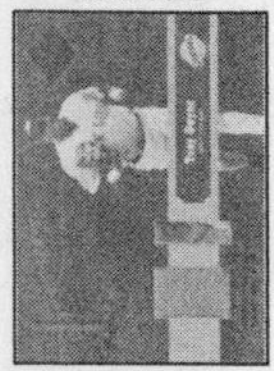

STATED PRINT RUN 10 SERIAL #'d SETS
N.RYAN PRINT RUN 5 SERIAL #'d CARDS
NO PRICING DUE TO SCARCITY

2003 Leaf Limited Leather and Lace Gold

STATED PRINT RUN 5 SERIAL #'d SETS
NO PRICING DUE TO SCARCITY

2003 Leaf Limited Lineups Bat

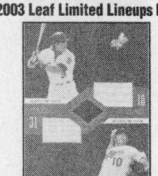

PRINT RUNS B/WN 25-50 COPIES PER
ALL ARE DUAL BAT CARDS UNLESS NOTED
CARD NUMBER 3 DOES NOT EXIST
1 Paul Molitor 15.00 40.00
Robin Yount/50
2 Don Mattingly 20.00 50.00
Bernie Williams/50
4 Hideki Matsui Ball 30.00 80.00
Derek Jeter Ball/25
5 Ryne Sandberg 20.00 50.00
Andre Dawson/50
6 George Brett 30.00 80.00
Bo Jackson/50
7 Reggie Jackson 15.00 40.00
Jose Canseco/50
8 Mark Grace 20.00 50.00
Ryne Sandberg/50
9 Rickey Henderson 15.00 40.00
Jose Canseco/50
10 Mike Piazza 15.00 40.00
Hideo Nomo/50

2003 Leaf Limited Lineups Button

STATED PRINT RUN 1 SERIAL #'d SET
NO PRICING DUE TO SCARCITY
2 Don Mattingly
Bernie Williams
3 Sammy Sosa
Hee Seop Choi
6 George Brett
Bo Jackson
10 Mike Piazza
Hideo Nomo

2003 Leaf Limited Lineups Jersey

PRINT RUNS B/WN 25
NO PRICING ON QTY OF 5 OR LESS
ALL ARE DUAL JSY CARDS UNLESS NOTED
1 Paul Molitor 15.00 40.00
Robin Yount/50
2 Don Mattingly 20.00 50.00
Bernie Williams/50
3 Sammy Sosa 15.00 40.00
Hee Seop Choi/50
4 Hideki Matsui Base 15.00 40.00
Derek Jeter Base/50
5 Ryne Sandberg 20.00 50.00
Andre Dawson/50
6 George Brett 30.00 80.00
Bo Jackson/50
7 Reggie Jackson
Jose Canseco/5
8 Mark Grace 20.00 50.00
Ryne Sandberg/50
9 Rickey Henderson
Jose Canseco/5
10 Mike Piazza 15.00 40.00
Hideo Nomo/50

2003 Leaf Limited Lineups Jersey Tag

PRINT RUNS B/WN 4-5 COPIES PER
NO PRICING DUE TO SCARCITY

2003 Leaf Limited Lumberjacks Barrel

PRINT RUNS B/WN 1-2 COPIES PER
NO PRICING DUE TO SCARCITY

2003 Leaf Limited Lumberjacks Bat

1-37 PRINT RUNS B/WN 1-25 COPIES PER
38-45 PRINT RUNS B/WN 1-25 COPIES PER
NO PRICING ON QTY OF 15 OR LESS
1 Babe Ruth/25 125.00 250.00
2 Lou Gehrig/25 75.00 150.00
3 Roberto Clemente/25 60.00 120.00
4 Stan Musial/25 25.00 60.00
5 Rogers Hornsby/25 30.00 80.00
6 Don Mattingly/25 25.00 60.00
7 Rickey Henderson/25 10.00 25.00
8 Cal Ripken/25 50.00 120.00
9 Yogi Berra/25 20.00 50.00
10 Reggie Jackson/25 15.00 40.00
11 George Brett/25 25.00 60.00
12 Mel Ott/25 25.00 60.00
13 Roger Maris/25 40.00 100.00
14 Ryne Sandberg/25 30.00 80.00
15 Eddie Mathews/15
16 Richie Ashburn/25 15.00 40.00
17 Mike Schmidt/25 25.00 60.00
18 Tony Gwynn/25 15.00 40.00
19 Ty Cobb/25 60.00 120.00
20 Thurman Munson/25 20.00 50.00
21 Jimmie Foxx/25 30.00 80.00
22 Duke Snider/25 15.00 40.00
23 Ernie Banks/1
24 Alex Rodriguez/25 15.00 40.00
25 Nomar Garciaparra/25 15.00 40.00
26 Hideki Matsui Base/25 30.00 80.00
27 Ichiro Suzuki Base/25 25.00 60.00
28 Barry Bonds Base/25 25.00 60.00
29 Mike Piazza/25 15.00 40.00
30 Alfonso Soriano/25 10.00 25.00
31 Al Kaline/25 20.00 50.00
32 Harmon Killebrew/5
33 Dale Murphy/25 15.00 40.00
34 Orlando Cepeda/5
35 Willie McCovey/25 10.00 25.00
36 Willie Stargell/5
37 Brooks Robinson/25 15.00 40.00
38 Hideki Matsui Base 60.00 120.00
Ichiro Suzuki Base/25
39 Ryne Sandberg
Ernie Banks/1
40 Don Mattingly 100.00 200.00
Lou Gehrig/25
41 Yogi Berra 30.00 80.00
Thurman Munson/25
42 Mike Schmidt 40.00 100.00
Richie Ashburn/25
43 Stan Musial 50.00 100.00
Rogers Hornsby/25
44 Don Mattingly 60.00 120.00
Roger Maris/25
45 Babe Ruth
Lou Gehrig/15

2003 Leaf Limited Lumberjacks Bat Black

PRINT RUNS B/WN 1-5 COPIES PER
NO PRICING DUE TO SCARCITY

2003 Leaf Limited Lumberjacks Bat Silver

PRINT RUNS B/WN 1-10 COPIES PER
NO PRICING DUE TO SCARCITY

2003 Leaf Limited Lumberjacks Bat-Jersey

1-37 PRINT RUNS B/WN 1-25 COPIES PER
38-45 PRINT RUNS B/WN 1-25 COPIES PER
NO PRICING ON QTY OF 15 OR LESS
ALL ARE BAT-JSY COMBOS UNLESS NOTED
1 Babe Ruth/5
2 Lou Gehrig/10
3 Roberto Clemente/10
4 Stan Musial/25 40.00 100.00
6 Don Mattingly/25 40.00 100.00
7 Rickey Henderson/5
8 Cal Ripken/25 60.00 150.00
9 Yogi Berra/25 25.00 60.00
10 Reggie Jackson/5
11 George Brett/25 40.00 100.00
12 Mel Ott/15
13 Roger Maris Bat-Pants/25 60.00 120.00
14 Ryne Sandberg/25 50.00 120.00
15 Eddie Mathews/25 25.00 60.00
17 Mike Schmidt/25 40.00 100.00
18 Tony Gwynn/25 25.00 60.00
19 Ty Cobb Bat-Pants/15
20 Thurman Munson/25 30.00 80.00
22 Duke Snider/15
23 Ernie Banks/1
24 Alex Rodriguez/25 25.00 60.00
25 Nomar Garciaparra/25 25.00 60.00
26 Hideki Matsui Base-Ball/25 50.00 100.00
27 Ichiro Suzuki Base-Ball/25 30.00 80.00
28 Barry Bonds Base-Ball/25 30.00 80.00
29 Mike Piazza/25 25.00 60.00
30 Alfonso Soriano/25 15.00 40.00
31 Al Kaline/10
32 Harmon Killebrew/10
33 Dale Murphy/25 20.00 50.00
34 Orlando Cepeda/5
35 Willie McCovey/25 12.50 30.00
36 Willie Stargell/25 20.00 50.00
37 Brooks Robinson/25 20.00 50.00
38A Hideki Matsui Base 60.00 120.00
Ichiro Suzuki Ball/25
38B Hideki Matsui Ball 60.00 120.00
Ichiro Suzuki Base/25
39A Ryne Sandberg Bat
Ernie Banks Jsy/5
39B Ryne Sandberg Jsy
Ernie Banks Bat/1
40A Don Mattingly Jsy
Lou Gehrig Bat/10
40B Don Mattingly Bat
Lou Gehrig Jsy/5
41A Yogi Berra Jsy 30.00 80.00
Thurman Munson Bat/25
41B Yogi Berra Bat 30.00 80.00
Thurman Munson Jsy/25
42 Mike Schmidt Jsy 40.00 100.00
Richie Ashburn Bat/25
43 Stan Musial Jsy 50.00 100.00
Rogers Hornsby Bat/25
44 Don Mattingly Bat
Roger Maris Pants/5
45A Babe Ruth Jsy
Lou Gehrig Bat/5
45B Babe Ruth Bat
Lou Gehrig Jsy/5

2003 Leaf Limited Lumberjacks Bat-Jersey Black

PRINT RUNS B/WN 1-5 COPIES PER
NO PRICING DUE TO SCARCITY

2003 Leaf Limited Lumberjacks Bat-Jersey Silver

PRINT RUNS B/WN 1-10 COPIES PER
NO PRICING DUE TO SCARCITY

2003 Leaf Limited Lumberjacks Jersey

1-37 PRINT RUNS B/WN 1-25 COPIES PER
38-45 PRINT RUNS B/WN 1-25 COPIES PER
NO PRICING ON QTY OF 15 OR LESS
1 Babe Ruth/5
2 Lou Gehrig/10
3 Roberto Clemente/10
4 Stan Musial/25 25.00 60.00
6 Don Mattingly/25 25.00 60.00
7 Rickey Henderson/10
8 Cal Ripken/25 50.00 120.00
9 Yogi Berra/25 15.00 40.00
10 Reggie Jackson/10
11 George Brett/25 25.00 60.00
12 Mel Ott/25 25.00 60.00
13 Roger Maris Pants/10
14 Ryne Sandberg/25 30.00 80.00
15 Eddie Mathews/25 15.00 40.00
17 Mike Schmidt/25 25.00 60.00
18 Tony Gwynn/25 15.00 40.00
19 Ty Cobb Pants/5
20 Thurman Munson/25 20.00 50.00
22 Duke Snider/25 12.50 30.00
23 Ernie Banks/5
24 Alex Rodriguez/25 15.00 40.00
25 Nomar Garciaparra/25 15.00 40.00
26 Hideki Matsui Ball/25 30.00 80.00
27 Ichiro Suzuki Ball/25 25.00 60.00
28 Barry Bonds Ball/25 25.00 60.00
29 Mike Piazza/25 15.00 40.00
30 Alfonso Soriano/25 10.00 25.00
31 Al Kaline/10
32 Harmon Killebrew/25 15.00 40.00
33 Dale Murphy/25 12.50 30.00
34 Orlando Cepeda/25 8.00 20.00
35 Willie McCovey/25 8.00 20.00
36 Willie Stargell/25 12.50 30.00
37 Brooks Robinson/25 12.50 30.00
38 Hideki Matsui Ball 60.00 120.00
Ichiro Suzuki Ball/25
39 Ryne Sandberg
Ernie Banks/5
40 Don Mattingly
Lou Gehrig/15
41 Yogi Berra 30.00 80.00
Thurman Munson/25
44 Don Mattingly
Roger Maris Pants/5
45 Babe Ruth
Lou Gehrig/5

2003 Leaf Limited Lumberjacks Jersey Black

PRINT RUNS B/WN 1-5 COPIES PER
NO PRICING DUE TO SCARCITY

2003 Leaf Limited Lumberjacks Jersey Silver

PRINT RUNS B/WN 3-10 COPIES PER
NO PRICING DUE TO SCARCITY

2003 Leaf Limited Player Threads

PRINT RUNS B/WN 5-50 COPIES PER
NO PRICING ON QTY OF 5 OR LESS
1 Roger Clemens/50 10.00 25.00
2 Alex Rodriguez/50 10.00 25.00
3 Pedro Martinez/50 6.00 15.00
4 Randy Johnson/50 6.00 15.00
5 Curt Schilling/50 4.00 10.00
6 Reggie Jackson/5
7 Nolan Ryan/50 25.00 60.00
8 Hideo Nomo/50 15.00 40.00
9 Mike Piazza/50 10.00 25.00
10 Rickey Henderson Padres/5
11 Rickey Henderson Mets/50 6.00 15.00
12 Ivan Rodriguez/50 6.00 15.00
13 Gary Sheffield/50 6.00 15.00
14 Jeff Kent/50 4.00 10.00
15 Roberto Alomar/50 6.00 15.00
16 Rafael Palmeiro/50 6.00 15.00
17 Juan Gonzalez/50 4.00 10.00
18 Shawn Green/50 4.00 10.00
19 Jason Giambi/50 4.00 10.00
20 Jim Thome/50 6.00 15.00
21 Scott Rolen/50 6.00 15.00
22 Mike Mussina/50 6.00 15.00
23 Tom Glavine/50 6.00 15.00
24 Sammy Sosa/50 6.00 15.00

2003 Leaf Limited Player Threads Prime

PRINT RUNS B/WN 5-10 COPIES PER
NO PRICING DUE TO SCARCITY

2003 Leaf Limited Player Threads Double

STATED PRINT RUN 50 SERIAL #'d SETS
CARD 6/10 PRINT RUN 5 SERIAL #'d SETS
1 R.Clemens Yanks-Sox 15.00 40.00
2 Alex Rodriguez Rgr-M's 15.00 40.00
3 P.Martinez Sox-Dodgers 10.00 25.00
4 Randy Johnson D'backs-Astros 10.00 25.00
5 C.Schilling D'backs-Phils 6.00 15.00
6 R.Jackson A's-Angels/5
7 Nolan Ryan Rgr-Astros 30.00 80.00
8 H.Nomo Dodgers-Sox 25.00 60.00
9 M.Piazza Mets-Dodgers 15.00 40.00
10 R.Henderson Padres-Sox/5
11 R.Henderson Mets-M's 10.00 25.00
12 I.Rodriguez Marlins-Rgr 10.00 25.00
13 G.Sheffield Braves-Dodgers 6.00 15.00
14 Jeff Kent Astros-Giants 6.00 15.00
15 R.Alomar Mets-Indians 10.00 25.00
16 Rafael Palmeiro Rgr-O's 10.00 25.00
17 J.Gonzalez Rgr-Indians 6.00 15.00
18 S.Green Dodgers-Jays 6.00 15.00
19 Jason Giambi Yanks-A's 6.00 15.00
20 Jim Thome Phils-Indians 10.00 25.00
21 Scott Rolen Cards-Phils 10.00 25.00
22 Mike Mussina Yanks-O's 10.00 25.00
23 Tom Glavine Mets-Braves 10.00 25.00
24 Sammy Sosa Cubs-Sox 10.00 25.00

2003 Leaf Limited Player Threads Double Prime

PRINT RUNS B/WN 5-10 COPIES PER
NO PRICING DUE TO SCARCITY

2003 Leaf Limited Player Threads Triple

STATED PRINT RUN 50 SERIAL #'d SETS
HENDERSON PADRES-SOX-A'S 5 #'d CARDS
NO HENDERSON PADRES-SOX-A'S PRICING
4 R.John D'backs-Astros-M's 15.00 40.00
7 N.Ryan Rgr-Astros-Angels 40.00 100.00
8 H.Nomo Dodgers-Sox-Mets 40.00 100.00
10 R.Henderson Padres-Sox-A's/5
11 R.Henderson Mets-M's-Jays 15.00 40.00
13 G.Sheffield Braves-Dgr-Brew 10.00 25.00
14 J.Kent Astros-Giants-Jays 10.00 25.00
15 R.Alomar Mets-Indians-O's 15.00 40.00

2003 Leaf Limited Player Threads Triple Prime

PRINT RUNS B/WN 5-10 COPIES PER
NO PRICING DUE TO SCARCITY

2003 Leaf Limited Team Threads

PRINT RUNS B/WN 10-50 COPIES PER
NO PRICING ON QTY OF 10 OR LESS
25 Jackie Robinson
Duke Snider/10
26 Alex Rodriguez 30.00 80.00
Nolan Ryan/50
27 Mike Piazza 15.00 40.00
Hideo Nomo/50
28 Cal Ripken 40.00 100.00
Mike Mussina/50
29 Hideo Nomo 15.00 40.00
Kazuhisa Ishii/50
30 Nolan Ryan 20.00 50.00
Randy Johnson/50

2003 Leaf Limited Team Threads Prime

PRINT RUNS B/WN 5-10 COPIES PER
NO PRICING DUE TO SCARCITY

2003 Leaf Limited Team Trademarks Autographs

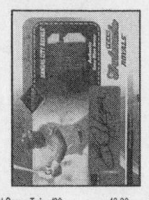

PRINT RUNS B/WN 5-25 COPIES PER
NO PRICING ON QTY OF 10 OR LESS
1 Alan Trammell/25 20.00 50.00
2 Joe Morgan/5
3 Jim Palmer/25 20.00 50.00
4 Bob Feller/5
5 Gary Carter/25 20.00 50.00
6 Andre Dawson/25 20.00 50.00
7 Duke Snider/5
8 Dale Murphy/25 30.00 60.00
9 Bo Jackson/5
10 Bobby Doerr/25 12.50 30.00
11 Brooks Robinson/25 30.00 60.00
12 Eric Davis/25 20.00 50.00
13 Fred Lynn/25 12.50 30.00
14 Harmon Killebrew/10
15 Jack Morris/25 12.50 30.00
16 Al Kaline/25 40.00 80.00
17 Deion Sanders/25 60.00 120.00
18 Luis Aparicio/25 12.50 30.00
19 Orlando Cepeda/5
20 Phil Rizzuto/25 30.00 60.00
21 Reggie Jackson/5
22 Robin Yount/5
23 Rod Carew Twins/5
24 Will Clark/25 60.00 120.00
25 Willie McCovey/5
26 Tony Gwynn/5
27 Nolan Ryan Astros/5
28 Cal Ripken/5
29 Stan Musial/5
30 Mike Schmidt/5
31 Rod Carew Angels/5
32 Nolan Ryan Rgr/5
33 George Brett/5
34 Nolan Ryan Angels/5
35 Alex Rodriguez/5
36 Roger Clemens/5
37 Greg Maddux/5
38 Albert Pujols/5
39 Alfonso Soriano/5
40 Mark Grace/5

2003 Leaf Limited Team Trademarks Autographs Jersey

PRINT RUNS B/WN 1-47 COPIES PER
NO PRICING ON QTY OF 24 OR LESS
12 Eric Davis/44 20.00 50.00
15 Jack Morris/47 15.00 40.00
19 Orlando Cepeda/30 20.00 50.00
23 Rod Carew Twins/29 40.00 80.00
24 Will Clark/22
25 Willie McCovey/44 30.00 60.00
26 Tony Gwynn/19
27 Nolan Ryan Astros/34 75.00 150.00
28 Cal Ripken/8
29 Stan Musial/6
30 Mike Schmidt/20
31 Rod Carew Angels/29 40.00 80.00
32 Nolan Ryan Rgr/34 75.00 150.00
33 George Brett/5
34 Nolan Ryan Angels/30 75.00 150.00
35 Alex Rodriguez/5
36 Roger Clemens/22
37 Greg Maddux/31 100.00 200.00
38 Albert Pujols/5
39 Alfonso Soriano/12
40 Mark Grace/17

2003 Leaf Limited Team Trademarks Threads Number

PRINT RUNS B/WN 1-47 COPIES PER
NO PRICING ON QTY OF 19 OR LESS
1 Alan Trammell/3
2 Joe Morgan/8
3 Jim Palmer/22 12.50 30.00
4 Bob Feller/19
5 Gary Carter/8
6 Andre Dawson/8
7 Duke Snider/4
8 Dale Murphy/3
9 Bo Jackson/16
10 Bobby Doerr/1
11 Brooks Robinson/5
12 Eric Davis/44 6.00 15.00
13 Fred Lynn/19
14 Harmon Killebrew/3
15 Jack Morris/47 6.00 15.00
16 Al Kaline/6
17 Deion Sanders/24 20.00 50.00
18 Luis Aparicio/11
19 Orlando Cepeda/30 10.00 25.00
20 Phil Rizzuto/10
21 Reggie Jackson/9
22 Robin Yount/19
23 Rod Carew Twins/29 15.00 40.00
24 Will Clark/22 40.00 100.00
25 Willie McCovey/44 6.00 15.00
26 Tony Gwynn/19
27 Nolan Ryan Astros/34 30.00 80.00
28 Cal Ripken/8
29 Stan Musial/6
30 Mike Schmidt/20 25.00 60.00
31 Rod Carew Angels/29 15.00 40.00
32 Nolan Ryan Rgr/34 30.00 80.00
33 George Brett/5
34 Nolan Ryan Angels/30 30.00 80.00
35 Alex Rodriguez/2
36 Roger Clemens/22 25.00 60.00
37 Greg Maddux/31 15.00 40.00
38 Albert Pujols/5
39 Alfonso Soriano/12
40 Mark Grace/17

2003 Leaf Limited Team Trademarks Threads Prime

PRINT RUNS B/WN 5-25 COPIES PER
NO PRICING ON QTY OF 10 OR LESS
1 Alan Trammell/25 15.00 40.00
2 Joe Morgan/25 15.00 40.00
3 Jim Palmer/25 15.00 40.00
4 Bob Feller/10
5 Gary Carter/25 15.00 40.00
6 Andre Dawson/25 15.00 40.00
7 Duke Snider/25 25.00 60.00
8 Dale Murphy/25 25.00 60.00
9 Bo Jackson/25 25.00 60.00
10 Bobby Doerr/20 20.00 50.00
11 Brooks Robinson/25 25.00 60.00
12 Eric Davis/25 15.00 40.00
13 Fred Lynn/25 10.00 25.00
14 Harmon Killebrew/25 30.00 80.00
15 Jack Morris/25 10.00 25.00
16 Al Kaline/5
17 Deion Sanders/25 25.00 60.00
18 Luis Aparicio/25 15.00 40.00
19 Orlando Cepeda/25 15.00 40.00
20 Phil Rizzuto/10
21 Reggie Jackson/5
22 Robin Yount/25 25.00 60.00
23 Rod Carew Twins/25 25.00 60.00
24 Will Clark/25 50.00 100.00
25 Willie McCovey/25 15.00 40.00

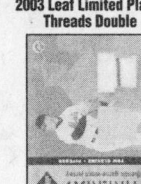

26 Tony Gwynn/25	25.00	60.00
27 Nolan Ryan Astros/25	50.00	100.00
28 Cal Ripken/25	60.00	120.00
29 Stan Musial/25	60.00	120.00
30 Mike Schmidt/25	40.00	100.00
31 Rod Carew Angels/25	25.00	60.00
32 Nolan Ryan Rgr/25	50.00	100.00
33 George Brett/25	40.00	100.00
34 Nolan Ryan Angels/25	50.00	100.00
35 Alex Rodriguez/25	25.00	60.00
36 Roger Clemens/20	30.00	80.00
37 Greg Maddux/25	25.00	60.00
38 Albert Pujols/25	40.00	100.00
39 Alfonso Soriano/25	15.00	40.00
40 Mark Grace/25	25.00	60.00

2004 Leaf Limited

This 275-card set was relased in October, 2004. The set was issued in four-card packs with an $70 SRP which came four packs to a box and 10 boxes to a case. The first 200 cards in this set and cards numbered 230 through 250 comprise the basic set. Cards numbered 201 through 229 feature retired greats that were issued to a stated print run of 499 serial numbered sets and cards numbered 251 through 275 are autographed rookie cards which were issued to a stated print run of 99 serial numbered sets.

COMMON CARD (1-200/230-250)	.60	1.50
1-200/230-250 PRINT RUN 749 #'d SETS		
COMMON CARD (201-229)	.75	2.00
201-229 PRINT RUN 499 SERIAL #'d SETS		
COMMON AUTO (251-275)	5.00	12.00
251-275: OVERALL AU-GU ONE PER PACK		
251-275 AUTO PRINT RUN 99 #'d SETS		
1 Adam Dunn A	1.00	2.50
2 Adrian Beltre	.60	1.50
3 Albert Pujols H	4.00	10.00
4 Alex Rodriguez Yanks	2.50	6.00
5 Alfonso Soriano Rgr	.60	1.50
6 Andruw Jones	.60	1.50
7 Andy Pettitte Astros	1.00	2.50
8 Angel Berroa	.60	1.50
9 Aramis Ramirez	.60	1.50
10 Aubrey Huff	.60	1.50
11 Austin Kearns	.60	1.50
12 Barry Larkin	1.00	2.50
13 Barry Zito H	.60	1.50
14 Bartolo Colon	.60	1.50
15 Ben Sheets	.60	1.50
16 Bernie Williams	1.00	2.50
17 Bobby Abreu	.60	1.50
18 Brandon Webb	.60	1.50
19 Brian Giles	.60	1.50
20 C.C. Sabathia	1.00	2.50
21 Carlos Beltran Royals A	.60	1.50
22 Carlos Delgado	.60	1.50
23 Chipper Jones H	1.50	4.00
24 Craig Biggio	1.00	2.50
25 Curt Schilling Sox	1.00	2.50
26 Darin Erstad	.60	1.50
27 Delmon Young	1.00	2.50
28 Derek Jeter	4.00	10.00
29 Derrek Lee	.60	1.50
30 Dontrelle Willis	.60	1.50
31 Edgar Renteria	.60	1.50
32 Eric Chavez	.60	1.50
33 Esteban Loaiza	.60	1.50
34 Frank Thomas	1.50	4.00
35 Fred McGriff	.60	1.50
36 Garret Anderson H	.60	1.50
37 Gary Sheffield Yanks	.60	1.50
38 Geoff Jenkins	.60	1.50
39 Greg Maddux Cubs	2.50	6.00
40 Hank Blalock H	.60	1.50
41 Hideki Matsui	2.50	6.00
42 Hideo Nomo Dodgers	1.50	4.00
43 Ichiro Suzuki	2.50	6.00
44 Ivan Rodriguez Tigers	1.00	2.50
45 J.D. Drew	.60	1.50
46 Jacque Jones	.60	1.50
47 Jae Weong Seo	.60	1.50
48 Jake Peavy	.60	1.50
49 Jamie Moyer	.60	1.50
50 Jason Giambi Yanks	.60	1.50
51 Jason Kendall	.60	1.50
52 Jason Schmidt	.60	1.50
53 Jason Varitek	1.50	4.00
54 Javier Vazquez	.60	1.50
55 Javy Lopez	.60	1.50
56 Jay Gibbons	.60	1.50
57 Jay Payton	.60	1.50
58 Jeff Bagwell H	1.00	2.50
59 Jeff Kent	.60	1.50
60 Jeremy Bonderman	.60	1.50
61 Jermaine Dye	.60	1.50
62 Jeromy Burnitz	.60	1.50
63 Jim Edmonds	1.00	2.50
64 Jim Thome Phils	1.00	2.50
65 Jimmy Rollins	1.00	2.50
66 Jody Gerut	.60	1.50
67 Johan Santana	1.50	4.00
68 John Olerud	.60	1.50
69 John Smoltz	1.50	4.00
70 Johnny Damon	1.00	2.50
71 Jorge Posada	1.00	2.50
72 Jose Contreras	.60	1.50
73 Jose Reyes	1.00	2.50
74 Jose Vidro	.60	1.50
75 Josh Beckett H	1.00	2.50
76 Juan Gonzalez Royals	.60	1.50
77 Juan Pierre	.60	1.50
78 Junior Spivey	.60	1.50
79 Kazuhisa Ishii	.60	1.50
80 Keith Foulke Sox	.60	1.50
81 Ken Griffey Jr. Reds	2.50	6.00
82 Ken Harvey	.60	1.50
83 Kenny Rogers	.60	1.50
84 Kerry Wood	.60	1.50
85 Kevin Brown Yanks	.60	1.50
86 Kevin Millwood	.60	1.50
87 Kip Wells	.60	1.50
88 Lance Berkman	1.00	2.50
89 Larry Bigbie	.60	1.50
90 Larry Walker	1.00	2.50
91 Laynce Nix	.60	1.50
92 Luis Castillo	.60	1.50
93 Luis Gonzalez	.60	1.50
94 Luis Matos	.60	1.50
95 Lyle Overbay	.60	1.50
96 Magglio Ordonez H	1.00	2.50
97 Manny Ramirez Sox	1.50	4.00
98 Marcus Giles	.60	1.50
99 Mark Buehrle	1.00	2.50
100 Mark Mulder	.60	1.50
101 Mark Prior H	1.00	2.50
102 Mark Teixeira	1.50	4.00
103 Marlon Byrd	.60	1.50
104 Matt Morris	.60	1.50
105 Melvin Mora	.60	1.50
106 Michael Young	.60	1.50
107 Miguel Cabrera Batting	1.50	4.00
108 Miguel Tejada O's	1.00	2.50
109 Mike Lowell	.60	1.50
110 Mike Mussina Yanks	1.00	2.50
111 Mike Piazza Mets	1.50	4.00
112 Mike Sweeney	.60	1.50
113 Milton Bradley	.60	1.50
114 Moises Alou	.60	1.50
115 Morgan Ensberg	.60	1.50
116 Nick Johnson	.60	1.50
117 Nomar Garciaparra	1.50	4.00
118 Omar Vizquel	1.00	2.50
119 Orlando Cabrera	.60	1.50
120 Pat Burrell	.60	1.50
121 Paul Konerko	1.00	2.50
122 Paul Lo Duca	.60	1.50
123 Pedro Martinez Sox	1.00	2.50
124 Preston Wilson H	.60	1.50
125 Rafael Furcal	.60	1.50
126 Rafael Palmeiro O's	1.00	2.50
127 Randy Johnson D'backs	1.50	4.00
128 Rich Harden	.60	1.50
129 Richard Hidalgo	.60	1.50
130 Richie Sexson	.60	1.50
131 Rickie Weeks	.60	1.50
132 Roberto Alomar	1.00	2.50
133 Robin Ventura	.60	1.50
134 Rocco Baldelli	.60	1.50
135 Roger Clemens Astros	2.00	5.00
136 Roy Halladay	1.50	4.00
137 Roy Oswalt A	1.00	2.50
138 Russ Ortiz	.60	1.50
139 Ryan Klesko	.60	1.50
140 Sammy Sosa H	1.50	4.00
141 Scott Podsednik	.60	1.50
142 Scott Rolen Cards A	1.00	2.50
143 Sean Burroughs	.60	1.50
144 Sean Casey	.60	1.50
145 Shannon Stewart	.60	1.50
146 Shawn Green Dodgers	.60	1.50
147 Shigetoshi Hasegawa	.60	1.50
148 Sidney Ponson	.60	1.50
149 Steve Finley	.60	1.50
150 Tim Hudson	1.00	2.50
151 Tim Salmon	.60	1.50
152 Tino Martinez	1.00	2.50
153 Todd Helton H	1.00	2.50
154 Tom Glavine Mets	1.00	2.50
155 Torii Hunter	.60	1.50
156 Trot Nixon	.60	1.50
157 Troy Glaus	.60	1.50
158 Vernon Wells H	.60	1.50
159 Victor Martinez A	1.00	2.50
160 Vinny Castilla	.60	1.50
161 Vladimir Guerrero Angels	1.50	4.00
162 Alex Rodriguez Rgr	2.50	6.00
163 Alfonso Soriano Yanks	.60	1.50
164 Andy Pettitte Yanks	1.00	2.50
165 Curt Schilling D'backs	1.00	2.50
166 Gary Sheffield Braves	.60	1.50
167 Greg Maddux Braves	2.50	6.00
168 Hideo Nomo Sox	1.50	4.00
169 Ivan Rodriguez Marlins	1.00	2.50
170 Jason Giambi A's	.60	1.50
171 Jim Thome Indians	1.00	2.50
172 Juan Gonzalez Rgr	.60	1.50
173 Ken Griffey Jr. M's	2.50	6.00
174 Kevin Brown Dodgers	.60	1.50
175 Manny Ramirez Indians	1.50	4.00
176 Miguel Tejada A's	1.00	2.50
177 Mike Mussina O's	1.00	2.50
178 Mike Piazza Dodgers	1.50	4.00
179 Pedro Martinez Expos	1.00	2.50
180 Rafael Palmeiro Rgr	1.00	2.50
181 Randy Johnson Astros	1.50	4.00
182 Roger Clemens Sox	2.00	5.00
183 Scott Rolen Phils	1.00	2.50
184 Shawn Green Jays	.60	1.50
185 Tom Glavine Braves	1.00	2.50
186 Vladimir Guerrero Expos	1.50	4.00
187 Alex Rodriguez M's	2.50	6.00
188 Mike Piazza Marlins	1.50	4.00
189 Randy Johnson M's	1.50	4.00
190 Roger Clemens Yanks	2.00	5.00
191 Albert Pujols A	4.00	10.00
192 Barry Zito A	.60	1.50
193 Chipper Jones A	1.50	4.00
194 Garret Anderson A	.60	1.50
195 Jeff Bagwell A	1.00	2.50
196 Josh Beckett A	1.00	2.50
197 Magglio Ordonez A	1.00	2.50
198 Mark Prior A	1.00	2.50
199 Sammy Sosa A	1.50	4.00
200 Todd Helton A	1.00	2.50
201 Andre Dawson RET	1.25	3.00
202 Babe Ruth RET	5.00	12.00
203 Bob Feller RET	.75	2.00
204 Bob Gibson RET	1.25	3.00
205 Bobby Doerr RET	.75	2.00
206 Cal Ripken RET	8.00	20.00
207 Dale Murphy RET	1.25	3.00
208 Don Mattingly RET	4.00	10.00
209 Gary Carter RET	.75	2.00
210 George Brett RET	4.00	10.00
211 Jackie Robinson RET	2.00	5.00
212 Lou Brock RET	1.25	3.00
213 Lou Gehrig RET	4.00	10.00
214 Mark Grace RET	1.25	3.00
215 Maury Wills RET	.75	2.00
216 Mike Schmidt RET	3.00	8.00
217 Nolan Ryan RET	6.00	15.00
218 Orel Hershiser RET	.75	2.00
219 Paul Molitor RET	2.00	5.00
220 Roberto Clemente RET	5.00	12.00
221 Rod Carew RET	1.25	3.00
222 Roy Campanella RET	2.00	5.00
223 Ryne Sandberg RET	4.00	10.00
224 Stan Musial RET	3.00	8.00
225 Ted Williams RET	5.00	12.00
226 Tony Gwynn RET	2.00	5.00
227 Ty Cobb RET	3.00	8.00
228 Whitey Ford RET	1.25	3.00
229 Yogi Berra RET	2.00	5.00
230 Carlos Beltran Astros H	.60	1.50
231 David Ortiz H	1.50	4.00
232 David Ortiz A	1.50	4.00
233 Carlos Zambrano	1.00	2.50
234 Carlos Lee	.60	1.50
235 Travis Hafner	.60	1.50
236 Brad Penny	.60	1.50
237 Wade Miller	.60	1.50
238 Edgar Martinez	1.00	2.50
239 Carl Crawford	1.00	2.50
240 Roy Oswalt H	1.00	2.50
241 Kazuo Matsui RC	1.00	2.50
242 Carlos Beltran Astros A	.60	1.50
243 Carlos Beltran Royals H	.60	1.50
244 Miguel Cabrera Fielding	1.50	4.00
245 Scott Rolen Cards H	1.00	2.50
246 Hank Blalock A	.60	1.50
247 Vernon Wells A	.60	1.50
248 Adam Dunn H	1.00	2.50
249 Preston Wilson A	.60	1.50
250 Victor Martinez H	1.00	2.50
251 Aarom Baldiris PH AU RC	5.00	12.00
252 Akinori Otsuka PH AU RC	10.00	25.00
253 Andres Blanco PH AU RC	5.00	12.00
254 Brad Halsey PH AU RC	5.00	12.00
255 Joey Gathright PH AU RC	5.00	12.00
256 Colby Miller PH AU RC	5.00	12.00
257 Fernando Nieve PH AU RC	5.00	12.00
258 Freddy Guzman PH AU RC	5.00	12.00
259 Hector Gimenez PH AU RC	5.00	12.00
260 Jake Woods PH AU RC	5.00	12.00
261 Jason Bartlett PH AU RC	6.00	15.00
262 John Gall PH AU RC	5.00	12.00
263 Jose Capellan PH AU RC	5.00	12.00
264 Josh Labandeira PH AU RC	5.00	12.00
265 Justin Germano PH AU RC	5.00	12.00
266 Kazuhito Tadano PH AU RC	12.50	30.00
267 Lance Cormier PH AU RC	5.00	12.00
268 Merkin Valdez PH AU RC	5.00	12.00
269 Mike Gosling PH AU RC	5.00	12.00
270 Ramon Ramirez PH AU RC	5.00	12.00
271 Rusty Tucker PH AU RC	5.00	12.00
272 Shawn Hill PH AU RC	5.00	12.00
273 Shingo Takatsu PH AU RC	10.00	25.00
274 William Bergolla PH AU RC	5.00	12.00
275 Yadier Molina PH AU RC	25.00	50.00

2004 Leaf Limited Bronze Spotlight

*BRONZE 1-200/230-250: .75X TO 2X
*BRONZE 201-229: .75X TO 2X
*BRONZE RC'S 1-200/230-250: .75X TO 2X
RANDOM INSERTS IN PACKS
STATED PRINT RUN 100 SERIAL #'d SETS

2004 Leaf Limited Gold Spotlight

*GOLD 1-200/230-250: 2X TO 5X
*GOLD 201-229: 2X TO 5X
RC'S 1-200/230-250: 2X TO 5X
RANDOM INSERTS IN PACKS
STATED PRINT RUN 25 SERIAL #'d SETS

2004 Leaf Limited Platinum Spotlight

STATED PRINT RUN 1 SERIAL #'d SET
NO PRICING DUE TO SCARCITY

2004 Leaf Limited Silver Spotlight

*SILVER 1-200/230-250: 1.25X TO 3X
*SILVER 201-229: 1.25X TO 3X
*SILVER RC'S 1-200/230-250: 1X TO 2.5X
RANDOM INSERTS IN PACKS
STATED PRINT RUN 50 SERIAL #'d SETS

2004 Leaf Limited Barrels

OVERALL AU-GU ODDS ONE PER PACK
PRINT RUNS B/WN 1-5 COPIES PER
NO PRICING DUE TO SCARCITY

2004 Leaf Limited Moniker Bronze

OVERALL AU-GU ODDS ONE PER PACK
PRINT RUNS B/WN 1-100 COPIES PER
NO PRICING ON QTY OF 10 OR LESS

1 Adam Dunn A/50	8.00	20.00
3 Albert Pujols H/25	150.00	250.00
5 Alfonso Soriano Rgr/100	10.00	25.00
6 Andruw Jones/50	12.50	30.00
7 Andy Pettitte Astros/10		
8 Angel Berroa/25	6.00	15.00
9 Aramis Ramirez/10		
10 Aubrey Huff/10		
11 Austin Kearns/50	5.00	12.00
12 Barry Larkin/1		
13 Barry Zito H/10		
15 Ben Sheets/10		
16 Bernie Williams/10		
17 Bobby Abreu/9		
18 Brandon Webb/21	6.00	15.00
20 C.C. Sabathia/10		
21 Carlos Beltran Royals A/50	8.00	20.00
23 Chipper Jones H/25	30.00	60.00
24 Craig Biggio/25	15.00	40.00
27 Delmon Young/10		
29 Derrek Lee/10		
30 Dontrelle Willis/25	15.00	40.00
31 Edgar Renteria/25	10.00	25.00
32 Eric Chavez/10		
33 Esteban Loaiza/10		
34 Frank Thomas/50	20.00	50.00
35 Fred McGriff/10		
36 Garret Anderson H/50	8.00	20.00
37 Gary Sheffield Yanks/50	12.50	30.00
39 Greg Maddux Cubs/25	50.00	100.00
40 Hank Blalock H/50	8.00	20.00
42 Hideo Nomo Dodgers/1		
46 Jacque Jones/25	10.00	25.00
48 Jake Peavy/10		
53 Jason Varitek/3		
54 Javier Vazquez/10		
56 Jay Gibbons/10		
57 Jay Payton/10		
58 Jeff Bagwell H/25	40.00	80.00
60 Jeremy Bonderman/10		
61 Jermaine Dye/10		
66 Jody Gerut/10		
67 Johan Santana/10		
71 Jorge Posada/25	20.00	50.00
72 Jose Contreras/10		
73 Jose Reyes/10		
74 Jose Vidro/10		
76 Juan Gonzalez Royals/25	10.00	25.00
79 Kazuhisa Ishii/25	10.00	25.00
80 Keith Foulke Sox/10		
82 Ken Harvey/10		
84 Kerry Wood/25	15.00	40.00
88 Lance Berkman/50	12.50	30.00
89 Larry Bigbie/10		
91 Laynce Nix/10		
94 Luis Matos/10		
95 Lyle Overbay/10		
97 Manny Ramirez Sox/10		
98 Marcus Giles/25	10.00	25.00
99 Mark Buehrle/10		
100 Mark Mulder/100	6.00	15.00
101 Mark Prior H/50	10.00	25.00
102 Mark Teixeira/50	12.50	30.00
105 Melvin Mora/10		
106 Michael Young/50	8.00	20.00
107 Miguel Cabrera Batting/50	12.50	30.00
109 Mike Lowell/25	10.00	25.00
110 Mike Mussina Yanks/10		
111 Mike Piazza Mets/1		
113 Milton Bradley/10		
115 Morgan Ensberg/10		
122 Paul Lo Duca/25	10.00	25.00
123 Pedro Martinez Sox/5		
125 Rafael Furcal/10		
127 Randy Johnson D'backs/10		
128 Rich Harden/10		
131 Rickie Weeks/25	10.00	25.00
132 Roberto Alomar/10		
133 Robin Ventura/10		
135 Roger Clemens Astros/5		
136 Roy Halladay/10		
137 Roy Oswalt A/50	8.00	20.00
140 Sammy Sosa H/25	50.00	100.00
141 Scott Podsednik/10		
142 Scott Rolen Cards A/25	15.00	40.00
143 Sean Burroughs/10		
144 Sean Casey/25	10.00	25.00
145 Shannon Stewart/25	10.00	25.00
146 Shawn Green Dodgers/10		
149 Steve Finley/5		
153 Todd Helton H/25	15.00	40.00
154 Tom Glavine Mets/10		
155 Torii Hunter/50	8.00	20.00
156 Trot Nixon/25	10.00	25.00
158 Vernon Wells H/25	10.00	25.00
159 Victor Martinez A/10		
163 Alfonso Soriano Yanks/100	10.00	25.00
164 Andy Pettitte Yanks/10		
166 Gary Sheffield Braves/50	12.50	30.00
167 Greg Maddux Braves/25	50.00	100.00
168 Hideo Nomo Sox/1		
172 Juan Gonzalez Rgr/25	10.00	25.00
175 Manny Ramirez Indians/10		
177 Mike Mussina O's/10		
178 Mike Piazza Dodgers/1		
179 Pedro Martinez Expos/5		
181 Randy Johnson Astros/10		
182 Roger Clemens Sox/5		
183 Scott Rolen Phils/25	15.00	40.00
184 Shawn Green Jays/10		
185 Tom Glavine Braves/10		
188 Mike Piazza Marlins/1		
189 Randy Johnson M's/10		
190 Roger Clemens Yanks/5		
191 Albert Pujols A/25	150.00	250.00
192 Barry Zito A/10		
193 Chipper Jones A/25	30.00	60.00
194 Garret Anderson A/50	8.00	20.00
195 Jeff Bagwell A/25	40.00	80.00
198 Mark Prior A/50	10.00	25.00
199 Sammy Sosa A/25	50.00	100.00
200 Todd Helton A/25	15.00	40.00
201 Andre Dawson RET/100	6.00	15.00
203 Bob Feller RET/100	10.00	25.00
204 Bob Gibson RET/100	10.00	25.00
205 Bobby Doerr RET/100	6.00	15.00
206 Cal Ripken RET/25	125.00	200.00
207 Dale Murphy RET/100	10.00	25.00
208 Don Mattingly RET/100	30.00	60.00
209 Gary Carter RET/100	6.00	15.00
210 George Brett RET/25	40.00	80.00
212 Lou Brock RET/100	10.00	25.00
214 Mark Grace RET/100	10.00	25.00
215 Maury Wills RET/100	6.00	15.00
216 Mike Schmidt RET/100	30.00	60.00
217 Nolan Ryan RET/100	50.00	100.00
218 Orel Hershiser RET/25	15.00	40.00
219 Paul Molitor RET/100	6.00	15.00
221 Rod Carew RET/100	10.00	25.00
223 Ryne Sandberg RET/100	20.00	50.00
224 Stan Musial RET/100	30.00	60.00
226 Tony Gwynn RET/100	15.00	40.00
228 Whitey Ford RET/10		
229 Yogi Berra RET/10		
230 Carlos Beltran Astros H/50	8.00	20.00
231 David Ortiz H/50	20.00	50.00
232 David Ortiz A/50	20.00	50.00
233 Carlos Zambrano/25	15.00	40.00
234 Carlos Lee/25	10.00	25.00
235 Travis Hafner/10		
236 Brad Penny/10		
237 Wade Miller/10		
238 Edgar Martinez/25	20.00	50.00
239 Carl Crawford/10		
240 Roy Oswalt H/50	8.00	20.00
242 Carlos Beltran Astros A/50	8.00	20.00
243 Carlos Beltran Royals H/50	8.00	20.00
244 Miguel Cabrera Fielding/50	12.50	30.00
245 Scott Rolen Cards H/25	15.00	40.00
246 Hank Blalock A/50	8.00	20.00
247 Vernon Wells A/25	10.00	25.00
248 Adam Dunn H/50	8.00	20.00
250 Victor Martinez H/10		

2004 Leaf Limited Moniker Gold

*1-220/230-250 p/r 25: .6X TO 1.5X p/r 100
*1-220/230-250 p/r 25: .5X TO 1.2X p/r 50
*201-229 p/r 25: .6X TO 1.5X p/r 100
OVERALL AU-GU ODDS ONE PER PACK
PRINT RUNS B/WN 1-25 COPIES PER
NO PRICING ON QTY OF 10 OR LESS

2004 Leaf Limited Moniker Platinum

OVERALL AU-GU ODDS ONE PER PACK
STATED PRINT RUN 1 SERIAL #'d SET
NO PRICING DUE TO SCARCITY

2004 Leaf Limited Moniker Silver

*1-200/230-250 p/r 50: .5X TO 1.2X p/r 100
*1-200/230-250 p/r 25: .5X TO 1.2X p/r 50
*201-229 p/r 50: .5X TO 1.2X p/r 100
OVERALL AU-GU ODDS ONE PER PACK
PRINT RUNS B/WN 1-50 COPIES PER
NO PRICING ON QTY OF 10 OR LESS

2004 Leaf Limited Moniker Bat

*1-200/230-250 p/r 40-50: .5X TO 1.2X Jsy/75
*1-200/230-250p/r40-50: .4X TO 1X Jsy/38-50
*1-200/230-250 p/r 40-50: .3X TO .8X Jsy/25
*1-200/230-250 p/r 25: .5X TO 1.2X Jsy/50
*1-200/230-250 p/r 25: .4X TO 1X Jsy/25
*1-200/230-250 p/r 15: .6X TO 1.5X Jsy/50
*1-200/230-250 p/r 15: .5X TO 1.2X Jsy/25
*201-229 p/r 100: .4X TO 1X Jsy/100
*201-229 p/r 50: .5X TO 1.2X Jsy/100
*201-229 p/r 50: .4X TO 1X Jsy/50
*201-229 p/r 50: .3X TO .8X Jsy/25
*201-229 p/r 25: .5X TO 1.2X Jsy/50
*201-229 p/r 25: .4X TO 1X Jsy/25
OVERALL AU-GU ODDS ONE PER PACK
PRINT RUNS B/WN 1-100 COPIES PER
NO PRICING ON QTY OF 10 OR LESS

27 Delmon Young/50	15.00	40.00
31 Edgar Renteria/25	12.50	30.00
37 Gary Sheffield Yanks/25	20.00	50.00
61 Jermaine Dye/25	12.50	30.00
106 Michael Young/50	10.00	25.00
131 Rickie Weeks/25	12.50	30.00
212 Lou Brock RET/50	15.00	40.00
214 Mark Grace RET/25	20.00	50.00
250 Victor Martinez H/25	12.50	30.00

2004 Leaf Limited Moniker Jersey

OVERALL AU-GU ODDS ONE PER PACK
PRINT RUNS B/WN 1-100 COPIES PER
NO PRICING ON QTY OF 10 OR LESS

1 Adam Dunn A/50	8.00	20.00
3 Albert Pujols H/10		
5 Alfonso Soriano Rgr/50	15.00	40.00
6 Andruw Jones/25	20.00	50.00
7 Andy Pettitte Astros/10		
8 Angel Berroa Pants/25	8.00	20.00
9 Aramis Ramirez/25	12.50	30.00
10 Aubrey Huff/25	12.50	30.00
11 Austin Kearns/25	8.00	20.00
12 Barry Larkin/1		
13 Barry Zito H/10		
15 Ben Sheets/25	12.50	30.00
16 Bernie Williams/10		
17 Bobby Abreu/5		
18 Brandon Webb/25	8.00	20.00
20 C.C. Sabathia/25	12.50	30.00
21 Carlos Beltran Royals A/50	10.00	25.00
23 Chipper Jones H/25	40.00	80.00
24 Craig Biggio/25	20.00	50.00
30 Dontrelle Willis/25	20.00	50.00
31 Edgar Renteria/10		
32 Eric Chavez/50	10.00	25.00
34 Frank Thomas/25	40.00	80.00
35 Fred McGriff/25	20.00	50.00
36 Garret Anderson H/50	10.00	25.00
39 Greg Maddux Cubs/10		
40 Hank Blalock H/50	10.00	25.00
42 Hideo Nomo Dodgers/1		
46 Jacque Jones/25	12.50	30.00
53 Jason Varitek/1		
56 Jay Gibbons/5		
58 Jeff Bagwell H/10		
60 Jeremy Bonderman/5		
63 Jim Edmonds/25	20.00	50.00
66 Jody Gerut/25	8.00	20.00
67 Johan Santana/25	20.00	50.00
71 Jorge Posada/25	30.00	60.00
73 Jose Reyes/5		
74 Jose Vidro/25	8.00	20.00
76 Juan Gonzalez Royals/10		
78 Junior Spivey/1		
79 Kazuhisa Ishii/10		
84 Kerry Wood/25	20.00	50.00
88 Lance Berkman/25	20.00	50.00
89 Larry Bigbie/25	12.50	30.00
94 Luis Matos/10		
97 Manny Ramirez Sox/10		
98 Marcus Giles/25	12.50	30.00
99 Mark Buehrle/25	30.00	60.00
100 Mark Mulder/75	8.00	20.00
101 Mark Prior H/50	12.50	30.00
102 Mark Teixeira/25	20.00	50.00
103 Marlon Byrd/1		
105 Melvin Mora/25	12.50	30.00
107 Miguel Cabrera Batting/38	15.00	40.00
109 Mike Lowell/25	12.50	30.00
110 Mike Mussina Yanks/5		
111 Mike Piazza Mets/5		
115 Morgan Ensberg/25	8.00	20.00
122 Paul Lo Duca/25	12.50	30.00
123 Pedro Martinez Sox/10		
124 Preston Wilson H/25	12.50	30.00
125 Rafael Furcal/10		
127 Randy Johnson D'backs/10		
128 Rich Harden/1		
135 Roger Clemens Astros/10		
137 Roy Oswalt A/25	12.50	30.00
140 Sammy Sosa H/10		
142 Scott Rolen Cards A/50	15.00	40.00
143 Sean Burroughs/25	8.00	20.00
144 Sean Casey/25	12.50	30.00
145 Shannon Stewart/25	12.50	30.00
146 Shawn Green Dodgers/10		
149 Steve Finley/25	12.50	30.00
153 Todd Helton H/25	20.00	50.00
154 Tom Glavine Mets/25	20.00	50.00
155 Torii Hunter/25	12.50	30.00
156 Trot Nixon/25	12.50	30.00
158 Vernon Wells H/50	10.00	25.00
159 Victor Martinez A/50	10.00	25.00
162 Alex Rodriguez Rgr/1		
163 Alfonso Soriano Yanks/50	15.00	40.00
164 Andy Pettitte Yanks/10		
166 Gary Sheffield Braves/25	20.00	50.00
167 Greg Maddux Braves/10		
168 Hideo Nomo Sox/1		
172 Juan Gonzalez Rgr/25	12.50	30.00
177 Mike Mussina O's/5		
178 Mike Piazza Dodgers/5		
179 Pedro Martinez Expos/10		
181 Randy Johnson Astros/10		
182 Roger Clemens Sox/10		
183 Scott Rolen Phils/50	15.00	40.00
184 Shawn Green Jays/10		
185 Tom Glavine Braves/25	20.00	50.00
187 Alex Rodriguez M's/1		
188 Mike Piazza Marlins/5		
189 Randy Johnson M's/10		
190 Roger Clemens Yanks/10		
191 Albert Pujols A/10		
192 Barry Zito A/10		
193 Chipper Jones A/25	40.00	80.00
194 Garret Anderson A/50	10.00	25.00
195 Jeff Bagwell A/10		
198 Mark Prior A/50	12.50	30.00
199 Sammy Sosa A/10		
200 Todd Helton A/25	20.00	50.00
201 Andre Dawson RET/50	10.00	25.00
203 Bob Feller RET Pants/5		
204 Bob Gibson RET/50	15.00	40.00
205 Bobby Doerr RET/50	10.00	25.00
206 Cal Ripken RET/10		
207 Dale Murphy RET/100	12.50	30.00
208 Don Mattingly RET/50	40.00	80.00
209 Gary Carter RET/100	8.00	20.00
210 George Brett RET/10		
212 Lou Brock RET/5		
214 Mark Grace RET/10		
216 Mike Schmidt RET/50	40.00	80.00
217 Nolan Ryan RET/100	60.00	120.00
218 Orel Hershiser RET/50	15.00	40.00
219 Paul Molitor RET/50	10.00	25.00
221 Rod Carew RET/50	15.00	40.00
223 Ryne Sandberg RET/25	50.00	100.00
224 Stan Musial RET/25	50.00	100.00
226 Tony Gwynn RET/100	20.00	50.00
228 Whitey Ford RET Pants/25	20.00	50.00
229 Yogi Berra RET/25	40.00	80.00
230 Carlos Beltran Astros H/50	10.00	25.00
231 David Ortiz H/50	30.00	60.00
232 David Ortiz A/50	30.00	60.00
234 Carlos Lee/50	10.00	25.00
235 Travis Hafner/25	12.50	30.00
236 Brad Penny/25	8.00	20.00
237 Wade Miller/25	8.00	20.00
238 Edgar Martinez/50	20.00	50.00
239 Carl Crawford/25	12.50	30.00
240 Roy Oswalt H/25	12.50	30.00
242 Carlos Beltran Astros A/50	10.00	25.00
243 Carlos Beltran Royals H/50	10.00	25.00
244 Miguel Cabrera Fielding/50	15.00	40.00
245 Scott Rolen Cards H/50	15.00	40.00
246 Hank Blalock A/50	10.00	25.00
247 Vernon Wells A/50	10.00	25.00
248 Adam Dunn H/50	8.00	20.00
249 Preston Wilson A/25	12.50	30.00

2004 Leaf Limited Moniker Jersey Prime

OVERALL AU-GU ODDS ONE PER PACK
STATED PRINT RUN 1 SERIAL #'d SET
NO PRICING DUE TO SCARCITY

2004 Leaf Limited Moniker Jersey Number

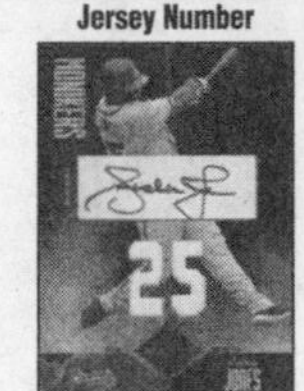

*1-200/230-250 p/r 75: .4X TO 1X Jsy/75
*1-200/230-250 p/r 50: .4X TO 1X Jsy/38-50
*1-200/230-250 p/r 25: .5X TO 1.2X Jsy/50
*1-200/230-250 p/r 25: .4X TO 1X Jsy/25
*201-229 p/r 100: .4X TO 1X Jsy/100
*201-229 p/r 50: .4X TO 1X Jsy/50
*201-229 p/r 25: .5X TO 1.2X Jsy/50
*201-229 p/r 25: .4X TO 1X Jsy/25
OVERALL AU-GU ODDS ONE PER PACK
PRINT RUNS B/WN 1-100 COPIES PER
NO PRICING ON QTY OF 10 OR LESS

140 Sammy Sosa H/25	50.00	100.00
199 Sammy Sosa A/25	50.00	100.00

2004 Leaf Limited Moniker Jersey Number Prime

OVERALL AU-GU ODDS ONE PER PACK
STATED PRINT RUN 1 SERIAL #'d SET
NO PRICING DUE TO SCARCITY

2004 Leaf Limited Threads Button

OVERALL AU-GU ODDS ONE PER PACK
PRINT RUNS B/WN 1-6 COPIES PER
NO PRICING DUE TO SCARCITY

2004 Leaf Limited Threads Jersey

OVERALL AU-GU ODDS ONE PER PACK
PRINT RUNS B/WN 1-100 COPIES PER
NO PRICING ON QTY OF 10 OR LESS

NO RC YR PRICING DUE TO SCARCITY
1 Adam Dunn A/25 5.00 12.00
2 Adrian Beltre/5
3 Albert Pujols H/50 10.00 25.00
5 Alfonso Soriano Rgr/25 5.00 12.00
6 Andruw Jones/25 8.00 20.00
7 Andy Pettitte Astros/5
8 Angel Berroa Pants/5
9 Aramis Ramirez/5
10 Aubrey Huff/5
11 Austin Kearns/25 5.00 12.00
12 Barry Larkin/25 8.00 20.00
13 Barry Zito H/25 5.00 12.00
15 Ben Sheets/5
16 Bernie Williams/50 5.00 12.00
17 Bobby Abreu/5
18 Brandon Webb/5
19 Brian Giles/5
20 C.C. Sabathia/5
21 Carlos Beltran Royals A/25 5.00 12.00
22 Carlos Delgado/25 5.00 12.00
23 Chipper Jones H/50 6.00 15.00
24 Craig Biggio/25 8.00 20.00
25 Curt Schilling Sox/25 8.00 20.00
26 Darin Erstad/10
30 Dontrelle Willis/25 8.00 20.00
31 Edgar Renteria/25 5.00 12.00
32 Eric Chavez/25 5.00 12.00
34 Frank Thomas/25 10.00 25.00
35 Fred McGriff/10
36 Garret Anderson H/25 5.00 12.00
38 Geoff Jenkins/5
39 Greg Maddux Cubs/50 8.00 20.00
40 Hank Blalock H/25 5.00 12.00
41 Hideki Matsui/50 20.00 50.00
42 Hideo Nomo Dodgers/50 6.00 15.00
44 Ivan Rodriguez Tigers/25 8.00 20.00
46 Jacque Jones/10
47 Jae Weong Seo/5
49 Jamie Moyer/5
50 Jason Giambi Yanks/50 3.00 8.00
51 Jason Kendall/5
53 Jason Varitek/5
55 Javy Lopez/25 5.00 12.00
56 Jay Gibbons/5
58 Jeff Bagwell H/50 5.00 12.00
59 Jeff Kent/50 3.00 8.00
60 Jeremy Bonderman/5
62 Jeromy Burnitz/1
63 Jim Edmonds/25 5.00 12.00
64 Jim Thome Phils/50 5.00 12.00
65 Jimmy Rollins/5
66 Jody Gerut/5
67 Johan Santana/5
68 John Olerud/10
69 John Smoltz/25 8.00 20.00
71 Jorge Posada/25 8.00 20.00
73 Jose Reyes/5
74 Jose Vidro/5
75 Josh Beckett H/25 5.00 12.00
76 Juan Gonzalez Royals/25 5.00 12.00
78 Junior Spivey/1
79 Kazuhisa Ishii/10
84 Kerry Wood/50 3.00 8.00
86 Kevin Millwood/10
88 Lance Berkman/50 3.00 8.00
89 Larry Bigbie/5
90 Larry Walker/25 5.00 12.00
92 Luis Castillo/5
93 Luis Gonzalez/25 5.00 12.00
94 Luis Matos/5
96 Magglio Ordonez H/25 5.00 12.00
97 Manny Ramirez Sox/50 5.00 12.00
98 Marcus Giles/5
99 Mark Buehrle/10
100 Mark Mulder/25 5.00 12.00
101 Mark Prior H/50 5.00 12.00
102 Mark Teixeira/10
103 Marlon Byrd/5
104 Matt Morris/10
105 Melvin Mora/5
107 Miguel Cabrera Batting/25 8.00 20.00
108 Miguel Tejada O's/25 5.00 12.00
109 Mike Lowell/1
110 Mike Mussina Yanks/50 5.00 12.00
111 Mike Piazza Mets/50 8.00 20.00
112 Mike Sweeney/25 5.00 12.00
115 Morgan Ensberg/5
118 Omar Vizquel/5
119 Orlando Cabrera/5
120 Pat Burrell/5
121 Paul Konerko/10
122 Paul Lo Duca/10
123 Pedro Martinez Sox/50 5.00 12.00
124 Preston Wilson H/5
125 Rafael Furcal/5
126 Rafael Palmeiro O's/25 8.00 20.00
127 Randy Johnson D'backs/25 10.00 25.00
128 Rich Harden/1
129 Richard Hidalgo Pants/5
130 Richie Sexson/10
134 Rocco Baldelli/10
135 Roger Clemens Astros/5
136 Roy Halladay/1
137 Roy Oswalt A/25 5.00 12.00
139 Ryan Klesko/5
140 Sammy Sosa H/50 6.00 15.00
142 Scott Rolen Cards A/25 8.00 20.00
143 Sean Burroughs/5
144 Sean Casey/5
145 Shannon Stewart/10
146 Shawn Green Dodgers/25 5.00 12.00
149 Steve Finley/5
150 Tim Hudson/25 5.00 12.00
151 Tim Salmon/5
152 Tino Martinez/5
153 Todd Helton H/50 5.00 12.00
154 Tom Glavine Mets/25 8.00 20.00
155 Torii Hunter/25 5.00 12.00
156 Trot Nixon/1
157 Troy Glaus/25 5.00 12.00
158 Vernon Wells H/25 5.00 12.00
159 Victor Martinez A/5
160 Vinny Castilla/5
161 Vladimir Guerrero Angels/25 10.00 25.00
162 Alex Rodriguez Rgr/100 5.00 12.00
163 Alfonso Soriano Yanks/50 3.00 8.00
164 Andy Pettitte Yanks/25 8.00 20.00
165 Curt Schilling D'backs/25 5.00 12.00
166 Gary Sheffield Braves/25 5.00 12.00
167 Greg Maddux Braves/50 8.00 20.00
168 Hideo Nomo Sox/25 10.00 25.00
169 Ivan Rodriguez Marlins/50 5.00 12.00
170 Jason Giambi A's/25 5.00 12.00
171 Jim Thome Indians/10
172 Juan Gonzalez Rgr/25 5.00 12.00
174 Kevin Brown Dodgers/25 5.00 12.00
176 Miguel Tejada A's/25 5.00 12.00
177 Mike Mussina O's/50 5.00 12.00
178 Mike Piazza Dodgers/25 12.50 30.00
179 Pedro Martinez Expos/25 8.00 20.00
180 Rafael Palmeiro Rgr/25 8.00 20.00
181 Randy Johnson Astros/50 6.00 15.00
182 Roger Clemens Sox/100 5.00 12.00
183 Scott Rolen Phils/25 8.00 20.00
184 Shawn Green Jays/25 5.00 12.00
185 Tom Glavine Braves/25 8.00 20.00
186 Vladimir Guerrero Expos/25 10.00 25.00
187 Alex Rodriguez M's/100 5.00 12.00
188 Mike Piazza Marlins/10
189 Randy Johnson M's/50 6.00 15.00
190 Roger Clemens Yanks/100 5.00 12.00
191 Albert Pujols A/50 10.00 25.00
192 Barry Zito A/25 5.00 12.00
193 Chipper Jones A/50 6.00 15.00
194 Garret Anderson A/25 5.00 12.00
195 Jeff Bagwell A/50 5.00 12.00
196 Josh Beckett A/25 5.00 12.00
197 Magglio Ordonez A/25 5.00 12.00
198 Mark Prior A/50 5.00 12.00
199 Sammy Sosa A/50 6.00 15.00
200 Todd Helton A/50 5.00 12.00
201 Andre Dawson RET/50 4.00 10.00
202 Babe Ruth RET/25 250.00 400.00
203 Bob Feller RET Pants/25 10.00 25.00
204 Bob Gibson RET/1
205 Bobby Doerr RET/50 4.00 10.00
206 Cal Ripken RET/100 20.00 50.00
207 Dale Murphy RET/100 5.00 12.00
208 Don Mattingly RET/50 12.50 30.00
209 Gary Carter RET/50 4.00 10.00
210 George Brett RET/100 8.00 20.00
211 J.Robinson RET Jkt/50 20.00 50.00
212 Lou Brock RET/25 10.00 25.00
213 Lou Gehrig RET/25 100.00 175.00
214 Mark Grace RET/25 10.00 25.00
215 Maury Wills RET/50 4.00 10.00
216 Mike Schmidt RET/100 8.00 20.00
217 Nolan Ryan RET/100 10.00 25.00
218 Orel Hershiser RET/25 10.00 25.00
219 Paul Molitor RET/50 4.00 10.00
220 Roberto Clemente RET/25 50.00 100.00
221 Rod Carew RET/100 5.00 12.00
222 R.Campanella RET Pants/50 8.00 20.00
223 Ryne Sandberg RET/50 12.50 30.00
224 Stan Musial RET/25 20.00 50.00
225 Ted Williams RET/50 30.00 80.00
226 Tony Gwynn RET/100 6.00 15.00
227 Ty Cobb RET Pants/100 40.00 80.00
228 Whitey Ford RET Pants/25 10.00 25.00
229 Yogi Berra RET/25 12.50 30.00
230 Carlos Beltran Astros H/25 5.00 12.00
231 David Ortiz H/25 10.00 25.00
232 David Ortiz A/25 10.00 25.00
234 Carlos Lee/10
235 Travis Hafner/5
236 Brad Penny/5
237 Wade Miller/5
238 Edgar Martinez/25 8.00 20.00
239 Carl Crawford/5
240 Roy Oswalt H/25 5.00 12.00
241 Kazuo Matsui/25
242 Carlos Beltran Astros A/25 5.00 12.00
243 Carlos Beltran Royals H/25 5.00 12.00
244 Miguel Cabrera Fielding/25 8.00 20.00
245 Scott Rolen Cards H/25 8.00 20.00
246 Hank Blalock A/25 5.00 12.00
247 Vernon Wells A/25 5.00 12.00
248 Adam Dunn H/25 5.00 12.00
249 Preston Wilson A/5

2004 Leaf Limited Threads Jersey Prime

OVERALL AU-GU ODDS ONE PER PACK
STATED PRINT RUN 1 SERIAL #'d SET
NO PRICING DUE TO SCARCITY

2004 Leaf Limited Threads Jersey Number

*1-200/230-250 p/r 100: .4X TO 1X Thrd/100
*1-200/230-250 p/r 50: .4X TO 1X Thrd/50
*1-200/230-250 p/r 25: .6X TO 1.5X Thrd/50
*1-200/230-250 p/r 25: .4X TO 1X Thrd/25
*201-229 p/r 100: .4X TO 1X Thrd/100
*201-229 p/r 100: .3X TO .8X Thrd/50
*201-229 p/r 50: .4X TO 1X Thrd/50
*201-229 p/r 25: .4X TO 1X Thrd/25
OVERALL AU-GU ODDS ONE PER PACK
PRINT RUNS B/WN 1-100 COPIES PER
NO PRICING ON QTY OF 10 OR LESS

2004 Leaf Limited Threads Jersey Number Prime

OVERALL AU-GU ODDS ONE PER PACK
STATED PRINT RUN 1 SERIAL #'d SET
NO PRICING DUE TO SCARCITY

2004 Leaf Limited Threads MLB Logo

OVERALL AU-GU ODDS ONE PER PACK
STATED PRINT RUN 1 SERIAL #'d SET
NO PRICING DUE TO SCARCITY

2004 Leaf Limited Timber

*1-200/230-250 p/r 100: .4X TO 1X Thrd/100
*1-200/230-250 p/r 50: .4X TO 1X Thrd/50
*1-200/230-250 p/r 25: 1X TO 2.5X Thrd/100
*1-200/230-250 p/r 25: .6X TO 1.5X Thrd/50
*1-200/230-250 p/r 25: .4X TO 1X Thrd/25
*201-229 p/r 100: .4X TO 1X Thrd/100
*201-229 p/r 100: .25X TO .6X Thrd/50
*201-229 p/r 100: .15X TO .4X Thrd/25
*201-229 p/r 50: .6X TO 1.5X Thrd/100
*201-229 p/r 50: .4X TO 1X Thrd/50
*201-229 p/r 25: 1X TO 2.5X Thrd/100
*201-229 p/r 25: .6X TO 1.5X Thrd/50
*201-229 p/r 25: .4X TO 1X Thrd/25
OVERALL AU-GU ODDS ONE PER PACK
PRINT RUNS B/WN 1-100 COPIES PER
NO PRICING ON QTY OF 10 OR LESS
4 Alex Rodriguez Yanks/100 5.00 12.00
7 Andy Pettitte Astros/25 8.00 20.00
35 Fred McGriff/25 8.00 20.00
37 Gary Sheffield Yanks/25 5.00 12.00
85 Kevin Brown Yanks/25 5.00 12.00
102 Mark Teixeira/25 8.00 20.00
106 Michael Young/25 5.00 12.00
109 Mike Lowell/25 5.00 12.00
116 Nick Johnson/25 5.00 12.00
117 Nomar Garciaparra/25 12.50 30.00
122 Paul Lo Duca/25 5.00 12.00
130 Richie Sexson/25 5.00 12.00
134 Rocco Baldelli/25 5.00 12.00
135 Roger Clemens Astros/25 12.50 30.00
156 Trot Nixon/25 5.00 12.00
171 Jim Thome Indians/25 8.00 20.00
175 Manny Ramirez Indians/25 8.00 20.00
186 Mike Piazza Marlins/25 12.50 30.00
202 Babe Ruth RET/100 75.00 150.00
213 Lou Gehrig RET/100 60.00 120.00
220 Roberto Clemente RET/100 40.00 80.00
225 Ted Williams RET/100 25.00 60.00

2004 Leaf Limited TNT

*1-200/230-250 p/r 100: .5X TO 1.2X Thrd/100
*1-200/230-250 p/r 100: .3X TO .8X Thrd/50
*1-200/230-250 p/r 50: .5X TO 1.2X Thrd/50
*1-200/230-250 p/r 50: .3X TO .8X Thrd/25
*1-200/230-250 p/r 25: .75X TO 2X Thrd/100
*1-200/230-250 p/r 25: .5X TO 1.2X Thrd/25
*201-229 p/r 100: .5X TO 1.2X Thrd/100
*201-229 p/r 100: .3X TO .8X Thrd/50
*201-229 p/r 50: .75X TO 2X Thrd/100
*201-229 p/r 50: .5X TO 1.2X Thrd/50
*201-229 p/r 25: .75X TO 2X Thrd/50
*201-229 p/r 25: .5X TO 1.2X Thrd/25
OVERALL AU-GU ODDS ONE PER PACK
PRINT RUNS B/WN 5-100 COPIES PER
NO PRICING ON QTY OF 10 OR LESS
102 Mark Teixeira Bat-Jsy/25 10.00 25.00
109 Mike Lowell Bat-Jsy/25 6.00 15.00

2004 Leaf Limited TNT Prime

OVERALL AU-GU ODDS ONE PER PACK
STATED PRINT RUN 1 SERIAL #'d SET
NO PRICING DUE TO SCARCITY

2004 Leaf Limited Cuts

OVERALL AU-GU ODDS ONE PER PACK
PRINT RUNS B/WN 50-100 COPIES PER
CUTS FABRIC IS NOT GAME-USED
1 Nolan Ryan/100 75.00 150.00
2 Bob Gibson/100 20.00 50.00
3 Harmon Killebrew/100 30.00 60.00
4 Duke Snider/100 15.00 40.00
5 George Brett/100 40.00 80.00
6 Stan Musial/100 50.00 100.00
7 Alan Trammell/100 10.00 25.00
8 Cal Ripken/100 100.00 200.00
9 Steve Carlton/50 12.50 30.00
10 Phil Rizzuto/100 15.00 40.00
11 Mark Prior/50 20.00 50.00
12 Will Clark/100 15.00 40.00
13 Lou Brock/100 15.00 40.00
14 Ozzie Smith/100 30.00 60.00
15 Bob Feller/100 15.00 40.00
16 Gary Carter/50 12.50 30.00
17 Al Kaline/100 20.00 50.00
18 Brooks Robinson/100 15.00 40.00
19 Tony Gwynn/100 30.00 60.00
20 Mike Schmidt/100 40.00 80.00
21 Ralph Kiner/50 20.00 50.00
22 Jim Palmer/50 20.00 50.00
23 Don Mattingly/100 40.00 80.00
24 Paul Molitor/50 12.50 30.00
25 Dale Murphy/100 15.00 40.00

2004 Leaf Limited Cuts Gold

*GOLD p/r 45: .4X TO 1X BASIC p/r 50
*GOLD p/r 20-35: .6X TO 1.5X BASIC p/r 100
*GOLD p/r 20-35: .5X TO 1.2X BASIC p/r 50
*GOLD p/r 19: .75X TO 2X BASIC p/r 100
OVERALL AU-GU ODDS ONE PER PACK
PRINT RUNS B/WN 1-45 COPIES PER
NO PRICING ON QTY OF 10 OR LESS
CUTS FABRIC IS NOT GAME-USED

2004 Leaf Limited Legends Material Number

PRINT RUNS B/WN 5-100 COPIES PER
*POSITION: .4X TO 1X NUMBER
POSITION PRINT RUNS B/WN 5-100 PER
OVERALL AU-GU ODDS ONE PER PACK
NO PRICING ON QTY OF 5 OR LESS
1 Al Kaline Pants/50 8.00 20.00
2 Babe Ruth Pants/50 125.00 200.00
3 Bob Feller Jsy/50 6.00 15.00
4 Bob Gibson Jsy/50 6.00 15.00
5 Brooks Robinson Jsy/5
6 Burleigh Grimes Pants/100 20.00 50.00
7 Carl Yastrzemski Jsy/100 8.00 20.00
8 Harmon Killebrew Jsy/25 12.50 30.00
9 Hoyt Wilhelm Jsy/100 3.00 8.00
10 Johnny Mize Pants/100 5.00 12.00
11 Ernie Banks Pants/50 8.00 20.00
12 Lou Brock Jsy/50 6.00 15.00
13 Luis Aparicio Pants/100 3.00 8.00
14 Pee Wee Reese Jsy/50 6.00 15.00
15 Reggie Jackson Jsy/50 5.00 12.00
16 Red Schoendienst Jsy/50 4.00 10.00
17 Roberto Clemente Jsy/25 50.00 100.00
18 Roger Maris Pants/100 12.50 30.00
19 Stan Musial Jsy/100 10.00 25.00
20 Ted Williams Jsy/50 30.00 80.00
21 Ty Cobb Pants/50 50.00 100.00
22 Warren Spahn Jsy/100 6.00 15.00
23 Whitey Ford Pants/100 5.00 12.00
24 Yogi Berra Jsy/25 8.00 20.00
25 Satchel Paige CO Jsy/100 30.00 60.00

2004 Leaf Limited Legends Material Autographs Number

PRINT RUNS B/WN 5-50 COPIES PER
*POSITION: .4X TO 1X NUMBER
POSITION PRINT RUNS B/WN 5-100 PER
OVERALL AU-GU ODDS ONE PER PACK
NO PRICING ON QTY OF 10 OR LESS
1 Al Kaline Pants/50 30.00 60.00
3 Bob Feller Jsy/50 15.00 40.00
4 Bob Gibson Jsy/50 15.00 40.00
5 Brooks Robinson Jsy/5
7 Carl Yastrzemski Jsy/25 50.00 100.00
8 Harmon Killebrew Jsy/25 50.00 100.00
9 Hoyt Wilhelm Jsy/25 20.00 50.00
12 Lou Brock Jsy/50 15.00 40.00
13 Luis Aparicio Pants/50 10.00 25.00
15 Reggie Jackson Jsy/50 30.00 60.00
16 Red Schoendienst Jsy/50 15.00 40.00
19 Stan Musial Jsy/50 40.00 80.00
22 Warren Spahn Jsy/10
23 Whitey Ford Pants/25 20.00 50.00
24 Yogi Berra Jsy/25 30.00 60.00

2004 Leaf Limited Lumberjacks

1-40 PRINT RUNS B/WN 16-714 PER
41-50 PRINT RUN 500 #'d SETS
RANDOM INSERTS IN PACKS
1 Al Kaline/399 1.50 4.00
2 Albert Pujols/114 6.00 15.00
3 Andre Dawson/438 1.00 2.50
4 Babe Ruth/714 4.00 10.00
5 Bo Jackson/141 2.00 5.00
6 Bobby Doerr/223 .75 2.00
7 Brooks Robinson/268 1.00 2.50
8 Cal Ripken/431 6.00 15.00
9 Carlton Fisk/376 1.00 2.50
10 Dale Murphy/398 1.00 2.50
11 Darryl Strawberry/335 .60 1.50
12 Don Mattingly/222 4.00 10.00
13 Duke Snider/407 1.00 2.50
14 Eddie Mathews/512 1.50 4.00
15 Eddie Murray/504 1.50 4.00
16 Frank Robinson/586 1.00 2.50
17 Frank Thomas/418 1.50 4.00
18 Gary Carter/324 .60 1.50
19 George Brett/317 3.00 8.00
20 Harmon Killebrew/573 1.50 4.00
21 Hideki Matsui/16 12.00 30.00
22 Lou Gehrig/493 3.00 8.00
23 Mark Grace/173 1.25 3.00
24 Mike Piazza/358 1.50 4.00
25 Mike Schmidt/548 2.50 6.00
26 Orlando Cepeda/379 .60 1.50
27 Rafael Palmeiro/528 1.00 2.50
28 Ralph Kiner/369 1.00 2.50
29 Reggie Jackson/563 1.00 2.50
30 Rickey Henderson/297 1.50 4.00
31 Roger Maris/275 1.50 4.00
32 Ryne Sandberg/282 3.00 8.00
33 Sammy Sosa/539 1.50 4.00
34 Scott Rolen/192 1.25 3.00
35 Stan Musial/475 2.50 6.00
36 Ted Williams/521 4.00 10.00
37 Thurman Munson/113 2.50 6.00
38 Vladimir Guerrero/234 2.00 5.00
39 Willie McCovey/521 1.00 2.50
40 Willie Stargell/475 1.00 2.50
41 Roberto Clemente / Stan Musial 4.00 10.00
42 Cal Ripken / Ernie Banks 6.00 15.00
43 Babe Ruth / Lou Gehrig 4.00 10.00
44 George Brett / Mike Schmidt 3.00 8.00
45 Frank Robinson / Jackie Robinson 1.50 4.00
46 Don Mattingly / Roger Maris 3.00 8.00
47 Nomar Garciaparra / Ted Williams 4.00 10.00
48 Johnny Bench / Mike Piazza 1.50 4.00
49 Reggie Jackson / Sammy Sosa 1.50 4.00
50 Mel Ott / Willie McCovey 1.50 4.00

2004 Leaf Limited Lumberjacks Black

*1-40 p/r 66: 1.5X TO 4X LJ p/r 251+
*1-40 p/r 37-61: 1.5X TO 4X LJ p/r 251+
*1-40 p/r 37-61: .75X TO 2X LJ p/r 126-250
*1-40 p/r 37-61: .6X TO 1.5X LJ p/r 66-125
*1-40 p/r 20-35: 2X TO 5X LJ p/r 251+
*1-40 p/r 20-35: 1.5X TO 4X LJ p/r 126-250
*1-40 p/r 20-35: 1.25X TO 3X LJ p/r 66-125
*1-40 p/r 16-17: 2X TO 5X LJ p/r 126-250
*1-40 p/r 16-17: .4X TO 1X LJ p/r 16
1-40 PRINT RUNS B/WN 16-66 COPIES PER
*BLACK 41-50: 1X TO 2.5X LJ 41-50
41-50 PRINT RUN 100 SERIAL #'d SETS

2004 Leaf Limited Lumberjacks Autographs

OVERALL AU-GU ODDS ONE PER PACK
PRINT RUNS B/WN 1-100 COPIES PER
NO PRICING ON QTY OF 10 OR LESS
1 Al Kaline/100 15.00 40.00
2 Albert Pujols/10
3 Andre Dawson/100 6.00 15.00
5 Bo Jackson/25 30.00 60.00
6 Bobby Doerr/100 6.00 15.00
7 Brooks Robinson/100 10.00 25.00
8 Cal Ripken/25 125.00 200.00
9 Carlton Fisk/25 15.00 40.00
10 Dale Murphy/100 10.00 25.00
11 Darryl Strawberry/100 6.00 15.00
12 Don Mattingly/25 40.00 80.00
13 Duke Snider/100 10.00 25.00
15 Eddie Murray/10
16 Frank Robinson/100 10.00 25.00
17 Frank Thomas/25 20.00 50.00
18 Gary Carter/100 6.00 15.00
19 George Brett/25 40.00 80.00
20 Harmon Killebrew/100 20.00 50.00
23 Mark Grace/25 15.00 40.00
24 Mike Piazza/10
25 Mike Schmidt/50 30.00 60.00
26 Orlando Cepeda/1
27 Rafael Palmeiro/1
28 Ralph Kiner/100 10.00 25.00
29 Reggie Jackson/25 30.00 60.00
30 Rickey Henderson/25 30.00 60.00
32 Ryne Sandberg/25 40.00 80.00
33 Sammy Sosa/10
34 Scott Rolen/25 15.00 40.00
35 Stan Musial/50 30.00 60.00
39 Willie McCovey/25 15.00 40.00

2004 Leaf Limited Lumberjacks Autographs Bat

*BAT p/r 100: .5X TO1.2X AU p/r 100
*BAT p/r 50: .6X TO1.5X AU p/r 100
*BAT p/r 50: .5X TO1.2X AU p/r 50
*BAT p/r 25: .75X TO2X AU p/r 100
*BAT p/r 25: .6X TO1.5X AU p/r 50
*BAT p/r 25: .5X TO1.2X AU p/r 25
*BAT p/r 17: .6X TO1.5X AU p/r 25
OVERALL AU-GU ODDS ONE PER PACK
PRINT RUNS B/WN 1-100 COPIES PER
NO PRICING ON QTY OF 10 OR LESS

2004 Leaf Limited Lumberjacks Autographs Jersey

*JSY p/r 100: .5X TO 1.2X AU p/r 100
*JSY p/r 50: .6X TO 1.5X AU p/r 100
*JSY p/r 50: .5X TO 1.2X AU p/r 50
*JSY p/r 50: .4X TO 1X AU p/r 25
*JSY p/r 25: .75X TO 2X AU p/r 100
*JSY p/r 25: .6X TO 1.5X AU p/r 50
*JSY p/r 25: .5X TO 1.2X AU p/r 25
*JSY p/r 17: .6X TO 1.5X AU p/r 25
OVERALL AU-GU ODDS ONE PER PACK
PRINT RUNS B/WN 5-100 COPIES PER
NO PRICING ON QTY OF 10 OR LESS
15 Eddie Murray/25 40.00 80.00
26 Orlando Cepeda Pants/50 10.00 25.00

2004 Leaf Limited Lumberjacks Barrel

OVERALL AU-GU ODDS ONE PER PACK
PRINT RUNS B/WN 1-5 COPIES PER
NO PRICING DUE TO SCARCITY

2004 Leaf Limited Lumberjacks Bat

OVERALL AU-GU ODDS ONE PER PACK
PRINT RUNS B/WN 25-100 COPIES PER
1 Al Kaline/100 6.00 15.00
2 Albert Pujols/100 6.00 15.00
3 Andre Dawson/25 6.00 15.00
4 Babe Ruth/100 100.00 175.00
5 Bo Jackson/50 8.00 20.00
6 Bobby Doerr/25 6.00 15.00
7 Brooks Robinson/100 5.00 12.00
8 Cal Ripken/100 20.00 50.00
9 Carlton Fisk/100 5.00 12.00
10 Dale Murphy/50 6.00 15.00
11 Darryl Strawberry/25 6.00 15.00
12 Don Mattingly/100 8.00 20.00
14 Eddie Mathews/100 6.00 15.00
15 Eddie Murray/100 6.00 15.00
16 Frank Robinson/100 3.00 8.00
17 Frank Thomas/25 10.00 25.00
18 Gary Carter/50 4.00 10.00
19 George Brett/100 8.00 20.00
20 Harmon Killebrew/100 6.00 15.00
21 Hideki Matsui/100 12.50 30.00
22 Lou Gehrig/100 60.00 120.00
23 Mark Grace/25 10.00 25.00
24 Mike Piazza/50 8.00 20.00
25 Mike Schmidt/100 8.00 20.00
26 Orlando Cepeda/50 4.00 10.00
27 Rafael Palmeiro/50 5.00 12.00
28 Ralph Kiner/100 3.00 8.00
29 Reggie Jackson/100 5.00 12.00
30 Rickey Henderson/100 6.00 15.00
31 Roger Maris/100 12.50 30.00
32 Ryne Sandberg/100 8.00 20.00
33 Sammy Sosa/100 4.00 10.00
34 Scott Rolen/25 8.00 20.00
35 Stan Musial/100 10.00 25.00
36 Ted Williams/100 25.00 60.00
37 Thurman Munson/100 10.00 25.00
38 Vladimir Guerrero/25 10.00 25.00
39 Willie McCovey/100 5.00 12.00
40 Willie Stargell/50 6.00 15.00
41 Roberto Clemente / Stan Musial /100 50.00 100.00
42 Cal Ripken / Ernie Banks /50 50.00 100.00
43 Babe Ruth / Lou Gehrig /25 175.00 300.00
44 George Brett / Mike Schmidt /50 20.00 50.00
46 Don Mattingly / Roger Maris /50 20.00 50.00
47 Nomar Garciaparra / Ted Williams /100 30.00 80.00
48 Johnny Bench / Mike Piazza /25 15.00 40.00
49 Reggie Jackson / Sammy Sosa /50 10.00 25.00
50 Mel Ott / Willie McCovey /100 15.00 40.00

2004 Leaf Limited Lumberjacks Jersey

*1-40 p/r 100: .4X TO 1X BAT p/r 100
*1-40 p/r 100: .25X TO .6X BAT p/r 50
*1-40 p/r 100: .15X TO .4X BAT p/r 25
*1-40 p/r 50: .6X TO 1.5X BAT p/r 100
*1-40 p/r 50: .4X TO 1X BAT p/r 50
*1-40 p/r 50: .25X TO .6X BAT p/r 25
*1-40 p/r 25: 1X TO 2.5X BAT p/r 100
*1-40 p/r 25: .4X TO 1X BAT p/r 25
*41-50 p/r 100: .25X TO .6X BAT p/r 50
*41-50 p/r 100: .15X TO .4X BAT p/r 25
*41-50 p/r 50: .6X TO 1.5X BAT p/r 100
*41-50 p/r 25: 1X TO 2.5X BAT p/r 100
*41-50 p/r 25: .4X TO 1X BAT p/r 25
OVERALL AU-GU ODDS ONE PER PACK
PRINT RUNS B/WN 4-100 COPIES PER
NO PRICING ON QTY OF 4 OR LESS

2004 Leaf Limited Lumberjacks Combos

*COMBO p/r 100: .5X TO 1.2X BAT p/r 100
*COMBO p/r 100: .3X TO .8X BAT p/r 50
*COMBO p/r 50: .75X TO 2X BAT p/r 100
*COMBO p/r 50: .5X TO 1.2X BAT p/r 50
*COMBO p/r 50: .3X TO .8X BAT p/r 25
*COMBO p/r 25: 1.25X TO 3X BAT p/r 100
*COMBO p/r 25: .5X TO 1.2X BAT p/r 25
*COMBO p/r 17: .6X TO 1.5X BAT p/r 25
OVERALL AU-GU ODDS ONE PER PACK
PRINT RUNS B/WN 17-100 COPIES PER

2004 Leaf Limited Matching Numbers

PRINT RUNS B/WN 25-100 COPIES PER
PRIME PRINT RUN 1 SERIAL #'d SET
NO PRIME PRICING DUE TO SCARCITY
OVERALL AU-GU ODDS ONE PER PACK
1 Bobby Doerr Jsy 6.00 15.00
Pee Wee Reese Jsy/100
2 Lou Gehrig Pants 125.00 200.00
Mel Ott Jsy/50
3 Albert Pujols Jsy 15.00 40.00
George Brett Jsy/100
4 Cal Ripken Jsy 30.00 60.00
Carl Yastrzemski Jsy/100
5 Dwight Gooden Jsy 8.00 20.00
Whitey Ford Pants/50
6 Mark Grace Jsy 12.50 30.00
Todd Helton Jsy/25
7 Robin Yount Jsy 20.00 50.00
Tony Gwynn Jsy/50
8 Frank Robinson Jsy 12.50 30.00
Mike Schmidt Jsy/100
9 Roberto Clemente Jsy 40.00 80.00
Sammy Sosa Jsy/100
10 Roger Clemens Jsy 12.50 30.00
Warren Spahn Pants/100
11 Mark Prior Jsy 12.50 30.00
Roger Clemens Jsy/50
12 Don Mattingly Jkt 15.00 40.00
Ryne Sandberg Jsy/100
13 Billy Williams Jsy 6.00 15.00
Wade Boggs Jsy/100
14 Catfish Hunter Jsy 6.00 15.00
Juan Marichal Jsy/50
15 Fergie Jenkins Pants 10.00 25.00
Greg Maddux Jsy/50
16 Kerry Wood Pants 15.00 40.00
Nolan Ryan Jsy/100
17 Rickey Henderson Jsy 15.00 40.00
Roger Maris Pants/100
18 Dontrelle Willis Jsy 8.00 20.00
Mike Mussina Jsy/50
19 Reggie Jackson Jsy 6.00 15.00
Willie McCovey Jsy/100
20 Bob Gibson Jsy 8.00 20.00
Pedro Martinez Jsy/50
21 Duke Snider Jsy 6.00 15.00
Paul Molitor Jsy/100
22 Johnny Bench Jsy 8.00 20.00
Lou Boudreau Jsy/100
23 Andre Dawson Jsy 8.00 20.00
Chipper Jones Jsy/100
24 Ernie Banks Jsy 8.00 20.00
Ken Boyer Jsy/100
25 Manny Ramirez Jsy 8.00 20.00
Rickey Henderson Jsy/100
26 Carlton Fisk Jsy 6.00 15.00
Scott Rolen Jsy/100
27 Nolan Ryan Jsy 12.50 30.00
Orlando Cepeda Pants/100
28 Roy Halladay Jsy 4.00 10.00
Steve Carlton Jsy/100
29 Eddie Mathews Jsy 8.00 20.00
Tom Seaver Jsy/100
30 Brandon Webb Jsy 6.00 15.00
Orel Hershiser Jsy/100

2004 Leaf Limited Player Threads Jersey Number

PRINT RUNS B/WN 10-100 COPIES PER
NO PRICING ON QTY OF 10 OR LESS
PRIME PRINT RUN 1 SERIAL #'d SET
NO PRIME PRICING DUE TO SCARCITY
OVERALL AU-GU ODDS ONE PER PACK
1 Mike Piazza/100 5.00 12.00
2 Roger Clemens/10
3 Nolan Ryan Jkt/100 10.00 25.00
4 Reggie Jackson/100 5.00 12.00
5 Wade Boggs/50 6.00 15.00
6 Steve Carlton Pants/100 3.00 8.00
7 Ivan Rodriguez/25 8.00 20.00
8 Pedro Martinez/50 5.00 12.00
9 R.Henderson Yanks/10
10 R.Hend Mets Pants/100 6.00 15.00
11 Randy Johnson/50 6.00 15.00
12 Curt Schilling/25 8.00 20.00
13 Roger Maris/50 20.00 50.00
14 Sammy Sosa/100 4.00 10.00
15 Gary Carter Pants/50 4.00 10.00
16 Gary Sheffield/25 5.00 12.00
17 Eddie Murray/50 8.00 20.00
18 Hideo Nomo/50 6.00 15.00
19 Rafael Palmeiro/50 5.00 12.00
20 Andre Dawson/50 4.00 10.00

2004 Leaf Limited Player Threads Double

*DBL p/r 100: .6X TO 1.5X PT p/r 100
*DBL p/r 100: .4X TO 1X PT p/r 50
*DBL p/r 100: .25X TO .6X PT p/r 25
*DBL p/r 50: .6X TO 1.5X PT p/r 50
*DBL p/r 50: .4X TO 1X PT p/r 25
OVERALL AU-GU ODDS ONE PER PACK
PRINT RUNS B/WN 50-100 COPIES PER
2 R.Clemens Sox-Yanks/100 10.00 25.00
9 R.Henderson A's-Jays/50 12.50 30.00

2004 Leaf Limited Player Threads Triple

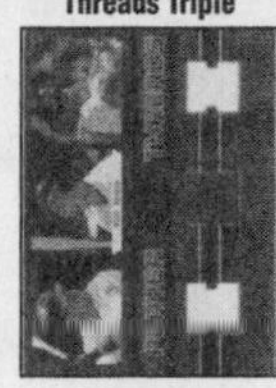

*TRIPLE p/r 50: 1.25X TO 3X PT p/r 100
*TRIPLE p/r 50: .75X TO 2X PT p/r 50
*TRIPLE p/r 25: 1.5X TO 4X PT p/r 100
*TRIPLE p/r 25: 1X TO 2.5X PT p/r 50
*TRIPLE p/r 25: .6X TO 1.5X PT p/r 25
OVERALL AU-GU ODDS ONE PER PACK
PRINT RUNS B/WN 10-50 COPIES PER
NO PRICING ON QTY OF 10 OR LESS
2 R.Clem Astros-Sox-Yanks/25 25.00 60.00
13 Roger Maris 75.00 150.00
A's Pants-Cards Bat-Yanks Jsy/25

2004 Leaf Limited Team Threads Jersey Number

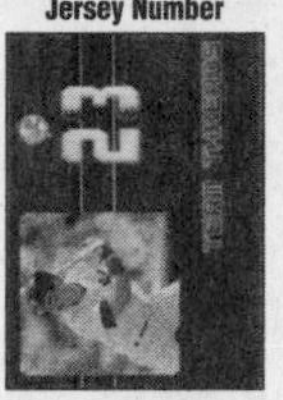

STATED PRINT RUN 100 SERIAL #'d SETS
PRIME PRINT RUN 1 SERIAL #'d SET
NO PRIME PRICING DUE TO SCARCITY
OVERALL AU-GU ODDS ONE PER PACK
ALL ARE DUAL JSY CARDS UNLESS NOTED
1 Stan Musial 20.00 50.00
Albert Pujols
2 Cal Ripken Jkt 20.00 50.00
Mike Mussina
3 Carlton Fisk 12.50 30.00
Roger Clemens
4 Dale Murphy 8.00 20.00
Chipper Jones
5 Tony Gwynn 12.50 30.00
Dave Winfield
6 Don Mattingly 30.00 60.00
Hideki Matsui
7 Lou Boudreau 8.00 20.00
Early Wynn
8 Ernie Banks 15.00 40.00
Sammy Sosa
9 Nolan Ryan Jkt 30.00 60.00
Jeff Bagwell
10 Mike Schmidt 12.50 30.00
Jim Thome

2004 Leaf Limited Team Trademarks

STATED PRINT RUN 100 SERIAL #'d SETS
GOLD PRINT RUN 10 SERIAL #'d SETS
NO GOLD PRICING DUE TO SCARCITY
RANDOM INSERTS IN PACKS
1 Bob Gibson 2.50 6.00
2 Cal Ripken 15.00 40.00
3 Carl Yastrzemski 4.00 10.00
4 Dale Murphy 2.50 6.00
5 Gary Carter 1.50 4.00
6 George Brett 8.00 20.00
7 Tom Seaver 2.50 6.00
8 Kerry Wood 1.50 4.00
9 Lou Brock 2.50 6.00
10 Luis Aparicio 1.50 4.00
11 Mike Piazza 4.00 10.00
12 Nolan Ryan Astros 12.00 30.00
13 Nolan Ryan Rgr 12.00 30.00
14 Randy Johnson 4.00 10.00
15 Reggie Jackson 2.50 6.00
16 Rickey Henderson 4.00 10.00
17 Robin Yount 4.00 10.00
18 Rod Carew 2.50 6.00
19 Ryne Sandberg 8.00 20.00
20 Steve Carlton 1.50 4.00
21 Steve Garvey 1.50 4.00
22 Johnny Bench 4.00 10.00
23 Tony Gwynn 4.00 10.00
24 Whitey Ford 2.50 6.00
25 Will Clark 2.50 6.00

2004 Leaf Limited Team Trademarks Autographs

OVERALL AU-GU ODDS ONE PER PACK
PRINT RUNS B/WN 5-100 COPIES PER
NO PRICING ON QTY OF 10 OR LESS
1 Bob Gibson/100 10.00 25.00
2 Cal Ripken/25 125.00 200.00
3 Carl Yastrzemski/25 40.00 80.00
4 Dale Murphy/100 10.00 25.00
5 Gary Carter/100 6.00 15.00
6 George Brett/25 40.00 80.00
7 Tom Seaver/25 30.00 60.00
8 Kerry Wood/25 15.00 40.00
9 Lou Brock/100 10.00 25.00
10 Luis Aparicio/100 6.00 15.00
11 Mike Piazza/5
12 Nolan Ryan Astros/25 60.00 120.00
13 Nolan Ryan Rgr/25 60.00 120.00
14 Randy Johnson/5
15 Reggie Jackson/25 30.00 60.00
16 Rickey Henderson/10
17 Robin Yount/50 30.00 60.00
18 Rod Carew/50 12.50 30.00
19 Ryne Sandberg/25 40.00 80.00
20 Steve Carlton/100 6.00 15.00
21 Steve Garvey/50 8.00 20.00
22 Johnny Bench/25 30.00 60.00
23 Tony Gwynn/100 15.00 40.00
24 Whitey Ford/25 15.00 40.00
25 Will Clark/34 15.00 40.00

2004 Leaf Limited Team Trademarks Autographs Jersey Number

*JSY NBR p/r 84-100: .5X TO 1.2X AU p/r 100
*JSY NBR p/r 84-100: .3X TO .8X AU p/r 25-34
*JSY NBR p/r 50: .6X TO 1.5X AU p/r 100
*JSY NBR p/r 50: .5X TO 1.2X AU p/r 50
*JSY NBR p/r 50: .4X TO 1X AU p/r 25-34
*JSY NBR p/r 25: .75X TO 2X AU p/r 100
*JSY NBR p/r 25: .5X TO 1.2X AU p/r 25-34
PRINT RUNS B/WN 5-100 COPIES PER
NO PRICING ON QTY OF 10 OR LESS
PRIME PRINT RUN 1 SERIAL #'d SET
NO PRIME PRICING DUE TO SCARCITY
OVERALL AU-GU ODDS ONE PER PACK

2004 Leaf Limited Team Trademarks Jersey Number

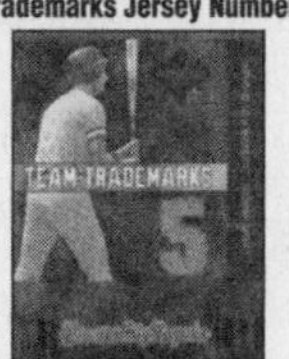

PRINT RUNS B/WN 6-100 COPIES PER
NO PRICING ON QTY OF 6 OR LESS
PRIME PRINT RUN 1 SERIAL #'d SET
NO PRIME PRICING DUE TO SCARCITY
OVERALL AU-GU ODDS ONE PER PACK
1 Bob Gibson/100 5.00 12.00
2 Cal Ripken Pants/100 20.00 50.00
3 Carl Yastrzemski/100 8.00 20.00
4 Dale Murphy/100 5.00 12.00
5 Gary Carter/100 3.00 8.00
6 George Brett/100 8.00 20.00
7 Tom Seaver/100 5.00 12.00
8 Kerry Wood Pants/50 3.00 8.00
9 Lou Brock/100 5.00 12.00
10 Luis Aparicio Pants/100 3.00 8.00
11 Mike Piazza/50 8.00 20.00
12 Nolan Ryan Astros/100 10.00 25.00
13 Nolan Ryan Rgr/100 10.00 25.00
14 Randy Johnson/50 6.00 15.00
15 Reggie Jackson Pants/100 5.00 12.00
16 Rickey Henderson/100 6.00 15.00
17 Robin Yount/100 6.00 15.00
18 Rod Carew Jkt/100 5.00 12.00
19 Ryne Sandberg/100 8.00 20.00
20 Steve Carlton/50 4.00 10.00
21 Steve Garvey/6
22 Johnny Bench/100 6.00 15.00
23 Tony Gwynn/100 6.00 15.00
24 Whitey Ford/100 5.00 12.00
25 Will Clark/50 6.00 15.00

2005 Leaf Limited

This 204-card set was released in August, 2005. The set was issued in four-card tins with an $70 SRP which were issued one pack per box and 10 boxes per case. The first 150 cards in the set feature active veterans with the 1st 20 cards featuring players in home and away uniforms. Each of those cards were issued to a stated print run of 699 serial numbered sets. Cards numbered 151 through 168 feature retired greats, while cards 169-175 feature active players in uniforms they wore during key parts of their career. The set concludes with cards number 176 through 204 which feature signed Rookie Cards (with the exception of Tadahito Iguchi). All cards numbered 151 through 205 were issued to a stated print run of 99 serial numbered sets except for a couple exceptions which we have notated in our checklist. Cards numbered 176 through 205 were issued at a stated rate of one in two. Card number 204 was not issued.

COMMON CARD (1-150) 1.00 2.50
1-150 PRINT RUN 699 SERIAL #'d SETS
COMMON CARD (151-168) 1.25 3.00
COMMON CARD (169-175) 1.25 3.00
COMMON CARD (197) 2.00 5.00
151-175/197 PRINT RUN 99 #'d SETS
COM.AU (176-196/198-200) 6.00 15.00
176-196/198-200 PRINT RUN 99 #'d SETS
COM.AU CUT (201-205) 10.00 25.00
201-205 PRINTS B/WN 70-99 COPIES PER
176-205: OVERALL AU ODDS 1:2
201-205 CUTS FABRIC IS NOT GAME-USED
CARD 204 DOES NOT EXIST
1 Roger Clemens H 3.00 8.00
2 Roger Clemens A 3.00 8.00
3 Ichiro Suzuki H 4.00 10.00
4 Ichiro Suzuki A 4.00 10.00
5 Todd Helton H 1.50 4.00
6 Todd Helton A 1.50 4.00
7 Vladimir Guerrero H 2.50 6.00
8 Vladimir Guerrero A 2.50 6.00
9 Miguel Cabrera H 2.50 6.00
10 Miguel Cabrera A 2.50 6.00
11 Albert Pujols H 6.00 15.00
12 Albert Pujols A 6.00 15.00
13 Mark Prior H 1.50 4.00
14 Mark Prior A 1.50 4.00
15 Chipper Jones H 2.50 6.00
16 Chipper Jones A 2.50 6.00
17 Jeff Bagwell H 1.50 4.00
18 Jeff Bagwell A 1.50 4.00
19 Kerry Wood H 1.00 2.50
20 Kerry Wood A 1.00 2.50
21 Gary Sheffield 1.00 2.50
22 Carl Crawford 1.50 4.00
23 Mariano Rivera 2.50 6.00
24 Curt Schilling 1.50 4.00
25 Ben Sheets 1.00 2.50
26 Jimmy Rollins 1.50 4.00
27 Melvin Mora 1.00 2.50
28 Corey Patterson 1.00 2.50
29 Rafael Furcal 1.00 2.50
30 Jim Thome 1.50 4.00
31 Derek Jeter 6.00 15.00
32 Jake Peavy 1.00 2.50
33 Francisco Cordero 1.00 2.50
34 Aramis Ramirez 1.00 2.50
35 Javy Lopez 1.00 2.50
36 Aaron Rowand 1.00 2.50
37 Jason Bay 1.00 2.50
38 Michael Young 1.50 4.00
39 Ivan Rodriguez 1.50 4.00
40 Joe Nathan 1.00 2.50
41 Oliver Perez 1.00 2.50
42 Adam Dunn 1.50 4.00
43 Eric Chavez 1.00 2.50
44 Pedro Martinez 1.50 4.00
45 Roy Oswalt 1.50 4.00
46 Carlos Delgado 1.00 2.50
47 Jeff Kent 1.00 2.50
48 Johnny Damon 1.50 4.00
49 Edgar Renteria 1.00 2.50
50 Mark Buehrle 1.50 4.00
51 Carl Pavano 1.00 2.50
52 J.D. Drew 1.00 2.50
53 Hank Blalock 1.00 2.50
54 Moises Alou 1.00 2.50
55 Brad Radke 1.00 2.50
56 Brad Wilkerson 1.00 2.50
57 Sean Casey 1.00 2.50
58 Mike Lowell 1.00 2.50
59 Octavio Dotel 1.00 2.50
60 Francisco Rodriguez 1.50 4.00
61 Jose Guillen 1.00 2.50
62 Greg Maddux 4.00 10.00
63 A.J. Burnett 1.50 4.00
64 Chris Carpenter 2.50 6.00
65 Jose Reyes 1.50 4.00
66 Travis Hafner 1.00 2.50
67 Rich Harden 1.00 2.50
68 Bret Boone 1.00 2.50
69 Scott Podsednik 1.00 2.50
70 Andruw Jones 1.00 2.50
71 Milton Bradley 1.00 2.50
72 Zack Greinke 1.50 4.00
73 Torii Hunter 1.00 2.50
74 Paul Konerko 1.50 4.00
75 David Wells 1.00 2.50
76 Tim Hudson 1.50 4.00
77 Sammy Sosa 2.50 6.00
78 Jason Varitek 2.50 6.00
79 Lance Berkman 1.50 4.00
80 Justin Morneau 2.50 6.00
81 Troy Glaus 1.00 2.50
82 Jose Vidro 1.00 2.50
83 Joe Mauer 2.50 6.00
84 Josh Beckett 1.50 4.00
85 Craig Biggio 1.50 4.00
86 Luis Gonzalez 1.00 2.50
87 Larry Walker 1.50 4.00
88 Barry Zito 1.00 2.50
89 Jacque Jones 1.00 2.50
90 Lyle Overbay 1.00 2.50
91 Roy Halladay 2.50 6.00
92 Orlando Cabrera 1.00 2.50
93 Magglio Ordonez 1.50 4.00
94 Mike Sweeney 1.00 2.50
95 Rafael Palmeiro 1.50 4.00
96 Brandon Webb 1.50 4.00
97 Preston Wilson 1.00 2.50
98 Shannon Stewart 1.00 2.50
99 Trot Nixon 1.00 2.50
100 Mike Piazza 2.50 6.00
101 Dontrelle Willis 1.00 2.50
102 Ken Griffey Jr. 4.00 10.00
103 Andy Pettitte 1.50 4.00
104 Kazuo Matsui 1.00 2.50
105 Bobby Crosby 1.00 2.50
106 Shawn Green 1.00 2.50
107 Alfonso Soriano 1.50 4.00
108 Carlos Zambrano 1.50 4.00
109 Keith Foulke 1.00 2.50
110 Aubrey Huff 1.00 2.50
111 Adrian Beltre 1.00 2.50
112 Mark Teixeira 2.50 6.00
113 Randy Johnson 2.50 6.00
114 Miguel Tejada 1.50 4.00
115 Alex Rodriguez 4.00 10.00
116 Carlos Beltran 1.00 2.50
117 Bobby Abreu 1.00 2.50
118 Johan Santana 2.50 6.00
119 Manny Ramirez 2.50 6.00
120 Juan Pierre 1.00 2.50
121 Scott Rolen 1.50 4.00
122 Livan Hernandez 1.00 2.50
123 Carlos Lee 1.00 2.50
124 Derrek Lee 1.00 2.50
125 Brian Giles 1.00 2.50
126 Nomar Garciaparra 2.50 6.00
127 John Smoltz 2.50 6.00
128 Jim Edmonds 1.50 4.00
129 Bartolo Colon 1.00 2.50
130 Garret Anderson 1.00 2.50
131 Austin Kearns 1.00 2.50
132 Shingo Takatsu 1.00 2.50
133 Omar Vizquel 1.50 4.00
134 Tom Glavine 1.50 4.00
135 Mark Mulder 1.00 2.50
136 Bernie Williams 1.50 4.00
137 Richie Sexson 1.00 2.50
138 Mike Mussina 1.50 4.00
139 Mark Loretta 1.00 2.50
140 Vernon Wells 1.00 2.50
141 David Wright 4.00 10.00
142 Marcus Giles 1.00 2.50
143 David Ortiz 2.50 6.00
144 Victor Martinez 1.50 4.00
145 Hideki Matsui 4.00 10.00
146 C.C. Sabathia 1.50 4.00
147 Angel Berroa 1.00 2.50
148 Troy Percival 1.00 2.50
149 Paul Lo Duca 1.00 2.50
150 Jorge Posada 1.50 4.00
151 Willie Mays LGD 6.00 15.00
152 Ryne Sandberg LGD 6.00 15.00
153 Rickey Henderson LGD 2.00 5.00
154 Ted Williams LGD 6.00 15.00
155 Roberto Clemente LGD 8.00 20.00
156 George Brett LGD 6.00 15.00
157 Whitey Ford LGD 2.00 5.00
158 Duke Snider LGD 2.00 5.00
159 Don Mattingly LGD 6.00 15.00
160 Bob Gibson LGD 2.00 5.00
161 Hank Aaron LGD 6.00 15.00
162 Al Kaline LGD 3.00 8.00
163 Nolan Ryan LGD 8.00 20.00
164 Stan Musial LGD 5.00 12.00
165 George Kell LGD 1.25 3.00
166 Harmon Killebrew LGD 3.00 8.00
167 Cal Ripken LGD 12.00 30.00
168 Babe Ruth LGD 8.00 20.00
169 Roger Clemens Sox SP 4.00 10.00
170 Curt Schilling D'backs SP 2.00 5.00
171 Rafael Palmeiro Rgr SP 2.00 5.00
172 Randy Johnson M's SP 3.00 8.00
173 Mike Piazza Dgr SP 3.00 8.00
174 Greg Maddux Braves SP 5.00 12.00
175 Sammy Sosa Cubs SP 3.00 8.00
176 Hayden Penn PH AU RC 10.00 25.00
177 A.Concepcion PH AU RC 6.00 15.00
178 Casey Rogowski PH AU RC 8.00 20.00
179 Prince Fielder PH AU RC 30.00 60.00
180 Geovany Soto PH AU RC 12.50 30.00
181 W.Balentien PH AU RC 10.00 25.00
182 Jason Hammel PH AU RC 6.00 15.00
183 Keiichi Yabu PH AU RC 10.00 25.00
184 B.McCarthy PH AU RC 20.00 50.00
185 Ubaldo Jimenez PH AU RC 12.50 30.00
186 Keiichi Yabu PH AU RC 10.00 25.00
187 Miguel Negron PH AU RC 8.00 20.00
188 Mike Morse PH AU RC 6.00 15.00
189 Nate McLouth PH AU RC 10.00 25.00
190 N.Nakamura PH AU RC 15.00 40.00
191 B.McCarthy PH AU RC 20.00 50.00
192 Tony Pena PH AU RC 6.00 15.00
193 A.Concepcion PH AU RC 6.00 15.00
194 Raul Tablado PH AU RC 6.00 15.00
195 Hayden Penn PH AU RC 10.00 25.00
196 Sean Thompson PH AU RC 6.00 15.00
197 Tadahito Iguchi PH RC 3.00 8.00
198 Ubaldo Jimenez PH AU RC 12.50 30.00
199 W.Balentien PH AU RC 10.00 25.00
200 Prince Fielder PH AU RC 30.00 60.00
201 P.Humber PHC AU/99 RC 20.00 50.00
202 J.Niemann PHC AU/95 RC 20.00 50.00
203 J.Verlander PHC AU/70 RC 75.00 150.00
205 Y.Betan PHC AU/99 RC 50.00 80.00

2005 Leaf Limited Bronze Spotlight

*BRZ 1-150: .6X TO 1.5X BASIC
*BRZ 151-168: .4X TO 1X BASIC
*BRZ 169-175: .4X TO 1X BASIC
*BRZ 176-196/298-200: .12X TO .3X BASIC AU
*BRZ 197: .3X TO .8X BASIC
OVERALL INSERT ODDS ONE PER PACK
STATED PRINT RUN 99 SERIAL #'d SETS
179 Prince Fielder PH 6.00 15.00
180 Geovany Soto PH 6.00 15.00
185 Ubaldo Jimenez PH 4.00 10.00
198 Ubaldo Jimenez PH 4.00 10.00
200 Prince Fielder PH 6.00 15.00

2005 Leaf Limited Gold Spotlight

*GOLD 1-150: 1.5X TO 4X BASIC
*GOLD 151-168: 1X TO 2.5X BASIC
*GOLD 169-175: 1X TO 2.5X BASIC
OVERALL INSERT ODDS ONE PER PACK
1-200 PRINT RUN 25 SERIAL #'d SETS
201-205 AU PRINTS B/WN 5-25 COPIES PER
176-205 NO PRICING DUE TO SCARCITY
201-205 CUTS FABRIC IS NOT GAME-USED
CARD 204 DOES NOT EXIST

2005 Leaf Limited Platinum Spotlight

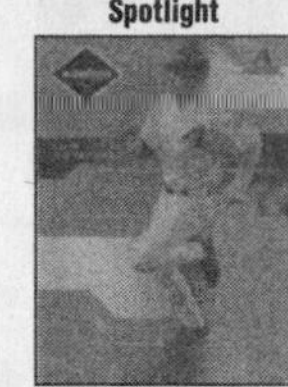

OVERALL INSERT ODDS ONE PER PACK
STATED PRINT RUN 1 SERIAL #'d SET
NO PRICING DUE TO SCARCITY
201-205 CUTS FABRIC IS NOT GAME-USED
CARD 204 DOES NOT EXIST

2005 Leaf Limited Silver Spotlight

*SILV 1-150: .75X TO 2X BASIC
*SILV 151-168: .5X TO 1.2X BASIC
*SILV 169-175: .5X TO 1.2X BASIC
COMMON CARD (176-200) 1.50 4.00
SEMISTARS 176-200 2.50 6.00
UNLISTED STARS 176-200 4.00 10.00
*SILV 176-196/298-200: .15X TO .4X BASE AU
*SILV 197: .4X TO 1X BASIC
OVERALL INSERT ODDS ONE PER PACK
STATED PRINT RUN 50 SERIAL #'d SETS
179 Prince Fielder PH 8.00 20.00
180 Geovany Soto PH 8.00 20.00
186 Keiichi Yabu PH 1.50 4.00
198 Ubaldo Jimenez PH 5.00 12.00
200 Prince Fielder PH 8.00 20.00

2005 Leaf Limited Monikers Bronze

OVERALL AU-GU ODDS ONE PER PACK
PRINT RUNS B/WN 1-100 COPIES PER
1-175 NO PRICING ON QTY OF 12 OR LESS
176-200 NO PRICING ON QTY 20 OR LESS
1 Roger Clemens H/1
2 Roger Clemens A/1
5 Todd Helton H/1
6 Todd Helton A/1
9 Miguel Cabrera H/100 10.00 25.00
10 Miguel Cabrera A/100 10.00 25.00
11 Albert Pujols H/1
12 Albert Pujols A/1
13 Mark Prior H/50 10.00 25.00
14 Mark Prior A/50 10.00 25.00
15 Chipper Jones H/10
16 Chipper Jones A/10
17 Jeff Bagwell H/1
18 Jeff Bagwell A/1
21 Gary Sheffield/1
22 Carl Crawford/4
24 Curt Schilling/1
25 Ben Sheets/100 6.00 15.00
27 Melvin Mora/50 8.00 20.00
29 Rafael Furcal/25 10.00 25.00
32 Jake Peavy/50 12.50 30.00
33 Francisco Cordero/25 10.00 25.00
37 Jason Bay/10
38 Michael Young/25 10.00 25.00
40 Joe Nathan/25 10.00 25.00
43 Eric Chavez/25 10.00 25.00
44 Pedro Martinez/1
45 Roy Oswalt/50 8.00 20.00
49 Edgar Renteria/25 10.00 25.00
50 Mark Buehrle/25 20.00 50.00
57 Sean Casey/50 8.00 20.00
59 Octavio Dotel/25 6.00 15.00
60 Francisco Rodriguez/25 15.00 40.00
61 Jose Guillen/25 10.00 25.00
62 Greg Maddux/1
66 Travis Hafner/50 8.00 20.00
67 Rich Harden/50 8.00 20.00
71 Milton Bradley/25 10.00 25.00
73 Torii Hunter/25 10.00 25.00
74 Paul Konerko/50 12.50 30.00
76 Tim Hudson/25 15.00 40.00
80 Justin Morneau/100 6.00 15.00
82 Jose Vidro/25 10.00 25.00
84 Josh Beckett/25 15.00 40.00
85 Craig Biggio/25 15.00 40.00
88 Barry Zito/1
89 Jacque Jones/50 8.00 20.00
91 Roy Halladay/25 15.00 40.00
92 Orlando Cabrera/10
93 Magglio Ordonez/100 6.00 15.00
95 Rafael Palmeiro/1
96 Brandon Webb/50 5.00 12.00
97 Preston Wilson/50 8.00 20.00
98 Shannon Stewart/50 8.00 20.00
99 Trot Nixon/50 12.50 30.00
100 Mike Piazza/1
101 Dontrelle Willis/10
105 Bobby Crosby/40 8.00 20.00
106 Shawn Green/1
107 Alfonso Soriano/25 10.00 25.00
108 Carlos Zambrano/50 15.00 40.00
109 Keith Foulke/25 15.00 40.00
110 Aubrey Huff/50 8.00 20.00
111 Adrian Beltre/10
112 Mark Teixeira/100 10.00 25.00
116 Carlos Beltran/25 10.00 25.00
118 Johan Santana/100 12.50 30.00
119 Manny Ramirez/1
121 Scott Rolen/25 15.00 40.00
122 Livan Hernandez/5
123 Carlos Lee/50 8.00 20.00
124 Derrek Lee/50 12.50 30.00
128 Jim Edmonds/1
130 Garret Anderson/100 6.00 15.00
131 Austin Kearns/100 4.00 10.00
132 Shingo Takatsu/5
133 Omar Vizquel/50 12.50 30.00
135 Mark Mulder/50 8.00 20.00
139 Mark Loretta/25 6.00 15.00
140 Vernon Wells/12
141 David Wright/50 20.00 50.00
144 Victor Martinez/25 10.00 25.00
147 Angel Berroa/5
148 Troy Percival/5
149 Paul Lo Duca/5
151 Willie Mays LGD/25 100.00 175.00
152 Ryne Sandberg LGD/25 30.00 60.00
153 Rickey Henderson LGD/1
156 George Brett LGD/1
157 Whitey Ford LGD/5
158 Duke Snider LGD/50 12.50 30.00
159 Don Mattingly LGD/25 30.00 60.00
160 Bob Gibson LGD/50 12.50 30.00
161 Hank Aaron LGD/1
162 Al Kaline LGD/50 15.00 40.00
163 Nolan Ryan LGD/25 50.00 100.00
164 Stan Musial LGD/25 30.00 60.00
165 George Kell LGD/50 12.50 30.00
166 Harmon Killebrew LGD/50 20.00 50.00
167 Cal Ripken LGD/25 60.00 120.00
169 Roger Clemens Sox/1
170 Curt Schilling D'backs/1
171 Rafael Palmeiro Rgr/1
173 Mike Piazza Dgr/1
174 Greg Maddux Braves/1
176 Hayden Penn PH/50 12.50 30.00
177 Ambiorix Concepcion PH/50 6.00 15.00
178 Casey Rogowski PH/20
179 Prince Fielder PH/50 40.00 80.00
180 Geovany Soto PH/10
181 Wladimir Balentien PH/50 12.50 30.00
182 Jason Hammel PH/50 6.00 15.00
183 Keiichi Yabu PH/50 15.00 40.00
184 Brandon McCarthy PH/50 30.00 60.00
185 Ubaldo Jimenez PH/50 15.00 40.00
186 Keiichi Yabu PH/50 15.00 40.00
187 Miguel Negron PH/50 10.00 25.00
188 Mike Morse PH/50 8.00 20.00
189 Nate McLouth PH/50 15.00 40.00
190 Norihiro Nakamura PH/50 20.00 50.00
191 Brandon McCarthy PH/50 30.00 60.00
192 Tony Pena PH/50 6.00 15.00
193 Ambiorix Concepcion PH/50 6.00 15.00
194 Raul Tablado PH/50 6.00 15.00
195 Hayden Penn PH/50 12.50 30.00
196 Sean Thompson PH/50 6.00 15.00
198 Ubaldo Jimenez PH/50 15.00 40.00
199 Wladimir Balentien PH/50 12.50 30.00
200 Prince Fielder PH/50 40.00 80.00

2005 Leaf Limited Monikers Gold

*1-175 p/r 25: .6X TO 1.5X BRZ p/r 100
*1-175 p/r 25: .5X TO 1.2X BRZ p/r 40-50
*1-175 p/r 25: .4X TO 1X BRZ p/r 25
OVERALL AU-GU ODDS ONE PER PACK
PRINT RUNS B/WN 1-25 COPIES PER
1-175 NO PRICING ON QTY OF 10 OR LESS
176-200 NO PRICING DUE TO SCARCITY
21 Gary Sheffield/25 15.00 40.00
37 Jason Bay/25 10.00 25.00
88 Barry Zito/25 10.00 25.00
90 Lyle Overbay/25 6.00 15.00
151 Willie Mays LGD/25 100.00 175.00
163 Nolan Ryan LGD/25 50.00 100.00
167 Cal Ripken LGD/25 60.00 120.00

2005 Leaf Limited Monikers Platinum

OVERALL AU-GU ODDS ONE PER PACK
STATED PRINT RUN 1 SERIAL #'d SET
NO PRICING DUE TO SCARCITY

2005 Leaf Limited Monikers Silver

*1-175 p/r 50: .5X TO 1.2X BRZ p/r 100
*1-175 p/r 50: .4X TO 1X BRZ p/r 40-50
*1-175 p/r 25: .5X TO 1.2X BRZ p/r 40-50
*1-175 p/r 25: .4X TO 1X BRZ p/r 25
OVERALL AU-GU ODDS ONE PER PACK
PRINT RUNS B/WN 1-50 COPIES PER
1-175 NO PRICING ON QTY OF 10 OR LESS
176-200 NO PRICING DUE TO SCARCITY
151 Willie Mays LGD/25 100.00 175.00
163 Nolan Ryan LGD/25 50.00 100.00
167 Cal Ripken LGD/25 60.00 120.00

2005 Leaf Limited Monikers Material Bat Bronze

*1-175 p/r 100: .5X TO 1.2X BRZ p/r 100
*1-175 p/r 100: .4X TO 1X BRZ p/r 40-50
*1-175 p/r 100: .3X TO .8X BRZ p/r 25
*1-175 p/r 50: .6X TO 1.5X BRZ p/r 100
*1-175 p/r 50: .5X TO 1.2X BRZ p/r 40-50
*1-175 p/r 50: .4X TO 1X BRZ p/r 25
*1-175 p/r 25: .6X TO 1.5X BRZ p/r 40-50
*1-175 p/r 25: .5X TO 1.2X BRZ p/r 25
OVERALL AU-GU ODDS ONE PER PACK
PRINT RUNS B/WN 1-100 COPIES PER
NO PRICING ON QTY OF 10 OR LESS
34 Aramis Ramirez/100 8.00 20.00
37 Jason Bay/100 8.00 20.00
111 Adrian Beltre/25 12.50 30.00
140 Vernon Wells/50 10.00 25.00
143 David Ortiz/50 20.00 50.00
147 Angel Berroa/100 5.00 12.00

2005 Leaf Limited Monikers Material Bat Platinum

OVERALL AU-GU ODDS ONE PER PACK
STATED PRINT RUN 1 SERIAL #'d SET
NO PRICING DUE TO SCARCITY

2005 Leaf Limited Monikers Material Button Gold

PRINT RUNS B/WN 1-5 COPIES PER
PLATINUM PRINT RUN 1 SERIAL #'d SET
OVERALL AU-GU ODDS ONE PER PACK
NO PRICING DUE TO SCARCITY

2005 Leaf Limited Monikers Material Jersey Prime Gold

*1-175 p/r 100: .5X TO 1.2X BRZ p/r 40-50
*1-175 p/r 100: .4X TO 1X BRZ p/r 25
*1-175 p/r 50: .75X TO 2X BRZ p/r 100
*1-175 p/r 50: .6X TO 1.5X BRZ p/r 40-50
*1-175 p/r 50: .5X TO 1.2X BRZ p/r 25
*1-175 p/r 20-30: 1X TO 2.5X BRZ p/r 100
*1-175 p/r 20-30: .75X TO 2X BRZ p/r 40-50
*1-175 p/r 20-30: .6X TO 1.5X BRZ p/r 25
PRINT RUNS B/WN 1-100 COPIES PER
NO PRICING ON QTY OF 10 OR LESS
PLATINUM PRINT RUN 1 SERIAL #'d SET
NO PLATINUM PRICING DUE TO SCARCITY
OVERALL AU-GU ODDS ONE PER PACK
34 Aramis Ramirez/100 10.00 25.00
70 Andruw Jones/50 15.00 40.00
88 Barry Zito/25 15.00 40.00
103 Andy Pettitte/25 30.00 60.00
117 Bobby Abreu/100 10.00 25.00
128 Jim Edmonds/25 30.00 60.00
140 Vernon Wells/50 12.50 30.00
163 Nolan Ryan LGD/25 60.00 120.00
167 Cal Ripken LGD/25 125.00 200.00

2005 Leaf Limited Monikers Material Jersey Number Silver

*1-175 p/r 75: .5X TO 1.2X BRZ p/r 100
*1-175 p/r 75: .4X TO 1X BRZ p/r 40-50
*1-175 p/r 75: .3X TO .8X BRZ p/r 25
*1-175 p/r 50: .6X TO 1.5X BRZ p/r 100
*1-175 p/r 50: .5X TO 1.2X BRZ p/r 40-50
*1-175 p/r 50: .4X TO 1X BRZ p/r 25
*1-175 p/r 24-25: .6X TO 1.5X BRZ p/r 40-50
*1-175 p/r 24-25: .5X TO 1.2X BRZ p/r 25
*1-175 p/r 15: 1X TO 2.5X BRZ p/r 100
PRINT RUNS B/WN 1-75 COPIES PER
NO PRICING ON QTY OF 10 OR LESS
PRIME PLATINUM PRINT RUN 1 #'d SET
NO PRIME PLAT.PRICING DUE TO SCARCITY
OVERALL AU-GU ODDS ONE PER PACK
34 Aramis Ramirez/75 8.00 20.00
70 Andruw Jones/25 20.00 50.00
90 Lyle Overbay/75 5.00 12.00
101 Dontrelle Willis/24 12.50 30.00
117 Bobby Abreu/75 8.00 20.00
128 Jim Edmonds/25 20.00 50.00
140 Vernon Wells/50 10.00 25.00
143 David Ortiz/75 15.00 40.00
163 Nolan Ryan LGD/25 50.00 100.00
167 Cal Ripken LGD/25 75.00 150.00

2005 Leaf Limited Threads Button

OVERALL AU-GU ODDS ONE PER PACK
PRINT RUNS B/WN 1-7 COPIES PER
NO PRICING DUE TO SCARCITY

2005 Leaf Limited Threads Jersey Prime

OVERALL AU-GU ODDS ONE PER PACK
PRINT RUNS B/WN 5-100 COPIES PER
NO PRICING ON QTY OF 5
PRICES ARE FOR 2 COLOR PATCHES
REDUCE 20% FOR 1-COLOR PATCH
ADD 20% FOR 3-4 COLOR PATCH
ADD 50% FOR 5-COLOR+ PATCH
1 Roger Clemens H/25 12.50 30.00
5 Todd Helton H/100 5.00 12.00
6 Todd Helton A/100 5.00 12.00
7 Vladimir Guerrero H/100 6.00 15.00
8 Vladimir Guerrero A Jkt/30 10.00 25.00
9 Miguel Cabrera H/100 5.00 12.00
10 Miguel Cabrera A/100 5.00 12.00
12 Albert Pujols A/50 15.00 40.00
13 Mark Prior H/100 5.00 12.00
14 Mark Prior A/25 8.00 20.00
15 Chipper Jones H/100 6.00 15.00
16 Chipper Jones A/100 6.00 15.00
17 Jeff Bagwell H/100 5.00 12.00
18 Jeff Bagwell A/100 5.00 12.00
19 Kerry Wood H/100 3.00 8.00
22 Carl Crawford/100 3.00 8.00
23 Mariano Rivera/60 8.00 20.00
25 Ben Sheets/100 3.00 8.00
27 Melvin Mora/25 5.00 12.00
28 Corey Patterson/100 3.00 8.00
29 Rafael Furcal/100 3.00 8.00
30 Jim Thome/100 5.00 12.00
34 Aramis Ramirez/50 4.00 10.00
35 Javy Lopez/100 3.00 8.00
38 Michael Young/100 3.00 8.00
39 Ivan Rodriguez/100 5.00 12.00
42 Adam Dunn/100 3.00 8.00
43 Eric Chavez/100 3.00 8.00
45 Roy Oswalt/100 3.00 8.00
48 Johnny Damon/50 6.00 15.00
50 Mark Buehrle/50 4.00 10.00
53 Hank Blalock/100 3.00 8.00
55 Brad Radke/50 4.00 10.00
57 Sean Casey/50 4.00 10.00
58 Mike Lowell/100 3.00 8.00
60 Francisco Rodriguez/100 3.00 8.00
62 Greg Maddux/25 12.50 30.00
63 A.J. Burnett/75 3.00 8.00
66 Travis Hafner/100 3.00 8.00
68 Bret Boone/100 3.00 8.00
70 Andruw Jones/100 5.00 12.00
73 Torii Hunter/100 3.00 8.00
74 Paul Konerko/100 3.00 8.00
79 Lance Berkman/100 3.00 8.00
80 Justin Morneau/100 3.00 8.00
82 Jose Vidro/100 3.00 8.00
84 Josh Beckett/100 3.00 8.00
86 Luis Gonzalez/100 3.00 8.00
88 Barry Zito/100 3.00 8.00
91 Roy Halladay/100 3.00 8.00
94 Mike Sweeney/100 3.00 8.00
95 Rafael Palmeiro/100 5.00 12.00
97 Preston Wilson/100 3.00 8.00
98 Shannon Stewart/50 4.00 10.00
99 Trot Nixon/25 5.00 12.00
100 Mike Piazza/100 6.00 15.00
101 Dontrelle Willis/100 3.00 8.00
103 Andy Pettitte/50 6.00 15.00
104 Kazuo Matsui/100 3.00 8.00
107 Alfonso Soriano/100 3.00 8.00
110 Aubrey Huff/100 3.00 8.00
111 Adrian Beltre/50 4.00 10.00
112 Mark Teixeira/60 6.00 15.00
114 Miguel Tejada/100 3.00 8.00
117 Bobby Abreu/100 3.00 8.00
119 Manny Ramirez/60 6.00 15.00
121 Scott Rolen/100 5.00 12.00
124 Derrek Lee/50 5.00 12.00
127 John Smoltz/100 5.00 12.00
128 Jim Edmonds/100 3.00 8.00
130 Garret Anderson/60 4.00 10.00
131 Austin Kearns/100 3.00 8.00
138 Mike Mussina/50 6.00 15.00
140 Vernon Wells/100 3.00 8.00
141 David Wright/100 12.50 30.00
142 Marcus Giles/100 3.00 8.00
144 Victor Martinez/75 3.00 8.00
145 Hideki Matsui/100 20.00 50.00
146 C.C. Sabathia/100 3.00 8.00
150 Jorge Posada/75 5.00 12.00
152 Ryne Sandberg LGD/50 12.50 30.00
153 Rickey Henderson LGD/25 12.50 30.00
154 Ted Williams LGD/5
156 George Brett LGD/50 12.50 30.00
159 Don Mattingly LGD/50 12.50 30.00
160 Bob Gibson LGD/25 10.00 25.00
161 Hank Aaron LGD/25 40.00 80.00
163 Nolan Ryan LGD/100 12.50 30.00
167 Cal Ripken LGD/100 15.00 40.00
169 Roger Clemens Sox/50 10.00 25.00
170 Curt Schilling D'backs/100 3.00 8.00
171 Rafael Palmeiro Rgr/100 5.00 12.00
173 Mike Piazza Dgr/100 6.00 15.00
174 Greg Maddux Braves/100 8.00 20.00
175 Sammy Sosa Cubs/100 6.00 15.00

2005 Leaf Limited Threads Jersey Number

*151-168 p/r 50: .3X TO .8X JPR p/r 100
*151-168 p/r 50: .25X TO .6X JPR p/r 50
OVERALL AU-GU ODDS ONE PER PACK
PRINT RUNS B/WN 1-100 COPIES PER
NO PRICING ON QTY OF 10 OR LESS
154 Ted Williams LGD/25 30.00 60.00
157 Whitey Ford LGD/50 5.00 12.00
158 Duke Snider LGD/25 6.00 15.00
164 Stan Musial LGD/25 12.50 30.00
166 Harmon Killebrew LGD/50 6.00 15.00
168 Babe Ruth LGD/25 175.00 300.00

2005 Leaf Limited Threads MLB Logo

OVERALL AU-GU ODDS ONE PER PACK
STATED PRINT RUN 1 SERIAL #'d SET
NO PRICING DUE TO SCARCITY

2005 Leaf Limited Timber Barrel

OVERALL AU-GU ODDS ONE PER PACK
PRINT RUNS B/WN 1-3 COPIES PER
NO PRICING DUE TO SCARCITY

2005 Leaf Limited TNT

*1-150/169-175p/r50: .4XTO1X JPRp/r75-100
*1-150/169-175p/r50: .3XTO.8X JPRp/r50-60
*1-150/169-175p/r50: .25XTO.6XJPRp/r25-30
*1-150 p/r 25-30: .5X TO 1.2X JPR p/r 75-100
*1-150 p/r 25-30: .3X TO .8X JPR p/r 25-30
*151-168 p/r 50: .4X TO 1X JPR p/r 50
*151-168 p/r 50: .3X TO .8X JPR p/r 50
*151-168 p/r 50: .25X TO .6X JPR p/r 25
*151-168 p/r 25: .3X TO .8X JPR p/r 25
OVERALL AU-GU ODDS ONE PER PACK
PRINT RUNS B/WN 1-50 COPIES PER
NO PRICING ON QTY OF 10 OR LESS
11 Albert Pujols H Bat-Jsy/50 12.50 30.00
143 David Ortiz Bat-Jsy/50 5.00 12.00
151 Willie Mays LGD Bat-Jsy/25 30.00 60.00
154 T.Williams LGD Bat-Jsy/25 50.00 100.00
164 S.Musial LGD Bat-Jsy/25 15.00 40.00
166 H.Killebrew LGD Bat-Jsy/25 10.00 25.00
172 R.Johnson M's Bat-Jsy/25 8.00 20.00

2005 Leaf Limited TNT Prime

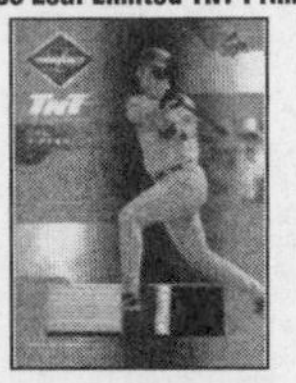

*1-150/169-75p/r75-100: .4XTO1XJPRpr 75-100
*1-150 p/r 75-100: .3X TO .8X JPR p/r 50-60
*1-150/169-175p/r40-60: .5XTO1.2Xpr75-100
*1-150/169-175p/r40-60: .4XTO1XJPRpr50-60
*1-150 p/r 40-60: .3X TO .8X JPR p/r25-30
*1-150 p/r 25: .6X TO 1.5X JPR p/r 75-100
*1-150 p/r 25: .5X TO 1.2X JPR p/r 50-60
*1-150 p/r 25: .4X TO 1X JPR p/r 25-30
*1-150 p/r 15: .6X TO 1.5X JPR p/r 50-60
*151-168 p/r 100: .4X TO 1X JPR p/r 100
*151-168 p/r 50: .5X TO 1.2X JPR p/r 100
*151-168 p/r 50: .4X TO 1X JPR p/r 50
*151-168 p/r 25: .4X TO 1X JPR p/r 25
OVERALL AU-GU ODDS ONE PER PACK
PRINT RUNS B/WN 1-100 COPIES PER
NO PRICING ON QTY OF 10 OR LESS
PRICES ARE FOR 2-COLOR PATCHES
REDUCE 20% FOR 1-COLOR PATCH
ADD 20% FOR 3-4 COLOR PATCH
ADD 50% FOR 5-COLOR+ PATCH

2005 Leaf Limited Cuts Gold

*GOLD p/r 22-30: .6X TO 1.5X SILVER p/r 99
*GOLD p/r 22-30: .4X TO 1X SILVER p/r 20-34
OVERALL AU-GU ODDS ONE PER PACK
PRINT RUNS B/WN 3-30 COPIES PER
NO PRICING ON QTY OF 12 OR LESS
CUTS FABRIC IS NOT GAME-USED
4 Sandy Koufax/30 250.00 400.00
20 Craig Biggio/25 20.00 50.00

2005 Leaf Limited Cuts Silver

PRINT RUNS B/WN 7-99 COPIES PER
NO PRICING ON QTY OF 7
PLATINUM PRINT RUN 1 SERIAL #'d SET
NO PLATINUM PRICING DUE TO SCARCITY
OVERALL AU-GU ODDS ONE PER PACK
CUTS FABRIC IS NOT GAME-USED
1 Orlando Cepeda/30 15.00 40.00
2 Hank Aaron/44 175.00 300.00
3 Willie Mays/24 125.00 200.00
4 Sandy Koufax/32 250.00 400.00
5 Cal Ripken/25 100.00 175.00
6 Nolan Ryan/34 60.00 120.00
7 Jim Palmer/22 15.00 40.00
8 Tony Gwynn/19 30.00 60.00
9 Rod Carew/29 20.00 50.00
10 Ryne Sandberg/23 40.00 80.00
11 Stan Musial/28 40.00 80.00
12 Steve Carlton/32 15.00 40.00
14 Mike Schmidt/20 40.00 80.00
15 Harmon Killebrew/25 40.00 80.00
17 Duke Snider/53 20.00 50.00
18 Don Mattingly/25 40.00 80.00
19 Dale Murphy/25 20.00 50.00
20 Craig Biggio/7
21 Juan Marichal/99 10.00 25.00
22 Greg Maddux/36 100.00 175.00
23 Lou Brock/20 20.00 50.00
24 Paul Molitor/25 15.00 40.00
25 Wade Boggs/26 20.00 50.00
26 Mark Prior/27 15.00 40.00
28 Al Kaline/28 30.00 60.00
29 Minnie Minoso/25 20.00 50.00

2005 Leaf Limited Legends

STATED PRINT RUN 50 SERIAL #'d SETS
FOIL PRINT RUN 10 SERIAL #'d SETS
NO FOIL PRICING DUE TO SCARCITY
OVERALL INSERT ODDS ONE PER PACK
1 Billy Martin 2.00 5.00
2 Bobby Doerr 1.25 3.00
3 Carlton Fisk 2.00 5.00
4 Harmon Killebrew 3.00 8.00
5 Duke Snider 2.00 5.00
6 George Brett 6.00 15.00
7 Johnny Bench 3.00 8.00
8 Lou Boudreau 1.25 3.00
9 Brooks Robinson 2.00 5.00
10 Al Kaline 3.00 8.00
11 Stan Musial 5.00 12.00
12 Burleigh Grimes 2.00 5.00
13 Cal Ripken 12.00 30.00
14 Carl Yastrzemski 4.00 10.00
15 Willie Stargell 2.00 5.00
16 Yogi Berra 3.00 8.00
17 Enos Slaughter 1.25 3.00
18 Phil Rizzuto 2.00 5.00
19 Luis Aparicio 1.25 3.00
20 Ernie Banks 3.00 8.00
21 Hal Newhouser 2.00 5.00
22 Whitey Ford 2.00 5.00
23 Tony Gwynn 4.00 10.00
24 Bob Feller 1.25 3.00
25 Don Sutton 1.25 3.00
26 Lou Brock 2.00 5.00
27 Jim Palmer 1.25 3.00
28 Billy Williams 1.25 3.00
29 Juan Marichal 1.25 3.00
30 Rod Carew 2.00 5.00
31 Catfish Hunter 1.25 3.00
32 Maury Wills 1.25 3.00
33 Joe Cronin 1.25 3.00
34 Fergie Jenkins 1.25 3.00
35 Sandy Koufax 10.00 25.00
36 Steve Carlton 1.25 3.00
37 Eddie Murray 3.00 8.00
38 Roger Maris 3.00 8.00
39 Gaylord Perry 1.25 3.00
40 Bob Gibson 2.00 5.00
41 Tom Seaver 2.00 5.00
42 Dennis Eckersley 1.25 3.00
43 Reggie Jackson 3.00 8.00
44 Willie McCovey 2.00 5.00
45 Willie Mays NY 6.00 15.00
46 Willie Mays SF 6.00 15.00
47 Rickey Henderson M's 2.00 5.00
48 Rickey Henderson Mets 2.00 5.00
49 Nolan Ryan Angels 8.00 20.00
50 Nolan Ryan Mets 8.00 20.00

2005 Leaf Limited Legends Jersey Number

OVERALL AU-GU ODDS ONE PER PACK
PRINT RUNS B/WN 1-50 COPIES PER
NO PRICING ON QTY OF 14 OR LESS
1 Billy Martin/1
2 Bobby Doerr Pants/1
3 Carlton Fisk/50 5.00 12.00
4 Harmon Killebrew/3
5 Duke Snider/4
6 George Brett/5
7 Johnny Bench Pants/5
8 Lou Boudreau/5
9 Brooks Robinson/5
10 Al Kaline Pants/5
11 Stan Musial/6
12 Burleigh Grimes Pants/25 40.00 80.00
13 Cal Ripken/1
14 Carl Yastrzemski/8
15 Willie Stargell/8
16 Yogi Berra Pants/8
17 Enos Slaughter/9
18 Phil Rizzuto Pants/10
19 Luis Aparicio/11
20 Ernie Banks/14
21 Hal Newhouser/16 5.00 12.00
22 Whitey Ford/16 8.00 20.00
23 Tony Gwynn/1
24 Bob Feller Pants/19 8.00 20.00
25 Don Sutton/20 4.00 10.00
26 Lou Brock/20 6.00 15.00
27 Jim Palmer/22 4.00 10.00
28 Billy Williams/26 4.00 10.00
29 Juan Marichal/27 4.00 10.00
30 Rod Carew/29 6.00 15.00
31 Catfish Hunter Pants/29 4.00 10.00
32 Maury Wills/1
33 Joe Cronin/4
34 Fergie Jenkins/31 4.00 10.00
35 Sandy Koufax/32 75.00 150.00
36 Steve Carlton/32 4.00 10.00
37 Eddie Murray/33 8.00 20.00
38 Roger Maris Pants/1
39 Gaylord Perry/36 3.00 8.00
40 Bob Gibson/45 5.00 12.00
41 Tom Seaver/41 5.00 12.00
42 Dennis Eckersley/43 3.00 8.00
43 Reggie Jackson Pants/44 5.00 12.00
44 Willie McCovey/44 5.00 12.00
45 Willie Mays NY/24 15.00 40.00
46 Willie Mays SF/24 15.00 40.00
47 Rickey Henderson M's/1
48 Rickey Henderson Mets/1
49 Nolan Ryan Angels/30 12.50 30.00
50 Nolan Ryan Mets/30 12.50 30.00

2005 Leaf Limited Legends Jersey Number Prime

*PRIME p/r 25: .75X TO 2X NBR p/r 36-50
*PRIME p/r 25: .6X TO 1.5X NBR p/r 20-33
*PRIME p/r 15: .75X TO 2X NBR p/r 20-33
OVERALL AU-GU ODDS ONE PER PACK
PRINT RUNS B/WN 1-25 COPIES PER
NO PRICING ON QTY OF 10 OR LESS

PRICES ARE FOR 2 COLOR PATCHES
REDUCE 20% FOR 1-COLOR PATCH
ADD 20% FOR 3-4 COLOR PATCH
ADD 50% FOR 5-COLOR+ PATCH
6 George Brett/25 15.00 40.00
7 Johnny Bench/15 15.00 40.00
11 Stan Musial/25 20.00 50.00
13 Cal Ripken/25 30.00 60.00
14 Carl Yastrzemski/25 12.50 30.00
15 Willie Stargell/25 10.00 25.00
20 Ernie Banks/25 15.00 40.00
23 Tony Gwynn/25 12.50 30.00
47 Rickey Henderson M's/25 12.50 30.00
48 Rickey Henderson Mets/25 12.50 30.00

2005 Leaf Limited Legends Signature

OVERALL AU-GU ODDS ONE PER PACK
PRINT RUNS B/WN 2-50 COPIES PER
NO PRICING ON QTY OF 10 OR LESS
2 Bobby Doerr/50 8.00 20.00
3 Carlton Fisk/10
4 Harmon Killebrew/50 20.00 50.00
5 Duke Snider/25 15.00 40.00
6 George Brett/5
7 Johnny Bench/10
9 Brooks Robinson/50 12.50 30.00
10 Al Kaline/50 15.00 40.00
11 Stan Musial/10
13 Cal Ripken/8
18 Phil Rizzuto/50 12.50 30.00
19 Luis Aparicio/50 8.00 20.00
20 Ernie Banks/4
22 Whitey Ford/5
23 Tony Gwynn/10
24 Bob Feller/50 8.00 20.00
25 Don Sutton/50 8.00 20.00
26 Lou Brock/50 12.50 30.00
27 Jim Palmer/50 8.00 20.00
28 Billy Williams/25 10.00 25.00
29 Juan Marichal/50 8.00 20.00
30 Rod Carew/25 15.00 40.00
32 Maury Wills/50 8.00 20.00
34 Fergie Jenkins/50 8.00 20.00
35 Sandy Koufax/5
36 Steve Carlton/50 8.00 20.00
39 Gaylord Perry/50 8.00 20.00
40 Bob Gibson/25 15.00 40.00
41 Tom Seaver/10
42 Dennis Eckersley/50 8.00 20.00
43 Reggie Jackson/5
44 Willie McCovey/10
45 Willie Mays NY/5
46 Willie Mays SF/5
47 Rickey Henderson M's/5
48 Rickey Henderson Mets/2
49 Nolan Ryan Angels/5
50 Nolan Ryan Mets/5

2005 Leaf Limited Legends Signature Jersey Number

*NBR p/r 20-30: .6X TO 1.5X SIG p/r 50
*NBR p/r 20-30: .5X TO 1.2X SIG p/r 25
*NBR p/r 15-16: .6X TO 1.5X SIG p/r 25
OVERALL AU-GU ODDS ONE PER PACK
PRINT RUNS B/WN 5-30 COPIES PER
NO PRICING ON QTY OF 14 OR LESS
11 Stan Musial/25 40.00 80.00
13 Cal Ripken/25 75.00 150.00
22 Whitey Ford/16 30.00 60.00
23 Tony Gwynn/19 20.00 50.00
44 Willie McCovey/25 20.00 50.00
45 Willie Mays NY/24 125.00 200.00
46 Willie Mays SF/24 125.00 200.00
49 Nolan Ryan Angels/30 50.00 100.00
50 Nolan Ryan Mets/30 50.00 100.00

2005 Leaf Limited Legends Signature Jersey Number Prime

*PRIME p/r 20-25: .75X TO 2X SIG p/r 50
*PRIME p/r 20-25: .6X TO 1.5X SIG p/r 25
*PRIME p/r 15: 1X TO 2.5X SIG p/r 50
OVERALL AU-GU ODDS ONE PER PACK
PRINT RUNS B/WN 1-25 COPIES PER
NO PRICING ON QTY OF 14 OR LESS
3 Carlton Fisk/15 40.00 80.00
11 Stan Musial/25 60.00 120.00
13 Cal Ripken/25 125.00 200.00
23 Tony Gwynn/25 30.00 60.00
44 Willie McCovey/20 30.00 60.00

2005 Leaf Limited Lettermen

A.BELTRE p/r 20 60.00 120.00
A.BELTRE p/r 10 75.00 150.00
C.BIGGIO p/r 10 150.00 250.00
C.BIGGIO p/r 5 175.00 300.00
C.JONES p/r 5 175.00 300.00
C.RIPKEN p/r 8 300.00 450.00
D.MATTINGLY p/r 10 150.00 250.00
D.MATTINGLY p/r 5 175.00 300.00
D.SNIDER p/r 11 125.00 200.00
D.MURPHY p/r 20 75.00 150.00
M.CABRERA p/r 20 125.00 200.00
M.CABRERA p/r 10 150.00 250.00
M.SCHMIDT p/r 4-5 150.00 250.00
N.RYAN p/r 21 150.00 250.00
P.MOLITOR p/r 10 75.00 150.00
P.MOLITOR p/r 5 125.00 200.00
R.SANDBERG p/r 11 150.00 250.00
S.MUSIAL p/r 6 150.00 250.00
T.GWYNN p/r 21 125.00 200.00
T.GWYNN p/r 10-11 175.00 300.00
OVERALL AU-GU ODDS ONE PER PACK
PRINT RUNS B/WN 4-21 COPIES PER
LETTERMEN FABRIC IS NOT GAME-USED

2005 Leaf Limited Lumberjacks

STATED PRINT RUN 50 SERIAL #'d SETS
FOIL PRINT RUN 10 SERIAL #'d SETS
NO FOIL PRICING DUE TO SCARCITY
OVERALL INSERT ODDS ONE PER PACK
1 Al Kaline 3.00 8.00
2 Albert Pujols 8.00 20.00
3 Andre Dawson 2.00 5.00
4 Babe Ruth 8.00 20.00
5 Cal Ripken 12.00 30.00
6 Chipper Jones 3.00 8.00
7 Dale Murphy 1.25 3.00
8 Dave Winfield 1.25 3.00
9 Don Mattingly 6.00 15.00
10 Duke Snider 2.00 5.00
11 Eddie Murray 3.00 8.00
12 Frank Robinson 2.00 5.00
13 Frank Thomas 3.00 8.00
14 Gary Carter 1.25 3.00
15 Hack Wilson 2.00 5.00
16 Hank Aaron 6.00 15.00
17 Harmon Killebrew 3.00 8.00
18 Joe Morgan 1.25 3.00
19 Johnny Bench 3.00 8.00
20 Kirby Puckett 3.00 8.00
21 Kirk Gibson 1.25 3.00
22 Manny Ramirez 3.00 8.00
23 Mark Grace 2.00 5.00
24 Mike Piazza 3.00 8.00
25 Mike Schmidt 6.00 15.00
26 Orlando Cepeda 1.25 3.00
27 Paul Molitor 3.00 8.00
28 Rafael Palmeiro 2.00 5.00
29 Ralph Kiner 1.25 3.00
30 Reggie Jackson 3.00 8.00
31 Richie Ashburn 2.00 5.00
32 Rickey Henderson 2.00 5.00
33 Robin Yount 3.00 8.00
34 Rod Carew 2.00 5.00
35 Ryne Sandberg 6.00 15.00
36 Stan Musial 5.00 12.00
37 Ted Williams 6.00 15.00
38 Tony Gwynn 4.00 10.00
39 Vladimir Guerrero 3.00 8.00
40 Willie Mays 6.00 15.00
41 Ernie Banks 3.00 8.00
Billy Williams
42 Ted Williams 6.00 15.00
Joe Cronin
43 George Brett 6.00 15.00
Bo Jackson
44 John Kruk 2.00 5.00
Jim Thome
45 Willie Mays 6.00 15.00
Jim Thorpe
46 Wade Boggs 2.00 5.00
Johnny Damon
47 Matt Williams 2.00 5.00
Will Clark
48 Willie Stargell 2.00 5.00
Dave Parker
49 Ichiro Suzuki 5.00 12.00
Edgar Martinez
50 Carl Yastrzemski 4.00 10.00
Carlton Fisk

2005 Leaf Limited Lumberjacks Barrel

OVERALL AU-GU ODDS ONE PER PACK
PRINT RUNS B/WN 1-5 COPIES PER
NO PRICING DUE TO SCARCITY

2005 Leaf Limited Lumberjacks Bat

1-40 PRINT RUNS B/WN 1-50 COPIES PER
41-50 PRINT RUNS B/WN 5-50 COPIES PER
OVERALL AU-GU ODDS ONE PER PACK
NO PRICING ON QTY OF 5 OR LESS
1 Al Kaline/50 6.00 15.00
2 Albert Pujols/1
3 Andre Dawson Pants/1
4 Babe Ruth/25 125.00 200.00
6 Chipper Jones/1
7 Dale Murphy/1
8 Dave Winfield/50 3.00 8.00
9 Don Mattingly/1
11 Eddie Murray/25 10.00 25.00
12 Frank Robinson/50 3.00 8.00
13 Frank Thomas/1
14 Gary Carter/25 5.00 12.00
15 Hack Wilson/50 20.00 50.00
16 Hank Aaron/50 15.00 40.00
17 Harmon Killebrew/3
18 Joe Morgan/25 5.00 12.00
19 Johnny Bench/50 6.00 15.00
20 Kirby Puckett/50 6.00 15.00
21 Kirk Gibson/1
22 Manny Ramirez/1
23 Mark Grace/1
24 Mike Piazza/1
25 Mike Schmidt/50 8.00 20.00
26 Orlando Cepeda/25 5.00 12.00
27 Paul Molitor/50 3.00 8.00
28 Rafael Palmeiro/1
29 Ralph Kiner/25 8.00 20.00
30 Reggie Jackson/1
31 Richie Ashburn/25 8.00 20.00
32 Rickey Henderson/1
33 Robin Yount/25 10.00 25.00
34 Rod Carew/1
35 Ryne Sandberg/25 10.00 25.00
36 Stan Musial/50 10.00 25.00
37 Ted Williams/50 20.00 50.00
38 Tony Gwynn/1
39 Vladimir Guerrero/1
40 Willie Mays/50 12.50 30.00
43 George Brett 10.00 25.00
Bo Jackson/50
46 Wade Boggs
Johnny Damon/5
47 Matt Williams 8.00 20.00
Will Clark/50
48 Willie Stargell 8.00 20.00
Dave Parker/50
50 Carl Yastrzemski 10.00 25.00
Carlton Fisk/50

2005 Leaf Limited Lumberjacks Combos

*COMBO p/r 50: .5X TO 1.2X BAT p/r 50
*COMBO p/r 50: .4X TO 1X BAT p/r 25
*COMBO p/r 25: .6X TO 1.5X BAT p/r 50
*COMBO p/r 25: .5X TO 1.2X BAT p/r 25
OVERALL AU-GU ODDS ONE PER PACK
PRINT RUNS B/WN 1-50 COPIES PER
NO PRICING ON QTY OF 10 OR LESS
2 Albert Pujols Bat-Jsy/50 12.50 30.00
4 Babe Ruth Bat-Jsy/25 300.00 500.00
5 Cal Ripken Bat-Jsy/50 15.00 40.00
6 Chipper Jones Bat-Jsy/25 10.00 25.00
7 Dale Murphy Bat-Jsy/50 6.00 15.00
13 Frank Thomas Bat-Jsy/25 10.00 25.00
21 Kirk Gibson Bat-Jsy/50 4.00 10.00
22 Manny Ramirez Bat-Jsy/50 6.00 15.00
23 Mark Grace Bat-Jsy/50 6.00 15.00
24 Mike Piazza Bat-Jsy/50 8.00 20.00

2005 Leaf Limited Lumberjacks Combos Prime

*PRIME p/r 50: .6X TO 1.5X BAT p/r 50
*PRIME p/r 50: .5X TO 1.2X BAT p/r 25
*PRIME p/r 25: .6X TO 1.5X BAT p/r 25
OVERALL AU-GU ODDS ONE PER PACK
PRINT RUNS B/WN 1-50 COPIES PER
NO PRICING ON QTY OF 10 OR LESS
PRICES ARE FOR 2-COLOR PATCHES
REDUCE 20% FOR 1-COLOR PATCH
ADD 20% FOR 3-4 COLOR PATCH
ADD 50% FOR 5-COLOR+ PATCH
2 Albert Pujols Bat-Jsy/50 15.00 40.00
3 Andre Dawson Bat-Jsy/50 4.00 10.00
5 Cal Ripken Bat-Jsy/25 30.00 60.00
6 Chipper Jones Bat-Jsy/50 8.00 20.00
13 Frank Thomas Bat-Jsy/50 8.00 20.00
21 Kirk Gibson Bat-Jsy/50 4.00 10.00
22 Manny Ramirez Bat-Jsy/25 8.00 20.00
24 Mike Piazza Bat-Jsy/50 8.00 20.00
28 Rafael Palmeiro Bat-Jsy/50 6.00 15.00
32 R.Henderson Bat-Jsy/25 10.00 25.00
34 Rod Carew Bat-Jsy/50 6.00 15.00
39 V.Guerrero Bat-Jsy/50 8.00 20.00

2005 Leaf Limited Lumberjacks Jersey

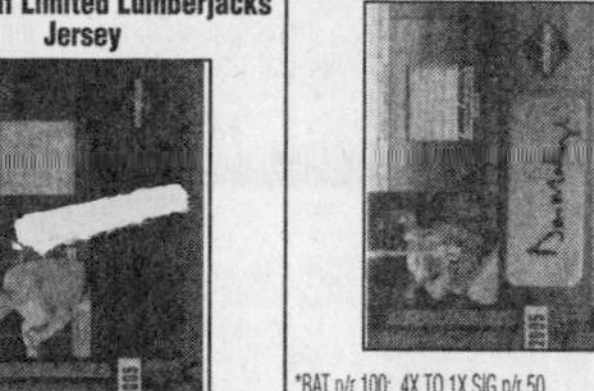

*JSY 1-40 p/r 50: .4X TO 1X BAT p/r 50
*JSY 1-40 p/r 50: .3X TO .8X BAT p/r 25
*JSY 1-40 p/r 25: .5X TO 1.2X BAT p/r 50
*JSY 1-40 p/r 25: .4X TO 1X BAT p/r 25
1-40 PRINT RUNS B/WN 1-50 COPIES PER
*JSY 41-50 p/r 50: .4X TO 1X BAT p/r 50
*JSY 41-50 p/r 25: .5X TO 1.2X BAT p/r 50
41-50 PRINT RUNS B/WN 5-50 COPIES PER
OVERALL AU-GU ODDS ONE PER PACK
NO PRICING ON QTY OF 5 OR LESS
4 Babe Ruth/25 175.00 300.00
10 Duke Snider Pants/50 5.00 12.00
30 Reggie Jackson/50 5.00 12.00
41 Ernie Banks 15.00 40.00
Billy Williams/25
42 Ted Williams 30.00 60.00
Joe Cronin/25
44 John Kruk 10.00 25.00
Jim Thome/25
45 Willie Mays 125.00 200.00
Jim Thorpe/25
46 Wade Boggs 8.00 20.00
Johnny Damon/50

2005 Leaf Limited Lumberjacks Jersey Prime

*PRIME 1-40 p/r 50: .5X TO 1.2X BAT p/r 25
*PRIME 1-40 p/r 25: .75X TO 2X BAT p/r 50
*PRIME 1-40 p/r 25: .6X TO 1.5X BAT p/r 25
1-40 PRINT RUNS B/WN 1-50 COPIES PER
41-50 PRINT RUNS B/WN 1-5 COPIES PER
OVERALL AU-GU ODDS ONE PER PACK
NO PRICING ON QTY OF 10 OR LESS
PRICES ARE FOR 2 COLOR PATCHES
REDUCE 20% FOR 1-COLOR PATCH
ADD 20% FOR 3-4 COLOR PATCH
ADD 50% FOR 5-COLOR+ PATCH
2 Albert Pujols/25 20.00 50.00
3 Andre Dawson/50 5.00 12.00
5 Cal Ripken/25 30.00 60.00
6 Chipper Jones/50 10.00 25.00
13 Frank Thomas/50 10.00 25.00
21 Kirk Gibson/50 5.00 12.00
24 Mike Piazza/50 10.00 25.00
28 Rafael Palmeiro/50 8.00 20.00
32 Rickey Henderson/25 12.50 30.00
34 Rod Carew/50 8.00 20.00
38 Tony Gwynn/50 10.00 25.00
39 Vladimir Guerrero/25 10.00 25.00

2005 Leaf Limited Lumberjacks Signature

OVERALL AU-GU ODDS ONE PER PACK
PRINT RUNS B/WN 1-50 COPIES PER
NO PRICING ON QTY OF 10 OR LESS
1 Al Kaline/50 15.00 40.00
2 Albert Pujols/1
3 Andre Dawson/25 10.00 25.00
5 Cal Ripken/21 60.00 120.00
6 Chipper Jones/10
7 Dale Murphy/50 12.50 30.00
8 Dave Winfield/1
9 Don Mattingly/50 20.00 50.00
10 Duke Snider/50 12.50 30.00
11 Eddie Murray/10
12 Frank Robinson/50 8.00 20.00
13 Frank Thomas/25 20.00 50.00
14 Gary Carter/50 8.00 20.00
16 Hank Aaron/10
17 Harmon Killebrew/50 20.00 50.00
18 Joe Morgan/25 10.00 25.00
19 Johnny Bench/50 15.00 40.00
20 Kirby Puckett/25 50.00 100.00
21 Kirk Gibson/10
22 Manny Ramirez/1
23 Mark Grace/25 15.00 40.00
25 Mike Schmidt/50 20.00 50.00
26 Orlando Cepeda/1
27 Paul Molitor/50 8.00 20.00
29 Ralph Kiner/50 12.50 30.00
30 Reggie Jackson/1
32 Rickey Henderson/10
33 Robin Yount/10
34 Rod Carew/50 12.50 30.00
35 Ryne Sandberg/50 20.00 50.00
36 Stan Musial/50 20.00 50.00
38 Tony Gwynn/50 15.00 40.00
40 Willie Mays/25 100.00 175.00

2005 Leaf Limited Lumberjacks Signature Bat

*BAT p/r 100: .4X TO 1X SIG p/r 50
*BAT p/r 100: .3X TO .8X SIG p/r 21-25
*BAT p/r 50: .5X TO 1.2X SIG p/r 50
*BAT p/r 50: .4X TO 1X SIG p/r 21-25
*BAT p/r 25: .6X TO 1.5X SIG p/r 50
*BAT p/r 25: .5X TO 1.2X SIG p/r 21-25
OVERALL AU-GU ODDS ONE PER PACK
PRINT RUNS B/WN 1-100 COPIES PER
NO PRICING ON QTY OF 10 OR LESS
21 Kirk Gibson/25 12.50 30.00
26 Orlando Cepeda/100 8.00 20.00
33 Robin Yount/25 30.00 60.00

2005 Leaf Limited Lumberjacks Signature Combos

*COMBO p/r 100: .4X TO 1X SIG p/r 50
*COMBO p/r 100: .3X TO .8X SIG p/r 21-25
*COMBO p/r 50: .5X TO 1.2X SIG p/r 50
*COMBO p/r 25: .6X TO 1.5X SIG p/r 50
*COMBO p/r 25: .5X TO 1.2X SIG p/r 21-25
OVERALL AU-GU ODDS ONE PER PACK
PRINT RUNS B/WN 1-100 COPIES PER
NO PRICING ON QTY OF 10 OR LESS

2005 Leaf Limited Lumberjacks Signature Combos Prime

*PRIME p/r 25: .75X TO 2X SIG p/r 50
*PRIME p/r 25: .6X TO 1.5X SIG p/r 21-25
OVERALL AU-GU ODDS ONE PER PACK
PRINT RUNS B/WN 1-25 COPIES PER
NO PRICING ON QTY OF 10 OR LESS
5 Cal Ripken Bat-Jsy/25 125.00 200.00

2005 Leaf Limited Lumberjacks Signature Jersey

*JSY p/r 100: .4X TO 1X SIG p/r 50
*JSY p/r 100: .3X TO .8X SIG p/r 21-25
*JSY p/r 50: .5X TO 1.2X SIG p/r 50
*JSY p/r 25: .6X TO 1.5X SIG p/r 50
*JSY p/r 25: .5X TO 1.2X SIG p/r 21-25
OVERALL AU-GU ODDS ONE PER PACK
PRINT RUNS B/WN 1-100 COPIES PER
NO PRICING ON QTY OF 10 OR LESS
30 Reggie Jackson/25 30.00 60.00
33 Robin Yount/25 30.00 60.00

2005 Leaf Limited Lumberjacks Signature Jersey Prime

*PRIME p/r 25: .75X TO 2X SIG p/r 50
*PRIME p/r 25: .6X TO 1.5X SIG p/r 21-25
OVERALL AU-GU ODDS ONE PER PACK
PRINT RUNS B/WN 1-25 COPIES PER
NO PRICING ON QTY OF 10 OR LESS
5 Cal Ripken/25 125.00 200.00
33 Robin Yount/25 40.00 80.00

2005 Leaf Limited Matching Numbers

PRINT RUNS B/WN 5-50 COPIES PER
NO PRICING ON QTY OF 5
PRIME PRINT RUNS 1-5 COPIES PER
NO PRIME PRICING DUE TO SCARCITY
OVERALL AU-GU ODDS ONE PER PACK
1 Ted Williams Jsy 100.00 200.00
Roger Maris Jsy/25
2 Nolan Ryan Jsy 15.00 40.00
Kerry Wood Jsy/50
3 Cal Ripken Jsy 20.00 50.00
Gary Carter Jsy/50
4 Willie Mays Pants 40.00 80.00
Rickey Henderson Jsy/25
5 Johnny Bench Pants 15.00 40.00
Albert Pujols Jsy/50
6 Roger Clemens Jsy 15.00 40.00
Will Clark Jsy/50
7 Willie McCovey Jsy 10.00 25.00
Reggie Jackson Jsy/25
8 Ryne Sandberg Jsy 15.00 40.00
Don Mattingly Jsy/50
9 Duke Snider Pants 12.50 30.00
Joe Cronin Pants/25
10 Roberto Clemente Jsy
Roger Clemens Jsy/5

2005 Leaf Limited Team Trademarks

STATED PRINT RUN 50 SERIAL #'d SETS
FOIL PRINT RUN 10 SERIAL #'d SETS
NO FOIL PRICING DUE TO SCARCITY
OVERALL INSERT ODDS ONE PER PACK
1 Ryne Sandberg 6.00 15.00
2 George Brett 6.00 15.00
3 Steve Carlton 1.25 3.00
4 Reggie Jackson 3.00 8.00
5 Edgar Martinez 2.00 5.00
6 Barry Larkin 2.00 5.00
7 Ozzie Smith 5.00 12.00
8 Carlton Fisk 2.00 5.00
9 Wade Boggs 2.00 5.00
10 Will Clark 2.00 5.00
11 Nolan Ryan 8.00 20.00
12 Gary Carter 1.25 3.00
13 Don Mattingly 6.00 15.00
14 Willie Stargell 2.00 5.00
15 Don Sutton 1.25 3.00
16 Kirk Gibson 1.25 3.00
17 Kirby Puckett 3.00 8.00
18 Dale Murphy 1.25 3.00
19 Rickey Henderson 2.00 5.00
20 Willie Mays 6.00 15.00
21 Cal Ripken 12.00 30.00
22 Paul Molitor 3.00 8.00
23 Tony Gwynn 4.00 10.00
24 Andre Dawson 2.00 5.00
25 Bob Feller 1.25 3.00
26 Alan Trammell 1.25 3.00
27 Dave Parker 1.25 3.00
28 Dave Righetti 1.25 3.00
29 Dwight Gooden 1.25 3.00
30 Harold Baines 1.25 3.00
31 Jack Morris 1.25 3.00
32 John Kruk 1.25 3.00
33 Lee Smith 1.25 3.00
34 Lenny Dykstra 1.25 3.00
35 Luis Tiant 1.25 3.00
36 Matt Williams 2.00 5.00
37 Ron Guidry 1.25 3.00
38 Tony Oliva 1.25 3.00

2005 Leaf Limited Team Trademarks Jersey Number

*NBR p/r 44-50: .25X TO .6X PRIME p/r 40-50
*NBR p/r 20-32: .3X TO .8X PRIME p/r 40-50
*NBR p/r 20-32: .25X TO .6X PRIME p/r 25-26
OVERALL AU-GU ODDS ONE PER PACK
PRINT RUNS B/WN 1-50 COPIES PER
NO PRICING ON QTY OF 8 OR LESS
20 Willie Mays/24 15.00 40.00
25 Bob Feller/19 8.00 20.00

2005 Leaf Limited Team Trademarks Jersey Number Prime

OVERALL AU-GU ODDS ONE PER PACK
PRINT RUNS B/WN 1-50 COPIES PER
NO PRICING ON QTY OF 1
PRICES ARE FOR 2 COLOR PATCHES
REDUCE 20% FOR 1-COLOR PATCH
ADD 20% FOR 3-4 COLOR PATCH
ADD 50% FOR 5-COLOR+ PATCH
1 Ryne Sandberg/50 12.50 30.00
2 George Brett/50 12.50 30.00
3 Steve Carlton/50 5.00 12.00
4 Reggie Jackson/50 8.00 20.00
5 Edgar Martinez/50 8.00 20.00
6 Barry Larkin/50 8.00 20.00
7 Ozzie Smith/50 10.00 25.00
8 Carlton Fisk/50 8.00 20.00
9 Wade Boggs/50 8.00 20.00
10 Will Clark/50 8.00 20.00
11 Nolan Ryan/50 12.50 30.00
12 Gary Carter/50 5.00 12.00
13 Don Mattingly/40 12.50 30.00
14 Willie Stargell/50 8.00 20.00
15 Don Sutton/25 6.00 15.00
16 Kirk Gibson/50 5.00 12.00
17 Kirby Puckett/1
18 Dale Murphy/50 8.00 20.00
19 Rickey Henderson/50 10.00 25.00
21 Cal Ripken/25 30.00 60.00
23 Tony Gwynn/50 10.00 25.00
24 Andre Dawson/25 6.00 15.00
26 Alan Trammell/25 6.00 15.00
27 Dave Parker/50 5.00 12.00
29 Dwight Gooden/50 5.00 12.00
30 Harold Baines/25 6.00 15.00
31 Jack Morris/47 5.00 12.00
32 John Kruk/25 10.00 25.00
33 Lee Smith/47 5.00 12.00
34 Lenny Dykstra/25 6.00 15.00
38 Tony Oliva/26 6.00 15.00

2005 Leaf Limited Team Trademarks Signature

OVERALL AU-GU ODDS ONE PER PACK
PRINT RUNS B/WN 5-100 COPIES PER
NO PRICING ON QTY OF 5
1 Ryne Sandberg/25 30.00 60.00
2 George Brett/5
3 Steve Carlton/25 10.00 25.00
4 Reggie Jackson/25 20.00 50.00
5 Edgar Martinez/50 12.50 30.00
6 Barry Larkin/50 12.50 30.00
7 Ozzie Smith/50 15.00 40.00
8 Carlton Fisk/50 12.50 30.00
9 Wade Boggs/25 15.00 40.00
10 Will Clark/50 12.50 30.00
11 Nolan Ryan/50 40.00 80.00
12 Gary Carter/50 8.00 20.00
13 Don Mattingly/25 30.00 60.00
15 Don Sutton/100 6.00 15.00
16 Kirk Gibson/50 8.00 20.00
17 Kirby Puckett/25 50.00 100.00
18 Dale Murphy/100 10.00 25.00
19 Rickey Henderson/5
20 Willie Mays/25 100.00 175.00
21 Cal Ripken/50 50.00 100.00
22 Paul Molitor/25 10.00 25.00
23 Tony Gwynn/25 20.00 50.00
24 Andre Dawson/100 6.00 15.00
25 Bob Feller/50 8.00 20.00
26 Alan Trammell/25 10.00 25.00
27 Dave Parker/50 8.00 20.00
28 Dave Righetti/25 10.00 25.00
29 Dwight Gooden/50 8.00 20.00
30 Harold Baines/50 8.00 20.00
31 Jack Morris/50 8.00 20.00
32 John Kruk/25 15.00 40.00
33 Lee Smith/50 8.00 20.00
34 Lenny Dykstra/25 10.00 25.00
35 Luis Tiant/50 8.00 20.00
36 Matt Williams/50 12.50 30.00
37 Ron Guidry/25 10.00 25.00
38 Tony Oliva/50 8.00 20.00

2005 Leaf Limited Team Trademarks Signature Jersey Number

*NBR p/r 72: .4X TO 1X SIG p/r 50
*NBR p/r 39-49: .5X TO 1.2X SIG p/r 50
*NBR p/r 39-49: .4X TO 1X SIG p/r 25
*NBR p/r 20-34: .75X TO 2X SIG p/r 100
*NBR p/r 20-34: .6X TO 1.5X SIG p/r 50
*NBR p/r 20-34: .5X TO 1.2X SIG p/r 25
*NBR p/r 16-19: .75X TO 2X SIG p/r 50
*NBR p/r 16-19: .6X TO 1.5X SIG p/r 25
OVERALL AU-GU ODDS ONE PER PACK
PRINT RUNS B/WN 1-72 COPIES PER
NO PRICING ON QTY OF 11 OR LESS
11 Nolan Ryan Pants/34 50.00 100.00
19 Rickey Henderson/24 30.00 60.00
20 Willie Mays/24 125.00 200.00

2005 Leaf Limited Team Trademarks Signature Jersey Number Prime

*PRIME p/r 39-47: .6X TO 1.5X SIG p/r 50
*PRIME p/r 25-29: 1X TO 2.5X SIG p/r 100
*PRIME p/r 25-29: .75X TO 2X SIG p/r 50
*PRIME p/r 25-29: .6X TO 1.5X SIG p/r 25
*PRIME p/r 16: 1X TO 2.5X SIG p/r 50
OVERALL AU-GU ODDS ONE PER PACK
PRINT RUNS B/WN 1-47 COPIES PER
NO PRICING ON QTY OF 10 OR LESS

2011 Leaf Muhammad Ali Fans of Ali Autographs Bronze

OVERALL NON-ALI AUTO ODDS TWO PER PACK
CARD FAU7 NOT ISSUED
FAU5 Nolan Ryan 60.00 120.00

2011 Leaf Muhammad Ali Fans of Ali Autographs Gold

STATED PRINT RUN 5 SER. #'d SETS
UNPRICED DUE TO SCARCITY
CARD FAU7 NOT ISSUED

2011 Leaf Muhammad Ali Fans of Ali Autographs Silver

*SILVER: .6X TO 1.2X BRONZE
STATED PRINT RUN 25 SER. #'d SETS
CARD FAU7 NOT ISSUED

1998 Leaf Rookies and Stars

The 1998 Leaf Rookies and Stars set was issued in one series totalling 339 cards. The nine-card packs retailed for $2.99 each. The product was released very late in the year going live in December, 1998. This late release allowed for the inclusion of several rookies added to the 40 man roster at the end of the 1998 season. The set contains the topical subsets: Power Tools (131-160), Team Line-Up (161-190), and Rookies (191-300). Cards 131-230 were shortprinted, being seeded at a rate of 1:2 packs. In addition, 39 cards were tacked on to the end of the set (301-339) just prior to release. These cards were seeded at noticeably shorter rates (approximately 1:8 packs) than other subsets. Several key Rookie Cards, including J.D. Drew, Troy Glaus, Gabe Kapler and Ruben Mateo appear within this run of "high series" cards. Though not confirmed by the manufacturer, it is believed that card number 317 Ryan Minor was printed in a lesser amount than the other cards in the high series. All card fronts feature full-bleed color action photos. The featured player's name lines the bottom of the card with his jersey number in the lower left corner. This product was originally created by Pinnacle in their final days as a card manufacturer. After Playoff went out of business, Playoff paid for the right to distribute this product and release it late in 1998 as much of the product had already been created. Because of the especially strong selection of Rookie Cards and an large number of shortprints, this set endured to become one of the more popular and notable base brand issues of the late 1990's.

COMPLETE SET (339) 125.00 250.00
COMP.SET w/o SP's (200) 10.00 25.00
COMMON (1-130/231-300) .10 .30
COMMON (131-190) .40 1.00
COMMON (191-230) .75 2.00
COMMON RC (191-230) .75 2.00
COMMON (301-339) 1.00 2.50
COMMON RC (301-339) 1.00 2.50
1 Andy Pettitte .20 .50
2 Roberto Alomar .20 .50
3 Randy Johnson .30 .75
4 Manny Ramirez .20 .50
5 Paul Molitor .10 .30
6 Mike Mussina .20 .50
7 Jim Thome .20 .50
8 Tino Martinez .20 .50
9 Gary Sheffield .10 .30
10 Chuck Knoblauch .10 .30
11 Bernie Williams .20 .50
12 Tim Salmon .20 .50
13 Sammy Sosa .30 .75
14 Wade Boggs .20 .50
15 Andres Galarraga .10 .30
16 Pedro Martinez .20 .50
17 David Justice .10 .30
18 Chan Ho Park .10 .30
19 Jay Buhner .10 .30
20 Ryan Klesko .10 .30
21 Barry Larkin .20 .50
22 Will Clark .20 .50
23 Raul Mondesi .10 .30
24 Rickey Henderson .30 .75
25 Jim Edmonds .10 .30
26 Ken Griffey Jr. .50 1.25
27 Frank Thomas .30 .75
28 Cal Ripken 1.00 2.50
29 Alex Rodriguez .50 1.25
30 Mike Piazza .50 1.25
31 Greg Maddux .50 1.25
32 Chipper Jones .30 .75
33 Tony Gwynn .40 1.00
34 Derek Jeter .75 2.00
35 Jeff Bagwell .20 .50
36 Juan Gonzalez .10 .30
37 Nomar Garciaparra .50 1.25
38 Andruw Jones .20 .50
39 Hideo Nomo .30 .75
40 Roger Clemens .60 1.50
41 Mark McGwire .75 2.00
42 Scott Rolen .20 .50
43 Vladimir Guerrero .30 .75
44 Barry Bonds .75 2.00
45 Darin Erstad .10 .30
46 Albert Belle .10 .30
47 Kenny Lofton .10 .30
48 Mo Vaughn .10 .30
49 Ivan Rodriguez .20 .50
50 Jose Cruz Jr. .10 .30
51 Tony Clark .10 .30
52 Larry Walker .10 .30
53 Mark Grace .20 .50
54 Edgar Martinez .20 .50
55 Fred McGriff .20 .50
56 Rafael Palmeiro .20 .50
57 Matt Williams .10 .30
58 Craig Biggio .20 .50
59 Ken Caminiti .10 .30
60 Jose Canseco .20 .50
61 Brady Anderson .10 .30
62 Moises Alou .10 .30
63 Justin Thompson .10 .30
64 John Smoltz .20 .50
65 Carlos Delgado .10 .30
66 J.T. Snow .10 .30
67 Jason Giambi .10 .30
68 Garret Anderson .10 .30
69 Rondell White .10 .30
70 Eric Karros .10 .30
71 Javier Lopez .10 .30
72 Pat Hentgen .10 .30
73 Dante Bichette .10 .30
74 Charles Johnson .10 .30
75 Tom Glavine .20 .50
76 Rusty Greer .10 .30
77 Travis Fryman .10 .30
78 Todd Hundley .10 .30
79 Ray Lankford .10 .30
80 Denny Neagle .10 .30
81 Henry Rodriguez .10 .30
82 Sandy Alomar Jr. .10 .30
83 Robin Ventura .10 .30
84 John Olerud .10 .30
85 Omar Vizquel .20 .50
86 Darren Dreifort .10 .30
87 Kevin Brown .10 .30
88 Curt Schilling .10 .30
89 Francisco Cordova .10 .30
90 Brad Radke .10 .30
91 David Cone .10 .30
92 Paul O'Neill .20 .50
93 Vinny Castilla .10 .30
94 Marquis Grissom .10 .30
95 Brian L.Hunter .10 .30
96 Kevin Appier .10 .30
97 Bobby Bonilla .10 .30
98 Eric Young .10 .30
99 Jason Kendall .10 .30
100 Shawn Green .10 .30
101 Edgardo Alfonzo .10 .30
102 Alan Benes .10 .30
103 Bobby Higginson .10 .30
104 Todd Greene .10 .30
105 Jose Guillen .10 .30
106 Neifi Perez .10 .30
107 Edgar Renteria .10 .30
108 Chris Stynes .10 .30
109 Todd Walker .10 .30
110 Brian Jordan .10 .30
111 Joe Carter .10 .30
112 Ellis Burks .10 .30
113 Brett Tomko .10 .30
114 Mike Cameron .10 .30
115 Shannon Stewart .10 .30
116 Kevin Orie .10 .30
117 Brian Giles .10 .30
118 Hideki Irabu .10 .30
119 Delino DeShields .10 .30
120 David Segui .10 .30
121 Dustin Hermanson .10 .30
122 Kevin Young .10 .30
123 Jay Bell .10 .30
124 Doug Glanville .10 .30
125 John Roskos RC .10 .30
126 Damon Hollins .10 .30
127 Matt Stairs .10 .30
128 Cliff Floyd .10 .30
129 Derek Bell .10 .30
130 Darryl Strawberry .10 .30
131 Ken Griffey Jr. PT SP 1.50 4.00
132 Tim Salmon PT SP .60 1.50
133 M.Ramirez PT SP .60 1.50
134 Paul Konerko PT SP .40 1.00
135 Frank Thomas PT SP 1.00 2.50
136 Todd Helton PT SP .60 1.50
137 Larry Walker PT SP .40 1.00
138 Mo Vaughn PT SP .40 1.00
139 Travis Lee PT SP .40 1.00
140 Ivan Rodriguez PT SP .60 1.50
141 Ben Grieve PT SP .40 1.00
142 Brad Fullmer PT SP .40 1.00
143 Alex Rodriguez PT SP 1.50 4.00
144 Mike Piazza PT SP 1.50 4.00
145 Greg Maddux PT SP 1.50 4.00
146 Chipper Jones PT SP 1.00 2.50
147 Kenny Lofton PT SP .40 1.00
148 Albert Belle PT SP .40 1.00
149 Barry Bonds PT SP 2.50 6.00
150 V.Guerrero PT SP 1.00 2.50
151 Tony Gwynn PT SP 1.25 3.00
152 Derek Jeter PT SP 2.50 6.00
153 Jeff Bagwell PT SP .60 1.50
154 Juan Gonzalez PT SP .40 1.00
155 N.Garciaparra PT SP 1.50 4.00
156 Andruw Jones PT SP .60 1.50
157 Hideo Nomo PT SP 1.00 2.50
158 Roger Clemens PT SP 2.00 5.00
159 Mark McGwire PT SP 2.50 6.00
160 Scott Rolen PT SP .60 1.50
161 Travis Lee TLU SP .40 1.00
162 Ben Grieve TLU SP .40 1.00
163 Jose Guillen TLU SP .40 1.00
164 Mike Piazza TLU SP 1.50 4.00
165 Kevin Appier TLU SP .40 1.00
166 M.Grissom TLU SP .40 1.00
167 Rusty Greer TLU SP .40 1.00
168 Ken Caminiti TLU SP .40 1.00
169 Craig Biggio TLU SP .60 1.50
170 K.Griffey Jr. TLU SP 1.50 4.00
171 Larry Walker TLU SP .40 1.00
172 Barry Larkin TLU SP .60 1.50
173 A.Galarraga TLU SP .40 1.00
174 Wade Boggs TLU SP .60 1.50
175 Sammy Sosa TLU SP 1.00 2.50
176 T.Dunwoody TLU SP .40 1.00
177 Jim Thome TLU SP .60 1.50
178 Paul Molitor TLU SP .40 1.00
179 Tony Clark TLU SP .40 1.00
180 Jose Cruz Jr. TLU SP .40 1.00
181 Darin Erstad TLU SP .40 1.00
182 Barry Bonds TLU SP 2.50 6.00
183 Vlad.Guerrero TLU SP 1.00 2.50
184 Scott Rolen TLU SP .60 1.50
185 M.McGwire TLU SP 2.50 6.00

1998 Leaf Rookies and Stars

186 N.Garciaparra TLU SP 1.50 4.00
187 Gary Sheffield TLU SP .40 1.00
188 Cal Ripken TLU SP 3.00 8.00
189 F.Thomas TLU SP 1.00 2.50
190 Andy Pettitte TLU SP .60 1.50
191 Paul Konerko SP .75 2.00
192 Todd Helton SP 1.25 3.00
193 Mark Kotsay SP .75 2.00
194 Brad Fullmer SP .75 2.00
195 K.Millwood SP RC 3.00 8.00
196 David Ortiz SP 5.00 12.00
197 Kerry Wood SP 1.00 2.50
198 Miguel Tejada SP 2.00 5.00
199 Fernando Tatis SP .75 2.00
200 Jaret Wright SP .75 2.00
201 Ben Grieve SP .75 2.00
202 Travis Lee SP .75 2.00
203 Wes Helms SP .75 2.00
204 Geoff Jenkins SP 4.00 10.00
205 Russell Branyan SP .75 2.00
206 Esteban Yan SP RC 1.25 3.00
207 Ben Ford SP RC .75 2.00
208 Rich Butler SP RC .75 2.00
209 Ryan Jackson SP RC .75 2.00
210 A.J. Hinch SP .75 2.00
211 Magglio Ordonez RC 10.00 25.00
212 Dave Dellucci SP RC 2.00 5.00
213 Billy McMillon SP .75 2.00
214 Mike Lowell SP RC 4.00 10.00
215 Todd Erdos SP RC .75 2.00
216 C.Mendoza SP RC .75 2.00
217 F.Catalanotto SP RC 2.00 5.00
218 Julio Ramirez SP RC 1.25 3.00
219 John Halama SP RC 1.25 3.00
220 Wilson Delgado SP .75 2.00
221 Mike Judd SP RC 1.25 3.00
222 Rolando Arrojo SP RC 1.25 3.00
223 Jason LaRue SP RC 1.25 3.00
224 Manny Aybar SP RC 1.25 3.00
225 Jorge Velandia SP .75 2.00
226 Mike Kinkade SP RC 1.25 3.00
227 Carlos Lee SP RC 6.00 15.00
228 Bobby Hughes SP .75 2.00
229 R.Christenson SP RC .75 2.00
230 Masato Yoshii SP RC 1.25 3.00
231 Richard Hidalgo .10 .30
232 Rafael Medina .10 .30
233 Damian Jackson .10 .30
234 Derek Lowe .10 .30
235 Mario Valdez .10 .30
236 Eli Marrero .10 .30
237 Juan Encarnacion .10 .30
238 Livan Hernandez .10 .30
239 Bruce Chen .10 .30
240 Eric Milton .10 .30
241 Jason Varitek .30 .75
242 Scott Elarton .10 .30
243 Manuel Barrios RC .10 .30
244 Mike Caruso .10 .30
245 Tom Evans .10 .30
246 Pat Cline .10 .30
247 Matt Clement .10 .30
248 Karim Garcia .10 .30
249 Richie Sexson .10 .30
250 Sidney Ponson .10 .30
251 Randall Simon .10 .30
252 Tony Saunders .10 .30
253 Javier Valentin .10 .30
254 Danny Clyburn .10 .30
255 Michael Coleman .10 .30
256 Hanley Frias RC .10 .30
257 Miguel Cairo .10 .30
258 Rob Stanifer RC .10 .30
259 Lou Collier .10 .30
260 Abraham Nunez .10 .30
261 Ricky Ledee .10 .30
262 Carl Pavano .10 .30
263 Derrek Lee .20 .50
264 Jeff Abbott .10 .30
265 Bob Abreu .10 .30
266 Bartolo Colon .10 .30
267 Mike Drumright .10 .30
268 Daryle Ward .10 .30
269 Gabe Alvarez .10 .30
270 Josh Booty .10 .30
271 Damian Moss .10 .30
272 Brian Rose .10 .30
273 Jarrod Washburn .10 .30
274 Bobby Estalella .10 .30
275 Enrique Wilson .10 .30
276 Derrick Gibson .10 .30
277 Ken Cloude .10 .30
278 Kevin Witt .10 .30
279 Donnie Sadler .10 .30
280 Sean Casey .10 .30
281 Jacob Cruz .10 .30
282 Ron Wright .10 .30
283 Jeremi Gonzalez .10 .30
284 Desi Relaford .10 .30
285 Bobby Smith .10 .30
286 Javier Vazquez .10 .30
287 Steve Woodard .10 .30
288 Greg Norton .10 .30
289 Cliff Politte .10 .30
290 Felix Heredia .10 .30
291 Braden Looper .10 .30
292 Felix Martinez .10 .30
293 Brian Meadows .10 .30
294 Edwin Diaz .10 .30
295 Pat Watkins .10 .30
296 Marc Pisciotta RC .10 .30
297 Rick Gorecki .10 .30
298 DaRond Stovall .10 .30
299 Andy Larkin .10 .30
300 Felix Rodriguez .10 .30
301 Blake Stein SP 1.00 2.50
302 John Rocker SP RC 2.50 6.00
303 J.Baughman SP RC 1.00 2.50
304 Jesus Sanchez SP RC 1.50 4.00
305 Randy Winn SP 1.00 2.50
306 Lou Merloni SP 1.00 2.50
307 Jim Parque SP RC 1.50 4.00
308 Dennis Reyes SP 1.00 2.50
309 O.Hernandez SP RC 4.00 10.00
310 Jason Johnson SP 1.00 2.50
311 Torii Hunter SP 1.00 2.50
312 M.Piazza Marlins SP 4.00 10.00
313 Mike Frank SP RC 1.00 2.50
314 Troy Glaus SP RC 15.00 40.00
315 Jin Ho Cho SP RC 1.50 4.00
316 Ruben Mateo SP RC 1.00 2.50
317 Ryan Minor SP RC 1.50 4.00
318 Aramis Ramirez SP 1.00 2.50
319 Adrian Beltre SP 1.00 2.50
320 Matt Anderson SP RC 1.00 2.50
321 Gabe Kapler SP RC 2.50 6.00
322 Jeremy Giambi SP RC 1.50 4.00
323 Carlos Beltran SP 3.00 8.00
324 Dermal Brown SP 1.00 2.50
325 Ben Davis SP 1.00 2.50
326 Eric Chavez SP 1.00 2.50
327 Bobby Howry SP RC 1.00 2.50
328 Roy Halladay SP 5.00 12.00
329 George Lombard SP 1.00 2.50
330 Michael Barrett SP 1.00 2.50
331 F. Seguignol SP RC 1.00 2.50
332 J.D. Drew SP RC 5.00 12.00
333 Odalis Perez SP RC 4.00 10.00
334 Alex Cora SP RC 1.50 4.00
335 P.Polanco SP RC 2.00 5.00
336 Armando Rios SP RC 1.50 4.00
337 Sammy Sosa HR SP 2.50 6.00
338 Mark McGwire HR SP 6.00 15.00
339 Sammy Sosa 4.00 10.00
Mark McGwire CL SP

1998 Leaf Rookies and Stars Longevity

Randomly inserted in packs, this 339-card set is a parallel to the Leaf Rookies and Stars base set. The set is serially numbered to 50 (although only 49 sets were actually produced because the first set - cards numbered "1/50" were given a holographic foil coating) and printed on foil board with foil stamping.

*STARS 1-130/231-300: 15X TO 40X BASIC
*RC's 1-130/231-300: 25X TO 50X BASIC
*STARS 131-190: 3X TO 8X BASIC
*STARS 191-230: 3X TO 8X BASIC
*RC's 191-230: 2X TO 4X BASIC
*STARS 301-339: 2.5X TO 6X BASIC
*RC's 301-339: 1.5X TO 3X BASIC
314 Troy Glaus 125.00 200.00

1998 Leaf Rookies and Stars True Blue

Randomly inserted in packs, this 339-card set is a parallel to the Leaf Rookies and Stars base set. Only 500 sets were printed (though the cards are not serial numbered - instead, they say "1 of 500" on back) and each card features blue foil stamping accents.

*STARS 1-130/231-300: 6X TO 15X BASIC
*ROOKIES 1-130/231-300: 3X TO 8X BASIC CARDS
*LO SP STARS 131-190: 1X TO 2.5X BASIC
*LO SP STARS 191-230: 2X TO 5X BASIC
*ROOKIES 191-230: .5X TO 1.2X BASIC
*STARS 301-339: .75X TO 2X BASIC
*ROOKIES 301-339: .4X TO 1X BASIC

1998 Leaf Rookies and Stars Crosstraining

Randomly inserted in packs, this 10-card set is an insert to the Leaf Rookies and Stars brand. The set is sequentially numbered to 1000. The cards are printed on foil board. Each card front highlights a color action player photo surrounded by a crosstraining shoe sole design. The same player is highlighted on the back with information on his different skills.

COMPLETE SET (10) 50.00 120.00
1 Kenny Lofton 1.50 4.00
2 Ken Griffey Jr. 6.00 15.00
3 Alex Rodriguez 6.00 15.00
4 Greg Maddux 6.00 15.00
5 Barry Bonds 10.00 25.00
6 Ivan Rodriguez 2.50 6.00
7 Chipper Jones 4.00 10.00
8 Jeff Bagwell 2.50 6.00
9 Nomar Garciaparra 6.00 15.00
10 Derek Jeter 10.00 25.00

1998 Leaf Rookies and Stars Crusade Update Green

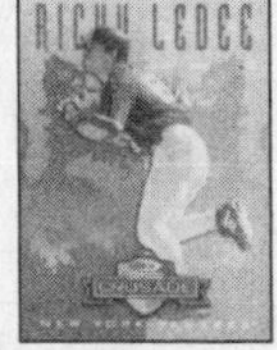

Randomly inserted in packs, this 30-card set is an insert to the Leaf Rookies and Stars brand and was intended as an update to the 100 Crusade insert cards seeded in 1998 Donruss Update, 1998 Leaf and 1998 Donruss packs (thus the numbering 101-130). The set is sequentially numbered to 250. The fronts feature color action photos placed on a background of a Crusade shield design. The set features three parallel versions printed with a "Spectra-tech" holographic technology. First year serial-numbered cards of Kevin Millwood and Magglio Ordonez are featured in this set.

COMPLETE SET (30) 125.00 300.00
101 Richard Hidalgo 4.00 10.00
102 Paul Konerko 6.00 15.00
103 Miguel Tejada 10.00 25.00
104 Fernando Tatis 4.00 10.00
105 Travis Lee 4.00 10.00
106 Wes Helms 4.00 10.00
107 Rich Butler 4.00 10.00
108 Mark Kotsay 6.00 15.00
109 Eli Marrero 4.00 10.00
110 David Ortiz 12.50 30.00
111 Juan Encarnacion 4.00 10.00
112 Jaret Wright 4.00 10.00
113 Livan Hernandez 6.00 15.00
114 Ron Wright 4.00 10.00
115 Ryan Christenson 4.00 10.00
116 Eric Milton 4.00 10.00
117 Brad Fullmer 4.00 10.00
118 Karim Garcia 4.00 10.00
119 Abraham Nunez 4.00 10.00
120 Ricky Ledee 4.00 10.00
121 Carl Pavano 6.00 15.00
122 Derrek Lee 8.00 20.00
123 A.J. Hinch 4.00 10.00
124 Brian Rose 4.00 10.00
125 Bobby Estalella 4.00 10.00
126 Kevin Millwood 10.00 25.00
127 Kerry Wood 6.00 15.00
128 Sean Casey 6.00 15.00
129 Russell Branyan 4.00 10.00
130 Magglio Ordonez 15.00 40.00

1998 Leaf Rookies and Stars Crusade Update Purple

Randomly inserted in packs, this 30-card set is a parallel insert to the Leaf Rookies and Stars Crusade Update set. The set is sequentially numbered to 100.

*PURPLE: .75X TO 2X GREEN
*PURPLE: .75X TO 2X GREEN RC'S

1998 Leaf Rookies and Stars Extreme Measures

Randomly inserted in packs, this 10-card set is an insert to the Leaf Rookies and Stars brand. The cards are printed on foil board and sequentially numbered to 1000. However, a parallel version was created wherby a specific amount of each card was die cut to a featured statistic. The result, was varying print runs of the non-die cut cards. Specific print runs for each card are provided in our checklist after the player's name. Card fronts feature color action photos and highlights the featured player's extreme statistics.

COMPLETE SET (10) 50.00 120.00
1 Ken Griffey Jr./944 6.00 15.00
2 Frank Thomas/653 4.00 10.00
3 Tony Gwynn/628 5.00 12.00
4 Mark McGwire/942 10.00 25.00
5 Larry Walker/280 2.50 6.00
6 Mike Piazza/960 6.00 15.00
7 Roger Clemens/708 8.00 20.00
8 Greg Maddux/980 6.00 15.00
9 Jeff Bagwell/873 2.50 6.00
10 Nomar Garciaparra/989 6.00 15.00

1998 Leaf Rookies and Stars Extreme Measures Die Cuts

Randomly inserted in packs, this 10-card set is a parallel insert to the Leaf Rookies and Stars Extreme Measures set. The set is sequentially numbered to 1000. The low serial numbered cards are die-cut to showcase a specific statistic for each player. For example, Ken Griffey hit 56 home runs last year, so the 1st 56 of his cards are die-cut and cards serial numbered from 57 through 1000 are not.

NO PRICING ON 11 OR LESS
1 Ken Griffey Jr./56 20.00 50.00
2 Frank Thomas/347 6.00 15.00
3 Tony Gwynn/372 6.00 15.00
4 Mark McGwire/58 40.00 80.00
5 Larry Walker/720 4.00 10.00
6 Mike Piazza/40 20.00 50.00
7 Roger Clemens/292 10.00 25.00
8 Greg Maddux/20
9 Jeff Bagwell/127 8.00 20.00
10 Nomar Garciaparra/11

1998 Leaf Rookies and Stars Freshman Orientation Samples

To preview the late-released 1998 Leaf Rookies and Stars product, all dealer wholesale order forms contained one sample card from four different insert sets (Freshman Orientation, Great American Heroes. Major League Hard Drives and Standing Ovations). The samples each feature the large "SAMPLE" text printed

diagonally across the card back and a blank area intended for serial numbering on back. Apparently, MLB disallowed Donruss/Leaf the rights to use the word "chase" in a product name, fearing it insinuated aspects of gambling. However, the name was officially changed after Playoff took over Pinnacle's bankruptcy assets.

COMPLETE SET (20) 16.00 40.00
1 Todd Helton 2.00 5.00
2 Ben Grieve .40 1.00
3 Travis Lee .40 1.00
4 Paul Konerko 1.50 4.00
5 Jaret Wright .40 1.00
6 Livan Hernandez .75 2.00
7 Brad Fullmer .40 1.00
8 Carl Pavano .40 1.00
9 Richard Hidalgo .40 1.00
10 Miguel Tejada 1.50 4.00
11 Mark Kotsay .40 1.00
12 David Ortiz 1.50 4.00
13 Juan Encarnacion .60 1.50
14 Fernando Tatis .60 1.50
15 Kevin Millwood 2.00 5.00
16 Kerry Wood 1.25 3.00
17 Magglio Ordonez 4.00 10.00
18 Derrek Lee 1.50 4.00
19 Jose Cruz Jr. .60 1.50
20 A.J. Hinch .40 1.00

1998 Leaf Rookies and Stars Freshman Orientation

Randomly inserted in packs, this 20-card set is an insert to the Leaf Rookies and Stars brand. The set is sequentially numbered to 5000 and printed with holographic foil. The fronts feature color photos of the top up and coming stars in the game today surrounded by a background of banners and baseballs. The backs highlight the date of the featured player's Major League debut.

COMPLETE SET (20) 10.00 25.00
1 Todd Helton .75 2.00
2 Ben Grieve .40 1.00
3 Travis Lee .40 1.00
4 Paul Konerko .60 1.50
5 Jaret Wright .40 1.00
6 Livan Hernandez .60 1.50
7 Brad Fullmer .40 1.00
8 Carl Pavano .60 1.50
9 Richard Hidalgo .40 1.00
10 Miguel Tejada 1.25 3.00
11 Mark Kotsay .60 1.50
12 David Ortiz 1.50 4.00
13 Juan Encarnacion .40 1.00
14 Fernando Tatis .40 1.00
15 Kevin Millwood 1.25 3.00
16 Kerry Wood .60 1.50
17 Magglio Ordonez 1.50 4.00
18 Derrek Lee .75 2.00
19 Jose Cruz Jr. .40 1.00
20 A.J. Hinch .40 1.00

1998 Leaf Rookies and Stars Great American Heroes Samples

To preview the late-released 1998 Leaf Rookies and Stars product, all dealer wholesale order forms contained one sample card from four different insert sets (Freshman Orientation, Great American Heroes. Major League Hard Drives and Standing Ovations). The samples each feature the large "SAMPLE" text printed diagonally across the card back and a blank area intended for serial numbering on back. Apparently, MLB disallowed Donruss/Leaf the rights to use the word "chase" in a product name, fearing it insinuated aspects of gambling. However, the name was officially changed after Playoff took over Pinnacle's bankruptcy assets.

COMPLETE SET (20) 32.00 80.00
1 Frank Thomas 1.00 2.50
2 Cal Ripken 4.00 10.00
3 Ken Griffey Jr. 2.00 5.00
4 Alex Rodriguez 2.50 6.00
5 Greg Maddux 2.00 5.00
6 Mike Piazza 2.50 6.00
7 Chipper Jones 2.00 5.00
8 Tony Gwynn 1.50 4.00
9 Jeff Bagwell 1.00 2.50
10 Juan Gonzalez .75 2.00
11 Hideo Nomo 2.00 5.00
12 Roger Clemens 2.00 5.00
13 Mark McGwire 2.50 6.00
14 Barry Bonds 2.00 5.00
15 Kenny Lofton .40 1.00
16 Larry Walker .30 .75
17 Paul Molitor 1.00 2.50
18 Wade Boggs 1.00 2.50
19 Barry Larkin .60 1.50
20 Andres Galarraga .40 1.00

1998 Leaf Rookies and Stars Great American Heroes

Randomly inserted in packs, this 20-card set is an insert to the Leaf Rookies and Stars brand. The set is sequentially numbered to 2500 and stamped with holographic foil. The fronts feature color player photos placed in an open star with "Great American Heroes" written in the upper right corner. In remembrance of his turbulent 1998 season, Mike Piazza is featured on three different versions (pictured separately as a Dodger, Marlin and Met).

COMPLETE SET (20) 60.00 150.00
1 Frank Thomas 2.50 6.00
2 Cal Ripken 8.00 20.00
3 Ken Griffey Jr. 4.00 10.00
4 Alex Rodriguez 4.00 10.00
5 Greg Maddux 4.00 10.00
6 Mike Piazza Dodgers 4.00 10.00
6B Mike Piazza Marlins 4.00 10.00
6C Mike Piazza Mets 4.00 10.00
7 Chipper Jones 2.50 6.00
8 Tony Gwynn 3.00 8.00
9 Jeff Bagwell 1.50 4.00
10 Juan Gonzalez 1.00 2.50
11 Hideo Nomo 2.50 6.00
12 Roger Clemens 5.00 12.00
13 Mark McGwire 6.00 15.00
14 Barry Bonds 6.00 15.00
15 Kenny Lofton 1.00 2.50
16 Larry Walker 1.00 2.50
17 Paul Molitor 1.00 2.50
18 Wade Boggs 1.50 4.00
19 Barry Larkin 1.50 4.00
20 Andres Galarraga 1.00 2.50

1998 Leaf Rookies and Stars Greatest Hits

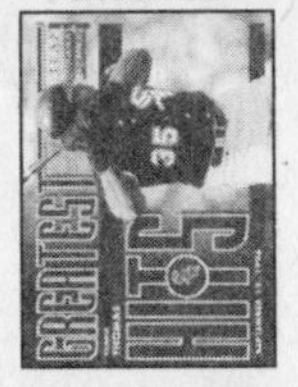

Randomly inserted in packs, this 20-card set features color photos of the season's great rookies as well as stars of the game. The backs carry player information. Only 2500 serially numbered sets were produced.

COMPLETE SET (20) 50.00 120.00
1 Ken Griffey Jr. 4.00 10.00
2 Frank Thomas 2.50 6.00
3 Cal Ripken 8.00 20.00
4 Alex Rodriguez 4.00 10.00
5 Ben Grieve 2.50 6.00
6 Mike Piazza 4.00 10.00
7 Chipper Jones 2.50 6.00
8 Tony Gwynn 3.00 8.00
9 Derek Jeter 6.00 15.00
10 Jeff Bagwell 1.50 4.00
11 Tino Martinez 1.50 4.00
12 Juan Gonzalez 1.00 2.50
13 Nomar Garciaparra 4.00 10.00
14 Mark McGwire 6.00 15.00
15 Scott Rolen 1.50 4.00
16 David Justice 1.00 2.50
17 Darin Erstad 1.00 2.50
18 Mo Vaughn 1.00 2.50
19 Ivan Rodriguez 1.50 4.00
20 Travis Lee 1.50 4.00

1998 Leaf Rookies and Stars Home Run Derby

Randomly inserted in packs, this 20-card set is an insert to the Leaf Rookies and Stars brand. The set is sequentially numbered to 2500 and printed on foil board. The card fronts feature color player photos of today's top homerun hitters surrounded by a nostalgic bordered background that takes a look at the TV show from the 50's with the same name.

COMPLETE SET (20) 40.00 100.00
1 Tino Martinez 1.50 4.00
2 Jim Thome 1.50 4.00
3 Larry Walker 1.00 2.50
4 Tony Clark 1.00 2.50
5 Jose Cruz Jr. 1.00 2.50
6 Barry Bonds 6.00 15.00
7 Scott Rolen 1.50 4.00
8 Paul Konerko 1.00 2.50
9 Travis Lee 1.00 2.50
10 Todd Helton 2.50 6.00
11 Mark McGwire 6.00 15.00
12 Andruw Jones 1.50 4.00
13 Nomar Garciaparra 4.00 10.00
14 Juan Gonzalez 1.00 2.50
15 Jeff Bagwell 1.50 4.00
16 Chipper Jones 2.50 6.00
17 Mike Piazza 4.00 10.00
18 Frank Thomas 2.50 6.00
19 Ken Griffey Jr. 4.00 10.00
20 Albert Belle 1.00 2.50

1998 Leaf Rookies and Stars Leaf MVP's

Randomly inserted in packs, this 20-card set is an insert to the Leaf Rookies and Stars brand. Each card is printed on foil board, with a red background and sequentially numbered to 5000 - although the first 500 of each card was die cut for a parallel set. Thus, only cards serial numbered from 501 through 5000 are featured in this set. The fronts feature color action photos on top of an "MVP" logo in the background.

COMPLETE SET (20) 30.00 80.00
*PENNANT ED: 1.5X TO 4X BASIC LEAF MVP
PENNANT ED.1ST 500 SERIAL #'d SETS
RANDOM INSERTS IN PACKS
1 Frank Thomas 1.50 4.00
2 Chuck Knoblauch .60 1.50
3 Cal Ripken 5.00 12.00
4 Alex Rodriguez 2.50 6.00
5 Ivan Rodriguez 1.00 2.50
6 Albert Belle .60 1.50
7 Ken Griffey Jr. 2.50 6.00
8 Juan Gonzalez .60 1.50
9 Roger Clemens 3.00 8.00
10 Mo Vaughn .60 1.50
11 Jeff Bagwell 1.00 2.50
12 Craig Biggio 1.00 2.50
13 Chipper Jones 1.50 4.00
14 Barry Larkin 1.00 2.50
15 Mike Piazza 2.50 6.00
16 Barry Bonds 4.00 10.00
17 Andruw Jones 1.00 2.50
18 Tony Gwynn 2.00 5.00
19 Greg Maddux 2.50 6.00
20 Mark McGwire 4.00 10.00

1998 Leaf Rookies and Stars Major League Hard Drives Samples

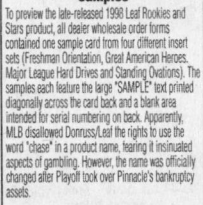

To preview the late-released 1998 Leaf Rookies and Stars product, all dealer wholesale order forms contained one sample card from four different insert sets (Freshman Orientation, Great American Heroes. Major League Hard Drives and Standing Ovations). The samples each feature the large "SAMPLE" text printed diagonally across the card back and a blank area intended for serial numbering on back. Apparently, MLB disallowed Donruss/Leaf the rights to use the word "chase" in a product name, fearing it insinuated aspects of gambling. However, the name was officially changed after Playoff took over Pinnacle's bankruptcy assets.

COMPLETE SET (20) 24.00 60.00
1 Jeff Bagwell 1.00 2.50
2 Juan Gonzalez .75 2.00
3 Nomar Garciaparra 2.50 6.00
4 Ken Griffey Jr. 2.00 5.00
5 Frank Thomas 1.00 2.50
6 Cal Ripken 4.00 10.00
7 Alex Rodriguez 2.50 6.00
8 Mike Piazza 2.50 6.00
9 Chipper Jones 2.00 5.00
10 Tony Gwynn 1.50 4.00
11 Derek Jeter 4.00 10.00
12 Mo Vaughn .30 .75
13 Ben Grieve .20 .50
14 Manny Ramirez 1.00 2.50
15 Vladimir Guerrero 1.25 3.00
16 Scott Rolen .60 1.50
17 Darin Erstad .60 1.50
18 Kenny Lofton .40 1.00
19 Brad Fullmer .20 .50
20 David Justice .40 1.00

1998 Leaf Rookies and Stars Major League Hard Drives

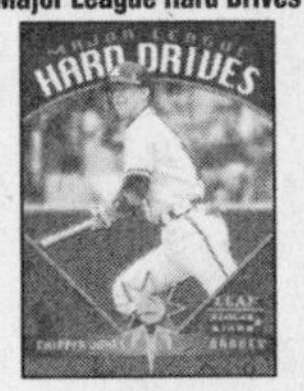

Randomly inserted in packs, this 20-card set is an insert to the Leaf Rookies and Stars brand. The set is printed with holographic foil stamping and sequentially numbered to 2500. The fronts feature color action photos of some of today's hottest hitting machines placed in a baseball diamond background. In remembrance of his turbulent 1998 season, Mike Piazza is featured on three different versions (pictured separately as a Dodger, Marlin and Met). All three versions of the Piazza card had 2500 cards printed.

COMPLETE SET (20) 60.00 150.00
1 Jeff Bagwell 1.50 4.00
2 Juan Gonzalez 1.00 2.50
3 Nomar Garciaparra 4.00 10.00
4 Ken Griffey Jr. 4.00 10.00
5 Frank Thomas 2.50 6.00
6 Cal Ripken 8.00 20.00
7 Alex Rodriguez 4.00 10.00
8 Mike Piazza Dodgers 4.00 10.00
8B Mike Piazza Marlins 4.00 10.00
8C Mike Piazza Mets 4.00 10.00
9 Chipper Jones 2.50 6.00
10 Tony Gwynn 3.00 8.00
11 Derek Jeter 6.00 15.00
12 Mo Vaughn 1.00 2.50
13 Ben Grieve 2.50 6.00
14 Manny Ramirez 1.50 4.00
15 Vladimir Guerrero 2.50 6.00
16 Scott Rolen 1.50 4.00
17 Darin Erstad 1.00 2.50
18 Kenny Lofton 1.00 2.50
19 Brad Fullmer 1.00 2.50
20 David Justice 1.00 2.50

1998 Leaf Rookies and Stars Standing Ovations Samples

To preview the late-released 1998 Leaf Rookies and Stars product, all dealer wholesale order forms contained one sample card from four different insert sets (Freshman Orientation, Great American Heroes. Major League Hard Drives and Standing Ovations). The samples each feature the large "SAMPLE" text printed diagonally across the card back and a blank area intended for serial numbering on back. Apparently, MLB disallowed Donruss/Leaf the rights to use the word "chase" in a product name, fearing it insinuated

aspects of gambling. However, the name was officially changed after Playoff took over Pinnacle's bankruptcy assets.

COMPLETE SET (10) 20.00 50.00
1 Barry Bonds 2.00 5.00
2 Mark McGwire 2.50 6.00
3 Ken Griffey Jr. 2.00 5.00
4 Frank Thomas 1.00 2.50
5 Tony Gwynn 1.50 4.00
6 Cal Ripken 4.00 10.00
7 Greg Maddux 2.50 6.00
8 Roger Clemens 2.00 5.00
9 Paul Molitor 1.00 2.50
10 Ivan Rodriguez 1.00 2.50

1998 Leaf Rookies and Stars Standing Ovations

Randomly inserted in packs, this 10-card set is an insert to the Leaf Rookies and Stars brand set. The set is sequentially numbered to 5000 and printed with holographic foil stamping. The fronts feature full-bleed color photos. The featured player's ovation deserved accomplishments are found lining the bottom of the card along with his name and team.

COMPLETE SET (10) 20.00 50.00
1 Barry Bonds 4.00 10.00
2 Mark McGwire 4.00 10.00
3 Ken Griffey Jr. 2.50 6.00
4 Frank Thomas 1.50 4.00
5 Tony Gwynn 2.00 5.00
6 Cal Ripken 5.00 12.00
7 Greg Maddux 2.50 6.00
8 Roger Clemens 3.00 8.00
9 Paul Molitor .60 1.50
10 Ivan Rodriguez 1.00 2.50

1998 Leaf Rookies and Stars Ticket Masters

Randomly inserted in packs, this 20-card set is an insert to the Leaf Rookies and Stars base set. The set is sequentially numbered to 2500, but the first 250 cards were die cut for a parallel set. This double-sided set is printed on foil board and features color photos of players from the same team.

COMPLETE SET (20) 60.00 150.00
*DIE CUTS: 1.25X TO 3X BASIC TICKET
DIE CUTS 1ST 250 SERIAL #'d SETS
RANDOM INSERTS IN PACKS
1 Ken Griffey Jr. 5.00 12.00
Alex Rodriguez
2 Frank Thomas 3.00 8.00
Albert Belle
3 Cal Ripken 10.00 25.00
Roberto Alomar
4 Greg Maddux 5.00 12.00
Chipper Jones
5 Tony Gwynn 4.00 10.00
Ken Caminiti
6 Derek Jeter 8.00 20.00
Andy Pettitte
7 Jeff Bagwell 2.00 5.00
Craig Biggio
8 Juan Gonzalez 2.00 5.00
Ivan Rodriguez
9 Nomar Garciaparra 5.00 12.00
Mo Vaughn
10 Vladimir Guerrero 3.00 8.00
Brad Fullmer
11 Andruw Jones 2.00 5.00
Andres Galarraga
12 Tino Martinez 2.00 5.00
Chuck Knoblauch
13 Raul Mondesi 1.25 3.00
Paul Konerko
14 Roger Clemens 6.00 15.00
Jose Cruz Jr.
15 Mark McGwire 8.00 20.00
Brian Jordan
16 Kenny Lofton 2.00 5.00
Manny Ramirez
17 Larry Walker 1.25 3.00
Todd Helton
18 Darin Erstad 1.25 3.00
Tim Salmon
19 Travis Lee 1.25 3.00
Matt Williams
20 Ben Grieve 1.25 3.00
Jason Giambi

2001 Leaf Rookies and Stars Samples

Inserted one per sealed Beckett Baseball Card Monthly issue number 202, these 100 cards feature veterans from the Leaf Rookies and Stars set. Each card has the word Sample stamped on the back.

*SINGLES: 1.5X TO 4X BASIC CARDS

2001 Leaf Rookies and Stars

This 300 card set was issued in five card packs. All cards numbered over 100 were shortprinted. Cards numbered 101-200 were inserted at a rate of one in four while cards numbered 201-300 were inserted at a rate of one in 24.

Card	Low	High
COMP.SET w/o SP'S (100)	8.00	20.00
COMMON CARD (1-100)	.10	.30
COMMON (101-200)	1.25	3.00
COMMON (201-300)	2.00	5.00
1 Alex Rodriguez	.50	1.25
2 Derek Jeter	.75	2.00
3 Aramis Ramirez	.10	.30
4 Cliff Floyd	.10	.30
5 Nomar Garciaparra	.50	1.25
6 Craig Biggio	.20	.50
7 Ivan Rodriguez	.20	.50
8 Cal Ripken	1.00	2.50
9 Fred McGriff	.20	.50
10 Chipper Jones	.30	.75
11 Roberto Alomar	.20	.50
12 Moises Alou	.10	.30
13 Freddy Garcia	.10	.30
14 Bobby Abreu	.10	.30
15 Shawn Green	.10	.30
16 Jason Giambi	.10	.30
17 Todd Helton	.20	.50
18 Robert Fick	.10	.30
19 Tony Gwynn	.40	1.00
20 Luis Gonzalez	.10	.30
21 Sean Casey	.10	.30
22 Roger Clemens	.60	1.50
23 Brian Giles	.10	.30
24 Manny Ramirez Sox	.20	.50
25 Barry Bonds	.75	2.00
26 Richard Hidalgo	.10	.30
27 Vladimir Guerrero	.30	.75
28 Kevin Brown UER Batting headers for stats	.10	.30
29 Mike Sweeney	.10	.30
30 Ken Griffey Jr.	.50	1.25
31 Mike Piazza	.50	1.25
32 Richie Sexson	.10	.30
33 Matt Morris	.10	.30
34 Jorge Posada	.20	.50
35 Eric Chavez	.10	.30
36 Mark Buehrle	.20	.50
37 Jeff Bagwell	.20	.50
38 Curt Schilling	.10	.30
39 Bartolo Colon	.10	.30
40 Mark Quinn	.10	.30
41 Tony Clark	.10	.30
42 Brad Radke	.10	.30
43 Gary Sheffield	.10	.30
44 Doug Mientkiewicz	.10	.30
45 Pedro Martinez	.20	.50
46 Carlos Lee	.10	.30
47 Troy Glaus	.10	.30
48 Preston Wilson	.10	.30
49 Phil Nevin	.10	.30
50 Chan Ho Park	.10	.30
51 Randy Johnson	.30	.75
52 Jermaine Dye	.10	.30
53 Terrence Long	.10	.30
54 Joe Mays	.10	.30
55 Scott Rolen	.20	.50
56 Miguel Tejada	.10	.30
57 Jim Thome	.20	.50
58 Jose Vidro	.10	.30
59 Gabe Kapler	.10	.30
60 Darin Erstad	.10	.30
61 Jim Edmonds	.10	.30
62 Jarrod Washburn	.10	.30
63 Tom Glavine	.20	.50
64 Adrian Beltre	.10	.30
65 Sammy Sosa	.30	.75
66 Juan Gonzalez	.10	.30
67 Rafael Furcal	.10	.30
68 Mike Mussina	.20	.50
69 Mark McGwire	.75	2.00
70 Ryan Kiesko	.10	.30
71 Raul Mondesi	.10	.30
72 Trot Nixon	.10	.30
73 Barry Larkin	.20	.50
74 Rafael Palmeiro	.20	.50
75 Mark Mulder	.10	.30
76 Carlos Delgado	.10	.30
77 Mike Hampton	.10	.30
78 Carl Everett	.10	.30
79 Paul Konerko	.10	.30
80 Larry Walker	.10	.30
81 Kerry Wood	.10	.30
82 Frank Thomas	.30	.75
83 Andruw Jones	.20	.50
84 Eric Milton	.10	.30
85 Ben Grieve	.10	.30
86 Carlos Beltran	.10	.30
87 Tim Hudson	.10	.30
88 Hideo Nomo	.30	.75
89 Greg Maddux	.50	1.25
90 Edgar Martinez	.20	.50
91 Lance Berkman	.10	.30
92 Pat Burrell	.10	.30
93 Jeff Kent	.10	.30
94 Magglio Ordonez	.10	.30
95 Cristian Guzman	.10	.30
96 Jose Canseco	.20	.50
97 J.D. Drew	.10	.30
98 Bernie Williams	.20	.50
99 Kazuhiro Sasaki	.10	.30
100 Rickey Henderson	.30	.75
101 Wilson Guzman RC	1.25	3.00
102 Nick Neugebauer	1.25	3.00
103 Lance Davis RC	1.25	3.00
104 Felipe Lopez	1.25	3.00
105 Toby Hall	1.25	3.00
106 Jack Cust	1.25	3.00
107 Jason Karnuth RC	1.25	3.00
108 Bart Miadich RC	1.25	3.00
109 Brian Roberts RC	3.00	8.00
110 Brandon Larson RC	1.25	3.00
111 Sean Douglass RC	1.25	3.00
112 Joe Crede	2.00	5.00
113 Tim Redding	1.25	3.00
114 Adam Johnson	1.25	3.00
115 Marcus Giles	1.25	3.00
116 Jose Ortiz	1.25	3.00
117 Jose Mieses RC	1.25	3.00
118 Nick Maness RC	1.25	3.00
119 Les Walrond RC	1.25	3.00
120 Travis Phelps RC	1.25	3.00
121 Troy Mattes RC	1.25	3.00
122 Carlos Garcia RC	1.25	3.00
123 Bill Ortega RC	1.25	3.00
124 Gene Altman RC	1.25	3.00
125 Nate Frese RC	1.25	3.00
126 Alfonso Soriano	2.00	5.00
127 Jose Nunez RC	1.25	3.00
128 Bob File RC	1.25	3.00
129 Dan Wright	1.25	3.00
130 Nick Johnson	1.25	3.00
131 Brent Abernathy	1.25	3.00
132 Steve Green RC	1.25	3.00
133 Billy Sylvester RC	1.25	3.00
134 Scott MacRae RC	1.25	3.00
135 Kris Keller RC	1.25	3.00
136 Scott Stewart RC	1.25	3.00
137 Henry Mateo RC	1.25	3.00
138 Timo Perez	1.25	3.00
139 Nate Teut RC	1.25	3.00
140 Jason Michaels RC	1.25	3.00
141 Junior Spivey RC	2.00	5.00
142 Carlos Pena	1.25	3.00
143 Wilmy Caceres RC	1.25	3.00
144 David Lundquist	1.25	3.00
145 Jack Wilson RC	2.00	5.00
146 Jeremy Fikac RC	1.25	3.00
147 Alex Escobar	1.25	3.00
148 Abraham Nunez	1.25	3.00
149 Xavier Nady	1.25	3.00
150 Michael Cuddyer	1.25	3.00
151 Greg Miller RC	1.25	3.00
152 Eric Munson	1.25	3.00
153 Aubrey Huff	1.25	3.00
154 Tim Christman RC	1.25	3.00
155 Erick Almonte RC	1.25	3.00
156 Mike Penney RC	1.25	3.00
157 Delvin James RC	1.25	3.00
158 Ben Sheets	2.00	5.00
159 Jason Hart	1.25	3.00
160 Jose Acevedo RC	1.25	3.00
161 Will Ohman RC	1.25	3.00
162 Erik Hiljus RC	1.25	3.00
163 Juan Moreno RC	1.25	3.00
164 Mike Koplove RC	1.25	3.00
165 Pedro Santana RC	1.25	3.00
166 Jimmy Rollins	1.25	3.00
167 Matt White RC	1.25	3.00
168 Cesar Crespo RC	1.25	3.00
169 Carlos Hernandez	1.25	3.00
170 Chris George	1.25	3.00
171 Brad Voyles RC	1.25	3.00
172 Luis Pineda RC	1.25	3.00
173 Carlos Zambrano RC	2.00	5.00
174 Nate Cornejo	1.25	3.00
175 Jason Smith RC	1.25	3.00
176 Craig Monroe RC	3.00	8.00
177 Cody Ransom RC	1.25	3.00
178 John Grabow RC	1.25	3.00
179 Pedro Feliz	1.25	3.00
180 Jeremy Owens RC	1.25	3.00
181 Kurt Ainsworth	1.25	3.00
182 Luis Lopez	1.25	3.00
183 Stubby Clapp RC	1.25	3.00
184 Ryan Freel RC	3.00	8.00
185 Duaner Sanchez RC	1.25	3.00
186 Jason Jennings	1.25	3.00
187 Kyle Lohse RC	2.00	5.00
188 Jerrod Riggan RC	1.25	3.00
189 Joe Beimel RC	1.25	3.00
190 Nick Punto RC	1.25	3.00
191 Willie Harris RC	1.25	3.00
192 Ryan Jensen RC	1.25	3.00
193 Adam Pettyjohn RC	1.25	3.00
194 Donaldo Mendez RC	1.25	3.00
195 Bret Prinz RC	1.25	3.00
196 Paul Phillips RC	1.25	3.00
197 Brian Lawrence RC	1.25	3.00
198 Cesar Izturis	1.25	3.00
199 Blaine Neal RC	1.25	3.00
200 Josh Fogg RC	2.00	5.00
201 Josh Towers RC	3.00	8.00
202 T.Spooneybarger RC	2.00	5.00
203 Michael Rivera RC	2.00	5.00
204 Juan Cruz RC	2.00	5.00
205 Albert Pujols RC	60.00	120.00
206 Josh Beckett	3.00	8.00
207 Roy Oswalt	3.00	8.00
208 Elpidio Guzman RC	2.00	5.00
209 Horacio Ramirez RC	3.00	8.00
210 Corey Patterson	2.00	5.00
211 Geronimo Gil RC	2.00	5.00
212 Jay Gibbons RC	3.00	8.00
213 O.Woodards RC	2.00	5.00
214 David Espinosa	2.00	5.00
215 Angel Berroa RC	3.00	8.00
216 B.Duckworth RC	2.00	5.00
217 Brian Reith RC	2.00	5.00
218 David Brous RC	2.00	5.00
219 Bud Smith RC	2.00	5.00
220 Ramon Vazquez RC	2.00	5.00
221 Mark Teixeira RC	15.00	40.00
222 Justin Atchley RC	2.00	5.00
223 Tony Cogan RC	2.00	5.00
224 Grant Balfour RC	2.00	5.00
225 Ricardo Rodriguez RC	2.00	5.00
226 Brian Rogers RC	2.00	5.00
227 Adam Dunn	3.00	8.00
228 Wilson Betemit RC	3.00	8.00
229 Juan Diaz RC	2.00	5.00
230 Jackson Melian RC	2.00	5.00
231 Claudio Vargas RC	2.00	5.00
232 Wilkin Ruan RC	2.00	5.00
233 J.Duchscherer RC	2.00	5.00
234 Kevin Olsen RC	2.00	5.00
235 Tony Fiore RC	2.00	5.00
236 Jeremy Affeldt RC	2.00	5.00
237 Mike Maroth RC	2.00	5.00
238 C.C. Sabathia	2.00	5.00
239 Cory Aldridge RC	2.00	5.00
240 Zach Day RC	2.00	5.00
241 Brett Jodie RC	2.00	5.00
242 Winston Abreu RC	2.00	5.00
243 Travis Hafner RC	10.00	25.00
244 Joe Kennedy RC	3.00	8.00
245 Rick Bauer RC	2.00	5.00
246 Mike Young	3.00	8.00
247 Ken Vining RC	2.00	5.00
248 Doug Nickle RC	2.00	5.00
249 Pablo Ozuna	2.00	5.00
250 Dustan Mohr RC	2.00	5.00
251 Ichiro Suzuki RC	20.00	50.00
252 Ryan Drese RC	3.00	8.00
253 Morgan Ensberg RC	3.00	8.00
254 George Perez RC	2.00	5.00
255 Roy Smith RC	2.00	5.00
256 Juan Uribe RC	3.00	8.00
257 Dewon Brazelton RC	2.00	5.00
258 Endy Chavez RC	2.00	5.00
259 Kris Foster	2.00	5.00
260 Eric Knott RC	2.00	5.00
261 Corky Miller RC	2.00	5.00
262 Larry Bigbie	2.00	5.00
263 Andres Torres RC	2.00	5.00
264 Adrian Hernandez RC	2.00	5.00
265 Johnny Estrada RC	3.00	8.00
266 David Williams RC	2.00	5.00
267 Steve Lomasney	2.00	5.00
268 Victor Zambrano RC	3.00	8.00
269 Keith Ginter	2.00	5.00
270 Casey Fossum RC	2.00	5.00
271 Josue Perez RC	2.00	5.00
272 Josh Phelps	2.00	5.00
273 Mark Prior RC	10.00	25.00
274 Brandon Berger RC	2.00	5.00
275 Scott Podsednik RC	5.00	12.00
276 Jorge Julio RC	2.00	5.00
277 Esix Snead RC	2.00	5.00
278 Brandon Knight RC	2.00	5.00
279 Saul Rivera RC	2.00	5.00
280 Benito Baez RC	2.00	5.00
281 Rob MacKowiak RC	3.00	8.00
282 Eric Hinske RC	3.00	8.00
283 Juan Rivera	2.00	5.00
284 Kevin Joseph RC	2.00	5.00
285 Juan A. Pena RC	2.00	5.00
286 Brandon Lyon RC	2.00	5.00
287 Adam Everett	2.00	5.00
288 Eric Valent	2.00	5.00
289 Ken Harvey	2.00	5.00
290 Bert Snow RC	2.00	5.00
291 Wily Mo Pena	2.00	5.00
292 Rafael Soriano RC	2.00	5.00
293 Carlos Valderrama RC	2.00	5.00
294 Christian Parker RC	2.00	5.00
295 Tsuyoshi Shinjo RC	3.00	8.00
296 Martin Vargas RC	2.00	5.00
297 Luke Hudson RC	2.00	5.00
298 Dee Brown	2.00	5.00
299 Alexis Gomez RC	2.00	5.00
300 Angel Santos RC	2.00	5.00

2001 Leaf Rookies and Stars Autographs

Randomly inserted in packs, these 76 cards feature signed cards of some of the prospects and rookies included in the Leaf Rookie and Stars set. According to Donruss/Playoff most players signed 250 cards for inclusion in this product. A few signed 100 cards so we have included that information in our checklist next to the player's name.

Card	Low	High
107 Jason Karnuth/250 *	4.00	10.00
110 Brandon Larson/100 *	6.00	15.00
117 Jose Mieses/250 *	4.00	10.00
118 Nick Maness/250 *	4.00	10.00
119 Les Walrond/250 *	4.00	10.00
122 Carlos Garcia/250 *	4.00	10.00
123 Bill Ortega/250 *	4.00	10.00
124 Gene Altman/250 *	4.00	10.00
125 Nate Frese/250 *	4.00	10.00
130 Nick Johnson/100 *	10.00	25.00
133 Billy Sylvester/250 *	4.00	10.00
135 Kris Keller/250 *	4.00	10.00
139 Nate Teut/250 *	4.00	10.00
140 Jason Michaels/250 *	4.00	10.00
143 Wilmy Caceres/250 *	4.00	10.00
145 Jack Wilson/100 *	10.00	25.00
151 Greg Miller/250 *	4.00	10.00
155 Erick Almonte/250 *	4.00	10.00
156 Mike Penney/250 *	4.00	10.00
157 Delvin James/250 *	4.00	10.00
161 Will Ohman/250 *	4.00	10.00
167 Matt White/250 *	4.00	10.00
180 Jeremy Owens/250 *	4.00	10.00
184 Ryan Freel/250 *	10.00	25.00
185 Duaner Sanchez/250 *	4.00	10.00
193 Adam Pettyjohn/100 *	6.00	15.00
194 Donaldo Mendez/100 *	6.00	15.00
196 Paul Phillips/250 *	4.00	10.00
197 Brian Lawrence/100 *	6.00	15.00
199 Blaine Neal/250 *	4.00	10.00
201 Josh Towers/100 *	6.00	15.00
203 Michael Rivera/250 *	4.00	10.00
204 Juan Cruz/100 *	6.00	15.00
205 Albert Pujols/50 *		
207 Roy Oswalt/50 *	30.00	60.00
208 Elpidio Guzman/100 *	6.00	15.00
209 Horacio Ramirez/250 *	6.00	15.00
210 Corey Patterson/50 *	10.00	25.00
211 Geronimo Gil/250 *	4.00	10.00
212 Jay Gibbons/100 *	10.00	25.00
213 Orlando Woodards/250 *	4.00	10.00
215 Angel Berroa/100 *	10.00	25.00
216 Brandon Duckworth/100 *	6.00	15.00
218 David Brous/250 *	4.00	10.00
219 Bud Smith/50 *	10.00	25.00
221 Mark Teixeira/100 *	150.00	250.00
223 Tony Cogan/250 *	4.00	10.00
225 Ricardo Rodriguez/250 *	4.00	10.00
226 Brian Rogers/250 *	4.00	10.00
227 Adam Dunn/50 *	20.00	50.00
228 Wilson Betemit/100 *	15.00	40.00
231 Claudio Vargas/250 *	4.00	10.00
232 Wilkin Ruan/250 *	4.00	10.00
234 Kevin Olsen/250 *	4.00	10.00
236 Jeremy Affeldt/250 *	4.00	10.00
237 Mike Maroth/250 *	6.00	15.00
238 C.C. Sabathia/50 *	10.00	25.00
239 Cory Aldridge/250 *	4.00	10.00
240 Zach Day/250 *	4.00	10.00
243 Travis Hafner/250 *	20.00	50.00
244 Joe Kennedy/100 *	6.00	15.00
254 George Perez/250 *	4.00	10.00
256 Juan Uribe/250 *	6.00	15.00
257 Dewon Brazelton/100 *	6.00	15.00
261 Corky Miller/100 *	6.00	15.00
263 Andres Torres/100 *	6.00	15.00
265 Johnny Estrada/100 *	6.00	15.00
266 David Williams/250 *	4.00	10.00
270 Casey Fossum/250 *	4.00	10.00
273 Mark Prior/100 *	125.00	200.00
274 Brandon Berger/250 *	4.00	10.00
277 Esix Snead/250 *	4.00	10.00
282 Eric Hinske/250 *	6.00	15.00
292 Rafael Soriano/250 *	6.00	15.00
293 Carlos Valderrama/250 *	4.00	10.00
299 Alexis Gomez/250 *	4.00	10.00

2001 Leaf Rookies and Stars Longevity

Randomly inserted into packs, these cards parallel the Leaf Rookie and Stars set. Cards numbered 1-100 are serial numbered to 50 while cards numbered 101-300 are serial numbered to 25.

*LONGEVITY: 1-100: 12.5X TO 30X BASIC CARDS

2001 Leaf Rookies and Stars Dress for Success

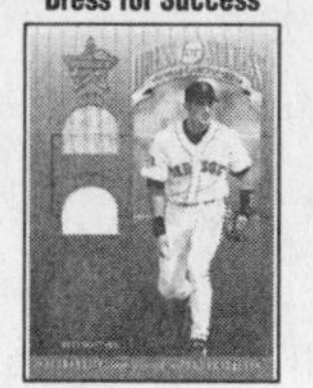

Inserted one per 96 packs, these 25 cards feature two swatches of game-used memorabilia on each card.

Card	Low	High
DFS1 Cal Ripken	20.00	50.00
DFS2 Mike Piazza	10.00	25.00
DFS3 Barry Bonds	20.00	50.00
DFS4 Frank Thomas	8.00	20.00
DFS5 Nomar Garciaparra	12.50	30.00
DFS6 Richie Sexson	6.00	15.00
DFS7 Brian Giles	6.00	15.00
DFS8 Todd Helton	8.00	20.00
DFS9 Ivan Rodriguez	8.00	20.00
DFS10 Andruw Jones	8.00	20.00
DFS11 Juan Gonzalez	6.00	15.00
DFS12 Vladimir Guerrero	8.00	20.00
DFS13 Greg Maddux	10.00	25.00
DFS14 Tony Gwynn	10.00	25.00
DFS15 Randy Johnson	8.00	20.00
DFS16 Jeff Bagwell	8.00	20.00
DFS17 Kerry Wood SP		
DFS18 Roberto Alomar	8.00	20.00
DFS19 Chipper Jones	8.00	20.00
DFS20 Pedro Martinez	8.00	20.00
DFS21 Shawn Green	6.00	15.00
DFS22 Magglio Ordonez	6.00	15.00
DFS23 Darin Erstad SP		
DFS24 Rafael Palmeiro SP		
DFS25 Edgar Martinez	8.00	20.00

2001 Leaf Rookies and Stars Dress for Success Prime Cuts

Randomly inserted into packs, these cards parallel the Dress for Success insert set. Each card had a stated print run of 50 serial numbered sets.

*PRIME CUTS: 1.25X TO 3X BASIC DRESS

Card	Low	High
DFS17 Kerry Wood	15.00	40.00
DFS23 Darin Erstad	15.00	40.00
DFS24 Rafael Palmeiro	20.00	50.00

2001 Leaf Rookies and Stars Freshman Orientation

Inserted into packs at odds of one in 96, these 25 cards feature leading prospects along with a piece of game-used memorabilia. The Dunn, Pujols and Gibbons cards are shortprinted compared to the rest of the set.

Card	Low	High
F01 Adam Dunn Bat SP		
F02 Josh Towers Pants	6.00	15.00
F03 Vernon Wells Jsy	4.00	10.00
F04 Corey Patterson Pants	4.00	10.00
F05 Albert Pujols Bat SP		
F06 Ben Sheets Jsy	6.00	15.00
F07 Pedro Feliz Bat	4.00	10.00
F08 Keith Ginter Bat	4.00	10.00
F09 Luis Rivas Bat	4.00	10.00
F010 Andres Torres Bat	4.00	10.00
F011 Carlos Valderrama Jsy	4.00	10.00
F012 Brandon Inge Jsy	4.00	10.00
F013 Jay Gibbons Cap SP		
F014 Cesar Izturis Bat	4.00	10.00
F015 Marcus Giles Jsy	4.00	10.00
F016 Tsuyoshi Shinjo Jsy	6.00	15.00
F017 Eric Valent Bat	4.00	10.00
F018 David Espinosa Bat	4.00	10.00
F019 Aubrey Huff Jsy	4.00	10.00
F020 Wilmy Caceres Jsy	4.00	10.00
F021 Bud Smith Jsy	4.00	10.00
F022 Ricardo Rodriguez Pants	4.00	10.00
F023 Wes Helms Jsy	4.00	10.00
F024 Jason Hart Bat	4.00	10.00
F025 Dee Brown Jsy	4.00	10.00

2001 Leaf Rookies and Stars Freshman Orientation Autographs

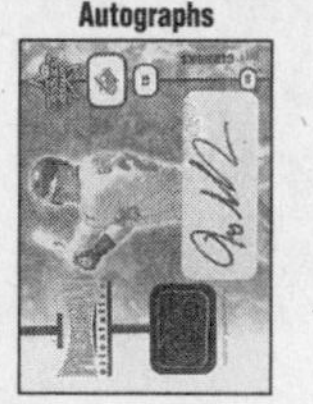

Randomly inserted into packs, these 21 cards parallel the Freshman Orientation insert set. Each of these players signed 100 cards or less for this product. If the player signed less than 100 cards we have notated that with an SP in our checklist.

Card	Low	High
F01 Adam Dunn Bat SP		
F02 Josh Towers Pants SP		
F04 Corey Patterson Pants SP		
F05 Albert Pujols Bat SP		
F06 Ben Sheets Jsy SP		
F07 Pedro Feliz Bat	8.00	20.00
F08 Keith Ginter Bat	8.00	20.00
F09 Luis Rivas Bat	8.00	20.00
F010 Andres Torres Bat	8.00	20.00
F011 Carlos Valderrama Jsy	8.00	20.00
F013 Jay Gibbons Cap	10.00	25.00
F014 Cesar Izturis Bat	8.00	20.00
F015 Marcus Giles Jsy	8.00	20.00
F017 Eric Valent Bat	8.00	20.00
F018 David Espinosa Bat	8.00	20.00
F019 Aubrey Huff Jsy	8.00	20.00
F020 Wilmy Caceres Jsy	8.00	20.00
F021 Bud Smith Jsy SP		
F022 Ricardo Rodriguez Pants	8.00	20.00
F024 Jason Hart Bat	8.00	20.00
F025 Dee Brown Jsy	8.00	20.00

2001 Leaf Rookies and Stars Freshman Orientation Class Officers

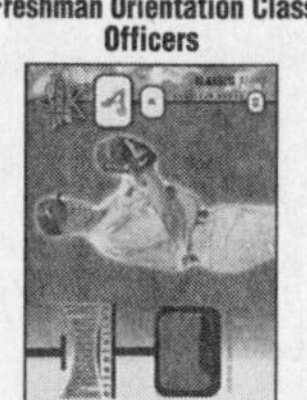

Randomly inserted into packs, these cards parallel the Freshman Orientation insert set. Each card had a stated print run of 50 serial numbered sets.

*CLASS OFFICER: .75X TO 2X BASIC FRESH

Card	Low	High
F01 Adam Dunn Bat	8.00	20.00
F05 Albert Pujols Bat	150.00	250.00
F013 Jay Gibbons Cap	8.00	20.00

2001 Leaf Rookies and Stars Great American Treasures

Inserted at a rate of one in 1,120 packs, these 20 cards feature pieces of memorabilia from key moments in a players career.

PRINT RUN INFO PROVIDED BY DONRUSS
CARDS ARE NOT SERIAL-NUMBERED
NO PRICING ON QTY OF 25 DUE TO SCARCITY

Card	Low	High
GT1 B.Bonds 517 HR Jsy/50 *	125.00	200.00
GT2 M.Ordonez HR Bat/200 *	15.00	40.00
GT3 D.Jeter 1st Game Ball/25 *		
GT4 N.Ryan 7th No-Hit Ball/25 *		
GT5 S.Sosa June HR Ball/25 *		
GT6 T.Glavine 96 WS Jsy/100 *	30.00	60.00
GT7 I.Rod 99 MVP Bat/200 *	20.00	50.00
GT8 P.Martinez 300 K Ball/25 *		
GT9 M.McGwire 60 HR Ball/25 *		
GT10 T.Williams 517 HR Ball/25 *		
GT11 R.Sandberg 91 AS Bat/200 *	40.00	80.00
GT12 B.Bonds 500 HR Ball/25 *		
GT13 H.Nomo No-Hit Ball/25 *		
GT14 R.Maris 61 HR Ball/25 *		
GT15 T.Cobb 09 WS Ball/25 *		
GT16 H.Killebrew 570 HR Bat/50 *	40.00	80.00
GT17 M.Ordonez 00 AS Cap/100 *	20.00	50.00
GT18 W.Boggs WS Bat/200 *	20.00	50.00
GT19 H.Aaron 755 HR Cap/25 *		
GT20 D.Cone Perfect Game Ball/25 *		

2001 Leaf Rookies and Stars Great American Treasures Autograph

This four card parallel to the Great American Treasure set features signed cards by these players on cards relating to a key event in their career. Due to scarcity, no pricing information is provided.

GT6 Tom Glavine 96 WS Jsy
GT11 Ryne Sandberg 91 AS Bat
GT16 Harmon Killebrew 570 HR Bat
GT18 Wade Boggs WS Bat

2001 Leaf Rookies and Stars Players Collection

Randomly inserted into packs, these 15 cards feature four different types of memorabilia from three key superstars. Each player also had a quad card with one piece each of the four types of memorabilia featured. Each card is serial numbered to 100 except for the quad cards which are serial numbered to 25.

Card	Low	High
PC1 Tony Gwynn Bat SP	10.00	25.00
PC2 Tony Gwynn Jsy	10.00	25.00
PC3 Tony Gwynn Pants	10.00	25.00
PC4 Tony Gwynn Shoe	10.00	25.00
PC5 Tony Gwynn Quad/25		
PC6 Cal Ripken White Jsy SP	30.00	60.00
PC7 Cal Ripken Bat SP	30.00	60.00
PC8 Cal Ripken Glove	30.00	60.00
PC9 Cal Ripken Gray Jsy	30.00	60.00
PC10 Cal Ripken Quad		
PC11 Barry Bonds Jsy	20.00	50.00
PC12 Barry Bonds Shoe	20.00	50.00
PC13 Barry Bonds Pants	20.00	50.00
PC14 Barry Bonds Bat	20.00	50.00
PC15 Barry Bonds Quad/25		

2001 Leaf Rookies and Stars Players Collection Autographs

Randomly inserted into packs, these three cards feature signed cards of the players along with a memorabilia piece. Due to market scarcity, no pricing is provided.

PC1 Tony Gwynn Bat
PC6 Cal Ripken Jsy
PC7 Cal Ripken Bat

2001 Leaf Rookies and Stars Slideshow

Randomly inserted into packs, each card features a jersey swatch along with a snapshot of major league action. Most players have 100 serial numbered cards but a few have less and we have notated those players with an SP.

VIEW MASTER PRINT RUN 25 #'d SETS
NO V'MASTER PRICING DUE TO SCARCITY

Card	Low	High
S1 Cal Ripken	20.00	50.00
S2 Chipper Jones SP	10.00	25.00
S3 Jeff Bagwell	10.00	25.00
S4 Larry Walker	6.00	15.00
S5 Greg Maddux SP	10.00	25.00
S6 Ivan Rodriguez	10.00	25.00
S7 Andruw Jones SP	10.00	25.00
S8 Lance Berkman SP	6.00	15.00
S9 Luis Gonzalez SP	6.00	15.00
S10 Tony Gwynn	10.00	25.00
S11 Troy Glaus SP	6.00	15.00
S12 Todd Helton	10.00	25.00
S13 Roberto Alomar	10.00	25.00
S14 Barry Bonds	20.00	50.00
S15 Vladimir Guerrero SP	10.00	25.00
S16 Sean Casey SP	6.00	15.00
S17 Curt Schilling SP	6.00	15.00
S18 Frank Thomas	10.00	25.00
S19 Pedro Martinez	10.00	25.00
S20 Juan Gonzalez	6.00	15.00
S21 Randy Johnson	10.00	25.00
S22 Kerry Wood SP	6.00	15.00
S23 Mike Sweeney	6.00	15.00
S24 Magglio Ordonez	6.00	15.00
S25 Kazuhiro Sasaki	6.00	15.00
S26 Manny Ramirez Sox	10.00	25.00
S27 Roger Clemens	15.00	40.00
S28 Albert Pujols SP	90.00	150.00
S29 Hideo Nomo	10.00	25.00
S30 Miguel Tejada SP	6.00	15.00

2001 Leaf Rookies and Stars Statistical Standouts

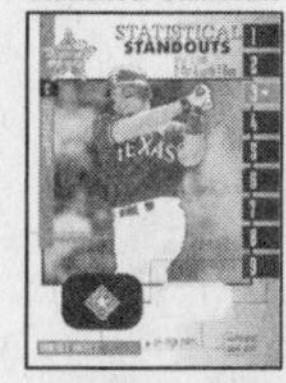

Inserted at packs at a rate of one in 96, these 25 cards feature star players along with a swatch of game-used materials. A few of these cards were printed in shorter quantites than the others and we have notated those with an SP.

*SUPER: 1X TO 2.5X BASIC STAT. STANDOUT
SUPER STATED PRINT RUN 50 SERIAL #'D SETS

Card	Low	High
SS1 Ichiro Suzuki	15.00	40.00
SS2 Barry Bonds SP		
SS3 Ivan Rodriguez	6.00	15.00
SS4 Jeff Bagwell	6.00	15.00
SS5 Vladimir Guerrero SP		
SS6 Mike Sweeney	4.00	10.00
SS7 Miguel Tejada	4.00	10.00
SS8 Mike Piazza SP		
SS9 Darin Erstad	4.00	10.00
SS10 Alex Rodriguez	10.00	25.00
SS11 Jason Giambi	4.00	10.00
SS12 Cal Ripken	15.00	40.00
SS13 Albert Pujols	20.00	50.00
SS14 Carlos Delgado	4.00	10.00
SS15 Rafael Palmeiro	6.00	15.00
SS16 Lance Berkman	4.00	10.00
SS17 Luis Gonzalez SP		
SS18 Sammy Sosa SP		
SS19 Andruw Jones SP		
SS20 Derek Jeter	15.00	40.00
SS21 Edgar Martinez	6.00	15.00
SS22 Troy Glaus	4.00	10.00
SS23 Magglio Ordonez	4.00	10.00
SS24 Mark McGwire	15.00	40.00
SS25 Manny Ramirez Sox	6.00	15.00

2001 Leaf Rookies and Stars Statistical Standouts Super

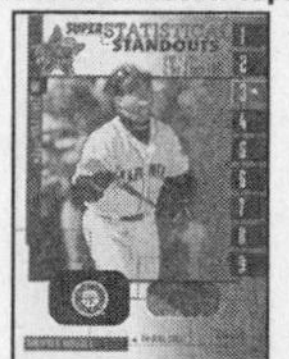

This parallel to the Statistical Standout set was randomly inserted into packs. Each of these cards are serial numbered to 50.

*SUPER: 1X TO 2.5X BASIC STAT.STAND

2001 Leaf Rookies and Stars Triple Threads

Randomly inserted into packs, each of these cards feature three swatches of game-worn jerseys from players of the same franchise. Each of these cards are serial numbered to 100.

Card	Low	High
TT1 Pedro Martinez Manny Ramirez Sox Nomar Garciaparra	20.00	50.00
TT2 Frank Robinson Cal Ripken	30.00	80.00

Brooks Robinson
TT3 Babe Ruth 350.00 500.00
Lou Gehrig
Yogi Berra
TT4 Andre Dawson 12.50 30.00
Ryne Sandberg
Ernie Banks
TT5 Warren Spahn 30.00 80.00
Hank Aaron
Eddie Mathews
TT6 Greg Maddux 20.00 50.00
Chipper Jones
Andruw Jones
TT7 Nolan Ryan 30.00 80.00
Ivan Rodriguez
Juan Gonzalez
TT8 Lance Berkman 15.00 40.00
Jeff Bagwell
Craig Biggio
TT9 Rod Carew 30.00 80.00
Harmon Killebrew
Kirby Puckett
TT10 Luis Gonzalez 15.00 40.00
Curt Schilling
Randy Johnson

2002 Leaf Rookies and Stars Samples

20 Trot Nixon .60 1.50
45 Chuck Knoblauch .60 1.50
96 Brent Abernathy .60 1.50
97 Chan Ho Park 1.00 2.50
98 Alex Rodriguez 2.50 6.00
99 Juan Gonzalez .60 1.50
100 Rafael Palmeiro 1.00 2.50

2002 Leaf Rookies and Stars

This 502 card set was issued in November, 2002. This set was issued in six card packs which came 24 packs to a box and 20 boxes to a case with an SRP of $3 per pack. Originally designed as a 400 card set, this set mushroomed to 501 when 101 variations of some of the basic cards were discovered upon release. These cards feature some of the players who have been on more-than one team with cards from their time with that earlier team. Those variation cards were inserted at stated odds of one in four. In addition, cards numbered 301 through 400, which featured a mix of rookies and prospects, were issued at stated odds of one in two. Another subset, which was not printed in shorter supply, was an award winner group from cards numbered 251 through 300.

COMP.SET w/o SP's (300) 15.00 40.00
COMMON CARD (1-300) .10 .30
COMMON SP (1-300) .75 2.00
COMMON CARD (301-400) .40 1.00
1 Darin Erstad .10 .30
2 Garret Anderson .10 .30
3 Troy Glaus .10 .30
4 David Eckstein .10 .30
5 Adam Kennedy .10 .30
6 Kevin Appier Angels .10 .30
6A Kevin Appier Mets SP .75 2.00
6B Kevin Appier Royals SP .75 2.00
7 Jarrod Washburn .10 .30
8 David Segui .10 .30
9 Jay Gibbons .10 .30
10 Tony Batista .10 .30
11 Scott Erickson .10 .30
12 Jeff Conine .10 .30
13 Melvin Mora .10 .30
14 Shea Hillenbrand .10 .30
15 Manny Ramirez Red Sox .20 .50
15A Manny Ramirez Indians SP 1.00 2.50
16 Pedro Martinez Red Sox .20 .50
16A Ped. Martinez Dodgers SP 1.00 2.50
16B Pedro Martinez Expos SP 1.00 2.50
17 Nomar Garciaparra .50 1.25
18 Rickey Henderson Red Sox .30 .75
18A Ri. Henderson Angels SP 1.50 4.00
18B Rickey Henderson A's SP 1.50 4.00
18C Ri. Henderson Bl.Jays SP 1.50 4.00
18D Rickey Henderson M's SP 1.50 4.00
18E Rickey Henderson Mets SP 1.50 4.00
18F Ri. Henderson Padres SP 1.50 4.00
18G Ri. Henderson Yanks SP 1.50 4.00
19 Johnny Damon Red Sox .20 .50
19A Johnny Damon A's SP 1.00 2.50
19B Johnny Damon Royals SP 1.00 2.50
20 Trot Nixon .10 .30
21 Derek Lowe .10 .30
22 Jason Varitek .30 .75
23 Tim Wakefield .10 .30
24 Frank Thomas .30 .75
25 Kenny Lofton White Sox .10 .30
25A Kenny Lofton Indians SP .75 2.00
25B Kenny Lofton Giants SP .75 2.00
26 Magglio Ordonez .10 .30
27 Ray Durham .10 .30
28 Mark Buehrle .10 .30
29 Paul Konerko White Sox .10 .30
29A Paul Konerko Dodgers SP .75 2.00
29B Paul Konerko Reds SP .75 2.00
30 Jose Valentin .10 .30
31 C.C. Sabathia .10 .30
32 Ellis Burks Indians .10 .30
32A Ellis Burks Giants SP .75 2.00
32B Ellis Burks Red Sox SP .75 2.00
32C Ellis Burks Rockies SP .75 2.00
33 Omar Vizquel Indians .20 .50
33A Omar Vizquel Mariners SP 1.00 2.50
34 Jim Thome .20 .50
35 Matt Lawton .10 .30
36 Travis Fryman Indians .10 .30
36A Travis Fryman Tigers SP .75 2.00
37 Robert Fick .10 .30
38 Bobby Higginson .10 .30
39 Steve Sparks .10 .30
40 Mike Rivera .10 .30
41 Wendell Magee .10 .30
42 Randall Simon .10 .30
43 Carlos Pena Tigers .10 .30
43A Carlos Pena A's SP .75 2.00
43B Carlos Pena Rangers SP .75 2.00
44 Mike Sweeney .10 .30
45 Chuck Knoblauch .10 .30
46 Carlos Beltran .10 .30
47 Joe Randa .10 .30
48 Paul Byrd .10 .30
49 Mac Suzuki .10 .30
50 Torii Hunter .10 .30
51 Jacque Jones .10 .30
52 David Ortiz .30 .75
53 Corey Koskie .10 .30
54 Brad Radke .10 .30
55 Doug Mientkiewicz .10 .30
56 A.J. Pierzynski .10 .30
57 Dustan Mohr .10 .30
58 Derek Jeter .75 2.00
59 Bernie Williams .20 .50
60 Roger Clemens Yankees .60 1.50
60A R.Clemens Blue Jays SP 3.00 8.00
60B R.Clemens Red Sox SP 3.00 8.00
61 Mike Mussina Yankees .20 .50
61A Mike Mussina Orioles SP 1.00 2.50
62 Jorge Posada .20 .50
63 Alfonso Soriano .10 .30
64 Jason Giambi Yankees .10 .30
64A Jason Giambi A's SP .75 2.00
65 Robin Ventura Yankees .10 .30
65A Robin Ventura Mets SP .75 2.00
65B Robin Ventura White Sox SP .75 2.00
66 Andy Pettitte .20 .50
67 David Wells Yankees .10 .30
67A David Wells Blue Jays SP .75 2.00
67B David Wells Tigers SP .75 2.00
68 Nick Johnson .10 .30
69 Jeff Weaver Yankees .10 .30
69A Jeff Weaver Tigers SP .75 2.00
70 Raul Mondesi Yankees .10 .30
70A R.Mondesi Blue Jays SP .75 2.00
70B Raul Mondesi Dodgers SP .75 2.00
71 Tim Hudson .10 .30
72 Barry Zito .10 .30
73 Mark Mulder .10 .30
74 Miguel Tejada .10 .30
75 Eric Chavez .10 .30
76 Billy Koch A's .10 .30
76A Billy Koch Blue Jays SP .75 2.00
77 Jermaine Dye A's .10 .30
77A Jermaine Dye Royals SP .75 2.00
78 Scott Hatteberg .10 .30
79 Ichiro Suzuki .60 1.50
80 Edgar Martinez .20 .50
81 Mike Cameron Mariners .10 .30
81A M.Cameron White Sox SP .75 2.00
82 John Olerud Mariners .10 .30
82A John Olerud Blue Jays SP .75 2.00
82B John Olerud Mets SP .75 2.00
83 Bret Boone .10 .30
84 Dan Wilson .10 .30
85 Freddy Garcia .10 .30
86 Jamie Moyer .10 .30
87 Carlos Guillen .10 .30
88 Ruben Sierra .10 .30
89 Kazuhiro Sasaki .10 .30
90 Mark McLemore .10 .30
91 Ben Grieve .10 .30
92 Aubrey Huff .10 .30
93 Steve Cox .10 .30
94 Toby Hall .10 .30
95 Randy Winn .10 .30
96 Brent Abernathy .10 .30
97 Chan Ho Park Rangers .10 .30
97A Chan Ho Park Dodgers SP .75 2.00
98 Alex Rodriguez Rangers .50 1.25
98A A.Rodriguez Mariners SP 2.50 6.00
99 Juan Gonzalez Rangers .10 .30
99A Juan Gonzalez Indians SP .75 2.00
99B Juan Gonzalez Tigers SP .75 2.00
100 Rafael Palmeiro Rangers .20 .50
100A Rafael Palmeiro Cubs SP 1.00 2.50
100B Raf. Palmeiro Orioles SP 1.00 2.50
101 Ivan Rodriguez .20 .50
102 Rusty Greer .10 .30
103 Kenny Rogers Rangers .10 .30
103A Kenny Rogers A's SP .75 2.00
103B Ken. Rogers Yankees SP .75 2.00
104 Hank Blalock .20 .50
105 Mark Teixeira .30 .75
106 Carlos Delgado .10 .30
107 Shannon Stewart .10 .30
108 Eric Hinske .10 .30
109 Roy Halladay .10 .30
110 Felipe Lopez .10 .30
111 Vernon Wells .10 .30
112 Curt Schilling D'backs .10 .30
112A Curt Schilling Phillies SP .75 2.00
113 Randy Johnson D'backs .30 .75
113A Randy Johnson Astros SP 1.50 4.00
113B Randy Johnson Expos SP 1.50 4.00
113C R.Johnson Mariners SP 1.50 4.00
114 Luis Gonzalez D'backs .10 .30
114A Luis Gonzalez Astros SP .75 2.00
114B Luis Gonzalez Cubs SP .75 2.00
115 Mark Grace D'backs .20 .50
115A Mark Grace Cubs SP 1.00 2.50
116 Junior Spivey .10 .30
117 Tony Womack .10 .30
118 Matt Williams D'backs .10 .30
118A Matt Williams Giants SP .75 2.00
118B Matt Williams Indians SP .75 2.00
119 Danny Bautista .10 .30
120 Byung-Hyun Kim .10 .30
121 Craig Counsell .10 .30
122 Greg Maddux Braves .50 1.25
122A Greg Maddux Cubs SP 2.50 6.00
123 Tom Glavine .20 .50
124 John Smoltz Braves .20 .50
124A John Smoltz Tigers SP 1.00 2.50
125 Chipper Jones .30 .75
126 Gary Sheffield .10 .30
127 Andruw Jones .20 .50
128 Vinny Castilla .10 .30
129 Damian Moss .10 .30
130 Rafael Furcal .10 .30
131 Kerry Wood .10 .30
132 Fred McGriff Cubs .20 .50
132A F.McGriff Blue Jays SP 1.00 2.50
132B Fred McGriff Braves SP 1.00 2.50
132C F.McGriff Devil Rays SP 1.00 2.50
132D Fred McGriff Padres SP 1.00 2.50
133 Sammy Sosa Cubs .30 .75
133A Sammy Sosa Rangers SP 1.50 4.00
133B S.Sosa White Sox SP 1.50 4.00
134 Alex Gonzalez .10 .30
135 Corey Patterson .10 .30
136 Moises Alou .10 .30
137 Mark Prior 2.00 5.00
138 Jon Lieber .10 .30
139 Matt Clement .10 .30
140 Ken Griffey Jr. Reds .50 1.25
140A K.Griffey Jr. Mariners SP 2.50 6.00
141 Barry Larkin .20 .50
142 Adam Dunn .10 .30
143 Sean Casey Reds .10 .30
143A Sean Casey Indians SP .75 2.00
144 Jose Rijo .10 .30
145 Elmer Dessens .10 .30
146 Austin Kearns .10 .30
147 Corky Miller .10 .30
148 Todd Walker Reds .10 .30
148A Todd Walker Rockies SP .75 2.00
149 Chris Reitsma .10 .30
150 Ryan Dempster .10 .30
151 Larry Walker Rockies .10 .30
151A Larry Walker Expos SP .75 2.00
152 Todd Helton .20 .50
153 Juan Uribe .10 .30
154 Juan Pierre .10 .30
155 Mike Hampton .10 .30
156 Todd Zeile .10 .30
157 Josh Beckett .10 .30
158 Mike Lowell Marlins .10 .30
158A Mike Lowell Yankees SP .75 2.00
159 Derrek Lee .20 .50
160 A.J. Burnett .10 .30
161 Luis Castillo .10 .30
162 Tim Raines .10 .30
163 Preston Wilson .10 .30
164 Juan Encarnacion .10 .30
165 Jeff Bagwell .20 .50
166 Craig Biggio .20 .50
167 Lance Berkman .10 .30
168 Wade Miller .10 .30
169 Roy Oswalt .10 .30
170 Richard Hidalgo .10 .30
171 Carlos Hernandez .10 .30
172 Daryle Ward .10 .30
173 Shawn Green Dodgers .10 .30
173A S.Green Blue Jays SP .75 2.00
174 Adrian Beltre .10 .30
175 Paul Lo Duca .10 .30
176 Eric Karros .10 .30
177 Kevin Brown .10 .30
178 Hideo Nomo Dodgers .30 .75
178A Hideo Nomo Brewers SP 1.50 4.00
178B Hideo Nomo Mets SP 1.50 4.00
178C Hideo Nomo Red Sox SP 1.50 4.00
178D Hideo Nomo Tigers SP 1.50 4.00
179 Odalis Perez .10 .30
180 Eric Gagne .10 .30
181 Brian Jordan .10 .30
182 Cesar Izturis .10 .30
183 Geoff Jenkins .10 .30
184 Richie Sexson Brewers .10 .30
184A Richie Sexson Indians SP .75 2.00
185 Jose Hernandez .10 .30
186 Ben Sheets .10 .30
187 Ruben Quevedo .10 .30
188 Jeffrey Hammonds .10 .30
189 Alex Sanchez .10 .30
190 Vladimir Guerrero .30 .75
191 Jose Vidro .10 .30
192 Orlando Cabrera .10 .30
193 Michael Barrett .10 .30
194 Javier Vazquez .10 .30
195 Tony Armas Jr. .10 .30
196 Andres Galarraga .10 .30
197 Tomo Ohka .10 .30
198 Bartolo Colon Expos .10 .30
198A Bartolo Colon Indians SP .75 2.00
199 Cliff Floyd Expos .10 .30
199A Cliff Floyd Marlins SP .75 2.00
199B Cliff Floyd Red Sox SP .75 2.00
200 Mike Piazza Mets .50 1.25
200A Mike Piazza Dodgers SP 2.50 6.00
200B Mike Piazza Marlins SP 2.50 6.00
201 Jeromy Burnitz .10 .30
202 Roberto Alomar Mets .20 .50
202A Rob. Alomar Bl.Jays SP 1.00 2.50
202B Ro. Alomar Indians SP 1.00 2.50
202C Ro. Alomar Orioles SP 1.00 2.50
202D Ro. Alomar Padres SP 1.00 2.50
203 Mo Vaughn Mets .10 .30
203A Mo Vaughn Angels SP .75 2.00
203B Mo Vaughn Red Sox SP .75 2.00
204 Al Leiter Mets .10 .30
204A Al Leiter Blue Jays SP .75 2.00
205 Pedro Astacio .10 .30
206 Edgardo Alfonzo .10 .30
207 Armando Benitez .10 .30
208 Scott Rolen .20 .50
209 Pat Burrell .10 .30
210 Bobby Abreu Phillies .10 .30
210A Bobby Abreu Astros SP .75 2.00
211 Mike Lieberthal .10 .30
212 Brandon Duckworth .10 .30
213 Jimmy Rollins .10 .30
214 Jeremy Giambi .10 .30
215 Vicente Padilla .10 .30
216 Travis Lee .10 .30
217 Jason Kendall .10 .30
218 Brian Giles Pirates .10 .30
218A Brian Giles Indians SP .75 2.00
219 Aramis Ramirez .10 .30
220 Pokey Reese .10 .30
221 Kip Wells .10 .30
222 Josh Fogg Pirates .10 .30
222A Josh Fogg White Sox SP .75 2.00
223 Mike Williams .10 .30
224 Ryan Klesko Padres .10 .30
224A Ryan Klesko Braves SP .75 2.00
225 Phil Nevin Padres .10 .30
225A Phil Nevin Tigers SP .75 2.00
226 Brian Lawrence .10 .30
227 Mark Kotsay .10 .30
228 Brett Tomko .10 .30
229 Trevor Hoffman Padres .10 .30
229A Tr. Hoffman Marlins SP .75 2.00
230 Barry Bonds Giants .75 2.00
230A Barry Bonds Pirates SP 4.00 10.00
231 Jeff Kent Giants .10 .30
231A Jeff Kent Blue Jays SP .75 2.00
232 Rich Aurilia .10 .30
233 Tsuyoshi Shinjo Giants .10 .30
233A Tsuyoshi Shinjo Mets SP .75 2.00
234 Benito Santiago Giants .10 .30
234A Ben. Santiago Padres SP .75 2.00
235 Kirk Rueter .10 .30
236 Kurt Ainsworth .10 .30
237 Livan Hernandez .10 .30
238 Russ Ortiz .10 .30
239 David Bell .10 .30
240 Jason Schmidt .10 .30
241 Reggie Sanders .10 .30
242 Jim Edmonds Cardinals .10 .30
242A Jim Edmonds Angels SP .75 2.00
243 J.D. Drew .10 .30
244 Albert Pujols .60 1.50
245 Fernando Vina .10 .30
246 Tino Martinez Cardinals .20 .50
246A T.Martinez Mariners SP 1.00 2.50
246B T.Martinez Yankees SP 1.00 2.50
247 Edgar Renteria .10 .30
248 Matt Morris .10 .30
249 Woody Williams .10 .30
250 Jason Isringhausen Cards .10 .30
250A J.Isringhausen A's SP .75 2.00
251 Cal Ripken 82 ROY 1.00 2.50
252 Cal Ripken 83 MVP 1.00 2.50
253 Cal Ripken 91 MVP 1.00 2.50
254 Cal Ripken 91 AS 1.00 2.50
255 Ryne Sandberg 84 MVP .60 1.50
256 Don Mattingly 85 MVP .60 1.50
257 Don Mattingly 85-94 GLV .60 1.50
258 Roger Clemens 01 CY .60 1.50
259 Roger Clemens 87 CY .60 1.50
260 Roger Clemens 91 CY .60 1.50
261 Roger Clemens 97 CY .60 1.50
262 Roger Clemens 98 CY .60 1.50
263 Roger Clemens 86 CY .60 1.50
264 Roger Clemens 86 MVP .60 1.50
265 Rickey Henderson 90 MVP .30 .75
266 Rickey Henderson 81 GLV .30 .75
267 Jose Canseco 88 MVP .20 .50
268 Barry Bonds 01 MVP .75 2.00
269 Barry Bonds 90 MVP .75 2.00
270 Barry Bonds 92 MVP .75 2.00
271 Barry Bonds 93 MVP .75 2.00
272 Jeff Bagwell 94 MVP .10 .30
273 Kirby Puckett 91 ALCS .30 .75
274 Kirby Puckett 93 AS .30 .75
275 Greg Maddux 95 CY .50 1.25
276 Greg Maddux 92 CY .50 1.25
277 Greg Maddux 93 CY .50 1.25
278 Greg Maddux 94 CY .50 1.25
279 Ken Griffey Jr. 97 MVP .50 1.25
280 Mike Piazza 93 ROY .50 1.25
281 Kirby Puckett 86-89 GLV .30 .75
282 Mike Piazza 96 AS .50 1.25
283 Frank Thomas 93 MVP .20 .50
284 Hideo Nomo 95 ROY .20 .50
285 Randy Johnson 01 CY .20 .50
286 Juan Gonzalez 96 MVP .10 .30
287 Derek Jeter 96 ROY .75 2.00
288 Derek Jeter 00 WS .75 2.00
289 Derek Jeter 00 AS .75 2.00
290 Nomar Garciaparra 97 ROY .50 1.25
291 Pedro Martinez 00 CY .20 .50
292 Kerry Wood 98 ROY .10 .30
293 Sammy Sosa 98 MVP .20 .50
294 Chipper Jones 99 MVP .20 .50
295 Ivan Rodriguez 99 MVP .10 .30
296 Ivan Rodriguez 92-01 GLV .10 .30
297 Albert Pujols 01 ROY .60 1.50
298 Ichiro Suzuki 01 ROY .60 1.50
299 Ichiro Suzuki 01 MVP .60 1.50
300 Ichiro Suzuki 01 GLV .60 1.50
301 So Taguchi RS RC .50 1.25
302 Kazuhisa Ishii RS RC .50 1.25
303 Jeremy Lambert RS RC .40 1.00
304 Sean Burroughs RS .40 1.00
305 P.J. Bevis RS RC .40 1.00
306 Jon Rauch RS .40 1.00
307 Scotty Layfield RS RC .40 1.00
308 Miguel Asencio RS RC .40 1.00
309 Franklyn German RS RC .40 1.00
310 Luis Ugueto RS RC .40 1.00
311 Jorge Sosa RS RC .50 1.25
312 Felix Escalona RS RC .40 1.00
313 Jose Valverde RS RC .40 1.00
314 Jeremy Ward RS RC .40 1.00
315 Kevin Gryboski RS RC .40 1.00
316 Francis Beltran RS RC .40 1.00
317 Joe Thurston RS .40 1.00
318 Cliff Lee RS RC 6.00 15.00
319 Takahito Nomura RS RC .40 1.00
320 Bill Hall RS .40 1.00
321 Marlon Byrd RS .40 1.00
322 Andy Shibilo RS RC .40 1.00
323 Edwin Almonte RS RC .40 1.00
324 Brandon Backe RS RC .50 1.25
325 Chone Figgins RS RC .75 2.00
326 Brian Mallette RS RC .40 1.00
327 Rodrigo Rosario RS RC .40 1.00
328 Anderson Machado RS RC .40 1.00
329 Jorge Padilla RS RC .40 1.00
330 Allan Simpson RS RC .40 1.00
331 Doug Devore RS RC .40 1.00
332 Drew Henson RS .40 1.00
333 Raul Chavez RS RC .40 1.00
334 Tom Shearn RS RC .40 1.00
335 Ben Howard RS RC .40 1.00
336 Chris Baker RS RC .40 1.00
337 Travis Hughes RS RC .40 1.00
338 Kevin Mench RS .40 1.00
339 Brian Tallet RS RC .40 1.00
340 Mike Moriarty RS RC .40 1.00
341 Corey Thurman RS RC .40 1.00
342 Terry Pearson RS RC .40 1.00
343 Steve Kent RS RC .40 1.00
344 Satoru Komiyama RS RC .40 1.00
345 Jason Lane RS .40 1.00
346 Freddy Sanchez RS RC 1.25 3.00
347 Brandon Puffer RS RC .40 1.00
348 Clay Condrey RS RC .40 1.00
349 Rene Reyes RS RC .40 1.00
350 Hee Seop Choi RS .40 1.00
351 Rodrigo Lopez RS .40 1.00
352 Colin Young RS RC .40 1.00
353 Jason Simontacchi RS RC .40 1.00
354 Oliver Perez RS RC .75 2.00
355 Kirk Saarloos RS RC .40 1.00
356 Marcus Thames RS .40 1.00
357 Jeff Austin RS RC .40 1.00
358 Justin Kaye RS .40 1.00
359 Julio Mateo RS RC .40 1.00
360 Mike A. Smith RS RC .40 1.00
361 Chris Snelling RS RC .60 1.50
362 Dennis Tankersley RS .40 1.00
363 Runelvys Hernandez RS RC .40 1.00
364 Aaron Cook RS RC .40 1.00
365 Joe Borchard RS .40 1.00
366 Earl Snyder RS RC .40 1.00
367 Shane Nance RS RC .40 1.00
368 Aaron Guiel RS RC .40 1.00
369 Steve Bechler RS RC .40 1.00
370 Tim Kalita RS RC .40 1.00
371 Shawn Sedlacek RS RC .40 1.00
372 Eric Good RS RC .40 1.00
373 Eric Junge RS RC .40 1.00
374 Matt Thornton RS RC .40 1.00
375 Travis Driskill RS RC .40 1.00
376 Mitch Wylie RS RC .40 1.00
377 John Ennis RS RC .40 1.00
378 Reed Johnson RS RC .75 2.00
379 Juan Brito RS RC .40 1.00
380 Ron Calloway RS RC .40 1.00
381 Adrian Burnside RS RC .40 1.00
382 Josh Bard RS RC .40 1.00
383 Matt Childers RS RC .40 1.00
384 Gustavo Chacin RS RC .75 2.00
385 Luis Martinez RS RC .40 1.00
386 Trey Hodges RS RC .40 1.00
387 Hansel Izquierdo RS RC .40 1.00
388 Jeriome Robertson RS RC .40 1.00
389 Victor Alvarez RS RC .40 1.00
390 David Ross RS RC .50 1.25
391 Ron Chiavacci RS .40 1.00
392 Adam Walker RS RC .40 1.00
393 Mike Gonzalez RS RC .40 1.00
394 John Foster RS RC .40 1.00
395 Kyle Kane RS RC .40 1.00
396 Cam Esslinger RS RC .40 1.00
397 Kevin Frederick RS RC .40 1.00
398 Franklin Nunez RS RC .40 1.00
399 Todd Donovan RS RC .40 1.00
400 Kevin Cash RS RC .40 1.00

2002 Leaf Rookies and Stars Great American Signings

Randomly inserted into packs, this is a partial parallel to the basic Leaf Rookies and Stars set. These cards feature the basic card along with the attached "sticker" autograph. Since cards were issued to different stated print runs, we have notated that information next to the player's name in our checklist. If a card has a stated print run of 25 or fewer it is not printed due to market scarcity.

9 Jay Gibbons/150 4.00 10.00
18 Rickey Henderson/20
40 Mike Rivera/175 4.00 10.00
49 Mac Suzuki/100 15.00 40.00
59 Bernie Williams/15
60 Roger Clemens/10
63 Alfonso Soriano/25
68 Nick Johnson/175 6.00 15.00
92 Aubrey Huff/175 6.00 15.00
96 Brent Abernathy/175 4.00 10.00
108 Eric Hinske/175 4.00 10.00
131 Kerry Wood/25
141 Barry Larkin/25
142 Adam Dunn/25
146 Austin Kearns/75 6.00 15.00
169 Roy Oswalt/100 6.00 15.00
182 Cesar Izturis/175 4.00 10.00
190 Vladimir Guerrero/25
210 Bobby Abreu/25
221 Kip Wells/175 4.00 10.00
226 Brian Lawrence/175 4.00 10.00
244 Albert Pujols/25
256 Don Mattingly/25
301 So Taguchi/50 15.00 40.00
302 Kazuhisa Ishii/25
309 Franklyn German/175 4.00 10.00
310 Luis Ugueto/175 4.00 10.00
312 Felix Escalona/100 6.00 15.00
316 Francis Beltran/175 4.00 10.00
320 Bill Hall/175 6.00 15.00
324 Brandon Backe/175 6.00 15.00
327 Rodrigo Rosario/175 4.00 10.00
328 Anderson Machado/175 4.00 10.00
329 Jorge Padilla/175 4.00 10.00
331 Doug Devore/175 4.00 10.00
332 Drew Henson/50 6.00 15.00
333 Raul Chavez/175 4.00 10.00
334 Tom Shearn/175 4.00 10.00
335 Ben Howard/175 4.00 10.00
336 Chris Baker/175 4.00 10.00
337 Travis Hughes/175 4.00 10.00
341 Corey Thurman/175 4.00 10.00
344 Satoru Komiyama/75 10.00 25.00
345 Jason Lane/150 6.00 15.00
346 Rene Reyes/175 4.00 10.00
354 Oliver Perez/175 15.00 40.00
361 Chris Snelling/175 8.00 20.00
362 Dennis Tankersley/175 4.00 10.00

2002 Leaf Rookies and Stars Longevity

Randomly inserted into packs, this is a parallel to the basic Leaf Rookie and Stars set. Cards numbered between 1-300 (and including all of the variations) were printed to a stated print run of 100 serial numbered sets while cards 301 through 400 were printed to a stated print run of 25 serial numbered sets.

*LONGEVITY 1-300: 6X TO 15X BASIC
*LONGEVITY 1-300: 1.25X TO 3X BASIC SP'S
*RETIRED STARS 251-300: 12.5X TO 30X

2002 Leaf Rookies and Stars BLC Homers

Randomly inserted into packs, these 30 cards feature pieces of baseball's used during the Big League Challenge held in Las Vegas before the 2002 season began. Each card has a stated print run of 25 serial numbered sets.

LUIS GONZALEZ (1-3) 10.00 25.00
TODD HELTON (4-11) 15.00 40.00
JIM THOME (12-14) 15.00 40.00
RAFAEL PALMEIRO (15-19) 15.00 40.00
TROY GLAUS (20-22) 10.00 25.00
GARY SHEFFIELD (23-25) 10.00 25.00
MIKE PIAZZA (26-30) 20.00 50.00

2002 Leaf Rookies and Stars Dress for Success

Randomly inserted into packs, these 15 cards feature two game-used memorabilia pieces from the featured players. Each card was also issued to a stated print run of 250 serial numbered sets.

1 Mike Piazza Jsy-Jsy 10.00 25.00
2 Cal Ripken Jsy-Jsy 30.00 60.00
3 Carlos Delgado Jsy-Jsy 8.00 20.00
4 Chipper Jones Jsy-Jsy 10.00 25.00
5 Bernie Williams Jsy-Shoe 10.00 25.00
6 Carlos Beltran Jsy-Shoe 8.00 20.00
7 Curt Schilling Jsy-Jsy 8.00 20.00
8 Greg Maddux Jsy-Jsy 10.00 25.00
9 Ivan Rodriguez Jsy-Jsy 10.00 25.00
10 Alex Rodriguez Jsy-Jsy 15.00 40.00
11 Roger Clemens Jsy-Jsy 15.00 40.00
12 Todd Helton Jsy-Jsy 10.00 25.00
13 Jim Edmonds Shoe-Jsy 8.00 20.00
14 Manny Ramirez Jsy-Fld Glv 10.00 25.00
15 Mark Buehrle Jsy-Shoe 8.00 20.00

2002 Leaf Rookies and Stars Freshman Orientation

Inserted in packs at a stated rate of one in 142, these 20 cards feature not only players who debuted during the 2002 season but also a game-used memorabilia piece from that player.

*CLASS OFFICERS: .6X TO 1.5X BASIC
CLASS OFFICERS PRINT RUN 50 #'d SETS
1 Andres Torres Bat 4.00 10.00
2 Mark Ellis Jsy 4.00 10.00
3 Erik Bedard Bat 4.00 10.00
4 Delvin James Jsy 4.00 10.00
5 Austin Kearns Bat 4.00 10.00
6 Josh Pearce Bat 4.00 10.00
7 Rafael Soriano Jsy 4.00 10.00
8 Jason Lane Bat 4.00 10.00
9 Mark Prior Jsy 4.00 10.00
10 Alfredo Amezaga Bat 4.00 10.00
11 Ryan Ludwick Bat 4.00 10.00
12 So Taguchi Bat 6.00 15.00
13 Duaner Sanchez Bat 4.00 10.00
14 Kazuhisa Ishii Jsy 6.00 15.00
15 Zach Day Pants 4.00 10.00
16 Eric Cyr Bat 4.00 10.00
17 Francis Beltran Jsy 4.00 10.00
18 Joe Borchard Jsy 4.00 10.00
19 Jeremy Affeldt Shoe 4.00 10.00
20 Alexis Gomez Shoe 4.00 10.00

2002 Leaf Rookies and Stars Statistical Standouts

Issued at stated odds of one in 12, these 50 cards feature some of the leading players in baseball.

1 Adam Dunn 1.00 2.50
2 Alex Rodriguez 4.00 10.00
3 Andruw Jones 1.50 4.00
4 Brian Giles 1.00 2.50
5 Chipper Jones 2.50 6.00
6 Cliff Floyd 1.00 2.50
7 Craig Biggio 1.50 4.00
8 Frank Thomas 2.50 6.00
9 Fred McGriff 1.50 4.00
10 Garret Anderson 1.00 2.50
11 Greg Maddux 4.00 10.00
12 Luis Gonzalez 1.00 2.50
13 Magglio Ordonez 1.00 2.50
14 Ivan Rodriguez 1.50 4.00
15 Ken Griffey Jr. 4.00 10.00
16 Ichiro Suzuki 5.00 12.00
17 Jason Giambi 1.00 2.50
18 Derek Jeter 6.00 15.00
19 Sammy Sosa 2.50 6.00
20 Albert Pujols 5.00 12.00
21 J.D. Drew 1.00 2.50
22 Jeff Bagwell 1.50 4.00
23 Jim Edmonds 1.00 2.50
24 Jose Vidro 1.00 2.50
25 Juan Encarnacion 1.00 2.50
26 Kerry Wood 1.00 2.50
27 Al Leiter 1.00 2.50
28 Curt Schilling 1.00 2.50
29 Manny Ramirez 1.50 4.00
30 Lance Berkman 1.00 2.50
31 Miguel Tejada 1.00 2.50
32 Mike Piazza 4.00 10.00
33 Nomar Garciaparra 4.00 10.00
34 Omar Vizquel 1.50 4.00
35 Pat Burrell 1.00 2.50
36 Paul Konerko 1.00 2.50
37 Rafael Palmeiro 1.50 4.00
38 Randy Johnson 2.50 6.00
39 Richie Sexson 1.00 2.50
40 Roger Clemens 5.00 12.00
41 Shawn Green 1.00 2.50
42 Todd Helton 1.50 4.00
43 Tom Glavine 1.50 4.00
44 Troy Glaus 1.00 2.50
45 Vladimir Guerrero 2.50 6.00
46 Mike Sweeney 1.00 2.50
47 Alfonso Soriano 1.00 2.50
48 Barry Zito 1.00 2.50
49 John Smoltz 1.50 4.00
50 Ellis Burks 1.00 2.50

2002 Leaf Rookies and Stars Statistical Standouts Materials

Randomly inserted into packs, this is a parallel to the basic Statistical Standouts insert set. These cards feature a game-used memorabilia piece from each player. Please note that some cards were issued in shorter supply and we have notated that information along with the stated print run information next to the player's name in our checklist.

SUPER PRINT RUN 25 SERIAL #'d SETS
SUPER: NO PRICING DUE TO SCARCITY
1 Adam Dunn Bat/200 4.00 10.00
2 Alex Rodriguez Bat/200 8.00 20.00
3 Andruw Jones Bat/200 6.00 15.00
4 Brian Giles Bat 4.00 10.00
5 Chipper Jones Bat/200 6.00 15.00
6 Cliff Floyd Jsy 4.00 10.00
7 Craig Biggio Pants 6.00 15.00
8 Frank Thomas Jsy/125 6.00 15.00
9 Fred McGriff Bat 6.00 15.00
10 Garret Anderson Bat
11 Greg Maddux Jsy/200 8.00 20.00
12 Luis Gonzalez Jsy 4.00 10.00
13 Magglio Ordonez Bat/150 4.00 10.00
14 Ivan Rodriguez Bat/100
15 Ken Griffey Jr. Base/100 10.00 25.00
16 Ichiro Suzuki Base/100
17 Jason Giambi Base 4.00 10.00
18 Derek Jeter Base/100
19 Sammy Sosa Base/100 6.00 15.00
20 Albert Pujols Base/100
21 J.D. Drew Bat/150 4.00 10.00
22 Jeff Bagwell Pants/150
23 Jim Edmonds Bat 4.00 10.00
24 Jose Vidro Bat 4.00 10.00
25 Juan Encarnacion Bat 4.00 10.00
26 Kerry Wood Jsy/200 4.00 10.00
27 Al Leiter Jsy 4.00 10.00
28 Curt Schilling Jsy/225
29 Manny Ramirez Bat/100 6.00 15.00
30 Lance Berkman Bat/150
31 Miguel Tejada Jsy 4.00 10.00
32 Mike Piazza Bat/200 8.00 20.00
33 Nomar Garciaparra Bat/200 10.00 25.00
34 Omar Vizquel Jsy 6.00 15.00
35 Pat Burrell Bat 4.00 10.00
36 Paul Konerko Jsy 4.00 10.00

37 Rafael Palmeiro Bat 6.00 15.00
38 Randy Johnson Jsy/200 6.00 15.00
39 Richie Sexson Jsy 4.00 10.00
40 Roger Clemens Jsy/200 12.50 30.00
41 Shawn Green Jsy 4.00 10.00
42 Todd Helton Jsy/175 6.00 15.00
43 Tom Glavine Jsy/125 6.00 15.00
44 Troy Glaus Jsy 4.00 10.00
45 Vladimir Guerrero Jsy 6.00 15.00
46 Mike Sweeney Bat 4.00 10.00
47 Alfonso Soriano Jsy/200 4.00 10.00
48 Barry Zito Jsy/100 4.00 10.00
49 John Smoltz Jsy
50 Ellis Burks Jsy/50 4.00 10.00

2002 Leaf Rookies and Stars Triple Threads

Randomly inserted into packs, this 10 card set featured three players who have something in common along with a memorabilia piece of each player featured on the card. Each card was also issued to a stated print run of 100 serial numbered sets.

1 Reggie Jackson 50.00 100.00
Alfonso Soriano
Don Mattingly
2 Alex Rodriguez 30.00 60.00
Rafael Palmeiro
Ivan Rodriguez
3 Mike Piazza 30.00 60.00
Gary Carter
Rickey Henderson
4 Dale Murphy 20.00 50.00
Andruw Jones
Chipper Jones
5 Mike Schmidt 50.00 100.00
Steve Carlton
Scott Rolen
6 Rickey Henderson 20.00 50.00
Rickey Henderson
Rickey Henderson
7 Johnny Bench 40.00 80.00
Joe Morgan
Tom Seaver
8 Randy Johnson 20.00 50.00
Pedro Martinez
Vladimir Guerrero
9 Nolan Ryan 50.00 100.00
Rod Carew
Troy Glaus
10 Lou Brock 50.00 100.00
J.D Drew
Stan Musial

2002 Leaf Rookies and Stars View Masters

Randomly inserted into packs, these 20 cards feature some of the leading players in the game in a style reminiscent of the old "View Masters" which became popular in the 1950's. Each of these cards were printed to a stated print run of 100 serial numbered sets and have a game used-memorabilia piece attached to them.

SLIDESHOW PRINT 25 SERIAL #'d SETS
SLIDESHOW: NO PRICE DUE TO SCARCITY
1 Carlos Delgado 6.00 15.00
2 Todd Helton 10.00 25.00
3 Tony Gwynn 15.00 40.00
4 Bernie Williams 10.00 25.00
5 Luis Gonzalez 6.00 15.00
6 Larry Walker 6.00 15.00
7 Troy Glaus 6.00 15.00
8 Alfonso Soriano 6.00 15.00
9 Curt Schilling 6.00 15.00
10 Chipper Jones 10.00 25.00
11 Vladimir Guerrero 10.00 25.00
12 Adam Dunn 6.00 15.00
13 Rickey Henderson 10.00 25.00
14 Miguel Tejada 6.00 15.00
15 Kazuhisa Ishii 10.00 25.00
16 Greg Maddux 15.00 40.00
17 Pedro Martinez 10.00 25.00
18 Nomar Garciaparra 20.00 50.00
19 Mike Piazza 15.00 40.00
20 Lance Berkman 6.00 15.00

1996 Leaf Signature

The 1996 Leaf Signature Set was issued by Donruss in two series totalling 150 cards. The four-card packs carried a suggested retail price of $9.99 each. It's interesting to note that the Extended Series was the last of the 1996 releases. In fact, it was released in January, 1997 - so late in the year that it's categorization as a 1996 issue was a bit of a stretch at that time. Production for the Extended Series was only 40 percent that of the regular issue. Extended Series packs actually contained a mix of both series cards, thus the Extended Series cards are somewhat scarcer. Card fronts feature borderless color action player photos with the card name printed in a silver foil emblem. The backs carry player information. Rookie Cards include Darin Erstad. This product was a benchmark release in hobby history due to it's inclusion of one or more autograph cards per pack (explaining it's high suggested retail pack price). The product was highly successful upon release and opened the doors for wide incorporation of autograph cards into a wide array of brands from that point forward.

COMPLETE SET (150) 40.00 100.00
COMP. SERIES 1 (100) 25.00 60.00
COMPLETE SERIES 2 (50) 15.00 40.00
COMMON CARD (1-100) .20 .50
COMMON (101-150) .10 .30
1 Mike Piazza .75 2.00
2 Juan Gonzalez .20 .50
3 Greg Maddux .75 2.00
4 Marc Newfield .20 .50
5 Wade Boggs .30 .75
6 Ray Lankford .20 .50
7 Frank Thomas .50 1.25
8 Rico Brogna .20 .50
9 Tim Salmon .30 .75
10 Ken Griffey Jr. .75 2.00
11 Manny Ramirez .30 .75
12 Cecil Fielder .20 .50
13 Gregg Jefferies .20 .50
14 Rondell White .20 .50
15 Cal Ripken 1.50 4.00
16 Alex Rodriguez 1.00 2.50
17 Bernie Williams .30 .75
18 Andres Galarraga .20 .50
19 Mike Mussina .30 .75
20 Chuck Knoblauch .20 .50
21 Joe Carter .20 .50
22 Jeff Bagwell .30 .75
23 Mark McGwire 1.25 3.00
24 Sammy Sosa .50 1.25
25 Reggie Sanders .20 .50
26 Chipper Jones .50 1.25
27 Jeff Cirillo .20 .50
28 Roger Clemens 1.00 2.50
29 Craig Biggio .30 .75
30 Gary Sheffield .20 .50
31 Paul O'Neill .30 .75
32 Johnny Damon .30 .75
33 Jason Isringhausen .20 .50
34 Jay Bell .20 .50
35 Henry Rodriguez .20 .50
36 Matt Williams .20 .50
37 Randy Johnson .50 1.25
38 Fred McGriff .30 .75
39 Jason Giambi .20 .50
40 Ivan Rodriguez .30 .75
41 Raul Mondesi .20 .50
42 Barry Larkin .30 .75
43 Ryan Klesko .20 .50
44 Joey Hamilton .20 .50
45 Todd Hundley .20 .50
46 Jim Edmonds .20 .50
47 Dante Bichette .20 .50
48 Roberto Alomar .30 .75
49 Mark Grace .30 .75
50 Brady Anderson .20 .50
51 Hideo Nomo .50 1.25
52 Ozzie Smith .75 2.00
53 Robin Ventura .20 .50
54 Andy Pettitte .30 .75
55 Kenny Lofton .20 .50
56 John Mabry .20 .50
57 Paul Molitor .20 .50
58 Rey Ordonez .20 .50
59 Albert Belle .20 .50
60 Charles Johnson .20 .50
61 Edgar Martinez .30 .75
62 Derek Bell .20 .50
63 Carlos Delgado .20 .50
64 Raul Casanova .20 .50
65 Ismael Valdes .20 .50
66 J.T. Snow .20 .50
67 Derek Jeter 1.25 3.00
68 Jason Kendall .20 .50
69 John Smoltz .30 .75
70 Chad Mottola .20 .50
71 Jim Thome .30 .75
72 Will Clark .30 .75
73 Mo Vaughn .20 .50
74 John Wasdin .20 .50
75 Rafael Palmeiro .30 .75
76 Mark Grudzielanek .20 .50
77 Larry Walker .20 .50
78 Alan Benes .20 .50
79 Michael Tucker .20 .50
80 Billy Wagner .20 .50
81 Paul Wilson .20 .50
82 Greg Vaughn .20 .50
83 Dean Palmer .20 .50
84 Ryne Sandberg .75 2.00
85 Eric Young .20 .50
86 Jay Buhner .20 .50
87 Tony Clark .20 .50
88 Jermaine Dye .20 .50
89 Barry Bonds 1.25 3.00
90 Ugueth Urbina .20 .50
91 Charles Nagy .20 .50
92 Ruben Rivera .20 .50
93 Todd Hollandsworth .20 .50
94 Darin Erstad RC 1.50 4.00
95 Brooks Kieschnick .20 .50
96 Edgar Renteria .20 .50
97 Lenny Dykstra .20 .50
98 Tony Gwynn .60 1.50
99 Kirby Puckett .50 1.25
100 Checklist .20 .50
101 Andruw Jones 1.00 2.50
102 Alex Ochoa .10 .30
103 David Cone .20 .50
104 Rusty Greer .20 .50
105 Jose Canseco .30 .75
106 Ken Caminiti .20 .50
107 Mariano Rivera 1.00 2.50
108 Ron Gant .20 .50
109 Darryl Strawberry .20 .50
110 Vladimir Guerrero 1.25 3.00
111 George Arias .10 .30
112 Jeff Conine .20 .50
113 Bobby Higginson .20 .50
114 Eric Karros .20 .50
115 Brian Hunter .10 .30
116 Eddie Murray .50 1.25
117 Todd Walker .10 .30
118 Chan Ho Park .20 .50
119 John Jaha .10 .30
120 Dave Justice .20 .50
121 Makoto Suzuki .10 .30
122 Scott Rolen .50 1.25
123 Tino Martinez .30 .75
124 Kimera Bartee .10 .30
125 Garret Anderson .20 .50
126 Brian Jordan .20 .50
127 Andre Dawson .20 .50
128 Javier Lopez .20 .50
129 Bill Pulsipher .10 .30
130 Dwight Gooden .20 .50
131 Al Martin .10 .30
132 Terrell Wade .10 .30
133 Steve Gibralter .10 .30
134 Tom Glavine .30 .75
135 Kevin Appier .20 .50
136 Tim Raines .20 .50
137 Curtis Pride .10 .30
138 Todd Greene .10 .30
139 Bobby Bonilla .20 .50
140 Trey Beamon .10 .30
141 Marty Cordova .10 .30
142 Rickey Henderson .50 1.25
143 Ellis Burks .20 .50
144 Dennis Eckersley .20 .50
145 Kevin Brown .20 .50
146 Carlos Baerga .10 .30
147 Brett Butler .20 .50
148 Marquis Grissom .20 .50
149 Karim Garcia .10 .30
150 Frank Thomas CL .30 .75

1996 Leaf Signature Gold Press Proofs

Randomly inserted in first series packs at an approximate rate of one in 12 and second series packs at an approximate rate of one in 8, this 150-card set is parallel to the regular version. The design is similar to the regular card with the exception of the card name being printed in a gold foil emblem and the words "Press Proof" printed in gold foil vertically down the side.

COMPLETE SET (150) 700.00 1100.00
*SER.1 STARS: 4X TO 10X BASIC CARDS
*SER.1 ROOKIES: 1.25X TO 3X BASIC CARDS
*SER.2 STARS: 3X TO 8X BASIC CARDS
STATED ODDS 1:12
67 Derek Jeter 20.00 50.00

1996 Leaf Signature Platinum Press Proofs

Randomly inserted exclusively into Extended Series packs at the rate of one in 24, this 150-card set is parallel to the regular Leaf Signature Set. Only 150 sets were produced. Unlike the multi-series base set and Gold Press Proofs, these scarce Platinum cards were issued in one comprehensive series. The cards are similar in design to the regular set with the exception of holographic platinum foil stamping.

*SER.1 STARS: 10X TO 25X BASIC CARDS
*SER. 1 ROOKIES: 2.5X TO 6X BASIC CARDS
*SER.2 STARS: 8X TO 20X BASIC CARDS
67 Derek Jeter 100.00 200.00

1996 Leaf Signature Autographs

Inserted into 1996 Leaf Signature Series first series packs, these unnumbered cards were one of the first major autograph issues featured in an MLB-licensed trading card set. First series packs contained at least one autograph, with the chance of getting more. Donruss/Leaf reports that all but 10 players in the Leaf Signature Series signed close to 5,000 total autographs (3,500 bronze, 1,000 silver, 500 gold). The 10 players who signed 1,000 (700 bronze, 200 silver, 100 gold) are: Roberto Alomar, Wade Boggs, Derek Jeter, Kenny Lofton, Paul Molitor, Raul Mondesi, Manny Ramirez, Alex Rodriguez, Frank Thomas and Mo Vaughn. It's also important to note that six additional players did not submit their cards in time to be included in first series packs. Thus, their cards were thrown into Extended series packs. Those six players are as follows: Brian L.Hunter, Carlos Delgado, Phil Plantier, Jim Thome, Terrell Wade and Ernie Young. Thome signed only silver and gold foil cards, thus the Bronze set is considered complete at 251 cards. Prices below refer exclusively to Bronze versions. Blue and black ink variations have been found for Carlos Delgado, Alex Rodriguez and Michael Tucker. No consistent premiums for these variations has been tracked. Finally, an autographed jumbo silver foil version of the Frank Thomas card was distributed to dealers in March, 1997. Dealers received either this first series or the Extended Series jumbo Thomas for every Extended Series case ordered. Each Thomas jumbo is individually serial numbered to 1,500. A standard-size promo card of Frank Thomas with a fascimile signature was also created and released several weeks before this set's release. An Otis Nixon card surfaced in the secondary market in 2005. Nixon's cards were never seeded into packs, but it's believed that the cards were printed and sent to Nixon, of whom signed them but failed to return them to the manufacturer.

1 Kurt Abbott 2.00 5.00
2 Juan Acevedo 2.00 5.00
3 Terry Adams 2.00 5.00
4 Manny Alexander 2.00 5.00
5 Roberto Alomar SP 20.00 50.00
6 Moises Alou 6.00 15.00
7 Wilson Alvarez 2.00 5.00
8 Garret Anderson 6.00 15.00
9 Shane Andrews 2.00 5.00
10 Andy Ashby 2.00 5.00
11 Pedro Astacio 2.00 5.00
12 Brad Ausmus 6.00 15.00
13 Bobby Ayala 2.00 5.00
14 Carlos Baerga 4.00 10.00
15 Harold Baines 4.00 10.00
16 Jason Bates 2.00 5.00
17 Allen Battle 2.00 5.00
18 Rich Becker 2.00 5.00
19 David Bell 2.00 5.00
20 Rafael Belliard 4.00 10.00
21 Andy Benes 2.00 5.00
22 Armando Benitez 2.00 5.00
23 Jason Bere 2.00 5.00
24 Geronimo Berroa 2.00 5.00
25 Willie Blair 2.00 5.00
26 Mike Blowers 2.00 5.00
27 Wade Boggs SP 30.00 60.00
28 Ricky Bones 2.00 5.00
29 Mike Bordick 4.00 10.00
30 Toby Borland 2.00 5.00
31 Ricky Bottalico 2.00 5.00
32 Darren Bragg 2.00 5.00
33 Jeff Branson 2.00 5.00
34 Tilson Brito 2.00 5.00
35 Rico Brogna 2.00 5.00
36 Scott Brosius 8.00 20.00
37 Damon Buford 2.00 5.00
38 Mike Busby 2.00 5.00
39 Tom Candiotti 4.00 10.00
40 Frank Castillo 2.00 5.00
41 Andujar Cedeno 2.00 5.00
42 Domingo Cedeno 2.00 5.00
43 Roger Cedeno 2.00 5.00
44 Norm Charlton 2.00 5.00
45 Jeff Cirillo 4.00 10.00
46 Will Clark 4.00 10.00
47 Jeff Conine 4.00 10.00
48 Steve Cooke 2.00 5.00
49 Joey Cora 2.00 5.00
50 Marty Cordova 2.00 5.00
51 Rheal Cormier 2.00 5.00
52 Felipe Crespo 2.00 5.00
53 Chad Curtis 2.00 5.00
54 Johnny Damon 6.00 15.00
55 Russ Davis 2.00 5.00
56 Andre Dawson 8.00 20.00
57 Carlos Delgado 4.00 10.00
58 Doug Drabek 2.00 5.00
59 Darren Dreifort 2.00 5.00
60 Shawon Dunston 2.00 5.00
61 Ray Durham 4.00 10.00
62 Jim Edmonds 5.00 12.00
63 Joey Eischen 2.00 5.00
64 Jim Eisenreich 2.00 5.00
65 Sal Fasano 2.00 5.00
66 Jeff Fassero 2.00 5.00
67 Alex Fernandez 2.00 5.00
68 Darrin Fletcher 2.00 5.00
69 Chad Fonville 2.00 5.00
70 Kevin Foster 2.00 5.00
71 John Franco 4.00 10.00
72 Julio Franco 5.00 12.00
73 Marvin Freeman 2.00 5.00
74 Travis Fryman 4.00 10.00
75 Gary Gaetti 4.00 10.00
76 Carlos Garcia 2.00 5.00
77 Jason Giambi 4.00 10.00
78 Benji Gil 2.00 5.00
79 Greg Gohr 2.00 5.00
80 Chris Gomez 2.00 5.00
81 Leo Gomez 2.00 5.00
82 Tom Goodwin 2.00 5.00
83 Mike Grace 2.00 5.00
84 Mike Greenwell 6.00 15.00
85 Rusty Greer 4.00 10.00
86 Mark Grudzielanek 2.00 5.00
87 Mark Gubicza 2.00 5.00
88 Juan Guzman 2.00 5.00
89 Darryl Hamilton 2.00 5.00
90 Joey Hamilton 2.00 5.00
91 Chris Hammond 2.00 5.00
92 Mike Hampton 4.00 10.00
93 Chris Haney 2.00 5.00
94 Todd Haney 2.00 5.00
95 Erik Hanson 2.00 5.00
96 Pete Harnisch 2.00 5.00
97 LaTroy Hawkins 4.00 10.00
98 Charlie Hayes 2.00 5.00
99 Jimmy Haynes 2.00 5.00
100 Roberto Hernandez 2.00 5.00
101 Bobby Higginson 4.00 10.00
102 Glenallen Hill 2.00 5.00
103 Ken Hill 2.00 5.00
104 Sterling Hitchcock 2.00 5.00
105 Trevor Hoffman 8.00 20.00
106 Dave Hollins 2.00 5.00
107 Dwayne Hosey 2.00 5.00
108 Thomas Howard 2.00 5.00
109 Steve Howe 10.00 25.00
110 John Hudek 2.00 5.00
111 Rex Hudler 2.00 5.00
112 Brian L.Hunter 2.00 5.00
113 Butch Huskey 2.00 5.00
114 Mark Hutton 2.00 5.00
115 Jason Jacome 2.00 5.00
116 John Jaha 2.00 5.00
117 Reggie Jefferson 2.00 5.00
118 Derek Jeter SP 125.00 300.00
119 Bobby Jones 2.00 5.00
120 Todd Jones 4.00 10.00
121 Brian Jordan 4.00 10.00
122 Kevin Jordan 2.00 5.00
123 Jeff Juden 2.00 5.00
124 Ron Karkovice 2.00 5.00
125 Roberto Kelly 2.00 5.00
126 Mark Kiefer 2.00 5.00
127 Brooks Kieschnick 2.00 5.00
128 Jeff King 2.00 5.00
129 Mike Lansing 2.00 5.00
130 Matt Lawton 2.00 5.00
131 Al Leiter 4.00 10.00
132 Mark Leiter 2.00 5.00
133 Curtis Leskanic 4.00 10.00
134 Darren Lewis 2.00 5.00
135 Mark Lewis 2.00 5.00
136 Felipe Lira 2.00 5.00
137 Pat Listach 2.00 5.00
138 Keith Lockhart 2.00 5.00
139 Kenny Lofton SP 10.00 25.00
140 John Mabry 4.00 10.00
141 Mike Macfarlane 2.00 5.00
142 Kirt Manwaring 2.00 5.00
143 Al Martin 2.00 5.00
144 Norberto Martin 2.00 5.00
145 Dennis Martinez 4.00 10.00
146 Pedro Martinez 20.00 50.00
147 Sandy Martinez 2.00 5.00
148 Mike Matheny 2.00 5.00
149 T.J. Mathews 2.00 5.00
150 David McCarty 2.00 5.00
151 Ben McDonald 2.00 5.00
152 Pat Meares 2.00 5.00
153 Orlando Merced 2.00 5.00
154 Jose Mesa 2.00 5.00
155 Matt Mieske 2.00 5.00
156 Orlando Miller 2.00 5.00
157 Mike Mimbs 2.00 5.00
158 Paul Molitor SP 20.00 50.00
159 Raul Mondesi SP 15.00 40.00
160 Jeff Montgomery 2.00 5.00
161 Mickey Morandini 2.00 5.00
162 Lyle Mouton 2.00 5.00
163 James Mouton 2.00 5.00
164 Jamie Moyer 5.00 12.00
165 Rodney Myers 2.00 5.00
166 Denny Neagle 4.00 10.00
167 Robb Nen 4.00 10.00
168 Marc Newfield 2.00 5.00
169 Dave Nilsson 2.00 5.00
170 Otis Nixon * 50.00 100.00
171 Jon Nunnally 2.00 5.00
172 Chad Ogea 2.00 5.00
173 Troy O'Leary 2.00 5.00
174 Rey Ordonez 4.00 10.00
175 Jayhawk Owens 2.00 5.00
176 Tom Pagnozzi 2.00 5.00
177 Dean Palmer 2.00 5.00
178 Roger Pavlik 2.00 5.00
179 Troy Percival 2.00 5.00
180 Carlos Perez 2.00 5.00
181 Robert Perez 2.00 5.00
182 Andy Pettitte 30.00 60.00
183 Phil Plantier 2.00 5.00
184 Mike Potts 2.00 5.00
185 Curtis Pride 2.00 5.00
186 Ariel Prieto 2.00 5.00
187 Bill Pulsipher 2.00 5.00
188 Brad Radke 4.00 10.00
189 Manny Ramirez SP 10.00 25.00
190 Joe Randa 4.00 10.00
191 Pat Rapp 2.00 5.00
192 Bryan Rekar 2.00 5.00
193 Shane Reynolds 2.00 5.00
194 Arthur Rhodes 2.00 5.00
195 Mariano Rivera 100.00 200.00
196 Alex Rodriguez SP 100.00 175.00
197 Frank Rodriguez 2.00 5.00
198 Mel Rojas 2.00 5.00
199 Ken Ryan 2.00 5.00
200 Bret Saberhagen 4.00 10.00
201 Tim Salmon 6.00 15.00
202 Rey Sanchez 2.00 5.00
203 Scott Sanders 2.00 5.00
204 Steve Scarsone 2.00 5.00
205 Curt Schilling 10.00 25.00
206 Jason Schmidt 6.00 15.00
207 David Segui 4.00 10.00
208 Kevin Seitzer 2.00 5.00
209 Scott Servais 2.00 5.00
210 Don Slaught 2.00 5.00
211 Zane Smith 2.00 5.00
212 Paul Sorrento 2.00 5.00
213 Scott Stahoviak 2.00 5.00
214 Mike Stanley 2.00 5.00
215 Terry Steinbach 2.00 5.00
216 Kevin Stocker 2.00 5.00
217 Jeff Suppan 4.00 10.00
218 Bill Swift 2.00 5.00
219 Greg Swindell 2.00 5.00
220 Kevin Tapani 2.00 5.00
221 Danny Tartabull 2.00 5.00
222 Julian Tavarez 2.00 5.00
223 Frank Thomas SP 30.00 60.00
224 Ozzie Timmons 2.00 5.00
225 Michael Tucker 2.00 5.00
226 Ismael Valdes 2.00 5.00
227 Jose Valentin 2.00 5.00
228 Todd Van Poppel 2.00 5.00
229 Mo Vaughn SP 15.00 40.00
230 Quilvio Veras 2.00 5.00
231 Fernando Vina 2.00 5.00
232 Joe Vitiello 2.00 5.00
233 Jose Vizcaino 2.00 5.00
234 Omar Vizquel 10.00 25.00
235 Terrell Wade 2.00 5.00
236 Paul Wagner 2.00 5.00
237 Matt Walbeck 2.00 5.00
238 Jerome Walton 2.00 5.00
239 Turner Ward 2.00 5.00
240 Allen Watson 2.00 5.00
241 David Weathers 2.00 5.00
242 Walt Weiss 2.00 5.00
243 Turk Wendell 2.00 5.00
244 Rondell White 4.00 10.00
245 Brian Williams 2.00 5.00
246 George Williams 2.00 5.00
247 Paul Wilson 2.00 5.00
248 Bobby Witt 2.00 5.00
249 Bob Wolcott 2.00 5.00
250 Eric Young 2.00 5.00
251 Ernie Young 2.00 5.00
252 Greg Zaun 2.00 5.00
NNO F.Thomas Jumbo AU/1500 20.00 50.00
NNO Frank Thomas Sample .75 2.00
Fascimile Auto

1996 Leaf Signature Autographs Gold

Randomly inserted primarily in first series packs, this 252-card set is parallel to the regular set and is similar in design with the exception of the gold foil printing on each card front. Each player signed 500 cards, except for the SP's of which only 100 of each are signed. Jim Thome erroneously signed 514 Gold cards.

*GOLD: .6X TO 1.5X BRONZE CARDS
GOLD NON-SP PRINT RUN 500 SETS
223 Jim Thome SP/514 15.00 40.00

1996 Leaf Signature Autographs Silver

Randomly inserted primarily in first series packs, this 252-card set is parallel to the regular set and is similar in design with the exception of the silver foil printing on each card front. Each player signed 1000 silver cards, except for the SP's of which only 200 are signed. Jim Thome erroneously signed 410 Silver cards.

*SILVER: .4X TO 1X BRONZE CARDS
223 Jim Thome SP/410 15.00 40.00

1996 Leaf Signature Extended Autographs

At least two autographed cards from this 217-card set were inserted in every Extended Series pack. Super Packs with four autographed cards were seeded one in every 12 packs. Most players signed 5000 cards, but short prints (500-2500 of each) do exist. On average, one in every nine packs contains a short print. All short print cards are individually noted in our checklist. By mistake, Andruw Jones, Ryan Klesko, Andy Pettitte, Kirby Puckett and Frank Thomas signed a few hundred of each of their cards in blue ink instead of black. No difference in price has been noted. Also, the Juan Gonzalez, Andruw Jones and Alex Rodriguez cards available in packs were not signed. All three cards had information on the back on how to mail them into Donruss/Leaf for an actual signed version. The deadline to exchange these cards was December 31st, 1998. In addition, middle relievers Doug Creek and Steve Parris failed to sign all 5000 of their cards. Creek submitted 1,950 cards and Parris submitted 1,800. Finally, an autographed jumbo version of the Extended Series Frank Thomas card was distributed to dealers in March, 1997. Dealers received either this card or the first series jumbo Thomas for every Extended Series case ordered. Each Extended Thomas jumbo is individually serial numbered to 1,500. A very popular Sammy Sosa card, one of his only certified autographs, is the key card in the set.

1 Scott Aldred 2.00 5.00
2 Mike Aldrete 2.00 5.00
3 Rich Amaral 2.00 5.00
4 Alex Arias 2.00 5.00
5 Paul Assenmacher 2.00 5.00
6 Roger Bailey 2.00 5.00
7 Erik Bennett 2.00 5.00
8 Sean Bergman 2.00 5.00
9 Doug Bochtler 2.00 5.00
10 Tim Bogar 2.00 5.00
11 Pat Borders 2.00 5.00
12 Pedro Borbon 2.00 5.00
13 Shawn Boskie 2.00 5.00
14 Rafael Bournigal 2.00 5.00
15 Mark Brandenburg 2.00 5.00
16 John Briscoe 2.00 5.00
17 Jorge Brito 2.00 5.00
18 Doug Brocail 2.00 5.00
19 Jay Buhner SP/1000 15.00 40.00
20 Scott Bullett 2.00 5.00
21 Dave Burba 2.00 5.00
22 Ken Caminiti SP/1000 15.00 40.00
23 John Cangelosi 2.00 5.00
24 Cris Carpenter 2.00 5.00
25 Chuck Carr 2.00 5.00
26 Larry Casian 2.00 5.00
27 Tony Castillo 2.00 5.00
28 Jason Christiansen 2.00 5.00
29 Archi Cianfrocco 2.00 5.00
30 Mark Clark 2.00 5.00
31 Terry Clark 2.00 5.00
32 R. Clemens SP1000 100.00 175.00
33 Jim Converse 2.00 5.00
34 Dennis Cook 2.00 5.00
35 Francisco Cordova 2.00 5.00
36 Jim Corsi 2.00 5.00
37 Tim Crabtree 2.00 5.00
38 Doug Creek SP/1950 6.00 15.00
39 John Cummings 2.00 5.00
40 Omar Daal 2.00 5.00
41 Rich DeLucia 2.00 5.00
42 Mark Dewey 2.00 5.00
43 Alex Diaz 2.00 5.00
44 Jermaine Dye SP/2500 12.50 30.00
45 Ken Edenfield 2.00 5.00
46 Mark Eichhorn 2.00 5.00
47 John Ericks 2.00 5.00
48 Darin Erstad 10.00 25.00
49 Alvaro Espinoza 2.00 5.00
50 Jorge Fabregas 2.00 5.00
51 Mike Fetters 2.00 5.00
52 John Flaherty 2.00 5.00
53 Bryce Florie 2.00 5.00
54 Tony Fossas 2.00 5.00
55 Lou Frazier 2.00 5.00
56 Mike Gallego 2.00 5.00
57 Karim Garcia SP/2500 6.00 15.00
58 Jason Giambi 6.00 15.00
59 Ed Giovanola 2.00 5.00
60 Tom Glavine SP/1250 20.00 50.00
61 Juan Gonzalez SP/1000 10.00 25.00
62 Craig Grebeck 2.00 5.00
63 Buddy Groom 2.00 5.00
64 Kevin Gross 2.00 5.00
65 Eddie Guardado 4.00 10.00
66 Mark Guthrie 2.00 5.00
67 Tony Gwynn SP/1000 40.00 80.00
68 Chip Hale 2.00 5.00
69 Darren Hall 2.00 5.00
70 Lee Hancock 2.00 5.00
71 Dave Hansen 2.00 5.00
72 Bryan Harvey 2.00 5.00
73 Bill Haselman 2.00 5.00
74 Mike Henneman 2.00 5.00
75 Doug Henry 2.00 5.00
76 Gil Heredia 2.00 5.00
77 Carlos Hernandez 2.00 5.00
78 Jose Hernandez 2.00 5.00
79 Darren Holmes 2.00 5.00
80 Mark Holzemer 2.00 5.00
81 Rick Honeycutt 2.00 5.00
82 Chris Hook 2.00 5.00
83 Chris Howard 2.00 5.00
84 Jack Howell 2.00 5.00
85 David Hulse 2.00 5.00
86 Edwin Hurtado 2.00 5.00
87 Jeff Huson 2.00 5.00
88 Mike James 2.00 5.00
89 Derek Jeter SP/1000 100.00 200.00
90 Brian Johnson 2.00 5.00
91 R. Johnson SP1000 60.00 120.00
92 Mark Johnson 2.00 5.00
93 Andruw Jones SP/2000 10.00 25.00
94 Chris Jones 2.00 5.00
95 Ricky Jordan 2.00 5.00
96 Matt Karchner 2.00 5.00
97 Scott Karl 2.00 5.00
98 Jason Kendall SP/2500 10.00 25.00
99 Brian Keyser 2.00 5.00
100 Mike Kingery 2.00 5.00
101 Wayne Kirby 2.00 5.00
102 Ryan Klesko SP/1000 20.00 50.00
103 C. Knoblauch SP1000 15.00 40.00
104 Chad Kreuter 2.00 5.00
105 Tom Lampkin 2.00 5.00
106 Scott Leius 2.00 5.00
107 Jon Lieber 4.00 10.00
108 Nelson Liriano 2.00 5.00
109 Scott Livingstone 2.00 5.00
110 Graeme Lloyd 2.00 5.00
111 Kenny Lofton SP/1000 15.00 40.00
112 Luis Lopez 2.00 5.00
113 Torey Lovullo 2.00 5.00
114 Greg Maddux SP/500 150.00 300.00
115 Mike Maddux 2.00 5.00
116 Dave Magadan 2.00 5.00
117 Mike Magnante 2.00 5.00
118 Joe Magrane 2.00 5.00
119 Pat Mahomes 2.00 5.00
120 Matt Mantei 2.00 5.00
121 John Marzano 2.00 5.00
122 Terry Mathews 2.00 5.00
123 Chuck McElroy 2.00 5.00
124 Fred McGriff SP/1000 15.00 40.00
125 Mark McLemore 2.00 5.00
126 Greg McMichael 2.00 5.00
127 Blas Minor 2.00 5.00
128 Dave Mlicki 2.00 5.00
129 Mike Mohler 2.00 5.00
130 Paul Molitor SP/1000 12.50 30.00
131 Steve Montgomery 2.00 5.00
132 Mike Mordecai 2.00 5.00
133 Mike Morgan 2.00 5.00
134 Mike Munoz 2.00 5.00
135 Greg Myers 2.00 5.00
136 Jimmy Myers 2.00 5.00
137 Mike Myers 2.00 5.00
138 Bob Natal 2.00 5.00
139 Dan Naulty 2.00 5.00
140 Jeff Nelson 4.00 10.00
141 Warren Newson 2.00 5.00
142 Chris Nichting 2.00 5.00
143 Melvin Nieves 2.00 5.00
144 Charlie O'Brien 2.00 5.00
145 Alex Ochoa 2.00 5.00
146 Omar Olivares 2.00 5.00
147 Joe Oliver 2.00 5.00
148 Lance Painter 2.00 5.00
149 R. Palmeiro SP2000 20.00 50.00
150 Mark Parent 2.00 5.00
151 Steve Parris SP/1800 6.00 15.00
152 Bob Patterson 2.00 5.00
153 Tony Pena 2.00 5.00
154 Eddie Perez 2.00 5.00
155 Yorkis Perez 2.00 5.00
156 Robert Person 2.00 5.00
157 Mark Petkovsek 2.00 5.00
158 Andy Pettitte SP/1000 20.00 50.00
159 J.R. Phillips 2.00 5.00
160 Hipolito Pichardo 2.00 5.00
161 Eric Plunk 2.00 5.00
162 Jimmy Poole 2.00 5.00
163 K. Puckett SP/1000 125.00 250.00
164 Paul Quantrill 2.00 5.00
165 Tom Quinlan 2.00 5.00
166 Jeff Reboulet 2.00 5.00
167 Jeff Reed 2.00 5.00
168 Steve Reed 2.00 5.00
169 Carlos Reyes 2.00 5.00
170 Bill Risley 2.00 5.00
171 Kevin Ritz 2.00 5.00
172 Kevin Roberson 2.00 5.00
173 Rich Robertson 2.00 5.00
174 A. Rodriguez SP/500 100.00 200.00
175 I. Rodriguez SP1250 30.00 60.00
176 Bruce Ruffin 2.00 5.00
177 Juan Samuel 2.00 5.00
178 Tim Scott 2.00 5.00
179 Kevin Sefcik 2.00 5.00
180 Jeff Shaw 2.00 5.00
181 Danny Sheaffer 2.00 5.00
182 Craig Shipley 2.00 5.00
183 Dave Silvestri 2.00 5.00
184 Aaron Small 2.00 5.00
185 John Smoltz SP/1000 50.00 100.00
186 Luis Sojo 2.00 5.00
187 S. Sosa SP/1000 60.00 120.00
188 Steve Sparks 2.00 5.00
189 Tim Spehr 2.00 5.00
190 Russ Springer 2.00 5.00
191 Matt Stairs 2.00 5.00
192 Andy Stankiewicz 2.00 5.00
193 Mike Stanton 6.00 12.00
194 Kelly Stinnett 2.00 5.00
195 Doug Strange 2.00 5.00

196 Mark Sweeney 2.00 5.00
197 Jeff Tabaka 2.00 5.00
198 Jesus Tavarez 2.00 5.00
199 F. Thomas SP1000 30.00 60.00
200 Larry Thomas 2.00 5.00
201 Mark Thompson 2.00 5.00
202 Mike Timlin 6.00 15.00
203 Steve Trachsel 2.00 5.00
204 Tom Urbani 2.00 5.00
205 Julio Valera 2.00 5.00
206 Dave Valle 2.00 5.00
207 Wm. VanLandingham 2.00 5.00
208 Mo Vaughn SP/1000 15.00 40.00
209 Dave Veres 2.00 5.00
210 Ed Vosberg 2.00 5.00
211 Don Wengert 2.00 5.00
212 Matt Whiteside 2.00 5.00
213 Bob Wickman 4.00 10.00
214 M.Williams SP/1250 10.00 25.00
215 Mike Williams 2.00 5.00
216 Woody Williams 4.00 10.00
217 Craig Worthington 2.00 5.00
NNO F.Thomas Jumbo AU 15.00 40.00

1996 Leaf Signature Extended Autographs Century Marks

Randomly inserted exclusively into Extended Series packs, cards from this 31-card parallel set feature a selection of star and rising young prospect players taken from the more comprehensive 217-card Extended Autograph set. The cards differ by a special blue holographic foil treatment. Only 100 of each card exists. In addition, Juan Gonzalez, Derek Jeter, Andruw Jones, Rafael Palmeiro and Alex Rodriguez did not sign the cards distributed in packs. All of these players cards had information on the back on how to mail them into Leaf/Donruss to receive a signed version.

1 Jay Buhner 30.00 60.00
2 Ken Caminiti 60.00 120.00
3 Roger Clemens 250.00 400.00
4 Jermaine Dye 30.00 60.00
5 Darin Erstad 20.00 50.00
6 Karim Garcia 10.00 25.00
7 Jason Giambi 30.00 60.00
8 Tom Glavine 75.00 150.00
9 Juan Gonzalez 30.00 60.00
10 Tony Gwynn 75.00 150.00
11 Derek Jeter 300.00 450.00
12 Randy Johnson 75.00 150.00
13 Andruw Jones 60.00 120.00
14 Jason Kendall 30.00 60.00
15 Ryan Klesko 30.00 60.00
16 Chuck Knoblauch 30.00 60.00
17 Kenny Lofton 30.00 60.00
18 Greg Maddux 250.00 400.00
19 Fred McGriff 60.00 120.00
20 Paul Molitor 50.00 100.00
21 Alex Ochoa 10.00 25.00
22 Rafael Palmeiro 75.00 150.00
23 Andy Pettitte 75.00 150.00
24 Kirby Puckett 100.00 200.00
25 Alex Rodriguez 175.00 350.00
26 Ivan Rodriguez 50.00 100.00
27 John Smoltz 75.00 150.00
28 Sammy Sosa 250.00 400.00
29 Frank Thomas 75.00 150.00
30 Mo Vaughn 30.00 60.00
31 Matt Williams 30.00 60.00

1965 O-Pee-Chee

The cards in this 283-card set measure the standard size. This set is essentially the same as the regular 1965 Topps set, except that the words "Printed in Canada" appear on the bottom of the back. On a white border, the fronts feature color player photos with rounded corners. The team name appears within a pennant design below the photo. The player's name and position are also printed on the front. On a blue background, the horizontal backs carry player biography and statistics on a gray card stock. Remember the prices below apply only to the O-Pee-Chee cards -- NOT to the 1965 Topps cards which are much more plentiful. Notable Rookie Cards include Bert Campaneris, Denny McLain, Joe Morgan and Luis Tiant.

COMPLETE SET (283) 1250.00 2500.00
COMMON CARD (1-198) 1.50 4.00
COMMON (199-283) 2.50 6.00
1 Tony Oliva 12.50 30.00
Elston Howard
Brooks Robinson LL
2 Bob Clemente 15.00 40.00
Hank Aaron
Rico Carty LL
3 Harmon Killebrew 40.00 80.00
Mickey Mantle
Boog Powell LL
4 Willie Mays 10.00 25.00
Billy Williams
Jim Ray Hart
Orlando Cepeda
Johnny Callison LL
5 Brooks Robinson 30.00 60.00
Harmon Killebrew
Mickey Mantle
Dick Stuart LL
6 Ken Boyer 8.00 20.00
Willie Mays
Ron Santo LL
7 Dean Chance 4.00 10.00
Joel Horlen LL
8 Sandy Koufax 12.50 30.00
Don Drysdale LL
9 Dean Chance 4.00 10.00
Gary Peters
Dave Wickersham
Juan Pizarro
Wally Bunker LL
10 Larry Jackson 4.00 10.00
Ray Sadecki
Juan Marichal LL
11 Al Downing 4.00 10.00
Dean Chance
Camilo Pascual
12 Bob Veale 4.00 10.00
Don Drysdale
Bob Gibson LL
13 Pedro Ramos 2.50 6.00
14 Len Gabrielson 1.50 4.00
15 Robin Roberts 6.00 15.00
16 Joe Morgan RC 50.00 100.00
Sonny Jackson
17 John Romano 1.50 4.00
18 Bill McCool 1.50 4.00
19 Gates Brown 2.50 6.00
20 Jim Bunning 6.00 15.00
21 Don Blasingame 1.50 4.00
22 Charlie Smith 1.50 4.00
23 Bob Tiefenauer 1.50 4.00
24 Twins Team 4.00 10.00
25 Al McBean 1.50 4.00
26 Bob Knoop 1.50 4.00
27 Dick Bertell 1.50 4.00
28 Barney Schultz 1.50 4.00
29 Felix Mantilla 1.50 4.00
30 Jim Bouton 4.00 10.00
31 Mike White 1.50 4.00
32 Herman Franks MG 1.50 4.00
33 Jackie Brandt 1.50 4.00
34 Cal Koonce 1.50 4.00
35 Ed Charles 1.50 4.00
36 Bob Wine 1.50 4.00
37 Fred Gladding 1.50 4.00
38 Jim King 1.50 4.00
39 Gerry Arrigo 1.50 4.00
40 Frank Howard 3.00 8.00
41 Bruce Howard 1.50 4.00
Marv Staehle
42 Earl Wilson 2.50 6.00
43 Mike Shannon 2.50 6.00
44 Wade Blasingame 1.50 4.00
45 Roy McMillan 2.50 6.00
46 Bob Lee 1.50 4.00
47 Tommy Harper 2.50 6.00
48 Claude Raymond 2.50 6.00
49 Curt Blefary RC 2.50 6.00
John Miller
50 Juan Marichal 6.00 15.00
51 Bill Bryan 1.50 4.00
52 Ed Roebuck 1.50 4.00
53 Dick McAuliffe 2.50 6.00
54 Joe Gibbon 1.50 4.00
55 Tony Conigliaro 8.00 20.00
56 Ron Kline 1.50 4.00
57 Cardinals Team 4.00 10.00
58 Fred Talbot 1.50 4.00
59 Nate Oliver 1.50 4.00
60 Jim O'Toole 2.50 6.00
61 Chris Cannizzaro 1.50 4.00
62 Jim Kaat UER 3.00 8.00
(Misspelled Katt)
63 Ty Cline 1.50 4.00
64 Lou Burdette 2.50 6.00
65 Tony Kubek 6.00 15.00
66 Bill Rigney MG 1.50 4.00
67 Harvey Haddix 2.50 6.00
68 Del Crandall 2.50 6.00
69 Bill Virdon 2.50 6.00
70 Bill Skowron 3.00 8.00
71 John O'Donoghue 1.50 4.00
72 Tony Gonzalez 1.50 4.00
73 Dennis Ribant 1.50 4.00
74 Rico Petrocelli RC 6.00 15.00
Jerry Stephenson
75 Deron Johnson 2.50 6.00
76 Sam McDowell 3.00 8.00
77 Doug Camilli 1.50 4.00
78 Dal Maxvill 2.50 6.00
79 Checklist 1-88 4.00 10.00
80 Turk Farrell 1.50 4.00
81 Don Buford 2.50 6.00
82 Santos Alomar RC 3.00 8.00
John Braun
83 George Thomas 1.50 4.00
84 Ron Herbel 1.50 4.00
85 Willie Smith 1.50 4.00
86 Buster Narum 1.50 4.00
87 Nelson Mathews 1.50 4.00
88 Jack Lamabe 1.50 4.00
89 Mike Hershberger 1.50 4.00
90 Rich Rollins 2.50 6.00
91 Cubs Team 4.00 10.00
92 Dick Howser 2.50 6.00
93 Jack Fisher 1.50 4.00
94 Charlie Lau 2.50 6.00
95 Bill Mazeroski 6.00 15.00
96 Sonny Siebert 2.50 6.00
97 Pedro Gonzalez 1.50 4.00
98 Bob Miller 1.50 4.00
99 Gil Hodges MG 4.00 10.00
100 Ken Boyer 6.00 15.00
101 Fred Newman 1.50 4.00
102 Steve Boros 1.50 4.00
103 Harvey Kuenn 2.50 6.00
104 Checklist 89-176 4.00 10.00
105 Chico Salmon 1.50 4.00
106 Gene Oliver 1.50 4.00
107 Pat Corrales RC 2.50 6.00
Costen Shockley
108 Don Mincher 1.50 4.00
109 Walt Bond 1.50 4.00
110 Ron Santo 3.00 8.00
111 Lee Thomas 2.50 6.00
112 Derrell Griffith 1.50 4.00
113 Steve Barber 1.50 4.00
114 Jim Hickman 2.50 6.00
115 Bobby Richardson 6.00 15.00
116 Dave Dowling 2.50 6.00
Bob Tolan RC
117 Wes Stock 1.50 4.00
118 Hal Lanier 2.50 6.00
119 John Kennedy 1.50 4.00
120 Frank Robinson 30.00 60.00
121 Gene Alley 2.50 6.00
122 Bill Pleis 1.50 4.00
123 Frank Thomas 2.50 6.00
124 Tom Satriano 1.50 4.00
125 Juan Pizarro 1.50 4.00
126 Dodgers Team 4.00 10.00
127 Frank Lary 1.50 4.00
128 Vic Davalillo 1.50 4.00
129 Bennie Daniels 1.50 4.00
130 Al Kaline 30.00 60.00
131 Johnny Keane MG 1.50 4.00
132 Mike Shannon WS 4.00 10.00
133 Mel Stottlemyre WS 4.00 10.00
134 Mickey Mantle WS 60.00 120.00
135 Ken Boyer WS 6.00 15.00
136 Tim McCarver WS 4.00 10.00
137 Jim Bouton WS 4.00 10.00
138 Bob Gibson WS 8.00 20.00
139 WS Summary 4.00 10.00
Cards celebrate
140 Dean Chance 2.50 6.00
141 Charlie James 1.50 4.00
142 Bill Monbouquette 1.50 4.00
143 John Gelnar 1.50 4.00
Jerry May
144 Ed Kranepool 2.50 6.00
145 Luis Tiant RC 8.00 20.00
146 Ron Hansen 1.50 4.00
147 Dennis Bennett 1.50 4.00
148 Willie Kirkland 1.50 4.00
149 Wayne Schurr 1.50 4.00
150 Brooks Robinson 30.00 60.00
151 Athletics Team 4.00 10.00
152 Phil Ortega 1.50 4.00
153 Norm Cash 4.00 10.00
154 Bob Humphreys 1.50 4.00
155 Roger Maris 50.00 100.00
156 Bob Sadowski 1.50 4.00
157 Zoilo Versalles 2.50 6.00
158 Dick Sisler MG 1.50 4.00
159 Jim Duffalo 1.50 4.00
160 Roberto Clemente 125.00 250.00
161 Frank Baumann 1.50 4.00
162 Russ Nixon 1.50 4.00
163 John Briggs 1.50 4.00
164 Al Spangler 1.50 4.00
165 Dick Ellsworth 1.50 4.00
166 George Culver 3.00 8.00
Tommie Agee RC
167 Bill Wakefield 1.50 4.00
168 Dick Green 2.50 6.00
169 Dave Vineyard 1.50 4.00
170 Hank Aaron 100.00 200.00
171 Jim Roland 1.50 4.00
172 Jim Piersall 3.00 8.00
173 Tigers Team 4.00 10.00
174 Joe Jay 1.50 4.00
175 Bob Aspromonte 1.50 4.00
176 Willie McCovey 12.50 30.00
177 Pete Mikkelsen 1.50 4.00
178 Dalton Jones 1.50 4.00
179 Hal Woodeschick 1.50 4.00
180 Bob Allison 2.50 6.00
181 Don Loun 1.50 4.00
Joe McCabe
182 Mike de la Hoz 1.50 4.00
183 Dave Nicholson 1.50 4.00
184 John Boozer 1.50 4.00
185 Max Alvis 1.50 4.00
186 Bill Cowan 1.50 4.00
187 Casey Stengel MG 10.00 25.00
188 Sam Bowens 1.50 4.00
189 Checklist 177-264 4.00 10.00
190 Bill White 3.00 8.00
191 Phil Regan 2.50 6.00
192 Jim Coker 1.50 4.00
193 Gaylord Perry 10.00 25.00
194 Bill Kelso 2.50 6.00
Rick Reichardt
195 Bob Veale 2.50 6.00
196 Ron Fairly 2.50 6.00
197 Diego Segui 1.50 4.00
198 Smoky Burgess 2.50 6.00
199 Bob Heffner 2.50 6.00
200 Joe Torre 4.00 10.00
201 Sandy Valdespino 2.50 6.00
Cesar Tovar RC
202 Leo Burke 2.50 6.00
203 Dallas Green 2.50 6.00
204 Russ Snyder 2.50 6.00
205 Warren Spahn 20.00 50.00
206 Willie Horton 4.00 10.00
207 Pete Rose 125.00 250.00
208 Tommy John 4.00 10.00
209 Pirates Team 4.00 10.00
210 Jim Fregosi 3.00 8.00
211 Steve Ridzik 2.50 6.00
212 Ron Brand 2.50 6.00
213 Jim Davenport 2.50 6.00
214 Bob Purkey 2.50 6.00
215 Pete Ward 2.50 6.00
216 Al Worthington 2.50 6.00
217 Walt Alston MG 4.00 10.00
218 Dick Schofield 2.50 6.00
219 Bob Meyer 2.50 6.00
220 Billy Williams 6.00 15.00
221 John Tsitouris 2.50 6.00
222 Bob Tillman 2.50 6.00
223 Dan Osinski 2.50 6.00
224 Bob Chance 2.50 6.00
225 Bo Belinsky 3.00 8.00
226 Elvio Jimenez 3.00 8.00
Jake Gibbs
227 Bobby Klaus 2.50 6.00
228 Jack Sanford 2.50 6.00
229 Lou Clinton 2.50 6.00
230 Ray Sadecki 2.50 6.00
231 Jerry Adair 2.50 6.00
232 Steve Blass 2.50 6.00
233 Don Zimmer 3.00 8.00
234 White Sox Team 4.00 10.00
235 Chuck Hinton 2.50 6.00
236 Dennis McLain RC 15.00 40.00
237 Bernie Allen 2.50 6.00
238 Joe Moeller 2.50 6.00
239 Doc Edwards 2.50 6.00
240 Bob Bruce 2.50 6.00
241 Mack Jones 2.50 6.00
242 George Brunet 2.50 6.00
243 Ted Davidson 3.00 8.00
Tommy Helms RC
244 Lindy McDaniel 3.00 8.00
245 Joe Pepitone 3.00 8.00
246 Tom Butters 3.00 8.00
247 Wally Moon 3.00 8.00
248 Gus Triandos 2.50 6.00
249 Dave McNally 3.00 8.00
250 Willie Mays 100.00 200.00
251 Billy Herman MG 3.00 8.00
252 Pete Richert 2.50 6.00
253 Danny Cater 2.50 6.00
254 Roland Sheldon 2.50 6.00
255 Camilo Pascual 3.00 8.00
256 Tito Francona 2.50 6.00
257 Jim Wynn 3.00 8.00
258 Larry Bearnarth 2.50 6.00
259 Jim Northrup RC 4.00 10.00
Ray Oyler RC
260 Don Drysdale 12.50 30.00
261 Duke Carmel 2.50 6.00
262 Bud Daley 2.50 6.00
263 Marty Keough 2.50 6.00
264 Bob Buhl 2.50 6.00
265 Jim Pagliaroni 2.50 6.00
266 Bert Campaneris RC 5.00 12.00
267 Senators Team 4.00 10.00
268 Ken McBride 2.50 6.00
269 Frank Bolling 2.50 6.00
270 Milt Pappas 2.50 6.00
271 Don Wert 2.50 6.00
272 Chuck Schilling 2.50 6.00
273 4th Series Checklist 5.00 12.00
274 Lum Harris MG 2.50 6.00
275 Dick Groat 4.00 10.00
276 Hoyt Wilhelm 6.00 15.00
277 Johnny Lewis 2.50 6.00
278 Ken Retzer 2.50 6.00
279 Dick Tracewski 2.50 6.00
280 Dick Stuart 3.00 8.00
281 Bill Stafford 2.50 6.00
282 Dick Estelle 30.00 60.00
Masanori Murakami RC
283 Fred Whitfield 3.00 8.00

1966 O-Pee-Chee

The cards in this 196-card set measure 2 1/2" by 3 1/2". This set is essentially the same as the regular 1966 Topps set, except that the words "Printed in Canada" appear on the bottom of the back, and the background colors are slightly different. On a white border, the fronts feature color player photos. The team name appears within a tilted bar in the top right corner, while the player's name and position are printed inside a bar under the photo. The horizontal backs carry player biography and statistics. The set was issued in five-card nickel packs which came 36 to a box. Remember the prices below apply only to the O-Pee-Chee cards -- NOT to the 1966 Topps cards which are much more plentiful. Notable Rookie Cards include Jim Palmer.

COMPLETE SET (196) 750.00 1500.00
1 Willie Mays 200.00 400.00
2 Ted Abernathy 1.25 3.00
3 Sam Mele MG 1.25 3.00
4 Ray Culp 1.25 3.00
5 Jim Fregosi 1.50 4.00
6 Chuck Schilling 1.25 3.00
7 Tracy Stallard 1.25 3.00
8 Floyd Robinson 1.25 3.00
9 Clete Boyer 1.50 4.00
10 Tony Cloninger 1.25 3.00
11 Brant Alyea 1.50 4.00
Pete Craig
12 John Tsitouris 1.25 3.00
13 Lou Johnson 1.50 4.00
14 Norm Siebern 1.25 3.00
15 Vern Law 1.50 4.00
16 Larry Brown 1.25 3.00
17 John Stephenson 1.25 3.00
18 Roland Sheldon 1.25 3.00
19 Giants Team 2.50 6.00
20 Willie Horton 1.50 4.00
21 Don Nottebart 1.25 3.00
22 Joe Nossek 1.25 3.00
23 Jack Sanford 1.25 3.00
24 Don Kessinger RC 2.50 6.00
25 Pete Ward 1.50 4.00
26 Ray Sadecki 1.25 3.00
27 Darold Knowles 1.25 3.00
Andy Etchebarren
28 Phil Niekro 12.50 30.00
29 Mike Brumley 1.25 3.00
30 Pete Rose 75.00 150.00
31 Jack Cullen 1.50 4.00
32 Adolfo Phillips 1.25 3.00
33 Jim Pagliaroni 1.25 3.00
34 Checklist 1-88 5.00 12.00
35 Ron Swoboda 2.50 6.00
36 Jim Hunter 12.50 30.00
37 Billy Herman MG 1.50 4.00
38 Ron Nischwitz 1.25 3.00
39 Ken Henderson 1.25 3.00
40 Jim Grant 1.25 3.00
41 Don LeJohn 1.25 3.00
42 Aubrey Gatewood 1.25 3.00
43 Don Landrum 1.25 3.00
44 Bill Davis 1.25 3.00
Tom Kelley
45 Jim Gentile 1.50 4.00
46 Howie Koplitz 1.25 3.00
47 J.C. Martin 1.25 3.00
48 Paul Blair 1.50 4.00
49 Woody Woodward 1.50 4.00
50 Mickey Mantle 200.00 400.00
51 Gordon Richardson 1.25 3.00
52 Wes Covington 2.50 6.00
Johnny Callison
53 Bob Duliba 1.25 3.00
54 Jose Pagan 1.25 3.00
55 Ken Harrelson 1.50 4.00
56 Sandy Valdespino 1.25 3.00
57 Jim Lefebvre 1.50 4.00
58 Dave Wickersham 1.25 3.00
59 Reds Team 2.50 6.00
60 Curt Flood 3.00 8.00
61 Bob Bolin 1.25 3.00
62 Merritt Ranew 1.25 3.00
(with sold line)
63 Jim Stewart 1.25 3.00
64 Bob Bruce 1.25 3.00
65 Leon Wagner 1.25 3.00
66 Al Weis 1.25 3.00
67 Cleon Jones 2.50 6.00
Dick Selma
68 Hal Reniff 1.25 3.00
69 Ken Hamlin 1.25 3.00
70 Carl Yastrzemski 20.00 50.00
71 Frank Carpin 1.25 3.00
72 Tony Perez 15.00 40.00
73 Jerry Zimmerman 1.25 3.00
74 Don Mossi 1.50 4.00
75 Tommy Davis 1.50 4.00
76 Red Schoendienst MG 2.50 6.00
77 Johnny Orsino 1.25 3.00
78 Frank Linzy 1.25 3.00
79 Joe Pepitone 2.50 6.00
80 Richie Allen 3.00 8.00
81 Ray Oyler 1.25 3.00
82 Bob Hendley 1.25 3.00
83 Albie Pearson 1.50 4.00
84 Jim Beauchamp 1.25 3.00
Dick Kelley
85 Eddie Fisher 1.25 3.00
86 John Bateman 1.25 3.00
87 Dan Napoleon 1.25 3.00
88 Fred Whitfield 1.25 3.00
89 Ted Davidson 1.25 3.00
90 Luis Aparicio 5.00 12.00
91 Bob Uecker 6.00 15.00
(with traded line)
92 Yankees Team 10.00 25.00
93 Jim Lonborg 1.50 4.00
94 Matty Alou 1.50 4.00
95 Pete Richert 1.25 3.00
96 Felipe Alou 2.50 6.00
97 Jim Merritt 1.25 3.00
98 Don Demeter 1.25 3.00
99 Willie Stargell 3.00 8.00
Donn Clendenon
100 Sandy Koufax 75.00 150.00
101 Checklist 89-176 5.00 12.00
102 Ed Kirkpatrick 1.25 3.00
103 Dick Groat 1.50 4.00
(with traded line)
104 Alex Johnson 1.50 4.00
(with traded line)
105 Milt Pappas 1.50 4.00
106 Rusty Staub 2.50 6.00
107 Larry Stahl 1.25 3.00
Ron Tompkins
108 Bobby Klaus 1.25 3.00
109 Ralph Terry 1.50 4.00
110 Ernie Banks 20.00 50.00
111 Gary Peters 1.25 3.00
112 Manny Mota 1.50 4.00
113 Hank Aguirre 1.25 3.00
114 Jim Gosger 1.25 3.00
115 Bill Henry 1.25 3.00
116 Walt Alston MG 2.50 6.00
117 Jake Gibbs 1.25 3.00
118 Mike McCormick 1.25 3.00
119 Art Shamsky 1.25 3.00
120 Harmon Killebrew 10.00 25.00
121 Ray Herbert 1.25 3.00
122 Joe Gaines 1.25 3.00
123 Frank Bork 1.25 3.00
Jerry May
124 Tug McGraw 2.50 6.00
125 Lou Brock 12.50 30.00
126 Jim Palmer RC 75.00 150.00
127 Ken Berry 1.25 3.00
128 Jim Landis 1.25 3.00
129 Jack Kralick 1.25 3.00
130 Joe Torre 3.00 8.00
131 Angels Team 3.00 8.00
132 Orlando Cepeda 5.00 12.00
133 Don McMahon 1.25 3.00
134 Wes Parker 1.50 4.00
135 Dave Morehead 1.25 3.00
136 Woody Held 1.25 3.00
137 Pat Corrales 1.25 3.00
138 Roger Repoz 1.25 3.00
139 Byron Browne 1.25 3.00
Don Young
140 Jim Maloney 1.50 4.00
141 Tom McCraw 1.25 3.00
142 Don Dennis 1.25 3.00
143 Jose Tartabull 1.50 4.00
144 Don Schwall 1.25 3.00
145 Bill Freehan 1.50 4.00
146 George Altman 1.25 3.00
147 Lum Harris MG 1.25 3.00
148 Bob Johnson 1.25 3.00
149 Dick Nen 1.25 3.00
150 Rocky Colavito 5.00 12.00
151 Gary Wagner 1.25 3.00
152 Frank Malzone 1.50 4.00
153 Rico Carty 1.50 4.00
154 Chuck Hiller 1.25 3.00
155 Marcelino Lopez 1.25 3.00
156 Dick Schofield 1.25 3.00
Hal Lanier
157 Rene Lachemann 1.50 4.00
158 Jim Brewer 1.25 3.00
159 Chico Ruiz 1.25 3.00
160 Whitey Ford 20.00 50.00
161 Jerry Lumpe 1.25 3.00
162 Lee Maye 1.25 3.00
163 Tito Francona 1.25 3.00
164 Tommie Agee 1.50 4.00
Marv Staehle
165 Don Lock 1.25 3.00
166 Chris Krug 1.25 3.00
167 Boog Powell 3.00 8.00
168 Dan Osinski 1.25 3.00
169 Duke Sims 1.25 3.00
170 Cookie Rojas 1.50 4.00
171 Nick Willhite 1.25 3.00
172 Mets Team 3.00 8.00
173 Al Spangler 1.25 3.00
174 Ron Taylor 1.50 4.00
175 Bert Campaneris 2.50 6.00
176 Jim Davenport 1.25 3.00
177 Hector Lopez 1.25 3.00
178 Bob Tillman 1.25 3.00
179 Dennis Aust 1.50 4.00
Bob Tolan
180 Vada Pinson 2.50 6.00
181 Al Worthington 1.25 3.00
182 Jerry Lynch 1.25 3.00
183 Checklist 177-264 5.00 12.00
184 Denis Menke 1.25 3.00
185 Bob Buhl 1.50 4.00
186 Ruben Amaro 1.25 3.00
187 Chuck Dressen MG 1.50 4.00
188 Al Luplow 1.25 3.00
189 John Roseboro 1.50 4.00
190 Jimmie Hall 1.25 3.00
191 Darrell Sutherland 1.25 3.00
192 Vic Power 1.50 4.00
193 Dave McNally 1.50 4.00
194 Senators Team 3.00 8.00
195 Joe Morgan 10.00 25.00
196 Don Pavletich 1.50 4.00

1967 O-Pee-Chee

The cards in this 196-card set measure 2 1/2" by 3 1/2". This set is essentially the same as the regular 1967 Topps set, except that the words "Printed in Canada" appear on the bottom right corner of the back. On a white border, fronts feature color player photos with a thin black border. The player's name and position appear in the top part, while the team name is printed in big letters in the bottom part of the photo. On a green background, the backs carry player biography and statistics and two cartoon-like facts. Each checklist card features a small circular picture of a popular player included in that series. The set was issued in five card nickel packs which came 36 packs to a box. Remember the prices below apply only to the O-Pee-Chee cards -- NOT to the 1967 Topps cards which are much more plentiful.

COMPLETE SET (196) 600.00 1200.00
1 Frank Robinson 12.50 30.00
Hank Bauer MG
Brooks Robinson
2 Jack Hamilton 1.25 3.00
3 Duke Sims 1.25 3.00
4 Hal Lanier 1.25 3.00
5 Whitey Ford 10.00 25.00
6 Dick Simpson 1.25 3.00
7 Don McMahon 1.25 3.00
8 Chuck Harrison 1.25 3.00
9 Ron Hansen 1.25 3.00
10 Matty Alou 1.50 4.00
11 Barry Moore 1.25 3.00
12 Jim Campanis 1.50 4.00
Bill Singer
13 Joe Sparma 1.25 3.00
14 Phil Linz 1.50 4.00
15 Earl Battey 1.25 3.00
16 Bill Hands 1.25 3.00
17 Jim Gosger 1.25 3.00
18 Gene Oliver 1.25 3.00
19 Jim McGlothlin 1.25 3.00
20 Orlando Cepeda 4.00 10.00
21 Dave Bristol MG 1.25 3.00
22 Gene Brabender 1.25 3.00
23 Larry Elliot 1.25 3.00
24 Bob Allen 1.25 3.00
25 Elston Howard 2.50 6.00
26 Bob Priddy 1.25 3.00
(with traded line)
27 Bob Saverine 1.25 3.00
28 Barry Latman 1.25 3.00
29 Tommy McCraw 1.25 3.00
30 Al Kaline 10.00 25.00
31 Jim Brewer 1.25 3.00
32 Bob Bailey 1.50 4.00
33 Sal Bando RC 3.00 8.00
Randy Schwartz
34 Pete Cimino 1.25 3.00
35 Rico Carty 1.50 4.00
36 Bob Tillman 1.25 3.00
37 Rick Wise 1.50 4.00
38 Bob Johnson 1.25 3.00
39 Curt Simmons 1.50 4.00
40 Rick Reichardt 1.25 3.00
41 Joe Hoerner 1.25 3.00
42 Mets Team 5.00 12.00
43 Chico Salmon 1.25 3.00
44 Joe Nuxhall 1.50 4.00
45 Roger Maris 30.00 60.00
46 Lindy McDaniel 1.50 4.00
47 Ken McMullen 1.25 3.00
48 Bill Freehan 1.50 4.00
49 Roy Face 1.50 4.00
50 Tony Oliva 3.00 8.00
51 Dave Adlesh 1.25 3.00
Wes Bales
52 Dennis Higgins 1.25 3.00
53 Clay Dalrymple 1.25 3.00
54 Dick Green 1.25 3.00
55 Don Drysdale 8.00 20.00
56 Jose Tartabull 1.50 4.00
57 Pat Jarvis 1.50 4.00
58 Paul Schaal 1.25 3.00
59 Ralph Terry 1.50 4.00
60 Luis Aparicio 4.00 10.00
61 Gordy Coleman 1.25 3.00
62 Frank Robinson CL 5.00 12.00
63 Lou Brock 3.00 8.00
Curt Flood
64 Fred Valentine 1.25 3.00
65 Tom Haller 1.50 4.00
66 Manny Mota 1.50 4.00
67 Ken Berry 1.25 3.00
68 Bob Buhl 1.50 4.00
69 Vic Davalillo 1.25 3.00
70 Ron Santo 3.00 8.00
71 Camilo Pascual 1.50 4.00
72 George Korince 1.50 4.00
(photo actually
John Brown)
John (Tom) Matchick
73 Rusty Staub 3.00 8.00
74 Wes Stock 1.25 3.00
75 George Scott 1.50 4.00
76 Jim Barbieri 1.25 3.00
77 Dooley Womack 1.25 3.00
78 Pat Corrales 1.25 3.00
79 Bubba Morton 1.25 3.00
80 Jim Maloney 1.50 4.00
81 Eddie Stanky MG 1.50 4.00
82 Steve Barber 1.25 3.00
83 Ollie Brown 1.25 3.00
84 Tommie Sisk 1.25 3.00
85 Johnny Callison 1.50 4.00
86 Mike McCormick 1.50 4.00
(with traded line)
87 George Altman 1.25 3.00
88 Mickey Lolich 2.50 6.00
89 Felix Millan 1.50 4.00
90 Jim Nash 1.25 3.00
91 Johnny Lewis 1.25 3.00
92 Ray Washburn 1.25 3.00
93 Stan Bahnsen RC 2.50 6.00
Bobby Murcer
94 Ron Fairly 1.50 4.00
95 Sonny Siebert 1.25 3.00
96 Art Shamsky 1.25 3.00
97 Mike Cuellar 2.50 6.00
98 Rich Rollins 1.25 3.00
99 Lee Stange 1.25 3.00
100 Frank Robinson 8.00 20.00
101 Ken Johnson 1.25 3.00
102 Phillies Team 2.50 6.00
103 Mickey Mantle CL 10.00 25.00
104 Minnie Rojas 1.25 3.00
105 Ken Boyer 3.00 8.00
106 Randy Hundley 1.50 4.00
107 Joel Horlen 1.25 3.00
108 Alex Johnson 1.50 4.00
109 Rocky Colavito 3.00 8.00
Leon Wagner
110 Jack Aker 1.25 3.00
111 John Kennedy 1.25 3.00
112 Dave Wickersham 1.25 3.00
113 Dave Nicholson 1.25 3.00
114 Jack Baldschun 1.25 3.00
115 Paul Casanova 1.25 3.00
116 Herman Franks MG 1.25 3.00
117 Darrell Brandon 1.25 3.00
118 Bernie Allen 1.25 3.00
119 Wade Blasingame 1.25 3.00
120 Floyd Robinson 1.25 3.00
121 Ed Bressoud 1.25 3.00
122 George Brunet 1.25 3.00
123 Jim Price 1.50 4.00
Luke Walker
124 Jim Stewart 1.25 3.00
125 Moe Drabowsky 1.50 4.00
126 Tony Taylor 1.25 3.00
127 John O'Donoghue 1.25 3.00
128 Ed Spiezio 1.25 3.00
129 Phil Roof 1.25 3.00
130 Phil Regan 1.50 4.00
131 Yankees Team 5.00 12.00
132 Ozzie Virgil 1.25 3.00
133 Ron Kline 1.25 3.00
134 Gates Brown 1.25 3.00
135 Deron Johnson 1.50 4.00
136 Carroll Sembera 1.25 3.00
137 Ron Clark 1.25 3.00
Jim Ollom
138 Dick Kelley 1.25 3.00
139 Dalton Jones 1.25 3.00
140 Willie Stargell 10.00 25.00
141 John Miller 1.25 3.00
142 Jackie Brandt 1.25 3.00
143 Pete Ward 2.50 6.00
Don Buford
144 Bill Hepler 1.25 3.00
145 Larry Brown 1.25 3.00
146 Steve Carlton 30.00 60.00
147 Tom Egan 1.25 3.00
148 Adolfo Phillips 1.25 3.00
149 Joe Moeller 1.25 3.00
150 Mickey Mantle 200.00 400.00
151 Moe Drabowsky WS 2.50 6.00
152 Jim Palmer WS 4.00 10.00
153 Paul Blair WS 2.50 6.00
154 Brooks Robinson WS 2.50 6.00
Dave McNally
155 W.S. Summary 2.50 6.00
Winners celebrate
156 Ron Herbel 1.25 3.00
157 Danny Cater 1.25 3.00
158 Jimmie Coker 1.25 3.00
159 Bruce Howard 1.25 3.00
160 Willie Davis 1.50 4.00
161 Dick Williams MG 1.50 4.00
162 Billy O'Dell 1.25 3.00
163 Vic Roznovsky 1.25 3.00
164 Dwight Siebler 1.25 3.00
165 Cleon Jones 1.50 4.00
166 Eddie Mathews 8.00 20.00
167 Joe Coleman 1.25 3.00
Tim Cullen
168 Ray Culp 1.25 3.00
169 Horace Clarke 1.25 3.00
170 Dick McAuliffe 1.50 4.00
171 Calvin Koonce 1.25 3.00
172 Bill Heath 1.25 3.00
173 Cardinals Team 2.50 6.00
174 Dick Radatz 1.50 4.00
175 Bobby Knoop 1.25 3.00
176 Sammy Ellis 1.25 3.00
177 Tito Fuentes 1.25 3.00
178 John Buzhardt 1.25 3.00
179 Charles Vaughan 1.50 4.00
Cecil Upshaw
180 Curt Blefary 1.25 3.00
181 Terry Fox 1.25 3.00
182 Ed Charles 1.25 3.00
183 Jim Pagliaroni 1.25 3.00
184 George Thomas 1.25 3.00
185 Ken Holtzman RC 2.50 6.00
186 Ed Kranepool 2.50 6.00
Ron Swoboda
187 Pedro Ramos 1.25 3.00
188 Ken Harrelson 1.50 4.00
189 Chuck Hinton 1.25 3.00
190 Turk Farrell 1.25 3.00
191 Willie Mays CL 6.00 15.00
192 Fred Gladding 1.25 3.00
193 Jose Cardenal 1.50 4.00
194 Bob Allison 1.50 4.00
195 Al Jackson 1.25 3.00
196 Johnny Romano 1.50 4.00

1968 O-Pee-Chee

The cards in this 196-card set measure 2 1/2" by 3 1/2". This set is essentially the same as the regular 1968 Topps set, except that the words "Printed in Canada" appear on the bottom of the back and the backgrounds have a different color. The fronts feature color player photos with rounded corners. The player's name is printed under the photo, while his position and team name appear in a circle in the lower right. On a light brown background, the backs carry player biography and statistics and a cartoon-like trivia question. Each checklist card features a small circular picture of a popular player included in that series. Remember the prices below apply only to the O-Pee-Chee cards -- NOT to the 1968 Topps cards which are much more plentiful. The key card in the set is Nolan Ryan in his Rookie Card year. The first OPC cards of Hall of Famers Rod Carew and Tom Seaver also appear in this set.

COMPLETE SET (196) 1000.00 2000.00
1 Bob Clemente 15.00 40.00
Tony Gonzalez
Matty Alou LL
2 Carl Yastrzemski 8.00 20.00
Frank Robinson
Al Kaline LL
3 Orlando Cepeda 10.00 25.00
Bob Clemente
Hank Aaron LL
4 Carl Yastrzemski 8.00 20.00
Harmon Killebrew
Frank Robinson LL
5 Hank Aaron 4.00 10.00
Jim Wynn
Ron Santo
Willie McCovey LL
6 Carl Yastrzemski 4.00 10.00
Harmon Killebrew
Frank Howard LL
7 Phil Niekro 2.50 6.00
Jim Bunning
Chris Short LL
8 Joel Horlen 2.50 6.00
Gary Peters
Sonny Siebert LL
9 Mike McCormick 2.50 6.00
Ferguson Jenkins
Jim Bunning
Claude Osteen LL
10 Jim Lonborg 2.50 6.00
Earl Wilson
Dean Chance LL
11 Jim Bunning 3.00 8.00
Ferguson Jenkins
Gaylord Perry LL
12 Jim Lonborg 2.50 6.00
Sam McDowell
Dean Chance LL
13 Chuck Hartenstein 1.25 3.00
14 Jerry McNertney 1.25 3.00
15 Ron Hunt 1.25 3.00
16 Lou Piniella 3.00 8.00
Richie Scheinblum
17 Dick Hall 1.25 3.00
18 Mike Hershberger 1.25 3.00
19 Juan Pizarro 1.25 3.00
20 Brooks Robinson 12.50 30.00
21 Ron Davis 1.25 3.00
22 Pat Dobson 1.50 4.00
23 Chico Cardenas 1.50 4.00
24 Bobby Locke 1.25 3.00
25 Julian Javier 1.50 4.00
26 Darrell Brandon 1.25 3.00
27 Gil Hodges MG 4.00 10.00
28 Ted Uhlaender 1.25 3.00
29 Joe Verbanic 1.25 3.00
30 Joe Torre 3.00 8.00
31 Ed Stroud 1.25 3.00
32 Joe Gibbon 1.25 3.00
33 Pete Ward 1.50 4.00
34 Al Ferrara 1.25 3.00
35 Steve Hargan 1.25 3.00
36 Bob Moose 1.50 4.00
Bob Robertson
37 Billy Williams 4.00 10.00
38 Tony Pierce 1.25 3.00
39 Cookie Rojas 1.25 3.00
40 Denny McLain 4.00 10.00
41 Julio Gotay 1.25 3.00
42 Larry Haney 1.25 3.00
43 Gary Bell 1.25 3.00
44 Frank Kostro 1.25 3.00
45 Tom Seaver 30.00 60.00
46 Dave Ricketts 1.25 3.00
47 Ralph Houk MG 1.50 4.00
48 Ted Davidson 1.25 3.00
49 Ed Brinkman 1.25 3.00
50 Willie Mays 40.00 80.00
51 Bob Locker 1.25 3.00
52 Hawk Taylor 1.25 3.00
53 Gene Alley 1.50 4.00
54 Stan Williams 1.25 3.00
55 Felipe Alou 2.50 6.00
56 Dave Leonhard 1.25 3.00
Dave May RC
57 Dan Schneider 1.25 3.00
58 Ed Mathews 8.00 20.00
59 Don Lock 1.25 3.00
60 Ken Holtzman 1.50 4.00
61 Reggie Smith 2.50 6.00
62 Chuck Dobson 1.25 3.00
63 Dick Kenworthy 1.25 3.00
64 Jim Merritt 1.25 3.00
65 John Roseboro 1.50 4.00
66 Casey Cox 1.25 3.00
67 Jim Kaat CL 3.00 8.00
68 Ron Willis 1.25 3.00
69 Tom Tresh 1.50 4.00
70 Bob Veale 1.50 4.00
71 Vern Fuller 1.25 3.00
72 Tommy John 3.00 8.00
73 Jim Ray Hart 1.50 4.00
74 Milt Pappas 1.50 4.00
75 Don Mincher 1.25 3.00
76 Jim Britton 1.50 4.00
Ron Reed
77 Don Wilson 1.50 4.00
78 Jim Northrup 3.00 8.00
79 Ted Kubiak 1.25 3.00
80 Rod Carew 30.00 60.00
81 Larry Jackson 1.25 3.00
82 Sam Bowens 1.25 3.00
83 John Stephenson 1.25 3.00
84 Bob Tolan 1.25 3.00
85 Gaylord Perry 4.00 10.00
86 Willie Stargell 4.00 10.00
87 Dick Williams MG 1.50 4.00
88 Phil Regan 1.50 4.00
89 Jake Gibbs 1.50 4.00
90 Vada Pinson 2.50 6.00
91 Jim Ollom 1.25 3.00
92 Ed Kranepool 1.50 4.00
93 Tony Cloninger 1.25 3.00
94 Lee Maye 1.25 3.00
95 Bob Aspromonte 1.25 3.00
96 Frank Coggins 1.25 3.00
Dick Nold
97 Tom Phoebus 1.25 3.00
98 Gary Sutherland 1.25 3.00
99 Rocky Colavito 4.00 10.00
100 Bob Gibson 12.50 30.00
101 Glenn Beckert 1.50 4.00
102 Jose Cardenal 1.50 4.00
103 Don Sutton 4.00 10.00
104 Dick Dietz 1.25 3.00
105 Al Downing 1.50 4.00
106 Dalton Jones 1.25 3.00
107 Juan Marichal CL 3.00 8.00
108 Don Pavletich 1.25 3.00
109 Bert Campaneris 1.50 4.00
110 Hank Aaron 40.00 80.00
111 Rich Reese 1.25 3.00
112 Woody Fryman 1.25 3.00
113 Tom Matchick 1.50 4.00
Daryl Patterson
114 Ron Swoboda 1.50 4.00
115 Sam McDowell 1.50 4.00
116 Ken McMullen 1.25 3.00
117 Larry Jaster 1.25 3.00
118 Mark Belanger 1.50 4.00
119 Ted Savage 1.25 3.00
120 Mel Stottlemyre 2.50 6.00
121 Jimmie Hall 1.25 3.00
122 Gene Mauch MG 1.50 4.00
123 Jose Santiago 1.25 3.00
124 Nate Oliver 1.25 3.00
125 Joel Horlen 1.25 3.00
126 Bobby Etheridge 1.25 3.00
127 Paul Lindblad 1.25 3.00
128 Tom Dukes 1.25 3.00
Alonzo Harris
129 Mickey Stanley 3.00 8.00
130 Tony Perez 4.00 10.00
131 Frank Bertaina 1.25 3.00
132 Bud Harrelson 1.50 4.00
133 Fred Whitfield 1.25 3.00
134 Pat Jarvis 1.25 3.00
135 Paul Blair 1.50 4.00
136 Randy Hundley 1.50 4.00
137 Twins Team 2.50 6.00
138 Ruben Amaro 1.25 3.00
139 Chris Short 1.25 3.00
140 Tony Conigliaro 4.00 10.00
141 Dal Maxvill 1.25 3.00
142 Buddy Bradford 1.25 3.00
Bill Voss
143 Pete Cimino 1.25 3.00
144 Joe Morgan 6.00 15.00
145 Don Drysdale 6.00 15.00
146 Sal Bando 1.50 4.00
147 Frank Linzy 1.25 3.00
148 Dave Bristol MG 1.25 3.00
149 Bob Saverine 1.25 3.00
150 Bob Clemente 50.00 100.00
151 Lou Brock WS 5.00 12.00
152 Carl Yastrzemski WS 5.00 12.00
153 Nellie Briles WS 2.50 6.00
154 Bob Gibson WS 5.00 12.00
155 Jim Lonborg WS 2.50 6.00
156 Rico Petrocelli WS 2.50 6.00
157 World Series Game 7 2.50 6.00
St. Louis wins it
158 WS Summary 2.50 6.00
Cardinals celebrate
159 Don Kessinger 1.50 4.00
160 Earl Wilson 1.50 4.00
161 Norm Miller 1.25 3.00
162 Hal Gilson 1.50 4.00
Mike Torrez
163 Gene Brabender 1.25 3.00
164 Ramon Webster 1.25 3.00
165 Tony Oliva 3.00 8.00
166 Claude Raymond 1.50 4.00
167 Elston Howard 3.00 8.00
168 Dodgers Team 2.50 6.00
169 Bob Bolin 1.25 3.00
170 Jim Fregosi 1.50 4.00
171 Don Nottebart 1.25 3.00
172 Walt Williams 1.25 3.00
173 John Boozer 1.25 3.00
174 Bob Tillman 1.25 3.00
175 Maury Wills 3.00 8.00
176 Bob Allen 1.25 3.00
177 Jerry Koosman RC 300.00 600.00
Nolan Ryan RC
178 Don Wert 1.50 4.00
179 Bill Stoneman 1.25 3.00
180 Curt Flood 2.50 6.00
181 Jerry Zimmerman 1.25 3.00
182 Dave Giusti 1.25 3.00
183 Bob Kennedy MG 1.50 4.00
184 Lou Johnson 1.25 3.00
185 Tom Haller 1.25 3.00
186 Eddie Watt 1.25 3.00
187 Sonny Jackson 1.25 3.00
188 Cap Peterson 1.25 3.00
189 Bill Landis 1.25 3.00
190 Bill White 1.50 4.00
191 Dan Frisella 1.25 3.00
192 Carl Yastrzemski CL 4.00 10.00
193 Jack Hamilton 1.25 3.00
194 Don Buford 1.25 3.00
195 Joe Pepitone 1.50 4.00
196 Gary Nolan 1.50 4.00

1969 O-Pee-Chee

The cards in this 218-card set measure 2 1/2" by 3 1/2". This set is essentially the same as the regular 1969 Topps set, except that the words "Printed in Canada" appear on the bottom of the back and the backgrounds have a purple color. The fronts feature color player photos with rounded corners and thin black borders. The player's name and position are printed inside a circle in the top right corner, while the team name appears in the lower part of the photo. On a magenta background, the backs carry player biography and statistics. Each checklist card features a small circular picture of a popular player included in that series. Remember the prices below apply only to the O-Pee-Chee cards -- NOT to the 1969 Topps cards which are much more plentiful. Notable Rookie Cards include Graig Nettles.

COMPLETE SET (218) 500.00 1000.00
1 Carl Yastrzemski 8.00 20.00
Danny Cater
Tony Oliva LL
2 Pete Rose 4.00 10.00
Matty Alou
Felipe Alou LL
3 Ken Harrelson 2.50 6.00
Frank Howard
Jim Northrup LL
4 Willie McCovey 3.00 8.00
Ron Santo
Billy Williams LL
5 Frank Howard 2.50 6.00
Willie Horton
Ken Harrelson LL
6 Willie McCovey 3.00 8.00
Richie Allen
Ernie Banks LL
7 Luis Tiant 2.50 6.00
Sam McDowell
Dave McNally LL
8 Bob Gibson 3.00 8.00
Bobby Bolin
Bob Veale LL
9 Denny McLain 2.50 6.00
Dave McNally
Luis Tiant
Mel Stottlemyre LL
10 Juan Marichal 4.00 10.00
Bob Gibson
Fergie Jenkins LL
11 Sam McDowell 3.00 8.00
Denny McLain
Luis Tiant LL
12 Bob Gibson 2.50 6.00
Fergie Jenkins
Bill Singer LL
13 Mickey Stanley 1.50 4.00
14 Al McBean .75 2.00
15 Boog Powell 2.50 6.00
16 Cesar Gutierrez .75 2.00
Rich Robertson
17 Mike Marshall 1.50 4.00
18 Dick Schofield .75 2.00
19 Ken Suarez .75 2.00
20 Ernie Banks 10.00 25.00
21 Jose Santiago .75 2.00
22 Jesus Alou 1.50 4.00
23 Lew Krausse .75 2.00
24 Walt Alston MG 2.50 6.00
25 Roy White 1.50 4.00
26 Clay Carroll 1.50 4.00
27 Bernie Allen .75 2.00
28 Mike Ryan .75 2.00
29 Dave Morehead .75 2.00
30 Bob Allison 1.50 4.00
31 Gary Gentry RC 2.50 6.00
Amos Otis RC
32 Sammy Ellis .75 2.00
33 Wayne Causey .75 2.00
34 Gary Peters .75 2.00
35 Joe Morgan 5.00 12.00
36 Luke Walker .75 2.00
37 Curt Motton .75 2.00
38 Zoilo Versalles 1.50 4.00
39 Dick Hughes .75 2.00
40 Mayo Smith MG .75 2.00
41 Bob Barton .75 2.00
42 Tommy Harper 1.50 4.00
43 Joe Niekro 1.50 4.00
44 Danny Cater .75 2.00
45 Maury Wills 2.50 6.00
46 Fritz Peterson 1.50 4.00
47 Paul Popovich .75 2.00
48 Brant Alyea .75 2.00
49 Steve Jones .75 2.00
Ellie Rodriguez
50 Roberto Clemente 40.00 80.00
(Bob on card)
51 Woody Fryman 1.50 4.00
52 Mike Andrews .75 2.00
53 Sonny Jackson .75 2.00
54 Cisco Carlos .75 2.00
55 Jerry Grote 1.50 4.00
56 Rich Reese .75 2.00
57 Denny McLain CL 3.00 8.00
58 Fred Gladding .75 2.00
59 Jay Johnstone 1.50 4.00
60 Nelson Briles 1.50 4.00
61 Jimmie Hall .75 2.00
62 Chico Salmon .75 2.00
63 Jim Hickman .75 2.00
64 Bill Monbouquette .75 2.00
65 Willie Davis 1.50 4.00
66 Mike Adamson .75 2.00
Merv Rettenmund
67 Bill Stoneman 1.50 4.00
68 Dave Duncan 1.50 4.00
69 Steve Hamilton 1.50 4.00
70 Tommy Helms 1.50 4.00
71 Steve Whitaker 1.50 4.00
72 Ron Taylor 1.50 4.00
73 Johnny Briggs .75 2.00
74 Preston Gomez MG .75 2.00
75 Luis Aparicio 3.00 8.00
76 Norm Miller .75 2.00
77 Ron Perranoski 1.50 4.00
78 Tom Satriano .75 2.00
79 Milt Pappas 1.50 4.00
80 Norm Cash 1.50 4.00
81 Mel Queen .75 2.00
82 Rich Hebner RC 4.00 10.00
Al Oliver RC
83 Mike Ferraro 1.50 4.00
84 Bob Humphreys .75 2.00
85 Lou Brock 10.00 25.00
86 Pete Richert .75 2.00
87 Horace Clarke 1.50 4.00
88 Rich Nye .75 2.00
89 Russ Gibson .75 2.00
90 Jerry Koosman 2.50 6.00
91 Al Dark MG 1.50 4.00
92 Jack Billingham 1.50 4.00
93 Joe Foy .75 2.00
94 Hank Aguirre .75 2.00
95 Johnny Bench 30.00 60.00
96 Denver LeMaster .75 2.00
97 Buddy Bradford .75 2.00
98 Dave Giusti .75 2.00
99 Danny Morris 8.00 20.00
Graig Nettles RC
100 Hank Aaron 30.00 60.00
101 Daryl Patterson .75 2.00
102 Jim Davenport .75 2.00
103 Roger Repoz .75 2.00
104 Steve Blass .75 2.00
105 Rick Monday 1.50 4.00
106 Jim Hannan .75 2.00
107 Bob Gibson CL 3.00 8.00
108 Tony Taylor 1.50 4.00
109 Jim Lonborg 1.50 4.00
110 Mike Shannon 1.50 4.00
111 John Morris .75 2.00
112 J.C. Martin 1.50 4.00
113 Dave May .75 2.00
114 Alan Closter 1.50 4.00
John Cumberland
115 Bill Hands .75 2.00
116 Chuck Harrison .75 2.00
117 Jim Fairey 1.50 4.00
118 Stan Williams .75 2.00
119 Doug Rader 1.50 4.00
120 Pete Rose 30.00 60.00
121 Joe Grzenda .75 2.00
122 Ron Fairly 1.50 4.00
123 Wilbur Wood 1.50 4.00
124 Hank Bauer MG 1.50 4.00
125 Ray Sadecki .75 2.00
126 Dick Tracewski .75 2.00
127 Kevin Collins 1.50 4.00
128 Tommie Aaron 1.50 4.00
129 Bill McCool .75 2.00
130 Carl Yastrzemski 10.00 25.00
131 Chris Cannizzaro .75 2.00
132 Dave Baldwin .75 2.00
133 Johnny Callison 1.50 4.00
134 Jim Weaver .75 2.00
135 Tommy Davis 1.50 4.00
136 Steve Huntz .75 2.00
Mike Torrez
137 Wally Bunker .75 2.00
138 John Bateman .75 2.00
139 Andy Kosco .75 2.00
140 Jim Lefebvre 1.50 4.00
141 Bill Dillman .75 2.00
142 Woody Woodward .75 2.00
143 Joe Nossek .75 2.00
144 Bob Hendley .75 2.00
145 Max Alvis .75 2.00
146 Jim Perry 1.50 4.00
147 Leo Durocher MG 2.50 6.00
148 Lee Stange .75 2.00
149 Ollie Brown .75 2.00
150 Denny McLain 2.50 6.00
151 Clay Dalrymple 1.50 4.00
(Catching, Phillies)
152 Tommie Sisk .75 2.00
153 Ed Brinkman .75 2.00
154 Jim Britton .75 2.00
155 Pete Ward 1.50 4.00
156 Hal Gilson .75 2.00
Leon McFadden
157 Bob Rodgers 1.50 4.00
158 Joe Gibbon .75 2.00
159 Jerry Adair .75 2.00
160 Vada Pinson 2.50 6.00
161 John Purdin .75 2.00
162 Bob Gibson WS 4.00 10.00
fans 17
163 Willie Horton WS 3.00 8.00
164 Tim McCarver WS 6.00 15.00
with Roger Maris
165 Lou Brock WS 4.00 10.00
166 Al Kaline WS 4.00 10.00
167 Jim Northrup WS 3.00 8.00
168 Mickey Lolich WS 4.00 10.00
Bob Gibson
169 Tigers celebrate 3.00 8.00
Dick McAuliffe
Denny McLain
Willie Horton
170 Frank Howard 1.50 4.00
171 Glenn Beckert 1.50 4.00
172 Jerry Stephenson .75 2.00
173 Bob Christian .75 2.00
Gerry Nyman
174 Grant Jackson .75 2.00
175 Jim Bunning 3.00 8.00
176 Joe Azcue .75 2.00
177 Ron Reed .75 2.00
178 Ray Oyler 1.50 4.00
179 Don Pavletich .75 2.00
180 Willie Horton 1.50 4.00
181 Mel Nelson .75 2.00
182 Bill Rigney MG .75 2.00
183 Don Shaw 1.50 4.00
184 Roberto Pena .75 2.00
185 Tom Phoebus .75 2.00
186 John Edwards .75 2.00
187 Leon Wagner .75 2.00
188 Rick Wise 1.50 4.00
189 Joe Lahoud .75 2.00
John Thibodeau
190 Willie Mays 50.00 100.00
191 Lindy McDaniel 1.50 4.00
192 Jose Pagan .75 2.00
193 Don Cardwell 1.50 4.00
194 Ted Uhlaender .75 2.00
195 John Odom .75 2.00
196 Lum Harris MG .75 2.00
197 Dick Selma .75 2.00
198 Willie Smith .75 2.00
199 Jim French .75 2.00
200 Bob Gibson 6.00 15.00
201 Russ Snyder .75 2.00
202 Don Wilson 1.50 4.00
203 Dave Johnson 1.50 4.00
204 Jack Hiatt .75 2.00
205 Rick Reichardt .75 2.00
206 Larry Hisle 1.50 4.00
Barry Lersch
207 Roy Face 1.50 4.00
208 Donn Clendenon 1.50 4.00
(Montreal Expos)
209 Larry Haney UER .75 2.00
(Reversed negative)
210 Felix Millan .75 2.00
211 Galen Cisco .75 2.00
212 Tom Tresh 1.50 4.00
213 Gerry Arrigo .75 2.00
214 Checklist 3 3.00 8.00
With 69T deckle CL
on back (no player)
215 Rico Petrocelli 1.50 4.00
216 Don Sutton 3.00 8.00
217 John Donaldson .75 2.00
218 John Roseboro 1.50 4.00

1970 O-Pee-Chee

The cards in this 546-card set measure 2 1/2" by 3 1/2". This set is essentially the same as the regular 1970 Topps set, except that the words "Printed in Canada" appear on the backs and the backs are bilingual. On a gray border, the fronts feature color player photos with thin white borders. The player's name and position are printed under the photo, while the team name appears in the upper part of the picture. The horizontal backs carry player biography and statistics in French and English. The card stock is a deeper shade of yellow on the reverse for the O-Pee-Chee cards. The set was issued in eight-card dime packs which came 36 packs to a box. Remember the prices below apply only to the O-Pee-Chee cards -- NOT to the 1970 Topps cards which are much more plentiful. Notable Rookie Cards include Thurman Munson.

COMPLETE SET (546) 750.00 1500.00
COMMON CARD (1-459) .60 1.50
COMMON (460-546) 1.00 2.50
1 New York Mets 12.50 40.00
Team Card
2 Diego Segui .75 2.00
3 Darrel Chaney .60 1.50
4 Tom Egan .60 1.50
5 Wes Parker .75 2.00
6 Grant Jackson .60 1.50
7 Gary Boyd .60 1.50
Russ Nagelson
8 Jose Martinez .60 1.50
9 Checklist 1-132 6.00 15.00
10 Carl Yastrzemski 10.00 25.00
11 Nate Colbert .60 1.50
12 John Hiller .75 2.00
13 Jack Hiatt .60 1.50
14 Hank Allen .60 1.50
15 Larry Dierker .60 1.50
16 Charlie Metro MG .60 1.50
17 Hoyt Wilhelm 2.50 6.00
18 Carlos May .75 2.00
19 John Boccabella .60 1.50
20 Dave McNally .75 2.00
21 Vida Blue RC 2.50 6.00
Gene Tenace RC
22 Ray Washburn .60 1.50
23 Bill Robinson .75 2.00
24 Dick Selma .60 1.50
25 Cesar Tovar .60 1.50
26 Tug McGraw 1.50 4.00
27 Chuck Hinton .60 1.50
28 Billy Wilson .60 1.50
29 Sandy Alomar .75 2.00
30 Matty Alou .75 2.00
31 Marty Pattin .75 2.00
32 Harry Walker MG .60 1.50
33 Don Wert .60 1.50
34 Willie Crawford .60 1.50
35 Joel Horlen .60 1.50
36 Danny Breeden .75 2.00
Bernie Carbo
37 Dick Drago .60 1.50
38 Mack Jones .60 1.50
39 Mike Nagy .60 1.50
40 Rich Allen 1.50 4.00
41 George Lauzerique .60 1.50
42 Tito Fuentes .60 1.50
43 Jack Aker .60 1.50
44 Roberto Pena .60 1.50
45 Dave Johnson .75 2.00
46 Ken Rudolph .60 1.50
47 Bob Miller .60 1.50
48 Gil Garrido .60 1.50
49 Tim Cullen .60 1.50
50 Tommie Agee .75 2.00
51 Bob Christian .60 1.50
52 Bruce Dal Canton .60 1.50
53 John Kennedy .60 1.50
54 Jeff Torborg .75 2.00
55 John Odom .60 1.50
56 Joe Lis .60 1.50
Scott Reid
57 Pat Kelly .60 1.50
58 Dave Marshall .60 1.50
59 Dick Ellsworth .60 1.50
60 Jim Wynn .75 2.00
61 Pete Rose 6.00 15.00
Bob Clemente
Cleon Jones LL
62 Rod Carew 1.25 3.00
Reggie Smith
Tony Oliva LL
63 Willie McCovey 1.25 3.00
Ron Santo
Tony Perez LL
64 Harmon Killebrew 2.50 6.00
Boog Powell
Reggie Jackson LL
65 Willie McCovey 2.50 6.00
Hank Aaron
Lee May LL
66 Harmon Killebrew 2.50 6.00
Frank Howard
Reggie Jackson LL
67 Juan Marichal 3.00 8.00
Steve Carlton
Bob Gibson LL
68 Dick Bosman .75 2.00
Jim Palmer
Mike Cuellar LL
69 Tom Seaver 3.00 8.00
Phil Niekro
Fergie Jenkins
Juan Marichal LL
70 Dennis McLain .75 2.00
Mike Cuellar
Dave Boswell
Dave McNally
Jim Perry
Mel Stottlemyre LL
71 Fergie Jenkins 1.25 3.00
Bob Gibson
Bill Singer LL
72 Sam McDowell .75 2.00
Mickey Lolich
Andy Messersmith LL
73 Wayne Granger .60 1.50
74 Greg Washburn .60 1.50
Wally Wolf
75 Jim Kaat .75 2.00
76 Carl Taylor .60 1.50
77 Frank Linzy .60 1.50
78 Joe Lahoud .60 1.50
79 Clay Kirby .60 1.50
80 Don Kessinger .75 2.00
81 Dave May .60 1.50
82 Frank Fernandez .60 1.50
83 Don Cardwell .60 1.50
84 Paul Casanova .60 1.50
85 Max Alvis .60 1.50
86 Lum Harris MG .60 1.50
87 Steve Renko .75 2.00
88 Miguel Fuentes .75 2.00
Dick Baney
89 Juan Rios .60 1.50
90 Tim McCarver 1.25 3.00
91 Rich Morales .60 1.50
92 George Culver .60 1.50
93 Rick Renick .60 1.50
94 Fred Patek .75 2.00
95 Earl Wilson .75 2.00
96 Leron Lee 1.25 3.00
Jerry Reuss RC
97 Joe Moeller .60 1.50
98 Gates Brown .75 2.00
99 Bobby Pfeil .60 1.50
100 Mel Stottlemyre .75 2.00
101 Bobby Floyd .60 1.50
102 Joe Rudi .75 2.00
103 Frank Reberger .60 1.50
104 Gerry Moses .60 1.50
105 Tony Gonzalez .60 1.50
106 Darold Knowles .60 1.50
107 Bobby Etheridge .60 1.50
108 Tom Burgmeier .60 1.50
109 Garry Jestadt .75 2.00
Carl Morton
110 Bob Moose .60 1.50
111 Mike Hegan .75 2.00
112 Dave Nelson .60 1.50
113 Jim Ray .60 1.50
114 Gene Michael .75 2.00
115 Alex Johnson .75 2.00
116 Sparky Lyle 1.25 3.00
117 Don Young .60 1.50
118 George Mitterwald .60 1.50
119 Chuck Taylor .60 1.50
120 Sal Bando .75 2.00
121 Fred Beene .60 1.50
Terry Crowley
122 George Stone .60 1.50
123 Don Gutteridge MG .60 1.50
124 Larry Jaster .60 1.50
125 Deron Johnson .60 1.50
126 Marty Martinez .60 1.50
127 Joe Coleman .60 1.50
128 Checklist 133-263 3.00 8.00
129 Jimmie Price .60 1.50
130 Ollie Brown .60 1.50
131 Ray Lamb .60 1.50
Bob Stinson
132 Jim McGlothlin .60 1.50
133 Clay Carroll .60 1.50
134 Danny Walton .60 1.50
135 Dick Dietz .60 1.50
136 Steve Hargan .60 1.50
137 Art Shamsky .60 1.50
138 Joe Foy .60 1.50
139 Rich Nye .60 1.50
140 Reggie Jackson 30.00 60.00
141 Dave Cash RC .75 2.00
Johnny Jeter
142 Fritz Peterson .60 1.50
143 Phil Gagliano .60 1.50
144 Ray Culp .60 1.50
145 Rico Carty .75 2.00
146 Danny Murphy .60 1.50
147 Angel Hermoso .60 1.50
148 Earl Weaver MG 2.00 5.00
149 Billy Champion .60 1.50
150 Harmon Killebrew 4.00 10.00
151 Dave Roberts .60 1.50
152 Ike Brown .60 1.50
153 Gary Gentry .60 1.50
154 Jim Miles .60 1.50
Jan Dukes
155 Denis Menke .60 1.50
156 Eddie Fisher .60 1.50
157 Manny Mota 1.25 3.00
158 Jerry McNertney .75 2.00
159 Tommy Helms .75 2.00
160 Phil Niekro 2.50 6.00
161 Richie Scheinblum .60 1.50
162 Jerry Johnson .60 1.50
163 Syd O'Brien .60 1.50
164 Ty Cline .60 1.50
165 Ed Kirkpatrick .60 1.50
166 Al Oliver 1.50 4.00
167 Bill Burbach .60 1.50
168 Dave Watkins .60 1.50
169 Tom Hall .60 1.50
170 Billy Williams 3.00 8.00
171 Jim Nash .60 1.50
172 Garry Hill 1.25 3.00
Ralph Garr RC
173 Jim Hicks .60 1.50
174 Ted Sizemore .75 2.00
175 Dick Bosman .60 1.50
176 Jim Ray Hart .75 2.00
177 Jim Northrup .75 2.00
178 Denny LeMaster .60 1.50
179 Ivan Murrell .60 1.50
180 Tommy John 1.25 3.00
181 Sparky Anderson MG 3.00 8.00
182 Dick Hall .60 1.50
183 Jerry Grote .75 2.00
184 Ray Fosse .60 1.50
185 Don Mincher .75 2.00
186 Rick Joseph .60 1.50
187 Mike Hedlund .60 1.50
188 Manny Sanguillen .75 2.00
189 Thurman Munson RC 50.00 100.00
Dave McDonald
190 Joe Torre 1.50 4.00
191 Vicente Romo .60 1.50
192 Jim Qualls .60 1.50
193 Mike Wegener .60 1.50
194 Chuck Manuel RC 1.50 4.00
195 Tom Seaver NLCS 8.00 20.00
196 Ken Boswell NLCS 1.50 4.00
197 Nolan Ryan NLCS 12.50 40.00
198 Mets Celebrate 8.00 20.00
Includes Nolan Ryan
Tommie Agee
Wayne Garrett
199 Mike Cuellar ALCS 1.50 4.00
200 Boog Powell ALCS 1.50 4.00
201 Boog Powell ALCS 1.50 4.00
Andy Etchebarren
202 AL Playoff Summary 1.50 4.00
Orioles celebrate
203 Rudy May .60 1.50
204 Len Gabrielson .60 1.50
205 Bert Campaneris .75 2.00
206 Clete Boyer .75 2.00
207 Norman McRae .60 1.50
Bob Reed
208 Fred Gladding .60 1.50
209 Ken Suarez .60 1.50
210 Juan Marichal 3.00 8.00
211 Ted Williams MG 8.00 20.00
212 Al Santorini .60 1.50
213 Andy Etchebarren .60 1.50
214 Ken Boswell .60 1.50
215 Reggie Smith 1.25 3.00
216 Chuck Hartenstein .60 1.50
217 Ron Hansen .60 1.50
218 Ron Stone .60 1.50
219 Jerry Kenney .60 1.50
220 Steve Carlton 8.00 20.00
221 Ron Brand .60 1.50
222 Jim Rooker .60 1.50
223 Nate Oliver .60 1.50
224 Steve Barber .75 2.00
225 Lee May .75 2.00
226 Ron Perranoski .60 1.50
227 John Mayberry RC .75 2.00
Bob Watkins
228 Aurelio Rodriguez .60 1.50
229 Rich Robertson .60 1.50
230 Brooks Robinson 8.00 20.00
231 Luis Tiant 1.25 3.00
232 Bob Didier .60 1.50
233 Lew Krausse .60 1.50
234 Tommy Dean .60 1.50
235 Mike Epstein .60 1.50
236 Bob Veale .60 1.50
237 Russ Gibson .60 1.50
238 Jose Laboy .75 2.00
239 Ken Berry .60 1.50
240 Fergie Jenkins 3.00 8.00
241 Al Fitzmorris .60 1.50
Scott Northey
242 Walter Alston MG 1.50 4.00
243 Joe Sparma .75 2.00
244 Checklist 264-372 3.00 8.00
245 Leo Cardenas .60 1.50
246 Jim McAndrew .60 1.50
247 Lou Klimchock .60 1.50
248 Jesus Alou .60 1.50
249 Bob Locker .60 1.50
250 Willie McCovey 5.00 12.00
251 Dick Schofield .60 1.50
252 Lowell Palmer .60 1.50
253 Ron Woods .60 1.50
254 Camilo Pascual .60 1.50
255 Jim Spencer .60 1.50
256 Vic Davalillo .60 1.50
257 Dennis Higgins .60 1.50
258 Paul Popovich .60 1.50
259 Tommie Reynolds .60 1.50
260 Claude Osteen .75 2.00
261 Curt Motton .60 1.50
262 Jerry Morales .60 1.50
Jim Williams
263 Duane Josephson .60 1.50
264 Rich Hebner .60 1.50
265 Randy Hundley .60 1.50
266 Wally Bunker .60 1.50
267 Herman Hill .60 1.50
Paul Ratliff
268 Claude Raymond .75 2.00
269 Cesar Gutierrez .60 1.50
270 Chris Short .60 1.50
271 Greg Goossen .75 2.00
272 Hector Torres .60 1.50
273 Ralph Houk MG .75 2.00
274 Gerry Arrigo .60 1.50
275 Duke Sims .60 1.50
276 Ron Hunt .60 1.50
277 Paul Doyle .60 1.50
278 Tommie Aaron .60 1.50
279 Bill Lee 1.25 3.00
280 Donn Clendenon .75 2.00
281 Casey Cox .60 1.50
282 Steve Huntz .60 1.50

283 Angel Bravo	.60	1.50
284 Jack Baldschun	.60	1.50
285 Paul Blair	.75	2.00
286 Jack Jenkins	3.00	8.00
Bill Buckner RC		
287 Fred Talbot	.60	1.50
288 Larry Hisle	.75	2.00
289 Gene Brabender	.60	1.50
290 Rod Carew	10.00	25.00
291 Leo Durocher MG	1.50	4.00
292 Eddie Leon	.60	1.50
293 Bob Bailey	.75	2.00
294 Jose Azcue	.60	1.50
295 Cecil Upshaw	.60	1.50
296 Woody Woodward	.60	1.50
297 Curt Blefary	.60	1.50
298 Ken Henderson	.60	1.50
299 Buddy Bradford	.60	1.50
300 Tom Seaver	12.50	40.00
301 Chico Salmon	.60	1.50
302 Jeff James	.60	1.50
303 Brant Alyea	.60	1.50
304 Bill Russell RC	3.00	8.00
305 Don Buford WS	1.50	4.00
306 Donn Clendenon WS	1.50	4.00
307 Tommie Agee WS	1.50	4.00
308 J.C. Martin WS	1.50	4.00
309 Jerry Koosman WS	1.50	4.00
310 WS Celebration	3.00	8.00
Includes Ed Kranepool		
Tug McGraw		
Ed Charles		
311 Dick Green	.60	1.50
312 Mike Torrez	.60	1.50
313 Mayo Smith MG	.60	1.50
314 Bill McCool	.60	1.50
315 Luis Aparicio	3.00	8.00
316 Skip Guinn	.60	1.50
317 Billy Conigliaro	.75	2.00
Luis Alvarado		
318 Willie Smith	.60	1.50
319 Clay Dalrymple	.60	1.50
320 Jim Maloney	.75	2.00
321 Lou Piniella	1.25	3.00
322 Luke Walker	.60	1.50
323 Wayne Comer	.60	1.50
324 Tony Taylor	.75	2.00
325 Dave Boswell	.60	1.50
326 Bill Voss	.60	1.50
327 Hal King RC	.60	1.50
328 George Brunet	.60	1.50
329 Chris Cannizzaro	.60	1.50
330 Lou Brock	5.00	12.00
331 Chuck Dobson	.60	1.50
332 Bobby Wine	.75	2.00
333 Bobby Murcer	1.25	3.00
334 Phil Regan	.60	1.50
335 Bill Freehan	.75	2.00
336 Del Unser	.60	1.50
337 Mike McCormick	.75	2.00
338 Paul Schaal	.60	1.50
339 Johnny Edwards	.60	1.50
340 Tony Conigliaro	1.50	4.00
341 Bill Sudakis	.60	1.50
342 Wilbur Wood	.75	2.00
343 Checklist 373-459	3.00	8.00
344 Marcelino Lopez	.60	1.50
345 Al Ferrara	.60	1.50
346 Red Schoendienst MG	.75	2.00
347 Russ Snyder	.60	1.50
348 Mike Jorgensen	.75	2.00
Jesse Hudson		
349 Steve Hamilton	.60	1.50
350 Roberto Clemente	40.00	80.00
351 Tom Murphy	.60	1.50
352 Bob Barton	.60	1.50
353 Stan Williams	.60	1.50
354 Amos Otis	.75	2.00
355 Doug Rader	.60	1.50
356 Fred Lasher	.60	1.50
357 Bob Burda	.60	1.50
358 Pedro Borbon RC	.75	2.00
359 Phil Roof	.60	1.50
360 Curt Flood	1.25	3.00
361 Ray Jarvis	.60	1.50
362 Joe Hague	.60	1.50
363 Tom Shopay	.60	1.50
364 Dan McGinn	.75	2.00
365 Zoilo Versalles	.60	1.50
366 Barry Moore	.60	1.50
367 Mike Lum	.60	1.50
368 Ed Herrmann	.60	1.50
369 Alan Foster	.60	1.50
370 Tommy Harper	.75	2.00
371 Rod Gaspar	.60	1.50
372 Dave Giusti	.60	1.50
373 Roy White	.75	2.00
374 Tommie Sisk	.60	1.50
375 Johnny Callison	1.25	3.00
376 Lefty Phillips MG	.60	1.50
377 Bill Butler	.60	1.50
378 Jim Davenport	.60	1.50
379 Tom Tischinski	.60	1.50
380 Tony Perez	3.00	8.00
381 Bobby Brooks	.60	1.50
Mike Olivo		
382 Jack DiLauro	.60	1.50
383 Mickey Stanley	.75	2.00
384 Gary Neibauer	.60	1.50
385 George Scott	.75	2.00
386 Bill Dillman	.60	1.50
387 Orioles Team	1.50	4.00
388 Byron Browne	.60	1.50
389 Jim Shellenback	.60	1.50
390 Willie Davis	1.25	3.00
391 Larry Brown	.60	1.50
392 Walt Hriniak	.75	2.00
393 John Gelnar	.60	1.50
394 Gil Hodges MG	1.50	4.00
395 Walt Williams	.60	1.50
396 Steve Blass	.75	2.00
397 Roger Repoz	.60	1.50
398 Bill Stoneman	.60	1.50
399 Yankees Team	1.50	4.00
400 Denny McLain	1.50	4.00
401 John Harrell	.60	1.50
Bernie Williams		
402 Ellie Rodriguez	.60	1.50
403 Jim Bunning	3.00	8.00
404 Rich Reese	.60	1.50
405 Bill Hands	.60	1.50
406 Mike Andrews	.60	1.50
407 Bob Watson	.75	2.00
408 Paul Lindblad	.60	1.50
409 Bob Tolan	.60	1.50
410 Boog Powell	1.50	4.00
411 Dodgers Team	1.50	4.00
412 Larry Burchart	.60	1.50
413 Sonny Jackson	.60	1.50
414 Paul Edmondson	.60	1.50
415 Julian Javier	.75	2.00
416 Joe Verbanic	.60	1.50
417 John Bateman	.60	1.50
418 John Donaldson	.60	1.50
419 Ron Taylor	.75	2.00
420 Ken McMullen	.75	2.00
421 Pat Dobson	.75	2.00
422 Royals Team	1.50	4.00
423 Jerry May	.60	1.50
424 Mike Kilkenny	.75	2.00
425 Bobby Bonds	3.00	8.00
426 Bill Rigney MG	.60	1.50
427 Fred Norman	.60	1.50
428 Don Buford	.60	1.50
429 Randy Bobb	.60	1.50
Jim Cosman		
430 Andy Messersmith	.75	2.00
431 Ron Swoboda	.75	2.00
432 Checklist 460-546	3.00	8.00
433 Ron Bryant	.60	1.50
434 Felipe Alou	1.25	3.00
435 Nelson Briles	.75	2.00
436 Phillies Team	1.50	4.00
437 Danny Cater	.60	1.50
438 Pat Jarvis	.60	1.50
439 Lee Maye	.60	1.50
440 Bill Mazeroski	3.00	8.00
441 John O'Donoghue	.60	1.50
442 Gene Mauch MG	.75	2.00
443 Al Jackson	.60	1.50
444 Billy Farmer	.60	1.50
John Matias		
445 Vada Pinson	1.25	3.00
446 Billy Grabarkewitz	.60	1.50
447 Lee Stange	.60	1.50
448 Astros Team	1.50	4.00
449 Jim Palmer	6.00	15.00
450 Willie McCovey AS	3.00	8.00
451 Boog Powell AS	1.50	4.00
452 Felix Millan AS	1.25	3.00
453 Rod Carew AS	3.00	8.00
454 Ron Santo AS	1.50	4.00
455 Brooks Robinson AS	3.00	8.00
456 Don Kessinger AS	1.25	3.00
457 Rico Petrocelli AS	1.50	4.00
458 Pete Rose AS	8.00	20.00
459 Reggie Jackson AS	6.00	15.00
460 Matty Alou AS	1.50	4.00
461 Carl Yastrzemski AS	5.00	12.00
462 Hank Aaron AS	8.00	20.00
463 Frank Robinson AS	4.00	10.00
464 Johnny Bench AS	8.00	20.00
465 Bill Freehan AS	1.50	4.00
466 Juan Marichal AS	2.50	6.00
467 Denny McLain AS	2.50	6.00
468 Jerry Koosman AS	1.50	4.00
469 Sam McDowell AS	1.50	4.00
470 Willie Stargell	5.00	12.00
471 Chris Zachary	1.00	2.50
472 Braves Team	1.50	4.00
473 Don Bryant	1.00	2.50
474 Dick Kelley	1.00	2.50
475 Dick McAuliffe	1.50	4.00
476 Don Shaw	1.00	2.50
477 Al Severinsen	1.00	2.50
Roger Freed		
478 Bob Heise	1.00	2.50
479 Dick Woodson	1.00	2.50
480 Glenn Beckert	1.50	4.00
481 Jose Tartabull	1.00	2.50
482 Tom Hilgendorf	1.00	2.50
483 Gail Hopkins	1.00	2.50
484 Gary Nolan	1.50	4.00
485 Jay Johnstone	1.50	4.00
486 Terry Harmon	1.00	2.50
487 Cisco Carlos	1.00	2.50
488 J.C. Martin	1.00	2.50
489 Eddie Kasko MG	1.00	2.50
490 Bill Singer	1.50	4.00
491 Graig Nettles	2.50	6.00
492 Keith Lampard	1.00	2.50
Scipio Spinks		
493 Lindy McDaniel	1.50	4.00
494 Larry Stahl	1.00	2.50
495 Dave Morehead	1.00	2.50
496 Steve Whitaker	1.00	2.50
497 Eddie Watt	1.00	2.50
498 Al Weis	1.00	2.50
499 Skip Lockwood	1.00	2.50
500 Hank Aaron	30.00	60.00
501 White Sox Team	1.50	4.00
502 Rollie Fingers	5.00	12.00
503 Dal Maxvill	1.00	2.50
504 Don Pavletich	1.00	2.50
505 Ken Holtzman	1.50	4.00
506 Ed Stroud	1.00	2.50
507 Pat Corrales	1.00	2.50
508 Joe Niekro	1.50	4.00
509 Expos Team	2.50	6.00
510 Tony Oliva	2.50	6.00
511 Joe Hoerner	1.00	2.50
512 Billy Harris	1.00	2.50
513 Preston Gomez MG	1.00	2.50
514 Steve Hovley	1.00	2.50
515 Don Wilson	1.50	4.00
516 John Ellis	1.00	2.50
Jim Lyttle		
517 Joe Gibbon	1.00	2.50
518 Bill Melton	1.00	2.50
519 Don McMahon	1.00	2.50
520 Willie Horton	1.50	4.00
521 Cal Koonce	1.00	2.50
522 Angels Team	1.50	4.00
523 Jose Pena	1.00	2.50
524 Alvin Dark MG	1.50	4.00
525 Jerry Adair	1.00	2.50
526 Ron Herbel	1.00	2.50
527 Don Bosch	1.50	4.00
528 Elrod Hendricks	1.00	2.50
529 Bob Aspromonte	1.00	2.50
530 Bob Gibson	8.00	20.00
531 Ron Clark	1.00	2.50
532 Danny Murtaugh MG	1.50	4.00
533 Buzz Stephen	1.00	2.50
534 Twins Team	1.50	4.00
535 Andy Kosco	1.00	2.50
536 Mike Kekich	1.00	2.50
537 Joe Morgan	5.00	12.00
538 Bob Humphreys	1.00	2.50
539 Denny Doyle RC	4.00	10.00
Larry Bowa RC		
540 Gary Peters	1.00	2.50
541 Bill Heath	1.00	2.50
542 Checklist 547-633	3.00	8.00
543 Clyde Wright	1.00	2.50
544 Reds Team	2.50	6.00
545 Ken Harrelson	1.50	4.00
546 Ron Reed	1.50	4.00

1971 O-Pee-Chee

The cards in this 752-card set measure 2 1/2" by 3 1/2". The 1971 O-Pee-Chee set is a challenge to complete in "Mint" condition because the black borders are easily scratched and damaged. The O-Pee-Chee cards seem to have been cut (into individual cards) not as sharply as the Topps cards; the borders frequently appear slightly frayed. The players are also pictured in black and white on the back of the card. The next-to-last series (524-643) and the last series (644-752) are somewhat scarce. The O-Pee-Chee cards can be distinguished from Topps cards by the "Printed in Canada" on the bottom of the reverse. The reverse color is yellow instead of the green found on the backs of the 1971 Topps cards. The card backs are written in both French and English, except for cards 524-752 which were printed in English only. There are several cards which are different from the corresponding Topps card with a different pose or different team noted in bold type, i.e. "Recently Traded to ..." These changed cards are numbers 31, 32, 73, 144, 151, 161, 172, 182, 191, 202, 207, 248, 289 and 578. These cards were issued in eight-card dime packs which came 36 packs to a box. Remember, the prices below apply only to the 1971 O-Pee-Chee cards -- NOT Topps cards which are much more plentiful. Notable Rookie Cards include Dusty Baker and Don Baylor (Sharing the same card), Bert Blyleven, Dave Concepcion and Steve Garvey.

COMPLETE SET (752)	1250.00	2500.00
COMMON CARD (1-393)	.60	1.50
COMMON (394-523)	1.25	3.00
COMMON (524-643)	1.50	4.00
COMMON (644-752)	4.00	10.00
1 Orioles Team	10.00	25.00
2 Dock Ellis	.60	1.50
3 Dick McAuliffe	.75	2.00
4 Vic Davalillo	.60	1.50
5 Thurman Munson UER	75.00	150.00
American League is misspelled		
6 Ed Spiezio	.60	1.50
7 Jim Holt	.60	1.50
8 Mike McQueen	.60	1.50
9 George Scott	.75	2.00
10 Claude Osteen	.75	2.00
11 Elliott Maddox	.60	1.50
12 Johnny Callison	.75	2.00
13 Charlie Brinkman	.60	1.50
Dick Moloney		
14 Dave Concepcion RC	10.00	25.00
15 Andy Messersmith	.75	2.00
16 Ken Singleton RC	1.25	3.00
17 Billy Sorrell	.60	1.50
18 Norm Miller	.60	1.50
19 Skip Pitlock	.60	1.50
20 Reggie Jackson	30.00	60.00
21 Dan McGinn	.75	2.00
22 Phil Roof	.60	1.50
23 Oscar Gamble	.60	1.50
24 Rich Hand	.60	1.50
25 Clarence Gaston	.75	2.00
26 Bert Blyleven RC	10.00	25.00
27 Fred Cambria	.60	1.50
Gene Clines		
28 Ron Klimkowski	.60	1.50
29 Don Buford	.60	1.50
30 Phil Niekro	3.00	8.00
31 John Bateman	1.25	3.00
(different pose)		
32 Jerry DeVanon	.75	2.00
Recently Traded To Orioles		
33 Del Unser	.60	1.50
34 Sandy Vance	.60	1.50
35 Lou Piniella	1.25	3.00
36 Dean Chance	.75	2.00
37 Rich McKinney	.60	1.50
38 Jim Colborn	.60	1.50
39 Lerrin LaGrow	.75	2.00
Gene Lamont RC		
40 Lee May	.75	2.00
41 Rick Austin	.60	1.50
42 Boots Day	.75	2.00
43 Steve Kealey	.60	1.50
44 Johnny Edwards	.60	1.50
45 Jim Hunter	3.00	8.00
46 Dave Campbell	.75	2.00
47 Johnny Jeter	.60	1.50
48 Dave Baldwin	.60	1.50
49 Don Money	.60	1.50
50 Willie McCovey	5.00	12.00
51 Steve Kline	.60	1.50
52 Oscar Brown	.60	1.50
Earl Williams RC		
53 Paul Blair	.75	2.00
54 Checklist 1-132	4.00	10.00
55 Steve Carlton	10.00	25.00
56 Duane Josephson	.60	1.50
57 Von Joshua	.60	1.50
58 Bill Lee	.75	2.00
59 Gene Mauch MG	.75	2.00
60 Dick Bosman	.60	1.50
61 Alex Johnson	1.25	3.00
Carl Yastrzemski		
Tony Oliva LL		
62 Rico Carty	.75	2.00
Joe Torre		
Manny Sanguillen LL		
63 Frank Robinson	1.25	3.00
Tony Conigliaro		
Boog Powell LL		
64 Johnny Bench	3.00	8.00
Tony Perez		
Billy Williams LL		
65 Frank Howard	1.25	3.00
Harmon Killebrew		
Carl Yastrzemski LL		
66 Johnny Bench	3.00	8.00
Billy Williams		
Tony Perez LL		
67 Diego Segui	1.25	3.00
Jim Palmer		
Clyde Wright LL		
68 Tom Seaver	1.25	3.00
Wayne Simpson		
Luke Walker LL		
69 Mike Cuellar	.75	2.00
Dave McNally		
Jim Perry LL		
70 Bob Gibson	3.00	8.00
Gaylord Perry		
Fergie Jenkins LL		
71 Sam McDowell	.75	2.00
Mickey Lolich		
Bob Johnson LL		
72 Tom Seaver	3.00	8.00
Bob Gibson		
Fergie Jenkins LL		
73 George Brunet	.60	1.50
(St. Louis Cardinals)		
74 Pete Hamm	.60	1.50
Jim Nettles		
75 Gary Nolan	.75	2.00
76 Ted Savage	.60	1.50
77 Mike Compton	.60	1.50
78 Jim Spencer	.60	1.50
79 Wade Blasingame	.60	1.50
80 Bill Melton	.60	1.50
81 Felix Millan	.60	1.50
82 Casey Cox	.60	1.50
83 Tim Foli RC	.75	2.00
Randy Bobb		
84 Marcel Lachemann RC	.60	1.50
85 Bill Grabarkewitz	.60	1.50
86 Mike Kilkenny	.75	2.00
87 Jack Heidemann	.60	1.50
88 Hal King	.60	1.50
89 Ken Brett	.60	1.50
90 Joe Pepitone	.75	2.00
91 Bob Lemon MG	.75	2.00
92 Fred Wenz	.60	1.50
93 Norm McRae	.60	1.50
Denny Riddleberger		
94 Don Hahn	.75	2.00
95 Luis Tiant	.75	2.00
96 Joe Hague	.60	1.50
97 Floyd Wicker	.60	1.50
98 Joe Decker	.60	1.50
99 Mark Belanger	.75	2.00
100 Pete Rose	50.00	100.00
101 Les Cain	.60	1.50
102 Ken Forsch	.75	2.00
Larry Howard		
103 Rich Severson	.60	1.50
104 Dan Frisella	.60	1.50
105 Tony Conigliaro	.75	2.00
106 Tom Dukes	.60	1.50
107 Roy Foster	.60	1.50
108 John Cumberland	.60	1.50
109 Steve Hovley	.60	1.50
110 Bill Mazeroski	3.00	8.00
111 Loyd Colson	.60	1.50
Bobby Mitchell		
112 Manny Mota	.75	2.00
113 Jerry Crider	.60	1.50
114 Billy Conigliaro	.75	2.00
115 Donn Clendenon	.75	2.00
116 Ken Sanders	.60	1.50
117 Ted Simmons RC	4.00	10.00
118 Cookie Rojas	.75	2.00
119 Frank Lucchesi MG	.60	1.50
120 Willie Horton	.75	2.00
121 Jim Dunegan	.60	1.50
Roe Skidmore		
122 Eddie Watt	.60	1.50
123 Checklist 133-263	4.00	10.00
124 Don Gullett RC	.75	2.00
125 Ray Fosse	.60	1.50
126 Danny Coombs	.60	1.50
127 Danny Thompson	.75	2.00
128 Frank Johnson	.60	1.50
129 Aurelio Monteagudo	.60	1.50
130 Denis Menke	.60	1.50
131 Curt Blefary	.60	1.50
132 Jose Laboy	.75	2.00
133 Mickey Lolich	.75	2.00
134 Jose Arcia	.60	1.50
135 Rick Monday	.75	2.00
136 Duffy Dyer	.60	1.50
137 Marcelino Lopez	.60	1.50
138 Joe Lis	.75	2.00
Willie Montanez		
139 Paul Casanova	.60	1.50
140 Gaylord Perry	3.00	8.00
141 Frank Quilici MG	.60	1.50
142 Mack Jones	.75	2.00
143 Steve Blass	.75	2.00
144 Jackie Hernandez	.75	2.00
(Pittsburgh Pirates)		
145 Bill Singer	.75	2.00
146 Ralph Houk MG	.75	2.00
147 Bob Priddy	.60	1.50
148 John Mayberry	.75	2.00
149 Mike Hershberger	.60	1.50
150 Sam McDowell	.75	2.00
151 Tommy Davis	1.25	3.00
(Oakland A's)		
152 Lloyd Allen	.60	1.50
Winston Llenas		
153 Gary Ross	.60	1.50
154 Cesar Gutierrez	.60	1.50
155 Ken Henderson	.60	1.50
156 Bart Johnson	.60	1.50
157 Bob Bailey	1.25	3.00
158 Jerry Reuss	.75	2.00
159 Jarvis Tatum	.60	1.50
160 Tom Seaver	12.50	40.00
161 Ron Hunt	2.50	6.00
(different pose)		
162 Jack Billingham	.60	1.50
163 Buck Martinez	.75	2.00
164 Frank Duffy	.75	2.00
Milt Wilcox		
165 Cesar Tovar	.60	1.50
166 Joe Hoerner	.60	1.50
167 Tom Grieve RC	.75	2.00
168 Bruce Dal Canton	.60	1.50
169 Ed Herrmann	.60	1.50
170 Mike Cuellar	.75	2.00
171 Bobby Wine	.75	2.00
172 Duke Sims	.75	2.00
(Los Angeles Dodgers)		
173 Gil Garrido	.60	1.50
174 Dave LaRoche	.60	1.50
175 Jim Hickman	.60	1.50
176 Bob Montgomery RC	.75	2.00
Doug Griffin		
177 Hal McRae	.75	2.00
178 Dave Duncan	.75	2.00
179 Mike Corkins	.60	1.50
180 Al Kaline	10.00	25.00
181 Hal Lanier	.60	1.50
182 Al Downing	.75	2.00
(Los Angeles Dodgers)		
183 Gil Hodges MG	1.25	3.00
184 Stan Bahnsen	.60	1.50
185 Julian Javier	.60	1.50
186 Bob Spence	.60	1.50
187 Ted Abernathy	.60	1.50
188 Bob Valentine RC	3.00	8.00
Mike Strahler		
189 George Mitterwald	.60	1.50
190 Bob Tolan	.60	1.50
191 Mike Andrews	.75	2.00
(Chicago White Sox)		
192 Billy Wilson	.60	1.50
193 Bob Grich RC	1.25	3.00
194 Mike Lum	.60	1.50
195 Boog Powell ALCS	.75	2.00
196 Dave McNally ALCS	.75	2.00
197 Jim Palmer ALCS	1.25	3.00
198 AL Playoff Summary	.75	2.00
Orioles Celebrate		
199 Ty Cline NLCS	.75	2.00
200 Bobby Tolan NLCS	.75	2.00
201 Ty Cline NLCS	.75	2.00
202 Claude Raymond	2.50	6.00
(different pose)		
203 Larry Gura	.75	2.00
204 Bernie Smith	.60	1.50
George Kopacz		
205 Gerry Moses	.60	1.50
206 Checklist 264-393	5.00	12.00
207 Alan Foster	.75	2.00
(Cleveland Indians)		
208 Billy Martin MG	1.25	3.00
209 Steve Renko	.75	2.00
210 Rod Carew	8.00	20.00
211 Phil Hennigan	.60	1.50
212 Rich Hebner	.75	2.00
213 Frank Baker	.60	1.50
214 Al Ferrara	.60	1.50
215 Diego Segui	.60	1.50
216 Reggie Cleveland	.75	2.00
Luis Melendez		
217 Ed Stroud	.60	1.50
218 Tony Cloninger	.60	1.50
219 Elrod Hendricks	.60	1.50
220 Ron Santo	1.25	3.00
221 Dave Morehead	.60	1.50
222 Bob Watson	.75	2.00
223 Cecil Upshaw	.60	1.50
224 Alan Gallagher	.60	1.50
225 Gary Peters	.60	1.50
226 Bill Russell	.75	2.00
227 Floyd Weaver	.60	1.50
228 Wayne Garrett	.60	1.50
229 Jim Hannan	.60	1.50
230 Willie Stargell	8.00	20.00
231 Vince Colbert	.75	2.00
John Lowenstein RC		
232 John Strohmayer	.75	2.00
233 Larry Bowa	.75	2.00
234 Jim Lyttle	.60	1.50
235 Nate Colbert	.60	1.50
236 Bob Humphreys	.60	1.50
237 Cesar Cedeno RC	.75	2.00
238 Chuck Dobson	.60	1.50
239 Red Schoendienst MG	.75	2.00
240 Clyde Wright	.60	1.50
241 Dave Nelson	.60	1.50
242 Jim Ray	.60	1.50
243 Carlos May	.60	1.50
244 Bob Tillman	.60	1.50
245 Jim Kaat	.75	2.00
246 Tony Taylor	.60	1.50
247 Jerry Cram	.75	2.00
Paul Splittorff		
248 Hoyt Wilhelm	4.00	10.00
(Atlanta Braves)		
249 Chico Salmon	.60	1.50
250 Johnny Bench	30.00	60.00
251 Frank Reberger	.60	1.50
252 Eddie Leon	.60	1.50
253 Bill Sudakis	.60	1.50
254 Cal Koonce	.60	1.50
255 Bob Robertson	.75	2.00
256 Tony Gonzalez	.60	1.50
257 Nelson Briles	.75	2.00
258 Dick Green	.60	1.50
259 Dave Marshall	.60	1.50
260 Tommy Harper	.75	2.00
261 Darold Knowles	.60	1.50
262 Jim Williams	.60	1.50
Dave Robinson		
263 John Ellis	.60	1.50
264 Joe Morgan	4.00	10.00
265 Jim Northrup	.75	2.00
266 Bill Stoneman	.75	2.00
267 Rich Morales	.60	1.50
268 Phillies Team	1.25	3.00
269 Gail Hopkins	.60	1.50
270 Rico Carty	.75	2.00
271 Bill Zepp	.60	1.50
272 Tommy Helms	.75	2.00
273 Pete Richert	.60	1.50
274 Ron Slocum	.60	1.50
275 Vada Pinson	.75	2.00
276 Mike Davison	4.00	10.00
George Foster RC		
277 Gary Waslewski	.60	1.50
278 Jerry Grote	.75	2.00
279 Lefty Phillips MG	.60	1.50
280 Fergie Jenkins	3.00	8.00
281 Danny Walton	.60	1.50
282 Jose Pagan	.60	1.50
283 Dick Such	.60	1.50
284 Jim Gosger	.75	2.00
285 Sal Bando	.75	2.00
286 Jerry McNertney	.60	1.50
287 Mike Fiore	.60	1.50
288 Joe Moeller	.60	1.50
289 Rusty Staub	4.00	10.00
(Different pose)		
290 Tony Oliva	1.25	3.00
291 George Culver	.60	1.50
292 Jay Johnstone	.75	2.00
293 Pat Corrales	.75	2.00
294 Steve Dunning	.60	1.50
295 Bobby Bonds	2.50	6.00
296 Tom Timmermann	.60	1.50
297 Johnny Briggs	.60	1.50
298 Jim Nelson	.60	1.50
299 Ed Kirkpatrick	.60	1.50
300 Brooks Robinson	10.00	25.00
301 Earl Wilson	.60	1.50
302 Phil Gagliano	.60	1.50
303 Lindy McDaniel	.75	2.00
304 Ron Brand	.75	2.00
305 Reggie Smith	.75	2.00
306 Jim Nash	.60	1.50
307 Don Wert	.60	1.50
308 Cardinals Team	1.25	3.00
309 Dick Ellsworth	.60	1.50
310 Tommie Agee	.75	2.00
311 Lee Stange	.60	1.50
312 Harry Walker MG	.60	1.50
313 Tom Hall	.60	1.50
314 Jeff Torborg	.75	2.00
315 Ron Fairly	1.25	3.00
316 Fred Scherman	.60	1.50
317 Jim Driscoll	.60	1.50
Angel Mangual		
318 Rudy May	.60	1.50
319 Ty Cline	.60	1.50
320 Dave McNally	.75	2.00
321 Tom Matchick	.60	1.50
322 Jim Beauchamp	.60	1.50
323 Billy Champion	.60	1.50
324 Graig Nettles	1.25	3.00
325 Juan Marichal	4.00	10.00
326 Richie Scheinblum	.60	1.50
327 Boog Powell WS	.75	2.00
328 Don Buford WS	.75	2.00
329 Frank Robinson WS	1.25	3.00
330 World Series Game 4	.75	2.00
Reds stay alive		
331 Brooks Robinson WS	3.00	8.00
332 WS Summary	.75	2.00
Orioles Celebrate		
333 Clay Kirby	.60	1.50
334 Roberto Pena	.60	1.50
335 Jerry Koosman	.75	2.00
336 Tigers Team	1.25	3.00
337 Jesus Alou	.60	1.50
338 Gene Tenace	.75	2.00
339 Wayne Simpson	.60	1.50
340 Rico Petrocelli	.75	2.00
341 Steve Garvey RC	20.00	50.00
342 Frank Tepedino	.75	2.00
343 Ed Acosta	.75	2.00
Milt May RC		
344 Ellie Rodriguez	.60	1.50
345 Joel Horlen	.60	1.50
346 Lum Harris MG	.60	1.50
347 Ted Uhlaender	.60	1.50
348 Fred Norman	.60	1.50
349 Rich Reese	.60	1.50
350 Billy Williams	3.00	8.00
351 Jim Shellenback	.60	1.50
352 Denny Doyle	.60	1.50
353 Carl Taylor	.60	1.50
354 Don McMahon	.60	1.50
355 Bud Harrelson	1.25	3.00
356 Bob Locker	.60	1.50
357 Reds Team	1.25	3.00
358 Danny Cater	.60	1.50
359 Ron Reed	.60	1.50
360 Jim Fregosi	.75	2.00
361 Don Sutton	3.00	8.00
362 Mike Adamson	.60	1.50
Roger Freed		
363 Mike Nagy	.60	1.50
364 Tommy Dean	.60	1.50
365 Bob Johnson	.60	1.50
366 Ron Stone	.60	1.50
367 Dalton Jones	.60	1.50
368 Bob Veale	.75	2.00
369 Checklist 394-523	4.00	10.00
370 Joe Torre	2.50	6.00
371 Jack Hiatt	.60	1.50
372 Lew Krausse	.60	1.50
373 Tom McCraw	.60	1.50
374 Clete Boyer	.75	2.00
375 Steve Hargan	.60	1.50
376 Clyde Mashore	.75	2.00
Ernie McAnally		
377 Greg Garrett	.60	1.50
378 Tito Fuentes	.60	1.50
379 Wayne Granger	.60	1.50
380 Ted Williams MG	6.00	15.00
381 Fred Gladding	.60	1.50
382 Jake Gibbs	.60	1.50
383 Rod Gaspar	.60	1.50
384 Rollie Fingers	3.00	8.00
385 Maury Wills	2.50	6.00
386 Red Sox Team	1.25	3.00
387 Ron Herbel	.60	1.50
388 Al Oliver	1.25	3.00
389 Ed Brinkman	.60	1.50
390 Glenn Beckert	.75	2.00
391 Steve Brye	.75	2.00
Cotton Nash		
392 Grant Jackson	.60	1.50
393 Merv Rettenmund	.75	2.00
394 Clay Carroll	1.25	3.00
395 Roy White	1.50	4.00
396 Dick Schofield	1.25	3.00
397 Alvin Dark MG	1.50	4.00
398 Howie Reed	1.50	4.00
399 Jim French	1.25	3.00
400 Hank Aaron	40.00	80.00
401 Tom Murphy	1.25	3.00
402 Dodgers Team	2.50	6.00
403 Joe Coleman	1.25	3.00
404 Buddy Harris	1.25	3.00
Roger Metzger		
405 Leo Cardenas	1.25	3.00
406 Ray Sadecki	1.25	3.00
407 Joe Rudi	1.50	4.00
408 Rafael Robles	1.25	3.00
409 Don Pavletich	1.25	3.00
410 Ken Holtzman	1.50	4.00
411 George Spriggs	1.25	3.00
412 Jerry Johnson	1.25	3.00
413 Pat Kelly	1.25	3.00
414 Woodie Fryman	1.25	3.00
415 Mike Hegan	1.25	3.00
416 Gene Alley	1.25	3.00
417 Dick Hall	1.25	3.00
418 Adolfo Phillips	1.50	4.00
419 Ron Hansen	1.25	3.00
420 Jim Merritt	1.25	3.00
421 John Stephenson	1.25	3.00
422 Frank Bertaina	1.25	3.00
423 Dennis Saunders	1.25	3.00
Tim Marting		
424 Roberto Rodriquez	1.25	3.00
425 Doug Rader	1.50	4.00
426 Chris Cannizzaro	1.25	3.00
427 Bernie Allen	1.25	3.00
428 Jim McAndrew	1.25	3.00
429 Chuck Hinton	1.25	3.00
430 Wes Parker	1.50	4.00
431 Tom Burgmeier	1.25	3.00
432 Bob Didier	1.25	3.00
433 Skip Lockwood	1.25	3.00
434 Gary Sutherland	1.50	4.00
435 Jose Cardenal	1.50	4.00
436 Wilbur Wood	1.50	4.00
437 Danny Murtaugh MG	1.50	4.00
438 Mike McCormick	1.50	4.00
439 Greg Luzinski RC	2.50	6.00
Scott Reid		
440 Bert Campaneris	1.50	4.00
441 Milt Pappas	1.50	4.00
442 Angels Team	2.50	6.00
443 Rich Robertson	1.25	3.00
444 Jimmie Price	1.25	3.00
445 Art Shamsky	1.25	3.00
446 Bobby Bolin	1.25	3.00
447 Cesar Geronimo	1.50	4.00
448 Dave Roberts	1.25	3.00
449 Brant Alyea	1.25	3.00
450 Bob Gibson	8.00	20.00
451 Joe Keough	1.25	3.00
452 John Boccabella	1.50	4.00
453 Terry Crowley	1.25	3.00
454 Mike Paul	1.25	3.00
455 Don Kessinger	1.50	4.00
456 Bob Meyer	1.25	3.00
457 Willie Smith	1.25	3.00
458 Ron Lolich	1.25	3.00
Dave Lemonds		
459 Jim Lefebvre	1.25	3.00
460 Fritz Peterson	1.25	3.00
461 Jim Ray Hart	1.25	3.00
462 Senators Team	2.50	6.00
463 Tom Kelley	1.25	3.00
464 Aurelio Rodriguez	1.25	3.00
465 Tim McCarver	2.50	6.00
466 Ken Berry	1.25	3.00
467 Al Santorini	1.25	3.00
468 Frank Fernandez	1.25	3.00
469 Bob Aspromonte	1.25	3.00
470 Bob Oliver	1.25	3.00
471 Tom Griffin	1.25	3.00
472 Ken Rudolph	1.25	3.00
473 Gary Wagner	1.25	3.00
474 Jim Fairey	1.50	4.00
475 Ron Perranoski	1.25	3.00
476 Dal Maxvill	1.25	3.00
477 Earl Weaver MG	3.00	8.00
478 Bernie Carbo	1.25	3.00
479 Dennis Higgins	1.25	3.00
480 Manny Sanguillen	1.50	4.00
481 Daryl Patterson	1.25	3.00
482 Padres Team	2.50	6.00
483 Gene Michael	1.25	3.00
484 Don Wilson	1.25	3.00
485 Ken McMullen	1.25	3.00
486 Steve Huntz	1.25	3.00
487 Paul Schaal	1.25	3.00
488 Jerry Stephenson	1.25	3.00
489 Luis Alvarado	1.25	3.00
490 Deron Johnson	1.25	3.00
491 Jim Hardin	1.25	3.00
492 Ken Boswell	1.25	3.00
493 Dave May	1.25	3.00
494 Ralph Garr	1.50	4.00
Rick Kester		
495 Felipe Alou	1.50	4.00
496 Woody Woodward	1.25	3.00
497 Horacio Pina	1.25	3.00
498 John Kennedy	1.25	3.00
499 Checklist 524-643	3.00	8.00
500 Jim Perry	1.50	4.00
501 Andy Etchebarren	1.25	3.00
502 Cubs Team	2.50	6.00
503 Gates Brown	1.50	4.00
504 Ken Wright	1.25	3.00
505 Ollie Brown	1.25	3.00
506 Bobby Knoop	1.25	3.00
507 George Stone	1.25	3.00
508 Roger Repoz	1.25	3.00
509 Jim Grant	1.25	3.00
510 Ken Harrelson	1.50	4.00
511 Chris Short	1.50	4.00
512 Dick Mills	1.25	3.00
Mike Garman		
513 Nolan Ryan	100.00	200.00
514 Ron Woods	1.25	3.00
515 Carl Morton	1.50	4.00
516 Ted Kubiak	1.25	3.00
517 Charlie Fox MG	1.25	3.00
518 Joe Grzenda	1.25	3.00
519 Willie Crawford	1.25	3.00

520 Tommy John 2.50 6.00
521 Leron Lee 1.25 3.00
522 Twins Team 2.50 6.00
523 John Odom 1.25 3.00
524 Mickey Stanley 2.50 6.00
525 Ernie Banks 40.00 80.00
526 Ray Jarvis 1.50 4.00
527 Cleon Jones 2.50 6.00
528 Wally Bunker 1.50 4.00
529 Enzo Hernandez 2.50 6.00
Bill Buckner
Marty Perez
530 Carl Yastrzemski 20.00 50.00
531 Mike Torrez 1.50 4.00
532 Bill Rigney MG 1.50 4.00
533 Mike Ryan 1.50 4.00
534 Luke Walker 1.50 4.00
535 Curt Flood 2.50 6.00
536 Claude Raymond 2.50 6.00
537 Tom Egan 1.50 4.00
538 Angel Bravo 1.50 4.00
539 Larry Brown 1.50 4.00
540 Larry Dierker 2.50 6.00
541 Bob Burda 1.50 4.00
542 Bob Miller 1.50 4.00
543 Yankees Team 6.00 15.00
544 Vida Blue 2.50 6.00
545 Dick Dietz 1.50 4.00
546 John Matias 1.50 4.00
547 Pat Dobson 1.50 4.00
548 Don Mason 1.50 4.00
549 Jim Brewer 1.50 4.00
550 Harmon Killebrew 12.50 40.00
551 Frank Linzy 1.50 4.00
552 Buddy Bradford 1.50 4.00
553 Kevin Collins 1.50 4.00
554 Lowell Palmer 1.50 4.00
555 Walt Williams 1.50 4.00
556 Jim McGlothlin 1.50 4.00
557 Tom Satriano 1.50 4.00
558 Hector Torres 1.50 4.00
559 Terry Cox 1.50 4.00
Bill Gogolewski
Gary Jones
560 Rusty Staub 3.00 8.00
561 Syd O'Brien 1.50 4.00
562 Dave Giusti 1.50 4.00
563 Giants Team 3.00 8.00
564 Al Fitzmorris 1.50 4.00
565 Jim Wynn 2.50 6.00
566 Tim Cullen 1.50 4.00
567 Walt Alston MG 4.00 10.00
568 Sal Campisi 1.50 4.00
569 Ivan Murrell 1.50 4.00
570 Jim Palmer 20.00 50.00
571 Ted Sizemore 1.50 4.00
572 Jerry Kenney 1.50 4.00
573 Ed Kranepool 2.50 6.00
574 Jim Bunning 4.00 10.00
575 Bill Freehan 2.50 6.00
576 Adrian Garrett 1.50 4.00
Brock Davis
Garry Jestadt
577 Jim Lonborg 2.50 6.00
578 Eddie Kasko 2.50 6.00
(Topps 578 is
Ron Hunt)
579 Marty Pattin 1.50 4.00
580 Tony Perez 12.50 30.00
581 Roger Nelson 1.50 4.00
582 Dave Cash 2.50 6.00
583 Ron Cook 1.50 4.00
584 Indians Team 3.00 8.00
585 Willie Davis 2.50 6.00
586 Dick Woodson 1.50 4.00
587 Sonny Jackson 1.50 4.00
588 Tom Bradley 1.50 4.00
589 Bob Barton 1.50 4.00
590 Alex Johnson 2.50 6.00
591 Jackie Brown 1.50 4.00
592 Randy Hundley 2.50 6.00
593 Jack Aker 1.50 4.00
594 Bob Chlupsa 2.50 6.00
Bob Stinson
Al Hrabosky RC
595 Dave Johnson 2.50 6.00
596 Mike Jorgensen 1.50 4.00
597 Ken Suarez 1.50 4.00
598 Rick Wise 2.50 6.00
599 Norm Cash 2.50 6.00
600 Willie Mays 75.00 150.00
601 Ken Tatum 1.50 4.00
602 Marty Martinez 1.50 4.00
603 Pirates Team 3.00 8.00
604 John Gelnar 1.50 4.00
605 Orlando Cepeda 4.00 10.00
606 Chuck Taylor 1.50 4.00
607 Paul Ratliff 1.50 4.00
608 Mike Wegener 2.50 6.00
609 Leo Durocher MG 3.00 8.00
610 Amos Otis 2.50 6.00
611 Tom Phoebus 1.50 4.00
612 Lou Camilli 1.50 4.00
Ted Ford
Steve Mingori
613 Pedro Borbon 1.50 4.00
614 Billy Cowan 1.50 4.00
615 Mel Stottlemyre 2.50 6.00
616 Larry Hisle 2.50 6.00
617 Clay Dalrymple 1.50 4.00
618 Tug McGraw 2.50 6.00
619 Checklist 644-752 4.00 10.00
620 Frank Howard 2.50 6.00
621 Ron Bryant 1.50 4.00
622 Joe Lahoud 1.50 4.00
623 Pat Jarvis 1.50 4.00
624 Athletics Team 3.00 8.00
625 Lou Brock 20.00 50.00
626 Freddie Patek 2.50 6.00
627 Steve Hamilton 1.50 4.00
628 John Bateman 2.50 6.00
629 John Hiller 3.00 8.00
630 Roberto Clemente 100.00 200.00
631 Eddie Fisher 1.50 4.00
632 Darrel Chaney 1.50 4.00
633 Bobby Brooks 1.50 4.00
Pete Koegel
Scott Northey
634 Phil Regan 1.50 4.00
635 Bobby Murcer 2.50 6.00
636 Denny LeMaster 1.50 4.00
637 Dave Bristol MG 1.50 4.00
638 Stan Williams 1.50 4.00
639 Tom Haller 1.50 4.00
640 Frank Robinson 30.00 60.00
641 Mets Team 10.00 25.00
642 Jim Roland 1.50 4.00
643 Rick Reichardt 1.50 4.00
644 Jim Stewart 4.00 10.00
645 Jim Maloney 5.00 12.00
646 Bobby Floyd 4.00 10.00
647 Juan Pizarro 4.00 10.00
648 Rich Folkers 8.00 20.00
Ted Martinez
Jon Matlack RC
649 Sparky Lyle 6.00 15.00
650 Rich Allen 20.00 50.00
651 Jerry Robertson 4.00 10.00
652 Braves Team 6.00 15.00
653 Russ Snyder 4.00 10.00
654 Don Shaw 4.00 10.00
655 Mike Epstein 4.00 10.00
656 Gerry Nyman 4.00 10.00
657 Jose Azcue 4.00 10.00
658 Paul Lindblad 4.00 10.00
659 Byron Browne 4.00 10.00
660 Ray Culp 4.00 10.00
661 Chuck Tanner MG 6.00 15.00
662 Mike Hedlund 4.00 10.00
663 Marv Staehle 4.00 10.00
664 Archie Reynolds 6.00 15.00
Bob Reynolds
Ken Reynolds
665 Ron Swoboda 6.00 15.00
666 Gene Brabender 4.00 10.00
667 Pete Ward 5.00 12.00
668 Gary Neibauer 4.00 10.00
669 Ike Brown 4.00 10.00
670 Bill Hands 4.00 10.00
671 Bill Voss 4.00 10.00
672 Ed Crosby 4.00 10.00
673 Gerry Janeski 4.00 10.00
674 Expos Team 6.00 15.00
675 Dave Boswell 4.00 10.00
676 Tommie Reynolds 4.00 10.00
677 Jack DiLauro 4.00 10.00
678 George Thomas 4.00 10.00
679 Don O'Riley 4.00 10.00
680 Don Mincher 4.00 10.00
681 Bill Butler 4.00 10.00
682 Terry Harmon 4.00 10.00
683 Bill Burbach 4.00 10.00
684 Curt Motton 4.00 10.00
685 Moe Drabowsky 4.00 10.00
686 Chico Ruiz 4.00 10.00
687 Ron Taylor 5.00 12.00
688 Sparky Anderson MG 20.00 50.00
689 Frank Baker 4.00 10.00
690 Bob Moose 4.00 10.00
691 Bob Heise 4.00 10.00
692 Hal Haydel 4.00 10.00
Rogelio Moret
Wayne Twitchell
693 Jose Pena 4.00 10.00
694 Rick Renick 4.00 10.00
695 Joe Niekro 5.00 12.00
696 Jerry Morales 4.00 10.00
697 Rickey Clark 4.00 10.00
698 Brewers Team 8.00 20.00
699 Jim Britton 5.00 12.00
700 Boog Powell 12.50 40.00
701 Bob Garibaldi 4.00 10.00
702 Milt Ramirez 4.00 10.00
703 Mike Kekich 4.00 10.00
704 J.C. Martin 4.00 10.00
705 Dick Selma 4.00 10.00
706 Joe Foy 4.00 10.00
707 Fred Lasher 4.00 10.00
708 Russ Nagelson 4.00 10.00
709 Dusty Baker RC 60.00 120.00
Don Baylor RC
Tom Paciorek RC
710 Sonny Siebert 4.00 10.00
711 Larry Stahl 4.00 10.00
712 Jose Martinez 4.00 10.00
713 Mike Marshall 8.00 20.00
714 Dick Williams MG 6.00 15.00
715 Horace Clarke 4.00 10.00
716 Dave Leonhard 4.00 10.00
717 Tommie Aaron 5.00 12.00
718 Billy Wynne 4.00 10.00
719 Jerry May 4.00 10.00
720 Matty Alou 5.00 12.00
721 John Morris 4.00 10.00
722 Astros Team 8.00 20.00
723 Vicente Romo 4.00 10.00
724 Tom Tischinski 4.00 10.00
725 Gary Gentry 4.00 10.00
726 Paul Popovich 4.00 10.00
727 Ray Lamb 4.00 10.00
728 Wayne Redmond 4.00 10.00
Keith Lampard
Bernie Williams
729 Dick Billings 4.00 10.00
730 Jim Rooker 4.00 10.00
731 Jim Qualls 4.00 10.00
732 Bob Reed 4.00 10.00
733 Lee Maye 4.00 10.00
734 Rob Gardner 4.00 10.00
735 Mike Shannon 6.00 15.00
736 Mel Queen 4.00 10.00
737 Preston Gomez MG 4.00 10.00
738 Russ Gibson 4.00 10.00
739 Barry Lersch 4.00 10.00
740 Luis Aparicio 20.00 50.00
741 Skip Guinn 4.00 10.00
742 Royals Team 6.00 15.00
743 John O'Donoghue 5.00 12.00
744 Chuck Manuel 4.00 10.00
745 Sandy Alomar 5.00 12.00
746 Andy Kosco 4.00 10.00
747 Al Severinsen 4.00 10.00
Scipio Spinks
Balor Moore
748 John Purdin 4.00 10.00
749 Ken Szotkiewicz 4.00 10.00
750 Denny McLain 12.50 40.00
751 Al Weis 6.00 15.00
752 Dick Drago 5.00 12.00

1972 O-Pee-Chee

The cards in this 525-card set measure 2 1/2" by 3 1/2". The 1972 O-Pee-Chee set is very similar to the 1972 Topps set. On a white background, the fronts feature color player photos with multicolored frames, rounded bottom corners and the top part of the photo also rounded. The player's name and team name appear on the front. The horizontal backs carry player biography and statistics in French and English and have a different color than the 1972 Topps cards. Features appearing for the first time were "Boyhood Photos" (KP: 341-348 and 491-498) and "In Action" cards. The O-Pee-Chee cards can be distinguished from Topps cards by the "Printed in Canada" on the bottom of the back. This was the first year the cards denoted O.P.C. in the copyright line rather than T.C.G. There is one card in the set which is notably different from the corresponding Topps number on the back, No. 465 Gil Hodges, which notes his death in April of 1972. Remember, the prices below apply only to the O-Pee-Chee cards -- NOT Topps cards which are much more plentiful. The cards were packaged in 36 count boxes with eight cards per pack which cost ten cents each. Notable Rookie Cards include Carlton Fisk.

COMPLETE SET (525) 1000.00 2000.00
COMMON CARD (1-132) .40 1.00
COMMON PLAYER (133-263) .60 1.50
COMMON (264-394) .75 2.00
COMMON (395-525) 1.00 2.50
1 Pirates Team 5.00 12.00
2 Ray Culp .40 1.00
3 Bob Tolan .40 1.00
4 Checklist 1-132 2.50 6.00
5 John Bateman .75 2.00
6 Fred Scherman .40 1.00
7 Enzo Hernandez .40 1.00
8 Ron Swoboda .75 2.00
9 Stan Williams .40 1.00
10 Amos Otis .75 2.00
11 Bobby Valentine .75 2.00
12 Jose Cardenal .40 1.00
13 Joe Grzenda .40 1.00
14 Pete Koegel .40 1.00
Mike Anderson
Wayne Twitchell
15 Walt Williams .40 1.00
16 Mike Jorgensen .40 1.00
17 Dave Duncan .75 2.00
18 Juan Pizarro .40 1.00
19 Billy Cowan .40 1.00
20 Don Wilson .40 1.00
21 Braves Team .75 2.00
22 Rob Gardner .40 1.00
23 Ted Kubiak .40 1.00
24 Ted Ford .40 1.00
25 Bill Singer .40 1.00
26 Andy Etchebarren .40 1.00
27 Bob Johnson .40 1.00
28 Bob Gebhard .40 1.00
Steve Brye
Hal Haydel
29 Bill Bonham .40 1.00
30 Rico Petrocelli .75 2.00
31 Cleon Jones .75 2.00
32 Cleon Jones IA .40 1.00
33 Billy Martin MG 2.50 6.00
34 Billy Martin IA 1.50 4.00
35 Jerry Johnson .40 1.00
36 Jerry Johnson IA .40 1.00
37 Carl Yastrzemski 8.00 20.00
38 Carl Yastrzemski IA 3.00 8.00
39 Bob Barton .40 1.00
40 Bob Barton IA .40 1.00
41 Tommy Davis .75 2.00
42 Tommy Davis IA .40 1.00
43 Rick Wise .75 2.00
44 Rick Wise IA .40 1.00
45 Glenn Beckert .75 2.00
46 Glenn Beckert IA .40 1.00
47 John Ellis .40 1.00
48 John Ellis IA .40 1.00
49 Willie Mays 30.00 60.00
50 Willie Mays IA 12.50 30.00
51 Harmon Killebrew 5.00 12.00
52 Harmon Killebrew IA 2.50 6.00
53 Bud Harrelson .75 2.00
54 Bud Harrelson IA .40 1.00
55 Clyde Wright .40 1.00
56 Rich Chiles .40 1.00
57 Bob Oliver .40 1.00
58 Ernie McAnally .75 2.00
59 Fred Stanley .40 1.00
60 Manny Sanguillen .75 2.00
61 Burt Hooton RC .75 2.00
Gene Hiser
Earl Stephenson
62 Angel Mangual .40 1.00
63 Duke Sims .40 1.00
64 Pete Broberg .40 1.00
65 Cesar Cedeno .75 2.00
66 Ray Corbin .40 1.00
67 Red Schoendienst MG 1.50 4.00
68 Jim York .40 1.00
69 Roger Freed .40 1.00
70 Mike Cuellar .75 2.00
71 Angels Team .75 2.00
72 Bruce Kison .40 1.00
73 Steve Huntz .40 1.00
74 Cecil Upshaw .40 1.00
75 Bert Campaneris .75 2.00
76 Don Carrithers .40 1.00
77 Ron Theobald .40 1.00
78 Steve Arlin .40 1.00
79 Mike Garman 40.00 80.00
Cecil Cooper RC
Carlton Fisk RC
80 Tony Perez 3.00 8.00
81 Mike Hedlund .40 1.00
82 Ron Woods .75 2.00
83 Dalton Jones .40 1.00
84 Vince Colbert .40 1.00
85 Joe Torre 1.50 4.00
Ralph Garr
Glenn Beckert LL
86 Tony Oliva 1.50 4.00
Bobby Murcer
Merv Rettenmund LL
87 Joe Torre 2.50 6.00
Willie Stargell
Hank Aaron LL
88 Harmon Killebrew 2.50 6.00
Frank Robinson
Reggie Smith LL
89 Willie Stargell 1.50 4.00
Hank Aaron
Lee May LL
90 Bill Melton 1.50 4.00
Norm Cash
Reggie Jackson LL
91 Tom Seaver 1.50 4.00
Dave Roberts
photo actually
Danny Coombs
Don Wilson LL
92 Vida Blue 1.50 4.00
Wilbur Wood
Jim Palmer LL
93 Fergie Jenkins 2.50 6.00
Steve Carlton
Al Downing
Tom Seaver LL
94 Mickey Lolich 1.50 4.00
Vida Blue
Wilbur Wood LL
95 Tom Seaver 2.50 6.00
Fergie Jenkins
Bill Stoneman LL
96 Mickey Lolich 1.50 4.00
Vida Blue
Joe Coleman LL
97 Tom Kelley .40 1.00
98 Chuck Tanner MG .75 2.00
99 Ross Grimsley .40 1.00
100 Frank Robinson 4.00 10.00
101 Bill Greif 1.50 4.00
J.R. Richard RC
Ray Busse
102 Lloyd Allen .40 1.00
103 Checklist 133-263 2.50 6.00
104 Toby Harrah RC .75 2.00
105 Gary Gentry .40 1.00
106 Brewers Team .75 2.00
107 Jose Cruz RC .75 2.00
108 Gary Waslewski .40 1.00
109 Jerry May .40 1.00
110 Ron Hunt .75 2.00
111 Jim Grant .40 1.00
112 Greg Luzinski .75 2.00
113 Rogelio Moret .40 1.00
114 Bill Buckner .75 2.00
115 Jim Fregosi .75 2.00
116 Ed Farmer .40 1.00
117 Cleo James .40 1.00
118 Skip Lockwood .40 1.00
119 Marty Perez .40 1.00
120 Bill Freehan .75 2.00
121 Ed Sprague .40 1.00
122 Larry Biittner .40 1.00
123 Ed Acosta .40 1.00
124 Alan Closter .40 1.00
Rusty Torres
Roger Hambright
125 Dave Cash .75 2.00
126 Bart Johnson .40 1.00
127 Duffy Dyer .40 1.00
128 Eddie Watt .40 1.00
129 Charlie Fox MG .40 1.00
130 Bob Gibson 4.00 10.00
131 Jim Nettles .40 1.00
132 Joe Morgan 3.00 8.00
133 Joe Keough .60 1.50
134 Carl Morton 1.00 2.50
135 Vada Pinson 1.00 2.50
136 Darrel Chaney .60 1.50
137 Dick Williams MG 1.00 2.50
138 Mike Kekich .60 1.50
139 Tim McCarver 1.00 2.50
140 Pat Dobson 1.00 2.50
141 Buzz Capra 1.00 2.50
Leroy Stanton
Jon Matlack
142 Chris Chambliss RC 2.00 5.00
143 Garry Jestadt .60 1.50
144 Marty Pattin .60 1.50
145 Don Kessinger 1.00 2.50
146 Steve Kealey .60 1.50
147 Dave Kingman RC 3.00 8.00
148 Dick Billings .60 1.50
149 Gary Neibauer .60 1.50
150 Norm Cash 1.00 2.50
151 Jim Brewer .60 1.50
152 Gene Clines .60 1.50
153 Rick Auerbach .60 1.50
154 Ted Simmons 2.00 5.00
155 Larry Dierker 1.00 2.50
156 Twins Team 1.00 2.50
157 Don Gullett .60 1.50
158 Jerry Kenney .60 1.50
159 John Boccabella 1.00 2.50
160 Andy Messersmith 1.00 2.50
161 Brock Davis .60 1.50
162 Jerry Bell 1.00 2.50
Darrell Porter RC UER
Bob Reynolds
(Porter and Bell
photos switched)
163 Tug McGraw 2.00 5.00
164 Tug McGraw IA 1.00 2.50
165 Chris Speier RC 1.00 2.50
166 Chris Speier IA .60 1.50
167 Deron Johnson .60 1.50
168 Deron Johnson IA .60 1.50
169 Vida Blue 2.00 5.00
170 Vida Blue IA 1.00 2.50
171 Darrell Evans 2.00 5.00
172 Darrell Evans IA 1.00 2.50
173 Clay Kirby .60 1.50
174 Clay Kirby IA .60 1.50
175 Tom Haller .60 1.50
176 Tom Haller IA .60 1.50
177 Paul Schaal .60 1.50
178 Paul Schaal IA .60 1.50
179 Dock Ellis .60 1.50
180 Dock Ellis IA .60 1.50
181 Ed Kranepool 1.00 2.50
182 Ed Kranepool IA .60 1.50
183 Bill Melton .60 1.50
184 Bill Melton IA .60 1.50
185 Ron Bryant .60 1.50
186 Ron Bryant IA .60 1.50
187 Gates Brown .60 1.50
188 Frank Lucchesi MG .60 1.50
189 Gene Tenace 1.00 2.50
190 Dave Giusti .60 1.50
191 Jeff Burroughs RC 2.00 5.00
192 Cubs Team 1.00 2.50
193 Kurt Bevacqua .60 1.50
194 Fred Norman .60 1.50
195 Orlando Cepeda 3.00 8.00
196 Mel Queen .60 1.50
197 Johnny Briggs .60 1.50
198 Charlie Hough RC 3.00 8.00
Bob O'Brien
Mike Strahler
199 Mike Fiore .60 1.50
200 Lou Brock 4.00 10.00
201 Phil Roof .60 1.50
202 Scipio Spinks .60 1.50
203 Ron Blomberg .60 1.50
204 Tommy Helms .60 1.50
205 Dick Drago .60 1.50
206 Dal Maxvill .60 1.50
207 Tom Egan .60 1.50
208 Milt Pappas 1.00 2.50
209 Joe Rudi 1.00 2.50
210 Denny McLain 1.00 2.50
211 Gary Sutherland 1.00 2.50
212 Grant Jackson .60 1.50
213 Billy Parker .60 1.50
Art Kusnyer
Tom Silverio
214 Mike McQueen .60 1.50
215 Alex Johnson 1.00 2.50
216 Joe Niekro 1.00 2.50
217 Roger Metzger .60 1.50
218 Eddie Kasko MG .60 1.50
219 Rennie Stennett 1.00 2.50
220 Jim Perry 1.00 2.50
221 NL Playoffs 1.00 2.50
Bucs champs
222 B.Robinson ALCS 2.00 5.00
223 Dave McNally WS 1.00 2.50
224 Dave Johnson WS 1.00 2.50
Mark Belanger
225 Manny Sanguillen WS 1.00 2.50
226 Roberto Clemente WS 4.00 10.00
227 Nellie Briles WS 1.00 2.50
228 Frank Robinson WS 2.00 5.00
Manny Sanguillen
229 Steve Blass WS 1.00 2.50
230 WS Summary 1.00 2.50
Pirates celebrate
231 Casey Cox .60 1.50
232 Chris Arnold .60 1.50
Jim Barr
Dave Rader
233 Jay Johnstone 1.00 2.50
234 Ron Taylor 2.00 5.00
235 Merv Rettenmund .60 1.50
236 Jim McGlothlin .60 1.50
237 Yankees Team 1.00 2.50
238 Leron Lee .60 1.50
239 Tom Timmermann .60 1.50
240 Rich Allen 1.00 2.50
241 Rollie Fingers 3.00 8.00
242 Don Mincher .60 1.50
243 Frank Linzy .60 1.50
244 Steve Braun .60 1.50
245 Tommie Agee 1.00 2.50
246 Tom Burgmeier .60 1.50
247 Milt May .60 1.50
248 Tom Bradley .60 1.50
249 Harry Walker MG .60 1.50
250 Boog Powell 1.00 2.50
251 Checklist 264-394 2.50 6.00
252 Ken Reynolds .60 1.50
253 Sandy Alomar 1.00 2.50
254 Boots Day 1.00 2.50
255 Jim Lonborg 1.00 2.50
256 George Foster 1.00 2.50
257 Jim Foor .60 1.50
Tim Hosley
Paul Jata
258 Randy Hundley .60 1.50
259 Sparky Lyle 1.00 2.50
260 Ralph Garr 1.00 2.50
261 Steve Mingori .60 1.50
262 Padres Team 1.00 2.50
263 Felipe Alou 1.00 2.50
264 Tommy John 1.25 3.00
265 Wes Parker 1.25 3.00
266 Bobby Bolin .75 2.00
267 Dave Concepcion 2.50 6.00
268 Dwain Anderson .75 2.00
Chris Floethe
269 Don Hahn .75 2.00
270 Jim Palmer 4.00 10.00
271 Ken Rudolph .75 2.00
272 Mickey Rivers RC 1.25 3.00
273 Bobby Floyd .75 2.00
274 Al Severinsen .75 2.00
275 Cesar Tovar .75 2.00
276 Gene Mauch MG 1.25 3.00
277 Elliott Maddox .75 2.00
278 Dennis Higgins .75 2.00
279 Larry Brown .75 2.00
280 Willie McCovey 3.00 8.00
281 Bill Parsons .75 2.00
282 Astros Team 1.25 3.00
283 Darrell Brandon .75 2.00
284 Ike Brown .75 2.00
285 Gaylord Perry 4.00 10.00
286 Gene Alley .75 2.00
287 Jim Hardin .75 2.00
288 Johnny Jeter .75 2.00
289 Syd O'Brien .75 2.00
290 Sonny Siebert .75 2.00
291 Hal McRae 1.25 3.00
292 Hal McRae IA .75 2.00
293 Danny Frisella .75 2.00
294 Danny Frisella IA .75 2.00
295 Dick Dietz .75 2.00
296 Dick Dietz IA .75 2.00
297 Claude Osteen 1.25 3.00
298 Claude Osteen IA .75 2.00
299 Hank Aaron 30.00 60.00
300 Hank Aaron IA 12.50 30.00
301 George Mitterwald .75 2.00
302 George Mitterwald IA .75 2.00
303 Joe Pepitone 1.25 3.00
304 Joe Pepitone IA .75 2.00
305 Ken Boswell .75 2.00
306 Ken Boswell IA .75 2.00
307 Steve Renko 1.25 3.00
308 Steve Renko IA .75 2.00
309 Roberto Clemente 40.00 80.00
310 Roberto Clemente IA 12.50 40.00
311 Clay Carroll .75 2.00
312 Clay Carroll IA .75 2.00
313 Luis Aparicio 4.00 10.00
314 Luis Aparicio IA 2.50 6.00
315 Paul Splittorff .75 2.00
316 Jim Bibby 1.25 3.00
Jorge Roque
Santiago Guzman
317 Rich Hand .75 2.00
318 Sonny Jackson .75 2.00
319 Aurelio Rodriguez .75 2.00
320 Steve Blass 1.25 3.00
321 Joe Lahoud .75 2.00
322 Jose Pena .75 2.00
323 Earl Weaver MG 3.00 8.00
324 Mike Ryan .75 2.00
325 Mel Stottlemyre 1.25 3.00
326 Pat Kelly .75 2.00
327 Steve Stone RC 1.25 3.00
328 Red Sox Team 1.25 3.00
329 Roy Foster .75 2.00
330 Jim Hunter 4.00 10.00
331 Stan Swanson 1.25 3.00
332 Buck Martinez .75 2.00
333 Steve Barber .75 2.00
334 Bill Fahey .75 2.00
Jim Mason
Tom Ragland
335 Bill Hands .75 2.00
336 Marty Martinez .75 2.00
337 Mike Kilkenny 1.25 3.00
338 Bob Grich 1.25 3.00
339 Ron Cook .75 2.00
340 Roy White 1.25 3.00
341 Joe Torre KP 1.25 3.00
342 Wilbur Wood KP .75 2.00
343 Willie Stargell KP 1.25 3.00
344 Dave McNally KP .75 2.00
345 Rick Wise KP .75 2.00
346 Jim Fregosi KP .75 2.00
347 Tom Seaver KP 3.00 8.00
348 Sal Bando KP .75 2.00
349 Al Fitzmorris .75 2.00
350 Frank Howard 1.25 3.00
351 Tom House 1.25 3.00
Rick Kester
Jimmy Britton
352 Dave LaRoche .75 2.00
353 Art Shamsky .75 2.00
354 Tom Murphy .75 2.00
355 Bob Watson 1.25 3.00
356 Gerry Moses .75 2.00
357 Woodie Fryman .75 2.00
358 Sparky Anderson MG 3.00 8.00
359 Don Pavletich .75 2.00
360 Dave Roberts .75 2.00
361 Mike Andrews .75 2.00
362 Mets Team 2.50 6.00
363 Ron Klimkowski .75 2.00
364 Johnny Callison 1.25 3.00
365 Dick Bosman 1.25 3.00
366 Jimmy Rosario .75 2.00
367 Ron Perranoski .75 2.00
368 Danny Thompson .75 2.00
369 Jim LeFebvre 1.25 3.00
370 Don Buford .75 2.00
371 Denny LeMaster .75 2.00
372 Lance Clemons .75 2.00
Monty Montgomery
373 John Mayberry 1.25 3.00
374 Jack Heidemann .75 2.00
375 Reggie Cleveland 1.25 3.00
376 Andy Kosco .75 2.00
377 Terry Harmon .75 2.00
378 Checklist 395-525 3.00 8.00
379 Ken Berry .75 2.00
380 Earl Williams .75 2.00
381 White Sox Team 1.25 3.00
382 Joe Gibbon .75 2.00
383 Brant Alyea .75 2.00
384 Dave Campbell 1.25 3.00
385 Mickey Stanley 1.25 3.00
386 Jim Colborn .75 2.00
387 Horace Clarke 1.25 3.00
388 Charlie Williams .75 2.00
389 Bill Rigney MG .75 2.00
390 Willie Davis 1.25 3.00
391 Ken Sanders .75 2.00
392 Fred Cambria 1.25 3.00
Richie Zisk RC
393 Curt Motton .75 2.00
394 Ken Forsch 1.25 3.00
395 Matty Alou 1.25 3.00
396 Paul Lindblad 1.00 2.50
397 Phillies Team 2.50 6.00
398 Larry Hisle 1.25 3.00
399 Milt Wilcox 1.25 3.00
400 Tony Oliva 2.50 6.00
401 Jim Nash 1.00 2.50
402 Bobby Heise 1.00 2.50
403 John Cumberland 1.00 2.50
404 Jeff Torborg 1.25 3.00
405 Ron Fairly 1.25 3.00
406 George Hendrick RC 1.25 3.00
407 Chuck Taylor 1.00 2.50
408 Jim Northrup 1.25 3.00
409 Frank Baker 1.00 2.50
410 Fergie Jenkins 4.00 10.00
411 Bob Montgomery 1.00 2.50
412 Dick Kelley 1.00 2.50
413 Don Eddy 1.00 2.50
Dave Lemonds
414 Bob Miller 1.00 2.50
415 Cookie Rojas 1.00 2.50
416 Johnny Edwards 1.00 2.50
417 Tom Hall 1.00 2.50
418 Tom Shopay 1.00 2.50
419 Jim Spencer 1.00 2.50
420 Steve Carlton 12.50 30.00
421 Ellie Rodriguez 1.00 2.50
422 Ray Lamb 1.00 2.50
423 Oscar Gamble 1.25 3.00
424 Bill Gogolewski 1.00 2.50
425 Ken Singleton 1.25 3.00
426 Ken Singleton IA 1.00 2.50
427 Tito Fuentes 1.00 2.50
428 Tito Fuentes IA 1.00 2.50
429 Bob Robertson 1.00 2.50
430 Bob Robertson IA 1.00 2.50
431 Clarence Gaston 1.25 3.00
432 Clarence Gaston IA 1.00 2.50
433 Johnny Bench 12.50 40.00
434 Johnny Bench IA 8.00 20.00
435 Reggie Jackson 20.00 50.00
436 Reggie Jackson IA 10.00 25.00
437 Maury Wills 2.50 6.00
438 Maury Wills IA 1.25 3.00
439 Billy Williams 3.00 8.00
440 Billy Williams IA 2.50 6.00
441 Thurman Munson 10.00 25.00
442 Thurman Munson IA 5.00 12.00
443 Ken Henderson 1.00 2.50
444 Ken Henderson IA 1.00 2.50
445 Tom Seaver 20.00 50.00
446 Tom Seaver IA 10.00 25.00
447 Willie Stargell 4.00 10.00
448 Willie Stargell IA 2.50 6.00
449 Bob Lemon MG 1.25 3.00
450 Mickey Lolich 1.25 3.00
451 Tony LaRussa 3.00 8.00
452 Ed Herrmann 1.00 2.50
453 Barry Lersch 1.00 2.50
454 A's Team 2.50 6.00
455 Tommy Harper 1.25 3.00
456 Mark Belanger 1.25 3.00
457 Darcy Fast 1.00 2.50
Derrel Thomas
Mike Ivie
458 Aurelio Monteagudo 1.00 2.50
459 Rick Renick 1.00 2.50
460 Al Downing 1.00 2.50
461 Tim Cullen 1.00 2.50
462 Rickey Clark 1.00 2.50
463 Bernie Carbo 1.00 2.50
464 Jim Roland 1.00 2.50
465 Gil Hodges MG 12.50 40.00
(Mentions his
death on 4/2/72)
466 Norm Miller 1.00 2.50
467 Steve Kline 1.00 2.50
468 Richie Scheinblum 1.00 2.50
469 Ron Herbel 1.00 2.50
470 Ray Fosse 1.00 2.50
471 Luke Walker 1.00 2.50
472 Phil Gagliano 1.00 2.50
473 Dan McGinn 1.00 2.50
474 Don Baylor 10.00 25.00
Roric Harrison
Johnny Oates RC
475 Gary Nolan 1.00 2.50
476 Lee Richard 1.00 2.50
477 Tom Phoebus 1.00 2.50
478 Checklist 5th Series 3.00 8.00
479 Don Shaw 1.00 2.50
480 Lee May 1.25 3.00
481 Billy Conigliaro 1.00 2.50
482 Joe Hoerner 1.00 2.50
483 Ken Suarez 1.00 2.50
484 Lum Harris MG 1.00 2.50
485 Phil Regan 1.00 2.50
486 John Lowenstein 1.00 2.50
487 Tigers Team 2.50 6.00
488 Mike Nagy 1.00 2.50
489 Terry Humphrey 1.00 2.50
Keith Lampard
490 Dave McNally 1.25 3.00
491 Lou Piniella KP 1.25 3.00
492 Mel Stottlemyre KP 1.25 3.00
493 Bob Bailey KP 1.25 3.00
494 Willie Horton KP 1.25 3.00
495 Bill Melton KP 1.00 2.50
496 Bud Harrelson KP 1.25 3.00
497 Jim Perry KP 1.25 3.00
498 Brooks Robinson KP 2.50 6.00
499 Vicente Romo 1.00 2.50
500 Joe Torre 3.00 8.00
501 Pete Hamm 1.00 2.50
502 Jackie Hernandez 1.00 2.50
503 Gary Peters 1.00 2.50
504 Ed Spiezio 1.00 2.50
505 Mike Marshall 1.25 3.00
506 Terry Ley 1.25 3.00
Jim Moyer
Dick Tidrow
507 Fred Gladding 1.00 2.50
508 Ellie Hendricks 1.00 2.50
509 Don McMahon 1.00 2.50
510 Ted Williams MG 8.00 20.00
511 Tony Taylor 1.00 2.50
512 Paul Popovich 1.00 2.50
513 Lindy McDaniel 1.25 3.00
514 Ted Sizemore 1.00 2.50
515 Bert Blyleven 2.50 6.00
516 Oscar Brown 1.00 2.50
517 Ken Brett 1.00 2.50
518 Wayne Garrett 1.00 2.50
519 Ted Abernathy 1.00 2.50
520 Larry Bowa 1.25 3.00
521 Alan Foster 1.00 2.50
522 Dodgers Team 2.50 6.00
523 Chuck Dobson 1.00 2.50
524 Ed Armbrister 1.00 2.50
Mel Behney
525 Carlos May 1.25 3.00

1973 O-Pee-Chee

The cards in this 660-card set measure 2 1/2" by 3 1/2". This set is essentially the same as the regular 1973 Topps set, except that the words "Printed in Canada" appear on the backs and the backs are bilingual. On a white border, the fronts feature color player photos with rounded corners and thin black borders. The player's name and position and the team name are also printed on the front. An "All-Time

Leaders" series (471-478) appears in this set. Kid pictures appeared again for the second year in a row (341-346). The backs carry player biography and statistics in French and English. The cards are numbered on the back. The backs appear to be more "yellow" than the Topps backs. Remember, the prices below apply only to the O-Pee-Chee cards -- NOT Topps cards which are more plentiful. Unlike the 1973 Topps set, all cards in this set were issued equally and at the same time, i.e., there were no scarce series with the O-Pee-Chee cards. Although there are no scarce series, cards 529-660 attract a slight premium. Because of the premium that high series Topps cards attract, there is a perception that O-Pee-Chee cards of the same number sequence are less available. The key card in this set is the Mike Schmidt Rookie Card. The cards were packaged in 10 count packs with 36 cards in a box which cost 10 cents. Other Rookie Cards of note in this set include Bob Boone and Dwight Evans.

COMPLETE SET (660) 500.00 1000.00
COMMON CARD (1-528) .30 .75
COMMON (529-660) 1.25 3.00
1 Babe Ruth 20.00 50.00
Hank Aaron
Willie Mays ATL
2 Rich Hebner .60 1.50
3 Jim Lonborg .60 1.50
4 John Milner .30 .75
5 Ed Brinkman .30 .75
6 Mac Scarce .30 .75
7 Texas Rangers Team .60 1.50
8 Tom Hall .30 .75
9 Johnny Oates .30 .75
10 Don Sutton 2.50 6.00
11 Chris Chambliss .60 1.50
12 Don Zimmer MG .60 1.50
Dave Garcia CO
Johnny Podres CO
Bob Skinner CO
Whitey Wietelmann CO
13 George Hendrick .60 1.50
14 Sonny Siebert .30 .75
15 Ralph Garr .60 1.50
16 Steve Braun .30 .75
17 Fred Gladding .30 .75
18 Leroy Stanton .30 .75
19 Tim Foli .30 .75
20 Stan Bahnsen .30 .75
21 Randy Hundley .60 1.50
22 Ted Abernathy .30 .75
23 Dave Kingman .60 1.50
24 Al Santorini .30 .75
25 Roy White .60 1.50
26 Pirates Team .60 1.50
27 Bill Gogolewski .30 .75
28 Hal McRae .60 1.50
29 Tony Taylor .60 1.50
30 Tug McGraw .60 1.50
31 Buddy Bell RC 1.00 2.50
32 Fred Norman .30 .75
33 Jim Breazeale .30 .75
34 Pat Dobson .30 .75
35 Willie Davis .60 1.50
36 Steve Barber .30 .75
37 Bill Robinson .60 1.50
38 Mike Epstein .30 .75
39 Dave Roberts .30 .75
40 Reggie Smith .60 1.50
41 Tom Walker .30 .75
42 Mike Andrews .30 .75
43 Randy Moffitt .30 .75
44 Rick Monday .60 1.50
45 Ellie Rodriguez .30 .75
(photo actually
John Felske)
46 Lindy McDaniel .60 1.50
47 Luis Melendez .30 .75
48 Paul Splittorff .30 .75
49 Frank Quilici MG .60 1.50
Vern Morgan CO
Bob Rodgers CO
Ralph Rowe CO
Al Worthington CO
50 Roberto Clemente 20.00 50.00
51 Chuck Seelbach .30 .75
52 Denis Menke .30 .75
53 Steve Dunning .30 .75
54 Checklist 1-132 1.25 3.00
55 Jon Matlack .60 1.50
56 Merv Rettenmund .30 .75
57 Derrel Thomas .30 .75
58 Mike Paul .30 .75
59 Steve Yeager RC .60 1.50
60 Ken Holtzman .60 1.50
61 Billy Williams 1.50 4.00
Rod Carew LL
62 Johnny Bench 1.00 2.50
Dick Allen LL
Home Run Leaders
63 Johnny Bench 1.00 2.50
Dick Allen
RBI Leaders
64 Lou Brock .60 1.50
Bert Campaneris LL
65 Steve Carlton .60 1.50
Luis Tiant LL
66 Steve Carlton .60 1.50
Gaylord Perry
Wilbur Wood LL
67 Steve Carlton 12.50 40.00
Nolan Ryan LL
68 Clay Carroll .60 1.50
Sparky Lyle LL
69 Phil Gagliano .30 .75
70 Milt Pappas .60 1.50
71 Johnny Briggs .30 .75
72 Ron Reed .30 .75
73 Ed Herrmann .30 .75
74 Billy Champion .30 .75
75 Vada Pinson .60 1.50
76 Doug Rader .30 .75
77 Mike Torrez .60 1.50
78 Richie Scheinblum .30 .75
79 Jim Willoughby .30 .75
80 Tony Oliva 1.50 4.00
81 Whitey Lockman MG .60 1.50
Hank Aguirre CO
Ernie Banks CO
Larry Jansen CO
Pete Reiser CO
82 Fritz Peterson .30 .75
83 Leron Lee .30 .75
84 Rollie Fingers 2.50 6.00
85 Ted Simmons .60 1.50
86 Tom McCraw .30 .75
87 Ken Boswell .30 .75
88 Mickey Stanley .60 1.50
89 Jack Billingham .30 .75
90 Brooks Robinson 4.00 10.00
91 Dodgers Team .60 1.50
92 Jerry Bell .30 .75
93 Jesus Alou .30 .75
94 Dick Billings .30 .75
95 Steve Blass .60 1.50
96 Doug Griffin .30 .75
97 Willie Montanez .60 1.50
98 Dick Woodson .30 .75
99 Carl Taylor .30 .75
100 Hank Aaron 20.00 50.00
101 Ken Henderson .30 .75
102 Rudy May .30 .75
103 Celerino Sanchez .30 .75
104 Reggie Cleveland .60 1.50
105 Carlos May .30 .75
106 Terry Humphrey .30 .75
107 Phil Hennigan .30 .75
108 Bill Russell .60 1.50
109 Doyle Alexander .60 1.50
110 Bob Watson .60 1.50
111 Dave Nelson .30 .75
112 Gary Ross .30 .75
113 Jerry Grote .60 1.50
114 Lynn McGlothen .30 .75
115 Ron Santo 1.50 4.00
116 Ralph Houk MG .60 1.50
Jim Hegan CO
Elston Howard CO
Dick Howser CO
Jim Turner CO
117 Ramon Hernandez .30 .75
118 John Mayberry .60 1.50
119 Larry Bowa .60 1.50
120 Joe Coleman .30 .75
121 Dave Rader .30 .75
122 Jim Strickland .30 .75
123 Sandy Alomar .60 1.50
124 Jim Hardin .30 .75
125 Ron Fairly .60 1.50
126 Jim Brewer .30 .75
127 Brewers Team .60 1.50
128 Ted Sizemore .30 .75
129 Terry Forster .60 1.50
130 Pete Rose 12.50 40.00
131 Eddie Kasko MG .60 1.50
Doug Camilli CO
Don Lenhardt CO
Eddie Popowski CO
Lee Stange CO
132 Matty Alou .60 1.50
133 Dave Roberts .30 .75
134 Milt Wilcox .30 .75
135 Lee May .60 1.50
136 Earl Weaver MG 1.50 4.00
George Bamberger CO
Jim Frey CO
Billy Hunter CO
George Staller CO
137 Jim Beauchamp .30 .75
138 Horacio Pina .30 .75
139 Carmen Fanzone .30 .75
140 Lou Piniella 1.00 2.50
141 Bruce Kison .30 .75
142 Thurman Munson 4.00 10.00
143 John Curtis .30 .75
144 Marty Perez .30 .75
145 Bobby Bonds 1.50 4.00
146 Woodie Fryman .30 .75
147 Mike Anderson .30 .75
148 Dave Goltz .30 .75
149 Ron Hunt .30 .75
150 Wilbur Wood .60 1.50
151 Wes Parker .60 1.50
152 Dave May .30 .75
153 Al Hrabosky .60 1.50
154 Jeff Torborg .60 1.50
155 Sal Bando .60 1.50
156 Cesar Geronimo .30 .75
157 Denny Riddleberger .30 .75
158 Astros Team .60 1.50
159 Clarence Gaston .60 1.50
160 Jim Palmer 3.00 8.00
161 Ted Martinez .30 .75
162 Pete Broberg .30 .75
163 Vic Davalillo .30 .75
164 Monty Montgomery .30 .75
165 Luis Aparicio 2.50 6.00
166 Terry Harmon .30 .75
167 Steve Stone .60 1.50
168 Jim Northrup .60 1.50
169 Ron Schueler RC .60 1.50
170 Harmon Killebrew 2.50 6.00
171 Bernie Carbo .30 .75
172 Steve Kline .30 .75
173 Hal Breeden .60 1.50
174 Goose Gossage RC 3.00 8.00
175 Frank Robinson 3.00 8.00
176 Chuck Taylor .30 .75
177 Bill Plummer .30 .75
178 Don Rose .30 .75
179 Dick Williams MG .60 1.50
Jerry Adair CO
Vern Hoscheit CO
Irv Noren CO
Wes Stock CO
180 Fergie Jenkins 2.00 5.00
181 Jack Brohamer .30 .75
182 Mike Caldwell RC .60 1.50
183 Don Buford .30 .75
184 Jerry Koosman .60 1.50
185 Jim Wynn .60 1.50
186 Bill Fahey .30 .75
187 Luke Walker .30 .75
188 Cookie Rojas .60 1.50
189 Greg Luzinski 1.00 2.50
190 Bob Gibson 4.00 10.00
191 Tigers Team .60 1.50
192 Pat Jarvis .30 .75
193 Carlton Fisk 5.00 12.00
194 Jorge Orta .30 .75
195 Clay Carroll .30 .75
196 Ken McMullen .30 .75
197 Ed Goodson .30 .75
198 Horace Clarke .30 .75
199 Bert Blyleven 1.50 4.00
200 Billy Williams 2.50 6.00
201 G.Hendrick ALCS .60 1.50
202 George Foster NLCS .60 1.50
203 Gene Tenace WS .60 1.50
204 World Series Game 2 .60 1.50
A's two straight
205 Tony Perez WS 1.00 2.50
206 Gene Tenace WS .60 1.50
207 Blue Moon Odom WS .60 1.50
208 Johnny Bench WS 2.50 6.00
209 Bert Campaneris WS .60 1.50
210 W.S. Summary .60 1.50
World champions:
A's Win
211 Balor Moore .30 .75
212 Joe Lahoud .30 .75
213 Steve Garvey 2.50 6.00
214 Dave Hamilton .30 .75
215 Dusty Baker 1.50 4.00
216 Toby Harrah .60 1.50
217 Don Wilson .30 .75
218 Aurelio Rodriguez .30 .75
219 Cardinals Team .60 1.50
220 Nolan Ryan 50.00 100.00
221 Fred Kendall .30 .75
222 Rob Gardner .30 .75
223 Bud Harrelson .60 1.50
224 Bill Lee .60 1.50
225 Al Oliver .60 1.50
226 Ray Fosse .30 .75
227 Wayne Twitchell .30 .75
228 Bobby Darwin .30 .75
229 Roric Harrison .30 .75
230 Joe Morgan 3.00 8.00
231 Bill Parsons .30 .75
232 Ken Singleton .60 1.50
233 Ed Kirkpatrick .30 .75
234 Bill North .30 .75
235 Jim Hunter 2.50 6.00
236 Tito Fuentes .30 .75
237 Eddie Mathews MG 1.50 4.00
Lew Burdette CO
Jim Busby CO
Roy Hartsfield CO
Ken Silvestri CO
238 Tony Muser .30 .75
239 Pete Richert .30 .75
240 Bobby Murcer 1.00 2.50
241 Dwain Anderson .30 .75
242 George Culver .30 .75
243 Angels Team .60 1.50
244 Ed Acosta .30 .75
245 Carl Yastrzemski 5.00 12.00
246 Ken Sanders .30 .75
247 Del Unser .30 .75
248 Jerry Johnson .30 .75
249 Larry Biittner .30 .75
250 Manny Sanguillen .60 1.50
251 Roger Nelson .30 .75
252 Charlie Fox MG .60 1.50
Joe Amalfitano CO
Andy Gilbert CO
Don McMahon CO
John McNamara CO
253 Mark Belanger .60 1.50
254 Bill Stoneman .60 1.50
255 Reggie Jackson 8.00 20.00
256 Chris Zachary .30 .75
257 Yogi Berra MG 1.50 4.00
Roy McMillan CO
Joe Pignatano CO
Rube Walker CO
Eddie Yost CO
258 Tommy John 1.00 2.50
259 Jim Holt .30 .75
260 Gary Nolan .60 1.50
261 Pat Kelly .30 .75
262 Jack Aker .30 .75
263 George Scott .60 1.50
264 Checklist 133-264 1.00 2.50
265 Gene Michael .60 1.50
266 Mike Lum .30 .75
267 Lloyd Allen .30 .75
268 Jerry Morales .30 .75
269 Tim McCarver 1.00 2.50
270 Luis Tiant 1.00 2.50
271 Tom Hutton .30 .75
272 Ed Farmer .30 .75
273 Chris Speier .30 .75
274 Darold Knowles .30 .75
275 Tony Perez 2.50 6.00
276 Joe Lovitto .30 .75
277 Bob Miller .30 .75
278 Orioles Team .60 1.50
279 Mike Strahler .30 .75
280 Al Kaline 4.00 10.00
281 Mike Jorgensen .30 .75
282 Steve Hovley .30 .75
283 Ray Sadecki .30 .75
284 Glenn Borgmann .30 .75
285 Don Kessinger .60 1.50
286 Frank Linzy .30 .75
287 Eddie Leon .30 .75
288 Gary Gentry .30 .75
289 Bob Oliver .30 .75
290 Cesar Cedeno .60 1.50
291 Rogelio Moret .30 .75
292 Jose Cruz .60 1.50
293 Bernie Allen .30 .75
294 Steve Arlin .30 .75
295 Bert Campaneris .60 1.50
296 Sparky Anderson MG 1.50 4.00
Alex Grammas CO
Ted Kluszewski CO
George Scherger CO
Larry Shepard CO
297 Walt Williams .30 .75
298 Ron Bryant .30 .75
299 Ted Ford .30 .75
300 Steve Carlton 5.00 12.00
301 Billy Grabarkewitz .30 .75
302 Terry Crowley .30 .75
303 Nelson Briles .30 .75
304 Duke Sims .30 .75
305 Willie Mays 20.00 50.00
306 Tom Burgmeier .30 .75
307 Boots Day .30 .75
308 Skip Lockwood .30 .75
309 Paul Popovich .30 .75
310 Dick Allen 1.00 2.50
311 Joe Decker .30 .75
312 Oscar Brown .30 .75
313 Jim Ray .30 .75
314 Ron Swoboda .60 1.50
315 John Odom .30 .75
316 Padres Team .60 1.50
317 Danny Cater .30 .75
318 Jim McGlothlin .30 .75
319 Jim Spencer .30 .75
320 Lou Brock 4.00 10.00
321 Rich Hinton .30 .75
322 Garry Maddox RC .60 1.50
323 Billy Martin MG 1.00 2.50
Art Fowler CO
Charlie Silvera CO
Dick Tracewski CO
Joe Schultz CO ERR
Schultz name not printed on card
324 Al Downing .30 .75
325 Boog Powell .60 1.50
326 Darrell Brandon .30 .75
327 John Lowenstein .30 .75
328 Bill Bonham .30 .75
329 Ed Kranepool .60 1.50
330 Rod Carew 4.00 10.00
331 Carl Morton .30 .75
332 John Felske .30 .75
333 Gene Clines .30 .75
334 Freddie Patek .30 .75
335 Bob Tolan .30 .75
336 Tom Bradley .30 .75
337 Dave Duncan .60 1.50
338 Checklist 265-396 1.00 2.50
339 Dick Tidrow .30 .75
340 Nate Colbert .30 .75
341 Jim Palmer KP 1.00 2.50
342 Sam McDowell KP .60 1.50
343 Bobby Murcer KP .60 1.50
344 Jim Hunter KP 1.00 2.50
345 Chris Speier KP .30 .75
346 Gaylord Perry KP .60 1.50
347 Royals Team .60 1.50
348 Rennie Stennett .30 .75
349 Dick McAuliffe .30 .75
350 Tom Seaver 6.00 15.00
351 Jimmy Stewart .30 .75
352 Don Stanhouse .30 .75
353 Steve Brye .30 .75
354 Billy Parker .30 .75
355 Mike Marshall .60 1.50
356 Chuck Tanner MG .60 1.50
Joe Lonnett CO
Jim Mahoney CO
Al Monchak CO
Johnny Sain CO
357 Ross Grimsley .30 .75
358 Jim Nettles .30 .75
359 Cecil Upshaw .30 .75
360 Joe Rudi .60 1.50
(photo actually
Gene Tenace)
361 Fran Healy .30 .75
362 Eddie Watt .30 .75
363 Jackie Hernandez .30 .75
364 Rick Wise .30 .75
365 Rico Petrocelli .60 1.50
366 Brock Davis .30 .75
367 Burt Hooton .60 1.50
368 Bill Buckner .60 1.50
369 Lerrin LaGrow .30 .75
370 Willie Stargell 2.50 6.00
371 Mike Kekich .30 .75
372 Oscar Gamble .30 .75
373 Clyde Wright .30 .75
374 Darrell Evans 1.00 2.50
375 Larry Dierker .60 1.50
376 Frank Duffy .30 .75
377 Gene Mauch MG 1.00 2.50
Dave Bristol CO
Larry Doby CO
Cal McLish CO
Jerry Zimmerman CO
378 Lenny Randle .30 .75
379 Cy Acosta .30 .75
380 Johnny Bench 6.00 15.00
381 Vicente Romo .30 .75
382 Mike Hegan .30 .75
383 Diego Segui .30 .75
384 Don Baylor 1.50 4.00
385 Jim Perry .60 1.50
386 Don Money .30 .75
387 Jim Barr .30 .75
388 Ben Oglivie .60 1.50
389 Mets Team 2.00 5.00
390 Mickey Lolich .60 1.50
391 Lee Lacy RC .60 1.50
392 Dick Drago .30 .75
393 Jose Cardenal .30 .75
394 Sparky Lyle .60 1.50
395 Roger Metzger .30 .75
396 Grant Jackson .30 .75
397 Dave Cash .60 1.50
398 Rich Hand .30 .75
399 George Foster .60 1.50
400 Gaylord Perry 2.50 6.00
401 Clyde Mashore .30 .75
402 Jack Hiatt .30 .75
403 Sonny Jackson .30 .75
404 Chuck Brinkman .30 .75
405 Cesar Tovar .30 .75
406 Paul Lindblad .30 .75
407 Felix Millan .30 .75
408 Jim Colborn .30 .75
409 Ivan Murrell .30 .75
410 Willie McCovey 3.00 8.00
411 Ray Corbin .30 .75
412 Manny Mota .60 1.50
413 Tom Timmerman .30 .75
414 Ken Rudolph .30 .75
415 Marty Pattin .30 .75
416 Paul Schaal .30 .75
417 Scipio Spinks .30 .75
418 Bobby Grich .60 1.50
419 Casey Cox .30 .75
420 Tommie Agee .30 .75
421 Bobby Winkles MG .60 1.50
Tom Morgan CO
Salty Parker CO
Jimmie Reese CO
John Roseboro CO
422 Bob Robertson .30 .75
423 Johnny Jeter .30 .75
424 Denny Doyle .30 .75
425 Alex Johnson .30 .75
426 Dave LaRoche .30 .75
427 Rick Auerbach .30 .75
428 Wayne Simpson .30 .75
429 Jim Fairey .30 .75
430 Vida Blue .60 1.50
431 Gerry Moses .30 .75
432 Dan Frisella .30 .75
433 Willie Horton .60 1.50
434 Giants Team 1.00 2.50
435 Rico Carty .60 1.50
436 Jim McAndrew .30 .75
437 John Kennedy .30 .75
438 Enzo Hernandez .30 .75
439 Eddie Fisher .30 .75
440 Glenn Beckert .30 .75
441 Gail Hopkins .30 .75
442 Dick Dietz .30 .75
443 Danny Thompson .30 .75
444 Ken Brett .30 .75
445 Ken Berry .30 .75
446 Jerry Reuss .60 1.50
447 Joe Hague .30 .75
448 John Hiller .60 1.50
449 Ken Aspromonte MG 2.00 5.00
Rocky Colavito CO
Joe Lutz CO
Warren Spahn CO
450 Joe Torre 1.00 2.50
451 John Vuckovich .30 .75
452 Paul Casanova .30 .75
453 Checklist 397-528 1.00 2.50
454 Tom Haller .30 .75
455 Bill Melton .30 .75
456 Dick Green .30 .75
457 John Strohmayer .30 .75
458 Jim Mason .30 .75
459 Jimmy Howarth .30 .75
460 Bill Freehan .60 1.50
461 Mike Corkins .30 .75
462 Ron Blomberg .30 .75
463 Ken Tatum .30 .75
464 Chicago Cubs Team 1.00 2.50
465 Dave Giusti .30 .75
466 Jose Arcia .30 .75
467 Mike Ryan .30 .75
468 Tom Griffin .30 .75
469 Dan Monzon .30 .75
470 Mike Cuellar .60 1.50
471 Ty Cobb ATL 5.00 12.00
4191 Hits
472 Lou Gehrig ATL 8.00 20.00
23 Grand Slams
473 Hank Aaron ATL 5.00 12.00
6172 Total Bases
474 Babe Ruth ATL 10.00 25.00
2209 RBI's
475 Ty Cobb ATL 4.00 10.00
.367 Batting Average
476 Walter Johnson ATL 1.00 2.50
113 Shutouts
477 Cy Young ATL 1.00 2.50
511 Wins
478 Walter Johnson ATL 1.00 2.50
3508 Strikeouts
479 Hal Lanier .30 .75
480 Juan Marichal 2.50 6.00
481 White Sox Team Card 1.00 2.50
482 Rick Reuschel RC 1.00 2.50
483 Dal Maxvill .30 .75
484 Ernie McAnally .30 .75
485 Norm Cash .60 1.50
486 Danny Ozark MG .60 1.50
Carroll Beringer CO
Billy DeMars CO
Ray Rippelmeyer CO
Bobby Wine CO
487 Bruce Dal Canton .30 .75
488 Dave Campbell .60 1.50
489 Jeff Burroughs .60 1.50
490 Claude Osteen .60 1.50
491 Bob Montgomery .30 .75
492 Pedro Borbon .30 .75
493 Duffy Dyer .30 .75
494 Rich Morales .30 .75
495 Tommy Helms .30 .75
496 Ray Lamb .30 .75
497 Red Schoendienst MG 1.00 2.50
Vern Benson CO
George Kissell CO
Barney Schultz CO
498 Graig Nettles 1.50 4.00
499 Bob Moose .30 .75
500 Oakland A's Team 1.00 2.50
501 Larry Gura .30 .75
502 Bobby Valentine 1.00 2.50
503 Phil Niekro 2.50 6.00
504 Earl Williams .30 .75
505 Bob Bailey .30 .75
506 Bart Johnson .30 .75
507 Darrel Chaney .30 .75
508 Gates Brown .30 .75
509 Jim Nash .30 .75
510 Amos Otis .60 1.50
511 Sam McDowell .60 1.50
512 Dalton Jones .30 .75
513 Dave Marshall .30 .75
514 Jerry Kenney .30 .75
515 Andy Messersmith .60 1.50
516 Danny Walton .30 .75
517 Bill Virdon MG 1.00 2.50
Don Leppert CO
Bill Mazeroski CO
Dave Ricketts CO
Mel Wright CO
518 Bob Veale .30 .75
519 John Edwards .30 .75
520 Mel Stottlemyre .60 1.50
521 Atlanta Braves Team 1.00 2.50
522 Leo Cardenas .30 .75
523 Wayne Granger .30 .75
524 Gene Tenace .60 1.50
525 Jim Fregosi .60 1.50
526 Ollie Brown .30 .75
527 Dan McGinn .30 .75
528 Paul Blair .60 1.50
529 Milt May 1.25 3.00
530 Jim Kaat 1.50 4.00
531 Ron Woods 1.25 3.00
532 Steve Mingori 1.25 3.00
533 Larry Stahl 1.25 3.00
534 Dave Lemonds 1.25 3.00
535 John Callison 1.50 4.00
536 Phillies Team 2.50 6.00
537 Bill Slayback 1.25 3.00
538 Jim Ray Hart 1.50 4.00
539 Tom Murphy 1.25 3.00
540 Cleon Jones 1.50 4.00
541 Bob Bolin 1.25 3.00
542 Pat Corrales 1.50 4.00
543 Alan Foster 1.25 3.00
544 Von Joshua 1.25 3.00
545 Orlando Cepeda 4.00 10.00
546 Jim York 1.25 3.00
547 Bobby Heise 1.25 3.00
548 Don Durham 1.25 3.00
549 hitey Herzog MG 1.50 4.00
Chuck Estrada CO
Chuck Hiller CO
Jackie Moore CO
550 Dave Johnson 1.50 4.00
551 Mike Kilkenny 1.50 4.00
552 J.C. Martin 1.25 3.00
553 Mickey Scott 1.25 3.00
554 Dave Concepcion 2.50 6.00
555 Bill Hands 1.25 3.00
556 Yankees Team 2.50 6.00
557 Bernie Williams 1.25 3.00
558 Jerry May 1.25 3.00
559 Barry Lersch 1.25 3.00
560 Frank Howard 1.50 4.00
561 Jim Geddes 1.25 3.00
562 Wayne Garrett 1.25 3.00
563 Larry Haney 1.25 3.00
564 Mike Thompson 1.25 3.00
565 Jim Hickman 1.25 3.00
566 Lew Krausse 1.25 3.00
567 Bob Fenwick 1.25 3.00
568 Ray Newman 1.25 3.00
569 Walt Alston MG 3.00 8.00
Red Adams CO
Monty Basgall CO
Jim Gilliam CO
Tom Lasorda CO
570 Bill Singer 1.50 4.00
571 Rusty Torres 1.25 3.00
572 Gary Sutherland 1.25 3.00
573 Fred Beene 1.25 3.00
574 Bob Didier 1.25 3.00
575 Dock Ellis 1.25 3.00
576 Expos Team 3.00 8.00
577 Eric Soderholm 1.25 3.00
578 Ken Wright 1.25 3.00
579 Tom Grieve 1.50 4.00
580 Joe Pepitone 1.50 4.00
581 Steve Kealey 1.25 3.00
582 Darrell Porter 1.50 4.00
583 Bill Greif 1.25 3.00
584 Chris Arnold 1.25 3.00
585 Joe Niekro 1.50 4.00
586 Bill Sudakis 1.25 3.00
587 Rich McKinney 1.25 3.00
588 Checklist 529-660 8.00 20.00
589 Ken Forsch 1.25 3.00
590 Deron Johnson 1.25 3.00
591 Mike Hedlund 1.25 3.00
592 John Boccabella 1.25 3.00
593 Jack McKeon MG 1.25 3.00
Galen Cisco CO
Harry Dunlop CO
Charlie Lau CO
594 Vic Harris 1.25 3.00
595 Don Gullett 1.50 4.00
596 Red Sox Team 2.50 6.00
597 Mickey Rivers 1.50 4.00
598 Phil Roof 1.25 3.00
599 Ed Crosby 1.25 3.00
600 Dave McNally 1.50 4.00
601 Sergio Robles 1.50 4.00
George Pena
Rick Stelmaszek
602 Mel Behney 1.50 4.00
Ralph Garcia
Doug Rau
603 Terry Hughes 1.50 4.00
Bill McNulty
Ken Reitz
604 Jesse Jefferson 1.50 4.00
Dennis O'Toole
Bob Strampe
605 Enos Cabell RC 1.50 4.00
Pat Bourque
Gonzalo Marquez
606 Gary Matthews RC 2.50 6.00
Tom Paciorek
Jorge Roque
607 Pepe Frias 1.50 4.00
Ray Busse
Mario Guerrero
608 Steve Busby RC 2.50 6.00
Dick Colpaert
George Medich
609 Larvell Blanks 2.50 6.00
Pedro Garcia
Dave Lopes RC
610 Jimmy Freeman 1.50 4.00
Charlie Hough
Hank Webb
611 Rich Coggins 1.50 4.00
Jim Wohlford
Richie Zisk
612 Steve Lawson 1.50 4.00
Bob Reynolds
Brent Strom
613 Bob Boone RC 6.00 15.00
Skip Jutze
Mike Ivie
614 Al Bumbry 8.00 20.00
Dwight Evans RC
Charlie Spikes
615 Ron Cey 75.00 150.00
John Hilton
Mike Schmidt RC
616 Norm Angelini 1.50 4.00
Steve Blateric
Mike Garman
617 Rich Chiles 1.25 3.00
618 Andy Etchebarren 1.25 3.00
619 Billy Wilson 1.25 3.00
620 Tommy Harper 1.50 4.00
621 Joe Ferguson 1.50 4.00
622 Larry Hisle 1.50 4.00
623 Steve Renko 1.25 3.00
624 Leo Durocher MG 3.00 8.00
Preston Gomez CO
Grady Hatton CO
Hub Kittle CO
Jim Owens CO
625 Angel Mangual 1.25 3.00
626 Bob Barton 1.25 3.00
627 Luis Alvarado 1.25 3.00
628 Jim Slaton 1.25 3.00
629 Indians Team 2.50 6.00
630 Denny McLain 2.50 6.00
631 Tom Matchick 1.25 3.00
632 Dick Selma 1.25 3.00
633 Ike Brown 1.25 3.00
634 Alan Closter 1.25 3.00
635 Gene Alley 1.50 4.00
636 Rickey Clark 1.25 3.00
637 Norm Miller 1.25 3.00
638 Ken Reynolds 1.25 3.00
639 Willie Crawford 1.25 3.00
640 Dick Bosman 1.25 3.00
641 Reds Team 2.50 6.00
642 Jose Laboy 1.25 3.00
643 Al Fitzmorris 1.25 3.00
644 Jack Heidemann 1.25 3.00
645 Bob Locker 1.25 3.00
646 Del Crandall MG 1.50 4.00
Harvey Kuenn CO
Joe Nossek CO
Bob Shaw CO
Jim Walton CO
647 George Stone 1.25 3.00
648 Tom Egan 1.25 3.00
649 Rich Folkers 1.25 3.00
650 Felipe Alou 2.50 6.00
651 Don Carrithers 1.25 3.00
652 Ted Kubiak 1.25 3.00
653 Joe Hoerner 1.25 3.00
654 Twins Team 2.50 6.00
655 Clay Kirby 1.25 3.00
656 John Ellis 1.25 3.00
657 Bob Johnson 1.25 3.00
658 Elliott Maddox 1.25 3.00
659 Jose Pagan 1.25 3.00
660 Fred Scherman 2.50 6.00

1973 O-Pee-Chee Blue Team Checklists

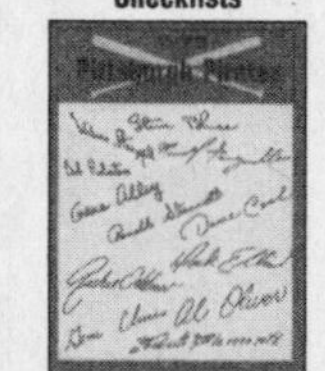

This 24-card standard-size set is somewhat difficult to find. These blue-bordered team checklist cards are very similar in design to the mass produced red trim team checklist cards issued by O-Pee-Chee the next year and obviously very similar to the Topps issue. The primary difference compared to the Topps issue is the existence of a little French language on the reverse of the O-Pee-Chee. The fronts feature facsimile autographs on a white background. On an orange background, the backs carry the team checklists. The words "Team Checklist" are printed in French and English. The cards are unnumbered and checklisted below in alphabetical order.

COMPLETE SET (24) 60.00 120.00
COMMON TEAM (1-24) 2.50 6.00

1974 O-Pee-Chee

The cards in this 660-card set measure 2 1/2" by 3 1/2". The 1974 O-Pee-Chee cards are very similar to the 1974 Topps cards. Since the O-Pee-Chee cards were printed substantially later than the Topps cards, there was no "San Diego rumored moving to Washington" problem in the O-Pee-Chee set. On a white background, the fronts feature color player photos with rounded corners and blue borders. The player's name and position and the team name also appear on the front. The horizontal backs are golden yellow instead of green like the 1974 Topps and carry player biography and statistics in French and English. There are a number of obverse differences between the two sets as well; they are numbers 3, 4, 5, 6, 7, 8, 9, 99, 166 and 196. The Aaron Specials generally feature two past cards per card instead of four as in the Topps. Remember, the prices below apply only to O-Pee-Chee cards -- they are NOT prices for Topps cards as the Topps cards are generally much more available. The cards were issued in eight card packs with 36 packs to a box. Notable Rookie Cards include Dave Parker and Dave Winfield.

COMPLETE SET (660)	600.00	1000.00
1 Hank Aaron	30.00	60.00
Complete ML record		
2 Aaron Special 54-57	5.00	12.00
Records on back		
3 Aaron Special 58-59	5.00	12.00
4 Aaron Special 60-61	5.00	12.00
5 Aaron Special 62-63	5.00	12.00
6 Aaron Special 64-65	5.00	12.00
7 Aaron Special 66-67	5.00	12.00
8 Aaron Special 68-69	5.00	12.00
9 Aaron Special 70-73	5.00	12.00
Milestone homers		
10 Johnny Bench	10.00	25.00
11 Jim Bibby	.40	1.00
12 Dave May	.40	1.00
13 Tom Hilgendorf	.40	1.00
14 Paul Popovich	.40	1.00
15 Joe Torre	1.50	4.00
16 Orioles Team	.75	2.00
17 Doug Bird	.40	1.00
18 Gary Thomasson	.40	1.00
19 Gerry Moses	.40	1.00
20 Nolan Ryan	40.00	80.00
21 Bob Gallagher	.40	1.00
22 Cy Acosta	.40	1.00
23 Craig Robinson	.40	1.00
24 John Hiller	.75	2.00
25 Ken Singleton	.75	2.00
26 Bill Campbell	.40	1.00
27 George Scott	.75	2.00
28 Manny Sanguillen	.75	2.00
29 Phil Niekro	2.50	6.00
30 Bobby Bonds	1.50	4.00
31 Preston Gomez MG	.75	2.00
Roger Craig CO		
Hub Kittle CO		
Grady Hatton CO		
Bob Lillis CO		
32 Johnny Grubb	.40	1.00
33 Don Newhauser	.40	1.00
34 Andy Kosco	.40	1.00
35 Gaylord Perry	2.50	6.00
36 Cardinals Team	.75	2.00
37 Dave Sells	.40	1.00
38 Don Kessinger	.75	2.00
39 Ken Suarez	.40	1.00
40 Jim Palmer	5.00	12.00
41 Bobby Floyd	.40	1.00
42 Claude Osteen	.75	2.00
43 Jim Wynn	.75	2.00
44 Mel Stottlemyre	.75	2.00
45 Dave Johnson	.75	2.00
46 Pat Kelly	.40	1.00
47 Dick Ruthven	.40	1.00
48 Dick Sharon	.40	1.00
49 Steve Renko	.75	2.00
50 Rod Carew	5.00	12.00
51 Bob Heise	.40	1.00
52 Al Oliver	.75	2.00
53 Fred Kendall	.40	1.00
54 Elias Sosa	.40	1.00
55 Frank Robinson	5.00	12.00
56 New York Mets Team	.75	2.00
57 Darold Knowles	.40	1.00
58 Charlie Spikes	.40	1.00
59 Ross Grimsley	.40	1.00
60 Lou Brock	4.00	10.00
61 Luis Aparicio	2.50	6.00
62 Bob Locker	.40	1.00
63 Bill Sudakis	.40	1.00
64 Doug Rau	.40	1.00
65 Amos Otis	.75	2.00
66 Sparky Lyle	.75	2.00
67 Tommy Helms	.40	1.00
68 Grant Jackson	.40	1.00
69 Del Unser	.40	1.00
70 Dick Allen	1.25	3.00
71 Dan Frisella	.40	1.00
72 Aurelio Rodriguez	.40	1.00
73 Mike Marshall	1.25	3.00
74 Twins Team	.75	2.00
75 Jim Colborn	.40	1.00
76 Mickey Rivers	.75	2.00
77 Rich Troedson	.40	1.00
78 Charlie Fox MG	.75	2.00
John McNamara CO		
Joe Amalfitano CO		
Andy Gilbert CO		
Don McMahon CO		
79 Gene Tenace	.75	2.00
80 Tom Seaver	8.00	20.00
81 Frank Duffy	.40	1.00
82 Dave Giusti	.40	1.00
83 Orlando Cepeda	2.50	6.00
84 Rick Wise	.40	1.00
85 Joe Morgan	5.00	12.00
86 Joe Ferguson	.75	2.00
87 Fergie Jenkins	2.50	6.00
88 Fred Patek	.75	2.00
89 Jackie Brown	.40	1.00
90 Bobby Murcer	.75	2.00
91 Ken Forsch	.40	1.00
92 Paul Blair	.75	2.00
93 Rod Gilbreath	.40	1.00
94 Tigers Team	.75	2.00
95 Steve Carlton	5.00	12.00
96 Jerry Hairston	.40	1.00
97 Bob Bailey	.75	2.00
98 Bert Blyleven	1.50	4.00
99 George Theodore	1.25	3.00
(Topps 99 is		
Brewers Leaders)		
100 Willie Stargell	5.00	12.00
101 Bobby Valentine	.75	2.00
102 Bill Greif	.40	1.00
103 Sal Bando	.75	2.00
104 Ron Bryant	.40	1.00
105 Carlton Fisk	8.00	20.00
106 Harry Parker	.40	1.00
107 Alex Johnson	.40	1.00
108 Al Hrabosky	.75	2.00
109 Bobby Grich	.75	2.00
110 Billy Williams	2.50	6.00
111 Clay Carroll	.40	1.00
112 Dave Lopes	1.25	3.00
113 Dick Drago	.40	1.00
114 Angels Team	.75	2.00
115 Willie Horton	.75	2.00
116 Jerry Reuss	.75	2.00
117 Ron Blomberg	.40	1.00
118 Bill Lee	.75	2.00
119 Danny Ozark MG	.75	2.00
Ray Rippelmeyer CO		
Bobby Wine CO		
Carroll Beringer CO		
Billy DeMars CO		
120 Wilbur Wood	.40	1.00
121 Larry Lintz	.40	1.00
122 Jim Holt	.40	1.00
123 Nellie Briles	.75	2.00
124 Bobby Coluccio	.40	1.00
125 Nate Colbert	.40	1.00
126 Checklist 1-132	2.00	6.00
127 Tom Paciorek	.75	2.00
128 John Ellis	.40	1.00
129 Chris Speier	.40	1.00
130 Reggie Jackson	10.00	25.00
131 Bob Boone	1.25	3.00
132 Felix Millan	.40	1.00
133 David Clyde	.40	1.00
134 Denis Menke	.40	1.00
135 Roy White	.75	2.00
136 Rick Reuschel	.75	2.00
137 Al Bumbry	.75	2.00
138 Eddie Brinkman	.40	1.00
139 Aurelio Monteagudo	.40	1.00
140 Darrell Evans	1.25	3.00
141 Pat Bourque	.40	1.00
142 Pedro Garcia	.40	1.00
143 Dick Woodson	.40	1.00
144 Walter Alston MG	1.50	4.00
Tom Lasorda CO		
Jim Gilliam CO		
Red Adams CO		
Monty Basgall CO		
145 Dock Ellis	.40	1.00
146 Ron Fairly	.75	2.00
147 Bart Johnson	.40	1.00
148 Dave Hilton	.40	1.00
149 Mac Scarce	.40	1.00
150 John Mayberry	.75	2.00
151 Diego Segui	.40	1.00
152 Oscar Gamble	.75	2.00
153 Jon Matlack	.75	2.00
154 Astros Team	.75	2.00
155 Bert Campaneris	.75	2.00
156 Randy Moffitt	.40	1.00
157 Vic Harris	.40	1.00
158 Jack Billingham	.40	1.00
159 Jim Ray Hart	.40	1.00
160 Brooks Robinson	5.00	12.00
161 Ray Burris	.75	2.00
162 Bill Freehan	.75	2.00
163 Ken Berry	.40	1.00
164 Tom House	.40	1.00
165 Willie Davis	.75	2.00
166 Mickey Lolich	1.50	4.00
(Topps 166 is		
Royals Leaders)		
167 Luis Tiant	1.25	3.00
168 Danny Thompson	.40	1.00
169 Steve Rogers RC	1.25	3.00
170 Bill Melton	.40	1.00
171 Eduardo Rodriguez	.40	1.00
172 Gene Clines	.40	1.00
173 Randy Jones RC	1.25	3.00
174 Bill Robinson	.75	2.00
175 Reggie Cleveland	.75	2.00
176 John Lowenstein	.40	1.00
177 Dave Roberts	.40	1.00
178 Garry Maddox	.75	2.00
179 Yogi Berra MG	3.00	8.00
Rube Walker CO		
Eddie Yost CO		
Roy McMillan CO		
Joe Pignatano CO		
180 Ken Holtzman	.75	2.00
181 Cesar Geronimo	.40	1.00
182 Lindy McDaniel	.75	2.00
183 Johnny Oates	.40	1.00
184 Rangers Team	.75	2.00
185 Jose Cardenal	.40	1.00
186 Fred Scherman	.40	1.00
187 Don Baylor	1.25	3.00
188 Rudy Meoli	.40	1.00
189 Jim Brewer	.40	1.00
190 Tony Oliva	1.25	3.00
191 Al Fitzmorris	.40	1.00
192 Mario Guerrero	.40	1.00
193 Tom Walker	.40	1.00
194 Darrell Porter	.75	2.00
195 Carlos May	.40	1.00
196 Jim Hunter	2.50	6.00
(Topps 196 is		
Jim Fregosi)		
197 Vicente Romo	.40	1.00
198 Dave Cash	.40	1.00
199 Mike Kekich	.40	1.00
200 Cesar Cedeno	.75	2.00
201 Rod Carew	3.00	8.00
Pete Rose LL		
202 Reggie Jackson	3.00	8.00
Willie Stargell LL		
203 Reggie Jackson	3.00	8.00
Willie Stargell LL		
204 Tommy Harper	1.25	3.00
Lou Brock LL		
205 Wilbur Wood	.75	2.00
Ron Bryant LL		
206 Jim Palmer	2.50	6.00
Tom Seaver LL		
207 Nolan Ryan	8.00	20.00
Tom Seaver LL		
208 John Hiller	.75	2.00
Mike Marshall LL		
209 Ted Sizemore	.40	1.00
210 Bill Singer	.40	1.00
211 Chicago Cubs Team	.75	2.00
212 Rollie Fingers	2.50	6.00
213 Dave Rader	.40	1.00
214 Bill Grabarkewitz	.40	1.00
215 Al Kaline	6.00	15.00
216 Ray Sadecki	.40	1.00
217 Tim Foli	.40	1.00
218 John Briggs	.40	1.00
219 Doug Griffin	.40	1.00
220 Don Sutton	2.50	6.00
221 Chuck Tanner MG	.75	2.00
Jim Mahoney CO		
Alex Monchak CO		
Johnny Sain CO		
Joe Lonnett CO		
222 Ramon Hernandez	.40	1.00
223 Jeff Burroughs	1.25	3.00
224 Roger Metzger	.40	1.00
225 Paul Splittorff	.40	1.00
226 Padres Team Card	1.25	3.00
227 Mike Lum	.40	1.00
228 Ted Kubiak	.40	1.00
229 Fritz Peterson	.40	1.00
230 Tony Perez	2.50	6.00
231 Dick Tidrow	.40	1.00
232 Steve Brye	.40	1.00
233 Jim Barr	.40	1.00
234 John Milner	.40	1.00
235 Dave McNally	.75	2.00
236 Red Schoendienst MG	1.50	4.00
Barney Schultz CO		
George Kissell CO		
Johnny Lewis CO		
Vern Benson CO		
237 Ken Brett	.40	1.00
238 Fran Healy	.40	1.00
239 Bill Russell	.75	2.00
240 Joe Coleman	.40	1.00
241 Glenn Beckert	.40	1.00
242 Bill Gogolewski	.40	1.00
243 Bob Oliver	.40	1.00
244 Carl Morton	.40	1.00
245 Cleon Jones	.40	1.00
246 Athletics Team	1.25	3.00
247 Rick Miller	.40	1.00
248 Tom Hall	.40	1.00
249 George Mitterwald	.40	1.00
250 Willie McCovey	4.00	10.00
251 Graig Nettles	1.25	3.00
252 Dave Parker RC	6.00	15.00
253 John Boccabella	.40	1.00
254 Stan Bahnsen	.40	1.00
255 Larry Bowa	.75	2.00
256 Tom Griffin	.40	1.00
257 Buddy Bell	1.25	3.00
258 Jerry Morales	.40	1.00
259 Bob Reynolds	.40	1.00
260 Ted Simmons	1.50	4.00
261 Jerry Bell	.40	1.00
262 Ed Kirkpatrick	.40	1.00
263 Checklist 133-264	1.50	4.00
264 Joe Rudi	.75	2.00
265 Tug McGraw	1.50	4.00
266 Jim Northrup	.75	2.00
267 Andy Messersmith	.75	2.00
268 Tom Grieve	.75	2.00
269 Bob Johnson	.40	1.00
270 Ron Santo	1.50	4.00
271 Bill Hands	.40	1.00
272 Paul Casanova	.40	1.00
273 Checklist 265-396	1.50	4.00
274 Fred Beene	.40	1.00
275 Ron Hunt	.40	1.00
276 Bobby Winkles MG	.75	2.00
John Roseboro CO		
Tom Morgan CO		
Jimmie Reese CO		
Salty Parker CO		
277 Gary Nolan	.75	2.00
278 Cookie Rojas	.75	2.00
279 Jim Crawford	.40	1.00
280 Carl Yastrzemski	8.00	20.00
281 Giants Team	.75	2.00
282 Doyle Alexander	.75	2.00
283 Mike Schmidt	12.50	40.00
284 Dave Duncan	.75	2.00
285 Reggie Smith	.75	2.00
286 Tony Muser	.40	1.00
287 Clay Kirby	.40	1.00
288 Gorman Thomas	1.25	3.00
289 Rick Auerbach	.40	1.00
290 Vida Blue	.75	2.00
291 Don Hahn	.40	1.00
292 Chuck Seelbach	.40	1.00
293 Milt May	.40	1.00
294 Steve Foucault	.40	1.00
295 Rick Monday	.75	2.00
296 Ray Corbin	.40	1.00
297 Hal Breeden	.40	1.00
298 Roric Harrison	.40	1.00
299 Gene Michael	.40	1.00
300 Pete Rose	12.50	30.00
301 Bob Montgomery	.40	1.00
302 Rudy May	.40	1.00
303 George Hendrick	.75	2.00
304 Don Wilson	.40	1.00
305 Tito Fuentes	.40	1.00
306 Earl Weaver MG	1.50	4.00
Jim Frey CO		
George Bamberger CO		
Billy Hunter CO		
George Staller CO		
307 Luis Melendez	.40	1.00
308 Bruce Dal Canton	.40	1.00
309 Dave Roberts	.40	1.00
310 Terry Forster	.75	2.00
311 Jerry Grote	.75	2.00
312 Deron Johnson	.40	1.00
313 Barry Lersch	.40	1.00
314 Brewers Team	.40	1.00
315 Ron Cey	1.25	3.00
316 Jim Perry	.75	2.00
317 Richie Zisk	.75	2.00
318 Jim Merritt	.40	1.00
319 Randy Hundley	.40	1.00
320 Dusty Baker	1.25	3.00
321 Steve Braun	.40	1.00
322 Ernie McAnally	.40	1.00
323 Richie Scheinblum	.40	1.00
324 Steve Kline	.40	1.00
325 Tommy Harper	.75	2.00
326 Sparky Anderson MG	1.50	4.00
Larry Shepard CO		
George Scherger CO		
Alex Grammas CO		
Ted Kluszewski CO		
327 Tom Timmermann	.40	1.00
328 Skip Jutze	.40	1.00
329 Mark Belanger	.75	2.00
330 Juan Marichal	2.50	6.00
331 Carlton Fisk	3.00	8.00
Johnny Bench AS		
332 Dick Allen	4.00	10.00
Hank Aaron AS		
333 Rod Carew	2.00	5.00
Joe Morgan AS		
334 Brooks Robinson	1.50	4.00
Ron Santo AS		
335 Bert Campaneris	.75	2.00
Chris Speier AS		
336 Bobby Murcer	2.50	6.00
Pete Rose AS		
337 Amos Otis	.75	2.00
Cesar Cedeno AS		
338 Reggie Jackson	3.00	8.00
Billy Williams AS		
339 Jim Hunter	1.50	4.00
Rick Wise AS		
340 Thurman Munson	5.00	12.00
341 Dan Driessen RC	.75	2.00
342 Jim Lonborg	.75	2.00
343 Royals Team	.75	2.00
344 Mike Caldwell	.40	1.00
345 Bill North	.40	1.00
346 Ron Reed	.40	1.00
347 Sandy Alomar	.75	2.00
348 Pete Richert	.40	1.00
349 John Vukovich	.40	1.00
350 Bob Gibson	4.00	10.00
351 Dwight Evans	1.50	4.00
352 Bill Stoneman	.40	1.00
353 Rich Coggins	.40	1.00
354 Whitey Lockman MG	.75	2.00
J.C. Martin CO		
Hank Aguirre CO		
Al Spangler CO		
Jim Marshall CO		
355 Dave Nelson	.40	1.00
356 Jerry Koosman	.75	2.00
357 Buddy Bradford	.40	1.00
358 Dal Maxvill	.40	1.00
359 Brent Strom	.40	1.00
360 Greg Luzinski	1.25	3.00
361 Don Carrithers	.40	1.00
362 Hal King	.40	1.00
363 Yankees Team	1.25	3.00
364 Cito Gaston	.75	2.00
365 Steve Busby	.75	2.00
366 Larry Hisle	.75	2.00
367 Norm Cash	1.25	3.00
368 Manny Mota	.75	2.00
369 Paul Lindblad	.40	1.00
370 Bob Watson	.75	2.00
371 Jim Slaton	.40	1.00
372 Ken Reitz	.40	1.00
373 John Curtis	.40	1.00
374 Marty Perez	.40	1.00
375 Earl Williams	.40	1.00
376 Jorge Orta	.40	1.00
377 Ron Woods	.40	1.00
378 Burt Hooton	.75	2.00
379 Billy Martin MG	1.25	3.00
Frank Lucchesi CO		
Art Fowler CO		
Charlie Silvera CO		
Jackie Moore CO		
380 Bud Harrelson	.75	2.00
381 Charlie Sands	.40	1.00
382 Bob Moose	.40	1.00
383 Phillies Team	.75	2.00
384 Chris Chambliss	.75	2.00
385 Don Gullett	.75	2.00
386 Gary Matthews	1.25	3.00
387 Rich Morales	.40	1.00
388 Phil Roof	.40	1.00
389 Gates Brown	.40	1.00
390 Lou Piniella	1.25	3.00
391 Billy Champion	.40	1.00
392 Dick Green	.40	1.00
393 Orlando Pena	.40	1.00
394 Ken Henderson	.40	1.00
395 Doug Rader	.40	1.00
396 Tommy Davis	.75	2.00
397 George Stone	.40	1.00
398 Duke Sims	.40	1.00
399 Mike Paul	.40	1.00
400 Harmon Killebrew	4.00	10.00
401 Elliott Maddox	.40	1.00
402 Jim Rooker	.40	1.00
403 Darrell Johnson MG	.75	2.00
Eddie Popowski CO		
Lee Stange CO		
Don Zimmer CO		
Don Bryant CO		
404 Jim Howarth	.40	1.00
405 Ellie Rodriguez	.40	1.00
406 Steve Arlin	.40	1.00
407 Jim Wohlford	.40	1.00
408 Charlie Hough	.75	2.00
409 Ike Brown	.40	1.00
410 Pedro Borbon	.40	1.00
411 Frank Baker	.40	1.00
412 Chuck Taylor	.40	1.00
413 Don Money	.75	2.00
414 Checklist 397-528	1.50	4.00
415 Gary Gentry	.40	1.00
416 White Sox Team	.75	2.00
417 Rich Folkers	.40	1.00
418 Walt Williams	.40	1.00
419 Wayne Twitchell	.40	1.00
420 Ray Fosse	.40	1.00
421 Dan Fife	.40	1.00
422 Gonzalo Marquez	.40	1.00
423 Fred Stanley	.40	1.00
424 Jim Beauchamp	.40	1.00
425 Pete Broberg	.40	1.00
426 Rennie Stennett	.40	1.00
427 Bobby Bolin	.40	1.00
428 Gary Sutherland	.40	1.00
429 Dick Lange	.40	1.00
430 Matty Alou	.75	2.00
431 Gene Garber RC	.75	2.00
432 Chris Arnold	.40	1.00
433 Lerrin LaGrow	.40	1.00
434 Ken McMullen	.40	1.00
435 Dave Concepcion	1.25	3.00
436 Don Hood	.40	1.00
437 Jim Lyttle	.40	1.00
438 Ed Herrmann	.40	1.00
439 Norm Miller	.40	1.00
440 Jim Kaat	1.50	4.00
441 Tom Ragland	.40	1.00
442 Alan Foster	.40	1.00
443 Tom Hutton	.40	1.00
444 Vic Davalillo	.40	1.00
445 George Medich	.40	1.00
446 Len Randle	.40	1.00
447 Frank Quilici MG	.75	2.00
Ralph Rowe CO		
Bob Rodgers CO		
Vern Morgan CO		
448 Ron Hodges	.40	1.00
449 Tom McCraw	.40	1.00
450 Rich Hebner	.75	2.00
451 Tommy John	1.50	4.00
452 Gene Hiser	.40	1.00
453 Balor Moore	.40	1.00
454 Kurt Bevacqua	.40	1.00
455 Tom Bradley	.40	1.00
456 Dave Winfield RC	30.00	60.00
457 Chuck Goggin	.40	1.00
458 Jim Ray	.40	1.00
459 Reds Team	1.25	3.00
460 Boog Powell	1.25	3.00
461 John Odom	.40	1.00
462 Luis Alvarado	.40	1.00
463 Pat Dobson	.40	1.00
464 Jose Cruz	1.25	3.00
465 Dick Bosman	.40	1.00
466 Dick Billings	.40	1.00
467 Winston Llenas	.40	1.00
468 Pepe Frias	.40	1.00
469 Joe Decker	.40	1.00
470 Reggie Jackson ALCS	3.00	8.00
471 Jon Matlack NLCS	.75	2.00
472 Darold Knowles WS	.75	2.00
473 Willie Mays WS	5.00	12.00
474 Bert Campaneris WS	.75	2.00
475 Rusty Staub WS	.75	2.00
476 Cleon Jones WS	.75	2.00
477 Reggie Jackson WS	3.00	8.00
478 Bert Campaneris WS	.75	2.00
479 WS Summary	.75	2.00
A's Celebrate; Win		
2nd cons. Championship		
480 Willie Crawford	.40	1.00
481 Jerry Terrell	.40	1.00
482 Bob Didier	.40	1.00
483 Braves Team	.75	2.00
484 Carmen Fanzone	.40	1.00
485 Felipe Alou	1.25	3.00
486 Steve Stone	.75	2.00
487 Ted Martinez	.40	1.00
488 Andy Etchebarren	.40	1.00
489 Danny Murtaugh MG	.75	2.00
Don Osborn CO		
Don Leppert CO		
Bill Mazeroski CO		
Bob Skinner CO		
490 Vada Pinson	1.25	3.00
491 Roger Nelson	.40	1.00
492 Mike Rogodzinski	.40	1.00
493 Joe Hoerner	.40	1.00
494 Ed Goodson	.40	1.00
495 Dick McAuliffe	.75	2.00
496 Tom Murphy	.40	1.00
497 Bobby Mitchell	.40	1.00
498 Pat Corrales	.40	1.00
499 Rusty Torres	.40	1.00
500 Lee May	.75	2.00
501 Eddie Leon	.40	1.00
502 Dave LaRoche	.40	1.00
503 Eric Soderholm	.40	1.00
504 Joe Niekro	.75	2.00
505 Bill Buckner	.75	2.00
506 Ed Farmer	.40	1.00
507 Larry Stahl	.40	1.00
508 Expos Team	1.25	3.00
509 Jesse Jefferson	.40	1.00
510 Wayne Garrett	.40	1.00
511 Toby Harrah	.75	2.00
512 Joe Lahoud	.40	1.00
513 Jim Campanis	.40	1.00
514 Paul Schaal	.40	1.00
515 Willie Montanez	.40	1.00
516 Horacio Pina	.40	1.00
517 Mike Hegan	.40	1.00
518 Derrel Thomas	.40	1.00
519 Bill Sharp	.40	1.00
520 Tim McCarver	1.25	3.00
521 Ken Aspromonte MG	.75	2.00
Clay Bryant CO		
Tony Pacheco CO		
522 J.R. Richard	1.25	3.00
523 Cecil Cooper	1.25	3.00
524 Bill Plummer	.40	1.00
525 Clyde Wright	.40	1.00
526 Frank Tepedino	.75	2.00
527 Bobby Darwin	.40	1.00
528 Bill Bonham	.40	1.00
529 Horace Clarke	.75	2.00
530 Mickey Stanley	.75	2.00
531 Gene Mauch MG	1.25	3.00
Dave Bristol CO		
Cal McLish CO		
Larry Doby CO		
Jerry Zimmerman CO		
532 Skip Lockwood	.40	1.00
533 Mike Phillips	.40	1.00
534 Eddie Watt	.40	1.00
535 Bob Tolan	.40	1.00
536 Duffy Dyer	.40	1.00
537 Steve Mingori	.40	1.00
538 Cesar Tovar	.40	1.00
539 Lloyd Allen	.40	1.00
540 Bob Robertson	.40	1.00
541 Indians Team	.75	2.00
542 Goose Gossage	1.25	3.00
543 Danny Cater	.40	1.00
544 Ron Schueler	.40	1.00
545 Billy Conigliaro	.75	2.00
546 Mike Corkins	.40	1.00
547 Glenn Borgmann	.40	1.00
548 Sonny Siebert	.40	1.00
549 Mike Jorgensen	.40	1.00
550 Sam McDowell	.75	2.00
551 Von Joshua	.40	1.00
552 Denny Doyle	.40	1.00
553 Jim Willoughby	.40	1.00
554 Tim Johnson	.40	1.00
555 Woody Fryman	.40	1.00
556 Dave Campbell	.75	2.00
557 Jim McGlothlin	.40	1.00
558 Bill Fahey	.40	1.00
559 Darrell Chaney	.40	1.00
560 Mike Cuellar	.75	2.00
561 Ed Kranepool	.75	2.00
562 Jack Aker	.40	1.00
563 Hal McRae	.75	2.00
564 Mike Ryan	.40	1.00
565 Milt Wilcox	.40	1.00
566 Jackie Hernandez	.40	1.00
567 Red Sox Team	.75	2.00
568 Mike Torrez	.75	2.00
569 Rick Dempsey	.75	2.00
570 Ralph Garr	.75	2.00
571 Rich Hand	.40	1.00
572 Enzo Hernandez	.40	1.00
573 Mike Adams	.40	1.00
574 Bill Parsons	.40	1.00
575 Steve Garvey	1.50	4.00
576 Scipio Spinks	.40	1.00
577 Mike Sadek	.40	1.00
578 Ralph Houk MG	.75	2.00
579 Cecil Upshaw	.40	1.00
580 Jim Spencer	.40	1.00
581 Fred Norman	.40	1.00
582 Bucky Dent RC	2.50	6.00
583 Marty Pattin	.40	1.00
584 Ken Rudolph	.40	1.00
585 Merv Rettenmund	.40	1.00
586 Jack Brohamer	.40	1.00
587 Larry Christenson	.40	1.00
588 Hal Lanier	.40	1.00
589 Boots Day	.75	2.00
590 Rogelio Moret	.40	1.00
591 Sonny Jackson	.40	1.00
592 Ed Bane	.40	1.00
593 Steve Yeager	.75	2.00
594 Leroy Stanton	.40	1.00
595 Steve Blass	.75	2.00
596 Wayne Garland	.40	1.00
Fred Holdsworth		
Mark Littell		
Dick Pole		
597 Dave Chalk	.75	2.00
John Gamble		
Pete MacKanin		
Manny Trillo		
598 Dave Augustine	6.00	15.00
Ken Griffey RC		
Steve Ontiveros		
Jim Tyrone		
599 Ron Diorio	1.25	3.00
Dave Freisleben		
Frank Riccelli		
Greg Shanahan		
600 Ron Cash	3.00	8.00
Jim Cox		
Bill Madlock RC		
Reggie Sanders		
601 Ed Armbrister	1.50	4.00
Rich Bladt		
Brian Downing RC		
Bake McBride RC		
602 Glenn Abbott	.75	2.00
Rick Henninger		
Craig Swan RC		
Dan Vossler		
603 Barry Foote	.75	2.00
Tom Lundstedt		
Charlie Moore		
Sergio Robles		
604 Terry Hughes	3.00	8.00
John Knox		
Andy Thornton RC		
Frank White RC		
605 Vic Albury	2.00	5.00
Ken Frailing		
Kevin Kobel		
Frank Tanana RC		
606 Jim Fuller	.75	2.00
Wilbur Howard		
Tommy Smith		
Otto Velez		
607 Leo Foster	.75	2.00
Tom Heintzelman		
Dave Rosello		
Frank Taveras		
608 Bob Apodaca UER	1.25	3.00
Dick Baney		
John D'Acquisto		
Mike Wallace		
Apodaca is spellled Apodaco		
609 Rico Petrocelli	.75	2.00
610 Dave Kingman	1.50	4.00
611 Rich Stelmaszek	.40	1.00
612 Luke Walker	.40	1.00
613 Dan Monzon	.40	1.00
614 Adrian Devine	.40	1.00
615 John Jeter	.40	1.00
616 Larry Gura	.40	1.00
617 Ted Ford	.40	1.00
618 Jim Mason	.40	1.00
619 Mike Anderson	.40	1.00
620 Al Downing	.40	1.00
621 Bernie Carbo	.40	1.00
622 Phil Gagliano	.40	1.00
623 Celerino Sanchez	.40	1.00
624 Bob Miller	.40	1.00
625 Ollie Brown	.40	1.00
626 Pirates Team	.75	2.00
627 Carl Taylor	.40	1.00
628 Ivan Murrell	.40	1.00
629 Rusty Staub	1.25	3.00
630 Tommy Agee	.75	2.00
631 Steve Barber	.40	1.00
632 George Culver	.40	1.00
633 Dave Hamilton	.40	1.00
634 Eddie Mathews MG	1.50	4.00
Herm Starrette CO		
Connie Ryan CO		
Jim Busby CO		
Ken Silvestri CO		
635 John Edwards	.40	1.00
636 Dave Goltz	.40	1.00
637 Checklist 529-660	1.50	4.00
638 Ken Sanders	.40	1.00
639 Joe Lovitto	.40	1.00
640 Milt Pappas	.75	2.00
641 Chuck Brinkman	.40	1.00
642 Terry Harmon	.40	1.00
643 Dodgers Team	.75	2.00
644 Wayne Granger	.40	1.00
645 Ken Boswell	.40	1.00
646 George Foster	1.25	3.00
647 Juan Beniquez	.40	1.00
648 Terry Crowley	.40	1.00
649 Fernando Gonzalez	.40	1.00
650 Mike Epstein	.40	1.00
651 Leron Lee	.40	1.00
652 Gail Hopkins	.40	1.00
653 Bob Stinson	.75	2.00
654 Jesus Alou	.75	2.00
655 Mike Tyson	.40	1.00
656 Adrian Garrett	.40	1.00
657 Jim Shellenback	.40	1.00
658 Lee Lacy	.40	1.00
659 Joe Lis	.40	1.00
660 Larry Dierker	1.25	3.00

1975 O-Pee-Chee

The cards in this 660-card set measure 2 1/2" by 3 1/2". The 1975 O-Pee-Chee cards are very similar to the 1975 Topps cards, yet rather different from previous years' issues. The most prominent change for the fronts is the use of a two-color fram colors surrounding the picture area rather than a single, subdued color. The fronts feature color player photos with rounded corners. The player's name and position, the team name and a facsimile autograph round out the front. The backs are printed in red and green on a yellow-vanilla card stock and carry player biography and statistics in French and English. Cards 189-212 depict the MVPs of both leagues from 1951 through 1974. The first six cards (1-6) feature players breaking records or achieving milestones during the previous season. Cards 306-313 picture league leaders in various statistical categories. Cards 459-466 depict the results of post-season action. Team cards feature a checklist back for players on that team. Remember, the prices below apply only to O-Pee-Chee cards -- they are NOT prices for Topps cards as the Topps cards are generally much more available. The cards were issued in eight card packs which cost 10 cents and came 48 packs to a box. Notable Rookie Cards include George Brett, Fred Lynn, Keith Hernandez, Jim Rice and Robin Yount.

COMPLETE SET (660)	500.00	1000.00
1 Hank Aaron HL	12.50	40.00
2 Lou Brock HL	1.50	4.00
3 Bob Gibson HL	1.50	4.00
4 Al Kaline HL	3.00	8.00
5 Nolan Ryan HL	12.50	30.00
6 Mike Marshall HL	.60	1.50
7 Steve Busby	5.00	12.00
Dick Bosman		
Nolan Ryan HL		
8 Rogelio Moret	.30	.75
9 Frank Tepedino	.60	1.50
10 Willie Davis	.60	1.50
11 Bill Melton	.30	.75
12 David Clyde	.30	.75
13 Gene Locklear	.60	1.50
14 Milt Wilcox	.30	.75
15 Jose Cardenal	.60	1.50
16 Frank Tanana	1.00	2.50
17 Dave Concepcion	1.00	2.50
18 Ralph Houk MG CL	1.00	2.50
19 Jerry Koosman	.60	1.50
20 Thurman Munson	4.00	10.00
21 Rollie Fingers	2.00	5.00
22 Dave Cash	.30	.75
23 Bill Russell	.60	1.50
24 Al Fitzmorris	.30	.75
25 Lee May	.60	1.50
26 Dave McNally	.60	1.50
27 Ken Reitz	.30	.75
28 Tom Murphy	.30	.75
29 Dave Parker	1.50	4.00
30 Bert Blyleven	1.00	2.50
31 Dave Rader	.30	.75
32 Reggie Cleveland	.60	1.50
33 Dusty Baker	1.00	2.50
34 Steve Renko	.30	.75
35 Ron Santo	.60	1.50
36 Joe Lovitto	.30	.75
37 Dave Freisleben	.30	.75
38 Buddy Bell	1.00	2.50
39 Andre Thornton	.60	1.50
40 Bill Singer	.30	.75
41 Cesar Geronimo	.60	1.50
42 Joe Coleman	.30	.75
43 Cleon Jones	.60	1.50
44 Pat Dobson	.30	.75
45 Joe Rudi	.60	1.50
46 Danny Ozark MG CL	1.00	2.50
47 Tommy John	1.00	2.50
48 Freddie Patek	.60	1.50
49 Larry Dierker	.60	1.50
50 Brooks Robinson	4.00	10.00
51 Bob Forsch	.60	1.50
52 Darrell Porter	.60	1.50
53 Dave Giusti	.30	.75
54 Eric Soderholm	.30	.75
55 Bobby Bonds	1.50	4.00
56 Rick Wise	.60	1.50
57 Dave Johnson	.60	1.50
58 Chuck Taylor	.30	.75
59 Ken Henderson	.30	.75
60 Fergie Jenkins	2.00	5.00
61 Dave Winfield	10.00	25.00
62 Fritz Peterson	.30	.75
63 Steve Swisher	.30	.75
64 Dave Chalk	.30	.75
65 Don Gullett	.60	1.50
66 Willie Horton	.60	1.50
67 Tug McGraw	1.00	2.50
68 Ron Blomberg	.30	.75
69 John Odom	.30	.75
70 Mike Schmidt	12.50	30.00
71 Charlie Hough	.60	1.50
72 Jack McKeon MG CL	1.00	2.50
73 J.R. Richard	.60	1.50
74 Mark Belanger	.60	1.50
75 Ted Simmons	1.00	2.50

76 Ed Sprague	.30	.75
77 Richie Zisk	.60	1.50
78 Ray Corbin	.30	.75
79 Gary Matthews	.60	1.50
80 Carlton Fisk	4.00	10.00
81 Ron Reed	.30	.75
82 Pat Kelly	.30	.75
83 Jim Merritt	.30	.75
84 Enzo Hernandez	.30	.75
85 Bill Bonham	.30	.75
86 Joe Lis	.30	.75
87 George Foster	1.00	2.50
88 Tom Egan	.30	.75
89 Jim Ray	.30	.75
90 Rusty Staub	1.00	2.50
91 Dick Green	.30	.75
92 Cecil Upshaw	.30	.75
93 Dave Lopes	1.00	2.50
94 Jim Lonborg	.60	1.50
95 John Mayberry	.60	1.50
96 Mike Cosgrove	.30	.75
97 Earl Williams	.30	.75
98 Rich Folkers	.30	.75
99 Mike Hegan	.30	.75
100 Willie Stargell	2.50	6.00
101 Gene Mauch MG CL	1.00	2.50
102 Joe Decker	.30	.75
103 Rick Miller	.30	.75
104 Bill Madlock	1.00	2.50
105 Buzz Capra	.30	.75
106 Mike Hargrove RC	1.50	4.00
107 Jim Barr	.30	.75
108 Tom Hall	.30	.75
109 George Hendrick	.60	1.50
110 Wilbur Wood	.30	.75
111 Wayne Garrett	.30	.75
112 Larry Hardy	.30	.75
113 Elliott Maddox	.30	.75
114 Dick Lange	.30	.75
115 Joe Ferguson	.30	.75
116 Lerrin LaGrow	.30	.75
117 Earl Weaver MG CL	1.50	4.00
118 Mike Anderson	.30	.75
119 Tommy Helms	.30	.75
120 Steve Busby	.60	1.50
(photo actually		
Fran Healy)		
121 Bill North	.30	.75
122 Al Hrabosky	.60	1.50
123 Johnny Briggs	.30	.75
124 Jerry Reuss	.60	1.50
125 Ken Singleton	.60	1.50
126 Checklist 1-132	1.50	4.00
127 Glenn Borgmann	.30	.75
128 Bill Lee	.60	1.50
129 Rick Monday	.60	1.50
130 Phil Niekro	1.50	4.00
131 Toby Harrah	.60	1.50
132 Randy Moffitt	.30	.75
133 Dan Driessen	.60	1.50
134 Ron Hodges	.30	.75
135 Charlie Spikes	.30	.75
136 Jim Mason	.30	.75
137 Terry Forster	.60	1.50
138 Del Unser	.30	.75
139 Horacio Pina	.30	.75
140 Steve Garvey	1.50	4.00
141 Mickey Stanley	.60	1.50
142 Bob Reynolds	.30	.75
143 Cliff Johnson RC	.60	1.50
144 Jim Wohlford	.30	.75
145 Ken Holtzman	.60	1.50
146 John McNamara MG CL	1.00	2.50
147 Pedro Garcia	.30	.75
148 Jim Rooker	.30	.75
149 Tim Foli	.30	.75
150 Bob Gibson	3.00	8.00
151 Steve Brye	.30	.75
152 Mario Guerrero	.30	.75
153 Rick Reuschel	.60	1.50
154 Mike Lum	.30	.75
155 Jim Bibby	.30	.75
156 Dave Kingman	1.00	2.50
157 Pedro Borbon	.60	1.50
158 Jerry Grote	.30	.75
159 Steve Arlin	.30	.75
160 Graig Nettles	1.00	2.50
161 Stan Bahnsen	.30	.75
162 Willie Montanez	.30	.75
163 Jim Brewer	.30	.75
164 Mickey Rivers	.60	1.50
165 Doug Rader	.60	1.50
166 Woodie Fryman	.30	.75
167 Rich Coggins	.30	.75
168 Bill Greif	.30	.75
169 Cookie Rojas	.30	.75
170 Bert Campaneris	.60	1.50
171 Ed Kirkpatrick	.30	.75
172 Darrell Johnson MG CL	1.50	4.00
173 Steve Rogers	.60	1.50
174 Bake McBride	.60	1.50
175 Don Money	.60	1.50
176 Burt Hooton	.60	1.50
177 Vic Correll	.30	.75
178 Cesar Tovar	.30	.75
179 Tom Bradley	.30	.75
180 Joe Morgan	3.00	8.00
181 Fred Beene	.30	.75
182 Don Hahn	.30	.75
183 Mel Stottlemyre	.60	1.50
184 Jorge Orta	.30	.75
185 Steve Carlton	4.00	10.00
186 Willie Crawford	.30	.75
187 Denny Doyle	.30	.75
188 Tom Griffin	.30	.75
189 Larry (Yogi) Berra	2.50	6.00
Roy Campanella MVP		
Campanella card never issued		
190 Bobby Shantz	1.00	2.50
Hank Sauer MVP		
191 Al Rosen	1.00	2.50
Roy Campanella MVP		
192 Yogi Berra	2.50	6.00
Willie Mays MVP		
193 Yogi Berra	1.50	4.00
Roy Campanella MVP		
(Campanella card never issued		
194 Mickey Mantle	6.00	15.00
Don Newcombe MVP		
195 Mickey Mantle	8.00	20.00
Hank Aaron MVP		
196 Jackie Jensen	1.00	2.50
Ernie Banks MVP		
197 Nellie Fox	1.50	4.00
Ernie Banks MVP		
198 Roger Maris	1.00	2.50
Dick Groat MVP		
199 Roger Maris	1.50	4.00
Frank Robinson MVP		
200 Mickey Mantle	6.00	15.00
Maury Wills MVP		
Wills card never issued		
201 Elston Howard	1.00	2.50
Sandy Koufax MVP		
202 Brooks Robinson	1.00	2.50
Ken Boyer MVP		
203 Zoilo Versalles	1.00	2.50
Willie Mays MVP		
204 Frank Robinson	3.00	8.00
Bob Clemente MVP		
205 Carl Yastrzemski	1.00	2.50
Orlando Cepeda MVP		
206 Denny McLain	1.00	2.50
Bob Gibson MVP		
207 Harmon Killebrew	1.00	2.50
Willie McCovey MVP		
208 Boog Powell	1.00	2.50
Johnny Bench MVP		
209 Vida Blue	1.00	2.50
Joe Torre MVP		
210 Rich Allen	1.00	2.50
Johnny Bench MVP		
211 Reggie Jackson	3.00	8.00
Pete Rose MVP		
212 Jeff Burroughs	1.00	2.50
Steve Garvey MVP		
213 Oscar Gamble	.60	1.50
214 Harry Parker	.30	.75
215 Bobby Valentine	.60	1.50
216 Wes Westrum MG CL	1.00	2.50
217 Lou Piniella	1.00	2.50
218 Jerry Johnson	.30	.75
219 Ed Herrmann	.30	.75
220 Don Sutton	1.50	4.00
221 Aurelio Rodriguez	.30	.75
222 Dan Spillner	.30	.75
223 Robin Yount RC	30.00	60.00
224 Ramon Hernandez	.30	.75
225 Bob Grich	.60	1.50
226 Bill Campbell	.30	.75
227 Bob Watson	.60	1.50
228 George Brett RC	50.00	100.00
229 Barry Foote	.60	1.50
230 Jim Hunter	2.00	5.00
231 Mike Tyson	.30	.75
232 Diego Segui	.30	.75
233 Billy Grabarkewitz	.30	.75
234 Tom Grieve	.60	1.50
235 Jack Billingham	.60	1.50
236 Dick Williams MG CL	1.00	2.50
237 Carl Morton	.30	.75
238 Dave Duncan	.60	1.50
239 George Stone	.30	.75
240 Garry Maddox	.60	1.50
241 Dick Tidrow	.30	.75
242 Jay Johnstone	.60	1.50
243 Jim Kaat	1.00	2.50
244 Bill Buckner	.60	1.50
245 Mickey Lolich	1.00	2.50
246 Red Schoendienst MG CL	1.00	2.50
247 Enos Cabell	.30	.75
248 Randy Jones	1.00	2.50
249 Danny Thompson	.30	.75
250 Ken Brett	.30	.75
251 Fran Healy	.30	.75
252 Fred Scherman	.30	.75
253 Jesus Alou	.30	.75
254 Mike Torrez	.60	1.50
255 Dwight Evans	1.00	2.50
256 Billy Champion	.30	.75
257 Checklist 133-264	1.50	4.00
258 Dave LaRoche	.30	.75
259 Len Randle	.30	.75
260 Johnny Bench	8.00	20.00
261 Andy Hassler	.30	.75
262 Rowland Office	.30	.75
263 Jim Perry	.60	1.50
264 John Milner	.30	.75
265 Ron Bryant	.30	.75
266 Sandy Alomar	.60	1.50
267 Dick Ruthven	.30	.75
268 Hal McRae	.60	1.50
269 Doug Rau	.30	.75
270 Ron Fairly	.60	1.50
271 Jerry Moses	.30	.75
272 Lynn McGlothen	.30	.75
273 Steve Braun	.30	.75
274 Vicente Romo	.30	.75
275 Paul Blair	.60	1.50
276 Chuck Tanner MG CL	1.00	2.50
277 Frank Taveras	.30	.75
278 Paul Lindblad	.30	.75
279 Milt May	.30	.75
280 Carl Yastrzemski	6.00	15.00
281 Jim Slaton	.30	.75
282 Jerry Morales	.30	.75
283 Steve Foucault	.30	.75
284 Ken Griffey Sr.	2.00	5.00
285 Ellie Rodriguez	.30	.75
286 Mike Jorgensen	.30	.75
287 Roric Harrison	.30	.75
288 Bruce Ellingsen	.30	.75
289 Ken Rudolph	.30	.75
290 Jon Matlack	.30	.75
291 Bill Sudakis	.30	.75
292 Ron Schueler	.30	.75
293 Dick Sharon	.30	.75
294 Geoff Zahn	.30	.75
295 Vada Pinson	1.00	2.50
296 Alan Foster	.30	.75
297 Craig Kusick	.30	.75
298 Johnny Grubb	.30	.75
299 Bucky Dent	1.00	2.50
300 Reggie Jackson	8.00	20.00
301 Dave Roberts	.30	.75
302 Rick Burleson	.60	1.50
303 Grant Jackson	.30	.75
304 Danny Murtaugh MG CL	1.00	2.50
305 Jim Colborn	.30	.75
306 Rod Carew	1.00	2.50
Ralph Garr LL		
307 Dick Allen	2.00	5.00
Mike Schmidt LL		
308 Jeff Burroughs	1.00	2.50
Johnny Bench LL		
309 Bill North	1.00	2.50
Lou Brock LL		
310 Jim Hunter	1.00	2.50
Fergie Jenkins		
Andy Messersmith		
Phil Niekro LL		
311 Jim Hunter	1.00	2.50
Buzz Capra LL		
312 Nolan Ryan	8.00	20.00
Steve Carlton LL		
313 Terry Forster	.60	1.50
Mike Marshall LL		
314 Buck Martinez	.30	.75
315 Don Kessinger	.60	1.50
316 Jackie Brown	.30	.75
317 Joe Lahoud	.30	.75
318 Ernie McAnally	.30	.75
319 Johnny Oates	.30	.75
320 Pete Rose	12.50	40.00
321 Rudy May	.30	.75
322 Ed Goodson	.30	.75
323 Fred Holdsworth	.30	.75
324 Ed Kranepool	.60	1.50
325 Tony Oliva	1.00	2.50
326 Wayne Twitchell	.30	.75
327 Jerry Hairston	.30	.75
328 Sonny Siebert	.30	.75
329 Ted Kubiak	.30	.75
330 Mike Marshall	.60	1.50
331 Frank Robinson MG CL	1.00	2.50
332 Fred Kendall	.30	.75
333 Dick Drago	.30	.75
334 Greg Gross	.30	.75
335 Jim Palmer	3.00	8.00
336 Rennie Stennett	.30	.75
337 Kevin Kobel	.30	.75
338 Rick Stelmaszek	.30	.75
339 Jim Fregosi	.60	1.50
340 Paul Splittorff	.30	.75
341 Hal Breeden	.30	.75
342 Leroy Stanton	.30	.75
343 Danny Frisella	.30	.75
344 Ben Oglivie	.60	1.50
345 Clay Carroll	.60	1.50
346 Bobby Darwin	.30	.75
347 Mike Caldwell	.30	.75
348 Tony Muser	.30	.75
349 Ray Sadecki	.30	.75
350 Bobby Murcer	.60	1.50
351 Bob Boone	1.00	2.50
352 Darold Knowles	.30	.75
353 Luis Melendez	.30	.75
354 Dick Bosman	.30	.75
355 Chris Cannizzaro	.30	.75
356 Rico Petrocelli	.60	1.50
357 Ken Forsch	.30	.75
358 Al Bumbry	.60	1.50
359 Paul Popovich	.30	.75
360 George Scott	.60	1.50
361 Walter Alston MG CL	1.00	2.50
362 Steve Hargan	.30	.75
363 Carmen Fanzone	.30	.75
364 Doug Bird	.30	.75
365 Bob Bailey	.30	.75
366 Ken Sanders	.30	.75
367 Craig Robinson	.30	.75
368 Vic Albury	.30	.75
369 Merv Rettenmund	.30	.75
370 Tom Seaver	6.00	15.00
371 Gates Brown	.30	.75
372 John D'Acquisto	.30	.75
373 Bill Sharp	.30	.75
374 Eddie Watt	.30	.75
375 Roy White	.60	1.50
376 Steve Yeager	.60	1.50
377 Tom Hilgendorf	.30	.75
378 Derrel Thomas	.30	.75
379 Bernie Carbo	.30	.75
380 Sal Bando	.60	1.50
381 John Curtis	.30	.75
382 Don Baylor	1.00	2.50
383 Jim York	.30	.75
384 Brewers Team CL	1.00	2.50
Del Crandall MG		
385 Dock Ellis	.30	.75
386 Checklist 265-396	1.50	4.00
387 Jim Spencer	.30	.75
388 Steve Stone	.60	1.50
389 Tony Solaita	.30	.75
390 Ron Cey	1.00	2.50
391 Don DeMola	.30	.75
392 Bruce Bochte RC	.60	1.50
393 Gary Gentry	.30	.75
394 Larvell Blanks	.30	.75
395 Bud Harrelson	.60	1.50
396 Fred Norman	.60	1.50
397 Bill Freehan	.60	1.50
398 Elias Sosa	.30	.75
399 Terry Harmon	.30	.75
400 Dick Allen	1.00	2.50
401 Mike Wallace	.30	.75
402 Bob Tolan	.30	.75
403 Tom Buskey	.30	.75
404 Ted Sizemore	.30	.75
405 John Montague	.30	.75
406 Bob Gallagher	.30	.75
407 Herb Washington RC	1.00	2.50
408 Clyde Wright	.30	.75
409 Bob Robertson	.30	.75
410 Mike Cueller	.60	1.50
sic, Cuellar		
411 George Mitterwald	.30	.75
412 Bill Hands	.30	.75
413 Marty Pattin	.30	.75
414 Manny Mota	.60	1.50
415 John Hiller	.60	1.50
416 Larry Lintz	.30	.75
417 Skip Lockwood	.30	.75
418 Leo Foster	.30	.75
419 Dave Goltz	.30	.75
420 Larry Bowa	1.00	2.50
421 Yogi Berra MG CL	1.50	4.00
422 Brian Downing	.60	1.50
423 Clay Kirby	.30	.75
424 John Lowenstein	.30	.75
425 Tito Fuentes	.30	.75
426 George Medich	.30	.75
427 Clarence Gaston	.60	1.50
428 Dave Hamilton	.30	.75
429 Jim Dwyer	.30	.75
430 Luis Tiant	1.00	2.50
431 Rod Gilbreath	.30	.75
432 Ken Berry	.30	.75
433 Larry Demery	.30	.75
434 Bob Locker	.30	.75
435 Dave Nelson	.30	.75
436 Ken Frailing	.30	.75
437 Al Cowens	.60	1.50
438 Don Carrithers	.30	.75
439 Ed Brinkman	.30	.75
440 Andy Messersmith	.60	1.50
441 Bobby Heise	.30	.75
442 Maximino Leon	.30	.75
443 Frank Quilici MG CL	1.00	2.50
444 Gene Garber	.60	1.50
445 Felix Millan	.30	.75
446 Bart Johnson	.30	.75
447 Terry Crowley	.30	.75
448 Frank Duffy	.30	.75
449 Charlie Williams	.30	.75
450 Willie McCovey	3.00	8.00
451 Rick Dempsey	.60	1.50
452 Angel Mangual	.30	.75
453 Claude Osteen	.60	1.50
454 Doug Griffin	.30	.75
455 Don Wilson	.30	.75
456 Bob Coluccio	.30	.75
457 Mario Mendoza	.30	.75
458 Ross Grimsley	.30	.75
459 1974 AL Champs	.60	1.50
A's over Orioles		
(Second base action pictured)		
460 Frank Taveras NCLS	1.00	2.50
Steve Garvey		
461 Reggie Jackson WS	2.50	6.00
462 World Series Game 2	.60	1.50
(Dodger dugout)		
463 Rollie Fingers WS	1.00	2.50
464 World Series Game 4	.60	1.50
(A's batter)		
465 Joe Rudi WS	.60	1.50
466 WS Summary:	1.00	2.50
A's do it again		
Win 3rd straight		
(A's group)		
467 Ed Halicki	.30	.75
468 Bobby Mitchell	.30	.75
469 Tom Dettore	.30	.75
470 Jeff Burroughs	.60	1.50
471 Bob Stinson	.30	.75
472 Bruce Dal Canton	.30	.75
473 Ken McMullen	.30	.75
474 Luke Walker	.30	.75
475 Darrell Evans	.60	1.50
476 Ed Figueroa	.30	.75
477 Tom Hutton	.30	.75
478 Tom Burgmeier	.30	.75
479 Ken Boswell	.30	.75
480 Carlos May	.30	.75
481 Will McEnaney	.60	1.50
482 Tom McCraw	.30	.75
483 Steve Ontiveros	.30	.75
484 Glenn Beckert	.60	1.50
485 Sparky Lyle	.60	1.50
486 Ray Fosse	.30	.75
487 Preston Gomez MG CL	1.00	2.50
488 Bill Travers	.30	.75
489 Cecil Cooper	1.00	2.50
490 Reggie Smith	.60	1.50
491 Doyle Alexander	.60	1.50
492 Rich Hebner	.60	1.50
493 Don Stanhouse	.30	.75
494 Pete LaCock	.30	.75
495 Nelson Briles	.60	1.50
496 Pepe Frias	.30	.75
497 Jim Nettles	.30	.75
498 Al Downing	.30	.75
499 Marty Perez	.30	.75
500 Nolan Ryan	40.00	80.00
501 Bill Robinson	.60	1.50
502 Pat Bourque	.30	.75
503 Fred Stanley	.30	.75
504 Buddy Bradford	.30	.75
505 Chris Speier	.30	.75
506 Leron Lee	.30	.75
507 Tom Carroll	.30	.75
508 Bob Hansen	.30	.75
509 Dave Hilton	.30	.75
510 Vida Blue	.60	1.50
511 Billy Martin MG CL	1.00	2.50
512 Larry Milbourne	.30	.75
513 Dick Pole	.30	.75
514 Jose Cruz	1.00	2.50
515 Manny Sanguillen	.60	1.50
516 Don Hood	.30	.75
517 Checklist 397-528	1.50	4.00
518 Leo Cardenas	.30	.75
519 Jim Todd	.30	.75
520 Amos Otis	.60	1.50
521 Dennis Blair	.30	.75
522 Gary Sutherland	.30	.75
523 Tom Paciorek	.60	1.50
524 John Doherty	.30	.75
525 Tom House	.30	.75
526 Larry Hisle	.60	1.50
527 Mac Scarce	.30	.75
528 Eddie Leon	.30	.75
529 Gary Thomasson	.30	.75
530 Gaylord Perry	1.50	4.00
531 Sparky Anderson MG CL	2.50	6.00
532 Gorman Thomas	.60	1.50
533 Rudy Meoli	.30	.75
534 Alex Johnson	.30	.75
535 Gene Tenace	.60	1.50
536 Bob Moose	.30	.75
537 Tommy Harper	.60	1.50
538 Duffy Dyer	.30	.75
539 Jesse Jefferson	.30	.75
540 Lou Brock	3.00	8.00
541 Roger Metzger	.30	.75
542 Pete Broberg	.30	.75
543 Larry Biittner	.30	.75
544 Steve Mingori	.30	.75
545 Billy Williams	1.50	4.00
546 John Knox	.30	.75
547 Von Joshua	.30	.75
548 Charlie Sands	.30	.75
549 Bill Butler	.30	.75
550 Ralph Garr	.60	1.50
551 Larry Christenson	.30	.75
552 Jack Brohamer	.30	.75
553 John Boccabella	.30	.75
554 Goose Gossage	1.00	2.50
555 Al Oliver	1.00	2.50
556 Tim Johnson	.30	.75
557 Larry Gura	.30	.75
558 Dave Roberts	.30	.75
559 Bob Montgomery	.30	.75
560 Tony Perez	2.00	5.00
561 Alvin Dark MG CL	1.00	2.50
562 Gary Nolan	.60	1.50
563 Wilbur Howard	.30	.75
564 Tommy Davis	.60	1.50
565 Joe Torre	1.00	2.50
566 Ray Burris	.30	.75
567 Jim Sundberg RC	1.00	2.50
568 Dale Murray	.30	.75
569 Frank White	.60	1.50
570 Jim Wynn	.60	1.50
571 Dave Lemanczyk	.30	.75
572 Roger Nelson	.30	.75
573 Orlando Pena	.30	.75
574 Tony Taylor	.30	.75
575 Gene Clines	.30	.75
576 Phil Roof	.30	.75
577 John Morris	.30	.75
578 Dave Tomlin	.30	.75
579 Skip Pitlock	.30	.75
580 Frank Robinson	3.00	8.00
581 Darrel Chaney	.30	.75
582 Eduardo Rodriguez	.30	.75
583 Andy Etchebarren	.30	.75
584 Mike Garman	.30	.75
585 Chris Chambliss	.60	1.50
586 Tim McCarver	1.00	2.50
587 Chris Ward	.30	.75
588 Rick Auerbach	.30	.75
589 Clyde King MG CL	1.00	2.50
590 Cesar Cedeno	.60	1.50
591 Glenn Abbott	.30	.75
592 Balor Moore	.30	.75
593 Gene Lamont	.30	.75
594 Jim Fuller	.30	.75
595 Joe Niekro	.60	1.50
596 Ollie Brown	.30	.75
597 Winston Llenas	.30	.75
598 Bruce Kison	.30	.75
599 Nate Colbert	.30	.75
600 Rod Carew	4.00	10.00
601 Juan Beniquez	.30	.75
602 John Vukovich	.30	.75
603 Lew Krausse	.30	.75
604 Oscar Zamora	.30	.75
605 John Ellis	.30	.75
606 Bruce Miller	.30	.75
607 Jim Holt	.30	.75
608 Gene Michael	.30	.75
609 Elrod Hendricks	.30	.75
610 Ron Hunt	.30	.75
611 Bill Virdon MG CL	1.00	2.50
612 Terry Hughes	.30	.75
613 Bill Parsons	.30	.75
614 Jack Kucek	.60	1.50
Dyar Miller		
Vern Ruhle		
Paul Siebert		
615 Pat Darcy	1.00	2.50
Dennis Leonard RC		
Tom Underwood		
Hank Webb		
616 Dave Augustine	8.00	20.00
Pepe Mangual		
Jim Rice RC		
John Scott		
617 Mike Cubbage	1.00	2.50
Doug DeCinces RC		
Reggie Sanders		
Manny Trillo		
618 Jamie Easterly	.60	1.50
Tom Johnson		
Scott McGregor RC		
Rick Rhoden		
619 Benny Ayala	.60	1.50
Nyls Nyman		
Tommy Smith		
Jerry Turner		
620 Gary Carter RC	10.00	25.00
Marc Hill		
Danny Meyer		
Leon Roberts		
621 John Denny RC	1.00	2.50
Rawly Eastwick		
Jim Kern		
Juan Veintidos		
622 Ed Armbrister	4.00	10.00
Fred Lynn RC		
Tom Poquette		
Terry Whitfield		
623 Phil Garner RC	5.00	12.00
Keith Hernandez		
Bob Sheldon		
Tom Veryzer		
624 Doug Konieczny	.60	1.50
Gary Lavelle		
Jim Otten		
Eddie Solomon		
625 Boog Powell	1.00	2.50
626 Larry Haney	.30	.75
(photo actually		
Dave Duncan)		
627 Tom Walker	.30	.75
628 Ron LeFlore RC	.60	1.50
629 Joe Hoerner	.30	.75
630 Greg Luzinski	1.00	2.50
631 Lee Lacy	.30	.75
632 Morris Nettles	.30	.75
633 Paul Casanova	.30	.75
634 Cy Acosta	.30	.75
635 Chuck Dobson	.30	.75
636 Charlie Moore	.30	.75
637 Ted Martinez	.30	.75
638 Jim Marshall MG CL	1.00	2.50
639 Steve Kline	.30	.75
640 Harmon Killebrew	3.00	8.00
641 Jim Northrup	.60	1.50
642 Mike Phillips	.30	.75
643 Brent Strom	.30	.75
644 Bill Fahey	.30	.75
645 Danny Cater	.30	.75
646 Checklist 529-660	1.50	4.00
647 C.Washington RC	1.00	2.50
648 Dave Pagan	.60	1.50
649 Jack Heidemann	.30	.75
650 Dave May	.30	.75
651 John Morlan	.30	.75
652 Lindy McDaniel	.60	1.50
653 Lee Richard	.30	.75
654 Jerry Terrell	.30	.75
655 Rico Carty	.60	1.50
656 Bill Plummer	.30	.75
657 Bob Oliver	.30	.75
658 Vic Harris	.30	.75
659 Bob Apodaca	.30	.75
660 Hank Aaron	12.50	40.00

1976 O-Pee-Chee

TIM McCARVER
PHILLIES

This is a 660-card standard-size set. The 1976 O-Pee-Chee cards are very similar to the 1976 Topps cards, yet rather different from previous years' issues. The most prominent change is that the backs are much brighter than their American counterparts. The cards parallel the American issue and it is a challenge to find well centered examples of these cards. Notable Rookie Cards include Dennis Eckersley and Ron Guidry.

COMPLETE SET (660)	400.00	800.00
1 Hank Aaron RB	10.00	25.00
2 Bobby Bonds RB	1.25	3.00
3 Mickey Lolich RB	.60	1.50
4 Dave Lopes RB	.60	1.50
5 Tom Seaver RB	3.00	8.00
6 Rennie Stennett RB	.60	1.50
7 Jim Umbarger	.30	.75
8 Tito Fuentes	.30	.75
9 Paul Lindblad	.30	.75
10 Lou Brock	3.00	8.00
11 Jim Hughes	.30	.75
12 Richie Zisk	.60	1.50
13 John Wockenfuss	.30	.75
14 Gene Garber	.60	1.50
15 George Scott	.60	1.50
16 Bob Apodaca	.30	.75
17 Billy Martin MG CL	1.25	3.00
18 Dale Murray	.30	.75
19 George Brett	30.00	60.00
20 Bob Watson	.60	1.50
21 Dave LaRoche	.30	.75
22 Bill Russell	.60	1.50
23 Brian Downing	.30	.75
24 Cesar Geronimo	.60	1.50
25 Mike Torrez	.60	1.50
26 Andre Thornton	.60	1.50
27 Ed Figueroa	.30	.75
28 Dusty Baker	1.25	3.00
29 Rick Burleson	.60	1.50
30 John Montefusco RC	.60	1.50
31 Len Randle	.30	.75
32 Danny Frisella	.30	.75
33 Bill North	.30	.75
34 Mike Garman	.30	.75
35 Tony Oliva	1.25	3.00
36 Frank Taveras	.30	.75
37 John Hiller	.60	1.50
38 Garry Maddox	.60	1.50
39 Pete Broberg	.30	.75
40 Dave Kingman	1.25	3.00
41 Tippy Martinez	.60	1.50
42 Barry Foote	.60	1.50
43 Paul Splittorff	.30	.75
44 Doug Rader	.60	1.50
45 Boog Powell	1.25	3.00
46 Walt Alston MG CL	1.25	3.00
47 Jesse Jefferson	.30	.75
48 Dave Concepcion	1.25	3.00
49 Dave Duncan	.60	1.50
50 Fred Lynn	1.25	3.00
51 Ray Burris	.30	.75
52 Dave Chalk	.30	.75
53 Mike Beard RC	.30	.75
54 Dave Rader	.30	.75
55 Gaylord Perry	2.00	5.00
56 Bob Tolan	.30	.75
57 Phil Garner	.60	1.50
58 Ron Reed	.30	.75
59 Larry Hisle	.60	1.50
60 Jerry Reuss	.60	1.50
61 Ron LeFlore	.60	1.50
62 Johnny Oates	.60	1.50
63 Bobby Darwin	.30	.75
64 Jerry Koosman	.60	1.50
65 Chris Chambliss	.60	1.50
66 Gus Bell FS	.60	1.50
Buddy Bell		
67 Ray Boone FS	.60	1.50
Bob Boone		
68 Joe Coleman FS	.30	.75
Joe Coleman Jr.		
69 Jim Hegan FS	.30	.75
Mike Hegan		
70 Roy Smalley FS	.60	1.50
Roy Smalley Jr.		
71 Steve Rogers	1.25	3.00
72 Hal McRae	.60	1.50
73 Earl Weaver MG CL	1.25	3.00
74 Oscar Gamble	.60	1.50
75 Larry Dierker	.60	1.50
76 Willie Crawford	.30	.75
77 Pedro Borbon	.60	1.50
78 Cecil Cooper	.60	1.50
79 Jerry Morales	.30	.75
80 Jim Kaat	1.50	4.00
81 Darrell Evans	.60	1.50
82 Von Joshua	.30	.75
83 Jim Spencer	.30	.75
84 Brent Strom	.30	.75
85 Mickey Rivers	.60	1.50
86 Mike Tyson	.30	.75
87 Tom Burgmeier	.30	.75
88 Duffy Dyer	.30	.75
89 Vern Ruhle	.30	.75
90 Sal Bando	.60	1.50
91 Tom Hutton	.30	.75
92 Eduardo Rodriguez	.30	.75
93 Mike Phillips	.30	.75
94 Jim Dwyer	.30	.75
95 Brooks Robinson	4.00	10.00
96 Doug Bird	.30	.75
97 Wilbur Howard	.30	.75
98 Dennis Eckersley RC	20.00	50.00
99 Lee Lacy	.30	.75
100 Jim Hunter	2.00	5.00
101 Pete LaCock	.30	.75
102 Jim Willoughby	.30	.75
103 Biff Pocoroba RC	.30	.75
104 Cincinnati Reds	1.50	4.00
Team Card CL		
Sparky Anderson MG		
105 Gary Lavelle	.30	.75
106 Tom Grieve	.60	1.50
107 Dave Roberts	.30	.75
108 Don Kirkwood	.30	.75
109 Larry Lintz	.30	.75
110 Carlos May	.30	.75
111 Danny Thompson	.30	.75
112 Kent Tekulve RC	1.25	3.00
113 Gary Sutherland	.30	.75
114 Jay Johnstone	.60	1.50
115 Ken Holtzman	.60	1.50
116 Charlie Moore	.30	.75
117 Mike Jorgensen	.30	.75
118 Darrell Johnson MG CL	1.25	3.00
119 Checklist 1-132	1.25	3.00
120 Rusty Staub	.60	1.50
121 Tony Solaita	.30	.75
122 Mike Cosgrove	.30	.75
123 Walt Williams	.30	.75
124 Doug Rau	.30	.75
125 Don Baylor	1.50	4.00
126 Tom Dettore	.30	.75
127 Larvell Blanks	.30	.75
128 Ken Griffey Sr.	1.50	4.00
129 Andy Etchebarren	.30	.75
130 Luis Tiant	1.25	3.00
131 Bill Stein	.30	.75
132 Don Hood	.30	.75
133 Gary Matthews	.60	1.50
134 Mike Ivie	.30	.75
135 Bake McBride	.60	1.50
136 Dave Goltz	.30	.75
137 Bill Robinson	.60	1.50
138 Lerrin LaGrow	.30	.75
139 Gorman Thomas	.60	1.50
140 Vida Blue	.60	1.50
141 Larry Parrish RC	1.25	3.00
142 Dick Drago	.30	.75
143 Jerry Grote	.30	.75
144 Al Fitzmorris	.30	.75
145 Larry Bowa	.60	1.50
146 George Medich	.30	.75
147 Bill Virdon MG CL	1.25	3.00
148 Stan Thomas	.30	.75
149 Tommy Davis	.60	1.50
150 Steve Garvey	1.50	4.00
151 Bill Bonham	.30	.75
152 Leroy Stanton	.30	.75
153 Buzz Capra	.30	.75
154 Bucky Dent	.60	1.50
155 Jack Billingham	.60	1.50
156 Rico Carty	.60	1.50
157 Mike Caldwell	.30	.75
158 Ken Reitz	.30	.75
159 Jerry Terrell	.30	.75
160 Dave Winfield	8.00	20.00
161 Bruce Kison	.30	.75
162 Jack Pierce	.30	.75
163 Jim Slaton	.30	.75
164 Pepe Mangual	.30	.75
165 Gene Tenace	.60	1.50
166 Skip Lockwood	.30	.75
167 Freddie Patek	.60	1.50
168 Tom Hilgendorf	.30	.75
169 Graig Nettles	1.25	3.00
170 Rick Wise	.30	.75
171 Greg Gross	.30	.75
172 Frank Lucchesi MG CL	1.25	3.00
173 Steve Swisher	.30	.75
174 Charlie Hough	.60	1.50
175 Ken Singleton	.60	1.50
176 Dick Lange	.30	.75
177 Marty Perez	.30	.75
178 Tom Buskey	.30	.75
179 George Foster	1.25	3.00
180 Goose Gossage	1.50	4.00
181 Willie Montanez	.30	.75
182 Harry Rasmussen	.30	.75
183 Steve Braun	.30	.75
184 Bill Greif	.30	.75
185 Dave Parker	1.50	4.00
186 Tom Walker	.30	.75
187 Pedro Garcia	.30	.75
188 Fred Scherman	.30	.75
189 Claudell Washington	.60	1.50
190 Jon Matlack	.30	.75
191 Bill Madlock	.60	1.50
Ted Simmons		
Manny Sanguillen LL		
192 Rod Carew	1.50	4.00
Fred Lynn		
Thurman Munson LL		
193 Mike Schmidt	2.00	5.00
Dave Kingman		
Greg Luzinski LL		
194 Reggie Jackson	2.00	5.00
George Scott		
John Mayberry LL		
195 Greg Luzinski	1.25	3.00
Johnny Bench		
Tony Perez LL		
196 George Scott	.60	1.50
John Mayberry		
Fred Lynn LL		
197 Dave Lopes	1.25	3.00
Joe Morgan		
Lou Brock LL		
198 Mickey Rivers	.60	1.50
Claudell Washington		
Amos Otis LL		
199 Tom Seaver	1.50	4.00
Randy Jones		
Andy Messersmith LL		

200 Jim Hunter	1.25	3.00
Jim Palmer		
Vida Blue LL		
201 Randy Jones	1.25	3.00
Andy Messersmith		
Tom Seaver LL		
202 Jim Palmer	2.00	5.00
Jim Hunter		
Dennis Eckersley LL		
203 Tom Seaver	1.50	4.00
John Montefusco		
Andy Messersmith LL		
204 Frank Tanana	.60	1.50
Bert Blyleven		
Gaylord Perry LL		
205 Al Hrabosky	.60	1.50
Rich Gossage LL		
206 Manny Trillo	.30	.75
207 Andy Hassler	.30	.75
208 Mike Lum	.30	.75
209 Alan Ashby	.60	1.50
210 Lee May	.60	1.50
211 Clay Carroll	.60	1.50
212 Pat Kelly	.30	.75
213 Dave Heaverlo	.30	.75
214 Eric Soderholm	.30	.75
215 Reggie Smith	.60	1.50
216 Karl Kuehl MG CL	1.25	3.00
217 Dave Freisleben	.30	.75
218 John Knox	.30	.75
219 Tom Murphy	.30	.75
220 Manny Sanguillen	.60	1.50
221 Jim Todd	.30	.75
222 Wayne Garrett	.30	.75
223 Ollie Brown	.30	.75
224 Jim York	.30	.75
225 Roy White	.60	1.50
226 Jim Sundberg	.60	1.50
227 Oscar Zamora	.30	.75
228 John Hale	.30	.75
229 Jerry Remy	.30	.75
230 Carl Yastrzemski	6.00	15.00
231 Tom House	.30	.75
232 Frank Duffy	.30	.75
233 Grant Jackson	.30	.75
234 Mike Sadek	.30	.75
235 Bert Blyleven	1.50	4.00
236 Whitey Herzog MG CL	1.25	3.00
237 Dave Hamilton	.30	.75
238 Larry Biittner	.30	.75
239 John Curtis	.30	.75
240 Pete Rose	12.50	40.00
241 Hector Torres	.30	.75
242 Dan Meyer	.30	.75
243 Jim Rooker	.30	.75
244 Bill Sharp	.30	.75
245 Felix Millan	.30	.75
246 Cesar Tovar	.30	.75
247 Terry Harmon	.30	.75
248 Dick Tidrow	.30	.75
249 Cliff Johnson	.60	1.50
250 Fergie Jenkins	2.00	5.00
251 Rick Monday	.60	1.50
252 Tim Nordbrook	.30	.75
253 Bill Buckner	.60	1.50
254 Rudy Meoli	.30	.75
255 Fritz Peterson	.30	.75
256 Rowland Office	.30	.75
257 Ross Grimsley	.30	.75
258 Nyls Nyman	.30	.75
259 Darrel Chaney	.30	.75
260 Steve Busby	.30	.75
261 Gary Thomasson	.30	.75
262 Checklist 133-264	1.25	3.00
263 Lyman Bostock RC	1.25	3.00
264 Steve Renko	.30	.75
265 Willie Davis	.60	1.50
266 Alan Foster	.30	.75
267 Aurelio Rodriguez	.30	.75
268 Del Unser	.30	.75
269 Rick Austin	.30	.75
270 Willie Stargell	2.00	5.00
271 Jim Lonborg	.60	1.50
272 Rick Dempsey	.60	1.50
273 Joe Niekro	.60	1.50
274 Tommy Harper	.60	1.50
275 Rick Manning	.30	.75
276 Mickey Scott	.30	.75
277 Jim Marshall MG CL	1.25	3.00
278 Bernie Carbo	.30	.75
279 Roy Howell	.30	.75
280 Burt Hooton	.60	1.50
281 Dave May	.30	.75
282 Dan Osborn	.30	.75
283 Merv Rettenmund	.30	.75
284 Steve Ontiveros	.30	.75
285 Mike Cuellar	.60	1.50
286 Jim Wohlford	.30	.75
287 Pete Mackanin	.30	.75
288 Bill Campbell	.30	.75
289 Enzo Hernandez	.30	.75
290 Ted Simmons	.60	1.50
291 Ken Sanders	.30	.75
292 Leon Roberts	.30	.75
293 Bill Castro	.30	.75
294 Ed Kirkpatrick	.30	.75
295 Dave Cash	.30	.75
296 Pat Dobson	.30	.75
297 Roger Metzger	.30	.75
298 Dick Bosman	.30	.75
299 Champ Summers	.30	.75
300 Johnny Bench	8.00	20.00
301 Jackie Brown	.30	.75
302 Rick Miller	.30	.75
303 Steve Foucault	.30	.75
304 Dick Williams MG CL	1.25	3.00
305 Andy Messersmith	.60	1.50
306 Rod Gilbreath	.30	.75
307 Al Bumbry	.60	1.50
308 Jim Barr	.30	.75
309 Bill Melton	.30	.75
310 Randy Jones	.60	1.50
311 Cookie Rojas	.30	.75
312 Don Carrithers	.30	.75
313 Dan Ford	.30	.75
314 Ed Kranepool	.30	.75
315 Al Hrabosky	.60	1.50
316 Robin Yount	10.00	25.00
317 John Candelaria RC	1.25	3.00
318 Bob Boone	1.25	3.00
319 Larry Gura	.30	.75
320 Willie Horton	.60	1.50
321 Jose Cruz	1.25	3.00
322 Glenn Abbott	.30	.75
323 Rob Sperring	.30	.75
324 Jim Bibby	.30	.75
325 Tony Perez	2.00	5.00
326 Dick Pole	.30	.75
327 Dave Moates	.30	.75
328 Carl Morton	.30	.75
329 Joe Ferguson	.30	.75
330 Nolan Ryan	20.00	50.00
331 John McNamara MG CL	1.25	3.00
332 Charlie Williams	.30	.75
333 Bob Coluccio	.30	.75
334 Dennis Leonard	.60	1.50
335 Bob Grich	.60	1.50
336 Vic Albury	.30	.75
337 Bud Harrelson	.60	1.50
338 Bob Bailey	.30	.75
339 John Denny	.60	1.50
340 Jim Rice	2.50	6.00
341 Lou Gehrig ATG	8.00	20.00
342 Rogers Hornsby ATG	1.50	4.00
343 Pie Traynor ATG	1.25	3.00
344 Honus Wagner ATG	3.00	8.00
345 Babe Ruth ATG	10.00	25.00
346 Ty Cobb ATG	8.00	20.00
347 Ted Williams ATG	8.00	20.00
348 Mickey Cochrane ATG	1.25	3.00
349 Walter Johnson ATG	3.00	8.00
350 Lefty Grove ATG	1.25	3.00
351 Randy Hundley	.60	1.50
352 Dave Giusti	.30	.75
353 Sixto Lezcano	.60	1.50
354 Ron Blomberg	.30	.75
355 Steve Carlton	4.00	10.00
356 Ted Martinez	.30	.75
357 Ken Forsch	.30	.75
358 Buddy Bell	.60	1.50
359 Rick Reuschel	.60	1.50
360 Jeff Burroughs	.60	1.50
361 Ralph Houk MG CL	1.25	3.00
362 Will McEnaney	.60	1.50
363 Dave Collins RC	.60	1.50
364 Elias Sosa	.30	.75
365 Carlton Fisk	3.00	8.00
366 Bobby Valentine	.60	1.50
367 Bruce Miller	.30	.75
368 Wilbur Wood	.30	.75
369 Frank White	.60	1.50
370 Ron Cey	.60	1.50
371 Ellie Hendricks	.30	.75
372 Rick Baldwin	.30	.75
373 Johnny Briggs	.30	.75
374 Dan Warthen	.30	.75
375 Ron Fairly	.60	1.50
376 Rich Hebner	.60	1.50
377 Mike Hegan	.30	.75
378 Steve Stone	.60	1.50
379 Ken Boswell	.30	.75
380 Bobby Bonds	1.50	4.00
381 Denny Doyle	.30	.75
382 Matt Alexander	.30	.75
383 John Ellis	.30	.75
384 Danny Ozark MG CL	1.25	3.00
385 Mickey Lolich	.60	1.50
386 Ed Goodson	.30	.75
387 Mike Miley	.30	.75
388 Stan Perzanowski	.30	.75
389 Glenn Adams	.30	.75
390 Don Gullett	.60	1.50
391 Jerry Hairston	.30	.75
392 Checklist 265-396	1.25	3.00
393 Paul Mitchell	.30	.75
394 Fran Healy	.30	.75
395 Jim Wynn	.60	1.50
396 Bill Lee	.30	.75
397 Tim Foli	.30	.75
398 Dave Tomlin	.30	.75
399 Luis Melendez	.30	.75
400 Rod Carew	3.00	8.00
401 Ken Brett	.30	.75
402 Don Money	.60	1.50
403 Geoff Zahn	.30	.75
404 Enos Cabell	.30	.75
405 Rollie Fingers	2.00	5.00
406 Ed Herrmann	.30	.75
407 Tom Underwood	.30	.75
408 Charlie Spikes	.30	.75
409 Dave Lemanczyk	.30	.75
410 Ralph Garr	.60	1.50
411 Bill Singer	.30	.75
412 Toby Harrah	.60	1.50
413 Pete Varney	.30	.75
414 Wayne Garland	.30	.75
415 Vada Pinson	1.50	4.00
416 Tommy John	1.50	4.00
417 Gene Clines	.30	.75
418 Jose Morales RC	.60	1.50
419 Reggie Cleveland	.30	.75
420 Joe Morgan	3.00	8.00
421 Oakland A's CL	1.25	3.00
422 Johnny Grubb	.30	.75
423 Ed Halicki	.30	.75
424 Phil Roof	.30	.75
425 Rennie Stennett	.30	.75
426 Bob Forsch	.30	.75
427 Kurt Bevacqua	.30	.75
428 Jim Crawford	.30	.75
429 Fred Stanley	.30	.75
430 Jose Cardenal	.60	1.50
431 Dick Ruthven	.30	.75
432 Tom Veryzer	.30	.75
433 Rick Waits	.30	.75
434 Morris Nettles	.30	.75
435 Phil Niekro	2.00	5.00
436 Bill Fahey	.30	.75
437 Terry Forster	.30	.75
438 Doug DeCinces	.60	1.50
439 Rick Rhoden	.60	1.50
440 John Mayberry	.60	1.50
441 Gary Carter	3.00	8.00
442 Hank Webb	.30	.75
443 San Francisco Giants CL	1.25	3.00
444 Gary Nolan	.60	1.50
445 Rico Petrocelli	.60	1.50
446 Larry Haney	.30	.75
447 Gene Locklear	.60	1.50
448 Tom Johnson	.30	.75
449 Bob Robertson	.30	.75
450 Jim Palmer	3.00	8.00
451 Buddy Bradford	.30	.75
452 Tom Hausman	.30	.75
453 Lou Piniella	1.25	3.00
454 Tom Griffin	.30	.75
455 Dick Allen	1.25	3.00
456 Joe Coleman	.30	.75
457 Ed Crosby	.30	.75
458 Earl Williams	.30	.75
459 Jim Brewer	.30	.75
460 Cesar Cedeno	.60	1.50
461 NL and AL Champs	.60	1.50
Reds sweep Bucs;		
Bosox surprise A's		
462 World Series	.60	1.50
Reds Champs		
463 Steve Hargan	.30	.75
464 Ken Henderson	.30	.75
465 Mike Marshall	.60	1.50
466 Bob Stinson	.30	.75
467 Woodie Fryman	.30	.75
468 Jesus Alou	.30	.75
469 Rawly Eastwick	.60	1.50
470 Bobby Murcer	.60	1.50
471 Jim Burton	.30	.75
472 Bob Davis	.30	.75
473 Paul Blair	.60	1.50
474 Ray Corbin	.30	.75
475 Joe Rudi	.60	1.50
476 Bob Moose	.30	.75
477 Frank Robinson MG CL	1.25	3.00
478 Lynn McGlothen	.30	.75
479 Bobby Mitchell	.30	.75
480 Mike Schmidt	10.00	25.00
481 Rudy May	.30	.75
482 Tim Hosley	.30	.75
483 Mickey Stanley	.30	.75
484 Eric Raich	.30	.75
485 Mike Hargrove	.60	1.50
486 Bruce Dal Canton	.30	.75
487 Leron Lee	.30	.75
488 Claude Osteen	.60	1.50
489 Skip Jutze	.30	.75
490 Frank Tanana	.60	1.50
491 Terry Crowley	.30	.75
492 Martin Pattin	.30	.75
493 Derrel Thomas	.30	.75
494 Craig Swan	.60	1.50
495 Nate Colbert	.30	.75
496 Juan Beniquez	.30	.75
497 Joe McIntosh	.30	.75
498 Glenn Borgmann	.30	.75
499 Mario Guerrero	.30	.75
500 Reggie Jackson	8.00	20.00
501 Billy Champion	.30	.75
502 Tim McCarver	1.25	3.00
503 Elliott Maddox	.30	.75
504 Danny Murtaugh MG CL	1.25	3.00
505 Mark Belanger	.60	1.50
506 George Mitterwald	.30	.75
507 Ray Bare	.30	.75
508 Duane Kuiper	.30	.75
509 Bill Hands	.30	.75
510 Amos Otis	.60	1.50
511 Jamie Easterley	.30	.75
512 Ellie Rodriguez	.30	.75
513 Bart Johnson	.30	.75
514 Dan Driessen	.60	1.50
515 Steve Yeager	.60	1.50
516 Wayne Granger	.30	.75
517 John Milner	.30	.75
518 Doug Flynn	.30	.75
519 Steve Brye	.30	.75
520 Willie McCovey	3.00	8.00
521 Jim Colborn	.30	.75
522 Ted Sizemore	.30	.75
523 Bob Montgomery	.30	.75
524 Pete Falcone	.30	.75
525 Billy Williams	2.00	5.00
526 Checklist 397-528	1.25	3.00
527 Mike Anderson	.30	.75
528 Dock Ellis	.30	.75
529 Deron Johnson	.30	.75
530 Don Sutton	2.00	5.00
531 Joe Frazier MG CL	1.25	3.00
532 Milt May	.30	.75
533 Lee Richard	.30	.75
534 Stan Bahnsen	.30	.75
535 Dave Nelson	.30	.75
536 Mike Thompson	.30	.75
537 Tony Muser	.30	.75
538 Pat Darcy	.30	.75
539 John Balaz	.30	.75
540 Bill Freehan	.60	1.50
541 Steve Mingori	.30	.75
542 Keith Hernandez	1.25	3.00
543 Wayne Twitchell	.30	.75
544 Pepe Frias	.30	.75
545 Sparky Lyle	.60	1.50
546 Dave Rosello	.30	.75
547 Roric Harrison	.30	.75
548 Manny Mota	.60	1.50
549 Randy Tate	.30	.75
550 Hank Aaron	12.50	40.00
551 Jerry DaVanon	.30	.75
552 Terry Humphrey	.30	.75
553 Randy Moffitt	.30	.75
554 Ray Fosse	.30	.75
555 Dyar Miller	.30	.75
556 Gene Mauch MG CL	1.25	3.00
557 Dan Spillner	.30	.75
558 Clarence Gaston	.60	1.50
559 Clyde Wright	.30	.75
560 Jorge Orta	.30	.75
561 Tom Carroll	.30	.75
562 Adrian Garrett	.30	.75
563 Larry Demery	.30	.75
564 Bubble Gum Champ:	1.25	3.00
Kurt Bevacqua		
565 Tug McGraw	1.25	3.00
566 Ken McMullen	.30	.75
567 George Stone	.30	.75
568 Rob Andrews	.30	.75
569 Nelson Briles	.60	1.50
570 George Hendrick	.60	1.50
571 Don DeMola	.30	.75
572 Rich Coggins	.30	.75
573 Bill Travers	.30	.75
574 Don Kessinger	.60	1.50
575 Dwight Evans	1.25	3.00
576 Maximino Leon	.30	.75
577 Marc Hill	.30	.75
578 Ted Kubiak	.30	.75
579 Clay Kirby	.30	.75
580 Bert Campaneris	.60	1.50
581 Red Schoendienst MG CL	1.25	3.00
582 Mike Kekich	.30	.75
583 Tommy Helms	.30	.75
584 Stan Wall	.30	.75
585 Joe Torre	1.50	4.00
586 Ron Schueler	.30	.75
587 Leo Cardenas	.30	.75
588 Kevin Kobel	.30	.75
589 Santo Alcala	1.25	3.00
Mike Flanagan RC		
Joe Pactwa		
Pablo Torrealba		
590 Henry Cruz	.60	1.50
Chet Lemon RC		
Ellis Valentine		
Terry Whitfield		
591 Steve Grilli	.60	1.50
Craig Mitchell		
Jose Sosa		
George Throop		
592 Willie Randolph RC	4.00	10.00
Dave McKay		
Jerry Royster		
Roy Staiger		
593 Larry Anderson	.60	1.50
Ken Crosby		
Mark Littell		
Butch Metzger		
594 Andy Merchant	.60	1.50
Ed Ott		
Royle Stillman		
Jerry White		
595 Art DeFillipis	.60	1.50
Randy Lerch		
Sid Monge		
Steve Barr		
596 Craig Reynolds	.60	1.50
Lamar Johnson		
Johnnie LeMaster		
Jerry Manuel		
597 Don Aase	.60	1.50
Jack Kucek		
Frank LaCorte		
Mike Pazik		
598 Hector Cruz	.60	1.50
Jamie Quirk		
Jerry Turner		
Joe Wallis		
599 Rob Dressler	5.00	12.00
Ron Guidry RC		
Bob McClure		
Pat Zachry		
600 Tom Seaver	6.00	15.00
601 Ken Rudolph	.30	.75
602 Doug Konieczny	.30	.75
603 Jim Holt	.30	.75
604 Joe Lovitto	.30	.75
605 Al Downing	.30	.75
606 Alex Grammas MG CL	1.25	3.00
607 Rich Hinton	.30	.75
608 Vic Correll	.30	.75
609 Fred Norman	.30	.75
610 Greg Luzinski	1.25	3.00
611 Rich Folkers	.30	.75
612 Joe Lahoud	.30	.75
613 Tim Johnson	.30	.75
614 Fernando Arroyo	.30	.75
615 Mike Cubbage	.30	.75
616 Buck Martinez	.60	1.50
617 Darold Knowles	.30	.75
618 Jack Brohamer	.30	.75
619 Bill Butler	.30	.75
620 Al Oliver	.60	1.50
621 Tom Hall	.30	.75
622 Rick Auerbach	.30	.75
623 Bob Allietta	.30	.75
624 Tony Taylor	.30	.75
625 J.R. Richard	.60	1.50
626 Bob Sheldon	.30	.75
627 Bill Plummer	.30	.75
628 John D'Acquisto	.30	.75
629 Sandy Alomar	.60	1.50
630 Chris Speier	.30	.75
631 Dave Bristol MG CL	1.25	3.00
632 Rogelio Moret	.30	.75
633 John Stearns RC	.60	1.50
634 Larry Christenson	.30	.75
635 Jim Fregosi	.60	1.50
636 Joe Decker	.30	.75
637 Bruce Bochte	.30	.75
638 Doyle Alexander	.60	1.50
639 Fred Kendall	.30	.75
640 Bill Madlock	1.25	3.00
641 Tom Paciorek	.60	1.50
642 Dennis Blair	.30	.75
643 Checklist 529-660	1.25	3.00
644 Tom Bradley	.30	.75
645 Darrell Porter	.60	1.50
646 John Lowenstein	.30	.75
647 Ramon Hernandez	.30	.75
648 Al Cowens	.30	.75
649 Dave Roberts	.30	.75
650 Thurman Munson	4.00	10.00
651 John Odom	.30	.75
652 Ed Armbrister	.30	.75
653 Mike Norris RC	.60	1.50
654 Doug Griffin	.30	.75
655 Mike Vail	.30	.75
656 Chuck Tanner MG CL	1.25	3.00
657 Roy Smalley RC	.60	1.50
658 Jerry Johnson	.30	.75
659 Ben Oglivie	.60	1.50
660 Dave Lopes	1.25	3.00

1977 O-Pee-Chee

The 1977 O-Pee-Chee set of 264 standard-size cards is not only much smaller numerically than its American counterpart, but also contains many different poses and is loaded with players from the two Canadian teams, including many players from the inaugural year of the Blue Jays and many single cards of players who were on multiplayer rookie cards. On a white background, the fronts feature color player photos with thin black borders. The player's name and position, a facsimile autograph, and the team name also appear on the front. The horizontal backs carry player biography and statistics in French and English. The numbering of this set is different than the U.S. issue, the backs have different colors and the words "O-Pee-Chee Printed in Canada" are printed on the back.

COMPLETE SET (264)	150.00	300.00
1 George Brett	4.00	10.00
Bill Madlock LL		
2 Graig Nettles	.75	2.00
Mike Schmidt LL		
3 Lee May	.60	1.50
George Foster LL		
4 Bill North	.30	.75
Dave Lopes LL		
5 Jim Palmer	.60	1.50
Randy Jones LL		
6 Nolan Ryan	8.00	20.00
Tom Seaver LL		
7 Mark Fidrych	.30	.75
John Denny LL		
8 Bill Campbell	.30	.75
Rawly Eastwick LL		
9 Mike Jorgensen	.30	.75
10 Jim Hunter	1.00	2.50
11 Ken Griffey Sr.	.60	1.50
12 Bill Campbell	.12	.30
13 Otto Velez	.30	.75
14 Milt May	.12	.30
15 Dennis Eckersley	2.00	5.00
16 John Mayberry	.30	.75
17 Larry Bowa	.30	.75
18 Don Carrithers	.30	.75
19 Ken Singleton	.30	.75
20 Bill Stein	.12	.30
21 Ken Brett	.12	.30
22 Gary Woods	.30	.75
23 Steve Swisher	.12	.30
24 Don Sutton	1.00	2.50
25 Willie Stargell	1.00	2.50
26 Jerry Koosman	.30	.75
27 Del Unser	.30	.75
28 Bob Grich	.30	.75
29 Jim Slaton	.12	.30
30 Thurman Munson	2.00	5.00
31 Dan Driessen	.12	.30
32 Tom Bruno	.30	.75
33 Larry Hisle	.30	.75
34 Phil Garner	.12	.30
35 Mike Hargrove	.30	.75
36 Jackie Brown	.30	.75
37 Carl Yastrzemski	3.00	8.00
38 Dave Roberts	.12	.30
39 Ray Fosse	.12	.30
40 Dave McKay	.30	.75
41 Paul Splittorff	.12	.30
42 Garry Maddox	.12	.30
43 Phil Niekro	1.00	2.50
44 Roger Metzger	.12	.30
45 Gary Carter	1.00	2.50
46 Jim Spencer	.12	.30
47 Ross Grimsley	.12	.30
48 Bob Bailor	.30	.75
49 Chris Chambliss	.30	.75
50 Will McEnaney	.30	.75
51 Lou Brock	1.50	4.00
52 Rollie Fingers	1.00	2.50
53 Chris Speier	.12	.30
54 Bombo Rivera	.30	.75
55 Pete Broberg	.12	.30
56 Bill Madlock	.75	2.00
57 Rick Rhoden	.30	.75
58 Don Leppert CO	.30	.75
Bob Miller CO		
Jackie Moore CO		
Harry Warner CO		
59 John Candelaria	.12	.30
60 Ed Kranepool	.12	.30
61 Dave LaRoche	.12	.30
62 Jim Rice	.75	2.00
63 Don Stanhouse	.30	.75
64 Jason Thompson RC	.30	.75
65 Nolan Ryan	12.50	40.00
66 Tom Poquette	.12	.30
67 Leon Hooten	.30	.75
68 Bob Boone	.30	.75
69 Mickey Rivers	.30	.75
70 Gary Nolan	.12	.30
71 Sixto Lezcano	.12	.30
72 Larry Parrish	.30	.75
73 Dave Goltz	.12	.30
74 Bert Campaneris	.30	.75
75 Vida Blue	.30	.75
76 Rick Cerone	.30	.75
77 Ralph Garr	.30	.75
78 Ken Forsch	.12	.30
79 Willie Montanez	.12	.30
80 Jim Palmer	1.50	4.00
81 Jerry White	.30	.75
82 Gene Tenace	.30	.75
83 Bobby Murcer	.30	.75
84 Garry Templeton	.60	1.50
85 Bill Singer	.30	.75
86 Buddy Bell	.30	.75
87 Luis Tiant	.30	.75
88 Rusty Staub	.60	1.50
89 Sparky Lyle	.30	.75
90 Jose Morales	.30	.75
91 Dennis Leonard	.30	.75
92 Tommy Smith	.12	.30
93 Steve Carlton	2.00	5.00
94 John Scott	.30	.75
95 Bill Bonham	.12	.30
96 Dave Lopes	.30	.75
97 Jerry Reuss	.30	.75
98 Dave Kingman	.60	1.50
99 Dan Warthen	.30	.75
100 Johnny Bench	4.00	10.00
101 Bert Blyleven	.60	1.50
102 Cecil Cooper	.30	.75
103 Mike Willis	.30	.75
104 Dan Ford	.12	.30
105 Frank Tanana	.30	.75
106 Bill North	.12	.30
107 Joe Ferguson	.12	.30
108 Dick Williams MG	.30	.75
109 John Denny	.30	.75
110 Willie Randolph	.60	1.50
111 Reggie Cleveland	.30	.75
112 Doug Howard	.30	.75
113 Randy Jones	.12	.30
114 Rico Carty	.30	.75
115 Mark Fidrych RC	2.00	5.00
116 Darrell Porter	.30	.75
117 Wayne Garrett	.30	.75
118 Greg Luzinski	.60	1.50
119 Jim Barr	.12	.30
120 George Foster	.60	1.50
121 Phil Roof	.30	.75
122 Bucky Dent	.30	.75
123 Steve Braun	.12	.30
124 Checklist 1-132	.60	1.50
125 Lee May	.30	.75
126 Woodie Fryman	.30	.75
127 Jose Cardenal	.30	.75
128 Doug Rau	.12	.30
129 Rennie Stennett	.12	.30
130 Pete Vuckovich RC	.30	.75
131 Cesar Cedeno	.30	.75
132 Jon Matlack	.12	.30
133 Don Baylor	.60	1.50
134 Darrel Chaney	.12	.30
135 Tony Perez	1.00	2.50
136 Aurelio Rodriguez	.12	.30
137 Carlton Fisk	2.50	6.00
138 Wayne Garland	.12	.30
139 Dave Hilton	.30	.75
140 Rawly Eastwick	.12	.30
141 Amos Otis	.30	.75
142 Tug McGraw	.30	.75
143 Rod Carew	2.50	6.00
144 Mike Torrez	.30	.75
145 Sal Bando	.30	.75
146 Dock Ellis	.12	.30
147 Jose Cruz	.30	.75
148 Alan Ashby	.30	.75
149 Gaylord Perry	1.00	2.50
150 Keith Hernandez	.30	.75
151 Dave Pagan	.12	.30
152 Richie Zisk	.12	.30
153 Steve Rogers	.30	.75
154 Mark Belanger	.30	.75
155 Andy Messersmith	.30	.75
156 Dave Winfield	6.00	15.00
157 Chuck Hartenstein	.30	.75
158 Manny Trillo	.12	.30
159 Steve Yeager	.30	.75
160 Cesar Geronimo	.12	.30
161 Jim Rooker	.12	.30
162 Tim Foli	.30	.75
163 Fred Lynn	.30	.75
164 Ed Figueroa	.12	.30
165 Johnny Grubb	.12	.30
166 Pedro Garcia	.30	.75
167 Ron LeFlore	.30	.75
168 Rich Hebner	.30	.75
169 Larry Herndon RC	.30	.75
170 George Brett	12.50	30.00
171 Joe Kerrigan	.30	.75
172 Bud Harrelson	.30	.75
173 Bobby Bonds	.75	2.00
174 Bill Travers	.12	.30
175 John Lowenstein	.30	.75
176 Butch Wynegar RC	.30	.75
177 Pete Falcone	.12	.30
178 Claudell Washington	.30	.75
179 Checklist 133-264	.60	1.50
180 Dave Cash	.30	.75
181 Fred Norman	.12	.30
182 Roy White	.30	.75
183 Marty Perez	.12	.30
184 Jesse Jefferson	.30	.75
185 Jim Sundberg	.30	.75
186 Dan Meyer	.30	.75
187 Fergie Jenkins	1.00	2.50
188 Tom Veryzer	.12	.30
189 Dennis Blair	.30	.75
190 Rick Manning	.12	.30
191 Doug Bird	.12	.30
192 Al Bumbry	.30	.75
193 Dave Roberts	.12	.30
194 Larry Christenson	.12	.30
195 Chet Lemon	.30	.75
196 Ted Simmons	.30	.75
197 Ray Burris	.12	.30
198 Jim Brewer CO	.30	.75
Billy Gardner CO		
Mickey Vernon CO		
Ozzie Virgil CO		
199 Ron Cey	.30	.75
200 Reggie Jackson	4.00	10.00
201 Pat Zachry	.12	.30
202 Doug Ault	.30	.75
203 Al Oliver	.30	.75
204 Robin Yount	4.00	10.00
205 Tom Seaver	3.00	8.00
206 Joe Rudi	.30	.75
207 Barry Foote	.30	.75
208 Toby Harrah	.30	.75
209 Jeff Burroughs	.30	.75
210 George Scott	.30	.75
211 Jim Mason	.30	.75
212 Vern Ruhle	.12	.30
213 Fred Kendall	.12	.30
214 Rick Reuschel	.30	.75
215 Hal McRae	.30	.75
216 Chip Lang	.30	.75
217 Graig Nettles	.60	1.50
218 George Hendrick	.30	.75
219 Glenn Abbott	.12	.30
220 Joe Morgan	2.00	5.00
221 Sam Ewing	.30	.75
222 George Medich	.12	.30
223 Reggie Smith	.30	.75
224 Dave Hamilton	.12	.30
225 Pepe Frias	.30	.75
226 Jay Johnstone	.30	.75
227 J.R. Richard	.30	.75
228 Doug DeCinces	.30	.75
229 Dave Lemanczyk	.30	.75
230 Rick Monday	.30	.75
231 Manny Sanguillen	.30	.75
232 John Montefusco	.12	.30
233 Duane Kuiper	.12	.30
234 Ellis Valentine	.30	.75
235 Dick Tidrow	.12	.30
236 Ben Oglivie	.30	.75
237 Rick Burleson	.30	.75
238 Roy Hartsfield MG	.30	.75
239 Lyman Bostock	.30	.75
240 Pete Rose	8.00	20.00
241 Mike Ivie	.12	.30
242 Dave Parker	.60	1.50
243 Bill Greif	.30	.75
244 Freddie Patek	.30	.75
245 Mike Schmidt	6.00	15.00
246 Brian Downing	.30	.75
247 Steve Hargan	.12	.30
248 Dave Collins	.30	.75
249 Felix Millan	.12	.30
250 Don Gullett	.30	.75
251 Jerry Royster	.12	.30
252 Earl Williams	.30	.75
253 Frank Duffy	.12	.30
254 Tippy Martinez	.12	.30
255 Steve Garvey	.75	2.00
256 Alvis Woods	.30	.75
257 John Hiller	.30	.75
258 Dave Concepcion	.60	1.50
259 Dwight Evans	.60	1.50
260 Pete MacKanin	.30	.75
261 George Brett RB	5.00	12.00
262 Minnie Minoso RB	.30	.75
263 Jose Morales RB	.30	.75
264 Nolan Ryan RB	6.00	15.00

1978 O-Pee-Chee

The 242 standard-size cards comprising the 1978 O-Pee-Chee set differ from the cards of the 1978 Topps set by having a higher ratio of cards of players from the two Canadian teams, a practice begun by O-Pee-Chee in 1977 and continued to 1988. The fronts feature white-bordered color player photos, each framed by a colored line. The player's name appears in black lettering at the right of lower white margin. His team name appears in colored cursive lettering, interrupting the framing line at the bottom left of the photo; his position appears within a white baseball icon in an upper corner. The tan and brown horizontal backs carry the player's name, team and position in the brown border at the bottom. Biography, major league statistics, career highlights in both French and English and a bilingual result of an "at bat" in the "Play Ball" game also appear. The asterisked cards have an extra line on the front indicating team change. Double-printed (DP) cards are also noted below. The key card in this set is the Eddie Murray Rookie Card.

COMPLETE SET (242)	100.00	200.00
COMMON CARD (1-242)	.10	.25
COMMON DP (1-242)	.08	.20
1 Dave Parker	.60	1.50
Rod Carew LL		
2 George Foster	.25	.60
Jim Rice LL DP		
3 George Foster	.25	.60
Larry Hisle LL		
4 Frank Taveras	.10	.25
Freddie Patek LL DP		
5 Steve Carlton	1.00	2.50
Dave Goltz		
Dennis Leonard		
Jim Palmer LL		
6 Phil Niekro	2.50	6.00
Nolan Ryan LL DP		
7 John Candelaria	.25	.60
Frank Tanana LL DP		
8 Rollie Fingers	.50	1.25
Bill Campbell LL		
9 Steve Rogers DP	.12	.30
10 Graig Nettles DP	.30	.75
11 Doug Capilla	.10	.25
12 George Scott	.25	.60
13 Gary Woods	.25	.60
14 Tom Veryzer	.25	.60
Now with Cleveland as of 12-9-77		
15 Wayne Garland	.10	.25
16 Amos Otis	.25	.60
17 Larry Christenson	.10	.25
18 Dave Cash	.25	.60
19 Jim Barr	.10	.25
20 Ruppert Jones	.10	.25
21 Eric Soderholm	.10	.25
22 Jesse Jefferson	.25	.60
23 Jerry Morales	.10	.25
24 Doug Rau	.10	.25
25 Rennie Stennett	.10	.25
26 Lee Mazzilli	.10	.25
27 Dick Williams MG	.25	.60
28 Joe Rudi	.25	.60
29 Robin Yount	4.00	10.00
30 Don Gullett DP	.10	.25
31 Roy Howell DP	.08	.20
32 Cesar Geronimo	.10	.25
33 Rick Langford DP	.08	.20
34 Dan Ford	.10	.25
35 Gene Tenace	.25	.60
36 Santo Alcala	.25	.60
37 Rick Burleson	.25	.60
38 Dave Rozema	.10	.25
39 Duane Kuiper	.10	.25
40 Ron Fairly	.25	.60
Now with California as of 12-8-77		
41 Dennis Leonard	.25	.60
42 Greg Luzinski	.50	1.25
43 Willie Montanez	.25	.60
Now with N.Y. Mets as of 12-8-77		
44 Enos Cabell	.10	.25
45 Ellis Valentine	.25	.60
46 Steve Stone	.25	.60
47 Lee May DP	.12	.30

48 Roy White .25 .60
49 Jerry Garvin .10 .25
50 Johnny Bench 3.00 8.00
51 Garry Templeton .25 .60
52 Doyle Alexander .25 .60
53 Steve Henderson .10 .25
54 Stan Bahnsen .10 .25
55 Dan Meyer .10 .25
56 Rick Reuschel .25 .60
57 Reggie Smith .25 .60
58 Blue Jays Team DP CL .30 .75
59 John Montefusco .10 .25
60 Dave Parker .50 1.25
61 Jim Bibby .10 .25
62 Fred Lynn .25 .60
63 Jose Morales .25 .60
64 Aurelio Rodriguez .10 .25
65 Frank Tanana .25 .60
66 Darrell Porter .25 .60
67 Otto Velez .10 .25
68 Larry Bowa .50 1.25
69 Jim Hunter 1.00 2.50
70 George Foster .50 1.25
71 Cecil Cooper DP .12 .30
72 Gary Alexander DP .08 .20
73 Paul Thormodsgard .10 .25
74 Toby Harrah .25 .60
75 Mitchell Page .10 .25
76 Alan Ashby .10 .25
77 Jorge Orta .10 .25
78 Dave Winfield 4.00 10.00
79 Andy Messersmith .25 .60
Now with N.Y. Yankees as of 12-8-77
80 Ken Singleton .25 .60
81 Will McEnaney .25 .60
82 Lou Piniella .25 .60
83 Bob Forsch .10 .25
84 Dan Driessen .10 .25
85 Dave Lemanczyk .10 .25
86 Paul Dade .10 .25
87 Bill Campbell .10 .25
88 Ron LeFlore .25 .60
89 Bill Madlock .25 .60
90 Tony Perez DP .50 1.25
91 Freddie Patek .25 .60
92 Glenn Abbott .10 .25
93 Garry Maddox .10 .25
94 Steve Staggs .10 .25
95 Bobby Murcer .25 .60
96 Don Sutton 1.00 2.50
97 Al Oliver 1.00 2.50
Now with Texas Rangers as of 12-8-77
98 Jon Matlack .25 .60
Now with Texas Rangers as of 12-8-77
99 Sam Mejias .25 .60
100 Pete Rose DP 5.00 12.00
101 Randy Jones .10 .25
102 Sixto Lezcano .10 .25
103 Jim Clancy DP .12 .30
104 Butch Wynegar .10 .25
105 Nolan Ryan 12.50 40.00
106 Wayne Gross .10 .25
107 Bob Watson .25 .60
108 Joe Kerrigan .25 .60
Now with Baltimore as of 12-8-77
109 Keith Hernandez .25 .60
110 Reggie Jackson 3.00 8.00
111 Denny Doyle .10 .25
112 Sam Ewing .25 .60
113 Bert Blyleven 1.00 2.50
Now with Pittsburgh as of 12-8-77
114 Andre Thornton .25 .60
115 Milt May .10 .25
116 Jim Colborn .10 .25
117 Warren Cromartie RC .50 1.25
118 Ted Sizemore .10 .25
119 Checklist 1-121 .50 1.25
120 Tom Seaver 2.50 6.00
121 Luis Gomez .25 .60
122 Jim Spencer .25 .60
Now with N.Y. Yankees as of 12-12-77
123 Leroy Stanton .10 .25
124 Luis Tiant .25 .60
125 Mark Belanger .25 .60
126 Jackie Brown .10 .25
127 Bill Buckner .25 .60
128 Bill Robinson .25 .60
129 Rick Cerone .25 .60
130 Ron Cey .50 1.25
131 Jose Cruz .25 .60
132 Len Randle DP .08 .20
133 Bob Grich .25 .60
134 Jeff Burroughs .25 .60
135 Gary Carter 1.00 2.50
136 Milt Wilcox .10 .25
137 Carl Yastrzemski 2.50 6.00
138 Dennis Eckersley 1.25 3.00
139 Tim Nordbrook .10 .25
140 Ken Griffey Sr. .50 1.25
141 Bob Boone .50 1.25
142 Dave Goltz DP .08 .20
143 Al Cowens .10 .25
144 Bill Atkinson .10 .25
145 Chris Chambliss .25 .60
146 Jim Slaton .25 .60
Now with Detroit Tigers as of 12-9-77
147 Bill Stein .10 .25
148 Bob Bailor .25 .60
149 J.R. Richard .25 .60
150 Ted Simmons .25 .60
151 Rick Manning .10 .25
152 Lerrin LaGrow .10 .25
153 Larry Parrish .50 1.25
154 Eddie Murray RC 30.00 60.00
155 Phil Niekro 1.00 2.50
156 Bake McBride .25 .60
157 Pete Vuckovich .25 .60
158 Ivan DeJesus .10 .25
159 Rick Rhoden .25 .60
160 Joe Morgan 1.25 3.00
161 Ed Ott .10 .25
162 Don Stanhouse .25 .60
163 Jim Rice .50 1.25
164 Bucky Dent .25 .60
165 Jim Kern .10 .25
166 Doug Rader .10 .25
167 Steve Kemp .10 .25
168 John Mayberry .25 .60
169 Tim Foli .25 .60
Now with N.Y. Mets as of 12-7-77
170 Steve Carlton 1.50 4.00
171 Pepe Frias .25 .60
172 Pat Zachry .10 .25
173 Don Baylor .50 1.25
174 Sal Bando DP .12 .30
175 Alvis Woods .25 .60
176 Mike Hargrove .25 .60
177 Vida Blue .25 .60
178 George Hendrick .25 .60
179 Jim Palmer 1.25 3.00
180 Andre Dawson 5.00 12.00
181 Paul Moskau .10 .25
182 Mickey Rivers .25 .60
183 Checklist 122-242 .50 1.25
184 Jerry Johnson .25 .60
185 Willie McCovey 1.25 3.00
186 Enrique Romo .10 .25
187 Butch Hobson .10 .25
188 Rusty Staub .50 1.25
189 Wayne Twitchell .25 .60
190 Steve Garvey 1.00 2.50
191 Rick Waits .10 .25
192 Doug DeCinces .25 .60
193 Tom Murphy .10 .25
194 Rich Hebner .25 .60
195 Ralph Garr .25 .60
196 Bruce Sutter .50 1.25
197 Tom Poquette .10 .25
198 Wayne Garrett .10 .25
199 Pedro Borbon .10 .25
200 Thurman Munson 1.50 4.00
201 Rollie Fingers 1.00 2.50
202 Doug Ault .25 .60
203 Phil Garner DP .08 .20
204 Lou Brock 1.25 3.00
205 Ed Kranepool .25 .60
206 Bobby Bonds .50 1.25
Now with White Sox as of 12-15-77
207 Expos Team DP CL .50 1.25
208 Bump Wills .10 .25
209 Gary Matthews .25 .60
210 Carlton Fisk 1.50 4.00
211 Jeff Byrd .25 .60
212 Jason Thompson .25 .60
213 Larvell Blanks .10 .25
214 Sparky Lyle .25 .60
215 George Brett 8.00 20.00
216 Del Unser .10 .25
217 Manny Trillo .10 .25
218 Roy Hartsfield MG .25 .60
219 Carlos Lopez .25 .60
Now with Baltimore as of 12-7-77
220 Dave Concepcion .50 1.25
221 John Candelaria .25 .60
222 Dave Lopes .25 .60
223 Tim Blackwell DP .12 .30
Now with Chicago Cubs as of 2-1-78
224 Chet Lemon .25 .60
225 Mike Schmidt 5.00 12.00
226 Cesar Cedeno .25 .60
227 Mike Willis .25 .60
228 Willie Randolph .50 1.25
229 Doug Bair .10 .25
230 Rod Carew 1.50 4.00
231 Mike Flanagan .25 .60
232 Chris Speier .10 .25
233 Don Aase .25 .60
Now with California as of 12-8-77
234 Buddy Bell .25 .60
235 Mark Fidrych 1.00 2.50
236 Lou Brock RB 1.25 3.00
237 Sparky Lyle RB .25 .60
238 Willie McCovey RB 1.00 2.50
239 Brooks Robinson RB 1.00 2.50
240 Pete Rose RB 3.00 8.00
241 Nolan Ryan RB 6.00 15.00
242 Reggie Jackson RB 1.50 4.00

1979 O-Pee-Chee

This set is an abridgement of the 1979 Topps set. The 374 standard-size cards comprising the 1979 O-Pee-Chee set differ from the cards of the 1979 Topps set by having a higher ratio of cards of players from the two Canadian teams, a practice begun by O-Pee-Chee in 1977 and continued to 1988. The 1979 O-Pee-Chee set was the largest (374) original baseball card set issued (up to that time) by O-Pee-Chee. The fronts feature white-bordered color player photos. The player's name, position, and team appear in colored lettering within the lower white margin. The green and white horizontal backs carry the player's name, team and position at the top. Biography, major league statistics, career highlights in both French and English and a bilingual trivia question and answer also appear. The asterisked cards have an extra line on the front indicating team change. Double-printed (DP) cards are also noted below. The fronts have an O-Pee-Chee logo in the lower left corner comparable to the Topps logo on the 1979 American Set. The cards are sequenced in the same order as the Topps cards; the O-Pee-Chee cards are in effect a compressed version of the Topps set. The key card in this set is the Ozzie Smith Rookie Card. This set was issued in 15 cent wax packs which came 24 boxes to a case.

COMPLETE SET (374) 100.00 200.00
COMMON CARD (1-374) .10 .25
COMMON DP (1-374) .08 .20
1 Lee May .40 1.00
2 Dick Drago .10 .25
3 Paul Dade .10 .25
4 Ross Grimsley .10 .25
5 Joe Morgan DP 1.00 2.50
6 Kevin Kobel .10 .25
7 Terry Forster .10 .25
8 Paul Molitor 6.00 15.00
9 Steve Carlton 1.50 4.00
10 Dave Goltz .10 .25
11 Dave Winfield 2.50 6.00
12 Dave Rozema .10 .25
13 Ed Figueroa .10 .25
14 Alan Ashby .20 .50
Trade with Blue Jays 11-28-78
15 Dale Murphy 1.50 4.00
16 Dennis Eckersley .75 2.00
17 Ron Blomberg .10 .25
18 Wayne Twitchell .20 .50
Free Agent as of 3-1-79
19 Al Hrabosky .10 .25
20 Fred Norman .10 .25
21 Steve Garvey DP .40 1.00
22 Willie Stargell .75 2.00
23 John Hale .10 .25
24 Mickey Rivers .20 .50
25 Jack Brohamer .10 .25
26 Tom Underwood .10 .25
27 Mark Belanger .20 .50
28 Elliott Maddox .10 .25
29 John Candelaria .20 .50
30 Shane Rawley .10 .25
31 Steve Yeager .20 .50
32 Warren Cromartie .40 1.00
33 Jason Thompson .20 .50
34 Roger Erickson .10 .25
35 Gary Matthews .20 .50
36 Pete Falcone .10 .25
Traded 12-5-78
37 Dick Tidrow .10 .25
38 Bob Boone .40 1.00
39 Jim Bibby .10 .25
40 Len Barker .20 .50
Trade with Rangers 10-3-78
41 Robin Yount 2.50 6.00
42 Sam Mejias .20 .50
Traded 12-14-78
43 Ray Burris .10 .25
44 Tom Seaver DP 2.00 5.00
45 Roy Howell .10 .25
46 Jim Todd .20 .50
Free Agent 3-1-79
47 Frank Duffy .10 .25
48 Joel Youngblood .10 .25
49 Vida Blue .20 .50
50 Cliff Johnson .10 .25
51 Nolan Ryan 12.50 30.00
52 Ozzie Smith RC 40.00 80.00
53 Jim Sundberg .20 .50
54 Mike Paxton .10 .25
55 Lou Whitaker 2.50 6.00
56 Dan Schatzeder .10 .25
57 Rick Burleson .10 .25
58 Doug Bair .10 .25
59 Ted Martinez .10 .25
60 Bob Watson .20 .50
61 Jim Clancy .20 .50
62 Rowland Office .10 .25
63 Bobby Murcer .20 .50
64 Don Gullett .20 .50
65 Tom Paciorek .10 .25
66 Rick Rhoden .10 .25
67 Duane Kuiper .10 .25
68 Bruce Boisclair .10 .25
69 Manny Sarmiento .10 .25
70 Wayne Cage .10 .25
71 John Hiller .20 .50
72 Rick Cerone .10 .25
73 Dwight Evans .40 1.00
74 Buddy Solomon .10 .25
75 Roy White .20 .50
76 Mike Flanagan .40 1.00
77 Tom Johnson .10 .25
78 Glenn Burke .10 .25
79 Frank Taveras .10 .25
80 Don Sutton .75 2.00
81 Leon Roberts .10 .25
82 George Hendrick .40 1.00
83 Aurelio Rodriguez .10 .25
84 Ron Reed .10 .25
85 Alvis Woods .10 .25
86 Jim Beattie DP .08 .20
87 Larry Hisle .10 .25
88 Mike Garman .10 .25
89 Tim Johnson .10 .25
90 Paul Splittorff .10 .25
91 Darrel Chaney .10 .25
92 Mike Torrez .20 .50
93 Eric Soderholm .10 .25
94 Ron Cey .20 .50
95 Randy Jones .10 .25
96 Bill Madlock .20 .50
97 Steve Kemp DP .08 .20
98 Bob Apodaca .10 .25
99 Johnny Grubb .10 .25
100 Larry Milbourne .10 .25
101 Johnny Bench DP 2.50 6.00
102 Dave Lemanczyk .10 .25
103 Reggie Cleveland .10 .25
104 Larry Bowa .20 .50
105 Denny Martinez .60 1.50
106 Bill Travers .10 .25
107 Willie McCovey 1.00 2.50
108 Wilbur Wood .10 .25
109 Dennis Leonard .20 .50
110 Roy Smalley .20 .50
111 Cesar Geronimo .10 .25
112 Jesse Jefferson .20 .50
113 Dave Revering .10 .25
114 Goose Gossage .40 1.00
115 Steve Stone .20 .50
Free Agent 11-25-78
116 Doug Flynn .10 .25
117 Bob Forsch .10 .25
118 Paul Mitchell .10 .25
119 Toby Harrah .20 .50
Traded 12-8-78
120 Steve Rogers .20 .50
121 Checklist 1-125 DP .08 .20
122 Balor Moore .10 .25
123 Rick Reuschel .20 .50
124 Jeff Burroughs .20 .50
125 Willie Randolph .20 .50
126 Bob Stinson .10 .25
127 Rick Wise .10 .25
128 Luis Gomez .20 .50
129 Tommy John .60 1.50
Signed as Free Agent 11-22-78
130 Richie Zisk .10 .25
131 Mario Guerrero .10 .25
132 Oscar Gamble .20 .50
Trade with Padres 10-25-78
133 Don Money .10 .25
134 Joe Rudi .20 .50
135 Woodie Fryman .10 .25
136 Butch Hobson .20 .50
137 Jim Colborn .10 .25
138 Tom Grieve .20 .50
Traded 12-5-78
139 Andy Messersmith .20 .50
Free Agent 2-7-79
140 Andre Thornton .10 .25
141 Ken Kravec .10 .25
142 Bobby Bonds .60 1.50
Trade with Rangers 10-3-78
143 Jose Cruz .40 1.00
144 Dave Lopes .20 .50
145 Jerry Garvin .10 .25
146 Pepe Frias .10 .25
147 Mitchell Page .10 .25
148 Ted Sizemore .20 .50
Traded 2-23-79
149 Rich Gale .10 .25
150 Steve Ontiveros .10 .25
151 Rod Carew 1.50 4.00
Traded 2-5-79
152 Lary Sorensen DP .08 .20
153 Willie Montanez .10 .25
154 Floyd Bannister .20 .50
Traded 12-8-78
155 Bert Blyleven .40 1.00
156 Ralph Garr .10 .25
157 Thurman Munson 1.50 4.00
158 Bob Robertson .20 .50
Free Agent 3-1-79
159 Jon Matlack .10 .25
160 Carl Yastrzemski 2.50 6.00
161 Gaylord Perry .75 2.00
162 Mike Tyson .10 .25
163 Cecil Cooper .20 .50
164 Pedro Borbon .10 .25
165 Art Howe DP .08 .20
166 Joe Coleman .20 .50
Free Agent 3-1-79
167 George Brett 8.00 20.00
168 Gary Alexander .10 .25
169 Chet Lemon .20 .50
170 Craig Swan .10 .25
171 Chris Chambliss .20 .50
172 John Montague .10 .25
173 Ron Jackson .20 .50
Traded 12-4-78
174 Jim Palmer 1.25 3.00
175 Willie Upshaw .40 1.00
176 Tug McGraw .20 .50
177 Bill Buckner .20 .50
178 Doug Rau .10 .25
179 Andre Dawson 2.50 6.00
180 Jim Wright .10 .25
181 Garry Templeton .20 .50
182 Bill Bonham .10 .25
183 Lee Mazzilli .10 .25
184 Alan Trammell 3.00 8.00
185 Amos Otis .20 .50
186 Tom Dixon .10 .25
187 Mike Cubbage .10 .25
188 Sparky Lyle .40 1.00
Traded 11-10-78
189 Juan Bernhardt .10 .25
190 Bump Wills .40 1.00
(Texas Rangers)
191 Dave Kingman .40 1.00
192 Lamar Johnson .10 .25
193 Lance Rautzhan .10 .25
194 Ed Herrmann .10 .25
195 Bill Campbell .10 .25
196 Gorman Thomas .20 .50
197 Paul Moskau .10 .25
198 Dale Murray .10 .25
199 John Mayberry .20 .50
200 Phil Garner .10 .25
201 Dan Ford .20 .50
Traded 12-4-78
202 Gary Thomasson .20 .50
Traded 2-15-79
203 Rollie Fingers .75 2.00
204 Al Oliver .20 .50
205 Doug Ault .20 .50
206 Scott McGregor .20 .50
207 Dave Cash .10 .25
208 Bill Plummer .10 .25
209 Ivan DeJesus .10 .25
210 Jim Rice .40 1.00
211 Ray Knight .40 1.00
212 Paul Hartzell .20 .50
Traded 2-5-79
213 Tim Foli .10 .25
214 Butch Wynegar DP .08 .20
215 Darrell Evans .40 1.00
216 Ken Griffey Sr. .20 .50
217 Doug DeCinces .20 .50
218 Ruppert Jones .10 .25
219 Bob Montgomery .10 .25
220 Rick Manning .10 .25
221 Chris Speier .10 .25
222 Bobby Valentine .10 .25
223 Dave Parker .20 .50
224 Larry Biittner .10 .25
225 Ken Clay .10 .25
226 Gene Tenace .20 .50
227 Frank White .20 .50
228 Rusty Staub .40 1.00
229 Lee Lacy .10 .25
230 Doyle Alexander .10 .25
231 Bruce Bochte .10 .25
232 Steve Henderson .10 .25
233 Jim Lonborg .20 .50
234 Dave Concepcion .40 1.00
235 Jerry Morales .20 .50
Traded 12-4-78
236 Len Randle .10 .25
237 Bill Lee DP .12 .30
Traded 12-7-78
238 Bruce Sutter .75 2.00
239 Jim Essian .10 .25
240 Graig Nettles .40 1.00
241 Otto Velez .10 .25
242 Checklist 126-250 DP .08 .20
243 Reggie Smith .20 .50
244 Stan Bahnsen DP .08 .20
245 Garry Maddox DP .08 .20
246 Joaquin Andujar .20 .50
247 Dan Driessen .10 .25
248 Bob Grich .20 .50
249 Fred Lynn .20 .50
250 Skip Lockwood .10 .25
251 Craig Reynolds .20 .50
Traded 12-5-78
252 Willie Horton .20 .50
253 Rick Waits .10 .25
254 Bucky Dent .20 .50
255 Bob Knepper .10 .25
256 Miguel Dilone .10 .25
257 Bob Owchinko .10 .25
258 Al Cowens .10 .25
259 Bob Bailor .10 .25
260 Larry Christenson .10 .25
261 Tony Perez .75 2.00
262 Roy Hartsfield MG CL .60 1.50
263 Glenn Abbott .10 .25
264 Ron Guidry .20 .50
265 Ed Kranepool .10 .25
266 Charlie Hough .20 .50
267 Ted Simmons .40 1.00
268 Jack Clark .20 .50
269 Enos Cabell .10 .25
270 Gary Carter .75 2.00
271 Sam Ewing .10 .25
272 Tom Burgmeier .10 .25
273 Freddie Patek .10 .25
274 Frank Tanana .20 .50
275 Leroy Stanton .10 .25
276 Ken Forsch .10 .25
277 Ellis Valentine .10 .25
278 Greg Luzinski .20 .50
279 Rick Bosetti .10 .25
280 John Stearns .10 .25
281 Enrique Romo .20 .50
Traded 12-5-78
282 Bob Bailey .10 .25
283 Sal Bando .20 .50
284 Matt Keough .10 .25
285 Biff Pocoroba .10 .25
286 Mike Lum .20 .50
Free Agent 3-1-79
287 Jay Johnstone .20 .50
288 John Montefusco .10 .25
289 Ed Ott .10 .25
290 Dusty Baker .40 1.00
291 Rico Carty .40 1.00
Waivers from A's 10-2-78
292 Nino Espinosa .10 .25
293 Rich Hebner .20 .50
294 Cesar Cedeno .20 .50
295 Darrell Porter .20 .50
296 Rod Gilbreath .10 .25
297 Jim Kern .20 .50
Trade with Indians 10-3-78
298 Claudell Washington .20 .50
299 Luis Tiant .40 1.00
Signed as Free Agent 11-14-78
300 Mike Parrott .10 .25
301 Pete Broberg .20 .50
Free Agent 3-1-79
302 Greg Gross .20 .50
Traded 2-23-79
303 Darold Knowles .20 .50
Free Agent 2-12-79
304 Paul Blair .20 .50
305 Julio Cruz .10 .25
306 Hal McRae .40 1.00
307 Ken Reitz .10 .25
308 Tom Murphy .10 .25
309 Terry Whitfield .10 .25
310 J.R. Richard .20 .50
311 Mike Hargrove .40 1.00
Trade with Rangers 10-25-78
312 Rick Dempsey .20 .50
313 Phil Niekro .75 2.00
314 Bob Stanley .10 .25
315 Jim Spencer .10 .25
316 George Foster .20 .50
317 Dave LaRoche .10 .25
318 Rudy May .10 .25
319 Jeff Newman .10 .25
320 Rick Monday DP .08 .20
321 Omar Moreno .10 .25
322 Dave McKay .20 .50
323 Mike Schmidt 4.00 10.00
324 Ken Singleton .20 .50
325 Jerry Remy .10 .25
326 Bert Campaneris .20 .50
327 Pat Zachry .10 .25
328 Larry Herndon .10 .25
329 Mark Fidrych .60 1.50
330 Del Unser .10 .25
331 Gene Garber .20 .50
332 Bake McBride .20 .50
333 Jorge Orta .10 .25
334 Don Kirkwood .10 .25
335 Don Baylor .40 1.00
336 Bill Robinson .20 .50
337 Manny Trillo .20 .50
Traded 2-23-79
338 Eddie Murray 10.00 25.00
339 Tom Hausman .10 .25
340 George Scott DP .08 .20
341 Rick Sweet .10 .25
342 Lou Piniella .20 .50
343 Pete Rose 6.00 15.00
Free Agent 12-5-79
344 Stan Papi .20 .50
Traded 12-7-78
345 Jerry Koosman .40 1.00
Traded 12-8-78
346 Hosken Powell .10 .25
347 George Medich .10 .25
348 Ron LeFlore DP .08 .20
349 Dick Williams MG CL .60 1.50
350 Lou Brock 1.25 3.00
351 Bill North .10 .25
352 Jim Hunter DP .60 1.50
353 Checklist 251-374 DP .12 .30
354 Ed Halicki .10 .25
355 Tom Hutton .10 .25
356 Mike Caldwell .10 .25
357 Larry Parrish .40 1.00
358 Geoff Zahn .10 .25
359 Derrel Thomas .20 .50
Signed as Free Agent 11-14-78
360 Carlton Fisk 1.25 3.00
361 John Henry Johnson .20 .50
362 Dave Chalk .10 .25
363 Dan Meyer DP .08 .20
364 Sixto Lezcano .20 .50
365 Rennie Stennett .10 .25
366 Mike Willis .20 .50
367 Buddy Bell DP .08 .20
Traded 12-8-78
368 Mickey Stanley .10 .25
369 Dave Rader .20 .50
Traded 2-23-79
370 Burt Hooton .20 .50
371 Keith Hernandez .40 1.00
372 Bill Stein .10 .25
373 Hal Dues .10 .25
374 Reggie Jackson DP 2.50 6.00

1980 O-Pee-Chee

This set is an abridgement of the 1980 Topps set. The cards are printed on white stock rather than the gray stock used by Topps. The 374 standard-size cards also differ from their Topps counterparts by having a higher ratio of cards of players from the two Canadian teams, a practice begun by O-Pee-Chee in 1977 and continued to 1988. The fronts feature white-bordered color player photos framed by a colored line. The player's name appears in the white border at the top and also as a simulated autograph across the photo. The player's position appears within a colored banner at the upper left; his team name appears within a colored banner at the lower right. The blue and white horizontal backs carry the player's name, team and position at the top. Biography, major league statistics and career highlights in both French and English also appear. The cards are numbered on the back. The asterisked cards have an extra line, "Now with (new team name)" on the front indicating team change. Color changes, to correspond to the new team, are apparent on the pennant name and frame on the front. Double-printed (DP) cards are also noted below. The cards in this set were produced in lower quantities than other O-Pee-Chee sets of this era reportedly due to the company being on strike. The cards are sequenced in the same order as the Topps cards.

COMPLETE SET (374) 75.00 150.00
COMMON CARD (1-374) .08 .25
COMMON DP (1-374) .02 .10
1 Craig Swan .08 .25
2 Dennis Martinez .40 1.00
3 Dave Cash .15 .40
Now With Padres
4 Bruce Sutter .60 1.50
5 Ron Jackson .08 .25
6 Balor Moore .15 .40
7 Dan Ford .08 .25
8 Pat Putnam .08 .25
9 Derrel Thomas .08 .25
10 Jim Slaton .08 .25
11 Lee Mazzilli .15 .40
12 Del Unser .08 .25
13 Mark Wagner .08 .25
14 Vida Blue .30 .75
15 Jay Johnstone .15 .40
16 Julio Cruz DP .02 .10
17 Tony Scott .08 .25
18 Jeff Newman DP .02 .10
19 Luis Tiant .15 .40
20 Carlton Fisk 1.25 3.00
21 Dave Palmer .08 .25
22 Bombo Rivera .08 .25
23 Bill Fahey .08 .25
24 Frank White .30 .75
25 Rico Carty .15 .40
26 Bill Bonham DP .02 .10
27 Rick Miller .08 .25
28 J.R. Richard .15 .40
29 Joe Ferguson DP .02 .10
30 Bill Madlock .15 .40
31 Pete Vuckovich .08 .25
32 Doug Flynn .08 .25
33 Bucky Dent .15 .40
34 Mike Ivie .08 .25
35 Bob Stanley .08 .25
36 Al Bumbry .15 .40
37 Gary Carter .75 2.00
38 John Milner DP .02 .10
39 Sid Monge .08 .25
40 Bill Russell .15 .40
41 John Stearns .08 .25
42 Dave Stieb .40 1.00
43 Ruppert Jones .15 .40
Now with Yankees
44 Bob Owchinko .08 .25
45 Ron LeFlore .30 .75
Now with Expos
46 Ted Sizemore .08 .25
47 Ted Simmons .15 .40
48 Pepe Frias .15 .40
Now with Rangers
49 Ken Landreaux .08 .25
50 Manny Trillo .15 .40
51 Rick Dempsey .15 .40
52 Cecil Cooper .15 .40
53 Bill Lee .15 .40
54 Victor Cruz .08 .25
55 Johnny Bench 2.00 5.00
56 Rich Dauer .08 .25
57 Frank Tanana .15 .40
58 Francisco Barrios .08 .25
59 Bob Horner .15 .40
60 Fred Lynn DP .07 .20
61 Bob Knepper .15 .40
62 Sparky Lyle .15 .40
63 Larry Cox .08 .25
64 Dock Ellis .15 .40
Now with Pirates
65 Phil Garner .15 .40
66 Greg Luzinski .15 .40
67 Checklist 1-125 .30 .75
68 Dave Lemanczyk .08 .25
69 Tony Perez .60 1.50
Now with Red Sox
70 Gary Thomasson .08 .25
71 Craig Reynolds .08 .25
72 Amos Otis .15 .40
73 Biff Pocoroba .08 .25
74 Matt Keough .08 .25
75 Bill Buckner .15 .40
76 John Castino .08 .25
77 Goose Gossage .40 1.00
78 Gary Alexander .08 .25
79 Phil Huffman .08 .25
80 Bruce Bochte .08 .25
81 Darrell Evans .15 .40
82 Terry Puhl .15 .40
83 Jason Thompson .08 .25
84 Lary Sorensen .08 .25
85 Jerry Remy .08 .25
86 Tony Brizzolara .08 .25
87 Willie Wilson DP .07 .20
88 Eddie Murray 6.00 12.00
89 Larry Christenson .08 .25
90 Bob Randall .08 .25
91 Greg Pryor .08 .25
92 Glenn Abbott .08 .25
93 Jack Clark .15 .40
94 Rick Waits .08 .25
95 Luis Gomez .15 .40
Now with Braves
96 Burt Hooton .15 .40
97 John Henry Johnson .08 .25
98 Ray Knight .15 .40
99 Rick Reuschel .15 .40
100 Champ Summers .08 .25
101 Ron Davis .08 .25
102 Warren Cromartie .15 .40
103 Ken Reitz .08 .25
104 Hal McRae .15 .40
105 Alan Ashby .08 .25
106 Kevin Kobel .08 .25
107 Buddy Bell .15 .40
108 Dave Goltz .15 .40
Now with Dodgers
109 John Montefusco .08 .25
110 Lance Parrish .15 .40
111 Mike LaCoss .08 .25
112 Jim Rice .15 .40
113 Steve Carlton 1.25 3.00
114 Sixto Lezcano .08 .25
115 Ed Halicki .08 .25
116 Jose Morales .08 .25
117 Dave Concepcion .30 .75
118 Joe Cannon .08 .25
119 Willie Montanez .15 .40
Now with Padres
120 Lou Piniella .30 .75
121 Bill Stein .08 .25
122 Dave Winfield 2.00 5.00
123 Alan Trammell .75 2.00
124 Andre Dawson 1.25 3.00
125 Marc Hill .08 .25
126 Don Aase .08 .25
127 Dave Kingman .30 .75
128 Checklist 126-250 .30 .75
129 Dennis Lamp .08 .25
130 Phil Niekro .75 2.00
131 Tim Foli DP .02 .10
132 Jim Clancy .15 .40
133 Bill Atkinson .15 .40
Now with White Sox
134 Paul Dade DP .02 .10
135 Dusty Baker .15 .40
136 Al Oliver .30 .75
137 Dave Chalk .08 .25
138 Bill Robinson .08 .25
139 Robin Yount 2.50 6.00
140 Dan Schatzeder .15 .40
Now with Tigers
141 Mike Schmidt DP 2.00 5.00
142 Ralph Garr .15 .40
Now with Angels
143 Dale Murphy .75 2.00
144 Jerry Koosman .15 .40
145 Tom Veryzer .08 .25
146 Rick Bosetti .08 .25
147 Jim Spencer .08 .25
148 Gaylord Perry .75 2.00
Now with Rangers
149 Paul Blair .15 .40
150 Don Baylor .30 .75
151 Dave Rozema .08 .25
152 Steve Garvey .40 1.00
153 Elias Sosa .08 .25
154 Larry Gura .08 .25
155 Tim Johnson .08 .25
156 Steve Henderson .08 .25
157 Ron Guidry .15 .40
158 Mike Edwards .08 .25
159 Butch Wynegar .08 .25
160 Randy Jones .08 .25
161 Denny Walling .08 .25
162 Mike Hargrove .15 .40
163 Dave Parker .40 1.00
164 Roger Metzger .08 .25
165 Johnny Grubb .08 .25
166 Steve Kemp .08 .25
167 Bob Lacey .08 .25
168 Chris Speier .08 .25
169 Dennis Eckersley .60 1.50
170 Keith Hernandez .15 .40
171 Claudell Washington .15 .40
172 Tom Underwood .15 .40
Now with Yankees
173 Dan Driessen .08 .25
174 Al Cowens .15 .40
Now with Angels
175 Rich Hebner .15 .40
Now with Tigers
176 Willie McCovey .75 2.00
177 Carney Lansford .15 .40
178 Ken Singleton .15 .40
179 Jim Essian .08 .25
180 Mike Vail .08 .25
181 Randy Lerch .08 .25
182 Larry Parrish .15 .40
183 Checklist 251-374 .30 .75
184 George Hendrick .15 .40
185 Bob Davis .08 .25
186 Gary Matthews .15 .40
187 Lou Whitaker .75 2.00
188 Darrell Porter DP .07 .20
189 Wayne Gross .08 .25
190 Bobby Murcer .15 .40

191 Willie Aikens .15 .40
Now with Royals
192 Jim Kern .08 .25
193 Cesar Cedeno .15 .40
194 Joel Youngblood .08 .25
195 Ross Grimsley .08 .25
196 Jerry Mumphrey .15 .40
Now with Padres
197 Kevin Bell .08 .25
198 Garry Maddox .15 .40
199 Dave Freisleben .08 .25
200 Ed Ott .08 .25
201 Enos Cabell .08 .25
202 Pete LaCock .08 .25
203 Fergie Jenkins .75 2.00
204 Milt Wilcox .08 .25
205 Ozzie Smith 7.50 15.00
206 Ellis Valentine .15 .40
207 Dan Meyer .08 .25
208 Barry Foote .08 .25
209 George Foster .15 .40
210 Dwight Evans .15 .40
211 Paul Molitor 5.00 10.00
212 Tony Solaita .08 .25
213 Bill North .08 .25
214 Paul Splittorff .08 .25
215 Bobby Bonds .40 1.00
Now with Cardinals
216 Butch Hobson .08 .25
217 Mark Belanger .15 .40
218 Grant Jackson .08 .25
219 Tom Hutton DP .02 .10
220 Pat Zachry .08 .25
221 Duane Kuiper .08 .25
222 Larry Hisle DP .02 .10
223 Mike Krukow .08 .25
224 Johnnie LeMaster .08 .25
225 Billy Almon .15 .40
Now with Expos
226 Joe Niekro .15 .40
227 Dave Revering .08 .25
228 Don Sutton .60 1.50
229 John Hiller .15 .40
230 Alvis Woods .08 .25
231 Mark Fidrych .40 1.00
232 Duffy Dyer .08 .25
233 Nino Espinosa .08 .25
234 Doug Bair .08 .25
235 George Brett 7.50 16.00
236 Mike Torrez .08 .25
237 Frank Taveras .08 .25
238 Bert Blyleven .40 1.00
239 Willie Randolph .15 .40
240 Mike Sadek DP .02 .10
241 Jerry Royster .08 .25
242 John Denny .15 .40
Now with Indians
243 Rick Monday .08 .25
244 Jesse Jefferson .15 .40
245 Aurelio Rodriguez .15 .40
Now with Padres
246 Bob Boone .30 .75
247 Cesar Geronimo .08 .25
248 Bob Shirley .08 .25
249 Expos Checklist .40 1.00
250 Bob Watson .30 .75
Now with Yankees
251 Mickey Rivers .15 .40
252 Mike Tyson DP .07 .20
Now with Cubs
253 Wayne Nordhagen .08 .25
254 Roy Howell .08 .25
255 Lee May .15 .40
256 Jerry Martin .08 .25
257 Bake McBride .08 .25
258 Silvio Martinez .08 .25
259 Jim Mason .08 .25
260 Tom Seaver 2.00 5.00
261 Rich Wortham DP .02 .10
262 Mike Cubbage .08 .25
263 Gene Garber .15 .40
264 Bert Campaneris .15 .40
265 Tom Buskey .08 .25
266 Leon Roberts .08 .25
267 Ron Cey .30 .75
268 Steve Ontiveros .08 .25
269 Mike Caldwell .08 .25
270 Nelson Norman .08 .25
271 Steve Rogers .15 .40
272 Jim Morrison .08 .25
273 Clint Hurdle .15 .40
274 Dale Murray .08 .25
275 Jim Barr .08 .25
276 Jim Sundberg DP .07 .20
277 Willie Horton .15 .40
278 Andre Thornton .15 .40
279 Bob Forsch .08 .25
280 Joe Strain .08 .25
281 Rudy May .15 .40
Now with Yankees
282 Pete Rose 6.00 12.00
283 Jeff Burroughs .15 .40
284 Rick Langford .08 .25
285 Ken Griffey Sr. .30 .75
286 Bill Nahorodny .15 .40
Now with Braves
287 Art Howe .15 .40
288 Ed Figueroa .08 .25
289 Joe Rudi .15 .40
290 Alfredo Griffin .15 .40
291 Dave Lopes .15 .40
292 Rick Manning .08 .25
293 Dennis Leonard .15 .40
294 Bud Harrelson .15 .40
295 Skip Lockwood .15 .40
Now with Red Sox
296 Roy Smalley .08 .25
297 Kent Tekulve .15 .40
298 Scot Thompson .08 .25
299 Ken Kravec .08 .25
300 Blue Jays Checklist .40 1.00
301 Scott Sanderson .15 .40
302 Charlie Moore .08 .25
303 Nolan Ryan 12.50 25.00
Now with Astros
304 Bob Bailor .15 .40
305 Bob Stinson .08 .25
306 Al Hrabosky .15 .40
Now with Braves
307 Mitchell Page .08 .25
308 Garry Templeton .08 .25
309 Chet Lemon .15 .40
310 Jim Palmer .75 2.00
311 Rick Cerone .15 .40
Now with Yankees
312 Jon Matlack .08 .25
313 Don Money .08 .25
314 Reggie Jackson 2.50 6.00
315 Brian Downing .08 .25
316 Woodie Fryman .08 .25
317 Alan Bannister .08 .25
318 Ron Reed .08 .25
319 Willie Stargell .75 2.00
320 Jerry Garvin DP .02 .10
321 Cliff Johnson .08 .25
322 Doug DeCinces .15 .40
323 Gene Richards .08 .25
324 Joaquin Andujar .15 .40
325 Richie Zisk .08 .25
326 Bob Grich .15 .40
327 Gorman Thomas .15 .40
328 Chris Chambliss .30 .75
Now with Braves
329 Butch Edge .30 .75
Pat Kelly
Ted Wilborn
330 Larry Bowa .15 .40
331 Barry Bonnell .15 .40
Now with Blue Jays
332 John Candelaria .15 .40
333 Toby Harrah .15 .40
334 Larry Biittner .08 .25
335 Mike Flanagan .15 .40
336 Ed Kranepool .08 .25
337 Ken Forsch DP .02 .10
338 John Mayberry .15 .40
339 Rick Burleson .08 .25
340 Milt May .15 .40
Now with Giants
341 Roy White .15 .40
342 Joe Morgan .75 2.00
343 Rollie Fingers .75 2.00
344 Mario Mendoza .08 .25
345 Stan Bahnsen .08 .25
346 Tug McGraw .15 .40
347 Rusty Staub .15 .40
348 Tommy John .30 .75
349 Ivan DeJesus .08 .25
350 Reggie Smith .15 .40
351 Tony Bernazard RC .40 1.00
Randy Miller
John Tamargo
352 Floyd Bannister .08 .25
353 Rod Carew DP .60 1.50
354 Otto Velez .08 .25
355 Gene Tenace .15 .40
356 Freddie Patek .15 .40
Now with Angels
357 Elliott Maddox .08 .25
358 Pat Underwood .08 .25
359 Graig Nettles .30 .75
360 Rodney Scott .08 .25
361 Terry Whitfield .08 .25
362 Fred Norman .15 .40
Now with Expos
363 Sal Bando .15 .40
364 Greg Gross .08 .25
365 Carl Yastrzemski DP .75 2.00
366 Paul Hartzell .08 .25
367 Jose Cruz .15 .40
368 Shane Rawley .08 .25
369 Jerry White .08 .25
370 Rick Wise .15 .40
Now with Padres
371 Steve Yeager .30 .75
372 Omar Moreno .08 .25
373 Bump Wills .08 .25
374 Craig Kusick .15 .40
Now with Padres

1981 O-Pee-Chee

This set is an abridgement of the 1981 Topps set. The 374 standard-size cards comprising the 1981 O-Pee-Chee set differ from the cards of the 1981 Topps set by having a higher ratio of cards of players from the two Canadian teams, a practice begun by O-Pee-Chee in 1977 and continued to 1988. The fronts feature white-bordered color player photos framed by a colored line that is wider at the bottom. The player's name appears in that wider colored area. The player's position and team appear within a colored baseball cap icon at the lower left. The red and white horizontal backs carry the player's name and position at the top. Biography, major league statistics, and career highlights in both French and English also appear. In cases where a player changed teams or was traded before press time, a small line of print on the obverse makes note of the change. Double-printed (DP) cards are also noted below. The card backs are typically found printed on white card stock. There is, however, a "variation" set printed on gray card stock; gray backs are worth 50 percent more than corresponding white backs listed below. Notable Rookie Cards include Harold Baines, Kirk Gibson and Tim Raines.

COMPLETE SET (374) 30.00 60.00
COMMON CARD (1-374) .04 .10
COMMON DP (1-374) .02 .05
1 Frank Pastore .02 .10
2 Phil Huffman .02 .10
3 Len Barker .02 .10
4 Robin Yount .75 2.00
5 Dave Stieb .08 .25
6 Gary Carter .40 1.00
7 Butch Hobson .02 .10
Now with Angels
8 Lance Parrish .08 .25
9 Bruce Sutter .40 1.00
Now with Cardinals
10 Mike Flanagan .08 .25
11 Paul Mirabella .02 .10
12 Craig Reynolds .02 .10
13 Joe Charboneau .20 .50
14 Dan Driessen .02 .10
15 Larry Parrish .02 .10
16 Ron Davis .02 .10
17 Cliff Johnson .02 .10
Now with Athletics
18 Bruce Bochte .02 .10
19 Jim Clancy .02 .10
20 Bill Russell .02 .10
21 Ron Oester .02 .10
22 Danny Darwin .02 .10
23 Willie Aikens .02 .10
24 Don Stanhouse .02 .10
25 Sixto Lezcano .02 .10
Now with Cardinals
26 U.L. Washington .02 .10
27 Champ Summers DP .01 .05
28 Enrique Romo .02 .10
29 Gene Tenace .08 .25
30 Jack Clark .08 .25
31 Checklist 1-125 DP .01 .05
32 Ken Oberkfell .02 .10
33 Rick Honeycutt .02 .10
Now with Rangers
34 Al Bumbry .02 .10
35 John Tamargo DP .01 .05
36 Ed Farmer .02 .10
37 Gary Roenicke .02 .10
38 Tim Foli DP .01 .05
39 Eddie Murray 2.50 6.00
40 Roy Howell .02 .10
Now with Brewers
41 Bill Gullickson .20 .50
42 Jerry White DP .01 .05
43 Tim Blackwell .02 .10
44 Steve Henderson .02 .10
45 Enos Cabell .02 .10
Now with Giants
46 Rick Bosetti .02 .10
47 Bill North .02 .10
48 Rich Gossage .20 .50
49 Bob Shirley .02 .10
Now with Cardinals
50 Dave Lopes .08 .25
51 Shane Rawley .02 .10
52 Lloyd Moseby .08 .25
53 Burt Hooton .02 .10
54 Ivan DeJesus .02 .10
55 Mike Norris .02 .10
56 Del Unser .02 .10
57 Dave Revering .02 .10
58 Joel Youngblood .02 .10
59 Steve McCatty .02 .10
60 Willie Randolph .08 .25
61 Butch Wynegar .02 .10
62 Gary Lavelle .02 .10
63 Willie Montanez .02 .10
64 Terry Puhl .02 .10
65 Scott McGregor .02 .10
66 Buddy Bell .08 .25
67 Toby Harrah .08 .25
68 Jim Rice .08 .25
69 Darrell Evans .08 .25
70 Al Oliver DP .07 .20
71 Hal Dues .02 .10
72 Barry Evans DP .01 .05
73 Doug Bair .02 .10
74 Mike Hargrove .08 .25
75 Reggie Smith .08 .25
76 Mario Mendoza .02 .10
Now with Rangers
77 Mike Barlow .02 .10
78 Garth Iorg .02 .10
79 Jeff Reardon RC .40 1.00
80 Roger Erickson .02 .10
81 Dave Stapleton .02 .10
82 Barry Bonnell .02 .10
83 Dave Concepcion .08 .25
84 Johnnie LeMaster .02 .10
85 Mike Caldwell .02 .10
86 Wayne Gross .02 .10
87 Rick Camp .02 .10
88 Joe Lefebvre .02 .10
89 Darrell Jackson .02 .10
90 Bake McBride .02 .10
91 Tim Stoddard DP .01 .05
92 Mike Easler .02 .10
93 Jim Bibby .02 .10
94 Kent Tekulve .08 .25
95 Jim Sundberg .08 .25
96 Tommy John .20 .50
97 Chris Speier .02 .10
98 Clint Hurdle .08 .25
99 Phil Garner .08 .25
100 Rod Carew .60 1.50
101 Steve Stone .02 .10
102 Joe Niekro .02 .10
103 Jerry Martin .02 .10
Now with Giants
104 Ron LeFlore DP .02 .10
Now with White Sox
105 Jose Cruz .08 .25
106 Don Money .02 .10
107 Bobby Brown .02 .10
108 Larry Herndon .02 .10
109 Dennis Eckersley .40 1.00
110 Carl Yastrzemski .60 1.50
111 Greg Minton .02 .10
112 Dan Schatzeder .02 .10
113 George Brett 3.00 8.00
114 Tom Underwood .02 .10
115 Roy Smalley .02 .10
116 Carlton Fisk .75 2.00
Now with White Sox
117 Pete Falcone .02 .10
118 Dale Murphy .60 1.50
119 Tippy Martinez .02 .10
120 Larry Bowa .08 .25
121 Julio Cruz .02 .10
122 Jim Gantner .08 .25
123 Al Cowens .02 .10
124 Jerry Garvin .02 .10
125 Andre Dawson .75 2.00
126 Charlie Leibrandt RC .20 .50
127 Willie Stargell .30 .75
128 Andre Thornton .08 .25
129 Art Howe .02 .10
130 Larry Gura .02 .10
131 Jerry Remy .02 .10
132 Rick Dempsey .08 .25
133 Alan Trammell DP .30 .75
134 Mike LaCoss .02 .10
135 Gorman Thomas .02 .10
136 Tim Raines RC 2.50 6.00
Roberto Ramos
Bobby Pate
137 Bill Madlock .08 .25
138 Rich Dotson DP .02 .10
139 Oscar Gamble .02 .10
140 Bob Forsch .02 .10
141 Miguel Dilone .02 .10
142 Jackson Todd .02 .10
143 Dan Meyer .02 .10
144 Garry Templeton .02 .10
145 Mickey Rivers .08 .25
146 Alan Ashby .02 .10
147 Dale Berra .02 .10
148 Randy Jones .02 .10
Now with Mets
149 Joe Nolan .02 .10
150 Mark Fidrych .20 .50
151 Tony Armas .02 .10
152 Steve Kemp .02 .10
153 Jerry Reuss .08 .25
154 Rick Langford .02 .10
155 Chris Chambliss .08 .25
156 Bob McClure .02 .10
157 John Wathan .02 .10
158 John Curtis .02 .10
159 Steve Howe .08 .25
160 Garry Maddox .02 .10
161 Dan Graham .02 .10
162 Doug Corbett .02 .10
163 Rob Dressler .02 .10
164 Bucky Dent .08 .25
165 Alvis Woods .02 .10
166 Floyd Bannister .02 .10
167 Lee Mazzilli .02 .10
168 Don Robinson DP .01 .05
169 John Mayberry .02 .10
170 Woodie Fryman .02 .10
171 Gene Richards .02 .10
172 Rick Burleson .02 .10
Now with Angels
173 Bump Wills .02 .10
174 Glenn Abbott .02 .10
175 Dave Collins .02 .10
176 Mike Krukow .02 .10
177 Rick Monday .08 .25
178 Dave Parker .20 .50
179 Rudy May .02 .10
180 Pete Rose 1.25 3.00
181 Elias Sosa .02 .10
182 Bob Grich .08 .25
183 Fred Norman .02 .10
184 Jim Dwyer .02 .10
Now with Orioles
185 Dennis Leonard .02 .10
186 Gary Matthews .02 .10
187 Ron Hassey DP .01 .05
188 Doug DeCinces .08 .25
189 Craig Swan .02 .10
190 Cesar Cedeno .08 .25
191 Rick Sutcliffe .08 .25
192 Kiko Garcia .02 .10
193 Pete Vuckovich .02 .10
Now with Brewers
194 Tony Bernazard .02 .10
Now with White Sox
195 Keith Hernandez .08 .25
196 Jerry Mumphrey .02 .10
197 Jim Kern .02 .10
198 Jerry Dybzinski .02 .10
199 John Lowenstein .02 .10
200 George Foster .08 .25
201 Phil Niekro .30 .75
202 Bill Buckner .08 .25
203 Steve Carlton .60 1.50
204 John D'Acquisto .02 .10
Now with Angels
205 Rick Reuschel .08 .25
206 Dan Quisenberry .08 .25
207 Mike Schmidt DP .75 2.00
208 Bob Watson .08 .25
209 Jim Spencer .02 .10
210 Jim Palmer .30 .75
211 Derrel Thomas .02 .10
212 Steve Nicosia .02 .10
213 Omar Moreno .02 .10
214 Richie Zisk .02 .10
Now with Mariners
215 Larry Hisle .02 .10
216 Mike Torrez .02 .10
217 Rich Hebner .02 .10
218 Britt Burns RC .08 .25
219 Ken Landreaux .02 .10
220 Tom Seaver .75 2.00
221 Bob Davis .02 .10
Now with Angels
222 Jorge Orta .02 .10
223 Bobby Bonds .08 .25
224 Pat Zachry .02 .10
225 Ruppert Jones .02 .10
226 Duane Kuiper .02 .10
227 Rodney Scott .02 .10
228 Tom Paciorek .08 .25
229 Rollie Fingers .30 .75
Now with Brewers
230 George Hendrick .02 .10
231 Tony Perez .30 .75
232 Grant Jackson .02 .10
233 Damaso Garcia .02 .10
234 Lou Whitaker .50 1.25
235 Scott Sanderson .02 .10
236 Mike Ivie .02 .10
237 Charlie Moore .02 .10
238 Luis Leal .02 .10
Brian Milner
Ken Schrom
239 Rick Miller DP .01 .05
Now with Red Sox
240 Nolan Ryan 4.00 10.00
241 Checklist 126-250 DP .01 .05
242 Chet Lemon .02 .10
243 Dave Palmer .02 .10
244 Ellis Valentine .02 .10
245 Carney Lansford .08 .25
Now with Red Sox
246 Ed Ott DP .01 .05
247 Glenn Hubbard DP .01 .05
248 Joey McLaughlin .02 .10
249 Jerry Narron .02 .10
250 Ron Guidry .08 .25
251 Steve Garvey .20 .50
252 Victor Cruz .02 .10
253 Bobby Murcer .08 .25
254 Ozzie Smith 3.00 8.00
255 John Stearns .02 .10
256 Bill Campbell .02 .10
257 Rennie Stennett .02 .10
258 Rick Waits .02 .10
259 Gary Lucas .02 .10
260 Ron Cey .08 .25
261 Rickey Henderson 5.00 12.00
262 Sammy Stewart .02 .10
263 Brian Downing .02 .10
264 Mark Bomback .02 .10
265 John Candelaria .08 .25
266 Renie Martin .02 .10
267 Stan Bahnsen .02 .10
268 Montreal Expos CL .20 .50
269 Ken Forsch .02 .10
270 Greg Luzinski .08 .25
271 Ron Jackson .02 .10
272 Wayne Garland .02 .10
273 Milt May .02 .10
274 Rick Wise .02 .10
275 Dwight Evans .20 .50
276 Sal Bando .08 .25
277 Alfredo Griffin .02 .10
278 Rick Sofield .02 .10
279 Bob Knepper .02 .10
Now with Astros
280 Ken Griffey .08 .25
281 Ken Singleton .08 .25
282 Ernie Whitt .08 .25
283 Billy Sample .02 .10
284 Jack Morris .30 .75
285 Dick Ruthven .02 .10
286 Johnny Bench .75 2.00
287 Dave Smith .08 .25
288 Amos Otis .08 .25
289 Dave Goltz .02 .10
290 Bob Boone DP .07 .20
291 Aurelio Lopez .02 .10
292 Tom Hume .02 .10
293 Charlie Lea .02 .10
294 Bert Blyleven .20 .50
Now with Indians
295 Hal McRae .08 .25
296 Bob Stanley .02 .10
297 Bob Bailor .02 .10
Now with Mets
298 Jerry Koosman .08 .25
299 Elliott Maddox .02 .10
Now with Yankees
300 Paul Molitor 2.00 5.00
301 Matt Keough .02 .10
302 Pat Putnam .02 .10
303 Dan Ford .02 .10
304 John Castino .02 .10
305 Barry Foote .02 .10
306 Lou Piniella .08 .25
307 Gene Garber .02 .10
308 Rick Manning .02 .10
309 Don Baylor .20 .50
310 Vida Blue DP .07 .20
311 Doug Flynn .02 .10
312 Rick Rhoden .02 .10
313 Fred Lynn .08 .25
Now with Angels
314 Rich Dauer .02 .10
315 Kirk Gibson RC 2.00 5.00
316 Ken Reitz .02 .10
Now with Cubs
317 Lonnie Smith .08 .25
318 Steve Yeager .02 .10
319 Rowland Office .02 .10
320 Tom Burgmeier .02 .10
321 Leon Durham RC .08 .25
Now with Cubs
322 Neil Allen .02 .10
323 Ray Burris .02 .10
Now with Expos
324 Mike Willis .02 .10
325 Ray Knight .08 .25
326 Rafael Landestoy .02 .10
327 Moose Haas .02 .10
328 Ross Baumgarten .02 .10
329 Joaquin Andujar .08 .25
330 Frank White .08 .25
331 Toronto Blue Jays CL .08 .25
332 Dick Drago .02 .10
333 Sid Monge .02 .10
334 Joe Sambito .02 .10
335 Rick Cerone .02 .10
336 Eddie Whitson .02 .10
337 Sparky Lyle .08 .25
338 Checklist 251-374 .08 .25
339 Jon Matlack .02 .10
340 Ben Oglivie .02 .10
341 Dwayne Murphy .02 .10
342 Terry Crowley .02 .10
343 Frank Taveras .02 .10
344 Steve Rogers .02 .10
345 Warren Cromartie .02 .10
346 Bill Caudill .02 .10
347 Harold Baines RC 4.00 10.00
348 Frank LaCorte .02 .10
349 Glenn Hoffman .02 .10
350 J.R. Richard .02 .10
351 Otto Velez .02 .10
352 Ted Simmons .08 .25
Now with Brewers
353 Terry Kennedy .02 .10
Now with Padres
354 Al Hrabosky .02 .10
355 Bob Horner .08 .25
356 Cecil Cooper .08 .25
357 Bob Welch .08 .25
358 Paul Moskau .02 .10
359 Dave Rader .02 .10
Now with Angels
360 Willie Wilson .08 .25
361 Dave Kingman DP .08 .25
362 Joe Rudi .02 .10
Now with Red Sox
363 Rich Gale .02 .10
364 Steve Trout .02 .10
365 Graig Nettles DP .10 .30
366 Lamar Johnson .08 .25
367 Denny Martinez .30 .75
368 Manny Trillo .02 .10
369 Frank Tanana .08 .25
Now with Red Sox
370 Reggie Jackson .75 2.00
371 Bill Lee .08 .25
372 Jay Johnstone .08 .25
373 Jason Thompson .02 .10
374 Tom Hutton .02 .10

1982 O-Pee-Chee

This set is an abridgement of the 1982 Topps set. The 396 standard-size cards comprising the 1982 O-Pee-Chee set differ from the cards of the 1982 Topps set by having a higher ratio of cards of players from the two Canadian teams, a practice begun by O-Pee-Chee in 1977 and continued to 1988. The set contains virtually the same pictures for the players also featured in the 1982 Topps issue, but the O-Pee-Chee photos appear brighter. The fronts feature white-bordered color player photos with colored lines within the wide white margin on the left. The player's name, team and bilingual position appear in colored lettering within the wide bottom margin. The player's name also appears as a simulated autograph across the photo. The blue print on green horizontal backs carry the player's name, bilingual position and biography at the top. The player's major league statistics follow below. The cards are numbered on the back. The asterisked cards have an extra line on the front inside the picture area indicating team change. In Action (IA) and All-Star (AS) cards are indicated in the checklist below; these are included in the set in addition to the player's regular card. The 396 cards in the set were the largest "original" or distinct set total printed up to that time by O-Pee-Chee; the previous high had been 374 in 1979, 1980 and 1981.

COMPLETE SET (396) 18.00 45.00
1 Dan Spillner .02 .10
2 Ken Singleton AS .02 .10
3 John Candelaria .02 .10
4 Frank Tanana .08 .25
Traded to Rangers Jan. 15/82
5 Reggie Smith .08 .25
6 Rick Monday .02 .10
7 Scott Sanderson .02 .10
8 Rich Dauer .02 .10
9 Ron Guidry .08 .25
10 Ron Guidry IA .02 .10
11 Tom Brookens .02 .10
12 Moose Haas .02 .10
13 Chet Lemon .08 .25
Traded to Tigers Nov. 27/81
14 Steve Howe .02 .10
15 Ellis Valentine .02 .10
16 Toby Harrah .08 .25
17 Darrell Evans .08 .25
18 Johnny Bench .75 2.00
19 Ernie Whitt .08 .25
20 Garry Maddox .02 .10
21 Graig Nettles IA .08 .25
22 Al Oliver IA .08 .25
23 Bob Boone .08 .25
Traded to Angels Dec. 9/81
24 Pete Rose IA .60 1.50
25 Jerry Remy .02 .10
26 Jorge Orta .08 .25
Traded to Dodgers Dec 9/81
27 Bobby Bonds .08 .25
28 Jim Clancy .02 .10
29 Dwayne Murphy .02 .10
30 Tom Seaver .75 2.00
31 Tom Seaver IA .40 1.00
32 Claudell Washington .02 .10
33 Bob Shirley .02 .10
34 Bob Forsch .02 .10
35 Willie Aikens .02 .10
36 Rod Carew AS .30 .75
37 Willie Randolph .08 .25
38 Charlie Lea .02 .10
39 Lou Whitaker .30 .75
40 Dave Parker .08 .25
41 Dave Parker IA .02 .10
42 Mark Belanger .08 .25
Traded to Dodgers Dec. 24/81
43 Rick Langford .02 .10
44 Rollie Fingers IA .20 .50
45 Rick Cerone .02 .10
46 Johnny Wockenfuss .02 .10
47 Jack Morris AS .08 .25
48 Cesar Cedeno .02 .10
Traded to Reds Dec. 18/81
49 Alvis Woods .02 .10
50 Buddy Bell .08 .25
51 Mickey Rivers IA .02 .10
52 Steve Rogers .02 .10
53 John Mayberry .08 .25
Dave Stieb TL CL
54 Ron Hassey .02 .10
55 Rick Burleson .02 .10
56 Harold Baines .20 .50
57 Craig Reynolds .02 .10
58 Carlton Fisk AS .30 .75
59 Jim Kern .02 .10
Traded to Reds Feb. 10/82
60 Tony Armas .02 .10
61 Warren Cromartie .02 .10
62 Graig Nettles .08 .25
63 Jerry Koosman .08 .25
64 Pat Zachry .02 .10
65 Terry Kennedy .02 .10
66 Richie Zisk .02 .10
67 Rich Gale .08 .25
Traded to Giants Dec. 10/81
68 Steve Carlton .60 1.50
69 Greg Luzinski IA .08 .25
70 Tim Raines .75 2.00
71 Roy Lee Jackson .02 .10
72 Carl Yastrzemski .60 1.50
73 John Castino .02 .10
74 Joe Niekro .08 .25
75 Tommy John .20 .50
76 Dave Winfield AS .30 .75
77 Miguel Dilone .02 .10
78 Gary Gray .02 .10
79 Tom Hume .02 .10
80 Jim Palmer .50 1.25
81 Jim Palmer IA .30 .75
82 Vida Blue IA .08 .25
83 Garth Iorg .02 .10
84 Rennie Stennett .02 .10
85 Dave Lopes IA .08 .25
Traded to A's Feb. 8/82
86 Dave Concepcion .08 .25
87 Matt Keough .02 .10
88 Jim Spencer .02 .10
89 Steve Henderson .02 .10
90 Nolan Ryan 4.00 10.00
91 Carney Lansford .08 .25
92 Bake McBride .02 .10
93 Dave Stapleton .02 .10
94 Warren Cromartie .08 .25
Bill Gullickson TL CL
95 Ozzie Smith 4.00 10.00
Traded to Cardinals Feb. 11/82
96 Rich Hebner .02 .10
97 Tim Foli .02 .10
Traded to Angels Dec. 11/82
98 Darrell Porter .02 .10
99 Barry Bonnell .02 .10
100 Mike Schmidt 1.25 3.00
101 Mike Schmidt IA .60 1.50
102 Dan Briggs .02 .10
103 Al Cowens .02 .10
104 Grant Jackson .08 .25
Traded to Royals Jan. 19/82
105 Kirk Gibson .30 .75
106 Dan Schatzeder .08 .25
Traded to Giants Dec. 9/81
107 Juan Berenguer .02 .10
108 Jack Morris .20 .50
109 Dave Revering .02 .10
110 Carlton Fisk .60 1.50
111 Carlton Fisk IA .30 .75
112 Billy Sample .02 .10
113 Steve McCatty .02 .10
114 Ken Landreaux .02 .10
115 Gaylord Perry .40 1.00
116 Elias Sosa .02 .10
117 Rich Gossage IA .08 .25
118 Terry Francona RC 2.00 5.00
Brad Mills
Bryn Smith
119 Billy Almon .02 .10
120 Gary Lucas .02 .10
121 Ken Oberkfell .02 .10
122 Steve Carlton IA .30 .75
123 Jeff Reardon .20 .50
124 Bill Buckner .08 .25
125 Danny Ainge .60 1.50
Voluntarily Retired Nov. 30/81
126 Paul Splittorff .02 .10
127 Lonnie Smith .02 .10
Traded to Cardinals Nov. 19/81
128 Rudy May .02 .10
129 Checklist 1-132 .02 .10
130 Julio Cruz .02 .10
131 Stan Bahnsen .02 .10
132 Pete Vuckovich .02 .10
133 Luis Salazar .02 .10
134 Dan Ford .08 .25
Traded to Orioles Jan. 28/82
135 Denny Martinez .30 .75
136 Lary Sorensen .02 .10
137 Fergie Jenkins .40 1.00
Traded to Cubs Dec. 15/81
138 Rick Camp .02 .10
139 Wayne Nordhagen .02 .10
140 Ron LeFlore .08 .25
141 Rick Sutcliffe .08 .25
142 Rick Waits .02 .10
143 Mookie Wilson .30 .75
144 Greg Minton .02 .10
145 Bob Horner .08 .25
146 Joe Morgan IA .30 .75
147 Larry Gura .02 .10
148 Alfredo Griffin .02 .10
149 Pat Putnam .02 .10
150 Ted Simmons .08 .25
151 Gary Matthews .08 .25
152 Greg Luzinski .08 .25
153 Mike Flanagan .08 .25
154 Jim Morrison .02 .10
155 Otto Velez .02 .10
156 Frank White .08 .25
157 Doug Corbett .02 .10
158 Brian Downing .02 .10
159 Willie Randolph IA .08 .25
160 Luis Tiant .08 .25
161 Andre Thornton .02 .10
162 Amos Otis .08 .25
163 Paul Mirabella .02 .10
164 Bert Blyleven .20 .50
165 Rowland Office .02 .10
166 Gene Tenace .08 .25
167 Cecil Cooper .08 .25
168 Bruce Benedict .02 .10
169 Mark Clear .02 .10
170 Jim Bibby .02 .10
171 Ken Griffey IA .08 .25
Traded to Yankees Nov 4/81
172 Bill Gullickson .02 .10
173 Mike Scioscia .02 .10
174 Doug DeCinces .08 .25
Traded to Angels Jan 28/82
175 Jerry Mumphrey .02 .10
176 Rollie Fingers .40 1.00
177 George Foster IA .08 .25
Traded to Mets Feb 10/82
178 Mitchell Page .02 .10
179 Steve Garvey .30 .75
180 Steve Garvey IA .08 .25
181 Woodie Fryman .02 .10
182 Larry Herndon .02 .10
Traded to Tigers Dec. 9/81
183 Frank White IA .08 .25
184 Alan Ashby .02 .10
185 Phil Niekro .40 1.00
186 Leon Roberts .02 .10

187 Rod Carew .60 1.50
188 Willie Stargell IA .30 .75
189 Joel Youngblood .02 .10
190 J.R. Richard .02 .10
191 Tim Wallach .30 .75
192 Broderick Perkins .02 .10
193 Johnny Grubb .02 .10
194 Larry Bowa .08 .25
Traded to Cubs Jan. 27/82
195 Paul Molitor 1.25 3.00
196 Willie Upshaw .02 .10
197 Roy Smalley .02 .10
198 Chris Speier .02 .10
199 Don Aase .02 .10
200 George Brett 2.50 6.00
201 George Brett IA 1.25 3.00
202 Rick Manning .02 .10
203 Jesse Barfield RC .30 .75
Brian Milner
Boomer Wells
204 Rick Reuschel .08 .25
205 Neil Allen .02 .10
206 Leon Durham .02 .10
207 Jim Gantner .08 .25
208 Joe Morgan .30 .75
209 Gary Lavelle .02 .10
210 Keith Hernandez .08 .25
211 Joe Charboneau .02 .10
212 Mario Mendoza .02 .10
213 Willie Randolph AS .08 .25
214 Lance Parrish .20 .50
215 Mike Krukow .02 .10
Traded to Phillies Dec. 8/81
216 Ron Cey .08 .25
217 Ruppert Jones .02 .10
218 Dave Lopes .08 .25
Traded to A's Feb. 8/82
219 Steve Yeager .02 .10
220 Manny Trillo .02 .10
221 Dave Concepcion IA .08 .25
222 Butch Wynegar .02 .10
223 Lloyd Moseby .02 .10
224 Bruce Bochte .02 .10
225 Ed Ott .02 .10
226 Checklist 133-264 .02 .10
227 Ray Burris .02 .10
228 Reggie Smith IA .08 .25
229 Oscar Gamble .02 .10
230 Willie Wilson .02 .10
231 Brian Kingman .02 .10
232 John Stearns .02 .10
233 Duane Kuiper .02 .10
Traded to Giants Nov. 16/81
234 Don Baylor .08 .25
235 Mike Easler .02 .10
236 Lou Piniella .08 .25
237 Robin Yount .60 1.50
238 Kevin Saucier .02 .10
239 Jon Matlack .02 .10
240 Bucky Dent .08 .25
241 Bucky Dent IA .02 .10
242 Milt May .02 .10
243 Lee Mazzilli .02 .10
244 Gary Carter .40 1.00
245 Ken Reitz .02 .10
246 Scott McGregor AS .02 .10
247 Pedro Guerrero .08 .25
248 Art Howe .02 .10
249 Dick Tidrow .02 .10
250 Tug McGraw .08 .25
251 Fred Lynn .08 .25
252 Fred Lynn IA .02 .10
253 Gene Richards .02 .10
254 George Bell RC .40 1.00
255 Tony Perez .40 1.00
256 Tony Perez IA .20 .50
257 Rich Dotson .02 .10
258 Bo Diaz .02 .10
Traded to Phillies Nov. 19/81
259 Rodney Scott .02 .10
260 Bruce Sutter .40 1.00
261 George Brett AS 1.25 3.00
262 Rick Dempsey .08 .25
263 Mike Phillips .02 .10
264 Jerry Garvin .02 .10
265 Al Bumbry .02 .10
266 Hubie Brooks .02 .10
267 Vida Blue .08 .25
268 Rickey Henderson 2.00 5.00
269 Rick Peters .02 .10
270 Rusty Staub .08 .25
271 Sixto Lezcano .02 .10
Traded to Padres Dec. 10/81
272 Bump Wills .02 .10
273 Gary Allenson .02 .10
274 Randy Jones .02 .10
275 Bob Watson .08 .25
276 Dave Kingman .08 .25
277 Terry Puhl .02 .10
278 Jerry Reuss .08 .25
279 Sammy Stewart .02 .10
280 Ben Oglivie .02 .10
281 Kent Tekulve .08 .25
282 Ken Macha .08 .25
283 Ron Davis .02 .10
284 Bob Grich .08 .25
285 Sparky Lyle .08 .25
286 Rich Gossage AS .08 .25
287 Dennis Eckersley .40 1.00
288 Garry Templeton .02 .10
Traded to Padres Dec. 10/81
289 Bob Stanley .02 .10
290 Ken Singleton .02 .10
291 Mickey Hatcher .02 .10
292 Dave Palmer .02 .10
293 Damaso Garcia .02 .10
294 Don Money .02 .10
295 George Hendrick .02 .10
296 Steve Kemp .02 .10
Traded to White Sox Nov. 27/81
297 Dave Smith .02 .10
298 Bucky Dent AS .02 .10
299 Steve Trout .02 .10
300 Reggie Jackson 1.25 3.00
Traded to Angels Jan. 26/82
301 Reggie Jackson IA .60 1.50
Traded to Angels Jan. 26/82
302 Doug Flynn .08 .25
Traded to Rangers Dec. 14/81
303 Wayne Gross .02 .10
304 Johnny Bench IA .30 .75
305 Don Sutton .40 1.00
306 Don Sutton IA .30 .75
307 Mark Bomback .02 .10
308 Charlie Moore .02 .10
309 Jeff Burroughs .02 .10
310 Mike Hargrove .08 .25
311 Enos Cabell .02 .10
312 Lenny Randle .02 .10
313 Ivan DeJesus .02 .10
Traded to Phillies Jan. 27/82
314 Buck Martinez .02 .10
315 Burt Hooton .02 .10
316 Scott McGregor .02 .10
317 Dick Ruthven .02 .10
318 Mike Heath .02 .10
319 Ray Knight .08 .25
Traded to Astros Dec. 18/81
320 Chris Chambliss .02 .10
321 Chris Chambliss IA .02 .10
322 Ross Baumgarten .02 .10
323 Bill Lee .08 .25
324 Gorman Thomas .02 .10
325 Jose Cruz .08 .25
326 Al Oliver .08 .25
327 Jackson Todd .02 .10
328 Ed Farmer .02 .10
Traded to Phillies Jan. 28/82
329 U.L. Washington .02 .10
330 Ken Griffey .08 .25
Traded to Yankees Nov. 4/81
331 John Milner .02 .10
332 Don Robinson .02 .10
333 Cliff Johnson .02 .10
334 Fernando Valenzuela .30 .75
335 Jim Sundberg .08 .25
336 George Foster .08 .25
Traded to Mets Feb. 10/82
337 Pete Rose AS .60 1.50
338 Dave Lopes AS .08 .25
Traded to A's Feb. 8/82
339 Mike Schmidt AS .60 1.50
340 Dave Concepcion AS .02 .10
341 Andre Dawson AS .30 .75
342 George Foster AS .08 .25
Traded to Mets Feb. 10/82
343 Dave Parker AS .08 .25
344 Gary Carter AS .08 .25
345 Fernando Valenzuela AS .20 .50
346 Tom Seaver AS .30 .75
347 Bruce Sutter AS .20 .50
348 Darrell Porter IA .02 .10
349 Dave Collins .02 .10
Traded to Yankees Dec. 23/81
350 Amos Otis IA .02 .10
351 Frank Taveras .02 .10
Traded to Expos Dec. 14/81
352 Dave Winfield .60 1.50
353 Larry Parrish .02 .10
354 Roberto Ramos .02 .10
355 Dwight Evans .08 .25
356 Mickey Rivers .02 .10
357 Butch Hobson .02 .10
358 Carl Yastrzemski IA .30 .75
359 Ron Jackson .02 .10
360 Len Barker .02 .10
361 Pete Rose 1.25 3.00
362 Kevin Hickey RC .02 .10
363 Rod Carew IA .30 .75
364 Hector Cruz .02 .10
365 Bill Madlock .08 .25
366 Jim Rice .08 .25
367 Ron Cey IA .08 .25
368 Luis Leal .04 .10
369 Dennis Leonard .02 .10
370 Mike Norris .02 .10
371 Tom Paciorek .08 .25
Traded to White Sox Dec. 11/81
372 Willie Stargell .40 1.00
373 Dan Driessen .02 .10
374 Larry Bowa IA .08 .25
Traded to Cubs Jan. 27/82
375 Dusty Baker .08 .25
376 Joey McLaughlin .02 .10
377 Reggie Jackson AS .60 1.50
Traded to Angels Jan. 26/82
378 Mike Caldwell .02 .10
379 Andre Dawson .60 1.50
380 Dave Stieb .02 .10
381 Alan Trammell .30 .75
382 John Mayberry .02 .10
383 John Wathan .02 .10
384 Hal McRae .08 .25
385 Ken Forsch .02 .10
386 Jerry White .02 .10
387 Tom Veryzer .02 .10
Traded to Mets Jan. 8/82
388 Joe Rudi .02 .10
Traded to A's Dec. 4/81
389 Bob Knepper .02 .10
390 Eddie Murray 1.50 4.00
391 Dale Murphy .30 .75
392 Bob Boone IA .08 .25
Traded to Angels Dec. 6/81
393 Al Hrabosky .02 .10
394 Checklist 265-396 .02 .10
395 Omar Moreno .02 .10
396 Rich Gossage .30 .75

1983 O-Pee-Chee

This set is an abridgement of the 1983 Topps set. The 396 standard-size cards comprising the 1983 O-Pee-Chee set differ from the cards of the 1983 Topps set by having a higher ratio of cards of players from the two Canadian teams, a practice begun by O-Pee-Chee in 1977 and continued to 1988. The set contains virtually the same pictures for the players also featured in the 1983 Topps issue. The fronts feature white-bordered color player action photos framed by a colored line. A circular color player head shot also appears on the front at the lower right. The player's name, team and bilingual position appear at the lower left. The pink and white horizontal backs carry the player's name and biography at the top. The player's major league statistics and bilingual career highlights follow below. The asterisked cards have an extra line on the front inside the picture area indicating team change. The O-Pee-Chee logo appears on the front of every card. Super Veteran (SV) and All-Star (AS) cards are indicated in the checklist below; these are included in the set in addition to the player's regular card. The 1983 O-Pee-Chee set was issued in nine-card packs which cost 25 cents Canadian at time of issue. The set features Rookie Cards of Tony Gwynn and Ryne Sandberg.

COMPLETE SET (396) 24.00 60.00
1 Rusty Staub .07 .20
2 Larry Parrish .02 .10
3 George Brett 1.50 4.00
4 Carl Yastrzemski .50 1.25
5 Al Oliver SV .07 .20
6 Bill Virdon MG .02 .10
7 Gene Richards .02 .10
8 Steve Balboni .02 .10
9 Joey McLaughlin .02 .10
10 Gorman Thomas .02 .10
11 Chris Chambliss .07 .20
12 Ray Burris .02 .10
13 Larry Herndon .02 .10
14 Ozzie Smith 1.00 2.50
15 Ron Cey .07 .20
Now with Cubs
16 Willie Wilson .07 .20
17 Kent Tekulve .02 .10
18 Kent Tekulve SV .02 .10
19 Oscar Gamble .02 .10
20 Carlton Fisk .40 1.00
21 Dale Murphy AS .20 .50
22 Randy Lerch .02 .10
23 Dale Murphy .20 .50
24 Steve Mura .07 .20
Now with White Sox
25 Hal McRae .07 .20
26 Dennis Lamp .02 .10
27 Ron Washington .02 .10
28 Bruce Bochte .02 .10
29 Randy Jones .07 .20
Now with Pirates
30 Jim Rice .07 .20
31 Bill Gullickson .07 .20
32 Dave Concepcion AS .07 .20
33 Ted Simmons SV .07 .20
34 Bobby Cox MG .02 .10
35 Rollie Fingers .20 .50
36 Rollie Fingers SV .10 .30
37 Mike Hargrove .07 .20
38 Roy Smalley .02 .10
39 Terry Puhl .02 .10
40 Fernando Valenzuela .20 .50
41 Garry Maddox .02 .10
42 Dale Murray .07 .20
Now with Yankees
43 Bob Dernier .02 .10
44 Don Robinson .02 .10
45 John Mayberry .02 .10
46 Richard Dotson .02 .10
47 Wayne Nordhagen .02 .10
Now with Cubs
48 Lary Sorensen .02 .10
49 Willie McGee RC 1.25 3.00
50 Bob Horner .02 .10
51 Rusty Staub SV .07 .20
52 Tom Seaver 1.00 2.50
Now with Mets
53 Chet Lemon .02 .10
54 Scott Sanderson .02 .10
55 Mookie Wilson .07 .20
56 Reggie Jackson .60 1.50
57 Tim Blackwell .02 .10
58 Keith Moreland .02 .10
59 Alvis Woods .07 .20
Now with Athletics
60 Johnny Bench .60 1.50
61 Johnny Bench SV .30 .75
62 Jim Gott .02 .10
63 Rick Monday .02 .10
64 Gary Matthews .07 .20
65 Jack Morris .07 .20
66 Lou Whitaker .20 .50
67 U.L. Washington .02 .10
68 Eric Show .02 .10
69 Lee Lacy .02 .10
70 Steve Carlton .40 1.00
71 Steve Carlton SV .30 .75
72 Tom Paciorek .02 .10
73 Manny Trillo .07 .20
Now with Indians
74 Tony Perez SV .10 .30
75 Amos Otis .07 .20
76 Rick Mahler .02 .10
77 Hosken Powell .02 .10
78 Bill Caudill .02 .10
79 Dan Petry .02 .10
80 George Foster .07 .20
81 Joe Morgan .20 .50
Now with Phillies
82 Burt Hooton .02 .10
83 Ryne Sandberg RC 6.00 15.00
84 Alan Ashby .02 .10
85 Ken Singleton .07 .20
86 Tom Hume .02 .10
87 Dennis Leonard .02 .10
88 Jim Gantner .07 .20
89 Leon Roberts .07 .20
Now with Royals
90 Jerry Reuss .07 .20
91 Ben Oglivie .02 .10
92 Sparky Lyle SV .07 .20
93 John Castino .02 .10
94 Phil Niekro .20 .50
95 Alan Trammell .20 .50
96 Gaylord Perry .20 .50
97 Tom Herr .02 .10
98 Vance Law .02 .10
99 Dickie Noles .02 .10
100 Pete Rose 1.00 2.50
101 Pete Rose SV .50 1.25
102 Dave Concepcion .07 .20
103 Darrell Porter .02 .10
104 Ron Guidry .07 .20
105 Don Baylor .07 .20
Now with Yankees
106 Steve Rogers AS .02 .10
107 Greg Minton .02 .10
108 Glenn Hoffman .02 .10
109 Luis Leal .02 .10
110 Ken Griffey .07 .20
111 Al Oliver .07 .20
Steve Rogers TL CL
112 Luis Pujols .02 .10
113 Julio Cruz .02 .10
114 Jim Slaton .02 .10
115 Chili Davis .20 .50
116 Pedro Guerrero .07 .20
117 Mike Ivie .02 .10
118 Chris Welsh .02 .10
119 Frank Pastore .02 .10
120 Len Barker .02 .10
121 Chris Speier .02 .10
122 Bobby Murcer .07 .20
123 Bill Russell .02 .10
124 Lloyd Moseby .02 .10
125 Leon Durham .02 .10
126 Carl Yastrzemski SV .20 .50
127 John Candelaria .02 .10
128 Phil Garner .07 .20
129 Checklist 1-132 .02 .10
130 Dave Stieb .02 .10
131 Geoff Zahn .02 .10
132 Todd Cruz .02 .10
133 Tony Pena .02 .10
134 Hubie Brooks .02 .10
135 Dwight Evans .07 .20
136 Willie Aikens .02 .10
137 Woodie Fryman .02 .10
138 Rick Dempsey .07 .20
139 Bruce Berenyi .02 .10
140 Willie Randolph .07 .20
141 Eddie Murray 1.00 2.50
142 Mike Caldwell .02 .10
143 Tony Gwynn RC 10.00 25.00
144 Tommy John SV .07 .20
145 Don Sutton .40 1.00
146 Don Sutton SV .20 .50
147 Rick Manning .02 .10
148 George Hendrick .02 .10
149 Johnny Ray .02 .10
150 Bruce Sutter .07 .20
151 Bruce Sutter SV .07 .20
152 Jay Johnstone .07 .20
153 Jerry Koosman .07 .20
154 Johnnie LeMaster .02 .10
155 Dan Quisenberry .07 .20
156 Luis Salazar .02 .10
157 Steve Bedrosian .07 .20
158 Jim Sundberg .02 .10
159 Gaylord Perry SV .10 .30
160 Dave Kingman .10 .30
161 Dave Kingman SV .02 .10
162 Mark Clear .02 .10
163 Cal Ripken 4.00 10.00
164 Dave Palmer .02 .10
165 Dan Driessen .02 .10
166 Tug McGraw .10 .30
167 Dennis Martinez .07 .20
168 Juan Eichelberger .07 .20
Now with Indians
169 Doug Flynn .02 .10
170 Steve Howe .02 .10
171 Frank White .07 .20
172 Mike Flanagan .07 .20
173 Andre Dawson AS .10 .30
174 Manny Trillo AS .07 .20
Now with Indians
175 Bo Diaz .02 .10
176 Dave Righetti .07 .20
177 Harold Baines .20 .50
178 Vida Blue .07 .20
179 Luis Tiant SV .07 .20
180 Rickey Henderson 1.00 2.50
181 Rick Rhoden .02 .10
182 Fred Lynn .07 .20
183 Ed VandeBerg .02 .10
184 Dwayne Murphy .02 .10
185 Tim Lollar .02 .10
186 Dave Tobik .02 .10
187 Tug McGraw SV .07 .20
188 Rick Miller .02 .10
189 Dan Schatzeder .02 .10
190 Cecil Cooper .07 .20
191 Jim Beattie .02 .10
192 Rich Dauer .02 .10
193 Al Cowens .02 .10
194 Roy Lee Jackson .02 .10
195 Mike Gates .02 .10
196 Tommy John .20 .50
197 Bob Forsch .02 .10
198 Steve Garvey .20 .50
Now with Padres
199 Brad Mills .02 .10
200 Rod Carew .40 1.00
201 Rod Carew SV .20 .50
202 Dave Stieb .07 .20
Damaso Garcia TL CL
203 Floyd Bannister .07 .20
Now with White Sox
204 Bruce Benedict .02 .10
205 Dave Parker .07 .20
206 Ken Oberkfell .02 .10
207 Graig Nettles SV .07 .20
208 Sparky Lyle .07 .20
209 Jason Thompson .02 .10
210 Jack Clark .07 .20
211 Jim Kaat .07 .20
212 John Stearns .02 .10
213 Tom Burgmeier .02 .10
214 Jerry White .02 .10
215 Mario Soto .02 .10
216 Scott McGregor .02 .10
217 Tim Stoddard .02 .10
218 Bill Laskey .02 .10
219 Reggie Jackson SV .20 .50
220 Dusty Baker .07 .20
221 Joe Niekro .07 .20
222 Damaso Garcia .02 .10
223 John Montefusco .02 .10
224 Mickey Rivers .02 .10
225 Enos Cabell .02 .10
226 LaMarr Hoyt .02 .10
227 Tim Raines .20 .50
228 Joaquin Andujar .02 .10
229 Tim Wallach .07 .20
230 Fergie Jenkins .40 1.00
231 Fergie Jenkins SV .20 .50
232 Tom Brunansky .07 .20
233 Ivan DeJesus .02 .10
234 Bryn Smith .02 .10
235 Claudell Washington .02 .10
236 Steve Renko .02 .10
237 Dan Norman .02 .10
238 Cesar Cedeno .07 .20
239 Dave Stapleton .02 .10
240 Rich Gossage .20 .50
241 Rich Gossage SV .10 .30
242 Bob Stanley .02 .10
243 Rich Gale .07 .20
Now with Reds
244 Sixto Lezcano .02 .10
245 Steve Sax .07 .20
246 Jerry Mumphrey .02 .10
247 Dave Smith .02 .10
248 Bake McBride .02 .10
249 Checklist 133-264 .02 .10
250 Bill Buckner .07 .20
251 Kent Hrbek .20 .50
252 Gene Tenace .02 .10
Now with Pirates
253 Charlie Lea .02 .10
254 Rick Cerone .02 .10
255 Gene Garber .02 .10
256 Gene Garber SV .02 .10
257 Jesse Barfield .07 .20
258 Dave Winfield .40 1.00
259 Don Money .02 .10
260 Steve Kemp .02 .10
Now with Yankees
261 Steve Yeager .02 .10
262 Keith Hernandez .07 .20
263 Tippy Martinez .02 .10
264 Joe Morgan SV .20 .50
Now with Phillies
265 Joel Youngblood .02 .10
Now with Giants
266 Bruce Sutter AS .20 .50
267 Terry Francona .07 .20
268 Neil Allen .02 .10
269 Ron Oester .02 .10
270 Dennis Eckersley .40 1.00
271 Dale Berra .02 .10
272 Al Bumbry .02 .10
273 Lonnie Smith .02 .10
274 Terry Kennedy .02 .10
275 Ray Knight .02 .10
276 Mike Norris .02 .10
277 Rance Mulliniks .02 .10
278 Dan Spillner .02 .10
279 Bucky Dent .07 .20
280 Bert Blyleven .20 .50
281 Barry Bonnell .02 .10
282 Reggie Smith .07 .20
283 Reggie Smith SV .07 .20
284 Ted Simmons .07 .20
285 Lance Parrish .07 .20
286 Larry Christenson .02 .10
287 Ruppert Jones .02 .10
288 Bob Welch .07 .20
289 John Wathan .02 .10
290 Jeff Reardon .07 .20
291 Dave Revering .02 .10
292 Craig Swan .02 .10
293 Graig Nettles .07 .20
294 Alfredo Griffin .02 .10
295 Jerry Remy .02 .10
296 Joe Sambito .02 .10
297 Ron LeFlore .02 .10
298 Brian Downing .02 .10
299 Jim Palmer .20 .50
300 Mike Schmidt .75 2.00
301 Mike Schmidt SV .40 1.00
302 Ernie Whitt .02 .10
303 Andre Dawson .20 .50
304 Bobby Murcer SV .07 .20
305 Larry Bowa .07 .20
306 Lee Mazzilli .02 .10
Now with Pirates
307 Lou Piniella .07 .20
308 Buck Martinez .07 .20
309 Jerry Martin .02 .10
310 Greg Luzinski .07 .20
311 Al Oliver .07 .20
312 Mike Torrez .02 .10
Now with Mets
313 Dick Ruthven .02 .10
314 Gary Carter AS .20 .50
315 Rick Burleson .02 .10
316 Phil Niekro SV .10 .30
317 Moose Haas .02 .10
318 Carney Lansford .07 .20
Now with Athletics
319 Tim Foli .02 .10
320 Steve Rogers .02 .10
321 Kirk Gibson .20 .50
322 Glenn Hubbard .02 .10
323 Luis DeLeon .02 .10
324 Mike Marshall .02 .10
325 Von Hayes .02 .10
Now with Phillies
326 Garth Iorg .02 .10
327 Jose Cruz .07 .20
328 Jim Palmer SV .10 .30
329 Darrell Evans .07 .20
330 Buddy Bell .07 .20
331 Mike Krukow .02 .10
Now with Giants
332 Omar Moreno .02 .10
Now with Astros
333 Dave LaRoche .02 .10
334 Dave LaRoche SV .02 .10
335 Bill Madlock .07 .20
336 Garry Templeton .02 .10
337 John Lowenstein .02 .10
338 Willie Upshaw .02 .10
339 Dave Hostetler RC .02 .10
340 Larry Gura .02 .10
341 Doug DeCinces .07 .20
342 Mike Schmidt AS .40 1.00
343 Charlie Hough .07 .20
344 Andre Thornton .02 .10
345 Jim Clancy .02 .10
346 Ken Forsch .02 .10
347 Sammy Stewart .02 .10
348 Alan Bannister .02 .10
349 Checklist 265-396 .02 .10
350 Robin Yount .40 1.00
351 Warren Cromartie .02 .10
352 Tim Raines AS .20 .50
353 Tony Armas .02 .10
Now with Red Sox
354 Tom Seaver SV .50 1.25
Now with Mets
355 Tony Perez .30 .75
Now with Phillies
356 Toby Harrah .02 .10
357 Dan Ford .02 .10
358 Charlie Puleo .02 .10
Now with Reds
359 Dave Collins .02 .10
Now with Blue Jays
360 Nolan Ryan 3.00 8.00
361 Nolan Ryan SV 1.50 4.00
362 Bill Almon .02 .10
Now with Athletics
363 Eddie Milner .02 .10
364 Gary Lucas .02 .10
365 Dave Lopes .07 .20
366 Bob Boone .07 .20
367 Biff Pocoroba .02 .10
368 Richie Zisk .02 .10
369 Tony Bernazard .02 .10
370 Gary Carter .40 1.00
371 Paul Molitor .50 1.25
372 Art Howe .02 .10
373 Pete Rose AS .50 1.25
374 Glenn Adams .02 .10
375 Pete Vuckovich .02 .10
376 Gary Lavelle .02 .10
377 Lee May .07 .20
378 Lee May SV .07 .20
379 Butch Wynegar .02 .10
380 Ron Davis .02 .10
381 Bob Grich .07 .20
382 Gary Roenicke .02 .10
383 Jim Kaat SV .07 .20
384 Steve Carlton AS .20 .50
385 Mike Easler .02 .10
386 Rod Carew AS .20 .50
387 Bob Grich AS .07 .20
388 George Brett AS .75 2.00
389 Robin Yount AS .20 .50
390 Reggie Jackson AS .20 .50
391 Rickey Henderson AS .20 .50
392 Fred Lynn AS .07 .20
393 Carlton Fisk AS .20 .50
394 Pete Vuckovich AS .02 .10
395 Larry Gura AS .02 .10
396 Dan Quisenberry AS .02 .10

1984 O-Pee-Chee

This set is an abridgement of the 1984 Topps set. The 396 standard-size cards comprising the 1984 O-Pee-Chee set differ from the cards of the 1984 Topps set by having a higher ratio of cards of players from the two Canadian teams, a practice begun by O-Pee-Chee in 1977 and continued to 1988. The set contains virtually the same pictures for the players also featured in the 1984 Topps issue. The fronts feature white-bordered color player action photos. A color player head shot also appears on the front at the lower left. The player's name and position appear in colored lettering within the white margin at the lower right. His team name appears in vertical colored lettering within the white margin on the left. The red, white and blue horizontal backs carry the player's name and biography at the top. The player's major league statistics and bilingual career highlights follow below. The asterisked cards have an extra line on the front inside the picture area indicating team change. The O-Pee-Chee logo appears on the front of every card. All-Star (AS) cards are indicated in the checklist below; they are included in the set in addition to the player's regular card. The O-Pee-Chee set came in 12-card packs which cost 35 cents Canadian at time of issue. Notable Rookie Cards include Don Mattingly and Darryl Strawberry.

COMPLETE SET (396) 14.00 35.00
1 Pascual Perez .01 .05
2 Cal Ripken AS 1.25 3.00
3 Lloyd Moseby AS .01 .05
4 Mel Hall .01 .05
5 Willie Wilson .01 .05
6 Mike Morgan .01 .05
7 Gary Lucas .02 .10
Now with Expos
8 Don Mattingly RC 6.00 15.00
9 Jim Gott .01 .05
10 Robin Yount .20 .50
11 Joey McLaughlin .01 .05
12 Billy Sample .01 .05
13 Oscar Gamble .01 .05
14 Bill Russell .01 .05
15 Burt Hooton .01 .05
16 Omar Moreno .01 .05
17 Dave Lopes .02 .10
18 Dale Berra .01 .05
19 Rance Mulliniks .01 .05
20 Greg Luzinski .02 .10
21 Doug Sisk .01 .05
22 Don Robinson .01 .05
23 Keith Moreland .01 .05
24 Richard Dotson .01 .05
25 Glenn Hubbard .01 .05
26 Rod Carew .40 1.00
27 Alan Wiggins .01 .05
28 Frank Viola .20 .50
29 Phil Niekro .40 1.00
Now with Yankees
30 Wade Boggs 1.25 3.00
31 Dave Parker .08 .25
Now with Reds
32 Bobby Ramos .01 .05
33 Tom Burgmeier .01 .05
34 Eddie Milner .01 .05
35 Don Sutton .30 .75
36 Glenn Wilson .01 .05
37 Mike Krukow .01 .05
38 Dave Collins .01 .05
39 Garth Iorg .01 .05
40 Dusty Baker .08 .25
41 Tony Bernazard .02 .10
Now with Indians
42 Claudell Washington .01 .05
43 Cecil Cooper .02 .10
44 Dan Driessen .01 .05
45 Jerry Mumphrey .01 .05
46 Rick Rhoden .01 .05
47 Rudy Law .01 .05
48 Julio Franco .20 .50
49 Mike Norris .01 .05
50 Chris Chambliss .01 .05
51 Pete Falcone .01 .05
52 Mike Marshall .01 .05
53 Amos Otis .02 .10
Now with Pirates
54 Jesse Orosco .02 .10
55 Dave Concepcion .02 .10
56 Gary Allenson .01 .05
57 Dan Schatzeder .01 .05
58 Jerry Remy .01 .05
59 Carney Lansford .02 .10
60 Paul Molitor .40 1.00
61 Chris Codiroli .01 .05
62 Dave Hostetler .01 .05
63 Ed VandeBerg .01 .05
64 Ryne Sandberg 1.50 4.00
65 Kirk Gibson .20 .50
66 Nolan Ryan 2.50 6.00
67 Gary Ward .01 .05
Now with Rangers
68 Luis Salazar .01 .05
69 Dan Quisenberry AS .01 .05
70 Gary Matthews .01 .05
71 Pete O'Brien .02 .10
72 John Wathan .01 .05
73 Jody Davis .01 .05
74 Kent Tekulve .01 .05
75 Bob Forsch .01 .05
76 Alfredo Griffin .01 .05
77 Bryn Smith .01 .05
78 Mike Torrez .01 .05
79 Mike Hargrove .02 .10
80 Steve Rogers .01 .05
81 Bake McBride .01 .05
82 Doug DeCinces .01 .05
83 Richie Zisk .01 .05
84 Randy Bush .01 .05
85 Atlee Hammaker .01 .05
86 Chet Lemon .01 .05
87 Frank Pastore .01 .05
88 Alan Trammell .20 .50
89 Terry Francona .02 .10
90 Pedro Guerrero .02 .10
91 Dan Spillner .01 .05
92 Lloyd Moseby .01 .05
93 Bob Knepper .01 .05
94 Ted Simmons AS .02 .10
95 Aurelio Lopez .01 .05
96 Bill Buckner .02 .10
97 LaMarr Hoyt .01 .05
98 Tom Brunansky .02 .10
99 Ron Oester .01 .05
100 Reggie Jackson .50 1.25
101 Ron Davis .01 .05
102 Ken Oberkfell .01 .05
103 Dwayne Murphy .01 .05
104 Jim Slaton .01 .05
Now with Angels
105 Tony Armas .01 .05
106 Ernie Whitt .02 .10
107 Johnnie LeMaster .01 .05
108 Randy Moffitt .01 .05
109 Terry Forster .01 .05
110 Ron Guidry .02 .10
111 Bill Virdon MG .01 .05
112 Doyle Alexander .01 .05
113 Lonnie Smith .01 .05
114 Checklist 1-132 .01 .05
115 Andre Thornton .01 .05
116 Jeff Reardon .02 .10
117 Tom Herr .02 .10
118 Charlie Hough .02 .10
119 Phil Garner .02 .10
120 Keith Hernandez .08 .25
121 Rich Gossage .20 .50
Now with Padres
122 Ted Simmons .02 .10
123 Butch Wynegar .01 .05
124 Damaso Garcia .01 .05
125 Britt Burns .01 .05
126 Bert Blyleven .02 .10
127 Carlton Fisk .20 .50
128 Rick Manning .01 .05
129 Bill Laskey .01 .05
130 Ozzie Smith .75 2.00
131 Bo Diaz .01 .05
132 Tom Paciorek .01 .05
133 Dave Rozema .01 .05
134 Dave Stieb .01 .05
135 Brian Downing .01 .05
136 Rick Camp .01 .05
137 Willie Aikens .02 .10
Now with Blue Jays
138 Charlie Moore .01 .05
139 George Frazier .02 .10
Now with Indians
140 Storm Davis .01 .05
141 Glenn Hoffman .01 .05
142 Charlie Lea .01 .05
143 Mike Vail .01 .05
144 Steve Sax .02 .10
145 Gary Lavelle .01 .05
146 Gorman Thomas .02 .10
Now with Mariners
147 Dan Petry .01 .05
148 Mark Clear .01 .05
149 Dave Beard .02 .10
Now with Mariners
150 Dale Murphy .20 .50
151 Steve Trout .01 .05
152 Tony Pena .02 .10
153 Geoff Zahn .01 .05
154 Dave Henderson .01 .05

155 Frank White .02 .10
156 Dick Ruthven .01 .05
157 Gary Gaetti .08 .25
158 Lance Parrish .02 .10
159 Joe Price .01 .05
160 Mario Soto .01 .05
161 Tug McGraw .08 .25
162 Bob Ojeda .01 .05
163 George Hendrick .01 .05
164 Scott Sanderson .01 .05
Now with Cubs
165 Ken Singleton .01 .05
166 Terry Kennedy .01 .05
167 Gene Garber .01 .05
168 Juan Bonilla .01 .05
169 Larry Parrish .02 .10
170 Jerry Reuss .02 .10
171 John Tudor .02 .10
Now with Pirates
172 Dave Kingman .02 .10
173 Garry Templeton .01 .05
174 Bob Boone .02 .10
175 Graig Nettles .02 .10
176 Lee Smith .20 .50
177 LaMarr Hoyt AS .01 .05
178 Bill Krueger .01 .05
179 Buck Martinez .01 .05
180 Manny Trillo .02 .10
Now with Giants
181 Lou Whitaker AS .02 .10
182 Darryl Strawberry RC 1.25 3.00
183 Neil Allen .01 .05
184 Jim Rice AS .02 .10
185 Sixto Lezcano .01 .05
186 Tom Hume .01 .05
187 Garry Maddox .01 .05
188 Bryan Little .01 .05
189 Jose Cruz .02 .10
190 Ben Oglivie .01 .05
191 Cesar Cedeno .02 .10
192 Nick Esasky .01 .05
193 Ken Forsch .01 .05
194 Jim Palmer .20 .50
195 Jack Morris .02 .10
196 Steve Howe .01 .05
197 Harold Baines .02 .10
198 Bill Doran .02 .10
199 Willie Hernandez .02 .10
200 Andre Dawson .20 .50
201 Bruce Kison .01 .05
202 Bobby Cox MG .01 .05
203 Matt Keough .01 .05
204 Ron Guidry AS .02 .10
205 Greg Minton .01 .05
206 Al Holland .01 .05
207 Luis Leal .01 .05
208 Jose Oquendo RC .01 .05
209 Leon Durham .01 .05
210 Joe Morgan .30 .75
Now with Athletics
211 Lou Whitaker .02 .10
212 George Brett 1.25 3.00
213 Bruce Hurst .01 .05
214 Steve Carlton .40 1.00
215 Tippy Martinez .01 .05
216 Ken Landreaux .01 .05
217 Alan Ashby .01 .05
218 Dennis Eckersley .20 .50
219 Craig McMurtry .01 .05
220 Fernando Valenzuela .02 .10
221 Cliff Johnson .01 .05
222 Rick Honeycutt .01 .05
223 George Brett AS .60 1.50
224 Rusty Staub .02 .10
225 Lee Mazzilli .01 .05
226 Pat Putnam .01 .05
227 Bob Welch .02 .10
228 Rick Cerone .01 .05
229 Lee Lacy .01 .05
230 Rickey Henderson .75 2.00
231 Gary Redus .01 .05
232 Tim Wallach .02 .10
233 Checklist 133-264 .01 .05
234 Rafael Ramirez .01 .05
235 Matt Young RC .01 .05
236 Ellis Valentine .01 .05
237 John Castino .01 .05
238 Eric Show .01 .05
239 Bob Horner .01 .05
240 Eddie Murray .50 1.25
241 Billy Almon .01 .05
242 Greg Brock .01 .05
243 Bruce Sutter .02 .10
244 Dwight Evans .02 .10
245 Rick Sutcliffe .02 .10
246 Terry Crowley .01 .05
247 Fred Lynn .02 .10
248 Bill Dawley .01 .05
249 Dave Stapleton .01 .05
250 Bill Madlock .01 .05
251 Jim Sundberg .02 .10
Now with Brewers
252 Steve Yeager .01 .05
253 Jim Wohlford .01 .05
254 Shane Rawley .01 .05
255 Bruce Benedict .01 .05
256 Dave Geisel .01 .05
Now with Mariners
257 Julio Cruz .01 .05
258 Luis Sanchez .01 .05
259 Von Hayes .01 .05
260 Scott McGregor .01 .05
261 Tom Seaver .75 2.00
Now with White Sox
262 Doug Flynn .01 .05
263 Wayne Gross .01 .05
Now with Orioles
264 Larry Gura .01 .05
265 John Montefusco .01 .05
266 Dave Winfield AS .20 .50
267 Tim Lollar .01 .05
268 Ron Washington .01 .05
269 Mickey Rivers .01 .05
270 Mookie Wilson .02 .10
271 Moose Haas .01 .05
272 Rick Dempsey .02 .10
273 Dan Quisenberry .01 .05
274 Steve Henderson .01 .05
275 Len Matuszek .01 .05
276 Frank Tanana .02 .10
277 Dave Righetti .01 .05
278 Jorge Bell .08 .25
279 Ivan DeJesus .01 .05
280 Floyd Bannister .01 .05
281 Dale Murray .01 .05
282 Andre Robertson .01 .05
283 Rollie Fingers .20 .50
284 Tommy John .08 .25
285 Darrell Porter .01 .05
286 Lary Sorensen .02 .10
Now with Athletics
287 Warren Cromartie .02 .10
Now playing in Japan
288 Jim Beattie .01 .05
289 Blue Jays Leaders .02 .10
Lloyd Moseby
Dave Stieb
(Team checklist back)
290 Dave Dravecky .02 .10
291 Eddie Murray AS .20 .50
292 Greg Bargar .01 .05
293 Tom Underwood .02 .10
Now with Orioles
294 U.L. Washington .01 .05
295 Mike Flanagan .01 .05
296 Rich Gedman .01 .05
297 Bruce Berenyi .01 .05
298 Jim Gantner .02 .10
299 Bill Caudill .02 .10
Now with Athletics
300 Pete Rose 1.00 2.50
Now with Expos
301 Steve Kemp .01 .05
302 Barry Bonnell .02 .10
Now with Mariners
303 Joel Youngblood .01 .05
304 Rick Langford .01 .05
305 Roy Smalley .01 .05
306 Ken Griffey .02 .10
307 Al Oliver .02 .10
308 Ron Hassey .01 .05
309 Len Barker .01 .05
310 Willie McGee .08 .25
311 Jerry Koosman .02 .10
Now with Phillies
312 Jorge Orta .02 .10
Now with Royals
313 Pete Vuckovich .01 .05
314 George Wright .01 .05
315 Bob Grich .02 .10
316 Jesse Barfield .02 .10
317 Willie Upshaw .01 .05
318 Bill Gullickson .01 .05
319 Ray Burris .02 .10
Now with Athletics
320 Bob Stanley .01 .05
321 Ray Knight .01 .05
322 Ken Schrom .01 .05
323 Johnny Ray .01 .05
324 Brian Giles .01 .05
325 Darrell Evans .02 .10
Now with Tigers
326 Mike Caldwell .01 .05
327 Ruppert Jones .01 .05
328 Chris Speier .01 .05
329 Bobby Castillo .01 .05
330 John Candelaria .01 .05
331 Bucky Dent .02 .10
332 Expos Leaders .02 .10
Al Oliver
Charlie Lea
(Team checklist back)
333 Larry Herndon .01 .05
334 Chuck Rainey .01 .05
335 Don Baylor .02 .10
336 Bob James .01 .05
337 Jim Clancy .01 .05
338 Duane Kuiper .01 .05
339 Roy Lee Jackson .01 .05
340 Hal McRae .02 .10
341 Larry McWilliams .01 .05
342 Tim Foli .02 .10
Now with Yankees
343 Fergie Jenkins .20 .50
344 Dickie Thon .01 .05
345 Kent Hrbek .08 .25
346 Larry Bowa .02 .10
347 Buddy Bell .02 .10
348 Toby Harrah .02 .10
Now with Yankees
349 Dan Ford .01 .05
350 George Foster .02 .10
351 Lou Piniella .02 .10
352 Dave Stewart .20 .50
353 Mike Easler .02 .10
Now with Red Sox
354 Jeff Burroughs .01 .05
355 Jason Thompson .01 .05
356 Glenn Abbott .01 .05
357 Ron Cey .02 .10
358 Bob Dernier .01 .05
359 Jim Acker .01 .05
360 Willie Randolph .02 .10
361 Mike Schmidt .60 1.50
362 David Green .01 .05
363 Cal Ripken 2.50 6.00
364 Jim Rice .02 .10
365 Steve Bedrosian .01 .05
366 Gary Carter .20 .50
367 Chili Davis .02 .10
368 Hubie Brooks .01 .05
369 Steve McCatty .01 .05
370 Tim Raines .20 .50
371 Joaquin Andujar .01 .05
372 Gary Roenicke .01 .05
373 Ron Kittle .01 .05
374 Rich Dauer .01 .05
375 Dennis Leonard .01 .05
376 Rick Burleson .01 .05
377 Eric Rasmussen .01 .05
378 Dave Winfield .20 .50
379 Checklist 265-396 .01 .05
380 Steve Garvey .08 .25
381 Jack Clark .02 .10
382 Odell Jones .01 .05
383 Terry Puhl .01 .05
384 Joe Niekro .02 .10
385 Tony Perez .30 .75
Now with Reds
386 George Hendrick AS .01 .05
387 Johnny Ray AS .01 .05
388 Mike Schmidt AS .20 .50
389 Ozzie Smith AS .40 1.00
390 Tim Raines AS .08 .25
391 Dale Murphy AS .08 .25
392 Andre Dawson AS .08 .25
393 Gary Carter AS .02 .10
394 Steve Rogers AS .01 .05
395 Steve Carlton AS .20 .50
396 Jesse Orosco AS .01 .05

1985 O-Pee-Chee

This set is an abridgement of the 1985 Topps set. The 396 standard-size cards comprising the 1985 O-Pee-Chee set differ from the cards of the 1985 Topps set by having a higher ratio of cards of players from the two Canadian teams, a practice begun by O-Pee-Chee in 1977 and continued to 1988. The set contains virtually the same pictures for the players also featured in the 1985 Topps issue. The fronts feature white-bordered color player photos. The player's name, position and team name and logo appear at the bottom of the photo. The green and white horizontal backs carry the player's name and biography at the top. The player's major league statistics and bilingual profile follow below. A bilingual trivia question and answer round out the back. The O-Pee-Chee logo appears on the front of every card. Notable Rookie Cards include Dwight Gooden and Kirby Puckett.

COMPLETE SET (396) 10.00 25.00
1 Tom Seaver .20 .50
2 Gary Lavelle .02 .10
Traded to Blue Jays 1-26-85
3 Tim Wallach .02 .10
4 Jim Wohlford .01 .05
5 Jeff Robinson .01 .05
6 Willie Wilson .01 .05
7 Cliff Johnson .02 .10
Free Agent with Rangers 12-20-84
8 Willie Randolph .02 .10
9 Larry Herndon .01 .05
10 Kirby Puckett RC 3.00 8.00
11 Mookie Wilson .02 .10
12 Dave Lopes .02 .10
Traded to Cubs 8-31-84
13 Tim Lollar .02 .10
Traded to White Sox 12-6-84
14 Chris Bando .01 .05
15 Jerry Koosman .02 .10
16 Bobby Meacham .01 .05
17 Mike Scott .01 .05
18 Rich Gedman .01 .05
19 George Frazier .01 .05
20 Chet Lemon .01 .05
21 Dave Concepcion .02 .10
22 Jason Thompson .01 .05
23 Bret Saberhagen RC* .40 1.00
24 Jesse Barfield .02 .10
25 Steve Bedrosian .01 .05
26 Roy Smalley .02 .10
Traded to Twins 2-19-85
27 Bruce Berenyi .01 .05
28 Butch Wynegar .01 .05
29 Alan Ashby .01 .05
30 Cal Ripken 1.50 4.00
31 Luis Leal .01 .05
32 Dave Dravecky .02 .10
33 Tito Landrum .01 .05
34 Pedro Guerrero .02 .10
35 Graig Nettles .02 .10
36 Fred Breining .01 .05
37 Roy Lee Jackson .01 .05
38 Steve Henderson .01 .05
39 Gary Pettis UER .02 .10
Photo actually
Lynn Pettis
40 Phil Niekro .20 .50
41 Dwight Gooden RC .75 2.00
42 Luis Sanchez .01 .05
43 Lee Smith .20 .50
44 Dickie Thon .01 .05
45 Greg Minton .01 .05
46 Mike Flanagan .01 .05
47 Bud Black .01 .05
48 Tony Fernandez .20 .50
49 Carlton Fisk .20 .50
50 John Candelaria .01 .05
51 Bob Watson .02 .10
Announced his Retirement
52 Rick Leach .01 .05
53 Rick Rhoden .01 .05
54 Cesar Cedeno .02 .10
55 Frank Tanana .02 .10
56 Larry Bowa .02 .10
57 Willie McGee .02 .10
58 Rich Dauer .01 .05
59 Jorge Bell .02 .10
60 George Hendrick .02 .10
Traded to Pirates 12-12-84
61 Donnie Moore .02 .10
Drafted by Angels 1-24-85
62 Mike Ramsey .01 .05
63 Nolan Ryan 1.25 3.00
64 Mark Bailey .01 .05
65 Bill Buckner .02 .10
66 Jerry Reuss .01 .05
67 Mike Schmidt .40 1.00
68 Von Hayes .01 .05
69 Phil Bradley .02 .10
70 Don Baylor .02 .10
71 Julio Cruz .01 .05
72 Rick Sutcliffe .01 .05
73 Storm Davis .01 .05
74 Mike Krukow .01 .05
75 Willie Upshaw .01 .05
76 Craig Lefferts .01 .05
77 Lloyd Moseby .01 .05
78 Ron Davis .01 .05
79 Rick Mahler .01 .05
80 Keith Hernandez .02 .10
81 Vance Law .02 .10
Traded to Expos 12-7-84
82 Joe Price .01 .05
83 Dennis Lamp .01 .05
84 Gary Ward .01 .05
85 Mike Marshall .01 .05
86 Marvell Wynne .01 .05
87 David Green .01 .05
88 Bryn Smith .01 .05
89 Sixto Lezcano .02 .10
Free Agent with Pirates 1-26-85
90 Rich Gossage .02 .10
91 Jeff Burroughs .02 .10
Purchased by Blue Jays 12-22-84
92 Bobby Brown .01 .05
93 Oscar Gamble .01 .05
94 Rick Dempsey .02 .10
95 Jose Cruz .02 .10
96 Johnny Ray .01 .05
97 Joel Youngblood .01 .05
98 Eddie Whitson .02 .10
Free Agent with 12-28-84
99 Milt Wilcox .01 .05
100 George Brett 1.25 3.00
101 Jim Acker .01 .05
102 Jim Sundberg .02 .10
Traded to Royals 1-18-85
103 Ozzie Virgil .01 .05
104 Mike Fitzgerald .02 .10
Traded to Expos 12-10-84
105 Ron Kittle .01 .05
106 Pascual Perez .01 .05
107 Barry Bonnell .01 .05
108 Lou Whitaker .08 .25
109 Gary Roenicke .01 .05
110 Alejandro Pena .01 .05
111 Doug DeCinces .01 .05
112 Doug Flynn .01 .05
113 Tom Herr .02 .10
114 Bob James .02 .10
Traded to White Sox 12-7-84
115 Rickey Henderson 1.25 3.00
Traded to Yankees 12-8-84
116 Pete Rose .20 .50
117 Greg Gross .01 .05
118 Eric Show .01 .05
119 Buck Martinez .01 .05
120 Steve Kemp .01 .05
Traded to Pirates 12-20-84
121 Checklist 1-132 .01 .05
122 Tom Brunansky .02 .10
123 Dave Kingman .02 .10
124 Garry Templeton .01 .05
125 Kent Tekulve .01 .05
126 Darryl Strawberry .20 .50
127 Mark Gubicza RC .02 .10
128 Ernie Whitt .01 .05
129 Don Robinson .01 .05
130 Al Oliver .02 .10
Traded to Dodgers 2-4-85
131 Mario Soto .01 .05
132 Jeff Leonard .01 .05
133 Andre Dawson .20 .50
134 Bruce Hurst .01 .05
135 Bobby Cox MG CL .01 .05
136 Matt Young .01 .05
137 Bob Forsch .01 .05
138 Ron Darling .02 .10
139 Steve Trout .01 .05
140 Geoff Zahn .01 .05
141 Ken Forsch .01 .05
142 Jerry Willard .01 .05
143 Bill Gullickson .01 .05
144 Mike Mason .01 .05
145 Alvin Davis .02 .10
146 Gary Redus .01 .05
147 Willie Aikens .01 .05
148 Steve Yeager .01 .05
149 Dickie Noles .01 .05
150 Jim Rice .02 .10
151 Moose Haas .01 .05
152 Steve Balboni .01 .05
153 Frank LaCorte .01 .05
154 Angel Salazar .02 .10
Drafted by Cardinals 1-24-85
155 Bob Grich .02 .10
156 Craig Reynolds .01 .05
157 Bill Madlock .02 .10
158 Pat Tabler .01 .05
159 Don Slaught .02 .10
Traded to Rangers 1-18-85
160 Lance Parrish .02 .10
161 Ken Schrom .01 .05
162 Wally Backman .01 .05
163 Dennis Eckersley .20 .50
164 Dave Collins .02 .10
Traded to A's 12-8-84
165 Dusty Baker .08 .25
166 Claudell Washington .01 .05
167 Rick Camp .01 .05
168 Garth Iorg .01 .05
169 Shane Rawley .01 .05
170 George Foster .02 .10
171 Tony Bernazard .01 .05
172 Don Sutton .30 .75
Traded to A's 12-8-84
173 Jerry Remy .01 .05
174 Rick Honeycutt .02 .10
175 Dave Parker .02 .10
176 Buddy Bell .02 .10
177 Steve Garvey .08 .25
178 Miguel Dilone .01 .05
179 Tommy John .08 .25
180 Dave Winfield .20 .50
181 Alan Trammell .08 .25
182 Rollie Fingers .20 .50
183 Larry McWilliams .01 .05
184 Carmen Castillo .01 .05
185 Al Holland .01 .05
186 Jerry Mumphrey .02 .10
187 Chris Chambliss .02 .10
188 Jim Clancy .01 .05
189 Glenn Wilson .02 .10
190 Rusty Staub .02 .10
191 Ozzie Smith .75 2.00
192 Howard Johnson .08 .25
Traded to Mets 12-7-84
193 Jimmy Key RC .20 .50
194 Terry Kennedy .01 .05
195 Glenn Hubbard .01 .05
196 Pete O'Brien .01 .05
197 Keith Moreland .01 .05
198 Eddie Milner .01 .05
199 Dave Engle .01 .05
200 Reggie Jackson .20 .50
201 Burt Hooton .02 .10
Free Agent with Rangers 1-3-85
202 Gorman Thomas .01 .05
203 Larry Parrish .01 .05
204 Bob Stanley .01 .05
205 Steve Rogers .01 .05
206 Phil Garner .01 .05
207 Ed VandeBerg .01 .05
208 Jack Clark .08 .25
Traded to Cardinals 2-1-85
209 Bill Campbell .01 .05
210 Gary Matthews .01 .05
211 Dave Palmer .01 .05
212 Tony Perez .20 .50
213 Sammy Stewart .01 .05
214 John Tudor .02 .10
Traded to Cardinals 12-12-84
215 Bob Brenly .02 .10
216 Jim Gantner .01 .05
217 Bryan Clark .01 .05
218 Doyle Alexander .01 .05
219 Bo Diaz .01 .05
220 Fred Lynn .02 .10
Free Agent with Orioles 12-11-84
221 Eddie Murray .20 .50
222 Hubie Brooks .01 .05
Traded to Expos 12-10-84
223 Tom Hume .01 .05
224 Al Cowens .01 .05
225 Mike Boddicker .01 .05
226 Len Matuszek .01 .05
227 Danny Darwin .02 .10
Traded to Brewers 1-18-85
228 Scott McGregor .01 .05
229 Dave LaPoint .02 .10
Traded to Giants 2-1-85
230 Gary Carter .30 .75
Traded to Mets 12-10-84
231 Joaquin Andujar .01 .05
232 Rafael Ramirez .01 .05
233 Wayne Gross .01 .05
234 Neil Allen .01 .05
235 Garry Maddox .01 .05
236 Mark Thurmond .01 .05
237 Julio Franco .08 .25
238 Ray Burris .02 .10
Traded to Brewers 12-8-84
239 Tim Teufel .01 .05
240 Dave Stieb .01 .05
241 Brett Butler .02 .10
242 Greg Brock .01 .05
243 Barbaro Garbey .01 .05
244 Greg Walker .01 .05
245 Chili Davis .02 .10
246 Darrell Porter .01 .05
247 Tippy Martinez .01 .05
248 Terry Forster .01 .05
249 Harold Baines .08 .25
250 Jesse Orosco .02 .10
251 Brad Gulden .01 .05
252 Mike Hargrove .02 .10
253 Nick Esasky .01 .05
254 Frank Williams .01 .05
255 Lonnie Smith .01 .05
256 Daryl Sconiers .01 .05
257 Bryan Little .02 .10
Traded to White Sox 12-7-84
258 Terry Francona .02 .10
259 Mark Langston RC .20 .50
260 Dave Righetti .02 .10
261 Checklist 133-264 .02 .10
262 Bob Horner .01 .05
263 Mel Hall .01 .05
264 John Shelby .01 .05
265 Juan Samuel .01 .05
266 Frank Viola .02 .10
267 Jim Fanning MG .01 .05
Now Vice President
Player Development and Scouting
268 Dick Ruthven .01 .05
269 Bobby Ramos .01 .05
270 Dan Quisenberry .01 .05
271 Dwight Evans .02 .10
272 Andre Thornton .01 .05
273 Orel Hershiser .75 2.00
274 Ray Knight .01 .05
275 Bill Caudill .02 .10
Traded to Blue Jays 12-8-84
276 Charlie Hough .02 .10
277 Tim Raines .08 .25
278 Mike Squires .01 .05
279 Alex Trevino .01 .05
280 Ron Romanick .01 .05
281 Tom Niedenfuer .01 .05
282 Mike Stenhouse .02 .10
Traded to Twins 1-9-85
283 Terry Puhl .01 .05
284 Hal McRae .01 .05
285 Dan Driessen .01 .05
286 Rudy Law .01 .05
287 Walt Terrell .02 .10
Traded to Tigers 12-7-84
288 Jeff Kunkel .01 .05
289 Bob Knepper .01 .05
290 Cecil Cooper .01 .05
291 Bob Welch .01 .05
292 Frank Pastore .01 .05
293 Dan Schatzeder .01 .05
294 Tom Nieto .01 .05
295 Joe Niekro .01 .05
296 Ryne Sandberg .75 2.00
297 Gary Lucas .01 .05
298 John Castino .01 .05
299 Bill Doran .01 .05
300 Rod Carew .20 .50
301 John Montefusco .01 .05
302 Johnnie LeMaster .01 .05
303 Jim Beattie .01 .05
304 Gary Gaetti .02 .10
305 Dale Berra .01 .05
Traded to Yankees 12-20-84
306 Rick Reuschel .02 .10
307 Ken Oberkfell .01 .05
308 Kent Hrbek .02 .10
309 Mike Witt .01 .05
310 Manny Trillo .01 .05
311 Jim Gott .01 .05
Traded to Giants 1-26-85
312 LaMarr Hoyt .02 .10
Traded to Padres 12-6-84
313 Dave Schmidt .01 .05
314 Ron Oester .01 .05
315 Doug Sisk .01 .05
316 John Lowenstein .01 .05
317 Derrel Thomas .02 .10
Traded to Angels 9-6-84
318 Ted Simmons .02 .10
319 Darrell Evans .02 .10
320 Dale Murphy .08 .25
321 Ricky Horton .01 .05
322 Ken Phelps .01 .05
323 Lee Mazzilli .02 .10
324 Don Mattingly 1.50 4.00
325 John Denny .01 .05
326 Ken Singleton .01 .05
327 Brook Jacoby .01 .05
328 Greg Luzinski .02 .10
Announced his Retirement
329 Bob Ojeda .01 .05
330 Leon Durham .01 .05
331 Bill Laskey .01 .05
332 Ben Oglivie .01 .05
333 Willie Hernandez .01 .05
334 Bob Dernier .01 .05
335 Bruce Benedict .01 .05
336 Rance Mulliniks .01 .05
337 Rick Cerone .02 .10
Traded to Braves 12-6-84
338 Britt Burns .01 .05
339 Danny Heep .01 .05
340 Robin Yount .20 .50
341 Andy Van Slyke .08 .25
342 Curt Wilkerson .01 .05
343 Bill Russell .01 .05
344 Dave Henderson .01 .05
345 Charlie Lea .01 .05
346 Terry Pendleton RC .20 .50
347 Carney Lansford .01 .05
348 Bob Boone .02 .10
349 Mike Easler .01 .05
350 Wade Boggs .40 1.00
351 Atlee Hammaker .01 .05
352 Joe Morgan .20 .50
353 Damaso Garcia .01 .05
354 Floyd Bannister .01 .05
355 Bert Blyleven .02 .10
356 John Butcher .01 .05
357 Fernando Valenzuela .02 .10
358 Tony Pena .02 .10
359 Mike Smithson .01 .05
360 Steve Carlton .20 .50
361 Alfredo Griffin .02 .10
Traded to A's 12-8-84
362 Craig McMurtry .01 .05
363 Bill Dawley .01 .05
364 Richard Dotson .01 .05
365 Carmelo Martinez .01 .05
366 Ron Cey .02 .10
367 Tony Scott .01 .05
368 Dave Bergman .01 .05
369 Steve Sax .01 .05
370 Bruce Sutter .02 .10
371 Mickey Rivers .01 .05
372 Kirk Gibson .02 .10
373 Scott Sanderson .01 .05
374 Brian Downing .01 .05
375 Jeff Reardon .02 .10
376 Frank DiPino .01 .05
377 Checklist 265-396 .01 .05
378 Alan Wiggins .01 .05
379 Charles Hudson .01 .05
380 Ken Griffey .02 .10
381 Tom Paciorek .01 .05
382 Jack Morris .02 .10
383 Tony Gwynn 1.25 3.00
384 Jody Davis .01 .05
385 Jose DeLeon .01 .05
386 Bob Kearney .01 .05
387 George Wright .01 .05
388 Ron Guidry .02 .10
389 Rick Manning .01 .05
390 Sid Fernandez .02 .10
391 Bruce Bochte .01 .05
392 Dan Petry .01 .05
393 Tim Stoddard .02 .10
Free Agent with Padres 1-2-85
394 Tony Armas .01 .05
395 Paul Molitor .20 .50
396 Mike Heath .01 .05

1986 O-Pee-Chee

This set is an abridgement of the 1986 Topps set. The 396 standard-size cards comprising the 1986 O-Pee-Chee set differ from the cards of the 1986 Topps set by having a higher ratio of cards of players from the two Canadian teams, a practice begun by O-Pee-Chee in 1977 and continued to 1988. The fronts feature black-and white-bordered color player photos. The player's name appears within the white margin at the bottom. His team name appears within the black margin at the top and his position appears within a colored circle at the photo's lower left. The red horizontal backs carry the player's name and biography at the top. The player's major league statistics follow below. Some backs also have bilingual career highlights, some have bilingual baseball facts and still others have neither. The asterisked cards have an extra line on the front inside the picture area indicating team change. The O-Pee-Chee logo appears on the front of every card.

COMPLETE SET (396) 4.80 12.00
1 Pete Rose .75 2.00
2 Ken Landreaux .01 .05
3 Rob Picciolo .01 .05
4 Steve Garvey .05 .15
5 Andy Hawkins .01 .05
6 Rudy Law .01 .05
7 Lonnie Smith .01 .05
8 Dwayne Murphy .01 .05
9 Moose Haas .01 .05
10 Tony Gwynn .60 1.50
11 Bob Ojeda .02 .10
Now with Mets
12 Jose Uribe .01 .05
13 Bob Kearney .01 .05
14 Julio Cruz .01 .05
15 Eddie Whitson .01 .05
16 Rick Schu .01 .05
17 Mike Stenhouse .02 .10
Now with Red Sox
18 Lou Thornton .01 .05
19 Ryne Sandberg .30 .75
20 Lou Whitaker .02 .10
21 Mark Brouhard .01 .05
22 Gary Lavelle .01 .05
23 Manny Lee .01 .05
24 Don Slaught .01 .05
25 Willie Wilson .01 .05
26 Mike Marshall .01 .05
27 Ray Knight .01 .05
28 Mario Soto .01 .05
29 Dave Anderson .01 .05
30 Eddie Murray .30 .75
31 Dusty Baker .02 .10
32 Steve Yeager .02 .10
Now with Mariners
33 Andy Van Slyke .02 .10
34 Dave Righetti .01 .05
35 Jeff Reardon .02 .10
36 Burt Hooton .01 .05
37 Johnny Ray .01 .05
38 Glenn Hoffman .01 .05
39 Rick Mahler .01 .05
40 Ken Griffey .02 .10
41 Brad Wellman .01 .05
42 Joe Hesketh .01 .05
43 Mark Salas .01 .05
44 Jorge Orta .01 .05
45 Damaso Garcia .01 .05
46 Jim Acker .01 .05
47 Bill Madlock .02 .10
48 Bill Almon .01 .05
49 Rick Manning .01 .05
50 Dan Quisenberry .01 .05
51 Jim Gantner .01 .05
52 Kevin Bass .01 .05
53 Len Dykstra RC .40 1.00
54 John Franco .05 .15
55 Fred Lynn .02 .10
56 Jim Morrison .01 .05
57 Bill Doran .01 .05
58 Leon Durham .01 .05
59 Andre Thornton .01 .05
60 Dwight Evans .02 .10
61 Larry Herndon .01 .05
62 Bob Boone .02 .10
63 Kent Hrbek .05 .15
64 Floyd Bannister .01 .05
65 Harold Baines .05 .15
66 Pat Tabler .01 .05
67 Carmelo Martinez .01 .05
68 Ed Lynch .01 .05
69 George Foster .02 .10
70 Dave Winfield .15 .40
71 Ken Schrom .01 .05
Now with Indians
72 Toby Harrah .01 .05
73 Jackie Gutierrez .01 .05
Now with Orioles
74 Rance Mulliniks .01 .05
75 Jose DeLeon .01 .05
76 Ron Romanick .01 .05
77 Charlie Leibrandt .01 .05
78 Bruce Benedict .01 .05
79 Dave Schmidt .01 .05
Now with White Sox
80 Darryl Strawberry .05 .15
81 Wayne Krenchicki .01 .05
82 Tippy Martinez .01 .05
83 Phil Garner .02 .10
84 Darrell Porter .02 .10
Now with Rangers
85 Tony Perez .15 .40
Eric Davis also
shown in photo
86 Tom Waddell .01 .05
87 Tim Hulett .01 .05
88 Barbaro Garbey .01 .05
Now with A's
89 Randy St. Claire .01 .05
90 Garry Templeton .01 .05
91 Tim Teufel .02 .10
Now with Mets
92 Al Cowens .01 .05
93 Scot Thompson .01 .05
94 Tom Herr .01 .05
95 Ozzie Virgil .02 .10
Now with Braves
96 Jose Cruz .01 .05
97 Gary Gaetti .02 .10
98 Roger Clemens 2.00 5.00
99 Vance Law .01 .05
100 Nolan Ryan .60 1.50
101 Mike Smithson .01 .05
102 Rafael Santana .01 .05
103 Darrell Evans .02 .10
104 Rich Gossage .08 .25
105 Gary Ward .01 .05
106 Jim Gott .01 .05
107 Rafael Ramirez .01 .05
108 Ted Power .01 .05
109 Ron Guidry .02 .10
110 Scott McGregor .01 .05
111 Mike Scioscia .02 .10
112 Glenn Hubbard .01 .05
113 U.L. Washington .01 .05
114 Al Oliver .02 .10
115 Jay Howell .01 .05
116 Brook Jacoby .01 .05
117 Willie McGee .02 .10
118 Jerry Royster .01 .05
119 Barry Bonnell .01 .05
120 Steve Carlton .15 .40
121 Alfredo Griffin .01 .05
122 David Green .02 .10
Now with Brewers
123 Greg Walker .01 .05

124 Frank Tanana .01 .05
125 Dave Lopes .02 .10
126 Mike Krukow .01 .05
127 Jack Howell .01 .05
128 Greg Harris .01 .05
129 Herm Winningham .01 .05
130 Alan Trammell .05 .15
131 Checklist 1-132 .01 .05
132 Razor Shines .01 .05
133 Bruce Sutter .15 .40
134 Carney Lansford .01 .05
135 Joe Niekro .02 .10
136 Ernie Whitt .01 .05
137 Charlie Moore .01 .05
138 Mel Hall .01 .05
139 Roger McDowell .01 .05
140 John Candelaria .01 .05
141 Bob Rodgers MG CL .01 .05
142 Manny Trillo .02 .10
Now with Cubs
143 Dave Palmer .02 .10
Now with Braves
144 Robin Yount .08 .25
145 Pedro Guerrero .02 .10
146 Von Hayes .01 .05
147 Lance Parrish .02 .10
148 Mike Heath .02 .10
Now with Cardinals
149 Brett Butler .02 .10
150 Joaquin Andujar .02 .10
Now with A's
151 Graig Nettles .02 .10
152 Pete Vuckovich .01 .05
153 Jason Thompson .01 .05
154 Bert Roberge .01 .05
155 Bob Grich .02 .10
156 Roy Smalley .01 .05
157 Ron Hassey .01 .05
158 Bob Stanley .01 .05
159 Orel Hershiser .15 .40
160 Chet Lemon .01 .05
161 Terry Puhl .01 .05
162 Dave LaPoint .02 .10
Now with Tigers
163 Onix Concepcion .01 .05
164 Steve Balboni .01 .05
165 Mike Davis .01 .05
166 Dickie Thon .01 .05
167 Zane Smith .01 .05
168 Jeff Burroughs .01 .05
169 Alex Trevino .02 .10
Now with Dodgers
170 Gary Carter .15 .40
171 Tito Landrum .01 .05
172 Sammy Stewart .02 .10
Now with Red Sox
173 Wayne Gross .01 .05
174 Britt Burns .02 .10
Now with Yankees
175 Steve Sax .01 .05
176 Jody Davis .01 .05
177 Joel Youngblood .01 .05
178 Fernando Valenzuela .02 .10
179 Storm Davis .01 .05
180 Don Mattingly .50 1.25
181 Steve Bedrosian .02 .10
Now with Phillies
182 Jesse Orosco .02 .10
183 Gary Roenicke .02 .10
Now with Yankees
184 Don Baylor .02 .10
185 Rollie Fingers .15 .40
186 Ruppert Jones .01 .05
187 Scott Fletcher .02 .10
Now with Rangers
188 Bob Dernier .01 .05
189 Mike Mason .01 .05
190 George Hendrick .01 .05
191 Wally Backman .01 .05
192 Oddibe McDowell .01 .05
193 Bruce Hurst .01 .05
194 Ron Cey .02 .10
195 Dave Concepcion .02 .10
196 Doyle Alexander .01 .05
197 Dale Murphy .20 .50
198 Mark Langston .02 .10
199 Dennis Eckersley .15 .40
200 Mike Schmidt .15 .40
201 Nick Esasky .01 .05
202 Ken Dayley .01 .05
203 Rick Cerone .01 .05
204 Larry McWilliams .01 .05
205 Brian Downing .01 .05
206 Danny Darwin .01 .05
207 Bill Caudill .01 .05
208 Dave Rozema .01 .05
209 Eric Show .01 .05
210 Brad Komminsk .01 .05
211 Chris Bando .01 .05
212 Chris Speier .01 .05
213 Jim Clancy .01 .05
214 Randy Bush .01 .05
215 Frank White .02 .10
216 Dan Petry .01 .05
217 Tim Wallach .01 .05
218 Mitch Webster .01 .05
219 Dennis Lamp .01 .05
220 Bob Horner .01 .05
221 Dave Henderson .01 .05
222 Dave Smith .01 .05
223 Willie Upshaw .01 .05
224 Cesar Cedeno .02 .10
225 Ron Darling .01 .05
226 Lee Lacy .01 .05
227 John Tudor .01 .05
228 Jim Presley .01 .05
229 Bill Gullickson .02 .10
Now with Reds
230 Terry Kennedy .01 .05
231 Bob Knepper .01 .05
232 Rick Rhoden .01 .05
233 Richard Dotson .01 .05
234 Jesse Barfield .01 .05
235 Butch Wynegar .01 .05
236 Jerry Reuss .02 .10
237 Juan Samuel .01 .05
238 Larry Parrish .01 .05
239 Bill Buckner .02 .10
240 Pat Sheridan .01 .05
241 Tony Fernandez .05 .15
242 Rich Thompson .01 .05
Now with Brewers
243 Rickey Henderson .20 .50
244 Craig Lefferts .01 .05
245 Jim Sundberg .01 .05
246 Phil Niekro .15 .40
247 Terry Harper .01 .05
248 Spike Owen .01 .05
249 Bret Saberhagen .08 .25
250 Dwight Gooden .08 .25
251 Rich Dauer .01 .05
252 Keith Hernandez .02 .10
253 Bo Diaz .01 .05
254 Ozzie Guillen RC .60 1.50
255 Tony Armas .01 .05
256 Andre Dawson .08 .25
257 Doug DeCinces .01 .05
258 Tim Burke .01 .05
259 Dennis Boyd .01 .05
260 Tony Pena .01 .05
261 Sal Butera .02 .10
Now with Reds
262 Wade Boggs .30 .75
263 Checklist 133-264 .01 .05
264 Ron Oester .01 .05
265 Ron Davis .01 .05
266 Keith Moreland .01 .05
267 Paul Molitor .20 .50
268 John Denny .02 .10
Now with Reds
269 Frank Viola .02 .10
270 Jack Morris .02 .10
271 Dave Collins .02 .10
Now with Tigers
272 Bert Blyleven .02 .10
273 Jerry Willard .01 .05
274 Matt Young .01 .05
275 Charlie Hough .02 .10
276 Dave Dravecky .02 .10
277 Garth Iorg .01 .05
278 Hal McRae .01 .05
279 Curt Wilkerson .01 .05
280 Tim Raines .02 .10
281 Bill Laskey .02 .10
Now with Giants
282 Jerry Mumphrey .02 .10
Now with Cubs
283 Pat Clements .01 .05
284 Bob James .01 .05
285 Buddy Bell .02 .10
286 Tom Brookens .01 .05
287 Dave Parker .02 .10
288 Ron Kittle .01 .05
289 Johnnie LeMaster .01 .05
290 Carlton Fisk .15 .40
291 Jimmy Key .05 .15
292 Gary Matthews .01 .05
293 Marvell Wynne .01 .05
294 Danny Cox .01 .05
295 Kirk Gibson .02 .10
296 Mariano Duncan RC .05 .15
297 Ozzie Smith .40 1.00
298 Craig Reynolds .01 .05
299 Bryn Smith .01 .05
300 George Brett .40 1.00
301 Walt Terrell .01 .05
302 Greg Gross .01 .05
303 Claudell Washington .01 .05
304 Howard Johnson .02 .10
305 Phil Bradley .01 .05
306 R.J. Reynolds .01 .05
307 Bob Brenly .01 .05
308 Hubie Brooks .01 .05
309 Alvin Davis .01 .05
310 Donnie Hill .01 .05
311 Dick Schofield .01 .05
312 Tom Filer .01 .05
313 Mike Fitzgerald .01 .05
314 Marty Barrett .01 .05
315 Mookie Wilson .02 .10
316 Alan Knicely .01 .05
317 Ed Romero .01 .05
Now with Red Sox
318 Glenn Wilson .01 .05
319 Bud Black .01 .05
320 Jim Rice .02 .10
321 Terry Pendleton .05 .15
322 Dave Kingman .02 .10
323 Gary Pettis .01 .05
324 Dan Schatzeder .01 .05
325 Juan Beniquez .02 .10
Now with Orioles
326 Kent Tekulve .01 .05
327 Mike Pagliarulo .01 .05
328 Pete O'Brien .01 .05
329 Kirby Puckett .75 2.00
330 Rick Sutcliffe .01 .05
331 Alan Ashby .01 .05
332 Willie Randolph .02 .10
333 Tom Henke .02 .10
334 Ken Oberkfell .01 .05
335 Don Sutton .15 .40
336 Dan Gladden .01 .05
337 George Vukovich .01 .05
338 Jorge Bell .02 .10
339 Jim Dwyer .01 .05
340 Cal Ripken .60 1.50
341 Willie Hernandez .01 .05
342 Gary Redus .02 .10
Now with Phillies
343 Jerry Koosman .02 .10
344 Jim Wohlford .01 .05
345 Donnie Moore .01 .05
346 Floyd Youmans .01 .05
347 Gorman Thomas .01 .05
348 Cliff Johnson .01 .05
349 Ken Howell .01 .05
350 Jack Clark .02 .10
351 Gary Lucas .02 .10
Now with Angels
352 Bob Clark .01 .05
353 Dave Stieb .01 .05
354 Tony Bernazard .01 .05
355 Lee Smith .08 .25
356 Mickey Hatcher .01 .05
357 Ed VandeBerg .02 .10
Now with Dodgers
358 Rick Dempsey .01 .05
359 Bobby Cox MG CL .02 .10
Now General Manager of Atlanta Braves
360 Lloyd Moseby .01 .05
361 Shane Rawley .01 .05
362 Garry Maddox .01 .05
363 Buck Martinez .02 .10
364 Ed Nunez .01 .05
365 Luis Leal .01 .05
366 Dale Berra .01 .05
367 Mike Boddicker .01 .05
368 Greg Brock .01 .05
369 Al Holland .01 .05
370 Vince Coleman RC .08 .25
371 Rod Carew .15 .40
372 Ben Oglivie .01 .05
373 Lee Mazzilli .01 .05
374 Terry Francona .02 .10
375 Rich Gedman .01 .05
376 Charlie Lea .01 .05
377 Joe Carter .40 1.00
378 Bruce Bochte .01 .05
379 Bobby Meacham .01 .05
380 LaMarr Hoyt .01 .05
381 Jeff Leonard .01 .05
382 Ivan Calderon RC .02 .10
383 Chris Brown RC .01 .05
384 Steve Trout .01 .05
385 Cecil Cooper .02 .10
386 Cecil Fielder RC .60 1.50
387 Tim Flannery .01 .05
388 Chris Codiroli .01 .05
389 Glenn Davis .01 .05
390 Tom Seaver .15 .40
391 Julio Franco .05 .15
392 Tom Brunansky .01 .05
393 Rob Wilfong .01 .05
394 Reggie Jackson .15 .40
395 Scott Garrelts .01 .05
396 Checklist 265-396 .01 .05

1987 O-Pee-Chee

This set is an abridgement of the 1987 Topps set. The 396 standard-size cards comprising the 1987 O-Pee-Chee set differ from the cards of the 1987 Topps set by having a higher ratio of cards of players from the two Canadian teams, a practice begun by O-Pee-Chee in 1977 and continued to 1988. The fronts feature wood grain bordered color player photos. The player's name appears in the colored rectangle at the lower right. His team logo appears at the upper left. The yellow, white and blue horizontal backs carry the player's name and bilingual position at the top. The player's major league statistics follow below. Some backs also have bilingual career highlights, some have bilingual baseball facts and still others have both or neither. The asterisked cards have an extra line on the front inside the picture area indicating team change. The O-Pee-Chee logo appears on the front of every card. Notable Rookie Cards include Barry Bonds.

COMPLETE SET (396) 6.00 15.00
1 Ken Oberkfell .01 .05
2 Jack Howell .01 .05
3 Hubie Brooks .01 .05
4 Bob Grich .02 .10
5 Rick Leach .01 .05
6 Phil Niekro .15 .40
7 Rickey Henderson .20 .50
8 Terry Pendleton .02 .10
9 Jay Tibbs .01 .05
10 Cecil Cooper .02 .10
11 Mario Soto .01 .05
12 George Bell .01 .05
13 Nick Esasky .01 .05
14 Larry McWilliams .01 .05
15 Dan Quisenberry .01 .05
16 Ed Lynch .01 .05
17 Pete O'Brien .01 .05
18 Luis Aguayo .01 .05
19 Matt Young .02 .10
Now with Dodgers
20 Gary Carter .15 .40
21 Tom Paciorek .01 .05
22 Doug DeCinces .01 .05
23 Lee Smith .05 .15
24 Jesse Barfield .01 .05
25 Bert Blyleven .02 .10
26 Greg Brock .02 .10
Now with Brewers
27 Dan Petry .01 .05
28 Rick Dempsey .02 .10
Now with Indians
29 Jimmy Key .05 .15
30 Tim Raines .02 .10
31 Bruce Hurst .01 .05
32 Manny Trillo .01 .05
33 Andy Van Slyke .02 .10
34 Ed VandeBerg .02 .10
Now with Indians
35 Sid Bream .01 .05
36 Dave Winfield .15 .40
37 Scott Garrelts .01 .05
38 Dennis Leonard .01 .05
39 Marty Barrett .01 .05
40 Dave Righetti .01 .05
41 Bo Diaz .01 .05
42 Gary Redus .01 .05
43 Tom Niedenfuer .01 .05
44 Greg Harris .01 .05
45 Jim Presley .01 .05
46 Danny Gladden .01 .05
47 Roy Smalley .01 .05
48 Wally Backman .01 .05
49 Tom Seaver .15 .40
50 Dave Smith .01 .05
51 Mel Hall .01 .05
52 Tim Flannery .01 .05
53 Julio Cruz .01 .05
54 Dick Schofield .01 .05
55 Tim Wallach .01 .05
56 Glenn Davis .01 .05
57 Darren Daulton .05 .15
58 Chico Walker .01 .05
59 Garth Iorg .01 .05
60 Tony Pena .01 .05
61 Ron Hassey .01 .05
62 Dave Dravecky .01 .05
63 Jorge Orta .01 .05
64 Al Nipper .01 .05
65 Tom Browning .01 .05
66 Marc Sullivan .01 .05
67 Todd Worrell .02 .10
68 Glenn Hubbard .01 .05
69 Carney Lansford .02 .10
70 Charlie Hough .01 .05
71 Lance McCullers .01 .05
72 Walt Terrell .01 .05
73 Bob Kearney .01 .05
74 Dan Pasqua .01 .05
75 Ron Darling .01 .05
76 Robin Yount .15 .40
77 Pat Tabler .01 .05
78 Tom Foley .01 .05
79 Juan Nieves .01 .05
80 Wally Joyner RC .20 .50
81 Wayne Krenchicki .01 .05
82 Kirby Puckett .30 .75
83 Bob Ojeda .01 .05
84 Mookie Wilson .02 .10
85 Kevin Bass .01 .05
86 Kent Tekulve .01 .05
87 Mark Salas .01 .05
88 Brian Downing .01 .05
89 Ozzie Guillen .02 .10
90 Dave Stieb .02 .10
91 Rance Mulliniks .01 .05
92 Mike Witt .01 .05
93 Charlie Moore .01 .05
94 Jose Uribe .01 .05
95 Oddibe McDowell .01 .05
96 Ray Soff .01 .05
97 Glenn Wilson .01 .05
98 Brook Jacoby .01 .05
99 Darryl Motley .02 .10
Now with Braves
100 Steve Garvey .05 .15
101 Frank White .02 .10
102 Mike Moore .01 .05
103 Rick Aguilera .02 .10
104 Buddy Bell .02 .10
105 Floyd Youmans .01 .05
106 Lou Whitaker .02 .10
107 Ozzie Smith .30 .75
108 Jim Gantner .01 .05
109 R.J. Reynolds .01 .05
110 John Tudor .01 .05
111 Alfredo Griffin .01 .05
112 Mike Flanagan .01 .05
113 Neil Allen .01 .05
114 Ken Griffey .02 .10
115 Donnie Moore .01 .05
116 Bob Horner .01 .05
117 Ron Shepherd .01 .05
118 Cliff Johnson .01 .05
119 Vince Coleman .01 .05
120 Eddie Murray .15 .40
121 Dwayne Murphy .01 .05
122 Jim Clancy .01 .05
123 Ken Landreaux .01 .05
124 Tom Nieto .02 .10
Now with Twins
125 Bob Brenly .01 .05
126 George Brett .30 .75
127 Vance Law .01 .05
128 Checklist 1-132 .01 .05
129 Bob Knepper .01 .05
130 Dwight Gooden .05 .15
131 Juan Bonilla .01 .05
132 Tim Burke .01 .05
133 Bob McClure .01 .05
134 Scott Bailes .01 .05
135 Mike Easler .02 .10
Now with Phillies
136 Ron Romanick .02 .10
Now with Yankees
137 Rich Gedman .01 .05
138 Bob Dernier .01 .05
139 John Denny .01 .05
140 Bret Saberhagen .02 .10
141 Herm Winningham .01 .05
142 Rick Sutcliffe .01 .05
143 Ryne Sandberg .15 .40
144 Mike Scioscia .02 .10
145 Charlie Kerfeld .01 .05
146 Jim Rice .02 .10
147 Steve Trout .01 .05
148 Jesse Orosco .02 .10
149 Mike Boddicker .01 .05
150 Wade Boggs .15 .40
151 Dane Iorg .01 .05
152 Rick Burleson .02 .10
Now with Orioles
153 Duane Ward RC .02 .10
154 Rick Reuschel .01 .05
155 Nolan Ryan .60 1.50
156 Bill Caudill .01 .05
157 Danny Darwin .01 .05
158 Ed Romero .01 .05
159 Bill Almon .01 .05
160 Julio Franco .02 .10
161 Kent Hrbek .02 .10
162 Chili Davis .05 .15
163 Kevin Gross .01 .05
164 Carlton Fisk .15 .40
165 Jeff Reardon .05 .15
Now with Twins
166 Bob Boone .02 .10
167 Rick Honeycutt .01 .05
168 Dan Schatzeder .01 .05
169 Jim Wohlford .01 .05
170 Phil Bradley .01 .05
171 Ken Schrom .01 .05
172 Ron Oester .01 .05
173 Juan Beniquez .02 .10
Now with Royals
174 Tony Armas .01 .05
175 Bob Stanley .01 .05
176 Steve Buechele .01 .05
177 Keith Moreland .01 .05
178 Cecil Fielder .05 .15
179 Gary Gaetti .02 .10
180 Chris Brown .01 .05
181 Tom Herr .01 .05
182 Lee Lacy .01 .05
183 Ozzie Virgil .01 .05
184 Paul Molitor .15 .40
185 Roger McDowell .01 .05
186 Mike Marshall .01 .05
187 Ken Howell .01 .05
188 Rob Deer .01 .05
189 Joe Hesketh .01 .05
190 Jim Sundberg .01 .05
191 Kelly Gruber .01 .05
192 Cory Snyder .01 .05
193 Dave Concepcion .02 .10
194 Kirk McCaskill .01 .05
195 Mike Pagliarulo .01 .05
196 Rick Manning .01 .05
197 Brett Butler .02 .10
198 Tony Gwynn .50 1.25
199 Mariano Duncan .01 .05
200 Pete Rose .15 .40
201 John Cangelosi .01 .05
202 Danny Cox .01 .05
203 Butch Wynegar .02 .10
Now with Angels
204 Chris Chambliss .02 .10
205 Graig Nettles .02 .10
206 Chet Lemon .01 .05
207 Don Aase .01 .05
208 Mike Mason .01 .05
209 Alan Trammell .05 .15
210 Lloyd Moseby .01 .05
211 Richard Dotson .01 .05
212 Mike Fitzgerald .01 .05
213 Darrell Porter .01 .05
214 Checklist 265-396 .01 .05
215 Mark Langston .01 .05
216 Steve Farr .01 .05
217 Dann Bilardello .01 .05
218 Gary Ward .02 .10
Now with Yankees
219 Cecilio Guante .02 .10
Now with Yankees
220 Joe Carter .08 .25
221 Ernie Whitt .01 .05
222 Denny Walling .01 .05
223 Charlie Leibrandt .01 .05
224 Wayne Tolleson .01 .05
225 Mike Smithson .01 .05
226 Zane Smith .01 .05
227 Terry Puhl .01 .05
228 Eric Davis .05 .15
229 Don Mattingly .30 .75
230 Don Baylor .02 .10
231 Frank Tanana .01 .05
232 Tom Brookens .01 .05
233 Steve Bedrosian .01 .05
234 Wallace Johnson .01 .05
235 Alvin Davis .01 .05
236 Tommy John .02 .10
237 Jim Morrison .01 .05
238 Ricky Horton .01 .05
239 Shane Rawley .01 .05
240 Steve Balboni .01 .05
241 Mike Krukow .01 .05
242 Rick Mahler .01 .05
243 Bill Doran .01 .05
244 Mark Clear .01 .05
245 Willie Upshaw .01 .05
246 Hal McRae .01 .05
247 Jose Canseco .60 1.50
248 George Hendrick .01 .05
249 Doyle Alexander .01 .05
250 Teddy Higuera .01 .05
251 Tom Hume .01 .05
252 Denny Martinez .02 .10
253 Eddie Milner .02 .10
Now with Giants
254 Steve Sax .01 .05
255 Juan Samuel .01 .05
256 Dave Bergman .01 .05
257 Bob Forsch .01 .05
258 Steve Yeager .01 .05
259 Don Sutton .15 .40
260 Vida Blue .05 .15
Now with A's
261 Tom Brunansky .01 .05
262 Joe Sambito .01 .05
263 Mitch Webster .01 .05
264 Checklist 133-264 .01 .05
265 Darrell Evans .02 .10
266 Dave Kingman .02 .10
267 Howard Johnson .01 .05
268 Greg Pryor .01 .05
269 Tippy Martinez .01 .05
270 Jody Davis .01 .05
271 Steve Carlton .15 .40
272 Andres Galarraga .20 .50
273 Fernando Valenzuela .02 .10
274 Jeff Hearron .01 .05
275 Ray Knight .02 .10
Now with Orioles
276 Bill Madlock .02 .10
277 Tom Henke .01 .05
278 Gary Pettis .01 .05
279 Jimy Williams MG CL .01 .05
280 Jeffrey Leonard .01 .05
281 Bryn Smith .01 .05
282 John Cerutti .01 .05
283 Gary Roenicke .02 .10
Now with Braves
284 Joaquin Andujar .01 .05
285 Dennis Boyd .01 .05
286 Tim Hulett .01 .05
287 Craig Lefferts .01 .05
288 Tito Landrum .01 .05
289 Manny Lee .01 .05
290 Leon Durham .01 .05
291 Johnny Ray .01 .05
292 Franklin Stubbs .01 .05
293 Bob Rodgers MG CL .01 .05
294 Terry Francona .02 .10
295 Len Dykstra .05 .15
296 Tom Candiotti .01 .05
297 Frank DiPino .01 .05
298 Craig Reynolds .01 .05
299 Jerry Hairston .01 .05
300 Reggie Jackson .20 .50
Now with A's
301 Luis Aquino .01 .05
302 Greg Walker .01 .05
303 Terry Kennedy .02 .10
Now with Orioles
304 Phil Garner .02 .10
305 John Franco .02 .10
306 Bill Buckner .02 .10
307 Kevin Mitchell RC .08 .25
Now with Padres
308 Don Slaught .01 .05
309 Harold Baines .02 .10
310 Frank Viola .01 .05
311 Dave Lopes .02 .10
312 Cal Ripken .60 1.50
313 John Candelaria .01 .05
314 Bob Sebra .01 .05
315 Bud Black .01 .05
316 Brian Fisher .02 .10
Now with Pirates
317 Clint Hurdle .02 .10
318 Earnest Riles .01 .05
319 Dave LaPoint .02 .10
Now with Cardinals
320 Barry Bonds RC 4.00 10.00
321 Tim Stoddard .01 .05
322 Ron Cey .05 .15
Now with A's
323 Al Newman .01 .05
324 Jerry Royster .02 .10
Now with White Sox
325 Garry Templeton .01 .05
326 Mark Gubicza .01 .05
327 Andre Thornton .01 .05
328 Bob Welch .02 .10
329 Tony Fernandez .02 .10
330 Mike Scott .01 .05
331 Jack Clark .02 .10
332 Danny Tartabull .02 .10
Now with Royals
333 Greg Minton .01 .05
334 Ed Correa .01 .05
335 Candy Maldonado .01 .05
336 Dennis Lamp .02 .10
Now with Indians
337 Sid Fernandez .01 .05
338 Greg Gross .01 .05
339 Willie Hernandez .01 .05
340 Roger Clemens .50 1.25
341 Mickey Hatcher .01 .05
342 Bob James .01 .05
343 Jose Cruz .02 .10
344 Bruce Sutter .15 .40
345 Andre Dawson .08 .25
346 Shawon Dunston .01 .05
347 Scott McGregor .01 .05
348 Carmelo Martinez .01 .05
349 Storm Davis .02 .10
Now with Padres
350 Keith Hernandez .02 .10
351 Andy McGaffigan .01 .05
352 Dave Parker .02 .10
353 Ernie Camacho .01 .05
354 Eric Show .01 .05
355 Don Carman .01 .05
356 Floyd Bannister .01 .05
357 Willie McGee .02 .10
358 Atlee Hammaker .01 .05
359 Dale Murphy .08 .25
360 Pedro Guerrero .01 .05
361 Will Clark RC .40 1.00
362 Bill Campbell .01 .05
363 Alejandro Pena .01 .05
364 Dennis Rasmussen .01 .05
365 Rick Rhoden .02 .10
Now with Yankees
366 Randy St. Claire .01 .05
367 Willie Wilson .02 .10
368 Dwight Evans .02 .10
369 Moose Haas .01 .05
370 Fred Lynn .02 .10
371 Mark Eichhorn .01 .05
372 Dave Schmidt .02 .10
Now with Orioles
373 Jerry Reuss .01 .05
374 Lance Parrish .02 .10
375 Ron Guidry .02 .10
376 Jack Morris .02 .10
377 Willie Randolph .02 .10
378 Joel Youngblood .01 .05
379 Darryl Strawberry .05 .15
380 Rich Gossage .08 .25
381 Dennis Eckersley .15 .40
382 Gary Lucas .01 .05
383 Ron Davis .01 .05
384 Pete Incaviglia .02 .10
385 Orel Hershiser .02 .10
386 Kirk Gibson .02 .10
387 Don Robinson .01 .05
388 Darnell Coles .01 .05
389 Von Hayes .01 .05
390 Gary Matthews .01 .05
391 Jay Howell .01 .05
392 Tim Laudner .01 .05
393 Rod Scurry .01 .05
394 Tony Bernazard .01 .05
395 Damaso Garcia .02 .10
Now with Braves
396 Mike Schmidt .15 .40

1988 O-Pee-Chee

This set is an abridgement of the 1988 Topps set. The 396 standard-size cards comprising the 1988 O-Pee-Chee set differ from the cards of the 1988 Topps set by having a higher ratio of cards of players from the two Canadian teams, a practice begun by O-Pee-Chee in 1977 and continued to 1988. The fronts feature white-bordered color player photos framed by a colored line. The player's name appears in the colored diagonal stripe at the lower right. His team name appears at the top. The orange horizontal backs carry the player's name, position and biography printed across the row of baseball icons at the top. The player's major league statistics follow below. Some backs also have bilingual career highlights, some have bilingual baseball facts and still others have both or neither. The asterisked cards have an extra line on the front inside the picture area indicating team change. They are styled like the 1988 Topps regular issue cards. The O-Pee-Chee logo appears on the front of every card. This set includes the first two 1987 draft picks of both the Montreal Expos and the Toronto Blue Jays.

COMPLETE SET (396) 4.00 10.00
1 Chris James .01 .05
2 Steve Buechele .01 .05
3 Mike Henneman .02 .10
4 Eddie Murray .15 .40
5 Bret Saberhagen .02 .10
6 Nathan Minchey .01 .05
7 Harold Reynolds .02 .10
8 Bo Jackson .08 .25
9 Mike Easler .01 .05
10 Ryne Sandberg .15 .40
11 Mike Young .01 .05
12 Tony Phillips .01 .05
13 Andres Thomas .01 .05
14 Tim Burke .01 .05
15 Chili Davis .05 .15
Now with Angels
16 Jim Lindeman .01 .05
17 Ron Oester .01 .05
18 Craig Reynolds .01 .05
19 Juan Samuel .01 .05
20 Kevin Gross .01 .05
21 Cecil Fielder .02 .10
22 Greg Swindell .01 .05
23 Jose DeLeon .01 .05
24 Jim Deshaies .01 .05
25 Andres Galarraga .08 .25
26 Mitch Williams .01 .05
27 R.J. Reynolds .01 .05
28 Jose Nunez .01 .05
29 Angel Salazar .01 .05
30 Sid Fernandez .01 .05
31 Keith Moreland .01 .05
32 John Kruk .02 .10
33 Rob Deer .01 .05
34 Ricky Horton .01 .05
35 Harold Baines .05 .15
36 Jamie Moyer .02 .10
37 Kevin McReynolds .01 .05
38 Ron Darling .01 .05
39 Ozzie Smith .20 .50
40 Orel Hershiser .02 .10
41 Bob Melvin .02 .10
42 Alfredo Griffin .02 .10
Now with Dodgers
43 Dick Schofield .01 .05
44 Terry Steinbach .01 .05
45 Kent Hrbek .02 .10
46 Darnell Coles .01 .05
47 Jimmy Key .02 .10
48 Alan Ashby .01 .05
49 Julio Franco .02 .10
50 Hubie Brooks .01 .05
51 Chris Bando .01 .05
52 Fernando Valenzuela .02 .10
53 Kal Daniels .01 .05
54 Jim Clancy .01 .05
55 Phil Bradley .02 .10
Now with Phillies
56 Andy McGaffigan .01 .05
57 Mike LaValliere .01 .05
58 Dave Magadan .01 .05
59 Danny Cox .01 .05
60 Rickey Henderson .15 .40
61 Jim Rice .02 .10
62 Calvin Schiraldi .02 .10
Now with Cubs
63 Jerry Mumphrey .01 .05
64 Ken Caminiti RC .75 2.00
65 Leon Durham .01 .05
66 Shane Rawley .01 .05
67 Ken Oberkfell .01 .05
68 Keith Hernandez .02 .10
69 Bob Brenly .01 .05
70 Roger Clemens .40 1.00
71 Gary Pettis .02 .10
Now with Tigers
72 Dennis Eckersley .15 .40
73 Dave Smith .01 .05
74 Cal Ripken .60 1.50
75 Joe Carter .08 .25
76 Denny Martinez .02 .10
77 Juan Beniquez .01 .05
78 Tim Laudner .01 .05
79 Ernie Whitt .01 .05
80 Mark Langston .01 .05
81 Dale Sveum .01 .05
82 Dion James .01 .05
83 Dave Valle .01 .05
84 Bill Wegman .01 .05
85 Howard Johnson .01 .05
86 Benito Santiago .01 .05
87 Casey Candaele .01 .05
88 Delino DeShields XRC .20 .50
89 Dave Winfield .15 .40
90 Dale Murphy .08 .25
91 Jay Howell .02 .10
Now with Dodgers
92 Ken Williams RC .05 .15
93 Bob Sebra .01 .05
94 Tim Wallach .01 .05
95 Lance Parrish .01 .05
96 Todd Benzinger .01 .05
97 Scott Garrelts .01 .05
98 Jose Guzman .01 .05
99 Jeff Reardon .02 .10
100 Jack Clark .02 .10
101 Tracy Jones .01 .05
102 Barry Larkin .30 .75
103 Curt Young .01 .05
104 Juan Nieves .01 .05
105 Terry Pendleton .02 .10
106 Rob Ducey .01 .05
107 Scott Bailes .01 .05
108 Eric King .01 .05
109 Mike Pagliarulo .01 .05
110 Teddy Higuera .01 .05
111 Pedro Guerrero .01 .05
112 Chris Brown .01 .05
113 Kelly Gruber .01 .05
114 Jack Howell .01 .05
115 Johnny Ray .01 .05

Card	Low	High
116 Mark Eichhorn	.01	.05
117 Tony Pena	.01	.05
118 Bob Welch	.02	.10
Now with Athletics		
119 Mike Kingery	.01	.05
120 Kirby Puckett	.30	.75
121 Charlie Hough	.02	.10
122 Tony Bernazard	.01	.05
123 Tom Candiotti	.01	.05
124 Ray Knight	.01	.05
125 Bruce Hurst	.01	.05
126 Steve Jeltz	.01	.05
127 Ron Guidry	.02	.10
128 Duane Ward	.01	.05
129 Greg Minton	.01	.05
130 Buddy Bell	.02	.10
131 Denny Walling	.01	.05
132 Donnie Hill	.01	.05
133 Wayne Tolleson	.01	.05
134 Bob Rodgers MG CL	.01	.05
135 Todd Worrell	.02	.10
136 Brian Dayett	.01	.05
137 Chris Bosio	.01	.05
138 Mitch Webster	.01	.05
139 Jerry Browne	.01	.05
140 Jesse Barfield	.01	.05
141 Doug DeCinces	.02	.10
Now with Cardinals		
142 Andy Van Slyke	.02	.10
143 Doug Drabek	.02	.10
144 Jeff Parrett	.01	.05
145 Bill Madlock	.02	.10
146 Larry Herndon	.01	.05
147 Bill Buckner	.02	.10
148 Carmelo Martinez	.01	.05
149 Ken Howell	.01	.05
150 Eric Davis	.02	.10
151 Randy Ready	.01	.05
152 Jeffrey Leonard	.01	.05
153 Dave Stieb	.02	.10
154 Jeff Stone	.01	.05
155 Dave Righetti	.01	.05
156 Gary Matthews	.02	.10
157 Gary Carter	.15	.40
158 Bob Boone	.02	.10
159 Glenn Davis	.01	.05
160 Willie McGee	.02	.10
161 Bryn Smith	.01	.05
162 Mark McLemore RC	.02	.10
163 Dale Mohorcic	.01	.05
164 Mike Flanagan	.01	.05
165 Robin Yount	.15	.40
166 Bill Doran	.01	.05
167 Rance Mulliniks	.01	.05
168 Wally Joyner	.05	.15
169 Cory Snyder	.01	.05
170 Rich Gossage	.08	.25
171 Rick Mahler	.01	.05
172 Henry Cotto	.01	.05
173 George Bell	.01	.05
174 B.J. Surhoff	.02	.10
175 Kevin Bass	.01	.05
176 Jeff Reed	.01	.05
177 Frank Tanana	.01	.05
178 Darryl Strawberry	.02	.10
179 Lou Whitaker	.02	.10
180 Terry Kennedy	.01	.05
181 Mariano Duncan	.01	.05
182 Ken Phelps	.01	.05
183 Bob Dernier	.02	.10
Now with Phillies		
184 Ivan Calderon	.01	.05
185 Rick Rhoden	.01	.05
186 Rafael Palmeiro	.20	.50
187 Kelly Downs	.01	.05
188 Spike Owen	.01	.05
189 Bobby Bonilla	.02	.10
190 Candy Maldonado	.01	.05
191 John Cerutti	.01	.05
192 Devon White	.02	.10
193 Brian Fisher	.01	.05
194 Alex Sanchez	.01	.05
Blue Jays 1st Draft		
195 Dan Quisenberry	.01	.05
196 Dave Engle	.01	.05
197 Lance McCullers	.01	.05
198 Franklin Stubbs	.01	.05
199 Scott Bradley	.01	.05
200 Wade Boggs	.15	.40
201 Kirk Gibson	.02	.10
202 Brett Butler	.02	.10
Now with Giants		
203 Dave Anderson	.01	.05
204 Donnie Moore	.01	.05
205 Nelson Liriano	.01	.05
206 Danny Gladden	.01	.05
207 Dan Pasqua	.02	.10
Now with White Sox		
208 Robby Thompson	.01	.05
209 Richard Dotson	.02	.10
Now with Yankees		
210 Willie Randolph	.02	.10
211 Danny Tartabull	.01	.05
212 Greg Brock	.01	.05
213 Albert Hall	.01	.05
214 Dave Schmidt	.01	.05
215 Von Hayes	.01	.05
216 Herm Winningham	.01	.05
217 Mike Davis	.02	.10
Now with Dodgers		
218 Charlie Leibrandt	.01	.05
219 Mike Stanley	.02	.10
220 Tom Henke	.01	.05
221 Dwight Evans	.02	.10
222 Willie Wilson	.01	.05
223 Stan Jefferson	.01	.05
224 Mike Dunne	.01	.05
225 Mike Scioscia	.02	.10
226 Larry Parrish	.01	.05
227 Mike Scott	.01	.05
228 Wallace Johnson	.01	.05
229 Jeff Musselman	.01	.05
230 Pat Tabler	.01	.05
231 Paul Molitor	.15	.40
232 Bob James	.01	.05
233 Joe Niekro	.01	.05
234 Oddibe McDowell	.01	.05
235 Gary Ward	.01	.05
236 Ted Power	.02	.10
Now with Royals		
237 Pascual Perez	.01	.05
238 Luis Polonia	.01	.05
239 Mike Diaz	.01	.05
240 Lee Smith	.02	.10
Now with Red Sox		
241 Willie Upshaw	.01	.05
242 Tom Niedenfuer	.01	.05
243 Tim Raines	.02	.10
244 Jeff D. Robinson	.01	.05
245 Rich Gedman	.01	.05
246 Scott Bankhead	.01	.05
247 Andre Dawson	.08	.25
248 Brook Jacoby	.01	.05
249 Mike Marshall	.01	.05
250 Nolan Ryan	.60	1.50
251 Tom Foley	.01	.05
252 Bob Brower	.01	.05
253 Checklist	.01	.05
254 Scott McGregor	.01	.05
255 Ken Griffey	.02	.10
256 Ken Schrom	.01	.05
257 Gary Gaetti	.02	.10
258 Ed Nunez	.01	.05
259 Frank Viola	.01	.05
260 Vince Coleman	.01	.05
261 Reid Nichols	.01	.05
262 Tim Flannery	.01	.05
263 Glenn Braggs	.01	.05
264 Garry Templeton	.01	.05
265 Bo Diaz	.01	.05
266 Matt Nokes	.01	.05
267 Barry Bonds	.60	1.50
268 Bruce Ruffin	.01	.05
269 Ellis Burks RC	.20	.50
270 Mike Witt	.01	.05
271 Ken Gerhart	.01	.05
272 Lloyd Moseby	.01	.05
273 Garth Iorg	.01	.05
274 Mike Greenwell	.01	.05
275 Kevin Seitzer	.02	.10
276 Luis Salazar	.01	.05
277 Shawon Dunston	.01	.05
278 Rick Reuschel	.01	.05
279 Randy St.Claire	.01	.05
280 Pete Incaviglia	.01	.05
281 Mike Boddicker	.01	.05
282 Jay Tibbs	.01	.05
283 Shane Mack	.01	.05
284 Walt Terrell	.01	.05
285 Jim Presley	.01	.05
286 Greg Walker	.01	.05
287 Dwight Gooden	.02	.10
288 Jim Morrison	.01	.05
289 Gene Garber	.01	.05
290 Tony Fernandez	.05	.15
291 Ozzie Virgil	.01	.05
292 Carney Lansford	.02	.10
293 Jim Acker	.01	.05
294 Tommy Hinzo	.01	.05
295 Bert Blyleven	.08	.25
296 Ozzie Guillen	.05	.15
297 Zane Smith	.01	.05
298 Milt Thompson	.01	.05
299 Len Dykstra	.02	.10
300 Don Mattingly	.30	.75
301 Bud Black	.01	.05
302 Jose Uribe	.01	.05
303 Manny Lee	.01	.05
304 Sid Bream	.01	.05
305 Steve Sax	.01	.05
306 Billy Hatcher	.01	.05
307 John Shelby	.01	.05
308 Lee Mazzilli	.01	.05
309 Bill Long	.01	.05
310 Tom Herr	.01	.05
311 Derek Bell XRC	.15	.40
312 George Brett	.30	.75
313 Bob McClure	.01	.05
314 Jimy Williams MG CL	.01	.05
315 Dave Parker	.02	.10
Now with Athletics		
316 Doyle Alexander	.01	.05
317 Dan Plesac	.01	.05
318 Mel Hall	.01	.05
319 Ruben Sierra	.01	.05
320 Alan Trammell	.05	.15
321 Mike Schmidt	.15	.40
322 Wally Ritchie	.01	.05
323 Rick Leach	.01	.05
324 Danny Jackson	.01	.05
Now with Reds		
325 Glenn Hubbard	.01	.05
326 Frank White	.02	.10
327 Larry Sheets	.01	.05
328 John Cangelosi	.01	.05
329 Bill Gullickson	.01	.05
330 Eddie Whitson	.01	.05
331 Brian Downing	.01	.05
332 Gary Redus	.01	.05
333 Wally Backman	.01	.05
334 Dwayne Murphy	.01	.05
335 Claudell Washington	.01	.05
336 Dave Concepcion	.02	.10
337 Jim Gantner	.01	.05
338 Marty Barrett	.01	.05
339 Mickey Hatcher	.01	.05
340 Jack Morris	.02	.10
341 John Franco	.02	.10
342 Ron Robinson	.01	.05
343 Greg Gagne	.01	.05
344 Steve Bedrosian	.01	.05
345 Scott Fletcher	.01	.05
346 Vance Law	.02	.10
Now with Cubs		
347 Joe Johnson	.02	.10
Now with Angels		
348 Jim Eisenreich	.08	.25
349 Alvin Davis	.01	.05
350 Will Clark	.20	.50
351 Mike Aldrete	.01	.05
352 Billy Ripken	.01	.05
353 Dave Stewart	.02	.10
354 Neal Heaton	.01	.05
355 Roger McDowell	.01	.05
356 John Tudor	.01	.05
357 Floyd Bannister	.02	.10
Now with Royals		
358 Rey Quinones	.01	.05
359 Glenn Wilson	.02	.10
Now with Mariners		
360 Tony Gwynn	.30	.75
361 Greg Maddux	1.00	2.50
362 Juan Castillo	.01	.05
363 Willie Fraser	.01	.05
364 Nick Esasky	.01	.05
365 Floyd Youmans	.01	.05
366 Chet Lemon	.01	.05
367 Matt Young	.02	.10
Now with A's		
368 Gerald Young	.01	.05
369 Bob Stanley	.01	.05
370 Jose Canseco	.15	.40
371 Joe Hesketh	.01	.05
372 Rick Sutcliffe	.02	.10
373 Checklist 133-264	.01	.05
374 Checklist 265-396	.01	.05
375 Tom Brunansky	.01	.05
376 Jody Davis	.01	.05
377 Sam Horn RC	.01	.05
378 Mark Gubicza	.01	.05
379 Rafael Ramirez	.02	.10
Now with Astros		
380 Joe Magrane	.01	.05
381 Pete O'Brien	.01	.05
382 Lee Guetterman	.01	.05
383 Eric Bell	.01	.05
384 Gene Larkin	.02	.10
385 Carlton Fisk	.15	.40
386 Mike Fitzgerald	.01	.05
387 Kevin Mitchell	.02	.10
388 Jim Winn	.01	.05
389 Mike Smithson	.01	.05
390 Darrell Evans	.02	.10
391 Terry Leach	.01	.05
392 Charlie Kerfeld	.01	.05
393 Mike Krukow	.01	.05
394 Mark McGwire	1.25	3.00
395 Fred McGriff	.20	.50
396 DeWayne Buice	.01	.05

1989 O-Pee-Chee

The 1989 O-Pee-Chee baseball set contains 396 standard-size cards that feature white bordered color player photos framed by colored lines. The player's name and team appear at the lower right. The bilingual pinkish horizontal backs are bordered in black and carry the player's biography and statistics.

Card	Low	High
COMPLETE SET (396)	8.00	15.00
COMP. FACT. SET (396)	10.00	15.00
1 Brook Jacoby	.01	.05
2 Atlee Hammaker	.05	.15
3 Jack Clark	.01	.05
4 Dave Stieb	.02	.10
5 Bud Black	.01	.05
6 Damon Berryhill	.01	.05
7 Mike Scioscia	.02	.10
8 Jose Uribe	.01	.05
9 Mike Aldrete	.01	.05
10 Andre Dawson	.08	.25
11 Bruce Sutter	.15	.40
12 Dale Sveum	.01	.05
13 Dan Quisenberry	.01	.05
14 Tom Niedenfuer	.01	.05
15 Robby Thompson	.01	.05
16 Ron Robinson	.01	.05
17 Brian Downing	.01	.05
18 Rick Rhoden	.01	.05
19 Greg Gagne	.01	.05
20 Allan Anderson	.01	.05
21 Eddie Whitson	.01	.05
22 Billy Ripken	.01	.05
23 Mike Fitzgerald	.01	.05
24 Shane Rawley	.01	.05
25 Frank White	.02	.10
26 Don Mattingly	.40	1.00
27 Fred Lynn	.01	.05
28 Mike Moore	.01	.05
29 Kelly Gruber	.01	.05
30 Dwight Gooden	.02	.10
31 Dan Pasqua	.01	.05
32 Dennis Rasmussen	.01	.05
33 B.J. Surhoff	.02	.10
34 Sid Fernandez	.01	.05
35 John Tudor	.01	.05
36 Mitch Webster	.01	.05
37 Doug Drabek	.01	.05
38 Bobby Witt	.01	.05
39 Mike Maddux	.01	.05
40 Steve Sax	.01	.05
41 Orel Hershiser	.02	.10
42 Pete Incaviglia	.01	.05
43 Guillermo Hernandez	.01	.05
44 Kevin Coffman	.01	.05
45 Kal Daniels	.01	.05
46 Carlton Fisk	.15	.40
47 Carney Lansford	.02	.10
48 Tim Burke	.01	.05
49 Alan Trammell	.60	1.50
50 George Bell	.01	.05
51 Tony Gwynn	.50	1.25
52 Bob Brenly	.01	.05
53 Ruben Sierra	.02	.10
54 Otis Nixon	.01	.05
55 Julio Franco	.02	.10
56 Pat Tabler	.01	.05
57 Alvin Davis	.01	.05
58 Kevin Seitzer	.01	.05
59 Mark Davis	.01	.05
60 Tom Brunansky	.01	.05
61 Jeff Treadway	.01	.05
62 Alfredo Griffin	.01	.05
63 Keith Hernandez	.02	.10
64 Alex Trevino	.01	.05
65 Rick Reuschel	.01	.05
66 Bob Walk	.01	.05
67 Dave Palmer	.01	.05
68 Pedro Guerrero	.01	.05
69 Jose Oquendo	.01	.05
70 Mark McGwire	.60	1.50
71 Mike Boddicker	.01	.05
72 Wally Backman	.01	.05
73 Pascual Perez	.01	.05
74 Joe Hesketh	.01	.05
75 Tom Henke	.01	.05
76 Nelson Liriano	.01	.05
77 Doyle Alexander	.01	.05
78 Tim Wallach	.01	.05
79 Scott Bankhead	.01	.05
80 Cory Snyder	.01	.05
81 Dave Magadan	.01	.05
82 Randy Ready	.01	.05
83 Steve Buechele	.01	.05
84 Bo Jackson	.08	.25
85 Kevin McReynolds	.01	.05
86 Jeff Reardon	.02	.10
87 Tim Raines	.02	.10
(Named Rock on card)		
88 Melido Perez	.01	.05
89 Dave LaPoint	.01	.05
90 Vince Coleman	.01	.05
91 Floyd Youmans	.01	.05
92 Buddy Bell	.02	.10
93 Andres Galarraga	.08	.25
94 Tony Pena	.01	.05
95 Gerald Young	.01	.05
96 Rick Cerone	.01	.05
97 Ken Oberkfell	.01	.05
98 Larry Sheets	.01	.05
99 Chuck Crim	.01	.05
100 Mike Schmidt	.15	.40
101 Ivan Calderon	.01	.05
102 Kevin Bass	.01	.05
103 Chili Davis	.02	.10
104 Randy Myers	.02	.10
105 Ron Darling	.01	.05
106 Willie Upshaw	.01	.05
107 Jose DeLeon	.01	.05
108 Fred Manrique	.01	.05
109 Johnny Ray	.01	.05
110 Paul Molitor	.15	.40
111 Rance Mulliniks	.01	.05
112 Jim Presley	.01	.05
113 Lloyd Moseby	.01	.05
114 Lance Parrish	.01	.05
115 Jody Davis	.01	.05
116 Matt Nokes	.01	.05
117 Dave Anderson	.01	.05
118 Checklist 1-132	.01	.05
119 Rafael Belliard	.01	.05
120 Frank Viola	.01	.05
121 Roger Clemens	.40	1.00
122 Luis Salazar	.01	.05
123 Mike Stanley	.01	.05
124 Jim Traber	.01	.05
125 Mike Krukow	.01	.05
126 Sid Bream	.01	.05
127 Joel Skinner	.01	.05
128 Milt Thompson	.01	.05
129 Terry Clark	.01	.05
130 Gerald Perry	.01	.05
131 Bryn Smith	.01	.05
132 Kirby Puckett	.40	1.00
133 Bill Long	.01	.05
134 Jim Gantner	.01	.05
135 Jose Rijo	.01	.05
136 Joey Meyer	.01	.05
137 Geno Petralli	.01	.05
138 Wallace Johnson	.01	.05
139 Mike Flanagan	.01	.05
140 Shawon Dunston	.01	.05
141 Eric Plunk	.01	.05
142 Bobby Bonilla	.02	.10
143 Jack McDowell	.15	.40
144 Mookie Wilson	.01	.05
145 Dave Stewart	.02	.10
146 Gary Pettis	.01	.05
147 Eric Show	.01	.05
148 Eddie Murray	.15	.40
149 Lee Smith	.02	.10
150 Fernando Valenzuela	.02	.10
151 Bob Walk	.01	.05
152 Harold Baines	.05	.15
153 Albert Hall	.01	.05
154 Don Carman	.01	.05
155 Marty Barrett	.01	.05
156 Chris Sabo	.01	.05
157 Bret Saberhagen	.15	.40
158 Danny Cox	.01	.05
159 Tom Foley	.01	.05
160 Jeffrey Leonard	.01	.05
161 Brady Anderson RC	.30	.75
162 Rich Gossage	.02	.10
163 Greg Brock	.01	.05
164 Joe Carter	.05	.15
165 Mike Dunne	.01	.05
166 Jeff Russell	.01	.05
167 Dan Plesac	.01	.05
168 Willie Wilson	.01	.05
169 Mike Jackson	.02	.10
170 Tony Fernandez	.05	.15
171 Jamie Moyer	.05	.15
172 Jim Gott	.01	.05
173 Mel Hall	.01	.05
174 Mark McGwire	.60	1.50
175 John Shelby	.01	.05
176 Jeff Parrett	.01	.05
177 Tim Belcher	.01	.05
178 Rich Gedman	.01	.05
179 Ozzie Virgil	.01	.05
180 Mike Scott	.01	.05
181 Dickie Thon	.01	.05
182 Rob Murphy	.01	.05
183 Oddibe McDowell	.01	.05
184 Wade Boggs	.15	.40
185 Claudell Washington	.01	.05
186 Randy Johnson RC	1.25	3.00
187 Paul O'Neill	.02	.10
188 Todd Benzinger	.01	.05
189 Kevin Mitchell	.02	.10
190 Mike Witt	.01	.05
191 Sil Campusano	.01	.05
192 Ken Gerhart	.01	.05
193 Bob Rodgers MG	.01	.05
194 Floyd Bannister	.01	.05
195 Ozzie Guillen	.05	.15
196 Ron Gant	.02	.10
197 Neal Heaton	.01	.05
198 Bill Swift	.01	.05
199 Dave Parker	.02	.10
200 George Brett	.30	.75
201 Bo Diaz	.01	.05
202 Brad Moore	.01	.05
203 Rob Ducey	.01	.05
204 Bert Blyleven	.08	.25
205 Dwight Evans	.02	.10
206 Roberto Alomar	.30	.75
207 Henry Cotto	.01	.05
208 Harold Reynolds	.02	.10
209 Jose Guzman	.01	.05
210 Dale Murphy	.08	.25
211 Mike Pagliarulo	.01	.05
212 Jay Howell	.01	.05
213 Rene Gonzales	.01	.05
214 Scott Garrelts	.01	.05
215 Kevin Gross	.01	.05
216 Jack Howell	.01	.05
217 Kurt Stillwell	.01	.05
218 Mike LaValliere	.01	.05
219 Jim Clancy	.01	.05
220 Gary Gaetti	.02	.10
221 Hubie Brooks	.01	.05
222 Bruce Ruffin	.01	.05
223 Jay Buhner	.08	.25
224 Cecil Fielder	.02	.10
225 Willie McGee	.02	.10
226 Bill Doran	.01	.05
227 John Farrell	.01	.05
228 Nelson Santovenia	.01	.05
229 Jimmy Key	.02	.10
230 Ozzie Smith	.30	.75
231 Dave Schmidt	.02	.10
232 Jody Reed	.01	.05
233 Gregg Jefferies	.01	.05
234 Tom Browning	.01	.05
235 John Kruk	.02	.10
236 Charles Hudson	.01	.05
237 Todd Stottlemyre	.02	.10
238 Don Slaught	.01	.05
239 Tim Laudner	.01	.05
240 Greg Maddux	.50	1.25
241 Brett Butler	.02	.10
242 Checklist 133-264	.01	.05
243 Bob Boone	.02	.10
244 Willie Randolph	.02	.10
245 Jim Rice	.02	.10
246 Rey Quinones	.01	.05
247 Checklist 265-396	.01	.05
248 Stan Javier	.01	.05
249 Tim Leary	.01	.05
250 Cal Ripken	.60	1.50
251 John Dopson	.01	.05
252 Billy Hatcher	.01	.05
253 Robin Yount	.15	.40
254 Mickey Hatcher	.01	.05
255 Bob Horner	.01	.05
256 Benny Santiago	.02	.10
257 Luis Rivera	.01	.05
258 Fred McGriff	.08	.25
259 Dave Wells	.01	.05
260 Dave Winfield	.15	.40
261 Rafael Ramirez	.01	.05
262 Nick Esasky	.01	.05
263 Barry Bonds	.40	1.00
264 Joe Magrane	.05	.15
265 Kent Hrbek	.02	.10
266 Jack Morris	.02	.10
267 Jeff M. Robinson	.01	.05
268 Ron Kittle	.01	.05
269 Candy Maldonado	.01	.05
270 Wally Joyner	.02	.10
271 Glenn Braggs	.01	.05
272 Ron Hassey	.01	.05
273 Jose Lind	.01	.05
274 Mark Eichhorn	.01	.05
275 Danny Tartabull	.01	.05
276 Paul Kilgus	.01	.05
277 Mike Davis	.01	.05
278 Andy McGaffigan	.01	.05
279 Scott Bradley	.01	.05
280 Bob Knepper	.01	.05
281 Gary Redus	.01	.05
282 Rickey Henderson	.02	.10
283 Andy Allanson	.01	.05
284 Rick Leach	.01	.05
285 John Candelaria	.01	.05
286 Dick Schofield	.01	.05
287 Bryan Harvey	.01	.05
288 Randy Bush	.01	.05
289 Ernie Whitt	.01	.05
290 John Franco	.02	.10
291 Todd Worrell	.01	.05
292 Teddy Higuera	.01	.05
293 Keith Moreland	.01	.05
294 Juan Berenguer	.01	.05
295 Scott Fletcher	.01	.05
296 Roger McDowell	.02	.10
Now with Indians 12-6-88		
297 Mark Grace	.30	.75
298 Chris James	.01	.05
299 Frank Tanana	.01	.05
300 Darryl Strawberry	.02	.10
301 Charlie Leibrandt	.01	.05
302 Gary Ward	.01	.05
303 Brian Fisher	.01	.05
304 Terry Steinbach	.01	.05
305 Dave Smith	.01	.05
306 Greg Minton	.01	.05
307 Lance McCullers	.01	.05
308 Phil Bradley	.01	.05
309 Terry Kennedy	.01	.05
310 Rafael Palmeiro	.08	.25
311 Ellis Burks	.05	.15
312 Doug Jones	.01	.05
313 Denny Martinez	.02	.10
314 Pete O'Brien	.01	.05
315 Greg Swindell	.01	.05
316 Walt Weiss	.01	.05
317 Pete Stanicek	.01	.05
318 Gene Nelson	.01	.05
319 Danny Jackson	.01	.05
320 Lou Whitaker	.02	.10
321 Will Clark	.08	.25
322 John Smiley	.01	.05
323 Mike Marshall	.01	.05
324 Gary Carter	.15	.40
325 Jesse Barfield	.01	.05
326 Dennis Boyd	.01	.05
327 Dave Henderson	.01	.05
328 Chet Lemon	.01	.05
329 Bob Melvin	.02	.10
330 Eric Davis	.02	.10
331 Ted Power	.01	.05
332 Carmelo Martinez	.01	.05
333 Bob Ojeda	.01	.05
334 Steve Lyons	.02	.10
335 Dave Righetti	.02	.10
336 Steve Balboni	.01	.05
337 Calvin Schiraldi	.01	.05
338 Vance Law	.01	.05
339 Zane Smith	.01	.05
340 Kirk Gibson	.02	.10
341 Jim Deshaies	.01	.05
342 Tom Brookens	.01	.05
343 Pat Borders	.75	2.00
344 Devon White	.02	.10
345 Charlie Hough	.02	.10
346 Rex Hudler	.01	.05
347 John Cerutti	.01	.05
348 Kirk McCaskill	.01	.05
349 Len Dykstra	.02	.10
350 Andy Van Slyke	.02	.10
351 Jeff D. Robinson	.01	.05
352 Rick Schu	.01	.05
353 Bruce Benedict	.01	.05
354 Bill Wegman	.01	.05
355 Mark Langston	.01	.05
356 Steve Farr	.01	.05
357 Richard Dotson	.01	.05
358 Andres Thomas	.01	.05
359 Alan Ashby	.01	.05
360 Ryne Sandberg	.30	.75
361 Kelly Downs	.01	.05
362 Jeff Musselman	.01	.05
363 Barry Larkin	.08	.25
364 Rob Deer	.01	.05
365 Mike Henneman	.01	.05
366 Nolan Ryan	.60	1.50
367 Johnny Paredes	.01	.05
368 Bobby Thigpen	.01	.05
369 Mickey Brantley	.01	.05
370 Dennis Eckersley	.15	.40
371 Manny Lee	.01	.05
372 Juan Samuel	.01	.05
373 Tracy Jones	.01	.05
374 Mike Greenwell	.01	.05
375 Terry Pendleton	.02	.10
376 Steve Lombardozzi	.01	.05
377 Mitch Williams	.01	.05
378 Glenn Davis	.01	.05
379 Mark Gubicza	.01	.05
380 Orel Hershiser WS	.20	.50
381 Jimy Williams MG	.01	.05
382 Kirk Gibson WS	.75	2.00
383 Howard Johnson	.01	.05
384 David Cone	.08	.25
385 Von Hayes	.01	.05
386 Luis Polonia	.01	.05
387 Danny Gladden	.01	.05
388 Pete Smith	.01	.05
389 Jose Canseco	.20	.50
390 Mickey Hatcher	.01	.05
391 Wil Tejada	.01	.05
392 Duane Ward	.01	.05
393 Rick Mahler	.01	.05
394 Rick Sutcliffe	.02	.10
395 Dave Martinez	.01	.05
396 Ken Dayley	.01	.05

1990 O-Pee-Chee

The 1990 O-Pee-Chee baseball set was a 792-card standard-size set. For the first time since 1976, O-Pee-Chee issued the exact same set as Topps. The only distinctions are the bilingual text and the O-Pee-Chee copyright on the backs. The fronts feature color player photos bordered in various colors. The player's name appears at the bottom and his team name is printed at the top. The yellow horizontal backs carry the player's name, biography and position at the top, followed below by major league statistics. Cards 385-407 feature All-Stars, while cards 661-665 are Turn Back the Clock cards. Notable Rookie Cards include Juan Gonzalez, Sammy Sosa, Frank Thomas and Bernie Williams.

Card	Low	High
COMPLETE SET (792)	8.00	20.00
COMP.FACT.SET (792)	10.00	25.00
1 Nolan Ryan	.75	2.00
2 Nolan Ryan Salute	.40	1.00
3 Nolan Ryan Salute	.40	1.00
4 Nolan Ryan Salute	.40	1.00
5 Nolan Ryan Salute UER	.40	1.00
(Says Texas Stadium		
rather than		
Arlington Stadium)		
6 Vince Coleman RB	.01	.05
7 Rickey Henderson RB	.08	.25
8 Cal Ripken RB	.30	.75
9 Eric Plunk	.01	.05
10 Barry Larkin	.08	.25
11 Paul Gibson	.01	.05
12 Joe Girardi	.02	.10
13 Mark Williamson	.01	.05
14 Mike Fetters	.01	.05
15 Teddy Higuera	.01	.05
16 Kent Anderson	.01	.05
17 Kelly Downs	.01	.05
18 Carlos Quintana	.01	.05
19 Al Newman	.01	.05
20 Mark Gubicza	.01	.05
21 Jeff Torborg MG	.01	.05
22 Bruce Ruffin	.01	.05
23 Randy Velarde	.01	.05
24 Joe Hesketh	.01	.05
25 Willie Randolph	.02	.10
26 Don Slaught	.02	.10
Now with Pirates		
12/4/89		
27 Rick Leach	.01	.05
28 Duane Ward	.01	.05
29 John Cangelosi	.01	.05
30 David Cone	.08	.25
31 Henry Cotto	.01	.05
32 John Farrell	.01	.05
33 Greg Walker	.01	.05
34 Tony Fossas	.01	.05
35 Benito Santiago	.02	.10
36 John Costello	.01	.05
37 Domingo Ramos	.01	.05
38 Wes Gardner	.01	.05
39 Curt Ford	.01	.05
40 Jay Howell	.01	.05
41 Matt Williams	.05	.15
42 Jeff M. Robinson	.01	.05
43 Dante Bichette	.02	.10
44 Roger Salkeld FDP RC	.01	.05
45 Dave Parker UER	.05	.15
Born in Jackson		
not Calhoun		
46 Rob Dibble	.01	.05
47 Brian Harper	.01	.05
48 Zane Smith	.01	.05
49 Tom Lawless	.01	.05
50 Glenn Davis	.01	.05
51 Doug Rader MG	.01	.05
52 Jack Daugherty	.01	.05
53 Mike LaCoss	.01	.05
54 Joel Skinner	.01	.05
55 Darrell Evans UER	.02	.10
HR total should be		
414, not 424		
56 Franklin Stubbs	.01	.05
57 Greg Vaughn	.08	.25
58 Keith Miller	.01	.05
59 Ted Power	.02	.10
Now with Pirates		
11/21/89		
60 George Brett	.30	.75
61 Deion Sanders	.08	.25
62 Ramon Martinez	.02	.10
63 Mike Pagliarulo	.01	.05
64 Danny Darwin	.01	.05
65 Devon White	.01	.05
66 Greg Litton	.01	.05
67 Scott Sanderson	.02	.10
Now with Athletics		
12/13/89		
68 Dave Henderson	.01	.05
69 Todd Frohwirth	.01	.05
70 Mike Greenwell	.01	.05
71 Allan Anderson	.01	.05
72 Jeff Huson	.01	.05
73 Bob Milacki	.01	.05
74 Jeff Jackson FDP RC	.01	.05
75 Doug Jones	.01	.05
76 Dave Valle	.01	.05
77 Dave Bergman	.01	.05
78 Mike Flanagan	.01	.05
79 Ron Kittle	.01	.05
80 Jeff Russell	.01	.05
81 Bob Rodgers MG	.01	.05
82 Scott Terry	.01	.05
83 Hensley Meulens	.01	.05
84 Ray Searage	.01	.05
85 Juan Samuel	.02	.10
Now with Dodgers		
12/20/89		
86 Paul Kilgus	.02	.10
Now with Blue Jays		
12/7/89		
87 Rick Luecken	.02	.10
Now with Braves		
12/17/89		
88 Glenn Braggs	.01	.05
89 Clint Zavaras	.01	.05
90 Jack Clark	.02	.10
91 Steve Frey	.01	.05
92 Mike Stanley	.01	.05
93 Shawn Hillegas	.01	.05
94 Herm Winningham	.01	.05
95 Todd Worrell	.01	.05
96 Jody Reed	.01	.05
97 Curt Schilling	.60	1.50
98 Jose Gonzalez	.01	.05
99 Rich Monteleone	.01	.05
100 Will Clark	.08	.25
101 Shane Rawley	.01	.05
Now with Red Sox		
1/9/90		
102 Stan Javier	.01	.05
103 Marvin Freeman	.01	.05
104 Bob Knepper	.01	.05
105 Randy Myers	.02	.10
Now with Reds		
12/8/89		
106 Charlie O'Brien	.01	.05
107 Fred Lynn	.02	.10
Now with Padres		
12/7/89		
108 Rod Nichols	.01	.05
109 Roberto Kelly	.01	.05
110 Tommy Helms MG	.01	.05
111 Ed Whited	.01	.05
112 Glenn Wilson	.01	.05
113 Manny Lee	.01	.05
114 Mike Bielecki	.01	.05
115 Tony Pena	.02	.10
Now with Red Sox		
11/28/89		
116 Floyd Bannister	.01	.05
117 Mike Sharperson	.01	.05
118 Erik Hanson	.01	.05
119 Billy Hatcher	.01	.05
120 John Franco	.05	.15
Now with Mets		
12/8/89		
121 Robin Ventura	.08	.25
122 Shawn Abner	.01	.05
123 Rich Gedman	.01	.05
124 Dave Dravecky	.01	.05
125 Kent Hrbek	.02	.10
126 Randy Kramer	.01	.05
127 Mike Devereaux	.01	.05
128 Checklist 1	.01	.05
129 Ron Jones	.01	.05
130 Bert Blyleven	.08	.25
131 Matt Nokes	.01	.05
132 Lance Blankenship	.01	.05
133 Ricky Horton	.01	.05
134 E.Cunningham FDP RC	.01	.05
135 Dave Magadan	.01	.05
136 Kevin Brown	.08	.25
137 Marty Pevey	.01	.05

138 Al Leiter .08 .25
139 Greg Brock .01 .05
140 Andre Dawson .08 .25
141 John Hart MG .01 .05
142 Jeff Wetherby .01 .05
143 Rafael Belliard .01 .05
144 Bud Black .01 .05
145 Terry Steinbach .01 .05
146 Rob Richie .01 .05
147 Chuck Finley .02 .10
148 Edgar Martinez .05 .15
149 Steve Farr .01 .05
150 Kirk Gibson .02 .10
151 Rick Mahler .01 .05
152 Lonnie Smith .01 .05
153 Randy Milligan .01 .05
154 Mike Maddux .02 .10
Now with Dodgers
12/21/89
155 Ellis Burks .05 .15
156 Ken Patterson .01 .05
157 Craig Biggio .08 .25
158 Craig Lefferts .02 .10
Now with Padres
12/7/89
159 Mike Felder .01 .05
160 Dave Righetti .01 .05
161 Harold Reynolds .02 .10
162 Todd Zeile .05 .15
163 Phil Bradley .01 .05
164 Jeff Juden FDP RC .01 .05
165 Walt Weiss .01 .05
166 Bobby Witt .01 .05
167 Kevin Appier .05 .15
168 Jose Lind .01 .05
169 Richard Dotson .02 .10
Now with Royals
12/6/89
170 George Bell .01 .05
171 Russ Nixon MG .01 .05
172 Tom Lampkin .01 .05
173 Tim Belcher .01 .05
174 Jeff Kunkel .01 .05
175 Mike Moore .01 .05
176 Luis Quinones .01 .05
177 Mike Henneman .01 .05
178 Chris James .01 .05
Now with Indians
12/6/89
179 Brian Holton .01 .05
180 Tim Raines .02 .10
181 Juan Agosto .01 .05
182 Mookie Wilson .02 .10
183 Steve Lake .01 .05
184 Danny Cox .01 .05
185 Ruben Sierra .02 .10
186 Dave LaPoint .01 .05
187 Rick Wrona .01 .05
188 Mike Smithson .02 .10
Now with Angels
12/19/89
189 Dick Schofield .01 .05
190 Rick Reuschel .01 .05
191 Pat Borders .01 .05
192 Don August .01 .05
193 Andy Benes .02 .10
194 Glenallen Hill .01 .05
195 Tim Burke .01 .05
196 Gerald Young .01 .05
197 Doug Drabek .01 .05
198 Mike Marshall .02 .10
Now with Mets
12/20/89
199 Sergio Valdez .01 .05
200 Don Mattingly .40 1.00
201 Cito Gaston MG .01 .05
202 Mike Macfarlane .01 .05
203 Mike Roesler .01 .05
204 Bob Dernier .01 .05
205 Mark Davis .02 .10
Now with Royals
12/11/89
206 Nick Esasky .02 .10
Now with Braves
11/17/89
207 Bob Ojeda .01 .05
208 Brook Jacoby .01 .05
209 Greg Mathews .01 .05
210 Ryne Sandberg .20 .50
211 John Cerutti .01 .05
212 Joe Orsulak .01 .05
213 Scott Bankhead .01 .05
214 Terry Francona .02 .10
215 Kirk McCaskill .01 .05
216 Ricky Jordan .01 .05
217 Don Robinson .01 .05
218 Wally Backman .01 .05
219 Donn Pall .01 .05
220 Barry Bonds .40 1.00
221 Gary Mielke .01 .05
222 Kurt Stillwell UER .01 .05
Graduate misspelled
as gradute
223 Tommy Gregg .01 .05
224 Delino DeShields RC .08 .25
225 Jim Deshaies .01 .05
226 Mickey Hatcher .01 .05
227 Kevin Tapani RC .08 .25
228 Dave Martinez .01 .05
229 David Wells .08 .25
230 Keith Hernandez .05 .15
Now with Indians
12/7/89
231 Jack McKeon MG .02 .10
232 Darnell Coles .01 .05
233 Ken Hill .02 .10
234 Mariano Duncan .01 .05
235 Jeff Reardon .02 .10
Now with Red Sox
12/6/89
236 Hal Morris .01 .05
Now with Reds
12/12/89
237 Kevin Ritz .01 .05
238 Felix Jose .01 .05
239 Eric Show .01 .05
240 Mark Grace .08 .25
241 Mike Krukow .01 .05
242 Fred Manrique .01 .05
243 Barry Jones .01 .05
244 Bill Schroeder .01 .05
245 Roger Clemens .40 1.00
246 Jim Eisenreich .01 .05
247 Jerry Reed .01 .05
248 Dave Anderson .02 .10
Now with Giants&(11/29/89
249 Mike(Texas) Smith .01 .05
250 Jose Canseco .15 .40
251 Jeff Blauser .01 .05
252 Otis Nixon .01 .05
253 Mark Portugal .01 .05
254 Francisco Cabrera .01 .05
255 Bobby Thigpen .01 .05
256 Marvell Wynne .01 .05
257 Jose DeLeon .01 .05
258 Barry Lyons .01 .05
259 Lance McCullers .01 .05
260 Eric Davis .02 .10
261 Whitey Herzog MG .02 .10
262 Checklist 2 .01 .05
263 Mel Stottlemyre Jr. .01 .05
264 Bryan Clutterbuck .01 .05
265 Pete O'Brien .02 .10
Now with Mariners
12/7/89
266 German Gonzalez .01 .05
267 Mark Davidson .01 .05
268 Rob Murphy .01 .05
269 Dickie Thon .01 .05
270 Dave Stewart .02 .10
271 Chet Lemon .01 .05
272 Bryan Harvey .01 .05
273 Bobby Bonilla .01 .05
274 Mauro Gozzo .01 .05
275 Mickey Tettleton .02 .10
276 Gary Thurman .01 .05
277 Lenny Harris .01 .05
278 Pascual Perez .02 .10
Now with Yankees
11/27/89
279 Steve Buechele .01 .05
280 Lou Whitaker .02 .10
281 Kevin Bass .02 .10
Now with Giants
11/20/89
282 Derek Lilliquist .01 .05
283 Joey Belle .08 .25
284 Mark Gardner .01 .05
285 Willie McGee .02 .10
286 Lee Guetterman .01 .05
287 Vance Law .01 .05
288 Greg Briley .01 .05
289 Norm Charlton .01 .05
290 Robin Yount .20 .50
291 Dave Johnson MG .02 .10
292 Jim Gott .02 .10
Now with Dodgers
12/7/89
293 Mike Gallego .01 .05
294 Craig McMurtry .01 .05
295 Fred McGriff .08 .25
296 Jeff Ballard .01 .05
297 Tom Herr .01 .05
298 Dan Gladden .01 .05
299 Adam Peterson .01 .05
300 Bo Jackson .08 .25
301 Don Aase .01 .05
302 Marcus Lawton .01 .05
303 Rick Cerone .02 .10
Now with Yankees
12/19/89
304 Marty Clary .01 .05
305 Eddie Murray .15 .40
306 Tom Niedenfuer .01 .05
307 Bip Roberts .01 .05
308 Jose Guzman .01 .05
309 Eric Yelding .01 .05
310 Steve Bedrosian .01 .05
311 Dwight Smith .01 .05
312 Dan Quisenberry .01 .05
313 Gus Polidor .01 .05
314 Donald Harris FDP .01 .05
315 Bruce Hurst .01 .05
316 Carney Lansford .02 .10
317 Mark Guthrie .01 .05
318 Wallace Johnson .01 .05
319 Dion James .01 .05
320 Dave Stieb .02 .10
321 Joe Morgan MG .01 .05
322 Junior Ortiz .01 .05
323 Willie Wilson .01 .05
324 Pete Harnisch .01 .05
325 Robby Thompson .01 .05
326 Tom McCarthy .01 .05
327 Ken Williams .02 .10
328 Curt Young .01 .05
329 Oddibe McDowell .01 .05
330 Ron Darling .01 .05
331 Juan Gonzalez RC .60 1.50
332 Paul O'Neill .08 .25
333 Bill Wegman .01 .05
334 Johnny Ray .01 .05
335 Andy Hawkins .01 .05
336 Ken Griffey Jr. .60 1.50
337 Lloyd McClendon .01 .05
338 Dennis Lamp .01 .05
339 Dave Clark .02 .10
Now with Cubs
11/20/89
340 Fernando Valenzuela .02 .10
341 Tom Foley .01 .05
342 Alex Trevino .01 .05
343 Frank Tanana .01 .05
344 George Canale .01 .05
345 Harold Baines .05 .15
346 Jim Presley .01 .05
347 Junior Felix .01 .05
348 Gary Wayne .01 .05
349 Steve Finley .08 .25
350 Bret Saberhagen .02 .10
351 Roger Craig MG .01 .05
352 Bryn Smith .02 .10
Now with Cardinals
11/28/89
353 Sandy Alomar Jr. .05 .15
Now with Indians
12/6/89
354 Stan Belinda .01 .05
355 Marty Barrett .01 .05
356 Randy Ready .01 .05
357 Dave West .01 .05
358 Andres Thomas .01 .05
359 Jimmy Jones .01 .05
360 Paul Molitor .15 .40
361 Randy McCament .01 .05
362 Damon Berryhill .01 .05
363 Dan Petry .01 .05
364 Rolando Roomes .01 .05
365 Ozzie Guillen .02 .10
366 Mike Heath .01 .05
367 Mike Morgan .01 .05
368 Bill Doran .01 .05
369 Todd Burns .01 .05
370 Tim Wallach .01 .05
371 Jimmy Key .02 .10
372 Terry Kennedy .01 .05
373 Alvin Davis .01 .05
374 Steve Cummings RC .01 .05
375 Dwight Evans .02 .10
376 Checklist 3 UER .01 .05
Higuera misalphabet-
ized in Brewer list
377 Mickey Weston .01 .05
378 Luis Salazar .01 .05
379 Steve Rosenberg .01 .05
380 Dave Winfield .15 .40
381 Frank Robinson MG .05 .15
382 Jeff Musselman .01 .05
383 John Morris .01 .05
384 Pat Combs .01 .05
385 Fred McGriff AS .02 .10
386 Julio Franco AS .01 .05
387 Wade Boggs AS .08 .25
388 Cal Ripken AS .30 .75
389 Robin Yount AS .08 .25
390 Ruben Sierra AS .01 .05
391 Kirby Puckett AS .08 .25
392 Carlton Fisk AS .08 .25
393 Bret Saberhagen AS .01 .05
394 Jeff Ballard AS .01 .05
395 Jeff Russell AS .01 .05
396 A.Bartlett Giamatti RC .08 .25
COMM MEM
397 Will Clark AS .02 .10
398 Ryne Sandberg AS .08 .25
399 Howard Johnson AS .01 .05
400 Ozzie Smith AS .08 .25
401 Kevin Mitchell AS .01 .05
402 Eric Davis AS .01 .05
403 Tony Gwynn AS .08 .25
404 Craig Biggio AS .05 .15
405 Mike Scott AS .01 .05
406 Joe Magrane AS .01 .05
407 Mark Davis AS .01 .05
408 Trevor Wilson .01 .05
409 Tom Brunansky .01 .05
410 Joe Boever .01 .05
411 Ken Phelps .01 .05
412 Jamie Moyer .01 .05
413 Brian DuBois .01 .05
414 F.Thomas FDP RC 1.25 3.00
415 Shawon Dunston .01 .05
416 Dave Johnson (P) .01 .05
417 Jim Gantner .01 .05
418 Tom Browning .01 .05
419 Beau Allred RC .01 .05
420 Carlton Fisk .15 .40
421 Greg Minton .01 .05
422 Pat Sheridan .01 .05
423 Fred Toliver .02 .10
Now with Yankees
9/27/89
424 Jerry Reuss .01 .05
425 Bill Landrum .01 .05
426 Jeff Hamilton UER .01 .05
Stats say he fanned
197 times in 1987
but he only had 147 at bats
427 Carmen Castillo .01 .05
428 Steve Davis .02 .10
Now with Dodgers
12/12/89
429 Tom Kelly MG .01 .05
430 Pete Incaviglia .01 .05
431 Randy Johnson .30 .75
432 Damaso Garcia .02 .10
Now with Yankees
12/22/89
433 Steve Olin .02 .10
434 Mark Carreon .01 .05
435 Kevin Seitzer .01 .05
436 Mel Hall .01 .05
437 Les Lancaster .01 .05
438 Greg Myers .01 .05
439 Jeff Parrett .01 .05
440 Alan Trammell .05 .15
441 Bob Kipper .01 .05
442 Jerry Browne .01 .05
443 Cris Carpenter .01 .05
444 Kyle Abbott FDP .01 .05
445 Danny Jackson .01 .05
446 Dan Pasqua .01 .05
447 Atlee Hammaker .01 .05
448 Greg Gagne .01 .05
449 Dennis Rasmussen .01 .05
450 Rickey Henderson .30 .75
451 Mark Lemke .01 .05
452 Luis DeLosSantos .01 .05
453 Jody Davis .01 .05
454 Jeff King .01 .05
455 Jeffrey Leonard .01 .05
456 Chris Gwynn .01 .05
457 Gregg Jefferies .01 .05
458 Bob McClure .01 .05
459 Jim Lefebvre MG .01 .05
460 Mike Scott .01 .05
461 Carlos Martinez .01 .05
462 Denny Walling .01 .05
463 Drew Hall .01 .05
464 Jerome Walton .01 .05
465 Kevin Gross .01 .05
466 Rance Mulliniks .01 .05
467 Juan Nieves .01 .05
468 Bill Ripken .01 .05
469 John Kruk .02 .10
470 Frank Viola .01 .05
471 Mike Brumley .02 .10
Now with Orioles
1/10/90
472 Jose Uribe .01 .05
473 Joe Price .01 .05
474 Rich Thompson .01 .05
475 Bob Welch .01 .05
476 Brad Komminsk .01 .05
477 Willie Fraser .01 .05
478 Mike LaValliere .01 .05
479 Frank White .02 .10
480 Sid Fernandez .01 .05
481 Garry Templeton .01 .05
482 Steve Carter .01 .05
483 Alejandro Pena .02 .10
Now with Mets
12/20/89
484 Mike Fitzgerald .01 .05
485 John Candelaria .01 .05
486 Jeff Treadway .01 .05
487 Steve Searcy .01 .05
488 Ken Oberkfell .02 .10
Now with Astros
12/6/89
489 Nick Leyva MG .01 .05
490 Dan Plesac .01 .05
491 Dave Cochrane RC .01 .05
492 Ron Oester .01 .05
493 Jason Grimsley .01 .05
494 Terry Puhl .01 .05
495 Lee Smith .02 .10
496 Cecil Espy UER .01 .05
'88 stats have 3 SB's
should be 33
497 Dave Schmidt .02 .10
Now with Expos
12/13/89
498 Rick Schu .01 .05
499 Bill Long .01 .05
500 Kevin Mitchell .01 .05
501 Matt Young .02 .10
Now with Mariners
12/8/89
502 Mitch Webster .02 .10
Now with Indians
11/20/89
503 Randy St.Claire .01 .05
504 Tom O'Malley .01 .05
505 Kelly Gruber .01 .05
506 Tom Glavine .08 .25
507 Gary Redus .01 .05
508 Terry Leach .01 .05
509 Tom Pagnozzi .01 .05
510 Dwight Gooden .02 .10
511 Clay Parker .01 .05
512 Gary Pettis .02 .10
Now with Rangers
11/24/89
513 Mark Eichhorn .02 .10
Now with Angels
12/13/89
514 Andy Allanson .01 .05
515 Len Dykstra .02 .10
516 Tim Leary .01 .05
517 Roberto Alomar .08 .25
518 Bill Krueger .01 .05
519 Bucky Dent MG .01 .05
520 Mitch Williams .01 .05
521 Craig Worthington .01 .05
522 Mike Dunne .02 .10
Now with Padres
12/4/89
523 Jay Bell .01 .05
524 Daryl Boston .01 .05
525 Wally Joyner .02 .10
526 Checklist 4 .01 .05
527 Ron Hassey .01 .05
528 Kevin Wickander UER .01 .05
Monthly scoreboard
strikeout total was 2.2
that was his innings
pitched total
529 Greg A. Harris .01 .05
530 Mark Langston .02 .10
Now with Angels
12/4/89
531 Ken Caminiti .08 .25
532 Cecilio Guante .02 .10
Now with Indians
11/21/89
533 Tim Jones .01 .05
534 Louie Meadows .01 .05
535 John Smoltz .08 .25
536 Bob Geren .01 .05
537 Mark Grant .01 .05
538 Bill Spiers UER .01 .05
Photo actually George Canale
539 Neal Heaton .01 .05
540 Danny Tartabull .01 .05
541 Pat Perry .01 .05
542 Darren Daulton .02 .10
543 Nelson Liriano .01 .05
544 Dennis Boyd .02 .10
Now with Expos
12/7/89
545 Kevin McReynolds .01 .05
546 Kevin Hickey .01 .05
547 Jack Howell .01 .05
548 Pat Clements .01 .05
549 Don Zimmer MG .01 .05
550 Julio Franco .01 .05
551 Tim Crews .01 .05
552 Mike(Miss.) Smith .01 .05
553 Scott Scudder UER .01 .05
Cedar Rapids
554 Jay Buhner .08 .25
555 Jack Morris .02 .10
556 Gene Larkin .01 .05
557 Jeff Innis .01 .05
558 Rafael Ramirez .01 .05
559 Andy McGaffigan .01 .05
560 Steve Sax .01 .05
561 Ken Dayley .01 .05
562 Chad Kreuter .01 .05
563 Alex Sanchez .01 .05
564 Tyler Houston FDP RC .01 .05
565 Scott Fletcher .01 .05
566 Mark Knudson .01 .05
567 Ron Gant .02 .10
568 John Smiley .01 .05
569 Ivan Calderon .01 .05
570 Cal Ripken .60 1.50
571 Brett Butler .02 .10
572 Greg W. Harris .01 .05
573 Danny Heep .01 .05
574 Bill Swift .01 .05
575 Lance Parrish .01 .05
576 Mike Dyer RC .01 .05
577 Charlie Hayes .01 .05
578 Joe Magrane .01 .05
579 Art Howe MG .01 .05
580 Joe Carter .02 .10
581 Ken Griffey Sr. .02 .10
582 Rick Honeycutt .01 .05
583 Bruce Benedict .01 .05
584 Phil Stephenson .01 .05
585 Kal Daniels .01 .05
586 Edwin Nunez .01 .05
587 Lance Johnson .01 .05
588 Rick Rhoden .01 .05
589 Mike Aldrete .01 .05
590 Ozzie Smith .20 .50
591 Todd Stottlemyre .01 .05
592 R.J. Reynolds .01 .05
593 Scott Bradley .01 .05
594 Luis Sojo .01 .05
595 Greg Swindell .01 .05
596 Jose DeJesus .01 .05
597 Chris Bosio .01 .05
598 Brady Anderson .08 .25
599 Frank Williams .01 .05
600 Darryl Strawberry .02 .10
601 Luis Rivera .01 .05
602 Scott Garrelts .01 .05
603 Tony Armas .01 .05
604 Ron Robinson .01 .05
605 Mike Scioscia .02 .10
606 Storm Davis .02 .10
Now with Royals
12/7/89
607 Steve Jeltz .01 .05
608 Eric Anthony .01 .05
609 Sparky Anderson MG .02 .10
610 Pedro Guerrero .01 .05
611 Walt Terrell .02 .10
Now with Pirates
11/29/89
612 Dave Gallagher .01 .05
613 Jeff Pico .01 .05
614 Nelson Santovenia .01 .05
615 Rob Deer .01 .05
616 Brian Holman .01 .05
617 Geronimo Berroa .01 .05
618 Ed Whitson .01 .05
619 Rob Ducey .01 .05
620 Tony Castillo .01 .05
621 Melido Perez .01 .05
622 Sid Bream .01 .05
623 Jim Corsi .01 .05
624 Darrin Jackson .01 .05
625 Roger McDowell .01 .05
626 Bob Melvin .01 .05
627 Jose Rijo .01 .05
628 Candy Maldonado .02 .10
Now with Indians
11/28/89
629 Eric Hetzel .01 .05
630 Gary Gaetti .02 .10
631 John Wetteland .08 .25
632 Scott Lusader .01 .05
633 Dennis Cook .01 .05
634 Luis Polonia .01 .05
635 Brian Downing .01 .05
636 Jesse Orosco .02 .10
637 Craig Reynolds .01 .05
638 Jeff Montgomery .02 .10
639 Tony LaRussa MG .02 .10
640 Rick Sutcliffe .02 .10
641 Doug Strange .01 .05
642 Jack Armstrong .01 .05
643 Alfredo Griffin .01 .05
644 Paul Assenmacher .01 .05
645 Jose Oquendo .01 .05
646 Checklist 5 .01 .05
647 Rex Hudler .02 .10
648 Jim Clancy .01 .05
649 Dan Murphy .01 .05
650 Mike Witt .01 .05
651 Rafael Santana .02 .10
Now with Indians
1/10/90
652 Mike Boddicker .01 .05
653 John Moses .01 .05
654 Paul Coleman FDP RC .01 .05
655 Gregg Olson .01 .05
656 Mackey Sasser .01 .05
657 Terry Mulholland .01 .05
658 Donell Nixon .01 .05
659 Greg Cadaret .01 .05
660 Vince Coleman .01 .05
661 Dick Howser TBC'85 .01 .05
UER
Seaver's 300th on 7/11/85
should be 8/4/85
662 Mike Schmidt TBC'80 .08 .25
663 Fred Lynn TBC'75 .01 .05
664 Johnny Bench TBC'70 .08 .25
665 Sandy Koufax TBC'65 .20 .50
666 Brian Fisher .01 .05
667 Curt Wilkerson .01 .05
668 Joe Oliver .01 .05
669 Tom Lasorda MG .08 .25
670 Dennis Eckersley .15 .40
671 Bob Boone .02 .10
672 Roy Smith .01 .05
673 Joey Meyer .01 .05
674 Spike Owen .01 .05
675 Jim Abbott .05 .15
676 Randy Kutcher .01 .05
677 Jay Tibbs .01 .05
678 Kirt Manwaring UER .01 .05
'88 Phoenix stats repeated
679 Gary Ward .01 .05
680 Howard Johnson .01 .05
681 Mike Schooler .01 .05
682 Dann Bilardello .01 .05
683 Kenny Rogers .02 .10
684 Julio Machado .01 .05
685 Tony Fernandez .02 .10
686 Carmelo Martinez .02 .10
Now with Phillies
12/4/89
687 Tim Birtsas .01 .05
688 Milt Thompson .02 .10
689 Rich Yett .02 .10
Now with Twins
12/26/89
690 Mark McGwire .30 .75
691 Chuck Cary .01 .05
692 Sammy Sosa RC 1.50 4.00
693 Calvin Schiraldi .01 .05
694 Mike Stanton .01 .05
695 Tom Henke .01 .05
696 B.J. Surhoff .02 .10
697 Mike Davis .01 .05
698 Omar Vizquel .08 .25
699 Jim Leyland MG .01 .05
700 Kirby Puckett .30 .75
701 Bernie Williams RC .60 1.50
702 Tony Phillips .01 .05
Now with Tigers
12/5/89
703 Jeff Brantley .01 .05
704 Chip Hale .01 .05
705 Claudell Washington .01 .05
706 Geno Petralli .01 .05
707 Luis Aquino .01 .05
708 Larry Sheets .02 .10
Now with Tigers
1/10/90
709 Juan Berenguer .01 .05
710 Von Hayes .01 .05
711 Rick Aguilera .04 .10
712 Todd Benzinger .01 .05
713 Tim Drummond .01 .05
714 Marquis Grissom RC .20 .50
715 Greg Maddux .40 1.00
716 Steve Balboni .01 .05
717 Ron Karkovice .01 .05
718 Gary Sheffield .20 .50
719 Wally Whitehurst .01 .05
720 Andres Galarraga .08 .25
721 Lee Mazzilli .01 .05
722 Felix Fermin .01 .05
723 Jeff D. Robinson .01 .05
Now with Yankees
12/4/89
724 Juan Bell .01 .05
725 Terry Pendleton .02 .10
726 Gene Nelson .01 .05
727 Pat Tabler .01 .05
728 Jim Acker .01 .05
729 Bobby Valentine MG .01 .05
730 Tony Gwynn .30 .75
731 Don Carman .01 .05
732 Ernest Riles .01 .05
733 John Dopson .01 .05
734 Kevin Elster .01 .05
735 Charlie Hough .02 .10
736 Rick Dempsey .01 .05
737 Chris Sabo .01 .05
738 Gene Harris .01 .05
739 Dale Sveum .01 .05
740 Jesse Barfield .01 .05
741 Steve Wilson .01 .05
742 Ernie Whitt .01 .05
743 Tom Candiotti .01 .05
744 Kelly Mann .01 .05
745 Hubie Brooks .01 .05
746 Dave Smith .01 .05
747 Randy Bush .01 .05
748 Doyle Alexander .01 .05
749 Mark Parent UER .01 .05
'87 BA .80, should be .080
750 Dale Murphy .08 .25
751 Steve Lyons .02 .10
752 Tom Gordon .05 .15
753 Chris Speier .01 .05
754 Bob Walk .01 .05
755 Rafael Palmeiro .08 .25
756 Ken Howell .01 .05
757 Larry Walker RC .60 1.50
758 Mark Thurmond .01 .05
759 Tom Trebelhorn MG .01 .05
760 Wade Boggs .15 .40
761 Mike Jackson .02 .10
762 Doug Dascenzo .01 .05
763 Dennis Martinez .02 .10
764 Tim Teufel .01 .05
765 Chili Davis .02 .10
766 Brian Meyer .01 .05
767 Tracy Jones .01 .05
768 Chuck Crim .01 .05
769 Greg Hibbard .01 .05
770 Cory Snyder .01 .05
771 Pete Smith .01 .05
772 Jeff Reed .01 .05
773 Dave Leiper .01 .05
774 Ben McDonald .01 .05
775 Andy Van Slyke .02 .10
776 Charlie Leibrandt .02 .10
Now with Braves
12/17/89
777 Tim Laudner .01 .05
778 Mike Jeffcoat .01 .05
779 Lloyd Moseby .02 .10
Now with Tigers
12/7/89
780 Orel Hershiser .02 .10
781 Mario Diaz .01 .05
782 Jose Alvarez .02 .10
Now with Giants
12/4/89
783 Checklist 6 .01 .05
784 Scott Bailes .02 .10
Now with Angels
1/9/90
785 Jim Rice .02 .10
786 Eric King .01 .05
787 Rene Gonzales .01 .05
788 Frank DiPino .01 .05
789 John Wathan MG .01 .05
790 Gary Carter .15 .40
791 Alvaro Espinoza .01 .05
792 Gerald Perry .01 .05

1991 O-Pee-Chee

The 1991 O-Pee-Chee baseball set contains 792 standard-size cards. For the second time since 1976, O-Pee-Chee issued the exact same set as Topps. The only distinctions are the bilingual text and the O-Pee-Chee copyright on the backs. The fronts feature white-bordered color action player photos framed by two different colored lines. The player's name and position appear at the bottom of the photo, with his team name appearing just above. The Topps 40th anniversary logo appears in the upper left corner. The traded players have their new teams and dates of trade printed on the photo. The pinkish horizontal backs present player biography, statistics and bilingual career highlights. Cards 386-407 are an All-Star subset. Notable Rookie Cards include Carl Everett and Chipper Jones.

COMPLETE SET (792) 10.00 15.00
COMP. FACT.SET (792) 10.00 20.00
1 Nolan Ryan .75 2.00
2 George Brett RB .15 .40
3 Carlton Fisk RB .08 .25
4 Kevin Maas RB .01 .05
5 Cal Ripken RB .30 .75
6 Nolan Ryan RB .40 1.00
7 Ryne Sandberg RB .08 .25
8 Bobby Thigpen RB .01 .05
9 Darrin Fletcher .01 .05
10 Gregg Olson .01 .05
11 Roberto Kelly .01 .05
12 Paul Assenmacher .01 .05
13 Mariano Duncan .01 .05
14 Dennis Lamp .01 .05
15 Von Hayes .01 .05
16 Mike Heath .01 .05
17 Jeff Brantley .01 .05
18 Nelson Liriano .01 .05
19 Jeff D. Robinson .01 .05
20 Pedro Guerrero .01 .05
21 Joe Morgan MG .01 .05
22 Storm Davis .01 .05
23 Jim Gantner .01 .05
24 Dave Martinez .01 .05
25 Tim Belcher .01 .05
26 Luis Sojo UER .01 .05
Born in Barquisimeto
not Caracas
Now with Angels
12/2/90
27 Bobby Witt .01 .05
28 Alvaro Espinoza .01 .05
29 Bob Walk .01 .05
30 Gregg Jefferies .01 .05
31 Colby Ward .01 .05
32 Mike Simms .01 .05
33 Barry Jones .01 .05
34 Atlee Hammaker .01 .05
35 Greg Maddux .40 1.00
36 Donnie Hill .01 .05
37 Tom Bolton .01 .05
38 Scott Bradley .01 .05
39 Jim Neidlinger .01 .05
40 Kevin Mitchell .01 .05
41 Ken Dayley .02 .10
Now with Blue Jays
11/26/90
42 Chris Hoiles .01 .05
43 Roger McDowell .01 .05
44 Mike Felder .01 .05
45 Chris Sabo .01 .05
46 Tim Drummond .01 .05
47 Brook Jacoby .01 .05
48 Dennis Boyd .01 .05
49 Pat Borders .01 .05
50 Bob Welch .01 .05
51 Art Howe MG .01 .05
52 Francisco Oliveras .01 .05
53 Mike Sharperson UER .01 .05
Born in 1961, not 1960
54 Gary Mielke .01 .05
55 Jeffrey Leonard .01 .05
56 Jeff Parrett .01 .05
57 Jack Howell .01 .05
58 Mel Stottlemyre Jr. .01 .05
59 Eric Yelding .01 .05
60 Frank Viola .01 .05
61 Stan Javier .01 .05
62 Lee Guetterman .01 .05
63 Milt Thompson .01 .05
64 Tom Herr .01 .05
65 Bruce Hurst .01 .05
66 Terry Kennedy .01 .05
67 Rick Honeycutt .01 .05
68 Gary Sheffield .20 .50
69 Steve Wilson .01 .05
70 Ellis Burks .02 .10
71 Jim Acker .01 .05
72 Junior Ortiz .01 .05
73 Craig Worthington .01 .05
74 Shane Andrews RC .01 .05
75 Jack Morris .02 .10
76 Jerry Browne .01 .05
77 Drew Hall .01 .05
78 Geno Petralli .01 .05
79 Frank Thomas .25 .60
80 Fernando Valenzuela .02 .10
81 Cito Gaston MG .01 .05
82 Tom Glavine .15 .40
83 Daryl Boston .01 .05
84 Bob McClure .01 .05
85 Jesse Barfield .01 .05
86 Les Lancaster .01 .05
87 Tracy Jones .01 .05
88 Bob Tewksbury .01 .05
89 Darren Daulton .02 .10
90 Danny Tartabull .01 .05
91 Greg Colbrunn .01 .05
92 Danny Jackson .02 .10
Now with Cubs
11/21/90
93 Ivan Calderon .01 .05
94 John Dopson .01 .05
95 Paul Molitor .15 .40
96 Trevor Wilson .01 .05
97 Brady Anderson .08 .25
98 Sergio Valdez .01 .05
99 Chris Gwynn .01 .05
100 Don Mattingly .40 1.00
101 Rob Ducey .01 .05

102 Gene Larkin .01 .05
103 Tim Costo .01 .05
104 Don Robinson .01 .05
105 Kevin McReynolds .01 .05
106 Ed Nunez .02 .10
Now with Brewers
12/4/90
107 Luis Polonia .01 .05
108 Matt Young .02 .10
Now with Red Sox
12/4/90
109 Greg Riddoch MG .01 .05
110 Tom Henke .01 .05
111 Andres Thomas .01 .05
112 Frank DiPino .01 .05
113 Carl Everett RC .40 1.00
114 Lance Dickson .01 .05
115 Hubie Brooks .02 .10
Now with Mets
12/15/90
116 Mark Davis .01 .05
117 Dion James .01 .05
118 Tom Edens .01 .05
119 Carl Nichols .01 .05
120 Joe Carter .05 .15
Now with Blue Jays
12/5/90
121 Eric King .02 .10
Now with Indians
12/4/90
122 Paul O'Neill .15 .40
123 Greg A. Harris .01 .05
124 Randy Bush .01 .05
125 Steve Bedrosian .02 .10
Now with Twins
12/5/90
126 Bernard Gilkey .02 .10
127 Joe Price .01 .05
128 Travis Fryman .08 .25
Front has SS, back has SS-3B
129 Mark Eichhorn .01 .05
130 Ozzie Smith .20 .50
131 Checklist 1 .01 .05
132 Jamie Quirk .01 .05
133 Greg Briley .01 .05
134 Kevin Elster .01 .05
135 Jerome Walton .01 .05
136 Dave Schmidt .01 .05
137 Randy Ready .01 .05
138 Jamie Moyer .05 .15
Now with Cardinals
1/10/91
139 Jeff Treadway .01 .05
140 Fred McGriff .08 .25
Now with Padres
12/5/90
141 Nick Leyva MG .01 .05
142 Curt Wilkerson .02 .10
Now with Pirates
1/9/91
143 John Smiley .01 .05
144 Dave Henderson .01 .05
145 Lou Whitaker .02 .10
146 Dan Plesac .01 .05
147 Carlos Baerga .01 .05
148 Rey Palacios .01 .05
149 Al Osuna RC UER .01 .05
Shown with glove on
right hand
bio says throws right
150 Cal Ripken .60 1.50
151 Tom Browning .01 .05
152 Mickey Hatcher .01 .05
153 Bryan Harvey .01 .05
154 Jay Buhner .02 .10
155 Dwight Evans .05 .15
Now with Orioles
12/6/90
156 Carlos Martinez .01 .05
157 John Smoltz .08 .25
158 Jose Uribe .01 .05
159 Joe Boever .01 .05
160 Vince Coleman .01 .05
161 Tim Leary .01 .05
162 Ozzie Canseco .01 .05
163 Dave Johnson .01 .05
164 Edgar Diaz .01 .05
165 Sandy Alomar Jr. .02 .10
166 Harold Baines .05 .15
167 Randy Tomlin .01 .05
168 John Olerud .08 .25
169 Luis Aquino .01 .05
170 Carlton Fisk .15 .40
171 Tony LaRussa MG .02 .10
172 Pete Incaviglia .01 .05
173 Jason Grimsley .01 .05
174 Ken Caminiti .08 .25
175 Jack Armstrong .01 .05
176 John Orton .01 .05
177 Reggie Harris .01 .05
178 Dave Valle .01 .05
179 Pete Harnisch .01 .05
Now with Astros
1/10/91
180 Tony Gwynn .30 .75
181 Duane Ward .01 .05
182 Junior Noboa .01 .05
183 Clay Parker .01 .05
184 Gary Green .01 .05
185 Joe Magrane .01 .05
186 Rod Booker .01 .05
187 Greg Cadaret .01 .05
188 Damon Berryhill .01 .05
189 Daryl Irvine .01 .05
190 Matt Williams .05 .15
191 Willie Blair .02 .10
Now with Indians
11/6/90
192 Rob Deer .02 .10
Now with Tigers
11/21/90
193 Felix Fermin .01 .05
194 Xavier Hernandez .01 .05
195 Wally Joyner .02 .10
196 Jim Vatcher .01 .05
197 Chris Nabholz .01 .05
198 R.J. Reynolds .01 .05
199 Mike Hartley .01 .05
200 Darryl Strawberry .05 .15
Now with Dodgers
11/8/90
201 Tom Kelly MG .01 .05
202 Jim Leyritz .01 .05
203 Gene Harris .01 .05
204 Herm Winningham .01 .05
205 Mike Perez .01 .05
206 Carlos Quintana .01 .05
207 Gary Wayne .01 .05
208 Willie Wilson .01 .05
209 Ken Howell .01 .05
210 Lance Parrish .01 .05
211 Brian Barnes .01 .05
212 Steve Finley .08 .25
Now with Astros
1/10/91
213 Frank Wills .01 .05
214 Joe Girardi .02 .10
215 Dave Smith .02 .10
Now with Cubs
12/17/90
216 Greg Gagne .01 .05
217 Chris Bosio .01 .05
218 Rick Parker .01 .05
219 Jack McDowell .01 .05
220 Tim Wallach .01 .05
221 Don Slaught .01 .05
222 Brian McRae RC .08 .25
223 Allan Anderson .01 .05
224 Juan Gonzalez .08 .25
225 Randy Johnson .25 .60
226 Alfredo Griffin .01 .05
227 Steve Avery UER .01 .05
Pitched 13 games for
Durham in 1989, not 2
228 Rex Hudler .01 .05
229 Rance Mulliniks .01 .05
230 Sid Fernandez .01 .05
231 Doug Rader MG .01 .05
232 Jose DeJesus .01 .05
233 Al Leiter .01 .05
234 Scott Erickson .01 .05
235 Dave Parker .02 .10
236 Frank Tanana .01 .05
237 Rick Cerone .01 .05
238 Mike Dunne .01 .05
239 Darren Lewis .02 .10
Now with Giants
12/4/90
240 Mike Scott .01 .05
241 Dave Clark UER .01 .05
Career totals 19 HR and 5 3B
should be 22 and 3
242 Mike LaCoss .01 .05
243 Lance Johnson .01 .05
244 Mike Jeffcoat .01 .05
245 Kal Daniels .01 .05
246 Kevin Wickander .01 .05
247 Jody Reed .01 .05
248 Tom Gordon .02 .10
249 Bob Melvin .02 .10
250 Dennis Eckersley .15 .40
251 Mark Lemke .01 .05
252 Mel Rojas .02 .10
253 Garry Templeton .01 .05
254 Shawn Boskie .01 .05
255 Brian Downing .01 .05
256 Greg Hibbard .01 .05
257 Tom O'Malley .01 .05
258 Chris Hammond .01 .05
259 Hensley Meulens .01 .05
260 Harold Reynolds .02 .10
261 Bud Harrelson MG .01 .05
262 Tim Jones .01 .05
263 Checklist 2 .01 .05
264 Dave Hollins .01 .05
265 Mark Gubicza .01 .05
266 Carmelo Castillo .01 .05
267 Mark Knudson .01 .05
268 Tom Brookens .01 .05
269 Joe Hesketh .01 .05
270 Mark McGwire .30 .75
271 Omar Olivares .01 .05
272 Jeff King .01 .05
273 Johnny Ray .01 .05
274 Ken Williams .02 .10
275 Alan Trammell .05 .15
276 Bill Swift .01 .05
277 Scott Coolbaugh .02 .10
Now with Padres
12/12/90
278 Alex Fernandez UER .01 .05
No '90 White Sox stats
279 Jose Gonzalez .01 .05
280 Bret Saberhagen .02 .10
281 Larry Sheets .01 .05
282 Don Carman .01 .05
283 Marquis Grissom .02 .10
284 Billy Spiers .01 .05
285 Jim Abbott .02 .10
286 Ken Oberkfell .01 .05
287 Mark Grant .01 .05
288 Derrick May .01 .05
289 Tim Birtsas .01 .05
290 Steve Sax .01 .05
291 John Wathan MG .01 .05
292 Bud Black .01 .05
293 Jay Bell .01 .05
294 Mike Moore .01 .05
295 Rafael Palmeiro .08 .25
296 Mark Williamson .01 .05
297 Manny Lee .01 .05
298 Omar Vizquel .08 .25
299 Scott Radinsky .01 .05
300 Kirby Puckett .25 .60
301 Steve Farr .02 .10
Now with Yankees
11/26/90
302 Tim Teufel .01 .05
303 Mike Boddicker .02 .10
Now with Royals
11/21/90
304 Kevin Reimer .01 .05
305 Mike Scioscia .02 .10
306 Lonnie Smith .01 .05
307 Andy Benes .01 .05
308 Tom Pagnozzi .01 .05
309 Norm Charlton .01 .05
310 Gary Carter .15 .40
311 Jeff Pico .01 .05
312 Charlie Hayes .01 .05
313 Ron Robinson .01 .05
314 Gary Pettis .01 .05
315 Roberto Alomar .15 .40
316 Gene Nelson .01 .05
317 Mike Fitzgerald .01 .05
318 Rick Aguilera .02 .10
319 Jeff McKnight .01 .05
320 Tony Fernandez .02 .10
Now with Padres
12/5/90
321 Bob Rodgers MG .01 .05
322 Terry Shumpert .01 .05
323 Cory Snyder .01 .05
324 Ron Kittle .01 .05
325 Brett Butler .02 .10
Now with Dodgers
12/15/90
326 Ken Patterson .01 .05
327 Ron Hassey .01 .05
328 Walt Terrell .01 .05
329 Dave Justice UER .15 .40
Drafted third round on card
should say fourth pick
330 Dwight Gooden .02 .10
331 Eric Anthony .01 .05
332 Kenny Rogers .05 .15
Now with White Sox
12/4/90
333 C.Jones FDP RC 2.00 5.00
334 Todd Benzinger .01 .05
335 Mitch Williams .01 .05
336 Matt Nokes .01 .05
337 Keith Comstock .01 .05
338 Luis Rivera .01 .05
339 Larry Walker .08 .25
340 Ramon Martinez .01 .05
341 John Moses .01 .05
342 Mickey Morandini .01 .05
343 Jose Oquendo .01 .05
344 Jeff Russell .01 .05
345 Len Dykstra .02 .10
346 Jesse Orosco .02 .10
347 Greg Vaughn .08 .25
348 Todd Stottlemyre .02 .10
349 Dave Gallagher .02 .10
Now with Angels
12/4/90
350 Glenn Davis .01 .05
351 Joe Torre MG .02 .10
352 Frank White .02 .10
353 Tony Castillo .01 .05
354 Sid Bream .02 .10
Now with Braves
12/5/90
355 Chili Davis .02 .10
356 Mike Marshall .01 .05
357 Jack Savage .01 .05
358 Mark Parent .02 .10
Now with Rangers
12/12/90
359 Chuck Cary .01 .05
360 Tim Raines .05 .15
Now with White Sox
12/23/90
361 Scott Garrelts .01 .05
362 Hector Villanueva .01 .05
363 Rick Mahler .01 .05
364 Dan Pasqua .01 .05
365 Mike Schooler .01 .05
366 Checklist 3 .01 .05
367 Dave Walsh RC .01 .05
368 Felix Jose .01 .05
369 Steve Searcy .01 .05
370 Kelly Gruber .01 .05
371 Jeff Montgomery .01 .05
372 Spike Owen .01 .05
373 Darrin Jackson .01 .05
374 Larry Casian .01 .05
375 Tony Pena .01 .05
376 Mike Harkey .01 .05
377 Rene Gonzales .01 .05
378 Wilson Alvarez .08 .25
379 Randy Velarde .01 .05
380 Willie McGee .05 .15
Now with Giants
12/3/90
381 Jim Leyland MG .01 .05
382 Mackey Sasser .01 .05
383 Pete Smith .01 .05
384 Gerald Perry .02 .10
Now with Cardinals
12/13/90
385 Mickey Tettleton .02 .10
Now with Tigers
1/12/90
386 Cecil Fielder AS .02 .10
387 Julio Franco AS .01 .05
388 Kelly Gruber AS .01 .05
389 Alan Trammell AS .02 .10
390 Jose Canseco AS .08 .25
391 Rickey Henderson AS .15 .40
392 Ken Griffey Jr. AS .30 .75
393 Carlton Fisk AS .02 .10
394 Bob Welch AS .01 .05
395 Chuck Finley AS .01 .05
396 Bobby Thigpen AS .01 .05
397 Eddie Murray AS .02 .10
398 Ryne Sandberg AS .05 .15
399 Matt Williams AS .05 .15
400 Barry Larkin AS .02 .10
401 Barry Bonds AS .20 .50
402 Darryl Strawbery AS .02 .10
403 Bobby Bonilla AS .01 .05
404 Mike Scioscia AS .01 .05
405 Doug Drabek AS .01 .05
406 Frank Viola AS .01 .05
407 John Franco AS .01 .05
408 Earnie Riles .02 .10
Now with Athletics
12/4/90
409 Mike Stanley .01 .05
410 Dave Righetti .02 .10
Now with Giants
12/4/90
411 Lance Blankenship .01 .05
412 Dave Bergman .01 .05
413 Terry Mulholland .01 .05
414 Sammy Sosa .15 .40
415 Rick Sutcliffe .02 .10
416 Randy Milligan .01 .05
417 Bill Krueger .01 .05
418 Nick Esasky .01 .05
419 Jeff Reed .01 .05
420 Bobby Thigpen .01 .05
421 Alex Cole .01 .05
422 Rick Reuschel .01 .05
423 Rafael Ramirez UER .01 .05
Born 1959, not 1958
424 Calvin Schiraldi .01 .05
425 Andy Van Slyke .01 .05
426 Joe Grahe .01 .05
427 Rick Dempsey .01 .05
428 John Barfield .01 .05
429 Stump Merrill MG .01 .05
430 Gary Gaetti .02 .10
431 Paul Gibson .01 .05
432 Delino DeShields .02 .10
433 Pat Tabler .01 .05
Now with Blue Jays
12/5/90
434 Julio Machado .01 .05
435 Kevin Maas .01 .05
436 Scott Bankhead .01 .05
437 Doug Dascenzo .01 .05
438 Vicente Palacios .01 .05
439 Dickie Thon .01 .05
440 George Bell .01 .05
Now with Cubs
12/6/90
441 Zane Smith .01 .05
442 Charlie O'Brien .01 .05
443 Jeff Innis .01 .05
444 Glenn Braggs .01 .05
445 Greg Swindell .01 .05
446 Craig Grebeck .01 .05
447 John Burkett .01 .05
448 Craig Lefferts .01 .05
449 Juan Berenguer .01 .05
450 Wade Boggs .15 .40
451 Neal Heaton .01 .05
452 Bill Schroeder .01 .05
453 Lenny Harris .01 .05
454 Kevin Appier .02 .10
455 Walt Weiss .01 .05
456 Charlie Leibrandt .01 .05
457 Todd Hundley .08 .25
458 Brian Holman .01 .05
459 Tom Trebelhorn MG .01 .05
460 Dave Stieb .02 .10
461 Robin Ventura .08 .25
462 Steve Frey .01 .05
463 Dwight Smith .01 .05
464 Steve Buechele .01 .05
465 Ken Griffey Sr. .02 .10
466 Charles Nagy .02 .10
467 Dennis Cook .01 .05
468 Tim Hulett .01 .05
469 Chet Lemon .01 .05
470 Howard Johnson .01 .05
471 Mike Lieberthal RC .20 .50
472 Kirt Manwaring .01 .05
473 Curt Young .01 .05
474 Phil Plantier .01 .05
475 Teddy Higuera .01 .05
476 Glenn Wilson .01 .05
477 Mike Fetters .01 .05
478 Kurt Stillwell .01 .05
479 Bob Patterson .01 .05
480 Dave Magadan .01 .05
481 Eddie Whitson .01 .05
482 Tino Martinez .08 .25
483 Mike Aldrete .01 .05
484 Dave LaPoint .01 .05
485 Terry Pendleton .05 .15
Now with Braves
12/3/90
486 Tommy Greene .01 .05
487 Rafael Belliard .02 .10
Now with Braves
12/18/90
488 Jeff Manto .01 .05
489 Bobby Valentine MG .01 .05
490 Kirk Gibson .05 .15
Now with Royals
12/1/90
491 Kurt Miller .01 .05
492 Ernie Whitt .01 .05
493 Jose Rijo .01 .05
494 Chris James .01 .05
495 Charlie Hough .05 .15
Now with White Sox
12/20/90
496 Marty Barrett .01 .05
497 Ben McDonald .01 .05
498 Mark Salas .01 .05
499 Melido Perez .01 .05
500 Will Clark .15 .40
501 Mike Bielecki .01 .05
502 Carney Lansford .02 .10
503 Roy Smith .01 .05
504 Julio Valera .01 .05
505 Chuck Finley .02 .10
506 Darnell Coles .01 .05
507 Steve Jeltz .01 .05
508 Mike York .01 .05
509 Glenallen Hill .01 .05
510 John Franco .02 .10
511 Steve Balboni .01 .05
512 Jose Mesa .01 .05
513 Jerald Clark .01 .05
514 Mike Stanton .01 .05
515 Alvin Davis .01 .05
516 Karl Rhodes .01 .05
517 Joe Oliver .01 .05
518 Cris Carpenter .01 .05
519 Sparky Anderson MG .02 .10
520 Mark Grace .15 .40
521 Joe Orsulak .01 .05
522 Stan Belinda .01 .05
523 Rodney McCray .01 .05
524 Darrel Akerfelds .01 .05
525 Willie Randolph .02 .10
526 Moises Alou .02 .10
527 Checklist 4 .01 .05
528 Denny Martinez .02 .10
529 Marc Newfield .01 .05
530 Roger Clemens .40 1.00
531 Dave Rohde .01 .05
532 Kirk McCaskill .01 .05
533 Oddibe McDowell .01 .05
534 Mike Jackson .02 .10
535 Ruben Sierra .02 .10
536 Mike Witt .01 .05
537 Jose Lind .01 .05
538 Bip Roberts .01 .05
539 Scott Terry .01 .05
540 George Brett .30 .75
541 Domingo Ramos .01 .05
542 Rob Murphy .01 .05
543 Junior Felix .01 .05
544 Alejandro Pena .01 .05
545 Dale Murphy .15 .40
546 Jeff Ballard .01 .05
547 Mike Pagliarulo .01 .05
548 Jaime Navarro .01 .05
549 John McNamara MG .01 .05
550 Eric Davis .02 .10
551 Bob Kipper .01 .05
552 Jeff Hamilton .01 .05
553 Joe Klink .01 .05
554 Brian Harper .01 .05
555 Turner Ward .01 .05
556 Gary Ward .01 .05
557 Wally Whitehurst .01 .05
558 Otis Nixon .02 .10
559 Adam Peterson .01 .05
560 Greg Smith .02 .10
Now with Dodgers
12/14/90
561 Tim McIntosh .01 .05
562 Jeff Kunkel .01 .05
563 Brent Knackert .01 .05
564 Dante Bichette .02 .10
565 Craig Biggio .05 .15
566 Craig Wilson .01 .05
567 Dwayne Henry .01 .05
568 Ron Karkovice .01 .05
569 Curt Schilling .25 .60
Now with Astros
1/10/91
570 Barry Bonds .30 .75
571 Pat Combs .01 .05
572 Dave Anderson .01 .05
573 Rich Rodriguez UER .01 .05
Stats say drafted 4th
but bio says 9th round
574 John Marzano .01 .05
575 Robin Yount .15 .40
576 Jeff Kaiser .01 .05
577 Bill Doran .01 .05
578 Dave West .01 .05
579 Roger Craig MG .01 .05
580 Dave Stewart .02 .10
581 Luis Quinones .01 .05
582 Marty Clary .01 .05
583 Tony Phillips .01 .05
584 Kevin Brown .05 .15
585 Pete O'Brien .01 .05
586 Fred Lynn .01 .05
587 Jose Offerman UER .01 .05
Text says signed 7/24/88
but bio says 1986
588 Mark Whiten .01 .05
589 Scott Ruskin .01 .05
590 Eddie Murray .15 .40
591 Ken Hill .01 .05
592 B.J. Surhoff .02 .10
593 Mike Walker .01 .05
594 Rich Garces .01 .05
595 Bill Landrum .01 .05
596 Ronnie Walden .01 .05
597 Jerry Don Gleaton .01 .05
598 Sam Horn .01 .05
599 Greg Myers .01 .05
600 Bo Jackson .08 .25
601 Bob Ojeda .02 .10
Now with Dodgers
12/15/90
602 Casey Candaele .01 .05
603 Wes Chamberlain .01 .05
604 Billy Hatcher .01 .05
605 Jeff Reardon .02 .10
606 Jim Gott .01 .05
607 Edgar Martinez .05 .15
608 Todd Burns .01 .05
609 Jeff Torborg MG .01 .05
610 Andres Galarraga .08 .25
611 Dave Eiland .01 .05
612 Steve Lyons .02 .10
613 Eric Show .02 .10
Now with Athletics
12/10/90
614 Luis Salazar .01 .05
615 Bert Blyleven .02 .10
616 Todd Zeile .02 .10
617 Bill Wegman .01 .05
618 Sil Campusano .01 .05
619 David Wells .05 .15
620 Ozzie Guillen .02 .10
621 Ted Power .02 .10
Now with Reds
12/14/90
622 Jack Daugherty .01 .05
623 Jeff Blauser .01 .05
624 Tom Candiotti .01 .05
625 Terry Steinbach .01 .05
626 Gerald Young .01 .05
627 Tim Layana .01 .05
628 Greg Litton .01 .05
629 Wes Gardner .02 .10
Now with Padres
12/15/90
630 Dave Winfield .15 .40
631 Mike Morgan .01 .05
632 Lloyd Moseby .01 .05
633 Kevin Tapani .01 .05
634 Henry Cotto .01 .05
635 Andy Hawkins .01 .05
636 Geronimo Pena .01 .05
637 Bruce Ruffin .01 .05
638 Mike Macfarlane .01 .05
639 Frank Robinson MG .08 .25
640 Andre Dawson .08 .25
641 Mike Henneman .01 .05
642 Hal Morris .01 .05
643 Jim Presley .01 .05
644 Chuck Crim .01 .05
645 Juan Samuel .01 .05
646 Andujar Cedeno .01 .05
647 Mark Portugal .01 .05
648 Lee Stevens .01 .05
649 Bill Sampen .01 .05
650 Jack Clark .05 .15
Now with Red Sox
12/15/90
651 Alan Mills .01 .05
652 Kevin Romine .01 .05
653 Anthony Telford .01 .05
654 Paul Sorrento .02 .10
655 Erik Hanson .01 .05
656 Checklist 5 .01 .05
657 Mike Kingery .01 .05
658 Scott Aldred .01 .05
659 Oscar Azocar .01 .05
660 Lee Smith .02 .10
661 Steve Lake .01 .05
662 Rob Dibble .01 .05
663 Greg Brock .01 .05
664 John Farrell .01 .05
665 Mike LaValliere .01 .05
666 Danny Darwin .01 .05
Now with Red Sox
12/19/90
667 Kent Anderson .01 .05
668 Bill Long .01 .05
669 Lou Piniella MG .02 .10
670 Rickey Henderson .30 .75
671 Andy McGaffigan .01 .05
672 Shane Mack .01 .05
673 Greg Olson UER .01 .05
6 RBI in '88 at Tidewater
and 2 RBI in '87
should be 48 and 15
674 Kevin Gross .02 .10
Now with Dodgers
12/3/90
675 Tom Brunansky .01 .05
676 Scott Chiamparino .01 .05
677 Billy Ripken .01 .05
678 Mark Davidson .01 .05
679 Bill Bathe .01 .05
680 David Cone .08 .25
681 Jeff Schaefer .01 .05
682 Ray Lankford .08 .25
683 Derek Lilliquist .01 .05
684 Milt Cuyler .01 .05
685 Doug Drabek .01 .05
686 Mike Gallego .01 .05
687 John Cerutti .01 .05
688 Rosario Rodriguez .02 .10
Now with Pirates
12/20/90
689 John Kruk .02 .10
690 Orel Hershiser .02 .10
691 Mike Blowers .01 .05
692 Efrain Valdez .01 .05
693 Francisco Cabrera .01 .05
694 Randy Veres .01 .05
695 Kevin Seitzer .01 .05
696 Steve Olin .01 .05
697 Shawn Abner .01 .05
698 Mark Guthrie .01 .05
699 Jim Lefebvre MG .01 .05
700 Jose Canseco .15 .40
701 Pascual Perez .01 .05
702 Tim Naehring .01 .05
703 Juan Agosto .02 .10
Now with Cardinals
12/14/90
704 Devon White .05 .15
Now with Blue Jays
12/2/90
705 Robby Thompson .01 .05
706 Brad Arnsberg .01 .05
707 Jim Eisenreich .01 .05
708 John Mitchell .01 .05
709 Matt Sinatro .01 .05
710 Kent Hrbek .02 .10
711 Jose DeLeon .01 .05
712 Ricky Jordan .01 .05
713 Scott Scudder .01 .05
714 Marvell Wynne .01 .05
715 Tim Burke .01 .05
716 Bob Geren .01 .05
717 Phil Bradley .01 .05
718 Steve Crawford .01 .05
719 Keith Miller .01 .05
720 Cecil Fielder .02 .10
721 Mark Lee .01 .05
722 Wally Backman .01 .05
723 Candy Maldonado .01 .05
724 David Segui .01 .05
725 Ron Gant .02 .10
726 Phil Stephenson .01 .05
727 Mookie Wilson .02 .10
728 Scott Sanderson .02 .10
Now with Yankees
12/31/90
729 Don Zimmer MG .01 .05
730 Barry Larkin .15 .40
731 Jeff Gray .01 .05
732 Franklin Stubbs .02 .10
Now with Brewers
12/5/90
733 Kelly Downs .01 .05
734 John Russell .01 .05
735 Ron Darling .01 .05
736 Dick Schofield .01 .05
737 Tim Crews .01 .05
738 Mel Hall .01 .05
739 Russ Swan .01 .05
740 Ryne Sandberg .20 .50
741 Jimmy Key .02 .10
742 Tommy Gregg .01 .05
743 Bryn Smith .01 .05
744 Nelson Santovenia .01 .05
745 Doug Jones .01 .05
746 John Shelby .01 .05
747 Tony Fossas .01 .05
748 Al Newman .01 .05
749 Greg W. Harris .01 .05
750 Bobby Bonilla .01 .05
751 Wayne Edwards .01 .05
752 Kevin Bass .01 .05
753 Paul Marak UER .01 .05
Stats say drafted in May
but bio says Jan.
754 Bill Pecota .01 .05
755 Mark Langston .01 .05
756 Jeff Huson .01 .05
757 Mark Gardner .01 .05
758 Mike Devereaux .01 .05
759 Bobby Cox MG .02 .10
760 Benny Santiago .02 .10
761 Larry Andersen .02 .10
Now with Padres
12/21/90
762 Mitch Webster .01 .05
763 Dana Kiecker .01 .05
764 Mark Carreon .01 .05
765 Shawon Dunston .01 .05
766 Jeff M. Robinson .02 .10
Now with Orioles
1/12/91
767 Dan Wilson RC .08 .25
768 Donn Pall .01 .05
769 Tim Sherrill .01 .05
770 Jay Howell .01 .05
771 Gary Redus UER .01 .05
Born in Tanner, should say Athens
772 Kent Mercker UER .01 .05
Born in Indianapolis
should say Dublin, Ohio
773 Tom Foley .01 .05
774 Dennis Rasmussen .01 .05
775 Julio Franco .02 .10
776 Brent Mayne .01 .05
777 John Candelaria .01 .05
778 Dan Gladden .01 .05
779 Carmelo Martinez .01 .05
780 Randy Myers .02 .10
781 Darryl Hamilton .01 .05
782 Jim Deshaies .01 .05
783 Joel Skinner .01 .05
784 Willie Fraser .02 .10
Now with Blue Jays
12/2/90
785 Scott Fletcher .01 .05
786 Eric Plunk .01 .05
787 Checklist 6 .01 .05
788 Bob Milacki .01 .05
789 Tom Lasorda MG .15 .40
790 Ken Griffey Jr. .60 1.50
791 Mike Benjamin .01 .05
792 Mike Greenwell .01 .05

1992 O-Pee-Chee

The 1992 O-Pee-Chee set contains 792 standard-size cards. These cards were sold in ten-card wax packs with a stick of bubble gum. The fronts have either posed or action color player photos on a white card face. Different color stripes frame the pictures, and the player's name and team name appear in two short color stripes respectively at the bottom. In English and French, the horizontally oriented backs have biography and complete career batting or pitching record. In addition, some of the cards have a picture of a baseball field and stadium on the back. Special subsets included are Record Breakers (2-5), Prospects (58, 126, 179, 473, 551, 591, 618, 656, 676) and a five-card tribute to Gary Carter (45, 387, 389, 399, 402). Each wax pack wrapper served as an entry blank offering each collector the chance to win one of 1,000 complete factory sets of 1992 O-Pee-Chee Premier baseball cards.

COMPLETE SET (792) 10.00 25.00
COMP. FACT.SET (792) 20.00 30.00
1 Nolan Ryan .75 2.00
2 Rickey Henderson RB .15 .40
(Some cards have print
marks that show 1.991
on the front)
3 Jeff Reardon RB .01 .05
4 Nolan Ryan RB .40 1.00
5 Dave Winfield RB .05 .15
6 Brien Taylor RC .01 .05
7 Jim Olander .01 .05
8 Bryan Hickerson .01 .05
9 Jon Farrell .01 .05
10 Wade Boggs .15 .40
11 Jack McDowell .01 .05
12 Luis Gonzalez .15 .40
13 Mike Scioscia .02 .10
14 Wes Chamberlain .01 .05
15 Dennis Martinez .02 .10
16 Jeff Montgomery .02 .10
17 Randy Milligan .01 .05
18 Greg Cadaret .01 .05
19 Jamie Quirk .01 .05
20 Bip Roberts .01 .05
21 Buck Rodgers MG .01 .05
22 Bill Wegman .01 .05
23 Chuck Knoblauch .08 .25
24 Randy Myers .02 .10
25 Ron Gant .01 .05
26 Mike Bielecki .01 .05
27 Juan Gonzalez .08 .25
28 Mike Schooler .01 .05
29 Mickey Tettleton .01 .05
30 John Kruk .02 .10
31 Bryn Smith .01 .05
32 Chris Nabholz .01 .05
33 Carlos Baerga .01 .05
34 Jeff Juden .01 .05
35 Dave Righetti .01 .05
36 Scott Ruffcorn .01 .05
37 Luis Polonia .01 .05
38 Tom Candiotti .02 .10
Now with Dodgers
12-3-91
39 Greg Olson .01 .05
40 Cal Ripken 1.50 4.00
Lou Gehrig
41 Craig Lefferts .01 .05
42 Mike Macfarlane .01 .05
43 Jose Lind .01 .05
44 Rick Aguilera .02 .10
45 Gary Carter .20 .50
46 Steve Farr .01 .05
47 Rex Hudler .02 .10
48 Scott Scudder .01 .05
49 Damon Berryhill .01 .05
50 Ken Griffey Jr. .40 1.00
51 Tom Runnells MG .01 .05

52 Juan Bell .01 .05
53 Tommy Gregg .01 .05
54 David Wells .05 .15
55 Rafael Palmeiro .15 .40
56 Charlie O'Brien .01 .05
57 Donn Pall .01 .05
58 Brad Ausmus RC .60 1.50
Jim Campanis Jr.
Dave Nilsson
Doug Robbins
59 Mo Vaughn .08 .25
60 Tony Fernandez .01 .05
61 Paul O'Neill .15 .40
62 Gene Nelson .01 .05
63 Randy Ready .01 .05
64 Bob Kipper .02 .10
Now with Twins
12-17-91
65 Willie McGee .02 .10
66 Scott Stahoviak .01 .05
67 Luis Salazar .01 .05
68 Marvin Freeman .01 .05
69 Kenny Lofton .15 .40
Now with Indians
12-10-91
70 Gary Gaetti .02 .10
71 Erik Hanson .01 .05
72 Eddie Zosky .01 .05
73 Brian Barnes .01 .05
74 Scott Leius .01 .05
75 Bret Saberhagen .02 .10
76 Mike Gallego .01 .05
77 Jack Armstrong .02 .10
Now with Indians
11-15-91
78 Ivan Rodriguez .20 .50
79 Jesse Orosco .01 .05
80 David Justice .05 .15
81 Ced Landrum .01 .05
82 Doug Simons .01 .05
83 Tommy Greene .01 .05
84 Leo Gomez .01 .05
85 Jose DeLeon .01 .05
86 Steve Finley .02 .10
87 Bob MacDonald .01 .05
88 Darrin Jackson .01 .05
89 Neal Heaton .01 .05
90 Robin Yount .15 .40
91 Jeff Reed .01 .05
92 Lenny Harris .01 .05
93 Reggie Jefferson .01 .05
94 Sammy Sosa .15 .40
95 Scott Bailes .01 .05
96 Tom McKinnon .01 .05
97 Luis Rivera .01 .05
98 Mike Harkey .01 .05
99 Jeff Treadway .01 .05
100 Jose Canseco .15 .40
101 Omar Vizquel .02 .10
102 Scott Kamieniecki .01 .05
103 Ricky Jordan .01 .05
104 Jeff Ballard .01 .05
105 Felix Jose .01 .05
106 Mike Boddicker .01 .05
107 Dan Pasqua .01 .05
108 Mike Timlin .01 .05
109 Roger Craig MG .01 .05
110 Ryne Sandberg .20 .50
111 Mark Carreon .01 .05
112 Oscar Azocar .01 .05
113 Mike Greenwell .01 .05
114 Mark Portugal .01 .05
115 Terry Pendleton .01 .05
116 Willie Randolph .02 .10
Now with Mets
12-20-91
117 Scott Terry .01 .05
118 Chili Davis .02 .10
119 Mark Gardner .01 .05
120 Alan Trammell .05 .15
121 Derek Bell .02 .10
122 Gary Varsho .01 .05
123 Bob Ojeda .01 .05
124 Shawn Livsey .01 .05
125 Chris Hoiles .01 .05
126 Ryan Klesko .08 .25
John Jaha
Rico Brogna
Dave Staton
127 Carlos Quintana .01 .05
128 Kurt Stillwell .01 .05
129 Melido Perez .01 .05
130 Alvin Davis .01 .05
131 Checklist 1-132 .01 .05
132 Eric Show .01 .05
133 Rance Mulliniks .01 .05
134 Darryl Kile .01 .05
135 Von Hayes .02 .10
Now with Angels
12-8-91
136 Bill Doran .01 .05
137 Jeff D. Robinson .01 .05
138 Monty Fariss .01 .05
139 Jeff Innis .01 .05
140 Mark Grace UER .15 .40
Home Calie., should be Calif.
141 Jim Leyland MG UER .01 .05
(No closed parenthesis
after East in 1991)
142 Todd Van Poppel .01 .05
143 Paul Gibson .01 .05
144 Bill Swift .01 .05
145 Danny Tartabull .02 .10
Now with Yankees
1-6-92
146 Al Newman .01 .05
147 Cris Carpenter .01 .05
148 Anthony Young .01 .05
149 Brian Bohanon .01 .05
150 Roger Clemens UER .40 1.00
(League leading ERA in
1990 not italicized)
151 Jeff Hamilton .01 .05
152 Charlie Leibrandt .01 .05
153 Ron Karkovice .01 .05
154 Hensley Meulens .01 .05
155 Scott Bankhead .01 .05
156 Manny Ramirez RC 2.00 5.00
157 Keith Miller .02 .10
Now with Royals
12-11-91
158 Todd Frohwirth .01 .05
159 Darrin Fletcher .02 .10
Now with Expos
12-9-91
160 Bobby Bonilla .01 .05
161 Casey Candaele .01 .05
162 Paul Faries .01 .05
163 Dana Kiecker .01 .05
164 Shane Mack .01 .05
165 Mark Langston .01 .05
166 Geronimo Pena .01 .05
167 Andy Allanson .01 .05
168 Dwight Smith .01 .05
169 Chuck Crim .02 .10
Now with Angels
12-10-91
170 Alex Cole .01 .05
171 Bill Plummer MG .01 .05
172 Juan Berenguer .01 .05
173 Brian Downing .01 .05
174 Steve Frey .01 .05
175 Orel Hershiser .02 .10
176 Ramon Garcia .01 .05
177 Dan Gladden .02 .10
Now with Tigers
12-19-91
178 Jim Acker .01 .05
179 Bobby DeJardin .01 .05
Cesar Bernhardt
Armando Moreno
Andy Stankiewicz
180 Kevin Mitchell .02 .10
181 Hector Villanueva .01 .05
182 Jeff Reardon .02 .10
183 Brent Mayne .01 .05
184 Jimmy Jones .01 .05
185 Benito Santiago .02 .10
186 Cliff Floyd .40 1.00
187 Ernie Riles .01 .05
188 Jose Guzman .01 .05
189 Junior Felix .01 .05
190 Glenn Davis .01 .05
191 Charlie Hough .02 .10
192 Dave Fleming .01 .05
193 Omar Olivares .01 .05
194 Eric Karros .08 .25
195 David Cone .08 .25
196 Frank Castillo .01 .05
197 Glenn Braggs .01 .05
198 Scott Aldred .01 .05
199 Jeff Blauser .01 .05
200 Len Dykstra .02 .10
201 Buck Showalter MG RC .08 .25
202 Rick Honeycutt .01 .05
203 Greg Myers .01 .05
204 Trevor Wilson .01 .05
205 Jay Howell .01 .05
206 Luis Sojo .01 .05
207 Jack Clark .02 .10
208 Julio Machado .01 .05
209 Lloyd McClendon .01 .05
210 Ozzie Guillen .02 .10
211 Jeremy Hernandez .01 .05
212 Randy Velarde .01 .05
213 Les Lancaster .01 .05
214 Andy Mota .01 .05
215 Rich Gossage .02 .10
216 Brent Gates .01 .05
217 Brian Harper .01 .05
218 Mike Flanagan .01 .05
219 Jerry Browne .01 .05
220 Jose Rijo .01 .05
221 Skeeter Barnes .01 .05
222 Jaime Navarro .01 .05
223 Mel Hall .01 .05
224 Bret Barberie .01 .05
225 Roberto Alomar .15 .40
226 Pete Smith .01 .05
227 Daryl Boston .01 .05
228 Eddie Whitson .01 .05
229 Shawn Boskie .01 .05
230 Dick Schofield .01 .05
231 Brian Drahman .01 .05
232 John Smiley .01 .05
233 Mitch Webster .01 .05
234 Terry Steinbach .01 .05
235 Jack Morris .05 .15
Now with Blue Jays
12-18-91
236 Bill Pecota .02 .10
Now with Mets
12-11-91
237 Jose Hernandez .01 .05
238 Greg Litton .01 .05
239 Brian Holman .01 .05
240 Andres Galarraga .08 .25
241 Gerald Young .01 .05
242 Mike Mussina .25 .60
243 Alvaro Espinoza .01 .05
244 Darren Daulton .02 .10
245 John Smoltz .08 .25
246 Jason Pruitt .01 .05
247 Chuck Finley .02 .10
248 Jim Gantner .01 .05
249 Tony Fossas .01 .05
250 Ken Griffey Sr. .02 .10
251 Kevin Elster .01 .05
252 Dennis Rasmussen .01 .05
253 Terry Kennedy .01 .05
254 Ryan Bowen .01 .05
255 Robin Ventura .01 .05
256 Mike Aldrete .01 .05
257 Jeff Russell .01 .05
258 Jim Lindeman .01 .05
259 Ron Darling .01 .05
260 Devon White .02 .10
261 Tom Lasorda MG .08 .25
262 Terry Lee .01 .05
263 Bob Patterson .01 .05
264 Checklist 133-264 .01 .05
265 Teddy Higuera .01 .05
266 Roberto Kelly .01 .05
267 Steve Bedrosian .01 .05
268 Brady Anderson .05 .15
269 Ruben Amaro Jr. .01 .05
270 Tony Gwynn .30 .75
271 Tracy Jones .01 .05
272 Jerry Don Gleaton .01 .05
273 Craig Grebeck .01 .05
274 Bob Scanlan .01 .05
275 Todd Zeile .02 .10
276 Shawn Green RC 1.50 4.00
277 Scott Chiamparino .01 .05
278 Darryl Hamilton .01 .05
279 Jim Clancy .01 .05
280 Carlos Martinez .01 .05
281 Kevin Appier .02 .10
282 John Wehner .01 .05
283 Reggie Sanders .02 .10
284 Gene Larkin .01 .05
285 Bob Welch .01 .05
286 Gilberto Reyes .01 .05
287 Pete Schourek .01 .05
288 Andujar Cedeno .01 .05
289 Mike Morgan .02 .10
Now with Cubs
12-3-91
290 Bo Jackson .02 .10
291 Phil Garner MG .01 .05
292 Ray Lankford .08 .25
293 Mike Henneman .01 .05
294 Dave Valle .01 .05
295 Alonzo Powell .01 .05
296 Tom Brunansky .01 .05
297 Kevin Brown .05 .15
298 Kelly Gruber .01 .05
299 Charles Nagy .01 .05
300 Don Mattingly .40 1.00
301 Kirk McCaskill .02 .10
Now with White Sox
12-28-91
302 Joey Cora .01 .05
303 Dan Plesac .01 .05
304 Joe Oliver .01 .05
305 Tom Glavine .15 .40
306 Al Shirley .01 .05
307 Bruce Ruffin .01 .05
308 Craig Shipley .01 .05
309 Dave Martinez .02 .10
Now with Reds
12-11-91
310 Jose Mesa .01 .05
311 Henry Cotto .01 .05
312 Mike LaValliere .01 .05
313 Kevin Tapani .01 .05
314 Jeff Huson .01 .05
315 Juan Samuel .01 .05
316 Curt Schilling .15 .40
317 Mike Bordick .02 .10
318 Steve Howe .01 .05
319 Tony Phillips .01 .05
320 George Bell .01 .05
321 Lou Piniella MG .02 .10
322 Tim Burke .01 .05
323 Milt Thompson .01 .05
324 Danny Darwin .01 .05
325 Joe Orsulak .01 .05
326 Eric King .01 .05
327 Jay Buhner .05 .15
328 Joel Johnston .01 .05
329 Franklin Stubbs .01 .05
330 Will Clark .15 .40
331 Steve Lake .01 .05
332 Chris Jones .02 .10
Now with Astros
12-19-91
333 Pat Tabler .01 .05
334 Kevin Gross .01 .05
335 Dave Henderson .01 .05
336 Greg Anthony .01 .05
337 Alejandro Pena .01 .05
338 Shawn Abner .01 .05
339 Tom Browning .01 .05
340 Otis Nixon .01 .05
341 Bob Geren .02 .10
Now with Reds
12-2-91
342 Tim Spehr .01 .05
343 John Vander Wal .01 .05
344 Jack Daugherty .01 .05
345 Zane Smith .01 .05
346 Rheal Cormier .01 .05
347 Kent Hrbek .02 .10
348 Rick Wilkins .01 .05
349 Steve Lyons .02 .10
350 Gregg Olson .01 .05
351 Greg Riddoch MG .01 .05
352 Ed Nunez .01 .05
353 Braulio Castillo .01 .05
354 Dave Bergman .01 .05
355 Warren Newson .01 .05
356 Luis Quinones .01 .05
Now with Twins
1-9-92
357 Mike Witt .01 .05
358 Ted Wood .01 .05
359 Mike Moore .01 .05
360 Lance Parrish .01 .05
361 Barry Jones .01 .05
362 Javier Ortiz .01 .05
363 John Candelaria .01 .05
364 Glenallen Hill .01 .05
365 Duane Ward .01 .05
366 Checklist 265-396 .01 .05
367 Rafael Belliard .01 .05
368 Bill Krueger .01 .05
369 Steve Whitaker .01 .05
370 Shawon Dunston .01 .05
371 Dante Bichette .02 .10
372 Kip Gross .02 .10
Now with Dodgers
11-27-91
373 Don Robinson .01 .05
374 Bernie Williams .15 .40
375 Bert Blyleven .02 .10
376 Chris Donnels .01 .05
377 Bob Zupcic .02 .10
378 Joel Skinner .01 .05
379 Steve Chitren .01 .05
380 Barry Bonds .40 1.00
381 Sparky Anderson MG .02 .10
382 Sid Fernandez .01 .05
383 Dave Hollins .01 .05
384 Mark Lee .01 .05
385 Tim Wallach .01 .05
386 Lance Blankenship .01 .05
387 Gary Carter TRIB .08 .25
388 Ron Tingley .01 .05
389 Gary Carter TRIB .08 .25
390 Gene Harris .01 .05
391 Jeff Schaefer .01 .05
392 Mark Grant .01 .05
393 Carl Willis .01 .05
394 Al Leiter .02 .10
395 Ron Robinson .01 .05
396 Tim Hulett .01 .05
397 Craig Worthington .01 .05
398 John Orton .01 .05
399 Gary Carter TRIB .08 .25
400 John Dopson .01 .05
401 Moises Alou .08 .25
402 Gary Carter TRIB .08 .25
403 Matt Young .01 .05
404 Wayne Edwards .01 .05
405 Nick Esasky .01 .05
406 Dave Eiland .01 .05
407 Mike Brumley .01 .05
408 Bob Milacki .01 .05
409 Geno Petralli .01 .05
410 Dave Stewart .02 .10
411 Mike Jackson .02 .10
412 Luis Aquino .01 .05
413 Tim Teufel .01 .05
414 Jeff Ware .01 .05
415 Jim Deshaies .01 .05
416 Ellis Burks .02 .10
417 Allan Anderson .01 .05
418 Alfredo Griffin .01 .05
419 Wally Whitehurst .01 .05
420 Sandy Alomar Jr. .02 .10
421 Juan Agosto .01 .05
422 Sam Horn .01 .05
423 Jeff Fassero .01 .05
424 Paul McClellan .01 .05
425 Cecil Fielder .02 .10
426 Tim Raines .02 .10
427 Eddie Taubensee .02 .10
428 Dennis Boyd .01 .05
429 Tony LaRussa MG .02 .10
430 Steve Sax .01 .05
431 Tom Gordon .01 .05
432 Billy Hatcher .01 .05
433 Cal Eldred .01 .05
434 Wally Backman .01 .05
435 Mark Eichhorn .01 .05
436 Mookie Wilson .02 .10
437 Scott Servais .01 .05
438 Mike Maddux .01 .05
439 Chico Walker .01 .05
440 Doug Drabek .01 .05
441 Rob Deer .01 .05
442 Dave West .01 .05
443 Spike Owen .01 .05
444 Tyrone Hill .01 .05
445 Matt Williams .05 .15
446 Mark Lewis .01 .05
447 David Segui .01 .05
448 Tom Pagnozzi .01 .05
449 Jeff Johnson .01 .05
450 Mark McGwire .40 1.00
451 Tom Henke .01 .05
452 Wilson Alvarez .02 .10
453 Gary Redus .01 .05
454 Darren Holmes .01 .05
455 Pete O'Brien .01 .05
456 Pat Combs .01 .05
457 Hubie Brooks .01 .05
Now with Angels
12-10-91
458 Frank Tanana .01 .05
459 Tom Kelly MG .01 .05
460 Andre Dawson .05 .15
461 Doug Jones .01 .05
462 Rich Rodriguez .01 .05
463 Mike Simms .01 .05
464 Mike Jeffcoat .01 .05
465 Barry Larkin .15 .40
466 Stan Belinda .01 .05
467 Lonnie Smith .01 .05
468 Greg A. Harris .01 .05
469 Jim Eisenreich .01 .05
470 Pedro Guerrero .01 .05
471 Jose DeJesus .01 .05
472 Rich Rowland .01 .05
473 Frank Bolick .15 .40
Craig Paquette
Tom Redington
Paul Russo UER
Line around top border
474 Mike Rossiter .01 .05
475 Robby Thompson .01 .05
476 Randy Bush .01 .05
477 Greg Hibbard .01 .05
478 Dale Sveum .02 .10
Now with Phillies
12-11-91
479 Chito Martinez .01 .05
480 Scott Sanderson .01 .05
481 Tino Martinez .08 .25
482 Jimmy Key .02 .10
483 Terry Shumpert .01 .05
484 Mike Hartley .01 .05
485 Chris Sabo .01 .05
486 Bob Walk .01 .05
487 John Cerutti .01 .05
488 Scott Cooper .01 .05
489 Bobby Cox MG .02 .10
490 Julio Franco .02 .10
491 Jeff Brantley .01 .05
492 Mike Devereaux .01 .05
493 Jose Offerman .01 .05
494 Gary Thurman .01 .05
495 Carney Lansford .02 .10
496 Joe Grahe .01 .05
497 Andy Ashby .01 .05
498 Gerald Perry .01 .05
499 Dave Otto .01 .05
500 Vince Coleman .01 .05
501 Rob Mallicoat .01 .05
502 Greg Briley .01 .05
503 Pascual Perez .01 .05
504 Aaron Sele RC .40 1.00
505 Bobby Thigpen .01 .05
506 Todd Benzinger .01 .05
507 Candy Maldonado .01 .05
508 Bill Gullickson .01 .05
509 Doug Dascenzo .01 .05
510 Frank Viola .01 .05
511 Kenny Rogers .01 .05
512 Mike Heath .01 .05
513 Kevin Bass .01 .05
514 Kim Batiste .01 .05
515 Delino DeShields .02 .10
516 Ed Sprague .01 .05
517 Jim Gott .01 .05
518 Jose Melendez .01 .05
519 Hal McRae MG .01 .05
520 Jeff Bagwell .30 .75
521 Joe Hesketh .01 .05
522 Milt Cuyler .01 .05
523 Shawn Hillegas .01 .05
524 Don Slaught .01 .05
525 Randy Johnson .20 .50
526 Doug Piatt .01 .05
527 Checklist 397-528 .01 .05
528 Steve Foster .01 .05
529 Joe Girardi .02 .10
530 Jim Abbott .02 .10
531 Larry Walker .05 .15
532 Mike Huff .01 .05
533 Mackey Sasser .01 .05
534 Benji Gil .01 .05
535 Dave Stieb .01 .05
536 Willie Wilson .01 .05
537 Mark Leiter .01 .05
538 Jose Uribe .01 .05
539 Thomas Howard .01 .05
540 Ben McDonald .01 .05
541 Jose Tolentino .01 .05
542 Keith Mitchell .01 .05
543 Jerome Walton .01 .05
544 Cliff Brantley .01 .05
545 Andy Van Slyke .02 .10
546 Paul Sorrento .01 .05
547 Herm Winningham .01 .05
548 Mark Guthrie .01 .05
549 Joe Torre MG .02 .10
550 Darryl Strawberry .02 .10
551 Wilfredo Cordero .75 2.00
Chipper Jones
Manny Alexander
Alex Arias UER
No line around top border
552 Dave Gallagher .01 .05
553 Edgar Martinez .05 .15
554 Donald Harris .01 .05
555 Frank Thomas .20 .50
556 Storm Davis .01 .05
557 Dickie Thon .01 .05
558 Scott Garrelts .01 .05
559 Steve Olin .01 .05
560 Rickey Henderson .30 .75
561 Jose Vizcaino .01 .05
562 Wade Taylor .01 .05
563 Pat Borders .01 .05
564 Jimmy Gonzalez .01 .05
565 Lee Smith .02 .10
566 Bill Sampen .01 .05
567 Dean Palmer .02 .10
568 Bryan Harvey .01 .05
569 Tony Pena .01 .05
570 Lou Whitaker .02 .10
571 Randy Tomlin .01 .05
572 Greg Vaughn .01 .05
573 Kelly Downs .01 .05
574 Steve Avery UER .01 .05
(Should be 13 games
for Durham in 1989)
575 Kirby Puckett .40 1.00
576 Heathcliff Slocumb .01 .05
577 Kevin Seitzer .01 .05
578 Lee Guetterman .01 .05
579 Johnny Oates MG .01 .05
580 Greg Maddux .40 1.00
581 Stan Javier .01 .05
582 Vicente Palacios .01 .05
583 Mel Rojas .01 .05
584 Wayne Rosenthal .01 .05
585 Lenny Webster .01 .05
586 Rod Nichols .01 .05
587 Mickey Morandini .01 .05
588 Russ Swan .01 .05
589 Mariano Duncan .01 .05
Now with Phillies
12-10-91
590 Howard Johnson .01 .05
591 Jeromy Burnitz .08 .25
Jacob Brumfield
Alan Cockrell
D.J. Dozier
592 Denny Neagle .02 .10
593 Steve Decker .01 .05
594 Brian Barber .01 .05
595 Bruce Hurst .01 .05
596 Kent Mercker .01 .05
597 Mike Magnante .01 .05
598 Jody Reed .01 .05
599 Steve Searcy .01 .05
600 Paul Molitor .15 .40
601 Dave Smith .01 .05
602 Mike Fetters .01 .05
603 Luis Mercedes .01 .05
604 Chris Gwynn .02 .10
Now with Royals
12-11-91
605 Scott Erickson .01 .05
606 Brook Jacoby .01 .05
607 Todd Stottlemyre .01 .05
608 Scott Bradley .01 .05
609 Mike Hargrove MG .02 .10
610 Eric Davis .01 .05
611 Brian Hunter .01 .05
612 Pat Kelly .01 .05
613 Pedro Munoz .01 .05
614 Al Osuna .01 .05
615 Matt Merullo .01 .05
616 Larry Andersen .01 .05
617 Junior Ortiz .01 .05
618 Cesar Hernandez .01 .05
Steve Hosey
Jeff McNeely
Dan Peltier
619 Danny Jackson .01 .05
620 George Brett .30 .75
621 Dan Gakeler .01 .05
622 Steve Buechele .01 .05
623 Bob Tewksbury .01 .05
624 Shawn Estes RC .40 1.00
625 Kevin McReynolds .01 .05
626 Chris Haney .01 .05
627 Mike Sharperson .01 .05
628 Mark Williamson .01 .05
629 Wally Joyner .02 .10
630 Carlton Fisk .15 .40
631 Armando Reynoso .01 .05
632 Felix Fermin .01 .05
633 Mitch Williams .01 .05
634 Manuel Lee .01 .05
635 Harold Baines .05 .15
636 Greg W. Harris .01 .05
637 Orlando Merced .01 .05
638 Chris Bosio .01 .05
639 Wayne Housie .01 .05
640 Xavier Hernandez .01 .05
641 David Howard .01 .05
642 Tim Crews .01 .05
643 Rick Cerone .01 .05
644 Terry Leach .01 .05
645 Deion Sanders .08 .25
646 Craig Wilson .01 .05
647 Marquis Grissom .02 .10
648 Scott Fletcher .01 .05
649 Norm Charlton .01 .05
650 Jesse Barfield .01 .05
651 Joe Slusarski .01 .05
652 Bobby Rose .01 .05
653 Dennis Lamp .01 .05
654 Allen Watson .01 .05
655 Brett Butler .02 .10
656 Rudy Pemberton .05 .15
Henry Rodriguez
Lee Tinsley
Gerald Williams
657 Dave Johnson .01 .05
658 Checklist 529-660 .01 .05
659 Brian McRae .01 .05
660 Fred McGriff .05 .15
661 Bill Landrum .01 .05
662 Juan Guzman .01 .05
663 Greg Gagne .01 .05
664 Ken Hill .02 .10
Now with Expos
11-25-91
665 Dave Haas .01 .05
666 Tom Foley .01 .05
667 Roberto Hernandez .02 .10
668 Dwayne Henry .01 .05
669 Jim Fregosi MG .01 .05
670 Harold Reynolds .02 .10
671 Mark Whiten .01 .05
672 Eric Plunk .01 .05
673 Todd Hundley .02 .10
674 Mo Sanford .01 .05
675 Bobby Witt .01 .05
676 Sam Militello .01 .05
Pat Mahomes
Turk Wendell
Roger Salkeld
677 John Marzano .01 .05
678 Joe Klink .01 .05
679 Pete Incaviglia .01 .05
680 Dale Murphy .15 .40
681 Rene Gonzales .01 .05
682 Andy Benes .01 .05
683 Jim Poole .01 .05
684 Trever Miller .01 .05
685 Scott Livingstone .01 .05
686 Rich DeLucia .01 .05
687 Harvey Pulliam .01 .05
688 Tim Belcher .01 .05
689 Mark Lemke .01 .05
690 John Franco .02 .10
691 Walt Weiss .01 .05
692 Scott Ruskin .02 .10
Now with Reds
12-11-91
693 Jeff King .01 .05
694 Mike Gardiner .01 .05
695 Gary Sheffield .20 .50
696 Joe Boever .01 .05
697 Mike Felder .01 .05
698 John Habyan .01 .05
699 Cito Gaston MG .01 .05
700 Ruben Sierra .02 .10
701 Scott Radinsky .01 .05
702 Lee Stevens .01 .05
703 Mark Wohlers .01 .05
704 Curt Young .01 .05
705 Dwight Evans .02 .10
706 Rob Murphy .01 .05
707 Gregg Jefferies .02 .10
Now with Royals
12-11-91
708 Tom Bolton .01 .05
709 Chris James .01 .05
710 Kevin Maas .01 .05
711 Ricky Bones .01 .05
712 Curt Wilkerson .01 .05
713 Roger McDowell .01 .05
714 Pokey Reese RC .15 .40
715 Craig Biggio .05 .15
716 Kirk Dressendorfer .01 .05
717 Ken Dayley .01 .05
718 B.J. Surhoff .02 .10
719 Terry Mulholland .01 .05
720 Kirk Gibson .02 .10
721 Mike Pagliarulo .01 .05
722 Walt Terrell .01 .05
723 Jose Oquendo .01 .05
724 Kevin Morton .01 .05
725 Dwight Gooden .02 .10
726 Kirt Manwaring .01 .05
727 Chuck McElroy .01 .05
728 Dave Burba .01 .05
729 Art Howe MG .01 .05
730 Ramon Martinez .01 .05
731 Donnie Hill .01 .05
732 Nelson Santovenia .01 .05
733 Bob Melvin .01 .05
734 Scott Hatteberg .02 .10
735 Greg Swindell .02 .10
Now with Reds
11-15-91
736 Lance Johnson .01 .05
737 Kevin Reimer .01 .05
738 Dennis Eckersley .15 .40
739 Rob Ducey .01 .05
740 Ken Caminiti .05 .15
741 Mark Gubicza .01 .05
742 Billy Spiers .01 .05
743 Darren Lewis .01 .05
744 Chris Hammond .01 .05
745 Dave Magadan .01 .05
746 Bernard Gilkey .01 .05
747 Willie Banks .01 .05
748 Matt Nokes .01 .05
749 Jerald Clark .01 .05
750 Travis Fryman .02 .10
751 Steve Wilson .01 .05
752 Billy Ripken .01 .05
753 Paul Assenmacher .01 .05
754 Charlie Hayes .01 .05
755 Alex Fernandez .01 .05
756 Gary Pettis .01 .05
757 Rob Dibble .01 .05
758 Tim Naehring .01 .05
759 Jeff Torborg MG .01 .05
760 Ozzie Smith .20 .50
761 Mike Fitzgerald .01 .05
762 John Burkett .01 .05
763 Kyle Abbott .01 .05
764 Tyler Green .01 .05
765 Pete Harnisch .01 .05
766 Mark Davis .01 .05
767 Kal Daniels .01 .05
768 Jim Thome .15 .40
769 Jack Howell .01 .05
770 Sid Bream .01 .05
771 Arthur Rhodes .01 .05
772 Garry Templeton .01 .05
773 Hal Morris .01 .05
774 Bud Black .01 .05
775 Ivan Calderon .01 .05
776 Doug Henry .01 .05
777 John Olerud .05 .15
778 Tim Leary .01 .05
779 Jay Bell .01 .05
780 Eddie Murray .20 .50
Now with Mets
11-27-91
781 Paul Abbott .01 .05
782 Phil Plantier .01 .05
783 Joe Magrane .01 .05
784 Ken Patterson .01 .05
785 Albert Belle .05 .15
786 Royce Clayton .01 .05
787 Checklist 661-792 .01 .05
788 Mike Stanton .01 .05
789 Bobby Valentine MG .01 .05
790 Joe Carter .02 .10
791 Danny Cox .01 .05
792 Dave Winfield .20 .50
Now with Blue Jays
12-19-91

1993 O-Pee-Chee

The 1993 O-Pee-Chee baseball set consists of 396 standard-size cards. This is the first year that the regular series does not parallel in design the series that Topps issued. The set was sold in wax packs with eight cards plus a random insert card from either a four-card World Series Heroes subset or an 18-card World Series Champions subset. The fronts features color action player photos with white borders. The player's name appears in a silver stripe across the bottom that overlaps the O-Pee-Chee logo. The backs display color close-ups next to a panel containing biographical data. The panel and a stripe at the bottom reflect the team colors. A white box in the center of the card contains statistics and bilingual (English and French) career highlights.

COMPLETE SET (396) 15.00 50.00
1 Jim Abbott .15 .40
Now with Yankees
12/6/92
2 Eric Anthony .02 .10
3 Harold Baines .07 .20
4 Roberto Alomar .25 .60
5 Steve Avery .02 .10
6 Jim Austin .02 .10
7 Mark Wohlers .02 .10
8 Steve Buechele .02 .10
9 Pedro Astacio .02 .10
10 Moises Alou .07 .20
11 Rod Beck .02 .10
12 Sandy Alomar Jr. .07 .20
13 Bret Boone .15 .40
14 Bryan Harvey .02 .10
15 Bobby Bonilla .07 .20
16 Brady Anderson .07 .20
17 Andy Benes .02 .10
18 Ruben Amaro Jr. .02 .10
19 Jay Bell .02 .10
20 Kevin Brown .15 .40
21 Scott Bankhead .07 .20
Now with Red Sox
12/8/92
22 Denis Boucher .02 .10
23 Kevin Appier .07 .20
24 Pat Kelly .02 .10
25 Rick Aguilera .02 .10
26 George Bell .02 .10
27 Steve Farr .02 .10
28 Chad Curtis .02 .10
29 Jeff Bagwell .60 1.50
30 Lance Blankenship .02 .10
31 Derek Bell .02 .10
32 Damon Berryhill .02 .10
33 Ricky Bones .02 .10
34 Rheal Cormier .02 .10
35 Andre Dawson .25 .60
Now with Red Sox
12/2/92
36 Brett Butler .07 .20
37 Sean Berry .02 .10
38 Bud Black .02 .10
39 Carlos Baerga .07 .20
40 Jay Buhner .15 .40
41 Charlie Hough .07 .20
42 Sid Fernandez .02 .10
43 Luis Mercedes .02 .10
44 Jerald Clark .07 .20
Now with Rockies

11/17/92
45 Wes Chamberlain .02 .10
46 Barry Bonds .75 2.00
Now with Giants
12/8/92
47 Jose Canseco .30 .75
48 Tim Belcher .02 .10
49 David Nied .02 .10
50 George Brett .60 1.50
51 Cecil Fielder .07 .20
52 Chili Davis .07 .20
Now with Angels
12/11/92
53 Alex Fernandez .02 .10
54 Charlie Hayes .07 .20
Now with Rockies
11/17/92
55 Rob Ducey .02 .10
56 Craig Biggio .25 .60
57 Mike Bordick .02 .10
58 Pat Borders .02 .10
59 Jeff Blauser .02 .10
60 Chris Bosio .07 .20
Now with Mariners
12/3/92
61 Bernard Gilkey .02 .10
62 Shawon Dunston .02 .10
63 Tom Candiotti .02 .10
64 Darrin Fletcher .02 .10
65 Jeff Brantley .07 .20
66 Albert Belle .07 .20
67 Dave Fleming .02 .10
68 John Franco .07 .20
69 Glenn Davis .02 .10
70 Tony Fernandez .07 .20
Now with Mets
10/26/92
71 Darren Daulton .07 .20
72 Doug Drabek .07 .20
Now with Astros
12/1/92
73 Julio Franco .07 .20
74 Tom Browning .02 .10
75 Tom Gordon .07 .20
76 Travis Fryman .07 .20
77 Scott Erickson .02 .10
78 Carlton Fisk .25 .60
79 Roberto Kelly .07 .20
Now with Reds
11/3/92
80 Gary DiSarcina .02 .10
81 Ken Caminiti .15 .40
82 Ron Darling .02 .10
83 Joe Carter .07 .20
84 Sid Bream .02 .10
85 Cal Eldred .02 .10
86 Mark Grace .15 .40
87 Eric Davis .07 .20
88 Ivan Calderon .07 .20
Now with Red Sox
12/8/92
89 John Burkett .02 .10
90 Felix Fermin .02 .10
91 Ken Griffey Jr. .75 2.00
92 Dwight Gooden .07 .20
93 Mike Devereaux .02 .10
94 Tony Gwynn .75 2.00
95 Mariano Duncan .02 .10
96 Jeff King .02 .10
97 Juan Gonzalez .25 .60
98 Norm Charlton .07 .20
Now with Mariners
11/17/92
99 Mark Gubicza .02 .10
100 Danny Gladden .02 .10
101 Greg Gagne .07 .20
Now with Royals
12/8/92
102 Ozzie Guillen .07 .20
103 Don Mattingly .75 2.00
104 Damion Easley .02 .10
105 Casey Candaele .02 .10
106 Dennis Eckersley .30 .75
107 David Cone .15 .40
Now with Royals
12/8/92
108 Ron Gant .02 .10
109 Mike Fetters .02 .10
110 Mike Harkey .02 .10
111 Kevin Gross .02 .10
112 Archi Cianfrocco .02 .10
113 Will Clark .25 .60
114 Glenallen Hill .02 .10
115 Erik Hanson .02 .10
116 Todd Hundley .07 .20
117 Leo Gomez .02 .10
118 Bruce Hurst .02 .10
119 Len Dykstra .07 .20
120 Jose Lind .07 .20
Now with Royals
11/19/92
121 Jose Guzman .07 .20
Now with Cubs
12/1/92
122 Rob Dibble .02 .10
123 Gregg Jefferies .02 .10
124 Bill Gullickson .02 .10
125 Brian Harper .02 .10
126 Roberto Hernandez .07 .20
127 Sam Militello .02 .10
128 Junior Felix .07 .20
Now with Marlins
11/17/92
129 Andujar Cedeno .02 .10
130 Rickey Henderson .40 1.00
131 Bob MacDonald .02 .10
132 Tom Glavine .30 .75
133 Scott Fletcher .07 .20
Now with Red Sox
11/30/92
134 Brian Jordan .07 .20
135 Greg Maddux 1.00 2.50
Now with Braves
12/9/92
136 Orel Hershiser .07 .20
137 Greg Colbrunn .02 .10
138 Royce Clayton .02 .10
139 Thomas Howard .02 .10
140 Randy Johnson .40 1.00
141 Jeff Innis .02 .10
142 Chris Hoiles .02 .10
143 Darrin Jackson .02 .10
144 Tommy Greene .02 .10
145 Mike LaValliere .02 .10
146 David Hulse .02 .10
147 Barry Larkin .15 .40
148 Wally Joyner .07 .20
149 Mike Henneman .02 .10
150 Kent Hrbek .07 .20
151 Bo Jackson .25 .60
152 Rich Monteleone .02 .10
153 Chuck Finley .07 .20
154 Steve Finley .07 .20
155 Dave Henderson .02 .10
156 Kelly Gruber .07 .20
Now with Angels
12/8/92
157 Brian Hunter .02 .10
158 Darryl Hamilton .02 .10
159 Derrick May .02 .10
160 Jay Howell .02 .10
161 Wil Cordero .02 .10
162 Bryan Hickerson .02 .10
163 Reggie Jefferson .02 .10
164 Edgar Martinez .15 .40
165 Nigel Wilson .02 .10
166 Howard Johnson .02 .10
167 Tim Hulett .02 .10
168 Mike Maddux .07 .20
Now with Mets
12/17/92
169 Dave Hollins .02 .10
170 Zane Smith .02 .10
171 Rafael Palmeiro .25 .60
172 Dave Martinez .07 .20
Now with Giants
12/9/92
173 Rusty Meacham .02 .10
174 Mark Leiter .02 .10
175 Chuck Knoblauch .25 .60
176 Lance Johnson .02 .10
177 Matt Nokes .02 .10
178 Luis Gonzalez .25 .60
179 Jack Morris .07 .20
180 David Justice .25 .60
181 Doug Henry .02 .10
182 Felix Jose .02 .10
183 Delino DeShields .02 .10
184 Rene Gonzales .02 .10
185 Pete Harnisch .02 .10
186 Mike Moore .07 .20
Now with Tigers
12/9/92
187 Juan Guzman .02 .10
188 John Olerud .15 .40
189 Ryan Klesko .07 .20
190 John Jaha .02 .10
191 Ray Lankford .07 .20
192 Jeff Fassero .02 .10
193 Darren Lewis .02 .10
194 Mark Lewis .02 .10
195 Alan Mills .02 .10
196 Wade Boggs .40 1.00
Now with Yankees
12/15/92
197 Hal Morris .02 .10
198 Ron Karkovice .02 .10
199 Joe Grahe .02 .10
200 Butch Henry .07 .20
Now with Rockies
11/17/92
201 Mark McGwire 1.00 2.50
202 Tom Henke .07 .20
Now with Rangers
12/15/92
203 Ed Sprague .02 .10
204 Charlie Leibrandt .07 .20
Now with Rangers
12/9/92
205 Pat Listach .02 .10
206 Omar Olivares .02 .10
207 Mike Morgan .02 .10
208 Eric Karros .15 .40
209 Marquis Grissom .07 .20
210 Willie McGee .07 .20
211 Derek Lilliquist .02 .10
212 Tino Martinez .25 .60
213 Jeff Kent .15 .40
214 Mike Mussina .25 .60
215 Randy Myers .07 .20
Now with Cubs
12/9/92
216 John Kruk .07 .20
217 Tom Brunansky .02 .10
218 Paul O'Neill .15 .40
Now with Yankees
11/3/92
219 Scott Livingstone .02 .10
220 John Valentin .02 .10
221 Eddie Zosky .02 .10
222 Pete Smith .02 .10
223 Bill Wegman .02 .10
224 Todd Zeile .07 .20
225 Tim Wallach .07 .20
Now with Dodgers
12/24/92
226 Mitch Williams .02 .10
227 Tim Wakefield .15 .40
228 Frank Viola .02 .10
229 Nolan Ryan 1.25 3.00
230 Kirk McCaskill .02 .10
231 Melido Perez .02 .10
232 Mark Langston .02 .10
233 Xavier Hernandez .02 .10
234 Jerry Browne .02 .10
235 Dave Stieb .07 .20
Now with White Sox
12/8/92
236 Mark Lemke .02 .10
237 Paul Molitor .25 .60
Now with Blue Jays
12/7/92
238 Geronimo Pena .02 .10
239 Ken Hill .02 .10
240 Jack Clark .02 .10
241 Greg Myers .02 .10
242 Pete Incaviglia .07 .20
Now with Phillies
12/8/92
243 Ruben Sierra .07 .20
244 Todd Stottlemyre .02 .10
245 Pat Hentgen .07 .20
246 Melvin Nieves .02 .10
247 Jaime Navarro .02 .10
248 Donovan Osborne .02 .10
249 Brian Barnes .02 .10
250 Cory Snyder .07 .20
Now with Dodgers
12/5/92
251 Kenny Lofton .15 .40
252 Kevin Mitchell .07 .20
Now with Reds
11/17/92
253 Dave Magadan .07 .20
Now with Marlins
12/8/92
254 Ben McDonald .02 .10
255 Fred McGriff .15 .40
256 Mickey Morandini .02 .10
257 Randy Tomlin .02 .10
258 Dean Palmer .07 .20
259 Roger Clemens .75 2.00
260 Joe Oliver .02 .10
261 Jeff Montgomery .07 .20
262 Tony Phillips .02 .10
263 Shane Mack .02 .10
264 Jack McDowell .02 .10
265 Mike Macfarlane .02 .10
266 Luis Polonia .02 .10
267 Doug Jones .02 .10
268 Terry Steinbach .02 .10
269 Jimmy Key .07 .20
Now with Yankees
12/10/92
270 Pat Tabler .02 .10
271 Otis Nixon .02 .10
272 Dave Nilsson .02 .10
273 Tom Pagnozzi .02 .10
274 Ryne Sandberg .60 1.50
275 Ramon Martinez .02 .10
276 Tim Laker .02 .10
277 Bill Swift .02 .10
278 Charles Nagy .02 .10
279 Harold Reynolds .15 .40
Now with Orioles
12/11/92
280 Eddie Murray .30 .75
281 Gregg Olson .02 .10
282 Frank Seminara .02 .10
283 Terry Mulholland .02 .10
284 Kevin Reimer .07 .20
Now with Brewers
11/17/92
285 Mike Greenwell .02 .10
286 Jose Rijo .02 .10
287 Brian McRae .02 .10
288 Frank Tanana .07 .20
Now with Mets
12/10/92
289 Pedro Munoz .02 .10
290 Tim Raines .07 .20
291 Andy Stankiewicz .02 .10
292 Tim Salmon .25 .60
293 Jimmy Jones .02 .10
294 Dave Stewart .07 .20
Now with Blue Jays
12/8/92
295 Mike Timlin .02 .10
296 Greg Olson .02 .10
297 Dan Plesac .07 .20
Now with Cubs
12/8/92
298 Mike Perez .02 .10
299 Jose Offerman .02 .10
300 Denny Martinez .07 .20
301 Robby Thompson .02 .10
302 Bret Saberhagen .07 .20
303 Joe Orsulak .07 .20
Now with Mets
12/18/92
304 Tim Naehring .02 .10
305 Bip Roberts .02 .10
306 Kirby Puckett .60 1.50
307 Steve Sax .02 .10
308 Danny Tartabull .02 .10
309 Jeff Juden .02 .10
310 Duane Ward .02 .10
311 Alejandro Pena .07 .20
Now with Pirates
12/10/92
312 Kevin Seitzer .02 .10
313 Ozzie Smith .40 1.00
314 Mike Piazza 1.25 3.00
315 Chris Nabholz .02 .10
316 Tony Pena .07 .20
317 Gary Sheffield .40 1.00
318 Mark Portugal .02 .10
319 Walt Weiss .07 .20
Now with Marlins
11/17/92
320 Manuel Lee .07 .20
Now with Rangers
12/19/92
321 David Wells .15 .40
322 Terry Pendleton .02 .10
323 Billy Spiers .02 .10
324 Lee Smith .07 .20
325 Bob Scanlan .02 .10
326 Mike Scioscia .07 .20
327 Spike Owen .07 .20
Now with Yankees
12/4/92
328 Mackey Sasser .07 .20
Now with Mariners
12/23/92
329 Arthur Rhodes .02 .10
330 Ben Rivera .02 .10
331 Ivan Rodriguez .40 1.00
332 Phil Plantier .07 .20
Now with Padres
12/10/92
333 Chris Sabo .02 .10
334 Mickey Tettleton .02 .10
335 John Smiley .07 .20
Now with Reds
11/30/92
336 Bobby Thigpen .02 .10
337 Randy Velarde .02 .10
338 Luis Sojo .07 .20
Now with Blue Jays
12/8/92
339 Scott Servais .02 .10
340 Bob Welch .02 .10
341 Devon White .02 .10
342 Jeff Reardon .07 .20
343 B.J. Surhoff .07 .20
344 Bob Tewksbury .02 .10
345 Jose Vizcaino .02 .10
346 Mike Sharperson .02 .10
347 Mel Rojas .02 .10
348 Matt Williams .15 .40
349 Steve Olin .02 .10
350 Mike Schooler .02 .10
351 Ryan Thompson .02 .10
352 Cal Ripken 1.25 3.00
353 Benito Santiago .15 .40
Now with Marlins
12/16/92
354 Curt Schilling .30 .75
355 Andy Van Slyke .02 .10
356 Kenny Rogers .02 .10
357 Jody Reed .07 .20
Now with Dodgers
11/17/92
358 Reggie Sanders .15 .40
359 Kevin McReynolds .02 .10
360 Alan Trammell .15 .40
361 Kevin Tapani .02 .10
362 Frank Thomas .30 .75
363 Bernie Williams .25 .60
364 John Smoltz .07 .20
365 Robin Yount .40 1.00
366 John Wetteland .07 .20
367 Bob Zupcic .02 .10
368 Julio Valera .02 .10
369 Brian Williams .02 .10
370 Willie Wilson .02 .10
Now with Cubs
12/18/92
371 Dave Winfield .40 1.00
Now with Twins
12/17/92
372 Deion Sanders .15 .40
373 Greg Vaughn .07 .20
374 Todd Worrell .07 .20
Now with Dodgers
12/9/92
375 Darryl Strawberry .07 .20
376 John Vander Wal .02 .10
377 Mike Benjamin .02 .10
378 Mark Whiten .02 .10
379 Omar Vizquel .07 .20
380 Anthony Young .02 .10
381 Rick Sutcliffe .02 .10
382 Candy Maldonado .07 .20
Now with Cubs
12/11/92
383 Francisco Cabrera .02 .10
384 Larry Walker .15 .40
385 Scott Cooper .02 .10
386 Gerald Williams .02 .10
387 Robin Ventura .15 .40
388 Carl Willis .02 .10
389 Lou Whitaker .07 .20
390 Hipolito Pichardo .02 .10
391 Rudy Seanez .02 .10
392 Greg Swindell .07 .20
Now with Astros
12/4/92
393 Mo Vaughn .25 .60
394 Checklist 1-132 .02 .10
395 Checklist 133-264 .02 .10
396 Checklist 265-396 .02 .10

1994 O-Pee-Chee

The 1994 O-Pee-Chee baseball set consists of 270 standard-size cards. Production was limited to 2,500 individually numbered cases. Each display box contained 36 packs and one 5" by 7" All-Star Jumbo card. Each foil pack contained 14 regular cards plus either one chase card or one redemption card.

COMPLETE SET (270) 6.00 15.00
1 Paul Molitor .15 .40
2 Kirt Manwaring .01 .05
3 Brady Anderson .02 .10
4 Scott Cooper .01 .05
5 Kevin Stocker .01 .05
6 Alex Fernandez .01 .05
7 Jeff Montgomery .02 .10
8 Danny Tartabull .01 .05
9 Damion Easley .01 .05
10 Andujar Cedeno .01 .05
11 Steve Karsay .01 .05
12 Dave Stewart .02 .10
13 Fred McGriff .05 .15
14 Jaime Navarro .01 .05
15 Allen Watson .01 .05
16 Ryne Sandberg .30 .75
17 Arthur Rhodes .01 .05
18 Marquis Grissom .02 .10
19 John Burkett .01 .05
20 Robby Thompson .01 .05
21 Denny Martinez .02 .10
22 Ken Griffey Jr. .60 1.50
23 Orestes Destrade .01 .05
24 Dwight Gooden .02 .10
25 Rafael Palmeiro .08 .25
26 Pedro A.Martinez .01 .05
27 Wes Chamberlain .01 .05
28 Juan Gonzalez .08 .25
29 Kevin Mitchell .01 .05
30 Dante Bichette .02 .10
31 Howard Johnson .01 .05
32 Mickey Tettleton .01 .05
33 Robin Ventura .05 .15
34 Terry Mulholland .01 .05
35 Bernie Williams .08 .25
36 Eduardo Perez .01 .05
37 Rickey Henderson .20 .50
38 Terry Pendleton .01 .05
39 John Smoltz .08 .25
40 Derrick May .01 .05
41 Pedro Martinez .20 .50
42 Mark Portugal .01 .05
43 Albert Belle .04 .10
44 Edgar Martinez .05 .15
45 Gary Sheffield .20 .50
46 Bret Saberhagen .02 .10
47 Ricky Gutierrez .01 .05
48 Orlando Merced .01 .05
49 Mike Greenwell .01 .05
50 Jose Rijo .01 .05
51 Jeff Granger .01 .05
52 Mike Henneman .01 .05
53 Dave Winfield .15 .40
54 Don Mattingly .40 1.00
55 J.T. Snow .02 .10
56 Todd Van Poppel .01 .05
57 Chipper Jones .30 .75
58 Darryl Hamilton .01 .05
59 Delino DeShields .01 .05
60 Rondell White .02 .10
61 Eric Anthony .01 .05
62 Charlie Hough .01 .05
63 Sid Fernandez .01 .05
64 Derek Bell .01 .05
65 Phil Plantier .01 .05
66 Curt Schilling .15 .40
67 Roger Clemens .40 1.00
68 Jose Lind .01 .05
69 Andres Galarraga .08 .25
70 Tim Belcher .01 .05
71 Ron Karkovice .01 .05
72 Alan Trammell .05 .15
73 Pete Harnisch .01 .05
74 Mark McGwire .50 1.25
75 Ryan Klesko .02 .10
76 Ramon Martinez .01 .05
77 Gregg Jefferies .01 .05
78 Steve Buechele .01 .05
79 Bill Swift .01 .05
80 Matt Williams .05 .15
81 Randy Johnson .20 .50
82 Mike Mussina .08 .25
83 Andy Benes .01 .05
84 Dave Staton .01 .05
85 Steve Cooke .01 .05
86 Andy Van Slyke .01 .05
87 Ivan Rodriguez .20 .50
88 Frank Viola .01 .05
89 Aaron Sele .02 .10
90 Ellis Burks .02 .10
91 Wally Joyner .02 .10
92 Rick Aguilera .01 .05
93 Kirby Puckett .40 1.00
94 Roberto Hernandez .01 .05
95 Mike Stanley .01 .05
96 Roberto Alomar .08 .25
97 James Mouton .01 .05
98 Chad Curtis .01 .05
99 Mitch Williams .01 .05
100 Carlos Delgado .20 .50
101 Greg Maddux .40 1.00
102 Brian Harper .01 .05
103 Tom Pagnozzi .01 .05
104 Jose Offerman .01 .05
105 John Wetteland .02 .10
106 Carlos Baerga .02 .10
107 Dave Magadan .01 .05
108 Bobby Jones .01 .05
109 Tony Gwynn .40 1.00
110 Jeromy Burnitz .05 .15
111 Bip Roberts .01 .05
112 Carlos Garcia .01 .05
113 Jeff Russell .01 .05
114 Armando Reynoso .01 .05
115 Ozzie Guillen .02 .10
116 Bo Jackson .05 .15
117 Terry Steinbach .01 .05
118 Deion Sanders .08 .25
119 Randy Myers .01 .05
120 Mark Whiten .01 .05
121 Manny Ramirez .20 .50
122 Ben McDonald .01 .05
123 Darren Daulton .02 .10
124 Kevin Young .01 .05
125 Barry Larkin .08 .25
126 Cecil Fielder .02 .10
127 Frank Thomas .20 .50
128 Luis Polonia .01 .05
129 Steve Finley .02 .10
130 John Olerud .02 .10
131 John Jaha .01 .05
132 Darren Lewis .01 .05
133 Orel Hershiser .02 .10
134 Chris Bosio .01 .05
135 Ryan Thompson .01 .05
136 Chris Sabo .01 .05
137 Tommy Greene .01 .05
138 Andre Dawson .08 .25
139 Roberto Kelly .01 .05
140 Ken Hill .01 .05
141 Greg Gagne .01 .05
142 Julio Franco .02 .10
143 Chili Davis .02 .10
144 Dennis Eckersley .15 .40
145 Joe Carter .02 .10
146 Mark Grace .05 .15
147 Mike Piazza .40 1.00
148 J.R. Phillips .01 .05
149 Rich Amaral .01 .05
150 Benny Santiago .02 .10
151 Jeff King .01 .05
152 Dean Palmer .02 .10
153 Hal Morris .01 .05
154 Mike Macfarlane .01 .05
155 Chuck Knoblauch .02 .10
156 Pat Kelly .01 .05
157 Greg Swindell .01 .05
158 Chuck Finley .02 .10
159 Devon White .02 .10
160 Duane Ward .01 .05
161 Sammy Sosa .25 .60
162 Javy Lopez .05 .15
163 Eric Karros .02 .10
164 Royce Clayton .01 .05
165 Salomon Torres .01 .05
166 Jeff Kent .02 .10
167 Chris Hoiles .01 .05
168 Len Dykstra .02 .10
169 Jose Canseco .15 .40
170 Bret Boone .02 .10
171 Charlie Hayes .01 .05
172 Lou Whitaker .02 .10
173 Jack McDowell .01 .05
174 Jimmy Key .02 .10
175 Mark Langston .01 .05
176 Darryl Kile .01 .05
177 Juan Guzman .01 .05
178 Pat Borders .01 .05
179 Cal Eldred .01 .05
180 Jose Guzman .01 .05
181 Ozzie Smith .25 .60
182 Rod Beck .01 .05
183 Dave Fleming .01 .05
184 Eddie Murray .15 .40
185 Cal Ripken .75 2.00
186 Dave Hollins .01 .05
187 Will Clark .08 .25
188 Otis Nixon .01 .05
189 Joe Oliver .01 .05
190 Roberto Mejia .01 .05
191 Felix Jose .01 .05
192 Tony Phillips .01 .05
193 Wade Boggs .20 .50
194 Tim Salmon .05 .15
195 Ruben Sierra .02 .10
196 Steve Avery .01 .05
197 B.J. Surhoff .02 .10
198 Todd Zeile .02 .10
199 Raul Mondesi .08 .25
200 Barry Bonds .40 1.00
201 Sandy Alomar .02 .10
202 Bobby Bonilla .01 .05
203 Mike Devereaux .01 .05
204 Ricky Bottalico RC .01 .05
205 Kevin Brown .05 .15
206 Jason Bere .01 .05
207 Reggie Sanders .02 .10
208 David Nied .01 .05
209 Travis Fryman .02 .10
210 James Baldwin .01 .05
211 Jim Abbott .02 .10
212 Jeff Bagwell .30 .75
213 Bob Welch .02 .10
214 Jeff Blauser .01 .05
215 Brett Butler .02 .10
216 Pat Listach .01 .05
217 Bob Tewksbury .01 .05
218 Mike Lansing .01 .05
219 Wayne Kirby .01 .05
220 Chuck Carr .01 .05
221 Harold Baines .02 .10
222 Jay Bell .01 .05
223 Cliff Floyd .05 .15
224 Rob Dibble .01 .05
225 Kevin Appier .02 .10
226 Eric Davis .02 .10
227 Matt Walbeck .01 .05
228 Tim Raines .02 .10
229 Paul O'Neill .02 .10
230 Craig Biggio .08 .25
231 Brent Gates .01 .05
232 Rob Butler .01 .05
233 David Justice .05 .15
234 Rene Arocha .01 .05
235 Mike Morgan .01 .05
236 Denis Boucher .01 .05
237 Kenny Lofton .02 .10
238 Jeff Conine .02 .10
239 Bryan Harvey .01 .05
240 Danny Jackson .01 .05
241 Al Martin .01 .05
242 Tom Henke .01 .05
243 Erik Hanson .01 .05
244 Walt Weiss .01 .05
245 Brian McRae .01 .05
246 Kevin Tapani .01 .05
247 David McCarty .01 .05
248 Doug Drabek .01 .05
249 Troy Neel .01 .05
250 Tom Glavine .08 .25
251 Ray Lankford .02 .10
252 Wil Cordero .01 .05
253 Larry Walker .05 .15
254 Charles Nagy .01 .05
255 Kirk Rueter .01 .05
256 John Franco .02 .10
257 John Kruk .02 .10
258 Alex Gonzalez .01 .05
259 Mo Vaughn .08 .25
260 David Cone .05 .15
261 Kent Hrbek .02 .10
262 Lance Johnson .01 .05
263 Luis Gonzalez .08 .25
264 Mike Bordick .01 .05
265 Ed Sprague .01 .05
266 Moises Alou .05 .15
267 Omar Vizquel .02 .10
268 Jay Buhner .02 .10
269 Checklist .01 .05
270 Checklist .01 .05

2009 O-Pee-Chee

COMPLETE SET (600) 60.00 120.00
COMMON CARD (1-560) .15 .40
COMMON RC (561-600) .40 1.00
RC ODDS 1:3 HOBBY/RETAIL
CL ODDS 1:3 HOBBY/RETAIL
MOMENT ODDS 1:6 HOBBY/RETAIL
LL ODDS 1:8 HOBBY/RETAIL
1 Melvin Mora .15 .40
2 Jim Thome .25 .60
3 Jonathan Sanchez .15 .40
4 Cesar Izturis .15 .40
5 A.J. Pierzynski .15 .40
6 Adam LaRoche .15 .40
7 J.D. Drew .15 .40
8 Brian Schneider .15 .40
9 John Grabow .15 .40
10 Jimmy Rollins .25 .60
11 Jeff Baker .15 .40
12 Daniel Cabrera .15 .40
13 Kyle Lohse .15 .40
14 Jason Giambi .15 .40
15 Nate McLouth .15 .40
16 Gary Matthews .15 .40
17 Cody Ross .15 .40
18 Justin Masterson .15 .40
19 Jose Lopez .15 .40
20 Brian Roberts .15 .40
21 Cla Meredith .15 .40
22 Ben Francisco .15 .40
23 Brian McCann .25 .60
24 Carlos Guillen .15 .40
25 Chien-Ming Wang .25 .60
26 Brandon Phillips .15 .40
27 Saul Rivera .15 .40
28 Torii Hunter .15 .40
29 Jamie Moyer .15 .40
30 Kevin Youkilis .25 .60
31 Martin Prado .15 .40
32 Magglio Ordonez .25 .60
33 Nomar Garciaparra .40 1.00
34 Takashi Saito .15 .40
35 Chase Headley .15 .40
36 Mike Pelfrey .15 .40
37 Ronny Cedeno .15 .40
38 Dallas McPherson .15 .40
39 Zack Greinke .25 .60
40 Matt Cain .15 .40
41 Xavier Nady .15 .40
42 Willie Aybar .15 .40
43 Edgar Gonzalez .15 .40
44 Gabe Gross .15 .40
45 Joey Votto .40 1.00
46 Jason Michaels .15 .40
47 Eric Chavez .15 .40
48 Jason Bartlett .15 .40
49 Jeremy Guthrie .15 .40
50 Matt Holliday .40 1.00
51 Ross Ohlendorf .15 .40
52 Gil Meche .15 .40
53 B.J. Upton .25 .60
54 Ryan Doumit .15 .40
55 Jay Bruce .25 .60
56 Huston Street .15 .40
57 Bobby Crosby .15 .40
58 Jose Valverde .15 .40
59 Brian Tallet .15 .40
60 Adam Dunn .25 .60
61 Victor Martinez .25 .60
62 Jeff Francoeur .25 .60
63 Emilio Bonifacio .15 .40
64 Chone Figgins .15 .40
65 Alexei Ramirez .25 .60
66 Brian Giles .15 .40
67 Khalil Greene .15 .40
68 Phil Hughes .25 .60
69 Mike Aviles .15 .40
70 Ryan Braun .50 1.25
71 Braden Looper .15 .40
72 Jhonny Peralta .15 .40
73 Ian Stewart .15 .40
74 James Loney .25 .60
75 Chase Utley .40 1.00
76 Reed Johnson .15 .40
77 Jorge Cantu .15 .40
78 Julio Lugo .15 .40
79 Raul Ibanez .25 .60
80 Lance Berkman .25 .60
81 Joel Peralta .15 .40
82 Mark Hendrickson .15 .40
83 Jeff Suppan .15 .40
84 Scott Olsen .15 .40
85 Joba Chamberlain .25 .60
86 Fausto Carmona .15 .40
87 Andy Pettitte .25 .60
88 Jim Johnson .15 .40
89 Chris Snyder .15 .40
90 Nick Swisher .40 1.00
91 Edgar Renteria .15 .40
92 Brandon Inge .15 .40
93 Aubrey Huff .15 .40
94 Stephen Drew .15 .40
95 Denard Span .15 .40
96 Carl Crawford .25 .60
97 Felix Pie .15 .40
98 Jeremy Sowers .15 .40
99 Trevor Hoffman .25 .60
100 Albert Pujols 1.00 2.50
101 Radhames Liz .15 .40
102 Doug Davis .15 .40
103 Joel Hanrahan .25 .60
104 Seth Smith .15 .40
105 Francisco Liriano .15 .40
106 Bobby Abreu .15 .40
107 Willie Harris .15 .40
108 Travis Ishikawa .15 .40
109 Travis Hafner .15 .40
110 Adrian Gonzalez .25 .60
111 Shin-Soo Choo .25 .60
112 Robinson Cano .40 1.00
113 Matt Capps .15 .40
114 Gerald Laird .15 .40
115 Max Scherzer .25 .60
116 Mike Jacobs .15 .40
117 Asdrubal Cabrera .25 .60
118 J.J. Hardy .15 .40
119 Justin Upton .25 .60
120 Mariano Rivera .40 1.00
121 Jack Cust .15 .40
122 Orlando Hudson .15 .40
123 Brian Wilson .40 1.00
124 Heath Bell .25 .60
125 Chipper Jones .40 1.00
126 Jason Marquis .15 .40
127 Rocco Baldelli .15 .40
128 Rafael Perez .15 .40
129 Carlos Gomez .15 .40
130 Kerry Wood .15 .40
131 Adam Wainwright .25 .60
132 Michael Bourn .15 .40
133 Cristian Guzman .15 .40
134 Dustin McGowan .15 .40
135 James Shields .15 .40
136 Matt Lindstrom .15 .40
137 Rick Ankiel .15 .40
138 J.P. Howell .15 .40
139 Ben Zobrist .15 .40
140 Tim Hudson .25 .60
141 Clayton Kershaw .40 1.00
142 Edwin Encarnacion .15 .40
143 Kevin Millwood .15 .40
144 Jack Hannahan .15 .40
145 Alex Gordon .25 .60
146 Chad Durbin .15 .40
147 Derrek Lee .15 .40
148 Kevin Gregg .15 .40
149 Clint Barmes .15 .40
150 Dustin Pedroia .50 1.25
151 Brad Hawpe .15 .40
152 Steven Shell .15 .40
153 Jesse Crain .15 .40

154 Edwar Ramirez .15 .40
155 Jair Jurrjens .15 .40
156 Matt Albers .15 .40
157 Endy Chavez .15 .40
158 Steve Pearce .15 .40
159 John Maine .15 .40
160 Ryan Theriot .15 .40
161 Eric Stults .15 .40
162 Cha-Seung Baek .15 .40
163 Alex Gonzalez .15 .40
164 Dan Haren .15 .40
165 Edwin Jackson .15 .40
166 Felipe Lopez .15 .40
167 David DeJesus .15 .40
168 Todd Wellemeyer .15 .40
169 Joey Gathright .15 .40
170 Roy Oswalt .25 .60
171 Carlos Pena .25 .60
172 Nick Hundley .15 .40
173 Adrian Beltre .15 .40
174 Omar Vizquel .25 .60
175 Cole Hamels .40 1.00
176 Jarrod Saltalamacchia .15 .40
177 Yuniesky Betancourt .15 .40
178 Placido Polanco .15 .40
179 Ryan Spilborghs .15 .40
180 Josh Beckett .25 .60
181 Cory Wade .15 .40
182 Aaron Laffey .15 .40
183 Kosuke Fukudome .40 1.00
184 Miguel Montero .15 .40
185 Edinson Volquez .15 .40
186 Jon Garland .15 .40
187 Andruw Jones .15 .40
188 Vernon Wells .15 .40
189 Zach Duke .15 .40
190 David Wright .50 1.25
191 Ryan Madson .15 .40
192 Hideki Okajima .15 .40
193 Ryan Church .15 .40
194 Adam Jones .25 .60
195 Geovany Soto .25 .60
196 Jeremy Hermida .15 .40
197 Juan Rivera .15 .40
198 David Weathers .15 .40
199 Jorge Campillo .15 .40
200 Derek Jeter 1.00 2.50
201 Brett Myers .15 .40
202 Brett Gardner .15 .40
203 Rafael Furcal .15 .40
204 Wandy Rodriguez .15 .40
205 Ricky Nolasco .15 .40
206 Ryan Freel .15 .40
207 Jeremy Bonderman .15 .40
208 Michael Wuertz .15 .40
209 Hank Blalock .15 .40
210 Alfonso Soriano .25 .60
211 Jeff Clement .15 .40
212 Garrett Atkins .15 .40
213 Luis Vizcaino .15 .40
214 Tim Redding .15 .40
215 Ryan Ludwick .25 .60
216 Mark Teahen .15 .40
217 Chris Young .15 .40
218 David Aardsma .15 .40
219 Ubaldo Jimenez .25 .60
220 Ryan Howard .50 1.25
221 Skip Schumaker .15 .40
222 Craig Counsell .15 .40
223 Chris Iannetta .15 .40
224 Jason Kubel .15 .40
225 Johan Santana .40 1.00
226 Luke Hochevar .15 .40
227 Jason Bay .25 .60
228 Alex Hinshaw .15 .40
229 Jon Rauch .15 .40
230 Carlos Quentin .25 .60
231 Coco Crisp .15 .40
232 Casey Blake .15 .40
233 Carlos Marmol .25 .60
234 Fernando Rodney .15 .40
235 Jed Lowrie .25 .60
236 Brad Penny .15 .40
237 Reggie Willits .15 .40
238 Mike Hampton .15 .40
239 Mike Lowell .15 .40
240 Randy Johnson .25 .60
241 Jarrod Washburn .15 .40
242 B.J. Ryan .15 .40
243 Javier Vazquez .15 .40
244 Todd Helton .25 .60
245 Matt Garza .15 .40
246 Ramon Hernandez .15 .40
247 Johnny Cueto .15 .40
248 Willy Taveras .15 .40
249 Carlos Silva .15 .40
250 Manny Ramirez .40 1.00
251 A.J. Burnett .25 .60
252 Aaron Cook .15 .40
253 Josh Bard .15 .40
254 Aaron Harang .15 .40
255 Jeff Samardzija .25 .60
256 Brad Lidge .15 .40
257 Pedro Feliz .15 .40
258 Kazuo Matsui .15 .40
259 Joe Blanton .15 .40
260 Ian Kinsler .25 .60
261 Rich Harden .15 .40
262 Kelly Johnson .15 .40
263 Anibal Sanchez .15 .40
264 Mike Adams .15 .40
265 Chad Billingsley .15 .40
266 Chris Davis .15 .40
267 Brandon Moss .15 .40
268 Matt Kemp .25 .60
269 Jose Arredondo .15 .40
270 Mark Teixeira .40 1.00
271 Glen Perkins .15 .40
272 Pat Burrell .15 .40
273 Luke Scott .15 .40
274 Scott Feldman .25 .60
275 Ichiro Suzuki .60 1.50
276 Cliff Floyd .15 .40
277 Bill Hall .15 .40
278 Bronson Arroyo .15 .40
279 Lyle Overbay .15 .40
280 Aramis Ramirez .15 .40
281 Jeff Keppinger .15 .40
282 Brandon Morrow .15 .40
283 Ryan Shealy .15 .40
284 Andy Sonnanstine .15 .40
285 Josh Johnson .25 .60
286 Carlos Ruiz .15 .40
287 Gregg Zaun .15 .40
288 Kenji Johjima .25 .60
289 Mike Gonzalez .15 .40
290 Carlos Delgado .15 .40
291 Gary Sheffield .15 .40
292 Brian Anderson .15 .40
293 Josh Hamilton .40 1.00
294 Tom Gorzelanny .15 .40
295 Yunel Escobar .15 .40
296 Scott Hairston .15 .40
297 Luis Castillo .15 .40
298 Gabe Kapler .15 .40
299 Nelson Cruz .25 .60
300 Tim Lincecum .60 1.50
301 Brian Bannister .15 .40
302 Frank Francisco .15 .40
303 Jose Guillen .15 .40
304 Erick Aybar .15 .40
305 Brad Ziegler .15 .40
306 John Baker .15 .40
307 Hong-Chih Kuo .15 .40
308 Jo Jo Reyes .15 .40
309 Josh Willingham .15 .40
310 Billy Wagner .15 .40
311 Nick Blackburn .15 .40
312 David Purcey .15 .40
313 Rafael Soriano .15 .40
314 Zach Miner .15 .40
315 Andre Ethier .25 .60
316 Rickie Weeks .25 .60
317 Akinori Iwamura .15 .40
318 Hideki Matsui .40 1.00
319 Ryan Rowland-Smith .15 .40
320 Miguel Cabrera .40 1.00
321 Manny Parra .15 .40
322 Jack Wilson .15 .40
323 Jeremy Reed .15 .40
324 Chris Coste .15 .40
325 Grady Sizemore .25 .60
326 Andy LaRoche .15 .40
327 Joel Pineiro .15 .40
328 Brian Buscher .15 .40
329 Randy Wolf .15 .40
330 Jake Peavy .15 .40
331 Curtis Granderson .25 .60
332 Kyle Kendrick .15 .40
333 Joe Saunders .15 .40
334 Russell Martin .15 .40
335 Conor Jackson .15 .40
336 Paul Konerko .25 .60
337 Kevin Slowey .25 .60
338 Mark DeRosa .25 .60
339 Garret Anderson .15 .40
340 Michael Young .25 .60
341 Greg Dobbs .15 .40
342 Brian Moehler .15 .40
343 Alex Rios .25 .60
344 Mike Napoli .25 .60
345 Bobby Jenks .15 .40
346 Daric Barton .15 .40
347 Jason Kendall .15 .40
348 Chad Qualls .15 .40
349 Milton Bradley .15 .40
350 Joe Mauer .40 1.00
351 Livan Hernandez .15 .40
352 Chris Ray .15 .40
353 Bob Howry .15 .40
354 Manny Corpas .15 .40
355 Ervin Santana .15 .40
356 Billy Butler .15 .40
357 Russ Springer .15 .40
358 Micah Owings .15 .40
359 Corey Hart .15 .40
360 Francisco Rodriguez .25 .60
361 Ted Lilly .15 .40
362 Adam Everett .15 .40
363 Scott Rolen .25 .60
364 Troy Tulowitzki .40 1.00
365 Jacoby Ellsbury .40 1.00
366 Jayson Werth .25 .60
367 Gio Gonzalez .15 .40
368 Mark Ellis .15 .40
369 Brendan Harris .15 .40
370 David Ortiz .25 .60
371 Carlos Lee .15 .40
372 Jonathan Broxton .15 .40
373 Jesse Litsch .15 .40
374 Barry Zito .15 .40
375 Daisuke Matsuzaka .40 1.00
376 Kevin Kouzmanoff .15 .40
377 Jesse Carlson .15 .40
378 Brian Fuentes .15 .40
379 Mark Reynolds .15 .40
380 Brandon Webb .25 .60
381 Scott Kazmir .15 .40
382 Blake DeWitt .15 .40
383 Kurt Suzuki .15 .40
384 Chris Volstad .15 .40
385 Gavin Floyd .15 .40
386 Paul Maholm .15 .40
387 Freddy Sanchez .15 .40
388 Scott Baker .15 .40
389 John Danks .15 .40
390 CC Sabathia .25 .60
391 Ryan Dempster .15 .40
392 Tim Wakefield .15 .40
393 Mike Cameron .15 .40
394 Aaron Rowand .15 .40
395 Howie Kendrick .15 .40
396 Marlon Byrd .15 .40
397 Dave Bush .15 .40
398 George Sherrill .15 .40
399 Francisco Cordero .15 .40
400 Evan Longoria .50 1.25
401 Hiroki Kuroda .15 .40
402 Sean Gallagher .15 .40
403 Yovani Gallardo .15 .40
404 Ryan Sweeney .15 .40
405 Chris Dickerson .15 .40
406 Jason Varitek .40 1.00
407 Erik Bedard .15 .40
408 J.J. Putz .15 .40
409 Wily Mo Pena .15 .40
410 Rich Hill .15 .40
411 Delmon Young .25 .60
412 David Eckstein .15 .40
413 Marcus Thames .15 .40
414 Dontrelle Willis .15 .40
415 Joakim Soria .15 .40
416 Chan Ho Park .25 .60
417 Jered Weaver .15 .40
418 Justin Duchscherer .15 .40
419 Casey Kotchman .15 .40
420 John Lackey .15 .40
421 Peter Moylan .15 .40
422 Bengie Molina .15 .40
423 Mark Loretta .15 .40
424 Dan Wheeler .15 .40
425 Ken Griffey Jr. .60 1.50
426 Justin Verlander .50 1.25
427 Troy Glaus .15 .40
428 Daniel Murphy RC 1.00 2.50
429 Brandon Backe .15 .40
430 Nick Markakis .40 1.00
431 Travis Metcalf .15 .40
432 Austin Kearns .15 .40
433 Adam Lind .15 .40
434 Jody Gerut .15 .40
435 Jonathan Papelbon .25 .60
436 Duaner Sanchez .15 .40
437 David Murphy .15 .40
438 Eddie Guardado .15 .40
439 Johnny Damon .25 .60
440 Derek Lowe .15 .40
441 Miguel Olivo .15 .40
442 Shaun Marcum .15 .40
443 Ty Wigginton .25 .60
444 Elijah Dukes .15 .40
445 Felix Hernandez .40 1.00
446 Joe Inglett .15 .40
447 Kelly Shoppach .15 .40
448 Eric Hinske .15 .40
449 Fred Lewis .15 .40
450 Cliff Lee .25 .60
451 Miguel Tejada .25 .60
452 Jensen Lewis .15 .40
453 Ryan Zimmerman .25 .60
454 Jon Lester .40 1.00
455 Justin Morneau .40 1.00
456 John Smoltz .40 1.00
457 Emmanuel Burriss .15 .40
458 Joe Nathan .15 .40
459 Jeff Niemann .15 .40
460 Roy Halladay .40 1.00
461 Matt Diaz .15 .40
462 Oscar Salazar .15 .40
463 Chris Perez .15 .40
464 Matt Joyce .15 .40
465 Dan Uggla .25 .60
466 Jermaine Dye .15 .40
467 Shane Victorino .15 .40
468 Chris Getz .15 .40
469 Chris B. Young .15 .40
470 Prince Fielder .25 .60
471 Juan Pierre .15 .40
472 Travis Buck .15 .40
473 Dioner Navarro .15 .40
474 Mark Buehrle .25 .60
475 Hanley Ramirez .40 1.00
476 John Lannan .15 .40
477 Lastings Milledge .15 .40
478 Dallas Braden .25 .60
479 Orlando Cabrera .15 .40
480 Jose Reyes .25 .60
481 Jorge Posada .25 .60
482 Jason Isringhausen .15 .40
483 Rich Aurilia .15 .40
484 Hunter Pence .25 .60
485 Carlos Zambrano .25 .60
486 Randy Winn .15 .40
487 Carlos Beltran .15 .40
488 Armando Galarraga .15 .40
489 Wilson Betemit .15 .40
490 Vladimir Guerrero .40 1.00
491 Ryan Garko .15 .40
492 Ian Snell .15 .40
493 Yadier Molina .25 .60
494 Tom Glavine .25 .60
495 Cameron Maybin .15 .40
496 Vicente Padilla .15 .40
497 Keiichi Yabu .15 .40
498 Oliver Perez .15 .40
499 Carlos Villanueva .15 .40
500 Alex Rodriguez .60 1.50
501 Baltimore Orioles CL .15 .40
502 Boston Red Sox CL .25 .60
503 Chicago White Sox CL .15 .40
504 Houston Astros CL .15 .40
505 Oakland Athletics CL .15 .40
506 Toronto Blue Jays CL .15 .40
507 Atlanta Braves CL .15 .40
508 Milwaukee Brewers CL .15 .40
509 St. Louis Cardinals CL .25 .60
510 Chicago Cubs CL .25 .60
511 Arizona Diamondbacks CL .15 .40
512 Los Angeles Dodgers CL .25 .60
513 San Francisco Giants CL .15 .40
514 Cleveland Indians CL .15 .40
515 Seattle Mariners CL .15 .40
516 Florida Marlins CL .15 .40
517 New York Mets CL .25 .60
518 Washington Nationals CL .15 .40
519 San Diego Padres CL .15 .40
520 Pittsburgh Pirates CL .15 .40
521 Tampa Bay Rays CL .15 .40
522 Cincinnati Reds CL .15 .40
523 Colorado Rockies CL .15 .40
524 Kansas City Royals CL .15 .40
525 Detroit Tigers CL .15 .40
526 Minnesota Twins CL .15 .40
527 New York Yankees CL .25 .60
528 Philadelphia Phillies CL .15 .40
529 Los Angeles Angels CL .15 .40
530 Texas Rangers CL .15 .40
531 Milton Bradley .50 1.25
Joe Mauer
Dustin Pedroia
532 Chipper Jones 1.00 2.50
Matt Holliday
Albert Pujols
533 Miguel Cabrera .40 1.00
Alex Rodriguez
Carlos Quentin
534 Carlos Delgado .25 .60
Adam Dunn
Ryan Howard
535 Justin Morneau .40 1.00
Josh Hamilton
Miguel Cabrera
536 Ryan Howard .50 1.25
David Wright
Adrian Gonzalez
537 Cliff Lee .40 1.00
Daisuke Matsuzaka
Roy Halladay
538 Johan Santana .15 .40
Jake Peavy
Tim Lincecum
539 Cliff Lee .40 1.00
Daisuke Matsuzaka
Roy Halladay
540 Tim Lincecum .60 1.50
Ryan Dempster
Brandon Webb
541 Ervin Santana .40 1.00
Roy Halladay
A.J. Burnett
542 Johan Santana .60 1.50
Tim Lincecum
Dan Haren
543 Grady Sizemore .25 .60
544 Ichiro Suzuki .60 1.50
545 Hanley Ramirez .40 1.00
546 Jose Reyes .25 .60
547 Johan Santana .40 1.00
548 Adrian Gonzalez .25 .60
549 Carlos Zambrano .25 .60
550 Jonathan Papelbon .25 .60
551 Josh Hamilton .40 1.00
552 Derek Jeter 1.00 2.50
553 Kevin Youkilis .25 .60
554 Joe Mauer .40 1.00
555 Kosuke Fukudome .40 1.00
556 Chipper Jones .40 1.00
557 Lance Berkman .25 .60
558 Michael Young .25 .60
559 Evan Longoria .50 1.25
560 Alex Rodriguez .60 1.50
561 Travis Snider RC .60 1.50
562 James McDonald RC .60 1.50
563 Brian Duensing RC .60 1.50
564 Josh Outman RC .60 1.50
565 Josh Geer (RC) .40 1.00
566 Kevin Jepsen (RC) .40 1.00
567 Scott Lewis (RC) .40 1.00
568 Jason Motte (RC) .60 1.50
569 Ricky Romero (RC) 1.00 2.50
570 Landon Powell (RC) .40 1.00
571 Scott Elbert (RC) .40 1.00
572 Bobby Parnell RC .60 1.50
573 Ryan Perry RC 1.00 2.50
574 Phil Coke RC .60 1.50
575 Trevor Cahill RC 1.00 2.50
576 Jesse Chavez RC .40 1.00
577 George Kottaras (RC) .40 1.00
578 Trevor Crowe RC .40 1.00
579 David Freese RC 3.00 8.00
580 Matt Tuiasosopo (RC) .40 1.00
581 Brett Anderson RC .60 1.50
582 Casey McGehee (RC) .40 1.00
583 Elvis Andrus RC .60 1.50
584 Shawn Kelley RC .60 1.50
585 Mike Hinckley (RC) .40 1.00
586 Donald Veal RC .60 1.50
587 Colby Rasmus (RC) 1.00 2.50
588 Shairon Martis RC .60 1.50
589 Walter Silva RC .60 1.50
590 Chris Jakubauskas RC .60 1.50
591 Brad Nelson (RC) .40 1.00
592 Alfredo Simon (RC) .40 1.00
593 Koji Uehara RC .60 1.50
594 Rick Porcello RC 1.25 3.00
595 Kenshin Kawakami RC .60 1.50
596 Dexter Fowler (RC) .60 1.50
597 Jordan Schafer (RC) .60 1.50
598 David Patton RC .60 1.50
599 Luis Cruz RC .40 1.00
600 Joe Martinez RC .60 1.50

2009 O-Pee-Chee Black

*BLACK VET: 1X TO 2.5X BASIC
*BLACK RC: .75X TO 2X BASIC
STATED ODDS 1:6 HOBBY/RETAIL

2009 O-Pee-Chee Black Blank Back

RANDOM INSERTS IN PACKS
NO PRICING DUE TO SCARCITY

2009 O-Pee-Chee Black Mini

*BLK MINI VET: 4X TO 10X BASIC
*BLK MINI RC: 1.5X TO 4X BASIC
STATED ODDS 1:216 HOBBY/RETAIL

2009 O-Pee-Chee All-Rookie Team

STATED ODDS 1:40 HOBBY/RETAIL
AR1 Geovany Soto .60 1.50
AR2 Joey Votto 1.00 2.50
AR3 Alexei Ramirez .60 1.50
AR4 Evan Longoria 1.25 3.00
AR5 Mike Aviles .40 1.00
AR6 Jacoby Ellsbury 1.00 2.50
AR7 Jay Bruce .60 1.50
AR8 Kosuke Fukudome 1.00 2.50
AR9 Jair Jurrjens .40 1.00
AR10 Denard Span .40 1.00

2009 O-Pee-Chee Box Bottoms

CARDS LISTED ALPHABETICALLY
1 Ryan Braun 1.25 3.00
2 Miguel Cabrera 1.00 2.50
3 Adrian Gonzalez .60 1.50
4 Vladimir Guerrero 1.00 2.50
5 Josh Hamilton 1.00 2.50
6 Derek Jeter 2.50 6.00
7 Chipper Jones 1.00 2.50
8 Clayton Kershaw 1.00 2.50
9 Evan Longoria 1.25 3.00
10 Dustin Pedroia 1.25 3.00
11 Albert Pujols 2.50 6.00
12 Hanley Ramirez 1.00 2.50
13 Grady Sizemore .60 1.50
14 Alfonso Soriano .60 1.50
15 Ichiro Suzuki 1.50 4.00
16 Chase Utley 1.00 2.50

2009 O-Pee-Chee Face of the Franchise

STATED ODDS 1:13 HOBBY/RETAIL
FF1 Vladimir Guerrero 1.00 2.50
FF2 Roy Oswalt .60 1.50
FF3 Eric Chavez .40 1.00
FF4 Roy Halladay 1.00 2.50
FF5 Chipper Jones 1.00 2.50
FF6 Ryan Braun 1.25 3.00
FF7 Albert Pujols 2.50 6.00
FF8 Carlos Zambrano .60 1.50
FF9 Brandon Webb .60 1.50
FF10 Russell Martin .40 1.00
FF11 Tim Lincecum 1.50 4.00
FF12 Grady Sizemore .60 1.50
FF13 Ichiro Suzuki 1.50 4.00
FF14 Hanley Ramirez 1.00 2.50
FF15 David Wright 1.25 3.00
FF16 Ryan Zimmerman .60 1.50
FF17 Brian Roberts .40 1.00
FF18 Adrian Gonzalez .60 1.50
FF19 Jimmy Rollins .60 1.50
FF20 Nate McLouth .40 1.00
FF21 Michael Young .60 1.50
FF22 Evan Longoria 1.25 3.00
FF23 David Ortiz .60 1.50
FF24 Jay Bruce .60 1.50
FF25 Troy Tulowitzki 1.00 2.50
FF26 Alex Gordon .60 1.50
FF27 Miguel Cabrera 1.00 2.50
FF28 Joe Mauer 1.00 2.50
FF29 Carlos Quentin .60 1.50
FF30 Derek Jeter 2.50 6.00

2009 O-Pee-Chee Highlights and Milestones

STATED ODDS 1:27 HOBBY/RETAIL
HM1 Brad Lidge .40 1.00
HM2 Ken Griffey Jr. 1.50 4.00
HM3 Melvin Mora .40 1.00
HM4 Derek Jeter 2.50 6.00
HM5 Josh Hamilton 1.00 2.50
HM6 Alfonso Soriano .60 1.50
HM7 Francisco Rodriguez .60 1.50
HM8 Jon Lester 1.00 2.50
HM9 Carlos Zambrano .60 1.50
HM10 Adrian Beltre .40 1.00
HM11 Carlos Gomez .40 1.00
HM12 Kelly Shoppach .40 1.00
HM13 Manny Ramirez 1.00 2.50
HM14 Carlos Delgado .40 1.00
HM15 CC Sabathia .60 1.50

2009 O-Pee-Chee Materials

STATED ODDS 1:108 HOBBY
STATED ODDS 1:216 RETAIL
BBP Brad Penny 4.00 10.00
Josh Beckett
A.J. Burnett
BHH Rocco Baldelli 4.00 10.00
Corey Hart
Jeremy Hermida
BMY Kevin Youkilis 8.00 20.00
Adrian Beltre
Melvin Mora
BYP Jonathan Papelbon 6.00 15.00
Kevin Youkilis
Josh Beckett
CBG Chad Billingsley 4.00 10.00
Fausto Carmona
Zack Greinke
CFM Nick Markakis 6.00 15.00
Jeff Francoeur
Michael Cuddyer
CKR Ian Kinsler 5.00 12.00
Brian Roberts
Robinson Cano
CSW Nick Swisher 6.00 15.00
Michael Cuddyer
Josh Willingham
DLO Magglio Ordonez 6.00 15.00
Carlos Lee
Jermaine Dye
EFG Jacoby Ellsbury 6.00 15.00
Curtis Granderson
Chone Figgins
ELK Matt Kemp 8.00 20.00
Andre Ethier
James Loney
FOD David Ortiz 5.00 12.00
Carlos Delgado
Prince Fielder
GDH J.J. Hardy 4.00 10.00
Stephen Drew
Khalil Greene
HAG Garrett Atkins 4.00 10.00
Carlos Gonzalez
Todd Helton
HMC Justin Morneau 6.00 15.00
Miguel Cabrera
Travis Hafner
HML Evan Longoria 8.00 20.00
Justin Morneau
Josh Hamilton
HMW Jake Westbrook 4.00 10.00
Travis Hafner
Victor Martinez
HRR Roy Halladay 8.00 20.00
Alex Rios
Scott Rolen
JCP Jorge Posada 10.00 25.00
Robinson Cano
Derek Jeter
KJN Jayson Nix 4.00 10.00
Kelly Johnson
Howie Kendrick
LRF Kosuke Fukudome 4.00 10.00
Derrek Lee
Aramis Ramirez
LWS Brad Lidge 4.00 10.00
Takashi Saito
Billy Wagner
MFJ Kelly Johnson 4.00 10.00
Jeff Francoeur
Brian McCann
MMM Russell Martin 6.00 15.00
Victor Martinez
Joe Mauer
NMC Joe Mauer 8.00 20.00
Joe Nathan
Michael Cuddyer
OHG Travis Hafner 4.00 10.00
David Ortiz
Jason Giambi
OHP Roy Halladay 5.00 12.00
Brad Penny
Roy Oswalt
PBO David Ortiz 5.00 12.00
Jonathan Papelbon
Clay Buchholz
PCF Albert Pujols 10.00 25.00
Prince Fielder
Miguel Cabrera
PHB Cole Hamels 5.00 12.00
Erik Bedard
Andy Pettitte
RPV Ivan Rodriguez 5.00 12.00
Jorge Posada
Jason Varitek
VWB Clay Buchholz 4.00 10.00
Justin Verlander
Jered Weaver
WHK Chien-Ming Wang
Ian Kennedy
Phil Hughes
YDR Chris B. Young 5.00 12.00
Mark Reynolds
Stephen Drew
YKM Michael Young 4.00 10.00
Ian Kinsler
Kevin Millwood

2009 O-Pee-Chee Midsummer Memories

STATED ODDS 1:27 HOBBY/RETAIL
MM1 Ken Griffey Jr. 1.50 4.00
MM2 Hank Blalock .40 1.00
MM3 Michael Young .60 1.50
MM4 Ichiro Suzuki 1.50 4.00
MM5 Miguel Tejada .60 1.50
MM6 Alfonso Soriano .60 1.50
MM7 Jimmy Rollins .60 1.50
MM8 Derek Jeter 2.50 6.00
MM9 Justin Morneau 1.00 2.50
MM10 J.D. Drew .40 1.00
MM11 Carl Crawford .60 1.50
MM12 Vladimir Guerrero 1.00 2.50
MM13 Mark Teixeira 1.00 2.50
MM14 David Ortiz .60 1.50
MM15 Manny Ramirez 1.00 2.50

2009 O-Pee-Chee New York New York

STATED ODDS 1:40 HOBBY/RETAIL
NY1 CC Sabathia 1.00 2.50
NY2 Jorge Posada 1.00 2.50
NY3 Derek Jeter 4.00 10.00
NY4 Alex Rodriguez 2.50 6.00
NY5 Chien-Ming Wang 1.00 2.50
NY6 Joba Chamberlain 1.00 2.50
NY7 A.J. Burnett 1.00 2.50
NY8 Mariano Rivera 1.50 4.00
NY9 Nick Swisher 1.50 4.00
NY10 Robinson Cano 1.50 4.00
NY11 Mark Teixeira 1.50 4.00
NY12 Johnny Damon 1.00 2.50
NY13 Hideki Matsui 1.50 4.00
NY14 Andy Pettitte 1.00 2.50
NY15 Xavier Nady .60 1.50
NY16 Jose Reyes 1.00 2.50
NY17 David Wright 2.00 5.00
NY18 John Maine .60 1.50
NY19 Daniel Murphy 1.50 4.00
NY20 Francisco Rodriguez 1.00 2.50
NY21 Carlos Delgado .60 1.50
NY22 Luis Castillo .60 1.50
NY23 Ryan Church .60 1.50
NY24 Brian Schneider .60 1.50
NY25 J.J. Putz .60 1.50
NY26 Mike Pelfrey .60 1.50
NY27 Oliver Perez .60 1.50
NY28 Jeremy Reed .60 1.50
NY29 Johan Santana 1.50 4.00
NY30 Carlos Beltran .60 1.50

2009 O-Pee-Chee New York New York Multi Sport

RANDOM INSERTS IN PACKS
MS1 CC Sabathia 1.50 4.00
MS2 Henrik Lundqvist 4.00 10.00
MS3 Jose Reyes 1.50 4.00
MS4 Derek Jeter 6.00 15.00
MS5 David Wright 3.00 8.00
MS6 Rick DiPietro 2.50 6.00
MS7 Joba Chamberlain 1.50 4.00
MS8 Alex Rodriguez 4.00 10.00
MS9 Johan Santana 2.50 6.00
MS10 Carlos Beltran 1.00 2.50

2009 O-Pee-Chee Retro

RM1 Sidney Crosby 8.00 20.00
RM2 Alexander Ovechkin 4.00 10.00
RM3 Carey Price 3.00 8.00
RM4 Henrik Lundqvist 2.50 6.00
RM5 Jonathan Toews 3.00 8.00
RM6 Martin Brodeur 3.00 8.00
RM7 Evgeni Malkin 5.00 12.00
RM8 Jarome Iginla 2.50 6.00
RM9 Henrik Zetterberg 2.50 6.00
RM10 Roberto Luongo 2.50 6.00
RM11 Travis Snider 1.25 3.00
RM12 Russell Martin .75 2.00
RM13 Justin Morneau 2.00 5.00
RM14 Joey Votto 2.00 5.00
RM15 Alex Rios 1.25 3.00
RM16 Jon Lester 2.00 5.00
RM17 Ryan Howard 2.50 6.00
RM18 Johan Santana 2.00 5.00
RM19 CC Sabathia 1.25 3.00
RM20 Roy Halladay 2.00 5.00
RM21 Chase Utley 2.00 5.00
RM22 Chipper Jones 2.00 5.00
RM23 Ryan Braun 2.50 6.00
RM24 Ken Griffey Jr. 3.00 8.00
RM25 B.J. Upton 1.25 3.00
RM26 Hanley Ramirez 2.00 5.00
RM27 Alex Rodriguez 3.00 8.00
RM28 Cole Hamels 2.00 5.00
RM29 Albert Pujols 5.00 12.00
RM30 Derek Jeter 5.00 12.00
RM31 Manny Ramirez 2.00 5.00
RM32 David Wright 2.50 6.00
RM33 Evan Longoria 2.50 6.00

2009 O-Pee-Chee Signatures

STATED ODDS 1:216 HOBBY
STATED ODDS 1:1080 RETAIL
SAJ Joaquin Arias 4.00 10.00
SAL Aaron Laffey 6.00 15.00
SAR Alexei Ramirez 10.00 25.00
SBJ Brandon Jones 3.00 8.00
SBR Brian Barton 3.00 8.00
SCD Chris Duncan 10.00 25.00
SCH Corey Hart 5.00 12.00
SCS Clint Sammons 3.00 8.00
SCW Cory Wade 5.00 12.00
SDM David Murphy 3.00 8.00
SDP Dustin Pedroia
SDS Denard Span
SEC Eric Chavez
SED Elijah Dukes 4.00 10.00
SEV Edinson Volquez 6.00 15.00
SFC Fausto Carmona 3.00 8.00
SGA Garrett Atkins
SGP Glen Perkins
SHE Chase Headley 6.00 15.00
SHJ J.A. Happ 8.00 20.00
SIK Ian Kennedy 4.00 10.00
SJA Jonathan Albaladejo 4.00 10.00
SJB Jeremy Bonderman 15.00 40.00
SJC Jeff Clement 6.00 15.00
SJH Justin Hampson 3.00 8.00
SJL Jed Lowrie 4.00 10.00
SJM John Maine
SKJ Kelly Johnson 3.00 8.00
SKK Kevin Kouzmanoff 3.00 8.00
SKM Kyle McClellan 6.00 15.00
SKS Kurt Suzuki 6.00 15.00
SLB Lance Broadway
SMB Michael Bourn 8.00 20.00
SME Mark Ellis
SMG Matt Garza
SMH Micah Hoffpauir 8.00 20.00
SML Matt Lindstrom
SMP Mike Pelfrey
SMR Mike Rabelo 10.00 25.00
SNB Nick Blackburn 3.00 8.00
SRM Russell Martin
SRO Ross Ohlendorf 6.00 15.00
SSA Jarrod Saltalamacchia 6.00 15.00
SSK Kelly Shoppach
SSM Sean Marshall 5.00 12.00
SSP Steve Pearce 3.00 8.00
SWB Wladimir Balentien

2009 O-Pee-Chee The Award Show

STATED ODDS 1:20 HOBBY/RETAIL
AW1 Yadier Molina .60 1.50
AW2 Adrian Gonzalez .60 1.50
AW3 Brandon Phillips .40 1.00
AW4 David Wright 1.25 3.00
AW5 Jimmy Rollins .60 1.50
AW6 Carlos Beltran .40 1.00
AW7 Shane Victorino .40 1.00
AW8 Geovany Soto .60 1.50
AW9 Tim Lincecum 1.50 4.00
AW10 Albert Pujols 2.50 6.00
AW11 Joe Mauer 1.00 2.50
AW12 Carlos Pena .60 1.50
AW13 Dustin Pedroia 1.25 3.00
AW14 Adrian Beltre .40 1.00
AW15 Torii Hunter .40 1.00
AW16 Grady Sizemore .60 1.50
AW17 Ichiro Suzuki 1.50 4.00
AW18 Evan Longoria 1.25 3.00
AW19 Cliff Lee .60 1.50
AW20 Dustin Pedroia 1.25 3.00

2009 O-Pee-Chee Walk-Off Winners

STATED ODDS 1:40 HOBBY/RETAIL
WK1 Ryan Braun 1.25 3.00
WK2 Ryan Zimmerman .60 1.50
WK3 Michael Young .60 1.50
WK4 J.D. Drew .40 1.00
WK5 Carlos Ruiz .40 1.00
WK6 Dan Uggla .60 1.50
WK7 Johnny Damon .60 1.50
WK8 Jed Lowrie .60 1.50
WK9 Ryan Ludwick .60 1.50
WK10 Dioner Navarro .40 1.00

1887-90 Old Judge N172

The Goodwin Company's baseball series depicts hundreds of ballplayers from more than 40 major and minor league teams as well as boxers and wrestlers. The cards (approximately 1 1/2" by 2 1/2") are actually photographs from the Hall studio in New York which were pasted onto thick cardboard. The pictures are sepia in color with either a white or pink cast, and the cards are blank backed. They are found either numbered or unnumbered, with or without a copyright date, and with hand printed or machine printed names. All known cards have the name "Goodwin Co., New York" at the base. The cards were marketed during the period 1887-1890 in packs of "Old Judge" and "Gypsy Queen" cigarettes (cards marked with the latter brand are worth double the values listed below). They have been listed alphabetically and assigned numbers in the checklist below for simplicity's sake; the various poses known for some players also have not been listed for the same reason. Some of the players are pictured in horizontal (HOR) poses. In all, more than 2300 different Goodwin cards are known to collectors, with more being discovered every year. Cards from the "Spotted Tie" sub-series are denoted in the checklist below by SPOT. The Lee Gibson and Egyptian Healey cards are currently considered unique and are not priced due to market scarcity. The Stephen Behel card is drawing extra interest as there is debate as to whether or not he is the first Jewish player depicted on a card.

COMP.SET 500000.001000000.00
COMMON CARD 150.00 300.00
COMMON (DOUBLE) 200.00 400.00
COM.BROWNS CHAMP 250.00 500.00
COMMON CARD (PCL) 20000.00 50000.00
COMMON SPOTTED TIE 500.00 1000.00
1 Gus Albert 300.00 500.00
2 Charles Alcott 300.00 500.00
3 Alexander 300.00 500.00

4 Myron Allen 300.00 500.00
5 Bob Allen 300.00 500.00
6 Uncle Bill Alvord 300.00 500.00
7 Varney Anderson 300.00 500.00
8 Ed Andrews: Phila. 300.00 500.00
9 Ed Andrews and Buster Hoover 350.00 600.00
10 Wally Andrews 300.00 500.00
11 Bill Annis 300.00 500.00
12A Cap Anson: Chicago (In uniform)
12B Cap Anson: Chicago (Not in uniform) 5000.00 8000.00
13 Old Hoss Ardner 300.00 500.00
14 Tug Arundel: Indianapolis-Whites 300.00 500.00
15 Jersey Bakley: Cleve. 300.00 500.00
16 Clarence Baldwin: Cincinnati 300.00 500.00
17 Mark(Fido) Baldwin: Chicago-Columbus 300.00 500.00
18 Lady Baldwin: Detroit 350.00 600.00
19 James Banning: Wash. 300.00 500.00
20 Samuel Barkley: Pittsburgh-K.C. 300.00 500.00
21 Bald Billy Barnie: Mgr. Baltimore 350.00 600.00
22 Charles Bassett: Indianapolis-N.Y. 300.00 500.00
23 Charles Bastian: Phila.-Chicago 300.00 500.00
24 Charles Bastian and Schriver: Philadelphia 350.00 600.00
25 Ebenezer Beatin: Cleve. 300.00 500.00
26 Jake Beckley: Eagle Eye Whites-Pittsburgh 2500.00 4000.00
27 Stephen Behel SPOT 6000.00 10000.00
28 Charles Bennett: Detroit-Boston 300.00 500.00
29 Louis Bierbauer: A's 300.00 500.00
30 Louis Bierbauer and Robert Gamble: Athletics 350.00 600.00
31 Bill Bishop: Pittsburgh-Syracuse 300.00 500.00
32 William Blair: A's-Hamiltons 300.00 500.00
33 Ned Bligh: Columbus 300.00 500.00
34 Bogart: Indianapolis 300.00 500.00
35 Boyce: Washington 300.00 500.00
36 Jake Boyd: Maroons 350.00 600.00
37 Honest John Boyle: St. Louis-Chicago 300.00 500.00
38 Handsome Henry Boyle Indianapolis-N.Y. 300.00 500.00
39 Nick Bradley: K.C.- Worchester 300.00 500.00
40 George(Grin) Bradley Sioux City 300.00 500.00
41 Stephen Brady SPOT 900.00 1500.00
42 E.L. Breckinridge: Sacramento PCL
43 Timothy Brosnan: Minneapolis 300.00 500.00
44 Timothy Brosnan Sioux City 300.00 500.00
45 Cal Broughton: St. Paul 300.00 500.00
46 Big Dan Brouthers: Detroit-Boston 1500.00 2500.00
47 Thomas Brown: Pittsburgh-Boston 300.00 500.00
48 California Brown: New York 300.00 500.00
49 Pete Browning: Gladiator Louisville 3000.00 5000.00
50 Charles Brynan: Chicago-Des Moines 300.00 500.00
51 Al Buckenberger MG: Columbus 300.00 500.00
52 Dick Buckley: Indianapolis-N.Y. 300.00 500.00
53 Charles Buffington: Philadelphia 300.00 500.00
54 Ernest Burch: Brooklyn-Whites 300.00 500.00
55 Bill Burdick: Omaha-Indianapolis 300.00 500.00
56 Black Jack Burdock: Boston-Brooklyn 300.00 500.00
57 Robert Burks: Sioux City 300.00 500.00
58 George Burnham Watch Mgr. Indianapolis 350.00 600.00
59 Burns: Omaha 300.00 500.00
60 Jimmy Burns: K.C. 300.00 500.00
61 Tommy(Oyster) Burns Baltimore-Brooklyn 350.00 600.00
62 Thomas E. Burns: Chicago 300.00 500.00
63 Doc Bushong: Brook. 300.00 500.00
64 Doc Bushong: Browns Champs 500.00 800.00
65 Patsy Cahill: Ind. 300.00 500.00
66 Count Campau: Kansas City-Detroit 300.00 500.00
67 Jimmy Canavan: Omaha 300.00 500.00
68 Bart Cantz: Whites-Baltimore 300.00 500.00
69 Handsome Jack Carney Washington 300.00 500.00
70 Hick Carpenter Cincinnati 300.00 500.00
71 Cliff Carroll: Wash. 300.00 500.00
72 Scrappy Carroll: St.Paul-Chicago 300.00 500.00
73 Frederick Carroll: Pitts. 300.00 500.00
74 Jumbo Cartwright: Kansas City-St. Joe 300.00 500.00
75 Bob Caruthers: Parisian Brooklyn 500.00 800.00
76 Bob Caruthers: Parisian Browns Champs 500.00 800.00
77 Daniel Casey: Phila. 300.00 500.00
78 Icebox Chamberlain: St. Louis 300.00 500.00
79 Cupid Childs: Phila.-Syracuse 300.00 500.00
80 Bob Clark: Washington 300.00 500.00
81 Owen Clark: Washington 300.00 500.00
82 William H. Clarke and Mickey Hughes: Brooklyn HOR 350.00 600.00
83 William(Dad) Clarke: Chicago-Omaha 300.00 500.00
84 Pete Connell: Des Moines 300.00 500.00
85 John Clarkson: Chicago-Boston 1200.00 2000.00
86 Jack Clements: Philadelphia 300.00 500.00
87 Elmer Cleveland: Omaha-New York 300.00 500.00
88 Monk Cline: K.C.-Sioux City 300.00 500.00
89 Mike Cody: Des Moines 300.00 500.00
90 John Coleman: Pittsburgh - A's 300.00 500.00
91 Bill Collins: New York-Newark 300.00 500.00
92 Hub Collins: Louisville-Brooklyn 300.00 500.00
93 Charles Comiskey: Browns Champs 2500.00 4000.00
94 Commy Comiskey: St. Louis-Chicago 1800.00 3000.00
95 Roger Connor: Script 2500.00 4000.00
96 Roger Connor: New York 2500.00 4000.00
97 Richard Conway: Boston-Worchester 300.00 500.00
98 Peter Conway: Det.-Pitts.-Ind. 300.00 500.00
99 James Conway: K.C. 300.00 500.00
100 Paul Cook: Louisville 300.00 500.00
101 Jimmy Cooney: Omaha-Chicago 300.00 500.00
102 Larry Corcoran: Indianapolis-London 500.00 800.00
103 Pop Corkhill: Cincinnati-Brooklyn 300.00 500.00
104 Cannon Ball Crane: New York 300.00 500.00
105 Samuel Crane: Wash. 300.00 500.00
106 Jack Crogan Maroons 350.00 600.00
107 John Crooks: Whites-Omaha 300.00 500.00
108 Lave Cross: Louisville-A's-Phila. 300.00 500.00
109 Bill Crossley: Milw. 300.00 500.00
110 Joe Crotty SPOT 900.00 1500.00
111 Joe Crotty: Sioux City 300.00 500.00
112 Billy Crowell: Cleveland-St. Joe 300.00 500.00
113 Jim Cudworth: St. Louis-Worchester 300.00 500.00
114 Bert Cunningham: Baltimore-Phila. 300.00 500.00
115 Tacks Curtis: St. Joe 300.00 500.00
116 Ed Cushman SPOT 900.00 1500.00
117 Ed Cushman: Toledo 300.00 500.00
118 Tony Cusick: Mil. 300.00 500.00
119 Vincent Dailey Oakland PCL
120 Edward Dailey: Phil.-Wash.-Columbus 300.00 500.00
121 Edward Dailey: Columbus 500.00 800.00
122 Bill Daley: Boston 300.00 500.00
123 Con Daley: Boston-Indianapolis 300.00 500.00
124 Abner Dalrymple: Pittsburgh-Denver 300.00 500.00
125 Tom Daly: Chicago-Wash.-Cleve. 350.00 600.00
126 James Daly: Minn. 300.00 500.00
127 Law Daniels: K.C. 300.00 500.00
128 Dell Darling: Chicago 300.00 500.00
129 Wm. Darnbrough: Denver 300.00 500.00
130 D. Davin: Milwaukee 300.00 1500.00
131 Jumbo Davis: K.C. 300.00 500.00
132 Pat Dealey: Wash 300.00 500.00
133 Thomas Deasley: New York-Washington Throwing 300.00 500.00
134 Thomas Deasley Fielding 300.00 500.00
135 Edward Decker: Phil. 300.00 500.00
136 Big Ed Delahanty: Philadelphia 5000.00 8000.00
137 Jeremiah Denny: Indianapolis-New York 300.00 500.00
138 James Devlin: St.L. 300.00 500.00
139 Thomas Dolan: Whites-St. Louis-Denver 300.00 500.00
140 Jack Donahue: San Francisco PCL
141 James Donahue SPOT 900.00 1500.00
142 James Donahue: K.C. 300.00 500.00
143 James Donnelly: Washington 300.00 500.00
144 Charles Dooley Oakland PCL
145 J. Doran: Omaha 500.00 800.00
146 Michael Dorgan: N.Y. 300.00 500.00
147 Cornelius Doyle San Fran. PCL
148 Homerun Dufle: St.L. 300.00 500.00
149 Hugh Duffy: Chicago 1500.00 2500.00
150 Dan Dugdale: Maroons-Minneapolis 350.00 600.00
151 Duck Duke: Minn. 300.00 500.00
152 Sure Shot Dunlap: Pittsburgh 300.00 500.00
153 J. Dunn: Maroons 350.00 600.00
154 Jesse(Cyclone)Duryea St. Paul-Cinc. 300.00 500.00
155 John Dwyer: Chicago Maroons 350.00 600.00
156 Billy Earle: Cincinnati-St.Paul 300.00 500.00
157 Buck Ebright: Wash. 300.00 500.00
158 Red Ehret: Louisville 300.00 500.00
159 R. Emmerke: Des Moines 300.00 500.00
160 Dude Esterbrook: Louisville-Ind.-New York-All Star 300.00 500.00
161 Henry Esterday: K.C.-Columbus 300.00 500.00
162 Long John Ewing: Louisville-N.Y. 300.00 500.00
163 Buck Ewing New York 1500.00 2500.00
164 Buck Ewing and Mascot: New York 1500.00 2500.00
165 Jay Faatz: Cleveland 300.00 500.00
166 Clinkgers Fagan: Kansas City-Denver 300.00 500.00
167 William Farmer: Pittsburgh-St. Paul 300.00 500.00
168 Sidney Farrar: Philadelphia 350.00 600.00
169 John(Moose) Farrell: Wash.-Baltimore 300.00 500.00
170 Charles(Duke)Farrell Chicago 300.00 500.00
171 Frank Fennelly: Cincinnati-A's 300.00 500.00
172 Chas. Ferguson: Phila. 300.00 500.00
173 Colonel Ferson: Washington 300.00 500.00
174 Wallace Fessenden: Umpire National 350.00 600.00
175 Jocko Fields: Pitts. 300.00 500.00
176 Fischer: Maroons 350.00 600.00
177 Thomas Flanigan: Cleve.-Sioux City 300.00 500.00
178 Silver Flint: Chicago 300.00 500.00
179 Thomas Flood: St. Joe 300.00 500.00
180 Flynn: Omaha 1500.00
181 James Fogarty: Philadelphia 300.00 500.00
182 Frank(Monkey)Foreman Baltimore-Cinc. 300.00 500.00
183 Thomas Forster: Milwaukee-Hartford 300.00 500.00
184 Elmer E. Foster SPOT 900.00 1500.00
185 Elmer Foster: New York-Chicago 300.00 500.00
186 F.W. Foster SPOT T.W. Forster (Sic) 900.00 1500.00
187 Scissors Foutz: Browns Champ 500.00 800.00
188 Scissors Foutz: Brooklyn 300.00 500.00
189 Julie Freeman: St.L.-Milwaukee 300.00 500.00
190 Will Fry: St. Joe 300.00 500.00
191 Fred Fudger Oakland PCL
192 William Fuller: Milwaukee 300.00 500.00
193 Shorty Fuller: St.Louis 300.00 500.00
194 Christopher Fullmer: Baltimore 300.00 500.00
195 Christopher Fullmer and Tom Tucker: Baltimore HOR 350.00 600.00
196 Honest John Gaffney: Mgr. Washington 500.00 800.00
197 Pud Galvin: Pitts. 1800.00 3000.00
198 Robert Gamble: A's 300.00 500.00
199 Charles Ganzel: Detroit-Boston 300.00 500.00
200 Frank(Gid) Gardner: Phila.-Washington 300.00 500.00
201 Gid Gardner and Miah Murray: Washington HOR 350.00 600.00
202 Hank Gastreich: Columbus 300.00 500.00
203 Emil Geiss: Chicago 300.00 500.00
204 Frenchy Genins: Sioux City 300.00 500.00
205 William George: N.Y. 300.00 500.00
206 Move Up Joe Gerhardt All Star-Jersey City 300.00 500.00
207 Pretzels Getzein: Detroit-Ind. 300.00 500.00
208 Lee Gibson: A's 300.00 500.00
209 Robert Gilks: Cleve. 300.00 500.00
210 Pete Gillespie: N.Y. 300.00 500.00
211 Barney Gilligan Washington-Detroit 300.00 500.00
212 Frank Gilmore: Wash. 300.00 500.00
213 Pebbly Jack Glasscock Indianapolis-N.Y. 500.00 800.00
214 Kid Gleason: Phila. 500.00 800.00
215 Brother Bill Gleason A's-Louisville 500.00 800.00
216 William Bill Gleason Browns Champs 500.00 800.00
217 Mouse Glenn: Sioux City 300.00 500.00
218 Michael Goodfellow: Cleveland-Detroit 300.00 500.00
219 George Gore (Pianolegs) New York 300.00 500.00
220 Frank Graves: Minn. 300.00 500.00
221 William Greenwood: Baltimore-Columbus 300.00 500.00
222 Michael Greer: Cleveland-Brooklyn 300.00 500.00
223 Mike Griffin: Baltimore-Phila NL 300.00 500.00
224 Clark Griffith: Milwaukee 1800.00 3000.00
225 Henry Gruber: Cleve. 300.00 500.00
226 Addison Gumbert: Chicago-Boston 300.00 500.00
227 Thomas Gunning: Philadelphia-A's 300.00 500.00
228 Joseph Gunson: K.C. 300.00 500.00
229 George Haddock: Washington 300.00 500.00
230 William Hafner: K.C. 300.00 500.00
231 Willie Hahm: Chicago Mascot 300.00 500.00
232 William Hallman: Philadelphia 300.00 500.00
233 Billy Hamilton: Kansas City-Phila. 1200.00 2000.00
234 Willie Hamm and Ned Williamson: Chicago 500.00 800.00
235 Frank Hankinson: SPOT 900.00 1500.00
236 Frank Hankinson: Kansas City 300.00 500.00
237 Ned Hanlon: Det.-Boston-Pitts. 1200.00 2000.00
238 William Hanrahan: Maroons-Minn. 350.00 600.00
239 A.G. Hapeman: Sacramento PCL
240 Pa Harkins: Brooklyn-Baltimore 300.00 500.00
241 William Hart: Cinc.-Des Moines 300.00 500.00
242 Wm. Hasamdear: K.C. 300.00 500.00
243 Colonel Hatfield: New York 300.00 500.00
244 Egyptian Healey: Wash.-Indianapolis 300.00 500.00
245 Egyptian Healey Washington 300.00 500.00
246 J.C. Healy: Omaha-Denver 300.00 500.00
247 Guy Hecker: Louisville 300.00 500.00
248 Tony Hellman: Sioux City 300.00 500.00
249 Hardie Henderson: Brook.-Pitts.-Balt. 300.00 500.00
250 Hardie Henderson and Michael Greer: Brooklyn 350.00 600.00
251 Moxie Hengle: Maroons-Minneapolis 350.00 600.00
252 John Henry: Phila. 300.00 500.00
253 Edward Herr: Whites-Milwaukee 300.00 500.00
254 Hunkey Hines: Whites 300.00 500.00
255 Paul Hines: Wash.-Indianapolis 300.00 500.00
256 Texas Wonder Hoffman: Denver 300.00 500.00
257 Eddie Hogan: Cleve. 300.00 500.00
258 William Holbert SPOT 900.00 1500.00
259 William Holbert: Brooklyn-Mets-Jersey City 300.00 500.00
260 James(Bugs) Holliday: Des Moines-Cinc. 300.00 500.00
261 Charles Hoover: Maroons-Chi.-K.C. 350.00 600.00
262 Buster Hoover: Phila.-Toronto 300.00 500.00
263 Jack Horner: Milwaukee-New Haven 300.00 500.00
264 Jack Horner and E.H. Warner: Milwaukee 350.00 600.00
265 Michael Horning: Boston-Balt.-N.Y. 300.00 500.00
266 Pete Hotaling: Cleveland 300.00 500.00
267 William Howes: Minn.-St. Paul 300.00 500.00
268 Dummy Hoy: Washington 1800.00 3000.00
269 Nat Hudson: Browns Champ 500.00 800.00
270 Nat Hudson: St. Louis 300.00 500.00
271 Mickey Hughes: Brk. 300.00 500.00
272 Hungler: Sioux City 300.00 500.00
273 Wild Bill Hutchinson: Chicago 300.00 500.00
274 John Irwin: Wash.-Wilkes Barre 300.00 500.00
275 Cutrate Irwin: Phila.-Boston-Wash. 300.00 500.00
276 A.C. Jantzen: Minn. 300.00 500.00
277 Frederick Jevne: Minn.-St. Paul 300.00 500.00
278 John Johnson: K.C.-Columbus 300.00 500.00
279 Richard Johnston: Boston 300.00 500.00
280 Jordan Minneapolis 300.00 500.00
281 Heinie Kappell: Columbus-Cincinnati 300.00 500.00
282 Sir Timothy Keefe: New York 1200.00 2000.00
283 Tim Keefe and Danny Richardson: Stealing 2nd Base New York HOR 700.00 1200.00
284 George Keefe: Wash. 300.00 500.00
285 James Keenan: Cinc. 300.00 500.00
286 Mike King Kelly 10,000 Chic-Boston 3000.00 5000.00
287 Honest John Kelly: Mgr. Louisville 500.00 800.00
288 Kelly: (Umpire) Western Association 350.00 600.00
289 Charles Kelly: Philadelphia 600.00 1000.00
290 Kelly and Powell: Umpire and Manager Sioux City 350.00 600.00
291 Rudolph Kemmler: Browns Champ 500.00 800.00
292 Rudolph Kemmler: St. Paul 300.00 500.00
293 Theodore Kennedy: Des Moines-Omaha 350.00 600.00
294 J.J. Kenyon: Whites-Des Moines 300.00 500.00
295 John Kerins: Louisville 300.00 500.00
296 Matthew Kilroy: Baltimore-Boston 300.00 500.00
297 Charles King: St.L.-Chi. 300.00 500.00
298 Aug. Kloff: Minn.-St.Joe 300.00 500.00
299 William Klusman: Milwaukee-Denver 300.00 500.00
300 Phillip Knell: St. Joe-Phila. 300.00 500.00
301 Fred Knouf: St. Louis 300.00 500.00
302 Charles Kremmeyer: Sacramento PCL
303 William Krieg: Wash.-St. Joe-Minn. 300.00 500.00
304 William Krieg and Aug. Kloff: Minneapolis 350.00 600.00
305 Gus Krock: Chicago 300.00 500.00
306 Willie Kuehne: Pittsburgh 300.00 500.00
307 Frederick Lange: Maroons 350.00 600.00
308 Ted Larkin: A's 300.00 500.00
309 Arlie Latham: Browns Champ 600.00 1000.00
310 Arlie Latham: St. Louis-Chicago 500.00 800.00
311 John Lauer: Pittsburgh 300.00 500.00
312 John Leighton Omaha 300.00 500.00
313 Rube Levy San Fran. PCL
314 Tom Loftus MG: Whites-Cleveland 300.00 500.00
315 Herman(Germany)Long Maroons-K.C. 500.00 800.00
316 Danny Long Oak. PCL
317 Tom Lovett: Omaha-Brooklyn 300.00 500.00
318 Bobby(Link) Lowe: Milwaukee 500.00 800.00
319 Jack Lynch SPOT 900.00 1500.00
320 John Lynch: All Stars 300.00 500.00
321 Dennis Lyons: A's 300.00 500.00
322 Harry Lyons: St. L. 300.00 500.00
323 Connie Mack: Wash. 3500.00 6000.00
324 Joe(Reddie) Mack: Louisville 300.00 500.00
325 James(Little Mack) Macullar: Des Moines-Milwaukee 300.00 500.00
326 Kid Madden: Boston 300.00 500.00
327 Daniel Mahoney: St. Joe 300.00 500.00
328 Willard(Grasshopper) Maines: St. Paul 300.00 500.00
329 Fred Mann: St.Louis-Hartford 300.00 500.00
330 Jimmy Manning: K.C. 300.00 500.00
331 Charles(Lefty) Marr: Col.-Cinc. 300.00 500.00
332 Mascot(Willie Breslin): New York 350.00 600.00
333 Samuel Maskery: Milwaukee-Des Moines 300.00 500.00
334 Bobby Mathews: A's 300.00 500.00
335 Michael Mattimore: New York-A's 300.00 500.00
336 Albert Maul: Pitts. 300.00 500.00
337 Albert Mays SPOT 900.00 1500.00
338 Albert Mays: Columbus 300.00 500.00
339 James McAleer: Cleveland 500.00 800.00
340 Thomas McCarthy: Phila.-St. Louis 1500.00 2500.00
341 John McCarthy: K.C. 300.00 500.00
342 James McCauley: Maroons-Phila. 350.00 600.00
343 William McClellan: Brooklyn-Denver 300.00 500.00
344 John McCormack: Whites 300.00 500.00
345 Big Jim McCormick: Chicago-Pittsburgh 300.00 500.00
346 McCreachery: Mgr. Indianapolis 300.00 500.00
347 James(Chippy)McGarr: St. Louis-K.C. 300.00 500.00
348 Jack McGeachy: Ind. 300.00 500.00
349 John McGlone: Cleveland-Detroit 300.00 500.00
350 James(Deacon)McGuire Phila.-Toronto 300.00 500.00
351 Bill McGunnigle: Mgr. Brooklyn 500.00 800.00
352 Ed McKean: Cleveland 300.00 500.00
353 Alex McKinnon: Pittsburgh 300.00 500.00
354 Thomas McLaughlin SPOT 900.00 1500.00
355 John(Bid) McPhee: Cincinnati 3000.00 5000.00
356 James McQuaid: Denver 300.00 500.00
357 John McQuaid: Umpire Amer. Assoc. 350.00 600.00
358 Jame McTamany: Brook.-Col.-K.C. 300.00 500.00
359 George McVey: Mil.-Denver-St. Joe 300.00 500.00
360 Peter Meegan San Fran. PCL
361 John Messitt: Omaha 300.00 500.00
362 George(Doggie)Miller Pittsburgh 300.00 500.00
363 Joseph Miller: Omaha-Minneapolis 300.00 500.00
364 Jocko Milligan: St. Louis-Phila. 300.00 500.00
365 E.L. Mills: Milwaukee 300.00 500.00
366 Daniel (Minahan) Minnehan: Minneapolis 300.00 500.00
367 Samuel Moffet: Ind. 300.00 500.00
368 Honest Morrell: Boston-Washington 300.00 500.00
369 Ed Morris (Cannonball): Pittsburgh 300.00 500.00
370 Morrisey: St. Paul 300.00 500.00
371 Tony(Count) Mullane: Cincinnati 500.00 800.00
372 Joseph Mulvey: Philadelphia 300.00 500.00
373 P.L. Murphy: St. Paul 300.00 500.00
374 Pat J. Murphy: New York 300.00 500.00
375 Miah Murray: Wash. 300.00 500.00
376 James(Truthful) Mutrie: Mgr. N.Y. 350.00 600.00
377 George Myers: Indianapolis-Phila. 300.00 500.00
378 Al(Cod) Myers: Washington 300.00 500.00
379 Thomas Nagle: Omaha-Chi. 300.00 500.00
380 Billy Nash: Boston 300.00 500.00
381 Jack(Candy) Nelson: SPOT 900.00 1500.00
382 Kid Nichols: Omaha 2500.00 4000.00
383 Samuel Nichols: Pittsburgh 300.00 500.00
384 J.W. Nicholson Maroons-Minn. 350.00 600.00
385 Tom Nicholson (Parson) Whites-Cleveland 300.00 500.00
386 Nicholls Nicol Browns Champ 500.00 800.00
387 Hugh Nicol: Cinc. 300.00 500.00
388 Hugh Nicol and Long John Reilly: Cincinnati 350.00 600.00
389 Frederick Nyce Whites-Burlington 300.00 500.00
390 Doc Oberlander Cleveland-Syracuse 300.00 500.00
391 Jack O'Brien Brooklyn-Baltimore 300.00 500.00
392 William O'Brien: Washington 300.00 500.00
393 William O'Brien and John Irwin: Washington 350.00 600.00
394 Darby O'Brien: Brooklyn 300.00 500.00
395 John O'Brien: Cleve. 300.00 500.00
396 P.J. O'Connell: Omaha-Des Moines 300.00 500.00
397 John O'Connor: Cincinnati-Columbus 300.00 500.00
398 Hank O'Day: Washington-New York 500.00 800.00
399 O'Day Sacramento 300.00 500.00
400 James O'Neil: St. Louis-Chicago 300.00 500.00
401 James O'Neil: Browns Champs 500.00 800.00
402 Norris Tip O'Neill Oakland PCL
403 Jim O'Rourke: New York 1800.00 3000.00
404 Thomas O'Rourke: Boston-Jersey City 300.00 500.00
405 David Orr SPOT 900.00 1500.00
406 David Orr: All Star-Brooklyn-Columbus 300.00 500.00
407 Parsons: Minneapolis 300.00 500.00
408 Owen Patton: Minn.-Des Moines 300.00 500.00
409 James Peeples: Brooklyn-Columbus 300.00 500.00
410 James Peeples and Hardie Henderson: Brooklyn 350.00 600.00
411 Hip Perrier: San Francisco PCL
412 Patrick Pettee: Milwaukee-London 300.00 500.00
413 Patrick Pettee and Bobby Lowe: Milwaukee 350.00 600.00
414 Dandelion Pfeffer: Chi. 300.00 500.00
415 Dick Phelan: Des Moines 300.00 500.00
416 William Phillips: Brooklyn-Kansas City 300.00 500.00
417 John Pickett: St. Paul-K.C.-Phila. 300.00 500.00
418 George Pinkney: Brooklyn 300.00 500.00
419 Thomas Poorman: A's-Milwaukee 500.00 800.00
420 Henry Porter: Brooklyn-Kansas City 300.00 500.00
421 James Powell: Sioux City 300.00 500.00
422 Tom Powers: San Francisco PCL
423 Bill Purcell: (Blondie) Baltimore-A's 300.00 500.00
424 Thomas Quinn: Baltimore 300.00 500.00
425 Joseph Quinn: Des Moines-Boston 300.00 500.00
426 Old Hoss Radbourne: Boston (Portrait) 2500.00 4000.00
427 Old Hoss Radbourne: Boston (Non-portrait) 2500.00 4000.00
428 Shorty Radford: Brooklyn-Cleveland 300.00 500.00
429 Tom Ramsey: Louisville 300.00 500.00
430 Rehse: Minneapolis 300.00 500.00
431 Long John Reilly: Cincinnati 300.00 500.00
432 Charles Reilly (Princeton) St.Paul 300.00 500.00
433 Charles Reynolds: Kansas City 300.00 500.00
434 Hardie Richardson Detroit-Boston 300.00 500.00
435 Danny Richardson: New York 300.00 500.00
436 Charles Ripslager SPOT 900.00 1500.00
437 John Roach New York 300.00 500.00
438 Wilbert Robinson Uncle Robbie: A's 1500.00 2500.00
439 M.C. Robinson: Minn. 300.00 500.00
440 Yank Robinson: St. Louis 300.00 500.00
441 Wm.(Yank) Robinson: Browns Champs 500.00 800.00
442 George Rooks: Maroons-Detroit 350.00 600.00
443 James(Chief) Roseman SPOT 900.00 1500.00
444 Davis Rowe: Mgr. K.C.-Denver 300.00 500.00
445 Jack Rowe: Detroit-Pittsburgh 300.00 500.00
446 Amos (Hoosier Thunderbolt) Rusie: Indianapolis 3500.00 6000.00
447 Amos Rusie New York 3500.00 6000.00
448 James Ryan: Chicago 500.00 800.00
449 Henry Sage: Des Moines-Toledo 300.00 500.00
450 Henry Sage and William Van Dyke: Des Moines-Toledo 350.00 600.00
451 Sanders: Omaha 300.00 500.00
452 Al(Ben) Sanders: Philadelphia 300.00 500.00
453 Frank Scheibeck: Detroit 300.00 500.00
454 Albert Schellhase: St. Joseph 300.00 500.00
455 William Schenkle: Milwaukee 300.00 500.00
456 Bill Schildknecht: Des Moines-Milwaukee 300.00 500.00
457 Gus(Pink Whiskers) Schmelz Mgr. Cincinnati 300.00 500.00
458 Lewis Schoeneck (Jumbo): Maroons-Indianapolis 350.00 600.00
459 Pop Schriver: Phila. 300.00 500.00
460 John Seery: Ind. 300.00 500.00
461 William Serad Cincinnati-Toronto 300.00 500.00
462 Edward Seward: A's 300.00 500.00
463 George(Orator)Shafer Des Moines 300.00 500.00
464 Frank Shafer: St. Paul 300.00 500.00
465 Daniel Shannon: Omaha-L'ville-Phila. 300.00 500.00
466 William Sharsig: Mgr. Athletics 350.00 600.00
467 Samuel Shaw: Baltimore-Newark 300.00 500.00
468 John Shaw: Minneapolis 300.00 500.00
469 William Shindle: Baltimore-Phila. 300.00 500.00
470 George Shock: Wash. 300.00 500.00
471 Otto Shomberg: Ind. 300.00 500.00
472 Lev Shreve: Ind. 300.00 500.00
473 Ed(Baldy) Silch: Brooklyn-Denver 300.00 500.00
474 Michael Slattery: New York 300.00 500.00
475 Sam(Skyrocket)Smith: Louisville 300.00 500.00
476 John(Phenomenal) Smith (Portrait) 1500.00 2500.00
477 John(Phenomenal) Smith: Balt.-A's (Non-portrait) 300.00 500.00
478 Elmer Smith: Cincinnati 300.00 500.00
479 Fred(Sam) Smith: Des Moines 300.00 500.00
480 George Smith (Germany) Brooklyn 300.00 500.00
481 Pop Smith: Pitt.-Bos.-Phila. 300.00 500.00
482 Nick Smith: St. Joe 300.00 500.00
483 P.T. Somers: St. Louis 300.00 500.00
484 Joe Sommer: Balt. 300.00 500.00
485 Pete Sommers: Chicago-New York 300.00 500.00
486 William Sowders: Boston-Pittsburgh 300.00 500.00
487 John Sowders: St. Paul-Kansas City 300.00 500.00
488 Charles Sprague: Maroons-Chi.-Cleve. 350.00 600.00
489 Edward Sproat: Whites 300.00 500.00
490 Harry Staley: Whites-Pittsburgh 300.00 500.00
491 Daniel Stearns: Des Moines-K.C. 300.00 500.00
492 Billy(Cannonball) Stemmyer: Boston-Cleveland 300.00 500.00
493 B.F. Stephens: Milw. 300.00 500.00
494 John C. Sterling: Minneapolis 300.00 500.00

495 Leonard Stockwell S.F. PCL
496 Harry Stovey: A's-Boston 600.00 1000.00
497 C. Scott Stratton: Louisville 300.00 500.00
498 Joseph Straus: Omaha-Milwaukee 300.00 500.00
499 John(Cub) Stricker: Cleveland 300.00 500.00
500 Marty Sullivan: Chicago-Ind. 300.00 500.00
501 Michael Sullivan: A's 300.00 500.00
502 Billy Sunday: Chicago-Pittsburgh 900.00 1500.00
503 Sy Sutcliffe: Cleve. 300.00 500.00
504 Ezra Sutton: Boston-Milwaukee 300.00 500.00
505 Ed Cyrus Swartwood: Brook.-D.Moines-Ham. 300.00 500.00
506 Parke Swartzel: K.C. 300.00 500.00
507 Peter Sweeney: Wash. 300.00 500.00
508 Louis Sylvester Sacramento PCL
509 Ed(Dimples) Tate: Boston-Baltimore 300.00 500.00
510 Patsy Tebeau: Chi.-Cleve.-Minn. 500.00 800.00
511 John Tener: Chicago 350.00 600.00
512 Bill(Adonis) Terry: Brooklyn 300.00 500.00
513 Big Sam Thompson: Detroit-Philadelphia 1500.00 2500.00
514 Silent Mike Tiernan: New York 350.00 600.00
515 Ledell Titcomb: N.Y. 300.00 500.00
516 Phillip Tomney: Louisville 300.00 500.00
517 Stephen Toole: Brooklyn-K.C.-Rochester 300.00 500.00
518 George Townsend A's 300.00 500.00
519 William Traffley: Des Moines 300.00 500.00
520 George Treadway: St. Paul-Denver 300.00 500.00
521 Samuel Trott: Baltimore-Newark 300.00 500.00
522 Sam Trott and Tommy(Oyster) Burns: Baltimore HOR 350.00 600.00
523 Tom(Foghorn) Tucker: Baltimore 300.00 500.00
524 William Tuckerman: St. Paul 300.00 500.00
525 Turner: Minneapolis 300.00 500.00
526 Lawrence Twitchell: Detroit-Cleveland 300.00 500.00
527 James Tyng: Phila. 300.00 500.00
528 William Van Dyke: Des Moines-Toledo 300.00 500.00
529 George(Rip) VanHaltren Chicago 300.00 500.00
530 Harry Vaughn: (Farmer) Louisville-New York 300.00 500.00
531 Peek-a-Boo Veach: St. Paul 500.00 800.00
532 Veach: Sacra. PCL
533 Leon Viau: Cincinnati 300.00 500.00
534 William Vinton: Minneapolis 300.00 500.00
535 Joseph Visner: Brooklyn 300.00 500.00
536 Christian Von Der Ahe Owner Browns Champs 500.00 800.00
537 Joseph Walsh Omaha 300.00 500.00
538 John (Monte) Ward: New York 1800.00 3000.00
539 E.H. Warner: Milwaukee 500.00 800.00
540 William Watkins: Mgr. Detroit-Kansas City 350.00 600.00
541 Bill Weaver: (Farmer) Louisville 300.00 500.00
542 Charles Weber: Sioux City 300.00 500.00
543 George Weidman (Stump): Detroit-New York 300.00 500.00
544 William Weidner: Columbus 300.00 500.00
545 Curtis Welch: Browns Champ 500.00 800.00
546 Curtis Welch: A's 350.00 600.00
547 Curtis Welch and Bill Gleason: Athletics 500.00 800.00
548 Smilin'Mickey Welch: All Star-New York 1800.00 3000.00
549 Jake Wells: K.C. 300.00 500.00
550 Frank Wells: Des Moines-Mil. 350.00 600.00
551 Joseph Werrick: Louisville-St. Paul 300.00 500.00
552 Milton(Buck) West: Minneapolis 300.00 500.00
553 Gus(Cannonball) Weyhing: A's 300.00 500.00
554 John Weyhing: Athletics-Columbus 300.00 500.00
555 Bobby Wheelock: Boston-Detroit 300.00 500.00
556 Whitacre: A's 300.00 500.00
557 Pat Whitaker: Balt. 300.00 500.00
558 Deacon White: Detroit-Pittsburgh 500.00 800.00
559 William White: Louisville 300.00 500.00
560 Jim(Grasshopper) Whitney: Wash.-Indianapolis 300.00 500.00
561 Arthur Whitney: Pittsburgh-New York 300.00 500.00
562 G. Whitney: St. Joseph 300.00 500.00
563 James Williams: Mgr. Cleveland 350.00 600.00
564 Ned Williamson: Chi. 500.00 800.00
565 Williamson and Mascot 350.00 600.00
566 C.H. Willis: Omaha 300.00 500.00
567 Walt Wilmot: Washington-Chicago 300.00 500.00
568 George Winkleman: Minneapolis-Hartford Issued only in 1889 600.00 1000.00
569 Samuel Wise: Boston-Washington 300.00 500.00
570 William Wolf (Chicken) Louisville 300.00 500.00
571 George(Dandy) Wood: Philadelphia 300.00 500.00
572 Peter Wood: Phila. 300.00 500.00
573 Harry Wright: Mgr. Philadelphia 5000.00 8000.00
574 Charles Zimmer (Chief) Cleveland 300.00 500.00
575 Frank Zinn: Athletics 300.00 500.00
576 John Barnes (Barns) MG 500.00 800.00

2010 Panini Century Air Mail Bats

STATED PRINT RUN 3-250
NO PRICING QTY 5 OR LESS
1 Joe Jackson/50 60.00 120.00
2 Pete Rose/250 12.50 30.00
3 Cal Ripken Jr./3
4 Eddie Mathews/250 4.00 10.00
5 Robin Yount/5
6 Joe Morgan/250 3.00 8.00
8 Mike Schmidt/250 4.00 10.00
9 Minnie Minoso/250 5.00 12.00
11 Orlando Cepeda/250 4.00 10.00
12 Reggie Jackson/250 3.00 8.00

2010 Panini Century Air Mail Jerseys

STATED PRINT RUN 3-250
NO PRICING ON QTY 25 OR LESS
3 Cal Ripken Jr./20
4 Eddie Mathews/250 4.00 10.00
5 Robin Yount/40 20.00 50.00
8 Mike Schmidt/25
12 Reggie Jackson/150 4.00 10.00
14 Duke Snider/50 6.00 15.00
15 George Brett/3

2010 Panini Century Air Mail Bats Autographs

STATED PRINT RUN 1-50
NO PRICING ON QTY 25 OR LESS
2 Pete Rose/50 60.00 120.00
11 Orlando Cepeda/50 15.00 40.00
13 Brooks Robinson/27 20.00 50.00

2010 Panini Century Air Mail Jerseys Autographs

STATED PRINT RUN 1-25
NO PRICING DUE TO SCARCITY

2010 Panini Century Ballpark Autographs

STATED PRINT RUN 5-50
NO PRICING ON QTY 25 OR LESS
11 Andre Dawson/50 12.50 30.00

2010 Panini Century Ballpark Materials

STATED PRINT RUN 1-250
NO PRICING ON QTY 25 OR LESS
3 Duke Snider/50 6.00 15.00
5 Steve Carlton/250 3.00 8.00
6 Rod Carew/200 3.00 8.00
7 Frank Robinson/99 4.00 10.00
8 Dale Murphy/99 5.00 12.00
9 Tom Seaver/1
10 Lou Brock/250 3.00 8.00
11 Andre Dawson/99 3.00 8.00
12 Willie McCovey/25
13 Carlton Fisk/15
14 Wade Boggs/250 3.00 8.00

2010 Panini Century Ballpark Materials Prime

STATED PRINT RUN 2-30
NO PRICING ON QTY 25 OR LESS
8 Dale Murphy/30 10.00 25.00

2010 Panini Century Ballpark Materials Autographs

STATED PRINT RUN 2-49
NO PRICING ON QTY 25 OR LESS

2010 Panini Century Ballpark Materials Prime Autographs

STATED PRINT RUN 1-50
NO PRICING ON QTY 25 OR LESS
8 Dale Murphy/50 40.00 80.00
15 Joe Morgan/50 15.00 40.00

2010 Panini Century Baseball Six Cent Stamp Autographs

STATED PRINT RUN 2-50
NO PRICING ON QTY 25 OR LESS
3 Billy Williams/32 10.00 25.00
7 Dennis Eckersley/50 12.50 30.00
15 Johnny Pesky/50 12.50 30.00
31 Steve Carlton/32 15.00 40.00
47 Carlton Fisk/38 12.50 30.00
48 Gary Carter/50 10.00 25.00
54 Brooks Robinson/50 15.00 40.00
68 Frank Howard/31 10.00 25.00
69 Dale Murphy/26 20.00 50.00
75 Joe Morgan/50 12.50 30.00

2010 Panini Century Baseball Six Cent Stamp Materials

STATED PRINT RUN 1-250
NO PRICING ON QTY 25 OR LESS
2 Orel Hershiser/100 3.00 8.00
14 Joe Jackson/50 60.00 120.00
17 Lou Brock/100 6.00 15.00
24 Pete Rose/100 12.50 30.00
25 Phil Niekro/50 4.00 10.00
27 Robin Yount/50 20.00 50.00
28 Rod Carew/50 5.00 12.00
45 Tony Gwynn/250 6.00 15.00
63 Dave Winfield/99 3.00 8.00
69 Dale Murphy/30 10.00 25.00
71 Fergie Jenkins/33 5.00 12.00

2010 Panini Century Baseball Six Cent Stamp Materials Autographs

STATED PRINT RUN 1-34
NO PRICING ON QTY 25 OR LESS
74 Harmon Killebrew/34 60.00 120.00
75 Joe Morgan/1

2010 Panini Century Baseball Six Cent Stamp Materials Prime Autographs

STATED PRINT RUN 1-20
NO PRICING DUE TO SCARCITY

2010 Panini Century Baseball Three Cent Stamp Autographs

STATED PRINT RUN 1-42
NO PRICING ON QTY 25 OR LESS
7 Dennis Eckersley/40 12.50 30.00
40 Don Mattingly/34 40.00 80.00
48 Gary Carter/37 12.50 30.00
54 Brooks Robinson/34 20.00 50.00
75 Joe Morgan/28 15.00 40.00

2010 Panini Century Baseball Three Cent Stamp Materials

STATED PRINT RUN 1-250
NO PRICING ON QTY 25 OR LESS
2 Orel Hershiser/50 4.00 10.00
14 Joe Jackson/50 60.00 120.00
24 Pete Rose/100 12.50 30.00
25 Phil Niekro/50 4.00 10.00
27 Robin Yount/50 20.00 50.00
28 Rod Carew/50 5.00 12.00
45 Tony Gwynn/250 6.00 15.00
63 Dave Winfield/31 4.00 10.00

2010 Panini Century Baseball Three Cent Stamp Materials Autographs

STATED PRINT RUN 1-25
NO PRICING DUE TO SCARCITY

2010 Panini Century Baseball Three Cent Stamp Materials Prime Autographs

STATED PRINT RUN 1-10
NO PRICING DUE TO SCARCITY

2010 Panini Century Bats

NO PRICING ON QTY 25 OR LESS
1 Bo Jackson/50 6.00 15.00
6 Arky Vaughan/250 8.00 20.00
8 Reggie Jackson/250 3.00 8.00
10 Wade Boggs/250 3.00 8.00
15 Rod Carew/25
17 Orlando Cepeda/100 6.00 15.00
19 Will Clark/250 4.00 10.00
21 Andre Dawson/100 3.00 8.00
35 Pete Rose/100 12.50 30.00
40 Joe Jackson/50 60.00 120.00
41 Reggie Jackson/250 3.00 8.00
47 Pete Rose/100 12.50 30.00
53 Eddie Mathews/250 4.00 10.00
54 Don Mattingly/25
59 Minnie Minoso/250 5.00 12.00
61 Joe Morgan/50
63 Dale Murphy/50 6.00 15.00
64 Eddie Murray/250 3.00 8.00
69 Dave Parker/100 4.00 10.00
78 Frank Robinson/25
79 Pete Rose/100 12.50 30.00
82 Ryne Sandberg/250 5.00 12.00
83 Deion Sanders/25
85 Mike Schmidt/100 5.00 12.00
90 Willie Stargell/250 5.00 12.00
94 Larry Walker/100 3.00 8.00

2010 Panini Century Bats Autographs

STATED PRINT RUN 1-99
NO PRICING ON QTY 25 OR LESS
17 Orlando Cepeda/50 15.00 40.00
18 Gary Carter/50 6.00 15.00
19 Will Clark/10
21 Andre Dawson/50 10.00 25.00
22 Bobby Doerr/50 12.50 30.00
27 Carlton Fisk/50 12.50 30.00
30 Steve Garvey/20
32 Kirk Gibson/5
33 Dwight Gooden/99 6.00 15.00
34 Tony Gwynn/1
35 Pete Rose/50 60.00 120.00
46 Harmon Killebrew/20
47 Pete Rose/50 60.00 120.00
69 Dave Parker/50 8.00 20.00
79 Pete Rose/50 60.00 120.00

2010 Panini Century Blast from the Past Bats

STATED PRINT RUN 1-250
NO PRICING ON QTY 25 OR LESS
1 Reggie Jackson/250 3.00 8.00
2 Ryne Sandberg/150 6.00 15.00
3 Mike Schmidt/250 4.00 10.00
4 Cal Ripken Jr./3
5 Paul Molitor/150 4.00 10.00
6 Don Mattingly/30
7 Barry Larkin/99 4.00 10.00
9 Wade Boggs/250 3.00 8.00
10 Fred Lynn/1
12 Jim Rice/1
13 Tony Perez/1
14 Carlton Fisk/27 5.00 12.00
15 Kirk Gibson/40 4.00 10.00
16 Will Clark/250 4.00 10.00
18 Dale Murphy/99 5.00 12.00
20 Joe Morgan/250 3.00 8.00

2010 Panini Century Blast from the Past Jerseys

STATED PRINT RUN 1-250
NO PRICING ON QTY 25 OR LESS
1 Reggie Jackson/250 3.00 8.00
2 Ryne Sandberg/100 6.00 15.00
3 Mike Schmidt/50 6.00 15.00
4 Cal Ripken Jr./5
6 Don Mattingly/5
7 Barry Larkin/99 4.00 10.00
8 Tony Gwynn/250 6.00 15.00
9 Wade Boggs/175 4.00 10.00
10 Fred Lynn/10
11 Jim Palmer/50 4.00 10.00
12 Jim Rice/250 4.00 10.00
13 Tony Perez/20
14 Carlton Fisk/10
16 Will Clark/250 4.00 10.00
18 Dale Murphy/99 5.00 12.00
19 Tom Seaver/1

2010 Panini Century Blast from the Past Bats Autographs

STATED PRINT RUN 1-25
NO PRICING DUE TO SCARCITY

2010 Panini Century Blast from the Past Jerseys Autographs

STATED PRINT RUN 1-25
NO PRICING DUE TO SCARCITY

2010 Panini Century Cut Autographs

STATED PRINT RUN 1-100
NO PRICING ON QTY 25 OR LESS
1 Al Barlick/100 12.50 30.00
3 Babe Ruth/1
5 Bill Dickey/15
6 Bill Terry/65 30.00 60.00
7 Bob Lemon/55 20.00 50.00
8 Buck Leonard/35
9 Burleigh Grimes/10
10 Carl Hubbell/30
11 Catfish Hunter/40 30.00 60.00
12 Charlie Gehringer/40 20.00 50.00
13 Dizzy Dean/1
14 Don Drysdale/23
15 Luke Appling/35
17 Eddie Mathews/21
18 Enos Slaughter/52 20.00 50.00
19 Fred Lindstrom/4
21 George Kell/100 8.00 20.00
23 Stanley Coveleski/28
24 Happy Chandler/34 30.00 60.00
25 Honus Wagner/1
27 Jackie Robinson/1
29 Joe Sewell/100 15.00 40.00
30 Johnny Mize/100 40.00 80.00
31 Judy Johnson/40
32 George L. Kelly/25
33 Lloyd Waner/24
34 Lou Boudreau/58 12.50 30.00
36 Billy Herman/50 15.00 40.00
37 Edd Roush/27 20.00 50.00
39 Pee Wee Reese/31 40.00 80.00
40 Phil Rizzuto/52 40.00 80.00
41 Pie Traynor/1
42 Rick Ferrell/88 15.00 40.00
43 Satchel Paige/1
44 Ted Williams/1
45 Ty Cobb/1
47 Waite Hoyt/35
48 Walter Johnson/1
50 Lefty Gomez/15

2010 Panini Century Jerseys

STATED PRINT RUN 15-250
NO PRICING ON QTY 25 OR LESS
1 Bo Jackson/50 6.00 15.00
3 Luis Aparicio/250 3.00 8.00
4 Richie Ashburn/250 5.00 12.00
8 Reggie Jackson/25
9 Bert Blyleven/100 5.00 12.00
10 Wade Boggs/100 5.00 12.00
11 Lou Boudreau/175 5.00 12.00
13 Lou Brock/25
15 Rod Carew/100 4.00 10.00
16 Steve Carlton/25
19 Will Clark/100 8.00 20.00
20 Joe Cronin/250 4.00 10.00
21 Andre Dawson/50 4.00 10.00
22 Bobby Doerr/250 4.00 10.00
23 Dennis Eckersley/25
27 Carlton Fisk/100 5.00 12.00
28 Whitey Ford/25
34 Tony Gwynn/250 6.00 15.00
36 Orel Hershiser/50 4.00 10.00
37 Gil Hodges/250 8.00 20.00
38 Frank Howard/250 4.00 10.00
46 Harmon Killebrew/25
47 Pete Rose/50 15.00 40.00
48 Barry Larkin/50
51 Juan Marichal/50 3.00 8.00
53 Eddie Mathews/250 4.00 10.00
58 Joe Medwick/15
62 Jack Morris/50 5.00 12.00
63 Dale Murphy/25
64 Eddie Murray/250 3.00 8.00
65 Stan Musial/25
66 Phil Niekro/25
67 Tony Oliva/100 6.00 15.00
69 Dave Parker/250 3.00 8.00
74 Jim Rice/250 4.00 10.00
81 Ozzie Smith/25
83 Deion Sanders/25
86 Red Schoendienst/25
89 Warren Spahn/250 4.00 10.00
90 Willie Stargell/100 6.00 15.00

2010 Panini Century Jerseys Prime

STATED PRINT RUN 5-50
NO PRICING ON QTY 25 OR LESS
4 Richie Ashburn/25
11 Lou Boudreau/25
20 Joe Cronin/25
37 Gil Hodges/5
53 Eddie Mathews/15
89 Warren Spahn/50
90 Willie Stargell/25

2010 Panini Century Jerseys Autographs

STATED PRINT RUN 1-100
NO PRICING ON QTY 25 OR LESS
1 Bo Jackson/30 40.00 80.00
21 Andre Dawson/50 10.00 25.00
22 Bobby Doerr/50 12.50 30.00
23 Dennis Eckersley/50 10.00 25.00
25 Bob Feller/50 20.00 50.00
33 Dwight Gooden/99 6.00 15.00
36 Orel Hershiser/50 12.50 30.00
38 Frank Howard/65 10.00 25.00
42 Fergie Jenkins/50 12.50 30.00
44 Al Kaline/45 12.50 30.00
46 Harmon Killebrew/25
47 Pete Rose/50 60.00 120.00
62 Jack Morris/100 8.00 20.00
68 Jim Palmer/50 8.00 20.00
69 Dave Parker/100 6.00 15.00
71 Gaylord Perry/99 6.00 15.00
74 Jim Rice/100 10.00 25.00
86 Red Schoendienst/50 10.00 25.00
92 Don Sutton/100 8.00 20.00
95 Billy Williams/30 20.00 50.00
100 Robin Yount/50 30.00 60.00

2010 Panini Century Jerseys Prime Autographs

STATED PRINT RUN 1-50
NO PRICING ON QTY 25 OR LESS
13 Lou Brock/50 20.00 50.00
18 Gary Carter/50 6.00 15.00
21 Andre Dawson/50 10.00 25.00
23 Dennis Eckersley/50 10.00 25.00
32 Kirk Gibson/50 15.00 40.00
33 Dwight Gooden/50 8.00 20.00
35 Pete Rose/40 60.00 120.00
36 Orel Hershiser/50 12.50 30.00
38 Frank Howard/50 12.50 30.00
42 Fergie Jenkins/45 12.50 30.00
51 Juan Marichal/50 10.00 25.00
62 Jack Morris/50 20.00 50.00
63 Dale Murphy/50 40.00 80.00
68 Jim Palmer/45 8.00 20.00
69 Dave Parker/50 8.00 20.00
74 Jim Rice/50 15.00 40.00
85 Mike Schmidt/35 20.00 50.00
87 Tom Seaver/35 30.00 60.00
92 Don Sutton/50 10.00 25.00
93 Alan Trammell/50 30.00 60.00
94 Larry Walker/30
95 Billy Williams/50 20.00 50.00
97 Maury Wills/10
98 Dave Winfield/25
99 Carl Yastrzemski/1
100 Robin Yount/50 30.00 60.00

2010 Panini Century Postcards Materials

STATED PRINT RUN 5-250
NO PRICING ON QTY 25 OR LESS
1 Andre Dawson/100 3.00 8.00
5 Harmon Killebrew/100 15.00 40.00
6 Stan Musial/99 8.00 20.00
7 Bob Gibson/25
8 Cal Ripken Jr./25
9 Mike Schmidt/20
10 Nolan Ryan/100 10.00 25.00
11 Whitey Ford/25
13 Reggie Jackson/25
15 Don Mattingly/20
16 Tony Gwynn/250 6.00 15.00
18 George Brett/5
19 Carl Yastrzemski/12
20 Paul Molitor/250 3.00 8.00

2010 Panini Century Postcards Materials Prime

STATED PRINT RUN 1-25
NO PRICING DUE TO SCARCITY

2010 Panini Century Postcards Materials Autographs

STATED PRINT RUN 1-50
NO PRICING ON QTY 25 OR LESS
1 Andre Dawson/50 10.00 25.00
10 Nolan Ryan/50 50.00 100.00

2010 Panini Century Postcards Materials Prime Autographs

STATED PRINT RUN 1-50
NO PRICING ON QTY 25 OR LESS
1 Andre Dawson/50 10.00 25.00
10 Nolan Ryan/50 50.00 100.00
20 Paul Molitor/50 15.00 40.00

2010 Panini Century Postmark Autographs Gold

STATED PRINT RUN 1-25
NO PRICING DUE TO SCARCITY

2010 Panini Century Postmark Autographs Platinum

STATED PRINT RUN 1 SER.#'d SET
NO PRICING DUE TO SCARCITY

2010 Panini Century Postmark Autographs Silver

STATED PRINT RUN 1-250
NO PRICING ON QTY 25 OR LESS
5 Harold Baines/163 6.00 15.00
14 Jim Bunning/79 6.00 15.00
16 Steve Carlton/50 10.00 25.00
17 Orlando Cepeda/25
18 Gary Carter/250 6.00 15.00
21 Andre Dawson/250 6.00 15.00
22 Bobby Doerr/250 6.00 15.00
23 Dennis Eckersley/250 6.00 15.00
24 Carl Erskine/250 6.00 15.00
25 Bob Feller/50 15.00 40.00
26 Mark Fidrych/50 15.00 40.00
33 Dwight Gooden/250 6.00 15.00
39 Monte Irvin/250 6.00 15.00
42 Fergie Jenkins/250 6.00 15.00
44 Al Kaline/250 10.00 25.00
45 George Kell/150 6.00 15.00
49 Don Larsen/38 5.00 12.00
52 Marty Marion/98 10.00 25.00
57 Denny McLain/43 10.00 25.00
62 Jack Morris/74 5.00 12.00
63 Dale Murphy/250 10.00 25.00
68 Jim Palmer/213 6.00 15.00
69 Dave Parker/75 6.00 15.00
70 Tony Perez/60 6.00 15.00
71 Gaylord Perry/250 5.00 12.00
72 Johnny Pesky/24
73 Tim Raines/75 5.00 12.00
74 Jim Rice/250 6.00 15.00
77 Brooks Robinson/50 15.00 40.00
86 Red Schoendienst/250 6.00 15.00
88 Duke Snider/40 15.00 40.00
91 Bruce Sutter/223 8.00 20.00
92 Don Sutton/149 5.00 12.00
93 Alan Trammell/226 12.50 30.00
97 Maury Wills/250 5.00 12.00

2010 Panini Century Sports Dual Stamp Combo Dual Memorabilia

STATED PRINT RUN 50-100

2010 Panini Century Sports Dual Stamp Combo Memorabilia

STATED PRINT RUN 49-100

2010 Panini Century Stamp Cut Autographs

STATED PRINT RUN 1 SER.#'d SET
NO PRICING DUE TO SCARCITY

1939 Play Ball

The cards in this 161-card set measure approximately 2 1/2" by 3 1/8". Gum Incorporated introduced a brief (war-shortened) but innovative era of baseball card production with its set of 1939. The combination of actual player photos (black and white), large card size, and extensive biography proved extremely popular. Player names are found either entirely capitalized or with initial caps only, and a "sample card" overprint is not uncommon. The "sample card" overprint variations are valued at double the prices below. Card number 126 was never issued, and cards 116-162 were produced in lesser quantities than cards 1-115. A card of Ted Williams in his rookie season as well as an early card of Joe DiMaggio are the key cards in the set.

COMPLETE SET (161) 6000.00 10000.00
COMMON CARD (1-115) 12.00 20.00
COMMON (116-162) 40.00 75.00
WRAPPER (1-CENT) 150.00 200.00
1 Jake Powell RC 30.00 60.00
2 Lee Grissom RC 12.00 20.00
3 Red Ruffing 40.00 75.00
4 Eldon Auker RC 12.00 20.00
5 Luke Sewell 15.00 25.00
6 Leo Durocher 60.00 100.00
7 Bobby Doerr RC 40.00 75.00
8 Henry Pippen RC 12.00 20.00
9 James Tobin RC 12.00 20.00
10 James DeShong 12.00 20.00
11 Johnny Rizzo RC 12.00 20.00
12 Hershel Martin RC 12.00 20.00
13 Luke Hamlin RC 12.00 20.00
14 Jim Tabor RC 12.00 20.00
15 Paul Derringer 18.00 30.00
16 John Peacock RC 12.00 20.00
17 Emerson Dickman RC 12.00 20.00
18 Harry Danning RC 12.00 20.00
19 Paul Dean RC 25.00 40.00
20 Joe Heving RC 12.00 20.00
21 Dutch Leonard RC 18.00 30.00
22 Bucky Walters RC 18.00 30.00
23 Burgess Whitehead RC 12.00 20.00
24 Richard Coffman 12.00 20.00
25 George Selkirk RC 25.00 40.00
26 Joe DiMaggio RC 900.00 1400.00
27 Fred Ostermueller 12.00 20.00
28 Sylvester Johnson RC 12.00 20.00
29 John(Jack) Wilson RC 12.00 20.00
30 Bill Dickey 75.00 125.00
31 Sam West 12.00 20.00
32 Bob Seeds RC 12.00 20.00
33 Del Young RC 12.00 20.00
34 Frank Demaree 12.00 20.00
35 Bill Jurges 12.00 20.00
36 Frank McCormick RC 12.00 20.00
37 Virgil Davis 12.00 20.00
38 Billy Myers RC 12.00 20.00
39 Rick Ferrell 40.00 75.00
40 James Bagby Jr. RC 12.00 20.00
41 Lon Warneke 15.00 25.00
42 Arndt Jorgens 12.00 20.00
43 Melo Almada RC 15.00 25.00
44 Don Heffner RC 12.00 20.00
45 Merrill May RC 12.00 20.00
46 Morris Arnovich RC 12.00 20.00
47 Buddy Lewis RC 12.00 20.00
48 Lefty Gomez 75.00 125.00
49 Eddie Miller RC 12.00 20.00
50 Charley Gehringer 75.00 125.00
51 Mel Ott 75.00 125.00
52 Tommy Henrich RC 25.00 40.00
53 Carl Hubbell 75.00 125.00
54 Harry Gumpert RC 12.00 20.00
55 Arky Vaughan 40.00 75.00
56 Hank Greenberg 125.00 200.00
57 Buddy Hassett RC 12.00 20.00
58 Lou Chiozza RC 12.00 20.00
59 Ken Chase RC 12.00 20.00
60 Schoolboy Rowe RC 25.00 40.00
61 Tony Cuccinello 15.00 25.00
62 Tom Carey RC 12.00 20.00
63 Emmett Mueller RC 12.00 20.00
64 Wally Moses RC 15.00 25.00
65 Harry Craft RC 15.00 25.00
66 Jimmy Ripple RC 12.00 20.00
67 Ed Joost RC 15.00 25.00
68 Fred Sington RC 12.00 20.00
69 Elbie Fletcher RC 12.00 20.00
70 Fred Frankhouse 12.00 20.00
71 Monte Pearson RC 18.00 30.00
72 Debs Garms RC 12.00 20.00
73 Hal Schumacher 15.00 25.00
74 Cookie Lavagetto RC 15.00 25.00
75 Stan Bordagaray RC 12.00 20.00
76 Goody Rosen RC 12.00 20.00
77 Lew Riggs RC 12.00 20.00
78 Julius Solters 12.00 20.00
79 Jo Jo Moore 12.00 20.00
80 Pete Fox 12.00 20.00
81 Babe Dahlgren RC 18.00 30.00
82 Chuck Klein 60.00 100.00
83 Gus Suhr 12.00 20.00
84 Skeeter Newsom RC 12.00 20.00
85 Johnny Cooney RC 12.00 20.00
86 Dolph Camilli 15.00 25.00
87 Milburn Shoffner RC 12.00 20.00
88 Charlie Keller RC 25.00 40.00
89 Lloyd Waner 40.00 75.00
90 Robert Klinger RC 12.00 20.00
91 John Knott RC 12.00 20.00
92 Ted Williams RC 1000.00 1800.00
93 Charles Gelbert RC 12.00 20.00
94 Heinie Manush 40.00 75.00
95 Whit Wyatt RC 15.00 25.00
96 Babe Phelps RC 12.00 20.00
97 Bob Johnson 18.00 30.00
98 Pinky Whitney RC 12.00 20.00
99 Wally Berger 18.00 30.00
100 Buddy Myer 15.00 25.00
101 Roger Cramer 15.00 25.00
102 Lem (Pep) Young RC 12.00 20.00
103 Moe Berg 75.00 125.00
104 Tom Bridges 15.00 25.00
105 Rabbit McNair RC 12.00 20.00
106 Dolly Stark UMP 18.00 30.00
107 Joe Vosmik 12.00 20.00
108 Frank Hayes RC 12.00 20.00
109 Myril Hoag 12.00 20.00
110 Fred Fitzsimmons 15.00 25.00
111 Van Lingle Mungo RC 18.00 30.00
112 Paul Waner 60.00 100.00
113 Al Schacht 18.00 30.00
114 Cecil Travis RC 15.00 25.00
115 Ralph Kress 12.00 20.00
116 Gene Desautels RC 40.00 75.00
117 Wayne Ambler RC 40.00 75.00
118 Lynn Nelson 40.00 75.00
119 Will Hershberger RC 50.00 100.00
120 Rabbit Warstler RC 40.00 75.00
121 Bill Posedel RC 40.00 75.00
122 George McQuinn RC 40.00 75.00
123 Ray T. Davis RC 40.00 75.00
124 Walter Brown 40.00 75.00
125 Cliff Melton RC 40.00 75.00
126 Not issued
127 Gil Brack RC 40.00 75.00
128 Joe Bowman RC 40.00 75.00
129 Bill Swift 40.00 75.00
130 Bill Brubaker RC 40.00 75.00
131 Mort Cooper RC 50.00 100.00
132 Jim Brown RC 40.00 75.00
133 Lynn Myers RC 40.00 75.00
134 Tot Presnell RC 40.00 75.00
135 Mickey Owen RC 50.00 100.00
136 Roy Bell RC 40.00 75.00
137 Pete Appleton 40.00 75.00
138 George Case RC 50.00 100.00
139 Vito Tamulis RC 40.00 75.00
140 Ray Hayworth RC 40.00 75.00
141 Pete Coscarart RC 40.00 75.00
142 Ira Hutchinson RC 40.00 75.00
143 Earl Averill 100.00 175.00
144 Zeke Bonura RC 50.00 100.00
145 Hugh Mulcahy RC 40.00 75.00
146 Tom Sunkel RC 40.00 75.00
147 George Coffman RC 40.00 75.00
148 Bill Trotter RC 40.00 75.00
149 Max West RC 40.00 75.00
150 James Walkup RC 40.00 75.00
151 Hugh Casey RC 50.00 100.00
152 Roy Weatherly RC 40.00 75.00
153 Dizzy Trout RC 50.00 100.00
154 Johnny Hudson RC 40.00 75.00
155 Jimmy Outlaw RC 40.00 75.00
156 Ray Berres RC 40.00 75.00
157 Don Padgett RC 40.00 75.00
158 Bud Thomas RC 40.00 75.00
159 Red Evans RC 40.00 75.00
160 Gene Moore RC 40.00 75.00
161 Lonnie Frey 40.00 75.00
162 Whitey Moore RC 50.00 100.00

1940 Play Ball

The cards in this 240-card series measure approximately 2 1/2" by 3 1/8". Gum Inc. improved upon its 1939 design by enclosing the 1940 black and white player photo with a frame line and printing the player's name in a panel below the picture (often using a nickname). The set included many Hall of Famers and Old Timers. Cards 1-114 are numbered in team groupings. Cards 181-240 are scarcer than cards 1-180. The backs contain an extensive biography and a dated copyright line. The key cards in the set are the cards of Joe DiMaggio, Shoeless Joe Jackson, and Ted Williams.

COMPLETE SET (240) 10000.00 15000.00
COMMON CARD (1-120) 12.00 20.00
COMMON (121-180) 12.00 20.00
COMMON (181-240) 35.00 70.00
WRAP.(1-CENT, DIFF. COLORS) 700.00 800.00
1 Joe DiMaggio 1500.00 2500.00
2 Art Jorgens 15.00 25.00
3 Babe Dahlgren 15.00 25.00
4 Tommy Henrich 25.00 50.00
5 Monte Pearson 15.00 25.00
6 Lefty Gomez 90.00 150.00
7 Bill Dickey 100.00 175.00
8 George Selkirk 15.00 25.00
9 Charlie Keller 25.00 50.00
10 Red Ruffing 50.00 90.00
11 Jake Powell 15.00 25.00
12 Johnny Schulte 12.00 20.00
13 Jack Knott 12.00 20.00
14 Rabbit McNair 12.00 20.00
15 George Case 15.00 25.00
16 Cecil Travis 15.00 25.00
17 Buddy Myer 15.00 25.00
18 Charlie Gelbert 12.00 20.00
19 Ken Chase 12.00 20.00
20 Buddy Lewis 12.00 20.00
21 Rick Ferrell 45.00 80.00
22 Sammy West 12.00 20.00
23 Dutch Leonard 15.00 25.00
24 Frank Hayes 12.00 20.00

25 Bob Johnson 15.00 25.00
26 Wally Moses 15.00 25.00
27 Ted Williams 800.00 1200.00
28 Gene Desautels 12.00 20.00
29 Doc Cramer 15.00 25.00
30 Moe Berg 90.00 150.00
31 Jack Wilson 12.00 20.00
32 Jim Bagby 12.00 20.00
33 Fritz Ostermueller 12.00 20.00
34 John Peacock 12.00 20.00
35 Joe Heving 12.00 20.00
36 Jim Tabor 12.00 20.00
37 Emerson Dickman 12.00 20.00
38 Bobby Doerr 50.00 90.00
39 Tom Carey 12.00 20.00
40 Hank Greenberg 100.00 200.00
41 Charley Gehringer 90.00 150.00
42 Bud Thomas 12.00 20.00
43 Pete Fox 12.00 20.00
44 Dizzy Trout 15.00 25.00
45 Red Kress 12.00 20.00
46 Earl Averill 50.00 90.00
47 Oscar Vitt RC 12.00 20.00
48 Luke Sewell 15.00 25.00
49 Stormy Weatherly 12.00 20.00
50 Hal Trosky 15.00 25.00
51 Don Heffner 12.00 20.00
52 Myril Hoag 12.00 20.00
53 George McQuinn 15.00 25.00
54 Bill Trotter 12.00 20.00
55 Slick Coffman 12.00 20.00
56 Eddie Miller RC 15.00 25.00
57 Max West 12.00 20.00
58 Bill Posedel 12.00 20.00
59 Rabbit Warstler 12.00 20.00
60 John Cooney 12.00 20.00
61 Tony Cuccinello 15.00 25.00
62 Buddy Hassett 12.00 20.00
63 Pete Coscarart 12.00 20.00
64 Van Lingle Mungo 15.00 25.00
65 Fred Fitzsimmons 15.00 25.00
66 Babe Phelps 12.00 20.00
67 Whit Wyatt 15.00 25.00
68 Dolph Camilli 15.00 25.00
69 Cookie Lavagetto 15.00 25.00
70 Luke Hamlin 12.00 20.00
(Hot Potato)
71 Mel Almada 12.00 20.00
72 Chuck Dressen RC 15.00 25.00
73 Bucky Walters 15.00 25.00
74 Paul(Duke) Derringer 15.00 25.00
75 Frank (Buck) McCormick 15.00 25.00
76 Lonny Frey 12.00 20.00
77 Willard Hershberger 15.00 25.00
78 Lew Riggs 12.00 20.00
79 Harry Craft 15.00 25.00
80 Billy Myers 12.00 20.00
81 Wally Berger 15.00 25.00
82 Hank Gowdy CO 15.00 25.00
83 Cliff Melton 12.00 20.00
84 Jo Jo Moore 12.00 20.00
85 Hal Schumacher 15.00 25.00
86 Harry Gumbert 12.00 20.00
87 Carl Hubbell 75.00 125.00
88 Mel Ott 100.00 175.00
89 Bill Jurges 12.00 20.00
90 Frank Demaree 12.00 20.00
91 Bob Seeds 12.00 20.00
92 Whitey Whitehead 12.00 20.00
93 Harry Danning 12.00 20.00
94 Gus Suhr 12.00 20.00
95 Hugh Mulcahy 12.00 20.00
96 Heinie Mueller 12.00 20.00
97 Morry Arnovich 12.00 20.00
98 Pinky May 12.00 20.00
99 Syl Johnson 12.00 20.00
100 Hersh Martin 12.00 20.00
101 Del Young 12.00 20.00
102 Chuck Klein 60.00 100.00
103 Elbie Fletcher 12.00 20.00
104 Paul Waner 50.00 90.00
105 Lloyd Waner 45.00 80.00
106 Pep Young 12.00 20.00
107 Arky Vaughan 45.00 80.00
108 Johnny Rizzo 12.00 20.00
109 Don Padgett 12.00 20.00
110 Tom Sunkel 12.00 20.00
111 Mickey Owen 15.00 25.00
112 Jimmy Brown 12.00 20.00
113 Mort Cooper 15.00 25.00
114 Lon Warneke 15.00 25.00
115 Mike Gonzalez CO 15.00 25.00
116 Al Schacht 15.00 25.00
117 Dolly Stark UMP 15.00 25.00
118 Waite Hoyt 50.00 90.00
119 Grover C. Alexander 100.00 175.00
120 Walter Johnson 100.00 200.00
121 Atley Donald RC 15.00 25.00
122 Sandy Sundra RC 15.00 25.00
123 Hildy Hildebrand 15.00 25.00
124 Earle Combs 60.00 100.00
125 Art Fletcher RC 15.00 25.00
126 Jake Solters 12.00 20.00
127 Muddy Ruel 12.00 20.00
128 Pete Appleton 12.00 20.00
129 Bucky Harris MG RC 45.00 80.00
130 Clyde Milan RC 15.00 25.00
131 Zeke Bonura 15.00 25.00
132 Connie Mack MG RC 75.00 150.00
133 Jimmie Foxx 100.00 200.00
134 Joe Cronin 60.00 100.00
135 Line Drive Nelson 12.00 20.00
136 Cotton Pippen 12.00 20.00
137 Bing Miller 12.00 20.00
138 Beau Bell 12.00 20.00
139 Elden Auker 12.00 20.00
140 Dick Coffman 12.00 20.00
141 Casey Stengel MG RC 100.00 175.00
142 George Kelly RC 50.00 90.00
143 Gene Moore 12.00 20.00
144 Joe Vosmik 12.00 20.00
145 Vito Tamulis 12.00 20.00
146 Tot Pressnell 12.00 20.00
147 Johnny Hudson 12.00 20.00
148 Hugh Casey 15.00 25.00
149 Pinky Shoffner 12.00 20.00
150 Whitey Moore 12.00 20.00
151 Edwin Joost 15.00 25.00
152 Jimmy Wilson 12.00 20.00
153 Bill McKechnie MG RC 45.00 80.00
154 Jumbo Brown 12.00 20.00
155 Ray Hayworth 12.00 20.00
156 Daffy Dean 25.00 50.00
157 Lou Chiozza 12.00 20.00
158 Travis Jackson 50.00 90.00
159 Pancho Snyder RC 12.00 20.00
160 Hans Lobert CO 12.00 20.00
161 Debs Garms 12.00 20.00
162 Joe Bowman 12.00 20.00
163 Spud Davis 12.00 20.00
164 Ray Berres 12.00 20.00
165 Bob Klinger 12.00 20.00
166 Bill Brubaker 12.00 20.00
167 Frankie Frisch MG 50.00 90.00
168 Honus Wagner CO 100.00 200.00
169 Gabby Street 12.00 20.00
170 Tris Speaker 100.00 175.00
171 Harry Heilmann 45.00 80.00
172 Chief Bender 45.00 80.00
173 Napoleon Lajoie 100.00 175.00
174 Johnny Evers 50.00 90.00
175 Christy Mathewson 150.00 250.00
176 Heinie Manush 50.00 90.00
177 Frank Baker 60.00 100.00
178 Max Carey 50.00 90.00
179 George Sisler 75.00 125.00
180 Mickey Cochrane 90.00 150.00
181 Spud Chandler RC 45.00 80.00
182 Knick Knickerbocker RC 35.00 70.00
183 Marvin Breuer RC 35.00 70.00
184 Mule Haas 35.00 70.00
185 Joe Kuhel 35.00 70.00
186 Taft Wright RC 35.00 70.00
187 Jimmy Dykes MG 45.00 80.00
188 Joe Krakauskas RC 35.00 70.00
189 Jim Bloodworth RC 35.00 70.00
190 Charley Berry 35.00 70.00
191 John Babich RC 35.00 70.00
192 Dick Siebert RC 35.00 70.00
193 Chubby Dean RC 35.00 70.00
194 Sam Chapman RC 35.00 70.00
195 Dee Miles RC 35.00 70.00
196 Red (Nonny) Nonnenkamp RC 35.00 70.00
197 Lou Finney RC 35.00 70.00
198 Denny Galehouse RC 35.00 70.00
199 Pinky Higgins 35.00 70.00
200 Soup Campbell RC 35.00 70.00
201 Barney McCosky RC 35.00 70.00
202 Al Milnar RC 35.00 70.00
203 Bad News Hale RC 35.00 70.00
204 Harry Eisenstat RC 35.00 70.00
205 Rollie Hemsley RC 35.00 70.00
206 Chet Laabs RC 35.00 70.00
207 Gus Mancuso 35.00 70.00
208 Lee Gamble RC 35.00 70.00
209 Hy Vandenberg RC 35.00 70.00
210 Bill Lohrman RC 35.00 70.00
211 Pop Joiner RC 35.00 70.00
212 Babe Young RC 35.00 70.00
213 John Rucker RC 35.00 70.00
214 Ken O'Dea RC 35.00 70.00
215 Johnnie McCarthy RC 35.00 70.00
216 Joe Marty RC 35.00 70.00
217 Walter Beck 35.00 70.00
218 Wally Millies RC 35.00 70.00
219 Russ Bauers RC 35.00 70.00
220 Mace Brown RC 35.00 70.00
221 Lee Handley RC 35.00 70.00
222 Max Butcher RC 35.00 70.00
223 Hughie Jennings 90.00 150.00
224 Pie Traynor 100.00 175.00
225 Joe Jackson 1500.00 2500.00
226 Harry Hooper 90.00 150.00
227 Jesse Haines 90.00 150.00
228 Charlie Grimm 45.00 80.00
229 Buck Herzog 35.00 70.00
230 Red Faber 100.00 175.00
231 Dolf Luque 60.00 100.00
232 Goose Goslin 90.00 150.00
233 George Earnshaw 45.00 80.00
234 Frank Chance 90.00 150.00
235 John McGraw 100.00 175.00
236 Jim Bottomley 90.00 150.00
237 Willie Keeler 100.00 175.00
238 Tony Lazzeri 100.00 175.00
239 George Uhle 35.00 70.00
240 Bill Atwood RC 60.00 100.00

1941 Play Ball

The cards in this 72-card set measure approximately 2 1/2" by 3 1/8". Many of the cards in the 1941 Play Ball series are simply color versions of pictures appearing in the 1940 set. This was the only color baseball card set produced by Gum, Inc.. Card numbers 49-72 are slightly more difficult to obtain as they were not issued until 1942. In 1942, numbers 1-48 were also reissued but without the copyright date. The cards were also printed on paper without a cardboard backing; these are generally encountered in sheets or strips. The set features a card of Pee Wee Reese in his rookie year.

COMPLETE SET (72) 6000.00 10000.00
COMMON CARD (1-48) 20.00 40.00
COMMON CARD (49-72) 30.00 60.00
WRAPPER (1-CENT) 700.00 800.00
1 Eddie Miller 75.00 125.00
2 Max West 20.00 40.00
3 Bucky Walters 25.00 45.00
4 Paul Derringer 30.00 50.00
5 Frank (Buck) McCormick 25.00 45.00
6 Carl Hubbell 100.00 175.00
7 Harry Danning 20.00 40.00
8 Mel Ott 125.00 225.00
9 Pinky May 20.00 40.00
10 Arky Vaughan 60.00 100.00
11 Debs Garms 20.00 40.00
12 Jimmy Brown 20.00 40.00
13 Jimmie Foxx 175.00 300.00
14 Ted Williams 900.00 1500.00
15 Joe Cronin 75.00 125.00
16 Hal Trosky 25.00 45.00
17 Roy Weatherly 20.00 40.00
18 Hank Greenberg 175.00 300.00
19 Charley Gehringer 125.00 200.00
20 Red Ruffing 75.00 125.00
21 Charlie Keller 35.00 60.00
22 Bob Johnson 30.00 50.00
23 George McQuinn 20.00 40.00
24 Dutch Leonard 25.00 45.00
25 Gene Moore 20.00 40.00
26 Harry Gumpert 20.00 40.00
27 Babe Young 20.00 40.00
28 Joe Marty 20.00 40.00
29 Jack Wilson 20.00 40.00
30 Lou Finney 20.00 40.00
31 Joe Kuhel 20.00 40.00
32 Taft Wright 20.00 40.00
33 Al Milnar 20.00 40.00
34 Rollie Hemsley 20.00 40.00
35 Pinky Higgins 25.00 45.00
36 Barney McCosky 20.00 40.00
37 Bruce Campbell RC 20.00 40.00
38 Atley Donald 30.00 50.00
39 Tommy Henrich 35.00 60.00
40 John Babich 20.00 40.00
41 Frank (Blimp) Hayes 20.00 40.00
42 Wally Moses 25.00 45.00
43 Al Brancato RC 20.00 40.00
44 Sam Chapman 20.00 40.00
45 Eldon Auker 20.00 40.00
46 Sid Hudson RC 20.00 40.00
47 Buddy Lewis 20.00 40.00
48 Cecil Travis 25.00 45.00
49 Babe Dahlgren 35.00 65.00
50 Johnny Cooney 30.00 60.00
51 Dolph Camilli 35.00 65.00
52 Kirby Higbe RC 30.00 60.00
53 Luke Hamlin 30.00 60.00
54 Pee Wee Reese RC 350.00 600.00
55 Whit Wyatt 35.00 65.00
56 Johnny VanderMeer RC 60.00 100.00
57 Moe Arnovich 30.00 60.00
58 Frank Demaree 30.00 60.00
59 Bill Jurges 30.00 60.00
60 Chuck Klein 90.00 150.00
61 Vince DiMaggio RC 125.00 225.00
62 Elbie Fletcher 30.00 60.00
63 Dom DiMaggio RC 150.00 250.00
64 Bobby Doerr 100.00 175.00
65 Tommy Bridges 35.00 65.00
66 Harland Clift RC 30.00 60.00
67 Walt Judnich RC 30.00 60.00
68 John Knott 30.00 60.00
69 George Case 35.00 65.00
70 Bill Dickey 250.00 400.00
71 Joe DiMaggio 1500.00 2500.00
72 Lefty Gomez 275.00 475.00

2008 Playoff Contenders

This set was released on February 4, 2009. The base set consists of 130 cards.

COMP.SET w/o AU's (50) 8.00 20.00
COMMON CARD (1-50) .25 .60
COMMON AU (51-130) 3.00 8.00
OVERALL AUTO ODDS 5 PER BOX
EXCHANGE DEADLINE 8/4/2010
1 Aaron Shafer .25 .60
2 Adrian Nieto .25 .60
3 Andrew Liebel .25 .60
4 Blake Tekotte .40 1.00
5 Brad Mills .25 .60
6 Brandon Waring .75 2.00
7 Brett Hunter .25 .60
8 Byron Wiley .25 .60
9 Caleb Gindl .25 .60
10 Carlos Peguero .40 1.00
11 Carson Blair .25 .60
12 Charlie Blackmon .25 .60
13 Chris Johnson 1.00 2.50
14 Cody Adams .40 1.00
15 Cody Satterwhite .40 1.00
16 Cole Rohrbough .25 .60
17 Cole St. Clair .25 .60
18 Daniel Thomas .25 .60
19 Dennis Raben .40 1.00
20 Derek Norris .40 1.00
21 Dominic Brown 4.00 10.00
22 Dusty Coleman .25 .60
23 Gerardo Parra .25 .60
24 Greg Halman .40 1.00
25 J.P. Ramirez .25 .60
26 James Darnell .40 1.00
27 Jason Knapp .25 .60
28 Jay Austin .25 .60
29 Jesus Montero 2.00 5.00
30 Jharmidy De Jesus .25 .60
31 Jose Duran .40 1.00
32 Josh Vitters .25 .60
33 Kenn Kasparek .60 1.50
34 L. J. Hoes .60 1.50
35 Logan Schafer .25 .60
36 Matt Harrison .25 .60
37 Matt Mitchell .25 .60
38 Max Ramirez .25 .60
39 Mike Cisco .25 .60
40 Niko Vasquez .60 1.50
41 Rolando Gomez .40 1.00
42 Ryan Kalish .60 1.50
43 Stolmy Pimentel .25 .60
44 T.J. Steele .40 1.00
45 Tim Murphy .25 .60
46 Tony Delmonico .40 1.00
47 Tyler Ladendorf .40 1.00
48 Tyler Sample .25 .60
49 Vance Worley 1.25 3.00
50 Xavier Avery .60 1.50
51 Aaron Cunningham AU/283 * 5.00 12.00
52 Alex Buchholz AU 3.00 8.00
53 Allan Dykstra AU 3.00 8.00
54 Andrew Cashner AU/216 * 8.00 20.00
55 Andrew Walker AU/288 * 3.00 8.00
56 Angel Morales AU 3.00 8.00
57 Angel Villalona AU 10.00 25.00
58 Anthony Hewitt AU 4.00 10.00
59 Brad Hand AU/274 * 4.00 10.00
60 Brad Holt AU/236 * 4.00 10.00
61 Brandon Crawford AU/339 * 4.00 10.00
62 Bryan Price AU/165 * 10.00 25.00
63 Buster Posey AU 40.00 80.00
64 Carlos Gutierrez AU/97 * 15.00 40.00
65 Chase D'Arnaud AU/304 * 3.00 8.00
66 Chris Davis AU 6.00 15.00
67 Chris Hicks AU/230 * 3.00 8.00
68 Christian Friedrich AU 6.00 15.00
69 Clark Murphy AU 3.00 8.00
70 Cord Phelps AU/244 * 3.00 8.00
71 Curtis Petersen AU/244 * 3.00 8.00
72 Daniel Cortes AU/292 * 4.00 10.00
73 Daniel Schlereth AU/317 * 4.00 10.00
74 Danny Carroll AU 3.00 8.00
75 Danny Espinosa AU/395 * 10.00 25.00
76 Dayan Viciedo AU/395 * 40.00 80.00
77 Derek Holland AU 6.00 15.00
78 Derrick Rose AU/88 * 150.00 300.00
79 Devaris Gordon AU 20.00 50.00
80 Engel Beltre AU 5.00 12.00
81 Evan Frederickson AU/177 * 5.00 12.00
82 Gordon Beckham AU 10.00 25.00
83 Greg Veloz AU/339 * 3.00 8.00
84 Ike Davis AU 12.50 30.00
85 Isaac Galloway AU 3.00 8.00
86 Jared Bolden AU 3.00 8.00
87 Jarek Cunningham AU/229 * 8.00 20.00
88 Jhoulys Chacin AU 5.00 12.00
89 Jon Jay AU 6.00 15.00
90 Jordan Danks AU/354 * 10.00 25.00
91 Josh Lindblom AU/288 * 4.00 10.00
92 Juan Carlos Sulbaran AU 3.00 8.00
93 Juan Ramirez AU/267 * 4.00 10.00
94 Justin Parker AU/229 * 6.00 15.00
95 Kirk Nieuwenhuis AU 4.00 10.00
96 Pat Venditte AU 10.00 25.00
97 Lance Lynn AU 3.00 8.00
98 Logan Forsythe AU/262 * 3.00 8.00
99 Logan Morrison AU/314 * 20.00 50.00
100 Marcus Lemon AU 3.00 8.00
101 Mark Sobolewski AU/277 * 3.00 8.00
102 Mat Gamel AU 10.00 25.00
103 Michael Beasley AU/88 * 30.00 60.00
104 Michael Kohn AU 3.00 8.00
105 Michael Taylor AU/362 * 10.00 25.00
106 Michel Inoa AU 5.00 12.00
107 Mike Jones AU 3.00 8.00
108 Mike Montgomery AU 6.00 15.00
109 Mike Stanton AU/149 * 300.00 400.00
110 Neftali Feliz AU/246 * 12.50 30.00
111 Neftali Soto AU/249 * 8.00 20.00
112 O.J. Mayo AU/88 * 40.00 80.00
113 Pedro Baez AU EXCH 3.00 8.00
114 Petey Paramore AU 3.00 8.00
115 Rafael Rodriguez AU 8.00 20.00
116 Rashun Dixon AU 6.00 15.00
117 Rick Porcello AU 10.00 25.00
118 Robbie Grossman AU/227 * 6.00 15.00
119 Roger Kieschnick AU/289 * 5.00 12.00
120 Ryan Perry AU 3.00 8.00
121 Shane Peterson AU/399 * 3.00 8.00
122 Shooter Hunt AU/52 * 50.00 100.00
123 Trey Haley AU/309 * 4.00 10.00
124 Tyler Chatwood AU 6.00 15.00
125 Tyson Ross AU 3.00 8.00
126 Wilin Rosario AU 4.00 10.00
127 Wilmer Flores AU/75 * EXCH 75.00 150.00
128 Yamaico Navarro AU 4.00 10.00
129 Zach Collier AU/200 * 5.00 12.00
130 Zach Putnam AU 3.00 8.00

2008 Playoff Contenders Black Box

96 Pat Venditte AU/2
110 Neftali Feliz AU/3

2008 Playoff Contenders Championship Ticket

RANDOM INSERTS IN PACKS
STATED PRINT RUN 1 SER.#'d SET
NO PRICING DUE TO SCARCITY
EXCHANGE DEADLINE 8/4/2010

2008 Playoff Contenders Playoff Ticket

COMMON CARD (51-130) 1.00 2.50

2008 Playoff Contenders Season Ticket Autographs

OVERALL AUTO ODDS 5 PER BOX
CARDS ARE NOT SERIAL NUMBERED
PRINT RUN INFO PROVIDED BY DLP
EXCHANGE DEADLINE 8/4/2010
1 Aaron Shafer/35 5.00 12.00
2 Adrian Nieto 3.00 8.00
3 Andrew Liebel/141 3.00 8.00
4 Blake Tekotte 5.00 12.00
5 Brad Mills/127 3.00 8.00
6 Brandon Waring/149 6.00 15.00
7 Brett Hunter/121 5.00 12.00
8 Byron Wiley 4.00 10.00
9 Caleb Gindl/134 12.50 30.00
10 Carlos Peguero/72 15.00 40.00
11 Carson Blair 3.00 8.00
12 Charlie Blackmon 3.00 8.00
13 Chris Johnson
14 Cody Adams 4.00 10.00
15 Cody Satterwhite/90 6.00 15.00
16 Cole Rohrbough 3.00 8.00
17 Cole St. Clair 3.00 8.00
18 Daniel Thomas 3.00 8.00
19 Dennis Raben/38 30.00 60.00
20 Derek Norris/39 75.00 150.00
21 Dominic Brown/98 175.00 350.00
22 Dusty Coleman 3.00 8.00
23 Gerardo Parra 5.00 12.00
24 Greg Halman/88 30.00 60.00
25 J.P. Ramirez 5.00 12.00
26 James Darnell 12.50 30.00
27 Jason Knapp/124 10.00 25.00
28 Jay Austin 4.00 10.00
29 Jesus Montero/39 100.00 200.00
30 Jharmidy De Jesus/53 50.00 100.00
31 Jose Duran 4.00 10.00
32 Josh Vitters 6.00 15.00
33 Kenn Kasparek 4.00 10.00
34 L. J. Hoes 8.00 20.00
35 Logan Schafer 3.00 8.00
36 Matt Harrison/114 3.00 8.00
37 Matt Mitchell 3.00 8.00
38 Max Ramirez/39 60.00 120.00
39 Mike Cisco/123 15.00 40.00
40 Niko Vasquez 6.00 15.00
41 Rolando Gomez/113 20.00 50.00
42 Ryan Kalish/55 125.00 250.00
43 Stolmy Pimentel/30 100.00 200.00
44 T.J. Steele 5.00 12.00
45 Tim Murphy/55 5.00 12.00
46 Tony Delmonico 3.00 8.00
47 Tyler Ladendorf 3.00 8.00
48 Tyler Sample 4.00 10.00
49 Vance Worley 15.00 40.00
50 Xavier Avery 8.00 20.00

2008 Playoff Contenders Draft Class

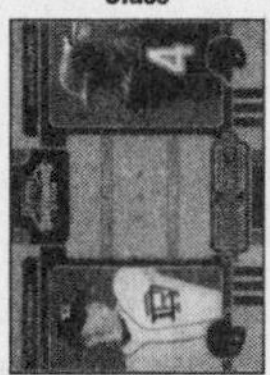

OVERALL INSERT ODDS 1:3
STATED PRINT RUN 1500 SER.#'d SETS
*BLACK: .75X TO 2X BASIC
BLACK PRINT RUN 100 SER.#'d SETS
*GOLD: .6X TO 1.5X BASIC
GOLD PRINT RUN 250 SER.#'d SETS
1 Ike Davis 3.00 8.00
Kirk Nieuwenhuis
2 Curtis Petersen 1.25 3.00
Isaac Galloway
3 Jon Jay 1.25 3.00
Lance Lynn
4 Clark Murphy 2.00 5.00
Chris Davis
5 Trey Haley .75 2.00
Zach Putnam

2008 Playoff Contenders Draft Class Autographs

RANDOM INSERTS IN PACKS
OVERALL AUTO ODDS 5 PER BOX
STATED PRINT RUN 25 SER.#'d SETS
NO PRICING DUE TO SCARCITY
EXCHANGE DEADLINE 8/4/2010

2008 Playoff Contenders Legendary Rookies

OVERALL INSERT ODDS 1:3
STATED PRINT RUN 1500 SER.#'d SETS
*BLACK: .75X TO 2X BASIC
BLACK PRINT RUN 100 SER.#'d SETS
*GOLD: .6X TO 1.5X BASIC
GOLD PRINT RUN 250 SER.#'d SETS
1 Willie Mays 2.00 5.00
2 Pete Rose 2.50 6.00
3 Cal Ripken Jr. 4.00 10.00
4 Mike Schmidt 1.50 4.00
5 Robin Yount 1.00 2.50

2008 Playoff Contenders Legendary Rookies Autographs

RANDOM INSERTS IN PACKS
OVERALL AUTO ODDS 5 PER BOX
STATED PRINT RUN 25 SER.#'d SETS
NO PRICING DUE TO SCARCITY
EXCHANGE DEADLINE 8/4/2010

2008 Playoff Contenders Rookie Roll Call

OVERALL INSERT ODDS 1:3
STATED PRINT RUN 1500 SER.#'d SETS
*BLACK: .75X TO 2X BASIC
BLACK PRINT RUN 100 SER.#'d SETS
*GOLD: .6X TO 1.5X BASIC
GOLD PRINT RUN 250 SER.#'d SETS
1 Mat Gamel 2.00 5.00
2 Michel Inoa 2.00 5.00
3 Rafael Rodriguez .75 2.00
4 Isaac Galloway 1.25 3.00
5 Angel Villalona 2.00 5.00

2008 Playoff Contenders Rookie Roll Call Autographs

RANDOM INSERTS IN PACKS
OVERALL AUTO ODDS 5 PER BOX
STATED PRINT RUN 25 SER.#'d SETS
NO PRICING DUE TO SCARCITY
EXCHANGE DEADLINE 8/4/2010

2008 Playoff Contenders Round Numbers

OVERALL INSERT ODDS 1:3
STATED PRINT RUN 1500 SER.#'d SETS
*BLACK: .75X TO 2X BASIC
BLACK PRINT RUN 100 SER.#'d SETS
*GOLD: .6X TO 1.5X BASIC
GOLD PRINT RUN 250 SER.#'d SETS
1 Buster Posey 2.50 6.00
Gordon Beckham
2 Daniel Schlereth 1.25 3.00
Ryan Perry
3 Allan Dykstra .75 2.00
Anthony Hewitt
4 Tyson Ross 1.25 3.00
Tyler Chatwood
5 Chase D'Arnaud 1.25 3.00
Brandon Crawford

2008 Playoff Contenders Round Numbers Autographs

RANDOM INSERTS IN PACKS
OVERALL AUTO ODDS 5 PER BOX
STATED PRINT RUN 25 SER.#'d SETS
NO PRICING DUE TO SCARCITY
EXCHANGE DEADLINE 8/4/2010

2003 Playoff Prestige

This 210 card set was issued in two separate series. The primary product - containing cards 1-200 from the basic set - was released in May, 2003. The set was issued in six-card packs which were issued 24 packs to a box and 20 boxes to a case. The first 180 cards in the set featured veterans while the final 20 cards featured leading rookies and prospects. Those final 20 cards were inserted at a stated rate of one in three. Cards 201-210 were issued in DLP Rookies and Traded packs of which was distributed in December, 2003.

COMP.LO SET (200) 15.00 40.00
COMP.LO SET w/o SP's (180) 10.00 25.00
COMP.UPDATE SET (10) 3.00 8.00
COMMON CARD (1-180) .15 .40
COMMON CARD (181-200) .60 1.50
COMMON CARD (201-210) .20 .50
201-210 ISSUED IN DLP R/T PACKS
1 Darin Erstad .15 .40
2 David Eckstein .15 .40
3 Garret Anderson .15 .40
4 Jarrod Washburn .15 .40
5 Tim Salmon .25 .60
6 Troy Glaus .15 .40
7 Jay Gibbons .15 .40
8 Marty Cordova .15 .40
9 Melvin Mora .15 .40
10 Rodrigo Lopez .15 .40
11 Tony Batista .15 .40
12 Cliff Floyd .15 .40
13 Derek Lowe .15 .40
14 Johnny Damon .25 .60
15 Manny Ramirez .25 .60
16 Nomar Garciaparra .60 1.50
17 Pedro Martinez .25 .60
18 Rickey Henderson .40 1.00
19 Shea Hillenbrand .15 .40
20 Carlos Lee .15 .40
21 Frank Thomas .40 1.00
22 Magglio Ordonez .15 .40
23 Mark Buehrle .15 .40
24 Paul Konerko .15 .40
25 C.C. Sabathia .15 .40
26 Danys Baez .15 .40
27 Ellis Burks .15 .40
28 Travis Hafner .15 .40
29 Omar Vizquel .25 .60
30 Bobby Higginson .15 .40
31 Carlos Pena .15 .40
32 Mark Redman .15 .40
33 Robert Fick .15 .40
34 Steve Sparks .15 .40
35 Carlos Beltran .15 .40
36 Joe Randa .15 .40
37 Mike Sweeney .15 .40
38 Paul Byrd .15 .40
39 Raul Ibanez .15 .40
40 Runelvys Hernandez .15 .40
41 Brad Radke .15 .40
42 Corey Koskie .15 .40
43 Cristian Guzman .15 .40
44 David Ortiz .40 1.00
45 Doug Mientkiewicz .15 .40
46 Dustin Mohr .15 .40
47 Jacque Jones .15 .40
48 Torii Hunter .15 .40
49 Alfonso Soriano .15 .40
50 Andy Pettitte .25 .60
51 Bernie Williams .25 .60
52 David Wells .15 .40
53 Derek Jeter 1.00 2.50
54 Jason Giambi .15 .40
55 Jeff Weaver .15 .40
56 Jorge Posada .25 .60
57 Mike Mussina .25 .60
58 Roger Clemens .75 2.00
59 Barry Zito .15 .40
60 David Justice .15 .40
61 Eric Chavez .15 .40
62 Jermaine Dye .15 .40
63 Mark Mulder .15 .40
64 Miguel Tejada .15 .40
65 Ray Durham .15 .40
66 Tim Hudson .15 .40
67 Bret Boone .15 .40
68 Chris Snelling .15 .40
69 Edgar Martinez .25 .60
70 Freddy Garcia .15 .40
71 Ichiro Suzuki .75 2.00
72 Jamie Moyer .15 .40
73 John Olerud .15 .40
74 Kazuhiro Sasaki .15 .40
75 Aubrey Huff .15 .40
76 Joe Kennedy .15 .40
77 Paul Wilson .15 .40
78 Alex Rodriguez .75 2.00
79 Chan Ho Park .15 .40
80 Hank Blalock .15 .40
81 Ivan Rodriguez .25 .60
82 Juan Gonzalez .15 .40
83 Kevin Mench .15 .40
84 Rafael Palmeiro .25 .60
85 Carlos Delgado .15 .40
86 Eric Hinske .15 .40
87 Jose Cruz Jr. .15 .40
88 Josh Phelps .15 .40
89 Roy Halladay .15 .40
90 Shannon Stewart .15 .40
91 Vernon Wells .15 .40
92 Curt Schilling .15 .40
93 Junior Spivey .15 .40
94 Luis Gonzalez .15 .40
95 Mark Grace .25 .60
96 Randy Johnson .40 1.00
97 Andruw Jones .25 .60
98 Chipper Jones .40 1.00
99 Gary Sheffield .15 .40
100 Greg Maddux .60 1.50
101 John Smoltz .25 .60
102 Kevin Millwood .15 .40
103 Mike Hampton .15 .40
104 Corey Patterson .15 .40
105 Fred McGriff .25 .60
106 Kerry Wood .15 .40
107 Mark Prior .25 .60
108 Moises Alou .15 .40
109 Sammy Sosa .40 1.00
110 Adam Dunn .15 .40
111 Austin Kearns .15 .40
112 Barry Larkin .25 .60
113 Ken Griffey Jr. .60 1.50
114 Sean Casey .15 .40
115 Jason Jennings .15 .40
116 Jay Payton .15 .40
117 Larry Walker .15 .40
118 Todd Helton .25 .60
119 A.J. Burnett .15 .40
120 Josh Beckett .15 .40
121 Juan Encarnacion .15 .40
122 Mike Lowell .15 .40
123 Craig Biggio .25 .60
124 Daryle Ward .15 .40
125 Jeff Bagwell .25 .60
126 Lance Berkman .15 .40
127 Roy Oswalt .15 .40
128 Adrian Beltre .15 .40
129 Hideo Nomo .40 1.00
130 Kazuhisa Ishii .15 .40
131 Kevin Brown .15 .40
132 Odalis Perez .15 .40
133 Paul Lo Duca .15 .40
134 Shawn Green .15 .40
135 Jeff Kent .15 .40
136 Ben Sheets .15 .40
137 Jeffrey Hammonds .15 .40
138 Jose Hernandez .15 .40
139 Richie Sexson .15 .40
140 Bartolo Colon .15 .40
141 Brad Wilkerson .15 .40
142 Javier Vazquez .15 .40
143 Jose Vidro .15 .40
144 Michael Barrett .15 .40
145 Vladimir Guerrero .40 1.00
146 Al Leiter .15 .40
147 Mike Piazza .60 1.50
148 Mo Vaughn .15 .40
149 Pedro Astacio .15 .40
150 Roberto Alomar .25 .60
151 Roger Cedeno .15 .40
152 Tom Glavine .25 .60
153 Bobby Abreu .15 .40
154 Jimmy Rollins .15 .40
155 Mike Lieberthal .15 .40
156 Pat Burrell .15 .40
157 Vicente Padilla .15 .40
158 Jim Thome .25 .60
159 Aramis Ramirez .15 .40
160 Brian Giles .15 .40
161 Jason Kendall .15 .40
162 Josh Fogg .15 .40
163 Kip Wells .15 .40
164 Mark Kotsay .15 .40
165 Oliver Perez .15 .40
166 Phil Nevin .15 .40
167 Ryan Klesko .15 .40
168 Sean Burroughs .15 .40
169 Trevor Hoffman .15 .40
170 Barry Bonds 1.00 2.50
171 Benito Santiago .15 .40
172 Reggie Sanders .15 .40
173 Rich Aurilia .15 .40
174 Russ Ortiz .15 .40
175 Albert Pujols .75 2.00
176 J.D. Drew .15 .40
177 Jim Edmonds .15 .40
178 Matt Morris .15 .40

179 Tino Martinez .25 .60
180 Scott Rolen .25 .60
181 Joe Borchard ROO .60 1.50
182 Freddy Sanchez ROO .60 1.50
183 Jose Contreras ROO RC .75 2.00
184 Jeff Baker ROO .60 1.50
185 Ryan Church ROO .60 1.50
186 Mario Ramos ROO .60 1.50
187 Corwin Malone ROO .60 1.50
188 Jimmy Gobble ROO .60 1.50
189 Jon Adkins ROO .60 1.50
190 Tim Kalita ROO .60 1.50
191 Nelson Castro ROO .60 1.50
192 Colin Young ROO .60 1.50
193 Luis Martinez ROO .60 1.50
194 Todd Donovan ROO .60 1.50
195 Jeremy Ward ROO .60 1.50
196 Wilson Valdez ROO .60 1.50
197 Hideki Matsui ROO RC 2.00 5.00
198 Mitch Wylie ROO .60 1.50
199 Adam Walker ROO .60 1.50
200 Cliff Bartosh ROO .60 1.50
201 Jeremy Bonderman ROO RC .75 2.00
202 Brandon Webb ROO RC .60 1.50
203 Adam Loewen ROO RC .20 .50
204 Chien-Ming Wang ROO RC .75 2.00
205 Hong-Chih Kuo ROO RC .75 2.00
206 Delmon Young ROO RC 1.25 3.00
207 Ryan Wagner ROO RC .20 .50
208 Dan Haren ROO RC .20 .50
209 Rickie Weeks ROO RC .60 1.50
210 Ramon Nivar ROO RC .20 .50

2003 Playoff Prestige Autographs

These 10 cards were inserted into the DLP Update Packs. It is interesting to note that although the Rookie Cards were issued in a parallel autograph form for the updates, there were no "parallel" autogaph cards issued as part of the regular issue.

201 J.Bonderman ROO/100 20.00 50.00
202 Brandon Webb ROO/100 10.00 25.00
203 Adam Loewen ROO/100 10.00 25.00
204 C.Wang ROO/50 75.00 150.00
205 Hong-Chih Kuo ROO/100 100.00 200.00
206 Delmon Young ROO/25
207 Ryan Wagner ROO/100 4.00 10.00
208 Dan Haren ROO/100 8.00 20.00
209 Rickie Weeks ROO/10
210 Ramon Nivar ROO/100 4.00 10.00

2003 Playoff Prestige Xtra Points Green

*GREEN 1-180: 3X TO 8X BASIC
1-180 PRINT RUN 150 SERIAL #'d SETS
*GREEN 181-200: 1.25X TO 3X BASIC
*GREEN 201-210: 5X TO 12X BASIC
181-210 PRINT RUN 50 SERIAL #'d SETS
204 Chien-Ming Wang ROO 20.00 50.00
205 Hong-Chih Kuo ROO 20.00 50.00

2003 Playoff Prestige Xtra Points Purple

*PURPLE 1-180: 3X TO 8X BASIC
1-180 PRINT RUN 150 SERIAL #'d SETS
*PURPLE 181-200: 1.25X TO 3X BASIC
*PURPLE 201-210: 5X TO 12X BASIC
181-200 PRINT RUN 50 SERIAL #'d SETS
204 Chien-Ming Wang ROO 20.00 50.00
205 Hong-Chih Kuo ROO 20.00 50.00

2003 Playoff Prestige Award Winners

SERIAL NUMBERED TO YEAR OF AWARD
1 Barry Zito CY/2002 1.25 3.00
2 Barry Bonds MVP/2001 3.00 8.00
3 Randy Johnson CY/2002 1.25 3.00
4 Roger Clemens CY/2001 2.50 6.00
5 Ichiro Suzuki MVP/2001 2.50 6.00
6 Chipper Jones MVP/1999 1.25 3.00
7 Ken Griffey Jr. MVP/1997 2.00 5.00
8 Miguel Tejada MVP/2002 1.25 3.00
9 Greg Maddux CY/1995 2.00 5.00
10 Jeff Bagwell MVP/1994 1.25 3.00
11 Rickey Henderson MVP/1990 1.25 3.00
12 Tom Glavine CY/1998 1.25 3.00
13 Albert Pujols ROY/2001 2.50 6.00
14 Nomar Garciaparra ROY/1997 2.00 5.00
15 Derek Jeter ROY/1996 3.00 8.00

2003 Playoff Prestige Connections

STATED ODDS 1:8 HOBBY/RETAIL
*PARALLEL 100: 1.5X TO 4X BASIC
PARALLEL 100 PRINT RUN 100 #'d SETS
1 Troy Glaus .75 2.00
Garret Anderson
2 Troy Glaus .75 2.00
Tim Salmon
3 Randy Johnson 1.00 2.50
Curt Schilling
4 Matt Williams .75 2.00
Luis Gonzalez
5 Greg Maddux 1.50 4.00
John Smoltz
6 Andruw Jones 1.00 2.50
Chipper Jones
7 Greg Maddux 1.50 4.00
Kevin Millwood
8 Tony Batista .75 2.00
Geronimo Gil
9 Pedro Martinez 1.50 4.00
Nomar Garciaparra
10 Manny Ramirez 1.50 4.00
Nomar Garciaparra
11 Nomar Garciaparra 1.50 4.00
Rickey Henderson
12 Trot Nixon .75 2.00
Manny Ramirez
13 Kerry Wood .75 2.00
Mark Prior
14 Sammy Sosa 1.00 2.50
Fred McGriff
15 Sammy Sosa 1.00 2.50
Corey Patterson
16 Frank Thomas 1.00 2.50
Magglio Ordonez
17 Joe Borchard .75 2.00
Magglio Ordonez
18 Adam Dunn .75 2.00
Austin Kearns
19 Barry Larkin 1.50 4.00
Ken Griffey Jr.
20 Adam Dunn .75 2.00
Barry Larkin
21 Adam Dunn 1.50 4.00
Ken Griffey Jr.
22 Victor Martinez .75 2.00
Omar Vizquel
23 C.C. Sabathia .75 2.00
Victor Martinez
24 Larry Walker .75 2.00
Todd Helton
25 Carlos Pena .75 2.00
Robert Fick
26 Josh Beckett .75 2.00
Juan Encarnacion
27 Jeff Bagwell .75 2.00
Craig Biggio
28 Lance Berkman .75 2.00
Roy Oswalt
29 Lance Berkman .75 2.00
Jeff Bagwell
30 Mike Sweeney .75 2.00
Carlos Beltran
31 Mike Sweeney .75 2.00
Angel Berroa
32 Kazuhisa Ishii .75 2.00
Shawn Green
33 Adrian Beltre .75 2.00
Shawn Green
34 Kazuhisa Ishii 1.00 2.50
Hideo Nomo
35 Richie Sexson .75 2.00
Ben Sheets
36 Jacque Jones .75 2.00
Torii Hunter
37 Doug Mientkiewicz 1.00 2.50
David Ortiz
38 Vladimir Guerrero 1.00 2.50
Jose Vidro
39 Derek Jeter 2.50 6.00
Jason Giambi
40 Derek Jeter 2.50 6.00
Bernie Williams
41 Roger Clemens 2.00 5.00
Mike Mussina
42 Alfonso Soriano .75 2.00
Jorge Posada
43 Derek Jeter 2.50 6.00
Alfonso Soriano
44 Mike Piazza 1.50 4.00
Roberto Alomar
45 Mike Piazza 1.50 4.00
Mo Vaughn
46 Eric Chavez .75 2.00
Miguel Tejada
47 Mark Mulder .75 2.00
Barry Zito
48 Tim Hudson .75 2.00
Barry Zito
49 Pat Burrell .75 2.00
Bobby Abreu
50 Jim Thome .75 2.00
Pat Burrell
51 Jim Thome .75 2.00
Marlon Byrd
52 Brian Giles .75 2.00
Aramis Ramirez
53 Ryan Klesko .75 2.00
Phil Nevin
54 Barry Bonds 2.50 6.00
Benito Santiago
55 Jeff Kent .75 2.00
Rich Aurilia
56 Barry Bonds 2.50 6.00
Jeff Kent
57 Ichiro Suzuki 2.00 5.00
Kazuhiro Sasaki
58 Edgar Martinez .75 2.00
John Olerud
59 Albert Pujols 2.00 5.00
Scott Rolen
60 Jim Edmonds .75 2.00
J.D. Drew
61 Albert Pujols 2.00 5.00
Jim Edmonds
62 Dewon Brazelton .75 2.00
Joe Kennedy
63 Alex Rodriguez 1.50 4.00
Ivan Rodriguez
64 Juan Gonzalez .75 2.00
Rafael Palmeiro
65 Mark Teixeira .75 2.00
Hank Blalock
66 Alex Rodriguez 1.50 4.00
Rafael Palmeiro
67 Alex Rodriguez 1.50 4.00
Juan Gonzalez
68 Shannon Stewart .75 2.00
Carlos Delgado
69 Josh Phelps .75 2.00
Eric Hinske
70 Vernon Wells .75 2.00
Roy Halladay

2003 Playoff Prestige Connections Materials

Randomly inserted into packs, this is a parallel to the Connections insert set. These cards feature a game-used memorabilia piece from each player pictured and were issued to a stated print run of 400 serial numbered sets.

1 Troy Glaus Jsy 4.00 10.00
Garret Anderson Bat
2 Troy Glaus Jsy 4.00 10.00
Tim Salmon Bat
4 Matt Williams Jsy 4.00 10.00
Luis Gonzalez Bat
5 Greg Maddux Jsy 6.00 15.00
John Smoltz Jsy
6 Andruw Jones Bat 4.00 10.00
Chipper Jones Bat
7 Greg Maddux Jsy 6.00 15.00
Kevin Millwood Jsy
8 Tony Batista Jsy 4.00 10.00
Geronimo Gil Bat
9 Pedro Martinez Jsy 8.00 20.00
Nomar Garciaparra Jsy
10 Manny Ramirez Bat 6.00 15.00
Nomar Garciaparra Bat
11 Nomar Garciaparra Bat 8.00 20.00
Rickey Henderson Bat
12 Trot Nixon Bat 4.00 10.00
Manny Ramirez Bat
13 Kerry Wood Jsy 4.00 10.00
Mark Prior Jsy
14 Sammy Sosa Base 4.00 10.00
Fred McGriff Base
15 Sammy Sosa Base 4.00 10.00
Corey Patterson Base
16 Frank Thomas Jsy 4.00 10.00
Magglio Ordonez Jsy
17 Joe Borchard Jsy 4.00 10.00
Magglio Ordonez Bat
18 Adam Dunn Bat 4.00 10.00
Austin Kearns Jsy
20 Adam Dunn Jsy 4.00 10.00
Barry Larkin Bat
22 Victor Martinez Bat 4.00 10.00
Omar Vizquel Bat
23 C.C. Sabathia Jsy 4.00 10.00
Victor Martinez Bat
24 Larry Walker Jsy 4.00 10.00
Todd Helton Bat
26 Josh Beckett Jsy 4.00 10.00
Juan Encarnacion Bat
27 Jeff Bagwell Pants 4.00 10.00
Craig Biggio Pants
28 Lance Berkman Jsy 4.00 10.00
Roy Oswalt Jsy
29 Lance Berkman Jsy 4.00 10.00
Jeff Bagwell Pants
30 Mike Sweeney Bat 4.00 10.00
Carlos Beltran Bat
31 Mike Sweeney Bat 4.00 10.00
Angel Berroa Pants
32 Kazuhisa Ishii Jsy 4.00 10.00
Shawn Green Bat
33 Adrian Beltre Bat 4.00 10.00
Shawn Green Jsy
34 Kazuhisa Ishii Jsy 6.00 15.00
Hideo Nomo Jsy
35 Richie Sexson Jsy 4.00 10.00
Ben Sheets Jsy
36 Jacque Jones Jsy 4.00 10.00
Torii Hunter Bat
37 Doug Mientkiewicz Bat 4.00 10.00
David Ortiz Jsy
38 Vladimir Guerrero Bat 4.00 10.00
Jose Vidro Jsy
39 Derek Jeter Base 6.00 15.00
Jason Giambi Bat
40 Derek Jeter Base 6.00 15.00
Bernie Williams Base
41 Roger Clemens Jsy 10.00 25.00
Mike Mussina Jsy
42 Alfonso Soriano Jsy 4.00 10.00
Jorge Posada Jsy
43 Derek Jeter Base 10.00 25.00
Alfonso Soriano Base
44 Mike Piazza Bat 6.00 15.00
Roberto Alomar Jsy
45 Mike Piazza Bat 6.00 15.00
Mo Vaughn Bat
46 Eric Chavez Jsy 4.00 10.00
Miguel Tejada Jsy
47 Mark Mulder Jsy 4.00 10.00
Barry Zito Jsy
48 Tim Hudson Jsy 4.00 10.00
Barry Zito Jsy
49 Pat Burrell Bat 4.00 10.00
Bobby Abreu Bat
50 Jim Thome Bat 4.00 10.00
Pat Burrell Bat
51 Jim Thome Bat 4.00 10.00
Marlon Byrd Jsy
52 Brian Giles Bat 4.00 10.00
Aramis Ramirez Jsy
53 Ryan Klesko Jsy 4.00 10.00
Phil Nevin Jsy
54 Barry Bonds Base 6.00 15.00
Benito Santiago Base
55 Jeff Kent Jsy 4.00 10.00
Rich Aurilia Jsy
56 Barry Bonds Base 6.00 15.00
Jeff Kent Base
57 Ichiro Suzuki Base 10.00 25.00
Kazuhiro Sasaki Base
58 Edgar Martinez Bat 4.00 10.00
John Olerud Jsy
59 Albert Pujols Base 6.00 15.00
Scott Rolen Base
60 Jim Edmonds Bat 4.00 10.00
J.D. Drew Jsy
61 Albert Pujols Base 6.00 15.00
Jim Edmonds Base
62 Dewon Brazelton Jsy 4.00 10.00
Joe Kennedy Jsy
63 Alex Rodriguez Jsy 6.00 15.00
Ivan Rodriguez Bat
64 Juan Gonzalez Pants 4.00 10.00
Rafael Palmeiro Pants
65 Mark Teixeira Bat 4.00 10.00
Hank Blalock Bat
66 Alex Rodriguez Jsy 6.00 15.00
Rafael Palmeiro Pants
67 Alex Rodriguez Bat 6.00 15.00
Juan Gonzalez Pants
68 Shannon Stewart Bat 4.00 10.00
Carlos Delgado Jsy
69 Josh Phelps Bat 4.00 10.00
Eric Hinske Bat
70 Vernon Wells Jsy 4.00 10.00
Roy Halladay Jsy

2003 Playoff Prestige Diamond Heritage

STATED ODDS 1:21 HOBBY, 1:43 RETAIL
*GOLDEN: 1.25X TO 3X BASIC
GOLDEN PRINT RUN 50 SERIAL #'d SETS
1 Larry Walker 1.50 4.00
2 Troy Glaus 1.50 4.00
3 Magglio Ordonez 1.50 4.00
4 Roy Oswalt 1.50 4.00
5 Barry Zito 1.50 4.00
6 Nomar Garciaparra 2.50 6.00
7 Kerry Wood 1.50 4.00
8 Roger Clemens 3.00 8.00
9 Pedro Martinez 1.50 4.00
10 Mark Prior 1.50 4.00
11 Sammy Sosa 1.50 4.00
12 Randy Johnson 1.50 4.00
13 Greg Maddux 2.50 6.00
14 Manny Ramirez 1.50 4.00
15 Torii Hunter 1.50 4.00
16 Alex Rodriguez 2.50 6.00
17 Mike Piazza 2.50 6.00
18 Vladimir Guerrero 1.50 4.00
19 Ivan Rodriguez 1.50 4.00
20 Lance Berkman 1.50 4.00
21 Miguel Tejada 1.50 4.00
22 Chipper Jones 1.50 4.00
23 Todd Helton 1.50 4.00
24 Shawn Green 1.50 4.00
25 Scott Rolen 1.50 4.00
26 Adam Dunn 1.50 4.00
27 Jim Thome 1.50 4.00
28 Rafael Palmeiro 1.50 4.00
29 Eric Chavez 1.50 4.00
30 Andruw Jones 1.50 4.00

2003 Playoff Prestige Diamond Heritage Material

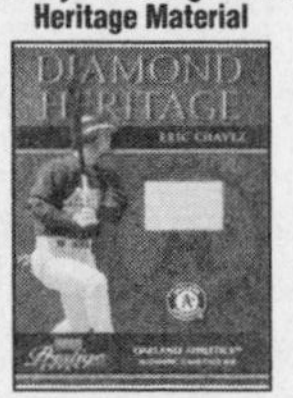

Randomly inserted into packs, this is a parallel ot the Diamond Heritage insert set. These cards were issued to a stated print run of 200 serial numbered sets for the jersey cards and 100 serial numbered sets for the bat cards.

*MULTI-COLOR PATCH 1-15: 1X TO 1.5X HI
1 Larry Walker Jsy 3.00 8.00
2 Troy Glaus Jsy 3.00 8.00
3 Magglio Ordonez Jsy 3.00 8.00
4 Roy Oswalt Jsy 3.00 8.00
5 Barry Zito Jsy 3.00 8.00
6 Nomar Garciaparra Jsy 6.00 15.00
7 Kerry Wood Jsy 3.00 8.00
8 Roger Clemens Jsy 8.00 20.00
9 Pedro Martinez Jsy 4.00 10.00
10 Mark Prior Jsy 4.00 10.00
11 Sammy Sosa Jsy 4.00 10.00
12 Randy Johnson Jsy 4.00 10.00
13 Greg Maddux Jsy 6.00 15.00
14 Manny Ramirez Jsy 4.00 10.00
15 Torii Hunter Jsy 3.00 8.00
16 Alex Rodriguez Bat 8.00 20.00
17 Mike Piazza Bat 6.00 15.00
18 Vladimir Guerrero Bat 6.00 15.00
19 Ivan Rodriguez Bat 6.00 15.00
20 Lance Berkman Bat 4.00 10.00
21 Miguel Tejada Bat 4.00 10.00
22 Chipper Jones Bat 6.00 15.00
23 Todd Helton Bat 6.00 15.00
24 Shawn Green Bat 4.00 10.00
25 Scott Rolen Bat 6.00 15.00
26 Adam Dunn Bat 4.00 10.00
27 Jim Thome Bat 6.00 15.00
28 Rafael Palmeiro Bat 6.00 15.00
29 Eric Chavez Bat 4.00 10.00
30 Andruw Jones Bat 6.00 15.00

2003 Playoff Prestige Diamond Heritage Material Autographs

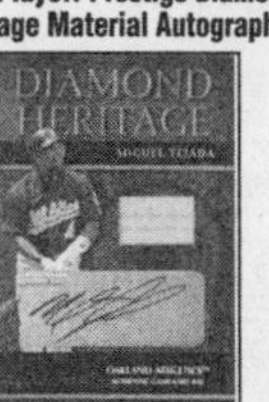

Randomly inserted into packs, this is a partial parallel to the Heritage Material insert set. These 10 cards feature not only a memorabilia piece but also an authentic signature from the player. Please note that since no card was issued to a stated print run of more than 25 cards, there is no pricing for this set.

2 Troy Glaus Jsy/15
3 Magglio Ordonez Jsy/25
7 Kerry Wood Jsy/15
15 Torii Hunter Jsy/25
20 Lance Berkman Bat/15
21 Miguel Tejada Bat/25
25 Scott Rolen Bat/15
26 Adam Dunn Bat/25
27 Jim Thome Bat/15
29 Eric Chavez Bat/25

2003 Playoff Prestige Draft Class Reunion

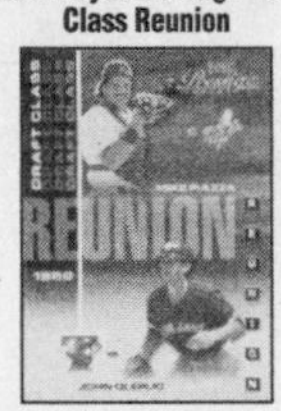

STATED ODDS 1:24 HOBBY, 1:42 RETAIL
1 Mike Piazza 2.00 5.00
John Olerud
2 Derek Jeter 3.00 8.00
Shannon Stewart
3 Alex Rodriguez 2.00 5.00
Torii Hunter
4 Nomar Garciaparra 1.25 3.00
Paul Konerko
5 Kerry Wood 1.25 3.00
Todd Helton
6 Eric Chavez 1.25 3.00
Billy Koch
7 Lance Berkman 1.25 3.00
Troy Glaus
8 Pat Burrell 1.25 3.00
Mark Mulder
9 Barry Zito 1.25 3.00
Jason Jennings
10 Mark Prior 1.25 3.00
Mark Teixeira

2003 Playoff Prestige Infield/Outfield Tandems Materials

Randomly inserted into packs, these cards feature an outfielder and infielder from the same team along with a game-used memorabilia piece from each player. These cards were issued to a stated print run of 100 serial numbered sets.

1 Troy Glaus Jsy 4.00 10.00
Garret Anderson Bat
2 Mark Grace Bat 6.00 15.00
Luis Gonzalez Jsy
3 Nomar Garciaparra Jsy 10.00 25.00
Manny Ramirez Jsy
4 Alfonso Soriano Jsy 6.00 15.00
Bernie Williams Jsy
5 Jeff Bagwell Jsy 6.00 15.00
Lance Berkman Jsy
6 Alex Rodriguez Jsy 10.00 25.00
Juan Gonzalez Jsy
7 Barry Larkin Jsy 4.00 10.00
Adam Dunn Jsy
8 Scott Rolen Bat 10.00 25.00
Jim Edmonds Jsy
9 Todd Helton Jsy 6.00 15.00
Larry Walker Jsy
10 Adrian Beltre Jsy 4.00 10.00
Shawn Green Jsy
11 Jose Vidro Jsy 6.00 15.00
Vladimir Guerrero Jsy
12 Mike Sweeney Jsy 4.00 10.00
Carlos Beltran Jsy
13 Josh Phelps Jsy 4.00 10.00
Vernon Wells Jsy
14 Paul Konerko Jsy 4.00 10.00
Magglio Ordonez Jsy
15 Phil Nevin Jsy 4.00 10.00
Ryan Klesko Jsy

2003 Playoff Prestige Inside the Numbers

STATED PRINT RUN 2002 SERIAL #'d SETS
*DIE CUT p/r 45-75: 2X TO 5X BASIC
*DIE CUT p/r 27-38: 2.5X TO 6X BASIC
DIE CUT PRINT RUN BASED ON UNIFORM
NO DIE CUT PRICING ON QTY OF 25 OR LESS
1 Roger Clemens 2.50 6.00
2 Greg Maddux 2.00 5.00
3 Miguel Tejada 1.25 3.00
4 Alex Rodriguez 2.00 5.00
5 Ichiro Suzuki 2.50 6.00
6 Sammy Sosa 1.25 3.00
7 Jim Thome 1.25 3.00
8 Derek Jeter 3.00 8.00
9 Randy Johnson 1.25 3.00
10 Barry Zito 1.25 3.00
11 Jason Giambi 1.25 3.00
12 Shawn Green 1.25 3.00
13 Curt Schilling 1.25 3.00
14 Albert Pujols 2.50 6.00
15 Vladimir Guerrero 1.25 3.00
16 Pedro Martinez 1.25 3.00
17 Alfonso Soriano 1.25 3.00
18 Barry Bonds 3.00 8.00
19 Magglio Ordonez 1.25 3.00
20 Chipper Jones 1.25 3.00
21 Pat Burrell 1.25 3.00
22 Luis Gonzalez 1.25 3.00
23 Jeff Bagwell 1.25 3.00
24 Garret Anderson 1.25 3.00
25 Larry Walker 1.25 3.00

2003 Playoff Prestige League Leaders

STATED PRINT RUN 2002 SERIAL #'d SETS
1 Manny Ramirez AVG 1.25 3.00
2 Sammy Sosa HR 1.25 3.00
3 Alex Rodriguez RBI 2.00 5.00
4 Alfonso Soriano Runs 1.25 3.00
5 Vladimir Guerrero Hits 1.25 3.00
6 Nomar Garciaparra 2B 2.00 5.00
7 Johnny Damon 3B 1.25 3.00
8 Alfonso Soriano SB 1.25 3.00
9 Barry Bonds Walks 3.00 8.00
10 Barry Zito Wins 1.25 3.00
11 Pedro Martinez ERA 1.25 3.00
12 John Smoltz SV 1.25 3.00
13 Randy Johnson CG 1.25 3.00
14 Lance Berkman RBI 1.25 3.00
15 Randy Johnson SO 1.25 3.00

2003 Playoff Prestige League Leaders Materials

STATED PRINT RUN 250 SERIAL #'d SETS
1 Manny Ramirez AVG Jsy 4.00 10.00
2 Sammy Sosa HR Base 4.00 10.00
3 Alex Rodriguez RBI Jsy 6.00 15.00
4 Alfonso Soriano Runs Jsy 3.00 8.00
5 Vladimir Guerrero Hits Jsy 4.00 10.00
6 Nomar Garciaparra 2B Jsy 8.00 20.00
7 Johnny Damon 3B Bat 4.00 10.00
8 Alfonso Soriano SB Jsy 3.00 8.00
9 Barry Bonds Walks Base 6.00 15.00
10 Barry Zito Wins Jsy 3.00 8.00
11 Pedro Martinez ERA Jsy 4.00 10.00
12 John Smoltz SV Jsy 4.00 10.00
13 Randy Johnson CG Jsy 4.00 10.00
14 Lance Berkman RBI Jsy 3.00 8.00
15 Randy Johnson SO Jsy 4.00 10.00

2003 Playoff Prestige Patches of MLB

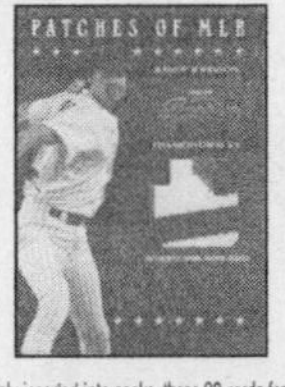

Randomly inserted into packs, these 20 cards feature patch pieces from the game-used jerseys used in this product. These cards were issued to a stated print run of 25 serial numbered sets and no pricing is available due to market scarcity.

2003 Playoff Prestige Patches of MLB Autographs

Randomly inserted into packs, these cards feature not only a game-used patch piece but also an authentic autograph from the featured player. Please note that since no card was issued to a stated print run of more than 10 copies, there is no pricing due to market scarcity.

2003 Playoff Prestige Player Collection

Randomly inserted into packs, these 100 cards feature leading players as well as various memorabilia pieces. Each of these cards was issued to a stated print run of 325 serial numbered sets. It is believed that this design on card style was used on more than one product issued by Playoff/Donruss during 2003 but each card was easily identifiable from what product it was pulled from.

*MULTI-COLOR PATCH: 1.25X TO 3X HI
1 Roberto Alomar Bat 4.00 10.00
2 Jeff Bagwell Bat 4.00 10.00
3 Jeff Bagwell Jsy 4.00 10.00
4 Jeff Bagwell Pants 4.00 10.00
5 Jay Bell Jsy 3.00 8.00
6 Adrian Beltre Jsy 3.00 8.00
7 Lance Berkman Jsy 3.00 8.00
8 Craig Biggio Bat 4.00 10.00
9 Craig Biggio Jsy 4.00 10.00
10 Bret Boone Jsy 3.00 8.00
11 Joe Borchard Jsy 3.00 8.00
12 Kevin Brown Jsy 3.00 8.00
13 Jeromy Burnitz Jsy 3.00 8.00
14 Pat Burrell Bat 3.00 8.00
15 Marlon Byrd Bat 3.00 8.00
16 Marlon Byrd Jsy 3.00 8.00
17 Roger Clemens Stand Jsy 6.00 15.00
18 Roger Clemens Throw Jsy 6.00 15.00
19 Doug Davis Jsy 3.00 8.00
20 Carlos Delgado Jsy 3.00 8.00
21 J.D. Drew Jsy 3.00 8.00
22 Adam Dunn Jsy 3.00 8.00
23 Jim Edmonds Jsy 3.00 8.00
24 Steve Finley Jsy 3.00 8.00
25 Freddy Garcia Jsy 3.00 8.00
26 Nomar Garciaparra Jsy 6.00 15.00
27 Jason Giambi Bat 3.00 8.00
28 Jason Giambi Jsy 3.00 8.00
29 Troy Glaus Jsy 3.00 8.00
30 Juan Gonzalez Bat 3.00 8.00
31 Juan Gonzalez Jsy 3.00 8.00
32 Luis Gonzalez Bat 3.00 8.00
33 Shawn Green Jsy 3.00 8.00
34 Ben Grieve Jsy 3.00 8.00
35 Vladimir Guerrero Jsy 4.00 10.00
36 Tony Gwynn Jsy 4.00 10.00
37 Toby Hall Jsy 3.00 8.00
38 Wes Helms Jsy 3.00 8.00
39 Todd Helton Bat 4.00 10.00
40 Todd Helton Jsy 4.00 10.00
41 Rickey Henderson Bat 4.00 10.00
42 Rickey Henderson Jsy 4.00 10.00
43 Rickey Henderson Pants 4.00 10.00
44 Tim Hudson Jsy 3.00 8.00
45 Jason Jennings Jsy 3.00 8.00
46 Andruw Jones Bat 4.00 10.00

47 Andruw Jones Jsy 4.00 10.00
48 Chipper Jones Jsy 4.00 10.00
49 Ryan Klesko Jsy 3.00 8.00
50 Paul Konerko Jsy 3.00 8.00
51 Barry Larkin Bat 4.00 10.00
52 Barry Larkin Jsy 4.00 10.00
53 Travis Lee Jsy 3.00 8.00
54 Paul Lo Duca Jsy 3.00 8.00
55 Terrence Long Jsy 3.00 8.00
56 Pedro Martinez Jsy 4.00 10.00
57 Joe Mays Jsy 3.00 8.00
58 Mark Mulder Jsy 3.00 8.00
59 John Olerud Jsy 3.00 8.00
60 Magglio Ordonez Bat 3.00 8.00
61 Magglio Ordonez Jsy 3.00 8.00
62 Roy Oswalt Jsy 3.00 8.00
63 Rafael Palmeiro Pants 4.00 10.00
64 Chan Ho Park Jsy 3.00 8.00
65 Jay Payton Jsy 3.00 8.00
66 Robert Person Jsy 3.00 8.00
67 Andy Pettitte Jsy 4.00 10.00
68 Mike Piazza Bat 4.00 10.00
69 Mike Piazza Jsy 4.00 10.00
70 Mark Prior Bat 4.00 10.00
71 Mark Prior Jsy 4.00 10.00
72 Manny Ramirez Bat 4.00 10.00
73 Manny Ramirez Jsy 4.00 10.00
74 Cal Ripken Jsy 15.00 40.00
75 Alex Rodriguez Bat 4.00 10.00
76 Alex Rodriguez M's Jsy 4.00 10.00
77 Alex Rodriguez Rgr Jsy 4.00 10.00
78 Ivan Rodriguez Bat 4.00 10.00
79 Ivan Rodriguez Jsy 4.00 10.00
80 C.C. Sabathia Jsy 3.00 8.00
81 Reggie Sanders Jsy 3.00 8.00
82 Kazuhiro Sasaki Jsy 3.00 8.00
83 Curt Schilling Jsy 3.00 8.00
84 Richie Sexson Jsy 3.00 8.00
85 Tsuyoshi Shinjo Jsy 3.00 8.00
86 Alfonso Soriano Bat 3.00 8.00
87 Alfonso Soriano Jsy 3.00 8.00
88 Sammy Sosa Jsy 4.00 10.00
89 Miguel Tejada Jsy 3.00 8.00
90 Frank Thomas Jsy 4.00 10.00
91 Jim Thome Jsy 6.00 15.00
92 Larry Walker Bat 3.00 8.00
93 Larry Walker Jsy 3.00 8.00
94 David Wells Jsy 3.00 8.00
95 Vernon Wells Jsy 3.00 8.00
96 Bernie Williams Jsy 4.00 10.00
97 Matt Williams Jsy 3.00 8.00
98 Preston Wilson Jsy 3.00 8.00
99 Kerry Wood Jsy 3.00 8.00
100 Barry Zito Jsy 3.00 8.00

2003 Playoff Prestige Signature Impressions

Randomly inserted into packs, these 50 cards feature authentic autographs from the player pictured on the card. These cards were printed to varying quantities and we have notated that information next to the player's name in our checklist.

1 A.J. Pierzynski/50 10.00 25.00
2 Adam Dunn/25
3 Barry Zito/25
4 Bobby Abreu/20
5 Brandon Phillips/25
6 Chipper Jones/5
7 Don Mattingly/15
8 Edgar Martinez/25
9 Eric Hinske/25
10 Greg Maddux/5
11 Joe Borchard/25
12 John Candelaria/50
13 Jose Canseco/10
14 Kerry Wood/5
15 Kevin Mench/25
16 Lance Berkman/25
17 Magglio Ordonez/5
18 Miguel Tejada/25
19 Nolan Ryan/5
20 Rafael Palmeiro/5
21 Roberto Alomar/5
22 Roy Oswalt/25
23 Bobby Doerr/25
24 Scott Rolen/5
25 Tim Hudson/15
26 Will Clark/10
27 Yogi Berra/15
28 Joe Kennedy/50 6.00 15.00
29 Johnny Bench/10
30 Lenny Dykstra/50 10.00 25.00
31 Mark Mulder/5
32 Mark Prior/25
33 Mike Schmidt/5
34 Ozzie Smith/5
35 Paul Lo Duca/25
36 Reggie Jackson/5
37 Roger Clemens/5
38 Steve Garvey/25
39 Toby Hall/50 6.00 15.00
40 Victor Martinez/25
41 Vladimir Guerrero/5
42 Adrian Beltre/15
43 Al Kaline/15
44 Albert Pujols/15
45 Barry Larkin/15
46 Brian Giles/15
47 C.C. Sabathia/15
48 Dale Murphy/15
49 George Brett/5
50 Jeremy Bonderman/100 20.00 50.00

2003 Playoff Prestige Stars of MLB Jersey

Randomly inserted into packs, these 20 cards feature game-used jersey swatches of the featured players. Each of these cards were issued to a stated print run of 150 serial numbered sets.

1 Roger Clemens 8.00 20.00
2 Randy Johnson 4.00 10.00
3 Sammy Sosa 4.00 10.00
4 Vladimir Guerrero 4.00 10.00
5 Lance Berkman 3.00 8.00
6 Alfonso Soriano 3.00 8.00
7 Alex Rodriguez 6.00 15.00
8 Roberto Alomar 4.00 10.00
9 Miguel Tejada 3.00 8.00
10 Pedro Martinez 4.00 10.00
11 Greg Maddux 6.00 15.00
12 Barry Zito 3.00 8.00
13 Magglio Ordonez 3.00 8.00
14 Chipper Jones 4.00 10.00
15 Manny Ramirez 4.00 10.00
16 Troy Glaus 3.00 8.00
17 Pat Burrell 3.00 8.00
18 Roy Oswalt 3.00 8.00
19 Mike Piazza 6.00 15.00
20 Nomar Garciaparra 8.00 20.00

2003 Playoff Prestige Stars of MLB Jersey Autographs

Randomly inserted into packs, these eight cards feature not only game-used jersey swatches but authentic autographs.from the player. Each of these cards were issued to a stated print run of 25 serial numbered sets and no pricing is available due to market scarcity.

4 Vladimir Guerrero
5 Lance Berkman
9 Miguel Tejada
12 Barry Zito
13 Magglio Ordonez
14 Chipper Jones
16 Troy Glaus
18 Roy Oswalt

2004 Playoff Prestige

This 200 card set was released in March, 2004. The set was issued in six card packs with an $3 SRP which came 24 packs to a box and 12 boxes to a case. Interspersed into this set are various prospect cards which were printed to the same quantity as the other cards.

COMPLETE SET (200) 15.00 40.00
COMMON CARD (1-200) .15 .40
COMMON PROSPECT .15 .40
PROSPECTS ARE NOT SHORT-PRINTED
1 Bengie Molina .15 .40
2 Garret Anderson .15 .40
3 Jarrod Washburn .15 .40
4 Scott Spiezio .15 .40
5 Tim Salmon .15 .40
6 Troy Glaus .15 .40
7 Alex Cintron .15 .40
8 Brandon Webb .15 .40
9 Curt Schilling .25 .60
10 Edgar Gonzalez PROS .15 .40
11 Luis Gonzalez .15 .40
12 Randy Johnson .40 1.00
13 Steve Finley .15 .40
14 Andruw Jones .15 .40
15 Bubba Nelson PROS .15 .40
16 Chipper Jones .40 1.00
17 Gary Sheffield .15 .40
18 Greg Maddux .60 1.50
19 Javy Lopez .15 .40
20 John Smoltz .40 1.00
21 Marcus Giles .15 .40
22 Rafael Furcal .15 .40
23 Brian Roberts .15 .40
24 Jason Johnson .15 .40
25 Jay Gibbons .15 .40
26 Luis Matos .15 .40
27 Melvin Mora .15 .40
28 Tony Batista .15 .40
29 Bill Mueller .15 .40
30 David Ortiz .40 1.00
31 Johnny Damon .25 .60
32 Kevin Youkilis PROS .25 .60
33 Manny Ramirez .40 1.00
34 Nomar Garciaparra .40 1.00
35 Pedro Martinez .25 .60
36 Trot Nixon .15 .40
37 Aramis Ramirez .15 .40
38 Brendan Harris PROS .15 .40
39 Carlos Zambrano .25 .60
40 Corey Patterson .15 .40
41 Kenny Lofton .15 .40
42 Kerry Wood .15 .40
43 Mark Prior .25 .60
44 Sammy Sosa .40 1.00
45 Bartolo Colon .15 .40
46 Carlos Lee .15 .40
47 Esteban Loaiza .15 .40
48 Frank Thomas .40 1.00
49 Joe Crede .15 .40
50 Magglio Ordonez .25 .60
51 Roberto Alomar .25 .60
52 Adam Dunn .25 .60
53 Austin Kearns .15 .40
54 Josh Hall .15 .40
55 Ken Griffey Jr. .60 1.50
56 Sean Casey .15 .40
57 Mike Nakamura .15 .40
58 C.C. Sabathia .25 .60
59 Casey Blake .15 .40
60 Jody Gerut .15 .40
61 Matt Lawton .15 .40
62 Milton Bradley .15 .40
63 Omar Vizquel .25 .60
64 Jason Jennings .15 .40
65 Jay Payton .15 .40
66 Larry Walker .25 .60
67 Preston Wilson .15 .40
68 Todd Helton .25 .60
69 Bobby Higginson .15 .40
70 Carlos Pena .25 .60
71 Dmitri Young .15 .40
72 Jeremy Bonderman .15 .40
73 Preston Larrison PROS .15 .40
74 Derrek Lee .15 .40
75 Dontrelle Willis .15 .40
76 Ivan Rodriguez .25 .60
77 Josh Beckett .25 .60
78 Juan Pierre .15 .40
79 Miguel Cabrera .40 1.00
80 Mike Lowell .15 .40
81 Chris Burke PROS .15 .40
82 Craig Biggio .25 .60
83 Jeff Bagwell .25 .60
84 Jeff Kent .15 .40
85 Lance Berkman .25 .60
86 Richard Hidalgo .15 .40
87 Roy Oswalt .25 .60
88 Aaron Guiel .15 .40
89 Angel Berroa .15 .40
90 Carlos Beltran .15 .40
91 Jeremy Affeldt .15 .40
92 Mike Sweeney .15 .40
93 Runelvys Hernandez .15 .40
94 Dave Roberts .15 .40
95 Eric Gagne .15 .40
96 Hideo Nomo .40 1.00
97 Kevin Brown .15 .40
98 Paul Lo Duca .15 .40
99 Shawn Green .15 .40
100 Ben Sheets .15 .40
101 Geoff Jenkins .15 .40
102 Richie Sexson .15 .40
103 Rickie Weeks PROS .15 .40
104 Scott Podsednik .15 .40
105 J.D. Durbin PROS .15 .40
106 Jacque Jones .15 .40
107 Jason Kubel PROS .15 .40
108 Shannon Stewart .15 .40
109 Torii Hunter .15 .40
110 Chad Cordero PROS .15 .40
111 Javier Vazquez .15 .40
112 Jose Vidro .15 .40
113 Livan Hernandez .15 .40
114 Orlando Cabrera .15 .40
115 Tony Armas Jr. .15 .40
116 Vladimir Guerrero .40 1.00
117 Al Leiter .15 .40
118 Cliff Floyd .15 .40
119 Jae Weong Seo .15 .40
120 Jose Reyes .25 .60
121 Mike Piazza .40 1.00
122 Tom Glavine .25 .60
123 Aaron Boone .15 .40
124 Alfonso Soriano .15 .40
125 Andy Pettitte .25 .60
126 Derek Jeter 1.00 2.50
127 Hideki Matsui .60 1.50
128 Jason Giambi .15 .40
129 Jorge Posada .25 .60
130 Jose Contreras .15 .40
131 Mike Mussina .25 .60
132 Barry Zito .15 .40
133 Eric Byrnes .15 .40
134 Eric Chavez .15 .40
135 Jose Guillen .15 .40
136 Mark Mulder .15 .40
137 Miguel Tejada .25 .60
138 Ramon Hernandez .15 .40
139 Rich Harden .15 .40
140 Tim Hudson .25 .60
141 Bobby Abreu .15 .40
142 Brett Myers .15 .40
143 Jim Thome .25 .60
144 Kevin Millwood .15 .40
145 Mike Lieberthal .15 .40
146 Ryan Howard PROS .50 1.25
147 Craig Wilson .15 .40
148 Jack Wilson .15 .40
149 Jason Kendall .15 .40
150 Kip Wells .15 .40
151 Reggie Sanders .15 .40
152 Albert Pujols 1.00 2.50
153 Edgar Renteria .15 .40
154 Jim Edmonds .25 .60
155 Matt Morris .15 .40
156 Scott Rolen .25 .60
157 Tino Martinez .25 .60
158 Woody Williams .15 .40
159 Brian Giles .15 .40
160 Freddy Guzman PROS RC .15 .40
161 Jake Peavy .15 .40
162 Khalil Greene PROS .25 .60
163 Phil Nevin .15 .40
164 Ryan Klesko .15 .40
165 Ray Durham .15 .40
166 Jason Schmidt .15 .40
167 Jerome Williams PROS .15 .40
168 Jesse Foppert .15 .40
169 Jose Cruz Jr. .15 .40
170 Marquis Grissom .15 .40
171 Merkin Valdez PROS RC .15 .40
172 Rich Aurilia .15 .40
173 Bret Boone .15 .40
174 Freddy Garcia .15 .40
175 Ichiro Suzuki .60 1.50
176 Jamie Moyer .15 .40
177 John Olerud .15 .40
178 Mike Cameron .15 .40
179 Randy Winn .15 .40
180 Aubrey Huff .15 .40
181 Carl Crawford .25 .60
182 Chad Gaudin PROS .15 .40
183 Rocco Baldelli .15 .40
184 Toby Hall .15 .40
185 Travis Lee .15 .40
186 Alex Rodriguez .60 1.50
187 Hank Blalock .15 .40
188 John Thomson .15 .40
189 Juan Gonzalez .15 .40
190 Mark Teixeira .40 1.00
191 Michael Young .15 .40
192 Rafael Palmeiro .25 .60
193 Ramon Nivar PROS .15 .40
194 Carlos Delgado .15 .40
195 Dustin McGowan PROS .15 .40
196 Frank Catalanotto .15 .40
197 Vinny Chulk .15 .40
198 Orlando Hudson .15 .40
199 Roy Halladay .40 1.00
200 Vernon Wells .15 .40

2004 Playoff Prestige Autographs

RANDOM INSERTS IN PACKS
PRINT RUNS B/WN 4-500 COPIES PER
PRINT RUNS PROVIDED BY DONRUSS
CARDS ARE NOT SERIAL-NUMBERED
SEE BECKETT.COM OPG FOR PRINT RUNS
NO PRICING ON QTY OF 25 OR LESS
8 Brandon Webb/100 4.00 10.00
10 Edgar Gonzalez PROS/150 4.00 10.00
15 Bubba Nelson PROS/250 4.00 10.00
25 Jay Gibbons/50 5.00 12.00
32 Kevin Youkilis PROS/100 4.00 10.00
38 Brendan Harris PROS/400 4.00 10.00
57 Mike Nakamura/250 4.00 10.00
60 Jody Gerut/50 5.00 12.00
73 Preston Larrison PROS/250 4.00 10.00
79 Miguel Cabrera/100 10.00 25.00
81 Chris Burke PROS/250 6.00 15.00
93 Runelvys Hernandez/50 5.00 12.00
105 J.D. Durbin PROS/500 4.00 10.00
106 Jacque Jones/50 5.00 12.00
107 Jason Kubel PROS/400 4.00 10.00
108 Shannon Stewart/50 5.00 12.00
133 Eric Byrnes/50 5.00 12.00
139 Rich Harden/50 8.00 20.00
146 Ryan Howard PROS/400 30.00 60.00
193 Ramon Nivar PROS/100 4.00 10.00
195 Dustin McGowan PROS/100 4.00 10.00
197 Vinny Chulk/112 4.00 10.00
198 Orlando Hudson/100 4.00 10.00

2004 Playoff Prestige Xtra Bases Black

*XB BLACK: 5X TO 12X BASIC
*XB BLACK: 5X TO 12X BASIC PROS
STATED PRINT RUN 75 SERIAL #'d SETS

2004 Playoff Prestige Xtra Bases Black Autographs

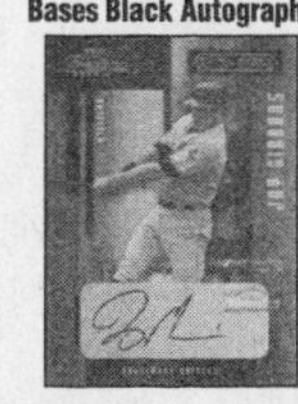

STATED PRINT RUN 25 SERIAL #'d SETS
NO PRICING DUE TO SCARCITY

2004 Playoff Prestige Xtra Bases Green

*XB GREEN: 3X TO 8X BASIC
*XB GREEN: 3X TO 8X BASIC PROS
STATED PRINT RUN 150 SERIAL #'d SETS

2004 Playoff Prestige Xtra Bases Green Autographs

STATED PRINT RUN 100 SERIAL #'d SETS
10 Edgar Gonzalez PROS 4.00 10.00
15 Bubba Nelson PROS 4.00 10.00
38 Brendan Harris PROS 4.00 10.00
57 Mike Nakamura 4.00 10.00
81 Chris Burke PROS 6.00 15.00
105 J.D. Durbin PROS 4.00 10.00
107 Jason Kubel PROS 4.00 10.00
146 Ryan Howard PROS 20.00 50.00
195 Dustin McGowan PROS 4.00 10.00

2004 Playoff Prestige Xtra Bases Purple

*XB PURPLE: 3X TO 8X BASIC
*XB PURPLE: 3X TO 8X BASIC PROS
STATED PRINT RUN 150 SERIAL #'d SETS

2004 Playoff Prestige Xtra Bases Purple Autographs

STATED PRINT RUN 100 SERIAL #'d SETS
10 Edgar Gonzalez PROS 4.00 10.00
15 Bubba Nelson PROS 4.00 10.00
32 Kevin Youkilis PROS 4.00 10.00
38 Brendan Harris PROS 4.00 10.00
57 Mike Nakamura 4.00 10.00
73 Preston Larrison PROS 4.00 10.00
79 Miguel Cabrera 10.00 25.00
81 Chris Burke PROS 6.00 15.00
105 J.D. Durbin PROS 4.00 10.00
107 Jason Kubel PROS 4.00 10.00
146 Ryan Howard PROS 20.00 50.00
193 Ramon Nivar PROS 4.00 10.00
195 Dustin McGowan PROS 4.00 10.00
198 Orlando Hudson 4.00 10.00

2004 Playoff Prestige Xtra Bases Red

STATED PRINT RUN 25 SERIAL #'d SETS
NO PRICING DUE TO SCARCITY

2004 Playoff Prestige Xtra Bases Red Autographs

STATED PRINT RUN 25 SERIAL #'d SETS
NO PRICING DUE TO SCARCITY

2004 Playoff Prestige Achievements

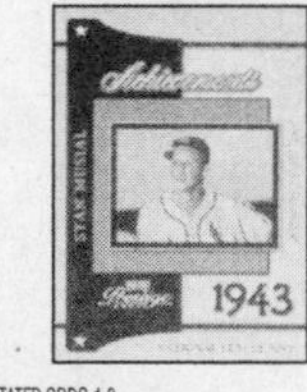

STATED ODDS 1:8
1 Hideo Nomo 95 ROY 1.00 2.50
2 Don Mattingly 85 MVP 2.00 5.00
3 Roger Clemens 86 CY/MVP 1.25 3.00
4 Greg Maddux 95 CY 1.50 4.00
5 Stan Musial 43 MVP 1.50 4.00
6 Roberto Clemente 66 MVP 2.50 6.00
7 Derek Jeter 96 ROY 2.50 6.00
8 Albert Pujols 01 ROY 2.50 6.00
9 Cal Ripken 91 MVP 4.00 10.00
10 George Brett 80 MVP 2.00 5.00
11 Carl Yastrzemski 67 MVP 1.00 2.50
12 Rickey Henderson 90 MVP 1.00 2.50
13 Sammy Sosa 98 MVP 1.00 2.50
14 Randy Johnson 02 CY 1.00 2.50
15 Bob Gibson 68 CY/MVP .60 1.50

2004 Playoff Prestige Changing Stripes

STATED ODDS 1:11
*FOIL: .75X TO 2X BASIC
FOIL PRINT RUN 150 SERIAL #'d SETS
*HOLO-FOIL: 1.5X TO 4X BASIC
HOLO-FOIL PRINT RUN 50 SERIAL #'d SETS
FOIL/HOLO-FOIL RANDOM IN PACKS
1 Rickey Henderson A's-Yanks 1.00 2.50
2 Mike Mussina O's-Yanks .60 1.50
3 Jim Thome Indians-Phils .60 1.50
4 Hideo Nomo Sox-Dodgers 1.00 2.50
5 Scott Rolen Phils-Cards .60 1.50
6 Jason Giambi A's-Yanks .40 1.00
7 R.Johnson Astros-D'backs 1.00 2.50
8 Shawn Green Jays-Dodgers .40 1.00
9 Curt Schilling Phils-D'backs .60 1.50
10 Alex Rodriguez M's-Rangers 1.50 4.00
11 Greg Maddux Cubs-Braves 1.50 4.00
12 Randy Johnson M's-Astros 1.00 2.50
13 Hideo Nomo Dodgers-Mets 1.00 2.50
14 Ivan Rodriguez Rgr-Marlins .60 1.50
15 Juan Gonzalez Indians-Rangers .40 1.00
16 Manny Ramirez Indians-Sox 1.00 2.50
17 Mike Piazza Dodgers-Mets 1.00 2.50
18 Nolan Ryan Angels-Astros 3.00 8.00
19 Nolan Ryan Astros-Rangers 3.00 8.00
20 Pedro Martinez Expos-Sox .60 1.50
21 Reg Jackson Yanks-Angels .60 1.50
22 Roberto Alomar Mets-Sox .60 1.50
23 Rod Carew Twins-Angels .60 1.50
24 Roger Clemens Sox-Yanks 1.25 3.00
25 Sammy Sosa Sox-Cubs 1.00 2.50

2004 Playoff Prestige Changing Stripes Dual Jersey

STATED PRINT RUN 150 SERIAL #'d SETS
PRIME PRINT RUN 25 SERIAL #'d SETS
NO PRIME PRICING DUE TO SCARCITY
1 Rickey Henderson A's-Yanks 6.00 15.00
2 Mike Mussina O's-Yanks 6.00 15.00
3 Jim Thome Indians-Phils 6.00 15.00
4 Hideo Nomo Sox-Dodgers 10.00 25.00
5 Scott Rolen Phils-Cards 6.00 15.00
6 Jason Giambi A's-Yanks 4.00 10.00
7 R.Johnson Astros-D'backs 6.00 15.00
8 Shawn Green Jays-Dodgers 4.00 10.00
9 Curt Schilling Phils-D'backs 4.00 10.00
10 Alex Rodriguez M's-Rangers 6.00 15.00
12 Randy Johnson M's-Astros 6.00 15.00
13 Hideo Nomo Dodgers-Mets 10.00 25.00
14 Ivan Rodriguez Rgr-Marlins 6.00 15.00
15 Juan Gonzalez Indians-Rangers 4.00 10.00
16 Manny Ramirez Indians-Sox 6.00 15.00
17 Mike Piazza Dodgers-Mets 6.00 15.00
18 Nolan Ryan Angels-Astros 20.00 50.00
19 Nolan Ryan Astros-Rangers 20.00 50.00
20 Pedro Martinez Expos-Sox 6.00 15.00
22 Roberto Alomar Mets-Sox 6.00 15.00
23 Rod Carew Twins-Angels 6.00 15.00
24 Roger Clemens Sox-Yanks 8.00 20.00
25 Sammy Sosa Sox-Cubs 6.00 15.00

2004 Playoff Prestige Connections

STATED ODDS 1:9
*FOIL: 1.5X TO 4X BASIC
FOIL PRINT RUN 100 SERIAL #'d SETS
HOLO-FOIL PRINT RUN 21 SERIAL #'d SETS
NO HOLO-FOIL PRICING DUE TO SCARCITY
1 Derek Jeter / Alfonso Soriano 2.50 6.00
2 Greg Maddux / Chipper Jones 1.50 4.00
3 Albert Pujols / Scott Rolen 2.50 6.00
4 Randy Johnson / Curt Schilling 1.00 2.50
5 Nomar Garciaparra / Manny Ramirez 1.00 2.50
6 Alex Rodriguez / Mark Teixeira 1.50 4.00
7 Barry Zito / Tim Hudson .60 1.50
8 Sammy Sosa / Mark Prior 1.00 2.50
9 Derek Jeter / Jason Giambi 2.50 6.00
10 Roger Clemens / Mike Mussina 1.25 3.00
11 Mark Prior / Kerry Wood .60 1.50
12 Alex Rodriguez / Hank Blalock 1.50 4.00
13 Frank Thomas / Magglio Ordonez .60 1.50
14 Nomar Garciaparra / Pedro Martinez 1.00 2.50
15 Carlos Delgado / Vernon Wells .40 1.00
16 Miguel Tejada / Eric Chavez .60 1.50
17 Jeff Bagwell / Lance Berkman .60 1.50
18 Jim Thome / Bobby Abreu .60 1.50
19 Todd Helton / Preston Wilson .60 1.50
20 Vladimir Guerrero / Javier Vazquez 1.00 2.50

2004 Playoff Prestige Connections Material

STATED PRINT RUN 250 SERIAL #'d SETS
1 Derek Jeter Bat / Alfonso Soriano Bat 10.00 25.00
2 Greg Maddux Bat / Chipper Jones Jsy 6.00 15.00
3 Albert Pujols Bat / Scott Rolen Bat 8.00 20.00
4 Randy Johnson Bat / Curt Schilling Bat 6.00 15.00
5 Nomar Garciaparra Bat / Manny Ramirez Bat 6.00 15.00
6 Alex Rodriguez Bat / Mark Texeira Bat 6.00 15.00
7 Barry Zito Bat / Tim Hudson Bat 4.00 10.00
8 Sammy Sosa Bat / Mark Prior Bat 6.00 15.00
9 Derek Jeter Bat / Jason Giambi Bat 10.00 25.00
10 Roger Clemens Jsy / Mike Mussina Bat 8.00 20.00
11 Mark Prior Bat / Kerry Wood Bat 6.00 15.00
12 Alex Rodriguez Bat / Hank Blalock Bat 6.00 15.00
13 Frank Thomas Bat / Magglio Ordonez Bat 6.00 15.00
14 Nomar Garciaparra Bat / Pedro Martinez Bat 10.00 25.00
15 Carlos Delgado Bat / Vernon Wells Bat 4.00 10.00
16 Miguel Tejada Bat / Eric Chavez Bat 4.00 10.00
17 Jeff Bagwell Bat / Lance Berkman Bat 6.00 15.00
18 Jim Thome Jsy / Bobby Abreu Bat 6.00 15.00
19 Todd Helton Bat / Preston Wilson Bat 6.00 15.00
20 Vladimir Guerrero Bat / Javier Vazquez Jsy 6.00 15.00

2004 Playoff Prestige Diamond Heritage

STATED ODDS 1:13
1 Mike Piazza 1.00 2.50
2 Greg Maddux 1.50 4.00
3 Nomar Garciaparra 1.00 2.50
4 Chipper Jones 1.00 2.50
5 Albert Pujols 2.50 6.00
6 Derek Jeter 2.50 6.00
7 Shawn Green .40 1.00
8 Alex Rodriguez 1.50 4.00
9 Jim Thome .60 1.50
10 Jason Giambi .40 1.00
11 Sammy Sosa 1.00 2.50
12 Hank Blalock .40 1.00
13 Garret Anderson .40 1.00
14 Manny Ramirez 1.00 2.50
15 Scott Rolen .60 1.50
16 Jeff Bagwell .60 1.50
17 Randy Johnson 1.00 2.50
18 Ichiro Suzuki 1.50 4.00
19 Ivan Rodriguez .60 1.50
20 Alfonso Soriano .40 1.00

2004 Playoff Prestige Diamond Heritage Material

STATED ODDS 1:92
1 Mike Piazza Bat 6.00 15.00
2 Greg Maddux Bat 6.00 15.00
3 Nomar Garciaparra Bat 6.00 15.00
4 Chipper Jones Jsy 4.00 10.00
5 Albert Pujols Bat 8.00 20.00
6 Derek Jeter Jsy 10.00 25.00
7 Shawn Green Bat 3.00 8.00
8 Alex Rodriguez Bat 6.00 15.00
9 Jim Thome Jsy 4.00 10.00
10 Jason Giambi Bat 3.00 8.00
11 Sammy Sosa Bat 4.00 10.00
12 Hank Blalock Bat 3.00 8.00
13 Garret Anderson Bat 3.00 8.00
14 Manny Ramirez Bat 4.00 10.00
15 Scott Rolen Bat 4.00 10.00
16 Jeff Bagwell Bat 4.00 10.00
17 Randy Johnson Bat 4.00 10.00
19 Ivan Rodriguez Bat 4.00 10.00
20 Alfonso Soriano Bat 3.00 8.00

2004 Playoff Prestige League Leaders Single

STATED ODDS 1:18
*FOIL: 1.5X TO 4X BASIC
FOIL PRINT RUN 100 SERIAL #'d SETS
HOLO-FOIL PRINT RUN 25 SERIAL #'d SETS
NO HOLO-FOIL PRICING DUE TO SCARCITY
FOIL/HOLO-FOIL RANDOM IN PACKS
1 Alex Rodriguez AL HR 1.50 4.00
2 Albert Pujols NL Hit 2.50 6.00
3 Albert Pujols NL Avg 2.50 6.00
4 Nomar Garciaparra AL Hit 1.00 2.50
5 Mark Prior NL ERA .60 1.50
6 Pedro Martinez AL ERA .60 1.50
7 Kerry Wood NL SO .40 1.00
8 Derek Jeter AL Avg 2.50 6.00
9 Jason Giambi AL BB .40 1.00
10 Roger Clemens AL SO 1.25 3.00

2004 Playoff Prestige League Leaders Single Material

STATED PRINT RUN 250 SERIAL #'d SETS
1 Alex Rodriguez AL HR Bat 4.00 10.00
2 Albert Pujols NL Hit Bat 6.00 15.00
3 Albert Pujols NL Avg Bat 6.00 15.00
4 Nomar Garciaparra AL Hit Bat 4.00 10.00
5 Mark Prior NL ERA Jsy 4.00 10.00
6 Pedro Martinez AL ERA Jsy 4.00 10.00
7 Kerry Wood NL SO Jsy 3.00 8.00
8 Derek Jeter AL Avg Jsy 8.00 20.00
9 Jason Giambi AL BB Jsy 3.00 8.00
10 Roger Clemens AL SO Jsy

2004 Playoff Prestige League Leaders Double

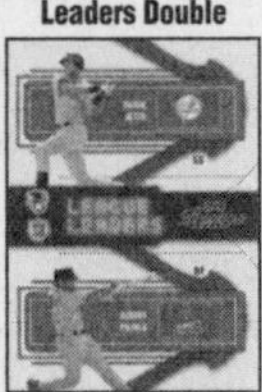

STATED PRINT RUN 500 SERIAL #'d SETS
*FOIL: .75X TO 2X BASIC
FOIL PRINT RUN 75 SERIAL #'d SETS
HOLO-FOIL PRINT RUN 10 SERIAL #'d SETS
NO HOLO-FOIL PRICING DUE TO SCARCITY
1 Alex Rodriguez 2.50 6.00
Jim Thome HR
2 Mark Prior 1.00 2.50
Pedro Martinez ERA
3 Roger Clemens 2.00 5.00
Kerry Wood SO
4 Nomar Garciaparra 4.00 10.00
Albert Pujols Hit
5 Derek Jeter 4.00 10.00
Albert Pujols Avg

2004 Playoff Prestige League Leaders Double Material

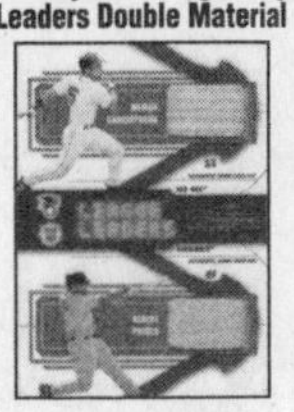

STATED PRINT RUN 100 SERIAL #'d SETS
1 Alex Rodriguez Bat 10.00 25.00
Jim Thome Bat HR
2 Mark Prior Jsy 10.00 25.00
Pedro Martinez Jsy ERA
3 Roger Clemens Jsy 12.50 30.00
Kerry Wood Jsy SO
4 Nomar Garciaparra Bat 12.50 30.00
Albert Pujols Bat Hits
5 Derek Jeter Jsy 15.00 40.00
Albert Pujols Bat Avg

2004 Playoff Prestige League Leaders Quad

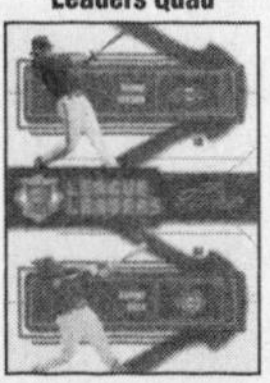

STATED PRINT RUN 250 SERIAL #'d SETS
*FOIL: .75X TO 2X BASIC
FOIL PRINT RUN 50 SERIAL #'d SETS
HOLO-FOIL PRINT RUN 5 SERIAL #'d SETS
NO HOLO-FOIL PRICING DUE TO SCARCITY
1 Albert Pujols 4.00 10.00
Todd Helton
Edgar Renteria
Gary Sheffield NL Avg
2 Derek Jeter 4.00 10.00
Manny Ramirez
Nomar Garciaparra
Ichiro Suzuki AL Avg
3 Mark PriorCurt Schilling 1.50 4.00
Hideo Nomo
Kevin Brown NL ERA
4 Richie Sexson 4.00 10.00
Sammy Sosa
Albert Pujols
Jim Thome NL HR
5 Alex Rodriguez 2.50 6.00
Frank Thomas
Jason Giambi
Carlos Delgado AL HR

2004 Playoff Prestige League Leaders Quad Material

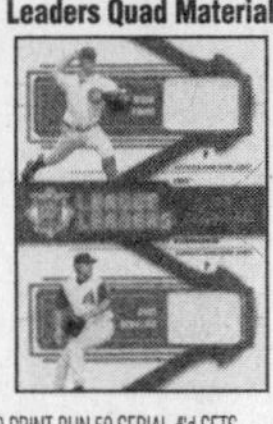

STATED PRINT RUN 50 SERIAL #'d SETS
1 Albert Pujols Bat 15.00 40.00
Todd Helton Bat
Edgar Renteria Jsy
Gary Sheffield Jsy NL Avg
3 Mark Prior Jsy 15.00 40.00
Curt Schilling Jsy
Hideo Nomo Jsy
Kevin Brown Jsy NL ERA
4 Richie Sexson Jsy 20.00 50.00
Sammy Sosa Bat
Albert Pujols Bat
Jim Thome Bat NL HR
5 Alex Rodriguez Jsy 15.00 40.00
Frank Thomas Jsy
Jason Giambi Jsy
Carlos Delgado Jsy AL HR

2004 Playoff Prestige Players Collection Jersey

STATED ODDS 1:79
*PLATINUM: .75X TO 2X BASIC
PLATINUM RANDOM INSERTS IN PACKS
PLATINUM PRINT RUN 50 SERIAL #'d SETS
1 Adam Dunn AS 2.00 5.00
2 Adam Dunn Gray 2.00 5.00
3 Adam Dunn White 2.00 5.00
4 Alex Rodriguez M's 4.00 10.00
5 Alex Rodriguez Rgr AS 4.00 10.00
6 Alex Rodriguez Rgr Blue 4.00 10.00
7 Alex Rodriguez Rgr White 4.00 10.00
8 Andruw Jones Home 3.00 8.00
9 Andruw Jones Road 3.00 8.00
10 Austin Kearns 2.00 5.00
11 Brandon Webb 2.00 5.00
12 C.C. Sabathia 2.00 5.00
13 Cal Ripken 15.00 40.00
14 Carlos Beltran 2.00 5.00
15 Carlos Delgado 2.00 5.00
16 Carlos Lee 2.00 5.00
17 Chipper Jones Home 3.00 8.00
18 Chipper Jones Road 3.00 8.00
19 Craig Biggio 3.00 8.00
20 Curt Schilling 2.00 5.00
21 David Wells 2.00 5.00
22 Don Mattingly 6.00 15.00
23 Dontrelle Willis 3.00 8.00
24 Frank Thomas Black 3.00 8.00
25 Frank Thomas White 3.00 8.00
26 Fred McGriff 3.00 8.00
27 Garret Anderson AS 2.00 5.00
28 Gary Sheffield Braves 2.00 5.00
29 Gary Sheffield Dodgers 2.00 5.00
30 Greg Maddux Gray 4.00 10.00
31 Hank Blalock Home 2.00 5.00
32 Hank Blalock Road 2.00 5.00
33 Hee Seop Choi 2.00 5.00
34 Hideo Nomo Mets 3.00 8.00
35 Hideo Nomo Dodgers Gray 3.00 8.00
36 Hideo Nomo Dodgers White 3.00 8.00
37 Ivan Rodriguez Marlins 3.00 8.00
38 Ivan Rodriguez Rgr 3.00 8.00
39 Jason Giambi Home 2.00 5.00
40 Jim Edmonds 2.00 5.00
41 Jim Thome 3.00 8.00
42 John Olerud 2.00 5.00
43 John Smoltz 3.00 8.00
44 Josh Beckett 2.00 5.00
45 Josh Phelps 2.00 5.00
46 Juan Gonzalez Rgr 2.00 5.00
47 Juan Gonzalez Indians 2.00 5.00
48 Kazuhisa Ishii 2.00 5.00
49 Lance Berkman White 2.00 5.00
50 Larry Walker Home 2.00 5.00
51 Larry Walker Road 2.00 5.00
52 Luis Gonzalez AS 2.00 5.00
53 Magglio Ordonez Home 2.00 5.00
54 Magglio Ordonez Road 2.00 5.00
55 Manny Ramirez 3.00 8.00
56 Manny Ramirez AS 3.00 8.00
57 Mark Prior Home 3.00 8.00
58 Mark Prior Road 3.00 8.00
59 Mark Teixeira 3.00 8.00
60 Mike Mussina 3.00 8.00
61 Mike Piazza AS 4.00 10.00
62 Mike Piazza Black 4.00 10.00
63 Mike Piazza White 4.00 10.00
64 Nomar Garciaparra Gray 4.00 10.00
65 Nomar Garciaparra White 4.00 10.00
66 Pat Burrell 2.00 5.00
67 Paul Konerko 2.00 5.00
68 Paul Lo Duca 2.00 5.00
69 Pedro Martinez 3.00 8.00
70 Rafael Furcal 2.00 5.00
71 Rafael Palmeiro Blue 3.00 8.00
72 Rafael Palmeiro Gray 3.00 8.00
73 Ramon Hernandez 2.00 5.00
74 Rickey Henderson 3.00 8.00
75 Rickey Henderson Black 3.00 8.00
76 Rickey Henderson White 3.00 8.00
77 Roberto Alomar Indians 3.00 8.00
78 Roberto Alomar Mets 3.00 8.00
79 Robin Ventura AS 2.00 5.00
80 Roger Clemens Away 6.00 15.00
81 Roger Clemens Home 6.00 15.00
82 Roy Halladay 2.00 5.00
83 Sammy Sosa AS 3.00 8.00
84 Sammy Sosa Gray 3.00 8.00
85 Sammy Sosa White 3.00 8.00
86 Scott Rolen 3.00 8.00
87 Shannon Stewart 2.00 5.00
88 Shawn Green Blue 2.00 5.00
89 Shawn Green Gray 2.00 5.00
90 Shawn Green White 2.00 5.00
91 Terrence Long 2.00 5.00
92 Tim Hudson 2.00 5.00
93 Todd Helton Away 3.00 8.00
94 Todd Helton Home 3.00 8.00
95 Tom Glavine Braves 3.00 8.00
96 Tom Glavine Mets 3.00 8.00
97 Torii Hunter 2.00 5.00
98 Vernon Wells 2.00 5.00
99 Vladimir Guerrero 3.00 8.00
100 Vladimir Guerrero AS 3.00 8.00

2004 Playoff Prestige Prestigious Pros

STATED ODDS 1:23
1 Mark Prior .60 1.50
2 Derek Jeter 2.50 6.00
3 Mike Mussina .60 1.50
4 Nomar Garciaparra 1.00 2.50
5 Roger Clemens 1.25 3.00
6 Jason Giambi .40 1.00
7 Randy Johnson 1.00 2.50
8 Rafael Palmeiro .60 1.50
9 Barry Zito .40 1.00
10 Pat Burrell .40 1.00

2004 Playoff Prestige Stars of MLB

STATED ODDS 1:36
*FOIL: .75X TO 2X BASIC
FOIL PRINT RUN 100 SERIAL #'d SETS
HOLO-FOIL PRINT RUN 25 SERIAL #'d SETS
NO HOLO-FOIL PRICING DUE TO SCARCITY
FOIL/HOLO-FOIL RANDOM IN PACKS
1 Albert Pujols 2.50 6.00
2 Derek Jeter 2.50 6.00
3 Mike Piazza 1.00 2.50
4 Greg Maddux 1.50 4.00
5 Ichiro Suzuki 1.50 4.00
6 Nomar Garciaparra 1.00 2.50
7 Ivan Rodriguez .60 1.50
8 Randy Johnson 1.00 2.50
9 Alex Rodriguez 1.50 4.00
10 Sammy Sosa 1.00 2.50
11 Alfonso Soriano .40 1.00
12 Vladimir Guerrero 1.00 2.50
13 Jason Giambi .40 1.00
14 Mark Prior .60 1.50
15 Chipper Jones 1.00 2.50

2004 Playoff Prestige Stars of MLB Jersey

STATED PRINT RUN 250 SERIAL #'d SETS
*PRIME: 1X TO 2.5X BASIC
PRIME PRINT RUN 50 SERIAL #'d SETS
RANDOM INSERTS IN PACKS
1 Albert Pujols 6.00 15.00
2 Derek Jeter 8.00 20.00
3 Mike Piazza 4.00 10.00
4 Greg Maddux 4.00 10.00
6 Nomar Garciaparra 4.00 10.00
7 Ivan Rodriguez 4.00 10.00
8 Randy Johnson 4.00 10.00
9 Alex Rodriguez 4.00 10.00
10 Sammy Sosa 4.00 10.00
11 Alfonso Soriano 3.00 8.00
12 Vladimir Guerrero 4.00 10.00
13 Jason Giambi 3.00 8.00
14 Mark Prior 4.00 10.00
15 Chipper Jones 4.00 10.00

2004 Playoff Prestige Stars of MLB Jersey Autographs

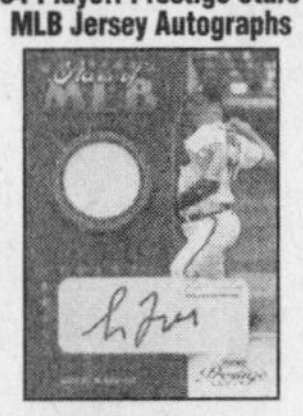

PRINT RUNS B/WN 1-50 COPIES PER
NO PRICING ON QTY OF 25 OR LESS
14 Mark Prior/50 20.00 50.00

2005 Playoff Prestige

This 200-card set was released in March, 2005. The set was issued in eight-card packs with an $3 SRP which came 12 packs to box and 16 boxes to a case. While there are no short prints in this set, please note that cards 1-185 feature active veterans and cards 186-200 feature retired greats.

COMPLETE SET (200) 15.00 40.00
COMMON CARD (1-185) .15 .40
COMMON RC (1-185) .30 .75
COMMON CARD (186-200) .20 .50
1 Rafael Furcal .15 .40
2 Derek Jeter 1.00 2.50
3 Edgar Renteria .15 .40
4 Jeff Bagwell .25 .60
5 Nomar Garciaparra .40 1.00
6 Melvin Mora .15 .40
7 Craig Biggio .25 .60
8 Brad Penny .15 .40
9 Hank Blalock .15 .40
10 Vernon Wells .15 .40
11 Gary Sheffield .15 .40
12 Jeff Kent .15 .40
13 Carl Crawford .25 .60
14 Paul Konerko .25 .60
15 Carlos Beltran .15 .40
16 Garret Anderson .15 .40
17 Todd Helton .25 .60
18 Javy Lopez .15 .40
19 Mike Lowell .15 .40
20 Robb Quinlan .15 .40
21 Andy Pettitte .25 .60
22 Roger Clemens .50 1.25
23 Mark Teixeira .40 1.00
24 Miguel Cabrera .40 1.00
25 Andruw Jones .15 .40
26 Josh Beckett .25 .60
27 Scott Rolen .25 .60
28 J.J. Putz .15 .40
29 Adrian Beltre .15 .40
30 Magglio Ordonez .25 .60
31 Mike Piazza .40 1.00
32 Danny Graves .15 .40
33 Larry Walker .25 .60
34 Kerry Wood .15 .40
35 Mike Mussina .25 .60
36 Joe Nathan .15 .40
37 Chone Figgins .15 .40
38 Curt Schilling .25 .60
39 Brett Myers .15 .40
40 Jae Weong Seo .15 .40
41 Danny Kolb .15 .40
42 Mariano Rivera .40 1.00
43 Francisco Cordero .15 .40
44 Adam Dunn .25 .60
45 Pedro Martinez .25 .60
46 Frank Thomas .40 1.00
47 Tom Glavine .25 .60
48 Torii Hunter .15 .40
49 Ben Sheets .15 .40
50 Shawn Green .15 .40
51 Randy Johnson .40 1.00
52 C.C. Sabathia .25 .60
53 Bobby Abreu .15 .40
54 Octavio Dotel .15 .40
55 Hideki Matsui .60 1.50
56 Mark Buehrle .25 .60
57 Johan Santana .40 1.00
58 Brandon Inge .15 .40
59 Dewon Brazelton .15 .40
60 Ryan Wagner .15 .40
61 Kevin Brown .15 .40
62 Laynce Nix .15 .40
63 Jason Bay .15 .40
64 J.D. Drew .15 .40
65 Jacque Jones .15 .40
66 Jason Schmidt .15 .40
67 Joe Kennedy .15 .40
68 Miguel Tejada .25 .60
69 Hideo Nomo .40 1.00
70 Michael Young .25 .60
71 Lyle Overbay .15 .40
72 Omar Vizquel .25 .60
73 Johnny Estrada .15 .40
74 Khalil Greene .15 .40
75 Barry Zito .15 .40
76 Wilson Valdez .15 .40
77 Nick Green .15 .40
78 Bucky Jacobsen .15 .40
79 Keith Foulke .15 .40
80 Sean Burroughs .15 .40
81 Carlos Zambrano .25 .60
82 Orlando Cabrera .15 .40
83 Shigetoshi Hasegawa .15 .40
84 Troy Glaus .15 .40
85 Mike Sweeney .15 .40
86 Jason Giambi .15 .40
87 Derrek Lee .15 .40
88 Carlos Delgado .15 .40
89 Kazuo Matsui .15 .40
90 Lew Ford .15 .40
91 Akinori Otsuka .15 .40
92 Bobby Crosby .15 .40
93 Jose Reyes .25 .60
94 Jose Vidro .15 .40
95 Shingo Takatsu .15 .40
96 Sean Casey .15 .40
97 Tim Olson .15 .40
98 Jeff Suppan .15 .40
99 Rafael Palmeiro .25 .60
100 Esteban Loaiza .15 .40
101 Brian Roberts .15 .40
102 Jack Wilson .15 .40
103 Eric Chavez .15 .40
104 Eric Milton .15 .40
105 Albert Pujols 1.00 2.50
106 Jake Peavy .15 .40
107 Ivan Rodriguez .25 .60
108 Chad Cordero .15 .40
109 Jody Gerut .15 .40
110 Chipper Jones .40 1.00
111 Barry Larkin .25 .60
112 Alfonso Soriano .25 .60
113 Alex Rodriguez .60 1.50
114 Paul Lo Duca .15 .40
115 Jim Edmonds .25 .60
116 Aramis Ramirez .15 .40
117 Lance Berkman .25 .60
118 Johnny Damon .25 .60
119 Aubrey Huff .15 .40
120 Mark Mulder .15 .40
121 Sammy Sosa .40 1.00
122 Mark Prior .25 .60
123 Shannon Stewart .15 .40
124 Manny Ramirez .40 1.00
125 Jim Thome .25 .60
126 Doug Devore .15 .40
127 Vladimir Guerrero .40 1.00
128 Ken Harvey .15 .40
129 Jacob Cruz .15 .40
130 Ken Griffey Jr. .60 1.50
131 Greg Maddux .60 1.50
132 Derek Lowe .15 .40
133 Craig Monroe .15 .40
134 David Ortiz .40 1.00
135 Dontrelle Willis .15 .40
136 Tom Gordon .15 .40
137 David Dellucci .15 .40
138 Vance Wilson .15 .40
139 Milton Bradley .15 .40
140 Ichiro Suzuki .60 1.50
141 Victor Martinez .25 .60
142 Wade Miller .15 .40
143 Francisco Rodriguez .25 .60
144 Roy Oswalt .25 .60
145 Carlos Lee .15 .40
146 Kazuhisa Ishii .15 .40
147 Tim Hudson .25 .60
148 Travis Hafner .15 .40
149 Jermaine Dye .15 .40
150 Steve Finley .15 .40
151 Justin Verlander RC 6.00 15.00
152 Yadier Molina .25 .60
153 Andy Green .15 .40
154 Nick Swisher .40 1.00
155 Clint Nageotte .15 .40
156 Grady Sizemore .25 .60
157 Gavin Floyd .15 .40
158 Josh Kroeger .15 .40
159 Russ Adams .15 .40
160 Jeff Baker .15 .40
161 Dioner Navarro .15 .40
162 Shawn Hill .15 .40
163 Ryan Howard .75 2.00
164 Scott Proctor .15 .40
165 Jason Kubel .15 .40
166 Jose Lopez .15 .40
167 Ryan Church .15 .40
168 Yhency Brazoban .15 .40
169 Jeff Francis .15 .40
170 Angel Guzman .15 .40
171 John Van Benschoten .15 .40
172 Adrian Gonzalez .25 .60
173 Casey Kotchman .15 .40
174 David Wright .60 1.50
175 B.J. Upton .25 .60
176 Dallas McPherson .15 .40
177 Rene Rivera .15 .40
178 Denny Bautista .15 .40
179 Logan Kensing .15 .40
180 Matt Peterson .15 .40
181 Jeremy Reed .15 .40
182 Jairo Garcia .15 .40
183 Val Majewski .15 .40
184 Victor Diaz .15 .40
185 Dave Krynzel .15 .40
186 Ron Cey .20 .50
187 Bill Madlock .20 .50
188 Dave Stewart .20 .50
189 Billy Ripken .20 .50
190 Gary Carter .20 .50
191 Darryl Strawberry .20 .50
192 Dave Parker .20 .50
193 Ron Guidry .20 .50
194 Gaylord Perry .20 .50
195 Fred Lynn .20 .50
196 Jack Morris .20 .50
197 Steve Garvey .20 .50
198 Andre Dawson .30 .75
199 Nolan Ryan 1.25 3.00
200 Paul Molitor .50 1.25

2005 Playoff Prestige Red Foil

*RED FOIL: 8X TO 20X BASIC
RANDOM INSERTS IN RETAIL PACKS
STATED PRINT RUN 25 SERIAL #'d SETS
NO RC PRICING DUE TO SCARCITY

2005 Playoff Prestige Xtra Bases Black

*BLACK: 8X TO 20X BASIC
RANDOM INSERTS IN PACKS
STATED PRINT RUN 25 SERIAL #'d SETS
NO RC PRICING DUE TO SCARCITY

2005 Playoff Prestige Xtra Bases Green

*GREEN: 5X TO 12X BASIC
*GREEN: 3X TO 8X BASIC RC's
RANDOM INSERTS IN PACKS
STATED PRINT RUN 50 SERIAL #'d SETS

2005 Playoff Prestige Xtra Bases Purple

*PURPLE: 4X TO 10X BASIC
*PURPLE: 2.5X TO 6X BASIC RC's
RANDOM INSERTS IN PACKS
STATED PRINT RUN 100 SERIAL #'d SETS

2005 Playoff Prestige Xtra Bases Red

*RED: 3X TO 8X BASIC
*RED: 2X TO 5X BASIC RC's
RANDOM INSERTS IN PACKS
STATED PRINT RUN 150 SERIAL #'d SETS

2005 Playoff Prestige Autographs

OVERALL AU-GU ODDS 1:12
SP INFO PROVIDED BY DONRUSS
SP's APPROXIMATELY 3X TOUGHER
20 Robb Quinlan 4.00 10.00
28 J.J. Putz 4.00 10.00
58 Brandon Inge SP 6.00 15.00
67 Joe Kennedy 4.00 10.00
76 Wilson Valdez 4.00 10.00
77 Nick Green 4.00 10.00
78 Bucky Jacobsen 4.00 10.00
97 Tim Olson 4.00 10.00
98 Jeff Suppan SP 10.00 25.00
126 Doug Devore 4.00 10.00
129 Jacob Cruz 4.00 10.00
133 Craig Monroe 4.00 10.00
138 Vance Wilson 4.00 10.00
153 Andy Green 4.00 10.00
164 Scott Proctor 4.00 10.00

2005 Playoff Prestige Signature Xtra Bases Black

OVERALL AU-GU ODDS 1:12
PRINT RUNS B/WN 3-10 COPIES PER
NO PRICING DUE TO SCARCITY

2005 Playoff Prestige Signature Xtra Bases Purple

*PURPLE p/r 50: .4X TO 1X AUTO
*PURPLE p/r 50: .4X TO 1X AUTO SP
*PURPLE p/r 25: .6X TO 1.5X AUTO
OVERALL AU-GU ODDS 1:12
PRINT RUNS B/WN 5-50 COPIES PER
NO PRICING ON QTY OF 10 OR LESS
6 Melvin Mora/25 10.00 25.00
8 Brad Penny/50 4.00 10.00
13 Carl Crawford/25 10.00 25.00
32 Danny Graves/50 4.00 10.00
36 Joe Nathan/50 10.00 25.00
37 Chone Figgins/50 4.00 10.00
39 Brett Myers/50 6.00 15.00
41 Danny Kolb/50 4.00 10.00
43 Francisco Cordero/50 4.00 10.00
52 C.C. Sabathia/25 10.00 25.00
54 Octavio Dotel/50 6.00 15.00
56 Mark Buehrle/25 20.00 50.00
59 Dewon Brazelton/50 4.00 10.00
60 Ryan Wagner/50 4.00 10.00
62 Laynce Nix/50 4.00 10.00
63 Jason Bay/50 6.00 15.00
65 Jacque Jones/25 10.00 25.00
71 Lyle Overbay/25 6.00 15.00
73 Johnny Estrada/50 4.00 10.00
79 Keith Foulke/50 10.00 25.00
81 Carlos Zambrano/25 15.00 40.00
82 Orlando Cabrera/25 10.00 25.00
90 Lew Ford/50 4.00 10.00
92 Bobby Crosby/50 6.00 15.00
100 Esteban Loaiza/50 6.00 15.00
101 Brian Roberts/50 6.00 15.00
102 Jack Wilson/50 6.00 15.00
106 Jake Peavy/25 15.00 40.00
108 Chad Cordero/50 6.00 15.00
109 Jody Gerut/25 6.00 15.00
128 Ken Harvey/50 4.00 10.00
136 Tom Gordon/50 6.00 15.00
137 David Dellucci/50 10.00 25.00
139 Milton Bradley/50 6.00 15.00
141 Victor Martinez/25 10.00 25.00
142 Wade Miller/50 6.00 15.00
145 Carlos Lee/25 10.00 25.00
148 Travis Hafner/50 6.00 15.00
149 Jermaine Dye/50 6.00 15.00
152 Yadier Molina/25 10.00 25.00
161 Dioner Navarro/50 6.00 15.00
162 Shawn Hill/50 4.00 10.00
165 Jason Kubel/50 4.00 10.00
168 Yhency Brazoban/50 4.00 10.00
170 Angel Guzman/50 4.00 10.00
172 Adrian Gonzalez/50 10.00 25.00
173 Casey Kotchman/50 6.00 15.00
187 Bill Madlock/25 10.00 25.00
189 Billy Ripken/25 6.00 15.00
190 Gary Carter/25 10.00 25.00
191 Darryl Strawberry/25 10.00 25.00
192 Dave Parker/25 15.00 40.00
195 Fred Lynn/25 10.00 25.00
196 Jack Morris/25 10.00 25.00
198 Andre Dawson/25 10.00 25.00

2005 Playoff Prestige Changing Stripes

STATED ODDS 1:8
*FOIL: 1.25X TO 3X BASIC
FOIL PRINT RUN 100 SERIAL #'d SETS
*HOLO-FOIL: 2.5X TO 6X BASIC
HOLO-FOIL PRINT RUN 25 SERIAL #'d SETS
FOIL/HOLO-FOIL RANDOM IN PACKS
1 I.Rod Marlins-Tigers .60 1.50
2 Roger Clemens Yanks-Astros 1.25 3.00
3 Curt Schilling D'backs-Sox .60 1.50
4 Alex Rodriguez Rgr-Yanks 1.50 4.00
5 Greg Maddux Braves-Cubs 1.50 4.00
6 Juan Gonzalez Rgr-Royals .40 1.00
7 Pedro Martinez Dgr-Expos .60 1.50
8 Roberto Alomar Indians-Mets .60 1.50
9 Randy Johnson Expos-M's 1.00 2.50
10 Ken Griffey Jr. M's-Reds 1.50 4.00
11 Carlos Beltran Royals-Astros .40 1.00
12 Andy Pettitte Yanks-Astros .60 1.50
13 Tom Glavine Braves-Mets .60 1.50
14 Miguel Tejada A's-O's .60 1.50
15 Alfonso Soriano Yanks-Rgr .60 1.50

16 Shannon Stewart Jays-Twins .40 1.00
17 Nomar Garciaparra Sox-Cubs 1.00 2.50
18 Jeff Kent Giants-Astros .40 1.00
19 David Ortiz Twins-Sox 1.00 2.50
20 Sean Casey Indians-Reds .40 1.00
21 Rickey Henderson Mets-M's .60 1.50
22 Carlton Fisk R.Sox-W.Sox .60 1.50
23 Phil Niekro Braves-Yanks .40 1.00
24 Dale Murphy Braves-Phils .40 1.00
25 Reggie Jackson A's-Yanks 1.00 2.50

2005 Playoff Prestige Changing Stripes Material Dual Jersey

OVERALL AU-GU ODDS 1:12
PRINT RUNS B/WN 12-250 COPIES PER
NO PRICING ON QTY OF 12
1 I.Rod Marlins-Tigers/250 6.00 15.00
2 R.Clemens Yanks-Astros/50 10.00 25.00
3 C.Schilling D'backs-Sox/250 6.00 15.00
6 J.Gonzalez Rgr-Royals/250 4.00 10.00
7 P.Martinez Dgr-Expos/100 8.00 20.00
8 R.Alomar Indians-Mets/250 6.00 15.00
9 R.Johnson Expos-M's/100 8.00 20.00
11 C.Beltran Royals-Astros/100 5.00 12.00
12 A.Pettitte Yanks-Astros/250 6.00 15.00
13 T.Glavine Braves-Mets/50 10.00 25.00
14 M.Tejada A's-O's/250 4.00 10.00
15 A.Soriano Yanks-Rgr/100 5.00 12.00
16 S.Stewart Jays-Twins/100 5.00 12.00
18 J.Kent Giants-Astros/12
19 D.Ortiz Twins-Sox/100 8.00 20.00
20 S.Casey Indians-Reds/50 6.00 15.00
21 R.Henderson Mets-M's/250 8.00 20.00
22 C.Fisk R.Sox-W.Sox Jkt/250 8.00 20.00
23 P.Niekro Braves-Yanks/250 5.00 12.00
24 D.Murphy Braves-Phils/250 8.00 20.00
25 R.Jack A's Jkt-Yanks/100 10.00 25.00

2005 Playoff Prestige Changing Stripes Material Dual Jersey Prime

*PRIME p/r 25: 1.25X TO 3X JSY p/r 250
*PRIME p/r 25: 1X TO 2.5X JSY p/r 100
*PRIME p/r 25: .75X TO 2X JSY p/r 50
OVERALL AU-GU ODDS 1:12
PRINT RUNS B/WN 10-25 COPIES PER
NO PRICING ON QTY OF 10
5 G.Maddux Braves-Cubs/25 20.00 50.00

2005 Playoff Prestige Connections

STATED ODDS 1:8
*FOIL: 1.5X TO 4X BASIC
FOIL PRINT RUN 100 SERIAL #'d SETS
*HOLO-FOIL: 3X TO 8X BASIC
HOLO-FOIL PRINT RUN 25 SERIAL #'d SETS
FOIL/HOLO-FOIL RANDOM IN PACKS
1 Josh Beckett .60 1.50
Dontrelle Willis
2 Andruw Jones .40 1.00
Chipper Jones
3 Kazuo Matsui .60 1.50
Jose Reyes
4 Bobby Abreu .60 1.50
Jim Thome
5 Jeff Bagwell .60 1.50
Lance Berkman
6 Roger Clemens .60 1.50
Roy Oswalt
7 Scott Rolen .60 1.50
Larry Walker
8 Albert Pujols 2.50 6.00
Jim Edmonds
9 Greg Maddux 1.50 4.00
Sammy Sosa
10 Mark Prior 1.00 2.50
Nomar Garciaparra
11 Barry Larkin .60 1.50
Sean Casey
12 Shawn Green .40 1.00
Adrian Beltre
13 Alex Rodriguez 2.50 6.00
Derek Jeter
14 Jason Varitek 1.00 2.50
Manny Ramirez
15 Miguel Tejada .60 1.50
Javy Lopez
16 B.J. Upton .60 1.50
Carl Crawford
17 Frank Thomas .60 1.50
Paul Konerko
18 Joe Mauer 1.00 2.50
Justin Morneau
19 Victor Martinez .60 1.50
Jody Gerut
20 Bobby Crosby .40 1.00
Barry Zito
21 Mark Teixeira 1.00 2.50
Hank Blalock
22 Reggie Jackson 1.00 2.50
Rod Carew
23 Rickey Henderson 1.25 3.00
Tony Gwynn
24 Tom Seaver 1.00 2.50
Johnny Bench
25 Don Mattingly 2.00 5.00
Dave Righetti

2005 Playoff Prestige Connections Material Dual Bat

*BAT p/r 250: .4X TO 1X JSY p/r 250
*BAT p/r 250: .3X TO .8X JSY p/r 100
*BAT p/r 100: .5X TO 1.2X JSY p/r 250
*BAT p/r 100: .4X TO 1X JSY p/r 100
*BAT p/r 100: .3X TO .8X JSY p/r 50
OVERALL AU-GU ODDS 1:12
PRINT RUNS B/WN 25-250 COPIES PER
10 Mark Prior 6.00 15.00
Nomar Garciaparra/100
19 Victor Martinez 6.00 15.00
Jody Gerut/25

2005 Playoff Prestige Connections Material Dual Jersey

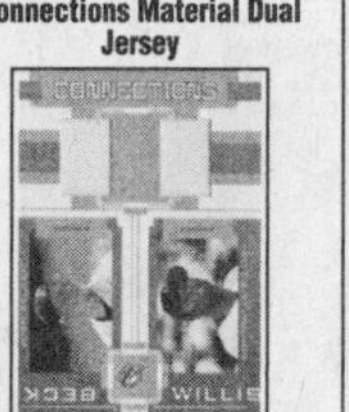

PRINT RUNS B/WN 10-250 COPIES PER
NO PRICING ON QTY OF 10
*PRIME p/r 25: 1X TO 2.5X JSY p/r 250
*PRIME p/r 25: .75X TO 2X JSY p/r 100
PRIME PRINT RUNS B/WN 10-25 PER
NO PRIME PRICING ON QTY OF 10
OVERALL AU-GU ODDS 1:12
1 Josh Beckett 3.00 8.00
Dontrelle Willis/250
2 Andruw Jones 5.00 12.00
Chipper Jones/250
3 Kazuo Matsui 6.00 15.00
Jose Reyes/100
4 Bobby Abreu 5.00 12.00
Jim Thome/250
5 Jeff Bagwell 5.00 12.00
Lance Berkman/250
6 Roger Clemens 6.00 15.00
Roy Oswalt/250
8 Albert Pujols 10.00 25.00
Jim Edmonds/250
11 Barry Larkin 8.00 20.00
Sean Casey/50
12 Shawn Green 3.00 8.00
Adrian Beltre/250
14 Jason Varitek 8.00 20.00
Manny Ramirez/50
15 Miguel Tejada 5.00 12.00
Javy Lopez/50
17 Frank Thomas Pants 5.00 12.00
Paul Konerko/250
19 Victor Martinez
Jody Gerut/10
20 Bobby Crosby 3.00 8.00
Barry Zito/250
21 Mark Teixeira 6.00 15.00
Hank Blalock/100
22 Reggie Jackson 6.00 15.00
Rod Carew Jkt/250
23 Rickey Henderson 10.00 25.00
Tony Gwynn/250
24 Tom Seaver 8.00 20.00
Johnny Bench Pants/100
25 Don Mattingly 12.50 30.00
Dave Righetti/250

2005 Playoff Prestige Diamond Heritage

STATED ODDS 1:12
1 Pedro Martinez .60 1.50
2 Mark Teixeira 1.00 2.50
3 Lance Berkman .60 1.50
4 Vladimir Guerrero 1.00 2.50
5 Albert Pujols 2.50 6.00
6 Roger Clemens 1.25 3.00
7 Manny Ramirez 1.00 2.50
8 Mike Piazza 1.00 2.50
9 Jim Thome .60 1.50
10 Mark Prior .60 1.50
11 Gary Sheffield .40 1.00
12 Sammy Sosa 1.00 2.50
13 Tim Hudson .60 1.50
14 Hideki Matsui 1.50 4.00
15 Jim Edmonds .60 1.50

2005 Playoff Prestige Diamond Heritage Material Jersey

STATED PRINT RUN 100 SERIAL #'d SETS
*BAT: .4X TO 1X JSY
BAT PRINT RUN 100 SERIAL #'d SETS
OVERALL AU-GU ODDS 1:12
1 Pedro Martinez 4.00 10.00
2 Mark Teixeira 4.00 10.00
3 Lance Berkman 3.00 8.00
4 Vladimir Guerrero 4.00 10.00
5 Albert Pujols 10.00 25.00
6 Roger Clemens 6.00 15.00
7 Manny Ramirez 4.00 10.00
8 Mike Piazza 4.00 10.00
9 Jim Thome 4.00 10.00
10 Mark Prior 4.00 10.00
11 Gary Sheffield 3.00 8.00
12 Sammy Sosa 4.00 10.00
13 Tim Hudson 3.00 8.00
14 Hideki Matsui Pants 10.00 25.00
15 Jim Edmonds 3.00 8.00

2005 Playoff Prestige Fans of the Game

STATED ODDS 1:24
1 Tony Hawk 1.25 3.00
2 Tia Carrere .75 2.00
3 Matthew Modine .75 2.00

2005 Playoff Prestige Fans of the Game Signature Silver

*GOLD: .6X TO 1.2X BASIC
GOLD PRINT RUN 100 SERIAL #'d SETS
*PLATINUM: .75X TO 1.5X BASIC
PLATINUM PRINT RUN 50 SERIAL #'d SETS
OVERALL AU-GU ODDS 1:12
1 Tony Hawk 40.00 80.00
2 Tia Carrere 40.00 80.00
3 Matthew Modine 15.00 40.00

2005 Playoff Prestige League Leaders Single

STATED ODDS 1:21
*FOIL: 1.5X TO 4X BASIC
FOIL PRINT RUN 100 SERIAL #'d SETS
*HOLO-FOIL: 3X TO 8X BASIC
HOLO-FOIL PRINT RUN 25 SERIAL #'d SETS
FOIL/HOLO-FOIL RANDOM IN PACKS
1 Gary Sheffield .40 1.00
2 Ben Sheets .40 1.00
3 Adrian Beltre .40 1.00
4 Scott Rolen .60 1.50
5 George Brett 2.00 5.00
6 Johan Santana 1.00 2.50
7 Manny Ramirez 1.00 2.50
8 Cal Ripken 4.00 10.00
9 Carlos Zambrano .60 1.50
10 Tony Gwynn 1.25 3.00

2005 Playoff Prestige League Leaders Single Material Bat

*BAT: .4X TO 1X JSY p/r 250
*BAT: .6X TO 1.5X JSY p/r 50
OVERALL AU-GU ODDS 1:12
STATED PRINT RUN 250 SERIAL #'d SETS

2005 Playoff Prestige League Leaders Single Material Jersey

OVERALL AU-GU ODDS 1:12
PRINT RUNS B/WN 25-250 COPIES PER
1 Gary Sheffield/250 3.00 8.00
2 Ben Sheets/250 3.00 8.00
3 Adrian Beltre/50 4.00 10.00
4 Scott Rolen/250 4.00 10.00
5 George Brett/250 6.00 15.00
6 Johan Santana/25 10.00 25.00
7 Manny Ramirez/250 4.00 10.00
8 Cal Ripken/250 12.50 30.00
9 Carlos Zambrano/250 3.00 8.00
10 Tony Gwynn/250 4.00 10.00

2005 Playoff Prestige League Leaders Double

STATED ODDS 1:39
*FOIL: 1.25X TO 3X BASIC
FOIL PRINT RUN 100 SERIAL #'d SETS
*HOLO-FOIL: 2.5X TO 6X BASIC
HOLO-FOIL PRINT RUN 25 SERIAL #'d SETS
FOIL/HOLO-FOIL RANDOM IN PACKS
1 Tim Hudson .60 1.50
Roy Oswalt
2 Ivan Rodriguez .60 1.50
Todd Helton
3 Mark Teixeira 1.00 2.50
Jim Edmonds
4 Nolan Ryan 2.50 6.00
Roger Clemens
5 Sammy Sosa 1.00 2.50
Troy Glaus

2005 Playoff Prestige League Leaders Double Material Bat

OVERALL AU-GU ODDS 1:12
STATED PRINT RUN 250 SERIAL #'d SETS
1 Tim Hudson 4.00 10.00
Roy Oswalt
2 Ivan Rodriguez 6.00 15.00
Todd Helton
3 Mark Teixeira 6.00 15.00
Jim Edmonds
4 Nolan Ryan 12.50 30.00
Roger Clemens
5 Sammy Sosa 6.00 15.00
Troy Glaus

2005 Playoff Prestige League Leaders Double Material Jersey

*JSY p/r 250: .4X TO 1X BAT
*JSY p/r 100: .5X TO 1.2X BAT
*JSY p/r 50: .6X TO 1.5X BAT
OVERALL AU-GU ODDS 1:12
PRINT RUNS B/WN 50-250 COPIES PER

2005 Playoff Prestige League Leaders Quad

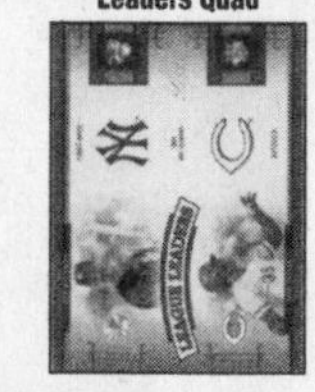

STATED ODDS 1:39
*FOIL: 1X TO 2.5X BASIC
FOIL PRINT RUN 100 SERIAL #'d SETS
*HOLO-FOIL: 2X TO 5X BASIC
HOLO-FOIL PRINT RUN 25 SERIAL #'d SETS
FOIL/HOLO-FOIL RANDOM IN PACKS
1 Wade Boggs 1.00 2.50
Paul Molitor
Alan Trammell
Kirby Puckett
2 Dale Murphy 2.00 5.00
Mike Schmidt
Gary Carter
Darryl Strawberry
3 Jose Canseco 1.00 2.50
Kirby Puckett
Will Clark
Darryl Strawberry
4 Pedro Martinez 1.25 3.00
Kevin Brown
Randy Johnson
Roger Clemens
5 Don Mattingly 2.00 5.00
Dave Parker
Eddie Murray
Dale Murphy

2005 Playoff Prestige League Leaders Quad Material Jersey

STATED PRINT RUN 100 SERIAL #'d SETS
*BAT: .4X TO 1X JSY
BAT PRINT RUN 100 SERIAL #'d SETS
OVERALL AU-GU ODDS 1:12
1 Wade Boggs 15.00 40.00
Paul Molitor
Alan Trammell
Kirby Puckett
2 Dale Murphy 15.00 40.00
Mike Schmidt
Gary Carter
Darryl Strawberry Pants
3 Jose Canseco 15.00 40.00
Kirby Puckett
Will Clark
Darryl Strawberry Pants
4 Pedro Martinez 15.00 40.00
Kevin Brown
Randy Johnson Pants
Roger Clemens
5 Don Mattingly 20.00 50.00
Dave Parker
Eddie Murray
Dale Murphy

2005 Playoff Prestige Playoff Champions Combos Division

*DIVISION: .4X TO 1X WILD CARD
OVERALL PC COMBO ODDS 1:93

2005 Playoff Prestige Playoff Champions Combos Wild Card

WILD CARD STATED ODDS 1:391
*DIVISION COMBO: .4X TO 1X BASIC
*LEAGUE COMBO: .4X TO 1X BASIC
*WORLD SERIES COMBO: .4X TO 1X BASIC
OVERALL PC COMBO ODDS 1:93
EXCHANGE DEADLINE 04/15/06
1 Andruw Jones .75 2.00
Chipper Jones
Johnny Estrada
2 Miguel Cabrera 2.00 5.00
Josh Beckett
Dontrelle Willis
3 Chad Cordero .75 2.00
Brad Wilkerson
Nick Johnson
4 Jim Thome 1.25 3.00
Bobby Abreu
Chase Utley
5 Mike Piazza 3.00 8.00
Kazuo Matsui
David Wright
6 Albert Pujols 5.00 12.00
Scott Rolen
Jim Edmonds
7 Kerry Wood 1.25 3.00
Mark Prior
Carlos Zambrano
8 Ben Sheets .75 2.00
Geoff Jenkins
Lyle Overbay
9 Kip Wells .75 2.00
Jack Wilson
Jason Bay
10 Austin Kearns 1.25 3.00
Adam Dunn
Ken Griffey Jr.
11 Jeff Bagwell 1.25 3.00
Lance Berkman
Roy Oswalt
12 Jason Jennings 2.00 5.00
Matt Holliday
Todd Helton
13 Eric Gagne 1.25 3.00
Jason Werth
Milton Bradley
14 Alex Cintron 1.25 3.00
Brandon Webb
Luis Gonzalez
15 Jason Schmidt 4.00 10.00
Edgardo Alfonzo
Kirk Rueter
16 Khalil Greene .75 2.00
Jake Peavy
Trevor Hoffman
17 Manny Ramirez 2.00 5.00
Curt Schilling
David Ortiz
18 Miguel Tejada 1.25 3.00
Melvin Mora
Javy Lopez
19 Roy Halladay 2.00 5.00
Alexis Rios
Gabe Gross
20 Alex Rodriguez 5.00 12.00
Derek Jeter
Hideki Matsui
21 B.J. Upton 1.25 3.00
Scott Kazmir
Carl Crawford
22 Frank Thomas 2.00 5.00
Shingo Takatsu
Aaron Rowand
23 Victor Martinez 1.25 3.00
C.C. Sabathia
Travis Hafner
24 Torii Hunter 2.00 5.00
Johan Santana
Justin Morneau
25 Zack Greinke 1.25 3.00
Mike Sweeney
Ken Harvey
26 Ivan Rodriguez 1.25 3.00
Jeremy Bonderman
Carlos Guillen
27 Rich Harden .75 2.00
Bobby Crosby
Barry Zito
28 Bret Boone 3.00 8.00
Ichiro Suzuki
Jeremy Reed
29 Michael Young 1.25 3.00
Mark Teixeira
Hank Blalock
30 Vladimir Guerrero 2.00 5.00
Darin Erstad
Garret Anderson

2005 Playoff Prestige Playoff MLB Game-Worn Jersey Collection

STATED ODDS 1:8 EXCEL RETAIL

2005 Playoff Prestige Prestigious Pros Blue

STATED PRINT RUN 900 SERIAL #'d SETS
BLACK PRINT RUN 10 SERIAL #'d SETS
NO BLACK PRICING DUE TO SCARCITY
*BRONZE: 1.25X TO 3X BLUE
BRONZE PRINT RUN 100 SERIAL #'d SETS
*GOLD: 1.5X TO 4X BLUE
GOLD PRINT RUN 50 SERIAL #'d SETS
*GREEN: .75X TO 2X BLUE
GREEN PRINT RUN 350 SERIAL #'d SETS
*ORANGE: .6X TO 1.5X BLUE
ORANGE PRINT RUN 500 SERIAL #'d SETS
*PLATINUM: 2.5X TO 6X BLUE
PLATINUM PRINT RUN 25 SERIAL #'d SETS
*PURPLE: 1X TO 2.5X BLUE
PURPLE PRINT RUN 200 SERIAL #'d SETS
*RED: .5X TO 1.2X BLUE
RED PRINT RUN 700 SERIAL #'d SETS
*SILVER: 1.25X TO 3X BLUE
SILVER PRINT RUN 75 SERIAL #'d SETS
1 Ozzie Smith 1.50 4.00
2 Derek Jeter 2.50 6.00
3 Eric Chavez .40 1.00
4 Paul Molitor 1.00 2.50
5 Jeff Bagwell .60 1.50
6 Melvin Mora .40 1.00
7 Craig Biggio .60 1.50
8 Cal Ripken 4.00 10.00
9 Hank Blalock .40 1.00
10 Miguel Tejada .60 1.50
11 Jacque Jones .40 1.00
12 Alfonso Soriano .60 1.50
13 Omar Vizquel .60 1.50
14 Paul Konerko .60 1.50
15 Tim Hudson .60 1.50
16 Garret Anderson .40 1.00
17 Lance Berkman .60 1.50
18 Randy Johnson 1.00 2.50
19 Robin Yount 1.00 2.50
20 Mark Mulder .40 1.00
21 Sean Casey .40 1.00
22 Jim Palmer .40 1.00
23 Don Mattingly 2.00 5.00
24 Manny Ramirez 1.00 2.50
25 Rafael Palmeiro .60 1.50
26 Vernon Wells .40 1.00
27 Vladimir Guerrero 1.00 2.50
28 Ken Harvey .40 1.00
29 Rod Carew .60 1.50
30 Nolan Ryan 2.50 6.00
31 Mike Piazza 1.00 2.50
32 Steve Carlton .40 1.00
33 Miguel Cabrera 1.00 2.50
34 Kerry Wood .40 1.00
35 Mike Mussina .60 1.50
36 Gaylord Perry .40 1.00
37 Gary Sheffield .40 1.00
38 Curt Schilling .60 1.50
39 Don Sutton .40 1.00
40 Roger Clemens 1.25 3.00
41 Victor Martinez .60 1.50
42 Jason Giambi .40 1.00
43 Dennis Eckersley .40 1.00
44 Adam Dunn .60 1.50
45 Pedro Martinez .60 1.50
46 Tony Perez .40 1.00
47 Tom Glavine .60 1.50
48 Torii Hunter .40 1.00
49 Hideo Nomo 1.00 2.50
50 Scott Rolen .60 1.50
51 Ichiro Suzuki 1.50 4.00
52 C.C. Sabathia .60 1.50
53 George Brett 2.00 5.00
54 David Ortiz 1.00 2.50
55 Hideki Matsui 1.50 4.00
56 Nomar Garciaparra 1.00 2.50
57 Johan Santana 1.00 2.50
58 Phil Niekro .40 1.00
59 Dontrelle Willis .40 1.00
60 Magglio Ordonez .40 1.00
61 Livan Hernandez .40 1.00
62 Edgar Renteria .40 1.00
63 Todd Helton .60 1.50
64 Carlos Beltran .40 1.00
65 Sammy Sosa 1.00 2.50
66 Albert Pujols 2.50 6.00
67 Mike Lowell .40 1.00
68 Mark Prior .60 1.50
69 Ivan Rodriguez .60 1.50
70 Jake Peavy .40 1.00
71 Jim Thome .60 1.50
72 Mark Teixeira 1.00 2.50
73 Shawn Green .40 1.00
74 Rollie Fingers .40 1.00
75 Barry Zito .40 1.00
76 Jose Vidro .40 1.00
77 Ben Sheets .40 1.00
78 Roy Halladay 1.00 2.50
79 Frank Thomas 1.00 2.50
80 Chipper Jones 1.00 2.50
81 Jason Bay .40 1.00
82 Tony Gwynn 1.25 3.00
83 Shannon Stewart .40 1.00
84 Carl Crawford .60 1.50
85 Andruw Jones .40 1.00
86 Greg Maddux 1.50 4.00
87 Barry Larkin .60 1.50
88 Alex Rodriguez 1.50 4.00
89 Rickey Henderson .60 1.50
90 Troy Glaus .40 1.00
91 Roy Oswalt .40 1.00
92 Michael Young .60 1.50
93 Carlos Lee .40 1.00
94 Jim Edmonds .60 1.50
95 Fergie Jenkins .40 1.00
96 Paul Lo Duca .40 1.00
97 Aubrey Huff .40 1.00
98 Ken Griffey Jr. 1.50 4.00
99 Carlos Delgado .40 1.00
100 Mike Schmidt 2.00 5.00

2005 Playoff Prestige Prestigious Pros Material Bat Silver

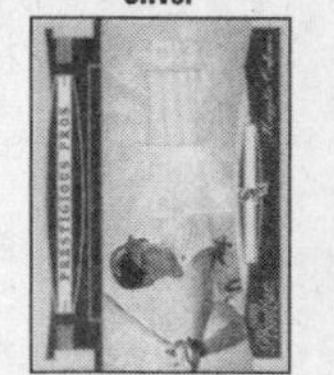

*BAT p/r 50: .4X TO 1X JSY p/r 50
*BAT p/r 50: .3X TO .8X JSY p/r 25
*BAT p/r 25: .4X TO 1X JSY p/r 25
OVERALL AU-GU ODDS 1:12
PRINT RUNS B/WN 5-50 COPIES PER
NO PRICING ON QTY OF 10 OR LESS
9 Hank Blalock/25 5.00 12.00
16 Garret Anderson/25 5.00 12.00
25 Rafael Palmeiro/25 8.00 20.00
44 Adam Dunn/25 5.00 12.00
47 Tom Glavine/25 8.00 20.00
48 Torii Hunter/50 4.00 10.00
54 David Ortiz/50 6.00 15.00
56 Nomar Garciaparra/25 10.00 25.00
64 Carlos Beltran/25 5.00 12.00
67 Mike Lowell/25 5.00 12.00
69 Ivan Rodriguez/50 6.00 15.00
76 Jose Vidro/25 5.00 12.00
83 Shannon Stewart/25 5.00 12.00
91 Roy Oswalt/25 5.00 12.00
96 Paul Lo Duca/25 5.00 12.00

2005 Playoff Prestige Prestigious Pros Material Jersey Gold

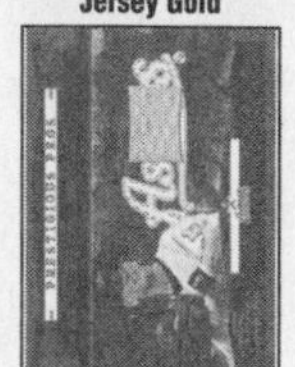

PRINT RUNS B/WN 5-50 COPIES PER
NO PRICING ON QTY OF 10 OR LESS
PATCH PLATINUM PRINTS B/WN 5-10 PER
NO PATCH PLAT.PRICING AVAILABLE
OVERALL AU-GU ODDS 1:12
1 Ozzie Smith/50 12.50 30.00
3 Eric Chavez/25 5.00 12.00
4 Paul Molitor/50 4.00 10.00
5 Jeff Bagwell/50 6.00 15.00
6 Melvin Mora/25 5.00 12.00
7 Craig Biggio/25 8.00 20.00
8 Cal Ripken/50 30.00 60.00
9 Hank Blalock/10
10 Miguel Tejada/25 5.00 12.00

11 Jacque Jones/10
12 Alfonso Soriano/10
13 Omar Vizquel/25 8.00 20.00
14 Paul Konerko/25 5.00 12.00
15 Tim Hudson/25 5.00 12.00
16 Garret Anderson/10
17 Lance Berkman/50 4.00 10.00
18 Randy Johnson/25 10.00 25.00
19 Robin Yount/50 10.00 25.00
20 Mark Mulder/20 5.00 12.00
21 Sean Casey/25 5.00 12.00
22 Jim Palmer/50 4.00 10.00
23 Don Mattingly/50 15.00 40.00
24 Manny Ramirez/10
25 Rafael Palmeiro/10
26 Vernon Wells/25 5.00 12.00
27 Vladimir Guerrero/25 10.00 25.00
28 Ken Harvey/25 5.00 12.00
29 Rod Carew/50 6.00 15.00
30 Nolan Ryan/50 20.00 50.00
31 Mike Piazza/25 10.00 25.00
32 Steve Carlton/50 4.00 10.00
33 Miguel Cabrera/10
34 Kerry Wood/25 5.00 12.00
35 Mike Mussina/25 8.00 20.00
36 Gaylord Perry/50 4.00 10.00
37 Gary Sheffield/25 5.00 12.00
38 Curt Schilling/25 8.00 20.00
39 Don Sutton/50 4.00 10.00
40 Roger Clemens/25 12.50 30.00
41 Victor Martinez/25 5.00 12.00
42 Jason Giambi/25 5.00 12.00
43 Dennis Eckersley/50 4.00 10.00
44 Adam Dunn/10
45 Pedro Martinez/25 8.00 20.00
46 Tony Perez/50 4.00 10.00
47 Tom Glavine/5
48 Torii Hunter/10
49 Hideo Nomo/25 10.00 25.00
50 Scott Rolen/25 8.00 20.00
52 C.C. Sabathia/25 5.00 12.00
53 George Brett/50 15.00 40.00
54 David Ortiz/10
55 Hideki Matsui/25 20.00 50.00
57 Johan Santana/5
58 Phil Niekro/50 4.00 10.00
59 Dontrelle Willis/25 5.00 12.00
60 Magglio Ordonez/25 5.00 12.00
61 Livan Hernandez/25 5.00 12.00
62 Edgar Renteria/25 5.00 12.00
63 Todd Helton/25 8.00 20.00
64 Carlos Beltran/10
65 Sammy Sosa/25 10.00 25.00
66 Albert Pujols/25 15.00 40.00
67 Mike Lowell/10
68 Mark Prior/25 8.00 20.00
71 Jim Thome/25 8.00 20.00
72 Mark Teixeira/25 8.00 20.00
73 Shawn Green/25 5.00 12.00
74 Rollie Fingers/50 4.00 10.00
75 Barry Zito/10
76 Jose Vidro/10
77 Ben Sheets/25 5.00 12.00
78 Roy Halladay/25 5.00 12.00
79 Frank Thomas/25 10.00 25.00
80 Chipper Jones/25 10.00 25.00
81 Jason Bay/25 5.00 12.00
82 Tony Gwynn/50 10.00 25.00
83 Shannon Stewart/5
84 Carl Crawford/25 5.00 12.00
85 Andruw Jones/25 8.00 20.00
86 Greg Maddux/25 12.50 30.00
87 Barry Larkin/25 8.00 20.00
89 Rickey Henderson/50 10.00 25.00
90 Troy Glaus/25 5.00 12.00
91 Roy Oswalt/10
92 Michael Young/25 5.00 12.00
93 Carlos Lee/25 5.00 12.00
94 Jim Edmonds/25 5.00 12.00
95 Fergie Jenkins/50 4.00 10.00
97 Aubrey Huff/25 5.00 12.00
99 Carlos Delgado/25 5.00 12.00
100 Mike Schmidt/50 15.00 40.00

2005 Playoff Prestige Prestigious Pros Signature Black

OVERALL AU-GU ODDS 1:12
STATED PRINT RUN 5 SERIAL #'d SETS
NO PRICING DUE TO SCARCITY

2005 Playoff Prestige Stars of MLB

STATED ODDS 1:12
*FOIL: 1.5X TO 4X BASIC
FOIL PRINT RUN 100 SERIAL #'d SETS
*HOLO-FOIL: 3X TO 8X BASIC
HOLO-FOIL PRINT RUN 25 SERIAL #'d SETS
FOIL/HOLO-FOIL RANDOM IN PACKS
1 Randy Johnson 1.00 2.50
2 Adrian Beltre .40 1.00
3 Eric Chavez .40 1.00
4 Mike Mussina .60 1.50
5 Todd Helton .60 1.50
6 Curt Schilling .60 1.50
7 Miguel Cabrera 1.00 2.50
8 Kerry Wood .40 1.00
9 David Ortiz 1.00 2.50
10 Michael Young .60 1.50
11 Mark Mulder .40 1.00
12 Victor Martinez .60 1.50
13 Johan Santana 1.00 2.50
14 Scott Rolen .60 1.50
15 Carlos Beltran .40 1.00

2005 Playoff Prestige Stars of MLB Material Bat

*BAT p/r 100: .4X TO 1X STARS JSY
*BAT p/r 50: .5X TO 1.2X STARS JSY
OVERALL AU-GU ODDS 1:12
PRINT RUNS B/WN 50-100 COPIES PER

2005 Playoff Prestige Stars of MLB Material Jersey

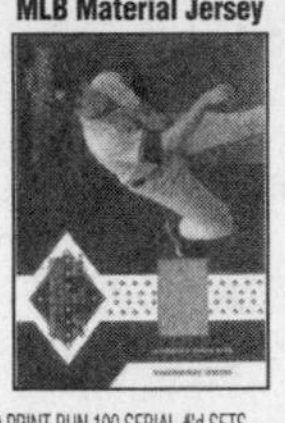

STATED PRINT RUN 100 SERIAL #'d SETS
*PRIME: .75X TO 2X JSY
PRIME PRINT RUN 25 SERIAL #'d SETS
OVERALL AU-GU ODDS 1:12
1 Randy Johnson Pants 5.00 12.00
2 Adrian Beltre 3.00 8.00
3 Eric Chavez 3.00 8.00
4 Mike Mussina 5.00 12.00
5 Todd Helton 5.00 12.00
6 Curt Schilling 5.00 12.00
7 Miguel Cabrera 5.00 12.00
8 Kerry Wood 3.00 8.00
9 David Ortiz 5.00 12.00
10 Michael Young 3.00 8.00
11 Mark Mulder 3.00 8.00
12 Victor Martinez 3.00 8.00
13 Johan Santana 5.00 12.00
14 Scott Rolen 5.00 12.00
15 Carlos Beltran 3.00 8.00

2005 Playoff Prestige Stars of MLB Signature Material Bat

*BAT p/r 50: .4X TO 1X JSY p/r 50
*BAT p/r 25: .4X TO 1X JSY p/r 25
OVERALL AU-GU ODDS 1:12
PRINT RUNS B/WN 10-50 COPIES PER
NO PRICING ON QTY OF 10

2005 Playoff Prestige Stars of MLB Signature Material Jersey

PRINT RUNS B/WN 10-50 COPIES PER
NO PRICING ON QTY OF 10
PRIME PRINT RUN 5 SERIAL #'d SETS
NO PRIME PRICING DUE TO SCARCITY
OVERALL AU-GU ODDS 1:12
1 Randy Johnson Pants/10
2 Adrian Beltre/50 10.00 25.00
3 Eric Chavez/50 10.00 25.00
4 Mike Mussina/10
5 Todd Helton/10
6 Curt Schilling/10
8 Kerry Wood/25 20.00 50.00
9 David Ortiz/50 20.00 50.00
10 Michael Young/50 10.00 25.00
12 Victor Martinez/50 10.00 25.00
13 Johan Santana/50 15.00 40.00
15 Carlos Beltran/25 12.50 30.00

2004 Prime Cuts

This 50-card set was released in November, 2003. Each four-card pack retailed for $150 and contained four cards per pack along with an encased (but not Graded) BGS card. Each case continued fifteen of these one-pack boxes. Please note a Babe Ruth "Santa" card was randomly inserted into packs and is not considered part of the basic set.

COMPLETE SET (50) 100.00 200.00
COMMON CARD (1-50) .75 2.00
STATED PRINT RUN 949 SERIAL #'d SETS
B.RUTH SANTA STATED ODDS 1:15
1 Roger Clemens Yanks 2.50 6.00
2 Nomar Garciaparra 2.00 5.00
3 Albert Pujols 5.00 12.00
4 Sammy Sosa 2.00 5.00
5 Greg Maddux Braves 3.00 8.00
6 Jason Giambi .75 2.00
7 Hideo Nomo Dodgers 2.00 5.00
8 Mike Piazza Mets 2.00 5.00
9 Ichiro Suzuki 3.00 8.00
10 Jeff Bagwell 1.25 3.00
11 Derek Jeter 5.00 12.00
12 Manny Ramirez 2.00 5.00
13 R.Henderson Dodgers 2.00 5.00
14 Alex Rodriguez Rgr 3.00 8.00
15 Troy Glaus .75 2.00
16 Mike Mussina 1.25 3.00
17 Kerry Wood .75 2.00
18 Kazuhisa Ishii .75 2.00
19 Hideki Matsui 3.00 8.00
20 Frank Thomas 2.00 5.00
21 Barry Bonds Giants 4.00 10.00
22 Adam Dunn 1.25 3.00
23 Randy Johnson D'backs 2.00 5.00
24 Alfonso Soriano .75 2.00
25 Pedro Martinez Sox 1.25 3.00
26 Andruw Jones .75 2.00
27 Mark Prior 1.25 3.00
28 Vladimir Guerrero 2.00 5.00
29 Chipper Jones 2.00 5.00
30 Todd Helton 1.25 3.00
31 Rafael Palmeiro 1.25 3.00
32 Mark Grace 1.25 3.00
33 Pedro Martinez Dodgers 1.25 3.00
34 Randy Johnson M's 2.00 5.00
35 Randy Johnson Astros 2.00 5.00
36 Roger Clemens Sox 2.50 6.00
37 Roger Clemens Jays 2.50 6.00
38 Alex Rodriguez M's 3.00 8.00
39 Greg Maddux Cubs 3.00 8.00
40 Mike Piazza Dodgers 2.00 5.00
41 Mike Piazza Marlins 2.00 5.00
42 Hideo Nomo Mets 2.00 5.00
43 R.Henderson Yanks 2.00 5.00
44 Rickey Henderson A's 2.00 5.00
45 Barry Bonds Pirates 4.00 10.00
46 Ivan Rodriguez 1.25 3.00
47 George Brett 4.00 10.00
48 Cal Ripken 8.00 20.00
49 Nolan Ryan 6.00 15.00
50 Don Mattingly 4.00 10.00
BRS1 Babe Ruth Santa 5.00 12.00

2004 Prime Cuts Century

*CENTURY 1-46: .75X TO 2X BASIC
*CENTURY MATSUI: .75X TO 2X BASIC
*CENTURY 47-50: .75X TO 2X BASIC
STATED PRINT RUN 100 SERIAL #'d SETS

2004 Prime Cuts Century Gold

STATED PRINT RUN 10 SERIAL #'d SETS
NO PRICING DUE TO SCARCITY

2004 Prime Cuts Century Proofs

STATED PRINT RUN 1 SERIAL #'d SET
NO PRICING DUE TO SCARCITY

2004 Prime Cuts Material

RANDOM INSERTS IN PACKS
PRINT RUNS B/WN 10-50 COPIES PER
NO PRICING ON QTY OF 10 OR LESS
ALL CARDS FEATURE PRIME SWATCHES
1 Roger Clemens Yanks Jsy/50 15.00 40.00
2 Nomar Garciaparra Jsy/50 15.00 40.00
3 Albert Pujols Jsy/50 20.00 50.00
4 Sammy Sosa Jsy/50 10.00 25.00
5 Greg Maddux Jsy/50 15.00 40.00
6 Jason Giambi Jsy/25 10.00 25.00
7 H.Nomo Dodgers Jsy/50 15.00 40.00
8 Mike Piazza Mets Jsy/50 15.00 40.00
9 Ichiro Suzuki Base/25 40.00 80.00
10 Jeff Bagwell Jsy/25 15.00 40.00
11 Derek Jeter Base/25 40.00 80.00
12 Manny Ramirez Jsy/25 15.00 40.00
13 R.Henderson Dodgers Jsy/50 10.00 25.00
14 Alex Rodriguez Rgr Jsy/25 20.00 50.00
15 Troy Glaus Jsy/25 10.00 25.00
16 Mike Mussina Jsy/10
17 Kerry Wood Jsy/25 10.00 25.00
18 Kazuhisa Ishii Jsy/25 10.00 25.00
19 Hideki Matsui Base/25 40.00 80.00
20 Frank Thomas Jsy/25 15.00 40.00
21 Barry Bonds Base/25 40.00 80.00
22 Adam Dunn Jsy/25 10.00 25.00
23 R.Johnson D'backs Jsy/25 15.00 40.00
24 Alfonso Soriano Jsy/35 6.00 15.00
25 Pedro Martinez Sox Jsy/25 15.00 40.00
26 Andruw Jones Jsy/25 15.00 40.00
27 Mark Prior Jsy/50 10.00 25.00
28 Vladimir Guerrero Jsy/25 15.00 40.00
29 Chipper Jones Jsy/25 15.00 40.00
30 Todd Helton Jsy/25 15.00 40.00
31 Rafael Palmeiro Jsy/25 15.00 40.00
32 Mark Grace Jsy/25 15.00 40.00
33 P.Martinez Dodgers Jsy/25 15.00 40.00
34 Randy Johnson M's Jsy/25 15.00 40.00
35 R.Johnson Astros Jsy/25 15.00 40.00
36 Roger Clemens Sox Jsy/50 15.00 40.00
38 Alex Rodriguez M's Jsy/25 30.00 60.00
40 Mike Piazza Dodgers Jsy/50 15.00 40.00
42 Hideo Nomo Mets Jsy/50 15.00 40.00
43 R.Henderson Yanks Jsy/50 10.00 25.00
44 R.Henderson A's Jsy/50 10.00 25.00
46 Ivan Rodriguez Jsy/25 15.00 40.00
47 George Brett Jsy/50 20.00 50.00
48 Cal Ripken Jsy/50 30.00 60.00
49 Nolan Ryan Jsy/50 20.00 50.00
50 Don Mattingly Jsy/50 20.00 50.00

2004 Prime Cuts Material Combos

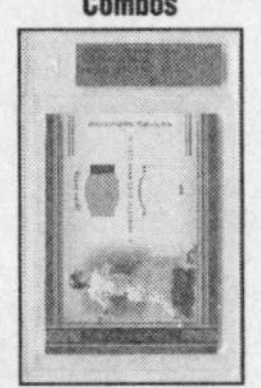

STATED PRINT RUN 25 SERIAL #'d SETS
ALL CARDS FEATURE PRIME SWATCHES
1 R.Clemens Yanks Bat-Jsy 30.00 60.00
2 Nomar Garciaparra Bat-Jsy 30.00 60.00
3 Albert Pujols Bat-Jsy 50.00 100.00
4 Sammy Sosa Bat-Jsy 20.00 50.00
5 Greg Maddux Bat-Jsy 30.00 60.00
6 Jason Giambi Bat-Jsy 15.00 40.00
7 H.Nomo Dodgers Bat-Jsy 30.00 60.00
8 Mike Piazza Mets Bat-Jsy 30.00 60.00
9 Ichiro Suzuki Ball-Base 40.00 80.00
10 Jeff Bagwell Bat-Jsy 20.00 50.00
11 Derek Jeter Ball-Base 40.00 80.00
12 Manny Ramirez Bat-Jsy 20.00 50.00
13 R.Henderson Dodgers Bat-Jsy 20.00 50.00
14 Alex Rodriguez Rgr Bat-Jsy 30.00 60.00
15 Troy Glaus Bat-Jsy 15.00 40.00
16 Mike Mussina Bat-Jsy 20.00 50.00
17 Kerry Wood Bat-Jsy 15.00 40.00
18 Kazuhisa Ishii Bat-Jsy 15.00 40.00
19 Hideki Matsui Ball-Base 50.00 100.00
20 Frank Thomas Bat-Jsy 20.00 50.00
21 Barry Bonds Ball-Base 50.00 100.00
22 Adam Dunn Bat-Jsy 15.00 40.00
23 R.Johnson D'backs Bat-Jsy 20.00 50.00
24 Alfonso Soriano Bat-Jsy 15.00 40.00
25 Pedro Martinez Sox Bat-Jsy 20.00 50.00
26 Andruw Jones Bat-Jsy 20.00 50.00
27 Mark Prior Bat-Jsy 20.00 50.00
28 Vladimir Guerrero Bat-Jsy 20.00 50.00
29 Chipper Jones Bat-Jsy 20.00 50.00
30 Todd Helton Bat-Jsy 20.00 50.00
31 Rafael Palmeiro Bat-Jsy 20.00 50.00
32 Mark Grace Bat-Jsy 20.00 50.00
33 P.Martinez Dodgers Bat-Jsy 20.00 50.00
34 Randy Johnson M's Bat-Jsy 20.00 50.00
35 R.Johnson Astros Bat-Jsy 20.00 50.00
36 Roger Clemens Sox Bat-Jsy 30.00 60.00
38 Alex Rodriguez M's Bat-Jsy 30.00 60.00
40 M.Piazza Dodgers Bat-Jsy 30.00 60.00
42 Hideo Nomo Mets Bat-Jsy 30.00 60.00
43 R.Henderson Yanks Bat-Jsy 20.00 50.00
44 R.Henderson A's Bat-Jsy 20.00 50.00
46 Ivan Rodriguez Bat-Jsy 20.00 50.00
47 George Brett Bat-Jsy 50.00 100.00
48 Cal Ripken Bat-Jsy 60.00 120.00
49 Nolan Ryan Bat-Jsy 50.00 100.00
50 Don Mattingly Bat-Jsy 50.00 100.00

2004 Prime Cuts Material Signature

RANDOM INSERTS IN PACKS
PRINT RUNS B/WN 5-50 COPIES PER
NO PRICING ON QTY OF 10 OR LESS
ALL CARDS FEATURE PRIME SWATCHES
1 R.Clemens Yanks Jsy/25 150.00 250.00
3 Albert Pujols Jsy/25 175.00 250.00
5 Greg Maddux Jsy/25 75.00 150.00
7 H.Nomo Dodgers Jsy/10
8 Mike Piazza Mets Jsy/10
10 Jeff Bagwell Jsy/25 50.00 100.00
12 Manny Ramirez Jsy/25 50.00 100.00
13 R.Hend Dodgers Jsy/25 50.00 100.00
14 Alex Rodriguez Rgr Jsy/25 100.00 200.00
15 Troy Glaus Jsy/50 30.00 60.00
16 Mike Mussina Jsy/25 40.00 80.00
17 Kerry Wood Jsy/25 40.00 80.00
18 Kazuhisa Ishii Jsy/50 15.00 40.00
20 Frank Thomas Jsy/25 50.00 100.00
22 Adam Dunn Jsy/50 30.00 60.00
23 R.Johnson D'backs Jsy/10
24 Alfonso Soriano Jsy/25 40.00 80.00
25 Pedro Martinez Sox Jsy/10
26 Andruw Jones Jsy/25 40.00 80.00
27 Mark Prior Jsy/50 20.00 50.00
28 Vladimir Guerrero Jsy/50 40.00 80.00
29 Chipper Jones Jsy/50 40.00 80.00
30 Todd Helton Jsy/50 30.00 60.00
31 Rafael Palmeiro Jsy/25 50.00 100.00
32 Mark Grace Jsy/50 40.00 80.00
33 P.Martinez Dodgers Jsy/10
34 Randy Johnson M's Jsy/10
35 R.Johnson Astros Jsy/10
36 Roger Clemens Sox Jsy/25 150.00 250.00
38 Alex Rodriguez M's Jsy/25 100.00 200.00
40 Mike Piazza Dodgers Jsy/10
42 Hideo Nomo Mets Jsy/5
43 R.Henderson Yanks Jsy/5
44 R.Henderson A's Jsy/25 50.00 100.00
46 Ivan Rodriguez Jsy/25 50.00 100.00
47 George Brett Jsy/50 75.00 150.00
48 Cal Ripken Jsy/50 150.00 250.00
49 Nolan Ryan Jsy/50 125.00 200.00
50 Don Mattingly Jsy/50 75.00 150.00

2004 Prime Cuts MLB Icons Material

RANDOM INSERTS IN PACKS
PRINT RUNS B/WN 9-50 COPIES PER
NO PRICING ON QTY OF 9 OR LESS
1 Ty Cobb Pants/9
2 Babe Ruth Pants/9
3 Lou Gehrig Pants/9
4 Johnny Bench Jsy/50 20.00 50.00
5 Lefty Grove A's Hat/25 75.00 150.00
6 Carlton Fisk Jsy/50 15.00 40.00
7 Mel Ott Jsy/25 50.00 100.00
8 Bob Feller Jsy/25 15.00 40.00
9 Jackie Robinson Jsy/25 60.00 120.00
10 Ted Williams Jsy/50 60.00 120.00
11 Roy Campanella Pants/50 30.00 60.00
12 Stan Musial Jsy/50 30.00 60.00
13 Yogi Berra Jsy/50 20.00 50.00
14 Babe Ruth Jsy/25 800.00 1200.00
15 Roberto Clemente Jsy/50 75.00 150.00
16 Warren Spahn Jsy/50 20.00 50.00
17 Ernie Banks Jsy/50 20.00 50.00
18 Eddie Mathews Jsy/50 20.00 50.00
19 Ryne Sandberg Jsy/50 30.00 60.00
20 Rod Carew Angels Jsy/50 15.00 40.00
21 Duke Snider Jsy/50 15.00 40.00
22 Jim Palmer Jsy/50 10.00 25.00
24 Frank Robinson Jsy/50 10.00 25.00
25 Brooks Robinson Jsy/50 15.00 40.00
26 Harmon Killebrew Jsy/50 20.00 50.00
27 Carl Yastrzemski Jsy/50 30.00 60.00
28 Reggie Jackson A's Jsy/50 15.00 40.00
29 Mike Schmidt Jsy/50 20.00 50.00
30 Robin Yount Jsy/50 20.00 50.00
31 George Brett Jsy/50 20.00 50.00
32 Nolan Ryan Rgr Jsy/50 30.00 60.00
33 Kirby Puckett Jsy/50 20.00 50.00
34 Cal Ripken Jsy/50 40.00 80.00
35 Don Mattingly Jsy/50 20.00 50.00
36 Tony Gwynn Jsy/19 40.00 80.00
37 Deion Sanders Jsy/19 20.00 50.00
38 Dave Winfield Yanks Jsy/19 15.00 40.00
39 Eddie Murray Jsy/19 30.00 60.00
40 Tom Seaver Jsy/19 20.00 50.00
41 Willie Stargell Jsy/19 20.00 50.00
42 Wade Boggs Yanks Jsy/19 20.00 50.00
43 Ozzie Smith Jsy/19 30.00 60.00
44 Willie McCovey Jsy/19 15.00 40.00
45 R.Jackson Angels Jsy/19 20.00 50.00
46 Whitey Ford Jsy/19 20.00 50.00
47 Lou Brock Jsy/19 20.00 50.00
48 Lou Boudreau Jsy/19 15.00 40.00
49 Steve Carlton Jsy/19 15.00 40.00
50 Rod Carew Twins Jsy/19 20.00 50.00
51 Bob Gibson Jsy/19 20.00 50.00
52 Thurman Munson Jsy/19 30.00 60.00
53 Roger Maris Jsy/19 60.00 120.00
54 Nolan Ryan Astros Jsy/50 30.00 60.00
55 Nolan Ryan Angels Jsy/50 30.00 60.00
56 Bo Jackson Jsy/19 30.00 60.00
57 Joe Morgan Jsy/19 15.00 40.00
58 Phil Rizzuto Jsy/19 20.00 50.00
59 Gary Carter Jsy/19 15.00 40.00
60 Paul Molitor Jsy/19 15.00 40.00
61 Don Drysdale Jsy/19 30.00 60.00
62 Catfish Hunter Jsy/19 20.00 50.00
63 Fergie Jenkins Pants/19 15.00 40.00
64 Pee Wee Reese Jsy/19 20.00 50.00
65 Dave Winfield Padres Jsy/19 15.00 40.00
66 Wade Boggs Sox Jsy/19 20.00 50.00
67 Lefty Grove Sox Hat/19 75.00 150.00
68 Rickey Henderson Jsy/19 30.00 60.00
69 Roger Clemens Sox Jsy/19 30.00 60.00
70 R.Clemens Yanks Jsy/19 30.00 60.00

2004 Prime Cuts MLB Icons Material Combos Prime

PRINT RUNS B/WN 1-25 COPIES PER
NO PRICING ON QTY OF 15 OR LESS
1 Ty Cobb Bat-Pants/9
2 Babe Ruth Bat-Pants/9
3 Lou Gehrig Bat-Pants/9

4 Johnny Bench Bat-Jsy/5
6 Carlton Fisk Bat-Jsy/25 40.00 80.00
7 Mel Ott Bat-Jsy/25
10 Ted Williams Bat-Jsy/9
11 R.Campanella Bat-Pants/25 50.00 100.00
12 Stan Musial Bat-Jsy/1
13 Yogi Berra Bat-Jsy/1
15 R.Clemente Bat-Jsy/25 100.00 200.00
17 Ernie Banks Bat-Jsy/25 50.00 100.00
18 Eddie Mathews Bat-Jsy/25 50.00 100.00
19 Ryne Sandberg Bat-Jsy/25 60.00 120.00
20 R.Carew Angels Bat-Jsy/25 40.00 80.00
21 Duke Snider Bat-Jsy/15
24 Frank Robinson Bat-Jsy/25 30.00 60.00
25 Brooks Robinson Bat-Jsy/25 40.00 80.00
26 Harmon Killebrew Bat-Jsy/5
27 Carl Yastrzemski Bat-Jsy/25 75.00 150.00
28 R.Jackson A's Bat-Jsy/25 40.00 80.00
29 Mike Schmidt Bat-Jsy/25 50.00 100.00
30 Robin Yount Bat-Jsy/25 50.00 100.00
31 George Brett Bat-Jsy/25 50.00 100.00
32 Nolan Ryan Rgr Bat-Jsy/25 60.00 120.00
33 Kirby Puckett Bat-Jsy/25 50.00 100.00
34 Cal Ripken Bat-Jsy/25 75.00 150.00
35 Don Mattingly Bat-Jsy/25 50.00 100.00
36 Tony Gwynn Bat-Jsy/19 60.00 120.00
37 Deion Sanders Bat-Jsy/19 40.00 80.00
38 D.Winfield Yanks Bat-Jsy/19 30.00 60.00
39 Eddie Murray Bat-Jsy/19 60.00 120.00
41 Willie Stargell Bat-Jsy/19 40.00 80.00
42 W.Boggs Yanks Bat-Jsy/19 40.00 80.00
43 Ozzie Smith Bat-Jsy/19 75.00 150.00
44 Willie McCovey Bat-Jsy/19 30.00 60.00
45 R.Jackson Angels Bat-Jsy/19 40.00 80.00
46 Whitey Ford Jsy-Pants/19 40.00 80.00
47 Lou Brock Bat-Jsy/19 50.00 100.00
48 Lou Boudreau Jsy-Jsy/19 30.00 60.00
49 Steve Carlton Bat-Jsy/19 30.00 60.00
50 Rod Carew Twins Bat-Jsy/19 40.00 80.00
52 T.Munson Bat-Jsy/19 60.00 120.00
53 Roger Maris Bat-Jsy/19 100.00 200.00
54 N.Ryan Astros Bat-Jsy/19 75.00 150.00
55 N.Ryan Angels Bat-Jsy/19 75.00 150.00
56 Bo Jackson Bat-Jsy/19 50.00 100.00
57 Joe Morgan Bat-Jsy/19 30.00 60.00
58 Phil Rizzuto Bat-Pants/19 40.00 80.00
59 Gary Carter Bat-Jsy/19 30.00 60.00
60 Paul Molitor Bat-Jsy/19 30.00 60.00
63 F.Jenkins Fld Glv-Pants/19 30.00 60.00
64 P.Reese Bat-Jsy/19 50.00 100.00
65 D.Winfield Padres Bat-Jsy/19 30.00 60.00
66 W.Boggs Sox Bat-Jsy/19 40.00 80.00
68 R.Henderson Bat-Jsy/19 50.00 100.00
69 R.Clemens Sox Bat-Jsy/19 50.00 100.00
70 R.Clemens Yanks Bat-Jsy/19 50.00 100.00

2004 Prime Cuts MLB Icons Material Prime

PRINT RUNS B/WN 1-25 COPIES PER
NO PRICING ON QTY OF 9 OR LESS
1 Ty Cobb Pants/9
2 Babe Ruth Pants/9
3 Lou Gehrig Pants/9
4 Johnny Bench Jsy/1
5 Lefty Grove A's Hat/9
6 Carlton Fisk Jsy/25 30.00 60.00
7 Mel Ott Jsy/25 100.00 200.00
8 Bob Feller Jsy/5
9 Jackie Robinson Jsy/9
10 Ted Williams Jsy/9
11 Roy Campanella Pants/25 40.00 80.00
12 Stan Musial Jsy/1
13 Yogi Berra Jsy/1
15 Roberto Clemente Jsy/25 100.00 200.00
16 Warren Spahn Jsy/25 60.00 120.00
17 Ernie Banks Jsy/25 40.00 80.00
18 Eddie Mathews Jsy/25 40.00 80.00
19 Ryne Sandberg Jsy/25 50.00 100.00
20 Rod Carew Angels Jsy/25 30.00 60.00
21 Duke Snider Jsy/9
22 Jim Palmer Jsy/25 20.00 50.00
24 Frank Robinson Jsy/25 20.00 50.00
25 Brooks Robinson Jsy/25 30.00 60.00
26 Harmon Killebrew Jsy/8
27 Carl Yastrzemski Jsy/25 50.00 100.00
28 Reggie Jackson A's Jsy/25 30.00 60.00
29 Mike Schmidt Jsy/25 40.00 80.00
30 Robin Yount Jsy/25 40.00 80.00
31 George Brett Jsy/25 40.00 80.00
32 Nolan Ryan Rgr Jsy/25 50.00 100.00
33 Kirby Puckett Jsy/25 40.00 80.00
34 Cal Ripken Jsy/25 60.00 120.00
35 Don Mattingly Jsy/25 40.00 80.00
36 Tony Gwynn Jsy/19 50.00 100.00
37 Deion Sanders Jsy/19 30.00 60.00
38 Dave Winfield Yanks Jsy/19 20.00 50.00
39 Eddie Murray Jsy/19 50.00 100.00
40 Tom Seaver Jsy/19 30.00 60.00
41 Willie Stargell Jsy/19 30.00 60.00
42 Wade Boggs Yanks Jsy/19 30.00 60.00
43 Ozzie Smith Jsy/19 40.00 80.00
44 Willie McCovey Jsy/19 20.00 50.00
45 R.Jackson Angels Jsy/19 30.00 60.00
46 Whitey Ford Jsy/19 30.00 60.00
47 Lou Brock Jsy/19 40.00 80.00
48 Lou Boudreau Jsy/19 20.00 50.00
49 Steve Carlton Jsy/19 20.00 50.00
50 Rod Carew Twins Jsy/19 30.00 60.00
51 Bob Gibson Jsy/19 40.00 80.00
52 Thurman Munson Jsy/19 50.00 100.00
53 Roger Maris Jsy/19 75.00 150.00
54 Nolan Ryan Astros Jsy/19 50.00 100.00
55 Nolan Ryan Angels Jsy/19 50.00 100.00
56 Bo Jackson Jsy/19 40.00 80.00
57 Joe Morgan Jsy/19 20.00 50.00
58 Phil Rizzuto Jsy/5
59 Gary Carter Jsy/19 20.00 50.00
60 Paul Molitor Jsy/19 20.00 50.00
61 Don Drysdale Jsy/19 50.00 100.00
62 Catfish Hunter Jsy/19 30.00 60.00
63 Fergie Jenkins Pants/19 20.00 50.00
64 Pee Wee Reese Jsy/19 30.00 60.00
65 Dave Winfield Padres Jsy/19 20.00 50.00
66 Wade Boggs Sox Jsy/19 30.00 60.00
67 Lefty Grove Sox Hat/19 90.00 180.00
68 Rickey Henderson Jsy/19 40.00 80.00
69 Roger Clemens Sox Jsy/19 40.00 80.00
70 R.Clemens Yanks Jsy/19 40.00 80.00

2004 Prime Cuts MLB Icons Material Signature

RANDOM INSERTS IN PACKS
PRINT RUNS B/WN 16-45 COPIES PER
4 Johnny Bench Jsy/18 75.00 150.00
8 Bob Feller Jsy/45 40.00 80.00
12 Stan Musial Jsy/30 75.00 150.00
13 Yogi Berra Jsy/42 60.00 120.00
21 Duke Snider Jsy/35 50.00 100.00
26 Harmon Killebrew Jsy/30 75.00 150.00
33 Kirby Puckett Jsy/16 75.00 150.00
69 Roger Clemens Sox Jsy/25 125.00 200.00

2004 Prime Cuts MLB Icons Material Signature Prime

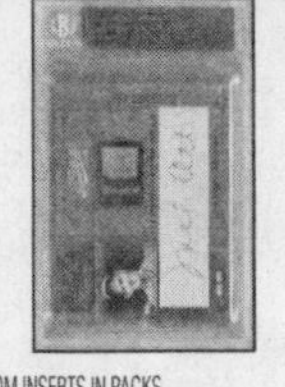

RANDOM INSERTS IN PACKS
PRINT RUNS B/WN 1-50 COPIES PER
NO PRICING ON QTY OF 15 OR LESS
1 Ty Cobb Pants/1
2 Babe Ruth Pants/1
3 Lou Gehrig Pants/1
4 Johnny Bench Jsy/5
5 Lefty Grove A's Hat/1
6 Carlton Fisk Jsy/50 40.00 80.00
7 Mel Ott Jsy/1
8 Bob Feller Jsy/5
9 Jackie Robinson Jsy/1
10 Ted Williams Jsy/1
11 Roy Campanella Pants/1
12 Stan Musial Jsy/20 125.00 200.00
13 Yogi Berra Jsy/8
16 Warren Spahn Jsy/25 125.00 200.00
17 Ernie Banks Jsy/50 60.00 120.00
18 Eddie Mathews Jsy/1
19 Ryne Sandberg Jsy/50 75.00 150.00
20 Rod Carew Angels Jsy/50 40.00 80.00
21 Duke Snider Jsy/15
22 Jim Palmer Jsy/50 30.00 60.00
24 Frank Robinson Jsy/50 30.00 60.00
25 Brooks Robinson Jsy/50 40.00 80.00
26 Harmon Killebrew Jsy/20 100.00 200.00
27 Carl Yastrzemski Jsy/50 75.00 150.00
28 Reggie Jackson A's Jsy/50 50.00 100.00
29 Mike Schmidt Jsy/20 125.00 200.00
30 Robin Yount Jsy/50 60.00 120.00
31 George Brett Jsy/50 75.00 150.00
32 Nolan Ryan Rgr Jsy/50 125.00 200.00
33 Kirby Puckett Jsy/34 50.00 100.00
34 Cal Ripken Jsy/50 150.00 250.00
35 Don Mattingly Jsy/50 75.00 150.00
36 Tony Gwynn Jsy/50 50.00 100.00
37 Deion Sanders Jsy/50 60.00 120.00
38 Dave Winfield Yanks Jsy/50 40.00 80.00
39 Eddie Murray Jsy/50 60.00 120.00
40 Tom Seaver Jsy/10
41 Willie Stargell Jsy/1
42 Wade Boggs Yanks Jsy/50 50.00 100.00
43 Ozzie Smith Jsy/50 75.00 150.00
44 Willie McCovey Jsy/50 40.00 80.00
45 R.Jackson Angels Jsy/50 50.00 100.00
46 Whitey Ford Jsy/50 50.00 100.00
47 Lou Brock Jsy/25 50.00 100.00
48 Lou Boudreau Jsy/50 75.00 150.00
49 Steve Carlton Jsy/50 30.00 60.00
50 Rod Carew Twins Jsy/50 40.00 80.00
51 Bob Gibson Jsy/50 60.00 120.00
52 Thurman Munson Jsy/1
53 Roger Maris Jsy/1
54 Nolan Ryan Astros Jsy/50 125.00 200.00
55 Nolan Ryan Angels Jsy/50 125.00 200.00
56 Bo Jackson Jsy/50 60.00 120.00
57 Joe Morgan Jsy/50 30.00 60.00
58 Phil Rizzuto Pants/50 40.00 80.00
59 Gary Carter Jsy/50 30.00 60.00
60 Paul Molitor Jsy/50 30.00 60.00
61 Don Drysdale Jsy/1
62 Catfish Hunter Jsy/1
63 Fergie Jenkins Pants/50 30.00 60.00
64 Pee Wee Reese Jsy/1
65 D.Winfield Padres Jsy/50 40.00 80.00
66 Wade Boggs Sox Jsy/50 50.00 100.00
67 Lefty Grove Sox Hat/1

68 Rickey Henderson Jsy/50 75.00 150.00
69 Roger Clemens Sox Jsy/25 150.00 250.00
70 R.Clemens Yanks Jsy/50 125.00 200.00

2004 Prime Cuts MLB Icons Signature

RANDOM INSERTS IN PACKS
PRINT RUNS B/WN 1-50 COPIES PER
NO PRICING ON QTY OF 12 OR LESS
4 Johnny Bench/50 40.00 80.00
6 Carlton Fisk/50 30.00 60.00
8 Bob Feller/50 20.00 50.00
12 Stan Musial/50 50.00 100.00
13 Yogi Berra/50 40.00 80.00
16 Warren Spahn/25 75.00 150.00
17 Ernie Banks/50 50.00 100.00
18 Eddie Mathews/12
19 Ryne Sandberg/50 60.00 120.00
20 Rod Carew Angels/5
21 Duke Snider/25 40.00 80.00
22 Jim Palmer/25 30.00 60.00
24 Frank Robinson/50 20.00 50.00
25 Brooks Robinson/50 30.00 60.00
26 Harmon Killebrew/25 75.00 150.00
27 Carl Yastrzemski/50 50.00 100.00
28 Reggie Jackson A's/50 40.00 80.00
29 Mike Schmidt/20 60.00 120.00
30 Robin Yount/25 60.00 120.00
31 George Brett/25 60.00 120.00
32 Nolan Ryan Rgr/50 75.00 150.00
33 Kirby Puckett/25 50.00 100.00
34 Cal Ripken/25 150.00 250.00
35 Don Mattingly/50 50.00 100.00
36 Tony Gwynn/25 50.00 100.00
37 Deion Sanders/10
38 Dave Winfield Yanks/25 40.00 80.00
39 Eddie Murray/25 60.00 120.00
40 Tom Seaver/25
42 Wade Boggs Yanks/25 50.00 100.00
43 Ozzie Smith/25 75.00 150.00
44 Willie McCovey/25 40.00 80.00
45 Reggie Jackson Angels/25 50.00 100.00
46 Whitey Ford/10
47 Lou Brock/25 40.00 80.00
48 Lou Boudreau/25 75.00 150.00
49 Steve Carlton/10
50 Rod Carew Twins/5
51 Bob Gibson/25 40.00 80.00
53 Roger Maris/1
54 Nolan Ryan Astros/10
55 Nolan Ryan Angels/10
56 Bo Jackson/25 60.00 120.00
57 Joe Morgan/25 30.00 60.00
58 Phil Rizzuto/10
59 Gary Carter/25 30.00 60.00
60 Paul Molitor/25 30.00 60.00
61 Don Drysdale/1
62 Catfish Hunter/1
63 Fergie Jenkins/10
64 Pee Wee Reese/1
65 Dave Winfield Padres/25 40.00 80.00
66 Wade Boggs Sox/25 50.00 100.00
67 Lefty Grove/1
68 Rickey Henderson A's/10
69 Roger Clemens Sox/10
70 Roger Clemens Yanks/10

2004 Prime Cuts MLB Icons Signature Proofs

STATED PRINT RUN 1 SERIAL #'d SET
NO PRICING DUE TO SCARCITY

2004 Prime Cuts Signature

PRINT RUNS B/WN 5-25 COPIES PER
NO PRICING ON QTY OF 14 OR LESS
1 Roger Clemens Yanks/25 75.00 150.00
3 Albert Pujols/25 150.00 250.00
5 Greg Maddux Braves/10
7 Hideo Nomo Dodgers/10
8 Mike Piazza Mets/10
10 Jeff Bagwell/25 40.00 80.00
12 Manny Ramirez/14
13 R.Henderson Dodgers/25 40.00 80.00
14 Alex Rodriguez Rgr/25 60.00 120.00
15 Troy Glaus/25 30.00 60.00
16 Mike Mussina/25 30.00 60.00
17 Kerry Wood/25 30.00 60.00
18 Kazuhisa Ishii/25 15.00 40.00
20 Frank Thomas/25 40.00 80.00
22 Adam Dunn/25 15.00 40.00
23 Randy Johnson D'backs/10
24 Alfonso Soriano/25 30.00 60.00
25 Pedro Martinez Sox/10
26 Andruw Jones/25 30.00 60.00
27 Mark Prior/25 20.00 50.00
28 Vladimir Guerrero/25 40.00 80.00
29 Chipper Jones/25 40.00 80.00
30 Todd Helton/17 30.00 60.00
31 Rafael Palmeiro/25 40.00 80.00
32 Mark Grace/25 40.00 80.00
33 Pedro Martinez Dodgers/10
34 Randy Johnson M's/10
35 Randy Johnson Astros/10
36 Roger Clemens Sox/25 75.00 150.00
37 Roger Clemens Jays/25 75.00 150.00
38 Alex Rodriguez M's/25 60.00 120.00
39 Greg Maddux Cubs/10
40 Mike Piazza Dodgers/10
41 Mike Piazza Marlins/5
42 Hideo Nomo Mets/5
43 Rickey Henderson Yanks/25 40.00 80.00
44 Rickey Henderson A's/25 40.00 80.00
46 Ivan Rodriguez/25 40.00 80.00
47 George Brett/25 75.00 150.00
48 Cal Ripken/25 100.00 200.00
49 Nolan Ryan/25 75.00 150.00
50 Don Mattingly/25 60.00 120.00

2004 Prime Cuts Signature Proofs

STATED PRINT RUN 1 SERIAL #'d SET
NO PRICING DUE TO SCARCITY

2004 Prime Cuts Timeline Dual Achievements Material

PRINT RUNS B/WN 9-19 COPIES PER
NO PRICING ON QTY OF 9 OR LESS
1 Roy Campanella Pants
Yogi Berra Jsy/9
2 Jackie Robinson Jsy
Ted Williams Jsy/9
3 Stan Musial Jsy 125.00 200.00
Ted Williams Jsy/19
4 Mike Schmidt Jsy 60.00 120.00
George Brett Jsy/19
5 Dale Murphy Jsy 60.00 120.00
Cal Ripken Jsy/19
6 Roger Clemens Jsy 50.00 100.00
Mike Schmidt Jsy/19
7 Ty Cobb Pants
Babe Ruth Pants/9
8 Roy Campanella Pants
Stan Musial Jsy/9
10 George Brett Jsy 60.00 120.00
Nolan Ryan Jsy/19
11 Jackie Robinson Jsy
Roy Campanella Pants/9
12 Al Kaline Pants 40.00 80.00
Duke Snider Jsy/19

2004 Prime Cuts Timeline Dual Achievements Material Combos

PRINT RUNS B/WN 1-19 COPIES PER
NO PRICING ON QTY OF 15 OR LESS
1 Roy Campanella Bat-Pants
Yogi Berra Bat-Jsy/1
3 Stan Musial Bat-Jsy
Ted Williams Bat-Jsy/1
4 Mike Schmidt Bat-Jsy 150.00 250.00
George Brett Bat-Jsy/19
5 Dale Murphy Bat-Jsy 100.00 200.00
Cal Ripken Bat-Jsy/19
6 Roger Clemens Bat-Jsy 75.00 150.00
Mike Schmidt Bat-Jsy/19
7 Ty Cobb Bat-Pants
Babe Ruth Bat-Pants/9
8 Roy Campanella Bat-Pants
Stan Musial Bat-Jsy/2
10 George Brett Bat-Jsy 150.00 250.00
Nolan Ryan Bat-Jsy/19
12 Al Kaline Bat-Pants
Duke Snider Bat-Jsy/15

2004 Prime Cuts Timeline Dual Achievements Material Prime

PRINT RUNS B/WN 1-19 COPIES PER
NO PRICING ON QTY OF 15 OR LESS
1 Roy Campanella Pants
Yogi Berra Jsy/1
2 Jackie Robinson Jsy
Ted Williams Jsy/9
3 Stan Musial Jsy
Ted Williams Jsy/2
4 Mike Schmidt Jsy 100.00 200.00
George Brett Jsy/19
5 Dale Murphy Jsy 100.00 200.00
Cal Ripken Jsy/19
6 Roger Clemens Jsy 75.00 150.00
Mike Schmidt Jsy/19
7 Ty Cobb Pants
Babe Ruth Pants/9
8 Roy Campanella Pants
Stan Musial Jsy/2
10 George Brett Jsy 100.00 200.00
Nolan Ryan Jsy/19
11 Jackie Robinson Jsy
Roy Campanella Pants/9
12 Al Kaline Pants
Duke Snider Jsy/15

2004 Prime Cuts Timeline Dual Achievements Material Signature

PRINT RUNS B/WN 1-25 COPIES PER
NO PRICING ON QTY OF 15 OR LESS
2 Jackie Robinson Jsy
Ted Williams Jsy/1
3 Stan Musial Jsy
Ted Williams Jsy/1
4 Mike Schmidt Jsy 175.00 300.00
George Brett Jsy/24
5 Dale Murphy Jsy 175.00 300.00
Cal Ripken Jsy/25
6 Roger Clemens Jsy 175.00 300.00
Mike Schmidt Jsy/24
7 Ty Cobb Pants
Babe Ruth Pants/1
10 George Brett Jsy 200.00 350.00
Nolan Ryan Jsy/25
12 Al Kaline Pants
Duke Snider Jsy/15

2004 Prime Cuts Timeline Dual Achievements Signature

PRINT RUNS B/WN 24-25 COPIES PER
4 Mike Schmidt 150.00 250.00
George Brett/24
5 Dale Murphy 150.00 250.00
Cal Ripken/25
6 Roger Clemens 150.00 250.00
Mike Schmidt/24
10 George Brett 175.00 300.00
Nolan Ryan/25
12 Al Kaline 75.00 150.00
Duke Snider/25

2004 Prime Cuts Timeline Dual Achievements Signature Proofs

STATED PRINT RUN 1 SERIAL #'d SET
NO PRICING DUE TO SCARCITY

2004 Prime Cuts Timeline Dual League Leaders Material

PRINT RUNS B/WN 9-19 COPIES PER
NO PRICING ON QTY OF 9 OR LESS
1 Mel Ott Jsy
Lou Gehrig Pants/9
2 Mel Ott Jsy
Ted Williams Jsy/9
4 Steve Carlton Jsy 30.00 60.00
Jim Palmer Jsy/19
6 Roberto Clemente Jsy
Carl Yastrzemski Jsy/9
7 Steve Carlton Jsy 50.00 100.00
Nolan Ryan Jsy/19
8 Don Mattingly Jsy 50.00 100.00
Tony Gwynn Jsy/19
9 Roger Clemens Jsy 60.00 120.00
Nolan Ryan Jsy/19
10 Babe Ruth Pants
Lou Gehrig Pants/9

2004 Prime Cuts Timeline Dual League Leaders Material Combos

PRINT RUNS B/WN 9-19 COPIES PER
NO PRICING ON QTY OF 9 OR LESS
1 Mel Ott Bat-Jsy
Lou Gehrig Bat-Pants/9

2 Mel Ott Bat-Jsy
Ted Williams Bat-Jsy/9
6 Roberto Clemente Bat-Jsy
Carl Yastrzemski Bat-Jsy/9
7 Steve Carlton Bat-Jsy 75.00 150.00
Nolan Ryan Bat-Jsy/19
8 Don Mattingly Bat-Jsy 75.00 150.00
Tony Gwynn Bat-Jsy/19
9 Roger Clemens Bat-Jsy 100.00 200.00
Nolan Ryan Bat-Jsy/19
10 Babe Ruth Bat-Pants
Lou Gehrig Bat-Pants/9

2004 Prime Cuts Timeline Dual League Leaders Material Prime

PRINT RUNS B/WN 9-19 COPIES PER
NO PRICING DUE TO SCARCITY
1 Mel Ott Jsy
Lou Gehrig Pants/9
2 Mel Ott Jsy
Ted Williams Jsy/9
4 Steve Carlton Jsy 50.00 100.00
Jim Palmer Jsy/19
6 Roberto Clemente Jsy
Carl Yastrzemski Jsy/9
7 Steve Carlton Jsy 75.00 150.00
Nolan Ryan Jsy/19
8 Don Mattingly Jsy 75.00 150.00
Tony Gwynn Jsy/19
9 Roger Clemens Jsy 100.00 200.00
Nolan Ryan Jsy/19
10 Babe Ruth Pants
Lou Gehrig Pants/9

2004 Prime Cuts Timeline Dual League Leaders Material Signature

PRINT RUNS B/WN 1-50 COPIES PER
NO PRICING ON QTY OF 1
1 Mel Ott Jsy
Lou Gehrig Pants/1
2 Mel Ott Jsy
Ted Williams Jsy/1
4 Steve Carlton Jsy 60.00 120.00
Jim Palmer Jsy/50
6 Roberto Clemente Jsy
Carl Yastrzemski Jsy/1
7 Steve Carlton Jsy 150.00 250.00
Nolan Ryan Jsy/25
8 Don Mattingly Jsy 150.00 250.00
Tony Gwynn Jsy/25
9 Roger Clemens Jsy 300.00 500.00
Nolan Ryan Jsy/25
10 Babe Ruth Pants
Lou Gehrig Pants/1

2004 Prime Cuts Timeline Dual League Leaders Signature

PRINT RUNS B/WN 25-50 COPIES PER
4 Steve Carlton 50.00 100.00
Jim Palmer/50
7 Steve Carlton 125.00 200.00
Nolan Ryan/25
8 Don Mattingly 125.00 200.00
Tony Gwynn/25
9 Roger Clemens 250.00 400.00
Nolan Ryan/25

2004 Prime Cuts Timeline Dual League Leaders Signature Proofs

STATED PRINT RUN 1 SERIAL #'d SET
NO PRICING DUE TO SCARCITY

2004 Prime Cuts Timeline Material

RANDOM INSERTS IN PACKS
NO PRICING ON QTY OF 9 OR LESS
1 Ty Cobb Pants/9
2 Babe Ruth Pants/9
3 Lou Gehrig Pants/9

4 Ted Williams TC Jsy/50 60.00 120.00
5 Roy Campanella Pants/50 30.00 60.00
6 Stan Musial MVP Jsy/50 30.00 60.00
7 Yogi Berra 51M Jsy/50 20.00 50.00
9 R.Clemente MVP Jsy/50 75.00 150.00
10 Will Clark Jsy/25 20.00 50.00
12 Carl Yastrzemski Jsy/50 30.00 60.00
13 Mike Schmidt Jsy/50 20.00 50.00
14 George Brett MVP Jsy/50 20.00 50.00
15 Nolan Ryan WIN Jsy/50 30.00 60.00
16 Stan Musial BA Jsy/50 30.00 60.00
17 Ted Williams BA Jsy/50 60.00 120.00
18 R.Clemente BTG Jsy/50 75.00 150.00
19 Greg Maddux Jsy/50 20.00 50.00
21 Robin Yount Jsy/50 20.00 50.00
22 Nolan Ryan HOF Jsy/50 30.00 60.00
23 Ted Williams RET Jsy/50 60.00 120.00
24 George Brett RET Jsy/50 20.00 50.00
25 Yogi Berra 55M Jsy/50 20.00 50.00
26 Rod Carew Jsy/50 15.00 40.00
27 Dale Murphy Jsy/25 20.00 50.00

2004 Prime Cuts Timeline Material Combos

PRINT RUNS B/WN 1-19 COPIES PER
NO PRICING ON QTY OF 9 OR LESS
1 Ty Cobb Bat-Pants/9
2 Babe Ruth Bat-Pants/9
3 Lou Gehrig Bat-Pants/9
4 Ted Williams TC Bat-Jsy/9
5 Roy Campanella Bat-Pants/9
6 Stan Musial MVP Bat-Jsy/1
7 Yogi Berra 51M Bat-Jsy/2
9 R.Clemente MVP Bat-Jsy/9
10 Will Clark Bat-Jsy/19 75.00 150.00
12 Carl Yastrzemski Bat-Jsy/19 75.00 150.00
13 Mike Schmidt Bat-Jsy/19 60.00 120.00
14 G.Brett MVP Bat-Jsy/19 60.00 120.00
15 N.Ryan WIN Bat-Jsy/19 75.00 150.00
16 Stan Musial BA Bat-Jsy/1
17 Ted Williams BA Bat-Jsy/9
18 R.Clemente BTG Bat-Jsy/9
19 Greg Maddux Bat-Jsy/19 50.00 100.00
21 Robin Yount Bat-Jsy/19 50.00 100.00
22 N.Ryan HOF Bat-Jsy/19 75.00 150.00
23 Ted Williams RET Bat-Jsy/9
24 G.Brett RET Bat-Jsy/19 60.00 120.00
25 Yogi Berra 55M Bat-Jsy/2
26 Rod Carew Bat-Jsy/19 40.00 80.00
27 Dale Murphy Bat-Jsy/19 40.00 80.00

2004 Prime Cuts Timeline Material Prime

PRINT RUNS B/WN 1-25 COPIES PER
NO PRICING ON QTY OF 9 OR LESS
1 Ty Cobb Pants/9
2 Babe Ruth Pants/9
3 Lou Gehrig Pants/9
4 Ted Williams TC Jsy/9
5 Roy Campanella Pants/25 40.00 80.00
6 Stan Musial MVP Jsy/2
7 Yogi Berra 51M Jsy/1
9 R.Clemente MVP Jsy/25 75.00 150.00
10 Will Clark Jsy/25 40.00 80.00
12 Carl Yastrzemski Jsy/25 60.00 120.00
13 Mike Schmidt Jsy/25 50.00 100.00
14 George Brett MVP Jsy/25 50.00 100.00
15 Nolan Ryan WIN Jsy/25 50.00 100.00
16 Stan Musial BA Jsy/2
17 Ted Williams BA Jsy/9
18 R.Clemente BTG Jsy/25 75.00 150.00
19 Greg Maddux Jsy/25 40.00 80.00
21 Robin Yount Jsy/25 40.00 80.00
22 Nolan Ryan HOF Jsy/25 50.00 100.00
23 Ted Williams RET Jsy/9
24 George Brett RET Jsy/25 50.00 100.00
25 Yogi Berra 55M Jsy/1
26 Rod Carew Jsy/25 40.00 80.00
27 Dale Murphy Jsy/25 40.00 80.00

2004 Prime Cuts Timeline Material Signature

PRINT RUNS B/WN 33-42 COPIES PER
6 Stan Musial MVP Jsy/33 75.00 150.00
7 Yogi Berra 51M Jsy/42 60.00 120.00
16 Stan Musial BA Jsy/38 75.00 150.00
25 Yogi Berra 55M Jsy/42 60.00 120.00

2004 Prime Cuts Timeline Material Signature Prime

RANDOM INSERTS IN PACKS
PRINT RUNS B/WN 1-50 COPIES PER
NO PRICING ON QTY OF 10 OR LESS
1 Ty Cobb Pants/1

2 Babe Ruth Pants/1
3 Lou Gehrig Pants/1
6 Stan Musial MVP Jsy/10
7 Yogi Berra 51M Jsy/8
9 Roberto Clemente Jsy/1
10 Will Clark Jsy/50 60.00 120.00
12 Carl Yastrzemski Jsy/50 75.00 150.00
13 Mike Schmidt Jsy/20 125.00 200.00
14 George Brett MVP Jsy/25 125.00 200.00
15 Nolan Ryan WIN Jsy/50 125.00 200.00
16 Stan Musial BA Jsy/10
19 Greg Maddux Jsy/50 125.00 200.00
21 Robin Yount Jsy/50 60.00 120.00
22 Nolan Ryan HOF Jsy/50 125.00 200.00
24 George Brett RET Jsy/25 125.00 200.00
25 Yogi Berra 55M Jsy/8
26 Rod Carew Jsy/50 40.00 80.00
27 Dale Murphy Jsy/50 40.00 80.00

2004 Prime Cuts Timeline Signature

RANDOM INSERTS IN PACKS
PRINT RUNS B/WN 10-50 COPIES PER
NO PRICING ON QTY OF 20 OR LESS
6 Stan Musial MVP/50 50.00 100.00
7 Yogi Berra 51M/50 40.00 80.00
10 Will Clark/25 75.00 150.00
12 Carl Yastrzemski/50 50.00 100.00
13 Mike Schmidt/20 60.00 120.00
14 George Brett MVP/25 60.00 120.00
15 Nolan Ryan WIN/50 75.00 150.00
16 Stan Musial BA/50 50.00 100.00
19 Greg Maddux/31 75.00 150.00
21 Robin Yount/25 60.00 120.00
22 Nolan Ryan HOF/50 75.00 150.00
24 George Brett RET/25 60.00 120.00
25 Yogi Berra 55M/50 40.00 80.00
26 Rod Carew/10
27 Dale Murphy/25 40.00 80.00

2004 Prime Cuts Timeline Signature Proofs

STATED PRINT RUN 1 SERIAL #'d SET
NO PRICING DUE TO SCARCITY

2004 Prime Cuts II

This 100-card set was released in November, 2004. The set was issued in four-card packs with an $150 SRP which were packed 1 to a box and 15 box-packs to a case. Each pack included a card which were put into special holders. The first 91 cards of the basic set feature active veterans while cards numbered 92-100 feature retired greats and all of these cards have a stated print run of 699 serial numbered sets.

COMMON CARD (1-91) .75 2.00
COMMON RC 1-91 .75 2.00
COMMON CARD (92-100) .75 2.00
STATED PRINT RUN 699 SERIAL #'d SETS
1 Mark Prior 1.25 3.00
2 Derek Jeter 5.00 12.00
3 Eric Chavez .75 2.00
4 Carlos Delgado .75 2.00
5 Albert Pujols 5.00 12.00
6 Miguel Cabrera 2.00 5.00
7 Ivan Rodriguez 1.25 3.00
8 Javy Lopez .75 2.00
9 Hank Blalock .75 2.00
10 Chipper Jones 2.00 5.00
11 Gary Sheffield .75 2.00
12 Alfonso Soriano .75 2.00
13 Alex Rodriguez Yanks 3.00 8.00
14 Edgar Renteria .75 2.00
15 Jim Edmonds 1.25 3.00
16 Garret Anderson .75 2.00
17 Lance Berkman 1.25 3.00
18 Brandon Webb .75 2.00
19 Mike Lowell .75 2.00
20 Mark Mulder .75 2.00
21 Sammy Sosa 2.00 5.00
22 Roger Clemens Astros 2.50 6.00
23 Mark Teixeira 2.00 5.00
24 Manny Ramirez 2.00 5.00
25 Rafael Palmeiro 1.25 3.00
26 Ichiro Suzuki 3.00 8.00
27 Vladimir Guerrero 2.00 5.00
28 Austin Kearns .75 2.00
29 Troy Glaus .75 2.00
30 Ken Griffey Jr. 3.00 8.00
31 Greg Maddux 3.00 8.00
32 Roy Halladay 2.00 5.00
33 Roy Oswalt 1.25 3.00
34 Kerry Wood .75 2.00
35 Mike Mussina Yanks 1.25 3.00
36 Michael Young .75 2.00
37 Juan Gonzalez .75 2.00
38 Curt Schilling 1.25 3.00
39 Shannon Stewart .75 2.00
40 Todd Helton 1.25 3.00
41 Larry Walker Cards 1.25 3.00
42 Mariano Rivera 2.00 5.00
43 Nomar Garciaparra 2.00 5.00
44 Adam Dunn 1.25 3.00
45 Pedro Martinez Sox 1.25 3.00
46 Bernie Williams 1.25 3.00
47 Tom Glavine 1.25 3.00
48 Torii Hunter .75 2.00
49 David Ortiz 2.00 5.00
50 Frank Thomas 2.00 5.00
51 Randy Johnson D'backs 2.00 5.00
52 Jason Giambi .75 2.00
53 Carlos Lee .75 2.00
54 Mike Sweeney .75 2.00
55 Hideki Matsui 3.00 8.00
56 Dontrelle Willis .75 2.00
57 Tim Hudson 1.25 3.00
58 Jose Vidro .75 2.00
59 Jeff Bagwell 1.25 3.00
60 Rocco Baldelli .75 2.00
61 Craig Biggio 1.25 3.00
62 Mike Piazza Mets 2.00 5.00
63 Magglio Ordonez 1.25 3.00
64 Hideo Nomo 2.00 5.00
65 Miguel Tejada 1.25 3.00
66 Vernon Wells .75 2.00
67 Barry Larkin 1.25 3.00
68 Jacque Jones .75 2.00
69 Scott Rolen 1.25 3.00
70 Jeff Kent .75 2.00
71 Steve Finley .75 2.00
72 Kazuo Matsui RC 1.25 3.00
73 Carlos Beltran .75 2.00
74 Shawn Green .75 2.00
75 Barry Zito .75 2.00
76 Aramis Ramirez .75 2.00
77 Paul Lo Duca .75 2.00
78 Kazuhisa Ishii .75 2.00
79 Aubrey Huff .75 2.00
80 Jim Thome 1.25 3.00
81 Andy Pettitte Astros 1.25 3.00
82 Andruw Jones .75 2.00
83 Josh Beckett 1.25 3.00
84 Sean Casey .75 2.00
85 Alex Rodriguez M's 3.00 8.00
86 Roger Clemens Yanks 2.50 6.00
87 Mike Mussina O's 1.25 3.00
88 Pedro Martinez Dgr 1.25 3.00
89 Randy Johnson Astros 2.00 5.00
90 Mike Piazza Dgr 2.00 5.00
91 Andy Pettitte Yanks 1.25 3.00
92 Cal Ripken 8.00 20.00
93 Dale Murphy 1.25 3.00
94 Don Mattingly 4.00 10.00
95 Gary Carter .75 2.00
96 George Brett 4.00 10.00
97 Nolan Ryan 6.00 15.00
98 Ozzie Smith 3.00 8.00
99 Steve Carlton .75 2.00
100 Tony Gwynn 2.00 5.00

2004 Prime Cuts II Century Gold

*GOLD 1-91: 1X TO 2.5X BASIC
*GOLD 92-100: 1X TO 2.5X BASIC
STATED PRINT RUN 25 SERIAL #'d SETS
NO RC YR PRICING DUE TO SCARCITY

2004 Prime Cuts II Century Platinum

STATED PRINT RUN 1 SERIAL #'d SET
NO PRICING DUE TO SCARCITY

2004 Prime Cuts II Century Silver

*SILVER 1-91: .6X TO 1.5X BASIC
*SILVER 92-100: .6X TO 1.5X BASIC
STATED PRINT RUN 50 SERIAL #'d SETS

2004 Prime Cuts II Material Number

*1-91 p/r 25: .3X TO .8X COMBO p/r 22
*92-100 p/r 25: .3X TO .8X COMBO p/r 25
OVERALL AU-GU ODDS 1:1
PRINT RUNS B/WN 1-25 COPIES PER
NO PRICING ON QTY OF 10 OR LESS

2004 Prime Cuts II Material Prime

OVERALL AU-GU ODDS 1:1
PRINT RUNS B/WN 1-10 COPIES PER
NO PRICING DUE TO SCARCITY

2004 Prime Cuts II Material Combo

OVERALL AU-GU ODDS 1:1
PRINT RUNS B/WN 1-35 COPIES PER
NO PRICING ON QTY OF 10 OR LESS
1 Mark Prior Hat-Jsy/22 10.00 25.00
3 Eric Chavez Bat-Jsy/3
4 Carlos Delgado Bat-Jsy/1
5 Albert Pujols Bat-Jsy/5
6 Miguel Cabrera Bat-Jsy/5
7 Ivan Rodriguez Bat-Jsy/7
8 Javy Lopez Bat-Jsy/5
9 Hank Blalock Bat-Jsy/1
10 Chipper Jones Bat-Jsy/10
12 Alfonso Soriano Bat-Jsy/25 6.00 15.00
14 Edgar Renteria Bat-Jsy/1
15 Jim Edmonds Bat-Jsy/15 8.00 20.00
16 Garret Anderson Bat-Jsy/16 8.00 20.00
17 Lance Berkman Hat-Jsy/17 8.00 20.00
19 Mike Lowell Bat-Jsy/1
20 Mark Mulder Bat-Jsy/1
21 Sammy Sosa Bat-Jsy/21 12.50 30.00
22 R.Clem Astros Bat-Jsy/22 20.00 50.00
23 Mark Teixeira Fld Glv-Jsy/1
24 Manny Ramirez Bat-Jsy/24 10.00 25.00
25 Rafael Palmeiro Bat-Jsy/25 10.00 25.00
27 Vlad Guerrero Bat-Jsy/27 12.50 30.00
29 Troy Glaus Bat-Jsy/1
31 Greg Maddux Bat-Jsy/31 20.00 50.00
35 M.Muss Yanks Bat-Jsy/35 10.00 25.00
40 Todd Helton Bat-Jsy/17 12.50 30.00
86 R.Clem Ynk Fld Glv-Jsy/22 20.00 50.00
92 Cal Ripken Bat-Jsy/25 50.00 100.00
93 Dale Murphy Bat-Jsy/25 12.50 30.00
94 Don Mattingly Bat-Jsy/25 30.00 60.00
95 Gary Carter Jkt-Jsy/10
96 George Brett Bat-Jsy/25 30.00 60.00
97 Nolan Ryan Bat-Jkt/25 30.00 60.00
98 Ozzie Smith Bat-Jsy/25 20.00 50.00

2004 Prime Cuts II Material Combo Prime

PRINT RUNS B/WN 1-9 COPIES PER
NO PRICING DUE TO SCARCITY

2004 Prime Cuts II Signature Century Gold

*1-91 p/r 15-19: .5X TO 1.2X SILV p/r 25
*92-100 p/r 15-19: .5X TO 1.2X SILV p/r 25
OVERALL AU-GU ODDS 1:1
PRINT RUNS B/WN 1-19 COPIES PER
NO PRICING ON QTY OF 11 OR LESS

2004 Prime Cuts II Signature Century Platinum

OVERALL AU-GU ODDS 1:1
STATED PRINT RUN 1 SERIAL #'d SET
NO PRICING DUE TO SCARCITY

2004 Prime Cuts II Signature Century Silver

OVERALL AU-GU ODDS 1:1
PRINT RUNS B/WN 1- COPIES PER
NO PRICING ON QTY OF OR LESS
1 Mark Prior/22 12.50 30.00
3 Eric Chavez/10
5 Albert Pujols/10
6 Miguel Cabrera/24 15.00 40.00
9 Hank Blalock/25 10.00 25.00
10 Chipper Jones/1
11 Gary Sheffield/25 15.00 40.00
14 Edgar Renteria/10
15 Jim Edmonds/25 15.00 40.00
16 Garret Anderson/25 10.00 25.00
17 Lance Berkman/25 15.00 40.00
19 Mike Lowell/19 12.50 30.00
20 Mark Mulder/20 10.00 25.00
21 Sammy Sosa/21 50.00 100.00
22 Roger Clemens Astros/10
23 Mark Teixeira/23 15.00 40.00
24 Manny Ramirez/24 40.00 80.00
25 Rafael Palmeiro/25 30.00 60.00
27 Vladimir Guerrero/5
31 Greg Maddux/31 60.00 120.00
34 Kerry Wood/34 15.00 40.00
35 Mike Mussina Yanks/35 15.00 40.00
37 Juan Gonzalez/22 10.00 25.00
38 Curt Schilling/10
40 Todd Helton/17 20.00 50.00
44 Adam Dunn/44 12.50 30.00
45 Pedro Martinez Sox/10
46 Bernie Williams/10
48 Torii Hunter/10
49 David Ortiz/34 20.00 50.00
50 Frank Thomas/35 20.00 50.00
51 Randy Johnson D'backs/10
56 Dontrelle Willis/10
57 Tim Hudson/15 20.00 50.00
59 Jeff Bagwell/10
61 Craig Biggio/25 15.00 40.00
62 Mike Piazza Mets/10
63 Magglio Ordonez/30 10.00 25.00
64 Hideo Nomo/1
66 Vernon Wells/25 10.00 25.00
67 Barry Larkin/11
69 Scott Rolen/27 15.00 40.00
73 Carlos Beltran/15 12.50 30.00
74 Shawn Green/15 20.00 50.00
75 Barry Zito/10
78 Kazuhisa Ishii/17 12.50 30.00
81 Andy Pettitte Astros/10
82 Andruw Jones/25 15.00 40.00
83 Josh Beckett/21 15.00 40.00
84 Sean Casey/10
86 Roger Clemens Yanks/10
87 Mike Mussina O's/35 15.00 40.00
88 Pedro Martinez Dgr/10
89 Randy Johnson Astros/10
90 Mike Piazza Dgr/10
91 Andy Pettitte Yanks/10
92 Cal Ripken/25 100.00 200.00
93 Dale Murphy/25 15.00 40.00
94 Don Mattingly/23 40.00 80.00
95 Gary Carter/25 10.00 25.00
96 George Brett/10
97 Nolan Ryan/34 60.00 120.00
98 Ozzie Smith/10
99 Steve Carlton/32 10.00 25.00
100 Tony Gwynn/25 30.00 60.00

2004 Prime Cuts II Signature Material Number

*1-91 p/r 20-35: .5X TO 1.2X SILV p/r 20-35
*1-91 p/r 15-19: .6X TO 1.5X SILV p/r 20-25
*1-91 p/r 15-19: .5X TO 1.2X SILV p/r 15-19
*92-100 p/r 20-35: .5X TO 1.2X SILV p/r 20-35
*92-100 p/r 15-19: .6X TO 1.5X SILV p/r 20-25
OVERALL AU-GU ODDS 1:1
PRINT RUNS B/WN 1- COPIES PER
NO PRICING ON QTY OF OR LESS

2004 Prime Cuts II Signature Material Prime

OVERALL AU-GU ODDS 1:1
PRINT RUNS B/WN 1-9 COPIES PER
NO PRICING DUE TO SCARCITY

2004 Prime Cuts II Signature Material Combo

*1-91 p/r 20-35: .6X TO 1.5X SILV p/r 20-35
*1-91 p/r 15-19: .75X TO 2X SILV p/r 20-35
*1-91 p/r 15-19: .6X TO 1.5X SILV p/r 15-19
*92-100 p/r 20-35: .6X TO 1.5X SILV p/r 20-35
OVERALL AU-GU ODDS 1:1
PRINT RUNS B/WN 1-25 COPIES PER
NO PRICING ON QTY OF 10 OR LESS

2004 Prime Cuts II Signature Material Combo Prime

OVERALL AU-GU ODDS 1:1
PRINT RUNS B/WN 1-9 COPIES PER
NO PRICING DUE TO SCARCITY

2004 Prime Cuts II MLB Icons

RANDOM INSERTS IN PACKS
STATED PRINT RUN 50 SERIAL #'d SETS
1 Dale Murphy 2.50 6.00
2 Eddie Mathews 4.00 10.00
3 Brooks Robinson 2.50 6.00
4 Cal Ripken Right 15.00 40.00
5 Cal Ripken Left 15.00 40.00
6 Eddie Murray 4.00 10.00
7 Frank Robinson 2.50 6.00
8 Jim Palmer 1.50 4.00
9 Bobby Doerr 1.50 4.00
10 Carl Yastrzemski 4.00 10.00
11 Carlton Fisk R.Sox 2.50 6.00
12 Dennis Eckersley 1.50 4.00
13 Luis Aparicio 1.50 4.00
14 Luis Tiant 1.50 4.00
15 Ted Williams 10.00 25.00
16 Wade Boggs Sox 2.50 6.00
17 Duke Snider Dgr 2.50 6.00
18 Jackie Robinson 4.00 10.00
19 Pee Wee Reese 2.50 6.00
20 Burleigh Grimes 1.50 4.00
21 Nolan Ryan Angels 12.00 30.00
22 Reggie Jackson Angels 2.50 6.00
23 Rod Carew White 2.50 6.00
24 Rod Carew Navy 2.50 6.00
25 Billy Williams 1.50 4.00
26 Ernie Banks 4.00 10.00
27 Mark Grace 2.50 6.00
28 Ron Santo 2.50 6.00
29 Paul Molitor Brew 4.00 10.00
30 Bo Jackson Sox 4.00 10.00
31 Carlton Fisk W.Sox 2.50 6.00
32 Johnny Bench 4.00 10.00
33 Tom Seaver Reds 2.50 6.00
34 Tony Perez 1.50 4.00
35 Bob Feller 1.50 4.00
36 Lou Boudreau 1.50 4.00
37 Al Kaline 4.00 10.00
38 Alan Trammell 1.50 4.00
39 Ty Cobb 6.00 15.00
40 Don Sutton 1.50 4.00
41 Nolan Ryan Astros 12.00 30.00
42 Roger Maris A's 4.00 10.00
43 Bo Jackson Royals 4.00 10.00
44 George Brett Gray 8.00 20.00
45 George Brett White 8.00 20.00
46 Maury Wills 1.50 4.00
47 Warren Spahn 2.50 6.00
48 Robin Yount 4.00 10.00
49 Harmon Killebrew Twins 4.00 10.00
50 Kirby Puckett 4.00 10.00
51 Paul Molitor Twins 4.00 10.00
52 Andre Dawson 2.50 6.00
53 Mel Ott Pinstripe 4.00 10.00
54 Mel Ott White 4.00 10.00
55 Duke Snider Mets 2.50 6.00
56 Rickey Henderson Mets 4.00 10.00
57 Tom Seaver Mets 2.50 6.00
58 Babe Ruth w/Bats 10.00 25.00
59 Babe Ruth Gray 10.00 25.00
60 Catfish Hunter 1.50 4.00
61 Dave Righetti 1.50 4.00
62 Dave Winfield Yanks 1.50 4.00
63 Don Mattingly White 8.00 20.00
64 Don Mattingly Navy 8.00 20.00
65 Lou Gehrig w/o Cap 8.00 20.00
66 Lou Gehrig w/Cap 8.00 20.00
67 Phil Niekro 1.50 4.00
68 Phil Rizzuto 2.50 6.00
69 Reggie Jackson Yanks 2.50 6.00
70 Rickey Henderson Yanks 4.00 10.00
71 Roger Maris Yanks 4.00 10.00
72 Thurman Munson w/Bat 4.00 10.00
73 Thurman Munson w/o Bat 4.00 10.00
74 Wade Boggs Yanks 2.50 6.00
75 Whitey Ford 2.50 6.00
76 Yogi Berra 4.00 10.00
77 Lefty Grove 1.50 4.00
78 Mike Schmidt w/Bat 6.00 15.00
79 Mike Schmidt w/o Bat 6.00 15.00
80 Steve Carlton Phils 1.50 4.00
81 Ralph Kiner 2.50 6.00
82 Roberto Clemente w/Bat 10.00 25.00
83 Roberto Clemente w/o Bat 10.00 25.00
84 Dave Winfield Padres 1.50 4.00
85 Rickey Henderson Padres 4.00 10.00
86 Steve Garvey 1.50 4.00
87 Tony Gwynn Gray 4.00 10.00
88 Tony Gwynn White 4.00 10.00
89 Gaylord Perry 1.50 4.00
90 Joe Morgan 1.50 4.00
91 Juan Marichal 1.50 4.00
92 Steve Carlton Giants 1.50 4.00
93 Will Clark 2.50 6.00
94 Willie McCovey 2.50 6.00
95 Bob Gibson 2.50 6.00
96 Lou Brock 2.50 6.00
97 Stan Musial 6.00 15.00
98 Fergie Jenkins 1.50 4.00
99 Nolan Ryan Rgr 12.00 30.00
100 Harmon Killebrew Senators 4.00 10.00

2004 Prime Cuts II MLB Icons Century Gold

STATED PRINT RUN 10 SERIAL #'d SETS
NO PRICING DUE TO SCARCITY

2004 Prime Cuts II MLB Icons Century Platinum

STATED PRINT RUN 1 SERIAL #'d SET
NO PRICING DUE TO SCARCITY

2004 Prime Cuts II MLB Icons Century Silver

*SILVER: .6X TO 1.5X BASIC
STATED PRINT RUN 25 SERIAL #'d SETS

2004 Prime Cuts II MLB Icons Material Number

*RUTH SWATCH W/P'STRIPE: ADD 25%
OVERALL AU-GU ODDS 1:1
PRINT RUNS B/WN 1- COPIES PER
NO PRICING ON QTY OF OR LESS
1 Dale Murphy Jsy/25 10.00 25.00
2 Eddie Mathews Jsy/5
3 Brooks Robinson Jsy/25 10.00 25.00
4 Cal Ripken Jsy/25 40.00 80.00
5 Cal Ripken Jkt/25 40.00 80.00
6 Eddie Murray Jsy/25 15.00 40.00
7 Frank Robinson Jsy/25 6.00 15.00
8 Jim Palmer Jsy/25 6.00 15.00
9 Bobby Doerr Jsy/25 6.00 15.00
10 Carl Yastrzemski Jsy/25 20.00 50.00
11 Carlton Fisk R.Sox Jsy/25 10.00 25.00
12 Dennis Eckersley Jsy/10
13 Luis Aparicio Jsy/10
14 Luis Tiant Jsy/1
15 Ted Williams Jsy/50 50.00 100.00
16 Wade Boggs Sox Jsy/10
17 Duke Snider Dgr Jsy/25 10.00 25.00
18 Jackie Robinson Jkt/50 40.00 80.00
19 Pee Wee Reese Jsy/25 10.00 25.00
20 Burleigh Grimes Pants/25 30.00 60.00
21 Nolan Ryan Angels Jsy/25 20.00 50.00
22 R.Jackson Angels Jsy/25 10.00 25.00
23 Rod Carew Jsy/25 10.00 25.00
24 Rod Carew Jkt/25 10.00 25.00
25 Billy Williams Jsy/25 6.00 15.00
26 Ernie Banks Jsy/25 12.50 30.00
27 Mark Grace Jsy/1
28 Ron Santo Bat/10
29 Paul Molitor Brew Pants/25 6.00 15.00
30 Bo Jackson Sox Jsy/1
31 Carlton Fisk W.Sox Jsy/25 10.00 25.00
32 Johnny Bench Jsy/25 12.50 30.00
33 Tom Seaver Reds Jsy/25 10.00 25.00
35 Bob Feller Jsy/25 6.00 15.00
36 Lou Boudreau Jsy/25 12.50 30.00
37 Al Kaline Pants/6
38 Alan Trammell Jsy/3
39 Ty Cobb Pants/50 60.00 120.00
40 Don Sutton Jsy/5
41 Nolan Ryan Astros Jsy/25 20.00 50.00
42 Roger Maris A's Jsy/25 30.00 60.00
43 Bo Jackson Royals Jsy/10
44 George Brett Jsy/25 20.00 50.00
45 George Brett Jsy/25 20.00 50.00
46 Maury Wills Jsy/1
47 Warren Spahn Jsy/25 12.50 30.00
48 Robin Yount Jsy/25 12.50 30.00
49 H.Killebrew Twins Jsy/25 15.00 40.00
50 Kirby Puckett Jsy/25 12.50 30.00
51 Paul Molitor Twins Jsy/25 6.00 15.00
52 Andre Dawson Jsy/1
53 Mel Ott Jsy/25 20.00 50.00
54 Mel Ott Pants/25 20.00 50.00
55 Duke Snider Mets Jsy/25 10.00 25.00
56 R.Henderson Mets Jsy/1
57 Tom Seaver Mets Jsy/5
58 Babe Ruth Jsy/25 200.00 350.00
59 Babe Ruth Pants/50 150.00 250.00
60 Catfish Hunter Jsy/25 10.00 25.00
61 Dave Righetti Jsy/1
62 D.Winfield Yanks Pants/10
63 Don Mattingly Jsy/25 20.00 50.00
64 Don Mattingly Jkt/25 20.00 50.00
65 Lou Gehrig Jsy/25 100.00 200.00
66 Lou Gehrig Pants/50 75.00 150.00
67 Phil Niekro Jsy/5
68 Phil Rizzuto Pants/25 10.00 25.00
69 R.Jackson Yanks Jsy/25 10.00 25.00
70 R.Henderson Yanks Jsy/1
71 R.Maris Yanks Pants/25 20.00 50.00
72 Thurman Munson Jsy/50 15.00 40.00
73 Thurman Munson Pants/50 15.00 40.00
74 Wade Boggs Yanks Jsy/10
75 Whitey Ford Pants/16 15.00 40.00
76 Yogi Berra Jsy/8
77 Lefty Grove Hat/25 75.00 150.00
78 Mike Schmidt Jsy/20 20.00 50.00
79 Mike Schmidt Jkt/20 20.00 50.00
80 S.Carlton Phils Pants/10
81 Ralph Kiner Bat/10
82 Roberto Clemente Jsy/21 75.00 150.00
83 Roberto Clemente Hat/21 75.00 150.00
84 Dave Winfield Padres Jsy/10
85 R.Henderson Padres Jsy/1
86 Steve Garvey Jsy/6
87 Tony Gwynn White Jsy/10
88 Tony Gwynn Navy Jsy/10
89 Gaylord Perry Jsy/10
90 Joe Morgan Jsy/8
91 Juan Marichal Jsy/25 6.00 15.00
92 Steve Carlton Giants Jsy/10
93 Will Clark Jsy/22 10.00 25.00
94 Willie McCovey Jsy/25 10.00 25.00
95 Bob Gibson Jsy/25 10.00 25.00
96 Lou Brock Jkt/20 10.00 25.00
97 Stan Musial Jsy/6
98 Fergie Jenkins Hat/10
99 Nolan Ryan Rgr Pants/25 20.00 50.00
100 H.Killebrew Senators Jsy/25 15.00 40.00

2004 Prime Cuts II MLB Icons Material Prime

OVERALL AU-GU ODDS 1:1
PRINT RUNS B/WN 1-10 COPIES PER
NO PRICING DUE TO SCARCITY

2004 Prime Cuts II MLB Icons Material Combo

*p/r 20-25: .6X TO 1.5X NBR p/r 50
*p/r 20-25: .5X TO 1.2X NBR p/r 25
*p/r 16-19: .6X TO 1.5X NBR p/r 25
*p/r 16-19: .5X TO 1.2X NBR p/r 16
OVERALL AU-GU ODDS 1:1
PRINT RUNS B/WN 1-25 COPIES PER
NO PRICING ON QTY OF 14 OR LESS
39 Ty Cobb Bat-Pants/25 125.00 200.00
58 Babe Ruth Bat-Jsy/25 250.00 400.00
59 Babe Ruth Bat-Pants/25 200.00 350.00
65 Lou Gehrig Bat-Jsy/25 175.00 300.00
66 Lou Gehrig Bat-Pants/25 150.00 250.00

2004 Prime Cuts II MLB Icons Material Combo Prime

OVERALL AU-GU ODDS 1:1
PRINT RUNS B/WN 1-10 COPIES PER
NO PRICING DUE TO SCARCITY

2004 Prime Cuts II MLB Icons Signature Century Gold

*p/r 20-25: .5X TO 1.2X SILV p/r 36-50
*p/r 20-25: .4X TO 1X SILV p/r 20-35
*p/r 16-19: .6X TO 1.5X SILV p/r 36-50
*p/r 16-19: .5X TO 1.2X SILV p/r 20-35
OVERALL AU-GU ODDS 1:1
PRINT RUNS B/WN 1-25 COPIES PER
NO PRICING ON QTY OF 11 OR LESS

2004 Prime Cuts II MLB Icons Signature Century Platinum

STATED PRINT RUN 1 SERIAL #'d SET
NO PRICING DUE TO SCARCITY

2004 Prime Cuts II MLB Icons Signature Century Silver

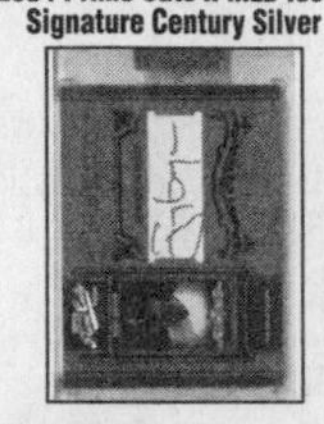

OVERALL AU-GU ODDS 1:1
PRINT RUNS B/WN 1-50 COPIES PER
NO PRICING ON QTY OF 12 OR LESS
1 Dale Murphy/25 15.00 40.00
3 Brooks Robinson/50 12.50 30.00
4 Cal Ripken Right/25 100.00 200.00
5 Cal Ripken Left/25 100.00 200.00
6 Eddie Murray/25 30.00 60.00
7 Frank Robinson/50 12.50 30.00
8 Jim Palmer/50 12.50 30.00
9 Bobby Doerr/25 10.00 25.00
10 Carl Yastrzemski/25 40.00 80.00
11 Carlton Fisk R.Sox/27 15.00 40.00
12 Dennis Eckersley/43 12.50 30.00
13 Luis Aparicio/25 10.00 25.00
14 Luis Tiant/1
16 Wade Boggs Sox/26 15.00 40.00
17 Duke Snider Dgr/50 12.50 30.00
21 Nolan Ryan Angels/30 60.00 120.00
22 Reggie Jackson Angels/25 30.00 60.00
23 Rod Carew White/29 15.00 40.00
24 Rod Carew Navy/29 15.00 40.00
25 Billy Williams/26 10.00 25.00
27 Mark Grace/1
28 Ron Santo/1
29 Paul Molitor Brew/25 10.00 25.00
30 Bo Jackson Sox/25 30.00 60.00
31 Carlton Fisk W.Sox/25 15.00 40.00
32 Johnny Bench/50 20.00 50.00
33 Tom Seaver Reds/25 15.00 40.00
34 Tony Perez/25 15.00 40.00
35 Bob Feller/25 10.00 25.00
37 Al Kaline/50 20.00 50.00
38 Alan Trammell/1
40 Don Sutton/20 10.00 25.00
41 Nolan Ryan Astros/34 60.00 120.00
43 Bo Jackson Royals/25 30.00 60.00
44 George Brett Gray/25 50.00 100.00
45 George Brett White/25 50.00 100.00
46 Maury Wills/1
47 Warren Spahn/1
48 Robin Yount/19 40.00 80.00
49 H.Killebrew Twins/50 30.00 60.00
50 Kirby Puckett/10
51 Paul Molitor Twins/50 8.00 20.00
52 Andre Dawson/1
55 Duke Snider Mets/50 12.50 30.00
56 Rickey Henderson Mets/24 30.00 60.00
57 Tom Seaver Mets/25 15.00 40.00
62 Dave Winfield Yanks/31 15.00 40.00
63 Don Mattingly White/50 30.00 60.00
64 Don Mattingly Navy/50 30.00 60.00
67 Phil Niekro/35 10.00 25.00
68 Phil Rizzuto/25 15.00 40.00
69 Reggie Jackson Yanks/25 30.00 60.00
70 Rickey Henderson Yanks/24 30.00 60.00
74 Wade Boggs Yanks/12
75 Whitey Ford/25 30.00 60.00
76 Yogi Berra/25 30.00 60.00
78 Mike Schmidt w/Bat/20 40.00 80.00
79 Mike Schmidt w/o Bat/20 40.00 80.00
80 Steve Carlton Phils/32 10.00 25.00
81 Ralph Kiner/25 15.00 40.00
84 Dave Winfield Padres/31 15.00 40.00
85 R.Henderson Padres/24 30.00 60.00
86 Steve Garvey/1
87 Tony Gwynn Gray/50 20.00 50.00
88 Tony Gwynn White/50 20.00 50.00
89 Gaylord Perry/36 8.00 20.00
90 Joe Morgan/24 10.00 25.00
91 Juan Marichal/27 10.00 25.00
92 Steve Carlton Giants/32 10.00 25.00
93 Will Clark/22 15.00 40.00
94 Willie McCovey/25 15.00 40.00
95 Bob Gibson/45 12.50 30.00
96 Lou Brock/50 12.50 30.00
97 Stan Musial/50 40.00 80.00
98 Fergie Jenkins/31 10.00 25.00
99 Nolan Ryan Rgr/34 60.00 120.00
100 H.Killebrew Senators/50 30.00 60.00

2004 Prime Cuts II MLB Icons Signature Material Number

*p/r 36-50: .5X TO 1.2X SILV p/r 36-50
*p/r 36-50: .4X TO 1X SILV p/r 20-35
*p/r 20-35: .6X TO 1.5X SILV p/r 36-50
*p/r 20-35: .5X TO 1.2X SILV p/r 20-35
*p/r 20-35: .4X TO 1X SILV p/r 15-19
*p/r 15-19: .75X TO 2X SILV p/r 36-50
*p/r 15-19: .6X TO 1.5X SILV p/r 20-35
OVERALL AU-GU ODDS 1:1
PRINT RUNS B/WN 1-45 COPIES PER
NO PRICING ON QTY OF 12 OR LESS
27 Mark Grace Jsy/17 30.00 60.00

2004 Prime Cuts II MLB Icons Signature Material Prime

OVERALL AU-GU ODDS 1:1
PRINT RUNS B/WN 1-10 COPIES PER
NO PRICING DUE TO SCARCITY

2004 Prime Cuts II MLB Icons Signature Material Combo

*p/r 20-35: .75X TO 2X SILV p/r 36-50
*p/r 20-35: .6X TO 1.5X SILV p/r 20-35
*p/r 15-19: 1X TO 2.5X SILV p/r 36-50
*p/r 15-19: .75X TO 2X SILV p/r 20-35
*p/r 15-19: .6X TO 1.5X SILV p/r 15-19
OVERALL AU-GU ODDS 1:1
PRINT RUNS B/WN 1-32 COPIES PER
NO PRICING ON QTY OF 11 OR LESS

2004 Prime Cuts II MLB Icons Signature Material Combo Prime

OVERALL AU-GU ODDS 1:1
PRINT RUNS B/WN 1-10 COPIES PER
NO PRICING DUE TO SCARCITY

2004 Prime Cuts II Timeline

RANDOM INSERTS IN PACKS
STATED PRINT RUN 50 SERIAL #'d SETS
1 Al Kaline 4.00 10.00
2 Alex Rodriguez 6.00 15.00
3 Andre Dawson 2.50 6.00
4 Babe Ruth 10.00 25.00
5 Barry Zito 1.50 4.00
6 Bob Feller 1.50 4.00
7 Bob Gibson 2.50 6.00
8 Bobby Doerr 1.50 4.00
9 Brooks Robinson 2.50 6.00
10 Cal Ripken 15.00 40.00
11 Carl Hubbell 1.50 4.00

12 Carl Yastrzemski	4.00	10.00
13 Carlton Fisk	2.50	6.00
14 Catfish Hunter	1.50	4.00
15 Chipper Jones	4.00	10.00
16 Cy Young	2.50	6.00
17 Dale Murphy	2.50	6.00
18 Dave Parker	1.50	4.00
19 Dennis Eckersley	1.50	4.00
20 Don Drysdale	2.50	6.00
21 Don Mattingly	8.00	20.00
22 Duke Snider	2.50	6.00
23 Dwight Gooden	1.50	4.00
24 Early Wynn	1.50	4.00
25 Eddie Mathews	4.00	10.00
26 Eddie Murray	4.00	10.00
27 Enos Slaughter	1.50	4.00
28 Ernie Banks	4.00	10.00
29 Fergie Jenkins	1.50	4.00
30 Frank Robinson	2.50	6.00
31 Frank Thomas	4.00	10.00
32 Frankie Frisch	2.50	6.00
33 Fred Lynn	1.50	4.00
34 Gary Carter	1.50	4.00
35 Gaylord Perry	1.50	4.00
36 George Brett	8.00	20.00
37 Greg Maddux	6.00	15.00
38 Hal Newhouser	1.50	4.00
39 Harmon Killebrew	4.00	10.00
40 Honus Wagner	4.00	10.00
41 Hoyt Wilhelm	1.50	4.00
42 Ivan Rodriguez	2.50	6.00
43 Jackie Robinson	4.00	10.00
44 Jason Giambi	1.50	4.00
45 Jeff Bagwell	2.50	6.00
46 Jim Palmer	1.50	4.00
47 Jimmie Foxx	4.00	10.00
48 Joe Morgan	1.50	4.00
49 Johnny Bench	4.00	10.00
50 Johnny Mize	1.50	4.00
51 Jose Canseco	2.50	6.00
52 Juan Gonzalez	1.50	4.00
53 Juan Marichal	1.50	4.00
54 Keith Hernandez	1.50	4.00
55 Kirby Puckett	4.00	10.00
56 Lefty Grove	1.50	4.00
57 Lou Boudreau	1.50	4.00
58 Lou Brock	2.50	6.00
59 Lou Gehrig	8.00	20.00
60 Luis Aparicio	1.50	4.00
61 Marty Marion	1.50	4.00
62 Mel Ott	4.00	10.00
63 Miguel Tejada	2.50	6.00
64 Mike Schmidt	6.00	15.00
65 Nellie Fox	2.50	6.00
66 Nolan Ryan	12.00	30.00
67 Orel Hershiser	1.50	4.00
68 Orlando Cepeda	1.50	4.00
69 Paul Molitor	4.00	10.00
70 Pedro Martinez	2.50	6.00
71 Pee Wee Reese	2.50	6.00
72 Phil Niekro	1.50	4.00
73 Phil Rizzuto	2.50	6.00
74 Ralph Kiner	2.50	6.00
75 Randy Johnson	4.00	10.00
76 Red Schoendienst	1.50	4.00
77 Reggie Jackson	2.50	6.00
78 Rickey Henderson	4.00	10.00
79 Roberto Clemente	10.00	25.00
80 Robin Yount	4.00	10.00
81 Rod Carew	2.50	6.00
82 Roger Clemens	5.00	12.00
83 Roger Maris	4.00	10.00
84 Rogers Hornsby	2.50	6.00
85 Roy Campanella	4.00	10.00
86 Ozzie Smith	6.00	15.00
87 Sammy Sosa	4.00	10.00
88 Satchel Paige	4.00	10.00
89 Stan Musial	6.00	15.00
90 Steve Carlton	1.50	4.00
91 Ted Williams	10.00	25.00
92 Thurman Munson	4.00	10.00
93 Tom Seaver	2.50	6.00
94 Ty Cobb	6.00	15.00
95 Walter Johnson	2.50	6.00
96 Warren Spahn	2.50	6.00
97 Whitey Ford	2.50	6.00
98 Willie McCovey	2.50	6.00
99 Willie Stargell	2.50	6.00
100 Yogi Berra	4.00	10.00

2004 Prime Cuts II Timeline Century Gold

STATED PRINT RUN 10 SERIAL #'d SETS
NO PRICING DUE TO SCARCITY

2004 Prime Cuts II Timeline Century Platinum

STATED PRINT RUN 1 SERIAL #'d SET
NO PRICING DUE TO SCARCITY

2004 Prime Cuts II Timeline Century Silver

*SILVER: .6X TO 1.5X BASIC
STATED PRINT RUN 25 SERIAL #'d SETS

2004 Prime Cuts II Timeline Material Number

*RUTH SWATCH W/P'STRIPE: ADD 25%
OVERALL AU-GU ODDS 1:1
PRINT RUNS B/WN 1-42 COPIES PER
NO PRICING ON QTY OF 11 OR LESS

1 Al Kaline Pants/6		
4 Babe Ruth Jsy/25	250.00	400.00
6 Bob Feller Pants/19	8.00	20.00
7 Bob Gibson Jsy/25	10.00	25.00
8 Bobby Doerr Jsy/5		
9 Brooks Robinson Jsy/5		
10 Cal Ripken Jsy/25	40.00	80.00
12 Carl Yastrzemski Jsy/25	20.00	50.00
13 Carlton Fisk Jsy/27	10.00	25.00
14 Catfish Hunter Jsy/27	10.00	25.00
17 Dale Murphy Jsy/10		
20 Don Drysdale Jsy/25	20.00	50.00
21 Don Mattingly Pants/10		
22 Duke Snider Pants/25	10.00	25.00
24 Early Wynn Jsy/24	6.00	15.00
25 Eddie Mathews Jsy/25	15.00	40.00
26 Eddie Murray Jsy/25	15.00	40.00
27 Enos Slaughter Jsy/9		
28 Ernie Banks Jsy/25	12.50	30.00
29 Fergie Jenkins Pants/1		
30 Frank Robinson Jsy/5		
32 Frankie Frisch Jkt/25	15.00	40.00
34 Gary Carter Jsy/8		
36 George Brett Jsy/25	20.00	50.00
38 Hal Newhouser Jsy/16	15.00	40.00
39 Harmon Killebrew Jsy/25	15.00	40.00
41 Hoyt Wilhelm Jsy/5		
43 Jackie Robinson Jkt/42	40.00	80.00
46 Jim Palmer Jsy/22	6.00	15.00
47 Jimmie Foxx Fld Glv/25	50.00	100.00
48 Joe Morgan Jsy/8		
49 Johnny Bench Jsy/25	12.50	30.00
50 Johnny Mize Pants/10		
53 Juan Marichal Jsy/25	6.00	15.00
55 Kirby Puckett Jsy/25	12.50	30.00
56 Lefty Grove Hat/10		
57 Lou Boudreau Jsy/5		
58 Lou Brock Jsy/20	10.00	25.00
59 Lou Gehrig Jsy/25	100.00	200.00
60 Luis Aparicio Jsy/11		
61 Marty Marion Jsy/4		
62 Mel Ott Pants/25	20.00	50.00
64 Mike Schmidt Jsy/20	20.00	50.00
65 Nellie Fox Bat/2		
66 Nolan Ryan Jsy/25	20.00	50.00
67 Orel Hershiser Jsy/5		
68 Orlando Cepeda Pants/25	6.00	15.00
69 Paul Molitor Jsy/4		
71 Pee Wee Reese Jsy/25	10.00	25.00
72 Phil Niekro Jsy/5		
73 Phil Rizzuto Pants/10		
74 Ralph Kiner Bat/25	6.00	15.00
76 Red Schoendienst Jsy/2		
77 Reggie Jackson Jsy/25	10.00	25.00
78 Rickey Henderson Jsy/5		
79 Roberto Clemente Jsy/5		
80 Robin Yount Jsy/19	15.00	40.00
81 Rod Carew Jsy/25	10.00	25.00
82 Roger Clemens Jsy/21	12.50	30.00
83 Roger Maris Jsy/25	30.00	60.00
84 Rogers Hornsby Bat/25	40.00	80.00
85 Roy Campanella Pants/25	12.50	30.00
86 Ozzie Smith Jsy/25	15.00	40.00
87 Sammy Sosa Jsy/21	10.00	25.00
88 Satchel Paige CO Jsy/25	40.00	80.00
89 Stan Musial Jsy/6		
90 Steve Carlton Jsy/25	6.00	15.00
91 Ted Williams Jsy/25	60.00	120.00
92 Thurman Munson Jsy/25	20.00	50.00
93 Tom Seaver Pants/25	10.00	25.00
94 Ty Cobb Pants/25	75.00	150.00
96 Warren Spahn Jsy/21	12.50	30.00
97 Whitey Ford Jsy/16	15.00	40.00
98 Willie McCovey Jsy/25	10.00	25.00
99 Willie Stargell Jsy/8		
100 Yogi Berra Jsy/8		

2004 Prime Cuts II Timeline Material Position

*RET p/r 36-50: .4X TO 1X NBR p/r 36-50
*ACT p/r 20-35: .4X TO 1X NBR p/r 20-35
*RET p/r 20-35: .4X TO 1X NBR p/r 20-35
*RET p/r 15-19: .5X TO 1.2X NBR p/r 20-35
*RET p/r 15-19: .4X TO 1X NBR p/r 15-19
OVERALL AU-GU ODDS 1:1
PRINT RUNS B/WN 1-42 COPIES PER
NO PRICING ON QTY OF 11 OR LESS

4 Babe Ruth Jsy/25	250.00	400.00
59 Lou Gehrig Jsy/25	100.00	200.00

2004 Prime Cuts II Timeline Material Prime

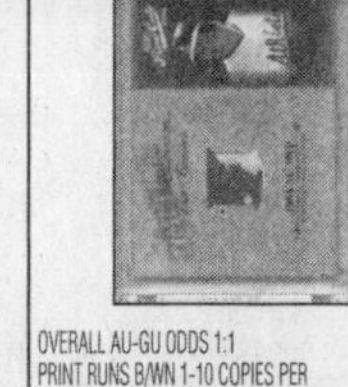

OVERALL AU-GU ODDS 1:1
PRINT RUNS B/WN 1-10 COPIES PER
NO PRICING DUE TO SCARCITY

2004 Prime Cuts II Timeline Material Combo

*RET p/r 36-50: .5X TO 1.2X NBR p/r 36-50
*RET p/r 36-50: .4X TO 1X NBR p/r 20-35
*ACT p/r 20-35: .5X TO 1.2X NBR p/r 20-35
*RET p/r 20-35: .5X TO 1.2X NBR p/r 20-35
*RET p/r 15-19: .6X TO 1.5X NBR p/r 20-35
*RET p/r 15-19: .5X TO 1.2X NBR p/r 15-19
OVERALL AU-GU ODDS 1:1
PRINT RUNS B/WN 1-42 COPIES PER
NO PRICING ON QTY OF 14 OR LESS

4 Babe Ruth Jsy-Jsy/25	300.00	500.00
17 Dale Murphy Bat-Jsy/25	12.50	30.00
21 D.Matt Btg Glv-Pants/25	30.00	60.00
59 Lou Gehrig Jsy-Pants/25	175.00	300.00
79 R.Clemente Hat-Jsy/21	100.00	200.00

2004 Prime Cuts II Timeline Material Combo CY

*ACT p/r 20-35: .5X TO 1.2X NBR p/r 20-35
*RET p/r 20-35: .5X TO 1.2X NBR p/r 20-35
*RET p/r 15-19: .5X TO 1.2X NBR p/r 15-19
OVERALL AU-GU ODDS 1:1
PRINT RUNS B/WN 1-32 COPIES PER
NO PRICING ON QTY OF 10 OR LESS

70 Pedro Martinez Bat-Jsy/25	30.00	60.00

2004 Prime Cuts II Timeline Material Trio

*ACT p/r 20-35: .6X TO 1.5X NBR p/r 20-35
*RET p/r 20-35: .6X TO 1.5X NBR p/r 20-35
*RET p/r 15-19: .75X TO 2X NBR p/r 20-35
*RET p/r 15-19: .6X TO 1.5X NBR p/r 15-19
OVERALL AU-GU ODDS 1:1
PRINT RUNS B/WN 1-25 COPIES PER
NO PRICING ON QTY OF 10 OR LESS

17 Dale Murphy Bat-Jsy-Jsy/25	15.00	40.00
21 D.Matt Bat-Jkt-Pants/25	40.00	80.00
26 E.Murray Bat-Jsy-Shoe/25	60.00	120.00

2004 Prime Cuts II Timeline Material Trio HOF

OVERALL AU-GU ODDS 1:1
PRINT RUNS B/WN 1-9 COPIES PER
NO PRICING DUE TO SCARCITY

2004 Prime Cuts II Timeline Material Trio HOF Presidential Edition

94 Ty Cobb Bat-Pants-Pants/1

2004 Prime Cuts II Timeline Material Trio MVP

*RET p/r 15-19: .75X TO 2X NBR p/r 20-35
OVERALL AU-GU ODDS 1:1
PRINT RUNS B/WN 1-15 COPIES PER
NO PRICING ON QTY OF 10 OR LESS

2004 Prime Cuts II Timeline Material Trio Stats

*RET p/r 15-19: .75X TO 2X NBR p/r 20-35
OVERALL AU-GU ODDS 1:1
PRINT RUNS B/WN 1-15 COPIES PER
NO PRICING ON QTY OF 10 OR LESS

2004 Prime Cuts II Timeline Material Quad

OVERALL AU-GU ODDS 1:1
PRINT RUNS B/WN 1-25 COPIES PER
NO PRICING ON QTY OF 10 OR LESS
B ='s Bat, BG ='s Btg Glv, FG ='s Fld Glv
H ='s Hat, J ='s Jsy, JK ='s Jkt, P ='s Pants

4 Babe Ruth B-J-J-P/25	600.00	1000.00
91 Ted Williams B-JK-J-J/25	175.00	300.00

2004 Prime Cuts II Timeline Signature Century Gold

OVERALL AU-GU ODDS 1:1
PRINT RUNS B/WN 1-5 COPIES PER
NO PRICING DUE TO SCARCITY

2004 Prime Cuts II Timeline Signature Century Platinum

OVERALL AU-GU ODDS 1:1
STATED PRINT RUN 1 SERIAL #'d SET
NO PRICING DUE TO SCARCITY

2004 Prime Cuts II Timeline Signature Century Silver

OVERALL AU-GU ODDS 1:1
PRINT RUNS B/WN 1-10 COPIES PER
NO PRICING DUE TO SCARCITY

2004 Prime Cuts II Timeline Signature Material Number

OVERALL AU-GU ODDS 1:1
PRINT RUNS B/WN 1-34 COPIES PER
NO PRICING ON QTY OF 11 OR LESS

1 Al Kaline Pants/6		
3 Andre Dawson Jsy/8		
4 Babe Ruth Jsy/1		
5 Barry Zito Jsy/5		
6 Bob Feller Pants/19	15.00	40.00
7 Bob Gibson Jsy/25	20.00	50.00
8 Bobby Doerr Jsy/25	12.50	30.00
9 Brooks Robinson Jsy/5		
10 Cal Ripken Jsy/1		
12 Carl Yastrzemski Jsy/8		
13 Carlton Fisk Jsy/5		
15 Chipper Jones Jsy/10		
17 Dale Murphy Jsy/3		
18 Dave Parker Jsy/1		
20 Don Drysdale Jsy/1		
21 Don Mattingly Pants/23	50.00	100.00
22 Duke Snider Pants/4		
23 Dwight Gooden Jsy/5		
26 Eddie Murray Jsy/1		
27 Enos Slaughter Jsy/1		
29 Fergie Jenkins Pants/1		
30 Frank Robinson Jsy/5		
31 Frank Thomas Jsy/5		
32 Frankie Frisch Jkt/1		
33 Fred Lynn Jsy/1		
34 Gary Carter Jsy/8		
35 Gaylord Perry Jsy/10		
36 George Brett Jsy/5		
37 Greg Maddux Jsy/5		
38 Hal Newhouser Jsy/1		
39 Harmon Killebrew Jsy/3		
41 Hoyt Wilhelm Jsy/5		
45 Jeff Bagwell Jsy/5		
46 Jim Palmer Jsy/22	20.00	50.00
47 Jimmie Foxx Fld Glv/1		
48 Joe Morgan Jsy/8		
49 Johnny Bench Jsy/5		
50 Johnny Mize Pants/1		
51 Jose Canseco Jsy/5		
52 Juan Gonzalez Jsy/5		
53 Juan Marichal Jsy/27	12.50	30.00
54 Keith Hernandez Jsy/5		
54 Keith Hernandez Jsy/5		
55 Kirby Puckett Jsy/1		
56 Lefty Grove Hat/1		
57 Lou Boudreau Jsy/1		
58 Lou Brock Jsy/20	20.00	50.00
60 Luis Aparicio Jsy/11		
61 Marty Marion Jsy/1		
64 Mike Schmidt Jsy/5		
66 Nolan Ryan Jsy/34	75.00	150.00
67 Orel Hershiser Jsy/5		
68 Orlando Cepeda Pants/1		
69 Paul Molitor Jsy/4		
70 Pedro Martinez Jsy/1		
71 Pee Wee Reese Jsy/1		
72 Phil Niekro Jsy/5		
73 Phil Rizzuto Pants/10		
74 Ralph Kiner Bat/4		
75 Randy Johnson Jsy/1		
76 Red Schoendienst Jsy/2		
77 Reggie Jackson Jsy/9		
78 Rickey Henderson Jsy/1		
79 Roberto Clemente Jsy/1		
80 Robin Yount Jsy/5		
81 Rod Carew Jsy/5		
82 Roger Clemens Jsy/1		
84 Rogers Hornsby Bat/1		
86 Ozzie Smith Jsy/1		
87 Sammy Sosa Jsy/1		
88 Satchel Paige CO Jsy/1		
89 Stan Musial Jsy/6		
90 Steve Carlton Jsy/32	12.50	30.00
91 Ted Williams Jsy/1		
93 Tom Seaver Pants/5		
94 Ty Cobb Pants/1		
96 Warren Spahn Jsy/1		
97 Whitey Ford Jsy/5		
98 Willie McCovey Jsy/4		
100 Yogi Berra Jsy/8		

2004 Prime Cuts II Timeline Signature Material Position

*RET p/r 20-35: .4X TO 1X NBR p/r 20-35
*RET p/r 15-19: .4X TO 1X NBR p/r 15-19
OVERALL AU-GU ODDS 1:1
PRINT RUNS B/WN 1-34 COPIES PER
NO PRICING ON QTY OF 11 OR LESS

2004 Prime Cuts II Timeline Signature Material Prime

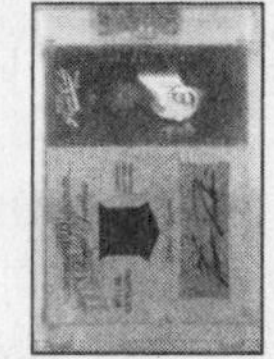

OVERALL AU-GU ODDS 1:1
PRINT RUNS B/WN 1-9 COPIES PER
NO PRICING DUE TO SCARCITY

2004 Prime Cuts II Timeline Signature Material Combo

*RET p/r 20-35: .5X TO 1.2X NBR p/r 20-35
OVERALL AU-GU ODDS 1:1
PRINT RUNS B/WN 1-25 COPIES PER
NO PRICING ON QTY OF 11 OR LESS

2004 Prime Cuts II Timeline Signature Material Combo CY

*RET p/r 20-35: .5X TO 1.2X NBR p/r 20-35
OVERALL AU-GU ODDS 1:1
PRINT RUNS B/WN 1-25 COPIES PER
NO PRICING ON QTY OF 5 OR LESS

2004 Prime Cuts II Timeline Signature Material Trio

OVERALL AU-GU ODDS 1:1
PRINT RUNS B/WN 1-9 COPIES PER
NO PRICING DUE TO SCARCITY

2004 Prime Cuts II Timeline Signature Material Trio HOF

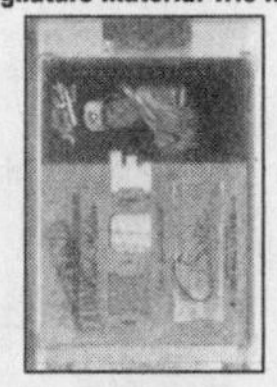

OVERALL AU-GU ODDS 1:1
PRINT RUNS B/WN 1-9 COPIES PER
NO PRICING DUE TO SCARCITY

2004 Prime Cuts II Timeline Signature Material Trio MVP

OVERALL AU-GU ODDS 1:1
PRINT RUNS B/WN 1-8 COPIES PER
NO PRICING DUE TO SCARCITY

2004 Prime Cuts II Timeline Signature Material Trio Stats

OVERALL AU-GU ODDS 1:1
PRINT RUNS B/WN 1-9 COPIES PER
NO PRICING DUE TO SCARCITY

2004 Prime Cuts II Timeline Signature Material Quad

OVERALL AU-GU ODDS 1:1
PRINT RUNS B/WN 1-25 COPIES PER
NO PRICING ON QTY OF OR LESS
B ='s Bat, BG ='s Btg Glv, FG ='s Fld Glv
H ='s Hat, J ='s Jsy, JK ='s Jkt, P ='s Pants

17 Dale Murphy B-J-J-J/25	60.00	120.00

2005 Prime Cuts

This 100-card set was released in October, 2005. The set was issued in six-card packs which came one pack to a box and 15 boxes to a case. Cards numbered 1-91 feature active players while cards numbered 92 through 100 feature retired players. All cards in this set were issued to stated print runs of 399, 449 or 499 cards issued. We have placed next to the player's name what print run that card is.

COMMON CARD (1-91)	.75	2.00
COMMON CARD (92-100)	.75	2.00
PRINT RUNS B/WN 399-499 COPIES PER		
1 Vladimir Guerrero Angels/499	2.00	5.00
2 Roger Clemens Astros/499	2.50	6.00
3 Carlos Beltran/499	.75	2.00
4 Johan Santana/499	2.00	5.00
5 Alfonso Soriano/499	1.25	3.00
6 Derek Jeter/499	5.00	12.00
7 Chipper Jones/499	2.00	5.00
8 David Ortiz/499	2.00	5.00
9 Josh Beckett/499	1.25	3.00
10 Mike Piazza Mets/499	2.00	5.00
11 Alex Rodriguez/449	3.00	8.00
12 Albert Pujols/449	5.00	12.00
13 Mike Sweeney/449	.75	2.00
14 Miguel Tejada/449	1.25	3.00
15 Barry Zito/449	.75	2.00
16 Mark Mulder/449	.75	2.00
17 Tim Hudson/449	1.25	3.00
18 Troy Glaus/449	.75	2.00
19 Ichiro Suzuki/449	3.00	8.00
20 Ken Griffey Jr./449	3.00	8.00
21 Miguel Cabrera/449	2.00	5.00
22 Jeff Bagwell/449	1.25	3.00
23 Todd Helton/449	1.25	3.00
24 Mark Buehrle/449	1.25	3.00
25 Greg Maddux Cubs/449	3.00	8.00
26 Ivan Rodriguez/449	1.25	3.00
27 Carlos Lee/449	.75	2.00
28 Nick Johnson/449	.75	2.00
29 Mike Mussina/449	1.25	3.00
30 Mark Teixeira/499	2.00	5.00
31 Adrian Beltre/499	.75	2.00
32 Torii Hunter/499	.75	2.00
33 Jim Edmonds/499	1.25	3.00
34 Manny Ramirez/499	2.00	5.00
35 Pedro Martinez/499	1.25	3.00
36 Jim Thome/499	1.25	3.00
37 Craig Biggio/499	1.25	3.00
38 Garret Anderson/499	.75	2.00
39 Paul Konerko/499	1.25	3.00
40 Adam Dunn/499	1.25	3.00
41 Brian Roberts/449	.75	2.00
42 Derrek Lee/449	.75	2.00
43 Hank Blalock/449	.75	2.00
44 Justin Morneau/449	2.00	5.00
45 David Wright/449	3.00	8.00
46 Richie Sexson/449	.75	2.00
47 Ben Sheets/449	.75	2.00
48 Gary Sheffield/449	.75	2.00
49 Pat Burrell/449	.75	2.00
50 Larry Walker/449	1.25	3.00
51 Johnny Damon/449	1.25	3.00
52 Jeff Kent/449	.75	2.00
53 Aubrey Huff/449	.75	2.00
54 Shawn Green/449	.75	2.00
55 Milton Bradley/449	.75	2.00
56 Magglio Ordonez/449	1.25	3.00
57 J.T. Snow/449	.75	2.00
58 Scott Rolen/449	1.25	3.00
59 Michael Young/449	1.25	3.00
60 Roy Oswalt/449	1.25	3.00
61 Carlos Zambrano/499	1.25	3.00
62 Dontrelle Willis/499	.75	2.00
63 Curt Schilling/499	1.25	3.00
64 Roy Halladay/499	2.00	5.00
65 Eric Chavez/499	.75	2.00
66 Randy Johnson Yanks/499	2.00	5.00
67 Mark Prior/499	1.25	3.00
68 Victor Martinez/399	1.25	3.00
69 Sammy Sosa O's/399	2.00	5.00
70 Lance Berkman/399	1.25	3.00
71 Jeremy Bonderman/399	.75	2.00
72 Frank Thomas/399	2.00	5.00
73 Jake Peavy/399	.75	2.00
74 Jason Schmidt/399	.75	2.00
75 Carlos Delgado/399	.75	2.00
76 Andruw Jones/399	.75	2.00
77 Vernon Wells/399	.75	2.00
78 Sean Casey/399	.75	2.00
79 Jason Bay/399	.75	2.00
80 Hideki Matsui/399	3.00	8.00
81 Jason Varitek/399	2.00	5.00
82 Kerry Wood/399	.75	2.00
83 Moises Alou/399	.75	2.00
84 Joe Mauer/399	2.00	5.00
85 Rafael Palmeiro/399	1.25	3.00
86 Mike Piazza Dgr/399	2.00	5.00
87 Sammy Sosa Cubs/399	2.00	5.00
88 Randy Johnson Astros/399	2.00	5.00
89 Vladimir Guerrero Expos/399	2.00	5.00
90 Greg Maddux Braves/399	3.00	8.00
91 Roger Clemens Yanks/399	2.50	6.00
92 Nolan Ryan/399	5.00	12.00
93 Cal Ripken/399	8.00	20.00
94 Tony Gwynn/399	2.50	6.00
95 Wade Boggs/449	1.25	3.00
96 Ryne Sandberg/449	4.00	10.00
97 Dale Murphy/449	.75	2.00
98 Mike Schmidt/449	4.00	10.00
99 Don Mattingly/449	4.00	10.00
100 Willie Mays/449	4.00	10.00

2005 Prime Cuts Century Gold

*GOLD 1-91: 1X TO 2.5X BASIC
*GOLD 92-100: 1X TO 2.5X BASIC
STATED PRINT RUN 25 SERIAL #'d SETS

2005 Prime Cuts Century Platinum

STATED PRINT RUN 1 SERIAL #'d SET
NO PRICING DUE TO SCARCITY

2005 Prime Cuts Century Silver

*SILVER 1-91: .6X TO 1.5X BASIC
*SILVER 92-100: .6X TO 1.5X BASIC
STATED PRINT RUN 50 SERIAL #'d SETS

2005 Prime Cuts Material Bat

*1-91 p/r 48-50: .4X TO 1X JSY p/r 50
*92-100 p/r 50: .4X TO 1X JSY p/r 50
OVERALL AU-GU ODDS ONE PER PACK
PRINT RUNS B/WN 1-50 COPIES PER
NO PRICING ON QTY OF 7 OR LESS

1 Vladimir Guerrero Angels/50 5.00 12.00
3 Carlos Beltran/50 3.00 8.00
16 Mark Mulder/50 3.00 8.00
17 Tim Hudson/30 4.00 10.00
18 Troy Glaus/50 3.00 8.00
24 Mark Buehrle/50 3.00 8.00
26 Ivan Rodriguez/50 4.00 10.00
27 Carlos Lee/50 3.00 8.00
28 Nick Johnson/50 3.00 8.00
29 Mike Mussina/48 4.00 10.00
35 Pedro Martinez/50 4.00 10.00
40 Adam Dunn/50 3.00 8.00
46 Richie Sexson/50 3.00 8.00
50 Larry Walker/18 6.00 15.00
52 Jeff Kent/50 3.00 8.00
54 Shawn Green/50 3.00 8.00
56 Magglio Ordonez/50 3.00 8.00
66 Randy Johnson Yanks/50 5.00 12.00
69 Sammy Sosa O's/50 5.00 12.00
81 Jason Varitek/50 5.00 12.00
83 Moises Alou/50 3.00 8.00
95 Wade Boggs/50 5.00 12.00

2005 Prime Cuts Material Jersey

OVERALL AU-GU ODDS ONE PER PACK
PRINT RUNS B/WN 11-50 COPIES PER
NO PRICING ON QTY OF 13 OR LESS

2 Roger Clemens Astros/50 6.00 15.00
4 Johan Santana/50 5.00 12.00
5 Alfonso Soriano/50 3.00 8.00
7 Chipper Jones/50 5.00 12.00
8 David Ortiz/50 4.00 10.00
9 Josh Beckett/50 3.00 8.00
10 Mike Piazza Mets/50 5.00 12.00
12 Albert Pujols/50 8.00 20.00
13 Mike Sweeney/50 3.00 8.00
14 Miguel Tejada/50 3.00 8.00
15 Barry Zito/50 3.00 8.00
21 Miguel Cabrera/50 4.00 10.00
22 Jeff Bagwell/50 4.00 10.00
23 Todd Helton/50 4.00 10.00
24 Mark Buehrle/13
25 Greg Maddux Cubs/50 6.00 15.00
26 Ivan Rodriguez/27 5.00 12.00
29 Mike Mussina/50 4.00 10.00
30 Mark Teixeira/50 4.00 10.00
31 Adrian Beltre/50 3.00 8.00
32 Torii Hunter/50 3.00 8.00
33 Jim Edmonds/50 3.00 8.00
34 Manny Ramirez/50 4.00 10.00
36 Jim Thome/50 4.00 10.00
37 Craig Biggio/50 4.00 10.00
38 Garret Anderson/50 3.00 8.00
39 Paul Konerko/50 3.00 8.00
40 Adam Dunn/11
41 Brian Roberts/50 3.00 8.00
42 Derrek Lee/50 4.00 10.00
43 Hank Blalock/50 3.00 8.00
44 Justin Morneau/50 3.00 8.00
45 David Wright/50 6.00 15.00
47 Ben Sheets/50 3.00 8.00
48 Gary Sheffield/50 3.00 8.00
49 Pat Burrell/50 3.00 8.00
50 Larry Walker/50 4.00 10.00
53 Aubrey Huff/50 3.00 8.00
57 J.T. Snow/50 3.00 8.00
58 Scott Rolen/50 4.00 10.00
59 Michael Young/50 3.00 8.00
60 Roy Oswalt/50 3.00 8.00
61 Carlos Zambrano/50 3.00 8.00
62 Dontrelle Willis/50 3.00 8.00
63 Curt Schilling/50 4.00 10.00
64 Roy Halladay/22 4.00 10.00
65 Eric Chavez/50 3.00 8.00
67 Mark Prior/50 4.00 10.00
68 Victor Martinez/50 3.00 8.00
70 Lance Berkman/50 3.00 8.00
72 Frank Thomas/50 5.00 12.00
75 Carlos Delgado/50 3.00 8.00
76 Andruw Jones/50 4.00 10.00
77 Vernon Wells/50 3.00 8.00
78 Sean Casey/50 3.00 8.00
79 Jason Bay/50 3.00 8.00
80 Hideki Matsui/50 12.50 30.00
82 Kerry Wood/50 3.00 8.00
85 Rafael Palmeiro/50 4.00 10.00
86 Mike Piazza Dgr/50 5.00 12.00
87 Sammy Sosa Cubs/50 5.00 12.00
88 Randy Johnson Astros/50 5.00 12.00
89 Vladimir Guerrero Expos/50 5.00 12.00
90 Greg Maddux Braves/50 6.00 15.00
91 Roger Clemens Yanks/50 6.00 15.00
92 Nolan Ryan/38 10.00 25.00
93 Cal Ripken/50 10.00 25.00
94 Tony Gwynn/50 6.00 15.00
96 Ryne Sandberg/50 8.00 20.00
97 Dale Murphy/50 5.00 12.00
98 Mike Schmidt/50 6.00 15.00
99 Don Mattingly/50 6.00 15.00
100 Willie Mays/50 10.00 25.00

2005 Prime Cuts Material Jersey Number

*1-91 p/r 50: .4X TO 1X JSY p/r 50
*1-91 p/r 50: .3X TO .8X JSY p/r 27
*92-100 p/r 50: .4X TO 1X JSY p/r 50
STATED PRINT RUN 50 SERIAL #'d SETS
PRIME PRINT RUN B/WN 5-10 COPIES PER
NO PRIME PRICING DUE TO SCARCITY
OVERALL AU-GU ODDS ONE PER PACK

1 Vladimir Guerrero Angels 5.00 12.00
24 Mark Buehrle 3.00 8.00
40 Adam Dunn 3.00 8.00

2005 Prime Cuts Material Jersey Position

*1-91 p/r 50: .4X TO 1X JSY p/r 50
*1-91 p/r 50: .3X TO .8X JSY p/r 22-27
*1-91 p/r 25: .5X TO 1.2X JSY p/r 50
*92-100 p/r 50: .4X TO 1X JSY p/r 38-50
OVERALL AU-GU ODDS ONE PER PACK
PRINT RUNS B/WN 25-50 COPIES PER

1 Vladimir Guerrero Angels/50 5.00 12.00
24 Mark Buehrle/50 3.00 8.00
40 Adam Dunn/50 3.00 8.00
71 Jeremy Bonderman/50 3.00 8.00

2005 Prime Cuts Material Combo

*1-91 p/r 50: .5X TO 1.2X JSY p/r 50
*1-91 p/r 25: .6X TO 1.5X JSY p/r 50
*1-91 p/r 25: .5X TO 1.2X JSY p/r 22-27
*92-100 p/r 50: .5X TO 1.2X JSY p/r 50
PRINT RUNS B/WN 1-50 COPIES PER
NO PRICING ON QTY OF 10 OR LESS
PRIME PRINT RUN B/WN 1-10 COPIES PER
NO PRIME PRICING DUE TO SCARCITY
OVERALL AU-GU ODDS ONE PER PACK

24 Mark Buehrle Bat-Jsy/50 4.00 10.00
40 Adam Dunn Bat-Jsy/18 6.00 15.00
51 Johnny Damon Bat-Jsy/15 8.00 20.00

2005 Prime Cuts Signature Century Gold

*GOLD p/r 25: .4X TO 1X SILVER p/r 25
OVERALL AU-GU ODDS ONE PER PACK
PRINT RUNS B/WN 1-25 COPIES PER
NO PRICING ON QTY OF 10 OR LESS

2005 Prime Cuts Signature Century Platinum

OVERALL AU-GU ODDS ONE PER PACK
STATED PRINT RUN 1 SERIAL #'d SET
NO PRICING DUE TO SCARCITY

2005 Prime Cuts Signature Century Silver

OVERALL AU-GU ODDS ONE PER PACK
PRINT RUNS B/WN 1-25 COPIES PER
NO PRICING ON QTY OF 10 OR LESS

2 Roger Clemens Astros/10
3 Carlos Beltran/25 10.00 25.00
4 Johan Santana/25 15.00 40.00
5 Alfonso Soriano/25 10.00 25.00
21 Miguel Cabrera/25 15.00 40.00

2005 Prime Cuts Signature Material Jersey Number

PRINT RUNS B/WN 1-10 COPIES PER
PRIME PRINT RUN B/WN 1-10 COPIES PER
OVERALL AU-GU ODDS ONE PER PACK
NO PRICING DUE TO SCARCITY

2005 Prime Cuts Signature Material Combo

PRINT RUNS B/WN 1-10 COPIES PER
PRIME PRINT RUN B/WN 1-10 COPIES PER
OVERALL AU-GU ODDS ONE PER PACK
NO PRICING DUE TO SCARCITY

2005 Prime Cuts MLB Icons

STATED PRINT RUN 100 SERIAL #'d SETS
*GOLD: .75X TO 2X BASIC
GOLD PRINT RUN 25 SERIAL #'d SETS
PLATINUM PRINT RUN 1 SERIAL #'d SET
NO PLATINUM PRICING DUE TO SCARCITY
*SILVER: .5X TO 1.2X BASIC
SILVER PRINT RUN 50 SERIAL #'d SETS
RANDOM INSERTS IN PACKS

1 Andre Dawson 2.00 5.00
2 Babe Ruth 8.00 20.00
3 Billy Williams 1.25 3.00
4 Bob Feller 1.25 3.00
5 Bob Gibson 2.00 5.00
6 Bobby Doerr 1.25 3.00
7 Brooks Robinson 2.00 5.00
8 Burleigh Grimes 2.00 5.00
9 Cal Ripken 12.00 30.00
10 Carlton Fisk 2.00 5.00
11 Dale Murphy 1.25 3.00
12 Don Mattingly 6.00 15.00
13 Don Sutton 1.25 3.00
14 Ted Williams 6.00 15.00
15 Ernie Banks 3.00 8.00
16 Frank Robinson 2.00 5.00
17 Gary Carter 1.25 3.00
18 Gaylord Perry 1.25 3.00
19 Hank Aaron 6.00 15.00
20 Harmon Killebrew 3.00 8.00
21 Jim Palmer 1.25 3.00
22 Jim Thorpe 5.00 12.00
23 Babe Ruth 8.00 20.00
24 Johnny Bench 3.00 8.00
25 Juan Marichal 1.25 3.00
26 Kirby Puckett 3.00 8.00
27 Lou Brock 2.00 5.00
28 Luis Aparicio 1.25 3.00
29 Marty Marion 1.25 3.00
30 Mike Schmidt 6.00 15.00
31 Nolan Ryan 8.00 20.00
32 Red Schoendienst 1.25 3.00
33 Rickey Henderson 2.00 5.00
34 Roberto Clemente 8.00 20.00
35 Rod Carew 2.00 5.00
36 Sandy Koufax 10.00 25.00
37 Stan Musial 5.00 12.00
38 Steve Carlton 1.25 3.00
39 Steve Garvey 1.25 3.00
40 Ted Williams 6.00 15.00
41 Tom Seaver 2.00 5.00
42 Tony Gwynn 4.00 10.00
43 Whitey Ford 2.00 5.00
44 Willie Mays 6.00 15.00
45 Willie McCovey 2.00 5.00

2005 Prime Cuts MLB Icons Material Bat

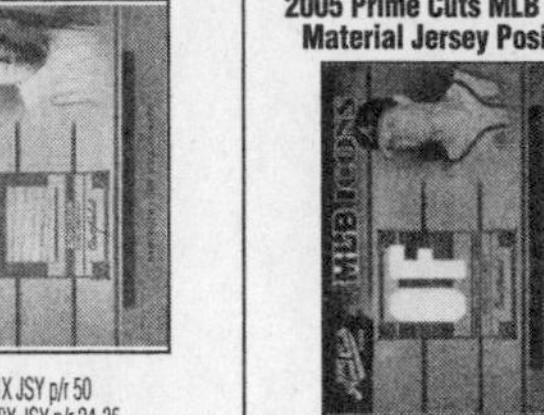

*BAT p/r 50: .4X TO 1X JSY p/r 50
*BAT p/r 50: .3X TO .8X JSY p/r 24-35
OVERALL AU-GU ODDS ONE PER PACK
PRINT RUNS B/WN 13-50 COPIES PER
NO PRICING ON QTY OF 13

2 Babe Ruth/50 100.00 175.00
7 Brooks Robinson/50 5.00 12.00
23 Babe Ruth/50 100.00 175.00
26 Kirby Puckett/50 6.00 15.00
27 Lou Brock/50 5.00 12.00
28 Luis Aparicio/50 4.00 10.00
32 Red Schoendienst/50 4.00 10.00
34 Roberto Clemente/50 30.00 60.00

2005 Prime Cuts MLB Icons Material Jersey

OVERALL AU-GU ODDS ONE PER PACK
PRINT RUNS B/WN 1-50 COPIES PER
NO PRICING ON QTY OF 12 OR LESS

1 Andre Dawson/50 4.00 10.00
2 Babe Ruth/25 200.00 300.00
3 Billy Williams/50 4.00 10.00
4 Bob Feller/8
5 Bob Gibson/25 6.00 15.00
6 Bobby Doerr Pants/50 4.00 10.00
7 Brooks Robinson/11
8 Burleigh Grimes Pants/50 30.00 60.00
9 Cal Ripken/50 10.00 25.00
10 Carlton Fisk/50 5.00 12.00
11 Dale Murphy/50 5.00 12.00
12 Don Mattingly/50 6.00 15.00
13 Don Sutton/24 5.00 12.00
14 Ted Williams/25 30.00 60.00
15 Ernie Banks/25 8.00 20.00
16 Frank Robinson/25 5.00 12.00
17 Gary Carter/50 4.00 10.00
18 Gaylord Perry/50 4.00 10.00
19 Hank Aaron/25 20.00 50.00
20 Harmon Killebrew/50 6.00 15.00
22 Jim Thorpe/50 100.00 175.00
23 Babe Ruth/25 200.00 300.00
24 Johnny Bench/50 6.00 15.00
25 Juan Marichal/50 4.00 10.00
26 Kirby Puckett/12
28 Luis Aparicio/1
30 Mike Schmidt/35 8.00 20.00
31 Nolan Ryan Pants/50 10.00 25.00
32 Red Schoendienst/10
33 Rickey Henderson/50 6.00 15.00
34 Roberto Clemente/5
35 Rod Carew/50 5.00 12.00
36 Sandy Koufax/5
37 Stan Musial/50 8.00 20.00
38 Steve Carlton/30 5.00 12.00
39 Steve Garvey/50 4.00 10.00
40 Ted Williams/25 30.00 60.00
41 Tom Seaver/50 5.00 12.00
42 Tony Gwynn/50 6.00 15.00
43 Whitey Ford/50 5.00 12.00
44 Willie Mays/50 10.00 25.00
45 Willie McCovey/50 5.00 12.00

2005 Prime Cuts MLB Icons Material Jersey Number

*NBR p/r 25: .5X TO 1.2X JSY p/r 50
*NBR p/r 25: .4X TO 1X JSY p/r 25
OVERALL AU-GU ODDS ONE PER PACK
PRINT RUNS B/WN 5-25 COPIES PER
NO PRICING ON QTY OF 10 OR LESS

23 Babe Ruth/25 200.00 300.00
36 Sandy Koufax/25 75.00 150.00

2005 Prime Cuts MLB Icons Material Jersey Number Prime

*PRIME p/r 20-25: .75X TO 2X JSY p/r 50
*PRIME p/r 20-25: .6X TO 1.5X JSY p/r 24-35
*PRIME p/r 15: 1X TO 2.5X JSY p/r 50
OVERALL AU-GU ODDS ONE PER PACK
PRINT RUNS B/WN 1-25 COPIES PER
NO PRICING ON QTY OF 10 OR LESS

2005 Prime Cuts MLB Icons Material Jersey Position

*POS p/r 50: .4X TO 1X JSY p/r 50
*POS p/r 50: .3X TO .8X JSY p/r 24-35
OVERALL AU-GU ODDS ONE PER PACK
PRINT RUNS B/WN 25-50 COPIES PER

2 Babe Ruth/50 175.00 300.00
4 Bob Feller Pants/50 4.00 10.00
22 Jim Thorpe/50 100.00 175.00
23 Babe Ruth/50 175.00 300.00
28 Luis Aparicio/25 5.00 12.00
29 Marty Marion/50 4.00 10.00
34 Roberto Clemente/25 40.00 80.00

2005 Prime Cuts MLB Icons Material Combo

*COMBO p/r 25: .6X TO 1.5X JSY p/r 50
*COMBO p/r 25: .5X TO 1.2X JSY p/r 25
PRINT RUNS B/WN 1-25 COPIES PER
NO PRICING ON QTY OF 10 OR LESS
PRIME PRINT RUN B/WN 1-10 COPIES PER
NO PRIME PRICING DUE TO SCARCITY
OVERALL AU-GU ODDS ONE PER PACK

2005 Prime Cuts MLB Icons Material Trio MLB

PRINT RUNS B/WN 1-25 COPIES PER
NO PRICING ON QTY OF 10 OR LESS
PRIME PRINT RUN B/WN 1-10 COPIES PER
NO PRIME PRICING DUE TO SCARCITY
OVERALL AU-GU ODDS ONE PER PACK
B=Bat; BG=Btg Glv; H=Hat; J=Jsy; JK=Jkt
P=Pants; S=Shoe

22 Jim Thorpe J-J-J/25 200.00 300.00
34 Roberto Clemente B-B-H/25 75.00 150.00

2005 Prime Cuts MLB Icons Signature Century Gold

OVERALL AU-GU ODDS ONE PER PACK
PRINT RUNS B/WN 1-15 COPIES PER
NO PRICING ON QTY OF 10 OR LESS

36 Sandy Koufax/15 300.00 400.00

2005 Prime Cuts MLB Icons Signature Century Platinum

OVERALL AU-GU ODDS ONE PER PACK
STATED PRINT RUN 1 SERIAL #'d SET
NO PRICING DUE TO SCARCITY

2005 Prime Cuts MLB Icons Signature Century Silver

OVERALL AU-GU ODDS ONE PER BOX
PRINT RUNS B/WN 1-32 COPIES PER
NO PRICING ON QTY OF 10 OR LESS

1 Andre Dawson/10
3 Billy Williams/25 10.00 25.00
4 Bob Feller/25 10.00 25.00
5 Bob Gibson/25 15.00 40.00
6 Bobby Doerr/25 10.00 25.00
7 Brooks Robinson/25 15.00 40.00
9 Cal Ripken/1
10 Carlton Fisk/25 15.00 40.00
11 Dale Murphy/10
12 Don Mattingly/20 30.00 60.00
13 Don Sutton/25 10.00 25.00
15 Ernie Banks/20 20.00 50.00
16 Frank Robinson/25 10.00 25.00
17 Gary Carter/25 10.00 25.00
18 Gaylord Perry/25 10.00 25.00
19 Hank Aaron/15 125.00 200.00
20 Harmon Killebrew/25 50.00 100.00
21 Jim Palmer/25 10.00 25.00
24 Johnny Bench/25 20.00 50.00
25 Juan Marichal/25 10.00 25.00
26 Kirby Puckett/25 50.00 100.00
27 Lou Brock/25 15.00 40.00
28 Luis Aparicio/25 10.00 25.00
29 Marty Marion/25 10.00 25.00
30 Mike Schmidt/25 30.00 60.00
31 Nolan Ryan/25 50.00 100.00
32 Red Schoendienst/25 10.00 25.00
33 Rickey Henderson/10
35 Rod Carew/25 15.00 40.00
36 Sandy Koufax/32 225.00 300.00
37 Stan Musial/25 30.00 60.00
38 Steve Carlton/25 10.00 25.00
39 Steve Garvey/10
41 Tom Seaver/25 20.00 50.00
42 Tony Gwynn/25 20.00 50.00
43 Whitey Ford/25 15.00 40.00
44 Willie Mays/10
45 Willie McCovey/25 15.00 40.00

2005 Prime Cuts MLB Icons Signature Material Jersey Number

OVERALL AU-GU ODDS ONE PER BOX
PRINT RUNS B/WN 1-25 COPIES PER
NO PRICING ON QTY OF 10 OR LESS

9 Cal Ripken/25 75.00 150.00

2005 Prime Cuts MLB Icons Signature Material Jersey Number Prime

*PRIME p/r 20: .6X TO 1.5X SILV p/r 20-32
*PRIME p/r 15: .75X TO 2X SILV p/r 20-32
OVERALL AU-GU ODDS ONE PER PACK
PRINT RUNS B/WN 1-25 COPIES PER
NO PRICING ON QTY OF 10 OR LESS

9 Cal Ripken/25 75.00 150.00

2005 Prime Cuts MLB Icons Signature Material Combo

*COMBO p/r 25: .5X TO 1.2X SILV p/r 20-32
PRINT RUNS B/WN 1-25 COPIES PER
NO PRICING ON QTY OF 10 OR LESS
PRIME PRINT RUN B/WN 1-10 COPIES PER
NO PRIME PRICING DUE TO SCARCITY
OVERALL AU-GU ODDS ONE PER PACK

11 Dale Murphy Bat-Jsy/25 20.00 50.00

2005 Prime Cuts MLB Icons Signature Material Trio MLB

PRINT RUNS B/WN 1-10 COPIES PER
NO PRICING DUE TO SCARCITY
PRIME PRINT RUN B/WN 1-10 COPIES PER

NO PRIME PRICING DUE TO SCARCITY
OVERALL AU-GU ODDS ONE PER PACK

2005 Prime Cuts Souvenir Cuts

OVERALL AU-GU ODDS ONE PER PACK
PRINT RUNS B/WN 1-50 COPIES PER
NO PRICING ON QTY OF 12 OR LESS

1 Tony Lazzeri/2
2 Al Barlick/7
3 Al Lopez/50 60.00 120.00
4 Bill Terry/50 100.00 175.00
5 Billy Herman/4
6 Buck Leonard/50 100.00 175.00
7 Bucky Harris/3
8 Cal Hubbard/26 75.00 150.00
9 Carl Hubbell/50 75.00 150.00
10 Charlie Gehringer/50 75.00 150.00
11 Connie Mack/3
12 Cool Papa Bell/5
13 David Bancroft/2
14 Earl Averill/47 60.00 120.00
15 Earle Combs/3
16 Edd Roush/48 60.00 120.00
17 Eddie Collins/1
18 Sam Rice/27 125.00 200.00
19 Ernie Lombardi/50 75.00 150.00
20 Ford Frick/50 100.00 175.00
21 Gabby Hartnett/50 150.00 250.00
22 George Kelly/50 75.00 150.00
23 Grover C. Alexander/1
24 Harry Caray/1
25 Heinie Manush/33 125.00 200.00
26 Hugh Duffy/1
27 Joe McCarthy/44 125.00 200.00
28 Joe Medwick/50 125.00 200.00
29 Joe Sewell/4
31 Kenesaw Landis/1
32 Lefty Gomez/32 100.00 175.00
33 Leo Durocher/1
34 Leon Day/1
35 Luke Appling/35 75.00 150.00
36 Max Carey/2
37 Mel Allen/1
38 Paul Waner/1
39 Pie Traynor/1
40 Ray Schalk/2
41 Sam Crawford/1
42 Ted Lyons/2
43 Waite Hoyt/50 75.00 150.00
44 Walter Alston/22 125.00 200.00
45 William Harridge/1
46 Jocko Conlan/35 75.00 150.00
47 Lloyd Waner/50 100.00 175.00
48 Rube Marquard/50 75.00 150.00
49 Hank Greenberg/43 200.00 350.00
50 Travis Jackson/50 75.00 150.00
51 Joe Cronin/50 75.00 150.00
52 Bill Dickey/26 125.00 200.00
53 Red Ruffing/26 175.00 300.00
54 Jesse Haines/50 150.00 250.00
55 Chick Hafey/50 125.00 200.00
102 Hal Newhouser/24 75.00 150.00
103 Hoyt Wilhelm/9
104 Lou Boudreau/48 60.00 120.00
105 Pee Wee Reese/28 150.00 250.00
106 Richie Ashburn/2
107 Roberto Clemente/2
108 Ted Williams/9
109 Willie Stargell/23 75.00 150.00
110 Roger Maris/3
111 Buck Leonard/50 100.00 175.00
112 Carl Hubbell/50 75.00 150.00
113 Charlie Gehringer/40 75.00 150.00
114 Gabby Hartnett/12
115 Joe Medwick/32 125.00 200.00
116 Lloyd Waner/10
117 Rube Marquard/37 75.00 150.00
118 Travis Jackson/7
119 Joe Cronin/3
120 Jesse Haines/27 150.00 250.00
121 Chick Hafey/25 125.00 200.00

2005 Prime Cuts Timeline

STATED PRINT RUN 100 SERIAL #'d SETS
*GOLD: .75X TO 2X BASIC
GOLD PRINT RUN 25 SERIAL #'d SETS
PLATINUM PRINT RUN 1 SERIAL #'d SET
NO PLATINUM PRICING DUE TO SCARCITY
*SILVER: .5X TO 1.2X BASIC
SILVER PRINT RUN 50 SERIAL #'d SETS
RANDOM INSERTS IN PACKS

1 Dale Murphy 1.25 3.00
2 Dennis Eckersley 1.25 3.00

3 Fergie Jenkins 1.25 3.00
4 Greg Maddux 5.00 12.00
5 Orel Hershiser 1.25 3.00
6 Stan Musial 5.00 12.00
7 Don Mattingly 6.00 15.00
8 Willie Mays NY Giants 6.00 15.00
9 Ozzie Smith 5.00 12.00
10 Roger Clemens Yanks 4.00 10.00
11 Cal Ripken 12.00 30.00
12 Duke Snider 2.00 5.00
13 Hank Aaron 6.00 15.00
14 Lou Brock 2.00 5.00
15 Paul Molitor 3.00 8.00
16 Ted Williams 6.00 15.00
17 Dwight Gooden 1.25 3.00
18 Frankie Frisch 2.00 5.00
19 Pedro Martinez 2.00 5.00
20 Robin Yount 3.00 8.00
21 Babe Ruth 8.00 20.00
22 Carl Yastrzemski 4.00 10.00
23 Rod Carew 2.00 5.00
24 Willie Mays SF Giants 6.00 15.00
25 Eddie Murray 3.00 8.00
26 Ivan Rodriguez 2.00 5.00
27 Roger Clemens Sox 4.00 10.00
28 Willie McCovey 2.00 5.00
29 Bob Feller 1.25 3.00
30 Catfish Hunter 1.25 3.00
31 Gaylord Perry 1.25 3.00
32 Wade Boggs 2.00 5.00
33 Phil Rizzuto 2.00 5.00
34 Roger Maris 3.00 8.00
35 Bob Gibson 2.00 5.00
36 Chipper Jones 3.00 8.00
37 Ernie Banks 3.00 8.00
38 George Brett 6.00 15.00
39 Keith Hernandez 1.25 3.00
40 Ryne Sandberg 6.00 15.00
41 Reggie Jackson 3.00 8.00
42 Sandy Koufax 10.00 25.00
43 Warren Spahn 2.00 5.00
44 Nolan Ryan Mets 8.00 20.00
45 Yogi Berra 3.00 8.00
46 Cal Ripken 12.00 30.00
47 Willie Mays NY Mets 6.00 15.00
48 Nolan Ryan Angels 8.00 20.00
49 Stan Musial 5.00 12.00
50 Roberto Clemente 8.00 20.00

2005 Prime Cuts Timeline Material Bat

*BAT p/r 50: .4X TO 1X JSY p/r 49-50
*BAT p/r 50: .3X TO .8X JSY p/r 24-35
*BAT p/r 22: .4X TO 1X JSY p/r 24-35
*BAT p/r 15: .6X TO 1.5X JSY p/r 49-50
OVERALL AU-GU ODDS ONE PER PACK
PRINT RUNS B/WN 3-50 COPIES PER
NO PRICING ON QTY OF 3
8 Willie Mays NY Giants/50 10.00 25.00
14 Lou Brock/50 5.00 12.00
21 Babe Ruth/50 100.00 175.00
50 Roberto Clemente/50 30.00 60.00

2005 Prime Cuts Timeline Material Jersey

OVERALL AU-GU ODDS ONE PER PACK
PRINT RUNS B/WN 5-50 COPIES PER
NO PRICING ON QTY OF 5
1 Dale Murphy/50 5.00 12.00
2 Dennis Eckersley/50 4.00 10.00
3 Fergie Jenkins/50 4.00 10.00
4 Greg Maddux/50 6.00 15.00
5 Orel Hershiser/50 4.00 10.00
6 Stan Musial/50 8.00 20.00
7 Don Mattingly/49 6.00 15.00
9 Ozzie Smith/17 12.50 30.00
10 Roger Clemens Yanks/50 6.00 15.00
11 Cal Ripken/50 10.00 25.00
12 Duke Snider/24 6.00 15.00
13 Hank Aaron/50 15.00 40.00
15 Paul Molitor/50 4.00 10.00
16 Ted Williams/50 20.00 50.00
17 Dwight Gooden/50 4.00 10.00
19 Pedro Martinez/50 5.00 12.00
20 Robin Yount/50 6.00 15.00
21 Babe Ruth/25 250.00 350.00
22 Carl Yastrzemski/50 8.00 20.00
23 Rod Carew/50 5.00 12.00
24 Willie Mays SF Giants/50 10.00 25.00
25 Eddie Murray/50 6.00 15.00
26 Ivan Rodriguez/50 5.00 12.00
27 Roger Clemens Sox/50 6.00 15.00
28 Willie McCovey/50 5.00 12.00
32 Wade Boggs/50 5.00 12.00
33 Phil Rizzuto/50 5.00 12.00
34 Roger Maris/50 15.00 40.00
35 Bob Gibson/50 5.00 12.00
36 Chipper Jones/50 6.00 15.00
37 Ernie Banks/50 6.00 15.00
38 George Brett/50 6.00 15.00
39 Keith Hernandez/5
40 Ryne Sandberg/50 8.00 20.00
41 Reggie Jackson/35 6.00 15.00
42 Sandy Koufax/5
43 Warren Spahn/50 5.00 12.00
44 Nolan Ryan Mets/50 10.00 25.00
45 Yogi Berra/50 6.00 15.00
46 Cal Ripken/50 10.00 25.00
47 Willie Mays NY Mets/50 10.00 25.00
48 Nolan Ryan Angels/50 10.00 25.00
49 Stan Musial/25 10.00 25.00

2005 Prime Cuts Timeline Material Jersey Number Prime

*PRIME p/r 25: .75X TO 2X JSY p/r 49-50
*PRIME p/r 15: .6X TO 1.5X JSY p/r 17
PRINT RUNS B/WN 1-25 COPIES PER
NO PRICING ON QTY OF 10 OR LESS
NBR PRINT RUN B/WN 1-10 COPIES PER
NO NUMBER PRICING DUE TO SCARCITY
OVERALL AU-GU ODDS ONE PER PACK
39 Keith Hernandez/25 8.00 20.00

2005 Prime Cuts Timeline Material Jersey Position

*POS p/r 23-25: .5X TO 1.2X JSY p/r 49-50
*POS p/r 23-25: .4X TO 1X JSY p/r 24-35
OVERALL AU-GU ODDS ONE PER PACK
PRINT RUNS B/WN 10-25 COPIES PER
NO PRICING ON QTY OF 12 OR LESS
14 Lou Brock Jkt/25 6.00 15.00
18 Frankie Frisch Jkt/23 8.00 20.00
21 Babe Ruth/25 200.00 300.00
30 Catfish Hunter/18 6.00 15.00
39 Keith Hernandez/25 5.00 12.00

2005 Prime Cuts Timeline Material Combo

*COMBO p/r 25: .6X TO 1.5X JSY p/r 49-50
*COMBO p/r 25: .5X TO 1.2X JSY p/r 24-35
OVERALL AU-GU ODDS ONE PER PACK
PRINT RUNS B/WN 1-25 COPIES PER
NO PRICING ON QTY OF 10 OR LESS
21 Babe Ruth Bat-Jsy/25 350.00 450.00

2005 Prime Cuts Timeline Material Combo Prime

*PRIME p/r 25: .75X TO 2X JSY p/r 49-50
OVERALL AU-GU ODDS ONE PER PACK
PRINT RUNS B/WN 1-25 COPIES PER
NO PRICING ON QTY OF 10 OR LESS
14 Lou Brock Bat-Jsy/25 12.50 30.00
39 Keith Hernandez Bat-Jsy/15 12.50 30.00

2005 Prime Cuts Timeline Material Combo CY HR

*CY HR p/r 25: .6X TO 1.5X JSY p/r 49-50
*CY HR p/r 25: .5X TO 1.2X JSY p/r 24-35
*CY HR p/r 25: .4X TO 1X JSY p/r 17
OVERALL AU-GU ODDS ONE PER PACK
PRINT RUNS B/WN 1-25 COPIES PER
NO PRICING ON QTY OF 10 OR LESS
8 W.Mays NYG Bat-Jsy/25 15.00 40.00
14 Lou Brock Bat-Jkt/25 8.00 20.00
18 Frankie Frisch Jkt-Jkt/25 10.00 25.00
21 Babe Ruth Bat-Pants/25 250.00 400.00
42 Sandy Koufax Jsy-Jsy/25 75.00 150.00

2005 Prime Cuts Timeline Material Combo CY HR Prime

*PRIME p/r 25: .75X TO 2X JSY p/r 49-50
OVERALL AU-GU ODDS ONE PER PACK
PRINT RUNS B/WN 1-25 COPIES PER
NO PRICING ON QTY OF 10 OR LESS

2005 Prime Cuts Timeline Material Trio

PRINT RUNS B/WN 1-10 COPIES PER
PRIME PRINT RUN B/WN 1-10 COPIES PER
OVERALL AU-GU ODDS ONE PER PACK
NO PRICING DUE TO SCARCITY

2005 Prime Cuts Timeline Material Trio HOF

PRINT RUNS B/WN 1-10 COPIES PER
PRIME PRINT RUN B/WN 1-10 COPIES PER
OVERALL AU-GU ODDS ONE PER PACK
NO PRICING DUE TO SCARCITY

2005 Prime Cuts Timeline Material Trio MVP

*MVP p/r 50: .6X TO 1.5X JSY p/r 49-50
*MVP p/r 50: .5X TO 1.2X JSY p/r 24-35
*MVP p/r 25: .75X TO 2X JSY p/r 49-50
PRINT RUNS B/WN 1-50 COPIES PER
NO PRICING ON QTY OF 10 OR LESS
PRIME PRINT RUN B/WN 1-10 COPIES PER
NO PRIME PRICING DUE TO SCARCITY
OVERALL AU-GU ODDS ONE PER PACK
21 Babe Ruth B-J-P/50 400.00 550.00
50 Roberto Clemente B-B-B/50 50.00 100.00

2005 Prime Cuts Timeline Material Trio Stats

PRINT RUNS B/WN 1-5 COPIES PER
PRIME PRINT RUN B/WN 1-5 COPIES PER
OVERALL AU-GU ODDS ONE PER PACK
NO PRICING DUE TO SCARCITY

2005 Prime Cuts Timeline Material Quad

PRINT RUNS B/WN 1-5 COPIES PER
PRIME PRINT RUN B/WN 1-5 COPIES PER
OVERALL AU-GU ODDS ONE PER PACK
NO PRICING DUE TO SCARCITY

2005 Prime Cuts Timeline Material Custom Names

*NAME 3P p/r 50: .2X TO .5X NBR 4P p/r 25
*NAME 4P p/r 50: .5X TO 1.2X NBR 3P p/r 50
*NAME 4P p/r 50: .4X TO 1X NBR 4P p/r 50
*NAME 4P p/r 25: .6X TO 1.5X NBR 4P p/r 50
*NAME 4P p/r 15: .5X TO 1.2X NBR 4P p/r 25
PRINT RUNS B/WN 1-50 COPIES PER

NO PRICING ON QTY OF 1
PRIME PRINT RUN B/WN 1-5 COPIES PER
NO PRIME PRICING DUE TO SCARCITY
OVERALL AU-GU ODDS ONE PER PACK
16 Ted Williams B-J-J-J/50 125.00 200.00
21 Babe Ruth B-B-J-P/50 500.00 800.00
34 Roger Maris B-B-J-P/50 50.00 100.00

2005 Prime Cuts Timeline Material Custom Nicknames

*NICK 3P p/r 50: .4X TO 1X NBR 3P p/r 50
*NICK 4P p/r 50: .4X TO 1X NBR 4P p/r 50
PRINT RUNS B/WN 5-50 COPIES PER
NO PRICING ON QTY OF 10 OR LESS
PRIME PRINT RUN B/WN 1-5 COPIES PER
NO PRIME PRICING DUE TO SCARCITY
OVERALL AU-GU ODDS ONE PER PACK
6 S.Musial B-B-J-J-P-P/50 60.00 120.00
21 Babe Ruth B-J-J-P/50 600.00 900.00
24 W.Mays SF B-B-B-J-J-J/50 75.00 150.00
37 E.Banks B-B-H-J-J/50 50.00 100.00
47 W.Mays NY B-B-B-J-J-J/50 75.00 150.00

2005 Prime Cuts Timeline Material Custom Numbers

PRINT RUNS B/WN 1-50 COPIES PER
NO PRICING ON QTY OF 10 OR LESS
PRIME PRINT RUN B/WN 1-10 COPIES PER
NO PRIME PRICING DUE TO SCARCITY
OVERALL AU-GU ODDS ONE PER PACK
1 D.Murphy B-B-J-J/50 10.00 25.00
2 D.Eckersley J-P-P/50 6.00 15.00
3 Fergie Jenkins Fld Glv-Fld Glv-Jsy-Jsy/5
4 G.Maddux B-J-J/50 20.00 50.00
5 O.Hershiser J-J-J/50 6.00 15.00
6 Stan Musial B-B-J-P/50 30.00 60.00
7 D.Mattingly B/BG-H-JK-J/25 40.00 80.00
8 Willie Mays NY Giants Bat-Bat-Jsy-Jsy/1
9 Ozzie Smith Bat-Bat-Pants-Pants/5
10 R.Clem Yanks B-B-J-J/50 20.00 50.00
11 C.Ripken B-H-J-P/50 40.00 80.00
12 Duke Snider J-J-P-P/50 15.00 40.00
13 Hank Aaron B-B-J-J/50 40.00 80.00
14 Lou Brock B-B-J-J/25 15.00 40.00
15 P.Molitor B-J-P-S/50 8.00 20.00
16 T.Williams B-JK-J-J/50 60.00 120.00
17 D.Gooden B-FG-H-J/50 8.00 20.00
18 F.Frisch JK-JK-JK-JK/50 20.00 50.00
19 P.Martinez B-B-J-P/50 10.00 25.00
20 Robin Yount Bat-Bat-Jsy-Jsy/10
21 Babe Ruth B-B-J-P/50 500.00 800.00
22 C.Yaz B-H-J-P/50 30.00 60.00
23 R.Carew B-J-J-S/25 15.00 40.00
24 W.Mays SFG B-B-J-J/50 30.00 60.00
25 E.Murray B-J-P-S/50 15.00 40.00
26 I.Rod B-FG-J-S/50 10.00 25.00
27 R.Clem Sox B-B-J-J/50 20.00 50.00
28 W.McCovey J-J-P-P/50 10.00 25.00
29 Bob Feller Jsy-Jsy-Jsy-Jsy/1
30 Catfish Hunter Jsy-Jsy-Jsy-Jsy/1
32 Wade Boggs B-H-J-J/50 10.00 25.00
33 Phil Rizzuto Jsy-Jsy-Pants-Pants/5
34 Roger Maris B-B-J-P/50 50.00 100.00
35 Bob Gibson Hat-Jsy-Jsy-Jsy/1
36 C.Jones B-FG-J-J/50 20.00 50.00
37 Ernie Banks B-B-H-J/50 20.00 50.00
38 G.Brett B-H-J-J/50 30.00 60.00
39 Keith Hernandez Bat-Bat-Jsy-Jsy/1
40 R.Sandberg B-FG-H-J/50 40.00 80.00
41 Reggie Jackson Jkt-Jsy-Jsy-Jsy/5
42 Sandy Koufax Jsy-Jsy-Jsy-Jsy/5
43 W.Spahn J-J-P-P/50 20.00 50.00
44 N.Ryan Mets B-B-J-J/25 40.00 80.00
45 Yogi Berra B-J-P-P/50 30.00 60.00
46 C.Ripken B-H-J-P/50 40.00 80.00
47 W.Mays NYM B-B-J-J/50 30.00 60.00
50 R.Clemente B-B-H-J/25 150.00 250.00

2005 Prime Cuts Timeline Signature Century Gold

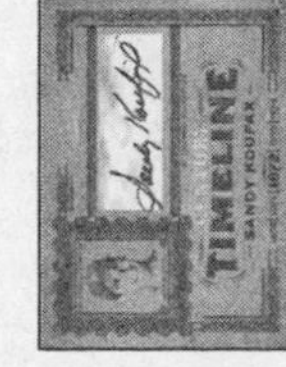

OVERALL AU-GU ODDS ONE PER PACK
PRINT RUNS B/WN 1-8 COPIES PER
NO PRICING DUE TO SCARCITY

2005 Prime Cuts Timeline Signature Century Platinum

OVERALL AU-GU ODDS ONE PER PACK
STATED PRINT RUN 1 SERIAL #'d SET
NO PRICING DUE TO SCARCITY

2005 Prime Cuts Timeline Signature Century Silver

OVERALL AU-GU ODDS ONE PER PACK
PRINT RUNS B/WN 1-32 COPIES PER
NO PRICING ON QTY OF 10 OR LESS
1 Dale Murphy/10
2 Dennis Eckersley/25 10.00 25.00
3 Fergie Jenkins/25 10.00 25.00
4 Greg Maddux/10
5 Orel Hershiser/10
6 Stan Musial/25 30.00 60.00
7 Don Mattingly/10
8 Willie Mays NY Giants/5
9 Ozzie Smith/25 20.00 50.00
10 Roger Clemens Yanks/10
11 Cal Ripken/1
12 Duke Snider/25 15.00 40.00
13 Hank Aaron/15 125.00 200.00
14 Lou Brock/25 15.00 40.00
15 Paul Molitor/25 10.00 25.00
17 Dwight Gooden/10
19 Pedro Martinez/5
20 Robin Yount/5
23 Rod Carew/25 15.00 40.00
24 Willie Mays SF Giants/5
27 Roger Clemens Sox/10
28 Willie McCovey/25 15.00 40.00
29 Bob Feller/25 10.00 25.00
31 Gaylord Perry/25 10.00 25.00
32 Wade Boggs/25 15.00 40.00
33 Phil Rizzuto/25 15.00 40.00
35 Bob Gibson/25 15.00 40.00
36 Chipper Jones/25 20.00 50.00
37 Ernie Banks/5
38 George Brett/25 40.00 80.00
39 Keith Hernandez/10
40 Ryne Sandberg/25 40.00 80.00
42 Sandy Koufax/32 225.00 300.00
44 Nolan Ryan Mets/25 50.00 100.00
46 Cal Ripken/1
47 Willie Mays NY Mets/5
48 Nolan Ryan Angels/25 50.00 100.00
49 Stan Musial/25 30.00 60.00

2005 Prime Cuts Timeline Signature Material Jersey Number

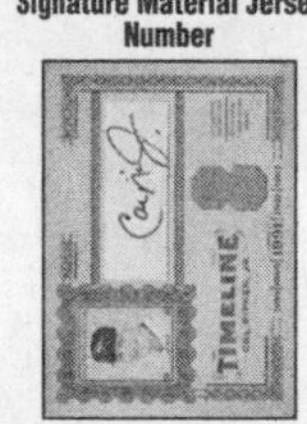

PRINT RUNS B/WN 1-10 COPIES PER
PRIME PRINT RUN B/WN 1-10 COPIES PER
OVERALL AU-GU ODDS ONE PER PACK
NO PRICING DUE TO SCARCITY

2005 Prime Cuts Timeline Signature Material Combo

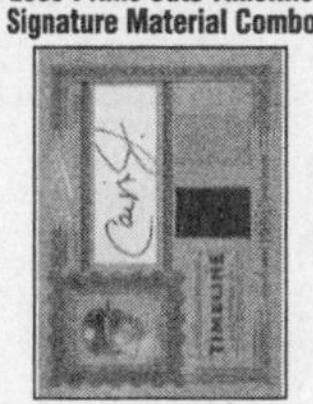

PRINT RUNS B/WN 1-10 COPIES PER
PRIME PRINT RUN B/WN 1-10 COPIES PER
OVERALL AU-GU ODDS ONE PER PACK
NO PRICING DUE TO SCARCITY

2005 Prime Cuts Timeline Signature Material Combo CY HR

*CY HR: .5X TO 1.2X SILVER
OVERALL AU-GU ODDS ONE PER PACK
PRINT RUNS B/WN 5-25 COPIES PER
NO PRICING ON QTY OF 10 OR LESS
1 Dale Murphy Bat-Jsy/25 20.00 50.00
7 Don Mattingly Jsy-Jsy/25 40.00 80.00
11 Cal Ripken Bat-Jsy/25 75.00 150.00
13 Hank Aaron Bat-Jsy/25 125.00 200.00
17 D.Gooden Jsy-Jsy/25 12.50 30.00

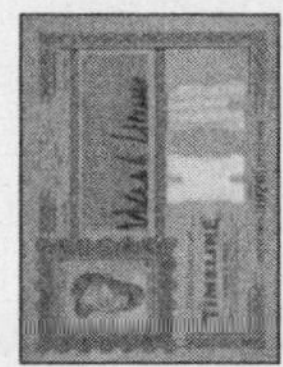

24 W.Mays SFG Bat-Jsy/25 100.00 175.00
46 Cal Ripken Jsy-Pants/25 75.00 150.00
47 W.Mays NYM Bat-Jsy/25 100.00 175.00

2005 Prime Cuts Timeline Signature Material Combo CY HR Prime

*PRIME p/r 25: .75X TO 2X SILVER p/r 25
OVERALL AU-GU ODDS ONE PER PACK
PRINT RUNS B/WN 1-25 COPIES PER
NO PRICING ON QTY OF 10 OR LESS
24 W.Mays SFG Bat-Jsy/25 150.00 250.00
47 W.Mays NYM Bat-Jsy/25 150.00 250.00

2005 Prime Cuts Timeline Signature Material Trio

PRINT RUNS B/WN 1-10 COPIES PER
PRIME PRINT RUN B/WN 1-5 COPIES PER
OVERALL AU-GU ODDS ONE PER PACK
NO PRICING DUE TO SCARCITY

2005 Prime Cuts Timeline Signature Material Trio HOF

PRINT RUNS B/WN 1-10 COPIES PER
PRIME PRINT RUN B/WN 1-10 COPIES PER
OVERALL AU-GU ODDS ONE PER PACK
NO PRICING DUE TO SCARCITY

2005 Prime Cuts Timeline Signature Material Trio MVP

PRINT RUNS B/WN 1-10 COPIES PER
PRIME PRINT RUN B/WN 1-10 COPIES PER
OVERALL AU-GU ODDS ONE PER PACK
NO PRICING DUE TO SCARCITY

2005 Prime Cuts Timeline Signature Material Trio Stats

PRINT RUNS B/WN 1-5 COPIES PER
PRIME PRINT RUN B/WN 1-5 COPIES PER
OVERALL AU-GU ODDS ONE PER PACK
NO PRICING DUE TO SCARCITY

2005 Prime Cuts Timeline Signature Material Quad

PRINT RUNS B/WN 1-5 COPIES PER
PRIME PRINT RUN B/WN 1-5 COPIES PER
OVERALL AU-GU ODDS ONE PER PACK
NO PRICING DUE TO SCARCITY

2005 Prime Cuts Timeline Signature Material Custom Names

PRINT RUNS B/WN 1-50 COPIES PER
NO PRICING ON QTY OF 5 OR LESS
PRIME PRINT RUN B/WN 1-5 COPIES PER
NO PRIME PRICING DUE TO SCARCITY
OVERALL AU-GU ODDS ONE PER PACK
11 Cal Ripken B-H-J-P/50 125.00 200.00
24 Willie Mays SFG B-H-J-J/50 125.00 200.00

2005 Prime Cuts Timeline Signature Material Custom Numbers

PRINT RUNS B/WN 1-50 COPIES PER
NO PRICING ON QTY OF 10 OR LESS
PRIME PRINT RUN B/WN 1-10 COPIES PER
NO PRIME PRICING DUE TO SCARCITY
OVERALL AU-GU ODDS ONE PER PACK
24 Willie Mays SFG B-B-J-J/50 125.00 200.00
46 Cal Ripken B-H-J-P/50 150.00 250.00
47 Willie Mays NYM B-B-J-J/50 125.00 200.00

2008 Prime Cuts

This set was released on December 22, 2008.

COMMON CARD (1-100) .40 1.00
TWO BASE CARDS PER BOX
1-100 PRINT RUN 249 SER.#'d SETS
COMMON AUTO (101-152) 3.00 8.00
OVERALL AU/MEM ODDS 4 PER BOX
AUTO PRINT RUN 249 SER.#'d SETS
EXCHANGE DEADLINE 6/26/2010
1 Al Kaline 1.00 2.50
2 Alan Trammell .40 1.00
3 Andre Dawson .60 1.50
4 Barry Larkin .60 1.50
5 Billy Williams .40 1.00
6 Bo Jackson 1.00 2.50
7 Bob Feller .40 1.00
8 Bob Gibson .60 1.50
9 Bobby Doerr .40 1.00
10 Brooks Robinson .60 1.50
11 Bruce Sutter .40 1.00
12 Cal Ripken Jr. 4.00 10.00
13 Carl Erskine .40 1.00
14 Carl Yastrzemski 1.50 4.00
15 Carlton Fisk .60 1.50
16 Dale Murphy .60 1.50
17 Dave Winfield .40 1.00
18 Deion Sanders .60 1.50
19 Dennis Eckersley .40 1.00
20 Denny McLain .40 1.00
21 Dwight Gooden .40 1.00
22 Don Drysdale .60 1.50
23 Don Larsen .40 1.00
24 Don Mattingly 2.00 5.00
25 Don Sutton .40 1.00
26 Duke Snider .60 1.50
27 Eddie Mathews 1.00 2.50
28 Eddie Murray 1.00 2.50
29 Ernie Banks 1.00 2.50
30 Fergie Jenkins .40 1.00
31 Frank Howard .40 1.00
32 Frank Robinson .40 1.00
33 Fred Lynn .40 1.00
34 Gary Carter .40 1.00
35 Gaylord Perry .40 1.00
36 George Brett 2.00 5.00
37 George Kell .40 1.00
38 Gil Hodges .60 1.50
39 Hank Aaron 2.00 5.00
40 Harmon Killebrew 1.00 2.50
41 Jackie Robinson 1.00 2.50
42 Jim Palmer .40 1.00
43 Jim Rice .40 1.00
44 Jim Thorpe 1.00 2.50
45 Joe Cronin .40 1.00
46 Joe Jackson 2.00 5.00
47 Joe Medwick 1.00 2.50
48 Joe Morgan .40 1.00
49 Johnny Bench 1.00 2.50
50 Johnny Pesky .40 1.00
51 Juan Marichal .40 1.00
52 Arky Vaughan .40 1.00
53 Kirk Gibson .40 1.00
54 Larry Walker .60 1.50
55 Lou Boudreau .40 1.00
56 Lou Brock .60 1.50
57 Lou Gehrig 2.00 5.00
58 Luis Aparicio .40 1.00
59 Mark Fidrych .40 1.00
60 Marty Marion .40 1.00
61 Maury Wills .40 1.00
62 Mike Schmidt 1.50 4.00
63 Monte Irvin .40 1.00
64 Nellie Fox .60 1.50
65 Nolan Ryan 3.00 8.00
66 Orlando Cepeda .40 1.00
67 Ozzie Smith 1.50 4.00
68 Paul Molitor 1.00 2.50
69 Pete Rose 2.50 6.00

70 Phil Niekro .40 1.00
72 Randy Jones .40 1.00
73 Red Schoendienst .40 1.00
74 Reggie Jackson .60 1.50
75 Richie Ashburn .60 1.50
77 Roberto Clemente 2.00 5.00
78 Robin Roberts .40 1.00
79 Robin Yount 1.00 2.50
80 Rod Carew .60 1.50
81 Roger Maris 1.00 2.50
82 Ryne Sandberg 2.00 5.00
83 Satchel Paige 1.00 2.50
84 Sparky Anderson .40 1.00
85 Stan Musial 1.50 4.00
86 Steve Carlton .40 1.00
87 Steve Garvey .40 1.00
88 Ted Williams 2.50 6.00
89 Tim Raines .40 1.00
90 Tom Seaver .60 1.50
91 Tony Gwynn 1.00 2.50
92 Tony Perez .40 1.00
93 Wade Boggs .60 1.50
94 Warren Spahn .60 1.50
95 Whitey Ford .60 1.50
96 Will Clark .60 1.50
97 Willie Mays 2.00 5.00
98 Willie McCovey .60 1.50
99 Willie Stargell .60 1.50
100 Yogi Berra 1.00 2.50
101 Mike Stanton AU/249 40.00 80.00
102 Logan Morrison AU/249 15.00 40.00
103 Daniel Cortes AU/249 5.00 12.00
104 Jhoulys Chacin AU/249 6.00 15.00
105 Brandon Crawford AU/249 4.00 10.00
106a Rick Porcello AU/249 10.00 25.00
106b Rick Porcello Jsy AU/249 12.50 30.00
107 Neftali Feliz AU/249 12.50 30.00
108a Buster Posey AU/249 50.00 100.00
108b Buster Posey Jsy AU/249 50.00 100.00
109a Gordon Beckham AU/249 8.00 20.00
109b Gordon Beckham Jsy AU/249 8.00 20.00
110a Ike Davis AU/249 15.00 40.00
110b Ike Davis Bat AU/249 20.00 50.00
111a Andrew Cashner AU/249 6.00 15.00
111b Andrew Cashner Jsy AU/249 8.00 20.00
112 Ryan Perry AU/249 4.00 10.00
113 Anthony Hewitt AU/249 4.00 10.00
114 Daniel Schlereth AU/249 4.00 10.00
115 Carlos Gutierrez AU/249 3.00 8.00
116 Shooter Hunt AU/249 6.00 15.00
117 Brad Holt AU/249 5.00 12.00
118 Zach Collier AU/249 5.00 12.00
119 Evan Fredrickson AU/249 3.00 8.00
120 Christian Friedrich AU/249 4.00 10.00
121 Cord Phelps AU/249 4.00 10.00
122 Danny Espinosa AU/249 12.50 30.00
124 Bryan Price AU/249 5.00 12.00
125 Juan Ramirez AU/249 3.00 8.00
126 Xavier Avery AU/249 5.00 12.00
127 Brad Hand AU/249 5.00 12.00
128 Jay Austin AU/249 3.00 8.00
129 Tyson Ross AU/249 3.00 8.00
130 Michael Taylor AU/249 12.50 30.00
131 Tyler Ladendorf AU/249 3.00 8.00
132 Rashun Dixon AU/249 12.50 30.00
133 Cody Adams AU/249 3.00 8.00
134 Michel Inoa AU/249 12.50 30.00
135 Wilin Rosario AU/249 4.00 10.00
136 Dennis Raben AU/249 5.00 12.00
137 Cody Satterwhite Jsy AU/249 6.00 15.00
138 Wilmer Flores AU/249 EXCH 30.00 60.00
139 Zeke Spruill AU/249 EXCH 5.00 12.00
140 Jason Knapp AU/249 5.00 12.00
141 Charlie Blackmon AU/249 4.00 10.00
142 Tyler Chatwood AU/187 5.00 12.00
143 Logan Schafer AU/249 4.00 10.00
144 Isaac Galloway AU/249 4.00 10.00
145 T.J. Steele AU/249 4.00 10.00
146 Chase D'Arnaud AU/249 3.00 8.00
147 Rolando Gomez AU/249 3.00 8.00
148 Anthony Gose AU/249 4.00 10.00
149 Adrian Nieto AU/249 3.00 8.00
150 Allan Dykstra AU/249 5.00 12.00

2008 Prime Cuts Century Gold

OVERALL INSERT ODDS 1 PER BOX
STATED PRINT RUN 5 SER.#'d SETS
NO PRICING DUE TO SCARCITY

2008 Prime Cuts Century Platinum

OVERALL INSERT ODDS 1 PER BOX
STATED PRINT RUN 1 SER.#'d SET
NO PRICING DUE TO SCARCITY

2008 Prime Cuts Century Silver

OVERALL INSERT ODDS 1 PER BOX
STATED PRINT RUN 25 SER.#'d SETS
NO PRICING DUE TO SCARCITY

2008 Prime Cuts Auto Biography

OVERALL AU/MEM ODDS 4 PER BOX
PRINT RUNS B/WN 1-50 COPIES PER
NO PRICING ON SOME DUE TO SCARCITY
EXCHANGE DEADLINE 6/26/2010
3 Ted Williams/1
9 Willie Mays/25 75.00 150.00
14 Cal Ripken Jr./25 50.00 100.00
15 Nolan Ryan/50 60.00 120.00
18 Mike Schmidt/50 30.00 60.00
19 Reggie Jackson/50 20.00 50.00
24 Ted Williams/1
29 Willie Mays/25 75.00 150.00
35 Cal Ripken Jr./24 50.00 100.00

2008 Prime Cuts Bats

OVERALL AU/MEM ODDS 4 PER BOX
PRINT RUNS B/WN 1-99 COPIES PER
NO PRICING ON QTY 25 OR LESS
2 Alan Trammell/99 5.00 12.00
3 Andre Dawson/99 4.00 10.00
4 Barry Larkin/99 3.00 8.00
5 Billy Williams/10
6 Bo Jackson/99 5.00 12.00
9 Bobby Doerr/20
10 Brooks Robinson/99 4.00 10.00
12 Cal Ripken Jr./30 15.00 40.00
14 Carl Yastrzemski/13
15 Carlton Fisk/27 4.00 10.00
16 Dale Murphy/99 6.00 15.00
17 Dave Winfield/20
18 Deion Sanders/49 6.00 15.00
21 Dwight Gooden/49 3.00 8.00
24 Don Mattingly/99 5.00 12.00
27 Eddie Mathews/99 6.00 15.00
28 Eddie Murray/99 4.00 10.00
29 Ernie Banks/5
32 Frank Robinson/5
33 Fred Lynn/10
34 Gary Carter/30 6.00 15.00
36 George Brett/30 10.00 25.00
40 Harmon Killebrew/31 6.00 15.00
43 Jim Rice/1
46 Joe Jackson/13
48 Joe Morgan/99 3.00 8.00
49 Johnny Bench/35 4.00 10.00
52 Arky Vaughan/99 15.00 40.00
53 Kirk Gibson/5
54 Larry Walker/19
56 Lou Brock/20
57 Lou Gehrig/1
62 Mike Schmidt/5
64 Nellie Fox/49 12.50 30.00
65 Nolan Ryan/15
66 Orlando Cepeda/99 3.00 8.00
68 Paul Molitor/49 3.00 8.00
73 Red Schoendienst/10
74 Reggie Jackson/10
75 Richie Ashburn/20
77 Roberto Clemente/50 20.00 50.00
79 Robin Yount/49 4.00 10.00
80 Rod Carew/5
81 Roger Maris/99 12.50 30.00
82 Ryne Sandberg/10
85 Stan Musial/1
86 Steve Carlton/29 4.00 10.00
87 Steve Garvey/6
88 Ted Williams/5
91 Tony Gwynn/49 5.00 12.00
92 Tony Perez/10
93 Wade Boggs/5
94 Warren Spahn/99
96 Will Clark/99 4.00 10.00
98 Willie McCovey/3
99 Willie Stargell/99 4.00 10.00
100 Yogi Berra/1

2008 Prime Cuts Biography

OVERALL INSERT ODDS 1 PER BOX
1 Lou Gehrig 4.00 10.00
2 Jackie Robinson 2.00 5.00
3 Ted Williams 5.00 12.00
4 Pete Rose 5.00 12.00
5 Jim Thorpe 2.00 5.00
6 Joe Jackson 4.00 10.00
7 Joe Medwick 2.00 5.00
8 Eddie Mathews 2.00 5.00
9 Willie Mays 4.00 10.00
10 Hank Aaron 4.00 10.00
11 Pete Rose 5.00 12.00
12 Gil Hodges 1.25 3.00
13 Roberto Clemente 4.00 10.00
14 Cal Ripken Jr. 8.00 20.00
15 Nolan Ryan 6.00 15.00
16 Satchel Paige 2.00 5.00
17 Roger Maris 2.00 5.00
18 Mike Schmidt 3.00 8.00
19 Reggie Jackson 1.25 3.00
20 George Brett 4.00 10.00
21 Pete Rose 5.00 12.00
22 Lou Gehrig 4.00 10.00
23 Jackie Robinson 2.00 5.00
24 Ted Williams 5.00 12.00
25 Jim Thorpe 2.00 5.00
26 Joe Jackson 4.00 10.00
27 Joe Medwick 2.00 5.00
28 Eddie Mathews 2.00 5.00
29 Willie Mays 4.00 10.00
30 Arky Vaughan .75 2.00
31 Gil Hodges 1.25 3.00
32 Roberto Clemente 4.00 10.00
33 Satchel Paige 2.00 5.00
34 Roger Maris 2.00 5.00
35 Cal Ripken Jr. 8.00 20.00

2008 Prime Cuts Biography Materials

OVERALL AU/MEM ODDS 4 PER BOX
PRINT RUNS B/WN 5-50 COPIES PER
NO PRICING ON MANY DUE TO SCARCITY
1 Lou Gehrig/10
2 Jackie Robinson/10
3 Ted Williams/25 50.00 100.00
4 Pete Rose/5
5 Jim Thorpe/5
6 Joe Jackson/25 125.00 250.00
7 Joe Medwick/50 20.00 50.00
8 Eddie Mathews/50 15.00 40.00
9 Willie Mays/5
10 Hank Aaron/5
11 Pete Rose/5
12 Gil Hodges/25 20.00 50.00
13 Roberto Clemente/50 30.00 60.00
14 Cal Ripken Jr./40 15.00 40.00
15 Nolan Ryan/10
16 Satchel Paige/25 40.00 80.00
17 Roger Maris/50 20.00 50.00
18 Mike Schmidt/15
19 Reggie Jackson/10
20 George Brett/50 12.50 30.00
21 Pete Rose/5
22 Lou Gehrig/10
23 Jackie Robinson/10
24 Ted Williams/25 50.00 100.00
25 Jim Thorpe/5
26 Joe Jackson/25 125.00 250.00
27 Joe Medwick/50 20.00 50.00
28 Eddie Mathews/50 15.00 40.00
29 Willie Mays/5
30 Arky Vaughan/50 20.00 50.00
31 Gil Hodges/25 20.00 50.00
32 Roberto Clemente/50 20.00 50.00
33 Satchel Paige/20 40.00 80.00
34 Roger Maris/50 20.00 50.00
35 Cal Ripken Jr./20 15.00 40.00

2008 Prime Cuts Biography Materials Prime

OVERALL AU/MEM ODDS 4 PER BOX
PRINT RUNS B/WN 1-25 COPIES PER
NO PRICING DUE TO SCARCITY

2008 Prime Cuts Colossal

OVERALL AU/MEM ODDS 4 PER BOX
PRINT RUNS B/WN 1-50 COPIES PER
NO PRICING ON MOST DUE TO SCARCITY
7 Nolan Ryan/30 20.00 50.00
21 Gil Hodges/50 20.00 50.00
23 Joe Medwick/49 30.00 60.00

2008 Prime Cuts Colossal Prime

OVERALL AU/MEM ODDS 4 PER BOX
PRINT RUNS B/WN 1-25 COPIES PER
NO PRICING DUE TO SCARCITY

2008 Prime Cuts Colossal Jersey Location

OVERALL AU/MEM ODDS 4 PER BOX
PRINT RUNS B/WN 1-99 COPIES PER
NO PRICING ON QTY 25 OR LESS
3 Jackie Robinson/20
16 Tony Gwynn/99 8.00 20.00
21 Gil Hodges/50 15.00 40.00
23 Joe Medwick/49 15.00 40.00

2008 Prime Cuts Colossal Jersey Location Prime

OVERALL AU/MEM ODDS 4 PER BOX
PRINT RUNS B/WN 1-25 COPIES PER
NO PRICING DUE TO SCARCITY

2008 Prime Cuts Colossal Jersey Number

OVERALL AU/MEM ODDS 4 PER BOX
PRINT RUNS B/WN 1-50 COPIES PER
NO PRICING ON QTY 25 OR LESS
21 Gil Hodges/50 15.00 40.00
23 Joe Medwick/49 20.00 50.00

2008 Prime Cuts Colossal Jersey Position

OVERALL AU/MEM ODDS 4 PER BOX
PRINT RUNS B/WN 1-50 COPIES PER
NO PRICING ON QTY 25 OR LESS
16 Tony Gwynn/99 8.00 20.00
21 Gil Hodges/50 15.00 40.00
23 Joe Medwick/49 20.00 50.00

2008 Prime Cuts Colossal Jersey Position Prime

OVERALL AU/MEM ODDS 4 PER BOX
PRINT RUNS B/WN 1-25 COPIES PER
NO PRICING DUE TO SCARCITY

2008 Prime Cuts Dual Materials

OVERALL AU/MEM ODDS 4 PER BOX
PRINT RUNS B/WN 1-99 COPIES PER
NO PRICING ON QTY 25 OR LESS
2 Alan Trammell/60 10.00 25.00
16 Dale Murphy/50 12.50 30.00
21 Dwight Gooden/49 3.00 8.00
25 Don Sutton/99 3.00 8.00
34 Gary Carter/30 6.00 15.00
45 Joe Cronin/49 10.00 25.00
46 Joe Jackson/25
47 Joe Medwick/5
48 Joe Morgan/99 3.00 8.00
51 Juan Marichal/1
52 Arky Vaughan/99 20.00 50.00
68 Paul Molitor/49 4.00 10.00
73 Red Schoendienst/29 3.00 8.00
81 Roger Maris/49 20.00 50.00
86 Steve Carlton/29 4.00 10.00
91 Tony Gwynn/49 5.00 12.00
92 Tony Perez/49 5.00 12.00
93 Wade Boggs/26 10.00 25.00
99 Willie Stargell/99 4.00 10.00

2008 Prime Cuts Icons

OVERALL INSERT ODDS 1 PER BOX
STATED PRINT RUN 25 SER.#'d SETS
NO PRICING DUE TO SCARCITY

2008 Prime Cuts Icons Gold

OVERALL INSERT ODDS 1 PER BOX
STATED PRINT RUN 5 SER.#'d SETS
NO PRICING DUE TO SCARCITY

2008 Prime Cuts Icons Platinum

OVERALL INSERT ODDS 1 PER BOX
STATED PRINT RUN 1 SER.#'d SET
NO PRICING DUE TO SCARCITY

2008 Prime Cuts Icons Silver

OVERALL INSERT ODDS 1 PER BOX
STATED PRINT RUN 10 SER.#'d SETS
NO PRICING DUE TO SCARCITY

2008 Prime Cuts Icons Bats

OVERALL AU/MEM ODDS 4 PER BOX
PRINT RUNS B/WN 1-99 COPIES PER
NO PRICING ON QTY 19 OR LESS
7 Brooks Robinson/60 5.00 12.00
17 Joe Morgan/50 4.00 10.00
21 Dale Murphy/99 6.00 15.00
22 Robin Yount/39 8.00 20.00
29 Barry Larkin/75 3.00 8.00
31 Roberto Clemente/50 15.00 40.00
32 Eddie Mathews/99 6.00 15.00
41 Roger Maris/99 12.50 30.00
45 Tony Gwynn/99 5.00 12.00
50 Will Clark/49 8.00 20.00

2008 Prime Cuts Icons Jersey Number

OVERALL AU/MEM ODDS 4 PER BOX
PRINT RUNS B/WN 1-99 COPIES PER
NO PRICING ON QTY 19 OR LESS
17 Joe Morgan/50 3.00 8.00
28 Dennis Eckersley/43 3.00 8.00
45 Tony Gwynn/99 4.00 10.00
49 Ozzie Smith/99 8.00 20.00
50 Will Clark/5

2008 Prime Cuts Icons Jersey Number Prime

OVERALL AU/MEM ODDS 4 PER BOX
PRINT RUNS B/WN 1-40 COPIES PER
NO PRICING ON QTY 25 OR LESS
23 Cal Ripken Jr./40 20.00 50.00

2008 Prime Cuts Icons Jersey Position

OVERALL AU/MEM ODDS 4 PER BOX
PRINT RUNS B/WN 1-99 COPIES PER
NO PRICING ON QTY 20 OR LESS
17 Joe Morgan/50 3.00 8.00
23 Cal Ripken Jr./35 15.00 40.00
45 Tony Gwynn/99 4.00 10.00
49 Ozzie Smith/90 8.00 20.00
50 Will Clark/5

2008 Prime Cuts Icons Materials Combos

OVERALL AU/MEM ODDS 4 PER BOX
PRINT RUNS B/WN 1-49 COPIES PER
NO PRICING ON QTY 20 OR LESS
17 Joe Morgan/49 4.00 10.00
21 Dale Murphy/49 10.00 25.00
30 Larry Walker/49 4.00 10.00
41 Roger Maris/49 20.00 50.00
45 Tony Gwynn/49 6.00 15.00

2008 Prime Cuts Icons Materials HOF

OVERALL AU/MEM ODDS 4 PER BOX
PRINT RUNS B/WN 1-99 COPIES PER
NO PRICING ON QTY 20 OR LESS
17 Joe Morgan/30 4.00 10.00
28 Dennis Eckersley/35 5.00 12.00
45 Tony Gwynn/99 5.00 12.00

2008 Prime Cuts Icons Materials HOF Prime

OVERALL AU/MEM ODDS 4 PER BOX
PRINT RUNS B/WN 1-25 COPIES PER
NO PRICING DUE TO SCARCITY

2008 Prime Cuts Icons Materials Icon

OVERALL AU/MEM ODDS 4 PER BOX
PRINT RUNS B/WN 1-49 COPIES PER
NO PRICING ON QTY 20 OR LESS
28 Dennis Eckersley/35 3.00 8.00
29 Barry Larkin/30 10.00 25.00
45 Tony Gwynn/99 6.00 15.00

2008 Prime Cuts Icons Materials MVP

OVERALL AU/MEM ODDS 4 PER BOX
PRINT RUNS B/WN 1-50 COPIES PER
NO PRICING ON QTY 20 OR LESS
17 Joe Morgan/50 3.00 8.00

2008 Prime Cuts Icons Signature Century Platinum

OVERALL AU/MEM ODDS 4 PER BOX
STATED PRINT RUN 1 SER.#'d SET
NO PRICING DUE TO SCARCITY
EXCHANGE DEADLINE 6/26/2010

2008 Prime Cuts Icons Signature Jersey Number

OVERALL AU/MEM ODDS 4 PER BOX
PRINT RUNS B/WN 1-25 COPIES PER
NO PRICING DUE TO SCARCITY
EXCHANGE DEADLINE 6/26/2010

2008 Prime Cuts Icons Signature Jersey Number Prime

OVERALL AU/MEM ODDS 4 PER BOX
PRINT RUNS B/WN 1-15 COPIES PER
NO PRICING DUE TO SCARCITY
EXCHANGE DEADLINE 6/26/2010

2008 Prime Cuts Icons Signature Materials Combos Prime

OVERALL AU/MEM ODDS 4 PER BOX
PRINT RUNS B/WN 1-8 COPIES PER
NO PRICING DUE TO SCARCITY
EXCHANGE DEADLINE 6/26/2010

2008 Prime Cuts Icons Signature Materials HOF

OVERALL AU/MEM ODDS 4 PER BOX
PRINT RUNS B/WN 1-25 COPIES PER
NO PRICING DUE TO SCARCITY
EXCHANGE DEADLINE 6/26/2010

2008 Prime Cuts Icons Signature Materials HOF Prime

OVERALL AU/MEM ODDS 4 PER BOX
PRINT RUNS B/WN 1-6 COPIES PER
NO PRICING DUE TO SCARCITY
EXCHANGE DEADLINE 6/26/2010

2008 Prime Cuts Icons Signature Materials Icon

OVERALL AU/MEM ODDS 4 PER BOX
PRINT RUNS B/WN 1-20 COPIES PER
NO PRICING DUE TO SCARCITY
EXCHANGE DEADLINE 6/26/2010

2008 Prime Cuts Icons Signature Materials MVP

OVERALL AU/MEM ODDS 4 PER BOX
PRINT RUNS B/WN 1-49 COPIES PER
NO PRICING ON MOST DUE TO SCARCITY
EXCHANGE DEADLINE 6/26/2010
17 Joe Morgan/49 12.50 30.00
28 Dennis Eckersley/30 8.00 20.00

2008 Prime Cuts Icons Signature Materials MVP Prime

OVERALL AU/MEM ODDS 4 PER BOX
PRINT RUNS B/WN 1-49 COPIES PER
NO PRICING ON MOST TO SCARCITY
EXCHANGE DEADLINE 6/26/2010
21 Dale Murphy/49 20.00 50.00

2008 Prime Cuts Jersey Number

OVERALL AU/MEM ODDS 4 PER BOX
PRINT RUNS B/WN 1-99 COPIES PER
NO PRICING ON QTY 25 OR LESS
1 Al Kaline/10
2 Alan Trammell/75 6.00 15.00
3 Andre Dawson/50 4.00 10.00
4 Barry Larkin/11
5 Billy Williams/75 3.00 8.00
6 Bo Jackson/8
7 Bob Feller/49 6.00 15.00
8 Bob Gibson/15
9 Bobby Doerr/49 5.00 12.00
9 Bobby Doerr/49 5.00 12.00
10 Brooks Robinson/30 10.00 25.00
12 Cal Ripken Jr./30 20.00 50.00
16 Dale Murphy/75 10.00 25.00
17 Dave Winfield/31 4.00 10.00
18 Deion Sanders/75 5.00 12.00
21 Dwight Gooden/99 3.00 8.00
25 Don Sutton/99 3.00 8.00
28 Eddie Murray/33 6.00 15.00
35 Gaylord Perry/36 3.00 8.00
45 Joe Cronin/49 5.00 12.00
48 Joe Morgan/50 3.00 8.00
67 Ozzie Smith/75 6.00 15.00
68 Paul Molitor/49 4.00 10.00
70 Phil Niekro/49 3.00 8.00
86 Steve Carlton/49 3.00 8.00
91 Tony Gwynn/50 4.00 10.00
94 Warren Spahn/99 6.00 15.00
99 Willie Stargell/99 4.00 10.00

2008 Prime Cuts Jersey Position

OVERALL AU/MEM ODDS 4 PER BOX
PRINT RUNS B/WN 1-99 COPIES PER
NO PRICING ON QTY 25 OR LESS
1 Al Kaline/10
2 Alan Trammell/75 6.00 15.00
3 Andre Dawson/99 3.00 8.00
4 Barry Larkin/20
5 Billy Williams/75 3.00 8.00
6 Bo Jackson/25
7 Bob Feller/49 6.00 15.00
8 Bob Gibson/15
9 Bobby Doerr/49 5.00 12.00
10 Brooks Robinson/3
12 Cal Ripken Jr./30 20.00 50.00
14 Carl Yastrzemski/3
15 Carlton Fisk/5
16 Dale Murphy/49 10.00 25.00
17 Dave Winfield/25
18 Deion Sanders/99 5.00 12.00
19 Dennis Eckersley/5
21 Dwight Gooden/99 3.00 8.00
22 Don Drysdale/10
24 Don Mattingly/49 6.00 15.00
25 Don Sutton/99 3.00 8.00
45 Joe Cronin/49 5.00 12.00
48 Joe Morgan/50 3.00 8.00
67 Ozzie Smith/75 6.00 15.00
68 Paul Molitor/49 4.00 10.00
70 Phil Niekro/49 3.00 8.00
86 Steve Carlton/49 3.00 8.00
91 Tony Gwynn/99 4.00 10.00
92 Tony Perez/49 5.00 12.00
94 Warren Spahn/99 6.00 15.00
99 Willie Stargell/99 4.00 10.00

2008 Prime Cuts Leaf Limited Phenoms Autographs

OVERALL AU/MEM ODDS 4 PER BOX
EXCHANGE DEADLINE 6/26/2010
1 Rick Porcello 60.00 120.00
2 Buster Posey 50.00 100.00
3 Gordon Beckham 30.00 60.00
4 Ike Davis 20.00 50.00
5 Andrew Cashner 8.00 20.00
6 Jhoulys Chacin 8.00 20.00
7 Neftali Feliz 15.00 40.00
8 Ryan Perry 4.00 10.00
9 Anthony Hewitt 4.00 10.00
10 Daniel Schlereth 4.00 10.00
11 Michel Inoa 8.00 20.00
12 Logan Schafer 4.00 10.00
13 Rafael Rodriguez 15.00 40.00
14 Allan Dykstra 4.00 10.00
15 Neftali Soto 10.00 25.00
16 Wilson Ramos 8.00 20.00
17 Anthony Gose 4.00 10.00
18 Tyler Sample 4.00 10.00
19 Danny Espinosa 12.50 30.00
20 Rashun Dixon 6.00 15.00
21 Kyle Hudson 4.00 10.00
22 Tim Murphy 4.00 10.00
23 Jharmidy De Jesus 4.00 10.00
24 Will Smith 4.00 10.00
25 Derek Norris 8.00 20.00

2008 Prime Cuts Material Combos

OVERALL AU/MEM ODDS 4 PER BOX
PRINT RUNS B/WN 25-99 COPIES PER
NO PRICING ON QTY 25 OR LESS
5 Ted Williams 20.00 50.00
Lou Boudreau/99
9 Ted Williams 20.00 50.00
Tony Gwynn/99
10 Joe Medwick 15.00 40.00
Carl Yastrzemski/99

2008 Prime Cuts Material Combos Prime

OVERALL AU/MEM ODDS 4 PER BOX
PRINT RUNS B/WN 1-5 COPIES PER
NO PRICING DUE TO SCARCITY

2008 Prime Cuts Material Triples

OVERALL AU/MEM ODDS 4 PER BOX
PRINT RUNS B/WN 5-50 COPIES PER
NO PRICING ON QTY 25 OR LESS
1 Pete Rose 40.00 80.00
Pete Rose
Pete Rose/50

2008 Prime Cuts Material Quads

OVERALL AU/MEM ODDS 4 PER BOX
PRINT RUNS B/WN 5-99 COPIES PER
NO PRICING ON QTY 25 OR LESS
3 Johnny Bench 20.00 50.00
Mike Schmidt
Willie Mays
Paul Molitor/99

2008 Prime Cuts Material Quads Prime

OVERALL AU/MEM ODDS 4 PER BOX
PRINT RUNS B/WN 1-5 COPIES PER
NO PRICING DUE TO SCARCITY

2008 Prime Cuts Playoff Contenders Autographs

OVERALL AU/MEM ODDS 4 PER BOX
EXCHANGE DEADLINE 6/26/2010
1 Rick Porcello 60.00 120.00
2 Buster Posey 60.00 120.00
3 Gordon Beckham 30.00 60.00
4 Ike Davis 20.00 50.00
5 Andrew Cashner 8.00 20.00
6 Jhoulys Chacin 6.00 15.00
7 Neftali Feliz 20.00 50.00
8 Ryan Perry 3.00 8.00
9 Anthony Hewitt 4.00 10.00
10 Daniel Schlereth 3.00 8.00
11 Michel Inoa 10.00 25.00
12 Logan Schafer 4.00 10.00
13 Rafael Rodriguez 20.00 50.00
14 Allan Dykstra 4.00 10.00
15 T.J. Steele 4.00 10.00
16 Aaron Shafer 3.00 8.00
17 Dennis Raben 4.00 10.00
18 Cody Satterwhite 8.00 20.00
19 James Darnell 4.00 10.00
20 Zeke Spruill EXCH 8.00 20.00
21 Jason Knapp 3.00 8.00
22 Charlie Blackmon 3.00 8.00
23 O.J. Mayo 30.00 60.00
24 Michael Beasley 15.00 40.00
25 Derrick Rose 150.00 300.00

2008 Prime Cuts Signature Century

OVERALL AU/MEM ODDS 4 PER BOX
PRINT RUNS B/WN 1-99 COPIES PER
NO PRICING ON QTY ON 25 OR LESS
EXCHANGE DEADLINE 6/26/2010
1 Al Kaline/28 15.00 40.00
10 Brooks Robinson/74 15.00 40.00
12 Cal Ripken Jr./29 60.00 120.00
25 Don Sutton/53 10.00 25.00
37 George Kell/99 10.00 25.00
51 Juan Marichal/43 10.00 25.00
60 Marty Marion/94 6.00 15.00
65 Nolan Ryan/32 40.00 80.00
85 Stan Musial/99 30.00 60.00
95 Whitey Ford/26 20.00 50.00

2008 Prime Cuts Signature Century Platinum

RANDOM INSERTS IN PACKS
STATED PRINT RUN 1 SER.#'d SET
NO PRICING DUE TO SCARCITY
EXCHANGE DEADLINE 6/26/2010

2008 Prime Cuts Signature Colossal

RANDOM INSERTS IN PACKS
PRINT RUNS B/WN 1-19 COPIES PER
NO PRICING DUE TO SCARCITY
EXCHANGE DEADLINE 6/26/2010

2008 Prime Cuts Signature Colossal Prime

RANDOM INSERTS IN PACKS
PRINT RUNS B/WN 1-25 COPIES PER
NO PRICING DUE TO SCARCITY
EXCHANGE DEADLINE 6/26/2010

2008 Prime Cuts Signature Colossal Jersey Location

RANDOM INSERTS IN PACKS
PRINT RUNS B/WN 1-19 COPIES PER
NO PRICING DUE TO SCARCITY
EXCHANGE DEADLINE 6/26/2010

2008 Prime Cuts Signature Colossal Jersey Location Prime

RANDOM INSERTS IN PACKS
PRINT RUNS B/WN 5-25 COPIES PER
NO PRICING DUE TO SCARCITY
EXCHANGE DEADLINE 6/26/2010
16 Tony Gwynn/25
24 Ozzie Smith/5

2008 Prime Cuts Signature Colossal Jersey Number

RANDOM INSERTS IN PACKS
PRINT RUNS B/WN 1-19 COPIES PER
NO PRICING DUE TO SCARCITY
EXCHANGE DEADLINE 6/26/2010

2008 Prime Cuts Signature Colossal Jersey Number Prime

RANDOM INSERTS IN PACKS
PRINT RUNS B/WN 5-19 COPIES PER
NO PRICING DUE TO SCARCITY
EXCHANGE DEADLINE 6/26/2010
16 Tony Gwynn/19
24 Ozzie Smith/5

2008 Prime Cuts Signature Colossal Jersey Position

RANDOM INSERTS IN PACKS
PRINT RUNS B/WN 1-19 COPIES PER
NO PRICING DUE TO SCARCITY
EXCHANGE DEADLINE 6/26/2010

2008 Prime Cuts Signature Colossal Jersey Position Prime

RANDOM INSERTS IN PACKS
PRINT RUNS B/WN 5-25 COPIES PER
NO PRICING DUE TO SCARCITY
EXCHANGE DEADLINE 6/26/2010
16 Tony Gwynn/25
24 Ozzie Smith/5

2008 Prime Cuts Signature Combos

OVERALL AU/MEM ODDS 4 PER BOX
STATED PRINT RUN 10 SER.#'d SETS
NO PRICING DUE TO SCARCITY
EXCHANGE DEADLINE 6/26/2010

2008 Prime Cuts Signature Trios

OVERALL AU/MEM ODDS 4 PER BOX
STATED PRINT RUN 10 SER.#'d SETS
NO PRICING DUE TO SCARCITY
EXCHANGE DEADLINE 6/26/2010

2008 Prime Cuts Signature Quads

OVERALL AU/MEM ODDS 4 PER BOX
STATED PRINT RUN 10 SER.#'d SETS
NO PRICING DUE TO SCARCITY
EXCHANGE DEADLINE 6/26/2010

2008 Prime Cuts Souvenir Cuts

OVERALL AU/MEM ODDS 4 PER BOX
PRINT RUNS B/WN 1-250 COPIES PER
NO PRICING ON MOST DUE TO SCARCITY
EXCHANGE DEADLINE 6/26/2010
98 Joe DiMaggio/250 200.00 300.00

2008 Prime Cuts Stadium Souvenir Cuts

OVERALL AU/MEM ODDS 4 PER BOX
PRINT RUNS B/WN 1-250 COPIES PER
NO PRICING ON MOST DUE TO SCARCITY
EXCHANGE DEADLINE 6/26/2010
2 Joe DiMaggio/250 200.00 300.00

2008 Prime Cuts Timeline

OVERALL INSERT ODDS 1 PER BOX
STATED PRINT RUN 50 SER.#'d SETS
1 Stan Musial 5.00 12.00
2 Yogi Berra 3.00 8.00
3 Willie Mays 6.00 15.00
4 Hank Aaron 6.00 15.00
5 Ernie Banks 3.00 8.00
6 Frank Robinson 1.25 3.00
7 Brooks Robinson 2.00 5.00
8 Frank Robinson 1.25 3.00
9 Orlando Cepeda 1.25 3.00
10 Carl Yastrzemski 5.00 12.00
11 Bob Gibson 2.00 5.00
12 Willie McCovey 2.00 5.00
13 Harmon Killebrew 3.00 8.00
14 Johnny Bench 3.00 8.00
15 Pete Rose 8.00 20.00
16 Reggie Jackson 2.00 5.00
17 Joe Morgan 1.25 3.00
18 Rod Carew 2.00 5.00
19 Mike Schmidt 5.00 12.00
20 George Brett 6.00 15.00
21 Robin Yount 3.00 8.00
22 Cal Ripken Jr. 12.00 30.00
23 Ryne Sandberg 6.00 15.00
24 Don Mattingly 6.00 15.00
25 Roberto Clemente 6.00 15.00
26 Eddie Mathews 3.00 8.00
27 Gil Hodges 2.00 5.00
28 Jackie Robinson 3.00 8.00
29 Jim Thorpe 3.00 8.00
30 Joe Jackson 6.00 15.00
31 Joe Medwick 3.00 8.00
32 Lou Gehrig 6.00 15.00
33 Nellie Fox 2.00 5.00
34 Nolan Ryan 10.00 25.00
35 Roger Maris 3.00 8.00
36 Satchel Paige 3.00 8.00
37 Ted Williams 8.00 20.00
38 Tom Seaver 2.00 5.00
39 Tony Gwynn 3.00 8.00
40 Whitey Ford 2.00 5.00
41 Reggie Jackson 2.00 5.00
42 Casey Stengel 1.25 3.00
43 Early Wynn 1.25 3.00
44 Billy Martin 2.00 5.00
45 Don Drysdale 2.00 5.00
46 Lefty Grove 2.00 5.00
47 Enos Slaughter 1.25 3.00
48 Catfish Hunter 1.25 3.00
49 Carlton Fisk 2.00 5.00
50 Eddie Murray 3.00 8.00

2008 Prime Cuts Timeline Gold

OVERALL INSERT ODDS 1 PER BOX
STATED PRINT RUN 5 SER.#'d SETS
NO PRICING DUE TO SCARCITY

2008 Prime Cuts Timeline Platinum

OVERALL INSERT ODDS 1 PER BOX
STATED PRINT RUN 1 SER.#'d SET
NO PRICING DUE TO SCARCITY

2008 Prime Cuts Timeline Silver

OVERALL INSERT ODDS 1 PER BOX
STATED PRINT RUN 10 SER.#'d SETS
NO PRICING DUE TO SCARCITY

2008 Prime Cuts Timeline Bats

OVERALL AU/MEM ODDS 4 PER BOX
PRINT RUNS B/WN 3-99 COPIES PER
NO PRICING ON QTY 25 OR LESS
1 Stan Musial/5
2 Yogi Berra/8
5 Ernie Banks/5
6 Frank Robinson/5
7 Brooks Robinson/60 5.00 12.00
8 Frank Robinson/5
9 Orlando Cepeda/29 5.00 12.00
10 Carl Yastrzemski/67 5.00 12.00
12 Willie McCovey/5
13 Harmon Killebrew/10
14 Johnny Bench/25
16 Reggie Jackson/10
17 Joe Morgan/50 4.00 10.00
18 Rod Carew/10
19 Mike Schmidt/5
20 George Brett/9
21 Robin Yount/25
22 Cal Ripken Jr./25
23 Ryne Sandberg/10
24 Don Mattingly/60 5.00 12.00
25 Roberto Clemente/50 20.00 50.00
26 Eddie Mathews/99 6.00 15.00
30 Joe Jackson/25
32 Lou Gehrig/3
33 Nellie Fox/5
34 Nolan Ryan/10
35 Roger Maris/99 12.50 30.00
37 Ted Williams/5
38 Tom Seaver/3
39 Tony Gwynn/49 5.00 12.00
41 Reggie Jackson/10
49 Carlton Fisk/10
50 Eddie Murray/99 4.00 10.00

2008 Prime Cuts Timeline Jersey Location

OVERALL AU/MEM ODDS 4 PER BOX
PRINT RUNS B/WN 1-99 COPIES PER
NO PRICING ON QTY 25 OR LESS
17 Joe Morgan/50 4.00 10.00
39 Tony Gwynn/99 5.00 12.00
49 Carlton Fisk/35 4.00 10.00
50 Eddie Murray/5

2008 Prime Cuts Timeline Jersey Number

OVERALL AU/MEM ODDS 4 PER BOX
PRINT RUNS B/WN 1-99 COPIES PER
NO PRICING ON QTY 25 OR LESS
17 Joe Morgan/50 4.00 10.00
22 Cal Ripken Jr./35 10.00 25.00
39 Tony Gwynn/99 5.00 12.00
49 Carlton Fisk/27 4.00 10.00

2008 Prime Cuts Timeline Jersey Number Prime

OVERALL AU/MEM ODDS 4 PER BOX
PRINT RUNS B/WN 1-25 COPIES PER
NO PRICING DUE TO SCARCITY

2008 Prime Cuts Timeline Jersey Position

OVERALL AU/MEM ODDS 4 PER BOX
PRINT RUNS B/WN 1-99 COPIES PER
NO PRICING ON QTY 25 OR LESS
17 Joe Morgan/99 4.00 10.00
22 Cal Ripken Jr./35 10.00 25.00
39 Tony Gwynn/99 5.00 12.00
49 Carlton Fisk/49 4.00 10.00

2008 Prime Cuts Timeline Materials Combos

OVERALL AU/MEM ODDS 4 PER BOX
PRINT RUNS B/WN 1-99 COPIES PER
NO PRICING ON QTY 25 OR LESS
17 Joe Morgan/50 4.00 10.00
39 Tony Gwynn/99 5.00 12.00
42 Casey Stengel/30 10.00 25.00

2008 Prime Cuts Timeline Materials Trios

OVERALL AU/MEM ODDS 4 PER BOX
PRINT RUNS B/WN 1-99 COPIES PER
NO PRICING ON QTY 25 OR LESS
17 Joe Morgan/40 4.00 10.00
39 Tony Gwynn/99 5.00 12.00
42 Casey Stengel/30 10.00 25.00

2008 Prime Cuts Timeline Materials Trios HOF

OVERALL AU/MEM ODDS 4 PER BOX
PRINT RUNS B/WN 1-99 COPIES PER
NO PRICING ON QTY 25 OR LESS
39 Tony Gwynn/99 5.00 12.00

2008 Prime Cuts Timeline Materials Trios HOF Prime

OVERALL AU/MEM ODDS 4 PER BOX
PRINT RUNS B/WN 1-25 COPIES PER
NO PRICING DUE TO SCARCITY

2008 Prime Cuts Timeline Materials Trios MVP

OVERALL AU/MEM ODDS 4 PER BOX
PRINT RUNS B/WN 1-25 COPIES PER
NO PRICING DUE TO SCARCITY

2008 Prime Cuts Timeline Materials Trios Stats

OVERALL AU/MEM ODDS 4 PER BOX
PRINT RUNS B/WN 1-99 COPIES PER
NO PRICING ON QTY 25 OR LESS
39 Tony Gwynn/99 5.00 12.00

2008 Prime Cuts Timeline Materials Quads

OVERALL AU/MEM ODDS 4 PER BOX
PRINT RUNS B/WN 1-99 COPIES PER
NO PRICING ON QTY 25 OR LESS
39 Tony Gwynn/99 5.00 12.00

2008 Prime Cuts Timeline Materials Custom Nicknames

OVERALL AU/MEM ODDS 4 PER BOX
PRINT RUNS B/WN 1-99 COPIES PER
NO PRICING ON QTY 25 OR LESS
9 Orlando Cepeda/99 5.00 12.00
27 Gil Hodges/50 10.00 25.00
30 Joe Jackson/50 125.00 250.00
33 Nellie Fox/50 30.00 60.00
39 Tony Gwynn/99 5.00 12.00

2008 Prime Cuts Timeline Materials Custom Nicknames Prime

OVERALL AU/MEM ODDS 4 PER BOX
PRINT RUNS B/WN 1-25 COPIES PER
NO PRICING DUE TO SCARCITY

2008 Prime Cuts Timeline Materials Custom Numbers

OVERALL AU/MEM ODDS 4 PER BOX
PRINT RUNS B/WN 1-25 COPIES PER
NO PRICING DUE TO SCARCITY

2008 Prime Cuts Timeline Materials CY HR

OVERALL AU/MEM ODDS 4 PER BOX
PRINT RUNS B/WN 1-99 COPIES PER
NO PRICING ON QTY 25 OR LESS
17 Joe Morgan/50 4.00 10.00
30 Joe Jackson/50 100.00 200.00
39 Tony Gwynn/99 5.00 12.00

2008 Prime Cuts Timeline Signature Materials Quads Custom Numbers

OVERALL AU/MEM ODDS 4 PER BOX
PRINT RUNS B/W 1-49 COPIES PER
NO PRICING ON MOST DUE TO SCARCITY
EXCHANGE DEADLINE 6/26/2010
9 Orlando Cepeda/49 20.00 50.00

1988 Score

COMP.FACT.SET (660) 7.50 15.00
1 Don Mattingly .25 .60
2 Wade Boggs .05 .15
3 Tim Raines .02 .10
4 Andre Dawson .02 .10
5 Mark McGwire .60 1.50
6 Kevin Seitzer .01 .05
7 Wally Joyner .02 .10
8 Jesse Barfield .02 .10
9 Pedro Guerrero .02 .10
10 Eric Davis .02 .10
11 George Brett .20 .50
12 Ozzie Smith .10 .30
13 Rickey Henderson .07 .20
14 Jim Rice .02 .10
15 Matt Nokes RC .08 .25
16 Mike Schmidt .20 .50
17 Dave Parker .02 .10
18 Eddie Murray .07 .20
19 Andres Galarraga .02 .10
20 Tony Fernandez .01 .05
21 Kevin McReynolds .01 .05
22 B.J. Surhoff .02 .10
23 Pat Tabler .01 .05
24 Kirby Puckett .07 .20
25 Benny Santiago .02 .10
26 Ryne Sandberg .15 .40
27 Kelly Downs .01 .05
28 Jose Cruz .02 .10
29 Pete O'Brien .01 .05
30 Mark Langston .01 .05
31 Lee Smith .02 .10
32 Juan Samuel .01 .05
33 Kevin Bass .01 .05
34 R.J. Reynolds .01 .05
35 Steve Sax .01 .05
36 John Kruk .02 .10
37 Alan Trammell .02 .10
38 Chris Bosio .01 .05
39 Brook Jacoby .01 .05
40 Willie McGee UER .02 .10
(Excited misspelled
as excild)
41 Dave Magadan .01 .05
42 Fred Lynn .02 .10
43 Kent Hrbek .02 .10
44 Brian Downing .02 .10
45 Jose Canseco .20 .50
46 Jim Presley .01 .05
47 Mike Stanley .01 .05
48 Tony Pena .01 .05
49 David Cone .02 .10
50 Rick Sutcliffe .02 .10
51 Doug Drabek .01 .05
52 Bill Doran .01 .05
53 Mike Scioscia .02 .10
54 Candy Maldonado .01 .05
55 Dave Winfield .02 .10
56 Lou Whitaker .02 .10
57 Tom Henke .01 .05
58 Ken Gerhart .01 .05
59 Glenn Braggs .01 .05
60 Julio Franco .02 .10
61 Charlie Leibrandt .01 .05
62 Gary Gaetti .02 .10
63 Bob Boone .02 .10
64 Luis Polonia RC .08 .25
65 Dwight Evans .05 .15
66 Phil Bradley .01 .05
67 Mike Boddicker .01 .05
68 Vince Coleman .01 .05
69 Howard Johnson .02 .10
70 Tim Wallach .01 .05
71 Keith Moreland .01 .05
72 Barry Larkin .05 .15
73 Alan Ashby .01 .05
74 Rick Rhoden .01 .05
75 Darrell Evans .02 .10
76 Dave Stieb .02 .10
77 Dan Plesac .01 .05
78 Will Clark UER .07 .20
(Born 3/17/64,
should be 3/13/64)
79 Frank White .02 .10
80 Joe Carter .02 .10
81 Mike Witt .01 .05
82 Terry Steinbach .02 .10
83 Alvin Davis .01 .05
84 Tommy Herr .02 .10
85 Vance Law .01 .05
86 Kal Daniels .01 .05
87 Rick Honeycutt UER .01 .05
(Wrong years for
stats on back)
88 Alfredo Griffin .01 .05
89 Bret Saberhagen .02 .10
90 Bert Blyleven .02 .10
91 Jeff Reardon .02 .10
92 Cory Snyder .01 .05
93A Greg Walker ERR .75 2.00
(93 of 66)
93B Greg Walker COR .01 .05
(93 of 660)
94 Joe Magrane RC .08 .25
95 Rob Deer .01 .05
96 Ray Knight .02 .10
97 Casey Candaele .01 .05
98 John Cerutti .01 .05
99 Buddy Bell .02 .10
100 Jack Clark .02 .10
101 Eric Bell .01 .05
102 Willie Wilson .02 .10
103 Dave Schmidt .01 .05
104 Dennis Eckersley UER .05 .15
(Complete games stats
are wrong)
105 Don Sutton .02 .10
106 Danny Tartabull .01 .05
107 Fred McGriff .07 .20
108 Les Straker .01 .05
109 Lloyd Moseby .01 .05
110 Roger Clemens .40 1.00
111 Glenn Hubbard .01 .05
112 Ken Williams RC .01 .05
113 Ruben Sierra .02 .10
114 Stan Jefferson .01 .05
115 Milt Thompson .01 .05
116 Bobby Bonilla .02 .10
117 Wayne Tolleson .01 .05
118 Matt Williams RC .30 .75
119 Chet Lemon .02 .10
120 Dale Sveum .01 .05
121 Dennis Boyd .01 .05
122 Brett Butler .02 .10
123 Terry Kennedy .01 .05
124 Jack Howell .01 .05
125 Curt Young .01 .05
126A Dave Valle ERR .02 .10
(Misspelled Dale
on card front)
126B Dave Valle COR .01 .05
127 Curt Wilkerson .01 .05
128 Tim Teufel .01 .05
129 Ozzie Virgil .01 .05
130 Brian Fisher .01 .05
131 Lance Parrish .02 .10
132 Tom Browning .01 .05
133A Larry Andersen ERR .02 .10
(Misspelled Anderson
on card front)
133B Larry Andersen COR .01 .05
134A Bob Brenly ERR .02 .10
(Misspelled Brenley
on card front)
134B Bob Brenly COR .01 .05
135 Mike Marshall .01 .05
136 Gerald Perry .01 .05
137 Bobby Meacham .01 .05
138 Larry Herndon .01 .05
139 Fred Manrique .01 .05
140 Charlie Hough .02 .10
141 Ron Darling .02 .10
142 Herm Winningham .01 .05
143 Mike Diaz .01 .05
144 Mike Jackson RC .08 .25
145 Denny Walling .01 .05
146 Robby Thompson .01 .05
147 Franklin Stubbs .01 .05
148 Albert Hall .01 .05
149 Bobby Witt .01 .05
150 Lance McCullers .01 .05
151 Scott Bradley .01 .05
152 Mark McLemore .01 .05
153 Tim Laudner .01 .05
154 Greg Swindell .01 .05
155 Marty Barrett .01 .05
156 Mike Heath .01 .05
157 Gary Ward .01 .05
158A Lee Mazzilli ERR .02 .10
(Misspelled Mazilli
on card front)
158B Lee Mazzilli COR .02 .10
159 Tom Foley .01 .05
160 Robin Yount .10 .30
161 Steve Bedrosian .01 .05
162 Bob Walk .01 .05
163 Nick Esasky .01 .05
164 Ken Caminiti RC .75 2.00
165 Jose Uribe .01 .05
166 Dave Anderson .01 .05
167 Ed Whitson .01 .05
168 Ernie Whitt .01 .05
169 Cecil Cooper .02 .10
170 Mike Pagliarulo .01 .05
171 Pat Sheridan .01 .05
172 Chris Bando .01 .05
173 Lee Lacy .01 .05
174 Steve Lombardozzi .01 .05
175 Mike Greenwell .01 .05
176 Greg Minton .01 .05
177 Moose Haas .01 .05
178 Mike Kingery .01 .05
179 Greg A. Harris .01 .05
180 Bo Jackson .07 .20
181 Carmelo Martinez .01 .05
182 Alex Trevino .01 .05
183 Ron Oester .01 .05
184 Danny Darwin .01 .05
185 Mike Krukow .01 .05
186 Rafael Palmeiro .15 .40
187 Tim Burke .01 .05
188 Roger McDowell .01 .05
189 Garry Templeton .02 .10
190 Terry Pendleton .02 .10
191 Larry Parrish .01 .05
192 Rey Quinones .01 .05
193 Joaquin Andujar .02 .10
194 Tom Brunansky .01 .05
195 Donnie Moore .01 .05
196 Dan Pasqua .01 .05
197 Jim Gantner .01 .05
198 Mark Eichhorn .01 .05
199 John Grubb .01 .05
200 Bill Ripken RC .08 .25
201 Sam Horn RC .02 .10
202 Todd Worrell .01 .05
203 Terry Leach .01 .05
204 Garth Iorg .01 .05
205 Brian Dayett .01 .05
206 Bo Diaz .01 .05
207 Craig Reynolds .01 .05
208 Brian Holton .01 .05
209 Marvell Wynne UER .01 .05
(Misspelled Marvelle
on card front)
210 Dave Concepcion .02 .10
211 Mike Davis .01 .05
212 Devon White .02 .10
213 Mickey Brantley .01 .05
214 Greg Gagne .01 .05
215 Oddibe McDowell .01 .05
216 Jimmy Key .02 .10
217 Dave Bergman .01 .05
218 Calvin Schiraldi .01 .05
219 Larry Sheets .01 .05
220 Mike Easler .01 .05
221 Kurt Stillwell .01 .05
222 Chuck Jackson .01 .05
223 Dave Martinez .01 .05
224 Tim Leary .01 .05
225 Steve Garvey .02 .10
226 Greg Mathews .01 .05
227 Doug Sisk .01 .05
228 Dave Henderson .01 .05
(Wearing Red Sox uniform;
Red Sox logo on back)
229 Jimmy Dwyer .01 .05
230 Larry Owen .01 .05
231 Andre Thornton .01 .05
232 Mark Salas .01 .05
233 Tom Brookens .01 .05
234 Greg Brock .01 .05
235 Rance Mulliniks .01 .05
236 Bob Brower .01 .05
237 Joe Niekro .01 .05
238 Scott Bankhead .01 .05
239 Doug DeCinces .01 .05
240 Tommy John .02 .10
241 Rich Gedman .01 .05
242 Ted Power .01 .05
243 Dave Meads .01 .05
244 Jim Sundberg .02 .10
245 Ken Oberkfell .01 .05
246 Jimmy Jones .01 .05
247 Ken Landreaux .01 .05
248 Jose Oquendo .01 .05
249 John Mitchell RC .02 .10
250 Don Baylor .02 .10
251 Scott Fletcher .01 .05
252 Al Newman .01 .05
253 Carney Lansford .02 .10
254 Johnny Ray .01 .05
255 Gary Pettis .01 .05
256 Ken Phelps .01 .05
257 Rick Leach .01 .05
258 Tim Stoddard .01 .05
259 Ed Romero .01 .05
260 Sid Bream .01 .05
261A T.Niedenfuer ERR .02 .10
Misspelled Neidenfuer
on card front
261B T.Niedenfuer COR .01 .05
262 Rick Dempsey .01 .05
263 Lonnie Smith .01 .05
264 Bob Forsch .01 .05
265 Barry Bonds .75 2.00
266 Willie Randolph .02 .10
267 Mike Ramsey .01 .05
268 Don Slaught .01 .05
269 Mickey Tettleton .01 .05
270 Jerry Reuss .01 .05
271 Marc Sullivan .01 .05
272 Jim Morrison .01 .05
273 Steve Balboni .01 .05
274 Dick Schofield .01 .05
275 John Tudor .02 .10
276 Gene Larkin RC .08 .25
277 Harold Reynolds .02 .10
278 Jerry Browne .01 .05
279 Willie Upshaw .01 .05
280 Ted Higuera .01 .05
281 Terry McGriff .01 .05
282 Terry Puhl .01 .05
283 Mark Wasinger .01 .05
284 Luis Salazar .01 .05
285 Ted Simmons .02 .10
286 John Shelby .01 .05
287 John Smiley RC .08 .25
288 Curt Ford .01 .05
289 Steve Crawford .01 .05
290 Dan Quisenberry .01 .05
291 Alan Wiggins .01 .05
292 Randy Bush .01 .05
293 John Candelaria .01 .05
294 Tony Phillips .01 .05
295 Mike Morgan .01 .05
296 Bill Wegman .01 .05
297A Terry Francona ERR .02 .10
(Misspelled Franconia
on card front)
297B Terry Francona COR .02 .10
298 Mickey Hatcher .01 .05
299 Andres Thomas .01 .05
300 Bob Stanley .01 .05
301 Al Pedrique .01 .05
302 Jim Lindeman .01 .05
303 Wally Backman .01 .05
304 Paul O'Neill .05 .15
305 Hubie Brooks .01 .05
306 Steve Buechele .01 .05
307 Bobby Thigpen .01 .05
308 George Hendrick .02 .10
309 John Moses .01 .05
310 Ron Guidry .02 .10
311 Bill Schroeder .01 .05
312 Jose Nunez .01 .05
313 Bud Black .01 .05
314 Joe Sambito .01 .05
315 Scott McGregor .01 .05
316 Rafael Santana .01 .05
317 Frank Williams .01 .05
318 Mike Fitzgerald .01 .05
319 Rick Mahler .01 .05
320 Jim Gott .01 .05
321 Mariano Duncan .01 .05
322 Jose Guzman .01 .05
323 Lee Guetterman .01 .05
324 Dan Gladden .01 .05
325 Gary Carter .02 .10
326 Tracy Jones .01 .05
327 Floyd Youmans .01 .05
328 Bill Dawley .01 .05
329 Paul Noce .01 .05
330 Angel Salazar .01 .05
331 Goose Gossage .02 .10
332 George Frazier .01 .05
333 Ruppert Jones .01 .05
334 Billy Joe Robidoux .01 .05
335 Mike Scott .02 .10
336 Randy Myers .02 .10
337 Bob Sebra .01 .05
338 Eric Show .01 .05
339 Mitch Williams .01 .05
340 Paul Molitor .02 .10
341 Gus Polidor .01 .05
342 Steve Trout .01 .05
343 Jerry Don Gleaton .01 .05
344 Bob Knepper .01 .05
345 Mitch Webster .01 .05
346 John Morris .01 .05
347 Andy Hawkins .01 .05
348 Dave Leiper .01 .05
349 Ernest Riles .01 .05
350 Dwight Gooden .02 .10
351 Dave Righetti .02 .10
352 Pat Dodson .01 .05
353 John Habyan .01 .05
354 Jim Deshaies .01 .05
355 Butch Wynegar .01 .05
356 Bryn Smith .01 .05
357 Matt Young .01 .05
358 Tom Pagnozzi RC .02 .10
359 Floyd Rayford .01 .05
360 Darryl Strawberry .02 .10
361 Sal Butera .01 .05
362 Domingo Ramos .01 .05
363 Chris Brown .01 .05
364 Jose Gonzalez .01 .05
365 Dave Smith .01 .05
366 Andy McGaffigan .01 .05
367 Stan Javier .01 .05
368 Henry Cotto .01 .05
369 Mike Birkbeck .01 .05
370 Len Dykstra .02 .10
371 Dave Collins .01 .05
372 Spike Owen .01 .05
373 Geno Petralli .01 .05
374 Ron Karkovice .01 .05
375 Shane Rawley .01 .05
376 DeWayne Buice .01 .05
377 Bill Pecota RC .02 .10
378 Leon Durham .01 .05
379 Ed Olwine .01 .05
380 Bruce Hurst .01 .05
381 Bob McClure .01 .05
382 Mark Thurmond .01 .05
383 Buddy Biancalana .01 .05
384 Tim Conroy .01 .05
385 Tony Gwynn .10 .30
386 Greg Gross .01 .05
387 Barry Lyons .01 .05
388 Mike Felder .01 .05
389 Pat Clements .01 .05
390 Ken Griffey .02 .10
391 Mark Davis .01 .05
392 Jose Rijo .02 .10
393 Mike Young .01 .05
394 Willie Fraser .01 .05
395 Dion James .01 .05
396 Steve Shields .01 .05
397 Randy St.Claire .01 .05
398 Danny Jackson .01 .05
399 Cecil Fielder .02 .10
400 Keith Hernandez .02 .10
401 Don Carman .01 .05
402 Chuck Crim .01 .05
403 Rob Woodward .01 .05
404 Junior Ortiz .01 .05
405 Glenn Wilson .01 .05
406 Ken Howell .01 .05
407 Jeff Kunkel .01 .05
408 Jeff Reed .01 .05
409 Chris James .01 .05
410 Zane Smith .01 .05
411 Ken Dixon .01 .05
412 Ricky Horton .01 .05
413 Frank DiPino .01 .05
414 Shane Mack .01 .05
415 Danny Cox .01 .05
416 Andy Van Slyke .05 .15
417 Danny Heep .01 .05
418 John Cangelosi .01 .05
419A J.Christensen ERR .02 .10
Christiansen
on card front
419B J.Christensen COR .01 .05
420 Joey Cora RC .08 .25
421 Mike LaValliere .01 .05
422 Kelly Gruber .01 .05
423 Bruce Benedict .01 .05
424 Len Matuszek .01 .05
425 Kent Tekulve .01 .05
426 Rafael Ramirez .01 .05
427 Mike Flanagan .01 .05
428 Mike Gallego .01 .05
429 Juan Castillo .01 .05
430 Neal Heaton .01 .05
431 Phil Garner .02 .10
432 Mike Dunne .01 .05
433 Wallace Johnson .01 .05
434 Jack O'Connor .01 .05
435 Steve Jeltz .01 .05
436 Donell Nixon .01 .05
437 Jack Lazorko .01 .05
438 Keith Comstock .01 .05
439 Jeff D. Robinson .01 .05
440 Graig Nettles .02 .10
441 Mel Hall .01 .05
442 Gerald Young .01 .05
443 Gary Redus .01 .05
444 Charlie Moore .01 .05
445 Bill Madlock .02 .10
446 Mark Clear .01 .05
447 Greg Booker .01 .05
448 Rick Schu .01 .05
449 Ron Kittle .01 .05
450 Dale Murphy .05 .15
451 Bob Dernier .01 .05
452 Dale Mohorcic .01 .05
453 Rafael Belliard .01 .05
454 Charlie Puleo .01 .05
455 Dwayne Murphy .01 .05
456 Jim Eisenreich .01 .05
457 David Palmer .01 .05
458 Dave Stewart .02 .10
459 Pascual Perez .01 .05
460 Glenn Davis .01 .05
461 Dan Petry .01 .05
462 Jim Winn .01 .05
463 Darrell Miller .01 .05
464 Mike Moore .01 .05
465 Mike LaCoss .01 .05
466 Steve Farr .01 .05
467 Jerry Mumphrey .01 .05
468 Kevin Gross .01 .05
469 Bruce Bochy .01 .05
470 Orel Hershiser .02 .10
471 Eric King .01 .05
472 Ellis Burks RC .15 .40
473 Darren Daulton .02 .10
474 Mookie Wilson .02 .10
475 Frank Viola .02 .10
476 Ron Robinson .01 .05
477 Bob Melvin .01 .05
478 Jeff Musselman .01 .05
479 Charlie Kerfeld .01 .05
480 Richard Dotson .01 .05
481 Kevin Mitchell .02 .10
482 Gary Roenicke .01 .05
483 Tim Flannery .01 .05
484 Rich Yett .01 .05
485 Pete Incaviglia .01 .05
486 Rick Cerone .01 .05
487 Tony Armas .02 .10
488 Jerry Reed .01 .05
489 Dave Lopes .02 .10
490 Frank Tanana .02 .10
491 Mike Loynd .01 .05
492 Bruce Ruffin .01 .05
493 Chris Speier .01 .05
494 Tom Hume .01 .05
495 Jesse Orosco .01 .05
496 Robbie Wine UER .01 .05
(Misspelled Robby
on card front)
497 Jeff Montgomery RC .08 .25
498 Jeff Dedmon .01 .05
499 Luis Aguayo .01 .05
500 Reggie Jackson A's .05 .15
501 Reggie Jackson O's .05 .15
502 Reggie Jackson Yanks .05 .15
503 Reggie Jackson Angels .05 .15
504 Reggie Jackson A's .05 .15
505 Billy Hatcher .01 .05
506 Ed Lynch .01 .05
507 Willie Hernandez .01 .05
508 Jose DeLeon .01 .05
509 Joel Youngblood .01 .05
510 Bob Welch .02 .10
511 Steve Ontiveros .01 .05
512 Randy Ready .01 .05
513 Juan Nieves .01 .05
514 Jeff Russell .01 .05
515 Von Hayes .01 .05
516 Mark Gubicza .01 .05
517 Ken Dayley .01 .05
518 Don Aase .01 .05
519 Rick Reuschel .02 .10
520 Mike Henneman RC .08 .25
521 Rick Aguilera .01 .05
522 Jay Howell .01 .05
523 Ed Correa .01 .05
524 Manny Trillo .01 .05
525 Kirk Gibson .07 .20
526 Wally Ritchie .01 .05
527 Al Nipper .01 .05
528 Atlee Hammaker .01 .05
529 Shawon Dunston .01 .05
530 Jim Clancy .01 .05
531 Tom Paciorek .01 .05
532 Joel Skinner .01 .05
533 Scott Garrelts .01 .05
534 Tom O'Malley .01 .05
535 John Franco .02 .10
536 Paul Kilgus .01 .05
537 Darrell Porter .01 .05
538 Walt Terrell .01 .05
539 Bill Long .01 .05
540 George Bell .02 .10
541 Jeff Sellers .01 .05
542 Joe Boever .01 .05
543 Steve Howe .01 .05
544 Scott Sanderson .01 .05
545 Jack Morris .02 .10
546 Todd Benzinger RC .08 .25
547 Steve Henderson .01 .05
548 Eddie Milner .01 .05
549 Jeff M. Robinson .01 .05
550 Cal Ripken .30 .75
551 Jody Davis .01 .05
552 Kirk McCaskill .01 .05
553 Craig Lefferts .01 .05
554 Darnell Coles .01 .05
555 Phil Niekro .02 .10
556 Mike Aldrete .01 .05
557 Pat Perry .01 .05
558 Juan Agosto .01 .05
559 Rob Murphy .01 .05
560 Dennis Rasmussen .01 .05
561 Manny Lee .01 .05
562 Jeff Blauser RC .08 .25
563 Bob Ojeda .01 .05
564 Dave Dravecky .01 .05
565 Gene Garber .01 .05
566 Ron Roenicke .01 .05
567 Tommy Hinzo .01 .05
568 Eric Nolte .01 .05
569 Ed Hearn .01 .05
570 Mark Davidson .01 .05
571 Jim Walewander .01 .05
572 Donnie Hill UER .01 .05
(84 Stolen Base
total listed as 7)
573 Jamie Moyer .02 .10
574 Ken Schrom .01 .05
575 Nolan Ryan .40 1.00
576 Jim Acker .01 .05
577 Jamie Quirk .01 .05
578 Jay Aldrich .01 .05
579 Claudell Washington .01 .05
580 Jeff Leonard .01 .05
581 Carmen Castillo .01 .05
582 Daryl Boston .01 .05
583 Jeff DeWillis .01 .05
584 John Marzano .01 .05
585 Bill Gullickson .01 .05
586 Andy Allanson .01 .05
587 Lee Tunnell UER .01 .05
(1987 stat line
reads .4.84 ERA)
588 Gene Nelson .01 .05
589 Dave LaPoint .01 .05
590 Harold Baines .02 .10
591 Bill Buckner .02 .10
592 Carlton Fisk .05 .15
593 Rick Manning .01 .05
594 Doug Jones RC .08 .25
595 Tom Candiotti .01 .05
596 Steve Lake .01 .05
597 Jose Lind RC .08 .25
598 Ross Jones .01 .05
599 Gary Matthews .02 .10
600 Fernando Valenzuela .02 .10
601 Dennis Martinez .02 .10
602 Les Lancaster .01 .05
603 Ozzie Guillen .02 .10
604 Tony Bernazard .01 .05
605 Chili Davis .02 .10
606 Roy Smalley .01 .05
607 Ivan Calderon .01 .05
608 Jay Tibbs .01 .05
609 Guy Hoffman .01 .05
610 Doyle Alexander .01 .05
611 Mike Bielecki .01 .05
612 Shawn Hillegas .01 .05
613 Keith Atherton .01 .05
614 Eric Plunk .01 .05
615 Sid Fernandez .01 .05
616 Dennis Lamp .01 .05
617 Dave Engle .01 .05
618 Harry Spilman .01 .05
619 Don Robinson .01 .05
620 John Farrell RC .02 .10
621 Nelson Liriano .01 .05
622 Floyd Bannister .01 .05
623 Randy Milligan RC .02 .10
624 Kevin Elster .01 .05
625 Jody Reed RC .08 .25
626 Shawn Abner .01 .05
627 Kirt Manwaring RC .08 .25
628 Pete Stanicek .01 .05
629 Rob Ducey .01 .05
630 Steve Kiefer .01 .05
631 Gary Thurman .01 .05
632 Darrel Akerfelds .01 .05
633 Dave Clark .01 .05
634 Roberto Kelly RC .08 .25
635 Keith Hughes .01 .05
636 John Davis .01 .05
637 Mike Devereaux RC .08 .25
638 Tom Glavine RC 1.00 2.50
639 Keith A. Miller RC .08 .25
640 Chris Gwynn UER RC .08 .25
(Wrong batting and
throwing on back)
641 Tim Crews RC .08 .25
642 Mackey Sasser RC .08 .25
643 Vicente Palacios .01 .05
644 Kevin Romine .01 .05
645 Gregg Jefferies RC .08 .25
646 Jeff Treadway RC .08 .25
647 Ron Gant RC .15 .40
648 Mark McGwire .30 .75
Matt Nokes
649 Eric Davis .02 .10
Tim Raines
650 Don Mattingly .10 .30
Jack Clark
651 Tony Fernandez .08 .25
Alan Trammell
Cal Ripken
652 Vince Coleman HL .01 .05
653 Kirby Puckett HL .05 .15
654 Benito Santiago HL .01 .05
655 Juan Nieves HL .01 .05
656 Steve Bedrosian HL .01 .05
657 Mike Schmidt HL .07 .20
658 Don Mattingly HL .10 .30
659 Mark McGwire HL .30 .75
660 Paul Molitor HL .01 .05

1988 Score Rookie/Traded

This 110-card standard-size set issued exclusively in a boxes factory-set form features traded players (1-65) and rookies (66-110) for the 1988 season. The cards are distinguishable from the regular Score set by the orange borders and by the fact that the numbering on the back has a T suffix. Apparently Score's first attempt at a Rookie/Traded set was produced very conservatively, resulting in a set which is now recognized as being much tougher to find than the other Rookie/Traded sets from the other major companies of that year. Extended Rookie Cards in this set include Roberto Alomar, Brady Anderson, Craig Biggio, Jay Buhner and Mark Grace.

COMP.FACT.SET (110) 15.00 40.00
1T Jack Clark .30 .75
2T Danny Jackson .08 .25
3T Brett Butler .30 .75
4T Kurt Stillwell .08 .25
5T Tom Brunansky .08 .25
6T Dennis Lamp .08 .25
7T Jose DeLeon .08 .25
8T Tom Herr .08 .25
9T Keith Moreland .08 .25
10T Kirk Gibson .75 2.00
11T Bud Black .08 .25
12T Rafael Ramirez .08 .25
13T Luis Salazar .08 .25
14T Goose Gossage .30 .75
15T Bob Welch .30 .75
16T Vance Law .08 .25
17T Ray Knight .30 .75
18T Dan Quisenberry .08 .25
19T Don Slaught .08 .25
20T Lee Smith .30 .75
21T Rick Cerone .08 .25
22T Pat Tabler .08 .25
23T Larry McWilliams .08 .25
24T Ricky Horton .08 .25
25T Graig Nettles .30 .75
26T Dan Petry .08 .25
27T Jose Rijo .30 .75
28T Chili Davis .30 .75
29T Dickie Thon .08 .25
30T Mackey Sasser .08 .25
31T Mickey Tettleton .08 .25
32T Rick Dempsey .08 .25
33T Ron Hassey .08 .25
34T Phil Bradley .08 .25
35T Jay Howell .08 .25
36T Bill Buckner .30 .75
37T Alfredo Griffin .08 .25
38T Gary Pettis .08 .25
39T Calvin Schiraldi .08 .25
40T John Candelaria .08 .25
41T Joe Orsulak .08 .25
42T Willie Upshaw .08 .25
43T Herm Winningham .08 .25
44T Ron Kittle .08 .25
45T Bob Dernier .08 .25
46T Steve Balboni .08 .25
47T Steve Shields .08 .25
48T Henry Cotto .08 .25
49T Dave Henderson .08 .25
50T Dave Parker .30 .75
51T Mike Young .08 .25
52T Mark Salas .08 .25
53T Mike Davis .08 .25
54T Rafael Santana .08 .25
55T Don Baylor .30 .75
56T Dan Pasqua .08 .25
57T Ernest Riles .08 .25
58T Glenn Hubbard .08 .25
59T Mike Smithson .08 .25
60T Richard Dotson .08 .25
61T Jerry Reuss .08 .25
62T Mike Jackson .30 .75
63T Floyd Bannister .08 .25
64T Jesse Orosco .08 .25
65T Larry Parrish .08 .25
66T Jeff Bittiger .08 .25
67T Ray Hayward .08 .25
68T Ricky Jordan XRC .30 .75
69T Tommy Gregg .08 .25
70T Brady Anderson XRC .50 1.25
71T Jeff Montgomery .30 .75
72T Darryl Hamilton XRC .30 .75
73T Cecil Espy XRC .08 .25
74T Greg Briley XRC .08 .25
75T Joey Meyer .08 .25
76T Mike Macfarlane XRC .30 .75

77T Oswald Peraza .08 .25
78T Jack Armstrong XRC .08 .25
79T Don Heinkel .08 .25
80T Mark Grace XRC 3.00 8.00
81T Steve Curry .08 .25
82T Damon Berryhill XRC .30 .75
83T Steve Ellsworth .08 .25
84T Pete Smith XRC .08 .25
85T Jack McDowell XRC .50 1.25
86T Rob Dibble XRC .50 1.25
87T Bryan Harvey XRC .30 .75
UER Games Pitched 47,
Innings 5) XRC
88T John Dopson .08 .25
89T Dave Gallagher .08 .25
90T Todd Stottlemyre XRC .30 .75
91T Mike Schooler .08 .25
92T Don Gordon .08 .25
93T Sil Campusano .08 .25
94T Jeff Pico .08 .25
95T Jay Buhner XRC .75 2.00
96T Nelson Santovenia .08 .25
97T Al Leiter XRC 1.25 3.00
98T Luis Alicea XRC .30 .75
99T Pat Borders XRC .30 .75
100T Chris Sabo XRC .50 1.25
101T Tim Belcher .08 .25
102T Walt Weiss XRC .50 1.25
103T Craig Biggio XRC 5.00 12.00
104T Don August .08 .25
105T Roberto Alomar XRC 4.00 10.00
106T Todd Burns .08 .25
107T John Costello .08 .25
108T Melido Perez XRC .30 .75
109T Darrin Jackson XRC .08 .25
110T O.Destrade XRC .08 .25

1988 Score Rookie/Traded Glossy

This 110-card standard-size set was issued as a parallel vesion to the regular Score Rookie/Traded set. This set was issued only in boxed factory-set form. According to published reports, only 3,000 of these sets were created. The sets were sold solely through Score's dealer's accounts of the time.

COMP.FACT.SET (110) 75.00 150.00
*STARS: 1X TO 2.5X BASIC CARDS
*ROOKIES: 1X TO 2.5X BASIC CARDS
DISTRIBUTED ONLY IN FACTORY SET FORM

1989 Score

This 660-card standard-size set was distributed by Major League Marketing. Cards were issued primarily in fin-wrapped plastic packs and factory sets. Cards feature six distinctive inner border (inside a white outer border) colors on the front. Subsets include Highlights (652-660) and Rookie Prospects (621-651). Rookie Cards in this set include Brady Anderson, Craig Biggio, Randy Johnson, Gary Sheffield, and John Smoltz.

COMPLETE SET (660) 6.00 15.00
COMP.FACT.SET (660) 6.00 15.00
1 Jose Canseco .08 .25
2 Andre Dawson .02 .10
3 Mark McGwire UER .40 1.00
4 Benito Santiago .02 .10
5 Rick Reuschel .02 .10
6 Fred McGriff .05 .15
7 Kal Daniels .01 .05
8 Gary Gaetti .02 .10
9 Ellis Burks .02 .10
10 Darryl Strawberry .02 .10
11 Julio Franco .02 .10
12 Lloyd Moseby .01 .05
13 Jeff Pico .01 .05
14 Johnny Ray .01 .05
15 Cal Ripken .30 .75
16 Dick Schofield .01 .05
17 Mel Hall .01 .05
18 Bill Ripken .01 .05
19 Brook Jacoby .01 .05
20 Kirby Puckett .08 .25
21 Bill Doran .01 .05
22 Pete O'Brien .01 .05
23 Matt Nokes .01 .05
24 Brian Fisher .01 .05
25 Jack Clark .02 .10
26 Gary Pettis .01 .05
27 Dave Valle .01 .05
28 Willie Wilson .02 .10
29 Curt Young .01 .05
30 Dale Murphy .05 .15
31 Barry Larkin .05 .15
32 Dave Stewart .02 .10
33 Mike LaValliere .01 .05
34 Glenn Hubbard .01 .05
35 Ryne Sandberg .15 .40
36 Tony Pena .01 .05
37 Greg Walker .01 .05
38 Von Hayes .01 .05
39 Kevin Mitchell .02 .10
40 Tim Raines .02 .10
41 Keith Hernandez .02 .10
42 Keith Moreland .01 .05
43 Ruben Sierra .02 .10
44 Chet Lemon .02 .10
45 Willie Randolph .02 .10
46 Andy Allanson .01 .05
47 Candy Maldonado .01 .05
48 Sid Bream .01 .05
49 Denny Walling .01 .05
50 Dave Winfield .02 .10
51 Alvin Davis .01 .05
52 Cory Snyder .01 .05
53 Hubie Brooks .01 .05
54 Chili Davis .02 .10
55 Kevin Seitzer .01 .05
56 Jose Uribe .01 .05
57 Tony Fernandez .01 .05
58 Tim Teufel .01 .05
59 Oddibe McDowell .01 .05
60 Les Lancaster .01 .05
61 Billy Hatcher .01 .05
62 Dan Gladden .01 .05
63 Marty Barrett .01 .05
64 Nick Esasky .01 .05
65 Wally Joyner .02 .10
66 Mike Greenwell .01 .05
67 Ken Williams .01 .05
68 Bob Horner .02 .10
69 Steve Sax .01 .05
70 Rickey Henderson .08 .25
71 Mitch Webster .01 .05
72 Rob Deer .01 .05
73 Jim Presley .01 .05
74 Albert Hall .01 .05
75 George Brett COR .25 .60
(At age 35)
75A George Brett ERR .40 1.00
(At age 33)
76 Brian Downing .02 .10
77 Dave Martinez .01 .05
78 Scott Fletcher .01 .05
79 Phil Bradley .01 .05
80 Ozzie Smith .15 .40
81 Larry Sheets .01 .05
82 Mike Aldrete .01 .05
83 Darnell Coles .01 .05
84 Len Dykstra .02 .10
85 Jim Rice .02 .10
86 Jeff Treadway .01 .05
87 Jose Lind .01 .05
88 Willie McGee .02 .10
89 Mickey Brantley .01 .05
90 Tony Gwynn .10 .30
91 R.J. Reynolds .01 .05
92 Milt Thompson .01 .05
93 Kevin McReynolds .01 .05
94 Eddie Murray UER .08 .25
('86 batting .205,
should be .305)
95 Lance Parrish .02 .10
96 Ron Kittle .01 .05
97 Gerald Young .01 .05
98 Ernie Whitt .01 .05
99 Jeff Reed .01 .05
100 Don Mattingly .25 .60
101 Gerald Perry .01 .05
102 Vance Law .01 .05
103 John Shelby .01 .05
104 Chris Sabo RC .15 .40
105 Danny Tartabull .01 .05
106 Glenn Wilson .01 .05
107 Mark Davidson .01 .05
108 Dave Parker .02 .10
109 Eric Davis .02 .10
110 Alan Trammell .02 .10
111 Ozzie Virgil .01 .05
112 Frank Tanana .02 .10
113 Rafael Ramirez .01 .05
114 Dennis Martinez .02 .10
115 Jose DeLeon .01 .05
116 Bob Ojeda .01 .05
117 Doug Drabek .01 .05
118 Andy Hawkins .01 .05
119 Greg Maddux .20 .50
120 Cecil Fielder UER .02 .10
Reversed Photo on back
121 Mike Scioscia .02 .10
122 Dan Petry .01 .05
123 Terry Kennedy .01 .05
124 Kelly Downs .01 .05
125 Greg Gross UER .01 .05
(Gregg on back)
126 Fred Lynn .02 .10
127 Barry Bonds .60 1.50
128 Harold Baines .02 .10
129 Doyle Alexander .01 .05
130 Kevin Elster .01 .05
131 Mike Heath .01 .05
132 Teddy Higuera .01 .05
133 Charlie Leibrandt .01 .05
134 Tim Laudner .01 .05
135A Ray Knight ERR .02 .10
(Reverse negative)
135B Ray Knight COR .02 .10
136 Howard Johnson .02 .10
137 Terry Pendleton .02 .10
138 Andy McGaffigan .01 .05
139 Ken Oberkfell .01 .05
140 Butch Wynegar .01 .05
141 Rob Murphy .01 .05
142 Rich Renteria .01 .05
143 Jose Guzman .01 .05
144 Andres Galarraga .02 .10
145 Ricky Horton .01 .05
146 Frank DiPino .01 .05
147 Glenn Braggs .01 .05
148 John Kruk .02 .10
149 Mike Schmidt .20 .50
150 Lee Smith .02 .10
151 Robin Yount .15 .40
152 Mark Eichhorn .01 .05
153 DeWayne Buice .01 .05
154 B.J. Surhoff .02 .10
155 Vince Coleman .01 .05
156 Tony Phillips .01 .05
157 Willie Fraser .01 .05
158 Lance McCullers .01 .05
159 Greg Gagne .01 .05
160 Jesse Barfield .02 .10
161 Mark Langston .01 .05
162 Kurt Stillwell .01 .05
163 Dion James .01 .05
164 Glenn Davis .01 .05
165 Walt Weiss .01 .05
166 Dave Concepcion .02 .10
167 Alfredo Griffin .01 .05
168 Don Heinkel .01 .05
169 Luis Rivera .01 .05
170 Shane Rawley .01 .05
171 Darrell Evans .02 .10
172 Robby Thompson .01 .05
173 Jody Davis .01 .05
174 Andy Van Slyke .05 .15
175 Wade Boggs UER .05 .15
(Bio says .364,
should be .356)
176 Garry Templeton .02 .10
('85 stats
off-centered)
177 Gary Redus .01 .05
178 Craig Lefferts .01 .05
179 Carney Lansford .02 .10
180 Ron Darling .02 .10
181 Kirk McCaskill .01 .05
182 Tony Armas .02 .10
183 Steve Farr .01 .05
184 Tom Brunansky .01 .05
185 B.Harvey RC UER .08 .25
'87 games 47,
should be 3
186 Mike Marshall .01 .05
187 Bo Diaz .01 .05
188 Willie Upshaw .01 .05
189 Mike Pagliarulo .01 .05
190 Mike Krukow .01 .05
191 Tommy Herr .01 .05
192 Jim Pankovits .01 .05
193 Dwight Evans .05 .15
194 Kelly Gruber .01 .05
195 Bobby Bonilla .02 .10
196 Wallace Johnson .01 .05
197 Dave Stieb .02 .10
198 Pat Borders RC .08 .25
199 Rafael Palmeiro .08 .25
200 Dwight Gooden .02 .10
201 Pete Incaviglia .01 .05
202 Chris James .01 .05
203 Marvell Wynne .01 .05
204 Pat Sheridan .01 .05
205 Don Baylor .02 .10
206 Paul O'Neill .05 .15
207 Pete Smith .01 .05
208 Mark McLemore .01 .05
209 Henry Cotto .01 .05
210 Kirk Gibson .02 .10
211 Claudell Washington .01 .05
212 Randy Bush .01 .05
213 Joe Carter .02 .10
214 Bill Buckner .02 .10
215 Bert Blyleven UER .02 .10
(Wrong birth year)
216 Brett Butler .02 .10
217 Lee Mazzilli .02 .10
218 Spike Owen .01 .05
219 Bill Swift .01 .05
220 Tim Wallach .01 .05
221 David Cone .02 .10
222 Don Carman .01 .05
223 Rich Gossage .02 .10
224 Bob Walk .01 .05
225 Dave Righetti .02 .10
226 Kevin Bass .01 .05
227 Kevin Gross .01 .05
228 Tim Burke .01 .05
229 Rick Mahler .01 .05
230 Lou Whitaker UER .02 .10
(252 games in '85,
should be 152)
231 Luis Alicea RC .08 .25
232 Roberto Alomar .08 .25
233 Bob Boone .02 .10
234 Dickie Thon .01 .05
235 Shawon Dunston .01 .05
236 Pete Stanicek .01 .05
237 Craig Biggio RC 1.50 4.00
(Inconsistent design,
portrait on front)
238 Dennis Boyd .01 .05
239 Tom Candiotti .01 .05
240 Gary Carter .02 .10
241 Mike Stanley .01 .05
242 Ken Phelps .01 .05
243 Chris Bosio .01 .05
244 Les Straker .01 .05
245 Dave Smith .01 .05
246 John Candelaria .01 .05
247 Joe Orsulak .01 .05
248 Storm Davis .01 .05
249 Floyd Bannister UER .01 .05
(ML Batting Record)
250 Jack Morris .02 .10
251 Bret Saberhagen .02 .10
252 Tom Niedenfuer .01 .05
253 Neal Heaton .01 .05
254 Eric Show .01 .05
255 Juan Samuel .01 .05
256 Dale Sveum .01 .05
257 Jim Gott .01 .05
258 Scott Garrelts .01 .05
259 Larry McWilliams .01 .05
260 Steve Bedrosian .01 .05
261 Jack Howell .01 .05
262 Jay Tibbs .01 .05
263 Jamie Moyer .02 .10
264 Doug Sisk .01 .05
265 Todd Worrell .01 .05
266 John Farrell .01 .05
267 Dave Collins .01 .05
268 Sid Fernandez .01 .05
269 Tom Brookens .01 .05
270 Shane Mack .01 .05
271 Paul Kilgus .01 .05
272 Chuck Crim .01 .05
273 Bob Knepper .01 .05
274 Mike Moore .01 .05
275 Guillermo Hernandez .01 .05
276 Dennis Eckersley .05 .15
277 Graig Nettles .02 .10
278 Rich Dotson .01 .05
279 Larry Herndon .01 .05
280 Gene Larkin .01 .05
281 Roger McDowell .01 .05
282 Greg Swindell .01 .05
283 Juan Agosto .01 .05
284 Jeff M. Robinson .01 .05
285 Mike Dunne .01 .05
286 Greg Mathews .01 .05
287 Kent Tekulve .01 .05
288 Jerry Mumphrey .01 .05
289 Jack McDowell .02 .10
290 Frank Viola .02 .10
291 Mark Gubicza .01 .05
292 Dave Schmidt .01 .05
293 Mike Henneman .01 .05
294 Jimmy Jones .01 .05
295 Charlie Hough .02 .10
296 Rafael Santana .01 .05
297 Chris Speier .01 .05
298 Mike Witt .01 .05
299 Pascual Perez .01 .05
300 Nolan Ryan .40 1.00
301 Mitch Williams .01 .05
302 Mookie Wilson .02 .10
303 Mackey Sasser .01 .05
304 John Cerutti .01 .05
305 Jeff Reardon .02 .10
306 Randy Myers UER .02 .10
(6 hits in '87,
should be 61)
307 Greg Brock .01 .05
308 Bob Welch .02 .10
309 Jeff D. Robinson .01 .05
310 Harold Reynolds .02 .10
311 Jim Walewander .01 .05
312 Dave Magadan .01 .05
313 Jim Gantner .01 .05
314 Walt Terrell .01 .05
315 Wally Backman .01 .05
316 Luis Salazar .01 .05
317 Rick Rhoden .01 .05
318 Tom Henke .01 .05
319 Mike Macfarlane RC .08 .25
320 Dan Plesac .01 .05
321 Calvin Schiraldi .01 .05
322 Stan Javier .01 .05
323 Devon White .02 .10
324 Scott Bradley .01 .05
325 Bruce Hurst .01 .05
326 Manny Lee .01 .05
327 Rick Aguilera .01 .05
328 Bruce Ruffin .01 .05
329 Ed Whitson .01 .05
330 Bo Jackson .08 .25
331 Ivan Calderon .01 .05
332 Mickey Hatcher .01 .05
333 Barry Jones .01 .05
334 Ron Hassey .01 .05
335 Bill Wegman .01 .05
336 Damon Berryhill .01 .05
337 Steve Ontiveros .01 .05
338 Dan Pasqua .01 .05
339 Bill Pecota .01 .05
340 Greg Cadaret .01 .05
341 Scott Bankhead .01 .05
342 Ron Guidry .02 .10
343 Danny Heep .01 .05
344 Bob Brower .01 .05
345 Rich Gedman .01 .05
346 Nelson Santovenia .01 .05
347 George Bell .02 .10
348 Ted Power .01 .05
349 Mark Grant .01 .05
350 Roger Clemens COR .40 1.00
(78 career wins)
350A Roger Clemens ERR .75 2.00
(778 career wins)
351 Bill Long .01 .05
352 Jay Bell .02 .10
353 Steve Balboni .01 .05
354 Bob Kipper .01 .05
355 Steve Jeltz .01 .05
356 Jesse Orosco .01 .05
357 Bob Dernier .01 .05
358 Mickey Tettleton .01 .05
359 Duane Ward .01 .05
360 Darrin Jackson .02 .10
361 Rey Quinones .01 .05
362 Mark Grace .08 .25
363 Steve Lake .01 .05
364 Pat Perry .01 .05
365 Terry Steinbach .02 .10
366 Alan Ashby .01 .05
367 Jeff Montgomery .01 .05
368 Steve Buechele .01 .05
369 Chris Brown .01 .05
370 Orel Hershiser .02 .10
371 Todd Benzinger .01 .05
372 Ron Gant .02 .10
373 Paul Assenmacher .01 .05
374 Joey Meyer .01 .05
375 Neil Allen .01 .05
376 Mike Davis .01 .05
377 Jeff Parrett .01 .05
378 Jay Howell .01 .05
379 Rafael Belliard .01 .05
380 Luis Polonia UER .01 .05
(2 triples in '87,
should be 10)
381 Keith Atherton .01 .05
382 Kent Hrbek .02 .10
383 Bob Stanley .01 .05
384 Dave LaPoint .01 .05
385 Rance Mulliniks .01 .05
386 Melido Perez .01 .05
387 Doug Jones .01 .05
388 Steve Lyons .01 .05
389 Alejandro Pena .01 .05
390 Frank White .02 .10
391 Pat Tabler .01 .05
392 Eric Plunk .01 .05
393 Mike Maddux .01 .05
394 Allan Anderson .01 .05
395 Bob Brenly .01 .05
396 Rick Cerone .01 .05
397 Scott Terry .01 .05
398 Mike Jackson .01 .05
399 Bobby Thigpen UER .01 .05
Bio says 37 saves in
'88, should be 34
400 Don Sutton .02 .10
401 Cecil Espy .01 .05
402 Junior Ortiz .01 .05
403 Mike Smithson .01 .05
404 Bud Black .01 .05
405 Tom Foley .01 .05
406 Andres Thomas .01 .05
407 Rick Sutcliffe .02 .10
408 Brian Harper .01 .05
409 John Smiley .01 .05
410 Juan Nieves .01 .05
411 Shawn Abner .01 .05
412 Wes Gardner .01 .05
413 Darren Daulton .02 .10
414 Juan Berenguer .01 .05
415 Charles Hudson .01 .05
416 Rick Honeycutt .01 .05
417 Greg Booker .01 .05
418 Tim Belcher .01 .05
419 Don August .01 .05
420 Dale Mohorcic .01 .05
421 Steve Lombardozzi .01 .05
422 Atlee Hammaker .01 .05
423 Jerry Don Gleaton .01 .05
424 Scott Bailes .01 .05
425 Bruce Sutter .02 .10
426 Randy Ready .01 .05
427 Jerry Reed .01 .05
428 Bryn Smith .01 .05
429 Tim Leary .01 .05
430 Mark Clear .01 .05
431 Terry Leach .01 .05
432 John Moses .01 .05
433 Ozzie Guillen .02 .10
434 Gene Nelson .01 .05
435 Gary Ward .01 .05
436 Luis Aguayo .01 .05
437 Fernando Valenzuela .02 .10
438 Jeff Russell UER .01 .05
(Saves total does
not add up correctly)
439 Cecilio Guante .01 .05
440 Don Robinson .01 .05
441 Rick Anderson .01 .05
442 Tom Glavine .08 .25
443 Daryl Boston .01 .05
444 Joe Price .01 .05
445 Stu Cliburn .01 .05
446 Manny Trillo .01 .05
447 Joel Skinner .01 .05
448 Charlie Puleo .01 .05
449 Carlton Fisk .05 .15
450 Will Clark .05 .15
451 Otis Nixon .01 .05
452 Rick Schu .01 .05
453 Todd Stottlemyre UER .01 .05
(ML Batting Record)
454 Tim Birtsas .01 .05
455 Dave Gallagher .01 .05
456 Barry Lyons .01 .05
457 Fred Manrique .01 .05
458 Ernest Riles .01 .05
459 Doug Jennings .01 .05
460 Joe Magrane .01 .05
461 Jamie Quirk .01 .05
462 Jack Armstrong RC .08 .25
463 Bobby Witt .01 .05
464 Keith A. Miller .01 .05
465 Todd Burns .01 .05
466 John Dopson .01 .05
467 Rich Yett .01 .05
468 Craig Reynolds .01 .05
469 Dave Bergman .01 .05
470 Rex Hudler .01 .05
471 Eric King .01 .05
472 Joaquin Andujar .02 .10
473 Sil Campusano .01 .05
474 Terry Mulholland .01 .05
475 Mike Flanagan .01 .05
476 Greg A. Harris .01 .05
477 Tommy John .02 .10
478 Dave Anderson .01 .05
479 Fred Toliver .01 .05
480 Jimmy Key .02 .10
481 Donell Nixon .01 .05
482 Mark Portugal .01 .05
483 Tom Pagnozzi .01 .05
484 Jeff Kunkel .01 .05
485 Frank Williams .01 .05
486 Jody Reed .01 .05
487 Roberto Kelly .01 .05
488 Shawn Hillegas UER .01 .05
(165 innings in '87,
should be 165.2)
489 Jerry Reuss .01 .05
490 Mark Davis .01 .05
491 Jeff Sellers .01 .05
492 Zane Smith .01 .05
493 Al Newman .01 .05
494 Mike Young .01 .05
495 Larry Parrish .01 .05
496 Herm Winningham .01 .05
497 Carmen Castillo .01 .05
498 Joe Hesketh .01 .05
499 Darrell Miller .01 .05
500 Mike LaCoss .01 .05
501 Charlie Lea .01 .05
502 Bruce Benedict .01 .05
503 Chuck Finley .02 .10
504 Brad Wellman .01 .05
505 Tim Crews .01 .05
506 Ken Gerhart .01 .05
507A Brian Holton ERR .01 .05
(Born 1/25/65 Denver,
should be 11/29/59
in McKeesport)
507B Brian Holton COR .75 2.00
508 Dennis Lamp .01 .05
509 Bobby Meacham UER .01 .05
('84 games 099)
510 Tracy Jones .01 .05
511 Mike R. Fitzgerald .01 .05
512 Jeff Bittiger .01 .05
513 Tim Flannery .01 .05
514 Ray Hayward .01 .05
515 Dave Leiper .01 .05
516 Rod Scurry .01 .05
517 Carmelo Martinez .01 .05
518 Curtis Wilkerson .01 .05
519 Stan Jefferson .01 .05
520 Dan Quisenberry .01 .05
521 Lloyd McClendon .01 .05
522 Steve Trout .01 .05
523 Larry Andersen .01 .05
524 Don Aase .01 .05
525 Bob Forsch .01 .05
526 Geno Petralli .01 .05
527 Angel Salazar .01 .05
528 Mike Schooler .01 .05
529 Jose Oquendo .01 .05
530 Jay Buhner UER .02 .10
(Wearing 43 on front,
listed as 34 on back)
531 Tom Bolton .01 .05
532 Al Nipper .01 .05
533 Dave Henderson .01 .05
534 John Costello .01 .05
535 Donnie Moore .01 .05
536 Mike Laga .01 .05
537 Mike Gallego .01 .05
538 Jim Clancy .01 .05
539 Joel Youngblood .01 .05
540 Rick Leach .01 .05
541 Kevin Romine .01 .05
542 Mark Salas .01 .05
543 Greg Minton .01 .05
544 Dave Palmer .01 .05
545 Dwayne Murphy UER .01 .05
(Game-sinning)
546 Jim Deshaies .01 .05
547 Don Gordon .01 .05
548 Ricky Jordan RC .08 .25
549 Mike Boddicker .01 .05
550 Mike Scott .02 .10
551 Jeff Ballard .01 .05
552A Jose Rijo ERR .02 .10
(Uniform lisied as
27 on back)
552B Jose Rijo COR .02 .10
(Uniform listed as
24 on back)
553 Danny Darwin .01 .05
554 Tom Browning .01 .05
555 Danny Jackson .01 .05
556 Rick Dempsey .01 .05
557 Jeffrey Leonard .01 .05
558 Jeff Musselman .01 .05
559 Ron Robinson .01 .05
560 John Tudor .02 .10
561 Don Slaught UER .01 .05
(237 games in 1987)
562 Dennis Rasmussen .01 .05
563 Brady Anderson RC .15 .40
564 Pedro Guerrero .02 .10
565 Paul Molitor .02 .10
566 Terry Clark .01 .05
567 Terry Puhl .01 .05
568 Mike Campbell .01 .05
569 Paul Mirabella .01 .05
570 Jeff Hamilton .01 .05
571 Oswald Peraza .01 .05
572 Bob McClure .01 .05
573 Jose Bautista RC .02 .10
574 Alex Trevino .01 .05
575 John Franco .02 .10
576 Mark Parent .01 .05
577 Nelson Liriano .01 .05
578 Steve Shields .01 .05
579 Odell Jones .01 .05
580 Al Leiter .08 .25
581 Dave Stapleton .01 .05
582 Orel Hershiser .08 .25
Jose Canseco
Kirk Gibson
Dave Stewart WS
583 Donnie Hill .01 .05
584 Chuck Jackson .01 .05
585 Rene Gonzales .01 .05
586 Tracy Woodson .01 .05
587 Jim Adduci .01 .05
588 Mario Soto .02 .10
589 Jeff Blauser .01 .05
590 Jim Traber .01 .05
591 Jon Perlman .01 .05
592 Mark Williamson .01 .05
593 Dave Meads .01 .05
594 Jim Eisenreich .01 .05
595A Paul Gibson P1 .40 1.00
595B Paul Gibson P2 .01 .05
(Airbrushed leg on
player in background)
596 Mike Birkbeck .01 .05
597 Terry Francona .02 .10
598 Paul Zuvella .01 .05
599 Franklin Stubbs .01 .05
600 Gregg Jefferies .01 .05
601 John Cangelosi .01 .05
602 Mike Sharperson .01 .05
603 Mike Diaz .01 .05
604 Gary Varsho .01 .05
605 Terry Blocker .01 .05
606 Charlie O'Brien .01 .05
607 Jim Eppard .01 .05
608 John Davis .01 .05
609 Ken Griffey Sr. .02 .10
610 Buddy Bell .02 .10
611 Ted Simmons UER .02 .10
('78 stats Cardinal)
612 Matt Williams .08 .25
613 Danny Cox .01 .05
614 Al Pedrique .01 .05
615 Ron Oester .01 .05
616 John Smoltz RC .60 1.50
617 Bob Melvin .01 .05
618 Rob Dibble RC .15 .40
619 Kirt Manwaring .01 .05
620 Felix Fermin .01 .05
621 Doug Dascenzo .01 .05
622 Bill Brennan .01 .05
623 Carlos Quintana RC .02 .10
624 Mike Harkey RC UER .02 .10
(13 and 31 walks in '88,
should be 35 and 33
625 Gary Sheffield RC .60 1.50
626 Tom Prince .01 .05
627 Steve Searcy .01 .05
628 Charlie Hayes RC .08 .25
(Listed as outfielder)
629 Felix Jose RC UER .02 .10
(Modesto misspelled
as Modesta)
630 Sandy Alomar Jr. RC .15 .40
(Inconsistent design,
portrait on front)
631 Derek Lilliquist RC .02 .10
632 Geronimo Berroa .01 .05
633 Luis Medina .01 .05
634 Tom Gordon RC UER .20 .50
Height 6'0"
635 Ramon Martinez RC .08 .25
636 Craig Worthington .01 .05
637 Edgar Martinez .08 .25
638 Chad Kreuter RC .08 .25
639 Ron Jones .02 .10
640 Van Snider RC .02 .10
641 Lance Blankenship RC .02 .10
642 Dwight Smith RC UER .08 .25
10 HR's in '87, should be 18
643 Cameron Drew .01 .05
644 Jerald Clark RC .02 .10
645 Randy Johnson RC 1.00 2.50
646 Norm Charlton RC .08 .25
647 Todd Frohwirth UER .01 .05
(Southpaw on back)
648 Luis De Los Santos .01 .05
649 Tim Jones .01 .05
650 Dave West RC UER .02 .10
ML hits 3
should be 6
651 Bob Milacki .01 .05
652 Wrigley Field HL .02 .10
653 Orel Hershiser HL .01 .05
654A W.Boggs HL ERR .05 .15
('seaason' on back
654B W.Boggs HL COR .02 .10
655 Jose Canseco HL .08 .25
656 Doug Jones HL .01 .05
657 Rickey Henderson HL .05 .15
658 Tom Browning HL .01 .05
659 Mike Greenwell HL .01 .05
660 Boston Red Sox HL .01 .05

1989 Score Rookie/Traded

The 1989 Score Rookie and Traded set contains 110 standard-size cards. The set was issued exclusively in factory set form through hobby dealers. The set was distributed in a blue box with 10 Magic Motion trivia cards. The fronts have coral green borders with pink diamonds at the bottom. Cards 1-80 feature traded players; cards 81-110 feature 1989 rookies. Rookie Cards in this set include Jim Abbott, Joey (Albert) Belle, Ken Griffey Jr. and John Wetteland.

COMP.FACT.SET (110) 6.00 15.00
1T Rafael Palmeiro .08 .25
2T Nolan Ryan .60 1.50
3T Jack Clark .02 .10
4T Dave LaPoint .01 .05
5T Mike Moore .01 .05
6T Pete O'Brien .01 .05
7T Jeffrey Leonard .01 .05
8T Rob Murphy .01 .05
9T Tom Herr .01 .05
10T Claudell Washington .01 .05
11T Mike Pagliarulo .01 .05
12T Steve Lake .01 .05
13T Spike Owen .01 .05
14T Andy Hawkins .01 .05
15T Todd Benzinger .01 .05
16T Mookie Wilson .02 .10
17T Bert Blyleven .02 .10
18T Jeff Treadway .01 .05
19T Bruce Hurst .01 .05
20T Steve Sax .01 .05
21T Juan Samuel .01 .05
22T Jesse Barfield .02 .10
23T Carmen Castillo .01 .05
24T Terry Leach .01 .05
25T Mark Langston .01 .05
26T Eric King .01 .05
27T Steve Balboni .01 .05
28T Len Dykstra .02 .10
29T Keith Moreland .01 .05
30T Terry Kennedy .01 .05
31T Eddie Murray .08 .25
32T Mitch Williams .01 .05
33T Jeff Parrett .01 .05
34T Wally Backman .01 .05
35T Julio Franco .02 .10
36T Lance Parrish .02 .10
37T Nick Esasky .01 .05
38T Luis Polonia .01 .05
39T Kevin Gross .01 .05
40T John Dopson .01 .05
41T Willie Randolph .02 .10
42T Jim Clancy .01 .05
43T Tracy Jones .01 .05
44T Phil Bradley .01 .05
45T Milt Thompson .01 .05
46T Chris James .01 .05
47T Scott Fletcher .01 .05
48T Kal Daniels .01 .05
49T Steve Bedrosian .01 .05
50T Rickey Henderson .08 .25
51T Dion James .01 .05
52T Tim Leary .01 .05
53T Roger McDowell .01 .05
54T Mel Hall .01 .05
55T Dickie Thon .01 .05
56T Zane Smith .01 .05
57T Danny Heep .01 .05
58T Bob McClure .01 .05
59T Brian Holton .01 .05
60T Randy Ready .01 .05
61T Bob Melvin .01 .05
62T Harold Baines .02 .10
63T Lance McCullers .01 .05
64T Jody Davis .01 .05
65T Darrell Evans .02 .10
66T Joel Youngblood .01 .05
67T Frank Viola .02 .10
68T Mike Aldrete .01 .05
69T Greg Cadaret .01 .05
70T John Kruk .02 .10
71T Pat Sheridan .01 .05
72T Oddibe McDowell .01 .05
73T Tom Brookens .01 .05
74T Bob Boone .02 .10
75T Walt Terrell .01 .05

76T Joel Skinner .01 .05
77T Randy Johnson .60 1.50
78T Felix Fermin .01 .05
79T Rick Mahler .01 .05
80T Richard Dotson .01 .05
81T Cris Carpenter RC .02 .10
82T Bill Spiers RC .08 .25
83T Junior Felix RC .02 .10
84T Joe Girardi RC .15 .40
85T Jerome Walton RC .08 .25
86T Greg Litton .01 .05
87T Greg W.Harris RC .02 .10
88T Jim Abbott RC .40 1.00
89T Kevin Brown .08 .25
90T John Wetteland RC .15 .40
91T Gary Wayne .01 .05
92T Rich Monteleone .01 .05
93T Bob Geren RC .01 .05
94T Clay Parker .01 .05
95T Steve Finley RC .30 .75
96T Gregg Olson RC .08 .25
97T Ken Patterson .01 .05
98T Ken Hill RC .08 .25
99T Scott Scudder RC .02 .10
100T Ken Griffey Jr. RC 2.50 6.00
101T Jeff Brantley RC .08 .25
102T Donn Pall .01 .05
103T Carlos Martinez RC .02 .10
104T Joe Oliver RC .08 .25
105T Omar Vizquel RC .40 1.00
106T Joey Belle RC .40 1.00
107T Kenny Rogers RC .75 2.00
108T Mark Carreon .01 .05
109T Rolando Roomes .01 .05
110T Pete Harnisch RC .08 .25

1990 Score

The 1990 Score set contains 704 standard-size cards. Cards were distributed in plastic-wrap packs and factory sets. The front borders are red, blue, green or white. The vertically oriented backs are white with borders that match the fronts, and feature color mugshots. Subsets include Draft Picks (661-682) and Dream Team (683-695). A special black and white horizontal-designed card of Bo Jackson in football pads holding a bat above his shoulders was a big hit in 1990. That card traded for as much as $10 but has since cooled off. Nevertheless, it remains one of the most noteworthy cards issued in the early 1990's. Rookie Cards of note include Juan Gonzalez, Dave Justice, Chuck Knoblauch, Dean Palmer, Sammy Sosa, Frank Thomas, Mo Vaughn, Larry Walker and Bernie Williams. A ten-card set of Dream Team Rookies was inserted into each hobby factory set, but was not included in retail factory sets.

COMPLETE SET (704) 6.00 15.00
COMP.RETAIL SET (704) 6.00 15.00
COMP.HOBBY SET (714) 6.00 15.00
1 Don Mattingly .25 .60
2 Cal Ripken .30 .75
3 Dwight Evans .05 .15
4 Barry Bonds .40 1.00
5 Kevin McReynolds .01 .05
6 Ozzie Guillen .02 .10
7 Terry Kennedy .01 .05
8 Bryan Harvey .01 .05
9 Alan Trammell .02 .10
10 Cory Snyder .01 .05
11 Jody Reed .01 .05
12 Roberto Alomar .05 .15
13 Pedro Guerrero .01 .05
14 Gary Redus .01 .05
15 Marty Barrett .01 .05
16 Ricky Jordan .01 .05
17 Joe Magrane .01 .05
18 Sid Fernandez .01 .05
19 Richard Dotson .01 .05
20 Jack Clark .02 .10
21 Bob Walk .01 .05
22 Ron Karkovice .01 .05
23 Lenny Harris .01 .05
24 Phil Bradley .01 .05
25 Andres Galarraga .02 .10
26 Brian Downing .01 .05
27 Dave Martinez .01 .05
28 Eric King .01 .05
29 Barry Lyons .01 .05
30 Dave Schmidt .01 .05
31 Mike Boddicker .01 .05
32 Tom Foley .01 .05
33 Brady Anderson .02 .10
34 Jim Presley .01 .05
35 Lance Parrish .01 .05
36 Von Hayes .01 .05
37 Lee Smith .02 .10
38 Herm Winningham .01 .05
39 Alejandro Pena .01 .05
40 Mike Scott .01 .05
41 Joe Orsulak .01 .05
42 Rafael Ramirez .01 .05
43 Gerald Young .01 .05
44 Dick Schofield .01 .05
45 Dave Smith .01 .05
46 Dave Magadan .01 .05
47 Dennis Martinez .02 .10
48 Greg Minton .01 .05
49 Milt Thompson .01 .05
50 Orel Hershiser .02 .10
51 Bip Roberts .01 .05
52 Jerry Browne .01 .05
53 Bob Ojeda .01 .05
54 Fernando Valenzuela .02 .10
55 Matt Nokes .01 .05
56 Brook Jacoby .01 .05
57 Frank Tanana .01 .05
58 Scott Fletcher .01 .05
59 Ron Oester .01 .05
60 Bob Boone .02 .10
61 Dan Gladden .01 .05
62 Darnell Coles .01 .05
63 Gregg Olson .02 .10
64 Todd Burns .01 .05
65 Todd Benzinger .01 .05
66 Dale Murphy .05 .15
67 Mike Flanagan .01 .05
68 Jose Oquendo .01 .05
69 Cecil Espy .01 .05
70 Chris Sabo .01 .05
71 Shane Rawley .01 .05
72 Tom Brunansky .01 .05
73 Vance Law .01 .05
74 B.J. Surhoff .02 .10
75 Lou Whitaker .02 .10
76 Ken Caminiti UER .02 .10
Euclid and Ohio should be
Hanford and California
77 Nelson Liriano .01 .05
78 Tommy Gregg .01 .05
79 Don Slaught .01 .05
80 Eddie Murray .08 .25
81 Joe Boever .01 .05
82 Charlie Leibrandt .01 .05
83 Jose Lind .01 .05
84 Tony Phillips .01 .05
85 Mitch Webster .01 .05
86 Dan Plesac .01 .05
87 Rick Mahler .01 .05
88 Steve Lyons .01 .05
89 Tony Fernandez .01 .05
90 Ryne Sandberg .15 .40
91 Nick Esasky .01 .05
92 Luis Salazar .01 .05
93 Pete Incaviglia .01 .05
94 Ivan Calderon .01 .05
95 Jeff Treadway .01 .05
96 Kurt Stillwell .01 .05
97 Gary Sheffield .08 .25
98 Jeffrey Leonard .01 .05
99 Andres Thomas .01 .05
100 Roberto Kelly .01 .05
101 Alvaro Espinoza .01 .05
102 Greg Gagne .01 .05
103 John Farrell .01 .05
104 Willie Wilson .01 .05
105 Glenn Braggs .01 .05
106 Chet Lemon .01 .05
107A Jamie Moyer ERR .02 .10
(Scintilating)
107B Jamie Moyer COR .20 .50
(Scintillating)
108 Chuck Crim .01 .05
109 Dave Valle .01 .05
110 Walt Weiss .01 .05
111 Larry Sheets .01 .05
112 Don Robinson .01 .05
113 Danny Heep .01 .05
114 Carmelo Martinez .01 .05
115 Dave Gallagher .01 .05
116 Mike LaValliere .01 .05
117 Bob McClure .01 .05
118 Rene Gonzales .01 .05
119 Mark Parent .01 .05
120 Wally Joyner .02 .10
121 Mark Gubicza .01 .05
122 Tony Pena .01 .05
123 Carmelo Castillo .01 .05
124 Howard Johnson .01 .05
125 Steve Sax .01 .05
126 Tim Belcher .01 .05
127 Tim Burke .01 .05
128 Al Newman .01 .05
129 Dennis Rasmussen .01 .05
130 Doug Jones .01 .05
131 Fred Lynn .01 .05
132 Jeff Hamilton .01 .05
133 German Gonzalez .01 .05
134 John Morris .01 .05
135 Dave Parker .02 .10
136 Gary Pettis .01 .05
137 Dennis Boyd .01 .05
138 Candy Maldonado .01 .05
139 Rick Cerone .01 .05
140 George Brett .25 .60
141 Dave Clark .01 .05
142 Dickie Thon .01 .05
143 Junior Ortiz .01 .05
144 Don August .01 .05
145 Gary Gaetti .02 .10
146 Kirt Manwaring .01 .05
147 Jeff Reed .01 .05
148 Jose Alvarez .01 .05
149 Mike Schooler .01 .05
150 Mark Grace .05 .15
151 Geronimo Berroa .01 .05
152 Barry Jones .01 .05
153 Geno Petralli .01 .05
154 Jim Deshaies .01 .05
155 Barry Larkin .05 .15
156 Alfredo Griffin .01 .05
157 Tom Henke .01 .05
158 Mike Jeffcoat .01 .05
159 Bob Welch .01 .05
160 Julio Franco .02 .10
161 Henry Cotto .01 .05
162 Terry Steinbach .01 .05
163 Damon Berryhill .01 .05
164 Tim Crews .01 .05
165 Tom Browning .01 .05
166 Fred Manrique .01 .05
167 Harold Reynolds .02 .10
168A Ron Hassey ERR .01 .05
(27 on back)
168B Ron Hassey COR .20 .50
(24 on back)
169 Shawon Dunston .01 .05
170 Bobby Bonilla .02 .10
171 Tommy Herr .01 .05
172 Mike Heath .01 .05
173 Rich Gedman .01 .05
174 Bill Ripken .01 .05
175 Pete O'Brien .01 .05
176A L.McClendon ERR .01 .05
Uniform number on
back listed as 1
176B L.McClendon COR .20 .50
Uniform number on
back listed as 10
177 Brian Holton .01 .05
178 Jeff Blauser .01 .05
179 Jim Eisenreich .01 .05
180 Bert Blyleven .02 .10
181 Rob Murphy .01 .05
182 Bill Doran .01 .05
183 Curt Ford .01 .05
184 Mike Henneman .01 .05
185 Eric Davis .02 .10
186 Lance McCullers .01 .05
187 Steve Davis RC .01 .05
188 Bill Wegman .01 .05
189 Brian Harper .01 .05
190 Mike Moore .01 .05
191 Dale Mohorcic .01 .05
192 Tim Wallach .01 .05
193 Keith Hernandez .02 .10
194 Dave Righetti .01 .05
195A B.Saberhagen ERR .02 .10
Joke
195B B.Saberhagen COR .20 .50
Joker
196 Paul Kilgus .01 .05
197 Bud Black .01 .05
198 Juan Samuel .01 .05
199 Kevin Seitzer .01 .05
200 Darryl Strawberry .02 .10
201 Dave Stieb .02 .10
202 Charlie Hough .02 .10
203 Jack Morris .02 .10
204 Rance Mulliniks .01 .05
205 Alvin Davis .01 .05
206 Jack Howell .01 .05
207 Ken Patterson .01 .05
208 Terry Pendleton .02 .10
209 Craig Lefferts .01 .05
210 Kevin Brown UER .02 .10
(First mention of '89
Rangers should be '88)
211 Dan Petry .01 .05
212 Dave Leiper .01 .05
213 Daryl Boston .01 .05
214 Kevin Hickey .01 .05
215 Mike Krukow .01 .05
216 Terry Francona .02 .10
217 Kirk McCaskill .01 .05
218 Scott Bailes .01 .05
219 Bob Forsch .01 .05
220A Mike Aldrete ERR .01 .05
(25 on back)
220B Mike Aldrete COR .20 .50
(24 on back)
221 Steve Buechele .01 .05
222 Jesse Barfield .01 .05
223 Juan Berenguer .01 .05
224 Andy McGaffigan .01 .05
225 Pete Smith .01 .05
226 Mike Witt .01 .05
227 Jay Howell .01 .05
228 Scott Bradley .01 .05
229 Jerome Walton .01 .05
230 Greg Swindell .01 .05
231 Atlee Hammaker .01 .05
232A Mike Devereaux ERR .01 .05
(RF on front)
232B M.Devereaux COR .20 .50
CF on front
233 Ken Hill .02 .10
234 Craig Worthington .01 .05
235 Scott Terry .01 .05
236 Brett Butler .02 .10
237 Doyle Alexander .01 .05
238 Dave Anderson .01 .05
239 Bob Milacki .01 .05
240 Dwight Smith .01 .05
241 Otis Nixon .01 .05
242 Pat Tabler .01 .05
243 Derek Lilliquist .01 .05
244 Danny Tartabull .01 .05
245 Wade Boggs .05 .15
246 Scott Garrelts .01 .05
(Should say Relief
Pitcher on front)
247 Spike Owen .01 .05
248 Norm Charlton .01 .05
249 Gerald Perry .01 .05
250 Nolan Ryan .40 1.00
251 Kevin Gross .01 .05
252 Randy Milligan .01 .05
253 Mike LaCoss .01 .05
254 Dave Bergman .01 .05
255 Tony Gwynn .10 .30
256 Felix Fermin .01 .05
257 Greg W. Harris .01 .05
258 Junior Felix .01 .05
259 Mark Davis .01 .05
260 Vince Coleman .01 .05
261 Paul Gibson .01 .05
262 Mitch Williams .01 .05
263 Jeff Russell .01 .05
264 Omar Vizquel .08 .25
265 Andre Dawson .02 .10
266 Storm Davis .01 .05
267 Guillermo Hernandez .01 .05
268 Mike Felder .01 .05
269 Tom Candiotti .01 .05
270 Bruce Hurst .01 .05
271 Fred McGriff .08 .25
272 Glenn Davis .01 .05
273 John Franco .02 .10
274 Rich Yett .01 .05
275 Craig Biggio .08 .25
276 Gene Larkin .01 .05
277 Rob Dibble .02 .10
278 Randy Bush .01 .05
279 Kevin Bass .01 .05
280A Bo Jackson ERR .08 .25
(Watham)
280B Bo Jackson COR .30 .75
(Wathan)
281 Wally Backman .01 .05
282 Larry Andersen .01 .05
283 Chris Bosio .01 .05
284 Juan Agosto .01 .05
285 Ozzie Smith .15 .40
286 George Bell .01 .05
287 Rex Hudler .01 .05
288 Pat Borders .01 .05
289 Danny Jackson .01 .05
290 Carlton Fisk .05 .15
291 Tracy Jones .01 .05
292 Allan Anderson .01 .05
293 Johnny Ray .01 .05
294 Lee Guetterman .01 .05
295 Paul O'Neill .05 .15
296 Carney Lansford .02 .10
297 Tom Brookens .01 .05
298 Claudell Washington .01 .05
299 Hubie Brooks .01 .05
300 Will Clark .05 .15
301 Kenny Rogers .02 .10
302 Darrell Evans .02 .10
303 Greg Briley .01 .05
304 Donn Pall .01 .05
305 Teddy Higuera .01 .05
306 Dan Pasqua .01 .05
307 Dave Winfield .02 .10
308 Dennis Powell .01 .05
309 Jose DeLeon .01 .05
310 Roger Clemens UER .40 1.00
(Dominate, should
say dominant)
311 Melido Perez .01 .05
312 Devon White .02 .10
313 Dwight Gooden .02 .10
314 Carlos Martinez .01 .05
315 Dennis Eckersley .02 .10
316 Clay Parker UER .01 .05
(Height 6'11-inch)
317 Rick Honeycutt .01 .05
318 Tim Laudner .01 .05
319 Joe Carter .02 .10
320 Robin Yount .15 .40
321 Felix Jose .01 .05
322 Mickey Tettleton .01 .05
323 Mike Gallego .01 .05
324 Edgar Martinez .05 .15
325 Dave Henderson .01 .05
326 Chili Davis .02 .10
327 Steve Balboni .01 .05
328 Jody Davis .01 .05
329 Shawn Hillegas .01 .05
330 Jim Abbott .05 .15
331 John Dopson .01 .05
332 Mark Williamson .01 .05
333 Jeff D. Robinson .01 .05
334 John Smiley .01 .05
335 Bobby Thigpen .01 .05
336 Garry Templeton .01 .05
337 Marvell Wynne .01 .05
338A Ken Griffey Sr. ERR .02 .10
(Uniform number on
back listed as 25)
338B Ken Griffey Sr. COR .20 .50
(Uniform number on
back listed as 30)
339 Steve Finley .02 .10
340 Ellis Burks .05 .15
341 Frank Williams .01 .05
342 Mike Morgan .01 .05
343 Kevin Mitchell .01 .05
344 Joel Youngblood .01 .05
345 Mike Greenwell .01 .05
346 Glenn Wilson .01 .05
347 John Costello .01 .05
348 Wes Gardner .01 .05
349 Jeff Ballard .01 .05
350 Mark Thurmond UER .01 .05
(ERA is 192,
should be 1.92)
351 Randy Myers .02 .10
352 Shawn Abner .01 .05
353 Jesse Orosco .01 .05
354 Greg Walker .01 .05
355 Pete Harnisch .01 .05
356 Steve Farr .01 .05
357 Dave LaPoint .01 .05
358 Willie Fraser .01 .05
359 Mickey Hatcher .01 .05
360 Rickey Henderson .08 .25
361 Mike Fitzgerald .01 .05
362 Bill Schroeder .01 .05
363 Mark Carreon .01 .05
364 Ron Jones .01 .05
365 Jeff Montgomery .02 .10
366 Bill Krueger .01 .05
367 John Cangelosi .01 .05
368 Jose Gonzalez .01 .05
369 Greg Hibbard RC .02 .10
370 John Smoltz .08 .25
371 Jeff Brantley .01 .05
372 Frank White .02 .10
373 Ed Whitson .01 .05
374 Willie McGee .02 .10
375 Jose Canseco .05 .15
376 Randy Ready .01 .05
377 Don Aase .01 .05
378 Tony Armas .01 .05
379 Steve Bedrosian .01 .05
380 Chuck Finley .02 .10
381 Kent Hrbek .02 .10
382 Jim Gantner .01 .05
383 Mel Hall .01 .05
384 Mike Marshall .01 .05
385 Mark McGwire .40 1.00
386 Wayne Tolleson .01 .05
387 Brian Holman .01 .05
388 John Wetteland .08 .25
389 Darren Daulton .02 .10
390 Rob Deer .01 .05
391 John Moses .01 .05
392 Todd Worrell .01 .05
393 Chuck Cary .01 .05
394 Stan Javier .01 .05
395 Willie Randolph .02 .10
396 Bill Buckner .01 .05
397 Robby Thompson .01 .05
398 Mike Scioscia .01 .05
399 Lonnie Smith .01 .05
400 Kirby Puckett .08 .25
401 Mark Langston .01 .05
402 Danny Darwin .01 .05
403 Greg Maddux .15 .40
404 Lloyd Moseby .01 .05
405 Rafael Palmeiro .05 .15
406 Chad Kreuter .01 .05
407 Jimmy Key .02 .10
408 Tim Birtsas .01 .05
409 Tim Raines .02 .10
410 Dave Stewart .02 .10
411 Eric Yelding RC .01 .05
412 Kent Anderson .01 .05
413 Les Lancaster .01 .05
414 Rick Dempsey .01 .05
415 Randy Johnson .20 .50
416 Gary Carter .02 .10
417 Rolando Roomes .01 .05
418 Dan Schatzeder .01 .05
419 Bryn Smith .01 .05
420 Ruben Sierra .02 .10
421 Steve Jeltz .01 .05
422 Ken Oberkfell .01 .05
423 Sid Bream .01 .05
424 Jim Clancy .01 .05
425 Kelly Gruber .01 .05
426 Rick Leach .01 .05
427 Len Dykstra .02 .10
428 Jeff Pico .01 .05
429 John Cerutti .01 .05
430 David Cone .02 .10
431 Jeff Kunkel .01 .05
432 Luis Aquino .01 .05
433 Ernie Whitt .01 .05
434 Bo Diaz .01 .05
435 Steve Lake .01 .05
436 Pat Perry .01 .05
437 Mike Davis .01 .05
438 Cecilio Guante .01 .05
439 Duane Ward .01 .05
440 Andy Van Slyke .05 .15
441 Gene Nelson .01 .05
442 Luis Polonia .01 .05
443 Kevin Elster .01 .05
444 Keith Moreland .01 .05
445 Roger McDowell .01 .05
446 Ron Darling .01 .05
447 Ernest Riles .01 .05
448 Mookie Wilson .02 .10
449A Billy Spiers ERR .01 .05
(No birth year)
449B Billy Spiers COR .20 .50
(Born in 1966)
450 Rick Sutcliffe .02 .10
451 Nelson Santovenia .01 .05
452 Andy Allanson .01 .05
453 Bob Melvin .01 .05
454 Benito Santiago .02 .10
455 Jose Uribe .01 .05
456 Bill Landrum .01 .05
457 Bobby Witt .01 .05
458 Kevin Romine .01 .05
459 Lee Mazzilli .01 .05
460 Paul Molitor .02 .10
461 Ramon Martinez .01 .05
462 Frank DiPino .01 .05
463 Walt Terrell .01 .05
464 Bob Geren .01 .05
465 Rick Reuschel .01 .05
466 Mark Grant .01 .05
467 John Kruk .02 .10
468 Gregg Jefferies .02 .10
469 R.J. Reynolds .01 .05
470 Harold Baines .02 .10
471 Dennis Lamp .01 .05
472 Tom Gordon .02 .10
473 Terry Puhl .01 .05
474 Curt Wilkerson .01 .05
475 Dan Quisenberry .01 .05
476 Oddibe McDowell .01 .05
477A Zane Smith ERR .01 .05
(Career ERA .393)
477B Zane Smith COR .20 .50
(career ERA 3.93)
478 Franklin Stubbs .01 .05
479 Wallace Johnson .01 .05
480 Jay Tibbs .01 .05
481 Tom Glavine .05 .15
482 Manny Lee .01 .05
483 Joe Hesketh UER .01 .05
Says Rookiess on back,
should say Rookies
484 Mike Bielecki .01 .05
485 Greg Brock .01 .05
486 Pascual Perez .01 .05
487 Kirk Gibson .02 .10
488 Scott Sanderson .01 .05
489 Domingo Ramos .01 .05
490 Kal Daniels .01 .05
491A David Wells ERR .02 .10
(Reverse negative
photo on card back)
491B David Wells COR .20 .50
492 Jerry Reed .01 .05
493 Eric Show .01 .05
494 Mike Pagliarulo .01 .05
495 Ron Robinson .01 .05
496 Brad Komminsk .01 .05
497 Greg Litton .01 .05
498 Chris James .01 .05
499 Luis Quinones .01 .05
500 Frank Viola .01 .05
501 Tim Teufel UER .01 .05
(Twins '85, the s is
lower case, should
be upper case)
502 Terry Leach .01 .05
503 Matt Williams UER .02 .10
(Wearing 10 on front,
listed as 9 on back)
504 Tim Leary .01 .05
505 Doug Drabek .01 .05
506 Mariano Duncan .01 .05
507 Charlie Hayes .01 .05
508 Joey Belle .08 .25
509 Pat Sheridan .01 .05
510 Mackey Sasser .01 .05
511 Jose Rijo .01 .05
512 Mike Smithson .01 .05
513 Gary Ward .01 .05
514 Dion James .01 .05
515 Jim Gott .01 .05
516 Drew Hall .01 .05
517 Doug Bair .01 .05
518 Scott Scudder .01 .05
519 Rick Aguilera .02 .10
520 Rafael Belliard .01 .05
521 Jay Buhner .02 .10
522 Jeff Reardon .02 .10
523 Steve Rosenberg .01 .05
524 Randy Velarde .01 .05
525 Jeff Musselman .01 .05
526 Bill Long .01 .05
527 Gary Wayne .01 .05
528 Dave Wayne Johnson RC .01 .05
529 Ron Kittle .01 .05
530 Erik Hanson UER .01 .05
(5th line on back
says seson, should
say season)
531 Steve Wilson .01 .05
532 Joey Meyer .01 .05
533 Curt Young .01 .05
534 Kelly Downs .01 .05
535 Joe Girardi .05 .15
536 Lance Blankenship .01 .05
537 Greg Mathews .01 .05
538 Donell Nixon .01 .05
539 Mark Knudson .01 .05
540 Jeff Wetherby RC .01 .05
541 Darrin Jackson .01 .05
542 Terry Mulholland .01 .05
543 Eric Hetzel .01 .05
544 Rick Reed RC .08 .25
545 Dennis Cook .01 .05
546 Mike Jackson .01 .05
547 Brian Fisher .01 .05
548 Gene Harris .01 .05
549 Jeff King .01 .05
550 Dave Dravecky .08 .25
551 Randy Kutcher .01 .05
552 Mark Portugal .01 .05
553 Jim Corsi .01 .05
554 Todd Stottlemyre .02 .10
555 Scott Bankhead .01 .05
556 Ken Dayley .01 .05
557 Rick Wrona .01 .05
558 Sammy Sosa RC 1.00 2.50
559 Keith Miller .01 .05
560 Ken Griffey Jr. .30 .75
561A R.Sandberg HL ERR 3.00 8.00
Position on front
listed as 3B
561B R.Sandberg HL COR .08 .25
562 Billy Hatcher .01 .05
563 Jay Bell .02 .10
564 Jack Daugherty RC .01 .05
565 Rich Monteleone .01 .05
566 Bo Jackson AS-MVP .02 .10
567 Tony Fossas RC .01 .05
568 Roy Smith .01 .05
569 Jaime Navarro .01 .05
570 Lance Johnson .01 .05
571 Mike Dyer RC .01 .05
572 Kevin Ritz RC .01 .05
573 Dave West .01 .05
574 Gary Mielke RC .01 .05
575 Scott Lusader .01 .05
576 Joe Oliver .01 .05
577 Sandy Alomar Jr. .02 .10
578 Andy Benes UER .02 .10
(Extra comma between
day and year)
579 Tim Jones .01 .05
580 Randy McCament RC .01 .05
581 Curt Schilling .40 1.00
582 John Orton RC .02 .10
583A Milt Cuyler ERR RC .02 .10
(998 games)
583B Milt Cuyler COR .20 .50
(98 games; the extra 9
was ghosted out and
may still be visible)
584 Eric Anthony RC .02 .10
585 Greg Vaughn .01 .05
586 Deion Sanders .08 .25
587 Jose DeJesus .01 .05
588 Chip Hale RC .01 .05
589 John Olerud RC .20 .50
590 Steve Olin RC .08 .25
591 Marquis Grissom RC .15 .40
592 Moises Alou RC .30 .75
593 Mark Lemke .01 .05
594 Dean Palmer RC .08 .25
595 Robin Ventura .08 .25
596 Tino Martinez .20 .50
597 Mike Huff RC .01 .05
598 Scott Hemond RC .02 .10
599 Wally Whitehurst .01 .05
600 Todd Zeile .02 .10
601 Glenallen Hill .01 .05
602 Hal Morris .01 .05
603 Juan Bell .01 .05
604 Bobby Rose .01 .05
605 Matt Merullo .01 .05
606 Kevin Maas RC .08 .25
607 Randy Nosek RC .01 .05
608A Billy Bates RC .01 .05
(Text mentions 12
triples in tenth line)
608B Billy Bates .01 .05
(Text has no mention
of triples)
609 Mike Stanton RC .08 .25
610 Mauro Gozzo RC .01 .05
611 Charles Nagy .01 .05
612 Scott Coolbaugh RC .01 .05
613 Jose Vizcaino RC .08 .25
614 Greg Smith RC .01 .05
615 Jeff Huson RC .02 .10
616 Mickey Weston RC .01 .05
617 John Pawlowski .01 .05
618A Joe Skalski ERR .01 .05
(27 on back)
618B Joe Skalski COR .20 .50
(67 on back)
619 Bernie Williams RC .60 1.50
620 Shawn Holman RC .01 .05
621 Gary Eave RC .01 .05
622 Darrin Fletcher UER .02 .10
Elmherst, should be Elmhurst
623 Pat Combs .01 .05
624 Mike Blowers RC .02 .10
625 Kevin Appier .02 .10
626 Pat Austin .01 .05
627 Kelly Mann RC .01 .05
628 Matt Kinzer RC .01 .05
629 Chris Hammond RC .02 .10
630 Dean Wilkins RC .01 .05
631 Larry Walker UER RC .40 1.00
Uniform number 55 on front
and 33 on back;
Home is Maple Ridge,
not Maple River
632 Blaine Beatty RC .01 .05
633A Tommy Barrett ERR .01 .05
(29 on back)
633B Tommy Barrett COR .20 .50
(14 on back)
634 Stan Belinda RC .02 .10
635 Mike (Texas) Smith RC .01 .05
636 Hensley Meulens .01 .05
637 J.Gonzalez UER RC .40 1.00
Sarasots on back,
should be Sarasota
638 Lenny Webster RC .02 .10
639 Mark Gardner RC .02 .10
640 Tommy Greene RC .02 .10
641 Mike Hartley RC .01 .05
642 Phil Stephenson .01 .05
643 Kevin Mmahat RC .01 .05
644 Ed Whited RC .01 .05
645 Delino DeShields RC .08 .25
646 Kevin Blankenship .01 .05
647 Paul Sorrento RC .08 .25
648 Mike Roesler RC .01 .05
649 Jason Grimsley RC .02 .10
650 Dave Justice RC .20 .50
651 Scott Cooper RC .02 .10
652 Dave Eiland .01 .05
653 Mike Munoz RC .01 .05
654 Jeff Fischer RC .01 .05
655 Terry Jorgensen RC .01 .05
656 George Canale RC .01 .05
657 Brian DuBois UER RC .01 .05
(Misspelled Dubois
on card)
658 Carlos Quintana .01 .05
659 Luis de los Santos .01 .05
660 Jerald Clark .01 .05
661 Donald Harris RC .01 .05
662 Paul Coleman RC .02 .10
663 Frank Thomas RC .75 2.00
664 Brent Mayne DC RC .08 .25
665 Eddie Zosky RC .02 .10
666 Steve Hosey RC .02 .10
667 Scott Bryant RC .02 .10
668 Tom Goodwin RC .08 .25
669 Cal Eldred RC .08 .25
670 Earl Cunningham RC .02 .10
671 Alan Zinter DC RC .02 .10
672 Chuck Knoblauch RC .15 .40
673 Kyle Abbott RC .01 .05
674 Roger Salkeld RC .01 .05
675 Mo Vaughn RC .20 .50
676 Keith (Kiki) Jones RC .01 .05
677 Tyler Houston RC .08 .25
678 Jeff Jackson RC .02 .10
679 Greg Gohr RC .02 .10
680 Ben McDonald DC RC .08 .25
681 Greg Blosser RC .02 .10
682 Willie Greene UER RC .08 .25
Name spelled as Green
683A W.Boggs DT ERR .02 .10
Text says 215 hits in
'89, should be 205
683B W.Boggs DT COR .20 .50
Text says 205 hits in '89
684 Will Clark DT .02 .10
685 Tony Gwynn DT UER .05 .15
(Text reads battling
instead of batting)
686 Rickey Henderson DT .05 .15
687 Bo Jackson DT .02 .10
688 Mark Langston DT .01 .05
689 Barry Larkin DT .02 .10
690 Kirby Puckett DT .05 .15
691 Ryne Sandberg DT .08 .25
692 Mike Scott DT .01 .05
693A Terry Steinbach DT .01 .05
ERR (cathers)
693B Terry Steinbach DT .01 .05
COR (catchers)
694 Bobby Thigpen DT .01 .05
695 Mitch Williams DT .01 .05
696 Nolan Ryan HL .15 .40
697 Bo Jackson FB/BB .20 .50
698 Rickey Henderson .05 .15
ALCS-MVP
699 Will Clark .02 .10
NLCS-MVP
700 Dave Stewart .02 .10
Mike Moore WS
701 Lights Out .08 .25
702 Carney Lansford .05 .15
Rickey Henderson
Jose Canseco
Dave Henderson WS
703 WS Game 4/Wrap-up .01 .05
704 Wade Boggs HL .02 .10

1990 Score Rookie/Traded

The standard-size 110-card 1990 Score Rookie and Traded set marked the third consecutive year Score had issued an end of the year set to note trades and give rookies early cards. The set was issued through hobby accounts and only in factory set form. The first 66 cards are traded players while the last 44 cards are rookie cards. Hockey star Eric Lindros is included in this set. Rookie Cards in the set include Derek Bell, Todd Hundley and Ray Lankford.

COMP.FACT.SET (110) 1.25 3.00
1T Dave Winfield .02 .10
2T Kevin Bass .01 .05
3T Nick Esasky .01 .05
4T Mitch Webster .01 .05
5T Pascual Perez .01 .05
6T Gary Pettis .01 .05
7T Tony Pena .01 .05
8T Candy Maldonado .01 .05
9T Cecil Fielder .02 .10
10T Carmelo Martinez .01 .05
11T Mark Langston .01 .05
12T Dave Parker .02 .10
13T Don Slaught .01 .05

14T Tony Phillips .01 .05
15T John Franco .02 .10
16T Randy Myers .02 .10
17T Jeff Reardon .02 .10
18T Sandy Alomar Jr. .02 .10
19T Joe Carter .02 .10
20T Fred Lynn .01 .05
21T Storm Davis .01 .05
22T Craig Lefferts .01 .05
23T Pete O'Brien .01 .05
24T Dennis Boyd .01 .05
25T Lloyd Moseby .01 .05
26T Mark Davis .01 .05
27T Tim Leary .01 .05
28T Gerald Perry .01 .05
29T Don Aase .01 .05
30T Ernie Whitt .01 .05
31T Dale Murphy .05 .15
32T Alejandro Pena .01 .05
33T Juan Samuel .01 .05
34T Hubie Brooks .01 .05
35T Gary Carter .02 .10
36T Jim Presley .01 .05
37T Wally Backman .01 .05
38T Matt Nokes .01 .05
39T Dan Petry .01 .05
40T Franklin Stubbs .01 .05
41T Jeff Huson .01 .05
42T Billy Hatcher .01 .05
43T Terry Leach .01 .05
44T Phil Bradley .01 .05
45T Claudell Washington .01 .05
46T Luis Polonia .01 .05
47T Daryl Boston .01 .05
48T Lee Smith .02 .10
49T Tom Brunansky .01 .05
50T Mike Witt .01 .05
51T Willie Randolph .02 .10
52T Stan Javier .01 .05
53T Brad Komminsk .01 .05
54T John Candelaria .01 .05
55T Bryn Smith .01 .05
56T Glenn Braggs .01 .05
57T Keith Hernandez .02 .10
58T Ken Oberkfell .01 .05
59T Steve Jeltz .01 .05
60T Chris James .01 .05
61T Scott Sanderson .01 .05
62T Bill Long .01 .05
63T Rick Cerone .01 .05
64T Scott Bailes .01 .05
65T Larry Sheets .01 .05
66T Junior Ortiz .01 .05
67T Francisco Cabrera .01 .05
68T Gary DiSarcina RC .08 .25
69T Greg Olson (C) RC .01 .05
70T Beau Allred RC .01 .05
71T Oscar Azocar RC .01 .05
72T Kent Mercker RC .08 .25
73T John Burkett .01 .05
74T Carlos Baerga RC .08 .25
75T Dave Hollins RC .08 .25
76T Todd Hundley RC .08 .25
77T Rick Parker RC .01 .05
78T Steve Cummings RC .01 .05
79T Bill Sampen RC .01 .05
80T Jerry Kutzler RC .01 .05
81T Derek Bell RC .08 .25
82T Kevin Tapani RC .08 .25
83T Jim Leyritz RC .08 .25
84T Ray Lankford RC .15 .40
85T Wayne Edwards RC .01 .05
86T Frank Thomas .75 2.00
87T Tim Naehring RC .02 .10
88T Willie Blair RC .02 .10
89T Alan Mills RC .02 .10
90T Scott Radinsky RC .02 .10
91T Howard Farmer RC .01 .05
92T Julio Machado RC .01 .05
93T Rafael Valdez RC .01 .05
94T Shawn Boskie RC .02 .10
95T David Segui RC .15 .40
96T Chris Hoiles RC .08 .25
97T D.J. Dozier RC .02 .10
98T Hector Villanueva RC .01 .05
99T Eric Gunderson RC .01 .05
100T Eric Lindros .40 1.00
101T Dave Otto .01 .05
102T Dana Kiecker RC .01 .05
103T Tim Drummond RC .01 .05
104T Mickey Pina RC .01 .05
105T Craig Grebeck RC .02 .10
106T Bernard Gilkey RC .08 .25
107T Tim Layana RC .01 .05
108T Scott Chiamparino RC .01 .05
109T Steve Avery .01 .05
110T Terry Shumpert RC .01 .05

1991 Score

The 1991 Score set contains 893 standard-size cards issued in two separate series of 441 and 452 cards each. This set marks the fourth consecutive year that Score issued a major set but the first time Score issued the set in two series. Cards were distributed in plastic-wrap packs, blister packs and factory sets. The card fronts feature one of four different solid color borders (black, blue, teal and white) framing the full-color photo of the cards. Subsets include Rookie Prospects (331-379), First Draft Picks (380-391, 671-682), AL All-Stars (392-401), Master Blasters (402-406, 689-693), K-Men (407-411, 684-688), Rifleman (412-416, 694-698), NL All-Stars (661-670), No-Hitters (699-707), Franchise (849-874), Award Winners (875-881) and Dream Team (882-893). An American Flag card (737) was issued to honor the American soldiers involved in Desert Storm. Rookie Cards in the set include Carl Everett, Jeff Conine, Chipper Jones, Mike Mussina and Rondell White. There are a number of pitchers whose card backs show Innings Pitched totals which do not equal the added year-by-year total; the following card numbers were affected, 4, 24, 29, 30, 51, 81, 109, 111, 118, 141, 150, 156, 177, 204, 218, 232, 235, 255, 287, 289, 311, and 328.

COMPLETE SET (893) 8.00 20.00
COMP.FACT.SET (900) 10.00 25.00
1 Jose Canseco .05 .15
2 Ken Griffey Jr. .20 .50
3 Ryne Sandberg .15 .40
4 Nolan Ryan .40 1.00
5 Bo Jackson .08 .25
6 Bret Saberhagen UER .01 .05
(In bio, missed
misspelled as mised)
7 Will Clark .05 .15
8 Ellis Burks .02 .10
9 Joe Carter .02 .10
10 Rickey Henderson .08 .25
11 Ozzie Guillen .02 .10
12 Wade Boggs .05 .15
13 Jerome Walton .01 .05
14 John Franco .02 .10
15 Ricky Jordan UER .01 .05
(League misspelled
as legue)
16 Wally Backman .01 .05
17 Rob Dibble .02 .10
18 Glenn Braggs .01 .05
19 Cory Snyder .01 .05
20 Kal Daniels .01 .05
21 Mark Langston .01 .05
22 Kevin Gross .01 .05
23 Don Mattingly UER .25 .60
First line, ' is missing from Yankee
24 Dave Righetti .02 .10
25 Roberto Alomar .05 .15
26 Robby Thompson .01 .05
27 Jack McDowell .01 .05
28 Bip Roberts UER .01 .05
(Bio reads playd)
29 Jay Howell .01 .05
30 Dave Stieb UER .01 .05
(17 wins in bio,
18 in stats)
31 Johnny Ray .01 .05
32 Steve Sax .01 .05
33 Terry Mulholland .01 .05
34 Lee Guetterman .01 .05
35 Tim Raines .02 .10
36 Scott Fletcher .01 .05
37 Lance Parrish .02 .10
38 Tony Phillips UER .01 .05
(Born 4/15
should be 4/25)
39 Todd Stottlemyre .01 .05
40 Alan Trammell .02 .10
41 Todd Burns .01 .05
42 Mookie Wilson .02 .10
43 Chris Bosio .01 .05
44 Jeffrey Leonard .01 .05
45 Doug Jones .01 .05
46 Mike Scott UER .01 .05
(In first line,
dominate should
read dominating)
47 Andy Hawkins .01 .05
48 Harold Reynolds .02 .10
49 Paul Molitor .02 .10
50 John Farrell .01 .05
51 Danny Darwin .01 .05
52 Jeff Blauser .01 .05
53 John Tudor UER .01 .05
(41 wins in '81)
54 Milt Thompson .01 .05
55 Dave Justice .02 .10
56 Greg Olson .01 .05
57 Willie Blair .01 .05
58 Rick Parker .01 .05
59 Shawn Boskie .01 .05
60 Kevin Tapani .01 .05
61 Dave Hollins .01 .05
62 Scott Radinsky .01 .05
63 Francisco Cabrera .01 .05
64 Tim Layana .01 .05
65 Jim Leyritz .01 .05
66 Wayne Edwards .01 .05
67 Lee Stevens .01 .05
68 Bill Sampen UER .01 .05
Fourth line, long is spelled along
69 Craig Grebeck UER .01 .05
Born in Cerritos, not Johnstown
70 John Burkett .01 .05
71 Hector Villanueva .01 .05
72 Oscar Azocar .01 .05
73 Alan Mills .01 .05
74 Carlos Baerga .01 .05
75 Charles Nagy .01 .05
76 Tim Drummond .01 .05
77 Dana Kiecker .01 .05
78 Tom Edens RC .01 .05
79 Kent Mercker .01 .05
80 Steve Avery .01 .05
81 Lee Smith .02 .10
82 Dave Martinez .01 .05
83 Dave Winfield .02 .10
84 Bill Spiers .01 .05
85 Dan Pasqua .01 .05
86 Randy Milligan .01 .05
87 Tracy Jones .01 .05
88 Greg Myers .01 .05
89 Keith Hernandez .02 .10
90 Todd Benzinger .01 .05
91 Mike Jackson .01 .05
92 Mike Stanley .01 .05
93 Candy Maldonado .01 .05
94 John Kruk UER .02 .10
(No decimal point
before 1990 BA)
95 Cal Ripken UER .30 .75
(Genius spelled genuis)
96 Willie Fraser .01 .05
97 Mike Felder .01 .05
98 Bill Landrum .01 .05
99 Chuck Crim .01 .05
100 Chuck Finley .02 .10
101 Kirt Manwaring .01 .05
102 Jaime Navarro .01 .05
103 Dickie Thon .01 .05
104 Brian Downing .01 .05
105 Jim Abbott .05 .15
106 Tom Brookens .01 .05
107 Darryl Hamilton UER .01 .05
(Bio info is for
Jeff Hamilton)
108 Bryan Harvey .01 .05
109 Greg A. Harris UER .01 .05
Shown pitching lefty, bio says righty
110 Greg Swindell .01 .05
111 Juan Berenguer .01 .05
112 Mike Heath .01 .05
113 Scott Bradley .01 .05
114 Jack Morris .02 .10
115 Barry Jones .01 .05
116 Kevin Romine .01 .05
117 Garry Templeton .01 .05
118 Scott Sanderson .01 .05
119 Roberto Kelly .01 .05
120 George Brett .25 .60
121 Oddibe McDowell .01 .05
122 Jim Acker .01 .05
123 Bill Swift UER .01 .05
(Born 12/27/61,
should be 10/27)
124 Eric King .01 .05
125 Jay Buhner .02 .10
126 Matt Young .01 .05
127 Alvaro Espinoza .01 .05
128 Greg Hibbard .01 .05
129 Jeff M. Robinson .01 .05
130 Mike Greenwell .01 .05
131 Dion James .01 .05
132 Donn Pall UER .01 .05
(1988 ERA in stats 0.00)
133 Lloyd Moseby .01 .05
134 Randy Velarde .01 .05
135 Allan Anderson .01 .05
136 Mark Davis .01 .05
137 Eric Davis .02 .10
138 Phil Stephenson .01 .05
139 Felix Fermin .01 .05
140 Pedro Guerrero .02 .10
141 Charlie Hough .02 .10
142 Mike Henneman .01 .05
143 Jeff Montgomery .01 .05
144 Lenny Harris .01 .05
145 Bruce Hurst .01 .05
146 Eric Anthony .01 .05
147 Paul Assenmacher .01 .05
148 Jesse Barfield .01 .05
149 Carlos Quintana .01 .05
150 Dave Stewart .02 .10
151 Roy Smith .01 .05
152 Paul Gibson .01 .05
153 Mickey Hatcher .01 .05
154 Jim Eisenreich .01 .05
155 Kenny Rogers .02 .10
156 Dave Schmidt .01 .05
157 Lance Johnson .01 .05
158 Dave West .01 .05
159 Steve Balboni .01 .05
160 Jeff Brantley .01 .05
161 Craig Biggio .05 .15
162 Brook Jacoby .01 .05
163 Dan Gladden .01 .05
164 Jeff Reardon UER .02 .10
(Total IP shown as
943.2, should be 943.1)
165 Mark Carreon .01 .05
166 Mel Hall .01 .05
167 Gary Mielke .01 .05
168 Cecil Fielder .02 .10
169 Darrin Jackson .01 .05
170 Rick Aguilera .02 .10
171 Walt Weiss .01 .05
172 Steve Farr .01 .05
173 Jody Reed .01 .05
174 Mike Jeffcoat .01 .05
175 Mark Grace .05 .15
176 Larry Sheets .01 .05
177 Bill Gullickson .01 .05
178 Chris Gwynn .01 .05
179 Melido Perez .01 .05
180 Sid Fernandez UER .01 .05
(779 runs in 1990)
181 Tim Burke .01 .05
182 Gary Pettis .01 .05
183 Rob Murphy .01 .05
184 Craig Lefferts .01 .05
185 Howard Johnson .01 .05
186 Ken Caminiti .02 .10
187 Tim Belcher .01 .05
188 Greg Cadaret .01 .05
189 Matt Williams .02 .10
190 Dave Magadan .01 .05
191 Geno Petralli .01 .05
192 Jeff D. Robinson .01 .05
193 Jim Deshaies .01 .05
194 Willie Randolph .02 .10
195 George Bell .01 .05
196 Hubie Brooks .01 .05
197 Tom Gordon .01 .05
198 Mike Fitzgerald .01 .05
199 Mike Pagliarulo .01 .05
200 Kirby Puckett .08 .25
201 Shawon Dunston .01 .05
202 Dennis Boyd .01 .05
203 Junior Felix UER .01 .05
(Text has him in NL)
204 Alejandro Pena .01 .05
205 Pete Smith .01 .05
206 Tom Glavine UER .05 .15
(Lefty spelled leftie)
207 Luis Salazar .01 .05
208 John Smoltz .05 .15
209 Doug Dascenzo .01 .05
210 Tim Wallach .01 .05
211 Greg Gagne .01 .05
212 Mark Gubicza .01 .05
213 Mark Parent .01 .05
214 Ken Oberkfell .01 .05
215 Gary Carter .02 .10
216 Rafael Palmeiro .05 .15
217 Tom Niedenfuer .01 .05
218 Dave LaPoint .01 .05
219 Jeff Treadway .01 .05
220 Mitch Williams UER .01 .05
('89 ERA shown as 2.76,
should be 2.64)
221 Jose DeLeon .01 .05
222 Mike LaValliere .01 .05
223 Darrel Akerfelds .01 .05
224A Kent Anderson ERR .02 .10
(First line& flachy
should read flashy)
224B Kent Anderson COR .02 .10
(Corrected in
factory sets)
225 Dwight Evans .05 .15
226 Gary Redus .01 .05
227 Paul O'Neill .05 .15
228 Marty Barrett .01 .05
229 Tom Browning .01 .05
230 Terry Pendleton .02 .10
231 Jack Armstrong .01 .05
232 Mike Boddicker .01 .05
233 Neal Heaton .01 .05
234 Marquis Grissom .02 .10
235 Bert Blyleven .02 .10
236 Curt Young .01 .05
237 Don Carman .01 .05
238 Charlie Hayes .01 .05
239 Mark Knudson .01 .05
240 Todd Zeile .01 .05
241 Larry Walker UER .08 .25
(Maple River, should
be Maple Ridge)
242 Jerald Clark .01 .05
243 Jeff Ballard .01 .05
244 Jeff King .01 .05
245 Tom Brunansky .01 .05
246 Darren Daulton .02 .10
247 Scott Terry .01 .05
248 Rob Deer .01 .05
249 Brady Anderson UER .02 .10
(1990 Hagerstown 1 hit,
should say 13 hits)
250 Len Dykstra .02 .10
251 Greg W. Harris .01 .05
252 Mike Hartley .01 .05
253 Joey Cora .01 .05
254 Ivan Calderon .01 .05
255 Ted Power .01 .05
256 Sammy Sosa .08 .25
257 Steve Buechele .01 .05
258 Mike Devereaux UER .01 .05
(No comma between
city and state)
259 Brad Komminsk UER .01 .05
(Last text line,
Ba should be BA)
260 Ted Higuera .01 .05
261 Shawn Abner .01 .05
262 Dave Valle .01 .05
263 Jeff Huson .01 .05
264 Edgar Martinez .05 .15
265 Carlton Fisk .05 .15
266 Steve Finley .02 .10
267 John Wetteland .02 .10
268 Kevin Appier .02 .10
269 Steve Lyons .01 .05
270 Mickey Tettleton .01 .05
271 Luis Rivera .01 .05
272 Steve Jeltz .01 .05
273 R.J. Reynolds .01 .05
274 Carlos Martinez .01 .05
275 Dan Plesac .01 .05
276 Mike Morgan UER .01 .05
Total IP shown as
1149.1, should be 1149
277 Jeff Russell .01 .05
278 Pete Incaviglia .01 .05
279 Kevin Seitzer UER .01 .05
Bio has 200 hits twice
and .300 four times,
should be once and
three times
280 Bobby Thigpen .01 .05
281 Stan Javier UER .01 .05
(Born 1/9,
should say 9/1)
282 Henry Cotto .01 .05
283 Gary Wayne .01 .05
284 Shane Mack .01 .05
285 Brian Holman .01 .05
286 Gerald Perry .01 .05
287 Steve Crawford .01 .05
288 Nelson Liriano .01 .05
289 Don Aase .01 .05
290 Randy Johnson .10 .30
291 Harold Baines .02 .10
292 Kent Hrbek .02 .10
293A Les Lancaster ERR .01 .05
(No comma between
Dallas and Texas)
293B Les Lancaster COR .01 .05
(Corrected in
factory sets)
294 Jeff Musselman .01 .05
295 Kurt Stillwell .01 .05
296 Stan Belinda .01 .05
297 Lou Whitaker .02 .10
298 Glenn Wilson .01 .05
299 Omar Vizquel UER .05 .15
Born 5/15, should be
4/24, there is a decimal
before GP total for '90
300 Ramon Martinez .01 .05
301 Dwight Smith .01 .05
302 Tim Crews .01 .05
303 Lance Blankenship .01 .05
304 Sid Bream .01 .05
305 Rafael Ramirez .01 .05
306 Steve Wilson .01 .05
307 Mackey Sasser .01 .05
308 Franklin Stubbs .01 .05
309 Jack Daugherty UER .01 .05
(Born 6/3/60,
should say July)
310 Eddie Murray .08 .25
311 Bob Welch .01 .05
312 Brian Harper .01 .05
313 Lance McCullers .01 .05
314 Dave Smith .01 .05
315 Bobby Bonilla .02 .10
316 Jerry Don Gleaton .01 .05
317 Greg Maddux .15 .40
318 Keith Miller .01 .05
319 Mark Portugal .01 .05
320 Robin Ventura .02 .10
321 Bob Ojeda .01 .05
322 Mike Harkey .01 .05
323 Jay Bell .02 .10
324 Mark McGwire .30 .75
325 Gary Gaetti .02 .10
326 Jeff Pico .01 .05
327 Kevin McReynolds .01 .05
328 Frank Tanana .01 .05
329 Eric Yelding UER .01 .05
(Listed as 6'3
should be 5'11
330 Barry Bonds .40 1.00
331 Brian McRae UER RC .08 .25
(No comma between
city and state)
332 Pedro Munoz RC .02 .10
333 Daryl Irvine RC .01 .05
334 Chris Hoiles .01 .05
335 Thomas Howard .01 .05
336 Jeff Schulz RC .01 .05
337 Jeff Manto .01 .05
338 Beau Allred .01 .05
339 Mike Bordick RC .15 .40
340 Todd Hundley .01 .05
341 Jim Vatcher UER RC (Height 6'9
should be 5'9) .01 .05
342 Luis Sojo .01 .05
343 Jose Offerman UER .01 .05
(Born 1969, should
say 1968)
344 Pete Coachman RC .01 .05
345 Mike Benjamin .01 .05
346 Ozzie Canseco .01 .05
347 Tim McIntosh .01 .05
348 Phil Plantier RC .02 .10
349 Terry Shumpert .01 .05
350 Darren Lewis .01 .05
351 David Walsh RC .01 .05
352A Scott Chiamparino .02 .10
ERR
Bats left, should be right
352B Scott Chiamparino .02 .10
COR
corrected in factory sets
353 Julio Valera .01 .05
UER (Progressed mis-
spelled as progessed)
354 Anthony Telford RC .01 .05
355 Kevin Wickander .01 .05
356 Tim Naehring .01 .05
357 Jim Poole .01 .05
358 Mark Whiten UER .01 .05
Shown hitting lefty, bio says righty
359 Terry Wells RC .01 .05
360 Rafael Valdez .01 .05
361 Mel Stottlemyre Jr. .01 .05
362 David Segui .01 .05
363 Paul Abbott RC .01 .05
364 Steve Howard .01 .05
365 Karl Rhodes .01 .05
366 Rafael Novoa RC .01 .05
367 Joe Grahe RC .01 .05
368 Darren Reed .01 .05
369 Jeff McKnight .01 .05
370 Scott Leius .01 .05
371 Mark Dewey RC .01 .05
372 Mark Lee UER RC .02 .10
(Shown hitting left,
bio says righty,
born in Dakota,
should say North Dakota)
373 Rosario Rodriguez UER RC .01 .05
Shown hitting lefty, bio says righty)
374 Chuck McElroy .01 .05
375 Mike Bell RC .01 .05
376 Mickey Morandini .01 .05
377 Bill Haselman RC .01 .05
378 Dave Pavlas RC .01 .05
379 Derrick May .01 .05
380 Jeromy Burnitz RC .15 .40
381 Donald Peters RC .01 .05
382 Alex Fernandez FDP .01 .05
383 Mike Mussina RC .75 2.00
384 Dan Smith RC .02 .10
385 Lance Dickson RC .02 .10
386 Carl Everett RC .20 .50
387 Tom Nevers RC .02 .10
388 Adam Hyzdu RC .08 .25
389 Todd Van Poppel RC .08 .25
390 Rondell White RC .15 .40
391 Marc Newfield RC .02 .10
392 Julio Franco AS .01 .05
393 Wade Boggs AS .02 .10
394 Ozzie Guillen AS .01 .05
395 Cecil Fielder AS .01 .05
396 Ken Griffey Jr. AS .08 .25
397 Rickey Henderson AS .05 .15
398 Jose Canseco AS .02 .10
399 Roger Clemens AS .15 .40
400 Sandy Alomar Jr. AS .01 .05
401 Bobby Thigpen AS .01 .05
402 Bobby Bonilla MB .01 .05
403 Eric Davis MB .01 .05
404 Fred McGriff MB .02 .10
405 Glenn Davis MB .01 .05
406 Kevin Mitchell MB .01 .05
407 Rob Dibble KM .01 .05
408 Ramon Martinez KM .01 .05
409 David Cone KM .01 .05
410 Bobby Witt KM .01 .05
411 Mark Langston KM .01 .05
412 Bo Jackson RIF .02 .10
413 Shawon Dunston RIF .01 .05
UER
In the baseball, should say in baseball
414 Jesse Barfield RIF .01 .05
415 Ken Caminiti RIF .01 .05
416 Benito Santiago RIF .01 .05
417 Nolan Ryan HL .20 .50
418 B.Thigpen HL UER .01 .05
Back refers to Hal
McRae Jr., should
say Brian McRae
419 Ramon Martinez HL .01 .05
420 Bo Jackson HL .02 .10
421 Carlton Fisk HL .02 .10
422 Jimmy Key .02 .10
423 Junior Noboa .01 .05
424 Al Newman .01 .05
425 Pat Borders .01 .05
426 Von Hayes .01 .05
427 Tim Teufel .01 .05
428 Eric Plunk UER .01 .05
Text says Eric's had, no apostrophe needed
429 John Moses .01 .05
430 Mike Witt .01 .05
431 Otis Nixon .01 .05
432 Tony Fernandez .01 .05
433 Rance Mulliniks .01 .05
434 Dan Petry .01 .05
435 Bob Geren .01 .05
436 Steve Frey .01 .05
437 Jamie Moyer .02 .10
438 Junior Ortiz .01 .05
439 Tom O'Malley .01 .05
440 Pat Combs .01 .05
441 Jose Canseco DT .05 .15
442 Alfredo Griffin .01 .05
443 Andres Galarraga .02 .10
444 Bryn Smith .01 .05
445 Andre Dawson .02 .10
446 Juan Samuel .01 .05
447 Mike Aldrete .01 .05
448 Ron Gant .02 .10
449 Fernando Valenzuela .02 .10
450 Vince Coleman UER .01 .05
Should say topped
majors in steals four
times, not three times
451 Kevin Mitchell .01 .05
452 Spike Owen .01 .05
453 Mike Bielecki .01 .05
454 Dennis Martinez .02 .10
455 Brett Butler .02 .10
456 Ron Darling .01 .05
457 Dennis Rasmussen .01 .05
458 Ken Howell .01 .05
459 Steve Bedrosian .01 .05
460 Frank Viola .02 .10
461 Jose Lind .01 .05
462 Chris Sabo .01 .05
463 Dante Bichette .02 .10
464 Rick Mahler .01 .05
465 John Smiley .01 .05
466 Devon White .02 .10
467 John Orton .01 .05
468 Mike Stanton .01 .05
469 Billy Hatcher .01 .05
470 Wally Joyner .02 .10
471 Gene Larkin .01 .05
472 Doug Drabek .01 .05
473 Gary Sheffield .02 .10
474 David Wells .02 .10
475 Andy Van Slyke .05 .15
476 Mike Gallego .01 .05
477 B.J. Surhoff .02 .10
478 Gene Nelson .01 .05
479 Mariano Duncan .01 .05
480 Fred McGriff .05 .15
481 Jerry Browne .01 .05
482 Alvin Davis .01 .05
483 Bill Wegman .01 .05
484 Dave Parker .02 .10
485 Dennis Eckersley .02 .10
486 Erik Hanson UER .01 .05
(Basketball misspelled
as baseketball)
487 Bill Ripken .01 .05
488 Tom Candiotti .01 .05
489 Mike Schooler .01 .05
490 Gregg Olson .01 .05
491 Chris James .01 .05
492 Pete Harnisch .01 .05
493 Julio Franco .02 .10
494 Greg Briley .01 .05
495 Ruben Sierra .02 .10
496 Steve Olin .01 .05
497 Mike Fetters .01 .05
498 Mark Williamson .01 .05
499 Bob Tewksbury .01 .05
500 Tony Gwynn .10 .30
501 Randy Myers .01 .05
502 Keith Comstock .01 .05
503 C.Worthington UER .01 .05
DeCinces misspelled
DiCinces on back
504 Mark Eichhorn UER .01 .05
Stats incomplete,
doesn't have '89 Braves stint
505 Barry Larkin .05 .15
506 Dave Johnson .01 .05
507 Bobby Witt .01 .05
508 Joe Orsulak .01 .05
509 Pete O'Brien .01 .05
510 Brad Arnsberg .01 .05
511 Storm Davis .01 .05
512 Bob Milacki .01 .05
513 Bill Pecota .01 .05
514 Glenallen Hill .01 .05
515 Danny Tartabull .01 .05
516 Mike Moore .01 .05
517 Ron Robinson UER .01 .05
(577 K's in 1990)
518 Mark Gardner .01 .05
519 Rick Wrona .01 .05
520 Mike Scioscia .01 .05
521 Frank Wills .01 .05
522 Greg Brock .01 .05
523 Jack Clark .02 .10
524 Bruce Ruffin .01 .05
525 Robin Yount .15 .40
526 Tom Foley .01 .05
527 Pat Perry .01 .05
528 Greg Vaughn .01 .05
529 Wally Whitehurst .01 .05
530 Norm Charlton .01 .05
531 Marvell Wynne .01 .05
532 Jim Gantner .01 .05
533 Greg Litton .01 .05
534 Manny Lee .01 .05
535 Scott Bailes .01 .05
536 Charlie Leibrandt .01 .05
537 Roger McDowell .01 .05
538 Andy Benes .01 .05
539 Rick Honeycutt .01 .05
540 Dwight Gooden .02 .10
541 Scott Garrelts .01 .05
542 Dave Clark .01 .05
543 Lonnie Smith .01 .05
544 Rick Reuschel .01 .05
545 Delino DeShields UER .02 .10
(Rockford misspelled
as Rock Ford in '88)
546 Mike Sharperson .01 .05
547 Mike Kingery .01 .05
548 Terry Kennedy .01 .05
549 David Cone .02 .10
550 Orel Hershiser .02 .10
551 Matt Nokes .01 .05
552 Eddie Williams .01 .05
553 Frank DiPino .01 .05
554 Fred Lynn .01 .05
555 Alex Cole .01 .05
556 Terry Leach .01 .05
557 Chet Lemon .01 .05
558 Paul Mirabella .01 .05
559 Bill Long .01 .05
560 Phil Bradley .01 .05
561 Duane Ward .01 .05
562 Dave Bergman .01 .05
563 Eric Show .01 .05
564 Xavier Hernandez .01 .05
565 Jeff Parrett .01 .05
566 Chuck Cary .01 .05
567 Ken Hill .01 .05
568 Bob Welch Hand .01 .05
(Complement should be
compliment) UER
569 John Mitchell .01 .05
570 Travis Fryman .02 .10
571 Derek Lilliquist .01 .05
572 Steve Lake .01 .05
573 John Barfield .01 .05
574 Randy Bush .01 .05
575 Joe Magrane .01 .05
576 Eddie Diaz .01 .05
577 Casey Candaele .01 .05
578 Jesse Orosco .01 .05
579 Tom Henke .01 .05
580 Rick Cerone UER .01 .05
(Actually his third
go-round with Yankees)
581 Drew Hall .01 .05
582 Tony Castillo .01 .05
583 Jimmy Jones .01 .05
584 Rick Reed .01 .05
585 Joe Girardi .01 .05
586 Jeff Gray RC .01 .05
587 Luis Polonia .01 .05
588 Joe Klink .01 .05
589 Rex Hudler .01 .05
590 Kirk McCaskill .01 .05
591 Juan Agosto .01 .05
592 Wes Gardner .01 .05
593 Rich Rodriguez RC .01 .05
594 Mitch Webster .01 .05
595 Kelly Gruber .01 .05
596 Dale Mohorcic .01 .05
597 Willie McGee .02 .10
598 Bill Krueger .01 .05
599 Bob Walk UER .01 .05
Cards says he's 33,
but actually he's 34
600 Kevin Maas .01 .05
601 Danny Jackson .01 .05
602 Craig McMurtry UER .01 .05
(Anonymously misspelled
anonimously)
603 Curtis Wilkerson .01 .05
604 Adam Peterson .01 .05
605 Sam Horn .01 .05
606 Tommy Gregg .01 .05
607 Ken Dayley .01 .05
608 Carmelo Castillo .01 .05
609 John Shelby .01 .05
610 Don Slaught .01 .05
611 Calvin Schiraldi .01 .05
612 Dennis Lamp .01 .05
613 Andres Thomas .01 .05
614 Jose Gonzalez .01 .05
615 Randy Ready .01 .05
616 Kevin Bass .01 .05
617 Mike Marshall .01 .05
618 Daryl Boston .01 .05
619 Andy McGaffigan .01 .05
620 Joe Oliver .01 .05
621 Jim Gott .01 .05
622 Jose Oquendo .01 .05
623 Jose DeJesus .01 .05
624 Mike Brumley .01 .05
625 John Olerud .02 .10
626 Ernest Riles .01 .05
627 Gene Harris .01 .05
628 Jose Uribe .01 .05
629 Darnell Coles .01 .05
630 Carney Lansford .02 .10
631 Tim Leary .01 .05
632 Tim Hulett .01 .05
633 Kevin Elster .01 .05
634 Tony Fossas .01 .05
635 Francisco Oliveras .01 .05
636 Bob Patterson .01 .05
637 Gary Ward .01 .05
638 Rene Gonzales .01 .05
639 Don Robinson .01 .05
640 Darryl Strawberry .02 .10
641 Dave Anderson .01 .05
642 Scott Scudder .01 .05
643 Reggie Harris UER .01 .05
(Hepatitis misspelled
as hepititis)
644 Dave Henderson .01 .05
645 Ben McDonald .01 .05
646 Bob Kipper .01 .05
647 Hal Morris UER .01 .05
(It's should be its)
648 Tim Birtsas .01 .05
649 Steve Searcy .01 .05
650 Dale Murphy .05 .15
651 Ron Oester .01 .05
652 Mike LaCoss .01 .05
653 Ron Jones .01 .05
654 Kelly Downs .01 .05
655 Roger Clemens .30 .75
656 Herm Winningham .01 .05
657 Trevor Wilson .01 .05
658 Jose Rijo .01 .05
659 Dann Bilardello UER .01 .05
Bio has 13 games, 1 hit,
and 32 AB, stats show 19, 2, and 37
660 Gregg Jefferies .01 .05
661 Doug Drabek AS UER .01 .05
(Through is mis-
spelled though)
662 Randy Myers AS .01 .05
663 Benny Santiago AS .01 .05
664 Will Clark AS .02 .10
665 Ryne Sandberg AS .08 .25
666 Barry Larkin AS UER .02 .10
Line 13, coolly misspelled cooly
667 Matt Williams AS .01 .05
668 Barry Bonds AS .20 .50
669 Eric Davis AS .01 .05
670 Bobby Bonilla AS .01 .05
671 Chipper Jones RC 1.50 4.00
672 Eric Christopherson RC .02 .10
673 Robbie Beckett RC .02 .10
674 Shane Andrews RC .08 .25
675 Steve Karsay RC .08 .25

676 Aaron Holbert RC .02 .10
677 Donovan Osborne RC .02 .10
678 Todd Ritchie RC .08 .25
679 Ronnie Walden RC .02 .10
680 Tim Costo RC .02 .10
681 Dan Wilson RC .08 .25
682 Kurt Miller RC .02 .10
683 Mike Lieberthal RC .15 .40
684 Roger Clemens KM .15 .40
685 Dwight Gooden KM .01 .05
686 Nolan Ryan KM .20 .50
687 Frank Viola KM .01 .05
688 Erik Hanson MB .01 .05
689 Matt Williams MB .01 .05
690 J.Canseco MB UER .02 .10
Mammoth misspelled as monmouth
691 Darryl Strawberry MB .01 .05
692 Bo Jackson MB .02 .10
693 Cecil Fielder MB .01 .05
694 Sandy Alomar Jr. RF .01 .05
695 Cory Snyder RF .01 .05
696 Eric Davis RF .01 .05
697 Ken Griffey Jr. RF .08 .25
698 A.Van Slyke RF UER .02 .10
Line 2, outfielders does not need
699 Mark Langston NH .01 .05
Mike Witt
700 Randy Johnson NH .05 .15
701 Nolan Ryan NH .20 .50
702 Dave Stewart NH .01 .05
703 F.Valenzuela NH .01 .05
704 Andy Hawkins NH .01 .05
705 Melido Perez NH .01 .05
706 Terry Mulholland NH .01 .05
707 Dave Stieb NH .01 .05
708 Brian Barnes RC .01 .05
709 Bernard Gilkey .01 .05
710 Steve Decker RC .01 .05
711 Paul Faries RC .01 .05
712 Paul Marak RC .01 .05
713 Wes Chamberlain RC .02 .10
714 Kevin Belcher RC .01 .05
715 Dan Boone UER .01 .05
(IP adds up to 101, but card has 101.2)
716 Steve Adkins RC .01 .05
717 Geronimo Pena .01 .05
718 Howard Farmer .01 .05
719 Mark Leonard RC .01 .05
720 Tom Lampkin .01 .05
721 Mike Gardiner RC .01 .05
722 Jeff Conine RC .15 .40
723 Efrain Valdez RC .01 .05
724 Chuck Malone .01 .05
725 Leo Gomez .01 .05
726 Paul McClellan RC .01 .05
727 Mark Leiter RC .02 .10
728 Rich DeLucia UER .01 .05
(Line 2, all told is written alltold)
729 Mel Rojas .01 .05
730 Hector Wagner RC .01 .05
731 Ray Lankford .02 .10
732 Turner Ward RC .02 .10
733 Gerald Alexander RC .01 .05
734 Scott Anderson RC .01 .05
735 Tony Perezchica .01 .05
736 Jimmy Kremers .01 .05
737 American Flag .08 .25
(Pray for Peace)
738 Mike York RC .01 .05
739 Mike Rochford .01 .05
740 Scott Aldred .01 .05
741 Rico Brogna .01 .05
742 Dave Burba RC .08 .25
743 Ray Stephens RC .01 .05
744 Eric Gunderson .01 .05
745 Troy Afenir RC .01 .05
746 Jeff Shaw .01 .05
747 Orlando Merced RC .02 .10
748 O.Olivares UER RC .02 .10
Line 9, league is misspelled legaue
749 Jerry Kutzler .01 .05
750 Mo Vaughn UER .02 .10
(44 SB's in 1990)
751 Matt Stark RC .01 .05
752 Randy Hennis RC .01 .05
753 Andujar Cedeno .01 .05
754 Kelvin Torve .01 .05
755 Joe Kraemer .01 .05
756 Phil Clark RC .02 .10
757 Ed Vosberg RC .01 .05
758 Mike Perez RC .02 .10
759 Scott Lewis RC .01 .05
760 Steve Chitren RC .01 .05
761 Ray Young RC .01 .05
762 Andres Santana .01 .05
763 Rodney McCray RC .01 .05
764 Sean Berry UER RC .02 .10
(Name misspelled Barry on card front)
765 Brent Mayne .01 .05
766 Mike Simms RC .01 .05
767 Glenn Sutko RC .01 .05
768 Gary DiSarcina .01 .05
769 George Brett HL .08 .25
770 Cecil Fielder HL .01 .05
771 Jim Presley .01 .05
772 John Dopson .01 .05
773 Bo Jackson Breaker .02 .10
774 Brent Knackert UER .01 .05
Born in 1954, shown throwing righty, but bio says lefty
775 Bill Doran UER .01 .05
(Reds in NL East)
776 Dick Schofield .01 .05
777 Nelson Santovenia .01 .05
778 Mark Guthrie .01 .05
779 Mark Lemke .01 .05
780 Terry Steinbach .01 .05
781 Tom Bolton .01 .05
782 Randy Tomlin RC .02 .10
783 Jeff Kunkel .01 .05
784 Felix Jose .01 .05
785 Rick Sutcliffe .02 .10
786 John Cerutti .01 .05
787 Jose Vizcaino UER .01 .05
(Offerman, not Opperman)
788 Curt Schilling .08 .25
789 Ed Whitson .01 .05
790 Tony Pena .01 .05
791 John Candelaria .01 .05
792 Carmelo Martinez .01 .05
793 Sandy Alomar Jr. UER .01 .05
(Indian's should say Indians')
794 Jim Neidlinger RC .01 .05
795 Barry Larkin WS .02 .10
and Chris Sabo
796 Paul Sorrento .01 .05
797 Tom Pagnozzi .01 .05
798 Tino Martinez .08 .25
799 Scott Ruskin UER .01 .05
(Text says first three seasons but lists averages for four)
800 Kirk Gibson .02 .10
801 Walt Terrell .01 .05
802 John Russell .01 .05
803 Chili Davis .02 .10
804 Chris Nabholz .01 .05
805 Juan Gonzalez .08 .25
806 Ron Hassey .01 .05
807 Todd Worrell .01 .05
808 Tommy Greene .01 .05
809 Joel Skinner UER .01 .05
Joel, not Bob, was drafted in 1979
810 Benito Santiago .02 .10
811 Pat Tabler UER .01 .05
Line 3, always misspelled alwasy
812 Scott Erickson UER RC .01 .05
813 Moises Alou .02 .10
814 Dale Sveum .01 .05
815 R.Sandberg MANYR .08 .25
816 Rick Dempsey .01 .05
817 Scott Bankhead .01 .05
818 Jason Grimsley .01 .05
819 Doug Jennings .01 .05
820 Tom Herr .01 .05
821 Rob Ducey .01 .05
822 Luis Quinones .01 .05
823 Greg Minton .01 .05
824 Mark Grant .01 .05
825 Ozzie Smith UER .15 .40
(Shortstop misspelled shortsop)
826 Dave Eiland .01 .05
827 Danny Heep .01 .05
828 Hensley Meulens .01 .05
829 Charlie O'Brien .01 .05
830 Glenn Davis .01 .05
831 John Marzano UER .01 .05
(International misspelled Internaional)
832 Steve Ontiveros .01 .05
833 Ron Karkovice .01 .05
834 Jerry Goff .01 .05
835 Ken Griffey Sr. .02 .10
836 Kevin Reimer .01 .05
837 Randy Kutcher UER .01 .05
(Infectious misspelled infectous)
838 Mike Blowers .01 .05
839 Mike Macfarlane .01 .05
840 Frank Thomas UER .08 .25
1989 Sarasota stats, 15 games but 188 AB
841 Ken Griffey Jr. .15 .40
Ken Griffey Sr.
842 Jack Howell .01 .05
843 Goose Gozzo .01 .05
844 Gerald Young .01 .05
845 Zane Smith .01 .05
846 Kevin Brown .02 .10
847 Sil Campusano .01 .05
848 Larry Andersen .01 .05
849 Cal Ripken FRAN .15 .40
850 Roger Clemens FRAN .15 .40
851 S.Alomar Jr. FRAN .01 .05
852 Alan Trammell FRAN .02 .10
853 George Brett FRAN .08 .25
854 Robin Yount FRAN .08 .25
855 Kirby Puckett FRAN .05 .15
856 Don Mattingly FRAN .10 .30
857 R.Henderson FRAN .05 .15
858 Ken Griffey Jr. FRAN .08 .25
859 Ruben Sierra FRAN .01 .05
860 John Olerud FRAN .01 .05
861 Dave Justice FRAN .01 .05
862 Ryne Sandberg FRAN .08 .25
863 Eric Davis FRAN .01 .05
864 D.Strawberry FRAN .01 .05
865 Tim Wallach FRAN .01 .05
866 Dwight Gooden FRAN .01 .05
867 Len Dykstra FRAN .01 .05
868 Barry Bonds FRAN .20 .50
869 Todd Zeile FRAN UER .01 .05
(Powerful misspelled as poweful)
870 Benito Santiago FRAN .01 .05
871 Will Clark FRAN .02 .10
872 Craig Biggio FRAN .02 .10
873 Wally Joyner FRAN .01 .05
874 Frank Thomas FRAN .05 .15
875 R.Henderson MVP .05 .15
876 Barry Bonds MVP .20 .50
877 Bob Welch CY .01 .05
878 Doug Drabek CY .01 .05
879 S.Alomar Jr. ROY .01 .05
880 Dave Justice ROY .01 .05
881 Damon Berryhill .01 .05
882 Frank Viola DT .01 .05
883 Dave Stewart DT .01 .05
884 Doug Jones DT .01 .05
885 Randy Myers DT .01 .05
886 Will Clark DT .02 .10
887 Roberto Alomar DT .02 .10
888 Barry Larkin DT .02 .10
889 Wade Boggs DT .05 .15
890 Rickey Henderson DT .08 .25
891 Kirby Puckett DT .05 .15
892 Ken Griffey Jr DT .20 .50
893 Benny Santiago DT .02 .10

1991 Score Mantle

This seven-card standard-size set features Mickey Mantle at various points in his career. The fronts are full-color glossy shots of Mantle while the backs are in a horizontal format with a full-color photo and some narrative information. The cards were randomly inserted in second series packs. 2,500 serial numbered cards were actually signed by Mantle and stamped with certification press. A similar version of this set was also released to dealers and media members on Score's mailing list and was individually to 5,000 numbered on the back. The cards were sent in seven-card packs. The card number and the set serial number appear on the back.

COMPLETE SET (7) 50.00 100.00
COMMON MANTLE (1-7) 6.00 15.00
RANDOM INSERTS IN SER.2 PACKS
AU Mickey Mantle AU/2500 350.00 600.00

1991 Score Rookie/Traded

The 1991 Score Rookie and Traded contains 110 standard-size player cards and was issued exclusively in factory set form along with 10 "World Series II" magic motion trivia cards through hobby dealers. The front design is identical to the regular issue 1991 Score set except for the distinctive mauve borders and T-suffixed numbering. Cards 81T-110T focus on rookies. Rookie Cards in the set include Jeff Bagwell and Ivan Rodriguez.

COMP.FACT.SET (110) 2.00 5.00
1T Bo Jackson .20 .50
2T Mike Flanagan .02 .10
3T Pete Incaviglia .02 .10
4T Jack Clark .08 .25
5T Hubie Brooks .02 .10
6T Ivan Calderon .02 .10
7T Glenn Davis .02 .10
8T Wally Backman .02 .10
9T Dave Smith .02 .10
10T Tim Raines .08 .25
11T Joe Carter .08 .25
12T Sid Bream .02 .10
13T George Bell .02 .10
14T Steve Bedrosian .02 .10
15T Willie Wilson .02 .10
16T Darryl Strawberry .08 .25
17T Danny Jackson .02 .10
18T Kirk Gibson .08 .25
19T Willie McGee .08 .25
20T Junior Felix .02 .10
21T Steve Farr .02 .10
22T Pat Tabler .02 .10
23T Brett Butler .08 .25
24T Danny Darwin .02 .10
25T Mickey Tettleton .02 .10
26T Gary Carter .08 .25
27T Mitch Williams .02 .10
28T Candy Maldonado .02 .10
29T Otis Nixon .02 .10
30T Brian Downing .02 .10
31T Tom Candiotti .02 .10
32T John Candelaria .02 .10
33T Rob Murphy .02 .10
34T Deion Sanders .15 .40
35T Willie Randolph .08 .25
36T Pete Harnisch .02 .10
37T Dante Bichette .08 .25
38T Garry Templeton .02 .10
39T Gary Gaetti .08 .25
40T John Cerutti .02 .10
41T Rick Cerone .02 .10
42T Mike Pagliarulo .02 .10
43T Ron Hassey .02 .10
44T Roberto Alomar .15 .40
45T Mike Boddicker .02 .10
46T Bud Black .02 .10
47T Rob Deer .02 .10
48T Devon White .08 .25
49T Luis Sojo .02 .10
50T Terry Pendleton .08 .25
51T Kevin Gross .02 .10
52T Mike Huff .02 .10
53T Dave Righetti .08 .25
54T Matt Young .02 .10
55T Earnest Riles .02 .10
56T Bill Gullickson .02 .10
57T Vince Coleman .02 .10
58T Fred McGriff .15 .40
59T Franklin Stubbs .02 .10
60T Eric King .02 .10
61T Cory Snyder .02 .10
62T Dwight Evans .15 .40
63T Gerald Perry .02 .10
64T Eric Show .02 .10
65T Shawn Hillegas .02 .10
66T Tony Fernandez .02 .10
67T Tim Teufel .02 .10
68T Mitch Webster .02 .10
69T Mike Heath .02 .10
70T Chili Davis .08 .25
71T Larry Andersen .02 .10
72T Gary Varsho .02 .10
73T Juan Berenguer .02 .10
74T Jack Morris .08 .25
75T Barry Jones .02 .10
76T Rafael Belliard .02 .10
77T Steve Buechele .02 .10
78T Scott Sanderson .02 .10
79T Bob Ojeda .02 .10
80T Curt Schilling .20 .50
81T Brian Drahman RC .02 .10
82T Ivan Rodriguez RC .75 2.00
83T David Howard RC .02 .10
84T H.Slocumb RC .08 .25
85T Mike Timlin RC .08 .25
86T Darryl Kile .08 .25
87T Pete Schourek RC .02 .10
88T Bruce Walton RC .02 .10
89T Al Osuna RC .02 .10
90T Gary Scott RC .02 .10
91T Doug Simons RC .02 .10
92T Chris Jones RC .02 .10
93T Chuck Knoblauch .08 .25
94T Dana Allison RC .02 .10
95T Erik Pappas RC .02 .10
96T Jeff Bagwell RC .60 1.50
97T K.Dressendorfer RC .02 .10
98T Freddie Benavides RC .02 .10
99T Luis Gonzalez RC .20 .50
100T Wade Taylor RC .02 .10
101T Ed Sprague .02 .10
102T Bob Scanlan RC .02 .10
103T Rick Wilkins RC .02 .10
104T Chris Donnels RC .02 .10
105T Joe Slusarski RC .02 .10
106T Mark Lewis .02 .10
107T Pat Kelly RC .02 .10
108T John Briscoe RC .02 .10
109T Luis Lopez RC .02 .10
110T Jeff Johnson RC .02 .10

1991 Score Rookies

This 40-card standard-sized set was distributed with five magic motion trivia cards. The fronts feature high glossy color action player photos, on a blue card face with meandering green lines.

COMP.FACT.SET (40) 1.50 4.00
1 Mel Rojas .01 .05
2 Ray Lankford .10 .30
3 Scott Aldred .01 .05
4 Turner Ward .01 .05
5 Omar Olivares .01 .05
6 Mo Vaughn .60 1.50
7 Phil Clark .01 .05
8 Brent Mayne .01 .05
9 Scott Lewis .01 .05
10 Brian Barnes .01 .05
11 Bernard Gilkey .01 .05
12 Steve Decker .01 .05
13 Paul Marak .01 .05
14 Wes Chamberlain .01 .05
15 Kevin Belcher .01 .05
16 Steve Adkins .01 .05
17 Geronimo Pena .01 .05
18 Mark Leonard .01 .05
19 Jeff Conine .02 .10
20 Leo Gomez .02 .10
21 Chuck Malone .01 .05
22 Beau Allred .01 .05
23 Todd Hundley .10 .30
24 Lance Dickson .01 .05
25 Mike Benjamin .01 .05
26 Jose Offerman .01 .05
27 Terry Shumpert .01 .05
28 Darren Lewis .01 .05
29 Scott Chiamparino .01 .05
30 Tim Naehring .01 .05
31 David Segui .02 .10
32 Karl Rhodes .01 .05
33 Mickey Morandini .01 .05
34 Chuck McElroy .01 .05
35 Tim McIntosh .01 .05
36 Derrick May .01 .05
37 Rich DeLucia .01 .05
38 Tino Martinez .40 1.00
39 Hensley Meulens .01 .05
40 Andujar Cedeno .01 .05

1992 Score

The 1992 Score set marked the second year that Score released their set in two different series. The first series contains 442 cards while the second series contains 451 cards. Cards were distributed in plastic wrapped packs, blister packs, jumbo packs and factory sets. Each pack included a special "World Series II" trivia card. Topical subsets include Rookie Prospects (395-424/736-772/814-877), No-Hit Club (425-428/784-787), Highlights (429-430), AL All-Stars (431-440; with color montages displaying Chris Greco's player caricatures), Dream Team (441-442/883-893), NL All-Stars (773-782), Highlights (783, 795-797), Draft Picks (799-810), and Memorabilia (878-882). The memorabilia cards all feature items from the famed Barry Halper collection. Halper was a part-owner of Score at the time. All of the Rookie Prospects (736-772) can be found with or without the Rookie Prospect stripe. Rookie Cards in the set include Vinny Castilla and Manny Ramirez. Chuck Knoblauch, 1991 American League Rookie of the Year, autographed 3,000 of his own 1990 Score Draft Pick cards (card number 672) in gold ink, 2,989 were randomly inserted in Series two poly packs, while the other 11 were given away in a sweepstakes. The backs of these Knoblauch autograph cards have special holograms to differentiate them.

COMPLETE SET (893) 6.00 15.00
COMP.FACT.SET (910) 8.00 20.00
COMP. SERIES 1 (442) 3.00 8.00
COMP. SERIES 2 (451) 3.00 8.00
1 Ken Griffey Jr. .15 .40
2 Nolan Ryan .40 1.00
3 Will Clark .05 .15
4 Dave Justice .02 .10
5 Dave Henderson .01 .05
6 Bret Saberhagen .02 .10
7 Fred McGriff .05 .15
8 Erik Hanson .01 .05
9 Darryl Strawberry .02 .10
10 Dwight Gooden .02 .10
11 Juan Gonzalez .05 .15
12 Mark Langston .01 .05
13 Lonnie Smith .01 .05
14 Jeff Montgomery .01 .05
15 Roberto Alomar .05 .15
16 Delino DeShields .01 .05
17 Steve Bedrosian .01 .05
18 Terry Pendleton .02 .10
19 Mark Carreon .01 .05
20 Mark McGwire .25 .60
21 Roger Clemens .20 .50
22 Chuck Crim .01 .05
23 Don Mattingly .25 .60
24 Dickie Thon .01 .05
25 Ron Gant .02 .10
26 Milt Cuyler .01 .05
27 Mike Macfarlane .01 .05
28 Dan Gladden .01 .05
29 Melido Perez .01 .05
30 Willie Randolph .02 .10
31 Albert Belle .02 .10
32 Dave Winfield .02 .10
33 Jimmy Jones .01 .05
34 Kevin Gross .01 .05
35 Andres Galarraga .02 .10
36 Mike Devereaux .01 .05
37 Chris Bosio .01 .05
38 Mike LaValliere .01 .05
39 Gary Gaetti .02 .10
40 Felix Jose .01 .05
41 Alvaro Espinoza .01 .05
42 Rick Aguilera .02 .10
43 Mike Gallego .01 .05
44 Eric Davis .02 .10
45 George Bell .01 .05
46 Tom Brunansky .01 .05
47 Steve Farr .01 .05
48 Duane Ward .01 .05
49 David Wells .02 .10
50 Cecil Fielder .02 .10
51 Walt Weiss .01 .05
52 Todd Zeile .01 .05
53 Doug Jones .01 .05
54 Bob Walk .01 .05
55 Rafael Palmeiro .05 .15
56 Rob Deer .01 .05
57 Paul O'Neill .05 .15
58 Jeff Reardon .02 .10
59 Randy Ready .01 .05
60 Scott Erickson .01 .05
61 Paul Molitor .02 .10
62 Jack McDowell .01 .05
63 Jim Acker .01 .05
64 Jay Buhner .02 .10
65 Travis Fryman .02 .10
66 Marquis Grissom .02 .10
67 Mike Harkey .01 .05
68 Luis Polonia .01 .05
69 Ken Caminiti .02 .10
70 Chris Sabo .01 .05
71 Gregg Olson .01 .05
72 Carlton Fisk .05 .15
73 Juan Samuel .01 .05
74 Todd Stottlemyre .01 .05
75 Andre Dawson .02 .10
76 Alvin Davis .01 .05
77 Bill Doran .01 .05
78 B.J. Surhoff .02 .10
79 Kirk McCaskill .01 .05
80 Dale Murphy .05 .15
81 Jose DeLeon .01 .05
82 Alex Fernandez .01 .05
83 Ivan Calderon .01 .05
84 Brent Mayne .01 .05
85 Jody Reed .01 .05
86 Randy Tomlin .01 .05
87 Randy Milligan .01 .05
88 Pascual Perez .01 .05
89 Hensley Meulens .01 .05
90 Joe Carter .02 .10
91 Mike Moore .01 .05
92 Ozzie Guillen .02 .10
93 Shawn Hillegas .01 .05
94 Chili Davis .02 .10
95 Vince Coleman .01 .05
96 Jimmy Key .02 .10
97 Billy Ripken .01 .05
98 Dave Smith .01 .05
99 Tom Bolton .01 .05
100 Barry Larkin .05 .15
101 Kenny Rogers .02 .10
102 Mike Boddicker .01 .05
103 Kevin Elster .01 .05
104 Ken Hill .01 .05
105 Charlie Leibrandt .01 .05
106 Pat Combs .01 .05
107 Hubie Brooks .01 .05
108 Julio Franco .02 .10
109 Vicente Palacios .01 .05
110 Kal Daniels .01 .05
111 Bruce Hurst .01 .05
112 Willie McGee .02 .10
113 Ted Power .01 .05
114 Milt Thompson .01 .05
115 Doug Drabek .01 .05
116 Rafael Belliard .01 .05
117 Scott Garrelts .01 .05
118 Terry Mulholland .01 .05
119 Jay Howell .01 .05
120 Danny Jackson .01 .05
121 Scott Ruskin .01 .05
122 Robin Ventura .02 .10
123 Bip Roberts .01 .05
124 Jeff Russell .01 .05
125 Hal Morris .01 .05
126 Teddy Higuera .01 .05
127 Luis Sojo .01 .05
128 Carlos Baerga .01 .05
129 Jeff Ballard .01 .05
130 Tom Gordon .01 .05
131 Sid Bream .01 .05
132 Rance Mulliniks .01 .05
133 Andy Benes .01 .05
134 Mickey Tettleton .01 .05
135 Rich DeLucia .01 .05
136 Tom Pagnozzi .01 .05
137 Harold Baines .02 .10
138 Danny Darwin .01 .05
139 Kevin Bass .01 .05
140 Chris Nabholz .01 .05
141 Pete O'Brien .01 .05
142 Jeff Treadway .01 .05
143 Mickey Morandini .01 .05
144 Eric King .01 .05
145 Danny Tartabull .01 .05
146 Lance Johnson .01 .05
147 Casey Candaele .01 .05
148 Felix Fermin .01 .05
149 Rich Rodriguez .01 .05
150 Dwight Evans .05 .15
151 Joe Klink .01 .05
152 Kevin Reimer .01 .05
153 Orlando Merced .01 .05
154 Mel Hall .01 .05
155 Randy Myers .01 .05
156 Greg A. Harris .01 .05
157 Jeff Brantley .01 .05
158 Jim Eisenreich .01 .05
159 Luis Rivera .01 .05
160 Cris Carpenter .01 .05
161 Bruce Ruffin .01 .05
162 Omar Vizquel .05 .15
163 Gerald Alexander .01 .05
164 Mark Guthrie .01 .05
165 Scott Lewis .01 .05
166 Bill Sampen .01 .05
167 Dave Anderson .01 .05
168 Kevin McReynolds .01 .05
169 Jose Vizcaino .01 .05
170 Bob Geren .01 .05
171 Mike Morgan .01 .05
172 Jim Gott .01 .05
173 Mike Pagliarulo .01 .05
174 Mike Jeffcoat .01 .05
175 Craig Lefferts .01 .05
176 Steve Finley .02 .10
177 Wally Backman .01 .05
178 Kent Mercker .01 .05
179 John Cerutti .01 .05
180 Jay Bell .02 .10
181 Dale Sveum .01 .05
182 Greg Gagne .01 .05
183 Donnie Hill .01 .05
184 Rex Hudler .01 .05
185 Pat Kelly .01 .05
186 Jeff D. Robinson .01 .05
187 Jeff Gray .01 .05
188 Jerry Willard .01 .05
189 Carlos Quintana .01 .05
190 Dennis Eckersley .02 .10
191 Kelly Downs .01 .05
192 Gregg Jefferies .01 .05
193 Darrin Fletcher .01 .05
194 Mike Jackson .01 .05
195 Eddie Murray .08 .25
196 Bill Landrum .01 .05
197 Eric Yelding .01 .05
198 Devon White .02 .10
199 Larry Walker .05 .15
200 Ryne Sandberg .15 .40
201 Dave Magadan .01 .05
202 Steve Chitren .01 .05
203 Scott Fletcher .01 .05
204 Dwayne Henry .01 .05
205 Scott Coolbaugh .01 .05
206 Tracy Jones .01 .05
207 Von Hayes .01 .05
208 Bob Melvin .01 .05
209 Scott Scudder .01 .05
210 Luis Gonzalez .02 .10
211 Scott Sanderson .01 .05
212 Chris Donnels .01 .05
213 Heathcliff Slocumb .01 .05
214 Mike Timlin .01 .05
215 Brian Harper .01 .05
216 Juan Berenguer UER .01 .05
(Decimal point missing in IP total)
217 Mike Henneman .01 .05
218 Bill Spiers .01 .05
219 Scott Terry .01 .05
220 Frank Viola .02 .10
221 Mark Eichhorn .01 .05
222 Ernest Riles .01 .05
223 Ray Lankford .02 .10
224 Pete Harnisch .01 .05
225 Bobby Bonilla .02 .10
226 Mike Scioscia .01 .05
227 Joel Skinner .01 .05
228 Brian Holman .01 .05
229 Gilberto Reyes .01 .05
230 Matt Williams .02 .10
231 Jaime Navarro .01 .05
232 Jose Rijo .01 .05
233 Atlee Hammaker .01 .05
234 Tim Teufel .01 .05
235 John Kruk .02 .10
236 Kurt Stillwell .01 .05
237 Dan Pasqua .01 .05
238 Tim Crews .01 .05
239 Dave Gallagher .01 .05
240 Leo Gomez .01 .05
241 Steve Avery .01 .05
242 Bill Gullickson .01 .05
243 Mark Portugal .01 .05
244 Lee Guetterman .01 .05
245 Benito Santiago .02 .10
246 Jim Gantner .01 .05
247 Robby Thompson .01 .05
248 Terry Shumpert .01 .05
249 Mike Bell .01 .05
250 Harold Reynolds .02 .10
251 Mike Felder .01 .05
252 Bill Pecota .01 .05
253 Bill Krueger .01 .05
254 Alfredo Griffin .01 .05
255 Lou Whitaker .02 .10
256 Roy Smith .01 .05
257 Jerald Clark .01 .05
258 Sammy Sosa .08 .25
259 Tim Naehring .01 .05
260 Dave Righetti .02 .10
261 Paul Gibson .01 .05
262 Chris James .01 .05
263 Larry Andersen .01 .05
264 Storm Davis .01 .05
265 Jose Lind .01 .05
266 Greg Hibbard .01 .05
267 Norm Charlton .01 .05
268 Paul Kilgus .01 .05
269 Greg Maddux .15 .40
270 Ellis Burks .02 .10
271 Frank Tanana .01 .05
272 Gene Larkin .01 .05
273 Ron Hassey .01 .05
274 Jeff M. Robinson .01 .05
275 Steve Howe .01 .05
276 Daryl Boston .01 .05
277 Mark Lee .01 .05
278 Jose Segura .01 .05
279 Lance Blankenship .01 .05
280 Don Slaught .01 .05
281 Russ Swan .01 .05
282 Bob Tewksbury .01 .05
283 Geno Petralli .01 .05
284 Shane Mack .01 .05
285 Bob Scanlan .01 .05
286 Tim Leary .01 .05
287 John Smoltz .05 .15
288 Pat Borders .01 .05
289 Mark Davidson .01 .05
290 Sam Horn .01 .05
291 Lenny Harris .01 .05
292 Franklin Stubbs .01 .05
293 Thomas Howard .01 .05
294 Steve Lyons .01 .05
295 Francisco Oliveras .01 .05
296 Terry Leach .01 .05
297 Barry Jones .01 .05
298 Lance Parrish .02 .10
299 Wally Whitehurst .01 .05
300 Bob Welch .01 .05
301 Charlie Hayes .01 .05
302 Charlie Hough .02 .10
303 Gary Redus .01 .05
304 Scott Bradley .01 .05
305 Jose Oquendo .01 .05
306 Pete Incaviglia .01 .05
307 Marvin Freeman .01 .05
308 Gary Pettis .01 .05
309 Joe Slusarski .01 .05
310 Kevin Seitzer .01 .05
311 Jeff Reed .01 .05
312 Pat Tabler .01 .05
313 Mike Maddux .01 .05
314 Bob Milacki .01 .05
315 Eric Anthony .01 .05
316 Dante Bichette .02 .10
317 Steve Decker .01 .05
318 Jack Clark .02 .10
319 Doug Dascenzo .01 .05
320 Scott Leius .01 .05
321 Jim Lindeman .01 .05
322 Bryan Harvey .01 .05
323 Spike Owen .01 .05
324 Roberto Kelly .01 .05
325 Stan Belinda .01 .05
326 Joey Cora .01 .05
327 Jeff Innis .01 .05
328 Willie Wilson .01 .05
329 Juan Agosto .01 .05
330 Charles Nagy .01 .05
331 Scott Bailes .01 .05
332 Pete Schourek .01 .05
333 Mike Flanagan .01 .05
334 Omar Olivares .01 .05
335 Dennis Lamp .01 .05
336 Tommy Greene .01 .05
337 Randy Velarde .01 .05
338 Tom Lampkin .01 .05
339 John Russell .01 .05
340 Bob Kipper .01 .05
341 Todd Burns .01 .05
342 Ron Jones .01 .05
343 Dave Valle .01 .05
344 Mike Heath .01 .05
345 John Olerud .02 .10
346 Gerald Young .01 .05
347 Ken Patterson .01 .05
348 Les Lancaster .01 .05
349 Steve Crawford .01 .05
350 John Candelaria .01 .05
351 Mike Aldrete .01 .05
352 Mariano Duncan .01 .05
353 Julio Machado .01 .05
354 Ken Williams .01 .05
355 Walt Terrell .01 .05
356 Mitch Williams .01 .05
357 Al Newman .01 .05
358 Bud Black .01 .05
359 Joe Hesketh .01 .05
360 Paul Assenmacher .01 .05
361 Bo Jackson .08 .25
362 Jeff Blauser .01 .05
363 Mike Brumley .01 .05
364 Jim Deshaies .01 .05
365 Brady Anderson .02 .10
366 Chuck McElroy .01 .05
367 Matt Merullo .01 .05
368 Tim Belcher .01 .05
369 Luis Aquino .01 .05
370 Joe Oliver .01 .05
371 Greg Swindell .01 .05
372 Lee Stevens .01 .05
373 Mark Knudson .01 .05
374 Bill Wegman .01 .05
375 Jerry Don Gleaton .01 .05
376 Pedro Guerrero .02 .10
377 Randy Bush .01 .05
378 Greg W. Harris .01 .05
379 Eric Plunk .01 .05
380 Jose DeJesus .01 .05
381 Bobby Witt .01 .05
382 Curtis Wilkerson .01 .05
383 Gene Nelson .01 .05
384 Wes Chamberlain .01 .05

Card	Low	High
385 Tom Henke	.01	.05
386 Mark Lemke	.01	.05
387 Greg Briley	.01	.05
388 Rafael Ramirez	.01	.05
389 Tony Fossas	.01	.05
390 Henry Cotto	.01	.05
391 Tim Hulett	.01	.05
392 Dean Palmer	.02	.10
393 Glenn Braggs	.01	.05
394 Mark Salas	.01	.05
395 Rusty Meacham	.01	.05
396 Andy Ashby	.01	.05
397 Jose Melendez	.01	.05
398 Warren Newson	.01	.05
399 Frank Castillo	.01	.05
400 Chito Martinez	.01	.05
401 Bernie Williams	.05	.15
402 Derek Bell	.02	.10
403 Javier Ortiz	.01	.05
404 Tim Sherrill	.01	.05
405 Rob MacDonald	.01	.05
406 Phil Plantier	.01	.05
407 Troy Afenir	.01	.05
408 Gino Minutelli	.01	.05
409 Reggie Jefferson	.01	.05
410 Mike Remlinger	.01	.05
411 Carlos Rodriguez	.01	.05
412 Joe Redfield	.01	.05
413 Alonzo Powell	.01	.05
414 S.Livingstone UER	.01	.05
(Travis Fryman, not Woodie, should be referenced on back		
415 Scott Kamieniecki	.01	.05
416 Tim Spehr	.01	.05
417 Brian Hunter	.01	.05
418 Ced Landrum	.01	.05
419 Bret Barberie	.01	.05
420 Kevin Morton	.01	.05
421 Doug Henry RC	.02	.10
422 Doug Piatt	.01	.05
423 Pat Rice	.01	.05
424 Juan Guzman	.01	.05
425 Nolan Ryan NH	.20	.50
426 Tommy Greene NH	.01	.05
427 Bob Milacki and Mike Flanagan NH (Mark Williamson and Gregg Olson)	.01	.05
428 Wilson Alvarez NH	.01	.05
429 Otis Nixon HL	.01	.05
430 Rickey Henderson HL	.05	.15
431 Cecil Fielder AS	.01	.05
432 Julio Franco AS	.01	.05
433 Cal Ripken AS	.15	.40
434 Wade Boggs AS	.02	.10
435 Joe Carter AS	.01	.05
436 Ken Griffey Jr. AS	.08	.25
437 Ruben Sierra AS	.01	.05
438 Scott Erickson AS	.01	.05
439 Tom Henke AS	.01	.05
440 Terry Steinbach AS	.01	.05
441 Rickey Henderson DT	.08	.25
442 Ryne Sandberg DT	.15	.40
443 Otis Nixon	.01	.05
444 Scott Radinsky UER	.01	.05
Photo on front is Tom Drees		
445 Mark Grace	.05	.15
446 Tony Pena	.01	.05
447 Billy Hatcher	.01	.05
448 Glenallen Hill	.01	.05
449 Chris Gwynn	.01	.05
450 Tom Glavine	.05	.15
451 John Habyan	.01	.05
452 Al Osuna	.01	.05
453 Tony Phillips	.01	.05
454 Greg Cadaret	.01	.05
455 Rob Dibble	.02	.10
456 Rick Honeycutt	.01	.05
457 Jerome Walton	.01	.05
458 Mookie Wilson	.02	.10
459 Mark Gubicza	.01	.05
460 Craig Biggio	.05	.15
461 Dave Cochrane	.01	.05
462 Keith Miller	.01	.05
463 Alex Cole	.01	.05
464 Pete Smith	.01	.05
465 Brett Butler	.02	.10
466 Jeff Huson	.01	.05
467 Steve Lake	.01	.05
468 Lloyd Moseby	.01	.05
469 Tim McIntosh	.01	.05
470 Dennis Martinez	.02	.10
471 Greg Myers	.01	.05
472 Mackey Sasser	.01	.05
473 Junior Ortiz	.01	.05
474 Greg Olson	.01	.05
475 Steve Sax	.01	.05
476 Ricky Jordan	.01	.05
477 Max Venable	.01	.05
478 Brian McRae	.01	.05
479 Doug Simons	.01	.05
480 Rickey Henderson	.08	.25
481 Gary Varsho	.01	.05
482 Carl Willis	.01	.05
483 Rick Wilkins	.01	.05
484 Donn Pall	.01	.05
485 Edgar Martinez	.05	.15
486 Tom Foley	.01	.05
487 Mark Williamson	.01	.05
488 Jack Armstrong	.01	.05
489 Gary Carter	.02	.10
490 Ruben Sierra	.02	.10
491 Gerald Perry	.01	.05
492 Rob Murphy	.01	.05
493 Zane Smith	.01	.05
494 Darryl Kile	.02	.10
495 Kelly Gruber	.01	.05
496 Jerry Browne	.01	.05
497 Darryl Hamilton	.01	.05
498 Mike Stanton	.01	.05
499 Mark Leonard	.01	.05
500 Jose Canseco	.05	.15
501 Dave Martinez	.01	.05
502 Jose Guzman	.01	.05
503 Terry Kennedy	.01	.05
504 Ed Sprague	.01	.05
505 Frank Thomas UER	.08	.25
(His Gulf Coast League stats are wrong)		
506 Darren Daulton	.02	.10
507 Kevin Tapani	.01	.05
508 Luis Salazar	.01	.05
509 Paul Faries	.01	.05
510 Sandy Alomar Jr.	.01	.05
511 Jeff King	.01	.05
512 Gary Thurman	.01	.05
513 Chris Hammond	.01	.05
514 Pedro Munoz	.01	.05
515 Alan Trammell	.02	.10
516 Geronimo Pena	.01	.05
517 Rodney McCray UER	.01	.05
Stole 6 bases in 1990, not 5; career totals are correct at 7		
518 Manny Lee	.01	.05
519 Junior Felix	.01	.05
520 Kirk Gibson	.02	.10
521 Darrin Jackson	.01	.05
522 John Burkett	.01	.05
523 Jeff Johnson	.01	.05
524 Jim Corsi	.01	.05
525 Robin Yount	.15	.40
526 Jamie Quirk	.01	.05
527 Bob Ojeda	.01	.05
528 Mark Lewis	.01	.05
529 Bryn Smith	.01	.05
530 Kent Hrbek	.02	.10
531 Dennis Boyd	.01	.05
532 Ron Karkovice	.01	.05
533 Don August	.01	.05
534 Todd Frohwirth	.01	.05
535 Wally Joyner	.02	.10
536 Dennis Rasmussen	.01	.05
537 Andy Allanson	.01	.05
538 Rich Gossage	.02	.10
539 John Marzano	.01	.05
540 Cal Ripken	.30	.75
541 Bill Swift UER	.01	.05
(Brewers logo on front)		
542 Kevin Appier	.02	.10
543 Dave Bergman	.01	.05
544 Bernard Gilkey	.01	.05
545 Mike Greenwell	.01	.05
546 Jose Uribe	.01	.05
547 Jesse Orosco	.01	.05
548 Bob Patterson	.01	.05
549 Mike Stanley	.01	.05
550 Howard Johnson	.01	.05
551 Joe Orsulak	.01	.05
552 Dick Schofield	.01	.05
553 Dave Hollins	.01	.05
554 David Segui	.01	.05
555 Barry Bonds	.40	1.00
556 Mo Vaughn	.02	.10
557 Craig Wilson	.01	.05
558 Bobby Rose	.01	.05
559 Rod Nichols	.01	.05
560 Len Dykstra	.02	.10
561 Craig Grebeck	.01	.05
562 Darren Lewis	.01	.05
563 Todd Benzinger	.01	.05
564 Ed Whitson	.01	.05
565 Jesse Barfield	.01	.05
566 Lloyd McClendon	.01	.05
567 Dan Plesac	.01	.05
568 Danny Cox	.01	.05
569 Skeeter Barnes	.01	.05
570 Bobby Thigpen	.01	.05
571 Deion Sanders	.05	.15
572 Chuck Knoblauch	.02	.10
573 Matt Nokes	.01	.05
574 Herm Winningham	.01	.05
575 Tom Candiotti	.01	.05
576 Jeff Bagwell	.08	.25
577 Brook Jacoby	.01	.05
578 Chico Walker	.01	.05
579 Brian Downing	.01	.05
580 Dave Stewart	.02	.10
581 Francisco Cabrera	.01	.05
582 Rene Gonzales	.01	.05
583 Stan Javier	.01	.05
584 Randy Johnson	.08	.25
585 Chuck Finley	.02	.10
586 Mark Gardner	.01	.05
587 Mark Whiten	.01	.05
588 Garry Templeton	.01	.05
589 Gary Sheffield	.02	.10
590 Ozzie Smith	.15	.40
591 Candy Maldonado	.01	.05
592 Mike Sharperson	.01	.05
593 Carlos Martinez	.01	.05
594 Scott Bankhead	.01	.05
595 Tim Wallach	.01	.05
596 Tino Martinez	.05	.15
597 Roger McDowell	.01	.05
598 Cory Snyder	.01	.05
599 Andujar Cedeno	.01	.05
600 Kirby Puckett	.08	.25
601 Rick Parker	.01	.05
602 Todd Hundley	.01	.05
603 Greg Litton	.01	.05
604 Dave Johnson	.01	.05
605 John Franco	.02	.10
606 Mike Fetters	.01	.05
607 Luis Alicea	.01	.05
608 Trevor Wilson	.01	.05
609 Rob Ducey	.01	.05
610 Ramon Martinez	.01	.05
611 Dave Burba	.01	.05
612 Dwight Smith	.01	.05
613 Kevin Maas	.01	.05
614 John Costello	.01	.05
615 Glenn Davis	.01	.05
616 Shawn Abner	.01	.05
617 Scott Hemond	.01	.05
618 Tom Prince	.01	.05
619 Wally Ritchie	.01	.05
620 Jim Abbott	.05	.15
621 Charlie O'Brien	.01	.05
622 Jack Daugherty	.01	.05
623 Tommy Gregg	.01	.05
624 Jeff Shaw	.01	.05
625 Tony Gwynn	.10	.30
626 Mark Leiter	.01	.05
627 Jim Clancy	.01	.05
628 Tim Layana	.01	.05
629 Jeff Schaefer	.01	.05
630 Lee Smith	.02	.10
631 Wade Taylor	.01	.05
632 Mike Simms	.01	.05
633 Terry Steinbach	.01	.05
634 Shawon Dunston	.01	.05
635 Tim Raines	.02	.10
636 Kirt Manwaring	.01	.05
637 Warren Cromartie	.01	.05
638 Luis Quinones	.01	.05
639 Greg Vaughn	.01	.05
640 Kevin Mitchell	.01	.05
641 Chris Hoiles	.01	.05
642 Tom Browning	.01	.05
643 Mitch Webster	.01	.05
644 Steve Olin	.01	.05
645 Tony Fernandez	.01	.05
646 Juan Bell	.01	.05
647 Joe Boever	.01	.05
648 Carney Lansford	.02	.10
649 Mike Benjamin	.01	.05
650 George Brett	.25	.60
651 Tim Burke	.01	.05
652 Jack Morris	.02	.10
653 Orel Hershiser	.02	.10
654 Mike Schooler	.01	.05
655 Andy Van Slyke	.05	.15
656 Dave Stieb	.01	.05
657 Dave Clark	.01	.05
658 Ben McDonald	.01	.05
659 John Smiley	.01	.05
660 Wade Boggs	.05	.15
661 Eric Bullock	.01	.05
662 Eric Show	.01	.05
663 Lenny Webster	.01	.05
664 Mike Huff	.01	.05
665 Rick Sutcliffe	.02	.10
666 Jeff Manto	.01	.05
667 Mike Fitzgerald	.01	.05
668 Matt Young	.01	.05
669 Dave West	.01	.05
670 Mike Hartley	.01	.05
671 Curt Schilling	.05	.15
672 Brian Bohanon	.01	.05
673 Cecil Espy	.01	.05
674 Joe Grahe	.01	.05
675 Sid Fernandez	.01	.05
676 Edwin Nunez	.01	.05
677 Hector Villanueva	.01	.05
678 Sean Berry	.01	.05
679 Dave Eiland	.01	.05
680 David Cone	.02	.10
681 Mike Bordick	.01	.05
682 Tony Castillo	.01	.05
683 John Barfield	.01	.05
684 Jeff Hamilton	.01	.05
685 Ken Dayley	.01	.05
686 Carmelo Martinez	.01	.05
687 Mike Capel	.01	.05
688 Scott Chiamparino	.01	.05
689 Rich Gedman	.01	.05
690 Rich Monteleone	.01	.05
691 Alejandro Pena	.01	.05
692 Oscar Azocar	.01	.05
693 Jim Poole	.01	.05
694 Mike Gardiner	.01	.05
695 Steve Buechele	.01	.05
696 Rudy Seanez	.01	.05
697 Paul Abbott	.01	.05
698 Steve Searcy	.01	.05
699 Jose Offerman	.01	.05
700 Ivan Rodriguez	.08	.25
701 Joe Girardi	.01	.05
702 Tony Perezchica	.01	.05
703 Paul McClellan	.01	.05
704 David Howard	.01	.05
705 Dan Petry	.01	.05
706 Jack Howell	.01	.05
707 Jose Mesa	.01	.05
708 Randy St. Claire	.01	.05
709 Kevin Brown	.02	.10
710 Ron Darling	.01	.05
711 Jason Grimsley	.01	.05
712 John Orton	.01	.05
713 Shawn Boskie	.01	.05
714 Pat Clements	.01	.05
715 Brian Barnes	.01	.05
716 Luis Lopez	.01	.05
717 Bob McClure	.01	.05
718 Mark Davis	.01	.05
719 Dann Bilardello	.01	.05
720 Tom Edens	.01	.05
721 Willie Fraser	.01	.05
722 Curt Young	.01	.05
723 Neal Heaton	.01	.05
724 Craig Worthington	.01	.05
725 Mel Rojas	.01	.05
726 Daryl Irvine	.01	.05
727 Roger Mason	.01	.05
728 Kirk Dressendorfer	.01	.05
729 Scott Aldred	.01	.05
730 Willie Blair	.01	.05
731 Allan Anderson	.01	.05
732 Dana Kiecker	.01	.05
733 Jose Gonzalez	.01	.05
734 Brian Drahman	.01	.05
735 Brad Komminsk	.01	.05
736 Arthur Rhodes	.01	.05
737 Terry Mathews	.01	.05
738 Jeff Fassero	.01	.05
739 Mike Magnante RC	.02	.10
740 Kip Gross	.01	.05
741 Jim Hunter	.01	.05
742 Jose Mota	.01	.05
743 Joe Bitker	.01	.05
744 Tim Mauser	.01	.05
745 Ramon Garcia	.01	.05
746 Rod Beck RC	.08	.25
747 Jim Austin RC	.01	.05
748 Keith Mitchell	.01	.05
749 Wayne Rosenthal	.01	.05
750 Bryan Hickerson RC	.02	.10
751 Bruce Egloff	.01	.05
752 John Wehner	.01	.05
753 Darren Holmes	.01	.05
754 Dave Hansen	.01	.05
755 Mike Mussina	.08	.25
756 Anthony Young	.01	.05
757 Ron Tingley	.01	.05
758 Ricky Bones	.01	.05
759 Mark Wohlers	.01	.05
760 Wilson Alvarez	.01	.05
761 Harvey Pulliam	.01	.05
762 Ryan Bowen	.01	.05
763 Terry Bross	.01	.05
764 Joel Johnston	.01	.05
765 Terry McDaniel	.01	.05
766 Esteban Beltre	.01	.05
767 Rob Maurer	.01	.05
768 Ted Wood	.01	.05
769 Mo Sanford	.01	.05
770 Jeff Carter	.01	.05
771 Gil Heredia RC	.08	.25
772 Monty Fariss	.01	.05
773 Will Clark AS	.02	.10
774 Ryne Sandberg AS	.08	.25
775 Barry Larkin AS	.02	.10
776 Howard Johnson AS	.01	.05
777 Barry Bonds AS	.20	.50
778 Brett Butler AS	.01	.05
779 Tony Gwynn AS	.05	.15
780 Ramon Martinez AS	.01	.05
781 Lee Smith AS	.01	.05
782 Mike Scioscia AS	.01	.05
783 D.Martinez HL UER	.01	.05
Card has both 13th and 15th perfect game in Major League history		
784 Dennis Martinez NH	.01	.05
785 Mark Gardner NH	.01	.05
786 Bret Saberhagen NH	.01	.05
787 Kent Mercker NH	.01	.05
Mark Wohlers		
Alejandro Pena		
788 Cal Ripken MVP	.15	.40
789 Terry Pendleton MVP	.01	.05
790 Roger Clemens CY	.08	.25
791 Tom Glavine CY	.02	.10
792 C.Knoblauch ROY	.01	.05
793 Jeff Bagwell ROY	.05	.15
794 Cal Ripken MANYR	.15	.40
795 David Cone HL	.01	.05
796 Kirby Puckett HL	.05	.15
797 Steve Avery HL	.01	.05
798 Jack Morris HL	.01	.05
799 Allen Watson RC	.02	.10
800 Manny Ramirez RC	1.50	4.00
801 Cliff Floyd RC	.30	.75
802 Al Shirley RC	.02	.10
803 Brian Barber RC	.02	.10
804 Jon Farrell RC	.02	.10
805 Brent Gates RC	.02	.10
806 Scott Ruffcorn RC	.02	.10
807 Tyrone Hill RC	.02	.10
808 Benji Gil RC	.08	.25
809 Aaron Sele RC	.08	.25
810 Tyler Green RC	.02	.10
811 Chris Jones	.01	.05
812 Steve Wilson	.01	.05
813 Freddie Benavides	.01	.05
814 Don Wakamatsu	.01	.05
815 Mike Humphreys	.01	.05
816 Scott Servais	.01	.05
817 Rico Rossy	.01	.05
818 John Ramos	.01	.05
819 Rob Mallicoat	.01	.05
820 Milt Hill	.01	.05
821 Carlos Garcia	.01	.05
822 Stan Royer	.01	.05
823 Jeff Plympton	.01	.05
824 Braulio Castillo	.01	.05
825 David Haas	.01	.05
826 Luis Mercedes	.01	.05
827 Eric Karros	.02	.10
828 Shawn Hare RC	.02	.10
829 Reggie Sanders	.02	.10
830 Tom Goodwin	.01	.05
831 Dan Gakeler	.01	.05
832 Stacy Jones	.01	.05
833 Kim Batiste	.01	.05
834 Cal Eldred	.01	.05
835 Chris George	.01	.05
836 Wayne Housie	.01	.05
837 Mike Ignasiak	.01	.05
838 Josias Manzanillo RC	.02	.10
839 Jim Olander	.01	.05
840 Gary Cooper	.01	.05
841 Royce Clayton	.01	.05
842 Hector Fajardo RC	.02	.10
843 Blaine Beatty	.01	.05
844 Jorge Pedre	.01	.05
845 Kenny Lofton	.05	.15
846 Scott Brosius RC	.20	.50
847 Chris Cron	.01	.05
848 Denis Boucher	.01	.05
849 Kyle Abbott	.01	.05
850 Bob Zupcic RC	.02	.10
851 Rheal Cormier	.01	.05
852 Jimmy Lewis RC	.01	.05
853 Anthony Telford	.01	.05
854 Cliff Brantley	.01	.05
855 Kevin Campbell	.01	.05
856 Craig Shipley	.01	.05
857 Chuck Carr	.01	.05
858 Tony Eusebio	.02	.10
859 Jim Thome	.08	.25
860 Vinny Castilla RC	.40	1.00
861 Dann Howitt	.01	.05
862 Kevin Ward	.01	.05
863 Steve Wapnick	.01	.05
864 Rod Brewer RC	.02	.10
865 Todd Van Poppel	.01	.05
866 Jose Hernandez RC	.08	.25
867 Amalio Carreno	.01	.05
868 Calvin Jones	.01	.05
869 Jeff Gardner	.01	.05
870 Jarvis Brown	.01	.05
871 Eddie Taubensee RC	.08	.25
872 Andy Mota	.01	.05
873 Chris Haney	.01	.05
874 Roberto Hernandez	.01	.05
875 Laddie Renfroe	.01	.05
876 Scott Cooper	.01	.05
877 Armando Reynoso RC	.08	.25
878 Ty Cobb MEMO	.08	.25
879 Babe Ruth MEMO	.20	.50
880 Honus Wagner MEMO	.08	.25
881 Lou Gehrig MEMO	.15	.40
882 Satchel Paige MEMO	.08	.25
883 Will Clark DT	.02	.10
884 Cal Ripken DT	.75	2.00
885 Wade Boggs DT	.02	.10
886 Kirby Puckett DT	.05	.15
887 Tony Gwynn DT	.05	.15
888 Craig Biggio DT	.02	.10
889 Scott Erickson DT	.01	.05
890 Tom Glavine DT	.02	.10
891 Rob Dibble DT	.02	.10
892 Mitch Williams DT	.01	.05
893 Frank Thomas DT	.05	.15
X672 Chuck Knoblauch	10.00	25.00
1990 Score AU/3000		

1992 Score Rookie/Traded

The 1992 Score Rookie and Traded set contains 110 standard-size cards featuring traded veterans and rookies. This set was issued in complete set form and was released through hobby dealers. The set is arranged numerically such that cards 1T-79T are traded players and cards 80T-110T feature rookies. Notable Rookie Cards in this set include Brian Jordan and Jeff Kent.

Card	Low	High
COMP.FACT.SET (110)	3.00	8.00
1T Gary Sheffield	.10	.30
2T Kevin Seitzer	.07	.20
3T Danny Tartabull	.07	.20
4T Steve Sax	.07	.20
5T Bobby Bonilla	.10	.30
6T Frank Viola	.10	.30
7T Dave Winfield	.10	.30
8T Rick Sutcliffe	.10	.30
9T Jose Canseco	.20	.50
10T Greg Swindell	.07	.20
11T Eddie Murray	.30	.75
12T Randy Myers	.07	.20
13T Wally Joyner	.10	.30
14T Kenny Lofton	.20	.50
15T Jack Morris	.10	.30
16T Charlie Hayes	.07	.20
17T Pete Incaviglia	.07	.20
18T Kevin Mitchell	.07	.20
19T Kurt Stillwell	.07	.20
20T Bret Saberhagen	.10	.30
21T Steve Buechele	.07	.20
22T John Smiley	.07	.20
23T Sammy Sosa	.30	.75
24T George Bell	.07	.20
25T Curt Schilling	.20	.50
26T Dick Schofield	.07	.20
27T David Cone	.10	.30
28T Dan Gladden	.07	.20
29T Kirk McCaskill	.07	.20
30T Mike Gallego	.07	.20
31T Kevin McReynolds	.07	.20
32T Bill Swift	.07	.20
33T Dave Martinez	.07	.20
34T Storm Davis	.07	.20
35T Willie Randolph	.10	.30
36T Melido Perez	.07	.20
37T Mark Carreon	.07	.20
38T Doug Jones	.07	.20
39T Gregg Jefferies	.07	.20
40T Mike Jackson	.07	.20
41T Dickie Thon	.07	.20
42T Eric King	.07	.20
43T Herm Winningham	.07	.20
44T Derek Lilliquist	.07	.20
45T Dave Anderson	.07	.20
46T Jeff Reardon	.10	.30
47T Scott Bankhead	.07	.20
48T Cory Snyder	.07	.20
49T Al Newman	.07	.20
50T Keith Miller	.07	.20
51T Dave Burba	.07	.20
52T Bill Pecota	.07	.20
53T Chuck Crim	.07	.20
54T Mariano Duncan	.07	.20
55T Dave Gallagher	.07	.20
56T Chris Gwynn	.07	.20
57T Scott Ruskin	.07	.20
58T Jack Armstrong	.07	.20
59T Gary Carter	.10	.30
60T Andres Galarraga	.10	.30
61T Ken Hill	.07	.20
62T Eric Davis	.10	.30
63T Ruben Sierra	.10	.30
64T Darrin Fletcher	.07	.20
65T Tim Belcher	.07	.20
66T Mike Morgan	.07	.20
67T Scott Scudder	.07	.20
68T Tom Candiotti	.07	.20
69T Hubie Brooks	.07	.20
70T Kal Daniels	.07	.20
71T Bruce Ruffin	.07	.20
72T Billy Hatcher	.07	.20
73T Bob Melvin	.07	.20
74T Lee Guetterman	.07	.20
75T Rene Gonzales	.07	.20
76T Kevin Bass	.07	.20
77T Tom Bolton	.07	.20
78T John Wetteland	.10	.30
79T Bip Roberts	.07	.20
80T Pat Listach RC	.15	.40
81T John Doherty RC	.07	.20
82T Sam Militello	.07	.20
83T Brian Jordan RC	.25	.60
84T Jeff Kent RC	1.25	3.00
85T Dave Fleming	.07	.20
86T Jeff Tackett	.07	.20
87T Chad Curtis RC	.15	.40
88T Eric Fox RC	.07	.20
89T Denny Neagle	.10	.30
90T Donovan Osborne	.07	.20
91T Carlos Hernandez	.07	.20
92T Tim Wakefield RC	1.25	3.00
93T Tim Salmon	.20	.50
94T Dave Nilsson	.07	.20
95T Mike Perez	.07	.20
96T Pat Hentgen	.07	.20
97T Frank Seminara RC	.07	.20
98T Ruben Amaro	.07	.20
99T Archi Cianfrocco RC	.07	.20
100T Andy Stankiewicz	.07	.20
101T Jim Bullinger	.07	.20
102T Pat Mahomes RC	.15	.40
103T Hipolito Pichardo RC	.07	.20
104T Bret Boone	.20	.50
105T John Vander Wal	.07	.20
106T Vince Horsman	.07	.20
107T Jim Austin	.07	.20
108T Brian Williams RC	.07	.20
109T Dan Walters	.07	.20
110T Wil Cordero	.07	.20

1992 Score Rookies

This 40-card boxed set measures the standard size and features glossy color action player photos on a kelly green face with meandering purple stripes.

Card	Low	High
COMP.FACT SET (40)	1.60	4.00
1 Todd Van Poppel	.01	.05
2 Kyle Abbott	.01	.05
3 Derek Bell	.01	.05
4 Jim Thome	.60	1.50
5 Mark Wohlers	.01	.05
6 Todd Hundley	.08	.25
7 Arthur Lee Rhodes	.01	.05
8 John Ramos	.01	.05
9 Chris George	.01	.05
10 Kenny Lofton	.40	1.00
11 Ted Wood	.01	.05
12 Royce Clayton	.01	.05
13 Scott Cooper	.01	.05
14 Anthony Young	.01	.05
15 Joel Johnston	.01	.05
16 Andy Mota	.01	.05
17 Lenny Webster	.01	.05
18 Andy Ashby	.01	.05
19 Jose Mota	.01	.05
20 Tim McIntosh	.01	.05
21 Terry Bross	.01	.05
22 Harvey Pulliam	.01	.05
23 Hector Fajardo	.01	.05
24 Esteban Beltre	.01	.05
25 Gary DiSarcina	.01	.05
26 Mike Humphreys	.01	.05
27 Jarvis Brown	.01	.05
28 Gary Cooper	.01	.05
29 Chris Donnels	.01	.05
30 Monty Fariss	.01	.05
31 Eric Karros	.30	.75
32 Braulio Castillo	.01	.05
33 Cal Eldred	.01	.05
34 Tom Goodwin	.01	.05
35 Reggie Sanders	.20	.50
36 Scott Servais	.01	.05
37 Kim Batiste	.01	.05
38 Eric Wedge	.08	.25
39 Willie Banks	.01	.05
40 Mo Sanford	.01	.05

1993 Score

The 1993 Score baseball set consists of 660 standard-size cards issued in one single series. The cards were distributed in 16-card poly packs and 35-card jumbo superpacks. Topical subsets featured are Award Winners (481-486), Draft Picks (487-501), All-Star Caricature (502-512 [AL], 522-531 [NL]), Highlights (513-519), World Series Highlights (520-521), Dream Team (532-542) and Rookies (sprinkled throughout the set). Rookie Cards in this set include Derek Jeter, Jason Kendall and Shannon Stewart.

Card	Low	High
COMPLETE SET (660)	15.00	40.00
1 Ken Griffey Jr.	.30	.75
2 Gary Sheffield	.07	.20
3 Frank Thomas	.20	.50
4 Ryne Sandberg	.30	.75
5 Larry Walker	.07	.20
6 Cal Ripken Jr.	.60	1.50
7 Roger Clemens	.40	1.00
8 Bobby Bonilla	.07	.20
9 Carlos Baerga	.02	.10
10 Darren Daulton	.07	.20
11 Travis Fryman	.07	.20
12 Andy Van Slyke	.10	.30
13 Jose Canseco	.10	.30
14 Roberto Alomar	.10	.30
15 Tom Glavine	.10	.30
16 Barry Larkin	.10	.30
17 Gregg Jefferies	.02	.10
18 Craig Biggio	.10	.30
19 Shane Mack	.02	.10
20 Brett Butler	.07	.20
21 Dennis Eckersley	.07	.20
22 Will Clark	.10	.30
23 Don Mattingly	.50	1.25
24 Tony Gwynn	.25	.60
25 Ivan Rodriguez	.10	.30
26 Shawon Dunston	.02	.10
27 Mike Mussina	.10	.30
28 Marquis Grissom	.07	.20
29 Charles Nagy	.02	.10
30 Len Dykstra	.07	.20
31 Cecil Fielder	.07	.20
32 Jay Bell	.07	.20
33 B.J. Surhoff	.07	.20
34 Bob Tewksbury	.02	.10
35 Danny Tartabull	.02	.10
36 Terry Pendleton	.07	.20
37 Jack Morris	.07	.20
38 Hal Morris	.02	.10
39 Luis Polonia	.02	.10
40 Ken Caminiti	.07	.20
41 Robin Ventura	.07	.20
42 Darryl Strawberry	.07	.20
43 Wally Joyner	.07	.20
44 Fred McGriff	.10	.30
45 Kevin Tapani	.02	.10
46 Matt Williams	.07	.20
47 Robin Yount	.30	.75
48 Ken Hill	.02	.10
49 Edgar Martinez	.10	.30
50 Mark Grace	.10	.30
51 Juan Gonzalez	.07	.20
52 Curt Schilling	.07	.20
53 Dwight Gooden	.07	.20
54 Chris Hoiles	.02	.10
55 Frank Viola	.07	.20
56 Ray Lankford	.07	.20
57 George Brett	.50	1.25
58 Kenny Lofton	.07	.20
59 Nolan Ryan	.75	2.00
60 Mickey Tettleton	.02	.10
61 John Smoltz	.10	.30
62 Howard Johnson	.02	.10
63 Eric Karros	.07	.20
64 Rick Aguilera	.02	.10
65 Steve Finley	.07	.20
66 Mark Langston	.02	.10
67 Bill Swift	.02	.10
68 John Olerud	.07	.20
69 Kevin McReynolds	.02	.10
70 Jack McDowell	.02	.10
71 Rickey Henderson	.20	.50
72 Brian Harper	.02	.10
73 Mike Morgan	.02	.10
74 Rafael Palmeiro	.10	.30
75 Dennis Martinez	.07	.20
76 Tino Martinez	.10	.30
77 Eddie Murray	.20	.50
78 Ellis Burks	.07	.20
79 John Kruk	.07	.20
80 Gregg Olson	.02	.10
81 Bernard Gilkey	.02	.10
82 Milt Cuyler	.02	.10
83 Mike LaValliere	.02	.10
84 Albert Belle	.07	.20
85 Bip Roberts	.02	.10
86 Melido Perez	.02	.10
87 Otis Nixon	.02	.10
88 Bill Spiers	.02	.10
89 Jeff Bagwell	.10	.30
90 Orel Hershiser	.07	.20
91 Andy Benes	.02	.10
92 Devon White	.07	.20
93 Willie McGee	.07	.20
94 Ozzie Guillen	.07	.20
95 Ivan Calderon	.02	.10
96 Keith Miller	.02	.10
97 Steve Buechele	.02	.10
98 Kent Hrbek	.07	.20
99 Dave Hollins	.02	.10
100 Mike Bordick	.02	.10
101 Randy Tomlin	.02	.10
102 Omar Vizquel	.10	.30
103 Lee Smith	.07	.20
104 Leo Gomez	.02	.10
105 Jose Rijo	.02	.10
106 Mark Whiten	.02	.10
107 Dave Justice	.07	.20
108 Eddie Taubensee	.02	.10
109 Lance Johnson	.02	.10
110 Felix Jose	.02	.10
111 Mike Harkey	.02	.10
112 Randy Milligan	.02	.10
113 Anthony Young	.02	.10
114 Rico Brogna	.02	.10
115 Bret Saberhagen	.07	.20
116 Sandy Alomar Jr.	.02	.10
117 Terry Mulholland	.02	.10
118 Darryl Hamilton	.02	.10
119 Todd Zeile	.02	.10
120 Bernie Williams	.10	.30
121 Zane Smith	.02	.10
122 Derek Bell	.02	.10
123 Deion Sanders	.10	.30
124 Luis Sojo	.02	.10
125 Joe Oliver	.02	.10
126 Craig Grebeck	.02	.10
127 Andujar Cedeno	.02	.10
128 Brian McRae	.02	.10
129 Jose Offerman	.02	.10
130 Pedro Munoz	.02	.10
131 Bud Black	.02	.10
132 Mo Vaughn	.07	.20
133 Bruce Hurst	.02	.10
134 Dave Henderson	.02	.10
135 Tom Pagnozzi	.02	.10
136 Erik Hanson	.02	.10
137 Orlando Merced	.02	.10
138 Dean Palmer	.07	.20
139 John Franco	.07	.20
140 Brady Anderson	.07	.20
141 Ricky Jordan	.02	.10
142 Jeff Blauser	.02	.10
143 Sammy Sosa	.20	.50
144 Bob Walk	.02	.10
145 Delino DeShields	.02	.10
146 Kevin Brown	.07	.20
147 Mark Lemke	.02	.10
148 Chuck Knoblauch	.07	.20
149 Chris Sabo	.02	.10
150 Bobby Witt	.02	.10
151 Luis Gonzalez	.07	.20
152 Ron Karkovice	.02	.10
153 Jeff Brantley	.02	.10
154 Kevin Appier	.07	.20
155 Darrin Jackson	.02	.10
156 Kelly Gruber	.02	.10
157 Royce Clayton	.02	.10
158 Chuck Finley	.07	.20
159 Jeff King	.02	.10
160 Greg Vaughn	.02	.10
161 Geronimo Pena	.02	.10
162 Steve Farr	.02	.10
163 Jose Oquendo	.02	.10
164 Mark Lewis	.02	.10
165 John Wetteland	.07	.20
166 Mike Henneman	.02	.10
167 Todd Hundley	.02	.10
168 Wes Chamberlain	.02	.10
169 Steve Avery	.02	.10
170 Mike Devereaux	.02	.10
171 Reggie Sanders	.07	.20
172 Jay Buhner	.07	.20
173 Eric Anthony	.02	.10
174 John Burkett	.02	.10
175 Tom Candiotti	.02	.10
176 Phil Plantier	.02	.10
177 Doug Henry	.02	.10
178 Scott Leius	.02	.10
179 Kirt Manwaring	.02	.10
180 Jeff Parrett	.02	.10
181 Don Slaught	.02	.10
182 Scott Radinsky	.02	.10
183 Luis Alicea	.02	.10

184 Tom Gordon .02 .10
185 Rick Wilkins .02 .10
186 Todd Stottlemyre .02 .10
187 Moises Alou .07 .20
188 Joe Grahe .02 .10
189 Jeff Kent .20 .50
190 Bill Wegman .02 .10
191 Kim Batiste .02 .10
192 Matt Nokes .02 .10
193 Mark Wohlers .02 .10
194 Paul Sorrento .02 .10
195 Chris Hammond .02 .10
196 Scott Livingstone .02 .10
197 Doug Jones .02 .10
198 Scott Cooper .02 .10
199 Ramon Martinez .02 .10
200 Dave Valle .02 .10
201 Mariano Duncan .02 .10
202 Ben McDonald .02 .10
203 Darren Lewis .02 .10
204 Kenny Rogers .07 .20
205 Manuel Lee .02 .10
206 Scott Erickson .02 .10
207 Dan Gladden .02 .10
208 Bob Welch .02 .10
209 Greg Olson .02 .10
210 Dan Pasqua .02 .10
211 Tim Wallach .02 .10
212 Jeff Montgomery .02 .10
213 Derrick May .02 .10
214 Ed Sprague .02 .10
215 David Haas .02 .10
216 Darrin Fletcher .02 .10
217 Brian Jordan .07 .20
218 Jaime Navarro .02 .10
219 Randy Velarde .02 .10
220 Ron Gant .07 .20
221 Paul Quantrill .02 .10
222 Damion Easley .02 .10
223 Charlie Hough .07 .20
224 Brad Brink .02 .10
225 Barry Manuel .02 .10
226 Kevin Koslofski .02 .10
227 Ryan Thompson .02 .10
228 Mike Munoz .02 .10
229 Dan Wilson .07 .20
230 Peter Hoy .02 .10
231 Pedro Astacio .02 .10
232 Matt Stairs .02 .10
233 Jeff Reboulet .02 .10
234 Manny Alexander .02 .10
235 Willie Banks .02 .10
236 John Jaha .02 .10
237 Scooter Tucker .02 .10
238 Russ Springer .02 .10
239 Paul Miller .02 .10
240 Dan Peltier .02 .10
241 Ozzie Canseco .02 .10
242 Ben Rivera .02 .10
243 John Valentin .02 .10
244 Henry Rodriguez .02 .10
245 Derek Parks .02 .10
246 Carlos Garcia .02 .10
247 Tim Pugh RC .02 .10
248 Melvin Nieves .02 .10
249 Rich Amaral .02 .10
250 Willie Greene .02 .10
251 Tim Scott .02 .10
252 Dave Silvestri .02 .10
253 Rob Mallicoat .02 .10
254 Donald Harris .02 .10
255 Craig Colbert .02 .10
256 Jose Guzman .02 .10
257 Domingo Martinez RC .02 .10
258 William Suero .02 .10
259 Juan Guerrero .02 .10
260 J.T. Snow RC .20 .50
261 Tony Pena .02 .10
262 Tim Fortugno .02 .10
263 Tom Marsh .02 .10
264 Kurt Knudsen .02 .10
265 Tim Costo .02 .10
266 Steve Shifflett .02 .10
267 Billy Ashley .02 .10
268 Jerry Nielsen .02 .10
269 Pete Young .02 .10
270 Johnny Guzman .02 .10
271 Greg Colbrunn .02 .10
272 Jeff Nelson .02 .10
273 Kevin Young .07 .20
274 Jeff Frye .02 .10
275 J.T. Bruett .02 .10
276 Todd Pratt RC .08 .25
277 Mike Butcher .02 .10
278 John Flaherty .02 .10
279 John Patterson .02 .10
280 Eric Hillman .02 .10
281 Bien Figueroa .02 .10
282 Shane Reynolds .02 .10
283 Rich Rowland .02 .10
284 Steve Foster .02 .10
285 Dave Mlicki .02 .10
286 Mike Piazza 1.25 3.00
287 Mike Trombley .02 .10
288 Jim Pena .02 .10
289 Bob Ayrault .02 .10
290 Henry Mercedes .02 .10
291 Bob Wickman .02 .10
292 Jacob Brumfield .02 .10
293 David Hulse RC .02 .10
294 Ryan Klesko .07 .20
295 Doug Linton .02 .10
296 Steve Cooke .02 .10
297 Eddie Zosky .02 .10
298 Gerald Williams .02 .10
299 Jonathan Hurst .02 .10
300 Larry Carter RC .02 .10
301 William Pennyfeather .02 .10
302 Cesar Hernandez .02 .10
303 Steve Hosey .02 .10
304 Blas Minor .02 .10
305 Jeff Grotewold .02 .10
306 Bernardo Brito .02 .10
307 Rafael Bournigal .02 .10
308 Jeff Branson .02 .10
309 Tom Quinlan RC .02 .10
310 Pat Gomez RC .02 .10
311 Sterling Hitchcock RC .08 .25
312 Kent Bottenfield .02 .10
313 Alan Trammell .07 .20
314 Cris Colon .02 .10
315 Paul Wagner .02 .10
316 Matt Maysey .02 .10
317 Mike Stanton .02 .10
318 Rick Trlicek .02 .10
319 Kevin Rogers .02 .10
320 Mark Clark .02 .10
321 Pedro Martinez .40 1.00
322 Al Martin .02 .10
323 Mike Macfarlane .02 .10
324 Rey Sanchez .02 .10
325 Roger Pavlik .02 .10
326 Troy Neel .02 .10
327 Kerry Woodson .02 .10
328 Wayne Kirby .02 .10
329 Ken Ryan RC .08 .25
330 Jesse Levis .02 .10
331 Jim Austin .02 .10
332 Dan Walters .02 .10
333 Brian Williams .02 .10
334 Wil Cordero .02 .10
335 Bret Boone .07 .20
336 Hipolito Pichardo .02 .10
337 Pat Mahomes .02 .10
338 Andy Stankiewicz .02 .10
339 Jim Bullinger .02 .10
340 Archi Cianfrocco .02 .10
341 Ruben Amaro .02 .10
342 Frank Seminara .02 .10
343 Pat Hentgen .02 .10
344 Dave Nilsson .02 .10
345 Mike Perez .02 .10
346 Tim Salmon .10 .30
347 Tim Wakefield .20 .50
348 Carlos Hernandez .02 .10
349 Donovan Osborne .02 .10
350 Denny Neagle .07 .20
351 Sam Militello .02 .10
352 Eric Fox .02 .10
353 John Doherty .02 .10
354 Chad Curtis .02 .10
355 Jeff Tackett .02 .10
356 Dave Fleming .02 .10
357 Pat Listach .02 .10
358 Kevin Wickander .02 .10
359 John Vander Wal .02 .10
360 Arthur Rhodes .02 .10
361 Bob Scanlan .02 .10
362 Bob Zupcic .02 .10
363 Mel Rojas .02 .10
364 Jim Thome .10 .30
365 Bill Pecota .02 .10
366 Mark Carreon .02 .10
367 Mitch Williams .02 .10
368 Cal Eldred .02 .10
369 Stan Belinda .02 .10
370 Pat Kelly .02 .10
371 Rheal Cormier .02 .10
372 Juan Guzman .02 .10
373 Damon Berryhill .02 .10
374 Gary DiSarcina .02 .10
375 Norm Charlton .02 .10
376 Roberto Hernandez .02 .10
377 Scott Kamieniecki .02 .10
378 Rusty Meacham .02 .10
379 Kurt Stillwell .02 .10
380 Lloyd McClendon .02 .10
381 Mark Leonard .02 .10
382 Jerry Browne .02 .10
383 Glenn Davis .02 .10
384 Randy Johnson .20 .50
385 Mike Greenwell .02 .10
386 Scott Chiamparino .02 .10
387 George Bell .02 .10
388 Steve Olin .02 .10
389 Chuck McElroy .02 .10
390 Mark Gardner .02 .10
391 Rod Beck .02 .10
392 Dennis Rasmussen .02 .10
393 Charlie Leibrandt .02 .10
394 Julio Franco .07 .20
395 Pete Harnisch .02 .10
396 Sid Bream .02 .10
397 Milt Thompson .02 .10
398 Glenallen Hill .02 .10
399 Chico Walker .02 .10
400 Alex Cole .02 .10
401 Trevor Wilson .02 .10
402 Jeff Conine .07 .20
403 Kyle Abbott .02 .10
404 Tom Browning .02 .10
405 Jerald Clark .02 .10
406 Vince Horsman .02 .10
407 Kevin Mitchell .02 .10
408 Pete Smith .02 .10
409 Jeff Innis .02 .10
410 Mike Timlin .02 .10
411 Charlie Hayes .02 .10
412 Alex Fernandez .02 .10
413 Jeff Russell .02 .10
414 Jody Reed .02 .10
415 Mickey Morandini .02 .10
416 Darnell Coles .02 .10
417 Xavier Hernandez .02 .10
418 Steve Sax .02 .10
419 Joe Girardi .02 .10
420 Mike Fetters .02 .10
421 Danny Jackson .02 .10
422 Jim Gott .02 .10
423 Tim Belcher .02 .10
424 Jose Mesa .02 .10
425 Junior Felix .02 .10
426 Thomas Howard .02 .10
427 Julio Valera .02 .10
428 Dante Bichette .07 .20
429 Mike Sharperson .02 .10
430 Darryl Kile .07 .20
431 Lonnie Smith .02 .10
432 Monty Fariss .02 .10
433 Reggie Jefferson .02 .10
434 Bob McClure .02 .10
435 Craig Lefferts .02 .10
436 Duane Ward .02 .10
437 Shawn Abner .02 .10
438 Roberto Kelly .02 .10
439 Paul O'Neill .10 .30
440 Alan Mills .02 .10
441 Roger Mason .02 .10
442 Gary Pettis .02 .10
443 Steve Lake .02 .10
444 Gene Larkin .02 .10
445 Larry Andersen .02 .10
446 Doug Dascenzo .02 .10
447 Daryl Boston .02 .10
448 John Candelaria .02 .10
449 Storm Davis .02 .10
450 Tom Edens .02 .10
451 Mike Maddux .02 .10
452 Tim Naehring .02 .10
453 John Orton .02 .10
454 Joey Cora .02 .10
455 Chuck Crim .02 .10
456 Dan Plesac .02 .10
457 Mike Bielecki .02 .10
458 Terry Jorgensen .02 .10
459 John Habyan .02 .10
460 Pete O'Brien .02 .10
461 Jeff Treadway .02 .10
462 Frank Castillo .02 .10
463 Jimmy Jones .02 .10
464 Tommy Greene .02 .10
465 Tracy Woodson .02 .10
466 Rich Rodriguez .02 .10
467 Joe Hesketh .02 .10
468 Greg Myers .02 .10
469 Kirk McCaskill .02 .10
470 Ricky Bones .02 .10
471 Lenny Webster .02 .10
472 Francisco Cabrera .02 .10
473 Turner Ward .02 .10
474 Dwayne Henry .02 .10
475 Al Osuna .02 .10
476 Craig Wilson .02 .10
477 Chris Nabholz .02 .10
478 Rafael Belliard .02 .10
479 Terry Leach .02 .10
480 Tim Teufel .02 .10
481 Dennis Eckersley AW .07 .20
482 Barry Bonds AW .30 .75
483 Dennis Eckersley AW .07 .20
484 Greg Maddux AW .20 .50
485 Pat Listach AW .02 .10
486 Eric Karros AW .07 .20
487 Jamie Arnold DP RC .02 .10
488 B.J. Wallace DP .02 .10
489 Derek Jeter DP RC 8.00 20.00
490 Jason Kendall DP RC .40 1.00
491 Rick Helling DP .02 .10
492 Derek Wallace DP RC .02 .10
493 Sean Lowe DP RC .02 .10
494 S.Stewart DP RC .30 .75
495 Benji Grigsby DP RC .02 .10
496 T.Steverson DP RC .02 .10
497 Dan Serafini DP RC .02 .10
498 Michael Tucker DP .02 .10
499 Chris Roberts DP .02 .10
500 Pete Janicki DP RC .02 .10
501 Jeff Schmidt DP RC .02 .10
502 Edgar Martinez AS .07 .20
503 Omar Vizquel AS .07 .20
504 Ken Griffey Jr. AS .20 .50
505 Kirby Puckett AS .10 .30
506 Joe Carter AS .02 .10
507 Ivan Rodriguez AS .07 .20
508 Jack Morris AS .02 .10
509 Dennis Eckersley AS .02 .10
510 Frank Thomas AS .10 .30
511 Roberto Alomar AS .07 .20
512 Mickey Morandini AS .02 .10
513 Dennis Eckersley HL .07 .20
514 Jeff Reardon HL .02 .10
515 Danny Tartabull HL .02 .10
516 Bip Roberts HL .02 .10
517 George Brett HL .25 .60
518 Robin Yount HL .10 .30
519 Kevin Gross HL .02 .10
520 Ed Sprague WS .02 .10
521 Dave Winfield WS .02 .10
522 Ozzie Smith AS .20 .50
523 Barry Bonds AS .30 .75
524 Andy Van Slyke AS .07 .20
525 Tony Gwynn AS .10 .30
526 Darren Daulton AS .02 .10
527 Greg Maddux AS .20 .50
528 Fred McGriff AS .10 .30
529 Lee Smith AS .02 .10
530 Ryne Sandberg AS .20 .50
531 Gary Sheffield AS .02 .10
532 Ozzie Smith DT .20 .50
533 Kirby Puckett DT .10 .30
534 Gary Sheffield DT .02 .10
535 Andy Van Slyke DT .07 .20
536 Ken Griffey Jr. DT .20 .50
537 Ivan Rodriguez DT .07 .20
538 Charles Nagy DT .02 .10
539 Tom Glavine DT .07 .20
540 Dennis Eckersley DT .07 .20
541 Frank Thomas DT .10 .30
542 Roberto Alomar DT .07 .20
543 Sean Berry .02 .10
544 Mike Schooler .02 .10
545 Chuck Carr .02 .10
546 Lenny Harris .02 .10
547 Gary Scott .02 .10
548 Derek Lilliquist .02 .10
549 Brian Hunter .02 .10
550 Kirby Puckett MOY .10 .30
551 Jim Eisenreich .02 .10
552 Andre Dawson .07 .20
553 David Nied .02 .10
554 Spike Owen .02 .10
555 Greg Gagne .02 .10
556 Sid Fernandez .02 .10
557 Mark McGwire .50 1.25
558 Bryan Harvey .02 .10
559 Harold Reynolds .07 .20
560 Barry Bonds .60 1.50
561 Eric Wedge RC .08 .25
562 Ozzie Smith .30 .75
563 Rick Sutcliffe .07 .20
564 Jeff Reardon .07 .20
565 Alex Arias .02 .10
566 Greg Swindell .02 .10
567 Brook Jacoby .02 .10
568 Pete Incaviglia .02 .10
569 Butch Henry .02 .10
570 Eric Davis .07 .20
571 Kevin Seitzer .02 .10
572 Tony Fernandez .02 .10
573 Steve Reed RC .02 .10
574 Cory Snyder .02 .10
575 Joe Carter .07 .20
576 Greg Maddux .30 .75
577 Bert Blyleven UER (Should say 3701 career strikeouts) .07 .20
578 Kevin Bass .02 .10
579 Carlton Fisk .10 .30
580 Doug Drabek .02 .10
581 Mark Gubicza .02 .10
582 Bobby Thigpen .02 .10
583 Chili Davis .07 .20
584 Scott Bankhead .02 .10
585 Harold Baines .07 .20
586 Eric Young .07 .20
587 Lance Parrish .07 .20
588 Juan Bell .02 .10
589 Bob Ojeda .02 .10
590 Joe Orsulak .02 .10
591 Benito Santiago .07 .20
592 Wade Boggs .10 .30
593 Robby Thompson .02 .10
594 Eric Plunk .02 .10
595 Hensley Meulens .02 .10
596 Lou Whitaker .07 .20
597 Dale Murphy .10 .30
598 Paul Molitor .07 .20
599 Greg W. Harris .02 .10
600 Darren Holmes .02 .10
601 Dave Martinez .02 .10
602 Tom Henke .02 .10
603 Mike Benjamin .02 .10
604 Rene Gonzales .02 .10
605 Roger McDowell .02 .10
606 Kirby Puckett .20 .50
607 Randy Myers .02 .10
608 Ruben Sierra .07 .20
609 Wilson Alvarez .02 .10
610 David Segui .02 .10
611 Juan Samuel .02 .10
612 Tom Brunansky .02 .10
613 Willie Randolph .07 .20
614 Tony Phillips .02 .10
615 Candy Maldonado .02 .10
616 Chris Bosio .02 .10
617 Bret Barberie .02 .10
618 Scott Sanderson .02 .10
619 Ron Darling .02 .10
620 Dave Winfield .07 .20
621 Mike Felder .02 .10
622 Greg Hibbard .02 .10
623 Mike Scioscia .02 .10
624 John Smiley .02 .10
625 Alejandro Pena .02 .10
626 Terry Steinbach .02 .10
627 Freddie Benavides .02 .10
628 Kevin Reimer .02 .10
629 Braulio Castillo .02 .10
630 Dave Stieb .02 .10
631 Dave Magadan .02 .10
632 Scott Fletcher .02 .10
633 Cris Carpenter .02 .10
634 Kevin Maas .02 .10
635 Todd Worrell .02 .10
636 Rob Deer .02 .10
637 Dwight Smith .02 .10
638 Chito Martinez .02 .10
639 Jimmy Key .07 .20
640 Greg A. Harris .02 .10
641 Mike Moore .02 .10
642 Pat Borders .02 .10
643 Bill Gullickson .02 .10
644 Gary Gaetti .07 .20
645 David Howard .02 .10
646 Jim Abbott .10 .30
647 Willie Wilson .02 .10
648 David Wells .07 .20
649 Andres Galarraga .07 .20
650 Vince Coleman .02 .10
651 Rob Dibble .07 .20
652 Frank Tanana .02 .10
653 Steve Decker .02 .10
654 David Cone .07 .20
655 Jack Armstrong .02 .10
656 Dave Stewart .07 .20
657 Billy Hatcher .02 .10
658 Tim Raines .07 .20
659 Walt Weiss .02 .10
660 Jose Lind .02 .10

1993 Score Boys of Summer

Randomly inserted exclusively into one in every four 1993 Score 35-card super packs, cards from this standard-size set feature 30 rookies expected to be the best in their class. Early cards of Pedro Martinez and Mike Piazza highlight this set.

COMPLETE SET (30) 25.00 50.00
RANDOM INSERTS IN JUMBO PACKS
1 Billy Ashley .60 1.50
2 Tim Salmon 1.25 3.00
3 Pedro Martinez 4.00 10.00
4 Luis Mercedes .60 1.50
5 Mike Piazza 4.00 10.00
6 Troy Neel .60 1.50
7 Melvin Nieves .60 1.50
8 Ryan Klesko .75 2.00
9 Ryan Thompson .60 1.50
10 Kevin Young .75 2.00
11 Gerald Williams .60 1.50
12 Willie Greene .60 1.50
13 John Patterson .60 1.50
14 Carlos Garcia .60 1.50
15 Ed Zosky .60 1.50
16 Sean Berry .60 1.50
17 Rico Brogna .60 1.50
18 Larry Carter .60 1.50
19 Bobby Ayala .60 1.50
20 Alan Embree .60 1.50
21 Donald Harris .60 1.50
22 Sterling Hitchcock .75 2.00
23 David Nied .60 1.50
24 Henry Mercedes .60 1.50
25 Ozzie Canseco .60 1.50
26 David Hulse .60 1.50
27 Al Martin .60 1.50
28 Dan Wilson .60 1.50
29 Paul Miller .60 1.50
30 Rich Rowland .60 1.50

1993 Score Franchise

This 28-card set honors the top player on each of the major league teams. These cards were randomly inserted into one in every 24 16-card packs. The set is arranged in alphabetical team order by league, with the exception of cards 29 and 30 which honor a player from the 1993 expansion teams.

COMPLETE SET (28) 50.00 120.00
STATED ODDS 1:24
1 Cal Ripken 10.00 25.00
2 Roger Clemens 6.00 15.00
3 Mark Langston .60 1.50
4 Frank Thomas 3.00 8.00
5 Carlos Baerga .60 1.50
6 Cecil Fielder 1.25 3.00
7 Gregg Jefferies .60 1.50
8 Robin Yount 5.00 12.00
9 Kirby Puckett 3.00 8.00
10 Don Mattingly 8.00 20.00
11 Dennis Eckersley 1.25 3.00
12 Ken Griffey Jr. 5.00 12.00
13 Juan Gonzalez 1.25 3.00
14 Roberto Alomar 2.00 5.00
15 Terry Pendleton 1.25 3.00
16 Ryne Sandberg 5.00 12.00
17 Barry Larkin 2.00 5.00
18 Jeff Bagwell 2.00 5.00
19 Brett Butler 1.25 3.00
20 Larry Walker 1.25 3.00
21 Bobby Bonilla 1.25 3.00
22 Darren Daulton 1.25 3.00
23 Andy Van Slyke 2.00 5.00
24 Ray Lankford 1.25 3.00
25 Gary Sheffield 1.25 3.00
26 Will Clark 2.00 5.00
27 Bryan Harvey .60 1.50
28 David Nied .60 1.50

1993 Score Gold Dream Team

Cards from this 12-card standard-size set feature Score's selection of the best players in baseball at each position. The cards were available only through a mail-in offer. Each card front features sepia tone photos of the players out of uniform, with the exception of Griffey's card (of whom is pictured in his Mariners togs). The photo edges are rounded with an airbrush effect.

COMPLETE SET (12) 2.00 5.00
SETS DISTRIBUTED VIA MAIL-IN OFFER
1 Ozzie Smith .30 .75
2 Kirby Puckett .20 .50
3 Gary Sheffield .07 .20
4 Andy Van Slyke .10 .30
5 Ken Griffey Jr. .30 .75
6 Ivan Rodriguez .10 .30
7 Charles Nagy .02 .10
8 Tom Glavine .10 .30
9 Dennis Eckersley .07 .20
10 Frank Thomas .20 .50
11 Roberto Alomar .10 .30
NNO Header Card .02 .10

1994 Score

The 1994 Score set of 660 standard-size cards was issued in two series of 330. Cards were distributed in 14-card hobby and retail packs. Each pack contained 13 basic cards plus one Gold Rush parallel card. Cards were also distributed in retail Jumbo packs. 4,875 cases of 1994 Score baseball were printed for the hobby. This figure does not take into account additional product printed for retail outlets. Among the subsets are American League stadiums (317-330) and National League stadiums (647-660). Rookie Cards include Trot Nixon and Billy Wagner.

COMPLETE SET (660) 10.00 24.00
COMP.SERIES 1 (330) 5.00 12.00
COMP.SERIES 2 (330) 5.00 12.00
1 Barry Bonds .60 1.50
2 John Olerud .07 .20
3 Ken Griffey Jr. .30 .75
4 Jeff Bagwell .10 .30
5 John Burkett .02 .10
6 Jack McDowell .02 .10
7 Albert Belle .07 .20
8 Andres Galarraga .07 .20
9 Mike Mussina .10 .30
10 Will Clark .10 .30
11 Travis Fryman .07 .20
12 Tony Gwynn .25 .60
13 Robin Yount .30 .75
14 Dave Magadan .02 .10
15 Paul O'Neill .10 .30
16 Ray Lankford .07 .20
17 Damion Easley .02 .10
18 Andy Van Slyke .10 .30
19 Brian McRae .02 .10
20 Ryne Sandberg .30 .75
21 Kirby Puckett .20 .50
22 Dwight Gooden .07 .20
23 Don Mattingly .50 1.25
24 Kevin Mitchell .02 .10
25 Roger Clemens .40 1.00
26 Eric Karros .07 .20
27 Juan Gonzalez .07 .20
28 John Kruk .07 .20
29 Gregg Jefferies .02 .10
30 Tom Glavine .10 .30
31 Ivan Rodriguez .10 .30
32 Jay Bell .07 .20
33 Randy Johnson .20 .50
34 Darren Daulton .07 .20
35 Rickey Henderson .20 .50
36 Eddie Murray .20 .50
37 Brian Harper .02 .10
38 Delino DeShields .02 .10
39 Jose Lind .02 .10
40 Benito Santiago .07 .20
41 Frank Thomas .20 .50
42 Mark Grace .10 .30
43 Roberto Alomar .10 .30
44 Andy Benes .02 .10
45 Luis Polonia .02 .10
46 Brett Butler .07 .20
47 Terry Steinbach .02 .10
48 Craig Biggio .10 .30
49 Greg Vaughn .02 .10
50 Charlie Hayes .02 .10
51 Mickey Tettleton .02 .10
52 Jose Rijo .02 .10
53 Carlos Baerga .02 .10
54 Jeff Blauser .02 .10
55 Leo Gomez .02 .10
56 Bob Tewksbury .02 .10
57 Mo Vaughn .07 .20
58 Orlando Merced .02 .10
59 Tino Martinez .10 .30
60 Lenny Dykstra .07 .20
61 Jose Canseco .10 .30
62 Tony Fernandez .02 .10
63 Donovan Osborne .02 .10
64 Ken Hill .02 .10
65 Kent Hrbek .07 .20
66 Bryan Harvey .02 .10
67 Wally Joyner .07 .20
68 Derrick May .02 .10
69 Lance Johnson .02 .10
70 Willie McGee .07 .20
71 Mark Langston .02 .10
72 Terry Pendleton .07 .20
73 Joe Carter .07 .20
74 Barry Larkin .10 .30
75 Jimmy Key .07 .20
76 Joe Girardi .02 .10
77 B.J. Surhoff .07 .20
78 Pete Harnisch .02 .10
79 Lou Whitaker UER (Milt Cuyler pictured on front) .07 .20
80 Cory Snyder .02 .10
81 Kenny Lofton .07 .20
82 Fred McGriff .10 .30
83 Mike Greenwell .02 .10
84 Mike Perez .02 .10
85 Cal Ripken .60 1.50
86 Don Slaught .02 .10
87 Omar Vizquel .10 .30
88 Curt Schilling .07 .20
89 Chuck Knoblauch .07 .20
90 Moises Alou .07 .20
91 Greg Gagne .02 .10
92 Bret Saberhagen .07 .20
93 Ozzie Guillen .07 .20
94 Matt Williams .07 .20
95 Chad Curtis .02 .10
96 Mike Harkey .02 .10
97 Devon White .07 .20
98 Walt Weiss .02 .10
99 Kevin Brown .07 .20
100 Gary Sheffield .07 .20
101 Wade Boggs .10 .30
102 Orel Hershiser .07 .20
103 Tony Phillips .02 .10
104 Andujar Cedeno .02 .10
105 Bill Spiers .02 .10
106 Otis Nixon .02 .10
107 Felix Fermin .02 .10
108 Bip Roberts .02 .10
109 Dennis Eckersley .07 .20
110 Dante Bichette .07 .20
111 Ben McDonald .02 .10
112 Jim Poole .02 .10
113 John Dopson .02 .10
114 Rob Dibble .07 .20
115 Jeff Treadway .02 .10
116 Ricky Jordan .02 .10
117 Mike Henneman .02 .10
118 Willie Blair .02 .10
119 Doug Henry .02 .10
120 Gerald Perry .02 .10
121 Greg Myers .02 .10
122 John Franco .07 .20
123 Roger Mason .02 .10
124 Chris Hammond .02 .10
125 Hubie Brooks .02 .10
126 Kent Mercker .02 .10
127 Jim Abbott .10 .30
128 Kevin Bass .02 .10
129 Rick Aguilera .02 .10
130 Mitch Webster .02 .10
131 Eric Plunk .02 .10
132 Mark Carreon .02 .10
133 Dave Stewart .07 .20
134 Willie Wilson .02 .10
135 Dave Fleming .02 .10
136 Jeff Tackett .02 .10
137 Geno Petralli .02 .10
138 Gene Harris .02 .10
139 Scott Bankhead .02 .10
140 Trevor Wilson .02 .10
141 Alvaro Espinoza .02 .10
142 Ryan Bowen .02 .10
143 Mike Moore .02 .10
144 Bill Pecota .02 .10
145 Jaime Navarro .02 .10
146 Jack Daugherty .02 .10
147 Bob Wickman .02 .10
148 Chris Jones .02 .10
149 Todd Stottlemyre .02 .10
150 Brian Williams .02 .10
151 Chuck Finley .07 .20
152 Lenny Harris .02 .10
153 Alex Fernandez .02 .10
154 Candy Maldonado .02 .10
155 Jeff Montgomery .02 .10
156 David West .02 .10
157 Mark Williamson .02 .10
158 Milt Thompson .02 .10
159 Ron Darling .02 .10
160 Stan Belinda .02 .10
161 Henry Cotto .02 .10
162 Mel Rojas .02 .10
163 Doug Strange .02 .10
164 Rene Arocha .02 .10
165 Tim Hulett .02 .10
166 Steve Avery .02 .10
167 Jim Thome .10 .30
168 Tom Browning .02 .10
169 Mario Diaz .02 .10
170 Steve Reed .02 .10
171 Scott Livingstone .02 .10
172 Chris Donnels .02 .10
173 John Jaha .02 .10
174 Carlos Hernandez .02 .10
175 Dion James .02 .10
176 Bud Black .02 .10
177 Tony Castillo .02 .10
178 Jose Guzman .02 .10
179 Torey Lovullo .02 .10
180 John Vander Wal .02 .10
181 Mike LaValliere .02 .10
182 Sid Fernandez .02 .10
183 Brent Mayne .02 .10
184 Terry Mulholland .02 .10
185 Willie Banks .02 .10
186 Steve Cooke .02 .10
187 Brent Gates .02 .10
188 Erik Pappas .02 .10
189 Bill Haselman .02 .10
190 Fernando Valenzuela .07 .20
191 Gary Redus .02 .10
192 Danny Darwin .02 .10
193 Mark Portugal .02 .10
194 Derek Lilliquist .02 .10
195 Charlie O'Brien .02 .10
196 Matt Nokes .02 .10
197 Danny Sheaffer .02 .10
198 Bill Gullickson .02 .10
199 Alex Arias .02 .10
200 Mike Fetters .02 .10
201 Brian Jordan .07 .20
202 Joe Grahe .02 .10
203 Tom Candiotti .02 .10
204 Jeremy Hernandez .02 .10
205 Mike Stanton .02 .10
206 David Howard .02 .10
207 Darren Holmes .02 .10
208 Rick Honeycutt .02 .10
209 Danny Jackson .02 .10
210 Rich Amaral .02 .10
211 Blas Minor .02 .10
212 Kenny Rogers .07 .20
213 Jim Leyritz .02 .10
214 Mike Morgan .02 .10
215 Dan Gladden .02 .10
216 Randy Velarde .02 .10
217 Mitch Williams .02 .10
218 Hipolito Pichardo .02 .10
219 Dave Burba .02 .10
220 Wilson Alvarez .02 .10
221 Bob Zupcic .02 .10
222 Francisco Cabrera .02 .10
223 Julio Valera .02 .10
224 Paul Assenmacher .02 .10
225 Jeff Branson .02 .10
226 Todd Frohwirth .02 .10
227 Armando Reynoso .02 .10
228 Rich Rowland .02 .10
229 Freddie Benavides .02 .10
230 Wayne Kirby .02 .10
231 Darryl Kile .07 .20
232 Skeeter Barnes .02 .10
233 Ramon Martinez .02 .10
234 Tom Gordon .02 .10
235 Dave Gallagher .02 .10
236 Ricky Bones .02 .10
237 Larry Andersen .02 .10
238 Pat Meares .02 .10
239 Zane Smith .02 .10
240 Tim Leary .02 .10
241 Phil Clark .02 .10
242 Danny Cox .02 .10
243 Mike Jackson .02 .10
244 Mike Gallego .02 .10
245 Lee Smith .07 .20
246 Todd Jones .02 .10
247 Steve Bedrosian .02 .10
248 Troy Neel .02 .10
249 Jose Bautista .02 .10
250 Steve Frey .02 .10
251 Jeff Reardon .07 .20
252 Stan Javier .02 .10
253 Mo Sanford .02 .10
254 Steve Sax .02 .10
255 Luis Aquino .02 .10
256 Domingo Jean .02 .10
257 Scott Servais .02 .10
258 Brad Pennington .02 .10
259 Dave Hansen .02 .10
260 Rich Gossage .07 .20
261 Jeff Fassero .02 .10
262 Junior Ortiz .02 .10
263 Anthony Young .02 .10
264 Chris Bosio .02 .10
265 Ruben Amaro .02 .10
266 Mark Eichhorn .02 .10
267 Dave Clark .02 .10
268 Gary Thurman .02 .10
269 Les Lancaster .02 .10
270 Jamie Moyer .07 .20
271 Ricky Gutierrez .02 .10
272 Greg A. Harris .02 .10
273 Mike Benjamin .02 .10
274 Gene Nelson .02 .10
275 Damon Berryhill .02 .10
276 Scott Radinsky .02 .10
277 Mike Aldrete .02 .10
278 Jerry DiPoto .02 .10
279 Chris Haney .02 .10
280 Richie Lewis .02 .10

281 Jarvis Brown .02 .10
282 Juan Bell .02 .10
283 Joe Klink .02 .10
284 Graeme Lloyd .02 .10
285 Casey Candaele .02 .10
286 Bob MacDonald .02 .10
287 Mike Sharperson .02 .10
288 Gene Larkin .02 .10
289 Brian Barnes .02 .10
290 David McCarty .02 .10
291 Jeff Innis .02 .10
292 Bob Patterson .02 .10
293 Ben Rivera .02 .10
294 John Habyan .02 .10
295 Rich Rodriguez .02 .10
296 Edwin Nunez .02 .10
297 Rod Brewer .02 .10
298 Mike Timlin .02 .10
299 Jesse Orosco .02 .10
300 Gary Gaetti .07 .20
301 Todd Benzinger .02 .10
302 Jeff Nelson .02 .10
303 Rafael Belliard .02 .10
304 Matt Whiteside .02 .10
305 Vinny Castilla .07 .20
306 Matt Turner .02 .10
307 Eduardo Perez .02 .10
308 Joel Johnston .02 .10
309 Chris Gomez .02 .10
310 Pat Rapp .02 .10
311 Jim Tatum .02 .10
312 Kirk Rueter .02 .10
313 John Flaherty .02 .10
314 Tom Kramer .02 .10
315 Mark Whiten .02 .10
316 Chris Bosio .02 .10
317 Baltimore Orioles CL .02 .10
318 Bos.Red Sox CL UER .02 .10
Viola listed as 316; should be 331
319 California Angels CL .02 .10
320 Chicago White Sox CL .02 .10
321 Cleveland Indians CL .02 .10
322 Detroit Tigers CL .02 .10
323 KC Royals CL .02 .10
324 Milw. Brewers CL .02 .10
325 Minnesota Twins CL .02 .10
326 New York Yankees CL .02 .10
327 Oakland Athletics CL .02 .10
328 Seattle Mariners CL .02 .10
329 Texas Rangers CL .02 .10
330 Toronto Blue Jays CL .02 .10
331 Frank Viola .07 .20
332 Ron Gant .07 .20
333 Charles Nagy .02 .10
334 Roberto Kelly .02 .10
335 Brady Anderson .07 .20
336 Alex Cole .02 .10
337 Alan Trammell .07 .20
338 Derek Bell .02 .10
339 Bernie Williams .10 .30
340 Jose Offerman .02 .10
341 Bill Wegman .02 .10
342 Ken Caminiti .07 .20
343 Pat Borders .02 .10
344 Kirt Manwaring .02 .10
345 Chili Davis .07 .20
346 Steve Buechele .02 .10
347 Robin Ventura .07 .20
348 Teddy Higuera .02 .10
349 Jerry Browne .02 .10
350 Scott Kamieniecki .02 .10
351 Kevin Tapani .02 .10
352 Marquis Grissom .07 .20
353 Jay Buhner .07 .20
354 Dave Hollins .02 .10
355 Dan Wilson .02 .10
356 Bob Walk .02 .10
357 Chris Hoiles .02 .10
358 Todd Zeile .02 .10
359 Kevin Appier .07 .20
360 Chris Sabo .02 .10
361 David Segui .02 .10
362 Jerald Clark .02 .10
363 Tony Pena .02 .10
364 Steve Finley .07 .20
365 Roger Pavlik .02 .10
366 John Smoltz .10 .30
367 Scott Fletcher .02 .10
368 Jody Reed .02 .10
369 David Wells .07 .20
370 Jose Vizcaino .02 .10
371 Pat Listach .02 .10
372 Orestes Destrade .02 .10
373 Danny Tartabull .02 .10
374 Greg W. Harris .02 .10
375 Juan Guzman .02 .10
376 Larry Walker .07 .20
377 Gary DiSarcina .02 .10
378 Bobby Bonilla .07 .20
379 Tim Raines .07 .20
380 Tommy Greene .02 .10
381 Chris Gwynn .02 .10
382 Jeff King .02 .10
383 Shane Mack .02 .10
384 Ozzie Smith .30 .75
385 Eddie Zambrano RC .02 .10
386 Mike Devereaux .02 .10
387 Erik Hanson .02 .10
388 Scott Cooper .02 .10
389 Dean Palmer .07 .20
390 John Wetteland .07 .20
391 Reggie Jefferson .02 .10
392 Mark Lemke .02 .10
393 Cecil Fielder .07 .20
394 Reggie Sanders .07 .20
395 Darryl Hamilton .02 .10
396 Daryl Boston .02 .10
397 Pat Kelly .02 .10
398 Joe Orsulak .02 .10
399 Ed Sprague .02 .10
400 Eric Anthony .02 .10
401 Scott Sanderson .02 .10
402 Jim Gott .02 .10
403 Ron Karkovice .02 .10
404 Phil Plantier .02 .10
405 David Cone .07 .20
406 Robby Thompson .02 .10
407 Dave Winfield .07 .20
408 Dwight Smith .02 .10
409 Ruben Sierra .07 .20
410 Jack Armstrong .02 .10
411 Mike Felder .02 .10
412 Wil Cordero .02 .10
413 Julio Franco .07 .20
414 Howard Johnson .02 .10
415 Mark McLemore .02 .10
416 Pete Incaviglia .02 .10
417 John Valentin .02 .10
418 Tim Wakefield .10 .30
419 Jose Mesa .02 .10
420 Bernard Gilkey .02 .10
421 Kirk Gibson .07 .20
422 Dave Justice .07 .20
423 Tom Brunansky .02 .10
424 John Smiley .02 .10
425 Kevin Maas .02 .10
426 Doug Drabek .02 .10
427 Paul Molitor .07 .20
428 Darryl Strawberry .07 .20
429 Tim Naehring .02 .10
430 Bill Swift .02 .10
431 Ellis Burks .07 .20
432 Greg Hibbard .02 .10
433 Felix Jose .02 .10
434 Bret Barberie .02 .10
435 Pedro Munoz .02 .10
436 Darrin Fletcher .02 .10
437 Bobby Witt .02 .10
438 Wes Chamberlain .02 .10
439 Mackey Sasser .02 .10
440 Mark Whiten .02 .10
441 Harold Reynolds .07 .20
442 Greg Olson .02 .10
443 Billy Hatcher .02 .10
444 Joe Oliver .02 .10
445 Sandy Alomar Jr. .02 .10
446 Tim Wallach .02 .10
447 Karl Rhodes .02 .10
448 Royce Clayton .02 .10
449 Cal Eldred .02 .10
450 Rick Wilkins .02 .10
451 Mike Stanley .02 .10
452 Charlie Hough .07 .20
453 Jack Morris .07 .20
454 Jon Ratliff RC .02 .10
455 Rene Gonzales .02 .10
456 Eddie Taubensee .02 .10
457 Roberto Hernandez .02 .10
458 Todd Hundley .02 .10
459 Mike Macfarlane .02 .10
460 Mickey Morandini .02 .10
461 Scott Erickson .02 .10
462 Lonnie Smith .02 .10
463 Dave Henderson .02 .10
464 Ryan Klesko .07 .20
465 Edgar Martinez .10 .30
466 Tom Pagnozzi .02 .10
467 Charlie Leibrandt .02 .10
468 Brian Anderson RC .08 .25
469 Harold Baines .07 .20
470 Tim Belcher .02 .10
471 Andre Dawson .07 .20
472 Eric Young .02 .10
473 Paul Sorrento .02 .10
474 Luis Gonzalez .07 .20
475 Rob Deer .02 .10
476 Mike Piazza .40 1.00
477 Kevin Reimer .02 .10
478 Jeff Gardner .02 .10
479 Melido Perez .02 .10
480 Darren Lewis .02 .10
481 Duane Ward .02 .10
482 Rey Sanchez .02 .10
483 Mark Lewis .02 .10
484 Jeff Conine .07 .20
485 Joey Cora .02 .10
486 Trot Nixon RC .40 1.00
487 Kevin McReynolds .02 .10
488 Mike Lansing .02 .10
489 Mike Pagliarulo .02 .10
490 Mariano Duncan .02 .10
491 Mike Bordick .02 .10
492 Kevin Young .02 .10
493 Dave Valle .02 .10
494 Wayne Gomes RC .02 .10
495 Rafael Palmeiro .10 .30
496 Deion Sanders .10 .30
497 Rick Sutcliffe .07 .20
498 Randy Milligan .02 .10
499 Carlos Quintana .02 .10
500 Chris Turner .02 .10
501 Thomas Howard .02 .10
502 Greg Swindell .02 .10
503 Chad Kreuter .02 .10
504 Eric Davis .07 .20
505 Dickie Thon .02 .10
506 Matt Drews RC .02 .10
507 Spike Owen .02 .10
508 Rod Beck .02 .10
509 Pat Hentgen .02 .10
510 Sammy Sosa .20 .50
511 J.T. Snow .07 .20
512 Chuck Carr .02 .10
513 Bo Jackson .20 .50
514 Dennis Martinez .07 .20
515 Phil Hiatt .02 .10
516 Jeff Kent .10 .30
517 Brooks Kieschnick RC .02 .10
518 Kirk Presley RC .02 .10
519 Kevin Seitzer .02 .10
520 Carlos Garcia .02 .10
521 Mike Blowers .02 .10
522 Luis Alicea .02 .10
523 David Hulse .02 .10
524 Greg Maddux UER .30 .75
(career strikeout totals listed as 113; should be 1134)
525 Gregg Olson .02 .10
526 Hal Morris .02 .10
527 Daron Kirkreit .02 .10
528 David Nied .02 .10
529 Jeff Russell .02 .10
530 Kevin Gross .02 .10
531 John Doherty .02 .10
532 Matt Brunson RC .02 .10
533 Dave Nilsson .02 .10
534 Randy Myers .02 .10
535 Steve Farr .02 .10
536 Billy Wagner RC .50 1.25
537 Darnell Coles .02 .10
538 Frank Tanana .02 .10
539 Tim Salmon .10 .30
540 Kim Batiste .02 .10
541 George Bell .02 .10
542 Tom Henke .02 .10
543 Sam Horn .02 .10
544 Doug Jones .02 .10
545 Scott Leius .02 .10
546 Al Martin .02 .10
547 Bob Welch .02 .10
548 Scott Christman RC .02 .10
549 Norm Charlton .02 .10
550 Mark McGwire .50 1.25
551 Greg McMichael .02 .10
552 Tim Costo .02 .10
553 Rodney Bolton .02 .10
554 Pedro Martinez .20 .50
555 Marc Valdes .02 .10
556 Darrell Whitmore .02 .10
557 Tim Bogar .02 .10
558 Steve Karsay .02 .10
559 Danny Bautista .02 .10
560 Jeffrey Hammonds .02 .10
561 Aaron Sele .02 .10
562 Russ Springer .02 .10
563 Jason Bere .02 .10
564 Billy Brewer .02 .10
565 Sterling Hitchcock .02 .10
566 Bobby Munoz .02 .10
567 Craig Paquette .02 .10
568 Bret Boone .07 .20
569 Dan Peltier .02 .10
570 Jeromy Burnitz .07 .20
571 John Wasdin RC .02 .10
572 Chipper Jones .20 .50
573 Jamey Wright RC .02 .10
574 Jeff Granger .02 .10
575 Jay Powell RC .02 .10
576 Ryan Thompson .02 .10
577 Lou Frazier .02 .10
578 Paul Wagner .02 .10
579 Brad Ausmus .10 .30
580 Jack Voigt .02 .10
581 Kevin Rogers .02 .10
582 Damon Buford .02 .10
583 Paul Quantrill .02 .10
584 Marc Newfield .02 .10
585 Derrek Lee RC .60 1.50
586 Shane Reynolds .02 .10
587 Cliff Floyd .07 .20
588 Jeff Schwarz .02 .10
589 Ross Powell RC .02 .10
590 Gerald Williams .02 .10
591 Mike Trombley .02 .10
592 Ken Ryan .02 .10
593 John O'Donoghue .02 .10
594 Rod Correia .02 .10
595 Darrell Sherman .02 .10
596 Steve Scarsone .02 .10
597 Sherman Obando .02 .10
598 Kurt Abbott RC .02 .10
599 Dave Telgheder .02 .10
600 Rick Trlicek .02 .10
601 Carl Everett .07 .20
602 Luis Ortiz .02 .10
603 Larry Luebbers .02 .10
604 Kevin Roberson .02 .10
605 Butch Huskey .02 .10
606 Benji Gil .02 .10
607 Todd Van Poppel .02 .10
608 Mark Hutton .02 .10
609 Chip Hale .02 .10
610 Matt Maysey .02 .10
611 Scott Ruffcorn .02 .10
612 Hilly Hathaway .02 .10
613 Allen Watson .02 .10
614 Carlos Delgado .10 .30
615 Roberto Mejia .02 .10
616 Turk Wendell .02 .10
617 Tony Tarasco .02 .10
618 Raul Mondesi .07 .20
619 Kevin Stocker .02 .10
620 Javier Lopez .07 .20
621 Keith Kessinger .02 .10
622 Bob Hamelin .02 .10
623 John Roper .02 .10
624 Lenny Dykstra WS .02 .10
625 Joe Carter WS .02 .10
626 Jim Abbott HL .07 .20
627 Lee Smith HL .02 .10
628 Ken Griffey Jr. HL .20 .50
629 Dave Winfield HL .02 .10
630 Darryl Kile HL .02 .10
631 F.Thomas AL MVP .10 .30
632 Barry Bonds NL MVP .30 .75
633 Jack McDowell AL CY .02 .10
634 Greg Maddux NL CY .20 .50
635 Tim Salmon AL ROY .07 .20
636 Mike Piazza NL ROY .20 .50
637 Brian Turang RC .02 .10
638 Rondell White .07 .20
639 Nigel Wilson .02 .10
640 Torii Hunter RC .40 1.00
641 Salomon Torres .02 .10
642 Kevin Higgins .02 .10
643 Eric Wedge .02 .10
644 Roger Salkeld .02 .10
645 Manny Ramirez .20 .50
646 Jeff McNeely .02 .10
647 Atlanta Braves CL .02 .10
648 Chicago Cubs CL .02 .10
649 Cincinnati Reds CL .02 .10
650 Colorado Rockies CL .02 .10
651 Florida Marlins CL .02 .10
652 Houston Astros CL .02 .10
653 L.A. Dodgers CL .02 .10
654 Montreal Expos CL .02 .10
655 New York Mets CL .02 .10
656 Phi. Phillies CL .02 .10
657 Pittsburgh Pirates CL .02 .10
658 St. Louis Cardinals CL .02 .10
659 San Diego Padres CL .02 .10
660 S.F. Giants CL .02 .10

1994 Score Gold Rush

This 660-card standard-size set is parallel to the basic Score issue. This set features metallicized and gold-bordered fronts. Gold Rush cards came one per 14-card pack or super pack. They were also issued two per jumbo. These cards were inserted into both hobby and retail packs.

COMPLETE SET (660) 60.00 120.00

COMP. SERIES 1 (330) 30.00 60.00
COMP. SERIES 2 (330) 30.00 60.00
*STARS: 1.5X TO 4X BASIC CARDS
*ROOKIES: 1.25X TO 3X BASIC
TWO PER JUMBO

1994 Score Boys of Summer

Randomly inserted in super packs at a rate of one in four, this 60-card set features top young stars and hopefuls. The set was issued in two series of 30 cards.

COMPLETE SET (60) 25.00 60.00
COMPLETE SERIES 1 (30) 10.00 25.00
COMPLETE SERIES 2 (30) 15.00 35.00
STATED ODDS 1:4 SUPER PACKS
1 Jeff Conine .75 2.00
2 Aaron Sele .40 1.00
3 Kevin Stocker .40 1.00
4 Pat Meares .40 1.00
5 Jeromy Burnitz .75 2.00
6 Mike Piazza 3.00 8.00
7 Allen Watson .40 1.00
8 Jeffrey Hammonds .40 1.00
9 Kevin Roberson .40 1.00
10 Hilly Hathaway .40 1.00
11 Kirk Rueter .40 1.00
12 Eduardo Perez .40 1.00
13 Ricky Gutierrez .40 1.00
14 Domingo Jean .40 1.00
15 David Nied .40 1.00
16 Wayne Kirby .40 1.00
17 Mike Lansing .40 1.00
18 Jason Bere .40 1.00
19 Brent Gates .40 1.00
20 Javier Lopez .75 2.00
21 Greg McMichael .40 1.00
22 David Hulse .40 1.00
23 Roberto Mejia .40 1.00
24 Tim Salmon 1.25 3.00
25 Rene Arocha .40 1.00
26 Bret Boone .75 2.00
27 David McCarty .40 1.00
28 Todd Van Poppel .40 1.00
29 Lance Painter .40 1.00
30 Erik Pappas .40 1.00
31 Chuck Carr .40 1.00
32 Mark Hutton .40 1.00
33 Jeff McNeely .40 1.00
34 Willie Greene .40 1.00
35 Nigel Wilson .40 1.00
36 Rondell White .75 2.00
37 Brian Turang .40 1.00
38 Manny Ramirez 2.00 5.00
39 Salomon Torres .40 1.00
40 Melvin Nieves .40 1.00
41 Ryan Klesko .75 2.00
42 Keith Kessinger .40 1.00
43 Brad Ausmus 1.25 3.00
44 Bob Hamelin .40 1.00
45 Carlos Delgado 1.25 3.00
46 Marc Newfield .40 1.00
47 Raul Mondesi .75 2.00
48 Tim Costo .40 1.00
49 Pedro Martinez 2.00 5.00
50 Steve Karsay .40 1.00
51 Danny Bautista .40 1.00
52 Butch Huskey .40 1.00
53 Kurt Abbott .40 1.00
54 Darrell Sherman .40 1.00
55 Damon Buford .40 1.00
56 Ross Powell .40 1.00
57 Darrell Whitmore .40 1.00
58 Chipper Jones 2.00 5.00
59 Jeff Granger .40 1.00
60 Cliff Floyd .75 2.00

1994 Score Cycle

This 20-card set was randomly inserted in second series foil at a rate of one in 72 and jumbo packs at a rate of one in 36. The set is arranged according to players with the most singles (1-5), doubles (6-10), triples (11-15) and home runs (16-20). The cards are number with a "TC" prefix.

COMPLETE SET (20) 60.00 150.00
SER.2 STATED ODDS 1:72, 1:36 JUM
TC1 Brett Butler 2.00 5.00
TC2 Kenny Lofton 2.00 5.00
TC3 Paul Molitor 2.00 5.00
TC4 Carlos Baerga 1.00 2.50
TC5 Gregg Jefferies 1.00 2.50
Tony Phillips
TC6 John Olerud 2.00 5.00
TC7 Charlie Hayes 1.00 2.50
TC8 Lenny Dykstra 2.00 5.00
TC9 Dante Bichette 2.00 5.00
TC10 Devon White 2.00 5.00
TC11 Lance Johnson 1.00 2.50
TC12 Joey Cora 2.00 5.00
Steve Finley
TC13 Tony Fernandez 1.00 2.50
TC14 David Hulse 2.00 5.00
Brett Butler
TC15 Jay Bell 2.00 5.00
Brian McRae
Mickey Morandini
TC16 Juan Gonzalez 15.00 40.00
Barry Bonds
TC17 Ken Griffey Jr. 8.00 20.00
TC18 Frank Thomas 5.00 12.00
TC19 Dave Justice 2.00 5.00
TC20 Matt Williams 2.00 5.00
Albert Belle

1994 Score Dream Team

Randomly inserted in first series foil and jumbo packs at a rate of one in 72, this ten-card set feature's baseball's Dream Team as selected by Pinnacle Brands. Banded by forest green stripes above and below, the player photos on the fronts feature ten of baseball's best players sporting historical team uniforms from the 1930's. A Barry Larkin promo card was distributed to dealers and hobby media to preview the set.

COMPLETE SET (10) 25.00 60.00
SER.1 STATED ODDS 1:72, 1:36 JUM
1 Mike Mussina 3.00 8.00
2 Tom Glavine 3.00 8.00
3 Don Mattingly 12.50 30.00
4 Carlos Baerga 1.00 2.50
5 Barry Larkin 3.00 8.00
6 Matt Williams 2.00 5.00
7 Juan Gonzalez 2.00 5.00
8 Andy Van Slyke 3.00 8.00
9 Larry Walker 2.00 5.00
10 Mike Stanley 1.00 2.50
S5 Barry Larkin Sample .40 1.00

1994 Score Gold Stars

Randomly inserted at a rate of one in every 18 hobby packs, this 60-card set features National and American stars. Split into two series of 30 cards, the first series (1-30) comprises of National League players and the second series (31-60) American Leaguers.

COMPLETE SET (60) 100.00 250.00
COMPLETE NL (30) 40.00 100.00
COMPLETE AL (30) 60.00 150.00
STATED ODDS 1:18 HOBBY
1 Barry Bonds 10.00 25.00
2 Orlando Merced .60 1.50
3 Mark Grace 2.00 5.00
4 Darren Daulton 1.25 3.00
5 Jeff Blauser .60 1.50
6 Deion Sanders 2.00 5.00
7 John Kruk 1.25 3.00
8 Jeff Bagwell 2.00 5.00
9 Gregg Jefferies .60 1.50
10 Matt Williams 1.25 3.00
11 Andres Galarraga 1.25 3.00
12 Jay Bell 1.25 3.00
13 Mike Piazza 6.00 15.00
14 Ron Gant 1.25 3.00
15 Barry Larkin 2.00 5.00
16 Tom Glavine 2.00 5.00
17 Lenny Dykstra 1.25 3.00
18 Fred McGriff 2.00 5.00
19 Andy Van Slyke 2.00 5.00
20 Gary Sheffield 1.25 3.00
21 John Burkett .60 1.50
22 Dante Bichette 1.25 3.00
23 Tony Gwynn 4.00 10.00
24 Dave Justice 1.25 3.00
25 Marquis Grissom 1.25 3.00
26 Bobby Bonilla 1.25 3.00
27 Larry Walker 1.25 3.00
28 Brett Butler 1.25 3.00
29 Robby Thompson .60 1.50
30 Jeff Conine 1.25 3.00
31 Joe Carter 1.25 3.00
32 Ken Griffey Jr. 5.00 12.00
33 Juan Gonzalez 1.25 3.00
34 Rickey Henderson 3.00 8.00
35 Bo Jackson 3.00 8.00
36 Cal Ripken 10.00 25.00
37 John Olerud 1.25 3.00
38 Carlos Baerga .60 1.50
39 Jack McDowell .60 1.50
40 Cecil Fielder 1.25 3.00
41 Kenny Lofton 1.25 3.00
42 Roberto Alomar 2.00 5.00
43 Randy Johnson 3.00 8.00
44 Tim Salmon 2.00 5.00
45 Frank Thomas 3.00 8.00
46 Albert Belle 1.25 3.00
47 Greg Vaughn .60 1.50
48 Travis Fryman 1.25 3.00
49 Don Mattingly 8.00 20.00
50 Wade Boggs 2.00 5.00
51 Mo Vaughn 1.25 3.00
52 Kirby Puckett 3.00 8.00
53 Devon White 1.25 3.00
54 Tony Phillips .60 1.50
55 Brian Harper .60 1.50
56 Chad Curtis .60 1.50
57 Paul Molitor 1.25 3.00
58 Ivan Rodriguez 2.00 5.00
59 Rafael Palmeiro 2.00 5.00
60 Brian McRae .60 1.50

1994 Score Rookie/Traded

The 1994 Score Rookie and Traded set consists of 165 standard-size cards featuring rookie standouts, traded players, and new young prospects. The set is delineated by traded players (RT1-RT70) and rookies/young prospects (RT71-RT163). The set closes with checklists (RT164-RT165). Each foil pack contained one Gold Rush card. The cards are numbered on the back with an "RT" prefix. Several leading dealers are under the belief that Jose Lima's card (number RT158) was short-printed. Conversely, extra cards of John Mabry are typically found in place of the short Lima's. A special unnumbered September Call-Up Redemption card could be exchanged for an Alex Rodriguez card. The expiration date was January 31st, 1995. Odds of finding a redemption card were approximately one in 240 retail and hobby packs. Rookie Cards include Jose Lima and Chan Ho Park.

COMPLETE SET (165) 6.00 15.00
ACTUAL CARD REDEEMED IN 1995
RT1 Will Clark .20 .50
RT2 Lee Smith .10 .30
RT3 Bo Jackson .30 .75
RT4 Ellis Burks .10 .30
RT5 Eddie Murray .30 .75
RT6 Delino DeShields .05 .15
RT7 Erik Hanson .05 .15
RT8 Rafael Palmeiro .20 .50
RT9 Luis Polonia .05 .15
RT10 Omar Vizquel .20 .50
RT11 Kurt Abbott .05 .15
RT12 Vince Coleman .05 .15
RT13 Rickey Henderson .30 .75
RT14 Terry Mulholland .05 .15
RT15 Greg Hibbard .05 .15
RT16 Walt Weiss .05 .15
RT17 Chris Sabo .05 .15
RT18 Dave Henderson .05 .15
RT19 Rick Sutcliffe .10 .30
RT20 Harold Reynolds .10 .30
RT21 Jack Morris .10 .30
RT22 Dan Wilson .05 .15
RT23 Dave Magadan .05 .15
RT24 Dennis Martinez .10 .30
RT25 Wes Chamberlain .05 .15
RT26 Otis Nixon .05 .15
RT27 Eric Anthony .05 .15
RT28 Randy Milligan .05 .15
RT29 Julio Franco .10 .30
RT30 Kevin McReynolds .05 .15
RT31 Anthony Young .05 .15
RT32 Brian Harper .05 .15
RT33 Gene Harris .05 .15
RT34 Eddie Taubensee .05 .15
RT35 David Segui .05 .15
RT36 Stan Javier .05 .15
RT37 Felix Fermin .05 .15
RT38 Darrin Jackson .05 .15
RT39 Tony Fernandez .05 .15
RT40 Jose Vizcaino .05 .15
RT41 Willie Banks .05 .15
RT42 Brian Hunter .05 .15
RT43 Reggie Jefferson .05 .15
RT44 Junior Felix .05 .15
RT45 Jack Armstrong .05 .15
RT46 Bip Roberts .05 .15
RT47 Jerry Browne .05 .15
RT48 Marvin Freeman .05 .15
RT49 Jody Reed .05 .15
RT50 Alex Cole .05 .15
RT51 Sid Fernandez .05 .15
RT52 Pete Smith .05 .15
RT53 Xavier Hernandez .05 .15
RT54 Scott Sanderson .05 .15
RT55 Turner Ward .05 .15
RT56 Rex Hudler .05 .15
RT57 Deion Sanders .20 .50
RT58 Sid Bream .05 .15
RT59 Tony Pena .05 .15
RT60 Bret Boone .10 .30
RT61 Bobby Ayala .05 .15
RT62 Pedro Martinez .30 .75
RT63 Howard Johnson .05 .15
RT64 Mark Portugal .05 .15
RT65 Roberto Kelly .05 .15
RT66 Spike Owen .05 .15
RT67 Jeff Treadway .05 .15
RT68 Mike Harkey .05 .15
RT69 Doug Jones .05 .15
RT70 Steve Farr .05 .15
RT71 Billy Taylor RC .05 .15
RT72 Manny Ramirez .30 .75
RT73 Bob Hamelin .05 .15
RT74 Steve Karsay .05 .15
RT75 Ryan Klesko .10 .30
RT76 Cliff Floyd .10 .30
RT77 Jeffrey Hammonds .05 .15
RT78 Javier Lopez .10 .30
RT79 Roger Salkeld .05 .15
RT80 Hector Carrasco .05 .15
RT81 Gerald Williams .05 .15
RT82 Raul Mondesi .10 .30
RT83 Sterling Hitchcock .05 .15
RT84 Danny Bautista .05 .15
RT85 Chris Turner .05 .15
RT86 Shane Reynolds .05 .15
RT87 Rondell White .10 .30
RT88 Salomon Torres .05 .15
RT89 Turk Wendell .05 .15
RT90 Tony Tarasco .05 .15
RT91 Shawn Green .30 .75
RT92 Greg Colbrunn .05 .15
RT93 Eddie Zambrano .05 .15
RT94 Rich Becker .05 .15
RT95 Chris Gomez .05 .15
RT96 John Patterson .05 .15
RT97 Derek Parks .05 .15
RT98 Rich Rowland .05 .15
RT99 James Mouton .05 .15
RT100 Tim Hyers RC .05 .15
RT101 Jose Valentin .05 .15
RT102 Carlos Delgado .20 .50
RT103 Robert Eenhoorn .05 .15
RT104 John Hudek RC .05 .15
RT105 Domingo Cedeno .05 .15
RT106 Denny Hocking .05 .15
RT107 Greg Pirkl .05 .15
RT108 Mark Smith .05 .15
RT109 Paul Shuey .05 .15
RT110 Jorge Fabregas .05 .15
RT111 Rikkert Faneyte RC .05 .15
RT112 Rob Butler .05 .15
RT113 Darren Oliver RC .10 .30
RT114 Troy O'Leary .05 .15
RT115 Scott Brow .05 .15
RT116 Tony Eusebio .05 .15
RT117 Carlos Reyes .05 .15
RT118 J.R. Phillips .05 .15
RT119 Alex Diaz .05 .15
RT120 Charles Johnson .10 .30
RT121 Nate Minchey .05 .15
RT122 Scott Sanders .05 .15
RT123 Daryl Boston .05 .15
RT124 Joey Hamilton .05 .15
RT125 Brian Anderson .10 .30
RT126 Dan Miceli .05 .15
RT127 Tom Brunansky .05 .15
RT128 Dave Staton .05 .15
RT129 Mike Oquist .05 .15
RT130 John Mabry RC .10 .30
RT131 Norberto Martin .05 .15
RT132 Hector Fajardo .05 .15
RT133 Mark Hutton .05 .15
RT134 Fernando Vina .05 .15
RT135 Lee Tinsley .05 .15
RT136 Chan Ho Park RC .20 .50
RT137 Paul Spoljaric .05 .15
RT138 Matias Carrillo .05 .15
RT139 Mark Kiefer .05 .15
RT140 Stan Royer .05 .15
RT141 Bryan Eversgerd .05 .15
RT142 Brian L. Hunter .05 .15
RT143 Joe Hall .05 .15
RT144 Johnny Ruffin .05 .15
RT145 Alex Gonzalez .05 .15
RT146 Keith Lockhart RC .10 .30
RT147 Tom Marsh .05 .15
RT148 Tony Longmire .05 .15
RT149 Keith Mitchell .05 .15
RT150 Melvin Nieves .05 .15
RT151 Kelly Stinnett RC .05 .15
RT152 Miguel Jimenez .05 .15
RT153 Jeff Juden .05 .15
RT154 Matt Walbeck .05 .15
RT155 Marc Newfield .05 .15
RT156 Matt Mieske .05 .15
RT157 Marcus Moore .05 .15
RT158 Jose Lima SP RC 2.00 5.00
RT159 Mike Kelly .05 .15
RT160 Jim Edmonds .30 .75
RT161 Steve Trachsel .05 .15
RT162 Greg Blosser .05 .15
RT163 Marc Acre RC .05 .15
RT164 AL Checklist .05 .15
RT165 NL Checklist .05 .15
HC1 Alex Rodriguez 150.00 300.00
Call-Up Redemption
NNO Sept. Call-Up Trade EXP .75 2.00

1994 Score Rookie/Traded Gold Rush

Issued one per pack, these cards are a gold foil version of the 165-card Rookie/Traded set. The differences between the basic card and Gold Rush version are the gold foil borders that surround a metallicized player photo. The only difference on the back is a Gold Rush logo.

COMPLETE SET (165) 20.00 50.00
*STARS: 1X TO 2.5X BASIC CARDS
*ROOKIES: 1X TO 2.5X BASIC CARDS

1994 Score Rookie/Traded Changing Places

Randomly inserted in both retail and hobby packs at a rate of one in 36 Rookie/Traded packs, this 10-card standard-size set focuses on ten veteran superstar players who were traded prior to or during the 1994 season. Cards fronts feature a color photo with a slanted design. The backs have a short write-up and a distorted photo.

COMPLETE SET (10) 15.00 30.00
STATED ODDS 1:36 HOB/RET
CP1 Will Clark 2.50 6.00
CP2 Rafael Palmeiro 2.50 6.00
CP3 Roberto Kelly .75 2.00
CP4 Bo Jackson 4.00 10.00
CP5 Otis Nixon .75 2.00
CP6 Rickey Henderson 4.00 10.00
CP7 Ellis Burks 1.50 4.00
CP8 Lee Smith 1.50 4.00
CP9 Delino DeShields .75 2.00
CP10 Deion Sanders 2.50 6.00

1994 Score Rookie/Traded Super Rookies

Randomly inserted in hobby packs at a rate of one in 36, this 18-card standard-size set focuses on top rookies of 1994. Odds of finding one of these cards is approximately one in 36 hobby packs. Designed much like the Gold Rush, the cards have an all-foil design. The fronts have a player photo and the backs have a photo that serves as background to the Super Rookies logo and text.

COMPLETE SET (18) 40.00 80.00
STATED ODDS 1:36 HOBBY
SU1 Carlos Delgado 3.00 8.00
SU2 Manny Ramirez 4.00 10.00
SU3 Ryan Klesko 2.00 5.00
SU4 Raul Mondesi 2.00 5.00
SU5 Bob Hamelin 1.50 4.00
SU6 Steve Karsay 1.50 4.00
SU7 Jeffrey Hammonds 1.50 4.00
SU8 Cliff Floyd 2.00 5.00
SU9 Kurt Abbott 1.50 4.00
SU10 Marc Newfield 1.50 4.00
SU11 Javier Lopez 2.00 5.00
SU12 Rich Becker 1.50 4.00
SU13 Greg Pirkl 1.50 4.00
SU14 Rondell White 2.00 5.00
SU15 James Mouton 1.50 4.00
SU16 Tony Tarasco 1.50 4.00
SU17 Brian Anderson 2.00 5.00
SU18 Jim Edmonds 4.00 10.00

1995 Score

The 1995 Score set consists of 605 standard-size cards issued in hobby, retail and jumbo packs. Hobby packs featured a special signed Ryan Klesko (RG1)card. Retail packs also had a Klesko card (SG1) but these were not signed.

COMPLETE SET (605) 10.00 24.00
COMP. SERIES 1 (330) 5.00 12.00
COMP. SERIES 2 (275) 5.00 12.00
1 Frank Thomas .20 .50
2 Roberto Alomar .10 .30

3 Cal Ripken .60 1.50
4 Jose Canseco .10 .30
5 Matt Williams .07 .20
6 Esteban Beltre .02 .10
7 Domingo Cedeno .02 .10
8 John Valentin .02 .10
9 Glenallen Hill .02 .10
10 Rafael Belliard .02 .10
11 Randy Myers .02 .10
12 Mo Vaughn .07 .20
13 Hector Carrasco .02 .10
14 Chili Davis .07 .20
15 Dante Bichette .07 .20
16 Darrin Jackson .02 .10
17 Mike Piazza .30 .75
18 Junior Felix .02 .10
19 Moises Alou .07 .20
20 Mark Gubicza .02 .10
21 Bret Saberhagen .07 .20
22 Lenny Dykstra .07 .20
23 Steve Howe .02 .10
24 Mark Dewey .02 .10
25 Brian Harper .02 .10
26 Ozzie Smith .30 .75
27 Scott Erickson .02 .10
28 Tony Gwynn .25 .60
29 Bob Welch .02 .10
30 Barry Bonds .60 1.50
31 Leo Gomez .02 .10
32 Greg Maddux .30 .75
33 Mike Greenwell .02 .10
34 Sammy Sosa .20 .50
35 Darnell Coles .02 .10
36 Tommy Greene .02 .10
37 Will Clark .10 .30
38 Steve Ontiveros .02 .10
39 Stan Javier .02 .10
40 Bip Roberts .02 .10
41 Paul O'Neill .10 .30
42 Bill Haselman .02 .10
43 Shane Mack .02 .10
44 Orlando Merced .02 .10
45 Kevin Seitzer .02 .10
46 Trevor Hoffman .07 .20
47 Greg Gagne .02 .10
48 Jeff Kent .07 .20
49 Tony Phillips .02 .10
50 Ken Hill .02 .10
51 Carlos Baerga .02 .10
52 Henry Rodriguez .02 .10
53 Scott Sanderson .02 .10
54 Jeff Conine .07 .20
55 Chris Turner .02 .10
56 Ken Caminiti .07 .20
57 Harold Baines .07 .20
58 Charlie Hayes .02 .10
59 Roberto Kelly .02 .10
60 John Olerud .07 .20
61 Tim Davis .02 .10
62 Rich Rowland .02 .10
63 Rey Sanchez .02 .10
64 Junior Ortiz .02 .10
65 Ricky Gutierrez .02 .10
66 Rex Hudler .02 .10
67 Johnny Ruffin .02 .10
68 Jay Buhner .07 .20
69 Tom Pagnozzi .02 .10
70 Julio Franco .07 .20
71 Eric Young .02 .10
72 Mike Bordick .02 .10
73 Don Slaught .02 .10
74 Goose Gossage .07 .20
75 Lonnie Smith .02 .10
76 Jimmy Key .07 .20
77 Dave Hollins .02 .10
78 Mickey Tettleton .02 .10
79 Luis Gonzalez .07 .20
80 Dave Winfield .07 .20
81 Ryan Thompson .02 .10
82 Felix Jose .02 .10
83 Rusty Meacham .02 .10
84 Darryl Hamilton .02 .10
85 John Wetteland .07 .20
86 Tom Brunansky .02 .10
87 Mark Lemke .02 .10
88 Spike Owen .02 .10
89 Shawon Dunston .02 .10
90 Wilson Alvarez .02 .10
91 Lee Smith .07 .20
92 Scott Kamieniecki .02 .10
93 Jacob Brumfield .02 .10
94 Kirk Gibson .07 .20
95 Joe Girardi .02 .10
96 Mike Macfarlane .02 .10
97 Greg Colbrunn .02 .10
98 Ricky Bones .02 .10
99 Delino DeShields .02 .10
100 Pat Meares .02 .10
101 Jeff Fassero .02 .10
102 Jim Leyritz .02 .10
103 Gary Redus .02 .10
104 Terry Steinbach .02 .10
105 Kevin McReynolds .02 .10
106 Felix Fermin .02 .10
107 Danny Jackson .02 .10
108 Chris James .02 .10
109 Jeff King .02 .10
110 Pat Hentgen .02 .10
111 Gerald Perry .02 .10
112 Tim Raines .07 .20
113 Eddie Williams .02 .10
114 Jamie Moyer .07 .20
115 Bud Black .02 .10
116 Chris Gomez .02 .10
117 Luis Lopez .02 .10
118 Roger Clemens .40 1.00
119 Javier Lopez .07 .20
120 Dave Nilsson .02 .10
121 Karl Rhodes .02 .10
122 Rick Aguilera .02 .10
123 Tony Fernandez .02 .10
124 Bernie Williams .10 .30
125 James Mouton .02 .10
126 Mark Langston .02 .10
127 Mike Lansing .02 .10
128 Tino Martinez .10 .30
129 Joe Orsulak .02 .10
130 David Hulse .02 .10
131 Pete Incaviglia .02 .10
132 Mark Clark .02 .10
100 Tony Eusebio .02 .10
134 Chuck Finley .07 .20
135 Lou Frazier .02 .10
136 Craig Grebeck .02 .10
137 Kelly Stinnett .02 .10
138 Paul Shuey .02 .10
139 David Nied .02 .10
140 Billy Brewer .02 .10
141 Dave Weathers .02 .10
142 Scott Leius .02 .10
143 Brian Jordan .07 .20
144 Melido Perez .02 .10
145 Tony Tarasco .02 .10
146 Dan Wilson .02 .10
147 Rondell White .07 .20
148 Mike Henneman .02 .10
149 Brian Johnson .02 .10
150 Tom Henke .02 .10
151 John Patterson .02 .10
152 Bobby Witt .02 .10
153 Eddie Taubensee .02 .10
154 Pat Borders .02 .10
155 Ramon Martinez .02 .10
156 Mike Kingery .02 .10
157 Zane Smith .02 .10
158 Benito Santiago .07 .20
159 Matias Carrillo .02 .10
160 Scott Brosius .07 .20
161 Dave Clark .02 .10
162 Mark McLemore .02 .10
163 Curt Schilling .07 .20
164 J.T. Snow .07 .20
165 Rod Beck .02 .10
166 Scott Fletcher .02 .10
167 Bob Tewksbury .02 .10
168 Mike LaValliere .02 .10
169 Dave Hansen .02 .10
170 Pedro Martinez .10 .30
171 Kirk Rueter .02 .10
172 Jose Lind .02 .10
173 Luis Alicea .02 .10
174 Mike Moore .02 .10
175 Andy Ashby .02 .10
176 Jody Reed .02 .10
177 Darryl Kile .07 .20
178 Carl Willis .02 .10
179 Jeromy Burnitz .07 .20
180 Mike Gallego .02 .10
181 Bill VanLandingham .02 .10
182 Sid Fernandez .02 .10
183 Kim Batiste .02 .10
184 Greg Myers .02 .10
185 Steve Avery .02 .10
186 Steve Farr .02 .10
187 Robb Nen .07 .20
188 Dan Pasqua .02 .10
189 Bruce Ruffin .02 .10
190 Jose Valentin .02 .10
191 Willie Banks .02 .10
192 Mike Aldrete .02 .10
193 Randy Milligan .02 .10
194 Steve Karsay .02 .10
195 Mike Stanley .02 .10
196 Jose Mesa .02 .10
197 Tom Browning .02 .10
198 John Vander Wal .02 .10
199 Kevin Brown .07 .20
200 Mike Oquist .02 .10
201 Greg Swindell .02 .10
202 Eddie Zambrano .02 .10
203 Joe Boever .02 .10
204 Gary Varsho .02 .10
205 Chris Gwynn .02 .10
206 David Howard .02 .10
207 Jerome Walton .02 .10
208 Danny Darwin .02 .10
209 Darryl Strawberry .07 .20
210 Todd Van Poppel .02 .10
211 Scott Livingstone .02 .10
212 Dave Fleming .02 .10
213 Todd Worrell .02 .10
214 Carlos Delgado .07 .20
215 Bill Pecota .02 .10
216 Jim Lindeman .02 .10
217 Rick White .02 .10
218 Jose Oquendo .02 .10
219 Tony Castillo .02 .10
220 Fernando Vina .02 .10
221 Jeff Bagwell .10 .30
222 Randy Johnson .20 .50
223 Albert Belle .07 .20
224 Chuck Carr .02 .10
225 Mark Leiter .02 .10
226 Hal Morris .02 .10
227 Robin Ventura .07 .20
228 Mike Munoz .02 .10
229 Jim Thome .10 .30
230 Mario Diaz .02 .10
231 John Doherty .02 .10
232 Bobby Jones .02 .10
233 Raul Mondesi .07 .20
234 Ricky Jordan .02 .10
235 John Jaha .02 .10
236 Carlos Garcia .02 .10
237 Kirby Puckett .20 .50
238 Orel Hershiser .07 .20
239 Don Mattingly .50 1.25
240 Sid Bream .02 .10
241 Brent Gates .02 .10
242 Tony Longmire .02 .10
243 Robby Thompson .02 .10
244 Rick Sutcliffe .07 .20
245 Dean Palmer .07 .20
246 Marquis Grissom .07 .20
247 Paul Molitor .07 .20
248 Mark Carreon .02 .10
249 Jack Voigt .02 .10
250 Greg McMichael UER .02 .10
(photo on front is Mike Stanton)
251 Damon Berryhill .02 .10
252 Brian Dorsett .02 .10
253 Jim Edmonds .10 .30
254 Barry Larkin .10 .30
255 Jack McDowell .02 .10
256 Wally Joyner .07 .20
257 Eddie Murray .20 .50
258 Lenny Webster .02 .10
259 Milt Cuyler .02 .10
260 Todd Benzinger .02 .10
261 Vince Coleman .02 .10
262 Todd Stottlemyre .02 .10
263 Turner Ward .02 .10
264 Ray Lankford .07 .20
265 Matt Walbeck .02 .10
266 Deion Sanders .10 .30
267 Gerald Williams .02 .10
268 Jim Gott .02 .10
269 Jeff Frye .02 .10
270 Jose Rijo .02 .10
271 Dave Justice .07 .20
272 Ismael Valdes .02 .10
273 Ben McDonald .02 .10
274 Darren Lewis .02 .10
275 Graeme Lloyd .02 .10
276 Luis Ortiz .02 .10
277 Julian Tavarez .02 .10
278 Mark Dalesandro .02 .10
279 Brett Merriman .02 .10
280 Ricky Bottalico .02 .10
281 Robert Eenhoorn .02 .10
282 Rikkert Faneyte .02 .10
283 Mike Kelly .02 .10
284 Mark Smith .02 .10
285 Turk Wendell .02 .10
286 Greg Blosser .02 .10
287 Garey Ingram .02 .10
288 Jorge Fabregas .02 .10
289 Blaise Ilsley .02 .10
290 Joe Hall .02 .10
291 Orlando Miller .02 .10
292 Jose Lima .02 .10
293 Greg O'Halloran RC .02 .10
294 Mark Kiefer .02 .10
295 Jose Oliva .02 .10
296 Rich Becker .02 .10
297 Brian L. Hunter .02 .10
298 Dave Silvestri .02 .10
299 Armando Benitez .02 .10
300 Darren Dreifort .02 .10
301 John Mabry .02 .10
302 Greg Pirkl .02 .10
303 J.R. Phillips .02 .10
304 Shawn Green .07 .20
305 Roberto Petagine .02 .10
306 Keith Lockhart .02 .10
307 Jonathan Hurst .02 .10
308 Paul Spoljaric .02 .10
309 Mike Lieberthal .07 .20
310 Garret Anderson .07 .20
311 John Johnstone .02 .10
312 Alex Rodriguez .50 1.25
313 Kent Mercker HL .02 .10
314 John Valentin HL .02 .10
315 Kenny Rogers HL .07 .20
316 Fred McGriff HL .07 .20
317 Team Checklists .02 .10
318 Team Checklists .02 .10
319 Team Checklists .02 .10
320 Team Checklists .02 .10
321 Team Checklists .02 .10
322 Team Checklists .02 .10
323 Team Checklists .02 .10
324 Team Checklists .02 .10
325 Team Checklists .02 .10
326 Team Checklists .02 .10
327 Team Checklists .02 .10
328 Team Checklists .02 .10
329 Team Checklists .02 .10
330 Team Checklists .02 .10
331 Pedro Munoz .02 .10
332 Ryan Klesko .07 .20
333 Andre Dawson .07 .20
334 Derrick May .02 .10
335 Aaron Sele .02 .10
336 Kevin Mitchell .02 .10
337 Steve Trachsel .02 .10
338 Andres Galarraga .07 .20
339 Terry Pendleton .07 .20
340 Gary Sheffield .07 .20
341 Travis Fryman .07 .20
342 Bo Jackson .20 .50
343 Gary Gaetti .07 .20
344 Brett Butler .07 .20
345 B.J. Surhoff .07 .20
346 Larry Walker .07 .20
347 Kevin Tapani .02 .10
348 Rick Wilkins .02 .10
349 Wade Boggs .10 .30
350 Mariano Duncan .02 .10
351 Ruben Sierra .07 .20
352 Andy Van Slyke .10 .30
353 Reggie Jefferson .02 .10
354 Gregg Jefferies .02 .10
355 Tim Naehring .02 .10
356 John Roper .02 .10
357 Joe Carter .07 .20
358 Kurt Abbott .02 .10
359 Lenny Harris .02 .10
360 Lance Johnson .02 .10
361 Brian Anderson .02 .10
362 Jim Eisenreich .02 .10
363 Jerry Browne .02 .10
364 Mark Grace .10 .30
365 Devon White .07 .20
366 Reggie Sanders .07 .20
367 Ivan Rodriguez .10 .30
368 Kirt Manwaring .02 .10
369 Pat Kelly .02 .10
370 Ellis Burks .07 .20
371 Charles Nagy .02 .10
372 Kevin Bass .02 .10
373 Lou Whitaker .07 .20
374 Rene Arocha .02 .10
375 Derek Parks .02 .10
376 Mark Whiten .02 .10
377 Mark McGwire .50 1.25
378 Doug Drabek .02 .10
379 Greg Vaughn .02 .10
380 Al Martin .02 .10
381 Ron Darling .02 .10
382 Tim Wallach .02 .10
383 Alan Trammell .07 .20
384 Randy Velarde .02 .10
385 Chris Sabo .02 .10
386 Wil Cordero .02 .10
387 Darrin Fletcher .02 .10
388 David Segui .02 .10
389 Steve Buechele .02 .10
390 Dave Gallagher .02 .10
391 Thomas Howard .02 .10
392 Chad Curtis .02 .10
393 Cal Eldred .02 .10
394 Jason Bere .02 .10
395 Bret Barberie .02 .10
396 Paul Sorrento .02 .10
397 Steve Finley .07 .20
398 Cecil Fielder .07 .20
399 Eric Karros .07 .20
400 Jeff Montgomery .02 .10
401 Cliff Floyd .07 .20
402 Matt Mieske .02 .10
403 Brian Hunter .02 .10
404 Alex Cole .02 .10
405 Kevin Stocker .02 .10
406 Eric Davis .07 .20
407 Marvin Freeman .02 .10
408 Dennis Eckersley .07 .20
409 Todd Zeile .02 .10
410 Keith Mitchell .02 .10
411 Andy Benes .02 .10
412 Juan Bell .02 .10
413 Royce Clayton .02 .10
414 Ed Sprague .02 .10
415 Mike Mussina .10 .30
416 Todd Hundley .02 .10
417 Pat Listach .02 .10
418 Joe Oliver .02 .10
419 Rafael Palmeiro .10 .30
420 Tim Salmon .10 .30
421 Brady Anderson .07 .20
422 Kenny Lofton .07 .20
423 Craig Biggio .10 .30
424 Bobby Bonilla .07 .20
425 Kenny Rogers .07 .20
426 Derek Bell .02 .10
427 Scott Cooper .02 .10
428 Ozzie Guillen .07 .20
429 Omar Vizquel .10 .30
430 Phil Plantier .02 .10
431 Chuck Knoblauch .07 .20
432 Darren Daulton .07 .20
433 Bob Hamelin .02 .10
434 Tom Glavine .10 .30
435 Walt Weiss .02 .10
436 Jose Vizcaino .02 .10
437 Ken Griffey Jr. .30 .75
438 Jay Bell .07 .20
439 Juan Gonzalez .07 .20
440 Jeff Blauser .02 .10
441 Rickey Henderson .20 .50
442 Bobby Ayala .02 .10
443 David Cone .07 .20
444 Pedro Martinez .10 .30
445 Manny Ramirez .10 .30
446 Mark Portugal .02 .10
447 Damion Easley .02 .10
448 Gary DiSarcina .02 .10
449 Roberto Hernandez .02 .10
450 Jeffrey Hammonds .02 .10
451 Jeff Treadway .02 .10
452 Jim Abbott .10 .30
453 Carlos Rodriguez .02 .10
454 Joey Cora .02 .10
455 Bret Boone .07 .20
456 Danny Tartabull .02 .10
457 John Franco .07 .20
458 Roger Salkeld .02 .10
459 Fred McGriff .10 .30
460 Pedro Astacio .02 .10
461 Jon Lieber .02 .10
462 Luis Polonia .02 .10
463 Geronimo Pena .02 .10
464 Tom Gordon .02 .10
465 Brad Ausmus .07 .20
466 Willie McGee .07 .20
467 Doug Jones .02 .10
468 John Smoltz .10 .30
469 Troy Neel .02 .10
470 Luis Sojo .02 .10
471 John Smiley .02 .10
472 Rafael Bournigal .02 .10
473 Bill Taylor .02 .10
474 Juan Guzman .02 .10
475 Dave Magadan .02 .10
476 Mike Devereaux .02 .10
477 Andujar Cedeno .02 .10
478 Edgar Martinez .10 .30
479 Milt Thompson .02 .10
480 Allen Watson .02 .10
481 Ron Karkovice .02 .10
482 Joey Hamilton .02 .10
483 Vinny Castilla .07 .20
484 Tim Belcher .02 .10
485 Bernard Gilkey .02 .10
486 Scott Servais .02 .10
487 Cory Snyder .02 .10
488 Mel Rojas .02 .10
489 Carlos Reyes .02 .10
490 Chip Hale .02 .10
491 Bill Swift .02 .10
492 Pat Rapp .02 .10
493 Brian McRae .02 .10
494 Mickey Morandini .02 .10
495 Tony Pena .02 .10
496 Danny Bautista .02 .10
497 Armando Reynoso .02 .10
498 Ken Ryan .02 .10
499 Billy Ripken .02 .10
500 Pat Mahomes .02 .10
501 Mark Acre .02 .10
502 Geronimo Berroa .02 .10
503 Norberto Martin .02 .10
504 Chad Kreuter .02 .10
505 Howard Johnson .02 .10
506 Eric Anthony .02 .10
507 Mark Wohlers .02 .10
508 Scott Sanders .02 .10
509 Pete Harnisch .02 .10
510 Wes Chamberlain .02 .10
511 Tom Candiotti .02 .10
512 Albie Lopez .02 .10
513 Denny Neagle .07 .20
514 Sean Berry .02 .10
515 Billy Hatcher .02 .10
516 Todd Jones .02 .10
517 Wayne Kirby .02 .10
518 Butch Henry .02 .10
519 Sandy Alomar Jr. .02 .10
520 Kevin Appier .07 .20
521 Roberto Mejia .02 .10
522 Steve Cooke .02 .10
523 Terry Shumpert .02 .10
524 Mike Jackson .02 .10
525 Kent Mercker .02 .10
526 David Wells .07 .20
527 Juan Samuel .02 .10
528 Salomon Torres .02 .10
529 Duane Ward .02 .10
530 Rob Dibble .07 .20
531 Mike Blowers .02 .10
532 Mark Eichhorn .02 .10
533 Alex Diaz .02 .10
534 Dan Miceli .02 .10
535 Jeff Branson .02 .10
536 Dave Stevens .02 .10
537 Charlie O'Brien .02 .10
538 Shane Reynolds .02 .10
539 Rich Amaral .02 .10
540 Rusty Greer .07 .20
541 Alex Arias .02 .10
542 Eric Plunk .02 .10
543 John Hudek .02 .10
544 Kirk McCaskill .02 .10
545 Jeff Reboulet .02 .10
546 Sterling Hitchcock .02 .10
547 Warren Newson .02 .10
548 Bryan Harvey .02 .10
549 Mike Huff .02 .10
550 Lance Parrish .07 .20
551 Ken Griffey Jr. HIT .20 .50
552 Matt Williams HIT .02 .10
553 R.Alomar HIT UER .07 .20
Card says he's a NL All-Star
He plays in the AL
554 Jeff Bagwell HIT .07 .20
555 Dave Justice HIT .02 .10
556 Cal Ripken Jr. HIT .30 .75
557 Albert Belle HIT .02 .10
558 Mike Piazza HIT .15 .40
559 Kirby Puckett HIT .10 .30
560 Wade Boggs HIT .07 .20
561 Tony Gwynn HIT UER .10 .30
card has him winning AL batting titles
he's played whole career in the NL
562 Barry Bonds HIT .30 .75
563 Mo Vaughn HIT .02 .10
564 Don Mattingly HIT .25 .60
565 Carlos Baerga HIT .02 .10
566 Paul Molitor HIT .02 .10
567 Raul Mondesi HIT .02 .10
568 Manny Ramirez HIT .07 .20
569 Alex Rodriguez HIT .20 .50
570 Will Clark HIT .07 .20
571 Frank Thomas HIT .10 .30
572 Moises Alou HIT .02 .10
573 Jeff Conine HIT .02 .10
574 Joe Ausanio .02 .10
575 Charles Johnson .07 .20
576 Ernie Young .02 .10
577 Jeff Granger .02 .10
578 Robert Perez .02 .10
579 Melvin Nieves .02 .10
580 Gar Finnvold .02 .10
581 Duane Singleton .02 .10
582 Chan Ho Park .07 .20
583 Fausto Cruz .02 .10
584 Dave Staton .02 .10
585 Denny Hocking .02 .10
586 Nate Minchey .02 .10
587 Marc Newfield .02 .10
588 Jayhawk Owens UER .02 .10
Front Photo is Jim Tatum
589 Darren Bragg .02 .10
590 Kevin King .02 .10
591 Kurt Miller .02 .10
592 Aaron Small .02 .10
593 Troy O'Leary .02 .10
594 Phil Stidham .02 .10
595 Steve Dunn .02 .10
596 Cory Bailey .02 .10
597 Alex Gonzalez .02 .10
598 Jim Bowie RC .02 .10
599 Jeff Cirillo .02 .10
600 Mark Hutton .02 .10
601 Russ Davis .02 .10
602 Checklist .02 .10
603 Checklist .02 .10
604 Checklist .02 .10
605 Checklist .02 .10
RG1 R.Klesko Rook.Great. .40 1.00
SG1 Ryan Klesko AU/6100 4.00 10.00

1995 Score Gold Rush

Parallel to the basic Score issue, these cards were inserted one per foil pack and two per jumbo pack. The fronts were printed in gold foil and the backs contain the Gold Rush logo. As part of the Gold Rush program, one Platinum Team Redemption card was randomly inserted in Score packs at a rate of one in 36. This redemption card and up to four Gold Rush team sets (and $2) could be redeemed for platinum versions of the team set(s). The Gold Rush sets that were sent in would be returned with a stamp indicating they were already used for redemption purposes. The Platinum Upgrade offer was good through 7/13/95 for series 1, 10/1/95 for series 2.

COMPLETE SET (605) 40.00 100.00
COMP. SERIES 1 (330) 20.00 50.00
COMP. SERIES 2 (275) 20.00 50.00
*STARS: 2X TO 5X BASIC CARDS

1995 Score Platinum Team Sets

After completing a Score Gold Rush team set in either series, a collector could mail in those cards along with a platinum redemption card. In return, the collector would receive a complete Platinum Team Set. The cards are similar to the gold cards except they have sparkling platinum-foil fronts and come in a small card case. The top card is the certificate for the team set. Only 4,950 of each platinum team set was produced.

*STARS: 5X TO 12X BASIC CARDS

1995 Score You Trade Em

This skip-numbered 11-card set was available only by redeeming the randomly inserted Score You Trade Em redemption card. The set features a selection of veteran players that were traded to new teams at the beginning of the 1995 season. The numbering and card design parallel the corresponding cards within the regular issue 1995 Score set, but these Trade cards feature the players in their new uniforms.

COMPLETE SET (11) .60 1.50
333T Andre Dawson UER .15 .40
position listed as DH
339T Terry Pendleton .15 .40
344T Brett Butler .15 .40
346T Larry Walker .15 .40
352T Andy Van Slyke .25 .60
392T Chad Curtis .07 .20
427T Scott Cooper .07 .20
443T David Cone .15 .40
452T Jim Abbott .25 .60
493T Brian McRae .07 .20
530T Rob Dibble .15 .40
NNO Expired Trade Card .20 .50

1995 Score Airmail

This 18-card set was randomly inserted in series two jumbo packs at a rate of one in 24.

COMPLETE SET (18) 25.00 50.00
SER.2 STATED ODDS 1:24 JUMBO
AM1 Bob Hamelin .60 1.50
AM2 John Mabry .60 1.50
AM3 Marc Newfield .60 1.50
AM4 Jose Oliva .60 1.50
AM5 Charles Johnson 1.00 2.50
AM6 Russ Davis .60 1.50
AM7 Ernie Young .60 1.50
AM8 Billy Ashley .60 1.50
AM9 Ryan Klesko 1.00 2.50
AM10 J.R. Phillips .60 1.50
AM11 Cliff Floyd 1.00 2.50
AM12 Carlos Delgado 1.00 2.50
AM13 Melvin Nieves .60 1.50
AM14 Raul Mondesi 1.00 2.50
AM15 Manny Ramirez 1.50 4.00
AM16 Mike Kelly .60 1.50
AM17 Alex Rodriguez 6.00 15.00
AM18 Rusty Greer 1.00 2.50

1995 Score Contest Redemption

These cards were mailed to collectors who correctly identified intentional errors in two Pinnacle print ads depicting baseball scenes. The Alex Rodriguez card was the prize for the first ad, the Ivan Rodriguez card for the second ad.

COMPLETE SET (2) 3.20 8.00
AD1 Alex Rodriguez 2.50 6.00
AD2 Ivan Rodriguez 1.25 3.00

1995 Score Double Gold Champs

This 12-card set was randomly inserted in second series hobby packs at a rate of one in 36.

COMPLETE SET (12) 30.00 80.00
SER.2 STATED ODDS 1:36 HOBBY
GC1 Frank Thomas 2.00 5.00
GC2 Ken Griffey Jr. 3.00 8.00
GC3 Barry Bonds 6.00 15.00
GC4 Tony Gwynn 2.50 6.00
GC5 Don Mattingly 5.00 12.00
GC6 Greg Maddux 3.00 8.00
GC7 Roger Clemens 4.00 10.00
GC8 Kenny Lofton .75 2.00
GC9 Jeff Bagwell 1.25 3.00
GC10 Matt Williams .75 2.00
GC11 Kirby Puckett 2.00 5.00
GC12 Cal Ripken 6.00 15.00

1995 Score Draft Picks

Randomly inserted in first series hobby packs at a rate of one in 36, this 18-card set takes a look at top picks

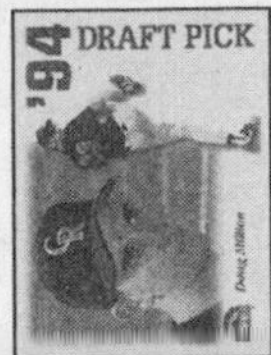

selected in June of 1994. The cards are numbered with a "DP" prefix.

COMPLETE SET (18) 10.00 25.00
SER.1 STATED ODDS 1:36 HOBBY
DP1 McKay Christensen .40 1.00
DP2 Bret Wagner .40 1.00
DP3 Paul Wilson .40 1.00
DP4 C.J. Nitkowski .40 1.00
DP5 Josh Booty .40 1.00
DP6 Antone Williamson .40 1.00
DP7 Paul Konerko 2.00 5.00
DP8 Scott Elarton .60 1.50
DP9 Jacob Shumate .40 1.00
DP10 Terrence Long .40 1.00
DP11 Mark Johnson .60 1.50
DP12 Ben Grieve .40 1.00
DP13 Doug Million .40 1.00
DP14 Jayson Peterson .40 1.00
DP15 Dustin Hermanson .40 1.00
DP16 Matt Smith .40 1.00
DP17 Kevin Witt .40 1.00
DP18 Brian Buchanan .40 1.00

1995 Score Dream Team

Randomly inserted in first series hobby and retail packs at a rate of one in 72 packs, this 12-card hologram set showcases top performers from the 1994 season. The cards are numbered with a "DG" prefix.

COMPLETE SET (12) 40.00 100.00
RANDOM INSERTS IN SER.1 HOB. AND RET.PACKS
DG1 Frank Thomas 3.00 8.00
DG2 Roberto Alomar 2.00 5.00
DG3 Cal Ripken 10.00 25.00
DG4 Matt Williams 1.25 3.00
DG5 Mike Piazza 5.00 12.00
DG6 Albert Belle 1.25 3.00
DG7 Ken Griffey Jr. 5.00 12.00
DG8 Tony Gwynn 4.00 10.00
DG9 Paul Molitor 1.25 3.00
DG10 Jimmy Key 1.25 3.00
DG11 Greg Maddux 5.00 12.00
DG12 Lee Smith 1.25 3.00

1995 Score Hall of Gold

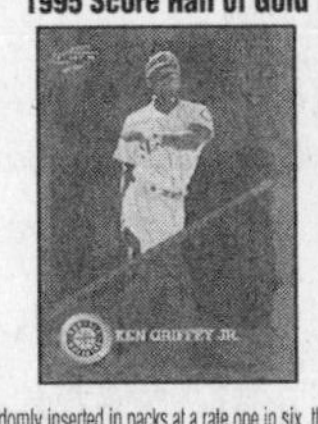

Randomly inserted in packs at a rate one in six, this 110-card multi-series set is a collection of top stars and young hopefuls. Cards numbered one through 55 were seeded in first series packs and cards 56-100 were seeded in second series packs.

COMPLETE SET (110) 30.00 80.00
COMP. SERIES 1 (55) 20.00 50.00
COMP.SERIES 2 (55) 12.50 30.00
STATED ODDS 1:6H/R, 1:4J, 1:3ANCO
*YTE CARDS: .4X TO 1X BASIC HALL
ONE YTE SET VIA MAIL PER YTE TRADE CARD
HG1 Ken Griffey Jr. 2.00 5.00
HG2 Matt Williams .50 1.25
HG3 Roberto Alomar .75 2.00
HG4 Jeff Bagwell .75 2.00
HG5 Dave Justice .50 1.25
HG6 Cal Ripken 4.00 10.00
HG7 Randy Johnson 1.25 3.00
HG8 Barry Larkin .75 2.00
HG9 Albert Belle .50 1.25
HG10 Mike Piazza 2.00 5.00
HG11 Kirby Puckett 1.25 3.00
HG12 Moises Alou .50 1.25
HG13 Jose Canseco .75 2.00
HG14 Tony Gwynn 1.50 4.00
HG15 Roger Clemens 2.50 6.00
HG16 Barry Bonds 4.00 10.00
HG17 Mo Vaughn .50 1.25
HG18 Greg Maddux 2.00 5.00
HG19 Dante Bichette .50 1.25
HG20 Will Clark .75 2.00
HG21 Lenny Dykstra .50 1.25
HG22 Don Mattingly 3.00 8.00
HG23 Carlos Baerga .25 .60
HG24 Ozzie Smith 2.00 5.00
HG25 Paul Molitor .50 1.25
HG26 Paul O'Neill .75 2.00
HG27 Deion Sanders .75 2.00
HG28 Jeff Conine .50 1.25
HG29 John Olerud .50 1.25
HG30 Jose Rijo .25 .60
HG31 Sammy Sosa 1.25 3.00
HG32 Robin Ventura .50 1.25
HG33 Raul Mondesi .50 1.25
HG34 Eddie Murray 1.25 3.00
HG35 Marquis Grissom .50 1.25
HG36 Darryl Strawberry .50 1.25

HG37 Dave Nilsson .25 .60
HG38 Manny Ramirez .75 2.00
HG39 Delino DeShields .25 .60
HG40 Lee Smith .50 1.25
HG41 Alex Rodriguez 3.00 8.00
HG42 Julio Franco .50 1.25
HG43 Bret Saberhagen .50 1.25
HG44 Ken Hill .25 .60
HG45 Roberto Kelly .25 .60
HG46 Hal Morris .25 .60
HG47 Jimmy Key .50 1.25
HG48 Terry Steinbach .25 .60
HG49 Mickey Tettleton .25 .60
HG50 Tony Phillips .25 .60
HG51 Carlos Garcia .25 .60
HG52 Jim Edmonds .75 2.00
HG53 Rod Beck .25 .60
HG54 Shane Mack .25 .60
HG55 Ken Caminiti .50 1.25
HG56 Frank Thomas 1.25 3.00
HG57 Kenny Lofton .50 1.25
HG58 Juan Gonzalez .50 1.25
HG59 Jason Bere .25 .60
HG60 Joe Carter .50 1.25
HG61 Gary Sheffield .50 1.25
HG62 Andres Galarraga .50 1.25
HG63 Ellis Burks .50 1.25
HG64 Bobby Bonilla .50 1.25
HG65 Tom Glavine .75 2.00
HG66 John Smoltz .75 2.00
HG67 Fred McGriff .75 2.00
HG68 Craig Biggio .75 2.00
HG69 Reggie Sanders .50 1.25
HG70 Kevin Mitchell .25 .60
HG71 Larry Walker .50 1.25
HG72 Carlos Delgado .50 1.25
HG73 Alex Gonzalez .25 .60
HG74 Ivan Rodriguez .75 2.00
HG75 Ryan Klesko .50 1.25
HG76 John Kruk .25 .60
HG77 Brian McRae .25 .60
HG78 Tim Salmon .75 2.00
HG79 Travis Fryman .50 1.25
HG80 Chuck Knoblauch .50 1.25
HG81 Jay Bell .50 1.25
HG82 Cecil Fielder .50 1.25
HG83 Cliff Floyd .50 1.25
HG84 Ruben Sierra .50 1.25
HG85 Mike Mussina .75 2.00
HG86 Mark Grace .75 2.00
HG87 Dennis Eckersley .50 1.25
HG88 Dennis Martinez .25 .60
HG89 Rafael Palmeiro .75 2.00
HG90 Ben McDonald .25 .60
HG91 Dave Hollins .25 .60
HG92 Steve Avery .25 .60
HG93 David Cone .50 1.25
HG94 Darren Daulton .50 1.25
HG95 Bret Boone .50 1.25
HG96 Wade Boggs .75 2.00
HG97 Doug Drabek .25 .60
HG98 Andy Benes .25 .60
HG99 Jim Thome .75 2.00
HG100 Chili Davis .50 1.25
HG101 J.Hammonds .25 .60
HG102 R.Henderson 1.25 3.00
HG103 Brett Butler .50 1.25
HG104 Tim Wallach .25 .60
HG105 Wil Cordero .25 .60
HG106 Mark Whiten .25 .60
HG107 Bob Hamelin .25 .60
HG108 Rondell White .50 1.25
HG109 Devon White .50 1.25
HG110 Tony Tarasco .25 .60

1995 Score Hall of Gold You Trade Em

This skip-numbered five-card set was available only by redeeming the randomly inserted Hall of Gold Trade card inserted in second series packs of 1995 Score. The set features a selection of veterans that joined new teams prior to the 1995 season. The design and numbering of the cards parallel the regular Hall of Gold inserts.

HG71T Larry Walker .50 1.25
HG76T John Kruk .25 .60
HG77T Brian McRae .25 .60
HG93T David Cone .50 1.25
HG110T Tony Tarasco .25 .60
NNO Exp. Hall of Gold Trade Card .20 .50

1995 Score Rookie Dream Team

This 12-card set was randomly inserted in second series retail and hobby packs at a rate of one in 12. The cards are numbered with a "RDT" prefix.

COMPLETE SET (12) 30.00 60.00
SER.2 STAT.ODDS 1:72 HOB/RET, 1:43 ANCO
RDT1 J.R. Phillips 1.00 2.50
RDT2 Alex Gonzalez 1.00 2.50
RDT3 Alex Rodriguez 8.00 20.00
RDT4 Jose Oliva 1.00 2.50
RDT5 Charles Johnson 2.00 5.00
RDT6 Shawn Green 2.00 5.00
RDT7 Brian Hunter 1.00 2.50
RDT8 Garret Anderson 2.00 5.00
RDT9 Julian Tavarez 1.00 2.50
RDT10 Jose Lima 1.00 2.50
RDT11 Armando Benitez 1.00 2.50
RDT12 Ricky Bottalico 1.00 2.50

1995 Score Rules

Randomly inserted in first series jumbo packs, this 30-card standard-size set features top big league players. The cards are numbered with an "SR" prefix.

COMPLETE SET (30) 50.00 120.00
SER.1 STATED ODDS 1:8 JUMBO
*JUMBO'S: .5X TO 1.2X
JUMBOS ISSUED ONE PER COLLECTOR KIT
SR1 Ken Griffey Jr. 3.00 8.00
SR2 Frank Thomas 2.00 5.00
SR3 Mike Piazza 3.00 8.00
SR4 Jeff Bagwell 1.25 3.00
SR5 Alex Rodriguez 5.00 12.00
SR6 Albert Belle .75 2.00
SR7 Matt Williams .75 2.00
SR8 Roberto Alomar 1.25 3.00
SR9 Barry Bonds 6.00 15.00
SR10 Raul Mondesi .75 2.00
SR11 Jose Canseco 1.25 3.00
SR12 Kirby Puckett 2.00 5.00
SR13 Fred McGriff 1.25 3.00
SR14 Kenny Lofton .75 2.00
SR15 Greg Maddux 3.00 8.00
SR16 Juan Gonzalez .75 2.00
SR17 Cliff Floyd .75 2.00
SR18 Cal Ripken Jr. 6.00 15.00
SR19 Will Clark 1.25 3.00
SR20 Tim Salmon 1.25 3.00
SR21 Paul O'Neill 1.25 3.00
SR22 Jason Bere .40 1.00
SR23 Tony Gwynn 2.50 6.00
SR24 Manny Ramirez 1.25 3.00
SR25 Don Mattingly 5.00 12.00
SR26 Dave Justice .75 2.00
SR27 Javier Lopez .75 2.00
SR28 Ryan Klesko .75 2.00
SR29 Carlos Delgado .75 2.00
SR30 Mike Mussina 1.25 3.00

1996 Score

This set consists of 517 standard-size cards. These cards were issued in packs of 10 that retailed for 99 cents per pack. The fronts feature an action photo surrounded by white borders. The "Score 96" logo is in the upper left, while the player is identified on the bottom. The backs have season and career stats as well as a player photo and some text. A Cal Ripken tribute card was issued at a rate of 1 every 300 packs.

COMPLETE SET (517) 10.00 24.00
COMP. SERIES 1 (275) 5.00 12.00
COMP. SERIES 2 (242) 5.00 12.00
1 Will Clark .10 .30
2 Rich Becker .07 .20
3 Ryan Klesko .07 .20
4 Jim Edmonds .07 .20
5 Barry Larkin .10 .30
6 Jim Thome .10 .30
7 Raul Mondesi .07 .20
8 Don Mattingly .50 1.25
9 Jeff Conine .07 .20
10 Rickey Henderson .20 .50
11 Chad Curtis .07 .20
12 Darren Daulton .07 .20
13 Larry Walker .07 .20
14 Carlos Garcia .07 .20
15 Carlos Baerga .07 .20
16 Tony Gwynn .25 .60
17 Jon Nunnally .07 .20
18 Deion Sanders .10 .30
19 Mark Grace .10 .30
20 Alex Rodriguez .40 1.00
21 Frank Thomas .20 .50
22 Brian Jordan .07 .20
23 J.T. Snow .07 .20
24 Shawn Green .07 .20
25 Tim Wakefield .07 .20
26 Curtis Goodwin .07 .20
27 John Smoltz .10 .30
28 Devon White .07 .20
29 Brian L. Hunter .07 .20
30 Rusty Greer .07 .20
31 Rafael Palmeiro .10 .30
32 Bernard Gilkey .07 .20
33 John Valentin .07 .20
34 Randy Johnson .20 .50
35 Garret Anderson .07 .20
36 Rikkert Faneyte .07 .20
37 Ray Durham .07 .20
38 Bip Roberts .07 .20
39 Jaime Navarro .07 .20
40 Mark Johnson .07 .20
41 Darren Lewis .07 .20
42 Tyler Green .07 .20
43 Bill Pulsipher .07 .20
44 Jason Giambi .07 .20
45 Kevin Ritz .07 .20
46 Jack McDowell .07 .20
47 Felipe Lira .07 .20
48 Rico Brogna .07 .20
49 Terry Pendleton .07 .20
50 Rondell White .07 .20
51 Andre Dawson .07 .20
52 Kirby Puckett .20 .50
53 Wally Joyner .07 .20
54 B.J. Surhoff .07 .20
55 Randy Velarde .07 .20
56 Greg Vaughn .07 .20
57 Roberto Alomar .10 .30
58 David Justice .07 .20
59 Kevin Seitzer .07 .20
60 Cal Ripken .60 1.50
61 Ozzie Smith .30 .75
62 Mo Vaughn .07 .20
63 Ricky Bones .07 .20
64 Gary DiSarcina .07 .20
65 Matt Williams .07 .20
66 Wilson Alvarez .07 .20
67 Lenny Dykstra .07 .20
68 Brian McRae .07 .20
69 Todd Stottlemyre .07 .20
70 Bret Boone .07 .20
71 Sterling Hitchcock .07 .20
72 Albert Belle .07 .20
73 Todd Hundley .07 .20
74 Vinny Castilla .07 .20
75 Moises Alou .07 .20
76 Cecil Fielder .07 .20
77 Brad Radke .07 .20
78 Quilvio Veras .07 .20
79 Eddie Murray .20 .50
80 James Mouton .07 .20
81 Pat Listach .07 .20
82 Mark Gubicza .07 .20
83 Dave Winfield .07 .20
84 Fred McGriff .10 .30
85 Darryl Hamilton .07 .20
86 Jeffrey Hammonds .07 .20
87 Pedro Munoz .07 .20
88 Craig Biggio .10 .30
89 Cliff Floyd .07 .20
90 Tim Naehring .07 .20
91 Brett Butler .07 .20
92 Kevin Foster .07 .20
93 Pat Kelly .07 .20
94 John Smiley .07 .20
95 Terry Steinbach .07 .20
96 Orel Hershiser .07 .20
97 Darrin Fletcher .07 .20
98 Walt Weiss .07 .20
99 John Wetteland .07 .20
100 Alan Trammell .07 .20
101 Steve Avery .07 .20
102 Tony Eusebio .07 .20
103 Sandy Alomar Jr. .07 .20
104 Joe Girardi .07 .20
105 Rick Aguilera .07 .20
106 Tony Tarasco .07 .20
107 Chris Hammond .07 .20
108 Mike Macfarlane .07 .20
109 Doug Drabek .07 .20
110 Derek Bell .07 .20
111 Ed Sprague .07 .20
112 Todd Hollandsworth .07 .20
113 Otis Nixon .07 .20
114 Keith Lockhart .07 .20
115 Donovan Osborne .07 .20
116 Dave Magadan .07 .20
117 Edgar Martinez .10 .30
118 Chuck Carr .07 .20
119 J.R. Phillips .07 .20
120 Sean Bergman .07 .20
121 Andujar Cedeno .07 .20
122 Eric Young .07 .20
123 Al Martin .07 .20
124 Mark Lemke .07 .20
125 Jim Eisenreich .07 .20
126 Benito Santiago .07 .20
127 Ariel Prieto .07 .20
128 Jim Bullinger .07 .20
129 Russ Davis .07 .20
130 Jim Abbott .10 .30
131 Jason Isringhausen .07 .20
132 Carlos Perez .07 .20
133 David Segui .07 .20
134 Troy O'Leary .07 .20
135 Pat Meares .07 .20
136 Chris Hoiles .07 .20
137 Ismael Valdes .07 .20
138 Jose Oliva .07 .20
139 Carlos Delgado .07 .20
140 Tom Goodwin .07 .20
141 Bob Tewksbury .07 .20
142 Chris Gomez .07 .20
143 Jose Oquendo .07 .20
144 Mark Lewis .07 .20
145 Salomon Torres .07 .20
146 Luis Gonzalez .07 .20
147 Mark Carreon .07 .20
148 Lance Johnson .07 .20
149 Melvin Nieves .07 .20
150 Lee Smith .07 .20
151 Jacob Brumfield .07 .20
152 Armando Benitez .07 .20
153 Curt Schilling .07 .20
154 Javier Lopez .07 .20
155 Frank Rodriguez .07 .20
156 Alex Gonzalez .07 .20
157 Todd Worrell .07 .20
158 Benji Gil .07 .20
159 Greg Gagne .07 .20
160 Tom Henke .07 .20
161 Randy Myers .07 .20
162 Joey Cora .07 .20
163 Scott Ruffcorn .07 .20
164 W. VanLandingham .07 .20
165 Tony Phillips .07 .20
166 Eddie Williams .07 .20
167 Bobby Bonilla .07 .20
168 Denny Neagle .07 .20
169 Troy Percival .07 .20
170 Billy Ashley .07 .20
171 Andy Van Slyke .10 .30
172 Jose Offerman .07 .20
173 Mark Parent .07 .20
174 Edgardo Alfonzo .07 .20
175 Trevor Hoffman .07 .20
176 David Cone .07 .20
177 Dan Wilson .07 .20
178 Steve Ontiveros .07 .20
179 Dean Palmer .07 .20
180 Mike Kelly .07 .20
181 Jim Leyritz .07 .20
182 Ron Karkovice .07 .20
183 Kevin Brown .07 .20
184 Jose Valentin .07 .20
185 Jorge Fabregas .07 .20
186 Jose Mesa .07 .20
187 Brent Mayne .07 .20
188 Carl Everett .07 .20
189 Paul Sorrento .07 .20
190 Pete Schourek .07 .20
191 Scott Kamieniecki .07 .20
192 Roberto Hernandez .07 .20
193 Randy Johnson RR .10 .30
194 Greg Maddux RR .20 .50
195 Hideo Nomo RR .10 .30
196 David Cone RR .07 .20
197 Mike Mussina RR .07 .20
198 Andy Benes RR .07 .20
199 Kevin Appier RR .07 .20
200 John Smoltz RR .07 .20
201 John Wetteland RR .07 .20
202 Mark Wohlers RR .07 .20
203 Stan Belinda .07 .20
204 Brian Anderson .07 .20
205 Mike Devereaux .07 .20
206 Mark Wohlers .07 .20
207 Omar Vizquel .10 .30
208 Jose Rijo .07 .20
209 Willie Blair .07 .20
210 Jamie Moyer .07 .20
211 Craig Shipley .07 .20
212 Shane Reynolds .07 .20
213 Chad Fonville .07 .20
214 Jose Vizcaino .07 .20
215 Sid Fernandez .07 .20
216 Andy Ashby .07 .20
217 Frank Castillo .07 .20
218 Kevin Tapani .07 .20
219 Kent Mercker .07 .20
220 Karim Garcia .07 .20
221 Antonio Osuna .07 .20
222 Tim Unroe .07 .20
223 Johnny Damon .10 .30
224 LaTroy Hawkins .07 .20
225 Mariano Rivera .40 1.00
226 Jose Alberro .07 .20
227 Angel Martinez .07 .20
228 Jason Schmidt .10 .30
229 Tony Clark .07 .20
230 Kevin Jordan UER .07 .20
Ricky Jordan pictured on both sides
231 Mark Thompson .07 .20
232 Jim Dougherty .07 .20
233 Roger Cedeno .07 .20
234 Ugueth Urbina .07 .20
235 Ricky Otero .07 .20
236 Mark Smith .07 .20
237 Brian Barber .07 .20
238 Kevin Flora .07 .20
239 Joe Rosselli .07 .20
240 Derek Jeter .50 1.25
241 Michael Tucker .07 .20
242 Ben Blomdahl .07 .20
243 Joe Vitiello .07 .20
244 Todd Steverson .07 .20
245 James Baldwin .07 .20
246 Alan Embree .07 .20
247 Shannon Penn .07 .20
248 Chris Stynes .07 .20
249 Oscar Munoz .07 .20
250 Jose Herrera .07 .20
251 Scott Sullivan .07 .20
252 Reggie Williams .07 .20
253 Mark Grudzielanek .07 .20
254 Steve Rodriguez .07 .20
255 Terry Bradshaw .07 .20
256 F.P. Santangelo .07 .20
257 Lyle Mouton .07 .20
258 George Williams .07 .20
259 Larry Thomas .07 .20
260 Rudy Pemberton .07 .20
261 Jim Pittsley .07 .20
262 Les Norman .07 .20
263 Ruben Rivera .07 .20
264 Cesar Devarez .07 .20
265 Greg Zaun .07 .20
266 Dustin Hermanson .07 .20
267 John Frascatore .07 .20
268 Joe Randa .07 .20
269 Jeff Bagwell CL .07 .20
270 Mike Piazza CL .20 .50
271 Dante Bichette CL .07 .20
272 Frank Thomas CL .10 .30
273 Ken Griffey Jr. CL .20 .50
274 Cal Ripken CL .30 .75
275 Greg Maddux CL .07 .20
Albert Belle
276 Greg Maddux .30 .75
277 Pedro Martinez .10 .30
278 Bobby Higginson .07 .20
279 Ray Lankford .07 .20
280 Shawon Dunston .07 .20
281 Gary Sheffield .07 .20
282 Ken Griffey Jr. .30 .75
283 Paul Molitor .07 .20
284 Kevin Appier .07 .20
285 Chuck Knoblauch .07 .20
286 Alex Fernandez .07 .20
287 Steve Finley .07 .20
288 Jeff Blauser .07 .20
289 Charles Johnson .07 .20
290 John Franco .07 .20
291 Mark Langston .07 .20
292 Bret Saberhagen .07 .20
293 John Mabry .07 .20
294 Ramon Martinez .07 .20
295 Mike Blowers .07 .20
296 Paul O'Neill .10 .30
297 Dave Nilsson .07 .20
298 Dante Bichette .07 .20
299 Marty Cordova .07 .20
300 Jay Bell .07 .20
301 Mike Mussina .10 .30
302 Ivan Rodriguez .10 .30
303 Jose Canseco .10 .30
304 Jeff Bagwell .10 .30
305 Manny Ramirez .10 .30
306 Dennis Martinez .07 .20
307 Charlie Hayes .07 .20
308 Joe Carter .07 .20
309 Travis Fryman .07 .20
310 Mark McGwire .50 1.25
311 Reggie Sanders UER .07 .20
Photo on front is John Roper
312 Julian Tavarez .07 .20
313 Jeff Montgomery .07 .20
314 Andy Benes .07 .20
315 John Jaha .07 .20
316 Jeff Kent .07 .20
317 Mike Piazza .30 .75
318 Erik Hanson .07 .20
319 Kenny Rogers .07 .20
320 Hideo Nomo .20 .50
321 Gregg Jefferies .07 .20
322 Chipper Jones .20 .50
323 Jay Buhner .07 .20
324 Dennis Eckersley .07 .20
325 Kenny Lofton .07 .20
326 Robin Ventura .07 .20
327 Tom Glavine .10 .30
328 Tim Salmon .10 .30
329 Andres Galarraga .07 .20
330 Hal Morris .07 .20
331 Brady Anderson .07 .20
332 Chili Davis .07 .20
333 Roger Clemens .40 1.00
334 Marquis Grissom .07 .20
335 Mike Greenwell UER .07 .20
Name spelled Jeff on Front
336 Sammy Sosa .20 .50
337 Ron Gant .07 .20
338 Ken Caminiti .07 .20
339 Danny Tartabull .07 .20
340 Barry Bonds .60 1.50
341 Ben McDonald .07 .20
342 Ruben Sierra .07 .20
343 Bernie Williams .10 .30
344 Wil Cordero .07 .20
345 Wade Boggs .10 .30
346 Gary Gaetti .07 .20
347 Greg Colbrunn .07 .20
348 Juan Gonzalez .07 .20
349 Marc Newfield .07 .20
350 Charles Nagy .07 .20
351 Robby Thompson .07 .20
352 Roberto Petagine .07 .20
353 Darryl Strawberry .07 .20
354 Tino Martinez .10 .30
355 Eric Karros .07 .20
356 Cal Ripken SS .30 .75
357 Cecil Fielder SS .07 .20
358 Kirby Puckett SS .10 .30
359 Jim Edmonds SS .07 .20
360 Matt Williams SS .07 .20
361 Alex Rodriguez SS .20 .50
362 Barry Larkin SS .07 .20
363 Rafael Palmeiro SS .07 .20
364 David Cone SS .07 .20
365 Roberto Alomar SS .07 .20
366 Eddie Murray SS .10 .30
367 Randy Johnson SS .10 .30
368 Ryan Klesko SS .07 .20
369 Raul Mondesi SS .07 .20
370 Mo Vaughn SS .07 .20
371 Will Clark SS .07 .20
372 Carlos Baerga SS .07 .20
373 Frank Thomas SS .10 .30
374 Larry Walker SS .07 .20
375 Garret Anderson SS .07 .20
376 Edgar Martinez SS .07 .20
377 Don Mattingly SS .25 .60
378 Tony Gwynn SS .10 .30
379 Albert Belle SS .07 .20
380 J.Isringhausen SS .07 .20
381 Ruben Rivera SS .07 .20
382 Johnny Damon SS .07 .20
383 Karim Garcia SS .07 .20
384 Derek Jeter SS .25 .60
385 David Justice SS .07 .20
386 Royce Clayton .07 .20
387 Mark Whiten .07 .20
388 Mickey Tettleton .07 .20
389 Steve Trachsel .07 .20
390 Danny Bautista .07 .20
391 Midre Cummings .07 .20
392 Scott Leius .07 .20
393 Manny Alexander .07 .20
394 Brent Gates .07 .20
395 Rey Sanchez .07 .20
396 Andy Pettitte .10 .30
397 Jeff Cirillo .07 .20
398 Kurt Abbott .07 .20
399 Lee Tinsley .07 .20
400 Paul Assenmacher .07 .20
401 Scott Erickson .07 .20
402 Todd Zeile .07 .20
403 Tom Pagnozzi .07 .20
404 Ozzie Guillen .07 .20
405 Jeff Frye .07 .20
406 Kirt Manwaring .07 .20
407 Chad Ogea .07 .20
408 Harold Baines .07 .20
409 Jason Bere .07 .20
410 Chuck Finley .07 .20
411 Jeff Fassero .07 .20
412 Joey Hamilton .07 .20
413 John Olerud .07 .20
414 Kevin Stocker .07 .20
415 Eric Anthony .07 .20
416 Aaron Sele .07 .20
417 Chris Bosio .07 .20
418 Michael Mimbs .07 .20
419 Orlando Miller .07 .20
420 Stan Javier .07 .20
421 Matt Mieske .07 .20
422 Jason Bates .07 .20
423 Orlando Merced .07 .20
424 John Flaherty .07 .20
425 Reggie Jefferson .07 .20
426 Scott Stahoviak .07 .20
427 John Burkett .07 .20
428 Rod Beck .07 .20
429 Bill Swift .07 .20
430 Scott Cooper .07 .20
431 Mel Rojas .07 .20
432 Todd Van Poppel .07 .20
433 Bobby Jones .07 .20
434 Mike Harkey .07 .20
435 Sean Berry .07 .20
436 Glenallen Hill .07 .20
437 Ryan Thompson .07 .20
438 Luis Alicea .07 .20
439 Esteban Loaiza .07 .20
440 Jeff Reboulet .07 .20
441 Vince Coleman .07 .20
442 Ellis Burks .07 .20
443 Allen Battle .07 .20
444 Jimmy Key .07 .20
445 Ricky Bottalico .07 .20
446 Delino DeShields .07 .20
447 Albie Lopez .07 .20
448 Mark Petkovsek .07 .20
449 Tim Raines .07 .20
450 Bryan Harvey .07 .20
451 Pat Hentgen .07 .20
452 Tim Laker .07 .20
453 Tom Gordon .07 .20
454 Phil Plantier .07 .20
455 Ernie Young .07 .20
456 Pete Harnisch .07 .20
457 Roberto Kelly .07 .20
458 Mark Portugal .07 .20
459 Mark Leiter .07 .20
460 Tony Pena .07 .20
461 Roger Pavlik .07 .20
462 Jeff King .07 .20
463 Bryan Rekar .07 .20
464 Al Leiter .07 .20
465 Phil Nevin .07 .20
466 Jose Lima .07 .20
467 Mike Stanley .07 .20
468 David McCarty .07 .20
469 Herb Perry .07 .20
470 Geronimo Berroa .07 .20
471 David Wells .07 .20
472 Vaughn Eshelman .07 .20
473 Greg Swindell .07 .20
474 Steve Sparks .07 .20
475 Luis Sojo .07 .20
476 Derrick May .07 .20
477 Joe Oliver .07 .20
478 Alex Arias .07 .20
479 Brad Ausmus .07 .20
480 Gabe White .07 .20
481 Pat Rapp .07 .20
482 Damon Buford .07 .20
483 Turk Wendell .07 .20
484 Jeff Brantley .07 .20
485 Curtis Leskanic .07 .20
486 Robb Nen .07 .20
487 Lou Whitaker .07 .20
488 Melido Perez .07 .20
489 Luis Polonia .07 .20
490 Scott Brosius .07 .20
491 Robert Perez .07 .20
492 Mike Sweeney RC .30 .75
493 Mark Loretta .07 .20
494 Alex Ochoa .07 .20
495 Matt Lawton RC .07 .20
496 Shawn Estes .07 .20
497 John Wasdin .07 .20
498 Marc Kroon .07 .20
499 Chris Snopek .07 .20
500 Jeff Suppan .07 .20
501 Terrell Wade .07 .20
502 Marvin Benard RC .07 .20
503 Chris Widger .07 .20
504 Quinton McCracken .07 .20
505 Bob Wolcott .07 .20
506 C.J. Nitkowski .07 .20
507 Aaron Ledesma .07 .20
508 Scott Hatteberg .07 .20
509 Jimmy Haynes .07 .20
510 Howard Battle .07 .20
511 Marty Cordova CL .07 .20
512 Randy Johnson CL .10 .30
513 Mo Vaughn CL .07 .20
514 Hideo Nomo CL .07 .20
515 Greg Maddux CL .20 .50
516 Barry Larkin CL .07 .20
517 Tom Glavine CL .07 .20
NNO Cal Ripken 2131 8.00 20.00

1996 Score All-Stars

Randomly inserted in second series jumbo packs at a rate of one in nine, this 20-card set was printed in rainbow holographic prismatic foil.

COMPLETE SET (20) 25.00 60.00
SER.2 STATED ODDS 1:9 JUMBO
1 Frank Thomas 1.25 3.00
2 Albert Belle .50 1.25
3 Ken Griffey Jr. 2.00 5.00
4 Cal Ripken 4.00 10.00
5 Mo Vaughn .50 1.25
6 Matt Williams .50 1.25
7 Barry Bonds 4.00 10.00
8 Dante Bichette .50 1.25
9 Tony Gwynn 1.50 4.00
10 Greg Maddux 2.00 5.00
11 Randy Johnson 1.25 3.00
12 Hideo Nomo 1.25 3.00
13 Tim Salmon .75 2.00
14 Jeff Bagwell .75 2.00
15 Edgar Martinez .75 2.00
16 Reggie Sanders .50 1.25
17 Larry Walker .50 1.25
18 Chipper Jones 1.25 3.00
19 Manny Ramirez .75 2.00
20 Eddie Murray 1.25 3.00

1996 Score Big Bats

This 20-card set was randomly inserted in retail packs at a rate of approximately one in 31. The cards are numbered "X" of 20 in the upper left corner.

COMPLETE SET (20) 40.00 100.00
SER.1 STATED ODDS 1:31 RETAIL
1 Cal Ripken 6.00 15.00
2 Ken Griffey Jr. 3.00 8.00
3 Frank Thomas 2.00 5.00
4 Jeff Bagwell 1.25 3.00
5 Mike Piazza 3.00 8.00
6 Barry Bonds 6.00 15.00
7 Matt Williams .75 2.00
8 Raul Mondesi .75 2.00
9 Tony Gwynn 2.50 6.00
10 Albert Belle .75 2.00
11 Manny Ramirez 1.25 3.00
12 Carlos Baerga .75 2.00
13 Mo Vaughn .75 2.00
14 Derek Bell .75 2.00
15 Larry Walker .75 2.00
16 Kenny Lofton .75 2.00
17 Edgar Martinez 1.25 3.00
18 Reggie Sanders .75 2.00
19 Eddie Murray 2.00 5.00
20 Chipper Jones 2.00 5.00

1996 Score Diamond Aces

This 30-card set features some of baseball's best players. These cards were inserted approximately one every eight jumbo packs.

COMPLETE SET (30) 50.00 120.00
SER.1 STATED ODDS 1:8 JUMBO
1 Hideo Nomo 2.00 5.00
2 Brian L.Hunter .75 2.00
3 Ray Durham .75 2.00
4 Frank Thomas 2.00 5.00
5 Cal Ripken 6.00 15.00
6 Barry Bonds 6.00 15.00
7 Greg Maddux 3.00 8.00
8 Chipper Jones 2.00 5.00
9 Raul Mondesi .75 2.00
10 Mike Piazza 3.00 8.00
11 Derek Jeter 5.00 12.00
12 Bill Pulsipher .75 2.00
13 Larry Walker .75 2.00
14 Ken Griffey Jr. 3.00 8.00
15 Alex Rodriguez 4.00 10.00
16 Manny Ramirez 1.25 3.00
17 Mo Vaughn .75 2.00
18 Reggie Sanders .75 2.00
19 Derek Bell .75 2.00
20 Jim Edmonds .75 2.00
21 Albert Belle .75 2.00
22 Eddie Murray 2.00 5.00
23 Tony Gwynn 2.50 6.00
24 Jeff Bagwell 1.25 3.00
25 Carlos Baerga .75 2.00
26 Matt Williams .75 2.00
27 Garret Anderson .75 2.00
28 Todd Hollandsworth .75 2.00
29 Johnny Damon .75 2.00
30 Tim Salmon 1.25 3.00

1996 Score Dream Team

This nine-card set was randomly inserted in approximately one in 72 packs. This set features a leading player at each position. The cards are numbered in the upper right as "X" of nine.

COMPLETE SET (9) 25.00 60.00
SER.1 STATED ODDS 1:72 HOB/RET
1 Cal Ripken 6.00 15.00
2 Frank Thomas 2.00 5.00
3 Carlos Baerga .75 2.00
4 Matt Williams .75 2.00
5 Mike Piazza 3.00 8.00
6 Barry Bonds 6.00 15.00
7 Ken Griffey Jr. 3.00 8.00
8 Manny Ramirez 1.25 3.00
9 Greg Maddux 3.00 8.00

1996 Score Dugout Collection

This set is a mini-parallel to the regular issue. Only 110 cards of each Series 1 and Series 2 were selected. Randomly inserted approximately one in every three packs, these cards have all gold foil printing that gives them a shiny copper cast. The words "Dugout Collection" are printed on the back.

COMP. SERIES 1 (110) 20.00 50.00
COMP. SERIES 2 (110) 20.00 50.00
*DUGOUT: 1.5X TO 4X BASIC
STATED ODDS 1:3 HOB/RET
*AP DUGOUT: 10X TO 25X BASIC
AP STATED ODDS 1:36 HOB/RET

1996 Score Dugout Collection Artist's Proofs

This set is a parallel to the Dugout Collection set. These cards are different from the regular Dugout Collection as they have the words Artist Proof printed on the front. Randomly inserted one in every 36 packs, this set was printed using Gold Rush all gold-foil card technology .

*STARS: 2.5X TO 6X BASIC DUGOUT
STATED ODDS 1:36

1996 Score Future Franchise

Randomly inserted in retail packs at a rate of one in 72, this 16-card set honors young stars of the game.

COMPLETE SET (16) 40.00 100.00
SER.2 STATED ODDS 1:72 HOB/RET
1 Jason Isringhausen 1.50 4.00
2 Chipper Jones 4.00 10.00
3 Derek Jeter 10.00 25.00
4 Alex Rodriguez 8.00 20.00
5 Alex Ochoa 1.50 4.00
6 Manny Ramirez 2.50 6.00
7 Johnny Damon 1.50 4.00
8 Ruben Rivera 1.50 4.00
9 Karim Garcia 1.50 4.00
10 Garret Anderson 1.50 4.00
11 Marty Cordova 1.50 4.00
12 Bill Pulsipher 1.50 4.00
13 Hideo Nomo 4.00 10.00
14 Marc Newfield 1.50 4.00
15 Charles Johnson 1.50 4.00
16 Raul Mondesi 1.50 4.00

1996 Score Gold Stars

Randomly inserted in packs at a rate of one in 15, this 30-card set features borderless color action player photos with a special sepia player cutout inserted behind a gold foil stamp designating the star player.

COMPLETE SET (30)	20.00	50.00
SER.2 STATED ODDS 1:15 HOB/RET		
1 Ken Griffey Jr.	1.50	4.00
2 Frank Thomas	1.00	2.50
3 Reggie Sanders	.40	1.00
4 Tim Salmon	.60	1.50
5 Mike Piazza	1.50	4.00
6 Tony Gwynn	1.25	3.00
7 Gary Sheffield	.40	1.00
8 Matt Williams	.40	1.00
9 Bernie Williams	.60	1.50
10 Jason Isringhausen	.40	1.00
11 Albert Belle	.40	1.00
12 Chipper Jones	1.00	2.50
13 Edgar Martinez	.60	1.50
14 Barry Larkin	.60	1.50
15 Barry Bonds	3.00	8.00
16 Jeff Bagwell	.60	1.50
17 Greg Maddux	1.50	4.00
18 Mo Vaughn	.40	1.00
19 Ryan Klesko	.40	1.00
20 Sammy Sosa	1.00	2.50
21 Darren Daulton	.40	1.00
22 Ivan Rodriguez	.60	1.50
23 Dante Bichette	.40	1.00
24 Hideo Nomo	1.00	2.50
25 Cal Ripken	3.00	8.00
26 Rafael Palmeiro	.60	1.50
27 Larry Walker	.40	1.00
28 Carlos Baerga	.40	1.00
29 Randy Johnson	1.00	2.50
30 Manny Ramirez	.60	1.50

1996 Score Numbers Game

This 30-card set was inserted approximately one in every 15 packs. The cards are numbered as "X" of 30 in the upper left corner.

COMPLETE SET (30)	25.00	60.00
SER.1 STATED ODDS 1:15 HOB/RET		
1 Cal Ripken	3.00	8.00
2 Frank Thomas	1.00	2.50
3 Ken Griffey Jr.	1.50	4.00
4 Mike Piazza	1.50	4.00
5 Barry Bonds	3.00	8.00
6 Greg Maddux	1.50	4.00
7 Jeff Bagwell	.60	1.50
8 Derek Bell	.40	1.00
9 Tony Gwynn	1.25	3.00
10 Hideo Nomo	1.00	2.50
11 Raul Mondesi	.40	1.00
12 Manny Ramirez	.60	1.50
13 Albert Belle	.40	1.00
14 Matt Williams	.40	1.00
15 Jim Edmonds	.40	1.00
16 Edgar Martinez	.60	1.50
17 Mo Vaughn	.40	1.00
18 Reggie Sanders	.40	1.00
19 Chipper Jones	1.00	2.50
20 Larry Walker	.40	1.00
21 Juan Gonzalez	.40	1.00
22 Kenny Lofton	.40	1.00
23 Don Mattingly	2.50	6.00
24 Ivan Rodriguez	.60	1.50
25 Randy Johnson	1.00	2.50
26 Derek Jeter	2.50	6.00
27 J.T. Snow	.40	1.00
28 Will Clark	.60	1.50
29 Rafael Palmeiro	.60	1.50
30 Alex Rodriguez	2.00	5.00

1996 Score Power Pace

Randomly inserted in retail packs at a rate of one in 31, this 18-card set features homerun hitters.

COMPLETE SET (18)	25.00	60.00
SER.2 STATED ODDS 1:31 RETAIL		
1 Mark McGwire	4.00	10.00
2 Albert Belle	.60	1.50
3 Jay Buhner	.60	1.50
4 Frank Thomas	1.50	4.00
5 Matt Williams	.60	1.50
6 Gary Sheffield	.60	1.50
7 Mike Piazza	2.50	6.00
8 Larry Walker	.60	1.50
9 Mo Vaughn	.60	1.50
10 Rafael Palmeiro	1.00	2.50
11 Dante Bichette	.60	1.50
12 Ken Griffey Jr.	2.50	6.00
13 Barry Bonds	5.00	12.00
14 Manny Ramirez	1.00	2.50
15 Sammy Sosa	1.50	4.00
16 Tim Salmon	1.00	2.50
17 Dave Justice	.60	1.50
18 Eric Karros	.60	1.50

1996 Score Reflextions

This 20-card set was randomly inserted approximately one in every 31 hobby packs. Two players per card are featured, a veteran player and a younger star playing the same position.

COMPLETE SET (20)	40.00	100.00
SER.1 STATED ODDS 1:15 HOBBY		
1 Cal Ripken	6.00	15.00
Chipper Jones		
2 Ken Griffey Jr.	3.00	8.00
Alex Rodriguez		
3 Frank Thomas	2.00	5.00
Mo Vaughn		
4 Kenny Lofton	.75	2.00
Brian L.Hunter		
5 Don Mattingly	5.00	12.00
J.T.Snow		
6 Manny Ramirez	1.25	3.00
Raul Mondesi		
7 Tony Gwynn	2.50	6.00
Garret Anderson		
8 Roberto Alomar	1.25	3.00
Carlos Baerga		
9 Andre Dawson	.75	2.00
Larry Walker		
10 Barry Larkin	5.00	12.00
Derek Jeter		
11 Barry Bonds	6.00	15.00
Reggie Sanders		
12 Mike Piazza	3.00	8.00
Albert Belle		
13 Wade Boggs	1.25	3.00
Edgar Martinez		
14 David Cone	.75	2.00
John Smoltz		
15 Will Clark	1.25	3.00
Jeff Bagwell		
16 Mark McGwire	5.00	12.00
Cecil Fielder		
17 Greg Maddux	3.00	8.00
Mike Mussina		
18 Randy Johnson	2.00	5.00
Hideo Nomo		
19 Jim Thome	1.25	3.00
Dean Palmer		
20 Chuck Knoblauch	1.25	3.00
Craig Biggio		

1996 Score Titanic Taters

Randomly inserted in hobby packs at a rate of one in 31, this 18-card set features long home run hitters.

COMPLETE SET (18)	30.00	80.00
SER.2 STATED ODDS 1:31 HOBBY		
1 Albert Belle	.75	2.00
2 Frank Thomas	2.00	5.00
3 Mo Vaughn	.75	2.00
4 Ken Griffey Jr.	3.00	8.00
5 Matt Williams	.75	2.00
6 Mark McGwire	5.00	12.00
7 Dante Bichette	.75	2.00
8 Tim Salmon	1.25	3.00
9 Jeff Bagwell	1.25	3.00
10 Rafael Palmeiro	1.25	3.00
11 Mike Piazza	3.00	8.00
12 Cecil Fielder	.75	2.00
13 Larry Walker	.75	2.00
14 Sammy Sosa	2.00	5.00
15 Manny Ramirez	1.25	3.00
16 Gary Sheffield	.75	2.00
17 Barry Bonds	6.00	15.00
18 Jay Buhner	.75	2.00

1997 Score

The 1997 Score set has a total of 550 cards. With cards 1-330 distributed in series one packs and cards 331-550 in series two packs. The 10-card Series one packs and the 12-card Series two packs carried a suggested retail price of $.99 each and were distributed exclusively to retail outlets. The fronts feature color player action photos in a white border. The backs carry player information and career statistics. The Hideki Irabu card (551A and B) is shortprinted (about twice as tough to pull as a basic card). One final note on the Irabu card, in the retail packs and factory sets, the card text is in English. In the Hobby Reserve packs, text is in Japanese. Notable Rookie Cards include Brian Giles.

COMPLETE SET (551)	15.00	40.00
COMP.FACT.SET (551)	15.00	40.00
COMP.SERIES 1 (330)	6.00	15.00
COMP.SERIES 2 (221)	10.00	25.00
1 Jeff Bagwell	.12	.30
2 Mickey Tettleton	.07	.20
3 Johnny Damon	.12	.30
4 Jeff Conine	.07	.20
5 Bernie Williams	.12	.30
6 Will Clark	.12	.30
7 Ryan Klesko	.07	.20
8 Cecil Fielder	.07	.20
9 Paul Wilson	.07	.20
10 Gregg Jefferies	.07	.20
11 Chili Davis	.07	.20
12 Albert Belle	.07	.20
13 Ken Hill	.07	.20
14 Cliff Floyd	.07	.20
15 Jaime Navarro	.07	.20
16 Ismael Valdes	.07	.20
17 Jeff King	.07	.20
18 Chris Bosio	.07	.20
19 Reggie Sanders	.07	.20
20 Darren Daulton	.07	.20
21 Ken Caminiti	.07	.20
22 Mike Piazza	.20	.50
23 Chad Mottola	.07	.20
24 Darin Erstad	.07	.20
25 Dante Bichette	.07	.20
26 Frank Thomas	.20	.50
27 Ben McDonald	.07	.20
28 Raul Casanova	.07	.20
29 Kevin Ritz	.07	.20
30 Garret Anderson	.07	.20
31 Jason Kendall	.07	.20
32 Billy Wagner	.07	.20
33 Dave Justice	.07	.20
34 Marty Cordova	.07	.20
35 Derek Jeter	.50	1.25
36 Trevor Hoffman	.07	.20
37 Geronimo Berroa	.07	.20
38 Walt Weiss	.07	.20
39 Kirt Manwaring	.07	.20
40 Alex Gonzalez	.07	.20
41 Sean Berry	.07	.20
42 Kevin Appier	.07	.20
43 Rusty Greer	.07	.20
44 Pete Incaviglia	.07	.20
45 Rafael Palmeiro	.07	.20
46 Eddie Murray	.12	.30
47 Moises Alou	.07	.20
48 Mark Lewis	.07	.20
49 Hal Morris	.07	.20
50 Edgar Renteria	.07	.20
51 Rickey Henderson	.20	.50
52 Pat Listach	.07	.20
53 John Wasdin	.07	.20
54 James Baldwin	.07	.20
55 Brian Jordan	.07	.20
56 Edgar Martinez	.12	.30
57 Wil Cordero	.07	.20
58 Danny Tartabull	.07	.20
59 Keith Lockhart	.07	.20
60 Rico Brogna	.07	.20
61 Ricky Bottalico	.07	.20
62 Terry Pendleton	.07	.20
63 Bret Boone	.07	.20
64 Charlie Hayes	.07	.20
65 Marc Newfield	.07	.20
66 Sterling Hitchcock	.07	.20
67 Roberto Alomar	.12	.30
68 John Jaha	.07	.20
69 Greg Colbrunn	.07	.20
70 Sal Fasano	.07	.20
71 Brooks Kieschnick	.07	.20
72 Pedro Martinez	.12	.30
73 Kevin Elster	.07	.20
74 Ellis Burks	.07	.20
75 Chuck Finley	.07	.20
76 John Olerud	.07	.20
77 Jay Bell	.07	.20
78 Allen Watson	.07	.20
79 Darryl Strawberry	.07	.20
80 Orlando Miller	.07	.20
81 Jose Herrera	.07	.20
82 Andy Pettitte	.12	.30
83 Juan Guzman	.07	.20
84 Alan Benes	.07	.20
85 Jack McDowell	.07	.20
86 Ugueth Urbina	.07	.20
87 Rocky Coppinger	.07	.20
88 Jeff Cirillo	.07	.20
89 Tom Glavine	.12	.30
90 Robby Thompson	.07	.20
91 Barry Bonds	.40	1.00
92 Carlos Delgado	.07	.20
93 Mo Vaughn	.07	.20
94 Ryne Sandberg	.30	.75
95 Alex Rodriguez	.30	.75
96 Brady Anderson	.07	.20
97 Scott Brosius	.07	.20
98 Dennis Eckersley	.07	.20
99 Brian McRae	.07	.20
100 Rey Ordonez	.07	.20
101 John Valentin	.07	.20
102 Brett Butler	.07	.20
103 Eric Karros	.07	.20
104 Harold Baines	.07	.20
105 Javier Lopez	.07	.20
106 Alan Trammell	.07	.20
107 Jim Thome	.12	.30
108 Frank Rodriguez	.07	.20
109 Bernard Gilkey	.07	.20
110 Reggie Jefferson	.07	.20
111 Scott Stahoviak	.07	.20
112 Steve Gibralter	.07	.20
113 Todd Hollandsworth	.07	.20
114 Ruben Rivera	.07	.20
115 Dennis Martinez	.07	.20
116 Mariano Rivera	.12	.30
117 John Smoltz	.12	.30
118 John Mabry	.07	.20
119 Tom Gordon	.07	.20
120 Alex Ochoa	.07	.20
121 Jamey Wright	.07	.20
122 Dave Nilsson	.07	.20
123 Bobby Bonilla	.07	.20
124 Al Leiter	.07	.20
125 Rick Aguilera	.07	.20
126 Jeff Brantley	.07	.20
127 Kevin Brown	.07	.20
128 George Arias	.07	.20
129 Darren Oliver	.07	.20
130 Bill Pulsipher	.07	.20
131 Roberto Hernandez	.07	.20
132 Delino DeShields	.07	.20
133 Mark Grudzielanek	.07	.20
134 John Wetteland	.07	.20
135 Carlos Baerga	.07	.20
136 Paul Sorrento	.07	.20
137 Leo Gomez	.07	.20
138 Andy Ashby	.07	.20
139 Julio Franco	.07	.20
140 Brian Hunter	.07	.20
141 Jermaine Dye	.07	.20
142 Tony Clark	.07	.20
143 Ruben Sierra	.07	.20
144 Donovan Osborne	.07	.20
145 Mark McLemore	.07	.20
146 Terry Steinbach	.07	.20
147 Bob Wells	.07	.20
148 Chan Ho Park	.07	.20
149 Tim Salmon	.07	.20
150 Paul O'Neill	.12	.30
151 Cal Ripken	.75	2.00
152 Wally Joyner	.07	.20
153 Omar Vizquel	.12	.30
154 Mike Mussina	.12	.30
155 Andres Galarraga	.07	.20
156 Ken Griffey Jr.	.30	.75
157 Kenny Lofton	.07	.20
158 Ray Durham	.07	.20
159 Hideo Nomo	.12	.30
160 Ozzie Guillen	.07	.20
161 Roger Pavlik	.07	.20
162 Manny Ramirez	.12	.30
163 Mark Lemke	.07	.20
164 Mike Stanley	.07	.20
165 Chuck Knoblauch	.07	.20
166 Kimera Bartee	.07	.20
167 Wade Boggs	.12	.30
168 Jay Buhner	.07	.20
169 Eric Young	.07	.20
170 Jose Canseco	.12	.30
171 Dwight Gooden	.07	.20
172 Fred McGriff	.12	.30
173 Sandy Alomar Jr.	.07	.20
174 Andy Benes	.07	.20
175 Dean Palmer	.07	.20
176 Larry Walker	.07	.20
177 Charles Nagy	.07	.20
178 David Cone	.07	.20
179 Mark Grace	.12	.30
180 Robin Ventura	.07	.20
181 Roger Clemens	.30	.75
182 Bobby Witt	.07	.20
183 Vinny Castilla	.07	.20
184 Gary Sheffield	.07	.20
185 Dan Wilson	.07	.20
186 Roger Cedeno	.07	.20
187 Mark McGwire	.25	.60
188 Darren Bragg	.07	.20
189 Quinton McCracken	.07	.20
190 Randy Myers	.07	.20
191 Jeromy Burnitz	.07	.20
192 Randy Johnson	.20	.50
193 Chipper Jones	.20	.50
194 Greg Vaughn	.07	.20
195 Travis Fryman	.07	.20
196 Tim Naehring	.07	.20
197 B.J. Surhoff	.07	.20
198 Juan Gonzalez	.07	.20
199 Terrell Wade	.07	.20
200 Jeff Frye	.07	.20
201 Joey Cora	.07	.20
202 Raul Mondesi	.07	.20
203 Ivan Rodriguez	.12	.30
204 Armando Reynoso	.07	.20
205 Jeffrey Hammonds	.07	.20
206 Darren Dreifort	.07	.20
207 Kevin Seitzer	.07	.20
208 Tino Martinez	.12	.30
209 Jim Bruske	.07	.20
210 Jeff Suppan	.07	.20
211 Mark Carreon	.07	.20
212 Wilson Alvarez	.07	.20
213 John Burkett	.07	.20
214 Tony Phillips	.07	.20
215 Greg Maddux	.30	.75
216 Mark Whiten	.07	.20
217 Curtis Pride	.07	.20
218 Lyle Mouton	.07	.20
219 Todd Hundley	.07	.20
220 Greg Gagne	.07	.20
221 Rich Amaral	.07	.20
222 Tom Goodwin	.07	.20
223 Chris Hoiles	.07	.20
224 Jayhawk Owens	.07	.20
225 Kenny Rogers	.07	.20
226 Mike Greenwell	.07	.20
227 Mark Wohlers	.07	.20
228 Henry Rodriguez	.07	.20
229 Robert Perez	.07	.20
230 Jeff Kent	.07	.20
231 Darryl Hamilton	.07	.20
232 Alex Fernandez	.07	.20
233 Ron Karkovice	.07	.20
234 Jimmy Haynes	.07	.20
235 Craig Biggio	.12	.30
236 Ray Lankford	.07	.20
237 Lance Johnson	.07	.20
238 Matt Williams	.07	.20
239 Chad Curtis	.07	.20
240 Mark Thompson	.07	.20
241 Jason Giambi	.07	.20
242 Barry Larkin	.12	.30
243 Paul Molitor	.20	.50
244 Sammy Sosa	.12	.30
245 Kevin Tapani	.07	.20
246 Marquis Grissom	.07	.20
247 Joe Carter	.07	.20
248 Ramon Martinez	.07	.20
249 Tony Gwynn	.20	.50
250 Andy Fox	.07	.20
251 Troy O'Leary	.07	.20
252 Warren Newson	.07	.20
253 Troy Percival	.07	.20
254 Jamie Moyer	.07	.20
255 Danny Graves	.07	.20
256 David Wells	.07	.20
257 Todd Zeile	.07	.20
258 Raul Ibanez	.07	.20
259 Tyler Houston	.07	.20
260 LaTroy Hawkins	.07	.20
261 Joey Hamilton	.07	.20
262 Mike Sweeney	.07	.20
263 Brant Brown	.07	.20
264 Pat Hentgen	.07	.20
265 Mark Johnson	.07	.20
266 Robb Nen	.07	.20
267 Justin Thompson	.07	.20
268 Ron Gant	.07	.20
269 Jeff D'Amico	.07	.20
270 Shawn Estes	.07	.20
271 Derek Bell	.07	.20
272 Fernando Valenzuela	.07	.20
273 Tom Pagnozzi	.07	.20
274 John Burke	.07	.20
275 Ed Sprague	.07	.20
276 F.P. Santangelo	.07	.20
277 Todd Greene	.07	.20
278 Butch Huskey	.07	.20
279 Steve Finley	.07	.20
280 Eric Davis	.07	.20
281 Shawn Green	.07	.20
282 Al Martin	.07	.20
283 Michael Tucker	.07	.20
284 Shane Reynolds	.07	.20
285 Matt Mieske	.07	.20
286 Jose Rosado	.07	.20
287 Mark Langston	.07	.20
288 Ralph Milliard	.07	.20
289 Mike Lansing	.07	.20
290 Scott Servais	.07	.20
291 Royce Clayton	.07	.20
292 Mike Grace	.07	.20
293 James Mouton	.07	.20
294 Charles Johnson	.07	.20
295 Gary Gaetti	.07	.20
296 Kevin Mitchell	.07	.20
297 Carlos Garcia	.07	.20
298 Desi Relaford	.07	.20
299 Jason Thompson	.07	.20
300 Osvaldo Fernandez	.07	.20
301 Fernando Vina	.07	.20
302 Jose Offerman	.07	.20
303 Yamil Benitez	.07	.20
304 J.T. Snow	.07	.20
305 Rafael Bournigal	.07	.20
306 Jason Isringhausen	.07	.20
307 Bobby Higginson	.07	.20
308 Nerio Rodriguez RC	.07	.20
309 Brian Giles RC	.40	1.00
310 Andruw Jones	.12	.30
311 Tony Graffanino	.07	.20
312 Arquimedez Pozo	.07	.20
313 Jermaine Allensworth	.07	.20
314 Jeff Darwin	.07	.20
315 George Williams	.07	.20
316 Karim Garcia	.07	.20
317 Trey Beamon	.07	.20
318 Mac Suzuki	.07	.20
319 Robin Jennings	.07	.20
320 Danny Patterson	.07	.20
321 Damon Mashore	.07	.20
322 Wendell Magee	.07	.20
323 Dax Jones	.07	.20
324 Todd Walker	.07	.20
325 Marvin Benard	.07	.20
326 Mike Cameron	.07	.20
327 Marcus Jensen	.07	.20
328 Eddie Murray CL	.12	.30
329 Paul Molitor CL	.20	.50
330 Todd Hundley CL	.07	.20
331 Norm Charlton	.07	.20
332 Bruce Ruffin	.07	.20
333 John Wetteland	.07	.20
334 Marquis Grissom	.07	.20
335 Sterling Hitchcock	.07	.20
336 John Olerud	.07	.20
337 David Wells	.07	.20
338 Chili Davis	.07	.20
339 Mark Lewis	.07	.20
340 Kenny Lofton	.07	.20
341 Alex Fernandez	.07	.20
342 Ruben Sierra	.07	.20
343 Delino DeShields	.07	.20
344 John Wasdin	.07	.20
345 Dennis Martinez	.07	.20
346 Kevin Elster	.07	.20
347 Bobby Bonilla	.07	.20
348 Jaime Navarro	.07	.20
349 Chad Curtis	.07	.20
350 Terry Steinbach	.07	.20
351 Ariel Prieto	.07	.20
352 Jeff Kent	.07	.20
353 Carlos Garcia	.07	.20
354 Mark Whiten	.07	.20
355 Todd Zeile	.07	.20
356 Eric Davis	.07	.20
357 Greg Colbrunn	.07	.20
358 Moises Alou	.07	.20
359 Allen Watson	.07	.20
360 Jose Canseco	.12	.30
361 Matt Williams	.07	.20
362 Jeff King	.07	.20
363 Darryl Hamilton	.07	.20
364 Mark Clark	.07	.20
365 J.T. Snow	.07	.20
366 Kevin Mitchell	.07	.20
367 Orlando Miller	.07	.20
368 Rico Brogna	.07	.20
369 Mike James	.07	.20
370 Brad Ausmus	.07	.20
371 Darryl Kile	.07	.20
372 Edgardo Alfonzo	.07	.20
373 Julian Tavarez	.07	.20
374 Darren Lewis	.07	.20
375 Steve Karsay	.07	.20
376 Lee Stevens	.07	.20
377 Albie Lopez	.07	.20
378 Orel Hershiser	.07	.20
379 Lee Smith	.07	.20
380 Rick Helling	.07	.20
381 Carlos Perez	.07	.20
382 Tony Tarasco	.07	.20
383 Melvin Nieves	.07	.20
384 Benji Gil	.07	.20
385 Devon White	.07	.20
386 Armando Benitez	.07	.20
387 Bill Swift	.07	.20
388 John Smiley	.07	.20
389 Midre Cummings	.07	.20
390 Tim Belcher	.07	.20
391 Tim Raines	.07	.20
392 Todd Worrell	.07	.20
393 Quilvio Veras	.07	.20
394 Matt Lawton	.07	.20
395 Aaron Sele	.07	.20
396 Bip Roberts	.07	.20
397 Denny Neagle	.07	.20
398 Tyler Green	.07	.20
399 Hipolito Pichardo	.07	.20
400 Scott Erickson	.07	.20
401 Bobby Jones	.07	.20
402 Jim Edmonds	.07	.20
403 Chad Ogea	.07	.20
404 Cal Eldred	.07	.20
405 Pat Listach	.07	.20
406 Todd Stottlemyre	.07	.20
407 Phil Nevin	.07	.20
408 Otis Nixon	.07	.20
409 Billy Ashley	.07	.20
410 Jimmy Key	.07	.20
411 Mike Timlin	.07	.20
412 Joe Vitiello	.07	.20
413 Rondell White	.07	.20
414 Jeff Fassero	.07	.20
415 Rex Hudler	.07	.20
416 Curt Schilling	.07	.20
417 Rich Becker	.07	.20
418 W.Van Landingham	.07	.20
419 Chris Snopek	.07	.20
420 David Segui	.07	.20
421 Eddie Murray	.12	.30
422 Shane Andrews	.07	.20
423 Gary DiSarcina	.07	.20
424 Brian Hunter	.07	.20
425 Willie Greene	.07	.20
426 Felipe Crespo	.07	.20
427 Jason Bates	.07	.20
428 Albert Belle	.07	.20
429 Rey Sanchez	.07	.20
430 Roger Clemens	.30	.75
431 Deion Sanders	.12	.30
432 Ernie Young	.07	.20
433 Jay Bell	.07	.20
434 Jeff Blauser	.07	.20
435 Lenny Dykstra	.07	.20
436 Chuck Carr	.07	.20
437 Russ Davis	.07	.20
438 Carl Everett	.07	.20
439 Damion Easley	.07	.20
440 Pat Kelly	.07	.20
441 Pat Rapp	.07	.20
442 Dave Justice	.07	.20
443 Graeme Lloyd	.07	.20
444 Damon Buford	.07	.20
445 Jose Valentin	.07	.20
446 Jason Schmidt	.07	.20
447 Dave Martinez	.07	.20
448 Danny Tartabull	.07	.20
449 Jose Vizcaino	.07	.20
450 Steve Avery	.07	.20
451 Mike Devereaux	.07	.20
452 Jim Eisenreich	.07	.20
453 Mark Leiter	.07	.20
454 Roberto Kelly	.07	.20
455 Benito Santiago	.07	.20
456 Steve Trachsel	.07	.20
457 Gerald Williams	.07	.20
458 Pete Schourek	.07	.20
459 Esteban Loaiza	.07	.20
460 Mel Rojas	.07	.20
461 Tim Wakefield	.07	.20
462 Tony Fernandez	.07	.20
463 Doug Drabek	.07	.20
464 Joe Girardi	.07	.20
465 Mike Bordick	.07	.20
466 Jim Leyritz	.07	.20
467 Erik Hanson	.07	.20
468 Michael Tucker	.07	.20
469 Tony Womack RC	.07	.20
470 Doug Glanville	.07	.20
471 Rudy Pemberton	.07	.20
472 Keith Lockhart	.07	.20
473 Nomar Garciaparra	.20	.50
474 Scott Rolen	.12	.30
475 Jason Dickson	.07	.20
476 Glendon Rusch	.07	.20
477 Todd Walker	.07	.20
478 Dmitri Young	.07	.20
479 Rod Myers	.07	.20
480 Wilton Guerrero	.07	.20
481 Jorge Posada	.12	.30
482 Brant Brown	.07	.20
483 Bubba Trammell RC	.07	.20
484 Jose Guillen	.07	.20
485 Scott Spiezio	.07	.20
486 Bob Abreu	.12	.30
487 Chris Holt	.07	.20
488 Deivi Cruz RC	.07	.20
489 Vladimir Guerrero	.20	.50
490 Julio Santana	.07	.20
491 Ray Montgomery RC	.07	.20
492 Kevin Orie	.07	.20
493 Todd Hundley GY	.07	.20
494 Tim Salmon GY	.07	.20
495 Albert Belle GY	.07	.20
496 Manny Ramirez GY	.12	.30
497 Rafael Palmeiro GY	.07	.20
498 Juan Gonzalez GY	.07	.20
499 Ken Griffey Jr. GY	.30	.75
500 Andruw Jones GY	.12	.30
501 Mike Piazza GY	.20	.50
502 Jeff Bagwell GY	.12	.30
503 Bernie Williams GY	.12	.30
504 Barry Bonds GY	.40	1.00
505 Ken Caminiti GY	.07	.20
506 Darin Erstad GY	.07	.20
507 Alex Rodriguez GY	.30	.75
508 Frank Thomas GY	.20	.50
509 Chipper Jones GY	.20	.50
510 Mo Vaughn GY	.07	.20
511 Mark McGwire GY	.25	.60
512 Fred McGriff GY	.12	.30
513 Jay Buhner GY	.07	.20
514 Jim Thome GY	.12	.30
515 Gary Sheffield GY	.07	.20
516 Dean Palmer GY	.07	.20
517 Henry Rodriguez GY	.07	.20
518 Andy Pettitte RF	.12	.30
519 Mike Mussina RF	.12	.30
520 Greg Maddux RF	.30	.75
521 John Smoltz RF	.12	.30
522 Hideo Nomo RF	.12	.30
523 Troy Percival RF	.07	.20
524 John Wetteland RF	.07	.20
525 Roger Clemens RF	.30	.75
526 Charles Nagy RF	.07	.20
527 Mariano Rivera RF	.12	.30
528 Tom Glavine RF	.12	.30
529 Randy Johnson RF	.20	.50
530 J.Isringhausen RF	.07	.20
531 Alex Fernandez RF	.07	.20
532 Kevin Brown RF	.07	.20
533 Chuck Knoblauch TG	.07	.20
534 Rusty Greer TG	.07	.20
535 Tony Gwynn TG	.20	.50
536 Ryan Klesko TG	.07	.20
537 Ryne Sandberg TG	.30	.75
538 Barry Larkin TG	.12	.30
539 Will Clark TG	.12	.30
540 Kenny Lofton TG	.07	.20
541 Paul Molitor TG	.20	.50
542 Roberto Alomar TG	.12	.30
543 Rey Ordonez TG	.07	.20
544 Jason Giambi TG	.07	.20
545 Derek Jeter TG	.50	1.25
546 Cal Ripken TG	.75	2.00
547 Ivan Rodriguez TG	.12	.30
548 Ken Griffey Jr. CL	.30	.75
549 Frank Thomas CL	.20	.50
550 Mike Piazza CL	.20	.50
551A Hideki Irabu SP	1.00	2.50
551B Hideki Irabu	1.00	2.50
Japanese SP		

1997 Score Artist's Proofs White Border

Artist's Proofs White Border cards were randomly inserted exclusively into Score Series 1 retail packs. The cards share the similar "Artist's Proof" logo as seen on the more commonly traded Showcase Series Artist's Proofs. Unlike the silver-foiled Showcase Series Artist's Proofs, however, the White Border cards have plain white stock card fronts - making them easy to misidentify with a basic issue Score card. Please note that Series 2 Artist Proofs do not exist.

*STARS: 12.5X TO 30X BASIC CARDS
*ROOKIES: 4X TO 10X BASIC CARDS

1997 Score Hobby Reserve

*HOBBY RESERVE: .6X TO 1.5X		
HR1 Jeff Bagwell	2.00	5.00
HR2 Mickey Tettleton	1.25	3.00
HR3 Johnny Damon	2.00	5.00
HR4 Jeff Conine	1.25	3.00
HR5 Bernie Williams	2.00	5.00
HR6 Will Clark	2.00	5.00
HR7 Ryan Klesko	1.25	3.00
HR8 Cecil Fielder	1.25	3.00
HR9 Paul Wilson	1.25	3.00
HR10 Gregg Jefferies	1.25	3.00
HR11 Chili Davis	1.25	3.00
HR12 Albert Belle	1.25	3.00
HR13 Ken Hill	1.25	3.00
HR14 Cliff Floyd	1.25	3.00
HR15 Jaime Navarro	1.25	3.00
HR16 Ismael Valdes	1.25	3.00
HR17 Jeff King	1.25	3.00
HR18 Chris Bosio	1.25	3.00
HR19 Reggie Sanders	1.25	3.00
HR20 Darren Daulton	1.25	3.00
HR21 Ken Caminiti	1.25	3.00
HR22 Mike Piazza	3.00	8.00
HR23 Chad Mottola	1.25	3.00
HR24 Darin Erstad	1.25	3.00
HR25 Dante Bichette	1.25	3.00
HR26 Frank Thomas	3.00	8.00
HR27 Ben McDonald	1.25	3.00
HR28 Raul Casanova	1.25	3.00
HR29 Kevin Ritz	1.25	3.00
HR30 Garret Anderson	1.25	3.00
HR31 Jason Kendall	1.25	3.00
HR32 Billy Wagner	1.25	3.00
HR33 Dave Justice	1.25	3.00
HR34 Marty Cordova	1.25	3.00
HR35 Derek Jeter	8.00	20.00
HR36 Trevor Hoffman	1.25	3.00
HR37 Geronimo Berroa	1.25	3.00
HR38 Walt Weiss	1.25	3.00
HR39 Kirt Manwaring	1.25	3.00
HR40 Alex Gonzalez	1.25	3.00
HR41 Sean Berry	1.25	3.00
HR42 Kevin Appier	1.25	3.00
HR43 Rusty Greer	1.25	3.00
HR44 Pete Incaviglia	1.25	3.00
HR45 Rafael Palmeiro	1.25	3.00
HR46 Eddie Murray	2.00	5.00
HR47 Moises Alou	1.25	3.00
HR48 Mark Lewis	1.25	3.00
HR49 Hal Morris	1.25	3.00
HR50 Edgar Renteria	1.25	3.00
HR51 Rickey Henderson	3.00	8.00
HR52 Pat Listach	1.25	3.00
HR53 John Wasdin	1.25	3.00
HR54 James Baldwin	1.25	3.00
HR55 Brian Jordan	1.25	3.00
HR56 Edgar Martinez	2.00	5.00
HR57 Wil Cordero	1.25	3.00
HR58 Danny Tartabull	1.25	3.00
HR59 Keith Lockhart	1.25	3.00
HR60 Rico Brogna	1.25	3.00
HR61 Ricky Bottalico	1.25	3.00
HR62 Terry Pendleton	1.25	3.00
HR63 Bret Boone	1.25	3.00
HR64 Charlie Hayes	1.25	3.00
HR65 Marc Newfield	1.25	3.00
HR66 Sterling Hitchcock	1.25	3.00
HR67 Roberto Alomar	2.00	5.00
HR68 John Jaha	1.25	3.00
HR69 Greg Colbrunn	1.25	3.00
HR70 Sal Fasano	1.25	3.00
HR71 Brooks Kieschnick	1.25	3.00
HR72 Pedro Martinez	2.00	5.00
HR73 Kevin Elster	1.25	3.00
HR74 Ellis Burks	1.25	3.00
HR75 Chuck Finley	1.25	3.00
HR76 John Olerud	1.25	3.00
HR77 Jay Bell	1.25	3.00
HR78 Allen Watson	1.25	3.00
HR79 Darryl Strawberry	1.25	3.00
HR80 Orlando Miller	1.25	3.00
HR81 Jose Herrera	1.25	3.00
HR82 Andy Pettitte	2.00	5.00
HR83 Juan Guzman	1.25	3.00
HR84 Alan Benes	1.25	3.00
HR85 Jack McDowell	1.25	3.00
HR86 Ugueth Urbina	1.25	3.00
HR87 Rocky Coppinger	1.25	3.00
HR88 Jeff Cirillo	1.25	3.00
HR89 Tom Glavine	2.00	5.00
HR90 Robby Thompson	1.25	3.00
HR91 Barry Bonds	6.00	15.00
HR92 Carlos Delgado	1.25	3.00
HR93 Mo Vaughn	1.25	3.00
HR94 Ryne Sandberg	5.00	12.00
HR95 Alex Rodriguez	5.00	12.00
HR96 Brady Anderson	1.25	3.00
HR97 Scott Brosius	1.25	3.00
HR98 Dennis Eckersley	1.25	3.00
HR99 Brian McRae	1.25	3.00
HR100 Rey Ordonez	1.25	3.00
HR101 John Valentin	1.25	3.00

HR102 Brett Butler 1.25 3.00
HR103 Eric Karros 1.25 3.00
HR104 Harold Baines 1.25 3.00
HR105 Javier Lopez 1.25 3.00
HR106 Alan Trammell 1.25 3.00
HR107 Jim Thome 2.00 5.00
HR108 Frank Rodriguez 1.25 3.00
HR109 Bernard Gilkey 1.25 3.00
HR110 Reggie Jefferson 1.25 3.00
HR111 Scott Stahoviak 1.25 3.00
HR112 Steve Gibralter 1.25 3.00
HR113 Todd Hollandsworth 1.25 3.00
HR114 Ruben Rivera 1.25 3.00
HR115 Dennis Martinez 1.25 3.00
HR116 Mariano Rivera 2.00 5.00
HR117 John Smoltz 2.00 5.00
HR118 John Mabry 1.25 3.00
HR119 Tom Gordon 1.25 3.00
HR120 Alex Ochoa 1.25 3.00
HR121 Jamey Wright 1.25 3.00
HR122 Dave Nilsson 1.25 3.00
HR123 Bobby Bonilla 1.25 3.00
HR124 Al Leiter 1.25 3.00
HR125 Rick Aguilera 1.25 3.00
HR126 Jeff Brantley 1.25 3.00
HR127 Kevin Brown 1.25 3.00
HR128 George Arias 1.25 3.00
HR129 Darren Oliver 1.25 3.00
HR130 Bill Pulsipher 1.25 3.00
HR131 Roberto Hernandez 1.25 3.00
HR132 Delino DeShields 1.25 3.00
HR133 Mark Grudzielanek 1.25 3.00
HR134 John Wetteland 1.25 3.00
HR135 Carlos Baerga 1.25 3.00
HR136 Paul Sorrento 1.25 3.00
HR137 Leo Gomez 1.25 3.00
HR138 Andy Ashby 1.25 3.00
HR139 Julio Franco 1.25 3.00
HR140 Brian Hunter 1.25 3.00
HR141 Jermaine Dye 1.25 3.00
HR142 Tony Clark 1.25 3.00
HR143 Ruben Sierra 1.25 3.00
HR144 Donovan Osborne 1.25 3.00
HR145 Mark McLemore 1.25 3.00
HR146 Terry Steinbach 1.25 3.00
HR147 Bob Wells 1.25 3.00
HR148 Chan Ho Park 1.25 3.00
HR149 Tim Salmon 1.25 3.00
HR150 Paul O'Neill 2.00 5.00
HR151 Cal Ripken 12.00 30.00
HR152 Wally Joyner 1.25 3.00
HR153 Omar Vizquel 2.00 5.00
HR154 Mike Mussina 2.00 5.00
HR155 Andres Galarraga 1.25 3.00
HR156 Ken Griffey Jr. 5.00 12.00
HR157 Kenny Lofton 1.25 3.00
HR158 Ray Durham 1.25 3.00
HR159 Hideo Nomo 2.00 5.00
HR160 Ozzie Guillen 1.25 3.00
HR161 Roger Pavlik 1.25 3.00
HR162 Manny Ramirez 2.00 5.00
HR163 Mark Lemke 1.25 3.00
HR164 Mike Stanley 1.25 3.00
HR165 Chuck Knoblauch 1.25 3.00
HR166 Kimera Bartee 1.25 3.00
HR167 Wade Boggs 2.00 5.00
HR168 Jay Buhner 1.25 3.00
HR169 Eric Young 1.25 3.00
HR170 Jose Canseco 2.00 5.00
HR171 Dwight Gooden 1.25 3.00
HR172 Fred McGriff 2.00 5.00
HR173 Sandy Alomar Jr. 1.25 3.00
HR174 Andy Benes 1.25 3.00
HR175 Dean Palmer 1.25 3.00
HR176 Larry Walker 1.25 3.00
HR177 Charles Nagy 1.25 3.00
HR178 David Cone 1.25 3.00
HR179 Mark Grace 2.00 5.00
HR180 Robin Ventura 1.25 3.00
HR181 Roger Clemens 5.00 12.00
HR182 Bobby Witt 1.25 3.00
HR183 Vinny Castilla 1.25 3.00
HR184 Gary Sheffield 1.25 3.00
HR185 Dan Wilson 1.25 3.00
HR186 Roger Cedeno 1.25 3.00
HR187 Mark McGwire 4.00 10.00
HR188 Darren Bragg 1.25 3.00
HR189 Quinton McCracken 1.25 3.00
HR190 Randy Myers 1.25 3.00
HR191 Jeromy Burnitz 1.25 3.00
HR192 Randy Johnson 3.00 8.00
HR193 Chipper Jones 3.00 8.00
HR194 Greg Vaughn 1.25 3.00
HR195 Travis Fryman 1.25 3.00
HR196 Tim Naehring 1.25 3.00
HR197 B.J. Surhoff 1.25 3.00
HR198 Juan Gonzalez 1.25 3.00
HR199 Terrell Wade 1.25 3.00
HR200 Jeff Frye 1.25 3.00
HR201 Joey Cora 1.25 3.00
HR202 Raul Mondesi 1.25 3.00
HR203 Ivan Rodriguez 2.00 5.00
HR204 Armando Reynoso 1.25 3.00
HR205 Jeffrey Hammonds 1.25 3.00
HR206 Darren Dreifort 1.25 3.00
HR207 Kevin Seitzer 1.25 3.00
HR208 Tino Martinez 2.00 5.00
HR209 Jim Bruske SP 1.25 3.00
HR210 Jeff Suppan 1.25 3.00
HR211 Mark Carreon 1.25 3.00
HR212 Wilson Alvarez 1.25 3.00
HR213 John Burkett 1.25 3.00
HR214 Tony Phillips
HR215 Greg Maddux 5.00 12.00
HR216 Mark Whiten 1.25 3.00
HR217 Curtis Pride 1.25 3.00
HR218 Lyle Mouton 1.25 3.00
HR219 Todd Hundley 1.25 3.00
HR220 Greg Gagne 1.25 3.00
HR221 Rich Amaral 1.25 3.00
HR222 Tom Goodwin 1.25 3.00
HR223 Chris Hoiles 1.25 3.00
HR224 Jayhawk Owens 1.25 3.00
HR225 Kenny Rogers 1.25 3.00
HR226 Mike Greenwell 1.25 3.00
HR227 Mark Wohlers 1.25 3.00
HR228 Henry Rodriguez 1.25 3.00
HR229 Robert Perez 1.25 3.00
HR230 Jeff Kent 1.25 3.00
HR231 Darryl Hamilton 1.25 3.00
HR232 Alex Fernandez 1.25 3.00
HR233 Ron Karkovice 1.25 3.00
HR234 Jimmy Haynes 1.25 3.00
HR235 Craig Biggio 2.00 5.00
HR236 Ray Lankford 1.25 3.00
HR237 Lance Johnson 1.25 3.00
HR238 Matt Williams 1.25 3.00
HR239 Chad Curtis 1.25 3.00
HR240 Mark Thompson 1.25 3.00
HR241 Jason Giambi 1.25 3.00
HR242 Barry Larkin 2.00 5.00
HR243 Paul Molitor 3.00 8.00
HR244 Sammy Sosa 2.00 5.00
HR245 Kevin Tapani 1.25 3.00
HR246 Marquis Grissom 1.25 3.00
HR247 Joe Carter 1.25 3.00
HR248 Ramon Martinez 1.25 3.00
HR249 Tony Gwynn 3.00 8.00
HR250 Andy Fox 1.25 3.00
HR251 Troy O'Leary 1.25 3.00
HR252 Warren Newson 1.25 3.00
HR253 Troy Percival 1.25 3.00
HR254 Jamie Moyer 1.25 3.00
HR255 Danny Graves 1.25 3.00
HR256 David Wells 1.25 3.00
HR257 Todd Zeile 1.25 3.00
HR258 Raul Ibanez 1.25 3.00
HR259 Tyler Houston 1.25 3.00
HR260 LaTroy Hawkins 1.25 3.00
HR261 Joey Hamilton 1.25 3.00
HR262 Mike Sweeney 1.25 3.00
HR263 Brant Brown 1.25 3.00
HR264 Pat Hentgen 1.25 3.00
HR265 Mark Johnson 1.25 3.00
HR266 Robb Nen 1.25 3.00
HR267 Justin Thompson 1.25 3.00
HR268 Ron Gant 1.25 3.00
HR269 Jeff D'Amico 1.25 3.00
HR270 Shawn Estes 1.25 3.00
HR271 Derek Bell 1.25 3.00
HR272 Fernando Valenzuela 1.25 3.00
HR273 Tom Pagnozzi 1.25 3.00
HR274 John Burke
HR275 Ed Sprague 1.25 3.00
HR276 F.P. Santangelo 1.25 3.00
HR277 Todd Greene 1.25 3.00
HR278 Butch Huskey 1.25 3.00
HR279 Steve Finley 1.25 3.00
HR280 Eric Davis 1.25 3.00
HR281 Shawn Green 1.25 3.00
HR282 Al Martin 1.25 3.00
HR283 Michael Tucker 1.25 3.00
HR284 Shane Reynolds 1.25 3.00
HR285 Matt Mieske 1.25 3.00
HR286 Jose Rosado 1.25 3.00
HR287 Mark Langston 1.25 3.00
HR288 Ralph Milliard 1.25 3.00
HR289 Mike Lansing 1.25 3.00
HR290 Scott Servais 1.25 3.00
HR291 Royce Clayton 1.25 3.00
HR292 Mike Grace 1.25 3.00
HR293 James Mouton 1.25 3.00
HR294 Charles Johnson 1.25 3.00
HR295 Gary Gaetti 1.25 3.00
HR296 Kevin Mitchell 1.25 3.00
HR297 Carlos Garcia 1.25 3.00
HR298 Desi Relaford 1.25 3.00
HR299 Jason Thompson 1.25 3.00
HR300 Osvaldo Fernandez 1.25 3.00
HR301 Fernando Vina 1.25 3.00
HR302 Jose Offerman 1.25 3.00
HR303 Yamil Benitez 1.25 3.00
HR304 J.T. Snow 1.25 3.00
HR305 Rafael Bournigal 1.25 3.00
HR306 Jason Isringhausen 1.25 3.00
HR307 Bobby Higginson 1.25 3.00
HR308 Nerio Rodriguez 1.25 3.00
HR309 Brian Giles 6.00 15.00
HR310 Andruw Jones 2.00 5.00
HR311 Tony Graffanino
HR312 Arquimedez Pozo 1.25 3.00
HR313 Jermaine Allensworth 1.25 3.00
HR314 Jeff Darwin 1.25 3.00
HR315 George Williams 1.25 3.00
HR316 Karim Garcia 1.25 3.00
HR317 Trey Beamon 1.25 3.00
HR318 Mac Suzuki 1.25 3.00
HR319 Robin Jennings 1.25 3.00
HR320 Danny Patterson 1.25 3.00
HR321 Damon Mashore 1.25 3.00
HR322 Wendell Magee 1.25 3.00
HR323 Dax Jones 1.25 3.00
HR324 Todd Walker 1.25 3.00
HR325 Marvin Benard 1.25 3.00
HR326 Mike Cameron
HR327 Marcus Jensen 1.25 3.00
HR328 Eddie Murray CL 2.00 5.00
HR329 Paul Molitor CL 3.00 8.00
HR330 Todd Hundley CL 1.25 3.00
HR331 Norm Charlton 1.25 3.00
HR332 Bruce Ruffin 1.25 3.00
HR333 John Wetteland 1.25 3.00
HR334 Marquis Grissom 1.25 3.00
HR335 Sterling Hitchcock 1.25 3.00
HR336 John Olerud 1.25 3.00
HR337 David Wells 1.25 3.00
HR338 Chili Davis 1.25 3.00
HR339 Mark Lewis 1.25 3.00
HR340 Kenny Lofton 1.25 3.00
HR341 Alex Fernandez 1.25 3.00
HR342 Ruben Sierra 1.25 3.00
HR343 Delino DeShields 1.25 3.00
HR344 John Wasdin 1.25 3.00
HR345 Dennis Martinez 1.25 3.00
HR346 Kevin Elster 1.25 3.00
HR347 Bobby Bonilla 1.25 3.00
HR348 Jaime Navarro 1.25 3.00
HR349 Chad Curtis 1.25 3.00
HR350 Terry Steinbach 1.25 3.00
HR351 Ariel Prieto 1.25 3.00
HR352 Jeff Kent 1.25 3.00
HR353 Carlos Garcia 1.25 3.00
HR354 Mark Whiten 1.25 3.00
HR355 Todd Zeile 1.25 3.00
HR356 Eric Davis 1.25 3.00
HR357 Greg Colbrunn 1.25 3.00
HR358 Moises Alou 1.25 3.00
HR359 Allen Watson 1.25 3.00
HR360 Jose Canseco 2.00 5.00
HR361 Matt Williams 1.25 3.00
HR362 Jeff King 1.25 3.00
HR363 Darryl Hamilton 1.25 3.00
HR364 Mark Clark 1.25 3.00
HR365 J.T. Snow 1.25 3.00
HR366 Kevin Mitchell 1.25 3.00
HR367 Orlando Miller 1.25 3.00
HR368 Rico Brogna 1.25 3.00
HR369 Mike James 1.25 3.00
HR370 Brad Ausmus 1.25 3.00
HR371 Darryl Kile 1.25 3.00
HR372 Edgardo Alfonzo 1.25 3.00
HR373 Julian Tavarez 1.25 3.00
HR374 Darren Lewis 1.25 3.00
HR375 Steve Karsay 1.25 3.00
HR376 Lee Stevens 1.25 3.00
HR377 Albie Lopez 1.25 3.00
HR378 Orel Hershiser 1.25 3.00
HR379 Lee Smith 1.25 3.00
HR380 Rick Helling 1.25 3.00
HR381 Carlos Perez 1.25 3.00
HR382 Tony Tarasco 1.25 3.00
HR383 Melvin Nieves 1.25 3.00
HR384 Benji Gil 1.25 3.00
HR385 Devon White 1.25 3.00
HR386 Armando Benitez 1.25 3.00
HR387 Bill Swift 1.25 3.00
HR388 John Smiley 1.25 3.00
HR389 Midre Cummings 1.25 3.00
HR390 Tim Belcher 1.25 3.00
HR391 Tim Raines 1.25 3.00
HR392 Todd Worrell 1.25 3.00
HR393 Quilvio Veras 1.25 3.00
HR394 Matt Lawton 1.25 3.00
HR395 Aaron Sele 1.25 3.00
HR396 Bip Roberts 1.25 3.00
HR397 Denny Neagle 1.25 3.00
HR398 Tyler Green 1.25 3.00
HR399 Hipolito Pichardo 1.25 3.00
HR400 Scott Erickson 1.25 3.00
HR401 Bobby Jones 1.25 3.00
HR402 Jim Edmonds 1.25 3.00
HR403 Chad Ogea 1.25 3.00
HR404 Cal Eldred 1.25 3.00
HR405 Pat Listach 1.25 3.00
HR406 Todd Stottlemyre 1.25 3.00
HR407 Phil Nevin 1.25 3.00
HR408 Otis Nixon 1.25 3.00
HR409 Billy Ashley 1.25 3.00
HR410 Jimmy Key 1.25 3.00
HR411 Mike Timlin 1.25 3.00
HR412 Joe Vitiello 1.25 3.00
HR413 Rondell White 1.25 3.00
HR414 Jeff Fassero 1.25 3.00
HR415 Rex Hudler 1.25 3.00
HR416 Curt Schilling 1.25 3.00
HR417 Rich Becker 1.25 3.00
HR418 William Van Landingham 1.25 3.00
HR419 Chris Snopek 1.25 3.00
HR420 David Segui 1.25 3.00
HR421 Eddie Murray 2.00 5.00
HR422 Shane Andrews 1.25 3.00
HR423 Gary DiSarcina 1.25 3.00
HR424 Brian Hunter 1.25 3.00
HR425 Willie Greene 1.25 3.00
HR426 Felipe Crespo 1.25 3.00
HR427 Jason Bates 1.25 3.00
HR428 Albert Belle 1.25 3.00
HR429 Rey Sanchez 1.25 3.00
HR430 Roger Clemens 5.00 12.00
HR431 Deion Sanders 2.00 5.00
HR432 Ernie Young
HR433 Jay Bell 1.25 3.00
HR434 Jeff Blauser 1.25 3.00
HR435 Lenny Dykstra 1.25 3.00
HR436 Chuck Carr 1.25 3.00
HR437 Russ Davis 1.25 3.00
HR438 Carl Everett 1.25 3.00
HR439 Damion Easley 1.25 3.00
HR440 Pat Kelly 1.25 3.00
HR441 Pat Rapp 1.25 3.00
HR442 Dave Justice 1.25 3.00
HR443 Graeme Lloyd 1.25 3.00
HR444 Damon Buford 1.25 3.00
HR445 Jose Valentin 1.25 3.00
HR446 Jason Schmidt 1.25 3.00
HR447 Dave Martinez 1.25 3.00
HR448 Danny Tartabull 1.25 3.00
HR449 Jose Vizcaino 1.25 3.00
HR450 Steve Avery 1.25 3.00
HR451 Mike Devereaux 1.25 3.00
HR452 Jim Eisenreich 1.25 3.00
HR453 Mark Leiter 1.25 3.00
HR454 Roberto Kelly 1.25 3.00
HR455 Benito Santiago 1.25 3.00
HR456 Steve Trachsel 1.25 3.00
HR457 Gerald Williams 1.25 3.00
HR458 Pete Schourek 1.25 3.00
HR459 Esteban Loaiza 1.25 3.00
HR460 Mel Rojas 1.25 3.00
HR461 Tim Wakefield 1.25 3.00
HR462 Tony Fernandez 1.25 3.00
HR463 Doug Drabek 1.25 3.00
HR464 Joe Girardi 1.25 3.00
HR465 Mike Bordick 1.25 3.00
HR466 Jim Leyritz 1.25 3.00
HR467 Erik Hanson 1.25 3.00
HR468 Michael Tucker 1.25 3.00
HR469 Tony Womack 1.25 3.00
HR470 Doug Glanville 1.25 3.00
HR471 Rudy Pemberton 1.25 3.00
HR472 Keith Lockhart 1.25 3.00
HR473 Nomar Garciaparra 3.00 8.00
HR474 Scott Rolen 2.00 5.00
HR475 Jason Dickson 1.25 3.00
HR476 Glendon Rusch 1.25 3.00
HR477 Todd Walker 1.25 3.00
HR478 Dmitri Young 1.25 3.00
HR479 Rod Myers 1.25 3.00
HR480 Wilton Guerrero 1.25 3.00
HR481 Jorge Posada 2.00 5.00
HR482 Brant Brown 1.25 3.00
HR483 Bubba Trammell 1.25 3.00
HR484 Jose Guillen 1.25 3.00
HR485 Scott Spiezio 1.25 3.00
HR486 Bob Abreu 2.00 5.00
HR487 Chris Holt 1.25 3.00
HR488 Deivi Cruz 1.25 3.00
HR489 Vladimir Guerrero 3.00 8.00
HR490 Julio Santana 1.25 3.00
HR491 Ray Montgomery 1.25 3.00
HR492 Kevin Orie 1.25 3.00
HR493 Todd Hundley GY 1.25 3.00
HR494 Tim Salmon GY 1.25 3.00
HR495 Albert Belle GY 1.25 3.00
HR496 Manny Ramirez GY 2.00 5.00
HR497 Rafael Palmeiro GY 1.25 3.00
HR498 Juan Gonzalez GY 1.25 3.00
HR499 Ken Griffey Jr. GY 5.00 12.00
HR500 Andruw Jones GY 2.00 5.00
HR501 Mike Piazza GY 3.00 8.00
HR502 Jeff Bagwell GY 2.00 5.00
HR503 Bernie Williams GY 2.00 5.00
HR504 Barry Bonds GY 6.00 15.00
HR505 Ken Caminiti GY 1.25 3.00
HR506 Darin Erstad GY 1.25 3.00
HR507 Alex Rodriguez GY 5.00 12.00
HR508 Frank Thomas GY 3.00 8.00
HR509 Chipper Jones GY 3.00 8.00
HR510 Mo Vaughn GY 1.25 3.00
HR511 Mark McGwire GY 4.00 10.00
HR512 Fred McGriff GY 2.00 5.00
HR513 Jay Buhner GY 1.25 3.00
HR514 Jim Thome GY 2.00 5.00
HR515 Gary Sheffield GY 1.25 3.00
HR516 Dean Palmer GY 1.25 3.00
HR517 Henry Rodriguez GY 1.25 3.00
HR518 Andy Pettitte RF 2.00 5.00
HR519 Mike Mussina RF 2.00 5.00
HR520 Greg Maddux RF 5.00 12.00
HR521 John Smoltz RF 2.00 5.00
HR522 Hideo Nomo RF 2.00 5.00
HR523 Troy Percival RF 1.25 3.00
HR524 John Wetteland RF 1.25 3.00
HR525 Roger Clemens RF 5.00 12.00
HR526 Charles Nagy RF 1.25 3.00
HR527 Mariano Rivera RF 2.00 5.00
HR528 Tom Glavine RF 2.00 5.00
HR529 Randy Johnson RF 3.00 8.00
HR530 Jason Isringhausen RF 1.25 3.00
HR531 Alex Fernandez RF 1.25 3.00
HR532 Kevin Brown RF 1.25 3.00
HR533 Chuck Knoblauch TG 1.25 3.00
HR534 Rusty Greer TG 1.25 3.00
HR535 Tony Gwynn TG 3.00 8.00
HR536 Ryan Klesko TG 1.25 3.00
HR537 Ryne Sandberg TG 5.00 12.00
HR538 Barry Larkin TG 2.00 5.00
HR539 Will Clark TG 2.00 5.00
HR540 Kenny Lofton TG 1.25 3.00
HR541 Paul Molitor TG 3.00 8.00
HR542 Roberto Alomar TG 2.00 5.00
HR543 Rey Ordonez TG 1.25 3.00
HR544 Jason Giambi TG 1.25 3.00
HR545 Derek Jeter TG 8.00 20.00
HR546 Cal Ripken TG 12.00 30.00
HR547 Ivan Rodriguez TG 2.00 5.00
HR548 Ken Griffey Jr. CL 5.00 12.00
HR549 Frank Thomas CL 3.00 8.00
HR550 Mike Piazza CL 3.00 8.00

1997 Score Premium Stock

A special Premium Stock version of the base series one set was produced exclusively for hobby outlets. The cards parallel the regular issue set except for a grey border, thicker card stock and a prominent gold foil "Premium Stock" logo on front. The cards were distributed in Premium Stock hobby packs. Second series Premium Stock cards were called "Hobby Reserve."

COMPLETE SET (551) 30.00 80.00
COMP.SERIES 1 (330) 15.00 40.00
COMP.SERIES 2 (221) 15.00 40.00
*STARS: .75X TO 2X BASIC CARDS
*ROOKIES: .6X TO 1.5X BASIC CARDS
*IRABU: .4X TO 1X BASIC IRABU

1997 Score Reserve Collection

Randomly inserted in second series hobby reserve packs only at a rate of one in 11, this set is parallel to the regular second series set. The cards are printed on thick 20 pt. foil card stock with screen printing for a raised ink effect. A large grey "Reserve Collection" logo is printed on each card back.

*STARS: 5X TO 12X BASIC CARDS
*ROOKIES: 2.5X TO 6X BASIC CARDS
*IRABU: 1.5X TO 3X BASIC IRABU
SER.2 ODDS 1:11 HOBBY

1997 Score Showcase Series

Randomly inserted in first series packs at a rate of one in seven hobby packs, one in two jumbo packs, one in four magazine and one in seven retail packs, and second series packs at a rate of one in five hobby packs and one in seven retail packs, cards from this set are silver-coated parallel versions of the regular Score set.

*STARS: 3X TO 8X BASIC CARDS
*ROOKIES: 1.5X TO 4X BASIC CARDS
*IRABU: .5X TO 1.2X BASIC IRABU
SER.1 ODDS 1:7 H/R, 1:2 JUM, 1:4 MAG
SER.2 ODDS 1:5 HOBBY, 1:7 RETAIL

1997 Score Showcase Series Artist's Proofs

Randomly inserted in first series hobby and retail packs at a rate of one in 35, and second series hobby 1:23 and second series retail 1:35, cards from this 551-card set are parallel to the more common Showcase Series set. The cards are printed on holographic laminated card stock with a prismatic foil background and stamped with an Artist's Proof logo on front.

*STARS: 10X TO 25X BASIC CARDS
*ROOKIES: 4X TO 10X BASIC CARDS
*IRABU: 2X TO 5X BASIC IRABU
SER.1 ODDS 1:35 H/R, 1:7 JUM, 1:17 MAG
SER.2 ODDS 1:23 HOBBY, 1:35 RETAIL

1997 Score All-Star Fanfest

This 20-card insert set features players that were involved in the 1996 All-Star game. The cards were available at a rate of 1:29 in special retail Score I boxes.

COMPLETE SET (20) 40.00 80.00
1 Frank Thomas 1.50 4.00
2 Jeff Bagwell 2.00 5.00
3 Chuck Knoblauch .75 2.00
4 Ryne Sandberg 2.00 5.00
5 Alex Rodriguez 4.00 10.00
6 Chipper Jones 3.00 8.00
7 Jim Thome 1.25 3.00
8 Ken Caminiti .60 1.50
9 Albert Belle .60 1.50
10 Tony Gwynn 3.00 8.00
11 Ken Griffey Jr. 4.00 10.00
12 Andruw Jones 2.50 6.00
13 Juan Gonzalez 1.25 3.00
14 Brian Jordan .60 1.50
15 Ivan Rodriguez 2.00 5.00
16 Mike Piazza 4.00 10.00
17 Andy Pettitte .75 2.00
18 John Smoltz 1.25 3.00
19 John Wetteland .60 1.50
20 Mark Wohlers .40 1.00

1997 Score Blast Masters

Randomly inserted in second series packs at a rate of 1:35 (retail) and 1:23 (hobby reserve), this 18-card set features color player photos on a gold prismatic foil card.

COMPLETE SET (18) 40.00 100.00
SER.2 ODDS 1:35 RETAIL, 1:23 HOBBY
1 Mo Vaughn .75 2.00
2 Mark McGwire 5.00 12.00
3 Juan Gonzalez .75 2.00
4 Albert Belle .75 2.00
5 Barry Bonds 6.00 15.00
6 Ken Griffey Jr. 3.00 8.00
7 Andruw Jones 1.25 3.00
8 Chipper Jones 2.00 5.00
9 Mike Piazza 3.00 8.00
10 Jeff Bagwell 1.25 3.00
11 Dante Bichette .75 2.00
12 Alex Rodriguez 3.00 8.00
13 Gary Sheffield .75 2.00
14 Ken Caminiti .75 2.00
15 Sammy Sosa 2.00 5.00
16 Vladimir Guerrero 2.00 5.00
17 Brian Jordan .75 2.00
18 Tim Salmon 1.25 3.00

1997 Score Franchise

Randomly inserted in series one hobby packs only at a rate of one in 72, this nine-card set honors superstar players for their irreplaceable contribution to their team. The fronts display sepia player portraits on a white baseball replica background. The backs carry an action player photo with a sentence about the player which explains why he was selected for this set.

COMPLETE SET (9) 8.00 20.00
SER.1 ODDS 1:72 H/R, 1:17 JUM, 1:35 MAG
*GLOWING: 1.25X TO 3X BASIC FRANCHISE
GLOW.SER.1 ODDS 1:240H/R, 1:79J, 1:120M
1 Ken Griffey Jr. .75 2.00
2 John Smoltz .30 .75
3 Cal Ripken 1.50 4.00
4 Chipper Jones .50 1.25
5 Mike Piazza .75 2.00
6 Albert Belle .20 .50
7 Frank Thomas .50 1.25
8 Sammy Sosa .50 1.25
9 Roberto Alomar .30 .75

1997 Score Heart of the Order

Randomly inserted in packs at a rate of 1:23 (retail) and 1:15 (hobby reserve), this 36-card set features color photos of players on six teams with a panorama of the stadium in the background. Each team's three cards form one collectible unit. Eighteen of these cards are found in retail packs, and eighteen in Hobby Reserve packs.

COMPLETE SET (36) 40.00 100.00
STATED ODDS 1:23 RETAIL, 1:15 HOBBY
1 Will Clark 1.00 2.50
2 Ivan Rodriguez 1.00 2.50
3 Juan Gonzalez .60 1.50
4 Frank Thomas 1.50 4.00
5 Albert Belle .60 1.50
6 Robin Ventura .60 1.50
7 Alex Rodriguez 2.50 6.00
8 Jay Buhner .60 1.50
9 Ken Griffey Jr. 2.50 6.00
10 Rafael Palmeiro 1.00 2.50
11 Roberto Alomar 1.00 2.50
12 Cal Ripken 5.00 12.00
13 Manny Ramirez 1.00 2.50
14 Matt Williams .60 1.50
15 Jim Thome 1.00 2.50
16 Derek Jeter 4.00 10.00
17 Wade Boggs 1.00 2.50
18 Bernie Williams 1.00 2.50
19 Chipper Jones 1.50 4.00
20 Andruw Jones 1.00 2.50
21 Ryan Klesko .60 1.50
22 Mike Piazza 2.50 6.00
23 Wilton Guerrero .60 1.50
24 Raul Mondesi .60 1.50
25 Tony Gwynn 2.00 5.00
26 Greg Vaughn .60 1.50
27 Ken Caminiti .60 1.50
28 Brian Jordan .60 1.50
29 Ron Gant .60 1.50
30 Dmitri Young .60 1.50
31 Darin Erstad .60 1.50
32 Tim Salmon 1.00 2.50
33 Jim Edmonds .60 1.50
34 Chuck Knoblauch .60 1.50
35 Paul Molitor .60 1.50
36 Todd Walker .60 1.50

1997 Score Highlight Zone

Randomly inserted in series one hobby packs only at a rate of one in 35, this 18-card set honors those mega-stars who have the incredible ability to consistently make the highlight films. The set is printed on thicker card stock with special foil stamping and a dot matrix holographic background.

COMPLETE SET (18) 60.00 150.00
SER.1 ODDS 1:35 HOBBY, 1:9 JUMBO PS
1 Frank Thomas 2.50 6.00
2 Ken Griffey Jr. 4.00 10.00
3 Mo Vaughn 1.00 2.50
4 Albert Belle 1.00 2.50
5 Mike Piazza 4.00 10.00
6 Barry Bonds 8.00 20.00
7 Greg Maddux 4.00 10.00
8 Sammy Sosa 2.50 6.00
9 Jeff Bagwell 1.50 4.00
10 Alex Rodriguez 4.00 10.00
11 Chipper Jones 2.50 6.00
12 Brady Anderson 1.00 2.50
13 Ozzie Smith 1.00 2.50
14 Edgar Martinez 1.50 4.00
15 Cal Ripken 8.00 20.00
16 Ryan Klesko 1.00 2.50
17 Randy Johnson 2.50 6.00
18 Eddie Murray 2.50 6.00

1997 Score Pitcher Perfect

Randomly inserted in series one packs at a rate of one in 23, this 15-card set features players photographed by Randy Johnson in unique poses and foil stamping. The backs carry player information.

COMPLETE SET (15) 2.00 5.00
SER.1 ODDS 1:23 H/R,1:11 MAG,1:15 JUM PS
1 Cal Ripken .60 1.50
2 Alex Rodriguez .30 .75
3 Alex Rodriguez 1.25 3.00
Cal Ripken
4 Edgar Martinez .10 .30
5 Ivan Rodriguez .10 .30
6 Mark McGwire .50 1.25
7 Tim Salmon .10 .30
8 Chili Davis .07 .20
9 Joe Carter .07 .20
10 Frank Thomas .20 .50
11 Will Clark .10 .30
12 Mo Vaughn .07 .20
13 Wade Boggs .10 .30
14 Ken Griffey Jr. .30 .75
15 Randy Johnson .20 .50

1997 Score Stand and Deliver

Randomly inserted in series two packs at a rate of 1:71 (retail) and 1:47 (hobby reserve), this 24-card set features color player photos printed on silver foil card stock. The set is broken into six separate 4-card groupings. Groups contain players from the following teams: 1-4 (Braves), 5-8 (Mariners), 9-12 (Yankees), 13-16 (Dodgers), 17-20 (Indians) and 21-24 (Wild Card). The four players featured within the Wild Card group are from "lesser" teams not given a shot at winning the World Series. Each of these cards, unlike cards 1-20, has a "Wild Card" logo stamped on front. Collectors were then supposed to gather up the particular group that won the 1997 World Series, in this case - the Florida Marlins. Since none of the featured teams won, the 4-card Wild Card group was designated as the winner. The winning cards could then be mailed into Pinnacle for a special gold upgrade version of the set, framed in glass.

COMPLETE SET (24) 100.00 250.00
SER.2 ODDS 1:41 HOBBY, 1:71 RETAIL
1 Andruw Jones 2.50 6.00
2 Greg Maddux 6.00 15.00
3 Chipper Jones 4.00 10.00
4 John Smoltz 2.50 6.00
5 Ken Griffey Jr. 6.00 15.00
6 Alex Rodriguez 6.00 15.00
7 Jay Buhner 1.50 4.00
8 Randy Johnson 4.00 10.00
9 Derek Jeter 10.00 25.00
10 Andy Pettitte 2.50 6.00
11 Bernie Williams 2.50 6.00
12 Mariano Rivera 4.00 10.00
13 Mike Piazza 6.00 15.00
14 Hideo Nomo 4.00 10.00
15 Raul Mondesi 1.50 4.00
16 Todd Hollandsworth 1.50 4.00
17 Manny Ramirez 2.50 6.00
18 Jim Thome 2.50 6.00
19 Dave Justice 1.50 4.00
20 Matt Williams 1.50 4.00
21 Juan Gonzalez W 1.50 4.00
22 Jeff Bagwell W 2.50 6.00
23 Cal Ripken W 12.50 30.00
24 Frank Thomas W 4.00 10.00

1997 Score Stellar Season

Randomly inserted in series one pre-priced magazine packs only at a rate of one in 35, this 18-card set features players who had a star season. The cards are printed using dot matrix holographic printing.

COMPLETE SET (18) 25.00 60.00
SER.1 STATED ODDS 1:35 MAGAZINE
1 Juan Gonzalez .60 1.50
2 Chuck Knoblauch .60 1.50
3 Jeff Bagwell 1.00 2.50
4 John Smoltz 1.00 2.50
5 Mark McGwire 4.00 10.00
6 Ken Griffey Jr. 2.50 6.00
7 Frank Thomas 1.50 4.00
8 Alex Rodriguez 2.50 6.00
9 Mike Piazza 2.50 6.00
10 Albert Belle .60 1.50
11 Roberto Alomar 1.00 2.50
12 Sammy Sosa 1.50 4.00
13 Mo Vaughn .60 1.50
14 Brady Anderson .60 1.50
15 Henry Rodriguez .60 1.50
16 Eric Young .60 1.50
17 Gary Sheffield .60 1.50
18 Ryan Klesko .60 1.50

1997 Score Titanic Taters

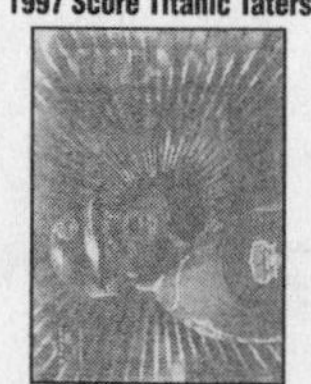

Randomly inserted in series one retail packs only at a rate of one in 35, this 18-card set honors the long-ball ability of some of the league's top sluggers and uses dot matrix holographic printing.

COMPLETE SET (18) 50.00 120.00
SER.1 STATED ODDS 1:35 RETAIL
1 Mark McGwire 6.00 15.00
2 Mike Piazza 4.00 10.00
3 Ken Griffey Jr. 4.00 10.00
4 Juan Gonzalez 1.00 2.50
5 Frank Thomas 2.50 6.00
6 Albert Belle 1.00 2.50
7 Sammy Sosa 2.50 6.00
8 Jeff Bagwell 1.50 4.00
9 Todd Hundley 1.00 2.50
10 Ryan Klesko 1.00 2.50
11 Brady Anderson 1.00 2.50
12 Mo Vaughn 1.00 2.50
13 Jay Buhner 1.00 2.50
14 Chipper Jones 2.50 6.00
15 Barry Bonds 8.00 20.00
16 Gary Sheffield 1.00 2.50
17 Alex Rodriguez 4.00 10.00
18 Cecil Fielder 1.00 2.50

1998 Score

This 270-card set was distributed in 10-card packs exclusively to retail outlets with a suggested retail price of $.99. The fronts feature color player photos in a thin white border. The backs carry player information and statistics. In addition, two unnumbered checklist cards were created. The first card was available only in regular issue packs and provided listings for the standard 270-card set. A blank-backed checklist card was randomly seeded exclusively into All-Star Edition packs (released about three months after the regular packs went live). This checklist card provided listings only for the three insert sets exclusively distributed in All-Star Edition packs (First Pitch, Loaded Lineup and New Season).

COMPLETE SET (270) 15.00 40.00
1 Andruw Jones .10 .30
2 Dan Wilson .07 .20
3 Hideo Nomo .20 .50
4 Chuck Carr .07 .20
5 Barry Bonds .60 1.50
6 Jack McDowell .07 .20
7 Albert Belle .07 .20
8 Francisco Cordova .07 .20
9 Greg Maddux .30 .75
10 Alex Rodriguez .30 .75
11 Steve Avery .07 .20
12 Chuck McElroy .07 .20
13 Larry Walker .07 .20
14 Hideki Irabu .07 .20
15 Roberto Alomar .10 .30
16 Neifi Perez .07 .20
17 Jim Thome .10 .30
18 Rickey Henderson .20 .50

19 Andres Galarraga	.07	.20
20 Jeff Fassero	.07	.20
21 Kevin Young	.07	.20
22 Derek Jeter	.50	1.25
23 Andy Benes	.07	.20
24 Mike Piazza	.30	.75
25 Todd Stottlemyre	.07	.20
26 Michael Tucker	.07	.20
27 Denny Neagle	.07	.20
28 Javier Lopez	.07	.20
29 Aaron Sele	.07	.20
30 Ryan Klesko	.07	.20
31 Dennis Eckersley	.07	.20
32 Quinton McCracken	.07	.20
33 Brian Anderson	.07	.20
34 Ken Griffey Jr.	.30	.75
35 Shawn Estes	.07	.20
36 Tim Wakefield	.07	.20
37 Jimmy Key	.07	.20
38 Jeff Bagwell	.10	.30
39 Edgardo Alfonzo	.07	.20
40 Mike Cameron	.07	.20
41 Mark McGwire	.50	1.25
42 Tino Martinez	.10	.30
43 Cal Ripken	.60	1.50
44 Curtis Goodwin	.07	.20
45 Bobby Ayala	.07	.20
46 Sandy Alomar Jr.	.07	.20
47 Bobby Jones	.07	.20
48 Omar Vizquel	.10	.30
49 Roger Clemens	.40	1.00
50 Tony Gwynn	.25	.60
51 Chipper Jones	.20	.50
52 Ron Coomer	.07	.20
53 Dmitri Young	.07	.20
54 Brian Giles	.07	.20
55 Steve Finley	.07	.20
56 David Cone	.07	.20
57 Andy Pettitte	.10	.30
58 Wilton Guerrero	.07	.20
59 Deion Sanders	.10	.30
60 Carlos Delgado	.07	.20
61 Jason Giambi	.07	.20
62 Ozzie Guillen	.07	.20
63 Jay Bell	.07	.20
64 Barry Larkin	.10	.30
65 Sammy Sosa	.20	.50
66 Bernie Williams	.10	.30
67 Terry Steinbach	.07	.20
68 Scott Rolen	.10	.30
69 Melvin Nieves	.07	.20
70 Craig Biggio	.10	.30
71 Todd Greene	.07	.20
72 Greg Gagne	.07	.20
73 Shigetoshi Hasegawa	.07	.20
74 Mark McLemore	.07	.20
75 Darren Bragg	.07	.20
76 Brett Butler	.07	.20
77 Ron Gant	.07	.20
78 Mike Difelice RC	.07	.20
79 Charles Nagy	.07	.20
80 Scott Hatteberg	.07	.20
81 Brady Anderson	.07	.20
82 Jay Buhner	.07	.20
83 Todd Hollandsworth	.07	.20
84 Geronimo Berroa	.07	.20
85 Jeff Suppan	.07	.20
86 Pedro Martinez	.10	.30
87 Roger Cedeno	.07	.20
88 Ivan Rodriguez	.10	.30
89 Jaime Navarro	.07	.20
90 Chris Hoiles	.07	.20
91 Nomar Garciaparra	.30	.75
92 Rafael Palmeiro	.10	.30
93 Darin Erstad	.07	.20
94 Kenny Lofton	.07	.20
95 Mike Timlin	.07	.20
96 Chris Clemons	.07	.20
97 Vinny Castilla	.07	.20
98 Charlie Hayes	.07	.20
99 Lyle Mouton	.07	.20
100 Jason Dickson	.07	.20
101 Justin Thompson	.07	.20
102 Pat Kelly	.07	.20
103 Chan Ho Park	.07	.20
104 Ray Lankford	.07	.20
105 Frank Thomas	.20	.50
106 Jermaine Allensworth	.07	.20
107 Doug Drabek	.07	.20
108 Todd Hundley	.07	.20
109 Carl Everett	.07	.20
110 Edgar Martinez	.10	.30
111 Robin Ventura	.07	.20
112 John Wetteland	.07	.20
113 Mariano Rivera	.20	.50
114 Jose Rosado	.07	.20
115 Ken Caminiti	.07	.20
116 Paul O'Neill	.10	.30
117 Tim Salmon	.10	.30
118 Eduardo Perez	.07	.20
119 Mike Jackson	.07	.20
120 John Smoltz	.10	.30
121 Brant Brown	.07	.20
122 John Mabry	.07	.20
123 Chuck Knoblauch	.07	.20
124 Reggie Sanders	.07	.20
125 Ken Hill	.07	.20
126 Mike Mussina	.10	.30
127 Chad Curtis	.07	.20
128 Todd Worrell	.07	.20
129 Chris Widger	.07	.20
130 Damon Mashore	.07	.20
131 Kevin Brown	.10	.30
132 Bip Roberts	.07	.20
133 Tim Naehring	.07	.20
134 Dave Martinez	.07	.20
135 Jeff Blauser	.07	.20
136 David Justice	.07	.20
137 Dave Hollins	.07	.20
138 Pat Hentgen	.07	.20
139 Darren Daulton	.07	.20
140 Ramon Martinez	.07	.20
141 Raul Casanova	.07	.20
142 Tom Glavine	.10	.30
143 J.T. Snow	.07	.20
144 Tony Graffanino	.07	.20
145 Randy Johnson	.20	.50
146 Orlando Merced	.07	.20
147 Jeff Juden	.07	.20
148 Darryl Kile	.07	.20
149 Ray Durham	.07	.20
150 Alex Fernandez	.07	.20
151 Joey Cora	.07	.20
152 Royce Clayton	.07	.20
153 Randy Myers	.07	.20
154 Charles Johnson	.07	.20
155 Alan Benes	.07	.20
156 Mike Bordick	.07	.20
157 Heathcliff Slocumb	.07	.20
158 Roger Bailey	.07	.20
159 Reggie Jefferson	.07	.20
160 Ricky Bottalico	.07	.20
161 Scott Erickson	.07	.20
162 Matt Williams	.07	.20
163 Robb Nen	.07	.20
164 Matt Stairs	.07	.20
165 Ismael Valdes	.07	.20
166 Lee Stevens	.07	.20
167 Gary DiSarcina	.07	.20
168 Brad Radke	.07	.20
169 Mike Lansing	.07	.20
170 Armando Benitez	.07	.20
171 Mike James	.07	.20
172 Russ Davis	.07	.20
173 Lance Johnson	.07	.20
174 Joey Hamilton	.07	.20
175 John Valentin	.07	.20
176 David Segui	.07	.20
177 David Wells	.07	.20
178 Delino DeShields	.07	.20
179 Eric Karros	.07	.20
180 Jim Leyritz	.07	.20
181 Raul Mondesi	.07	.20
182 Travis Fryman	.07	.20
183 Todd Zeile	.07	.20
184 Brian Jordan	.07	.20
185 Rey Ordonez	.07	.20
186 Jim Edmonds	.07	.20
187 Terrell Wade	.07	.20
188 Marquis Grissom	.07	.20
189 Chris Snopek	.07	.20
190 Shane Reynolds	.07	.20
191 Jeff Frye	.07	.20
192 Paul Sorrento	.07	.20
193 James Baldwin	.07	.20
194 Brian McRae	.07	.20
195 Fred McGriff	.10	.30
196 Troy Percival	.07	.20
197 Rich Amaral	.07	.20
198 Juan Guzman	.07	.20
199 Cecil Fielder	.07	.20
200 Willie Blair	.07	.20
201 Chili Davis	.07	.20
202 Gary Gaetti	.07	.20
203 B.J. Surhoff	.07	.20
204 Steve Cooke	.07	.20
205 Chuck Finley	.07	.20
206 Jeff Kent	.07	.20
207 Ben McDonald	.07	.20
208 Jeffrey Hammonds	.07	.20
209 Tom Goodwin	.07	.20
210 Billy Ashley	.07	.20
211 Wil Cordero	.07	.20
212 Shawon Dunston	.07	.20
213 Tony Phillips	.07	.20
214 Jamie Moyer	.07	.20
215 John Jaha	.07	.20
216 Troy O'Leary	.07	.20
217 Brad Ausmus	.07	.20
218 Garret Anderson	.07	.20
219 Wilson Alvarez	.07	.20
220 Kent Mercker	.07	.20
221 Wade Boggs	.10	.30
222 Mark Wohlers	.07	.20
223 Kevin Appier	.07	.20
224 Tony Fernandez	.07	.20
225 Ugueth Urbina	.07	.20
226 Gregg Jefferies	.07	.20
227 Mo Vaughn	.07	.20
228 Arthur Rhodes	.07	.20
229 Jorge Fabregas	.07	.20
230 Mark Gardner	.07	.20
231 Shane Mack	.07	.20
232 Jorge Posada	.10	.30
233 Jose Cruz Jr.	.07	.20
234 Paul Konerko	.07	.20
235 Derrek Lee	.10	.30
236 Steve Woodard	.07	.20
237 Todd Dunwoody	.07	.20
238 Fernando Tatis	.07	.20
239 Jacob Cruz	.07	.20
240 Pokey Reese	.07	.20
241 Mark Kotsay	.07	.20
242 Matt Morris	.07	.20
243 Antone Williamson	.07	.20
244 Ben Grieve	.07	.20
245 Ryan McGuire	.07	.20
246 Lou Collier	.07	.20
247 Shannon Stewart	.07	.20
248 Brett Tomko	.07	.20
249 Bobby Estalella	.07	.20
250 Livan Hernandez	.07	.20
251 Todd Helton	.10	.30
252 Jaret Wright	.07	.20
253 Darryl Hamilton IM	.07	.20
254 Stan Javier IM	.07	.20
255 Glenallen Hill IM	.07	.20
256 Mark Gardner IM	.07	.20
257 Cal Ripken IM	.30	.75
258 Mike Mussina IM	.07	.20
259 Mike Piazza IM	.20	.50
260 Sammy Sosa IM	.10	.30
261 Todd Hundley IM	.07	.20
262 Eric Karros IM	.07	.20
263 Denny Neagle IM	.07	.20
264 Jeromy Burnitz IM	.07	.20
265 Greg Maddux IM	.20	.50
266 Tony Clark IM	.07	.20
267 Vladimir Guerrero IM	.10	.30
268 Cal Ripken CL UER	.30	.75
269 Ken Griffey Jr. CL	.20	.50
270 Mark McGwire CL	.25	.60
NNO CL Regular Issue	.07	.20
NNO CL All-Star Edition	.10	.30

1998 Score Showcase Series

Randomly inserted in packs at the rate of one in seven, this 160-card set is an all silver-foil partial parallel rendition of the base set.

*SHOWCASE: 2X TO 5X BASIC CARDS
STATED ODDS 1:7

1998 Score Showcase Series Artist's Proofs

Randomly inserted in packs at the rate of one in 35, this 160-card set is a partial parallel to the base set and features color player photos printed on full prismatic foil with the "Artist Proof" stamp on the fronts.

*STARS: 1.5X TO 4X BASIC SHOWCASE
STATED ODDS 1:35

1998 Score All Score Team

Randomly inserted in packs at the rate of one in 35, this 20-card set features color player images on a metallic foil background. The backs carry a small player head photo with information stating why the player was selected to this appear in this set.

COMPLETE SET (20)	40.00	100.00
STATED ODDS 1:35		
1 Mike Piazza	3.00	8.00
2 Ivan Rodriguez	1.25	3.00
3 Frank Thomas	2.00	5.00
4 Mark McGwire	5.00	12.00
5 Ryne Sandberg	2.00	5.00
6 Roberto Alomar	1.25	3.00
7 Cal Ripken	6.00	15.00
8 Barry Larkin	1.25	3.00
9 Paul Molitor	2.00	5.00
10 Travis Fryman	.75	2.00
11 Kirby Puckett	4.00	10.00
12 Tony Gwynn	2.50	6.00
13 Ken Griffey Jr.	3.00	8.00
14 Juan Gonzalez	2.00	5.00
15 Barry Bonds	6.00	15.00
16 Andruw Jones	1.25	3.00
17 Roger Clemens	4.00	10.00
18 Randy Johnson	2.00	5.00
19 Greg Maddux	3.00	8.00
20 Dennis Eckersley	.75	2.00

1998 Score All-Score Team Gold Jones Autograph

This special autographed card was created as a prize for Pinnacle's 1998 "Score with Score" hobby shop promotion. Dealers that ordered 1998 Score 1 baseball direct from Pinnacle or through one of their distributors were automatically entered into Pinnacle's hobby shop locator program. In December of 1997, all eligible shops were mailed a "Score with Score" contest ballot box and collector entry forms. Over the next several months, store customers could then fill out and submit forms. In the Spring of 1998, 600 lucky collectors were randomly selected winners. 100 people won actual Interleague game-used baseballs and 500 people won this special Andruw Jones autographed All-Score Team Gold card. The card is easy to differentiate from the more common All-Score Team inserts by it's bold gold (rather than silver) foil front and Jones' black ink signature.

1 Andruw Jones Gold AU/500 *	20.00	50.00

1998 Score Complete Players

Randomly inserted in packs at the rate of one in 23, this 30-card set features three photos of each of the ten listed players with full holographic foil stamping.

COMPLETE SET (30)	60.00	150.00
STATED ODDS 1:23		
*GOLD: .4X TO 1X BASIC COMP.PLAY.		
GOLD: RANDOM IN SCORE TEAM SETS		
1A Ken Griffey Jr.	2.50	6.00
2A Mark McGwire	4.00	10.00
3A Derek Jeter	4.00	10.00
4A Cal Ripken	5.00	12.00
5A Mike Piazza	2.50	6.00
6A Darin Erstad	.60	1.50
7A Frank Thomas	1.50	4.00
8A Andruw Jones	1.00	2.50
9A Nomar Garciaparra	2.50	6.00
10A Manny Ramirez	1.50	4.00

1998 Score First Pitch

This 20 card insert set features star players anxiously awaiting opening day. The player's name is at top with the "First Pitch" words on the bottom of the card. These cards were inserted one every 11 All-Star Edition packs.

COMPLETE SET (20)	25.00	60.00
STATED ODDS 1:11 AS EDIT.		
1 Ken Griffey Jr.	1.50	4.00
2 Frank Thomas	1.00	2.50
3 Alex Rodriguez	1.50	4.00
4 Cal Ripken	3.00	8.00
5 Chipper Jones	1.00	2.50
6 Juan Gonzalez	1.00	2.50
7 Derek Jeter	2.50	6.00
8 Mike Piazza	1.50	4.00
9 Andruw Jones	.60	1.50
10 Nomar Garciaparra	1.50	4.00
11 Barry Bonds	3.00	8.00
12 Jeff Bagwell	.60	1.50
13 Scott Rolen	.60	1.50
14 Hideo Nomo	1.00	2.50
15 Roger Clemens	2.00	5.00
16 Mark McGwire	2.50	6.00
17 Greg Maddux	1.50	4.00
18 Albert Belle	.40	1.00
19 Ivan Rodriguez	.60	1.50
20 Mo Vaughn	.40	1.00

1998 Score Andruw Jones Icon Order Card

This one-card set features a white bordered color photo of Andruw Jones kneeling with his right arm resting on his bat. The card was always inserted on the top of the prepriced 1998 Score 27-card blister packs. The backs carry instructions on how to order a Pinnacle Icon display.

1 Andruw Jones	.40	1.00

1998 Score Loaded Lineup

This 10-card set was inserted one every 45 Score All-Star Edition packs. The cards feature a player for each position and the cards are printed on all-foil micro etched cards.

COMPLETE SET (10)	25.00	60.00
STATED ODDS 1:45 AS EDIT.		
LL1 Chuck Knoblauch	.75	2.00
LL2 Tony Gwynn	2.50	6.00
LL3 Frank Thomas	2.00	5.00
LL4 Ken Griffey Jr.	3.00	8.00
LL5 Mike Piazza	3.00	8.00
LL6 Barry Bonds	6.00	15.00
LL7 Cal Ripken	6.00	15.00
LL8 Paul Molitor	2.00	5.00
LL9 Nomar Garciaparra	3.00	8.00
LL10 Greg Maddux	3.00	8.00

1998 Score New Season

This 15 card insert set features a mix of young and veteran players waiting for the new season to begin. The players photo take up most of the borderless cards with his name on top and the words "New Season" on the bottom.

COMPLETE SET (15)	20.00	50.00
STATED ODDS 1:23 AS EDIT.		
NS1 Kenny Lofton	.75	2.00
NS2 Nomar Garciaparra	2.50	6.00
NS3 Todd Helton	1.00	2.50
NS4 Miguel Tejada	1.25	3.00
NS5 Jaret Wright	.60	1.50
NS6 Alex Rodriguez	2.50	6.00
NS7 Vladimir Guerrero	1.25	3.00
NS8 Ken Griffey Jr.	3.00	8.00
NS9 Ben Grieve	.60	1.50
NS10 Travis Lee	.60	1.50
NS11 Jose Cruz Jr.	.60	1.50
NS12 Paul Konerko	.75	2.00
NS13 Frank Thomas	1.25	3.00
NS14 Chipper Jones	1.25	3.00
NS15 Cal Ripken	5.00	12.00

1998 Score Rookie Traded

The 1998 Score Rookie and Traded set was issued in one series totalling 270 cards. The 10-card packs retail for $.99 each. The set contains the subset: Spring Training (253-267). Cards numbered one through 50 were inserted one per pack making them short prints compared to the other cards in the set. Paul Konerko signed 500 cards which were also randomly seeded into packs. Notable Rookie Cards include Magglio Ordonez.

COMPLETE SET (270)	15.00	40.00
COMMON SP (1-50)	.10	.30
COMMON CARD (51-270)	.07	.20
COMMON RC (51-270)	.07	.20
1 Tony Clark	.10	.30
2 Juan Gonzalez	.10	.30
3 Frank Thomas	.30	.75
4 Greg Maddux	.50	1.25
5 Barry Larkin	.20	.50
6 Derek Jeter	.75	2.00
7 Randy Johnson	.30	.75
8 Roger Clemens	.60	1.50
9 Tony Gwynn	.40	1.00
10 Barry Bonds	.75	2.00
11 Jim Edmonds	.10	.30
12 Bernie Williams	.20	.50
13 Ken Griffey Jr.	.50	1.25
14 Tim Salmon	.20	.50
15 Mo Vaughn	.10	.30
16 David Justice	.10	.30
17 Jose Cruz Jr.	.10	.30
18 Andruw Jones	.20	.50
19 Sammy Sosa	.30	.75
20 Jeff Bagwell	.20	.50
21 Scott Rolen	.20	.50
22 Darin Erstad	.10	.30
23 Andy Pettitte	.20	.50
24 Mike Mussina	.20	.50
25 Mark McGwire	.75	2.00
26 Hideo Nomo	.30	.75
27 Chipper Jones	.30	.75
28 Cal Ripken	1.00	2.50
29 Chuck Knoblauch	.10	.30
30 Alex Rodriguez	.50	1.25
31 Jim Thome	.20	.50
32 Mike Piazza	.50	1.25
33 Ivan Rodriguez	.20	.50
34 Roberto Alomar	.20	.50
35 Nomar Garciaparra	.50	1.25
36 Albert Belle	.10	.30
37 Vladimir Guerrero	.30	.75
38 Raul Mondesi	.10	.30
39 Larry Walker	.10	.30
40 Manny Ramirez	.20	.50
41 Tino Martinez	.20	.50
42 Craig Biggio	.20	.50
43 Jay Buhner	.10	.30
44 Kenny Lofton	.10	.30
45 Pedro Martinez	.20	.50
46 Edgar Martinez	.20	.50
47 Gary Sheffield	.10	.30
48 Jose Guillen	.10	.30
49 Ken Caminiti	.10	.30
50 Bobby Higginson	.10	.30
51 Alan Benes	.07	.20
52 Shawn Green	.07	.20
53 Ron Coomer	.07	.20
54 Charles Nagy	.07	.20
55 Steve Karsay	.07	.20
56 Matt Morris	.07	.20
57 Bobby Jones	.07	.20
58 Jason Kendall	.07	.20
59 Jeff Conine	.07	.20
60 Joe Girardi	.07	.20
61 Mark Kotsay	.07	.20
62 Eric Karros	.07	.20
63 Bartolo Colon	.07	.20
64 Mariano Rivera	.20	.50
65 Alex Gonzalez	.07	.20
66 Scott Spiezio	.07	.20
67 Luis Castillo	.07	.20
68 Joey Cora	.07	.20
69 Mark McLemore	.07	.20
70 Reggie Jefferson	.07	.20
71 Lance Johnson	.07	.20
72 Damian Jackson	.07	.20
73 Jeff D'Amico	.07	.20
74 David Ortiz	.30	.75
75 J.T. Snow	.07	.20
76 Todd Hundley	.07	.20
77 Billy Wagner	.07	.20
78 Vinny Castilla	.07	.20
79 Ismael Valdes	.07	.20
80 Neifi Perez	.07	.20
81 Derek Bell	.07	.20
82 Ryan Klesko	.07	.20
83 Rey Ordonez	.07	.20
84 Carlos Garcia	.07	.20
85 Curt Schilling	.07	.20
86 Robin Ventura	.07	.20
87 Pat Hentgen	.07	.20
88 Glendon Rusch	.07	.20
89 Hideki Irabu	.07	.20
90 Antone Williamson	.07	.20
91 Denny Neagle	.07	.20
92 Kevin Orie	.07	.20
93 Reggie Sanders	.07	.20
94 Brady Anderson	.07	.20
95 Andy Benes	.07	.20
96 John Valentin	.07	.20
97 Bobby Bonilla	.07	.20
98 Walt Weiss	.07	.20
99 Robin Jennings	.07	.20
100 Marty Cordova	.07	.20
101 Brad Ausmus	.07	.20
102 Brian Rose	.07	.20
103 Calvin Maduro	.07	.20
104 Raul Casanova	.07	.20
105 Jeff King	.07	.20
106 Sandy Alomar Jr.	.07	.20
107 Tim Naehring	.07	.20
108 Mike Cameron	.07	.20
109 Omar Vizquel	.10	.30
110 Brad Radke	.07	.20
111 Jeff Fassero	.07	.20
112 Deivi Cruz	.07	.20
113 Dave Hollins	.07	.20
114 Dean Palmer	.07	.20
115 Esteban Loaiza	.07	.20
116 Brian Giles	.07	.20
117 Steve Finley	.07	.20
118 Jose Canseco	.10	.30
119 Al Martin	.07	.20
120 Eric Young	.07	.20
121 Curtis Goodwin	.07	.20
122 Ellis Burks	.07	.20
123 Mike Hampton	.07	.20
124 Lou Collier	.07	.20
125 John Olerud	.07	.20
126 Ramon Martinez	.07	.20
127 Todd Dunwoody	.07	.20
128 Jermaine Allensworth	.07	.20
129 Eduardo Perez	.07	.20
130 Dante Bichette	.07	.20
131 Edgar Renteria	.07	.20
132 Bob Abreu	.07	.20
133 Rondell White	.07	.20
134 Michael Coleman	.07	.20
135 Jason Giambi	.07	.20
136 Brant Brown	.07	.20
137 Michael Tucker	.07	.20
138 Dave Nilsson	.07	.20
139 Benito Santiago	.07	.20
140 Ray Durham	.07	.20
141 Jeff Kent	.07	.20
142 Matt Stairs	.07	.20
143 Kevin Young	.07	.20
144 Eric Davis	.07	.20
145 John Wetteland	.07	.20
146 Esteban Yan RC	.10	.30
147 Wilton Guerrero	.07	.20
148 Moises Alou	.07	.20
149 Edgardo Alfonzo	.07	.20
150 Andy Ashby	.07	.20
151 Todd Walker	.07	.20
152 Jermaine Dye	.07	.20
153 Brian Hunter	.07	.20
154 Shawn Estes	.07	.20
155 Bernard Gilkey	.07	.20
156 Tony Womack	.07	.20
157 John Smoltz	.10	.30
158 Delino DeShields	.07	.20
159 Jacob Cruz	.07	.20
160 Javier Valentin	.07	.20
161 Chris Hoiles	.07	.20
162 Garret Anderson	.07	.20
163 Dan Wilson	.07	.20
164 Paul O'Neill	.10	.30
165 Matt Williams	.07	.20
166 Travis Fryman	.07	.20
167 Javier Lopez	.07	.20
168 Ray Lankford	.07	.20
169 Bobby Estalella	.07	.20
170 Henry Rodriguez	.07	.20
171 Quinton McCracken	.07	.20
172 Jaret Wright	.07	.20
173 Darryl Kile	.07	.20
174 Wade Boggs	.10	.30
175 Orel Hershiser	.07	.20
176 B.J. Surhoff	.07	.20
177 Fernando Tatis	.07	.20
178 Carlos Delgado	.07	.20
179 Jorge Fabregas	.07	.20
180 Tony Saunders	.07	.20
181 Devon White	.07	.20
182 Dmitri Young	.07	.20
183 Ryan McGuire	.07	.20
184 Mark Bellhorn	.07	.20
185 Joe Carter	.07	.20
186 Kevin Stocker	.07	.20
187 Mike Lansing	.07	.20
188 Jason Dickson	.07	.20
189 Charles Johnson	.07	.20
190 Will Clark	.10	.30
191 Shannon Stewart	.07	.20
192 Johnny Damon	.10	.30
193 Todd Greene	.07	.20
194 Carlos Baerga	.07	.20
195 David Cone	.07	.20
196 Pokey Reese	.07	.20
197 Livan Hernandez	.07	.20
198 Tom Glavine	.10	.30
199 Geronimo Berroa	.07	.20
200 Darryl Hamilton	.07	.20
201 Terry Steinbach	.07	.20
202 Robb Nen	.07	.20
203 Ron Gant	.07	.20
204 Rafael Palmeiro	.10	.30
205 Rickey Henderson	.20	.50
206 Justin Thompson	.07	.20
207 Jeff Suppan	.07	.20
208 Kevin Brown	.10	.30
209 Jimmy Key	.07	.20
210 Brian Jordan	.07	.20
211 Aaron Sele	.07	.20
212 Fred McGriff	.10	.30
213 Jay Bell	.07	.20
214 Andres Galarraga	.07	.20
215 Mark Grace	.10	.30
216 Brett Tomko	.07	.20
217 Francisco Cordova	.07	.20
218 Rusty Greer	.07	.20
219 Bubba Trammell	.07	.20
220 Derrek Lee	.10	.30
221 Brian Anderson	.07	.20
222 Mark Grudzielanek	.07	.20
223 Marquis Grissom	.07	.20
224 Gary DiSarcina	.07	.20
225 Jim Leyritz	.07	.20
226 Jeffrey Hammonds	.07	.20
227 Karim Garcia	.07	.20
228 Chan Ho Park	.07	.20
229 Brooks Kieschnick	.07	.20
230 Trey Beamon	.07	.20
231 Kevin Appier	.07	.20
232 Wally Joyner	.07	.20
233 Richie Sexson	.07	.20
234 Frank Catalanotto RC	.20	.50
235 Rafael Medina	.07	.20
236 Travis Lee	.07	.20
237 Eli Marrero	.07	.20
238 Carl Pavano	.07	.20
239 Enrique Wilson	.07	.20
240 Richard Hidalgo	.07	.20
241 Todd Helton	.10	.30
242 Ben Grieve	.07	.20
243 Mario Valdez	.07	.20
244 Magglio Ordonez RC	.60	1.50
245 Juan Encarnacion	.07	.20
246 Russell Branyan	.07	.20
247 Sean Casey	.07	.20
248 Abraham Nunez	.07	.20
249 Brad Fullmer	.07	.20
250 Paul Konerko	.07	.20
251 Miguel Tejada	.20	.50
252 Mike Lowell RC	.40	1.00
253 Ken Griffey Jr. ST	.20	.50
254 Frank Thomas ST	.10	.30
255 Alex Rodriguez ST	.20	.50
256 Jose Cruz Jr. ST	.07	.20
257 Jeff Bagwell ST	.20	.50
258 Chipper Jones ST	.10	.30
259 Mo Vaughn ST	.07	.20
260 Nomar Garciaparra ST	.20	.50
261 Jim Thome ST	.07	.20
262 Derek Jeter ST	.25	.60
263 Mike Piazza ST	.20	.50
264 Tony Gwynn ST	.10	.30
265 Scott Rolen ST	.10	.30
266 Andruw Jones ST	.10	.30
267 Cal Ripken ST	.30	.75
268 Checklist 1	.07	.20
269 Checklist 2	.07	.20
270 Checklist 3	.07	.20
S250 Paul Konerko AU/500	6.00	15.00

1998 Score Rookie Traded Showcase Series

Randomly inserted in packs at a rate of one in seven, this 160-card set is a parallel to the Score Rookie Traded base set.

*STARS 1-50: 1.25X TO 3X BASIC CARDS
*SHOWCASE 51-270: 2X TO 5X BASIC
*SHOWCASE RC'S 51-270: 1.5X TO 4X BASIC
STATED ODDS 1:7

1998 Score Rookie Traded Showcase Series Artist's Proofs

Randomly inserted in packs at a rate of one in 35, this 160-card set is a parallel to the Score Rookie Traded base set.

*SHOWCASE AP 1-50: 5X TO 12X BASIC
*SHOWCASE AP 51-270: 8X TO 20X BASIC
*SHOWCASE AP RC'S 51-270: 3X TO 8X BASIC
STATED ODDS 1:35

1998 Score Rookie Traded Showcase Series Artist's Proofs 1 of 1's

These extremely scarce parallel Artist's Proofs cards were randomly seeded into Rookie Traded hobby packs. Only one of each card was produced. They're easy to spot due to the gold foil circular logo directly on the middle of the card front that says "SCORE ONE OF ONE . . . 001/001". Due to scarcity no pricing is provided.

RANDOM INSERTS IN HOBBY PACKS
STATED PRINT RUN 1 SET
NO PRICING DUE TO SCARCITY

1998 Score Rookie Traded Complete Players

Randomly inserted in packs at a rate of one in 11, this 30-card set is an insert to the Score Rookie Traded base set. The card fronts feature special holographic foil stamping. Each player has three different cards highlighting his own power, speed and approach to the game. Put them together and form the Complete Player.

COMPLETE SET (30)	20.00	50.00
STATED ODDS 1:11		
THREE CARDS PER PLAYER		
ALL 3 VERSIONS SAME PRICE		
1A Ken Griffey Jr.	1.25	3.00
2A Larry Walker	.30	.75
3A Alex Rodriguez	1.25	3.00
4A Jose Cruz Jr.	.30	.75
5A Jeff Bagwell	.50	1.25
6A Greg Maddux	1.25	3.00
7A Ivan Rodriguez	.50	1.25
8A Roger Clemens	1.50	4.00
9A Chipper Jones	.75	2.00
10A Hideo Nomo	.75	2.00

1998 Score Rookie Traded Star Gazing

Randomly inserted in packs at a rate of one in 35, this 20-card set is an insert to the Score Rookie Traded base set. The fronts feature color action photos printed on a diamond-shaped star-gazing background. The player's name sits atop the player photo with the Score logo in the upper right corner.

COMPLETE SET (20)	10.00	25.00

STATED ODDS 1:35
1 Ken Griffey Jr. 1.00 2.50
2 Frank Thomas .60 1.50
3 Chipper Jones .60 1.50
4 Mark McGwire 1.50 4.00
5 Cal Ripken 2.00 5.00
6 Mike Piazza 1.00 2.50
7 Nomar Garciaparra 1.00 2.50
8 Derek Jeter 1.50 4.00
9 Juan Gonzalez .25 .60
10 Vladimir Guerrero .60 1.50
11 Alex Rodriguez 1.00 2.50
12 Tony Gwynn .75 2.00
13 Andruw Jones .40 1.00
14 Scott Rolen .40 1.00
15 Jose Cruz Jr. .25 .60
16 Mo Vaughn .25 .60
17 Bernie Williams .40 1.00
18 Greg Maddux 1.00 2.50
19 Tony Clark .25 .60
20 Ben Grieve .15 .40

2000 SkyBox

The 2000 SkyBox product was released in late May, 2000 as a 250-card set that featured 200-player cards, and 50-short printed prospect cards. The set also includes a horizontal parallel version of each of the 50 prospect cards (1:8). The last ten cards in the set feature dual player cards of some of the hottest prospects in baseball. The horizontal parallel version of these ten cards were inserted at one in 12 packs. Each pack contained 10-cards and carried a suggested retail price of 2.99.

COMP.MASTER SET (300) 60.00 120.00
COMP.SET w/o SP's (250) 15.00 40.00
COMMON CARD (1-200) .10 .30
COMMON (201S-240S) .75 2.00
COMMON (241S-250S) .30 .75
1 Cal Ripken 1.00 2.50
2 Ivan Rodriguez .20 .50
3 Chipper Jones .30 .75
4 Dean Palmer .10 .30
5 Devon White .10 .30
6 Ugueth Urbina .10 .30
7 Doug Glanville .10 .30
8 Damian Jackson .10 .30
9 Jose Canseco .20 .50
10 Billy Koch .10 .30
11 Brady Anderson .10 .30
12 Vladimir Guerrero .30 .75
13 Dan Wilson .10 .30
14 Kevin Brown .20 .50
15 Eddie Taubensee .10 .30
16 Jose Lima .10 .30
17 Greg Maddux .50 1.25
18 Manny Ramirez .20 .50
19 Brad Fullmer .10 .30
20 Ron Gant .10 .30
21 Edgar Martinez .20 .50
22 Pokey Reese .10 .30
23 Jason Varitek .30 .75
24 Neifi Perez .10 .30
25 Shane Reynolds .10 .30
26 Robin Ventura .20 .50
27 Scott Rolen .20 .50
28 Trevor Hoffman .20 .50
29 John Valentin .10 .30
30 Shannon Stewart .10 .30
31 Troy Glaus .10 .30
32 Kevin Millwood .10 .30
33 Jim Thome .20 .50
34 Rafael Roque .10 .30
35 Tino Martinez .20 .50
36 Jeffrey Hammonds .10 .30
37 Orlando Hernandez .10 .30
38 Kris Benson .10 .30
39 Fred McGriff .20 .50
40 Brian Jordan .10 .30
41 Trot Nixon .10 .30
42 Matt Clement .10 .30
43 Ray Durham .10 .30
44 Johnny Damon .20 .50
45 Todd Hollandsworth .10 .30
46 Edgardo Alfonzo .10 .30
47 Tim Hudson .10 .30
48 Tony Gwynn .40 1.00
49 Barry Bonds .75 2.00
50 Andruw Jones .20 .50
51 Pedro Martinez .20 .50
52 Mike Hampton .10 .30
53 Miguel Tejada .10 .30
54 Kevin Young .10 .30
55 J.T. Snow .10 .30
56 Carlos Delgado .10 .30
57 Bobby Howry .10 .30
58 Andres Galarraga .10 .30
59 Paul Konerko .10 .30
60 Mike Cameron .10 .30
61 Jeremy Giambi .10 .30
62 Todd Hundley .10 .30
63 Al Leiter .10 .30
64 Matt Stairs .10 .30
65 Edgar Renteria .10 .30
66 Jeff Kent .10 .30
67 John Wetteland .10 .30
68 Nomar Garciaparra .50 1.25
69 Jeff Weaver .10 .30
70 Matt Williams .10 .30
71 Kyle Farnsworth .10 .30
72 Brad Radke .10 .30
73 Eric Chavez .10 .30
74 J.D. Drew .10 .30
75 Steve Finley .10 .30
76 Pete Harnisch .10 .30
77 Chad Kreuter .10 .30
78 Todd Pratt .10 .30
79 John Jaha .10 .30
80 Armando Rios .10 .30
81 Luis Gonzalez .10 .30
82 Ryan Minor .10 .30
83 Juan Gonzalez .10 .30
84 Rickey Henderson .30 .75
85 Jason Giambi .10 .30
86 Shawn Estes .10 .30
87 Chad Curtis .10 .30
88 Jeff Cirillo .10 .30
89 Juan Encarnacion .10 .30
90 Tony Womack .10 .30
91 Mike Mussina .20 .50
92 Jeff Bagwell .20 .50
93 Rey Ordonez .10 .30
94 Joe McEwing .10 .30
95 Robb Nen .10 .30
96 Will Clark .20 .50
97 Chris Singleton .10 .30
98 Jason Kendall .10 .30
99 Ken Griffey Jr. .50 1.25
100 Rusty Greer .10 .30
101 Charles Johnson .10 .30
102 Carlos Lee .10 .30
103 Brad Ausmus .10 .30
104 Preston Wilson .10 .30
105 Ronnie Belliard .10 .30
106 Mike Lieberthal .10 .30
107 Alex Rodriguez .50 1.25
108 Jay Bell .10 .30
109 Frank Thomas .30 .75
110 Adrian Beltre .10 .30
111 Ron Coomer .10 .30
112 Ben Grieve .10 .30
113 Darryl Kile .10 .30
114 Erubiel Durazo .10 .30
115 Magglio Ordonez .10 .30
116 Gary Sheffield .10 .30
117 Joe Mays .10 .30
118 Fernando Tatis .10 .30
119 David Wells .10 .30
120 Tim Salmon .20 .50
121 Troy O'Leary .10 .30
122 Roberto Alomar .20 .50
123 Damion Easley .10 .30
124 Brant Brown .10 .30
125 Carlos Beltran .10 .30
126 Eric Karros .10 .30
127 Geoff Jenkins .10 .30
128 Roger Clemens .60 1.50
129 Warren Morris .10 .30
130 Eric Owens .10 .30
131 Jose Cruz Jr. .10 .30
132 Mo Vaughn .10 .30
133 Eric Young .10 .30
134 Kenny Lofton .10 .30
135 Marquis Grissom .10 .30
136 A.J. Burnett .10 .30
137 Bernie Williams .20 .50
138 Javy Lopez .10 .30
139 Jose Offerman .10 .30
140 Sean Casey .10 .30
141 Alex Gonzalez .10 .30
142 Carlos Febles .10 .30
143 Mike Piazza .50 1.25
144 Curt Schilling .10 .30
145 Ben Davis .10 .30
146 Rafael Palmeiro .20 .50
147 Scott Williamson .10 .30
148 Darin Erstad .10 .30
149 Joe Girardi .10 .30
150 Gerald Williams .10 .30
151 Richie Sexson .10 .30
152 Corey Koskie .10 .30
153 Paul O'Neill .20 .50
154 Chad Hermansen .10 .30
155 Randy Johnson .30 .75
156 Henry Rodriguez .10 .30
157 Bartolo Colon .10 .30
158 Tony Clark .10 .30
159 Mike Lowell .10 .30
160 Moises Alou .10 .30
161 Todd Walker .10 .30
162 Mariano Rivera .30 .75
163 Mark McGwire .75 2.00
164 Roberto Hernandez .10 .30
165 Larry Walker .10 .30
166 Albert Belle .10 .30
167 Barry Larkin .20 .50
168 Rolando Arrojo .10 .30
169 Mark Kotsay .10 .30
170 Ken Caminiti .10 .30
171 Dermal Brown .10 .30
172 Michael Barrett .10 .30
173 Jay Buhner .10 .30
174 Ruben Mateo .10 .30
175 Jim Edmonds .10 .30
176 Sammy Sosa .30 .75
177 Omar Vizquel .20 .50
178 Todd Helton .20 .50
179 Kevin Barker .10 .30
180 Derek Jeter .75 2.00
181 Brian Giles .10 .30
182 Greg Vaughn .10 .30
183 Roy Halladay .10 .30
184 Tom Glavine .20 .50
185 Craig Biggio .20 .50
186 Jose Vidro .10 .30
187 Andy Ashby .10 .30
188 Freddy Garcia .10 .30
189 Garret Anderson .10 .30
190 Mark Grace .20 .50
191 Travis Fryman .10 .30
192 Jeromy Burnitz .10 .30
193 Jacque Jones .10 .30
194 David Cone .10 .30
195 Ryan Rupe .10 .30
196 John Smoltz .20 .50
197 Daryle Ward .10 .30
198 Rondell White .10 .30
199 Bobby Abreu .10 .30
200 Justin Thompson .10 .30
201 Norm Hutchins .10 .30
201S Norm Hutchins SP .75 2.00
202 Ramon Ortiz .10 .30
202S Ramon Ortiz SP .75 2.00
203 Dan Wheeler .10 .30
203S Dan Wheeler SP .75 2.00
204 Matt Riley .10 .30
204S Matt Riley SP .75 2.00
205 Steve Lomasney .10 .30
205S Steve Lomasney SP .75 2.00
206 Chad Meyers .10 .30
206S Chad Meyers SP .75 2.00
207 Gary Glover RC .20 .50
207S Gary Glover SP .75 2.00
208 Joe Crede .40 1.00
208S Joe Crede SP 2.00 5.00
209 Kip Wells .10 .30
209S Kip Wells SP .75 2.00
210 Travis Dawkins .10 .30
210S Travis Dawkins SP .75 2.00
211 Denny Stark RC .20 .50
211S Denny Stark SP .75 2.00
212 Ben Petrick .10 .30
212S Ben Petrick SP .75 2.00
213 Eric Munson .10 .30
213S Eric Munson SP .75 2.00
214 Josh Beckett .30 .75
214S Josh Beckett SP 1.50 4.00
215 Pablo Ozuna .10 .30
215S Pablo Ozuna SP .75 2.00
216 Brad Penny .10 .30
216S Brad Penny SP .75 2.00
217 Julio Ramirez .10 .30
217S Julio Ramirez SP .75 2.00
218 Danny Peoples .10 .30
218S Danny Peoples SP .75 2.00
219 W.Rodriguez RC .20 .50
219S W.Rodriguez SP .75 2.00
220 Julio Lugo .10 .30
220S Julio Lugo SP .75 2.00
221 Mark Quinn .10 .30
221S Mark Quinn SP .75 2.00
222 Eric Gagne .40 1.00
222S Eric Gagne SP 1.50 4.00
223 Chad Green .10 .30
223S Chad Green SP .75 2.00
224 Tony Armas Jr. .10 .30
224S Tony Armas Jr. SP .75 2.00
225 Milton Bradley .10 .30
225S Milton Bradley SP .75 2.00
226 Rob Bell .10 .30
226S Rob Bell SP .75 2.00
227 Alfonso Soriano .30 .75
227S Alfonso Soriano SP 1.50 4.00
228 Wily Pena .10 .30
228S Wily Pena SP .75 2.00
229 Nick Johnson .10 .30
229S Nick Johnson SP .75 2.00
230 Ed Yarnall .10 .30
230S Ed Yarnall SP .75 2.00
231 Ryan Bradley .10 .30
231S Ryan Bradley SP .75 2.00
232 Adam Piatt .10 .30
232S Adam Piatt SP .75 2.00
233 Chad Harville .10 .30
233S Chad Harville SP .75 2.00
234 Alex Sanchez .10 .30
234S Alex Sanchez SP .75 2.00
235 Michael Coleman .10 .30
235S Michael Coleman SP .75 2.00
236 Pat Burrell .10 .30
236S Pat Burrell SP .75 2.00
237 Wascar Serrano RC .20 .50
237S Wascar Serrano SP .75 2.00
238 Rick Ankiel .10 .30
238S Rick Ankiel SP .75 2.00
239 Mike Lamb RC .30 .75
239S Mike Lamb SP 1.00 2.50
240 Vernon Wells .10 .30
240S Vernon Wells SP .75 2.00
241 Jorge Toca Geofrey Tomlinson .10 .30
241S Jorge Toca Geofrey Tomlinson SP .30 .75
242 Josh Phelps RC Shea Hillenbrand .20 .50
242S Josh Phelps Shea Hillenbrand SP .50 1.25
243 Aaron Myette Doug Davis .10 .30
243S Aaron Myette Doug Davis SP .50 1.25
244 Brett Laxton Rob Ramsay .10 .30
244S Brett Laxton Rob Ramsay SP .30 .75
245 B.J. Ryan Corey Lee .10 .30
245S B.J.Ryan Corey Lee SP .50 1.25
246 Chris Haas Wilton Veras .10 .30
246S Chris Haas Wilton Veras SP .30 .75
247 Jimmy Anderson Kyle Peterson .10 .30
247S Jimmy Anderson Kyle Peterson SP .30 .75
248 Jason Dewey Giuseppe Chiaramonte .10 .30
248S Jason Dewey Giuseppe Chiaramonte SP .30 .75
249 Guillermo Mota Orber Moreno .10 .30
249S Guillermo Mota Orber Moreno SP .30 .75
250 Julio Zuleta Steve Cox .20 .50
250S Julio Zuleta Steve Cox SP .30 .75

2000 SkyBox Star Rubies

Randomly inserted into packs at one in 12, this set parallels the 250-card base issued Skybox set. Card fronts feature red foil. Card backs carry a "SR" prefix.

*STARS: 4X TO 10X BASIC CARDS
*ROOKIES: 2X TO 5X BASIC VERTICAL

2000 SkyBox Star Rubies Extreme

Randomly inserted into packs, this set parallels the 250-card base issued Skybox set. There were 50 serial numbered sets produced. Card fronts feature red foil. Card backs carry a "SRE" prefix.

*STARS: 15X TO 40X BASIC CARDS
*ROOKIES: 6X TO 15X BASIC CARDS

2000 SkyBox Autographics

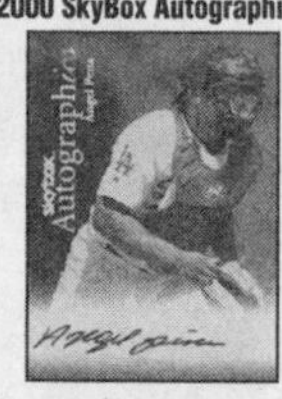

Randomly inserted in numerous Fleer/SkyBox brands insert set features autographed cards of a wide array of major league veterans and youngsters. Stated odds per brand are as follows: Dominion 1:144, E-X 1:24, Impact 1:216, Metal 1:96 and SkyBox 1:72.

*PURPLE FOIL: 1X TO 2.5X BASIC
PURPLE STATED PRINT RUN 50 #'d SETS
1 Bobby Abreu EX-IM-MT 10.00 25.00
2 Chad Allen MT 4.00 10.00
3 Moises Alou EX 6.00 15.00
4 Marlon Anderson IM-MT 4.00 10.00
5 Rick Ankiel DM-EX-IM-MT-SB 10.00 25.00
6 Glen Barker MT 4.00 10.00
7 Michael Barrett EX-SB 4.00 10.00
8 Josh Beckett EX-SB 8.00 20.00
9 Rob Bell EX-IM-MT-SB 4.00 10.00
10 Mark Bellhorn MT 20.00 50.00
11 Carlos Beltran EX-IM 6.00 15.00
12 Adrian Beltre EX-SB 8.00 20.00
13 Peter Bergeron DM-MT-SB 4.00 10.00
14 Lance Berkman MT-SB 10.00 25.00
15 Wade Boggs DM-EX-IM-MT 10.00 25.00
16 Barry Bonds DM-EX-IM-MT 100.00 175.00
17 Kent Bottenfield EX-MT 4.00 10.00
18 Milton Bradley EX-IM 6.00 15.00
19 Rico Brogna SB 6.00 15.00
20 Pat Burrell DM-EX-IM-MT-SB 6.00 15.00
21 Orlando Cabrera IM-SB 6.00 15.00
22 Miguel Cairo DM-MT 4.00 10.00
23 Mike Cameron DM-MT-SB 6.00 15.00
24 Chris Carpenter EX-IM-MT 12.50 30.00
25 Sean Casey EX-IM 6.00 15.00
26 Roger Cedeno MT-SB 4.00 10.00
27 Eric Chavez EX-SB 6.00 15.00
28 Bruce Chen SB 4.00 10.00
29 Will Clark EX 10.00 25.00
30 Johnny Damon EX-SB 8.00 20.00
31 Mike Darr EX-MT 6.00 15.00
32 Ben Davis EX-DM-SB 4.00 10.00
33 Russ Davis EX-DM 4.00 10.00
34 Carlos Delgado EX-IM 10.00 25.00
35 Jason Dewey EX-SB 4.00 10.00
36 Einar Diaz DM-MT 4.00 10.00
37 Octavio Dotel EX-SB 4.00 10.00
38 J.D. Drew EX-IM-MT-SB 6.00 15.00
39 Erubiel Durazo MT-SB 4.00 10.00
40 Ray Durham EX-IM-MT 6.00 15.00
41 Damion Easley EX-MT 4.00 10.00
42 Scott Elarton DM-MT 4.00 10.00
43 Kelvim Escobar EX-IM 4.00 10.00
44 Carlos Febles EX 4.00 10.00
45 Freddy Garcia EX 6.00 15.00
46 Jason Giambi SB 10.00 25.00
47 Jeremy Giambi DM-EX-MT 4.00 10.00
48 Doug Glanville MT-SB 6.00 15.00
49 Troy Glaus SB 10.00 25.00
50 Alex Gonzalez SB 4.00 10.00
51 Shawn Green MT-SB 10.00 25.00
52 Todd Greene DM-EX 4.00 10.00
53 Jason Grilli EX-SB 4.00 10.00
54 Vladimir Guerrero DM-EX-IM 10.00 25.00
55 Tony Gwynn DM-EX-IM-SB 20.00 50.00
56 Jerry Hairston Jr. EX-IM-MT 4.00 10.00
57 Mike Hampton EX-SB 6.00 15.00
58 Todd Helton EX-IM 8.00 20.00
59 Trevor Hoffman EX 10.00 25.00
60 Bobby Howry DM-MT 4.00 10.00
61 Tim Hudson DM-EX-SB 6.00 15.00
62 Norm Hutchins MT-SB 4.00 10.00
63 John Jaha EX-SB 4.00 10.00
64 Derek Jeter EX-SB 75.00 150.00
65 D'Angelo Jimenez EX-SB 4.00 10.00
66 Nick Johnson IM 6.00 15.00
67 Russ Johnson DM-EX-MT-SB 40.00 80.00
68 Andruw Jones DM-SB 10.00 25.00
69 Jacque Jones DM-MT 6.00 15.00
70 Gabe Kapler MT-SB 6.00 15.00
71 Jason Kendall EX-IM-SB 6.00 15.00
72 Adam Kennedy EX-SB 4.00 10.00
73 Cesar King EX-MT-SB 4.00 10.00
74 Paul Konerko EX-SB 8.00 20.00
75 Mark Kotsay EX-IM-MT-SB 6.00 15.00
76 Ray Lankford EX 6.00 15.00
77 Jason LaRue DM-EX 4.00 10.00
78 Matt Lawton DM-EX 4.00 10.00
79 Carlos Lee EX-SB 6.00 15.00
80 Mike Lieberthal EX-SB 6.00 15.00
81 Cole Liniak EX-IM-MT 4.00 10.00
82 Steve Lomasney EX-SB 4.00 10.00
83 Jose Macias EX-IM 4.00 10.00
84 Greg Maddux DM-EX-MT-SB-IM 75.00 150.00
85 Edgar Martinez EX-SB 15.00 40.00
86 Pedro Martinez DM-EX-MT 50.00 100.00
87 Ruben Mateo EX-IM-MT 4.00 10.00
88 Gary Matthews Jr. EX 4.00 10.00
89 Aaron McNeal EX-SB 4.00 10.00
90 Kevin Millwood SB 6.00 15.00
91 Raul Mondesi EX-SB 6.00 15.00
92 Orber Moreno EX-IM 4.00 10.00
93 Warren Morris EX-MT 4.00 10.00
94 Eric Munson EX-IM 4.00 10.00
95 Heath Murray EX-MT 4.00 10.00
96 Mike Mussina EX 10.00 25.00
97 Joe Nathan EX-IM-MT-SB 6.00 15.00
98 Magglio Ordonez SB 10.00 25.00
99 Eric Owens SB 4.00 10.00
100 Rafael Palmeiro EX-SB 20.00 50.00
101 Jim Parque EX-MT 4.00 10.00
102 Angel Pena EX-IM-MT-SB 4.00 10.00
103 Adam Piatt IM 4.00 10.00
104 Wily Pena EX-SB 12.50 30.00
105 Pokey Reese DM-EX 6.00 15.00
106 Matt Riley EX-IM 4.00 10.00
107 Cal Ripken EX-IM-MT-SB 60.00 120.00
108 Alex Rodriguez DM-EX-IM-MT-SB 40.00 80.00
109 Scott Rolen EX-IM-SB 10.00 25.00
110 Jimmy Rollins EX-IM-SB 12.50 30.00
111 Ryan Rupe DM-MT 4.00 10.00
112 B.J. Ryan EX-IM-SB 6.00 15.00
113 Tim Salmon SB 10.00 25.00
114 Randall Simon EX-MT 4.00 10.00
115 Chris Singleton EX-MT-SB 4.00 10.00
116 J.T. Snow DM-SB 6.00 15.00
117 Alfonso Soriano EX-IM 8.00 20.00
118 Shannon Stewart EX 6.00 15.00
119 Mike Sweeney EX-MT-SB 6.00 15.00
120 Miguel Tejada EX 10.00 25.00
121 Frank Thomas EX-IM 20.00 50.00
122 Wilton Veras EX-IM-MT 4.00 10.00
123 Jose Vidro DM-SB 4.00 10.00
124 Billy Wagner EX-IM 10.00 25.00
125 Jeff Weaver EX-IM 6.00 15.00
126 Rondell White EX-SB 6.00 15.00
127 Scott Williamson EX-IM-MT 4.00 10.00
128 Randy Wolf EX-MT 6.00 15.00
129 Tony Womack DM-MT 4.00 10.00
130 Jaret Wright EX-SB 4.00 10.00
131 Ed Yarnall DM-EX 4.00 10.00
132 Kevin Young DM-EX 4.00 10.00

2000 SkyBox E-Ticket

Randomly inserted into packs at one in four, this 15-card insert features players that are Hall of Fame bound. Card backs carry an "ET" prefix.

COMPLETE SET (15) 8.00 20.00
*STAR RUBY: 8X TO 20X BASIC E-TICKET
STAR RUBIES PR.RUN 100 SERIAL #'d SETS
ET1 Alex Rodriguez .60 1.50
ET2 Derek Jeter 1.00 2.50
ET3 Nomar Garciaparra .60 1.50
ET4 Cal Ripken 1.25 3.00
ET5 Sean Casey .15 .40
ET6 Mark McGwire 1.00 2.50
ET7 Sammy Sosa .40 1.00
ET8 Ken Griffey Jr. .60 1.50
ET9 Tony Gwynn .50 1.25
ET10 Pedro Martinez .25 .60
ET11 Chipper Jones .40 1.00
ET12 Vladimir Guerrero .40 1.00
ET13 Roger Clemens .75 2.00
ET14 Mike Piazza .60 1.50
ET15 Randy Johnson .40 1.00

2000 SkyBox Genuine Coverage

This insert features game-used jersey cards of 10 of the major league's top athletes. All cards are unnumbered and checklisted below alphabetically by player name. The set was split into two five card groups for hobby and retail distribution. The five "common" cards - tagged with an "HR" in the checklist below - were distributed in both hobby and retail packs at a rate of 1:399. The five "hobby-only" cards - tagged with an "H" in the checklist below - were seeded hobby packs at a rate of 1:144. In addition, Cal Ripken and Alex Rodriguez each signed 20 serial numbered copies of their jersey cards. These rare cards were seeded exclusively into hobby packs and are listed at the end of the checklist.

AU PRINT RUN 20 SERIAL #'d SETS
NO AU PRICING DUE TO SCARCITY
1 Jose Canseco H 6.00 15.00
2 J.D. Drew H 4.00 10.00
3 Troy Glaus HR 4.00 10.00
4 Manny Ramirez H 6.00 15.00
5 Cal Ripken HR 15.00 40.00
6 Alex Rodriguez HR 10.00 25.00
7 Ivan Rodriguez H 6.00 15.00
8 Frank Thomas H 6.00 15.00
9 Robin Ventura HR 4.00 10.00
10 Matt Williams HR 4.00 10.00
AU1 Cal Ripken AU/20
AU2 Alex Rodriguez AU 20

2000 SkyBox Higher Level

Randomly inserted into packs at one in 24, this insert features 10 players that take their game to the next level. Card backs carry a "HL" prefix.

COMPLETE SET (10) 20.00 50.00
*STAR RUBIES: 5X TO 12X BASIC HIGH LEVEL
STAR RUBIES PRINT RUN 50 SERIAL #'d SETS
HL1 Cal Ripken 4.00 10.00
HL2 Derek Jeter 3.00 8.00
HL3 Nomar Garciaparra 2.00 5.00
HL4 Chipper Jones 1.25 3.00
HL5 Mike Piazza 2.00 5.00
HL6 Ivan Rodriguez .75 2.00
HL7 Ken Griffey Jr. 2.00 5.00
HL8 Sammy Sosa 1.25 3.00
HL9 Alex Rodriguez 2.00 5.00
HL10 Mark McGwire 3.00 8.00

2000 SkyBox Preeminence

Randomly inserted into packs at one in 24, this insert set features 10 of major league baseball's top athletes. Card backs carry a "P" prefix.

COMPLETE SET (10) 15.00 40.00
*STAR RUBIES: 5X TO 12X BASIC PRE-EM
STAR RUBIES PRINT RUN 50 SERIAL #'d SETS
P1 Pedro Martinez .75 2.00
P2 Derek Jeter 3.00 8.00
P3 Nomar Garciaparra 2.00 5.00
P4 Alex Rodriguez 2.00 5.00
P5 Mark McGwire 3.00 8.00
P6 Sammy Sosa 1.25 3.00
P7 Sean Casey .50 1.25
P8 Mike Piazza 2.00 5.00
P9 Chipper Jones 1.25 3.00
P10 Ivan Rodriguez .75 2.00

2000 SkyBox Skylines

Randomly inserted into packs at one in 11, this insert set features ten MLB stars against the backdrop of the city they play in. Card backs carry a "SL" prefix.

COMPLETE SET (10) 10.00 25.00
*STAR RUBIES: 10X TO 25X BASIC SKYLINES
STAR RUBIES PRINT RUN 50 SERIAL #'d SETS
SL1 Cal Ripken 2.00 5.00
SL2 Mark McGwire 1.50 4.00
SL3 Alex Rodriguez 1.00 2.50
SL4 Sammy Sosa .60 1.50
SL5 Derek Jeter 1.50 4.00
SL6 Mike Piazza 1.00 2.50
SL7 Nomar Garciaparra 1.00 2.50
SL8 Chipper Jones .60 1.50
SL9 Ken Griffey Jr. 1.00 2.50
SL10 Manny Ramirez .40 1.00

2000 SkyBox Speed Merchants

Randomly inserted into packs at one in 8, this set features 10 players who exhibit speed including baserunning, bat speed, pitching and fielding. Card backs carry a "SM" prefix.

COMPLETE SET (10) 8.00 20.00
*STAR RUBIES: 6X TO 15X BASIC MERCHANT
STAR RUBIES PRINT RUN 100 SERIAL #'d SETS
SM1 Derek Jeter 1.25 3.00
SM2 Sammy Sosa .50 1.25
SM3 Nomar Garciaparra .75 2.00
SM4 Alex Rodriguez .75 2.00
SM5 Randy Johnson .50 1.25
SM6 Ken Griffey Jr. .75 2.00
SM7 Pedro Martinez .30 .75
SM8 Pat Burrell .20 .50
SM9 Barry Bonds 1.25 3.00
SM10 Mark McGwire 1.25 3.00

2000 SkyBox Technique

Randomly inserted into packs at one in 11, this insert set features 15 players that get the job done with their exceptional fundamentals and technique. Card backs carry a "T" prefix.

COMPLETE SET (15) 15.00 40.00
*STAR RUBIES: 6X TO 20X BASIC TECHNIQUE
STAR RUBIES PRINT RUN 50 SERIAL #'d SETS
T1 Alex Rodriguez 1.25 3.00
T2 Tony Gwynn 1.00 2.50
T3 Sean Casey .30 .75
T4 Mark McGwire 2.00 5.00
T5 Sammy Sosa .75 2.00
T6 Ken Griffey Jr. 1.25 3.00
T7 Mike Piazza 1.25 3.00
T8 Nomar Garciaparra 1.25 3.00
T9 Derek Jeter 2.00 5.00
T10 Vladimir Guerrero .75 2.00
T11 Cal Ripken 2.50 6.00
T12 Chipper Jones .75 2.00
T13 Frank Thomas .75 2.00
T14 Manny Ramirez .50 1.25
T15 Jeff Bagwell .50 1.25

2000 SkyBox Hobby Bullpen

These 15 standard-size cards were given away by Fleer executives at 15 different promotional stops as part of the Fleer Traveling Road Show. These are parallel cards to the regular SkyBox cards and they feature a red "Fleer Hobby Bullpen" logo.

COMPLETE SET (15) 12.00 30.00
1 Cal Ripken 2.00 5.00
2 Ivan Rodriguez .50 1.25
3 Chipper Jones .80 2.00
12 Vladimir Guerrero .60 1.50
17 Greg Maddux 1.00 2.50
18 Manny Ramirez .50 1.25
48 Tony Gwynn 1.00 2.50
49 Barry Bonds .75 2.00
51 Pedro Martinez .50 1.25
68 Nomar Garciaparra .80 2.00
98 Jason Kendall .20 .50
99 Ken Griffey Jr. 1.00 2.50
163 Mark McGwire 1.00 2.50
176 Sammy Sosa .75 2.00
180 Derek Jeter 2.00 5.00

2000 SkyBox National

This six-card standard-size set was distributed at the 2000 National Convention in Anaheim,CA in July, 2000. The set features cards from the 2000 SkyBox set with a special "NSCC" stamp on the front right corner.

COMPLETE SET (6) 8.00 20.00
1 Cal Ripken 2.00 5.00
2 Ken Griffey Jr. 1.00 2.50
3 Derek Jeter 2.00 5.00
4 Alex Rodriguez 1.20 3.00
5 Mark McGwire 1.25 3.00
6 Mike Piazza 1.25 3.00

2004 SkyBox Autographics

This 100 card set was released in April, 2004. The set was issued in five-card hobby packs with an $34.99 SRP which came four packs to a hobby box and four boxes to a case. Cards numbered 1 through 65 feature veterans while cards numbered 66 through 100 feature leading rookies and prospects. Those prospect cards were issued at a stated rate of one per hobby pack and one per 72 retail packs and were issued to a stated print run of 1500 serial numbered sets.

COMP.SET w/o SP's (65) 15.00 40.00
COMMON CARD (1-65) .30 .75
COMMON CARD (66-100) .75 2.00
66-100 ODDS 1:1 HOBBY, 1:72 RETAIL
66-100 PRINT RUN 1500 SERIAL #'d SETS
1 Albert Pujols 2.00 5.00
2 Richie Sexson .30 .75
3 Scott Rolen .50 1.25
4 Rafael Palmeiro .50 1.25
5 Ichiro Suzuki 1.25 3.00
6 Craig Biggio .50 1.25
7 Todd Helton .50 1.25
8 Miguel Cabrera .75 2.00
9 Ken Griffey Jr. 1.25 3.00
10 Pat Burrell .30 .75
11 Jose Reyes .50 1.25
12 Hideki Matsui 1.25 3.00
13 Geoff Jenkins .30 .75
14 Mark Prior .50 1.25
15 Gary Sheffield .30 .75
16 Nomar Garciaparra .75 2.00
17 Luis Gonzalez .30 .75
18 Troy Glaus .30 .75
19 Rocco Baldelli .30 .75
20 Hank Blalock .30 .75
21 Bret Boone .30 .75
22 Mike Sweeney .30 .75
23 Dmitri Young .30 .75
24 Dontrelle Willis .30 .75
25 Austin Kearns .30 .75
26 Jason Kendall .30 .75
27 Derek Jeter 2.00 5.00
28 Miguel Tejada .50 1.25
29 Torii Hunter .30 .75
30 Sammy Sosa .75 2.00
31 Chipper Jones .75 2.00
32 Pedro Martinez .50 1.25
33 Curt Schilling .50 1.25
34 Roy Halladay .75 2.00
35 Jim Edmonds .50 1.25
36 Alex Rodriguez Yanks 1.25 3.00
37 Jason Schmidt .30 .75
38 Jeff Bagwell .50 1.25
39 Omar Vizquel .50 1.25
40 Ivan Rodriguez .50 1.25
41 Magglio Ordonez .50 1.25
42 Jim Thome .50 1.25
43 Mike Piazza .75 2.00
44 Alfonso Soriano .30 .75
45 Hideo Nomo .75 2.00
46 Kerry Wood .30 .75
47 Greg Maddux 1.25 3.00
48 Tony Batista .30 .75
49 Randy Johnson .75 2.00
50 Garret Anderson .30 .75
51 Mark Teixeira .75 2.00
52 Carlos Delgado .30 .75
53 Darin Erstad .30 .75
54 Shawn Green .30 .75
55 Josh Beckett .50 1.25
56 Lance Berkman .50 1.25
57 Adam Dunn .50 1.25
58 Brian Giles .30 .75
59 Jason Giambi .30 .75
60 Barry Zito .30 .75
61 Vladimir Guerrero .75 2.00
62 Frank Thomas .75 2.00
63 Jay Gibbons .30 .75
64 Manny Ramirez .75 2.00
65 Andruw Jones .30 .75
66 Rickie Weeks PR .75 2.00
67 Chad Bentz PR RC .75 2.00
68 Bobby Crosby PR .75 2.00
69 Greg Dobbs PR RC .75 2.00
70 John Gall PR RC .75 2.00
71 Kaz Matsui PR RC 1.25 3.00
72 Dallas McPherson PR .75 2.00
73 Brandon Watson PR .75 2.00

74 Jerry Gil PR RC .75 2.00
75 Garrett Atkins PR .75 2.00
76 Cory Sullivan PR RC .75 2.00
77 Khalil Greene PR 1.25 3.00
78 Shawn Hill PR RC .75 2.00
79 Graham Koonce PR .75 2.00
80 Chien-Ming Wang PR 4.00 10.00
81 John Labandeira PR RC .75 2.00
82 Jonny Gomes PR .75 2.00
83 Edwin Jackson PR .75 2.00
84 Alfredo Simon PR RC .75 2.00
85 Delmon Young PR 1.25 3.00
86 Jason Bartlett PR RC 2.50 6.00
87 Angel Chavez PR RC .75 2.00
88 Angel Guzman PR .75 2.00
89 Ryan Howard PR 2.50 6.00
90 Scott Hairston PR .75 2.00
91 Ronny Cedeno PR RC .75 2.00
92 Don Kelly PR RC 1.25 3.00
93 Ivan Ochoa PR RC .75 2.00
94 Edwin Encarnacion PR 1.25 3.00
95 Byron Gettis PR .75 2.00
96 Kevin Youkilis PR 1.25 3.00
97 Grady Sizemore PR 1.25 3.00
98 Mariano Gomez PR RC .75 2.00
99 Hector Gimenez PR RC .75 2.00
100 Ruddy Yan PR .75 2.00

2004 SkyBox Autographics Insignia

*INSIGNIA 1-65: 1.25X TO 3X BASIC
*INSIGNIA 66-100: .6X TO 1.5X BASIC
OVERALL PARALLEL ODDS 1:4 H, 1:192 R
STATED PRINT RUN 150 SERIAL #'d SETS
INSIGNIA IS SILVER BACKGROUND

2004 SkyBox Autographics Royal Insignia

*ROYAL INS. 1-65: 3X TO 8X BASIC
*ROYAL INS. 66-100: 1X TO 2.5X BASIC
OVERALL PARALLEL ODDS 1:4 H, 1:192 R
STATED PRINT RUN 25 SERIAL #'d SETS
ROYAL INSIGNIA IS PURPLE BACKGROUND

2004 SkyBox Autographics Autoclassics

STATED ODDS 1:12 HOBBY/RETAIL
1 Johnny Bench 1.00 2.50
2 Steve Carlton .40 1.00
3 Carlton Fisk .60 1.50
4 Bill Mazeroski .60 1.50
5 Jim Palmer .40 1.00
6 Warren Spahn .60 1.50
7 Duke Snider .60 1.50
8 Wade Boggs .60 1.50
9 Nolan Ryan 3.00 8.00
10 Mike Schmidt 1.50 4.00
11 Albert Chandler .40 1.00
12 Ty Cobb 1.50 4.00
13 Sal Maglie .40 1.00
14 George Kelly .40 1.00
15 Joe Sewell .40 1.00

2004 SkyBox Autographics Autoclassics Memorabilia

OVERALL AU-GU ODDS 1:1 HOB, 1:24 RET
STATED PRINT RUN 350 SERIAL #'d SETS
BM Bill Mazeroski Bat 6.00 15.00
CF Carlton Fisk Jsy 6.00 15.00
DS Duke Snider Jsy 6.00 15.00
JB Johnny Bench Jsy 6.00 15.00
JP Jim Palmer Jsy 4.00 10.00
MS Mike Schmidt Bat 6.00 15.00
NR Nolan Ryan Jsy 10.00 25.00
SC Steve Carlton Jsy 4.00 10.00
WB Wade Boggs Jsy 6.00 15.00
WS Warren Spahn Jsy 6.00 15.00

2004 SkyBox Autographics Autoclassics Signature

OVERALL AU-GU ODDS 1:1 HOB, 1:24 RET
PRINT RUNS B/WN 3-50 COPIES PER
NO PRICING ON QTY OF 3 OR LESS
AC Albert Chandler/25 75.00 150.00
BM Bill Mazeroski/50 15.00 40.00
CF Carlton Fisk/50 15.00 40.00
DS Duke Snider/50 15.00 40.00
GK George Kelly/25 100.00 175.00
JB Johnny Bench/50 20.00 50.00
JP Jim Palmer/50 10.00 25.00
JS Joe Sewell/25 75.00 150.00
NR Nolan Ryan/38 75.00 150.00
SC Steve Carlton/50 10.00 25.00
SM Mike Schmidt/25 60.00 120.00
SM Sal Maglie/25 100.00 175.00
TC Ty Cobb/3
WB Wade Boggs/50 15.00 40.00
WS Warren Spahn/50 20.00 50.00

2004 SkyBox Autographics Jerseygraphics Blue

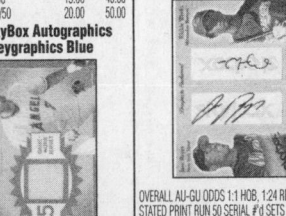

STATED PRINT RUN 250 SERIAL #'d SETS
*GOLD: 1X TO 2.5X BLUE
GOLD PRINT RUN 25 SERIAL #'d SETS
PURPLE PRINT RUN 1 SERIAL #'d SET
NO PURPLE PRICING DUE TO SCARCITY
*SILVER: .5X TO 1.2X BLUE
SILVER PRINT RUN 100 SERIAL #'d SETS
OVERALL AU-GU ODDS 1:1 HOB, 1:24 RET
AD Adam Dunn 3.00 8.00
AJ Andruw Jones 4.00 10.00
AK Austin Kearns 3.00 8.00
AP Albert Pujols 6.00 15.00
AR Alex Rodriguez 5.00 12.00
AS Alfonso Soriano 3.00 8.00
BA Bobby Abreu 3.00 8.00
BZ Barry Zito 3.00 8.00
CB Craig Biggio 4.00 10.00
CD Carlos Delgado 3.00 8.00
CJ Chipper Jones 4.00 10.00
CS Curt Schilling 3.00 8.00
DE Darin Erstad 3.00 8.00
DJ Derek Jeter 8.00 20.00
DO David Ortiz 4.00 10.00
DW Dontrelle Willis 4.00 10.00
FT Frank Thomas 4.00 10.00
GM Greg Maddux 5.00 12.00
HB Hank Blalock 3.00 8.00
HN Hideo Nomo 4.00 10.00
IR Ivan Rodriguez 4.00 10.00
JB Josh Beckett 3.00 8.00
JE Jim Edmonds 3.00 8.00
JG1 Jason Giambi 3.00 8.00
JG2 Jay Gibbons 3.00 8.00
JR Jose Reyes 3.00 8.00
JT Jim Thome 4.00 10.00
KM Kevin Millwood 3.00 8.00
KW Kerry Wood 3.00 8.00
LB Lance Berkman 3.00 8.00
MC Miguel Cabrera 4.00 10.00
MO Magglio Ordonez 3.00 8.00
MP1 Mike Piazza 5.00 12.00
MP2 Mark Prior 4.00 10.00
MR Manny Ramirez 4.00 10.00
MT1 Mark Teixeira 4.00 10.00
MT2 Miguel Tejada 3.00 8.00
NG Nomar Garciaparra 5.00 12.00
PB Pat Burrell 3.00 8.00
PM Pedro Martinez 4.00 10.00
RB Rocco Baldelli 3.00 8.00
RH Roy Halladay 3.00 8.00
RP Rafael Palmeiro 4.00 10.00
SG Shawn Green 3.00 8.00
SR Scott Rolen 4.00 10.00
SS Sammy Sosa 4.00 10.00
TG Troy Glaus 3.00 8.00
TH1 Todd Helton 4.00 10.00
TH2 Torii Hunter 3.00 8.00
VG Vladimir Guerrero 4.00 10.00

2004 SkyBox Autographics Jeter Legacy Collection

OVERALL AU-GU ODDS 1:1 HOB, 1:24 RET
STATED PRINT RUN 25 SERIAL #'d CARDS
DJ Derek Jeter AU/25

2004 SkyBox Autographics Prospects Endorsed

STATED ODDS 1:4 HOBBY, 1:8 RETAIL
1 Albert Pujols 2.50 6.00
Delmon Young
2 Eric Gagne .40 1.00
Bobby Jenks
3 Barry Larkin .60 1.50
Kaz Matsui
4 Andruw Jones .40 1.00
Jonny Gomes
5 Hideo Nomo 2.00 5.00
Chien-Ming Wang
6 Gary Sheffield .40 1.00
Cory Sullivan
7 Billy Wagner 1.25 3.00
Ryan Howard
8 Jorge Posada .60 1.50
Koyie Hill
9 Curt Schilling .60 1.50
Ryan Wagner
10 Jose Reyes .60 1.50
Rickie Weeks
11 Alfonso Soriano .40 1.00
Matt Kata
12 Barry Zito .40 1.00
Rich Harden
13 Randy Johnson 1.00 2.50
Brandon Webb
14 Alex Rodriguez 1.50 4.00
Angel Berroa
15 Dontrelle Willis .40 1.00
Edwin Jackson

2004 SkyBox Autographics Prospects Endorsed Dual Autograph

OVERALL AU-GU ODDS 1:1 HOB, 1:24 RET
STATED PRINT RUN 50 SERIAL #'d SETS
AJJG Andruw Jones 15.00 40.00
Jonny Gomes
APDY Albert Pujols 175.00 300.00
Delmon Young
BLEE Barry Larkin 15.00 40.00
Edwin Encarnacion
BWRH Billy Wagner 50.00 100.00
Ryan Howard
EGBJ Eric Gagne 15.00 40.00
Bobby Jenks
GSCS Gary Sheffield 10.00 25.00
Cory Sullivan
JRRW Jose Reyes 15.00 40.00
Rickie Weeks

2004 SkyBox Autographics Prospects Endorsed Dual Jersey

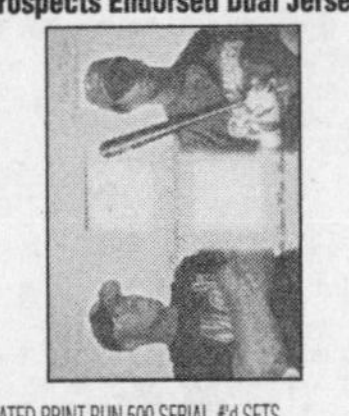

STATED PRINT RUN 500 SERIAL #'d SETS
*PATCH: 1.25X TO 3X BASIC
PATCH PRINT RUN 50 SERIAL #'d SETS
OVERALL AU-GU ODDS 1:1 HOB, 1:24 RET
APDY Albert Pujols 6.00 15.00
Delmon Young
ARAB Alex Rodriguez 4.00 10.00
Angel Berroa
ASMK Alfonso Soriano 3.00 8.00
Matt Kata
BLKM Barry Larkin 4.00 10.00
Kaz Matsui Bat
BZRH Barry Zito 3.00 8.00
Rich Harden
CSRW Curt Schilling 4.00 10.00
Ryan Wagner
DWEJ Dontrelle Willis 4.00 10.00
Edwin Jackson
HNCW Hideo Nomo 30.00 60.00
Chein-Ming Wang
JRRW Jose Reyes 3.00 8.00
Rickie Weeks
RJBW Randy Johnson 4.00 10.00
Brandon Webb

2004 SkyBox Autographics Signatures Blue

PRINT RUNS B/WN 100-485 COPIES PER
*GOLD: 1X TO 2X BLUE p/r 200-485
*GOLD: 1X TO 2X BLUE p/r 100-197
GOLD PRINT RUN 25 SERIAL #'d SETS
*ON LOCATION: .4X TO 1X BLUE p/r 200-485
*ON LOCATION: .4X TO 1X BLUE p/r 100-197
ON LOCATION PRINT 99 SERIAL #'d SETS
PURPLE PRINT RUN 1 SERIAL #'d SET
NO PURPLE PRICING DUE TO SCARCITY
*SILVER: .4X TO 1X BLUE p/r 200-485
*SILVER: .4X TO 1X BLUE p/r 100-197
SILVER PRINT RUN 100 SERIAL #'d SETS
OVERALL AU-GU ODDS 1:1 HOB, 1:24 RET
AB1 Angel Berroa/182 4.00 10.00
AB2 A.J. Burnett/485 6.00 15.00
AH Aubrey Huff/296 6.00 15.00
AK Austin Kearns/275 4.00 10.00
AM Aaron Miles/140 4.00 10.00
AP Albert Pujols/103 100.00 175.00
BJ Bobby Jenks/307 6.00 15.00
BL Barry Larkin/195 10.00 25.00
BW1 Billy Wagner/180 10.00 25.00
BW2 Brandon Webb/310 4.00 10.00
CP Corey Patterson/220 4.00 10.00
CS1 Chris Snelling/200 4.00 10.00
CS2 Cory Sullivan/170 4.00 10.00
CW Chien-Ming Wang/195 60.00 120.00
DH Dan Haren/176 4.00 10.00
DM Dallas McPherson/179 6.00 15.00
DW Dontrelle Willis/225 10.00 25.00
DY Delmon Young/205 10.00 25.00
EE Edwin Encarnacion/188 6.00 15.00
EG Eric Gagne/225 10.00 25.00
EJ Edwin Jackson/224 4.00 10.00
GA Garrett Atkins/175 4.00 10.00
GK Graham Koonce/190 4.00 10.00
GS Gary Sheffield/210 10.00 25.00
HB Hank Blalock/205 6.00 15.00
JB Josh Beckett/100 10.00 25.00
JG Jonny Gomes/265 6.00 15.00
JP Juan Pierre/220 6.00 15.00
JR1 Jose Reyes/195 6.00 15.00
JR2 Juan Richardson/345 4.00 10.00
JV Javier Vazquez/210 6.00 15.00
KG Khalil Greene/190 10.00 25.00
KH Koyie Hill/240 4.00 10.00
KW Kerry Wood/191 10.00 25.00
LN Laynce Nix/185 4.00 10.00
MB Marlon Byrd/240 4.00 10.00
MK Matt Kata/197 4.00 10.00
MM Mark Mulder/186 6.00 15.00
RB Rocco Baldelli/255 6.00 15.00
RH1 Rich Harden/185 6.00 15.00
RH2 Ryan Howard/170 15.00 40.00
RW Rickie Weeks/187 6.00 15.00
SH Shea Hillenbrand/213 6.00 15.00
SP Scott Podsednik/210 10.00 25.00
SS Shannon Stewart/340 6.00 15.00
TH1 Tim Hudson/169 10.00 25.00
TH2 Torii Hunter/215 6.00 15.00
TN Trot Nixon/210 6.00 15.00

2004 SkyBox Autographics Signatures Game Jersey

STATED PRINT RUN 125 SERIAL #'d SETS
*PATCH: 1X TO 2X BASIC
PATCH PRINT RUN 25 SERIAL #'d SETS
OVERALL AU-GU ODDS 1:1 HOB, 1:24 RET
AP Albert Pujols 100.00 175.00
BW1 Billy Wagner 15.00 40.00
BW2 Brandon Webb 6.00 15.00
CP Corey Patterson 6.00 15.00
DW Dontrelle Willis 15.00 40.00
HB Hank Blalock 10.00 25.00
JB Josh Beckett 8.00 20.00
RB Rocco Baldelli 10.00 25.00
TH2 Torii Hunter 10.00 25.00

2005 SkyBox Autographics

COMP.SET w/o SP's (60) 15.00 40.00
COMMON CARD (1-60) .30 .75
1-60 GOLD FOIL FACSIMILE SIGS ON ALL
COMMON CARD (61-90) 1.00 2.50
61-90 STATED ODDS 1:6 H
61-90 PRINT RUN 750 SERIAL #'d SETS
61-90 BLACK FOIL FACSIMILE SIGS ON ALL
COMMON CARD (91-115) .50 1.25
91-115 STATED ODDS 1:6
91-115 PRINT RUN 750 SERIAL #'d SETS
SUBSETS 61-115/PARALLEL ODDS 1:6 R
1 Vladimir Guerrero .75 2.00
2 Garret Anderson .30 .75
3 Troy Glaus .30 .75
4 Shawn Green .30 .75
5 Chipper Jones .75 2.00
6 Andruw Jones .30 .75
7 Miguel Tejada .50 1.25
8 Melvin Mora .30 .75
9 Manny Ramirez .75 2.00
10 Curt Schilling .50 1.25
11 Nomar Garciaparra .75 2.00
12 Mark Prior .50 1.25
13 Sammy Sosa .75 2.00
14 Frank Thomas .75 2.00
15 Paul Konerko .50 1.25
16 Adam Dunn .50 1.25
17 Ken Griffey Jr. 1.25 3.00
18 Victor Martinez .50 1.25
19 Travis Hafner .30 .75
20 Todd Helton .50 1.25
21 Ivan Rodriguez .50 1.25
22 Carlos Guillen .30 .75
23 Miguel Cabrera .75 2.00
24 Juan Pierre .30 .75
25 Roger Clemens 1.00 2.50
26 Jeff Bagwell .50 1.25
27 Lance Berkman .50 1.25
28 Mike Sweeney .30 .75
29 Eric Gagne .30 .75
30 J.D. Drew .30 .75
31 Ben Sheets .30 .75
32 Lyle Overbay .30 .75
33 Johan Santana .75 2.00
34 Torii Hunter .30 .75
35 Mike Piazza .75 2.00
36 Pedro Martinez .50 1.25
37 Carlos Beltran .30 .75
38 Derek Jeter 2.00 5.00
39 Alex Rodriguez 1.25 3.00
40 Hideki Matsui 1.25 3.00
41 Randy Johnson .75 2.00
42 Eric Chavez .30 .75
43 Jim Thome .50 1.25
44 Craig Wilson .30 .75
45 Khalil Greene .30 .75
46 Jake Peavy .30 .75
47 Jason Schmidt .30 .75
48 Ichiro Suzuki 1.25 3.00
49 Adrian Beltre .30 .75
50 Albert Pujols 2.00 5.00
51 Scott Rolen .50 1.25
52 Carl Crawford .50 1.25
53 Rocco Baldelli .30 .75
54 Alfonso Soriano .50 1.25
55 Hank Blalock .30 .75
56 Vernon Wells .30 .75
57 Jose Vidro .30 .75
58 David Ortiz .75 2.00
59 Bobby Abreu .30 .75
60 Gary Sheffield .30 .75
61 Nolan Ryan GT 6.00 15.00
62 Mike Schmidt GT 5.00 12.00
63 Johnny Bench GT 2.50 6.00
64 Lou Brock GT 1.50 4.00
65 Dennis Eckersley GT 1.00 2.50
66 Carlton Fisk GT 1.50 4.00
67 Bob Gibson GT 1.50 4.00
68 Reggie Jackson GT 2.50 6.00
69 Al Kaline GT 2.50 6.00
70 Bill Mazeroski GT 1.50 4.00
71 Willie McCovey GT 1.50 4.00
72 Jim Palmer GT 1.00 2.50
73 Phil Rizzuto GT 1.50 4.00
74 Warren Spahn GT 1.50 4.00
75 Brooks Robinson GT 1.50 4.00
76 Willie Stargell GT 1.50 4.00
77 Catfish Hunter GT 1.00 2.50
78 Tony Perez GT 1.00 2.50
79 George Kell GT 1.00 2.50
80 Robin Yount GT 2.50 6.00
81 Fergie Jenkins GT 1.00 2.50
82 Tom Seaver GT 1.50 4.00
83 Eddie Mathews GT 1.50 4.00
84 Enos Slaughter GT 1.00 2.50
85 Pee Wee Reese GT 1.50 4.00
86 Harmon Killebrew GT 2.50 6.00
87 Eddie Murray GT 2.50 6.00
88 Orlando Cepeda GT 1.00 2.50
89 Billy Williams GT 1.00 2.50
90 Ralph Kiner GT 1.00 2.50
91 Ryan Raburn ROO .50 1.25
92 Justin Morneau ROO 1.25 3.00
93 Zack Greinke ROO .75 2.00
94 David Aardsma ROO .50 1.25
95 B.J. Upton ROO .75 2.00
96 Gavin Floyd ROO .50 1.25
97 David Wright ROO 2.00 5.00
98 Russ Adams ROO .50 1.25
99 Jose Lopez ROO .50 1.25
100 Scott Kazmir ROO 1.25 3.00
101 Mike Gosling ROO .50 1.25
102 Jeff Keppinger ROO .50 1.25
103 Dave Krynzel ROO .50 1.25
104 Jeff Niemann ROO RC 1.25 3.00
105 Ruben Gotay ROO .50 1.25
106 Dioner Navarro ROO .50 1.25
107 Nick Swisher ROO 1.25 3.00
108 Yadier Molina ROO .75 2.00
109 Joey Gathright ROO .50 1.25
110 Jon Knott ROO .50 1.25
111 J.D. Durbin ROO .50 1.25
112 Andres Blanco ROO .50 1.25
113 Charlton Jimerson ROO .50 1.25
114 Sean Burnett ROO .50 1.25
115 Justin Verlander ROO RC 10.00 25.00

2005 SkyBox Autographics Insignia

*1-60: 1.25X TO 3X BASIC
*61-90: .6X TO 1.5X BASIC
*91-115: 1.2X TO 3X BASIC
OVERALL PARALLEL ODDS 1:6 H
SUBSETS 61-115/PARALLEL ODDS 1:6 R
STATED PRINT RUN 150 SERIAL #'d SETS
GOLD FOIL FACSIMILE SIGS ON ALL

2005 SkyBox Autographics Royal Insignia

*1-60: 3X TO 8X BASIC
*61-90: 1X TO 2.5X BASIC
*91-115: 2X TO 5X BASIC
OVERALL PARALLEL ODDS 1:6 H
SUBSETS 61-115/PARALLEL ODDS 1:6 R
STATED PRINT RUN 25 SERIAL #'d SETS
NO PRICING AVAIL.ON CARDS 104 AND 115
PURPLE FOIL FACSIMILE SIGS ON ALL

2005 SkyBox Autographics Future Signs

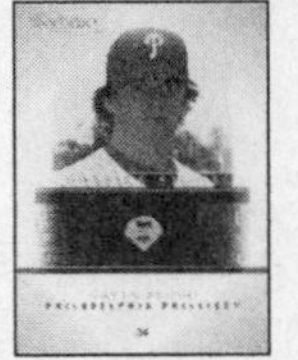

STATED ODDS 1:6 H, 1:12 R
1 Bobby Crosby .75 2.00
2 David Aardsma .75 2.00
3 Russ Adams .75 2.00
4 J.D. Durbin .75 2.00
5 Johnny Estrada .75 2.00
6 Chone Figgins .75 2.00
7 Jason Bay .75 2.00
8 Gavin Floyd .75 2.00
9 Lew Ford .75 2.00
10 Victor Martinez 1.25 3.00
11 Joe Mauer 2.00 5.00
12 Justin Morneau 2.00 5.00
13 Laynce Nix .75 2.00
14 Sean Burnett .75 2.00
15 B.J. Upton 1.25 3.00
16 Justin Verlander 15.00 40.00
17 David Wright 3.00 8.00
18 Delmon Young 2.00 5.00
19 Michael Young 1.25 3.00
20 Zack Greinke 1.25 3.00

2005 SkyBox Autographics Future Signs Autograph Blue

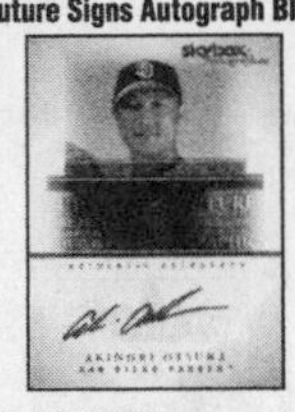

STATED ODDS 1:25 HOBBY
PRINT RUNS B/WN 8-639 COPIES PER
CARDS ARE NOT SERIAL-NUMBERED
PRINT RUN INFO PROVIDED BY UD
NO PRICING ON QTY OF 8
AO Akinori Otsuka/639 * 6.00 15.00
DW David Wright/8 *
JB Jason Bay/264 * 6.00 15.00
JM Justin Morneau/224 * 8.00 20.00
JV Justin Verlander/505 * 20.00 50.00
VM Victor Martinez/500 * 6.00 15.00
ZG Zack Greinke/264 * 8.00 20.00

2005 SkyBox Autographics Future Signs Autograph Gold

*GOLD: .5X TO 1.2X BLUE
OVERALL AU ODDS 1:4 H, AU-GU 1:24 R
STATED PRINT RUN 65 SERIAL #'d SETS
AS Alfredo Simon/30 UER 5.00 12.00
BU B.J. Upton 8.00 20.00
DW David Wright 30.00 60.00
EE Edwin Encarnacion 8.00 20.00
JD J.D. Durbin 5.00 12.00
RW Rickie Weeks 8.00 20.00
SB Sean Burnett 5.00 12.00
SH Scott Hairston/31 UER 5.00 12.00
VMJ Val Majewski 5.00 12.00

2005 SkyBox Autographics Future Signs Autograph Gold Embossed

*GOLD EMB: .5X TO 1.2X BLUE
OVERALL AU ODDS 1:4 H, AU-GU 1:24 R
STATED PRINT RUN 45 SERIAL #'d SETS
AS Alfredo Simon/30 UER 5.00 12.00
BU B.J. Upton 8.00 20.00
DW David Wright 30.00 60.00
DY Delmon Young 12.50 30.00
EE Edwin Encarnacion 8.00 20.00
JD J.D. Durbin 5.00 12.00
RW Rickie Weeks 8.00 20.00
SB Sean Burnett 5.00 12.00
SH Scott Hairston/28 UER 5.00 12.00
VMJ Val Majewski 5.00 12.00

2005 SkyBox Autographics Future Signs Autograph Platinum

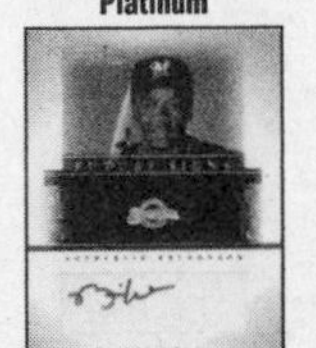

*PLAT: .6X TO 1.5X BLUE
STATED PRINT RUN 25 SERIAL #'d SETS
NO PRICING AVAIL ON CARDS JN AND JV
EMBOSSED PLAT.PRINT RUN 5 #'d SETS
NO EMB.PLAT.PRICING DUE TO SCARCITY
OVERALL AU ODDS 1:4 H, AU-GU 1:24 R
AS Alfredo Simon 6.00 15.00
BU B.J. Upton 10.00 25.00
DW David Wright 40.00 80.00
DY Delmon Young 15.00 40.00
EE Edwin Encarnacion 10.00 25.00
JD J.D. Durbin 6.00 15.00
RW Rickie Weeks 10.00 25.00
SB Sean Burnett 6.00 15.00
SH Scott Hairston 6.00 15.00
VMJ Val Majewski 6.00 15.00

2005 SkyBox Autographics Future Signs Autograph Silver

*SILVER: .4X TO 1X BLUE
OVERALL AU ODDS 1:4 H, AU-GU 1:24 R
STATED PRINT RUN 100 SERIAL #'d SETS
AS Alfredo Simon/54 UER 4.00 10.00
BU B.J. Upton/34 UER 6.00 15.00
DW David Wright 20.00 50.00
EE Edwin Encarnacion/95 UER 6.00 15.00
JD J.D. Durbin/53 UER 4.00 10.00
RW Rickie Weeks/36 UER 6.00 15.00
SB Sean Burnett/51 UER 4.00 10.00
VMJ Val Majewski/55 UER 4.00 10.00

2005 SkyBox Autographics Future Signs Autograph Silver Embossed

*SILVER EMB: .4X TO 1X BLUE
OVERALL AU ODDS 1:4 H, AU-GU 1:24 R
STATED PRINT RUN 65 SERIAL #'d SETS
AS Alfredo Simon/40 UER 4.00 10.00
BU B.J. Upton 6.00 15.00
DW David Wright 20.00 50.00
DY Delmon Young/29 UER 10.00 25.00
EE Edwin Encarnacion 6.00 15.00
JD J.D. Durbin/70 UER 4.00 10.00
RW Rickie Weeks 6.00 15.00
SB Sean Burnett/60 UER 4.00 10.00
SH Scott Hairston/40 UER 4.00 10.00
VMJ Val Majewski 4.00 10.00

2005 SkyBox Autographics Jerseygraphics Blue

STATED ODDS 1:40 RETAIL
*GOLD: .75X TO 2X BLUE
GOLD STATED ODDS 1:240 RETAIL
*SILVER: .5X TO 1.2X BLUE
SILVER STATED ODDS 1:80 RETAIL
AB Adrian Beltre 2.00 5.00
AD Adam Dunn 2.00 5.00
AK Austin Kearns 2.00 5.00
BG Brian Giles 2.00 5.00
BS Ben Sheets 2.00 5.00
CD Carlos Delgado 2.00 5.00
EG Eric Gagne 2.00 5.00
GA Garret Anderson 2.00 5.00
HB Hank Blalock 2.00 5.00
JB Jeff Bagwell 3.00 8.00
JBE Josh Beckett 2.00 5.00
JR Jose Reyes 2.00 5.00
MB Marlon Byrd 2.00 5.00
MC Miguel Cabrera 3.00 8.00
MO Magglio Ordonez 2.00 5.00
MT Mark Teixeira 3.00 8.00
RB Rocco Baldelli 2.00 5.00
TG Troy Glaus 2.00 5.00
TGL Tom Glavine 2.00 5.00
TH Torii Hunter 2.00 5.00

2005 SkyBox Autographics Jerseygraphics Silver

AB Adrian Beltre 2.50 6.00

2005 SkyBox Autographics Master Collection

STATED PRINT RUN 25 SERIAL #'d SETS
ALL CARDS ARE JSY-JSY-PATCH COMBOS
ONE OF A KIND PRINT RUN 1 #'d SET
ALL ONE OF A KIND ARE JSY-PATCH-LOGO
OVERALL AU ODDS 1:4 H, AU-GU 1:24 R
NO PRICING DUE TO SCARCITY

2005 SkyBox Autographics Signature Moments

STATED ODDS 1:12 H, 1:24 R

Card	Low	High
1 Manny Ramirez	2.00	5.00
2 Derek Jeter	4.00	10.00
3 Ichiro Suzuki	3.00	8.00
4 Roger Clemens	3.00	8.00
5 Albert Pujols	4.00	10.00
6 Nolan Ryan	4.00	10.00
7 Reggie Jackson	2.00	5.00
8 Carlton Fisk	2.00	5.00
9 Mike Schmidt	4.00	10.00
10 Johnny Bench	2.00	5.00

2005 SkyBox Autographics Signatures Blue

STATED ODDS 1:19 H
PRINT RUNS B/WN 137-590 COPIES PER
CARDS ARE NOT SERIAL-NUMBERED
PRINT RUN INFO PROVIDED BY UD

Card	Low	High
AE Adam Everett/590 *	4.00	10.00
BL Brad Lidge/164 *	10.00	25.00
CC Carl Crawford/150 *	6.00	15.00
CK Casey Kotchman/227 *	6.00	15.00
CP Corey Patterson/329 *	4.00	10.00
DE David Eckstein/546 *	15.00	40.00
EP Eduardo Perez/584 *	4.00	10.00
JB Jeremy Bonderman/369 *	6.00	15.00
JK Jason Kubel/137 *	4.00	10.00
JO John Olerud/446 *	10.00	25.00
JS Johan Santana/200 *	12.50	30.00
LG Luis Gonzalez/187 *	6.00	15.00
MC Miguel Cabrera/250 *	10.00	25.00
MCA Mike Cameron/200 *	4.00	10.00
OH Orlando Hudson/231 *	4.00	10.00
SK Scott Kazmir/231 *	8.00	20.00
TH Trevor Hoffman/590 *	6.00	15.00
THA Travis Hafner/246 *	6.00	15.00

2005 SkyBox Autographics Signatures Game Jersey Gold

*JSY GOLD: .6X TO 1.5X BLUE
OVERALL AU ODDS 1:4 H, AU-GU 1:24 R
STATED PRINT RUN 45 SERIAL #'d SETS

Card	Low	High
MG Marcus Giles	10.00	25.00
MT Mark Teixeira	15.00	40.00
RB Rocco Baldelli/40 UER	10.00	25.00
RH Roy Halladay	10.00	25.00
SS Shannon Stewart	6.00	15.00

2005 SkyBox Autographics Signatures Game Jersey Gold Embossed

*JSY GOLD EMB: .75X TO 2X BLUE
OVERALL AU ODDS 1:4 H, AU-GU 1:24 R
STATED PRINT RUN 30 SERIAL #'d SETS

Card	Low	High
MG Marcus Giles	12.50	30.00
MT Mark Teixeira	20.00	50.00
RB Rocco Baldelli	12.50	30.00
SS Shannon Stewart	12.50	30.00

2005 SkyBox Autographics Signatures Game Jersey Silver

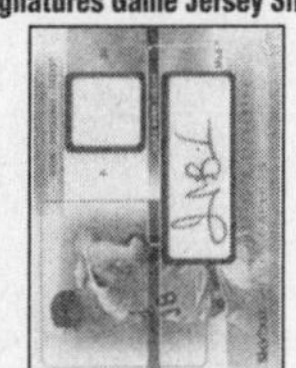

*JSY SILVER: .5X TO 1.2X BLUE
OVERALL AU ODDS 1:4 H, AU-GU 1:24 R
STATED PRINT RUN 100 SERIAL #'d SETS

Card	Low	High
MT Mark Teixeira/70 UER	12.50	30.00
RB Rocco Baldelli/58 UER	8.00	20.00
SS Shannon Stewart	5.00	12.00

2005 SkyBox Autographics Signatures Game Jersey Silver Embossed

*JSY SILVER EMB: .5X TO 1.2X BLUE
OVERALL AU ODDS 1:4 H, AU-GU 1:24 R
STATED PRINT RUN 75 SERIAL #'d SETS

Card	Low	High
MG Marcus Giles	8.00	20.00
MT Mark Teixeira	12.50	30.00
RB Rocco Baldelli/50 UER	8.00	20.00
SS Shannon Stewart	5.00	12.00

2005 SkyBox Autographics Signatures Game Patch Gold

STATED PRINT RUN 5 SERIAL #'d SETS
GOLD EMBOSSED PRINT RUN 15 #'d SETS
OVERALL AU ODDS 1:4 H, AU-GU 1:24 R
NO PRICING DUE TO SCARCITY

2005 SkyBox Autographics Signatures Game Patch Masterpiece Embossed

OVERALL AUTO ODDS 1:4 H
STATED PRINT RUN 1 SERIAL #'d SET
NO PRICING DUE TO SCARCITY

2005 SkyBox Autographics Signatures Game Patch Silver

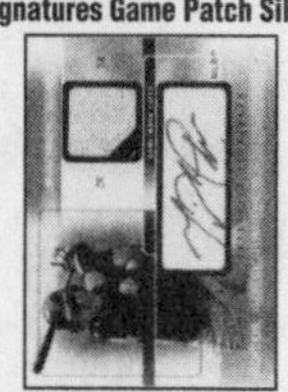

*PATCH SILVER: 1X TO 2.5X BLUE
OVERALL AUTO ODDS 1:4 H
STATED PRINT RUN 25 SERIAL #'d SETS
NO GILES PRICING DUE TO SCARCITY

Card	Low	High
MG Marcus Giles/10 UER		
MT Mark Teixeira	25.00	60.00
RB Rocco Baldelli	15.00	40.00
SS Shannon Stewart	15.00	40.00

1999 SkyBox Premium

The 1999 SkyBox Premium set was issued in one series for a total of 350 cards and distributed in eight-card packs with a suggested retail price of $2.69. The set features color action player photos with a team colored action-trail and gold-foil stamping. The set contains the following subsets: Spring Fling (273-297) and two versions of the 50 Rookies. In an effoty to satisfy fans of both complete sets and short-printed Rookie Cards, dual version rookie and prospect cards were created. The commonly available versions feature close-up shots of the players and these are considered the true Rookie Card. The short-printed versions feature full-body action shots and are seeded at a rate of one in eight packs. Both versions of these cards are numbered but we've added an "S" suffix on the short-prints for checklisting purposes. Notable Rookie Cards include Pat Burrell and Freddy Garcia.

Card	Low	High
COMP.MASTER SET (350)	100.00	200.00
COMP.SET w/o SP's (300)	10.00	25.00
COMMON (1-222/273-300)	.07	.20
COMMON (223-272)	.10	.30
COMMON SP (223-272)	.75	2.00
1 Alex Rodriguez	.50	1.25
2 Sidney Ponson	.07	.20
3 Shawn Green	.10	.30
4 Dan Wilson	.07	.20
5 Rolando Arrojo	.07	.20
6 Roberto Alomar	.20	.50
7 Matt Anderson	.07	.20
8 David Segui	.07	.20
9 Alex Gonzalez	.07	.20
10 Edgar Renteria	.10	.30
11 Benito Santiago	.10	.30
12 Todd Stottlemyre	.07	.20
13 Rico Brogna	.07	.20
14 Troy Glaus	.20	.50
15 Al Leiter	.10	.30
16 Pedro Martinez	.20	.50
17 Paul O'Neill	.20	.50
18 Manny Ramirez	.20	.50
19 Scott Rolen	.20	.50
20 Curt Schilling	.10	.30
21 Bob Abreu	.10	.30
22 Robb Nen	.10	.30
23 Andy Pettitte	.20	.50
24 John Wetteland	.10	.30
25 Bobby Bonilla	.10	.30
26 Darin Erstad	.10	.30
27 Shawn Estes	.07	.20
28 John Franco	.10	.30
29 Nomar Garciaparra	.50	1.25
30 Rick Helling	.07	.20
31 David Justice	.10	.30
32 Chuck Knoblauch	.10	.30
33 Quinton McCracken	.07	.20
34 Kenny Rogers	.10	.30
35 Brian Giles	.10	.30
36 Armando Benitez	.07	.20
37 Trevor Hoffman	.10	.30
38 Charles Johnson	.10	.30
39 Travis Lee	.07	.20
40 Tom Glavine	.20	.50
41 Rondell White	.10	.30
42 Orlando Hernandez	.10	.30
43 Mickey Morandini	.07	.20
44 Darryl Kile	.10	.30
45 Greg Vaughn	.07	.20
46 Gregg Jefferies	.07	.20
47 Mark McGwire	.75	2.00
48 Kerry Wood	.10	.30
49 Jeromy Burnitz	.10	.30
50 Ron Gant	.10	.30
51 Vinny Castilla	.10	.30
52 Doug Glanville	.07	.20
53 Juan Guzman	.07	.20
54 Dustin Hermanson	.07	.20
55 Jose Hernandez	.07	.20
56 Bobby Higginson	.10	.30
57 A.J. Hinch	.07	.20
58 Randy Johnson	.30	.75
59 Eli Marrero	.07	.20
60 Rafael Palmeiro	.20	.50
61 Carl Pavano	.10	.30
62 Brett Tomko	.07	.20
63 Jose Guillen	.10	.30
64 Mike Lieberthal	.10	.30
65 Jim Abbott	.20	.50
66 Dante Bichette	.10	.30
67 Jeff Cirillo	.07	.20
68 Eric Davis	.10	.30
69 Delino DeShields	.07	.20
70 Steve Finley	.10	.30
71 Mark Grace	.20	.50
72 Jason Kendall	.10	.30
73 Jeff Kent	.10	.30
74 Desi Relaford	.07	.20
75 Ivan Rodriguez	.20	.50
76 Shannon Stewart	.10	.30
77 Geoff Jenkins	.07	.20
78 Ben Grieve	.07	.20
79 Cliff Floyd	.10	.30
80 Jason Giambi	.10	.30
81 Rod Beck	.07	.20
82 Derek Bell	.07	.20
83 Will Clark	.20	.50
84 David Dellucci	.07	.20
85 Joey Hamilton	.07	.20
86 Livan Hernandez	.10	.30
87 Barry Larkin	.20	.50
88 Matt Mantei	.07	.20
89 Dean Palmer	.10	.30
90 Chan Ho Park	.10	.30
91 Jim Thome	.20	.50
92 Miguel Tejada	.10	.30
93 Justin Thompson	.07	.20
94 David Wells	.10	.30
95 Bernie Williams	.20	.50
96 Jeff Bagwell	.20	.50
97 Derrek Lee	.20	.50
98 Devon White	.10	.30
99 Jeff Shaw	.07	.20
100 Brad Radke	.10	.30
101 Mark Grudzielanek	.07	.20
102 Javy Lopez	.10	.30
103 Mike Sirotka	.07	.20
104 Robin Ventura	.10	.30
105 Andy Ashby	.07	.20
106 Juan Gonzalez	.10	.30
107 Albert Belle	.10	.30
108 Andy Benes	.07	.20
109 Jay Buhner	.10	.30
110 Ken Caminiti	.10	.30
111 Roger Clemens	.60	1.50
112 Mike Hampton	.10	.30
113 Pete Harnisch	.07	.20
114 Mike Piazza	.50	1.25
115 J.T. Snow	.10	.30
116 John Olerud	.10	.30
117 Tony Womack	.07	.20
118 Todd Zeile	.10	.30
119 Tony Gwynn	.40	1.00
120 Brady Anderson	.10	.30
121 Sean Casey	.10	.30
122 Jose Cruz Jr.	.07	.20
123 Carlos Delgado	.10	.30
124 Edgar Martinez	.20	.50
125 Jose Mesa	.07	.20
126 Shane Reynolds	.07	.20
127 John Valentin	.07	.20
128 Mo Vaughn	.10	.30
129 Kevin Young	.10	.30
130 Jay Bell	.10	.30
131 Aaron Boone	.10	.30
132 John Smoltz	.20	.50
133 Mike Stanley	.07	.20
134 Bret Saberhagen	.10	.30
135 Tim Salmon	.20	.50
136 Mariano Rivera	.30	.75
137 Ken Griffey Jr.	.50	1.25
138 Jose Offerman	.07	.20
139 Troy Percival	.10	.30
140 Greg Maddux	.50	1.25
141 Frank Thomas	.30	.75
142 Steve Avery	.07	.20
143 Kevin Millwood	.10	.30
144 Sammy Sosa	.30	.75
145 Larry Walker	.10	.30
146 Matt Williams	.10	.30
147 Mike Caruso	.07	.20
148 Todd Helton	.20	.50
149 Andruw Jones	.20	.50
150 Ray Lankford	.10	.30
151 Craig Biggio	.20	.50
152 Ugueth Urbina	.07	.20
153 Wade Boggs	.20	.50
154 Derek Jeter	.75	2.00
155 Wally Joyner	.10	.30
156 Mike Mussina	.20	.50
157 Gregg Olson	.07	.20
158 Henry Rodriguez	.07	.20
159 Reggie Sanders	.10	.30
160 Fernando Tatis	.07	.20
161 Dmitri Young	.10	.30
162 Rick Aguilera	.07	.20
163 Marty Cordova	.07	.20
164 Johnny Damon	.20	.50
165 Ray Durham	.10	.30
166 Brad Fullmer	.07	.20
167 Chipper Jones	.30	.75
168 Bobby Smith	.07	.20
169 Omar Vizquel	.20	.50
170 Todd Hundley	.07	.20
171 David Cone	.10	.30
172 Royce Clayton	.07	.20
173 Ryan Klesko	.10	.30
174 Jeff Montgomery	.07	.20
175 Magglio Ordonez	.10	.30
176 Billy Wagner	.10	.30
177 Masato Yoshii	.07	.20
178 Jason Christiansen	.07	.20
179 Chuck Finley	.10	.30
180 Tom Gordon	.07	.20
181 Wilton Guerrero	.07	.20
182 Rickey Henderson	.30	.75
183 Sterling Hitchcock	.07	.20
184 Kenny Lofton	.10	.30
185 Tino Martinez	.20	.50
186 Fred McGriff	.20	.50
187 Matt Stairs	.07	.20
188 Neifi Perez	.07	.20
189 Bob Wickman	.07	.20
190 Barry Bonds	.75	2.00
191 Jose Canseco	.20	.50
192 Damion Easley	.07	.20
193 Jim Edmonds	.10	.30
194 Juan Encarnacion	.07	.20
195 Travis Fryman	.10	.30
196 Tom Goodwin	.07	.20
197 Rusty Greer	.10	.30
198 Roberto Hernandez	.07	.20
199 B.J. Surhoff	.10	.30
200 Scott Brosius	.10	.30
201 Brian Jordan	.10	.30
202 Paul Konerko	.10	.30
203 Ismael Valdes	.07	.20
204 Eric Milton	.07	.20
205 Adrian Beltre	.10	.30
206 Tony Clark	.07	.20
207 Bartolo Colon	.10	.30
208 Cal Ripken	1.00	2.50
209 Moises Alou	.10	.30
210 Wilson Alvarez	.07	.20
211 Kevin Brown	.20	.50
212 Orlando Cabrera	.10	.30
213 Vladimir Guerrero	.30	.75
214 Jose Rosado	.07	.20
215 Raul Mondesi	.10	.30
216 David Nilsson	.07	.20
217 Carlos Perez	.07	.20
218 Jason Schmidt	.10	.30
219 Richie Sexson	.10	.30
220 Gary Sheffield	.10	.30
221 Fernando Vina	.07	.20
222 Todd Walker	.07	.20
223 Scott Sauerbeck RC	.10	.30
223S Scott Sauerbeck SP	.75	2.00
224 Pascual Matos RC	.10	.30
224S Pascual Matos SP	.75	2.00
225 Kyle Farnsworth RC	.10	.30
225S Kyle Farnsworth SP	.75	2.00
226 Freddy Garcia RC	.30	.75
226S Freddy Garcia SP	1.25	3.00
227 David Lundquist RC	.10	.30
227S David Lundquist SP	.75	2.00
228 Jolbert Cabrera RC	.10	.30
228S Jolbert Cabrera SP	.75	2.00
229 Dan Perkins RC	.10	.30
229S Dan Perkins SP	.75	2.00
230 Warren Morris	.10	.30
230S Warren Morris SP	.75	2.00
231 Carlos Febles	.10	.30
231S Carlos Febles SP	.75	2.00
232 Brett Hinchliffe RC	.10	.30
232S Brett Hinchliffe SP	.75	2.00
233 Jason Phillips RC	.10	.30
233S Jason Phillips SP	.75	2.00
234 Glen Barker RC	.10	.30
234S Glen Barker SP	.75	2.00
235 Jose Macias RC	.10	.30
235S Jose Macias SP	.75	2.00
236 Joe Mays RC	.10	.30
236S Joe Mays SP	.75	2.00
237 Chad Allen RC	.10	.30
237S Chad Allen SP	.75	2.00
238 Miguel Del Toro RC	.10	.30
238S Miguel Del Toro SP	.75	2.00
239 Chris Singleton	.10	.30
239S Chris Singleton SP	.75	2.00
240 Jesse Garcia RC	.10	.30
240S Jesse Garcia SP	.75	2.00
241 Kris Benson	.10	.30
241S Kris Benson SP	.75	2.00
242 Clay Bellinger RC	.10	.30
242S Clay Bellinger SP	.75	2.00
243 Scott Williamson	.10	.30
243S Scott Williamson SP	.75	2.00
244 Masao Kida RC	.10	.30
244S Masao Kida SP	.75	2.00
245 Guillermo Garcia RC	.10	.30
245S Guillermo Garcia SP	.75	2.00
246 A.J. Burnett RC	.30	.75
246S A.J. Burnett SP	1.25	3.00
247 Bo Porter RC	.10	.30
247S Bo Porter SP	.75	2.00
248 Pat Burrell RC	.60	1.50
248S Pat Burrell SP	2.50	6.00
249 Carlos Lee	.10	.30
249S Carlos Lee SP	.75	2.00
250 Jeff Weaver RC	.20	.50
250S Jeff Weaver SP	.75	2.00
251 Ruben Mateo	.10	.30
251S Ruben Mateo SP	.75	2.00
252 J.D. Drew	.10	.30
252S J.D. Drew SP	.75	2.00
253 Jeremy Giambi	.10	.30
253S Jeremy Giambi SP	.75	2.00
254 Gary Bennett RC	.10	.30
254S Gary Bennett SP	.75	2.00
255 Edwards Guzman RC	.10	.30
255S Edwards Guzman SP	.75	2.00
256 Ramon E.Martinez RC	.10	.30
256S RamonE.Martinez SP	.75	2.00
257 Giomar Guevara RC	.10	.30
257S Giomar Guevara SP	.75	2.00
258 Joe McEwing RC	.10	.30
258S Joe McEwing SP	.75	2.00
259 Tom Davey RC	.10	.30
259S Tom Davey SP	.75	2.00
260 Gabe Kapler	.10	.30
260S Gabe Kapler SP	.75	2.00
261 Ryan Rupe RC	.10	.30
261S Ryan Rupe SP	.75	2.00
262 Kelly Dransfeldt RC	.10	.30
262S Kelly Dransfeldt SP	.75	2.00
263 Michael Barrett	.10	.30
263S Michael Barrett SP	.75	2.00
264 Eric Chavez	.10	.30
264S Eric Chavez SP	.75	2.00
265 Orber Moreno RC	.10	.30
265S Orber Moreno SP	.75	2.00
266 Marlon Anderson	.10	.30
266S Marlon Anderson SP	.75	2.00
267 Carlos Beltran	.20	.50
267S Carlos Beltran SP	.75	2.00
268 D.Mientkiewicz RC	.20	.50
268S D.Mientkiewicz SP	.75	2.00
269 Roy Halladay	.30	.75
269S Roy Halladay SP	2.00	5.00
270 Torii Hunter	.10	.30
270S Torii Hunter SP	.75	2.00
271 Stan Spencer	.10	.30
271S Stan Spencer SP	.75	2.00
272 Alex Gonzalez	.10	.30
272S Alex Gonzalez SP	.75	2.00
273 Mark McGwire SF	.40	1.00
274 Scott Rolen SF	.10	.30
275 Jeff Bagwell SF	.10	.30
276 Derek Jeter SF	.40	1.00
277 Tony Gwynn SF	.20	.50
278 Frank Thomas SF	.20	.50
279 Sammy Sosa SF	.20	.50
280 Nomar Garciaparra SF	.30	.75
281 Cal Ripken SF	.50	1.25
282 Albert Belle SF	.07	.20
283 Kerry Wood SF	.10	.30
284 Greg Maddux SF	.30	.75
285 Barry Bonds SF	.40	1.00
286 Juan Gonzalez SF	.07	.20
287 Ken Griffey Jr. SF	.30	.75
288 Alex Rodriguez SF	.30	.75
289 Ben Grieve SF	.07	.20
290 Travis Lee SF	.07	.20
291 Mo Vaughn SF	.07	.20
292 Mike Piazza SF	.30	.75
293 Roger Clemens SF	.30	.75
294 J.D. Drew SF	.07	.20
295 Randy Johnson SF	.20	.50
296 Chipper Jones SF	.20	.50
297 Vladimir Guerrero SF	.20	.50
298 Nomar Garciaparra CL	.30	.75
299 Ken Griffey Jr. CL	.30	.75
300 Mark McGwire CL	.40	1.00
S83 Ben Grieve Sample	.40	1.00

1999 SkyBox Premium Star Rubies

Randomly inserted into packs, this 300-card set is parallel to the base set. Only 50 serial-numbered sets were produced with the short-printed full-body action shot rookie and prospect cards sequentially numbered to just 15. Like the rest of the cards in this set, the close-up rookie and prospect cards are serial numbered to 50.

Card	Low	High
COMMON CARD (1-300)	4.00	8.00

*STARS 1-300: 12.5X TO 30X BASIC CARDS
*PROSPECTS 223-272: 12.5X TO 30X BASIC
*ROOKIES 223-272: 8X TO 20X BASIC RC'S

1999 SkyBox Premium Autographics

Randomly inserted in packs at the rate of one in 68, this 52-card set features autographed color photos of top players. The cards are unnumbered and checklisted in alphabetical order.

STATED ODDS 1:68

Card	Low	High
1 Roberto Alomar	10.00	25.00
2 Paul Bako	4.00	10.00
3 Michael Barrett	4.00	10.00
4 Kris Benson	6.00	15.00
5 Micah Bowie	4.00	10.00
6 Roosevelt Brown	4.00	10.00
7 A.J. Burnett	10.00	25.00
8 Pat Burrell	10.00	25.00
9 Ken Caminiti	15.00	40.00
10 Royce Clayton	4.00	10.00
11 Edgard Clemente	4.00	10.00
12 Bartolo Colon	6.00	15.00
13 J.D. Drew	6.00	15.00
14 Damion Easley	4.00	10.00
15 Derrin Ebert	4.00	10.00
16 Mario Encarnacion	4.00	10.00
17 Juan Encarnacion	6.00	15.00
18 Troy Glaus	15.00	40.00
19 Tom Glavine	15.00	40.00
20 Juan Gonzalez SP	60.00	120.00
21 Shawn Green	10.00	25.00
22 Wilton Guerrero	4.00	10.00
23 Jose Guillen	6.00	15.00
24 Tony Gwynn	20.00	50.00
25 Mark Harriger	4.00	10.00
26 Todd Hollandsworth	4.00	10.00
27 Scott Hunter	4.00	10.00
28 Gabe Kapler	6.00	15.00
29 Scott Karl	4.00	10.00
30 Mike Kinkade	4.00	10.00
31 Ray Lankford	6.00	15.00
32 Barry Larkin	10.00	25.00
33 Matt Lawton	4.00	10.00
34 Ricky Ledee	4.00	10.00
35 Travis Lee	4.00	10.00
36 Eli Marrero	4.00	10.00
37 Ruben Mateo	4.00	10.00
38 Joe McEwing	4.00	10.00
39 Doug Mientkiewicz	6.00	15.00
40 Russ Ortiz	4.00	10.00
41 Jim Parque	4.00	10.00
42 Robert Person	4.00	10.00
43 Alex Rodriguez	50.00	100.00
44 Scott Rolen	10.00	25.00
45 Benj Sampson	4.00	10.00
46 Luis Saturria	4.00	10.00
47 Curt Schilling	20.00	50.00
48 David Segui	6.00	15.00
49 Fernando Tatis	4.00	10.00
50 Peter Tucci	4.00	10.00
51 Javier Vazquez	6.00	15.00
52 Robin Ventura	6.00	15.00

1999 SkyBox Premium Autographics Blue Ink

Randomly inserted in packs, this 52-card set is a blue ink parallel version of the regular insert set. Only 50 serial-numbered sets were produced.

*BLUE INK STARS: 1X TO 2.5X BASIC AU'S
*BLUE INK RC's: .75X TO 2X BASIC AU'S

1999 SkyBox Premium Diamond Debuts

Randomly inserted in packs at the rate of one in 49, this 15-card set features color photos of the best rookies of 1999 printed on silver rainbow holo-foil and etched cards.

Card	Low	High
COMPLETE SET (15)	40.00	80.00
STATED ODDS 1:49		
1 Eric Chavez	3.00	8.00
2 Kyle Farnsworth	3.00	8.00
3 Ryan Rupe	3.00	8.00
4 Jeremy Giambi	3.00	8.00
5 Marlon Anderson	3.00	8.00
6 J.D. Drew	3.00	8.00
7 Carlos Febles	3.00	8.00
8 Joe McEwing	3.00	8.00
9 Jeff Weaver	5.00	12.00
10 Alex Gonzalez	2.00	5.00
11 Chad Allen	3.00	8.00
12 Michael Barrett	3.00	8.00
13 Gabe Kapler	3.00	8.00
14 Carlos Lee	3.00	8.00
15 Edwards Guzman	3.00	8.00

1999 SkyBox Premium Intimidation Nation

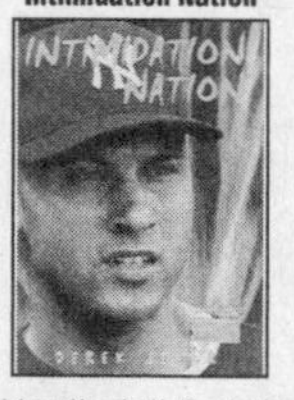

Randomly inserted in packs, this 15-card set features color photos of top players stamped on gold rainbow holo-foil cards. Only 99 serial-numbered sets were produced.

Card	Low	High
1 Cal Ripken	40.00	100.00
2 Tony Gwynn	15.00	40.00
3 Nomar Garciaparra	20.00	50.00
4 Frank Thomas	12.50	30.00
5 Mike Piazza	20.00	50.00
6 Mark McGwire	30.00	80.00
7 Scott Rolen	8.00	20.00
8 Chipper Jones	12.50	30.00
9 Greg Maddux	20.00	50.00
10 Ken Griffey Jr.	20.00	50.00
11 Juan Gonzalez	8.00	20.00
12 Derek Jeter	30.00	80.00
13 J.D. Drew	8.00	20.00
14 Roger Clemens	25.00	60.00
15 Alex Rodriguez	20.00	50.00

1999 SkyBox Premium Live Bats

Randomly inserted in packs at the rate of one in seven, this 15-card set features color photos of some of baseball's best hitters on foil stamped cards.

Card	Low	High
COMPLETE SET (15)	10.00	25.00
STATED ODDS 1:7		
1 Juan Gonzalez	.20	.50
2 Mark McGwire	1.25	3.00
3 Jeff Bagwell	.30	.75
4 Frank Thomas	.50	1.25
5 Mike Piazza	.75	2.00
6 Nomar Garciaparra	.75	2.00
7 Alex Rodriguez	.75	2.00
8 Scott Rolen	.30	.75
9 Travis Lee	.10	.30
10 Tony Gwynn	.60	1.50
11 Derek Jeter	1.25	3.00
12 Ben Grieve	.10	.30
13 Chipper Jones	.50	1.25
14 Ken Griffey Jr.	.75	2.00
15 Cal Ripken	1.50	4.00

1999 SkyBox Premium Show Business

Randomly inserted in packs at the rate of one in 70, this 15-card set features top players printed on double foil-stamped cards.

Card	Low	High
COMPLETE SET (15)	100.00	200.00
STATED ODDS 1:70		
1 Mark McGwire	8.00	20.00
2 Tony Gwynn	4.00	10.00
3 Nomar Garciaparra	5.00	12.00
4 Juan Gonzalez	1.25	3.00
5 Roger Clemens	6.00	15.00
6 Chipper Jones	3.00	8.00
7 Cal Ripken	10.00	25.00
8 Alex Rodriguez	5.00	12.00
9 Orlando Hernandez	1.25	3.00
10 Greg Maddux	5.00	12.00
11 Mike Piazza	5.00	12.00
12 Frank Thomas	3.00	8.00
13 Ken Griffey Jr.	5.00	12.00
14 Scott Rolen	2.00	5.00
15 Derek Jeter	8.00	20.00

1999 SkyBox Premium Soul of the Game

Randomly inserted into packs at the rate of one in 14, this 15-card set features players who are fan favorites printed on rainbow foil stamped cards.

Card	Low	High
COMPLETE SET (15)	30.00	60.00
STATED ODDS 1:14		
1 Alex Rodriguez	1.50	4.00
2 Vladimir Guerrero	1.00	2.50
3 Chipper Jones	1.00	2.50
4 Derek Jeter	2.50	6.00
5 Tony Gwynn	1.25	3.00
6 Scott Rolen	.60	1.50
7 Juan Gonzalez	.40	1.00
8 Mark McGwire	2.50	6.00
9 Ken Griffey Jr.	1.50	4.00
10 Jeff Bagwell	.60	1.50
11 Cal Ripken	3.00	8.00
12 Frank Thomas	1.00	2.50
13 Mike Piazza	1.50	4.00
14 Nomar Garciaparra	1.50	4.00
15 Sammy Sosa	1.00	2.50

1993 SP

Card	Low	High
COMMON CARD (1-270)	.20	.50
COMMON FOIL (271-290)	.40	1.00
1 Roberto Alomar AS	.50	1.25
2 Wade Boggs AS	.50	1.25
3 Joe Carter AS	.20	.50
4 Ken Griffey Jr. AS	1.25	3.00
5 Mark Langston AS	.20	.50
6 John Olerud AS	.30	.75
7 Kirby Puckett AS	.75	2.00
8 Cal Ripken Jr. AS	2.50	6.00
9 Ivan Rodriguez AS	.50	1.25
10 Barry Bonds AS	2.00	5.00
11 Darren Daulton AS	.30	.75
12 Marquis Grissom AS	.30	.75
13 David Justice AS	.30	.75
14 John Kruk AS	.30	.75
15 Barry Larkin AS	.50	1.25
16 Terry Mulholland AS	.20	.50
17 Ryne Sandberg AS	1.25	3.00
18 Gary Sheffield AS	.30	.75
19 Chad Curtis	.20	.50
20 Chili Davis	.30	.75

21 Gary DiSarcina	.20	.50
22 Damion Easley	.20	.50
23 Chuck Finley	.30	.75
24 Luis Polonia	.20	.50
25 Tim Salmon	.50	1.25
26 J.T. Snow RC	.50	1.25
27 Russ Springer	.20	.50
28 Jeff Bagwell	.50	1.25
29 Craig Biggio	.50	1.25
30 Ken Caminiti	.30	.75
31 Andujar Cedeno	.20	.50
32 Doug Drabek	.20	.50
33 Steve Finley	.30	.75
34 Luis Gonzalez	.30	.75
35 Pete Harnisch	.20	.50
36 Darryl Kile	.30	.75
37 Mike Bordick	.20	.50
38 Dennis Eckersley	.30	.75
39 Brent Gates	.20	.50
40 Rickey Henderson	.75	2.00
41 Mark McGwire	2.00	5.00
42 Craig Paquette	.20	.50
43 Ruben Sierra	.30	.75
44 Terry Steinbach	.20	.50
45 Todd Van Poppel	.20	.50
46 Pat Borders	.20	.50
47 Tony Fernandez	.20	.50
48 Juan Guzman	.20	.50
49 Pat Hentgen	.20	.50
50 Paul Molitor	.30	.75
51 Jack Morris	.30	.75
52 Ed Sprague	.20	.50
53 Duane Ward	.20	.50
54 Devon White	.30	.75
55 Steve Avery	.20	.50
56 Jeff Blauser	.20	.50
57 Ron Gant	.30	.75
58 Tom Glavine	.50	1.25
59 Greg Maddux	1.25	3.00
60 Fred McGriff	.50	1.25
61 Terry Pendleton	.30	.75
62 Deion Sanders	.50	1.25
63 John Smoltz	.50	1.25
64 Cal Eldred	.20	.50
65 Darryl Hamilton	.20	.50
66 John Jaha	.20	.50
67 Pat Listach	.20	.50
68 Jaime Navarro	.20	.50
69 Kevin Reimer	.20	.50
70 B.J. Surhoff	.30	.75
71 Greg Vaughn	.20	.50
72 Robin Yount	1.25	3.00
73 Rene Arocha RC	.30	.75
74 Bernard Gilkey	.20	.50
75 Gregg Jefferies	.20	.50
76 Ray Lankford	.30	.75
77 Tom Pagnozzi	.20	.50
78 Lee Smith	.30	.75
79 Ozzie Smith	1.25	3.00
80 Bob Tewksbury	.20	.50
81 Mark Whiten	.20	.50
82 Steve Buechele	.20	.50
83 Mark Grace	.50	1.25
84 Jose Guzman	.20	.50
85 Derrick May	.20	.50
86 Mike Morgan	.20	.50
87 Randy Myers	.20	.50
88 Kevin Roberson RC	.20	.50
89 Sammy Sosa	.75	2.00
90 Rick Wilkins	.20	.50
91 Brett Butler	.30	.75
92 Eric Davis	.30	.75
93 Orel Hershiser	.30	.75
94 Eric Karros	.30	.75
95 Ramon Martinez	.20	.50
96 Raul Mondesi	.30	.75
97 Jose Offerman	.20	.50
98 Mike Piazza	2.00	5.00
99 Darryl Strawberry	.30	.75
100 Moises Alou	.30	.75
101 Wil Cordero	.20	.50
102 Delino DeShields	.20	.50
103 Darrin Fletcher	.20	.50
104 Ken Hill	.20	.50
105 Mike Lansing RC	.30	.75
106 Dennis Martinez	.30	.75
107 Larry Walker	.30	.75
108 John Wetteland	.30	.75
109 Rod Beck	.20	.50
110 John Burkett	.20	.50
111 Will Clark	.50	1.25
112 Royce Clayton	.20	.50
113 Darren Lewis	.20	.50
114 Willie McGee	.30	.75
115 Bill Swift	.20	.50
116 Robby Thompson	.20	.50
117 Matt Williams	.30	.75
118 Sandy Alomar Jr.	.20	.50
119 Carlos Baerga	.20	.50
120 Albert Belle	.30	.75
121 Reggie Jefferson	.20	.50
122 Wayne Kirby	.20	.50
123 Kenny Lofton	.30	.75
124 Carlos Martinez	.20	.50
125 Charles Nagy	.20	.50
126 Paul Sorrento	.20	.50
127 Rich Amaral	.20	.50
128 Jay Buhner	.30	.75
129 Norm Charlton	.20	.50
130 Dave Fleming	.20	.50
131 Erik Hanson	.20	.50
132 Randy Johnson	.75	2.00
133 Edgar Martinez	.50	1.25
134 Tino Martinez	.50	1.25
135 Omar Vizquel	.50	1.25
136 Bret Barberie	.20	.50
137 Chuck Carr	.20	.50
138 Jeff Conine	.30	.75
139 Orestes Destrade	.20	.50
140 Chris Hammond	.20	.50
141 Bryan Harvey	.20	.50
142 Benito Santiago	.30	.75
143 Walt Weiss	.20	.50
144 Darrell Whitmore RC	.20	.50
145 Tim Bogar RC	.20	.50
146 Bobby Bonilla	.30	.75
147 Jeromy Burnitz	.30	.75
148 Vince Coleman	.20	.50
149 Dwight Gooden	.30	.75
150 Todd Hundley	.20	.50
151 Howard Johnson	.20	.50
152 Eddie Murray	.75	2.00
153 Bret Saberhagen	.30	.75
154 Brady Anderson	.30	.75
155 Mike Devereaux	.20	.50
156 Jeffrey Hammonds	.20	.50
157 Chris Hoiles	.20	.50
158 Ben McDonald	.20	.50
159 Mark McLemore	.20	.50
160 Mike Mussina	.50	1.25
161 Gregg Olson	.20	.50
162 David Segui	.20	.50
163 Derek Bell	.20	.50
164 Andy Benes	.20	.50
165 Archi Cianfrocco	.20	.50
166 Ricky Gutierrez	.20	.50
167 Tony Gwynn UER	1.00	2.50
Photo is Tracy Sanders		
168 Gene Harris	.20	.50
169 Trevor Hoffman	.75	2.00
170 Ray McDavid RC	.20	.50
171 Phil Plantier	.20	.50
172 Mariano Duncan	.20	.50
173 Len Dykstra	.30	.75
174 Tommy Greene	.20	.50
175 Dave Hollins	.20	.50
176 Pete Incaviglia	.20	.50
177 Mickey Morandini	.20	.50
178 Curt Schilling	.30	.75
179 Kevin Stocker	.20	.50
180 Mitch Williams	.20	.50
181 Stan Belinda	.20	.50
182 Jay Bell	.30	.75
183 Steve Cooke	.20	.50
184 Carlos Garcia	.20	.50
185 Jeff King	.20	.50
186 Orlando Merced	.20	.50
187 Don Slaught	.20	.50
188 Andy Van Slyke	.50	1.25
189 Kevin Young	.30	.75
190 Kevin Brown	.30	.75
191 Jose Canseco	.50	1.25
192 Julio Franco	.30	.75
193 Benji Gil	.20	.50
194 Juan Gonzalez	.30	.75
195 Tom Henke	.20	.50
196 Rafael Palmeiro	.50	1.25
197 Dean Palmer	.30	.75
198 Nolan Ryan	3.00	8.00
199 Roger Clemens	1.50	4.00
200 Scott Cooper	.20	.50
201 Andre Dawson	.30	.75
202 Mike Greenwell	.20	.50
203 Carlos Quintana	.20	.50
204 Jeff Russell	.20	.50
205 Aaron Sele	.20	.50
206 Mo Vaughn	.30	.75
207 Frank Viola	.30	.75
208 Rob Dibble	.30	.75
209 Roberto Kelly	.20	.50
210 Kevin Mitchell	.20	.50
211 Hal Morris	.20	.50
212 Joe Oliver	.20	.50
213 Jose Rijo	.20	.50
214 Bip Roberts	.20	.50
215 Chris Sabo	.20	.50
216 Reggie Sanders	.30	.75
217 Dante Bichette	.30	.75
218 Jerald Clark	.20	.50
219 Alex Cole	.20	.50
220 Andres Galarraga	.30	.75
221 Joe Girardi	.20	.50
222 Charlie Hayes	.20	.50
223 Roberto Mejia RC	.20	.50
224 Armando Reynoso	.20	.50
225 Eric Young	.20	.50
226 Kevin Appier	.30	.75
227 George Brett	2.00	5.00
228 David Cone	.30	.75
229 Phil Hiatt	.20	.50
230 Felix Jose	.20	.50
231 Wally Joyner	.30	.75
232 Mike Macfarlane	.20	.50
233 Brian McRae	.20	.50
234 Jeff Montgomery	.20	.50
235 Rob Deer	.20	.50
236 Cecil Fielder	.30	.75
237 Travis Fryman	.30	.75
238 Mike Henneman	.20	.50
239 Tony Phillips	.20	.50
240 Mickey Tettleton	.20	.50
241 Alan Trammell	.30	.75
242 David Wells	.30	.75
243 Lou Whitaker	.30	.75
244 Rick Aguilera	.20	.50
245 Scott Erickson	.20	.50
246 Brian Harper	.20	.50
247 Kent Hrbek	.30	.75
248 Chuck Knoblauch	.30	.75
249 Shane Mack	.20	.50
250 David McCarty	.20	.50
251 Pedro Munoz	.20	.50
252 Dave Winfield	.30	.75
253 Alex Fernandez	.20	.50
254 Ozzie Guillen	.30	.75
255 Bo Jackson	.75	2.00
256 Lance Johnson	.20	.50
257 Ron Karkovice	.20	.50
258 Jack McDowell	.20	.50
259 Tim Raines	.30	.75
260 Frank Thomas	.75	2.00
261 Robin Ventura	.30	.75
262 Jim Abbott	.50	1.25
263 Steve Farr	.20	.50
264 Jimmy Key	.30	.75
265 Don Mattingly	2.00	5.00
266 Paul O'Neill	.50	1.25
267 Mike Stanley	.20	.50
268 Danny Tartabull	.20	.50
269 Bob Wickman	.20	.50
270 Bernie Williams	.50	1.25
271 Jason Bere FOIL	.40	1.00
272 R.Cedeno FOIL RC	.60	1.50
273 J.Damon FOIL RC	3.00	8.00
274 Russ Davis FOIL RC	.60	1.50
275 Carlos Delgado FOIL	1.50	4.00
276 Carl Everett FOIL	.60	1.50
277 Cliff Floyd FOIL	.30	.75
278 Alex Gonzalez FOIL	.40	1.00
279 Derek Jeter FOIL RC	75.00	150.00
280 Chipper Jones FOIL	1.50	4.00
281 Javier Lopez FOIL	.50	1.25
282 Chad Mottola FOIL RC	.40	1.00
283 Marc Newfield FOIL	.40	1.00
284 Eduardo Perez FOIL	.40	1.00
285 Manny Ramirez FOIL	2.00	5.00
286 T.Steverson FOIL RC	.40	1.00
287 Michael Tucker FOIL	.40	1.00
288 Allen Watson FOIL	.40	1.00
289 Rondell White FOIL	.60	1.50
290 Dmitri Young FOIL	.60	1.50

1993 SP Platinum Power

Cards from this 20-card standard-size were inserted one every nine packs and feature power hitters from the American and National Leagues.

COMPLETE SET (20)	30.00	80.00
STATED ODDS 1:9		
PP1 Albert Belle	.75	2.00
PP2 Barry Bonds	5.00	12.00
PP3 Joe Carter	.50	1.25
PP4 Will Clark	1.25	3.00
PP5 Darren Daulton	.75	2.00
PP6 Cecil Fielder	.75	2.00
PP7 Ron Gant	.75	2.00
PP8 Juan Gonzalez	.75	2.00
PP9 Ken Griffey Jr.	3.00	8.00
PP10 Dave Hollins	.50	1.25
PP11 David Justice	.75	2.00
PP12 Fred McGriff	1.25	3.00
PP13 Mark McGwire	5.00	12.00
PP14 Dean Palmer	.75	2.00
PP15 Mike Piazza	5.00	12.00
PP16 Tim Salmon	1.25	3.00
PP17 Ryne Sandberg	3.00	8.00
PP18 Gary Sheffield	.75	2.00
PP19 Frank Thomas	2.00	5.00
PP20 Matt Williams	.75	2.00

1994 SP Previews

These 15 cards were distributed regionally as inserts in second series Upper Deck hobby packs. They were inserted at a rate of one in 35. The manner of distribution was five cards per Central, East and West region. The cards are nearly identical to the basic SP issue. Card fronts differ in that the region is at bottom right where the team name is located on the SP cards.

COMPLETE SET (15)	65.00	160.00
COMPLETE CENTRAL (5)	25.00	60.00
COMPLETE EAST (5)	15.00	40.00
COMPLETE WEST (5)	25.00	60.00
STATED ODDS 1:35 REG'L SER.2 UD HOBBY		
CR1 Jeff Bagwell	2.00	5.00
CR2 Michael Jordan	6.00	15.00
CR3 Kirby Puckett	3.00	8.00
CR4 Manny Ramirez	3.00	8.00
CR5 Frank Thomas	3.00	8.00
ER1 Roberto Alomar	2.00	5.00
ER2 Cliff Floyd	1.25	3.00
ER3 Javier Lopez	1.25	3.00
ER4 Don Mattingly	8.00	20.00
ER5 Cal Ripken	10.00	25.00
WR1 Barry Bonds	8.00	20.00
WR2 Juan Gonzalez	1.25	3.00
WR3 Ken Griffey Jr.	5.00	12.00
WR4 Mike Piazza	6.00	15.00
WR5 Tim Salmon	2.00	5.00

1994 SP

This 200-card standard-size set distributed in foil packs contains the game's top players and prospects. The first 20 cards in the set are Foil Prospects which are brighter and more metallic than the rest of the set. These cards therefore are highly condition sensitive. Cards 21-200 are in alphabetical order by team nickname. Rookie Cards include Brad Fullmer, Derrek Lee, Chan Ho Park and Alex Rodriguez.

COMPLETE SET (200)	75.00	150.00
COMMON CARD (21-200)	.07	.20
COMMON FOIL (1-20)	.20	.50
1 Mike Bell FOIL RC	.20	.50
2 D.J. Boston FOIL RC	.20	.50
3 Johnny Damon FOIL	.75	2.00
4 Brad Fullmer FOIL RC	.40	1.00
5 Joey Hamilton FOIL	.20	.50
6 T.Hollandsworth FOIL	.20	.50
7 Brian L. Hunter FOIL	.20	.50
8 L.Hawkins FOIL RC	.40	1.00
9 B.Kieschnick FOIL RC	.20	.50
10 Derrek Lee FOIL RC	5.00	12.00
11 Trot Nixon FOIL RC	1.50	4.00
12 Alex Ochoa FOIL	.20	.50
13 Chan Ho Park FOIL RC	.75	2.00
14 Kirk Presley FOIL RC	.20	.50
15 A.Rodriguez FOIL RC	40.00	80.00
16 Jose Silva FOIL RC	.20	.50
17 Terrell Wade FOIL RC	.20	.50
18 Billy Wagner FOIL RC	1.50	4.00
19 G.Williams FOIL RC	.20	.50
20 Preston Wilson FOIL	.40	1.00
21 Brian Anderson RC	.15	.40
22 Chad Curtis	.07	.20
23 Chili Davis	.15	.40
24 Bo Jackson	.40	1.00
25 Mark Langston	.07	.20
26 Tim Salmon	.25	.60
27 Jeff Bagwell	.25	.60
28 Craig Biggio	.25	.60
29 Ken Caminiti	.15	.40
30 Doug Drabek	.07	.20
31 John Hudek RC	.07	.20
32 Greg Swindell	.07	.20
33 Brent Gates	.07	.20
34 Rickey Henderson	.40	1.00
35 Steve Karsay	.07	.20
36 Mark McGwire	1.00	2.50
37 Ruben Sierra	.15	.40
38 Terry Steinbach	.07	.20
39 Roberto Alomar	.25	.60
40 Joe Carter	.15	.40
41 Carlos Delgado	.25	.60
42 Alex Gonzalez	.07	.20
43 Juan Guzman	.07	.20
44 Paul Molitor	.15	.40
45 John Olerud	.15	.40
46 Devon White	.15	.40
47 Steve Avery	.07	.20
48 Jeff Blauser	.07	.20
49 Tom Glavine	.25	.60
50 David Justice	.15	.40
51 Roberto Kelly	.07	.20
52 Ryan Klesko	.15	.40
53 Javier Lopez	.15	.40
54 Greg Maddux	.60	1.50
55 Fred McGriff	.25	.60
56 Ricky Bones	.07	.20
57 Cal Eldred	.07	.20
58 Brian Harper	.07	.20
59 Pat Listach	.07	.20
60 B.J. Surhoff	.15	.40
61 Greg Vaughn	.07	.20
62 Bernard Gilkey	.07	.20
63 Gregg Jefferies	.07	.20
64 Ray Lankford	.15	.40
65 Ozzie Smith	.60	1.50
66 Bob Tewksbury	.07	.20
67 Mark Whiten	.07	.20
68 Todd Zeile	.07	.20
69 Mark Grace	.25	.60
70 Randy Myers	.07	.20
71 Ryne Sandberg	.60	1.50
72 Sammy Sosa	.40	1.00
73 Steve Trachsel	.07	.20
74 Rick Wilkins	.07	.20
75 Brett Butler	.15	.40
76 Delino DeShields	.07	.20
77 Orel Hershiser	.15	.40
78 Eric Karros	.15	.40
79 Raul Mondesi	.15	.40
80 Mike Piazza	.75	2.00
81 Tim Wallach	.07	.20
82 Moises Alou	.15	.40
83 Cliff Floyd	.15	.40
84 Marquis Grissom	.15	.40
85 Pedro Martinez	.40	1.00
86 Larry Walker	.15	.40
87 John Wetteland	.15	.40
88 Rondell White	.15	.40
89 Rod Beck	.07	.20
90 Barry Bonds	1.00	2.50
91 John Burkett	.07	.20
92 Royce Clayton	.07	.20
93 Billy Swift	.07	.20
94 Robby Thompson	.07	.20
95 Matt Williams	.15	.40
96 Carlos Baerga	.07	.20
97 Albert Belle	.15	.40
98 Kenny Lofton	.15	.40
99 Dennis Martinez	.15	.40
100 Eddie Murray	.40	1.00
101 Manny Ramirez	.40	1.00
102 Eric Anthony	.07	.20
103 Chris Bosio	.07	.20
104 Jay Buhner	.15	.40
105 Ken Griffey Jr.	.60	1.50
106 Randy Johnson	.40	1.00
107 Edgar Martinez	.25	.60
108 Chuck Carr	.07	.20
109 Jeff Conine	.15	.40
110 Carl Everett	.15	.40
111 Chris Hammond	.07	.20
112 Bryan Harvey	.07	.20
113 Charles Johnson	.15	.40
114 Gary Sheffield	.15	.40
115 Bobby Bonilla	.15	.40
116 Dwight Gooden	.15	.40
117 Todd Hundley	.07	.20
118 Bobby Jones	.07	.20
119 Jeff Kent	.25	.60
120 Bret Saberhagen	.15	.40
121 Jeffrey Hammonds	.07	.20
122 Chris Hoiles	.07	.20
123 Ben McDonald	.07	.20
124 Mike Mussina	.25	.60
125 Rafael Palmeiro	.25	.60
126 Cal Ripken Jr.	1.25	3.00
127 Lee Smith	.15	.40
128 Derek Bell	.07	.20
129 Andy Benes	.07	.20
130 Tony Gwynn	.50	1.25
131 Trevor Hoffman	.25	.60
132 Phil Plantier	.07	.20
133 Bip Roberts	.07	.20
134 Darren Daulton	.15	.40
135 Lenny Dykstra	.15	.40
136 Dave Hollins	.07	.20
137 Danny Jackson	.07	.20
138 John Kruk	.15	.40
139 Kevin Stocker	.07	.20
140 Jay Bell	.15	.40
141 Carlos Garcia	.07	.20
142 Jeff King	.07	.20
143 Orlando Merced	.07	.20
144 Andy Van Slyke	.25	.60
145 Rick White	.07	.20
146 Jose Canseco	.25	.60
147 Will Clark	.25	.60
148 Juan Gonzalez	.15	.40
149 Rick Helling	.07	.20
150 Dean Palmer	.15	.40
151 Ivan Rodriguez	.25	.60
152 Roger Clemens	.75	2.00
153 Scott Cooper	.07	.20
154 Andre Dawson	.15	.40
155 Mike Greenwell	.07	.20
156 Aaron Sele	.07	.20
157 Mo Vaughn	.15	.40
158 Bret Boone	.15	.40
159 Barry Larkin	.25	.60
160 Kevin Mitchell	.07	.20
161 Jose Rijo	.07	.20
162 Deion Sanders	.25	.60
163 Reggie Sanders	.15	.40
164 Dante Bichette	.15	.40
165 Ellis Burks	.15	.40
166 Andres Galarraga	.15	.40
167 Charlie Hayes	.07	.20
168 David Nied	.07	.20
169 Walt Weiss	.07	.20
170 Kevin Appier	.15	.40
171 David Cone	.15	.40
172 Jeff Granger	.07	.20
173 Felix Jose	.07	.20
174 Wally Joyner	.15	.40
175 Brian McRae	.07	.20
176 Cecil Fielder	.15	.40
177 Travis Fryman	.15	.40
178 Mike Henneman	.07	.20
179 Tony Phillips	.07	.20
180 Mickey Tettleton	.07	.20
181 Alan Trammell	.15	.40
182 Rick Aguilera	.07	.20
183 Rich Becker	.07	.20
184 Scott Erickson	.07	.20
185 Chuck Knoblauch	.15	.40
186 Kirby Puckett	.40	1.00
187 Dave Winfield	.15	.40
188 Wilson Alvarez	.07	.20
189 Jason Bere	.07	.20
190 Alex Fernandez	.07	.20
191 Julio Franco	.15	.40
192 Jack McDowell	.07	.20
193 Frank Thomas	.40	1.00
194 Robin Ventura	.15	.40
195 Jim Abbott	.25	.60
196 Wade Boggs	.25	.60
197 Jimmy Key	.15	.40
198 Don Mattingly	1.00	2.50
199 Paul O'Neill	.25	.60
200 Danny Tartabull	.07	.20
P24 Ken Griffey Jr. Promo	.75	2.00

1994 SP Die Cuts

This 200-card die-cut set is parallel to that of the basic SP issue. The cards were inserted one per SP pack. The difference, of course, is the unique die-cut shape. The backs have a silver Upper Deck hologram as opposed to gold on the basic issue.

COMPLETE SET (200)	75.00	150.00
*STARS: .75X TO 2X BASIC CARDS		
*ROOKIES: .6X TO 1.5X BASIC CARDS		
10 Derrek Lee FOIL	6.00	15.00
15 Alex Rodriguez FOIL	50.00	100.00

1994 SP Holoviews

Randomly inserted in SP foil packs at a rate of one in five, this 38-card set contains top stars and prospects.

STATED ODDS 1:5		
1 Roberto Alomar	1.25	3.00
2 Kevin Appier	.75	2.00
3 Jeff Bagwell	1.25	3.00
4 Jose Canseco	1.25	3.00
5 Roger Clemens	4.00	10.00
6 Carlos Delgado	1.25	3.00
7 Cecil Fielder	.75	2.00
8 Cliff Floyd	.75	2.00
9 Travis Fryman	.75	2.00
10 Andres Galarraga	.75	2.00
11 Juan Gonzalez	.75	2.00
12 Ken Griffey Jr.	3.00	8.00
13 Tony Gwynn	2.50	6.00
14 Jeffrey Hammonds	.60	1.50
15 Bo Jackson	2.00	5.00
16 Michael Jordan	6.00	15.00
17 David Justice	.75	2.00
18 Steve Karsay	.60	1.50
19 Jeff Kent	1.25	3.00
20 Brooks Kieschnick	.60	1.50
21 Ryan Klesko	.75	2.00
22 John Kruk	.75	2.00
23 Barry Larkin	1.25	3.00
24 Pat Listach	.60	1.50
25 Don Mattingly	5.00	12.00
26 Mark McGwire	5.00	12.00
27 Raul Mondesi	.75	2.00
28 Trot Nixon	2.50	6.00
29 Mike Piazza	3.00	8.00
30 Kirby Puckett	2.00	5.00
31 Manny Ramirez	2.00	5.00
32 Cal Ripken	6.00	15.00
33 Alex Rodriguez	20.00	50.00
34 Tim Salmon	1.25	3.00
35 Gary Sheffield	.75	2.00
36 Ozzie Smith	3.00	8.00
37 Sammy Sosa	2.00	5.00
38 Andy Van Slyke	1.25	3.00

1994 SP Holoviews Die Cuts

Parallel to the blue Holoview set, this 38-card red-bordered issue was also randomly inserted in SP packs. They are much more difficult to pull than the blue version with an insertion rate of one in 75.

*DIE CUTS: 4X TO 10X BASIC HOLO

*DIE CUTS: 2.5X TO 6X BASIC HOLO RC YR		
STATED ODDS 1:75		
16 Michael Jordan	75.00	150.00
28 Trot Nixon	15.00	40.00
33 Alex Rodriguez	250.00	500.00

1995 SP

This set consists of 207 cards being sold in eight-card, hobby-only packs with a suggested retail price of $3.99. Subsets featured are Salute (1-4) and Premier Prospects (5-24). The only notable Rookie Card in this set is Hideo Nomo. Dealers who ordered a certain quantity of Upper Deck baseball cases received as a bonus, a certified autographed SP card of Ken Griffey Jr.

COMPLETE SET (207)	15.00	40.00
COMMON CARD (1-207)	.07	.20
COMMON FOIL (5-24)	.20	.50
GRIFFEY AU SENT TO DEALERS AS BONUS		
1 Cal Ripken Salute	1.25	3.00
2 Nolan Ryan Salute	1.50	4.00
3 George Brett Salute	1.00	2.50
4 Mike Schmidt Salute	.60	1.50
5 Dustin Hermanson FOIL	.20	.50
6 Antonio Osuna FOIL	.20	.50
7 M.Grudzielanek FOIL RC	.50	1.25
8 Ray Durham FOIL	.30	.75
9 Ugueth Urbina FOIL	.20	.50
10 Ruben Rivera FOIL	.20	.50
11 Curtis Goodwin FOIL	.20	.50
12 Jimmy Hurst FOIL	.20	.50
13 Jose Malave FOIL	.20	.50
14 Hideo Nomo FOIL RC	1.50	4.00
15 Juan Acevedo RC FOIL	.20	.50
16 Tony Clark FOIL	.20	.50
17 Jim Pittsley FOIL	.20	.50
18 Freddy A. Garcia RC FOIL	.20	.50
19 Carlos Perez RC FOIL	.30	.75
20 R.Casanova FOIL RC	.20	.50
21 Quilvio Veras FOIL	.20	.50
22 Edgardo Alfonzo FOIL	.20	.50
23 Marty Cordova FOIL	.20	.50
24 C.J. Nitkowski FOIL	.20	.50
25 Wade Boggs CL	.15	.40
26 Dave Winfield CL	.07	.20
27 Eddie Murray CL	.25	.60
28 David Justice	.15	.40
29 Marquis Grissom	.15	.40
30 Fred McGriff	.25	.60
31 Greg Maddux	.60	1.50
32 Tom Glavine	.25	.60
33 Steve Avery	.07	.20
34 Chipper Jones	.40	1.00
35 Sammy Sosa	.40	1.00
36 Jaime Navarro	.07	.20
37 Randy Myers	.07	.20
38 Mark Grace	.25	.60
39 Todd Zeile	.07	.20
40 Brian McRae	.07	.20
41 Reggie Sanders	.15	.40
42 Ron Gant	.15	.40
43 Deion Sanders	.25	.60
44 Bret Boone	.15	.40
45 Barry Larkin	.25	.60
46 Jose Rijo	.07	.20
47 Jason Bates	.07	.20
48 Andres Galarraga	.15	.40
49 Bill Swift	.07	.20
50 Larry Walker	.15	.40
51 Vinny Castilla	.15	.40
52 Dante Bichette	.15	.40
53 Jeff Conine	.15	.40
54 John Burkett	.07	.20
55 Gary Sheffield	.15	.40
56 Andre Dawson	.15	.40
57 Terry Pendleton	.15	.40
58 Charles Johnson	.15	.40
59 Brian L. Hunter	.07	.20
60 Jeff Bagwell	.25	.60
61 Craig Biggio	.25	.60
62 Phil Nevin	.15	.40
63 Doug Drabek	.07	.20
64 Derek Bell	.07	.20
65 Raul Mondesi	.15	.40
66 Eric Karros	.15	.40
67 Roger Cedeno	.07	.20
68 Delino DeShields	.07	.20
69 Ramon Martinez	.07	.20
70 Mike Piazza	.60	1.50
71 Billy Ashley	.07	.20
72 Jeff Fassero	.07	.20
73 Shane Andrews	.07	.20
74 Wil Cordero	.07	.20
75 Tony Tarasco	.07	.20
76 Rondell White	.15	.40
77 Pedro Martinez	.25	.60
78 Moises Alou	.15	.40
79 Rico Brogna	.07	.20
80 Bobby Bonilla	.15	.40
81 Jeff Kent	.15	.40
82 Brett Butler	.15	.40
83 Bobby Jones	.07	.20
84 Bill Pulsipher	.07	.20
85 Bret Saberhagen	.15	.40
86 Gregg Jefferies	.07	.20
87 Lenny Dykstra	.15	.40
88 Dave Hollins	.07	.20
89 Charlie Hayes	.07	.20
90 Darren Daulton	.15	.40
91 Curt Schilling	.15	.40
92 Heathcliff Slocumb	.07	.20
93 Carlos Garcia	.07	.20
94 Denny Neagle	.15	.40
95 Jay Bell	.15	.40
96 Orlando Merced	.07	.20
97 Dave Clark	.07	.20
98 Bernard Gilkey	.07	.20
99 Scott Cooper	.07	.20
100 Ozzie Smith	.60	1.50
101 Tom Henke	.07	.20
102 Ken Hill	.07	.20
103 Brian Jordan	.15	.40
104 Ray Lankford	.15	.40
105 Tony Gwynn	.50	1.25
106 Andy Benes	.07	.20
107 Ken Caminiti	.15	.40
108 Steve Finley	.15	.40
109 Joey Hamilton	.07	.20
110 Bip Roberts	.07	.20
111 Eddie Williams	.07	.20
112 Rod Beck	.07	.20
113 Matt Williams	.15	.40
114 Glenallen Hill	.07	.20
115 Barry Bonds	1.00	2.50
116 Robby Thompson	.07	.20
117 Mark Portugal	.07	.20
118 Brady Anderson	.15	.40
119 Mike Mussina	.25	.60
120 Rafael Palmeiro	.25	.60
121 Chris Hoiles	.07	.20
122 Harold Baines	.15	.40
123 Jeffrey Hammonds	.07	.20
124 Tim Naehring	.07	.20
125 Mo Vaughn	.15	.40
126 Mike Macfarlane	.07	.20
127 Roger Clemens	.75	2.00
128 John Valentin	.07	.20
129 Aaron Sele	.07	.20
130 Jose Canseco	.25	.60
131 J.T. Snow	.15	.40
132 Mark Langston	.07	.20
133 Chili Davis	.15	.40
134 Chuck Finley	.15	.40
135 Tim Salmon	.25	.60
136 Tony Phillips	.07	.20
137 Jason Bere	.07	.20
138 Robin Ventura	.15	.40
139 Tim Raines	.15	.40
140 Frank Thomas COR	.40	1.00
Career stats correct, example is RBI career total is 484		
140A Frank Thomas ERR	.40	1.00
Career stats alll messed up		
141 Alex Fernandez	.07	.20
142 Jim Abbott	.25	.60
143 Wilson Alvarez	.07	.20
144 Carlos Baerga	.07	.20
145 Albert Belle	.15	.40
146 Jim Thome	.25	.60
147 Dennis Martinez	.15	.40
148 Eddie Murray	.40	1.00
149 Dave Winfield	.15	.40
150 Kenny Lofton	.15	.40
151 Manny Ramirez	.25	.60
152 Chad Curtis	.07	.20
153 Lou Whitaker	.15	.40
154 Alan Trammell	.15	.40
155 Cecil Fielder	.15	.40
156 Kirk Gibson	.15	.40
157 Michael Tucker	.07	.20
158 Jon Nunnally	.07	.20
159 Wally Joyner	.15	.40
160 Kevin Appier	.15	.40
161 Jeff Montgomery	.07	.20
162 Greg Gagne	.07	.20
163 Ricky Bones	.07	.20
164 Cal Eldred	.07	.20
165 Greg Vaughn	.07	.20
166 Kevin Seitzer	.07	.20
167 Jose Valentin	.07	.20
168 Joe Oliver	.07	.20
169 Rick Aguilera	.07	.20
170 Kirby Puckett	.40	1.00
171 Scott Stahoviak	.07	.20
172 Kevin Tapani	.07	.20
173 Chuck Knoblauch	.15	.40
174 Rich Becker	.07	.20
175 Don Mattingly	1.00	2.50
176 Jack McDowell	.07	.20
177 Jimmy Key	.15	.40
178 Paul O'Neill	.25	.60
179 John Wetteland	.15	.40
180 Wade Boggs	.25	.60
181 Derek Jeter	1.00	2.50
182 Rickey Henderson	.40	1.00
183 Terry Steinbach	.07	.20
184 Ruben Sierra	.15	.40
185 Mark McGwire	1.00	2.50
186 Todd Stottlemyre	.07	.20
187 Dennis Eckersley	.15	.40
188 Alex Rodriguez	1.00	2.50
189 Randy Johnson	.40	1.00
190 Ken Griffey Jr.	.60	1.50
191 Tino Martinez UER	.25	.60
Mike Blowers pictured on back		
192 Jay Buhner	.15	.40
193 Edgar Martinez	.25	.60
194 Mickey Tettleton	.07	.20
195 Juan Gonzalez	.15	.40
196 Benji Gil	.07	.20
197 Dean Palmer	.15	.40
198 Ivan Rodriguez	.25	.60
199 Kenny Rogers	.15	.40
200 Will Clark	.25	.60
201 Roberto Alomar	.25	.60
202 David Cone	.15	.40
203 Paul Molitor	.15	.40
204 Shawn Green	.15	.40
205 Joe Carter	.15	.40
206 Alex Gonzalez	.07	.20
207 Pat Hentgen	.07	.20
P100 K.Griffey Jr. Promo	.75	2.00
AU190 Ken Griffey Jr. AU	100.00	175.00

1995 SP Silver

This 207-card set parallels that of the regular SP set and was inserted one per pack. The only difference between the regular 180 cards in the two sets is that the chevron of the parallel version on the left side of the front uses rainbow-colored foil instead of blue or red. The subset cards have a die-cut design to differentiate them from the regular edition cards. The only other difference is the silver (rather than gold) hologram on the back.

COMPLETE SET (207) 50.00 100.00
*STARS: 1X TO 2.5X BASIC CARDS
*ROOKIES: .6X to 1.5X BASIC CARDS

1995 SP Platinum Power

This 20-card set was randomly inserted in packs at a rate of one in five. This die-cut set is comprised of the top home run hitters in baseball.

COMPLETE SET (20) 8.00 20.00
STATED ODDS 1:5
PP1 Jeff Bagwell .30 .75
PP2 Barry Bonds 1.25 3.00
PP3 Ron Gant .20 .50
PP4 Fred McGriff .30 .75
PP5 Raul Mondesi .20 .50
PP6 Mike Piazza .75 2.00
PP7 Larry Walker .20 .50
PP8 Matt Williams .20 .50
PP9 Albert Belle .20 .50
PP10 Cecil Fielder .20 .50
PP11 Juan Gonzalez .20 .50
PP12 Ken Griffey Jr. .75 2.00
PP13 Mark McGwire 1.25 3.00
PP14 Eddie Murray .50 1.25
PP15 Manny Ramirez .30 .75
PP16 Cal Ripken 1.50 4.00
PP17 Tim Salmon .30 .75
PP18 Frank Thomas .50 1.25
PP19 Jim Thome .30 .75
PP20 Mo Vaughn .20 .50

1995 SP Special FX

This 48-card set was randomly inserted in packs at a rate of one in 75. The set is comprised of the top names in baseball. The cards are numbered on the back "X/48."

COMPLETE SET (48) 125.00 300.00
STATED ODDS 1:75
1 Jose Canseco 4.00 10.00
2 Roger Clemens 12.50 30.00
3 Mo Vaughn 2.50 6.00
4 Tim Salmon 4.00 10.00
5 Chuck Finley 2.50 6.00
6 Robin Ventura 2.50 6.00
7 Jason Bere 1.25 3.00
8 Carlos Baerga 1.25 3.00
9 Albert Belle 2.50 6.00
10 Kenny Lofton 2.50 6.00
11 Manny Ramirez 4.00 10.00
12 Jeff Montgomery 1.25 3.00
13 Kirby Puckett 6.00 15.00
14 Wade Boggs 4.00 10.00
15 Don Mattingly 15.00 40.00
16 Cal Ripken 20.00 50.00
17 Ruben Sierra 2.50 6.00
18 Ken Griffey Jr. 10.00 25.00
19 Randy Johnson 6.00 15.00
20 Alex Rodriguez 15.00 40.00
21 Will Clark 4.00 10.00
22 Juan Gonzalez 2.50 6.00
23 Roberto Alomar 4.00 10.00
24 Joe Carter 2.50 6.00
25 Alex Gonzalez 1.25 3.00
26 Paul Molitor 2.50 6.00
27 Ryan Klesko 2.50 6.00
28 Fred McGriff 4.00 10.00
29 Greg Maddux 10.00 25.00
30 Sammy Sosa 6.00 15.00
31 Bret Boone 2.50 6.00
32 Barry Larkin 4.00 10.00
33 Reggie Sanders 2.50 6.00
34 Dante Bichette 2.50 6.00
35 Andres Galarraga 2.50 6.00
36 Charles Johnson 2.50 6.00
37 Gary Sheffield 2.50 6.00
38 Jeff Bagwell 4.00 10.00
39 Craig Biggio 4.00 10.00
40 Eric Karros 2.50 6.00
41 Billy Ashley 1.25 3.00
42 Raul Mondesi 2.50 6.00
43 Mike Piazza 10.00 25.00
44 Rondell White 2.50 6.00
45 Bret Saberhagen 2.50 6.00
46 Tony Gwynn 8.00 20.00
47 Melvin Nieves 1.25 3.00
48 Matt Williams 2.50 6.00

1996 SP

The 1996 SP set was issued in one series totalling 188 cards. The eight-card packs retailed for $4.19 each. Cards number 1-20 feature color action player photos with "Premier Prospects" printed in silver foil across the top and the player's name and team at the bottom in the border. The backs carry player information and statistics. Cards number 21-185 display unique player photos with an outer wood-grain border and inner thin platinum foil border as well as a small inset player shot. The only notable Rookie Card in this set is Darin Erstad.

COMPLETE SET (188) 15.00 40.00
1 Rey Ordonez FOIL .15 .40
2 George Arias FOIL .15 .40
3 Osvaldo Fernandez FOIL .15 .40
4 Darin Erstad FOIL RC 2.00 5.00
5 Paul Wilson FOIL .15 .40
6 Richard Hidalgo FOIL .15 .40
7 Justin Thompson FOIL .15 .40
8 Jimmy Haynes FOIL .15 .40
9 Edgar Renteria FOIL .15 .40
10 Ruben Rivera FOIL .15 .40
11 Chris Snopek FOIL .15 .40
12 Billy Wagner FOIL .15 .40
13 Mike Grace FOIL RC .15 .40
14 Todd Greene FOIL .15 .40
15 Karim Garcia FOIL .15 .40
16 John Wasdin FOIL .15 .40
17 Jason Kendall FOIL .15 .40
18 Bob Abreu FOIL .40 1.00
19 Jermaine Dye FOIL .15 .40
20 Jason Schmidt FOIL .25 .60
21 Javy Lopez .15 .40
22 Ryan Klesko .15 .40
23 Tom Glavine .25 .60
24 John Smoltz .25 .60
25 Greg Maddux .60 1.50
26 Chipper Jones .40 1.00
27 Fred McGriff .25 .60
28 David Justice .15 .40
29 Roberto Alomar .25 .60
30 Cal Ripken 1.25 3.00
31 B.J. Surhoff .15 .40
32 Bobby Bonilla .15 .40
33 Mike Mussina .25 .60
34 Randy Myers .15 .40
35 Rafael Palmeiro .25 .60
36 Brady Anderson .15 .40
37 Tim Naehring .15 .40
38 Jose Canseco .25 .60
39 Roger Clemens .75 2.00
40 Mo Vaughn .15 .40
41 John Valentin .15 .40
42 Kevin Mitchell .15 .40
43 Chili Davis .15 .40
44 Garret Anderson .15 .40
45 Tim Salmon .25 .60
46 Chuck Finley .15 .40
47 Troy Percival .15 .40
48 Jim Abbott .25 .60
49 J.T. Snow .15 .40
50 Jim Edmonds .15 .40
51 Sammy Sosa .40 1.00
52 Brian McRae .15 .40
53 Ryne Sandberg .60 1.50
54 Jaime Navarro .15 .40
55 Mark Grace .25 .60
56 Harold Baines .15 .40
57 Robin Ventura .15 .40
58 Tony Phillips .15 .40
59 Alex Fernandez .15 .40
60 Frank Thomas .40 1.00
61 Ray Durham .15 .40
62 Bret Boone .15 .40
63 Reggie Sanders .15 .40
64 Pete Schourek .15 .40
65 Barry Larkin .25 .60
66 John Smiley .15 .40
67 Carlos Baerga .15 .40
68 Jim Thome .25 .60
69 Eddie Murray .40 1.00
70 Albert Belle .15 .40
71 Dennis Martinez .15 .40
72 Jack McDowell .15 .40
73 Kenny Lofton .15 .40
74 Manny Ramirez .25 .60
75 Dante Bichette .15 .40
76 Vinny Castilla .15 .40
77 Andres Galarraga .15 .40
78 Walt Weiss .15 .40
79 Ellis Burks .15 .40
80 Larry Walker .15 .40
81 Cecil Fielder .15 .40
82 Melvin Nieves .15 .40
83 Travis Fryman .15 .40
84 Chad Curtis .15 .40
85 Alan Trammell .15 .40
86 Gary Sheffield .15 .40
87 Charles Johnson .15 .40
88 Andre Dawson .15 .40
89 Jeff Conine .15 .40
90 Greg Colbrunn .15 .40
91 Derek Bell .15 .40
92 Brian L.Hunter .15 .40
93 Doug Drabek .15 .40
94 Craig Biggio .25 .60
95 Jeff Bagwell .25 .60
96 Kevin Appier .15 .40
97 Jeff Montgomery .15 .40
98 Michael Tucker .15 .40
99 Bip Roberts .15 .40
100 Johnny Damon .25 .60
101 Eric Karros .15 .40
102 Raul Mondesi .15 .40
103 Ramon Martinez .15 .40
104 Ismael Valdes .15 .40
105 Mike Piazza .60 1.50
106 Hideo Nomo .40 1.00
107 Chan Ho Park .15 .40
108 Ben McDonald .15 .40
109 Kevin Seitzer .15 .40
110 Greg Vaughn .15 .40
111 Jose Valentin .15 .40
112 Rick Aguilera .15 .40
113 Marty Cordova .15 .40
114 Brad Radke .15 .40
115 Kirby Puckett .40 1.00
116 Chuck Knoblauch .15 .40
117 Paul Molitor .15 .40
118 Pedro Martinez .25 .60
119 Mike Lansing .15 .40
120 Rondell White .15 .40
121 Moises Alou .15 .40
122 Mark Grudzielanek .15 .40
123 Jeff Fassero .15 .40
124 Rico Brogna .15 .40
125 Jason Isringhausen .15 .40
126 Jeff Kent .15 .40
127 Bernard Gilkey .15 .40
128 Todd Hundley .15 .40
129 David Cone .15 .40
130 Andy Pettitte .25 .60
131 Wade Boggs .25 .60
132 Paul O'Neill .25 .60
133 Ruben Sierra .15 .40
134 John Wetteland .15 .40
135 Derek Jeter 1.00 2.50
136 Geronimo Berroa .15 .40
137 Terry Steinbach .15 .40
138 Ariel Prieto .15 .40
139 Scott Brosius .15 .40
140 Mark McGwire 1.00 2.50
141 Lenny Dykstra .15 .40
142 Todd Zeile .15 .40
143 Benito Santiago .15 .40
144 Mickey Morandini .15 .40
145 Gregg Jefferies .15 .40
146 Denny Neagle .15 .40
147 Orlando Merced .15 .40
148 Charlie Hayes .15 .40
149 Carlos Garcia .15 .40
150 Jay Bell .15 .40
151 Ray Lankford .15 .40
152 Alan Benes .15 .40
Andy Benes
153 Dennis Eckersley .15 .40
154 Gary Gaetti .15 .40
155 Ozzie Smith .60 1.50
156 Ron Gant .15 .40
157 Brian Jordan .15 .40
158 Ken Caminiti .15 .40
159 Rickey Henderson .40 1.00
160 Tony Gwynn .50 1.25
161 Wally Joyner .15 .40
162 Andy Ashby .15 .40
163 Steve Finley .15 .40
164 Glenallen Hill .15 .40
165 Matt Williams .15 .40
166 Barry Bonds 1.00 2.50
167 W. VanLandingham .15 .40
168 Rod Beck .15 .40
169 Randy Johnson .40 1.00
170 Ken Griffey Jr. .60 1.50
171 Alex Rodriguez .75 2.00
172 Edgar Martinez .25 .60
173 Jay Buhner .15 .40
174 Russ Davis .15 .40
175 Juan Gonzalez .15 .40
176 Mickey Tettleton .15 .40
177 Will Clark .25 .60
178 Ken Hill .15 .40
179 Dean Palmer .15 .40
180 Ivan Rodriguez .25 .60
181 Carlos Delgado .15 .40
182 Alex Gonzalez .15 .40
183 Shawn Green .15 .40
184 Juan Guzman .15 .40
185 Joe Carter .15 .40
186 Hideo Nomo CL UER .25 .60
Checklist lists Livan Hernandez as #4
187 Cal Ripken CL .60 1.50
188 Ken Griffey Jr. CL .40 1.00

1996 SP Baseball Heroes

This 10-card set was randomly inserted at the rate of one in 96 packs. It continues the insert set that was started in 1990 featuring ten of the top players in baseball. Please note these cards are condition sensitive and trade for premiums in Mint.

COMPLETE SET (10) 60.00 150.00
STATED ODDS 1:96
82 Frank Thomas 5.00 12.00
83 Albert Belle 2.00 5.00
84 Barry Bonds 12.50 30.00
85 Chipper Jones 5.00 12.00
86 Hideo Nomo 5.00 12.00
87 Mike Piazza 8.00 20.00
88 Manny Ramirez 3.00 8.00
89 Greg Maddux 8.00 20.00
90 Ken Griffey Jr. 8.00 20.00
NNO Ken Griffey Jr. HDR 8.00 20.00

1996 SP Marquee Matchups

Randomly inserted at the rate of one in five packs, this 20-card set highlights two superstars' cards with a common matching stadium background photograph in a blue border.

COMPLETE SET (20) 15.00 40.00
STATED ODDS 1:5
*DIE CUTS: 2X TO 5X BASIC MARQUEE
DC STATED ODDS 1:61
MM1 Ken Griffey Jr. 1.25 3.00
MM2 Hideo Nomo .75 2.00
MM3 Derek Jeter 2.00 5.00
MM4 Rey Ordonez .30 .75
MM5 Tim Salmon .50 1.25
MM6 Mike Piazza 1.25 3.00
MM7 Mark McGwire 2.00 5.00
MM8 Barry Bonds 2.00 5.00
MM9 Cal Ripken 2.50 6.00
MM10 Greg Maddux 1.25 3.00
MM11 Albert Belle .30 .75
MM12 Barry Larkin .50 1.25
MM13 Jeff Bagwell .50 1.25
MM14 Juan Gonzalez .30 .75
MM15 Frank Thomas .75 2.00
MM16 Sammy Sosa .75 2.00
MM17 Mike Mussina .50 1.25
MM18 Chipper Jones .75 2.00
MM19 Roger Clemens 1.50 4.00
MM20 Fred McGriff .50 1.25

1996 SP Special FX

Randomly inserted at the rate of one in five packs, this 48-card set features a color action player cutout on a gold foil background with a holoview diamond shaped insert containing a black-and-white player portrait.

COMPLETE SET (48) 60.00 150.00
STATED ODDS 1:5
*DIE CUTS: 2X TO 5X BASIC SPECIAL FX
DIE CUTS STATED ODDS 1:75
1 Greg Maddux 3.00 8.00
2 Eric Karros .75 2.00
3 Mike Piazza 3.00 8.00
4 Raul Mondesi .75 2.00
5 Hideo Nomo 2.00 5.00
6 Jim Edmonds .75 2.00
7 Jason Isringhausen .75 2.00
8 Jay Buhner .75 2.00
9 Barry Larkin 1.25 3.00
10 Ken Griffey Jr. 3.00 8.00
11 Gary Sheffield .75 2.00
12 Craig Biggio 1.25 3.00
13 Paul Wilson .75 2.00
14 Rondell White .75 2.00
15 Chipper Jones 2.00 5.00
16 Kirby Puckett 2.00 5.00
17 Ron Gant .75 2.00
18 Wade Boggs 1.25 3.00
19 Fred McGriff 1.25 3.00
20 Cal Ripken 6.00 15.00
21 Jason Kendall .75 2.00
22 Johnny Damon 1.25 3.00
23 Kenny Lofton .75 2.00
24 Roberto Alomar 1.25 3.00
25 Barry Bonds 5.00 12.00
26 Dante Bichette .75 2.00
27 Mark McGwire 5.00 12.00
28 Rafael Palmeiro 1.25 3.00
29 Juan Gonzalez .75 2.00
30 Albert Belle .75 2.00
31 Randy Johnson 2.00 5.00
32 Jose Canseco 1.25 3.00
33 Sammy Sosa 2.00 5.00
34 Eddie Murray 2.00 5.00
35 Frank Thomas 2.00 5.00
36 Tom Glavine 1.25 3.00
37 Matt Williams .75 2.00
38 Roger Clemens 4.00 10.00
39 Paul Molitor .75 2.00
40 Tony Gwynn 2.50 6.00
41 Mo Vaughn .75 2.00
42 Tim Salmon 1.25 3.00
43 Manny Ramirez 1.25 3.00
44 Jeff Bagwell 1.25 3.00
45 Edgar Martinez 1.25 3.00
46 Rey Ordonez .75 2.00
47 Osvaldo Fernandez .75 2.00
48 Derek Jeter 5.00 12.00

1997 SP

The 1997 SP set was issued in one series totalling 183 cards and was distributed in eight-card packs with a suggested retail of $4.39. Although unconfirmed by the manufacturer, it is perceived in some circles that cards numbered between 160 and 180 are in slightly shorter supply. Notable Rookie Cards include Jose Cruz Jr. and Hideki Irabu.

COMPLETE SET (184) 15.00 40.00
1 Andruw Jones FOIL .40 1.00
2 Kevin Orie FOIL .20 .50
3 Nomar Garciaparra FOIL 1.00 2.50
4 Jose Guillen FOIL .30 .75
5 Todd Walker FOIL .20 .50
6 Derrick Gibson FOIL .20 .50
7 Aaron Boone FOIL .30 .75
8 Bartolo Colon FOIL .30 .75
9 Derrek Lee FOIL .40 1.00
10 Vladimir Guerrero FOIL .60 1.50
11 Wilton Guerrero FOIL .20 .50
12 Luis Castillo FOIL .20 .50
13 Jason Dickson FOIL .20 .50
14 B.Trammell FOIL RC .30 .75
15 Jose Cruz Jr. FOIL RC .30 .75
16 Eddie Murray .40 1.00
17 Darin Erstad .15 .40
18 Garret Anderson .15 .40
19 Jim Edmonds .15 .40
20 Tim Salmon .25 .60
21 Chuck Finley .15 .40
22 John Smoltz .25 .60
23 Greg Maddux .60 1.50
24 Kenny Lofton .15 .40
25 Chipper Jones .40 1.00
26 Ryan Klesko .15 .40
27 Javy Lopez .15 .40
28 Fred McGriff .25 .60
29 Roberto Alomar .25 .60
30 Rafael Palmeiro .25 .60
31 Mike Mussina .25 .60
32 Brady Anderson .15 .40
33 Rocky Coppinger .15 .40
34 Cal Ripken 1.25 3.00
35 Mo Vaughn .15 .40
36 Steve Avery .15 .40
37 Tom Gordon .15 .40
38 Tim Naehring .15 .40
39 Troy O'Leary .15 .40
40 Sammy Sosa .40 1.00
41 Brian McRae .15 .40
42 Mel Rojas .15 .40
43 Ryne Sandberg .60 1.50
44 Mark Grace .25 .60
45 Albert Belle .15 .40
46 Robin Ventura .15 .40
47 Roberto Hernandez .15 .40
48 Ray Durham .15 .40
49 Harold Baines .15 .40
50 Frank Thomas .40 1.00
51 Bret Boone .15 .40
52 Reggie Sanders .15 .40
53 Deion Sanders .25 .60
54 Hal Morris .15 .40
55 Barry Larkin .25 .60
56 Jim Thome .25 .60
57 Marquis Grissom .15 .40
58 David Justice .15 .40
59 Charles Nagy .15 .40
60 Manny Ramirez .25 .60
61 Matt Williams .15 .40
62 Jack McDowell .15 .40
63 Vinny Castilla .15 .40
64 Dante Bichette .15 .40
65 Andres Galarraga .15 .40
66 Ellis Burks .15 .40
67 Larry Walker .15 .40
68 Eric Young .15 .40
69 Brian L. Hunter .15 .40
70 Travis Fryman .15 .40
71 Tony Clark .15 .40
72 Bobby Higginson .15 .40
73 Melvin Nieves .15 .40
74 Jeff Conine .15 .40
75 Gary Sheffield .15 .40
76 Moises Alou .15 .40
77 Edgar Renteria .15 .40
78 Alex Fernandez .15 .40
79 Charles Johnson .15 .40
80 Bobby Bonilla .15 .40
81 Darryl Kile .15 .40
82 Derek Bell .15 .40
83 Shane Reynolds .15 .40
84 Craig Biggio .25 .60
85 Jeff Bagwell .25 .60
86 Billy Wagner .15 .40
87 Chili Davis .15 .40
88 Kevin Appier .15 .40
89 Jay Bell .15 .40
90 Johnny Damon .25 .60
91 Jeff King .15 .40
92 Hideo Nomo .40 1.00
93 Todd Hollandsworth .15 .40
94 Eddie Murray .40 1.00
95 Mike Piazza .60 1.50
96 Ramon Martinez .15 .40
97 Todd Worrell .15 .40
98 Raul Mondesi .15 .40
99 Dave Nilsson .15 .40
100 John Jaha .15 .40
101 Jose Valentin .15 .40
102 Jeff Cirillo .15 .40
103 Jeff D'Amico .15 .40
104 Ben McDonald .15 .40
105 Paul Molitor .15 .40
106 Rich Becker .15 .40
107 Frank Rodriguez .15 .40
108 Marty Cordova .15 .40
109 Terry Steinbach .15 .40
110 Chuck Knoblauch .15 .40
111 Mark Grudzielanek .15 .40
112 Mike Lansing .15 .40
113 Pedro Martinez .25 .60
114 Henry Rodriguez .15 .40
115 Rondell White .15 .40
116 Rey Ordonez .15 .40
117 Carlos Baerga .15 .40
118 Lance Johnson .15 .40
119 Bernard Gilkey .15 .40
120 Todd Hundley .15 .40
121 John Franco .15 .40
122 Bernie Williams .25 .60
123 David Cone .15 .40
124 Cecil Fielder .15 .40
125 Derek Jeter 1.00 2.50
126 Tino Martinez .25 .60
127 Mariano Rivera .40 1.00
128 Andy Pettitte .25 .60
129 Wade Boggs .25 .60
130 Mark McGwire 1.00 2.50
131 Jose Canseco .25 .60
132 Geronimo Berroa .15 .40
133 Jason Giambi .15 .40
134 Ernie Young .15 .40
135 Scott Rolen .25 .60
136 Ricky Bottalico .15 .40
137 Curt Schilling .15 .40
138 Gregg Jefferies .15 .40
139 Mickey Morandini .15 .40
140 Jason Kendall .15 .40
141 Kevin Elster .15 .40
142 Al Martin .15 .40
143 Joe Randa .15 .40
144 Jason Schmidt .15 .40
145 Ray Lankford .15 .40
146 Brian Jordan .15 .40
147 Andy Benes .15 .40
148 Alan Benes .15 .40
149 Gary Gaetti .15 .40
150 Ron Gant .15 .40
151 Dennis Eckersley .15 .40
152 Rickey Henderson .40 1.00
153 Joey Hamilton .15 .40
154 Ken Caminiti .15 .40
155 Tony Gwynn .50 1.25
156 Steve Finley .15 .40
157 Trevor Hoffman .15 .40
158 Greg Vaughn .15 .40
159 J.T.Snow .15 .40
160 Barry Bonds 1.00 2.50
161 Glenallen Hill .15 .40
162 Bill Van Landingham .15 .40
163 Jeff Kent .15 .40
164 Jay Buhner .15 .40
165 Ken Griffey Jr. .60 1.50
166 Alex Rodriguez .60 1.50
167 Randy Johnson .40 1.00
168 Edgar Martinez .25 .60
169 Dan Wilson .15 .40
170 Ivan Rodriguez .25 .60
171 Roger Pavlik .15 .40
172 Will Clark .25 .60
173 Dean Palmer .15 .40
174 Rusty Greer .15 .40
175 Juan Gonzalez .15 .40
176 John Wetteland .15 .40
177 Joe Carter .15 .40
178 Ed Sprague .15 .40
179 Carlos Delgado .15 .40
180 Roger Clemens .75 2.00
181 Juan Guzman .15 .40
182 Pat Hentgen .15 .40
183 Ken Griffey Jr. CL .40 1.00
184 Hideki Irabu RC .15 .40

1997 SP Game Film

Randomly inserted in packs, this 10-card set features actual game film that highlights the accomplishments of some of the League's greatest players. Only 500 of each card in this crash numbered, limited edition set were produced.

COMPLETE SET (10) 75.00 200.00
GF1 Alex Rodriguez 10.00 25.00
GF2 Frank Thomas 6.00 15.00
GF3 Andruw Jones 6.00 15.00
GF4 Cal Ripken 20.00 50.00
GF5 Mike Piazza 10.00 25.00
GF6 Derek Jeter 15.00 40.00
GF7 Mark McGwire 15.00 40.00
GF8 Chipper Jones 6.00 15.00
GF9 Barry Bonds 15.00 40.00
GF10 Ken Griffey Jr. 10.00 25.00

1997 SP Griffey Heroes

This 10-card continuation insert set pays special tribute to one of the game's most talented players and features color photos of Ken Griffey Jr. Only 2,000 of each card in this crash numbered, limited edition set were produced.

COMPLETE SET (10) 20.00 50.00
COMMON CARD (91-100) 3.00 8.00

1997 SP Inside Info

Inserted one in every 30-pack box, this 25-card set features color player photos on original cards with an exclusive pull-out panel that details the accomplishments of the League's brightest stars. Please note these cards are condition sensitive and trade for premium values in Mint condition.

COMPLETE SET (25) 60.00 150.00
1 Ken Griffey Jr. 4.00 10.00
2 Mark McGwire 6.00 15.00
3 Kenny Lofton 1.00 2.50
4 Paul Molitor 1.00 2.50
5 Frank Thomas 2.50 6.00
6 Greg Maddux 4.00 10.00
7 Mo Vaughn 1.00 2.50
8 Cal Ripken 8.00 20.00
9 Jeff Bagwell 1.50 4.00
10 Alex Rodriguez 4.00 10.00
11 John Smoltz 1.50 4.00
12 Manny Ramirez 1.50 4.00
13 Sammy Sosa 2.50 6.00
14 Vladimir Guerrero 4.00 10.00
15 Albert Belle 1.00 2.50
16 Mike Piazza 4.00 10.00
17 Derek Jeter 6.00 15.00
18 Scott Rolen 1.50 4.00
19 Tony Gwynn 3.00 8.00
20 Barry Bonds 6.00 15.00
21 Ken Caminiti 1.00 2.50
22 Chipper Jones 2.50 6.00
23 Juan Gonzalez 1.00 2.50
24 Roger Clemens 5.00 12.00
25 Andruw Jones 2.50 6.00

1997 SP Marquee Matchups

Randomly inserted in packs at a rate of one in five, this 20-card set features color player images on die-cut cards that match-up the best pitchers and hitters from around the League.

COMPLETE SET (20) 20.00 50.00
STATED ODDS 1:5
MM1 Ken Griffey Jr. 1.25 3.00
MM2 Andres Galarraga .30 .75
MM3 Barry Bonds 2.00 5.00
MM4 Mark McGwire 2.00 5.00
MM5 Mike Piazza 1.25 3.00
MM6 Tim Salmon .50 1.25
MM7 Tony Gwynn 1.00 2.50
MM8 Alex Rodriguez 1.25 3.00
MM9 Chipper Jones .75 2.00
MM10 Derek Jeter 2.00 5.00
MM11 Manny Ramirez .50 1.25
MM12 Jeff Bagwell .50 1.25
MM13 Greg Maddux 1.25 3.00
MM14 Cal Ripken 2.50 6.00
MM15 Mo Vaughn .30 .75
MM16 Gary Sheffield .30 .75
MM17 Jim Thome .50 1.25
MM18 Barry Larkin .50 1.25
MM19 Frank Thomas .75 2.00
MM20 Sammy Sosa .75 2.00

1997 SP Special FX

Randomly inserted in packs at a rate of one in nine, this 48-card set features color player photos on Holoview cards with the Special F/X die-cut design. Cards numbers 1-47 are from 1997 with card number 49 featuring a design from 1996. There is no card number 48.

COMPLETE SET (48) 80.00 200.00
STATED ODDS 1:9
1 Ken Griffey Jr. 3.00 8.00
2 Frank Thomas 2.00 5.00
3 Barry Bonds 5.00 12.00
4 Albert Belle .75 2.00
5 Mike Piazza 3.00 8.00
6 Greg Maddux 3.00 8.00
7 Chipper Jones 2.00 5.00
8 Cal Ripken 6.00 15.00
9 Jeff Bagwell 1.25 3.00
10 Alex Rodriguez 3.00 8.00
11 Mark McGwire 5.00 12.00
12 Kenny Lofton .75 2.00
13 Juan Gonzalez .75 2.00
14 Mo Vaughn .75 2.00
15 John Smoltz 1.25 3.00
16 Derek Jeter 5.00 12.00
17 Tony Gwynn 2.50 6.00
18 Ivan Rodriguez 1.25 3.00
19 Barry Larkin 1.25 3.00
20 Sammy Sosa 2.00 5.00
21 Mike Mussina 1.25 3.00
22 Gary Sheffield .75 2.00
23 Brady Anderson .75 2.00
24 Roger Clemens 4.00 10.00
25 Ken Caminiti .75 2.00
26 Roberto Alomar 1.25 3.00
27 Hideo Nomo 2.00 5.00
28 Bernie Williams 1.25 3.00
29 Todd Hundley .75 2.00
30 Manny Ramirez 1.25 3.00
31 Eric Karros .75 2.00
32 Tim Salmon 1.25 3.00
33 Jay Buhner .75 2.00
34 Andy Pettitte 1.25 3.00
35 Jim Thome 1.25 3.00
36 Ryne Sandberg 3.00 8.00
37 Matt Williams .75 2.00
38 Ryan Klesko .75 2.00
39 Jose Canseco 1.25 3.00
40 Paul Molitor 1.25 3.00
41 Eddie Murray 2.00 5.00
42 Darin Erstad .75 2.00
43 Todd Walker 1.00 2.50
44 Wade Boggs 1.25 3.00
45 Andruw Jones 2.00 5.00
46 Scott Rolen 1.25 3.00
47 Vladimir Guerrero 3.00 8.00
49 Alex Rodriguez '96 4.00 10.00

1997 SP SPx Force

Randomly inserted in packs, this 10-card die-cut set features head photos of four of the very best players on each card with an "X" in the background and players' and teams' names on one side. Only 500 of each card in this crash numbered, limited edition set were produced.

COMPLETE SET (10) 80.00 200.00
1 Ken Griffey Jr. 10.00 25.00
Jay Buhner
Andres Galarraga
Dante Bichette
2 Albert Belle 15.00 40.00
Brady Anderson
Mark McGwire
Cecil Fielder
3 Mo Vaughn 6.00 15.00
Ken Caminiti
Frank Thomas
Jeff Bagwell
4 Gary Sheffield 6.00 15.00
Sammy Sosa
Barry Bonds
Jose Canseco
5 Greg Maddux 10.00 25.00
Roger Clemens
John Smoltz
Randy Johnson
6 Alex Rodriguez 15.00 40.00
Derek Jeter
Chipper Jones
Rey Ordonez
7 Todd Hollandsworth 10.00 25.00
Mike Piazza
Raul Mondesi
Hideo Nomo
8 Juan Gonzalez 4.00 10.00

Manny Ramirez		
Roberto Alomar		
Ivan Rodriguez		
9 Tony Gwynn	8.00	20.00
Wade Boggs		
Eddie Murray		
Paul Molitor		
10 Andruw Jones	10.00	25.00
Vladimir Guerrero		
Todd Walker		
Scott Rolen		

1997 SP SPx Force Autographs

Randomly inserted in packs, this 10-card set is an autographed parallel version of the regular SPx Force set. Only 100 of each card in this crash numbered, limited edition set were produced. Mo Vaughn packed out as an exchange card.

1 Ken Griffey Jr.	150.00	250.00
2 Albert Belle	15.00	40.00
3 Mo Vaughn	15.00	40.00
4 Gary Sheffield	20.00	50.00
5 Greg Maddux	75.00	150.00
6 Alex Rodriguez	100.00	175.00
7 Todd Hollandsworth	10.00	25.00
8 Roberto Alomar	20.00	50.00
9 Tony Gwynn	40.00	80.00
10 Andruw Jones	20.00	50.00

1997 SP Vintage Autographs

Randomly inserted in packs, this set features authenticated original 1993-1996 SP cards that have been autographed by the pictured player. The print runs are listed after year following the player's name in our checklist. Some of the very short printed autographs are listed but not priced. Each card came in the pack along with a standard size certificate of authenticity. These certificates are usually included when these autographed cards are traded. The 1997 Mo Vaughn card was available only as a mail-in exchange. Upper Deck seeded 250 '97 SP Vaughn cards into packs each carrying a large circular sticker on front. UD sent Mo 300 cards to sign, hoping that he'd sign at least 250 cards and actually received 293 cards back. The additional 43 cards were sent to UD's Quality Assurance area. An additional Mo Vaughn card, hailing from 1995, surfaced in early 2001. This set now stands as one of the most important issues of the 1990's in that it was the first to feature the popular "buy-back" concept widely used in the 2000's.

1 Jeff Bagwell 93/7		
2 Jeff Bagwell 95/173	30.00	60.00
3 Jeff Bagwell 96/292	20.00	50.00
4 Jeff Bagwell 96 MM/23		
5 Jay Buhner 95/57	15.00	40.00
6 Jay Buhner 96/79	15.00	40.00
7 Jay Buhner 96 FX/27	20.00	50.00
8 Ken Griffey Jr. 93/16		
9 Ken Griffey Jr. 93 PP/5		
10 Ken Griffey Jr. 94/103	40.00	80.00
11 Ken Griffey Jr. 95/38	75.00	150.00
12 Ken Griffey Jr. 96/312	40.00	80.00
13 Tony Gwynn 93/17		
14 Tony Gwynn 94/367	15.00	40.00
15 Tony Gwynn 94 HV/31	60.00	120.00
16 Tony Gwynn 95/64	30.00	60.00
17 Tony Gwynn 96/20		
18 Todd Hollandsworth 94/167	6.00	15.00
19 Chipper Jones 93/34	50.00	100.00
20 Chipper Jones 95/60	40.00	80.00
21 Chipper Jones 96/102	30.00	60.00
22 Rey Ordonez 96/111	6.00	15.00
23 R.Ordonez '96 MM/40	10.00	25.00
24 Alex Rodriguez 94/94	1000.00	1600.00
25 Alex Rodriguez 95/63	60.00	120.00
26 Alex Rodriguez 96/73	60.00	120.00
27 Gary Sheffield 94/130	15.00	40.00
28 Gary Sheffield 94 HVDC/4		
29 Gary Sheffield 95/221	10.00	25.00
30 Gary Sheffield 96/58	30.00	60.00
31 Mo Vaughn 95/75	6.00	15.00
32 Mo Vaughn 97/293	6.00	15.00

1998 SP Authentic

The 1998 SP Authentic set was issued in one series totalling 198 cards. The five-card packs retailed for $4.99 each. The set contains the topical subset: Future Watch (1-30). Rookie Cards include Magglio Ordonez. A sample card featuring Ken Griffey Jr. was issued prior to the product's release and distributed along with dealer order forms. The card is identical to the basic issue Griffey Jr. card (number 123) except for the term "SAMPLE" in red print running diagonally against the card back.

COMPLETE SET (198)	15.00	40.00
1 Travis Lee FOIL	.15	.40
2 Mike Caruso FOIL	.15	.40
3 Kerry Wood FOIL	.20	.50
4 Mark Kotsay FOIL	.15	.40
5 Magglio Ordonez FOIL RC	5.00	12.00
6 Scott Elarton FOIL	.15	.40
7 Carl Pavano FOIL	.15	.40
8 A.J. Hinch FOIL	.15	.40
9 Rolando Arrojo FOIL RC	.15	.40
10 Ben Grieve FOIL	.15	.40
11 Gabe Alvarez FOIL	.15	.40
12 Mike Kinkade FOIL RC	.15	.40
13 Bruce Chen FOIL	.15	.40
14 Juan Encarnacion FOIL	.15	.40
15 Todd Helton FOIL	.25	.60
16 Aaron Boone FOIL	.15	.40
17 Sean Casey FOIL	.15	.40
18 R.Hernandez FOIL	.15	.40
19 Daryle Ward FOIL	.15	.40
20 Paul Konerko FOIL	.15	.40
21 David Ortiz FOIL	.50	1.25
22 Derrek Lee FOIL	.25	.60
23 Brad Fullmer FOIL	.15	.40
24 Javier Vazquez FOIL	.15	.40
25 Miguel Tejada FOIL	.40	1.00
26 Dave Dellucci FOIL RC	.25	.60
27 Alex Gonzalez FOIL	.15	.40
28 Matt Clement FOIL	.15	.40
29 Masato Yoshii FOIL RC	.15	.40
30 Russell Branyan FOIL	.15	.40
31 Chuck Finley	.15	.40
32 Jim Edmonds	.15	.40
33 Darin Erstad	.15	.40
34 Jason Dickson	.15	.40
35 Tim Salmon	.25	.60
36 Cecil Fielder	.15	.40
37 Todd Greene	.15	.40
38 Andy Benes	.15	.40
39 Jay Bell	.15	.40
40 Matt Williams	.15	.40
41 Brian Anderson	.15	.40
42 Karim Garcia	.15	.40
43 Javy Lopez	.15	.40
44 Tom Glavine	.25	.60
45 Greg Maddux	.60	1.50
46 Andruw Jones	.25	.60
47 Chipper Jones	.40	1.00
48 Ryan Klesko	.15	.40
49 John Smoltz	.25	.60
50 Andres Galarraga	.15	.40
51 Rafael Palmeiro	.25	.60
52 Mike Mussina	.25	.60
53 Roberto Alomar	.25	.60
54 Joe Carter	.15	.40
55 Cal Ripken	1.25	3.00
56 Brady Anderson	.15	.40
57 Mo Vaughn	.15	.40
58 John Valentin	.15	.40
59 Dennis Eckersley	.15	.40
60 Nomar Garciaparra	.60	1.50
61 Pedro Martinez	.25	.60
62 Jeff Blauser	.15	.40
63 Kevin Orie	.15	.40
64 Henry Rodriguez	.15	.40
65 Mark Grace	.25	.60
66 Albert Belle	.15	.40
67 Mike Cameron	.15	.40
68 Robin Ventura	.15	.40
69 Frank Thomas	.40	1.00
70 Barry Larkin	.25	.60
71 Brett Tomko UER	.15	.40
1 Yr Total is Wrong		
72 Willie Greene	.15	.40
73 Reggie Sanders	.15	.40
74 Sandy Alomar Jr.	.15	.40
75 Kenny Lofton	.15	.40
76 Jaret Wright	.15	.40
77 David Justice	.15	.40
78 Omar Vizquel	.25	.60
79 Manny Ramirez	.25	.60
80 Jim Thome	.25	.60
81 Travis Fryman	.15	.40
82 Neifi Perez	.15	.40
83 Mike Lansing	.15	.40
84 Vinny Castilla	.15	.40
85 Larry Walker	.15	.40
86 Dante Bichette	.15	.40
87 Darryl Kile	.15	.40
88 Justin Thompson	.15	.40
89 Damion Easley	.15	.40
90 Tony Clark	.15	.40
91 Bobby Higginson	.15	.40
92 Brian Hunter	.15	.40
93 Edgar Renteria	.15	.40
94 Craig Counsell	.15	.40
95 Mike Piazza	.60	1.50
96 Livan Hernandez	.15	.40
97 Todd Zeile	.15	.40
98 Richard Hidalgo	.15	.40
99 Moises Alou	.15	.40
100 Jeff Bagwell	.25	.60
101 Mike Hampton	.15	.40
102 Craig Biggio	.25	.60
103 Dean Palmer	.15	.40
104 Tim Belcher	.15	.40
105 Jeff King	.15	.40
106 Jeff Conine	.15	.40
107 Johnny Damon	.25	.60
108 Hideo Nomo	.40	1.00
109 Raul Mondesi	.15	.40
110 Gary Sheffield	.15	.40
111 Ramon Martinez	.15	.40
112 Chan Ho Park	.15	.40
113 Eric Young	.15	.40
114 Charles Johnson	.15	.40
115 Eric Karros	.15	.40
116 Bobby Bonilla	.15	.40
117 Jeromy Burnitz	.15	.40
118 Cal Eldred	.15	.40
119 Jeff D'Amico	.15	.40
120 Marquis Grissom	.15	.40
121 Dave Nilsson	.15	.40
122 Brad Radke	.15	.40
123 Marty Cordova	.15	.40
124 Ron Coomer	.15	.40
125 Paul Molitor	.15	.40
126 Todd Walker	.15	.40
127 Rondell White	.15	.40
128 Mark Grudzielanek	.15	.40
129 Carlos Perez	.15	.40
130 Vladimir Guerrero	.40	1.00
131 Dustin Hermanson	.15	.40
132 Butch Huskey	.15	.40
133 John Franco	.15	.40
134 Rey Ordonez	.15	.40
135 Todd Hundley	.15	.40
136 Edgardo Alfonzo	.15	.40
137 Bobby Jones	.15	.40
138 John Olerud	.15	.40
139 Chili Davis	.15	.40
140 Tino Martinez	.25	.60
141 Andy Pettitte	.25	.60
142 Chuck Knoblauch	.15	.40
143 Bernie Williams	.25	.60
144 David Cone	.15	.40
145 Derek Jeter	1.00	2.50
146 Paul O'Neill	.25	.60
147 Rickey Henderson	.40	1.00
148 Jason Giambi	.15	.40
149 Kenny Rogers	.15	.40
150 Scott Rolen	.25	.60
151 Curt Schilling	.15	.40
152 Ricky Bottalico	.15	.40
153 Mike Lieberthal	.15	.40
154 Francisco Cordova	.15	.40
155 Jose Guillen	.15	.40
156 Jason Schmidt	.15	.40
157 Jason Kendall	.15	.40
158 Kevin Young	.15	.40
159 Delino DeShields	.15	.40
160 Mark McGwire	1.00	2.50
161 Ray Lankford	.15	.40
162 Brian Jordan	.15	.40
163 Ron Gant	.15	.40
164 Todd Stottlemyre	.15	.40
165 Ken Caminiti	.15	.40
166 Kevin Brown	.25	.60
167 Trevor Hoffman	.15	.40
168 Steve Finley	.15	.40
169 Wally Joyner	.15	.40
170 Tony Gwynn	.50	1.25
171 Shawn Estes	.15	.40
172 J.T. Snow	.15	.40
173 Jeff Kent	.15	.40
174 Robb Nen	.15	.40
175 Barry Bonds	1.00	2.50
176 Randy Johnson	.40	1.00
177 Edgar Martinez	.25	.60
178 Jay Buhner	.15	.40
179 Alex Rodriguez	.60	1.50
180 Ken Griffey Jr.	.60	1.50
181 Ken Cloude	.15	.40
182 Wade Boggs	.25	.60
183 Tony Saunders	.15	.40
184 Wilson Alvarez	.15	.40
185 Fred McGriff	.25	.60
186 Roberto Hernandez	.15	.40
187 Kevin Stocker	.15	.40
188 Fernando Tatis	.15	.40
189 Will Clark	.25	.60
190 Juan Gonzalez	.15	.40
191 Rusty Greer	.15	.40
192 Ivan Rodriguez	.25	.60
193 Jose Canseco	.25	.60
194 Carlos Delgado	.15	.40
195 Roger Clemens	.75	2.00
196 Pat Hentgen	.15	.40
197 Randy Myers	.15	.40
198 Ken Griffey Jr. CL	.40	1.00
S123 Ken Griffey Jr. Sample	.75	2.00

1998 SP Authentic Chirography

Randomly inserted in packs at a rate of one in 25, this 31-card set is autographed by the league's top players. The Ken Griffey Jr. card was actually not available in packs. Instead, an exchange card was printed and seeded into packs. Collectors had until July 27th, 1999 to redeem these Griffey exchange cards. A selection of players were short-printed to 400 or 800 copies. These cards, however, are not serial numbered.

STATED ODDS 1:25		
AJ Andruw Jones	6.00	15.00
AR Alex Rodriguez SP/800	50.00	100.00
BG Ben Grieve	6.00	15.00
CJ Charles Johnson	6.00	15.00
CP Chipper Jones SP/800	20.00	50.00
DE Darin Erstad	6.00	15.00
GS Gary Sheffield	10.00	25.00
IR Ivan Rodriguez	15.00	40.00
JC Jose Cruz Jr.	6.00	15.00
JW Jaret Wright	6.00	15.00
KG Ken Griffey Jr. SP/400	50.00	100.00
KGEX K.Griffey Jr. EXCH	6.00	15.00
LH Livan Hernandez	6.00	15.00
MK Mark Kotsay	6.00	15.00
MM Mike Mussina	10.00	25.00
MT Miguel Tejada	6.00	15.00
MV Mo Vaughn SP800	6.00	15.00
NG N. Garciaparra SP400	60.00	120.00
PK Paul Konerko	6.00	15.00
PM Paul Molitor SP/800	6.00	15.00
RA R. Alomar SP/800	10.00	25.00
RB Russell Branyan	6.00	15.00
RC R. Clemens SP/400	60.00	120.00
RL Ray Lankford	6.00	15.00
SC Sean Casey	6.00	15.00
SR Scott Rolen	6.00	15.00
TC Tony Clark	6.00	15.00
TG Tony Gwynn SP/850	15.00	40.00
TH Todd Helton	10.00	25.00
TL Travis Lee	6.00	15.00
VG Vladimir Guerrero	10.00	25.00

1998 SP Authentic Griffey 300th HR Redemption

This 5" by 7" card is the redemption one received for mailing in the Ken Griffey Jr. 300 Home Run card available in the SP Authentic packs.

300 Ken Griffey Jr.	12.50	30.00

1998 SP Authentic Game Jersey 5 x 7

These attractive 5" by 7" memorabilia cards are the items one received when redeeming the SP Authentic Trade Cards (of which were randomly seeded into 1998 SP Authentic packs at a rate of 1:291). The 5 x 7 cards feature a larger swatch of the jersey on them as compared to a standard size Game Jersey card. The exchange deadline expired back on August 1st, 1999.

1 Ken Griffey Jr./125	40.00	80.00
2 Gary Sheffield/125	10.00	25.00
3 Greg Maddux/125	40.00	80.00
4 Alex Rodriguez/125	40.00	80.00
5 Tony Gwynn/415	20.00	50.00
6 Jay Buhner/125	10.00	25.00

1998 SP Authentic Sheer Dominance

Randomly inserted in packs at a rate of one in three, this 42-card set has a mix of stars and young players and were issued in three different versions.

COMPLETE SET (42)	40.00	100.00
STATED ODDS 1:3		
*GOLD: 1.25X TO 3X BASIC DOMINANCE		
GOLD: RANDOM INSERTS IN PACKS		
GOLD PRINT RUN 2000 SERIAL #'d SETS		
*TITANIUM: 3X TO 8X BASIC DOMINANCE		
TITANIUM: RANDOM INSERTS IN PACKS		
TITANIUM PRINT RUN 100 SERIAL #'d SETS		
SD1 Ken Griffey Jr.	1.50	4.00
SD2 Rickey Henderson	1.00	2.50
SD3 Jaret Wright	.40	1.00
SD4 Craig Biggio	.60	1.50
SD5 Travis Lee	.40	1.00
SD6 Kenny Lofton	.40	1.00
SD7 Raul Mondesi	.40	1.00
SD8 Cal Ripken	3.00	8.00
SD9 Matt Williams	.40	1.00
SD10 Mark McGwire	2.50	6.00
SD11 Alex Rodriguez	1.50	4.00
SD12 Fred McGriff	.60	1.50
SD13 Scott Rolen	.60	1.50
SD14 Paul Molitor	.40	1.00
SD15 Nomar Garciaparra	1.50	4.00
SD16 Vladimir Guerrero	1.00	2.50
SD17 Andruw Jones	.60	1.50
SD18 Manny Ramirez	.60	1.50
SD19 Tony Gwynn	1.25	3.00
SD20 Barry Bonds	2.50	6.00
SD21 Ben Grieve	.40	1.00
SD22 Ivan Rodriguez	.60	1.50
SD23 Jose Cruz Jr.	1.00	2.50
SD24 Pedro Martinez	.60	1.50
SD25 Chipper Jones	1.00	2.50
SD26 Albert Belle	.40	1.00
SD27 Todd Helton	.60	1.50
SD28 Paul Konerko	.40	1.00
SD29 Sammy Sosa	1.00	2.50
SD30 Frank Thomas	1.00	2.50
SD31 Greg Maddux	1.50	4.00
SD32 Randy Johnson	1.00	2.50
SD33 Larry Walker	.40	1.00
SD34 Roberto Alomar	.60	1.50
SD35 Roger Clemens	2.00	5.00
SD36 Mo Vaughn	.40	1.00
SD37 Jim Thome	.60	1.50
SD38 Jeff Bagwell	.60	1.50
SD39 Tino Martinez	.60	1.50
SD40 Mike Piazza	1.50	4.00
SD41 Derek Jeter	2.50	6.00
SD42 Juan Gonzalez	.40	1.00

1998 SP Authentic Trade Cards

Randomly seeded into packs at a rate of 1:291, these fifteen different trade cards could be redeemed for an assortion of UDA material. Specific quantities for each item are detailed below after each player name. The deadline to redeem these cards was August 1st, 1999. It is important to note that the redemption items came from UDA back stock and in many cases the card is far mor valuable than the redemption prize.

COMMON CARD (B1-B5)	6.00	15.00
COMMON CARD (J1-J6)	6.00	15.00
COMMON CARD (KG1-KG4)	6.00	15.00
STATED ODDS 1:291		
B1 Roberto Alomar	10.00	25.00
Ball 100		
B2 Albert Belle	6.00	15.00
Ball 100		
B3 Brian Jordan	6.00	15.00
Ball 50		
B4 Raul Mondesi	6.00	15.00
Ball 100		
B5 Robin Ventura	10.00	25.00
Ball 50		
J1 Jay Buhner	6.00	15.00
Jersey Card 125		
J2 Ken Griffey Jr.	[illegible]	[illegible]
Jersey Card 125		
J3 Tony Gwynn	10.00	25.00
Jersey Card 415		
J4 Greg Maddux	25.00	60.00
Jersey Card 125		
J5 Alex Rodriguez	20.00	50.00
Jersey Card 125		
J6 Gary Sheffield	6.00	15.00
Jersey Card 125		
KG1 Ken Griffey Jr.	6.00	15.00
300 Card 1000 made		
KG2 Ken Griffey Jr.		
Auto Glove 30		
KG3 Ken Griffey Jr.		
Auto Jersey 30		
KG4 Ken Griffey Jr.	10.00	25.00
Standee 200		

1999 SP Authentic

The 1999 SP Authentic set was issued in one series totalling 135 cards and distributed in five-card packs with a suggested retail price of $4.99. The fronts feature color action player photos with player information printed on the backs. The set features the following limited edition subsets: Future Watch (91-120) serially numbered to 2700 and Season to Remember (121-135) numbered to 2700 also. 350 Ernie Banks A Piece of History 500 Club bat cards were randomly seeded into packs. Also, Banks signed and numbered twenty additional copies. Pricing for these bat cards can be referenced under 1999 Upper Deck A Piece of History 500 Club.

COMP.SET w/o SP's (90)	10.00	25.00
COMMON CARD (1-90)	.15	.40
COMMON FW (91-120)	4.00	10.00
COMMON STR (121-135)	1.25	3.00
1 Mo Vaughn	.15	.40
2 Jim Edmonds	.15	.40
3 Darin Erstad	.15	.40
4 Travis Lee	.15	.40
5 Matt Williams	.15	.40
6 Randy Johnson	.40	1.00
7 Chipper Jones	.40	1.00
8 Greg Maddux	.60	1.50
9 Andruw Jones	.25	.60
10 Andres Galarraga	.15	.40
11 Tom Glavine	.25	.60
12 Cal Ripken	1.25	3.00
13 Brady Anderson	.15	.40
14 Albert Belle	.15	.40
15 Nomar Garciaparra	.60	1.50
16 Donnie Sadler	.15	.40
17 Pedro Martinez	.25	.60
18 Sammy Sosa	.40	1.00
19 Kerry Wood	.15	.40
20 Mark Grace	.25	.60
21 Mike Caruso	.15	.40
22 Frank Thomas	.40	1.00
23 Paul Konerko	.15	.40
24 Sean Casey	.15	.40
25 Barry Larkin	.25	.60
26 Kenny Lofton	.15	.40
27 Manny Ramirez	.25	.60
28 Jim Thome	.25	.60
29 Bartolo Colon	.15	.40
30 Jaret Wright	.15	.40
31 Larry Walker	.15	.40
32 Todd Helton	.25	.60
33 Tony Clark	.15	.40
34 Dean Palmer	.15	.40
35 Mark Kotsay	.15	.40
36 Cliff Floyd	.15	.40
37 Ken Caminiti	.15	.40
38 Craig Biggio	.25	.60
39 Jeff Bagwell	.25	.60
40 Moises Alou	.15	.40
41 Johnny Damon	.25	.60
42 Larry Sutton	.15	.40
43 Kevin Brown	.25	.60
44 Gary Sheffield	.15	.40
45 Raul Mondesi	.15	.40
46 Jeromy Burnitz	.15	.40
47 Jeff Cirillo	.15	.40
48 Todd Walker	.15	.40
49 David Ortiz	.40	1.00
50 Brad Radke	.15	.40
51 Vladimir Guerrero	.40	1.00
52 Rondell White	.15	.40
53 Brad Fullmer	.15	.40
54 Mike Piazza	.60	1.50
55 Robin Ventura	.15	.40
56 John Olerud	.15	.40
57 Derek Jeter	1.00	2.50
58 Tino Martinez	.25	.60
59 Bernie Williams	.25	.60
60 Roger Clemens	.75	2.00
61 Ben Grieve	.15	.40
62 Miguel Tejada	.15	.40
63 A.J. Hinch	.15	.40
64 Scott Rolen	.25	.60
65 Curt Schilling	.15	.40
66 Doug Glanville	.15	.40
67 Aramis Ramirez	.15	.40
68 Tony Womack	.15	.40
69 Jason Kendall	.15	.40
70 Tony Gwynn	.50	1.25
71 Wally Joyner	.15	.40
72 Greg Vaughn	.15	.40
73 Barry Bonds	1.00	2.50
74 Ellis Burks	.15	.40
75 Jeff Kent	.15	.40
76 Ken Griffey Jr.	.60	1.50
77 Alex Rodriguez	.60	1.50
78 Edgar Martinez	.25	.60
79 Mark McGwire	1.00	2.50
80 Eli Marrero	.15	.40
81 Matt Morris	.15	.40
82 Rolando Arrojo	.15	.40
83 Quinton McCracken	.15	.40
84 Jose Canseco	.25	.60
85 Ivan Rodriguez	.25	.60
86 Juan Gonzalez	.15	.40
87 Royce Clayton	.15	.40
88 Shawn Green	.15	.40
89 Jose Cruz Jr.	.15	.40
90 Carlos Delgado	.15	.40
91 Troy Glaus FW	5.00	12.00
92 George Lombard FW	4.00	10.00
93 Ryan Minor FW	4.00	10.00
94 Calvin Pickering FW	4.00	10.00
95 Jin Ho Cho FW	4.00	10.00
96 Russ Branyan FW	4.00	10.00
97 Derrick Gibson FW	4.00	10.00
98 Gabe Kapler FW	4.00	10.00
99 Matt Anderson FW	4.00	10.00
100 Preston Wilson FW	4.00	10.00
101 Alex Gonzalez FW	4.00	10.00
102 Carlos Beltran FW	4.00	10.00
103 Dee Brown FW	4.00	10.00
104 Jeremy Giambi FW	4.00	10.00
105 Angel Pena FW	4.00	10.00
106 Geoff Jenkins FW	4.00	10.00
107 Corey Koskie FW	4.00	10.00
108 A.J. Pierzynski FW	4.00	10.00
109 Michael Barrett FW	4.00	10.00
110 F.Seguignol FW	4.00	10.00
111 Mike Kinkade FW	4.00	10.00
112 Ricky Ledee FW	4.00	10.00
113 Mike Lowell FW	4.00	10.00
114 Eric Chavez FW	4.00	10.00
115 Matt Clement FW	4.00	10.00
116 Shane Monahan FW	4.00	10.00
117 J.D. Drew FW	4.00	10.00
118 Bubba Trammell FW	4.00	10.00
119 Kevin Witt FW	4.00	10.00
120 Roy Halladay FW	10.00	25.00
121 Mark McGwire STR	5.00	12.00
122 Mark McGwire STR	4.00	10.00
Sammy Sosa		
123 Sammy Sosa STR	2.00	5.00
124 Ken Griffey Jr. STR	3.00	8.00
125 Cal Ripken STR	6.00	15.00
126 Juan Gonzalez STR	1.25	3.00
127 Kerry Wood STR	1.25	3.00
128 Trevor Hoffman STR	1.25	3.00
129 Barry Bonds STR	5.00	12.00
130 Alex Rodriguez STR	3.00	8.00
131 Ben Grieve STR	1.25	3.00
132 Tom Glavine STR	1.25	3.00
133 David Wells STR	1.25	3.00
134 Mike Piazza STR	3.00	8.00
135 Scott Brosius STR	1.25	3.00

1999 SP Authentic Chirography

Randomly inserted in packs at the rate of one in 24, this 39-card set features color player photos with the pictured player's autograph at the bottom of the photo. Exchange cards for Ken Griffey Jr., Cal Ripken, Ruben Rivera and Scott Rolen were seeded into packs. The expiration date for the exchange cards was February 24th, 2000. Prices in our checklist refer to the actual autograph cards.

STATED ODDS 1:24		
AG Alex Gonzalez	3.00	8.00
BC Bruce Chen	3.00	8.00
BF Brad Fullmer	3.00	8.00
BG Ben Grieve	3.00	8.00
CB Carlos Beltran	8.00	20.00
CJ Chipper Jones	30.00	60.00
CK Corey Koskie	4.00	10.00
CP Calvin Pickering	3.00	8.00
CR Cal Ripken	60.00	120.00
EC Eric Chavez	4.00	10.00
GK Gabe Kapler	4.00	10.00
GL George Lombard	3.00	8.00
GM Greg Maddux	75.00	150.00
GMJ Gary Matthews Jr.	3.00	8.00
GV Greg Vaughn	3.00	8.00
IR Ivan Rodriguez	15.00	40.00
JD J.D. Drew	4.00	10.00
JG Jeremy Giambi	3.00	8.00
JR Ken Griffey Jr.	50.00	100.00
JT Jim Thome	15.00	40.00
KW Kevin Witt	3.00	8.00
KW Kerry Wood	10.00	25.00
MA Matt Anderson	3.00	8.00
MK Mike Kinkade	3.00	8.00
ML Mike Lowell	5.00	12.00
NG Nomar Garciaparra	20.00	50.00
RB Russell Branyan	3.00	8.00
RH Richard Hidalgo	3.00	8.00
RL Ricky Ledee	3.00	8.00
RM Ryan Minor	3.00	8.00
RR Ruben Rivera	3.00	8.00
SM Shane Monahan	3.00	8.00
SR Scott Rolen	10.00	25.00
TG Tony Gwynn	15.00	40.00
TGL Troy Glaus	5.00	12.00
TH Todd Helton	8.00	20.00
TL Travis Lee	3.00	8.00
TW Todd Walker	4.00	10.00
VG Vladimir Guerrero	15.00	40.00
CRX Cal Ripken EXCH	4.00	10.00
JRX Ken Griffey Jr. EXCH	5.00	12.00
RRX Ruben Rivera EXCH	.40	1.00
SRX Scott Rolen EXCH	1.00	2.50

1999 SP Authentic Chirography Gold

These scarce parallel versions of the Chirography cards were all serial numbered to the featured player's jersey number. The serial numbering was done by hand and is on the front of the card. In addition, gold ink was used on the card fronts (a flat grey front was used on the more common basic Chirography cards). While we only have pricing on some of the cards in this set, we are printing the checklist so collectors can know how many cards are available of each player. The same four players featured on exchange cards in the basic chirography (Griffey, Ripken, Rivera and Rolen) also had exchange cards in this set. The deadline for redeeming these cards was February 24th, 2000. Our listed price refers to the actual autograph cards.

AG Alex Gonzalez/22		
BC Bruce Chen/48	10.00	25.00
BF Brad Fullmer/20		
BG Ben Grieve/14		
CB Carlos Beltran/36	20.00	50.00
CJ Chipper Jones/10		
CK Corey Koskie/47	15.00	40.00
CP Calvin Pickering/6		
CR Cal Ripken/8		
EC Eric Chavez/30	15.00	40.00
GK Gabe Kapler/51	15.00	40.00
GL George Lombard/26	10.00	25.00
GM Greg Maddux/31	125.00	250.00
GMJ G.Matthews Jr./68	10.00	25.00
GV Greg Vaughn/23		
IR Ivan Rodriguez/7		
JD J.D. Drew/8		
JG Jeremy Giambi/15		
JR Ken Griffey Jr./24		
JT Jim Thome/25		
KW Kevin Witt/6		
KW Kerry Wood/34	30.00	60.00
MA Matt Anderson/14		
MK Mike Kinkade/33	10.00	25.00
ML Mike Lowell/60	20.00	50.00
NG Nomar Garciaparra/5		
RB Russ Branyan/66	10.00	25.00
RH Richard Hidalgo/15		
RL Ricky Ledee/38	10.00	25.00
RM Ryan Minor/10		
RR Ruben Rivera/28	10.00	25.00
SM Shane Monahan/12		
SR Scott Rolen/17		
TG Tony Gwynn/19		
TGL Troy Glaus/14		
TH Todd Helton/17		
TL Travis Lee/16		
TW Todd Walker/12		
VG Vladimir Guerrero/27	60.00	120.00
CRX Cal Ripken EXCH		
JRX Ken Griffey Jr. EXCH		
RRX Ruben Rivera EXCH		
SRX Scott Rolen EXCH		

1999 SP Authentic Epic Figures

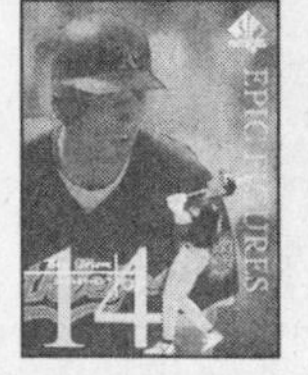

Randomly inserted in packs at the rate of one in seven, this 30-card set features action color photos of some of the game's most impressive players.

COMPLETE SET (30)	40.00	100.00
STATED ODDS 1:7		
E1 Mo Vaughn	.60	1.50
E2 Travis Lee	.60	1.50
E3 Andres Galarraga	.60	1.50
E4 Andruw Jones	1.00	2.50
E5 Chipper Jones	1.50	4.00
E6 Greg Maddux	2.50	6.00
E7 Cal Ripken	5.00	12.00
E8 Nomar Garciaparra	2.50	6.00
E9 Sammy Sosa	1.50	4.00
E10 Frank Thomas	1.50	4.00
E11 Kerry Wood	.60	1.50
E12 Kenny Lofton	.60	1.50
E13 Manny Ramirez	1.00	2.50
E14 Larry Walker	.60	1.50
E15 Jeff Bagwell	1.00	2.50
E16 Paul Molitor	1.50	4.00
E17 Vladimir Guerrero	1.50	4.00
E18 Derek Jeter	4.00	10.00
E19 Tino Martinez	1.00	2.50
E20 Mike Piazza	2.50	6.00
E21 Ben Grieve	.60	1.50
E22 Scott Rolen	1.00	2.50
E23 Mark McGwire	4.00	10.00
E24 Tony Gwynn	2.00	5.00
E25 Barry Bonds	4.00	10.00
E26 Ken Griffey Jr.	2.50	6.00
E27 Alex Rodriguez	2.50	6.00
E28 J.D. Drew	.60	1.50
E29 Juan Gonzalez	.60	1.50
E30 Kevin Brown	1.00	2.50

1999 SP Authentic Home Run Chronicles

Inserted one per pack, this 70-card set features action color photos of players who were the leading sluggers of the 1998 season.

COMPLETE SET (70) 30.00 60.00
*DIE CUTS: 5X TO 12X BASIC HR CHRON.
DIE CUTS RANDOM INSERTS IN PACKS
DIE CUT PRINT RUN 70 SERIAL #'d SETS
HR1 Mark McGwire 1.50 4.00
HR2 Sammy Sosa .40 1.00
HR3 Ken Griffey Jr. .60 1.50
HR4 Mark McGwire 1.00 2.50
HR5 Mark McGwire 1.00 2.50
HR6 Albert Belle .15 .40
HR7 Jose Canseco .25 .60
HR8 Juan Gonzalez .15 .40
HR9 Manny Ramirez .25 .60
HR10 Rafael Palmeiro .40 1.00
HR11 Mo Vaughn .15 .40
HR12 Carlos Delgado .15 .40
HR13 Nomar Garciaparra .60 1.50
HR14 Barry Bonds 1.00 2.50
HR15 Alex Rodriguez .60 1.50
HR16 Tony Clark .15 .40
HR17 Jim Thome .25 .60
HR18 Edgar Martinez .25 .60
HR19 Frank Thomas .40 1.00
HR20 Greg Vaughn .15 .40
HR21 Vinny Castilla .15 .40
HR22 Andres Galarraga .15 .40
HR23 Moises Alou .15 .40
HR24 Jeromy Burnitz .15 .40
HR25 Vladimir Guerrero .40 1.00
HR26 Jeff Bagwell .25 .60
HR27 Chipper Jones .40 1.00
HR28 Javier Lopez .15 .40
HR29 Mike Piazza .60 1.50
HR30 Andruw Jones .25 .60
HR31 Henry Rodriguez .15 .40
HR32 Jeff Kent .15 .40
HR33 Ray Lankford .15 .40
HR34 Scott Rolen .25 .60
HR35 Raul Mondesi .15 .40
HR36 Ken Caminiti .15 .40
HR37 J.D. Drew .15 .40
HR38 Troy Glaus .25 .60
HR39 Gabe Kapler .15 .40
HR40 Alex Rodriguez .60 1.50
HR41 Ken Griffey Jr. .60 1.50
HR42 Sammy Sosa .40 1.00
HR43 Mark McGwire 1.00 2.50
HR44 Sammy Sosa .40 1.00
HR45 Mark McGwire 1.00 2.50
HR46 Vinny Castilla .15 .40
HR47 Sammy Sosa .40 1.00
HR48 Mark McGwire 1.00 2.50
HR49 Sammy Sosa .40 1.00
HR50 Greg Vaughn .15 .40
HR51 Sammy Sosa .40 1.00
HR52 Mark McGwire 1.00 2.50
HR53 Sammy Sosa .40 1.00
HR54 Mark McGwire 1.00 2.50
HR55 Sammy Sosa .40 1.00
HR56 Ken Griffey Jr. .60 1.50
HR57 Sammy Sosa .40 1.00
HR58 Mark McGwire 1.00 2.50
HR59 Sammy Sosa .40 1.00
HR60 Mark McGwire 1.00 2.50
HR61 Mark McGwire 1.50 4.00
HR62 Mark McGwire 2.00 5.00
HR63 Mark McGwire 1.00 2.50
HR64 Mark McGwire 1.00 2.50
HR65 Mark McGwire 1.00 2.50
HR66 Sammy Sosa 2.00 5.00
HR67 Mark McGwire 1.00 2.50
HR68 Mark McGwire 1.00 2.50
HR69 Mark McGwire 1.00 2.50
HR70 Mark McGwire 4.00 10.00

1999 SP Authentic Redemption Cards

Randomly inserted in packs at the rate of one in 864, this 10-card set features hand-numbered cards that could be redeemed for various items autographed by the player named on the card. The expiration date for these cards was March 1st, 2000.

STATED ODDS 1:864
1 K.Griffey Jr. AU Jersey/25
2 K.Griffey Jr. AU Baseball/75
3 K.Griffey Jr. AU SI Cover/75
4 K.Griffey Jr. AU Mini Helmet/75
5 M.McGwire AU 62 Ticket/1
6 M.McGwire AU 70 Ticket/3
7 Ken Griffey Jr. Standee/300 5.00 12.00
8 Ken Griffey Jr. Glove Card/200 15.00 40.00
9 Ken Griffey Jr. HE Cel Card/346 10.00 25.00
10 Ken Griffey Jr. SI Cover/200 8.00 20.00

1999 SP Authentic Reflections

Randomly inserted in packs at the rate of one in 23, this 30-card set features color action photos of some of the game's best players and printed using Dot Matrix technology.

COMPLETE SET (30) 150.00 300.00
STATED ODDS 1:23

R1 Mo Vaughn 1.25 3.00
R2 Travis Lee 1.25 3.00
R3 Andres Galarraga 1.25 3.00
R4 Andruw Jones 2.00 5.00
R5 Chipper Jones 3.00 8.00
R6 Greg Maddux 5.00 12.00
R7 Cal Ripken 10.00 25.00
R8 Nomar Garciaparra 5.00 12.00
R9 Sammy Sosa 3.00 8.00
R10 Frank Thomas 3.00 8.00
R11 Kerry Wood 1.25 3.00
R12 Kenny Lofton 1.25 3.00
R13 Manny Ramirez 2.00 5.00
R14 Larry Walker 1.25 3.00
R15 Jeff Bagwell 2.00 5.00
R16 Paul Molitor 3.00 8.00
R17 Vladimir Guerrero 3.00 8.00
R18 Derek Jeter 8.00 20.00
R19 Tino Martinez 2.00 5.00
R20 Mike Piazza 5.00 12.00
R21 Ben Grieve 1.25 3.00
R22 Scott Rolen 2.00 5.00
R23 Mark McGwire 8.00 20.00
R24 Tony Gwynn 4.00 10.00
R25 Barry Bonds 8.00 20.00
R26 Ken Griffey Jr 5.00 12.00
R27 Alex Rodriguez 5.00 12.00
R28 J.D. Drew 1.25 3.00
R29 Juan Gonzalez 1.25 3.00
R30 Roger Clemens 6.00 15.00

2000 SP Authentic

The 2000 SP Authentic product was initially released in late July, 2000 as a 135-card set. Each pack contained five cards and carried a suggested retail price of $4.99. The basic set features 90 veteran players, a 15-card SP Superstars subset serial numbered to 2500, and a 30-card Future Watch subset also serial numbered to 2500. In late December, Upper Deck released their UD Rookie Update brand, which contained a selection of cards to append the 2000 SP Authentic, SPx and UD Pros and Prospects brands. For SP Authentic, sixty new cards were intended, but card number 165 was never created due to problems at the manufacturer. Cards 136-164 are devoted to an extension of the Future Watch prospect subset established in the basic set. Similar to the basic set's FW cards, these Update cards are serial numbered, but only 1,700 copies of each card were produced (as compared to the 2,500 print run for the "first series" cards). Cards 166-195 feature a selection of established veterans either initially not included in the basic set or traded to new teams. Notable Rookie Cards include Xavier Nady, Kazuhiro Sasaki and Barry Zito. Also, a selection of A Piece of History 3000 Club Tris Speaker and Paul Waner memorabilia cards were randomly seeded into packs. 350 bat cards and five hand-numbered, combination bat chip and autograph cut cards for each player were produced. Pricing for these memorabilia cards can be referenced under 2000 Upper Deck A Piece of History 3000 Club. Finally, a Ken Griffey Jr. sample card was distributed to dealers and hobby media in June, 2000 (several weeks prior to the basic product's national release). The card can be readily distinguished by the large "SAMPLE" text running diagonally across the back.

COMP.BASIC w/o SP's (90) 10.00 25.00
COMP.UPDATE w/o SP'S (30) 4.00 10.00
COMMON CARD (1-90) .15 .40
COMMON SUP (91-105) 1.25 3.00
COMMON FW (106-135) 2.00 5.00
COMMON FW (136-164) 2.00 5.00
COMMON (166-195) .25 .60
1 Mo Vaughn .15 .40
2 Troy Glaus .15 .40
3 Jason Giambi .15 .40
4 Tim Hudson .15 .40
5 Eric Chavez .15 .40
6 Shannon Stewart .15 .40
7 Raul Mondesi .15 .40
8 Carlos Delgado .15 .40
9 Jose Canseco .25 .60
10 Vinny Castilla .15 .40
11 Greg Vaughn .15 .40
12 Manny Ramirez .25 .60
13 Roberto Alomar .25 .60
14 Jim Thome .25 .60
15 Richie Sexson .15 .40
16 Alex Rodriguez .60 1.50
17 Freddy Garcia .15 .40
18 John Olerud .15 .40
19 Albert Belle .15 .40
20 Cal Ripken 1.25 3.00
21 Mike Mussina .25 .60
22 Ivan Rodriguez .25 .60
23 Gabe Kapler .15 .40
24 Rafael Palmeiro .25 .60
25 Nomar Garciaparra .60 1.50
26 Pedro Martinez .25 .60
27 Carl Everett .15 .40
28 Carlos Beltran .15 .40
29 Jermaine Dye .15 .40
30 Juan Gonzalez .15 .40
31 Dean Palmer .15 .40
32 Corey Koskie .15 .40
33 Jacque Jones .15 .40
34 Frank Thomas .40 1.00
35 Paul Konerko .15 .40
36 Magglio Ordonez .15 .40
37 Bernie Williams .25 .60
38 Derek Jeter 1.00 2.50
39 Roger Clemens .75 2.00
40 Mariano Rivera .40 1.00
41 Jeff Bagwell .25 .60
42 Craig Biggio .25 .60
43 Jose Lima .15 .40
44 Moises Alou .15 .40
45 Chipper Jones .40 1.00
46 Greg Maddux .60 1.50
47 Andruw Jones .25 .60
48 Andres Galarraga .15 .40
49 Jeromy Burnitz .15 .40
50 Geoff Jenkins .15 .40
51 Mark McGwire 1.00 2.50
52 Fernando Tatis .15 .40
53 J.D. Drew .15 .40
54 Sammy Sosa .40 1.00
55 Kerry Wood .15 .40
56 Mark Grace .25 .60
57 Matt Williams .15 .40
58 Randy Johnson .40 1.00
59 Erubiel Durazo .15 .40
60 Gary Sheffield .15 .40
61 Kevin Brown .25 .60
62 Shawn Green .15 .40
63 Vladimir Guerrero .40 1.00
64 Michael Barrett .15 .40
65 Barry Bonds 1.00 2.50
66 Jeff Kent .15 .40
67 Russ Ortiz .15 .40
68 Preston Wilson .15 .40
69 Mike Lowell .15 .40
70 Mike Piazza .60 1.50
71 Mike Hampton .15 .40
72 Robin Ventura .15 .40
73 Edgardo Alfonzo .15 .40
74 Tony Gwynn .50 1.25
75 Ryan Klesko .15 .40
76 Trevor Hoffman .15 .40
77 Scott Rolen .25 .60
78 Bob Abreu .15 .40
79 Mike Lieberthal .15 .40
80 Curt Schilling .15 .40
81 Jason Kendall .15 .40
82 Brian Giles .15 .40
83 Kris Benson .15 .40
84 Ken Griffey Jr. .60 1.50
85 Sean Casey .15 .40
86 Pokey Reese .15 .40
87 Barry Larkin .25 .60
88 Larry Walker .15 .40
89 Todd Helton .25 .60
90 Jeff Cirillo .15 .40
91 Ken Griffey Jr. SUP 3.00 8.00
92 Mark McGwire SUP 5.00 12.00
93 Chipper Jones SUP 2.00 5.00
94 Derek Jeter SUP 5.00 12.00
95 Shawn Green SUP 1.25 3.00
96 Pedro Martinez SUP 1.25 3.00
97 Mike Piazza SUP 3.00 8.00
98 Alex Rodriguez SUP 3.00 8.00
99 Jeff Bagwell SUP 1.25 3.00
100 Cal Ripken SUP 6.00 15.00
101 Sammy Sosa SUP 2.00 5.00
102 Barry Bonds SUP 5.00 12.00
103 Jose Canseco SUP 1.25 3.00
104 N.Garciaparra SUP 3.00 8.00
105 Ivan Rodriguez SUP 1.25 3.00
106 Rick Ankiel FW 3.00 8.00
107 Pat Burrell FW 1.25 3.00
108 Vernon Wells FW 2.00 5.00
109 Nick Johnson FW 2.00 5.00
110 Kip Wells FW 2.00 5.00
111 Matt Riley FW 2.00 5.00
112 Alfonso Soriano FW 3.00 8.00
113 Josh Beckett FW 3.00 8.00
114 Danys Baez FW RC 2.00 5.00
115 Travis Dawkins FW 2.00 5.00
116 Eric Gagne FW 3.00 8.00
117 Mike Lamb FW RC 3.00 8.00
118 Eric Munson FW 2.00 5.00
119 W.Rodriguez FW RC 2.00 5.00
120 K.Sasaki FW RC 3.00 8.00
121 Chad Hutchinson FW 2.00 5.00
122 Peter Bergeron FW 2.00 5.00
123 W.Serrano FW RC 2.00 5.00
124 Tony Armas Jr. FW 2.00 5.00
125 Ramon Ortiz FW 2.00 5.00
126 Adam Kennedy FW 2.00 5.00
127 Joe Crede FW 4.00 10.00
128 Roosevelt Brown FW 2.00 5.00
129 Mark Mulder FW 2.00 5.00
130 Brad Penny FW 2.00 5.00
131 Terrence Long FW 2.00 5.00
132 Ruben Mateo FW 2.00 5.00
133 Wily Mo Pena FW 2.00 5.00
134 Rafael Furcal FW 2.00 5.00
135 M.Encarnacion FW 2.00 5.00
136 Barry Zito FW RC 8.00 20.00
137 Aaron McNeal FW RC 2.00 5.00
138 Timo Perez FW RC 2.00 5.00
139 Sun Woo Kim FW RC 2.00 5.00
140 Xavier Nady FW RC 4.00 10.00
141 M.Wheatland FW RC 2.00 5.00
142 B.Abernathy FW RC 2.00 5.00
143 Cory Vance FW RC 2.00 5.00
144 Scott Heard FW RC 2.00 5.00
145 Mike Meyers FW RC 2.00 5.00
146 Ben Diggins FW RC 2.00 5.00
147 Luis Matos FW RC 2.00 5.00
148 Ben Sheets FW RC 5.00 12.00
149 K.Ainsworth FW RC 2.00 5.00
150 Dave Krynzel FW RC 2.00 5.00
151 Alex Cabrera FW RC 2.00 5.00
152 Mike Tonis FW RC 2.00 5.00
153 Dane Sardinha FW RC 2.00 5.00
154 Keith Ginter FW RC 2.00 5.00
155 D.Espinosa FW RC 2.00 5.00
156 Joe Torres FW RC 2.00 5.00
157 Daylan Holt FW RC 2.00 5.00
158 Koyie Hill FW RC 2.00 5.00
159 B.Wilkerson FW RC 3.00 8.00
160 Juan Pierre FW RC 3.00 8.00
161 Matt Ginter FW RC 2.00 5.00
162 Dane Artman FW RC 2.00 5.00
163 Jon Rauch FW RC 2.00 5.00
164 Sean Burnett FW RC 2.00 5.00
165 Does Not Exist
166 Darin Erstad .25 .60
167 Ben Grieve .25 .60
168 David Wells .25 .60
169 Fred McGriff .40 1.00
170 Bob Wickman .25 .60
171 Al Martin .25 .60
172 Melvin Mora .25 .60
173 Ricky Ledee .25 .60
174 Dante Bichette .25 .60
175 Mike Sweeney .25 .60
176 Bobby Higginson .25 .60
177 Matt Lawton .25 .60
178 Charles Johnson .25 .60
179 David Justice .25 .60
180 Richard Hidalgo .25 .60
181 B.J. Surhoff .25 .60
182 Richie Sexson .25 .60
183 Jim Edmonds .25 .60
184 Rondell White .25 .60
185 Curt Schilling .25 .60
186 Tom Goodwin .25 .60
187 Jose Vidro .25 .60
188 Ellis Burks .25 .60
189 Henry Rodriguez .25 .60
190 Mike Bordick .25 .60
191 Eric Owens .25 .60
192 Travis Lee .25 .60
193 Kevin Young .25 .60
194 Aaron Boone .25 .60
195 Todd Hollandsworth .25 .60
SPA K.Griffey Jr. Sample .75 2.00

2000 SP Authentic Limited

Randomly inserted into packs, this 135-card set is a complete parallel of the 2000 SP Authentic base set. These cards are individually serial numbered to 100.

*STARS 1-90: 8X TO 20X BASIC CARDS
*SUP 91-105: 1.25X TO 3X BASIC SUP
*FW 106-135: 1X TO 2.5X BASIC FW
*FW 106-135 RC: 1X TO 2.5X BASIC FW RC

2000 SP Authentic Buybacks

Representatives at Upper Deck purchased back a selection of vintage SP brand trading cards from 1993-1999, featuring 29 different players. The "vintage" cards were all purchased in 2000 through hobby dealers. Each card was then hand-numbered in blue ink sharpie on front (please see listings for print runs), affixed with a serial numbered UDA hologram on back and packaged with a 2 1/2" by 3 1/2" UDA Certificate of Authenticity (of which had a hologram with a matching serial number of the signed card). The Certificate of Authenticity and the signed card were placed together in a soft plastic "penny" sleeve and then randomly seeded into 2000 SP Authentic packs at a rate of 1:95. Jeff Bagwell, Ken Griffey, Andruw Jones, Chipper Jones, Manny Ramirez and Alex Rodriguez did not manage to sign their cards in time for packout, thus exchange cards were created and seeded into packs for these players. The exchange cards did NOT specify the actual vintage card that the bearer would receive back in the mail. The deadline to redeem the exchange cards was March 30th, 2001. Pricing for cards with production of 25 or fewer cards is not provided due to scarcity.

1 Jeff Bagwell 93/58 20.00 50.00
2 Jeff Bagwell 94/46 20.00 50.00
3 Jeff Bagwell 95/60 20.00 50.00
4 Jeff Bagwell 96/74 20.00 50.00
5 Jeff Bagwell 97/53 20.00 50.00
6 Jeff Bagwell 98/38 20.00 50.00
7 Jeff Bagwell 99/539 20.00 50.00
9 Craig Biggio 93/59 15.00 40.00
10 Craig Biggio 94/69 15.00 40.00
11 Craig Biggio 95/171 10.00 25.00
12 Craig Biggio 96/71 15.00 40.00
13 Craig Biggio 97/46 15.00 40.00
14 Craig Biggio 98/40 15.00 40.00
15 Craig Biggio 99/125 10.00 25.00
22 Barry Bonds 99/520 100.00 175.00
23 Jose Canseco 93/29 20.00 50.00
29 Jose Canseco 99/502 10.00 25.00
31 Sean Casey 99/139 6.00 15.00
32 Roger Clemens 93/68 60.00 120.00
33 Roger Clemens 94/60 60.00 120.00
34 Roger Clemens 95/68 60.00 120.00
35 Roger Clemens 96/68 60.00 120.00
38 Roger Clemens 99/134 50.00 100.00
39 Jason Giambi 97/34 20.00 50.00
41 Tom Glavine 93/99 15.00 40.00
42 Tom Glavine 94/107 15.00 40.00
43 Tom Glavine 95/97 15.00 40.00
44 Tom Glavine 96/42 20.00 50.00
45 Tom Glavine 98/40 20.00 50.00
46 Tom Glavine 99/138 15.00 40.00
47 Shawn Green 96/55 15.00 40.00
48 Shawn Green 99/530 10.00 25.00
55 Ken Griffey Jr. 99/403 40.00 80.00
63 Tony Gwynn 99/129 15.00 40.00
64 Tony Gwynn 99/369 10.00 25.00
70 Derek Jeter 99/119 100.00 200.00
71 Randy Johnson 93/60 40.00 80.00
72 Randy Johnson 94/45 40.00 80.00
73 Randy Johnson 95/70 40.00 80.00
74 Randy Johnson 96/60 40.00 80.00
77 Randy Johnson 99/113 40.00 80.00
78 Andruw Jones 97/70 10.00 25.00
79 Andruw Jones 98/56 15.00 40.00
80 Andruw Jones 99/531 10.00 25.00
85 Chipper Jones 97/63 30.00 60.00
87 Chipper Jones 99/541 15.00 40.00
89 Kenny Lofton 94/100 10.00 25.00
90 Kenny Lofton 95/84 10.00 25.00
91 Kenny Lofton 96/34 20.00 50.00
92 Kenny Lofton 97/82 10.00 25.00
94 Kenny Lofton 99/99 10.00 25.00
95 Javy Lopez 93/106 6.00 15.00
96 Javy Lopez 94/160 6.00 15.00
97 Javy Lopez 96/99 6.00 15.00
98 Javy Lopez 97/61 10.00 25.00
99 Javy Lopez 98/26 12.50 30.00
106 Greg Maddux 99/504 40.00 80.00
107 Paul O'Neill 93/110 10.00 25.00
108 Paul O'Neill 94/97 10.00 25.00
109 Paul O'Neill 95/142 10.00 25.00
110 Paul O'Neill 96/70 10.00 25.00
111 Paul O'Neill 98/23
112 Manny Ramirez 93/6
113 Manny Ramirez 94/7
114 Manny Ramirez 95/22
115 Manny Ramirez 96/13
116 Manny Ramirez 97/42 20.00 50.00
117 Manny Ramirez 98/36 20.00 50.00
118 M. Ramirez 99/532 50.00 100.00
120 Cal Ripken 93/7
121 Cal Ripken 94/22
122 Cal Ripken 95/10
123 Cal Ripken 96/12
124 Cal Ripken 97/12
125 Cal Ripken 98/13
126 Cal Ripken 99/510 50.00 100.00
127 Alex Rodriguez 94/5
128 Alex Rodriguez 95/57 60.00 120.00
129 Alex Rodriguez 96/37 60.00 120.00
130 Alex Rodriguez 97/10
131 Alex Rodriguez 98/22
132 A.Rodriguez 99/408 50.00 100.00
134 Ivan Rodriguez 93/29 30.00 60.00
135 Ivan Rodriguez 94/16
136 Ivan Rodriguez 95/18
137 Ivan Rodriguez 96/22
138 Ivan Rodriguez 97/14
139 Ivan Rodriguez 98/27 30.00 60.00
140 Ivan Rodriguez 99/2
141 Scott Rolen 97/23
142 Scott Rolen 98/31 20.00 50.00
143 Frank Thomas 93/1
144 Frank Thomas 94/20
145 Frank Thomas 95/5
146 Frank Thomas 96/10
147 Frank Thomas 97/20
148 Frank Thomas 98/29 30.00 60.00
149 F.Thomas 99/100 15.00 40.00
150 Greg Vaughn 93/79 4.00 10.00
151 Greg Vaughn 94/75 4.00 10.00
152 Greg Vaughn 95/155 4.00 10.00
153 Greg Vaughn 96/113 4.00 10.00
154 Greg Vaughn 97/29 8.00 20.00
155 Greg Vaughn 99/527 4.00 10.00
156 Mo Vaughn 93/119 6.00 15.00
157 Mo Vaughn 94/96 6.00 15.00
158 Mo Vaughn 95/121 6.00 15.00
159 Mo Vaughn 96/114 6.00 15.00
160 Mo Vaughn 97/61 10.00 25.00
161 Mo Vaughn 98/29 12.50 30.00
162 Mo Vaughn 99/537 4.00 10.00
163 Robin Ventura 93/59 10.00 25.00
164 Robin Ventura 94/49 10.00 25.00
165 R.Ventura 95/125 6.00 15.00
166 Robin Ventura 96/55 10.00 25.00
167 Robin Ventura 97/44 10.00 25.00
168 Robin Ventura 98/28 12.50 30.00
169 R.Ventura 99/370 6.00 15.00
170 Matt Williams 93/55 15.00 40.00
171 Matt Williams 94/50 15.00 40.00
172 Matt Williams 95/137 10.00 25.00
173 Matt Williams 96/77 10.00 25.00
174 Matt Williams 97/54 15.00 40.00
175 Matt Williams 98/29 20.00 50.00
176 Matt Williams 99/529 10.00 25.00
177 P.Wilson 94/249 6.00 15.00
178 P.Wilson 99/195 6.00 15.00
179 Authentication Card .20 .50

2000 SP Authentic Chirography

Randomly inserted into packs at one in 23, this 42-card insert features autographed cards of modern superstar players. Please note that there were also autographs of Sandy Koutax inserted into this set. There were a number of cards in this set that packed out as exchange cards, the exchange cards must be sent to Upper Deck by 03/30/01.

AJ Andruw Jones 10.00 25.00
AR Alex Rodriguez 50.00 100.00
AS Alfonso Soriano 8.00 20.00
BB Barry Bonds 100.00 175.00
BP Ben Petrick 4.00 10.00
CBE Carlos Beltran 4.00 10.00
CJ Chipper Jones 20.00 50.00
CR Cal Ripken 60.00 120.00
DJ Derek Jeter 75.00 150.00
EC Eric Chavez 6.00 15.00
ED Erubiel Durazo 4.00 10.00
EM Eric Munson 4.00 10.00
EY Ed Yarnall 4.00 10.00
IR Ivan Rodriguez 8.00 20.00
JB Jeff Bagwell 20.00 50.00
JC Jose Canseco 10.00 25.00
JD J.D. Drew 6.00 15.00
JG Jason Giambi 10.00 25.00
JK Josh Kalinowski 4.00 10.00
JL Jose Lima 10.00 25.00
JMA Joe Mays 4.00 10.00
JMO Jim Morris 10.00 25.00
JOB John Bale 4.00 10.00
KL Kenny Lofton 10.00 25.00
MQ Mark Quinn 4.00 10.00
MR Manny Ramirez 20.00 50.00
MRI Matt Riley 4.00 10.00
MV Mo Vaughn 6.00 15.00
NJ Nick Johnson 6.00 15.00
PB Pat Burrell 6.00 15.00
RA Rick Ankiel 10.00 25.00
RC Roger Clemens 60.00 120.00
RF Rafael Furcal 4.00 10.00
RP Robert Person 4.00 10.00
SC Sean Casey 6.00 15.00
SK Sandy Koufax 175.00 300.00
SR Scott Rolen 10.00 25.00
TG Tony Gwynn 20.00 50.00
TGL Troy Glaus 10.00 25.00
VG Vladimir Guerrero 12.50 30.00
VW Vernon Wells 4.00 10.00
WG Wilton Guerrero 4.00 10.00

2000 SP Authentic Chirography Gold

GAS Alfonso Soriano/53 10.00 25.00
GED Erubiel Durazo/44 6.00 15.00
GEY Ed Yarnall/41 6.00 15.00
GJC Jose Canseco/33 30.00 60.00
GJK Josh Kalinowski/62 6.00 15.00
GJL Jose Lima/42 15.00 40.00
GJMA Joe Mays/53 6.00 15.00
GJMO Jim Morris/63 15.00 40.00
GJOB John Bale/49 6.00 15.00
GMV Mo Vaughn/42 10.00 25.00
GNJ Nick Johnson/63 10.00 25.00
GPB Pat Burrell/33 15.00 40.00
GRA Rick Ankiel/66 10.00 25.00
GRP Robert Person/31 10.00 25.00
GVG V.Guerrero/27 50.00 100.00

2000 SP Authentic Cornerstones

Randomly inserted into packs at one in 23, this seven-card insert features players that are the cornerstones of their teams. Card backs carry a "C" prefix.

COMPLETE SET (7) 25.00 60.00
C1 Ken Griffey Jr 2.50 6.00
C2 Cal Ripken 5.00 12.00
C3 Mike Piazza 2.50 6.00
C4 Derek Jeter 4.00 10.00
C5 Mark McGwire 4.00 10.00
C6 Nomar Garciaparra 2.50 6.00
C7 Sammy Sosa 1.50 4.00

2000 SP Authentic DiMaggio Memorabilia

Randomly inserted into packs, this three-card insert features game-used memorabilia cards of Joe DiMaggio. This set features a Game-Used Jersey card (numbered to 500), a Game-Used Jersey card Gold (numbered to 56), and a Game-Used Jersey/Cut Autograph card (numbered to 5).

1 Joe DiMaggio Jsy/500 60.00 120.00
2 Joe DiMaggio Jsy Gold/56 100.00 200.00
3 Joe DiMaggio Jsy-Cut AU/5

2000 SP Authentic Midsummer Classics

Randomly inserted into packs at one in 12, this 10-card insert features perennial All-Stars. Card backs carry a "MC" prefix.

COMPLETE SET (10) 12.50 30.00
MC1 Cal Ripken 3.00 8.00
MC2 Roger Clemens 2.00 5.00
MC3 Jeff Bagwell .60 1.50
MC4 Barry Bonds 2.50 6.00
MC5 Jose Canseco .60 1.50
MC6 Frank Thomas 1.00 2.50
MC7 Mike Piazza 1.50 4.00
MC8 Tony Gwynn 1.25 3.00
MC9 Juan Gonzalez .40 1.00
MC10 Greg Maddux 1.50 4.00

2000 SP Authentic Premier Performers

Randomly inserted into packs at one in 12, this 10-card insert features prime-time players that leave it all on the field and hold nothing back. Card backs carry a "PP" prefix.

COMPLETE SET (10) 20.00 50.00
PP1 Mark McGwire 2.50 6.00
PP2 Alex Rodriguez 1.50 4.00
PP3 Cal Ripken 3.00 8.00
PP4 Nomar Garciaparra 1.50 4.00
PP5 Ken Griffey Jr. 1.50 4.00
PP6 Chipper Jones 1.00 2.50
PP7 Derek Jeter 2.50 6.00
PP8 Ivan Rodriguez .60 1.50
PP9 Vladimir Guerrero 1.00 2.50
PP10 Sammy Sosa 1.00 2.50

2000 SP Authentic Supremacy

Randomly inserted into packs at one in 23, this seven-card insert features players that any team would like to have. Card backs carry a "S" prefix.

COMPLETE SET (7) 12.50 30.00
S1 Alex Rodriguez 2.50 6.00
S2 Shawn Green .60 1.50
S3 Pedro Martinez 1.00 2.50
S4 Chipper Jones 1.50 4.00
S5 Tony Gwynn 2.00 5.00
S6 Ivan Rodriguez 1.00 2.50
S7 Jeff Bagwell 1.00 2.50

2000 SP Authentic United Nations

Randomly inserted into packs at one in four, this 10-card insert features players that have come from other countries to play in the Major Leagues. Card backs carry a "UN" prefix.

COMPLETE SET (10) 4.00 10.00
UN1 Sammy Sosa .50 1.25
UN2 Ken Griffey Jr. .75 2.00
UN3 Orlando Hernandez .20 .50
UN4 Andres Galarraga .20 .50
UN5 Kazuhiro Sasaki .30 .75
UN6 Larry Walker .20 .50
UN7 Vinny Castilla .20 .50
UN8 Andruw Jones .30 .75
UN9 Ivan Rodriguez .30 .75
UN10 Chan Ho Park .20 .50

2001 SP Authentic

SP Authentic was initially released as a 180-card set in September, 2001. An additional 60-card Update set was distributed within Upper Deck Rookie Update packs in late December, 2001. Each basic sealed box contained 24 packs plus two three-card bonus packs (one entitled Stars of Japan and another entitled Mantle Pinstripe Exclusives). Each basic pack of SP Authentic contained five cards and carried a suggested retail price of $4.99. Upper Deck Rookie Update packs contained four cards and carried an SRP of $4.99. The basic set is broken into the following components: basic veterans (1-90), Future Watch (91-135) and Superstars (136-180). Each Future Watch and Superstar subset card from the first series is serial numbered of 1250 copies. Though odds were not released by the manufacturer, information supplied by dealers breaking several cases indicate on average one in every 18 basic packs contains one of these serial-numbered cards. The Update set is broken down as follows: basic veterans (181-210) and Future Watch (211-240). Each Update Future Watch is serial numbered to 1500 copies. Notable Rookie Cards in the basic set include Albert Pujols, Tsuyoshi Shinjo and Ichiro Suzuki. Notable Rookie Cards in the Update set include Mark Prior and Mark Teixeira.

COMP.BASIC w/o SP's (90) 10.00 25.00
COMP.UPDATE w/o SP's (30) 4.00 10.00
COMMON CARD (1-90) .15 .40
COMMON FW (91-135) 3.00 8.00
COMMON SS (136-180) 2.00 5.00
COMMON (181-210) .25 .60
COMMON (211-240) 2.50 6.00
1 Troy Glaus .15 .40
2 Darin Erstad .15 .40
3 Jason Giambi .15 .40
4 Tim Hudson .15 .40
5 Eric Chavez .15 .40
6 Miguel Tejada .15 .40
7 Jose Ortiz .15 .40
8 Carlos Delgado .15 .40
9 Tony Batista .15 .40
10 Raul Mondesi .15 .40
11 Aubrey Huff .15 .40
12 Greg Vaughn .15 .40
13 Roberto Alomar .25 .60
14 Juan Gonzalez .15 .40
15 Jim Thome .25 .60
16 Omar Vizquel .25 .60
17 Edgar Martinez .25 .60
18 Freddy Garcia .15 .40
19 Cal Ripken 1.25 3.00
20 Ivan Rodriguez .25 .60
21 Rafael Palmeiro .25 .60
22 Alex Rodriguez .60 1.50
23 Manny Ramirez Sox .25 .60
24 Pedro Martinez .25 .60
25 Nomar Garciaparra .60 1.50
26 Mike Sweeney .15 .40
27 Jermaine Dye .15 .40
28 Bobby Higginson .15 .40
29 Dean Palmer .15 .40
30 Matt Lawton .15 .40
31 Eric Milton .15 .40
32 Frank Thomas .40 1.00
33 Magglio Ordonez .15 .40
34 David Wells .15 .40
35 Paul Konerko .15 .40
36 Derek Jeter 1.00 2.50
37 Bernie Williams .25 .60
38 Roger Clemens .75 2.00
39 Mike Mussina .25 .60
40 Jorge Posada .25 .60
41 Jeff Bagwell .25 .60
42 Richard Hidalgo .15 .40
43 Craig Biggio .25 .60
44 Greg Maddux .60 1.50
45 Chipper Jones .40 1.00
46 Andruw Jones .25 .60
47 Rafael Furcal .15 .40
48 Tom Glavine .25 .60
49 Jeromy Burnitz .15 .40
50 Jeffrey Hammonds .15 .40
51 Mark McGwire 1.00 2.50
52 Jim Edmonds .15 .40
53 Rick Ankiel .15 .40
54 J.D. Drew .15 .40
55 Sammy Sosa .40 1.00
56 Corey Patterson .15 .40
57 Kerry Wood .15 .40
58 Randy Johnson .40 1.00
59 Luis Gonzalez .15 .40
60 Curt Schilling .15 .40
61 Gary Sheffield .15 .40
62 Shawn Green .15 .40
63 Kevin Brown .15 .40
64 Vladimir Guerrero .40 1.00
65 Jose Vidro .15 .40
66 Barry Bonds 1.00 2.50
67 Jeff Kent .15 .40
68 Livan Hernandez .15 .40
69 Preston Wilson .15 .40
70 Charles Johnson .15 .40
71 Ryan Dempster .15 .40
72 Mike Piazza .60 1.50
73 Al Leiter .15 .40
74 Edgardo Alfonzo .15 .40
75 Robin Ventura .15 .40
76 Tony Gwynn .50 1.25
77 Phil Nevin .15 .40
78 Trevor Hoffman .15 .40
79 Scott Rolen .25 .60
80 Pat Burrell .15 .40

81 Bob Abreu .15 .40
82 Jason Kendall .15 .40
83 Brian Giles .15 .40
84 Kris Benson .15 .40
85 Ken Griffey Jr. .60 1.50
86 Barry Larkin .25 .60
87 Sean Casey .15 .40
88 Todd Helton .25 .60
89 Mike Hampton .15 .40
90 Larry Walker .15 .40
91 Ichiro Suzuki FW RC 60.00 120.00
92 Wilson Betemit FW RC 6.00 15.00
93 A. Hernandez FW RC 3.00 8.00
94 Juan Uribe FW RC 4.00 10.00
95 Travis Hafner FW RC 20.00 50.00
96 M. Ensberg FW RC 6.00 15.00
97 Sean Douglass FW RC 3.00 8.00
98 Juan Diaz FW RC 3.00 8.00
99 Erick Almonte FW RC 3.00 8.00
100 Ryan Freel FW RC 3.00 8.00
101 E. Guzman FW RC 3.00 8.00
102 C. Parker FW RC 3.00 8.00
103 Josh Fogg FW RC 3.00 8.00
104 Bert Snow FW RC 3.00 8.00
105 H. Ramirez FW RC 4.00 10.00
106 R. Rodriguez FW RC 3.00 8.00
107 Tyler Walker FW RC 3.00 8.00
108 Jose Mieses FW RC 3.00 8.00
109 Billy Sylvester FW RC 3.00 8.00
110 Martin Vargas FW RC 3.00 8.00
111 Andres Torres FW RC 3.00 8.00
112 Greg Miller FW RC 3.00 8.00
113 Alexis Gomez FW RC 3.00 8.00
114 Grant Balfour FW RC 3.00 8.00
115 Henry Mateo FW RC 3.00 8.00
116 Esix Snead FW RC 3.00 8.00
117 J. Melian FW RC 3.00 8.00
118 Nate Teut FW RC 3.00 8.00
119 T. Shinjo FW RC 4.00 10.00
120 C. Valderrama FW RC 3.00 8.00
121 J. Estrada FW RC 4.00 10.00
122 J. Michaels FW RC 3.00 8.00
123 William Ortega FW RC 3.00 8.00
124 Jason Smith FW RC 3.00 8.00
125 B. Lawrence FW RC 3.00 8.00
126 Albert Pujols FW RC 200.00 500.00
127 Wilkin Ruan FW RC 3.00 8.00
128 Josh Towers FW RC 4.00 10.00
129 Kris Keller FW RC 3.00 8.00
130 Nick Maness FW RC 3.00 8.00
131 Jack Wilson FW RC 4.00 10.00
132 B. Duckworth FW RC 3.00 8.00
133 Mike Penney FW RC 3.00 8.00
134 Jay Gibbons FW RC 4.00 10.00
135 Cesar Crespo FW RC 3.00 8.00
136 Ken Griffey Jr. SS 4.00 10.00
137 Mark McGwire SS 6.00 15.00
138 Derek Jeter SS 6.00 15.00
139 Alex Rodriguez SS 4.00 10.00
140 Sammy Sosa SS 2.50 6.00
141 Carlos Delgado SS 2.00 5.00
142 Cal Ripken SS 8.00 20.00
143 Pedro Martinez SS 2.00 5.00
144 Frank Thomas SS 2.50 6.00
145 Juan Gonzalez SS 2.00 5.00
146 Troy Glaus SS 2.00 5.00
147 Jason Giambi SS 2.00 5.00
148 Ivan Rodriguez SS 2.00 5.00
149 Chipper Jones SS 2.50 6.00
150 Vladimir Guerrero SS 2.50 6.00
151 Mike Piazza SS 4.00 10.00
152 Jeff Bagwell SS 2.00 5.00
153 Randy Johnson SS 2.50 6.00
154 Todd Helton SS 2.00 5.00
155 Gary Sheffield SS 2.00 5.00
156 Tony Gwynn SS 3.00 8.00
157 Barry Bonds SS 6.00 15.00
158 N. Garciaparra SS 4.00 10.00
159 Bernie Williams SS 2.00 5.00
160 Greg Vaughn SS 2.00 5.00
161 David Wells SS 2.00 5.00
162 Roberto Alomar SS 2.00 5.00
163 Jermaine Dye SS 2.00 5.00
164 Rafael Palmeiro SS 2.00 5.00
165 Andruw Jones SS 2.00 5.00
166 Preston Wilson SS 2.00 5.00
167 Edgardo Alfonzo SS 2.00 5.00
168 Pat Burrell SS 2.00 5.00
169 Jim Edmonds SS 2.00 5.00
170 Mike Hampton SS 2.00 5.00
171 Jeff Kent SS 2.00 5.00
172 Kevin Brown SS 2.00 5.00
173 Manny Ramirez Sox SS 2.00 5.00
174 Magglio Ordonez SS 2.00 5.00
175 Roger Clemens SS 5.00 12.00
176 Jim Thome SS 2.00 5.00
177 Barry Zito SS 2.00 5.00
178 Brian Giles SS 2.00 5.00
179 Rick Ankiel SS 2.00 5.00
180 Corey Patterson SS 2.00 5.00
181 Garret Anderson .25 .60
182 Jermaine Dye .25 .60
183 Shannon Stewart .25 .60
184 Ben Grieve .25 .60
185 Ellis Burks .25 .60
186 John Olerud .25 .60
187 Tony Batista .25 .60
188 Ruben Sierra .25 .60
189 Carl Everett .25 .60
190 Neifi Perez .25 .60
191 Tony Clark .25 .60
192 Doug Mientkiewicz .25 .60
193 Carlos Lee .25 .60
194 Jorge Posada .40 1.00
195 Lance Berkman 2.00 5.00
196 Ken Caminiti .25 .60
197 Ben Sheets .40 1.00
198 Matt Morris .25 .60
199 Fred McGriff .40 1.00
200 Mark Grace .40 1.00
201 Paul LoDuca .25 .60
202 Tony Armas Jr. .25 .60
203 Andres Galarraga .25 .60
204 Cliff Floyd .25 .60
205 Matt Lawton .25 .60
206 Ryan Klesko .25 .60
207 Jimmy Rollins .25 .60
208 Aramis Ramirez .25 .60
209 Aaron Boone .25 .60
210 Jose Ortiz .25 .60
211 Mark Prior FW RC 6.00 15.00
212 Mark Teixeira FW RC 40.00 80.00
213 Bud Smith FW RC 2.50 6.00
214 W.Caceres FW RC 2.50 6.00
215 Dave Williams FW RC 2.50 6.00
216 Delvin James FW RC 2.50 6.00
217 Endy Chavez FW RC 2.50 6.00
218 Doug Nickle FW RC 2.50 6.00
219 Bret Prinz FW RC 2.50 6.00
220 Troy Mattes FW RC 2.50 6.00
221 D.Sanchez FW RC 2.50 6.00
222 D.Brazelton FW RC 2.50 6.00
223 Brian Rowles FW RC 2.50 6.00
224 D.Mendez FW RC 2.50 6.00
225 Jorge Julio FW RC 2.50 6.00
226 Matt White FW RC 2.50 6.00
227 Casey Fossum FW RC 2.50 6.00
228 Mike Rivera FW RC 2.50 6.00
229 Joe Kennedy FW RC 3.00 8.00
230 Kyle Lohse FW RC 3.00 8.00
231 Juan Cruz FW RC 2.50 6.00
232 Jeremy Affeldt FW RC 2.50 6.00
233 Brandon Lyon FW RC 2.50 6.00
234 Brian Roberts FW RC 8.00 20.00
235 Willie Harris FW RC 2.50 6.00
236 Pedro Santana FW RC 2.50 6.00
237 Rafael Soriano FW RC 2.50 6.00
238 Steve Green FW RC 2.50 6.00
239 Junior Spivey FW RC 3.00 8.00
240 R.Mackowiak FW RC 3.00 8.00
NNO K.Griffey Jr. Promo .75 2.00

2001 SP Authentic Limited

This 180-card set is a straight parallel of the basic set. Only fifty sets were produced and each card features serial-numbering in thin gold foil on front and a gold foil brand logo (basic cards feature silver foil brand logos).

*STARS 1-90: 10X TO 25X BASIC 1-90
*FW 91-135: 1X TO 2.5X BASIC 91-135
*SS 136-180: 1.5X TO 4X BASIC 136-180
91 Ichiro Suzuki FW 175.00 300.00
126 Albert Pujols FW 600.00 800.00

2001 SP Authentic BuyBacks

For the third time in the history of the brand (including 1997 and 2000), Upper Deck incorporated Buyback cards into SP Authentic packs. Representatives from UD purchased varying quantities of actual previously released SP Authentic cards ranging from 1993 to 2000. The cards were then signed by the featured ballplayer, hand-numbered in blue ink on front and affixed with a serial-numbered hologram sticker on back (note: it's believed all 2001 hologram sticker numbers begin with the letters "AAA"). In addition to the actual signed card, each Buyback was distributed with a 2 1/2" by 3 1/2" Authenticity Guarantee card. Each of these cards featured a hologram with a matching serial-number and a note of congratulations from Upper Deck's CEO Richard McWilliam. Our listings for these cards feature the year of the card followed by the quantity produced. Thus, "Edgardo Alfonzo 95/77" indicates a 1995 SP Authentic Edgardo Alfonzo card of which 77 copies were made. Please note that several Buyback cards are too scarce for us to provide accurate pricing. Please see our magazine or website for pricing information on these cards as it's made available. The following players were seeded into packs as exchange cards: Roger Clemens, Cal Ripken and Frank Thomas. Collectors did not know which card of these players they would receive until it was mailed to them. Exchange deadline was 8/30/04.

1 Edgardo Alfonzo 95/77 10.00 25.00
2 Edgardo Alfonzo 98/15
3 Edgardo Alfonzo 00/280 6.00 15.00
4 Barry Bonds 93/75 100.00 175.00
5 Barry Bonds 94/103 100.00 175.00
6 Barry Bonds 95/31 100.00 175.00
7 Barry Bonds 95 Silver/2
8 Barry Bonds 96/49 100.00 175.00
9 Barry Bonds 97/15
10 Barry Bonds 98/15
11 Barry Bonds 00/146 100.00 175.00
12 Roger Clemens 00/145 50.00 100.00
13 R.Clemens 99/150 EXCH 50.00 100.00
15 Carlos Delgado 93/24
16 Carlos Delgado 94/272 6.00 15.00
17 Carlos Delgado 96/81 10.00 25.00
18 Carlos Delgado 97/8
19 Carlos Delgado 98/29 20.00 50.00
20 Carlos Delgado 00/169 6.00 15.00
21 Jim Edmonds 96/72 15.00 40.00
22 Jim Edmonds 97/38 30.00 60.00
23 Jim Edmonds 98/23
24 Jason Giambi 97/14
25 Jason Giambi 98/6
26 Jason Giambi 00/290 6.00 15.00
27 Troy Glaus 00/340 10.00 25.00
28 Shawn Green 00/340 10.00 25.00
29 Ken Griffey Jr. 93/34 75.00 150.00
30 Ken Griffey Jr. 94/182 40.00 80.00
31 Ken Griffey Jr. 95/116 40.00 80.00
32 Ken Griffey Jr. 95 Silver/2
33 Ken Griffey Jr. 96/53 60.00 120.00
34 Ken Griffey Jr. 97/7
35 Ken Griffey Jr. 98/8
36 Ken Griffey Jr. 00/333 40.00 80.00
37 Tony Gwynn 93/101 10.00 25.00
38 Tony Gwynn 94/88 10.00 25.00
39 Tony Gwynn 95/179 10.00 25.00
40 Tony Gwynn 96/92 10.00 25.00
41 Tony Gwynn 97/9
42 Tony Gwynn 98/16
43 Tony Gwynn 00/95 10.00 25.00
44 Todd Helton 00/194 10.00 25.00
45 Tim Hudson 00/291 10.00 25.00
46 Randy Johnson 93/97 50.00 100.00
47 Randy Johnson 94/146 20.00 60.00
48 Randy Johnson 95/121 30.00 60.00
49 Randy Johnson 95 Silver/6
50 Randy Johnson 96/78 50.00 100.00
51 Randy Johnson 97/8
52 Randy Johnson 98/12
53 Randy Johnson 00/213 30.00 60.00
54 Andruw Jones 97/20
55 Andruw Jones 98/12
56 Andruw Jones 00/336 10.00 25.00
57 Chipper Jones 93/13
58 Chipper Jones 95/118 20.00 50.00
59 Chipper Jones 96/72 30.00 60.00
60 Chipper Jones 97/15
61 Chipper Jones 98/11
62 Chipper Jones 00/303 20.00 50.00
63 Cal Ripken 93/22
64 Cal Ripken 94/99 60.00 120.00
65 Cal Ripken 95/37 75.00 150.00
66 Cal Ripken 96/16
67 Cal Ripken 96 CL/10
68 Cal Ripken 97/23
69 Cal Ripken 98/11
70 Cal Ripken 00/266 60.00 120.00
72 Alex Rodriguez 95/117 100.00 175.00
73 Alex Rodriguez 95 Silver/2
74 Alex Rodriguez 96/72 100.00 175.00
75 Alex Rodriguez 97/14
76 Alex Rodriguez 98/11
77 Alex Rodriguez 00/332 100.00 175.00
78 Ivan Rodriguez 93/89 20.00 50.00
79 Ivan Rodriguez 95/16
80 Ivan Rodriguez 95 Silver/2
81 Ivan Rodriguez 96/64 40.00 80.00
82 Ivan Rodriguez 97/8
83 Ivan Rodriguez 98/13
84 Ivan Rodriguez 00/163 15.00 40.00
85 Gary Sheffield 93/82 8.00 20.00
86 Gary Sheffield 94/3
87 Gary Sheffield 95/70 8.00 20.00
88 Gary Sheffield 96/67 8.00 20.00
89 Gary Sheffield 97/43 12.50 30.00
90 Gary Sheffield 98/27 15.00 40.00
91 Gary Sheffield 00/146 5.00 12.00
92 Sammy Sosa 93/73 50.00 100.00
93 Sammy Sosa 94/19
94 Sammy Sosa 95/30 50.00 100.00
95 Sammy Sosa 96/9
96 Sammy Sosa 97/14
97 Fernando Tatis 00/267 4.00 10.00
98 Frank Thomas 93/79 50.00 100.00
99 Frank Thomas 94/165 50.00 100.00
100 Frank Thomas 95/3
101 Frank Thomas 97/34 50.00 100.00
102 Frank Thomas 98/10
103 Frank Thomas 00/302 50.00 100.00
105 Mo Vaughn 93/94 10.00 25.00
106 Mo Vaughn 94/102 10.00 25.00
107 Mo Vaughn 95/129 6.00 15.00
108 Mo Vaughn 95 Silver/3
109 Mo Vaughn 96/81 10.00 25.00
110 Mo Vaughn 97/36 15.00 40.00
111 Mo Vaughn 98/23
112 Mo Vaughn 00/309 6.00 15.00
113 Robin Ventura 00/340 6.00 15.00
114 Matt Williams 00/340 10.00 25.00
115 Authentication Card

2001 SP Authentic Chirography

Signed Chirography inserts were brought back for the fourth straight year within SP Authentic. Over 40 players were featured in the 2001 issue, with announced odds of 1:72 packs. Each card features a horizontal design and a small black and white action photo of the player at the side to allow the maximum amount of room for the featured player's autograph (of which is typically found signed in blue ink). Quantities produced for each card varied dramatically and shortly after the product was released, representatives at Upper Deck publicly announced print runs on a selection of the toughest cards to obtain. Those quantities have been added to our checklist following the featured player's name.

AB Albert Belle 6.00 15.00
AJ Andruw Jones 4.00 10.00
AP Albert Pujols 400.00 600.00
AR Alex Rodriguez SP/229 50.00 100.00
BS Ben Sheets 10.00 25.00
CB Carlos Beltran 12.50 30.00
CD Carlos Delgado 12.50 30.00
CF Cliff Floyd 6.00 15.00
CJ Chipper Jones SP/184 20.00 50.00
CR Cal Ripken SP/109 40.00 80.00
DD Darren Dreifort SP/206 4.00 10.00
DER Darin Erstad 6.00 15.00
DES David Espinosa 4.00 10.00
DJ David Justice 6.00 15.00
DS Dane Sardinha 4.00 10.00
DW David Wells 6.00 15.00
EA Edgardo Alfonzo 6.00 15.00
JC Jose Canseco 10.00 25.00
JD J.D. Drew 8.00 20.00
JE Jim Edmonds 10.00 25.00
JG Jason Giambi 6.00 15.00
KG Ken Griffey Jr. SP/126 50.00 100.00
LG Luis Gonzalez SP/271 10.00 25.00
MB Milton Bradley 6.00 15.00
MK Mark Kotsay SP/228 6.00 15.00
MS Mike Sweeney 6.00 15.00
MV Mo Vaughn SP/103 6.00 15.00
MW Matt Williams 10.00 25.00
PB Pat Burrell 6.00 15.00
RF Rafael Furcal SP/222 6.00 15.00
RH Rick Helling SP/211 4.00 10.00
RJ R. Johnson SP/143 30.00 60.00
RV Robin Ventura SP/92
RW Rondell White 6.00 15.00
SG Shawn Green SP/82 15.00 40.00
SS Sammy Sosa SP/76 50.00 100.00
TIH Tim Hudson 4.00 10.00
TL Travis Lee SP/226 4.00 10.00
TOG Tony Gwynn SP/76 20.00 50.00
TOH Todd Helton SP/152 10.00 25.00
TRG Troy Glaus 10.00 25.00

2001 SP Authentic Chirography Gold

These scarce autograph cards are a straight parallel of the more commonly available Chirography cards. The Gold cards, however, were all produced to quantities mirroring the featured player's uniform number. Furthermore, the cards are individually numbered on front in blue ink and the imagery and design accents are printed in a subdued gold color (rather than the black and white design used on the basic Chirography cards). Many of these cards are too scarce for us to provide accurate pricing on.

GAB Albert Belle/88 20.00 50.00
GDD Darren Dreifort/37 10.00 25.00
GDES David Espinosa/79 10.00 25.00
GDJ David Justice/28 20.00 50.00
GDS Dane Sardinha/50 10.00 25.00
GDW David Wells/33 20.00 50.00
GKG Ken Griffey Jr./30 75.00 150.00
GMS Mike Sweeney/29 20.00 50.00
GMV Mo Vaughn/42 20.00 50.00
GRH Rick Helling/32 10.00 25.00
GRJ Randy Johnson/51 50.00 100.00

2001 SP Authentic Chirography Update

Randomly inserted into Upper Deck Rookie Update packs, thse eight cards feature autographs from leading players in the game. Cal Ripken and Ichiro Suuzki did not return their cards in time for inclusion in these packs and these cards are available as exchange cards. Those cards could be redeemed until September 13th, 2004. These cards are serial numbered to 250.

SPCR Cal Ripken 75.00 150.00
SPDM Doug Mientkiewicz 6.00 15.00
SPIS Ichiro Suzuki 250.00 400.00
SPJP Jorge Posada 15.00 40.00
SPKG Ken Griffey Jr. 40.00 80.00
SPLB Lance Berkman 10.00 25.00
SPMS Mike Sweeney 6.00 15.00
SPTG Tony Gwynn 15.00 40.00

2001 SP Authentic Chirography Update Silver

Randomly inserted into Upper Deck Rookie Update packs, thse eight cards parallel the Chirography Update insert set and feature autographs from leading players in the game. Cal Ripken Jr. and Ichiro Suuzki did not return their cards in time for inclusion in these packs and these cards are available as exchange cards. These cards are serial numbered to 100.

SPCR Cal Ripken
SPDM Doug Mientkiewicz 10.00 25.00
SPIS Ichiro Suzuki
SPJP Jorge Posada 15.00 40.00
SPKG Ken Griffey Jr. 60.00 120.00
SPLB Lance Berkman 15.00 40.00
SPMS Mike Sweeney 10.00 25.00
SPTG Tony Gwynn 30.00 60.00

2001 SP Authentic Cooperstown Calling Game Jersey

This 22-card set features a selection of players that were voted in (or were soon to be voted in) to the baseball Hall of Fame in Cooperstown, NY. Each card features a swatch of game-used jersey incorporated into an attractive horizontal design. Though specific odds per pack were not released for this set, Upper Deck did release cumulative odds of 1:24 packs for finding a game-used jersey card from either of the Cooperstown Calling, UD Exclusives or UD Exclusives Combos sets within the SP Authentic product.

CCAD Andre Dawson 4.00 10.00
CCBM Bill Mazeroski 6.00 15.00
CCCR Cal Ripken 15.00 40.00
CCDM Don Mattingly 15.00 40.00
CCDW Dave Winfield 4.00 10.00
CCEM Eddie Murray 6.00 15.00
CCGC Gary Carter 4.00 10.00
CCGG Goose Gossage 4.00 10.00
CCJB Jeff Bagwell 6.00 15.00
CCKP Kirby Puckett 6.00 15.00
CCKS Kazuhiro Sasaki 4.00 10.00
CCMP Mike Piazza SP 10.00 25.00
CCMR M. Ramirez Sox SP 6.00 15.00
[illegible] Ozzie Smith [illegible] [illegible]
CCPM Pedro Martinez SP 6.00 15.00
CCPM Paul Molitor 4.00 10.00
CCRC Roger Clemens 15.00 40.00
CCRM R. Maris SP/243 40.00 80.00
CCRS Ryne Sandberg 12.50 30.00
CCSG Steve Garvey 4.00 10.00
CCTG Tony Gwynn 8.00 20.00
CCWB Wade Boggs 6.00 15.00

2001 SP Authentic Stars of Japan

This 30-card dual player set features a selection of Japanese stars active in Major League baseball at the time of issue. The cards were distributed in special Stars of Japan packs of which were available as a bonus pack within each sealed box of 2001 SP Authentic baseball. Each Stars of Japan pack contained three cards and one in every 12 packs contained a memorabilia card.

COMPLETE SET (30) 20.00 50.00
RS1 Ichiro Suzuki / Tsuyoshi Shinjo 3.00 8.00
RS2 Shigetoshi Hasegawa / Hideki Irabu .75 2.00
RS3 Tomo Ohka / Mac Suzuki .75 2.00
RS4 Tsuyoshi Shinjo / Hideki Irabu .75 2.00
RS5 Ichiro Suzuki / Hideo Nomo 4.00 10.00
RS6 Tsuyoshi Shinjo / Mac Suzuki .75 2.00
RS7 Tsuyoshi Shinjo / Kazuhiro Sasaki .75 2.00
RS8 Hideo Nomo / Tomo Ohka .75 2.00
RS9 Ichiro Suzuki / Mac Suzuki 3.00 8.00
RS10 Hideo Nomo / Shigetoshi Hasegawa .75 2.00
RS11 Hideo Nomo / Masato Yoshii .75 2.00
RS12 Hideo Nomo / Hideki Irabu .75 2.00
RS13 Shig. Hasegawa / Kazuhiro Sasaki .75 2.00
RS14 Shig. Hasegawa / Mac Suzuki .75 2.00
RS15 Tsuyoshi Shinjo / Hideo Nomo .75 2.00
RS16 Tsuyoshi Shinjo / Tomo Ohka .75 2.00
RS17 Ichiro Suzuki / Kazuhiro Sasaki 4.00 10.00
RS18 Masato Yoshii / Hideki Irabu .75 2.00
RS19 Ichiro Suzuki / Tomo Ohka 3.00 8.00
RS20 Hideki Irabu / Kazuhiro Sasaki .75 2.00
RS21 Tsuyoshi Shinjo / Masato Yoshii .75 2.00
RS22 Ichiro Suzuki / Shigetoshi Hasegawa 3.00 8.00
RS23 Mac Suzuki / Kazuhiro Sasaki .75 2.00
RS24 Ichiro Suzuki / Hideki Irabu 3.00 8.00
RS25 Tomo Ohka / Kazuhiro Sasaki .75 2.00
RS26 Tsuyoshi Shinjo / Shigetoshi Hasegawa .75 2.00
RS27 Masato Yoshii / Kazuhiro Sasaki .75 2.00
RS28 Hideo Nomo / Kazuhiro Sasaki .75 2.00
RS29 Ichiro Suzuki / Masato Yoshii 3.00 8.00
RS30 Hideo Nomo / Mac Suzuki .75 2.00

2001 SP Authentic Stars of Japan Game Ball

This six-card set features a selection of Japanese stars actively playing in the Major Leagues at the time of issue. Each card features a patch of game-used baseball. The cards were distributed in special Stars of Japan packs. Each sealed box of 2001 SP Authentic contained one three-card Stars of Japan pack inside.Though individual Jersey card odds were not announced, the cumulative odds of finding a memorabilia card (ball, base, bat or jersey) from a Stars of Japan packs was 1:12.

GOLD PRINT RUN 25 SERIAL #'d SETS
GOLD NO PRICING DUE TO SCARCITY
BBHI Hideki Irabu 4.00 10.00
BBIS Ichiro Suzuki 40.00 80.00
BBKS Kazuhiro Sasaki 4.00 10.00
BBMY Masato Yoshii 4.00 10.00
BBSH Shig. Hasegawa SP/30
BBTS T. Shinjo SP/50 6.00 15.00

2001 SP Authentic Stars of Japan Game Ball-Base Combos

This 14-card dual player set features a selection of Japanese stars actively playing in the Major Leagues at the time of issue. Each card features a piece of a game-used baseball coupled with a piece of game-used base. The cards were distributed in special Stars of Japan packs. Each sealed box of 2001 SP Authentic contained one three-card Stars of Japan pack inside.Though individual Jersey card odds were not announced, the cumulative odds of finding a memorabilia card (ball, base, bat or jersey) from a Stars of Japan packs was 1:12.

GOLD PRINT RUN 25 SERIAL #'d SETS
GOLD NO PRICING DUE TO SCARCITY
HIKS Hideki Irabu / Kazuhiro Sasaki SP/30
HNKS Hideo Nomo / Kazuhiro Sasaki SP/50 40.00 80.00
HNSH Hideo Nomo / Shigetosi Hasegawa 10.00 25.00
ISKS Ichiro Suzuki / Kazuhiro Sasaki SP/30
ISMY Ichiro Suzuki / Masato Yoshii 40.00 80.00
ISSH Ichiro Suzuki / Shigestosi Hasegawa SP/72 60.00 120.00
ISTS Ichiro Suzuki / Tsuyoshi Shinjo SP/40
MSKS Mac Suzuki / Kazuhiro Sasaki SP/30
MYKS Masato Yoshii / Kazuhiro Sasaki SP/30
SHKS S. Hasegawa / Kazuhiro Sasaki SP/30
TOKS Tomokazu Ohka / Kazuhiro Sasaki 4.00 10.00
TSHI Tsuyoshi Shinjo / Hideki Irabu SP/30
TSKS Tsuyoshi Shinjo / Kazuhiro Sasaki SP/30
TSSH Tsuyoshi Shinjo / Shigetosi Hasegawa SP/30

2001 SP Authentic Stars of Japan Game Ball-Base Trio

This card features the three greatest Japanese stars actively playing in the Major Leagues at the time of issue. The card features two pieces of game-used bases and one piece of a game-used baseball from the highlighted players. The card was distributed in special Stars of Japan packs. Each sealed box of 2001 SP Authentic contained one three-card Stars of Japan pack inside.Though individual Jersey card odds were not announced, the cumulative odds of finding a memorabilia card (ball, base, bat or jersey) from a Stars of Japan packs was 1:12.

GOLD PRINT RUN 25 SERIAL #'d SETS
GOLD NO PRICING DUE TO SCARCITY
RS Kazuhiro Sasaki / Ichiro Suzuki / Hideo Nomo SP/30

2001 SP Authentic Stars of Japan Game Base

This eight-card set features a selection of Japanese stars actively playing in the Major Leagues at the time of issue. Each card features a piece of game used base. The cards were distributed in special Stars of Japan packs. Each sealed box of 2001 SP Authentic contained one three-card Stars of Japan pack inside.Though individual Jersey card odds were not announced, the cumulative odds of finding a memorabilia card (ball, base, bat or jersey) from a Stars of Japan packs was 1:12.

OVERALL MEMORABILIA ODDS 1:12 SOJ
SP PRINT RUNS PROVIDED BY UD
NO PRICING ON QTY OF 40 OR LESS
GOLD PRINT RUN 25 SERIAL #'d SETS
GOLD NO PRICING DUE TO SCARCITY
HI Hideki Irabu SP/33
IS Ichiro Suzuki SP/23
KS Kazuhiro Sasaki SP/33
MS Mac Suzuki SP/23
MY Masato Yoshii SP/33
SH S. Hasegawa SP/33
TO Tomokazu Ohka SP/33
TS Tsuyoshi Shinjo SP/33

2001 SP Authentic Stars of Japan Game Bat

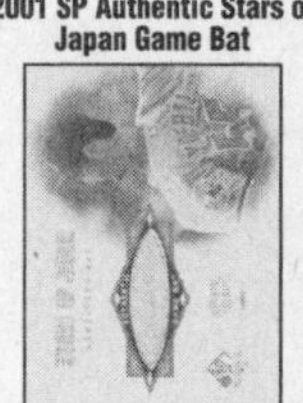

This three-card set features a selection of Japanese stars actively playing in the Major Leagues at the time of issue. Each card features a piece of game-used bat. The cards were distributed in special Stars of Japan packs. Each sealed box of 2001 SP Authentic contained one three-card Stars of Japan pack inside.Though individual Jersey card odds were not announced, the cumulative odds of finding a memorabilia card (ball, base, bat or jersey) from a Stars of Japan packs was 1:12.

GOLD PRINT RUN 25 SERIAL #'d SETS
GOLD NO PRICING DUE TO SCARCITY
BHN Hideo Nomo SP/30
BMY Masato Yoshii 4.00 10.00
BTS T. Shinjo SP/30

2001 SP Authentic Stars of Japan Game Bat-Jersey Combos

This 4-card dual player set features a selection of Japanese stars actively playing in the Major Leagues at the time of issue. Each card features a combination of a game-used bat chip or game-used jersey swatch from the featured players. The cards were distributed in special Stars of Japan packs. Each sealed box of 2001 SP Authentic contained one 3-card Stars of Japan pack inside.Though individual Jersey card odds were not announced, the cumulative odds of finding a memorabilia card (ball, base, bat or jersey) from a Stars of Japan packs was 1:12.

GOLD PRINT RUN 25 SERIAL #'d SETS
GOLD NO PRICING DUE TO SCARCITY
BBHS S. Hasegawa / Tsuyoshi Shinjo 10.00 25.00
JBNN Hideo Nomo / Hideo Nomo 30.00 60.00
JBSN Kazuhiro Sasaki / Hideo Nomo 10.00 25.00
JJSH Kazuhiro Sasaki / Shigetosi Hasegawa 6.00 15.00

2001 SP Authentic Stars of Japan Game Jersey

This six-card set features a selection of Japanese stars actively playing in the Major Leagues at the time of issue. Each card features a swatch of game-used jersey. The cards were distributed in special Stars of Japan packs. Each sealed box of 2001 SP Authentic contained one three-card Stars of Japan pack inside. Though individual Jersey card odds were not announced, the cumulative odds of finding a memorabilia card (ball, base, bat or jersey) from a Stars of Japan packs was 1:12. Ichiro Suzuki's jersey card was not available at time of packout and an exchange card was seeded into packs in it's place. The exchange card had a redemption deadline of August 30th, 2004. Though not serial-numbered, officials at Upper Deck announced that only 260 copies of Ichiro's jersey card were produced.

GOLD PRINT RUN 25 SERIAL #'d SETS
NO GOLD PRICING DUE TO SCARCITY
JHN Hideo Nomo 6.00 15.00
JIS Ichiro Suzuki SP/260 50.00 100.00
JKS Kazuhiro Sasaki 4.00 10.00
JMY Masato Yoshii 4.00 10.00
JSH S. Hasegawa 4.00 10.00
JTS Tsuyoshi Shinjo 6.00 15.00

2001 SP Authentic Stars of Japan Game Jersey Gold

These Gold cards are straight parallels to the standard Stars of Japan Game Jersey inserts. However, only 25 Gold sets were produced and each card carries gold-foil serial-numbering "XX/25" on front. In addition, gold ink design highlights on the card fronts and backs replace the silver ink highlights seen on the standard Stars of Japan memorabilia cards. The cards were randomly inserted into Stars of Japan packs at an unspecified ratio. No Ichiro Suzuki game jersey gold card was issued.

JHN Hideo Nomo
JKS Kazuhiro Sasaki
JMY Masato Yoshii
JSH S. Hasegawa
JTS Tsuyoshi Shinjo

2001 SP Authentic Sultan of Swatch Memorabilia

This 21-card set features a selection of significant achievements from legendary slugger Babe Ruth's storied career. Each card features a swatch of game-used uniform (most likely pants) and is hand-numbered in blue ink on front to the year or statistical figure of the featured event (i.e. card SOS3 highlights Ruth's 94 career wins as a pitcher, thus only 94 hand-numbered copies of that card were produced). Quantities on each card vary from as many as 94 copies to as few as 14 copies. The cards were randomly inserted into packs at an unspecified ratio.

SOS1 B.Ruth Red Sox/14
SOS2 B.Ruth 29.2 Inn/29 250.00 400.00
SOS3 B.Ruth 94 Wins/94 250.00 400.00
SOS4 B.Ruth 54 HRs/54 250.00 400.00
SOS5 B.Ruth 59 HRs/59 250.00 400.00
SOS6 Babe Ruth 250.00 400.00
3 HRs WS/26
SOS7 B.Ruth 60 HRs/27 250.00 400.00
SOS8 Babe Ruth 250.00 400.00
Called Shot/32
SOS9 B.Ruth HR Title/20
SOS10 B.Ruth HR Title/21
SOS11 B.Ruth Christens/23
SOS12 B.Ruth 46 HRs/24
SOS13 B.Ruth 40 HRs/26 250.00 400.00
SOS14 B.Ruth HR Title/27 250.00 400.00
SOS15 B.Ruth 50 HRs/28 250.00 400.00
SOS16 Babe Ruth 250.00 400.00
Leads Way/29
SOS17 B.Ruth 49 HRs/30 250.00 400.00
SOS18 Babe Ruth 250.00 400.00
Last Title/31
SOS19 Babe Ruth 250.00 400.00
1st AS/33
SOS20 B.Ruth 1st HOF/36 250.00 400.00
SOS21 B.Ruth House/48 250.00 400.00

2001 SP Authentic Sultan of Swatch Memorabilia Signature Cuts

Each of these cards features an actual Babe Ruth autograph taken from an autographed "cut" (an industry term for a signed piece of paper - often old checks or 3 x 5 note cards) incorporated directly into the card through a window of cardboard. Though only one copy of each card was made for this set, three cards are actually identical parallels of each other save for the SOS-prefixed card numbering on back and the variations in the cut signatures used for each. The signature on card SOS2 has been verified as "Babe Ruth" and for card SOS3 as "G.H. Ruth". Due to the extreme scarcity of these cards, we cannot provide an accurate value as they rarely are seen for public sale.

JC1 Babe Ruth Jsy-Cut AU/1
JC2 Babe Ruth Jsy-Cut AU
Cut signed as Babe Ruth
JC3 Babe Ruth Jsy-Cut AU
Cut signed as G.H. Ruth

2001 SP Authentic UD Exclusives Game Jersey

This 6-card set features a selection of superstars signed exclusively to Upper Deck for the rights to produce game-used jersey cards. Each card features a swatch of game-used jersey incorporated into an attractive horizontal design. Though specific odds per pack were not released for this set, Upper Deck did release cumulative odds of 1:24 packs for finding a game-used jersey card from either of the Cooperstown Calling, UD Exclusives or UD Exclusives Combos sets within the SP Authentic product. Shortly after release, representatives at Upper Deck publicly released print run information on several short prints. These quantities have been added to the end of the card description within our checklist.

AR Alex Rodriguez 6.00 15.00
GS Gary Sheffield 4.00 10.00
JD J.DiMaggio SP/243 50.00 100.00
KG Ken Griffey Jr. 6.00 15.00
MM M.Mantle SP/243 75.00 150.00
SS Sammy Sosa 6.00 15.00

2001 SP Authentic UD Exclusives Game Jersey Combos

This six-card set features a selection of superstars signed exclusively to Upper Deck for the rights to produce game-used jersey cards. Each card features a swatch of game-used jersey from each featured player incorporated into an attractive horizontal design. Though specific odds per pack were not released for this set, Upper Deck did release cumulative odds of 1:24 packs for finding a game-used jersey card from either of the Cooperstown Calling, UD Exclusives or UD Exclusives Combos sets within the SP Authentic product. Shortly after release, representatives at Upper Deck publicly released print run information on several short prints. These quantities have been added to the end of the card description within our checklist.

GD Ken Griffey Jr. 100.00 175.00
Joe DiMaggio SP/98
MD Mickey Mantle 175.00 300.00
Joe DiMaggio SP/98
MG Mickey Mantle 75.00 150.00
Ken Griffey Jr. SP/98
RS Alex Rodriguez 20.00 50.00
Ozzie Smith
SD Sammy Sosa 10.00 25.00
Andre Dawson
SW Gary Sheffield 10.00 25.00
Dave Winfield

2002 SP Authentic

This 230 card set was released in two separate series. The basic SP Authentic product (containing cards 1-170) was issued in September, 2002. Update cards 171-230 were distributed within packs of 2002 Upper Deck Rookie Update in mid-December, 2002. SP Authentic packs were issued in five card packs with a $5 SRP. Boxes contained 24 packs and were packed five to a case. Cards numbered 1 through 90 featured veterans while cards number 91 through 135 were part of the Future Watch subset and were printed to a stated print run of 1999 serial numbered sets. Cards numbered 136 through 170 were signed by the player and most of the cards were printed to a stated print run of 999 serial numbered sets. Cards number 146, 152 and 157 were printed to a stated print run of 249 serial numbered sets. Update cards 201-230 continued the Future Watch subset (focusing on rookies and prospects) and each card was serial numbered to 1999. Though pack odds for these cards was never released, we estimate the cards were seeded at an approximate rate of 1:7 Rookie Update packs. In addition, an exchange card with a redemption deadline of August 8th, 2005, good for a signed Joe DiMaggio poster was randomly inserted into SP Authentic packs.

COMP.LOW w/o SP's (90) 6.00 15.00
COMP.UPDATE w/o SP's (30) 4.00 10.00
COMMON CARD (1-90) .15 .40
COMMON (91-135/201-230) 2.00 5.00
COMMON CARD (136-170) 4.00 10.00
COMMON CARD (171-200) .25 .60
1 Troy Glaus .15 .40
2 Darin Erstad .15 .40
3 Barry Zito .15 .40
4 Eric Chavez .15 .40
5 Tim Hudson .15 .40
6 Miguel Tejada .15 .40
7 Carlos Delgado .15 .40
8 Shannon Stewart .15 .40
9 Ben Grieve .15 .40
10 Jim Thome .25 .60
11 C.C. Sabathia .15 .40
12 Ichiro Suzuki .75 2.00
13 Freddy Garcia .15 .40
14 Edgar Martinez .25 .60
15 Bret Boone .15 .40
16 Jeff Conine .15 .40
17 Alex Rodriguez .60 1.50
18 Juan Gonzalez .15 .40
19 Ivan Rodriguez .25 .60
20 Rafael Palmeiro .25 .60
21 Hank Blalock .25 .60
22 Pedro Martinez .25 .60
23 Manny Ramirez .25 .60
24 Nomar Garciaparra .60 1.50
25 Carlos Beltran .15 .40
26 Mike Sweeney .15 .40
27 Randall Simon .15 .40
28 Dmitri Young .15 .40
29 Bobby Higginson .15 .40
30 Corey Koskie .15 .40
31 Eric Milton .15 .40
32 Torii Hunter .15 .40
33 Joe Mays .15 .40
34 Frank Thomas .40 1.00
35 Mark Buehrle .15 .40
36 Magglio Ordonez .15 .40
37 Kenny Lofton .15 .40
38 Roger Clemens .75 2.00
39 Derek Jeter 1.00 2.50
40 Jason Giambi .15 .40
41 Bernie Williams .25 .60
42 Alfonso Soriano .25 .60
43 Lance Berkman .15 .40
44 Roy Oswalt .15 .40
45 Jeff Bagwell .25 .60
46 Craig Biggio .25 .60
47 Chipper Jones .40 1.00
48 Greg Maddux .60 1.50
49 Gary Sheffield .15 .40
50 Andruw Jones .25 .60
51 Ben Sheets .15 .40
52 Richie Sexson .15 .40
53 Albert Pujols .75 2.00
54 Matt Morris .15 .40
55 J.D. Drew .15 .40
56 Sammy Sosa .40 1.00
57 Kerry Wood .15 .40
58 Corey Patterson .15 .40
59 Mark Prior .25 .60
60 Randy Johnson .40 1.00
61 Luis Gonzalez .15 .40
62 Curt Schilling .15 .40
63 Shawn Green .15 .40
64 Kevin Brown .15 .40
65 Hideo Nomo .40 1.00
66 Vladimir Guerrero .40 1.00
67 Jose Vidro .15 .40
68 Barry Bonds 1.00 2.50
69 Jeff Kent .15 .40
70 Rich Aurilia .15 .40
71 Preston Wilson .15 .40
72 Josh Beckett .15 .40
73 Mike Lowell .15 .40
74 Roberto Alomar .25 .60
75 Mo Vaughn .15 .40
76 Jeromy Burnitz .15 .40
77 Mike Piazza .60 1.50
78 Sean Burroughs .15 .40
79 Phil Nevin .15 .40
80 Bobby Abreu .15 .40
81 Pat Burrell .15 .40
82 Scott Rolen .25 .60
83 Jason Kendall .15 .40
84 Brian Giles .15 .40
85 Ken Griffey Jr. .60 1.50
86 Adam Dunn .15 .40
87 Sean Casey .15 .40
88 Todd Helton .25 .60
89 Larry Walker .15 .40
90 Mike Hampton .15 .40
91 Brandon Puffer FW 2.00 5.00
92 Tom Shearn FW RC 2.00 5.00
93 Chris Baker FW RC 2.00 5.00
94 Gustavo Chacin FW RC 3.00 8.00
95 Joe Orloski FW RC 2.00 5.00
96 Mike Smith FW RC 2.00 5.00
97 John Ennis FW RC 2.00 5.00
98 John Foster FW RC 2.00 5.00
99 Kevin Gryboski FW RC 2.00 5.00
100 Brian Mallette FW RC 2.00 5.00
101 Takahito Nomura FW RC 2.00 5.00
102 So Taguchi FW RC 3.00 8.00
103 Jeremy Lambert FW RC 2.00 5.00
104 J.Simontacchi FW RC 2.00 5.00
105 Jorge Sosa FW RC 3.00 8.00
106 Brandon Backe FW RC 3.00 8.00
107 P.J. Bevis FW RC 2.00 5.00
108 Jeremy Ward FW RC 2.00 5.00
109 Doug Devore FW RC 2.00 5.00
110 Ron Chiavacci FW 2.00 5.00
111 Ron Calloway FW RC 2.00 5.00
112 Nelson Castro FW RC 2.00 5.00
113 Deivis Santos FW 2.00 5.00
114 Earl Snyder FW RC 2.00 5.00
115 Julio Mateo FW RC 2.00 5.00
116 J.J. Putz FW RC 2.00 5.00
117 Allan Simpson FW RC 2.00 5.00
118 Satoru Komiyama FW RC 2.00 5.00
119 Adam Walker FW RC 2.00 5.00
120 Oliver Perez FW RC 3.00 8.00
121 Cliff Bartosh FW RC 2.00 5.00
122 Todd Donovan FW RC 2.00 5.00
123 Elio Serrano FW RC 2.00 5.00
124 Pete Zamora FW RC 2.00 5.00
125 Mike Gonzalez FW RC 2.00 5.00
126 Travis Hughes FW RC 2.00 5.00
127 J.De La Rosa FW RC 2.00 5.00
128 An.Martinez FW RC 2.00 5.00
129 Colin Young FW RC 2.00 5.00
130 Nate Field FW RC 2.00 5.00
131 Tim Kalita FW RC 2.00 5.00
132 Julius Matos FW RC 2.00 5.00
133 Terry Pearson FW RC 2.00 5.00
134 Kyle Kane FW RC 2.00 5.00
135 Mitch Wylie FW RC 2.00 5.00
136 Rodrigo Rosario AU RC 4.00 10.00
137 Franklyn German AU RC 4.00 10.00
138 Reed Johnson AU RC 8.00 20.00
139 Luis Martinez AU RC 4.00 10.00
140 Michael Crudale AU RC 4.00 10.00
141 Francis Beltran AU RC 4.00 10.00
142 Steve Kent AU RC 4.00 10.00
143 Felix Escalona AU RC 4.00 10.00
144 Jose Valverde AU RC 6.00 15.00
145 Victor Alvarez AU RC 4.00 10.00
146 Kazuhisa Ishii AU/249 RC 15.00 40.00
147 Jorge Nunez AU RC 4.00 10.00
148 Eric Good AU RC 4.00 10.00
149 Luis Ugueto AU RC 4.00 10.00
150 Matt Thornton AU RC 4.00 10.00
151 Wilson Valdez AU RC 4.00 10.00
152 Han Izquierdo AU/249 RC 15.00 40.00
153 Jaime Cerda AU RC 4.00 10.00
154 Mark Corey AU RC 4.00 10.00
155 Tyler Yates AU RC 4.00 10.00
156 Steve Bechler AU RC 4.00 10.00
157 Ben Howard AU/249 RC 15.00 40.00
158 And. Machado AU RC 4.00 10.00
159 Jorge Padilla AU RC 4.00 10.00
160 Eric Junge AU RC 4.00 10.00
161 Adrian Burnside AU RC 4.00 10.00
162 Josh Hancock AU RC 8.00 20.00
163 Chris Booker AU RC 4.00 10.00
164 Cam Esslinger AU RC 4.00 10.00
165 Rene Reyes AU RC 4.00 10.00
166 Aaron Cook AU RC 6.00 15.00
167 Juan Brito AU RC 4.00 10.00
168 Miguel Ascencio AU RC 4.00 10.00
169 Kevin Frederick AU RC 4.00 10.00
170 Edwin Almonte AU RC 4.00 10.00
171 Erubiel Durazo .25 .60
172 Junior Spivey .25 .60
173 Geronimo Gil .25 .60
174 Cliff Floyd .25 .60
175 Brandon Larson .25 .60
176 Aaron Boone .25 .60
177 Shawn Estes .25 .60
178 Austin Kearns .25 .60
179 Joe Borchard .25 .60
180 Russell Branyan .25 .60
181 Jay Payton .25 .60
182 Andres Torres .25 .60
183 Andy Van Hekken .25 .60
184 Alex Sanchez .25 .60
185 Endy Chavez .25 .60
186 Bartolo Colon .25 .60
187 Raul Mondesi .25 .60
188 Robin Ventura .25 .60
189 Mike Mussina .40 1.00
190 Jorge Posada .40 1.00
191 Ted Lilly .25 .60
192 Ray Durham .25 .60
193 Brett Myers .25 .60
194 Marlon Byrd .25 .60
195 Vicente Padilla .25 .60
196 Josh Fogg .25 .60
197 Kenny Lofton .25 .60
198 Scott Rolen .40 1.00
199 Jason Lane .25 .60
200 Josh Phelps .25 .60
201 Travis Driskill FW RC 2.00 5.00
202 Howie Clark FW RC 2.00 5.00
203 Mike Mahoney FW 2.00 5.00
204 Brian Tallet FW RC 2.00 5.00
205 Kirk Saarloos FW RC 2.00 5.00
206 Barry Wesson FW RC 2.00 5.00
207 Aaron Guiel FW RC 2.00 5.00
208 Shawn Sedlacek FW RC 2.00 5.00
209 Jose Diaz FW RC 2.00 5.00
210 Jorge Nunez FW 2.00 5.00
211 Danny Mota FW RC 2.00 5.00
212 David Ross FW RC 3.00 8.00
213 Jayson Durocher FW RC 2.00 5.00
214 Shane Nance FW RC 2.00 5.00
215 Wil Nieves FW RC 2.00 5.00
216 Freddy Sanchez FW RC 4.00 10.00
217 Alex Pelaez FW RC 2.00 5.00
218 Jamey Carroll FW RC 3.00 8.00
219 J.J. Trujillo FW RC 2.00 5.00
220 Kevin Pickford FW RC 2.00 5.00
221 Clay Condrey FW RC 2.00 5.00
222 Chris Snelling FW RC 2.50 6.00
223 Cliff Lee FW RC 50.00 100.00
224 Jeremy Hill FW RC 2.00 5.00
225 Jose Rodriguez FW RC 2.00 5.00
226 Lance Carter FW RC 2.00 5.00
227 Ken Huckaby FW RC 2.00 5.00
228 Scott Wiggins FW RC 2.00 5.00
229 Corey Thurman FW RC 2.00 5.00
230 Kevin Cash FW RC 2.00 5.00
RJD Joe DiMaggio AU Poster 125.00 200.00

2002 SP Authentic Limited

Randomly inserted into packs, this is a parallel to the basic 170-card SP Authentic first series set. These cards have a stated print run of 125 serial numbered sets.

*LTD 1-90: 5X TO 12X BASIC
*LTD 91-135: .6X TO 1.5X BASIC
*LTD 136-170: .4X TO 1X BASIC
*LTD 146/152/157: .3X TO .8X BASIC
146 Kazuhisa Ishii FW AU 15.00 40.00

2002 SP Authentic Limited Gold

Randomly inserted into packs, this is a parallel to the basic 170-card SP Authentic first series set. These cards have a stated print run of 50 serial numbered sets.

*GOLD 1-90: 10X TO 25X BASIC
*GOLD 91-135: 1X TO 2.5X BASIC
*GOLD 136-170: .6X TO 1.5X BASIC
*GOLD 146/152/157: .5X TO 1.2X BASIC
146 Kazuhisa Ishii FW AU 30.00 60.00

2002 SP Authentic Big Mac Missing Link

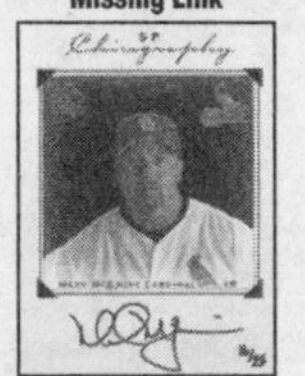

Randomly inserted into packs, these five cards feature autographs of Mark McGwire. Each card was issued to a stated print run of 25 serial numbered sets and thus no pricing is available due to market scarcity.

MMC Mark McGwire 98
MM Mark McGwire 99
MAM Mark McGwire 00
SPMM Mark McGwire 01
MAMC Mark McGwire 02

2002 SP Authentic Chirography

Bret Boone and Tony Gwynn are available only in the basic Chirography set. No Gold parallels were created for them. The following players packed out as redemption cards: Alex Rodriguez, Bret Boone, Sammy Sosa and Tony Gwynn. The deadline for exchange cards to be received by Upper Deck was September 10th, 2005.

AD Adam Dunn/348 10.00 25.00
AG Alex Graman/418 4.00 10.00
AR Alex Rodriguez/391 50.00 100.00
BB Barry Bonds/112 100.00 175.00
BBo Bret Boone/500 6.00 15.00
BZ Barry Zito/419 10.00 25.00
CF Cliff Floyd/313 6.00 15.00
CS C.C. Sabathia/442 10.00 25.00
DE Darin Erstad/80 6.00 15.00
DM Doug Mientkiewicz/478 6.00 15.00
FG Freddy Garcia/456 6.00 15.00
HB Hank Blalock/282 6.00 15.00
IS Ichiro Suzuki/78 300.00 500.00
JB John Buck/427 4.00 10.00
JG Jason Giambi/244 6.00 15.00
JL Jon Lieber/462 6.00 15.00
JM Joe Mays/469 4.00 10.00
KG Ken Griffey Jr./238 50.00 100.00
MBr Milton Bradley/470 6.00 15.00
MBu Mark Buehrle/438 12.50 30.00
MM Mark McGwire/50 200.00 400.00
MS Mike Sweeney/265 6.00 15.00
RS Richie Sexson/483 6.00 15.00
SB Sean Burroughs/275 4.00 10.00
SS Sammy Sosa/247 50.00 100.00
TG Tom Glavine/376 15.00 40.00
TGw Tony Gwynn/75 20.00 50.00

2002 SP Authentic Chirography Gold

Gold parallel cards were not created for Tony Gwynn and Bret Boone. Sammy Sosa and Alex Rodriguez packed out as exchange cards with a redemption deadline of September 10th, 2005.

AD Adam Dunn/44 20.00 50.00
AG Alex Graman/76 6.00 15.00
AR Alex Rodriguez/3
BB Barry Bonds/25
BZ Barry Zito/75 15.00 40.00
CF Cliff Floyd/30 15.00 40.00
CS C.C. Sabathia/52 20.00 50.00
DE Darin Erstad/17
DM Doug Mientkiewicz/16
FG Freddy Garcia/34 15.00 40.00
HB Hank Blalock/12
IS Ichiro Suzuki/51 1000.00 2000.00
JB John Buck/67
JG Jason Giambi/25
JL Jon Lieber/32 15.00 40.00
JM Joe Mays/25
KG Ken Griffey Jr./30 100.00 200.00
MBr Milton Bradley/24
MBu Mark Buehrle/56 30.00 60.00
MM Mark McGwire/25
MS Mike Sweeney/29 15.00 40.00
RS Richie Sexson/11
SB Sean Burroughs/21
SS Sammy Sosa/21
TG Tom Glavine/47 30.00 60.00

2002 SP Authentic Excellence

Randomly inserted into packs, theis card features signatures of many of Upper Deck's spokespeople. This card was issued to a stated print run of 25 serial numbered sets and no pricing is available due to market scarcity. Please note that this card was issued as an exchange card and was redeemable until September 10, 2005.

AE Ken Griffey Jr.
Sammy Sosa
Cal Ripken
Jason Giambi
Mark McGwire
Ichiro Suzuki

2002 SP Authentic Game Jersey

Inserted into packs at stated odds of one in 24, these 38 cards feature some of the leading players along with a game-used memorabilia swatch. A few cards were issued in shorter supply and we have notated that in our checklist along with a stated print run when available.

JAJ Andruw Jones 6.00 15.00
JAP Andy Pettitte 6.00 15.00
JAR Alex Rodriguez 8.00 20.00
JBW Bernie Williams 6.00 15.00
JBZ Barry Zito 4.00 10.00
JCC C.C. Sabathia 4.00 10.00
JCD Carlos Delgado 4.00 10.00
JCJ Chipper Jones 6.00 15.00
JCS Curt Schilling 4.00 10.00
JDE Darin Erstad 4.00 10.00
JGM Greg Maddux 6.00 15.00
JGS Gary Sheffield 4.00 10.00
JIR Ivan Rodriguez 6.00 15.00
JIS Ichiro Suzuki SP 30.00 60.00
JJBA Jeff Bagwell 6.00 15.00
JJBU Jeromy Burnitz SP 6.00 15.00
JJE Jim Edmonds 4.00 10.00
JJGO Juan Gonzalez 4.00 10.00
JJGR Jason Giambi 4.00 10.00
JJK Jason Kendall 4.00 10.00
JJT Jim Thome 6.00 15.00
JKG Ken Griffey Jr. SP/95 15.00 40.00
JKI Kazuhisa Ishii 6.00 15.00
JMM Mark McGwire SP 75.00 150.00
JMO Magglio Ordonez 4.00 10.00
JMP Mike Piazza 6.00 15.00
JMR Manny Ramirez 6.00 15.00
JOV Omar Vizquel 6.00 15.00
JPW Preston Wilson 4.00 10.00
JRA Roberto Alomar 6.00 15.00
JRC Roger Clemens 8.00 20.00
JRJ Randy Johnson 6.00 15.00
JRV Robin Ventura 4.00 10.00
JSG Shawn Green 4.00 10.00
JSR Scott Rolen 6.00 15.00
JSS Sammy Sosa 6.00 15.00
JTH Todd Helton 6.00 15.00
JTS Tsuyoshi Shinjo 4.00 10.00

2002 SP Authentic Game Jersey Gold

Randomly inserted into packs, this is a parallel to the Game Jersey insert set. Each of these cards have a stated print run which matches the featured player's uniform number and we have notated that information in our checklist. If a card was issued to a stated print run of 25 or fewer, it is not priced due to market scarcity.

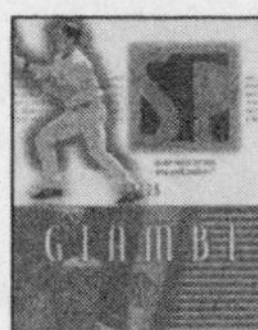

JAJ Andruw Jones/25
JAP Andy Pettitte/46 12.50 30.00
JAR Alex Rodriguez/3
JBW Bernie Williams/51 12.50 30.00
JBZ Barry Zito/75 8.00 20.00
JCC C.C. Sabathia/52 8.00 20.00
JCD Carlos Delgado/25
JCJ Chipper Jones/10
JCS Curt Schilling/38 10.00 25.00
JDE Darin Erstad/17
JGM Greg Maddux/31 40.00 80.00
JGS Gary Sheffield/11
JIR Ivan Rodriguez/7
JIS Ichiro Suzuki/51 60.00 120.00
JJBA Jeff Bagwell/5
JJBU Jeromy Burnitz/20
JJE Jim Edmonds/15
JJGO Juan Gonzalez/19
JJGR Jason Giambi/25
JJK Jason Kendall/18
JJT Jim Thome/25
JKG Ken Griffey Jr./30 40.00 80.00
JKI Kazuhisa Ishii/17
JMM Mark McGwire/25
JMO Magglio Ordonez/30 10.00 25.00
JMP Mike Piazza/31 40.00 80.00
JMR Manny Ramirez/24
JOV Omar Vizquel/13
JPW Preston Wilson/44 8.00 20.00
JRA Roberto Alomar/12
JRC Roger Clemens/22
JRJ Randy Johnson/51 15.00 40.00
JRV Robin Ventura/19
JSG Shawn Green/15
JSR Scott Rolen/17
JSS Sammy Sosa/21
JTH Todd Helton/17
JTS Tsuyoshi Shinjo/5

2002 SP Authentic Prospects Signatures

Inserted into packs at a stated rate of one in 36, these 12 cards feature signed cards of some leading baseball prospects.

PAG Alex Graman 3.00 8.00
PBH Bill Hall 4.00 10.00
PDM Dustan Mohr 3.00 8.00
PDW Danny Wright 3.00 8.00
PJC Jose Cueto 3.00 8.00
PJDE Jeff Deardorff 3.00 8.00
PJDI Jose Diaz 3.00 8.00
PKH Ken Huckaby 3.00 8.00
PMG Matt Guerrier 3.00 8.00
PMS Marcos Scutaro 3.00 8.00
PST Steve Torrealba 3.00 8.00
PXN Xavier Nady 3.00 8.00

2002 SP Authentic Signed Big Mac

Randomly inserted into packs, these 10 cards feature authentic autographs of retired superstar Mark McGwire. Each of these cards were signed to a different stated print run and we have notated that information in our checklist. If a card was signed to 25 or fewer copies, there is no pricing provided due to market scarcity.

MM1 Mark McGwire/1
MM2 Mark McGwire/25
MM3 Mark McGwire/5
MM4 Mark McGwire/4
MM5 Mark McGwire/12
MM6 Mark McGwire/70 200.00 350.00
MM7 Mark McGwire/4
MM8 Mark McGwire/7
MM9 Mark McGwire/5
MM10 Mark McGwire/16

2002 SP Authentic Signs of Greatness

Randomly inserted into packs, this card features five autographs and only one copy was produced. An exchange card with a redemption deadline of September 10th, 2005 was placed into packs whereby the lucky collector received the actual signed card directly from Upper Deck via mail. There is no pricing due to scarcity.

2002 SP Authentic USA Future Watch

Randomly inserted into packs, these 22 cards feature players from the USA National Team. Each card was issued to a stated print run of 1999 serial numbered sets.

USA1 Chad Cordero 4.00 10.00
USA2 Philip Humber 3.00 8.00
USA3 Grant Johnson 2.00 5.00
USA4 Wes Littleton 2.00 5.00
USA5 Kyle Sleeth 2.00 5.00
USA6 Huston Street 4.00 10.00
USA7 Brad Sullivan 2.00 5.00
USA8 Bob Zimmermann 2.00 5.00
USA9 Abe Alvarez 2.00 5.00
USA10 Kyle Bakker 2.00 5.00
USA11 Landon Powell 2.00 5.00
USA12 Clint Sammons 2.00 5.00
USA13 Michael Aubrey 3.00 8.00
USA14 Aaron Hill 4.00 10.00
USA15 Conor Jackson 6.00 15.00
USA16 Eric Patterson 3.00 8.00
USA17 Dustin Pedroia 10.00 25.00
USA18 Rickie Weeks 10.00 25.00
USA19 Shane Costa 2.00 5.00
USA20 Mark Jurich 2.00 5.00
USA21 Sam Fuld 6.00 15.00
USA22 Carlos Quentin 3.00 8.00

2002 SP Authentic Hawaii Sign of the Times Duke Snider

This card was distributed on February 27th, 2002 at Upper Deck's poolside reception during the Hawaii Trade Conference. Each attendee received either this signed Duke Snider card or a signed card of NFL legend John Riggins, both of which were hand-numbered to 500 copies in blue ink. Snider signed each card in blue ink sharpie across the front.

DS Duke Snider/500 8.00 20.00

2003 SP Authentic

This 239-card set was distributed in two separate series. The primary SP Authentic product was originally issued as a 189-card set released in May, 2003. These cards were issued in five card packs with an $5 SRP which were issued 24 packs to a box and 12 boxes to a case. Update cards 190-239 were issued randomly within packs of 2003 Upper Deck Finite and released in December, 2003. Cards numbered 1-90 featured commonly seeded veterans while cards 91-123 featured what was titled SP Rookie Archives (RA) and those cards were issued to a stated print run of 2500 serial numbered sets. Cards numbered 124 to 150 feature a subset called Back to 93 and those cards were issued to a stated print run of 1993 serial numbered sets. Cards numbered 151 through 189 feature Future Watch prospects (with 181 to 189 being autographed). Please note that cards numbered 151-180 were also issued to a stated print run of 2003 serial numbered sets and cards numbered 181-189 were issued to a stated print run of 500 serial numbered sets. The Jose Contreras signed card was issued either as a live card or an exchange card. The Contreras exchange card could be redeemed until May 21, 2006. Cards 190-239 (released at year's end) continued the Future Watch subset but each card was serial numbered to 699 copies.

COMP.LO SET w/o SP's (90) 6.00 15.00
COMMON CARD (1-90) .15 .40
COMMON CARD (91-123) 1.25 3.00
COMMON CARD (124-150) 1.25 3.00
COMMON CARD (151-180) 2.00 5.00
COMMON CARD (181-189) 6.00 15.00
91-189 RANDOM INSERTS IN PACKS
COMMON CARD (190-239) 2.00 5.00
190-239 RANDOM IN 03 UD FINITE PACKS
190-239 PRINT RUN 699 SERIAL #'d SETS

1 Darin Erstad .15 .40
2 Garret Anderson .15 .40
3 Troy Glaus .15 .40
4 Eric Chavez .15 .40
5 Barry Zito .15 .40
6 Miguel Tejada .15 .40
7 Eric Hinske .15 .40
8 Carlos Delgado .15 .40
9 Josh Phelps .15 .40
10 Ben Grieve .15 .40
11 Carl Crawford .15 .40
12 Omar Vizquel .25 .60
13 Matt Lawton .15 .40
14 C.C. Sabathia .15 .40
15 Ichiro Suzuki .75 2.00
16 John Olerud .15 .40
17 Freddy Garcia .15 .40
18 Jay Gibbons .15 .40
19 Tony Batista .15 .40
20 Melvin Mora .15 .40
21 Alex Rodriguez .60 1.50
22 Rafael Palmeiro .25 .60
23 Hank Blalock .15 .40
24 Nomar Garciaparra .60 1.50
25 Pedro Martinez .25 .60
26 Johnny Damon .25 .60
27 Mike Sweeney .15 .40
28 Carlos Febles .15 .40
29 Carlos Beltran .15 .40
30 Carlos Pena .15 .40
31 Eric Munson .15 .40
32 Bobby Higginson .15 .40
33 Torii Hunter .15 .40
34 Doug Mientkiewicz .15 .40
35 Jacque Jones .15 .40
36 Paul Konerko .15 .40
37 Bartolo Colon .15 .40
38 Magglio Ordonez .15 .40
39 Derek Jeter 1.00 2.50
40 Bernie Williams .25 .60
41 Jason Giambi .15 .40
42 Alfonso Soriano .15 .40
43 Roger Clemens .75 2.00
44 Jeff Bagwell .25 .60
45 Jeff Kent .15 .40
46 Lance Berkman .15 .40
47 Chipper Jones .40 1.00
48 Andruw Jones .25 .60
49 Gary Sheffield .15 .40
50 Ben Sheets .15 .40
51 Richie Sexson .15 .40
52 Geoff Jenkins .15 .40
53 Jim Edmonds .15 .40
54 Albert Pujols .75 2.00
55 Scott Rolen .25 .60
56 Sammy Sosa .40 1.00
57 Kerry Wood .15 .40
58 Eric Karros .15 .40
59 Luis Gonzalez .15 .40
60 Randy Johnson .40 1.00
61 Curt Schilling .15 .40
62 Fred McGriff .25 .60
63 Shawn Green .15 .40
64 Paul Lo Duca .15 .40
65 Vladimir Guerrero .40 1.00
66 Jose Vidro .15 .40
67 Barry Bonds 1.00 2.50
68 Rich Aurilia .15 .40
69 Edgardo Alfonzo .15 .40
70 Ivan Rodriguez .25 .60
71 Mike Lowell .15 .40
72 Derrek Lee .25 .60
73 Tom Glavine .25 .60
74 Mike Piazza .60 1.50
75 Roberto Alomar .25 .60
76 Ryan Klesko .15 .40
77 Phil Nevin .15 .40
78 Mark Kotsay .15 .40
79 Jim Thome .25 .60
80 Pat Burrell .15 .40
81 Bobby Abreu .15 .40
82 Jason Kendall .15 .40
83 Brian Giles .15 .40
84 Aramis Ramirez .15 .40
85 Austin Kearns .15 .40
86 Ken Griffey Jr. .60 1.50
87 Adam Dunn .15 .40
88 Larry Walker .15 .40
89 Todd Helton .25 .60
90 Preston Wilson .15 .40
91 Derek Jeter RA 3.00 8.00
92 Johnny Damon RA 1.25 3.00
93 Chipper Jones RA 1.25 3.00
94 Manny Ramirez RA 1.25 3.00
95 Trot Nixon RA 1.25 3.00
96 Alex Rodriguez RA 2.00 5.00
97 Chan Ho Park RA 1.25 3.00
98 Brad Fullmer RA 1.25 3.00
99 Billy Wagner RA 1.25 3.00
100 Hideo Nomo RA 1.25 3.00
101 Freddy Garcia RA 1.25 3.00
102 Darin Erstad RA 1.25 3.00
103 Jose Cruz Jr. RA 1.25 3.00
104 Nomar Garciaparra RA 2.00 5.00
105 Magglio Ordonez RA 1.25 3.00
106 Kerry Wood RA 1.25 3.00
107 Troy Glaus RA 1.25 3.00
108 J.D. Drew RA 1.25 3.00
109 Alfonso Soriano RA 1.25 3.00
110 Danys Baez RA 1.25 3.00
111 Kazuhiro Sasaki RA 1.25 3.00
112 Barry Zito RA 1.25 3.00
113 Brent Abernathy RA 1.25 3.00
114 Ben Diggins RA 1.25 3.00
115 Ben Sheets RA 1.25 3.00
116 Brad Wilkerson RA 1.25 3.00
117 Juan Pierre RA 1.25 3.00
118 Jon Rauch RA 1.25 3.00
119 Ichiro Suzuki RA 2.50 6.00
120 Albert Pujols RA 2.50 6.00
121 Mark Prior RA 1.25 3.00
122 Mark Teixeira RA 1.25 3.00
123 Kazuhisa Ishii RA 1.25 3.00
124 Troy Glaus B93 1.25 3.00
125 Randy Johnson B93 1.25 3.00
126 Curt Schilling B93 1.25 3.00
127 Chipper Jones B93 1.25 3.00
128 Greg Maddux B93 2.00 5.00
129 Nomar Garciaparra B93 2.00 5.00
130 Pedro Martinez B93 1.25 3.00
131 Sammy Sosa B93 1.25 3.00
132 Mark Prior B93 1.25 3.00
133 Ken Griffey Jr. B93 2.00 5.00
134 Adam Dunn B93 1.25 3.00
135 Jeff Bagwell B93 1.25 3.00
136 Vladimir Guerrero B93 1.25 3.00
137 Mike Piazza B93 2.00 5.00
138 Tom Glavine B93 1.25 3.00
139 Derek Jeter B93 3.00 8.00
140 Roger Clemens B93 2.50 6.00
141 Jason Giambi B93 1.25 3.00
142 Alfonso Soriano B93 1.25 3.00
143 Miguel Tejada B93 1.25 3.00
144 Barry Zito B93 1.25 3.00
145 Jim Thome B93 1.25 3.00
146 Barry Bonds B93 3.00 8.00
147 Ichiro Suzuki B93 2.50 6.00
148 Albert Pujols B93 2.50 6.00
149 Alex Rodriguez B93 2.00 5.00
150 Carlos Delgado B93 1.25 3.00
151 Rich Fischer FW RC 2.00 5.00
152 Brandon Webb FW RC 10.00 25.00
153 Rob Hammock FW RC 2.00 5.00
154 Matt Kata FW RC 2.00 5.00
155 Tim Olson FW RC 2.00 5.00
156 Oscar Villarreal FW RC 2.00 5.00
157 Michael Hessman FW RC 2.00 5.00
158 Daniel Cabrera FW RC 3.00 8.00
159 Jon Leicester FW RC 2.00 5.00
160 Todd Wellemeyer FW RC 2.00 5.00
161 Felix Sanchez FW RC 2.00 5.00
162 David Sanders FW RC 2.00 5.00
163 Josh Stewart FW RC 2.00 5.00
164 Arnie Munoz FW RC 2.00 5.00
165 Ryan Cameron FW RC 2.00 5.00
166 Clint Barmes FW RC 2.00 5.00
167 Josh Willingham FW RC 4.00 10.00
169 Willie Eyre FW RC 2.00 5.00
170 Brent Hoard FW RC 2.00 5.00
171 Termel Sledge FW RC 2.00 5.00
172 Phil Seibel FW RC 2.00 5.00
173 Craig Brazell FW RC 2.00 5.00
174 Jeff Duncan FW RC 2.00 5.00
176 Bernie Castro FW RC 2.00 5.00
177 Mike Nicolas FW RC 2.00 5.00
178 Rett Johnson FW RC 2.00 5.00
179 Bobby Madritsch FW RC 2.00 5.00
180 Chris Capuano FW RC 10.00 25.00
181 Hid Matsui FW AU RC 175.00 300.00
182 J.Contreras FW AU RC 12.50 30.00
183 Lew Ford FW AU RC 10.00 25.00
184 Jer. Griffiths FW AU RC 6.00 15.00
185 G.Quiroz FW AU RC 6.00 15.00
186 Alej Machado FW AU RC 6.00 15.00
187 Fran Cruceta FW AU RC 6.00 15.00
188 Pr. Redman FW AU RC 6.00 15.00
189 S.Bazzell FW AU RC 6.00 15.00
190 Aaron Looper FW RC 2.00 5.00
191 Alex Prieto FW RC 2.00 5.00
192 Alfredo Gonzalez FW RC 2.00 5.00
193 Andrew Brown FW RC 3.00 8.00
194 Anthony Ferrari FW RC 2.00 5.00
195 Aquilino Lopez FW RC 2.00 5.00
196 Beau Kemp FW RC 2.00 5.00
197 Bo Hart FW RC 2.00 5.00
198 Chad Gaudin FW RC 2.00 5.00
199 Colin Porter FW RC 2.00 5.00
200 D.J. Carrasco FW RC 2.00 5.00
201 Dan Haren FW RC 3.00 8.00
202 Danny Garcia FW RC 2.00 5.00
203 Jon Switzer FW 2.00 5.00
204 Edwin Jackson FW RC 3.00 8.00
205 Fernando Cabrera FW RC 2.00 5.00
206 Garrett Atkins FW 2.00 5.00
207 Gerald Laird FW 2.00 5.00
208 Greg Jones FW RC 2.00 5.00
209 Ian Ferguson FW RC 2.00 5.00
210 Jason Roach FW RC 2.00 5.00
211 Jason Shiell FW RC 2.00 5.00
212 Jeremy Bonderman FW RC 10.00 25.00
213 Jeremy Wedel FW RC 2.00 5.00
214 Jhonny Peralta FW 3.00 8.00
215 Delmon Young FW RC 6.00 15.00
216 Jorge DePaula FW 2.00 5.00
217 Josh Hall FW RC 2.00 5.00
218 Julio Manon FW RC 2.00 5.00
219 Kevin Correia FW RC 2.00 5.00
220 Kevin Ohme FW RC 2.00 5.00
221 Kevin Tolar FW RC 2.00 5.00
222 Luis Ayala FW RC 2.00 5.00
223 Luis De Los Santos FW 2.00 5.00
224 Chad Cordero FW RC 4.00 10.00
225 Mark Malaska FW RC 2.00 5.00
226 Khalil Greene FW 3.00 8.00
227 Michael Nakamura FW RC 2.00 5.00
228 Michel Hernandez FW RC 2.00 5.00
229 Miguel Ojeda FW RC 2.00 5.00
230.Mike Neu FW RC 2.00 5.00
231 Nate Bland FW RC 2.00 5.00
232 Pete LaForest FW RC 2.00 5.00
233 Rickie Weeks FW RC 5.00 12.00
234 Rosman Garcia FW RC 2.00 5.00
235 Ryan Wagner FW RC 2.00 5.00
236 Lance Niekro FW 2.00 5.00
237 Tom Gregorio FW RC 2.00 5.00
238 Tommy Phelps FW 2.00 5.00
239 Wilfredo Ledezma FW RC 2.00 5.00

2003 SP Authentic Matsui Future Watch Autograph Parallel

PRINT RUNS B/WN 10-75 COPIES PER
NO PRICING ON QTY OF 25 OR LESS
181A H.Matsui Bronze/75 175.00 300.00
181B H.Matsui Silver/25
181C H.Matsui Gold/10

2003 SP Authentic 500 HR Club

Randomly inserted into packs, this card featured members of the 500 homer club along with a game-

used memorablia piece from each player. A gold parallel was also issued for this card and that card was issued to a stated print run of 25 serial numbered sets. The gold version is not priced due to market scarcity.

500 Sammy Sosa Jsy/Pants 125.00 250.00
  Ted Williams Pants
  Mickey Mantle Jsy/Pants
  Mark McGwire Jsy/Pants
  Barry Bonds Base
500G Sammy Sosa Jsy/Pants
  Ted Williams Pants
  Mickey Mantle Jsy/Pants
  Mark McGwire Jsy/Pants
  Barry Bonds Base Gold/25

2003 SP Authentic Chirography

Randomly inserted into packs, these cards feature authentic autographs from the player pictured on the card. These cards marked the debut of Upper Deck using the "Band-Aid" approach to putting autographs on cards. What that means is that the player does not actually sign the card, instead the player signs a sticker which is then attached to the card. Please note that since these cards were issued to varying print runs, we have notated the stated print run next to the player's name in our checklist. Several players did not get their cards signed in time for inclusion in this product and those exchange cards could be redeemed until April 21, 2006. Please note that many cards in the various sets have notations but neither Mark Prior nor Corey Patterson used whatever notations they were supposed to throughout the course of this product.

AD Adam Dunn/170 10.00 25.00
BA Jeff Bagwell/175 30.00 60.00
CR Cal Ripken/250 60.00 120.00
FC Rafael Furcal/150 6.00 15.00
FG Freddy Garcia/345 6.00 15.00
FL Cliff Floyd/125 4.00 10.00
GA1 Garret Anderson/350 6.00 15.00
GI Jason Giambi/250 6.00 15.00
GJ Ken Griffey Jr./350 40.00 80.00
GL Brian Giles/225 6.00 15.00
IC Ichiro Suzuki/85 350.00 500.00
IS Ichiro Suzuki/75 350.00 500.00
JD Johnny Damon/245 6.00 15.00
JE2 Jim Edmonds/350 10.00 25.00
JM Joe Mays/245 4.00 10.00
JR Ken Griffey Jr./350 40.00 80.00
JT1 Jim Thome/250 15.00 40.00
KE Jason Kendall/145 6.00 15.00
LG1 Luis Gonzalez/195 6.00 15.00
MM Mark McGwire/50 175.00 300.00
RO Scott Rolen/345 15.00 40.00
RS Richie Sexson/245 6.00 15.00
SA Sammy Sosa/335 40.00 80.00
SO Sammy Sosa/335 40.00 80.00
SW Mike Sweeney/125 6.00 15.00
TO Torii Hunter/245 6.00 15.00
TS Tim Salmon/350 10.00 25.00

2003 SP Authentic Chirography Bronze

Randomly inserted into packs, this is a partial parallel to the Chirography insert set. A few of these cards have special notations and we have noted that information in our checklist. Again, a few cards were issued as exchange cards and those cards could be redeemed until May 21, 2006.

AD Adam Dunn/50 15.00 40.00
BA Jeff Bagwell/50 40.00 100.00
CR Cal Ripken/75 75.00 150.00
FC Rafael Furcal/50 10.00 25.00
FG Freddy Garcia/100 10.00 25.00
FL Cliff Floyd/50 6.00 15.00
GI Jason Giambi/50 10.00 25.00
GJ Ken Griffey Jr./100 50.00 100.00
GL Brian Giles/50 10.00 25.00
IC Ichiro Suzuki ROY/50 1000.00 2000.00
IS Ichiro Suzuki MVP/50 1000.00 2000.00
JD Johnny Damon/100 10.00 25.00
JM Joe Mays/100 6.00 15.00
JR Ken Griffey Jr./100 50.00 100.00
KE Jason Kendall/50 10.00 25.00
MM Mark McGwire/25
RO Scott Rolen/100 25.00 60.00
RS Richie Sexson 10.00 25.00
  Milwaukee Notation/100
SA Sammy Sosa/100 50.00 100.00
SO Sammy Sosa/100 50.00 100.00
SW Mike Sweeney/75 10.00 25.00
TO Torii Hunter/100 10.00 25.00
  Gold Glove Notation

2003 SP Authentic Chirography Silver

AD Adam Dunn/25
BA Jeff Bagwell/25
CR Cal Ripken/25
FC Rafael Furcal/25
FG Freddy Garcia/50 15.00 40.00
FL Cliff Floyd/25
GI Jason Giambi/25
GJ Ken Griffey Jr./25
GL Brian Giles/25
IC Ichiro Suzuki/25
IS Ichiro Suzuki/25
JD Johnny Damon/50 15.00 40.00
JM Joe Mays/50 10.00 25.00
JR Ken Griffey Jr./25
KE Jason Kendall/25
MM Mark McGwire/15
RO Scott Rolen/50 40.00 100.00
RS Richie Sexson/50 15.00 40.00
SA Sammy Sosa/50 50.00 100.00
SO Sammy Sosa/50 50.00 100.00
SW Mike Sweeney/25
TO Torii Hunter/50 15.00 40.00

2003 SP Authentic Chirography Dodgers Stars

Randomly inserted in packs, these 11 cards feature retired Dodger stars and were issued to varying print runs. We have noted the stated print run in our checklist next to the player's name.

BB Bill Buckner/245 6.00 15.00
BI Bill Russell/245 6.00 15.00
CE Ron Cey/345 6.00 15.00
DL Davey Lopes/245 6.00 15.00
DN Don Newcombe/345 6.00 15.00
DS Duke Snider/345 15.00 40.00
JN Tommy John/170 6.00 15.00
MW Maury Wills/320 6.00 15.00
SG Steve Garvey/320 10.00 25.00
SU Don Sutton/245 6.00 15.00
SY Steve Yeager/345 6.00 15.00

2003 SP Authentic Chirography Dodgers Stars Bronze

Randomly inserted in packs, this is a partial parallel to the Dodgers Stars insert set. Please note that all of these cards have the word "Dodgers" as an inscription.

*BRONZE: .6X TO 1.5X BASIC DODGER

2003 SP Authentic Chirography Dodgers Stars Silver

Randomly inserted into packs, this is a partial parallel to the Dodgers Stars insert set. Each of these cards were issued to a stated print run of 50 serial numbered sets and most of these cards had a 1981 WS Champs Notation. Please note that the player's who signed cards for this set and were not on the 81 Dodgers used different notations which we have identified in our checklist.

*SILVER: .75X TO 2X BASIC DODGER

2003 SP Authentic Chirography Doubles

Randomly inserted into packs, these 15 cards feature signatures from two different players, who had a reason for commonality. These cards were issued to a stated print run of anywhere from 10 to 150 copies and we have placed that information next to the player's name in our checklist. Please note that cards with a stated print run of 25 or fewer are not priced due to market scarcity. In addition, a few cards were issued as exchange cards and those cards could be redeemed until May 21, 2006.

FB Whitey Ford 75.00 150.00
  Yogi Berra/75
FC Carlton Fisk 40.00 [illegible]
  Dwight Evans/75
FM Carlton Fisk 30.00 60.00
  Bill Mazeroski/75
GG Ken Griffey Jr. 60.00 120.00
  Jason Giambi/75
GR Steve Garvey 30.00 60.00
  Ron Cey/75
JI Ken Griffey Jr. 400.00 600.00
  Ichiro Suzuki/125
KR Tony Kubek 50.00 100.00
  Bobby Richardson/75
KT Jerry Koosman 40.00 80.00
  Tom Seaver/75
MG Don Mattingly
  Jason Giambi/25
MJ Mark McGwire
  Ken Griffey Jr./10
MS Mark McGwire
  Sammy Sosa/15
RT Nolan Ryan
  Tom Seaver/25
SE Tim Salmon
  Darin Erstad/25
SJ Sammy Sosa 60.00 120.00
  Jason Giambi/75
WB Mookie Wilson 20.00 50.00
  Bill Buckner/150

2003 SP Authentic Chirography Flashback

Randomly inserted into packs, these cards feature an important moment from the player's career as well as authentic autograph. Most of these cards were issued to a stated print run of 350 copies but a few were issued to differing amounts so we have noted the print run information next to the player's name in our checklist. In addition, some players did not return their autograph in time and those cards could be exchanged until May 21, 2006.

BN Brian Giles/245 6.00 15.00
CF1 Cliff Floyd/350 6.00 15.00
GM Ken Griffey Jr./350 40.00 80.00
JA Jason Giambi/350 6.00 15.00
JE1 Jim Edmonds/350 10.00 25.00
LA Luis Gonzalez/200 8.00 20.00
MA Mark McGwire/55 150.00 300.00
SR Sammy Sosa/245 50.00 100.00

2003 SP Authentic Chirography Flashback Bronze

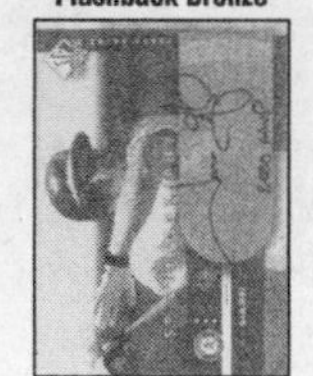

Randomly inserted in packs, this is a partial parallel to the Flashback insert set. All of the cards live at the time of issue had special notations and we have noted those notations in our checklist. These cards were issued to varying print runs and we have identified the stated print runs in our checklist. Ken Griffey Jr and Sammy Sosa did not return their autographs in time for inclusion and those exchange cards could be redeemed until May 21, 2006.

BN Brian Giles/50 10.00 25.00
GM Ken Griffey Jr./100 50.00 100.00
JA Jason Giambi 10.00 25.00
  2000 MVP/100
LA Luis Gonzalez 12.50 30.00
  2001 Champs/75
MA Mark McGwire
  500 HR Club/25
SR Sammy Sosa/100 50.00 100.00

2003 SP Authentic Chirography Flashback Silver

Randomly inserted into packs, this is a partial parallel to the Flashback insert set. These cards were issued to stated print runs of between 15 and 50 copies and for those copies with stated print runs fo 25 or fewer, no pricing is provided due to market scarcity.

NO PRICING ON QTY OF 25 OR LESS
BN Brian Giles/25
GM Ken Griffey Jr./25
JA0 Jason Giambi A's/50 12.50 30.00
LA Luis Gonzalez 25
MA Mark McGwire/15
SR Sammy Sosa/50 60.00 120.00

2003 SP Authentic Chirography Hall of Famers

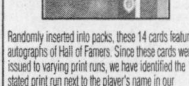

Randomly inserted into packs, these 14 cards feature autographs of Hall of Famers. Since these cards were issued to varying print runs, we have identified the stated print run next to the player's name in our checklist.

BG Bob Gibson/245 15.00 40.00
CF Carlton Fisk/240 15.00 40.00
DS Duke Snider/250 15.00 40.00
DW2 Dave Winfield/350 10.00 25.00
GC1 Gary Carter/350 10.00 25.00
JB1 Johnny Bench/350 20.00 50.00
NR Nolan Ryan/170 75.00 150.00
OC Orlando Cepeda/245 10.00 25.00
RF Rollie Fingers/170 10.00 25.00
RR Robin Roberts/170 15.00 40.00
RY Robin Yount/350 20.00 50.00
TP Tony Perez/320 10.00 25.00
TS Tom Seaver/170 15.00 40.00
WF Whitey Ford/150 15.00 40.00

2003 SP Authentic Chirography Hall of Famers Bronze

Randomly inserted into packs, this is a partial parallel to the Hall of Famers insert set. These cards all feature an HOF (or some close variation) notation as part of the autograph. These cards were issued to stated print runs between 50 and 100 copies and we have noted the specific information next to the player's name in our checklist.

BG Bob Gibson/100 25.00 60.00
CF Carlton Fisk/100 25.00 60.00
DS Duke Snider/100 25.00 60.00
NR Nolan Ryan/50 100.00 200.00
OC Orlando Cepeda/100 15.00 40.00
RF Rollie Fingers/50 15.00 40.00
RR Robin Roberts/50 25.00 60.00
TP Tony Perez/100 15.00 40.00
TS Tom Seaver/75 25.00 60.00
WF Whitey Ford/75 25.00 60.00

2003 SP Authentic Chirography Hall of Famers Silver

Randomly inserted into packs, this is a partial parallel to the Hall of Famers insert set. All of these cards have the HOF (and specific year of the player's induction) notation. These cards were issued to a stated print run of either 25 or 50 copies. Please note that for cards with a stated print run of 25 copies there is no pricing due to market scarcity.

BG Bob Gibson/50 30.00 80.00
CF Carlton Fisk/50 30.00 80.00
DS Duke Snider/50 30.00 80.00
NR Nolan Ryan/25
OC Orlando Cepeda/50 20.00 50.00
RF Rollie Fingers/25
RR Robin Roberts/25
TP Tony Perez/50 20.00 50.00
TS Tom Seaver/50 30.00 80.00
WF Whitey Ford/25

2003 SP Authentic Chirography Triples

Randomly inserted in packs, these 12 cards feature autographs from three leading players. These cards were issued to stated print runs of anywhere from 10 to 75 copies and we are only providing pricing for cards with a stated print run of more than 10 copies. The following cards were available only as an exchange and those cards could be redeemed until May 21, 2006: Berra/Kubek/Richardson, Fisk/Carter/Gibson, Griffey Jr./Ichiro/Sosa, Griffey Jr./Sosa/Giambi, Giambi/Sosa/Griffey Jr., Ichiro/Sosa/Giambi, McGwire/Sosa/Griffey Jr., McGwire/Sosa/Ichiro and Seaver/Koosman/McGraw.

BKR Yogi Berra 100.00 200.00
  Tony Kubek
  Bobby Richardson/75
FCG Carlton Fisk 60.00 120.00
  Gary Carter
  Kirk Gibson/75 EXCH
GIS Ken Griffey Jr. 400.00 600.00
  Ichiro Suzuki
  Sammy Sosa/75 EXCH
GLO Steve Garvey 50.00 100.00
  Davy Lopes
  Ron Cey/75
GRC Steve Garvey 50.00 100.00
  Bill Russell
  Ron Cey/75
GSG Ken Griffey Jr. 150.00 250.00
  Sammy Sosa
  Jason Giambi/75 EXCH
GSJ Jason Giambi 75.00 150.00
  Sammy Sosa
  Ken Griffey Jr./75
ISG Ichiro Suzuki 250.00 500.00
  Sammy Sosa
  Jason Giambi/75
MSG Mark McGwire
  Sammy Sosa
  Ken Griffey Jr./10
MSI Mark McGwire
  Sammy Sosa
  Ichiro Suzuki/10
SEA Tim Salmon 60.00 120.00
  Darin Erstad
  Garret Anderson/75
SKM Tom Seaver 75.00 150.00
  Jerry Koosman
  Tug McGraw/75 EXCH

2003 SP Authentic Chirography World Series Heroes

Randomly inserted into packs, these 17 cards feature players who were leading players in at least one World Series. Each of these cards were issued to varying print runs and we have identified the stated print run next to the player's name in our checklist. Andruw Jones did not return his cards in time for inclusion in this product so those exchange cards could be redeemed until May 21, 2006.

AJ1 Andruw Jones/350 10.00 25.00
BM Bill Mazeroski/245 10.00 25.00
CF Carlton Fisk/200 15.00 40.00
CR Cal Ripken/295 60.00 120.00
CS Curt Schilling/345 15.00 40.00
DE Darin Erstad/245 8.00 20.00
DJ David Justice/170 10.00 25.00
ER Edgar Renteria/220 8.00 20.00
GA Garret Anderson/245 10.00 25.00
GC Gary Carter/345 8.00 20.00
GO Luis Gonzalez/225 8.00 20.00
GS Ken Griffey Sr./295 8.00 20.00
JK Jerry Koosman/170 10.00 25.00
JP Jorge Posada/350 15.00 40.00
KG Kirk Gibson/145 10.00 25.00
TI Tim Salmon/245 10.00 25.00
TM Tug McGraw/170 20.00 50.00

2003 SP Authentic Chirography World Series Heroes Bronze

Randomly inserted into packs, this is a partial parallel to the World Series Heroes insert set. Each of these cards have not only an autograph but a notation identifying a key world series this player's career. Each of these cards were issued to a stated print run of between 50 and 100 copies.

BM Bill Mazeroski/100 15.00 40.00
CF Carlton Fisk/75 25.00 60.00
CS Curt Schilling/100 25.00 60.00
DE Darin Erstad/100 12.50 30.00
DJ David Justice/75 15.00 40.00
ER Edgar Renteria/75 12.50 30.00
GA Garret Anderson/100 15.00 40.00
GC Gary Carter/100 12.50 30.00
GO Luis Gonzalez/100 12.50 30.00
GS Ken Griffey Sr./100 12.50 30.00
JK Jerry Koosman/75 15.00 40.00
KG Kirk Gibson/50 15.00 40.00
TI Tim Salmon/100 15.00 40.00
TM Tug McGraw/100 30.00 80.00

2003 SP Authentic Chirography World Series Heroes Silver

Randomly inserted into packs, this is a partial parallel to the World Series Heroes insert set. These cards feature not only the player's autograph but also in most cases a notation which we have identified in our checklist. Please note that these cards have stated print runs of either 25 or 50 cards. Cards with stated print runs of 25 are not printed due to market scarcity. Of note, Tug McGraw's card, inscribed "Ya Gotta Believe" took on a much deeper meaning after his unfortunate death less than a year after the card was issued.

BM Bill Mazeroski Buc's 60/50	20.00	50.00
CF Carlton Fisk Home Run/25		
CS Curt Schilling/50	30.00	80.00
DE Darin Erstad/50	15.00	40.00
DJ David Justice/50	20.00	50.00
ER Edgar Renteria Marlins 97/25		
GA Garret Anderson/50	20.00	50.00
GC Gary Carter Mets Champs/50	15.00	40.00
GO Luis Gonzalez D-Backs 01/50	15.00	40.00
GS Ken Griffey Sr. Big Red Machine/50	15.00	40.00
JK Jerry Koosman/50	20.00	50.00
KG Kirk Gibson Home Run/25		
TI Tim Salmon 2002 Champs/50	20.00	50.00
TM Tug McGraw Ya Gotta Believe/50	50.00	100.00

2003 SP Authentic Chirography Yankees Stars

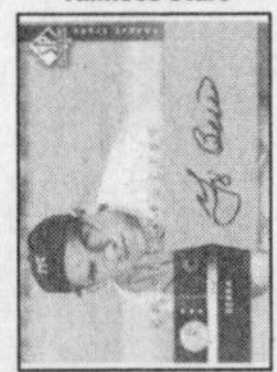

Randomly inserted into packs, these 14 cards feature not only Yankee stars of the past and present but also authentic autographs of the featured players. Since these cards were issued to varying print runs, we have identified the stated print run next to the player's name in our checklist.

BR Bobby Richardson/320	10.00	25.00
DM Don Mattingly/295	30.00	60.00
DW1 Dave Winfield/350	10.00	25.00
HK Ralph Houk/245	6.00	15.00
JB Jim Bouton/345	6.00	15.00
JG Jason Giambi/275	6.00	15.00
KS Ken Griffey Sr./350	6.00	15.00
RC Roger Clemens/210	50.00	100.00
SL Sparky Lyle/345	6.00	15.00
ST Mel Stottlemyre/345	6.00	15.00
TH Tommy Henrich/345	6.00	15.00
TJ Tommy John/245	6.00	15.00
TK Tony Kubek/345	10.00	25.00
YB Yogi Berra/320	15.00	40.00

2003 SP Authentic Chirography Yankees Stars Bronze

Randomly inserted into packs, this is a partial parallel to the Yankee Stars insert set. Most of these cards were issued to a stated print run of 100 copies and most have an "Yankees" inscription. Please note that for the few players who did not put an Yankees inscription we put a NO next to the player's name. In addition, since a few cards have a print run of fewer than 100 copies we have noted all print runs in our checklist.

BR Bobby Richardson/100	15.00	40.00
DM Don Mattingly NO/100	40.00	100.00
HK Ralph Houk/100	10.00	25.00
JB Jim Bouton/100	10.00	25.00
JG Jason Giambi/60	10.00	25.00
KS Ken Griffey Sr./100	10.00	25.00
RC Roger Clemens NO/75	60.00	120.00
SL Sparky Lyle/100	10.00	25.00
ST Mel Stottlemyre/100	10.00	25.00
TH Tommy Henrich/100	10.00	25.00
TJ Tommy John/100	10.00	25.00
TK Tony Kubek/100	15.00	40.00
YB Yogi Berra NO/100	25.00	60.00

2003 SP Authentic Chirography Yankees Stars Silver

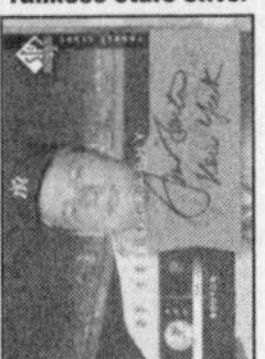

Randomly inserted into packs, this is a partial parallel to the Yankee Stars insert set. Each of these cards were issued to a stated print run of either 25 or 50 copies and we have noted that information in our checklist. Since there is a mix in this set about cards with notations, what the notations are -- we have put the notation information, when it exists, in our checklist.

NO PRICING ON QTY OF 25 OR LESS

BR Bobby Richardson New York/50	20.00	50.00
DM Don Mattingly/50	50.00	120.00
HK Ralph Houk New York/50	12.50	30.00
JB Jim Bouton New York/50	12.50	30.00
JG Jason Giambi/25		
KS Ken Griffey Sr./25		
RC Roger Clemens/50	60.00	120.00
SL Sparky Lyle/50	12.50	30.00
ST Mel Stottlemyre/50	12.50	30.00
TH Tommy Henrich Yankees/50	12.50	30.00
TJ Tommy John/50	12.50	30.00
TK Tony Kubek New York/50	20.00	50.00
YB Yogi Berra/75	30.00	80.00

2003 SP Authentic Chirography Young Stars

Randomly inserted into packs, these 25 cards feature autographs of some of the leading young stars in baseball. These cards were issued to stated print runs of between 150 and 350 cards and we have notated that information in our checklist. Please note that Hee Seop Choi did not return his autographs in time for pack out and those exchange cards could be redeemed until May 21, 2006.

AP A.J. Pierzynski/245	6.00	15.00
BO Joe Borchard/245	4.00	10.00
BP1 Brandon Phillips/350	4.00	10.00
BZ Barry Zito/350	10.00	25.00
CP Corey Patterson/245	4.00	10.00
DH Drew Henson/245	4.00	10.00
DI1 Ben Diggins/350	4.00	10.00
EH Eric Hinske/245	4.00	10.00
FS Freddy Sanchez/350	6.00	15.00
HB Hank Blalock/245	6.00	15.00
JJ Jacque Jones/245	6.00	15.00
JJ1 Jimmy Journell/350	4.00	10.00
JL Jason Lane/245	6.00	15.00
JP Josh Phelps/245	4.00	10.00
JS Jayson Werth/350	4.00	10.00
MB Marlon Byrd/245	4.00	10.00
MI Doug Mientkiewicz/245	6.00	15.00
MP Mark Prior/150	10.00	25.00
MY Brett Myers/245	6.00	15.00
OH Orlando Hudson/245	4.00	10.00
OP Oliver Perez/245	6.00	15.00
PE Carlos Pena/245	4.00	10.00
SB Sean Burroughs/245	4.00	10.00
TX Mark Teixeira/245	10.00	25.00

2003 SP Authentic Chirography Young Stars Bronze

Randomly inserted into packs, this is a partial parallel to the Young Stars insert set. Please note that most of these cards (with the exception of the Mark Prior card) were issued to a stated print run of 100 serial numbered sets and most of these cards had a notation of what city the player was playing in at the time of issue for this set. We have put the city information when applicable in our checklist.

*BRONZE: .6X TO 1.5X BASIC YS
*BRONZE PRIOR: .75X TO 2X BASIC YS

2003 SP Authentic Chirography Young Stars Silver

Randomly inserted into packs, this is a partial parallel to the Young Stars insert set. Most of these cards have a team notation and we have put that information next to tha players name in our checklist. Please note that most of these cards, with the exception of Mark Prior was issued to a stated print run of 50 serial numbered sets. The Prior card was issued to a stated print run of 25 serial numbered sets and there is no pricing due to market scarcity on that card.

*SILVER: .75X TO 2X BASIC YS

2003 SP Authentic Simply Splendid

COMMON CARD (TW1-TW30)	3.00	8.00

STATED PRINT RUN 406 SERIAL #'d SETS

2003 SP Authentic Splendid Jerseys

STATED PRINT RUN 406 SERIAL #'d SETS

SJTW Ted Williams	50.00	100.00

2003 SP Authentic Splendid Signatures

Randomly inserted in packs, these two cards feature autographs of current Red Sox star Nomar Garciaparra and retired Red Sox legend Ted Williams. Please note, that since these cards were issued after Williams passed on, that the Williams autographs are "cuts" while the Nomar autographs were signed for this product. Since the Williams card was issued to a stated print run of five serial numbered copies, no pricing is available for that card.

GA Nomar Garciaparra/406	30.00	60.00
TWSIG Ted Williams/5		

2003 SP Authentic Splendid Signatures Pairs

Randomly inserted into packs, these six cards feature a Ted Williams autograph "cut" to go with an autograph of an modern star. Each of these cards were issued to a stated print run of 3 serial numbered copies and no pricing is available due to market scarcity. Of note, all three copies of the Ken Griffey Jr./Ted Williams combo signature actually packed erroneously featuring Ken Griffey Sr. signatures. It's been verified that at least one of the three copies was returned to Upper Deck by a dealer and a Griffey Jr. signature was switched out.

2003 SP Authentic Splendid Swatches Pairs

Randomly inserted into packs, these nine cards feature a game-worn jersey swatch of retired Red Sox legend Ted Williams along with a game-used jersey swatch of another star. Each of the these cards were issued to a stated print run of 406 serial numbered sets. The two Williams/Nomar cards were not ready for pack-out and those were issued as a exchange cards with a redemption date of May 21, 2006.

IS Ted Williams Ichiro Suzuki	50.00	100.00
JG Ted Williams Jason Giambi	30.00	60.00
KG Ted Williams Ken Griffey Jr.	40.00	80.00
MM Ted Williams Mark McGwire	60.00	120.00
NM1 Ted Williams Nomar Garciaparra	30.00	60.00
NM2 Ted Williams Nomar Garciaparra	30.00	60.00
SS Ted Williams Sammy Sosa	20.00	50.00
TW Ted Williams Mickey Mantle	100.00	200.00

2003 SP Authentic Superstar Flashback

STATED PRINT RUN 2003 SERIAL #'d SETS

SF1 Tim Salmon	1.25	3.00
SF2 Darin Erstad	1.25	3.00
SF3 Troy Glaus	1.25	3.00
SF4 Randy Johnson	1.25	3.00
SF5 Curt Schilling	1.25	3.00
SF6 Steve Finley	1.25	3.00
SF7 Greg Maddux	2.00	5.00
SF8 Chipper Jones	1.25	3.00
SF9 Andruw Jones	1.25	3.00
SF10 Gary Sheffield	1.25	3.00
SF11 Manny Ramirez	1.25	3.00
SF12 Pedro Martinez	1.25	3.00
SF13 Nomar Garciaparra	2.00	5.00
SF14 Sammy Sosa	1.25	3.00
SF15 Frank Thomas	1.25	3.00
SF16 Kerry Wood	1.25	3.00
SF17 Paul Konerko	1.25	3.00
SF18 Corey Patterson	1.25	3.00
SF19 Mark Prior	1.25	3.00
SF20 Ken Griffey Jr.	2.00	5.00
SF21 Adam Dunn	1.25	3.00
SF22 Larry Walker	1.25	3.00
SF23 Preston Wilson	1.25	3.00
SF24 Todd Helton	1.25	3.00
SF25 Ivan Rodriguez	1.25	3.00
SF26 Josh Beckett	1.25	3.00
SF27 Jeff Bagwell	1.25	3.00
SF28 Jeff Kent	1.25	3.00
SF29 Lance Berkman	1.25	3.00
SF30 Carlos Beltran	1.25	3.00
SF31 Shawn Green	1.25	3.00
SF32 Richie Sexson	1.25	3.00
SF33 Vladimir Guerrero	1.25	3.00
SF34 Mike Piazza	2.00	5.00
SF35 Roberto Alomar	1.25	3.00
SF36 Roger Clemens	2.50	6.00
SF37 Derek Jeter	3.00	8.00
SF38 Jason Giambi	1.25	3.00
SF39 Bernie Williams	1.25	3.00
SF40 Nick Johnson	1.25	3.00
SF41 Alfonso Soriano	1.25	3.00
SF42 Miguel Tejada	1.25	3.00
SF43 Eric Chavez	1.25	3.00
SF44 Barry Zito	1.25	3.00
SF45 Jim Thome	1.25	3.00
SF46 Pat Burrell	1.25	3.00
SF47 Marlon Byrd	1.25	3.00
SF48 Jason Kendall	1.25	3.00
SF49 Aramis Ramirez	1.25	3.00
SF50 Brian Giles	1.25	3.00
SF51 Phil Nevin	1.25	3.00
SF52 Barry Bonds	3.00	8.00
SF53 Ichiro Suzuki	2.50	6.00
SF54 Scott Rolen	1.25	3.00
SF55 J.D. Drew	1.25	3.00
SF56 Albert Pujols	2.50	6.00
SF57 Mark Teixeira	1.25	3.00
SF58 Hank Blalock	1.25	3.00
SF59 Carlos Delgado	1.25	3.00
SF60 Roy Halladay	1.25	3.00

2004 SP Authentic

This 191 card set was released in June, 2004. The set was issued in five card packs with an $5 SRP which came 24 packs to a box and 12 boxes to a case. Cards numbered 1 through 90 featured veterans while cards numbered 91 through 132 and 178 through 191 feature rookies.With the exception of card 180, there were parallel versions issued of these cards and those cards all begin their serial numbering with 296. Card number 180 featuring Kazuo Matsui has a straight serial print run of card 1 through 999. Cards numbered 133 through 177 feature a mix of active and retired players with All-Star game memories and those cards were inserted at a stated rate of one in 24 with a stated print run of 999 serial numbered sets.

COMP.SET w/o SP's (90)	6.00	15.00
COMMON CARD (1-90)	.15	.40
COMMON (91-132/178-191)	1.25	3.00
91-132/178-191 OVERALL FW ODDS 1:24		
91-132/178-179/181-191 PRINT 704 #'d SETS		
91-132/178-179/181-191 #'d FROM 296-999		
CARD 180 PRINT RUN 999 #'d COPIES		
CARD 180 #'d FROM 1-999		
COMMON CARD (133-177)	.40	1.00
133-177 STATED ODDS 1:24		
133-177 PRINT RUN 999 SERIAL #'d SETS		
1 Bret Boone	.15	.40
2 Gary Sheffield	.15	.40
3 Rafael Palmeiro	.25	.60
4 Jorge Posada	.25	.60
5 Derek Jeter	1.00	2.50
6 Garret Anderson	.15	.40
7 Bartolo Colon	.15	.40
8 Kevin Brown	.15	.40
9 Shea Hillenbrand	.15	.40
10 Ryan Klesko	.15	.40
11 Bobby Abreu	.15	.40
12 Scott Rolen	.25	.60
13 Alfonso Soriano	.15	.40
14 Jason Giambi	.15	.40
15 Tom Glavine	.25	.60
16 Hideo Nomo	.40	1.00
17 Johan Santana	.40	1.00
18 Sammy Sosa	.40	1.00
19 Rickie Weeks	.15	.40
20 Barry Zito	.15	.40
21 Kerry Wood	.15	.40
22 Austin Kearns	.15	.40
23 Shawn Green	.15	.40
24 Miguel Cabrera	.40	1.00
25 Richard Hidalgo	.15	.40
26 Andruw Jones	.15	.40
27 Randy Wolf	.15	.40
28 David Ortiz	.40	1.00
29 Roy Oswalt	.25	.60
30 Vernon Wells	.15	.40
31 Ben Sheets	.15	.40
32 Mike Lowell	.15	.40
33 Todd Helton	.25	.60
34 Jacque Jones	.15	.40
35 Mike Sweeney	.15	.40
36 Hank Blalock	.15	.40
37 Jason Schmidt	.15	.40
38 Jeff Kent	.15	.40
39 Josh Beckett	.25	.60
40 Manny Ramirez	.40	1.00
41 Torii Hunter	.15	.40
42 Brian Giles	.15	.40
43 Javier Vazquez	.15	.40
44 Jim Edmonds	.25	.60
45 Dmitri Young	.15	.40
46 Preston Wilson	.15	.40
47 Jeff Bagwell	.25	.60
48 Pedro Martinez	.25	.60
49 Eric Chavez	.15	.40
50 Ken Griffey Jr.	.60	1.50
51 Shannon Stewart	.15	.40
52 Rafael Furcal	.15	.40
53 Brandon Webb	.15	.40
54 Juan Pierre	.15	.40
55 Roger Clemens	.50	1.25
56 Geoff Jenkins	.15	.40
57 Lance Berkman	.25	.60
58 Albert Pujols	1.00	2.50
59 Frank Thomas	.40	1.00
60 Edgar Martinez	.25	.60
61 Tim Hudson	.25	.60
62 Eric Gagne	.15	.40
63 Richie Sexson	.15	.40
64 Corey Patterson	.15	.40
65 Nomar Garciaparra	.40	1.00
66 Hideki Matsui	.60	1.50
67 Mark Teixeira	.40	1.00
68 Troy Glaus	.15	.40
69 Carlos Lee	.15	.40
70 Mike Mussina	.25	.60
71 Magglio Ordonez	.25	.60
72 Roy Halladay	.40	1.00
73 Ichiro Suzuki	.60	1.50
74 Randy Johnson	.40	1.00
75 Luis Gonzalez	.15	.40
76 Mark Prior	.25	.60
77 Carlos Beltran	.15	.40
78 Ivan Rodriguez	.25	.60
79 Alex Rodriguez	.60	1.50
80 Dontrelle Willis	.15	.40
81 Mike Piazza	.40	1.00
82 Curt Schilling	.25	.60
83 Vladimir Guerrero	.40	1.00
84 Greg Maddux	.60	1.50
85 Jim Thome	.25	.60
86 Miguel Tejada	.25	.60
87 Carlos Delgado	.15	.40
88 Jose Reyes	.25	.60
89 Matt Morris	.15	.40
90 Mark Mulder	.15	.40
91 Angel Chavez FW RC	1.25	3.00
92 Brandon Medders FW RC	1.25	3.00
93 Carlos Vasquez FW RC	1.25	3.00
94 Chris Aguila FW RC	1.25	3.00
95 Colby Miller FW RC	1.25	3.00
96 Dave Crouthers FW RC	1.25	3.00
97 Dennis Sarfate FW RC	1.25	3.00
98 Donnie Kelly FW RC	2.00	5.00
99 Merkin Valdez FW RC	1.25	3.00
100 Eddy Rodriguez FW RC	1.25	3.00
101 Edwin Moreno FW RC	1.25	3.00
102 Enemencio Pacheco FW RC	1.25	3.00
103 Roberto Novoa FW RC	1.25	3.00
104 Greg Dobbs FW RC	1.25	3.00
105 Hector Gimenez FW RC	1.25	3.00
106 Ian Snell FW RC	1.25	3.00
107 Jake Woods FW RC	1.25	3.00
108 Jamie Brown FW RC	1.25	3.00
109 Jason Frasor FW RC	1.25	3.00
110 Jerome Gamble FW RC	1.25	3.00
111 Jerry Gil FW RC	1.25	3.00
112 Jesse Harper FW RC	1.25	3.00
113 Jorge Vasquez FW RC	1.25	3.00
114 Jose Capellan FW RC	1.25	3.00
115 Josh Labandeira FW RC	1.25	3.00
116 Justin Hampson FW RC	1.25	3.00
117 Justin Huisman FW RC	1.25	3.00
118 Justin Leone FW RC	1.25	3.00
119 Lincoln Holdzkom FW RC	1.25	3.00
120 Lino Urdaneta FW RC	1.25	3.00
121 Mike Gosling FW RC	1.25	3.00
122 Mike Johnston FW RC	1.25	3.00
123 Mike Rouse FW RC	1.25	3.00
124 Scott Proctor FW RC	1.25	3.00
125 Roman Colon FW RC	1.25	3.00
126 Ronny Cedeno FW RC	1.25	3.00
127 Ryan Meaux FW RC	1.25	3.00
128 Scott Dohmann FW RC	1.25	3.00
129 Sean Henn FW RC	1.25	3.00
130 Tim Bausher FW RC	1.25	3.00
131 Tim Bittner FW RC	1.25	3.00
132 William Bergolla FW RC	1.25	3.00
133 Rick Ferrell ASM	.40	1.00
134 Joe DiMaggio ASM	2.50	6.00
135 Bob Feller ASM	.40	1.00
136 Ted Williams ASM	2.50	6.00
137 Stan Musial ASM	1.50	4.00
138 Larry Doby ASM	.40	1.00
139 Red Schoendienst ASM	.40	1.00
140 Enos Slaughter ASM	.40	1.00
141 Stan Musial ASM	1.50	4.00
142 Mickey Mantle ASM	3.00	8.00
143 Ted Williams ASM	2.50	6.00
144 Mickey Mantle ASM	3.00	8.00
145 Stan Musial ASM	1.50	4.00
146 Tom Seaver ASM	.60	1.50
147 Willie McCovey ASM	.60	1.50
148 Bob Gibson ASM	.60	1.50
149 Frank Robinson ASM	.60	1.50
150 Joe Morgan ASM	.40	1.00
151 Billy Williams ASM	.40	1.00
152 Catfish Hunter ASM	.40	1.00
153 Joe Morgan ASM	.40	1.00
154 Joe Morgan ASM	.40	1.00
155 Mike Schmidt ASM	1.50	4.00
156 Tommy Lasorda ASM	.40	1.00
157 Robin Yount ASM	1.00	2.50
158 Nolan Ryan ASM	3.00	8.00
159 John Franco ASM	.40	1.00
160 Nolan Ryan ASM	3.00	8.00
161 Ken Griffey Jr. ASM	1.50	4.00
162 Cal Ripken ASM	4.00	10.00
163 Ken Griffey Jr. ASM	1.50	4.00
164 Gary Sheffield ASM	.40	1.00
165 Fred McGriff ASM	.40	1.00
166 Hideo Nomo ASM	1.00	2.50
167 Mike Piazza ASM	1.00	2.50
168 Sandy Alomar Jr. ASM	.40	1.00
169 Roberto Alomar ASM	.60	1.50
170 Ted Williams ASM	2.50	6.00
171 Pedro Martinez ASM	.60	1.50
172 Derek Jeter ASM	2.50	6.00
173 Cal Ripken ASM	4.00	10.00
174 Torii Hunter ASM	.40	1.00
175 Alfonso Soriano ASM	.40	1.00
176 Hank Blalock ASM	.40	1.00
177 Ichiro Suzuki ASM	1.50	4.00
178 Orlando Rodriguez FW RC	1.25	3.00
179 Ramon Ramirez FW RC	1.25	3.00
180 Kazuo Matsui FW RC	2.00	5.00
181 Kevin Cave FW RC	1.25	3.00
182 John Gall FW RC	1.25	3.00
183 Freddy Guzman FW RC	1.25	3.00
184 Chris Oxspring FW RC	1.25	3.00
185 Rusty Tucker FW RC	1.25	3.00
186 Jorge Sequea FW RC	1.25	3.00
187 Carlos Hines FW RC	1.25	3.00
188 Michael Vento FW RC	1.25	3.00
189 Ryan Wing FW RC	1.25	3.00
190 Jeff Bennett FW RC	1.25	3.00
191 Luis A. Gonzalez FW RC	1.25	3.00

2004 SP Authentic 199/99

*199/99 1-90: 3X TO 8X BASIC
*199/99 91-132/178-191: 1X TO 2.5X BASIC
1-132/178-191 PRINT RUN SER. 99 #'d SETS
*199/99 133-177: .75X TO 2X BASIC
133-177 PRINT RUN 199 SERIAL #'d SETS
OVERALL PARALLEL ODDS 1:8

2004 SP Authentic 499/249

*499/249 1-90: 1.5X TO 4X BASIC
*499/249 133-177: .6X TO 1.5X BASIC
1-90/133-177 PRINT RUN 499 #'d SETS
*499/249 91-132/178-191: .75X TO 2X BASIC
91-132/178-191 PRINT RUN 249 #'d SETS
OVERALL PARALLEL ODDS 1:8

2004 SP Authentic Future Watch Autograph

STATED PRINT RUN 295 SERIAL #'d SETS
*AUTO 195: .5X TO 1.2X BASIC
AUTO 195 PRINT RUN 195 SERIAL #'d SETS
OVERALL FUTURE WATCH ODDS 1:24

91 Angel Chavez FW	4.00	10.00
92 Brandon Medders FW	4.00	10.00
93 Carlos Vasquez FW	6.00	15.00
94 Chris Aguila FW	4.00	10.00
95 Colby Miller FW	4.00	10.00
96 Dave Crouthers FW	4.00	10.00
97 Dennis Sarfate FW	4.00	10.00
98 Donnie Kelly FW	4.00	10.00
99 Merkin Valdez FW	4.00	10.00
100 Eddy Rodriguez FW	6.00	15.00
101 Edwin Moreno FW	4.00	10.00
102 Enemencio Pacheco FW	4.00	10.00
103 Roberto Novoa FW	4.00	10.00
104 Greg Dobbs FW	4.00	10.00
105 Hector Gimenez FW	4.00	10.00
106 Ian Snell FW	10.00	25.00
107 Jake Woods FW	4.00	10.00
108 Jamie Brown FW	4.00	10.00
109 Jason Frasor FW	4.00	10.00
110 Jerome Gamble FW	4.00	10.00
111 Jerry Gil FW	4.00	10.00
112 Jesse Harper FW	4.00	10.00
113 Jorge Vasquez FW	4.00	10.00
114 Jose Capellan FW	4.00	10.00
115 Josh Labandeira FW	4.00	10.00
116 Justin Hampson FW	4.00	10.00
117 Justin Huisman FW	4.00	10.00
118 Justin Leone FW	6.00	15.00
119 Lincoln Holdzkom FW	4.00	10.00
120 Lino Urdaneta FW	4.00	10.00
121 Mike Gosling FW	4.00	10.00
122 Mike Johnston FW	4.00	10.00
123 Mike Rouse FW	4.00	10.00
124 Scott Proctor FW	6.00	15.00
125 Roman Colon FW	4.00	10.00
126 Ronny Cedeno FW	6.00	15.00
127 Ryan Meaux FW	4.00	10.00
128 Scott Dohmann FW	4.00	10.00
129 Sean Henn FW	4.00	10.00
130 Tim Bausher FW	4.00	10.00
131 Tim Bittner FW	4.00	10.00
132 William Bergolla FW	4.00	10.00
178 Orlando Rodriguez FW	4.00	10.00
179 Ramon Ramirez FW	4.00	10.00
181 Kevin Cave FW	4.00	10.00
182 John Gall FW	6.00	15.00
183 Freddy Guzman FW	4.00	10.00
184 Chris Oxspring FW	4.00	10.00
185 Rusty Tucker FW	6.00	15.00
186 Jorge Sequea FW	4.00	10.00
187 Carlos Hines FW	4.00	10.00
188 Michael Vento FW	6.00	15.00
189 Ryan Wing FW	4.00	10.00
190 Jeff Bennett FW	4.00	10.00
191 Luis A. Gonzalez FW	6.00	15.00

2004 SP Authentic Game-Dated

OVERALL GAME DATED ODDS 1:288
STATED PRINT RUN 1 SERIAL #'d SET
MULTIPLE VERSIONS OF EACH CARD EXIST
NO PRICING DUE TO SCARCITY

2004 SP Authentic Game-Dated Autographs

OVERALL GAME DATED ODDS 1:288
STATED PRINT RUN 1 SERIAL #'d SET
CL: 1/5/6/10/11/19-20/22/24-25/27/29
CL: 31/34/36/43/49-50/59-60/62/67/69
CL: 72/76/78/80/86-88
MULTIPLE VERSIONS OF EACH CARD EXIST
NO PRICING DUE TO SCARCITY

2004 SP Authentic Buybacks

Jorge Posada did not return his cards in time for pack out and those cards could be redeemed until June 4, 2007.

OVERALL AUTO INSERT ODDS 1:12
PRINT RUNS B/WN 1-105 COPIES PER
NO PRICING ON QTY OF 14 OR LESS

AB1 Angel Berroa 04 VIN/70	4.00	10.00
AD1 Andre Dawson 04 SSC/50	6.00	15.00
AKE1 Austin Kearns 03 40M/5		
AKE2 Austin Kearns 03 CP/1		
AKE3 Austin Kearns 03 PC/1		
AKE4 Austin Kearns 03 SPx/1		
AKE5 Austin Kearns 03 SS/5		
AKE6 Austin Kearns 03 UDA/1		
AKE7 Austin Kearns 04 DAS/1		
AKE8 Austin Kearns 04 VIN/5		
AK1 Al Kaline 03 SP LC/20	30.00	60.00
AK2 Al Kaline 04 SSC/70	20.00	50.00
AL1 Al Leiter 04 FP/80	6.00	15.00
AL2 Al Leiter 04 UD/60	6.00	15.00
BA1 Bobby Abreu 03 CP/63	6.00	15.00
BA2 Bobby Abreu 03 HR/53		
BA3 Bobby Abreu 03 SPx/63	6.00	15.00
BA4 Bobby Abreu 03 SS/64	6.00	15.00
BA5 Bobby Abreu 03 UDA/63	6.00	15.00
BA6 Bobby Abreu 04 DAS/53	6.00	15.00
BA7 Bobby Abreu 04 FP/53	6.00	15.00
BA8 Bobby Abreu 04 UD/65	6.00	15.00
BA9 Bobby Abreu 04 VIN/53	6.00	15.00
BB1 Bret Boone 03 CP/66	15.00	40.00
BB2 Bret Boone 03 PC/15	30.00	60.00
BB3 Bret Boone 03 SPx/29	20.00	50.00
BB4 Bret Boone 03 SS/44	15.00	40.00
BB5 Bret Boone 03 UDA/63	15.00	40.00
BB6 Bret Boone 04 DAS/57	15.00	40.00
BB7 Bret Boone 04 VIN/53	15.00	40.00
BD1 Bobby Doerr 03 SP LCB/50	6.00	15.00
BD2 Bobby Doerr 04 SSC/73	6.00	15.00
BG1 Bob Gibson 04 SSC/23	15.00	40.00
BHI1 Bobby Hill 03 40M/40	4.00	10.00
BHI2 Bobby Hill 03 UDA/17	8.00	20.00
BHI3 Bobby Hill 04 FP/17	8.00	20.00
BHI4 Bobby Hill 04 UD/17	8.00	20.00
BHI5 Bobby Hill 04 VIN/34	6.00	15.00
BH1 Bo Hart 03 SPx/50	4.00	10.00
BH2 Bo Hart 04 VIN/45	4.00	10.00
BL1 Barry Larkin 03 FP/10		
BR1 B.Robinson 03 SP LC/50	10.00	25.00
BR2 B.Robinson 04 SSC/70	10.00	25.00
BS1 Ben Sheets 03 40M/25	10.00	25.00
BS2 Ben Sheets 03 CP/15	12.50	30.00
BS3 Ben Sheets 03 PC/15	12.50	30.00
BS4 Ben Sheets 03 SPx/15	12.50	30.00
BS5 Ben Sheets 04 DAS/15	12.50	30.00
BS6 Ben Sheets 04 FP/15		
BS7 Ben Sheets 04 UD/25	10.00	25.00
BS8 Ben Sheets 04 VIN/15	12.50	30.00
BW1 Brandon Webb 03 SPx/20	6.00	15.00
BW2 Brandon Webb 03 UD/65	4.00	10.00
BW3 Brandon Webb 03 UDA/10		
BW4 Brandon Webb 04 DAS/50	4.00	10.00
BW5 Brandon Webb 04 FP/30	10.00	25.00
BW6 Brandon Webb 04 VIN/85	4.00	10.00
BZ1 Barry Zito 03 40M/30	15.00	40.00
BZ2 Barry Zito 03 CP/41	10.00	25.00
BZ3 Barry Zito 03 HR/60	10.00	25.00
BZ4 Barry Zito 03 PC/15	20.00	50.00
BZ5 Barry Zito 03 SPx/46	10.00	25.00
BZ6 Barry Zito 03 SS/63	10.00	25.00
BZ7 Barry Zito 03 UDA/40	10.00	25.00
BZ8 Barry Zito 04 FP/69	10.00	25.00
BZ9 Barry Zito 04 UD/61	10.00	25.00

BZ10 Barry Zito 04 VIN/50 10.00 25.00
CB1 Carlos Beltran 03 40M/25
CB2 Carlos Beltran 03 CP/15 12.50 30.00
CB3 Carlos Beltran 03 PC/15 12.50 30.00
CB4 Carlos Beltran 03 SPx/15
CB5 Carlos Beltran 03 SS/15 12.50 30.00
CB6 Carlos Beltran 04 DAS/15 12.50 30.00
CB7 Carlos Beltran 04 VIN/15 12.50 30.00
CD1 Carlos Delgado 03 CP/1
CD2 Carlos Delgado 03 HR/1
CD3 Carlos Delgado 03 SPx/1
CD4 Carlos Delgado 03 SS/1
CD5 C.Delgado 03 UDA/40 6.00 15.00
CD6 Carlos Delgado 04 DAS/1
CD7 Carlos Delgado 04 VIN/1
CF1 C.Fisk 03 SP LC/38 15.00 40.00
CF2 C.Fisk 03 SP LCB/55 15.00 40.00
CLL1 Cliff Lee 04 FP/40 30.00 60.00
CLL2 Cliff Lee 04 UD/50 30.00 60.00
CL1 Carlos Lee 04 FP/70 6.00 15.00
CL2 Carlos Lee 04 UD/70 6.00 15.00
CL3 Carlos Lee 04 VIN/70 6.00 15.00
CPO1 Colin Porter 03 CP/60 4.00 10.00
CPO2 Colin Porter 03 SS/10
CPO3 Colin Porter 04 FP/70 4.00 10.00
CP1 C.Patterson 03 40M/20 6.00 15.00
CP2 C.Patterson 03 PC/20 6.00 15.00
CP3 C.Patterson 03 SPx/20 6.00 15.00
CP4 C.Patterson 03 SS/20 6.00 15.00
CP5 C.Patterson 04 FP/20 6.00 15.00
CP6 C.Patterson 04 UD/20 6.00 15.00
CP7 C.Patterson 04 VIN/20 6.00 15.00
CR1 Cal Ripken 04 SSC/45 75.00 150.00
CW1 C.Wang 04 FP/26 75.00 150.00
CY1 C.Yastrzemski 04 SSC/22 40.00 80.00
CZ1 C.Zambrano 04 VIN/70 10.00 25.00
DJ1 Derek Jeter 03 40M/30 90.00 180.00
DJ2 Derek Jeter 03 CP/2
DJ3 Derek Jeter 03 HR/25 100.00 200.00
DJ4 Derek Jeter 03 PC/25 100.00 200.00
DJ5 Derek Jeter 03 SPx/2
DJ6 Derek Jeter 03 SS/30 90.00 180.00
DJ7 Derek Jeter 03 UDA/2
DJ8 Derek Jeter 04 DAS/12
DJ9 Derek Jeter 04 FP/12
DJ10 Derek Jeter 04 UD/25 100.00 200.00
DJ11 Derek Jeter 04 VIN/25 100.00 200.00
DS1 Duke Snider 04 SSC/23 20.00 50.00
DW1 D.Willis 04 DAS/70 10.00 25.00
DW2 D.Willis 04 FP/80 10.00 25.00
DW3 D.Willis 04 UD SR/45 10.00 25.00
DW4 D.Willis 04 VIN/105 10.00 25.00
DY1 Delmon Young 04 DAS/5
DY2 Delmon Young 04 FP/5
DY3 Delmon Young 04 VIN/35 15.00 40.00
EC1 Eric Chavez 03 40M/30 10.00 25.00
EC2 Eric Chavez 03 CP/3
EC3 Eric Chavez 03 HR/3
EC4 Eric Chavez 03 SPx/3
EC5 Eric Chavez 03 SS/25 10.00 25.00
EC6 Eric Chavez 04 FP/3
EC7 Eric Chavez 04 DAS/2
EC8 Eric Chavez 04 UD/3
EC9 Eric Chavez 04 VIN/3
EG1 Eric Gagne 03 40M/38 10.00 25.00
EG2 Eric Gagne 04 FP/26 15.00 40.00
EG3 Eric Gagne 04 UD/38 10.00 25.00
EG4 Eric Gagne 04 VIN/38 10.00 25.00
EM1 E.Martinez 04 DAS/70 15.00 40.00
GA1 G.Anderson 03 40M/30 10.00 25.00
GA2 G.Anderson 03 CP/16
GA3 G.Anderson 03 SPx/2
GA4 G.Anderson 03 SS/20 10.00 25.00
GA5 G.Anderson 04 DAS/16 12.50 30.00
GA6 G.Anderson 04 VIN/16 12.50 30.00
HB1 Hank Blalock 03 40M/20 10.00 25.00
HB2 Hank Blalock 03 CP/9
HB3 Hank Blalock 03 PC/9
HB4 Hank Blalock 03 SPx/9
HB5 Hank Blalock 03 SS/15 12.50 30.00
HB6 Hank Blalock 04 FP/10
HB7 Hank Blalock 04 UD/9
HB8 Hank Blalock 04 VIN/9
HK1 H.Killebrew 03 SP LC/20 40.00 80.00
HK2 Harmon Killebrew 04 SSC/3
HR1 H.Ramirez 03 40M/25 6.00 15.00
HR2 Horacio Ramirez 04 FP/5
HR3 Horacio Ramirez 04 UD/15 8.00 20.00
JB1 Josh Beckett 03 40M/21 15.00 40.00
JB2 Josh Beckett 03 CP/5
JB3 Josh Beckett 03 HR/21 15.00 40.00
JB4 Josh Beckett 03 PC/12
JB5 Josh Beckett 03 SPx/5
JB6 Josh Beckett 03 SS/21 15.00 40.00
JB7 Josh Beckett 04 VIN/5
JE1 Jim Edmonds 03 CP/25 15.00 40.00
JE2 Jim Edmonds 03 HR/15 20.00 50.00
JE3 Jim Edmonds 03 SPx/25 15.00 40.00
JE4 Jim Edmonds 03 SS/45 10.00 25.00
JE5 Jim Edmonds 03 UDA/25 15.00 40.00
JE6 Jim Edmonds 04 DAS/15 20.00 50.00
JE7 Jim Edmonds 04 FP/15 20.00 50.00
JE8 Jim Edmonds 04 UD/25 15.00 40.00
JE9 Jim Edmonds 04 VIN/15 20.00 50.00
JGE1 Jody Gerut 04 DAS/70 4.00 10.00
JGE2 Jody Gerut 04 VIN/70 4.00 10.00
JG1 Juan Gonzalez 03 40M/19 12.50 30.00
JG2 Juan Gonzalez 03 CP/19
JG3 Juan Gonzalez 03 PC/19 12.50 30.00
JG4 Juan Gonzalez 03 SS/19 12.50 30.00
JG5 Juan Gonzalez 04 FP/5
JG6 Juan Gonzalez 04 UD/19 12.50 30.00
JG7 Juan Gonzalez 04 VIN/20 10.00 25.00
JJ1 Jacque Jones 03 40M/40 6.00 15.00
JJ2 Jacque Jones 03 CP/11
JJ3 Jacque Jones 03 SPx/35 10.00 25.00
JJ4 Jacque Jones 03 SS/35 10.00 25.00
JJ5 Jacque Jones 03 UDA/11
JJ6 Jacque Jones 04 DAS/2
JJ7 Jacque Jones 04 VIN/11
JL1 Javy Lopez 03 40M/30 10.00 25.00
JL2 Javy Lopez 04 FP/18 12.50 30.00
JL3 Javy Lopez 04 UD/29 10.00 25.00
JL4 Javy Lopez 04 VIN/18 12.50 30.00
JO1 John Olerud 03 CP/50 10.00 25.00
JO2 John Olerud 03 SS/45 10.00 25.00
JO3 John Olerud 04 VIN/70 10.00 25.00
JR1 Jose Reyes 04 DAS/7
JS1 John Smoltz 04 FP/67 30.00 60.00
JS2 John Smoltz 04 UD/67 30.00 60.00
JS3 John Smoltz 04 VIN/70 30.00 60.00
JT1 Joe Torre 04 SSC/70 10.00 25.00
JV1 Javier Vazquez 04 DAS/70 6.00 15.00
JV2 Javier Vazquez 04 VIN/70 6.00 15.00
JWS1 Jae Seo 03 SS/10
JWS2 Jae Seo 04 FP/5
JWS3 Jae Seo 04 UD/15 12.50 30.00
JWS4 Jae Seo 04 VIN/15 12.50 30.00
JW1 Jer.Williams 04 UD/70 4.00 10.00
JW2 Jer.Williams 04 VIN/60 4.00 10.00
KG1 K.Grif 02 SUP Silv/45 50.00 100.00
KG2 K.Grif 02 SUP SK 92 AS/6
KG3 K.Grif 02 SUP SK Blue/19 75.00 150.00
KG4 K.Grif 03 40M Blue/20 60.00 120.00
KG5 K.Grif 03 40M Red/10
KG6 K.Grif 03 40M 92 AS/18 75.00 150.00
KG7 K.Grif 03 40M 97 AL/18 75.00 150.00
KG8 K.Grif 03 40MHR94 Blk/31 60.00 120.00
KG9 K.Grif 03 40MHR94 Blu/27 60.00 120.00
KG10 K.Grif 03 40MHR98 Sil/28 60.00 120.00
KG11 K.Grif 03 40M HR98 AS/12
KG12 K.Grif 03 40M HR98 GG/14
KG13 K.Grif 03 40M HR99 Sil/48 50.00 100.00
KG14 K.Grif 03 40M T40 Blu/35 60.00 120.00
KG15 K.Grif 03 40M T40 AL/29 50.00 100.00
KG16 K.Grif 03 GF Black/40 50.00 100.00
KG17 K.Grif 03 GF Blue/23 60.00 120.00
KG18 K.Grif 03 GF Red/10
KG19 K.Grif 03 GF 92AS/19 75.00 150.00
KG20 K.Grif 03 HR 92AS/15 75.00 150.00
KG21 K.Grif 03 HR 97AL/37 60.00 120.00
KG22 K.Grif 03 HR Red/10
KG23 K.Grif 03 MVP Blk/56 50.00 100.00
KG24 K.Grif 03 MVP Red/10
KG25 K.Grif 03 MVP GG/15 75.00 150.00
KG26 K.Grif 03 MVP GG92/1
KG27 K.Grif 03 PC Black/27 60.00 120.00
KG28 K.Grif 03 PC Blue/7
KG29 K.Grif 03 PC 92 AS/8
KG30 K.Grif 03 PB Black/15 75.00 150.00
KG31 K.Grif 03 PB Blue/11
KG32 K.Grif 03 PB 56 HR/15 75.00 150.00
KG33 K.Grif 03 PB 92 AS/9
KG34 K.Grif 03 SPA 56 HR/15 75.00 150.00
KG35 K.Grif 03 SPA 92 AS/20 60.00 120.00
KG36 K.Grif 03 SPA B93/20 60.00 120.00
KG37 K.Grif 03 SPA B93 AS MVP/1
KG38 K.Grif 03 SPA Red/5
KG39 K.Grif 03 SPx 97 AL/26 60.00 120.00
KG40 K.Grif 03 SS 97 AL/32 50.00 120.00
KG41 K.Grif 03 UDA Red/5
KG42 K.Grif 03 VIC Blk/57 50.00 100.00
KG43 K.Grif 03 VIC 92 AS/18 75.00 150.00
KW1 Kerry Wood 03 40M/34 15.00 40.00
KW6 Kerry Wood 03 SS/34 15.00 40.00
KW7 Kerry Wood 03 UDA/5
KW8 Kerry Wood 04 DAS/1
KW9 Kerry Wood 04 VIN/5
LA1 L.Aparicio 03 SP LC/20 10.00 25.00
LA2 Luis Aparicio 04 SSC/3
LG1 L.Gonzalez 03 40M HR/25 10.00 25.00
LG2 Luis Gonzalez 03 CP/20 10.00 25.00
LG3 Luis Gonzalez 03 HR/20 10.00 25.00
LG4 Luis Gonzalez 03 SPx/1
LG5 Luis Gonzalez 03 SS/40 6.00 15.00
LG6 Luis Gonzalez 03 UDA/1
LG7 Luis Gonzalez 04 FP/20
LG8 Luis Gonzalez 04 UD/10
LG9 Luis Gonzalez 04 VIN/20 10.00 25.00
MB1 Marlon Byrd 04 VIN/70 4.00 10.00
MC1 M.Cabrera 03 SPx/25 15.00 40.00
MC2 M.Cabrera 04 DAS/20 15.00 40.00
MC3 M.Cabrera 04 FP/20 15.00 40.00
MC4 M.Cabrera 04 VIN/20 15.00 40.00
ME1 M.Ensberg 04 FP/70 6.00 15.00
ME2 M.Ensberg 04 UD/70 6.00 15.00
ME3 M.Ensberg 04 VIN/70 6.00 15.00
MG1 Marcus Giles 04 VIN/70 6.00 15.00
MH1 Mike Hampton 03 UDA/60 4.00 10.00
MH2 Mike Hampton 04 FP/34 6.00 15.00
MH3 Mike Hampton 04 UD/47 4.00 10.00
MI1 Monte Irvin 03 SP LC/20 10.00 25.00
MI2 Monte Irvin 04 SSC/3
ML1 Mike Lowell 03 40M/19 8.00 20.00
ML2 Mike Lowell 04 DAS/19 8.00 20.00
ML3 Mike Lowell 04 FP/19 8.00 20.00
ML4 Mike Lowell 04 UD/19 8.00 20.00
ML5 Mike Lowell 04 VIN/19 8.00 20.00
MM1 Mike Mussina 03 CP/45
MM2 Mike Mussina 03 HR/20 15.00 40.00
MM3 Mike Mussina 03 HR/25 15.00 40.00
MM4 Mike Mussina 03 SPx/45
MM5 Mike Mussina 03 SS/60 10.00 25.00
MM6 Mike Mussina 03 UDA/45 10.00 25.00
MM7 Mike Mussina 04 FP/58 10.00 25.00
MM8 Mike Mussina 04 UD/45 10.00 25.00
MM9 Mike Mussina 04 VIN/45 10.00 25.00
MP1 Mark Prior 03 40M/22 12.50 30.00
MP2 Mark Prior 03 40M RWB/5
MP3 Mark Prior 03 CP/5
MP4 Mark Prior 03 HR/22 12.50 30.00
MP5 Mark Prior 03 PC/22 12.50 30.00
MP6 Mark Prior 03 SPx/22 12.50 30.00
MP7 Mark Prior 03 SS/22 12.50 30.00
MP8 Mark Prior 03 UDA/10
MP9 Mark Prior 04 DAS/4
MP10 Mark Prior 04 FP/22 12.50 30.00
MP11 Mark Prior 04 UD/22 12.50 30.00
MP12 Mark Prior 04 VIN/22 12.50 30.00
MS1 M.Schmidt 03 SP LC/20 50.00 100.00
MS2 Mike Schmidt 04 SSC/3
MTE1 Miguel Tejada 03 CP/38 10.00 25.00
MTE2 Miguel Tejada 03 HR/36 10.00 25.00
MTE3 M.Tejada 03 SPx/30 15.00 40.00
MTE4 M.Tejada 03 UDA/58 10.00 25.00
MTE5 Miguel Tejada 04 DAS/37 10.00 25.00
MTE6 Miguel Tejada 04 VIN/70 6.00 15.00
MT1 M.Teix 03 40M RWB/45 10.00 25.00
MT2 Mark Teixeira 03 CP/23
MT3 Mark Teixeira 03 PC/3
MT4 Mark Teixeira 03 SPx/40 10.00 25.00
MT5 Mark Teixeira 03 SS/23 15.00 40.00
MT6 Mark Teixeira 03 SS/25 15.00 40.00
MT7 Mark Teixeira 03 UDA/21 15.00 40.00
MT8 Mark Teixeira 04 DAS/5
MT9 Mark Teixeira 04 FP/10
MT10 Mark Teixeira 04 UD/23 15.00 40.00
MT11 Mark Teixeira 04 VIN/23
MW1 Maury Wills 04 SSC/70 6.00 15.00
NR1 Nolan Ryan 03 UDA/20 75.00 150.00
NR2 Nolan Ryan 04 SSC/3
OD1 Octavio Dotel 04 FP/70 4.00 10.00
OD2 Octavio Dotel 04 UD/70 4.00 10.00
OD3 Octavio Dotel 04 VIN/70 4.00 10.00
PB1 Pat Burrell 03 CP/50 6.00 15.00
PB2 Pat Burrell 03 HR/25 10.00 25.00
PB3 Pat Burrell 03 SS/50 6.00 15.00
PB4 Pat Burrell 03 UDA/50 6.00 15.00
PB5 Pat Burrell 04 VIN/68 6.00 15.00
PL1 P.LoDuca 03 40M RWB/60 6.00 15.00
PL2 Paul Lo Duca 04 VIN/60 6.00 15.00
PL3 P.Lo Duca 04 VIN BW/20 10.00 25.00
PR1 Phil Rizzuto 03 SP LC/21 15.00 40.00
PR2 Phil Rizzuto 04 SSC/2
RB1 Rocco Baldelli 03 40M/20
RB2 Rocco Baldelli 03 PC/20
RB3 Rocco Baldelli 03 SPx/15 12.50 30.00
RB4 Rocco Baldelli 03 UDA/10
RB5 Rocco Baldelli 04 DAS/5
RB6 Rocco Baldelli 04 FP/10
RB7 R.Baldelli 04 PB Red/25 10.00 25.00
RB8 R.Baldelli 04 PB Blue/25 10.00 25.00
RB9 Rocco Baldelli 04 UD/5
RB10 Rocco Baldelli 04 VIN/5
RF1 Rollie Fingers 03 SP LC/1
RF2 Rollie Fingers 03 UDA/5
RF3 Rollie Fingers 04 SSC/10
RHL1 Roy Halladay 03 40M/32 20.00 50.00
RHL2 Roy Halladay 03 HR/10
RHL3 Roy Halladay 04 DAS/10
RHL4 Roy Halladay 04 FP/10
RHL5 Roy Halladay 04 UD/32 20.00 50.00
RHL6 Roy Halladay 04 VIN/1
RHM1 R.Hammock 03 40M/35 6.00 15.00
RHM2 R.Hammock 03 PC/15 8.00 20.00
RHM3 R.Hammock 04 FP/7
RHM4 R.Hammock 04 UD/30 6.00 15.00
RHM5 R.Hammock 04 VIN/7
RHR1 R.Hernandez 03 40M/55 4.00 10.00
RHR2 R.Hernandez 03 UDA/40 4.00 10.00
RI1 Raul Ibanez 04 FP/70 8.00 20.00
RI2 Raul Ibanez 04 UD/65 8.00 20.00
RI3 Raul Ibanez 04 VIN/70 8.00 20.00
RK1 Ralph Kiner 03 SP LC/20 15.00 40.00
RK2 Ralph Kiner 04 SSC/3
RO1 Roy Oswalt 03 40M/44 6.00 15.00
RO2 Roy Oswalt 03 HR/55 6.00 15.00
RO3 Roy Oswalt 03 SS/20 10.00 25.00
RO4 Roy Oswalt 04 UD/52 6.00 15.00
RR1 R.Roberts 03 SP LC/15 12.50 30.00
RR2 Robin Roberts 03 UDA/5
RR3 Robin Roberts 04 SSC/3
RW1 Rickie Weeks 03 UD/30 15.00 40.00
RW2 Rickie Weeks 04 FP/15 12.50 30.00
RW3 Rickie Weeks 04 VIN/50 6.00 15.00
RY1 Robin Yount 03 SP LC/20 50.00 100.00
RY2 Robin Yount 04 SSC/3
SG1 Shawn Green 03 CP/2
SG2 Shawn Green 03 HR/10
SG3 Shawn Green 03 SS/15 20.00 50.00
SG4 Shawn Green 03 UDA/5
SG5 Shawn Green 04 DAS/5
SG6 Shawn Green 04 FP/15 20.00 50.00
SG7 Shawn Green 04 UD/1
SG8 Shawn Green 04 VIN/15 20.00 50.00
SM1 S.Musial 03 SP LC/16 50.00 100.00
SM2 Stan Musial 03 UDA/6
SM3 Stan Musial 04 SSC/1
THO1 T.Hoffman 04 FP/67 10.00 25.00
THO2 T.Hoffman 04 UD/51 10.00 25.00
TH1 Travis Hafner 03 40M/32 6.00 15.00
TH2 Travis Hafner 03 HR/10
TH3 Travis Hafner 03 SPx/1
TH4 Travis Hafner 03 SS/32 6.00 15.00
TH5 Travis Hafner 03 UDA/5
TH6 Travis Hafner 04 VIN/10
TP1 Tony Perez 03 SP LC/20
TP2 Tony Perez 04 SSC/3
TS1 Tom Seaver 03 SP LC/15 30.00 60.00
TS2 Tom Seaver 03 UDA/6
TS3 Tom Seaver 04 SSC/2
VG1 Vlad Guerrero 03 CP/20 20.00 50.00
VG2 Vlad Guerrero 03 HR/27
VG3 Vlad Guerrero 03 SPx/34 20.00 50.00
VG4 Vlad Guerrero 03 SS/27 20.00 50.00
VG5 Vlad Guerrero 03 UDA/54 15.00 40.00
VG6 Vlad Guerrero 04 DAS/27 20.00 50.00
VG7 Vlad Guerrero 04 FP/28 20.00 50.00
VG8 Vlad Guerrero 04 UD/27
VG9 Vlad Guerrero 04 VIN/27 20.00 50.00
VW1 Vernon Wells 03 40M/15 12.50 30.00
WE1 Willie Eyre 03 40M/45 4.00 10.00
WE2 W.Eyre 03 40M RWB/45 4.00 10.00
YB1 Yogi Berra 03 SP LC/23 30.00 60.00

2004 SP Authentic Chirography

Jorge Posada and Ken Griffey Jr. did not return their cards in time for pack out and those cards could be redeemed until June 4, 2007. It is interesting to note that Griffey did return his buy-backed cards in time for inclusion in this product.

STATED PRINT RUN 75 SERIAL #'d SETS
BASIC CHIRO. HAVE RED BACKGROUNDS
*DT w/NOTE: .5X TO 1.2X BASIC
*DT w/o NOTE: .4X TO 1X BASIC
DUO TONE PRINT RUN 75 SERIAL #'d SETS
MOST DT FEATURE UNIFORM # NOTATION

*BRONZE: .4X TO 1X BASIC
BRONZE PRINT RUN 65 SERIAL #'d SETS
*BRONZE DT w/NOTE: .5X TO 1.2X BASIC
*BRONZE DT w/o NOTE: .4X TO 1X BASIC
BRONZE DUO TONE PRINT RUN 60 #'d SETS
MOST BRONZE DT FEATURE TEAM NAMES
*SILVER: .4X TO 1X BASIC
SILVER PRINT RUN 60 SERIAL #'d SETS
*SILVER DT w/NOTE: .6X TO 1.5X BASIC
*SILVER DT w/o NOTE: .5X TO 1.2X BASIC
SILVER DT PRINT RUN 30 SERIAL #'d SETS
MOST SILVER DT HAVE KEY ACHIEVEMENT
OVERALL AUTO INSERT ODDS 1:12

AK Austin Kearns 5.00 12.00
BA Bobby Abreu 8.00 20.00
BB Bret Boone 12.50 30.00
BH Bo Hart 5.00 12.00
BS Ben Sheets 8.00 20.00
BW Brandon Webb 6.00 15.00
BZ Barry Zito 12.50 30.00
CB Carlos Beltran 8.00 20.00
CL Cliff Lee 15.00 40.00
CP Colin Porter 5.00 12.00
CR Cal Ripken 60.00 120.00
CW Chien-Ming Wang 75.00 150.00
DE Dennis Eckersley 12.50 30.00
DJ Derek Jeter 100.00 200.00
DW Dontrelle Willis 12.50 30.00
DY Delmon Young 6.00 15.00
EC Eric Chavez 8.00 20.00
EG Eric Gagne 12.50 30.00
GA Garret Anderson 8.00 20.00
HA Robby Hammock 5.00 12.00
HB Hank Blalock 8.00 20.00
HE Runelvys Hernandez 5.00 12.00
HI Bobby Hill 5.00 12.00
HR Horacio Ramirez 5.00 12.00
HY Roy Halladay 30.00 60.00
JB Josh Beckett 12.50 30.00
JG Juan Gonzalez 8.00 20.00
JJ Jacque Jones 11 8.00 20.00
JL Javy Lopez 12.50 30.00
JR Jose Reyes 15.00 40.00
JS Jae Weong Seo 8.00 20.00
JV Javier Vazquez 8.00 20.00
JW Jerome Williams 5.00 12.00
KW Kerry Wood 12.50 30.00
MC Miguel Cabrera 12.50 30.00
ML Mike Lowell 8.00 20.00
MP Mark Prior 12.50 30.00
MT Mark Teixeira 12.50 30.00
PA Corey Patterson 5.00 12.00
PI Mike Piazza 90.00 180.00
PL Paul Lo Duca 8.00 20.00
RB Rocco Baldelli 8.00 20.00
RO Roy Oswalt 5.00 12.00
RW Rickie Weeks 8.00 20.00
TH Travis Hafner 5.00 12.00
VW Vernon Wells 8.00 20.00
WE Willie Eyre 5.00 12.00

2004 SP Authentic Chirography Gold

*GOLD p/r 40: .5X TO 1.2X BASIC
STATED PRINT RUN 40 SERIAL #'d SETS
EDGAR/LEITER/SMOLTZ 75 #'d COPIES PER
*GLD DT p/r 20 w/NOTE: .6X TO 1.5X p/r 40
*GLD DT p/r20 w/o NOTE:.5X TO 1.2X p/r 40
*GOLD DT p/r 75: .4X TO 1X GOLD p/r 75
GOLD DT PRINT RUN 20 SERIAL #'d SETS
MOST GOLD DT HAVE KEY ACHIEVEMENT
OVERALL AUTO INSERT ODDS 1:12
EXCHANGE DEADLINE 06/04/07

AL Al Leiter/75 8.00 20.00
AR Alex Rodriguez 100.00 175.00
EM Edgar Martinez/75 12.50 30.00
SM John Smoltz/75 20.00 50.00

2004 SP Authentic Chirography Dual

A few cards were not ready in time for pack out and those cards could be exchanged until June 4, 2007.

OVERALL AUTO INSERT ODDS 1:12
STATED PRINT RUN 50 SERIAL #'d SETS

BC Bret Boone 30.00 60.00
Eric Chavez
BL Josh Beckett 30.00 60.00
Mike Lowell
BP Carlos Beltran 20.00 50.00
Corey Patterson
BT Hank Blalock 30.00 60.00
Mark Teixeira

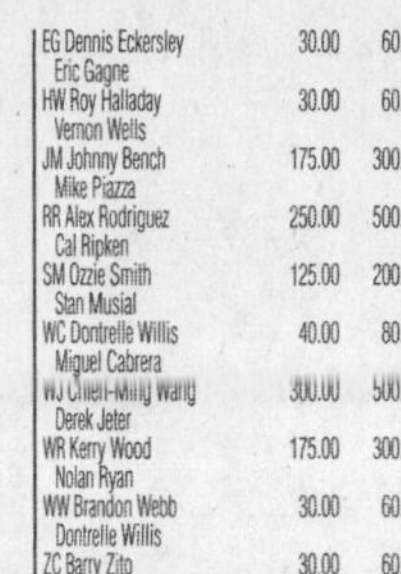

EG Dennis Eckersley 30.00 60.00
Eric Gagne
HW Roy Halladay 30.00 60.00
Vernon Wells
JM Johnny Bench 175.00 300.00
Mike Piazza
RR Alex Rodriguez 250.00 500.00
Cal Ripken
SM Ozzie Smith 125.00 200.00
Stan Musial
WC Dontrelle Willis 40.00 80.00
Miguel Cabrera
WJ Chien-Ming Wang 300.00 500.00
Derek Jeter
WR Kerry Wood 175.00 300.00
Nolan Ryan
WW Brandon Webb 30.00 60.00
Dontrelle Willis
ZC Barry Zito 30.00 60.00
Eric Chavez

2004 SP Authentic Chirography Hall of Famers

STATED PRINT RUN 40 SERIAL #'d SETS
*DUO TONE: .5X TO 1.2X BASIC
DUO TONE PRINT RUN 25 SERIAL #'d SETS
SOME DT FEATURE HOF NOTATION
OVERALL AUTO INSERT ODDS 1:12

AK Al Kaline 30.00 60.00
BD Bobby Doerr 10.00 25.00
BG Bob Gibson 15.00 40.00
BR B.Robinson UER B/W 15.00 40.00
CF Carlton Fisk 15.00 40.00
CY Carl Yastrzemski HOF 89 50.00 100.00
DE Dennis Eckersley 15.00 40.00
DS Duke Snider 15.00 40.00
HK Harmon Killebrew 40.00 80.00
JB Johnny Bench 30.00 60.00
KP Kirby Puckett 50.00 100.00
LA Luis Aparicio Hall of Famer 10.00 25.00
MI Monte Irvin 10.00 25.00
MS Mike Schmidt 60.00 120.00
NR Nolan Ryan 75.00 150.00
OS Ozzie Smith 50.00 100.00
PM Paul Molitor 10.00 25.00
PR Phil Rizzuto Hall of Famer 15.00 40.00
RK Ralph Kiner HOF 1975 10.00 25.00
RR Robin Roberts Hall of Famer 15.00 40.00
RY Robin Yount 50.00 100.00
SM Stan Musial 60.00 120.00
TP Tony Perez Hall of Famer 10.00 25.00
TS Tom Seaver 15.00 40.00
YB Yogi Berra 30.00 60.00

2004 SP Authentic Chirography Quad

OVERALL AUTO INSERT ODDS 1:12
STATED PRINT RUN 10 SERIAL #'d SETS
NO PRICING DUE TO SCARCITY
EXCHANGE DEADLINE 06/04/07

2004 SP Authentic Chirography Triple

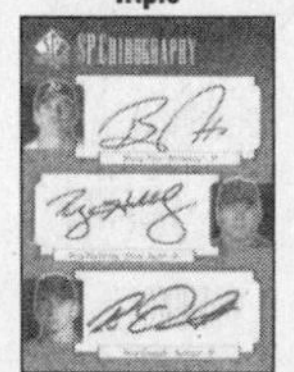

A couple of cards were not totally ready at pack-out time and those cards could be exchanged until June 4, 2007.

OVERALL AUTO INSERT ODDS 1:12
STATED PRINT RUN 25 SERIAL #'d SETS

BWR Josh Beckett 150.00 250.00
Kerry Wood
Nolan Ryan
FBB Carlton Fisk 200.00 350.00
Johnny Bench
Yogi Berra
GSM Bob Gibson 175.00 300.00
Ozzie Smith
Stan Musial
JVB Derek Jeter 250.00 400.00
Javier Vazquez
Yogi Berra
PRC Colin Porter 40.00 80.00
Jose Reyes
Miguel Cabrera
RBT Alex Rodriguez 125.00 250.00
Hank Blalock
Mark Teixeira
RRR Alex Rodriguez 400.00 600.00
Cal Ripken
Phil Rizzuto
SJB Ichiro Suzuki 250.00 400.00
Jacque Jones
Rocco Baldelli
WLE Chien-Ming Wang 250.00 400.00
Cliff Lee
Willie Eyre
WPB Brandon Webb 75.00 150.00
Mark Prior
Josh Beckett
YYM Carl Yastrzemski 250.00 400.00
Robin Yount
Stan Musial
ZHO Barry Zito 60.00 120.00
Roy Halladay
Roy Oswalt

2004 SP Authentic USA Signatures 445

STATED PRINT RUN 445 SERIAL #'d SETS
*USA SIG 50: .6X TO 1.5X BASIC
USA SIG 50 PRINT RUN 50 #'d SETS
OVERALL AUTO INSERT ODDS 1:12

1 Ernie Young 4.00 10.00
2 Chris Burke 6.00 15.00
3 Jesse Crain 6.00 15.00
4 Justin Duchscherer 6.00 15.00
5 J.D. Durbin 4.00 10.00
6 Gerald Laird 6.00 15.00
7 John Grabow 4.00 10.00
8 Gabe Gross 6.00 15.00
9 J.J. Hardy 15.00 40.00
10 Jeremy Reed 6.00 15.00
11 Graham Koonce 4.00 10.00
12 Mike Lamb 4.00 10.00
13 Justin Leone 6.00 15.00
14 Ryan Madson 4.00 10.00
15 Joe Mauer 20.00 50.00
16 Todd Williams 4.00 10.00
17 Horacio Ramirez 4.00 10.00
18 Mike Rouse 4.00 10.00
19 Jason Stanford 4.00 10.00
20 John Van Benschoten 4.00 10.00
21 Grady Sizemore 12.50 30.00

2004 SP Authentic USA Signatures 50

9 J.J. Hardy 40.00 80.00

2005 SP Authentic

This set was released within two separate products . . . SP Collection in October, 2005 (containing cards 1-100) and Upper Deck Update in February, 2006 (containing cards 101-186) . The SP Collection packs had five cards in each pack with an $6 SRP and those packs came 20 packs to a box and 16 boxes to a case. Upper Deck Update packs contained 5 cards and carried a $4.99 SRP. 24 packs were issued in each box. Of note, cards 105, 115, 118-119, 142, 154, 161, 180, 183 and 186 do not exist.

COMP.BASIC SET (100) 10.00 25.00
COMMON CARD (1-100) .15 .40
COMMON RETIRED 1-100 .15 .40
1-100 ISSUED IN 05 SP COLLECTION PACKS
COMMON AUTO (101-186) 4.00 10.00
101-186 ODDS APPX 1:8 '05 UD UPDATE
101-186 PRINT RUN 185 SERIAL #'d SETS
105, 115, 118-119, 142, 154 DO NOT EXIST
161, 180, 183, 186 DO NOT EXIST

1 A.J. Burnett .25 .60
2 Aaron Rowand .15 .40
3 Adam Dunn .25 .60
4 Adrian Beltre .15 .40
5 Adrian Gonzalez .25 .60
6 Akinori Otsuka .15 .40
7 Albert Pujols 1.00 2.50
8 Andre Dawson .25 .60
9 Andruw Jones .15 .40
10 Aramis Ramirez .15 .40
11 Barry Larkin .25 .60
12 Ben Sheets .15 .40
13 Bo Jackson .40 1.00
14 Bobby Abreu .15 .40
15 Bobby Crosby .15 .40
16 Bronson Arroyo .15 .40
17 Cal Ripken 1.50 4.00
18 Carl Crawford .25 .60
19 Carlos Zambrano .25 .60
20 Casey Kotchman .15 .40
21 Cesar Izturis .15 .40
22 Chone Figgins .15 .40
23 Corey Patterson .15 .40
24 Craig Biggio .25 .60
25 Dale Murphy .15 .40
26 Dallas McPherson .15 .40
27 Danny Haren .15 .40
28 Darryl Strawberry .15 .40
29 David Ortiz .40 1.00
30 David Wright .60 1.50
31 Derek Jeter 1.00 2.50
32 Derrek Lee .15 .40
33 Don Mattingly .75 2.00
34 Dwight Gooden .15 .40
35 Edgar Renteria .15 .40
36 Eric Chavez .15 .40
37 Eric Gagne .15 .40
38 Gary Sheffield .15 .40
39 Gavin Floyd .15 .40
40 Pedro Martinez .25 .60
41 Greg Maddux .60 1.50
42 Hank Blalock .15 .40
43 Huston Street .15 .40
44 J.D. Drew .15 .40
45 Jake Peavy .15 .40
46 Jake Westbrook .15 .40
47 Jason Bay .15 .40
48 Austin Kearns .15 .40
49 Jeremy Reed .15 .40
50 Jim Rice .15 .40
51 Jimmy Rollins .25 .60
52 Joe Blanton .15 .40
53 Joe Mauer .40 1.00
54 Johan Santana .40 1.00
55 John Smoltz .40 1.00
56 Johnny Estrada .15 .40
57 Jose Reyes .25 .60
58 Ken Griffey Jr. .60 1.50
59 Kerry Wood .15 .40
60 Khalil Greene .15 .40
61 Marcus Giles .15 .40
62 Melvin Mora .15 .40
63 Mark Grace .25 .60
64 Mark Mulder .15 .40
65 Mark Prior .25 .60
66 Mark Teixeria .40 1.00
67 Matt Clement .15 .40
68 Michael Young .25 .60
69 Miguel Cabrera .40 1.00
70 Miguel Tejada .25 .60
71 Mike Piazza .40 1.00
72 Mike Schmidt .75 2.00
73 Nolan Ryan 1.00 2.50
74 Oliver Perez .15 .40
75 Nick Johnson .15 .40
76 Paul Molitor .40 1.00
77 Rafael Palmeiro .25 .60
78 Randy Johnson .40 1.00
79 Reggie Jackson .40 1.00
80 Rich Harden .15 .40
81 Rickie Weeks .25 .60
82 Robin Yount .40 1.00
83 Roger Clemens .50 1.25
84 Roy Oswalt .25 .60
85 Ryan Howard .75 2.00
86 Ryne Sandberg .75 2.00
87 Scott Kazmir .40 1.00
88 Scott Rolen .25 .60
89 Sean Burroughs .15 .40
90 Sean Casey .15 .40
91 Shingo Takatsu .15 .40
92 Tim Hudson .25 .60
93 Tony Gwynn .50 1.25
94 Torii Hunter .15 .40
95 Travis Hafner .15 .40
96 Victor Martinez .25 .60
97 Vladimir Guerrero .40 1.00
98 Wade Boggs .25 .60
99 Will Clark .25 .60
100 Yadier Molina .25 .60
101 Adam Shabala AU RC 4.00 10.00
102 Ambiorix Burgos AU RC 4.00 10.00
103 Ambiorix Concepcion AU RC 4.00 10.00
104 Anibal Sanchez AU RC 15.00 40.00
106 Brandon McCarthy AU RC 15.00 40.00
107 Brian Burres AU RC 4.00 10.00
108 Carlos Ruiz AU RC 10.00 25.00
109 Casey Rogowski AU RC 6.00 15.00
110 Chad Orvella AU RC 4.00 10.00
111 Chris Resop AU RC 6.00 15.00
112 Chris Roberson AU RC 4.00 10.00
113 Chris Seddon AU RC 4.00 10.00
114 Colter Bean AU RC 6.00 15.00
116 Dave Gassner AU RC 4.00 10.00
117 Brian Anderson AU RC 15.00 40.00
120 Devon Lowery AU RC 4.00 10.00
121 Enrique Gonzalez AU RC 6.00 15.00
122 Eude Brito AU RC 4.00 10.00
123 Francisco Butto AU RC 4.00 10.00
124 Franquelis Osoria AU RC 4.00 10.00
125 Garrett Jones AU RC 50.00 100.00
126 Geovany Soto AU RC 75.00 150.00
127 Hayden Penn AU RC 10.00 25.00
128 Ismael Ramirez AU RC 4.00 10.00
129 Jared Gothreaux AU RC 4.00 10.00
130 Jason Hammel AU RC 4.00 10.00
131 Jeff Miller AU RC 4.00 10.00
132 Jeff Niemann AU RC 12.50 30.00
133 Joel Peralta AU RC 4.00 10.00
134 John Hattig AU RC 4.00 10.00
135 Jorge Campillo AU RC 4.00 10.00
136 Juan Morillo AU RC 4.00 10.00
137 Justin Verlander AU RC 100.00 200.00
138 Ryan Garko AU RC 25.00 50.00
139 Keiichi Yabu AU RC 6.00 15.00
140 Kendry Morales AU RC 40.00 80.00
141 Luis Hernandez AU RC 4.00 10.00
143 Luis O.Rodriguez AU RC 4.00 10.00
144 Luke Scott AU RC 30.00 60.00
145 Marcos Carvajal AU RC 4.00 10.00
146 Mark Woodyard AU RC 4.00 10.00
147 Matt A.Smith AU RC 4.00 10.00
148 Matthew Lindstrom AU RC 4.00 10.00
149 Miguel Negron AU RC 6.00 15.00
150 Mike Morse AU RC 15.00 40.00
151 Nate McLouth AU RC 50.00 100.00
152 Nelson Cruz AU RC 60.00 120.00
153 Nick Masset AU RC 4.00 10.00
155 Paulino Reynoso AU RC 4.00 10.00
156 Pedro Lopez AU RC 4.00 10.00

Card	Low	High
157 Pete Orr AU RC	4.00	10.00
158 Philip Humber AU RC	12.50	30.00
159 Prince Fielder AU RC	225.00	300.00
160 Randy Messenger AU RC	4.00	10.00
162 Raul Tablado AU RC	4.00	10.00
163 Ronny Paulino AU RC	10.00	25.00
164 Russ Rohlicek AU RC	4.00	10.00
165 Russell Martin AU RC	60.00	120.00
166 Scott Baker AU RC	6.00	15.00
167 Scott Munter AU RC	4.00	10.00
168 Sean Thompson AU RC	4.00	10.00
169 Sean Tracey AU RC	4.00	10.00
170 Shane Costa AU RC	4.00	10.00
171 Stephen Drew AU RC	30.00	60.00
172 Steve Schmoll AU RC	4.00	10.00
173 Tadahito Iguchi AU RC	20.00	50.00
174 Tony Giarratano AU RC	4.00	10.00
175 Tony Pena AU RC	4.00	10.00
176 Travis Bowyer AU RC	4.00	10.00
177 Ubaldo Jimenez AU RC	12.50	30.00
178 Wladimir Balentien AU RC	50.00	100.00
179 Yorman Bazardo AU RC	4.00	10.00
181 Ryan Zimmerman AU RC	150.00	225.00
182 Chris Denorfia AU RC	10.00	25.00
184 Jermaine Van Buren AU	4.00	10.00
185 Mark McLemore AU RC	4.00	10.00

2005 SP Authentic Gold

APPX AU ODDS 1:8 '05 UD UPDATE
STATED PRINT RUN 10 SERIAL #'d SETS
105, 115, 118-119, 142, 154 DO NOT EXIST
161, 180, 183, 186 DO NOT EXIST
NO PRICING DUE TO SCARCITY

2005 SP Authentic Jersey

STATED PRINT RUN 199 SERIAL #'d SETS
*GOLD: .5X TO 1.2X BASIC
GOLD PRINT RUN 99 SERIAL #'d SETS
ISSUED IN 05 SP COLLECTION PACKS
OVERALL GAME-USED ODDS 1:10

Card	Low	High
1 A.J. Burnett	2.00	5.00
2 Aaron Rowand	2.00	5.00
3 Adam Dunn	2.00	5.00
4 Adrian Beltre	2.00	5.00
5 Adrian Gonzalez	2.00	5.00
6 Akinori Otsuka	2.00	5.00
7 Albert Pujols	6.00	15.00
8 Andre Dawson	3.00	8.00
9 Andruw Jones	3.00	8.00
10 Aramis Ramirez	2.00	5.00
11 Barry Larkin	3.00	8.00
12 Ben Sheets	2.00	5.00
13 Bo Jackson	4.00	10.00
14 Bobby Abreu	2.00	5.00
15 Bobby Crosby	2.00	5.00
16 Bronson Arroyo	2.00	5.00
17 Cal Ripken Pants	8.00	20.00
18 Carl Crawford	2.00	5.00
19 Carlos Zambrano	2.00	5.00
20 Casey Kotchman	2.00	5.00
21 Cesar Izturis	2.00	5.00
22 Chone Figgins	2.00	5.00
23 Corey Patterson	2.00	5.00
24 Craig Biggio	3.00	8.00
25 Dale Murphy	4.00	10.00
26 Dallas McPherson	2.00	5.00
27 Danny Haren	2.00	5.00
28 Darryl Strawberry	3.00	8.00
29 David Ortiz	3.00	8.00
30 David Wright	4.00	10.00
31 Derek Jeter Pants	8.00	20.00
32 Derrek Lee	3.00	8.00
33 Don Mattingly	6.00	15.00
34 Dwight Gooden	3.00	8.00
35 Edgar Renteria	2.00	5.00
36 Eric Chavez	2.00	5.00
37 Eric Gagne	2.00	5.00
38 Gary Sheffield	2.00	5.00
39 Gavin Floyd	2.00	5.00
40 Pedro Martinez	3.00	8.00
41 Greg Maddux	4.00	10.00
42 Hank Blalock	2.00	5.00
43 Huston Street	3.00	8.00
44 J.D. Drew	2.00	5.00
45 Jake Peavy	2.00	5.00
46 Jake Westbrook	2.00	5.00
47 Jason Bay	2.00	5.00
48 Austin Kearns	2.00	5.00
49 Jeremy Reed	2.00	5.00
50 Jim Rice	3.00	8.00
51 Jimmy Rollins	2.00	5.00
52 Joe Blanton	2.00	5.00
53 Joe Mauer	4.00	10.00
54 Johan Santana	4.00	10.00
55 John Smoltz	3.00	8.00
56 Johnny Estrada	2.00	5.00
57 Jose Reyes	2.00	5.00
58 Ken Griffey Jr.	6.00	15.00
59 Kerry Wood	2.00	5.00
60 Khalil Greene	3.00	8.00
61 Marcus Giles	2.00	5.00
62 Melvin Mora	2.00	5.00
63 Mark Grace	4.00	10.00
64 Mark Mulder	2.00	5.00
65 Mark Prior	3.00	8.00
66 Mark Teixeria	3.00	8.00
67 Matt Clement	2.00	5.00
68 Michael Young	2.00	5.00
69 Miguel Cabrera	3.00	8.00
70 Miguel Tejada	2.00	5.00
71 Mike Piazza	4.00	10.00
72 Mike Schmidt	6.00	15.00
73 Nolan Ryan Pants	8.00	20.00
74 Oliver Perez	2.00	5.00
75 Nick Johnson	2.00	5.00
76 Paul Molitor	3.00	8.00
77 Rafael Palmeiro	4.00	10.00
78 Randy Johnson	4.00	10.00
79 Reggie Jackson	4.00	10.00
80 Rich Harden	2.00	5.00
81 Rickie Weeks	2.00	5.00
82 Robin Yount	4.00	10.00
83 Roger Clemens Pants	4.00	10.00
84 Roy Oswalt	2.00	5.00
85 Ryan Howard	10.00	25.00
86 Ryne Sandberg	6.00	15.00
87 Scott Kazmir	2.00	5.00
88 Scott Rolen	3.00	8.00
89 Sean Burroughs	2.00	5.00
90 Sean Casey	2.00	5.00
91 Shingo Takatsu	2.00	5.00
92 Tim Hudson	2.00	5.00
93 Tony Gwynn	4.00	10.00
94 Torii Hunter	2.00	5.00
95 Travis Hafner	2.00	5.00
96 Victor Martinez	2.00	5.00
97 Vladimir Guerrero	4.00	10.00
98 Wade Boggs	4.00	10.00
99 Will Clark	4.00	10.00
100 Yadier Molina	2.00	5.00

2005 SP Authentic Signature

PRINT RUNS B/WN 25-550 COPIES PER
GOLD PRINT RUN 10 SERIAL #'d SETS
NO GOLD PRICING DUE TO SCARCITY
ISSUED IN 05 SP COLLECTION PACKS
OVERALL AUTO ODDS 1:10

Card	Low	High
2 Aaron Rowand/550	10.00	25.00
3 Adam Dunn/25	10.00	25.00
4 Adrian Beltre/125	6.00	15.00
5 Adrian Gonzalez/550	10.00	25.00
6 Akinori Otsuka/475	6.00	15.00
7 Albert Pujols/25	150.00	250.00
8 Andre Dawson/125	6.00	15.00
9 Andruw Jones/25	20.00	50.00
10 Aramis Ramirez/475	6.00	15.00
11 Barry Larkin/125	15.00	40.00
12 Ben Sheets/350	6.00	15.00
13 Bo Jackson/25	40.00	80.00
15 Bobby Crosby/350	6.00	15.00
16 Bronson Arroyo/550	6.00	15.00
18 Carl Crawford/475	6.00	15.00
20 Casey Kotchman/550	6.00	15.00
21 Cesar Izturis/550	4.00	10.00
22 Chone Figgins/550	6.00	15.00
23 Corey Patterson/350	4.00	10.00
24 Craig Biggio/125	15.00	40.00
25 Dale Murphy/350	10.00	25.00
26 Dallas McPherson/550	4.00	10.00
27 Danny Haren/550	4.00	10.00
28 Darryl Strawberry/125	6.00	15.00
30 David Wright/350	20.00	50.00
31 Derek Jeter/150	90.00	150.00
32 Derrek Lee/350	10.00	25.00
33 Don Mattingly/25	40.00	80.00
34 Dwight Gooden/475	6.00	15.00
36 Eric Chavez/75	8.00	20.00
38 Gary Sheffield/25	15.00	40.00
39 Gavin Floyd/550	4.00	10.00
42 Hank Blalock/25	10.00	25.00
43 Huston Street/550	10.00	25.00
45 Jake Peavy/475	6.00	15.00
46 Jake Westbrook/550	4.00	10.00
47 Jason Bay/475	6.00	15.00
48 Austin Kearns/75	5.00	12.00
49 Jeremy Reed/550	4.00	10.00
50 Jim Rice/350	6.00	15.00
52 Joe Blanton/550	4.00	10.00
53 Joe Mauer/350	20.00	50.00
55 John Smoltz/25	20.00	50.00
57 Jose Reyes/475	6.00	15.00
59 Kerry Wood/25	10.00	25.00
60 Khalil Greene/350	10.00	25.00
62 Melvin Mora/475	6.00	15.00
63 Mark Grace/25	15.00	40.00
64 Mark Mulder/350	6.00	15.00
65 Mark Prior/25	10.00	25.00
66 Mark Teixeria/125	10.00	25.00
67 Matt Clement/350	6.00	15.00
68 Michael Young/475	6.00	15.00
69 Miguel Cabrera/125	10.00	25.00
70 Miguel Tejada/25	10.00	25.00
71 Mike Piazza/25	50.00	100.00
72 Mike Schmidt/25	40.00	80.00
73 Nolan Ryan/25	50.00	100.00
74 Oliver Perez/475	4.00	10.00
75 Nick Johnson/550	6.00	15.00
76 Paul Molitor/25	10.00	25.00
77 Rafael Palmeiro/25	15.00	40.00
78 Randy Johnson/25	50.00	100.00
79 Reggie Jackson/25	15.00	40.00
83 Roger Clemens/25	125.00	200.00
84 Roy Oswalt/125	6.00	15.00
85 Ryan Howard/550	30.00	60.00
86 Ryne Sandberg/25	40.00	80.00
87 Scott Kazmir/475	10.00	25.00
89 Sean Burroughs/475	4.00	10.00
91 Shingo Takatsu/550	6.00	15.00
92 Tim Hudson/25	10.00	25.00
93 Tony Gwynn/25	30.00	60.00
94 Torii Hunter/125	6.00	15.00
97 Vladimir Guerrero/25	40.00	80.00
98 Wade Boggs/25	15.00	40.00
99 Will Clark/25	20.00	50.00

2005 SP Authentic Signature Jersey Gold

ISSUED IN 05 SP COLLECTION PACKS
OVERALL PREMIUM AU-GU ODDS 1:20
STATED PRINT RUN 10 SERIAL #'d SETS
NO PRICING DUE TO SCARCITY

2005 SP Authentic Chirography

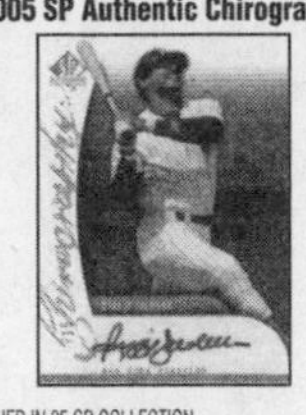

ISSUED IN 05 SP COLLECTION
OVERALL AUTO ODDS 1:10
STATED PRINT RUN 15 SERIAL #'d SETS
NO PRICING DUE TO SCARCITY

2005 SP Authentic Chirography Triple

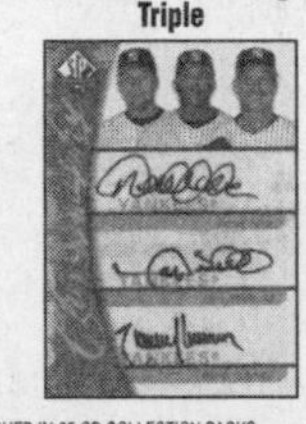

ISSUED IN 05 SP COLLECTION PACKS
OVERALL PREMIUM AU-GU ODDS 1:20
STATED PRINT RUN 5 SERIAL #'d SETS
NO PRICING DUE TO SCARCITY

2005 SP Authentic Honors

ISSUED IN 05 SP COLLECTION PACKS
OVERALL INSERT ODDS 1:10
STATED PRINT RUN 299 SERIAL #'d SETS

Card	Low	High
AB Adrian Beltre	.60	1.50
AP Albert Pujols	4.00	10.00
AR Aramis Ramirez	.60	1.50
BC Bobby Crosby	.60	1.50
BJ Bo Jackson	1.50	4.00
BL Barry Larkin	1.00	2.50
BO Jeremy Bonderman	.60	1.50
BS Ben Sheets	.60	1.50
BU B.J. Upton	1.00	2.50
CA Miguel Cabrera	1.50	4.00
CC Carl Crawford	1.00	2.50
CP Corey Patterson	.60	1.50
CR Cal Ripken	6.00	15.00
CZ Carlos Zambrano	1.00	2.50
DG Dwight Gooden	.60	1.50
DJ Derek Jeter	4.00	10.00
DM Dale Murphy	.60	1.50
DO David Ortiz	1.50	4.00
DW David Wright	2.50	6.00
GR Khalil Greene	.60	1.50
JB Jason Bay	.60	1.50
JM Joe Mauer	1.50	4.00
JP Jake Peavy	.60	1.50
JR Jimmy Rollins	1.00	2.50
JS Johan Santana	1.50	4.00
JW Jake Westbrook	.60	1.50
KG Ken Griffey Jr.	2.50	6.00
MC Dallas McPherson	.60	1.50
MG Marcus Giles	.60	1.50
MO Justin Morneau	1.50	4.00
MS Mike Schmidt	3.00	8.00
MT Mark Teixeria	1.50	4.00
MY Michael Young	1.00	2.50
NR Nolan Ryan	4.00	10.00
OP Oliver Perez	.60	1.50
PM Paul Molitor	1.50	4.00
RC Roger Clemens	2.00	5.00
RE Jose Reyes	1.00	2.50
RH Rich Harden	.60	1.50
RS Ryne Sandberg	3.00	8.00
SK Scott Kazmir	1.50	4.00
SM John Smoltz	1.50	4.00
ST Shingo Takatsu	.60	1.50
TE Miguel Tejada	1.00	2.50
TG Tony Gwynn	2.00	5.00
TH Travis Hafner	.60	1.50
VM Victor Martinez	1.00	2.50
WB Wade Boggs	1.00	2.50
WC Will Clark	1.00	2.50
ZG Zack Greinke	1.00	2.50

2005 SP Authentic Honors Jersey

ISSUED IN 05 SP COLLECTION PACKS
OVERALL PREMIUM AU-GU ODDS 1:20
STATED PRINT RUN 130 SERIAL #'d SETS

Card	Low	High
AB Adrian Beltre	2.00	5.00
AP Albert Pujols	6.00	15.00
AR Aramis Ramirez	2.00	5.00
BC Bobby Crosby	2.00	5.00
BJ Bo Jackson	4.00	10.00
BL Barry Larkin	3.00	8.00
BO Jeremy Bonderman	2.00	5.00
BS Ben Sheets	2.00	5.00
BU B.J. Upton	2.00	5.00
CA Miguel Cabrera	3.00	8.00
CC Carl Crawford	2.00	5.00
CP Corey Patterson	2.00	5.00
CR Cal Ripken Pants	8.00	20.00
CZ Carlos Zambrano	2.00	5.00
DG Dwight Gooden	3.00	8.00
DJ Derek Jeter Pants	8.00	20.00
DM Dale Murphy	4.00	10.00
DO David Ortiz	3.00	8.00
DW David Wright	4.00	10.00
GR Khalil Greene	3.00	8.00
JB Jason Bay	2.00	5.00
JM Joe Mauer	4.00	10.00
JP Jake Peavy	2.00	5.00
JR Jimmy Rollins	2.00	5.00
JS Johan Santana	4.00	10.00
JW Jake Westbrook	2.00	5.00
KG Ken Griffey Jr.	6.00	15.00
MC Dallas McPherson	2.00	5.00
MG Marcus Giles	2.00	5.00
MO Justin Morneau	2.00	5.00
MS Mike Schmidt	6.00	15.00
MT Mark Teixeria	3.00	8.00
MY Michael Young	2.00	5.00
NR Nolan Ryan Pants	8.00	20.00
OP Oliver Perez	2.00	5.00
PM Paul Molitor	3.00	8.00
RC Roger Clemens Pants	4.00	10.00
RE Jose Reyes	2.00	5.00
RH Rich Harden	2.00	5.00
RS Ryne Sandberg	6.00	15.00
SK Scott Kazmir	2.00	5.00
SM John Smoltz	3.00	8.00
ST Shingo Takatsu	2.00	5.00
TE Miguel Tejada	2.00	5.00
TG Tony Gwynn	4.00	10.00
TH Travis Hafner	2.00	5.00
VM Victor Martinez	2.00	5.00
WB Wade Boggs	4.00	10.00
WC Will Clark	4.00	10.00
ZG Zack Greinke	2.00	5.00

2005 SP Authentic Honors Signature

ISSUED IN 05 SP COLLECTION PACKS
OVERALL PREMIUM AU-GU ODDS 1:20
STATED PRINT RUN 5 SERIAL #'d SETS
NO PRICING DUE TO SCARCITY

2006 SP Authentic

This 300-card set was released in December, 2006. The set was issued in five-card packs, with an $4.99 SRP, which came 24 packs to a box and 12 boxes to a case. The first 100 cards of the set all feature veterans while cards 101-200 were inserted at a stated rate of one in eight and were issued to a stated print run of 899 serial numbered cards. The final 100-cards in this set all feature 2006 rookies and had between 125 and 899 serial numbered copies produced. These autograph cards were issued at a stated rate of one in 16. A few players did not return their signatures in time for pack out and those autographs could be redeemed until December 5, 2009.

Card	Low	High
COMP.SET w/o SP's (100)	6.00	15.00
101-200 STATED ODDS 1:8		
101-200 PRINT RUN 899 #'d SETS		
201-300 AU STATED ODDS 1:16		
201-300 AU PRINTS B/WN 125-899 PER		
EXCH: 214/235/242/247/249/253/277		
EXCH: 279/280/291		
EXCHANGE DEADLINE 12/05/09		
1 Erik Bedard	.15	.40
2 Corey Patterson	.15	.40
3 Ramon Hernandez	.15	.40
4 Kris Benson	.15	.40
5 Miguel Batista	.15	.40
6 Orlando Hudson	.15	.40
7 Shawn Green	.15	.40
8 Jeff Francoeur	.40	1.00
9 Marcus Giles	.15	.40
10 Edgar Renteria	.15	.40
11 Tim Hudson	.25	.60
12 Tim Wakefield	.15	.40
13 Mark Loretta	.15	.40
14 Kevin Youkilis	.15	.40
15 Mike Lowell	.15	.40
16 Coco Crisp	.15	.40
17 Tadahito Iguchi	.15	.40
18 Scott Podsednik	.15	.40
19 Jermaine Dye	.15	.40
20 Jose Contreras	.15	.40
21 Carlos Zambrano	.25	.60
22 Aramis Ramirez	.15	.40
23 Jacque Jones	.15	.40
24 Austin Kearns	.15	.40
25 Felipe Lopez	.15	.40
26 Brandon Phillips	.15	.40
27 Aaron Harang	.15	.40
28 Cliff Lee	.25	.60
29 Jhonny Peralta	.15	.40
30 Jason Michaels	.15	.40
31 Clint Barmes	.15	.40
32 Brad Hawpe	.15	.40
33 Aaron Cook	.15	.40
34 Kenny Rogers	.15	.40
35 Carlos Guillen	.15	.40
36 Brian Moehler	.15	.40
37 Andy Pettitte	.25	.60
38 Wandy Rodriguez	.15	.40
39 Morgan Ensberg	.15	.40
40 Preston Wilson	.15	.40
41 Mark Grudzielanek	.15	.40
42 Angel Berroa	.15	.40
43 Jeremy Affeldt	.15	.40
44 Zack Greinke	.25	.60
45 Orlando Cabrera	.15	.40
46 Garret Anderson	.15	.40
47 Ervin Santana	.15	.40
48 Derek Lowe	.15	.40
49 Nomar Garciaparra	.40	1.00
50 J.D. Drew	.15	.40
51 Rafael Furcal	.15	.40
52 Rickie Weeks	.25	.60
53 Geoff Jenkins	.15	.40
54 Bill Hall	.15	.40
55 Chris Capuano	.15	.40
56 Derrick Turnbow	.15	.40
57 Justin Morneau	.40	1.00
58 Michael Cuddyer	.15	.40
59 Luis Castillo	.15	.40
60 Hideki Matsui	.40	1.00
61 Jason Giambi	.15	.40
62 Jorge Posada	.25	.60
63 Mariano Rivera	.40	1.00
64 Billy Wagner	.15	.40
65 Carlos Delgado	.15	.40
66 Jose Reyes	.25	.60
67 Nick Swisher	.40	1.00
68 Bobby Crosby	.15	.40
69 Frank Thomas	.40	1.00
70 Ryan Howard	.60	1.50
71 Pat Burrell	.15	.40
72 Jimmy Rollins	.25	.60
73 Craig Wilson	.15	.40
74 Freddy Sanchez	.15	.40
75 Sean Casey	.15	.40
76 Mike Piazza	.40	1.00
77 Dave Roberts	.15	.40
78 Chris Young	.15	.40
79 Noah Lowry	.15	.40
80 Armando Benitez	.15	.40
81 Pedro Feliz	.15	.40
82 Jose Lopez	.15	.40
83 Adrian Beltre	.15	.40
84 Jamie Moyer	.15	.40
85 Jason Isringhausen	.15	.40
86 Jason Marquis	.15	.40
87 David Eckstein	.15	.40
88 Juan Encarnacion	.15	.40
89 Julio Lugo	.15	.40
90 Ty Wigginton	.15	.40
91 Jorge Cantu	.15	.40
92 Akinori Otsuka	.15	.40
93 Hank Blalock	.15	.40
94 Kevin Mench	.15	.40
95 Lyle Overbay	.15	.40
96 Shea Hillenbrand	.15	.40
97 B.J. Ryan	.15	.40
98 Tony Armas	.15	.40
99 Chad Cordero	.15	.40
100 Jose Guillen	.15	.40
101 Miguel Tejada	1.00	2.50
102 Brian Roberts	.60	1.50
103 Melvin Mora	.60	1.50
104 Brandon Webb	1.00	2.50
105 Chad Tracy	.60	1.50
106 Luis Gonzalez	.60	1.50
107 Andruw Jones	.60	1.50
108 Chipper Jones	1.50	4.00
109 John Smoltz	1.50	4.00
110 Curt Schilling	1.00	2.50
111 Josh Beckett	1.00	2.50
112 David Ortiz	1.00	2.50
113 Manny Ramirez	1.50	4.00
114 Jason Varitek	1.50	4.00
115 Jim Thome	1.00	2.50
116 Paul Konerko	1.00	2.50
117 Javier Vazquez	.60	1.50
118 Mark Prior	1.00	2.50
119 Derrek Lee	.60	1.50
120 Greg Maddux	2.50	6.00
121 Ken Griffey Jr.	2.50	6.00
122 Adam Dunn	1.00	2.50
123 Bronson Arroyo	.60	1.50
124 Travis Hafner	.60	1.50
125 Victor Martinez	1.00	2.50
126 Grady Sizemore	1.00	2.50
127 C.C. Sabathia	1.00	2.50
128 Todd Helton	1.00	2.50
129 Matt Holliday	1.50	4.00
130 Garrett Atkins	.60	1.50
131 Jeff Francis	.60	1.50
132 Jeremy Bonderman	.60	1.50
133 Ivan Rodriguez	1.00	2.50
134 Chris Shelton	.60	1.50
135 Magglio Ordonez	1.00	2.50
136 Dontrelle Willis	.60	1.50
137 Miguel Cabrera	1.50	4.00
138 Roger Clemens	2.00	5.00
139 Roy Oswalt	1.00	2.50
140 Lance Berkman	1.00	2.50
141 Reggie Sanders	.60	1.50
142 Vladimir Guerrero	1.50	4.00
143 Bartolo Colon	.60	1.50
144 Chone Figgins	.60	1.50
145 Francisco Rodriguez	1.00	2.50
146 Brad Penny	.60	1.50
147 Jeff Kent	.60	1.50
148 Eric Gagne	.60	1.50
149 Carlos Lee	.60	1.50
150 Ben Sheets	.60	1.50
151 Johan Santana	1.50	4.00
152 Torii Hunter	.60	1.50
153 Joe Nathan	.60	1.50
154 Alex Rodriguez	2.50	6.00
155 Derek Jeter	4.00	10.00
156 Randy Johnson	1.50	4.00
157 Johnny Damon	1.00	2.50
158 Mike Mussina	1.00	2.50
159 Pedro Martinez	1.00	2.50
160 Tom Glavine	1.00	2.50
161 David Wright	2.50	6.00
162 Carlos Beltran	.60	1.50
163 Rich Harden	.60	1.50
164 Barry Zito	.60	1.50
165 Eric Chavez	.60	1.50
166 Huston Street	.60	1.50
167 Bobby Abreu	.60	1.50
168 Chase Utley	1.50	4.00
169 Brett Myers	.60	1.50
170 Jason Bay	.60	1.50
171 Zach Duke	.60	1.50
172 Jake Peavy	.60	1.50
173 Brian Giles	.60	1.50
174 Khalil Greene	.60	1.50
175 Trevor Hoffman	1.00	2.50
176 Jason Schmidt	.60	1.50
177 Randy Winn	.60	1.50
178 Omar Vizquel	1.00	2.50
179 Kenji Johjima	1.50	4.00
180 Ichiro Suzuki	2.50	6.00
181 Richie Sexson	.60	1.50
182 Felix Hernandez	1.50	4.00
183 Albert Pujols	4.00	10.00
184 Chris Carpenter	1.50	4.00
185 Jim Edmonds	1.00	2.50
186 Scott Rolen	1.00	2.50
187 Carl Crawford	1.00	2.50
188 Scott Kazmir	1.00	2.50
189 Jonny Gomes	.60	1.50
190 Mark Teixeira	1.50	4.00
191 Michael Young	1.00	2.50
192 Kevin Millwood	.60	1.50
193 Vernon Wells	.60	1.50
194 Troy Glaus	.60	1.50
195 Roy Halladay	1.50	4.00
196 Alex Rios	1.00	2.50
197 Nick Johnson	.60	1.50
198 Livan Hernandez	.60	1.50
199 Alfonso Soriano	1.00	2.50
200 Jose Vidro	.60	1.50
201 Aaron Rakers AU/399 (RC)	3.00	8.00
202 Angel Pagan AU/399 (RC)	6.00	15.00
203 Ben Hendrickson AU/399 (RC)	3.00	8.00
204 Bobby Livingston AU/399 (RC)	3.00	8.00
205 Darrell Rasner AU/399 (RC)	3.00	8.00
206 Brian Bannister AU/399 (RC)	12.50	30.00
207 Brian Wilson AU/899 RC	40.00	80.00
208 Bobby Keppel AU/199 (RC)	6.00	15.00
209 Choo Freeman AU/399 (RC)	3.00	8.00
210 Chris Booker AU/899 (RC)	3.00	8.00
211 Chris Britton AU/399 (RC)	4.00	10.00
212 Chris Demaria AU/329 RC	4.00	10.00
213 Chris Resop AU/899 (RC)	3.00	8.00
214 Tony Gwynn Jr. AU/399 (RC)	30.00	60.00
215 Eric Reed AU/399 (RC)	3.00	8.00
216 Fabio Castro AU/399 RC	8.00	20.00
217 Fernando Nieve AU/299 (RC)	4.00	10.00
218 Freddie Bynum AU/899 (RC)	3.00	8.00
219 Guillermo Quiroz AU/399 (RC)	3.00	8.00
220 Hong-Chih Kuo AU/899 (RC)	30.00	60.00
221 Ryan Theriot AU/399 RC	12.50	30.00
222 Jack Taschner AU/899 (RC)	3.00	8.00
223 Jason Bergmann AU/899 (RC)	3.00	8.00
224 Jason Hammel AU/899 (RC)	3.00	8.00
225 Jeff Harris AU/399 RC	3.00	8.00
226 Jeremy Accardo AU/399 RC	4.00	10.00
227 Ty Taubenheim AU/399 RC	12.50	30.00
228 Joel Zumaya AU/399 (RC)	15.00	40.00
229 John Koronka AU/399 (RC)	3.00	8.00
230 Erick Aybar AU/399 (RC)	3.00	8.00
231 Jordan Tata AU/399 RC	6.00	15.00
232 Russell Martin AU/399 (RC)	15.00	40.00
233 Josh Rupe AU/399 (RC)	3.00	8.00
234 Kevin Frandsen AU/399 (RC)	6.00	15.00
235 Martin Prado AU/399 (RC)	6.00	15.00
236 Matt Capps AU/399 (RC)	3.00	8.00
237 Agustin Montero AU/199 (RC)	4.00	10.00
238 Mike Thompson AU/399 RC	3.00	8.00
239 Nate McLouth AU/399 (RC)	8.00	20.00
240 Peter Moylan AU/399 RC	3.00	8.00
241 Reggie Abercrombie AU/399 (RC)	3.00	8.00
242 Carlos Quentin AU/399 (RC)	8.00	20.00
243 Ron Flores AU/399 RC	3.00	8.00
244 Ryan Shealy AU/399 (RC)	8.00	20.00
245 Mike Rouse AU/399 (RC)	3.00	8.00
246 Santiago Ramirez AU/399 (RC)	3.00	8.00
247 Clay Hensley AU/899 (RC)	3.00	8.00
248 Skip Schumaker AU/399 (RC)	4.00	10.00
249 Eliezer Alfonzo AU/899 RC	3.00	8.00
250 Steve Stemle AU/399 RC	3.00	8.00
251 Tim Hamulack AU/399 (RC)	3.00	8.00
252 Tony Pena Jr. AU/299 (RC)	4.00	10.00
253 Emiliano Fruto AU/899 RC	3.00	8.00
254 Wil Nieves AU/399 (RC)	4.00	10.00
255 Joey Devine AU/399 RC	4.00	10.00
256 Adam Wainwright AU/399 (RC)	12.50	30.00
257 Andre Ethier AU/399 (RC)	15.00	40.00
258 Ben Johnson AU/399 (RC)	3.00	8.00
259 Boone Logan AU/399 RC	6.00	15.00
260 Chris Denorfia AU/899 (RC)	4.00	10.00
261 Alay Soler AU/299 RC	6.00	15.00
262 Cody Ross AU/899 (RC)	8.00	20.00
263 David Gassner AU/399 (RC)	3.00	8.00
264 Fausto Carmona AU/399 (RC)	10.00	25.00
265 Jeremy Sowers AU/299 (RC)	10.00	25.00
266 Jason Kubel AU/399 (RC)	4.00	10.00
267 John Van Benschoten AU/399 (RC)	3.00	8.00
268 Jose Capellan AU/399 (RC)	3.00	8.00
269 Josh Wilson AU/399 (RC)	3.00	8.00
270 Kelly Shoppach AU/399 (RC)	3.00	8.00
271 Macay McBride AU/399 (RC)	4.00	10.00
272 Matt Cain AU/399 (RC)	10.00	25.00
273 Mike Jacobs AU/399 (RC)	6.00	15.00
274 Paul Maholm AU/399 (RC)	4.00	10.00
275 Chad Billingsley AU/399 (RC)	6.00	15.00
276 Ruddy Lugo AU/399 (RC)	3.00	8.00
277 Jon Lester AU/399 RC	30.00	60.00
278 Sean Marshall AU/383 (RC)	10.00	25.00
279 Melky Cabrera AU/399 (RC)	15.00	40.00
280 Yusmeiro Petit AU/399 (RC)	4.00	10.00
281 Anderson Hernandez AU/299 (RC)	4.00	10.00
282 Brian Anderson AU/699 (RC)	4.00	10.00
283 Cole Hamels AU/299 (RC)	15.00	40.00
284 Boof Bonser AU/299 (RC)	6.00	15.00
285 Dan Uggla AU/199 (RC)	20.00	50.00
286 Francisco Liriano AU/299 (RC)	15.00	40.00
287 Hanley Ramirez AU/199 (RC)	30.00	60.00
288 Ian Kinsler AU/299 (RC)	40.00	80.00
289 Jeremy Hermida AU/299 (RC)	6.00	15.00
290 Jonathan Papelbon AU/199 (RC)	30.00	60.00
291 Jered Weaver AU/199 (RC)	15.00	40.00
292 Josh Johnson AU/299 (RC)	40.00	80.00
293 Josh Willingham AU/199 (RC)	6.00	15.00
294 Justin Verlander AU/199 (RC)	30.00	60.00
295 Stephen Drew AU/299 (RC)	12.50	30.00
296 Prince Fielder AU/125 (RC)	60.00	120.00
297 Ryan Zimmerman AU/199 (RC)	40.00	70.00
298 Takashi Saito AU/283 RC	15.00	40.00
299 Taylor Buchholz AU/299 (RC)	4.00	10.00
300 Conor Jackson AU/299 (RC)	6.00	15.00

2006 SP Authentic Rookie Signatures Platinum

RANDOM INSERTS IN PACKS
STATED PRINT RUN 1 SERIAL #'d SET
NO PRICING DUE TO SCARCITY
CARD 242 DOES NOT EXIST

2006 SP Authentic Baseball Heroes

Card	Low	High
COMPLETE SET (70)	50.00	100.00
STATED ODDS 1:4		
1 Albert Pujols	2.50	6.00
2 Andruw Jones	.40	1.00
3 Aramis Ramirez	.40	1.00
4 Brian Roberts	.40	1.00
5 Carl Crawford	.60	1.50
6 Carlos Lee	.40	1.00
7 Vladimir Guerrero	1.00	2.50
8 Chris Carpenter	1.00	2.50
9 Craig Biggio	.60	1.50
10 David Ortiz	.60	1.50
11 David Wright	1.50	4.00
12 Derrek Lee	.40	1.00
13 Dontrelle Willis	.40	1.00
14 Felix Hernandez	1.00	2.50
15 Garrett Atkins	.40	1.00
16 Grady Sizemore	.60	1.50
17 Huston Street	.40	1.00
18 Jake Peavy	.40	1.00
19 Jason Bay	.40	1.00
20 Joe Mauer	1.00	2.50
21 John Smoltz	1.00	2.50
22 Jonny Gomes	.40	1.00
23 Jorge Cantu	.40	1.00
24 Ken Griffey Jr.	1.50	4.00
25 Marcus Giles	.40	1.00
26 Mark Teixeira	1.00	2.50
27 Matt Cain	1.00	2.50
28 Michael Young	.60	1.50
29 Miguel Cabrera	1.00	2.50
30 Johan Santana	1.00	2.50
31 Nick Swisher	1.00	2.50
32 Prince Fielder	1.50	4.00
33 Joe Blanton	.40	1.00
34 Roy Oswalt	.60	1.50
35 Ryan Howard	1.50	4.00
36 Scott Kazmir	.60	1.50
37 Tadahito Iguchi	.40	1.00
38 Travis Hafner	.40	1.00
39 Victor Martinez	.60	1.50
40 Jose Reyes	.60	1.50
41 Chris Carpenter Albert Pujols	2.50	6.00
42 Albert Pujols Miguel Cabrera	2.50	6.00
43 Ken Griffey Jr. Andruw Jones	1.50	4.00
44 Derrek Lee Aramis Ramirez	.40	1.00
45 Ryan Howard Prince Fielder	1.50	4.00
46 Roy Oswalt Jake Peavy	.60	1.50
47 Craig Biggio Morgan Ensberg	.60	1.50
48 Travis Hafner David Ortiz	.60	1.50
49 Derek Jeter David Wright	2.50	6.00
50 Ken Griffey Jr. Derek Jeter	2.50	6.00
51 Derek Jeter Michael Young	.60	1.50
52 Scott Kazmir Dontrelle Willis	.60	1.50
53 Grady Sizemore Jason Bay	.60	1.50
54 Michael Young Mark Teixeira	.60	1.50
55 Brian Roberts Tadahito Iguchi	.40	1.00

56 Chien-Ming Wang 1.00 2.50
Matt Cain
Felix Hernandez
57 Derrek Lee 2.50 6.00
Albert Pujols
Mark Teixeira
58 Ken Griffey Jr. 2.50 6.00
Albert Pujols
Miguel Cabrera
59 Andruw Jones 1.00 2.50
John Smoltz
Marcus Giles
60 Kerry Wood .40 1.00
Derrek Lee
Aramis Ramirez
61 Aramis Ramirez 1.50 4.00
Morgan Ensberg
David Wright
62 Carl Crawford .60 1.50
Jorge Cantu
Jonny Gomes
63 John Smoltz 1.00 2.50
Chris Carpenter
Jake Peavy
64 Travis Hafner .60 1.50
Victor Martinez
Grady Sizemore
65 David Ortiz 1.50 4.00
Ryan Howard
Prince Fielder
66 John Smoltz 1.00 2.50
Chris Carpenter
Jake Peavy
Dontrelle Willis
67 Ken Griffey Jr. 2.50 6.00
Derek Jeter
David Ortiz
Albert Pujols
68 Andruw Jones 1.00 2.50
Derrek Lee
David Ortiz
Mark Teixeira
69 Craig Biggio .60 1.50
Brian Roberts
Marcus Giles
Tadahito Iguchi
70 David Wright 1.50 4.00
Mark Teixeira
Miguel Cabrera
Jason Bay

2006 SP Authentic By the Letter

STATED ODDS 1:24
PRINT RUNS B/WN 4-400 COPIES PER
EXCH: AJ, AR, CS, CZ, FH, FH2, GM, HO
EXCH: HU, JM, JR, JV, JW, KG, KG2, KG3
EXCH: KG4, KM, KW, MT, SM, TE
EXCHANGE DEADLINE 12/05/09
ABB A.J. Burnett B/50 20.00 40.00
ABE A.J. Burnett E/50 20.00 40.00
ABN A.J. Burnett N/50 20.00 40.00
ABR A.J. Burnett R/50 20.00 40.00
ABT A.J. Burnett T/100 20.00 40.00
ABU A.J. Burnett U/50 20.00 40.00
ADD Adam Dunn D/50 30.00 60.00
ADN Adam Dunn N/100 30.00 60.00
ADU Adam Dunn U/50 30.00 60.00
AGG Tony Gwynn Jr. G/150 20.00 40.00
AGN Tony Gwynn Jr. N/300 20.00 40.00
AGW Tony Gwynn Jr. W/150 20.00 40.00
AGY Tony Gwynn Jr. Y/150 20.00 40.00
AJE Andruw Jones E/20 60.00 120.00
AJJ Andruw Jones J/20 60.00 120.00
AJN Andruw Jones N/20 60.00 120.00
AJO Andruw Jones O/20 60.00 120.00
AJS Andruw Jones S/20 60.00 120.00
APJ Albert Pujols J/5 200.00 400.00
APL Albert Pujols L/5 200.00 400.00
APO Albert Pujols O/5 200.00 400.00
APP Albert Pujols P/5 200.00 400.00
APS Albert Pujols S/5 200.00 400.00
APU Albert Pujols U/5 200.00 400.00
AP2M Albert Pujols MVP M/10 200.00 400.00
AP2P Albert Pujols MVP P/10 200.00 400.00
AP2V Albert Pujols MVP V/10 200.00 400.00
ARI Alex Rios I/100 20.00 40.00
ARO Alex Rios O/100 20.00 40.00
ARR Alex Rios R/100 20.00 40.00
ARS Alex Rios S/100 20.00 40.00
BAA Bronson Arroyo A/80 10.00 25.00
BAO Bronson Arroyo O/160 10.00 25.00
BAR Bronson Arroyo R/160 10.00 25.00
BAY Bronson Arroyo Y/80 10.00 25.00
BIB Chad Billingsley B/75 10.00 25.00
BIE Chad Billingsley E/75 10.00 25.00
BIG Chad Billingsley G/75 10.00 25.00
BII Chad Billingsley I/150 10.00 25.00
BIL Chad Billingsley L/225 10.00 25.00
BIN Chad Billingsley N/75 10.00 25.00
BIS Chad Billingsley S/75 10.00 25.00
BIY Chad Billingsley Y/75 10.00 25.00
BRB Brian Roberts B/14 40.00 80.00
BRE Brian Roberts E/14 40.00 80.00
BRO Brian Roberts O/14 40.00 80.00
BRR Brian Roberts R/28 40.00 80.00
BRS Brian Roberts S/14 40.00 80.00
BRT Brian Roberts T/14 40.00 80.00
BSE Ben Sheets E/250 20.00 40.00
BSH Ben Sheets H/125 20.00 40.00
BSS Ben Sheets S/250 20.00 40.00
BST Ben Sheets T/125 20.00 40.00
BUN B.J. Upton N/20 25.00 50.00
BUO B.J. Upton O/20 25.00 50.00
BUP B.J. Upton P/20 25.00 50.00
BUT B.J. Upton T/20 25.00 50.00
BUU B.J. Upton U/20 25.00 50.00
CBB Craig Biggio B/55 40.00 80.00
CBG Craig Biggio G/110 40.00 80.00
CBI Craig Biggio I/110 40.00 80.00
CBO Craig Biggio O/55 40.00 80.00
CCA Chris Carpenter A/4 40.00 80.00
CCC Chris Carpenter C/4 40.00 80.00
CCE Chris Carpenter E/8 40.00 80.00
CCN Chris Carpenter N/4 40.00 80.00
CCP Chris Carpenter P/4 40.00 80.00
CCR Chris Carpenter R/8 40.00 80.00
CCT Chris Carpenter T/4 40.00 80.00
CC2C Chris Carpenter CY C/8 40.00 80.00
CC2G Chris Carpenter CY G/8 40.00 80.00
CC2N Chris Carpenter CY N/8 40.00 80.00
CC2U Chris Carpenter CY U/8 40.00 80.00
CC2U Chris Carpenter CY U/8 40.00 80.00
CC2Y Chris Carpenter CY Y/16 40.00 80.00
CHA Craig Hansen A/30 30.00 60.00
CHE Craig Hansen E/30 30.00 60.00
CHH Craig Hansen H/30 30.00 60.00
CHN Craig Hansen N/60 30.00 60.00
CHS Craig Hansen S/30 30.00 60.00
COA Cole Hamels A/120 40.00 80.00
COE Cole Hamels E/120 40.00 80.00
COH Cole Hamels H/120 40.00 80.00
COL Cole Hamels L/120 40.00 80.00
COM Cole Hamels M/120 40.00 80.00
COS Cole Hamels S/120 40.00 80.00
CSA C.C. Sabathia A/120 20.00 40.00
CSB C.C. Sabathia B/40 20.00 40.00
CSH C.C. Sabathia H/40 20.00 40.00
CSI C.C. Sabathia I/40 20.00 40.00
CSS C.C. Sabathia S/40 20.00 40.00
CST C.C. Sabathia T/40 20.00 40.00
CUE Chase Utley E/25 75.00 150.00
CUL Chase Utley L/25 75.00 150.00
CUT Chase Utley T/25 75.00 150.00
CUU Chase Utley U/25 75.00 150.00
CUY Chase Utley Y/25 75.00 150.00
CZA Carlos Zambrano A/34 50.00 100.00
CZB Carlos Zambrano B/17 50.00 100.00
CZM Carlos Zambrano M/17 50.00 100.00
CZN Carlos Zambrano N/17 50.00 100.00
CZO Carlos Zambrano O/17 50.00 100.00
CZR Carlos Zambrano R/17 50.00 100.00
CZZ Carlos Zambrano Z/17 50.00 100.00
DHA Danny Haren A/180 8.00 20.00
DHE Danny Haren E/180 8.00 20.00
DHH Danny Haren H/180 8.00 20.00
DHN Danny Haren N/180 8.00 20.00
DHR Danny Haren R/180 8.00 20.00
DJE Derek Jeter E/12 300.00 500.00
DJJ Derek Jeter J/6 300.00 500.00
DJR Derek Jeter R/6 300.00 500.00
DJT Derek Jeter T/6 300.00 500.00
DJ2A Derek Jeter Captain A/10 300.00 500.00
DJ2C Derek Jeter Captain C/5 300.00 500.00
DJ2I Derek Jeter Captain I/5 300.00 500.00
DJ2N Derek Jeter Captain N/5 300.00 500.00
DJ2P Derek Jeter Captain P/5 300.00 500.00
DJ2T Derek Jeter Captain T/5 300.00 500.00
DLE Derrek Lee E/400 25.00 50.00
DLL Derrek Lee L/200 25.00 50.00
DUA Dan Uggla A/100 12.50 30.00
DUG Dan Uggla G/200 12.50 30.00
DUL Dan Uggla L/100 12.50 30.00
DUU Dan Uggla U/100 12.50 30.00
DWI Dontrelle Willis I/300 6.00 15.00
DWL Dontrelle Willis L/300 6.00 15.00
DWS Dontrelle Willis S/150 6.00 15.00
DWW Dontrelle Willis W/150 6.00 15.00
ECA Eric Chavez A/75 20.00 40.00
ECC Eric Chavez C/75 20.00 40.00
ECE Eric Chavez E/75 20.00 40.00
ECH Eric Chavez H/75 20.00 40.00
ECV Eric Chavez V/75 20.00 40.00
ECZ Eric Chavez Z/75 20.00 40.00
FHA Felix Hernandez A/40 30.00 60.00
FHD Felix Hernandez D/40 30.00 60.00
FHE Felix Hernandez E/80 30.00 60.00
FHH Felix Hernandez H/40 30.00 60.00
FHN Felix Hernandez N/80 30.00 60.00
FHR Felix Hernandez R/40 30.00 60.00
FHZ Felix Hernandez Z/40 30.00 60.00
FH2G Felix Hernandez King G/75 30.00 60.00
FH2I Felix Hernandez King I/75 30.00 60.00
FH2K Felix Hernandez King K/75 30.00 60.00
FH2N Felix Hernandez King N/75 30.00 60.00
FLA Francisco Liriano A/100 8.00 20.00
FLI Francisco Liriano I/200 8.00 20.00
FLL Francisco Liriano L/100 8.00 20.00
FLN Francisco Liriano N/100 8.00 20.00
FLO Francisco Liriano O/100 8.00 20.00
FLR Francisco Liriano R/100 8.00 20.00
GMA Greg Maddux A/25 75.00 150.00
GMD Greg Maddux D/50 75.00 150.00
GMM Greg Maddux M/25 75.00 150.00
GMU Greg Maddux U/25 75.00 150.00
GMX Greg Maddux X/25 75.00 150.00
HBA Hank Blalock A/50 20.00 40.00
HBB Hank Blalock B/50 20.00 40.00
HBC Hank Blalock C/50 20.00 40.00
HBK Hank Blalock K/50 20.00 40.00
HBL Hank Blalock L/100 20.00 40.00
HBO Hank Blalock O/50 20.00 40.00
HKC Howie Kendrick C/75 25.00 50.00
HKD Howie Kendrick D/75 25.00 50.00
HKE Howie Kendrick E/75 25.00 50.00
HKI Howie Kendrick I/75 25.00 50.00
HKK Howie Kendrick K/150 25.00 50.00
HKN Howie Kendrick N/75 25.00 50.00
HKR Howie Kendrick R/75 25.00 50.00
HOA Trevor Hoffman A/8 40.00 80.00
HOF Trevor Hoffman F/16 40.00 80.00
HOH Trevor Hoffman H/8 40.00 80.00
HOM Trevor Hoffman M/8 40.00 80.00
HON Trevor Hoffman N/8 40.00 80.00
HOO Trevor Hoffman O/8 40.00 80.00
HRA Hanley Ramirez A/125 30.00 60.00
HRE Hanley Ramirez E/125 30.00 60.00
HRI Hanley Ramirez I/125 30.00 60.00
HRM Hanley Ramirez M/125 30.00 60.00
HRR Hanley Ramirez R/250 30.00 60.00
HRZ Hanley Ramirez Z/125 30.00 60.00
HSE Huston Street E/150 20.00 40.00
HSR Huston Street R/75 20.00 40.00
HSS Huston Street S/75 20.00 40.00
HST Huston Street T/150 20.00 40.00
HUD Tim Hudson D/50 20.00 40.00
HUH Tim Hudson H/50 20.00 40.00
HUN Tim Hudson N/50 20.00 40.00
HUO Tim Hudson O/50 20.00 40.00
HUS Tim Hudson S/50 20.00 40.00
HUU Tim Hudson U/50 20.00 40.00
IKE Ian Kinsler E/125 20.00 50.00
IKI Ian Kinsler I/125 20.00 50.00
IKK Ian Kinsler K/125 20.00 50.00
IKL Ian Kinsler L/125 20.00 50.00
IKN Ian Kinsler N/125 20.00 50.00
IKR Ian Kinsler R/125 20.00 50.00
IKS Ian Kinsler S/125 20.00 50.00
JBA Jason Bay A/110 25.00 50.00
JBB Jason Bay B/110 25.00 50.00
JBY Jason Bay Y/110 25.00 50.00
JB2O Jason Bay ROY O/50 25.00 50.00
JB2R Jason Bay ROY R/50 25.00 50.00
JB2Y Jason Bay ROY Y/50 25.00 50.00
JGE Jonny Gomes E/175 15.00 30.00
JGG Jonny Gomes G/175 15.00 30.00
JGM Jonny Gomes M/175 15.00 30.00
JGO Jonny Gomes O/175 15.00 30.00
JGS Jonny Gomes S/175 15.00 30.00
JHA Jeremy Hermida A/125 15.00 30.00
JHD Jeremy Hermida D/125 15.00 30.00
JHE Jeremy Hermida E/125 15.00 30.00
JHH Jeremy Hermida H/125 15.00 30.00
JHI Jeremy Hermida I/125 15.00 30.00
JHM Jeremy Hermida M/125 15.00 30.00
JHR Jeremy Hermida R/125 15.00 30.00
JMA Joe Mauer A/25 50.00 100.00
JME Joe Mauer E/25 50.00 100.00
JMM Joe Mauer M/25 50.00 100.00
JMR Joe Mauer R/25 50.00 100.00
JMU Joe Mauer U/25 50.00 100.00
JNA Joe Nathan A/200 15.00 30.00
JNH Joe Nathan H/100 15.00 30.00
JNN Joe Nathan N/200 15.00 30.00
JNT Joe Nathan T/100 15.00 30.00
JPA Jonathan Papelbon A/100 30.00 60.00
JPB Jonathan Papelbon B/100 30.00 60.00
JPE Jonathan Papelbon E/100 30.00 60.00
JPL Jonathan Papelbon L/100 30.00 60.00
JPN Jonathan Papelbon N/100 30.00 60.00
JPO Jonathan Papelbon O/100 30.00 60.00
JPP Jonathan Papelbon P/200 30.00 60.00
JRE Jose Reyes E/150 40.00 80.00
JRR Jose Reyes R/75 40.00 80.00
JRS Jose Reyes S/75 40.00 80.00
JRY Jose Reyes Y/75 40.00 80.00
JSE Jeremy Sowers E/50 25.00 50.00
JSO Jeremy Sowers O/50 25.00 50.00
JSR Jeremy Sowers R/50 25.00 50.00
JSS Jeremy Sowers S/100 25.00 50.00
JSW Jeremy Sowers W/50 25.00 50.00
JTE Jim Thome E/30 50.00 100.00
JTH Jim Thome H/30 50.00 100.00
JTM Jim Thome M/30 50.00 100.00
JTO Jim Thome O/30 50.00 100.00
JTT Jim Thome T/30 50.00 100.00
JVA Justin Verlander A/20 40.00 80.00
JVD Justin Verlander D/20 40.00 80.00
JVE Justin Verlander E/40 40.00 80.00
JVL Justin Verlander L/20 40.00 80.00
JVN Justin Verlander N/20 40.00 80.00
JVR Justin Verlander R/40 40.00 80.00
JVV Justin Verlander V/20 40.00 80.00
JWA Jered Weaver A/40 30.00 60.00
JWE Jered Weaver E/80 30.00 60.00
JWR Jered Weaver R/40 30.00 60.00
JWV Jered Weaver V/40 30.00 60.00
JWW Jered Weaver W/40 30.00 60.00
JZA Joel Zumaya A/250 25.00 50.00
JZM Joel Zumaya M/125 25.00 50.00
JZU Joel Zumaya U/125 25.00 50.00
JZY Joel Zumaya Y/125 25.00 50.00
JZZ Joel Zumaya Z/125 25.00 50.00
KGE Ken Griffey Jr. Reds E/25 90.00 150.00
KGF Ken Griffey Jr. Reds F/50 90.00 150.00
KGG Ken Griffey Jr. Reds G/25 90.00 150.00
KGI Ken Griffey Jr. Reds I/25 90.00 150.00
KGR Ken Griffey Jr. Reds R/25 90.00 150.00
KGY Ken Griffey Jr. Reds Y/25 90.00 150.00
KG2I Ken Griffey Jr. Junior I/25 90.00 150.00
KG2J Ken Griffey Jr. Junior J/25 90.00 150.00
KG2N Ken Griffey Jr. Junior N/25 90.00 150.00
KG2O Ken Griffey Jr. Junior O/25 90.00 150.00
KG2R Ken Griffey Jr. Junior R/25 90.00 150.00
KG2U Ken Griffey Jr. Junior U/25 90.00 150.00
KG3E Ken Griffey Jr. M's E/25 90.00 150.00
KG3F Ken Griffey Jr. M's F/50 90.00 150.00
KG3G Ken Griffey Jr. M's G/25 90.00 150.00
KG3I Ken Griffey Jr. M's I/25 90.00 150.00
KG3R Ken Griffey Jr. M's R/25 90.00 150.00
KG3Y Ken Griffey Jr. M's Y/25 90.00 150.00
KG4D Ken Griffey Jr. The Kid D/25 90.00 150.00
KG4E Ken Griffey Jr. The Kid E/25 90.00 150.00
KG4H Ken Griffey Jr. The Kid H/25 90.00 150.00
KG4I Ken Griffey Jr. The Kid I/25 90.00 150.00
KG4K Ken Griffey Jr. The Kid K/25 90.00 150.00
KG4T Ken Griffey Jr. The Kid T/25 90.00 150.00
KHE Khalil Greene E/225 15.00 30.00
KHG Khalil Greene G/75 15.00 30.00
KHN Khalil Greene N/75 15.00 30.00
KHR Khalil Greene R/75 15.00 30.00
KMA Kendry Morales A/20 25.00 50.00
KME Kendry Morales E/20 25.00 50.00
KML Kendry Morales L/20 25.00 50.00
KMM Kendry Morales M/20 25.00 50.00
KMO Kendry Morales O/20 25.00 50.00
KMR Kendry Morales R/20 25.00 50.00
KMS Kendry Morales S/20 25.00 50.00
KWD Kerry Wood D/10 40.00 80.00
KWO Kerry Wood O/20 40.00 80.00
KWW Kerry Wood W/10 40.00 80.00
LEE Carlos Lee E/50 20.00 40.00
LEL Carlos Lee L/25 20.00 40.00
MCA Miguel Cabrera A/70 30.00 60.00
MCB Miguel Cabrera B/35 30.00 60.00
MCC Miguel Cabrera C/35 30.00 60.00
MCE Miguel Cabrera E/35 30.00 60.00
MCR Miguel Cabrera R/70 30.00 60.00
MGE Marcus Giles E/136 15.00 30.00
MGG Marcus Giles G/136 15.00 30.00
MGI Marcus Giles I/136 15.00 30.00
MGL Marcus Giles L/136 15.00 30.00
MGS Marcus Giles S/136 15.00 30.00
MHA Matt Holliday A/37 15.00 40.00
MHD Matt Holliday D/37 15.00 40.00
MHH Matt Holliday H/37 15.00 40.00
MHI Matt Holliday I/37 15.00 40.00
MHL Matt Holliday L/74 15.00 40.00
MHO Matt Holliday O/37 15.00 40.00
MHY Matt Holliday Y/37 15.00 40.00
MMD Mark Mulder D/50 20.00 40.00
MME Mark Mulder E/50 20.00 40.00
MML Mark Mulder L/50 20.00 40.00
MMM Mark Mulder M/50 20.00 40.00
MMR Mark Mulder R/50 20.00 40.00
MMU Mark Mulder U/50 20.00 40.00
MOA Justin Morneau A/75 30.00 60.00
MOE Justin Morneau E/75 30.00 60.00
MOM Justin Morneau M/75 30.00 60.00
MON Justin Morneau N/75 30.00 60.00
MOO Justin Morneau O/75 30.00 60.00
MOR Justin Morneau R/75 30.00 60.00
MOU Justin Morneau U/75 30.00 60.00
MTA Mark Teixeira A/5 90.00 150.00
MTE Mark Teixeira E/10 90.00 150.00
MTI Mark Teixeira I/10 90.00 150.00
MTR Mark Teixeira R/5 90.00 150.00
MTT Mark Teixeira T/5 90.00 150.00
MTX Mark Teixeira X/5 90.00 150.00
MYG Michael Young G/50 25.00 50.00
MYN Michael Young N/50 25.00 50.00
MYO Michael Young O/50 25.00 50.00
MYU Michael Young U/50 25.00 50.00
MYY Michael Young Y/50 25.00 50.00
NSE Nick Swisher E/170 8.00 20.00
NSH Nick Swisher H/170 8.00 20.00
NSI Nick Swisher I/170 8.00 20.00
NSR Nick Swisher R/170 8.00 20.00
NSS Nick Swisher S/340 8.00 20.00
NSW Nick Swisher W/170 8.00 20.00
PEA Jake Peavy A/20 30.00 60.00
PEE Jake Peavy E/20 30.00 60.00
PEP Jake Peavy P/20 30.00 60.00
PEV Jake Peavy V/20 30.00 60.00
PEY Jake Peavy Y/20 30.00 60.00
RCC Roger Clemens C/15 100.00 150.00
RCE Roger Clemens E/30 100.00 150.00
RCL Roger Clemens L/15 100.00 150.00
RCM Roger Clemens M/15 100.00 150.00
RCN Roger Clemens N/15 100.00 150.00
RCS Roger Clemens S/15 100.00 150.00
RC2C Roger Clemens The Rocket C/15 100.00 150.00
RC2E Roger Clemens The Rocket E/30 100.00 150.00
RC2H Roger Clemens The Rocket H/15 100.00 150.00
RC2K Roger Clemens The Rocket K/15 100.00 150.00
RC2O Roger Clemens The Rocket O/15 100.00 150.00
RC2R Roger Clemens The Rocket R/15 100.00 150.00
RC2T Roger Clemens The Rocket T/30 100.00 150.00
ROA Roy Oswalt A/50 30.00 60.00
ROL Roy Oswalt L/50 30.00 60.00
ROO Roy Oswalt O/50 30.00 60.00
ROS Roy Oswalt S/50 30.00 60.00
ROT Roy Oswalt T/50 30.00 60.00
ROW Roy Oswalt W/50 30.00 60.00
RWE Rickie Weeks E/200 20.00 40.00
RWK Rickie Weeks K/100 20.00 40.00
RWS Rickie Weeks S/100 20.00 40.00
RWW Rickie Weeks W/100 20.00 40.00
RZA Ryan Zimmerman A/17 50.00 100.00
RZE Ryan Zimmerman E/17 50.00 100.00
RZI Ryan Zimmerman I/17 50.00 100.00
RZM Ryan Zimmerman M/51 50.00 100.00
RZN Ryan Zimmerman N/17 50.00 100.00
RZR Ryan Zimmerman R/17 50.00 100.00
RZZ Ryan Zimmerman Z/17 50.00 100.00
SKA Scott Kazmir A/6 50.00 100.00
SKI Scott Kazmir I/6 50.00 100.00
SKK Scott Kazmir K/6 50.00 100.00
SKM Scott Kazmir M/6 50.00 100.00
SKR Scott Kazmir R/6 50.00 100.00
SKZ Scott Kazmir Z/6 50.00 100.00
SML John Smoltz L/75 40.00 80.00
SMM John Smoltz M/75 40.00 80.00
SMO John Smoltz O/75 40.00 80.00
SMS John Smoltz S/75 40.00 80.00
SMT John Smoltz T/75 40.00 80.00
SMZ John Smoltz Z/75 40.00 80.00
TEA Miguel Tejada A/50 30.00 60.00
TED Miguel Tejada D/25 30.00 60.00
TEE Miguel Tejada E/25 30.00 60.00
TEJ Miguel Tejada J/25 30.00 60.00
TET Miguel Tejada T/25 30.00 60.00
THA Travis Hafner A/10 50.00 100.00
THE Travis Hafner E/10 50.00 100.00
THF Travis Hafner F/10 50.00 100.00
THH Travis Hafner H/10 50.00 100.00
THN Travis Hafner N/10 50.00 100.00
THR Travis Hafner R/10 50.00 100.00
TH2K Travis Hafner Pronk K/8 50.00 100.00
TH2N Travis Hafner Pronk N/8 50.00 100.00
TH2O Travis Hafner Pronk O/8 50.00 100.00
TH2P Travis Hafner Pronk P/8 50.00 100.00
TH2R Travis Hafner Pronk R/8 50.00 100.00
TIC Tadahito Iguchi C/20 30.00 60.00
TIG Tadahito Iguchi G/20 30.00 60.00
TIH Tadahito Iguchi H/20 30.00 60.00
TII Tadahito Iguchi I/40 30.00 60.00
TIU Tadahito Iguchi U/20 30.00 60.00
VGE Vladimir Guerrero E/50 40.00 80.00
VGG Vladimir Guerrero G/25 40.00 80.00
VGO Vladimir Guerrero O/25 40.00 80.00
VGR Vladimir Guerrero R/75 40.00 80.00
VGU Vladimir Guerrero U/25 40.00 80.00
VMA Victor Martinez A/75 10.00 25.00
VME Victor Martinez E/75 10.00 25.00
VMI Victor Martinez I/75 10.00 25.00
VMM Victor Martinez M/75 10.00 25.00
VMN Victor Martinez N/75 10.00 25.00
VMR Victor Martinez R/75 10.00 25.00
VMT Victor Martinez T/75 10.00 25.00
VMZ Victor Martinez Z/75 10.00 25.00
WIA Josh Willingham A/75 15.00 30.00
WIG Josh Willingham G/75 15.00 30.00
WIH Josh Willingham H/75 15.00 30.00
WII Josh Willingham I/150 15.00 30.00
WIL Josh Willingham L/150 15.00 30.00
WIM Josh Willingham M/75 15.00 30.00
WIN Josh Willingham N/75 15.00 30.00
WIW Josh Willingham W/75 15.00 30.00

2006 SP Authentic Chirography

STATED ODDS 1:96
PRINT RUNS B/WN 25-75 COPIES PER
NO PRICING ON QTY OF 25
EXCHANGE DEADLINE 12/05/09
AE Andre Ethier/75 12.50 30.00
AG Tony Gwynn Jr./75 15.00 40.00
AH Anderson Hernandez/75 4.00 10.00
AN Brian Anderson/75 4.00 10.00
AS Alfonso Soriano/75 20.00 50.00
AW Adam Wainwright/75 10.00 25.00
BA Brian Bannister/75 6.00 15.00

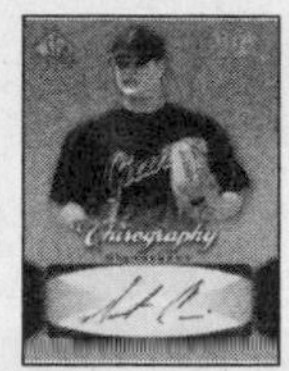

BB Brandon Backe/75 4.00 10.00
BC Bobby Crosby/75 6.00 15.00
BI Chad Billingsley/75 10.00 25.00
BL Boone Logan/75 4.00 10.00
BO Boof Bonser/75 6.00 15.00
BS Ben Sheets/75 10.00 25.00
CB Craig Biggio/75 30.00 60.00
CD Chris Denorfia/75 4.00 10.00
CF Choo Freeman/75 4.00 10.00
CG Carlos Guillen/75 10.00 25.00
CH Cole Hamels/75 10.00 25.00
CJ Conor Jackson/75 6.00 15.00
CK Casey Kotchman/75 4.00 10.00
CL Cliff Lee/75 15.00 40.00
CP Corey Patterson/75 6.00 15.00
CR Cody Ross/75 10.00 25.00
CS C.C. Sabathia/75 6.00 15.00
CU Chase Utley/25
DB Denny Bautista/75 4.00 10.00
DD David DeJesus/75 6.00 15.00
DG David Gassner/75 4.00 10.00
DJ Derek Jeter/75 100.00 175.00
DU Dan Uggla/75 6.00 15.00
DW Dontrelle Willis/75 10.00 25.00
FC Fausto Carmona/75 4.00 10.00
FH Felix Hernandez/25
FL Felipe Lopez/75 4.00 10.00
FT Frank Thomas/75 40.00 80.00
GA Garret Anderson/75 6.00 15.00
GR Ken Griffey Jr./75 60.00 120.00
HA Jeff Harris/75 4.00 10.00
HB Hank Blalock/75 6.00 15.00
HK Hong-Chih Kuo/75 50.00 100.00
HR Hanley Ramirez/75 10.00 25.00
IK Ian Kinsler/75 6.00 15.00
JB Joe Blanton/75 6.00 15.00
JC Jose Capellan/75 4.00 10.00
JD Joey Devine/75 4.00 10.00
JE Johnny Estrada/75 4.00 10.00
JF Jeff Francis/75 10.00 25.00
JH Jeremy Hermida/75 6.00 15.00
JJ Josh Johnson/75 10.00 25.00
JK Jason Kubel/75 4.00 10.00
JL Jon Lester/75 20.00 50.00
JN Joe Nathan/75 6.00 15.00
JP Jonathan Papelbon/75 20.00 50.00
JR Josh Rupe/75 4.00 10.00
JS Jeremy Sowers/75 6.00 15.00
JW Josh Willingham/75 4.00 10.00
KF Keith Foulke/75 6.00 15.00
KG Khalil Greene/75 10.00 25.00
KM Kevin Mench/75 6.00 15.00
KS Kelly Shoppach/75 4.00 10.00
KY Kevin Youkilis/75 6.00 15.00
LI Francisco Liriano/75 15.00 40.00
LO Lyle Overbay/40 6.00 15.00
MC Matt Cain/75 10.00 25.00
MM Macay McBride/75 4.00 10.00
NS Nick Swisher/75 6.00 15.00
OP Oliver Perez/75 6.00 15.00
PM Paul Maholm/75 4.00 10.00
RE Eric Reed/75 4.00 10.00
RH Rich Harden/75 6.00 15.00
RZ Ryan Zimmerman/75 20.00 50.00
SC Sean Casey/75 10.00 25.00
SD Stephen Drew/75 20.00 50.00
SH Chris Shelton/75 4.00 10.00
SK Scott Kazmir/25
SM Sean Marshall/75 12.50 30.00
SO Alay Soler/75 6.00 15.00
TB Taylor Buchholz/75 4.00 10.00
TH Travis Hafner/75 10.00 25.00
TP Tony Pena Jr./75 4.00 10.00
TS Takashi Saito/75 20.00 50.00
VA John Van Benschoten/75 4.00 10.00
VE Justin Verlander/75 50.00 100.00
VM Victor Martinez/75 10.00 25.00
WE Jered Weaver/75 30.00 60.00
WI Josh Wilson/75 4.00 10.00
WM Wily Mo Pena/75 6.00 15.00

2006 SP Authentic Chirography Dual

RANDOM INSERTS IN PACKS
STATED PRINT RUN 25 SERIAL #'d SETS
NO PRICING DUE TO SCARCITY
EXCHANGE DEADLINE 12/05/09

2006 SP Authentic Chirography Triple

RANDOM INSERTS IN PACKS
STATED PRINT RUN 15 SERIAL #'d SETS
NO PRICING DUE TO SCARCITY
EXCHANGE DEADLINE 12/05/09

2006 SP Authentic Sign of the Times

STATED ODDS 1:96
PRINT RUNS B/WN 25-75 COPIES PER
NO PRICING ON QTY OF 25
EXCHANGE DEADLINE 12/05/09
AE Andre Ethier/75 12.50 30.00
AH Anderson Hernandez/75 4.00 10.00
AJ Andruw Jones/75 15.00 40.00
AN Brian Anderson/75 4.00 10.00
AR Aramis Ramirez/75 6.00 15.00
AS Alay Soler/75 6.00 15.00
AW Adam Wainwright/75 10.00 25.00
BA Bobby Abreu/75 30.00 60.00
BB Boof Bonser/75 6.00 15.00
BI Chad Billingsley/75 10.00 25.00
BJ Ben Johnson/75 4.00 10.00
BL Boone Logan/75 4.00 10.00
BR Brian Bannister/75 6.00 15.00
CA Matt Cain/75 10.00 25.00
CB Chris Booker/75 4.00 10.00
CC Carl Crawford/75 6.00 15.00
CD Chris Demaria/75 4.00 10.00
CH Cole Hamels/75 20.00 50.00
CL Carlos Lee/25
CR Cody Ross/75 10.00 25.00
CS Curt Schilling/75 20.00 50.00
CY Clay Hensley/75 4.00 10.00
DE Chris Denorfia/75 4.00 10.00
DG David Gassner/75 4.00 10.00
DJ Derek Jeter/75 100.00 175.00
DL Derrek Lee/75 10.00 25.00
DU Dan Uggla/75 12.50 30.00
EG Eric Gagne/75 10.00 25.00
ER Eric Reed/75 4.00 10.00
FC Fausto Carmona/75 10.00 25.00
FL Francisco Liriano/75 15.00 40.00
FR Ron Flores/75 4.00 10.00
GM Greg Maddux/75 60.00 120.00
HA Tim Hamulack/75 4.00 10.00
HE Jeremy Hermida/75 6.00 15.00
HR Hanley Ramirez/75 10.00 25.00
IK Ian Kinsler/75 6.00 15.00
JA Conor Jackson/75 6.00 15.00
JC Jose Capellan/75 4.00 10.00
JD J.D. Drew/75 10.00 25.00
JE Jered Weaver/75 30.00 60.00
JG Jose Guillen/75 4.00 10.00
JH Jason Hammel/75 4.00 10.00
JJ Josh Johnson/75 10.00 25.00
JK Jason Kendall/75 6.00 15.00
JP Jake Peavy/75 6.00 15.00
JV John Van Benschoten/75 4.00 10.00
JW Josh Willingham/75 4.00 10.00
JY Jeremy Sowers/75 6.00 15.00
KG Ken Griffey Jr./75 60.00 120.00
KU Jason Kubel/75 4.00 10.00
MA Macay McBride/75 4.00 10.00
MC Miguel Cabrera/75 15.00 40.00
MI Mike Thompson/75 4.00 10.00
MJ Mike Jacobs/75 6.00 15.00
MK Mark Kotsay/75 6.00 15.00
MM Mark Mulder/75 6.00 15.00
MO Justin Morneau/75 6.00 15.00
MT Mark Teixeira/75 10.00 25.00
PA Jonathan Papelbon/75 20.00 50.00
PE Joel Peralta/75 4.00 10.00
PM Paul Maholm/75 4.00 10.00
RA Reggie Abercrombie/75 4.00 10.00
RF Rafael Furcal/75 6.00 15.00
RH Ramon Hernandez/75 10.00 25.00
RJ Randy Johnson/75 30.00 60.00
RM Russell Martin/75 6.00 15.00
RS Ryan Shealy/75 6.00 15.00
RW Rickie Weeks/75 10.00 25.00
RZ Ryan Zimmerman/75 20.00 50.00
SA Santiago Ramirez/75 4.00 10.00
SD Stephen Drew/75 20.00 50.00
SM Sean Marshall/75 10.00 25.00
SP Scott Podsednik/75 6.00 15.00
SS Skip Schumaker/75 4.00 10.00
ST Steve Stemle/75 4.00 10.00
TB Taylor Buchholz/75 4.00 10.00
TE Miguel Tejada/75 10.00 25.00
TH Tim Hudson/75 10.00 25.00
TP Tony Pena Jr./75 4.00 10.00
TS Takashi Saito/75 20.00 50.00
VE Justin Verlander/75 20.00 50.00
VG Vladimir Guerrero/75 20.00 50.00
VW Vernon Wells/75 6.00 15.00
WI Josh Wilson/75 4.00 10.00
YB Yuniesky Betancourt/75 6.00 15.00
ZG Zack Greinke/75 10.00 25.00

2006 SP Authentic Sign of the Times Dual

RANDOM INSERTS IN PACKS
STATED PRINT RUN 25 SERIAL #'d SETS
NO PRICING DUE TO SCARCITY
EXCHANGE DEADLINE 12/05/09

2006 SP Authentic Sign of the Times Triple

RANDOM INSERTS IN PACKS
STATED PRINT RUN 15 SERIAL #'d SETS

NO PRICING DUE TO SCARCITY
EXCHANGE DEADLINE 12/05/09

2006 SP Authentic WBC Future Watch

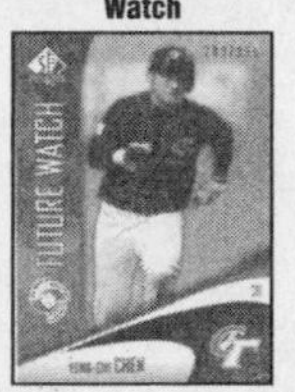

STATED ODDS 1:7
STATED PRINT RUN 999 SERIAL #'d SETS
1 Adrian Burnside 1.00 2.50
2 Gavin Fingleson 1.00 2.50
3 Bradley Harman 1.50 4.00
4 Brendan Kingman 1.00 2.50
5 Brett Roneberg 1.00 2.50
6 Paul Rutgers 1.00 2.50
7 Phil Stockman 1.00 2.50
8 Stubby Clapp 1.00 2.50
9 Steve Green 1.00 2.50
10 Pete LaForest 1.00 2.50
11 Adam Loewen 1.00 2.50
12 Ryan Radmanovich 1.00 2.50
13 Chenhao Li 1.00 2.50
14 Guangbiao Liu 1.00 2.50
15 Guogan Yang 1.00 2.50
16 Jingchao Wang 1.00 2.50
17 Lei Li 1.00 2.50
18 Lingfeng Sun 1.00 2.50
19 Nan Wang 1.00 2.50
20 Shuo Yang 1.00 2.50
21 Tao Bu 1.00 2.50
22 Wei Wang 1.00 2.50
23 Yi Feng 1.00 2.50
24 Chien-Ming Chiang 2.50 6.00
25 Yung-Chi Chen 1.50 4.00
26 Chia-Hsien Hseih 2.50 6.00
27 Chin-Lung Hu 3.00 8.00
28 En-Yu Lin 2.50 6.00
29 Wei-Lun Pan 2.50 6.00
30 Ariel Borrero 1.00 2.50
31 Yadel Marti 1.00 2.50
32 Yulieski Gourriel 2.50 6.00
33 Frederich Cepeda 1.00 2.50
34 Yadiel Pedroso 1.00 2.50
35 Pedro Luis Lazo 1.50 4.00
36 Elier Sanchez 1.00 2.50
37 Norberto Gonzalez 1.00 2.50
38 Carlos Tabares 1.00 2.50
39 Eduardo Paret 1.00 2.50
40 Osmany Urrutia 1.00 2.50
41 Alexi Ramirez 12.00 30.00
42 Yoandy Garlobo 1.00 2.50
43 Vicyohandry Odelin 1.00 2.50
44 Michel Enriquez 1.00 2.50
45 Ormari Romero 1.00 2.50
46 Ariel Pestano 1.00 2.50
47 Francisco Liriano 2.50 6.00
48 Dustin Delucchi 1.00 2.50
49 Tony Giarratano 1.00 2.50
50 Tom Gregorio 1.00 2.50
51 Mark Saccomanno 1.00 2.50
52 Takahiro Arai 1.50 4.00
53 Akinori Iwamura 3.00 8.00
54 Munenori Kawaski 2.50 6.00
55 Nobuhiko Matsunaka 1.50 4.00
56 Daisuke Matsuzaka 3.00 8.00
57 Shinya Miyamoto 1.50 4.00
58 Tsuyoshi Nishioka 6.00 15.00
59 Tomoya Satozaki 1.50 4.00
60 Koji Uehara 2.50 6.00
61 Shunsuke Watanabe 1.50 4.00
62 Sadaharu Oh 6.00 15.00
63 Byung Kyu Lee 1.00 2.50
64 Ji Man Song 1.00 2.50
65 Jin Man Park 1.00 2.50
66 Jong Beom Lee 1.00 2.50
67 Jong Kook Kim 1.00 2.50
68 Min Han Son 1.00 2.50
69 Min Jae Kim 1.00 2.50
70 Seung Yeop Lee 1.50 4.00
71 Luis A. Garcia 1.00 2.50
72 Mario Valenzuela 1.00 2.50
73 Sharnol Adriana 1.00 2.50
74 Rob Cordemans 1.00 2.50
75 Michael Duursma 1.00 2.50
76 Percy Isenia 1.00 2.50
77 Sidney de Jong 1.00 2.50
78 Dirk Klooster 1.00 2.50
79 Raylinoe Legito 1.00 2.50
80 Shairon Martis 1.00 2.50
81 Harvey Monte 1.00 2.50
82 Hainley Statia 1.00 2.50
83 Roger Deago 1.00 2.50
84 Audes De Leon 1.00 2.50
85 Freddy Herrera 1.00 2.50
86 Yoni Lasso 1.00 2.50
87 Orlando Miller 1.00 2.50
88 Len Pecota 1.00 2.50
89 Federico Baez 1.00 2.50
90 Dicky Gonzalez 1.00 2.50
91 Josue Matos 1.00 2.50
92 Orlando Roman 1.00 2.50
93 Paul Bell 1.00 2.50
94 Kyle Botha 1.00 2.50
95 Jason Cook 1.00 2.50
96 Nicholas Dempsey 1.00 2.50
97 Victor Moreno 1.00 2.50
98 Ricardo Palma 1.00 2.50

99 Huston Street 1.00 2.50
100 Chase Utley 2.50 6.00

2007 SP Authentic

COMP.SET w/o RCs (100) 6.00 15.00
COMMON CARD (1-100) .15 .40
COMMON AU RC (101-158) 5.00 12.00
OVERALL BY THE LETTER AUTOS 1:12
AU RC PRINT RUN B/WN 20-120 COPIES PER
EXCHANGE DEADLINE 11/08/2008
1 Chipper Jones .40 1.00
2 Andruw Jones .15 .40
3 John Smoltz .40 1.00
4 Carlos Quentin .15 .40
5 Randy Johnson .40 1.00
6 Brandon Webb .25 .60
7 Alfonso Soriano .25 .60
8 Derrek Lee .15 .40
9 Aramis Ramirez .15 .40
10 Carlos Zambrano .25 .60
11 Ken Griffey Jr. .60 1.50
12 Adam Dunn .25 .60
13 Josh Hamilton .60 1.50
14 Todd Helton .25 .60
15 Jeff Francis .15 .40
16 Matt Holliday .40 1.00
17 Hanley Ramirez .40 1.00
18 Dontrelle Willis .15 .40
19 Miguel Cabrera .40 1.00
20 Lance Berkman .25 .60
21 Roy Oswalt .25 .60
22 Carlos Lee .15 .40
23 Nomar Garciaparra .40 1.00
24 Derek Lowe .15 .40
25 Juan Pierre .15 .40
26 Rafael Furcal .15 .40
27 Rickie Weeks .25 .60
28 Prince Fielder .25 .60
29 Ben Sheets .15 .40
30 David Wright .60 1.50
31 Jose Reyes .25 .60
32 Tom Glavine .25 .60
33 Carlos Beltran .25 .60
34 Cole Hamels .40 1.00
35 Jimmy Rollins .25 .60
36 Ryan Howard .60 1.50
37 Jason Bay .25 .60
38 Freddy Sanchez .15 .40
39 Ian Snell .15 .40
40 Jake Peavy .15 .40
41 Greg Maddux .60 1.50
42 Trevor Hoffman .25 .60
43 Matt Cain .25 .60
44 Barry Zito .15 .40
45 Ray Durham .15 .40
46 Albert Pujols 1.00 2.50
47 Chris Carpenter .40 1.00
48 Jim Edmonds .25 .60
49 Scott Rolen .25 .60
50 Ryan Zimmerman .25 .60
51 Felipe Lopez .15 .40
52 Austin Kearns .15 .40
53 Miguel Tejada .25 .60
54 Erik Bedard .15 .40
55 Daniel Cabrera .15 .40
56 David Ortiz .25 .60
57 Curt Schilling .25 .60
58 Manny Ramirez .40 1.00
59 Jonathan Papelbon .40 1.00
60 Jim Thome .25 .60
61 Paul Konerko .25 .60
62 Bobby Jenks .15 .40
63 Grady Sizemore .25 .60
64 Victor Martinez .25 .60
65 Travis Hafner .15 .40
66 Ivan Rodriguez .25 .60
67 Justin Verlander .50 1.25
68 Joel Zumaya .25 .60
69 Jeremy Bonderman .15 .40
70 Gil Meche .15 .40
71 Mike Sweeney .15 .40
72 Mark Teahen .15 .40
73 Vladimir Guerrero .40 1.00
74 Howie Kendrick .15 .40
75 Francisco Rodriguez .25 .60
76 Johan Santana .40 1.00
77 Justin Morneau .40 1.00
78 Joe Mauer .40 1.00
79 Joe Nathan .15 .40
80a Alex Rodriguez .60 1.50
80b Alex Rodriguez
Angels Logo
80c Alex Rodriguez
Cubs Logo
80d Alex Rodriguez
Dodgers Logo
80e Alex Rodriguez
Mets Logo
80f Alex Rodriguez
Red Sox Logo
81 Derek Jeter 1.00 2.50
82 Johnny Damon .25 .60
83 Chien-Ming Wang .25 .60
84 Rich Harden .15 .40
85 Mike Piazza .40 1.00
86 Dan Haren .15 .40
87 Ichiro Suzuki .60 1.50
88 Felix Hernandez .40 1.00
89 Kenji Johjima .40 1.00
90 Adrian Beltre .15 .40
91 Carl Crawford .25 .60
92 Scott Kazmir .25 .60
93 Delmon Young .25 .60
94 Michael Young .40 1.00
95 Mark Teixeira .40 1.00
96 Eric Gagne .15 .40
97 Hank Blalock .15 .40
98 Vernon Wells .15 .40

99 Roy Halladay .40 1.00
100 Frank Thomas .40 1.00
101 Joaquin Arias AU/75 (RC) 5.00 12.00
102 Jeff Baker AU (RC) 5.00 12.00
103 Michael Bourn AU/75 (RC) 6.00 15.00
104 Brian Burres AU/75 (RC) 6.00 15.00
105 Jared Burton AU/75 RC 6.00 15.00
106 Ryan Braun AU/50 (RC) 20.00 50.00
109 Alex Gordon AU/50 RC 20.00 50.00
112 Sean Henn AU/75 (RC) 10.00 25.00
113 Phil Hughes AU (RC) 40.00 80.00
114 Kei Igawa AU/25 RC 30.00 60.00
115 Akinori Iwamura AU/20 RC 40.00 80.00
119 Adam Lind AU/75 (RC) 10.00 25.00
123 Brad Salmon AU/75 RC 5.00 12.00
127 Cesar Jimenez AU RC 5.00 12.00
129 Troy Tulowitzki AU (RC) 40.00 80.00
130 Chase Wright AU/75 RC 12.50 30.00
131 Delmon Young AU/20 (RC) 12.50 30.00
133 Brian Barden AU/75 RC 5.00 12.00
137 Billy Butler AU/75 (RC) 20.00 50.00
139 Kory Casto AU/75 (RC) 6.00 15.00
140 Matt Chico AU/75 (RC) 6.00 15.00
141 John Danks AU/75 RC 15.00 40.00
142 Andrew Miller AU/50 RC 8.00 20.00
145 Devern Hansack AU RC 6.00 15.00
146 Mike Rabelo AU/75 RC 8.00 20.00
150a Daisuke Matsuzaka AU/20 RC 125.00 250.00
152 Micah Owings AU/75 (RC) 20.00 50.00
153 Hunter Pence AU/75 (RC) 10.00 25.00
156 Danny Putnam AU/75 (RC) 6.00 15.00
159 Doug Slaten AU/75 RC 6.00 15.00
160 Joe Smith AU/75 RC 8.00 20.00
161 Justin Upton AU/120 RC 15.00 40.00
162 Joba Chamberlain AU/60 RC 10.00 25.00
107a Yovani Gallardo AU/75 (RC) 10.00 25.00
107b Yovani Gallardo AU/35 12.50 30.00
108a Hector Gimenez AU/75 (RC) 6.00 15.00
108b Hector Gimenez AU/50 6.00 15.00
110a Josh Hamilton AU/50 (RC) 15.00 40.00
110b Josh Hamilton AU/35 20.00 50.00
111a Justin Hampson AU/75 (RC) 5.00 12.00
111b Justin Hampson AU/50 5.00 12.00
116a Mark Reynolds AU/75 RC 20.00 50.00
116b Mark Reynolds AU/35 30.00 60.00
117a Homer Bailey AU/75 (RC) 10.00 25.00
117b Homer Bailey AU/50 (RC) 10.00 25.00
118a Kevin Kouzmanoff AU/75 (RC) 8.00 20.00
118b Kevin Kouzmanoff AU/40 8.00 20.00
120a Carlos Gomez AU/75 RC 20.00 50.00
120b Carlos Gomez AU/50 20.00 50.00
121a Glen Perkins AU/75 (RC) 6.00 15.00
121b Glen Perkins AU/50 6.00 15.00
122a Rick Vanden Hurk AU/75 RC 10.00 25.00
122b Rick Vanden Hurk AU/35 12.50 30.00
124a Zack Segovia AU/75 (RC) 5.00 12.00
124b Zack Segovia AU/50 5.00 12.00
125a Kurt Suzuki AU/75 (RC) 12.50 30.00
125b Kurt Suzuki AU/50 12.50 30.00
126a Chris Stewart AU/75 RC 5.00 12.00
126b Chris Stewart AU/50 5.00 12.00
128a Ryan Sweeney AU/50 (RC) 6.00 15.00
128b Ryan Sweeney AU/40 6.00 15.00
132a Tony Abreu AU/75 RC 10.00 25.00
132b Tony Abreu AU/57 10.00 25.00
132c Tony Abreu AU/50 10.00 25.00
134a Curtis Thigpen AU/75 (RC) 10.00 25.00
134b Curtis Thigpen AU/40 10.00 25.00
135a Jon Coutlangus AU/75 (RC) 5.00 12.00
135b Jon Coutlangus AU/55 5.00 12.00
136a Kevin Cameron AU/75 RC 5.00 12.00
136b Kevin Cameron AU/50 5.00 12.00
138a Alexi Casilla AU/75 RC 6.00 15.00
138b Alexi Casilla AU/50 6.00 15.00
143a Ben Francisco AU/75 (RC) 6.00 15.00
143b Ben Francisco AU/40 6.00 15.00
144a Andy Gonzalez AU/75 RC 5.00 12.00
144b Andy Gonzalez AU/50 5.00 12.00
147a Tim Lincecum AU/50 RC 75.00 150.00
147b Tim Lincecum AU/25 125.00 250.00
148a Matt Lindstrom AU/75 (RC) 6.00 15.00
148b Matt Lindstrom AU/40 6.00 15.00
149a Jay Marshall AU/75 RC 5.00 12.00
149b Jay Marshall AU/50 5.00 12.00
150b Daisuke Matsuzaka AU/10
151a Miguel Montero AU/75 (RC) 6.00 15.00
151b Miguel Montero AU/60 6.00 15.00
154a Brandon Wood AU/75 (RC) 6.00 15.00
155a Felix Pie AU/75 (RC) 12.50 30.00
155b Felix Pie AU/70 12.50 30.00
157a Andy LaRoche AU/50 (RC) 6.00 15.00
157b Andy LaRoche AU/40 6.00 15.00
158a Jarrod Saltalamacchia AU/75 (RC) 10.00 25.00
158b Jarrod Saltalamacchia AU/25 12.50 30.00

2007 SP Authentic Autograph Parallel

RANDOM INSERTS IN PACKS
STATED PRINT RUN 5 SER.#'d SETS
NO PRICING DUE TO SCARCITY
EXCHANGE DEADLINE 11/8/2008

2007 SP Authentic By the Letter Rookie Signatures Full Name Redemptions

RANDOM INSERTS IN PACKS
PRINT RUNS B/WN 1-5 COPIES PER
REDEMPTION CARDS ARE NOT SERIAL #'d
PRINT RUNS PROVIDED BY UPPER DECK
NO PRICING DUE TO SCARCITY
EXCHANGE DEADLINE 12/31/08

2007 SP Authentic By the Letter Signatures

OVERALL BY THE LETTER AUTOS 1:12
PRINT RUNS B/WN 5-199 COPIES PER
NO PRICING ON SOME DUE TO SCARCITY
EXCHANGE DEADLINE 11/08/2008
1 Derek Jeter 200.00 300.00
8 Josh Beckett/15 30.00 60.00
10 Aramis Ramirez/25 12.50 30.00
11 Austin Kearns/50 6.00 15.00
16 Felix Pie/75 12.50 30.00
17 Alex Gordon/25 10.00 25.00
22 Adam Lind/75 8.00 20.00
25 Dan Haren/25 8.00 20.00
26 David Ortiz/10 20.00 50.00
27 Felix Hernandez/10 30.00 60.00
2a Ken Griffey Jr./25 100.00 250.00
2b Ken Griffey Jr./20 100.00 250.00
35 Khalil Greene/25 10.00 25.00
41 Jonathan Papelbon/40 20.00 50.00
44 Victor Martinez/25 6.00 15.00
45 Roger Clemens/5 50.00 100.00
46 Ryan Zimmerman/25 50.00 100.00
48 Travis Hafner/25 30.00 60.00
4a Justin Verlander/25 40.00 80.00
4b Justin Verlander/15 40.00 80.00
51 Billy Butler/50 10.00 25.00
55 Hunter Pence/50 12.50 30.00
5a Adrian Gonzalez/50 12.50 30.00
5b Adrian Gonzalez/60 12.50 30.00
9a Carlos Quentin/75 12.50 30.00
9b Carlos Quentin/50 12.50 30.00
12a B.J. Upton/25 20.00 50.00
12b B.J. Upton/15 20.00 50.00
13a Boof Bonser/75 6.00 15.00
13b Boof Bonser/50 6.00 15.00
14a Bronson Arroyo/75 5.00 12.00
14b Bronson Arroyo/10 5.00 12.00
15a Troy Tulowitzki 15.00 40.00
15b Troy Tulowitzki 15.00 40.00
18a Chris Duffy/75 6.00 15.00
18b Chris Duffy 6.00 15.00
19a Chris Young/75 6.00 15.00
19b Chris Young/50 6.00 15.00
20a Cliff Lee/75 15.00 40.00
20b Cliff Lee/50 15.00 40.00
21a Cole Hamels/25 20.00 50.00
21b Cole Hamels/15 20.00 50.00
23a Akinori Iwamura/25 12.50 30.00
23b Akinori Iwamura/15 12.50 30.00
24a Dan Uggla/25 6.00 15.00
24b Dan Uggla/21 6.00 15.00
28a Tony Gwynn Jr. 10.00 25.00
28b Tony Gwynn Jr. 10.00 25.00
29a Josh Hamilton/75 15.00 40.00
29b Josh Hamilton/50 15.00 40.00
29c Josh Hamilton/10 30.00 60.00
30a Phil Hughes 12.50 30.00
30b Phil Hughes 12.50 30.00
32a Dontrelle Willis/25 6.00 15.00
32b Dontrelle Willis/20 6.00 15.00
33a Hanley Ramirez/50 15.00 40.00
33b Hanley Ramirez/25 20.00 50.00
34a Howie Kendrick/60 8.00 20.00
34b Howie Kendrick/50 8.00 20.00
35a Huston Street/50 6.00 15.00
35b Huston Street/25 8.00 20.00
37a Jason Bay/50 30.00 60.00
37b Jason Bay/25 40.00 80.00
40a Joe Mauer/25 75.00 150.00
40b Joe Mauer/15 75.00 150.00
42a Tim Lincecum/50 60.00 120.00
42b Tim Lincecum/40 60.00 120.00
43a Matt Cain/75 15.00 40.00
43b Matt Cain/40 15.00 40.00
47a Stephen Drew/25 12.50 30.00
47b Stephen Drew/10 15.00 40.00
49a Josh Willingham 6.00 15.00
49b Josh Willingham/50 6.00 15.00
50a Torii Hunter/25 12.50 30.00
52a Justin Morneau/25 30.00 60.00
52b Justin Morneau/15 30.00 60.00
53a Andy LaRoche/75 6.00 15.00
53b Andy LaRoche/60 6.00 15.00
53c Andy LaRoche/50 6.00 15.00
54a Brandon Wood/75 6.00 15.00
54b Brandon Wood/50 6.00 15.00
56a Devern Hansack 6.00 15.00
56b Devern Hansack/75 6.00 15.00
58a Derrek Lee/25 30.00 60.00
58b Derrek Lee/10 40.00 80.00
59a Prince Fielder/25 30.00 60.00
59b Prince Fielder/10 40.00 80.00
60a Kevin Kouzmanoff/50 8.00 20.00

2007 SP Authentic By the Letter Signatures Full Name Redemptions

RANDOM INSERTS IN PACKS
PRINT RUNS B/WN 2-5 COPIES PER
REDEMPTION CARDS ARE NOT SERIAL #'d
PRINT RUNS PROVIDED BY UPPER DECK
NO PRICING DUE TO SCARCITY
EXCHANGE DEADLINE 12/31/08

2007 SP Authentic Authentic Power

COMPLETE SET (50) 8.00 20.00
STATED ODDS 1:2
AP1 Adam Dunn .30 .75
AP2 Albert Pujols 1.25 3.00
AP3 Alex Rodriguez .75 2.00
AP4 Alfonso Soriano .30 .75
AP5 Andruw Jones .20 .50
AP6 Aramis Ramirez .20 .50
AP7 Bill Hall .20 .50
AP8 Carlos Beltran .20 .50
AP9 Carlos Delgado .20 .50
AP10 Carlos Lee .20 .50
AP11 Chase Utley .50 1.25
AP12 Chipper Jones .50 1.25
AP13 Dan Uggla .30 .75
AP14 David Ortiz .30 .75
AP15 David Wright .75 2.00
AP16 Derrek Lee .20 .50
AP17 Eric Chavez .20 .50
AP18 Frank Thomas .50 1.25
AP19 Garrett Atkins .20 .50
AP20 Gary Sheffield .20 .50
AP21 Hideki Matsui .50 1.25
AP22 J.D. Drew .20 .50
AP23 Jason Bay .30 .75
AP24 Jason Giambi .20 .50
AP25 Jeff Francoeur .50 1.25
AP26 Jermaine Dye .20 .50
AP27 Jim Thome .30 .75
AP28 Justin Morneau .50 1.25
AP29 Ken Griffey Jr. .75 2.00
AP30 Lance Berkman .20 .50
AP31 Magglio Ordonez .30 .75
AP32 Manny Ramirez .50 1.25
AP33 Mark Teixeira .50 1.25
AP34 Matt Holliday .50 1.25
AP35 Miguel Cabrera .50 1.25
AP36 Miguel Tejada .30 .75
AP37 Mike Piazza .50 1.25
AP38 Nick Swisher .50 1.25
AP39 Pat Burrell .20 .50
AP40 Paul Konerko .30 .75
AP41 Prince Fielder .30 .75
AP42 Richie Sexson .20 .50
AP43 Ryan Howard .75 2.00
AP44 Sammy Sosa .50 1.25
AP45 Todd Helton .30 .75
AP46 Travis Hafner .20 .50
AP47 Troy Glaus .20 .50
AP48 Vernon Wells .20 .50
AP49 Victor Martinez .30 .75
AP50 Vladimir Guerrero .50 1.25

2007 SP Authentic Authentic Speed

COMPLETE SET (50) 8.00 20.00
STATED ODDS 1:2
AS1 Alex Rios .30 .75
AS2 Alex Rodriguez .75 2.00
AS3 Alfonso Soriano .30 .75
AS4 B.J. Upton .20 .50
AS5 Bobby Abreu .20 .50
AS6 Brandon Phillips .20 .50
AS7 Brian Roberts .20 .50
AS8 Carl Crawford .30 .75
AS9 Carlos Beltran .20 .50
AS10 Chase Utley .50 1.25
AS11 Chone Figgins .20 .50
AS12 Chris Burke .20 .50
AS13 Chris Duffy .20 .50
AS14 Coco Crisp .20 .50
AS15 Corey Patterson .20 .50
AS16 Dave Roberts .20 .50
AS17 David Wright .75 2.00
AS18 Derek Jeter 1.25 3.00
AS19 Edgar Renteria .20 .50
AS20 Eric Byrnes .20 .50
AS21 Felipe Lopez .20 .50
AS22 Gary Matthews .20 .50
AS23 Grady Sizemore .30 .75
AS24 Hanley Ramirez .50 1.25
AS25 Ian Kinsler .30 .75
AS26 Ichiro Suzuki .75 2.00
AS27 Jacque Jones .20 .50
AS28 Jimmy Rollins .30 .75
AS29 Johnny Damon .30 .75
AS30 Jose Reyes .30 .75
AS31 Juan Pierre .20 .50
AS32 Julio Lugo .20 .50
AS33 Kenny Lofton .20 .50
AS34 Luis Castillo .20 .50
AS35 Marcus Giles .20 .50
AS36 Melky Cabrera .20 .50
AS37 Mike Cameron .20 .50
AS38 Orlando Cabrera .20 .50
AS39 Rafael Furcal .20 .50
AS40 Randy Winn .20 .50
AS41 Rickie Weeks .30 .75
AS42 Rocco Baldelli .20 .50
AS43 Ryan Freel .20 .50
AS44 Ryan Theriot .20 .50
AS45 Scott Podsednik .20 .50
AS46 Shane Victorino .20 .50
AS47 Tadahito Iguchi .20 .50
AS48 Torii Hunter .20 .50
AS49 Vernon Wells .20 .50
AS50 Willy Taveras .20 .50

2007 SP Authentic Chirography Dual

RANDOM INSERTS IN PACKS
PRINT RUNS B/WN 75-175 COPIES PER
EXCHANGE DEADLINE 11/05/2008
CL Tim Lincecum 125.00 250.00
Matt Cain/175
HD Adam Dunn 12.50 30.00
Travis Hafner/75
HW Dan Haren 10.00 25.00
Jered Weaver/175
MI Daisuke Matsuzaka 100.00 200.00
Akinori Iwamura/75
ML Andrew Miller 50.00 100.00
Tim Lincecum/175
MZ Nick Markakis 10.00 25.00
Ryan Zimmerman/75

2007 SP Authentic Chirography Quad

RANDOM INSERTS IN PACKS
STATED PRINT RUN 5 SER.#'d SETS
NO PRICING DUE TO SCARCITY
EXCHANGE DEADLINE 11/05/2008

2007 SP Authentic Sign of the Times Dual

RANDOM INSERTS IN PACKS
PRINT RUNS B/WN 75-175 COPIES PER
EXCHANGE DEADLINE 11/05/2008
BP Josh Beckett 30.00 60.00
Jonathan Papelbon/75
CJ Roger Clemens 200.00 250.00
Derek Jeter/75
TK Mark Teixeira 8.00 20.00
Ian Kinsler/75

2007 SP Authentic Sign of the Times Triple

RANDOM INSERTS IN PACKS
PRINT RUNS B/WN 25-75 COPIES PER
NO PRICING ON QTY OF 25 DUE TO SCARCITY
EXCHANGE DEADLINE 11/05/2008

2007 SP Authentic Sign of the Times Quad

RANDOM INSERTS IN PACKS
STATED PRINT RUN 5 SER.#'d SETS
NO PRICING DUE TO SCARCITY
EXCHANGE DEADLINE 11/05/2008

2008 SP Authentic

This set was released on October 14, 2008. The base set consists of 191 cards. Cards 1-100 feature veterans, and cards 101-191 are rookies serial numbered of various quantities. Some rookie cards feature autographs, jerseys, or both.

COMP.SET w/o RCs (100) 8.00 20.00
COMMON CARD .15 .40
COMMON AU RC (101-191) 3.00 8.00
AU PRINT RUNS 149-999 PER
OVERALL AU ODDS 1:8 HOBBY
COMMON JSY AU RC (101-191) 4.00 10.00
JSY AU PRINT RUN 299-999 PER
OVERALL AU ODDS 1:8 HOBBY
EXCH DEADLINE 9/18/2010
1 Ken Griffey Jr. .60 1.50
2 Derek Jeter 1.00 2.50
3 Albert Pujols 1.00 2.50
4 Ichiro Suzuki .60 1.50
5 Daisuke Matsuzaka .40 1.00
6 Vladimir Guerrero .40 1.00
7 Magglio Ordonez .25 .60
8 Eric Chavez .15 .40
9 Randy Johnson .40 1.00
10 Ryan Braun .50 1.25
11 Phil Hughes .40 1.00
12 Joba Chamberlain .25 .60
13 B.J. Upton .25 .60
14 Frank Thomas .40 1.00
15 Greg Maddux .50 1.25
16 Delmon Young .25 .60
17 Carlos Beltran .25 .60
18 Derrek Lee .15 .40
19 Aramis Ramirez .15 .40
20 Miguel Tejada .25 .60
21 Manny Ramirez .40 1.00
22 Justin Upton .25 .60
23 Miguel Cabrera .40 1.00
24 Prince Fielder .25 .60
25 Adam Dunn .25 .60
26 Jose Reyes .25 .60
27 Chase Utley .40 1.00
28 Jimmy Rollins .25 .60
29 Joe Blanton .15 .40
30 Mark Teixeira .40 1.00
31 Brian McCann .25 .60
32 Russell Martin .15 .40
33 Ian Kinsler .25 .60
34 Travis Hafner .15 .40
35 Victor Martinez .25 .60
36 Grady Sizemore .25 .60
37 Alex Rodriguez .60 1.50
38 David Wright .50 1.25
39 Ryan Howard .50 1.25
40 Carlos Lee .15 .40
41 Lance Berkman .25 .60
42 Hunter Pence .40 1.00
43 John Lackey .25 .60
44 C.C. Sabathia .25 .60
45 Michael Young .25 .60
46 Carl Crawford .25 .60
47 Carlos Pena .25 .60
48 Justin Verlander .50 1.25
49 Cole Hamels .40 1.00
50 Carlos Zambrano .25 .60
51 Jake Peavy .15 .40
52 Khalil Greene .15 .40
53 Chris Young .15 .40
54 Vernon Wells .15 .40
55 Alex Rios .25 .60
56 Roy Halladay .40 1.00
57 Roy Oswalt .25 .60
58 Ben Sheets .15 .40
59 J.J. Hardy .15 .40
60 Pedro Martinez .25 .60
61 Nick Swisher .40 1.00
62 Curtis Granderson .25 .60
63 Johnny Damon .25 .60
64 Mariano Rivera .40 1.00
65 Josh Beckett .25 .60
66 Erik Bedard .15 .40
67 Johan Santana .40 1.00
68 Joe Mauer .40 1.00
69 Justin Morneau .40 1.00
70 Torii Hunter .15 .40
71 Alex Gordon .25 .60
72 Jose Guillen .15 .40
73 Jim Thome .25 .60
74 Paul Konerko .25 .60
75 Josh Hamilton .40 1.00
76 Hanley Ramirez .40 1.00
77 Dontrelle Willis .15 .40
78 Dan Uggla .25 .60
79 Brandon Phillips .15 .40
80 Rich Ankiel .15 .40
81 Nick Markakis .40 1.00
82 Ryan Zimmerman .25 .60
83 Brian Roberts .15 .40
84 Lastings Milledge .15 .40
85 Freddy Sanchez .15 .40
86 Barry Zito .15 .40
87 Matt Cain .15 .40
88 Andruw Jones .15 .40
89 Dan Haren .15 .40
90 Chien-Ming Wang .25 .60
91 Jonathan Papelbon .25 .60
92 Felix Hernandez .40 1.00
93 David Ortiz .25 .60
94 Jason Bay .25 .60
95 Matt Holliday .40 1.00
96 Troy Tulowitzki .40 1.00
97 Hideki Matsui .40 1.00
98 Jeff Francoeur .25 .60
99 Alfonso Soriano .25 .60
100 Curt Schilling .25 .60
101 Alex Romero Jsy AU/799 (RC) 4.00 10.00
102 Matt Tolbert Jsy/699 RC 5.00 12.00
103 Bobby Wilson AU/699 RC 6.00 15.00
104 Brent Lillibridge AU/599 (RC) 5.00 12.00
105 Brian Barton AU/698 RC 6.00 15.00
106 Brian Bass Jsy AU/799 (RC) 8.00 20.00
107 Brian Bixler AU/698 (RC) 3.00 8.00
108 Brian Bocock Jsy AU/599 RC 4.00 10.00
109 Burke Badenhop AU/797 RC 3.00 8.00
110 Chin-Lung Hu Jsy AU/999 (RC) 10.00 25.00
111 Chris Perez AU/699 RC 5.00 12.00
112 Clay Buchholz Jsy AU/999 (RC) 8.00 20.00
113 Clayton Kershaw Jsy AU/699 RC EXCH 12.50 30.00
114 Colt Morton Jsy AU/574 RC 4.00 10.00
115 Daric Barton AU/799 (RC) 4.00 10.00
116 Darren O'Day AU/798 RC 3.00 8.00
117 David Purcey AU/599 (RC) 3.00 8.00
118 Denard Span Jsy AU/299 (RC) EXCH 8.00 20.00
119 Elliot Johnson AU/798 (RC) 3.00 8.00
120 Emmanuel Burriss AU/299 RC EXCH 4.00 10.00
121 Evan Longoria Jsy AU/499 RC 30.00 60.00
122 Evan Meek Jsy AU/649 RC 5.00 12.00
123 Felipe Paulino Jsy AU/799 RC 4.00 10.00
124 Carlos Gonzalez Jsy AU/599 (RC) EXCH 15.00 40.00
125 German Duran AU/699 RC 3.00 8.00
126 Greg Reynolds AU/149 RC 3.00 8.00
127 Greg Smith Jsy AU/799 RC 5.00 12.00
128 Harvey Garcia Jsy AU/799 RC 4.00 10.00
129 Hernan Iribarren Jsy AU/799 (RC) 4.00 10.00
130 Ian Kennedy Jsy AU/699 RC 12.50 30.00
131 J.R. Towles Jsy AU/499 RC 4.00 10.00
132 Jay Bruce Jsy AU/549 (RC) 12.50 30.00
133 Justin Nix Jsy AU/299 (RC) EXCH 4.00 10.00
134 Jed Lowrie AU/499 (RC) 10.00 25.00
135 Jeff Clement AU/399 (RC) 6.00 15.00
136 Jonathan Herrera AU/699 RC 3.00 8.00
137 Joey Votto Jsy AU/999 (RC) 40.00 80.00
138 Johnny Cueto Jsy AU/999 RC 8.00 20.00
139 Jonathan Albaladejo Jsy AU/799 RC 4.00 10.00
140 Justin Masterson AU/699 RC 20.00 50.00
141 Justin Ruggiano AU/149 RC 3.00 8.00
142 Kevin Hart Jsy AU/749 (RC) 4.00 10.00
143 Kosuke Fukudome Jsy/799 RC 12.50 30.00
144 Luis Mendoza Jsy AU/299 (RC) 4.00 10.00
145 Luke Carlin AU/699 RC 6.00 15.00
146 Luke Hochevar AU/798 RC 4.00 10.00
147 Max Scherzer Jsy AU/799 RC EXCH 12.50 30.00
148 Micah Hoffpauir AU/599 RC 8.00 20.00
149 Mike Parisi AU/699 RC 3.00 8.00
150 Nick Adenhart AU/599 (RC) 10.00 25.00
151 Nick Blackburn Jsy AU/799 RC 8.00 20.00
152 Nyjer Morgan Jsy AU/999 (RC) 4.00 10.00
153 Ramon Troncoso Jsy AU/399 RC 5.00 12.00
154 Randor Bierd Jsy AU/799 RC 4.00 10.00
155 Rich Thompson AU/398 RC 5.00 12.00
156 Rico Washington Jsy AU/799 (RC) 4.00 10.00
157 Ross Ohlendorf Jsy AU/999 RC 4.00 10.00
158 Steve Holm Jsy AU/999 RC 4.00 10.00
159 Wesley Wright Jsy AU/849 RC 4.00 10.00
160 Wladimir Balentien AU/599 (RC) 3.00 8.00
161 Alex Hinshaw AU/699 RC EXCH 5.00 12.00
162 Bobby Korecky AU/999 RC 5.00 12.00
163 Brad Harman AU/999 RC 5.00 12.00
164 Brandon Boggs AU/999 (RC) 3.00 8.00
165 Callix Crabbe AU/325 (RC) 3.00 8.00
166 Clay Timpner AU/849 (RC) 3.00 8.00
167 Clete Thomas AU/850 RC 6.00 15.00
168 Cory Wade AU/999 (RC) 3.00 8.00
169 Doug Mathis AU/999 RC 3.00 8.00
170 Eider Torres AU/999 (RC) 5.00 12.00
171 Gregorio Petit AU/999 RC 4.00 10.00
172 Michael Aubrey AU/699 RC EXCH 4.00 10.00
173 Jesse Carlson AU/999 RC 8.00 20.00
174 Billy Buckner AU/999 (RC) 3.00 8.00
175 Josh Newman AU/699 RC 3.00 8.00
176 Matt Tupman AU/999 RC 5.00 12.00
177 Matt Joyce AU/999 RC 12.50 30.00
178 Paul Janish AU/999 (RC) 5.00 12.00
179 Robinzon Diaz AU/999 (RC) 3.00 8.00
180 Fernando Hernandez AU/999 RC 3.00 8.00
181 Brandon Jones AU/999 RC 3.00 8.00
182 Eddie Bonine AU/899 RC 3.00 8.00
183 Chris Smith AU/384 (RC) 6.00 15.00
184 Jonathan Van Every AU/999 RC 4.00 10.00
185 Marino Salas AU/999 RC 4.00 10.00
186 Mike Aviles AU/899 RC 6.00 15.00
187 Mitchell Boggs AU/699 (RC) EXCH 6.00 15.00
188 Chris Carter AU/699 (RC) EXCH 5.00 12.00
189 Travis Denker AU/699 RC EXCH 3.00 8.00
190 Carlos Rosa AU/699 RC 5.00 12.00
191 Evan Longoria AU/350 (RC) 30.00 60.00

2008 SP Authentic Gold

*GOLD 1-100: 5X TO 12X BASIC
*GLD AU RC: .75X TO 2X BASIC
*GLD JSY AU RC: .75X TO 2X BASIC
RANDOM INSERTS IN PACKS
PRINT RUN B/WN 10-50 SER.#'d SETS
NO VOTTO PRICING AVAILABLE
EXCH DEADLINE 9/18/2010
2 Derek Jeter 20.00 50.00
4 Ichiro Suzuki 20.00 50.00
110 Chin-Lung Hu Jsy AU/50 40.00 80.00
121 Evan Longoria Jsy AU/50 125.00 250.00
147 Max Scherzer Jsy AU/50 40.00 80.00
150 Nick Adenhart AU/50 15.00 40.00
151 Nick Blackburn Jsy AU/50 20.00 50.00
191 Evan Longoria AU/50 125.00 250.00

2008 SP Authentic Authentic Achievements

STATED ODDS 1:2 HOBBY
AA1 Derek Jeter 2.00 5.00
AA2 Ken Griffey Jr. 1.25 3.00
AA3 Randy Johnson .75 2.00
AA4 Frank Thomas .75 2.00
AA5 Tom Glavine .50 1.25
AA6 Matt Holliday .75 2.00
AA7 Justin Verlander 1.00 2.50
AA8 Manny Ramirez .75 2.00
AA9 Scott Rolen .50 1.25
AA10 Brandon Webb .50 1.25
AA11 Erik Bedard .30 .75
AA12 Daisuke Matsuzaka .75 2.00
AA13 Johan Santana .75 2.00
AA14 Carlos Lee .30 .75
AA15 Alfonso Soriano .50 1.25
AA16 Grady Sizemore .50 1.25
AA17 Jose Reyes .50 1.25
AA18 Chase Utley .75 2.00
AA19 Roy Oswalt .50 1.25
AA20 David Ortiz .50 1.25
AA21 Jake Peavy .30 .75
AA22 Hanley Ramirez .75 2.00
AA23 Alex Rodriguez 1.25 3.00
AA24 Ryan Howard 1.00 2.50
AA25 David Wright 1.00 2.50
AA26 Trevor Hoffman .50 1.25
AA27 Prince Fielder .50 1.25
AA28 Ichiro Suzuki 1.25 3.00
AA29 Jimmy Rollins .50 1.25
AA30 Mariano Rivera .75 2.00
AA31 Pedro Martinez .50 1.25
AA32 Torii Hunter .30 .75
AA33 Ivan Rodriguez .50 1.25
AA34 Jim Thome .50 1.25
AA35 Chipper Jones .75 2.00
AA36 John Smoltz .75 2.00
AA37 Jeff Kent .30 .75
AA38 Albert Pujols 2.00 5.00
AA39 Lance Berkman .50 1.25
AA40 Justin Morneau .75 2.00
AA41 Andruw Jones .30 .75
AA42 Adam Dunn .50 1.25
AA43 Greg Maddux 1.00 2.50
AA44 Billy Wagner .30 .75
AA45 Vladimir Guerrero .75 2.00
AA46 C.C. Sabathia .50 1.25
AA47 Mark Teixeira .75 2.00
AA48 Mark Buehrle .50 1.25
AA49 Miguel Cabrera .75 2.00
AA50 Josh Beckett .50 1.25

2008 SP Authentic By The Letter Signatures

OVERALL AU ODDS 1:8 HOBBY
ANNCD PRINT RUNS LISTED
SER.# ON CARDS ARE DIFFERENT
EXCH DEADLINE 9/18/2010
AD Adam Dunn/140 * 10.00 25.00
Spells Dunn and Reds
AG Adrian Gonzalez/110 * 8.00 20.00
Spells Gonzalez and Padres
AS Alfonso Soriano/90 *
Spells Soriano and Cubs
BH Bill Hall/1570 * 8.00 20.00
Spells Bill Hall and Milwaukee Brewers
BP Brandon Phillips/1259 * 12.50 30.00
Spells Brandon Phillips and Cincinnati Reds
BR Brandon Webb/30 *

2007 SP Authentic

Spells Webb
BW Billy Wagner/125 * 20.00 50.00
Spells Wagner and New York Mets
CB Chad Billingsley/1306 * 6.00 15.00
Spells Chad Billingsley and Los Angeles Dodgers
CD Chris Duncan/480 *
Spells Chris Duncan and St Louis Cardinals
CJ Chipper Jones/100 * 50.00 100.00
Spells Chipper and Braves
CL Carlos Lee/160 * 10.00 25.00
Spells Lee and Houston Astros
CW Chien-Ming Wang/80 75.00 150.00
Spells Wang and Yankees
DA David Murphy/1837 * 10.00 25.00
Spells David Murphy and Texas Rangers
DE David Eckstein/510 *
Spells David Eckstein and Toronto Blue Jays
DJ Derek Jeter/240 * 125.00 250.00
Spells Jeter and Yankees EXCH
DM Daisuke Matsuzaka/125 * 60.00 120.00
Spells Matsuzaka and Red Sox
EE Edwin Encarnacion/1570 * 5.00 12.00
Spells Edwin Encarnacion and Cincinnati Reds
FC Fausto Carmona/844 * 8.00 20.00
Spells Fausto Carmona and Cleveland Indians
GA Garrett Atkins/588 * 10.00 25.00
Spells Garrett Atkins and Colorado Rockies
GJ Geoff Jenkins/1200 * 8.00 20.00
Spells Geoff Jenkins and Philadelphia Phillies
GM Gil Meche/380 *
Spells Gil Meche and Kansas City Royals
GS Grady Sizemore/240 * 20.00 50.00
Spells Sizemore and Indians
HK Howie Kendrick/175 *
Spells Howie Kendrick and Anaheim Angels
JB Joe Blanton/580 * 6.00 15.00
Spells Joe Blanton and Oakland Athletics
JE Jeff Francoeur/275 * 15.00 40.00
Spells Jeff Francoeur and Atlanta Braves
JF Jeff Francis/335 * 8.00 20.00
Spells Jeff Francis and Colorado Rockies
JG Jeremy Guthrie/985 * 12.50 30.00
Spells Jeremy Guthrie and Baltimore Orioles
JH Jeremy Hermida/505 *
Spells Jeremy Hermida and Florida Marlins
JL James Loney/1275 * 10.00 25.00
Spells James Loney and Los Angeles Dodgers EXCH
JN Joe Nathan/365 * 10.00 25.00
Spells Joe Nathan and Minnesota Twins
JO John Lackey/187 * 12.50 30.00
Spells John Lackey and Anaheim Angels
JP Jonathan Papelbon/550 * 20.00 50.00
Spells Papelbon and Red Sox
JS Jon Lester/235 * 60.00 120.00
Spells Jon Lester and Boston Red Sox
JT Jim Thome/35 *
Spells Thome and White Sox
JV Jason Varitek/110 *
Spells Varitek and Red Sox
KE Kevin Youkilis/365 * 30.00 60.00
Spells Kevin Youkilis and Boston Red Sox
KG Ken Griffey Jr./275 * 100.00 175.00
Spells Griffey and Reds EXCH
KJ Kelly Johnson/1399 * 5.00 12.00
Spells Kelly Johnson and Atlanta Braves
LB Lance Berkman/165 * 30.00 60.00
Spells Berkman and Astros
MC Miguel Cabrera/35 *
Spells Cabrera and Tigers
ME Mark Ellis/995 * 5.00 12.00
Spells Mark Ellis and Oakland Athletics
MG Matt Garza/235 * 8.00 20.00
Spells Matt Garza and Tampa Bay Rays
MK Matt Kemp/1369 * 10.00 25.00
Spells Matt Kemp and Los Angeles Dodgers
MM Melvin Mora/490 * 8.00 20.00
Spells Melvin Mora and Baltimore Orioles EXCH
NL Noah Lowry/1440 * 10.00 25.00
Spells Noah Lowry and San Francisco Giants
NM Nick Markakis/1100 *
Spells Nick Markakis and Baltimore Orioles
NS Nick Swisher/1150 * 6.00 15.00
Spells Nick Swisher and Chicago White Sox
PF Prince Fielder/245 * 20.00 50.00
Spells Fielder and Brewers EXCH
PH Phil Hughes/385 * 15.00 40.00
Spells Phil Hughes and New York Yankees
PK Paul Konerko/175 * 12.50 30.00
Spells Konerko and White Sox
RH Rich Hill/220 * 10.00 25.00
Spells Hill and Cubs
RM Russell Martin/265 * 20.00 50.00
Spells Martin and Dodgers
RO Roy Halladay/160 * 60.00 120.00
Spells Halladay and Blue Jays
SB Scott Baker/1248 * 6.00 15.00
Spells Scott Baker and Minnesota Twins
TG Tom Gorzelanny/1082 * 5.00 12.00
Spells Tom Gorzelanny and Pittsburgh Pirates
TH Tim Hudson/170 *
Spells Hudson and Braves
TT Troy Tulowitzki/252 * 12.50 30.00
Spells Tulowitzki and Rockies
YE Yunel Escobar/1342 *
Spells Yunel Escobar and Atlanta Braves

2008 SP Authentic Chirography Signatures Dual

OVERALL AU ODDS 1:8 HOBBY
PRINT RUNS B/WN 10-99 COPIES PER
NO PRICING ON MOST CARDS
EXCH DEADLINE 9/18/2010
BH Joe Blanton
Rich Harden/99
GB Tom Gorzelanny 12.50 30.00
Chad Billingsley/96
HK Phil Hughes 10.00 25.00
Ian Kennedy/99 EXCH
PE Brandon Phillips 6.00 15.00
Edwin Encarnacion/99

2008 SP Authentic Chirography Signatures Triple

OVERALL AU ODDS 1:8 HOBBY
PRINT RUNS B/WN 25-50 COPIES PER
NO PRICING DUE TO SCARCITY
EXCH DEADLINE 9/18/2010

2008 SP Authentic Chirography Signatures Quad

OVERALL AU ODDS 1:8 HOBBY
PRINT RUNS B/WN 5-15 COPIES PER
NO PRICING DUE TO SCARCITY
EXCH DEADLINE 9/18/2010

2008 SP Authentic Marquee Matchups

STATED ODDS 1:2 HOBBY
MM1 Derek Jeter 2.00 5.00
Curt Schilling
MM2 Josh Beckett 2.00 5.00
Derek Jeter
MM3 Albert Pujols 2.00 5.00
Brad Lidge
MM4 Daisuke Matsuzaka 1.25 3.00
Alex Rodriguez
MM5 Ken Griffey Jr. 1.25 3.00
John Smoltz
MM6 John Smoltz 1.00 2.50
David Wright
MM7 Jonathan Papelbon .50 1.25
Gary Sheffield
MM8 Ryan Braun .50 1.25
Roy Oswalt
MM9 Mariano Rivera .75 2.00
David Ortiz
MM10 Carlos Zambrano .50 1.25
Albert Pujols
MM11 Dontrelle Willis .30 .75
Travis Hafner
MM12 Felix Hernandez .50 1.25
Victor Martinez
MM13 Carlos Zambrano .50 1.25
Carlos Lee
MM14 Chien-Ming Wang .50 1.25
Manny Ramirez
MM15 Felix Hernandez .75 2.00
Justin Morneau
MM16 Ichiro Suzuki .50 1.25
Francisco Rodriguez
MM17 Grady Sizemore .50 1.25
Erik Bedard
MM18 Vladimir Guerrero 1.00 2.50
Justin Verlander
MM19 Daisuke Matsuzaka 1.25 3.00
Ichiro Suzuki
MM20 Alfonso Soriano .75 2.00
Chris Carpenter
MM21 Hanley Ramirez .75 2.00
Pedro Martinez
MM22 Chase Utley .75 2.00
Randy Johnson
MM23 Ken Griffey Jr. .50 1.25
Roy Oswalt
MM24 Randy Johnson 1.25 3.00
Ken Griffey Jr.
MM25 Jimmy Rollins .75 2.00
Johan Santana
MM26 Matt Cain .30 .75
Andruw Jones
MM27 Pedro Martinez 1.00 2.50
Ryan Howard
MM28 Cole Hamels .75 2.00
David Wright
MM29 Chipper Jones .75 2.00
Johan Santana
MM30 Billy Wagner .75 2.00
Mark Teixeira
MM31 C.C. Sabathia .50 1.25
Magglio Ordonez
MM32 Jose Reyes .50 1.25
Tom Glavine
MM33 Derek Jeter 2.00 5.00
Jonathan Papelbon
MM34 Johan Santana .75 2.00
Alex Rodriguez
MM35 Alfonso Soriano .30 .75
Jake Peavy
MM36 Johan Santana .75 2.00
Ryan Howard
MM37 Jake Peavy .30 .75
Russell Martin
MM38 Carlos Zambrano .50 1.25
Prince Fielder
MM39 Cole Hamels .75 2.00
Carlos Beltran
MM40 Josh Beckett 1.25 3.00
Alex Rodriguez
MM41 Roy Halladay 2.00 5.00
Derek Jeter
MM42 Hideki Matsui .75 2.00
Daisuke Matsuzaka
MM43 C.C. Sabathia .50 1.25
Joe Mauer
MM44 Francisco Rodriguez .50 1.25
Manny Ramirez
MM45 Jered Weaver .75 2.00
Miguel Cabrera
MM46 David Wright .30 .75
Jake Peavy
MM47 Greg Maddux 1.25 3.00
Ken Griffey Jr.
MM48 John Smoltz .75 2.00
Hanley Ramirez
MM49 Pedro Martinez 1.25 3.00
Alex Rodriguez
MM50 Trevor Hoffman .75 2.00
Matt Holliday

2008 SP Authentic Rookie Exclusives

RANDOM INSERTS IN PACKS
AH Alex Hinshaw 1.25 3.00
AR Alex Romero 1.25 3.00
BA Brian Barton 1.25 3.00
BB Brandon Boggs 1.25 3.00
BH Brad Harman 1.25 3.00
BI Brian Bixler .75 2.00
BK Bobby Korecky .75 2.00
BO Brian Bocock .75 2.00
BR Brian Bass .75 2.00
BU Burke Badenhop 1.25 3.00
BW Bobby Wilson .75 2.00
CB Clay Buchholz 2.00 5.00
CC Callix Crabbe .75 2.00
CM Colt Morton 1.25 3.00
CT Clay Timpner .75 2.00
CU Johnny Cueto 1.25 3.00
CW Cory Wade .75 2.00
DB Daric Barton .75 2.00
DM Doug Mathis .75 2.00
DS Denard Span 1.25 3.00
EB Emmanuel Burriss 1.25 3.00
EJ Elliot Johnson .75 2.00
EM Evan Meek .75 2.00
ET Eider Torres 1.25 3.00
FH Fernando Hernandez .75 2.00
FP Felipe Paulino 1.25 3.00
GD German Duran 1.25 3.00
GP Gregorio Petit 1.25 3.00
GS Greg Smith .75 2.00
HI Hernan Iribarren 1.25 3.00
IK Ian Kennedy 2.00 5.00
JA Jonathan Albaladejo 1.25 3.00
JB Jay Bruce 3.00 8.00
JC Jesse Carlson 1.25 3.00
JH Jonathan Herrera 1.25 3.00
JL Jed Lowrie 2.00 5.00
JN Jayson Nix .75 2.00
JT J.R. Towles 1.25 3.00
KH Kevin Hart .75 2.00
LC Luke Carlin .75 2.00
LM Luis Mendoza .75 2.00
MA Matt Tolbert 1.25 3.00
MH Micah Hoffpauir 2.50 6.00
MJ Matt Joyce 2.00 5.00
MP Mike Parisi 1.25 3.00
MT Matt Tupman .75 2.00
NA Nick Adenhart .75 2.00
NB Nick Blackburn 1.25 3.00
NE Josh Newman 1.25 3.00
NM Nyjer Morgan .75 2.00
RA Alexei Ramirez 3.00 8.00
RB Randor Bierd .75 2.00
RD Robinzon Diaz .75 2.00
RI Rich Thompson 1.25 3.00
RO Ross Ohlendorf 1.25 3.00
RT Ramon Troncoso .75 2.00
RW Rico Washington .75 2.00
SH Steve Holm .75 2.00
TH Clete Thomas 1.25 3.00
WB Wladimir Balentien .75 2.00
WW Wesley Wright .75 2.00

2008 SP Authentic Rookie Exclusives Autographs

OVERALL AU ODDS 1:8 HOBBY
NO PRICING DUE TO SCARCITY
EXCH DEADLINE 9/18/2010

2008 SP Authentic Sign of the Times Dual

OVERALL AU ODDS 1:8 HOBBY
PRINT RUNS B/WN 10-99 COPIES PER
MOST CARDS NOT PRICED
EXCH DEADLINE 9/18/2010
BB Clay Buchholz
Chad Billingsley/99 EXCH
DC Daisuke Matsuzaka
Chien-Ming Wang/10
FZ Jeff Francoeur
Ryan Zimmerman/25
GL Yovani Gallardo
Tim Lincecum/99
GM Alex Gordon
Gil Meche/99
HL Phil Hughes
Jon Lester/25
JE Kelly Johnson
Yunel Escobar/99
JH Derek Jeter
Phil Hughes/25
JT Derek Jeter
Troy Tulowitzki/25
KR Ian Kinsler
Mark Reynolds/99
NW Joe Nathan 10.00 25.00
Billy Wagner/74
PK Brandon Phillips
Howie Kendrick/99
PW Felix Pie 6.00 15.00
Josh Willingham/99
RJ Rich Hill
Jon Lester/99
UR B.J. Upton
Hanley Ramirez/25

2008 SP Authentic Sign of the Times Triple

OVERALL AU ODDS 1:8 HOBBY
PRINT RUNS B/WN 10-50 COPIES PER
NO PRICING DUE TO SCARCITY
EXCH DEADLINE 9/18/2010

2008 SP Authentic USA Junior National Team Jersey Autographs

OVERALL AU ODDS 1:8 HOBBY
STATED PRINT RUN 120 SER.#'d SETS
AA Andrew Aplin 10.00 25.00
AM Austin Maddox 30.00 60.00
CC Colton Cain 30.00 60.00
CG Cameron Garfield 12.50 30.00
CT Cecil Tanner 4.00 10.00
DN David Nick 20.00 50.00
DT Donovan Tate 50.00 100.00
FR Nick Franklin 5.00 12.00
HM Harold Martinez 10.00 25.00
JB Jake Barrett 6.00 15.00
MA Jeff Malm 6.00 15.00
ME Jonathan Meyer 8.00 20.00
MP Matthew Purke 8.00 20.00
MS Max Stassi 6.00 15.00
NF Nolan Fontana
RW Ryan Weber
TU Jacob Turner 20.00 50.00
WH Wes Hatton 10.00 25.00

2008 SP Authentic USA Junior National Team Patch Autographs

OVERALL AU ODDS 1:8 HOBBY
STATED PRINT RUN 50 SER.#'d SETS
AA Andrew Aplin 10.00 25.00
AM Austin Maddox
CC Colton Cain 10.00 25.00
CG Cameron Garfield
CT Cecil Tanner
DN David Nick 6.00 15.00
DT Donovan Tate
FR Nick Franklin
HM Harold Martinez
JB Jake Barrett 6.00 15.00
MA Jeff Malm
ME Jonathan Meyer
MP Matthew Purke
MS Max Stassi 30.00 60.00
NF Nolan Fontana 12.50 30.00
RW Ryan Weber 12.50 30.00
TU Jacob Turner 40.00 80.00
WH Wes Hatton 15.00 40.00

2008 SP Authentic USA National Team By the Letter Autographs

OVERALL AU ODDS 1:8 HOBBY
PRINT RUNS BW/N 50-181 PER
AG A.J. Griffin/105 6.00 15.00
AO Andrew Oliver/105
BS Blake Smith/105 8.00 20.00
CC Christian Colon/105 20.00 50.00
CH Chris Hernandez/180 12.50 30.00
DD Derek Dietrich/105 12.50 30.00
HM Hunter Morris/106
KD Kentrail Davis/103 20.00 50.00
KG Kyle Gibson/181 30.00 60.00
KR Kevin Rhoderick/172 6.00 15.00
KV Kendal Volz/105 8.00 20.00
MD Matt den Dekker/105 8.00 20.00
MG Micah Gibbs/180 6.00 15.00
ML Mike Leake/180 15.00 40.00
MM Mike Minor/105 6.00 15.00
RJ Ryan Jackson/104 8.00 20.00
RL Ryan Lipkin/50
SS Stephen Strasburg/105 150.00 300.00
TL Tyler Lyons/104 6.00 15.00

2009 SP Authentic

COMP.SET w/o AU's (200) 50.00 100.00
COMP.SET w/o SPs (100) 12.50 30.00
COMMON CARD (1-128) .15 .40
COMMON RC (129-170) 1.00 2.50
COMMON SP (171-200) .50 1.25
171-200 APPX.ODDS 1:8 HOBBY
COMMON SP (201-225) .60 1.50
201-225 RANDOMLY INSERTED
201-225 PRINT RUN 495 SER.#'d SETS
COMMON AUTO (226-250) 4.00 10.00
OVERALL AUTO ODDS 1:8 HOBBY
AUTO PRINT RUN B/WN 100-500 PER
1 Kosuke Fukudome .40 1.00
2 Derek Jeter 1.00 2.50
3 Evan Longoria .50 1.25
4 Yadier Molina .25 .60
5 Albert Pujols 1.00 2.50
6 Ryan Howard .50 1.25
7 Joe Mauer .40 1.00
8 Ryan Braun .50 1.25
9 Hunter Pence .25 .60
10 Gary Sheffield .15 .40
11 Ryan Zimmerman .25 .60
12 Alfonso Soriano .25 .60
13 Alex Rodriguez .60 1.50
14 Paul Konerko .25 .60
15 Dustin Pedroia .50 1.25
16 Brian McCann .25 .60
17 Lance Berkman .25 .60
18 Daisuke Matsuzaka .40 1.00
19 Josh Beckett .25 .60
20 Carlos Quentin .25 .60
21 Carlos Delgado .15 .40
22 Clayton Kershaw .40 1.00
23 Zack Greinke .25 .60
24 Ken Griffey Jr. .60 1.50
25 Mark Teixeira .40 1.00
26 Chase Utley .40 1.00
27 Vladimir Guerrero .40 1.00
28 Prince Fielder .25 .60
29 Adrian Beltre .15 .40
30 Magglio Ordonez .25 .60
31 Jon Lester .40 1.00
32 Josh Hamilton .40 1.00
33 Justin Morneau .40 1.00
34 Felix Hernandez .40 1.00
35 Cole Hamels .40 1.00
36 Edinson Volquez .15 .40
37 Hideki Okajima .15 .40
38 Carlos Zambrano .25 .60
39 Aaron Harang .15 .40
40 Chien-Ming Wang .25 .60
41 Shin-Soo Choo .25 .60
42 Mariano Rivera .40 1.00
43 Josh Johnson .25 .60
44 Roy Oswalt .25 .60
45 Carlos Lee .15 .40
46 Ryan Dempster .15 .40
47 Ryan Ludwick .25 .60
48 Joakim Soria .15 .40
49 Jair Jurrjens .15 .40
50 John Danks .15 .40
51 Ichiro Suzuki .60 1.50
52 CC Sabathia .25 .60
53 Yovani Gallardo .15 .40
54 Ervin Santana .15 .40
55 Tim Lincecum .60 1.50
56 Mark Buehrle .25 .60
57 Johan Santana .40 1.00
58 Chad Billingsley .15 .40
59 Francisco Liriano .15 .40
60 Joey Votto .40 1.00
61 Matt Kemp .25 .60
62 Joba Chamberlain .25 .60
63 Hiroki Kuroda .15 .40
64 Brian Roberts .15 .40
65 Randy Johnson .25 .60
66 Jay Bruce .25 .60
67 Curtis Granderson .25 .60
68 Hideki Matsui .40 1.00
69 Todd Helton .25 .60
70 Nick Markakis .40 1.00
71 Andy Pettitte .25 .60
72 Ian Kinsler .25 .60
73 Brandon Inge .15 .40
74 Adrian Gonzalez .25 .60
75 Francisco Rodriguez .25 .60
76 Derek Lowe .15 .40
77 Carlos Beltran .15 .40
78 Matt Holliday .40 1.00
79 Jake Peavy .15 .40
80 Scott Kazmir .15 .40
81 David Ortiz .25 .60
82 Dan Haren .15 .40
83 Hanley Ramirez .40 1.00
84 Jim Thome .25 .60
85 Brad Hawpe .15 .40
86 Vernon Wells .15 .40
87 B.J. Upton .25 .60
88 James Shields .15 .40
89 Jason Giambi .15 .40
90 Adam Dunn .25 .60
91 Brandon Webb .25 .60
92 Roy Halladay .40 1.00
93 Miguel Cabrera .40 1.00
94 Jose Reyes .25 .60
95 Chipper Jones .40 1.00
96 Grady Sizemore .25 .60
97 Jason Varitek .40 1.00
98 David Wright .50 1.25
99 Manny Ramirez .40 1.00
100 Kevin Youkilis .25 .60
101 Bengie Molina .15 .40
102 Ivan Rodriguez .25 .60
103 Andruw Jones .15 .40
104 Jorge Cantu .15 .40
105 Corey Hart .15 .40
106 Adam Wainwright .25 .60
107 Raul Ibanez .25 .60
108 Jason Bay .25 .60
109 Chris Volstad .15 .40
110 Jermaine Dye .15 .40
111 Torii Hunter .15 .40
112 Brad Ziegler .15 .40
113 Carl Crawford .25 .60
114 Troy Tulowitzki .40 1.00
115 Aramis Ramirez .15 .40
116 Nomar Garciaparra .40 1.00
117 Pedro Martinez .25 .60
118 Ryan Theriot .15 .40
119 Matt Cain .15 .40
120 Carlos Pena .25 .60
121 Nick Swisher .40 1.00
122 Javier Vazquez .15 .40
123 John Lackey .15 .40
124 Jack Cust .15 .40
125 Justin Upton .25 .60
126 Michael Young .25 .60
127 Jeff Samardzija .25 .60
128 John Smoltz .40 1.00
129 Josh Reddick RC 1.50 4.00
130 Chris Tillman RC 1.50 4.00
131 Aaron Cunningham RC 1.00 2.50
132 Andrew McCutchen (RC) 4.00 10.00
133 Anthony Ortega RC 1.00 2.50
134 Anthony Swarzak (RC) 1.00 2.50
135 Antonio Bastardo RC 1.00 2.50
136 Brad Bergesen (RC) 1.00 2.50
137 Brett Cecil RC 1.00 2.50
138 Neftali Feliz RC 3.00 8.00
139 Chris Coghlan RC 2.50 6.00
140 Daniel Bard RC 1.00 2.50
141 Daniel Schlereth RC 1.00 2.50
142 Donald Veal RC 1.50 4.00
143 Brad Mills RC 1.00 2.50
144 David Huff RC 1.00 2.50
145 Elvis Andrus RC 1.50 4.00
146 Everth Cabrera RC 1.50 4.00
147 Mat Latos RC 3.00 8.00
148 Shairon Martis RC 1.50 4.00
149 Jess Todd RC 1.00 2.50
150 Jonathon Niese RC 1.50 4.00
151 Jose Mijares RC 2.50 6.00
152 Jhoulys Chacin RC 1.50 4.00
153 Kyle Blanks RC 1.50 4.00
154 Kris Medlen RC 1.50 4.00
155 Fu-Te Ni RC 1.50 4.00
156 Bud Norris RC 1.00 2.50
157 Julio Borbon RC 1.50 4.00
158 Mat Gamel RC 2.50 6.00
159 Matt LaPorta RC 2.50 6.00
160 Michael Bowden (RC) 1.00 2.50
161 Michael Saunders RC 1.50 4.00
162 Ricky Romero (RC) 2.50 6.00
163 Marc Rzepczynski RC 1.50 4.00
164 Ryan Perry RC 2.50 6.00
165 Sean O'Sullivan RC 1.00 2.50
166 Sean West (RC) 1.50 4.00
167 Trevor Cahill RC 2.50 6.00
168 Mike Carp (RC) 1.50 4.00
169 Vin Mazzaro RC 1.00 2.50
170 Wilkin Ramirez RC 1.00 2.50
171 Albert Pujols FG SP 3.00 8.00
172 Alfonso Soriano FG SP .75 2.00
173 Brandon Webb FG SP .75 2.00
174 Carlos Quentin FG SP .75 2.00
175 Carlos Zambrano FG SP .75 2.00
176 CC Sabathia FG SP .75 2.00
177 Chase Utley FG SP 1.25 3.00
178 Chipper Jones FG SP 1.25 3.00
179 Cole Hamels FG SP 1.25 3.00
180 Daisuke Matsuzaka FG SP 1.25 3.00
181 David Wright FG SP 1.50 4.00
182 Derek Jeter FG SP 3.00 8.00
183 Derek Lowe FG SP .50 1.25
184 Dustin Pedroia FG SP 1.50 4.00
185 Felix Hernandez FG SP 1.25 3.00
186 Grady Sizemore FG SP .75 2.00
187 Jason Giambi FG SP .50 1.25
188 Joba Chamberlain FG SP .75 2.00
189 Joe Mauer FG SP 1.25 3.00
190 Johan Santana FG SP 1.25 3.00
191 Jose Reyes FG SP .75 2.00
192 Josh Beckett FG SP .75 2.00
193 Josh Hamilton FG SP 1.25 3.00
194 Ken Griffey Jr. FG SP 2.00 5.00
195 Manny Ramirez FG SP 1.25 3.00
196 Prince Fielder FG SP .75 2.00
197 Randy Johnson FG SP .75 2.00
198 Ryan Braun FG SP 1.50 4.00
199 Ryan Howard FG SP 1.50 4.00
200 Tim Lincecum FG SP 2.00 5.00
201 A.J. Burnett FW FB 1.00 2.50
202 Adam Dunn FW FB 1.00 2.50
203 Alex Rodriguez FW FB 2.50 6.00
204 Alfonso Soriano FW FB 1.00 2.50
205 Andy Pettitte FW FB 1.00 2.50
206 Bobby Abreu FW FB .60 1.50
207 Carlos Beltran FW FB .60 1.50
208 Chipper Jones FW FB 1.50 4.00
209 Dan Haren FW FB .60 1.50
210 Derek Jeter FW FB 4.00 10.00
211 Derek Lowe FW FB .60 1.50
212 Gary Sheffield FW FB .60 1.50
213 Ivan Rodriguez FW FB 1.00 2.50
214 Jamie Moyer FW FB .60 1.50
215 Jason Giambi FW FB .60 1.50
216 Jim Thome FW FB 1.00 2.50
217 Johan Santana FW FB 1.50 4.00
218 John Smoltz FW FB 1.50 4.00
219 Johnny Damon FW FB 1.00 2.50
220 Josh Beckett FW FB 1.00 2.50
221 Ken Griffey Jr. FW FB 2.50 6.00
222 Manny Ramirez FW FB 1.50 4.00
223 Mark Teixeira FW FB 1.50 4.00
224 Randy Johnson FW FB 1.00 2.50
225 Tim Wakefield FW FB .60 1.50
226 Aaron Poreda AU/300 RC 4.00 10.00
227 Brett Anderson AU/371 RC 5.00 12.00
228 Matt LaPorta AU/225 12.50 30.00
229 Colby Rasmus AU/300 (RC) 15.00 40.00
230 David Price AU/222 RC 20.00 50.00
231 Derek Holland AU/195 RC 8.00 20.00
232 Dexter Fowler AU/490 (RC) 4.00 10.00
233 Fernando Martinez AU/243 RC 6.00 15.00
234 Gerardo Parra AU/299 RC 5.00 12.00
235 Gordon Beckham AU/136 RC 15.00 40.00
236 James McDonald AU/500 RC 4.00 10.00
237 James Parr AU/500 (RC) 4.00 10.00
238 Jason Motte AU/415 (RC) 5.00 12.00
239 Jordan Schafer AU/475 (RC) 4.00 10.00
240 Jordan Zimmermann AU/417 RC 4.00 10.00
241 Kenshin Kawakami AU/425 RC 12.50 30.00
242 Koji Uehara AU/200 RC 40.00 80.00
243 Luis Perdomo AU/275 RC 4.00 10.00
244 Matt Tuiasosopo AU/500 (RC) 5.00 12.00
245 Matt Wieters AU/200 RC 30.00 60.00
246 Nolan Reimold AU/135 (RC) 15.00 40.00
247 Pablo Sandoval AU/230 (RC) 30.00 60.00
248 Rick Porcello AU/225 RC 30.00 60.00
249 Tommy Hanson AU/198 RC 15.00 40.00
250 Travis Snider AU/100 RC 20.00 50.00

2009 SP Authentic Copper

*1-128 COPPER: 2X TO 5X BASIC
1-128 PRINT RUN 99 SER.#'d SETS
*129-170 COPPER: ..6X TO 1.5X BASIC
129-170 PRINT RUN 99 SER.#'d SETS
*171-200 COPPER: .6X TO 1.5X BASIC
171-200 PRINT RUN 99 SER.#'d SETS
*201-225 COPPER: 1.2X TO 3X BASIC
1-225 RANDOMLY INSERTED IN PACKS
201-225 PRINT RUN 29 SER.#'d SETS
OVERALL AUTO ODDS 1:8 HOBBY
AU PRINT RUNS B/WN 10-50 COPIES
NO PRICING ON QTY 25 OR LESS
226 Aaron Poreda AU/50 8.00 20.00
227 Brett Anderson AU/50 10.00 25.00
228 Matt LaPorta AU/50 15.00 40.00
229 Colby Rasmus AU/50 20.00 50.00
230 David Price AU/50 40.00 80.00
231 Derek Holland AU/35 10.00 25.00
232 Dexter Fowler AU/50 8.00 20.00
233 Fernando Martinez AU/50 10.00 25.00
234 Gerardo Parra AU/50 8.00 20.00
235 Gordon Beckham AU/40 40.00 80.00
236 James McDonald AU/50 8.00 20.00
237 James Parr AU/50 8.00 20.00
238 Jason Motte AU/50 10.00 25.00
239 Jordan Schafer AU/50 8.00 20.00
240 Jordan Zimmermann AU/50 8.00 20.00
241 Kenshin Kawakami AU/50 50.00 100.00
242 Koji Uehara AU/10
243 Luis Perdomo AU/50 8.00 20.00
244 Matt Tuiasosopo AU/50 10.00 25.00
245 Matt Wieters AU/25
246 Nolan Reimold AU/25
247 Pablo Sandoval AU/50 60.00 120.00
248 Rick Porcello AU/25
249 Tommy Hanson AU/35 50.00 100.00
250 Travis Snider AU/25

2009 SP Authentic Gold

*1-128 GOLD: 1.5X TO 4X BASIC
1-128 PRINT RUN 299 SER.#'d SETS
*129-170 GOLD: .6X TO 1.5X BASIC
129-170 PRINT RUN 299 SER.#'d SETS
*171-200 GOLD: .5X TO 1.2X BASIC
171-200 PRINT RUN 299 SER.#'d SETS
*201-225 GOLD: .5X TO 1.2X BASIC
1-225 RANDOMLY INSERTED IN PACKS
201-225 PRINT RUN 99 SER.#'d SETS
OVERALL AUTO ODDS 1:8 HOBBY
AU PRINT RUNS B/WN 25-125 COPIES
NO PRICING ON QTY 25 OR LESS
226 Aaron Poreda AU/124 5.00 12.00
227 Brett Anderson AU/125 6.00 15.00
228 Matt LaPorta AU/125 12.50 30.00
229 Colby Rasmus AU/100 20.00 50.00
230 David Price AU/125 20.00 50.00
231 Derek Holland AU/90 8.00 20.00
232 Dexter Fowler AU/125 5.00 12.00
233 Fernando Martinez AU/125 6.00 15.00
234 Gerardo Parra AU/125 5.00 12.00
235 Gordon Beckham AU/85 30.00 60.00
236 James McDonald AU/125 5.00 12.00
237 James Parr AU/125 5.00 12.00
238 Jason Motte AU/125 6.00 15.00
239 Jordan Schafer AU/125 5.00 12.00
240 Jordan Zimmermann AU/125 5.00 12.00
241 Kenshin Kawakami AU/125 30.00 60.00
242 Koji Uehara AU/25
243 Luis Perdomo AU/125 5.00 12.00
244 Matt Tuiasosopo AU/125 6.00 15.00
245 Matt Wieters AU/50 100.00 175.00
246 Nolan Reimold AU/65 15.00 40.00
247 Pablo Sandoval AU/75 40.00 80.00
248 Rick Porcello AU/75 60.00 120.00
249 Tommy Hanson AU/65 40.00 80.00
250 Travis Snider AU/50 20.00 50.00

2009 SP Authentic Silver

*1-128 SILVER: 2.5X TO 6X BASIC
1-128 PRINT RUN 59 SER.#'d SETS
*129-170 SILVER: .75X TO 2X BASIC
129-170 PRINT RUN 59 SER.#'d SETS
*171-200 SILVER: 2.5X TO 6X BASIC
1-200 RANDOMLY INSERTED IN PACKS
171-200 PRINT RUN 59 SER.#'d SETS
OVERALL AUTO ODDS 1:8 HOBBY
226-250 AU PR B/WN 4-25 SER.#'d SETS
NO 201-250 PRICING DUE TO SCARCITY

2009 SP Authentic Titanium

RANDOM INSERTS IN PACKS
1-200 PRINT RUN 19 SER.#'d SETS
201-225 PRINT RUN 9 SER.#'d SETS
226-250 AU PR B/WN 1-10 SER.#'d SETS
NO PRICING DUE TO SCARCITY

2009 SP Authentic By The Letter Rookie Signatures

OVERALL LETTER AU ODDS 1:12
SER.#'d B/WN 11-100 COPIES PER
TOTAL PRINT RUNS LISTED BELOW
EXCHANGE DEADLINE 9/18/2011
BA Brett Anderson/599 * 6.00 15.00
Letters spell Rookie (each letter #'d to 100)
CR Colby Rasmus/450 * 20.00 50.00
Letters spell Rookie (each letter #'d/75)
DF David Freese/450 * 40.00 80.00
Letters spell Rookie (each letter #'d/75)
DH Derek Holland/270 * 8.00 20.00
Letters spell Rookie (each letter #'d/45)
DP David Patton/600 * 5.00 12.00
Letters spell Rookie (each letter #'d/100)
DV Donald Veal/715 * 5.00 12.00
Letters spell SP Authentic (each letter #'d/65)
EA Elvis Andrus/660 * 10.00 25.00
Letters spell SP Authentic (each letter #'d/60)
EC Everth Cabrera/715 * 5.00 12.00
Letters spell SP Authentic (each letter #'d/65)
FO Dexter Fowler/715 * 8.00 20.00
Letters spell SP Authentic (each letter #'d/65)
GK George Kottaras/715 * 5.00 12.00
Letters spell SP Authentic (each letter #'d/65)
JM James McDonald/715 * 5.00 12.00
Letters spell SP Authentic (each letter #'d/65)
JS Jordan Schafer/510 * 6.00 15.00
Letters spell Rookie (each letter #'d/85)
JZ Jordan Zimmermann/297 * 6.00 15.00
Letters spell SP Authentic (each letter #'d/27)
KJ Kevin Jepsen/600 * 5.00 12.00
Letters spell Rookie (each letter #'d/100)
KK Kenshin Kawakami/600 * 15.00 40.00
Letters spell Rookie (each letter #'d/100)
KU Koji Uehara/400 * 15.00 40.00
Letters spell Osaka (each letter #'d/80)
MO Jason Motte/600 * 6.00 15.00
Letters spell Rookie (each letter #'d/100)
MW Matt Wieters/165 * 40.00 80.00
Letters spell Matt Wieters (each letter #'d/15)
PC Phil Coke/709 * 5.00 12.00
Letters spell SP Authentic (each letter #'d/65)
PD David Price/168 * 15.00 40.00
Letters spell Tampa Bay Rays (each letter #'d/14)
PE Ryan Perry/300 * 10.00 25.00
Letters spell Rookie (each letter #'d/50)
PR David Price/140 * 15.00 40.00
Letters spell David Price (each letter #'d/14)
PS Pablo Sandoval/308 * 20.00 50.00
Letters spell SP Authentic (each letter #'d/11)
RP Rick Porcello/510 * 12.50 30.00
Letters spell Rookie (each letter #'d/85)
RR Ricky Romero/715 * 15.00 40.00
Letters spell SP Authentic (each letter #'d/65)
SM Shairon Martis/715 * 5.00 12.00
Letters spell SP Authentic (each letter #'d/65)
TC Trevor Cahill/510 * 5.00 12.00
Letters spell Rookie (each letter #'d/85)
TR Trevor Crowe/715 * 6.00 15.00
Letters spell SP Authentic (each letter #'d/65)
TS Travis Snider/540 * 10.00 25.00
Letters spell Travis Snider (each letter #'d/45)
UE Koji Uehara/190 * 20.00 50.00
Letters spell Koji Uehara (each letter #'d/19)

2009 SP Authentic By The Letter Signatures

OVERALL LETTER AU ODDS 1:12
SER.#'d B/WN 2-60 COPIES PER
TOTAL PRINT RUNS LISTED BELOW
EXCHANGE DEADLINE 9/18/2011
AH Alex Hinshaw/473 * 5.00 12.00
Letters spell Alex Hinshaw (each letter #'d/43)
AR Alex Romero/400 * 5.00 12.00
Letters spell Alex Romero (each letter #'d/40)
BJ Brandon Jones/360 * 8.00 20.00
Letters spell Brandon Jones (each letter #'d/30)
BM Brian McCann/220 * 12.50 30.00
Letters spell Brian McCann (each letter #'d/20)
BR Jay Bruce/350 * 12.50 30.00
Letters spell Cincinnati Reds (each letter #'d/25)
BU B.J. Upton/26 * 6.00 15.00
Letters spell Bossman Junior (each letter #'d/2)
CG Carlos Gonzalez/495 * 20.00 50.00
Letters spell Maracaibo (each letter #'d/55)
CH Chin-Lung Hu/120 * 12.50 30.00
Letters spell Hu (each letter #'d/60)
CJ Chipper Jones/24 * 100.00 200.00
Letters spell Chipper Jones (each letter #'d/2)
CK Clayton Kershaw/140 * 12.50 30.00
Letters spell Clayton Kershaw (each letter #'d/10)
CV Chris Volstad/300 * 5.00 12.00
Letters spell Chris Volstad (each letter #'d/25)
CW Chien-Ming Wang/60 * 90.00 150.00
Letters spell Tainan (each letter #'d/10)
DJ Derek Jeter/200 * 150.00 250.00
Letters spell Derek Jeter (each letter #'d/20)
DM Daniel Murphy/360 * 10.00 25.00
Letters spell Daniel Murphy (each letter #'d/30)
DP David Purcey/341 * 5.00 12.00
Letters spell David Purcey (each letter #'d/31)
DU Dustin Pedroia/390 * 15.00 40.00
Letters spell Dustin Pedroia (each letter #'d/30)
EB Emmanuel Burriss/375 * 5.00 12.00
Letters spell Emmanuel Burriss (each letter #'d/25)
EC Eric Chavez/54 * 12.50 30.00
Letters spell Lion Of Alameda County (each letter #'d/3)
EL Evan Longoria/60* 75.00 150.00
Letters spell Evan Longoria (each letter #'d/5)
FH Felix Hernandez/80 * EXCH 20.00 50.00
(Letters spell Valencia (each letter #'d/10)
GA Garrett Atkins/65 * 8.00 20.00
Letters spell Garrett Atkins (each letter #'d/5)
GF Gavin Floyd/400 * 6.00 15.00
Letters spell Gavin Floyd (each letter #'d/40)
GP Glen Perkins/385 * 5.00 12.00
Letters spell Glen Perkins (each letter #'d/35)
GS Geovany Soto/40 * 20.00 50.00
Letters spell Cubs (each letter #'d/10)
HA Cole Hamels/100 * 30.00 60.00
Letters spell Cole Hamels (each letter #'d/10)

HP Hunter Pence/48 * 15.00 40.00
Letters spell Astros (each letter #'d/8)
HR Hanley Ramirez/52 * 30.00 60.00
Letters spell Hanley Ramirez (each letter #'d/4)
HU Chin-Lung Hu/270 * 10.00 25.00
Letters spell Taiwan (each letter #'d/45)
JB Jay Bruce/494 * 10.00 25.00
Letters spell Bruce Almighty (each letter #'d/38)
JC Joba Chamberlain/150 * 30.00 60.00
Letters spell Joba Chamberlain (each letter #'d/10)
JJ Josh Johnson/297 * 10.00 25.00
Letters spell Josh Johnson (each letter #'d/27)
JN Joe Nathan/324 * 5.00 12.00
Letters spell Joe Nathan (each letter #'d/36)
JT J.R. Towles/400 * 5.00 12.00
Letters spell JR Towles (each letter #'d/50)
JV Jason Varitek/30 *
Letters spell Tek (each letter #'d/10)
JW Josh Willingham/420 *
Letters spell Josh Willingham (each letter #'d/30)
KG Ken Griffey Jr./144 * 75.00 150.00
Letters spell Junior (each letter #'d/24)
KM Kyle McClellan/390 * 5.00 12.00
Letters spell Kyle McClellan (each letter #'d/30)
KS Kelly Shoppach/494 * 5.00 12.00
Letters spell Kelly Shoppach (each letter #'d/38)
KY Kevin Youkilis/260 * 20.00 50.00
Letters spell Kevin Youkilis (each letter #'d/20)
LE Jon Lester/270 * 15.00 40.00
Letters spell Jon Lester (each letter #'d/30)
LJ Jed Lowrie/297 * 10.00 25.00
Letters spell Jed Lowrie (each letter #'d/33)
MA Mike Aviles/500 * 10.00 25.00
Letters spell Mike Aviles (each letter #'d/50)
MC Matt Cain/400 * 10.00 25.00
Letters spell Matt Cain (each letter #'d/50)
MD Daniel Murphy/385 * 10.00 25.00
Letters spell New York Mets (each letter #'d/35)
MG Matt Garza/450 * 10.00 25.00
Letters spell Matt Garza (each letter #'d/50)
MN Nick Markakis/315 * 15.00 40.00
Letters spell Baltimore Orioles (each letter #'d/21)
MO Nyjer Morgan/385 * 8.00 20.00
Letters spell Nyjer Morgan (each letter #'d/35)
MR Nick Markakis/360 * 12.50 30.00
Letters spell Nick Markakis (each letter #'d/30)
NA Joe Nathan/350 * 5.00 12.00
Letters spell Minnesota Twins (each letter #'d/25)
NM Nate McLouth/495 * 6.00 15.00
Letters spell Nate Mclouth (each letter #'d/45)
PE Dustin Pedroia/408 * 20.00 50.00
Letters spell Boston Red Sox (each letter #'d/34)
RB Ryan Braun/90 * 40.00 80.00
Letters spell Ryan Braun (each letter #'d/10)
RH Roy Halladay/110 * 40.00 80.00
Letters spell Roy Halladay (each letter #'d/10)
RJ Randy Johnson/21 * 100.00 175.00
Letters spell Big Unit (each letter #'d/3)
SI Grady Sizemore/130 *
Letters spell Grady Sizemore (each letter #'d/10)
TT Troy Tulowitzki/420 * 10.00 25.00
Letters spell Troy Tulowitzki (each letter #'d/30)
UB B.J. Upton/210 * 15.00 40.00
Letters spell BJ Upton (each letter #'d/30)
WA Cory Wade/400 * 6.00 15.00
Letters spell Cory Wade (each letter #'d/50)

2009 SP Authentic Derek Jeter 1993 SP Buyback Autograph

RANDOMLY INSERTED IN PACKS
STATED PRINT RUN 93 SER.#'d SETS
279 Derek Jeter/93 1000.00 1700.00

2009 SP Authentic Pennant Run Heroes

STATED ODDS 1:20 HOBBY
PR1 Alfonso Soriano .60 1.50
PR2 B.J. Upton .60 1.50
PR3 Brad Lidge .40 1.00
PR4 Brandon Webb .60 1.50
PR5 Carlos Quentin .60 1.50
PR6 Chad Billingsley .40 1.00
PR7 Chase Utley 1.00 2.50
PR8 Chris B. Young .40 1.00
PR9 Clayton Kershaw 1.00 2.50
PR10 Cole Hamels 1.00 2.50
PR11 David Ortiz .60 1.50
PR12 David Price 1.00 2.50
PR13 Derek Jeter 2.50 6.00
PR14 Evan Longoria 1.25 3.00
PR15 John Lackey .40 1.00
PR16 Jonathan Papelbon .60 1.50
PR17 Kevin Youkilis .60 1.50
PR18 Lance Berkman .60 1.50
PR19 Magglio Ordonez .60 1.50
PR20 Mariano Rivera 1.00 2.50

2009 SP Authentic Platinum Power

STATED ODDS 1:10 HOBBY
PP1 A.J. Burnett .60 1.50
PP2 Adam Dunn .60 1.50
PP3 Adrian Gonzalez .60 1.50
PP4 Albert Pujols 2.50 6.00
PP5 Alex Rodriguez 1.50 4.00
PP6 Alfonso Soriano .60 1.50
PP7 Brandon Webb .60 1.50
PP8 Bronson Arroyo .40 1.00
PP9 Carlos Delgado .40 1.00
PP10 Carlos Lee .40 1.00
PP11 Carlos Pena .60 1.50
PP12 Carlos Quentin .60 1.50
PP13 CC Sabathia .60 1.50
PP14 Chad Billingsley .40 1.00
PP15 Chase Utley 1.00 2.50
PP16 Cole Hamels 1.00 2.50
PP17 Dan Haren .40 1.00
PP18 David Wright 1.25 3.00
PP19 Edinson Volquez .40 1.00
PP20 Evan Longoria 1.25 3.00
PP21 Felix Hernandez 1.00 2.50
PP22 Grady Sizemore .60 1.50
PP23 Ian Kinsler .60 1.50
PP24 Jack Cust .40 1.00
PP25 Jake Peavy .40 1.00
PP26 James Shields .40 1.00
PP27 Jason Bay .60 1.50
PP28 Jason Giambi .40 1.00
PP29 Javier Vazquez .40 1.00
PP30 Jermaine Dye .40 1.00
PP31 Jim Thome .60 1.50
PP32 Joey Votto 1.00 2.50
PP33 Johan Santana 1.00 2.50
PP34 Josh Beckett .60 1.50
PP35 Josh Hamilton 1.00 2.50
PP36 Josh Johnson .60 1.50
PP37 Justin Verlander 1.25 3.00
PP38 Lance Berkman .60 1.50
PP39 Manny Ramirez 1.00 2.50
PP40 Mark Teixeira 1.00 2.50
PP41 Matt Cain .40 1.00
PP42 Miguel Cabrera 1.00 2.50
PP43 Mike Jacobs .40 1.00
PP44 Nick Markakis 1.00 2.50
PP45 Prince Fielder .60 1.50
PP46 Randy Johnson .60 1.50
PP47 Ricky Nolasco .40 1.00
PP48 Roy Halladay 1.00 2.50
PP49 Roy Oswalt .60 1.50
PP50 Ryan Braun 1.25 3.00
PP51 Ryan Dempster .40 1.00
PP52 Ryan Howard 1.25 3.00
PP53 Ryan Ludwick .60 1.50
PP54 Scott Kazmir .40 1.00
PP55 Tim Lincecum 1.50 4.00
PP56 Ubaldo Jimenez .60 1.50
PP57 Vladimir Guerrero 1.00 2.50
PP58 Wandy Rodriguez .40 1.00
PP59 Yovani Gallardo .40 1.00
PP60 Zack Greinke .60 1.50

2009 SP Authentic Signatures

OVERALL AUTO ODDS 1:8 HOBBY
SP INFO PROVIDED BY UD
SAG Alberto Gonzalez
SAH Aaron Harang SP
SAJ Josh Anderson
SAL Aaron Laffey
SAN Andy LaRoche SP 8.00 20.00
SAR Aaron Rowand SP 6.00 15.00
SAS Anibal Sanchez SP 3.00 8.00
SBA Burke Badenhop
SBI Brian Bixler
SBP Brandon Phillips SP
SBR Brian Roberts SP
SBY Marlon Byrd
SCB Chad Billingsley SP 5.00 12.00
SCF Chone Figgins SP
SCH Chase Headley SP 4.00 10.00
SCW Cory Wade SP 5.00 12.00
SDB Daric Barton SP 5.00 12.00
SDE David Eckstein SP 8.00 20.00
SDJ Derek Jeter SP 150.00 250.00
SDL Derek Lowe SP 3.00 8.00
SDM Dustin Moseley
SDS Denard Span
SDU Dan Uggla SP 4.00 10.00
SEB Emilio Bonifacio 3.00 8.00
SED Elijah Dukes
SEJ Edwin Jackson SP 5.00 12.00
SEM Evan Meek
SEV Edinson Volquez
SFC Fausto Carmona SP 3.00 8.00
SFJ Jeff Francoeur SP 3.00 8.00
SFL Felipe Lopez SP 3.00 8.00
SFP Felipe Paulino
SGG Greg Golson SP 3.00 8.00
SGP Glen Perkins SP 3.00 8.00
SHA Corey Hart
SHE Jeremy Hermida SP 4.00 10.00
SHJ Josh Hamilton SP 10.00 25.00
SHP Hunter Pence
SJA Jonathan Albaladejo
SJB Jason Bay SP
SJC Johnny Cueto SP
SJD John Danks SP 4.00 10.00
SJF Jesus Flores
SJG Josh Geer SP
SJH J.A. Happ 12.50 30.00
SJK Jeff Karstens
SJL Jed Lowrie
SJL John Lackey SP 20.00 50.00
SJM James McDonald
SJM Justin Masterson SP 8.00 20.00
SJP Jonathan Papelbon SP
SJS Joe Smith 3.00 8.00
SJS James Shields SP 5.00 12.00
SJW Josh Willingham
SKG Ken Griffey Jr. SP 75.00 150.00
SKM Kyle McClellan
SKO Kevin Kouzmanoff
SKS Kurt Suzuki SP 4.00 10.00
SKY Kevin Youkilis SP 8.00 20.00
SLA Adam Lind SP 4.00 10.00
SLI Jesse Litsch
SLS Luke Scott
SMA Daisuke Matsuzaka SP 100.00 200.00
SMB Michael Bourn
SMC Manny Corpas
SME Mark Ellis SP 3.00 8.00
SMG Matt Garza SP 4.00 10.00
SML Matt Lindstrom
SMN Nyjer Morgan
SMO Micah Owings
SMP Mike Pelfrey SP
SMR Mark Reynolds
SMT Matt Tolbert
SMU David Murphy SP 3.00 8.00
SNB Nick Blackburn
SNM Nick Markakis SP 15.00 40.00
SNS Nick Swisher SP 30.00 60.00
SPE Fernando Perez
SPI Felix Pie
SPJ Paul Janish
SRA Alexei Ramirez
SRC Ryan Church SP 3.00 8.00
SRH Ramon Hernandez SP
SRM Russell Martin SP 6.00 15.00
SRT Ryan Theriot 5.00 12.00
SSA Andy Sonnanstine
SSA Jarrod Saltalamacchia SP 3.00 8.00
SSB Scott Baker
SSH Steve Holm
SSL Kevin Slowey
SSM Sean Marshall 3.00 8.00
SSO Joakim Soria SP 5.00 12.00
STH Travis Hafner SP
STR Ramon Troncoso
STS Takashi Saito SP 20.00 50.00
SVE Eugenio Velez
SVM Victor Martinez SP 6.00 15.00
SWB Wladimir Balentien SP
SWW Wesley Wright
SYE Yunel Escobar

2009 SP Authentic Signatures Dual

OVERALL AUTO ODDS 1:8 HOBBY
STATED PRINT RUN 15 SER.#'d SETS
NO PRICING DUE TO SCARCITY

2009 SP Authentic Signatures Quad

OVERALL AUTO ODDS 1:8 HOBBY
STATED PRINT RUN 10 SER.#'d SETS
NO PRICING DUE TO SCARCITY

2009 SP Authentic Signatures Triple

OVERALL AUTO ODDS 1:8 HOBBY
STATED PRINT RUN 10 SER.#'d SETS
NO PRICING DUE TO SCARCITY

2001 SP Game Bat Edition

The 2001 SP Game Bat Edition product was released in late December, 2000 and featured a 90-card base set. Each pack contained four cards and carried a suggested retail price of $19.99 per pack. Please note that each pack contained one game-used memorabilia card.

COMPLETE SET (90) 20.00 50.00
1 Troy Glaus .40 1.00
2 Darin Erstad .40 1.00
3 Mo Vaughn .40 1.00
4 Jason Giambi .40 1.00
5 Ben Grieve .40 1.00
6 Eric Chavez .40 1.00
7 Carlos Delgado .40 1.00
8 Tony Batista .40 1.00
9 Shannon Stewart .40 1.00
10 Jose Cruz Jr. .40 1.00
11 Fred McGriff .60 1.50
12 Greg Vaughn .40 1.00
13 Roberto Alomar .60 1.50
14 Manny Ramirez .60 1.50
15 Jim Thome .60 1.50
16 Russell Branyan .40 1.00
17 Alex Rodriguez 1.50 4.00
18 John Olerud .40 1.00
19 Edgar Martinez .60 1.50
20 Cal Ripken 3.00 8.00
21 Albert Belle .40 1.00
22 Ivan Rodriguez .60 1.50
23 Rafael Palmeiro .60 1.50
24 Nomar Garciaparra 1.50 4.00
25 Carl Everett .40 1.00
26 Dante Bichette .40 1.00
27 Mike Sweeney .40 1.00
28 Jermaine Dye .40 1.00
29 Carlos Beltran .40 1.00
30 Juan Gonzalez .40 1.00
31 Dean Palmer .40 1.00
32 Bobby Higginson .40 1.00
33 Matt Lawton .40 1.00
34 Jacque Jones .40 1.00
35 Frank Thomas 1.00 2.50
36 Magglio Ordonez .40 1.00
37 Paul Konerko .40 1.00
38 Carlos Lee .40 1.00
39 Bernie Williams .60 1.50
40 Derek Jeter 2.50 6.00
41 Paul O'Neill .60 1.50
42 Jose Canseco .60 1.50
43 Ken Caminiti .40 1.00
44 Jeff Bagwell .60 1.50
45 Craig Biggio .60 1.50
46 Richard Hidalgo .40 1.00
47 Andruw Jones .60 1.50
48 Chipper Jones 1.00 2.50
49 Andres Galarraga .40 1.00
50 B.J. Surhoff .40 1.00
51 Jeromy Burnitz .40 1.00
52 Geoff Jenkins .40 1.00
53 Richie Sexson .40 1.00
54 Mark McGwire 2.50 6.00
55 Jim Edmonds .40 1.00
56 J.D. Drew .40 1.00
57 Fernando Tatis .40 1.00
58 Sammy Sosa 1.00 2.50
59 Mark Grace .60 1.50
60 Eric Young .40 1.00
61 Matt Williams .40 1.00
62 Luis Gonzalez .40 1.00
63 Steve Finley .40 1.00
64 Shawn Green .40 1.00
65 Gary Sheffield .40 1.00
66 Eric Karros .40 1.00
67 Vladimir Guerrero 1.00 2.50
68 Jose Vidro .40 1.00
69 Barry Bonds 2.50 6.00
70 Jeff Kent .40 1.00
71 Preston Wilson .40 1.00
72 Mike Lowell .40 1.00
73 Luis Castillo .40 1.00
74 Mike Piazza 1.50 4.00
75 Robin Ventura .40 1.00
76 Edgardo Alfonzo .40 1.00
77 Tony Gwynn 1.25 3.00
78 Eric Owens .40 1.00
79 Ryan Klesko .40 1.00
80 Scott Rolen .60 1.50
81 Bobby Abreu .40 1.00
82 Pat Burrell .40 1.00
83 Brian Giles .40 1.00
84 Jason Kendall .40 1.00
85 Aaron Boone .40 1.00
86 Ken Griffey Jr. 1.50 4.00
87 Barry Larkin .60 1.50
88 Todd Helton .60 1.50
89 Larry Walker .40 1.00
90 Jeffrey Hammonds .40 1.00

2001 SP Game Bat Edition Big League Hit Parade

Randomly inserted into packs at one in 15, this six-card set features some of the Major League's top hitters. Card backs carry a "HP" prefix.

COMPLETE SET (6) 12.50 30.00
HP1 Nomar Garciaparra 2.00 5.00
HP2 Ken Griffey Jr. 2.00 5.00
HP3 Sammy Sosa 1.25 3.00
HP4 Alex Rodriguez 2.00 5.00
HP5 Mark McGwire 3.00 8.00
HP6 Ivan Rodriguez 1.25 3.00

2001 SP Game Bat Edition In the Swing

Randomly inserted into packs at one in seven, this 15-card set features some sweetest swings in Major League Baseball. Card backs carry a "IS" prefix.

COMPLETE SET (15) 20.00 50.00
IS1 Ken Griffey Jr. 2.00 5.00
IS2 Jim Edmonds .50 1.25
IS3 Carlos Delgado .50 1.25
IS4 Frank Thomas 1.25 3.00
IS5 Barry Bonds 3.00 8.00
IS6 Nomar Garciaparra 2.00 5.00
IS7 Gary Sheffield .50 1.25
IS8 Vladimir Guerrero 1.25 3.00
IS9 Alex Rodriguez 2.00 5.00
IS10 Todd Helton .75 2.00
IS11 Darin Erstad .50 1.25
IS12 Derek Jeter 3.00 8.00
IS13 Sammy Sosa 1.25 3.00
IS14 Mark McGwire 3.00 8.00
IS15 Jason Giambi .50 1.25

2001 SP Game Bat Edition Line Up Time

Randomly inserted into packs at one in eight, this 11-card set features players that are always in the starting line up. Card backs carry a "LT" prefix.

COMPLETE SET (11) 20.00 50.00
LT1 Mark McGwire 3.00 8.00
LT2 Roberto Alomar 1.25 3.00
LT3 Alex Rodriguez 2.00 5.00
LT4 Chipper Jones 1.25 3.00
LT5 Ivan Rodriguez 1.25 3.00
LT6 Ken Griffey Jr. 2.00 5.00
LT7 Sammy Sosa 1.25 3.00
LT8 Barry Bonds 3.00 8.00
LT9 Frank Thomas 1.25 3.00
LT10 Pedro Martinez 1.25 3.00
LT11 Derek Jeter 3.00 8.00

2001 SP Game Bat Edition Lumber Yard

Randomly inserted into packs at one in 10, this 10-card set features some of the Major League's top power hitters. Card backs carry a "Y" prefix.

COMPLETE SET (10) 15.00 40.00
Y1 Jason Giambi .50 1.25
Y2 Chipper Jones 1.25 3.00
Y3 Carl Everett .50 1.25
Y4 Alex Rodriguez 2.00 5.00
Y5 Frank Thomas 1.25 3.00
Y6 Barry Bonds 3.00 8.00
Y7 Jeff Bagwell .75 2.00
Y8 Sammy Sosa 1.25 3.00
Y9 Carlos Delgado .50 1.25
Y10 Mike Piazza 2.00 5.00

2001 SP Game Bat Edition Piece of the Game

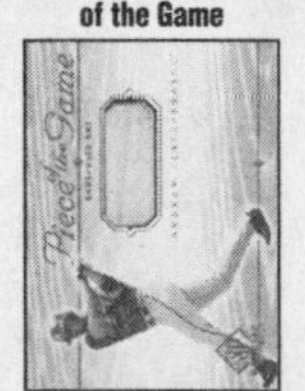

Inserted at one per pack, this 58-card set features actual game-used pieces of bat. Card backs carry the player's initials as numbering. Cards are listed below in alphabetical order for convenience. Upper Deck announced shortly after the product went live that fifteen cards were short-printed in comparison to others in the set. According to Upper Deck, all short-print cards have a production of 1,500 or fewer cards.

SP PRINT RUN 1500 OR FEWER OF EACH
GOLD PRINT RUN 25 SERIAL #'d SETS
NO GOLD PRICING DUE TO SCARCITY
AJ Andruw Jones 6.00 15.00
AR Alex Rodriguez 6.00 15.00
BB Barry Bonds 10.00 25.00
BG Bob Gibson SP 6.00 15.00
BW Bernie Williams 6.00 15.00
CB Carlos Beltran 4.00 10.00
CD Carlos Delgado 4.00 10.00
CJ Chipper Jones 6.00 15.00
CR Cal Ripken SP 20.00 50.00
DE Darin Erstad SP 4.00 10.00
DJ David Justice 4.00 10.00
EA Edgardo Alfonzo SP 4.00 10.00
EM Edgar Martinez 6.00 15.00
FM Fred McGriff SP 6.00 15.00
FT Frank Thomas 6.00 15.00
GM Greg Maddux 6.00 15.00
GS Gary Sheffield 4.00 10.00
GV Greg Vaughn 4.00 10.00
IR Ivan Rodriguez 6.00 15.00
JB Jeff Bagwell SP 6.00 15.00
JB Johnny Bench SP 6.00 15.00
JC Jose Canseco 6.00 15.00
JD J.D. Drew 4.00 10.00
JE Jim Edmonds 4.00 10.00
JO John Olerud 4.00 10.00
JOD Joe DiMaggio SP 60.00 120.00
KB Kevin Brown SP 4.00 10.00
KG Ken Griffey Jr. 6.00 15.00
KL Kenny Lofton 4.00 10.00
MG Mark Grace 6.00 15.00
MO Magglio Ordonez 4.00 10.00
MQ Mark Quinn SP 4.00 10.00
MR Manny Ramirez 6.00 15.00
MV Mo Vaughn 4.00 10.00
MW Matt Williams 4.00 10.00
NR Nolan Ryan SP 10.00 25.00
PB Pat Burrell 4.00 10.00
PN Phil Nevin SP 4.00 10.00
PO Paul O'Neill 6.00 15.00
PW Preston Wilson 4.00 10.00
RA Rick Ankiel 4.00 10.00
RA Roberto Alomar 6.00 15.00
REJ Reggie Jackson SP 6.00 15.00
RF Rafael Furcal 4.00 10.00
RJ Randy Johnson 6.00 15.00
RV Robin Ventura 4.00 10.00
SA Sandy Alomar Jr. 4.00 10.00
SAS Sammy Sosa SP 6.00 15.00
SG Shawn Green 4.00 10.00
SR Scott Rolen 6.00 15.00
SS Shannon Stewart 4.00 10.00
TGL Tom Glavine SP 6.00 15.00
TGW Tony Gwynn 6.00 15.00
TH Todd Helton 6.00 15.00
THU Todd Hundley SP 4.00 10.00
TM Tino Martinez 6.00 15.00
TS Tim Salmon SP 6.00 15.00
WC Will Clark 6.00 15.00

2001 SP Game Bat Edition Piece of the Game Autograph

Inserted into packs at one in 96, this nine-card insert features actual game-used pieces of bats, and are autographed by the players. Card backs carry a "S" prefix followed by the players initials. Please note that Frank Thomas, Ken Griffey Jr. and Sammy Sosa packed out as exchange cards. The deadline to exchange these cards is 09/22/01.

GOLD PRINT RUN 25 SERIAL #'d SETS
NO GOLD PRICING DUE TO SCARCITY
SAJ Andruw Jones 20.00 50.00
SAR Alex Rodriguez 60.00 120.00
SBB Barry Bonds 100.00 175.00
SFT Frank Thomas 40.00 80.00
SJC Jose Canseco 20.00 50.00
SKG Ken Griffey Jr. 60.00 120.00
SNR Nolan Ryan 60.00 120.00
SSS Sammy Sosa 50.00 100.00
STGW Tony Gwynn 40.00 80.00

2001 SP Game Bat Milestone

This ninety-six card set was issued in October, 2001. This set was issued in four-card packs with an SRP of $19.99 per pack. Cards numbered 91-96 were short printed and these cards were serial numbered to 500.

COMP.SET w/o SP's (90) 30.00 80.00
COMMON CARD (1-90) .40 1.00
COMMON BAT (91-96) 4.00 10.00
1 Troy Glaus .40 1.00
2 Darin Erstad .40 1.00
3 Jason Giambi .40 1.00
4 Jermaine Dye .40 1.00
5 Eric Chavez .40 1.00
6 Carlos Delgado .40 1.00
7 Raul Mondesi .40 1.00
8 Shannon Stewart .40 1.00
9 Greg Vaughn .40 1.00
10 Aubrey Huff .40 1.00
11 Juan Gonzalez .40 1.00
12 Roberto Alomar .60 1.50
13 Jim Thome .60 1.50
14 Omar Vizquel .60 1.50
15 Mike Cameron .40 1.00
16 Edgar Martinez .60 1.50
17 John Olerud .40 1.00
18 Bret Boone .40 1.00
19 Cal Ripken 3.00 8.00
20 Tony Batista .40 1.00
21 Alex Rodriguez 1.50 4.00
22 Ivan Rodriguez .60 1.50
23 Rafael Palmeiro .60 1.50
24 Manny Ramirez Sox .60 1.50
25 Pedro Martinez .60 1.50
26 Nomar Garciaparra 1.50 4.00
27 Carl Everett .40 1.00
28 Mike Sweeney .40 1.00
29 Neifi Perez .40 1.00
30 Mark Quinn .40 1.00
31 Bobby Higginson .40 1.00
32 Tony Clark .40 1.00
33 Doug Mientkiewicz .40 1.00
34 Cristian Guzman .40 1.00
35 Joe Mays .40 1.00
36 David Ortiz 1.00 2.50
37 Frank Thomas 1.00 2.50
38 Magglio Ordonez .40 1.00
39 Carlos Lee .40 1.00
40 Alfonso Soriano .60 1.50
41 Bernie Williams .60 1.50
42 Derek Jeter 2.50 6.00
43 Roger Clemens 2.00 5.00
44 Jeff Bagwell .60 1.50
45 Richard Hidalgo .40 1.00
46 Moises Alou .40 1.00
47 Chipper Jones 1.00 2.50
48 Greg Maddux 1.50 4.00
49 Rafael Furcal .40 1.00
50 Andruw Jones .60 1.50
51 Jeromy Burnitz .40 1.00
52 Geoff Jenkins .40 1.00
53 Richie Sexson .40 1.00
54 Edgar Renteria .40 1.00
55 Mark McGwire 2.50 6.00
56 Jim Edmonds .40 1.00
57 J.D. Drew .40 1.00
58 Sammy Sosa 1.00 2.50
59 Fred McGriff .60 1.50
60 Luis Gonzalez .40 1.00
61 Randy Johnson 1.00 2.50
62 Gary Sheffield .40 1.00
63 Shawn Green .40 1.00
64 Kevin Brown .40 1.00
65 Vladimir Guerrero 1.00 2.50
66 Jose Vidro .40 1.00
67 Fernando Tatis .40 1.00
68 Barry Bonds 2.50 6.00
69 Jeff Kent .40 1.00
70 Rich Aurilia .40 1.00
71 Preston Wilson .40 1.00
72 Charles Johnson .40 1.00
73 Cliff Floyd .40 1.00
74 Mike Piazza 1.50 4.00
75 Matt Lawton .40 1.00
76 Edgardo Alfonzo .40 1.00
77 Tony Gwynn 1.25 3.00
78 Phil Nevin .40 1.00
79 Scott Rolen .60 1.50
80 Pat Burrell .40 1.00
81 Bobby Abreu .40 1.00
82 Brian Giles .40 1.00
83 Jason Kendall .40 1.00
84 Aramis Ramirez .40 1.00
85 Sean Casey .40 1.00
86 Ken Griffey Jr. 1.50 4.00
87 Barry Larkin .60 1.50
88 Todd Helton .60 1.50
89 Mike Hampton .40 1.00
90 Larry Walker .40 1.00
91 Ichiro Suzuki BAT RC 30.00 60.00
92 Albert Pujols BAT RC 30.00 60.00
93 T. Shinjo BAT RC 6.00 15.00
94 Jack Wilson BAT RC 6.00 15.00
95 D. Mendez BAT RC 4.00 10.00
96 Junior Spivey BAT RC 6.00 15.00

2001 SP Game Bat Milestone Art of Hitting

Inserted at a rate of one in five and featured a mix of batting champions and other leading hitters who made hitting an art.

COMPLETE SET (12) 20.00 50.00
AH1 Tony Gwynn 1.50 4.00
AH2 Manny Ramirez Sox .75 2.00
AH3 Todd Helton .75 2.00
AH4 Nomar Garciaparra 2.00 5.00
AH5 Vladimir Guerrero 1.25 3.00
AH6 Ichiro Suzuki 8.00 20.00
AH7 Darin Erstad .75 2.00
AH8 Alex Rodriguez 2.00 5.00
AH9 Carlos Delgado .75 2.00
AH10 Edgar Martinez .75 2.00
AH11 Luis Gonzalez .75 2.00
AH12 Barry Bonds 3.00 8.00

2001 SP Game Bat Milestone Piece of Action Autographs

Inserted at a rate of one per 100 packs, these 13 cards feature signed cards of some of the leading players in the game. A few players were printed in lower quantities than the others and we have notated those players with both and SP and officially released print information from Upper Deck. Jose Vidro did not return his cards in time for inclusion in this product, these cards were available via exchange until October 12, 2004.

SAR A. Rodriguez SP/97 60.00 120.00
SCD C. Delgado SP/97 20.00 50.00
SGS G. Sheffield SP/194 30.00 60.00
SIS Ichiro Suzuki SP/53 900.00 1200.00
SJD J.D. Drew 15.00 40.00
SJD Jermaine Dye 15.00 40.00
SJK Jason Kendall 15.00 40.00
SJK Jeff Kent SP/194 30.00 60.00
SJV Jose Vidro 10.00 25.00
SLG Luis Gonzalez 15.00 40.00
SMT Miguel Tejada 30.00 60.00
SPW Preston Wilson 15.00 40.00
SRB Russell Branyan 10.00 25.00

2001 SP Game Bat Milestone Piece of Action Bound for the Hall

Randomly inserted in packs, these 16 cards feature bat clippings of players who look like they are on their way to enshriment in Cooperstown. A few players seemed to be available in larger supply, we have notated those players with an asterisk next to their name.

BAR A.Rodriguez Rangers 6.00 15.00
BBB Barry Bonds 10.00 25.00
BCD Carlos Delgado 4.00 10.00
BCR Cal Ripken 15.00 40.00
BEM Edgar Martinez 6.00 15.00
BFM Fred McGriff 6.00 15.00
BGM Greg Maddux 6.00 15.00
BIR Ivan Rodriguez 6.00 15.00
BJG Jason Giambi 4.00 10.00
BMP Mike Piazza 6.00 15.00
BRC R.Clemens SP/203 15.00 40.00
BRP Rafael Palmeiro 6.00 15.00
BSS Sammy Sosa 6.00 15.00
BTG Tony Gwynn 6.00 15.00
BKGM Ken Griffey Jr. M's* 8.00 20.00
BKGR K.Griffey Jr. Reds 8.00 20.00

2001 SP Game Bat Milestone Piece of Action Bound for the Hall Gold

Randomly inserted in packs, these 16 cards parallel the Piece of History Bound for the Hall insert set. These cards are serial numbered to 35.

BAR Alex Rodriguez 20.00 50.00
BBB Barry Bonds 25.00 60.00
BCD Carlos Delgado 10.00 25.00
BCR Cal Ripken 30.00 80.00
BEM Edgar Martinez 15.00 40.00
BFM Fred McGriff 15.00 40.00
BGM Greg Maddux 20.00 50.00
BIR Ivan Rodriguez 15.00 40.00
BJG Jason Giambi 10.00 25.00
BMP Mike Piazza 20.00 50.00
BRC Roger Clemens 20.00 50.00
BRP Rafael Palmeiro 15.00 40.00
BSS Sammy Sosa 15.00 40.00
BTG Tony Gwynn 20.00 50.00
BKGM K.Griffey Jr. Mariners 20.00 50.00
BKGR K.Griffey Jr. Reds 20.00 50.00

2001 SP Game Bat Milestone Piece of Action International

Randomly inserted into packs, these 16 cards feature bat pieces of some of the finest imports playing major league baseball. A couple of players were printed in lesser quantity then the other cards in this set and we have notated those with an SP as well as the print information. Omar Vizquel seems to have been printed in larger quantites and we have notated that with an asterisk.

IAB Adrian Beltre 4.00 10.00
IAJ Andruw Jones 6.00 15.00
IAP Albert Pujols 40.00 80.00
ICP Chan Ho Park 4.00 10.00
IHN Hideo Nomo SP/275 6.00 15.00
IIS Ichiro Suzuki SP/203 40.00 80.00
IJG Juan Gonzalez 4.00 10.00
IJP Jorge Posada 6.00 15.00
IMO Magglio Ordonez 4.00 10.00
IMR Manny Ramirez Sox 6.00 15.00
IMT Miguel Tejada 4.00 10.00
IOV Omar Vizquel * 6.00 15.00
IPM Pedro Martinez 6.00 15.00
IRA Roberto Alomar 6.00 15.00
IRF Rafael Furcal 4.00 10.00
ITS Tsuyoshi Shinjo 6.00 15.00

2001 SP Game Bat Milestone Piece of Action International Gold

Randomly inserted in packs, these 16 cards parallel the Piece of History International insert set. These cards are serial numbered to 35.

IAB Adrian Beltre 10.00 25.00
IAJ Andruw Jones 15.00 40.00
IAP Albert Pujols 150.00 250.00
ICP Chan Ho Park 10.00 25.00
IHN Hideo Nomo 15.00 40.00
IIS Ichiro Suzuki 60.00 120.00
IJG Juan Gonzalez 10.00 25.00
IJP Jorge Posada 15.00 40.00
IMO Magglio Ordonez 10.00 25.00
IMR Manny Ramirez Sox 15.00 40.00
IMT Miguel Tejada 10.00 25.00
IOV Omar Vizquel 15.00 40.00
IPM Pedro Martinez 15.00 40.00
IRA Roberto Alomar 15.00 40.00
IRF Rafael Furcal 10.00 25.00
ITS Tsuyoshi Shinjo 15.00 40.00

2001 SP Game Bat Milestone Piece of Action Milestone

Randomly inserted into packs, these 18 cards feature some of the best hitters in baseball. Each card features a bat sliver on it.

AR A.Rodriguez Mariners 6.00 15.00
BB Barry Bonds 10.00 25.00
CHJ Chipper Jones 6.00 15.00
CR Cal Ripken 15.00 40.00
DE Darin Erstad 4.00 10.00
FT Frank Thomas * 6.00 15.00
GS Gary Sheffield 4.00 10.00
IS Ichiro Suzuki SP/203 40.00 80.00
JB Jeff Bagwell 6.00 15.00
JBU Jeromy Burnitz 4.00 10.00
JT Jim Thome 6.00 15.00
KG Ken Griffey Jr. 8.00 20.00
LG Luis Gonzalez * 4.00 10.00
MP Mike Piazza 6.00 15.00
RB Russell Branyan 4.00 10.00
RC Roger Clemens 8.00 20.00
SS Sammy Sosa * 6.00 15.00
TH Todd Helton 6.00 15.00

2001 SP Game Bat Milestone Piece of Action Milestone Gold

Randomly inserted in packs, these 16 cards parallel the Piece of History Milestone set. These cards are serial numbered to 35.

AR Alex Rodriguez 25.00 60.00
BB Barry Bonds 30.00 80.00
CHJ Chipper Jones 15.00 40.00
CR Cal Ripken 40.00 100.00
DE Darin Erstad 10.00 25.00
FT Frank Thomas 15.00 40.00
GS Gary Sheffield 10.00 25.00
IS Ichiro Suzuki 60.00 120.00
JB Jeff Bagwell 15.00 40.00
JBU Jeromy Burnitz 10.00 25.00
JT Jim Thome 15.00 40.00
KG Ken Griffey Jr. 25.00 60.00
LG Luis Gonzalez 10.00 25.00
MP Mike Piazza 30.00 80.00
RB Russell Branyan 10.00 25.00
RC Roger Clemens 30.00 80.00
SS Sammy Sosa 15.00 40.00
TH Todd Helton 15.00 40.00

2001 SP Game Bat Milestone Piece of Action Quads

Inserted in packs at a rate of one in 50, these 15 cards feature four pieces of game-used bats from four different major league stars.

GDBS Ken Griffey Jr. 20.00 50.00
J.D. Drew
Jeromy Burnitz
Sammy Sosa
GGRR Ken Griffey Jr. 40.00 80.00
Ken Griffey Jr.
Alex Rodriguez
Alex Rodriguez
GHSK Luis Gonzalez 15.00 40.00
Todd Helton
Gary Sheffield
Jeff Kent
GRBM Tony Gwynn 60.00 120.00
Cal Ripken
Barry Bonds
Fred McGriff
GRSB Ken Griffey Jr. 60.00 120.00
Alex Rodriguez
Sammy Sosa
Barry Bonds
JJFM Chipper Jones 15.00 40.00
Andruw Jones
Rafael Furcal
Greg Maddux
JVBW Chipper Jones 15.00 40.00
Robin Ventura
Pat Burrell
Preston Wilson
OJCP Paul O'Neill 40.00 80.00
David Justice
Roger Clemens
Jorge Posada
ONRD Paul O'Neill 40.00 80.00
Hideo Nomo
Cal Ripken
Carlos Delgado
PWSG Kirby Puckett 15.00 40.00
Dave Winfield
Ozzie Smith
Steve Garvey
RGGM Alex Rodriguez 20.00 50.00
Troy Glaus
Jason Giambi
Edgar Martinez
RRPM Alex Rodriguez 20.00 50.00
Ivan Rodriguez
Rafael Palmeiro
Ruben Mateo
SGBP Gary Sheffield 10.00 25.00
Shawn Green
Adrian Beltre
Chan Ho Park
TDTA Frank Thomas 15.00 40.00
Jermaine Dye
Jim Thome
Roberto Alomar
TVAL Jim Thome 15.00 40.00
Omar Vizquel
Roberto Alomar
Kenny Lofton

2001 SP Game Bat Milestone Piece of Action Trios

Inserted in packs at a rate of one in 50, these 14 cards feature four pieces of game-used bats from three different major league stars.

CMG Roger Clemens 20.00 50.00
Greg Maddux
Tom Glavine
GBM Ken Griffey Jr. 15.00 40.00
Barry Bonds
Fred McGriff
GRB Tony Gwynn 30.00 60.00
Cal Ripken
Barry Bonds
GRS Ken Griffey Jr. 15.00 40.00
Alex Rodriguez
Sammy Sosa
JJF Chipper Jones 15.00 40.00
Andruw Jones
Rafael Furcal
KGR Jason Kendall 10.00 25.00
Brian Giles
Aramis Ramirez
OJC Paul O'Neill 20.00 50.00
David Justice
Roger Clemens
OTA Rey Ordonez 15.00 40.00
Frank Thomas
Sandy Alomar Jr.
PWS Kirby Puckett 15.00 40.00
Dave Winfield
Ozzie Smith
RRP Alex Rodriguez 20.00 50.00
Ivan Rodriguez
Rafael Palmeiro
SFR Alfonso Soriano 15.00 40.00
Rafael Furcal
Aramis Ramirez
SGB Gary Sheffield 10.00 25.00
Shawn Green
Adrian Beltre
TVA Jim Thome 15.00 40.00
Omar Vizquel
Roberto Alomar
VSA Robin Ventura 15.00 40.00
Tsuyoshi Shinjo
Edgardo Alfonzo

2001 SP Game Bat Milestone Slugging Sensations

Inserted in packs at a rate of one in five, these 12 cards feature the players who hit a baseball harder and farther than other players.

COMPLETE SET (12) 15.00 40.00
SS1 Troy Glaus .50 1.25
SS2 Mark McGwire 3.00 8.00
SS3 Sammy Sosa 1.25 3.00
SS4 Juan Gonzalez .50 1.25
SS5 Barry Bonds 3.00 8.00
SS6 Jeff Bagwell .75 2.00
SS7 Jason Giambi .50 1.25
SS8 Ivan Rodriguez .75 2.00
SS9 Mike Piazza 2.00 5.00
SS10 Chipper Jones 1.25 3.00
SS11 Ken Griffey Jr. 2.00 5.00
SS12 Gary Sheffield .50 1.25

2001 SP Game Bat Milestone Trophy Room

Inserted at a rate of one in ten, these six cards feature players who have won key awards during their career.

COMPLETE SET (6) 12.50 30.00
TR1 Sammy Sosa 1.25 3.00
TR2 Jason Giambi 1.25 3.00
TR3 Todd Helton 1.25 3.00
TR4 Alex Rodriguez 2.00 5.00
TR5 Mark McGwire 3.00 8.00
TR6 Ken Griffey Jr. 2.00 5.00

2001 SP Game Used Edition

This 90-card set was distributed in three-card packs with a suggested retail value of $29.99 and features color action player photos. The set includes the following subset: Super Prospects (61-90).

COMP.SET w/o SP's (60) 30.00 80.00
COMMON CARD (1-60) .50 1.25
COMMON CARD (61-90) 3.00 8.00
1 Garret Anderson .50 1.25
2 Troy Glaus .50 1.25
3 Darin Erstad .50 1.25
4 Jason Giambi .50 1.25
5 Tim Hudson .50 1.25
6 Johnny Damon .75 2.00
7 Carlos Delgado .50 1.25
8 Greg Vaughn .50 1.25
9 Juan Gonzalez .50 1.25
10 Roberto Alomar .75 2.00
11 Jim Thome .75 2.00
12 Edgar Martinez .75 2.00
13 Cal Ripken 4.00 10.00
14 Andres Galarraga .50 1.25
15 Alex Rodriguez 2.00 5.00
16 Rafael Palmeiro .75 2.00
17 Ivan Rodriguez .75 2.00
18 Manny Ramirez Sox .75 2.00
19 Nomar Garciaparra 2.00 5.00
20 Pedro Martinez .75 2.00
21 Jermaine Dye .50 1.25
22 Dean Palmer .50 1.25
23 Matt Lawton .50 1.25
24 Frank Thomas 1.25 3.00
25 David Wells .50 1.25
26 Magglio Ordonez .50 1.25
27 Derek Jeter 3.00 8.00
28 Bernie Williams .75 2.00
29 Roger Clemens 2.50 6.00
30 Jeff Bagwell .75 2.00
31 Richard Hidalgo .50 1.25
32 Chipper Jones 1.25 3.00
33 Andruw Jones .75 2.00
34 Greg Maddux 2.00 5.00
35 Jeffrey Hammonds .50 1.25
36 Mark McGwire 3.00 8.00
37 Jim Edmonds .50 1.25
38 Sammy Sosa 1.25 3.00
39 Corey Patterson .50 1.25
40 Randy Johnson 1.25 3.00
41 Luis Gonzalez .50 1.25
42 Gary Sheffield .50 1.25
43 Shawn Green .50 1.25
44 Kevin Brown .50 1.25
45 Vladimir Guerrero 1.25 3.00
46 Barry Bonds 3.00 8.00
47 Jeff Kent .50 1.25
48 Preston Wilson .50 1.25
49 Charles Johnson .50 1.25
50 Mike Piazza 2.00 5.00
51 Edgardo Alfonzo .50 1.25
52 Tony Gwynn 1.50 4.00
53 Scott Rolen .75 2.00
54 Pat Burrell .50 1.25
55 Brian Giles .50 1.25
56 Jason Kendall .50 1.25
57 Ken Griffey Jr. 2.00 5.00
58 Mike Hampton .50 1.25
59 Todd Helton .75 2.00
60 Larry Walker .50 1.25
61 Wilson Betemit RC 6.00 15.00
62 Travis Hafner RC 12.50 30.00
63 Ichiro Suzuki RC 40.00 80.00
64 Juan Diaz RC 3.00 8.00
65 Morgan Ensberg RC 6.00 15.00
66 Horacio Ramirez RC 4.00 10.00
67 Ricardo Rodriguez RC 3.00 8.00
68 Sean Douglass RC 3.00 8.00
69 Brandon Duckworth RC 3.00 8.00
70 Jackson Melian RC 3.00 8.00
71 Adrian Hernandez RC 3.00 8.00
72 Kyle Kessel RC 3.00 8.00
73 Jason Michaels RC 3.00 8.00
74 Esix Snead RC 3.00 8.00
75 Jason Smith RC 3.00 8.00
76 Tyler Walker RC 3.00 8.00
77 Juan Uribe RC 4.00 10.00
78 Adam Pettyjohn RC 3.00 8.00
79 Tsuyoshi Shinjo RC 4.00 10.00
80 Mike Penney RC 3.00 8.00
81 Josh Towers RC 4.00 10.00
82 Erick Almonte RC 3.00 8.00
83 Ryan Freel RC 4.00 10.00
84 Juan Pena 3.00 8.00
85 Albert Pujols RC 75.00 150.00
86 Henry Mateo RC 3.00 8.00
87 Greg Miller RC 3.00 8.00
88 Jose Mieses RC 3.00 8.00
89 Jack Wilson RC 4.00 10.00
90 Carlos Valderrama RC 3.00 8.00

2001 SP Game Used Edition Authentic Fabric

Randomly inserted one in every pack, this 82-card set features color player portraits with a swatch of a game-used jersey embedded in the card.

AH Aubrey Huff 4.00 10.00
AJ Andruw Jones 6.00 15.00
AL Al Leiter 4.00 10.00
AP Adam Piatt 4.00 10.00
ARH A.Rodriguez Rangers 6.00 15.00
ARM Alex Rodriguez Mariners DP 6.00 15.00
BB Barry Bonds 10.00 25.00
BG Brian Giles SP 10.00 25.00
BL Barry Larkin 6.00 15.00
CD Carlos Delgado SP 10.00 25.00
CJ Chipper Jones 6.00 15.00
CJO Charles Johnson 4.00 10.00
CR Cal Ripken 15.00 40.00
DE Darin Erstad 4.00 10.00
DW David Wells SP 10.00 25.00
DY Dmitri Young 4.00 10.00
EA Edgardo Alfonzo 4.00 10.00
EC Eric Chavez 4.00 10.00
EM Edgar Martinez DP 6.00 15.00
FM Fred McGriff 6.00 15.00
FTA Fernando Tatis 4.00 10.00
FTH Frank Thomas 6.00 15.00
GM Greg Maddux DP 6.00 15.00
GS Gary Sheffield 4.00 10.00
GV Greg Vaughn 4.00 10.00
IR Ivan Rodriguez 6.00 15.00
JB Jeromy Burnitz 4.00 10.00
JCB Jose Canseco BLC
JCH Jose Canseco 6.00 15.00
JCI Jeff Cirillo 4.00 10.00
JDI Joe DiMaggio SP/50 * 75.00 150.00
JDR J.D. Drew DP 4.00 10.00
JDY Jermaine Dye SP 10.00 25.00
JE Jim Edmonds DP 4.00 10.00
JG Jason Giambi 4.00 10.00
JI Jason Isringhausen SP 10.00 25.00
JK Jason Kendall 4.00 10.00
JK Jeff Kent 4.00 10.00
JO John Olerud 4.00 10.00
JT Jim Thome 6.00 15.00
JV Jose Vidro 4.00 10.00
KB Kevin Brown 4.00 10.00
KGH Ken Griffey Jr. Reds 6.00 15.00
KGM Ken Griffey Jr. Mariners DP 6.00 15.00
KGR Ken Griffey Jr. Road
KL Kenny Lofton 4.00 10.00
KM Kevin Millwood 4.00 10.00
LG Luis Gonzalez 4.00 10.00
MG Mark Grace 6.00 15.00
MH Mike Hampton 4.00 10.00
MM Mickey Mantle SP/50 * 150.00 250.00
MO Magglio Ordonez 4.00 10.00
MR Mariano Rivera 6.00 15.00
MT Miguel Tejada 4.00 10.00
MW Matt Williams 4.00 10.00
NR Nolan Ryan Rangers SP/50 * 40.00 80.00
NRA Nolan Ryan Astros SP/50 * 40.00 80.00
PB Pat Burrell 4.00 10.00
PN Phil Nevin 4.00 10.00
PW Preston Wilson 4.00 10.00
RA Rick Ankiel DP 4.00 10.00
RAL Roberto Alomar 6.00 15.00
RC Roger Clemens 6.00 15.00
RJ Randy Johnson 6.00 15.00
RM Roger Maris SP 20.00 50.00
RV Robin Ventura 4.00 10.00
SG Shawn Green 4.00 10.00
SR Scott Rolen 6.00 15.00
SSH Sammy Sosa Home 6.00 15.00
SSR Sammy Sosa Road 6.00 15.00
TB Tony Batista SP 6.00 15.00
TGL Troy Glaus 4.00 10.00
TGW Tony Gwynn DP 6.00 15.00
TH Tim Hudson 4.00 10.00
THE Todd Helton 6.00 15.00
TL Terrence Long 4.00 10.00
TM Tino Martinez 6.00 15.00
TOG Tom Glavine 6.00 15.00
TRH Trevor Hoffman 4.00 10.00
TS Tom Seaver Mets SP/50 * 15.00 40.00
TSR Tom Seaver Reds SP/50 * 15.00 40.00
TZ Todd Zeile 4.00 10.00

2001 SP Game Used Edition Authentic Fabric Autographs

Randomly inserted in packs, this 21-card set is an autographed, partial parallel version of the regular insert set. Only 50 serially numbered sets were produced. An exchange card was seeded into packs for Alex Rodriguez.

SAJ Andruw Jones 40.00 80.00
SAR Alex Rodriguez 100.00 175.00
SBB Barry Bonds 125.00 200.00
SCD Carlos Delgado 20.00 50.00
SCJ Chipper Jones 60.00 120.00
SCR Cal Ripken 125.00 200.00
SDW David Wells 20.00 50.00
SEA Edgardo Alfonzo 20.00 50.00
SFTH Frank Thomas 60.00 120.00
SIR Ivan Rodriguez 60.00 120.00
SJC Jose Canseco 40.00 80.00
SJDR J.D. Drew 20.00 50.00
SJG Jason Giambi 20.00 50.00
SKG Ken Griffey Jr. 75.00 150.00
SNR Nolan Ryan 125.00 200.00
SRA Rick Ankiel 30.00 60.00
SRJ Randy Johnson 60.00 120.00
SSS Sammy Sosa 50.00 100.00
STGL Troy Glaus 40.00 80.00
STH Tim Hudson 40.00 80.00
STS Tom Seaver Mets

2001 SP Game Used Edition Authentic Fabric Duos

Randomly inserted in packs, this 14-card set features color photos of two players to a card with two game jersey swatches embedded in each card. Only 50 serially numbered sets were produced.

2001 SP Game Used Edition Authentic Fabric Trios

Randomly inserted in packs, this six-card set features color photos of three players to a card with three game jersey swatches embedded in each card. Only 25 serially numbered sets were produced. Due to market scarcity, no pricing is provided for these cards.

DGS Joe DiMaggio
Ken Griffey Jr.
Sammy Sosa
DMM Joe DiMaggio
Mickey Mantle
Roger Maris
GRS Ken Griffey Jr.
Alex Rodriguez
Sammy Sosa
JBS Andruw Jones
Barry Bonds
Sammy Sosa
JSM Randy Johnson
Tom Seaver
Greg Maddux
MJJ Greg Maddux
Chipper Jones
Andruw Jones

2004 SP Game Used Hawaii Trade Conference

Given out by Upper Deck at the 2004 Hawaii Trade Conference, this set was sealed in one-card packages and distributed one-per to all paid attendees. Each card came sealed in a one-screw case where the screw was replaced with an un-tamperable piece of metal. Unless specified below, each card was serial numbered to 10. Due to market scarcity, no pricing is provided.

2004 SP Game Used Patch

The initial 119 card set was released in April, 2004. This set was issued in three-card pack with an $150 SRP which came one pack to box and 12 boxes to a case. Cards numbered 1 through 60 feature active veterans while cards 61 through 90 feature veterans in a significant number subset in which cards were issued to an important number of their career. Cards numbered 91 through 119 feature rookies and those cards were issued to a stated print run of 375 serial numbered sets. Cards 121-170 were issued as a complete sealed factory set randomly seeded into one in every 48 hobby boxes of 2004 Upper Deck Series 2 baseball in June, 2004. Please note, card 120 was never produced, thus the set is complete at 169 cards despite being checklisted from 1-170.

COMP.UPDATE SET (50) 40.00 100.00
COMMON CARD 1-60 .60 1.50
COMMON (61-90) p/r 400-684 .75 2.00
COMMON 61-90 p/r 262-384 .75 2.00
COMMON 61-90 p/r 165-236 .75 2.00
COMMON 61-90 p/r 86 .75 2.00
61-90 PRINT RUN B/WN 86-684 COPIES PER
COMMON CARD (91-119) 2.50 6.00
91-119 PRINT RUN 375 SERIAL #'d SETS
61-119 RANDOM INSERTS IN PACKS
COMMON CARD (121-135) .60 1.50
COMMON CARD (136-170) .75 2.00
ONE UPDATE SET PER 48 UD2 HOB.BOXES
1 Miguel Cabrera 1.50 4.00
2 Alex Rodriguez Yanks 2.50 6.00
3 Edgar Renteria .60 1.50
4 Juan Gonzalez .60 1.50
5 Mike Lowell .60 1.50
6 Andruw Jones .60 1.50
7 Eric Chavez .60 1.50
8 Jim Edmonds 1.00 2.50
9 Mike Piazza 1.50 4.00
10 Angel Berroa .60 1.50
11 Eric Gagne .60 1.50
12 Jody Gerut .60 1.50
13 Orlando Cabrera .60 1.50
14 Austin Kearns .60 1.50
15 Frank Thomas 1.50 4.00
16 Johan Santana 1.50 4.00
17 Randy Johnson 1.50 4.00
18 Preston Wilson .60 1.50
19 Garret Anderson .60 1.50
20 Jorge Posada 1.00 2.50
21 Rich Harden .60 1.50
22 Barry Zito .60 1.50
23 Gary Sheffield .60 1.50
24 Jose Reyes 1.00 2.50
25 Roy Halladay 1.50 4.00
26 Ben Sheets .60 1.50
27 Geoff Jenkins .60 1.50
28 Josh Beckett 1.00 2.50
29 Roy Oswalt 1.00 2.50
30 Bobby Abreu .60 1.50
31 Hank Blalock .60 1.50
32 Kerry Wood .60 1.50
33 Ryan Klesko .60 1.50
34 Rafael Furcal .60 1.50
35 Tom Glavine 1.00 2.50
36 Kevin Brown .60 1.50
37 Scott Rolen 1.00 2.50
38 Bret Boone .60 1.50
39 Ichiro Suzuki 2.50 6.00
40 Lance Berkman 1.00 2.50
41 Tim Hudson 1.00 2.50
42 Carlos Delgado .60 1.50
43 Ivan Rodriguez 1.00 2.50
44 Luis Gonzalez .60 1.50
45 Torii Hunter .60 1.50
46 Carlos Lee .60 1.50
47 Jacque Jones .60 1.50
48 Manny Ramirez 1.50 4.00
49 Troy Glaus .60 1.50
50 Corey Patterson .60 1.50
51 Jason Schmidt .60 1.50
52 Mark Mulder .60 1.50
53 Vernon Wells .60 1.50
54 Curt Schilling 1.00 2.50
55 Javy Lopez .60 1.50
56 Mark Prior 1.00 2.50
57 Dontrelle Willis .60 1.50
58 Derek Jeter 4.00 10.00
59 Jeff Bagwell 1.00 2.50
60 Marlon Byrd .60 1.50
61 Rafael Palmeiro SN/500 1.25 3.00
62 Kevin Millwood SN/165 .75 2.00
63 Greg Maddux SN/273 3.00 8.00
64 Adam Dunn SN/400 1.25 3.00
65 Richie Sexson SN/469 .75 2.00
66 Magglio Ordonez SN/567 1.25 3.00
67 Hideo Nomo SN/236 2.00 5.00
68 Albert Pujols SN/194 5.00 12.00
69 Rocco Baldelli SN/368 .75 2.00
70 Mark Teixeira SN/86 2.00 5.00
71 Jason Giambi SN/660 .75 2.00
72 Alfonso Soriano SN/230 .75 2.00
73 Roger Clemens SN/300 2.50 6.00
74 Miguel Tejada SN/359 1.25 3.00
75 Jeff Kent SN/684 .75 2.00
76 Bernie Williams SN/342 1.25 3.00
77 Sammy Sosa SN/470 2.00 5.00
78 Mike Mussina SN/641 1.25 3.00
79 Jim Thome SN/334 1.25 3.00
80 Brian Giles SN/506 .75 2.00
81 Shawn Green SN/234 .75 2.00
82 Mike Sweeney SN/340 .75 2.00
83 John Smoltz SN/262 2.00 5.00
84 Carlos Beltran SN/319 .75 2.00
85 Todd Helton SN/384 1.25 3.00
86 Nomar Garciaparra SN/372 2.00 5.00
87 Ken Griffey Jr. SN/481 3.00 8.00
88 Chipper Jones SN/633 2.00 5.00
89 Vladimir Guerrero SN/226 2.00 5.00
90 Pedro Martinez SN/313 1.25 3.00
91 Brandon Medders RD RC 2.50 6.00
92 Colby Miller RD RC 2.50 6.00
93 Dave Crouthers RD RC 2.50 6.00
94 Dennis Sarfate RD RC 2.50 6.00
95 Donald Kelly RD RC 4.00 10.00
96 Alec Zumwalt RD RC 2.50 6.00
97 Chris Aguila RD RC 2.50 6.00
98 Greg Dobbs RD RC 2.50 6.00
99 Ian Snell RD RC 2.50 6.00
100 Jake Woods RD RC 2.50 6.00
101 Jamie Brown RD RC 2.50 6.00
102 Jason Frasor RD RC 2.50 6.00
103 Jerome Gamble RD RC 2.50 6.00
104 Jesse Harper RD RC 2.50 6.00
105 Josh Labandeira RD RC 2.50 6.00
106 Justin Hampson RD RC 2.50 6.00
107 Justin Huisman RD RC 2.50 6.00
108 Justin Leone RD RC 2.50 6.00
109 Lincoln Holdzkom RD RC 2.50 6.00
110 Mike Bumatay RD RC 2.50 6.00
111 Mike Gosling RD RC 2.50 6.00
112 Mike Johnston RD RC 2.50 6.00
113 Mike Rouse RD RC 2.50 6.00
114 Nick Regilio RD RC 2.50 6.00
115 Ryan Meaux RD RC 2.50 6.00
116 Scott Dohmann RD RC 2.50 6.00
117 Sean Henn RD RC 2.50 6.00
118 Tim Bausher RD RC 2.50 6.00
119 Tim Bittner RD RC 2.50 6.00
121 Richie Sexson .60 1.50
122 Javier Vazquez .60 1.50
123 Alex Rodriguez Yanks 2.50 6.00
124 Javy Lopez .60 1.50
125 Miguel Tejada 1.00 2.50
126 Bartolo Colon .60 1.50
127 Ivan Rodriguez 1.00 2.50
128 Rafael Palmeiro 1.00 2.50
129 Kevin Brown .60 1.50
130 Gary Sheffield .60 1.50
131 Greg Maddux 2.50 6.00
132 Curt Schilling 1.00 2.50
133 Roger Clemens 2.00 5.00
134 Alfonso Soriano .60 1.50
135 Vladimir Guerrero 1.50 4.00
136 Carlos Vasquez RC .75 2.00
137 Roman Colon RC .75 2.00
138 William Bergolla RC .75 2.00
139 Jason Bartlett RC 2.50 6.00
140 Casey Daigle RC .75 2.00
141 Ryan Wing RC .75 2.00
142 Chris Saenz RC .75 2.00
143 Edwin Moreno RC .75 2.00
144 Shawn Hill RC .75 2.00
145 Eddy Rodriguez RC .75 2.00
146 Justin Knoedler RC .75 2.00
147 Renyel Pinto RC .75 2.00
148 Kevin Cave RC .75 2.00
149 Carlos Hines RC .75 2.00
150 Merkin Valdez RC .75 2.00
151 Tim Hamulack RC .75 2.00
152 Hector Gimenez RC .75 2.00
153 Mike Vento RC .75 2.00
154 Scott Proctor RC .75 2.00
155 Rusty Tucker RC .75 2.00
156 Akinori Otsuka RC .75 2.00
157 Ronny Cedeno RC .75 2.00
158 Jose Capellan RC .75 2.00
159 Justin Germano RC .75 2.00
160 Shingo Takatsu RC .75 2.00
161 Fernando Nieve RC .75 2.00
162 Michael Wuertz RC .75 2.00
163 Jerry Gil RC .75 2.00
164 Jorge Vasquez RC .75 2.00
165 Chad Bentz RC .75 2.00
166 Luis A. Gonzalez RC .75 2.00
167 Ivan Ochoa RC .75 2.00
168 Onil Joseph RC .75 2.00
169 Enemencio Pacheco RC .75 2.00
170 Kazuo Matsui RC 1.25 3.00

2004 SP Game Used Patch 1 of 1

STATED PRINT RUN 1 SERIAL #'d SET
NO PRICING DUE TO SCARCITY

2004 SP Game Used Patch 300 Win Club

STATED PRINT RUN 10 SERIAL #'d SETS
NO PRICING DUE TO SCARCITY

2004 SP Game Used Patch 300 Win Club Autograph

STATED PRINT RUN 10 SERIAL #'d SETS
NO PRICING DUE TO SCARCITY

2004 SP Game Used Patch 3000 Hit Club

STATED PRINT RUN 10 SERIAL #'d SETS
NO PRICING DUE TO SCARCITY
CR Cal Ripken
CY Carl Yastrzemski
SM Stan Musial
TG Tony Gwynn

2004 SP Game Used Patch 3000 Hit Club Autograph

STATED PRINT RUN 10 SERIAL #'d SETS
NO PRICING DUE TO SCARCITY

2004 SP Game Used Patch 500 HR Club

STATED PRINT RUN 10 SERIAL #'d SETS
NO PRICING DUE TO SCARCITY

2004 SP Game Used Patch 500 HR Club Autograph

STATED PRINT RUN 10 SERIAL #'d SETS
NO PRICING DUE TO SCARCITY

2004 SP Game Used Patch 500 HR Club Triple

STATED PRINT RUN 10 SERIAL #'d SETS
NO PRICING DUE TO SCARCITY
MSW Eddie Mathews
Sammy Sosa
Ted Williams
RKS Frank Robinson
Harmon Killebrew
Mike Schmidt

2004 SP Game Used Patch All-Star

STATED PRINT RUN 50 SERIAL #'d SETS
AP Albert Pujols 40.00 80.00
AR Alex Rodriguez 30.00 60.00
AS Alfonso Soriano 10.00 25.00
BZ Barry Zito 10.00 25.00
CD Carlos Delgado 10.00 25.00
CJ Chipper Jones 15.00 40.00
CS Curt Schilling 15.00 40.00
DJ Derek Jeter 50.00 100.00
EC Eric Chavez 10.00 25.00
FT Frank Thomas 15.00 40.00
GS Gary Sheffield 10.00 25.00
HE Todd Helton 15.00 40.00
HN Hideo Nomo 40.00 80.00
IS Ichiro Suzuki 50.00 100.00
JG Juan Gonzalez 10.00 25.00
JT Jim Thome 15.00 40.00
KG Ken Griffey Jr. 30.00 60.00
MP Mark Prior 15.00 40.00
SS Sammy Sosa 15.00 40.00
TH Tim Hudson 10.00 25.00
VW Vernon Wells 10.00 25.00

2004 SP Game Used Patch All-Star Number

RANDOM INSERTS IN PACKS
PRINT RUNS B/WN 3-50 COPIES PER
NO PRICING ON QTY OF 12 OR LESS
AJ Andruw Jones/25 20.00 50.00
AP Andy Pettitte/42 15.00 40.00
AR Alex Rodriguez/3
AS Alfonso Soriano/12
BZ Barry Zito/50 10.00 25.00
CD Carlos Delgado/25 15.00 40.00
CD1 Carlos Delgado/25 15.00 40.00
CJ Chipper Jones/10
CS Curt Schilling Sox/38 15.00 40.00
CS1 Curt Schilling D'backs/38 10.00 25.00
CY Carl Yastrzemski/8
EC Eric Chavez/3
EC1 Eric Chavez/3
FT Frank Thomas/35 15.00 40.00
GA Garret Anderson/16 15.00 40.00
GM Greg Maddux Braves/31 30.00 60.00
GM1 Greg Maddux Cubs/31 30.00 60.00
GS Gary Sheffield/11
HE Todd Helton/17 20.00 50.00
HN Hideo Nomo/10
IR Ivan Rodriguez/7
IS Ichiro Suzuki/50 50.00 100.00
JG Juan Gonzalez/19 15.00 40.00
JP Jorge Posada/20 20.00 50.00
JT Jim Thome/25 20.00 50.00
KG Ken Griffey Jr./30 40.00 80.00
MM Mike Mussina/35 15.00 40.00
MO Magglio Ordonez/30 10.00 25.00
MP Mark Prior/5
MT Miguel Tejada/4
PM Pedro Martinez/45 15.00 40.00
PU Albert Pujols/7
RC Roger Clemens/22 40.00 80.00
RH Roy Halladay/32 10.00 25.00
RP Rafael Palmeiro/25 20.00 50.00
SG Shawn Green/15 15.00 40.00
SR Scott Rolen/27 15.00 40.00
SS Sammy Sosa Cubs/21 20.00 50.00
SS1 Sammy Sosa Sox/21 20.00 50.00
TH Tim Hudson/15 15.00 40.00
TH1 Tim Hudson/15 15.00 40.00
VW Vernon Wells/10

2004 SP Game Used Patch All-Star Autograph

STATED PRINT RUN 10 SERIAL #'d SETS
NO PRICING DUE TO SCARCITY

2004 SP Game Used Patch All-Star Autograph Dual

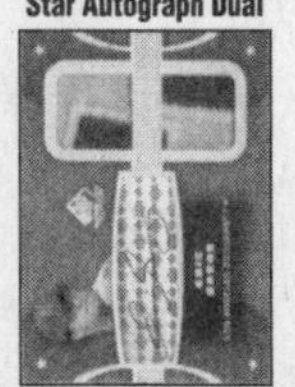

STATED PRINT RUN 10 SERIAL #'d SETS
NO PRICING DUE TO SCARCITY

2004 SP Game Used Patch Cut Signatures

PRINT RUNS B/WN 1-2 COPIES PER
NO PRICING DUE TO SCARCITY

2004 SP Game Used Patch Famous Nicknames

RANDOM INSERTS IN PACKS
PRINT RUNS B/WN 1-27 COPIES PER
NO PRICING ON QTY OF 14 OR LESS
AR Alex Rodriguez/10
BM Bill Mazeroski/1
BR Brooks Robinson/23 20.00 50.00
CR Cal Ripken Glove Down/21 100.00 200.00
CR1 Cal Ripken Glove Up/21 100.00 200.00
CY Carl Yastrzemski/23 40.00 80.00
DM Don Mattingly/14
DS Darryl Strawberry/17 15.00 40.00

DW Dontrelle Willis/1
ES Duke Snider/18 20.00 50.00
FT Frank Thomas/14
GA Sparky Anderson/27 10.00 25.00
GC Gary Carter/19 15.00 40.00
HK Harmon Killebrew/22 50.00 100.00
HM Hideki Matsui/1
IR Ivan Rodriguez/13
JB Jeff Bagwell/13
JD Joe DiMaggio/13
JF Nellie Fox/19 100.00 200.00
JG Juan Gonzalez/15 15.00 40.00
JH Catfish Hunter/15 20.00 50.00
KG Ken Griffey Jr./15 60.00 120.00
LB Yogi Berra/19 50.00 100.00
LJ Chipper Jones Hand Up/10
LJ1 Chipper Jones Arms Out/10
MU Mike Mussina Yanks/13
MU1 Mike Mussina O's/13
NR Nolan Ryan Astros/27 50.00 100.00
NR1 Nolan Ryan Rgr/27 50.00 100.00
OC Orlando Cepeda/17 15.00 40.00
OS Ozzie Smith/19 40.00 80.00
PN Phil Niekro/24 15.00 40.00
RC Roger Clemens/20 40.00 80.00
RI Phil Rizzuto/13
RJ Randy Johnson/16 20.00 50.00
RR Red Rolfe/10
RY Robin Yount/20 20.00 50.00
SM Stan Musial/22 75.00 150.00
SS Sammy Sosa Cubs/15 20.00 50.00
SS1 Sammy Sosa Sox/15 20.00 50.00
TS Tom Seaver/20 20.00 50.00
WS Willie Stargell/21 20.00 50.00

2004 SP Game Used Patch Famous Nicknames Autograph

STATED PRINT RUN 50 SERIAL #'d SETS
AD Andre Dawson 30.00 60.00
AR Alex Rodriguez Rgr 100.00 175.00
AR1 Alex Rodriguez M's 100.00 175.00
BM Bill Mazeroski 40.00 80.00
BR Brooks Robinson 40.00 80.00
DM Don Mattingly 75.00 150.00
FT Frank Thomas 50.00 100.00
HK Harmon Killebrew 60.00 120.00
HM Hideki Matsui 250.00 400.00
JB Jeff Bagwell 60.00 120.00
JG Juan Gonzalez 30.00 60.00
KG Ken Griffey Jr. 100.00 200.00
LJ Chipper Jones Hand Up 50.00 100.00
MM Mike Mussina 40.00 80.00
NR Nolan Ryan 125.00 200.00
OS Ozzie Smith 60.00 120.00
PN Phil Niekro 30.00 60.00
RC Roger Clemens 100.00 175.00
RY Robin Yount 60.00 120.00
TS Tom Seaver 40.00 80.00
WI Dontrelle Willis 40.00 80.00

2004 SP Game Used Patch HOF Numbers

RANDOM INSERTS IN PACKS
PRINT RUNS B/WN 1-50 COPIES PER
NO PRICING ON QTY OF 11 OR LESS
AJ Andruw Jones/25 20.00 50.00
AP Albert Pujols/5
AR Alex Rodriguez/3
BE Johnny Bench/5
BG Bob Gibson/45 15.00 40.00
BM Bill Mazeroski/1
BR Brooks Robinson/5
BW Billy Williams/26 15.00 40.00
CD Carlos Delgado/25 15.00 40.00
CH Catfish Hunter/27 15.00 40.00
CJ Chipper Jones/10
CL Roger Clemens/22 40.00 80.00
CR Cal Ripken/8
CS Curt Schilling/38 15.00 40.00
CY Carl Yastrzemski/8
DD Don Drysdale/50 30.00 60.00
DJ Derek Jeter Cap/2
DJ1 Derek Jeter No Cap/2
DS Don Sutton/20 15.00 40.00
EC Eric Chavez/3
EG Eric Gagne/38 10.00 25.00
EM Eddie Mathews/41 40.00 80.00
FR Frank Robinson/20 15.00 40.00
FT Frank Thomas/35 15.00 40.00
GC Gary Carter/8
GL Tom Glavine/47 15.00 40.00
GM Greg Maddux/31 30.00 60.00
GO Juan Gonzalez Royals/19 15.00 40.00
GO1 Juan Gonzalez Rgr/19 15.00 40.00
GP Gaylord Perry/36 10.00 25.00
GS Gary Sheffield/11
HE Todd Helton/17 20.00 50.00
HK Harmon Killebrew/3
HN Hideo Nomo/10
IR Ivan Rodriguez/7
IS Ichiro Suzuki/50 50.00 100.00
JB Jeff Bagwell/5
JC Jose Canseco/33 15.00 40.00
JD Joe DiMaggio/5
JG Jason Giambi/25 15.00 40.00
JI Jim Thome/25 20.00 50.00
JM Joe Morgan/8
JP Jim Palmer/22 15.00 40.00
JT Joe Torre/9
KG Ken Griffey Jr./30 40.00 80.00
LA Luis Aparicio/11
LD Leo Durocher/2
MA Juan Marichal/27 15.00 40.00
MP Mike Piazza/31 30.00 60.00
MR Manny Ramirez/24 20.00 50.00
MS Mike Schmidt/20 40.00 80.00
MZ Pedro Martinez/45 15.00 40.00
NF Nellie Fox/2
NG Nomar Garciaparra/5
NR Nolan Ryan/34 40.00 80.00
OC Orlando Cepeda/30 10.00 25.00
OS Ozzie Smith/1
PI Mark Prior Look Right/22 15.00 40.00
PI1 Mark Prior Look Left/22 15.00 40.00
PM Paul Molitor/4
PR Phil Rizzuto/10
RC Roberto Clemente/21 200.00 350.00
RF Rollie Fingers/34 10.00 25.00
RH Rickey Henderson/25 20.00 50.00
RP Rafael Palmeiro O's/25 20.00 50.00
RP1 Rafael Palmeiro Rgr/25 20.00 50.00
RY Robin Yount/19 20.00 50.00
SA Sparky Anderson/2
SC Steve Carlton/32 10.00 25.00
SG Shawn Green/15 15.00 40.00
SM Stan Musial/6
SN Duke Snider/4
SR Scott Rolen/27 15.00 40.00
SS Sammy Sosa Cubs/21 20.00 50.00
SS1 Sammy Sosa Sox/21 20.00 50.00
ST Willie Stargell/8
TG Tony Gwynn/19
TH Tim Hudson/15 15.00 40.00
TS Tom Seaver/41 15.00 40.00
WB Wade Boggs/26 15.00 40.00
WS Warren Spahn/21 40.00 80.00
YB Yogi Berra/8

2004 SP Game Used Patch HOF Numbers Autograph

STATED PRINT RUN 10 SERIAL #'d SETS
PUCKETT PRINT RUN 3 SERIAL #'d CARDS
NO PRICING DUE TO SCARCITY

2004 SP Game Used Patch HOF Numbers Autograph Dual

STATED PRINT RUN 10 SERIAL #'d SETS
NO PRICING DUE TO SCARCITY

2004 SP Game Used Patch Legendary Combo Cuts

STATED PRINT RUN 1 SERIAL #'d SET
NO PRICING DUE TO SCARCITY

2004 SP Game Used Patch Legendary Fabrics

PRINT RUNS B/WN 6-50 COPIES PER
NO PRICING ON QTY OF 10 OR LESS
BE Johnny Bench w/Mask/50 15.00 40.00
BE1 Johnny Bench Hitting/50 15.00 40.00
BG Bob Gibson/50 15.00 40.00
BR Brooks Robinson/9
BR1 Brooks Robinson/10
BW Billy Williams/50 10.00 25.00
CH Catfish Hunter/50 15.00 40.00
CR Cal Ripken Fielding/50 50.00 100.00
CR1 Cal Ripken Running/50 50.00 100.00

CY Carl Yastrzemski/31 30.00 60.00
EM Eddie Mathews/50 40.00 80.00
FR Frank Robinson O's/50 15.00 40.00
FR1 Frank Robinson Reds/50 15.00 40.00
GP Gaylord Perry/50 10.00 25.00
HK Harmon Killebrew Twins/50 40.00 80.00
HK1 H.Killebrew Senators/50 40.00 80.00
JC Jose Canseco/50 15.00 40.00
JM Joe Morgan Reds/50 10.00 25.00
JM1 Joe Morgan Giants/50 10.00 25.00
JP Jim Palmer/6
JP1 Jim Palmer/7
JT Joe Torre/50 10.00 25.00
LA Luis Aparicio/50 10.00 25.00
LD Leo Durocher/50 15.00 40.00
MS Mike Schmidt Bat Hand/50 30.00 60.00
MS1 Mike Schmidt Swing/50 30.00 60.00
NR Nolan Ryan Astros/50 30.00 60.00
NR1 Nolan Ryan Rgr/50 30.00 60.00
OC Orlando Cepeda/50 10.00 25.00
OS Ozzie Smith/50 20.00 50.00
PO Paul O'Neill/50 15.00 40.00
RF Rollie Fingers/50 10.00 25.00
RY Robin Yount Bat Up/50 15.00 40.00
RY1 Robin Yount Bat Down/50 15.00 40.00
SC Steve Carlton/50 10.00 25.00
TS Tom Seaver Mets/50 15.00 40.00
TS1 Tom Seaver Reds/50 15.00 40.00
WS W.Spahn Arms Down/50 20.00 50.00
WS1 W.Spahn Arms Up/50 20.00 50.00

2004 SP Game Used Patch Legendary Fabrics Autograph Dual

PRINT RUNS B/WN 10-25 COPIES PER
NO PRICING ON QTY OF 13 OR LESS
AD Andre Dawson/25 50.00 100.00
BE Johnny Bench/25 75.00 150.00
BM Bill Mazeroski/10
BR Brooks Robinson/25 60.00 120.00
BW Billy Williams/25 60.00 120.00
CR Cal Ripken/25 200.00 350.00
CY Carl Yastrzemski/17 125.00 200.00
DE Dwight Evans/25 60.00 120.00
DM Don Mattingly/25 150.00 250.00
DS Don Sutton/25 40.00 80.00
FL Fred Lynn/25 40.00 80.00
FR Frank Robinson/25 60.00 120.00
GP Gaylord Perry/25 40.00 80.00
HK Harmon Killebrew/25 100.00 200.00
JC Jose Canseco/25 60.00 120.00
JM Joe Morgan/25 50.00 100.00
JP Jim Palmer/25 50.00 100.00
JT Joe Torre Cards/25 50.00 100.00
JT1 Joe Torre Braves/25 50.00 100.00
KP Kirby Puckett/25 75.00 150.00
KP1 Kirby Puckett/12
LA Luis Aparicio/25 40.00 80.00
LB Lou Brock/13
NR Nolan Ryan Astros/25 150.00 250.00
NR1 Nolan Ryan Rgr/25 150.00 250.00
OC Orlando Cepeda/25 50.00 100.00
OS Ozzie Smith/25 100.00 175.00
PM Paul Molitor/25 50.00 100.00
PO Paul O'Neill/25 60.00 120.00
RC Roger Clemens/25 150.00 250.00
RF Rollie Fingers/25 50.00 100.00
RY Robin Yount Look Ahead/25 100.00 175.00
SG Steve Garvey/25 50.00 100.00
ST Darryl Strawberry/25 50.00 100.00
TG Tony Gwynn Look Left/25 75.00 150.00
TG1 Tony Gwynn Look Right/25 75.00 150.00
TS Tom Seaver Mets/25 60.00 120.00
TS1 Tom Seaver Reds/25 60.00 120.00
WB Wade Boggs Yanks/25 60.00 120.00
WB1 Wade Boggs Sox/25 60.00 120.00
WI Maury Wills/25 40.00 80.00
YO Robin Yount Look Right/25 100.00 175.00

2004 SP Game Used Patch Logo Threads

STATED PRINT RUN 1 SERIAL #'d SET
NO PRICING DUE TO SCARCITY

2004 SP Game Used Patch Logo Threads Autograph

STATED PRINT RUN 1 SERIAL #'d SET
NO PRICING DUE TO SCARCITY

2004 SP Game Used Patch Logo Threads Autograph Dual

STATED PRINT RUN 1 SERIAL #'d SET
NO PRICING DUE TO SCARCITY

2004 SP Game Used Patch MLB Masters

RANDOM INSERTS IN PACKS
PRINT RUNS B/WN 3-50 COPIES PER
NO PRICING ON QTY OF 12 OR LESS
AJ Andruw Jones/25 20.00 50.00
AP Albert Pujols/5
AR Alex Rodriguez/3
AS Alfonso Soriano/12
BE Josh Beckett/25 15.00 40.00
CD Carlos Delgado/25 15.00 40.00
CJ Chipper Jones/10
CS Curt Schilling/38 15.00 40.00
EC Eric Chavez/3
FT Frank Thomas/35 15.00 40.00
GM Greg Maddux Braves/31 30.00 60.00
GM1 Greg Maddux Cubs/31 30.00 60.00
GO Juan Gonzalez/19 15.00 40.00
GS Gary Sheffield/11
HE Todd Helton/17 20.00 50.00
HN Hideo Nomo Dodgers/10
HN1 Hideo Nomo Sox/10
IR Ivan Rodriguez/7
IS Ichiro Suzuki/50 50.00 100.00
JB Jeff Bagwell/5
JG Jason Giambi/25 15.00 40.00
JP Jorge Posada/20 20.00 50.00
JT Jim Thome Phils/25 20.00 50.00
JT1 Jim Thome Indians/25 20.00 50.00
KG Ken Griffey Jr./30 40.00 80.00
MO Magglio Ordonez/30 10.00 25.00
MP Mark Prior/22 20.00 50.00
MR Manny Ramirez/24 20.00 50.00
PI Mike Piazza/31 15.00 40.00
PM Pedro Martinez/45 15.00 40.00
RC Roger Clemens/22 40.00 80.00
RH Roy Halladay/32 10.00 25.00
SG Shawn Green/15 15.00 40.00
SR Scott Rolen/27 15.00 40.00
SS Sammy Sosa/21 20.00 50.00
TH Tim Hudson Glove Up/15 15.00 40.00
TH1 Tim Hudson Glove Down/15 15.00 40.00
VW Vernon Wells/10

2004 SP Game Used Patch MVP

STATED PRINT RUN 25 SERIAL #'d SETS
AR Alex Rodriguez 30.00 60.00
BR Brooks Robinson 20.00 50.00
BW Bernie Williams 20.00 50.00
CJ Chipper Jones 20.00 50.00
CR Cal Ripken 75.00 150.00
CS Curt Schilling 20.00 50.00
DJ Derek Jeter 60.00 120.00
FT Frank Thomas 20.00 50.00
GA Garret Anderson 15.00 40.00
IS Ichiro Suzuki 60.00 120.00
IV Ivan Rodriguez 20.00 50.00
JB Josh Beckett 15.00 40.00
JG Jason Giambi 15.00 40.00
KG Ken Griffey Jr. 40.00 80.00
MP Mike Piazza 30.00 60.00
MT Miguel Tejada 15.00 40.00
PM Pedro Martinez 20.00 50.00
RC Roger Clemens 40.00 80.00
RJ Randy Johnson 20.00 50.00
SS Sammy Sosa 20.00 50.00
TG Troy Glaus 15.00 40.00

2004 SP Game Used Patch Premium

RANDOM INSERTS IN PACKS
STATED PRINT RUN 50 SERIAL #'d SETS
GARCIAPARRA PRINT RUN 11 #'d CARDS
MATSUI PRINT RUN 17 #'d CARDS
SORIANO PRINT RUN 34 #'d CARDS
NO PRICING ON QTY OF 11 OR LESS
AD Adam Dunn 10.00 25.00
AP Albert Pujols 40.00 80.00
AR Alex Rodriguez Rgr 30.00 60.00
AR1 A.Rodriguez Yanks Cap 40.00 80.00
AR2 A.Rodriguez Yanks Helmet 40.00 80.00
AS Alfonso Soriano/34 10.00 25.00
BE Josh Beckett 10.00 25.00
BW Bernie Williams 15.00 40.00
BZ Barry Zito 10.00 25.00
CD Carlos Delgado 10.00 25.00
CJ Chipper Jones 15.00 40.00
CS Curt Schilling Glove Up 15.00 40.00
CS1 Curt Schilling Hand in Air 15.00 40.00
DJ Derek Jeter 40.00 100.00
DW Dontrelle Willis 15.00 40.00
EC Eric Chavez 10.00 25.00
FT Frank Thomas 15.00 40.00
GM Greg Maddux Braves 20.00 50.00
GM1 Greg Maddux Cubs 20.00 50.00
GO Juan Gonzalez 10.00 25.00
HM Hideki Matsui/17 125.00 200.00
IR Ivan Rodriguez 15.00 40.00
IS Ichiro Suzuki Profile 50.00 100.00
IS1 Ichiro Suzuki Arm Out 50.00 100.00
JB Jeff Bagwell 15.00 40.00
JG Jason Giambi 10.00 25.00
JP Jorge Posada 15.00 40.00
JT Jim Thome 15.00 40.00
KB Kevin Brown 10.00 25.00
KG Ken Griffey Jr. Arm Out 30.00 60.00
KG1 K.Griffey Jr. Red Helmet 30.00 60.00
MO Magglio Ordonez 10.00 25.00
MP Mark Prior 15.00 40.00
MR Manny Ramirez 15.00 40.00
MT Miguel Tejada 10.00 25.00
NG Nomar Garciaparra/11
NR Nolan Ryan 30.00 60.00
PI Mike Piazza 20.00 50.00
PM Pedro Martinez 15.00 40.00
RC Roger Clemens 20.00 50.00
RH Roy Halladay 10.00 25.00
RI Mariano Rivera 15.00 40.00
RJ Randy Johnson 15.00 40.00
RP Rafael Palmeiro 15.00 40.00
SG Shawn Green 10.00 25.00
SR Scott Rolen 15.00 40.00
SS Sammy Sosa Swing 15.00 40.00
SS1 Sammy Sosa Bat Down 15.00 40.00
TE Mark Teixeira 15.00 40.00
TG Tom Glavine 15.00 40.00
TH Tim Hudson 10.00 25.00

2004 SP Game Used Patch Premium Update

ONE PER SPGU UPDATE FACTORY SET
ONE UPDATE SET PER 48 UD2 HOB.BOXES
STATED PRINT RUN 20 SERIAL #'d SETS
V.WELLS PRINT RUN 21 SERIAL #'d CARDS
AK Austin Kearns 15.00 40.00
BA Bobby Abreu 15.00 40.00
BB Bret Boone 15.00 40.00
BC Bartolo Colon 15.00 40.00
BW Brandon Webb 15.00 40.00
CP Corey Patterson 15.00 40.00
EG Eric Gagne 15.00 40.00
EM Edgar Martinez 30.00 60.00
GA Garret Anderson 15.00 40.00
HB Hank Blalock 15.00 40.00
HN Hideo Nomo 40.00 80.00
JE Jim Edmonds 15.00 40.00
JJ Jacque Jones 15.00 40.00
JK Jeff Kent 15.00 40.00
JR Jose Reyes 15.00 40.00
KM Kevin Millwood 15.00 40.00
KW Kerry Wood 15.00 40.00
LB Lance Berkman 15.00 40.00
MM Mark Mulder 15.00 40.00
MS Mike Sweeney 15.00 40.00
RB Rocco Baldelli 15.00 40.00
RK Ryan Klesko 15.00 40.00
RO Roy Oswalt 15.00 40.00
RS Richie Sexson 15.00 40.00
TG Troy Glaus 15.00 40.00
TH Torii Hunter 15.00 40.00
VG Vladimir Guerrero 40.00 80.00
VW Vernon Wells /21 15.00 40.00

2004 SP Game Used Patch Premium Autograph

STATED PRINT RUN 50 SERIAL #'d SETS
GARCIAPARRA PRINT RUN 33 SERIAL #'d CARDS
AK Austin Kearns 30.00 60.00
AR Alex Rodriguez 100.00 175.00
BZ Barry Zito 10.00 25.00
CD Carlos Delgado 30.00 60.00
DW Dontrelle Willis 40.00 80.00
EC Eric Chavez 30.00 60.00
EG Eric Gagne 40.00 80.00
HM Hideki Matsui 250.00 400.00
IR Ivan Rodriguez 50.00 100.00
IS Ichiro Suzuki 1000.00 2000.00
KB Kevin Brown 30.00 60.00
KG Ken Griffey Jr. Reds 100.00 200.00
KG1 Ken Griffey Jr. M's 175.00 350.00
MP Mark Prior 30.00 60.00
MT Miguel Tejada 40.00 80.00
NG Nomar Garciaparra/33 75.00 150.00
RC Roger Clemens 100.00 175.00
SG Shawn Green 40.00 80.00
TG Troy Glaus 40.00 80.00
TH Tim Hudson 40.00 80.00
VG Vladimir Guerrero 50.00 100.00

2004 SP Game Used Patch Significant Numbers

RANDOM INSERTS IN PACKS
PRINT RUNS B/WN 1-27 COPIES PER
NO PRICING ON QTY OF 14 OR LESS

Card	Low	High
AJ Andruw Jones/8		
AP Albert Pujols/3		
AR Alex Rodriguez/10		
BE Josh Beckett/3		
BW Brandon Webb/1		
CD Carlos Delgado/11		
CJ Chipper Jones/10		
CR Cal Ripken/21	100.00	200.00
CS Curt Schilling/16	20.00	50.00
CY Carl Yastrzemski/23	40.00	80.00
DJ Derek Jeter/9		
DS Darryl Strawberry/17	15.00	40.00
EC Eric Chavez/6		
EG Eric Gagne/5		
EM Eddie Mathews/17	60.00	120.00
FT Frank Thomas/14		
GM Greg Maddux/18	40.00	80.00
GO Juan Gonzalez/15	15.00	40.00
GS Gary Sheffield/16	15.00	40.00
HM Hideki Matsui/1		
IS Ichiro Suzuki/3		
JB Jeff Bagwell/13		
JG Jason Giambi/9		
KG Ken Griffey Jr./15	60.00	120.00
MM Mike Mussina/13		
MP Mike Piazza/12		
MR Manny Ramirez/11		
MT Mark Teixeira/1		
NR Nolan Ryan/27	50.00	100.00
PM Pedro Martinez/12		
PO Paul O'Neill/17	20.00	50.00
PR Mark Prior/2		
RC Roger Clemens/20	40.00	80.00
RF Rollie Fingers/17	15.00	40.00
RH Roy Halladay/6		
RJ Randy Johnson/16	20.00	50.00
RP Rafael Palmeiro/18	20.00	50.00
SG Shawn Green/11		
SN Duke Snider/18	20.00	50.00
SS Sammy Sosa/15	20.00	50.00
TG Tom Glavine/17	20.00	50.00
TS Tom Seaver/20	20.00	50.00

2004 SP Game Used Patch Significant Numbers Autograph

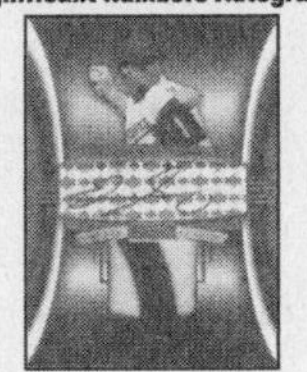

RANDOM INSERTS IN PACKS
STATED PRINT RUN 50 SERIAL #'d SETS
BROCK PRINT RUN 16 SERIAL #'d CARDS
PUCKETT PRINT RUN 3 SERIAL #'d CARDS
NO PUCKETT PRICING DUE TO SCARCITY

Card	Low	High
AR Alex Rodriguez Rgr	100.00	200.00
AR1 Alex Rodriguez M's	100.00	200.00
BA Bobby Abreu	30.00	60.00
BG Brian Giles	30.00	60.00
BW Bernie Williams	60.00	120.00
BZ Barry Zito	10.00	25.00
CD Carlos Delgado	30.00	60.00
CJ Chipper Jones	50.00	100.00
EC Eric Chavez	30.00	60.00
EG Eric Gagne	40.00	80.00
GM Greg Maddux	75.00	150.00
HE Todd Helton	40.00	80.00
HM Hideki Matsui	250.00	400.00
JG Juan Gonzalez Royals	30.00	60.00
JG1 Juan Gonzalez Rgr	30.00	60.00
KB Kevin Brown	30.00	60.00
KG Ken Griffey Jr. Reds	150.00	300.00
KG1 Ken Griffey Jr. M's	150.00	300.00
KP Kirby Puckett/3		
LB Lou Brock/16	50.00	100.00
LG Luis Gonzalez	30.00	60.00
MM Mike Mussina Yanks	40.00	80.00
MM1 Mike Mussina O's	20.00	50.00
MP Mike Piazza	150.00	250.00
MS Mike Schmidt	60.00	120.00
MT Miguel Tejada O's	40.00	80.00
MT1 Miguel Tejada A's	40.00	80.00
NR Nolan Ryan	125.00	200.00
PB Pat Burrell	30.00	60.00
PO Paul O'Neill	40.00	80.00
PR Mark Prior	30.00	60.00
RA Roberto Alomar	40.00	80.00
RB Rocco Baldelli	30.00	60.00
RF Rollie Fingers	30.00	60.00
RO Roy Oswalt Arm Up	15.00	40.00
RO1 Roy Oswalt Elbow Out	15.00	40.00
RP Rafael Palmeiro	50.00	100.00
RS Ryne Sandberg	60.00	120.00
SG Shawn Green	40.00	80.00
TG Tom Glavine	40.00	80.00
TH Tim Hudson	40.00	80.00
VG Vladimir Guerrero	50.00	100.00

2004 SP Game Used Patch Significant Numbers Autograph Dual

STATED PRINT RUN 25 SERIAL #'d SETS
BROCK PRINT RUN 14 SERIAL #'d CARDS
NO BROCK PRICING DUE TO SCARCITY

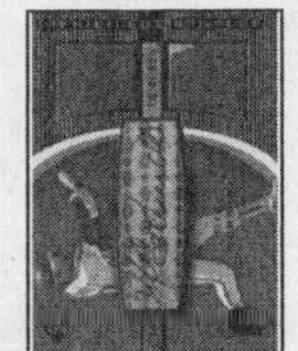

Card	Low	High
AR Alex Rodriguez Rgr	125.00	250.00
BA Bobby Abreu	50.00	100.00
BG Brian Giles	40.00	80.00
BW Bernie Williams	125.00	200.00
BZ Barry Zito	15.00	40.00
CD Carlos Delgado	50.00	100.00
CJ Chipper Jones	75.00	150.00
DW Dontrelle Willis	60.00	120.00
EC Eric Chavez	50.00	100.00
EG Eric Gagne	60.00	120.00
GI Bob Gibson	60.00	120.00
GM Greg Maddux	125.00	200.00
HE Todd Helton	60.00	120.00
HM Hideki Matsui	400.00	600.00
JG Juan Gonzalez Royals	50.00	100.00
JG1 Juan Gonzalez Rgr	50.00	100.00
KB Kevin Brown	50.00	100.00
KG Ken Griffey Jr. Reds	150.00	250.00
KP Kirby Puckett	75.00	150.00
LB Lou Brock/14		
LG Luis Gonzalez	40.00	80.00
MM Mike Mussina Yanks	60.00	120.00
MM1 Mike Mussina O's	60.00	120.00
MP Mike Piazza	200.00	350.00
MR Troy Glaus	60.00	120.00
MS Mike Schmidt	150.00	250.00
MT Miguel Tejada O's	40.00	80.00
MT1 Miguel Tejada A's	40.00	80.00
NR Nolan Ryan	90.00	150.00
PB Pat Burrell	50.00	100.00
PO Paul O'Neill	60.00	120.00
RA Roberto Alomar	60.00	120.00
RF Rollie Fingers	50.00	100.00
RP Rafael Palmeiro	75.00	150.00
RS Ryne Sandberg	150.00	250.00
SG Shawn Green Dodgers	60.00	120.00
SG1 Shawn Green Jays	60.00	120.00
TG Tom Glavine	60.00	120.00
TH Tim Hudson	60.00	120.00
TO Tony Gwynn	75.00	150.00
TS Tom Seaver	60.00	120.00
VG Vladimir Guerrero	75.00	150.00

2004 SP Game Used Patch Star Potential

PRINT RUNS B/WN 3-50 COPIES PER
NO PRICING ON QTY OF 12 OR LESS

Card	Low	High
AS Alfonso Soriano/12		
BW Brandon Webb/50	10.00	25.00
CP Corey Patterson/20	15.00	40.00
DW0 D.Willis Arm Up/35	15.00	40.00
DW1 D.Willis Arm Down/35	15.00	40.00
EC Eric Chavez/3		
HA Roy Halladay/32	10.00	25.00
HB Hank Blalock/9		
IS Ichiro Suzuki/50	50.00	100.00
JB Josh Beckett/21	15.00	40.00
JR Jose Reyes/7		
LB Lance Berkman/17	15.00	40.00
MM Mark Mulder/20	15.00	40.00
MP0 M.Prior Hand in Glove/22	20.00	50.00
MP1 Mark Prior Throwing/22	20.00	50.00
MT M.Teixeira Hands Back/23	20.00	50.00
MT1 M.Teixeira Hands Fwd/23	20.00	50.00
RB Rocco Baldelli/5		
RH Rich Harden/40	10.00	25.00
RO Roy Oswalt/44	10.00	25.00
RS Richie Sexson/11		
RW Rickie Weeks/23	15.00	40.00
TE Miguel Tejada/4		
TG Troy Glaus/25	15.00	40.00
TH Tim Hudson/15	15.00	40.00
VW Vernon Wells/10		

2004 SP Game Used Patch Stellar Combos Dual

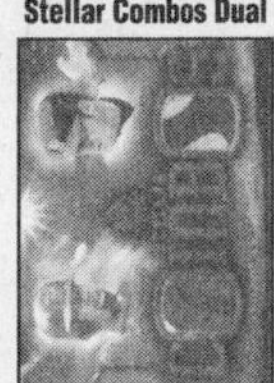

PRINT RUNS B/WN 1-25 COPIES PER
NO PRICING ON QTY OF 8 OR LESS

Card	Low	High
AD Alfonso Soriano Derek Jeter/8	60.00	120.00
AJ Alex Rodriguez Juan Gonzalez/25	40.00	80.00
AT Bobby Abreu Jim Thome/25	30.00	60.00
BK Jeff Bagwell Jeff Kent/25	30.00	60.00
BT Hank Blalock Mark Teixeira/25	30.00	60.00
CA Joe Carter Roberto Alomar/25	30.00	60.00
CO Roger Clemens Roy Oswalt/25	40.00	80.00
CR Curt Schilling Randy Johnson/25	30.00	60.00
DG Carlos Delgado Jason Giambi/25	20.00	50.00
DK Adam Dunn Austin Kearns/25	20.00	50.00
DL Derek Jeter Lou Gehrig/25		
GH Eric Gagne Trevor Hoffman/25	20.00	50.00
GT Greg Maddux Tom Glavine/25	50.00	100.00
JD Derek Jeter Joe DiMaggio/10		
JG Derek Jeter Nomar Garciaparra/3		
JJ Andruw Jones Chipper Jones/25	30.00	60.00
KR Jerry Koosman Nolan Ryan/25	100.00	175.00
LP Al Leiter Mike Piazza/25	40.00	80.00
LS Fred Lynn Ichiro Suzuki/25	60.00	120.00
MG Don Mattingly Jason Giambi/25	50.00	100.00
MM Hideki Matsui Mickey Mantle/1		
MN Hideki Matsui Hideo Nomo/5		
MT Edgar Martinez Frank Thomas/25	30.00	60.00
MY Paul Molitor Robin Yount/25	30.00	60.00
NB Hideo Nomo Kevin Brown/25	30.00	60.00
NY Alfonso Soriano Jose Reyes/25	20.00	50.00
PC Mark Prior Roger Clemens/25	50.00	100.00
PE Albert Pujols Jim Edmonds/25	60.00	120.00
PM Andy Pettitte Mike Mussina/25	30.00	60.00
PP Jorge Posada Mike Piazza/25	40.00	80.00
PS Rafael Palmeiro Sammy Sosa/25	30.00	60.00
RB Ivan Rodriguez Josh Beckett/25	30.00	60.00
RG1 Manny Ramirez Nomar Garciaparra/3		
RG2 Cal Ripken Lou Gehrig/25	300.00	500.00
RJ1 Alex Rodriguez Rgr Derek Jeter/25	75.00	150.00
RJ2 Alex Rodriguez Yanks Derek Jeter/25	100.00	200.00
RR Alex Rodriguez Cal Ripken/25	150.00	250.00
RS Brooks Robinson Mike Schmidt/25	40.00	80.00
SC Ichiro Suzuki Ty Cobb Pants/25	150.00	250.00
SG Duke Snider Shawn Green/25	30.00	60.00
SJ Gary Sheffield Randy Johnson/25	30.00	60.00
SM Curt Schilling Pedro Martinez/25	30.00	60.00
SR Curt Schilling Nolan Ryan/25	50.00	100.00
TO Frank Thomas Magglio Ordonez/25	30.00	60.00
WC David Wells Roger Clemens/25	40.00	80.00
WH Larry Walker Todd Helton/25	30.00	60.00
WS Billy Williams Sammy Sosa/25	30.00	60.00
WW Honus Wagner Pants Ted Williams/1		
ZH Barry Zito Tim Hudson/25	20.00	50.00

2004 SP Game Used Patch Team Threads Triple

STATED PRINT RUN 10 SERIAL #'d SETS
MANNY/NOMAR/PEDRO PRINT 3 #'d CARDS
A.ROD/JETER/MATSUI PRINT 5 #'d CARDS
NO PRICING DUE TO SCARCITY

2004 SP Game Used Patch Triple Authentic

STATED PRINT RUN 10 SERIAL #'d SETS
A.ROD/JETER/NOMAR PRINT 3 #'d CARDS
A.ROD/MANNY/NOMAR PRINT 3 #'d CARDS
NO PRICING DUE TO SCARCITY

2004 SP Game Used Patch World Series

RANDOM INSERTS IN PACKS
PRINT RUNS B/WN 15-50 COPIES PER

Card	Low	High
AJ Andruw Jones/50	15.00	40.00
AP Andy Pettitte/15	20.00	50.00
AS0 A.Soriano Hands on Bat/15	15.00	40.00
AS1 A.Soriano Hands Apart/15	15.00	40.00
BL Barry Larkin/50	15.00	40.00
BW Bernie Williams/50	15.00	40.00
CA Jose Canseco/50	15.00	40.00
CJ Chipper Jones/50	15.00	40.00
CS Curt Schilling D'backs/50	10.00	25.00
CS1 Curt Schilling Sox/50	15.00	40.00
CY Carl Yastrzemski/31	30.00	60.00
DW Dontrelle Willis/50	15.00	40.00
GA Garret Anderson/50	10.00	25.00
GL Troy Glaus Run/50	10.00	25.00
GL1 Troy Glaus Walk/50	10.00	25.00
GM Greg Maddux Arm Up/50	20.00	50.00
GM1 Greg Maddux Cubs/50	20.00	50.00
GM2 G.Maddux Glove Out/50	20.00	50.00
HM Hideki Matsui/17	125.00	200.00
IR Ivan Rodriguez/50	15.00	40.00
JB Josh Beckett Leaning/50	10.00	25.00
JB1 Josh Beckett Leg Kick/50	10.00	25.00
JE Derek Jeter Gray/50	40.00	100.00
JE1 Derek Jeter Stripes/50	40.00	100.00
JM Joe Morgan/50	10.00	25.00
JP Jorge Posada/50	15.00	40.00
JT Jim Thome Indians/50	15.00	40.00
JT1 Jim Thome Phils/50	15.00	40.00
KB Kevin Brown/50	10.00	25.00
MM Mike Mussina Yanks/50	15.00	40.00
MM1 Mike Mussina O's/43	15.00	40.00
MP Mike Piazza Mets/50	20.00	50.00
MP1 Mike Piazza Dodgers/50	20.00	50.00
MR Mariano Rivera/50	15.00	40.00
MS Mike Schmidt/50	30.00	60.00
PM Paul Molitor/50	10.00	25.00
PO Paul O'Neill/50	15.00	40.00
RC Roger Clemens/50	20.00	50.00
RF Rollie Fingers/50	15.00	40.00
RJ Randy Johnson/50	15.00	40.00
TG Tom Glavine/50	15.00	40.00

2004 SP Game Used Patch World Series Autograph

STATED PRINT RUN 1 SERIAL #'d SET
NO PRICING DUE TO SCARCITY

2004 SP Game Used Patch World Series Autograph Dual

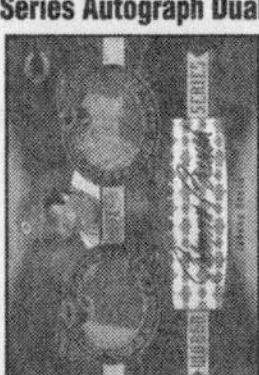

STATED PRINT RUN 1 SERIAL #'d SET
NO PRICING DUE TO SCARCITY

2001 SP Legendary Cuts

The SP Lengendary Cuts product was released in October, 2001 and featured a 90-card base set. Each pack contained four cards and carried a suggested retail price of $9.99.

Card	Low	High
COMPLETE SET (90)	10.00	25.00
1 Al Simmons	.10	.30
2 Jimmie Foxx	.30	.75
3 Mickey Cochrane	.20	.50
4 Phil Niekro	.10	.30

Card	Low	High
5 Eddie Mathews	.30	.75
6 Gary Matthews	.10	.30
7 Hank Aaron	.60	1.50
8 Joe Adcock	.10	.30
9 Warren Spahn	.20	.50
10 George Sisler	.10	.30
11 Stan Musial	.50	1.25
12 Dizzy Dean	.30	.75
13 Frankie Frisch	.10	.30
14 Harvey Haddix	.10	.30
15 Johnny Mize	.20	.50
16 Ken Boyer	.10	.30
17 Rogers Hornsby	.30	.75
18 Cap Anson	.30	.75
19 Andre Dawson	.10	.30
20 Billy Williams	.10	.30
21 Billy Herman	.10	.30
22 Hack Wilson	.20	.50
23 Ron Santo	.20	.50
24 Ryne Sandberg	.50	1.25
25 Ernie Banks	.30	.75
26 Burleigh Grimes	.10	.30
27 Don Drysdale	.20	.50
28 Gil Hodges	.30	.75
29 Jackie Robinson	.30	.75
30 Tommy Lasorda	.10	.30
31 Pee Wee Reese	.30	.75
32 Roy Campanella	.30	.75
33 Tommy Davis	.10	.30
34 Branch Rickey	.10	.30
35 Leo Durocher	.20	.50
36 Walt Alston	.10	.30
37 Bill Terry	.10	.30
38 Carl Hubbell	.20	.50
39 Eddie Stanky	.10	.30
40 George Kelly	.10	.30
41 Mel Ott	.30	.75
42 Juan Marichal	.10	.30
43 Rube Marquard	.10	.30
44 Travis Jackson	.10	.30
45 Bob Feller	.10	.30
46 Earl Averill	.10	.30
47 Elmer Flick	.10	.30
48 Ken Keltner	.10	.30
49 Lou Boudreau	.20	.50
50 Early Wynn	.20	.50
51 Satchel Paige	.30	.75
52 Ron Hunt	.10	.30
53 Tom Seaver	.20	.50
54 Richie Ashburn	.20	.50
55 Mike Schmidt	.60	1.50
56 Honus Wagner	.40	1.00
57 Lloyd Waner	.20	.50
58 Max Carey	.10	.30
59 Paul Waner	.20	.50
60 Roberto Clemente	.75	2.00
61 Nolan Ryan	.75	2.00
62 Bobby Doerr	.20	.50
63 Carlton Fisk	.20	.50
64 Joe Cronin	.10	.30
65 Joe Wood	.20	.50
66 Tony Conigliaro	.20	.50
67 Edd Roush	.10	.30
68 Johnny VanderMeer	.10	.30
69 Walter Johnson	.30	.75
70 Charlie Gehringer	.10	.30
71 Al Kaline	.30	.75
72 Ty Cobb	.50	1.25
73 Tony Oliva	.10	.30
74 Luke Appling	.10	.30
75 Minnie Minoso	.10	.30
76 Nellie Fox	.20	.50
77 Joe Jackson	.60	1.50
78 Babe Ruth	1.00	2.50
79 Bill Dickey	.20	.50
80 Elston Howard	.20	.50
81 Joe DiMaggio	.60	1.50
82 Lefty Gomez	.30	.75
83 Lou Gehrig	.60	1.50
84 Mickey Mantle	1.25	3.00
85 Reggie Jackson	.20	.50
86 Roger Maris	.30	.75
87 Whitey Ford	.20	.50
88 Waite Hoyt	.10	.30
89 Yogi Berra	.30	.75
90 Casey Stengel	.30	.75

2001 SP Legendary Cuts Autographs

Randomly inserted into packs at a rate of one in 252 (a.k.a. - one per case), this 85-card set features more than 3,300 autographs of deceased legends that were cut off of checks, contracts, letters, etc that Upper Deck purchased on the secondary market. The card backs carry the players initials as numbering. Cards with a print run of less than 25 are not priced due to scarcity. A couple of players, Joe DiMaggio and Ted Lyons, were printed to different quantities.

Card	Low	High
CBD Bill Dickey/28	300.00	450.00
CBG Burleigh Grimes/18		
CBHA Bucky Harris/10		
CBHE Billy Herman/88	75.00	150.00
CBL Bob Lemon/23		
CBM Bob Meusel/23		
CBRI Branch Rickey/16		
CBRU Babe Ruth/7		
CBS Bob Shawkey/39	150.00	250.00
CBT Bill Terry/184	150.00	250.00
CBW Bucky Walters/13		
CCA Cap Anson/2		
CCH Carl Hubbell/30	250.00	400.00
CCK Charlie Keller/16		
CCS Casey Stengel/10		
CDDE Dizzy Dean/56	400.00	800.00
CDDR Don Drysdale/12		
CEA Earl Averill/189	60.00	120.00
CEB Ed Barrow/16		
CEF Elmer Flick/22		
CEL Eddie Lopat/22		
CER Edd Roush/83	75.00	150.00
CFF Ford Frick/21		
CFF Frankie Frisch/3		
CFL Freddy Lindstrom/2		
CGA Grover Alexander/1		
CGH Gabby Hartnett/32	175.00	300.00
CGH Gil Hodges/6		
CGK George Kelly/52	125.00	200.00
CGS George Selkirk/15		
CGS George Sisler/1		
CHH Harvey Haddix/4		
CHH Harry Hooper/14		
CHM Heinie Manush/50	175.00	300.00
CHW Honus Wagner/24		
CHW Hack Wilson/4		
CJC Jocko Conlan/26	250.00	400.00
CJC Joe Cronin/12		
CJD1 Joe DiMaggio/25		
CJD2 Joe DiMaggio/50	400.00	600.00
CJD3 Joe DiMaggio/150	300.00	500.00
CJD4 Joe DiMaggio/275	300.00	500.00
CJF Jimmie Foxx/16		
CJJ Judy Johnson/9		
CJM Joe Medwick/18		
CJMC Joe McCarthy/40	300.00	500.00
CJMI Johnny Mize/84	150.00	250.00
CJR Jackie Robinson/147	1200.00	1600.00
CJS Joe Sewell/55	150.00	250.00
CJW Joe Wood/43	300.00	500.00
CKC Kiki Cuyler/6		
CKK Ken Keltner/11		
CKL Kenesaw Landis/4		
CLA Luke Appling/45	125.00	200.00
CLD Leo Durocher/45	175.00	300.00
CLG Lefty Grove/34	300.00	500.00
CLGE Lou Gehrig/7		
CLGO Lefty Gomez/85	175.00	300.00
CLW Lloyd Waner/217	125.00	250.00
CMC Max Carey/73	150.00	250.00
CMK Mark Koenig/30	250.00	400.00
CMM Mickey Mantle/8		
CMO Mel Ott/8		
CNF Nellie Fox/9		
CPW Paul Waner/4		
CRC Roberto Clemente/4		
CRF Rick Ferrell/8		
CRH Rogers Hornsby/4		
CROM Roger Maris/73	1000.00	1500.00
CRP R.Peckinpaugh/45	150.00	250.00
CRR Red Ruffing/5		
CRS Rip Sewell/39	150.00	250.00
CRUM Rube Marquard/23		
CSC Stanley Coveleski/42	125.00	200.00
CSM Sal Maglie/19		
CSP Satchel Paige/36	1200.00	1700.00
CTC Ty Cobb/24		
CTJ Travis Jackson/35	175.00	300.00
CTL1 Ted Lyons/2		
CTL2 Ted Lyons/59	125.00	200.00
CVM J. VanderMeer/65	150.00	250.00
CVR Vic Raschi/26	175.00	300.00
CWA Walt Alston/34	250.00	400.00
CWG Warren Giles/10		
CWH Waite Hoyt/38	150.00	250.00
CWJ Walter Johnson/113	2000.00	3000.00

2001 SP Legendary Cuts Debut Game Bat

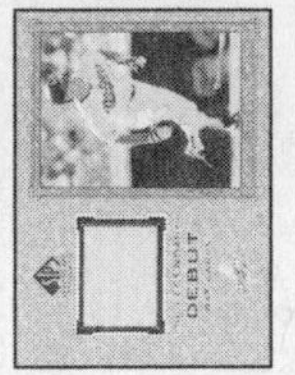

Randomly inserted into packs at one in 18, this 35-card set features the first game-used pieces of bat cards for each player. Card backs carry the player's intials as numbering. Cards with a perceived larger supply carry an asterisk and all short-print cards carry an SP designation.

Card	Low	High
BAT Alan Trammell *	4.00	10.00
BBB Bobby Bonds	4.00	10.00
BBF Bill Freehan	4.00	10.00
BGL Greg Luzinski	4.00	10.00
BLW Lou Whitaker	4.00	10.00
BSS Steve Sax *	4.00	10.00
BSY Steve Yeager	4.00	10.00
BWH Willie Horton	4.00	10.00
BWP Wes Parker *	4.00	10.00
DBB Bill Buckner *	4.00	10.00
DBD Bobby Doerr SP	10.00	25.00
DBF Bob Feller SP	15.00	40.00
DBH Billy Herman SP	10.00	25.00
DBM Bill Mazeroski	6.00	15.00
DBR B.Richardson SP	10.00	25.00
DCG Charlie Gehringer	40.00	80.00
DEH Elston Howard SP	10.00	25.00
DES Eddie Stanky	4.00	10.00
DFF Frankie Frisch SP	10.00	25.00
DGM Gary Matthews	4.00	10.00
DGS George Sisler	10.00	25.00
DHW Hack Wilson SP	50.00	100.00
DJA Joe Adcock SP	10.00	25.00
DJC Joe Cronin	6.00	15.00
DJJ Joe Jackson	200.00	400.00
DKB Ken Boyer SP	10.00	25.00
DLA Luke Appling SP	15.00	40.00
DLB Lou Boudreau	6.00	15.00
DMC Mickey Cochrane	60.00	120.00
DMM Minnie Minoso SP	10.00	25.00
DPW Paul Waner SP	30.00	60.00
DRA Richie Ashburn SP	15.00	40.00
DRH Ron Hunt	4.00	10.00
DTC Tony Conigliaro SP	50.00	100.00
DTO Tony Oliva	4.00	10.00

2001 SP Legendary Cuts Game Bat

Randomly inserted into packs at one in 18, this 36-card set features game-used pieces of bat cards for each player. Card backs carry the player's intials as numbering. Cards with a perceived larger supply carry an asterisk and all short-print cards carry an SP designation.

Card	Low	High
BAD Andre Dawson *	4.00	10.00
BAS Al Simmons SP	100.00	175.00
BBR Babe Ruth SP	125.00	200.00
BBT Bill Terry SP	30.00	60.00
BCF Carlton Fisk	6.00	15.00
BDD Don Drysdale SP	15.00	40.00
BDJ Davey Johnson	4.00	10.00
BEM Eddie Mathews	6.00	15.00
BGB George Brett *	6.00	15.00
BGH Gil Hodges SP	30.00	60.00
BHA Hank Aaron SP	20.00	50.00
BJD Joe DiMaggio SP	60.00	120.00
BJF Jimmie Foxx	30.00	60.00
BJR Jackie Robinson SP	30.00	60.00
BKC Kiki Cuyler	30.00	60.00
BMM Mickey Mantle SP	75.00	150.00
BMM Manny Mota	4.00	10.00
BMO Mel Ott SP	40.00	80.00
BMW Maury Wills *	4.00	10.00
BNF Nellie Fox	6.00	15.00
BNR Nolan Ryan SP	15.00	40.00
BPM Paul Molitor	4.00	10.00
BRC Rico Carty	4.00	10.00
BRCA R.Campanella SP	20.00	50.00
BRCL Roberto Clemente	30.00	60.00
BRJ Reggie Jackson *	6.00	15.00
BRM Roger Maris SP	40.00	80.00
BRS Ryne Sandberg *	10.00	25.00
BRY Robin Yount *	6.00	15.00
BTC Ty Cobb SP	75.00	150.00
BTD Tommy Davis SP	40.00	80.00
BTHO Tommy Holmes UER Eddie Mathews pictured	4.00	10.00
BVP Vada Pinson	4.00	10.00
BWB Wade Boggs *	6.00	15.00
BWMC Willie McCovey *	4.00	10.00
BYB Yogi Berra	6.00	15.00

2001 SP Legendary Cuts Game Jersey

Randomly inserted into packs at one in 18, this 35-card set features game-worn jersey or uniform pieces for each player. Card backs carry the player's intials as numbering. Cards with a perceived larger supply carry an asterisk and all short-print cards carry an SP designation.

SP'S NOT PRICED DUE TO SCARCITY

Card	Low	High
JBD Bill Dickey Uni	15.00	40.00
JBL Bob Lemon Uni	6.00	15.00
JBM B.Mazeroski Uni SP		
JBR B.Richardson Uni	4.00	10.00
JBR Babe Ruth Uni SP		
JBRO B.Robinson Uni	6.00	15.00
JBT Bobby Thomson Uni	6.00	15.00
JBW Billy Williams Jsy	4.00	10.00
JCS Casey Stengel Uni	6.00	15.00
JGH Gil Hodges Jsy	6.00	15.00
JGP Gaylord Perry Jsy	4.00	10.00
JHW H.Wagner Uni SP		
JJD Joe DiMaggio Uni SP		
JJF Jim Fregosi Jsy	4.00	10.00
JJM Juan Marichal Jsy *	4.00	10.00
JJN Joe Nuxhall Jsy	6.00	15.00
JLD Leo Durocher Jsy	15.00	40.00
JMM M. Mantle Uni SP		
JMW Maury Wills Jsy	4.00	10.00
JNF Nellie Fox Uni	6.00	15.00
JNR Nolan Ryan Jsy	15.00	40.00
JRC R. Clemente Jsy	50.00	100.00
JRJ Reggie Jackson Jsy	6.00	15.00
JRM Roger Maris Uni SP		
JRY Robin Yount Jsy	6.00	15.00
JTC Tony Conigliaro Jsy	6.00	15.00
JTC Ty Cobb Uni SP		
JTHO T.Holmes Uni*	4.00	10.00
JTK Ted Kluszewski Jsy	6.00	15.00
JTS Tom Seaver Jsy SP		
JVL Vic Lombardi Jsy	4.00	10.00
JWB Wade Boggs Jsy	6.00	15.00
JWF Whitey Ford Uni	6.00	15.00
JWM Willie McCovey Uni*	4.00	10.00
JYB Yogi Berra Uni	6.00	15.00

2002 SP Legendary Cuts

This 90 card set was released in October, 2002. The set was issued in four card packs which came 12 packs to a box and 16 boxes to a case. In addition to these basic cards, an exchange card for a Mark McGwire "private signings" card was randomly inserted into packs. That card has a stated print run of 100 copies inserted and a redemption deadline of 09/12/03.

COMPLETE SET (90)	10.00	25.00
1 Al Kaline	.60	1.50
2 Alvin Dark	.25	.60
3 Andre Dawson	.25	.60
4 Babe Ruth	2.00	5.00
5 Ernie Banks	.60	1.50
6 Bob Lemon	.40	1.00
7 Bobby Bonds	.25	.60
8 Carl Erskine	.25	.60
9 Carl Hubbell	.40	1.00
10 Casey Stengel	.60	1.50
11 Charlie Gehringer	.40	1.00
12 Christy Mathewson	.60	1.50
13 Dale Murphy	.40	1.00
14 Dave Concepcion	.25	.60
15 Dave Parker	.25	.60
16 Dazzy Vance	.25	.60
17 Dizzy Dean	.40	1.00
18 Don Baylor	.25	.60
19 Don Drysdale	.40	1.00
20 Duke Snider	.40	1.00
21 Earl Averill	.25	.60
22 Early Wynn	.25	.60
23 Edd Roush	.25	.60
24 Elston Howard	.25	.60
25 Ferguson Jenkins	.25	.60
26 Frank Crosetti	.25	.60
27 Frankie Frisch	.25	.60
28 Gaylord Perry	.25	.60
29 George Foster	.25	.60
30 George Kell	.25	.60
31 Gil Hodges	.40	1.00
32 Hank Greenberg	.60	1.50
33 Phil Niekro	.25	.60
34 Harvey Haddix	.25	.60
35 Harvey Kuenn	.25	.60
36 Honus Wagner	1.00	2.50
37 Jackie Robinson	.60	1.50
38 Orlando Cepeda	.25	.60
39 Joe Adcock	.25	.60
40 Joe Cronin	.25	.60
41 Joe DiMaggio	1.00	2.50
42 Joe Morgan	.25	.60
43 Johnny Mize	.25	.60
44 Lefty Gomez	.40	1.00
45 Lefty Grove	.40	1.00
46 Jim Palmer	.25	.60
47 Lou Boudreau	.25	.60
48 Lou Gehrig	1.00	2.50
49 Luke Appling	.25	.60
50 Mark McGwire	2.00	5.00
51 Mel Ott	.60	1.50
52 Mickey Cochrane	.40	1.00
53 Mickey Mantle	2.00	5.00
54 Minnie Minoso	.25	.60
55 Brooks Robinson	.40	1.00
56 Nellie Fox	.40	1.00
57 Nolan Ryan	1.50	4.00
58 Rollie Fingers	.25	.60
59 Pee Wee Reese	.40	1.00
60 Phil Rizzuto	.40	1.00
61 Ralph Kiner	.25	.60
62 Ray Dandridge	.25	.60
63 Richie Ashburn	.40	1.00
64 Robin Yount	.60	1.50
65 Rocky Colavito	.40	1.00
66 Roger Maris	.60	1.50
67 Rogers Hornsby	.60	1.50
68 Ron Santo	.25	.60
69 Ryne Sandberg	1.25	3.00
70 Stan Musial	1.00	2.50
71 Sam McDowell	.25	.60
72 Satchel Paige	.60	1.50
73 Willie McCovey	.25	.60
74 Steve Garvey	.25	.60
75 Ted Kluszewski	.40	1.00
76 Catfish Hunter	.40	1.00
77 Terry Moore	.15	.40
78 Thurman Munson	.60	1.50
79 Tom Seaver	.40	1.00
80 Tommy John	.25	.60
81 Tony Gwynn	.75	2.00
82 Tony Kubek	.40	1.00
83 Tony Lazzeri	.25	.60
84 Ty Cobb	1.00	2.50
85 Wade Boggs	.40	1.00
86 Waite Hoyt	.25	.60
87 Walter Johnson	.60	1.50
88 Willie Stargell	.40	1.00
89 Yogi Berra	.60	1.50
90 Zack Wheat	.25	.60
MM M.McGwire AU/100 EX		

2002 SP Legendary Cuts Autographs

Inserted in packs at stated odds of one in 128, these 97 cards feature "cut" autographs of a mix of retired greats and tough to track down early players dating back to the 1910's. Each card has a different stated serial numbered print run and we have notated that information next to the player's name in our checklist. Edd Roush has two different varieties issued. Also, if a player has a stated print run of 25 or fewer copies, there is no pricing provided due to market scarcity.

BDA Babe Dahlgren/51	125.00	200.00
BFA Bibb Falk/44	75.00	150.00
BGO Bill Goodman/53	75.00	150.00
BHA Buddy Hassett/56	75.00	150.00
BIL Bill Lee/40	75.00	150.00
BKA Bob Kahle/53	60.00	120.00
BOL Bob Lemon/91	75.00	150.00
BRU Babe Ruth/3		
BSC Bob Scheffing/19		
BSE Bill Serena/16		
BSH Bill Sherdel/10		
BSH Bob Shawkey/118	75.00	150.00
BSZ Billy Shantz/17		
BVE Bill Veeck/11		
BWA Bucky Walters/31	150.00	250.00
CGE Charlie Gehringer/3		
CHM Chet Morgan/27	125.00	200.00
CHRM Christy Mathewson/2		
CHU Carl Hubbell/17		
CKE Charlie Keller/29	150.00	250.00
CLA Cookie Lavagetto/22		
CST Casey Stengel/8		
DDE Dizzy Dean/4		
DDO Dick Donovan/23		
DDR Don Drysdale/14		
DVA Dazzy Vance/5		
EAV Earl Averill/22		
EJO Earl Johnson/31	125.00	200.00
ELO Ed Lopat/58	60.00	120.00
ERO Edd Roush/101	60.00	120.00
ERO2 Edd Roush/155	60.00	120.00
EWY Early Wynn/4		
FFR Frankie Frisch/35	250.00	400.00
FOF Ford Frick/1		
GBU Guy Bush/38	75.00	150.00
GCA George Case/35	125.00	200.00
GHO Gil Hodges/1		
GPI George Pipgras/34	125.00	200.00
HCH Happy Chandler/96	75.00	150.00
HGR Hank Greenberg/94	200.00	400.00
HHA Harvey Haddix/37	125.00	200.00
HKU Harvey Kuenn/23		
HMA Hank Majeski/21		
HNE Hal Newhouser/81	60.00	120.00
HSC Hal Schumacher/17		
HWA Honus Wagner/6		
JAD Joe Adcock/48	100.00	175.00
JBE Johnny Berardino/12		
JCO Johnny Cooney/64	60.00	120.00
JCR Joe Cronin/185	75.00	150.00
JDI Joe DiMaggio/103	350.00	500.00
JDU Joe Dugan/39	125.00	200.00
JJO Judy Johnson/86	125.00	200.00
JMI Johnny Mize/3		
JMO Johnny Moore/22		
JSE Joe Sewell/136	60.00	120.00
KKE Ken Keltner/11		
LAP Luke Appling/53	75.00	150.00
LBO Lou Boudreau/85	75.00	150.00
LGE Lou Gehrig/3		
LGO Lefty Gomez/3		
LGR Lefty Grove/194	150.00	250.00
LJA Larry Jackson/37	75.00	150.00
LRI Lance Richbourg/3		
LSE Luke Sewell/2		
MCO Mickey Cochrane/2		
MKO Mark Koenig/22		
MMA Mickey Mantle/2		
NFO Nellie Fox/1		
NJA Bucky Jacobs/44	125.00	200.00
ORO Oscar Roettger/9		
PRE Pete Reiser/73	100.00	175.00
PWE Pee Wee Reese/23		
PWI Pete Whisenant/13		
RAS Richie Ashburn/10		
RDA Ray Dandridge/179	60.00	120.00
RFE Rick Ferrell/19		
RHO Rogers Hornsby/1		
RMA Roger Maris/1		
RMC Roy McMillan/18		
RRE Rip Repulski/19		
SCH Spud Chandler/17		
SCO Stan Coveleski/85	75.00	150.00
SHA Stan Hack/36	150.00	250.00
SMA Sal Maglie/29	125.00	200.00
TDO Taylor Douthit/60	75.00	150.00
TKL Ted Kluszewski/23		
TMO Terry Moore/86	60.00	120.00
TYC Ty Cobb/2		
VRA Vic Raschi/98	75.00	150.00
VWE Vic Wertz/17		
WHO Waite Hoyt/61	75.00	150.00
WJO Walter Johnson/20		
WKA Willie Kamm/57	60.00	120.00
WSC Willard Schmidt/10		
WST Willie Stargell/153	75.00	150.00
ZWH Zack Wheat/127	200.00	300.00

2002 SP Legendary Cuts Buybacks

Randomly inserted into packs, this is a one card set featuring signed cards from the 1992 Upper Deck Ted Williams Heroes insert set. These Buyback cards have a stated print run of nine copies based upon information provided by the manufacturer and there is no pricing due to market scarcity. It's believed these Buyback cards have a rectangular foil sticker with a tracking code running verically along the back of the card on the right hand side. In addition, each Buyback comes with an additional certificate of Authenticity card.

NNO Ted Williams 92 Heroes AU/9

2002 SP Legendary Cuts Game Bat

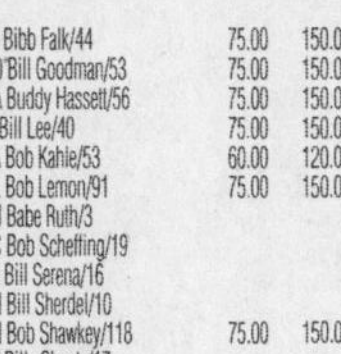

Inserted in packs at a stated rate of one in eight, these 36 cards feature game-used bat chips of some leading retired superstars. A few cards were issued in shorter supply and we have either notated that information with an SP next to the players name or an asterisk.

BADA Alvin Dark DP	4.00	10.00
BAND Andre Dawson DP	3.00	8.00
BBBO Bobby Bonds DP	3.00	8.00
BBRU Babe Ruth SP	100.00	175.00
BCRI Cal Ripken	12.50	30.00
BDBA Don Baylor DP	3.00	8.00
BDMU Dale Murphy DP	4.00	10.00
BDPA Dave Parker DP	3.00	8.00
BDSN Duke Snider	6.00	15.00
BEHO Elston Howard SP *	6.00	15.00
BEWY Early Wynn	4.00	10.00
BGFO George Foster DP	3.00	8.00
BGKE George Kell	4.00	10.00
BGPE Gaylord Perry	3.00	8.00
BHGR Hank Greenberg SP	20.00	50.00
BJAR Jackie Robinson SP *	20.00	50.00
BJMI Johnny Mize SP *	6.00	15.00
BLGR Lefty Grove	15.00	40.00
BMMA Mickey Mantle SP	100.00	175.00
BMMC Mark McGwire DP	30.00	60.00
BNFO Nellie Fox	6.00	15.00
BNRY Nolan Ryan	15.00	40.00
BPWE Pee Wee Reese DP	6.00	15.00
BRCO Rocky Colavito DP	6.00	15.00
BRKI Ralph Kiner	4.00	10.00
BRMA Roger Maris SP *	40.00	80.00
BRSA Ryne Sandberg DP	6.00	15.00
BRYO Robin Yount DP	6.00	15.00
BSGA Steve Garvey	3.00	8.00
BTGW Tony Gwynn SP *	8.00	20.00
BTKU Tony Kubek UER	6.00	15.00
Name spelled Tonk on the front		
BTLA Tony Lazzeri	4.00	10.00
BTMU Thurman Munson	10.00	25.00
BTSE Tom Seaver SP	8.00	20.00
BWST Willie Stargell	4.00	10.00
BYBE Yogi Berra SP	10.00	25.00

2002 SP Legendary Cuts Game Jersey

Inserted in packs at stated odds of one in 24, these 15 cards feature pieces of game-worn jerseys. A few players cards actually feature pant pieces and we have notated that next to their name in our checklist. In addition, a few cards were issued in shorter supply and we have notated that information in our checklist as well.

JAND Andre Dawson	3.00	8.00
JBBO Bobby Bonds Pants	3.00	8.00
JDBA Don Baylor	3.00	8.00
JDPA Dave Parker Pants DP	3.00	8.00
JFCR Frank Crosetti	4.00	10.00
JGFO George Foster	3.00	8.00
JJRO J.Robinson Pants SP *	20.00	50.00
JMMA M.Mantle Pants SP *	60.00	120.00
JNRY Nolan Ryan Pants	15.00	40.00
JPWE Pee Wee Reese	6.00	15.00
JRMA Roger Maris Pants	20.00	50.00
JRSA Ryne Sandberg SP *	10.00	25.00
JSGA Steve Garvey	3.00	8.00
JTSE Tom Seaver	4.00	10.00
JYBE Yogi Berra Pants DP	10.00	25.00

2002 SP Legendary Cuts Game Swatches

Inserted in packs at stated odds of one in 24, these 15 cards feature game-used memorabilia swatches of the featured players.

SCER Carl Erskine Pants	4.00	10.00
SCRJ Cal Ripken	10.00	25.00
SDBA Don Baylor	3.00	8.00
SDDR Don Drysdale Pants	10.00	25.00
SDPA Dave Parker	3.00	8.00
SFCR Frank Crosetti	4.00	10.00
SFJE Ferguson Jenkins Pants	3.00	8.00
SJMO Joe Morgan	3.00	8.00
SMMI Minnie Minoso	4.00	10.00
SMOT Mel Ott Pants	15.00	40.00
SRSA Ron Santo	6.00	15.00
SSMC Sam McDowell	3.00	8.00
STGW Tony Gwynn	6.00	15.00
STJO Tommy John	3.00	8.00
SWBO Wade Boggs	4.00	10.00

2003 SP Legendary Cuts

This 130-card set was released in December, 2003. This set was issued in four-card packs with an $10 SRP which came 12 packs to a box and 16 boxes to a case. Thirty cards in this set were short printed and each of those cards were issued to a stated print run of 1299 serial numbered sets and were inserted at a stated rate of one in 12.

COMP.SET w/o SP's (100)	15.00	40.00
COMMON CARD	.15	.40
COMMON SP	3.00	8.00
1 Luis Aparicio	.25	.60
2 Al Barlick	.15	.40
3 Al Lopez	.25	.60
4 Ernie Banks	.60	1.50
5 Alexander Cartwright	.25	.60
6 Lou Brock	.40	1.00
7 Babe Ruth/1299	6.00	15.00
8 Bill Dickey	.40	1.00
9 Bill Mazeroski	.40	1.00
10 Bob Feller	.25	.60
11 Billy Herman	.25	.60
12 Billy Williams	.25	.60
13 Bob Gibson/1299	4.00	10.00
14 Bob Lemon	.25	.60
15 Bobby Doerr	.25	.60
16 Branch Rickey	.25	.60
17 Gary Carter	.25	.60
18 Burleigh Grimes	.25	.60
19 Cap Anson	.40	1.00
20 Carl Hubbell	.40	1.00
21 Carlton Fisk	.40	1.00
22 Casey Stengel	.40	1.00
23 Charlie Gehringer	.25	.60
24 Chief Bender	.25	.60
25 Christy Mathewson/1299	4.00	10.00
26 Cy Young	.60	1.50
27 Dave Winfield	.25	.60
28 Dazzy Vance	.25	.60
29 Dizzy Dean/1299	4.00	10.00
30 Don Drysdale/1299	4.00	10.00
31 Duke Snider/1299	4.00	10.00
32 Earl Averill	.25	.60
33 Earle Combs	.25	.60
34 Edd Roush	.25	.60
35 Earl Weaver	.25	.60
36 Eddie Collins	.25	.60
37 Eddie Plank	.25	.60
38 Elmer Flick	.25	.60
39 Enos Slaughter	.25	.60
40 Ernie Lombardi	.25	.60
41 Ford Frick	.15	.40
42 Jim Hunter	.40	1.00
43 Frankie Frisch	.25	.60
44 Gabby Hartnett	.25	.60
45 George Kell	.25	.60
46 Early Wynn	.25	.60
47 Ferguson Jenkins	.25	.60
48 Al Kaline	.60	1.50
49 Harmon Killebrew	.60	1.50
50 Hal Newhouser	.25	.60
51 Hank Greenberg/1299	4.00	10.00
52 Harry Caray	.40	1.00
53 Tommy Lasorda	.25	.60
54 Honus Wagner/1299	4.00	10.00
55 Hoyt Wilhelm/1299	3.00	8.00
56 Jackie Robinson/1299	4.00	10.00
57 Jim Bottomley	.25	.60
58 Jim Bunning/1299	4.00	10.00
59 Jimmie Foxx/1299	4.00	10.00
60 Eddie Mathews	.60	1.50
61 Joe Cronin	.25	.60
62 Joe DiMaggio/1299	4.00	10.00
63 Joe McCarthy/1299	3.00	8.00
64 Joe Morgan/1299	3.00	8.00
65 Willie McCovey	.25	.60
66 Joe Tinker	.25	.60
67 Johnny Bench/1299	4.00	10.00
68 Johnny Evers/1299	3.00	8.00
69 Johnny Mize/1299	3.00	8.00
70 Josh Gibson/1299	4.00	10.00
71 Juan Marichal	.25	.60
72 Judy Johnson	.25	.60
73 Stan Musial	1.00	2.50
74 Kiki Cuyler	.25	.60
75 Larry Doby	.25	.60
76 Nap Lajoie	.40	1.00
77 Larry MacPhail	.15	.40
78 Phil Niekro	.25	.60
79 Lefty Gomez/1299	4.00	10.00
80 Lefty Grove/1299	4.00	10.00
81 Leo Durocher/1299	3.00	8.00
82 Leon Day	.25	.60
83 Gaylord Perry/1299	3.00	8.00
84 Lou Boudreau	.25	.60
85 Lou Gehrig	1.00	2.50
86 Luke Appling	.25	.60
87 Max Carey	.25	.60
88 Mel Allen/1299	3.00	8.00
89 Mel Ott/1299	4.00	10.00
90 Mickey Cochrane	.25	.60
91 Mickey Mantle	2.00	5.00
92 Brooks Robinson	.40	1.00
93 Monte Irvin	.25	.60
94 Nellie Fox	.40	1.00
95 Nolan Ryan/1299	5.00	12.00
96 Ozzie Smith/1299	4.00	10.00
97 Mike Schmidt	1.25	3.00
98 Pee Wee Reese/1299	4.00	10.00
99 Phil Rizzuto	.40	1.00
100 Ralph Kiner	.25	.60
101 Ray Dandridge	.25	.60
102 Richie Ashburn	.40	1.00
103 Rick Ferrell	.25	.60
104 Roberto Clemente	1.50	4.00
105 Robin Roberts	.25	.60
106 Robin Yount	.60	1.50
107 Rogers Hornsby	.60	1.50
108 Rollie Fingers	.25	.60
109 Roy Campanella	.60	1.50
110 Rube Marquard	.25	.60
111 Sam Crawford	.25	.60
112 Steve Carlton	.25	.60
113 Satchel Paige/1299	4.00	10.00
114 Sparky Anderson	.25	.60
115 Stan Coveleski	.25	.60
116 Red Schoendienst	.40	1.00
117 Ted Williams	1.25	3.00
118 Tom Seaver	.40	1.00
119 Tom Yawkey	.15	.40
120 Tony Lazzeri	.25	.60
121 Tony Perez	.25	.60
122 Tris Speaker	.60	1.50
123 Ty Cobb	1.00	2.50
124 Waite Hoyt/1299	3.00	8.00
125 Walter Alston	.25	.60
126 Walter Johnson	.60	1.50
127 Warren Spahn	.40	1.00
128 Whitey Ford	.40	1.00
129 Willie Stargell	.40	1.00
130 Yogi Berra	.60	1.50

2003 SP Legendary Cuts Blue

*BLUE POST-WAR: 2X TO 5X BASIC
*BLUE PRE-WAR: 1.5X TO 4X BASIC
*BLUE POST-WAR: .6X TO 1.5X BASIC SP
*BLUE PRE-WAR: .5X TO 1.2X BASIC SP
STATED PRINT RUN 275 SERIAL #'d SETS

2003 SP Legendary Cuts Green

STATED PRINT RUN 25 SERIAL #'d SETS
NO PRICING DUE TO SCARCITY

2003 SP Legendary Cuts Autographs

All the autograph cards in this insert set feature HOFers. After having a mix in 2002 of HOFers and retired players of varying note, Upper Deck decided that this product was better off with only HOFers involved in the cut signature insert set. Please note that several players: Bob Lemon, Charlie Gehringer, Carl Hubbell, Hal Newhouser, Joe DiMaggio and Ray Dandridge had two different varities in the main autograph set. in addition, for the first time, Upper Deck made some "color" variations in the autograph cut insert set. This set includes a "cut" signature of Alexander Cartwright who is believed by most historians to be the true founder of baseball.

OVERALL CUT SIG ODDS 1:196
PRINT RUNS B/WN 1-96 COPIES PER
NO PRICING ON QTY OF 25 OR LESS

AL Alexander Cartwright/1		
BD Bill Dickey/25		
BG Burleigh Grimes/34	175.00	300.00
BI Billy Herman/30	75.00	150.00
BL Bob Lemon/34	75.00	150.00
BL1 Bob Lemon/41	75.00	150.00
CG Charlie Gehringer/17		
CG1 Charlie Gehringer/20		
CH Carl Hubbell/47	150.00	250.00
CH1 Carl Hubbell/63	150.00	250.00
CS Casey Stengel/3		
CY Cy Young/2		
DD Dizzy Dean/8		
DO Don Drysdale/12		
DV Dazzy Vance/2		
EA Earl Averill/96	60.00	120.00
EC Earle Combs/45	150.00	250.00
EF Elmer Flick/6		
EL Ernie Lombardi/1		
ER Edd Roush/15		
ER1 Edd Roush/14		
ES Enos Slaughter/30	100.00	200.00
FF Ford Frick/10		
FR Frankie Frisch/4		
GH Gabby Hartnett/20		
HC Harry Caray/29	175.00	300.00
HC1 Harry Caray/35	175.00	300.00
HG Hank Greenberg/30	250.00	400.00
HN Hal Newhouser TC/22		
HN1 Hal Newhouser B2B/22		
HW Honus Wagner/1		
JB Jim Bottomley/2		
JC Joe Cronin/15		
JD Joe DiMaggio/50	300.00	500.00
JD1 Joe DiMaggio/28	350.00	550.00
JF Jimmie Foxx/3		
JJ Judy Johnson/23		
JM Johnny Mize/18		
JM1 Johnny Mize/12		
JO Joe McCarthy/22		
JR Jackie Robinson/4		
LA Leon Day/6		
LB Lou Boudreau/82	60.00	120.00
LB1 Lou Boudreau/49	75.00	150.00
LD Leo Durocher/20		
LE Lefty Grove/9		
LG Lefty Gomez/21		
LM Larry MacPhail/2		
LU Luke Appling/52	75.00	150.00
RM Rube Marquard/40	150.00	250.00
WA Walter Alston/30	100.00	200.00
WJ Walter Johnson/1		
WS Willie Stargell/4		
ZW Zack Wheat/19		

2003 SP Legendary Cuts Autographs Blue

OVERALL CUT SIG ODDS 1:196
PRINT RUNS B/WN 1-50 COPIES PER
NO PRICING ON QTY OF 25 OR LESS

EA Earl Averill/50	75.00	150.00
HC1 Harry Caray/35	175.00	300.00
HN1 Hal Newhouser B2B/29	75.00	150.00
JD1 Joe DiMaggio/40	300.00	500.00

2003 SP Legendary Cuts Autographs Green

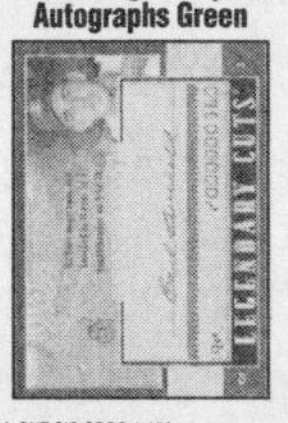

OVERALL CUT SIG ODDS 1:196
PRINT RUNS B/WN 1-5 COPIES PER
NO PRICING DUE TO SCARCITY

2003 SP Legendary Cuts Combo Cuts

OVERALL CUT SIG ODDS 1:196
STATED PRINT RUN 1 SERIAL #'d SET
NO PRICING DUE TO SCARCITY

2003 SP Legendary Cuts Etched in Time 400

STATED PRINT RUN 400 SERIAL #'d SETS
*ETCHED 300: .4X TO 1X BASIC 400
ETCHED 300 PRINT RUN 300 #'d SETS
*ETCHED 175: .5X TO 1.2X BASIC 400
ETCHED 175 PRINT RUN 175 #'d SETS
OVERALL ETCHED ODDS 1:12

AB Al Barlick	2.00	5.00
AC Alexander Cartwright	2.00	5.00
BR Babe Ruth	6.00	15.00
CG Charlie Gehringer	2.00	5.00
CH Carl Hubbell	3.00	8.00
CM Christy Mathewson	3.00	8.00
CS Casey Stengel	3.00	8.00
CY Cy Young	3.00	8.00
DD Dizzy Dean	3.00	8.00
DO Don Drysdale	3.00	8.00
EC Eddie Collins	2.00	5.00
EL Ernie Lombardi	2.00	5.00
GH Gabby Hartnett	2.00	5.00
HC Harry Caray	3.00	8.00
HG Hank Greenberg	3.00	8.00
HW Honus Wagner	3.00	8.00
JD Joe DiMaggio	4.00	10.00
JF Jimmie Foxx	3.00	8.00
JG Josh Gibson	3.00	8.00
JM Joe McCarthy	2.00	5.00
JO Johnny Mize	2.00	5.00
JR Jackie Robinson	3.00	8.00
LB Lou Boudreau	2.00	5.00
LD Leo Durocher	2.00	5.00
LE Lefty Grove	3.00	8.00
LG Lefty Gomez	3.00	8.00
LO Lou Gehrig	5.00	12.00
ME Mel Allen	2.00	5.00
MM Mickey Mantle	10.00	25.00
MO Mel Ott	3.00	8.00
PR Pee Wee Reese	3.00	8.00
RA Richie Ashburn	3.00	8.00
RC Roberto Clemente	6.00	15.00
RH Rogers Hornsby	3.00	8.00
RO Roy Campanella	3.00	8.00
SP Satchel Paige	3.00	8.00
TC Ty Cobb	4.00	10.00
TL Tony Lazzeri	2.00	5.00
TS Tris Speaker	3.00	8.00
TW Ted Williams	4.00	10.00

2003 SP Legendary Cuts Hall Marks Autographs

OVERALL HALL MARKS ODDS 1:196
BLACK INK PRINTS B/WN 10-99 COPIES PER
BLUE INK PRINTS B/WN 10-15 COPIES PER
RED INK PRINT RUN 5 #'d COPIES PER
NO PRICING ON QTY OF 15 OR LESS

BD1 Bobby Doerr Black/50	15.00	40.00
BD2 Bobby Doerr Blue/15		
BD3 Bobby Doerr Red/5		
BG1 Bob Gibson Black/30		
BG2 Bob Gibson Blue/15		
BG3 Bob Gibson Red/5		
BM1 Bill Mazeroski Black/50	30.00	60.00
BM2 Bill Mazeroski Blue/15		
BM3 Bill Mazeroski Red/5		
CF1 Carlton Fisk Black/50	30.00	60.00
CF2 Carlton Fisk Blue/15		
CF3 Carlton Fisk Red/5		
CY1 Carl Yastrzemski Black/45	50.00	100.00
CY2 Carl Yastrzemski Blue/15		
CY3 Carl Yastrzemski Red/5		
DS1 Duke Snider Black/50	30.00	60.00
DS2 Duke Snider Blue/15		
DS3 Duke Snider Red/5		
DW1 Dave Winfield Black/10		
DW2 Dave Winfield Blue/15		
DW3 Dave Winfield Red/5		
GC1 Gary Carter Black/50	30.00	60.00
GC2 Gary Carter Blue/15		
GC3 Gary Carter Red/5		
GK1 George Kell Black/50	20.00	50.00
GK2 George Kell Blue/15		
GK3 George Kell Red/5		
JB2 Johnny Bench Blue/10		
JB3 Johnny Bench Red/5		
JM1 Juan Marichal Black/50	15.00	40.00
JM2 Juan Marichal Blue/15		
JM3 Juan Marichal Red/5		
JO1 Joe Morgan Black/75	15.00	40.00
JO2 Joe Morgan Blue/15		
JO3 Joe Morgan Red/5		
LA1 Luis Aparicio Black/45	15.00	40.00
LA2 Luis Aparicio Blue/15		
LA3 Luis Aparicio Red/5		
MI1 Monte Irvin Black/85	20.00	50.00
MI2 Monte Irvin Blue/15		
MI3 Monte Irvin Red/5		
NR3 Nolan Ryan Red/5		
OS1 Ozzie Smith Black/45	50.00	100.00
OS2 Ozzie Smith Blue/15		
OS3 Ozzie Smith Red/5		
PR1 Phil Rizzuto Black/50	30.00	60.00
PR2 Phil Rizzuto Blue/15		
PR3 Phil Rizzuto Red/5		
RF1 Rollie Fingers Black/99	10.00	25.00
RF2 Rollie Fingers Blue/15		
RF3 Rollie Fingers Red/5		
RK1 Ralph Kiner Black/50	15.00	40.00
RK2 Ralph Kiner Blue/15		
RK3 Ralph Kiner Red/5		
RR1 Robin Roberts Black/65	30.00	60.00
RR2 Robin Roberts Blue/15		
RR3 Robin Roberts Red/5		
RY1 Robin Yount Black/45	50.00	100.00
RY2 Robin Yount Blue/15		
RY3 Robin Yount Red/5		
SA1 Sparky Anderson Black/30	15.00	40.00
SA2 Sparky Anderson Blue/15		
SA3 Sparky Anderson Red/5		
TP1 Tony Perez Black/50	15.00	40.00
TP2 Tony Perez Blue/15		
TP3 Tony Perez Red/5		
TS2 Tom Seaver Blue/10		
TS3 Tom Seaver Red/5		
WS1 Warren Spahn Black/35	40.00	80.00
WS2 Warren Spahn Blue/15		
WS3 Warren Spahn Red/5		
YB1 Yogi Berra Black/50	40.00	80.00
YB2 Yogi Berra Blue/15		
YB3 Yogi Berra Red/5		

2003 SP Legendary Cuts Hall Marks Autographs Blue

OVERALL HALL MARKS ODD 1:196
STATED PRINT RUN 25 SERIAL #'d SETS
NO PRICING DUE TO SCARCITY

2003 SP Legendary Cuts Hall Marks Autographs Green

OVERALL HALL MARKS ODDS 1:196
STATED PRINT RUN 10 SERIAL #'d SETS
NO PRICING DUE TO SCARCITY

2003 SP Legendary Cuts Historic Lumber

OVERALL GAME USED ODDS 1:12
PRINT RUNS B/WN 50-350 COPIES PER
BR Babe Ruth Away/150 75.00 150.00
BR1 Babe Ruth Home/150 75.00 150.00
CF Carlton Fisk R.Sox/50 10.00 25.00
CF1 Carlton Fisk W.Sox/50 10.00 25.00
CY C.Yastrzemski w/Bat/300 12.50 30.00
CY1 C.Yastrzemski w/Cap/350 12.50 30.00
CY2 C.Yaz w/Helmet/350 12.50 30.00
DW Dave Winfield Padres/350 4.00 10.00
DW1 Dave Winfield Yanks/350 4.00 10.00
FR Frank Robinson O's/300 6.00 15.00
FR1 Frank Robinson Reds/350 6.00 15.00
FR2 Frank Robinson Angels/350 6.00 15.00
GC Gary Carter Mets/300 4.00 10.00
GC1 G.Carter Helmet Expos/100 4.00 10.00
GC2 G.Carter Cap Expos/100 4.00 10.00
HK Harmon Killebrew/350 6.00 15.00
JB Johnny Bench w/Bat/350 6.00 15.00
JB1 Johnny Bench Swing/350 6.00 15.00
JM Joe Morgan Reds/350 4.00 10.00
JM1 Joe Morgan Astros/350 4.00 10.00
MM Mickey Mantle/300 40.00 80.00
NR Nolan Ryan Rgr/225 12.50 30.00
OS Ozzie Smith Cards/300 10.00 25.00
OS1 Ozzie Smith Padres/350 10.00 25.00
RS R.Schoen Look Right/165 6.00 15.00
RS1 R.Schoen Look Left/165 6.00 15.00
SC Steve Carlton/350 4.00 10.00
TP Tony Perez Swing/350 4.00 10.00
TP1 Tony Perez Portrait/350 4.00 10.00
TS Tom Seaver/100 6.00 15.00
TW Ted Williams w/3 Bats/150 40.00 80.00
TW1 Ted Williams Portrait/150 40.00 80.00
WS W.Stargell Arms Down/150 6.00 15.00
WS1 W.Stargell Arms Up/150 6.00 15.00
YB Yogi Berra Shoul/350 6.00 15.00
YB1 Yogi Berra w/Bat/350 6.00 15.00

2003 SP Legendary Cuts Historic Lumber Green

OVERALL GAME USED ODDS 1:12
PRINT RUNS BETWEEN 50-125 COPIES PER
BR Babe Ruth Away/75 100.00 200.00
BR1 Babe Ruth Home/75 100.00 200.00
CY C.Yastrzemski w/Bat/125 15.00 40.00
CY1 C.Yastrzemski w/Cap/125 15.00 40.00
CY2 C.Yaz w/Helmet/125 15.00 40.00
DW Dave Winfield Padres/125 4.00 10.00
DW1 Dave Winfield Yanks/125 4.00 10.00
FR Frank Robinson O's/125 6.00 15.00
FR1 Frank Robinson Reds/125 6.00 15.00
FR2 Frank Robinson Angels/125 6.00 15.00
GC Gary Carter Mets/125 4.00 10.00
GC1 G.Carter Helmet Expos/125 4.00 10.00
GC2 G.Carter Cap Expos/125 4.00 10.00
HK Harmon Killebrew/125 6.00 15.00
JB Johnny Bench w/Bat/125 6.00 15.00
JB1 Johnny Bench Swing/125 6.00 15.00
JM Joe Morgan Reds/125 4.00 10.00
JM1 Joe Morgan Astros/125 4.00 10.00
MM Mickey Mantle/75 50.00 100.00
NR Nolan Ryan Astros/50 30.00 60.00
OS Ozzie Smith Cards/125 12.50 30.00
OS1 Ozzie Smith Padres/125 12.50 30.00
RS R.Schoen Look Right/125 6.00 15.00
RS1 R.Schoen Look Left/125 6.00 15.00
SC Steve Carlton/125 4.00 10.00
TP Tony Perez Swing/125 4.00 10.00
TP1 Tony Perez Portrait/125 4.00 10.00
TS Tom Seaver/50 10.00 25.00
TW Ted Williams w/3 Bats/75 50.00 100.00
TW1 Ted Williams Portrait/75 50.00 100.00
WS W.Stargell Arms Down/125 6.00 15.00
WS1 W.Stargell Arms Up/125 6.00 15.00
YB Yogi Berra Shoul/125 6.00 15.00
YB1 Yogi Berra w/Bat/125 6.00 15.00

2003 SP Legendary Cuts Historic Swatches

OVERALL GAME USED ODDS 1:12
PRINT RUNS B/WN 48-350 COPIES PER
BG Bob Gibson CO Jsy/350 6.00 15.00
BM Bill Mazeroski Pants/50 10.00 25.00
BW Billy Williams Jsy/190 4.00 10.00
CF Carlton Fisk Pants/350 6.00 15.00
CM C.Mathewson Pants/300 75.00 150.00
CS Casey Stengel Jsy/275 6.00 15.00
CY Carl Yastrzemski Jsy/350 10.00 25.00
CY1 Carl Yastrzemski Pants/350 10.00 25.00
DS Duke Snider Jsy/350 6.00 15.00
DW1 D.Winfield Twins Jsy/300 4.00 10.00
FR F.Robinson O's Jsy/350 6.00 15.00
FR1 F.Robinson Angels Jsy/350 6.00 15.00
GC G.Carter Mets Jsy/350 4.00 10.00
GC1 G.Carter Expos Jsy/350 4.00 10.00
HW Honus Wagner Pants/275 75.00 150.00
JB Johnny Bench Jsy/150 6.00 15.00
JM Joe Morgan Jsy/350 4.00 10.00
JN Juan Marichal Pants/225 4.00 10.00
JN1 Juan Marichal Jsy/48 6.00 15.00
LA Luis Aparicio Jsy/230 4.00 10.00
LB Lou Boudreau Jsy/[illegible] 4.00 10.00
MM Mickey Mantle Pants/350 60.00 120.00
NR N.Ryan Rgr Pants/350 12.50 30.00
NR1 N.Ryan Astros Pants/350 12.50 30.00
OS Ozzie Smith Jsy/85 15.00 40.00
RF Rollie Fingers Jsy/105 4.00 10.00
RY R.Yount Portrait Jsy/350 6.00 15.00
RY1 R.Yount Swing Jsy/350 6.00 15.00
SA Sparky Anderson Jsy/350 4.00 10.00
SC Steve Carlton Jsy/350 4.00 10.00
SM Stan Musial Jsy/350 15.00 40.00
TC Ty Cobb Pants/350 50.00 100.00
TP Tony Perez Jsy/350 4.00 10.00
TS Tom Seaver Jsy/350 6.00 15.00
TS1 Tom Seaver Pants/350 6.00 15.00
TW Ted Williams Jsy/250 40.00 80.00
WA W.Alston Look Left Jsy/350 4.00 10.00
WA1 W.Alston Ahead Jsy/350 4.00 10.00
WI Willie Stargell Jsy/55 10.00 25.00
WS Warren Spahn CO Jsy/350 6.00 15.00
YB Yogi Berra Jsy/300 6.00 15.00

2003 SP Legendary Cuts Historic Swatches Blue

*BLUE: .5X TO 1.5X BASIC p/r 225-350
*BLUE: .5X TO 1.5X BASIC p/r 150-190
OVERALL GAME USED ODDS 1:12
STATED PRINT RUN 50 SERIAL #'d SETS

2003 SP Legendary Cuts Historic Swatches Green

*GREEN: .5X TO 1.2X BASIC SWATCH
OVERALL GAME USED ODDS 1:12
PRINT RUNS B/WN 160-250 COPIES PER
DW D.Winfield Yanks Jsy/160 4.00 10.00

2003 SP Legendary Cuts Historic Swatches Purple

*PURPLE p/r 150: .5X TO 1.2X BASIC
*PURPLE p/r 75-100: .6X TO 1.5X BASIC
OVERALL GAME USED ODDS 1:12
PRINT RUNS B/WN 75-150 COPIES PER

2003 SP Legendary Cuts Historical Impressions

STATED PRINT RUN 350 SERIAL #'d SETS
*GOLD 200: .6X TO 1.5X BASIC
GOLD 200 PRINT RUN 200 SERIAL #'d SETS
*GOLD 75: 1.25X TO 3X BASIC
GOLD 75 PRINT RUN 75 SERIAL #'d SETS
*SILVER: .75X TO 2X BASIC
SILVER PRINT RUN 250 SERIAL #'d SETS
OVERALL HIST.IMP.ODDS 1:12
AC Alexander Cartwright 3.00 8.00
BR Babe Ruth 8.00 20.00
CG Charlie Gehringer 3.00 8.00
CH Carl Hubbell 4.00 10.00
CM Christy Mathewson 4.00 10.00
CS Casey Stengel 4.00 10.00
CY Cy Young 4.00 10.00
DD Dizzy Dean 4.00 10.00
DO Don Drysdale 4.00 10.00
EC Eddie Collins 3.00 8.00
ES Enos Slaughter 3.00 8.00
GH Gabby Hartnett 3.00 8.00
HC Harry Caray 4.00 10.00
HG Hank Greenberg 4.00 10.00
HO Hoyt Wilhelm 3.00 8.00
HW Honus Wagner 4.00 10.00
JD Joe DiMaggio 5.00 12.00
JF Jimmie Foxx 4.00 10.00
JM Johnny Mize 3.00 8.00
JO Joe McCarthy 3.00 8.00
JR Jackie Robinson 4.00 10.00
LB Lou Boudreau 3.00 8.00
LD Leo Durocher 3.00 8.00
LE Lefty Grove 4.00 10.00
LG Lefty Gomez 4.00 10.00
LO Lou Gehrig 5.00 12.00
MA Mel Allen 3.00 8.00
MC Mickey Cochrane 3.00 8.00
MM Mickey Mantle 10.00 [illegible]
MO Mel Ott 4.00 10.00
PR Pee Wee Reese 4.00 10.00
RA Richie Ashburn 4.00 10.00
RC Roberto Clemente 8.00 20.00
RH Rogers Hornsby 4.00 10.00
RO Roy Campanella 4.00 10.00
SP Satchel Paige 4.00 10.00
TL Tony Lazzeri 3.00 8.00
TS Tris Speaker 4.00 10.00
TW Ted Williams 5.00 12.00
TY Ty Cobb 5.00 12.00

2003 SP Legendary Cuts Presidential Cut Signatures

Randomly inserted into packs, these cards featured autographs of deceased United States Presidents. It is believed that these cards were originally supposed to be included in the 2003 Upper Deck "American History" set which was never produced. We have put the stated print runs for these cards next to the President's name in our checklist. Please note that due to market scarcity, no pricing is provided for these cards. Many collectors were somewhat dismayed to discover that Upper Deck actually put their serial numbering on the cut itself.

2004 SP Legendary Cuts

This 126-card set was released in November, 2004. The set was issued in four card packs with an $10 SRP which came 12 packs to a box and 16 boxes to a case. The arrangement of this set was by first name of each player.

COMPLETE SET (126) 15.00 40.00
COMMON CARD (1-126) .20 .50
1 Al Kaline .50 1.25
2 Al Lopez .20 .50
3 Alan Trammell .20 .50
4 Andre Dawson .30 .75
5 Babe Ruth 1.25 3.00
6 Bert Campaneris .20 .50
7 Bill Mazeroski .30 .75
8 Bill Russell .20 .50
9 Billy Williams .30 .75
10 Bob Feller .20 .50
11 Bob Gibson .30 .75
12 Bob Lemon .20 .50
13 Bobby Doerr .20 .50
14 Brooks Robinson .30 .75
15 Cal Ripken 2.00 5.00
16 Carl Yastrzemski .50 1.25
17 Carlton Fisk .30 .75
18 Catfish Hunter .20 .50
19 Dale Murphy .30 .75
20 Darryl Strawberry .20 .50
21 Dave Concepcion .20 .50
22 Dave Winfield .20 .50
23 Dennis Eckersley .20 .50
24 Denny McLain .20 .50
25 Don Drysdale .30 .75
26 Don Larsen .20 .50
27 Don Mattingly 1.00 2.50
28 Don Sutton .20 .50
29 Duke Snider UER .30 .75
Tris Speaker's stats are on the back
30 Dusty Baker .20 .50
31 Dwight Gooden .20 .50
32 Earl Weaver .20 .50
33 Early Wynn .20 .50
34 Eddie Mathews .50 1.25
35 Eddie Murray .50 1.25
36 Enos Slaughter .20 .50
37 Ernie Banks .50 1.25
38 Fergie Jenkins .20 .50
39 Frank Robinson .30 .75
40 Fred Lynn .20 .50
41 Gary Carter .20 .50
42 Gaylord Perry .20 .50
43 George Brett 1.00 2.50
44 George Foster .20 .50
45 George Kell .20 .50
46 Greg Luzinski .20 .50
47 Hal Newhouser .20 .50
48 Hank Greenberg .50 1.25
49 Harmon Killebrew .50 1.25
50 Honus Wagner .50 1.25
51 Hoyt Wilhelm .20 .50
52 Jackie Robinson .50 1.25
53 Jim Bunning .20 .50
54 Jim Palmer .20 .50
55 Jimmie Foxx .50 1.25
56 Joe Carter .20 .50
57 Joe DiMaggio 1.25 3.00
58 Joe Morgan .20 .50
59 Joe Torre .30 .75
60 Johnny Bench .50 1.25
61 Johnny Podres .20 .50
62 Johnny Roseboro .20 .50
63 Johnny Sain .20 .50
64 Juan Marichal .20 .50
65 Keith Hernandez .20 .50
66 Kirby Puckett .50 1.25
67 Kirk Gibson .20 .50
68 Will Clark .30 .75
69 Jim Rice .30 .75
70 Larry Doby .20 .50
71 Lou Boudreau .20 .50
72 Lou Brock .30 .75
73 Lou Gehrig 1.00 2.50
74 Lou Piniella .20 .50
75 Luis Aparicio .20 .50
76 Mark Grace .30 .75
77 Mel Ott .50 1.25
78 Mickey Lolich .20 .50
79 Mickey Mantle 1.50 4.00
80 Mike Greenwell .20 .50
81 Mike Schmidt .75 2.00
82 Monte Irvin .20 .50
83 Nellie Fox .30 .75
84 Nolan Ryan 1.50 4.00
85 Orlando Cepeda .20 .50
86 Ozzie Smith .75 2.00
87 Paul Molitor .50 1.25
88 Pee Wee Reese .30 .75
89 Phil Niekro .20 .50
90 Phil Rizzuto .30 .75
91 Ralph Kiner .30 .75
92 Red Rolfe .20 .50
93 Red Schoendienst .20 .50
94 Reggie Smith .20 .50
95 Rich Gossage .20 .50
96 Richie Ashburn .30 .75
97 Rick Ferrell .20 .50
98 Elston Howard .20 .50
99 Roberto Clemente 1.25 3.00
100 Robin Roberts .20 .50
101 Robin Yount .50 1.25
102 Roger Maris .50 1.25
103 Rollie Fingers .20 .50
104 Ron Santo .30 .75
105 Roy Campanella .50 1.25
106 Ryne Sandberg 1.00 2.50
107 Sparky Anderson .20 .50
108 Sparky Lyle .20 .50
109 Stan Musial .75 2.00
110 Steve Carlton .20 .50
111 Steve Garvey .20 .50
112 Ted Williams 1.25 3.00
113 Thurman Munson .50 1.25
114 Tom Seaver .30 .75
115 Tommy Henrich .20 .50
116 Tommy Lasorda .20 .50
117 Tony Gwynn .50 1.25
118 Tony Perez .20 .50
119 Ty Cobb .75 2.00
120 Wade Boggs .30 .75
121 Warren Spahn .30 .75
122 Whitey Ford .30 .75
123 Willie McCovey .20 .50
124 Willie Randolph .20 .50
125 Willie Stargell .30 .75
126 Yogi Berra .50 1.25

2004 SP Legendary Cuts Significant Fact Memorabilia

COMMON CARD p/r 50-61 15.00 40.00
MINOR STARS p/r 50-61 15.00 40.00
SEMISTARS p/r 50-61 20.00 50.00
UNLISTED STARS p/r 50-61 30.00 60.00
STATED ODDS 1:96
B/WN 5-99 VARIATIONS PER CARD EXIST
VARIATION PRINT RUNS PROVIDED BY UD
DIFF.FACTS FEATURED ON EACH CARD
EACH VARIATION SERIAL #'d AS 1 OF 1
NO PRICING ON QTY OF 10 OR LESS
SEE BECKETT.COM FOR ALL PRINT RUNS
1 Al Kaline Bat/50 * 30.00 60.00
3 Alan Trammell Jsy/25 * 20.00 50.00
4 Andre Dawson Jsy/25 * 20.00 50.00
5 Babe Ruth Bat/10 *
7 Bill Mazeroski Bat/50 * 20.00 50.00
8 Bill Russell Pants/25 * 20.00 50.00
9 Billy Williams Jsy/99 * 10.00 25.00
11 Bob Gibson Jsy/99 * 15.00 40.00
13 Bobby Doerr Pants/99 * 10.00 25.00
14 Brooks Robinson Bat/99 * 15.00 40.00
15 Cal Ripken Jsy/99 * 125.00 200.00
16 Carl Yastrzemski Pants/99 * 30.00 60.00
17 Carlton Fisk Bat/99 * 15.00 40.00
18 Catfish Hunter Jsy/99 * 10.00 25.00
19 Dale Murphy Jsy/99 * 15.00 40.00
20 Darryl Strawberry Jsy/25 * 20.00 50.00
21 Dave Concepcion Jsy/99 * 10.00 25.00
22 Dave Winfield Jsy/99 * 10.00 25.00
23 Dennis Eckersley Jsy/25 * 20.00 50.00
25 Don Drysdale Jsy/99 * 20.00 50.00
26 Don Larsen Pants/50 * 20.00 50.00
27 Don Mattingly Jsy/99 * 75.00 150.00
28 Don Sutton Jsy/99 * 10.00 25.00
29 Duke Snider Jsy/99 * 15.00 40.00
30 Dusty Baker Jsy/50 * 15.00 40.00
31 Dwight Gooden Jsy/25 * 20.00 50.00
32 Earl Weaver Jsy/25 * 20.00 50.00
34 Eddie Mathews Jsy/99 * 20.00 50.00
35 Eddie Murray Jsy/99 * 75.00 150.00
36 Enos Slaughter Bat/10 *
37 Ernie Banks Jsy/99 * 20.00 50.00
38 Fergie Jenkins Pants/99 * 10.00 25.00
39 Frank Robinson Jsy/99 * 10.00 25.00
40 Fred Lynn Jsy/25 * 20.00 50.00
41 Gary Carter Jsy/99 * 10.00 25.00
42 Gaylord Perry Jsy/99 * 10.00 25.00
43 George Brett Jsy/99 * 60.00 120.00
49 Harmon Killebrew Jsy/99 * 20.00 50.00
50 Honus Wagner Pants/10 *
51 Hoyt Wilhelm Pants/99 * 15.00 40.00
52 Jackie Robinson Jsy/99 * 75.00 150.00
53 Jim Bunning Pants/25 * 20.00 50.00
54 Jim Palmer Jsy/25 * 20.00 50.00
55 Jimmie Foxx Bat/10 *
56 Joe Carter Jsy/99 * 50.00 100.00
57 Joe DiMaggio Pants/10 *
58 Joe Morgan Bat/50 * 15.00 40.00
59 Joe Torre Jsy/25 * 30.00 60.00
60 Johnny Bench Jsy/99 * 20.00 50.00
61 Johnny Podres Jsy/99 * 10.00 25.00
62 Johnny Roseboro Bat/50 * 15.00 40.00
63 Johnny Sain Jsy/25 * 20.00 50.00
64 Juan Marichal Jsy/99 * 10.00 25.00
66 Kirby Puckett Bat/50 * 50.00 100.00
69 Jim Rice Jsy/99 * 10.00 25.00
71 Lou Boudreau Bat/25 * 30.00 60.00
72 Lou Brock Bat/99 * 15.00 40.00
73 Lou Gehrig Pants/10 *
74 Lou Piniella Jsy/25 * 20.00 50.00
75 Luis Aparicio Jsy/25 * 20.00 50.00
76 Mark Grace Jsy/25 * 30.00 60.00
77 Mel Ott Pants/5 *
78 Mickey Lolich Jsy/25 * 20.00 50.00
79 Mickey Mantle Bat/25 * 200.00 350.00
81 Mike Schmidt Jsy/99 * 75.00 150.00
83 Nellie Fox Jsy/99 * 60.00 120.00
84 Nolan Ryan Pants/99 * 75.00 150.00
85 Orlando Cepeda Pants/99 * 10.00 25.00
86 Ozzie Smith Bat/99 * 40.00 80.00
87 Paul Molitor Pants/99 * 10.00 25.00
88 Pee Wee Reese Jsy/99 * 15.00 40.00
89 Phil Niekro Jsy/99 * 10.00 25.00
90 Phil Rizzuto Jsy/99 * 15.00 40.00
92 Red Rolfe Bat/25 * 20.00 50.00
94 Reggie Smith Jsy/10 *
95 Rich Gossage Jsy/50 * 15.00 40.00
98 Elston Howard Jsy/99 * 15.00 40.00
99 Roberto Clemente Jsy/10 *
101 Robin Yount Jsy/99 * 20.00 50.00
102 Roger Maris Pants/50 * 75.00 150.00
103 Rollie Fingers Jsy/99 * 10.00 25.00
104 Ron Santo Bat/10 *
105 Roy Campanella Pants/50 * 20.00 50.00
106 Ryne Sandberg Jsy/50 * 40.00 80.00
107 Sparky Anderson Jsy/50 * 15.00 40.00
108 Sparky Lyle Jsy/50 * 15.00 40.00
109 Stan Musial Pants/99 * 50.00 100.00
110 Steve Carlton Bat/99 * 10.00 25.00
111 Steve Garvey Jsy/99 * 10.00 25.00
112 Ted Williams Pants/10 *
113 Thurman Munson Jsy/99 * 20.00 50.00
114 Tom Seaver Jsy/61 * 20.00 50.00
115 Tommy Henrich Jsy/10 *
116 Tommy Lasorda Jsy/25 * 20.00 50.00
117 Tony Gwynn Jsy/99 * 30.00 60.00
118 Tony Perez Jsy/99 * 10.00 25.00
120 Wade Boggs Jsy/99 * 15.00 40.00
121 Warren Spahn Jsy/99 * 20.00 50.00
123 Willie McCovey Pants/99 * 15.00 40.00
124 Willie Randolph Jsy/25 * 20.00 50.00
125 Willie Stargell Jsy/99 * 15.00 40.00
126 Yogi Berra Jsy/99 * 20.00 50.00

2004 SP Legendary Cuts All-Time Autos

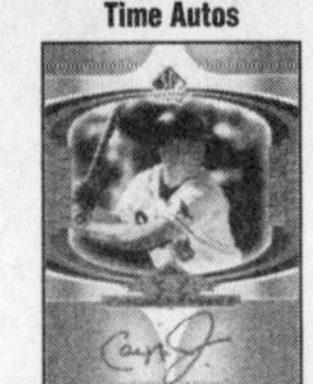

OVERALL AU ODDS 1:64
STATED PRINT RUN 50 SERIAL #'d SETS
EXCHANGE DEADLINE 11/19/07
AK Al Kaline 20.00 50.00
BD Bobby Doerr 10.00 25.00
BM Bill Mazeroski 15.00 40.00
CF Carlton Fisk 15.00 40.00
CR Cal Ripken 75.00 150.00
DE Dennis Eckersley 15.00 40.00
DM Dale Murphy 15.00 40.00
DN Don Newcombe 10.00 25.00
DS Don Sutton 10.00 25.00
FJ Fergie Jenkins 10.00 25.00
FL Fred Lynn 6.00 15.00
GC Gary Carter 10.00 25.00
GK George Kell 10.00 25.00
GP Gaylord Perry 10.00 25.00
HK Harmon Killebrew 30.00 60.00
JC Joe Carter 10.00 25.00
JP Johnny Podres 6.00 15.00
LA Luis Aparicio 10.00 25.00
MA Don Mattingly 40.00 80.00
MC Denny McLain 10.00 25.00
MI Monte Irvin 15.00 40.00
MW Maury Wills 10.00 25.00
NR Nolan Ryan 60.00 120.00
OC Orlando Cepeda 10.00 25.00
PN Phil Niekro 10.00 25.00
RF Rollie Fingers 10.00 25.00
RR Robin Roberts 20.00 50.00
RS Red Schoendienst 10.00 25.00
RY Robin Yount 30.00 60.00
SA Ryne Sandberg 40.00 80.00
SM Stan Musial 40.00 80.00
TG Tony Gwynn 20.00 50.00
TP Tony Perez 15.00 40.00
TS Tom Seaver 20.00 50.00
WB Wade Boggs 15.00 40.00
WC Will Clark 15.00 40.00
WF Whitey Ford 15.00 40.00
WM Willie McCovey 15.00 40.00
YB Yogi Berra 20.00 50.00

2004 SP Legendary Cuts Autographs

Some of the key players in this set include Adrian "Cap" Anson, "Gettysburg" Eddie Plank, Frank Chance, "Bullet" Joe Bush, Christy Mathewson and the original "Sad" Sam Jones. Many of these autographs, which were inserted at a stated rate of one in 128 are very tough to obtain.

OVERALL CUT AU ODDS 1:128
PRINT RUNS B/WN 1-199 COPIES PER
NO PRICING ON QTY OF 19 OR LESS
EXCHANGE DEADLINE 11/19/07
AN Cap Anson/1
AR Allie Reynolds/25 200.00 350.00
AS Al Simmons/10
AV Arky Vaughan/4
BD Bill Dickey/82 100.00 200.00
BG A. Bartlett Giamatti/2
BH Billy Herman/134 60.00 120.00
BJ Bob Johnson/32 150.00 250.00
BL Bob Lemon/199 40.00 80.00
BM Billy Martin/7
BO Jim Bottomley/2
BR Babe Ruth/13
BU Burleigh Grimes/83 100.00 200.00
BW Bobby Wallace/2
CA Max Carey/72 75.00 150.00
CB Chief Bender/6
CC Charlie Comiskey/2
CG Charlie Gehringer/171 60.00 120.00
CH Carl Hubbell/199 100.00 200.00
CJ Jack Coombs/1
CK Chuck Klein/5
CL Fred Clarke/2
CM Carl Mays/2
CO Eddie Collins/6
CR Joe Cronin/84 100.00 200.00
CS Casey Stengel/38 300.00 500.00
CY Cy Young/5
DD Dizzy Dean/33 500.00 800.00
DO Larry Doby/14
DR Don Drysdale/66 175.00 300.00
DU Joe Dugan/9
DV Dazzy Vance/5
EC Earle Combs/27 175.00 300.00
ED Ed Walsh/5
EH Elston Howard/2
EL Ernie Lombardi/39 175.00 300.00
EM Eddie Mathews/27 175.00 300.00
EPO Eddie Plank/1 UER
Signature was of the Eddie Plank who played in the 1970's
ER Edd Roush/129 40.00 80.00
ES Enos Slaughter/147 60.00 120.00
EW Early Wynn/54 150.00 250.00
FB Frank Baker/3
FC Frank Chance/1
FF Frankie Frisch/57 200.00 350.00
GA Grover Alexander/2
GE Lou Gehrig/7
GH Gaby Hartnett/19
GI Gil Hodges/9
GP George Pipgras/46 100.00 200.00
GR Lefty Grove/75 150.00 300.00
GS George Sisler/32 300.00 600.00
HG Hank Greenberg/37 250.00 400.00
HH Harry Heilmann/3
HK Harvey Kuenn/49 100.00 200.00
HM Heinie Manush/16
HN Hal Newhouser/51 75.00 150.00
HP Herb Pennock/2
HW Honus Wagner/17
JA Jack Buck/2
JB Joe Bush/1
JD Joe DiMaggio/111 350.00 500.00
JF Jimmie Foxx/15
JH Jim Hunter/25 150.00 250.00
JM Joe Medwick/32 250.00 400.00
JR Jackie Robinson/19
JS Joe Sewell/199 60.00 120.00
KC Kiki Cuyler/4
KN Kid Nichols/4
LA Tony Lazzeri/5
LB Lou Boudreau/199 50.00 100.00
LD Leo Durocher/75 150.00 300.00
LG Lefty Gomez/98 100.00 200.00
LU Luke Appling/108 60.00 120.00
MA Roger Maris/6
MB Mordecai Brown/2
MC Mickey Cochrane/2
MI Johnny Mize/118 75.00 150.00
MK Connie Mack/9
MM Mickey Mantle/19
MO Mel Ott/17
MW Christy Mathewson/1
NF Nellie Fox/14
NL Nap LaJoie/2
PB James Cool Papa Bell/47 350.00 500.00
PR Pee Wee Reese/35 175.00 300.00
PT Pie Traynor/6
PW Paul Waner/9
RA Richie Ashburn/31 175.00 300.00
RC Roy Campanella/3
RD Ray Dandridge/199 30.00 60.00
RF Rick Ferrell/43 60.00 120.00
RH Rogers Hornsby/5
RM Rabbit Maranville/5
RO Roberto Clemente/9
RR Red Ruffing/30 175.00 300.00
RU Rube Marquard/59 150.00 250.00
SC Sam Crawford/9
SJ Sam Jones/4
SM Stuffy McInnis/2
SP Satchel Paige/28 900.00 1300.00
SR Sam Rice/28 175.00 300.00
ST Stan Coveleski/102 75.00 150.00
SW Joe Wood/79 150.00 300.00
TC Ty Cobb/18
TL Ted Lyons/199 60.00 120.00
TM Thurman Munson/2
TS Tris Speaker/4
TW Ted Williams/[illegible] 1000.00 1200.00
WA Walter Alston/74 100.00 200.00
WF Wes Ferrell/36 150.00 250.00
WH Waite Hoyt/106 150.00 250.00
WI Hack Wilson/5
WJ Walter Johnson/14
WM Hoyt Wilhelm/115 60.00 120.00
WS Willie Stargell/39 100.00 200.00

2004 SP Legendary Cuts Game Graphs Memorabilia 25

OVERALL AU ODDS 1:64
STATED PRINT RUN 25 SERIAL #'d SETS
GRAPH 10 PRINT RUN 10 SERIAL #'d SETS
NO GRAPH 10 PRICING DUE TO SCARCITY
EXCHANGE DEADLINE 11/19/07
AK Al Kaline Bat 40.00 80.00
BG Bob Gibson Jsy 20.00 50.00
BM Bill Mazeroski Bat 20.00 50.00
BR Brooks Robinson Bat 20.00 50.00
CF Carlton Fisk Jsy 20.00 50.00
CR Cal Ripken Jsy 125.00 200.00
CY Carl Yastrzemski Jsy 50.00 100.00
DM Dale Murphy Jsy 20.00 50.00
DS Don Sutton Jsy 12.50 30.00
DW Dave Winfield Pants 20.00 50.00
EB Ernie Banks Jsy 40.00 80.00
EM Eddie Murray Jsy 50.00 100.00
FR Frank Robinson Jsy 20.00 50.00
GB George Brett Jsy 60.00 120.00
GC Gary Carter Jsy 15.00 40.00
HK Harmon Killebrew Jsy 50.00 100.00
JB Johnny Bench Jsy 20.00 50.00
JC Joe Carter Jsy 15.00 40.00
JM Juan Marichal Jsy 20.00 50.00
KP Kirby Puckett Bat 50.00 100.00
LA Luis Aparicio Jsy 15.00 40.00
LB Lou Brock Jsy 20.00 50.00
MA Don Mattingly Jsy 60.00 120.00
MO Joe Morgan Bat 15.00 40.00
MS Mike Schmidt Jsy 50.00 100.00
NR Nolan Ryan Jsy 75.00 150.00
OS Ozzie Smith Jsy 40.00 80.00
PM Paul Molitor Jsy 15.00 40.00
PN Phil Niekro Jsy 15.00 40.00
PR Phil Rizzuto Jsy 20.00 50.00
RF Rollie Fingers Jsy 12.50 30.00
RS Ryne Sandberg Jsy 60.00 120.00
RY Robin Yount Jsy 40.00 80.00
SM Stan Musial Jsy 50.00 100.00
SN Duke Snider Jsy 20.00 50.00
TG Tony Gwynn Jsy 40.00 80.00
WB Wade Boggs Jsy 40.00 80.00
WM Willie McCovey Pants 20.00 50.00
YB Yogi Berra Jsy 40.00 80.00

2004 SP Legendary Cuts Historic Patches

OVERALL GU ODDS 1:4
STATED PRINT RUN 25 SERIAL #'d SETS
BG Bob Gibson 15.00 40.00
CR Cal Ripken 60.00 120.00
CY Carl Yastrzemski 20.00 50.00
DD Don Drysdale 15.00 40.00
DS Duke Snider 15.00 40.00
EB Ernie Banks 30.00 60.00
EM Eddie Mathews 40.00 80.00
GB George Brett 20.00 50.00
JB Johnny Bench 15.00 40.00
MS Mike Schmidt 20.00 50.00
NR Nolan Ryan 40.00 80.00
RY Robin Yount 15.00 40.00
SM Stan Musial 40.00 80.00
TG Tony Gwynn 15.00 40.00
TS Tom Seaver 15.00 40.00

2004 SP Legendary Cuts Historic Quads Memorabilia

OVERALL GU ODDS 1:4
STATED PRINT RUN 10 SERIAL #'d SETS
NO PRICING DUE TO SCARCITY
B ='s BAT, J ='s JSY, P ='s PANTS

2004 SP Legendary Cuts Historic Quads Patch

OVERALL GU ODDS 1:4
STATED PRINT RUN 5 SERIAL #'d SETS
NO PRICING DUE TO SCARCITY

2004 SP Legendary Cuts Historic Swatches

OVERALL GU ODDS 1:4
SP INFO PROVIDED BY UPPER DECK

Card	Low	High
AN Sparky Anderson Jsy	3.00	8.00
BR Brooks Robinson Bat	4.00	10.00
CF Carlton Fisk Pants	4.00	10.00
CH Catfish Hunter Pants	4.00	10.00
CR Cal Ripken Jsy	10.00	25.00
DC Dave Concepcion Jsy	3.00	8.00
DD Don Drysdale Pants	4.00	10.00
DL Don Larsen Pants SP	6.00	15.00
DM Don Mattingly Jsy	6.00	15.00
DS Don Sutton Jsy	3.00	8.00
DW Dave Winfield Pants	3.00	8.00
EM Eddie Murray Jsy SP	6.00	15.00
FJ Fergie Jenkins Pants	3.00	8.00
GB George Brett Jsy	6.00	15.00
GC Gary Carter Pants	3.00	8.00
GF George Foster Bat	3.00	8.00
GP Gaylord Perry Jsy	3.00	8.00
HK Harmon Killebrew Jsy	4.00	10.00
HW Hoyt Wilhelm Pants	3.00	8.00
JB Johnny Bench Pants SP	6.00	15.00
JC Joe Carter Jsy	3.00	8.00
JM Joe Morgan Bat	3.00	8.00
JP Johnny Podres Jsy	3.00	8.00
JR Jim Rice Jsy	3.00	8.00
KP Kirby Puckett Bat	4.00	10.00
LB Lou Brock Jsy	4.00	10.00
MA Eddie Mathews Jsy	4.00	10.00
ML Mickey Lolich Jsy	3.00	8.00
MU Dale Murphy Jsy	4.00	10.00
NR Nolan Ryan Jsy	10.00	25.00
OS Ozzie Smith Jsy	6.00	15.00
PM Paul Molitor Jsy	3.00	8.00
PN Phil Niekro Jsy	3.00	8.00
RF Rollie Fingers Pants	3.00	8.00
RY Robin Yount Pants	4.00	10.00
SG Steve Garvey Jsy	3.00	8.00
SL Sparky Lyle Jsy	3.00	8.00
SM Stan Musial Pants	8.00	20.00
TM Thurman Munson Jsy	4.00	10.00
TS Tom Seaver Pants	4.00	10.00

2004 SP Legendary Cuts Historic Swatches 25

*SWATCH 25: .75X TO 2X BASIC
*SWATCH 25: .75X TO 2X BASIC SP
OVERALL GU ODDS 1:4
STATED PRINT RUN 25 SERIAL #'d SETS

Card	Low	High
CR Cal Ripken Jsy	40.00	80.00
PR Phil Rizzuto Jsy	8.00	20.00

2004 SP Legendary Cuts Historical Cuts

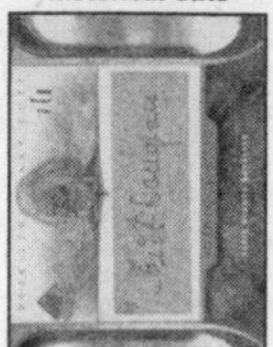

OVERALL CUT AU ODDS 1:128
PRINT RUNS B/WN
NO PRICING DUE TO SCARCITY

2004 SP Legendary Cuts Legendary Duels Memorabilia

OVERALL GU ODDS 1:4
STATED PRINT RUN 25 SERIAL #'d SETS

Card	Low	High
BG George Brett Jsy	30.00	60.00
Rich Gossage Jsy		
DW Joe DiMaggio Jsy	100.00	200.00
Ted Williams Jsy		
EG Dennis Eckersley Jsy	15.00	40.00
Kirk Gibson Bat		
FM Carlton Fisk Pants	15.00	40.00
Joe Morgan Bat		
GL Bob Gibson Jsy	15.00	40.00
Mickey Lolich Jsy		
MW Mickey Mantle Pants	150.00	250.00
Ted Williams Jsy		
PL Johnny Podres Jsy	15.00	40.00
Don Larsen Jsy		
RM John Roseboro Bat	10.00	25.00
Juan Marichal Pants		
RR Pee Wee Reese Jsy	15.00	40.00
Phil Rizzuto Pants		
SM Duke Snider Jsy	100.00	200.00
Mickey Mantle Pants		
SS Ozzie Smith Jsy	40.00	80.00
Ryne Sandberg Jsy		
WB Honus Wagner Pants	75.00	150.00
Ernie Banks Jsy		

2004 SP Legendary Cuts Legendary Duels Patch

OVERALL GU ODDS 1:4
STATED PRINT RUN 15 SERIAL #'d SETS
NO PRICING DUE TO SCARCITY

2004 SP Legendary Cuts Legendary Duos Memorabilia

OVERALL GU ODDS 1:4
STATED PRINT RUN 25 SERIAL #'d SETS

Card	Low	High
CM Dave Concepcion Jsy	10.00	25.00
Joe Morgan Bat		
DM Joe DiMaggio Jsy	175.00	300.00
Mickey Mantle Pants		
LB Don Larsen Jsy	40.00	80.00
Yogi Berra Jsy		
MB Mickey Mantle Pants	150.00	250.00
Yogi Berra Jsy		
MM Mickey Mantle Pants	175.00	300.00
Roger Maris Jsy		
MY Paul Molitor Jsy	20.00	50.00
Robin Yount Jsy		
PJ Pee Wee Reese Jsy	40.00	80.00
Jackie Robinson Jsy		
RR Brooks Robinson Bat	40.00	80.00
Cal Ripken Jsy		
RS Nolan Ryan Jsy	75.00	150.00
Tom Seaver Jsy		
SC Duke Snider Jsy	30.00	60.00
Roy Campanella Pants		
SS Johnny Sain Jsy	20.00	50.00
Warren Spahn Jsy		
WB Billy Williams Jsy	20.00	50.00
Ernie Banks Jsy		

2004 SP Legendary Cuts Legendary Duos Patch

OVERALL GU ODDS 1:4
STATED PRINT RUN 15 SERIAL #'d SETS
NO PRICING DUE TO SCARCITY

2004 SP Legendary Cuts Legendary Sigs

OVERALL AU ODDS 1:64
STATED PRINT RUN 50 SERIAL #'d SETS

Card	Low	High
AK Al Kaline	20.00	50.00
BD Bobby Doerr	10.00	25.00
BF Bob Feller	10.00	25.00
BG Bob Gibson	15.00	40.00
BR Brooks Robinson	15.00	40.00
CR Cal Ripken	75.00	150.00
CY Carl Yastrzemski	30.00	60.00
DE Dennis Eckersley	15.00	40.00
DM Dale Murphy	15.00	40.00
DN Don Newcombe	10.00	25.00
DS Don Sutton	10.00	25.00
EB Ernie Banks	30.00	60.00
EM Eddie Murray	50.00	100.00
FL Fred Lynn	6.00	15.00
GC Gary Carter	10.00	25.00
GK George Kell	20.00	50.00
GP Gaylord Perry	10.00	25.00
HK Harmon Killebrew UER	30.00	60.00
Killebrew misspelled Killewbrew on front)		
JB Johnny Bench	30.00	60.00
JC Joe Carter	10.00	25.00
JM Juan Marichal	10.00	25.00
JP Johnny Podres	6.00	15.00
LA Luis Aparicio	10.00	25.00
MA Don Mattingly	40.00	80.00
MC Denny McLain	10.00	25.00
MI Monte Irvin	15.00	40.00
MS Mike Schmidt	40.00	80.00
MW Maury Wills	10.00	25.00
OS Ozzie Smith	30.00	60.00
PA Jim Palmer	10.00	25.00
PR Phil Rizzuto	15.00	40.00
RF Rollie Fingers	10.00	25.00
RK Ralph Kiner	15.00	40.00
RR Robin Roberts	20.00	50.00
RS Red Schoendienst	10.00	25.00
SA Ryne Sandberg	40.00	80.00
SN Duke Snider	15.00	40.00
TG Tony Gwynn	20.00	50.00
WB Wade Boggs	15.00	40.00
WC Will Clark	15.00	40.00
WM Willie McCovey	15.00	40.00

2004 SP Legendary Cuts Legendary Swatches

SP INFO PROVIDED BY UPPER DECK
SWATCH 15 PRINT RUN 15 #'d SETS
NO SWATCH 15 PRICING DUE TO SCARCITY
OVERALL GU ODDS 1:4

Card	Low	High
AK Al Kaline Bat	4.00	10.00
BD Bobby Doerr Pants	3.00	8.00
BG Bob Gibson Jsy	4.00	10.00
BW Billy Williams Jsy	3.00	8.00
CF Carlton Fisk Pants	4.00	10.00
CH Catfish Hunter Jsy	4.00	10.00
CR Cal Ripken Jsy	10.00	25.00
CY Carl Yastrzemski Jsy	6.00	15.00
DD Don Drysdale Pants	4.00	10.00
DM Don Mattingly Jsy	6.00	15.00
DS Duke Snider Pants	4.00	10.00
DW Dave Winfield Jsy	3.00	8.00
EB Ernie Banks Jsy SP	6.00	15.00
EH Elston Howard Jsy	4.00	10.00
EM Eddie Mathews Jsy	4.00	10.00
FR Frank Robinson Pants	3.00	8.00
GB George Brett Jsy	6.00	15.00
HK Harmon Killebrew Jsy	4.00	10.00
JB Johnny Bench Jsy	4.00	10.00
JR Jim Rice Jsy	3.00	8.00
MA Juan Marichal Pants	3.00	8.00
MS Mike Schmidt Jsy	6.00	15.00
NF Nellie Fox Jsy	4.00	10.00
NR Nolan Ryan Jsy	10.00	25.00
OC Orlando Cepeda Pants	3.00	8.00
PO Johnny Podres Jsy	3.00	8.00
PR Pee Wee Reese Jsy	4.00	10.00
RC Roy Campanella Pants	4.00	10.00
RI Phil Rizzuto Pants	4.00	10.00
RY Robin Yount Pants	4.00	10.00
SC Steve Carlton Bat	3.00	8.00
SM Stan Musial Jsy	8.00	20.00
ST Willie Stargell Jsy	4.00	10.00
TG Tony Gwynn Pants	4.00	10.00
TM Thurman Munson Jsy	4.00	10.00
TP Tony Perez Jsy	3.00	8.00
TS Tom Seaver Jsy	4.00	10.00
WB Wade Boggs Pants	4.00	10.00
WM Willie McCovey Pants	4.00	10.00
WS Warren Spahn Jsy	4.00	10.00
YB Yogi Berra Jsy	4.00	10.00

2004 SP Legendary Cuts Marked for the Hall Autos

OVERALL AU ODDS 1:64
STATED PRINT RUN 50 SERIAL #'d SETS
EXCHANGE DEADLINE 11/19/07

Card	Low	High
AK Al Kaline	20.00	50.00
BD Bobby Doerr	10.00	25.00
BF Bob Feller	15.00	40.00
BG Bob Gibson	15.00	40.00
BM Bill Mazeroski	15.00	40.00
BR Brooks Robinson	15.00	40.00
CF Carlton Fisk	15.00	40.00
CY Carl Yastrzemski	30.00	60.00
DS Duke Snider	15.00	40.00
DW Dave Winfield	15.00	40.00
EB Ernie Banks	30.00	60.00
EM Eddie Murray	50.00	100.00
FR Frank Robinson	15.00	40.00
GB George Brett	40.00	80.00
GC Gary Carter	10.00	25.00
GP Gaylord Perry	10.00	25.00
HK Harmon Killebrew	30.00	60.00
JB Johnny Bench	30.00	60.00
JM Joe Morgan	10.00	25.00
JP Jim Palmer	10.00	25.00
KP Kirby Puckett	50.00	100.00
LA Luis Aparicio	10.00	25.00
LB Lou Brock	15.00	40.00
MA Juan Marichal	10.00	25.00
MS Mike Schmidt	40.00	80.00
NR Nolan Ryan	60.00	120.00
OC Orlando Cepeda	10.00	25.00
OS Ozzie Smith	30.00	60.00
PM Paul Molitor	10.00	25.00
PN Phil Niekro	10.00	25.00
PR Phil Rizzuto	15.00	40.00
RK Ralph Kiner	15.00	40.00
RR Robin Roberts	20.00	50.00
RY Robin Yount	30.00	60.00
SM Stan Musial	40.00	80.00
TP Tony Perez	15.00	40.00
TS Tom Seaver	20.00	50.00
WF Whitey Ford	15.00	40.00
WM Willie McCovey	15.00	40.00
YB Yogi Berra	20.00	50.00

2004 SP Legendary Cuts Marks of Greatness Autos

OVERALL AU ODDS 1:64
STATED PRINT RUN 50 SERIAL #'d SETS
EXCHANGE DEADLINE 11/19/07

Card	Low	High
AK Al Kaline	20.00	50.00
BG Bob Gibson	15.00	40.00
BR Brooks Robinson	15.00	40.00
CF Carlton Fisk	15.00	40.00
CR Cal Ripken	75.00	150.00
DM Dale Murphy	15.00	40.00
DN Don Newcombe	10.00	25.00
DS Duke Snider	15.00	40.00
DW Dave Winfield	15.00	40.00
EB Ernie Banks	30.00	60.00
FJ Fergie Jenkins	10.00	25.00
FL Fred Lynn	6.00	15.00
FR Frank Robinson	15.00	40.00
GB George Brett	40.00	80.00
HK Harmon Killebrew	30.00	60.00
JB Johnny Bench	30.00	60.00
JC Joe Carter	10.00	25.00
JM Joe Morgan	10.00	25.00
JP Jim Palmer	10.00	25.00
KP Kirby Puckett	75.00	150.00
LB Lou Brock	15.00	40.00
MA Don Mattingly	40.00	80.00
MC Denny McLain	10.00	25.00
MS Mike Schmidt	30.00	60.00
NR Nolan Ryan	60.00	120.00
OC Orlando Cepeda	10.00	25.00
OZ Ozzie Smith	30.00	60.00
PM Paul Molitor	10.00	25.00
PN Phil Niekro	10.00	25.00
RF Rollie Fingers	10.00	25.00
RS Ryne Sandberg	40.00	80.00
RY Robin Yount	30.00	60.00
SM Stan Musial	40.00	80.00
TG Tony Gwynn	20.00	50.00
TP Tony Perez	15.00	40.00
TS Tom Seaver	20.00	50.00
WB Wade Boggs	15.00	40.00
WC Will Clark	15.00	40.00
WF Whitey Ford	15.00	40.00
YB Yogi Berra	20.00	50.00

2004 SP Legendary Cuts Significant Swatches

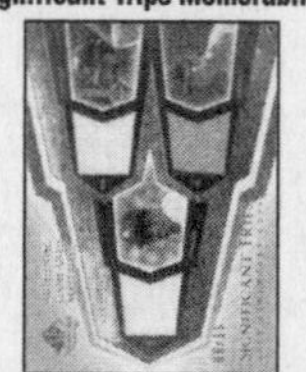

OVERALL GU ODDS 1:4
SP INFO PROVIDED BY UPPER DECK

Card	Low	High
BD Bobby Doerr Pants	3.00	8.00
BM Bill Mazeroski Bat	4.00	10.00
CF Carlton Fisk Pants	4.00	10.00
CH Catfish Hunter Pants	4.00	10.00
CR Cal Ripken Jsy	10.00	25.00
CY Carl Yastrzemski Jsy	6.00	15.00
DC Dave Concepcion Jsy	3.00	8.00
DD Don Drysdale Jsy	4.00	10.00
DM Dale Murphy Bat	4.00	10.00
DS Don Sutton Jsy	3.00	8.00
DW Dave Winfield Pants	3.00	8.00
EB Ernie Banks Pants SP	6.00	15.00
ED Eddie Mathews Jsy	4.00	10.00
EM Eddie Murray Jsy SP	6.00	15.00
FJ Fergie Jenkins Pants	3.00	8.00
FR Frank Robinson Jsy	3.00	8.00
GC Gary Carter Jsy	3.00	8.00
GF George Foster Bat	3.00	8.00
GP Gaylord Perry Jsy	3.00	8.00
HW Hoyt Wilhelm Pants	3.00	8.00
JC Joe Carter Jsy	3.00	8.00
JP Johnny Podres Jsy	3.00	8.00
LB Lou Brock Jsy SP	6.00	15.00
MA Don Mattingly Jsy	6.00	15.00
MS Mike Schmidt Pants	6.00	15.00
NR Nolan Ryan Jsy	10.00	25.00
OC Orlando Cepeda Pants	3.00	8.00
PM Paul Molitor Bat	3.00	8.00
PN Phil Niekro Jsy SP	4.00	10.00
RF Rollie Fingers Pants	3.00	8.00
RM Roger Maris Pants	12.50	30.00
RY Robin Yount Bat	4.00	10.00
SA Sparky Anderson Jsy	3.00	8.00
SG Steve Garvey Jsy	3.00	8.00
SL Sparky Lyle Jsy	3.00	8.00
SN Duke Snider Pants	4.00	10.00
ST Willie Stargell Jsy SP	6.00	15.00
TM Thurman Munson Pants	4.00	10.00
TP Tony Perez Jsy	3.00	8.00
TS Tom Seaver Pants	4.00	10.00
WM Willie McCovey Pants	4.00	10.00
WS Warren Spahn Jsy	4.00	10.00

2004 SP Legendary Cuts Significant Swatches 25

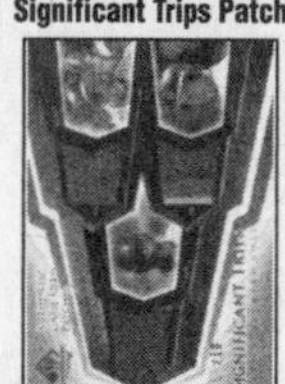

*SWATCH 25: .75X TO 2X BASIC
*SWATCH 25: .75X TO 2X BASIC SP
OVERALL GU ODDS 1:4
STATED PRINT RUN 25 SERIAL #'d SETS

Card	Low	High
CR Cal Ripken Jsy	40.00	80.00

2004 SP Legendary Cuts Significant Trips Memorabilia

OVERALL GU ODDS 1:4
STATED PRINT RUN 15 SERIAL #'d SETS
NO PRICING DUE TO SCARCITY
B ='s BAT, J ='s JSY, P ='s PANTS

2004 SP Legendary Cuts Significant Trips Patch

OVERALL GU ODDS 1:4
STATED PRINT RUN 10 SERIAL #'d SETS
NO PRICING DUE TO SCARCITY

2004 SP Legendary Cuts Ultimate Autos

OVERALL AU ODDS 1:64
STATED PRINT RUN 25 SERIAL #'d SETS
EXCHANGE DEADLINE 11/19/07

Card	Low	High
AK Al Kaline	30.00	60.00
BF Bob Feller	12.50	30.00
BG Bob Gibson	15.00	40.00
BM Bill Mazeroski	15.00	40.00
BR Brooks Robinson	15.00	40.00
CY Carl Yastrzemski	40.00	80.00
DE Dennis Eckersley	15.00	40.00
DM Don Mattingly	50.00	100.00
DS Don Sutton	10.00	25.00
DW Dave Winfield	15.00	40.00
EB Ernie Banks	30.00	60.00
EM Eddie Murray	40.00	80.00
FJ Fergie Jenkins	12.50	30.00
FR Frank Robinson	15.00	40.00
GB George Brett	50.00	100.00
GK George Kell	30.00	60.00
HK Harmon Killebrew	40.00	80.00
JB Johnny Bench	30.00	60.00
JM Joe Morgan	12.50	30.00
JP Johnny Podres	10.00	25.00
KP Kirby Puckett	50.00	100.00
LB Lou Brock	15.00	40.00
MA Juan Marichal	12.50	30.00
MI Monte Irvin	15.00	40.00
MS Mike Schmidt	40.00	80.00
MW Maury Wills	12.50	30.00
NR Nolan Ryan	60.00	120.00
OS Ozzie Smith	30.00	60.00
PA Jim Palmer	12.50	30.00
PM Paul Molitor	12.50	30.00
PR Phil Rizzuto	15.00	40.00
RK Ralph Kiner	15.00	40.00
RS Red Schoendienst	12.50	30.00
RY Robin Yount	30.00	60.00
SA Ryne Sandberg	50.00	100.00
SM Stan Musial	40.00	80.00
SN Duke Snider	15.00	40.00
TS Tom Seaver	30.00	60.00
WF Whitey Ford	15.00	40.00
YB Yogi Berra	30.00	60.00

2004 SP Legendary Cuts Ultimate Swatches

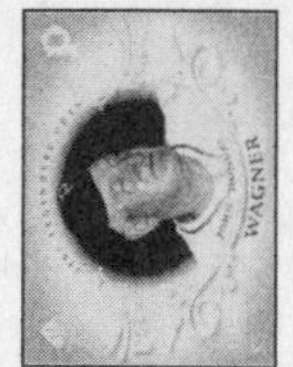

SP INFO PROVIDED BY UPPER DECK
SWATCH 10 PRINT RUN 10 #'d SETS
NO SWATCH 10 PRICING DUE TO SCARCITY
OVERALL GU ODDS 1:4

Card	Low	High
BG Bob Gibson Jsy	4.00	10.00
BR Brooks Robinson Bat	4.00	10.00
BW Billy Williams Jsy	3.00	8.00
CH Catfish Hunter Jsy	4.00	10.00
CR Cal Ripken Jsy	10.00	25.00
CY Carl Yastrzemski Jsy	6.00	15.00
DD Don Drysdale Jsy	4.00	10.00
DM Don Mattingly Jsy	6.00	15.00
DS Duke Snider Jsy SP	6.00	15.00
DW Dave Winfield Jsy	3.00	8.00
EB Ernie Banks Jsy	4.00	10.00
EM Eddie Mathews Jsy	4.00	10.00
FR Frank Robinson Pants	3.00	8.00
GB George Brett Jsy	6.00	15.00
HG Hank Greenberg Bat	10.00	25.00
HK Harmon Killebrew Jsy	4.00	10.00
HW Honus Wagner Pants SP	75.00	150.00
JB Johnny Bench Jsy	4.00	10.00
JD Joe DiMaggio Jsy SP	40.00	80.00
JR Jackie Robinson Jsy	15.00	40.00
KP Kirby Puckett Bat	4.00	10.00
MA Juan Marichal Jsy	3.00	8.00
MM Mickey Mantle Pants SP	75.00	150.00
MS Mike Schmidt Jsy	6.00	15.00
NF Nellie Fox Jsy	4.00	10.00
NR Nolan Ryan Jsy	10.00	25.00
OS Ozzie Smith Jsy	6.00	15.00
PR Pee Wee Reese Jsy	4.00	10.00
RC Roy Campanella Pants	4.00	10.00
RM Roger Maris Jsy	12.50	30.00
RY Robin Yount Jsy	4.00	10.00
SC Steve Carlton Bat	3.00	8.00
SM Stan Musial Jsy	8.00	20.00
TG Tony Gwynn Jsy	4.00	10.00
TM Thurman Munson Jsy	4.00	10.00
TS Tom Seaver Jsy SP	6.00	15.00
TW Ted Williams Pants SP	20.00	50.00
WB Wade Boggs Jsy	4.00	10.00
WM Willie McCovey Pants	4.00	10.00
WS Warren Spahn Jsy	4.00	10.00
YB Yogi Berra Pants	4.00	10.00

2005 SP Legendary Cuts

This 90-card set was released in November, 2005. The set was issued in four-card packs with an $10 SRP which came 12 packs to a box and 16 boxes to a case. Interestingly this set was sequenced in alphabetical order by the player's first name.

Card	Low	High
COMPLETE SET (90)	10.00	25.00
COMMON CARD (1-90)	.25	.60
1 Al Kaline	.60	1.50
2 Babe Ruth	1.50	4.00
3 Bill Mazeroski	.40	1.00
4 Billy Williams	.25	.60
5 Bob Feller	.25	.60
6 Bob Gibson	.40	1.00
7 Bob Lemon	.25	.60
8 Bobby Doerr	.25	.60
9 Brooks Robinson	.40	1.00
10 Carl Yastrzemski	.75	2.00
11 Carlton Fisk	.40	1.00
12 Casey Stengel	.25	.60
13 Catfish Hunter	.25	.60
14 Christy Mathewson	.60	1.50
15 Cy Young	.40	1.00
16 Dennis Eckersley	.25	.60
17 Dizzy Dean	.40	1.00
18 Don Drysdale	.40	1.00
19 Don Sutton	.25	.60
20 Duke Snider	.40	1.00
21 Early Wynn	.25	.60
22 Eddie Mathews	.40	1.00
23 Eddie Murray	.60	1.50
24 Enos Slaughter	.25	.60
25 Ernie Banks	.60	1.50
26 Fergie Jenkins	.25	.60
27 Frank Robinson	.40	1.00
28 Gary Carter	.25	.60
29 Gaylord Perry	.25	.60
30 Reggie Jackson	.60	1.50
31 George Kell	.25	.60
32 George Sisler	.25	.60
33 Hal Newhouser	.40	1.00
34 Harmon Killebrew	.60	1.50
35 Honus Wagner	.40	1.00
36 Jackie Robinson	.40	1.00
37 Jim Bunning	.25	.60
38 Jim Palmer	.25	.60
39 Jimmie Foxx	.40	1.00
40 Joe DiMaggio	1.50	4.00
41 Joe Morgan	.25	.60
42 Johnny Bench	.60	1.50
43 Johnny Mize	.40	1.00
44 Juan Marichal	.25	.60
45 Kirby Puckett	.60	1.50
46 Larry Doby	.25	.60
47 Lefty Grove	.25	.60
48 Lou Boudreau	.25	.60
49 Lou Brock	.40	1.00
50 Lou Gehrig	1.25	3.00
51 Luis Aparicio	.25	.60
52 Mel Ott	.60	1.50
53 Mickey Cochrane	.25	.60
54 Mickey Mantle	2.00	5.00
55 Mike Schmidt	1.25	3.00
56 Monte Irvin	.25	.60
57 Nolan Ryan	1.50	4.00
58 Orlando Cepeda	.25	.60
59 Ozzie Smith	1.00	2.50
60 Paul Molitor	.60	1.50
61 Pee Wee Reese	.40	1.00
62 Phil Niekro	.25	.60
63 Phil Rizzuto	.40	1.00
64 Ralph Kiner	.25	.60
65 Red Schoendienst	.25	.60
66 Richie Ashburn	.40	1.00
67 Rick Ferrell	.25	.60
68 Robin Roberts	.25	.60
69 Robin Yount	.60	1.50
70 Rod Carew	.40	1.00
71 Rogers Hornsby	.25	.60
72 Rollie Fingers	.25	.60
73 Roy Campanella	.40	1.00
74 Ryne Sandberg	1.25	3.00
75 Satchel Paige	.60	1.50
76 Stan Musial	1.00	2.50
77 Steve Carlton	.25	.60
78 Ted Williams	1.25	3.00
79 Thurman Munson	.40	1.00
80 Tom Seaver	.40	1.00
81 Tony Gwynn	.75	2.00
82 Tony Perez	.25	.60
83 Ty Cobb	1.00	2.50
84 Wade Boggs	.40	1.00
85 Walter Johnson	.40	1.00
86 Warren Spahn	.40	1.00
87 Whitey Ford	.40	1.00
88 Willie McCovey	.40	1.00
89 Willie Stargell	.40	1.00
90 Yogi Berra	.60	1.50

2005 SP Legendary Cuts HoloFoil

*HOLOFOIL: 2X TO 5X BASIC
STATED PRINT RUN 50 SERIAL #'d SETS

Card	Low	High
54 Mickey Mantle	10.00	25.00

2005 SP Legendary Cuts Autograph Cuts

OVERALL CUT AU ODDS 1:196
PRINT RUNS B/WN 1-108 COPIES PER
NO PRICING ON QTY OF 19 OR LESS

Card	Low	High
AN Cap Anson/1		
AS Al Simmons/7		
AV Arky Vaughan/1		
BC Ben Chapman/7		
BD Bill Dickey/95	75.00	150.00
BG A. Bartlett Giamatti/1		
BH Billy Herman/99	50.00	100.00
BJ Indian Bob Johnson/13		
BL Bob Lemon/108	20.00	50.00
BM Billy Martin/10		
BN Bill Nicholson/8		
BR Babe Ruth/3		

BU Burleigh Grimes/99 75.00 150.00
BW Bucky Walters/34 75.00 150.00
CA Roy Campanella/4
CB Chief Bender/2
CF Carl Furillo/25 150.00 250.00
CG Charlie Gehringer/97 60.00 120.00
CH Carl Hubbell/99 75.00 150.00
CJ Colby Jack Coombs/1
CK Charlie Keller/98 75.00 150.00
CM Christy Mathewson/1
CP Claude Passeau/1
CR Joe Cronin/76 75.00 150.00
CS Casey Stengel/61 200.00 400.00
CY Cy Young/2
DD Don Drysdale/50 100.00 175.00
DE Dizzy Dean/21 450.00 600.00
DM Dale Mitchell/7
DU Leo Durocher/57 75.00 150.00
DV Dazzy Vance/2
EA Earl Averill/91 50.00 100.00
EC Earle Combs/5
EL Ed Lopat/11
EM Eddie Mathews/80 100.00 175.00
ER Edd Roush/99 60.00 120.00
ES Enos Slaughter/99 60.00 120.00
EW Early Wynn/89 50.00 100.00
FE Rick Ferrell/80 75.00 150.00
FF Frankie Frisch/18
FL Curt Flood/7
FM Frank McCormick/15
GA Gene Autry/1
GH Gabby Hartnett/50 125.00 200.00
GO Lefty Gomez/68 100.00 175.00
GP George Pipgras/12
GR Lefty Grove/41 150.00 250.00
GS George Selkirk/5
HA Chick Hafey/52 100.00 175.00
HC Happy Chandler/39 60.00 120.00
HE Harry Heilmann/1
HG Hank Greenberg/44 250.00 400.00
HK Harvey Kuenn/33 75.00 150.00
HM Heinie Manush/25 125.00 200.00
HN Hal Newhouser/96 50.00 100.00
HO Gil Hodges/8
HU Catfish Hunter/65 60.00 120.00
HW Honus Wagner/1
JB Cool Papa Bell/78 200.00 350.00
JC Jocko Conlan/40 100.00 175.00
JD Joe DiMaggio/56 350.00 500.00
JF Jimmie Foxx/1
JG Joe Gordon/5
JH Jesse Haines/90 125.00 200.00
JJ Jackie Jensen/48 125.00 200.00
JM Joe Medwick/19
JO Judy Johnson/39 100.00 175.00
JR Jackie Robinson/4
JS Joe Sewell/76 40.00 80.00
JV Johnny Vander Meer/17
JW Hoyt Wilhelm/48 60.00 120.00
KC Kiki Cuyler/2
KL Chuck Klein/2
KN Kid Nichols/1
LA Luke Appling/55 60.00 120.00
LB Lou Boudreau/99 50.00 100.00
LD Larry Doby/32 100.00 200.00
LE Buck Leonard/71 100.00 175.00
LG Lou Gehrig/4
LI Fred Lindstrom/19
LO Ernie Lombardi/29 125.00 200.00
MA Connie Mack/6
MB Mordecai Brown/1
MC Max Carey/84 60.00 120.00
MI Johnny Mize/90 60.00 120.00
MM Mickey Mantle/7
MO Mel Ott/1
NF Nellie Fox/12
NL Nap Lajoie/1
PD Paul Derringer/3
PM Pepper Martin/3
PR Pee Wee Reese/69 100.00 175.00
PT Pie Traynor/9
PW Paul Waner/4
RA Rabbit Maranville/2
RC Roberto Clemente/5
RD1 Ray Dandridge/23 75.00 150.00
RD2 Ray Dandridge/76 60.00 120.00
RE Red Ruffing/22 250.00 400.00
RF Red Faber/5
RH Rogers Hornsby/1
RI Richie Ashburn/83 125.00 200.00
RM Roger Maris/9
RO Roy McMillan/23 75.00 150.00
RR Red Rolfe/8
RU Rube Marquard/80 100.00 175.00
RY Rudy York/4
SC Spud Chandler/14
SH Stan Hack/15
SI George Sisler/21 450.00 600.00
SJ Smokey Joe Wood/11
SP Satchel Paige/14
SR Sam Rice/41 125.00 200.00
ST Stan Coveleski/71 60.00 120.00
TC Ty Cobb/1
TJ Travis Jackson/16
TK Ted Kluszewski/50 150.00 250.00
TL Tony Lazzeri/1
TM Thurman Munson/2
TS Tris Speaker/1
TW Ted Williams/10
TY Tom Yawkey/3
VR Vic Raschi/21 75.00 150.00
VS Vern Stephens/10
WA Warren Spahn/92 60.00 120.00
WC Wahoo Sam Crawford/6
WF Wes Ferrell/1
WH Waite Hoyt/99 60.00 120.00
WI Hack Wilson/1
WJ Walter Johnson/1
WS Willie Stargell/63 75.00 150.00
ZV Zoilo Versalles/15
ZW Zack Wheat/15

2005 SP Legendary Cuts Autograph Dual Cuts

OVERALL CUT AU ODDS 1:196
PRINT RUNS B/WN 1-10 COPIES PER

NO PRICING DUE TO SCARCITY
EXCHANGE DEADLINE 11/10/08

2005 SP Legendary Cuts Autograph Quad Cuts

OVERALL CUT AU ODDS 1:196
STATED PRINT RUN 1 SERIAL #'d SET
NO PRICING DUE TO SCARCITY

2005 SP Legendary Cuts Battery Cuts

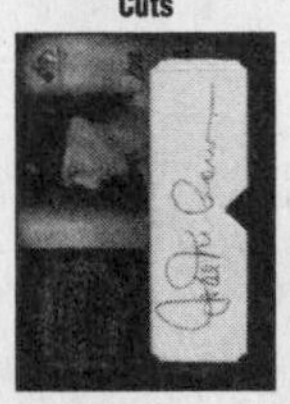

OVERALL CUT AU ODDS 1:196
PRINT RUNS B/WN 6-99 COPIES PER
NO PRICING ON QTY OF 9 OR LESS
BD Bill Dickey/22 125.00 200.00
CH Carl Hubbell/99 75.00 150.00
DD Don Drysdale/31 125.00 200.00
EL Ernie Lombardi/9
EW Early Wynn/32 75.00 150.00
GH Gabby Hartnett/9
HN Hal Newhouser/32 75.00 150.00
JH Jesse Haines/28 175.00 300.00
JV Johnny Vander Meer/8
LG Lefty Gomez/77 125.00 200.00
RR Red Ruffing/6
SC Stan Coveleski/25 100.00 175.00
WH Waite Hoyt/58 60.00 120.00
WS Warren Spahn/43 75.00 150.00

2005 SP Legendary Cuts Classic Careers

STATED PRINT RUN 399 SERIAL #'d SETS
*GOLD: .6X TO 1.5X BASIC
GOLD PRINT RUN 75 SERIAL #'d SETS
PLATINUM PRINT RUN 1 SERIAL #'d SET
NO PLATINUM PRICING DUE TO SCARCITY
OVERALL INSERT ODDS 1:6
AD Andre Dawson 1.00 2.50
AR Al Rosen .60 1.50
AV Andy Van Slyke .60 1.50
BD Bobby Doerr .60 1.50
BF Bill Freehan .60 1.50
BH Bob Horner .60 1.50
BL Barry Larkin 1.00 2.50
BM Bill Madlock .60 1.50
CA Jose Canseco 1.00 2.50
CE Carl Erskine .60 1.50
CF Carlton Fisk 1.00 2.50
CR Cal Ripken 6.00 15.00
CY Carl Yastrzemski 2.00 5.00
DC David Cone .60 1.50
DE Dennis Martinez .60 1.50
DG Dwight Gooden .60 1.50
DM Dale Murphy .60 1.50
DO Don Sutton .60 1.50
DS Darryl Strawberry .60 1.50
FJ Fergie Jenkins .60 1.50
GC Gary Carter .60 1.50
GF George Foster .60 1.50
GG Goose Gossage .60 1.50
GM Gary Matthews .60 1.50
GN Graig Nettles .60 1.50
GP Gaylord Perry .60 1.50
GU Don Gullett .60 1.50
HB Harold Baines .60 1.50
JB Jay Buhner .60 1.50
JC Jack Clark .60 1.50
JM Jack Morris .60 1.50
JP Johnny Podres .60 1.50
JR Jim Rice .60 1.50
KH Keith Hernandez .60 1.50
LA Luis Aparicio .60 1.50
LD Lenny Dykstra .60 1.50
LT Luis Tiant .60 1.50
MA Don Mattingly 3.00 8.00
MG Mark Grace 1.00 2.50
MU Bobby Murcer .60 1.50
OC Orlando Cepeda .60 1.50
PN Phil Niekro .60 1.50
RG Ron Guidry .60 1.50
SF Sid Fernandez .60 1.50
SL Sparky Lyle .60 1.50
ST Dave Stewart .60 1.50
SU Bruce Sutter .60 1.50
TO Tony Oliva .60 1.50
TR Tim Raines .60 1.50
WC Will Clark 1.00 2.50

2005 SP Legendary Cuts Classic Careers Material

OVERALL GAME-USED ODDS 1:6
*GOLD: .5X TO 1.2X BASIC
GOLD PRINT RUN 75 SERIAL #'d SETS
PLATINUM PRINT RUN 1 SERIAL #'d SET
NO PLATINUM PRICING DUE TO SCARCITY
OVERALL #'d GAME-USED ODDS 1:40
AD Andre Dawson Jsy 2.00 5.00
AR Al Rosen Pants 3.00 8.00
AV Andy Van Slyke Jsy 3.00 8.00
BD Bobby Doerr Jsy 2.00 5.00
BF Bill Freehan Jsy 2.00 5.00
BH Bob Horner Jsy 2.00 5.00
BL Barry Larkin Jsy 3.00 8.00
BM Bill Madlock Jsy 2.00 5.00
CA Jose Canseco Jsy 3.00 8.00
CE Carl Erskine Pants 3.00 8.00
CF Carlton Fisk Jsy 3.00 8.00
CR Cal Ripken Jsy 8.00 20.00
CY Carl Yastrzemski Jsy 4.00 10.00
DC David Cone Jsy 2.00 5.00
DE Dennis Martinez Jsy 2.00 5.00
DG Dwight Gooden Jsy 2.00 5.00
DM Dale Murphy Jsy 3.00 8.00
DO Don Sutton Jsy 2.00 5.00
DS Darryl Strawberry Jsy 2.00 5.00
FJ Fergie Jenkins Jsy 2.00 5.00
GC Gary Carter Jsy 2.00 5.00
GF George Foster Jsy 2.00 5.00
GG Goose Gossage Jsy 2.00 5.00
GM Gary Matthews Jsy 2.00 5.00
GN Graig Nettles Jsy 2.00 5.00
GP Gaylord Perry Jsy 2.00 5.00
GU Don Gullett Jsy 2.00 5.00
HB Harold Baines Jsy 2.00 5.00
JB Jay Buhner Jsy 3.00 8.00
JC Jack Clark Jsy 2.00 5.00
JM Jack Morris Jsy 2.00 5.00
JP Johnny Podres Jsy 3.00 8.00
JR Jim Rice Jsy 2.00 5.00
KH Keith Hernandez Jsy 2.00 5.00
LA Luis Aparicio Jsy 2.00 5.00
LD Lenny Dykstra Jsy 2.00 5.00
LT Luis Tiant Jsy 2.00 5.00
MA Don Mattingly Jsy 5.00 12.00
MG Mark Grace Jsy 3.00 8.00
MU Bobby Murcer Pants 3.00 8.00
OC Orlando Cepeda Jsy 2.00 5.00
PN Phil Niekro Jsy 2.00 5.00
RG Ron Guidry Pants 3.00 8.00
SF Sid Fernandez Jsy 2.00 5.00
SL Sparky Lyle Pants 2.00 5.00
ST Dave Stewart Jsy 2.00 5.00
SU Bruce Sutter Jsy 2.00 5.00
TO Tony Oliva Jsy 2.00 5.00
TR Tim Raines Jsy 2.00 5.00
WC Will Clark Jsy 3.00 8.00

2005 SP Legendary Cuts Classic Careers Patch

*PATCH p/r 50: 1X TO 2.5X MATERIAL
*PATCH p/r 20: 1.25X TO 3X MATERIAL
STATED PRINT RUN 50 SERIAL #'d SETS
J.BUHNER PRINT RUN 14 CARDS
D.MARTINEZ PRINT RUN 20 CARDS
NO BUHNER PRICING AVAILABLE
GOLD PRINT RUN 10 SERIAL #'d SETS
NO GOLD PRICING DUE TO SCARCITY
PLATINUM PRINT RUN 1 SERIAL #'d SET
NO PLATINUM PRICING DUE TO SCARCITY
OVERALL PATCH ODDS 1:96

2005 SP Legendary Cuts Classic Careers Autograph

STATED PRINT RUN 25 SERIAL #'d SETS
GOLD PRINT RUN 10 SERIAL #'d SETS
NO GOLD PRICING DUE TO SCARCITY
PLATINUM PRINT RUN 1 SERIAL #'d SET
NO PLATINUM PRICING DUE TO SCARCITY
OVERALL AUTO ODDS 1:96
EXCHANGE DEADLINE 11/10/08
AD Andre Dawson 10.00 25.00

AR Al Rosen 10.00 25.00
AV Andy Van Slyke 15.00 40.00
BD Bobby Doerr 6.00 15.00
BF Bill Freehan 10.00 25.00
BH Bob Horner 6.00 15.00
BL Barry Larkin 15.00 40.00
BM Bill Madlock 10.00 25.00
CA Jose Canseco 20.00 50.00
CE Carl Erskine 10.00 25.00
CF Carlton Fisk 15.00 40.00
CY Carl Yastrzemski 20.00 50.00
DC David Cone 6.00 15.00
DE Dennis Martinez 6.00 15.00
DG Dwight Gooden 6.00 15.00
DM Dale Murphy 15.00 40.00
DO Don Sutton 10.00 25.00
DS Darryl Strawberry 10.00 25.00
FJ Fergie Jenkins 10.00 25.00
GC Gary Carter 10.00 25.00
GF George Foster 10.00 25.00
GG Goose Gossage 10.00 25.00
GM Gary Matthews 6.00 15.00
GN Graig Nettles 10.00 25.00
GP Gaylord Perry 10.00 25.00
GU Don Gullett 6.00 15.00
HB Harold Baines 10.00 25.00
JB Jay Buhner 15.00 40.00
JC Jack Clark 10.00 25.00
JM Jack Morris 6.00 15.00
JP Johnny Podres 10.00 25.00
JR Jim Rice 10.00 25.00
KH Keith Hernandez 6.00 15.00
LA Luis Aparicio 10.00 25.00
LD Lenny Dykstra 6.00 15.00
LT Luis Tiant 6.00 15.00
MA Don Mattingly 30.00 60.00
MG Mark Grace 15.00 40.00
MU Bobby Murcer 15.00 40.00
OC Orlando Cepeda 10.00 25.00
PN Phil Niekro 10.00 25.00
RG Ron Guidry 15.00 40.00
SF Sid Fernandez 6.00 15.00
SL Sparky Lyle 6.00 15.00
ST Dave Stewart 6.00 15.00
SU Bruce Sutter 15.00 40.00
TO Tony Oliva 10.00 25.00
TR Tim Raines 10.00 25.00
WC Will Clark 15.00 40.00

2005 SP Legendary Cuts Classic Careers Autograph Material

*AUTO MAT: .4X TO 1X AUTO
STATED PRINT RUN 25 SERIAL #'d SETS
GOLD PRINT RUN 10 SERIAL #'d SETS
NO GOLD PRICING DUE TO SCARCITY
PLATINUM PRINT RUN 1 SERIAL #'d SET
NO PLATINUM PRICING DUE TO SCARCITY
OVERALL AU-GU ODDS 1:96
EXCHANGE DEADLINE 11/10/08

2005 SP Legendary Cuts Classic Careers Autograph Patch

*AUTO PATCH: .6X TO 1.5X AUTO
STATED PRINT RUN 25 SERIAL #'d SETS
GOLD PRINT RUN 5 SERIAL #'d SETS
NO GOLD PRICING DUE TO SCARCITY
PLATINUM PRINT RUN 1 SERIAL #'d SET
NO PLATINUM PRICING DUE TO SCARCITY
OVERALL AU-PATCH ODDS 1:96
EXCHANGE DEADLINE 11/10/08

2005 SP Legendary Cuts Cornerstone Cuts

OVERALL CUT AU ODDS 1:196
PRINT RUNS B/WN 1-79 COPIES PER
NO PRICING ON QTY OF 16 OR LESS
BL Buck Leonard/15
DC Dolph Camilli/79 75.00 150.00
EM Eddie Mathews/50 125.00 200.00
GH Gil Hodges/8
GS George Sisler/6
HG Hank Greenberg/10
JF Jimmie Foxx/1
JJ Judy Johnson/16
JM Johnny Mize/44 75.00 150.00
PT Pie Traynor/1
RD Ray Dandridge/27 75.00 150.00
RY Rudy York/5
TK Ted Kluszewski/16
WP Wally Pipp/1
WS Willie Stargell/36 100.00 175.00

2005 SP Legendary Cuts Glory Days

STATED PRINT RUN 399 SERIAL #'d SETS
*GOLD: .6X TO 1.5X BASIC
GOLD PRINT RUN 75 SERIAL #'d SETS
PLATINUM PRINT RUN 1 SERIAL #'d SET
NO PLATINUM PRICING DUE TO SCARCITY
OVERALL INSERT ODDS 1:6
AD Andre Dawson 1.00 2.50
AR Al Rosen .60 1.50
AV Andy Van Slyke .60 1.50
BD Bobby Doerr .60 1.50
BF Bill Freehan .60 1.50
BH Bob Horner .60 1.50
BL Barry Larkin 1.00 2.50
BM Bill Madlock .60 1.50
BS Bruce Sutter .60 1.50
CA Jose Canseco 1.00 2.50
CR Cal Ripken 6.00 15.00
DC David Cone .60 1.50
DE Dennis Martinez .60 1.50
DG Dwight Gooden .60 1.50
DM Dale Murphy .60 1.50
DS Darryl Strawberry .60 1.50
FJ Fergie Jenkins .60 1.50
FL Fred Lynn .60 1.50
GF George Foster .60 1.50
GM Gary Matthews .60 1.50
GN Graig Nettles .60 1.50
GU Don Gullett .60 1.50
HB Harold Baines .60 1.50
JB Jay Buhner .60 1.50
JC Jack Clark .60 1.50
JM Jack Morris .60 1.50
JP Jim Palmer .60 1.50
JR Jim Rice .60 1.50
KG Kirk Gibson .60 1.50
KH Keith Hernandez .60 1.50
LB Lou Brock 1.00 2.50
LD Lenny Dykstra .60 1.50
LT Luis Tiant .60 1.50
MA Juan Marichal .60 1.50
MU Bobby Murcer .60 1.50
NR Nolan Ryan 4.00 10.00
PM Paul Molitor 1.50 4.00
RG Ron Guidry .60 1.50
RS Red Schoendienst .60 1.50
RY Robin Yount 1.50 4.00
SF Sid Fernandez .60 1.50
SL Sparky Lyle UER .60 1.50
Name misspelled as Sparly
SN Duke Snider 1.00 2.50
ST Dave Stewart .60 1.50
TG Tony Gwynn 2.00 5.00
TO Tony Oliva .60 1.50
TR Tim Raines .60 1.50
WC Will Clark 1.00 2.50
WF Whitey Ford 1.00 2.50
YB Yogi Berra 1.50 4.00

2005 SP Legendary Cuts Glory Days Material

OVERALL GAME-USED ODDS 1:6
*GOLD: .5X TO 1.2X BASIC
GOLD PRINT RUN 75 SERIAL #'d SETS
PLATINUM PRINT RUN 1 SERIAL #'d SET
NO PLATINUM PRICING DUE TO SCARCITY
OVERALL #'d GAME-USED ODDS 1:40
AD Andre Dawson Jsy 2.00 5.00
AR Al Rosen Pants 3.00 8.00
AV Andy Van Slyke Jsy 3.00 8.00
BD Bobby Doerr Jsy 2.00 5.00
BF Bill Freehan Jsy 2.00 5.00
BH Bob Horner Jsy 2.00 5.00
BL Barry Larkin Jsy 3.00 8.00
BM Bill Madlock Jsy 2.00 5.00
BS Bruce Sutter Jsy 2.00 5.00
CA Jose Canseco Jsy 3.00 8.00
CR Cal Ripken Jsy 8.00 20.00
DC David Cone Jsy 2.00 5.00
DE Dennis Martinez Jsy 2.00 5.00
DG Dwight Gooden Jsy 2.00 5.00
DM Dale Murphy Jsy 3.00 8.00
DS Darryl Strawberry Jsy 2.00 5.00
FJ Fergie Jenkins Jsy 2.00 5.00
FL Fred Lynn Bat 2.00 5.00
GF George Foster Jsy 2.00 5.00
GM Gary Matthews Jsy 2.00 5.00
GN Graig Nettles Jsy 2.00 5.00
GU Don Gullett Jsy 2.00 5.00
HB Harold Baines Jsy 2.00 5.00
JB Jay Buhner Jsy 3.00 8.00
JC Jack Clark Jsy 2.00 5.00
JM Jack Morris Jsy 2.00 5.00
JP Jim Palmer Jsy 2.00 5.00
JR Jim Rice Jsy 2.00 5.00
KG Kirk Gibson Jsy 2.00 5.00
KH Keith Hernandez Jsy 2.00 5.00
LB Lou Brock Jsy * 3.00 8.00
LD Lenny Dykstra Jsy 2.00 5.00
LT Luis Tiant Jsy 2.00 5.00
MA Juan Marichal Jsy 3.00 8.00
MU Bobby Murcer Pants 3.00 8.00
NR Nolan Ryan Jsy 6.00 15.00
PM Paul Molitor Bat 2.00 5.00
RG Ron Guidry Pants 3.00 8.00
RS Red Schoendienst Jsy 3.00 8.00
RY Robin Yount Jsy 4.00 10.00
SF Sid Fernandez Jsy 2.00 5.00
SL Sparky Lyle Pants 2.00 5.00
SN Duke Snider Pants 4.00 10.00
ST Dave Stewart Jsy 2.00 5.00
TG Tony Gwynn Jsy 4.00 10.00
TO Tony Oliva Jsy 2.00 5.00
TR Tim Raines Jsy 2.00 5.00
WC Will Clark Jsy 3.00 8.00
WF Whitey Ford Jsy 5.00 12.00
YB Yogi Berra Pants 5.00 12.00

2005 SP Legendary Cuts Glory Days Patch

*PATCH: 1X TO 2.5X MATERIAL
STATED PRINT RUN 50 SERIAL #'d SETS
K.HERNANDEZ PRINT RUN 37 CARDS
L.TIANT PRINT RUN 40 CARDS
GOLD PRINT RUN 10 SERIAL #'d SETS
NO GOLD PRICING DUE TO SCARCITY
PLATINUM PRINT RUN 1 SERIAL #'d SET
NO PLATINUM PRICING DUE TO SCARCITY
OVERALL PATCH ODDS 1:96

2005 SP Legendary Cuts Glory Days Autograph

STATED PRINT RUN 25 SERIAL #'d SETS
GOLD PRINT RUN 10 SERIAL #'d SETS
NO GOLD PRICING DUE TO SCARCITY
PLATINUM PRINT RUN 1 SERIAL #'d SET
NO PLATINUM PRICING DUE TO SCARCITY
OVERALL AUTO ODDS 1:96
EXCHANGE DEADLINE 11/10/08
AD Andre Dawson 10.00 25.00
AR Al Rosen 10.00 25.00
AV Andy Van Slyke 15.00 40.00
BD Bobby Doerr 6.00 15.00
BF Bill Freehan 10.00 25.00
BH Bob Horner 6.00 15.00
BL Barry Larkin 15.00 40.00
BM Bill Madlock 10.00 25.00
BS Bruce Sutter 15.00 40.00
CA Jose Canseco 20.00 50.00
DC David Cone 6.00 15.00
DE Dennis Martinez 6.00 15.00
DG Dwight Gooden 6.00 15.00
DM Dale Murphy 15.00 40.00
DS Darryl Strawberry 10.00 25.00
FJ Fergie Jenkins 10.00 25.00
FL Fred Lynn 10.00 25.00
GF George Foster 10.00 25.00
GM Gary Matthews 6.00 15.00
GN Graig Nettles 10.00 25.00
GU Don Gullett 6.00 15.00
HB Harold Baines 10.00 25.00
JB Jay Buhner 15.00 40.00
JC Jack Clark 10.00 25.00
JM Jack Morris 6.00 15.00
JP Jim Palmer 10.00 25.00
JR Jim Rice 10.00 25.00
KG Kirk Gibson 10.00 25.00
KH Keith Hernandez 6.00 15.00
LB Lou Brock 15.00 40.00
LD Lenny Dykstra 6.00 15.00
LT Luis Tiant 6.00 15.00
MA Juan Marichal 10.00 25.00
NR Nolan Ryan 50.00 100.00
PM Paul Molitor 10.00 25.00
RG Ron Guidry 15.00 40.00
RS Red Schoendienst 10.00 25.00
RY Robin Yount 20.00 50.00
SF Sid Fernandez 6.00 15.00
SL Sparky Lyle 6.00 15.00
SN Duke Snider 20.00 50.00
ST Dave Stewart 6.00 15.00
TG Tony Gwynn 20.00 50.00
TO Tony Oliva 10.00 25.00
TR Tim Raines 10.00 25.00
WC Will Clark 15.00 40.00
WF Whitey Ford 15.00 40.00
YB Yogi Berra 30.00 60.00

2005 SP Legendary Cuts Glory Days Autograph Material

*AUTO MAT: .4X TO 1X AUTO
STATED PRINT RUN 25 SERIAL #'d SETS
GOLD PRINT RUN 10 SERIAL #'d SETS
NO GOLD PRICING DUE TO SCARCITY
PLATINUM PRINT RUN 1 SERIAL #'d SET
NO PLATINUM PRICING DUE TO SCARCITY
OVERALL AU-GU ODDS 1:96
EXCHANGE DEADLINE 11/10/08

2005 SP Legendary Cuts Glory Days Autograph Patch

*AUTO PATCH: .6X TO 1.5X AUTO
STATED PRINT RUN 25 SERIAL #'d SETS
D.GULLETT PRINT RUN 7 CARDS
NO D.GULLETT PRICING DUE TO SCARCITY
GOLD PRINT RUN 5 SERIAL #'d SETS
NO GOLD PRICING DUE TO SCARCITY
PLATINUM PRINT RUN 1 SERIAL #'d SET
NO PLATINUM PRICING DUE TO SCARCITY
OVERALL AU-PATCH ODDS 1:96

2005 SP Legendary Cuts Glovemen Cuts

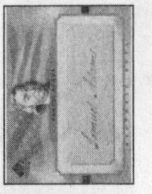

OVERALL CUT AU ODDS 1:196
PRINT RUNS B/WN 1-75 COPIES PER
NO PRICING ON QTY OF 19 OR LESS
CK Chuck Klein/1
CP Cool Papa Bell/29 300.00 400.00
EA Earl Averill/39 60.00 120.00
EC Earle Combs/12
ES Enos Slaughter/65 60.00 120.00
FL Fred Lindstrom/5
HM Heinie Manush/17
JD Joe DiMaggio/75 350.00 450.00
JM Joe Medwick/8
LD Larry Doby/16
MC Max Carey/50 75.00 150.00
MM Mickey Mantle/19
RA Richie Ashburn/20 150.00 250.00
TW Ted Williams/9

2005 SP Legendary Cuts Historic Cuts

OVERALL CUT AU ODDS 1:196
STATED PRINT RUN 1 SERIAL #'d SET
NO PRICING DUE TO SCARCITY

2005 SP Legendary Cuts Historic Quads Autograph

OVERALL AUTO ODDS 1:96
STATED PRINT RUN 5 SERIAL #'d SETS
NO PRICING DUE TO SCARCITY
EXCHANGE DEADLINE 11/10/08

2005 SP Legendary Cuts Historic Quads Material

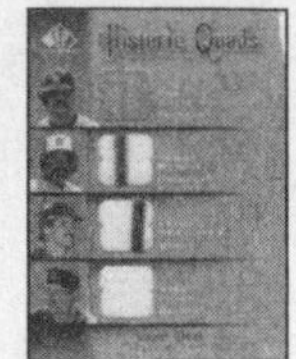

OVERALL #'d GAME-USED ODDS 1:40
STATED PRINT RUN 5 SERIAL #'d SETS
OVERALL PATCH ODDS 1:96
PATCH PRINT RUN 1 SERIAL #'d SET

2005 SP Legendary Cuts Lasting Legends

STATED PRINT RUN 399 SERIAL #'d SETS
*GOLD: .6X TO 1.5X BASIC
GOLD PRINT RUN 75 SERIAL #'d SETS
PLATINUM PRINT RUN 1 SERIAL #'d SET
NO PLATINUM PRICING DUE TO SCARCITY
OVERALL INSERT ODDS 1:6

AK Al Kaline 1.50 4.00
BD Bobby Doerr .60 1.50
BE Johnny Bench 1.50 4.00
BG Bob Gibson 1.00 2.50
BL Barry Larkin 1.00 2.50
BM Bill Mazeroski 1.00 2.50
BR Brooks Robinson 1.00 2.50
BS Bruce Sutter .60 1.50
CF Carlton Fisk 1.00 2.50
CR Cal Ripken 6.00 15.00
CY Carl Yastrzemski 2.00 5.00
DE Dennis Eckersley .60 1.50
DG Dwight Gooden .60 1.50
DM Don Mattingly 3.00 8.00
DS Don Sutton .60 1.50
EB Ernie Banks 1.50 4.00
EM Eddie Murray 1.50 4.00
FJ Fergie Jenkins .60 1.50
FR Frank Robinson 1.00 2.50
GC Gary Carter .60 1.50
GN Graig Nettles .60 1.50
GP Gaylord Perry .60 1.50
JM Joe Morgan .60 1.50
JP Jim Palmer .60 1.50
JR Jim Rice .60 1.50
KH Keith Hernandez .60 1.50
KP Kirby Puckett 1.50 4.00
LA Luis Aparicio .60 1.50
LB Lou Brock 1.00 2.50
MA Juan Marichal .60 1.50
MS Mike Schmidt 3.00 8.00
MU Dale Murphy .60 1.50
NR Nolan Ryan 4.00 10.00
OC Orlando Cepeda .60 1.50
OS Ozzie Smith 2.50 6.00
PM Paul Molitor 1.50 4.00
PN Phil Niekro .60 1.50
RC Rod Carew 1.00 2.50
RF Rollie Fingers .60 1.50
RS Red Schoendienst .60 1.50
RY Robin Yount 1.50 4.00
SA Ryne Sandberg 3.00 8.00
SC Steve Carlton .60 1.50
SM Stan Musial 2.50 6.00
SN Duke Snider 1.00 2.50
TG Tony Gwynn 2.00 5.00
TP Tony Perez .60 1.50
WB Wade Boggs 1.00 2.50
WF Whitey Ford 1.00 2.50
YB Yogi Berra 1.50 4.00

2005 SP Legendary Cuts Lasting Legends Material

OVERALL GAME-USED ODDS 1:6
*GOLD: .5X TO 1.2X BASIC
GOLD PRINT RUN 75 SERIAL #'d SETS
PLATINUM PRINT RUN 1 SERIAL #'d SET
NO PLATINUM PRICING DUE TO SCARCITY
OVERALL #'d GAME-USED ODDS 1:40

AK Al Kaline Bat 4.00 10.00
BD Bobby Doerr Pants 2.00 5.00
BE Johnny Bench Jsy 4.00 10.00
BG Bob Gibson Jsy 3.00 8.00
BL Barry Larkin Jsy 3.00 8.00
BM Bill Mazeroski Jsy 3.00 8.00
BR Brooks Robinson Jsy 3.00 8.00
BS Bruce Sutter Jsy 2.00 5.00
CF Carlton Fisk Jsy 3.00 8.00
CR Cal Ripken Jsy 8.00 20.00
CY Carl Yastrzemski Jsy 4.00 10.00
DE Dennis Eckersley Jsy 2.00 5.00
DG Dwight Gooden Jsy 2.00 5.00
DM Don Mattingly Jsy 5.00 12.00
DS Don Sutton Jsy 2.00 5.00
EB Ernie Banks Pants 4.00 10.00
EM Eddie Murray Jsy 4.00 10.00
FJ Fergie Jenkins Jsy 2.00 5.00
FR Frank Robinson Jsy 3.00 8.00
GC Gary Carter Jsy 2.00 5.00
GN Graig Nettles Jsy 2.00 5.00
GP Gaylord Perry Jsy 2.00 5.00
JM Joe Morgan Jsy 2.00 5.00
JP Jim Palmer Jsy 2.00 5.00
JR Jim Rice Jsy 2.00 5.00
KH Keith Hernandez Jsy 2.00 5.00
KP Kirby Puckett Jsy 4.00 10.00
LA Luis Aparicio Jsy 2.00 5.00
LB Lou Brock Jsy * 3.00 8.00
MA Juan Marichal Jsy 3.00 8.00
MS Mike Schmidt Jsy 5.00 12.00
MU Dale Murphy Jsy 3.00 8.00
NR Nolan Ryan Jsy 6.00 15.00
OC Orlando Cepeda Jsy 2.00 5.00
OS Ozzie Smith Jsy 4.00 10.00
PM Paul Molitor Bat 2.00 5.00
PN Phil Niekro Jsy 2.00 5.00
RC Rod Carew Jsy 3.00 8.00
RF Rollie Fingers Jsy 2.00 5.00
RS Red Schoendienst Jsy 3.00 8.00
RY Robin Yount Jsy 4.00 10.00
SA Ryne Sandberg Jsy 5.00 12.00
SC Steve Carlton Jsy 2.00 5.00
SM Stan Musial Jsy 6.00 15.00
SN Duke Snider Pants 4.00 10.00
TG Tony Gwynn Jsy 4.00 10.00
TP Tony Perez Jsy 2.00 5.00
WB Wade Boggs Jsy 3.00 8.00
WF Whitey Ford Jsy 5.00 12.00
YB Yogi Berra Pants 5.00 12.00

2005 SP Legendary Cuts Lasting Legends Patch

*PATCH: 1X TO 2.5X MATERIAL
STATED PRINT RUN 50 SERIAL #'d SETS
P.MOLITOR PRINT RUN 2 CARDS
B.ROBINSON PRINT RUN 43 CARDS
N.RYAN PRINT RUN 11 CARDS
NO MOLITOR/RYAN PRICING AVAILABLE
GOLD PRINT RUN 10 SERIAL #'d SETS
NO GOLD PRICING DUE TO SCARCITY
PLATINUM PRINT RUN 1 SERIAL #'d SET
NO PLATINUM PRICING DUE TO SCARCITY
OVERALL PATCH ODDS 1:96

2005 SP Legendary Cuts Lasting Legends Autograph

STATED PRINT RUN 25 SERIAL #'d SETS
GOLD PRINT RUN 10 SERIAL #'d SETS
NO GOLD PRICING DUE TO SCARCITY
PLATINUM PRINT RUN 1 SERIAL #'d SET
NO PLATINUM PRICING DUE TO SCARCITY
OVERALL AUTO ODDS 1:96
EXCHANGE DEADLINE 11/10/08

AK Al Kaline 20.00 50.00
BD Bobby Doerr 6.00 15.00
BE Johnny Bench 20.00 50.00
BG Bob Gibson 15.00 40.00
BL Barry Larkin 15.00 40.00
BM Bill Mazeroski 15.00 40.00
BR Brooks Robinson 15.00 40.00
BS Bruce Sutter 15.00 40.00
CF Carlton Fisk 15.00 40.00
CY Carl Yastrzemski 20.00 50.00
DE Dennis Eckersley 10.00 25.00
DG Dwight Gooden 6.00 15.00
DM Don Mattingly 30.00 60.00
DS Don Sutton 10.00 25.00
EB Ernie Banks 30.00 60.00
FJ Fergie Jenkins 10.00 25.00
FR Frank Robinson 10.00 25.00
GC Gary Carter 10.00 25.00
GN Graig Nettles 10.00 25.00
GP Gaylord Perry 10.00 25.00
JM Joe Morgan 10.00 25.00
JP Jim Palmer 10.00 25.00
JR Jim Rice 10.00 25.00
KH Keith Hernandez 6.00 15.00
KP Kirby Puckett 50.00 100.00
LA Luis Aparicio 10.00 25.00
LB Lou Brock 15.00 40.00
MA Juan Marichal 10.00 25.00
MS Mike Schmidt 30.00 60.00
MU Dale Murphy 15.00 40.00
NR Nolan Ryan 50.00 100.00
OC Orlando Cepeda 10.00 25.00
OS Ozzie Smith 20.00 50.00
PM Paul Molitor 10.00 25.00
PN Phil Niekro 10.00 25.00
RC Rod Carew 15.00 40.00
RF Rollie Fingers 10.00 25.00
RS Red Schoendienst 10.00 25.00
RY Robin Yount 20.00 50.00
SA Ryne Sandberg 30.00 60.00
SC Steve Carlton 10.00 25.00
SM Stan Musial 30.00 60.00
SN Duke Snider 20.00 50.00
TG Tony Gwynn 20.00 50.00
TP Tony Perez 10.00 25.00
WB Wade Boggs 15.00 40.00
WF Whitey Ford 15.00 40.00
YB Yogi Berra 30.00 60.00

2005 SP Legendary Cuts Lasting Legends Autograph Material

*AUTO MAT: .4X TO 1X AUTO
STATED PRINT RUN 25 SERIAL #'d SETS
C.FISK PRINT RUN 21 CARDS
GOLD PRINT RUN 10 SERIAL #'d SETS
NO GOLD PRICING DUE TO SCARCITY
PLATINUM PRINT RUN 1 SERIAL #'d SET
NO PLATINUM PRICING DUE TO SCARCITY
OVERALL AU-GU ODDS 1:96
EXCHANGE DEADLINE 11/10/08

2005 SP Legendary Cuts Lasting Legends Autograph Patch

*AUTO PATCH: .6X TO 1.5X AUTO
STATED PRINT RUN 25 SERIAL #'d SETS
L.BROCK PRINT RUN 6 CARDS
K.PUCKETT PRINT RUN 6 CARDS
NO BROCK/PUCKETT PRICING AVAILABLE
GOLD PRINT RUN 5 SERIAL #'d SETS
NO GOLD PRICING DUE TO SCARCITY
PLATINUM PRINT RUN 1 SERIAL #'d SET
NO PLATINUM PRICING DUE TO SCARCITY
OVERALL AU-PATCH ODDS 1:196

2005 SP Legendary Cuts Legendary Duels Autograph

OVERALL AUTO ODDS 1:96
STATED PRINT RUN 15 SERIAL #'d SETS
NO PRICING DUE TO SCARCITY

2005 SP Legendary Cuts Legendary Duels Material

OVERALL #'d GAME-USED ODDS 1:40
STATED PRINT RUN 25 SERIAL #'d SETS
OVERALL PATCH ODDS 1:96
PATCH PRINT RUN 10 SERIAL #'d SETS
NO PATCH PRICING DUE TO SCARCITY

BM Ernie Banks Pants 30.00 60.00
Stan Musial Jsy
CC Jose Canseco Jsy 15.00 40.00
Will Clark Jsy
DM Lenny Dykstra Jsy 6.00 15.00
Paul Molitor Jsy
EG Dennis Eckersley Jsy 10.00 25.00
Kirk Gibson Jsy
FB Carlton Fisk Jsy 15.00 40.00
Johnny Bench Jsy
FR George Foster Jsy 6.00 15.00
Jim Rice Jsy
JY Reggie Jackson Jsy 15.00 40.00
Carl Yastrzemski Jsy
MC Paul Molitor Pants 10.00 25.00
Rod Carew Jsy
MH Don Mattingly Jsy 15.00 40.00
Keith Hernandez Jsy
SF Duke Snider Pants 15.00 40.00
Whitey Ford Jsy
SG Don Sutton Jsy 10.00 25.00
Ron Guidry Pants
SS Ozzie Smith Jsy 30.00 60.00
Ryne Sandberg Jsy
YS Robin Yount Jsy 15.00 40.00
Mike Schmidt Jsy

2005 SP Legendary Cuts Legendary Duos Autograph

OVERALL AUTO ODDS 1:96
STATED PRINT RUN 15 SERIAL #'d SETS
NO PRICING DUE TO SCARCITY
EXCHANGE DEADLINE 11/10/08

2005 SP Legendary Cuts Legendary Duos Material

OVERALL #'d GAME-USED ODDS 1:40
STATED PRINT RUN 25 SERIAL #'d SETS
OVERALL PATCH ODDS 1:96
PATCH PRINT RUN 10 SERIAL #'d SETS
NO PATCH PRICING DUE TO SCARCITY

CO Rod Carew Jsy 10.00 25.00
Tony Oliva Jsy
ES Carl Erskine Jsy 10.00 25.00
Duke Snider Jsy
FB Whitey Ford Jsy 15.00 40.00
Yogi Berra Pants
GS Mark Grace Jsy 20.00 50.00
Ryne Sandberg Jsy
JG Reggie Jackson Jsy 10.00 25.00
Ron Guidry Pants
MB Joe Morgan Jsy 15.00 40.00
Johnny Bench Jsy
MY Paul Molitor Pants 15.00 40.00
Robin Yount Jsy
RB Jim Rice Jsy 10.00 25.00
Wade Boggs Jsy
RC Cal Ripken Jsy 20.00 50.00
Will Clark Jsy
RM Cal Ripken Jsy 30.00 60.00
Eddie Murray Jsy
RR Brooks Robinson Jsy 10.00 25.00
Frank Robinson Jsy
SC Mike Schmidt Jsy 15.00 40.00
Steve Carlton Jsy
SG Darryl Strawberry Jsy 6.00 15.00
Dwight Gooden Jsy

2005 SP Legendary Cuts Legendary Lineage

STATED PRINT RUN 399 SERIAL #'d SETS
*GOLD: .6X TO 1.5X BASIC
GOLD PRINT RUN 75 SERIAL #'d SETS
PLATINUM PRINT RUN 1 SERIAL #'d SET
NO PLATINUM PRICING DUE TO SCARCITY
OVERALL INSERT ODDS 1:6

AD Andre Dawson 1.00 2.50
AR Al Rosen .60 1.50
AV Andy Van Slyke .60 1.50
BD Bobby Doerr .60 1.50
BF Bill Freehan .60 1.50
BH Bob Horner .60 1.50
BL Barry Larkin 1.00 2.50
BM Bill Madlock .60 1.50
BR Brooks Robinson 1.00 2.50
CA Jose Canseco 1.00 2.50
CR Cal Ripken 6.00 15.00
DC David Cone .60 1.50
DE Dennis Martinez .60 1.50
DG Dwight Gooden .60 1.50
DM Dale Murphy .60 1.50
DS Dave Stewart .60 1.50
EC Dennis Eckersley .60 1.50
FJ Fergie Jenkins .60 1.50
GG Goose Gossage .60 1.50
GM Gary Matthews .60 1.50
GN Graig Nettles .60 1.50
GU Don Gullett .60 1.50
HB Harold Baines .60 1.50
JB Jay Buhner .60 1.50
JC Jack Clark .60 1.50
JM Jack Morris .60 1.50
JP Jim Palmer .60 1.50
JR Jim Rice .60 1.50
KH Keith Hernandez .60 1.50
KP Kirby Puckett 1.50 4.00
LD Lenny Dykstra .60 1.50
LT Luis Tiant .60 1.50
MA Don Mattingly 3.00 8.00
MG Mark Grace 1.00 2.50
MS Mike Schmidt 3.00 8.00
MU Bobby Murcer .60 1.50
OS Ozzie Smith 2.50 6.00
PM Paul Molitor 1.50 4.00
RG Ron Guidry .60 1.50
RJ Reggie Jackson 1.50 4.00
SC Steve Carlton .60 1.50
SF Sid Fernandez .60 1.50
SL Sparky Lyle .60 1.50
SN Duke Snider 1.00 2.50
ST Darryl Strawberry .60 1.50
SU Bruce Sutter .60 1.50
TG Tony Gwynn 2.00 5.00
TO Tony Oliva .60 1.50
TR Tim Raines .60 1.50
WC Will Clark 1.00 2.50

2005 SP Legendary Cuts Legendary Lineage Material

OVERALL GAME-USED ODDS 1:6
*GOLD: .5X TO 1.2X BASIC
GOLD PRINT RUN 75 SERIAL #'d SETS
PLATINUM PRINT RUN 1 SERIAL #'d SET
NO PLATINUM PRICING DUE TO SCARCITY
OVERALL #'d GAME-USED ODDS 1:40

AD Andre Dawson Jsy 2.00 5.00
AR Al Rosen Pants 3.00 8.00
AV Andy Van Slyke Jsy 3.00 8.00
BD Bobby Doerr Jsy 2.00 5.00
BF Bill Freehan Jsy 2.00 5.00
BH Bob Horner Jsy 2.00 5.00
BL Barry Larkin Jsy 3.00 8.00
BM Bill Madlock Jsy 2.00 5.00
BR Brooks Robinson Jsy 3.00 8.00
CA Jose Canseco Jsy 3.00 8.00
CR Cal Ripken Jsy 8.00 20.00
DC David Cone Jsy 2.00 5.00
DE Dennis Martinez Jsy 2.00 5.00
DG Dwight Gooden Jsy 2.00 5.00
DM Dale Murphy Jsy 3.00 8.00
DS Dave Stewart Jsy 2.00 5.00
EC Dennis Eckersley Jsy 2.00 5.00
FJ Fergie Jenkins Jsy 2.00 5.00
GG Goose Gossage Jsy 2.00 5.00
GM Gary Matthews Jsy 2.00 5.00
GN Graig Nettles Jsy 2.00 5.00
GU Don Gullett Jsy 2.00 5.00
HB Harold Baines Jsy 2.00 5.00
JB Jay Buhner Jsy 3.00 8.00
JC Jack Clark Jsy 2.00 5.00
JM Jack Morris Jsy 2.00 5.00
JP Jim Palmer Jsy 2.00 5.00
JR Jim Rice Jsy 2.00 5.00
KH Keith Hernandez Jsy 2.00 5.00
KP Kirby Puckett Jsy 4.00 10.00
LD Lenny Dykstra Jsy 2.00 5.00
LT Luis Tiant Jsy 2.00 5.00
MA Don Mattingly Jsy 5.00 12.00
MG Mark Grace Jsy 3.00 8.00
MS Mike Schmidt Jsy 5.00 12.00
MU Bobby Murcer Pants 3.00 8.00
OS Ozzie Smith Jsy 4.00 10.00
PM Paul Molitor Bat 2.00 5.00
RG Ron Guidry Pants 3.00 8.00
RJ Reggie Jackson Jsy 3.00 8.00
SC Steve Carlton Jsy 2.00 5.00
SF Sid Fernandez Jsy 2.00 5.00
SL Sparky Lyle Pants 2.00 5.00
SN Duke Snider Pants 4.00 10.00
ST Darryl Strawberry Jsy 2.00 5.00
SU Bruce Sutter Jsy 2.00 5.00
TG Tony Gwynn Jsy 4.00 10.00
TO Tony Oliva Jsy 2.00 5.00
TR Tim Raines Jsy 2.00 5.00
WC Will Clark Jsy 3.00 8.00

2005 SP Legendary Cuts Legendary Lineage Patch

*PATCH: 1X TO 2.5X MATERIAL
STATED PRINT RUN 50 SERIAL #'d SETS
K.HERNANDEZ PRINT RUN 39 CARDS
B.MADLOCK PRINT RUN 43 CARDS
P.MOLITOR PRINT RUN 5 CARDS
J.RICE PRINT RUN 12 CARDS
NO MOLITOR/RICE PRICING AVAILABLE
GOLD PRINT RUN 10 SERIAL #'d SETS
NO GOLD PRICING DUE TO SCARCITY
PLATINUM PRINT RUN 1 SERIAL #'d SET
NO PLATINUM PRICING DUE TO SCARCITY
OVERALL PATCH ODDS 1:96

2005 SP Legendary Cuts Legendary Lineage Autograph

STATED PRINT RUN 25 SERIAL #'d SETS
GOLD PRINT RUN 10 SERIAL #'d SETS
NO GOLD PRICING DUE TO SCARCITY
PLATINUM PRINT RUN 1 SERIAL #'d SET
NO PLATINUM PRICING DUE TO SCARCITY
OVERALL AUTO ODDS 1:96
EXCHANGE DEADLINE 11/10/08

AD Andre Dawson 10.00 25.00
AR Al Rosen 10.00 25.00
AV Andy Van Slyke 15.00 40.00
BD Bobby Doerr 6.00 15.00

BF Bill Freehan 10.00 25.00
BH Bob Horner 6.00 15.00
BL Barry Larkin 15.00 40.00
BM Bill Madlock 10.00 25.00
BR Brooks Robinson 15.00 40.00
CA Jose Canseco 20.00 50.00
DC David Cone 6.00 15.00
DE Dennis Martinez 6.00 15.00
DG Dwight Gooden 6.00 15.00
DM Dale Murphy 15.00 40.00
DS Dave Stewart 6.00 15.00
EC Dennis Eckersley 10.00 25.00
FJ Fergie Jenkins 10.00 25.00
GG Goose Gossage 10.00 25.00
GM Gary Matthews 6.00 15.00
GN Graig Nettles 10.00 25.00
GU Don Gullett 6.00 15.00
HB Harold Baines 10.00 25.00
JB Jay Buhner 15.00 40.00
JC Jack Clark 10.00 25.00
JM Jack Morris 6.00 15.00
JP Jim Palmer 10.00 25.00
JR Jim Rice 10.00 25.00
KH Keith Hernandez 6.00 15.00
KP Kirby Puckett 50.00 100.00
LD Lenny Dykstra 6.00 15.00
LT Luis Tiant 6.00 15.00
MA Don Mattingly 30.00 60.00
MG Mark Grace 15.00 40.00
MS Mike Schmidt 30.00 60.00
OS Ozzie Smith 20.00 50.00
PM Paul Molitor 10.00 25.00
RG Ron Guidry 15.00 40.00
RJ Reggie Jackson 20.00 50.00
SC Steve Carlton 10.00 25.00
SF Sid Fernandez 6.00 15.00
SL Sparky Lyle 6.00 15.00
SN Duke Snider 20.00 50.00
ST Darryl Strawberry 10.00 25.00
SU Bruce Sutter 15.00 40.00
TG Tony Gwynn 20.00 50.00
TO Tony Oliva 10.00 25.00
TR Tim Raines 10.00 25.00
WC Will Clark 15.00 40.00

2005 SP Legendary Cuts Legendary Lineage Autograph Material

*AUTO MAT: .4X TO 1X AUTO
STATED PRINT RUN 25 SERIAL #'d SETS
GOLD PRINT RUN 10 SERIAL #'d SETS
NO GOLD PRICING DUE TO SCARCITY
PLATINUM PRINT RUN 1 SERIAL #'d SET
NO PLATINUM PRICING DUE TO SCARCITY
OVERALL AU-GU ODDS 1:96
EXCHANGE DEADLINE 11/10/08

2005 SP Legendary Cuts Legendary Lineage Autograph Patch

*AUTO PATCH: .6X TO 1.5X AUTO
STATED PRINT RUN 25 SERIAL #'d SETS
T.OLIVA PRINT RUN 16 CARDS
NO T.OLIVA PRICING DUE TO SCARCITY
GOLD PRINT RUN 5 SERIAL #'d SETS
NO GOLD PRICING DUE TO SCARCITY
PLATINUM PRINT RUN 1 SERIAL #'d SET
NO PLATINUM PRICING DUE TO SCARCITY
OVERALL AU-PATCH ODDS 1:196
EXCHANGE DEADLINE 11/10/08

2005 SP Legendary Cuts Material

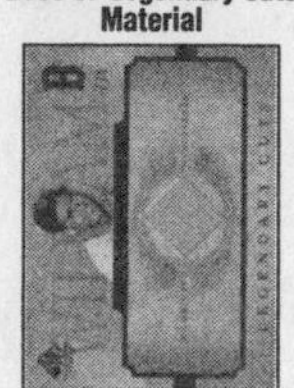

STATED PRINT RUN 75 SERIAL #'d SETS
H.WAGNER PRINT RUN 22 CARDS
GOLD PRINT RUN 15 SERIAL #'d SETS
GOLD H.WAGNER PRINT RUN 5 CARDS
NO GOLD PRICING DUE TO SCARCITY
OVERALL MATERIAL ODDS 1:196

BD Bill Dickey Jsy 15.00 40.00
BL Bob Lemon Jsy 10.00 25.00
BR Babe Ruth Bat 150.00 250.00
CA Roy Campanella Pants 15.00 40.00
CM Christy Mathewson Pants 75.00 150.00
CO Mickey Cochrane Bat 15.00 40.00
CR Joe Cronin Bat 10.00 25.00
CS Casey Stengel Jsy 15.00 40.00
DD Don Drysdale Pants 10.00 25.00
DE Dizzy Dean Jsy 40.00 80.00
EM Eddie Mathews Jsy 15.00 40.00
ES Enos Slaughter Bat 10.00 25.00
EW Early Wynn Pants 6.00 15.00
HG Hank Greenberg Bat 20.00 50.00
HO Gil Hodges Bat 20.00 50.00
HU Catfish Hunter Jsy 6.00 15.00
HW Honus Wagner Pants/22 90.00 150.00
JD Joe DiMaggio Jsy 60.00 120.00
JF Jimmie Foxx Bat 30.00 60.00
JR Jackie Robinson Pants 30.00 60.00
JW Hoyt Wilhelm Jsy 10.00 25.00
LG Lou Gehrig Pants 125.00 200.00
MI Johnny Mize Pants 10.00 25.00
MM Mickey Mantle Pants 100.00 175.00
MO Mel Ott Jsy 15.00 40.00
PR Pee Wee Reese Jsy 10.00 25.00
RC Roberto Clemente Pants 50.00 100.00
RH Rogers Hornsby Jkt 40.00 80.00
RM Roger Maris Pants 30.00 60.00
SI George Sisler Bat 15.00 40.00
SP Satchel Paige Pants 30.00 60.00
TC Ty Cobb Bat 75.00 150.00
TK Ted Kluszewski Jsy 10.00 25.00
TL Tony Lazzeri Bat 15.00 40.00
TM Thurman Munson Pants 15.00 40.00
TW Ted Williams Pants 40.00 80.00
WS Warren Spahn Jsy 15.00 40.00

2005 SP Legendary Cuts Middlemen Cuts

OVERALL CUT AU ODDS 1:196
PRINT RUNS B/WN 2-99 COPIES PER
NO PRICING ON QTY OF 18 OR LESS

AV Arky Vaughan/2
BH Billy Herman/90 60.00 120.00
CG Charlie Gehringer/95 75.00 150.00
FF Frankie Frisch/23 125.00 200.00
JC Joe Cronin/30 125.00 200.00
JS Joe Sewell/76 75.00 150.00
LA Luke Appling/32 100.00 175.00
LB Lou Boudreau/99 50.00 100.00
LD Leo Durocher/18
MC Roy McMillan/5
NF Nellie Fox/3
PW Pee Wee Reese/39 125.00 200.00
RM Rabbit Maranville/5
ZV Zoilo Versalles/4

2005 SP Legendary Cuts Significant Trips Autograph

OVERALL AUTO ODDS 1:96
STATED PRINT RUN 10 SERIAL #'d SETS
NO PRICING DUE TO SCARCITY
EXCHANGE DEADLINE 11/10/08

CSV Jack Clark
Ozzie Smith
Andy Van Slyke
DCR Andre Dawson
Gary Carter
Tim Raines
DGS Andre Dawson
Mark Grace
Ryne Sandberg
FLR Carlton Fisk
Fred Lynn
Jim Rice
HMM Bob Horner
Dale Murphy
Gary Matthews
MBP Joe Morgan
Johnny Bench
Tony Perez
RMP Cal Ripken
Eddie Murray
Jim Palmer
RRA Brooks Robinson
Frank Robinson
Luis Aparicio
SCH Keith Hernandez
Gary Carter
Darryl Strawberry
SEC Dave Stewart
Dennis Eckersley
Jose Canseco

2005 SP Legendary Cuts Significant Trips Material

OVERALL #'d GAME-USED ODDS 1:40
STATED PRINT RUN 10 SERIAL #'d SETS
OVERALL PATCH ODDS 1:96
PATCH PRINT RUN 5 SERIAL #'d SETS
NO PRICING DUE TO SCARCITY

2006 SP Legendary Cuts

This 200-card set was released in August, 2006. The product was issued in four-card packs with an $10 SRP, which came 12 packs to a box and 16 boxes to a case.

COMP.SET w/o SP's (100)	10.00	25.00
COMMON CARD (1-100)	.25	.60
COMMON CARD (101-200)	2.00	5.00

101-200: ONE BASIC OR BRONZE PER BOX
101-200 PRINT RUN 550 SERIAL #'d SETS
EXQUISITE EXCH ODDS 1:60
EXQUISITE EXCH DEADLINE 07/27/07

1 Juan Marichal	.25	.60
2 Monte Irvin	.25	.60
3 Will Clark	.40	1.00
4 Willie McCovey	.40	1.00
5 Eddie Gaedel	.25	.60
6 Ken Williams	.25	.60
7 Earl Battey	.25	.60
8 Rick Ferrell	.25	.60
9 Bob Gibson	.40	1.00
10 Elmer Flick	.25	.60
11 Joe Medwick	.25	.60
12 Lou Brock	.40	1.00
13 Ozzie Smith	1.00	2.50
14 Red Schoendienst	.25	.60
15 Stan Musial	1.00	2.50
16 Tony Oliva	.25	.60
17 Phil Niekro	.25	.60
18 Boog Powell	.25	.60
19 Brooks Robinson	.40	1.00
20 Cal Ripken	2.50	6.00
21 Eddie Murray	.60	1.50
22 Frank Robinson	.25	.60
23 Jim Palmer	.25	.60
24 Jocko Conlon	.25	.60
25 Carlton Fisk	.40	1.00
26 Dwight Evans	.25	.60
27 Fred Lynn	.25	.60
28 Jim Rice	.25	.60
29 Ted Williams	1.50	4.00
30 Wade Boggs	.40	1.00
31 Hugh Duffy	.25	.60
32 Kid Nichols	.25	.60
33 Johnny Vander Meer	.25	.60
34 Dolph Camilli	.25	.60
35 Carl Yastrzemski	1.00	2.50
36 Chick Hafey	.25	.60
37 Kirby Higbe	.25	.60
38 Pee Wee Reese	.40	1.00
39 Pete Reiser	.25	.60
40 Don Sutton	.25	.60
41 Rod Carew	.40	1.00
42 Andre Dawson	.40	1.00
43 Billy Herman	.25	.60
44 Billy Williams	.25	.60
45 Charley Root	.25	.60
46 Hack Wilson	.40	1.00
47 Ernie Banks	.60	1.50
48 Fergie Jenkins	.25	.60
49 Gabby Hartnett	.25	.60
50 Ken Hubbs	.25	.60
51 Kiki Cuyler	.25	.60
52 Mark Grace	.40	1.00
53 Ryne Sandberg	1.25	3.00
54 Harold Newhouser	.25	.60
55 Charlie Robertson	.25	.60
56 Harold Baines	.25	.60
57 Luis Aparicio	.25	.60
58 Luke Appling	.25	.60
59 Nellie Fox	.40	1.00
60 Ray Schalk	.25	.60
61 Red Faber	.25	.60
62 Sloppy Thurston	.25	.60
63 Freddie Lindstrom	.25	.60
64 Vern Kennedy	.25	.60
65 Barry Larkin	.40	1.00
66 Bucky Walters	.25	.60
67 Dolf Luque	.25	.60
68 Al Campanis	.25	.60
69 Ernie Lombardi	.25	.60
70 George Foster	.25	.60
71 Joe Morgan	.25	.60
72 Johnny Bench	.60	1.50
73 Ken Griffey Sr.	.25	.60
74 Ted Kluszewski	.40	1.00
75 Tony Perez	.25	.60
76 Wally Post	.25	.60
77 Bob Feller	.25	.60
78 Bob Lemon	.25	.60
79 Earl Averill	.25	.60
80 Joe Sewell	.25	.60
81 Johnny Hodapp	.25	.60
82 Larry Doby	.25	.60
83 Lou Boudreau	.25	.60
84 Rocky Colavito	.40	1.00
85 Stan Coveleski	.25	.60
86 Nap Lajoie	.40	1.00
87 Al Kaline	.60	1.50
88 Alan Trammell	.25	.60
89 Charlie Gehringer	.25	.60
90 Denny McLain	.25	.60
91 Hank Greenberg	.60	1.50
92 Jack Morris	.25	.60
93 Mark Fidrych	.25	.60
94 Ray Boone	.25	.60
95 Rudy York	.25	.60
96 Buck Leonard	.25	.60
97 Bo Jackson	.60	1.50
98 Zoilo Versalles	.25	.60
99 John Kruk	.25	.60
100 Don Drysdale	.40	1.00
101 Cecil Cooper	2.00	5.00
102 Vic Wertz	2.00	5.00
103 Kirk Gibson	2.00	5.00
104 Maury Wills	2.00	5.00
105 Steve Garvey	2.00	5.00
106 Warren Spahn	3.00	8.00
107 Paul Molitor	5.00	12.00
108 Robin Yount	3.00	8.00
109 Rollie Fingers	2.00	5.00
110 Bob Allison	2.00	5.00
111 Kirby Puckett	3.00	8.00
112 Tim Raines	2.00	5.00
113 George Pipgras	2.00	5.00
114 Eddie Grant	2.00	5.00
115 Hoyt Wilhelm	2.00	5.00
116 Sal Maglie	2.00	5.00
117 Ron Santo	[illegible]	[illegible]
118 Wally Joyner	2.00	5.00
119 Tom Seaver	3.00	8.00
120 Tommie Agee	2.00	5.00
121 Harmon Killebrew	3.00	8.00
122 Bill Dickey	2.00	5.00
123 Early Wynn	2.00	5.00
124 Bobby Murcer	2.00	5.00
125 Bucky Dent	2.00	5.00
126 Dave Winfield	2.00	5.00
127 Don Larsen	2.00	5.00
128 Don Mattingly	5.00	12.00
129 Earle Combs	2.00	5.00
130 Ed Lopat	2.00	5.00
131 Elston Howard	2.00	5.00
132 Everett Scott	2.00	5.00
133 Goose Gossage	2.00	5.00
134 Graig Nettles	2.00	5.00
135 Joe DiMaggio	6.00	15.00
136 Lou Piniella	2.00	5.00
137 Bill Skowron	2.00	5.00
138 Phil Rizzuto	3.00	8.00
139 Red Ruffing	2.00	5.00
140 Reggie Jackson	3.00	8.00
141 Roger Maris	3.00	8.00
142 Ron Guidry	2.00	5.00
143 Tiny Bonham	2.00	5.00
144 Bruce Sutter	2.00	5.00
145 Tony Lazzeri	2.00	5.00
146 Waite Hoyt	2.00	5.00
147 Whitey Ford	3.00	8.00
148 Steve Sax	2.00	5.00
149 Yogi Berra	3.00	8.00
150 Enos Slaughter	2.00	5.00
151 Catfish Hunter	2.00	5.00
152 Dennis Eckersley	2.00	5.00
153 Jose Canseco	3.00	8.00
154 Al Rosen	2.00	5.00
155 Al Simmons	2.00	5.00
156 Chief Bender	2.00	5.00
157 Cy Williams	2.00	5.00
158 Mike Schmidt	4.00	10.00
159 Richie Ashburn	3.00	8.00
160 Robin Roberts	2.00	5.00
161 Steve Carlton	2.00	5.00
162 Judy Johnson	2.00	5.00
163 Al Oliver	2.00	5.00
164 Bill Mazeroski	3.00	8.00
165 Dave Parker	2.00	5.00
166 Max Carey	2.00	5.00
167 Pie Traynor	2.00	5.00
168 Ralph Kiner	3.00	8.00
169 Roberto Clemente	8.00	20.00
170 Willie Stargell	3.00	8.00
171 Gaylord Perry	2.00	5.00
172 Tony Gwynn	3.00	8.00
173 Nolan Ryan	6.00	15.00
174 Joe Carter	2.00	5.00
175 Frank Howard	2.00	5.00
176 George Kell	2.00	5.00
177 Heinie Manush	2.00	5.00
178 Sam Rice	2.00	5.00
179 Babe Ruth	6.00	15.00
180 Casey Stengel	2.00	5.00
181 Christy Mathewson	3.00	8.00
182 Cy Young	3.00	8.00
183 Dizzy Dean	3.00	8.00
184 Eddie Mathews	3.00	8.00
185 George Sisler	2.00	5.00
186 Honus Wagner	3.00	8.00
187 Jackie Robinson	3.00	8.00
188 Jimmie Foxx	3.00	8.00
189 Johnny Mize	2.00	5.00
190 Lefty Gomez	2.00	5.00
191 Lou Gehrig	5.00	12.00
192 Mel Ott	2.00	5.00
193 Mickey Cochrane	2.00	5.00
194 Rogers Hornsby	3.00	8.00
195 Roy Campanella	3.00	8.00
196 Satchel Paige	3.00	8.00
197 Thurman Munson	3.00	8.00
198 Ty Cobb	4.00	10.00
199 Walter Johnson	3.00	8.00
200 Lefty Grove	2.00	5.00

2006 SP Legendary Cuts Bronze

*101-200 BRONZE: .6X TO 1.5X BASIC
101-200: ONE BASIC OR BRONZE PER BOX
STATED PRINT RUN 99 SERIAL #'d SETS

2006 SP Legendary Cuts A Place in History Cuts

OVERALL CUT AU ODDS 1:96
PRINT RUNS B/WN 1-98 COPIES PER
NO PRICING ON QTY OF 25 OR LESS

AD Abner Doubleday/1		
BA Bob Allison/94	40.00	80.00
BD Bill Dickey/29	125.00	250.00
BG Burleigh Grimes/43	75.00	150.00
BL Bob Lemon/47	30.00	60.00
BR Babe Ruth/1		
CA Roy Campanella/5		
CG Charlie Gehringer/57	60.00	120.00
CH Carl Hubbell/32	125.00	200.00
CM Connie Mack/7		
CO Chuck Connors/25		
CR Charley Root/1		
CW Cy Williams/29	150.00	250.00
CY Cy Young/1		
DD Don Drysdale/19		
DH Dick Howser/28	75.00	150.00
DL Leo Durocher/42	60.00	120.00
DU Joe Dugan/25		
EA Earl Averill/75	50.00	100.00
EM Eddie Mathews/34	60.00	120.00
ER Edd Roush/98	50.00	100.00
ES Everett Scott/1		
EW Early Wynn/36	40.00	80.00
FF Ford Frick/30	100.00	175.00
GB Garland Braxton/1		
GE Lou Gehrig/2		
GH Gabby Hartnett/15		
GS George Sisler/42	300.00	500.00
HC Happy Chandler/61	50.00	100.00
HG Hank Greenberg/31	125.00	250.00
HI Kirby Higbe/59	75.00	150.00
HM Heinie Manush/16		
HW Honus Wagner/2		
JC Joe Cronin/30	75.00	150.00
JD Joe DiMaggio/17		
JF Jimmie Foxx/8		
JH Johnny Hodapp/26	50.00	100.00
JJ Judy Johnson/20		
JM Joe McCarthy/58	125.00	250.00
JR Jackie Robinson/4		
JS Joe Sewell/87	50.00	100.00
KH Ken Hubbs/3		
KL Kenesaw Landis/2		
KW Ken Williams/3		
LA Luke Appling/94	60.00	120.00
LB Lou Boudreau/88	50.00	100.00
LG Lefty Gomez/30	100.00	175.00
LU Dolf Luque/1		
ME Joe Medwick/60	75.00	150.00
MO Mel Ott/5		
PR Pee Wee Reese/57	125.00	200.00
RA Richie Ashburn/3		
RC Roberto Clemente/3		
RD Ray Dandridge/43	60.00	120.00
RE Pete Reiser/75	75.00	150.00
RH Rogers Hornsby/3		
RM Roger Maris/11		
RO Charlie Robertson/42	75.00	150.00
RR Red Ruffing/16		
RS Ray Schalk Best/37	200.00	400.00
RS2 Ray Schalk/75	175.00	300.00
SM Sal Maglie/73	50.00	100.00
SP Satchel Paige/12		
ST Sloppy Thurston/15		
TA Tommie Agee/20		
TB Tiny Bonham/1		
TK Ted Kluszewski/24		
TL Tony Lazzeri/3		
TM Thurman Munson/1		
TS Tris Speaker/1		
TW Ted Williams/7		
TY Ty Cobb/2		
VK Vern Kennedy/61	60.00	120.00
WG Warren Giles/45	75.00	150.00
WI Hoyt Wilhelm/65	40.00	80.00
WS Warren Spahn/41	75.00	150.00
YO Rudy York/3		

2006 SP Legendary Cuts Baseball Chronology Gold

STATED PRINT RUN 550 SERIAL #'d SETS
*PLATINUM: .6X TO 1.5X BASIC
PLATINUM PRINT RUN 99 SERIAL #'d SETS
OVERALL CHRONOLOGY ODDS 1:12

AD Andre Dawson	.75	2.00
AK Al Kaline	1.25	3.00
AT Alan Trammell	.50	1.25
BD Bucky Dent	.50	1.25
BF Bob Feller	.50	1.25
BG Bob Gibson	.75	2.00
BL Bob Lemon	.50	1.25
BM Bill Mazeroski	.75	2.00
BO Bo Jackson	1.25	3.00
BR Babe Ruth	3.00	8.00
BR2 Babe Ruth	3.00	8.00
BR3 Babe Ruth	3.00	8.00
BW Billy Williams	.50	1.25
CA Rod Carew	.75	2.00
CF Carlton Fisk	.75	2.00
CH Catfish Hunter	.50	1.25
CL Roberto Clemente	4.00	10.00
CM Christy Mathewson	1.25	3.00
CN Joe Cronin	.50	1.25
CR Cal Ripken	5.00	12.00
CS Casey Stengel Yanks	.50	1.25
CS2 Casey Stengel Mets	.50	1.25
CY Cy Young	1.25	3.00
DD Don Drysdale	.75	2.00
DE Dennis Eckersley	.50	1.25
DL Don Larsen	.50	1.25
DM Don Mattingly	2.50	6.00
DS Don Sutton	.50	1.25
DZ Dizzy Dean	.75	2.00
EB Ernie Banks	1.25	3.00
EB2 Ernie Banks	1.25	3.00
EM Eddie Murray	1.25	3.00
ES Enos Slaughter	.50	1.25
FL Fred Lynn	.50	1.25
FR Frank Robinson	.50	1.25
GH Gil Hodges	.75	2.00
GP Gaylord Perry	.50	1.25
GS George Sisler	.50	1.25
HG Hank Greenberg	1.25	3.00
HW Honus Wagner	1.25	3.00
HY Hoyt Wilhelm	.50	1.25
JB Johnny Bench	1.25	3.00
JC Joe Carter	.50	1.25
JD Joe DiMaggio	3.00	8.00
JF Jimmie Foxx A's	1.25	3.00
JF2 Jimmie Foxx Sox	[illegible]	[illegible]
JM Johnny Mize	.50	1.25
JO Joe Morgan	.50	1.25
JR Jackie Robinson	1.25	3.00
KG Kirk Gibson	.50	1.25
KP Kirby Puckett	1.25	3.00
LB Lou Boudreau	.50	1.25
LG Lou Gehrig	2.50	6.00
LG2 Lou Gehrig	2.50	6.00
LO Lou Brock	.75	2.00
MC Mickey Cochrane	.50	1.25
MF Mark Fidrych	.50	1.25
MO Mel Ott	.50	1.25
MS Mike Schmidt	2.00	5.00
MW Maury Wills	.50	1.25
NL Nap Lajoie	.75	2.00
NR Nolan Ryan Angels	3.00	8.00
NR2 Nolan Ryan Rgr	3.00	8.00
NR3 Nolan Ryan Rgr	3.00	8.00
OS Ozzie Smith	2.00	5.00
PM Paul Molitor	1.25	3.00
PN Phil Niekro	.50	1.25
PW Pee Wee Reese	.75	2.00
RC Roy Campanella	1.25	3.00
RF Rollie Fingers	.50	1.25
RH Rogers Hornsby	.75	2.00
RI Jim Rice	.50	1.25
RJ Reggie Jackson	.75	2.00
RK Ralph Kiner	.75	2.00
RM Roger Maris	1.25	3.00
RO Brooks Robinson	.75	2.00
RS Ryne Sandberg	2.50	6.00
RY Robin Yount	1.25	3.00
SC Steve Carlton Cards	.50	1.25
SC2 Steve Carlton Phils	.50	1.25
SG Steve Garvey	.50	1.25
SM Stan Musial	2.00	5.00
SP Satchel Paige	1.25	3.00
ST Willie Stargell	.75	2.00
TC Ty Cobb Tigers	2.00	5.00
TC2 Ty Cobb A's	2.00	5.00
TG Tony Gwynn	1.25	3.00
TM Thurman Munson	1.25	3.00
TS Tom Seaver	.75	2.00
TW Ted Williams	3.00	8.00
TW2 Ted Williams	3.00	8.00
WB Wade Boggs Sox	.75	2.00
WB2 Wade Boggs Rays	.75	2.00
WC Will Clark	.75	2.00
WF Whitey Ford	.75	2.00
WJ Walter Johnson	1.25	3.00
WM Willie McCovey	.75	2.00
WS Warren Spahn	.75	2.00
YB Yogi Berra	1.25	3.00
YZ Carl Yastrzemski	2.00	5.00

2006 SP Legendary Cuts Baseball Chronology Materials

STATED ODDS 1:12
SP PRINT RUNS PROVIDED BY UD
NO PRICING ON QTY OF 25 OR LESS

AD Andre Dawson Pants	3.00	8.00
AK Al Kaline Bat	4.00	10.00
AT Alan Trammell Bat	3.00	8.00
BD Bucky Dent Jsy	3.00	8.00
BF Bob Feller Pants	4.00	10.00
BG Bob Gibson Jsy	3.00	8.00
BL Bob Lemon Jsy	3.00	8.00
BM Bill Mazeroski Bat SP/59 *	6.00	15.00
BO Bo Jackson Jsy	4.00	10.00
BR Babe Ruth Sox Pants SP/10 *		
BR2 B.Ruth 60 HR Pants SP/20 *		
BR3 B.Ruth 500 HR Pants SP/20 *		
BW Billy Williams Bat	3.00	8.00
CA Rod Carew Bat	3.00	8.00
CF Carlton Fisk Bat	3.00	8.00
CH Catfish Hunter Jsy	3.00	8.00
CL Roberto Clemente Pants SP/100 *	30.00	60.00
CM Christy Mathewson Pants SP/49 *	60.00	120.00
CN Joe Cronin Bat	4.00	10.00
CR Cal Ripken Pants	6.00	15.00
CS Casey Stengel Yanks Jsy SP/199 *	10.00	25.00
CS2 Casey Stengel Mets Jsy SP/100 *	10.00	25.00
DD Don Drysdale Jsy SP/94 *	10.00	25.00
DE Dennis Eckersley Jsy	3.00	8.00
DL Don Larsen Pants	3.00	8.00
DM Don Mattingly Pants	4.00	10.00
DS Don Sutton Jsy	3.00	8.00
DZ Dizzy Dean Jsy SP/100 *	30.00	60.00
EB Ernie Banks MVP Jsy	4.00	10.00
EB2 Ernie Banks 500 Jsy SP/100 *	6.00	15.00
EM Eddie Murray Jsy	3.00	8.00
ES Enos Slaughter Bat SP/100 *	6.00	15.00
FL Fred Lynn Bat	3.00	8.00
FR Frank Robinson Jsy	3.00	8.00
GH Gil Hodges Bat SP/50 *	10.00	25.00
GP Gaylord Perry Jsy	3.00	8.00
GS George Sisler Bat SP/100 *	8.00	20.00
HG Hank Greenberg Bat SP/198 *	10.00	25.00
HW Honus Wagner Pants SP/10 *		
HY Hoyt Wilhelm Jsy SP/46 *	4.00	10.00
JB Johnny Bench Jsy	4.00	10.00
JC Joe Carter Jsy	3.00	8.00
JD Joe DiMaggio Jsy SP/100 *	40.00	80.00
JF Jimmie Foxx A's Bat SP/50 *	30.00	60.00
JF2 Jimmie Foxx Sox Bat SP/100 *	30.00	60.00
JM Johnny Mize Pants	4.00	10.00
JO Joe Morgan Jsy	3.00	8.00
JR Jackie Robinson Pants SP/10 *		
KG Kirk Gibson Jsy	3.00	8.00
KP Kirby Puckett Bat	4.00	10.00
LB Lou Boudreau Jsy	4.00	10.00
LG L.Gehrig Speech Bat SP/20 *		
LG2 L.Gehrig MVP Bat SP/20 *		
LO Lou Brock Jsy	3.00	8.00
MF Mark Fidrych Jsy	3.00	8.00
MO Mel Ott Jsy SP/100 *	15.00	40.00
MS Mike Schmidt Bat	4.00	10.00
MW Maury Wills Bat	[illegible]	[illegible]
NR Nolan Ryan Angels Jsy SP/109 *	6.00	15.00
NR2 Nolan Ryan 5000 Jsy	6.00	15.00
NR3 Nolan Ryan 7th No-Hitter Jsy	6.00	15.00
OS Ozzie Smith Jkt-Jsy	4.00	10.00
PM Paul Molitor Bat	3.00	8.00
PN Phil Niekro Jsy	3.00	8.00
PW Pee Wee Reese Bat	4.00	10.00
RC Roy Campanella Pants SP/154 *	6.00	15.00
RF Rollie Fingers Jsy	3.00	8.00
RH Rogers Hornsby Bat SP/10 *		
RI Jim Rice Bat	3.00	8.00
RJ Reggie Jackson Jsy	4.00	10.00
RK Ralph Kiner Bat SP/154 *	4.00	10.00
RM Roger Maris Jsy	12.50	30.00
RO Brooks Robinson Bat	4.00	10.00
RS Ryne Sandberg Jsy	4.00	10.00
RY Robin Yount Pants	3.00	8.00
SC Steve Carlton Cards Bat	3.00	8.00
SC2 Steve Carlton Phils Bat	3.00	8.00
SG Steve Garvey Jsy	3.00	8.00
SM Stan Musial Bat	6.00	15.00
SP Satchel Paige Pants SP/50 *	30.00	60.00
ST Willie Stargell Bat	4.00	10.00
TC Ty Cobb Tigers Bat SP/25 *		
TC2 Ty Cobb A's Bat SP/25 *		
TG Tony Gwynn Jsy	3.00	8.00
TM Thurman Munson Jsy	8.00	20.00
TS Tom Seaver Jsy	3.00	8.00
TW Ted Williams Pants SP/198 *	20.00	50.00
TW2 Ted Williams Bat	20.00	50.00
WB Wade Boggs Jsy	3.00	8.00
WB2 Wade Boggs Bat	3.00	8.00
WC Will Clark Jsy	3.00	8.00
WM Willie McCovey Jsy	3.00	8.00
WS Warren Spahn Jsy	6.00	15.00
YB Yogi Berra Jsy	6.00	15.00
YZ Carl Yastrzemski Jsy	4.00	10.00

2006 SP Legendary Cuts Historical Cuts

OVERALL CUT AU ODDS 1:96
STATED PRINT RUN 1 SERIAL #'d SET
NO PRICING DUE TO SCARCITY

2006 SP Legendary Cuts Legendary Materials Gold

PRINT RUNS B/WN 99-225 COPIES PER
*BRONZE: .5X TO 1.2X GOLD
BRONZE PRINT RUNS B/WN 25-99 PER
NO BRONZE PRICING ON QTY OF 25
PLATINUM PRINT RUNS B/WN 5-15 PER
NO PLATINUM PRICING DUE TO SCARCITY
*SILVER: .4X TO 1X GOLD
SILVER PRINT RUNS B/WN 50-199 PER
OVERALL #'d GU ODDS 1:12

AD Andre Dawson Pants/225	3.00	8.00
AK Al Kaline Bat/225	4.00	10.00
AO Al Oliver Bat/225	3.00	8.00
AR Al Rosen Bat/225	3.00	8.00
BD Bucky Dent Jsy/225	3.00	8.00
BF Bob Feller Pants/225	4.00	10.00
BG Bob Gibson Jsy/225	3.00	8.00
BL Barry Larkin Bat/225	3.00	8.00
BM Bill Mazeroski Bat/225	4.00	10.00
BO Bo Jackson Bat/225	4.00	10.00
BP Boog Powell Bat/225	3.00	8.00
BR Babe Ruth Pants/99	150.00	250.00
BS Bruce Sutter Pants/225	3.00	8.00
BW Billy Williams Bat/225	3.00	8.00
CC Cecil Cooper Pants/225	3.00	8.00
CF Carlton Fisk Pants/225	3.00	8.00
CR Cal Ripken Pants/225	6.00	15.00
CW Rod Carew Pants/225	3.00	8.00
CY Carl Yastrzemski Pants/225	4.00	10.00
DC Dave Concepcion Bat/225	3.00	8.00
DE Dennis Eckersley Jsy/225	3.00	8.00
DE2 Dennis Eckersley Jsy/225	3.00	8.00
DL Don Larsen Pants/225	3.00	8.00
DP Dave Parker Jsy/225	3.00	8.00
DW Dave Winfield Bat/225	3.00	8.00
EB Ernie Banks Jsy/225	4.00	10.00
EM Eddie Murray Jsy/225	3.00	8.00
EV Dwight Evans Jsy/225	3.00	8.00
FH Frank Howard Bat/225	3.00	8.00
FJ Fergie Jenkins Jsy/225	3.00	8.00
FL Fred Lynn Pants/225	3.00	8.00
FR Frank Robinson Pants/225	3.00	8.00
FR2 Frank Robinson Bat/225	3.00	8.00
GF George Foster Bat/225	3.00	8.00
GG Goose Gossage Jsy/225	3.00	8.00
GN Graig Nettles Jsy/225	3.00	8.00
GP Gaylord Perry Jsy/225	3.00	8.00
GP2 Gaylord Perry Jsy/225	3.00	8.00
GU Ron Guidry Pants/225	3.00	8.00
HB Harold Baines Bat/225	3.00	8.00
JB Johnny Bench Jsy/225	4.00	10.00
JC Jose Canseco Jsy/225	4.00	10.00
JD Joe DiMaggio Jsy/99	40.00	80.00
JK John Kruk Bat/225	3.00	8.00
JM Jack Morris Jsy/225	3.00	8.00
JO Joe Morgan Jsy/225	3.00	8.00
JP Jim Palmer Jsy/225	3.00	8.00
JP2 Jim Palmer Jsy/225	3.00	8.00
JR Jim Rice Pants/225	3.00	8.00
JT Joe Torre Bat/225	4.00	10.00
JU Juan Marichal Jsy/225	[illegible]	[illegible]
KG Ken Griffey Sr. Pants/225	3.00	8.00
KI Kirk Gibson Jsy/225	3.00	8.00
KP Kirby Puckett Jsy/225	4.00	10.00
LB Lou Brock Jsy/225	3.00	8.00
LB2 Lou Brock Jsy/225	3.00	8.00
LP Lou Piniella Jsy/225	3.00	8.00
MA Don Mattingly Pants/225	4.00	10.00
MG Mark Grace Bat/225	3.00	8.00
MS Mike Schmidt Jsy/225	4.00	10.00
MU Bobby Murcer Bat/225	3.00	8.00
MW Maury Wills Bat/225	3.00	8.00
NR Nolan Ryan Jkt/225	6.00	15.00
OS Ozzie Smith Jsy/225	4.00	10.00
PM Paul Molitor Bat/225	3.00	8.00
PN Phil Niekro Jsy/225	3.00	8.00
PN2 Phil Niekro Jsy/225	3.00	8.00
PR Phil Rizzuto Jsy/99	5.00	12.00
RC Rocky Colavito Bat/225	6.00	15.00
RE Red Schoendienst Jsy/99	5.00	12.00
RF Rollie Fingers Jsy/225	3.00	8.00
RJ Reggie Jackson Bat/225	4.00	10.00
RK Ralph Kiner Bat/225	4.00	10.00
RN Ron Santo Jsy/125	4.00	10.00
RN2 Ron Santo Jsy/125	4.00	10.00
RO Brooks Robinson Jsy/175	4.00	10.00
RR Robin Roberts Pants/225	4.00	10.00
RS Ryne Sandberg Jsy/225	4.00	10.00
RY Robin Yount Jsy/225	3.00	8.00
SC Steve Carlton Bat/225	3.00	8.00
SC2 Steve Carlton Bat/225	3.00	8.00
SG Steve Garvey Jsy/225	3.00	8.00
SK Bill Skowron Bat/225	3.00	8.00
SM Stan Musial Bat/225	6.00	15.00
SS Steve Sax Jsy/225	3.00	8.00
SU Don Sutton Jsy/225	3.00	8.00
TG Tony Gwynn Jsy/225	3.00	8.00
TO Tony Oliva Bat/225	3.00	8.00
TP Tony Perez Pants/225	3.00	8.00
TS Tom Seaver Jsy/225	3.00	8.00
WB Wade Boggs Jsy/225	3.00	8.00
WC Will Clark Jsy/225	3.00	8.00
WC2 Will Clark Jsy/99	3.00	8.00
WJ Wally Joyner Jsy/225	3.00	8.00
WM Willie McCovey Jsy/225	3.00	8.00
YB Yogi Berra Bat/225	6.00	15.00

2006 SP Legendary Cuts Legendary Signature Cuts

OVERALL CUT AU ODDS 1:96
PRINT RUNS B/WN 1-90 COPIES PER
NO PRICING ON QTY OF 25 OR LESS

AS Al Simmons/4		
BD Bill Dickey/34	125.00	250.00
BG Burleigh Grimes/33	75.00	150.00
BL Bob Lemon/77	50.00	100.00
BR Babe Ruth/3		
BW Bucky Walters/52	60.00	120.00
CA Roy Campanella/6		
CB Chief Bender/1		
CG Charlie Gehringer/76	50.00	100.00
CH Catfish Hunter/24		
CM Mickey Cochrane/10		
CO Eddie Collins/3		
CR Charley Root/12		
CS Casey Stengel/35	250.00	400.00
CY Cy Young/1		
DC Dolph Camilli/58	60.00	120.00
DD Dizzy Dean/21		
DL Leo Durocher/22		
DR Don Drysdale/45	125.00	200.00
DU Joe Dugan/25		
EA Earl Averill/50	60.00	120.00
EB Ed Barrow/35	150.00	250.00
EC Earle Combs/65	150.00	250.00
EH Elston Howard/7		
EL Ed Lopat/32	100.00	175.00
EM Eddie Mathews/59	30.00	60.00
ER Edd Roush/90	50.00	100.00
EW Early Wynn/15		
FF Ford Frick/7		
GA Grover Alexander/1		
GE Lou Gehrig/1		
GH Gabby Hartnett/15		
GS George Sisler/14		
HD Hugh Duffy/2		
HE Billy Herman/87	50.00	100.00
HG Hank Greenberg/60	175.00	300.00
HK Harvey Kuehn/89	60.00	120.00
HM Heinie Manush/22		
HO Gil Hodges/3		
HW Honus Wagner/1		
JA Joe Adcock/47	75.00	150.00
JC Jocko Conlon/76	50.00	100.00
JD Joe DiMaggio/5		
JE Johnny Evers/1		
JF Jimmie Foxx/1		
JJ Judy Johnson/40	75.00	150.00
JM Joe McCarthy/67	100.00	200.00
JO Joe Cronin/30	50.00	100.00
JR Jackie Robinson/5		
JS Joe Sewell/83	50.00	100.00
KC Kiki Cuyler/6		
KN Kid Nichols/2		
LA Luke Appling/84	60.00	120.00
LB Lou Boudreau/86	40.00	80.00
LG Lefty Gomez/44	75.00	150.00
LO Ernie Lombardi/25		
MA Mel Allen/67	125.00	200.00
MC Max Carey/79	75.00	150.00
ME Joe Medwick/82	100.00	175.00
MH Miller Huggins/1		
MI Johnny Mize/90	60.00	120.00
MO Mel Ott/1		
NF Nellie Fox/12		
PR Pee Wee Reese/47	125.00	200.00
PT Pie Traynor/26	400.00	600.00
RA Richie Ashburn/22		
RB Ray Boone/51	60.00	120.00
RC Roberto Clemente/3		
RD Ray Dandridge/35	60.00	120.00
RF Red Faber/18		
RH Rogers Hornsby/4		
RM Rabbit Maranville/2		
RO Roger Maris/13		
RR Red Ruffing/72	125.00	200.00
SC Sam Crawford/8		
SP Satchel Paige/7		
SR Sam Rice/31	75.00	150.00
ST Stan Coveleski/81	60.00	120.00
TC Ty Cobb/1		
TK Ted Kluszewski/19		
TM Thurman Munson/2		
TO Tony Lazzeri/1		
TS Tris Speaker/1		
TW Ted Williams/9		
WA Walter Alston/27	50.00	100.00
WH Waite Hoyt/49	75.00	150.00
WI Hoyt Wilhelm/47	50.00	100.00
WJ Walter Johnson/1		
WP Wally Post/66	40.00	80.00
WS Warren Spahn/52	75.00	150.00

2006 SP Legendary Cuts Legendary Dual Cuts

OVERALL CUT AU ODDS 1:96
STATED PRINT RUN 1 SERIAL #'d SET
NO PRICING DUE TO SCARCITY

2006 SP Legendary Cuts Legendary Quad Cuts

OVERALL CUT AU ODDS 1:96
STATED PRINT RUN 1 SERIAL #'d SET
NO PRICING DUE TO SCARCITY

2006 SP Legendary Cuts Memorable Moments Autographs

OVERALL AU STATED ODDS 1:192
PRINT RUNS B/WN 1-99 COPIES PER
NO PRICING ON QTY OF 25 OR LESS

AD Andre Dawson/99	6.00	15.00
BL Barry Larkin/50	20.00	50.00
CC Cesar Cedeno/99	6.00	15.00
CE Cecil Cooper/99	5.00	12.00
DC David Cone/99	6.00	15.00
DM Don Mattingly/50	60.00	120.00
GP Gaylord Perry/99	6.00	15.00
JK John Kruk/99	6.00	15.00
PR Phil Rizzuto/99	15.00	40.00
RF Rollie Fingers/47	8.00	20.00
TR Tim Raines/50	20.00	50.00
TS Tom Seaver/44	30.00	60.00

2006 SP Legendary Cuts Memorable Moments Materials

OVERALL #'d GU ODDS 1:12
PRINT RUNS B/WN 223-225 COPIES PER

AD Andre Dawson Pants/225	3.00	8.00
BF Bob Feller Pants/225	4.00	10.00
BJ Bo Jackson Bat/225	4.00	10.00
BL Barry Larkin Pants/225	4.00	10.00
BM Bobby Murcer Pants/225	3.00	8.00
BS Bruce Sutter Pants/225	3.00	8.00
CC Cesar Cedeno Pants/225	3.00	8.00
CE Cecil Cooper Jsy/225	3.00	8.00
CF Carlton Fisk Pants/225	3.00	8.00
DC David Cone Jsy/225	3.00	8.00

DE Dwight Evans Jsy/225 3.00 8.00
DM Don Mattingly Pants/225 4.00 10.00
DP Dave Parker Jsy/225 3.00 8.00
DS Don Sutton Jsy/225 3.00 8.00
EM Eddie Mathews Pants/225 6.00 15.00
GF George Foster Bat/225 3.00 8.00
GG Goose Gossage Jsy/225 3.00 8.00
GP Gaylord Perry Bat/225 3.00 8.00
JB Johnny Bench Jsy/225 4.00 10.00
JK John Kruk Bat/225 3.00 8.00
JM Johnny Mize Pants/225 4.00 10.00
KG Kirk Gibson Jsy/225 3.00 8.00
MA Juan Marichal Jsy/225 3.00 8.00
MO Joe Morgan Jsy/225 3.00 8.00
MS Mike Schmidt Jsy/225 4.00 10.00
MU Eddie Murray Jsy/225 3.00 8.00
OS Ozzie Smith Jsy/225 4.00 10.00
PO Paul O'Neill Jsy/225 3.00 8.00
PR Phil Rizzuto Jsy/225 4.00 10.00
RC Rocky Colavito Bat/225 6.00 15.00
RF Rollie Fingers Jsy/225 3.00 8.00
RG Ron Guidry Jsy/223 3.00 8.00
RJ Reggie Jackson Jsy/225 4.00 10.00
RS Ron Santo Bat/225 4.00 10.00
RY Robin Yount Jsy/225 3.00 8.00
SG Steve Garvey Jsy/225 3.00 8.00
SM Stan Musial Bat/225 6.00 15.00
SS Steve Sax Jsy/223 3.00 8.00
TG Tony Gwynn Pants/225 3.00 8.00
TR Tim Raines Jsy/225 3.00 8.00
TS Tom Seaver Jsy/225 3.00 8.00

2006 SP Legendary Cuts Place in History Autographs

OVERALL AU STATED ODDS 1:192
PRINT RUNS B/WN 6-99 COPIES PER
NO PRICING ON QTY OF 25 OR LESS
AD Andre Dawson/99 6.00 15.00
AK Al Kaline/24
AR Al Rosen/99 6.00 15.00
BD Bucky Dent/99 6.00 15.00
BF Bob Feller/35 15.00 40.00
BG Bob Gibson/25
BL Barry Larkin/49 20.00 50.00
BM Bill Mazeroski/99 10.00 25.00
BO Bo Jackson/99 20.00 50.00
BP Boog Powell/99 6.00 15.00
BR Brooks Robinson/35 15.00 40.00
BR2 Brooks Robinson/35 15.00 40.00
BS Bruce Sutter/99 6.00 15.00
BW Billy Williams/99 6.00 15.00
CA Rod Carew/50
CC Cecil Cooper/99 5.00 12.00
CF Carlton Fisk/99 10.00 25.00
CR Cal Ripken/35 100.00 175.00
CY Carl Yastrzemski/45 20.00 50.00
DE Dennis Eckersley/99 6.00 15.00
DE2 Dennis Eckersley/99 6.00 15.00
DL Don Larsen/20
DP Dave Parker/26
DW Dave Winfield/12
EB Ernie Banks/25
EV Dwight Evans/99 10.00 25.00
FH Frank Howard/99 10.00 25.00
FJ Fergie Jenkins/99 6.00 15.00
FL Fred Lynn/99 6.00 15.00
FR Frank Robinson Reds/45 15.00 40.00
FR2 Frank Robinson O's/45 15.00 40.00
GF George Foster/56 6.00 15.00
GG Goose Gossage/25
GN Graig Nettles/99 12.50 30.00
GP Gaylord Perry Rgr/99 6.00 15.00
GP2 Gaylord Perry Giants/99 6.00 15.00
GU Ron Guidry/17
HB Harold Baines/45 8.00 20.00
JB Johnny Bench/42 30.00 60.00
JC Jose Canseco/99 20.00 50.00
JM Jack Morris/82 6.00 15.00
JO Joe Morgan/50 12.50 30.00
JP Jim Palmer/99 10.00 25.00
JR Jim Rice/75 10.00 25.00
JT Joe Torre/99 15.00 40.00
JU Juan Marichal/29 10.00 25.00
JY Johnny Podres/38 12.50 30.00
KG Ken Griffey Sr./99 6.00 15.00
KI Kirk Gibson/25
KP Kirby Puckett/99 60.00 120.00
LA Luis Aparicio/99 10.00 25.00
LA2 Luis Aparicio/99 10.00 25.00
LB Lou Brock/99 10.00 25.00
LB2 Lou Brock/99 10.00 25.00
LP Lou Piniella/99 10.00 25.00
MA Don Mattingly/50 60.00 120.00
MC Denny McLain/31 10.00 25.00
MG Mark Grace/99 10.00 25.00
MS Mike Schmidt/25
MU Bobby Murcer/6
MW Maury Wills/96 6.00 15.00
NR Nolan Ryan/21
OS Ozzie Smith/99 30.00 60.00
PM Paul Molitor/99 15.00 40.00
PN Phil Niekro/52 8.00 20.00
PN2 Phil Niekro/52 8.00 20.00
PR Phil Rizzuto/99 15.00 40.00
RD Red Schoendienst/99 15.00 40.00
RF Rollie Fingers/25
RJ Reggie Jackson/25
RK Ralph Kiner/99 15.00 40.00
RO Ron Santo/99 20.00 50.00
RO2 Ron Santo/99 20.00 50.00
RR Robin Roberts/55 12.50 30.00
RS Ryne Sandberg/25
RY Robin Yount/99 15.00 40.00
SC Steve Carlton/99 10.00 25.00
SC2 Steve Carlton/99 10.00 25.00
SG Steve Garvey/99 10.00 25.00
SM Stan Musial/45 30.00 60.00
SS Steve Sax/99 5.00 12.00
SU Don Sutton/24
TG Tony Gwynn/26 40.00 80.00
TO Tony Oliva/99 6.00 15.00
TO2 Tony Oliva/99 6.00 15.00
TP Tony Perez/24
TR Tim Raines/97 10.00 25.00
TS Tom Seaver/55 30.00 60.00
WB Wade Boggs/50 20.00 50.00
WC Will Clark/92 10.00 25.00
WC2 Will Clark/92 10.00 25.00
WF Whitey Ford/35 30.00 60.00
WJ Wally Joyner/99 10.00 25.00
WM Willie McCovey/25
YB Yogi Berra/25

2006 SP Legendary Cuts When It Was A Game Silver

STATED PRINT RUN 550 SERIAL #'d SETS
*GOLD: .6X TO 1.5X BASIC
GOLD PRINT RUN 99 SERIAL #'d SETS
OVERALL WIWAG ODDS 1:12
AD Andre Dawson .75 2.00
AK Al Kaline 1.25 3.00
AR Al Rosen .50 1.25
BF Bob Feller .50 1.25
BG Bob Gibson .50 1.25
BM Bill Mazeroski .75 2.00
BR Babe Ruth 3.00 8.00
BS Bruce Sutter .50 1.25
BW Billy Williams .50 1.25
CA Rod Carew .75 2.00
CF Carlton Fisk .75 2.00
CO Rocky Colavito .75 2.00
CR Cal Ripken 5.00 12.00
CY Cy Young 1.25 3.00
DD Don Drysdale .75 2.00
DE Dennis Eckersley .50 1.25
DL Don Larsen .50 1.25
DP Dave Parker .50 1.25
DY Denny McLain .50 1.25
EB Ernie Banks 1.25 3.00
ED Eddie Murray 1.25 3.00
EM Eddie Mathews 1.25 3.00
EV Dwight Evans .50 1.25
FH Frank Howard .50 1.25
FJ Fergie Jenkins .50 1.25
FL Fred Lynn .50 1.25
FR Frank Robinson Reds .50 1.25
FR2 Frank Robinson O's .50 1.25
GG Goose Gossage .50 1.25
GN Graig Nettles .50 1.25
GP Gaylord Perry .50 1.25
GS George Sisler .50 1.25
GU Ron Guidry .50 1.25
HB Harold Baines .50 1.25
HG Hank Greenberg 1.25 3.00
HO Rogers Hornsby .75 2.00
HW Honus Wagner 1.25 3.00
JB Johnny Bench 1.25 3.00
JD Joe DiMaggio 3.00 8.00
JF Jimmie Foxx 1.25 3.00
JK John Kruk .50 1.25
JM Jack Morris .50 1.25
JO Joe Morgan .50 1.25
JP Jim Palmer .50 1.25
JR Jackie Robinson 1.25 3.00
JT Joe Torre .75 2.00
JU Juan Marichal .50 1.25
KG Ken Griffey Sr. .50 1.25
KI Kirk Gibson .50 1.25
KP Kirby Puckett 1.25 3.00
LA Luis Aparicio .50 1.25
LB Lou Brock .75 2.00
LG Lou Gehrig 2.50 6.00
LP Lou Piniella .50 1.25
MA Don Mattingly 2.50 6.00
MC Mickey Cochrane .50 1.25
MO Mel Ott .50 1.25
MS Mike Schmidt 2.00 5.00
MU Bobby Murcer .50 1.25
MW Maury Wills .50 1.25
MZ Johnny Mize .75 2.00
NR Nolan Ryan 3.00 8.00
OS Ozzie Smith 2.00 5.00
PM Paul Molitor .50 1.25
PN Phil Niekro .50 1.25
PR Phil Rizzuto .75 2.00
PS Johnny Podres .50 1.25
RC Roberto Clemente 4.00 10.00
RF Rollie Fingers .50 1.25
RI Jim Rice .50 1.25
RJ Reggie Jackson .75 2.00
RK Ralph Kiner .75 2.00
RN Ron Santo .75 2.00
RO Brooks Robinson .75 2.00
RO2 Brooks Robinson .75 2.00
RR Robin Roberts .50 1.25
RS Red Schoendienst .50 1.25
RY Robin Yount 1.25 3.00
SA Ryne Sandberg 2.50 6.00
SC Steve Carlton .50 1.25
SC2 Steve Carlton .50 1.25
SG Steve Garvey .50 1.25
SK Bill Skowron .50 1.25
SM Stan Musial 2.00 5.00
SP Satchel Paige .75 2.00
SU Don Sutton .50 1.25
TG Tony Gwynn 1.25 3.00
TM Thurman Munson 1.25 3.00
TO Tony Oliva .50 1.25
TO2 Tony Oliva .50 1.25
TP Tony Perez .50 1.25
TR Tim Raines .50 1.25
TS Tom Seaver .75 2.00
WB Wade Boggs .75 2.00
WC Will Clark .75 2.00
WF Whitey Ford .75 2.00
WJ Wally Joyner .50 1.25
WM Willie McCovey .75 2.00
YB Yogi Berra 1.25 3.00
YZ Carl Yastrzemski 2.00 5.00

2006 SP Legendary Cuts When It Was A Game Materials

OVERALL #'d GU ODDS 1:12
PRINT RUNS B/WN 5-75 COPIES PER
NO PRICING ON QTY OF 25 OR LESS
AD Andre Dawson Pants/75 4.00 10.00
AK Al Kaline Pants/25
AR Al Rosen Pants/75 4.00 10.00
BF Bob Feller Pants/75 5.00 12.00
BG Bob Gibson Jsy/75 4.00 10.00
BM Bill Mazeroski Jsy/75 5.00 12.00
BR Babe Ruth Pants/25
BS Bruce Sutter Pants/75 4.00 10.00
BW Billy Williams Jsy/75 4.00 10.00
CA Rod Carew Jsy/75 4.00 10.00
CF Carlton Fisk Pants/75 4.00 10.00
CO Rocky Colavito Jsy/75 8.00 20.00
CR Cal Ripken Pants/75 8.00 20.00
DD Don Drysdale Pants/75 10.00 25.00
DE Dennis Eckersley Jsy/75 4.00 10.00
DL Don Larsen Pants/75 4.00 10.00
DP Dave Parker Jsy/75 4.00 10.00
EB Ernie Banks Jsy/75 5.00 12.00
ED Eddie Murray Jsy/75 4.00 10.00
EM Eddie Mathews Pants/75 8.00 20.00
EV Dwight Evans Jsy/25
FH Frank Howard Jsy/25
FJ Fergie Jenkins Jsy/75 4.00 10.00
FL Fred Lynn Jsy/75 4.00 10.00
FR Frank Robinson Reds Bat/75 4.00 10.00
FR2 Frank Robinson O's Bat/75 10.00 25.00
GG Goose Gossage Jsy/25
GN Graig Nettles Jsy/75 4.00 10.00
GP Gaylord Perry Bat/75 4.00 10.00
GS George Sisler Bat/75 10.00 25.00
GU Ron Guidry Jsy/75 4.00 10.00
HB Harold Baines Jsy/25
HG Hank Greenberg Bat/75 15.00 40.00
HO Rogers Hornsby Bat/75 15.00 40.00
JB Johnny Bench Jsy/75 5.00 12.00
JD Joe DiMaggio Jsy/75 40.00 80.00
JF Jimmie Foxx Bat/75 15.00 40.00
JK John Kruk Bat/75 4.00 10.00
JM Jack Morris Jsy/25
JO Joe Morgan Jsy/75 4.00 10.00
JP Jim Palmer Jsy/75 4.00 10.00
JR Jackie Robinson Jsy/75 20.00 50.00
JT Joe Torre Bat/75 5.00 12.00
JU Juan Marichal Jsy/75 5.00 12.00
KG Ken Griffey Sr. Jsy/75 4.00 10.00
KI Kirk Gibson Jsy/75 4.00 10.00
KP Kirby Puckett Jsy/75 5.00 12.00
LA Luis Aparicio Jsy/25
LB Lou Brock Jsy/25
LG Lou Gehrig Bat/75 75.00 150.00
LP Lou Piniella Jsy 4.00 10.00
MA Don Mattingly Pants/75 5.00 12.00
MC Mickey Cochrane Bat/25
MO Mel Ott Jsy/75 15.00 40.00
MS Mike Schmidt Jsy/75 8.00 20.00
MU Bobby Murcer Pants/75 4.00 10.00
MW Maury Wills Jsy/75 4.00 10.00
MZ Johnny Mize Pants/75 5.00 12.00
NR Nolan Ryan Jsy/25
OS Ozzie Smith Jkt-Jsy/75 5.00 12.00
PM Paul Molitor Bat/75 4.00 10.00
PN Phil Niekro Jsy/75 4.00 10.00
PR Phil Rizzuto Jsy/25
RC Roberto Clemente Jsy/75 40.00 80.00
RF Rollie Fingers Pants/75 4.00 10.00
RI Jim Rice Jsy/75 4.00 10.00
RJ Reggie Jackson Jsy/25
RK Ralph Kiner Bat/75 5.00 12.00
RN Ron Santo Jsy/75 5.00 12.00
RO Brooks Robinson Pants/25
RO2 Brooks Robinson Pants/25
RR Robin Roberts Pants/75 5.00 12.00
RS Red Schoendienst Jsy/75 5.00 12.00
RY Robin Yount Jsy/75 4.00 10.00
SA Ryne Sandberg Jsy/25
SC Steve Carlton Pants/75 4.00 10.00
SC2 Steve Carlton Pants/75 4.00 10.00
SG Steve Garvey Jsy/75 4.00 10.00
SK Bill Skowron Bat/75 4.00 10.00
SM Stan Musial Bat/75 8.00 20.00
SP Satchel Paige Pants/5
SU Don Sutton Jsy/75 4.00 10.00
TG Tony Gwynn Jsy/75 4.00 10.00
TM Thurman Munson Pants/75 10.00 25.00
TO Tony Oliva Jsy/75 4.00 10.00
TO2 Tony Oliva Jsy/75 4.00 10.00
TP Tony Perez Pants/75 4.00 10.00
TR Tim Raines Jsy/75 4.00 10.00
TS Tom Seaver Jsy/75 4.00 10.00
WB Wade Boggs Jsy/75 4.00 10.00
WC Will Clark Jsy/75 4.00 10.00
WJ Wally Joyner Jsy/75 4.00 10.00
WM Willie McCovey Jsy/75 4.00 10.00
YB Yogi Berra Pants/75 8.00 20.00
YZ Carl Yastrzemski Jsy-Pants/75 5.00 12.00

2006 SP Legendary Cuts When It Was A Game Cuts

OVERALL CUT AU ODDS 1:96
PRINT RUNS B/WN 2-99 COPIES PER
NO PRICING ON QTY OF 25 OR LESS
AC Al Campanis/30 150.00 250.00
BD Bill Dickey/24
BG Burleigh Grimes/56 50.00 100.00
BL Bob Lemon/79 50.00 100.00
CG Charlie Gehringer/64 30.00 60.00
CH Carl Hubbell/80 75.00 150.00
CR Joe Cronin/34 75.00 150.00
DC Dolph Camilli/2
DD Dizzy Dean/4

DR Don Drysdale/6
DU Leo Durocher/25
EA Earl Averill/67 15.00 40.00
EB Earl Battey/25
EF Elmer Flick/25
EL Ernie Lombardi/24
EM Eddie Mathews/33 100.00 175.00
ER Edd Roush/98 50.00 100.00
ES Enos Slaughter/8
EW Early Wynn/40 60.00 120.00
FF Ford Frick/30 100.00 175.00
FL Freddie Lindstrom/25
GH Gabby Hartnett/6
GP George Pipgras/25
GS George Sisler/37 300.00 500.00
HA Chick Hafey/12
HC Happy Chandler/64 50.00 100.00
HE Billy Herman/99 50.00 100.00
HG Hank Greenberg/27
HM Heinie Manush/29 125.00 250.00
HO Gil Hodges/5
HU Catfish Hunter/34 40.00 80.00
HW Hoyt Wilhelm/56 50.00 100.00
JA Joe Adcock/18
JC Jocko Conlon/73 50.00 100.00
JD Joe Dugan/30 125.00 200.00
JH Johnny Hodapp/17
JJ Judy Johnson/20
JM Joe McCarthy/51 125.00 250.00
JS Joe Sewell/78 50.00 100.00
JV Johnny Vander Meer/45 75.00 150.00
LA Luke Appling/83 60.00 120.00
LB Lou Boudreau/50 60.00 120.00
LG Lefty Gomez/36 100.00 200.00
LO Ed Lopat/28 100.00 175.00
MC Max Carey/71 40.00 80.00
ME Joe Medwick/57 125.00 200.00
MI Johnny Mize/70 60.00 120.00
PR Pee Wee Reese/52 125.00 200.00
RA Richie Ashburn/12
RB Ray Boone/68 60.00 120.00
RD Ray Dandridge/75 50.00 100.00
RF Rick Ferrell/25
RR Red Ruffing/44 150.00 250.00
SC Stan Coveleski/91 60.00 120.00
SE George Selkirk/30 125.00 200.00
SM Sal Maglie/68 60.00 120.00
SR Sam Rice/33 100.00 200.00
ST Willie Stargell/27 100.00 200.00
TA Tommie Agee/12
TK Ted Kluszewski/50 100.00 175.00
VK Vern Kennedy/85 60.00 120.00
VW Vic Wertz/30 125.00 200.00
WA Walter Alston/16
WH Waite Hoyt/70 60.00 120.00
WP Wally Post/66 60.00 120.00
WS Warren Spahn/78 60.00 120.00
ZV Zoilo Versalles/5

2007 SP Legendary Cuts

This 200-card set was released in September, 2007. The set was issued in four-card packs, with an $10 SRP, which came 12 packs per box and 16 boxes per case. While all cards in this set feature veterans, cards numbered 101-200 are a league leader subset and those cards were issued to a stated print run of 550 serial numbered sets.

COMP.SET w/o SP's (100) 10.00 25.00
COMMON CARD (1-100) .25 .60
COMMON CARD (101-200) 2.00 5.00
101-200 RANDOMLY INSERTED
101-200 PRINT RUN 550 SERIAL #'d SETS
1 Phil Niekro .25 .60
2 Brooks Robinson .40 1.00
3 Frank Robinson .40 1.00
4 Jim Palmer .25 .60
5 Cal Ripken Jr. 2.50 6.00
6 Warren Spahn .40 1.00
7 Cy Young .60 1.50
8 Carl Yastrzemski .60 1.50
9 Wade Boggs .40 1.00
10 Carlton Fisk .40 1.00
11 Joe Cronin .25 .60
12 Bobby Doerr .25 .60
13 Roy Campanella .60 1.50
14 Pee Wee Reese .40 1.00
15 Rod Carew .40 1.00
16 Ernie Banks .60 1.50
17 Fergie Jenkins .25 .60
18 Billy Williams .25 .60
19 Gabby Hartnett .25 .60
20 Luis Aparicio .25 .60
21 Nellie Fox .40 1.00
22 Luke Appling .25 .60
23 Joe Morgan .25 .60
24 Johnny Bench .60 1.50
25 Tony Perez .25 .60
26 George Foster .25 .60
27 Johnny Vander Meer .25 .60
28 Bob Feller .25 .60
29 Bob Lemon .25 .60
30 Lou Boudreau .25 .60
31 Early Wynn .25 .60
32 Charlie Gehringer .25 .60
33 George Kell .25 .60
34 Hal Newhouser .25 .60
35 Al Kaline .60 1.50
36 Ted Kluszewski .40 1.00
37 Harvey Kuenn .25 .60
38 Maury Wills .25 .60
39 Don Drysdale .40 1.00
40 Don Sutton .25 .60
41 Eddie Mathews .60 1.50
42 Joe Adcock .25 .60
43 Paul Molitor .60 1.50
44 Kirby Puckett .60 1.50
45 Harmon Killebrew .60 1.50
46 Monte Irvin .25 .60
47 Ralph Kiner .40 1.00
48 Christy Mathewson .60 1.50
49 Hoyt Wilhelm .25 .60
50 Tom Seaver .40 1.00
51 Allie Reynolds .25 .60
52 Joe DiMaggio 1.50 4.00
53 Lou Gehrig 1.25 3.00
54 Babe Ruth 1.50 4.00
55 Casey Stengel .25 .60
56 Phil Rizzuto .40 1.00
57 Thurman Munson .60 1.50
58 Johnny Mize .25 .60
59 Yogi Berra .60 1.50
60 Rube Marquard .25 .60
61 Don Mattingly 1.25 3.00
62 Ray Dandridge .25 .60
63 Rollie Fingers .25 .60
64 Roberto Clemente 2.00 5.00
65 Reggie Jackson .40 1.00
66 Dennis Eckersley .25 .60
67 Robin Yount .60 1.50
68 Jimmie Foxx .60 1.50
69 Lefty Grove .25 .60
70 Richie Ashburn .40 1.00
71 Jim Bunning .25 .60
72 Steve Carlton .25 .60
73 Robin Roberts .25 .60
74 Mike Schmidt 1.00 2.50
75 Willie Stargell .40 1.00
76 Ozzie Smith 1.00 2.50
77 Bill Mazeroski .40 1.00
78 Honus Wagner .60 1.50
79 Pie Traynor .25 .60
80 Tony Gwynn .60 1.50
81 Willie McCovey .40 1.00
82 Gaylord Perry .25 .60
83 Juan Marichal .25 .60
84 Orlando Cepeda .25 .60
85 Satchel Paige .60 1.50
86 George Sisler .25 .60
87 Ken Boyer .25 .60
88 Joe Medwick .25 .60
89 Travis Jackson .25 .60
90 Stan Musial 1.00 2.50
91 Dizzy Dean .40 1.00
92 Bob Gibson .40 1.00
93 Red Schoendienst .25 .60
94 Lou Brock .40 1.00
95 Enos Slaughter .25 .60
96 Nolan Ryan 1.50 4.00
97 Smokey Burgess .25 .60
98 Mickey Vernon .25 .60
99 Vern Stephens .25 .60
100 Rick Ferrell .25 .60
101 Phil Niekro LL 2.00 5.00
102 Brooks Robinson LL 3.00 8.00
103 Frank Robinson LL 3.00 8.00
104 Jim Palmer LL 2.00 5.00
105 Cal Ripken Jr. LL 5.00 12.00
106 Warren Spahn LL 3.00 8.00
107 Cy Young LL 3.00 8.00
108 Nellie Fox LL 3.00 8.00
109 Carl Yastrzemski LL 3.00 8.00
110 Joe Sewell LL 3.00 8.00
111 Wade Boggs LL 3.00 8.00
112 Carlton Fisk LL 3.00 8.00
113 Jackie Robinson LL 3.00 8.00
114 Roy Campanella LL 3.00 8.00
115 Pee Wee Reese LL 3.00 8.00
116 Earl Averill LL 2.00 5.00
117 Rod Carew LL 3.00 8.00
118 Ernie Banks LL 3.00 8.00
119 Fergie Jenkins LL 2.00 5.00
120 Billy Williams LL 2.00 5.00
121 Al Lopez LL 2.00 5.00
122 Luis Aparicio LL 2.00 5.00
123 Luke Appling LL 2.00 5.00
124 Joe Morgan LL 2.00 5.00
125 Johnny Bench LL 3.00 8.00
126 Tony Perez LL 2.00 5.00
127 George Foster LL 2.00 5.00
128 Bob Feller LL 2.00 5.00
129 Bob Lemon LL 2.00 5.00
130 Larry Doby LL 2.00 5.00
131 Lou Boudreau LL 2.00 5.00
132 George Kell LL 2.00 5.00
133 Hal Newhouser LL 2.00 5.00
134 Al Kaline LL 3.00 8.00
135 Ty Cobb LL 4.00 10.00
136 Charlie Keller LL 2.00 5.00
137 Buck Leonard LL 2.00 5.00
138 Maury Wills LL 2.00 5.00
139 Don Drysdale LL 3.00 8.00
140 Don Sutton LL 2.00 5.00
141 Eddie Mathews LL 3.00 8.00
142 Paul Molitor LL 3.00 8.00
143 Kirby Puckett LL 4.00 10.00
144 Harmon Killebrew LL 3.00 8.00
145 Monte Irvin LL 2.00 5.00
146 Mel Ott LL 3.00 8.00
147 Charlie Gehringer LL 2.00 5.00
148 Hoyt Wilhelm LL 2.00 5.00
149 Tom Seaver LL 3.00 8.00
150 Ted Kluszewski LL 3.00 8.00
151 Joe DiMaggio LL 4.00 10.00
152 Lou Gehrig LL 4.00 10.00
153 Babe Ruth LL 5.00 12.00
154 Casey Stengel LL 2.00 5.00
155 Phil Rizzuto LL 3.00 8.00
156 Thurman Munson LL 3.00 8.00
157 Johnny Mize LL 2.00 5.00
158 Yogi Berra LL 3.00 8.00
159 Roger Maris LL 3.00 8.00
160 Early Wynn LL 2.00 5.00
161 Bobby Doerr LL 2.00 5.00
162 Joe Cronin LL 2.00 5.00
163 Don Mattingly LL 4.00 10.00
164 Ray Dandridge LL 2.00 5.00
165 Rollie Fingers LL 2.00 5.00
166 Christy Mathewson LL 3.00 8.00
167 Reggie Jackson LL 3.00 8.00
168 Dennis Eckersley LL 2.00 5.00
169 Mickey Cochrane LL 2.00 5.00
170 Jimmie Foxx LL 3.00 8.00
171 Lefty Gomez LL 2.00 5.00
172 Jim Bunning LL 2.00 5.00
173 Steve Carlton LL 2.00 5.00
174 Robin Roberts LL 2.00 5.00
175 Richie Ashburn LL 3.00 8.00
176 Mike Schmidt LL 3.00 8.00
177 Ralph Kiner LL 3.00 8.00
178 Willie Stargell LL 3.00 8.00
179 Roberto Clemente LL 6.00 15.00
180 Bill Mazeroski LL 3.00 8.00
181 Honus Wagner LL 3.00 8.00
182 Pie Traynor LL 2.00 5.00
183 Tony Gwynn LL 3.00 8.00
184 Willie McCovey LL 3.00 8.00
185 Gaylord Perry LL 2.00 5.00
186 Juan Marichal LL 2.00 5.00
187 Orlando Cepeda LL 2.00 5.00
188 Satchel Paige LL 3.00 8.00
189 George Sisler LL 2.00 5.00
190 Rogers Hornsby LL 3.00 8.00
191 Stan Musial LL 3.00 8.00
192 Dizzy Dean LL 3.00 8.00
193 Bob Gibson LL 3.00 8.00
194 Red Schoendienst LL 3.00 8.00
195 Lou Brock LL 3.00 8.00
196 Enos Slaughter LL 2.00 5.00
197 Nolan Ryan LL 5.00 12.00
198 Mickey Vernon LL 2.00 5.00
199 Walter Johnson LL 3.00 8.00
200 Rick Ferrell LL 2.00 5.00

2007 SP Legendary Cuts A Stitch in Time Memorabilia

OVERALL AU-GU ODDS 1:12
BG Bob Gibson 3.00 8.00
BR Brooks Robinson 4.00 10.00
BW Billy Williams 3.00 8.00
CR Cal Ripken Jr. 6.00 15.00
DE Dwight Evans 3.00 8.00
DM Don Mattingly 4.00 10.00
EM Eddie Murray 3.00 8.00
GP Gaylord Perry 3.00 8.00
HK Harmon Killebrew 4.00 10.00
JB Johnny Bench 4.00 10.00
JR Jim Rice 3.00 8.00
KP Kirby Puckett 6.00 15.00
MS Mike Schmidt 5.00 12.00
PM Paul Molitor 3.00 8.00
RC Rod Carew 3.00 8.00
RJ Reggie Jackson 4.00 10.00
TG Tony Gwynn 4.00 10.00

2007 SP Legendary Cuts Enshrinement Cuts

OVERALL CUT ODDS 1:96
PRINT RUNS B/WN 1-86 COPIES PER
NO PRICING ON QTY 25 OR LESS
AB Al Barlick/44 50.00 100.00
BD Bill Dickey/5
BL Bob Lemon/53 30.00 60.00
BR Babe Ruth/1
CG Charlie Gehringer/65 40.00 80.00
CH Carl Hubbell/31 100.00 200.00
EA Earl Averill/6
EC Earle Combs/27 200.00 250.00
ER Edd Roush/65 30.00 60.00
EW Early Wynn/15
FF Frankie Frisch/2
GH Gabby Hartnett/31 90.00 150.00
HM Heinie Manush/10
HN Hal Newhouser/40 30.00 60.00
HU Catfish Hunter/17
HW Honus Wagner/1
JC Joe Cronin/86 40.00 80.00
JD Joe DiMaggio/19
JF Jimmie Foxx/1
LA Luke Appling/45 30.00 60.00
LB Lou Boudreau/30 30.00 60.00
MO Mel Ott/4
RH Rogers Hornsby/1
ST Willie Stargell/15
TC Ty Cobb/1
WH Waite Hoyt/33 50.00 100.00
WS Warren Spahn/35 60.00 120.00

2007 SP Legendary Cuts Historical Cuts

OVERALL CUT ODDS 1:96
STATED PRINT RUN 1 SER.#'d SET
NO PRICING DUE TO SCARCITY
AD Abner Doubleday
BR Babe Ruth
CL Charles Lindbergh

2007 SP Legendary Cuts Inside the Numbers Cuts

OVERALL CUT ODDS 1:96
PRINT RUNS B/WN 4-119 COPIES PER
NO PRICING ON QTY 25 OR LESS
BD Bill Dickey/28 60.00 120.00
BH Babe Herman/99 40.00 80.00

BL Bob Lemon/75 30.00 60.00
CG Charlie Gehringer/60 40.00 80.00
CH Carl Hubbell/70 50.00 100.00
CK Charlie Keller/38 50.00 100.00
EA Earl Averill/57 30.00 60.00
EL Ernie Lombardi/38 175.00 250.00
EM Eddie Mathews/70 60.00 120.00
ES Enos Slaughter/69 30.00 60.00
EW Early Wynn/34 40.00 80.00
FS Fred Snodgrass/75 75.00 150.00
GH Gabby Hartnett/25
GR Lefty Grove/73 150.00 200.00
HG Hank Greenberg/25
JC Joe Cronin/29 60.00 120.00
JM Joe Medwick/119 60.00 120.00
JV Johnny Vander Meer/39 60.00 120.00
LA Luke Appling/59
LB Lou Boudreau/13
LG Lefty Gomez/75 75.00 150.00
MC Max Carey/8
RA Richie Ashburn/4
RD Ray Dandridge/5
RH Rogers Hornsby/6
RM Rube Marquard/33 75.00 150.00
SC Stan Coveleski/72 50.00 100.00
ST Willie Stargell/6
VK Vern Kennedy/45
VS Vern Stephens/10
WH Waite Hoyt/65 40.00 80.00
WI Hoyt Wilhelm/55 40.00 80.00
WS Warren Spahn/55 50.00 100.00

2007 SP Legendary Cuts Legendary Americana

RANDOM INSERTS IN PACKS
STATED PRINT RUN 550 SER.#'d SETS
1 George Washington Carver 1.25 3.00
2 George Custer 1.25 3.00
3 Frederick Douglass 1.25 3.00
4 Crazy Horse UER 1.25 3.00
Photo is not Crazy Horse
5 William Cody 1.25 3.00
6 Abraham Lincoln 2.00 5.00
7 Thomas Edison 1.25 3.00
8 Andrew Carnegie 1.25 3.00
9 Eli Whitney 1.25 3.00
10 Harriet Tubman 1.25 3.00
11 Davy Crockett 1.25 3.00
12 Robert E. Lee 2.00 5.00
13 John D. Rockefeller 1.25 3.00
14 Billy the Kid 1.25 3.00
15 Ulysses S. Grant 2.00 5.00
16 Doc Holliday 1.25 3.00
17 Annie Oakley 1.25 3.00
18 Kit Carson 1.25 3.00
19 Francis Scott Key 1.25 3.00
20 Franklin Delano Roosevelt 1.25 3.00
21 Mark Twain 1.25 3.00
22 Thomas Paine 1.25 3.00
23 Walt Whitman 1.25 3.00
24 Alexander Graham Bell 1.25 3.00
25 Susan B. Anthony 1.25 3.00
26 Harriet Beecher Stowe 1.25 3.00
27 Eleanor Roosevelt 1.25 3.00
28 John F. Kennedy 2.00 5.00
29 P.T. Barnum 1.25 3.00
30 Frank Lloyd Wright 1.25 3.00
31 Wilbur Wright 1.25 3.00
32 Casey Jones 1.25 3.00
33 Theodore Roosevelt 1.25 3.00
34 Henry Ford 1.25 3.00
35 Dwight D. Eisenhower 1.25 3.00
36 Daniel Boone 1.25 3.00
37 Florence Nightingale 1.25 3.00
38 William Randolph Hearst 1.25 3.00
39 Charles Lindbergh 1.25 3.00
40 Wild Bill Hickok 1.25 3.00
41 William T. Sherman 2.00 5.00
42 Wyatt Earp 2.00 5.00
43 Jesse James 1.25 3.00
44 Boss Tweed 1.25 3.00
45 Daniel Webster 1.25 3.00
46 Joseph Pulitzer 1.25 3.00
47 Abner Doubleday 1.25 3.00
48 Harry Truman 1.25 3.00
49 Amelia Earhart 1.25 3.00
50 Eugene V. Debs 1.25 3.00
51 Bat Masterson 1.25 3.00
52 Will Rogers 1.25 3.00
53 Orville Wright 1.25 3.00
54 Johnny Appleseed 1.25 3.00
55 Jack London 1.25 3.00
56 Washington Irving 1.25 3.00
57 F. Scott Fitzgerald 1.25 3.00
58 Geronimo 4.00 10.00
59 Andrew Jackson 1.25 3.00
60 Zachary Taylor 1.25 3.00
61 George Eastman 1.25 3.00
62 Jefferson Davis 2.00 5.00
63 Sitting Bull 4.00 10.00
64 Clara Barton 1.25 3.00
65 Dorothea Dix 1.25 3.00
66 Booker T. Washington 1.25 3.00
67 Al Capone 4.00 10.00
68 Samuel F.B. Morse 1.25 3.00

69 Alexander Cartwright 1.25 3.00
70 John Marshall 1.25 3.00
71 William Seward 1.25 3.00
72 Andrew Johnson 1.25 3.00
73 Rutherford B. Hayes 1.25 3.00
74 James A. Garfield 1.25 3.00
75 Chester Arthur 1.25 3.00
76 Grover Cleveland 1.25 3.00
77 Benjamin Harrison 1.25 3.00
78 William McKinley 1.25 3.00
79 William H. Taft 1.25 3.00
80 Woodrow Wilson 1.25 3.00
81 Warren G. Harding 1.25 3.00
82 Calvin Coolidge 1.25 3.00
83 Herbert Hoover 1.25 3.00
84 Lyndon B. Johnson 1.25 3.00
85 Richard M. Nixon 1.25 3.00
86 Gerald Ford 1.25 3.00
87 Robert Johnson 1.25 3.00
88 Ronald Reagan 1.25 3.00
89 Chief Joseph 3.00 8.00
90 Butch Cassidy 2.00 5.00
91 Sundance Kid 2.00 5.00
92 Babe Ruth 5.00 12.00
93 Jackie Robinson 3.00 8.00
94 Frederick Winslow Taylor 1.25 3.00
95 Sojourner Truth 1.25 3.00
96 William Lloyd Garrison 1.25 3.00
97 Ira Hayes 1.25 3.00
98 Calamity Jane 1.25 3.00
99 Stonewall Jackson 2.00 5.00
100 Mary Harris Jones 1.25 3.00

2007 SP Legendary Cuts Legendary Cut Signatures

OVERALL CUT ODDS 1:96
PRINT RUNS B/WN 4-119 COPIES PER
NO PRICING ON QTY 25 OR LESS
AB Al Barlick/49 50.00 100.00
AH Happy Chandler/44 40.00 80.00
AR Allie Reynolds/40 60.00 120.00
BA Bob Allison/31 50.00 100.00
BD Bill Dickey/50 50.00 100.00
BG Burleigh Grimes/52 50.00 100.00
BH Babe Herman/99 40.00 80.00
BL Bob Lemon/23
BR Babe Ruth/1
BU Lew Burdette/50 30.00 60.00
BV Bill Veeck/47 200.00 300.00
CA Max Carey/40 50.00 100.00
CG Charlie Gehringer/50 40.00 80.00
CH Carl Hubbell/54 40.00 80.00
CM Connie Mack/6
CR Joe Cronin/28 60.00 120.00
CS Casey Stengel/20
CY Cy Young/1
DC Dolph Camilli/25
DD Dizzy Dean/11
DI Joe DiMaggio/52 400.00 500.00
DU Leo Durocher/84 60.00 120.00
EA Earl Averill/62 40.00 80.00
EB Ewell Blackwell/50 60.00 120.00
EC Earle Combs/11
EL Ed Lopat/66 60.00 120.00
EM Eddie Mathews/69 60.00 120.00
ER Edd Roush/50 30.00 60.00
ES Enos Slaughter/47 40.00 80.00
EW Early Wynn/40 40.00 80.00
FF Ford Frick/88 75.00 150.00
FL Freddy Lindstrom/45 125.00 175.00
GH Gabby Hartnett/50 75.00 150.00
GK George Kelly/95 40.00 80.00
GO Lefty Gomez/5
GP George Pipgras/70 50.00 100.00
GR Lefty Grove/66 150.00 200.00
GS George Sisler/18
HA Chick Hafey/10
HC Harry Caray/10
HG Hank Greenberg/59 175.00 250.00
HH Harvey Haddix/44 75.00 150.00
HK Harvey Kuenn/10
HN Hal Newhouser/14
HO Gil Hodges/25
HU Catfish Hunter/26 40.00 80.00
HW Honus Wagner/2
JA Joe Adcock/49 50.00 100.00
JC Jocko Conlan/54 30.00 60.00
JD Joe Dugan/46 60.00 120.00
JF Jimmie Foxx/4
JH Jesse Haines/25
JJ Jackie Jensen/19
JO Judy Johnson/54 60.00 120.00
JR Jackie Robinson/5
JS Joe Sewell/100 40.00 80.00
JV Johnny Vander Meer/49 60.00 120.00
KB Ken Boyer/19
KH Ken Hubbs/3
LA Luke Appling/92 40.00 80.00
LB Lou Boudreau/5
LD Larry Doby/50 50.00 100.00
LG Lou Gehrig/2
LO Ernie Lombardi/2
MC Mickey Cochrane/7
MI Johnny Mize/133 30.00 60.00
MO Mel Ott/2
NC Norm Cash/5
NF Nellie Fox/5
NL Nap Lajoie/2
PR Pee Wee Reese/39 100.00 150.00
PT Pie Traynor/2
RA Richie Ashburn/50 75.00 150.00
RC Roberto Clemente/3
RD Ray Dandridge/50 40.00 80.00
RF Red Faber/7
RH Rogers Hornsby/3
RI Branch Rickey/3
RM Rube Marquard/52 75.00 150.00
RS Ray Schalk/44 250.00 300.00
SC Stan Coveleski/84 50.00 100.00
SP Satchel Paige/15
SW Warren Spahn/95 30.00 60.00
TC Ty Cobb/2
TJ Travis Jackson/88 40.00 80.00
VD Vince DiMaggio/34 100.00 175.00
VS Vern Stephens/17
WA Walter Alston/48 40.00 80.00
WH Waite Hoyt/79 40.00 80.00
WI Hoyt Wilhelm/60 40.00 80.00
WJ Walter Johnson/1
WO Walter O'Malley/8
WS Willie Stargell/71 75.00 200.00

2007 SP Legendary Cuts Legendary Cut Signatures Dual

OVERALL CUT ODDS 1:96
STATED PRINT RUN 1 SER.#'d SET
NO PRICING DUE TO SCARCITY

2007 SP Legendary Cuts Legendary Cut Signatures Quad

OVERALL CUT ODDS 1:96
STATED PRINT RUN 1 SER.#'d SET
NO PRICING DUE TO SCARCITY

2007 SP Legendary Cuts Legendary Materials

OVERALL AU-GU ODDS 1:12
PRINT RUN B/WN 189-199 COPIES PER
AD1 Andre Dawson/199 3.00 8.00
AD2 Andre Dawson/199 3.00 8.00
AK1 Al Kaline/189 4.00 10.00
AK2 Al Kaline/199 4.00 10.00
AO Al Oliver/199 3.00 8.00
BJ Bo Jackson/199 4.00 10.00
BL Barry Larkin/199 4.00 10.00
BR1 Brooks Robinson/199 4.00 10.00
BR2 Brooks Robinson/199 4.00 10.00
BS Bruce Sutter/199 3.00 8.00
BW Billy Williams/199 3.00 8.00
CA Roy Campanella/199 4.00 10.00
CF1 Carlton Fisk/199 3.00 8.00
CF2 Carlton Fisk/199 3.00 8.00
CR1 Cal Ripken Jr./199 8.00 20.00
CR2 Cal Ripken Jr./199 8.00 20.00
CY1 Carl Yastrzemski/199 4.00 10.00
CY2 Carl Yastrzemski/199 4.00 10.00
DD Don Drysdale/199 4.00 10.00
DE Dwight Evans/199 3.00 8.00
DM1 Don Mattingly/199 4.00 10.00
DM2 Don Mattingly/199 4.00 10.00
DP Dave Parker/199 3.00 8.00
DS Don Sutton/199 3.00 8.00
DW1 Dave Winfield/199 3.00 8.00
DW2 Dave Winfield/199 3.00 8.00
EC Dennis Eckersley/199 3.00 8.00
EM1 Eddie Murray/199 3.00 8.00
EM2 Eddie Murray/199 3.00 8.00
FJ Fergie Jenkins/199 3.00 8.00
FL1 Fred Lynn/199 3.00 8.00
FL2 Fred Lynn/199 3.00 8.00
FR Frank Robinson/199 3.00 8.00
GF George Foster/199 3.00 8.00
GG Goose Gossage/199 3.00 8.00
GP1 Gaylord Perry/199 3.00 8.00
GP2 Gaylord Perry/199 3.00 8.00
HB Harold Baines/199 3.00 8.00
HK1 Harmon Killebrew/199 4.00 10.00
HK2 Harmon Killebrew/199 4.00 10.00
HU Catfish Hunter/199 3.00 8.00
JB1 Johnny Bench/199 4.00 10.00
JB2 Johnny Bench/199 4.00 10.00
JM1 Jack Morris/199 3.00 8.00
JM2 Jack Morris/199 3.00 8.00
JP Jim Palmer/199 3.00 8.00
JR1 Jim Rice/199 3.00 8.00
JR2 Jim Rice/199 3.00 8.00
JT Joe Torre/199 4.00 10.00
KG Ken Griffey Sr./199 3.00 8.00
KG1 Kirk Gibson/199 3.00 8.00
KG2 Kirk Gibson/199 3.00 8.00
KP1 Kirby Puckett/199 10.00 25.00
KP2 Kirby Puckett/199 10.00 25.00
LB1 Lou Brock/199 3.00 8.00
LB2 Lou Brock/199 3.00 8.00
MA Bill Madlock/199 3.00 8.00
MG Mark Grace/199 3.00 8.00
MS1 Mike Schmidt/199 5.00 12.00
MS2 Mike Schmidt/199 5.00 12.00
NR1 Nolan Ryan/199 8.00 20.00
NR2 Nolan Ryan/199 8.00 20.00
OS1 Ozzie Smith/199 5.00 12.00
OS2 Ozzie Smith/199 5.00 12.00
PM1 Paul Molitor/199 3.00 8.00
PM2 Paul Molitor/199 3.00 8.00
PN Phil Niekro/199 3.00 8.00
PO Paul O'Neill/199 3.00 8.00
PW Pee Wee Reese/199 5.00 12.00
RA Roberto Alomar/199 3.00 8.00
RC Roberto Clemente/199 20.00 50.00
RC1 Rod Carew/199 3.00 8.00
RC2 Rod Carew/199 3.00 8.00
RF Rollie Fingers/199 3.00 8.00
RG Ron Guidry/199 6.00 15.00
RJ1 Reggie Jackson/199 3.00 8.00
RJ2 Reggie Jackson/199 3.00 8.00
RM Roger Maris/199 10.00 25.00
RS Ryne Sandberg/199 5.00 12.00
RY1 Robin Yount/199 5.00 12.00
RY2 Robin Yount/199 5.00 12.00
SC Red Schoendienst/199 4.00 10.00
SC1 Steve Carlton/199 3.00 8.00
SC2 Steve Carlton/199 3.00 8.00
SG1 Steve Garvey/199 3.00 8.00
SG2 Steve Garvey/199 3.00 8.00
TG1 Tony Gwynn/199 4.00 10.00
TG2 Tony Gwynn/199 4.00 10.00
TO Tony Oliva/199 3.00 8.00
TP Tony Perez/199 3.00 8.00
WB1 Wade Boggs/199 3.00 8.00
WB2 Wade Boggs/199 3.00 8.00
WC1 Will Clark/199 3.00 8.00
WC2 Will Clark/199 3.00 8.00
WS Willie Stargell/199

2007 SP Legendary Cuts Legendary Materials Dual

*DUAL: .5X TO 1.2X BASIC
OVERALL AU-GU ODDS 1:12
PRINT RUN B/WN 63-125 COPIES PER
AK1 Al Kaline/125 8.00 20.00
AK2 Al Kaline/125 8.00 20.00
BJ Bo Jackson/125 8.00 20.00
CR1 Cal Ripken Jr./125 8.00 20.00
CR2 Cal Ripken Jr./125 8.00 20.00
EM Eddie Mathews/125 8.00 20.00
HK2 Harmon Killebrew/63 6.00 15.00
KP1 Kirby Puckett/125 10.00 25.00
KP2 Kirby Puckett/125 10.00 25.00

2007 SP Legendary Cuts Legendary Materials Triple

*TRIPLE: .6X TO 1.5X BASIC
OVERALL AU-GU ODDS 1:12
PRINT RUN B/WN 9-99 COPIES PER
NO PRICING ON QTY 25 OR LESS
AK1 Al Kaline/32 10.00 25.00
BJ Bo Jackson/99 10.00 25.00
CR1 Cal Ripken Jr./99 10.00 25.00
CR2 Cal Ripken Jr./99 10.00 25.00
KP1 Kirby Puckett/99 12.50 30.00
KP2 Kirby Puckett/99 12.50 30.00
RC Roberto Clemente/99 30.00 60.00

2007 SP Legendary Cuts Legendary Materials Quad

OVERALL AU-GU ODDS 1:12
PRINT RUNS B/WN 13-25 COPIES PER
NO PRICING DUE TO SCARCITY

2007 SP Legendary Cuts Legendary Signatures

OVERALL AU-GU ODDS 1:12
PRINT RUN B/WN 15-199 COPIES PER
NO PRICING ON QTY 25 OR LESS
ASTERISK EQUALS PARTIAL EXCH
EXCH DEADLINE 8/22/2010
AD1 Andre Dawson/199 6.00 15.00
AD2 Andre Dawson/199 6.00 15.00
AK1 Al Kaline/199 10.00 25.00
AK2 Al Kaline/199 10.00 25.00
BF1 Bob Feller/199 12.50 30.00
BF2 Bob Feller/199 12.50 30.00
BF3 Bob Feller/189 12.50 30.00
BG1 Bob Gibson/50 10.00 25.00
BG2 Bob Gibson/50 10.00 25.00
BG3 Bob Gibson/40 10.00 25.00
BJ1 Bo Jackson/100 20.00 50.00
BJ2 Bo Jackson/100 20.00 50.00
BM1 Bill Mazeroski/189 10.00 25.00
BM2 Bill Mazeroski/189 10.00 25.00
BR1 Brooks Robinson/150 10.00 25.00
BR2 Brooks Robinson/140 10.00 25.00
BW1 Billy Williams/199 8.00 20.00
BW2 Billy Williams/189 8.00 20.00
CF1 Carlton Fisk/75 12.50 30.00
CF2 Carlton Fisk/75 12.50 30.00
CF3 Carlton Fisk/65 12.50 30.00
CR3 Cal Ripken Jr./25
CY1 Carl Yastrzemski/25
CY2 Carl Yastrzemski/15
DM1 Don Mattingly/25
DM2 Don Mattingly/25
DM3 Don Mattingly/15
DW1 Dave Winfield/25
DW2 Dave Winfield/15
EB3 Ernie Banks/25
EM1 Eddie Murray/25
EM2 Eddie Murray/25
FJ1 Fergie Jenkins/125 5.00 12.00
FJ2 Fergie Jenkins/125 5.00 12.00
FJ3 Fergie Jenkins/125 5.00 12.00
FR1 Frank Robinson/50 8.00 20.00
FR2 Frank Robinson/50 8.00 20.00
FR3 Frank Robinson/40 8.00 20.00
GP1 Gaylord Perry/199 6.00 15.00
GP2 Gaylord Perry/199 6.00 15.00
HK1 Harmon Killebrew/100 30.00 60.00
HK2 Harmon Killebrew/90 30.00 60.00
JB1 Johnny Bench/25
JB2 Johnny Bench/25
JB3 Johnny Bench/15
JM1 Juan Marichal/199 5.00 12.00
JM2 Juan Marichal/199 5.00 12.00
JM3 Juan Marichal/189 5.00 12.00
JP1 Jim Palmer/199 6.00 15.00
JP2 Jim Palmer/199 6.00 15.00
JP3 Jim Palmer/199 6.00 15.00
JT Joe Torre/99 20.00 50.00
KG Kirk Gibson/199 8.00 20.00
LA1 Luis Aparicio/199 6.00 15.00
LA2 Luis Aparicio/186 6.00 15.00
MS1 Mike Schmidt/35 20.00 50.00
MS2 Mike Schmidt/35 20.00 50.00
MS3 Mike Schmidt/25
NR1 Nolan Ryan/25
NR2 Nolan Ryan/25
NR3 Nolan Ryan/15
OS1 Ozzie Smith/100 15.00 40.00
OS2 Ozzie Smith/100 15.00 40.00
OS3 Ozzie Smith/100 15.00 40.00
PM1 Paul Molitor/100 10.00 25.00
PM2 Paul Molitor/90 10.00 25.00
RC1 Rod Carew/35 20.00 50.00
RC2 Rod Carew/35 20.00 50.00
RJ1 Reggie Jackson/25
RJ2 Reggie Jackson/15
RS1 Ryne Sandberg/25
RS2 Ryne Sandberg/25
RS3 Ryne Sandberg/25
RY1 Robin Yount/35 20.00 50.00
RY2 Robin Yount/35 20.00 50.00
RY3 Robin Yount/25
SC1 Steve Carlton/199 10.00 25.00
SC2 Steve Carlton/199 10.00 25.00
SC3 Steve Carlton/189 10.00 25.00
SM1 Stan Musial/25
SM2 Stan Musial/25
TG1 Tony Gwynn/25
TG2 Tony Gwynn/25
TG3 Tony Gwynn/15
TP1 Tony Perez/199 5.00 12.00
TP2 Tony Perez/199 5.00 12.00
WB1 Wade Boggs/35 15.00 40.00
WB2 Wade Boggs/35 15.00 40.00
WB3 Wade Boggs/35 15.00 40.00
WC1 Will Clark/199 10.00 25.00
WC2 Will Clark/199 10.00 25.00
WM1 Willie McCovey/25
WM2 Willie McCovey/25
WM3 Willie McCovey/15
YB1 Yogi Berra/25
YB2 Yogi Berra/25
YB3 Yogi Berra/15

2007 SP Legendary Cuts Masterful Materials

OVERALL AU-GU ODDS 1:12
AD Andre Dawson 3.00 8.00
BJ Bo Jackson 4.00 10.00
BL Barry Larkin 3.00 8.00
BM Bill Madlock 3.00 8.00
BR Brooks Robinson 4.00 10.00
BS Bruce Sutter 3.00 8.00
CF Carlton Fisk 3.00 8.00
CR Cal Ripken Jr. 6.00 15.00
CY Carl Yastrzemski 4.00 10.00
DE Dwight Evans 3.00 8.00
DM Don Mattingly 4.00 10.00
DP Dave Parker 3.00 8.00
DS Don Sutton 3.00 8.00
DW Dave Winfield 3.00 8.00
EM Eddie Mathews 4.00 10.00
FL Fred Lynn 3.00 8.00
FR Frank Robinson 3.00 8.00
GP Gaylord Perry 3.00 8.00
JB Johnny Bench 4.00 10.00
JR Jim Rice 3.00 8.00
KG Ken Griffey Sr. 3.00 8.00
KP Kirby Puckett 6.00 15.00
MS Mike Schmidt 5.00 12.00
MU Eddie Murray 3.00 8.00
NR Nolan Ryan 8.00 20.00
PM Paul Molitor 3.00 8.00
RJ Reggie Jackson 4.00 10.00
RS Ryne Sandberg 4.00 10.00
RY Robin Yount 3.00 8.00
SC Steve Carlton 3.00 8.00
SG Steve Garvey 3.00 8.00
TG Tony Gwynn 4.00 10.00
WB Wade Boggs 3.00 8.00
WC Will Clark 3.00 8.00
WM Willie McCovey 4.00 10.00
YB Yogi Berra 5.00 12.00

2007 SP Legendary Cuts Quotation Cuts

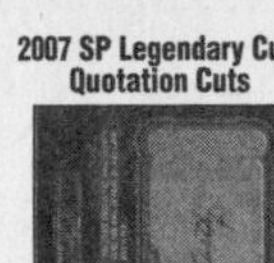

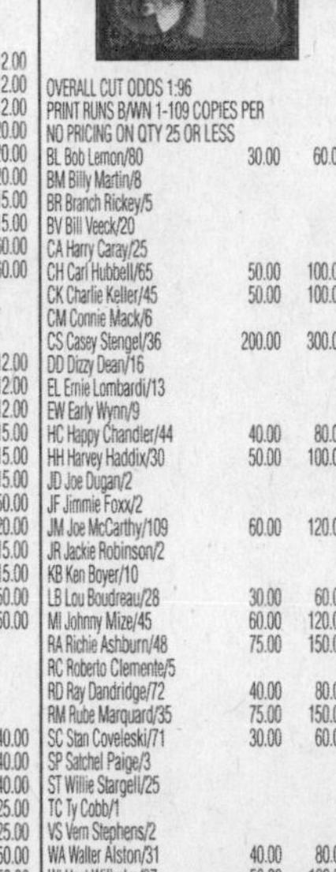

OVERALL CUT ODDS 1:96
PRINT RUNS B/WN 1-109 COPIES PER
NO PRICING ON QTY 25 OR LESS
BL Bob Lemon/80 30.00 60.00
BM Billy Martin/8
BR Branch Rickey/5
BV Bill Veeck/20
CA Harry Caray/25
CH Carl Hubbell/65 50.00 100.00
CK Charlie Keller/45 50.00 100.00
CM Connie Mack/6
CS Casey Stengel/36 200.00 300.00
DD Dizzy Dean/16
EL Ernie Lombardi/13
EW Early Wynn/9
HC Happy Chandler/44 40.00 80.00
HH Harvey Haddix/30 50.00 100.00
JD Joe Dugan/2
JF Jimmie Foxx/2
JM Joe McCarthy/109 60.00 120.00
JR Jackie Robinson/2
KB Ken Boyer/10
LB Lou Boudreau/28 30.00 60.00
MI Johnny Mize/45 60.00 120.00
RA Richie Ashburn/48 75.00 150.00
RC Roberto Clemente/5
RD Ray Dandridge/72 40.00 80.00
RM Rube Marquard/35 75.00 150.00
SC Stan Coveleski/71 30.00 60.00
SP Satchel Paige/3
ST Willie Stargell/25
TC Ty Cobb/1
VS Vern Stephens/2
WA Walter Alston/31 40.00 80.00
WI Hoyt Wilhelm/37 50.00 100.00
WS Warren Spahn/60 40.00 80.00

2007 SP Legendary Cuts Reel History Film Frame

STATED ODDS 1:576
CARDS SERIAL #'d TO ONE
BR Babe Ruth/785 * 60.00 120.00
LG Lou Gehrig/473 * 50.00 100.00

2007 SP Legendary Cuts When it Was a Game Memorabilia

OVERALL AU-GU ODDS 1:12
AT Alan Trammell 3.00 8.00
BF Bob Feller 3.00 8.00
BG Bob Gibson 3.00 8.00
BM Bill Mazeroski 4.00 10.00
BW Billy Williams 3.00 8.00
CF Carlton Fisk 3.00 8.00
CY Carl Yastrzemski 4.00 10.00
DE Dennis Eckersley 3.00 8.00
DM Don Mattingly 4.00 10.00
DW Dave Winfield 3.00 8.00
EM Eddie Murray 3.00 8.00
FJ Fergie Jenkins 3.00 8.00
FL Fred Lynn 3.00 8.00
FR Frank Robinson 3.00 8.00
GP Gaylord Perry 3.00 8.00
HK Harmon Killebrew 4.00 10.00
JP Jim Palmer 3.00 8.00
JR Jim Rice 3.00 8.00
KG Kirk Gibson 3.00 8.00
KP Kirby Puckett 6.00 15.00
LB Lou Brock 3.00 8.00
MS Mike Schmidt 5.00 12.00
NR Nolan Ryan 8.00 20.00
PM Paul Molitor 3.00 8.00
PW Pee Wee Reese 4.00 10.00
RF Rollie Fingers 3.00 8.00
RJ Reggie Jackson 4.00 10.00
RM Roger Maris 10.00 25.00
RS Red Schoendienst 3.00 8.00
TG Tony Gwynn 4.00 10.00

2008 SP Legendary Cuts

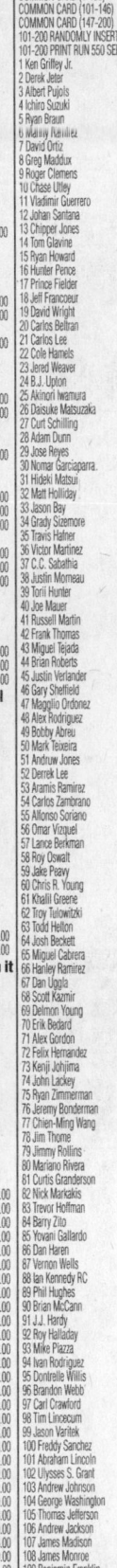

COMP.SET w/o SP's (100) 8.00 20.00
COMMON CARD (1-100) .20 .50
COMMON CARD (101-146) 2.00 5.00
COMMON CARD (147-200) 2.00 5.00
101-200 RANDOMLY INSERTED
101-200 PRINT RUN 550 SERIAL #'d SETS
1 Ken Griffey Jr. .75 2.00
2 Derek Jeter 1.25 3.00
3 Albert Pujols 1.25 3.00
4 Ichiro Suzuki .75 2.00
5 Ryan Braun .60 1.50
6 Manny Ramirez .50 1.25
7 David Ortiz .30 .75
8 Greg Maddux .60 1.50
9 Roger Clemens .60 1.50
10 Chase Utley .50 1.25
11 Vladimir Guerrero .50 1.25
12 Johan Santana .50 1.25
13 Chipper Jones .50 1.25
14 Tom Glavine .30 .75
15 Ryan Howard .60 1.50
16 Hunter Pence .50 1.25
17 Prince Fielder .30 .75
18 Jeff Francoeur .30 .75
19 David Wright .60 1.50
20 Carlos Beltran .20 .50
21 Carlos Lee .20 .50
22 Cole Hamels .50 1.25
23 Jered Weaver .20 .50
24 B.J. Upton .30 .75
25 Akinori Iwamura .20 .50
26 Daisuke Matsuzaka .50 1.25
27 Curt Schilling .30 .75
28 Adam Dunn .30 .75
29 Jose Reyes .30 .75
30 Nomar Garciaparra .50 1.25
31 Hideki Matsui .50 1.25
32 Matt Holliday .50 1.25
33 Jason Bay .30 .75
34 Grady Sizemore .30 .75
35 Travis Hafner .20 .50
36 Victor Martinez .30 .75
37 C.C. Sabathia .30 .75
38 Justin Morneau .50 1.25
39 Torii Hunter .20 .50
40 Joe Mauer .50 1.25
41 Russell Martin .20 .50
42 Frank Thomas .50 1.25
43 Miguel Tejada .30 .75
44 Brian Roberts .20 .50
45 Justin Verlander .60 1.50
46 Gary Sheffield .20 .50
47 Magglio Ordonez .30 .75
48 Alex Rodriguez .75 2.00
49 Bobby Abreu .20 .50
50 Mark Teixeira .50 1.25
51 Andruw Jones .20 .50
52 Derrek Lee .20 .50
53 Aramis Ramirez .20 .50
54 Carlos Zambrano .30 .75
55 Alfonso Soriano .30 .75
56 Omar Vizquel .30 .75
57 Lance Berkman .30 .75
58 Roy Oswalt .30 .75
59 Jake Peavy .20 .50
60 Chris R. Young .20 .50
61 Khalil Greene .20 .50
62 Troy Tulowitzki .50 1.25
63 Todd Helton .30 .75
64 Josh Beckett .30 .75
65 Miguel Cabrera .50 1.25
66 Hanley Ramirez .50 1.25
67 Dan Uggla .30 .75
68 Scott Kazmir .30 .75
69 Delmon Young .30 .75
70 Erik Bedard .20 .50
71 Alex Gordon .30 .75
72 Felix Hernandez .50 1.25
73 Kenji Johjima .20 .50
74 John Lackey .20 .50
75 Ryan Zimmerman .30 .75
76 Jeremy Bonderman .20 .50
77 Chien-Ming Wang .30 .75
78 Jim Thome .30 .75
79 Jimmy Rollins .30 .75
80 Mariano Rivera .50 1.25
81 Curtis Granderson .30 .75
82 Nick Markakis .50 1.25
83 Trevor Hoffman .30 .75
84 Barry Zito .30 .75
85 Yovani Gallardo .20 .50
86 Dan Haren .20 .50
87 Vernon Wells .20 .50
88 Ian Kennedy RC .50 1.25
89 Phil Hughes .50 1.25
90 Brian McCann .30 .75
91 J.J. Hardy .20 .50
92 Roy Halladay .50 1.25
93 Mike Piazza .50 1.25
94 Ivan Rodriguez .30 .75
95 Dontrelle Willis .20 .50
96 Brandon Webb .30 .75
97 Carl Crawford .30 .75
98 Tim Lincecum .75 2.00
99 Jason Varitek .50 1.25
100 Freddy Sanchez .20 .50
101 Abraham Lincoln 4.00 10.00
102 Ulysses S. Grant 3.00 8.00
103 Andrew Johnson 2.00 5.00
104 George Washington 3.00 8.00
105 Thomas Jefferson 2.00 5.00
106 Andrew Jackson 3.00 8.00
107 James Madison 2.00 5.00
108 James Monroe 2.00 5.00
109 Benjamin Franklin 2.50 6.00
110 Alexander Graham Bell 2.00 5.00
111 Thomas Edison 2.00 5.00
112 Red Baron 2.00 5.00
113 Robert E. Lee 3.00 8.00
114 Mark Twain 2.00 5.00
115 Arthur Conan Doyle 2.00 5.00
116 Bram Stoker 2.00 5.00
117 Jules Verne 2.00 5.00
118 Billy the Kid 2.50 6.00
119 Harriet Beecher Stowe 2.00 5.00
120 Andrew Carnegie 2.00 5.00
121 Lewis Carroll 2.00 5.00
122 Cornelius Vanderbilt 2.00 5.00
123 Brigham Young 2.00 5.00
124 Charles Dickens 2.00 5.00
125 Vincent Van Gogh 2.00 5.00
126 Claude Monet 2.00 5.00
127 Jesse James 2.50 6.00
128 John D. Rockefeller 2.00 5.00
129 Harry Longabaugh 2.00 5.00
130 John F. Kennedy 4.00 10.00
131 Richard Nixon 2.50 6.00
132 Lyndon B. Johnson 2.50 6.00
133 Dwight D. Eisenhower 2.00 5.00
134 Franklin D. Roosevelt 2.00 5.00
135 Harry Truman 2.00 5.00
136 Ronald Reagan 4.00 10.00
137 Bill Clinton 2.50 6.00
138 George H.W. Bush 2.50 6.00
139 Jimmy Carter 2.50 6.00
140 Gerald Ford 2.50 6.00
141 Herbert Hoover 2.00 5.00
142 Calvin Coolidge 2.00 5.00
143 Warren G. Harding 2.00 5.00
144 Woodrow Wilson 2.00 5.00
145 William Taft 2.00 5.00
146 Theodore Roosevelt 2.50 6.00
147 Phil Niekro 2.00 5.00
148 Brooks Robinson 3.00 8.00
149 Cal Ripken Jr. 6.00 15.00
150 Eddie Murray 3.00 8.00
151 Jim Palmer 2.00 5.00
152 Abner Doubleday 2.00 5.00
153 Wade Boggs 3.00 8.00
154 Carl Yastrzemski 5.00 12.00
155 Bobby Doerr 2.00 5.00
156 Carlton Fisk 3.00 8.00
157 Pee Wee Reese 3.00 8.00
158 Ernie Banks 3.00 8.00
159 Fergie Jenkins 2.00 5.00
160 Billy Williams 2.00 5.00
161 Ryne Sandberg 4.00 10.00
162 Luis Aparicio 2.00 5.00
163 Joe Morgan 2.00 5.00
164 Johnny Bench 3.00 8.00
165 Tony Perez 2.00 5.00
166 Bob Feller 2.00 5.00
167 Larry Doby 2.00 5.00
168 Bob Lemon 2.00 5.00
169 Al Kaline 3.00 8.00
170 Warren Spahn 3.00 8.00
171 Robin Yount 3.00 8.00
172 Rollie Fingers 2.00 5.00
173 Harmon Killebrew 3.00 8.00
174 Rod Carew 3.00 8.00
175 Babe Ruth 5.00 12.00
176 Monte Irvin 2.00 5.00
177 Tom Seaver 3.00 8.00
178 Phil Rizzuto 3.00 8.00
179 Jack Chesbro 2.00 5.00
180 Catfish Hunter 2.00 5.00
181 Babe Ruth 5.00 12.00
182 Reggie Jackson 3.00 8.00
183 Dennis Eckersley 2.00 5.00
184 Steve Carlton 2.00 5.00
185 Ed Delahanty 2.00 5.00
186 Mike Schmidt 4.00 10.00
187 Jim Bunning 2.00 5.00
188 Robin Roberts 2.00 5.00
189 Willie Stargell 3.00 8.00
190 Bill Mazeroski 3.00 8.00
191 Ralph Kiner 3.00 8.00
192 Tony Gwynn 5.00 12.00
193 Juan Marichal 2.00 5.00
194 Willie McCovey 3.00 8.00
195 Orlando Cepeda 2.00 5.00
196 Stan Musial 4.00 10.00
197 Ozzie Smith 4.00 10.00
198 Bob Gibson 3.00 8.00
199 Bruce Sutter 2.00 5.00
200 Nolan Ryan 5.00 12.00

2008 SP Legendary Cuts Memorable Moments

RANDOM INSERTS IN PACKS
STATED PRINT RUN 1 SER.#'d SET
MULTIPLE VERSIONS OF EACH CARD
NO PRICING DUE TO SCARCITY

2008 SP Legendary Cuts Baseball Headlines Cut Signatures

RANDOM INSERTS IN PACKS
NO PRICING DUE TO SCARCITY

2008 SP Legendary Cuts Classic Signatures

RANDOM INSERTS IN PACKS
STATED PRINT RUN 25 SER.#'d SETS
NO PRICING DUE TO SCARCITY

2008 SP Legendary Cuts Destination Stardom Memorabilia

RANDOM INSERTS IN PACKS
AG Alex Gordon 4.00 10.00
AI Akinori Iwamura 3.00 8.00
AM Andrew Miller 3.00 8.00
AR Alex Rios 3.00 8.00
BB Billy Butler 3.00 8.00
BM Brian McCann 3.00 8.00
BU B.J. Upton 3.00 8.00
CB Chad Billingsley 3.00 8.00
CD Chris Duncan 3.00 8.00
CG Curtis Granderson 3.00 8.00
CH Cole Hamels 3.00 8.00
DH Dan Haren 3.00 8.00
DM Daisuke Matsuzaka 5.00 12.00
DU Dan Uggla 3.00 8.00
DY Delmon Young 3.00 8.00
FH Felix Hernandez 3.00 8.00
FI Josh Fields 3.00 8.00
GA Garrett Atkins 3.00 8.00
GS Grady Sizemore 3.00 8.00
HA Corey Hart 3.00 8.00
HK Howie Kendrick 3.00 8.00
HP Hunter Pence 3.00 8.00
HR Hanley Ramirez 4.00 10.00
JF Jeff Francoeur 3.00 8.00
JH J.J. Hardy 3.00 8.00
JL James Loney 3.00 8.00
JM John Maine 3.00 8.00
JO Josh Hamilton 10.00 25.00
JP Jon Papelbon 4.00 10.00
JV Justin Verlander 3.00 8.00
JW Jered Weaver 3.00 8.00
KG Khalil Greene 3.00 8.00
LE Jon Lester 3.00 8.00
MH Matt Holliday 3.00 8.00
NM Nick Markakis 3.00 8.00
PF Prince Fielder 4.00 10.00
PH Phil Hughes 4.00 10.00
RB Ryan Braun 4.00 10.00
RG Ryan Garko 3.00 8.00
RH Rich Hill 3.00 8.00
RM Russell Martin 3.00 8.00
RZ Ryan Zimmerman 3.00 8.00
SD Stephen Drew 3.00 8.00
TB Travis Buck 3.00 8.00
TL Tim Lincecum 5.00 12.00
TT Troy Tulowitzki 3.00 8.00
YG Yovani Gallardo 3.00 8.00

2008 SP Legendary Cuts Destined for History Memorabilia

RANDOM INSERTS IN PACKS
AD Adam Dunn 3.00 8.00
AJ Andruw Jones 3.00 8.00
AP Albert Pujols 6.00 15.00
AP Andy Petitte 3.00 8.00
AR Alex Rodriguez 6.00 15.00
AS Alfonso Soriano 3.00 8.00
BW Brandon Webb 3.00 8.00
CB Carlos Beltran 3.00 8.00
CD Carlos Delgado 3.00 8.00
CJ Chipper Jones 4.00 10.00
CL Carlos Lee 3.00 8.00
CM Chien-Ming Wang 5.00 12.00
CS Curt Schilling 3.00 8.00
CZ Carlos Zambrano 3.00 8.00
DJ Derek Jeter 8.00 20.00
DL Derrek Lee 3.00 8.00
DO David Ortiz 4.00 10.00
DW Dontrelle Willis 3.00 8.00
FT Frank Thomas 4.00 10.00
GM Greg Maddux 4.00 10.00
GS Gary Sheffield 3.00 8.00
HA Travis Hafner 3.00 8.00
IR Ivan Rodriguez 3.00 8.00
JM Justin Morneau 3.00 8.00
JP Jake Peavy
JR Jimmy Rollins 3.00 8.00
JS John Smoltz 3.00 8.00
JT Jim Thome 3.00 8.00
MC Miguel Cabrera 3.00 8.00
MO Magglio Ordonez 3.00 8.00
MP Mike Piazza 4.00 10.00
MR Manny Ramirez 4.00 10.00
MT Mark Teixeira 3.00 8.00
MY Michael Young 3.00 8.00
OV Omar Vizquel 3.00 8.00
PM Pedro Martinez 3.00 8.00
RA Aramis Ramirez 3.00 8.00
RC Roger Clemens 4.00 10.00
RE Jose Reyes 3.00 8.00
RH Roy Halladay 3.00 8.00
RJ Randy Johnson 4.00 10.00
RO Roy Oswalt 3.00 8.00
SA Johan Santana 3.00 8.00
SS Sammy Sosa 3.00 8.00
TE Miguel Tejada 3.00 8.00
TG Tom Glavine 3.00 8.00
TH Todd Helton 3.00 8.00
TH Trevor Hoffman 3.00 8.00
VG Vladimir Guerrero 3.00 8.00

2008 SP Legendary Cuts Fall Classic Cut Signatures

RANDOM INSERTS IN PACKS
NO PRICING DUE TO SCARCITY

2008 SP Legendary Cuts Future Legends Signatures

RANDOM INSERTS IN PACKS
STATED PRINT RUN 99 SER.#'d SETS
BM Brian McCann 10.00 25.00
BU B.J. Upton 8.00 20.00
BW Brandon Wood 5.00 12.00
CB Clay Buchholz 10.00 25.00
CB Chad Billingsley 6.00 15.00
CD Chris Duncan 6.00 15.00
CH Chin-Lung Hu 15.00 40.00
CH Cole Hamels 15.00 40.00
CH Corey Hart 4.00 10.00
DB Daric Barton 5.00 12.00
DJ Derek Jeter
DM Daisuke Matsuzaka
DU Dan Uggla 6.00 15.00
FC Fausto Carmona 5.00 12.00
FH Felix Hernandez 10.00 25.00
GA Garrett Atkins 5.00 12.00
HK Hong-Chih Kuo 50.00 100.00
HR Hanley Ramirez 10.00 25.00
IK Ian Kennedy 10.00 25.00
IK2 Ian Kinsler 6.00 15.00
JF Jeff Francis 5.00 12.00
JH Josh Hamilton 15.00 40.00
JL Jon Lester 10.00 25.00
JM John Maine 6.00 15.00
JP Jonathan Papelbon 10.00 25.00
KG Ken Griffey Jr. 40.00 80.00
KY Kevin Youkilis 10.00 25.00
LH Luke Hochevar 6.00 15.00
MC Matt Cain 8.00 20.00
MG Matt Garza 5.00 12.00
NM Nick Markakis 8.00 20.00
PH Phil Hughes 10.00 25.00
RH Rich Hill 5.00 12.00
TH Travis Hafner 6.00 15.00
YG Yovani Gallardo 6.00 15.00

2008 SP Legendary Cuts Generations Dual Autographs

RANDOM INSERTS IN PACKS
ASTERISK EQUALS PARTIAL EXCHANGE
NO PRICING ON SOME DUE TO SCARCITY
EXCHANGE DEADLINE 5/22/2010
AR Luis Aparico 20.00 50.00
  Hanley Ramirez EXCH *
BC Johnny Bench
  Mickey Cochrane/2
BM Johnny Bench 30.00 60.00
  Russ Martin
CH Steve Carlton 60.00 120.00
  Cole Hamels
DR Larry Doby
  Frank Robinson/5
GC Lefty Grove
  Steve Carlton/1
GG Tony Gwynn 30.00 60.00
  Tony Gwynn Jr.
GM Ken Griffey Jr. 150.00 250.00
  Stan Musial
JJ Derek Jeter 125.00 250.00
  Reggie Jackson EXCH
MB Willie McCovey 30.00 60.00
  Lance Berkman
MH Paul Molitor 15.00 40.00
  Travis Hafner
PC Gaylord Perry 12.50 30.00
  Fausto Carmona
PK Jim Palmer 12.50 30.00
  Ian Kennedy
RC Brooks Robinson 12.50 30.00
  Eric Chavez
RG Cal Ripken Jr.
  Lou Gehrig/3
RM Nolan Ryan
  Daisuke Matsuzaka
YH Robin Yount 20.00 50.00
  Corey Hart EXCH *

2008 SP Legendary Cuts Generations Dual Memorabilia

RANDOM INSERTS IN PACKS
AR Luis Aparicio 5.00 12.00
  Hanley Ramirez
BC Lou Brock 4.00 10.00
  Carl Crawford
BL Ernie Banks 8.00 20.00
  Derrek Lee
BM Johnny Bench 5.00 12.00
  Victor Martinez
BM Johnny Bench 4.00 10.00
  Joe Mauer
BP Lance Berkman 4.00 10.00
  Hunter Pence
BY Wade Boggs 5.00 12.00
  Kevin Youkilis
CD Cal Ripken 12.50 30.00
  Derek Jeter
CG Roberto Clemente 15.00 40.00
  Vladimir Guerrero
CH Roger Clemens 4.00 10.00
  Philip Hughes
CK Rod Carew 4.00 10.00
  Howie Kendrick
CM Will Clark 4.00 10.00
  Justin Morneau
CP Orlando Cepeda 5.00 12.00
  Albert Pujols
CS Steve Carlton 4.00 10.00
  Johan Santana
DC Don Sutton 4.00 10.00
  Chad Billingsley
DD Don Mattingly 10.00 25.00
  Derek Jeter
DJ Joe DiMaggio 50.00 100.00
  Derek Jeter
DP Bill Dickey 10.00 25.00
  Jorge Posada
DS Andre Dawson 6.00 15.00
  Alfonso Soriano
DT Don Mattingly 4.00 10.00
  Todd Helton
EA Enos Slaughter 8.00 20.00
  Albert Pujols
EC Eddie Murray 4.00 10.00
  Chipper Jones
FF Frank Robinson 5.00 12.00
  Frank Thomas
FP Carlton Fisk 4.00 10.00
  Mike Piazza
FS Rollie Fingers 4.00 10.00
  Huston Street
FV Carlton Fisk 4.00 10.00
  Jason Varitek
GC Bob Gibson 6.00 15.00
  Chris Carpenter
GF Tony Gwynn 5.00 12.00
  Prince Fielder
GG Gaylord Perry 4.00 10.00
  Greg Maddux
GH Ken Griffey Jr. 20.00 50.00
  Josh Hamilton
GL Tom Glavine 4.00 10.00
  Jon Lester
GP Goose Gossage 4.00 10.00
  Jon Papelbon
GR Goose Gossage 5.00 12.00
  Mariano Rivera
HH Catfish Hunter 5.00 12.00
  Philip Hughes
HU Rogers Hornsby 20.00 50.00
  Chase Utley
JD Jim Rice 5.00 12.00
  David Ortiz
JG Frank Robinson 8.00 20.00
  Ken Griffey Jr.
JG Reggie Jackson 20.00 50.00
  Ken Griffey Jr.
JH Reggie Jackson 4.00 10.00
  Travis Hafner
JJ Reggie Jackson 15.00 40.00
  Derek Jeter
KB Ralph Kiner 10.00 25.00
  Jason Bay
KD Ted Kluszewski 5.00 12.00
  Adam Dunn
KH Harmon Killebrew 4.00 10.00
  Travis Hafner
KK Ken Griffey Sr. 12.50 30.00
  Ken Griffey Jr.
KT Harmon Killebrew 5.00 12.00
  Frank Thomas
LM Fred Lynn 4.00 10.00
  Nick Markakis
MA Mike Schmidt 6.00 15.00
  Albert Pujols
MB Paul Molitor 8.00 20.00
  Ryan Braun
MG Stan Musial
  Ken Griffey Jr.
MJ Roger Maris 15.00 40.00
  Derek Jeter
MM Juan Marichal 4.00 10.00
  Pedro Martinez
MS Bill Mazeroski 8.00 20.00
  Ryne Sandberg
NW Phil Niekro 4.00 10.00
  Tim Wakefield
OJ Ozzie Smith 5.00 12.00
  Jose Reyes
PB Jim Palmer 4.00 10.00
  Erik Bedard
PH Gaylord Perry 4.00 10.00
  Roy Halladay
PL Gaylord Perry 5.00 12.00
  Tim Lincecum
PM Mike Piazza 4.00 10.00
  Russell Martin
PO Dave Parker 5.00 12.00
  David Ortiz
PY Gaylord Perry 4.00 10.00
  Chris Young
RC Nolan Ryan 6.00 15.00
  Roger Clemens
RD Ryne Sandberg 4.00 10.00
  Dan Uggla
RJ Phil Rizzuto 12.50 30.00
  Derek Jeter
RM Cal Ripken 8.00 20.00
  Nick Markakis
RM Babe Ruth 100.00 200.00
  Roger Maris
RO Nolan Ryan 5.00 12.00
  Roy Oswalt
RR Randy Johnson 4.00 10.00
  Rich Hill
RT Cal Ripken 6.00 15.00
  Troy Tulowitzki
RV Nolan Ryan 5.00 12.00
  Justin Verlander
RW Nolan Ryan 5.00 12.00
  Jered Weaver
SA Stan Musial 15.00 40.00
  Albert Pujols
SB Mike Schmidt 8.00 20.00
  Ryan Braun
SC Steve Carlton 5.00 12.00
  Cole Hamels
SG Ben Sheets 4.00 10.00
  Yovani Gallardo
SJ Mike Schmidt 5.00 12.00
  Chipper Jones
SL John Smoltz 5.00 12.00
  Tim Lincecum
SM Tom Seaver 5.00 12.00
  John Maine
SP Tom Seaver 4.00 10.00
  Jake Peavy
SR Ron Santo 6.00 15.00
  Aramis Ramirez
SU Ryne Sandberg 6.00 15.00
  Chase Utley
SY Gary Sheffield 4.00 10.00
  Delmon Young
SZ Mike Schmidt 5.00 12.00
  Ryan Zimmerman
TM Todd Helton 5.00 12.00
  Matt Holliday
TR Cal Ripken 5.00 12.00
  Miguel Tejada
YH Robin Yount 5.00 12.00
  J.J. Hardy
YJ Robin Yount 8.00 20.00
  Derek Jeter
YO Carl Yastrzemski 6.00 15.00
  David Ortiz

2008 SP Legendary Cuts Headliners and Heroes Cut Signatures

RANDOM INSERTS IN PACKS
NO PRICING ON MOST DUE TO SCARCITY
AB Al Barlick/32 30.00 60.00
AL Al Lopez/45 30.00 60.00
BC Ben Chapman/28 100.00 200.00
BH Bucky Harris/18
BH Babe Herman/44 30.00 60.00
BH Billy Herman/76 30.00 60.00
BO Buck O'Neil/10
BT Bill Terry/94 75.00 150.00
CC Chuck Connors/9
CG Charlie Gehringer/40 30.00 60.00
EB Ed Barrow
EF Elmer Flick
EL Ed Lopal/46 40.00 80.00
ER Edd Roush/122 30.00 60.00
ES Enos Slaughter/36 30.00 60.00
EW Eugene Woodling/72 30.00 60.00
FC Frank Crosetti/24
FF Ford Frick
FL Freddie Lindstrom/21
FM Frank McCormick
GK George Kelly/77 30.00 60.00
GS George Selkirk
HC Happy Chandler/75 20.00 50.00
HH Harry Hooper/34 125.00 250.00
JA Joe Adcock
JB James Cool Papa Bell/23
JC Jocko Conlan/43
JD Joe DiMaggio
JH Jesse Haines/37 50.00 100.00
JJ Judy Johnson/38 40.00 80.00
JM Johnny Mize/41 40.00 80.00
JS Joe Sewell/59 30.00 60.00
JS Johnny Sain/50 50.00 100.00
KK Ken Keltner/10
LA Luke Appling/45 30.00 60.00
LB Lou Boudreau/52 30.00 60.00
LW Lloyd Waner
MC Max Carey/31 50.00 100.00
NL Nap Lajoie
PR Pee Wee Reese/52 75.00 150.00
RC Roy Campanella/37 300.00 600.00
RD Ray Dandridge/38 30.00 60.00
RF Red Faber
RM Rube Marquard
SB Smoky Burgess
SC Stan Coveleski/34
SH Stan Hack/10 60.00 120.00
SM Sal Maglie
TC Tony Conigliaro
TJ Travis Jackson/39 60.00 120.00
TL Ted Lyons/34 40.00 80.00
TS Tris Speaker/4
WG Warren Giles/9
ZW Zach Wheat/8
BL1 Buck Leonard/68 30.00 60.00
BL2 Buck Leonard/58 30.00 60.00
BL3 Bob Lemon/39 30.00 60.00

2008 SP Legendary Cuts Legendary Cut Signatures

RANDOM INSERTS IN PACKS
NO PRICING ON MOST DUE TO SCARCITY
AB Al Barlick/52 30.00 60.00
BD Bill Dickey/16
BH Babe Herman/30 40.00 80.00
BH Billy Herman/79 30.00 60.00
BL Bob Lemon 20.00 50.00
BL Buck Leonard 30.00 60.00
BR Babe Ruth/8
CF Curt Flood/26 175.00 300.00
CG Charlie Gehringer/45 30.00 60.00
CH Carl Hubbell/31 20.00 50.00
CK Charlie Keller/34 30.00 60.00
CM Connie Mack/6
CS Casey Stengel/10
DD Don Drysdale/2
DD Dizzy Dean/10
DH Dick Howser/3
EA Earl Averill/44 30.00 60.00
EL Ernie Lombardi/5
EM Eddie Mathews/6
ES Enos Slaughter
EW Early Wynn/37
GH Gabby Hartnett/8
HC Happy Chandler/55 30.00 60.00
HH Harvey Haddix/15
HN Hal Newhouser/52 30.00 60.00
HU Catfish Hunter/37 40.00 80.00
HW Hoyt Wilhelm 30.00 60.00
HW Honus Wagner/6
JC Jocko Conlan/40 20.00 50.00
JD Joe DiMaggio/25
JF Jimmie Foxx/3
JH Jesse Haines/40 40.00 80.00
JJ Judy Johnson/29 20.00 50.00
JM Johnny Mize/41
JM Joe McCarthy/27 40.00 80.00
JS Joe Sewell/46 30.00 60.00
LA Luke Appling/32 20.00 50.00
LB Lyman Bostock/15
LB Lou Boudreau/54 30.00 60.00
LB Lou Boudreau/50 30.00 60.00
LD Larry Doby/4
LD Leo Durocher/11
LG Lou Gehrig/3
LG Lefty Gomez/20
LW Lloyd Waner/60 40.00 80.00
PT Pie Traynor/6
RA Richie Ashburn/7
RC Roy Campanella/26 300.00 600.00
RF Rick Ferrell/108 30.00 60.00
RM Rube Marquard/40
RM Roger Maris/8
RR Red Ruffing
RS Ray Schalk/5
SB Smoky Burgess/28 30.00 60.00
SC Stan Coveleski/45 30.00 60.00
SP Satchel Paige/17
TL Ted Lyons/32 40.00 80.00
WH Waite Hoyt/18
WS Warren Spahn/39 40.00 80.00

2008 SP Legendary Cuts Legendary Cut Signatures Dual

RANDOM INSERTS IN PACKS
STATED PRINT RUN 1 SER.#'d SET
NO PRICING DUE TO SCARCITY
CB Harry Carey
  Jack Buck
LC Kenesaw Landis
  Charles Comiskey

2008 SP Legendary Cuts Legendary Memorabilia 99

RANDOM INSERTS IN PACKS
STATED PRINT RUN 99 SER.#'d SETS
AD Andre Dawson 4.00 10.00
BF Bob Feller 6.00 15.00
BR Brooks Robinson 4.00 10.00
BS Bruce Sutter 3.00 8.00
BW Billy Williams 4.00 10.00
CA Rod Carew 3.00 8.00
CF2 Carlton Fisk 4.00 10.00
CR Cal Ripken Jr. 6.00 15.00
CY Carl Yastrzemski 5.00 12.00
DM Don Mattingly 5.00 12.00
DP2 Dave Parker 3.00 8.00
DP2 Dave Parker 3.00 8.00
DS Don Sutton 3.00 8.00
DW Dave Winfield 3.00 8.00
EB Ernie Banks 5.00 12.00
EH Elston Howard 3.00 8.00
EM Eddie Murray 3.00 8.00
EW Early Wynn 3.00 8.00
FJ Fergie Jenkins 3.00 8.00
FL Fred Lynn 3.00 8.00
FR Frank Robinson 3.00 8.00
GG Goose Gossage 3.00 8.00
GP Gaylord Perry 3.00 8.00
HK Harmon Killebrew 5.00 12.00
JB Johnny Bench 3.00 8.00
JB2 Jim Bunning 3.00 8.00
JC Joe Carter 4.00 10.00
JM Juan Marichal 3.00 8.00
JM Joe Morgan 3.00 8.00
JT Joe Torre 4.00 10.00
LA Luis Aparicio 3.00 8.00
LE Bob Lemon 3.00 8.00
MA Edgar Martinez 4.00 10.00
MG Mark Grace 3.00 8.00
MS Mike Schmidt 4.00 10.00
NR Nolan Ryan 6.00 15.00
OS Ozzie Smith 4.00 10.00
OS2 Ozzie Smith 4.00 10.00
PM2 Paul Molitor 4.00 10.00
PN Phil Niekro 3.00 8.00
PO Paul O'Neill 3.00 8.00
RC Roberto Clemente 20.00 50.00
RF Rollie Fingers 3.00 8.00
RG Ron Guidry 4.00 10.00
RI Jim Rice 3.00 8.00
RJ Reggie Jackson 5.00 12.00
RM Roger Maris 12.50 30.00
RS Red Schoendienst 3.00 8.00
RS Ryne Sandberg 5.00 12.00
RY Robin Yount 4.00 10.00
SA Ron Santo 5.00 12.00
SM Stan Musial 6.00 15.00
ST Steve Carlton 3.00 8.00
TG2 Tony Gwynn 4.00 10.00
TP Tony Perez 3.00 8.00
TR Tim Raines 3.00 8.00
TS Tom Seaver 3.00 8.00
WB Wade Boggs 3.00 8.00
WC Will Clark 4.00 10.00
WF Whitey Ford 5.00 12.00

2008 SP Legendary Cuts Legendary Memorabilia 75

*MEM 75: .4X TO 1X MEM 99
RANDOM INSERTS IN PACKS
STATED PRINT RUN 75 SER.#'d SETS
BJ Bo Jackson 4.00 10.00
OC Orlando Cepeda 3.00 8.00

2008 SP Legendary Cuts Legendary Memorabilia 50

*MEM 50: .4X TO 1X MEM 99
RANDOM INSERTS IN PACKS
STATED PRINT RUN 50 SER.#'d SETS
BD Bill Dickey 5.00 12.00
BJ Bo Jackson 6.00 15.00
BM Bill Mazeroski 5.00 12.00
FM Fred McGriff 4.00 10.00
JD Joe DiMaggio 20.00 50.00
OC Orlando Cepeda 3.00 8.00

2008 SP Legendary Cuts Legendary Memorabilia 35

*MEM 35: .6X TO 1.5X MEM 99
RANDOM INSERTS IN PACKS
STATED PRINT RUN 35 SER.#'d SETS

2008 SP Legendary Cuts Legendary Memorabilia 25

RANDOM INSERTS IN PACKS
STATED PRINT RUN 25 SER.#'d SETS
NO PRICING DUE TO SCARCITY

2008 SP Legendary Cuts Legendary Memorabilia 15

RANDOM INSERTS IN PACKS
STATED PRINT RUN 15 SER.#'d SETS
NO PRICING DUE TO SCARCITY

2008 SP Legendary Cuts Legendary Memorabilia 10

RANDOM INSERTS IN PACKS
STATED PRINT RUN 10 SER.#'d SETS
NO PRICING DUE TO SCARCITY

2008 SP Legendary Cuts Midsummer Classic Cut Signatures

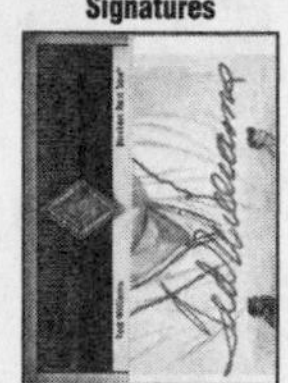

RANDOM INSERTS IN PACKS
NO PRICING DUE TO SCARCITY

2008 SP Legendary Cuts Mystery Cut Signatures

EXCHANGE DEADLINE 12/31/2010
AC Art Carney/27 50.00 100.00
CH Charlton Heston/31 75.00 150.00
EA2 Eddie Arcaro/136 50.00 100.00
EH J.Edgar Hoover/36 125.00 250.00
GF1 Gerald Ford/35 175.00 300.00
JG2 Sir John Gielgud/55 40.00 80.00
JH Jack Haley/34 50.00 100.00
KH Kim Hunter/31 15.00 40.00
LB1 Lucille Ball/51 125.00 250.00
MS1 Max Schmelling/30 60.00 120.00
VP Vincent Price/37 50.00 100.00
NNO Mystery EXCH 250.00 350.00

2009 SP Legendary Cuts

COMP.SET w/o SP's (100) 10.00 25.00
COMMON CARD (1-100) .15 .40
COMMON CARD (101-147) 2.00 5.00
COMMON CARD (148-200) 2.00 5.00
101-200 APPX.ODDS ONE PER BOX
101-200 PRINT RUN 550 SERIAL #'d SETS
1 Brian Roberts .15 .40
2 Derek Jeter 1.00 2.50
3 Evan Longoria .50 1.25
4 Brandon Phillips .15 .40
5 David Wright .50 1.25
6 Ryan Howard .50 1.25
7 Jose Reyes .25 .60
8 Ryan Braun .50 1.25
9 Jim Thome .25 .60
10 Chipper Jones .40 1.00
11 Jimmy Rollins .25 .60
12 Alfonso Soriano .25 .60
13 Alex Rodriguez .60 1.50
14 David Price RC .75 2.00
15 Carlos Beltran .15 .40
16 Aramis Ramirez .15 .40
17 Ken Griffey Jr. .60 1.50
18 Daisuke Matsuzaka .40 1.00
19 Josh Beckett .25 .60
20 Kevin Youkilis .25 .60
21 Carlos Delgado .15 .40
22 Clayton Kershaw .40 1.00
23 Adrian Gonzalez .25 .60
24 Grady Sizemore .25 .60
25 Mark Teixeira .40 1.00
26 Chase Utley .40 1.00
27 Vladimir Guerrero .40 1.00
28 Prince Fielder .25 .60
29 Jeff Samardzija .25 .60
30 Magglio Ordonez .25 .60
31 Cliff Lee .25 .60
32 Josh Hamilton .40 1.00
33 Justin Morneau .40 1.00
34 David Ortiz .25 .60
35 Cole Hamels .40 1.00
36 Edinson Volquez .15 .40
37 Nick Markakis .40 1.00
38 Carlos Zambrano .25 .60
39 Max Scherzer .25 .60
40 Rich Harden .15 .40
41 Ryan Doumit .15 .40
42 Mariano Rivera .40 1.00
43 Alexei Ramirez .25 .60
44 Jake Peavy .15 .40
45 Trevor Hoffman .25 .60
46 Ryan Dempster .15 .40
47 Francisco Liriano .15 .40
48 Travis Hafner .15 .40
49 Joakim Soria .15 .40
50 Albert Pujols 1.00 2.50
51 Ichiro Suzuki .60 1.50
52 CC Sabathia .25 .60
53 Ryan Ludwick .25 .60
54 Mike Lowell .15 .40
55 Tim Lincecum .60 1.50
56 Francisco Rodriguez .25 .60
57 Johan Santana .40 1.00
58 Jonathan Papelbon .25 .60
59 Geovany Soto .25 .60
60 Jacoby Ellsbury .40 1.00
61 Jon Lester .40 1.00
62 Joba Chamberlain .25 .60
63 Rick Ankiel .15 .40
64 Chad Billingsley .15 .40
65 Chien-Ming Wang .25 .60
66 Stephen Drew .15 .40
67 Roy Halladay .40 1.00
68 Ian Kinsler .25 .60
69 Scott Kazmir .15 .40
70 Miguel Tejada .25 .60
71 Carlos Lee .15 .40
72 Hanley Ramirez .40 1.00
73 Carlos Pena .25 .60
74 Alex Gordon .25 .60
75 Pat Burrell .15 .40
76 Dan Uggla .25 .60
77 Joe Mauer .40 1.00
78 Felix Hernandez .40 1.00
79 Jermaine Dye .15 .40
80 Carlos Quentin .25 .60
81 Lance Berkman .25 .60
82 Randy Johnson .25 .60
83 Matt Holliday .40 1.00
84 Curtis Granderson .25 .60
85 Miguel Cabrera .40 1.00
86 Matt Cain .15 .40
87 Troy Tulowitzki .40 1.00
88 Brian McCann .25 .60
89 Adam Dunn .25 .60
90 Matt Kemp .25 .60
91 B.J. Upton .25 .60
92 A.J. Burnett .25 .60
93 Carl Crawford .25 .60
94 Nate McLouth .15 .40
95 Derrek Lee .15 .40
96 Dustin Pedroia .50 1.25
97 Russell Martin .15 .40
98 John Lackey .15 .40
99 Manny Ramirez .40 1.00
100 Jay Bruce .25 .60
101 Ozzie Smith 4.00 10.00
102 Luis Aparicio 2.00 5.00
103 Johnny Bench 3.00 8.00
104 Yogi Berra 3.00 8.00
105 Lou Brock 2.50 6.00
106 Rod Carew 2.50 6.00
107 Whitey Ford 2.50 6.00
108 Dennis Eckersley 2.00 5.00
109 Bob Feller 2.00 5.00
110 Rollie Fingers 2.00 5.00
111 Carlton Fisk 2.50 6.00
112 Bob Gibson 2.50 6.00
113 Catfish Hunter 2.00 5.00
114 Reggie Jackson 2.50 6.00
115 Fergie Jenkins 2.00 5.00
116 Al Kaline 3.00 8.00
117 Harmon Killebrew 3.00 8.00
118 Ralph Kiner 2.50 6.00
119 Juan Marichal 2.00 5.00
120 Vince Coleman 2.00 5.00
121 Bill Mazeroski 2.50 6.00
122 Don Newcombe 2.00 5.00
123 Joe Morgan 2.00 5.00
124 Eddie Murray 3.00 8.00
125 Phil Niekro 2.00 5.00
126 Mike Schmidt 4.00 10.00
127 John Kruk 2.00 5.00
128 Steve Carlton 2.00 5.00
129 Brooks Robinson 2.50 6.00
130 Nolan Ryan 6.00 15.00
131 Dave Winfield 2.00 5.00
132 Bo Jackson 3.00 8.00
133 Paul Molitor 3.00 8.00
134 Billy Williams 2.00 5.00
135 Robin Yount 3.00 8.00
136 Don Mattingly 5.00 12.00
137 Cal Ripken Jr. 6.00 15.00
138 Bobby Doerr 2.00 5.00
139 Goose Gossage 2.00 5.00
140 Wade Boggs 2.50 6.00
141 Jim Palmer 2.00 5.00
142 Carl Yastrzemski 4.00 10.00
143 Frank Robinson 2.50 6.00
144 Joe Carter 2.00 5.00
145 Oil Can Boyd 2.00 5.00
146 Tony Perez 2.00 5.00
147 Gaylord Perry 2.00 5.00
148 Jules Verne 2.00 5.00
149 James K. Polk 2.00 5.00

150 William Henry Harrison 2.00 5.00
151 Manfred von Richthofen 2.00 5.00
152 William Jennings Bryan 2.00 5.00
153 Susan B. Anthony 2.00 5.00
154 Gentleman Jim Corbett 3.00 8.00
155 Cornelius Vanderbilt 2.00 5.00
156 John L. Sullivan 3.00 8.00
157 Daniel Boone 2.00 5.00
158 Davy Crockett 3.00 8.00
159 Edgar Allen Poe 2.00 5.00
160 George Custer 2.00 5.00
161 Harriet Tubman 2.00 5.00
162 Adolphus Busch 2.00 5.00
163 Bonnie Parker 2.00 5.00
164 Clyde Barrow 2.00 5.00
165 Winston Churchill 2.00 5.00
166 Sir Isaac Newton 2.00 5.00
167 Christopher Columbus 2.00 5.00
168 Doc Holliday 2.00 5.00
169 Wyatt Earp 2.00 5.00
170 Sam Houston 2.00 5.00
171 Francis Scott Key 2.00 5.00
172 Betsy Ross 2.00 5.00
173 John Hancock 2.00 5.00
174 Vincent Van Gogh 2.00 5.00
175 Charles Dickens 2.00 5.00
176 Pope John Paul II 3.00 8.00
177 Woodrow Wilson 2.00 5.00
178 James A. Garfield 2.00 5.00
179 Robert E. Lee 3.00 8.00
180 Julius Caesar 2.00 5.00
181 Napoleon Bonaparte 2.00 5.00
182 Alexander Hamilton 2.00 5.00
183 Frederick Douglass 2.00 5.00
184 Booker T. Washington 2.00 5.00
185 Paul Revere 2.00 5.00
186 Grover Cleveland 2.00 5.00
187 Andrew Johnson 2.00 5.00
188 Billy the Kid 2.00 5.00
189 Samuel Adams 2.00 5.00
190 Dwight D. Eisenhower 2.00 5.00
191 Theodore Roosevelt 2.00 5.00
192 Ulysses S. Grant 2.00 5.00
193 George Washington 4.00 10.00
194 John D. Rockefeller 2.00 5.00
195 Martin Van Buren 2.00 5.00
196 John Adams 2.00 5.00
197 Andrew Jackson 2.00 5.00
198 Jesse James 3.00 8.00
199 Thomas Jefferson 2.00 5.00
200 Abraham Lincoln 4.00 10.00

2009 SP Legendary Cuts Classic Signatures

RANDOM INSERTS IN PACKS
PRINT RUNS B/WN 10-25 COPIES PER
NO PRICING DUE TO SCARCITY

2009 SP Legendary Cuts Destination Stardom Memorabilia

OVERALL-MEM ODDS 1:3
BP Brandon Phillips 3.00 8.00
BS Ben Sheets 3.00 8.00
BU B.J. Upton 3.00 8.00
BW Brandon Webb 4.00 10.00
CB Carlos Beltran 3.00 8.00
CU Chase Utley 4.00 10.00
CZ Carlos Zambrano 3.00 8.00
DL Derrek Lee 3.00 8.00
DS Denard Span 3.00 8.00
EV Edinson Volquez 3.00 8.00
FH Felix Hernandez 3.00 8.00
FL Francisco Liriano 3.00 8.00
GS Grady Sizemore 3.00 8.00
JB Josh Beckett 4.00 10.00
JC Joba Chamberlain 4.00 10.00
JE Jacoby Ellsbury 5.00 12.00
JH Josh Hamilton 5.00 12.00
JM Joe Mauer 4.00 10.00
JP Jonathan Papelbon 3.00 8.00
JV Justin Verlander 3.00 8.00
MH Matt Holliday 3.00 8.00
MO Justin Morneau 3.00 8.00
MT Mark Teixeira 3.00 8.00
PE Jake Peavy 3.00 8.00
PF Prince Fielder 3.00 8.00
RC Robinson Cano 3.00 8.00
RM Russell Martin 3.00 8.00
SK Scott Kazmir 3.00 8.00

2009 SP Legendary Cuts Destined for History Memorabilia

OVERALL MEM ODDS 1:3
AP Albert Pujols 6.00 15.00
AR Aramis Ramirez 3.00 8.00
AS Alfonso Soriano 3.00 8.00
CD Carlos Delgado 3.00 8.00
CH Cole Hamels 4.00 10.00
CJ Chipper Jones 4.00 10.00
CS Curt Schilling 3.00 8.00
DJ Derek Jeter 10.00 25.00
DO David Ortiz 4.00 10.00
FT Frank Thomas 5.00 12.00
GS Gary Sheffield 3.00 8.00
HE Todd Helton 3.00 8.00
JG Jason Giambi 3.00 8.00
JP Jorge Posada 3.00 8.00
JS John Smoltz 3.00 8.00
JT Jim Thome 3.00 8.00
JV Jason Varitek 3.00 8.00
KG Ken Griffey Jr. 6.00 15.00
LB Lance Berkman 3.00 8.00
MO Magglio Ordonez 3.00 8.00
MR Mariano Rivera 6.00 15.00
PE Andy Pettitte 3.00 8.00
PM Pedro Martinez 3.00 8.00
RA Manny Ramirez 3.00 8.00
RH Roy Halladay 4.00 10.00
RJ Randy Johnson 4.00 10.00
RO Roy Oswalt 3.00 8.00
TG Tom Glavine 3.00 8.00
TH Trevor Hoffman 3.00 8.00
VG Vladimir Guerrero 3.00 8.00

2009 SP Legendary Cuts Future Legends Signatures

RANDOM INSERTS IN PACKS
PRINT RUNS B/WN 10-125 COPIES PER
NO PRICING ON QTY 25 OR LESS
AG Adrian Gonzalez/125 10.00 25.00
BE Josh Beckett/25
BM Brian McCann/125 10.00 25.00
BP Brandon Phillips/125 6.00 15.00
BU B.J. Upton/125 6.00 15.00
BZ Clay Buchholz/125 8.00 20.00
CG Carlos Gonzalez/125 50.00 100.00
CH Cole Hamels/25
CJ Chipper Jones/25
CK Clayton Kershaw/25
CL Carlos Lee/125 4.00 10.00
CW Chien-Ming Wang/25
CY Chris B. Young/34 10.00 25.00
DJ Derek Jeter/45 150.00 300.00
DL Derrek Lee/125
DM Daisuke Matsuzaka/10
DP Dustin Pedroia/125 20.00 50.00
EE Edwin Encarnacion/125 4.00 10.00
EL Evan Longoria/25
FH Felix Hernandez/125 10.00 25.00
GS Grady Sizemore/25
HR Hanley Ramirez/20
IK Ian Kennedy/125 4.00 10.00
JC Johnny Cueto/125 6.00 15.00
JF Jeff Francoeur/125 6.00 15.00
JL John Lackey/125 4.00 10.00
JN Joe Nathan/125 4.00 10.00
JP Jonathan Papelbon/125 10.00 25.00
JW Josh Willingham/125 6.00 15.00
KG Ken Griffey Jr./125 40.00 80.00
MK Matt Kemp/125 20.00 50.00
MU David Murphy/125 4.00 10.00
NM Nick Markakis/125
PF Prince Fielder/25
RZ Ryan Zimmerman/125 10.00 25.00
TT Troy Tulowitzki/125 10.00 25.00
VM Victor Martinez/125 10.00 25.00
YG Yovani Gallardo/125 8.00 20.00

2009 SP Legendary Cuts Generations Dual Memorabilia

OVERALL MEM ODDS 1:3
GM1B Jason Giambi 6.00 15.00
Don Mattingly
GMAV Jason Varitek 4.00 10.00
Luis Aparicio
GMBC Carlos Beltran 15.00 40.00
Roberto Clemente
GMBJ Derek Jeter 12.50 30.00
Ernie Banks
GMBL Evan Longoria 6.00 15.00
Wade Boggs
GMBO David Ortiz 4.00 10.00
Wade Boggs
GMBP Pedro Martinez 6.00 15.00
Bob Gibson
GMBR Ernie Banks 6.00 15.00
Hanley Ramirez
GMBS Brooks Robinson 4.00 10.00
Scott Rolen
GMBY Ryan Braun 10.00 25.00
Robin Yount
GMCG Roberto Clemente 15.00 40.00
Vladimir Guerrero
GMCH Cole Hamels 5.00 12.00
Steve Carlton
GMCM Cal Ripken Jr. 10.00 25.00
Miguel Tejada
GMCP Steve Carlton 4.00 10.00
Andy Pettitte
GMDB Joe DiMaggio 20.00 50.00
Carlos Beltran
GMDD Daisuke Matsuzaka 8.00 20.00
Don Sutton
GMDJ Derek Jeter 12.50 30.00
Bucky Dent
GMDM Eddie Murray 4.00 10.00
Carlos Delgado
GMDS Joe DiMaggio 20.00 50.00
Grady Sizemore
GMEA Ernie Banks 5.00 12.00
Aramis Ramirez
GMED Derrek Lee 4.00 10.00
Ernie Banks
GMEH Trevor Hoffman 4.00 10.00
Dennis Eckersley
GMEJ Edgar Martinez 4.00 10.00
Jason Bay
GMEP Jonathan Papelbon 4.00 10.00
Dennis Eckersley
GMES Dennis Eckersley 4.00 10.00
Huston Street
GMFM Carlton Fisk 4.00 10.00
Joe Mauer
GMFP Jorge Posada 4.00 10.00
Carlton Fisk
GMFV Carlton Fisk 4.00 10.00
Jason Varitek
GMGG Tony Gwynn 4.00 10.00
Brian Giles
GMGJ Goose Gossage 4.00 10.00
Jonathan Papelbon
GMGM Jason Giambi 4.00 10.00
Tino Martinez
GMGP Jake Peavy 6.00 15.00
Bob Gibson
GMGR Mariano Rivera 5.00 12.00
Goose Gossage
GMGY Carl Yastrzemski 8.00 20.00
Ken Griffey Jr.
GMHG Todd Helton 5.00 12.00
Mark Grace
GMHJ Josh Hamilton 5.00 12.00
Reggie Jackson
GMHY Robin Yount 5.00 12.00
J.J. Hardy
GMJB Brian McCann 4.00 10.00
Johnny Bench
GMJH Josh Hamilton 6.00 15.00
Bo Jackson
GMJJ Reggie Jackson 10.00 25.00
Derek Jeter
GMJO David Ortiz 5.00 12.00
Reggie Jackson
GMJP Bo Jackson 8.00 20.00
Albert Pujols
GMJR Nolan Ryan 12.50 30.00
Randy Johnson
GMJS Mike Schmidt 5.00 12.00
Chipper Jones
GMJV Johnny Bench 4.00 10.00
Victor Martinez
GMLA Don Sutton 4.00 10.00
Chad Billingsley
GMLG Mark Grace 5.00 12.00
Derrek Lee
GMLH Phil Hughes 4.00 10.00
Sparky Lyle
GMLR Sparky Lyle 4.00 10.00
Mariano Rivera
GMMB Paul Molitor 5.00 12.00
Ryan Braun
GMMH Matt Holliday 4.00 10.00
Edgar Martinez
GMMJ Don Mattingly 12.50 30.00
Derek Jeter
GMMK Joe Morgan 4.00 10.00
Ian Kinsler
GMMM Justin Morneau 4.00 10.00
Paul Molitor
GMMP Jake Peavy 4.00 10.00
Jack Morris
GMMR Brooks Robinson 8.00 20.00
Melvin Mora
GMMT Eddie Murray 5.00 12.00
Mark Teixeira
GMMU Chase Utley 4.00 10.00
Joe Morgan
GMMV Jack Morris 4.00 10.00
Justin Verlander
GMNC Graig Nettles 4.00 10.00
Robinson Cano
GMNY Joe DiMaggio 50.00 100.00
Derek Jeter
GMPB Josh Beckett 5.00 12.00
Jake Peavy
GMPF Dave Parker 4.00 10.00
Prince Fielder
GMPG Kirby Puckett 10.00 25.00
Ken Griffey Jr.
GMPL Gaylord Perry 4.00 10.00
John Lackey
GMPM Tino Martinez 4.00 10.00
Jorge Posada
GMPP Gaylord Perry 4.00 10.00
Jake Peavy
GMPV Jason Varitek 4.00 10.00
Tony Perez
GMRA Aramis Ramirez 10.00 25.00
Ron Santo
GMRB Ivan Rodriguez 4.00 10.00
Johnny Bench
GMRK Nolan Ryan 8.00 20.00
Scott Kazmir
GMRL Evan Longoria 10.00 25.00
Brooks Robinson
GMRN Graig Nettles 4.00 10.00
Aramis Ramirez
GMRO Roy Oswalt 8.00 20.00
Nolan Ryan
GMRR Cal Ripken Jr. 10.00 25.00
Hanley Ramirez
GMRT Cal Ripken Jr. 15.00 40.00
Troy Tulowitzki
GMSA Albert Pujols 15.00 40.00
Stan Musial
GMSB Pat Burrell 6.00 15.00
Mike Schmidt
GMSD Jake Peavy 4.00 10.00
Tony Gwynn
GMSG Khalil Greene 8.00 20.00
Ozzie Smith
GMSJ Ozzie Smith 15.00 40.00
Derek Jeter
GMSL Mike Schmidt 10.00 25.00
Evan Longoria
GMSP Ozzie Smith 12.50 30.00
Albert Pujols
GMSR Mike Schmidt 5.00 12.00
Aramis Ramirez
GMSS Derek Jeter 15.00 40.00
Cal Ripken Jr.
GMST Tom Glavine 4.00 10.00
Steve Carlton
GMSW Don Sutton 6.00 15.00
Brandon Webb
GMTA Adrian Gonzalez 4.00 10.00
Tino Martinez
GMTB Tom Glavine 4.00 10.00
Chad Billingsley
GMTC Carlos Beltran 4.00 10.00
Tony Perez
GMTJ Jose Reyes 4.00 10.00
Tim Raines
GMTX Nolan Ryan 10.00 25.00
Josh Beckett
GMWK Wade Boggs 5.00 12.00
Kevin Youkilis
GMWM Wade Boggs 4.00 10.00
Mike Lowell
GMYE Carl Yastrzemski 10.00 25.00
Jacoby Ellsbury
GMYO Carl Yastrzemski 5.00 12.00
David Ortiz

2009 SP Legendary Cuts Generations Signatures Dual

RANDOM INSERTS IN PACKS
PRINT RUNS B/WN 5-25 COPIES PER
NO PRICING DUE TO SCARCITY

2009 SP Legendary Cuts Legendary Cut Signatures

OVERALL CUT SIG ODDS TWO PER CASE
PRINT RUNS B/WN 5-55 COPIES PER
NO PRICING ON QTY 25 OR LESS
LC6 Wally Berger/50 30.00 60.00
LC107 Bob O'Farrell/26 30.00 60.00
LC109 Bill Stafford/26 50.00 100.00
LC201 Al Barlick/50 30.00 60.00
LC202 Luke Appling/33 30.00 60.00
LC203 Allie Reynolds/39 50.00 100.00
LC204 Aurelio Rodriguez/50 20.00 50.00
LC205 Bibb Falk/36 40.00 80.00
LC206 Bob Grim/37 40.00 80.00
LC207 Bill Hallahan/21
LC208 Billy Herman/50 30.00 60.00
LC209 Bowie Kuhn/5
LC210 Bob Lemon/50 30.00 60.00
LC211 Barney McCosky/43 30.00 60.00
LC212 Bill Rigney/10
LC213 Bob Buhl/44 20.00 50.00
LC214 Bucky Walters/42 40.00 80.00
LC215 Clete Boyer/42 40.00 80.00
LC216 Charlie Gehringer/36 40.00 80.00
LC217 Cecil Travis/8
LC218 Del Ennis/27 40.00 80.00
LC219 Harry Danning/37
LC220 Dick Donovan/31 30.00 60.00
LC221 Doc Cramer/39 40.00 80.00
LC222 Lou Gehrig/5
LC223 Dick Sisler/27 30.00 60.00
LC229 Frank McCormick/50 20.00 50.00
LC230 Charlie Grimm/50 30.00 60.00
LC231 George Kelly/26 30.00 60.00
LC232 Gus Suhr/55 30.00 60.00
LC233 Gene Woodling/47 30.00 60.00
LC234 Hank Borowy/33 40.00 80.00
LC235 Happy Chandler/28 30.00 60.00
LC236 Hoot Evers/20
LC237 Harvey Kuenn/32 40.00 80.00
LC238 Hank Sauer/33 30.00 60.00
LC239 Hal Trosky/34 50.00 100.00
LC240 Joe Adcock/30 50.00 100.00
LC241 Joe Black/23
LC242 Joe DiMaggio/27
LC243 Joe Kuhel/20
LC244 Joe Niekro/28 30.00 60.00
LC245 Joe Sewell/50 20.00 50.00
LC246 Jim Turner/32 30.00 60.00
LC247 Johnny Vander Meer/42 30.00 60.00
LC248 Ken Keltner/19
LC249 Clem Labine/26 40.00 80.00
LC250 Lew Fonseca/29 20.00 50.00
LC251 Luke Sewell/19
LC252 Lloyd Waner/50 75.00 150.00
LC253 Ted Lyons/30
LC254 Mel Harder/41 30.00 60.00
LC255 Marius Russo/21
LC256 Mickey Owen/16
LC257 Pete Runnels/28 50.00 100.00
LC258 Paul Waner/17
LC259 Ray Boone/37 30.00 60.00
LC260 Ray Dandridge/31 30.00 60.00
LC261 Roy McMillan/24
LC262 Roger Peckinpaugh/41 75.00 150.00
LC263 Rip Repulski/48 40.00 80.00
LC264 Smokey Burgess/25
LC265 Stan Coveleski/42 20.00 50.00
LC266 Riggs Stephenson/39 30.00 60.00
LC267 Birdie Tebbetts/20
LC268 Vic Raschi/19
LC269 Vic Wertz/43 30.00 60.00
LC270 Walker Cooper/44 20.00 50.00
LC271 Waite Hoyt/12
LC272 Wally Post/19
LC273 Willie Stargell/23
LC274 Whit Wyatt/20
LC275 Walter O'Malley/50 200.00 400.00
LC276 Buck Leonard/52 40.00 80.00
LC277 Cool Papa Bell/30 100.00 175.00
LC278 Catfish Hunter/40 30.00 60.00
LC279 Cookie Lavagetto/18
LC280 Dutch Leonard/27 40.00 80.00
LC281 Ewell Blackwell/48 30.00 60.00
LC282 Harry Brecheen/21
LC283 Hank Bauer/33 50.00 100.00
LC284 Hoyt Wilhelm/35 20.00 50.00
LC285 Harry Walker/45 30.00 60.00
LC286 Jim Busby/17
LC287 Johnny Callison/26 40.00 80.00
LC288 Johnny Hopp/23
LC289 Lou Boudreau/50 30.00 60.00
LC290 Larry French/45 30.00 60.00
LC291 Phil Rizzuto/50 40.00 80.00
LC292 Richie Ashburn/24
LC293 Rick Ferrell/5
LC294 Hal Schumacher/5
LC295 Spec Shea/22
LC296 Tony Cuccinello/37 40.00 80.00
LC297 Tommy Holmes/41 40.00 80.00
LC298 Terry Moore/50 30.00 60.00
LC299 Sammy White/28 30.00 60.00
LC300 Warren Spahn/39 30.00 60.00
LC309 Edd Roush/31 20.00 50.00
LC311 Enos Slaughter/43 30.00 60.00

2009 SP Legendary Cuts Legendary Cut Signatures Dual

OVERALL CUT SIG ODDS TWO PER CASE
STATED PRINT RUN 1 SER.#'d SET
NO PRICING DUE TO SCARCITY

2009 SP Legendary Cuts Legendary Cut Signatures Quad

OVERALL CUT SIG ODDS TWO PER CASE
STATED PRINT RUN 1 SER.#'d SET
NO PRICING DUE TO SCARCITY

2009 SP Legendary Cuts Legendary Memorabilia

OVERALL MEM ODDS 1:3
PRINT RUNS B/WN 40-125 COPIES PER
BD Bucky Dent/125 3.00 8.00
BG Bob Gibson/40 5.00 12.00
BO Bo Jackson/125 6.00 15.00
BR Brooks Robinson/125 5.00 12.00
BW Billy Williams/125 3.00 8.00
CA Rod Carew/125 3.00 8.00
CF Carlton Fisk/125 4.00 10.00
CR Cal Ripken Jr./125 12.50 30.00
CY Carl Yastrzemski/125 6.00 15.00
DE Dennis Eckersley/125 3.00 8.00
DM Don Mattingly/125 6.00 15.00
DS Don Sutton/125 3.00 8.00
DW Dave Winfield/125 3.00 8.00
EB Ernie Banks/125 5.00 12.00
EM Edgar Martinez/125 4.00 10.00
FR Frank Robinson/125 3.00 8.00
GG Goose Gossage/125 3.00 8.00
GK Kirk Gibson/125 5.00 12.00
GP Gaylord Perry/125 3.00 8.00
JB Johnny Bench/125 4.00 10.00
JC Joe Carter/125 3.00 8.00
JM Joe Morgan/125 3.00 8.00
JP Jim Palmer/125 4.00 10.00
JR Jim Rice/125 3.00 8.00
KG Ken Griffey Sr./125 3.00 8.00
LA Luis Aparicio/125 4.00 10.00
LB Lou Brock/125 5.00 12.00
MG Mark Grace/125 4.00 10.00
MO Jack Morris/125 4.00 10.00
MS Mike Schmidt/125 6.00 15.00
NR Nolan Ryan/125 8.00 20.00
OS Ozzie Smith/125 6.00 15.00
PM Paul Molitor/125 4.00 10.00
RJ Reggie Jackson/125 3.00 8.00
RS Ryne Sandberg/125 5.00 12.00
RY Robin Yount/125 4.00 10.00
SA Ron Santo/125 8.00 20.00
SC Steve Carlton/125 3.00 8.00
SL Sparky Lyle/125 3.00 8.00
SM Stan Musial/100 10.00 25.00
TG Tony Gwynn/125 5.00 12.00
TM Tino Martinez/125 4.00 10.00
TP Tony Perez/125 3.00 8.00
TR Tim Raines/125 4.00 10.00
TW Ted Williams/50 30.00 60.00
WB Wade Boggs/125 5.00 12.00
BG2 Bob Gibson/40 5.00 12.00
BO2 Bo Jackson/125 6.00 15.00
BR2 Brooks Robinson/125 5.00 12.00
BW2 Billy Williams/125 3.00 8.00
BW3 Billy Williams/125 3.00 8.00
CA2 Rod Carew/125 3.00 8.00
CA3 Rod Carew/125 3.00 8.00
CF2 Carlton Fisk/125 4.00 10.00
CF3 Carlton Fisk/125 4.00 10.00
CR2 Cal Ripken Jr./125 12.50 30.00
CR3 Cal Ripken Jr./125 12.50 30.00
CY2 Carl Yastrzemski/125 6.00 15.00
DE2 Dennis Eckersley/125 3.00 8.00
DM2 Don Mattingly/125 6.00 15.00
DM3 Don Mattingly/125 6.00 15.00
DS2 Don Sutton/125 3.00 8.00
EB2 Ernie Banks/125 5.00 12.00
GG2 Goose Gossage/125 3.00 8.00
GK2 Kirk Gibson/125 5.00 12.00
GP2 Gaylord Perry/125 3.00 8.00
GP3 Gaylord Perry/125 3.00 8.00
GP4 Gaylord Perry/125 3.00 8.00
JB2 Johnny Bench/125 4.00 10.00
JC2 Joe Carter/125 3.00 8.00
JM2 Joe Morgan/125 3.00 8.00
JP2 Jim Palmer/125 4.00 10.00
JR2 Jim Rice/125 3.00 8.00
LB2 Lou Brock/125 5.00 12.00
MG2 Mark Grace/125 4.00 10.00
MO2 Jack Morris/125 4.00 10.00
MS2 Mike Schmidt/125 6.00 15.00
NR2 Nolan Ryan/125 8.00 20.00
OS2 Ozzie Smith/125 6.00 15.00
OS3 Ozzie Smith/125 6.00 15.00
PM2 Paul Molitor/125 4.00 10.00
RJ2 Reggie Jackson/125 3.00 8.00
RS2 Ryne Sandberg/125 5.00 12.00
RY2 Robin Yount/125 4.00 10.00
SA2 Ron Santo/125 8.00 20.00
SC2 Steve Carlton/125 3.00 8.00
SL2 Sparky Lyle/125 3.00 8.00
SM2 Stan Musial/100 10.00 25.00
SM3 Stan Musial/100 10.00 25.00
TG2 Tony Gwynn/125 5.00 12.00
TM2 Tino Martinez/125 4.00 10.00
TP2 Tony Perez/125 3.00 8.00
TR2 Tim Raines/125 4.00 10.00
TW2 Ted Williams/50 30.00 60.00
WB2 Wade Boggs/125 5.00 12.00

2009 SP Legendary Cuts Legendary Memorabilia Blue

OVERALL MEM ODDS 1:3
PRINT RUNS B/WN 30-100 COPIES PER
BD Bucky Dent/100 3.00 8.00
BG Bob Gibson/30 5.00 12.00
BO Bo Jackson/100 6.00 15.00
BR Brooks Robinson/100 5.00 12.00
BW Billy Williams/100 3.00 8.00
CA Rod Carew/100 3.00 8.00
CF Carlton Fisk/100 4.00 10.00
CR Cal Ripken Jr./100 12.50 30.00
CY Carl Yastrzemski/100 6.00 15.00
DE Dennis Eckersley/100 3.00 8.00
DM Don Mattingly/100 6.00 15.00
DS Don Sutton/100 3.00 8.00
DW Dave Winfield/75 4.00 10.00
DW2 Dave Winfield/100 3.00 8.00
EB Ernie Banks/100 5.00 12.00
EM Edgar Martinez/100 4.00 10.00
FR Frank Robinson/100 3.00 8.00
GG Goose Gossage/100 3.00 8.00
GK Kirk Gibson/100 5.00 12.00
GP Gaylord Perry/100 3.00 8.00
JB Johnny Bench/100 4.00 10.00
JC Joe Carter/100 3.00 8.00
JM Joe Morgan/100 3.00 8.00
JR Jim Rice/100 3.00 8.00
KG Ken Griffey Sr./100 3.00 8.00
LA Luis Aparicio/100 4.00 10.00
LB Lou Brock/100 5.00 12.00
MG Mark Grace/100 4.00 10.00
MO Jack Morris/100 4.00 10.00
MS Mike Schmidt/100 6.00 15.00
OS Ozzie Smith/100 6.00 15.00
PM Paul Molitor/100 4.00 10.00
RJ Reggie Jackson/100 3.00 8.00
RS Ryne Sandberg/100 5.00 12.00
RY Robin Yount/100 4.00 10.00
SA Ron Santo/100 8.00 20.00
SC Steve Carlton/100 3.00 8.00
SL Sparky Lyle/100 3.00 8.00
SM Stan Musial/75 12.50 30.00
TG Tony Gwynn/100 5.00 12.00
TM Tino Martinez/100 4.00 10.00
TP Tony Perez/100 3.00 8.00
TR Tim Raines/100 4.00 10.00
TW Ted Williams/40 40.00 80.00
WB Wade Boggs/100 5.00 12.00
BG2 Bob Gibson/30 5.00 12.00
BO2 Bo Jackson/100 6.00 15.00
BR2 Brooks Robinson/100 5.00 12.00
BW2 Billy Williams/100 3.00 8.00
BW3 Billy Williams/100 3.00 8.00
CA2 Rod Carew/100 3.00 8.00
CA3 Rod Carew/100 3.00 8.00
CF2 Carlton Fisk/100 4.00 10.00
CF3 Carlton Fisk/100 4.00 10.00
CR2 Cal Ripken Jr./100 12.50 30.00
CR3 Cal Ripken Jr./100 12.50 30.00
CY2 Carl Yastrzemski/100 6.00 15.00
DE2 Dennis Eckersley/100 3.00 8.00
DM2 Don Mattingly/100 6.00 15.00
DM3 Don Mattingly/100 6.00 15.00
DS2 Don Sutton/100 3.00 8.00
EB2 Ernie Banks/100 5.00 12.00
GG2 Goose Gossage/100 3.00 8.00
GK2 Kirk Gibson/100 5.00 12.00
GP2 Gaylord Perry/100 3.00 8.00
GP3 Gaylord Perry/100 3.00 8.00
GP4 Gaylord Perry/100 3.00 8.00
JB2 Johnny Bench/100 4.00 10.00
JC2 Joe Carter/100 3.00 8.00
JM2 Joe Morgan/100 3.00 8.00
JP2 Jim Palmer/100 4.00 10.00
JR2 Jim Rice/100 3.00 8.00
LB2 Lou Brock/100 5.00 12.00
MG2 Mark Grace/100 4.00 10.00
MO2 Jack Morris/100 4.00 10.00
MS2 Mike Schmidt/100 6.00 15.00
OS2 Ozzie Smith/100 6.00 15.00
OS3 Ozzie Smith/100 6.00 15.00
PM2 Paul Molitor/100 4.00 10.00
RJ2 Reggie Jackson/100 3.00 8.00
RS2 Ryne Sandberg/100 5.00 12.00
RY2 Robin Yount/100 4.00 10.00
SA2 Ron Santo/100 8.00 20.00
SC2 Steve Carlton/100 3.00 8.00
SL2 Sparky Lyle/100 3.00 8.00
SM2 Stan Musial/75 12.50 30.00
SM3 Stan Musial/75 12.50 30.00
TG2 Tony Gwynn/100 5.00 12.00
TM2 Tino Martinez/100 4.00 10.00
TP2 Tony Perez/100 3.00 8.00
TR2 Tim Raines/100 4.00 10.00
TW2 Ted Williams/40 40.00 80.00
WB2 Wade Boggs/100 5.00 12.00

2009 SP Legendary Cuts Legendary Memorabilia Brown

OVERALL MEM ODDS 1:3
PRINT RUNS B/WN 20-50 COPIES PER
BD Bucky Dent 4.00 10.00
BG Bob Gibson/20 6.00 15.00
BO Bo Jackson 8.00 20.00
BR Brooks Robinson 6.00 15.00
BW Billy Williams 4.00 10.00
CA Rod Carew 4.00 10.00
CF Carlton Fisk 5.00 12.00
CR Cal Ripken Jr. 15.00 40.00
CY Carl Yastrzemski 8.00 20.00
DE Dennis Eckersley 4.00 10.00
DM Don Mattingly 8.00 20.00
DS Don Sutton 4.00 10.00
DW Dave Winfield 4.00 10.00
EB Ernie Banks 6.00 15.00
EM Edgar Martinez 5.00 12.00
FR Frank Robinson 4.00 10.00
GG Goose Gossage 4.00 10.00
GK Kirk Gibson 6.00 15.00
GP Gaylord Perry 4.00 10.00
JB Johnny Bench 5.00 12.00
JC Joe Carter 4.00 10.00
JM Joe Morgan 4.00 10.00
JP Jim Palmer 5.00 12.00
JR Jim Rice 4.00 10.00
KG Ken Griffey Sr. 4.00 10.00
LA Luis Aparicio 5.00 12.00
LB Lou Brock 6.00 15.00
MG Mark Grace 5.00 12.00
MO Jack Morris 5.00 12.00
MS Mike Schmidt 8.00 20.00
NR Nolan Ryan 10.00 25.00
OS Ozzie Smith 8.00 20.00
PM Paul Molitor 5.00 12.00
RC Roger Clemens 4.00 10.00
RC2 Roger Clemens 4.00 10.00
RJ Reggie Jackson 4.00 10.00
RS Ryne Sandberg 6.00 15.00
RY Robin Yount 5.00 12.00
SA Ron Santo 6.00 15.00
SC Steve Carlton 4.00 10.00
SL Sparky Lyle 4.00 10.00
SM Stan Musial 12.50 30.00
TG Tony Gwynn 6.00 15.00
TM Tino Martinez 5.00 12.00
TP Tony Perez 4.00 10.00
TR Tim Raines 5.00 12.00
TW Ted Williams 30.00 60.00
WB Wade Boggs 6.00 15.00
BG2 Bob Gibson/20 6.00 15.00
BO2 Bo Jackson 8.00 20.00
BR2 Brooks Robinson 6.00 15.00
BW2 Billy Williams 4.00 10.00
BW3 Billy Williams 4.00 10.00
CA2 Rod Carew 4.00 10.00
CA3 Rod Carew 4.00 10.00
CF2 Carlton Fisk 5.00 12.00
CF3 Carlton Fisk 5.00 12.00
CR2 Cal Ripken Jr. 15.00 40.00
CR3 Cal Ripken Jr. 15.00 40.00
CY2 Carl Yastrzemski 8.00 20.00
DE2 Dennis Eckersley 4.00 10.00
DM2 Don Mattingly 8.00 20.00
DM3 Don Mattingly 8.00 20.00
DS2 Don Sutton 4.00 10.00
EB2 Ernie Banks 6.00 15.00
GG2 Goose Gossage 4.00 10.00
GK2 Kirk Gibson 6.00 15.00
GP2 Gaylord Perry 4.00 10.00
GP3 Gaylord Perry 4.00 10.00
GP4 Gaylord Perry 4.00 10.00
JB2 Johnny Bench 5.00 12.00
JC2 Joe Carter 4.00 10.00
JM2 Joe Morgan 4.00 10.00
JP2 Jim Palmer 5.00 12.00
JR2 Jim Rice 4.00 10.00
LB2 Lou Brock 6.00 15.00
MG2 Mark Grace 5.00 12.00
MO2 Jack Morris 5.00 12.00
MS2 Mike Schmidt 8.00 20.00
NR2 Nolan Ryan 10.00 25.00
OS2 Ozzie Smith 8.00 20.00
OS3 Ozzie Smith 8.00 20.00
PM2 Paul Molitor 5.00 12.00
RJ2 Reggie Jackson 4.00 10.00
RS2 Ryne Sandberg 6.00 15.00
RY2 Robin Yount 5.00 12.00
SA2 Ron Santo 6.00 15.00
SC2 Steve Carlton 4.00 10.00
SL2 Sparky Lyle 4.00 10.00
SM2 Stan Musial 12.50 30.00
SM3 Stan Musial 12.50 30.00
TG2 Tony Gwynn 6.00 15.00
TM2 Tino Martinez 5.00 12.00
TP2 Tony Perez 4.00 10.00
TR2 Tim Raines 5.00 12.00
TW2 Ted Williams 30.00 60.00
WB2 Wade Boggs 6.00 15.00

2009 SP Legendary Cuts Legendary Memorabilia Red

OVERALL MEM ODDS 1:3
PRINT RUNS B/WN 25-75 COPIES PER
BD Bucky Dent 4.00 10.00
BG Bob Gibson/25 6.00 15.00
BO Bo Jackson 8.00 20.00
BR Brooks Robinson 6.00 15.00
BW Billy Williams 4.00 10.00
CA Rod Carew 4.00 10.00
CF Carlton Fisk 5.00 12.00
CR Cal Ripken Jr. 15.00 40.00
CY Carl Yastrzemski 8.00 20.00
DE Dennis Eckersley 4.00 10.00
DM Don Mattingly 8.00 20.00
DS Don Sutton 4.00 10.00
DW Dave Winfield 4.00 10.00
EB Ernie Banks 6.00 15.00
EM Edgar Martinez 5.00 12.00
FR Frank Robinson 4.00 10.00
GG Goose Gossage 4.00 10.00
GK Kirk Gibson 6.00 15.00
GP Gaylord Perry 4.00 10.00
JB Johnny Bench 5.00 12.00
JC Joe Carter 4.00 10.00
JM Joe Morgan 4.00 10.00
JP Jim Palmer 5.00 12.00
JR Jim Rice 4.00 10.00
KG Ken Griffey Sr. 4.00 10.00
LA Luis Aparicio 5.00 12.00
LB Lou Brock 6.00 15.00
MG Mark Grace 5.00 12.00
MO Jack Morris 5.00 12.00
MS Mike Schmidt 8.00 20.00
NR Nolan Ryan 10.00 25.00
OS Ozzie Smith 8.00 20.00
PM Paul Molitor 5.00 12.00
RJ Reggie Jackson 4.00 10.00
RS Ryne Sandberg 6.00 15.00
RY Robin Yount 5.00 12.00
SA Ron Santo 6.00 15.00
SC Steve Carlton 4.00 10.00
SL Sparky Lyle 4.00 10.00
SM Stan Musial 12.50 30.00
TG Tony Gwynn 6.00 15.00
TM Tino Martinez 5.00 12.00
TP Tony Perez 4.00 10.00
TR Tim Raines 5.00 12.00
TW Ted Williams 30.00 60.00
WB Wade Boggs 6.00 15.00
BG2 Bob Gibson/25 6.00 15.00
BO2 Bo Jackson 8.00 20.00
BR2 Brooks Robinson 6.00 15.00
BW2 Billy Williams 4.00 10.00
BW3 Billy Williams 4.00 10.00
CA2 Rod Carew 4.00 10.00
CA3 Rod Carew 4.00 10.00
CF2 Carlton Fisk 5.00 12.00
CF3 Carlton Fisk 5.00 12.00
CR2 Cal Ripken Jr. 15.00 40.00
CR3 Cal Ripken Jr. 15.00 40.00
CY2 Carl Yastrzemski 8.00 20.00
DE2 Dennis Eckersley 4.00 10.00
DM2 Don Mattingly 8.00 20.00
DM3 Don Mattingly 8.00 20.00
DS2 Don Sutton 4.00 10.00
EB2 Ernie Banks 6.00 15.00
GG2 Goose Gossage 4.00 10.00
GK2 Kirk Gibson 6.00 15.00
GP2 Gaylord Perry 4.00 10.00
GP3 Gaylord Perry 4.00 10.00
GP4 Gaylord Perry 4.00 10.00
JB2 Johnny Bench 5.00 12.00
JC2 Joe Carter 4.00 10.00
JM2 Joe Morgan 4.00 10.00
JP2 Jim Palmer 5.00 12.00
JR2 Jim Rice 4.00 10.00
LB2 Lou Brock 6.00 15.00
MG2 Mark Grace 5.00 12.00
MO2 Jack Morris 5.00 12.00
MS2 Mike Schmidt 8.00 20.00
NR2 Nolan Ryan 10.00 25.00
OS2 Ozzie Smith 8.00 20.00
OS3 Ozzie Smith 8.00 20.00
PM2 Paul Molitor 5.00 12.00
RJ2 Reggie Jackson 4.00 10.00
RS2 Ryne Sandberg 6.00 15.00
RY2 Robin Yount 5.00 12.00
SA2 Ron Santo 6.00 15.00
SC2 Steve Carlton 4.00 10.00
SL2 Sparky Lyle 4.00 10.00
SM2 Stan Musial 12.50 30.00
SM3 Stan Musial 12.50 30.00
TG2 Tony Gwynn 6.00 15.00
TM2 Tino Martinez 5.00 12.00
TP2 Tony Perez 4.00 10.00
TR2 Tim Raines 5.00 12.00
TW2 Ted Williams 30.00 60.00
WB2 Wade Boggs 6.00 15.00

2009 SP Legendary Cuts Legendary Memorabilia Violet

OVERALL MEM ODDS 1:3
STATED PRINT RUN 25 SER.#'d SETS
BD Bucky Dent 5.00 12.00
BG Bob Gibson 6.00 15.00
BO Bo Jackson 10.00 25.00
BR Brooks Robinson 8.00 20.00
BW Billy Williams 5.00 12.00
CA Rod Carew 5.00 12.00
CF Carlton Fisk 6.00 15.00
CR Cal Ripken Jr. 20.00 50.00
CY Carl Yastrzemski 10.00 25.00
DE Dennis Eckersley 5.00 12.00
DM Don Mattingly 10.00 25.00
DS Don Sutton 5.00 12.00
DW Dave Winfield 5.00 12.00
EB Ernie Banks 8.00 20.00
EM Edgar Martinez 6.00 15.00
FR Frank Robinson 5.00 12.00
GG Goose Gossage 5.00 12.00
GK Kirk Gibson 8.00 20.00
GP Gaylord Perry 5.00 12.00
JB Johnny Bench 6.00 15.00
JC Joe Carter 5.00 12.00
JM Joe Morgan 5.00 12.00
JP Jim Palmer 6.00 15.00
JR Jim Rice 5.00 12.00
KG Ken Griffey Sr. 5.00 12.00
LA Luis Aparicio 6.00 15.00
LB Lou Brock 8.00 20.00

MG Mark Grace 6.00 15.00
MO Jack Morris 6.00 15.00
MS Mike Schmidt 10.00 25.00
NR Nolan Ryan 12.50 30.00
OS Ozzie Smith 10.00 25.00
PM Paul Molitor 6.00 15.00
RC Roger Clemens 5.00 12.00
RJ Reggie Jackson 5.00 12.00
RS Ryne Sandberg 8.00 20.00
RY Robin Yount 6.00 15.00
SA Ron Santo 8.00 20.00
SC Steve Carlton 5.00 12.00
SL Sparky Lyle 5.00 12.00
SM Stan Musial 15.00 40.00
TG Tony Gwynn 8.00 20.00
TM Tino Martinez 6.00 15.00
TP Tony Perez 5.00 12.00
TR Tim Raines 6.00 15.00
TW Ted Williams 40.00 80.00
WB Wade Boggs 8.00 20.00
BG2 Bob Gibson 6.00 15.00
BO2 Bo Jackson 10.00 25.00
BR2 Brooks Robinson 8.00 20.00
BW2 Billy Williams 5.00 12.00
BW3 Billy Williams 5.00 12.00
CA2 Rod Carew 5.00 12.00
CA3 Rod Carew 5.00 12.00
CF2 Carlton Fisk 6.00 15.00
CF3 Carlton Fisk 6.00 15.00
CR2 Cal Ripken Jr. 20.00 50.00
CR3 Cal Ripken Jr. 20.00 50.00
CY2 Carl Yastrzemski 10.00 25.00
DE2 Dennis Eckersley 5.00 12.00
DM2 Don Mattingly 10.00 25.00
DM3 Don Mattingly 10.00 25.00
DS2 Don Sutton 5.00 12.00
EB2 Ernie Banks 8.00 20.00
GG2 Goose Gossage 5.00 12.00
GK2 Kirk Gibson 8.00 20.00
GP2 Gaylord Perry 5.00 12.00
GP3 Gaylord Perry 5.00 12.00
GP4 Gaylord Perry 5.00 12.00
JB2 Johnny Bench 6.00 15.00
JC2 Joe Carter 5.00 12.00
JM2 Joe Morgan 5.00 12.00
JP2 Jim Palmer 6.00 15.00
JR2 Jim Rice 5.00 12.00
LB2 Lou Brock 8.00 20.00
MG2 Mark Grace 6.00 15.00
MO2 Jack Morris 6.00 15.00
MS2 Mike Schmidt 10.00 25.00
NR2 Nolan Ryan 12.50 30.00
OS2 Ozzie Smith 10.00 25.00
OS3 Ozzie Smith 10.00 25.00
PM2 Paul Molitor 6.00 15.00
RJ2 Reggie Jackson 5.00 12.00
RS2 Ryne Sandberg 8.00 20.00
RY2 Robin Yount 6.00 15.00
SA2 Ron Santo 8.00 20.00
SC2 Steve Carlton 5.00 12.00
SL2 Sparky Lyle 5.00 12.00
SM2 Stan Musial 15.00 40.00
SM3 Stan Musial 15.00 40.00
TG2 Tony Gwynn 8.00 20.00
TM2 Tino Martinez 6.00 15.00
TP2 Tony Perez 5.00 12.00
TR2 Tim Raines 6.00 15.00
TW2 Ted Williams 40.00 80.00
WB2 Wade Boggs 8.00 20.00

2009 SP Legendary Cuts Mystery Cuts

STATED ODDS ONE PER CASE
NNO Exchange Card 175.00 350.00

2011 SP Legendary Cuts Legendary Signatures

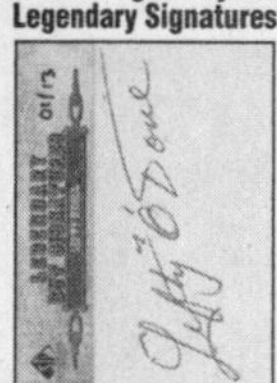

OVERALL AUTO ODDS 1:1
PRINT RUNS B/WN 5-36 COPIES PER
NO PRICING ON MOST QTY 25 OR LESS
1 Al Barlick/35 10.00 25.00
2 Al Lopez/35 12.50 30.00
9 Bill Dickey/35 50.00 100.00
11 Bill Terry/25 30.00 60.00
14 Billy Herman/35 15.00 40.00
16 Bob Lemon/34 10.00 25.00
22 Buck Leonard/35 20.00 50.00
23 Buck O'Neil/10 50.00 100.00
31 Carl Hubbell/35 40.00 80.00
33 Catfish Hunter/34 20.00 50.00
34 Charlie Gehringer/35 40.00 80.00
35 Charlie Grimm/15 30.00 60.00
40 Cool Papa Bell/24 90.00 150.00
42 Cy Williams/10 60.00 120.00
51 Duffy Lewis/13 75.00 150.00
52 Earl Averill/35 20.00 50.00
54 Earle Combs/12 100.00 175.00
55 Early Wynn/32 30.00 60.00
56 Ed Lopat/16 20.00 50.00
57 Edd Roush/35 30.00 60.00
58 Eddie Mathews/35 40.00 80.00
61 Enos Slaughter/35 20.00 50.00
63 Ernie Lombardi/10 90.00 150.00
66 Frank McCormick/15 20.00 50.00
68 Frankie Frisch/10 125.00 250.00
71 Freddie Lindstrom/15 60.00 120.00
74 Gene Benson/10 20.00 50.00
77 George Kell/35 20.00 50.00
78 George Kelly/33 20.00 50.00
82 George Uhle/15 15.00 40.00
84 Glenn Wright/17 30.00 60.00
85 Hal Newhouser/35 30.00 60.00
88 Happy Chandler/35 15.00 40.00
99 Jesse Haines/19 40.00 80.00
103 Jocko Conlan/34 20.00 50.00
105 Joe Cronin/15 20.00 50.00
106 Joe DiMaggio/35 250.00 350.00
113 Joe Sewell/35 40.00 80.00
115 Johnny Mize/33 40.00 80.00
116 Johnny Murphy/7 50.00 100.00
127 Lefty O'Doul/13 75.00 150.00
131 Lloyd Waner/36 50.00 100.00
133 Lou Boudreau/35 15.00 40.00
134 Luke Appling/35 20.00 50.00
138 Max Carey/35 30.00 60.00
139 Mel Allen/7 40.00 80.00
146 Pete Reiser/10 40.00 80.00
147 Phil Rizzuto/30 50.00 100.00
149 Ray Dandridge/25 15.00 40.00
150 Ray Schalk/10 200.00 400.00
153 Red Rolfe/12 90.00 150.00
156 Rick Ferrell/33 20.00 50.00
165 Rube Marquard/35 50.00 100.00
166 Rube Walberg/10 30.00 60.00
172 Spud Davis/13 30.00 60.00
173 Stan Coveleski/35 20.00 50.00
175 Ted Kluszewski/14 60.00 120.00
176 Ted Lyons/35 40.00 80.00
177 Ted Williams/23 400.00 600.00
180 Tommy Leach/10 30.00 60.00
182 Travis Jackson/25 30.00 60.00
187 Vern Stephens/10 50.00 100.00
191 Waite Hoyt/35 30.00 60.00
195 Warren Spahn/33 20.00 50.00

2011 SP Legendary Cuts Legendary Black Signatures

OVERALL AUTO ODDS 1:1
PRINT RUNS B/WN 1-40 COPIES PER
NO PRICING ON MOST QTY 25 OR LESS
NYBD Babe Dahlgren/33 40.00 80.00
NYBG Bob Grim/17 30.00 60.00
NYBJ Billy Johnson/37 15.00 40.00
NYCH Catfish Hunter/14 30.00 60.00
NYEL Ed Lopat/32 30.00 60.00
NYFC Frankie Crosetti/34 20.00 50.00
NYGW Gene Woodling/29 20.00 50.00
NYHB Hank Bauer/35 20.00 50.00
NYHR Hal Reniff/35 10.00 25.00
NYJD Joe DiMaggio/30 200.00 400.00
NYJL Johnny Lindell/18 30.00 60.00
NYMR Marius Russo/35 10.00 25.00
NYNE Nick Etten/28 10.00 25.00
NYOH Oral Hildebrand/11 30.00 60.00
NYPR Phil Rizzuto/17 40.00 80.00
NYSS Spec Shea/33 20.00 50.00
NYTB Tommy Byrne/14 30.00 60.00
NYTT Tom Tresh/40 15.00 40.00
BALMB Mark Belanger/13 30.00 60.00
BOSBW Bill Werber/38 15.00 40.00
BOSDC Doc Cramer/29 20.00 50.00
BOSPR Pete Runnels/35 20.00 50.00
CINER Edd Roush/17 20.00 50.00
CINJV Johnny Vander Meer/20 30.00 60.00
CLEES Elmer Smith/15 15.00 40.00
CLEJS Joe Sewell/20 20.00 40.00
DETBH Billy Hoeft/15 20.00 50.00
DETBM Barney McCoskey/25 20.00 50.00
DETHE Hoot Evers/25 20.00 50.00
DETHK Harvey Kuenn/27 20.00 50.00
DETJB Johnny Bassler/10 20.00 50.00
NLGBO Buck O'Neil/35 40.00 80.00
NLGLD Leon Day/15 50.00 100.00
NYBDI Bill Dickey/21 50.00 100.00
PHIEA Ethan Allen/26 20.00 50.00
PITGS Gus Suhr/10 30.00 60.00
PITVD Vince DiMaggio/10 40.00 80.00
STLAH Andy High/15 20.00 50.00
STLBO Bob O'Farrell/36 15.00 40.00
STLHB Harry Brecheen/35 15.00 40.00
STLHH Harvey Haddix/35 20.00 50.00
STLHW Harry Walker/33 15.00 40.00
STLJH Johnny Hopp/35 20.00 50.00
STLJR Jack Rothrock/16 40.00 80.00
STLMD Murry Dickson/33
STLSD Spud Davis/29 15.00 40.00
STLSJ Syl Johnson/36 15.00 40.00
STLTM Terry Moore/29 20.00 50.00
STLWC Walker Cooper/15 20.00 50.00
STLWK Whitey Kurowski/34 15.00 40.00
WASCT Cecil Travis/35 20.00 50.00
WASDL Dutch Leonard/26 20.00 50.00
WASOB Ossie Bluege/35 20.00 50.00
WASTC Tom Cheney/40 20.00 50.00
BOMIWB Wally Berger/35 20.00 50.00
BRLABH Babe Herman/35 20.00 50.00
BRLABP Babe Phelps/36 15.00 40.00
BRLADC Dolph Camilli/16 15.00 40.00
BRLAFB Frenchy Bordagaray/35 10.00 25.00
BRLAGC George Cutshaw/14 20.00 50.00
BRLAMO Mickey Owen/35 12.50 30.00
BRLATC Tony Cuccinello/32 15.00 40.00
BRLAWW Whit Wyatt/35 15.00 40.00
CHINAG Augie Galan/35 20.00 50.00
CHINBN Bill Nicholson/35 20.00 50.00
CHINHS Hank Sauer/35 20.00 50.00
CHINWE Woody English/32 20.00 50.00
CHISBF Bibb Falk/17 30.00 60.00
CHISRR Reb Russell/11 30.00 60.00
NYSFBJ Billy Jurges/40 20.00 50.00
NYSFBR Bill Rigney/30 10.00 25.00
NYSFCH Carl Hubbell/15 40.00 80.00
NYSFDB Dick Bartell/27 15.00 40.00
NYSFFF Freddie Fitzsimmons/35 20.00 50.00
NYSFGM Gus Mancuso/35 15.00 40.00
NYSFHC Hughie Critz/25 20.00 50.00
NYSFHD Harry Danning/25 20.00 40.00
NYSFJS Jack Sanford/27 20.00 50.00
NYSFSG Sid Gordon/15 40.00 80.00
NYSFWM Willard Marshall/29 15.00 40.00
NYSFWW Wes Westrum/30 12.50 30.00
PHKCPL Paddy Livingston/15 20.00 50.00
PHKCSC Sam Chapman/35 10.00 25.00
BRLACLV Cookie Lavagetto/37 20.00 50.00
BRLAJPO Johnny Podres/35 20.00 50.00
BRLAPRO Preacher Roe/35 40.00 80.00

2011 SP Legendary Cuts Legendary Dual Signatures

OVERALL AUTO ODDS 1:1
PRINT RUNS B/WN 1-25 COPIES PER
NO PRICING ON MOST DUE TO SCARCITY
FTWW Dixie Walker / Harry Walker/10 75.00 150.00
CHIAL Luke Appling / Ted Lyons/15 40.00 80.00
NLGDJ Ray Dandridge / Judy Johnson/15 60.00 120.00
UMPBC Al Barlick / Jocko Conlan/15 30.00 60.00
1948LS Bob Lemon / Johnny Sain/10 30.00 60.00
BR41CH Dolph Camilli / Billy Herman/10 30.00 60.00
CL48DL Larry Doby / Bob Lemon/10 50.00 100.00
DASHSW Enos Slaughter / Harry Walker/15 30.00 60.00
NY37DG Bill Dickey / Lefty Gomez/10 100.00 175.00
NY39KS Charlie Keller / George Selkirk/15 60.00 120.00
SPITCG Stan Coveleski / Burleigh Grimes/15 60.00 120.00
NYK20KT George Kelly / Bill Terry/10 50.00 100.00
NYK20LT Freddie Lindstrom / Bill Terry/15 75.00 150.00
NYK33HT Carl Hubbell / Bill Terry/15 75.00 150.00

2004 SP Prospects

This 437-card set was released in December, 2004. The set was issued in five card packs with an $5 SRP which came 24 packs to a box and 12 boxes to a case. The first 90 cards feature active veterans while cards 91 through 190 feature rookies. Cards numbere 191 through 290 feature players who were drafted and signed from the 2004 amateur draft and cards 291 through 447 feature players who were not only drafted and signed but also signed autographs for this product. SP Prospects was the Upper Deck product in which they put in those players who were involved in the 2004 amateur draft.

COMP.ROOKIES SET (198) 20.00 50.00
COMMON CARD (1-90) .30 .75
1-90 APPX. 2X TOUGHER THAN 91-290
COMMON CARD (91-190 .40 1.00
91-190 ODDS TWO PER PACK
COMMON CARD (191-290) .40 1.00
191-290 APPX.TWO PER PACK
COM.AU (291-447) p/r 500-600 3.00 8.00
COM.AU (291-447) p/r 325-499 3.00 8.00
OVERALL AU ODDS 1:5
AU PRINT RUNS B/WN 400-600 PER
233/237/345/438-443/445 DO NOT EXIST
1 Roger Clemens 1.00 2.50
2 Melvin Mora .30 .75
3 Dontrelle Willis .30 .75
4 Jose Vidro .30 .75
5 Oliver Perez .30 .75
6 Carlos Zambrano .50 1.25
7 Chipper Jones .75 2.00
8 Greg Maddux 1.25 3.00
9 Curt Schilling .50 1.25
10 Jose Reyes .50 1.25
11 David Ortiz .75 2.00
12 Mike Piazza .75 2.00
13 Jason Schmidt .30 .75
14 Randy Johnson .75 2.00
15 Magglio Ordonez .50 1.25
16 Mike Mussina .50 1.25
17 Jake Peavy .30 .75
18 Jim Edmonds .50 1.25
19 Ken Griffey Jr. 1.25 3.00
20 Jason Giambi .30 .75
21 Mike Sweeney .30 .75
22 Carlos Lee .30 .75
23 Craig Wilson .30 .75
24 Pedro Martinez .50 1.25
25 Bobby Abreu .30 .75
26 Mike Lowell .30 .75
27 Miguel Cabrera .75 2.00
28 Hank Blalock .30 .75
29 Frank Thomas .75 2.00
30 Manny Ramirez .75 2.00
31 Mark Mulder .30 .75
32 Scott Podsednik .30 .75
33 Albert Pujols 2.00 5.00
34 Preston Wilson .30 .75
35 Todd Helton .50 1.25
36 Victor Martinez .50 1.25
37 Kerry Wood .30 .75
38 Carlos Beltran .30 .75
39 Vernon Wells .30 .75
40 Sammy Sosa .75 2.00
41 Pat Burrell .30 .75
42 Tim Hudson .50 1.25
43 Eric Gagne .30 .75
44 Jim Thome .50 1.25
45 Vladimir Guerrero .75 2.00
46 Travis Hafner .30 .75
47 Rickie Weeks .30 .75
48 Miguel Tejada .50 1.25
49 Ivan Rodriguez .50 1.25
50 J.D. Drew .30 .75
51 Ben Sheets .30 .75
52 Garret Anderson .30 .75
53 Aubrey Huff .30 .75
54 Nomar Garciaparra .75 2.00
55 Luis Gonzalez .30 .75
56 Lance Berkman .50 1.25
57 Ichiro Suzuki 1.25 3.00
58 Torii Hunter .30 .75
59 Adam Dunn .50 1.25
60 Mark Teixeira .75 2.00
61 Bret Boone .30 .75
62 Roy Oswalt .50 1.25
63 Joe Mauer .75 2.00
64 Scott Rolen .50 1.25
65 Hideki Matsui 1.25 3.00
66 Richie Sexson .30 .75
67 Jeff Kent .30 .75
68 Barry Zito .30 .75
69 C.C. Sabathia .50 1.25
70 Carlos Delgado .30 .75
71 Gary Sheffield .30 .75
72 Shawn Green .30 .75
73 Jason Bay .50 1.25
74 Andruw Jones .30 .75
75 Jeff Bagwell .50 1.25
76 Rafael Palmeiro .50 1.25
77 Alex Rodriguez 1.25 3.00
78 Adrian Beltre .30 .75
79 Troy Glaus .30 .75
80 Tom Glavine .50 1.25
81 Paul Konerko .50 1.25
82 Alfonso Soriano .30 .75
83 Roy Halladay .75 2.00
84 Derek Jeter 2.00 5.00
85 Josh Beckett .50 1.25
86 Delmon Young .50 1.25
87 Brian Giles .30 .75
88 Eric Chavez .30 .75
89 Lyle Overbay .30 .75
90 Mark Prior .50 1.25
91 Shawn Camp RC .40 1.00
92 Travis Smith .40 1.00
93 Juan Padilla RC .40 1.00
94 Brad Halsey RC .40 1.00
95 Scott Kazmir RC 2.00 5.00
96 Sam Narron RC .40 1.00
97 Frank Francisco RC .40 1.00
98 Mike Johnston RC .40 1.00
99 Sam McConnell RC .40 1.00
100 Josh Labandeira RC .40 1.00
101 Kazuhito Tadano RC .40 1.00
102 Hector Gimenez RC .40 1.00
103 David Aardsma RC .40 1.00
104 Charles Thomas RC .40 1.00
105 Ian Snell RC .40 1.00
106 Jeff Keppinger RC .60 1.50
107 Michael Vento RC .40 1.00
108 Jerry Gil RC .40 1.00
109 Marty McLeary RC .40 1.00
110 Donnie Kelly RC .60 1.50
111 Roman Colon RC .40 1.00
112 Travis Blackley RC .40 1.00
113 Edwardo Sierra RC .40 1.00
114 Chris Shelton RC .40 1.00
115 Bartolome Fortunato RC .40 1.00
116 Brandon Medders RC .40 1.00
117 Merkin Valdez RC .40 1.00
118 Carlos Vasquez RC .40 1.00
119 Shingo Takatsu RC .40 1.00
120 Aarom Baldiris RC .40 1.00
121 Chris Aguila RC .40 1.00
122 Jimmy Serrano RC .40 1.00
123 Mike Gosling RC .40 1.00
124 Brian Dallimore RC .40 1.00
125 Ronald Belisario RC .40 1.00
126 George Sherrill RC .40 1.00
127 Fernando Nieve RC .40 1.00
128 Abe Alvarez RC .40 1.00
129 Jeff Bennett RC .40 1.00
130 Ryan Meaux RC .40 1.00
131 Edwin Moreno RC .40 1.00
132 Jesse Crain RC .40 1.00
133 Scott Dohmann RC .40 1.00
134 Ronny Cedeno RC .40 1.00
135 Orlando Rodriguez RC .40 1.00
136 Michael Wuertz RC .40 1.00
137 Justin Hampson RC .40 1.00
138 Matt Treanor RC .40 1.00
139 Andy Green RC .40 1.00
140 Yadier Molina RC 2.50 6.00
141 Joe Nelson RC .40 1.00
142 Justin Lehr RC .40 1.00
143 Ryan Wing RC .40 1.00
144 Kevin Cave RC .40 1.00
145 Evan Rust RC .40 1.00
146 Mike Rouse RC .40 1.00
147 Lance Cormier RC .40 1.00
148 Eduardo Villacis RC .40 1.00
149 Justin Knoedler RC .40 1.00
150 Freddy Guzman RC .40 1.00
151 Casey Daigle RC .40 1.00
152 Joey Gathright RC .40 1.00
153 Tim Bittner RC .40 1.00
154 Scott Atchison RC .40 1.00
155 Ivan Ochoa RC .40 1.00
156 Lincoln Holdzkom RC .40 1.00
157 Onil Joseph RC .40 1.00
158 Jason Bartlett RC 1.25 3.00
159 Jon Knott RC .40 1.00
160 Jake Woods RC .40 1.00
161 Jerome Gamble RC .40 1.00
162 Sean Henn RC .40 1.00
163 Kazuo Matsui RC .60 1.50
164 Roberto Novoa RC .40 1.00
165 Eddy Rodriguez RC .40 1.00
166 Ramon Ramirez RC .40 1.00
167 Enemencio Pacheco RC .40 1.00
168 Chad Bentz RC .40 1.00
169 Chris Oxspring RC .40 1.00
170 Justin Leone RC .40 1.00
171 Joe Horgan RC .40 1.00
172 Jose Capellan RC .40 1.00
173 Greg Dobbs RC .40 1.00
174 Jason Frasor RC .40 1.00
175 Shawn Hill RC .40 1.00
176 Carlos Hines RC .40 1.00
177 John Gall RC .40 1.00
178 Steve Andrade RC .40 1.00
179 Scott Proctor RC .40 1.00
180 Rusty Tucker RC .40 1.00
181 Dave Crouthers RC .40 1.00
182 Franklyn Gracesqui RC .40 1.00
183 Justin Germano RC .40 1.00
184 Alfredo Simon RC .40 1.00
185 Jorge Sequea RC .40 1.00
186 Nick Regilio RC .40 1.00
187 Justin Huisman RC .40 1.00
188 Akinori Otsuka RC .40 1.00
189 Luis Gonzalez RC .40 1.00
190 Renyel Pinto RC .40 1.00
191 Joshua Leblanc RC .40 1.00
192 Devin Ivany RC .40 1.00
193 Chad Blackwell RC .40 1.00
194 Brandon Burgess RC .40 1.00
195 Cory Patton RC .40 1.00
196 Daniel Batz RC .40 1.00
197 Adam Russell RC .40 1.00
198 Jarrett Hoffpauir RC .40 1.00
199 Patrick Bryant RC .40 1.00
200 Sean Gamble RC .40 1.00
201 Jermaine Brock RC .40 1.00
202 Ben Zobrist RC 1.00 2.50
203 Clay Meredith RC .40 1.00
204 Derek Tharpe RC .40 1.00
205 Bradley McCann RC .40 1.00
206 Justin Hedrick RC .40 1.00
207 Clint Sammons RC .40 1.00
208 Richard Steik RC .40 1.00
209 Fernando Perez RC .40 1.00
210 Mark Jecmen RC .40 1.00
211 Benjamin Harrison RC .40 1.00
212 Jason Quarles RC .40 1.00
213 William Layman RC .40 1.00
214 Koley Kolberg RC .40 1.00
215 Randy Dicken RC .40 1.00
216 Barry Richmond RC .40 1.00
217 Timothy Murphey RC .40 1.00
218 John Hardy RC .40 1.00
219 Sebastien Boucher RC .40 1.00
220 Andrew Alvarado RC .40 1.00
221 Patrick Perry RC .40 1.00
222 Jarod McAuliff RC .40 1.00
223 Jared Gaston RC .40 1.00
224 William Thompson RC .40 1.00
225 Lucas French RC .40 1.00
226 Brandon Parillo RC .40 1.00
227 Gregory Goetz RC .40 1.00
228 David Haehnel RC .40 1.00
229 James Miller RC .40 1.00
230 Mark Roberts RC .40 1.00
231 Eric Ridener RC .40 1.00
232 Freddy Sandoval RC .40 1.00
234 Carlos Medero-Stullz RC .40 1.00
235 Matthew Shepherd RC .40 1.00
236 Thomas Hubbard RC .40 1.00
238 Kyle Bono RC .40 1.00
239 Craig Moldrem RC .40 1.00
240 Brandon Timm RC UER .40 1.00
Photo is Cory Middleton
241 Mike Carp RC 1.25 3.00
242 Joseph Muro RC .40 1.00
243 Derek Decarlo RC .40 1.00
244 Christopher Niesel RC .40 1.00
245 Trevor Lawhorn RC .40 1.00
246 Joey Howell RC .40 1.00
247 Dustin Hahn RC .40 1.00
248 James Fasano RC .40 1.00
249 Hainley Statia RC .40 1.00
250 Brandon Conway RC .40 1.00
251 Christopher McConnell RC .40 1.00
252 Austin Shappi RC .40 1.00
253 Joseph Metropoulos RC .40 1.00
254 David Nicholson RC .40 1.00
255 Ryan McCarthy RC .40 1.00
256 Michael Parisi RC .40 1.00
257 Andrew Macfarlane RC .40 1.00
258 Jeffrey Dominguez RC .40 1.00
259 Troy Patton RC .40 1.00
260 Ryan Norwood RC .40 1.00
261 Chad Boyd RC .40 1.00
262 Grant Plumley RC .40 1.00
263 Jeffrey Katz RC .40 1.00
264 Cory Middleton RC .40 1.00
265 Andrew Moffitt RC .40 1.00
266 Jarrett Grube RC .40 1.00
267 Derek Hankins RC .40 1.00
268 Douglas Reinhardt RC .40 1.00
269 Duron Legrande RC .40 1.00
270 Steven Jackson RC .40 1.00
271 Brian Hall RC .40 1.00
272 Cory Wade RC .40 1.00
273 John Grogan RC .40 1.00
274 Robert Asanovich RC .40 1.00
275 Kevin Hart RC .40 1.00
276 Matthew Guillory RC .40 1.00
277 Clifton Remole RC .40 1.00
278 David Trahan RC .40 1.00
279 Kristian Bell RC .40 1.00
280 Christopher Westervelt RC .40 1.00
281 Garry Bakker RC .40 1.00
282 Jonathan Ash RC .40 1.00
283 Ryan Phillips RC .40 1.00
284 Wesley Letson RC UER .40 1.00
Name spelled Lesly on the back
285 Jeffrey Landing RC .40 1.00
286 Mark Worrell RC .40 1.00
287 Sean Gallagher RC .40 1.00
288 Nicholas Blasi RC .40 1.00
289 Kevin Frandsen RC .40 1.00
290 Richard Mercado RC .40 1.00
291 Matt Bush AU 400/RC 5.00 12.00
292 Mark Rogers AU 400/RC 10.00 25.00
293 Homer Bailey AU 400/RC 30.00 60.00
294 Chris Nelson AU 400/RC 6.00 15.00
295 T.Diamond AU 400/RC 3.00 8.00
296 Neil Walker AU 400/RC 8.00 20.00
297 Bill Bray AU 400/RC 3.00 8.00
298 David Purcey AU 400/RC 10.00 25.00
299 Scott Elbert AU 400/RC 6.00 15.00
300 Josh Fields AU 400/RC 6.00 15.00
301 Chris Lambert AU 400/RC 3.00 8.00
302 Trevor Plouffe AU 400/RC 12.50 30.00
303 Greg Golson AU 400/RC 6.00 15.00
304 Philip Hughes AU 400/RC 30.00 60.00
305 Kyle Waldrop AU 400/RC 3.00 8.00
306 Richie Robnett AU 350/RC 8.00 20.00
307 T.Tankersley AU 400/RC 5.00 12.00
308 Blake Dewitt AU 400/RC 12.50 30.00
309 Eric Hurley AU 400/RC 8.00 20.00
310 J.Howell AU 400/RC EX * 4.00 10.00
311 Zachary Jackson AU 400/RC 5.00 12.00
312 Justin Orenduff AU 400/RC 10.00 25.00
313 Tyler Lumsden AU 400/RC 3.00 8.00
314 Matthew Fox AU 600/RC 3.00 8.00
315 Danny Putnam AU 450/RC 6.00 15.00
316 Jon Poterson AU 400/RC 5.00 12.00
317 Gio Gonzalez AU 400/RC 12.50 30.00
318 Jay Rainville AU 475/RC 6.00 15.00
319 Huston Street AU 400/RC 4.00 10.00
320 Jeff Marquez AU 400/RC 20.00 50.00
321 Eric Beattie AU 500/RC 6.00 15.00
322 Reid Brignac AU 325/RC 10.00 25.00
323 Y.Gallardo AU 400/RC 30.00 60.00
324 Justin Hoyman AU 400/RC 3.00 8.00
325 B.J. Szymanski AU 400/RC 8.00 20.00
326 Seth Smith AU 600/RC 4.00 10.00
327 Karl Herren AU 600/RC 6.00 15.00
328 Brian Bixler AU 600/RC 3.00 8.00
329 Wesley Whisler AU 600/RC 3.00 8.00
330 E.San Pedro AU 400/RC 3.00 8.00
331 Billy Buckner AU 400/RC 3.00 8.00
332 Jon Zeringue AU 400/RC 6.00 15.00
333 Curtis Thigpen AU 400/RC 4.00 10.00
334 Blake Johnson AU 400/RC 5.00 12.00
335 Donald Lucy AU 400/RC 3.00 8.00
336 Michael Ferris AU 600/RC 5.00 12.00
337 A.Swarzak AU 600/RC 10.00 25.00
338 Jason Jaramillo AU 400/RC 3.00 8.00
339 Hunter Pence AU 600/RC 50.00 100.00
340 Dustin Pedroia AU 400/RC 30.00 60.00
341 Grant Johnson AU 400/RC 5.00 12.00
342 Kurt Suzuki AU 400/RC 8.00 20.00
343 Jason Vargas AU 600/RC 4.00 10.00
344 Raymond Liotta AU 400/RC 15.00 30.00
346 Eric Campbell AU 400/RC 5.00 12.00
347 Jeffrey Frazier AU 400/RC 3.00 8.00
348 G.Hernandez AU 400/RC 10.00 25.00
349 Wade Davis AU 600/RC 15.00 40.00
350 J.Wahpepah AU 400/RC 3.00 8.00
351 Scott Lewis AU 400/RC 12.50 30.00
352 Jeff Fiorentino AU 400/RC 3.00 8.00
353 S.Register AU 600/RC 3.00 8.00
354 Michael Schlact AU 400/RC 3.00 8.00
355 Eddie Prasch AU 400/RC 5.00 12.00
356 Adam Lind AU 400/RC 40.00 80.00
357 Ian Desmond AU 400/RC 12.50 30.00
358 Josh Johnson AU 575/RC 5.00 12.00
359 Garrett Mock AU 600/RC 3.00 8.00
360 Danny Hill AU 600/RC 3.00 8.00
361 Cory Dunlap AU 600/RC 4.00 10.00
362 Grant Hansen AU 600/RC 3.00 8.00
363 Eric Haberer AU 400/RC 3.00 8.00
364 E.Morlan AU 400/RC 3.00 8.00
365 James Happ AU 600/RC 8.00 20.00
366 M.Tuiasosopo AU 600/RC 8.00 20.00
367 Jordan Parraz AU 400/RC 5.00 12.00
368 Andrew Dobies AU 400/RC 8.00 20.00
369 Mark Reed AU 400/RC 10.00 25.00
370 Jason Windsor AU 400/RC 3.00 8.00
371 Gregory Burns AU 600/RC 3.00 8.00
372 Christian Garcia AU 600/RC 8.00 20.00
373 John Bowker AU 575/RC 6.00 15.00
374 J.C. Holt AU 550/RC 5.00 12.00
375 Daryl Jones AU 400/RC 3.00 8.00
376 Collin Mahoney AU 400/RC 5.00 12.00
377 A.Hathaway AU 400/RC 5.00 12.00
378 Matthew Spring AU 400/RC 3.00 8.00
379 Joshua Baker AU 400/RC 3.00 8.00
380 Charles Lofgren AU 400/RC 20.00 50.00
381 Raf Gonzalez AU 400/RC 10.00 25.00
382 Brad Bergesen AU 575/RC 8.00 20.00
383 Brandon Boggs AU 400/RC 8.00 20.00
384 J.Bauserman AU 400/RC 3.00 8.00
385 Collin Balester AU 500/RC 6.00 15.00
386 James Moore AU 400/RC 3.00 8.00
387 Robert Janssen AU 400/RC 10.00 25.00
388 Luis Guerra AU 400/RC 3.00 8.00
389 Lucas Harrell AU 550/RC 3.00 8.00
390 Donnie Smith AU 500/RC 5.00 12.00
391 Mark Robinson AU 525/RC 5.00 12.00
392 Louis Marson AU 550/RC 3.00 8.00
393 Rob Johnson AU 600/RC 3.00 8.00
394 L.Santangelo AU 600/RC 5.00 12.00
395 T.Hottovy AU 400/RC 3.00 8.00
396 Ryan Webb AU 400/RC 5.00 12.00
397 Jamar Walton AU 400/RC 3.00 8.00
398 Jason Jones AU 400/RC 10.00 25.00
399 Clay Timpner AU 600/RC 5.00 12.00
400 James Parr AU 400/RC 8.00 20.00
401 Sean Kazmar AU 400/RC 3.00 8.00
402 Andrew Kown AU 400/RC 5.00 12.00
403 Jacob McGee AU 600/RC 15.00 40.00
404 Michael Butia AU 600/RC 3.00 8.00
405 Paul Janish AU 500/RC 6.00 15.00
406 Matthew Macri AU 400/RC 10.00 25.00
407 Mike Nickeas AU 500/RC 6.00 15.00
408 Kyle Bloom AU 550/RC 4.00 10.00
409 Luis Rivera AU 500/RC 5.00 12.00
410 William Bunn AU 600/RC 10.00 25.00
411 Enrique Barrera AU 400/RC 10.00 25.00
412 R.Klosterman AU 400/RC 3.00 8.00
413 John Raglani AU 515/RC 8.00 20.00
414 Brandon Allen AU 500/RC 10.00 25.00
415 A.Baldwin AU 600/RC 3.00 8.00
416 Mark Lowe AU 400/RC 20.00 50.00
417 Mitch Einertson AU 400/RC 12.50 30.00
418 Ryan Schroyer AU 600/RC 5.00 12.00
419 Bradley Davis AU 400/RC 3.00 8.00
420 Jesse Hoover AU 500/RC 5.00 12.00
421 G.Broshuis AU 400/RC 8.00 20.00
422 Peter Pope AU 400/RC 8.00 20.00
423 Brent Dlugach AU 400/RC 5.00 12.00
424 Ryan Coultas AU 400/RC 5.00 12.00
425 Ryan Royster AU 400/RC 40.00 80.00
426 S.Chapman AU 400/RC 5.00 12.00
427 B.Chamberlin AU 400/RC 8.00 20.00
428 J.Koshansky AU 550/RC 12.50 30.00
429 William Susdorf AU 400/RC 3.00 8.00
430 A.J. Johnson AU 400/RC 8.00 20.00
431 Jeremy Sowers AU 400/RC 6.00 15.00
432 Justin Pekarek AU 400/RC 5.00 12.00
433 Brett Smith AU 400/RC 12.50 30.00
434 Matt Durkin AU 400/RC 5.00 12.00
435 Daniel Barone AU 400/RC 3.00 8.00
436 Scott Hyde AU 400/RC 3.00 8.00
437 T.Everidge AU 400/RC 20.00 50.00
444 Mark Trumbo AU 400/RC 50.00 100.00
446 Eric Patterson AU 400/RC 4.00 10.00
447 Michael Rozier AU 400/RC 5.00 12.00

2004 SP Prospects Gold

OVERALL AU ODDS 1:5
STATED PRINT RUN 10 SERIAL #'d SETS
NO PRICING DUE TO SCARCITY

2004 SP Prospects Platinum

OVERALL AU ODDS 1:5
STATED PRINT RUN 1 SERIAL #'d SET
NO PRICING DUE TO SCARCITY

2004 SP Prospects Autograph Bonus

OVERALL AU ODDS 1:5
PRINT RUNS B/WN 325-600 COPIES PER
AA Andrew Alvarado/400 3.00 8.00
AM Andrew Moffitt/400 3.00 8.00
AR Adam Russell/550 3.00 8.00
AS Austin Shappi/475 6.00 15.00
BB Brandon Burgess/400 6.00 15.00
BC Brandon Conway/400 3.00 8.00
BE Benjamin Harrison/387 3.00 8.00
BH Brian Hall/400 6.00 15.00
BL Chad Blackwell/400 3.00 8.00
BM Bradley McCann/400 10.00 25.00
BO Kyle Bono/400 3.00 8.00
BP Brandon Parillo/475 6.00 15.00
BR Barry Richmond/400 3.00 8.00
BT Brandon Timm/475 3.00 8.00
BZ Ben Zobrist/600 12.50 30.00
CA Mike Carp/400 20.00 50.00
CB Chad Boyd/475 3.00 8.00
CH Christopher McConnell/400 3.00 8.00
CL Clay Meredith/400 3.00 8.00
CM Cory Middleton/400 3.00 8.00
CN Christopher Niesel/475 6.00 15.00
CP Cory Patton/400 3.00 8.00
CR Clifton Remole/400 3.00 8.00
CS Clint Sammons/400 3.00 8.00
CW Cory Wade/400 6.00 15.00
DA David Haehnel/475 6.00 15.00
DB Daniel Batz/400 3.00 8.00
DD Derek Decarlo/400 3.00 8.00
DH Derek Hankins/400 3.00 8.00
DI Devin Ivany/550 3.00 8.00
DL Duron Legrande/400 3.00 8.00
DN David Nicholson/475 3.00 8.00
DR Douglas Reinhardt/400 3.00 8.00
DT Derek Tharpe/400 3.00 8.00
ER Eric Ridener/475 3.00 8.00
FP Fernando Perez/400 20.00 50.00
FS Freddy Sandoval/400 6.00 15.00
GA Jared Gaston/400 3.00 8.00
GB Garry Bakker/400 3.00 8.00
GG Gregory Goetz/400 3.00 8.00
GP Grant Plumley/475 3.00 8.00
GR John Grogan/400 3.00 8.00
HA Dustin Hahn/400 3.00 8.00
HE Justin Hedrick/400 3.00 8.00
HO Joey Howell/400 3.00 8.00
HS Hainley Statia/400 5.00 12.00
JA Jonathan Ash/400 8.00 20.00
JB Jermaine Brock/400 6.00 15.00
JD Jeffrey Dominguez/400 3.00 8.00
JF James Fasano/400 3.00 8.00
JG Jarrett Grube/400 3.00 8.00
JH Jarrett Hoffpauir/400 10.00 25.00
JK Jeffrey Katz/400 6.00 15.00
JL Joshua Leblanc/400 3.00 8.00
JM Joseph Metropoulos/400 6.00 15.00
JO John Hardy/475 3.00 8.00
JQ Jason Quarles/400 3.00 8.00
KB Kristian Bell/400 3.00 8.00
KF Kevin Frandsen/400 10.00 25.00
KH Kevin Hart/400 5.00 12.00
KK Koley Kolberg/400 3.00 8.00
LA Jeffrey Landing/400 3.00 8.00
LE Wesley Letson/400 3.00 8.00
LF Lucas French/400 6.00 15.00
MA Andrew Macfarlane/400 3.00 8.00
MC Jarod McAuliff/400 3.00 8.00
ME Carlos Medero-Stullz/400 3.00 8.00
MG Matthew Guillory/400 3.00 8.00
MI James Miller/475 3.00 8.00
MJ Mark Jecmen/600 3.00 8.00
MO Craig Moldrem/400 3.00 8.00
MP Michael Parisi/475 3.00 8.00
MR Mark Roberts/400 3.00 8.00
MS Matthew Shepherd/400 3.00 8.00
MU Joseph Muro/400 3.00 8.00
MW Mark Worrell/400 6.00 15.00
NB Nicholas Blasi/400 3.00 8.00
PB Patrick Bryant/400 3.00 8.00
PP Patrick Perry/475 6.00 15.00
RA Robert Asanovich/400 6.00 15.00
RD Randy Dicken/475 6.00 15.00
RI Richard Mercado/400 3.00 8.00
RM Ryan McCarthy/400 8.00 20.00
RN Ryan Norwood/400 10.00 25.00
RP Ryan Phillips/400 3.00 8.00
RS Richard Steik/400 3.00 8.00
SB Sebastien Boucher/325 6.00 15.00
SE Sean Gallagher/400 30.00 60.00
SG Sean Gamble/400 6.00 15.00
SJ Steven Jackson/475 3.00 8.00
TH Thomas Hubbard/400 3.00 8.00
TL Trevor Lawhorn/475 6.00 15.00
TM Timothy Murphey/400 3.00 8.00
TP Troy Patton/400 40.00 80.00
TR David Trahan/400 3.00 8.00
WE Christopher Westervelt/400 3.00 8.00
WL William Layman/400 3.00 8.00
WT William Thompson/475 3.00 8.00

2004 SP Prospects Autograph Bonus Gold

OVERALL AU ODDS 1:5
STATED PRINT RUN 10 SERIAL #'d SETS
NO PRICING DUE TO SCARCITY

2004 SP Prospects Draft Duos Dual Autographs

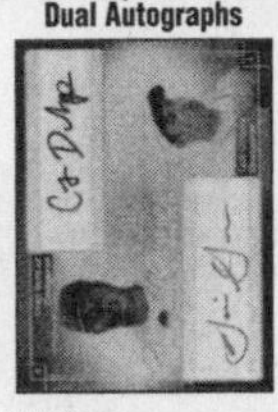

OVERALL AU ODDS 1:5
STATED PRINT RUN 175 SERIAL #'d SETS

BB Bill Bray	10.00	25.00
Collin Balester		
BG Homer Bailey	15.00	40.00
Rafael Gonzalez		
BH Matt Bush	20.00	50.00
Philip Hughes		
BI Bill Bray	10.00	25.00
Ian Desmond		
BJ Matt Bush	4.00	10.00
Daryl Jones		
BK Matt Bush	4.00	10.00
Sean Kazmar		
BM Billy Buckner	5.00	12.00
James Moore		
BN Matt Bush	15.00	40.00
Chris Nelson		
BP Matt Bush	10.00	25.00
Trevor Plouffe		
BR Reid Brignac	5.00	12.00
Ryan Royster		
BS Homer Bailey	15.00	40.00
B.J. Szymanski		
BT Thomas Diamond	4.00	10.00
Brandon Boggs		
CF Bryce Chamberlin	10.00	25.00
Jeff Fiorentino		
CH Ryan Coultas	5.00	12.00
Aaron Hathaway		
CL Justin Hoyman	12.50	30.00
Jeremy Sowers		
CO Steven Register	10.00	25.00
Seth Smith		
DB Blake Dewitt	4.00	10.00
Daniel Batz		
DG Cory Dunlap	5.00	12.00
Luis Guerra		
DH Thomas Diamond	10.00	25.00
Eric Hurley		
DR Blake Dewitt	5.00	12.00
John Raglani		
DZ David Purcey	4.00	10.00
Zachary Jackson		
EA Eric Beattie	5.00	12.00
Andrew Kown		
EC Eric Beattie	5.00	12.00
Collin Mahoney		
ED Scott Elbert	10.00	25.00
Blake Dewitt		
EJ Eric Campbell	15.00	40.00
J.C. Holt		
EM Eric Hurley	10.00	25.00
Michael Nickeas		
ER Scott Elbert	5.00	12.00
John Raglani		
FB Jeff Fiorentino	10.00	25.00
Brad Bergesen		
FH Josh Fields	15.00	40.00
Lucas Harrell		
FM Jeffrey Frazier	5.00	12.00
Collin Mahoney		
FW Josh Fields	4.00	10.00
Wesley Whisler		
GB Homer Bailey	15.00	40.00
Gregory Goetz		
GG Greg Golson	10.00	25.00
Sean Gamble		
GH Greg Golson	15.00	40.00
James Happ		
GM Giovanny Gonzalez	4.00	10.00
Timothy Murphey		
GW Yovani Gallardo	6.00	15.00
Joshua Wahpepah		
HB James Howell	4.00	10.00
Chad Blackwell		
HG Philip Hughes	20.00	50.00
Christian Garcia		
HH Gaby Hernandez	12.50	30.00
Aaron Hathaway		
HJ Hunter Pence	20.00	50.00
Jordan Parraz		
HM Jeff Marquez	20.00	50.00
Philip Hughes		
HP Philip Hughes	20.00	50.00
Jonathan Poterson		
HS Karl Herren	5.00	12.00
Michael Schlact		
JB Billy Buckner	4.00	10.00
Joshua Johnson		
JE Jeffrey Frazier	5.00	12.00
Eric Beattie		
JH James Howell	5.00	12.00
Joshua Johnson		
JJ Jonathan Poterson	5.00	12.00
Jason Jones		
JK Zachary Jackson	4.00	10.00
Ryan Klosterman		
JM Jason Jaramillo	5.00	12.00
Louis Marson		
JP Jay Rainville	10.00	25.00
Patrick Bryant		
JR Grant Johnson	10.00	25.00
Mark Reed		
JS Jeremy Sowers	5.00	12.00
Scott Lewis		
KB Kyle Waldrop	5.00	12.00
Patrick Bryant		
KH Matthew Durkin	4.00	10.00
Aaron Hathaway		
LA Raymond Liotta	5.00	12.00
Brandon Allen		
LF Chris Lambert	5.00	12.00
Michael Ferris		
LG Tyler Lumsden	4.00	10.00
Giovanny Gonzalez		
LH Donald Lucy	4.00	10.00
Grant Hansen		
LK Adam Lind	15.00	40.00
Ryan Klosterman		
LR Tyler Lumsden	5.00	12.00
Adam Russell		
LS Chris Lambert	4.00	10.00
Donnie Smith		
MH Jeff Marquez	5.00	12.00
Jesse Hoover		
MR Eduardo Morlan	5.00	12.00
Mark Robinson		
MS Jeff Marquez	5.00	12.00
Brett Smith		
NB Neil Walker	10.00	25.00
Brian Bixler		
NK Neil Walker	12.50	30.00
Kyle Bloom		
NM Chris Nelson	12.50	30.00
Matthew Macri		
NS Chris Nelson	10.00	25.00
Seth Smith		
OG Justin Orenduff	5.00	12.00
Luis Guerra		
OJ Justin Orenduff	5.00	12.00
Blake Johnson		
PB Eddie Prasch	5.00	12.00
Joseph Bauserman		
PD Dustin Pedroia	50.00	100.00
Andrew Dobies		
PI Erick San Pedro	5.00	12.00
Devin Ivany		
PJ David Purcey	4.00	10.00
Robert Janssen		
PR Trevor Plouffe	4.00	10.00
Mark Robinson		
PT Danny Putnam	5.00	12.00
Derek Tharpe		
PW Trevor Plouffe	10.00	25.00
Kyle Waldrop		
PZ Jordan Parraz	5.00	12.00
Ben Zobrist		
RB Mark Rogers	10.00	25.00
Joshua Baker		
RD Cory Dunlap	5.00	12.00
John Raglani		
RG Mark Rogers	6.00	15.00
Yovani Gallardo		
RH Richie Robnett	4.00	10.00
Huston Street		
RL Luis Rivera	5.00	12.00
William Layman		
RP Richie Robnett	5.00	12.00
Danny Putnam		
RS Jay Rainville	12.50	30.00
Anthony Swarzak		
RW Richie Robnett	5.00	12.00
Jason Windsor		
SB Jeremy Sowers	12.50	30.00
Homer Bailey		
SH Brett Smith	15.00	40.00
Phillip Hughes		
SJ B.J. Szymanski	5.00	12.00
Paul Janish		
SK Seth Smith	4.00	10.00
Joseph Koshansky		
SL Jeremy Sowers	15.00	40.00
Charles Lofgren		
SR Richie Robnett	10.00	25.00
Kurt Suzuki		
SS Huston Street	12.50	30.00
Kurt Suzuki		
SW Huston Street	4.00	10.00
Ryan Webb		
TD Taylor Tankersley	4.00	10.00
Bradley Davis		
TH Curtis Thigpen	5.00	12.00
Danny Hill UER(Photo of Thigpen is not him		
TV Taylor Tankersley	4.00	10.00
Jason Vargas		
WB Joshua Wahpepah	4.00	10.00
Joshua Baker		
WE Billy Buckner	4.00	10.00
Enrique Barrera		
WF Kyle Waldrop	5.00	12.00
Matthew Fox		
WJ Billy Buckner	4.00	10.00
James Howell		
WR Reid Brignac	20.00	50.00
Wade Davis		
ZM Jonathan Zeringue	10.00	25.00
Garrett Mock		
ZP Hunter Pence	30.00	60.00
Ben Zobrist		

2004 SP Prospects Draft Generations Triple Autographs

OVERALL AU ODDS 1:5
STATED PRINT RUN 25 SERIAL #'d SETS
NO PRICING DUE TO SCARCITY

2004 SP Prospects Link to the Future Dual Autographs

Card		
COMMON CARD	6.00	15.00
OVERALL AU ODDS 1:5		
STATED PRINT RUN 100 SERIAL #'d SETS		
BD Adrian Beltre	15.00	40.00
Blake Dewitt		
BG Carlos Beltran	6.00	15.00
Greg Golson		
BH Angel Berroa	10.00	25.00
James Howell		
CD Roger Clemens	20.00	50.00
Thomas Diamond		
CF Matt Clement	6.00	15.00
Matthew Fox		
EJ Eric Chavez	15.00	40.00
Josh Fields		
GB Nomar Garciaparra	30.00	60.00
Matt Bush		
GP Brian Giles	10.00	25.00
Danny Putnam		
GS Ken Griffey Jr.	30.00	60.00
B.J. Szymanski		
GZ Luis Gonzalez	10.00	25.00
Jonathan Zeringue		
HS Todd Helton	15.00	40.00
Seth Smith		
HW Rich Harden	10.00	25.00
Kyle Waldrop		
JB Jason Kendall	10.00	25.00
Brian Bixler		
JJ Edwin Jackson	6.00	15.00
Blake Johnson		
JR Andruw Jones	15.00	40.00
Richie Robnett		
KB Scott Kazmir	10.00	25.00
Reid Brignac		
KW Jason Kendall	15.00	40.00
Neil Walker		
LS Paul LoDuca	10.00	25.00
Erick San Pedro		
MB Mark Mulder	10.00	25.00
Bill Bray		
MH Mike Mussina	30.00	60.00
Philip Hughes		
MP Joe Mauer	40.00	80.00
Trevor Plouffe		
MS Mike Mussina	6.00	15.00
Brett Smith		
OH Magglio Ordonez	10.00	25.00
Karl Herren		
PE Odalis Perez	10.00	25.00
Scott Elbert		
PJ Mark Prior	15.00	40.00
Grant Johnson		
QT Guillermo Quiroz	6.00	15.00
Curtis Thigpen		
RE Roy Oswalt	10.00	25.00
Eric Hurley		
RF Scott Rolen	15.00	40.00
Michael Ferris		
RL Scott Rolen	6.00	15.00
Chris Lambert		
RP Alexis Rios	10.00	25.00
David Purcey		
SJ Johan Santana	15.00	40.00
Jay Rainville		
SR Ben Sheets	20.00	40.00
Mark Rogers		
SW Johan Santana	15.00	40.00
Kyle Waldrop		
TJ Tom Glavine	15.00	40.00
Jeremy Sowers		
TN Miguel Tejada	30.00	60.00
Chris Nelson		
TS Tim Hudson	15.00	40.00
Huston Street		
VD Victor Martinez	10.00	25.00
Donald Lucy		
VM Javier Vazquez	10.00	25.00
Jeff Marquez		
VP Javier Vazquez	6.00	15.00
Jonathan Poterson		
WB Kerry Wood	25.00	50.00
Homer Bailey		
WT Dontrelle Willis	10.00	25.00
Taylor Tankersley		

2004 SP Prospects Link to the Future Triple Autographs

OVERALL AU ODDS 1:5		
STATED PRINT RUN 50 SERIAL #'d SETS		
PRICING UNAVAILABLE AT THIS TIME		
JJB Edwin Jackson	10.00	25.00
Blake Johnson		
Daniel Batz		

2004 SP Prospects Link to the Past Dual Autographs

OVERALL AU ODDS 1:5
STATED PRINT RUN 50 SERIAL #'d SETS
NO PRICING DUE TO LOW VOLUME

2004 SP Prospects National Honors USA Jersey

STATED ODDS 1:12		
AG Alex Gordon	10.00	25.00
BC J. Brent Cox	3.00	8.00
BH Brett Hayes	3.00	8.00
CR Cesar Ramos	3.00	8.00
CV Chris Valaika	3.00	8.00
DB Daniel Bard	3.00	8.00
DS Drew Stubbs	3.00	8.00
IK Ian Kennedy	4.00	10.00
JC Jeff Clement	3.00	8.00
JD Joey Devine	3.00	8.00
JL Jed Lowrie	3.00	8.00
JM John Mayberry Jr.	3.00	8.00
LH Luke Hochevar	3.00	8.00
MP Mike Pelfrey	4.00	10.00
MR Mark Romanczuk	3.00	8.00
RR Ricky Romero	3.00	8.00
RZ Ryan Zimmerman	6.00	15.00
SK Stephen Kahn	3.00	8.00
TB Travis Buck	3.00	8.00
TC Trevor Crowe	3.00	8.00
TE Taylor Teagarden	3.00	8.00
TT Troy Tulowitzki	5.00	12.00

1999 SP Signature

The 1999 SP Signature set was issued in one series totalling 180 cards and distributed in three card packs with a suggested retail price of $19.99. The expensive SRP was due to the fact that there is one autograph card per pack. The set features color action player photos with player information on the cardback. Rookie Cards include A.J. Burnett and Pat Burrell. 350 Mel Ott A Piece of History 500 Club bat cards were randomly seeded into packs. Pricing for these bat cards can be referenced under 1999 Upper Deck A Piece of History 500 Club.

Card		
COMPLETE SET (180)	60.00	150.00
1 Nomar Garciaparra	1.50	4.00
2 Ken Griffey Jr.	1.50	4.00
3 J.D. Drew	.40	1.00
4 Alex Rodriguez	1.50	4.00
5 Juan Gonzalez	.40	1.00
6 Mo Vaughn	.40	1.00
7 Greg Maddux	1.50	4.00
8 Chipper Jones	1.00	2.50
9 Frank Thomas	1.00	2.50
10 Vladimir Guerrero	1.00	2.50
11 Mike Piazza	1.50	4.00
12 Eric Chavez	.40	1.00
13 Tony Gwynn	1.25	3.00
14 Orlando Hernandez	.40	1.00
15 Pat Burrell RC	3.00	8.00
16 Darin Erstad	.40	1.00
17 Greg Vaughn	.30	.75
18 Russ Branyan	.30	.75
19 Gabe Kapler	.40	1.00
20 Craig Biggio	.60	1.50
21 Troy Glaus	.60	1.50
22 Pedro Martinez	.60	1.50
23 Carlos Beltran	.60	1.50
24 Derrek Lee	.60	1.50
25 Manny Ramirez	.60	1.50
26 Shea Hillenbrand RC	1.50	4.00
27 Carlos Lee	.40	1.00
28 Angel Pena	.30	.75
29 Rafael Roque RC	.40	1.00
30 Octavio Dotel	.30	.75
31 Jeromy Burnitz	.40	1.00
32 Jeremy Giambi	.30	.75
33 Andruw Jones	.60	1.50
34 Todd Helton	.60	1.50
35 Scott Rolen	.60	1.50
36 Jason Kendall	.40	1.00
37 Trevor Hoffman	.40	1.00
38 Barry Bonds	2.50	6.00
39 Ivan Rodriguez	.60	1.50
40 Roy Halladay	1.00	2.50
41 Rickey Henderson	1.00	2.50
42 Ryan Minor	.30	.75
43 Brian Jordan	.40	1.00
44 Alex Gonzalez	.30	.75
45 Raul Mondesi	.40	1.00
46 Corey Koskie	.30	.75
47 Paul O'Neill	.60	1.50
48 Todd Walker	.30	.75
49 Carlos Febles	.30	.75
50 Travis Fryman	.40	1.00
51 Albert Belle	.40	1.00
52 Travis Lee	.30	.75
53 Bruce Chen	.30	.75
54 Reggie Taylor	.30	.75
55 Jerry Hairston Jr.	.30	.75
56 Carlos Guillen	.40	1.00
57 Michael Barrett	.30	.75
58 Jason Conti	.30	.75
59 Joe Lawrence	.30	.75
60 Jeff Cirillo	.30	.75
61 Juan Melo	.30	.75
62 Chad Hermansen	.30	.75
63 Ruben Mateo	.30	.75
64 Ben Davis	.30	.75
65 Mike Caruso	.30	.75
66 Jason Giambi	.40	1.00
67 Jose Canseco	.60	1.50
68 Chad Hutchinson RC	.60	1.50
69 Mitch Meluskey	.30	.75
70 Adrian Beltre	.40	1.00
71 Mark Kotsay	.40	1.00
72 Juan Encarnacion	.30	.75
73 Dermal Brown	.30	.75
74 Kevin Witt	.30	.75
75 Vinny Castilla	.40	1.00
76 Aramis Ramirez	.40	1.00
77 Marlon Anderson	.30	.75
78 Mike Kinkade	.30	.75
79 Kevin Barker	.30	.75
80 Ron Belliard	.30	.75
81 Chris Haas	.30	.75
82 Bob Henley	.30	.75
83 Fernando Seguignol	.30	.75
84 Damon Minor	.30	.75
85 A.J. Burnett RC	1.50	4.00
86 Calvin Pickering	.30	.75
87 Mike Darr	.30	.75
88 Cesar King	.30	.75
89 Rob Bell	.30	.75
90 Derrick Gibson	.30	.75
91 Orber Moreno RC	.40	1.00
92 Robert Fick	.30	.75
93 Doug Mientkiewicz RC	1.00	2.50
94 A.J. Pierzynski	.40	1.00
95 Orlando Palmeiro	.30	.75
96 Sidney Ponson	.30	.75
97 Ivanon Coffie RC	.40	1.00
98 Juan Pena RC	.40	1.00
99 Matt Karchner	.30	.75
100 Carlos Castillo	.30	.75
101 Bryan Ward RC	.40	1.00
102 Mario Valdez	.30	.75
103 Billy Wagner	.40	1.00
104 Miguel Tejada	.40	1.00
105 Jose Cruz Jr.	.30	.75
106 George Lombard	.30	.75
107 Geoff Jenkins	.30	.75
108 Ray Lankford	.40	1.00
109 Todd Stottlemyre	.30	.75
110 Mike Lowell	.40	1.00
111 Matt Clement	.40	1.00
112 Scott Brosius	.40	1.00
113 Preston Wilson	.40	1.00
114 Bartolo Colon	.40	1.00
115 Rolando Arrojo	.30	.75
116 Jose Guillen	.40	1.00
117 Ron Gant	.40	1.00
118 Ricky Ledee	.30	.75
119 Carlos Delgado	.40	1.00
120 Abraham Nunez	.30	.75
121 John Olerud	.40	1.00
122 Chan Ho Park	.40	1.00
123 Brad Radke	.40	1.00
124 Al Leiter	.40	1.00
125 Gary Matthews Jr.	.30	.75
126 F.P. Santangelo	.30	.75
127 Brad Fullmer	.30	.75
128 Matt Anderson	.30	.75
129 A.J. Hinch	.30	.75
130 Sterling Hitchcock	.30	.75
131 Edgar Martinez	.60	1.50
132 Fernando Tatis	.30	.75
133 Bobby Smith	.30	.75
134 Paul Konerko	.40	1.00
135 Sean Casey	.40	1.00
136 Donnie Sadler	.30	.75
137 Denny Neagle	.30	.75
138 Sandy Alomar Jr.	.30	.75
139 Mariano Rivera	1.00	2.50
140 Emil Brown	.30	.75
141 J.T. Snow	.40	1.00
142 Eli Marrero	.30	.75
143 Rusty Greer	.40	1.00
144 Johnny Damon	.60	1.50
145 Damion Easley	.30	.75
146 Eric Milton	.30	.75
147 Rico Brogna	.30	.75
148 Ray Durham	.40	1.00
149 Wally Joyner	.40	1.00
150 Royce Clayton	.30	.75
151 David Ortiz	1.00	2.50
152 Wade Boggs	.60	1.50
153 Ugueth Urbina	.30	.75
154 Richard Hidalgo	.30	.75
155 Bob Abreu	.40	1.00
156 Robb Nen	.40	1.00
157 David Segui	.30	.75
158 Sean Berry	.30	.75
159 Kevin Tapani	.30	.75
160 Jason Varitek	1.00	2.50
161 Fernando Vina	.30	.75
162 Jim Leyritz	.30	.75
163 Enrique Wilson	.30	.75
164 Jim Parque	.30	.75
165 Doug Glanville	.30	.75
166 Jesus Sanchez	.30	.75
167 Nolan Ryan	2.50	6.00
168 Robin Yount	1.50	4.00
169 Stan Musial	1.50	4.00
170 Tom Seaver	.60	1.50
171 Mike Schmidt	2.00	5.00
172 Willie Stargell	.60	1.50
173 Rollie Fingers	.40	1.00
174 Willie McCovey	.40	1.00
175 Harmon Killebrew	1.00	2.50
176 Eddie Mathews	1.00	2.50
177 Reggie Jackson	.60	1.50
178 Frank Robinson	.60	1.50
179 Ken Griffey Sr.	.40	1.00
180 Eddie Murray	1.00	2.50
S1 Ken Griffey Jr. Sample	.75	2.00

1999 SP Signature Autographs

Inserted one per pack, this 150-card set is a partial parallel autographed version of the base set. Though print runs were not released, the amount of cards each player signed varied greatly. Many of the active veteran stars are noticeably tougher to find than the other cards in the set. In addition, several players had exchange cards of which expired on May 12th, 2000. The following players originally packed out as exchange cards: A.J. Burnett, Sean Casey, Vinny Castilla, Bartolo Colon, Pedro Martinez, Ruben Mateo, Jim Parque, Mike Piazza, Scott Rolen, J.T. Snow and Willie Stargell.

Card		
AB Albert Belle	10.00	25.00
ABE Adrian Beltre	8.00	20.00
AG Alex Gonzalez	3.00	8.00
AJ Andruw Jones	10.00	25.00
AJB A.J. Burnett	6.00	15.00
AJP A.J. Pierzynski	6.00	15.00
AL Al Leiter	6.00	15.00
AN Abraham Nunez	3.00	8.00
AP Angel Pena	3.00	8.00
AR Alex Rodriguez	60.00	120.00
ARA Aramis Ramirez	6.00	15.00
BA Bob Abreu	6.00	15.00
BB Barry Bonds	100.00	200.00
BC Bruce Chen	3.00	8.00
BCO Bartolo Colon	6.00	15.00
BD Ben Davis	3.00	8.00
BF Brad Fullmer	3.00	8.00
BH Bob Henley	3.00	8.00
BR Brad Radke	6.00	15.00
BS Bobby Smith	3.00	8.00
BW Bryan Ward	3.00	8.00
BWA Billy Wagner	6.00	15.00
CBE Carlos Beltran	10.00	25.00
CC Carlos Castillo	3.00	8.00
CD Carlos Delgado	6.00	15.00
CF Carlos Febles	3.00	8.00
CH Chad Hermansen	3.00	8.00
CHA Chris Haas	3.00	8.00
CHU Chad Hutchinson	3.00	8.00
CJ Chipper Jones	30.00	60.00
CK Corey Koskie	6.00	15.00
CKI Cesar King	3.00	8.00
CL Carlos Lee	6.00	15.00
CP Calvin Pickering	3.00	8.00
DAM Damon Minor	3.00	8.00
DB Dermal Brown	3.00	8.00
DE Darin Erstad	3.00	8.00
DEA Damion Easley	3.00	8.00
DG Derrick Gibson	3.00	8.00
DGL Doug Glanville	3.00	8.00
DL Derrek Lee	6.00	15.00
DO David Ortiz	12.50	30.00
DOM Doug Mientkiewicz	3.00	8.00
DS Donnie Sadler	3.00	8.00
DSE David Segui	6.00	15.00
EB Emil Brown	3.00	8.00
EC Eric Chavez	3.00	8.00
ED Orlando Hernandez SP	60.00	120.00
ELI Eli Marrero	3.00	8.00
EM Edgar Martinez	10.00	25.00
EMA Eddie Mathews	50.00	100.00
EMI Eric Milton	3.00	8.00
EW Enrique Wilson	3.00	8.00
FR Frank Robinson	10.00	25.00
FS Fernando Seguignol	3.00	8.00
FT Frank Thomas	50.00	100.00
FTA Fernando Tatis	3.00	8.00
FV Fernando Vina	3.00	8.00
GJ Geoff Jenkins	6.00	15.00
GK Gabe Kapler	6.00	15.00
GM Greg Maddux	60.00	120.00
GMJ Gary Matthews Jr.	3.00	8.00
GV Greg Vaughn	3.00	8.00
HK Harmon Killebrew	30.00	60.00
IC Ivanon Coffie	3.00	8.00
JAG Jason Giambi	6.00	15.00
JC Jason Conti	3.00	8.00
JCI Jeff Cirillo	6.00	15.00
JD J.D. Drew	6.00	15.00
JDA Johnny Damon	10.00	25.00
JE Juan Encarnacion	6.00	15.00
JEG Jeremy Giambi	3.00	8.00
JG Jose Guillen	6.00	15.00
JHJ Jerry Hairston Jr.	3.00	8.00
JK Jason Kendall	6.00	15.00
JLA Joe Lawrence	3.00	8.00
JLE Jim Leyritz	3.00	8.00
JM Juan Melo	3.00	8.00
JO John Olerud	10.00	25.00
JOC Jose Canseco	15.00	40.00
JP Jim Parque	3.00	8.00
JR Ken Griffey Jr.	60.00	120.00
JS Jesus Sanchez	3.00	8.00
JT J.T. Snow	6.00	15.00
JV Jason Varitek	12.50	30.00
KB Kevin Barker	3.00	8.00
KW Kevin Witt	3.00	8.00
MA Marlon Anderson	3.00	8.00
MB Michael Barrett	3.00	8.00
MC Mike Caruso	3.00	8.00
MCL Matt Clement	6.00	15.00
MK Mark Kotsay	6.00	15.00
MKA Matt Karchner	3.00	8.00
MKI Mike Kinkade	3.00	8.00
MME Mitch Meluskey	3.00	8.00
MO Mo Vaughn	6.00	15.00
MP Mike Piazza	100.00	200.00
MR Manny Ramirez	10.00	25.00
MRI Mariano Rivera	100.00	175.00
MS Mike Schmidt	20.00	50.00
MT Miguel Tejada	6.00	15.00
MV Mario Valdez	3.00	8.00
NG Nomar Garciaparra	12.50	30.00
NR Nolan Ryan	75.00	150.00
OD Octavio Dotel	3.00	8.00
OP Orlando Palmeiro	3.00	8.00
PB Pat Burrell	6.00	15.00
PG Ivan Rodriguez	20.00	50.00
PK Paul Konerko	10.00	25.00
PM Pedro Martinez	60.00	120.00
PO Paul O'Neill	10.00	25.00
POP Willie Stargell	40.00	80.00
RB Russ Branyan	3.00	8.00
RBF Ron Belliard	3.00	8.00
RC Royce Clayton	3.00	8.00
RD Ray Durham	6.00	15.00
RGA Ron Gant SP	40.00	80.00
RGR Rusty Greer	6.00	15.00
RH Roy Halladay	50.00	100.00
RJ Reggie Jackson SP	30.00	60.00
RL Ray Lankford	6.00	15.00
RM Ryan Minor	3.00	8.00
RMA Ruben Mateo	3.00	8.00
RN Robb Nen	6.00	15.00
ROB Rob Bell	3.00	8.00
ROB Robert Fick	3.00	8.00
ROL Rollie Fingers	10.00	25.00
RR Rafael Roque	3.00	8.00
RT Reggie Taylor	3.00	8.00
RY Robin Yount	20.00	50.00
SA Sandy Alomar Jr.	3.00	8.00
SB Scott Brosius SP	60.00	120.00
SC Sean Casey	6.00	15.00
SHH Shea Hillenbrand	6.00	15.00
SM Stan Musial	60.00	120.00
SP Sidney Ponson	3.00	8.00
SR Ken Griffey Sr.	6.00	15.00
SR Scott Rolen	6.00	15.00
STH Sterling Hitchcock	3.00	8.00
TG Tony Gwynn	15.00	40.00
TGL Troy Glaus	3.00	8.00
THE Todd Helton	10.00	25.00
THO Trevor Hoffman	10.00	25.00
TSE Tom Seaver	15.00	40.00
TST Todd Stottlemyre	3.00	8.00
TW Todd Walker	6.00	15.00
VC Vinny Castilla	6.00	15.00
VG Vladimir Guerrero	12.50	30.00
WJ Wally Joyner	6.00	15.00
WMC Willie McCovey	15.00	40.00

1999 SP Signature Autographs Gold

Randomly inserted into packs, this 90-card set is a gold signature style partial parallel version of the base set. The only difference in design is a thin strip of gold foil squares on the card front. According to Upper Deck, 11 players did not sign their cards and are marked "NO AU" in the checklist below. Only 50 serial-numbered sets were produced. In addition, the following players had exchange cards of which expired on May 12th, 2000: Mike Piazza, Pedro Martinez, Scott Rolen and Vinny Castilla. Finally, a mere 20 copies of A.J. Burnett's cards packed out. All twenty made their way into packs as exchange cards with a May 12th, 2000 deadline. The Burnett card is not priced due to scarcity.

Card		
AB Albert Belle	8.00	20.00
ABE Adrian Beltre	10.00	25.00
AG Alex Gonzalez	6.00	15.00
AJ Andruw Jones	50.00	100.00
AJB A.J. Burnett SP/20		
AP Angel Pena	6.00	15.00
AR Alex Rodriguez	125.00	250.00
ARA Aramis Ramirez	8.00	20.00
BB Barry Bonds	225.00	350.00
BC Bruce Chen	6.00	15.00
BD Ben Davis	6.00	15.00
BH Bob Henley	6.00	15.00
BJ Brian Jordan NO AU	2.50	6.00
CB Craig Biggio NO AU	2.50	6.00
CBE Carlos Beltran	10.00	25.00
CF Carlos Febles	6.00	15.00
CG Carlos Guillen NO AU	2.50	6.00
CH Chad Hermansen	6.00	15.00
CHA Chris Haas	6.00	15.00
CHU Chad Hutchinson	6.00	15.00
CJ Chipper Jones	75.00	150.00
CK Corey Koskie	8.00	20.00
CKI Cesar King	6.00	15.00
CL Carlos Lee	8.00	20.00
CP Calvin Pickering	6.00	15.00
DAM Damon Minor	6.00	15.00
DB Dermal Brown	6.00	15.00
DE Darin Erstad	8.00	20.00
DG Derrick Gibson	6.00	15.00
DL Derrek Lee	6.00	15.00
EC Eric Chavez	8.00	20.00
ED Orlando Hernandez	125.00	200.00
FS Fernando Seguignol	6.00	15.00
FT Frank Thomas	125.00	200.00
GK Gabe Kapler	8.00	20.00
GM Greg Maddux	175.00	300.00
GV Greg Vaughn	6.00	15.00
JAG Jason Giambi	50.00	100.00
JB Jeromy Burnitz NO AU	2.50	6.00
JC Jason Conti	6.00	15.00
JCI Jeff Cirillo	6.00	15.00
JD J.D. Drew	8.00	20.00
JE Juan Encarnacion	8.00	20.00
JEG Jeremy Giambi NO AU	2.50	6.00
JHJ Jerry Hairston Jr.	6.00	15.00
JK Jason Kendall	6.00	15.00
JLA Joe Lawrence	6.00	15.00
JM Juan Melo	6.00	15.00
JOC Jose Canseco	50.00	100.00
JR Ken Griffey Jr.	150.00	250.00
JUG Juan Gonzalez NO AU	2.50	6.00
KB Kevin Barker	6.00	15.00
KW Kevin Witt	6.00	15.00
MA Marlon Anderson	6.00	15.00
MB Michael Barrett	6.00	15.00
MC Mike Caruso	6.00	15.00
MD Mike Darr NO AU	2.50	6.00
MK Mark Kotsay	6.00	15.00
MKI Mike Kinkade	6.00	15.00
MME Mitch Meluskey	6.00	15.00
MO Mo Vaughn	8.00	20.00
MP Mike Piazza	175.00	300.00
MR Manny Ramirez	75.00	150.00
NG Nomar Garciaparra	75.00	150.00
OD Octavio Dotel	6.00	15.00

PB Pat Burrell 50.00 100.00
PG Ivan Rodriguez 100.00 200.00
PM Pedro Martinez 100.00 200.00
PO Paul O'Neill 50.00 100.00
RB Russ Branyan 6.00 15.00
RBE Ron Belliard 6.00 15.00
RH Roy Halladay 150.00 400.00
RHE R. Henderson NO AU 2.50 6.00
RM Ryan Minor 6.00 15.00
RMA Ruben Mateo 6.00 15.00
RMO R.Mondesi NO AU 2.50 6.00
ROB Rob Bell 6.00 15.00
RR Rafael Roque 6.00 15.00
RT Reggie Taylor 6.00 15.00
SHH Shea Hillenbrand 6.00 15.00
SR Scott Rolen 50.00 100.00
TF Travis Fryman NO AU 2.50 6.00
TG Tony Gwynn 8.00 20.00
TGL Troy Glaus 50.00 100.00
THE Todd Helton 50.00 100.00
THO Trevor Hoffman 20.00 50.00
TL Travis Lee NO AU 2.50 6.00
TW Todd Walker 8.00 20.00
VC Vinny Castilla 8.00 20.00
VG Vladimir Guerrero 75.00 150.00

1999 SP Signature Legendary Cuts

Randomly inserted into packs, this eight-card set features a "cut" signature from one of baseball's legends. Only one of each card was produced. No pricing is available due to scarcity but a checklist is provided.

ROY Roy Campanella
XX Jimmie Foxx
LG Lefty Grove
W Walter Johnson
MEL1 Mel Ott
MEL2 Mel Ott
BR Babe Ruth
CY Cy Young

1933 Sport Kings

The cards in this 48-card set measure 2 3/8" by 2 7/8". The 1933 Sport Kings set, issued by the Goudey Gum Company, contains cards for the most famous athletic heroes of the times. No less than 18 different sports are represented in the set. The baseball cards of Cobb, Hubbell, and Ruth, and the football cards of Rockne, Grange and Thorpe command premium prices. The cards were issued in one-card penny packs which came 100 packs to a box along with a piece of gum. The catalog designation for this set is R338.

COMPLETE SET 10000.00 16000.00
1 Ty Cobb 1200.00 2000.00
(baseball)
2 Babe Ruth 2500.00 4000.00
(baseball)
42 Carl Hubbell 300.00 500.00
(baseball)

2007 Sportkings

COMPLETE SET (48) 600.00 900.00
THREE PER PACK
6 Roger Clemens 5.00 12.00
7 Roberto Clemente 15.00 30.00
24 Don Mattingly 6.00 15.00
25 Stan Musial 10.00 25.00
27 Jackie Robinson 10.00 25.00
28 Pete Rose 20.00 40.00
31 Nolan Ryan 10.00 25.00
34 Tom Seaver 4.00 10.00
45 Ted Williams 8.00 20.00
47 Carl Yastrzemski 6.00 15.00

2007 Sportkings Mini

*MINIS: 1X TO 2X BASIC
ONE PER PACK
ANNOUNCED PRINT RUN 93 SETS

2007 Sportkings Admit One Redemptions

RANDOM INSERTS IN PACKS
ANNOUNCED PRINT RUN 1 SET
NO PRICING DUE TO SCARCITY

2007 Sportkings Autograph Gold

*GOLD: 1.2X TO 2X BASIC
RANDOM INSERTS IN PACKS
ANNOUNCED PRINT RUN 10 SETS
ANR Nolan Ryan 90.00 150.00
APRO Pete Rose 400.00 600.00

2007 Sportkings Autograph Silver

RANDOM INSERTS IN PACKS
ANNOUNCED PRINT RUN B/WN 95-99 PER
ACY Carl Yastrzemski 25.00 50.00
ADM Don Mattingly 25.00 50.00
ANR Nolan Ryan 60.00 100.00
APRO Pete Rose 150.00 300.00
ARC Roger Clemens 50.00 80.00
ASM Stan Musial 40.00 80.00
ATS Tom Seaver 20.00 40.00

2007 Sportkings Autograph Memorabilia Gold

*GOLD/10: 1.2X TO 2X SILVER/40
ANNOUNCED PRINT RUN 10 SETS
AMNR Nolan Ryan Jsy 125.00 200.00
AMPRO Pete Rose Jsy

2007 Sportkings Autograph Memorabilia Silver

RANDOM INSERTS IN PACKS
ANNOUNCED PRINT RUN 40 SETS
AMCY Carl Yastrzemski Jsy 30.00 60.00
AMDM Don Mattingly Jsy 30.00 60.00
AMNR Nolan Ryan Jsy 70.00 120.00
AMPRO Pete Rose Jsy 300.00 500.00
AMRC Roger Clemens Jsy 60.00 100.00
AMSM Stan Musial Jsy 50.00 80.00
AMTS Tom Seaver Jsy 25.00 50.00

2007 Sportkings Cityscapes Silver

ANNOUNCED PRINT RUN 20 SETS
*GOLD: .5X TO 1.2X BASIC
GOLD ANNOUNCED PRINT RUN 10 SETS
RANDOM INSERTS IN PACKS
CS02 Pete Rose Jsy 100.00 175.00
Patrick Roy Jsy
Montreal
CS03 Roger Clemens Jsy 20.00 40.00
Milt Schmidt Jsy
Boston
CS04 Carl Yastrzemski Jsy 20.00 40.00
Larry Bird Jsy
Boston
CS05 Don Mattingly Jsy 25.00 50.00
Roger Clemens Jsy
New York
CS06 Ted Williams Jsy 40.00 80.00
Larry Bird Jsy
Boston
CS07 Roberto Clemente Pants 40.00 80.00
Mario Lemieux Jsy
Pittsburgh

2007 Sportkings Decades Silver

ANNOUNCED PRINT RUN 20 SETS
*GOLD: .5X TO 1.2X BASIC
GOLD ANNOUNCED PRINT RUN 10 SETS
RANDOM INSERTS IN PACKS
D01 Ted Williams Jsy 100.00 175.00
Maurice Richard Glove
Stan Musial Jsy
1940s
D02 Terry Sawchuk Jsy 40.00 80.00
Willie Shoemaker Silks
Milt Schmidt Jsy
1950s
D03 Carl Yastrzemski Jsy 50.00 100.00
Mario Andretti Uniform
Roberto Clemente Pants
1960s
D04 Pete Rose Jsy 90.00 150.00
Larry Holmes Robe
Evil Knievel Jkt
1970s
D05 Hulk Hogan Shirt 50.00 100.00
Don Mattingly Jsy
Magic Johnson Jsy
1980s
D06 Troy Aikman Jsy 40.00 80.00
Patrick Roy Jsy
Roger Clemens Jsy
1990s

2007 Sportkings Double Memorabilia Gold

*GOLD: .6X TO 1.5X BASIC
RANDOM INSERTS IN PACKS
ANNOUNCED PRINT RUN 10 SETS
DM15, DM16 ANNOUNCED PRINT RUN 1 PER
NO DM15, DM16 PRICING DUE TO SCARCITY
DM8 Pete Rose Jsy-Jsy 125.00 200.00

2007 Sportkings Double Memorabilia Silver

RANDOM INSERTS IN PACKS
ANNOUNCED PRINT RUN 4-40 SETS
DM15, DM16 ANNOUNCED PRINT RUN 4 PER
NO DM15, DM16 PRICING DUE TO SCARCITY
DM1 Don Mattingly Bat-Jsy 15.00 40.00
DM6 Nolan Ryan Jsy-Jsy 20.00 50.00
DM8 Pete Rose Jsy-Jsy 75.00 150.00
DM11 Roberto Clemente Hat-Pants 40.00 80.00
DM12 Roger Clemens Jsy-Jsy 12.50 30.00
DM13 Stan Musial Bat-Jsy 20.00 50.00

2007 Sportkings Fall Expo Memorabilia Silver

UNPRICED SILVER PRINT RUN 9
UNPRICED GOLD MEM PRINT RUN 1

2007 Sportkings Hats Off Silver

ANNOUNCED PRINT RUN 20 SETS
*GOLD: .5X TO 1.2X BASIC
GOLD ANNOUNCED PRINT RUN 10 SETS
RANDOM INSERTS IN PACKS
HO1 Nolan Ryan Houston 25.00 50.00
HO2 Nolan Ryan Texas 25.00 50.00
HO3 Carl Yastrzemski 20.00 40.00
HO4 Roberto Clemente 50.00 80.00
HO5 Tom Seaver 15.00 30.00
HO6 Pete Rose Philadelphia 50.00 80.00
HO7 Pete Rose Cincinnati 60.00 100.00
HO8 Pete Rose Triple 125.00 200.00

2007 Sportkings King-Sized Memorabilia

RANDOM INSERTS IN PACKS
ANNOUNCED PRINT RUN 1 SET
NO PRICING DUE TO SCARCITY

2007 Sportkings Logo Card

RANDOM INSERTS IN PACKS
ANNOUNCED PRINT RUN 1 SET
NO PRICING DUE TO SCARCITY

2007 Sportkings Lumber Gold

*GOLD: .75X TO 1.5 BASIC
RANDOM INSERTS IN PACKS
ANNOUNCED PRINT RUN 10 SETS
WORDED SWATCHES COMMAND PREMIUMS
L8 Pete Rose Barrel 175.00 300.00

2007 Sportkings Lumber Silver

RANDOM INSERTS IN PACKS
ANNOUNCED PRINT RUN 30 SETS
WORDED SWATCHES COMMAND PREMIUMS
L6 Stan Musial Bat 40.00 80.00
L7 Don Mattingly Bat 40.00 80.00
L8 Pete Rose Bat 150.00 250.00

2007 Sportkings Papercuts

RANDOM INSERTS IN PACKS
ANNOUNCED PRINT RUNS B/WN 1-10 PER
NO PRICING DUE TO SCARCITY
PCJR Jackie Robinson/4 *
PCRC Roberto Clemente/1 *
PCTW Ted Williams/5 *

2007 Sportkings Patch Silver

ANNOUNCED PRINT RUN 20 SETS
P28-P30 ANNOUNCED PRINT RUN 4 PER
NO P28-P30 PRICING DUE TO SCARCITY
*GOLD: .6X TO 1.2X BASIC
GOLD ANNOUNCED PRINT RUN 10 SETS
GOLD P28-P30 ANCD. PRINT RUN 1 PER
GOLD P28-P30 NO PRICING AVAILABLE
RANDOM INSERTS IN PACKS
P1 Carl Yastrzemski Jsy 20.00 50.00
P3 Don Mattingly Jsy 15.00 40.00
P15 Nolan Ryan Texas Jsy 30.00 60.00
P16 Nolan Ryan Houston Jsy 30.00 60.00
P18 Pete Rose Cincinnati Jsy 100.00 175.00
P19 Pete Rose Montreal Jsy 125.00 200.00
P22 Roger Clemens Jsy 15.00 40.00
P23 Stan Musial Jsy 30.00 60.00
P26 Tom Seaver Jsy 15.00 40.00
P30 Ted Williams Jsy/4 *

2007 Sportkings Quad Memorabilia Silver

ANNOUNCED PRINT RUN 10 SETS
GOLD ANNOUNCED PRINT RUN 1 SET
RANDOM INSERTS IN PACKS
NO PRICING DUE TO SCARCITY
QM01 Ted Williams Jsy
Roberto Clemente Pants
Don Mattingly Jsy
Pete Rose Jsy
QM03 Ted Williams Jsy
Milt Schmidt Jsy
Carl Yastrzemski Jsy
Larry Bird Jsy
QM07 Larry Bird Jsy
Roberto Clemente Pants
Martin Brodeur Jsy
Steve Young Jsy

2007 Sportkings Single Memorabilia Silver

RANDOM INSERTS IN PACKS
ANNOUNCED PRINT RUN 90 SETS
SM3, SM13 ANNOUNCED PRINT RUN 4 PER
NO SM3, SM13 PRICING DUE TO SCARCITY
SM02 Carl Yastrzemski Jsy 8.00 20.00
SM04 Don Mattingly Jsy 8.00 20.00
SM17 Pete Rose Cincinnati Jsy 40.00 80.00
SM22 Roberto Clemente Jsy 20.00 50.00
SM25 Stan Musial Jsy 10.00 25.00
SM27 Ted Williams Jsy 20.00 50.00
SM32 Roger Clemens Boston Jsy 6.00 15.00
SM33 Roger Clemens New York Jsy 6.00 15.00
SM41 Nolan Ryan Houston Jsy 10.00 25.00
SM44 Pete Rose Montreal Jsy 25.00 50.00
SM45 Tom Seaver Jsy 6.00 15.00
SM47 Nolan Ryan Texas Jsy 10.00 25.00

2007 Sportkings Triple Memorabilia Silver

ANNOUNCED PRINT RUN 10 SETS
TM7, TM8 ANNOUNCED PRINT RUN 4 PER
NO TM7, TM8 PRICING DUE TO SCARCITY
GOLD ANNOUNCED PRINT RUN 1 SET
NO GOLD PRICING DUE TO SCARCITY
RANDOM INSERTS IN PACKS
TM02 Nolan Ryan 50.00 100.00
Hat-Jsy-Pants
TM03 Pete Rose Bat-Hat-Jsy 175.00 300.00
TM11 Ted Williams Jsy
Roberto Clemente Pants
Pete Rose Jsy

2007 Sportkings National Convention Preview

2 Pete Rose

2008 Sportkings

FIVE CARDS PER BOX
54 Lou Brock 5.00 10.00
68 Bob Gibson 5.00 10.00
72 Johnny Bench 6.00 12.00
76 Tony Perez 4.00 8.00
79 Andre Dawson 4.00 8.00
98 Ernie Banks 6.00 12.00
99 Gary Carter 4.00 8.00
100 Ozzie Smith 6.00 12.00
102 Juan Marichal 4.00 8.00

2008 Sportkings Mini

*MINI: 1X TO 2X BASIC
ONE PER BOX

2008 Sportkings 1933 The Year

UNPRICED PRINT RUN 1

2008 Sportkings Admit One Redemptions

RANDOM INSERTS IN PACKS
ANNOUNCED PRINT RUN 1 SET
NO PRICING DUE TO SCARCITY

2008 Sportkings At the Movies

RANDOM INSERTS IN PACKS
STATED PRINT RUN 1 SERIAL #'d SET
NO PRICING DUE TO SCARCITY

2008 Sportkings Autograph Silver

ANNOUNCED PRINT RUN B/WN 20-90 PER
RANDOM INSERTS IN PACKS
AD Andre Dawson/80 * 15.00 30.00
BG Bob Gibson/70 * 20.00 40.00
EB Ernie Banks/40 * 30.00 60.00
GC Gary Carter/50 * 10.00 25.00
JM Juan Marichal/80 * 15.00 30.00
EB2 Ernie Banks/40 * 30.00 60.00
GC2 Gary Carter/50 * 10.00 25.00
LBR Lou Brock/80 * 20.00 40.00
OS1 Ozzie Smith/40 * 20.00 40.00
OS2 Ozzie Smith/40 * 20.00 40.00
PRO Pete Rose/95
TP1 Tony Perez/30 * 20.00 40.00
TP2 Tony Perez/30 * 20.00 40.00
JBEN1 Johnny Bench/25 * 25.00 50.00
JBEN2 Johnny Bench/25 * 25.00 50.00

2008 Sportkings Autograph Memorabilia Silver

ANNOUNCED PRINT RUN B/WN 15-50 PER
NO GOLD PRICING DUE TO SCARCITY
RANDOM INSERTS IN PACKS
AD Andre Dawson/40 * 20.00 40.00
BG Bob Gibson/40 * 25.00 50.00
EB Ernie Banks/40 * 40.00 80.00
GC Gary Carter/20 * 20.00 40.00
JB Jason Bay/40 * 15.00 30.00
JBEN1 Johnny Bench/25 * 40.00 80.00
JBEN2 Johnny Bench/25 * 40.00 80.00
JM Juan Marichal/40 * 25.00 50.00
JMO Justin Morneau/40 * 15.00 30.00
LBR Lou Brock/40 * 25.00 50.00
OS Ozzie Smith/40 * 25.00 50.00
TP1 Tony Perez/20 * 25.00 50.00
TP2 Tony Perez/20 * 25.00 50.00

2008 Sportkings AutoThread Silver

STATED PRINT RUN 9 SERIAL #'d SETS
GOLD PRINT RUN 1 SERIAL #'d SET
RANDOM INSERTS IN PACKS
NO PRICING DUE TO SCARCITY
TP Tony Perez

2008 Sportkings Cityscapes Double Silver

RANDOM INSERTS IN PACKS
3 Gary Carter 15.00 40.00
Jean Beliveau
Montreal
5 Ernie Banks 20.00 50.00
Bobby Hull
Chicago
6 Bob Gibson 15.00 40.00
Brett Hull
St. Louis
7 Hakeem Olajuwon
Nolan Ryan
Houston
9 Joe Montana 20.00 50.00
Juan Marichal
San Francisco

2008 Sportkings Cityscapes Triple Silver

RANDOM INSERTS IN PACKS
1 Larry Bird 30.00 60.00
Roger Clemens
Robert Parish
Boston
3 Pete Rose 50.00 100.00
Johnny Bench
Tony Perez
Cincinnati
4 Joe Montana 40.00 80.00
Steve Young
Juan Marichal
San Francisco
5 Gary Carter 30.00 60.00
Pete Rose
Jean Beliveau
Montreal
6 Mark Messier 75.00 125.00
Don Mattingly
Pelé
New York
7 Lou Brock 20.00 50.00
Ozzie Smith
Brett Hull
St. Louis

2008 Sportkings Decades Silver

RANDOM INSERTS IN PACKS
1 Ernie Banks 40.00 80.00
Jean Beliveau
Ben Hogan
2 Jim Brown 20.00 50.00
Jacque Plante
Juan Marichal

2008 Sportkings Double Memorabilia Silver

RANDOM INSERTS IN PACKS
2 Ozzie Smith 15.00 40.00
Lou Brock
13 Bo Jackson BB-FB 20.00 50.00
14 Deion Sanders BB-FB 15.00 40.00

2008 Sportkings Founding Fathers

RANDOM INSERTS IN PACKS
ANNOUNCED PRINT RUN 1 SET
NO PRICING DUE TO SCARCITY

2008 Sportkings Future Sportkings Autograph Silver

RANDOM INSERTS IN PACKS
JB1 Jason Bay/40 * 10.00 25.00
JB2 Jason Bay/40 * 10.00 25.00
JM1 Justin Morneau/40 * 10.00 25.00
JM2 Justin Morneau/40 * 10.00 25.00

2008 Sportkings King-Sized Memorabilia

RANDOM INSERTS IN PACKS
STATED PRINT RUN 1 SERIAL #'d SET
NO PRICING DUE TO SCARCITY

2008 Sportkings Logo Card

RANDOM INSERTS IN PACKS
ANNOUNCED PRINT RUN 1 SET
NO PRICING DUE TO SCARCITY

2008 Sportkings Lumber Silver

STATED PRINT RUN 9 SERIAL #'d SETS
GOLD PRINT RUN 1 SERIAL #'d SET
RANDOM INSERTS IN PACKS
NO PRICING DUE TO SCARCITY
7 Tony Perez Bat
8 Gary Carter Bat

2008 Sportkings Numerology Silver

STATED PRINT RUN 9 SERIAL #'d SETS
GOLD PRINT RUN 1 SERIAL #'d SET
RANDOM INSERTS IN PACKS
NO PRICING DUE TO SCARCITY

2008 Sportkings Passing the Torch Silver

RANDOM INSERTS IN PACKS
1 Ernie Banks 50.00 100.00
Pete Rose
9 Bob Gibson 15.00 40.00
Nolan Ryan

2008 Sportkings Patch Silver

RANDOM INSERTS IN PACKS
1 Andre Dawson 10.00 25.00
4 Bob Gibson 12.50 30.00
8 Gary Carter 10.00 25.00
11 Jason Bay 10.00 25.00
15 Justin Morneau 10.00 25.00
16 Lou Brock 10.00 25.00
21 Ozzie Smith 15.00 40.00
24 Tony Perez 12.50 30.00

2008 Sportkings Post Card Redemption Dual Memorabilia

ANNOUNCED PRINT RUN 1 SET
NO PRICING DUE TO SCARCITY

2008 Sportkings Presidents and Players

RANDOM INSERTS IN PACKS
STATED PRINT RUN 1 SERIAL #'d SET
NO PRICING DUE TO SCARCITY

2008 Sportkings Quad Memorabilia Silver

ANNOUNCED PRINT RUN 9 SETS
GOLD PRINT RUN 1 SET
RANDOM INSERTS IN PACKS
NO PRICING DUE TO SCARCITY

2008 Sportkings Single Memorabilia Silver

RANDOM INSERTS IN PACKS
1 Andre Dawson 6.00 15.00
8 Bob Gibson 8.00 20.00
13 Ernie Banks 10.00 25.00
14 Gary Carter 6.00 15.00
18 Jason Bay 6.00 15.00
25 Juan Marichal 6.00 15.00
26 Justin Morneau 6.00 15.00
27 Lou Brock 6.00 15.00
31 Ozzie Smith 10.00 25.00
40 Tony Perez 6.00 15.00

2008 Sportkings Triple Memorabilia Silver

RANDOM INSERTS IN PACKS
3 Pete Rose 90.00 150.00
Roberto Clemente
Ernie Banks

2008 Sportkings Vintage Memorabilia

RANDOM INSERTS IN PACKS
STATED PRINT RUN 1 SERIAL #'d SET
NO PRICING DUE TO SCARCITY

2008 Sportkings Vintage Papercuts

RANDOM INSERTS IN PACKS
STATED PRINT RUN 1 SERIAL #'d SET
NO PRICING DUE TO SCARCITY

2008 Sportkings National Convention Memorabilia Silver

UNPRICED SILVER PRINT RUN 9
UNPRICED GOLD PRINT RUN 1

2008 Sportkings National Convention VIP Promo

9 Pete Rose 3.00 8.00
Carl Hubbell

2009 Sportkings

COMPLETE SET (52) 250.00 450.00
COMMON CARD (109-160) 5.00 12.00
SEMISTARS 6.00 15.00
UNLISTED STARS 8.00 20.00
110 Reggie Jackson 6.00 15.00
111 Orlando Cepeda 6.00 15.00
138 Satchel Paige 8.00 20.00
152 Tony Oliva 6.00 15.00
153 Mike Schmidt 12.00 30.00

2009 Sportkings Mini

*MINI: .6X TO 1.5X BASIC CARDS
STATED ODDS ONE PER BOX
UNPRICED SILVER PRINT RUN 7 SETS
UNPRICED GOLD PRINT RUN 3 SETS

2009 Sportkings Admit One Redemptions

ANNOUNCED PRINT RUN 1 SET
NO PRICING DUE TO SCARCITY
1 Reggie Jackson's 500th Home Run
9/17/84
5 1973 World Series
6 1980 World Series
7 1962 World Series
9 1977 World Series
10 1974 World Series

2009 Sportkings Autograph Silver

ANNOUNCED PRINT RUN B/WN 15-70 PER
UNPRICED GOLD PRINT RUN 10
OC1 Orlando Cepeda/40* 20.00 40.00
OC2 Orlando Cepeda/40* 20.00 40.00
RJ1 Reggie Jackson/25* 50.00 100.00
RJ2 Reggie Jackson/25* 50.00 100.00
TO1 Tony Oliva/40* 20.00 40.00
TO2 Tony Oliva/40* 20.00 40.00
MSC1 Mike Schmidt/35* 50.00 100.00
MSC2 Mike Schmidt/35* 50.00 100.00

2009 Sportkings Autograph Memorabilia Silver

ANNOUNCED PRINT RUN B/WN 15-40 PER
UNPRICED GOLD PRINT RUN 10
RANDOM INSERTS IN PACKS
OC1 Orlando Cepeda Jsy/40* 15.00 30.00
OC2 Orlando Cepeda Jsy/40* 15.00 30.00
TO1 Tony Oliva Jsy/40* 20.00 40.00
TO2 Tony Oliva Jsy/40* 20.00 40.00
MSC1 Mike Schmidt Jsy/35* 60.00 120.00
MSC2 Mike Schmidt Jsy/35* 60.00 120.00
RJA1 Reggie Jackson Jsy/25* 40.00 80.00
RJA2 Reggie Jackson Jsy/25* 40.00 80.00

2009 Sportkings AutoThread Silver

ANNOUNCED PRINT RUN 9 SETS
GOLD PRINT RUN 1 SET
NO PRICING DUE TO SCARCITY
RANDOM INSERTS IN PACKS

2009 Sportkings Cityscapes Double Silver

ANNOUNCED PRINT RUN 19 SETS
UNPRICED GOLD PRINT RUN 1
RANDOM INSERTS IN PACKS
1 Reggie Jackson Jsy 25.00 50.00
Joe Namath Jsy
4 Mike Schmidt Jsy 25.00 50.00
Bernie Parent Jsy

2009 Sportkings Cityscapes Triple Silver

ANNOUNCED PRINT RUN 19 SETS
UNPRICED GOLD PRINT RUN 1
RANDOM INSERTS IN PACKS
1 Reggie Jackson Jsy 50.00 100.00
Joe Namath Jsy
Pele Jsy
2 Jerry Rice Jsy 60.00 120.00
Joe Montana Jsy
Orlando Cepeda Jsy
3 Lawrence Taylor Jsy 25.00 50.00
Reggie Jackson Jsy
Phil Esposito Jsy

2009 Sportkings Decades Silver

ANNOUNCED PRINT RUN 19 SETS
UNPRICED GOLD PRINT RUN 1
RANDOM INSERTS IN PACKS
1 Pele Jsy 50.00 100.00
Joe Namath Jsy
Orlando Cepeda Jsy
2 Vladislav Tretiak Jsy 50.00 100.00
Reggie Jackson Jsy
Bela Karolyi Shirt
3 Lawrence Taylor Jsy 40.00 80.00
Rusty Wallace Jsy
Mike Schmidt Jsy

2009 Sportkings Double Memorabilia Silver

ANNOUNCED PRINT RUN B/WN 1-19
UNPRICED GOLD PRINT RUN 1
RANDOM INSERTS IN PACKS
3 Reggie Jackson Jsy/19* 20.00 40.00
9 Mike Schmidt Jsy 30.00 60.00
Tony Oliva Jsy
10 Reggie Jackson Jsy/19* 30.00 60.00
Mike Schmidt Jsy

2009 Sportkings Eight Men Out Cut Autographs

RANDOM INSERTS IN PACKS
ANNOUNCED PRINT RUN 1 SET
NO PRICING DUE TO SCARCITY

2009 Sportkings Papercuts

RANDOM INSERTS IN PACKS
ANNOUNCED PRINT RUN 1 SET
NO PRICING DUE TO SCARCITY

2009 Sportkings Patch Silver

ANNOUNCED PRINT RUN B/WN 4-19
UNPRICED GOLD PRINT RUN 1
RANDOM INSERTS IN PACKS
3 Reggie Jackson/4*
4 Reggie Jackson/19* 20.00 40.00
5 Reggie Jackson/19* 20.00 40.00
13 Mike Schmidt/19* 20.00 40.00

2009 Sportkings Quad Memorabilia Silver

ANNOUNCED PRINT RUN B/WN 3-9 PER
GOLD PRINT RUN 1 SET
NO PRICING DUE TO SCARCITY
RANDOM INSERTS IN PACKS

2009 Sportkings Single Memorabilia Silver

ANNOUNCED PRINT RUN B/WN 4-29
UNPRICED GOLD PRINT RUN B/WN 1-4
RANDOM INSERTS IN PACKS
11 Orlando Cepeda Jsy/29* 6.00 15.00
13 Reggie Jackson Jsy/29* 12.00 30.00
17 Mike Schmidt Jsy/29* 30.00 60.00
21 Tony Oliva Jsy/29* 12.00 30.00

2009 Sportkings Triple Memorabilia Silver

ANNOUNCED PRINT RUN B/WN 3-19
UNPRICED GOLD PRINT RUN 1 SET
RANDOM INSERTS IN PACKS
5 Orlando Cepeda Jsy/19* 30.00 60.00
Reggie Jackson Jsy
Tony Oliva Jsy
8 Mike Schmidt Jsy/19* 20.00 40.00
Tony Oliva Jsy
Orlando Cepeda Jsy

2009 Sportkings National Convention Memorabilia Gold

STATED PRINT RUN 1 SER. #'d SET
2009 NAT'L CONVENTION EXCLUSIVE
UNPRICED DUE TO SCARCITY

2009 Sportkings National Convention Memorabilia Silver

STATED PRINT RUN 9 SER. #'d SETS
GOLD PRINT RUN 1 SER. #'d SET
2009 NAT'L CONVENTION EXCLUSIVE
UNPRICED DUE TO SCARCITY

2009 Sportkings National Convention VIP Promo

COMPLETE SET (7)
2 Lisa Leslie 5.00 12.00
Joe Namath
Doug Flutie
Vladislav Tretiak
Tony Oliva
Akebono Taro
3 Orlando Cepeda 4.00 10.00
Daniel Negreanu
Jersey Joe Walcott
Kelly Slater
Roddy Piper
Mike Schmidt
5 Lennox Lewis 5.00 12.00
Reggie Jackson
Ian Thorpe
Kurt Warner
Seabiscuit
Jackie Joyner-Kersee

2009 Sportkings Vintage Papercuts

RANDOM INSERTS IN PACKS
ANNOUNCED PRINT RUN 1 SET
NO PRICING DUE TO SCARCITY
BR Babe Ruth
CH Carl Hubbell

2010 Sportkings

COMPLETE SET (48) 150.00 300.00
COMP.SET w/o ALI SP (47) 100.00 200.00
162 Duke Snider 5.00 12.00
180 Tony Gwynn 5.00 12.00
186 Mark McGwire 6.00 15.00
194 Steve Carlton 5.00 12.00

2010 Sportkings Mini

COMPLETE SET (48) 175.00 350.00
*MINI: .5X TO 1.2X BASIC CARDS
STATED ODDS 1:2

2010 Sportkings Mini Gold

OVERALL GOLD/SILVER ODDS 1:19
UNPRICED GOLD PRINT RUN 3

2010 Sportkings Mini Silver

OVERALL GOLD/SILVER ODDS 1:19
UNPRICED SILVER PRINT RUN 7

2010 Sportkings Autograph Silver

ANNOUNCED PRINT RUN 10-50
UNPRICED GOLD PRINT RUN 5-10
ASC1 Steve Carlton/25* 20.00 40.00
ASC2 Steve Carlton/25* 20.00 40.00
ATG1 Tony Gwynn/20* 30.00 60.00
ATG2 Tony Gwynn/20* 30.00 60.00
ATG3 Tony Gwynn/20* 30.00 60.00
ADSN1 Duke Snider/20* 20.00 40.00
ADSN2 Duke Snider/25* 20.00 40.00
AMMC1 Mark McGwire/25* 125.00 225.00
AMMC2 Mark McGwire/25* 125.00 225.00

2010 Sportkings Autograph Memorabilia Silver

ANNOUNCED PRINT RUN 10-40
UNPRICED GOLD PRINT RUN 5-10
AMSC1 Steve Carlton Jsy/25* 20.00 40.00
AMSC2 Steve Carlton Jsy/25* 20.00 40.00
AMTG1 Tony Gwynn Jsy/15* 35.00 70.00
AMTG2 Tony Gwynn Jsy/15* 35.00 70.00
AMTG3 Tony Gwynn Jsy/15* 35.00 70.00
AMDSN1 Duke Snider Jsy/25* 20.00 40.00
AMDSN2 Duke Snider Jsy/25* 20.00 40.00
AMMMC1 Mark McGwire Jsy/25* 150.00 250.00
AMMMC2 Mark McGwire Jsy/25* 150.00 250.00

2010 Sportkings Patch Silver

STATED PRINT RUN 20
UNPRICED GOLD PRINT RUN 10
P3 Mark McGwire 25.00 60.00
P5 Steve Carlton 10.00 25.00
P9 Mark McGwire 25.00 60.00
P10 Tony Gwynn 20.00 50.00

2010 Sportkings Quad Memorabilia Silver

UNPRICED SILVER PRINT RUN 4-9
UNPRICED GOLD PRINT RUN 1

2010 Sportkings Single Memorabilia Gold

STATED PRINT RUN 10
UNPRICED DUE TO SCARCITY

2010 Sportkings Single Memorabilia Silver

STATED PRINT RUN 26 UNLESS NOTED
SM9 Duke Snider 10.00 20.00
SM15 Mark McGwire 25.00 50.00
SM16 Mark McGwire 25.00 50.00
SM27 Steve Carlton 12.00 25.00
SM28 Tony Gwynn 12.00 25.00

2010 Sportkings Triple Memorabilia Silver

SILVER PRINT RUN 4-20
UNPRICED GOLD PRINT RUN 1-10
TM6 Mark McGwire 25.00 50.00
Duke Snider
Tony Gwynn

2007 SP Rookie Edition

COMP.SET w/o RC's (100) 6.00 15.00
COMMON CARD (1-100) .12 .30
COMMON RC (101-142) .25 .60
COMMON SP (143-234) .40 1.00
SP ODDS 1:2
COMMON CARD (235-284) .25 .60
1 Chipper Jones .30 .75
2 Andruw Jones .12 .30
3 Jeff Francoeur .30 .75
4 Stephen Drew .12 .30
5 Randy Johnson .30 .75
6 Brandon Webb .20 .50
7 Alfonso Soriano .20 .50
8 Derrek Lee .20 .50
9 Aramis Ramirez .12 .30
10 Carlos Zambrano .20 .50
11 Ken Griffey Jr. .50 1.25
12 Adam Dunn .20 .50
13 Bronson Arroyo .12 .30
14 Todd Helton .20 .50
15 Jeff Francis .12 .30
16 Matt Holliday .30 .75
17 Hanley Ramirez .30 .75
18 Dontrelle Willis .12 .30
19 Miguel Cabrera .30 .75
20 Lance Berkman .20 .50
21 Roy Oswalt .20 .50
22 Carlos Lee .12 .30
23 Nomar Garciaparra .30 .75
24 Jason Schmidt .12 .30
25 Juan Pierre .12 .30
26 Rafael Furcal .20 .50
27 Rickie Weeks .20 .50
28 Prince Fielder .20 .50
29 Ben Sheets .12 .30
30 David Wright .50 1.25
31 Jose Reyes .20 .50
32 Pedro Martinez .20 .50
33 Carlos Beltran .20 .50
34 Cole Hamels .30 .75
35 Jimmy Rollins .20 .50
36 Ryan Howard .50 1.25
37 Jason Bay .20 .50
38 Freddy Sanchez .12 .30
39 Zach Duke .12 .30
40 Jake Peavy .12 .30

41 Greg Maddux	.50	1.25
42 Trevor Hoffman	.20	.50
43 Matt Cain	.20	.50
44 Barry Zito	.12	.30
45 Omar Vizquel	.20	.50
46 Albert Pujols	.75	2.00
47 Chris Carpenter	.30	.75
48 Jim Edmonds	.20	.50
49 Scott Rolen	.20	.50
50 Ryan Zimmerman	.20	.50
51 Felipe Lopez	.12	.30
52 Austin Kearns	.12	.30
53 Miguel Tejada	.20	.50
54 Erik Bedard	.12	.30
55 Chris Ray	.12	.30
56 David Ortiz	.20	.50
57 Curt Schilling	.20	.50
58 Manny Ramirez	.30	.75
59 Jonathan Papelbon	.30	.75
60 Jim Thome	.20	.50
61 Paul Konerko	.20	.50
62 Bobby Jenks	.12	.30
63 Grady Sizemore	.20	.50
64 Victor Martinez	.20	.50
65 C.C. Sabathia	.20	.50
66 Ivan Rodriguez	.20	.50
67 Justin Verlander	.40	1.00
68 Joel Zumaya	.20	.50
69 Jeremy Bonderman	.12	.30
70 Gil Meche	.12	.30
71 Mike Sweeney	.12	.30
72 Mark Teahen	.12	.30
73 Vladimir Guerrero	.30	.75
74 Howie Kendrick	.12	.30
75 Francisco Rodriguez	.20	.50
76 Johan Santana	.30	.75
77 Justin Morneau	.30	.75
78 Joe Mauer	.30	.75
79 Joe Nathan	.12	.30
80 Alex Rodriguez	.50	1.25
81 Derek Jeter	.75	2.00
82 Johnny Damon	.20	.50
83 Mariano Rivera	.30	.75
84 Rich Harden	.12	.30
85 Mike Piazza	.30	.75
86 Nick Swisher	.30	.75
87 Ichiro Suzuki	.50	1.25
88 Felix Hernandez	.30	.75
89 Kenji Johjima	.30	.75
90 Richie Sexson	.12	.30
91 Carl Crawford	.20	.50
92 Scott Kazmir	.20	.50
93 B.J. Upton	.12	.30
94 Michael Young	.20	.50
95 Mark Teixeira	.30	.75
96 Eric Gagne	.12	.30
97 Hank Blalock	.12	.30
98 Vernon Wells	.12	.30
99 Roy Halladay	.30	.75
100 Frank Thomas	.30	.75
101 Joaquin Arias (RC)	.25	.60
102 Jeff Baker (RC)	.25	.60
103 Brian Barden RC	.25	.60
104 Michael Bourn (RC)	.25	.60
105 Kevin Slowey (RC)	.60	1.50
106 Chase Wright RC	.60	1.50
107 Kory Casto (RC)	.25	.60
108 Matt Chico (RC)	.25	.60
109 Matt DeSalvo (RC)	.25	.60
110 Homer Bailey (RC)	.40	1.00
111 Ryan Braun (RC)	1.25	3.00
112 Felix Pie (RC)	.25	.60
113 Jesus Flores RC	.25	.60
114 Ryan Sweeney (RC)	.25	.60
115 Ryan Z. Braun RC	.25	.60
116 Alex Gordon RC	.75	2.00
117 Josh Hamilton (RC)	1.00	2.50
118 Sean Henn (RC)	.25	.60
119 Kei Igawa RC	.60	1.50
120 Akinori Iwamura RC	.60	1.50
121 Andy LaRoche (RC)	.25	.60
122 Kevin Kouzmanoff (RC)	.25	.60
123 Matt Lindstrom (RC)	.25	.60
124 Tim Lincecum RC	4.00	10.00
125 Daisuke Matsuzaka RC	1.00	2.50
126 Gustavo Molina RC	.25	.60
127 Miguel Montero (RC)	.25	.60
128 Brandon Morrow RC	1.25	3.00
129 Hideki Okajima RC	1.25	3.00
130 Adam Lind (RC)	.25	.60
131 Mike Rabelo RC	.25	.60
132 Micah Owings (RC)	.25	.60
133 Brandon Wood (RC)	.25	.60
134 Alexi Casilla RC	.40	1.00
135 Joe Smith RC	.25	.60
136 Hunter Pence (RC)	1.25	3.00
137 Glen Perkins (RC)	.25	.60
138 Chris Stewart RC	.25	.60
139 Troy Tulowitzki (RC)	1.50	4.00
140 Billy Butler (RC)	.40	1.00
141 Delmon Young (RC)	.40	1.00
142 Phil Hughes (RC)	1.25	3.00
143 Joaquin Arias 95	.40	1.00
144 Jeff Baker 95	.40	1.00
145 Brian Barden 95	.40	1.00
146 Michael Bourn 95	.40	1.00
147 Kevin Slowey 95	1.00	2.50
148 Chase Wright 95	1.00	2.50
149 Kory Casto 95	.40	1.00
150 Matt Chico 95	.40	1.00
151 Shawn Riggans 95	.40	1.00
152 Juan Salas 95	.40	1.00
153 Ryan Braun 95	2.00	5.00
154 Felix Pie 95	.40	1.00
155 Jesus Flores 95	.40	1.00
156 Ryan Sweeney 95	.40	1.00
157 Ryan Z. Braun 95	.40	1.00
158 Alex Gordon 95	1.25	3.00
159 Josh Hamilton 95	1.50	4.00
160 Sean Henn 95	.40	1.00
161 Kei Igawa 95	1.00	2.50
162 Akinori Iwamura 95	1.00	2.50
163 Andy LaRoche 95	.40	1.00
164 Kevin Kouzmanoff 95	.40	1.00
165 Matt Lindstrom 95	.40	1.00
166 Tim Lincecum 95	6.00	15.00
167 Daisuke Matsuzaka 95	1.50	4.00
168 Gustavo Molina 95	.40	1.00
169 Miguel Montero 95	.40	1.00
170 Brandon Morrow 95	2.00	5.00
171 Hideki Okajima 95	2.00	5.00
172 Adam Lind 95	.40	1.00
173 Mike Rabelo 95	.40	1.00
174 Micah Owings 95	.40	1.00
175 Brandon Wood 95	.40	1.00
176 Alexi Casilla 95	.60	1.50
177 Joe Smith 95	.40	1.00
178 Hunter Pence 95	2.00	5.00
179 Glen Perkins 95	.40	1.00
180 Chris Stewart 95	.40	1.00
181 Troy Tulowitzki 95	2.50	6.00
182 Billy Butler 95	.60	1.50
183 Delmon Young 95	.60	1.50
184 Phil Hughes 95	2.00	5.00
185 Joaquin Arias 93	.40	1.00
186 Jeff Baker 93	.40	1.00
187 Mark Reynolds 93	3.00	8.00
188 Joseph Bisenius 93	.40	1.00
189 Michael Bourn 93	.40	1.00
190 Zack Segovia 93	.40	1.00
191 Kevin Slowey 93	1.00	2.50
192 Chase Wright 93	1.00	2.50
193 Rocky Cherry 93	1.00	2.50
194 Danny Putnam 93	.40	1.00
195 Kory Casto 93	.40	1.00
196 Matt Chico 93	.40	1.00
197 John Danks 93	.60	1.50
198 Homer Bailey 93	.60	1.50
199 Ryan Braun 93	2.00	5.00
200 Felix Pie 93	.40	1.00
201 Jesus Flores 93	.40	1.00
202 Andy Gonzalez 93	.40	1.00
203 Ryan Sweeney 93	.40	1.00
204 Jarrod Saltalamacchia 93	.60	1.50
205 Alex Gordon 93	1.25	3.00
206 Josh Hamilton 93	1.50	4.00
207 Sean Henn 93	.40	1.00
208 Kei Igawa 93	1.00	2.50
209 Akinori Iwamura 93	1.00	2.50
210 Andy LaRoche 93	.40	1.00
211 Rick Vanden Hurk 93	.40	1.00
212 Kevin Kouzmanoff 93	.40	1.00
213 Matt Lindstrom 93	.40	1.00
214 Tim Lincecum 93	6.00	15.00
215 Daisuke Matsuzaka 93	1.50	4.00
216 Gustavo Molina 93	.40	1.00
217 Miguel Montero 93	.40	1.00
218 Brandon Morrow 93	2.00	5.00
219 Hideki Okajima 93	2.00	5.00
220 Adam Lind 93	.40	1.00
221 Mike Rabelo 93	.40	1.00
222 Brian Burres 93	.40	1.00
223 Micah Owings 93	.40	1.00
224 Brandon Wood 93	.40	1.00
225 Alexi Casilla 93	.60	1.50
226 Joe Smith 93	.40	1.00
227 Hunter Pence 93	2.00	5.00
228 Glen Perkins 93	.40	1.00
229 Chris Stewart 93	.40	1.00
230 Ben Francisco 93	.40	1.00
231 Troy Tulowitzki 93	2.50	6.00
232 Billy Butler 93	.60	1.50
233 Delmon Young 93	.60	1.50
234 Phil Hughes 93	2.00	5.00
235 Joaquin Arias 96	.25	.60
236 Jeff Baker 96	.25	.60
237 Mark Reynolds 96	2.00	5.00
238 Joseph Bisenius 96	.25	.60
239 Michael Bourn 96	.25	.60
240 Zack Segovia 96	.25	.60
241 Travis Buck 96	.25	.60
242 Chase Wright 96	.60	1.50
243 Rocky Cherry 96	.60	1.50
244 Danny Putnam 96	.25	.60
245 Kory Casto 96	.25	.60
246 Matt Chico 96	.25	.60
247 John Danks 96	.40	1.00
248 Juan Salas 96	.25	.60
249 Ryan Braun 96	1.25	3.00
250 Felix Pie 96	.25	.60
251 Jesus Flores 96	.25	.60
252 Andy Gonzalez 96	.25	.60
253 Ryan Sweeney 96	.25	.60
254 Jarrod Saltalamacchia 96	.40	1.00
255 Alex Gordon 96	.75	2.00
256 Josh Hamilton 96	1.00	2.50
257 Sean Henn 96	.25	.60
258 Kei Igawa 96	.60	1.50
259 Akinori Iwamura 96	.60	1.50
260 Andy LaRoche 96	.25	.60
261 Rick Vanden Hurk 96	.25	.60
262 Kevin Kouzmanoff 96	.25	.60
263 Matt Lindstrom 96	.25	.60
264 Tim Lincecum 96	4.00	10.00
265 Daisuke Matsuzaka 96	1.00	2.50
266 Gustavo Molina 96	.25	.60
267 Miguel Montero 96	.25	.60
268 Brandon Morrow 96	1.25	3.00
269 Hideki Okajima 96	1.25	3.00
270 Adam Lind 96	.25	.60
271 Mike Rabelo 96	.25	.60
272 Brian Burres 96	.25	.60
273 Micah Owings 96	.25	.60
274 Brandon Wood 96	.25	.60
275 Alexi Casilla 96	.40	1.00
276 Joe Smith 96	.25	.60
277 Hunter Pence 96	1.25	3.00
278 Glen Perkins 96	.25	.60
279 Chris Stewart 96	.25	.60
280 Ben Francisco 96	.25	.60
281 Troy Tulowitzki 96	1.50	4.00
282 Billy Butler 96	.40	1.00
283 Delmon Young 96	.40	1.00
284 Phil Hughes 96	1.25	3.00

2007 SP Rookie Edition Autographs

STATED ODDS 1:7
EXCH DEADLINE 8/17/2009
NO SP PRICING DUE TO SCARCITY

101 Joaquin Arias	3.00	8.00
102 Jeff Baker	3.00	8.00
103 Brian Barden	3.00	8.00
104 Michael Bourn	3.00	8.00
105 Kevin Slowey	6.00	15.00
106 Chase Wright	6.00	15.00
107 Kory Casto	3.00	8.00
108 Matt Chico	3.00	8.00
109 Matt DeSalvo	5.00	12.00
110 Homer Bailey	6.00	15.00
111 Ryan Braun	20.00	50.00
112 Felix Pie	5.00	12.00
113 Jesus Flores	4.00	10.00
114 Ryan Sweeney	4.00	10.00
115 Ryan Z. Braun	5.00	12.00
116 Alex Gordon SP		
117 Josh Hamilton	12.50	30.00
118 Sean Henn	3.00	8.00
119 Kei Igawa SP		
120 Akinori Iwamura SP		
121 Andy LaRoche	4.00	10.00
122 Kevin Kouzmanoff	4.00	10.00
123 Matt Lindstrom	3.00	8.00
124 Tim Lincecum SP		
125 Daisuke Matsuzaka SP		
126 Gustavo Molina	4.00	10.00
127 Miguel Montero	3.00	8.00
128 Brandon Morrow	5.00	12.00
130 Adam Lind	4.00	10.00
131 Mike Rabelo	3.00	8.00
132 Micah Owings	4.00	10.00
133 Brandon Wood	6.00	15.00
134 Alexi Casilla	4.00	10.00
135 Joe Smith	4.00	10.00
136 Hunter Pence SP		
137 Glen Perkins	3.00	8.00
138 Chris Stewart	3.00	8.00
139 Troy Tulowitzki SP		
140 Billy Butler	10.00	25.00
141 Delmon Young SP		
142 Phil Hughes SP		
143 Joaquin Arias 95	3.00	8.00
144 Jeff Baker 95	3.00	8.00
145 Brian Barden 95	3.00	8.00
146 Michael Bourn 95	3.00	8.00
147 Kevin Slowey 95	6.00	15.00
148 Chase Wright 95	6.00	15.00
149 Kory Casto 95	3.00	8.00
150 Matt Chico 95	3.00	8.00
151 Shawn Riggans 95	3.00	8.00
152 Juan Salas 95	3.00	8.00
153 Ryan Braun 95	30.00	60.00
154 Felix Pie 95	5.00	12.00
155 Jesus Flores 95	4.00	10.00
156 Ryan Sweeney 95	4.00	10.00
157 Ryan Z. Braun 95	5.00	12.00
158 Alex Gordon 95 SP		
159 Josh Hamilton 95	15.00	40.00
160 Sean Henn 95	3.00	8.00
161 Kei Igawa 95 SP		
162 Akinori Iwamura 95 SP		
163 Andy LaRoche 95	4.00	10.00
164 Kevin Kouzmanoff 95	4.00	10.00
165 Matt Lindstrom 95	3.00	8.00
166 Tim Lincecum 95 SP		
168 Gustavo Molina 95	4.00	10.00
169 Miguel Montero 95	3.00	8.00
170 Brandon Morrow 95	5.00	12.00
172 Adam Lind 95	4.00	10.00
173 Mike Rabelo 95	3.00	8.00
174 Micah Owings 95	4.00	10.00
175 Brandon Wood 95	6.00	15.00
176 Alexi Casilla 95	4.00	10.00
177 Joe Smith 95	4.00	10.00
178 Hunter Pence 95	20.00	50.00
179 Glen Perkins 95	3.00	8.00
180 Chris Stewart 95	3.00	8.00
181 Troy Tulowitzki 95	15.00	40.00
182 Billy Butler 95	10.00	25.00
183 Delmon Young 95 SP		
184 Phil Hughes 95 SP		
185 Joaquin Arias 93	3.00	8.00
186 Jeff Baker 93	3.00	8.00
187 Mark Reynolds 93		
188 Joseph Bisenius 93	3.00	8.00
189 Michael Bourn 93	3.00	8.00
190 Zack Segovia 93	3.00	8.00
191 Kevin Slowey 93	6.00	15.00
192 Chase Wright 93	6.00	15.00
193 Rocky Cherry 93	10.00	25.00
194 Danny Putnam 93	8.00	20.00
195 Kory Casto 93	3.00	8.00
196 Matt Chico 93	3.00	8.00
197 John Danks 93	3.00	8.00
198 Homer Bailey 93	6.00	15.00
199 Ryan Braun 93 SP		
200 Felix Pie 93	5.00	12.00
201 Jesus Flores 93	4.00	10.00
202 Andy Gonzalez 93	4.00	10.00
203 Ryan Sweeney 93 SP		
204 Jarrod Saltalamacchia 93	5.00	12.00
205 Alex Gordon 93 SP		
206 Josh Hamilton 93 SP		
207 Sean Henn 93	3.00	8.00
208 Kei Igawa 93 SP		
209 Akinori Iwamura 93 SP		
210 Andy LaRoche 93	4.00	10.00
211 Rick Vanden Hurk 93	3.00	8.00
212 Kevin Kouzmanoff 93	4.00	10.00
213 Matt Lindstrom 93	3.00	8.00
214 Tim Lincecum 93 SP		
215 Daisuke Matsuzaka 93		
216 Gustavo Molina 93	4.00	10.00
217 Miguel Montero 93	3.00	8.00
218 Brandon Morrow 93	5.00	12.00
220 Adam Lind 93	4.00	10.00
221 Mike Rabelo 93	3.00	8.00
222 Brian Burres 93	3.00	8.00
223 Micah Owings 93	4.00	10.00
224 Brandon Wood 93 SP		
225 Alexi Casilla 93	4.00	10.00
226 Joe Smith 93	4.00	10.00
227 Hunter Pence 93 SP		
228 Glen Perkins 93	3.00	8.00
229 Chris Stewart 93	3.00	8.00
230 Ben Francisco 93	3.00	8.00
231 Troy Tulowitzki 93 SP		
232 Billy Butler 93 SP		
233 Delmon Young 93 SP		
234 Phil Hughes 93 SP		
235 Joaquin Arias 96	3.00	8.00
236 Jeff Baker 96	3.00	8.00
237 Mark Reynolds 96		
238 Joseph Bisenius 96	3.00	8.00
239 Michael Bourn 96	3.00	8.00
240 Zack Segovia 96	3.00	8.00
241 Travis Buck 96 SP		
242 Chase Wright 96	6.00	15.00
243 Rocky Cherry 96	10.00	25.00
244 Danny Putnam 96	8.00	20.00
245 Kory Casto 96	3.00	8.00
246 Matt Chico 96	3.00	8.00
247 John Danks 96	3.00	8.00
248 Juan Salas 96	3.00	8.00
249 Ryan Braun 96 SP		
250 Felix Pie 96	5.00	12.00
251 Jesus Flores 96	4.00	10.00
252 Andy Gonzalez 96	4.00	10.00
253 Ryan Sweeney 96	4.00	10.00
254 Jarrod Saltalamacchia 96 SP		
255 Alex Gordon 96 SP		
256 Josh Hamilton 96	15.00	40.00
257 Sean Henn 96	3.00	8.00
258 Kei Igawa 96 SP		
259 Akinori Iwamura 96 SP		
260 Andy LaRoche 96	4.00	10.00
261 Rick Vanden Hurk 96	3.00	8.00
262 Kevin Kouzmanoff 96	4.00	10.00
263 Matt Lindstrom 96	3.00	8.00
264 Tim Lincecum 96 SP		
266 Gustavo Molina 96	4.00	10.00
267 Miguel Montero 96	3.00	8.00
268 Brandon Morrow 96	5.00	12.00
270 Adam Lind 96	4.00	10.00
271 Mike Rabelo 96	3.00	8.00
272 Brian Burres 96	3.00	8.00
273 Micah Owings 96	4.00	10.00
274 Brandon Wood 96	6.00	15.00
275 Alexi Casilla 96	4.00	10.00
276 Joe Smith 96	4.00	10.00
277 Hunter Pence 96 SP		
278 Glen Perkins 96	3.00	8.00
279 Chris Stewart 96	3.00	8.00
280 Ben Francisco 96	3.00	8.00
281 Troy Tulowitzki 96 SP		
282 Billy Butler 96 SP		
283 Delmon Young 96 SP		
284 Phil Hughes 96 SP		

1996 SPx

This 1996 SPx set (produced by Upper Deck) was issued in one series totalling 60 cards. The one-card packs had a suggested retail price of $3.49. Printed on 32 pt. card stock with Holoview technology and a perimeter diecut design, the set features color player photos with a Holography background on the fronts and decorative foil stamping on the back. Two special cards are included in the set: a Ken Griffey Jr. Commemorative card was inserted one in every 75 packs and a Mike Piazza Tribute card inserted one in every 95 packs. An autographed version of each of these cards was inserted at the rate of one in 2,000.

COMPLETE SET (60)	20.00	50.00
1 Greg Maddux	1.25	3.00
2 Chipper Jones	.75	2.00
3 Fred McGriff	.50	1.25
4 Tom Glavine	.50	1.25
5 Cal Ripken	2.50	6.00
6 Roberto Alomar	.50	1.25
7 Rafael Palmeiro	.50	1.25
8 Jose Canseco	.50	1.25
9 Roger Clemens	1.50	4.00
10 Mo Vaughn	.30	.75
11 Jim Edmonds	.30	.75
12 Tim Salmon	.50	1.25
13 Sammy Sosa	.75	2.00
14 Ryne Sandberg	1.25	3.00
15 Mark Grace	.50	1.25
16 Frank Thomas	.75	2.00
17 Barry Larkin	.50	1.25
18 Kenny Lofton	.30	.75
19 Albert Belle	.30	.75
20 Eddie Murray	.75	2.00
21 Manny Ramirez	.50	1.25
22 Dante Bichette	.30	.75
23 Larry Walker	.30	.75
24 Vinny Castilla	.30	.75
25 Andres Galarraga	.30	.75
26 Cecil Fielder	.30	.75
27 Gary Sheffield	.30	.75
28 Craig Biggio	.50	1.25
29 Jeff Bagwell	.50	1.25
30 Derek Bell	.30	.75
31 Johnny Damon	.50	1.25
32 Eric Karros	.30	.75
33 Mike Piazza	1.25	3.00
34 Raul Mondesi	.30	.75
35 Hideo Nomo	.75	2.00
36 Kirby Puckett	.75	2.00
37 Paul Molitor	.30	.75
38 Marty Cordova	.30	.75
39 Rondell White	.30	.75
40 Jason Isringhausen	.30	.75
41 Paul Wilson	.30	.75
42 Rey Ordonez	.30	.75
43 Derek Jeter	2.00	5.00
44 Wade Boggs	.50	1.25
45 Mark McGwire	2.00	5.00
46 Jason Kendall	.30	.75
47 Ron Gant	.30	.75
48 Ozzie Smith	1.25	3.00
49 Tony Gwynn	1.00	2.50
50 Ken Caminiti	.30	.75
51 Barry Bonds	2.00	5.00
52 Matt Williams	.30	.75
53 Osvaldo Fernandez	.30	.75
54 Jay Buhner	.30	.75
55 Ken Griffey Jr.	1.25	3.00
56 Randy Johnson	.75	2.00
57 Alex Rodriguez	1.50	4.00
58 Juan Gonzalez	.30	.75
59 Joe Carter	.30	.75
60 Carlos Delgado	.30	.75
KG1 K.Griffey Jr. Comm.	2.00	5.00
MP1 Mike Piazza Trib.	2.00	5.00
KGA1 Ken Griffey Jr. Auto.	150.00	250.00
MPA1 Mike Piazza Auto.	75.00	150.00

1996 SPx Gold

Parallel to the regular version, this 60-card set was randomly inserted in hobby packs only at a rate of one in seven. The design is similar to the regular set with the exception being the gold foil borders on front.

*STARS: 1.25X TO 3X BASIC CARDS
STATED ODDS 1:7

1996 SPx Bound for Glory

Randomly inserted in packs at a rate of one in 24, this 10-card set features players with a chance to be long remembered.

COMPLETE SET (10)	30.00	80.00
STATED ODDS 1:24		
1 Ken Griffey Jr.	3.00	8.00
2 Frank Thomas	2.00	5.00
3 Barry Bonds	5.00	12.00
4 Cal Ripken	6.00	15.00
5 Greg Maddux	3.00	8.00
6 Chipper Jones	2.00	5.00
7 Roberto Alomar	1.25	3.00
8 Manny Ramirez	1.25	3.00
9 Tony Gwynn	2.50	6.00
10 Mike Piazza	3.00	8.00

1997 SPx

The 1997 SPx set (produced by Upper Deck) was issued in one series totalling 50 cards and was distributed in three-card hobby only packs with a suggested retail price of $5.99. The fronts feature color player images on a Holoview perimeter die cut design. The backs carry a player photo, player information, and career statistics. A sample card featuring Ken Griffey Jr. was distribued to dealers and hobby media several weeks prior to the products release.

COMPLETE SET (50)	25.00	60.00
1 Eddie Murray	.60	1.50
2 Darin Erstad	.25	.60
3 Tim Salmon	.40	1.00
4 Andruw Jones	.40	1.00
5 Chipper Jones	.60	1.50
6 John Smoltz	.40	1.00
7 Greg Maddux	1.00	2.50
8 Kenny Lofton	.25	.60
9 Roberto Alomar	.40	1.00
10 Rafael Palmeiro	.40	1.00
11 Brady Anderson	.25	.60
12 Cal Ripken	2.00	5.00
13 Nomar Garciaparra	1.00	2.50
14 Mo Vaughn	.25	.60
15 Ryne Sandberg	1.00	2.50
16 Sammy Sosa	.60	1.50
17 Frank Thomas	.60	1.50
18 Albert Belle	.25	.60
19 Barry Larkin	.40	1.00
20 Deion Sanders	.40	1.00
21 Manny Ramirez	.40	1.00
22 Jim Thome	.40	1.00
23 Dante Bichette	.25	.60
24 Andres Galarraga	.25	.60
25 Larry Walker	.25	.60
26 Gary Sheffield	.25	.60
27 Jeff Bagwell	.40	1.00
28 Raul Mondesi	.25	.60
29 Hideo Nomo	.60	1.50
30 Mike Piazza	1.00	2.50
31 Paul Molitor	.25	.60
32 Todd Walker	.25	.60
33 Vladimir Guerrero	.60	1.50
34 Todd Hundley	.25	.60
35 Andy Pettitte	.40	1.00
36 Derek Jeter	1.50	4.00
37 Jose Canseco	.40	1.00
38 Mark McGwire	1.50	4.00
39 Scott Rolen	.40	1.00
40 Ron Gant	.25	.60
41 Ken Caminiti	.25	.60
42 Tony Gwynn	.75	2.00
43 Barry Bonds	1.50	4.00
44 Jay Buhner	.25	.60
45 Ken Griffey Jr.	1.00	2.50
46 Alex Rodriguez	1.00	2.50
47 Jose Cruz Jr. RC	.40	1.00
48 Juan Gonzalez	.25	.60
49 Ivan Rodriguez	.40	1.00
50 Roger Clemens	1.25	3.00
S45 Ken Griffey Jr. Sample	.75	2.00

1997 SPx Bronze

Randomly inserted in packs at the approximate rate of one in three, cards from this 50-card set are a parallel version of the base set with bronze etched foil enhancements.

*STARS: 1X TO 2.5X BASIC CARDS
*ROOKIES: .6X TO 1.5X BASIC CARDS

1997 SPx Gold

Randomly inserted in packs at the rate of one in 17, This 50-card set is parallel to the base set and features etched gold foil enhancements.

*STARS: 2.5X TO 6X BASIC CARDS
*ROOKIES: 1.5X TO 4X BASIC CARDS
STATED ODDS 1:17

1997 SPx Grand Finale

Randomly inserted in packs, cards from this 50-card set are an extremely limited edition parallel version of the base set and features an all gold holoview image. Only 50 of each card was produced. The set was entitled Grand Finale to signify the fact that this would be the last baseball product Upper Deck would ever use the holoview technology on.

*STARS: 12.5X TO 30X BASIC CARDS
*ROOKIES: 5X TO 12X BASIC CARDS

1997 SPx Silver

Randomly inserted in packs at an approximate rate of one in six, cards from this 50-card set are a parallel version of the base set with etched silver foil enhancements.

*STARS: 1.5X TO 4X BASIC CARDS
*ROOKIES: 1X TO 2.5X BASIC CARDS

1997 SPx Steel

Randomly inserted one in approximately one in every two packs, cards from this 50-card set are a parallel version of the base set. Many dealers and collectors believe that cards numbered 25-50 were printed in shorter supply. These cards can be distinguished from the similar looking silver cards by the holographic background behind the SPx logo and the player's number. Silvers lack the holographic background behind the SPx logo.

*STARS: .6X TO 1.5X BASIC CARDS
*ROOKIES: .5X TO 1.2X BASIC CARDS

1997 SPx Bound for Glory

Randomly inserted in packs, this 20-card set features color photos of promising great players on a Holoview die cut card design. Only 1,500 of each card was produced and are sequentially numbered.

COMPLETE SET (20)	100.00	250.00
1 Andruw Jones	2.50	6.00
2 Chipper Jones	4.00	10.00
3 Greg Maddux	6.00	15.00
4 Kenny Lofton	1.50	4.00
5 Cal Ripken	12.50	30.00
6 Mo Vaughn	1.50	4.00
7 Frank Thomas	4.00	10.00
8 Albert Belle	1.50	4.00
9 Manny Ramirez	2.50	6.00
10 Gary Sheffield	1.50	4.00
11 Jeff Bagwell	2.50	6.00
12 Mike Piazza	6.00	15.00
13 Derek Jeter	10.00	25.00
14 Mark McGwire	10.00	25.00
15 Tony Gwynn	5.00	12.00
16 Ken Caminiti	1.50	4.00
17 Barry Bonds	10.00	25.00
18 Alex Rodriguez	6.00	15.00
19 Ken Griffey Jr.	6.00	15.00
20 Juan Gonzalez	1.50	4.00

1997 SPx Bound for Glory Supreme Signatures

Randomly inserted in packs, this five-card set features unnumbered autographed Bound for Glory cards. Only 250 of each card was produced and signed and are sequentially numbered. The cards are checklisted below in alphabetical order.

1 Jeff Bagwell	30.00	60.00
2 Ken Griffey Jr.	100.00	175.00
3 Andruw Jones	10.00	25.00
4 Alex Rodriguez	100.00	200.00
5 Gary Sheffield	10.00	25.00

1997 SPx Cornerstones of the Game

Randomly inserted in packs, cards from this 10-card set display color photos of 20 top players. Two players are featured on each card using double Holoview technology. Only 500 of each card was produced and each is sequentially numbered on back.

COMPLETE SET (10)	100.00	250.00
1 Ken Griffey Jr. Barry Bonds	10.00	25.00
2 Frank Thomas	6.00	15.00

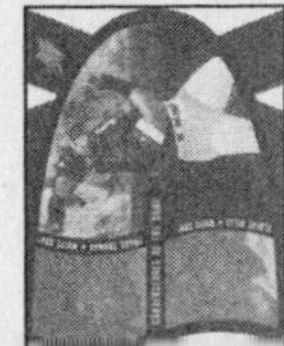

Albert Belle		
3 Chipper Jones Greg Maddux	10.00	25.00
4 Tony Gwynn Paul Molitor	8.00	20.00
5 Andruw Jones Vladimir Guerrero	6.00	15.00
6 Jeff Bagwell Ryne Sandberg	10.00	25.00
7 Mike Piazza Ivan Rodriguez	10.00	25.00
8 Cal Ripken Eddie Murray	20.00	50.00
9 Mo Vaughn Mark McGwire	15.00	40.00
10 Alex Rodriguez Derek Jeter	15.00	40.00

1998 SPx Finite Sample

A special Ken Griffey Jr. card serial numbered of 10,000 was issued as a promotional card and distributed within a silver foil wrapper along with a black and white information card to dealers with their first series order forms and at major industry events. The card is similar to Griffey's basic issue first series SPx Finite card (number 130) except for the lack of a card number on back, serial numbering to 10,000 coupled with the word "FINITE" running boldly across the back of the card in a diagonal manner.

1 Ken Griffey Jr.	2.00	5.00
2 Ken Griffey Jr.	2.00	5.00

1998 SPx Finite

The 1998 SPx Finite set contains a total of 180 cards, all serial numbered based upon specific subsets. The three-card packs retailed for $5.99 each and hit the market in June, 1998. The subsets and serial numbering are as follows: Youth Movement (1-30) - 5000 of each card, Power Explosion (31-50) - 4000 of each card, Basic Cards (51-140) - 9000 of each card, Star Focus (141-170) - 7000 of each card, Heroes of the Game (171-180) - 2000 of each card, Youth Movement (181-210) - 5000 of each card, Power Passion (211-240) - 7000 of each card, Basic Cards (241-330) - 9000 of each card, Tradewinds (331-350) - 4000 of each card and Cornerstones of the Game (351-360) -2000 of each card. Notable Rookie Cards include Kevin Millwood and Magglio Ordonez.

COMP.YM SER.1 (30)	15.00	40.00
COMMON YM (1-30)	.60	1.50
COMP.PE SER.1 (20)	50.00	120.00
COMMON PE (31-50)	1.00	2.50
COMP.BASIC SER.1 (90)	30.00	80.00
COMMON CARD (51-140)	.40	1.00
COMP.SF SER.1 (30)	40.00	100.00
COMMON SF (141-170)	.50	1.25
COMP.HG SER.1 (10)	60.00	150.00
COMMON HG (171-180)	1.50	4.00
COMP.YM SER.2 (30)	25.00	60.00
COMMON YM (181-210)	.60	1.50
COMP.PP SER.2 (30)	30.00	80.00
COMMON PP (211-240)	.50	1.25
COMP.BASIC SER.2 (90)	20.00	50.00
COMMON (241-330)	.40	1.00
COMP.TW SER.2 (20)	12.50	30.00
COMMON TW (331-350)	1.00	2.50
COMP.CG SER.2 (10)	60.00	150.00
COMMON CG (351-360)	1.50	4.00
1 Nomar Garciaparra YM	2.50	6.00
2 Miguel Tejada YM	1.50	4.00
3 Mike Cameron YM	.60	1.50
4 Ken Cloude YM	.60	1.50
5 Jaret Wright YM	.60	1.50
6 Mark Kotsay YM	.60	1.50
7 Craig Counsell YM	.60	1.50
8 Jose Guillen YM	.60	1.50
9 Neifi Perez YM	.60	1.50
10 Jose Cruz Jr. YM	.60	1.50
11 Brett Tomko YM	.60	1.50
12 Matt Morris YM	.60	1.50
13 Justin Thompson YM	.60	1.50
14 Jeremi Gonzalez YM	.60	1.50
15 Scott Rolen YM	1.00	2.50
16 Vladimir Guerrero YM	1.50	4.00
17 Brad Fullmer YM	.60	1.50
18 Brian Giles YM	.60	1.50
19 Todd Dunwoody YM	.60	1.50
20 Ben Grieve YM	.60	1.50
21 Juan Encarnacion YM	.60	1.50
22 Aaron Boone YM	.60	1.50
23 Richie Sexson YM	.60	1.50
24 Richard Hidalgo YM	.60	1.50

25 Andruw Jones YM	1.00	2.50
26 Todd Helton YM	1.00	2.50
27 Paul Konerko YM	.60	1.50
28 Dante Powell YM	.60	1.50
29 Eli Marrero YM	.60	1.50
30 Derek Jeter YM	4.00	10.00
31 Mike Piazza PE	4.00	10.00
32 Tony Clark PE	1.00	2.50
33 Larry Walker PE	1.00	2.50
34 Jim Thome PE	1.50	4.00
35 Juan Gonzalez PE	2.00	5.00
36 Jeff Bagwell PE	1.50	4.00
37 Jay Buhner PE	1.00	2.50
38 Tim Salmon PE	1.50	4.00
39 Albert Belle PE	1.00	2.50
40 Mark McGwire PE	6.00	15.00
41 Sammy Sosa PE	2.50	6.00
42 Mo Vaughn PE	1.00	2.50
43 Manny Ramirez PE	1.50	4.00
44 Tino Martinez PE	1.50	4.00
45 Frank Thomas PE	2.50	6.00
46 Nomar Garciaparra PE	4.00	10.00
47 Alex Rodriguez PE	4.00	10.00
48 Chipper Jones PE	2.50	6.00
49 Barry Bonds PE	6.00	15.00
50 Ken Griffey Jr. PE	4.00	10.00
51 Jason Dickson	.40	1.00
52 Jim Edmonds	.40	1.00
53 Darin Erstad	.40	1.00
54 Tim Salmon	.60	1.50
55 Chipper Jones	1.00	2.50
56 Ryan Klesko	.40	1.00
57 Tom Glavine	.60	1.50
58 Denny Neagle	.40	1.00
59 John Smoltz	.60	1.50
60 Javy Lopez	.40	1.00
61 Roberto Alomar	.60	1.50
62 Rafael Palmeiro	.60	1.50
63 Mike Mussina	.60	1.50
64 Cal Ripken	3.00	8.00
65 Mo Vaughn	.40	1.00
66 Tim Naehring	.40	1.00
67 John Valentin	.40	1.00
68 Mark Grace	.60	1.50
69 Kevin Orie	.40	1.00
70 Sammy Sosa	1.00	2.50
71 Albert Belle	.40	1.00
72 Frank Thomas	1.00	2.50
73 Robin Ventura	.40	1.00
74 David Justice	.40	1.00
75 Kenny Lofton	.40	1.00
76 Omar Vizquel	.60	1.50
77 Manny Ramirez	.60	1.50
78 Jim Thome	.60	1.50
79 Dante Bichette	.40	1.00
80 Larry Walker	.40	1.00
81 Vinny Castilla	.40	1.00
82 Ellis Burks	.40	1.00
83 Bobby Higginson	.40	1.00
84 Brian Hunter	.40	1.00
85 Tony Clark	.40	1.00
86 Mike Hampton	.40	1.00
87 Jeff Bagwell	.60	1.50
88 Craig Biggio	.60	1.50
89 Derek Bell	.40	1.00
90 Mike Piazza	1.50	4.00
91 Ramon Martinez	.40	1.00
92 Raul Mondesi	.40	1.00
93 Hideo Nomo	1.00	2.50
94 Eric Karros	.40	1.00
95 Paul Molitor	.40	1.00
96 Marty Cordova	.40	1.00
97 Brad Radke	.40	1.00
98 Mark Grudzielanek	.40	1.00
99 Carlos Perez	.40	1.00
100 Rondell White	.40	1.00
101 Todd Hundley	.40	1.00
102 Edgardo Alfonzo	.40	1.00
103 John Franco	.40	1.00
104 John Olerud	.40	1.00
105 Tino Martinez	.60	1.50
106 David Cone	.40	1.00
107 Paul O'Neill	.60	1.50
108 Andy Pettitte	.60	1.50
109 Bernie Williams	.60	1.50
110 Rickey Henderson	1.50	4.00
111 Jason Giambi	.40	1.00
112 Matt Stairs	.40	1.00
113 Gregg Jefferies	.40	1.00
114 Rico Brogna	.40	1.00
115 Curt Schilling	.40	1.00
116 Jason Schmidt	.40	1.00
117 Jose Guillen	.40	1.00
118 Kevin Young	.40	1.00
119 Ray Lankford	.40	1.00
120 Mark McGwire	2.50	6.00
121 Delino DeShields	.40	1.00
122 Ken Caminiti	.40	1.00
123 Tony Gwynn	1.25	3.00
124 Trevor Hoffman	.40	1.00
125 Barry Bonds	2.50	6.00
126 Jeff Kent	.40	1.00
127 Shawn Estes	.40	1.00
128 J.T. Snow	.40	1.00
129 Jay Buhner	.40	1.00
130 Ken Griffey Jr.	1.50	4.00
131 Dan Wilson	.40	1.00
132 Edgar Martinez	.60	1.50
133 Alex Rodriguez	1.50	4.00
134 Rusty Greer	.40	1.00
135 Juan Gonzalez	.40	1.00
136 Fernando Tatis	.40	1.00
137 Ivan Rodriguez	.60	1.50
138 Carlos Delgado	.40	1.00
139 Pat Hentgen	.40	1.00
140 Roger Clemens	2.00	5.00
141 Chipper Jones SF	1.25	3.00
142 Greg Maddux SF	2.00	5.00
143 Rafael Palmeiro SF	.75	2.00
144 Mike Mussina SF	.75	2.00
145 Cal Ripken SF	4.00	10.00
146 Nomar Garciaparra SF	2.00	5.00
147 Mo Vaughn SF	.50	1.25
148 Sammy Sosa SF	1.25	3.00
149 Albert Belle SF	.50	1.25
150 Frank Thomas SF	1.25	3.00
151 Jim Thome SF	.75	2.00
152 Kenny Lofton SF	.50	1.25
153 Manny Ramirez SF	.75	2.00
154 Larry Walker SF	.50	1.25
155 Jeff Bagwell SF	.75	2.00
156 Craig Biggio SF	.75	2.00
157 Mike Piazza SF	2.00	5.00
158 Paul Molitor SF	.50	1.25
159 Derek Jeter SF	3.00	8.00
160 Tino Martinez SF	.75	2.00
161 Curt Schilling SF	.50	1.25
162 Mark McGwire SF	3.00	8.00
163 Tony Gwynn SF	1.50	4.00
164 Barry Bonds SF	3.00	8.00
165 Ken Griffey Jr. SF	2.00	5.00
166 Randy Johnson SF	1.25	3.00
167 Alex Rodriguez SF	2.00	5.00
168 Juan Gonzalez SF	.50	1.25
169 Ivan Rodriguez SF	.75	2.00
170 Roger Clemens SF	2.50	6.00
171 Greg Maddux HG	6.00	15.00
172 Cal Ripken HG	12.50	30.00
173 Frank Thomas HG	4.00	10.00
174 Jeff Bagwell HG	2.50	6.00
175 Mike Piazza HG	6.00	15.00
176 Mark McGwire HG	10.00	25.00
177 Barry Bonds HG	10.00	25.00
178 Ken Griffey Jr. HG	6.00	15.00
179 Alex Rodriguez HG	6.00	15.00
180 Roger Clemens HG	8.00	20.00
181 Mike Caruso YM	.60	1.50
182 David Ortiz YM	2.00	5.00
183 Gabe Alvarez YM	.60	1.50
184 G.Matthews Jr. YM RC	1.00	2.50
185 Kerry Wood YM	.75	2.00
186 Carl Pavano YM	.60	1.50
187 Alex Gonzalez YM	.60	1.50
188 Masato Yoshii YM RC	.60	1.50
189 Larry Sutton YM	.60	1.50
190 Russell Branyan YM	.60	1.50
191 Bruce Chen YM	.60	1.50
192 R. Arrojo YM RC	.60	1.50
193 R.Christenson YM RC	.60	1.50
194 Cliff Politte YM	.60	1.50
195 A.J. Hinch YM	.60	1.50
196 Kevin Witt YM	.60	1.50
197 Daryle Ward YM	.60	1.50
198 Corey Koskie YM RC	1.00	2.50
199 Mike Lowell YM RC	4.00	10.00
200 Travis Lee YM	.60	1.50
201 K.Millwood YM RC	2.00	5.00
202 Robert Smith YM	.60	1.50
203 Magglio Ordonez YM RC	6.00	15.00
204 Eric Milton YM	.60	1.50
205 Geoff Jenkins YM	.60	1.50
206 Rich Butler YM RC	.60	1.50
207 Mike Kinkade YM RC	.60	1.50
208 Braden Looper YM	.60	1.50
209 Matt Clement YM	.60	1.50
210 Derrek Lee YM	1.00	2.50
211 Randy Johnson PP	1.25	3.00
212 John Smoltz PP	.75	2.00
213 Roger Clemens PP	2.50	6.00
214 Curt Schilling PP	.50	1.25
215 Pedro Martinez PP	.75	2.00
216 Vinny Castilla PP	.50	1.25
217 Jose Cruz Jr. PP	.50	1.25
218 Jim Thome PP	.75	2.00
219 Alex Rodriguez PP	2.00	5.00
220 Frank Thomas PP	1.25	3.00
221 Tim Salmon PP	.75	2.00
222 Larry Walker PP	.50	1.25
223 Albert Belle PP	.50	1.25
224 Manny Ramirez PP	.75	2.00
225 Mark McGwire PP	3.00	8.00
226 Mo Vaughn PP	.50	1.25
227 Andres Galarraga PP	.50	1.25
228 Scott Rolen PP	.75	2.00
229 Travis Lee PP	.50	1.25
230 Mike Piazza PP	2.00	5.00
231 N.Garciaparra PP	2.00	5.00
232 Andruw Jones PP	.75	2.00
233 Barry Bonds PP	3.00	8.00
234 Jeff Bagwell PP	.75	2.00
235 Juan Gonzalez PP	.50	1.25
236 Tino Martinez PP	.75	2.00
237 Vladimir Guerrero PP	1.25	3.00
238 Rafael Palmeiro PP	.75	2.00
239 Russell Branyan PP	.50	1.25
240 Ken Griffey Jr. PP	2.00	5.00
241 Cecil Fielder	.40	1.00
242 Chuck Finley	.40	1.00
243 Jay Bell	.40	1.00
244 Andy Benes	.40	1.00
245 Matt Williams	.40	1.00
246 Brian Anderson	.40	1.00
247 Dave Dellucci RC	.60	1.50
248 Andres Galarraga	.40	1.00
249 Andruw Jones	.60	1.50
250 Greg Maddux	1.50	4.00
251 Brady Anderson	.40	1.00
252 Joe Carter	.40	1.00
253 Eric Davis	.40	1.00
254 Pedro Martinez	.60	1.50
255 Nomar Garciaparra	1.50	4.00
256 Dennis Eckersley	.40	1.00
257 Henry Rodriguez	.40	1.00
258 Jeff Blauser	.40	1.00
259 Jaime Navarro	.40	1.00
260 Ray Durham	.40	1.00
261 Chris Stynes	.40	1.00
262 Willie Greene	.40	1.00
263 Reggie Sanders	.40	1.00
264 Bret Boone	.40	1.00
265 Barry Larkin	.60	1.50
266 Travis Fryman	.40	1.00
267 Charles Nagy	.40	1.00
268 Sandy Alomar Jr.	.40	1.00
269 Darryl Kile	.40	1.00
270 Mike Lansing	.40	1.00
271 Pedro Astacio	.40	1.00
272 Damion Easley	.40	1.00
273 Joe Randa	.40	1.00
274 Luis Gonzalez	.40	1.00
275 Mike Piazza	1.50	4.00
276 Todd Zeile	.40	1.00
277 Edgar Renteria	.40	1.00
278 Livan Hernandez	.40	1.00
279 Cliff Floyd	.40	1.00
280 Moises Alou	.40	1.00
281 Billy Wagner	.40	1.00
282 Jeff King	.40	1.00
283 Hal Morris	.40	1.00
284 Johnny Damon	.60	1.50
285 Dean Palmer	.40	1.00
286 Tim Belcher	.40	1.00
287 Eric Young	.40	1.00
288 Bobby Bonilla	.40	1.00
289 Gary Sheffield	.40	1.00
290 Chan Ho Park	.40	1.00
291 Charles Johnson	.40	1.00
292 Jeff Cirillo	.40	1.00
293 Jeromy Burnitz	.40	1.00
294 Jose Valentin	.40	1.00
295 Marquis Grissom	.40	1.00
296 Todd Walker	.40	1.00
297 Terry Steinbach	.40	1.00
298 Rick Aguilera	.40	1.00
299 Vladimir Guerrero	1.00	2.50
300 Rey Ordonez	.40	1.00
301 Butch Huskey	.40	1.00
302 Bernard Gilkey	.40	1.00
303 Mariano Rivera	1.00	2.50
304 Chuck Knoblauch	.40	1.00
305 Derek Jeter	2.50	6.00
306 Ricky Bottalico	.40	1.00
307 Bob Abreu	.40	1.00
308 Scott Rolen	.60	1.50
309 Al Martin	.40	1.00
310 Jason Kendall	.40	1.00
311 Brian Jordan	.40	1.00
312 Ron Gant	.40	1.00
313 Todd Stottlemyre	.40	1.00
314 Greg Vaughn	.40	1.00
315 Kevin Brown	.60	1.50
316 Wally Joyner	.40	1.00
317 Robb Nen	.40	1.00
318 Orel Hershiser	.40	1.00
319 Russ Davis	.40	1.00
320 Randy Johnson	1.00	2.50
321 Quinton McCracken	.40	1.00
322 Tony Saunders	.40	1.00
323 Wilson Alvarez	.40	1.00
324 Wade Boggs	.60	1.50
325 Fred McGriff	.60	1.50
326 Lee Stevens	.40	1.00
327 John Wetteland	.40	1.00
328 Jose Canseco	.60	1.50
329 Randy Myers	.40	1.00
330 Jose Cruz Jr.	.40	1.00
331 Matt Williams TW	1.00	2.50
332 Andres Galarraga TW	1.00	2.50
333 Walt Weiss TW	1.00	2.50
334 Joe Carter TW	1.00	2.50
335 Pedro Martinez TW	1.50	4.00
336 Henry Rodriguez TW	1.00	2.50
337 Travis Fryman TW	1.00	2.50
338 Darryl Kile TW	1.00	2.50
339 Mike Lansing TW	1.00	2.50
340 Mike Piazza TW	4.00	10.00
341 Moises Alou TW	1.00	2.50
342 Charles Johnson TW	1.00	2.50
343 Chuck Knoblauch TW	1.00	2.50
344 Rickey Henderson TW	2.50	6.00
345 Kevin Brown TW	1.50	4.00
346 Orel Hershiser TW	1.00	2.50
347 Wade Boggs TW	1.50	4.00
348 Fred McGriff TW	1.50	4.00
349 Jose Canseco TW	1.50	4.00
350 Gary Sheffield TW	1.00	2.50
351 Travis Lee CG	1.50	4.00
352 N.Garciaparra CG	6.00	15.00
353 Frank Thomas CG	4.00	10.00
354 Cal Ripken CG	12.50	30.00
355 Mark McGwire CG	10.00	25.00
356 Mike Piazza CG	6.00	15.00
357 Alex Rodriguez CG	6.00	15.00
358 Barry Bonds CG	10.00	25.00
359 Tony Gwynn CG	5.00	12.00
360 Ken Griffey Jr. CG	6.00	15.00

1998 SPx Finite Radiance

Randomly inserted in packs, this 360-card set is a parallel to the SPx Finite base set. Due to problems in the manufacturing process, exchange cards had to be inserted into packs for Power Explosion cards 40, 41 and 45. The deadline to redeem these exchange cards was June 2nd, 1999. Serial numbering of the various subsets is as follows: Youth Movement (1-30) - 2500 of each card, Power Explosion (31-50) - 1000 of each card, Basic Cards (51-140) - 4500 of each card, Star Focus (141-170) - 3500 of each card, Heroes of the Game (171-180) - 100 of each card, Youth Movement (181-210) - 2500 of each card, Power Passion (211-240) - 3500 of each card, Basic Cards (241-330) - 4500 of each card, Tradewinds (331-350) -1000 of each card, Cornerstones of the Game (351-360) -100 of each card.

*YOUTH: .6X TO 1.5X BASIC YOUTH
*PE RADIANCE: 1.25X TO 3X BASIC POW.EXP.
*BASIC RADIANCE: .75X TO 2X BASIC CARDS
*SF RADIANCE: .75X TO 2X BASIC SF
*HG RADIANCE: 2X TO 5X BASIC HG
*YM RADIANCE: .6X TO 1.5X BASIC YM
*YM RADIANCE RC's: .3X TO .8X BASIC YM
*PP RADIANCE: .6X TO 1.5X BASIC PP
*BASIC RADIANCE: .75X TO 2X BASIC CARDS
*TW RADIANCE: 1.25X TO 3X BASIC TW
*CG RADIANCE: 2X TO 5X BASIC CG

1998 SPx Finite Spectrum

Randomly inserted in packs, this 360-card set is a parallel to the SPx Finite base set. Due to problems in the manufacturing process, exchange cards had to be inserted into packs for Power Explosion cards 40, 41 and 45. The deadline to redeem these exchange cards was June 2nd, 1999. This version is the most difficult to obtain of the three varieties of SPx Finite. Serial numbering for the various subsets is as follows: Youth Movement (1-30) - 1250 of each card, Power Explosion (31-50) - 50 of each card, Basic Cards (51-140) - 2250 of each card, Star Focus (141-170) - 1750 of each card, Heroes of the Game (171-180) - 1 of each card, Youth Movement (181-210) - 1250 of each card, Power Passion (211-240) -1750 of each card, Basic Cards (241-330) - 2250 of each card, Tradewinds (331-350) - 50 of each card and Cornerstones of the Game (351-360) - 1 of each card. Neither the Heroes of the Game nor the Cornerstones of the Game subsets are priced due to scarcity.

*YM SPECTRUM: 1X TO 2.5X BASIC YM
*PE SPECTRUM: 5X TO 12X BASIC PE
*BASIC SPECTRUM: 1.25X TO 3X BASIC
*SF SPECTRUM: 1.25X TO 3X BASIC SF
*YM SPECTRUM: .75X TO 2X BASIC YM
*YM SPECTRUM RC's: .5X TO 1.2X BASIC YM
*PP SPECTRUM: 1.25X TO 3X BASIC PP
*BASIC SPECTRUM: 1.25X TO 3X BASIC
*TW SPECTRUM: 5X TO 12X BASIC TW

1998 SPx Finite Home Run Hysteria

Randomly seeded exclusively into second series packs, these ten different inserts chronicle the epic home run race of the 1998 season. Each card is serial numbered to 62 on back.

HR1 Ken Griffey Jr.	40.00	100.00
HR2 Mark McGwire	40.00	100.00
HR3 Sammy Sosa	20.00	50.00
HR4 Albert Belle	8.00	20.00
HR5 Alex Rodriguez	40.00	100.00
HR6 Greg Vaughn	8.00	20.00
HR7 Andres Galarraga	8.00	20.00
HR8 Vinny Castilla	8.00	20.00
HR9 Juan Gonzalez	8.00	20.00
HR10 Chipper Jones	20.00	50.00

1999 SPx

The 1999 SPx set (produced by Upper Deck) was issued in one series for a total of 120 cards and distributed in thee-card packs with a suggested retail price of $5.99. The set features color photos of 80 MLB verteran players (1-80) with 40 top rookies on subset cards (81-120) numbered to 1,999. J.D. Drew and Gabe Kapler autographed all 1,999 of their respective rookie cards. A Ken Griffey Jr. Sample card was distributed to dealers and hobby media several weeks prior to the product's release. This card is serial numbered "0000/0000" on front, has the word "SAMPLE" pasted across the back in red ink and is oddly numbered "24 East" on back (even though the basic cards have no regional references). Also, 350 Willie Mays A Piece of History 500 Home Run bat cards were randomly seeded into packs. Mays personally signed an additional 24 cards (matching his jersey number) - all of which were then serial numbered by hand and randomly seeded into packs. Pricing for these bat cards can be referenced under 1999 Upper Deck A Piece of History 500 Club.

COMP.SET w/o SP's (80)	10.00	25.00
COMMON (1-10)	.60	1.50
COMMON CARD (11-80)	.20	.50
COMMON SP (81-120)	4.00	10.00
1 Mark McGwire 61	1.25	3.00
2 Mark McGwire 62	1.25	3.00
3 Mark McGwire 63	.60	1.50
4 Mark McGwire 64	.60	1.50
5 Mark McGwire 65	.60	1.50
6 Mark McGwire 66	.60	1.50
7 Mark McGwire 67	.60	1.50
8 Mark McGwire 68	.60	1.50
9 Mark McGwire 69	.60	1.50
10 Mark McGwire 70	1.50	4.00
11 Mo Vaughn	.20	.50
12 Darin Erstad	.20	.50
13 Travis Lee	.20	.50
14 Randy Johnson	.50	1.25
15 Matt Williams	.20	.50
16 Chipper Jones	.50	1.25
17 Greg Maddux	.75	2.00
18 Andruw Jones	.30	.75
19 Andres Galarraga	.20	.50
20 Cal Ripken	1.50	4.00
21 Albert Belle	.20	.50
22 Mike Mussina	.30	.75
23 Nomar Garciaparra	.75	2.00
24 Pedro Martinez	.30	.75
25 John Valentin	.20	.50
26 Kerry Wood	.20	.50
27 Sammy Sosa	.50	1.25
28 Mark Grace	.30	.75
29 Frank Thomas	.50	1.25
30 Mike Caruso	.20	.50
31 Barry Larkin	.30	.75
32 Sean Casey	.20	.50
33 Jim Thome	.30	.75
34 Kenny Lofton	.20	.50
35 Manny Ramirez	.30	.75
36 Larry Walker	.20	.50
37 Todd Helton	.30	.75
38 Vinny Castilla	.20	.50
39 Tony Clark	.20	.50
40 Derrek Lee	.30	.75
41 Mark Kotsay	.20	.50
42 Jeff Bagwell	.30	.75
43 Craig Biggio	.30	.75
44 Moises Alou	.20	.50
45 Larry Sutton	.20	.50
46 Johnny Damon	.30	.75
47 Gary Sheffield	.20	.50
48 Raul Mondesi	.20	.50
49 Jeromy Burnitz	.20	.50
50 Todd Walker	.20	.50
51 David Ortiz	.50	1.25
52 Vladimir Guerrero	.50	1.25
53 Rondell White	.20	.50
54 Mike Piazza	.75	2.00
55 Derek Jeter	1.25	3.00
56 Tino Martinez	.30	.75
57 Roger Clemens	1.00	2.50
58 Ben Grieve	.20	.50
59 A.J. Hinch	.20	.50
60 Scott Rolen	.30	.75
61 Doug Glanville	.20	.50
62 Aramis Ramirez	.20	.50
63 Jose Guillen	.20	.50
64 Tony Gwynn	.60	1.50
65 Greg Vaughn	.20	.50
66 Ruben Rivera	.20	.50
67 Barry Bonds	1.25	3.00
68 J.T. Snow	.20	.50
69 Alex Rodriguez	.75	2.00
70 Ken Griffey Jr.	.75	2.00
71 Jay Buhner	.20	.50
72 Mark McGwire	1.25	3.00
73 Fernando Tatis	.20	.50
74 Quinton McCracken	.20	.50
75 Wade Boggs	.30	.75
76 Ivan Rodriguez	.30	.75
77 Juan Gonzalez	.20	.50
78 Rafael Palmeiro	.30	.75
79 Jose Cruz Jr.	.20	.50
80 Carlos Delgado	.20	.50
81 Troy Glaus SP	6.00	15.00
82 Vladimir Nunez SP	4.00	10.00
83 George Lombard SP	4.00	10.00
84 Bruce Chen SP	4.00	10.00
85 Ryan Minor SP	4.00	10.00
86 Calvin Pickering SP	4.00	10.00
87 Jin Ho Cho SP	4.00	10.00
88 Russ Branyan SP	4.00	10.00
89 Derrick Gibson SP	4.00	10.00
90 Gabe Kapler SP AU	6.00	15.00
91 Matt Anderson SP	4.00	10.00
92 Robert Fick SP	4.00	10.00
93 Juan Encarnacion SP	4.00	10.00
94 Preston Wilson SP	4.00	10.00
95 Alex Gonzalez SP	4.00	10.00
96 Carlos Beltran SP	6.00	15.00
97 Jeremy Giambi SP	4.00	10.00
98 Dee Brown SP	4.00	10.00
99 Adrian Beltre SP	4.00	10.00
100 Alex Cora SP	4.00	10.00
101 Angel Pena SP	4.00	10.00
102 Geoff Jenkins SP	4.00	10.00
103 Ronnie Belliard SP	4.00	10.00
104 Corey Koskie SP	4.00	10.00
105 A.J. Pierzynski SP	4.00	10.00
106 Michael Barrett SP	4.00	10.00
107 Fern.Seguignol SP	4.00	10.00
108 Mike Kinkade SP	4.00	10.00
109 Mike Lowell SP	4.00	10.00
110 Ricky Ledee SP	4.00	10.00
111 Eric Chavez SP	4.00	10.00
112 Abraham Nunez SP	4.00	10.00
113 Matt Clement SP	4.00	10.00
114 Ben Davis SP	4.00	10.00
115 Mike Darr SP	4.00	10.00
116 Ramon E.Martinez SP RC	4.00	10.00
117 Carlos Guillen SP	4.00	10.00
118 Shane Monahan SP	4.00	10.00
119 J.D. Drew SP AU	4.00	10.00
120 Kevin Witt SP	4.00	10.00
24EAST K.Griffey Jr. SAMP	.75	2.00

1999 SPx Finite Radiance

Randomly inserted in Finite Radiance Hot Packs only, this 120-card set is parallel to the SPx base set. Only 100 serial-numbered sets were produced.

*RADIANCE 1-10: 5X TO 12X BASIC 1-10
*RADIANCE 11-80: 8X TO 20X BASIC 11-80
*RADIANCE 81-120: .75X TO 2X BASIC 81-120

90 Gabe Kapler AU	10.00	25.00
119 J.D. Drew AU	10.00	25.00

1999 SPx Dominance

Randomly inserted into packs at the rate of one in 17, this 20-card set features color photos of some of the most dominant MLB superstars.

COMPLETE SET (20)	50.00	120.00
STATED ODDS 1:17		
FB1 Chipper Jones	2.50	6.00
FB2 Greg Maddux	4.00	10.00
FB3 Cal Ripken	8.00	20.00
FB4 Nomar Garciaparra	4.00	10.00
FB5 Mo Vaughn	1.00	2.50
FB6 Sammy Sosa	2.50	6.00
FB7 Albert Belle	1.00	2.50
FB8 Frank Thomas	2.50	6.00
FB9 Jim Thome	1.50	4.00
FB10 Jeff Bagwell	1.50	4.00
FB11 Vladimir Guerrero	2.50	6.00
FB12 Mike Piazza	4.00	10.00
FB13 Derek Jeter	6.00	15.00
FB14 Tony Gwynn	5.00	12.00
FB15 Barry Bonds	6.00	15.00
FB16 Ken Griffey Jr.	4.00	10.00
FB17 Alex Rodriguez	4.00	10.00
FB18 Mark McGwire	6.00	15.00
FB19 J.D. Drew	1.00	2.50
FB20 Juan Gonzalez	1.00	2.50

1999 SPx Power Explosion

Randomly inserted in packs at the rate of one in three, this 30-card set features color action photos of some of the top power hitters of the game.

COMPLETE SET (30)	15.00	40.00
STATED ODDS 1:3		
PE1 Troy Glaus	.50	1.25
PE2 Mo Vaughn	.30	.75
PE3 Travis Lee	.30	.75
PE4 Chipper Jones	.75	2.00
PE5 Andres Galarraga	.30	.75
PE6 Brady Anderson	.30	.75
PE7 Albert Belle	.30	.75
PE8 Nomar Garciaparra	1.25	3.00
PE9 Sammy Sosa	.75	2.00
PE10 Frank Thomas	.75	2.00
PE11 Jim Thome	.50	1.25
PE12 Manny Ramirez	.50	1.25
PE13 Larry Walker	.30	.75
PE14 Tony Clark	.30	.75
PE15 Jeff Bagwell	.50	1.25
PE16 Moises Alou	.30	.75
PE17 Ken Caminiti	.30	.75
PE18 Vladimir Guerrero	.75	2.00
PE19 Mike Piazza	1.25	3.00
PE20 Tino Martinez	.50	1.25
PE21 Ben Grieve	.30	.75
PE22 Scott Rolen	.50	1.25
PE23 Greg Vaughn	.30	.75
PE24 Barry Bonds	2.00	5.00
PE25 Ken Griffey Jr.	1.25	3.00
PE26 Alex Rodriguez	1.25	3.00
PE27 Mark McGwire	2.00	5.00
PE28 J.D. Drew	.30	.75
PE29 Juan Gonzalez	.30	.75
PE30 Ivan Rodriguez	.50	1.25

1999 SPx Premier Stars

Randomly inserted in packs at the rate of one in 17, this 30-card set features color action photos of some of the game's most powerful players captured on cards with a unique rainbow-foil design.

COMP. SET (PS1-PS30)	80.00	200.00
STATED ODDS 1:17		
PS1 Mark McGwire	8.00	20.00
PS2 Sammy Sosa	3.00	8.00
PS3 Frank Thomas	3.00	8.00
PS4 J.D. Drew	1.25	3.00
PS5 Kerry Wood	1.25	3.00
PS6 Moises Alou	1.25	3.00
PS7 Kenny Lofton	1.25	3.00
PS8 Jeff Bagwell	2.00	5.00
PS9 Tony Clark	1.25	3.00
PS10 Roberto Alomar	3.00	8.00
PS11 Cal Ripken	10.00	25.00
PS12 Derek Jeter	8.00	20.00
PS13 Mike Piazza	5.00	12.00
PS14 Jose Cruz Jr.	1.25	3.00
PS15 Chipper Jones	3.00	8.00
PS16 Nomar Garciaparra	5.00	12.00
PS17 Greg Maddux	5.00	12.00
PS18 Scott Rolen	2.00	5.00
PS19 Vladimir Guerrero	3.00	8.00
PS20 Albert Belle	1.25	3.00
PS21 Ken Griffey Jr.	5.00	12.00
PS22 Alex Rodriguez	5.00	12.00
PS23 Ben Grieve	1.25	3.00
PS24 Juan Gonzalez	1.25	3.00
PS25 Barry Bonds	8.00	20.00
PS26 Roger Clemens	6.00	15.00
PS27 Tony Gwynn	4.00	10.00
PS28 Randy Johnson	3.00	8.00
PS29 Travis Lee	1.25	3.00
PS30 Mo Vaughn	1.25	3.00

1999 SPx Star Focus

Randomly inserted in packs at the rate of one in eight, this 30-card set features action color photos of some of the brightest stars in the game beside a black-and-white portrait of the player.

COMPLETE SET (30)	50.00	120.00
STATED ODDS 1:8		
SF1 Chipper Jones	2.00	5.00

SF2 Greg Maddux	3.00	8.00
SF3 Cal Ripken	6.00	15.00
SF4 Nomar Garciaparra	3.00	8.00
SF5 Mo Vaughn	.75	2.00
SF6 Sammy Sosa	2.00	5.00
SF7 Albert Belle	.75	2.00
SF8 Frank Thomas	2.00	5.00
SF9 Jim Thome	1.25	3.00
SF10 Kenny Lofton	.75	2.00
SF11 Manny Ramirez	1.25	3.00
SF12 Larry Walker	.75	2.00
SF13 Jeff Bagwell	1.25	3.00
SF14 Craig Biggio	1.25	3.00
SF15 Randy Johnson	2.00	5.00
SF16 Vladimir Guerrero	2.00	5.00
SF17 Mike Piazza	3.00	8.00
SF18 Derek Jeter	5.00	12.00
SF19 Tino Martinez	1.25	3.00
SF20 Bernie Williams	2.00	5.00
SF21 Curt Schilling	.75	2.00
SF22 Tony Gwynn	2.50	6.00
SF23 Barry Bonds	5.00	12.00
SF24 Ken Griffey Jr.	3.00	8.00
SF25 Alex Rodriguez	3.00	8.00
SF26 Mark McGwire	5.00	12.00
SF27 J.D. Drew	.75	2.00
SF28 Juan Gonzalez	.75	2.00
SF29 Ivan Rodriguez	1.25	3.00
SF30 Ben Grieve	.75	2.00

1999 SPx Winning Materials

Randomly inserted into packs at the rate of one in 251, this eight-card set features color photos of top players with a piece of the player's game-worn jersey and game-used bat embedded in the card.

STATED ODDS 1:251		
IR Ivan Rodriguez	6.00	15.00
JD J.D. Drew	6.00	15.00
JR Ken Griffey Jr.	20.00	50.00
TG Tony Gwynn	15.00	40.00
TH Todd Helton	10.00	25.00
TL Travis Lee	4.00	10.00
VC Vinny Castilla	6.00	15.00
VG Vladimir Guerrero	10.00	25.00

2000 SPx

The 2000 SPx (produced by Upper Deck) set was initially released in May, 2000 as a 120-card set. Each pack contained four cards and carried a suggested retail price of $5.99. The set featured 90-player cards, and a 30-card "Young Stars" subset. There are three tiers within the Young Stars subset. Tier one cards are serial numbered to 1000, Tier two cards are serial numbered to 1500 and autographed by the player and Tier three cards are serial numbered to 500 and autographed by the player. Redemption cards were issued for several of the autograph cards and they were to be postmarked by 1/24/01 and received by 2/3/01 to be valid for exchange. In late December, 2000, Upper Deck issued a new product called Rookie Update which contained a selection of new cards for SP Authentic, SPx and UD Pros and Prospects. Rookie Update packs contained four cards and the collector was guaranteed one card from each featured brand, plus a fourth card. For SPx, these "high series" cards were numbered 121-196. The Young Stars subset was extended with cards 121-151 and cards 182-196. Cards 121-135 and 182-196 featured a selection of prospects each serial numbered to 1600. Cards 136-151 featured a selection of prospect cards signed by the player and each serial numbered to 1500. Cards 152-181 contained a selection of veteran players that were either initially not included in the basic 120-card "first series" set or traded to new teams. Notable Rookie Cards include Xavier Nady, Kazuhiro Sasaki, Ben Sheets and Barry Zito. Also, a selection of A Piece of History 3000 Club Ty Cobb memorabilia cards were randomly seeded into packs. 350 bat cards, three hand-numbered autograph cut cards and one hand-numbered, combination bat chip and autograph cut card were produced. Pricing for these memorabilia cards can be referenced under 2000 Upper Deck A Piece of History 3000 Club.

COMP.BASIC w/o SP's (90)	10.00	25.00
COMP.UPDATE w/o SP's (30)	4.00	10.00
COMMON CARD (1-90)	.20	.50
COMMON AU/1500 (91-120)	4.00	10.00
COMMON (121-135/182-196)	3.00	8.00
COMMON (136-151)	4.00	10.00
COMMON (152-181)	.30	.75
1 Troy Glaus	.20	.50
2 Mo Vaughn	.20	.50
3 Ramon Ortiz	.20	.50

4 Jeff Bagwell .30 .75
5 Moises Alou .20 .50
6 Craig Biggio .30 .75
7 Jose Lima .20 .50
8 Jason Giambi .20 .50
9 John Jaha .20 .50
10 Matt Stairs .20 .50
11 Chipper Jones .50 1.25
12 Greg Maddux .75 2.00
13 Andres Galarraga .20 .50
14 Andruw Jones .30 .75
15 Jeromy Burnitz .20 .50
16 Ron Belliard .20 .50
17 Carlos Delgado .20 .50
18 David Wells .20 .50
19 Tony Batista .20 .50
20 Shannon Stewart .20 .50
21 Sammy Sosa .50 1.25
22 Mark Grace .30 .75
23 Henry Rodriguez .20 .50
24 Mark McGwire 1.25 3.00
25 J.D. Drew .20 .50
26 Luis Gonzalez .20 .50
27 Randy Johnson .50 1.25
28 Matt Williams .20 .50
29 Steve Finley .20 .50
30 Shawn Green .20 .50
31 Kevin Brown .30 .75
32 Gary Sheffield .20 .50
33 Jose Canseco .30 .75
34 Greg Vaughn .20 .50
35 Vladimir Guerrero .50 1.25
36 Michael Barrett .20 .50
37 Russ Ortiz .20 .50
38 Barry Bonds 1.25 3.00
39 Jeff Kent .20 .50
40 Richie Sexson .20 .50
41 Manny Ramirez .30 .75
42 Jim Thome .30 .75
43 Roberto Alomar .30 .75
44 Edgar Martinez .30 .75
45 Alex Rodriguez .75 2.00
46 John Olerud .20 .50
47 Alex Gonzalez .20 .50
48 Cliff Floyd .20 .50
49 Mike Piazza .75 2.00
50 Al Leiter .20 .50
51 Robin Ventura .30 .75
52 Edgardo Alfonzo .20 .50
53 Albert Belle .20 .50
54 Cal Ripken 1.50 4.00
55 B.J. Surhoff .20 .50
56 Tony Gwynn .60 1.50
57 Trevor Hoffman .20 .50
58 Brian Giles .20 .50
59 Jason Kendall .20 .50
60 Kris Benson .20 .50
61 Bob Abreu .20 .50
62 Scott Rolen .30 .75
63 Curt Schilling .20 .50
64 Mike Lieberthal .20 .50
65 Sean Casey .20 .50
66 Dante Bichette .20 .50
67 Ken Griffey Jr. .75 2.00
68 Pokey Reese .20 .50
69 Mike Sweeney .20 .50
70 Carlos Febles .20 .50
71 Ivan Rodriguez .30 .75
72 Ruben Mateo .20 .50
73 Rafael Palmeiro .30 .75
74 Larry Walker .20 .50
75 Todd Helton .30 .75
76 Nomar Garciaparra .75 2.00
77 Pedro Martinez .30 .75
78 Troy O'Leary .20 .50
79 Jacque Jones .20 .50
80 Corey Koskie .20 .50
81 Juan Gonzalez .20 .50
82 Dean Palmer .20 .50
83 Juan Encarnacion .20 .50
84 Frank Thomas .50 1.25
85 Magglio Ordonez .20 .50
86 Paul Konerko .20 .50
87 Bernie Williams .30 .75
88 Derek Jeter 1.25 3.00
89 Roger Clemens 1.00 2.50
90 Orlando Hernandez .20 .50
91 Vernon Wells AU/1500 6.00 15.00
92 Rick Ankiel AU/1500 8.00 20.00
93 Eric Chavez AU/1500 10.00 25.00
94 A.Soriano/1500 AU 20.00 50.00
95 Eric Gagne AU/1500 6.00 15.00
96 Rob Bell AU/1500 4.00 10.00
97 Matt Riley AU/1500 4.00 10.00
98 Josh Beckett AU/1500 20.00 50.00
99 Ben Petrick AU/1500 4.00 10.00
100 Rob Ramsay AU/1500 4.00 10.00
101 Scott Williamson 4.00 10.00
1500 AU
102 Doug Davis AU/1500 6.00 15.00
103 E.Munson/1500 AU* 4.00 10.00
104 Pat Burrell AU/500 30.00 60.00
105 Jim Morris AU/1500 12.50 30.00
106 Gabe Kapler AU/500 15.00 40.00
107 Lance Berkman/1000 3.00 8.00
108 E.Durazo/1500 AU 4.00 10.00
109 Tim Hudson AU/1500 15.00 40.00
110 Ben Davis AU/1500 4.00 10.00
111 N.Johnson/1500 AU 6.00 15.00
112 O.Dotel/1500 AU 4.00 10.00
113 Jerry Hairston/1000 3.00 8.00
114 Ruben Mateo/1000 3.00 8.00
115 Chris Singleton/1000 3.00 8.00
116 Bruce Chen AU/1500 4.00 10.00
117 Derrick Gibson/1000 3.00 8.00
118 Carlos Beltran AU/500 12.50 30.00
119 F.Garcia/1500 AU 6.00 15.00
120 P.Wilson/1500 AU 6.00 15.00
121 B.Wilkerson/1600 RC 4.00 10.00
122 Roy Oswalt/1600 RC 20.00 50.00
123 W.Serrano/1600 RC 3.00 8.00
124 Sean Burnett/1600 RC 3.00 8.00
125 Alex Cabrera/1600 RC 3.00 8.00
126 Timo Perez/1600 RC 3.00 8.00
127 Juan Pierre/1600 RC 4.00 10.00
128 Daylan Holt/1600 RC 3.00 8.00
129 T.Ohka/1600 RC 3.00 8.00
130 K.Sasaki/1600 RC 4.00 10.00
131 K.Ainsworth/1600 RC 3.00 8.00
132 B.Abernathy/1600 RC 3.00 8.00
133 Danys Baez/1600 RC 3.00 8.00
134 Brad Cresse/1600 RC 3.00 8.00
135 R.Franklin/1600 RC 3.00 8.00
136 M.Lamb/1500 AU RC 6.00 15.00
137 David Espinosa 4.00 10.00
1500 AU RC
138 Matt Wheatland 4.00 10.00
1500 AU RC
139 X.Nady/1500 AU RC 8.00 20.00
140 S.Heard/1500 AU RC 4.00 10.00
141 P.Coco/1500 AU RC 4.00 10.00
Card erroneously numbered 54 instead of 141
142 J.Miller/1500 AU RC 4.00 10.00
143 Dave Krynzel 4.00 10.00
1500 AU RC
144 Dane Sardinha 4.00 10.00
1500 AU RC
145 B.Sheets/1500 AU RC 30.00 60.00
146 L.Estrella/1500 AU RC 4.00 10.00
147 Ben Diggins 4.00 10.00
1500 AU RC
148 B.Zito/1500 AU RC 12.50 30.00
149 J.Torres/1500 AU RC 4.00 10.00
150 Mike Meyers 4.00 10.00
1500 AU RC
151 K.Wilson/1500 AU RC 4.00 10.00
152 Darin Erstad .30 .75
153 Richard Hidalgo .30 .75
154 Eric Chavez .30 .75
155 B.J. Surhoff .30 .75
156 Richie Sexson .30 .75
157 Raul Mondesi .30 .75
158 Rondell White .30 .75
159 Jim Edmonds .30 .75
160 Curt Schilling .30 .75
161 Tom Goodwin .30 .75
162 Fred McGriff .50 1.25
163 Jose Vidro .30 .75
164 Ellis Burks .30 .75
165 David Segui .30 .75
166 Aaron Sele .30 .75
167 Henry Rodriguez .30 .75
168 Mike Bordick .30 .75
169 Mike Mussina .50 1.25
170 Ryan Klesko .30 .75
171 Kevin Young .30 .75
172 Travis Lee .30 .75
173 Aaron Boone .30 .75
174 Jermaine Dye .30 .75
175 Ricky Ledee .30 .75
176 Jeffrey Hammonds .30 .75
177 Carl Everett .30 .75
178 Matt Lawton .30 .75
179 Bobby Higginson .30 .75
180 Charles Johnson .30 .75
181 David Justice .30 .75
182 Joey Nation/1600 RC 3.00 8.00
183 Rico Washington 3.00 8.00
1600 RC
184 Luis Matos/1600 RC 3.00 8.00
185 C.Wakeland/1600 RC 3.00 8.00
186 SW Kim/1600 RC 3.00 8.00
187 Keith Ginter/1600 RC 3.00 8.00
188 G.Guzman/1600 RC 3.00 8.00
189 J.Spurgeon/1600 RC 3.00 8.00
190 Jace Brewer/1600 RC 3.00 8.00
191 J.Guzman/1600 RC 3.00 8.00
192 Ross Gload/1600 RC 3.00 8.00
193 P.Crawford/1600 RC 3.00 8.00
194 R.Kohlmeier/1600 RC 3.00 8.00
195 Julio Zuleta/1600 RC 3.00 8.00
196 Matt Ginter/1600 RC 3.00 8.00

2000 SPx Radiance

Randomly inserted into packs, this 135-card insert is a parallel of the SPx base set. Each card in the set is individually serial numbered to 100. Please note the cards with asterisks next to their name were not issued in the basic set but were prepared and accidentally issued in the 2000 SPx packs. They are numbered and packed out to 100 just like the other Radiance cards.

COMMON CARD (1-90) 1.50 4.00
*STARS 1-90: 6X TO 15X BASIC CARDS
COMMON CARD (91-120) 3.00 8.00
91 Vernon Wells 3.00 8.00
92 Rick Ankiel 3.00 8.00
93 Eric Chavez 3.00 8.00
94 Alfonso Soriano 6.00 15.00
95 Eric Gagne 10.00 25.00
96 Rob Bell 3.00 8.00
97 Matt Riley 3.00 8.00
98 Josh Beckett 6.00 15.00
98A John Bale * 3.00 8.00
98B Alex Escobar * 3.00 8.00
98C Joe Mays * 3.00 8.00
98D Calvin Pickering * 3.00 8.00
98E Dave Roberts * 3.00 8.00
98F Jared Sandberg * 3.00 8.00
98G Dernell Stenson * 3.00 8.00
98H Reggie Taylor * 3.00 8.00
98I Ed Yarnall * 3.00 8.00
99 Ben Petrick 3.00 8.00
100 Rob Ramsay 3.00 8.00
101 Scott Williamson 3.00 8.00
102 Doug Davis 3.00 8.00
103 Eric Munson 3.00 8.00
103A Tony Armas Jr. * 3.00 8.00
103B Travis Dawkins * 3.00 8.00
103C Mike Lamb * 4.00 10.00
103D Rico Washington * 3.00 8.00
104 Pat Burrell 3.00 8.00
105 Jim Morris 6.00 15.00
106 Gabe Kapler 3.00 8.00
106A Adam Piatt * 3.00 8.00
106B Mark Quinn * 3.00 8.00
107 Lance Berkman 3.00 8.00
108 Erubiel Durazo 3.00 8.00
109 Tim Hudson 3.00 8.00
110 Ben Davis 3.00 8.00
111 Nick Johnson 3.00 8.00
112 Octavio Dotel 3.00 8.00
113 Jerry Hairston 3.00 8.00
114 Ruben Mateo 3.00 8.00
115 Chris Singleton 3.00 8.00
116 Bruce Chen 3.00 8.00
117 Derrick Gibson 3.00 8.00
118 Carlos Beltran 3.00 8.00
119 Freddy Garcia 3.00 8.00
120 Preston Wilson 3.00 8.00

2000 SPx Foundations

Randomly inserted into packs at one 32, this 10-card insert features players that are the cornerstones teams build around. Card backs carry a "F" prefix.

COMPLETE SET (10) 40.00 100.00
F1 Ken Griffey Jr. 4.00 10.00
F2 Nomar Garciaparra 4.00 10.00
F3 Cal Ripken 8.00 20.00
F4 Chipper Jones 2.50 6.00
F5 Mike Piazza 4.00 10.00
F6 Derek Jeter 6.00 15.00
F7 Manny Ramirez 1.50 4.00
F8 Jeff Bagwell 1.50 4.00
F9 Tony Gwynn 3.00 8.00
F10 Larry Walker 1.00 2.50

2000 SPx Heart of the Order

Randomly inserted into packs at one in eight, this 20-card insert features players that can lift their teams to victory with one swing of the bat. Card backs carry a "H" prefix.

COMPLETE SET (20) 25.00 60.00
H1 Bernie Williams .75 2.00
H2 Mike Piazza 2.00 5.00
H3 Ivan Rodriguez .75 2.00
H4 Mark McGwire 3.00 8.00
H5 Manny Ramirez .75 2.00
H6 Ken Griffey Jr. 2.00 5.00
H7 Matt Williams .50 1.25
H8 Sammy Sosa 1.25 3.00
H9 Mo Vaughn .50 1.25
H10 Carlos Delgado .50 1.25
H11 Brian Giles .50 1.25
H12 Chipper Jones 1.25 3.00
H13 Sean Casey .50 1.25
H14 Tony Gwynn 1.50 4.00
H15 Barry Bonds 3.00 8.00
H16 Carlos Beltran .50 1.25
H17 Scott Rolen .75 2.00
H18 Juan Gonzalez .50 1.25
H19 Larry Walker .50 1.25
H20 Vladimir Guerrero 1.25 3.00

2000 SPx Highlight Heroes

Randomly inserted into packs at one in 16, this 10-card insert features players that have a flair for heroics. Card backs carry a "HH" prefix.

COMPLETE SET (10) 12.50 30.00
HH1 Pedro Martinez .75 2.00
HH2 Ivan Rodriguez .75 2.00
HH3 Carlos Beltran .50 1.25
HH4 Nomar Garciaparra 2.00 5.00
HH5 Ken Griffey Jr. 2.00 5.00
HH6 Randy Johnson 1.25 3.00
HH7 Chipper Jones 1.25 3.00
HH8 Scott Williamson .40 1.00
HH9 Larry Walker .50 1.25
HH10 Mark McGwire 3.00 8.00

2000 SPx Power Brokers

Randomly inserted into packs at one in eight, this 20-card insert features some of the greatest power hitters of all time. Card backs carry a "PB" prefix.

COMPLETE SET (20) 25.00 60.00
PB1 Rafael Palmeiro .75 2.00
PB2 Carlos Delgado .50 1.25
PB3 Ken Griffey Jr. 2.00 5.00
PB4 Matt Stairs .50 1.25
PB5 Mike Piazza 2.00 5.00
PB6 Vladimir Guerrero 1.25 3.00
PB7 Chipper Jones 1.25 3.00
PB8 Mark McGwire 3.00 8.00
PB9 Matt Williams .50 1.25
PB10 Juan Gonzalez .50 1.25
PB11 Shawn Green .50 1.25
PB12 Sammy Sosa 1.25 3.00
PB13 Brian Giles .50 1.25
PB14 Jeff Bagwell .75 2.00
PB15 Alex Rodriguez 2.00 5.00
PB16 Frank Thomas 1.25 3.00
PB17 Larry Walker .50 1.25
PB18 Albert Belle .50 1.25
PB19 Dean Palmer .50 1.25
PB20 Mo Vaughn .50 1.25

2000 SPx Signatures

Randomly inserted into packs at one in 179, this 15-card insert features autographed cards of some of the hottest players in major league baseball. The following players went out as stickered exchange cards: Jeff Bagwell (100 percent), Ken Griffey Jr. (100 percent), Tony Gwynn (25 percent), Vladimir Guerrero (50 percent), Manny Ramirez (100 percent) and Ivan Rodriguez (25 percent). The exchange deadline for the stickered cards was February 3rd, 2001. Card backs carry a "X" prefix followed by the players initials.

XBB Barry Bonds 100.00 175.00
XCJ Chipper Jones 20.00 50.00
XCR Cal Ripken 50.00 100.00
XDJ Derek Jeter 75.00 150.00
XIR I.Rodriguez EXCH * 15.00 40.00
XJB Jeff Bagwell 10.00 25.00
XJC Jose Canseco 10.00 25.00
XKG Ken Griffey Jr. 75.00 150.00
XMR M.Ramirez EXCH 15.00 40.00
XOH Orlando Hernandez 60.00 120.00
XRC Roger Clemens 60.00 120.00
XSC Sean Casey 6.00 15.00
XSR Scott Rolen 10.00 25.00
XTG Tony Gwynn 20.00 50.00
XVG V.Guerrero EXCH * 12.50 30.00

2000 SPx SPXcitement

Randomly inserted into packs at one in four, this 20-card insert features some of the most exciting players in the major leagues. Card backs carry a "XC" prefix.

COMPLETE SET (20) 12.50 30.00
XC1 Nomar Garciaparra 1.00 2.50
XC2 Mark McGwire 1.50 4.00
XC3 Derek Jeter 1.50 4.00
XC4 Cal Ripken 2.00 5.00
XC5 Barry Bonds 1.50 4.00
XC6 Alex Rodriguez 1.00 2.50
XC7 Scott Rolen .40 1.00
XC8 Pedro Martinez .40 1.00
XC9 Sean Casey .25 .60
XC10 Sammy Sosa .60 1.50
XC11 Randy Johnson .60 1.50
XC12 Ivan Rodriguez .40 1.00
XC13 Frank Thomas .60 1.50
XC14 Greg Maddux 1.00 2.50
XC15 Tony Gwynn .75 2.00
XC16 Ken Griffey Jr. 1.00 2.50
XC17 Carlos Beltran .25 .60
XC18 Mike Piazza 1.00 2.50
XC19 Chipper Jones .60 1.50
XC20 Craig Biggio .40 1.00

2000 SPx Untouchable Talents

Randomly inserted into packs at one in 96, this 10-card insert features players that have skills that are unmatched. Card backs carry a "UT" prefix.

COMPLETE SET (10) 80.00 200.00
UT1 Mark McGwire 15.00 40.00
UT2 Ken Griffey Jr. 10.00 25.00
UT3 Shawn Green 2.50 6.00
UT4 Ivan Rodriguez 4.00 10.00
UT5 Sammy Sosa 6.00 15.00
UT6 Derek Jeter 15.00 40.00
UT7 Sean Casey 2.50 6.00
UT8 Chipper Jones 6.00 15.00
UT9 Pedro Martinez 4.00 10.00
UT10 Vladimir Guerrero 6.00 15.00

2000 SPx Winning Materials

Randomly inserted into first series packs, this 30-card insert features game-used memorabilia cards from some of the top names in baseball. The set includes Bat/Jersey cards, Cap/Jersey cards, Ball/Jersey cards, and autographed Bat/Jersey cards. Card backs carry the players initals. Please note that the Ken Griffey Jr. autographed Bat/Jersey cards, and the Manny Ramirez autographed Bat/Jersey cards were both redemptions with an exchang deadline of 12/31/2000.

AR1 Alex Rodriguez 10.00 25.00
Bat-Jsy
AR2 Alex Rodriguez 20.00 50.00
Cap-Jsy/100
AR3 Alex Rodriguez 30.00 60.00
Ball-Jsy/50
BB1 Barry Bonds 15.00 40.00
Bat-Jsy
BB2 Barry Bonds 30.00 60.00
Cap-Jsy/100
BB3 Barry Bonds
Bat-Jsy AU/25
BW Bernie Williams 6.00 15.00
Bat-Jsy
DJ1 Derek Jeter 20.00 50.00
Bat-Jsy
DJ2 Derek Jeter 50.00 100.00
Ball-Jsy/50
DJ3 Derek Jeter
Bat-Jsy AU/2
EC1 Eric Chavez 4.00 10.00
Bat-Jsy
EC2 Eric Chavez 6.00 15.00
Cap-Jsy/100
GM Greg Maddux 10.00 25.00
Bat-Jsy
IR Ivan Rodriguez 6.00 15.00
Bat-Jsy
JB1 Jeff Bagwell 6.00 15.00
Bat-Jsy
JB2 Jeff Bagwell 15.00 40.00
Ball-Jsy/50
JC Jose Canseco 6.00 15.00
Bat-Jsy
JL1 Javy Lopez 4.00 10.00
Bat-Jsy
JL2 Javy Lopez 6.00 15.00
Cap-Jsy
KG1 Ken Griffey Jr. 20.00 50.00
Bat-Jsy
KG2 Ken Griffey Jr. 30.00 60.00
Ball-Jsy/50
KG3 Ken Griffey Jr.
Bat-Jsy AU/24
MM1 Mark McGwire 30.00 60.00
Ball-Base/250
MM2 Mark McGwire 30.00 60.00
Ball-Base/250
MR1 Manny Ramirez 6.00 15.00
Bat-Jsy
MR2 Manny Ramirez
Bat-Jsy AU/24
MW Matt Williams 4.00 10.00
Bat-Jsy
PM Pedro Martinez 10.00 25.00
Cap-Jsy/100
PO Paul O'Neill 6.00 15.00
Bat-Jsy
VG1 Vladimir Guerrero 6.00 15.00
Bat-Jsy
VG2 Vladimir Guerrero 10.00 25.00
Cap-Jsy/100
VG3 Vladimir Guerrero 15.00 40.00
Ball-Jsy/50
TGL Troy Glaus 4.00 10.00
Bat-Jsy
TGW1 Tony Gwynn 6.00 15.00
Bat-Jsy
TGW2 Tony Gwynn 20.00 50.00
Ball-Jsy/50
TGW3 Tony Gwynn 12.50 30.00
Cap-Jsy/100

2000 SPx Winning Materials Update

Randomly inserted into packs of 2000 Upper Deck Rookie Update (at an approximate rate of one per box), this 28-card insert features game-used memorabilia cards from some of baseball's top athletes. The set also includes a few members of the 2000 USA Olympic Baseball team. Card backs carry the player's initials as numbering.

MKGD Travis Dawkins 3.00 8.00
Mike Kinkade Bat-Bat
BAAE Brent Abernathy 3.00 8.00
Adam Everett Bat-Bat
BWEY Brad Wilkerson 4.00 10.00
Ernie Young Bat-Bat
CRTG Cal Ripken 15.00 40.00
Tony Gwynn Base-Base
DJAR Derek Jeter 15.00 40.00
Alex Rodriguez Base-Bat
DJNG Derek Jeter 20.00 50.00
Nomar Garciaparra Base-Bat
FTMO Frank Thomas 4.00 10.00
Magglio Ordonez Base-Base
GSR Ken Griffey Jr. 20.00 50.00
Sammy Sosa
Alex Rodriguez
Jsy-Jsy-Jsy
GWBS Ben Sheets 3.00 8.00
Ball-Jsy
GWDM D.Mientkiewicz 3.00 8.00
Bat-Base
GWEY Ernie Young 3.00 8.00
Bat-Base
GWJC John Cotton 3.00 8.00
Bat-Jsy
GWMN Mike Neill Bat-Jsy 3.00 8.00
GWSB Sean Burroughs 3.00 8.00
Bat-Jsy
IRRP Ivan Rodriguez 4.00 10.00
Rafael Palmeiro Ball-Ball
JGR Derek Jeter 60.00 120.00
Nomar Garciaparra
Alex Rodriguez
Base-Ball-Bat
JBCB Jeff Bagwell 4.00 10.00
Craig Biggio Base-Base
JCBB Jose Canseco 12.50 30.00
Barry Bonds Ball-Ball
KGSS Ken Griffey Jr. 12.50 30.00
Sammy Sosa Bat-Bat
MMKG Mark McGwire 15.00 40.00
Ken Griffey Jr. Ball-Bat
MMRA Mark McGwire 15.00 40.00
Rick Ankiel Base-Base
MMSS Mark McGwire 20.00 50.00
Sammy Sosa Ball-Ball
MPRV Mike Piazza 10.00 25.00
Robin Ventura Ball-Ball
NGPM N.Garciaparra 12.50 30.00
Pedro Martinez Ball-Ball
RCPM Roger Clemens 15.00 40.00
Pedro Martinez Ball-Ball
SBBS Sean Burroughs 3.00 8.00
Ben Sheets Bat-Base

2000 SPx Winning Materials Update Numbered

Randomly inserted into 2001 Rookie Update packs, this 3-card insert features game-used memorabilia from three different major leaguers on the same card. These rare gems are individually serial numbered to 50. Card backs carry the players initials as numbering

CBG Jose Canseco 60.00 120.00
Barry Bonds
Ken Griffey Jr
Ball-Ball-Bat
GSM Ken Griffey Jr. 50.00 100.00
Sammy Sosa
Mark McGwire
Bat-Ball-Base
JGR Derek Jeter 50.00 100.00
Nomar Garciaparra
Alex Rodriguez
Base-Ball-Bat

2001 SPx

The 2001 SPx product was initially released in early May, 2001, and featured a 150-card base set. 60 additional update cards (151-210) were distributed within Upper Deck Rookie Update packs in late December, 2001. The base set is broken into tiers as follows: Base Veterans (1-90), Young Stars (91-120) serial numbered to 2000, Rookie Jerseys (121-135), and Jersey Autographs (136-150). The Rookie Update SPx cards were broken into tiers as follows: base veterans (151-180) and Young Stars (181-210) serial numbered to 1500. Cards 206-210, in addition to being serial-numbered of 1,500 copies per, also feature on-card autographs. Each basic pack contained four cards and carried a suggested retail price of $6.99. Rookie Update packs contained four cards with an SRP of $4.99.

COMP.BASIC w/o SP's (90) 10.00 25.00
COMP.UPDATE w/o SP's (30) 4.00 10.00
COMMON CARD (1-90) .20 .50
COMMON YS (91-120) 2.00 5.00
COMMON JSY (121-135) 3.00 8.00
COMMON (136-150) 6.00 15.00
COMMON (151-180) .30 .75
COMMON (181-210) 2.00 5.00
1 Darin Erstad .20 .50
2 Troy Glaus .20 .50
3 Mo Vaughn .20 .50
4 Johnny Damon .30 .75
5 Jason Giambi .20 .50
6 Tim Hudson .20 .50
7 Miguel Tejada .20 .50
8 Carlos Delgado .20 .50
9 Raul Mondesi .20 .50
10 Tony Batista .20 .50
11 Ben Grieve .20 .50
12 Greg Vaughn .20 .50
13 Juan Gonzalez .20 .50
14 Jim Thome .30 .75
15 Roberto Alomar .30 .75
16 John Olerud .20 .50
17 Edgar Martinez .30 .75
18 Albert Belle .20 .50
19 Cal Ripken 1.50 4.00
20 Ivan Rodriguez .30 .75
21 Rafael Palmeiro .30 .75
22 Alex Rodriguez .75 2.00
23 Nomar Garciaparra .75 2.00
24 Pedro Martinez .30 .75
25 Manny Ramirez Sox .30 .75
26 Jermaine Dye .20 .50
27 Mark Quinn .20 .50
28 Carlos Beltran .20 .50
29 Tony Clark .20 .50
30 Bobby Higginson .20 .50
31 Eric Milton .20 .50
32 Matt Lawton .20 .50
33 Frank Thomas .50 1.25
34 Magglio Ordonez .20 .50
35 Ray Durham .20 .50
36 David Wells .20 .50
37 Derek Jeter 1.25 3.00
38 Bernie Williams .30 .75
39 Roger Clemens UER 1.00 2.50
Wrong uniform number on card
40 David Justice .20 .50
41 Jeff Bagwell .30 .75
42 Richard Hidalgo .20 .50
43 Moises Alou .20 .50
44 Chipper Jones .50 1.25
45 Andruw Jones .30 .75
46 Greg Maddux .75 2.00
47 Rafael Furcal .20 .50
48 Jeromy Burnitz .20 .50
49 Geoff Jenkins .20 .50
50 Mark McGwire 1.25 3.00
51 Jim Edmonds .20 .50
52 Rick Ankiel .20 .50
53 Edgar Renteria .20 .50
54 Sammy Sosa .50 1.25
55 Kerry Wood .20 .50
56 Rondell White .20 .50
57 Randy Johnson .50 1.25
58 Steve Finley .20 .50
59 Matt Williams .20 .50
60 Luis Gonzalez .20 .50
61 Kevin Brown .20 .50
62 Gary Sheffield .20 .50
63 Shawn Green .20 .50
64 Vladimir Guerrero .50 1.25
65 Jose Vidro .20 .50
66 Barry Bonds 1.25 3.00
67 Jeff Kent .20 .50
68 Livan Hernandez .20 .50
69 Preston Wilson .20 .50
70 Charles Johnson .20 .50
71 Cliff Floyd .20 .50
72 Mike Piazza .75 2.00
73 Edgardo Alfonzo .20 .50
74 Jay Payton .20 .50
75 Robin Ventura .20 .50
76 Tony Gwynn .60 1.50
77 Phil Nevin .20 .50
78 Ryan Klesko .20 .50
79 Scott Rolen .30 .75
80 Pat Burrell .20 .50
81 Bob Abreu .20 .50
82 Brian Giles .20 .50
83 Kris Benson .20 .50
84 Jason Kendall .20 .50
85 Ken Griffey Jr. .75 2.00
86 Barry Larkin .30 .75
87 Sean Casey .20 .50
88 Todd Helton .30 .75
89 Larry Walker .20 .50
90 Mike Hampton .20 .50
91 Billy Sylvester YS RC 2.00 5.00
92 Josh Towers YS RC 3.00 8.00
93 Zach Day YS RC 2.00 5.00
94 Martin Vargas YS RC 2.00 5.00
95 Adam Pettyjohn YS RC 2.00 5.00
96 Andres Torres YS RC 2.00 5.00
97 Kris Keller YS RC 2.00 5.00
98 Blaine Neal YS RC 2.00 5.00
99 Kyle Kessel YS RC 2.00 5.00
100 Greg Miller YS RC 2.00 5.00
101 Shawn Sonnier YS 2.00 5.00
102 Alexis Gomez YS RC 2.00 5.00
103 Grant Balfour YS RC 2.00 5.00
104 Henry Mateo YS RC 2.00 5.00
105 Wilken Ruan YS RC 2.00 5.00
106 Nick Maness YS RC 2.00 5.00
107 J. Michaels YS RC 2.00 5.00
108 Esix Snead YS RC 2.00 5.00
109 William Ortega YS RC 2.00 5.00
110 David Elder YS RC 2.00 5.00
111 J. Melian YS RC 2.00 5.00
112 Nate Teut YS RC 2.00 5.00
113 Jason Smith YS RC 2.00 5.00
114 Mike Penney YS RC 2.00 5.00
115 Jose Mieses YS RC 2.00 5.00
116 Juan Pena YS 2.00 5.00
117 B. Lawrence YS RC 2.00 5.00
118 Jeremy Owens YS RC 2.00 5.00
119 C. Valderrama YS RC 2.00 5.00
120 Rafael Soriano YS RC 2.00 5.00
121 H. Ramirez JSY RC 4.00 10.00
122 R. Rodriguez JSY RC 3.00 8.00
123 Juan Diaz JSY RC 3.00 8.00
124 Donnie Bridges JSY 3.00 8.00
125 Tyler Walker JSY RC 3.00 8.00
126 Erick Almonte JSY RC 3.00 8.00
127 Jesus Colome JSY 3.00 8.00
128 Ryan Freel JSY RC 4.00 10.00
129 Elpidio Guzman JSY RC 3.00 8.00
130 Jack Cust JSY 3.00 8.00
131 Eric Hinske JSY RC 4.00 10.00
132 Josh Fogg JSY RC 3.00 8.00
133 Juan Uribe JSY RC 4.00 10.00
134 Bert Snow JSY RC 3.00 8.00
135 Pedro Feliz JSY 3.00 8.00
136 W. Betemit JSY AU RC 6.00 15.00
137 S. Douglass JSY AU RC 6.00 15.00
138 D. Stenson JSY AU 6.00 15.00
139 Brandon Inge JSY AU 10.00 25.00
140 M. Ensberg JSY AU RC 15.00 40.00
141 Brian Cole JSY AU 6.00 15.00
142 A. Hernandez JSY AU RC 6.00 15.00
143 Brandon Duckworth 6.00 15.00
JSY AU RC
144 J. Wilson JSY AU RC 10.00 25.00
145 T. Hafner JSY AU RC 10.00 25.00
146 Carlos Pena JSY AU 10.00 25.00
147 C. Patterson JSY AU 6.00 15.00
148 Xavier Nady JSY AU 6.00 15.00
149 Jason Hart JSY AU 6.00 15.00
150 I.Suzuki JSY AU RC 900.00 1200.00
151 Garret Anderson .30 .75
152 Jermaine Dye .30 .75
153 Shannon Stewart .30 .75
154 Toby Hall .30 .75
155 C.C. Sabathia .30 .75
156 Bret Boone .30 .75
157 Tony Batista .30 .75
158 Gabe Kapler .30 .75
159 Carl Everett .30 .75
160 Mike Sweeney .30 .75
161 Dean Palmer .30 .75
162 Doug Mientkiewicz .30 .75
163 Carlos Lee .30 .75
164 Mike Mussina .50 1.25
165 Lance Berkman .30 .75
166 Ken Caminiti .30 .75
167 Ben Sheets .50 1.25
168 Matt Morris .30 .75
169 Fred McGriff .50 1.25
170 Curt Schilling .30 .75
171 Paul LoDuca .30 .75
172 Javier Vazquez .30 .75
173 Rich Aurilia .30 .75
174 A.J. Burnett .30 .75
175 Al Leiter .30 .75
176 Mark Kotsay .30 .75
177 Jimmy Rollins .30 .75
178 Aramis Ramirez .30 .75
179 Aaron Boone .30 .75
180 Jeff Cirillo .30 .75
181 J.Estrada YS RC 3.00 8.00
182 Dave Williams YS RC 2.00 5.00
183 D.Mendez YS RC 2.00 5.00
184 Junior Spivey YS RC 3.00 8.00
185 Jay Gibbons YS RC 3.00 8.00
186 Kyle Lohse YS RC 3.00 8.00
187 Willie Harris YS RC 2.00 5.00
188 Juan Cruz YS RC 2.00 5.00
189 Joe Kennedy YS RC 3.00 8.00
190 D.Sanchez YS RC 2.00 5.00
191 Jorge Julio YS RC 2.00 5.00
192 Cesar Crespo YS RC 2.00 5.00
193 Casey Fossum YS RC 2.00 5.00
194 Brian Roberts YS RC 6.00 15.00
195 Troy Mattes YS RC 2.00 5.00
196 R.Mackowiak YS RC 3.00 8.00
197 T.Shinjo YS RC 3.00 8.00
198 Nick Punto YS RC 2.00 5.00
199 Wilmy Caceres YS RC 2.00 5.00
200 Jeremy Affeldt YS RC 2.00 5.00
201 Bret Prinz YS RC 2.00 5.00
202 Delvin James YS RC 2.00 5.00
203 Luis Pineda YS RC 2.00 5.00
204 Matt White YS RC 2.00 5.00
205 B.Knight YS RC 2.00 5.00
206 Albert Pujols YS AU RC 500.00 700.00
207 M.Teixeira YS AU RC 60.00 120.00
208 Mark Prior YS AU RC 12.50 30.00
209 D.Brazelton YS AU RC 6.00 15.00
210 Bud Smith YS AU RC 6.00 15.00

2001 SPx Spectrum

Randomly inserted into packs, this 120-card insert is a partial parallel of the 2001 SPx base set. Please note that each card is individually serial numbered to 50.

*STARS 1-90: 12.5X TO 30X BASIC CARDS
*YS 91-120: 1X TO 2.5X BASIC CARDS

2001 SPx Foundations

Randomly inserted into packs at one in eight, this 12-card insert features players that are the major foundation that keeps their respective ballclubs together. Card backs carry a "F" prefix.

COMPLETE SET (12) 20.00 50.00
F1 Mark McGwire 3.00 8.00
F2 Jeff Bagwell .75 2.00
F3 Alex Rodriguez 2.00 5.00
F4 Ken Griffey Jr. 2.00 5.00
F5 Andruw Jones .75 2.00
F6 Cal Ripken 4.00 10.00
F7 Barry Bonds 3.00 8.00
F8 Derek Jeter 3.00 8.00
F9 Frank Thomas 1.25 3.00
F10 Sammy Sosa 1.25 3.00
F11 Tony Gwynn 1.50 4.00
F12 Vladimir Guerrero 1.25 3.00

2001 SPx SPXcitement

Randomly inserted into packs at one in eight, this 12-card insert features players that are known for bringing excitement to the game. Card backs carry an "X" prefix.

COMPLETE SET (12)	20.00	50.00
X1 Alex Rodriguez	2.00	5.00
X2 Jason Giambi	.75	2.00
X3 Ken Griffey Jr.	2.00	5.00
X4 Sammy Sosa	1.25	3.00
X5 Frank Thomas	1.25	3.00
X6 Todd Helton	.75	2.00
X7 Mark McGwire	3.00	8.00
X8 Mike Piazza	2.00	5.00
X9 Derek Jeter	3.00	8.00
X10 Vladimir Guerrero	1.25	3.00
X11 Carlos Delgado	.75	2.00
X12 Chipper Jones	1.25	3.00

2001 SPx Untouchable Talents

Randomly inserted into packs at one in 15, this six-card insert features players whose skills are unmatched. Card backs carry a "UT" prefix.

COMPLETE SET (6)	15.00	40.00
UT1 Ken Griffey Jr.	2.00	5.00
UT2 Mike Piazza	2.00	5.00
UT3 Mark McGwire	3.00	8.00
UT4 Alex Rodriguez	2.00	5.00
UT5 Sammy Sosa	2.00	5.00
UT6 Derek Jeter	3.00	8.00

2001 SPx Winning Materials Ball-Base

Randomly inserted into packs, this 13-card insert features actual swatches of both game-used baseball and base. Card backs carry a "B" prefix followed by the player's initials. Each card is individually serial numbered to 250.

BAJ Andruw Jones	10.00	25.00
BAR Alex Rodriguez	10.00	25.00
BBB Barry Bonds	20.00	50.00
BCJ Chipper Jones	10.00	25.00
BDJ Derek Jeter	20.00	50.00
BFT Frank Thomas	10.00	25.00
BKG Ken Griffey Jr.	15.00	40.00
BMM Mark McGwire	40.00	80.00
BMP Mike Piazza	10.00	25.00
BNG Nomar Garciaparra	10.00	25.00
BPM Pedro Martinez	10.00	25.00
BSS Sammy Sosa	10.00	25.00
BVG Vladimir Guerrero	10.00	25.00

2001 SPx Winning Materials Base Duos

Randomly inserted into packs, this 10-card insert features actual swatches of game-used bases. Card backs carry a "B2" prefix followed by the player's initials. Each card is individually serial numbered to 50.

B2GJ Nomar Garciaparra	50.00	100.00
Derek Jeter		
B2JG Derek Jeter	40.00	80.00
Jason Giambi		
B2JP Derek Jeter	50.00	100.00
Mike Piazza		
B2MG Mark McGwire	40.00	80.00
Ken Griffey Jr.		
B2MR Mark McGwire	40.00	80.00
Alex Rodriguez		
B2MS Mark McGwire	50.00	100.00
Sammy Sosa		
B2PB Mike Piazza	50.00	100.00
Barry Bonds		
B2PM Mike Piazza	40.00	80.00
Mark McGwire		
B2RJ Alex Rodriguez	50.00	100.00
Derek Jeter		
B2TR Frank Thomas	40.00	80.00
Alex Rodriguez		

2001 SPx Winning Materials Base Trios

Randomly inserted into packs, this five-card insert set features actual swatches of game-used bases. Card backs carry a "B3" prefix followed by the player's initials. Each card is individually serial numbered to 25. Due to market scarcity, no pricing is provided.

2001 SPx Winning Materials Bat-Jersey

Randomly inserted into packs, this 21-card insert features actual swatches of both game-used bats and jerseys. Card backs carry the player's initials as numbering.

AJ1 Andruw Jones AS	6.00	15.00
AJ2 Andruw Jones	6.00	15.00
AR1 Alex Rodriguez AS	6.00	15.00
AR2 Alex Rodriguez	6.00	15.00
BB1 Barry Bonds AS	10.00	25.00
BB2 Barry Bonds	10.00	25.00
CD Carlos Delgado AS *	4.00	10.00
CJ1 Chipper Jones AS	6.00	15.00
CJ2 Chipper Jones	6.00	15.00
CR Cal Ripken	15.00	40.00
FT Frank Thomas	6.00	15.00
IR1 Ivan Rodriguez AS	6.00	15.00
IR2 Ivan Rodriguez	6.00	15.00
JD Joe DiMaggio	75.00	150.00
JE Jim Edmonds *	4.00	10.00
KG1 Ken Griffey Jr. AS	6.00	15.00
KG2 Ken Griffey Jr.	6.00	15.00
RA Rick Ankiel *	4.00	10.00
RJ1 Randy Johnson AS	6.00	15.00
RJ2 Randy Johnson	6.00	15.00
SS Sammy Sosa	6.00	15.00

2001 SPx Winning Materials Jersey Duos

Randomly inserted into packs, this 13-card insert features actual swatches of game-used jerseys. Card backs carry both player's initials as numbering. Each card is individually serial numbered to 50.

AJCJ Andruw Jones	15.00	40.00
Chipper Jones		
ARCR Alex Rodriguez	50.00	100.00
Cal Ripken		
BBSS Barry Bonds	50.00	100.00
Sammy Sosa		
CJDW Chipper Jones	15.00	40.00
David Wells		
IRAR Ivan Rodriguez	40.00	80.00
Alex Rodriguez		
KGAR Ken Griffey Jr.	40.00	80.00
Alex Rodriguez AS		
KGBB Ken Griffey Jr.	50.00	100.00
Barry Bonds AS		
KGJD Ken Griffey Jr.	75.00	150.00
Joe DiMaggio		
KGKG Ken Griffey Jr.	40.00	80.00
Ken Griffey Jr. AS		
KGRJ Ken Griffey Jr.	40.00	80.00
Randy Johnson AS		
KGSS Ken Griffey Jr.	40.00	80.00
Sammy Sosa		
SSCD Sammy Sosa	15.00	40.00
Carlos Delgado		
SSFT Sammy Sosa	15.00	40.00
Frank Thomas		

2001 SPx Winning Materials Jersey Trios

Randomly inserted into packs, this seven-card insert set features actual swatches of game-used jerseys. Card backs carry the first letter of each player's last name as numbering. Each card is individually serial numbered to 25. Due to market scarcity, no pricing is provided for these cards.

2001 SPx Winning Materials Update Duos

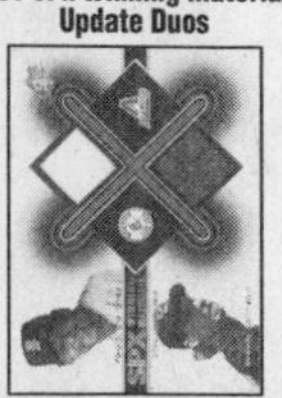

Inserted into 2001 Upper Deck Rookie Update packs at a rate of one in 15, these cards feature two players and a memorabilia piece from each of them.

GOLD PRINT RUN 25 SERIAL #'d SETS
NO GOLD PRICING DUE TO SCARCITY
EACH CARD FEATURES DUAL JSY SWATCH

APJE Albert Pujols	30.00	60.00
Jim Edmonds		
ASKS Aaron Sele	4.00	10.00
Kazuhiro Sasaki		
BBLG Barry Bonds	10.00	25.00
Luis Gonzalez		
BWMR Bernie Williams	6.00	15.00
Mariano Rivera		
BWRJ Bernie Williams	6.00	15.00
Reggie Jackson		
CPBK Chan Ho Park	4.00	10.00
Byung-Hyun Kim		
CPFV Chan Ho Park	6.00	15.00
Fernando Valenzuela		
CREM Cal Ripken	15.00	40.00
Eddie Murray		
CRX2 Cal Ripken	15.00	40.00
Cal Ripken		
CSRJ Curt Schilling	6.00	15.00
Randy Johnson		
EMJM Eric Milton	4.00	10.00
Joe Mays		
FTMO Frank Thomas	6.00	15.00
Magglio Ordonez		
GSSG Gary Sheffield	4.00	10.00
Shawn Green		
HNMY Hideo Nomo	6.00	15.00
Masato Yoshii		
IRAR Ivan Rodriguez	6.00	15.00
Alex Rodriguez		
JBCB Jeff Bagwell	6.00	15.00
Craig Biggio		
JBRY Jeromy Burnitz	6.00	15.00
Robin Yount		
JGBB Jason Giambi	10.00	25.00
Barry Bonds		
KGSC Ken Griffey Jr.	6.00	15.00
Sean Casey		
LWTH Larry Walker	6.00	15.00
Todd Helton		
MPEA Mike Piazza	6.00	15.00
Edgardo Alfonzo		
MRJG Manny Ramirez Sox	6.00	15.00
Juan Gonzalez		
PMGM Pedro Martinez	6.00	15.00
Greg Maddux		
PMRJ Pedro Martinez	6.00	15.00
Randy Johnson		
SRBA Scott Rolen	6.00	15.00
Bobby Abreu		
SSEB Sammy Sosa	10.00	25.00
Ernie Banks		
SSJG Sammy Sosa	6.00	15.00
Jason Giambi		
TGCR Tony Gwynn	15.00	40.00
Cal Ripken		
TGDW Tony Gwynn	6.00	15.00
Dave Winfield		
TGX2 Tony Gwynn	6.00	15.00
Tony Gwynn		
TSHN Tsuyoshi Shinjo	6.00	15.00
Hideo Nomo		

2001 SPx Winning Materials Update Trios

Inserted into 2001 Upper Deck Rookie Update Packs at a rate of one in 15, these 22 cards feature three players as well as a piece of game-worn jersey memorabilia from each one.

GOLD PRINT RUN 25 SERIAL #'d SETS
NO GOLD PRICING DUE TO SCARCITY
ALL FEATURE THREE JSY SWATCHES

BGG Barry Bonds	15.00	40.00
Luis Gonzalez		
Ken Griffey Jr.		
BTD Jeff Bagwell	6.00	15.00
Frank Thomas		
Carlos Delgado		
CHN Roger Clemens	10.00	25.00
Tim Hudson		
Hideo Nomo		
DEA J.D. Drew	4.00	10.00
Jim Edmonds		
Bobby Abreu		
DOP Carlos Delgado	30.00	60.00
Magglio Ordonez		
Albert Pujols		
GWS Luis Gonzalez	4.00	10.00
Matt Williams		
Curt Schilling		
GZH Jason Giambi	4.00	10.00
Barry Zito		
Tim Hudson		
HDG Todd Helton	6.00	15.00
Carlos Delgado		
Jason Giambi		
JAF Chipper Jones	6.00	15.00
Andruw Jones		
Rafael Furcal		
KBA Jeff Kent	10.00	25.00
Barry Bonds		
Rich Aurilia		
MGJ Greg Maddux	10.00	25.00
Tom Glavine		
Andruw Jones		
PPV Jay Payton	8.00	20.00
Mike Piazza		
Robin Ventura		
PWO Andy Pettitte	6.00	15.00
Bernie Williams		
Paul O'Neill		
RPK Ivan Rodriguez	8.00	20.00
Mike Piazza		
Jason Kendall		
RRK Alex Rodriguez	8.00	20.00
Ivan Rodriguez		
Gabe Kapler		
SJC Curt Schilling	15.00	40.00
Randy Johnson		
Roger Clemens		
SKB Gary Sheffield	4.00	10.00
Eric Karros		
Kevin Brown		
SSM Aaron Sele	12.50	30.00
Ichiro Suzuki		
Edgar Martinez		
SYN Kazuhiro Sasaki	6.00	15.00
Masato Yoshii		
Hideo Nomo		
TDK Frank Thomas	6.00	15.00
Ray Durham		
Paul Konerko		
TGA Jim Thome	4.00	10.00
Juan Gonzalez		
Roberto Alomar		
VRF Omar Vizquel	8.00	20.00
Alex Rodriguez		
Rafael Furcal		

2002 SPx

This 280-card set was issued in two separate brands. The SPx product itself was released in late April, 2002 and contained cards 1-250. These cards were issued in four card packs of which were distributed at a rate of 18 packs per box and 14 boxes per case. Cards numbered from 91 through 120 feature either a portrait or an action shot of a prospect. Both the portrait and the action shot were issued with separate stated print runs of 1800 serial numbered cards (for a total of 3,600 of each player in the subset). Cards 121-150 were not serial-numbered but instead feature autographs and were seeded into packs at a rate of 1:18. Cards numbered 151 through 190 were issued and featured jersey swatches of leading major league players. These cards had a stated print run of either 700 or 800 serial numbered cards. High series cards 191-250 were distributed in mid-December, 2002 within packs of 2002 Upper Deck Rookie Update. Cards 191-220 feature veterans on new teams and were commonly distributed in all packs. Cards 221-250 feature prospects and were signed by the player. In addition, the card were serial numbered to 825 copies. Though stated pack odds were not released by the manufacturer, we believe these signed cards were seeded at an approximate rate of 1:16 Upper Deck Rookie Update packs.

COMP.LOW w/o SP's (90)	10.00	25.00
COMP.UPDATE w/o SP's (30)	4.00	10.00
COMMON CARD (1-90)	.20	.50
COMMON ROOKIE (91-120)	3.00	8.00
COMMON CARD (121-150)	6.00	15.00
COMMON CARD (151-190)	3.00	8.00
COMMON CARD (191-220)	.30	.75
COMMON CARD (221-250)	4.00	10.00
1 Troy Glaus	.20	.50
2 Darin Erstad	.20	.50
3 David Justice	.20	.50
4 Tim Hudson	.20	.50
5 Miguel Tejada	.20	.50
6 Barry Zito	.20	.50
7 Carlos Delgado	.20	.50
8 Shannon Stewart	.20	.50
9 Greg Vaughn	.20	.50
10 Toby Hall	.20	.50
11 Jim Thome	.30	.75
12 C.C. Sabathia	.20	.50
13 Ichiro Suzuki	1.00	2.50
14 Edgar Martinez	.30	.75
15 Freddy Garcia	.20	.50
16 Mike Cameron	.20	.50
17 Jeff Conine	.20	.50
18 Tony Batista	.20	.50
19 Alex Rodriguez	.75	2.00
20 Rafael Palmeiro	.30	.75
21 Ivan Rodriguez	.30	.75
22 Carl Everett	.20	.50
23 Pedro Martinez	.30	.75
24 Manny Ramirez	.30	.75
25 Nomar Garciaparra	.75	2.00
26 Johnny Damon Sox	.30	.75
27 Mike Sweeney	.20	.50
28 Carlos Beltran	.20	.50
29 Dmitri Young	.20	.50
30 Joe Mays	.20	.50
31 Doug Mientkiewicz	.20	.50
32 Cristian Guzman	.20	.50
33 Corey Koskie	.20	.50
34 Frank Thomas	.50	1.25
35 Magglio Ordonez	.20	.50
36 Mark Buehrle	.20	.50
37 Bernie Williams	.30	.75
38 Roger Clemens	1.00	2.50
39 Derek Jeter	1.25	3.00
40 Jason Giambi	.20	.50
41 Mike Mussina	.30	.75
42 Lance Berkman	.20	.50
43 Jeff Bagwell	.30	.75
44 Roy Oswalt	.20	.50
45 Greg Maddux	.75	2.00
46 Chipper Jones	.50	1.25
47 Andruw Jones	.30	.75
48 Gary Sheffield	.20	.50
49 Geoff Jenkins	.20	.50
50 Richie Sexson	.20	.50
51 Ben Sheets	.20	.50
52 Albert Pujols	1.00	2.50
53 J.D. Drew	.20	.50
54 Jim Edmonds	.20	.50
55 Sammy Sosa	.50	1.25
56 Moises Alou	.20	.50
57 Kerry Wood	.20	.50
58 Jon Lieber	.20	.50
59 Fred McGriff	.30	.75
60 Randy Johnson	.50	1.25
61 Luis Gonzalez	.20	.50
62 Curt Schilling	.20	.50
63 Kevin Brown	.20	.50
64 Hideo Nomo	.50	1.25
65 Shawn Green	.20	.50
66 Vladimir Guerrero	.50	1.25
67 Jose Vidro	.20	.50
68 Barry Bonds	1.25	3.00
69 Jeff Kent	.20	.50
70 Rich Aurilia	.20	.50
71 Cliff Floyd	.20	.50
72 Josh Beckett	.20	.50
73 Preston Wilson	.20	.50
74 Mike Piazza	.75	2.00
75 Mo Vaughn	.20	.50
76 Jeromy Burnitz	.20	.50
77 Roberto Alomar	.30	.75
78 Phil Nevin	.20	.50
79 Ryan Klesko	.20	.50
80 Scott Rolen	.30	.75
81 Bobby Abreu	.20	.50
82 Jimmy Rollins	.20	.50
83 Brian Giles	.20	.50
84 Aramis Ramirez	.20	.50
85 Ken Griffey Jr.	.75	2.00
86 Sean Casey	.20	.50
87 Barry Larkin	.30	.75
88 Mike Hampton	.20	.50
89 Larry Walker	.20	.50
90 Todd Helton	.30	.75
91A Ron Calloway YS RC	3.00	8.00
91P Ron Calloway YS RC	3.00	8.00
92A Joe Orloski YS RC	3.00	8.00
92P Joe Orloski YS RC	3.00	8.00
93A An. Machado YS RC	3.00	8.00
93P An. Machado YS RC	3.00	8.00
94A Eric Good YS RC	3.00	8.00
94P Eric Good YS RC	3.00	8.00
95A Reed Johnson YS RC	4.00	10.00
95P Reed Johnson YS RC	4.00	10.00
96A Brendan Donnelly YS RC	3.00	8.00
96P Brendan Donnelly YS RC	3.00	8.00
97A Chris Baker YS RC	3.00	8.00
97P Chris Baker YS RC	3.00	8.00
98A Wilson Valdez YS RC	3.00	8.00
98P Wilson Valdez YS RC	3.00	8.00
99A Scotty Layfield YS RC	3.00	8.00
99P Scotty Layfield YS RC	3.00	8.00
100A P.J. Bevis YS RC	3.00	8.00
100P P.J. Bevis YS RC	3.00	8.00
101A Edwin Almonte YS RC	3.00	8.00
101P Edwin Almonte YS RC	3.00	8.00
102A Francis Beltran YS RC	3.00	8.00
102P Francis Beltran YS RC	3.00	8.00
103A Val Pascucci YS	3.00	8.00
103P Val Pascucci YS	3.00	8.00
104A Nelson Castro YS RC	3.00	8.00
104P Nelson Castro YS RC	3.00	8.00
105A Michael Crudale YS RC	3.00	8.00
105P Michael Crudale YS RC	3.00	8.00
106A Colin Young YS RC	3.00	8.00
106P Colin Young YS RC	3.00	8.00
107A Todd Donovan YS RC	3.00	8.00
107P Todd Donovan YS RC	3.00	8.00
108A Felix Escalona YS RC	3.00	8.00
108P Felix Escalona YS RC	3.00	8.00
109A Brandon Backe YS RC	4.00	10.00
109P Brandon Backe YS RC	4.00	10.00
110A Corey Thurman YS RC	3.00	8.00
110P Corey Thurman YS RC	3.00	8.00
111A Kyle Kane YS RC	3.00	8.00
111P Kyle Kane YS RC	3.00	8.00
112A Allan Simpson YS RC	3.00	8.00
112P Allan Simpson YS RC	3.00	8.00
113A Jose Valverde YS RC	3.00	8.00
113P Jose Valverde YS RC	6.00	15.00
114A Chris Booker YS RC	3.00	8.00
114P Chris Booker YS RC	3.00	8.00
115A Brandon Puffer YS RC	3.00	8.00
115P Brandon Puffer YS RC	3.00	8.00
116A John Foster YS RC	3.00	8.00
116P John Foster YS RC	3.00	8.00
117A Cliff Bartosh YS RC	3.00	8.00
117P Cliff Bartosh YS RC	3.00	8.00
118A Gustavo Chacin YS RC	4.00	10.00
118P Gustavo Chacin YS RC	4.00	10.00
119A Steve Kent YS RC	3.00	8.00
119P Steve Kent YS RC	3.00	8.00
120A Nate Field YS RC	3.00	8.00
120P Nate Field YS RC	3.00	8.00
121 Victor Alvarez AU RC	4.00	10.00
122 Steve Bechler AU RC	4.00	10.00
123 Adrian Burnside AU RC	4.00	10.00
124 Marlon Byrd AU	6.00	15.00
125 Jaime Cerda AU RC	4.00	10.00
126 Brandon Claussen AU	6.00	15.00
127 Mark Corey AU RC	4.00	10.00
128 Doug Devore AU RC	4.00	10.00
129 Kazuhisa Ishii AU SP RC	30.00	60.00
130 John Ennis AU RC	4.00	10.00
131 Kevin Frederick AU RC	4.00	10.00
132 Josh Hancock AU RC	8.00	20.00
133 Ben Howard AU RC	4.00	10.00
134 Orlando Hudson AU	6.00	15.00
135 Hansel Izquierdo AU RC	4.00	10.00
136 Eric Junge AU RC	4.00	10.00
137 Austin Kearns AU	6.00	15.00
138 Victor Martinez AU	8.00	20.00
139 Luis Martinez AU RC	4.00	10.00
140 Danny Mota AU RC	4.00	10.00
141 Jorge Padilla AU RC	4.00	10.00
142 Andy Pratt AU RC	4.00	10.00
143 Rene Reyes AU RC	4.00	10.00
144 Rodrigo Rosario AU RC	4.00	10.00
145 Tom Shearn AU RC	4.00	10.00
146 So Taguchi AU SP RC	10.00	25.00
147 Dennis Tankersley AU	6.00	15.00
148 Matt Thornton AU RC	4.00	10.00
149 Jeremy Ward AU RC	4.00	10.00
150 Mitch Wylie AU RC	4.00	10.00
151 Pedro Martinez JSY/800	4.00	10.00
152 Cal Ripken JSY/800	10.00	25.00
153 Roger Clemens JSY/800	6.00	15.00
154 Bernie Williams JSY/800	4.00	10.00
155 Jason Giambi JSY/700	3.00	8.00
156 Robin Ventura JSY/800	3.00	8.00
157 Carlos Delgado JSY/800	3.00	8.00
158 Frank Thomas JSY/800	4.00	10.00
159 Mag. Ordonez JSY/800	3.00	8.00
160 Jim Thome JSY/800	4.00	10.00
161 Darin Erstad JSY/800	3.00	8.00
162 Tim Salmon JSY/800	4.00	10.00
163 Tim Hudson JSY/800	3.00	8.00
164 Barry Zito JSY/800	3.00	8.00
165 Ichiro Suzuki JSY/800	10.00	25.00
166 Edgar Martinez JSY/800	4.00	10.00
167 Alex Rodriguez JSY/800	6.00	15.00
168 Ivan Rodriguez JSY/800	4.00	10.00
169 Juan Gonzalez JSY/800	3.00	8.00
170 Greg Maddux JSY/800	6.00	15.00
171 Chipper Jones JSY/800	4.00	10.00
172 Andruw Jones JSY/800	4.00	10.00
173 Tom Glavine JSY/800	4.00	10.00
174 Mike Piazza JSY/800	6.00	15.00
175 Roberto Alomar JSY/800	4.00	10.00
176 Scott Rolen JSY/800	4.00	10.00
177 Sammy Sosa JSY/800	4.00	10.00
178 Moises Alou JSY/800	3.00	8.00
179 Ken Griffey Jr. JSY/700	8.00	20.00
180 Jeff Bagwell JSY/800	4.00	10.00
181 Jim Edmonds JSY/800	3.00	8.00
182 J.D. Drew JSY/800	3.00	8.00
183 Brian Giles JSY/800	3.00	8.00
184 Randy Johnson JSY/800	4.00	10.00
185 Curt Schilling JSY/800	3.00	8.00
186 Luis Gonzalez JSY/800	3.00	8.00
187 Todd Helton JSY/800	4.00	10.00
188 Shawn Green JSY/800	3.00	8.00
189 David Wells JSY/800	3.00	8.00
190 Jeff Kent JSY/800	3.00	8.00
191 Tom Glavine	.50	1.25
192 Cliff Floyd	.30	.75
193 Mark Prior	.50	1.25
194 Corey Patterson	.30	.75
195 Paul Konerko	.30	.75
196 Adam Dunn	.30	.75
197 Joe Borchard	.30	.75
198 Carlos Pena	.30	.75
199 Juan Encarnacion	.30	.75
200 Luis Castillo	.30	.75
201 Torii Hunter	.30	.75
202 Hee Seop Choi	.30	.75
203 Bartolo Colon	.30	.75
204 Raul Mondesi	.30	.75
205 Jeff Weaver	.30	.75
206 Eric Munson	.30	.75
207 Alfonso Soriano	.30	.75
208 Ray Durham	.30	.75
209 Eric Chavez	.30	.75
210 Brett Myers	.30	.75
211 Jeremy Giambi	.30	.75
212 Vicente Padilla	.30	.75
213 Felipe Lopez	.30	.75
214 Sean Burroughs	.30	.75
215 Kenny Lofton	.30	.75
216 Scott Rolen	.50	1.25
217 Carl Crawford	.30	.75
218 Juan Gonzalez	.30	.75
219 Orlando Hudson	.30	.75
220 Eric Hinske	.30	.75
221 Adam Walker AU RC	4.00	10.00
222 Aaron Cook AU RC	6.00	15.00
223 Cam Esslinger AU RC	4.00	10.00
224 Kirk Saarloos AU RC	4.00	10.00
225 Jose Diaz AU RC	4.00	10.00
226 David Ross AU RC	10.00	25.00
227 Jayson Durocher AU RC	4.00	10.00
228 Brian Mallette AU RC	4.00	10.00
229 Aaron Guiel AU RC	4.00	10.00
230 Jorge Nunez AU RC	4.00	10.00
231 Satoru Komiyama AU RC	10.00	25.00
232 Tyler Yates AU RC	4.00	10.00
233 Pete Zamora AU RC	4.00	10.00
234 Mike Gonzalez AU RC	4.00	10.00
235 Oliver Perez AU RC	12.50	30.00
236 Julius Matos AU RC	4.00	10.00
237 Andy Shibilo AU RC	4.00	10.00
238 J.Simontacchi AU RC	4.00	10.00
239 Ron Chiavacci AU	4.00	10.00
240 Deivis Santos AU	4.00	10.00
241 Travis Driskill AU RC	4.00	10.00
242 Jorge De La Rosa AU RC	10.00	25.00
243 An. Martinez AU RC	4.00	10.00
244 Earl Snyder AU RC	4.00	10.00
245 Freddy Sanchez AU RC	12.50	30.00
246 Miguel Asencio AU RC	4.00	10.00
247 Juan Brito AU RC	4.00	10.00
248 Franklyn German AU RC	4.00	10.00
249 Chris Snelling AU RC	6.00	15.00
250 Ken Huckaby AU RC	4.00	10.00

2002 SPx SuperStars Swatches Gold

Randomly inserted in packs, these cards parallel the final forty cards of the base set. These cards were printed to a stated print run of 150 serial numbered sets.

*GOLD JSY: .6X TO 1.5X BASIC JSY

2002 SPx SuperStars Swatches Silver

Randomly inserted in packs, these cards parallel the final forty cards of the base set. These cards were printed to a stated print run of 400 serial numbered sets.

*SILVER JSY: .4X TO 1X BASIC JSY

2002 SPx Winning Materials 2-Player Base Combos

Randomly inserted into packs, these cards include bases used by both players featured on the card. These cards were issued to a stated print run of 200 serial numbered sets.

BBG Barry Bonds	15.00	40.00
Shawn Green		
BGR Troy Glaus	12.50	30.00
Alex Rodriguez		
BGS Ken Griffey Jr.	15.00	40.00
Sammy Sosa		
BIM Ichiro Suzuki	30.00	60.00
Edgar Martinez		
BPE Mike Piazza	10.00	25.00
Jim Edmonds		
BPI Albert Pujols	50.00	100.00
Ichiro Suzuki		
BRJ Alex Rodriguez	30.00	60.00
Derek Jeter		
BSG Sammy Sosa	10.00	25.00
Luis Gonzalez		
BSR Kazuhiro Sasaki	10.00	25.00
Mariano Rivera		
BWJ Bernie Williams	20.00	50.00
Derek Jeter		

2002 SPx Winning Materials 2-Player Jersey Combos

Inserted at stated odds of one in 18, these 29 cards feature not only the players but a jersey swatch from each player. A few players were issued in lesser quantities and we have notated that with an SP in our checklist. Other players were issued in larger quantities and we have notated that with an asterisk next to the player's name.

WMAR Alex Rodriguez	8.00	20.00
Ivan Rodriguez		
WMBA Jeromy Burnitz	4.00	10.00
Edgardo Alfonzo		
WMBG Jeff Bagwell	6.00	15.00
Juan Gonzalez		
WMBR Jeff Bagwell	6.00	15.00
Alex Rodriguez DP		
WMDH Jermaine Dye	4.00	10.00
Tim Hudson		
WMDS Carlos Delgado	4.00	10.00
Shannon Stewart		
WMED Jim Edmonds	4.00	10.00
J.D. Drew		
WMGC Ken Griffey Jr.	8.00	20.00
Sean Casey SP		
WMGK Shawn Green	4.00	10.00
Eric Karros		
WMGR Juan Gonzalez	6.00	15.00
Ivan Rodriguez		
WMHW Mike Hampton	4.00	10.00
Larry Walker		
WMJJ Chipper Jones	6.00	15.00
Andruw Jones		
WMJS Randy Johnson	6.00	15.00
Curt Schilling		
WMKG Jason Kendall	4.00	10.00
Brian Giles		
WMLH Al Leiter	4.00	10.00
Mike Hampton		
WMMC Edgar Martinez	6.00	15.00
Mike Cameron		
WMMJ Greg Maddux	10.00	25.00
Chipper Jones		
WMNM Hideo Nomo	10.00	25.00
Pedro Martinez SP		
WMPA Mike Piazza	6.00	15.00
Roberto Alomar DP		
WMRA Scott Rolen	6.00	15.00
Bob Abreu		
WMRP Ivan Rodriguez	6.00	15.00
Chan Ho Park		
WMSE Aaron Sele	4.00	10.00
Darin Erstad		
WMSH Kazuhiro Sasaki	4.00	10.00
Shigetoshi Hasegawa		
WMSP Sammy Sosa	6.00	15.00
Corey Patterson		
WMTO Frank Thomas	6.00	15.00
Maggio Ordonez		
WMTS Jim Thome	6.00	15.00
C.C. Sabathia DP		
WMVR Omar Vizquel	8.00	20.00
Alex Rodriguez		

WMWG Bernie Williams	6.00	15.00
Jason Giambi DP		
WMWP David Wells	6.00	15.00
Jorge PosadaDP		

2002 SPx Winning Materials USA Jersey Combos

Randomly inserted into packs, these 23 cards feature two uniform swatches from players who played for the USA National team. These cards had a stated print run of 150 serial numbered sets.

USAAH Brent Abernathy	6.00	15.00
Orlando Hudson		
USAAW Matt Anderson	6.00	15.00
Jeff Weaver		
USABT Sean Burroughs	10.00	25.00
MarkTeixeira		
USAGB Jason Giambi	6.00	15.00
Sean Burroughs		
USAGT Jason Giambi	10.00	25.00
Mark Teixeira		
USAHD Orlando Hudson	6.00	15.00
Jeff Deardorff		
USAHP Dustin Hermanson	6.00	15.00
Mark Prior		
USAJC Jacques Jones	6.00	15.00
Michael Cuddyer		
USAKB Austin Kearns	6.00	15.00
Sean Burroughs		
USAKC Aaron Kearns	6.00	15.00
Michael Cuddyer		
USAMG Doug Mientkiewicz	6.00	15.00
Jason Giambi		
USAMO Matt Morris	6.00	15.00
Roy Oswalt		
USAMP Matt Morris	6.00	15.00
Mark Prior		
USAMW Matt Morris	6.00	15.00
Jeff Weaver		
USAPB Mark Prior	6.00	15.00
Dewon Brazelton		
USARE Brian Roberts	6.00	15.00
Adam Everett		
USASD Mark Kotsay	6.00	15.00
Sean Burroughs		
USATB Brent Abernathy	6.00	15.00
Dewon Brazelton		
USATP Mark Teixeira	10.00	25.00
Mark Prior		
USAWB Jeff Weaver	6.00	15.00
Dewon Brazelton		
USAWH Jeff Weaver	6.00	15.00
Dustin Hermanson		
USAHOU Roy Oswalt	6.00	15.00
Adam Everett		
USAMIN Doug Mientkiewicz	6.00	15.00
Michael Cuddyer		

2003 SPx

This 199 card set was released in two series. The primary 178-card set was issued in August, 2003 followed up with 21 Update cards randomly seeded within a special rookie pack within sealed boxes of 2003 Upper Deck Finite baseball (of which was released in December, 2003). The primary SPx product was distributed in four card packs carrying an SRP of $7. Each sealed box contained 18 packs and each sealed case contained 14 boxes. Cards numbered 1 to 125 featured veterans with 25 short print cards inserted. Cards numbered 126 through 160 featured rookie cards which were issued to a stated print run of 999 serial numbered sets. Cards 161 and 162 featured New York Yankees rookies Hideki Matsui and Jose Contreras. The Matsui card was issued to a serial numbered print run of 864 copies while the Contreras was issued to a serial numbered print run of 800 copies. Both cards were signed while the Matsui also included a game-used jersey swatch. Cards numbered 163 through 178 featured both autographs and jersey swatches of the featured player and those cards were issued to a stated print run of 1224 cards. The Update cards 179-193 featured a selection of prospects and each card was serial numbered to 150 copies. For reasons unknown to us, the set then skipped to cards 381-387, of which featured additional prospects on cards enriched with both certified autographs and game jersey swatches. These "high number" cards were printed to a serial numbered quantity of 355 copies each.

COMP.LO SET w/o SP's (100)	10.00	25.00
COMP.LO SET w/ SP's (125)	50.00	100.00
COMMON CARD (1-125)	.20	.50
COMMON SP (1-125)	1.50	4.00
COMMON CARD (126-160)	3.00	8.00
COMMON CARD (161-178)	6.00	15.00
163-178 PRINT RUN 1224 SERIAL #'d SETS		
126-178 RANDOM INSERTS IN SPx PACKS		
COMMON CARD (179-193)	6.00	15.00
COMMON CARD (381-387)	6.00	15.00
1 Darin Erstad	.20	.50
2 Garret Anderson	.20	.50
3 Tim Salmon	.30	.75
4 Troy Glaus SP	1.50	4.00
5 Luis Gonzalez	.20	.50
6 Randy Johnson	.50	1.25
7 Curt Schilling	.20	.50
8 Lyle Overbay	.20	.50
9 Andruw Jones SP	1.50	4.00
10 Gary Sheffield	.20	.50
11 Rafael Furcal	.20	.50
12 Greg Maddux	.75	2.00
13 Chipper Jones SP	2.00	5.00
14 Tony Batista	.20	.50
15 Rodrigo Lopez	.20	.50
16 Jay Gibbons	.20	.50
17 Byung-Hyun Kim	.20	.50
18 Johnny Damon	.30	.75
19 Derek Lowe	.20	.50
20 Nomar Garciaparra SP	3.00	8.00
21 Pedro Martinez	.30	.75
22 Manny Ramirez SP	1.50	4.00
23 Mark Prior	.30	.75
24 Kerry Wood	.20	.50
25 Corey Patterson	.20	.50
26 Sammy Sosa SP	2.00	5.00
27 Moises Alou	.20	.50
28 Magglio Ordonez	.20	.50
29 Frank Thomas	.50	1.25
30 Paul Konerko	.20	.50
31 Bartolo Colon	.20	.50
32 Adam Dunn	.20	.50
33 Austin Kearns	.20	.50
34 Aaron Boone	.20	.50
35 Ken Griffey Jr. SP	3.00	8.00
36 Omar Vizquel	.30	.75
37 C.C. Sabathia	.20	.50
38 Jason Davis	.20	.50
39 Travis Hafner	.20	.50
40 Brandon Phillips	.20	.50
41 Larry Walker	.20	.50
42 Preston Wilson	.20	.50
43 Jay Payton	.20	.50
44 Todd Helton	.30	.75
45 Carlos Pena	.20	.50
46 Eric Munson	.20	.50
47 Ivan Rodriguez	.30	.75
48 Josh Beckett	.20	.50
49 Alex Gonzalez	.20	.50
50 Roy Oswalt	.20	.50
51 Craig Biggio	.30	.75
52 Jeff Bagwell	.30	.75
53 Dontrelle Willis SP	2.00	5.00
54 Mike Sweeney	.20	.50
55 Carlos Beltran	.20	.50
56 Brent Mayne	.20	.50
57 Hideo Nomo	.50	1.25
58 Rickey Henderson	.50	1.25
59 Adrian Beltre	.20	.50
60 Miguel Cabrera SP	2.00	5.00
61 Kazuhisa Ishii	.20	.50
62 Ben Sheets	.20	.50
63 Richie Sexson	.20	.50
64 Torii Hunter SP	1.50	4.00
65 Jacque Jones	.20	.50
66 Joe Mays	.20	.50
67 Corey Koskie	.20	.50
68 A.J. Pierzynski	.20	.50
69 Jose Vidro	.20	.50
70 Vladimir Guerrero SP	2.00	5.00
71 Tom Glavine	.30	.75
72 Jose Reyes SP	1.50	4.00
73 Aaron Heilman	.20	.50
74 Mike Piazza	.75	2.00
75 Jorge Posada	.30	.75
76 Mike Mussina	.30	.75
77 Robin Ventura	.20	.50
78 Mariano Rivera	.50	1.25
79 Roger Clemens SP	4.00	10.00
80 Jason Giambi	.20	.50
81 Bernie Williams	.30	.75
82 Alfonso Soriano SP	1.50	4.00
83 Derek Jeter SP	5.00	12.00
84 Miguel Tejada SP	1.50	4.00
85 Eric Chavez	.20	.50
86 Tim Hudson	.20	.50
87 Barry Zito	.20	.50
88 Mark Mulder	.20	.50
89 Erubiel Durazo	.20	.50
90 Pat Burrell	.20	.50
91 Jim Thome SP	1.50	4.00
92 Bobby Abreu	.20	.50
93 Brian Giles	.20	.50
94 Reggie Sanders SP	1.50	4.00
95 Kenny Lofton	.20	.50
96 Ryan Klesko	.20	.50
97 Sean Burroughs	.20	.50
98 Edgardo Alfonzo	.20	.50
99 Rich Aurilia	.20	.50
100 Jose Cruz Jr.	.20	.50
101 Barry Bonds SP	5.00	12.00
102 Mike Cameron	.20	.50
103 Kazuhiro Sasaki	.20	.50
104 Bret Boone	.20	.50
105 Ichiro Suzuki SP	4.00	10.00
106 J.D. Drew	.20	.50
107 Jim Edmonds	.20	.50
108 Scott Rolen SP	1.50	4.00
109 Matt Morris	.20	.50
110 Tino Martinez	.30	.75
111 Albert Pujols SP	4.00	10.00
112 Damian Rolls	.20	.50
113 Carl Crawford	.20	.50
114 Rocco Baldelli SP	1.50	4.00
115 Hank Blalock	.20	.50
116 Alex Rodriguez SP	3.00	8.00
117 Kevin Mench	.20	.50
118 Rafael Palmeiro	.30	.75
119 Mark Teixeira	.30	.75
120 Shannon Stewart	.20	.50
121 Vernon Wells	.20	.50
122 Josh Phelps	.20	.50
123 Eric Hinske	.20	.50
124 Orlando Hudson	.20	.50
125 Carlos Delgado SP	1.50	4.00
126 Jason Roach ROO RC	3.00	8.00
127 Dan Haren ROO RC	4.00	10.00
128 Luis Ayala ROO RC	3.00	8.00
129 Bo Hart ROO RC	3.00	8.00
130 Wil. Ledezma ROO RC	3.00	8.00
131 Rick Roberts ROO RC	3.00	8.00
132 Miguel Ojeda ROO RC	3.00	8.00
133 Aquilino Lopez ROO RC	3.00	8.00
134 Roger Deago ROO RC	3.00	8.00
135 Arnie Munoz ROO RC	3.00	8.00
136 Brent Hoard ROO RC	3.00	8.00
137 Termel Sledge ROO RC	3.00	8.00
138 Ryan Cameron ROO RC	3.00	8.00
139 Pr. Redman ROO RC	3.00	8.00
140 Clint Barmes ROO RC	2.50	6.00
141 Jeremy Griffiths ROO RC	3.00	8.00
142 Jon Leicester ROO RC	3.00	8.00
143 Brandon Webb ROO RC	5.00	12.00
144 T.Wellemeyer ROO RC	3.00	8.00
145 Felix Sanchez ROO RC	3.00	8.00
146 Anthony Ferrari ROO RC	3.00	8.00
147 Ian Ferguson ROO RC	3.00	8.00
148 Mi. Nakamura ROO RC	3.00	8.00
149 Lew Ford ROO RC	4.00	10.00
150 Nate Bland ROO RC	3.00	8.00
151 David Matranga ROO RC	3.00	8.00
152 Edgar Gonzalez ROO RC	3.00	8.00
153 Carlos Mendez ROO RC	3.00	8.00
154 Jason Gilfillan ROO RC	3.00	8.00
155 Mike Neu ROO RC	3.00	8.00
156 Jason Shiell ROO RC	3.00	8.00
157 Jeff Duncan ROO RC	3.00	8.00
158 Oscar Villarreal ROO RC	3.00	8.00
159 D.Markwell ROO RC	3.00	8.00
160 Joe Valentine ROO RC	3.00	8.00
161 H.Matsui AU JSY RC	150.00	250.00
162 Jose Contreras AU RC	20.00	40.00
163 Willie Eyre AU JSY RC	6.00	15.00
164 Matt Bruback AU JSY RC	6.00	15.00
165 Rett Johnson AU JSY RC	6.00	15.00
166 Jeremy Griffiths AU JSY	6.00	15.00
167 Fran Cruceta AU JSY RC	6.00	15.00
168 Fern Cabrera AU JSY RC	6.00	15.00
169 J.Peralta AU JSY	6.00	15.00
170 S.Bazzell AU JSY RC	6.00	15.00
171 B.Madritsch AU JSY RC	10.00	25.00
172 Phil Seibel AU JSY RC	6.00	15.00
173 J.Willingham AU JSY RC	6.00	15.00
174 R.Hammock AU JSY RC	6.00	15.00
175 A.Machado AU JSY RC	6.00	15.00
176 D.Sanders AU JSY RC	6.00	15.00
177 Matt Kata AU JSY RC	6.00	15.00
178 Heath Bell AU JSY RC	6.00	15.00
179 Chad Gaudin ROO RC	6.00	15.00
180 Chris Capuano ROO RC	10.00	25.00
181 Danny Garcia ROO RC	6.00	15.00
182 Delmon Young ROO	12.50	30.00
183 Edwin Jackson ROO RC	8.00	20.00
184 Greg Jones ROO RC	6.00	15.00
185 Jeremy Bonderman ROO RC	20.00	50.00
186 Jorge DePaula ROO	6.00	15.00
187 Khalil Greene ROO	8.00	20.00
188 Chad Cordero ROO RC	10.00	25.00
189 Miguel Cabrera ROO	8.00	20.00
190 Rich Harden ROO	8.00	20.00
191 Rickie Weeks ROO	15.00	40.00
192 Rosman Garcia ROO RC	6.00	15.00
193 Tom Gregorio ROO RC	6.00	15.00
381 Andrew Brown AU JSY RC	6.00	15.00
382 Delm Young AU JSY RC	30.00	60.00
383 Colin Porter AU JSY RC	6.00	15.00
385 Rickie Weeks AU JSY RC	30.00	60.00
386 David Matranga AU JSY RC	6.00	15.00
387 Bo Hart AU JSY	6.00	15.00

2003 SPx Spectrum

*SPECTRUM 1-125 p/r 51-75: 5X TO 12X		
*SPECTRUM 1-125 p/r 36-50: 6X TO 15X		
*SPECTRUM 1-125 p/r 26-35: 8X TO 20X		
*SPECTRUM 1-125 p/r 51-75: 1.25X TO 3X SP		
*SPECTRUM 1-125 p/r 36-50: 1.5X TO 4X SP		
*SPECTRUM 1-125 p/r 26-35: 2X TO 5X SP		
1-125 PRINT RUNS B/WN 1-75 COPIES PER		
*SPECTRUM 126-160: .6X TO 1.5X BASIC		
126-160 PRINT RUN 125 SERIAL #'d SETS		
161-178 PRINT RUN 25 SERIAL #'d SETS		
161-178 NO PRICING DUE TO SCARCITY		
143 Brandon Webb ROO	15.00	40.00

2003 SPx Game Used Combos

Randomly inserted into packs, these 42 cards feature two players along with game-used memorabilia of each player. Since these cards were issued in varying quantities, we have notated the print run next to the card in our checklist. Please note that if a card was issued to a print run of 25 or fewer copies, no pricing is provided due to market scarcity.

BK Jeff Bagwell Patch	15.00	40.00
Jeff Kent Patch/90		
BM Barry Bonds Base	100.00	175.00
Roger Maris Jsy/50		
BT Barry Bonds Base	150.00	250.00
Ted Williams Patch/50		
CA Cal Ripken Patch	125.00	200.00
Alex Rodriguez Patch/50		
CC Jose Contreras Base	20.00	50.00
Roger Clemens Patch/50		
CL Cal Ripken Patch	200.00	400.00
Lou Gehrig Pants/90		
CM Jose Contreras Base	15.00	40.00
Pedro Martinez Patch/90		
EG Darin Erstad Patch	10.00	25.00
Troy Glaus Patch/90		
FC Carlton Fisk Patch	15.00	40.00
Gary Carter Patch/90		
GC Greg Maddux Patch	20.00	50.00
Chipper Jones Patch/90		
GD Ken Griffey Jr. Patch	30.00	60.00
Adam Dunn Patch/90		
GR Ken Griffey Jr. Patch	30.00	60.00
Sammy Sosa Patch/90		
GS Jason Giambi Patch	10.00	25.00
Alfonso Soriano Patch/90		
HJ Hideki Matsui Patch	50.00	100.00
Jason Giambi Patch/50		
HM Hideki Matsui Patch		
Mickey Mantle Bat/10		
IA Ichiro Suzuki Patch	150.00	250.00
Albert Pujols Patch/50		
JJ Chipper Jones Patch	15.00	40.00
Andruw Jones Patch/90		
MB Mickey Mantle Bat	125.00	200.00
Barry Bonds Base/50		
MC Hideki Matsui Patch		
Jose Contreras Base/10		
MD Mickey Mantle Bat	150.00	250.00
Derek Jeter Base/50		
MG Pedro Martinez Patch	30.00	60.00
Nomar Garciaparra Base/90		
MJ Hideki Matsui Patch	60.00	120.00
Derek Jeter Base/90		
MR Mickey Mantle Bat		
Roger Maris Jsy/10		
MS Hideki Matsui Patch	250.00	400.00
Ichiro Suzuki Patch/50		
MW Mickey Mantle Bat	250.00	400.00
Ted Williams Jsy/50		
NI Hideo Nomo Patch	40.00	80.00
Kazuhisa Ishii Patch/50		
PM Rafael Palmeiro Patch	15.00	40.00
Fred McGriff Patch/90		
PS Rafael Palmeiro Patch		
Sammy Sosa Patch/10		
RC Nolan Ryan Patch	50.00	100.00
Roger Clemens Patch/90		
RG Alex Rodriguez Patch	30.00	60.00
Nomar Garciaparra Base/90		
RM Babe Ruth Bat		
Hideki Matsui Patch/10		
RR Cal Ripken Patch	50.00	100.00
Scott Rolen Patch/90		
RS Nolan Ryan Patch	75.00	150.00
Tom Seaver Patch/90		
RT Alex Rodriguez Patch	20.00	50.00
Miguel Tejada Patch/90		
RY Nolan Ryan Patch		
Pedro Martinez Patch/10		
SB Sammy Sosa Patch	30.00	60.00
Barry Bonds Base/90		
SJ Curt Schilling Patch	15.00	40.00
Randy Johnson Patch/90		
SN Ichiro Suzuki Patch	125.00	200.00
Hideo Nomo Patch/90		
SP Sammy Sosa Patch	15.00	40.00
Rafael Palmeiro Patch/90		
TB Thurman Munson Patch		
Yogi Berra Bat/10		
WG Ted Williams Patch		
Nomar Garciaparra Base/10		
WM Ted Williams Patch		
Pedro Martinez Patch/10		

2003 SPx Stars Autograph Jersey

Randomly inserted in packs, these cards feature both a game-used jersey swatch as well as an authentic signature. Since these cards were issued in varying print runs, we have notated the stated print run next to their name in our checklist.

SPECTRUM PRINT RUN 1 SERIAL #'d SET		
NO SPECTRUM PRICING DUE TO SCARCITY		
CJ0 Chipper Jones/195	40.00	80.00
CS Curt Schilling/490	12.50	30.00
JG Jason Giambi/315	15.00	40.00
KG Ken Griffey Jr./690	50.00	100.00
LB Lance Berkman/590	12.50	30.00
LG Luis Gonzalez/790	10.00	25.00
MP Mark Prior/490	15.00	40.00
NM Nomar Garciaparra/195	40.00	80.00
PB Pat Burrell/590	10.00	25.00
TG Troy Glaus/490	15.00	40.00
VG Vladimir Guerrero/390	12.50	30.00

2003 SPx Winning Materials 375

LOGO'S CONSECUTIVELY #'d FROM 41-375		
NUMBERS CONSECUTIVELY #'d FROM 1-40		
CARDS CUMULATIVELY SERIAL #'d TO 375		
*WIN.MAT.250: .5X TO 1.2X WIN.MAT.375		
NUMBERS CONSECUTIVELY #'d FROM 1-28		
LOGOS CONSECUTIVELY #'d FROM 29-250		
WM 250 CUMULATIVELY SERIAL #'d TO 250		
LOGO/NUMBER PRINTS PROVIDED BY UD		
AJ1A Andruw Jones Logo	4.00	10.00
AJ1B Andruw Jones Num	8.00	20.00
AP1A Albert Pujols Logo	10.00	25.00
AP1B Albert Pujols Num	20.00	50.00
AR1A Alex Rodriguez Logo	6.00	15.00
AR1B Alex Rodriguez Num	12.50	30.00
AS1A Alfonso Soriano Logo	3.00	8.00
AS1B Alfonso Soriano Num	6.00	15.00
BW1A Bernie Williams Logo	4.00	10.00
BW1B Bernie Williams Num	8.00	20.00
BZ1A Barry Zito Logo	3.00	8.00
BZ1B Barry Zito Num	6.00	15.00
CD1A Carlos Delgado Logo	3.00	8.00
CD1B Carlos Delgado Num	6.00	15.00
CJ1A Chipper Jones Logo	4.00	10.00
CJ1B Chipper Jones Num	8.00	20.00
CS1A Curt Schilling Logo	3.00	8.00
CS1B Curt Schilling Num	6.00	15.00
FT1A Frank Thomas Logo	4.00	10.00
FT1B Frank Thomas Num	8.00	20.00
GM1A Greg Maddux Logo	6.00	15.00
GM1B Greg Maddux Num	12.50	30.00
GS1A Gary Sheffield Logo	3.00	8.00
GS1B Gary Sheffield Num	6.00	15.00
HM1A Hideki Matsui Logo	10.00	25.00
HM1B Hideki Matsui Num	15.00	40.00
HN1A Hideo Nomo Logo	10.00	25.00
HN1B Hideo Nomo Num	20.00	50.00
IR1A Ivan Rodriguez Logo	4.00	10.00
IR1B Ivan Rodriguez Num	8.00	20.00
IS1A Ichiro Suzuki Logo	15.00	40.00
IS1B Ichiro Suzuki Num	40.00	80.00
JB1A Jeff Bagwell Logo	4.00	10.00
JB1B Jeff Bagwell Num	8.00	20.00
JG1A Jason Giambi Logo	3.00	8.00
JG1B Jason Giambi Num	6.00	15.00
JK1A Jeff Kent Logo	3.00	8.00
JK1B Jeff Kent Num	6.00	15.00
JT1A Jim Thome Logo	4.00	10.00
JT1B Jim Thome Num	8.00	20.00
KG1A Ken Griffey Jr. Logo	8.00	20.00
KG1B Ken Griffey Jr. Num	15.00	40.00
LB1A Lance Berkman Logo	3.00	8.00
LB1B Lance Berkman Num	6.00	15.00
LG1A Luis Gonzalez Logo	3.00	8.00
LG1B Luis Gonzalez Num	6.00	15.00
MA1A Mark Prior Logo	4.00	10.00
MA1B Mark Prior Num	8.00	20.00
MP1A Mike Piazza Logo	6.00	15.00
MP1B Mike Piazza Num	12.50	30.00
MR1A Manny Ramirez Logo	4.00	10.00
MR1B Manny Ramirez Num	8.00	20.00
MT1A Miguel Tejada Logo	3.00	8.00
MT1B Miguel Tejada Num	6.00	15.00
PB1A Pat Burrell Logo	3.00	8.00
PB1B Pat Burrell Num	6.00	15.00
PM1A Pedro Martinez Logo	4.00	10.00
PM1B Pedro Martinez Num	8.00	20.00
RA1A Roberto Alomar Logo	4.00	10.00
RA1B Roberto Alomar Num	8.00	20.00
RC1A Roger Clemens Logo	8.00	20.00
RC1B Roger Clemens Num	15.00	40.00
RF1A Rafael Furcal Logo	3.00	8.00
RF1B Rafael Furcal Num	6.00	15.00
RJ1A Randy Johnson Logo	4.00	10.00
RJ1B Randy Johnson Num	8.00	20.00
SG1A Shawn Green Logo	3.00	8.00
SG1B Shawn Green Num	6.00	15.00
SS1A Sammy Sosa Logo	4.00	10.00
SS1B Sammy Sosa Num	8.00	20.00
TG1A Tom Glavine Logo	4.00	10.00
TG1B Tom Glavine Num	8.00	20.00
TH1A Torii Hunter Logo	3.00	8.00
TH1B Torii Hunter Num	6.00	15.00
TO1A Todd Helton Logo	4.00	10.00
TO1B Todd Helton Num	8.00	20.00
TR1A Troy Glaus Logo	3.00	8.00
TR1B Troy Glaus Num	6.00	15.00
VG1A Vladimir Guerrero Logo	4.00	10.00
VG1B Vladimir Guerrero Num	8.00	20.00

2003 SPx Winning Materials 175

NUMBERS CONSECUTIVELY #'d FROM 1-20		
LOGOS CONSECUTIVELY #'d FROM 21-175		
CARDS CUMULATIVELY SERIAL #'d TO 175		
*WM LOGO 50: .75X TO 2X WM LOGO 175		
WM 50 NUMBERS CONSECUTIVELY #'d 1-10		
WM 50 LOGOS CONSECUTIVELY #'d 11-50		
WM 50 CUMULATIVELY SERIAL #'d TO 50		
NO NUMBER PRICING DUE TO SCARCITY		
LOGO/NUMBER PRINTS PROVIDED BY UD		
AJ2A Andruw Jones Logo	5.00	12.00
AP2A Albert Pujols Logo	12.50	30.00
AR2A Alex Rodriguez Logo	8.00	20.00
AS2A Alfonso Soriano Logo	4.00	10.00
BW2A Bernie Williams Logo	5.00	12.00
BZ2A Barry Zito Logo	4.00	10.00
CD2A Carlos Delgado Logo	4.00	10.00
CJ2A Chipper Jones Logo	5.00	12.00
CS2A Curt Schilling Logo	4.00	10.00
FT2A Frank Thomas Logo	5.00	12.00
GM2A Greg Maddux Logo	8.00	20.00
GS2A Gary Sheffield Logo	4.00	10.00
HM2A Hideki Matsui Logo	12.50	30.00
HN2A Hideo Nomo Logo	12.50	30.00
IR2A Ivan Rodriguez Logo	5.00	12.00
IS2A Ichiro Suzuki Logo	20.00	50.00
JB2A Jeff Bagwell Logo	5.00	12.00
JG2A Jason Giambi Logo	4.00	10.00
JK2A Jeff Kent Logo	4.00	10.00
JT2A Jim Thome Logo	5.00	12.00
KG2A Ken Griffey Jr. Logo	10.00	25.00
LB2A Lance Berkman Logo	4.00	10.00
LG2A Luis Gonzalez Logo	4.00	10.00
MM2A M.Mantle Pants Logo	75.00	150.00
MP2RA Mark Prior Logo	5.00	12.00
MP2A Mike Piazza Logo	8.00	20.00
MR2A Manny Ramirez Logo	5.00	12.00
MT2A Miguel Tejada Logo	4.00	10.00
PB2A Pat Burrell Logo	4.00	10.00
PM2A Pedro Martinez Logo	5.00	12.00
RA2A Roberto Alomar Logo	5.00	12.00
RC2A Roger Clemens Logo	10.00	25.00
RF2A Rafael Furcal Logo	4.00	10.00
RJ2A Randy Johnson Logo	5.00	12.00
SG2A Shawn Green Logo	4.00	10.00
SS2A Sammy Sosa Logo	5.00	12.00
TGL2A Troy Glaus Logo	4.00	10.00
TG2A Tom Glavine Logo	5.00	12.00
THE2A Todd Helton Logo	5.00	12.00
TH2A Torii Hunter Logo	4.00	10.00
TW2A T.Williams Pants Logo	40.00	80.00
VG2A Vladimir Guerrero Logo	5.00	12.00

2003 SPx Young Stars Autograph Jersey

20 of the 23 cards within this set were randomly inserted in 2003 SPx packs (released in August, 2003). Serial #'d print runs for the 20 low series cards range between 964-1460 copies each. An additional three cards (all of which are much scarcer with serial #'d print runs of only 355 copies per), were randomly seeded in packs of 2003 Upper Deck Finite of which was released in December, 2003. These cards feature game-used jersey swatches and authentic autographs from each player. Since these cards were issued in varying quantities, we have noted the stated print run next to the player's name in our checklist. Rocco Baldelli did not return his autographs prior to packout thus an exchange card with a redemption deadline of August 15th, 2006 was placed into packs.

SPECTRUM PRINT RUN 25 SERIAL #'d SETS		
NO SPECTRUM PRICING DUE TO SCARCITY		
AD Adam Dunn/1295	10.00	25.00
AK Austin Kearns/964	6.00	15.00
BM Brett Myers/1295	6.00	15.00
BP Brandon Phillips/1295	10.00	25.00
CG Chris George/1260	6.00	15.00
DW Dontrelle Willis/355	12.50	30.00
EH Eric Hinske/1295	6.00	15.00
HB Hank Blalock/1295	6.00	15.00
JA Jason Jennings/1295	6.00	15.00
JBA Josh Bard/1295	6.00	15.00
JJ Jacque Jones/1260	6.00	15.00
JP Josh Phelps/1295	6.00	15.00
KA Kurt Ainsworth/1460	6.00	15.00
KG Khalil Greene/355	20.00	50.00
KS Kirk Saarloos/1295	6.00	15.00
MD Michael Cuddyer/1156	6.00	15.00
MK Mike Kinkade/1295	6.00	15.00
MT Mark Teixeira/1295	12.50	30.00
NJ Nick Johnson/1295	6.00	15.00
RB Rocco Baldelli/1295	6.00	15.00
RH Rich Harden/355	6.00	15.00
RO Roy Oswalt/1295	6.00	15.00
SB Sean Burroughs/1295	6.00	15.00

2004 SPx

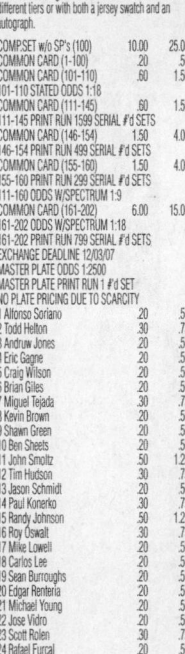

This 202-card set was released in December, 2004. The set was issued in four-card packs with an $7 SRP which came 18 packs to a box and 14 boxes to a case. The first 100 cards of this set feature active veterans while cards 101 through 110 feature retired greats. Cards 111 through 202 feature rookies either issued to different tiers or with both a jersey swatch and an autograph.

COMP.SET w/o SP's (100)	10.00	25.00
COMMON CARD (1-100)	.20	.50
COMMON CARD (101-110)	.60	1.50
101-110 STATED ODDS 1:18		
COMMON CARD (111-145)	.60	1.50
111-145 PRINT RUN 1599 SERIAL #'d SETS		
COMMON CARD (146-154)	1.50	4.00
146-154 PRINT RUN 499 SERIAL #'d SETS		
COMMON CARD (155-160)	1.50	4.00
155-160 PRINT RUN 299 SERIAL #'d SETS		
111-160 ODDS W/SPECTRUM 1:9		
COMMON CARD (161-202)	6.00	15.00
161-202 ODDS W/SPECTRUM 1:18		
161-202 PRINT RUN 799 SERIAL #'d SETS		
EXCHANGE DEADLINE 12/03/07		
MASTER PLATE ODDS 1:2500		
MASTER PLATE PRINT RUN 1 #'d SET		
NO PLATE PRICING DUE TO SCARCITY		
1 Alfonso Soriano	.20	.50
2 Todd Helton	.30	.75
3 Andruw Jones	.20	.50
4 Eric Gagne	.20	.50
5 Craig Wilson	.20	.50
6 Brian Giles	.20	.50
7 Miguel Tejada	.30	.75
8 Kevin Brown	.20	.50
9 Shawn Green	.20	.50
10 Ben Sheets	.20	.50
11 John Smoltz	.50	1.25
12 Tim Hudson	.30	.75
13 Jason Schmidt	.20	.50
14 Paul Konerko	.30	.75
15 Randy Johnson	.50	1.25
16 Roy Oswalt	.30	.75
17 Mike Lowell	.20	.50
18 Carlos Lee	.20	.50
19 Sean Burroughs	.20	.50
20 Edgar Renteria	.20	.50
21 Michael Young	.20	.50
22 Jose Vidro	.20	.50
23 Scott Rolen	.30	.75
24 Rafael Furcal	.20	.50
25 Tom Glavine	.30	.75
26 Scott Podsednik	.20	.50
27 Gary Sheffield	.20	.50
28 Eric Chavez	.20	.50
29 Mark Prior	.30	.75
30 Chipper Jones	.50	1.25
31 Frank Thomas	.50	1.25
32 Victor Martinez	.30	.75
33 Jake Peavy	.20	.50
34 Carlos Beltran	.20	.50
35 Roy Halladay	.50	1.25
36 Mark Teixeira	.50	1.25
37 Jacque Jones	.20	.50
38 Mike Sweeney	.20	.50
39 Troy Glaus	.20	.50
40 Pat Burrell	.20	.50
41 Ichiro Suzuki	.75	2.00
42 Vladimir Guerrero	.50	1.25
43 Bobby Abreu	.20	.50
44 Jim Edmonds	.30	.75
45 Garret Anderson	.20	.50
46 J.D. Drew	.20	.50
47 C.C. Sabathia	.30	.75
48 Joe Mauer	.50	1.25
49 Phil Nevin	.20	.50
50 Hank Blalock	.20	.50
51 Carlos Zambrano	.30	.75
52 Mike Piazza	.50	1.25
53 Manny Ramirez	.50	1.25
54 Lance Berkman	.30	.75
55 Delmon Young	.30	.75
56 Nomar Garciaparra	.50	1.25
57 Alex Rodriguez	.75	2.00
58 Rickie Weeks	.20	.50
59 Adrian Beltre	.20	.50
60 Albert Pujols	1.25	3.00
61 Richie Sexson	.20	.50
62 Magglio Ordonez	.30	.75
63 Derrek Lee	.20	.50
64 Sammy Sosa	.50	1.25
65 Jason Giambi	.20	.50
66 Curt Schilling	.30	.75
67 Jorge Posada	.30	.75
68 Rafael Palmeiro	.30	.75
69 Jeff Kent	.20	.50
70 Jose Reyes	.30	.75
71 David Ortiz	.50	1.25
72 Aubrey Huff	.20	.50
73 Jim Thome	.30	.75
74 Andy Pettitte	.30	.75
75 Barry Zito	.20	.50
76 Carlos Delgado	.20	.50
77 Hideki Matsui	.75	2.00
78 Sean Casey	.20	.50
79 Luis Gonzalez	.20	.50
80 Marcus Giles	.20	.50
81 Preston Wilson	.20	.50
82 Javy Lopez	.20	.50
83 Mark Mulder	.20	.50
84 Derek Jeter	1.25	3.00
85 Miguel Cabrera	.50	1.25
86 Vernon Wells	.20	.50
87 Roger Clemens	.60	1.50
88 Lyle Overbay	.20	.50
89 Bret Boone	.20	.50
90 Melvin Mora	.20	.50
91 Greg Maddux	.75	2.00
92 Kerry Wood	.20	.50
93 Ivan Rodriguez	.30	.75
94 Pedro Martinez	.30	.75
95 Jeff Bagwell	.30	.75
96 Torii Hunter	.20	.50
97 Ken Griffey Jr.	.75	2.00
98 Mike Mussina	.30	.75
99 Oliver Perez	.20	.50
100 Josh Beckett	.30	.75
101 Bob Gibson LGD	1.00	2.50
102 Cal Ripken LGD	6.00	15.00
103 Ted Williams LGD	4.00	10.00
104 Nolan Ryan LGD	5.00	12.00
105 Mickey Mantle LGD	5.00	12.00
106 Ernie Banks LGD	1.50	4.00
107 Joe DiMaggio LGD	4.00	10.00
108 Stan Musial LGD	2.50	6.00
109 Tom Seaver LGD	1.00	2.50
110 Mike Schmidt LGD	2.50	6.00
111 Jerry Gil T1 RC	.60	1.50
112 Dioner Navarro T1 RC	1.00	2.50
113 Bartolome Fortunato T1 RC	.60	1.50
114 Carlos Hines T1 RC	.60	1.50
115 Franklyn Gracesqui T1 RC	.60	1.50
116 Aarom Baldiris T1 RC	.60	1.50
117 Casey Daigle T1 RC	.60	1.50
118 Joey Gathright T1 RC	.60	1.50
119 William Bergolla T1 RC	.60	1.50
120 Jeff Bennett T1 RC	.60	1.50
121 Lincoln Holdzkom T1 RC	.60	1.50
122 Jorge Vasquez T1 RC	.60	1.50
123 Donnie Kelly T1 RC	1.00	2.50
124 Yadier Molina T1 RC	4.00	10.00
125 Ryan Wing T1 RC	.60	1.50
126 Justin Germano T1 RC	.60	1.50
127 Freddy Guzman T1 RC	.60	1.50
128 Onil Joseph T1 RC	.60	1.50
129 Roman Colon T1 RC	.60	1.50
130 Roberto Novoa T1 RC	.60	1.50
131 Renyel Pinto T1 RC	.60	1.50
132 Evan Rust T1 RC	.60	1.50
133 Orlando Rodriguez T1 RC	.60	1.50
134 Edwardo Sierra T1 RC	.60	1.50
135 Mike Rose T1 RC	.60	1.50
136 Phil Stockman T1 RC	.60	1.50
137 Greg Dobbs T1 RC	.60	1.50
138 Brad Halsey T1 RC	.60	1.50
139 David Aardsma T1 RC	.60	1.50
140 Joe Hietpas T1 RC	.60	1.50
141 Josh Labandeira T1 RC	.60	1.50
142 Mariano Gomez T1 RC	.60	1.50
143 Jeff Bajenaru T1 RC	.60	1.50
144 Travis Blackley T1 RC	.60	1.50
145 Abe Alvarez T1 RC	.60	1.50
146 Ramon Ramirez T2 RC	1.50	4.00
147 Edwin Moreno T2 RC	1.50	4.00
148 Ronny Cedeno T2 RC	1.50	4.00
149 Hector Gimenez T2 RC	1.50	4.00
150 Carlos Vasquez T2 RC	1.50	4.00
151 Jesse Crain T2 RC	1.50	4.00
152 Logan Kensing T2 RC	1.50	4.00
153 Sean Henn T2 RC	1.50	4.00
154 Rusty Tucker T2 RC	1.50	4.00
155 Justin Lehr T3 RC	1.50	4.00
156 Ian Snell T3 RC	1.50	4.00
157 Merkin Valdez T3 RC	1.50	4.00
158 Scott Proctor T3 RC	1.50	4.00
159 Jose Capellan T3 RC	1.50	4.00
160 Kazuo Matsui T3 RC	2.50	6.00
161 Chris Oxspring AU JSY RC	6.00	15.00

162 Jimmy Serrano AU JSY RC 6.00 15.00
163 Jeff Keppinger AU JSY RC 8.00 20.00
164 B.Medders AU JSY RC 6.00 15.00
165 Brian Dallimore AU JSY RC 6.00 15.00
166 Chad Bentz AU JSY RC 6.00 15.00
167 Chris Aguila AU JSY RC 6.00 15.00
168 Chris Saenz AU JSY RC 6.00 15.00
169 Frank Francisco AU JSY RC 6.00 15.00
170 Colby Miller AU JSY RC 6.00 15.00
172 Charles Thomas AU JSY RC 6.00 15.00
173 Dennis Sarfate AU JSY RC 6.00 15.00
174 Lance Cormier AU JSY RC 6.00 15.00
175 Joe Horgan AU JSY RC 6.00 15.00
176 Fernando Nieve AU JSY RC 6.00 15.00
177 Jake Woods AU JSY RC 6.00 15.00
178 Matt Treanor AU JSY RC 6.00 15.00
179 Jerome Gamble AU JSY RC 6.00 15.00
180 John Gall AU JSY RC 10.00 25.00
181 Jorge Sequea AU JSY RC 6.00 15.00
182 Justin Hampson AU JSY RC 6.00 15.00
183 Justin Huisman AU JSY RC 6.00 15.00
184 Justin Knoedler AU JSY RC 6.00 15.00
185 Justin Leone AU JSY RC 10.00 25.00
186 Scott Atchison AU JSY RC 6.00 15.00
187 Jon Knott AU JSY RC 6.00 15.00
188 Kevin Cave AU JSY RC 6.00 15.00
189 Jason Frasor AU JSY RC 6.00 15.00
190 George Sherrill AU JSY RC 6.00 15.00
191 Mike Gosling AU JSY RC 6.00 15.00
192 Mike Johnston AU JSY RC 6.00 15.00
193 Mike Rouse AU JSY RC 6.00 15.00
194 Nick Regilio AU JSY RC 6.00 15.00
195 Ryan Meaux AU JSY RC 6.00 15.00
196 Scott Dohmann AU JSY RC 6.00 15.00
197 Shawn Camp AU JSY RC 6.00 15.00
198 Shawn Hill AU JSY RC 6.00 15.00
199 Shingo Takatsu AU JSY RC 6.00 15.00
200 Tim Bausher AU JSY RC 6.00 15.00
201 Tim Bittner AU JSY RC 6.00 15.00
202 Scott Kazmir AU JSY RC 12.50 30.00

2004 SPx Spectrum

*SPEC 1-100: 6X TO 15X BASIC
*SPEC 101-110: 2X TO 5X
1-110 STATED ODDS 1:252
111-160 W/BASIC OVERALL ODDS 1:9
161-202 W/BASIC OVERALL ODDS 1:18
STATED PRINT RUN 25 SERIAL #'d SETS
111-202 NO PRICING DUE TO SCARCITY
EXCHANGE DEADLINE 12/03/07

2004 SPx SuperScripts Rookies

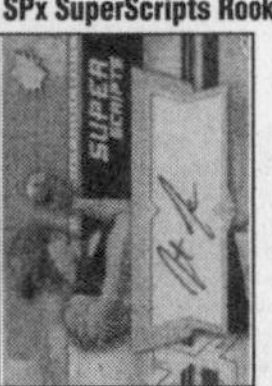

OVERALL SUPERSCRIPT ODDS 1:18
EXCHANGE DEADLINE 12/03/07
AS Alfredo Simon 4.00 10.00
CH Carlos Hines 4.00 10.00
CV Carlos Vasquez 6.00 15.00
DK Donnie Kelly 10.00 25.00
ES Edwardo Sierra 6.00 15.00
IO Ivan Ochoa 4.00 10.00
IS Ian Snell 8.00 20.00
JL Justin Lehr 4.00 10.00
LA Josh Labandeira 4.00 10.00
LH Lincoln Holdzkom 4.00 10.00
MG Mariano Gomez 4.00 10.00
MV Merkin Valdez 4.00 10.00
PS Phil Stockman 4.00 10.00
RR Ramon Ramirez 4.00 10.00
RU Evan Rust 4.00 10.00
SH Sean Henn 4.00 10.00
SP Scott Proctor 6.00 15.00
VE Michael Vento 6.00 15.00

2004 SPx SuperScripts Stars

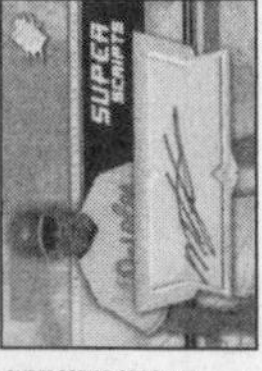

OVERALL SUPERSCRIPT ODDS 1:18
SP INFO PROVIDED BY UPPER DECK
AP Albert Pujols SP 150.00 250.00
CR Cal Ripken SP 75.00 150.00
DJ Derek Jeter SP 125.00 200.00
EC Eric Chavez 10.00 25.00
JB Josh Beckett 8.00 20.00
KG Ken Griffey Jr. 40.00 80.00
MP Mark Prior 15.00 40.00
NG Nomar Garciaparra SP 50.00 100.00
NR Nolan Ryan SP
TE Miguel Tejada 15.00 40.00

2004 SPx SuperScripts Young Stars

OVERALL SUPERSCRIPT ODDS 1:18
BC Bobby Crosby 6.00 15.00
BW Brandon Webb 6.00 15.00
DW Dontrelle Willis 6.00 15.00
DY Delmon Young 12.50 30.00

EJ Edwin Jackson 5.00 12.00
JM Joe Mauer 20.00 50.00
JR Jose Reyes 10.00 25.00
MC Miguel Cabrera 10.00 25.00
MT Mark Teixeira 10.00 25.00
RH Rich Harden 6.00 15.00
RO Roy Oswalt 6.00 15.00
RW Rickie Weeks 6.00 15.00

2004 SPx Swatch Supremacy Signatures Stars

STATED PRINT RUN 275 SERIAL #'d SETS
*SPECTRUM: .75X TO 1.5X BASIC
SPECTRUM PRINT RUN 25 #'d SETS
OVERALL SWATCH SUP.ODDS 1:18
AP Albert Pujols 100.00 200.00
CR Cal Ripken 75.00 150.00
DJ Derek Jeter 100.00 200.00
DL Derrek Lee 15.00 40.00
EC Eric Chavez 10.00 25.00
GA Garret Anderson 10.00 25.00
KG Ken Griffey Jr. 50.00 100.00
MP Mark Prior 15.00 40.00
NG Nomar Garciaparra 15.00 40.00
NR Nolan Ryan 60.00 120.00

2004 SPx Swatch Supremacy Signatures Young Stars

STATED PRINT RUN 999 SERIAL #'d SETS
*SPECTRUM: .75X TO 1.5X BASIC
SPECTRUM PRINT RUN 25 #'d SETS
OVERALL SWATCH SUP.ODDS 1:18
AB Angel Berroa 6.00 15.00
AE Adam Eaton 6.00 15.00
BC Bobby Crosby 6.00 15.00
BS Ben Sheets 6.00 15.00
BW Brandon Webb 6.00 15.00
CC Chad Cordero 6.00 15.00
CK Casey Kotchman 10.00 25.00
CL Cliff Lee 12.50 30.00
CP Corey Patterson 6.00 15.00
DW Dontrelle Willis 6.00 15.00
GR Khalil Greene 15.00 40.00
HB Hank Blalock 10.00 25.00
HR Horacio Ramirez 6.00 15.00
JB Josh Beckett 10.00 25.00
JM Joe Mauer 15.00 40.00
JP Jake Peavy 10.00 25.00
JR Jose Reyes 15.00 40.00
JW Jerome Williams 6.00 15.00
LO Lyle Overbay 6.00 15.00
MC Miguel Cabrera 12.50 30.00
MG Marcus Giles 10.00 25.00
MT Mark Teixeira 10.00 25.00
MY Michael Young 10.00 25.00
RB Rocco Baldelli 6.00 15.00
RH Rich Harden 6.00 15.00
RO Roy Oswalt 6.00 15.00
RW Rickie Weeks 10.00 25.00
SB Sean Burroughs 6.00 15.00
SP Scott Podsednik 15.00 40.00

2004 SPx Winning Materials Dual Jersey

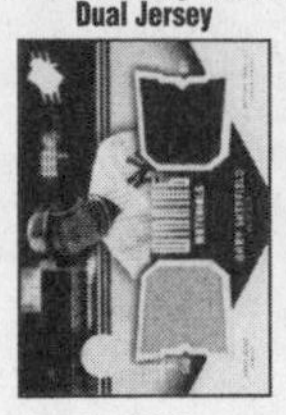

*SPECTRUM: .6X TO 1.5X BASIC
SPECTRUM PRINT RUN 25 #'d SETS
OVERALL WINNING MTL.ODDS 1:18
ALL HAVE GAME-WORN & BP SWATCHES
AP Albert Pujols 15.00 40.00
BE Josh Beckett 4.00 10.00
CD Carlos Delgado 4.00 10.00
CJ Chipper Jones 6.00 15.00
DJ Derek Jeter 8.00 20.00
EC Eric Chavez 4.00 10.00
GM Greg Maddux 10.00 25.00
GS Gary Sheffield 4.00 10.00
HB Hank Blalock 4.00 10.00
HM Hideki Matsui 20.00 50.00
IS Ichiro Suzuki 20.00 50.00
JB Jeff Bagwell 6.00 15.00
JG Jason Giambi 4.00 10.00
JP Jorge Posada 6.00 15.00
JR Jose Reyes 4.00 10.00
JT Jim Thome 6.00 15.00
KB Kevin Brown 4.00 10.00
MM Mike Mussina 6.00 15.00
MP Mark Prior 6.00 15.00
MR Manny Ramirez 6.00 15.00
PI Mike Piazza 10.00 25.00
RC Roger Clemens 10.00 25.00
RP Rafael Palmeiro 6.00 15.00
SG Shawn Green 4.00 10.00
SR Scott Rolen 6.00 15.00

SS Sammy Sosa 6.00 15.00
TE Miguel Tejada 4.00 10.00
TG Troy Glaus 4.00 10.00
VG Vladimir.Guerrero 6.00 15.00

2005 SPx

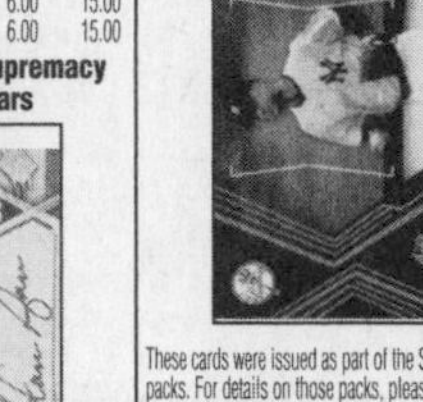

These cards were issued as part of the SP Collection packs. For details on those packs, please see the write-up for SP Authentic.

COMP.BASIC SET (100) 10.00 25.00
COMMON CARD (1-100) .15 .40
COMMON RC (1-100) .25 .60
1-100 ISSUED IN 05 SP COLLECTION PACKS
COMMON AUTO (101-180) 4.00 10.00
101-180 ODDS APPX 1:8 '05 UD UPDATE
101-180 PRINT RUN 185 SERIAL #'d SETS
105, 117, 139, 149, 155, 172 DO NOT EXIST
175, 178, 180 DO NOT EXIST
1 Aaron Harang .15 .40
2 Aaron Rowand .15 .40
3 Aaron Miles .15 .40
4 Adrian Gonzalez .25 .60
5 Alex Rios .25 .60
6 Angel Berroa .15 .40
7 B.J. Upton .25 .60
8 Brandon Claussen .15 .40
9 Andy Marte .25 .60
10 Brandon Webb .25 .60
11 Bronson Arroyo .15 .40
12 Casey Kotchman .15 .40
13 Cesar Izturis .15 .40
14 Chad Cordero .15 .40
15 Chad Tracy .15 .40
16 Charles Thomas .15 .40
17 Chase Utley .25 .60
18 Chone Figgins .15 .40
19 Chris Burke .15 .40
20 Cliff Lee .25 .60
21 Clint Barmes .15 .40
22 Coco Crisp .15 .40
23 Bill Hall .15 .40
24 Dallas McPherson .15 .40
25 Brad Halsey .15 .40
26 Daniel Cabrera .15 .40
27 Danny Haren .15 .40
28 Dave Bush .15 .40
29 David DeJesus .15 .40
30 D.J. Houlton RC .25 .60
31 Derek Jeter 1.00 2.50
32 Dewon Brazelton .15 .40
33 Edwin Jackson .15 .40
34 Brad Hawpe .15 .40
35 Brandon Inge .15 .40
36 Brett Myers .15 .40
37 Garrett Atkins .15 .40
38 Gavin Floyd .15 .40
39 Grady Sizemore .25 .60
40 Guillermo Mota .15 .40
41 Carlos Guillen .15 .40
42 Gustavo Chacin .15 .40
43 Huston Street .15 .40
44 Chris Duffy .15 .40
45 J.D. Closser .15 .40
46 J.J. Hardy .15 .40
47 Jason Bartlett .15 .40
48 Jason DuBois .15 .40
49 Chris Shelton .15 .40
50 Jason Lane .15 .40
51 Jayson Werth .25 .60
52 Jeff Baker .15 .40
53 Jeff Francis .15 .40
54 Jeremy Bonderman .15 .40
55 Jeremy Reed .15 .40
56 Jerome Williams .15 .40
57 Jesse Crain .15 .40
58 Chris Young .25 .60
59 Jhonny Peralta .15 .40
60 Joe Blanton .15 .40
61 Joe Crede .15 .40
62 Joel Pineiro .15 .40
63 Joey Gathright .15 .40
64 John Buck .15 .40
65 Jonny Gomes .15 .40
66 Jorge Cantu .15 .40
67 Dan Johnson .15 .40
68 Jose Valverde .15 .40
69 Ervin Santana .15 .40
70 Justin Morneau .40 1.00
71 Keiichi Yabu RC .25 .60
72 Ken Griffey Jr. .60 1.50
73 Jason Repko .15 .40
74 Kevin Youkilis .15 .40
75 Koyie Hill .15 .40
76 Laynce Nix .15 .40
77 Luke Scott RC .60 1.50
78 Juan Rivera .15 .40
79 Justin Duchscherer .15 .40
80 Mark Teahen .15 .40
81 Lance Niekro .15 .40
82 Michael Cuddyer .15 .40
83 Nick Swisher .40 1.00
84 Noah Lowry .15 .40
85 Matt Holliday .40 1.00
86 Reed Johnson .15 .40
87 Rich Harden .15 .40
88 Robb Quinlan .15 .40
89 Nick Johnson .15 .40
90 Ryan Howard .75 2.00
91 Nook Logan .15 .40
92 Steve Schmoll RC .25 .60
93 Tadahito Iguchi RC .40 1.00
94 Willy Taveras .15 .40
95 Wily Mo Pena .15 .40
96 Xavier Nady .15 .40
97 Yadier Molina .25 .60
98 Yhency Brazoban .15 .40
99 Ryan Freel .15 .40
100 Zack Greinke .25 .60
101 Adam Shabala AU RC 4.00 10.00
102 Ambiorix Burgos AU RC 4.00 10.00
103 Ambiorix Concepcion AU RC 4.00 10.00
104 Anibal Sanchez AU RC 15.00 40.00
106 Brandon McCarthy AU RC 12.50 30.00
107 Brian Burres AU RC 4.00 10.00
108 Carlos Ruiz AU RC 10.00 25.00
109 Casey Rogowski AU RC 6.00 15.00
110 Chad Orvella AU RC 4.00 10.00
111 Chris Resop AU RC 6.00 15.00
112 Chris Roberson AU RC 4.00 10.00
113 Chris Seddon AU RC 4.00 10.00
114 Colter Bean AU RC 6.00 15.00
115 Dave Gassner AU RC 4.00 10.00
116 Brian Anderson AU RC 15.00 40.00
118 Devon Lowery AU RC 4.00 10.00
119 Enrique Gonzalez AU RC 6.00 15.00
120 Eude Brito AU RC 4.00 10.00
121 Francisco Butto AU RC 4.00 10.00
122 Franquelis Osoria AU RC 4.00 10.00
123 Garrett Jones AU RC 30.00 60.00
124 Geovany Soto AU RC 60.00 120.00
125 Hayden Penn AU RC 8.00 20.00
126 Ismael Ramirez AU RC 4.00 10.00
127 Jared Gothreaux AU RC 4.00 10.00
128 Jason Hammel AU RC 4.00 10.00
129 Jeff Miller AU RC 4.00 10.00
130 Jeff Niemann AU RC 12.50 30.00
131 Joel Peralta AU RC 4.00 10.00
132 John Hattig AU RC 4.00 10.00
133 Jorge Campillo AU RC 4.00 10.00
134 Juan Morillo AU RC 4.00 10.00
135 Justin Verlander AU RC 90.00 150.00
136 Ryan Garko AU RC 15.00 40.00
137 Kendry Morales AU RC 30.00 60.00
138 Luis Hernandez AU RC 4.00 10.00
140 Luis O.Rodriguez AU RC 4.00 10.00
141 Mark Woodyard AU RC 4.00 10.00
142 Matt A.Smith AU RC 4.00 10.00
143 Matthew Lindstrom AU RC 4.00 10.00
144 Miguel Negron AU RC 6.00 15.00
145 Mike Morse AU RC 15.00 40.00
146 Nate McLouth AU RC 20.00 50.00
147 Nelson Cruz AU RC 30.00 60.00
148 Nick Masset AU RC 4.00 10.00
150 Paulino Reynoso AU RC 4.00 10.00
151 Pedro Lopez AU RC 4.00 10.00
152 Philip Humber AU RC 12.50 30.00
153 Prince Fielder AU RC 75.00 150.00
154 Randy Messenger AU RC 4.00 10.00
156 Raul Tablado AU RC 4.00 10.00
157 Ronny Paulino AU RC 6.00 15.00
158 Russ Rohlicek AU RC 4.00 10.00
159 Russell Martin AU RC 30.00 60.00
160 Scott Baker AU RC 6.00 15.00
161 Scott Munter AU RC 4.00 10.00
162 Sean Thompson AU RC 4.00 10.00
163 Sean Tracey AU RC 4.00 10.00
164 Shane Costa AU RC 4.00 10.00
165 Stephen Drew AU RC 30.00 60.00
166 Tony Giarratano AU RC 4.00 10.00
167 Tony Pena AU RC 4.00 10.00
168 Travis Bowyer AU RC 4.00 10.00
169 Ubaldo Jimenez AU RC 10.00 25.00
170 Wladimir Balentien AU RC 40.00 80.00
171 Yorman Bazardo AU RC 4.00 10.00
173 Ryan Zimmerman AU RC 60.00 120.00
174 Chris Denorfia AU RC 6.00 15.00
176 Jermaine Van Buren AU 4.00 10.00
177 Mark McLemore AU RC 4.00 10.00
179 Ryan Speier AU RC 4.00 10.00

2005 SPx Silver

APPX AU ODDS 1:8 '05 UD UPDATE
STATED PRINT RUN 10 SERIAL #'d SETS
NO PRICING DUE TO SCARCITY

2005 SPx Jersey

STATED PRINT RUN 199 SERIAL #'d SETS
*SPECTRUM: .5X TO 1.2X BASIC
SPECTRUM PRINT RUN 99 SERIAL #'d SETS
ISSUED IN 05 SP COLLECTION PACKS
OVERALL GAME-USED ODDS 1:10
1 Aaron Harang 2.00 5.00
2 Aaron Rowand 2.00 5.00
3 Aaron Miles 2.00 5.00
4 Adrian Gonzalez 2.00 5.00
5 Alex Rios 2.00 5.00
6 Angel Berroa 2.00 5.00
7 B.J. Upton 2.00 5.00
8 Brandon Claussen 2.00 5.00
9 Andy Marte 2.00 5.00
10 Brandon Webb 2.00 5.00
11 Bronson Arroyo 2.00 5.00
12 Casey Kotchman 2.00 5.00
13 Cesar Izturis 2.00 5.00
14 Chad Cordero 2.00 5.00
15 Chad Tracy 2.00 5.00
16 Charles Thomas 2.00 5.00
17 Chase Utley 3.00 8.00
18 Chone Figgins 2.00 5.00
19 Chris Burke 2.00 5.00
20 Cliff Lee 2.00 5.00
21 Clint Barmes 2.00 5.00
22 Coco Crisp 2.00 5.00
23 Bill Hall 2.00 5.00
24 Dallas McPherson 2.00 5.00
25 Brad Halsey 2.00 5.00
26 Daniel Cabrera 2.00 5.00
27 Danny Haren 2.00 5.00
28 Dave Bush 2.00 5.00
29 David DeJesus 2.00 5.00
30 D.J. Houlton 2.00 5.00
31 Derek Jeter Pants 8.00 20.00
32 Dewon Brazelton 2.00 5.00
33 Edwin Jackson 2.00 5.00
34 Brad Hawpe 2.00 5.00
35 Brandon Inge 2.00 5.00
36 Brett Myers 2.00 5.00
37 Garrett Atkins 2.00 5.00
38 Gavin Floyd 2.00 5.00
39 Grady Sizemore 3.00 8.00
40 Guillermo Mota 2.00 5.00
41 Carlos Guillen 2.00 5.00
42 Gustavo Chacin 2.00 5.00
43 Huston Street 3.00 8.00
44 Chris Duffy 2.00 5.00
45 J.D. Closser 2.00 5.00
46 J.J. Hardy 2.00 5.00
47 Jason Bartlett 2.00 5.00
48 Jason DuBois 2.00 5.00
49 Chris Shelton 4.00 10.00
50 Jason Lane 2.00 5.00
51 Jayson Werth 2.00 5.00
52 Jeff Baker 2.00 5.00
53 Jeff Francis 2.00 5.00
54 Jeremy Bonderman 2.00 5.00
55 Jeremy Reed 2.00 5.00
56 Jerome Williams 2.00 5.00
57 Jesse Crain 2.00 5.00
58 Chris Young 2.00 5.00
59 Jhonny Peralta 2.00 5.00
60 Joe Blanton 2.00 5.00
61 Joe Crede 2.00 5.00
62 Joel Pineiro 2.00 5.00
63 Joey Gathright 2.00 5.00
64 John Buck 2.00 5.00
65 Jonny Gomes 2.00 5.00
66 Jorge Cantu 2.00 5.00
67 Dan Johnson 2.00 5.00
68 Jose Valverde 2.00 5.00
69 Ervin Santana 2.00 5.00
70 Justin Morneau 2.00 5.00
71 Keiichi Yabu 2.00 5.00
72 Ken Griffey Jr. 6.00 15.00
73 Jason Repko 2.00 5.00
74 Kevin Youkilis 2.00 5.00
75 Koyie Hill 2.00 5.00
76 Laynce Nix 2.00 5.00
77 Luke Scott 4.00 10.00
78 Juan Rivera 2.00 5.00
79 Justin Duchscherer 2.00 5.00
80 Mark Teahen 2.00 5.00
81 Lance Niekro 2.00 5.00
82 Michael Cuddyer 2.00 5.00
83 Nick Swisher 2.00 5.00
84 Noah Lowry 2.00 5.00
85 Matt Holliday 2.50 6.00
86 Reed Johnson 2.00 5.00
87 Rich Harden 2.00 5.00
88 Robb Quinlan 2.00 5.00
89 Nick Johnson 2.00 5.00
90 Ryan Howard 10.00 25.00
91 Nook Logan 2.00 5.00
92 Steve Schmoll 2.00 5.00
93 Tadahito Iguchi 12.50 30.00
94 Willy Taveras 2.00 5.00
95 Wily Mo Pena 2.00 5.00
96 Xavier Nady 2.00 5.00
97 Yadier Molina 2.00 5.00
98 Yhency Brazoban 2.00 5.00
99 Ryan Freel 2.00 5.00
100 Zack Greinke 2.00 5.00

2005 SPx Signature

PRINT RUNS B/WN 50-350 COPIES PER
SPECTRUM PRINT RUN 10 SERIAL #'d SETS
NO SPECTRUM PRICING DUE TO SCARCITY
OVERALL AUTO ODDS 1:10
1 Aaron Harang/350 6.00 15.00
2 Aaron Rowand/150 10.00 25.00
4 Adrian Gonzalez/225 10.00 25.00
6 Angel Berroa/150 4.00 10.00
7 B.J. Upton/50 8.00 20.00
8 Brandon Claussen/350 4.00 10.00
9 Andy Marte/350 6.00 15.00
11 Bronson Arroyo/350 6.00 15.00
12 Casey Kotchman/225 6.00 15.00
13 Cesar Izturis/150 4.00 10.00
14 Chad Cordero/350 6.00 15.00
15 Chad Tracy/350 4.00 10.00
16 Charles Thomas/350 4.00 10.00
17 Chase Utley/50 20.00 50.00
18 Chone Figgins/150 6.00 15.00
19 Chris Burke/350 4.00 10.00
20 Cliff Lee/225 12.50 30.00
21 Clint Barmes/350 6.00 15.00
22 Coco Crisp/225 10.00 25.00
23 Bill Hall/350 4.00 10.00
24 Dallas McPherson/150 4.00 10.00
25 Brad Halsey/350 4.00 10.00
26 Daniel Cabrera/350 4.00 10.00
27 Danny Haren/225 4.00 10.00
28 Dave Bush/350 4.00 10.00
29 David DeJesus/225 4.00 10.00
30 D.J. Houlton/350 4.00 10.00
31 Derek Jeter/50 90.00 150.00
32 Dewon Brazelton/225 4.00 10.00
33 Edwin Jackson/150 4.00 10.00
34 Brad Hawpe/350 10.00 25.00
35 Brandon Inge/350 4.00 10.00
36 Brett Myers/150 6.00 15.00
37 Garrett Atkins/350 4.00 10.00
38 Gavin Floyd/150 4.00 10.00
39 Grady Sizemore/350 12.50 30.00
40 Guillermo Mota/225 4.00 10.00
41 Carlos Guillen/150 6.00 15.00
42 Gustavo Chacin/350 6.00 15.00
43 Huston Street/350 10.00 25.00
44 Chris Duffy/225 4.00 10.00
45 J.D. Closser/350 4.00 10.00
46 J.J. Hardy/350 20.00 50.00
47 Jason Bartlett/350 4.00 10.00
48 Jason DuBois/350 4.00 10.00
50 Jason Lane/350 4.00 10.00
51 Jayson Werth/350 4.00 10.00
52 Jeff Baker/350 4.00 10.00
53 Jeff Francis/150 4.00 10.00
54 Jeremy Bonderman/50 8.00 20.00
55 Jeremy Reed/150 6.00 15.00
56 Jerome Williams/50 8.00 20.00
57 Jesse Crain/350 4.00 10.00
59 Jhonny Peralta/350 6.00 15.00
60 Joe Blanton/350 4.00 10.00
61 Joe Crede/350 10.00 25.00
62 Joel Pineiro/150 6.00 15.00
63 Joey Gathright/350 4.00 10.00
64 John Buck/350 4.00 10.00
65 Jonny Gomes/350 6.00 15.00
66 Jorge Cantu/350 6.00 15.00
67 Dan Johnson/350 6.00 15.00
68 Jose Valverde/350 4.00 10.00
69 Ervin Santana/350 6.00 15.00
70 Justin Morneau/50 8.00 20.00
71 Keiichi Yabu/350 6.00 15.00
73 Jason Repko/350 10.00 25.00
74 Kevin Youkilis/225 8.00 20.00
75 Koyie Hill/350 4.00 10.00
76 Laynce Nix/150 4.00 10.00
77 Luke Scott/350 20.00 50.00
78 Juan Rivera/225 4.00 10.00
79 Justin Duchscherer/350 4.00 10.00
80 Mark Teahen/350 4.00 10.00
81 Lance Niekro/350 4.00 10.00
82 Michael Cuddyer/350 4.00 10.00
84 Noah Lowry/150 6.00 15.00
85 Matt Holliday/225 6.00 15.00
86 Reed Johnson/350 4.00 10.00
88 Robb Quinlan/350 4.00 10.00
89 Nick Johnson/150 6.00 15.00
90 Ryan Howard/225 20.00 50.00
91 Nook Logan/350 4.00 10.00
92 Steve Schmoll/350 4.00 10.00
93 Tadahito Iguchi/50 125.00 200.00
95 Wily Mo Pena/150 6.00 15.00
96 Xavier Nady/150 4.00 10.00
98 Yhency Brazoban/350 4.00 10.00
100 Zack Greinke/150 10.00 25.00

2005 SPx Signature Jersey Spectrum

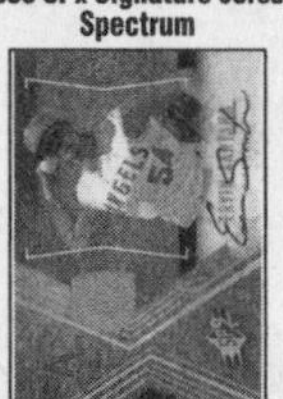

ISSUED IN 05 SP COLLECTION PACKS
OVERALL PREMIUM AU-GU ODDS 1:20
STATED PRINT RUN 10 SERIAL #'d SETS
NO PRICING DUE TO SCARCITY

2005 SPx SPxtreme Stats

ISSUED IN 05 SP COLLECTION PACKS
OVERALL INSERT ODDS 1:10
STATED PRINT RUN 299 SERIAL #'d SETS
AB Adrian Beltre .60 1.50
AD Adam Dunn 1.00 2.50
AJ Andruw Jones .60 1.50
AP Albert Pujols 4.00 10.00
AR Aramis Ramirez .60 1.50
BA Bobby Abreu .60 1.50
BC Bobby Crosby .60 1.50
BS Ben Sheets .60 1.50
CB Craig Biggio 1.00 2.50
CC Carl Crawford 1.00 2.50
CP Corey Patterson .60 1.50
CZ Carlos Zambrano 1.00 2.50
DJ Derek Jeter 4.00 10.00
DL Derrek Lee .60 1.50
DO David Ortiz 1.50 4.00
DW David Wright 2.50 6.00
EC Eric Chavez .60 1.50
EG Eric Gagne .60 1.50
ER Edgar Renteria .60 1.50
GM Greg Maddux 2.50 6.00
GR Khalil Greene .60 1.50
GS Gary Sheffield .60 1.50
HB Hank Blalock .60 1.50
HU Torii Hunter .60 1.50
JD J.D. Drew .60 1.50
JM Joe Mauer 1.50 4.00
JP Jake Peavy .60 1.50
JR Jose Reyes 1.00 2.50
KG Ken Griffey Jr. 2.50 6.00
KW Kerry Wood .60 1.50
MC Miguel Cabrera 1.50 4.00
MM Mark Mulder .60 1.50
MO Melvin Mora .60 1.50
MP Mark Prior 1.00 2.50
MT Mark Teixeria 1.50 4.00
MY Michael Young 1.00 2.50
OP Oliver Perez .60 1.50
PI Mike Piazza 1.50 4.00
RC Roger Clemens 2.00 5.00
RJ Randy Johnson 1.50 4.00
RO Roy Oswalt 1.00 2.50
RP Rafael Palmeiro 1.00 2.50
SA Johan Santana 1.50 4.00
SC Sean Casey .60 1.50
SM John Smoltz 1.50 4.00
SR Scott Rolen 1.00 2.50
TE Miguel Tejada 1.00 2.50
TH Tim Hudson 1.00 2.50
VG Vladimir Guerrero 1.50 4.00
VM Victor Martinez 1.00 2.50

2005 SPx SPxtreme Stats Jersey

ISSUED IN 05 SP COLLECTION PACKS
OVERALL PREMIUM AU-GU ODDS 1:20
STATED PRINT RUN 130 SERIAL #'d SETS
AB Adrian Beltre 2.00 5.00
AD Adam Dunn 2.00 5.00
AJ Andruw Jones 3.00 8.00
AP Albert Pujols 6.00 15.00
AR Aramis Ramirez 2.00 5.00
BA Bobby Abreu 2.00 5.00
BC Bobby Crosby 2.00 5.00
BS Ben Sheets 2.00 5.00
CB Craig Biggio 3.00 8.00
CC Carl Crawford 2.00 5.00
CP Corey Patterson 2.00 5.00
CZ Carlos Zambrano 2.00 5.00
DJ Derek Jeter Pants 8.00 20.00
DL Derrek Lee 3.00 8.00
DO David Ortiz 3.00 8.00
DW David Wright 4.00 10.00
EC Eric Chavez 2.00 5.00
EG Eric Gagne 2.00 5.00
ER Edgar Renteria 2.00 5.00
GM Greg Maddux 4.00 10.00
GR Khalil Greene 3.00 8.00
GS Gary Sheffield 2.00 5.00
HB Hank Blalock 2.00 5.00
HU Torii Hunter 2.00 5.00
JD J.D. Drew 2.00 5.00
JM Joe Mauer 4.00 10.00
JP Jake Peavy 2.00 5.00
JR Jose Reyes 2.00 5.00
KG Ken Griffey Jr. 6.00 15.00
KW Kerry Wood 2.00 5.00
MC Miguel Cabrera 3.00 8.00
MM Mark Mulder 2.00 5.00
MO Melvin Mora 2.00 5.00
MP Mark Prior 3.00 8.00
MT Mark Teixeria 3.00 8.00
MY Michael Young 2.00 5.00
OP Oliver Perez 2.00 5.00
PI Mike Piazza 4.00 10.00
RC Roger Clemens Pants 4.00 10.00
RJ Randy Johnson 4.00 10.00
RO Roy Oswalt 2.00 5.00
RP Rafael Palmeiro 3.00 8.00
SA Johan Santana 4.00 10.00
SC Sean Casey 2.00 5.00
SM John Smoltz 3.00 8.00
SR Scott Rolen 3.00 8.00
TE Miguel Tejada 2.00 5.00
TH Tim Hudson 2.00 5.00
VG Vladimir Guerrero 4.00 10.00
VM Victor Martinez 2.00 5.00

2005 SPx SPxtreme Stats Signature

ISSUED IN 05 SP COLLECTION PACKS
OVERALL PREMIUM AU-GU ODDS 1:20
STATED PRINT RUN 5 SERIAL #'d SETS
NO PRICING DUE TO SCARCITY

2005 SPx Superscripts

ISSUED IN 05 SP COLLECTION PACKS
OVERALL AUTO ODDS 1:10
STATED PRINT RUN 15 SERIAL #'d SETS
NO PRICING DUE TO SCARCITY

2005 SPx Superscripts Triple

ISSUED IN 05 SP COLLECTION PACKS
OVERALL PREMIUM AU-GU ODDS 1:20
STATED PRINT RUN 5 SERIAL #'d SETS
NO PRICING DUE TO SCARCITY

2005 SPx Winning Materials Dual Jersey

ISSUED IN 05 SP COLLECTION PACKS
OVERALL PREMIUM AU-GU ODDS 1:20
STATED PRINT RUN 20 SERIAL #'d SETS
NO PRICING DUE TO SCARCITY

2005 SPx Winning Materials Dual Jersey Signature

ISSUED IN 05 SP COLLECTION PACKS
OVERALL PREMIUM AU-GU ODDS 1:20
STATED PRINT RUN 5 SERIAL #'d SETS
NO PRICING DUE TO SCARCITY

2006 SPx

This 160-card set was released in September, 2006. The set was issued in four-card packs, which came 18 packs per box and 14 boxes per case. The first 100 cards feature veteran players which were sequenced in alphabetical order by team while the final 60 cards feature signed cards of 2006 rookies. Those cards were issued to stated print runs between 190 and 999 serial numbered copies and were inserted into packs at a stated rate of one in nine. A few players did not sign their cards in time for pack out and those autographs could be redeemed until September 7, 2008.

COMP.BASIC SET (100) 10.00 25.00
COMMON CARD (1-100) .15 .40
COMMON AU p/r 659-999 4.00 10.00
COMMON AU p/r 350-500 4.00 10.00
OVERALL 101-161 AU ODDS 1:9
101-161 AU EXCH DEADLINE 09/07/08
101-161 AU PRINT RUN B/WN 190-999 PER
101-161 PRINTING PLATE ODDS 1:224
101-161 PLATES PRINT RUN 1 SET PER CLR
101-161 PLATES FEATURE AUTOS
BLACK-CYAN-MAGENTA-YELLOW ISSUED
NO PLATE PRICING DUE TO SCARCITY
EXQUISITE EXCH ODDS 1:36
EXQUISITE EXCH DEADLINE 07/27/07
1 Luis Gonzalez .15 .40
2 Chad Tracy .15 .40
3 Brandon Webb .25 .60
4 Andruw Jones .15 .40
5 Chipper Jones .40 1.00
6 John Smoltz .40 1.00
7 Tim Hudson .25 .60
8 Miguel Tejada .25 .60
9 Brian Roberts .15 .40
10 Ramon Hernandez .15 .40
11 Curt Schilling .25 .60
12 David Ortiz .25 .60
13 Manny Ramirez .40 1.00
14 Jason Varitek .40 1.00
15 Josh Beckett .25 .60
16 Greg Maddux .60 1.50
17 Derrek Lee .25 .60
18 Mark Prior .25 .60
19 Aramis Ramirez .15 .40
20 Jim Thome .25 .60
21 Paul Konerko .25 .60
22 Scott Podsednik .15 .40
23 Jose Contreras .15 .40
24 Ken Griffey Jr. .60 1.50
25 Adam Dunn .25 .60
26 Felipe Lopez .15 .40
27 Travis Hafner .15 .40
28 Victor Martinez .25 .60
29 Grady Sizemore .25 .60
30 Jhonny Peralta .15 .40
31 Todd Helton .25 .60
32 Garrett Atkins .15 .40
33 Clint Barmes .15 .40
34 Ivan Rodriguez .25 .60
35 Chris Shelton .15 .40
36 Jeremy Bonderman .15 .40
37 Miguel Cabrera .40 1.00
38 Dontrelle Willis .15 .40
39 Lance Berkman .25 .60
40 Morgan Ensberg .15 .40
41 Roy Oswalt .25 .60
42 Reggie Sanders .15 .40
43 Mike Sweeney .15 .40
44 Vladimir Guerrero .40 1.00
45 Bartolo Colon .15 .40
46 Chone Figgins .15 .40
47 Nomar Garciaparra .40 1.00
48 Jeff Kent .15 .40
49 J.D. Drew .15 .40
50 Carlos Lee .15 .40
51 Ben Sheets .15 .40
52 Rickie Weeks .25 .60
53 Johan Santana .40 1.00
54 Torii Hunter .15 .40
55 Joe Mauer .40 1.00
56 Pedro Martinez .25 .60
57 David Wright .60 1.50
58 Carlos Beltran .15 .40
59 Carlos Delgado .15 .40
60 Jose Reyes .25 .60
61 Derek Jeter 1.00 2.50
62 Alex Rodriguez .60 1.50
63 Randy Johnson .40 1.00
64 Hideki Matsui .40 1.00
65 Gary Sheffield .15 .40
66 Rich Harden .15 .40
67 Eric Chavez .15 .40
68 Huston Street .15 .40
69 Bobby Crosby .15 .40
70 Bobby Abreu .15 .40
71 Ryan Howard .60 1.50
72 Chase Utley .40 1.00
73 Pat Burrell .15 .40
74 Jason Bay .15 .40
75 Sean Casey .15 .40
76 Mike Piazza .40 1.00
77 Jake Peavy .15 .40
78 Brian Giles .15 .40
79 Milton Bradley .15 .40
80 Omar Vizquel .25 .60
81 Jason Schmidt .15 .40
82 Ichiro Suzuki .60 1.50
83 Felix Hernandez .40 1.00
84 Richie Sexson .15 .40
85 Albert Pujols 1.00 2.50
86 Chris Carpenter .40 1.00
87 Scott Rolen .25 .60
88 Jim Edmonds .25 .60
89 Carl Crawford .25 .60
90 Jonny Gomes .15 .40
91 Scott Kazmir .25 .60
92 Mark Teixeira .40 1.00
93 Michael Young .25 .60
94 Phil Nevin .15 .40
95 Vernon Wells .15 .40
96 Roy Halladay .40 1.00
97 Troy Glaus .15 .40
98 Alfonso Soriano .25 .60
99 Nick Johnson .15 .40
100 Jose Vidro .15 .40
101 Conor Jackson AU/999 (RC) 6.00 15.00
103 Macay McBride AU/999 (RC) 4.00 10.00
104 Aaron Rakers AU/499 (RC) 4.00 10.00
105 Jonathan Papelbon AU/499 (RC) 8.00 20.00
106 Jason Bergmann AU/999 RC 4.00 10.00
107 Stephen Drew AU/350 (RC) 12.50 30.00
108 Chris Denorfia AU/999 (RC) 4.00 10.00
109 Kelly Shoppach AU/999 (RC) 4.00 10.00
110 Ryan Shealy AU/999 (RC) 4.00 10.00
111 Josh Wilson AU/999 (RC) 4.00 10.00
112 Brian Anderson AU/999 (RC) 4.00 10.00
113 Justin Verlander AU/749 (RC) 30.00 60.00
114 Jeremy Hermida AU/999 (RC) 6.00 15.00
115 Mike Jacobs AU/999 (RC) 6.00 15.00
116 Josh Johnson AU/999 (RC) 12.50 30.00
117 Hanley Ramirez AU/659 (RC) 20.00 50.00
118 Chris Resop AU/999 (RC) 4.00 10.00
119 Josh Willingham AU/999 (RC) 4.00 10.00
120 Cole Hamels AU/499 (RC) 12.50 30.00
121 Matt Cain AU/999 (RC) 8.00 20.00
122 Steve Stemle AU/999 RC 4.00 10.00
123 Tim Hamulack AU/999 (RC) 4.00 10.00
124 Choo Freeman AU/999 (RC) 4.00 10.00
125 Hong-Chih Kuo AU/999 (RC) 20.00 50.00
126 Cody Ross AU/999 (RC) 10.00 25.00
127 Jose Capellan AU/999 (RC) 4.00 10.00
128 Prince Fielder AU/190 (RC) 60.00 120.00
129 David Gassner AU/999 (RC) 4.00 10.00
130 Jason Kubel AU/999 (RC) 4.00 10.00
131 Francisco Liriano AU/299 (RC) 20.00 50.00
132 Anderson Hernandez AU/999 (RC) 6.00 15.00
133 Joey Devine AU/499 RC 4.00 10.00
134 Chris Booker AU/999 (RC) 4.00 10.00
135 Matt Capps AU/999 (RC) 4.00 10.00
136 Paul Maholm AU/999 (RC) 4.00 10.00
137 Nate McLouth AU/999 (RC) 8.00 20.00
138 John Van Benschoten AU/999 (RC) 4.00 10.00
139 Jeff Harris AU/999 RC 4.00 10.00
140 Ben Johnson AU/999 (RC) 4.00 10.00
141 Wil Nieves AU/999 (RC) 4.00 10.00
142 Guillermo Quiroz AU/999 (RC) 4.00 10.00
143 Josh Rupe AU/500 (RC) 4.00 10.00
144 Skip Schumaker AU/999 (RC) 4.00 10.00
145 Jack Taschner AU/999 (RC) 4.00 10.00
146 Adam Wainwright AU/999 (RC) 10.00 25.00
147 Alay Soler AU/499 RC 10.00 25.00
148 Kendry Morales AU/999 (RC) 6.00 15.00
149 Ian Kinsler AU/999 (RC) 12.50 30.00
150 Jason Hammel AU/999 (RC) 4.00 10.00
151 Chad Billingsley AU/499 (RC) 15.00 40.00
152 Boof Bonser AU/999 (RC) 6.00 15.00
153 Peter Moylan AU/999 RC 4.00 10.00
154 Chris Britton AU/999 RC 4.00 10.00
155 Takashi Saito AU/999 RC 12.50 30.00
156 Scott Dunn AU/999 (RC) 4.00 10.00
158 Dan Uggla AU/999 (RC) 12.50 30.00
159 Taylor Buchholz AU/999 (RC) 4.00 10.00

2006 SPx Spectrum

*SPECTRUM 1-100: 2X TO 5X BASIC
STATED ODDS 1:3

2006 SPx Rookie Signature Gold

RANDOM INSERTS IN PACKS
STATED PRINT RUN 5 SERIAL #'d SETS
NO PRICING DUE TO SCARCITY
EXCH DEADLINE 09/07/08

2006 SPx Rookie Signature Platinum

RANDOM INSERTS IN PACKS
STATED PRINT RUN 1 SERIAL #'d SET
NO PRICING DUE TO SCARCITY
EXCH DEADLINE 09/07/08

2006 SPx Next In Line

STATED ODDS 1:9
AW Adam Wainwright 1.50 4.00
BA Brian Anderson .60 1.50
BB Brian Bannister .60 1.50
BJ Ben Johnson .60 1.50
CJ Conor Jackson 1.00 2.50
DU Dan Uggla 1.50 4.00
FH Felix Hernandez 1.50 4.00
FL Francisco Liriano 1.50 4.00
HR Hanley Ramirez 1.50 4.00
HS Huston Street .60 1.50
IK Ian Kinsler 2.00 5.00
JB Josh Barfield .60 1.50
JE Jered Weaver 1.50 4.00
JH Jeremy Hermida .60 1.50
JL James Loney 1.00 2.50
JP Jonathan Papelbon 3.00 8.00
JS Jeremy Sowers .60 1.50
JV Justin Verlander 5.00 12.00
JW Josh Willingham .60 1.50
LE Jon Lester 2.50 6.00
MC Matt Cain 1.50 4.00
MJ Mike Jacobs .60 1.50
AS Alay Soler .60 1.50
PF Prince Fielder 2.50 6.00
RC Ryan Church .60 1.50
RH Ryan Howard 2.50 6.00
RZ Ryan Zimmerman 3.00 8.00
SO Scott Olsen .60 1.50
TB Taylor Buchholz .60 1.50
TI Travis Ishikawa .60 1.50

2006 SPx SPxtra Info

STATED ODDS 1:9
AJ Andruw Jones .60 1.50
AP Albert Pujols 4.00 10.00
BA Bobby Abreu .60 1.50
BG Brian Giles .60 1.50
CC Carl Crawford 1.00 2.50
CL Carlos Lee .60 1.50
DJ Derek Jeter 4.00 10.00
DL Derrek Lee .60 1.50
DO David Ortiz 1.00 2.50
DW Dontrelle Willis .60 1.50
EC Eric Chavez .60 1.50
HE Todd Helton 1.00 2.50
IR Ivan Rodriguez 1.00 2.50
IS Ichiro Suzuki 2.50 6.00
JB Jason Bay .60 1.50
JK Jeff Kent .60 1.50
JS Johan Santana 1.50 4.00
JT Jim Thome 1.00 2.50
KG Ken Griffey Jr. 2.50 6.00
LG Luis Gonzalez .60 1.50
MT Miguel Tejada 1.00 2.50
NJ Nick Johnson .60 1.50
PM Pedro Martinez 1.00 2.50
RO Roy Oswalt 1.00 2.50
RS Reggie Sanders .60 1.50
SC Jason Schmidt .60 1.50
TE Mark Teixeira 1.50 4.00
TH Travis Hafner .60 1.50
VG Vladimir Guerrero 1.50 4.00
VW Vernon Wells .60 1.50

2006 SPx SPxciting Signature

RANDOM INSERTS IN PACKS
PRINT RUNS B/WN 10-30 COPIES PER
NO PRICING DUE TO SCARCITY
EXCH DEADLINE 09/07/08
MC Matt Cain/30 12.50 30.00

2006 SPx SPxtreme Team

STATED ODDS 1:9
AD Adam Dunn 1.00 2.50
AJ Andruw Jones .60 1.50
AP Albert Pujols 4.00 10.00
AR Alex Rodriguez 2.50 6.00
AS Alfonso Soriano 1.00 2.50
BA Bobby Abreu .60 1.50
CC Chris Carpenter 1.50 4.00
CD Carlos Delgado .60 1.50
CL Carlos Lee .60 1.50
CR Carl Crawford 1.00 2.50
DJ Derek Jeter 4.00 10.00
DL Derrek Lee .60 1.50
DO David Ortiz 1.00 2.50
DW David Wright 2.50 6.00
GS Grady Sizemore 1.00 2.50
HA Travis Hafner .60 1.50
HM Hideki Matsui 1.50 4.00
HO Ryan Howard 2.50 6.00
IS Ichiro Suzuki 2.50 6.00
JB Jason Bay .60 1.50
JK Jeff Kent .60 1.50
JP Jake Peavy .60 1.50
JR Jose Reyes 1.00 2.50
JS Johan Santana 1.50 4.00
JT Jim Thome 1.00 2.50
KG Ken Griffey Jr. 2.50 6.00
LB Lance Berkman 1.00 2.50
MC Miguel Cabrera 1.50 4.00
MR Manny Ramirez 1.50 4.00
MT Mark Teixeira 1.50 4.00
MY Michael Young 1.00 2.50
PF Prince Fielder 2.50 6.00
PK Paul Konerko 1.00 2.50
PM Pedro Martinez 1.00 2.50
RH Rich Harden .60 1.50
TE Miguel Tejada 1.00 2.50
TH Todd Helton 1.00 2.50
VG Vladimir Guerrero 1.50 4.00
VM Victor Martinez 1.00 2.50
VW Vernon Wells .60 1.50

2006 SPx WBC All-World Team

STATED ODDS 1:9
1 Brett Willemburg .60 1.50
2 Bradley Harman 1.00 2.50
3 Adam Stern .60 1.50
4 Jason Bay .60 1.50
5 Adam Loewen .60 1.50
6 Wei Wang .60 1.50
7 Yi Feng .60 1.50
8 Yung Chi Chen 1.00 2.50
9 Chin-Lung Hu 2.00 5.00
10 Wei-Lun Pan 1.50 4.00
11 Yoandy Garlobo .60 1.50
12 Frederich Cepeda .60 1.50
13 Osmany Urrutia .60 1.50
14 Yulieski Gourriel 1.50 4.00
15 Yadel Marti .60 1.50
16 Pedro Luis Lazo 1.00 2.50
17 Adrian Beltre .60 1.50
18 David Ortiz 1.00 2.50
19 Albert Pujols 4.00 10.00
20 Bartolo Colon .60 1.50
21 Miguel Tejada 1.00 2.50
22 Mike Piazza 1.50 4.00
23 Jason Grilli .60 1.50
24 Nobuhiko Matsunaka 1.00 2.50
25 Tomoya Satozaki 1.00 2.50
26 Ichiro Suzuki 2.50 6.00
27 Hitoshi Tamura 1.00 2.50
28 Daisuke Matsuzaka 2.00 5.00
29 Koji Uehara 1.50 4.00
30 Jong Beom Lee .60 1.50
31 Seung Yeop Lee 1.00 2.50
32 Jae Seo .60 1.50
33 Min Han Son .60 1.50
34 Chan Ho Park 1.00 2.50
35 Jorge Cantu .60 1.50
36 Miguel Ojeda .60 1.50
37 Andruw Jones .60 1.50
38 Shairon Martis .60 1.50
39 Carlos Lee .60 1.50
40 Carlos Beltran .60 1.50
41 Javy Lopez .60 1.50
42 Javier Vazquez .60 1.50
43 Ken Griffey Jr. 2.50 6.00
44 Derek Jeter 4.00 10.00
45 Alex Rodriguez 2.50 6.00
46 Derrek Lee .60 1.50
47 Roger Clemens 2.00 5.00
48 Miguel Cabrera 1.50 4.00
49 Victor Martinez 1.00 2.50
50 Johan Santana 1.50 4.00

2006 SPx Winning Big Materials

STATED ODDS 1:252
PRINT RUNS B/WN 5-40 COPIES PER
NO PRICING ON QTY 26 OR LESS
PRICING IS FOR 2-3 CLR PATCHES
AB Adrian Beltre/40 50.00 100.00
AI Akinori Iwamura/30 200.00 300.00
AJ Andruw Jones/40 50.00 100.00
AP Ariel Pestano/30 50.00 100.00
AR Alex Rios/55 30.00 60.00
AS Alfonso Soriano/40 50.00 100.00
BA Bobby Abreu/40 50.00 100.00
BW Bernie Williams/40 75.00 120.00
CB Carlos Beltran/40 50.00 100.00
CD Carlos Delgado/40 30.00 60.00
CH Chin-Lung Hu/26
CL Carlos Lee/40 30.00 60.00
CZ Carlos Zambrano/40 75.00 150.00
DL Derrek Lee/40 50.00 100.00
DO David Ortiz/30 75.00 150.00
EB Erik Bedard/40 30.00 60.00
EP Eduardo Paret/30 30.00 60.00
FC Frederich Cepeda/30 50.00 100.00
GY Guogan Yang/52 30.00 60.00
HC Hee Seop Choi/32 50.00 100.00
HT Hitoshi Tamura/30 200.00 300.00
IR Ivan Rodriguez/40 30.00 60.00
IS Ichiro Suzuki/5
JB Jason Bay/40 50.00 100.00
JD Johnny Damon/40 50.00 100.00
JF Jeff Francis/40 30.00 60.00
JL Jong Beom Lee/20
JM Justin Morneau/25
JP Jin Man Park/22
JS Johan Santana/40 50.00 100.00
JV Jason Varitek/40 50.00 100.00
KG Ken Griffey Jr./5
KU Koji Uehara/30 250.00 400.00
LO Javy Lopez/40 30.00 60.00
MA Moises Alou/53 30.00 60.00
MC Miguel Cabrera/40 50.00 100.00
ME Michel Enriquez/30 50.00 100.00
MF Maikel Folch/30 50.00 100.00
MK Munenori Kawasaki/30 250.00 400.00
MO Michihiro Ogasawara/30 300.00 400.00
MP Mike Piazza/40 60.00 150.00
MS Min Han Son/24
MT Miguel Tejada/40 50.00 100.00
NM Nobuhiko Matsunaka/30 225.00 350.00
NS Naoyuki Shimizu/30 150.00 300.00
OU Osmany Urrutia/30 30.00 60.00
PE Wily Mo Pena/60 30.00 60.00
PL Pedro Luis Lazo/30 50.00 100.00
PU Albert Pujols/20
RO Alex Rodriguez/5
SW Shunsuke Watanabe/30 200.00 300.00
TN Tsuyoshi Nishioka/30 250.00 400.00
TW Tsuyoshi Wada/30 150.00 300.00
VM Victor Martinez/40 50.00 100.00
VO Vicyohandry Odelin/30 50.00 100.00
WL Wei-Chu Lin/45 200.00 400.00
WP Wei-Lun Pan/38 200.00 300.00
YG Yulieski Gourriel/30 50.00 100.00
YM Yunieski Maya/30 50.00 100.00

2006 SPx Winning Materials

STATED ODDS 1:18
AI Akinori Iwamura 8.00 20.00
AJ Andruw Jones 4.00 10.00
AP Ariel Pestano 3.00 8.00
AR Alex Rodriguez 6.00 15.00
AS Alfonso Soriano 3.00 8.00
BA Bobby Abreu 3.00 8.00
CB Carlos Beltran 3.00 8.00
CD Carlos Delgado 3.00 8.00
DL Derrek Lee 3.00 8.00
DO David Ortiz 4.00 10.00
EP Eduardo Paret 3.00 8.00
FC Frederich Cepeda 3.00 8.00
HC Hee Seop Choi 3.00 8.00
HT Hitoshi Tamura 8.00 20.00
IS Ichiro Suzuki 40.00 80.00
JB Jason Bay 3.00 8.00
JD Johnny Damon 3.00 8.00
JL Jong Beom Lee 3.00 8.00
JS Johan Santana 4.00 10.00
KG Ken Griffey Jr. 6.00 15.00
KU Koji Uehara 8.00 20.00
MC Miguel Cabrera 4.00 10.00
ME Michel Enriquez 3.00 8.00
MF Maikel Folch 3.00 8.00
MK Munenori Kawasaki 8.00 20.00
MO Michihiro Ogasawara 8.00 20.00
MP Mike Piazza 4.00 10.00
MS Min Han Son 4.00 10.00
MT Miguel Tejada 3.00 8.00
NM Nobuhiko Matsunaka 6.00 15.00
NS Naoyuki Shimizu 6.00 15.00
OU Osmany Urrutia 3.00 8.00
PL Pedro Luis Lazo 4.00 10.00
PU Albert Pujols 8.00 20.00
RC Roger Clemens 6.00 15.00
SW Shunsuke Watanabe 8.00 20.00
TN Tsuyoshi Nishioka 8.00 20.00
TW Tsuyoshi Wada 10.00 25.00
VM Victor Martinez 3.00 8.00
VO Vicyohandry Odelin 4.00 10.00
YG Yulieski Gourriel 3.00 8.00
YM Yunieski Maya 3.00 8.00

2007 SPx

This 150-card set was released in May, 2007. The set was issued in the hobby in three-card packs which came 10 packs per box and 10 boxes per case. Cards numbered 1-100 feature veterans while cards 101-150 (with the exception of Daisuke Matsuzaka (card #128) are signed rookie cards. The stated odds for the signed rookie cards were one in three packs. A few players did not return their signatures in time for pack out and those cards could be redeemed until May 10, 2010. The veteran cards were sequenced in alphabetical order by team.

COMMON CARD (1-100) .30 .75
COMMON AU RC (101-150) 3.00 8.00
OVERALL 101-150 AU RC ODDS 1:3
101-150 AU RC EXCH DEADLINE 05/10/2010
ASTERISK EQUALS PARTIAL EXCH
APPX.PRINTING PLATE ODDS 2 PER CASE
PLATES PRINT RUN 1 SET PER COLOR
BLACK-CYAN-MAGENTA-YELLOW ISSUED
NO PLATE PRICING DUE TO SCARCITY
1 Miguel Tejada .50 1.25
2 Brian Roberts .30 .75
3 Melvin Mora .30 .75
4 David Ortiz .50 1.25
5 Manny Ramirez .75 2.00
6 Jason Varitek .75 2.00
7 Curt Schilling .50 1.25
8 Jim Thome .50 1.25
9 Paul Konerko .50 1.25
10 Jermaine Dye .30 .75
11 Travis Hafner .30 .75
12 Victor Martinez .50 1.25
13 Grady Sizemore .50 1.25
14 C.C. Sabathia .50 1.25
15 Ivan Rodriguez .50 1.25
16 Magglio Ordonez .50 1.25
17 Carlos Guillen .30 .75
18 Justin Verlander 1.00 2.50
19 Shane Costa .30 .75
20 Emil Brown .30 .75
21 Mark Teahen .30 .75
22 Vladimir Guerrero .75 2.00
23 Jered Weaver .50 1.25
24 Juan Rivera .30 .75
25 Justin Morneau .75 2.00
26 Joe Mauer .75 2.00
27 Torii Hunter .30 .75
28 Johan Santana .75 2.00
29 Derek Jeter 2.00 5.00
30 Alex Rodriguez 1.25 3.00
31 Johnny Damon .50 1.25
32 Jason Giambi .30 .75
33 Bobby Crosby .30 .75
34 Nick Swisher .75 2.00
35 Eric Chavez .30 .75
36 Ichiro Suzuki 1.25 3.00
37 Raul Ibanez .50 1.25
38 Richie Sexson .30 .75
39 Carl Crawford .50 1.25
40 Rocco Baldelli .30 .75
41 Scott Kazmir .50 1.25
42 Michael Young .50 1.25
43 Mark Teixeira .75 2.00
44 Ian Kinsler .50 1.25
45 Troy Glaus .30 .75
46 Vernon Wells .30 .75
47 Roy Halladay .75 2.00
48 Lyle Overbay .30 .75
49 Brandon Webb .50 1.25
50 Conor Jackson .30 .75
51 Stephen Drew .30 .75
52 Chipper Jones .75 2.00
53 Andruw Jones .30 .75
54 Adam LaRoche .30 .75
55 John Smoltz .75 2.00
56 Derrek Lee .30 .75
57 Aramis Ramirez .30 .75
58 Carlos Zambrano .50 1.25
59 Ken Griffey Jr. 1.25 3.00
60 Adam Dunn .50 1.25
61 Aaron Harang .30 .75
62 Todd Helton .50 1.25
63 Matt Holliday .75 2.00
64 Garrett Atkins .30 .75
65 Miguel Cabrera .75 2.00
66 Hanley Ramirez .75 2.00
67 Dontrelle Willis .30 .75
68 Lance Berkman .50 1.25
69 Roy Oswalt .50 1.25
70 Craig Biggio .50 1.25
71 J.D. Drew .30 .75
72 Nomar Garciaparra .75 2.00
73 Rafael Furcal .30 .75
74 Jeff Kent .30 .75
75 Prince Fielder .50 1.25
76 Bill Hall .30 .75
77 Rickie Weeks .50 1.25
78 Jose Reyes .50 1.25
79 David Wright 1.25 3.00
80 Carlos Delgado .30 .75
81 Carlos Beltran .30 .75
82 Ryan Howard 1.25 3.00
83 Chase Utley .75 2.00
84 Jimmy Rollins .50 1.25
85 Jason Bay .50 1.25
86 Freddy Sanchez .30 .75
87 Zach Duke .30 .75
88 Trevor Hoffman .50 1.25
89 Adrian Gonzalez .50 1.25
90 Chris Young .30 .75
91 Ray Durham .30 .75
92 Omar Vizquel .50 1.25
93 Jason Schmidt .30 .75
94 Albert Pujols 2.00 5.00
95 Scott Rolen .50 1.25
96 Jim Edmonds .50 1.25
97 Chris Carpenter .75 2.00
98 Alfonso Soriano .50 1.25
99 Ryan Zimmerman .50 1.25
100 Nick Johnson .30 .75
101 Delmon Young AU (RC) 8.00 20.00
102 Andrew Miller AU RC 4.00 10.00
103 Troy Tulowitzki AU (RC) 10.00 25.00
104 Jeff Fiorentino AU (RC) 3.00 8.00
105 David Murphy AU (RC) 3.00 8.00
106 Tim Lincecum AU RC 60.00 120.00
108 Kevin Kouzmanoff AU (RC) 6.00 15.00
109 Adam Lind AU (RC) 3.00 8.00
111 Kevin Hooper AU (RC) 3.00 8.00
112 Mitch Maier AU RC 3.00 8.00
114 Dennis Sarfate AU (RC) 3.00 8.00
115 Drew Anderson AU RC 3.00 8.00
116 Miguel Montero AU (RC) 3.00 8.00
117 Glen Perkins AU (RC) 3.00 8.00
119 Tim Gradoville AU RC 3.00 8.00
120 Ryan Braun AU (RC) 30.00 60.00
121 Chris Narveson AU (RC) 3.00 8.00
122 Patrick Misch AU (RC) 3.00 8.00
123 Juan Salas AU (RC) 3.00 8.00
124 Beltran Perez AU (RC) 3.00 8.00
125 Joaquin Arias AU (RC) 3.00 8.00
126 Philip Humber AU (RC) 6.00 15.00
127 Kei Igawa AU RC 30.00 60.00
128 Daisuke Matsuzaka AU RC 40.00 80.00
129 Andy Cannizaro AU RC 6.00 15.00
130 Ubaldo Jimenez AU (RC) 12.50 30.00
131 Fred Lewis AU (RC) 6.00 15.00
132 Ryan Sweeney AU (RC) 3.00 8.00
133 Jeff Baker AU (RC) 3.00 8.00
134 Michael Bourn AU (RC) 3.00 8.00
135 Akinori Iwamura AU RC 6.00 15.00
136 Oswaldo Navarro AU RC 3.00 8.00
137 Hunter Pence AU (RC) 12.50 30.00
138 Jon Knott AU (RC) 3.00 8.00
139 Justin Hampson AU (RC) 3.00 8.00
140 Jeff Salazar AU (RC) 3.00 8.00
141 Juan Morillo AU (RC) 3.00 8.00
142 Delwyn Young AU (RC) 3.00 8.00
143 Brian Burres AU (RC) 5.00 12.00
144 Chris Stewart AU RC 3.00 8.00
145 Eric Stults AU RC 3.00 8.00
146 Carlos Maldonado AU (RC) 3.00 8.00
147 Angel Sanchez AU RC 3.00 8.00
148 Cesar Jimenez AU RC 3.00 8.00
149 Shawn Riggans AU (RC) 3.00 8.00
150 John Nelson AU RC 3.00 8.00

2007 SPx Spectrum

RANDOM INSERTS IN PACKS
STATED PRINT RUN 25 SER.#'d SETS
EXCH DEADLINE 05/10/2010
NO PRICING DUE TO SCARCITY

2007 SPx Autofacts Preview

ONE PER HOBBY BOX TOPPER
EXCH DEADLINE 05/10/2010
AI Akinori Iwamura 15.00 40.00
AL Adam Lind 5.00 12.00
AM Andrew Miller SP
AS Angel Sanchez 3.00 8.00
BP Beltran Perez 3.00 8.00
BR Jeremy Brown 3.00 8.00
CM Carlos Maldonado 3.00 8.00
CN Chris Narveson 3.00 8.00
CR Cal Ripken SP
CS C.C. Sabathia
DJ Derek Jeter
DM Daisuke Matsuzaka
DS Dennis Sarfate 3.00 8.00
DW Dewayne Wise 5.00 12.00
DY Delmon Young 6.00 15.00
ES Eric Stults 3.00 8.00
FL Fred Lewis 5.00 12.00
GP Glen Perkins 3.00 8.00
HG Hector Gimenez
HU Jon Huber
JA Joaquin Arias 3.00 8.00
JB Jeff Baker 3.00 8.00
JH Justin Hampson 3.00 8.00
JK Jon Knott 3.00 8.00
JM Juan Morillo 3.00 8.00
JN John Nelson 3.00 8.00
JS Juan Salas 3.00 8.00
JW Jason Wood 3.00 8.00
KG Ken Griffey Jr. SP
KH Kevin Hooper 3.00 8.00
KI Kei Igawa 6.00 15.00
KK Kevin Kouzmanoff 5.00 12.00
MB Michael Bourn 5.00 12.00
MM Miguel Montero 3.00 8.00

PH Philip Humber 5.00 12.00
PM Patrick Misch 3.00 8.00
RB Ryan Braun
SA Jeff Salazar 3.00 8.00
SR Shawn Riggans 3.00 8.00
ST Chris Stewart 3.00 8.00
TT Troy Tulowitzki 10.00 25.00
YO Delwyn Young 3.00 8.00

2007 SPx Iron Man

COMMON CARD 1.50 4.00
APPX.ODDS 1:3
STATED PRINT RUN 699 SER.#'d SETS
APPX.PRINTING PLATE ODDS 2 PER CASE
PLATES PRINT RUN 1 SET PER COLOR
BLACK-CYAN-MAGENTA-YELLOW ISSUED
NO PLATE PRICING DUE TO SCARCITY

2007 SPx Iron Man Platinum

COMMON CARD 15.00 40.00
RANDOM INSERTS IN PACKS
STATED PRINT RUN 1 SER.#'d SET

2007 SPx Iron Man Memorabilia

COMMON CARD 15.00 40.00
APPX. SIX GAME-USED PER BOX
STATED PRINT RUN 25 SER.#'d SETS

2007 SPx Iron Man Signatures

COMMON CARD 150.00 300.00
RANDOM INSERTS IN PACKS
STATED PRINT RUN 1 SER.#'d SET

2007 SPx Winning Materials 199 Bronze

APPX. SIX GAME-USED PER BOX
STATED PRINT RUN 199 SER.#'d SETS
APPX.PRINTING PLATE ODDS 2 PER CASE
PLATES PRINT RUN 1 SET PER COLOR
BLACK-CYAN-MAGENTA-YELLOW ISSUED
NO PLATE PRICING DUE TO SCARCITY
AB A.J. Burnett/199 3.00 8.00
AD Adam Dunn/199 3.00 8.00
AE Andre Ethier/199 3.00 8.00
AJ Andruw Jones/199 3.00 8.00
AL Adam LaRoche/199 3.00 8.00
AP Albert Pujols/199 6.00 15.00
AR Aramis Ramirez/199 3.00 8.00
AS Anibal Sanchez/199 3.00 8.00
BA Bobby Abreu/199 4.00 10.00
BG Brian Giles/199 3.00 8.00
BL Joe Blanton/199 3.00 8.00
BM Brian McCann/199 3.00 8.00
BO Jeremy Bonderman/199 3.00 8.00
BR Brian Roberts/199 3.00 8.00
BS Ben Sheets/199 3.00 8.00
BU B.J. Upton/199 3.00 8.00
CA Miguel Cabrera/199 3.00 8.00
CB Craig Biggio/199 4.00 10.00
CC Chris Carpenter/199 3.00 8.00
CF Chone Figgins/199 3.00 8.00
CH Cole Hamels/199 4.00 10.00
CJ Chipper Jones/199 4.00 10.00
CL Roger Clemens/199 6.00 15.00
CN Robinson Cano/199 4.00 10.00
CR Carl Crawford/199 3.00 8.00
CU Chase Utley/199 4.00 10.00
CW Chien-Ming Wang/199 6.00 15.00
DJ Derek Jeter/199 8.00 20.00
DJ2 Derek Jeter/199 8.00 20.00
DL Derrek Lee/199 3.00 8.00
DO David Ortiz/199 4.00 10.00
DU Dan Uggla/199 3.00 8.00
DW Dontrelle Willis/199 3.00 8.00
EC Eric Chavez/199 3.00 8.00
FH Felix Hernandez/199 4.00 10.00
FL Francisco Liriano/199 3.00 8.00
FS Freddy Sanchez/199 3.00 8.00
FT Frank Thomas/199 4.00 10.00
GA Garrett Atkins/199 3.00 8.00
HA Travis Hafner/199 3.00 8.00
HE Todd Helton/199 4.00 10.00
HI Rich Hill/199 3.00 8.00
HK Howie Kendrick/199 3.00 8.00
HN Rich Harden/199 3.00 8.00
HR Hanley Ramirez/199 4.00 10.00
HS Huston Street/199 3.00 8.00
IK Ian Kinsler/199 3.00 8.00
IR Ivan Rodriguez/199 4.00 10.00
JB Jason Bay/199 3.00 8.00
JE Jim Edmonds/199 3.00 8.00
JF Jeff Francoeur/199 4.00 10.00
JJ Josh Johnson/199 3.00 8.00
JL Chad Billingsley/199 3.00 8.00
JM Joe Mauer/199 4.00 10.00
JN Joe Nathan/199 3.00 8.00
JP Jake Peavy/199 3.00 8.00
JR Jose Reyes/199 3.00 8.00
JS Jeremy Sowers/199 3.00 8.00
JT Jim Thome/199 3.00 8.00
JV Justin Verlander/199 4.00 10.00
JW Jered Weaver/199 3.00 8.00
JZ Joel Zumaya/199 3.00 8.00
KG Ken Griffey Jr./199 6.00 15.00
KG2 Ken Griffey Jr./199 6.00 15.00
KH Khalil Greene/199 4.00 10.00
KU Hong-Chih Kuo/199 8.00 20.00
LE Jon Lester/199 4.00 10.00
LG Luis Gonzalez/199 3.00 8.00
MC Matt Cain/199 3.00 8.00
ME Melky Cabrera/199 3.00 8.00
MH Matt Holliday/199 4.00 10.00
MO Justin Morneau/199 3.00 8.00
MT Mark Teixeira/199 3.00 8.00
NM Nick Markakis/199 4.00 10.00
NS Nick Swisher/199 3.00 8.00
PA Jonathan Papelbon/199 4.00 10.00
PF Prince Fielder/199 4.00 10.00
PL Paul LoDuca/199 3.00 8.00
RC Cal Ripken /199 6.00 15.00
RI Alex Rios/199 3.00 8.00
RJ Randy Johnson/199 3.00 8.00
RO Roy Oswalt/199 3.00 8.00
RW Rickie Weeks/199 3.00 8.00
RZ Ryan Zimmerman/199 3.00 8.00
SA Alfonso Soriano/199 3.00 8.00
SD Stephen Drew/199 3.00 8.00
SH James Shields/199 3.00 8.00
SK Scott Kazmir/199 3.00 8.00
SM John Smoltz/199 4.00 10.00
SO Scott Olsen/199 3.00 8.00
SR Scott Rolen/199 4.00 10.00
TE Miguel Tejada/199 3.00 8.00
TG Tom Glavine/199 4.00 10.00
TH Trevor Hoffman/199 3.00 8.00
TO Torii Hunter/199 3.00 8.00
VG Vladimir Guerrero/199 4.00 10.00
VM Victor Martinez/199 3.00 8.00
WE David Wells/199 3.00 8.00
WI Josh Willingham/199 3.00 8.00
YB Yuniesky Betancourt/199 3.00 8.00

2007 SPx Winning Materials 199 Gold

*199 GOLD: .4X TO 1X 199 BRONZE
APPX. SIX GAME-USED PER BOX
STATED PRINT RUN 199 SER.#'d SETS

2007 SPx Winning Materials 199 Silver

*199 SILVER: .4X TO 1X 199 BRONZE
APPX. SIX GAME-USED PER BOX
STATED PRINT RUN 199 SER.#'d SETS

2007 SPx Winning Materials 175 Blue

*175 BLUE: .4X TO 1X 199 BRONZE
APPX. SIX GAME-USED PER BOX
STATED PRINT RUN 175 SER.#'d SETS

2007 SPx Winning Materials 175 Green

*175 GREEN: .4X TO 1X 199 BRONZE
APPX. SIX GAME-USED PER BOX
STATED PRINT RUN 175 SER.#'d SETS

2007 SPx Winning Materials 99 Gold

*99 GOLD: .5X TO 1.2X 199 BRONZE
APPX. SIX GAME-USED PER BOX
STATED PRINT RUN 99 SER.#'d SETS

2007 SPx Winning Materials 99 Silver

*99 SILVER: .5X TO 1.2X 199 BRONZE
APPX. SIX GAME-USED PER BOX
STATED PRINT RUN 99 SER.#'d SETS

2007 SPx Winning Materials Dual Gold

APPX. SIX GAME-USED PER BOX
STATED PRINT RUN 50 SER.#'d SETS
AB A.J. Burnett/50 5.00 12.00
AD Adam Dunn/50 5.00 12.00
AE Andre Ethier/50 5.00 12.00
AJ Andruw Jones/50 5.00 12.00
AL Adam LaRoche/50 5.00 12.00
AP Albert Pujols/50 10.00 25.00
AR Aramis Ramirez/50 5.00 12.00
AS Anibal Sanchez/50 5.00 12.00
BA Bobby Abreu/50 6.00 15.00
BG Brian Giles/50 5.00 12.00
BL Joe Blanton/50 5.00 12.00
BM Brian McCann/50 5.00 12.00
BO Jeremy Bonderman/50 5.00 12.00
BR Brian Roberts/50 5.00 12.00
BS Ben Sheets/50 5.00 12.00
BU B.J. Upton/50 5.00 12.00
CA Miguel Cabrera/50 5.00 12.00
CB Craig Biggio/50 6.00 15.00
CC Chris Carpenter/50 5.00 12.00
CF Chone Figgins/50 5.00 12.00
CH Cole Hamels/50 6.00 15.00
CJ Chipper Jones/50 6.00 15.00
CL Roger Clemens/50 10.00 25.00
CN Robinson Cano/50 6.00 15.00
CR Carl Crawford/50 5.00 12.00
CU Chase Utley/50 6.00 15.00
CW Chien-Ming Wang/50 10.00 25.00
DJ Derek Jeter/50 12.50 30.00
DJ2 Derek Jeter/50 12.50 30.00
DL Derrek Lee/50 5.00 12.00
DO David Ortiz/50 6.00 15.00
DU Dan Uggla/50 6.00 15.00
DW Dontrelle Willis/50 5.00 12.00
EC Eric Chavez/50 5.00 12.00
FH Felix Hernandez/50 6.00 15.00
FL Francisco Liriano/50 5.00 12.00
FS Freddy Sanchez/50 5.00 12.00
FT Frank Thomas/50 6.00 15.00
GA Garrett Atkins/50 5.00 12.00
HA Travis Hafner/50 5.00 12.00
HE Todd Helton/50 6.00 15.00
HI Rich Hill/50 5.00 12.00
HK Howie Kendrick/50 5.00 12.00
HN Rich Harden/50 5.00 12.00
HR Hanley Ramirez/50 6.00 15.00
HS Huston Street/50 5.00 12.00
IK Ian Kinsler/50 5.00 12.00
IR Ivan Rodriguez/50 6.00 15.00
JB Jason Bay/50 5.00 12.00
JE Jim Edmonds/50 5.00 12.00
JF Jeff Francoeur/50 6.00 15.00
JJ Josh Johnson/50 5.00 12.00
JL Chad Billingsley/50 5.00 12.00
JM Joe Mauer/50 6.00 15.00
JN Joe Nathan/50 5.00 12.00
JP Jake Peavy/50 5.00 12.00
JR Jose Reyes/50 5.00 12.00
JS Jeremy Sowers/50 5.00 12.00
JT Jim Thome/50 5.00 12.00
JV Justin Verlander/50 6.00 15.00
JW Jered Weaver/50 5.00 12.00
JZ Joel Zumaya/50 5.00 12.00
KG Ken Griffey Jr./50 10.00 25.00
KG2 Ken Griffey Jr./50 10.00 25.00
KH Khalil Greene/50 6.00 15.00
KU Hong-Chih Kuo/50 12.50 30.00
LE Jon Lester/50 6.00 15.00
LG Luis Gonzalez/50 5.00 12.00
MC Matt Cain/50 5.00 12.00
ME Melky Cabrera/50 5.00 12.00
MH Matt Holliday/50 6.00 15.00
MO Justin Morneau/50 5.00 12.00
MT Mark Teixeira/50 5.00 12.00
NM Nick Markakis/50 6.00 15.00
NS Nick Swisher/50 5.00 12.00
PA Jonathan Papelbon/50 6.00 15.00
PF Prince Fielder/50 6.00 15.00
PL Paul LoDuca/50 5.00 12.00
RC Cal Ripken /50 10.00 25.00
RI Alex Rios/50 5.00 12.00
RJ Randy Johnson/50 5.00 12.00
RO Roy Oswalt/50 5.00 12.00
RW Rickie Weeks/50 5.00 12.00
RZ Ryan Zimmerman/50 5.00 12.00
SA Alfonso Soriano/50 5.00 12.00
SD Stephen Drew/50 5.00 12.00
SH James Shields/50 5.00 12.00
SK Scott Kazmir/50 5.00 12.00
SM John Smoltz/50 5.00 12.00
SO Scott Olsen/50 5.00 12.00
SR Scott Rolen/50 5.00 12.00
TE Miguel Tejada/50 5.00 12.00
TG Tom Glavine/50 5.00 12.00
TH Trevor Hoffman/50 5.00 12.00
TO Torii Hunter/50 5.00 12.00
VG Vladimir Guerrero/50 6.00 15.00
VM Victor Martinez/50 5.00 12.00
WE David Wells/50 5.00 12.00
WI Josh Willingham/50 5.00 12.00
YB Yuniesky Betancourt/50 5.00 12.00

2007 SPx Winning Materials Dual Silver

*DUAL SILVER: .4X TO 1X DUAL GOLD
APPX. SIX GAME-USED PER BOX
STATED PRINT RUN 50 SER.#'d SETS

2007 SPx Winning Materials Dual Bronze

APPX. SIX GAME-USED PER BOX
STATED PRINT RUN 25 SER.#'d SETS
NO PRICING DUE TO SCARCITY

2007 SPx Winning Materials Dual Green

APPX. SIX GAME-USED PER BOX
STATED PRINT RUN 15 SER.#'d SETS
NO PRICING DUE TO SCARCITY

2007 SPx Winning Materials Patches Gold

APPX. SIX GAME-USED PER BOX
PRINT RUNS B/WN 3-99 COPIES PER
NO VERLANDER PRICING DUE TO SCARCITY
AB A.J. Burnett/99 4.00 10.00
AD Adam Dunn/99 4.00 10.00
AE Andre Ethier/99 5.00 12.00
AJ Andruw Jones/99 5.00 12.00
AL Adam LaRoche/99 4.00 10.00
AP Albert Pujols/99 15.00 40.00
AR Aramis Ramirez/99 4.00 10.00
AS Anibal Sanchez/54 4.00 10.00
BA Bobby Abreu/99 6.00 15.00
BG Brian Giles/99 4.00 10.00
BL Joe Blanton/99 4.00 10.00
BM Brian McCann/99 6.00 15.00
BO Jeremy Bonderman/99 6.00 15.00
BR Brian Roberts/99 4.00 10.00
BS Ben Sheets/99 4.00 10.00
BU B.J. Upton/99 10.00 25.00
CA Miguel Cabrera/99 5.00 12.00
CB Craig Biggio/99 6.00 15.00
CC Chris Carpenter/99 5.00 12.00
CF Chone Figgins/99 4.00 10.00
CH Cole Hamels/99 6.00 15.00
CJ Chipper Jones/99 6.00 15.00
CL Roger Clemens/99 15.00 40.00
CN Robinson Cano/99 6.00 15.00
CR Carl Crawford/99 5.00 12.00
CU Chase Utley/99 6.00 15.00
CW Chien-Ming Wang/99 15.00 40.00
DJ Derek Jeter/99 20.00 50.00
DJ2 Derek Jeter/99 20.00 50.00
DL Derrek Lee/99 4.00 10.00
DO David Ortiz/99 6.00 15.00
DU Dan Uggla/99 4.00 10.00
DW Dontrelle Willis/99 4.00 10.00
EC Eric Chavez/99 4.00 10.00
FH Felix Hernandez/99 5.00 12.00
FL Francisco Liriano/99 6.00 15.00
FS Freddy Sanchez/99 4.00 10.00
FT Frank Thomas/99 10.00 25.00
GA Garrett Atkins/99 4.00 10.00
HA Travis Hafner/99 4.00 10.00
HE Todd Helton/99 5.00 12.00
HI Rich Hill/99 4.00 10.00
HK Howie Kendrick/34 6.00 15.00
HN Rich Harden/99 4.00 10.00
HR Hanley Ramirez/99 5.00 12.00
HS Huston Street/99 4.00 10.00
IK Ian Kinsler/99 4.00 10.00
IR Ivan Rodriguez/99 5.00 12.00
JB Jason Bay/99 5.00 12.00
JE Jim Edmonds/99 5.00 12.00
JF Jeff Francoeur/99 10.00 25.00
JJ Josh Johnson/99 4.00 10.00
JL Chad Billingsley/99 4.00 10.00
JM Joe Mauer/99 5.00 12.00
JN Joe Nathan/99 4.00 10.00
JP Jake Peavy/99 4.00 10.00
JR Jose Reyes/99 6.00 15.00
JS Jeremy Sowers/99 4.00 10.00
JT Jim Thome/99 5.00 12.00
JV Justin Verlander/3
JW Jered Weaver/99 5.00 12.00
JZ Joel Zumaya/99 5.00 12.00
KG Ken Griffey Jr./99 12.50 30.00
KG2 Ken Griffey Jr./99 12.50 30.00
KH Khalil Greene/99 5.00 12.00
KU Hong-Chih Kuo/99 5.00 12.00
LE Jon Lester/99 5.00 12.00
LG Luis Gonzalez/99 4.00 10.00
MC Matt Cain/99 5.00 12.00
ME Melky Cabrera/99 4.00 10.00
MH Matt Holliday/99 5.00 12.00
MO Justin Morneau/99 4.00 10.00
MT Mark Teixeira/99 5.00 12.00
NM Nick Markakis/99 10.00 25.00
NS Nick Swisher/99 6.00 15.00
PA Jonathan Papelbon/99 6.00 15.00
PF Prince Fielder/99 6.00 15.00
PL Paul LoDuca/99 5.00 12.00
RC Cal Ripken /99 15.00 40.00
RI Alex Rios/99 4.00 10.00
RJ Randy Johnson/99 6.00 15.00
RO Roy Oswalt/99 5.00 12.00
RW Rickie Weeks/99 4.00 10.00
RZ Ryan Zimmerman/99 10.00 25.00
SA Alfonso Soriano/99 5.00 12.00
SD Stephen Drew/99 5.00 12.00
SH James Shields/99 4.00 10.00
SK Scott Kazmir/99 5.00 12.00
SM John Smoltz/99 10.00 25.00
SO Scott Olsen/99 4.00 10.00
SR Scott Rolen/99 10.00 25.00
TE Miguel Tejada/99 4.00 10.00
TG Tom Glavine/99 6.00 15.00
TH Trevor Hoffman/99 5.00 12.00
TO Torii Hunter/99 5.00 12.00
VG Vladimir Guerrero/99 10.00 25.00
VM Victor Martinez/99 4.00 10.00
WE David Wells/99 4.00 10.00
WI Josh Willingham/99 4.00 10.00
YB Yuniesky Betancourt/99 4.00 10.00

2007 SPx Winning Materials Patches Silver

*PATCH SILVER: .4X TO 1X PATCH GOLD
APPX. SIX GAME-USED PER BOX
PRINT RUN B/WN 3-99 COPIES PER
NO PRICING ON QTY 27 OR LESS
JV Justin Verlander/99 6.00 15.00
LE Jon Lester/37 6.00 15.00

2007 SPx Winning Materials Patches Bronze

*PATCH BRONZE: .5X TO 1.2X PATCH GOLD
APPX. SIX GAME-USED PER BOX
STATED PRINT RUN 50 SER.#'d SETS
AR Aramis Ramirez/50 4.00 10.00
JM Joe Mauer/50
LE Jon Lester/50 6.00 15.00
MH Matt Holliday/50 5.00 12.00
RI Alex Rios/50

2007 SPx Winning Materials Patches Triple

APPX. SIX GAME-USED PER BOX
STATED PRINT RUN 25 SER.#'d SETS
NO PRICING DUE TO SCARCITY

2007 SPx Winning Materials Triple Signatures

APPX. FOUR AUTOS PER BOX
PRINT RUNS B/WN 15-35
EXCH DEADLINE 05/10/2010
NO PRICING DUE TO SCARCITY

2007 SPx Winning Materials Triple Signatures Platinum

APPX. FOUR AUTOS PER BOX
PRINT RUNS B/WN 4-10 COPIES PER
EXCH DEADLINE 05/10/2010
NO PRICING DUE TO SCARCITY

2007 SPx Winning Trios Bronze

*BRONZE: .5X TO 1.2X GOLD
APPX. SIX GAME-USED PER BOX
STATED PRINT RUN 30 SER.#'d SETS

2007 SPx Winning Trios Gold

APPX. SIX GAME-USED PER BOX
STATED PRINT RUN 75 SER.#'d SETS
WT1 Ken Griffey Jr. 20.00 50.00
Albert Pujols
Derek Jeter
WT2 Dan Uggla 10.00 25.00
Hanley Ramirez
Josh Willingham
WT3 Dontrelle Willis 6.00 15.00
Josh Johnson
Anibal Sanchez
WT4 Lance Berkman 10.00 25.00
David Ortiz
Travis Hafner
WT5 Jake Peavy 6.00 15.00
Roy Oswalt
Ben Sheets
WT6 Justin Verlander 10.00 25.00
Jeremy Bonderman
Ivan Rodriguez
WT7 Jose Reyes 10.00 25.00
Hanley Ramirez
Stephen Drew
WT8 Miguel Cabrera 10.00 25.00
Ryan Zimmerman
B.J. Upton
WT9 Jered Weaver 10.00 25.00
Justin Verlander
Jonathan Papelbon
WT10 Derek Jeter 20.00 50.00
Randy Johnson
Bobby Abreu
WT11 Morgan Ensberg 6.00 15.00
Craig Biggio
Lance Berkman
WT12 Jeff Francoeur 10.00 25.00
Adam LaRoche
Brian McCann
WT13 Joe Mauer 10.00 25.00
Brian McCann
Victor Martinez
WT14 Carl Crawford 10.00 25.00
Grady Sizemore
Jose Reyes
WT15 Freddy Garcia 6.00 15.00
Carlos Zambrano
Johan Santana
WT16 Vladimir Guerrero 10.00 25.00
Bobby Abreu
Alfonso Soriano
WT17 Justin Morneau 10.00 25.00
Joe Mauer
Johan Santana
WT18 Carlos Delgado 6.00 15.00
Jose Reyes
Carlos Beltran
WT19 Chad Billingsley 10.00 25.00
Andre Ethier
Matt Kemp
WT20 Jim Thome 10.00 25.00
Jermaine Dye
Tadahito Iguchi
WT21 Chase Utley 10.00 25.00
Aaron Rowand
Jimmy Rollins
WT22 Magglio Ordonez 15.00 40.00
Ivan Rodriguez
Curtis Granderson
WT23 Albert Pujols 15.00 40.00
Chris Carpenter
Scott Rolen
WT24 James Shields 6.00 15.00
B.J. Upton
Carl Crawford
WT25 Howie Kendrick 6.00 15.00
Jered Weaver
Mike Napoli
WT26 Dan Uggla 6.00 15.00
Howie Kendrick
Ian Kinsler
WT27 Brian Roberts 10.00 25.00
Miguel Tejada
Nick Markakis
WT28 Jered Weaver 10.00 25.00
Justin Verlander
Mike Pelfrey
WT29 Cole Hamels 10.00 25.00
Rich Hill
Francisco Liriano
WT30 Anibal Sanchez 6.00 15.00
Derek Lowe
Randy Johnson
WT31 Ryan Zimmerman 10.00 25.00
Prince Fielder
Dan Uggla
WT32 Trevor Hoffman 6.00 15.00
Joe Nathan
Huston Street
WT33 A.J. Burnett 6.00 15.00
Alex Rios
Vernon Wells
WT34 Rickie Weeks 10.00 25.00
Prince Fielder
Ben Sheets
WT35 Yuniesky Betancourt 10.00 25.00
Adrian Beltre
Felix Hernandez
WT36 Justin Verlander 10.00 25.00
Joel Zumaya
Jeremy Bonderman
WT37 Billy Wagner 6.00 15.00
Jose Reyes
Paul LoDuca
WT38 Jeremy Sowers 6.00 15.00
C.C. Sabathia
Victor Martinez
WT39 Stephen Drew 6.00 15.00
Brandon Webb
Conor Jackson
WT40 Felix Hernandez 10.00 25.00
Jered Weaver
Justin Verlander
WT41 Ken Griffey Jr. 15.00 40.00
Frank Thomas
Ivan Rodriguez
WT42 Derek Jeter 30.00 60.00
Cal Ripken
Jose Reyes

2007 SPx Winning Trios Silver

*SILVER: .4X TO 1X GOLD
APPX. SIX GAME-USED PER BOX
STATED PRINT RUN 50 SER.#'d SETS

2007 SPx Winning Trios Patches

APPX. SIX GAME-USED PER BOX
PRINT RUNS B/WN 8-25 COPIES PER
NO PRICING DUE TO SCARCITY

2007 SPx Young Stars Signatures

STATED ODDS 1:12
EXCH DEADLINE 05/10/2010
APPX.PRINTING PLATE ODDS 2 PER CASE
PLATES PRINT RUN 1 SET PER COLOR
BLACK-CYAN-MAGENTA-YELLOW ISSUED
NO PLATE PRICING DUE TO SCARCITY
AE Andre Ethier 12.50 30.00
AG Adrian Gonzalez 10.00 25.00
AM Andrew Miller 10.00 25.00
AS Anibal Sanchez 3.00 8.00
BH Bill Hall
BU B.J. Upton 6.00 15.00
CA Matt Cain 6.00 15.00
CH Cole Hamels 6.00 15.00
CQ Carlos Quentin 8.00 20.00
CU Chase Utley
DJ Derek Jeter 100.00 175.00
DU Dan Uggla 10.00 25.00
DY Delmon Young 6.00 15.00
FH Felix Hernandez 8.00 20.00
FL Francisco Liriano 4.00 10.00
FS Freddy Sanchez
HA Rich Harden 5.00 12.00
HI Rich Hill 6.00 15.00
HK Howie Kendrick 6.00 15.00
HR Hanley Ramirez 6.00 15.00
HS Huston Street
IK Ian Kinsler
JB Jeremy Brown 3.00 8.00

JF Jeff Francoeur
JJ Josh Johnson 8.00 20.00
JL Jon Lester 8.00 20.00
JM Joe Mauer 20.00 50.00
JP Jonathan Papelbon 12.50 30.00
JR Jose Reyes 12.50 30.00
JS Jeremy Sowers 3.00 8.00
JV Justin Verlander 30.00 60.00
JW Jered Weaver 10.00 25.00
JZ Joel Zumaya 8.00 20.00
KG Ken Griffey Jr. 40.00 80.00
KU Hong-Chih Kuo 10.00 25.00
LO James Loney 10.00 25.00
MC Melky Cabrera
MO Justin Morneau 6.00 15.00
NM Nick Markakis 10.00 25.00
PF Prince Fielder
PH Philip Humber 5.00 12.00
RW Rickie Weeks 5.00 12.00
RY Jae Kuk Ryu
RZ Ryan Zimmerman 10.00 25.00
SC Shin-Soo Choo
SD Stephen Drew 5.00 12.00
SO Scott Olsen
ST Scott Thorman 5.00 12.00
TT Troy Tulowitzki 15.00 40.00
WI Josh Willingham 3.00 8.00

2007 SPx Young Stars Signatures Spectrum

APPX. FOUR AUTOS PER BOX
STATED PRINT RUN 25 SER.#'d SETS
EXCH DEADLINE 05/10/2010

2008 SPx

COMMON CARD (1-100) .25 .60
COMMON AU RC (101-150) 3.00 8.00
OVERALL AU ODDS FOUR PER BOX
1 Brandon Webb .40 1.00
2 Chris B. Young .25 .60
3 Eric Byrnes .25 .60
4 Dan Haren .25 .60
5 Mark Teixeira .60 1.50
6 Chipper Jones .60 1.50
7 John Smoltz .60 1.50
8 Erik Bedard .25 .60
9 Nick Markakis .60 1.50
10 Brian Roberts .25 .60
11 David Ortiz .40 1.00
12 Curt Schilling .40 1.00
13 Manny Ramirez .60 1.50
14 Daisuke Matsuzaka .60 1.50
15 Josh Beckett .40 1.00
16 Derrek Lee .25 .60
17 Alfonso Soriano .40 1.00
18 Carlos Zambrano .40 1.00
19 Aramis Ramirez .25 .60
20 Jermaine Dye .25 .60
21 Jim Thome .40 1.00
22 Nick Swisher .60 1.50
23 Ken Griffey Jr. 1.00 2.50
24 Adam Dunn .40 1.00
25 Brandon Phillips .25 .60
26 Grady Sizemore .40 1.00
27 Victor Martinez .40 1.00
28 C.C. Sabathia .40 1.00
29 Travis Hafner .25 .60
30 Matt Holliday .60 1.50
31 Todd Helton .40 1.00
32 Troy Tulowitzki .60 1.50
33 Magglio Ordonez .40 1.00
34 Gary Sheffield .25 .60
35 Justin Verlander .75 2.00
36 Curtis Granderson .40 1.00
37 Miguel Cabrera .60 1.50
38 Hanley Ramirez .60 1.50
39 Dan Uggla .40 1.00
40 Miguel Tejada .40 1.00
41 Lance Berkman .40 1.00
42 Hunter Pence .60 1.50
43 Carlos Lee .25 .60
44 Alex Gordon .40 1.00
45 David DeJesus .25 .60
46 Vladimir Guerrero .60 1.50
47 Jered Weaver .25 .60
48 Torii Hunter .25 .60
49 Andruw Jones .25 .60
50 Rafael Furcal .25 .60
51 Russell Martin .25 .60
52 Brad Penny .25 .60
53 Ryan Braun .75 2.00
54 Prince Fielder .60 1.50
55 J.J. Hardy .25 .60
56 Justin Morneau .60 1.50
57 Johan Santana .60 1.50
58 Joe Mauer .60 1.50
59 Delmon Young .40 1.00
60 Jose Reyes .40 1.00
61 David Wright .75 2.00
62 Carlos Beltran .25 .60
63 Pedro Martinez .40 1.00
64 Chien-Ming Wang .40 1.00
65 Alex Rodriguez 1.00 2.50
66 Derek Jeter 1.50 4.00
67 Robinson Cano .60 1.50
68 Hideki Matsui .60 1.50
69 Joe Blanton .25 .60
70 Jack Cust .25 .60
71 Cole Hamels .60 1.50
72 Jimmy Rollins .40 1.00
73 Ryan Howard .75 2.00
74 Chase Utley .60 1.50
75 Jason Bay .40 1.00
76 Freddy Sanchez .25 .60
77 Jake Peavy .25 .60
78 Greg Maddux .75 2.00
79 Adrian Gonzalez .40 1.00
80 Barry Zito .25 .60
81 Omar Vizquel .40 1.00
82 Tim Lincecum 1.00 2.50
83 Ichiro Suzuki 1.00 2.50
84 Felix Hernandez .60 1.50
85 Kenji Johjima .25 .60
86 Albert Pujols 1.50 4.00
87 Scott Rolen .40 1.00
88 Chris Carpenter .60 1.50
89 Rick Ankiel .25 .60
90 Scott Kazmir .40 1.00
91 Carl Crawford .40 1.00
92 B.J. Upton .40 1.00
93 Michael Young .40 1.00
94 Josh Hamilton .60 1.50
95 Hank Blalock .25 .60
96 Roy Halladay .60 1.50
97 Vernon Wells .25 .60
98 Alex Rios .40 1.00
99 Ryan Zimmerman .40 1.00
100 Dmitri Young .25 .60
101 Bill Murphy AU (RC) 3.00 8.00
102 Emilio Bonifacio AU RC 5.00 12.00
103 Brandon Jones AU RC 3.00 8.00
104 Clint Sammons AU (RC) 3.00 8.00
105 Clay Buchholz AU (RC) 10.00 25.00
106 Kevin Hart AU (RC) 3.00 8.00
107 Donny Lucy AU (RC) 3.00 8.00
108 Lance Broadway AU (RC) 3.00 8.00
109 Joey Votto AU (RC) 30.00 60.00
110 Ryan Hanigan AU RC 4.00 10.00
111 Joe Koshansky AU (RC) 3.00 8.00
112 Josh Newman AU RC 3.00 8.00
113 Seth Smith AU (RC) 3.00 8.00
114 Chris Seddon AU (RC) 3.00 8.00
115 Harvey Garcia AU (RC) 3.00 8.00
116 Felipe Paulino AU RC 3.00 8.00
117 J.R. Towles AU RC 4.00 10.00
118 Josh Anderson AU (RC) 3.00 8.00
119 Troy Patton AU (RC) 3.00 8.00
120 Billy Buckner AU (RC) 3.00 8.00
121 Luke Hochevar AU RC 3.00 8.00
122 Chin-Lung Hu AU (RC) 6.00 15.00
123 Jonathan Meloan AU RC
124 Jose Morales AU (RC) 6.00 15.00
125 Carlos Muniz AU RC
126 Alberto Gonzalez AU RC 3.00 8.00
127 Bronson Sardinha AU (RC) 3.00 8.00
128 Ian Kennedy AU RC 8.00 20.00
129 Ross Ohlendorf AU RC 3.00 8.00
130 Daric Barton AU (RC) 6.00 15.00
131 Jerry Blevins AU RC 3.00 8.00
132 Dave Davidson AU RC 3.00 8.00
133 Nyjer Morgan AU (RC) 3.00 8.00
134 Steve Pearce AU RC 3.00 8.00
135 Colt Morton AU RC 3.00 8.00
136 Eugenio Velez AU RC 3.00 8.00
137 Jeff Clement AU (RC)
138 Rob Johnson AU (RC) 3.00 8.00
139 Wladimir Balentien AU (RC) 3.00 8.00
140 Justin Ruggiano AU RC 3.00 8.00
141 Bill White AU RC 3.00 8.00
142 Luis Mendoza AU (RC) 3.00 8.00
143 Jonathan Albaladejo AU RC 3.00 8.00
144 Justin Maxwell AU RC
145 Ross Detwiler AU RC 6.00 15.00
146 Jay Bruce AU (RC) UER 8.00 20.00
Incorrectly refers to Bruce as A's young star
147 Carlos Gonzalez AU (RC) 75.00 150.00
148 Evan Longoria AU RC 20.00 50.00
149 Collin Balester AU (RC)
150 Max Scherzer AU RC 6.00 15.00
151 Clayton Kershaw AU RC 15.00 40.00
152 Alexei Ramirez AU RC

2008 SPx Silver

*SILVER AU: .4X TO 1X BASIC AU RC
RANDOM INSERT IN BOX TOPPER PACK
CARDS 146-150 DO NOT EXIST

2008 SPx Babe Ruth American Legend

COMMON RUTH 15.00 40.00
OVERALL ODDS ONE PER CASE
STATED PRINT RUN 1 SER.#'d SET

2008 SPx Ken Griffey Jr. American Hero

RANDOM INSERTS IN PACKS
STATED PRINT RUN 725 SER.#'d SETS

2008 SPx Ken Griffey Jr. American Hero Boxscore

OVERALL ODDS ONE PER CASE
STATED PRINT RUN 1 SER.#'d SET

2008 SPx Ken Griffey Jr. American Hero Memorabilia

COMMON GRIFFEY 20.00 50.00
OVERALL MEM ODDS SIX PER BOX
STATED PRINT RUN 25 SER.#'d SETS

2008 SPx Ken Griffey Jr. American Hero Signature

OVERALL AU ODDS FOUR PER BOX
STATED PRINT RUN 3 SER.#'d SETS
KG1 Ken Griffey Jr. 250.00 350.00

2008 SPx Mystery Rookie Redemptions

OVERALL ODDS TWO PER CASE
REDEEMABLE FOR BASE SET AU RC
EXCHANGE DEADLINE 6/30/2010
RR1 Jay Bruce #146 AU (RC)
RR2 Carlos Gonzalez #147 AU (RC)
RR3 Evan Longoria #148 AU RC
RR4 Collin Balester #149 AU (RC)
RR5 Max Scherzer #150 AU RC
RR6 Clayton Kershaw #151 AU RC
RR7 Alexei Ramirez #152 AU RC

2008 SPx Superstar Signatures

OVERALL AU ODDS FOUR PER BOX
EXCHANGE DEADLINE 4/28/2010
BW Brandon Webb 6.00 15.00
DJ Derek Jeter EXCH 75.00 150.00
DM Daisuke Matsuzaka 60.00 120.00
DU Dan Uggla 6.00 15.00
HR Hanley Ramirez 8.00 20.00
KG Ken Griffey Jr. 50.00 100.00
MH Matt Holliday 10.00 25.00
MT Mark Teixeira 10.00 25.00
PF Prince Fielder 12.50 30.00
PM Pedro Martinez
SR Scott Rolen 10.00 25.00
TG Tom Glavine 15.00 40.00
TH Travis Hafner 4.00 10.00
VG Vladimir Guerrero 15.00 40.00
VM Victor Martinez 8.00 20.00

2008 SPx Superstar Signatures Silver

RANDOM INSERT IN BOX TOPPER PACK
NO PRICING DUE TO SCARCITY
EXCHANGE DEADLINE 4/28/2010

2008 SPx Winning Materials SPx 150

OVERALL GU ODDS SIX PER BOX
STATED PRINT RUN 150 SER.#'d SETS
AB A.J. Burnett 3.00 8.00
AE Andre Ethier 3.00 8.00
AG Adrian Gonzalez 3.00 8.00
AH Aaron Harang 3.00 8.00
AJ Andruw Jones 3.00 8.00
AK Austin Kearns 3.00 8.00
AL Adam LaRoche 3.00 8.00
AP Albert Pujols 5.00 12.00
AP Andy Pettitte 4.00 10.00
AR Aaron Rowand 3.00 8.00
AS Alfonso Soriano 3.00 8.00
BA Bobby Abreu 3.00 8.00
BC Bartolo Colon 3.00 8.00
BE Adrian Beltre 3.00 8.00
BG Brian Giles 3.00 8.00
BM Brian McCann 3.00 8.00
BS Ben Sheets 3.00 8.00
BU B.J. Upton 3.00 8.00
BW Billy Wagner 4.00 10.00
CA Chris Carpenter 3.00 8.00
CB Carlos Beltran 3.00 8.00
CC Chad Cordero 3.00 8.00
CD Carlos Delgado 3.00 8.00
CG Carlos Guillen 3.00 8.00
CH Chris Burke 3.00 8.00
CJ Chipper Jones
CK Casey Kotchman 3.00 8.00
CL Carlos Lee 3.00 8.00
CS Curt Schilling 3.00 8.00
CU Chase Utley 5.00 12.00
CZ Carlos Zambrano 3.00 8.00
DH Dan Haren 3.00 8.00
DJ Derek Jeter 10.00 25.00
DL Derrek Lee 3.00 8.00
DO David Ortiz 3.00 8.00
DU Dan Uggla 3.00 8.00
DW Dontrelle Willis 3.00 8.00
DY Jermaine Dye 3.00 8.00
EC Eric Chavez 3.00 8.00
FH Felix Hernandez 3.00 8.00
FL Francisco Liriano 3.00 8.00
GA Garret Anderson 3.00 8.00
GA Garrett Atkins 3.00 8.00
GJ Geoff Jenkins 3.00 8.00
GM Greg Maddux 5.00 12.00
GO Alex Gordon 5.00 12.00
GR Curtis Granderson 3.00 8.00
GS Grady Sizemore 3.00 8.00
HA Cole Hamels 3.00 8.00
HB Hank Blalock 3.00 8.00
HE Todd Helton 3.00 8.00
HO Trevor Hoffman 3.00 8.00
HR Hanley Ramirez 3.00 8.00
HU Torii Hunter 3.00 8.00
IR Ivan Rodriguez 4.00 10.00
JA Conor Jackson 3.00 8.00
JB Josh Barfield 3.00 8.00
JD J.D. Drew 3.00 8.00
JE Jim Edmonds 4.00 10.00
JF Jeff Francoeur 4.00 10.00
JG Jason Giambi 3.00 8.00
JH Jhonny Peralta 3.00 8.00
JJ J.J. Hardy 3.00 8.00
JK Jeff Kent 3.00 8.00
JM Joe Mauer 3.00 8.00
JN Joe Nathan 3.00 8.00
JO Josh Beckett 4.00 10.00
JP Jake Peavy 3.00 8.00
JR Jose Reyes 3.00 8.00
JS Johan Santana 3.00 8.00
JT Jim Thome 3.00 8.00
JV Jason Varitek 4.00 10.00
KG Ken Griffey Jr.
KJ Kenji Johjima 3.00 8.00
KY Kevin Youkilis 4.00 10.00
LB Lance Berkman 3.00 8.00
LG Luis Gonzalez 3.00 8.00
MC Miguel Cabrera 3.00 8.00
MH Matt Holliday 3.00 8.00
MO Justin Morneau 3.00 8.00
MR Manny Ramirez 4.00 10.00
MT Mark Teixeira 3.00 8.00
MY Michael Young 3.00 8.00
OR Magglio Ordonez 3.00 8.00
PA Jonathan Papelbon 4.00 10.00
PF Prince Fielder 4.00 10.00
PM Pedro Martinez 3.00 8.00
PO Jorge Posada 3.00 8.00
RA Aramis Ramirez 3.00 8.00
RF Rafael Furcal
RH Roy Halladay 3.00 8.00
RJ Randy Johnson 3.00 8.00
RO Roy Oswalt 3.00 8.00
SM John Smoltz 4.00 10.00
TE Miguel Tejada 3.00 8.00
TH Tim Hudson 3.00 8.00
TR Travis Hafner 3.00 8.00
VE Justin Verlander 3.00 8.00
VG Vladimir Guerrero 3.00 8.00
VW Vernon Wells 3.00 8.00

2008 SPx Winning Materials Baseball 99

*BB 99: .4X TO 1X WM SPX 150
OVERALL GU ODDS SIX PER BOX
STATED PRINT RUN 99 SER.#'d SETS
KG Ken Griffey Jr. 5.00 12.00
RF Rafael Furcal 3.00 8.00

2008 SPx Winning Materials Dual Jersey Number

*DUAL JN: .5X TO 1.2X WM SPX 150
OVERALL GU ODDS SIX PER BOX
PRINT RUNS B/WN 35-46 COPIES PER
CJ Chipper Jones/46 5.00 12.00

2008 SPx Winning Materials Dual Limited Patch SPx

*DUAL LTD PATCH: .6X TO 1.5X LTD PATCH SPX
OVERALL GU ODDS SIX PER BOX
PRINT RUNS B/WN 23-50 COPIES PER
NO PRICING ON QTY 25 OR LESS
KG Ken Griffey Jr. 15.00 40.00

2008 SPx Winning Materials Dual Limited Patch Team Initials

OVERALL GU ODDS SIX PER BOX
STATED PRINT RUN 25 SER.#'d SETS
HANLEY PRINT RUN 5 SER.#'d SETS
NO PRICING DUE TO SCARCITY

2008 SPx Winning Materials Dual MLB 20

OVERALL GU ODDS SIX PER BOX
STATED PRINT RUN 20 SER.#'d SETS
NO PRICING DUE TO SCARCITY

2008 SPx Winning Materials Dual Position 20

OVERALL GU ODDS SIX PER BOX
STATED PRINT RUN 20 SER.#'d SETS
NO PRICING DUE TO SCARCITY

2008 SPx Winning Materials Dual SPx

*DUAL SPX: .5X TO 1.2X WM SPX 150
OVERALL GU ODDS SIX PER BOX
STATED PRINT RUN 50 SER.#'d SETS

2008 SPx Winning Materials Dual Team Initials 25

OVERALL GU ODDS SIX PER BOX
STATED PRINT RUN 25 SER.#'d SETS
NO PRICING DUE TO SCARCITY

2008 SPx Winning Materials Jersey Number 125

*JN 125: .4X TO 1X WM SPX 150
OVERALL GU ODDS SIX PER BOX
STATED PRINT RUN 125 SER.#'d SETS
RF Rafael Furcal 3.00 8.00

2008 SPx Winning Materials Limited Patch SPx

OVERALL GU ODDS SIX PER BOX
PRINT RUNS B/WN 72-99 COPIES PER
AB A.J. Burnett 4.00 10.00
AE Andre Ethier 4.00 10.00
AG Adrian Gonzalez 4.00 10.00
AH Aaron Harang 4.00 10.00
AJ Andruw Jones 4.00 10.00
AK Austin Kearns 4.00 10.00
AL Adam LaRoche 4.00 10.00
AP Albert Pujols 10.00 25.00
AR Aaron Rowand 4.00 10.00
AS Alfonso Soriano 4.00 10.00
AT Garrett Atkins 4.00 10.00
BA Bobby Abreu 4.00 10.00
BC Bartolo Colon 4.00 10.00
BE Adrian Beltre 4.00 10.00
BG Brian Giles 4.00 10.00
BM Brian McCann/72 4.00 10.00
BS Ben Sheets/97 4.00 10.00
BU B.J. Upton 4.00 10.00
BW Billy Wagner 5.00 12.00
CA Chris Carpenter 4.00 10.00
CB Carlos Beltran 3.00 8.00
CC Chad Cordero 3.00 8.00
CD Carlos Delgado 3.00 8.00
CG Carlos Guillen 4.00 10.00
CH Chris Burke 3.00 8.00
CJ Chipper Jones 5.00 12.00
CK Casey Kotchman 3.00 8.00
CL Carlos Lee 3.00 8.00
CS Curt Schilling 4.00 10.00
CU Chase Utley 5.00 12.00
CZ Carlos Zambrano 4.00 10.00
DH Dan Haren 4.00 10.00
DJ Derek Jeter/76 15.00 40.00
DL Derrek Lee 4.00 10.00
DO David Ortiz 5.00 12.00
DU Dan Uggla 4.00 10.00
DW Dontrelle Willis 4.00 10.00
DY Jermaine Dye 4.00 10.00
EC Eric Chavez 4.00 10.00
FH Felix Hernandez 4.00 10.00
FL Francisco Liriano 4.00 10.00
GA Garret Anderson 4.00 10.00
GJ Geoff Jenkins 4.00 10.00
GM Greg Maddux 6.00 15.00
GO Alex Gordon 6.00 15.00
GR Curtis Granderson 4.00 10.00
GS Grady Sizemore 4.00 10.00
HA Cole Hamels 4.00 10.00
HB Hank Blalock 4.00 10.00
HE Todd Helton 4.00 10.00
HO Trevor Hoffman 4.00 10.00
HR Hanley Ramirez 4.00 10.00
HU Torii Hunter 4.00 10.00
IR Ivan Rodriguez 5.00 12.00
JA Conor Jackson/80 4.00 10.00
JB Josh Barfield 4.00 10.00
JD J.D. Drew 4.00 10.00
JE Jim Edmonds 5.00 12.00
JF Jeff Francoeur 5.00 12.00
JG Jason Giambi 4.00 10.00
JH Jhonny Peralta 4.00 10.00
JJ J.J. Hardy 4.00 10.00
JK Jeff Kent 4.00 10.00
JM Joe Mauer 4.00 10.00
JN Joe Nathan 4.00 10.00
JO Josh Beckett 5.00 12.00
JP Jake Peavy 4.00 10.00
JR Jose Reyes 4.00 10.00
JS Johan Santana 4.00 10.00
JT Jim Thome 4.00 10.00
JV Jason Varitek 5.00 12.00
KG Ken Griffey Jr. 6.00 15.00
KJ Kenji Johjima 4.00 10.00
KY Kevin Youkilis 5.00 12.00
LB Lance Berkman 4.00 10.00
LG Luis Gonzalez 4.00 10.00
MC Miguel Cabrera 4.00 10.00
MH Matt Holliday 4.00 10.00
MO Justin Morneau 4.00 10.00
MR Manny Ramirez 5.00 12.00
MT Mark Teixeira 4.00 10.00
MY Michael Young 4.00 10.00
OR Magglio Ordonez 4.00 10.00
PA Jonathan Papelbon 5.00 12.00
PE Andy Pettitte 4.00 10.00
PF Prince Fielder 5.00 12.00
PM Pedro Martinez 4.00 10.00
PO Jorge Posada 4.00 10.00
RA Aramis Ramirez 4.00 10.00
RF Rafael Furcal 4.00 10.00
RH Roy Halladay 4.00 10.00
RJ Randy Johnson 4.00 10.00
RO Roy Oswalt 4.00 10.00
SM John Smoltz 5.00 12.00
TE Miguel Tejada/83 4.00 10.00
TH Tim Hudson 4.00 10.00
TR Travis Hafner 4.00 10.00
VE Justin Verlander 4.00 10.00
VG Vladimir Guerrero 4.00 10.00
VW Vernon Wells 4.00 10.00

2008 SPx Winning Materials Limited Patch Team Initials

*LTD PATCH TI: .5X TO 1.2X LTD PATCH SPX
OVERALL GU ODDS SIX PER BOX
PRINT RUNS B/WN 40-50 COPIES PER

2008 SPx Winning Materials MLB 125

*MLB 125: .4X TO 1X WM SPX 150
OVERALL GU ODDS SIX PER BOX
STATED PRINT RUN 125 SER.#'d SETS
RF Rafael Furcal 3.00 8.00

2008 SPx Winning Materials Position 75

*POS 75: .4X TO 1X WM SPX 150
OVERALL GU ODDS SIX PER BOX
STATED PRINT RUN 75 SER.#'d SETS

2008 SPx Winning Materials SPx Die Cut 150

*SPX DC 150: .4X TO 1X SPX 150
OVERALL GU ODDS SIX PER BOX
STATED PRINT RUN 150 SER.#'d SETS

2008 SPx Winning Materials Team Initials 99

*TI 99: .4X TO 1X WM SPX 150
OVERALL GU ODDS SIX PER BOX
STATED PRINT RUN 99 SER.#'d SETS
KG Ken Griffey Jr. 5.00 12.00
RF Rafael Furcal 3.00 8.00

2008 SPx Winning Materials Triple Limited Patch 15

OVERALL GU ODDS SIX PER BOX
STATED PRINT RUN 15 SER.#'d SETS
NO PRICING DUE TO SCARCITY

2008 SPx Winning Materials Triple SPx 15

OVERALL GU ODDS SIX PER BOX
STATED PRINT RUN 15 SER.#'d SETS
NO PRICING DUE TO SCARCITY

2008 SPx Winning Materials Triple Swatch Autographs

OVERALL AU ODDS FOUR PER BOX
STATED PRINT RUN 5 SER.#'d SETS
NO PRICING DUE TO SCARCITY
EXCHANGE DEADLINE 4/28/2010

2008 SPx Winning Materials Triple Team Initials 10

OVERALL GU ODDS SIX PER BOX
STATED PRINT RUN 10 SER.#'d SETS
NO PRICING DUE TO SCARCITY

2008 SPx Winning Materials UD Logo

*LOGO 99: .4X TO 1X WM SPX 150
OVERALL GU ODDS SIX PER BOX
PRINT RUNS B/WN 26-99 COPIES PER
KG Ken Griffey Jr./26 8.00 20.00
RF Rafael Furcal 3.00 8.00

2008 SPx Winning Trios

OVERALL GU ODDS SIX PER BOX
STATED PRINT RUN 75 SER.#'d SETS
GOLD 25 PRINT RUN 25 SER.#'d SETS
NO GOLD 25 PRICING DUE TO SCARCITY
GOLD 15 PRINT RUN 15 SER.#'d SETS
NO GOLD 15 PRICING DUE TO SCARCITY
LTD.PATCH PRINT RUN 25 SER.#'d SETS
NO LTD.PATCH PRICING DUE TO SCARCITY
AGK Garret Anderson 4.00 10.00
Vladimir Guerrero
Casey Kotchman
BHJ Adrian Beltre 4.00 10.00
Felix Hernandez
Kenji Johjima
BSS Josh Beckett 4.00 10.00
Johan Santana
C.C. Sabathia
CRP Chris Carpenter 6.00 15.00
Scott Rolen
Albert Pujols
CRU Miguel Cabrera 4.00 10.00
Hanley Ramirez
Dan Uggla
DBR Carlos Delgado 4.00 10.00
Carlos Beltran
Jose Reyes
DOP Carlos Delgado 8.00 20.00
David Ortiz
Albert Pujols
GHL Yovani Gallardo 6.00 15.00
Phil Hughes
Tim Lincecum
GIB Alex Gordon 20.00 50.00
Akinori Iwamura
Ryan Braun
GJP Ken Griffey Jr. 15.00 40.00
Derek Jeter
Albert Pujols
GMW Tom Glavine 8.00 20.00
Pedro Martinez
Billy Wagner
HAH Todd Helton 5.00 12.00
Garrett Atkins
Matt Holliday
HDF Travis Hafner 5.00 12.00
Adam Dunn
Prince Fielder
HFB J.J. Hardy 8.00 20.00
Prince Fielder
Ryan Braun
HRR J.J. Hardy 4.00 10.00
Jose Reyes
Hanley Ramirez
HSS Travis Hafner 4.00 10.00
Grady Sizemore
C.C. Sabathia
JBH Andruw Jones 4.00 10.00
Carlos Beltran
Torii Hunter
JDY Conor Jackson 4.00 10.00
Stephen Drew
Chris B. Young
JRR Chipper Jones 5.00 12.00
Scott Rolen
Aramis Ramirez
JST Chipper Jones 6.00 15.00
John Smoltz
Mark Teixeira
KFE Jeff Kent 5.00 12.00
Rafael Furcal
Andre Ethier
KUY Scott Kazmir 4.00 10.00
B.J. Upton
Delmon Young
LBO Carlos Lee 4.00 10.00
Lance Berkman
Roy Oswalt
LCL Noah Lowry 6.00 15.00
Matt Cain
Tim Lincecum
LSZ Derrek Lee 6.00 15.00
Alfonso Soriano
Carlos Zambrano
MGS Greg Maddux 15.00 40.00
Tom Glavine
John Smoltz
MHP Greg Maddux 6.00 15.00
Trevor Hoffman
Jake Peavy
MPB Victor Martinez 4.00 10.00
Jhonny Peralta
Josh Barfield
MSM Justin Morneau 5.00 12.00
Johan Santana
Joe Mauer
OGV Magglio Ordonez 10.00 25.00
Curtis Granderson
Justin Verlander
PJP Andy Pettitte 30.00 60.00
Derek Jeter
Jorge Posada
RJC Alex Rodriguez 30.00 60.00
Derek Jeter
Robinson Cano
RMM Ivan Rodriguez 5.00 12.00
Victor Martinez
Joe Mauer
SBP Curt Schilling 6.00 15.00
Josh Beckett
Jonathan Papelbon
SOH Ben Sheets 4.00 10.00
Roy Oswalt
Aaron Harang
SRG Gary Sheffield 6.00 15.00
Ivan Rodriguez
Carlos Guillen
TDB Jim Thome 5.00 12.00
Jermaine Dye
Mark Buehrle
UHR Chase Utley 6.00 15.00
Cole Hamels
Aaron Rowand
UKU Chase Utley 4.00 10.00
Ian Kinsler
Dan Uggla
VOY Jason Varitek 12.50 30.00
David Ortiz
Kevin Youkilis
WHB Vernon Wells 5.00 12.00
Roy Halladay
A.J. Burnett
ZPH Carlos Zambrano 4.00 10.00
Jake Peavy
Aaron Harang

2008 SPx Young Star Signatures

OVERALL AU ODDS FOUR PER BOX
EXCHANGE DEADLINE 4/28/2010
AC Alexi Casilla 3.00 8.00
AE Andre Ethier 10.00 25.00
BB Brian Bannister 4.00 10.00
BM Brian McCann 10.00 25.00
BU Brian Burres 4.00 10.00
CD Chris Duncan 6.00 15.00
CH Cole Hamels 8.00 20.00
CY Chris B. Young 5.00 12.00
FC Fausto Carmona 4.00 10.00
FL Francisco Liriano 4.00 10.00
IK Ian Kinsler 5.00 12.00
JA Joaquin Arias 3.00 8.00
JD John Danks 3.00 8.00
JJ Josh Johnson 3.00 8.00
JL James Loney 6.00 15.00
JS Jarrod Saltalamacchia 3.00 8.00
JV Justin Verlander 10.00 25.00
JW Josh Willingham 3.00 8.00
JZ Joel Zumaya 3.00 8.00
KK Kevin Kouzmanoff 3.00 8.00
MA Nick Markakis 10.00 25.00
MC Matt Chico 3.00 8.00
MF Mike Fontenot 5.00 12.00
MO Micah Owings 4.00 10.00
MR Mark Reynolds 5.00 12.00
NM Nate McLouth 5.00 12.00
PH Phil Hughes 6.00 15.00
RB Ryan Braun 15.00 40.00
RG Ryan Garko 3.00 8.00
RM Russell Martin 6.00 15.00
SD Stephen Drew 4.00 10.00
SH James Shields 5.00 12.00
TB Travis Buck 4.00 10.00
TG Tom Gorzelanny 3.00 8.00
TT Troy Tulowitzki 8.00 20.00

2008 SPx Young Star Signatures Silver

RANDOM INSERT IN BOX TOPPER PACK
NO PRICING DUE TO SCARCITY
EXCHANGE DEADLINE 4/28/2010

2009 SPx

This set was released on March 24, 2009. The base set consists of 123 cards.

COMP.SET w/o AU's (100) 12.50 30.00
COMMON CARD (1-100) .20 .50
COMMON AU RC (101-123) 4.00 10.00
OVERALL AUTO ODDS 1:18
AU RC PRINT RUN 99 SER.#'d SETS
1 Ichiro Suzuki .75 2.00
2 Rick Ankiel .20 .50
3 Garrett Atkins .20 .50
4 Jason Bay .30 .75
5 Josh Beckett .30 .75
6 Erik Bedard .20 .50
7 Carlos Beltran .30 .75
8 Lance Berkman .30 .75
9 Ryan Braun .60 1.50
10 Jay Bruce .30 .75
11 Miguel Cabrera .50 1.25
12 Matt Cain .20 .50
13 Joba Chamberlain .30 .75
14 Carl Crawford .30 .75
15 Jack Cust .20 .50
16 Joe DiMaggio 1.25 3.00
17 Ryan Doumit .20 .50
18 Justin Duchscherer .20 .50
19 Adam Dunn .30 .75
20 Prince Fielder .30 .75
21 Kosuke Fukudome .50 1.25
22 Troy Glaus .20 .50
23 Tom Glavine .30 .75
24 Adrian Gonzalez .30 .75
25 Alex Gordon .20 .50
26 Zack Greinke .30 .75
27 Ken Griffey Jr. .75 2.00
28 Vladimir Guerrero .50 1.25
29 Travis Hafner .20 .50
30 Roy Halladay .50 1.25
31 Cole Hamels .50 1.25
32 Josh Hamilton .50 1.25
33 Rich Harden .20 .50
34 Dan Haren .20 .50
35 Felix Hernandez .50 1.25
36 Trevor Hoffman .30 .75
37 Matt Holliday .50 1.25
38 Ryan Howard .60 1.50
39 Torii Hunter .20 .50
40 Derek Jeter 1.25 3.00
41 Randy Johnson .30 .75
42 Chipper Jones .50 1.25
43 Scott Kazmir .20 .50
44 Matt Kemp .30 .75
45 Clayton Kershaw .50 1.25
46 Ian Kinsler .30 .75
47 John Lackey .30 .75
48 Carlos Lee .20 .50
49 Derrek Lee .20 .50
50 Tim Lincecum .75 2.00
51 Evan Longoria .60 1.50
52 Nick Markakis .50 1.25
53 Russell Martin .20 .50
54 Victor Martinez .30 .75
55 Hideki Matsui .50 1.25
56 Daisuke Matsuzaka .50 1.25
57 Joe Mauer .50 1.25
58 Brian McCann .30 .75
59 Nate McLouth .20 .50
60 Lastings Milledge .20 .50
61 Justin Morneau .50 1.25
62 Magglio Ordonez .30 .75
63 David Ortiz .30 .75

64 Roy Oswalt .30 .75
65 Jonathan Papelbon .30 .75
66 Jake Peavy .20 .50
67 Dustin Pedroia .60 1.50
68 Brandon Phillips .20 .50
69 Albert Pujols 1.25 3.00
70 Carlos Quentin .30 .75
71 Aramis Ramirez .20 .50
72 Hanley Ramirez .50 1.25
73 Manny Ramirez .50 1.25
74 Jose Reyes .30 .75
75 Alex Rios .30 .75
76 Mariano Rivera .50 1.25
77 Brian Roberts .20 .50
78 Alex Rodriguez .75 2.00
79 Ivan Rodriguez .30 .75
80 Jimmy Rollins .30 .75
81 CC Sabathia .30 .75
82 Johan Santana .50 1.25
83 Grady Sizemore .30 .75
84 John Smoltz .50 1.25
85 Alfonso Soriano .30 .75
86 Mark Teixeira .50 1.25
87 Miguel Tejada .30 .75
88 Jim Thome .30 .75
89 Troy Tulowitzki .50 1.25
90 Dan Uggla .30 .75
91 B.J. Upton .30 .75
92 Chase Utley .50 1.25
93 Edinson Volquez .20 .50
94 Chien-Ming Wang .30 .75
95 Brandon Webb .30 .75
96 Vernon Wells .20 .50
97 David Wright .60 1.50
98 Michael Young .30 .75
99 Carlos Zambrano .30 .75
100 Ryan Zimmerman .30 .75
101 David Price AU RC 15.00 40.00
102 Aaron Cunningham AU RC 12.50 30.00
103 Angel Salome AU (RC) 10.00 25.00
104 Conor Gillaspie AU RC 12.50 30.00
105 Chris Lambert AU (RC) 8.00 20.00
106 Dexter Fowler AU (RC) 6.00 15.00
107 Francisco Cervelli AU RC EXCH 10.00 25.00
108 Greg Golson AU (RC) 8.00 20.00
109 Josh Geer AU (RC) 4.00 10.00
110 Josh Outman AU RC 4.00 10.00
111 James Parr AU (RC) 8.00 20.00
112 Kila Ka'aihue AU (RC) 6.00 15.00
113 Luis Cruz AU RC 10.00 25.00
114 Lou Marson AU (RC) 15.00 40.00
115 Matt Antonelli AU RC 10.00 25.00
116 Michael Bowden AU (RC) 6.00 15.00
117 Mat Gamel AU RC 20.00 50.00
118 Matt Tuiasosopo AU (RC) 15.00 40.00
119 Phil Coke AU RC 12.50 30.00
120 James McDonald AU RC 10.00 25.00
121 Shairon Martis AU RC EXCH 10.00 25.00
122 Travis Snider AU RC 75.00 150.00
123 Wade LeBlanc AU RC 4.00 10.00
124 Matt Wieters AU RC 15.00 40.00
125 Colby Rasmus AU (RC) 20.00 50.00
126 Josh Reddick AU RC 4.00 10.00
127 Mat Latos AU RC 8.00 20.00
128 Andrew McCutchen AU (RC) 30.00 60.00
129 Chris Tillman AU RC 6.00 15.00
130 Koji Uehara AU RC 30.00 60.00

2009 SPx Flashback Fabrics

OVERALL MEM ODDS 4 PER BOX
FFAG Adrian Gonzalez 3.00 8.00
FFAJ Andruw Jones 3.00 8.00
FFAP Andy Pettitte 3.00 8.00
FFBA Bobby Abreu 3.00 8.00
FFCC Coco Crisp 3.00 8.00
FFCD Carlos Delgado 3.00 8.00
FFCL Carlos Lee 3.00 8.00
FFCS Curt Schilling 3.00 8.00
FFDA Johnny Damon 3.00 8.00
FFFT Frank Thomas 4.00 10.00
FFGJ Geoff Jenkins 3.00 8.00
FFIR Ivan Rodriguez 4.00 10.00
FFJE Jim Edmonds 3.00 8.00
FFJV Jose Valverde 3.00 8.00
FFKM Kevin Millwood 3.00 8.00
FFLG Luis Gonzalez Pants 3.00 8.00
FFMA Moises Alou 3.00 8.00
FFMG Magglio Ordonez 3.00 8.00
FFMR Manny Ramirez 5.00 12.00
FFMT Mark Teixeira 4.00 10.00
FFOC Orlando Cabrera 3.00 8.00
FFPM Pedro Martinez 3.00 8.00
FFRJ Randy Johnson Pants 3.00 8.00
FFSR Scott Rolen 3.00 8.00
FFVG Vladimir Guerrero 3.00 8.00

2009 SPx Game Jersey

OVERALL MEM ODDS 4 PER BOX
GJBU B.J. Upton 3.00 8.00
GJCZ Carlos Zambrano 3.00 8.00
GJDJ Derek Jeter 10.00 25.00
GJDL Derrek Lee 3.00 8.00
GJDO David Ortiz 3.00 8.00
GJFL Francisco Liriano 3.00 8.00
GJGJ Geoff Jenkins 3.00 8.00
GJHR Hanley Ramirez 3.00 8.00
GJJD Jermaine Dye 3.00 8.00
GJJL John Lackey 3.00 8.00
GJJS John Smoltz 3.00 8.00
GJJT Jim Thome 3.00 8.00
GJJV Justin Verlander 3.00 8.00
GJKF Kosuke Fukudome 4.00 10.00
GJKW Kerry Wood 3.00 8.00
GJMR Manny Ramirez 3.00 8.00
GJMT Miguel Tejada 3.00 8.00
GJRH Roy Halladay 3.00 8.00
GJSA Johan Santana 3.00 8.00
GJTH Travis Hafner 3.00 8.00
GJTT Troy Tulowitzki 3.00 8.00

2009 SPx Game Jersey Autographs

OVERALL AUTO ODDS 1:18
GJAAE Andre Ethier 6.00 15.00
GJAAK Austin Kearns 4.00 10.00
GJAAL Adam LaRoche 4.00 10.00
GJAAM Andrew Miller 10.00 25.00
GJAAR Aaron Rowand 8.00 20.00
GJAAX Alex Romero 4.00 10.00
GJABA Brian Barton 4.00 10.00
GJABC Bobby Crosby 4.00 10.00
GJABE Josh Beckett 15.00 40.00
GJABG Brian Giles 4.00 10.00
GJABH Bill Hall 4.00 10.00
GJABM Brian McCann 12.50 30.00
GJABP Brandon Phillips 6.00 15.00
GJABR Brian Roberts 15.00 40.00
GJABW Brandon Webb 10.00 25.00
GJACB Chad Billingsley 8.00 20.00
GJACC Chris Carpenter 10.00 25.00
GJACD Chris Duncan 10.00 25.00
GJACF Chone Figgins 6.00 15.00
GJACH Cole Hamels 30.00 60.00
GJACJ Chipper Jones 50.00 100.00
GJACL Clay Buchholz 10.00 25.00
GJACR Coco Crisp 5.00 12.00
GJADL Derrek Lee 10.00 25.00
GJADS Denard Span 10.00 25.00
GJADU Dan Uggla 5.00 12.00
GJADW Dontrelle Willis
GJAEC Eric Chavez 4.00 10.00
GJAEM Evan Meek 4.00 10.00
GJAEV Edinson Volquez 6.00 15.00
GJAFC Fausto Carmona 4.00 10.00
GJAFH Felix Hernandez 12.50 30.00
GJAFL Francisco Liriano 5.00 12.00
GJAFP Felix Pie 4.00 10.00
GJAFT Frank Thomas 40.00 80.00
GJAGJ Geoff Jenkins 4.00 10.00
GJAHA Craig Hansen 4.00 10.00
GJAHC Hong-Chih Kuo 10.00 25.00
GJAHK Howie Kendrick 5.00 12.00
GJAHR Hanley Ramirez 15.00 40.00
GJAIK Ian Kinsler 10.00 25.00
GJAJB Jason Bay 10.00 25.00
GJAJC Johnny Cueto 10.00 25.00
GJAJH Jeremy Hermida 4.00 10.00
GJAJJ Josh Johnson 10.00 25.00
GJAJL John Lackey 5.00 12.00
GJAJN Joe Nathan 8.00 20.00
GJAJP Jonathan Papelbon 10.00 25.00
GJAJR J.R. Towles 4.00 10.00
GJAJV Joey Votto 15.00 40.00
GJAJZ Joel Zumaya 4.00 10.00
GJALA Andy LaRoche 4.00 10.00
GJALE Jon Lester 15.00 40.00
GJALS Luke Scott 4.00 10.00
GJAML Mark Loretta 4.00 10.00
GJAMO Justin Morneau 8.00 20.00
GJANS Nick Swisher 10.00 25.00
GJAPF Prince Fielder 12.50 30.00
GJAPH Phil Hughes 8.00 20.00
GJARA Aramis Ramirez 12.50 30.00
GJARH Ramon Hernandez 8.00 20.00
GJASD Stephen Drew 8.00 20.00
GJATH Travis Hafner 4.00 10.00
GJATT Troy Tulowitzki 6.00 15.00
GJAVE Justin Verlander 6.00 15.00
GJAVM Victor Martinez 5.00 12.00
GJAWI Josh Willingham 4.00 10.00
GJAZG Zack Greinke 12.50 30.00

2009 SPx Game Patch

OVERALL MEM ODDS 4 PER BOX
PRINT RUNS B/WN 50-99 COPIES PER
PRICING FOR 1-2 COLOR PATCHES
GJBU B.J. Upton 5.00 12.00
GJCZ Carlos Zambrano 6.00 15.00
GJDJ Derek Jeter/50 30.00 60.00
GJDL Derrek Lee 6.00 15.00
GJDO David Ortiz 5.00 12.00
GJFL Francisco Liriano 6.00 15.00
GJGJ Geoff Jenkins 5.00 12.00
GJHR Hanley Ramirez 6.00 15.00
GJJD Jermaine Dye 5.00 12.00
GJJL John Lackey 5.00 12.00
GJJS John Smoltz 8.00 20.00
GJJT Jim Thome 5.00 12.00
GJJV Justin Verlander 5.00 12.00
GJKF Kosuke Fukudome 8.00 20.00
GJKW Kerry Wood 5.00 12.00
GJMR Manny Ramirez 6.00 15.00
GJMT Miguel Tejada 5.00 12.00
GJRH Roy Halladay 6.00 15.00
GJSA Johan Santana 6.00 15.00
GJTH Travis Hafner 5.00 12.00
GJTT Troy Tulowitzki 5.00 12.00

2009 SPx Game Patch Autographs

PRINT RUNS B/WN 2-23 COPIES PER
NO PRICING DUE TO SCARCITY

2009 SPx Joe DiMaggio Career Highlights

COMMON DIMAGGIO (1-100) 3.00 8.00
STATED PRINT RUN 425 SER.#'d SETS

2009 SPx Mystery Rookie Redemption

RANDOM INSERTS IN PACKS
EXCHANGE DEADLINE 6/30/2011
NNO EXCH Card 20.00 50.00

2009 SPx Winning Materials

OVERALL MEM ODDS 4 PER BOX
WMAS Alfonso Soriano 3.00 8.00
WMCJ Chipper Jones 4.00 10.00
WMCW Chien-Ming Wang 4.00 10.00
WMDJ Derek Jeter 6.00 15.00
WMDM Daisuke Matsuzaka 6.00 15.00
WMJB Josh Beckett 3.00 8.00
WMJM Justin Morneau 3.00 8.00
WMJP Jake Peavy 3.00 8.00
WMJR Jose Reyes 3.00 8.00
WMLB Lance Berkman 3.00 8.00
WMMC Miguel Cabrera 3.00 8.00
WMMH Matt Holliday 3.00 8.00
WMMR Mariano Rivera 3.00 8.00
WMMT Mark Teixeira 3.00 8.00
WMPF Prince Fielder 3.00 8.00
WMRA Manny Ramirez 3.00 8.00
WMRB Ryan Braun 3.00 8.00
WMRL Ryan Ludwick 4.00 10.00
WMSK Scott Kazmir 3.00 8.00
WMTL Tim Lincecum 5.00 12.00

2009 SPx Winning Materials Patch

OVERALL MEM ODDS 4 PER BOX
PRINT RUNS B/WN 59-99 COPIES PER
PRICING FOR 1-2 COLOR PATCHES
WMAS Alfonso Soriano 6.00 15.00
WMCJ Chipper Jones 10.00 25.00
WMCW Chien-Ming Wang 8.00 20.00
WMDJ Derek Jeter 20.00 50.00
WMDM Daisuke Matsuzaka
WMJB Josh Beckett 6.00 15.00
WMJM Justin Morneau 5.00 12.00
WMJP Jake Peavy 5.00 12.00
WMJR Jose Reyes 10.00 25.00
WMLB Lance Berkman 5.00 12.00
WMMC Miguel Cabrera 5.00 12.00
WMMH Matt Holliday 5.00 12.00
WMMR Mariano Rivera 8.00 20.00
WMMT Mark Teixeira 5.00 12.00
WMPF Prince Fielder 5.00 12.00
WMRA Manny Ramirez 6.00 15.00
WMRB Ryan Braun/59 10.00 25.00
WMRL Ryan Ludwick 6.00 15.00
WMSK Scott Kazmir 5.00 12.00
WMTL Tim Lincecum 6.00 15.00

2009 SPx Winning Materials Dual

OVERALL MEM ODDS 4 PER BOX
BH A.J. Burnett 3.00 8.00
Roy Halladay
GE Ken Griffey Jr. 5.00 12.00
Jim Edmonds
GR Khalil Greene 4.00 10.00
Jose Reyes
GS Richie Sexson 3.00 8.00
Jason Giambi
HB Jeff Baker 3.00 8.00
Matt Holliday
JD Joe DiMaggio 40.00 80.00
Derek Jeter
JY Randy Johnson 4.00 10.00
Chris B. Young
KT Paul Konerko 3.00 8.00
Jim Thome
LL Adam LaRoche 3.00 8.00
Andy LaRoche
ML Daisuke Matsuzaka 5.00 12.00
Tim Lincecum
PS Jake Peavy 4.00 10.00
CC Sabathia
RB Jason Bay 4.00 10.00
Manny Ramirez
RO David Ortiz 4.00 10.00
Manny Ramirez
RP Jonathan Papelbon 4.00 10.00
Mariano Rivera

2009 SPx Winning Materials Quad

OVERALL MEM ODDS 4 PER BOX
BDBM Ryan Braun 8.00 20.00
Chris Duncan
Rocco Baldelli
Nick Markakis
BUUB Ryan Braun 4.00 10.00
Dan Uggla
Chase Utley
Lance Berkman
DJCP Joe DiMaggio 30.00 60.00
Derek Jeter
Robinson Cano
Jorge Posada
DTGS Jermaine Dye 5.00 12.00
Jim Thome
Ken Griffey Jr.
Nick Swisher
HFBS J.J. Hardy 5.00 12.00
Prince Fielder
Bill Hall
Ben Sheets
HHBN Matt Holliday 4.00 10.00
Todd Helton
Jeff Baker
Jayson Nix
HRBB Matt Holliday 4.00 10.00
Manny Ramirez
Pat Burrell
Ryan Braun
HRNB Trevor Hoffman 4.00 10.00
Mariano Rivera
Joe Nathan
Brad Lidge
HSLC Trevor Hoffman 4.00 10.00
Takashi Saito
Brad Lidge
Chad Cordero
JTJF Chipper Jones 5.00 12.00
Mark Teixeira
Andruw Jones
Rafael Furcal
KFSK Matt Kemp 4.00 10.00
Rafael Furcal
Takashi Saito
Hong-Chih Kuo
MMPV Brian McCann 4.00 10.00
Joe Mauer
Jorge Posada
Jason Varitek
OEYV David Ortiz 10.00 25.00
Jacoby Ellsbury
Kevin Youkilis
Jason Varitek
OGDF David Ortiz 4.00 10.00
Jason Giambi
Carlos Delgado
Prince Fielder
OGTS David Ortiz 4.00 10.00
Jason Giambi
Jim Thome
Gary Sheffield
PCLZ Albert Pujols 8.00 20.00
Chris Carpenter
Derrek Lee
Carlos Zambrano
PLKL Jake Peavy 8.00 20.00
Tim Lincecum
Scott Kazmir
Francisco Liriano
PMSL Jonathan Papelbon 20.00 50.00
Daisuke Matsuzaka
Curt Schilling
Jon Lester
PRMV Jorge Posada 5.00 12.00
Ivan Rodriguez
Joe Mauer
Jason Varitek
RGBN Manny Ramirez 5.00 12.00
Ken Griffey Jr.
Jason Bay
Xavier Nady
RLZW Aramis Ramirez 6.00 15.00
Derrek Lee
Carlos Zambrano
Kerry Wood
RRTD Jose Reyes 6.00 15.00
Hanley Ramirez
Troy Tulowitzki
Stephen Drew
RUJC Hanley Ramirez 10.00 25.00
Dan Uggla
Derek Jeter
Robinson Cano
SZCO Ben Sheets 4.00 10.00
Carlos Zambrano
Chris Carpenter
Roy Oswalt
UPRI Chase Utley 5.00 12.00
Brandon Phillips
Brian Roberts
Akinori Iwamura
VGSZ Justin Verlander 6.00 15.00
Curtis Granderson
Gary Sheffield
Joel Zumaya

2009 SPx Winning Materials Triple

OVERALL MEM ODDS 4 PER BOX
AKD Garrett Atkins 4.00 10.00
Kevin Kouzmanoff
Blake DeWitt
BCM Brian Barton 4.00 10.00
Chris Carpenter
Mark Mulder
CGV Miguel Cabrera 6.00 15.00
Curtis Granderson
Justin Verlander
DOF Jermaine Dye 4.00 10.00
Magglio Ordonez
Jeff Francoeur
FJH Prince Fielder 4.00 10.00
J.J. Hardy
Bill Hall
KCM Paul Konerko 4.00 10.00
Miguel Cabrera
Justin Morneau
KIB Scott Kazmir 4.00 10.00
Akinori Iwamura
Rocco Baldelli
KSB Jeff Kent 4.00 10.00
Freddy Sanchez
Josh Barfield
KSK Hiroki Kuroda 6.00 15.00
Takashi Saito
Hong-Chih Kuo
MBK Kevin Millwood 4.00 10.00
Hank Blalock
Ian Kinsler
MLY Joe Mauer 6.00 15.00
Francisco Liriano
Delmon Young
NLB Joe Nathan 4.00 10.00
Francisco Liriano
Scott Baker
PCS Jonathan Papelbon 4.00 10.00
Chad Cordero
Joakim Soria
PJG Andy Pettitte 4.00 10.00
Randy Johnson
Tom Glavine
PKD Brad Penny 5.00 12.00
Jeff Kent
Blake DeWitt
RBE Manny Ramirez 6.00 15.00
Jason Bay
Jacoby Ellsbury
RMD Manny Ramirez 8.00 20.00
Pedro Martinez
Johnny Damon
SBM Curt Schilling 5.00 12.00
Josh Beckett
Daisuke Matsuzaka
TCB Frank Thomas 10.00 25.00
Bobby Crosby
Travis Buck
TGB Mark Teahen 5.00 12.00
Zack Greinke
Billy Butler
WNP Kerry Wood 4.00 10.00
Joe Nathan
Jonathan Papelbon

1991 Stadium Club

COMP.SERIES 1 (300) 15.00 40.00
COMP.SERIES 2 (300) 8.00 20.00
1 Dave Stewart Tuxedo .20 .50
2 Wally Joyner .20 .50
3 Shawon Dunston .08 .25
4 Darren Daulton .20 .50
5 Will Clark .30 .75
6 Sammy Sosa .50 1.25
7 Dan Plesac .08 .25
8 Marquis Grissom .20 .50
9 Erik Hanson .08 .25
10 Geno Petralli .08 .25
11 Jose Rijo .08 .25
12 Carlos Quintana .08 .25
13 Junior Ortiz .08 .25
14 Bob Walk .08 .25
15 Mike Macfarlane .08 .25
16 Eric Yelding .08 .25
17 Bryn Smith .08 .25
18 Bip Roberts .08 .25
19 Mike Scioscia .08 .25
20 Mark Williamson .08 .25
21 Don Mattingly 1.25 3.00
22 John Franco .20 .50
23 Chet Lemon .08 .25
24 Tom Henke .08 .25
25 Jerry Browne .08 .25
26 Dave Justice .20 .50
27 Mark Langston .08 .25
28 Damon Berryhill .08 .25
29 Kevin Bass .08 .25
30 Scott Fletcher .08 .25
31 Moises Alou .20 .50
32 Dave Valle .08 .25
33 Jody Reed .08 .25
34 Dave West .08 .25
35 Kevin McReynolds .08 .25
36 Pat Combs .08 .25
37 Eric Davis .20 .50
38 Bret Saberhagen .20 .50
39 Stan Javier .08 .25
40 Chuck Cary .08 .25
41 Tony Phillips .08 .25
42 Lee Smith .20 .50
43 Tim Teufel .08 .25
44 Lance Dickson RC .15 .40
45 Greg Litton .08 .25
46 Ted Higuera .08 .25
47 Edgar Martinez .30 .75
48 Steve Avery .08 .25
49 Walt Weiss .08 .25
50 David Segui .08 .25
51 Andy Benes .08 .25
52 Karl Rhodes .08 .25
53 Neal Heaton .08 .25
54 Danny Gladden .08 .25
55 Luis Rivera .08 .25
56 Kevin Brown .20 .50
57 Frank Thomas .50 1.25
58 Terry Mulholland .08 .25
59 Dick Schofield .08 .25
60 Ron Darling .08 .25
61 Sandy Alomar Jr. .08 .25
62 Dave Stieb .08 .25
63 Alan Trammell .20 .50
64 Matt Nokes .08 .25
65 Lenny Harris .08 .25
66 Milt Thompson .08 .25
67 Storm Davis .08 .25
68 Joe Oliver .08 .25
69 Andres Galarraga .20 .50
70 Ozzie Guillen .20 .50
71 Ken Howell .08 .25
72 Garry Templeton .08 .25
73 Derrick May .08 .25
74 Xavier Hernandez .08 .25
75 Dave Parker .20 .50
76 Rick Aguilera .20 .50
77 Robby Thompson .08 .25
78 Pete Incaviglia .08 .25
79 Bob Welch .08 .25
80 Randy Milligan .08 .25
81 Chuck Finley .20 .50
82 Alvin Davis .08 .25
83 Tim Naehring .08 .25
84 Jay Bell .20 .50
85 Joe Magrane .08 .25
86 Howard Johnson .08 .25
87 Jack McDowell .08 .25
88 Kevin Seitzer .08 .25
89 Bruce Ruffin .08 .25
90 Fernando Valenzuela .20 .50
91 Terry Kennedy .08 .25
92 Barry Larkin .30 .75
93 Larry Walker .50 1.25
94 Luis Salazar .08 .25
95 Gary Sheffield .20 .50
96 Bobby Witt .08 .25
97 Lonnie Smith .08 .25
98 Bryan Harvey .08 .25
99 Mookie Wilson .20 .50
100 Dwight Gooden .20 .50
101 Lou Whitaker .20 .50
102 Ron Karkovice .08 .25
103 Jesse Barfield .08 .25
104 Jose DeJesus .08 .25
105 Benito Santiago .20 .50
106 Brian Holman .08 .25
107 Rafael Ramirez .08 .25
108 Ellis Burks .20 .50
109 Mike Bielecki .08 .25
110 Kirby Puckett .50 1.25
111 Terry Shumpert .08 .25
112 Chuck Crim .08 .25
113 Todd Benzinger .08 .25
114 Brian Barnes RC .15 .40
115 Carlos Baerga .08 .25
116 Kal Daniels .08 .25
117 Dave Johnson .08 .25
118 Andy Van Slyke .30 .75
119 John Burkett .08 .25
120 Rickey Henderson .50 1.25
121 Tim Jones .08 .25
122 Daryl Irvine RC .08 .25
123 Ruben Sierra .20 .50
124 Jim Abbott .30 .75
125 Daryl Boston .08 .25
126 Greg Maddux .75 2.00
127 Von Hayes .08 .25
128 Mike Fitzgerald .08 .25
129 Wayne Edwards .08 .25
130 Greg Briley .08 .25
131 Rob Dibble .20 .50
132 Gene Larkin .08 .25
133 David Wells .20 .50
134 Steve Balboni .08 .25
135 Greg Vaughn .08 .25
136 Mark Davis .08 .25
137 Dave Rhode .08 .25
138 Eric Show .08 .25
139 Bobby Bonilla .20 .50
140 Dana Kiecker .08 .25
141 Gary Pettis .08 .25
142 Dennis Boyd .08 .25
143 Mike Benjamin .08 .25
144 Luis Polonia .08 .25
145 Doug Jones .08 .25
146 Al Newman .08 .25
147 Alex Fernandez .08 .25
148 Bill Doran .08 .25
149 Kevin Elster .08 .25
150 Len Dykstra .20 .50
151 Mike Gallego .08 .25
152 Tim Belcher .08 .25
153 Jay Buhner .20 .50
154 Ozzie Smith UER .75 2.00
(Rookie card is 1979,
but card back says '78)
155 Jose Canseco .30 .75
156 Gregg Olson .08 .25
157 Charlie O'Brien .08 .25
158 Frank Tanana .08 .25
159 George Brett 1.25 3.00
160 Jeff Huson .08 .25
161 Kevin Tapani .08 .25
162 Jerome Walton .08 .25
163 Charlie Hayes .08 .25
164 Chris Bosio .08 .25
165 Chris Sabo .08 .25
166 Lance Parrish .20 .50
167 Don Robinson .08 .25
168 Manny Lee .08 .25
169 Dennis Rasmussen .08 .25
170 Wade Boggs .30 .75
171 Bob Geren .08 .25
172 Mackey Sasser .08 .25
173 Julio Franco .20 .50
174 Otis Nixon .08 .25
175 Bert Blyleven .20 .50
176 Craig Biggio .30 .75
177 Eddie Murray .50 1.25
178 Randy Tomlin RC .15 .40
179 Tino Martinez .50 1.25
180 Carlton Fisk .30 .75
181 Dwight Smith .08 .25
182 Scott Garrelts .08 .25
183 Jim Gantner .08 .25
184 Dickie Thon .08 .25
185 John Farrell .08 .25
186 Cecil Fielder .20 .50
187 Glenn Braggs .08 .25
188 Allan Anderson .08 .25
189 Kurt Stillwell .08 .25
190 Jose Oquendo .08 .25
191 Joe Orsulak .08 .25
192 Ricky Jordan .08 .25
193 Kelly Downs .08 .25
194 Delino DeShields .08 .25
195 Omar Vizquel .30 .75
196 Mark Carreon .08 .25
197 Mike Harkey .08 .25
198 Jack Howell .08 .25
199 Lance Johnson .08 .25
200 Nolan Ryan TUX 2.00 5.00
201 John Marzano .08 .25
202 Doug Drabek .08 .25
203 Mark Lemke .08 .25
204 Steve Sax .08 .25
205 Greg Harris .08 .25
206 B.J. Surhoff .20 .50
207 Todd Burns .08 .25
208 Jose Gonzalez .08 .25
209 Mike Scott .08 .25
210 Dave Magadan .08 .25
211 Dante Bichette .20 .50
212 Trevor Wilson .08 .25
213 Hector Villanueva .08 .25
214 Dan Pasqua .08 .25
215 Greg Colbrunn RC .25 .60
216 Mike Jeffcoat .08 .25
217 Harold Reynolds .20 .50
218 Paul O'Neill .30 .75
219 Mark Guthrie .08 .25
220 Barry Bonds 1.50 4.00
221 Jimmy Key .20 .50
222 Billy Ripken .08 .25
223 Tom Pagnozzi .08 .25
224 Bo Jackson .50 1.25
225 Sid Fernandez .08 .25
226 Mike Marshall .08 .25
227 John Kruk .20 .50
228 Mike Fetters .08 .25
229 Eric Anthony .08 .25
230 Ryne Sandberg .75 2.00
231 Carney Lansford .20 .50
232 Melido Perez .08 .25
233 Jose Lind .08 .25
234 Darryl Hamilton .08 .25
235 Tom Browning .08 .25
236 Spike Owen .08 .25
237 Juan Gonzalez .50 1.25
238 Felix Fermin .08 .25
239 Keith Miller .08 .25
240 Mark Gubicza .08 .25
241 Kent Anderson .08 .25
242 Alvaro Espinoza .08 .25
243 Dale Murphy .30 .75
244 Orel Hershiser .20 .50
245 Paul Molitor .20 .50
246 Eddie Whitson .08 .25
247 Joe Girardi .20 .50
248 Kent Hrbek .20 .50
249 Bill Sampen .08 .25
250 Kevin Mitchell .08 .25
251 Mariano Duncan .08 .25
252 Scott Bradley .08 .25
253 Mike Greenwell .08 .25
254 Tom Gordon .08 .25
255 Todd Zeile .08 .25
256 Bobby Thigpen .08 .25
257 Gregg Jefferies .08 .25
258 Kenny Rogers .20 .50
259 Shane Mack .08 .25
260 Zane Smith .08 .25
261 Mitch Williams .08 .25
262 Jim Deshaies .08 .25
263 Dave Winfield .20 .50
264 Ben McDonald .08 .25
265 Randy Ready .08 .25
266 Pat Borders .08 .25
267 Jose Uribe .08 .25
268 Derek Lilliquist .08 .25
269 Greg Brock .08 .25
270 Ken Griffey Jr. 1.00 2.50
271 Jeff Gray RC .08 .25
272 Danny Tartabull .08 .25
273 Dennis Martinez .20 .50
274 Robin Ventura .20 .50
275 Randy Myers .08 .25
276 Jack Daugherty .08 .25
277 Greg Gagne .08 .25
278 Jay Howell .08 .25
279 Mike LaValliere .08 .25
280 Rex Hudler .08 .25
281 Mike Simms RC .08 .25
282 Kevin Maas .08 .25
283 Jeff Ballard .08 .25
284 Dave Henderson .08 .25
285 Pete O'Brien .08 .25
286 Brook Jacoby .08 .25
287 Mike Henneman .08 .25
288 Greg Olson .08 .25
289 Greg Myers .08 .25
290 Mark Grace .30 .75
291 Shawn Abner .08 .25
292 Frank Viola .20 .50
293 Lee Stevens .08 .25
294 Jason Grimsley .08 .25
295 Matt Williams .20 .50
296 Ron Robinson .08 .25
297 Tom Brunansky .08 .25
298 Checklist 1-100 .08 .25
299 Checklist 101-200 .08 .25
300 Checklist 201-300 .08 .25
301 Darryl Strawberry .20 .50
302 Bud Black .08 .25
303 Harold Baines .20 .50
304 Roberto Alomar .30 .75
305 Norm Charlton .08 .25
306 Gary Thurman .08 .25
307 Mike Felder .08 .25
308 Tony Gwynn .60 1.50
309 Roger Clemens 1.50 4.00
310 Andre Dawson .20 .50
311 Scott Radinsky .08 .25
312 Bob Melvin .08 .25
313 Kirk McCaskill .08 .25
314 Pedro Guerrero .20 .50
315 Walt Terrell .08 .25
316 Sam Horn .08 .25
317 W.Chamberlain RC UER .25 .60
Card listed as 1989
Debut card, should be 1990)
318 Pedro Munoz RC .15 .40
319 Roberto Kelly .08 .25
320 Mark Portugal .08 .25
321 Tim McIntosh .08 .25
322 Jesse Orosco .08 .25
323 Gary Green .08 .25
324 Greg Harris .08 .25
325 Hubie Brooks .08 .25
326 Chris Nabholz .08 .25
327 Terry Pendleton .20 .50
328 Eric King .08 .25
329 Chili Davis .20 .50
330 Anthony Telford RC .08 .25
331 Kelly Gruber .08 .25
332 Dennis Eckersley .20 .50
333 Mel Hall .08 .25
334 Bob Kipper .08 .25
335 Willie McGee .20 .50
336 Steve Olin .08 .25
337 Steve Buechele .08 .25
338 Scott Leius .08 .25
339 Hal Morris .08 .25
340 Jose Offerman .08 .25
341 Kent Mercker .08 .25
342 Ken Griffey Sr. .20 .50
343 Pete Harnisch .08 .25
344 Kirk Gibson .20 .50
345 Dave Smith .08 .25
346 Dave Martinez .08 .25
347 Atlee Hammaker .08 .25
348 Brian Downing .08 .25
349 Todd Hundley .08 .25
350 Candy Maldonado .08 .25
351 Dwight Evans .30 .75
352 Steve Searcy .08 .25
353 Gary Gaetti .20 .50
354 Jeff Reardon .20 .50
355 Travis Fryman .20 .50
356 Dave Righetti .20 .50
357 Fred McGriff .30 .75
358 Don Slaught .08 .25
359 Gene Nelson .08 .25
360 Billy Spiers .08 .25
361 Lee Guetterman .08 .25
362 Darren Lewis .08 .25
363 Duane Ward .08 .25
364 Lloyd Moseby .08 .25
365 John Smoltz .30 .75
366 Felix Jose .08 .25
367 David Cone .20 .50
368 Wally Backman .08 .25
369 Jeff Montgomery .08 .25
370 Rich Garces RC .15 .40
371 Billy Hatcher .08 .25
372 Bill Swift .08 .25
373 Jim Eisenreich .08 .25
374 Rob Ducey .08 .25
375 Tim Crews .08 .25
376 Steve Finley .20 .50
377 Jeff Blauser .08 .25
378 Willie Wilson .08 .25
379 Gerald Perry .08 .25
380 Jose Mesa .08 .25
381 Pat Kelly RC .25 .60
382 Matt Merullo .08 .25
383 Ivan Calderon .08 .25
384 Scott Chiamparino .08 .25
385 Lloyd McClendon .08 .25
386 Dave Bergman .08 .25
387 Ed Sprague .08 .25
388 Jeff Bagwell RC 1.25 3.00
389 Brett Butler .20 .50
390 Larry Andersen .08 .25
391 Glenn Davis .08 .25
392 Alex Cole UER .08 .25
(Front photo actually
Otis Nixon)
393 Mike Heath .08 .25
394 Danny Darwin .08 .25
395 Steve Lake .08 .25
396 Tim Layana .08 .25
397 Terry Leach .08 .25
398 Bill Wegman .08 .25
399 Mark McGwire 1.50 4.00
400 Mike Boddicker .08 .25
401 Steve Howe .08 .25
402 Bernard Gilkey .08 .25
403 Thomas Howard .08 .25
404 Rafael Belliard .08 .25
405 Tom Candiotti .08 .25
406 Rene Gonzales .08 .25
407 Chuck McElroy .08 .25
408 Paul Sorrento .08 .25
409 Randy Johnson .60 1.50
410 Brady Anderson .20 .50
411 Dennis Cook .08 .25

412 Mickey Tettleton .08 .25
413 Mike Stanton .08 .25
414 Ken Oberkfell .08 .25
415 Rick Honeycutt .08 .25
416 Nelson Santovenia .08 .25
417 Bob Tewksbury .08 .25
418 Brent Mayne .08 .25
419 Steve Farr .08 .25
420 Phil Stephenson .08 .25
421 Jeff Russell .08 .25
422 Chris James .08 .25
423 Tim Leary .08 .25
424 Gary Carter .20 .50
425 Glenallen Hill .08 .25
426 Matt Young UER .08 .25
Card mentions 83T/Tr
as RC, but 84T shown)
427 Sid Bream .08 .25
428 Greg Swindell .08 .25
429 Scott Aldred .08 .25
430 Cal Ripken 1.50 4.00
431 Bill Landrum .08 .25
432 Earnest Riles .08 .25
433 Danny Jackson .08 .25
434 Casey Candaele .08 .25
435 Ken Hill .08 .25
436 Jaime Navarro .08 .25
437 Lance Blankenship .08 .25
438 Randy Velarde .08 .25
439 Frank DiPino .08 .25
440 Carl Nichols .08 .25
441 Jeff M. Robinson .08 .25
442 Deion Sanders .30 .75
443 Vicente Palacios .08 .25
444 Devon White .20 .50
445 John Cerutti .08 .25
446 Tracy Jones .08 .25
447 Jack Morris .20 .50
448 Mitch Webster .08 .25
449 Bob Ojeda .08 .25
450 Oscar Azocar .08 .25
451 Luis Aquino .08 .25
452 Mark Whiten .08 .25
453 Stan Belinda .08 .25
454 Ron Gant .20 .50
455 Jose DeLeon .08 .25
456 Mark Salas UER .08 .25
Back has 85T photo,
but calls it 86T
457 Junior Felix .08 .25
458 Wally Whitehurst .08 .25
459 Phil Plantier RC .25 .60
460 Juan Berenguer .08 .25
461 Franklin Stubbs .08 .25
462 Joe Boever .08 .25
463 Tim Wallach .08 .25
464 Mike Moore .08 .25
465 Albert Belle .20 .50
466 Mike Witt .08 .25
467 Craig Worthington .08 .25
468 Jerald Clark .08 .25
469 Scott Terry .08 .25
470 Milt Cuyler .08 .25
471 John Smiley .08 .25
472 Charles Nagy .08 .25
473 Alan Mills .08 .25
474 John Russell .08 .25
475 Bruce Hurst .08 .25
476 Andujar Cedeno .08 .25
477 Dave Eiland .08 .25
478 Brian McRae RC .25 .60
479 Mike LaCoss .08 .25
480 Chris Gwynn .08 .25
481 Jamie Moyer .20 .50
482 John Olerud .20 .50
483 Efrain Valdez RC .08 .25
484 Sil Campusano .08 .25
485 Pascual Perez .08 .25
486 Gary Redus .08 .25
487 Andy Hawkins .08 .25
488 Cory Snyder .08 .25
489 Chris Hoiles .08 .25
490 Ron Hassey .08 .25
491 Gary Wayne .08 .25
492 Mark Lewis .08 .25
493 Scott Coolbaugh .08 .25
494 Gerald Young .08 .25
495 Juan Samuel .08 .25
496 Willie Fraser .08 .25
497 Jeff Treadway .08 .25
498 Vince Coleman .08 .25
499 Cris Carpenter .08 .25
500 Jack Clark .20 .50
501 Kevin Appier .20 .50
502 Rafael Palmeiro .30 .75
503 Hensley Meulens .08 .25
504 George Bell .08 .25
505 Tony Pena .08 .25
506 Roger McDowell .08 .25
507 Luis Sojo .08 .25
508 Mike Schooler .08 .25
509 Robin Yount .75 2.00
510 Jack Armstrong .08 .25
511 Rick Cerone .08 .25
512 Curt Wilkerson .08 .25
513 Joe Carter .20 .50
514 Tim Burke .08 .25
515 Tony Fernandez .08 .25
516 Ramon Martinez .08 .25
517 Tim Hulett .08 .25
518 Terry Steinbach .08 .25
519 Pete Smith .08 .25
520 Ken Caminiti .20 .50
521 Shawn Boskie .08 .25
522 Mike Pagliarulo .08 .25
523 Tim Raines .20 .50
524 Alfredo Griffin .08 .25
525 Henry Cotto .08 .25
526 Mike Stanley .08 .25
527 Charlie Leibrandt .08 .25
528 Jeff King .08 .25
529 Eric Plunk .08 .25
530 Tom Lampkin .08 .25
531 Steve Bedrosian .08 .25
532 Tom Herr .08 .25
533 Craig Lefferts .08 .25
534 Jeff Reed .08 .25
535 Mickey Morandini .08 .25
536 Greg Cadaret .08 .25
537 Ray Lankford .20 .50
538 John Candelaria .08 .25
539 Rob Deer .08 .25
540 Brad Arnsberg .08 .25
541 Mike Sharperson .08 .25
542 Jeff D. Robinson .08 .25
543 Mo Vaughn .20 .50
544 Jeff Parrett .08 .25
545 Willie Randolph .20 .50
546 Herm Winningham .08 .25
547 Jeff Innis .08 .25
548 Chuck Knoblauch .20 .50
549 Tommy Greene UER .08 .25
(Born in North Carolina,
not South Carolina)
550 Jeff Hamilton .08 .25
551 Barry Jones .08 .25
552 Ken Dayley .08 .25
553 Rick Dempsey .08 .25
554 Greg Smith .08 .25
555 Mike Devereaux .08 .25
556 Keith Comstock .08 .25
557 Paul Faries RC .08 .25
558 Tom Glavine .30 .75
559 Craig Grebeck .08 .25
560 Scott Erickson .08 .25
561 Joel Skinner .08 .25
562 Mike Morgan .08 .25
563 Dave Gallagher .08 .25
564 Todd Stottlemyre .08 .25
565 Rich Rodriguez RC .08 .25
566 Craig Wilson RC .08 .25
567 Jeff Brantley .08 .25
568 Scott Kamieniecki RC .25 .60
569 Steve Decker RC .15 .40
570 Juan Agosto .08 .25
571 Tommy Gregg .08 .25
572 Kevin Wickander .08 .25
573 Jamie Quirk UER .08 .25
(Rookie card is 1976,
but card back is 1990)
574 Jerry Don Gleaton .08 .25
575 Chris Hammond .08 .25
576 Luis Gonzalez RC .60 1.50
577 Russ Swan .08 .25
578 Jeff Conine RC .40 1.00
579 Charlie Hough .20 .50
580 Jeff Kunkel .08 .25
581 Darrel Akerfelds .08 .25
582 Jeff Manto .08 .25
583 Alejandro Pena .08 .25
584 Mark Davidson .08 .25
585 Bob MacDonald RC .15 .40
586 Paul Assenmacher .08 .25
587 Dan Wilson RC .25 .60
588 Tom Bolton .08 .25
589 Brian Harper .08 .25
590 John Habyan .08 .25
591 John Orton .08 .25
592 Mark Gardner .08 .25
593 Turner Ward RC .25 .60
594 Bob Patterson .08 .25
595 Ed Nunez .08 .25
596 Gary Scott UER RC .15 .40
(Major League Batting
Record should be
Minor League)
597 Scott Bankhead .08 .25
598 Checklist 301-400 .08 .25
599 Checklist 401-500 .08 .25
600 Checklist 501-600 .08 .25

1991 Stadium Club Charter Member

This 50-card multi-sport standard-size set was sent to charter members in the Topps Stadium Club. The sports represented in the set are baseball (1-32), football (33-41), and hockey (42-50). The cards feature on the fronts full-bleed posed and action glossy color player photos. The player's name is shown in the light blue stripe that intersects the Stadium Club logo near the bottom of the picture. The words "Charter Member" are printed in gold foil lettering immediately below the stripe. The back design features a newspaper-like masthead (The Stadium Club Herald) complete with a headline announcing a major event in the player's season with copy below providing more information about the event. The cards are unnumbered and arranged below alphabetically within sports. Topps apparently made two printings of this set, which are most easily identifiable by the small asterisks on the bottom left of the card backs. The first printing cards have one asterisk, the second printing cards have two. The display box that contained the cards also included a Nolan Ryan bronze metallic card and a key chain. Very early members of the Stadium Club received a large size bronze metallic Nolan Ryan 1990 Topps card. It is valued below as well as the normal size Ryan metallic card. A third variation on the Ryan medallion has been found. This is another version of the 1991 Stadium Club charter member bronze medallion, except this one has a 24K logo on it. It is suspected that this might be a Home Shopping Newtork variety. No pricing is provided at this time for this piece due to lack of market information.

COMP.FACT.SET (50) 6.00 15.00
1 Sandy Alomar .10 .30
2 George Brett .60 1.50
3 Barry Bonds .40 1.00
4 Ellis Burks .10 .30
5 Eric Davis .10 .30
6 Delino DeShields .07 .20
7 Doug Drabek .07 .20
8 Cecil Fielder .10 .30
9 Carlton Fisk .20 .50
10 Ken Griffey Jr. 1.25 3.00
Ken Griffey Sr.
11 Billy Hatcher .07 .20
12 Andy Hawkins .07 .20
13 Rickey Henderson .20 .50
A.L. Recognizes
Rickey As MVP
14 Rickey Henderson .20 .50
A.L.'s Leading Thief
15 Randy Johnson .30 .75
16 Dave Justice .30 .75
17 Mark Langston .07 .20
Mike Witt
18 Kevin Maas .07 .20
19 Ramon Martinez .10 .30
20 Willie McGee .07 .20
21 Terry Mulholland .07 .20
22 Jose Offerman .07 .20
23 Melido Perez .07 .20
24 Nolan Ryan 1.25 3.00
A No-Hitter For
The Ages
25 Nolan Ryan 1.25 3.00
Earns 300th Career Win
26 Ryne Sandberg .60 1.50
27 Dave Stewart .10 .30
28 Dave Stieb .07 .20
29 Bobby Thigpen .07 .20
30 Fernando Valenzuela .10 .30
31 Frank Viola .07 .20
32 Bob Welch .10 .30
NNO Nolan Ryan Bronze 4.00 10.00
Medallion small
1991 Stadium Club
NNO Nolan Ryan Bronze 80.00 200.00
Medallion large
1990 Topps
NNO Nolan Ryan Bronze .75 2.00
Medallion small
1991 Stadium Club
24K gold

1991 Stadium Club Members Only

This 50-card multi-sport standard-size set was sent in three installments to members in the Topps Stadium Club. The first and second installments featured baseball players (card numbers 1-10 and 11-30), while the third spotlighted football (31-37) and hockey (38-50) players. The cards feature on the fronts full-bleed posed and action glossy color player photos. The player's name is shown in the light blue stripe that intersects the Stadium Club logo near the bottom of the picture. The words "Members Only" are printed in gold foil lettering immediately below the stripe. The back design features a newspaper-like masthead (The Stadium Club Herald) complete with a headline announcing a major event in the player's season with copy below providing more information about the event. The cards are unnumbered and arranged below alphabetically according to and within installments.

COMPLETE SET (50) 6.00 15.00
1 Wilson Alvarez .07 .20
2 Andy Ashby .07 .20
3 Tommy Greene .07 .20
4 Rickey Henderson .20 .50
Is Top Thief in History
5 Denny Martinez .07 .20
6 Paul Molitor .30 .75
7 Nolan Ryan 1.25 3.00
Extends Record
With 7th No-Hitter
8 Robby Thompson .07 .20
9 Dave Winfield .30 .75
10 Bob Milacki .07 .20
Mike Flanagan
Mark Williamson
Gregg Olson
Chris Hoiles
11 Jeff Bagwell 1.25 3.00
12 Roger Clemens .50 1.25
13 David Cone .08 .25
14 Carlton Fisk .20 .50
15 Julio Franco .07 .20
16 Tom Glavine .08 .25
17 Pete Harnisch .07 .20
18 Rickey Henderson .20 .50
Leads A.L. In
Thefts For 11th Time
19 Howard Johnson .07 .20
20 Chuck Knoblauch .07 .20
21 Ray Lankford .07 .20
22 Jack Morris .08 .25
23 Terry Pendleton .08 .25
NL's Leading Batsman
24 Terry Pendleton .08 .25
Close MVP Race
Favors Terry
25 Jeff Reardon .07 .20
26 Cal Ripken 1.25 3.00
27 Nolan Ryan 1.25 3.00
22nd Straight Year
With over 100 Strikeouts
28 Bret Saberhagen .07 .20
29 Cecil Fielder .15 .40
Jose Canseco
30 Kevin Mercker .07 .20
Mark Wohlers
Alejandro Pena

1992 Stadium Club Dome

The 1992 Stadium Club Dome set (issued by Topps) features 100 top draft picks, 56 1991 All-Star Game cards, 25 1991 Team U.S.A. cards, and 19 1991 Championship and World Series cards, all packaged in a factory set box inside a molded-plastic SkyDome display. Topps actually references this set as a 1991 set and the copyright lines on the card backs say 1991, but the set was released well into 1992. Rookie Cards in this set include Shawn Green and Manny Ramirez.

COMP.FACT.SET (200) 5.00 12.00
1 Terry Adams RC .20 .50
2 Tommy Adams RC .08 .25
3 Rick Aguilera .05 .15
4 Ron Allen RC .08 .25
5 Roberto Alomar .08 .25
6 Sandy Alomar Jr. .02 .10
7 Greg Anthony RC .08 .25
8 James Austin RC .08 .25
9 Steve Avery .02 .10
10 Harold Baines .05 .15
11 Brian Barber RC .08 .25
12 Jon Barnes RC .08 .25
13 George Bell .02 .10
14 Doug Bennett RC .08 .25
15 Sean Bergman RC .20 .50
16 Craig Biggio .08 .25
17 Bill Bliss RC .08 .25
18 Wade Boggs .08 .25
19 Bobby Bonilla .05 .15
20 Russell Brock RC .08 .25
21 Tarrik Brock RC .08 .25
22 Tom Browning .02 .10
23 Brett Butler .05 .15
24 Ivan Calderon .02 .10
25 Joe Carter .05 .15
26 Joe Caruso RC .08 .25
27 Dan Cholowsky RC .08 .25
28 Will Clark .08 .25
29 Roger Clemens .40 1.00
30 Shawn Curran RC .08 .25
31 Chris Curtis RC .08 .25
32 Chili Davis .05 .15
33 Andre Dawson .05 .15
34 Joe DeBerry RC .08 .25
35 John Dettmer .02 .10
36 Rob Dibble .05 .15
37 John Donati RC .08 .25
38 Dave Doorneweerd RC .08 .25
39 Darren Dreifort .02 .10
40 Mike Durant RC .08 .25
41 Chris Durkin RC .08 .25
42 Dennis Eckersley .05 .15
43 Brian Edmondson RC .08 .25
44 Vaughn Eshelman RC .08 .25
45 Shawn Estes RC .20 .50
46 Jorge Fabregas RC .20 .50
47 Jon Farrell RC .08 .25
48 Cecil Fielder .05 .15
49 Carlton Fisk .08 .25
50 Tim Flannelly RC .08 .25
51 Cliff Floyd RC .60 1.50
52 Julio Franco .05 .15
53 Greg Gagne .02 .10
54 Chris Gambs RC .08 .25
55 Ron Gant .05 .15
56 Brent Gates RC .08 .25
57 Dwayne Gerald RC .08 .25
58 Jason Giambi .40 1.00
59 Benji Gil RC .20 .50
60 Mark Gipner RC .08 .25
61 Danny Gladden .02 .10
62 Tom Glavine .08 .25
63 Jimmy Gonzalez RC .08 .25
64 Jeff Granger .02 .10
65 Dan Grapenthien RC .08 .25
66 Dennis Gray RC .08 .25
67 Shawn Green RC .75 2.00
68 Tyler Green RC .08 .25
69 Todd Greene .02 .10
70 Ken Griffey Jr. .30 .75
71 Kelly Gruber .02 .10
72 Ozzie Guillen .05 .15
73 Tony Gwynn .25 .60
74 Shane Halter RC .08 .25
75 Jeffrey Hammonds .05 .15
76 Larry Hanlon RC .08 .25
77 Pete Harnisch .02 .10
78 Mike Harrison RC .08 .25
79 Bryan Harvey .02 .10
80 Scott Hatteberg RC .20 .50
81 Rick Helling .02 .10
82 Dave Henderson .02 .10
83 Rickey Henderson .20 .50
84 Tyrone Hill RC .08 .25
85 T.Hollandsworth RC .20 .50
86 Brian Holliday RC .08 .25
87 Terry Horn RC .08 .25
88 Jeff Hostetler RC .08 .25
89 Kent Hrbek .05 .15
90 Mark Hubbard RC .08 .25
91 Charles Johnson .05 .15
92 Howard Johnson .02 .10
93 Todd Johnson .02 .10
94 Bobby Jones RC .20 .50
95 Dan Jones RC .08 .25
96 Felix Jose .02 .10
97 David Justice .05 .15
98 Jimmy Key .05 .15
99 Marc Kroon RC .08 .25
100 John Kruk .05 .15
101 Mark Langston .02 .10
102 Barry Larkin .08 .25
103 Mike LaValliere .02 .10
104 Scott Leius .02 .10
105 Mark Lemke .02 .10
106 Donnie Leshnock .02 .10
107 Jimmy Lewis RC .08 .25
108 Shane Livesy RC .08 .25
109 Ryan Long RC .08 .25
110 Trevor Mallory RC .08 .25
111 Dennis Martinez .05 .15
112 Justin Mashore RC .08 .25
113 Jason McDonald .02 .10
114 Jack McDowell .02 .10
115 Tom McKinnon RC .08 .25
116 Billy McMillon .02 .10
117 Buck McNabb RC .08 .25
118 Jim Mecir RC .08 .25
119 Dan Melendez .08 .25
120 Shawn Miller RC .08 .25
121 Trever Miller RC .08 .25
122 Paul Molitor .08 .25
123 Vincent Moore RC .08 .25
124 Mike Morgan .02 .10
125 Jack Morris WS .02 .10
126 Jack Morris AS .02 .10
127 Sean Mulligan RC .08 .25
128 Eddie Murray AS .20 .50
129 Mike Neill RC .08 .25
130 Phil Nevin .40 1.00
131 Mark O'Brien RC .08 .25
132 Alex Ochoa RC .08 .25
133 Chad Ogea RC .08 .25
134 Greg Olson .02 .10
135 Paul O'Neill .08 .25
136 Jared Osentowski RC .08 .25
137 Mike Pagliarulo .02 .10
138 Rafael Palmeiro .08 .25
139 Rodney Pedraza RC .08 .25
140 Tony Phillips (P) .02 .10
141 Scott Pisciotta RC .08 .25
142 C.Pritchett RC .08 .25
143 Jason Pruitt RC .08 .25
144 K.Puckett WS UER .20 .50
Championship series
AB and BA is wrong
145 Kirby Puckett AS .20 .50
146 Manny Ramirez RC 2.50 6.00
147 Eddie Ramos RC .08 .25
148 Mark Ratekin RC .08 .25
149 Jeff Reardon .05 .15
150 Sean Rees RC .08 .25
151 Pokey Reese RC .20 .50
152 Desmond Relaford RC .08 .25
153 Eric Richardson RC .08 .25
154 Cal Ripken .60 1.50
155 Chris Roberts .02 .10
156 Mike Robertson RC .08 .25
157 Steve Rodriguez .02 .10
158 Mike Rossiter RC .08 .25
159 Scott Ruffcorn RC .08 .25
160 Chris Sabo .02 .10
161 Juan Samuel .02 .10
162 Ryne Sandberg UER .30 .75
(On 5th line, prior
misspelled as prilor)
163 Scott Sanderson .02 .10
164 Benny Santiago .05 .15
165 Gene Schall RC .08 .25
166 Chad Schoenvogel RC .08 .25
167 Chris Seelbach RC .08 .25
168 Aaron Sele RC .20 .50
169 Basil Shabazz RC .08 .25
170 Al Shirley RC .08 .25
171 Paul Shuey .02 .10
172 Ruben Sierra .02 .10
173 John Smiley .02 .10
174 Lee Smith .05 .15
175 Ozzie Smith .30 .75
176 Tim Smith RC .08 .25
177 Zane Smith .02 .10
178 John Smoltz .08 .25
179 Scott Stahoviak RC .08 .25
180 Kennie Steenstra .02 .10
181 Kevin Stocker RC .08 .25
182 Chris Stynes RC .20 .50
183 Danny Tartabull .02 .10
184 Brien Taylor RC .20 .50
185 Todd Taylor .02 .10
186 Larry Thomas RC .08 .25
187 Ozzie Timmons RC .08 .25
(See also 188)
188 David Tuttle UER .02 .10
(Mistakenly numbered
as 187 on card)
189 Andy Van Slyke .08 .25
190 Frank Viola .05 .15
191 Michael Walkden RC .08 .25
192 Jeff Ware .02 .10
193 Allen Watson RC .08 .25
194 Steve Whitaker RC .08 .25
195 Jerry Willard .02 .10
196 Craig Wilson .02 .10
197 Chris Wimmer .02 .10
198 S.Wojciechowski RC .08 .25
199 Joel Wolfe RC .08 .25
200 Ivan Zweig .02 .10

1992 Stadium Club

The 1992 Stadium Club baseball card set consists of 900 standard-size cards issued in three series of 300 cards each. Cards were issued in plastic wrapped packs. A card-like application form for membership in Topps Stadium Club was inserted in each pack. Card numbers 591-610 form a "Members Choice" subset.

COMPLETE SET (900) 18.00 45.00
COMP.SERIES 1 (300) 6.00 15.00
COMP.SERIES 2 (300) 6.00 15.00
COMP.SERIES 3 (300) 6.00 15.00
1 Cal Ripken UER .60 1.50
(Misspelled Ripkin
on card back)
2 Eric Yelding .02 .10
3 Geno Petralli .02 .10
4 Wally Backman .02 .10
5 Milt Cuyler .02 .10
6 Kevin Bass .02 .10
7 Dante Bichette .05 .15
8 Ray Lankford .05 .15
9 Mel Hall .02 .10
10 Joe Carter .05 .15
11 Juan Samuel .02 .10
12 Jeff Montgomery .02 .10
13 Glenn Braggs .02 .10
14 Henry Cotto .02 .10
15 Deion Sanders .08 .25
16 Dick Schofield .02 .10
17 David Cone .05 .15
18 Chili Davis .05 .15
19 Tom Foley .02 .10
20 Ozzie Guillen .05 .15
21 Luis Salazar .02 .10
22 Terry Steinbach .02 .10
23 Chris James .02 .10
24 Jeff King .02 .10
25 Carlos Quintana .02 .10
26 Mike Maddux .02 .10
27 Tommy Greene .02 .10
28 Jeff Russell .02 .10
29 Steve Finley .05 .15
30 Mike Flanagan .02 .10
31 Darren Lewis .02 .10
32 Mark Lee .02 .10
33 Willie Fraser .02 .10
34 Mike Henneman .02 .10
35 Kevin Maas .02 .10
36 Dave Hansen .02 .10
37 Erik Hanson .02 .10
38 Bill Doran .02 .10
39 Mike Boddicker .02 .10
40 Vince Coleman .02 .10
41 Devon White .05 .15
42 Mark Gardner .02 .10
43 Scott Lewis .02 .10
44 Juan Berenguer .02 .10
45 Carney Lansford .05 .15
46 Curt Wilkerson .02 .10
47 Shane Mack .02 .10
48 Bip Roberts .02 .10
49 Greg A. Harris .02 .10
50 Ryne Sandberg .30 .75
51 Mark Whiten .02 .10
52 Jack McDowell .02 .10
53 Jimmy Jones .02 .10
54 Steve Lake .02 .10
55 Bud Black .02 .10
56 Dave Valle .02 .10
57 Kevin Reimer .02 .10
58 Rich Gedman UER .02 .10
(Wrong BARS chart used)
59 Travis Fryman .05 .15
60 Steve Avery .02 .10
61 Francisco de la Rosa .02 .10
62 Scott Hemond .02 .10
63 Hal Morris .02 .10
64 Hensley Meulens .02 .10
65 Frank Castillo .02 .10
66 Gene Larkin .02 .10
67 Jose DeLeon .02 .10
68 Al Osuna .02 .10
69 Dave Cochrane .02 .10
70 Robin Ventura .05 .15
71 John Cerutti .02 .10
72 Kevin Gross .02 .10
73 Ivan Calderon .02 .10
74 Mike Macfarlane .02 .10
75 Stan Belinda .02 .10
76 Shawn Hillegas .02 .10
77 Pat Borders .02 .10
78 Jim Vatcher .02 .10
79 Bobby Rose .02 .10
80 Roger Clemens .40 1.00
81 Craig Worthington .02 .10
82 Jeff Treadway .02 .10
83 Jamie Quirk .02 .10
84 Randy Bush .02 .10
85 Anthony Young .02 .10
86 Trevor Wilson .02 .10
87 Jaime Navarro .02 .10
88 Les Lancaster .02 .10
89 Pat Kelly .02 .10
90 Alvin Davis .02 .10
91 Larry Andersen .02 .10
92 Rob Deer .02 .10
93 Mike Sharperson .02 .10
94 Lance Parrish .05 .15
95 Cecil Espy .02 .10
96 Tim Spehr .02 .10
97 Dave Stieb .02 .10
98 Terry Mulholland .02 .10
99 Dennis Boyd .02 .10
100 Barry Larkin .08 .25
101 Ryan Bowen .02 .10
102 Felix Fermin .02 .10
103 Luis Alicea .02 .10
104 Tim Hulett .02 .10
105 Rafael Belliard .02 .10
106 Mike Gallego .02 .10
107 Dave Righetti .05 .15
108 Jeff Schaefer .02 .10
109 Ricky Bones .02 .10
110 Scott Erickson .02 .10
111 Matt Nokes .02 .10
112 Bob Scanlan .02 .10
113 Tom Candiotti .02 .10
114 Sean Berry .02 .10
115 Kevin Morton .02 .10
116 Scott Fletcher .02 .10
117 B.J. Surhoff .05 .15
118 Dave Magadan UER .02 .10
(Born Tampa, not Tamps)
119 Bill Gullickson .02 .10
120 Marquis Grissom .05 .15
121 Lenny Harris .02 .10
122 Wally Joyner .05 .15
123 Kevin Brown .05 .15
124 Braulio Castillo .02 .10
125 Eric King .02 .10
126 Mark Portugal .02 .10
127 Calvin Jones .02 .10
128 Mike Heath .02 .10
129 Todd Van Poppel .02 .10
130 Benny Santiago .05 .15
131 Gary Thurman .02 .10
132 Joe Girardi .02 .10
133 Dave Eiland .02 .10
134 Orlando Merced .02 .10
135 Joe Orsulak .02 .10
136 John Burkett .02 .10
137 Ken Dayley .02 .10
138 Ken Hill .02 .10
139 Walt Terrell .02 .10
140 Mike Scioscia .02 .10
141 Junior Felix .02 .10
142 Ken Caminiti .05 .15
143 Carlos Baerga .02 .10
144 Tony Fossas .02 .10
145 Craig Grebeck .02 .10
146 Scott Bradley .02 .10
147 Kent Mercker .02 .10
148 Derrick May .02 .10
149 Jerald Clark .02 .10
150 George Brett .50 1.25
151 Luis Quinones .02 .10
152 Mike Pagliarulo .02 .10
153 Jose Guzman .02 .10
154 Charlie O'Brien .02 .10
155 Darren Holmes .02 .10
156 Joe Boever .02 .10
157 Rich Monteleone .02 .10
158 Reggie Harris .02 .10
159 Roberto Alomar .08 .25
160 Robby Thompson .02 .10
161 Chris Hoiles .02 .10
162 Tom Pagnozzi .02 .10
163 Omar Vizquel .08 .25
164 John Candelaria .02 .10
165 Terry Shumpert .02 .10
166 Andy Mota .02 .10
167 Scott Bailes .02 .10
168 Jeff Blauser .02 .10
169 Steve Olin .02 .10
170 Doug Drabek .02 .10
171 Dave Bergman .02 .10
172 Eddie Whitson .02 .10
173 Gilberto Reyes .02 .10
174 Mark Grace .08 .25
175 Paul O'Neill .08 .25
176 Greg Cadaret .02 .10
177 Mark Williamson .02 .10
178 Casey Candaele .02 .10
179 Candy Maldonado .02 .10
180 Lee Smith .05 .15
181 Harold Reynolds .05 .15
182 David Justice .05 .15
183 Lenny Webster .02 .10
184 Donn Pall .02 .10
185 Gerald Alexander .02 .10
186 Jack Clark .05 .15
187 Stan Javier .02 .10
188 Ricky Jordan .02 .10
189 Franklin Stubbs .02 .10
190 Dennis Eckersley .05 .15
191 Danny Tartabull .02 .10
192 Pete O'Brien .02 .10
193 Mark Lewis .02 .10
194 Mike Felder .02 .10
195 Mickey Tettleton .02 .10
196 Dwight Smith .02 .10
197 Shawn Abner .02 .10
198 Jim Leyritz UER .02 .10
(Career totals less
than 1991 totals)
199 Mike Devereaux .02 .10
200 Craig Biggio .08 .25
201 Kevin Elster .02 .10
202 Rance Mulliniks .02 .10
203 Tony Fernandez .02 .10
204 Allan Anderson .02 .10
205 Herm Winningham .02 .10
206 Tim Jones .02 .10
207 Ramon Martinez .02 .10
208 Teddy Higuera .02 .10
209 John Kruk .05 .15
210 Jim Abbott .08 .25
211 Dean Palmer .05 .15
212 Mark Davis .02 .10
213 Jay Buhner .05 .15
214 Jesse Barfield .02 .10
215 Kevin Mitchell .02 .10
216 Mike LaValliere .02 .10
217 Mark Wohlers .02 .10
218 Dave Henderson .02 .10
219 Dave Smith .02 .10
220 Albert Belle .05 .15
221 Spike Owen .02 .10
222 Jeff Gray .02 .10
223 Paul Gibson .02 .10
224 Bobby Thigpen .02 .10
225 Mike Mussina .20 .50
226 Darrin Jackson .02 .10
227 Luis Gonzalez .05 .15
228 Greg Briley .02 .10
229 Brent Mayne .02 .10
230 Paul Molitor .05 .15
231 Al Leiter .05 .15
232 Andy Van Slyke .08 .25
233 Ron Tingley .02 .10
234 Bernard Gilkey .02 .10
235 Kent Hrbek .05 .15
236 Eric Karros .05 .15
237 Randy Velarde .02 .10
238 Andy Allanson .02 .10
239 Willie McGee .05 .15
240 Juan Gonzalez .08 .25
241 Karl Rhodes .02 .10
242 Luis Mercedes .02 .10
243 Bill Swift .02 .10
244 Tommy Gregg .02 .10
245 David Howard .02 .10
246 Dave Hollins .02 .10
247 Kip Gross .02 .10
248 Walt Weiss .02 .10
249 Mackey Sasser .02 .10
250 Cecil Fielder .05 .15
251 Jerry Browne .02 .10
252 Doug Dascenzo .02 .10
253 Darryl Hamilton .02 .10
254 Dann Bilardello .02 .10
255 Luis Rivera .02 .10
256 Larry Walker .08 .25
257 Ron Karkovice .02 .10
258 Bob Tewksbury .02 .10
259 Jimmy Key .05 .15
260 Bernie Williams .08 .25
261 Gary Wayne .02 .10
262 Mike Simms UER .02 .10
(Reversed negative)
263 John Orton .02 .10
264 Marvin Freeman .02 .10
265 Mike Jeffcoat .02 .10
266 Roger Mason .02 .10
267 Edgar Martinez .08 .25
268 Henry Rodriguez .02 .10
269 Sam Horn .02 .10
270 Brian McRae .02 .10
271 Kirt Manwaring .02 .10
272 Mike Bordick .02 .10
273 Chris Sabo .02 .10
274 Jim Olander .02 .10
275 Greg W. Harris .02 .10
276 Dan Gakeler .02 .10
277 Bill Sampen .02 .10
278 Joel Skinner .02 .10
279 Curt Schilling .08 .25
280 Dale Murphy .08 .25
281 Lee Stevens .02 .10
282 Lonnie Smith .02 .10
283 Manuel Lee .02 .10
284 Shawn Boskie .02 .10
285 Kevin Seitzer .02 .10
286 Stan Royer .02 .10
287 John Dopson .02 .10
288 Scott Bullett RC .02 .10
289 Ken Patterson .02 .10
290 Todd Hundley .02 .10
291 Tim Leary .02 .10
292 Brett Butler .05 .15
293 Gregg Olson .02 .10
294 Jeff Brantley .02 .10
295 Brian Holman .02 .10
296 Brian Harper .02 .10
297 Brian Bohanon .02 .10
298 Checklist 1-100 .02 .10
299 Checklist 101-200 .02 .10
300 Checklist 201-300 .02 .10

301 Frank Thomas	.20	.50
302 Lloyd McClendon	.02	.10
303 Brady Anderson	.05	.15
304 Julio Valera	.02	.10
305 Mike Aldrete	.02	.10
306 Joe Oliver	.02	.10
307 Todd Stottlemyre	.02	.10
308 Rey Sanchez RC	.05	.15
309 Gary Sheffield UER	.05	.15
310 Andujar Cedeno	.02	.10
311 Kenny Rogers	.05	.15
312 Bruce Hurst	.02	.10
313 Mike Schooler	.02	.10
314 Mike Benjamin	.02	.10
315 Chuck Finley	.05	.15
316 Mark Lemke	.02	.10
317 Scott Livingstone	.02	.10
318 Chris Nabholz	.02	.10
319 Mike Humphreys	.02	.10
320 Pedro Guerrero	.05	.15
321 Willie Banks	.02	.10
322 Tom Goodwin	.02	.10
323 Hector Wagner	.02	.10
324 Wally Ritchie	.02	.10
325 Mo Vaughn	.05	.15
326 Joe Klink	.02	.10
327 Cal Eldred	.02	.10
328 Daryl Boston	.02	.10
329 Mike Huff	.02	.10
330 Jeff Bagwell	.20	.50
331 Bob Milacki	.02	.10
332 Tom Prince	.02	.10
333 Pat Tabler	.02	.10
334 Ced Landrum	.02	.10
335 Reggie Jefferson	.02	.10
336 Mo Sanford	.02	.10
337 Kevin Ritz	.02	.10
338 Gerald Perry	.02	.10
339 Jeff Hamilton	.02	.10
340 Tim Wallach	.02	.10
341 Jeff Huson	.02	.10
342 Jose Melendez	.02	.10
343 Willie Wilson	.02	.10
344 Mike Stanton	.02	.10
345 Joel Johnston	.02	.10
346 Lee Guetterman	.02	.10
347 Francisco Oliveras	.02	.10
348 Dave Burba	.02	.10
349 Tim Crews	.02	.10
350 Scott Leius	.02	.10
351 Danny Cox	.02	.10
352 Wayne Housie	.02	.10
353 Chris Donnels	.02	.10
354 Chris George	.02	.10
355 Gerald Young	.02	.10
356 Roberto Hernandez	.02	.10
357 Neal Heaton	.02	.10
358 Todd Frohwirth	.02	.10
359 Jose Vizcaino	.02	.10
360 Jim Thome	.20	.50
361 Craig Wilson	.02	.10
362 Dave Haas	.02	.10
363 Billy Hatcher	.02	.10
364 John Barfield	.02	.10
365 Luis Aquino	.02	.10
366 Charlie Leibrandt	.02	.10
367 Howard Farmer	.02	.10
368 Bryn Smith	.02	.10
369 Mickey Morandini	.02	.10
370 Jose Canseco	.08	.25
(See also 597)		
371 Jose Uribe	.02	.10
372 Bob MacDonald	.02	.10
373 Luis Sojo	.02	.10
374 Craig Shipley	.02	.10
375 Scott Bankhead	.02	.10
376 Greg Gagne	.02	.10
377 Scott Cooper	.02	.10
378 Jose Offerman	.02	.10
379 Bill Spiers	.02	.10
380 John Smiley	.02	.10
381 Jeff Carter	.02	.10
382 Heathcliff Slocumb	.02	.10
383 Jeff Tackett	.02	.10
384 John Kiely	.02	.10
385 John Vander Wal	.02	.10
386 Omar Olivares	.02	.10
387 Ruben Sierra	.05	.15
388 Tom Gordon	.02	.10
389 Charles Nagy	.02	.10
390 Dave Stewart	.05	.15
391 Pete Harnisch	.02	.10
392 Tim Burke	.02	.10
393 Roberto Kelly	.02	.10
394 Freddie Benavides	.02	.10
395 Tom Glavine	.08	.25
396 Wes Chamberlain	.02	.10
397 Eric Gunderson	.02	.10
398 Dave West	.02	.10
399 Ellis Burks	.05	.15
400 Ken Griffey Jr.	.30	.75
401 Thomas Howard	.02	.10
402 Juan Guzman	.02	.10
403 Mitch Webster	.02	.10
404 Matt Merullo	.02	.10
405 Steve Buechele	.02	.10
406 Danny Jackson	.02	.10
407 Felix Jose	.02	.10
408 Doug Piatt	.02	.10
409 Jim Eisenreich	.02	.10
410 Bryan Harvey	.02	.10
411 Jim Austin	.02	.10
412 Jim Poole	.02	.10
413 Glenallen Hill	.02	.10
414 Gene Nelson	.02	.10
415 Ivan Rodriguez	.20	.50
416 Frank Tanana	.02	.10
417 Steve Decker	.02	.10
418 Jason Grimsley	.02	.10
419 Tim Layana	.02	.10
420 Don Mattingly	.50	1.25
421 Jerome Walton	.02	.10
422 Rob Ducey	.02	.10
423 Andy Benes	.02	.10
424 John Marzano	.02	.10
425 Gene Harris	.02	.10
426 Tim Raines	.05	.15
427 Bret Barberie	.02	.10
428 Harvey Pulliam	.02	.10
429 Cris Carpenter	.02	.10
430 Howard Johnson	.02	.10
431 Orel Hershiser	.05	.15
432 Brian Hunter	.02	.10
433 Kevin Tapani	.02	.10
434 Rick Reed	.02	.10
435 Ron Witmeyer RC	.02	.10
436 Gary Gaetti	.05	.15
437 Alex Cole	.02	.10
438 Chito Martinez	.02	.10
439 Greg Litton	.02	.10
440 Julio Franco	.05	.15
441 Mike Munoz	.02	.10
442 Erik Pappas	.02	.10
443 Pat Combs	.02	.10
444 Lance Johnson	.02	.10
445 Ed Sprague	.02	.10
446 Mike Greenwell	.02	.10
447 Milt Thompson	.02	.10
448 Mike Magnante RC	.02	.10
449 Chris Haney	.02	.10
450 Robin Yount	.30	.75
451 Rafael Ramirez	.02	.10
452 Gino Minutelli	.02	.10
453 Tom Lampkin	.02	.10
454 Tony Perezchica	.02	.10
455 Dwight Gooden	.05	.15
456 Mark Guthrie	.02	.10
457 Jay Howell	.02	.10
458 Gary DiSarcina	.02	.10
459 John Smoltz	.08	.25
460 Will Clark	.08	.25
461 Dave Otto	.02	.10
462 Rob Maurer	.02	.10
463 Dwight Evans	.08	.25
464 Tom Brunansky	.02	.10
465 Shawn Hare RC	.02	.10
466 Geronimo Pena	.02	.10
467 Alex Fernandez	.02	.10
468 Greg Myers	.02	.10
469 Jeff Fassero	.02	.10
470 Len Dykstra	.05	.15
471 Jeff Johnson	.02	.10
472 Russ Swan	.02	.10
473 Archie Corbin	.02	.10
474 Chuck McElroy	.02	.10
475 Mark McGwire	.50	1.25
476 Wally Whitehurst	.02	.10
477 Tim McIntosh	.02	.10
478 Sid Bream	.02	.10
479 Jeff Juden	.02	.10
480 Carlton Fisk	.08	.25
481 Jeff Plympton	.02	.10
482 Carlos Martinez	.02	.10
483 Jim Gott	.02	.10
484 Bob McClure	.02	.10
485 Tim Teufel	.02	.10
486 Vicente Palacios	.02	.10
487 Jeff Reed	.02	.10
488 Tony Phillips	.02	.10
489 Mel Rojas	.02	.10
490 Ben McDonald	.02	.10
491 Andres Santana	.02	.10
492 Chris Beasley	.02	.10
493 Mike Timlin	.02	.10
494 Brian Downing	.02	.10
495 Kirk Gibson	.05	.15
496 Scott Sanderson	.02	.10
497 Nick Esasky	.02	.10
498 Johnny Guzman RC	.02	.10
499 Mitch Williams	.02	.10
500 Kirby Puckett	.20	.50
501 Mike Harkey	.02	.10
502 Jim Gantner	.02	.10
503 Bruce Egloff	.02	.10
504 Josias Manzanillo RC	.02	.10
505 Delino DeShields	.02	.10
506 Rheal Cormier	.02	.10
507 Jay Bell	.05	.15
508 Rich Rowland RC	.02	.10
509 Scott Servais	.02	.10
510 Terry Pendleton	.05	.15
511 Rich DeLucia	.02	.10
512 Warren Newson	.02	.10
513 Paul Faries	.02	.10
514 Kal Daniels	.02	.10
515 Jarvis Brown	.02	.10
516 Rafael Palmeiro	.08	.25
517 Kelly Downs	.02	.10
518 Steve Chitren	.02	.10
519 Moises Alou	.05	.15
520 Wade Boggs	.08	.25
521 Pete Schourek	.02	.10
522 Scott Terry	.02	.10
523 Kevin Appier	.05	.15
524 Gary Redus	.02	.10
525 George Bell	.02	.10
526 Jeff Kaiser	.02	.10
527 Alvaro Espinoza	.02	.10
528 Luis Polonia	.02	.10
529 Darren Daulton	.05	.15
530 Norm Charlton	.02	.10
531 John Olerud	.05	.15
532 Dan Plesac	.02	.10
533 Billy Ripken	.02	.10
534 Rod Nichols	.02	.10
535 Joey Cora	.02	.10
536 Harold Baines	.05	.15
537 Bob Ojeda	.02	.10
538 Mark Leonard	.02	.10
539 Danny Darwin	.02	.10
540 Shawon Dunston	.02	.10
541 Pedro Munoz	.02	.10
542 Mark Gubicza	.02	.10
543 Kevin Baez	.02	.10
544 Todd Zeile	.02	.10
545 Don Slaught	.02	.10
546 Tony Eusebio	.05	.15
547 Alonzo Powell	.02	.10
548 Gary Pettis	.02	.10
549 Brian Barnes	.02	.10
550 Lou Whitaker	.05	.15
551 Keith Mitchell	.02	.10
552 Oscar Azocar	.02	.10
553 Stu Cole RC	.02	.10
554 Steve Wapnick	.02	.10
555 Derek Bell	.05	.15
556 Luis Lopez	.02	.10
557 Anthony Telford	.02	.10
558 Tim Mauser	.02	.10
559 Glen Sutko	.02	.10
560 Darryl Strawberry	.05	.15
561 Tom Bolton	.02	.10
562 Cliff Young	.02	.10
563 Bruce Walton	.02	.10
564 Chico Walker	.02	.10
565 John Franco	.05	.15
566 Paul McClellan	.02	.10
567 Paul Abbott	.02	.10
568 Gary Varsho	.02	.10
569 Carlos Maldonado RC	.02	.10
570 Kelly Gruber	.02	.10
571 Jose Oquendo	.02	.10
572 Steve Frey	.02	.10
573 Tino Martinez	.08	.25
574 Bill Haselman	.02	.10
575 Eric Anthony	.02	.10
576 John Habyan	.02	.10
577 Jeff McNeely	.02	.10
578 Chris Bosio	.02	.10
579 Joe Grahe	.02	.10
580 Fred McGriff	.08	.25
581 Rick Honeycutt	.02	.10
582 Matt Williams	.05	.15
583 Cliff Brantley	.02	.10
584 Rob Dibble	.05	.15
585 Skeeter Barnes	.02	.10
586 Greg Hibbard	.02	.10
587 Randy Milligan	.02	.10
588 Checklist 301-400	.02	.10
589 Checklist 401-500	.02	.10
590 Checklist 501-600	.02	.10
591 Frank Thomas MC	.08	.25
592 David Justice MC	.02	.10
593 Roger Clemens MC	.20	.50
594 Steve Avery MC	.02	.10
595 Cal Ripken MC	.30	.75
596 Barry Larkin MC UER	.05	.15
(Ranked in AL,		
should be NL)		
597 J.Canseco MC UER	.05	.15
Mistakenly numbered		
370 on card back		
598 Will Clark MC	.05	.15
599 Cecil Fielder MC	.02	.10
600 Ryne Sandberg MC	.20	.50
601 Chuck Knoblauch MC	.02	.10
602 Dwight Gooden MC	.02	.10
603 Ken Griffey Jr. MC	.20	.50
604 Barry Bonds MC	.40	1.00
605 Nolan Ryan MC	.30	.75
606 Jeff Bagwell MC	.08	.25
607 Robin Yount MC	.20	.50
608 Bobby Bonilla MC	.02	.10
609 George Brett MC	.25	.60
610 Howard Johnson MC	.02	.10
611 Esteban Beltre	.02	.10
612 Mike Christopher	.02	.10
613 Troy Afenir	.02	.10
614 Mariano Duncan	.02	.10
615 Doug Henry RC	.02	.10
616 Doug Jones	.02	.10
617 Alvin Davis	.02	.10
618 Craig Lefferts	.02	.10
619 Kevin McReynolds	.02	.10
620 Barry Bonds	.60	1.50
621 Turner Ward	.02	.10
622 Joe Magrane	.02	.10
623 Mark Parent	.02	.10
624 Tom Browning	.02	.10
625 John Smiley	.02	.10
626 Steve Wilson	.02	.10
627 Mike Gallego	.02	.10
628 Sammy Sosa	.20	.50
629 Rico Rossy	.02	.10
630 Royce Clayton	.02	.10
631 Clay Parker	.02	.10
632 Pete Smith	.02	.10
633 Jeff McKnight	.02	.10
634 Jack Daugherty	.02	.10
635 Steve Sax	.02	.10
636 Joe Hesketh	.02	.10
637 Vince Horsman	.02	.10
638 Eric King	.02	.10
639 Joe Boever	.02	.10
640 Jack Morris	.05	.15
641 Arthur Rhodes	.02	.10
642 Bob Melvin	.02	.10
643 Rick Wilkins	.02	.10
644 Scott Scudder	.02	.10
645 Bip Roberts	.02	.10
646 Julio Valera	.02	.10
647 Kevin Campbell	.02	.10
648 Steve Searcy	.02	.10
649 Scott Kamieniecki	.02	.10
650 Kurt Stillwell	.02	.10
651 Bob Welch	.02	.10
652 Andres Galarraga	.05	.15
653 Mike Jackson	.02	.10
654 Bo Jackson	.20	.50
655 Sid Fernandez	.02	.10
656 Mike Bielecki	.02	.10
657 Jeff Reardon	.05	.15
658 Wayne Rosenthal	.02	.10
659 Eric Bullock	.02	.10
660 Eric Davis	.05	.15
661 Randy Tomlin	.02	.10
662 Tom Edens	.02	.10
663 Rob Murphy	.02	.10
664 Leo Gomez	.02	.10
665 Greg Maddux	.30	.75
666 Greg Vaughn	.02	.10
667 Wade Taylor	.02	.10
668 Brad Arnsberg	.02	.10
669 Mike Moore	.02	.10
670 Mark Langston	.02	.10
671 Barry Jones	.02	.10
672 Bill Landrum	.02	.10
673 Greg Swindell	.02	.10
674 Wayne Edwards	.02	.10
675 Greg Olson	.02	.10
676 Bill Pulsipher RC	.02	.10
677 Bobby Witt	.02	.10
678 Mark Carreon	.02	.10
679 Patrick Lennon	.02	.10
680 Ozzie Smith	.30	.75
681 John Briscoe	.02	.10
682 Matt Young	.02	.10
683 Jeff Conine	.05	.15
684 Phil Stephenson	.02	.10
685 Ron Darling	.02	.10
686 Bryan Hickerson RC	.02	.10
687 Dale Sveum	.02	.10
688 Kirk McCaskill	.02	.10
689 Rich Amaral	.02	.10
690 Danny Tartabull	.02	.10
691 Donald Harris	.02	.10
692 Doug Davis	.02	.10
693 John Farrell	.02	.10
694 Paul Gibson	.02	.10
695 Kenny Lofton	.08	.25
696 Mike Fetters	.02	.10
697 Rosario Rodriguez	.02	.10
698 Chris Jones	.02	.10
699 Jeff Manto	.02	.10
700 Rick Sutcliffe	.05	.15
701 Scott Bankhead	.02	.10
702 Donnie Hill	.02	.10
703 Todd Worrell	.02	.10
704 Rene Gonzales	.02	.10
705 Rick Cerone	.02	.10
706 Tony Pena	.02	.10
707 Paul Sorrento	.02	.10
708 Gary Scott	.02	.10
709 Junior Noboa	.02	.10
710 Wally Joyner	.05	.15
711 Charlie Hayes	.02	.10
712 Rich Rodriguez	.02	.10
713 Rudy Seanez	.02	.10
714 Jim Bullinger	.02	.10
715 Jeff M. Robinson	.02	.10
716 Jeff Branson	.02	.10
717 Andy Ashby	.02	.10
718 Dave Burba	.02	.10
719 Rich Gossage	.05	.15
720 Randy Johnson	.20	.50
721 David Wells	.05	.15
722 Paul Kilgus	.02	.10
723 Dave Martinez	.02	.10
724 Denny Neagle	.05	.15
725 Andy Stankiewicz	.02	.10
726 Rick Aguilera	.05	.15
727 Junior Ortiz	.02	.10
728 Storm Davis	.02	.10
729 Don Robinson	.02	.10
730 Ron Gant	.05	.15
731 Paul Assenmacher	.02	.10
732 Mike Gardiner	.02	.10
733 Milt Hill	.02	.10
734 Jeremy Hernandez RC	.02	.10
735 Ken Hill	.02	.10
736 Xavier Hernandez	.02	.10
737 Gregg Jefferies	.02	.10
738 Dick Schofield	.02	.10
739 Ron Robinson	.02	.10
740 Sandy Alomar Jr.	.02	.10
741 Mike Stanley	.02	.10
742 Butch Henry RC	.02	.10
743 Floyd Bannister	.02	.10
744 Brian Drahman	.02	.10
745 Dave Winfield	.05	.15
746 Bob Walk	.02	.10
747 Chris James	.02	.10
748 Don Prybylinski RC	.02	.10
749 Dennis Rasmussen	.02	.10
750 Rickey Henderson	.20	.50
751 Chris Hammond	.02	.10
752 Bob Kipper	.02	.10
753 Dave Rohde	.02	.10
754 Hubie Brooks	.02	.10
755 Bret Saberhagen	.05	.15
756 Jeff D. Robinson	.02	.10
757 Pat Listach RC	.05	.15
758 Bill Wegman	.02	.10
759 John Wetteland	.05	.15
760 Phil Plantier	.02	.10
761 Wilson Alvarez	.02	.10
762 Scott Aldred	.02	.10
763 Armando Reynoso RC	.05	.15
764 Todd Benzinger	.02	.10
765 Kevin Mitchell	.02	.10
766 Gary Sheffield	.05	.15
767 Allan Anderson	.02	.10
768 Rusty Meacham	.02	.10
769 Rick Parker	.02	.10
770 Nolan Ryan	.75	2.00
771 Jeff Ballard	.02	.10
772 Cory Snyder	.02	.10
773 Denis Boucher	.02	.10
774 Jose Gonzalez	.02	.10
775 Juan Guerrero	.02	.10
776 Ed Nunez	.02	.10
777 Scott Ruskin	.02	.10
778 Terry Leach	.02	.10
779 Carl Willis	.02	.10
780 Bobby Bonilla	.05	.15
781 Duane Ward	.02	.10
782 Joe Slusarski	.02	.10
783 David Segui	.02	.10
784 Kirk Gibson	.05	.15
785 Frank Viola	.05	.15
786 Keith Miller	.02	.10
787 Mike Morgan	.02	.10
788 Kim Batiste	.02	.10
789 Sergio Valdez	.02	.10
790 Eddie Taubensee RC	.05	.15
791 Jack Armstrong	.02	.10
792 Scott Fletcher	.02	.10
793 Steve Farr	.02	.10
794 Dan Pasqua	.02	.10
795 Eddie Murray	.20	.50
796 John Morris	.02	.10
797 Francisco Cabrera	.02	.10
798 Mike Perez	.02	.10
799 Ted Wood	.02	.10
800 Jose Rijo	.02	.10
801 Danny Gladden	.02	.10
802 Archi Cianfrocco RC	.02	.10
803 Monty Fariss	.02	.10
804 Roger McDowell	.02	.10
805 Randy Myers	.02	.10
806 Kirk Dressendorfer	.02	.10
807 Zane Smith	.02	.10
808 Glenn Davis	.02	.10
809 Torey Lovullo	.02	.10
810 Andre Dawson	.05	.15
811 Bill Pecota	.02	.10
812 Ted Power	.02	.10
813 Willie Blair	.02	.10
814 Dave Fleming	.02	.10
815 Chris Gwynn	.02	.10
816 Jody Reed	.02	.10
817 Mark Dewey	.02	.10
818 Kyle Abbott	.02	.10
819 Tom Henke	.02	.10
820 Kevin Seitzer	.02	.10
821 Al Newman	.02	.10
822 Tim Sherrill	.02	.10
823 Chuck Crim	.02	.10
824 Darren Reed	.02	.10
825 Tony Gwynn	.25	.60
826 Steve Foster	.02	.10
827 Steve Howe	.02	.10
828 Brook Jacoby	.02	.10
829 Rodney McCray	.02	.10
830 Chuck Knoblauch	.05	.15
831 John Wehner	.02	.10
832 Scott Garrelts	.02	.10
833 Alejandro Pena	.02	.10
834 Jeff Parrett UER	.02	.10
(Kentucy)		
835 Juan Bell	.02	.10
836 Lance Dickson	.02	.10
837 Darryl Kile	.05	.15
838 Efrain Valdez	.02	.10
839 Bob Zupcic RC	.02	.10
840 George Bell	.02	.10
841 Dave Gallagher	.02	.10
842 Tim Belcher	.02	.10
843 Jeff Shaw	.02	.10
844 Mike Fitzgerald	.02	.10
845 Gary Carter	.05	.15
846 John Russell	.02	.10
847 Eric Hillman RC	.02	.10
848 Mike Witt	.02	.10
849 Curt Wilkerson	.02	.10
850 Alan Trammell	.05	.15
851 Rex Hudler	.02	.10
852 Mike Walkden RC	.02	.10
853 Kevin Ward	.02	.10
854 Tim Naehring	.02	.10
855 Bill Swift	.02	.10
856 Damon Berryhill	.02	.10
857 Mark Eichhorn	.02	.10
858 Hector Villanueva	.02	.10
859 Jose Lind	.02	.10
860 Dennis Martinez	.05	.15
861 Bill Krueger	.02	.10
862 Mike Kingery	.02	.10
863 Jeff Innis	.02	.10
864 Derek Lilliquist	.02	.10
865 Reggie Sanders	.05	.15
866 Ramon Garcia	.02	.10
867 Bruce Ruffin	.02	.10
868 Dickie Thon	.02	.10
869 Melido Perez	.02	.10
870 Ruben Amaro	.02	.10
871 Alan Mills	.02	.10
872 Matt Sinatro	.02	.10
873 Eddie Zosky	.02	.10
874 Pete Incaviglia	.02	.10
875 Tom Candiotti	.02	.10
876 Bob Patterson	.02	.10
877 Neal Heaton	.02	.10
878 Terrel Hansen RC	.02	.10
879 Dave Eiland	.02	.10
880 Von Hayes	.02	.10
881 Tim Scott	.02	.10
882 Otis Nixon	.02	.10
883 Herm Winningham	.02	.10
884 Dion James	.02	.10
885 Dave Wainhouse	.02	.10
886 Frank DiPino	.02	.10
887 Dennis Cook	.02	.10
888 Jose Mesa	.02	.10
889 Mark Leiter	.02	.10
890 Willie Randolph	.05	.15
891 Craig Colbert	.02	.10
892 Dwayne Henry	.02	.10
893 Jim Lindeman	.02	.10
894 Charlie Hough	.05	.15
895 Gil Heredia RC	.05	.15
896 Scott Chiamparino	.02	.10
897 Lance Blankenship	.02	.10
898 Checklist 601-700	.02	.10
899 Checklist 701-800	.02	.10
900 Checklist 801-900	.02	.10

1992 Stadium Club First Draft Picks

This three-card standard-size set, featuring Major League Baseball's Number 1 draft pick for 1990, 1991, and 1992, was randomly inserted into 1992 Stadium Club Series III packs at an approximate rate of 1:72. One card also was mailed to each member of Topps Stadium Club.

RANDOM INSERTS IN SER.3 PACKS		
ONE CARD SENT TO EACH ST.CLUB MEMBER		
1 Chipper Jones	2.00	5.00
2 Brien Taylor	.75	2.00
3 Phil Nevin	.75	2.00

1992 Stadium Club Master Photos

In the first package of materials sent to 1992 Topps Stadium Club members, along with an 11-card boxed set, members received a randomly chosen "Master Photo" printed on (approximately) 5" by 7" white card stock to demonstrate how the photos are cropped to create a borderless design. Each master photo has the Topps Stadium Club logo and the words "Master Photo" above a gold foil picture frame enclosing the color player photo. The backs are blank. The cards are unnumbered and checklisted below alphabetically. Master photos were also available through a special promotion at Walmart as an insert one-per-box in specially marked wax boxes of regular Topps Stadium Club cards.

COMPLETE SET (15)	8.00	20.00
1 Wade Boggs	.50	1.25
2 Barry Bonds	.75	2.00
3 Jose Canseco	.50	1.25
4 Will Clark	.40	1.00
5 Cecil Fielder	.20	.50
6 Dwight Gooden	.20	.50
7 Ken Griffey Jr.	1.00	2.50
8 Rickey Henderson	.60	1.50
9 Lance Johnson	.08	.25
10 Cal Ripken	2.00	5.00
11 Nolan Ryan	2.00	5.00
12 Deion Sanders	.40	1.00
13 Darryl Strawberry	.20	.50
14 Danny Tartabull	.08	.25
15 Frank Thomas	.60	1.50

1992 Stadium Club Members Only

This 50-card standard-size set was sent to 1992 Stadium Club members in four installments. In addition to the Stadium Club cards, the first installment included one "Top Draft Picks of the '90s" card (as a bonus) and a randomly chosen "Master Photo" printed on 5" by 7" white card stock. The third and fourth installments included hockey and football players in addition to baseball players. The cards feature full-bleed glossy color player photos. The fronts of the regular cards have the words "Members Only" printed in gold foil at the bottom along with the player's name and the Stadium Club logo. The backs feature a stadium scene with the scoreboard displaying, in yellow neon, a career highlight. The cards are unnumbered and checklisted below alphabetically, with the two-player cards listed at the end.

COMPLETE SET (50)	12.00	30.00
1 Carlos Baerga	.07	.20
2 Wade Boggs	.20	.50
3 Barry Bonds	.30	.75
4 Bret Boone	.07	.20
5 Pat Borders	.07	.20
6 George Brett	.40	1.00
7 George Brett	.40	1.00
8 Jim Bullinger	.07	.20
9 Gary Carter	.15	.40
10 Andujar Cedeno	.07	.20
11 Roger Clemens	.50	1.25
Matt Young		
12 Dennis Eckersley	.15	.40
13 Dennis Eckersley	.15	.40
14 Dave Eiland	.07	.20
15 Ken Griffey Jr.	1.25	3.00
16 Kevin Gross	.07	.20
17 Bo Jackson	.20	.50
18 Eric Karros	.07	.20
19 Pat Listach	.07	.20
20 Greg Maddux	.75	2.00
21 Mickey Morandini	.07	.20
22 Jack Morris	.15	.40
23 Eddie Murray	.20	.50
24 Eddie Murray	.20	.50
25 Bip Roberts	.07	.20
26 Nolan Ryan	1.00	2.50
27 Seasons		
27 Nolan Ryan	1.00	2.50
1993 Seasons His Finale		
28 Gary Sheffield	.15	.40
Dwight Gooden		
29 Gary Sheffield	.15	.40
Fred McGriff		
30 Lee Smith	.15	.40
31 Ozzie Smith	.50	1.25
(2,000th Hit)		
32 Ozzie Smith	.50	1.25
(7,000th Career Assist)		
33 Ozzie Smith	.50	1.25
34 Bobby Thigpen	.07	.20
35 Dave Winfield	.20	.50
36 Robin Yount	.20	.50

1993 Stadium Club Murphy

This 200-card boxed set features 1992 All-Star Game cards, 1992 Team USA cards, and 1992 Championship and World Series cards. Topps actually refers to this set as a 1992 issue, but the set was released in 1993. This set is housed in a replica of San Diego's Jack Murphy Stadium, site of the 1992 All-Star Game. Production was limited to 8,000 cases, with 16 boxes per case. The set includes 100 Draft Pick cards, 56 All-Star cards, 25 Team USA cards, and 19 cards commemorating the 1992 National and American League Championship Series and the World Series. Notable Rookie Cards in this set include Derek Jeter, Jason Kendall, Shannon Stewart and Preston Wilson. A second year Team USA Nomar Garciaparra is featured in this set as well.

COMP.FACT.SET (212)	90.00	150.00
COMPLETE SET (200)	60.00	120.00
COMMON CARD (1-200)	.05	.15
COMMON RC	.05	.15
STATED PRINT RUN 128,000 SETS		
1 Dave Winfield	.05	.15
2 Juan Guzman	.05	.15
3 Tony Gwynn	.40	1.00
4 Chris Roberts	.05	.15
5 Benny Santiago	.10	.30
6 Sherard Clinkscales RC	.05	.15
7 Jon Nunnally RC	.20	.50
8 Chuck Knoblauch	.10	.30
9 Bob Wolcott RC	.05	.15
10 Steve Rodriguez	.05	.15
11 Mark Williams RC	.05	.15
12 Danny Clyburn RC	.05	.15
13 Darren Dreifort	.05	.15
14 Andy Van Slyke	.20	.50
15 Wade Boggs	.20	.50
16 Scott Patton RC	.05	.15
17 Gary Sheffield	.10	.30
18 Ron Villone	.05	.15
19 Roberto Alomar	.20	.50
20 Marc Valdes	.05	.15
21 Daron Kirkreit	.05	.15
22 Jeff Granger	.05	.15
23 Levon Largusa RC	.05	.15
24 Jimmy Key	.10	.30
25 Kevin Pearson RC	.05	.15
26 Michael Moore RC	.05	.15
27 Preston Wilson RC	.60	1.50
28 Kirby Puckett	.30	.75
29 Tim Crabtree RC	.05	.15
30 Bip Roberts	.05	.15
31 Kelly Gruber	.05	.15
32 Tony Fernandez	.05	.15
33 Jason Angel RC	.05	.15
34 Calvin Murray	.05	.15
35 Chad McConnell	.05	.15
36 Jason Moler	.05	.15
37 Mark Lemke	.05	.15
38 Tom Knauss RC	.05	.15
39 Larry Mitchell RC	.05	.15
40 Doug Mirabelli RC	.20	.50
41 Everett Stull II RC	.05	.15
42 Chris Wimmer	.05	.15
43 Dan Serafini RC	.05	.15
44 Ryne Sandberg	.50	1.25
45 Steve Lyons RC	.05	.15
46 Ryan Freeburg RC	.05	.15
47 Ruben Sierra	.10	.30
48 David Mysel RC	.05	.15
49 Joe Hamilton RC	.05	.15
50 Steve Rodriguez	.05	.15
51 Tim Wakefield	.30	.75
52 Scott Gentile RC	.05	.15
53 Doug Jones	.05	.15
54 Willie Brown RC	.05	.15
55 Chad Mottola RC	.20	.50
56 Ken Griffey Jr.	.50	1.25
57 Jon Lieber RC	1.00	2.50
58 Dennis Martinez	.10	.30
59 Joe Petcka RC	.05	.15
60 Benji Simonton RC	.05	.15
61 Brett Backlund RC	.05	.15
62 Damon Berryhill	.05	.15
63 Juan Guzman	.05	.15
64 Doug Hecker RC	.05	.15
65 Jamie Arnold RC	.05	.15
66 Bob Tewksbury	.05	.15
67 Tim Leger RC	.05	.15
68 Todd Etler RC	.05	.15
69 Lloyd McClendon	.05	.15
70 Kurt Ehmann RC	.05	.15
71 Rick Magdaleno RC	.05	.15
72 Tom Pagnozzi	.05	.15
73 Jeffrey Hammonds	.05	.15
74 Joe Carter	.10	.30
75 Chris Holt RC	.10	.30
76 Charles Johnson	.10	.30
77 Bob Walk	.05	.15
78 Fred McGriff	.20	.50
79 Tom Evans RC	.05	.15
80 Scott Klingenbeck RC	.05	.15
81 Chad McConnell	.05	.15
82 Chris Eddy RC	.05	.15
83 Phil Nevin	.10	.30
84 John Kruk	.10	.30
85 Tony Sheffield RC	.05	.15
86 John Smoltz	.20	.50
87 Trevor Humphry RC	.05	.15
88 Charles Nagy	.05	.15
89 Sean Runyan RC	.05	.15
90 Mike Gulan RC	.05	.15
91 Darren Daulton	.10	.30
92 Otis Nixon	.05	.15
93 Nomar Garciaparra	2.00	5.00
94 Larry Walker	.10	.30
95 Hut Smith RC	.05	.15
96 Rick Helling	.05	.15
97 Roger Clemens	.60	1.50
98 Ron Gant	.10	.30
99 Kenny Felder RC	.05	.15
100 Steve Murphy RC	.05	.15
101 Mike Smith RC	.05	.15
102 Terry Pendleton	.10	.30
103 Tim Davis	.05	.15
104 Jeff Patzke RC	.05	.15
105 Craig Wilson	.05	.15
106 Tom Glavine	.20	.50
107 Mark Langston	.05	.15
108 Mark Thompson RC	.05	.15
109 Eric Owens RC	.05	.15
110 Keith Johnson RC	.05	.15
111 Robin Ventura	.10	.30
112 Ed Sprague	.05	.15
113 Jeff Schmidt RC	.05	.15
114 Don Wengert RC	.05	.15
115 Craig Biggio	.20	.50
116 Kenny Carlyle RC	.05	.15
117 Derek Jeter RC	50.00	100.00
118 Manuel Lee	.05	.15
119 Jeff Haas RC	.05	.15
120 Roger Bailey RC	.05	.15
121 Sean Lowe RC	.05	.15
122 Rick Aguilera	.05	.15
123 Sandy Alomar Jr.	.05	.15
124 Derek Wallace RC	.05	.15
125 B.J. Wallace	.05	.15
126 Greg Maddux	.50	1.25
127 Tim Moore RC	.05	.15
128 Lee Smith	.10	.30
129 Todd Steverson RC	.05	.15
130 Chris Widger RC	.20	.50
131 Paul Molitor	.10	.30
132 Chris Smith RC	.05	.15
133 Chris Gomez RC	.20	.50
134 Jimmy Baron RC	.05	.15
135 John Smoltz	.20	.50
136 Pat Borders	.05	.15
137 Donnie Leshnock	.05	.15
138 Gus Gandarillos RC	.05	.15
139 Will Clark	.20	.50

140 Ryan Luzinski RC .05 .15
141 Cal Ripken 1.00 2.50
142 B.J. Wallace .05 .15
143 Trey Beamon RC .20 .50
144 Norm Charlton .05 .15
145 Mike Mussina .20 .50
146 Billy Owens RC .05 .15
147 Ozzie Smith .50 1.25
148 Jason Kendall RC .60 1.50
149 Mike Matthews RC .05 .15
150 David Spykstra RC .05 .15
151 Benji Grigsby RC .05 .15
152 Sean Smith RC .05 .15
153 Mark McGwire .75 2.00
154 David Cone .10 .30
155 Shon Walker RC .05 .15
156 Jason Giambi .40 1.00
157 Jack McDowell .05 .15
158 Paxton Briley RC .05 .15
159 Edgar Martinez .20 .50
160 Brian Sackinsky RC .05 .15
161 Barry Bonds .75 2.00
162 Roberto Kelly .05 .15
163 Jeff Alkire .05 .15
164 Mike Sharperson .05 .15
165 Jamie Taylor RC .05 .15
166 John Saffer UER RC .05 .15
167 Jerry Browne .05 .15
168 Travis Fryman .10 .30
169 Brady Anderson .10 .30
170 Chris Roberts .05 .15
171 Lloyd Peever RC .05 .15
172 Francisco Cabrera .05 .15
173 Ramiro Martinez RC .05 .15
174 Jeff Alkire .05 .15
175 Ivan Rodriguez .20 .50
176 Kevin Brown .10 .30
177 Chad Roper RC .05 .15
178 Rod Henderson RC .05 .15
179 Dennis Eckersley .10 .30
180 Shannon Stewart RC .60 1.50
181 DeShawn Warren RC .05 .15
182 Lonnie Smith .05 .15
183 Willie Adams .05 .15
184 Jeff Montgomery .05 .15
185 Damon Hollins RC .20 .50
186 Byron Mathews RC .05 .15
187 Harold Baines .10 .30
188 Rick Greene .05 .15
189 Carlos Baerga .05 .15
190 Brandon Cromer RC .05 .15
191 Roberto Alomar .20 .50
192 Rich Ireland RC .05 .15
193 S.Montgomery RC .05 .15
194 Brant Brown RC .05 .15
195 Ritchie Moody RC .05 .15
196 Michael Tucker .05 .15
197 Jason Varitek 2.00 5.00
198 David Manning RC .05 .15
199 Marquis Riley RC .05 .15
200 Jason Giambi .40 1.00

1993 Stadium Club Murphy Master Photos

One Murphy Master Photo was included in each 1993 Stadium Club Murphy Special factory set. Each of these twelve uncropped Murphy Master Photos is inlaid in a 5" by 7" white frame and bordered with a prismatic foil trim. The photo within parallels the corresponding player's regular issue Murphy card. The cards are unnumbered and checklisted below in alphabetical order.

COMPLETE SET (12) 2.00 5.00
ONE MP SET PER MURPHY FACTORY SET
1 Sandy Alomar Jr. AS .05 .15
2 Tom Glavine AS .20 .50
3 Ken Griffey Jr. AS .50 1.25
4 Tony Gwynn AS .40 1.00
5 Chuck Knoblauch AS .10 .30
6 Chad Mottola .20 .50
7 Kirby Puckett AS .30 .75
8 Chris Roberts USA .05 .15
9 Ryne Sandberg AS .50 1.25
10 Gary Sheffield AS .10 .30
11 Larry Walker AS .10 .30
12 Preston Wilson .75 2.00

1993 Stadium Club

The 1993 Stadium Club baseball set consists of 750 standard-size cards issued in three series of 300, 300, and 150 cards respectively. Each series closes with a Members Choice subset (291-300, 591-600, and 746-750.

COMPLETE SET (750) 20.00 50.00
COMP.SERIES 1 (300) 6.00 15.00
COMP.SERIES 2 (300) 8.00 20.00
COMP.SERIES 3 (150) 6.00 15.00
1 Pat Borders .05 .15
2 Greg Maddux .50 1.25
3 Daryl Boston .05 .15
4 Bob Ayrault .05 .15
5 Tony Phillips IF .05 .15
6 Damion Easley .05 .15
7 Kip Gross .05 .15
8 Jim Thome .20 .50
9 Tim Belcher .05 .15
10 Gary Wayne .05 .15
11 Sam Militello .05 .15
12 Mike Magnante .05 .15
13 Tim Wakefield .30 .75
14 Tim Hulett .05 .15
15 Rheal Cormier .05 .15
16 Juan Guerrero .05 .15
17 Rich Gossage .10 .30
18 Tim Laker RC .05 .15
19 Darrin Jackson .05 .15
20 Jack Clark .10 .30
21 Roberto Hernandez .05 .15
22 Dean Palmer .10 .30
23 Harold Reynolds .10 .30
24 Dan Plesac .05 .15
25 Brent Mayne .05 .15
26 Pat Hentgen .05 .15
27 Luis Sojo .05 .15
28 Ron Gant .10 .30
29 Paul Gibson .05 .15
30 Bip Roberts .05 .15
31 Mickey Tettleton .05 .15
32 Randy Velarde .05 .15
33 Brian McRae .05 .15
34 Wes Chamberlain .05 .15
35 Wayne Kirby .05 .15
36 Rey Sanchez .05 .15
37 Jesse Orosco .05 .15
38 Mike Stanton .05 .15
39 Royce Clayton .05 .15
40 Cal Ripken UER 1.00 2.50
(Place of birth Havre de Grave;
should be Havre de Grace)
41 John Dopson .05 .15
42 Gene Larkin .05 .15
43 Tim Raines .10 .30
44 Randy Myers .05 .15
45 Clay Parker .05 .15
46 Mike Scioscia .05 .15
47 Pete Incaviglia .05 .15
48 Todd Van Poppel .05 .15
49 Ray Lankford .10 .30
50 Eddie Murray .30 .75
51 Barry Bonds COR .75 2.00
51A Barry Bonds ERR .75 2.00
(Missing four stars over
name to indicate NL MVP)
52 Gary Thurman .05 .15
53 Bob Wickman .05 .15
54 Joey Cora .05 .15
55 Kenny Rogers .10 .30
56 Mike Devereaux .05 .15
57 Kevin Seitzer .05 .15
58 Rafael Belliard .05 .15
59 David Wells .10 .30
60 Mark Clark .05 .15
61 Carlos Baerga .05 .15
62 Scott Brosius .10 .30
63 Jeff Grotewold .05 .15
64 Rick Wrona .05 .15
65 Kurt Knudsen .05 .15
66 Lloyd McClendon .05 .15
67 Omar Vizquel .20 .50
68 Jose Vizcaino .05 .15
69 Rob Ducey .05 .15
70 Casey Candaele .05 .15
71 Ramon Martinez .05 .15
72 Todd Hundley .05 .15
73 John Marzano .05 .15
74 Derek Parks .05 .15
75 Jack McDowell .05 .15
76 Tim Scott .05 .15
77 Mike Mussina .20 .50
78 Delino DeShields .05 .15
79 Chris Bosio .05 .15
80 Mike Bordick .05 .15
81 Rod Beck .05 .15
82 Ted Power .05 .15
83 John Kruk .10 .30
84 Steve Shifflett .05 .15
85 Danny Tartabull .05 .15
86 Mike Greenwell .05 .15
87 Jose Melendez .05 .15
88 Craig Wilson .05 .15
89 Melvin Nieves .05 .15
90 Ed Sprague .05 .15
91 Willie McGee .10 .30
92 Joe Orsulak .05 .15
93 Jeff King .05 .15
94 Dan Pasqua .05 .15
95 Brian Harper .05 .15
96 Joe Oliver .05 .15
97 Shane Turner .05 .15
98 Lenny Harris .05 .15
99 Jeff Parrett .05 .15
100 Luis Polonia .05 .15
101 Kent Bottenfield .05 .15
102 Albert Belle .10 .30
103 Mike Maddux .05 .15
104 Randy Tomlin .05 .15
105 Andy Stankiewicz .05 .15
106 Rico Rossy .05 .15
107 Joe Hesketh .05 .15
108 Dennis Powell .05 .15
109 Derrick May .05 .15
110 Pete Harnisch .05 .15
111 Kent Mercker .05 .15
112 Scott Fletcher .05 .15
113 Rex Hudler .05 .15
114 Chico Walker .05 .15
115 Rafael Palmeiro .20 .50
116 Mark Leiter .05 .15
117 Pedro Munoz .05 .15
118 Jim Bullinger .05 .15
119 Ivan Calderon .05 .15
120 Mike Timlin .05 .15
121 Rene Gonzales .05 .15
122 Greg Vaughn .05 .15
123 Mike Flanagan .05 .15
124 Mike Hartley .05 .15
125 Jeff Montgomery .05 .15
126 Mike Gallego .05 .15
127 Don Slaught .05 .15
128 Charlie O'Brien .05 .15
129 Jose Offerman .05 .15
(Can be found with home town
missing on back)
130 Mark Wohlers .05 .15
131 Eric Fox .05 .15
132 Doug Strange .05 .15
133 Jeff Frye .05 .15
134 Wade Boggs UER .20 .50
(Redundantly lists
lefty breakdown)
135 Lou Whitaker .10 .30
136 Craig Grebeck .05 .15
137 Rich Rodriguez .05 .15
138 Jay Bell .10 .30
139 Felix Fermin .05 .15
140 Dennis Martinez .10 .30
141 Eric Anthony .05 .15
142 Roberto Alomar .20 .50
143 Darren Lewis .05 .15
144 Mike Blowers .05 .15
145 Scott Bankhead .05 .15
146 Jeff Reboulet .05 .15
147 Frank Viola .10 .30
148 Bill Pecota .05 .15
149 Carlos Hernandez .05 .15
150 Bobby Witt .05 .15
151 Sid Bream .05 .15
152 Todd Zeile .05 .15
153 Dennis Cook .05 .15
154 Brian Bohanon .05 .15
155 Pat Kelly .05 .15
156 Milt Cuyler .05 .15
157 Juan Bell .05 .15
158 Randy Milligan .05 .15
159 Mark Gardner .05 .15
160 Pat Tabler .05 .15
161 Jeff Reardon .10 .30
162 Ken Patterson .05 .15
163 Bobby Bonilla .10 .30
164 Tony Pena .05 .15
165 Greg Swindell .05 .15
166 Kirk McCaskill .05 .15
167 Doug Drabek .05 .15
168 Franklin Stubbs .05 .15
169 Ron Tingley .05 .15
170 Willie Banks .05 .15
171 Sergio Valdez .05 .15
172 Mark Lemke .05 .15
173 Robin Yount .50 1.25
174 Storm Davis .05 .15
175 Dan Walters .05 .15
176 Steve Farr .05 .15
177 Curt Wilkerson .05 .15
178 Luis Alicea .05 .15
179 Russ Swan .05 .15
180 Mitch Williams .05 .15
181 Wilson Alvarez .05 .15
182 Carl Willis .05 .15
183 Craig Biggio .20 .50
184 Sean Berry .05 .15
185 Trevor Wilson .05 .15
186 Jeff Tackett .05 .15
187 Ellis Burks .10 .30
188 Jeff Branson .05 .15
189 Matt Nokes .05 .15
190 John Smiley .05 .15
191 Danny Gladden .05 .15
192 Mike Boddicker .05 .15
193 Roger Pavlik .05 .15
194 Paul Sorrento .05 .15
195 Vince Coleman .05 .15
196 Gary DiSarcina .05 .15
197 Rafael Bournigal .05 .15
198 Mike Schooler .05 .15
199 Scott Ruskin .05 .15
200 Frank Thomas .30 .75
201 Kyle Abbott .05 .15
202 Mike Perez .05 .15
203 Andre Dawson .10 .30
204 Bill Swift .05 .15
205 Alejandro Pena .05 .15
206 Dave Winfield .10 .30
207 Andujar Cedeno .05 .15
208 Terry Steinbach .05 .15
209 Chris Hammond .05 .15
210 Todd Burns .05 .15
211 Hipolito Pichardo .05 .15
212 John Kiely .05 .15
213 Tim Teufel .05 .15
214 Lee Guetterman .05 .15
215 Geronimo Pena .05 .15
216 Brett Butler .10 .30
217 Bryan Hickerson .05 .15
218 Rick Trlicek .05 .15
219 Lee Stevens .05 .15
220 Roger Clemens .60 1.50
221 Carlton Fisk .20 .50
222 Chili Davis .10 .30
223 Walt Terrell .05 .15
224 Jim Eisenreich .05 .15
225 Ricky Bones .05 .15
226 Henry Rodriguez .05 .15
227 Ken Hill .05 .15
228 Rick Wilkins .05 .15
229 Ricky Jordan .05 .15
230 Bernard Gilkey .05 .15
231 Tim Fortugno .05 .15
232 Geno Petralli .05 .15
233 Jose Rijo .05 .15
234 Jim Leyritz .05 .15
235 Kevin Campbell .05 .15
236 Al Osuna .05 .15
237 Pete Smith .05 .15
238 Pete Schourek .05 .15
239 Moises Alou .10 .30
240 Donn Pall .05 .15
241 Denny Neagle .10 .30
242 Dan Peltier .05 .15
243 Scott Scudder .05 .15
244 Juan Guzman .05 .15
245 Dave Burba .05 .15
246 Rick Sutcliffe .10 .30
247 Tony Fossas .05 .15
248 Mike Munoz .05 .15
249 Tim Salmon .20 .50
250 Rob Murphy .05 .15
251 Roger McDowell .05 .15
252 Lance Parrish .10 .30
253 Cliff Brantley .05 .15
254 Scott Leius .05 .15
255 Carlos Martinez .05 .15
256 Vince Horsman .05 .15
257 Oscar Azocar .05 .15
258 Craig Shipley .05 .15
259 Ben McDonald .05 .15
260 Jeff Brantley .05 .15
261 Damon Berryhill .05 .15
262 Joe Grahe .05 .15
263 Dave Hansen .05 .15
264 Rich Amaral .05 .15
265 Tim Pugh RC .05 .15
266 Dion James .05 .15
267 Frank Tanana .05 .15
268 Stan Belinda .05 .15
269 Jeff Kent .30 .75
270 Bruce Ruffin .05 .15
271 Xavier Hernandez .05 .15
272 Darrin Fletcher .05 .15
273 Tino Martinez .20 .50
274 Benny Santiago .10 .30
275 Scott Radinsky .05 .15
276 Mariano Duncan .05 .15
277 Kenny Lofton .10 .30
278 Dwight Smith .05 .15
279 Joe Carter .10 .30
280 Tim Jones .05 .15
281 Jeff Huson .05 .15
282 Phil Plantier .05 .15
283 Kirby Puckett .30 .75
284 Johnny Guzman .05 .15
285 Mike Morgan .05 .15
286 Chris Sabo .05 .15
287 Matt Williams .10 .30
288 Checklist 1-100 .05 .15
289 Checklist 101-200 .05 .15
290 Checklist 201-300 .05 .15
291 Dennis Eckersley MC .10 .30
292 Eric Karros MC .05 .15
293 Pat Listach MC .05 .15
294 Andy Van Slyke MC .10 .30
295 Robin Ventura MC .05 .15
296 Tom Glavine MC .10 .30
297 J.Gonzalez MC UER .05 .15
Misspelled Gonzales
298 Travis Fryman MC .05 .15
299 Larry Walker MC .10 .30
300 Gary Sheffield MC .05 .15
301 Chuck Finley .10 .30
302 Luis Gonzalez .10 .30
303 Darryl Hamilton .05 .15
304 Bien Figueroa .05 .15
305 Ron Darling .05 .15
306 Jonathan Hurst .05 .15
307 Mike Sharperson .05 .15
308 Mike Christopher .05 .15
309 Marvin Freeman .05 .15
310 Jay Buhner .10 .30
311 Butch Henry .05 .15
312 Greg W. Harris .05 .15
313 Darren Daulton .10 .30
314 Chuck Knoblauch .10 .30
315 Greg A. Harris .05 .15
316 John Franco .10 .30
317 John Wehner .05 .15
318 Donald Harris .05 .15
319 Benny Santiago .10 .30
320 Larry Walker .10 .30
321 Randy Knorr .05 .15
322 Ramon Martinez RC .05 .15
323 Mike Stanley .05 .15
324 Bill Wegman .05 .15
325 Tom Candiotti .05 .15
326 Glenn Davis .05 .15
327 Chuck Crim .05 .15
328 Scott Livingstone .05 .15
329 Eddie Taubensee .05 .15
330 George Bell .05 .15
331 Edgar Martinez .20 .50
332 Paul Assenmacher .05 .15
333 Steve Hosey .05 .15
334 Mo Vaughn .10 .30
335 Bret Saberhagen .10 .30
336 Mike Trombley .05 .15
337 Mark Lewis .05 .15
338 Terry Pendleton .10 .30
339 Dave Hollins .05 .15
340 Jeff Conine .10 .30
341 Bob Tewksbury .05 .15
342 Billy Ashley .05 .15
343 Zane Smith .05 .15
344 John Wetteland .10 .30
345 Chris Hoiles .05 .15
346 Frank Castillo .05 .15
347 Bruce Hurst .05 .15
348 Kevin McReynolds .05 .15
349 Dave Henderson .05 .15
350 Ryan Bowen .05 .15
351 Sid Fernandez .05 .15
352 Mark Whiten .05 .15
353 Nolan Ryan 1.25 3.00
354 Rick Aguilera .05 .15
355 Mark Langston .05 .15
356 Jack Morris .10 .30
357 Rob Deer .05 .15
358 Dave Fleming .05 .15
359 Lance Johnson .05 .15
360 Joe Millette .05 .15
361 Wil Cordero .05 .15
362 Chito Martinez .05 .15
363 Scott Servais .05 .15
364 Bernie Williams .20 .50
365 Pedro Martinez .60 1.50
366 Ryne Sandberg .50 1.25
367 Brad Ausmus .30 .75
368 Scott Cooper .05 .15
369 Rob Dibble .10 .30
370 Walt Weiss .05 .15
371 Mark Davis .05 .15
372 Orlando Merced .05 .15
373 Mike Jackson .05 .15
374 Kevin Appier .10 .30
375 Esteban Beltre .05 .15
376 Joe Slusarski .05 .15
377 William Suero .05 .15
378 Pete O'Brien .05 .15
379 Alan Embree .05 .15
380 Lenny Webster .05 .15
381 Eric Davis .10 .30
382 Duane Ward .05 .15
383 John Habyan .05 .15
384 Jeff Bagwell .20 .50
385 Ruben Amaro .05 .15
386 Julio Valera .05 .15
387 Robin Ventura .10 .30
388 Archi Cianfrocco .05 .15
389 Skeeter Barnes .05 .15
390 Tim Costo .05 .15
391 Luis Mercedes .05 .15
392 Jeremy Hernandez .05 .15
393 Shawon Dunston .05 .15
394 Andy Van Slyke .20 .50
395 Kevin Maas .05 .15
396 Kevin Brown .10 .30
397 J.T. Bruett .05 .15
398 Darryl Strawberry .10 .30
399 Tom Pagnozzi .05 .15
400 Sandy Alomar Jr. .05 .15
401 Keith Miller .05 .15
402 Rich DeLucia .05 .15
403 Shawn Abner .05 .15
404 Howard Johnson .05 .15
405 Mike Benjamin .05 .15
406 Roberto Mejia RC .05 .15
407 Mike Butcher .05 .15
408 Deion Sanders UER .20 .50
(Braves on front and Yankees on back)
409 Todd Stottlemyre .05 .15
410 Scott Kamieniecki .05 .15
411 Doug Jones .05 .15
412 John Burkett .05 .15
413 Lance Blankenship .05 .15
414 Jeff Parrett .05 .15
415 Barry Larkin .20 .50
416 Alan Trammell .10 .30
417 Mark Kiefer .05 .15
418 Gregg Olson .05 .15
419 Mark Grace .20 .50
420 Shane Mack .05 .15
421 Bob Walk .05 .15
422 Curt Schilling .10 .30
423 Erik Hanson .05 .15
424 George Brett .75 2.00
425 Reggie Jefferson .05 .15
426 Mark Portugal .05 .15
427 Ron Karkovice .05 .15
428 Matt Young .05 .15
429 Troy Neel .05 .15
430 Hector Fajardo .05 .15
431 Dave Righetti .10 .30
432 Pat Listach .05 .15
433 Jeff Innis .05 .15
434 Bob MacDonald .05 .15
435 Brian Jordan .10 .30
436 Jeff Blauser .05 .15
437 Mike Myers RC .05 .15
438 Frank Seminara .05 .15
439 Rusty Meacham .05 .15
440 Greg Briley .05 .15
441 Derek Lilliquist .05 .15
442 John Vander Wal .05 .15
443 Scott Erickson .05 .15
444 Bob Scanlan .05 .15
445 Todd Frohwirth .05 .15
446 Tom Goodwin .05 .15
447 William Pennyfeather .05 .15
448 Travis Fryman .10 .30
449 Mickey Morandini .05 .15
450 Greg Olson .05 .15
451 Trevor Hoffman .30 .75
452 Dave Magadan .05 .15
453 Shawn Jeter .05 .15
454 Andres Galarraga .10 .30
455 Ted Wood .05 .15
456 Freddie Benavides .05 .15
457 Junior Felix .05 .15
458 Alex Cole .05 .15
459 John Orton .05 .15
460 Eddie Zosky .05 .15
461 Dennis Eckersley .10 .30
462 Lee Smith .10 .30
463 John Smoltz .20 .50
464 Ken Caminiti .10 .30
465 Melido Perez .05 .15
466 Tom Marsh .05 .15
467 Jeff Nelson .05 .15
468 Jesse Levis .05 .15
469 Chris Nabholz .05 .15
470 Mike Macfarlane .05 .15
471 Reggie Sanders .10 .30
472 Chuck McElroy .05 .15
473 Kevin Gross .05 .15
474 Matt Whiteside RC .05 .15
475 Cal Eldred .05 .15
476 Dave Gallagher .05 .15
477 Len Dykstra .10 .30
478 Mark McGwire .75 2.00
479 David Segui .05 .15
480 Mike Henneman .05 .15
481 Bret Barberie .05 .15
482 Steve Sax .05 .15
483 Dave Valle .05 .15
484 Danny Darwin .05 .15
485 Devon White .10 .30
486 Eric Plunk .05 .15
487 Jim Gott .05 .15
488 Scooter Tucker .05 .15
489 Omar Olivares .05 .15
490 Greg Myers .05 .15
491 Brian Hunter .05 .15
492 Kevin Tapani .05 .15
493 Rich Monteleone .05 .15
494 Steve Buechele .05 .15
495 Bo Jackson .30 .75
496 Mike LaValliere .05 .15
497 Mark Leonard .05 .15
498 Daryl Boston .05 .15
499 Jose Canseco .20 .50
500 Brian Barnes .05 .15
501 Randy Johnson .30 .75
502 Tim McIntosh .05 .15
503 Cecil Fielder .10 .30
504 Derek Bell .10 .30
505 Kevin Koslofski .05 .15
506 Darren Holmes .05 .15
507 Brady Anderson .10 .30
508 John Valentin .05 .15
509 Jerry Browne .05 .15
510 Fred McGriff .20 .50
511 Pedro Astacio .05 .15
512 Gary Gaetti .10 .30
513 John Burke RC .05 .15
514 Dwight Gooden .10 .30
515 Thomas Howard .05 .15
516 D.Whitmore RC UER .05 .15
11 games played in 1992; should
be 121
517 Ozzie Guillen .10 .30
518 Darryl Kile .10 .30
519 Rich Rowland .05 .15
520 Carlos Delgado .30 .75
521 Doug Henry .05 .15
522 Greg Colbrunn .05 .15
523 Tom Gordon .05 .15
524 Ivan Rodriguez .20 .50
525 Kent Hrbek .10 .30
526 Eric Young .05 .15
527 Rod Brewer .05 .15
528 Eric Karros .10 .30
529 Marquis Grissom .10 .30
530 Rico Brogna .05 .15
531 Sammy Sosa .30 .75
532 Bret Boone .10 .30
533 Luis Rivera .05 .15
534 Hal Morris .05 .15
535 Monty Fariss .05 .15
536 Leo Gomez .05 .15
537 Wally Joyner .10 .30
538 Tony Gwynn .40 1.00
539 Mike Williams .05 .15
540 Juan Gonzalez .10 .30
541 Ryan Klesko .10 .30
542 Ryan Thompson .05 .15
543 Chad Curtis .05 .15
544 Orel Hershiser .10 .30
545 Carlos Garcia .05 .15
546 Bob Welch .05 .15
547 Vinny Castilla .05 .15
548 Ozzie Smith .50 1.25
549 Luis Salazar .05 .15
550 Mark Guthrie .05 .15
551 Charles Nagy .05 .15
552 Alex Fernandez .05 .15
553 Mel Rojas .05 .15
554 Orestes Destrade .05 .15
555 Mark Gubicza .05 .15
556 Steve Finley .10 .30
557 Don Mattingly .75 2.00
558 Rickey Henderson .30 .75
559 Tommy Greene .05 .15
560 Arthur Rhodes .05 .15
561 Alfredo Griffin .05 .15
562 Will Clark .20 .50
563 Bob Zupcic .05 .15
564 Chuck Carr .05 .15
565 Henry Cotto .05 .15
566 Billy Spiers .05 .15
567 Jack Armstrong .05 .15
568 Kurt Stillwell .05 .15
569 David McCarty .05 .15
570 Joe Vitiello .05 .15
571 Gerald Williams .05 .15
572 Dale Murphy .20 .50
573 Scott Aldred .05 .15
574 Bill Gullickson .05 .15
575 Bobby Thigpen .05 .15
576 Glenallen Hill .05 .15
577 Dwayne Henry .05 .15
578 Calvin Jones .05 .15
579 Al Martin .05 .15
580 Ruben Sierra .10 .30
581 Andy Benes .05 .15
582 Anthony Young .05 .15
583 Shawn Boskie .05 .15
584 Scott Pose RC .05 .15
585 Mike Piazza 1.25 3.00
586 Donovan Osborne .05 .15
587 Jim Austin .05 .15
588 Checklist 301-400 .05 .15
589 Checklist 401-500 .05 .15
590 Checklist 501-600 .05 .15
591 Ken Griffey Jr. MC .30 .75
592 Ivan Rodriguez MC .10 .30
593 Carlos Baerga MC .05 .15
594 Fred McGriff MC .10 .30
595 Mark McGwire MC .40 1.00
596 Roberto Alomar MC .10 .30
597 Kirby Puckett MC .20 .50
598 Marquis Grissom MC .05 .15
599 John Smoltz MC .10 .30
600 Ryne Sandberg MC .20 .50
601 Wade Boggs .20 .50
602 Jeff Reardon .10 .30
603 Billy Ripken .05 .15
604 Bryan Harvey .05 .15
605 Carlos Quintana .05 .15
606 Greg Hibbard .05 .15
607 Ellis Burks .10 .30
608 Greg Swindell .05 .15
609 Dave Winfield .10 .30
610 Charlie Hough .10 .30
611 Chili Davis .10 .30
612 Jody Reed .05 .15
613 Mark Williamson .05 .15
614 Phil Plantier .05 .15
615 Jim Abbott .20 .50
616 Dante Bichette .10 .30
617 Mark Eichhorn .05 .15
618 Gary Sheffield .10 .30
619 Richie Lewis RC .05 .15
620 Joe Girardi .05 .15
621 Jaime Navarro .05 .15
622 Willie Wilson .05 .15
623 Scott Fletcher .05 .15
624 Bud Black .05 .15
625 Tom Brunansky .05 .15
626 Steve Avery .05 .15
627 Paul Molitor .10 .30
628 Gregg Jefferies .05 .15
629 Dave Stewart .10 .30
630 Javier Lopez .20 .50
631 Greg Gagne .05 .15
632 Roberto Kelly .05 .15
633 Mike Fetters .05 .15
634 Ozzie Canseco .05 .15
635 Jeff Russell .05 .15
636 Pete Incaviglia .05 .15
637 Tom Henke .05 .15
638 Chipper Jones .30 .75
639 Jimmy Key .10 .30
640 Dave Martinez .05 .15
641 Dave Stieb .05 .15
642 Milt Thompson .05 .15
643 Alan Mills .05 .15
644 Tony Fernandez .05 .15
645 Randy Bush .05 .15
646 Joe Magrane .05 .15
647 Ivan Calderon .05 .15
648 Jose Guzman .05 .15
649 John Olerud .10 .30
650 Tom Glavine .20 .50
651 Julio Franco .10 .30
652 Armando Reynoso .05 .15
653 Felix Jose .05 .15
654 Ben Rivera .05 .15
655 Andre Dawson .10 .30
656 Mike Harkey .05 .15
657 Kevin Seitzer .05 .15
658 Lonnie Smith .05 .15
659 Norm Charlton .05 .15
660 David Justice .10 .30
661 Fernando Valenzuela .10 .30
662 Dan Wilson .10 .30
663 Mark Gardner .05 .15
664 Doug Dascenzo .05 .15
665 Greg Maddux .50 1.25
666 Harold Baines .10 .30
667 Randy Myers .05 .15
668 Harold Reynolds .10 .30
669 Candy Maldonado .05 .15
670 Al Leiter .10 .30
671 Jerald Clark .05 .15
672 Doug Drabek .05 .15
673 Kirk Gibson .10 .30
674 Steve Reed RC .05 .15
675 Mike Felder .05 .15
676 Ricky Gutierrez .05 .15
677 Spike Owen .05 .15
678 Otis Nixon .05 .15
679 Scott Sanderson .05 .15
680 Mark Carreon .05 .15
681 Troy Percival .20 .50
682 Kevin Stocker .05 .15
683 Jim Converse RC .05 .15
684 Barry Bonds .75 2.00
685 Greg Gohr .05 .15
686 Tim Wallach .05 .15
687 Matt Mieske .05 .15
688 Robby Thompson .05 .15
689 Brien Taylor .05 .15
690 Kirt Manwaring .05 .15
691 Mike Lansing RC .10 .30
692 Steve Decker .05 .15
693 Mike Moore .05 .15
694 Kevin Mitchell .05 .15
695 Phil Hiatt .05 .15
696 Tony Tarasco RC .05 .15
697 Benji Gil .05 .15
698 Jeff Juden .05 .15
699 Kevin Reimer .05 .15
700 Andy Ashby .05 .15
701 John Jaha .05 .15
702 Tim Bogar RC .05 .15
703 David Cone .10 .30
704 Willie Greene .05 .15
705 David Hulse RC .05 .15
706 Cris Carpenter .05 .15
707 Ken Griffey Jr. .50 1.25
708 Steve Bedrosian .05 .15
709 Dave Nilsson .05 .15
710 Paul Wagner .05 .15
711 B.J. Surhoff .10 .30
712 Rene Arocha RC .10 .30
713 Manuel Lee .05 .15
714 Brian Williams .05 .15
715 Sherman Obando RC .05 .15
716 Terry Mulholland .05 .15
717 Paul O'Neill .20 .50
718 David Nied .05 .15
719 J.T. Snow RC .20 .50
720 Nigel Wilson .05 .15
721 Mike Bielecki .05 .15
722 Kevin Young .10 .30
723 Charlie Leibrandt .05 .15
724 Frank Bolick .05 .15
725 Jon Shave RC .05 .15
726 Steve Cooke .05 .15
727 Domingo Martinez RC .05 .15
728 Todd Worrell .05 .15
729 Jose Lind .05 .15
730 Jim Tatum RC .05 .15
731 Mike Hampton .10 .30
732 Mike Draper .05 .15
733 Henry Mercedes .05 .15
734 John Johnstone RC .05 .15
735 Mitch Webster .05 .15
736 Russ Springer .05 .15
737 Rob Natal .05 .15
738 Steve Howe .05 .15
739 Darrell Sherman RC .05 .15
740 Pat Mahomes .05 .15
741 Alex Arias .05 .15
742 Damon Buford .05 .15
743 Charlie Hayes .05 .15
744 Guillermo Velasquez .05 .15
745 CL 601-750 UER .05 .15
650 Tom Glavine
746 Frank Thomas MC .20 .50
747 Barry Bonds MC .40 1.00
748 Roger Clemens MC .30 .75
749 Joe Carter MC .05 .15
750 Greg Maddux MC .30 .75

1993 Stadium Club First Day Issue

Two thousand of each 1993 Stadium Club baseball card were produced on the first day and then randomly inserted in packs at a rate of 1:24. These standard-size cards are identical to the regular-issue 1993 Stadium Club cards, except for the embossed prismatic-foil "1st Day Production" logo stamped in an upper corner. Some of the logos have been transferred from "common" 1st day cards to the fronts of better players.

*STARS: 8X TO 20X BASIC CARDS
STATED ODDS 1:24 H/R, 1:15 JUMBO

1993 Stadium Club Members Only Parallel

These standard-sized cards were issued in complete set form only through Topps' Stadium Club. These cards are the same as the regular Stadium Club cards except they are imprinted with the Stadium Club logo on the front. The set includes parallel versions of both the basic cards and the insert cards. Only the inserts cards have been priced below. Please use the multiplier for values on the basic cards. These sets were issued at an approximate cost of $200 to Stadium Club members. Even though, the set was issued at $200, the current market conditions makes this set available at less than original issue cost.

COMP.FACT.SET (760)	35.00	150.00
COMMON CARD (1-750)	.02	.25
*STARS: 2X TO 4X BASIC CARDS		
*ROOKIES: 1.5X to 3X BASIC CARDS		
MA1 Robin Yount	1.50	4.00
MA2 George Brett	3.00	8.00
MA3 David Nied	.40	1.00
MA4 Nigel Wilson	.40	1.00
MB1 Will Clark	3.00	8.00
Mark McGwire		
MB2 Dwight Gooden	1.50	4.00
Don Mattingly		
MB3 Ryne Sandberg	2.00	5.00
Frank Thomas		
MB4 Darryl Strawberry	2.00	5.00
Ken Griffey		
MC1 David Nied	.40	1.00
MC2 Charlie Hough	.60	1.50

1993 Stadium Club Inserts

This 10-card set was randomly inserted in all series of Stadium Club packs, the first four in series 1, the second four in series 2 and the last two in series 3. The themes of the standard-size cards differ from series to series, but the basic design -- borderless color action shots on the fronts -- remains the same throughout. The series 1 and 3 cards are numbered on the back, the series 2 cards are unnumbered. No matter what series, all of these inserts were included one every 15 packs.

COMPLETE SET (10)	5.00	12.00
COMPLETE SERIES 1 (4)	.75	2.00
COMPLETE SERIES 2 (4)	4.00	10.00
COMPLETE SERIES 3 (2)	.20	.50
COMMON SER.1 (A1-A4)	.10	.30
COMMON SER.2 (B1-B4)	.10	.30
COMMON SER.3 (C1-C2)	.10	.30
A1-A4 SER.1 STATED ODDS 1:15		
B1-B4 SER.2 STATED ODDS 1:15		
C1-C2 SER.3 STATED ODDS 1:15		
A1 Robin Yount	1.00	2.50
A2 George Brett	1.50	4.00
A3 David Nied FDP	.10	.30
A4 Nigel Wilson FDP	.10	.30
B1 Will Clark	1.50	4.00
Mark McGwire		
B2 Dwight Gooden	1.50	4.00
Don Mattingly		
B3 Ryne Sandberg	.60	1.50
Frank Thomas		
B4 Darryl Strawberry	1.00	2.50
Ken Griffey Jr.		
C1 David Nied UER	.10	.30
Colorado Rockies Firsts		
(Misspelled pitch-hitter on back)		
C2 Charlie Hough	.25	.60

1993 Stadium Club Master Photos

Each of the three Stadium Club series features Master Photos, uncropped versions of the regular Stadium Club cards. Each Master Photo is inlaid in a 5" by 7" white frame and bordered with a prismatic foil trim. The Master Photos were made available to the public in two ways. First, one in every 24 packs included a Master Photo winner card redeemable for a group of three Master Photos until Jan. 31, 1994. Second, each hobby box contained one Master Photo. The cards are unnumbered and checklisted below in alphabetical order within series I (1-12), II (13-24), and III (25-30). Two different versions of these master photos were issued, one with and one without the "Members Only" gold foil seal at the upper right corner. The "Members Only" Master Photos were only available with the direct-mail solicited 750-card Stadium Club Members Only set.

COMPLETE SET (30)	12.00	24.00
COMPLETE SERIES 1 (12)	2.50	6.00
COMPLETE SERIES 2 (12)	3.00	8.00
COMPLETE SERIES 3 (6)	4.00	10.00
STATED ODDS 1:24 HOB/RET, 1:15 JUM		
1 Carlos Baerga	.08	.25
2 Delino DeShields	.08	.25
3 Brian McRae	.08	.25
4 Sam Militello	.08	.25
5 Joe Oliver	.08	.25
6 Kirby Puckett	.50	1.25
7 Cal Ripken	1.50	4.00
8 Bip Roberts	.08	.25
9 Mike Scioscia	.08	.25
10 Rick Sutcliffe	.20	.50
11 Danny Tartabull	.08	.25
12 Tim Wakefield	.50	1.25
13 George Brett	1.25	3.00
14 Jose Canseco	.30	.75
15 Will Clark	.30	.75
16 Travis Fryman	.20	.50
17 Dwight Gooden	.20	.50
18 Mark Grace	.30	.75
19 Rickey Henderson	.50	1.25
20 Mark McGwire MC	1.25	3.00
21 Nolan Ryan	2.00	5.00
22 Ruben Sierra	.20	.50
23 Darryl Strawberry	.20	.50
24 Larry Walker	.20	.50
25 Barry Bonds	1.25	3.00
26 Ken Griffey Jr.	.75	2.00
27 Greg Maddux	.75	2.00
28 David Nied	.08	.25
29 J.T. Snow	.30	.75
30 Brien Taylor	.08	.25

1993 Stadium Club Members Only

This 59-card standard-size set was mailed out to Stadium Club Members in four separate mailings. Each box contained several sports. The fronts have full-bleed color action player photos with the words "Members Only" printed in gold foil at the bottom along with the player's name and the Stadium Club logo. On a multi-colored background, the horizontal backs carry player information and a computer generated drawing of a baseball player. The cards are unnumbered and checklisted below alphabetically according to sport as follows: baseball (1-28), basketball (29-44), football (45-53), and hockey (54-59).

COMPLETE SET (59)	10.00	20.00
1 Jim Abbott	.08	.25
2 Barry Bonds	.30	.75
3 Chris Bosio	.07	.20
4 George Brett	.50	1.25
5 Jay Buhner	.08	.25
6 Joe Carter	.08	.25
Belts 3 for Fifth		
Time in Career		
7 Joe Carter	.08	.25
Dramatics Give Jays Series Crown		
8 Carlton Fisk	.15	.40
9 Travis Fryman	.07	.20
10 Mark Grace	.08	.25
11 Ken Griffey Jr.	1.25	3.00
12 Darryl Kile	.07	.20
13 Darren Lewis	.07	.20
14 Greg Maddux	.75	2.00
15 Jack McDowell	.07	.20
16 Paul Molitor	.25	.60
17 Eddie Murray	.25	.60
18 Mike Piazza	1.25	3.00
Home Run Record		
for Rookie Catchers		
19 Mike Piazza	1.25	3.00
NL Rookie Honors		
20 Kirby Puckett	.50	1.25
21 Jeff Reardon	.08	.25
22 Tim Salmon	.08	.25
23 Curt Schilling	.25	.60
24 Lee Smith	.08	.25
25 Dave Stewart	.08	.25
26 Frank Thomas	1.00	2.50
27 Mark Whiten	.07	.20
28 Dave Winfield	.25	.60

1994 Stadium Club

The 720 standard-size cards comprising this set were issued two series of 270 and a third series of 180. There are a number of subsets including Home Run Club (258-268), Tale of Two Players (525/526), Division Leaders (527-532), Quick Starts (533-538), Career Contributors (541-543), Rookie Rocker (626-630), Rookie Rocket (631-634) and Fantastic Finishes (714-719). Rookie Cards include Jeff Cirillo and Chan Ho Park.

COMPLETE SET (720)	22.00	55.00
COMP.SERIES 1 (270)	8.00	20.00
COMP.SERIES 2 (270)	8.00	20.00
COMP.SERIES 3 (180)	6.00	15.00
1 Robin Yount	.50	1.25
2 Rick Wilkins	.05	.15
3 Steve Scarsone	.05	.15
4 Gary Sheffield	.10	.30
5 George Brett UER	.75	2.00
(birthdate listed as 1963; should be 1953)		
6 Al Martin	.05	.15
7 Joe Oliver	.05	.15
8 Stan Belinda	.05	.15
9 Denny Hocking	.05	.15
10 Roberto Alomar	.20	.50
11 Luis Polonia	.05	.15
12 Scott Hemond	.05	.15
13 Jody Reed	.05	.15
14 Mel Rojas	.05	.15
15 Junior Ortiz	.05	.15
16 Harold Baines	.10	.30
17 Brad Pennington	.05	.15
18 Jay Bell	.10	.30
19 Tom Henke	.05	.15
20 Jeff Branson	.05	.15
21 Roberto Mejia	.05	.15
22 Pedro Munoz	.05	.15
23 Matt Nokes	.05	.15
24 Jack McDowell	.05	.15
25 Cecil Fielder	.10	.30
26 Tony Fossas	.05	.15
27 Jim Eisenreich	.05	.15
28 Anthony Young	.05	.15
29 Chuck Carr	.05	.15
30 Jeff Treadway	.05	.15
31 Chris Nabholz	.05	.15
32 Tom Candiotti	.05	.15
33 Mike Maddux	.05	.15
34 Nolan Ryan	1.25	3.00
35 Luis Gonzalez	.10	.30
36 Tim Salmon	.20	.50
37 Mark Whiten	.05	.15
38 Roger McDowell	.05	.15
39 Royce Clayton	.05	.15
40 Troy Neel	.05	.15
41 Mike Harkey	.05	.15
42 Darrin Fletcher	.05	.15
43 Wayne Kirby	.05	.15
44 Rich Amaral	.05	.15
45 Robb Nen UER	.10	.30
(Nenn on back)		
46 Tim Teufel	.05	.15
47 Steve Cooke	.05	.15
48 Jeff McNeely	.05	.15
49 Jeff Montgomery	.05	.15
50 Skeeter Barnes	.05	.15
51 Scott Stahoviak	.05	.15
52 Pat Kelly	.05	.15
53 Brady Anderson	.10	.30
54 Mariano Duncan	.05	.15
55 Brian Bohanon	.05	.15
56 Jerry Spradlin	.05	.15
57 Ron Karkovice	.05	.15
58 Jeff Gardner	.05	.15
59 Bobby Bonilla	.10	.30
60 Tino Martinez	.20	.50
61 Todd Benzinger	.05	.15
62 Steve Trachsel	.05	.15
63 Brian Jordan	.10	.30
64 Steve Bedrosian	.05	.15
65 Brent Gates	.05	.15
66 Shawn Green	.30	.75
67 Sean Berry	.05	.15
68 Joe Klink	.05	.15
69 Fernando Valenzuela	.10	.30
70 Andy Tomberlin	.05	.15
71 Tony Pena	.05	.15
72 Eric Young	.05	.15
73 Chris Gomez	.05	.15
74 Paul O'Neill	.20	.50
75 Ricky Gutierrez	.05	.15
76 Brad Holman	.05	.15
77 Lance Painter	.05	.15
78 Mike Butcher	.05	.15
79 Sid Bream	.05	.15
80 Sammy Sosa	.30	.75
81 Felix Fermin	.05	.15
82 Todd Hundley	.05	.15
83 Kevin Higgins	.05	.15
84 Todd Pratt	.05	.15
85 Ken Griffey Jr.	.50	1.25
86 John O'Donoghue	.05	.15
87 Rick Renteria	.05	.15
88 John Burkett	.05	.15
89 Jose Vizcaino	.05	.15
90 Kevin Seitzer	.05	.15
91 Bobby Witt	.05	.15
92 Chris Turner	.05	.15
93 Omar Vizquel	.20	.50
94 David Justice	.10	.30
95 David Segui	.05	.15
96 Dave Hollins	.05	.15
97 Doug Strange	.05	.15
98 Jerald Clark	.05	.15
99 Mike Moore	.05	.15
100 Joey Cora	.05	.15
101 Scott Kamieniecki	.05	.15
102 Andy Benes	.05	.15
103 Chris Bosio	.05	.15
104 Rey Sanchez	.05	.15
105 John Jaha	.05	.15
106 Otis Nixon	.05	.15
107 Rickey Henderson	.30	.75
108 Jeff Bagwell	.20	.50
109 Gregg Jefferies	.05	.15
110 Roberto Alomar	.10	.30
Paul Molitor		
John Olerud		
111 Ron Gant	.10	.30
David Justice		
Fred McGriff		
112 Juan Gonzalez	.20	.50
Rafael Palmeiro		
Dean Palmer		
113 Greg Swindell	.05	.15
114 Bill Haselman	.05	.15
115 Phil Plantier	.05	.15
116 Ivan Rodriguez	.20	.50
117 Kevin Tapani	.05	.15
118 Mike LaValliere	.05	.15
119 Tim Costo	.05	.15
120 Mickey Morandini	.05	.15
121 Brett Butler	.10	.30
122 Tom Pagnozzi	.05	.15
123 Ron Gant	.10	.30
124 Damion Easley	.05	.15
125 Dennis Eckersley	.10	.30
126 Matt Mieske	.05	.15
127 Cliff Floyd	.10	.30
128 Julian Tavarez RC	.10	.30
129 Arthur Rhodes	.05	.15
130 Dave West	.05	.15
131 Tim Naehring	.05	.15
132 Freddie Benavides	.05	.15
133 Paul Assenmacher	.05	.15
134 David McCarty	.05	.15
135 Jose Lind	.05	.15
136 Reggie Sanders	.10	.30
137 Don Slaught	.05	.15
138 Andujar Cedeno	.05	.15
139 Rob Deer	.05	.15
140 Mike Piazza UER	.60	1.50
(listed as outfielder)		
141 Moises Alou	.10	.30
142 Tom Foley	.05	.15
143 Benito Santiago	.10	.30
144 Sandy Alomar Jr.	.05	.15
145 Carlos Hernandez	.05	.15
146 Luis Alicea	.05	.15
147 Tom Lampkin	.05	.15
148 Ryan Klesko	.10	.30
149 Juan Guzman	.05	.15
150 Scott Servais	.05	.15
151 Tony Gwynn	.40	1.00
152 Tim Wakefield	.20	.50
153 David Nied	.05	.15
154 Chris Haney	.05	.15
155 Danny Bautista	.05	.15
156 Randy Velarde	.05	.15
157 Darrin Jackson	.05	.15
158 J.R. Phillips	.05	.15
159 Greg Gagne	.05	.15
160 Luis Aquino	.05	.15
161 John Vander Wal	.05	.15
162 Randy Myers	.05	.15
163 Ted Power	.05	.15
164 Scott Brosius	.10	.30
165 Len Dykstra	.10	.30
166 Jacob Brumfield	.05	.15
167 Bo Jackson	.30	.75
168 Eddie Taubensee	.05	.15
169 Carlos Baerga	.05	.15
170 Tim Bogar	.05	.15
171 Jose Canseco	.20	.50
172 Greg Blosser UER	.05	.15
(Gregg on front)		
173 Chili Davis	.10	.30
174 Randy Knorr	.05	.15
175 Mike Perez	.05	.15
176 Henry Rodriguez	.05	.15
177 Brian Turang RC	.05	.15
178 Roger Pavlik	.05	.15
179 Aaron Sele	.05	.15
180 Fred McGriff	.20	.50
Gary Sheffield		
181 J.T. Snow	.20	.50
Tim Salmon		
182 Roberto Hernandez	.05	.15
183 Jeff Reboulet	.05	.15
184 John Doherty	.05	.15
185 Danny Sheaffer	.05	.15
186 Bip Roberts	.05	.15
187 Dennis Martinez	.10	.30
188 Darryl Hamilton	.05	.15
189 Eduardo Perez	.05	.15
190 Pete Harnisch	.05	.15
191 Rich Gossage	.10	.30
192 Mickey Tettleton	.05	.15
193 Lenny Webster	.05	.15
194 Lance Johnson	.05	.15
195 Don Mattingly	.75	2.00
196 Gregg Olson	.05	.15
197 Mark Gubicza	.05	.15
198 Scott Fletcher	.05	.15
199 Jon Shave	.05	.15
200 Tim Mauser	.05	.15
201 Jeromy Burnitz	.10	.30
202 Rob Dibble	.10	.30
203 Will Clark	.20	.50
204 Steve Buechele	.05	.15
205 Brian Williams	.05	.15
206 Carlos Garcia	.05	.15
207 Mark Clark	.05	.15
208 Rafael Palmeiro	.20	.50
209 Eric Davis	.10	.30
210 Pat Meares	.05	.15
211 Chuck Finley	.10	.30
212 Jason Bere	.05	.15
213 Gary DiSarcina	.05	.15
214 Tony Fernandez	.05	.15
215 B.J. Surhoff	.10	.30
216 Lee Guetterman	.05	.15
217 Tim Wallach	.05	.15
218 Kirt Manwaring	.05	.15
219 Albert Belle	.10	.30
220 Dwight Gooden	.10	.30
221 Archi Cianfrocco	.05	.15
222 Terry Mulholland	.05	.15
223 Hipolito Pichardo	.05	.15
224 Kent Hrbek	.10	.30
225 Craig Grebeck	.05	.15
226 Todd Jones	.05	.15
227 Mike Bordick	.05	.15
228 John Olerud	.10	.30
229 Jeff Blauser	.05	.15
230 Alex Arias	.05	.15
231 Bernard Gilkey	.05	.15
232 Denny Neagle	.10	.30
233 Pedro Borbon	.05	.15
234 Dick Schofield	.05	.15
235 Matias Carrillo	.05	.15
236 Juan Bell	.05	.15
237 Mike Hampton	.10	.30
238 Barry Bonds	.75	2.00
239 Cris Carpenter	.05	.15
240 Eric Karros	.10	.30
241 Greg McMichael	.05	.15
242 Pat Hentgen	.05	.15
243 Tim Pugh	.05	.15
244 Vinny Castilla	.10	.30
245 Charlie Hough	.10	.30
246 Bobby Munoz	.05	.15
247 Kevin Baez	.05	.15
248 Todd Frohwirth	.05	.15
249 Charlie Hayes	.05	.15
250 Mike Macfarlane	.05	.15
251 Danny Darwin	.05	.15
252 Ben Rivera	.05	.15
253 Dave Henderson	.05	.15
254 Steve Avery	.05	.15
255 Tim Belcher	.05	.15
256 Dan Plesac	.05	.15
257 Jim Thome	.20	.50
258 Albert Belle HR	.10	.30
259 Barry Bonds HR	.40	1.00
260 Ron Gant HR	.05	.15
261 Juan Gonzalez HR	.05	.15
262 Ken Griffey Jr. HR	.30	.75
263 David Justice HR	.05	.15
264 Fred McGriff HR	.10	.30
265 Rafael Palmeiro HR	.10	.30
266 Mike Piazza HR	.30	.75
267 Frank Thomas HR	.20	.50
268 Matt Williams HR	.05	.15
269 Checklist 1-135	.05	.15
270 Checklist 136-270	.05	.15
271 Mike Stanley	.05	.15
272 Tony Tarasco	.05	.15
273 Teddy Higuera	.05	.15
274 Ryan Thompson	.05	.15
275 Rick Aguilera	.05	.15
276 Ramon Martinez	.05	.15
277 Orlando Merced	.05	.15
278 Guillermo Velasquez	.05	.15
279 Mark Hutton	.05	.15
280 Larry Walker	.10	.30
281 Kevin Gross	.05	.15
282 Jose Offerman	.05	.15
283 Jim Leyritz	.05	.15
284 Jamie Moyer	.10	.30
285 Frank Thomas	.30	.75
286 Derek Bell	.05	.15
287 Derrick May	.05	.15
288 Dave Winfield	.10	.30
289 Curt Schilling	.10	.30
290 Carlos Quintana	.05	.15
291 Bob Natal	.05	.15
292 David Cone	.10	.30
293 Al Osuna	.05	.15
294 Bob Hamelin	.05	.15
295 Chad Curtis	.05	.15
296 Danny Jackson	.05	.15
297 Bob Welch	.05	.15
298 Felix Jose	.05	.15
299 Jay Buhner	.10	.30
300 Joe Carter	.10	.30
301 Kenny Lofton	.10	.30
302 Kirk Rueter	.05	.15
303 Kim Batiste	.05	.15
304 Mike Morgan	.05	.15
305 Pat Borders	.05	.15
306 Rene Arocha	.05	.15
307 Ruben Sierra	.10	.30
308 Steve Finley	.10	.30
309 Travis Fryman	.10	.30
310 Zane Smith	.05	.15
311 Willie Wilson	.05	.15
312 Trevor Hoffman	.20	.50
313 Terry Pendleton	.10	.30
314 Salomon Torres	.05	.15
315 Robin Ventura	.10	.30
316 Randy Tomlin	.05	.15
317 Dave Stewart	.10	.30
318 Mike Benjamin	.05	.15
319 Matt Turner	.05	.15
320 Manny Ramirez	.30	.75
321 Kevin Young	.05	.15
322 Ken Caminiti	.10	.30
323 Joe Girardi	.05	.15
324 Jeff McKnight	.05	.15
325 Gene Harris	.05	.15
326 Devon White	.10	.30
327 Darryl Kile	.10	.30
328 Craig Paquette	.05	.15
329 Cal Eldred	.05	.15
330 Bill Swift	.05	.15
331 Alan Trammell	.10	.30
332 Armando Reynoso	.05	.15
333 Brent Mayne	.05	.15
334 Chris Donnels	.05	.15
335 Darryl Strawberry	.10	.30
336 Dean Palmer	.10	.30
337 Frank Castillo	.05	.15
338 Jeff King	.05	.15
339 John Franco	.10	.30
340 Kevin Appier	.10	.30
341 Lance Blankenship	.05	.15
342 Mark McLemore	.05	.15
343 Pedro Astacio	.05	.15
344 Rich Batchelor	.05	.15
345 Ryan Bowen	.05	.15
346 Terry Steinbach	.05	.15
347 Troy O'Leary	.05	.15
348 Willie Blair	.05	.15
349 Wade Boggs	.20	.50
350 Tim Raines	.10	.30
351 Scott Livingstone	.05	.15
352 Rod Correia	.05	.15
353 Ray Lankford	.10	.30
354 Pat Listach	.05	.15
355 Milt Thompson	.05	.15
356 Miguel Jimenez	.05	.15
357 Marc Newfield	.05	.15
358 Mark McGwire	.75	2.00
359 Kirby Puckett	.30	.75
360 Kent Mercker	.05	.15
361 John Kruk	.10	.30
362 Jeff Kent	.20	.50
363 Hal Morris	.05	.15
364 Edgar Martinez	.20	.50
365 Dave Magadan	.05	.15
366 Dante Bichette	.10	.30
367 Chris Hammond	.05	.15
368 Bret Saberhagen	.10	.30
369 Billy Ripken	.05	.15
370 Bill Gullickson	.05	.15
371 Andre Dawson	.10	.30
372 Roberto Kelly	.05	.15
373 Cal Ripken	1.00	2.50
374 Craig Biggio	.20	.50
375 Dan Pasqua	.05	.15
376 Dave Nilsson	.05	.15
377 Duane Ward	.05	.15
378 Greg Vaughn	.05	.15
379 Jeff Fassero	.05	.15
380 Jerry DiPoto	.05	.15
381 John Patterson	.05	.15
382 Kevin Brown	.10	.30
383 Kevin Roberson	.05	.15
384 Joe Orsulak	.05	.15
385 Hilly Hathaway	.05	.15
386 Mike Greenwell	.05	.15
387 Orestes Destrade	.05	.15
388 Mike Gallego	.05	.15
389 Ozzie Guillen	.10	.30
390 Raul Mondesi	.10	.30
391 Scott Lydy	.05	.15
392 Tom Urbani	.05	.15
393 Wil Cordero	.05	.15
394 Tony Longmire	.05	.15
395 Todd Zeile	.05	.15
396 Scott Cooper	.05	.15
397 Ryne Sandberg	.50	1.25
398 Ricky Bones	.05	.15
399 Phil Clark	.05	.15
400 Orel Hershiser	.10	.30
401 Mike Henneman	.05	.15
402 Mark Lemke	.05	.15
403 Mark Grace	.20	.50
404 Ken Ryan	.05	.15
405 John Smoltz	.20	.50
406 Jeff Conine	.10	.30
407 Greg Harris	.05	.15
408 Doug Drabek	.05	.15
409 Dave Fleming	.05	.15
410 Danny Tartabull	.05	.15
411 Chad Kreuter	.05	.15
412 Brad Ausmus	.20	.50
413 Ben McDonald	.05	.15
414 Barry Larkin	.20	.50
415 Bret Barberie	.05	.15
416 Chuck Knoblauch	.10	.30
417 Ozzie Smith	.50	1.25
418 Ed Sprague	.05	.15
419 Matt Williams	.10	.30
420 Jeremy Hernandez	.05	.15
421 Jose Bautista	.05	.15
422 Kevin Mitchell	.05	.15
423 Manuel Lee	.05	.15
424 Mike Devereaux	.05	.15
425 Omar Olivares	.05	.15
426 Rafael Belliard	.05	.15
427 Richie Lewis	.05	.15
428 Ron Darling	.05	.15
429 Shane Mack	.05	.15
430 Tim Hulett	.05	.15
431 Wally Joyner	.10	.30
432 Wes Chamberlain	.05	.15
433 Tom Browning	.05	.15
434 Scott Radinsky	.05	.15
435 Rondell White	.10	.30
436 Rod Beck	.05	.15
437 Rheal Cormier	.05	.15
438 Randy Johnson	.30	.75
439 Pete Schourek	.05	.15
440 Mo Vaughn	.10	.30
441 Mike Timlin	.05	.15
442 Mark Langston	.05	.15
443 Lou Whitaker	.10	.30
444 Kevin Stocker	.05	.15
445 Ken Hill	.05	.15
446 John Wetteland	.10	.30
447 J.T. Snow	.10	.30
448 Erik Pappas	.05	.15
449 David Hulse	.05	.15
450 Darren Daulton	.10	.30
451 Chris Hoiles	.05	.15
452 Bryan Harvey	.05	.15
453 Darren Lewis	.05	.15
454 Andres Galarraga	.10	.30
455 Joe Hesketh	.05	.15
456 Jose Valentin	.05	.15
457 Dan Peltier	.05	.15
458 Joe Boever	.05	.15
459 Kevin Rogers	.05	.15
460 Craig Shipley	.05	.15
461 Alvaro Espinoza	.05	.15
462 Wilson Alvarez	.05	.15
463 Cory Snyder	.05	.15
464 Candy Maldonado	.05	.15
465 Blas Minor	.05	.15
466 Rod Bolton	.05	.15
467 Kenny Rogers	.10	.30
468 Greg Myers	.05	.15
469 Jimmy Key	.10	.30
470 Tony Castillo	.05	.15
471 Mike Stanton	.05	.15
472 Deion Sanders	.20	.50
473 Tito Navarro	.05	.15
474 Mike Gardiner	.05	.15
475 Steve Reed	.05	.15
476 John Roper	.05	.15
477 Mike Trombley	.05	.15
478 Charles Nagy	.05	.15
479 Larry Casian	.05	.15
480 Eric Hillman	.05	.15
481 Bill Wertz	.05	.15
482 Jeff Schwarz	.05	.15
483 John Valentin	.05	.15
484 Carl Willis	.05	.15
485 Gary Gaetti	.10	.30
486 Bill Pecota	.05	.15
487 John Smiley	.05	.15
488 Mike Mussina	.20	.50
489 Mike Ignasiak	.05	.15
490 Billy Brewer	.05	.15
491 Jack Voigt	.05	.15
492 Mike Munoz	.05	.15
493 Lee Tinsley	.05	.15
494 Bob Wickman	.05	.15
495 Roger Salkeld	.05	.15
496 Thomas Howard	.05	.15
497 Mark Davis	.05	.15
498 Dave Clark	.05	.15
499 Turk Wendell	.05	.15
500 Rafael Bournigal	.05	.15
501 Chip Hale	.05	.15
502 Matt Whiteside	.05	.15
503 Brian Koelling	.05	.15
504 Jeff Reed	.05	.15
505 Paul Wagner	.05	.15
506 Torey Lovullo	.05	.15
507 Curt Leskanic	.05	.15
508 Derek Lilliquist	.05	.15
509 Joe Magrane	.05	.15
510 Mackey Sasser	.05	.15
511 Lloyd McClendon	.05	.15
512 Jayhawk Owens	.05	.15
513 Woody Williams	.05	.15
514 Gary Redus	.05	.15
515 Tim Spehr	.05	.15
516 Jim Abbott	.20	.50
517 Lou Frazier	.05	.15
518 Erik Plantenberg RC	.05	.15
519 Tim Worrell	.05	.15
520 Brian McRae	.05	.15
521 Chan Ho Park RC	.30	.75
522 Mark Wohlers	.05	.15
523 Geronimo Pena	.05	.15
524 Andy Ashby	.05	.15
525 Tim Raines	.05	.15
Andre Dawson TALE		
526 Paul Molitor TALE	.05	.15
527 Joe Carter DL	.05	.15
528 F.Thomas DL UER	.20	.50
listed as third in RBI in 1993; was actually second		
529 Ken Griffey Jr. DL	.30	.75
530 David Justice DL	.05	.15
531 Gregg Jefferies DL	.05	.15
532 Barry Bonds DL	.40	1.00
533 John Kruk QS	.05	.15
534 Roger Clemens QS	.30	.75
535 Cecil Fielder QS	.05	.15
536 Ruben Sierra QS	.05	.15
537 Tony Gwynn QS	.20	.50
538 Tom Glavine QS	.10	.30
539 CL 271-405 UER	.05	.15
number on back is 269		
540 CL 406-540 UER	.05	.15
numbered 270 on back		
541 Ozzie Smith ATL	.30	.75
542 Eddie Murray ATL	.20	.50
543 Lee Smith ATL	.05	.15
544 Greg Maddux	.50	1.25
545 Denis Boucher	.05	.15
546 Mark Gardner	.05	.15
547 Bo Jackson	.30	.75
548 Eric Anthony	.05	.15
549 Delino DeShields	.05	.15
550 Turner Ward	.05	.15
551 Scott Sanderson	.05	.15
552 Hector Carrasco	.05	.15
553 Tony Phillips	.05	.15
554 Melido Perez	.05	.15
555 Mike Felder	.05	.15
556 Jack Morris	.10	.30
557 Rafael Palmeiro	.20	.50
558 Shane Reynolds	.05	.15
559 Pete Incaviglia	.05	.15
560 Greg Harris	.05	.15
561 Matt Walbeck	.05	.15
562 Todd Van Poppel	.05	.15
563 Todd Stottlemyre	.05	.15
564 Ricky Bones	.05	.15
565 Mike Jackson	.05	.15
566 Kevin McReynolds	.05	.15
567 Melvin Nieves	.05	.15
568 Juan Gonzalez	.10	.30
569 Frank Viola	.10	.30
570 Vince Coleman	.05	.15
571 Brian Anderson RC	.10	.30
572 Omar Vizquel	.20	.50
573 Bernie Williams	.20	.50
574 Tom Glavine	.20	.50
575 Mitch Williams	.05	.15
576 Shawon Dunston	.05	.15
577 Mike Lansing	.05	.15
578 Greg Pirkl	.05	.15
579 Sid Fernandez	.05	.15
580 Doug Jones	.05	.15
581 Walt Weiss	.05	.15
582 Tim Belcher	.05	.15
583 Alex Fernandez	.05	.15
584 Alex Cole	.05	.15
585 Greg Cadaret	.05	.15
586 Bob Tewksbury	.05	.15
587 Dave Hansen	.05	.15
588 Kurt Abbott RC	.05	.15
589 Rick White RC	.05	.15
590 Kevin Bass	.05	.15
591 Geronimo Berroa	.05	.15
592 Jaime Navarro	.05	.15
593 Steve Farr	.05	.15
594 Jack Armstrong	.05	.15
595 Steve Howe	.05	.15
596 Jose Rijo	.05	.15
597 Otis Nixon	.05	.15
598 Robby Thompson	.05	.15
599 Kelly Stinnett RC	.10	.30
600 Carlos Delgado	.20	.50
601 Brian Johnson RC	.05	.15
602 Gregg Olson	.05	.15
603 Jim Edmonds	.30	.75
604 Mike Blowers	.05	.15
605 Lee Smith	.10	.30
606 Pat Rapp	.05	.15
607 Mike Magnante	.05	.15
608 Karl Rhodes	.05	.15
609 Jeff Juden	.05	.15
610 Rusty Meacham	.05	.15
611 Pedro Martinez	.30	.75
612 Todd Worrell	.05	.15
613 Stan Javier	.05	.15
614 Mike Hampton	.10	.30
615 Jose Guzman	.05	.15
616 Xavier Hernandez	.05	.15
617 David Wells	.10	.30
618 John Habyan	.05	.15
619 Chris Nabholz	.05	.15
620 Bobby Jones	.05	.15
621 Chris James	.05	.15
622 Ellis Burks	.10	.30
623 Erik Hanson	.05	.15
624 Pat Meares	.05	.15
625 Harold Reynolds	.10	.30
626 Bob Hamelin RR	.05	.15
627 Manny Ramirez RR	.20	.50
628 Ryan Klesko RR	.05	.15
629 Carlos Delgado RR	.10	.30
630 Javier Lopez RR	.10	.30
631 Steve Karsay RR	.05	.15
632 Rick Helling RR	.05	.15
633 Steve Trachsel RR	.05	.15
634 Hector Carrasco RR	.05	.15
635 Andy Stankiewicz	.05	.15
636 Paul Sorrento	.05	.15
637 Scott Erickson	.05	.15
638 Chipper Jones	.30	.75
639 Luis Polonia	.05	.15
640 Howard Johnson	.05	.15
641 John Dopson	.05	.15
642 Jody Reed	.05	.15
643 Lonnie Smith UER	.05	.15
Card numbered 543		
644 Mark Portugal	.05	.15
645 Paul Molitor	.10	.30
646 Paul Assenmacher	.05	.15
647 Hubie Brooks	.05	.15
648 Gary Wayne	.05	.15
649 Sean Berry	.05	.15
650 Roger Clemens	.60	1.50
651 Brian R. Hunter	.05	.15
652 Wally Whitehurst	.05	.15
653 Allen Watson	.05	.15
654 Rickey Henderson	.30	.75
655 Sid Bream	.05	.15
656 Dan Wilson	.05	.15
657 Ricky Jordan	.05	.15
658 Sterling Hitchcock	.05	.15
659 Darrin Jackson	.05	.15
660 Junior Felix	.05	.15
661 Tom Brunansky	.05	.15
662 Jose Vizcaino	.05	.15
663 Mark Leiter	.05	.15
664 Gil Heredia	.05	.15
665 Fred McGriff	.20	.50
666 Will Clark	.20	.50
667 Al Leiter	.10	.30
668 James Mouton	.05	.15
669 Billy Bean	.05	.15
670 Scott Leius	.05	.15

671 Bret Boone .10 .30
672 Darren Holmes .05 .15
673 Dave Weathers .05 .15
674 Eddie Murray .30 .75
675 Felix Fermin .05 .15
676 Chris Sabo .05 .15
677 Billy Spiers .05 .15
678 Aaron Sele .05 .15
679 Juan Samuel .05 .15
680 Julio Franco .10 .30
681 Heathcliff Slocumb .05 .15
682 Dennis Martinez .10 .30
683 Jerry Browne .05 .15
684 Pedro Martinez RC .05 .15
685 Rex Hudler .05 .15
686 Willie McGee .10 .30
687 Andy Van Slyke .20 .50
688 Pat Mahomes .05 .15
689 Dave Henderson .05 .15
690 Tony Eusebio .05 .15
691 Rick Sutcliffe .10 .30
692 Willie Banks .05 .15
693 Alan Mills .05 .15
694 Jeff Treadway .05 .15
695 Alex Gonzalez .05 .15
696 David Segui .05 .15
697 Rick Helling .05 .15
698 Bip Roberts .05 .15
699 Jeff Cirillo RC .10 .30
700 Terry Mulholland .05 .15
701 Marvin Freeman .05 .15
702 Jason Bere .05 .15
703 Javier Lopez .10 .30
704 Greg Hibbard .05 .15
705 Tommy Greene .05 .15
706 Marquis Grissom .10 .30
707 Brian Harper .05 .15
708 Steve Karsay .05 .15
709 Jeff Brantley .05 .15
710 Jeff Russell .05 .15
711 Bryan Hickerson .05 .15
712 Jim Pittsley RC .05 .15
713 Bobby Ayala .05 .15
714 John Smoltz .20 .50
715 Jose Rijo .05 .15
716 Greg Maddux .30 .75
717 Matt Williams .05 .15
718 Frank Thomas .20 .50
719 Ryne Sandberg .30 .75
720 Checklist .05 .15

1994 Stadium Club First Day Issue

Randomly inserted in one of every 24 packs, these First Day Production cards are identical to the regular issues except for a special 1st Day foil stamp engraved on the front of each card. No more than 2,000 of each Stadium Club card was issued as First Day Issue. Some FDI logos have been transferred from "common" players to the front of "star" players.

*STARS: 8X TO 20X BASIC CARDS
*ROOKIES: 6X TO 15X BASIC CARDS
STATED ODDS 1:24 H/R, 1:15 JUMBO

1994 Stadium Club Golden Rainbow

Parallel to the basic Stadium Club set, Golden Rainbows differ in that the player's last name on front has gold refracting foil over it. The cards were inserted one per Stadium Club foil pack and two per jumbo.

COMPLETE SET (720) 75.00 160.00
COMP.SERIES 1 (270) 25.00 60.00
COMP.SERIES 2 (270) 25.00 60.00
COMP.SERIES 3 (180) 15.00 40.00
*STARS: 1.25X TO 3X BASIC CARDS
*ROOKIES: 1X TO 2.5X BASIC CARDS

1994 Stadium Club Members Only Parallel

This set, issued only to Topps Stadium Club Members, is a parallel of the regular Stadium Club set. This set was issued in factory set form only and includes parallel versions of both the basic issue and insert cards from the 1994 Stadium Club set. According to Topps, 5,000 sets were produced. However, some dealers believe less cards than that were actually produced. Only the insert cards have been listed below. Please use the multiplier for values on the basic issue cards.

COMP.FACT.SET (770) 27.50 200.00
*1ST SERIES MEMBERS ONLY: 4X BASIC CARDS
2ND AND 3RD SERIES MEMBERS ONLY STARS: 6X BASIC CARDS
F1 Jeff Bagwell 1.50 4.00
F2 Albert Belle .60 1.50
F3 Barry Bonds 3.00 8.00
F4 Juan Gonzalez 1.25 3.00
F5 Ken Griffey Jr. 5.00 12.00
F6 Marquis Grissom .40 1.00
F7 David Justice 1.25 3.00
F8 Mike Piazza 3.00 8.00
F9 Tim Salmon 1.25 3.00
F10 Frank Thomas 2.50 6.00
DD1 Mike Piazza 3.00 8.00
DD2 Dave Winfield 1.25 3.00
DD3 John Kruk .60 1.50
DD4 Cal Ripken 6.00 15.00
DD5 Jack McDowell 2.50 6.00
DD6 Barry Bonds 3.00 8.00
DD7 Ken Griffey Jr. 5.00 12.00
DD8 Tim Salmon 1.25 3.00
DD9 Frank Thomas 2.00 5.00
DD10 Jeff Kent 1.25 3.00
DD11 Randy Johnson 1.50 4.00
DD12 Darren Daulton .60 1.50
ST1 Jeff Blauser .30 .75
Terry Pendleton
ST2 Sammy Sosa .60 1.50
Derrick May
ST3 Reggie Sanders .40 1.00
Barry Larkin
ST4 Vinny Castilla .20 .50
Eric Young
ST5 Alex Arias .20 .50
ST6 Eric Anthony .30 .75
Steve Finley
ST7 Mike Piazza 2.00 5.00
ST8 Marquis Grissom .30 .75
ST9 Bobby Bonilla .20 .50
ST10 Mickey Morandini .20 .50
ST11 Andy Van Slyke .30 .75
Jay Bell
ST12 Todd Zeile .20 .50
Gregg Jefferies
ST13 Ricky Gutierrez .20 .50
ST14 Matt Williams .40 1.00
Kirt Manwaring
ST15 Cal Ripken 2.50 6.00
ST16 Luis Rivera .20 .50
John Valentin
ST17 Tim Salmon .60 1.50
ST18 Ozzie Guillen .20 .50
ST19 Kenny Lofton .40 1.00
Carlos Baerga
Albert Belle
ST20 Alan Trammell .30 .75
Tony Phillips
ST21 Jose Lind .20 .50
Curt Wilkerson
ST22 Pat Listach .20 .50
John Jaha
Cal Eldred
ST23 Kirby Puckett 1.25 3.00
Kent Hrbek
ST24 Don Mattingly 1.25 3.00
Bernie Williams
ST25 Mike Bordick .20 .50
Brent Gates
ST26 Jay Buhner .40 1.00
Mike Blowers
ST27 Ivan Rodriguez .60 1.50
Dean Palmer
Jose Canseco
Juan Gonzalez
ST28 John Olerud .20 .50

1994 Stadium Club Dugout Dirt

Randomly inserted at a rate of one per six packs, these standard-size cards feature some of baseball's most popular and colorful players by sports cartoonists Daniel Guidera and Steve Benson. The cards resemble basic Stadium Club cards except for a Dugout Dirt logo at the bottom. Backs contain a cartoon. Cards 1-4 were found in first series packs with cards 5-8 and 9-12 were inserted in second series and third series packs respectively.

COMPLETE SET (12) 4.00 10.00
COMPLETE SERIES 1 (4) 2.00 5.00
COMPLETE SERIES 2 (4) 1.25 3.00
COMPLETE SERIES 3 (4) 1.25 3.00
STATED ODDS 1:6 H/R, 1:3 JUM
DD1 Mike Piazza .60 1.50
DD2 Dave Winfield .10 .30
DD3 John Kruk .10 .30
DD4 Cal Ripken 1.00 2.50
DD5 Jack McDowell .05 .15
DD6 Barry Bonds .75 2.00
DD7 Ken Griffey Jr. .50 1.25
DD8 Tim Salmon .20 .50
DD9 Frank Thomas .30 .75
DD10 Jeff Kent .20 .50
DD11 Randy Johnson .30 .75
DD12 Darren Daulton .10 .30

1994 Stadium Club Finest

This set contains 10 standard-size metallic cards of top players. They were randomly inserted one in six third series packs. Jumbo versions measuring approximately five inches by seven inches were issued for retail repacks.

COMPLETE SET (10) 10.00 25.00
SER.3 STATED ODDS 1:6
*JUMBOS: .6X TO 1.5X BASIC SC FINEST
JUMBOS DISTRIBUTED IN RETAIL PACKS
F1 Jeff Bagwell .60 1.50
F2 Albert Belle .40 1.00
F3 Barry Bonds 2.50 6.00
F4 Juan Gonzalez .40 1.00
F5 Ken Griffey Jr. 1.50 4.00
F6 Marquis Grissom .40 1.00
F7 David Justice .40 1.00
F8 Mike Piazza 2.00 5.00
F9 Tim Salmon .60 1.50
F10 Frank Thomas 1.00 2.50

1994 Stadium Club Super Teams

Randomly inserted at a rate of one per 24 first series packs only, this 28-card standard-size features one card for each of the 28 MLB teams. Collectors holding team cards could redeem them for special prizes if those teams won a division title, a league championship, or the World Series. But, since the strike affected the 1994 season, Topps postponed the promotion until the 1995 season. The expiration was pushed back to January 31, 1996.

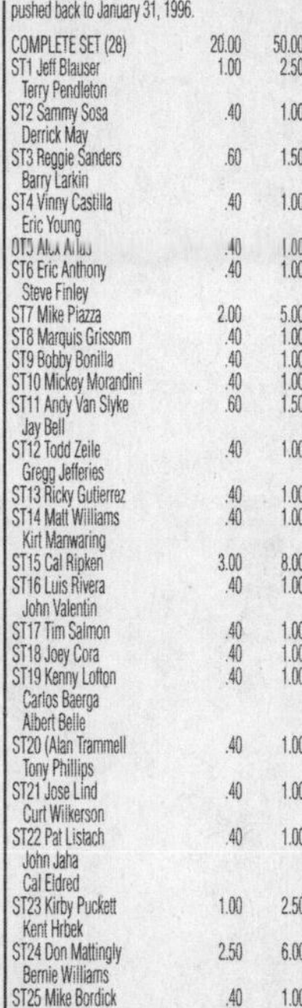

COMPLETE SET (28) 20.00 50.00
ST1 Jeff Blauser 1.00 2.50
Terry Pendleton
ST2 Sammy Sosa .40 1.00
Derrick May
ST3 Reggie Sanders .60 1.50
Barry Larkin
ST4 Vinny Castilla .40 1.00
Eric Young
ST5 Alex Arias .40 1.00
ST6 Eric Anthony .40 1.00
Steve Finley
ST7 Mike Piazza 2.00 5.00
ST8 Marquis Grissom .40 1.00
ST9 Bobby Bonilla .40 1.00
ST10 Mickey Morandini .40 1.00
ST11 Andy Van Slyke .60 1.50
Jay Bell
ST12 Todd Zeile .40 1.00
Gregg Jefferies
ST13 Ricky Gutierrez .40 1.00
ST14 Matt Williams .40 1.00
Kirt Manwaring
ST15 Cal Ripken 3.00 8.00
ST16 Luis Rivera .40 1.00
John Valentin
ST17 Tim Salmon .40 1.00
ST18 Joey Cora .40 1.00
ST19 Kenny Lofton .40 1.00
Carlos Baerga
Albert Belle
ST20 (Alan Trammell .40 1.00
Tony Phillips
ST21 Jose Lind .40 1.00
Curt Wilkerson
ST22 Pat Listach .40 1.00
John Jaha
Cal Eldred
ST23 Kirby Puckett 1.00 2.50
Kent Hrbek
ST24 Don Mattingly 2.50 6.00
Bernie Williams
ST25 Mike Bordick .40 1.00
Brent Gates
ST26 Jay Buhner .40 1.00
Mike Blowers
ST27 Ivan Rodriguez .40 1.00
Dean Palmer
Jose Canseco
Juan Gonzalez
ST28 John Olerud .40 1.00

1994 Stadium Club Members Only 50

Issued to Stadium Club members, this 50-card standard-size set features 45 regular Stadium Club cards as well as five Stadium Club Finest cards.

COMP. FACT SET (50) 8.00 20.00
1 Juan Gonzalez .30 .75
2 Tom Henke .02 .10
3 John Kruk .08 .25
4 Paul Molitor .30 .75
5 David Justice .08 .25
6 Rafael Palmeiro .25 .60
7 John Smoltz .25 .60
8 Matt Williams .15 .40
9 John Olerud .08 .25
10 Mark Grace .15 .40
11 Joe Carter .08 .25
12 Wilson Alvarez .08 .25
13 Len Dykstra .08 .25
14 Kevin Appier .08 .25
15 Andres Galarraga .25 .60
16 Mark Langston .02 .10
17 Ken Griffey Jr. .75 2.00
18 Albert Belle .08 .25
19 Gregg Jefferies .02 .10
20 Duane Ward .02 .10
21 Jack McDowell .02 .10
22 Randy Johnson .30 .75
23 Tom Glavine .25 .60
24 Barry Bonds .60 1.50
25 Chuck Carr .02 .10
26 Ron Gant .08 .25
27 Kenny Lofton .15 .40
28 Mike Piazza .60 1.50
29 Frank Thomas .40 1.00
30 Fred McGriff .15 .40
31 Bryan Harvey .02 .10
32 John Burkett .02 .10
33 Roberto Alomar .25 .60
34 Cecil Fielder .08 .25
35 Marquis Grissom .08 .25
36 Randy Myers .02 .10
37 Tony Phillips .02 .10
38 Rickey Henderson .30 .75
39 Luis Polonia .02 .10
40 Jose Rijo .02 .10
41 Jeff Montgomery .02 .10
42 Greg Maddux .75 2.00
43 Tony Gwynn .60 1.50
44 Rod Beck .02 .10
45 Carlos Baerga .08 .25
46 Wil Cordero FIN .20 .50
47 Tim Salmon FIN .75 2.00
48 Mike Lansing FIN .20 .50
49 J.T. Snow FIN .20 .50
50 Jeff Conine FIN .20 .50

1994 Stadium Club Team

This 360-card standard-size set features 30 players from 12 teams. The cards are checklisted alphabetically according to teams.

COMPLETE SET (360) 16.00 40.00
1 Barry Bonds .75 2.00
2 Royce Clayton .02 .10

3 Kirt Manwaring .02 .10
4 J.R. Phillips .02 .10
5 Robby Thompson .02 .10
6 Willie McGee .07 .20
7 Steve Hosey .02 .10
8 Dave Burba .02 .10
9 Steve Scarsone .02 .10
10 Salomon Torres .02 .10
11 Bryan Hickerson .02 .10
12 Mike Benjamin .02 .10
13 Mark Carreon .02 .10
14 Rich Monteleone .02 .10
15 Dave Martinez .02 .10
16 Bill Swift .02 .10
17 Jeff Reed .02 .10
18 John Patterson .02 .10
19 Darren Lewis .02 .10
20 Mark Portugal .02 .10
21 Trevor Wilson .02 .10
22 Matt Williams .15 .40
23 Kevin Rogers .02 .10
24 Luis Mercedes .02 .10
25 Mike Jackson .02 .10
26 Steve Frey .02 .10
27 Tony Menendez .02 .10
28 John Burkett .02 .10
29 Todd Benzinger .02 .10
30 Rod Beck .02 .10
31 Greg Maddux 1.00 2.50
32 Steve Avery .02 .10
33 Milt Hill .02 .10
34 Charlie O'Brien .02 .10
35 John Smoltz .07 .20
36 Jarvis Brown .02 .10
37 Dave Gallagher .02 .10
Wearing Mets Uniform
38 Ryan Klesko .15 .40
39 Kent Mercker .02 .10
40 Terry Pendleton .07 .20
41 Ron Gant .07 .20
42 Pedro Borbon Jr. .02 .10
43 Steve Bedrosian .02 .10
44 Ramon Caraballo .02 .10
45 Tyler Houston .02 .10
46 Mark Lemke .02 .10
47 Fred McGriff .15 .40
48 Jose Oliva .02 .10
49 David Justice .25 .60
50 Chipper Jones .75 2.00
51 Tony Tarasco .02 .10
52 Javier Lopez .15 .40
53 Mark Wohlers .02 .10
54 Deion Sanders .25 .60
55 Greg McMichael .02 .10
56 Tom Glavine .40 1.00
57 Bill Pecota .02 .10
58 Mike Stanton .02 .10
59 Rafael Belliard .02 .10
60 Jeff Blauser .02 .10
61 Bryan Harvey .02 .10
62 Bret Barberie .02 .10
63 Rick Renteria .02 .10
64 Chris Hammond .02 .10
65 Pat Rapp .02 .10
66 Nigel Wilson .02 .10
67 Gary Sheffield .40 1.00
68 Jerry Browne .02 .10
69 Charlie Hough .07 .20
70 Orestes Destrade .02 .10
71 Mario Diaz .02 .10
72 Ryan Bowen .02 .10
73 Carl Everett .07 .20
74 Richie Lewis .02 .10
75 Bob Natal .02 .10
76 Rich Rodriguez .02 .10
77 Darrell Whitmore .02 .10
78 Matt Turner .02 .10
79 Benito Santiago .07 .20
80 Robb Nen .07 .20
81 Dave Magadan .02 .10
82 Brian Drahman .02 .10
83 Mark Gardner .02 .10
84 Chuck Carr .02 .10
85 Alex Arias .02 .10
86 Kurt Abbott .02 .10
87 Joe Klink .02 .10
88 Jeff Mutis .02 .10
89 Dave Weathers .02 .10
90 Jeff Conine .07 .20
91 Andres Galarraga .07 .20
92 Vinny Castilla .07 .20
93 Roberto Mejia .02 .10
94 Darrell Sherman .02 .10
95 Mike Harkey .02 .10
96 Danny Sheaffer .02 .10
97 Pedro Castellano .02 .10
98 Walt Weiss .02 .10
99 Greg W. Harris .02 .10
100 Jayhawk Owens .02 .10
101 Bruce Ruffin .02 .10
102 Mike Munoz .02 .10
103 Armando Reynoso .02 .10
104 Eric Young .07 .20
105 Dante Bichette .07 .20
106 Marvin Freeman .02 .10
107 Joe Girardi .07 .20
108 Kent Bottenfield .02 .10
109 Howard Johnson .02 .10
110 Nelson Liriano .02 .10
111 David Nied .02 .10
112 Steve Reed .02 .10
113 Eric Wedge .02 .10
114 Charlie Hayes .02 .10
115 Ellis Burks .15 .40
116 Willie Blair .02 .10
117 Darren Holmes .02 .10
118 Curtis Leskanic .02 .10
119 Lance Painter .02 .10
120 Jim Tatum .02 .10
121 Frank Thomas .50 1.25
122 Jack McDowell .02 .10
123 Ron Karkovice .02 .10
124 Mike LaValliere .02 .10
125 Scott Radinsky .02 .10
126 Robin Ventura .15 .40
127 Scott Ruffcorn .02 .10
128 Steve Sax .02 .10
129 Roberto Hernandez .07 .20
130 Jose DeLeon .02 .10
131 Rod Bolton .02 .10
132 Wilson Alvarez .02 .10
133 Craig Grebeck .02 .10
134 Lance Johnson .02 .10
135 Kirk McCaskill .02 .10
136 Tim Raines .07 .20
137 Jeff Schwarz .02 .10
138 Warren Newson .02 .10
139 Norberto Martin .02 .10
140 Mike Huff .02 .10
141 Ozzie Guillen .15 .40
142 Alex Fernandez .02 .10
143 Joey Cora .02 .10
144 Jason Bere .02 .10
145 James Baldwin .07 .20
146 Esteban Beltre .02 .10
147 Julio Franco .07 .20
148 Matt Merullo .02 .10
149 Dan Pasqua .02 .10
150 Darrin Jackson .02 .10
151 Joe Carter .07 .20
152 Danny Cox .02 .10
153 Roberto Alomar .25 .60
154 Woody Williams .15 .40
155 Duane Ward .02 .10
156 Ed Sprague .02 .10
157 Domingo Martinez .02 .10
158 Pat Hentgen .07 .20
159 Shawn Green .40 1.00
160 Dick Schofield .02 .10
161 Paul Molitor .40 1.00
162 Darnell Coles .02 .10
163 Willie Canate .02 .10
164 Domingo Cedeno .02 .10
165 Pat Borders .02 .10
166 Greg Cadaret .02 .10
167 Tony Castillo .02 .10
168 Carlos Delgado .40 1.00
169 Scott Brow .02 .10
170 Juan Guzman .02 .10
171 Al Leiter .07 .20
172 John Olerud .15 .40
173 Todd Stottlemyre .02 .10
174 Devon White .07 .20
175 Paul Spoljaric .02 .10
176 Randy Knorr .02 .10
177 Huck Flener .02 .10
178 Rob Butler .02 .10
179 Dave Stewart .07 .20
180 Mike Timlin .02 .10
181 Don Mattingly .75 2.00
182 Mark Hutton .02 .10
183 Mike Gallego .02 .10
184 Jim Abbott .07 .20
185 Paul Gibson .02 .10
186 Scott Kamieniecki .02 .10
187 Sam Horn .02 .10
188 Melido Perez .02 .10
189 Randy Velarde .02 .10
190 Gerald Williams .02 .10
191 Dave Silvestri .02 .10
192 Jim Leyritz .02 .10
193 Steve Howe .02 .10
194 Russ Davis .02 .10
195 Paul Assenmacher .02 .10
196 Pat Kelly .02 .10
197 Mike Stanley .02 .10
198 Bernie Williams .30 .75
199 Paul O'Neill .25 .60
200 Donn Pall .02 .10
201 Xavier Hernandez .02 .10
202 Jim Austin .02 .10
203 Sterling Hitchcock .07 .20
204 Wade Boggs .40 1.00
205 Jimmy Key .07 .20
206 Matt Nokes .02 .10
207 Terry Mulholland .02 .10
208 Luis Polonia .02 .10
209 Danny Tartabull .07 .20
210 Bob Wickman .02 .10
211 Len Dykstra .07 .20
212 Kim Batiste .02 .10
213 Tony Longmire .02 .10
214 Bobby Munoz .02 .10
215 Pete Incaviglia .02 .10
216 Doug Jones .07 .20
217 Mariano Duncan .02 .10
218 Jeff Juden .02 .10
219 Milt Thompson .02 .10
220 Dave West .02 .10
221 Roger Mason .02 .10
222 Tommy Greene .02 .10
223 Larry Andersen .02 .10
224 Jim Eisenreich .02 .10
225 Dave Hollins .02 .10
226 John Kruk .07 .20
227 Todd Pratt .02 .10
228 Ricky Jordan .02 .10
229 Curt Schilling .60 1.50
230 Mike Williams .02 .10
231 Heathcliff Slocumb .02 .10
232 Ben Rivera .02 .10
233 Mike Lieberthal .07 .20
234 Mickey Morandini .02 .10
235 Danny Jackson .02 .10
236 Kevin Foster .02 .10
237 Darren Daulton .07 .20
238 Wes Chamberlain .02 .10
239 Tyler Green .02 .10
240 Kevin Stocker .02 .10
241 Juan Gonzalez .30 .75
242 Rick Honeycutt .02 .10
243 Bruce Hurst .02 .10
244 Steve Dreyer .02 .10
245 Brian Bohanon .02 .10
246 Benji Gil .02 .10
247 Jon Shave .02 .10
248 Manuel Lee .02 .10
249 Donald Harris .02 .10
250 Jose Canseco .30 .75
251 David Hulse .02 .10
252 Kenny Rogers .02 .10
253 Jeff Huson .02 .10
254 Dan Peltier .02 .10
255 Mike Scioscia .07 .20
256 Jack Armstrong .02 .10
257 Rob Ducey .02 .10
258 Will Clark .25 .60
259 Cris Carpenter .02 .10
260 Kevin Brown .15 .40
261 Jeff Frye .02 .10
262 Jay Howell .02 .10
263 Roger Pavlik .02 .10
264 Gary Redus .02 .10
265 Ivan Rodriguez .40 1.00
266 Matt Whiteside .02 .10
267 Doug Strange .02 .10
268 Billy Ripken .02 .10
269 Dean Palmer .07 .20
270 Tom Henke .02 .10
271 Cal Ripken 1.50 4.00
272 Mark McLemore .07 .20
273 Sid Fernandez .07 .20
274 Sherman Obando .02 .10
275 Paul Carey .02 .10
276 Mike Oquist .02 .10
277 Alan Mills .02 .10
278 Harold Baines .07 .20
279 Mike Mussina .40 1.00
280 Arthur Rhodes .02 .10
281 Kevin McGehee .02 .10
282 Mark Eichhorn .02 .10
283 Damon Buford .02 .10
284 Ben McDonald .02 .10
285 David Segui .02 .10
286 Brad Pennington .02 .10
287 Jamie Moyer .15 .40
288 Chris Hoiles .02 .10
289 Mike Cook .02 .10
290 Brady Anderson .07 .20
291 Chris Sabo .02 .10
292 Jack Voigt .02 .10
293 Jim Poole .02 .10
294 Jeff Tackett .02 .10
295 Rafael Palmeiro .30 .75
296 Alex Ochoa .02 .10
297 John O'Donoghue .02 .10
298 Tim Hulett .02 .10
299 Mike Devereaux .02 .10
300 Manny Alexander .02 .10
301 Ozzie Smith .40 1.00
302 Omar Olivares .02 .10
303 Rheal Cormier .02 .10
304 Donovan Osborne .02 .10
305 Mark Whiten .02 .10
306 Todd Zeile .07 .20
307 Geronimo Pena .02 .10
308 Brian Jordan .07 .20
309 Luis Alicea .02 .10
310 Ray Lankford .07 .20
311 Stan Royer .02 .10
312 Bob Tewksbury .02 .10
313 Jose Oquendo .02 .10
314 Steve Dixon .02 .10
315 Rene Arocha .02 .10
316 Bernard Gilkey .02 .10
317 Gregg Jefferies .02 .10
318 Rob Murphy .02 .10
319 Tom Pagnozzi .02 .10
320 Mike Perez .02 .10
321 Tom Urbani .02 .10
322 Allen Watson .02 .10
323 Erik Pappas .02 .10
324 Paul Kilgus .02 .10
325 John Habyan .02 .10
326 Rod Brewer .02 .10
327 Rich Batchelor .02 .10
328 Tripp Cromer .02 .10
329 Gerald Perry .02 .10
330 Les Lancaster .02 .10
331 Ryne Sandberg .75 2.00
332 Derrick May .02 .10
333 Steve Buechele .02 .10
334 Willie Banks .02 .10
335 Larry Luebbers .02 .10
336 Tommy Shields .02 .10
337 Eric Yelding .02 .10
338 Rey Sanchez .02 .10
339 Mark Grace .15 .40
340 Jose Bautista .02 .10
341 Frank Castillo .02 .10
342 Jose Guzman .02 .10
343 Rafael Novoa .02 .10
Wearing Milwaukee Brewer uniform
344 Karl Rhodes .02 .10
345 Steve Trachsel .02 .10
346 Rick Wilkins .02 .10
347 Sammy Sosa .60 1.50
348 Kevin Roberson .02 .10
349 Mark Parent .02 .10
350 Randy Myers .07 .20
351 Glenallen Hill .02 .10
352 Lance Dickson .02 .10
353 Shawn Boskie .02 .10
354 Shawon Dunston .07 .20
355 Dan Plesac .02 .10
356 Jose Vizcaino .02 .10
357 Willie Wilson .02 .10
358 Turk Wendell .02 .10
359 Mike Morgan .02 .10
360 Jim Bullinger .02 .10

1994 Stadium Club Team First Day Issue

This 360-card standard-size set features 30 players from 12 teams. First Day Issue cards were randomly packed one in every six 12-card packs; the odds of finding these insert cards in 20-card jumbo packs are one in three. Also one 1st Day Issue card was included in the 30-card team sets sold in blister packs. They are identical in design with the regular Stadium Club Team cards except for a holographic "1st Day Issue" emblem on the fronts.

*STARS: 10X to 20X BASIC CARDS
RANDOM INSERTS IN PACKS

1994 Stadium Club Team Finest

This 12-card standard-size set consists of one player from each of the 12 teams featured in the 1994 Stadium Club team series. The cards were randomly inserted in 12-card foil packs. Also one card was included in the 30-card team sets sold in blister packs. The cards are identical in design with the regular series, except for the metallic sheen characteristic of the Finest series.

COMPLETE SET (12) 12.00 30.00
1 Roberto Alomar .75 2.00
2 Barry Bonds 2.00 5.00
3 Len Dykstra .40 1.00
4 Andres Galarraga .75 2.00
5 Juan Gonzalez .75 2.00
6 David Justice .75 2.00
7 Don Mattingly 1.50 4.00
8 Cal Ripken 4.00 10.00
9 Ryne Sandberg 2.00 5.00
10 Gary Sheffield 1.00 2.50
11 Ozzie Smith 1.50 4.00
12 Frank Thomas .75 2.00

1994 Stadium Club Draft Picks

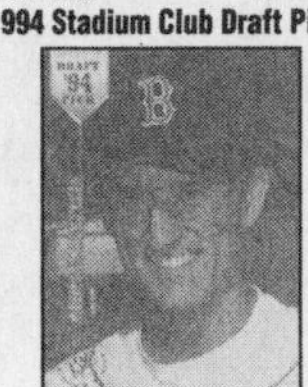

This 90-card standard-size set features players chosen in the June 1994 MLB draft and photographed in their major league uniforms. Each 24-pack box included four First Day Issue Draft Pick cards randomly packed, one in every six packs. Early cards of Nomar Garciaparra, Ben Grieve and Terrence Long are featured in this set.

COMPLETE SET (90) 4.00 10.00
1 Jacob Shumate XRC .08 .25
2 C.J. Nitkowski XRC .08 .25
3 Doug Million XRC .08 .25
4 Matt Smith XRC .08 .25
5 Kevin Lovinger XRC .08 .25
6 Alberto Castillo XRC .08 .25
7 Mike Russell XRC .08 .25
8 Dan Lock XRC .08 .25
9 Tom Szimanski XRC .08 .25
10 Aaron Boone XRC .20 .50
11 Jayson Peterson XRC .08 .25
12 Mark Johnson XRC .08 .25
13 Cade Gaspar XRC .08 .25
14 George Lombard XRC .08 .25
15 Russ Johnson .08 .25
16 Travis Miller XRC .08 .25
17 Jay Payton XRC .20 .50
18 Brian Buchanan XRC .08 .25
19 Jacob Cruz XRC .15 .40
20 Gary Rath XRC .08 .25
21 Ramon Castro XRC .08 .25
22 Tommy Davis XRC .08 .25
23 Tony Terry XRC .08 .25
24 Jerry Whittaker XRC .08 .25
25 Mike Darr XRC .08 .25
26 Doug Webb XRC .08 .25
27 Jason Camilli XRC .08 .25
28 Brad Rigby XRC .08 .25
29 Ryan Nye XRC .08 .25
30 Carl Dale XRC .08 .25
31 Andy Taulbee XRC .08 .25
32 Trey Moore XRC .08 .25
33 John Crowther XRC .08 .25
34 Joe Giuliano XRC .08 .25
35 Brian Rose XRC .08 .25
36 Paul Failla XRC .08 .25
37 Brian Meadows XRC .08 .25
38 Oscar Robles XRC .15 .40
39 Mike Metcalfe XRC .08 .25
40 Larry Barnes XRC .08 .25
41 Paul Ottavinia XRC .08 .25
42 Chris McBride XRC .08 .25
43 Ricky Stone XRC .08 .25
44 Billy Blythe XRC .08 .25
45 Eddie Priest XRC .08 .25
46 Scott Forster XRC .08 .25
47 Eric Pickett XRC .08 .25
48 Matt Beaumont .08 .25
49 Darrell Nicholas XRC .08 .25
50 Mike A. Hampton XRC .08 .25
51 Paul O'Malley XRC .08 .25
52 Steve Shoemaker XRC .08 .25
53 Jason Sikes XRC .08 .25
54 Bryan Farson XRC .08 .25
55 Yates Hall XRC .08 .25
56 Troy Brohawn XRC .08 .25
57 Dan Hower XRC .08 .25
58 Clay Caruthers XRC .08 .25
59 Pepe McNeal XRC .08 .25
60 Ray Ricken XRC .08 .25
61 Scott Shores XRC .08 .25
62 Eddie Brooks XRC .08 .25
63 Dave Kauflin XRC .08 .25
64 David Meyer XRC .08 .25
65 Geoff Blum XRC .20 .50

66 Roy Marsh XRC .08 .25
67 Ryan Beeney XRC .08 .25
68 Derek Dukart XRC .08 .25
69 Nomar Garciaparra 1.25 3.00
70 Jason Kelly XRC .08 .25
71 Jesse Ibarra XRC .08 .25
72 Bucky Buckles XRC .08 .25
73 Mark Little XRC .08 .25
74 Heath Murray XRC .08 .25
75 Greg Morris XRC .08 .25
76 Mike Halperlin XRC .08 .25
77 Wes Helms XRC .15 .40
78 Ray Brown XRC .08 .25
79 Kevin L.Brown XRC .15 .40
80 Paul Konerko XRC 2.00 5.00
81 Mike Thurman XRC .08 .25
82 Paul Wilson .08 .25
83 Terrence Long XRC .15 .40
84 Ben Grieve XRC .15 .40
85 Mark Farris XRC .08 .25
86 Bret Wagner .08 .25
87 Dustin Hermanson .08 .25
88 Kevin Witt XRC .15 .40
89 Corey Pointer XRC .08 .25
90 Tim Grieve XRC .08 .25

1994 Stadium Club Draft Picks First Day Issue

Randomly inserted in packs, this 90-card standard-size set is identical in design with the regular Stadium Club Draft Picks cards except for a holographic "1st Day Issue" emblem on the fronts.

*FIRST DAY: 1.25X TO 3X BASIC CARDS
RANDOM INSERTS IN PACKS

1994 Stadium Club Draft Picks Members Only

This parallel to the Stadium Club Draft Pick set was issued only in Factory set form and features a special "Members Only" logo on the card.

*MEMBERS ONLY: 1.25X TO 3X BASIC CARD

1995 Stadium Club

The 1995 Stadium Club baseball card set was issued in three series of 270, 225 and 135 standard-size cards for a total of 630. The cards were distributed in 14-card packs at a suggested retail price of $2.50 and contained 24 packs per box. Notable Rookie Cards include Mark Grudzielanek, Bobby Higginson and Hideo Nomo.

COMPLETE SET (630) 25.00 60.00
COMP.SERIES 1 (270) 10.00 25.00
COMP.SERIES 2 (225) 8.00 20.00
COMP.SERIES 3 (135) 6.00 15.00
1 Cal Ripken 1.00 2.50
2 Bo Jackson .30 .75
3 Bryan Harvey .05 .15
4 Curt Schilling .10 .30
5 Bruce Ruffin .05 .15
6 Travis Fryman .10 .30
7 Jim Abbott .20 .50
8 David McCarty .05 .15
9 Gary Gaetti .10 .30
10 Roger Clemens .60 1.50
11 Carlos Garcia .05 .15
12 Lee Smith .10 .30
13 Bobby Ayala .05 .15
14 Charles Nagy .05 .15
15 Lou Frazier .05 .15
16 Rene Arocha .05 .15
17 Carlos Delgado .10 .30
18 Steve Finley .10 .30
19 Ryan Klesko .10 .30
20 Cal Eldred .05 .15
21 Rey Sanchez .05 .15
22 Ken Hill .05 .15
23 Benito Santiago .10 .30
24 Julian Tavarez .05 .15
25 Jose Vizcaino .05 .15
26 Andy Benes .05 .15
27 Mariano Duncan .05 .15
28 Checklist A .05 .15
29 Shawon Dunston .05 .15
30 Rafael Palmeiro .20 .50
31 Dean Palmer .10 .30
32 Andres Galarraga .10 .30
33 Joey Cora .05 .15
34 Mickey Tettleton .05 .15
35 Barry Larkin .20 .50
36 Carlos Baerga .05 .15
37 Orel Hershiser .10 .30
38 Jody Reed .05 .15
39 Paul Molitor .10 .30
40 Jim Edmonds .20 .50
41 Bob Tewksbury .05 .15
42 John Patterson .05 .15
43 Ray McDavid .05 .15
44 Zane Smith .05 .15
45 Bret Saberhagen SE .05 .15
46 Greg Maddux SE .30 .75
47 Frank Thomas SE .20 .50
48 Carlos Baerga SE .05 .15
49 Billy Spiers .05 .15
50 Stan Javier .05 .15
51 Rex Hudler .05 .15
52 Denny Hocking .05 .15
53 Todd Worrell .05 .15
54 Mark Clark .05 .15
55 Hipolito Pichardo .05 .15
56 Bob Wickman .05 .15
57 Raul Mondesi .10 .30
58 Steve Cooke .05 .15
59 Rod Beck .05 .15
60 Tim Davis .05 .15
61 Jeff Kent .10 .30
62 John Valentin .05 .15
63 Alex Arias .05 .15
64 Steve Reed .05 .15
65 Ozzie Smith .50 1.25
66 Terry Pendleton .10 .30
67 Kenny Rogers .10 .30
68 Vince Coleman .05 .15
69 Tom Pagnozzi .05 .15
70 Roberto Alomar .20 .50
71 Darrin Jackson .05 .15
72 Dennis Eckersley .10 .30
73 Jay Buhner .10 .30
74 Darren Lewis .05 .15
75 Dave Weathers .05 .15
76 Matt Walbeck .05 .15
77 Brad Ausmus .10 .30
78 Danny Bautista .05 .15
79 Bob Hamelin .05 .15
80 Steve Trachsel .05 .15
81 Ken Ryan .05 .15
82 Chris Turner .05 .15
83 David Segui .05 .15
84 Ben McDonald .05 .15
85 Wade Boggs .20 .50
86 John Vander Wal .05 .15
87 Sandy Alomar Jr. .05 .15
88 Ron Karkovice .05 .15
89 Doug Jones .05 .15
90 Gary Sheffield .10 .30
91 Ken Caminiti .10 .30
92 Chris Bosio .05 .15
93 Kevin Tapani .05 .15
94 Walt Weiss .05 .15
95 Erik Hanson .05 .15
96 Ruben Sierra .10 .30
97 Nomar Garciaparra .75 2.00
98 Terrence Long .05 .15
99 Jacob Shumate .05 .15
100 Paul Wilson .05 .15
101 Kevin Witt .05 .15
102 Paul Konerko .40 1.00
103 Ben Grieve .05 .15
104 Mark Johnson RC .15 .40
105 Cade Gaspar RC .05 .15
106 Mark Farris .05 .15
107 Dustin Hermanson .05 .15
108 Scott Elarton RC .15 .40
109 Doug Million .05 .15
110 Matt Smith .05 .15
111 Brian Buchanan RC .05 .15
112 Jayson Peterson RC .05 .15
113 Bret Wagner .05 .15
114 C.J. Nitkowski RC .15 .40
115 Ramon Castro RC .15 .40
116 Rafael Bournigal .05 .15
117 Jeff Fassero .05 .15
118 Bobby Bonilla .10 .30
119 Ricky Gutierrez .05 .15
120 Roger Pavlik .05 .15
121 Mike Greenwell .05 .15
122 Deion Sanders .20 .50
123 Charlie Hayes .05 .15
124 Paul O'Neill .20 .50
125 Jay Bell .10 .30
126 Royce Clayton .05 .15
127 Willie Banks .05 .15
128 Mark Wohlers .05 .15
129 Todd Jones .05 .15
130 Todd Stottlemyre .05 .15
131 Will Clark .20 .50
132 Wilson Alvarez .05 .15
133 Chili Davis .10 .30
134 Dave Burba .05 .15
135 Chris Hoiles .05 .15
136 Jeff Blauser .05 .15
137 Jeff Reboulet .05 .15
138 Bret Saberhagen .10 .30
139 Kirk Rueter .05 .15
140 Dave Nilsson .05 .15
141 Pat Borders .05 .15
142 Ron Darling .05 .15
143 Derek Bell .05 .15
144 Dave Hollins .05 .15
145 Juan Gonzalez .10 .30
146 Andre Dawson .10 .30
147 Jim Thome .20 .50
148 Larry Walker .10 .30
149 Mike Piazza .50 1.25
150 Mike Perez .05 .15
151 Steve Avery .05 .15
152 Dan Wilson .05 .15
153 Andy Van Slyke .20 .50
154 Junior Felix .05 .15
155 Jack McDowell .05 .15
156 Danny Tartabull .05 .15
157 Willie Blair .05 .15
158 Wm.VanLandingham .05 .15
159 Robb Nen .10 .30
160 Lee Tinsley .05 .15
161 Ismael Valdes .05 .15
162 Juan Guzman .05 .15
163 Scott Servais .05 .15
164 Cliff Floyd .10 .30
165 Allen Watson .05 .15
166 Eddie Taubensee .05 .15
167 Scott Hemond .05 .15
168 Jeff Tackett .05 .15
169 Chad Curtis .05 .15
170 Rico Brogna .05 .15
171 Luis Polonia .05 .15
172 Checklist B .05 .15
173 Lance Johnson .05 .15
174 Sammy Sosa .30 .75
175 Mike Macfarlane .05 .15
176 Darryl Hamilton .05 .15
177 Rick Aguilera .05 .15
178 Dave West .05 .15
179 Mike Gallego .05 .15
180 Marc Newfield .05 .15
181 Steve Buechele .05 .15
182 David Wells .10 .30
183 Tom Glavine .20 .50
184 Joe Girardi .05 .15
185 Craig Biggio .20 .50
186 Eddie Murray .30 .75
187 Kevin Gross .05 .15
188 Sid Fernandez .05 .15
189 John Franco .10 .30
190 Bernard Gilkey .05 .15
191 Matt Williams .10 .30
192 Darrin Fletcher .05 .15
193 Jeff Conine .10 .30
194 Ed Sprague .05 .15
195 Eduardo Perez .05 .15
196 Scott Livingstone .05 .15
197 Ivan Rodriguez .20 .50
198 Orlando Merced .05 .15
199 Ricky Bones .05 .15
200 Javier Lopez .10 .30
201 Miguel Jimenez .05 .15
202 Terry McGriff .05 .15
203 Mike Lieberthal .10 .30
204 David Cone .10 .30
205 Todd Hundley .05 .15
206 Ozzie Guillen .10 .30
207 Alex Cole .05 .15
208 Tony Phillips .05 .15
209 Jim Eisenreich .05 .15
210 Greg Vaughn BES .05 .15
211 Barry Larkin BES .10 .30
212 Don Mattingly BES .40 1.00
213 Mark Grace BES .10 .30
214 Jose Canseco BES .10 .30
215 Joe Carter BES .05 .15
216 David Cone BES .05 .15
217 Sandy Alomar Jr. BES .05 .15
218 Al Martin BES .05 .15
219 Roberto Kelly BES .05 .15
220 Paul Sorrento .05 .15
221 Tony Fernandez .05 .15
222 Stan Belinda .05 .15
223 Mike Stanley .05 .15
224 Doug Drabek .05 .15
225 Todd Van Poppel .05 .15
226 Matt Mieske .05 .15
227 Tino Martinez .20 .50
228 Andy Ashby .05 .15
229 Midre Cummings .05 .15
230 Jeff Frye .05 .15
231 Hal Morris .05 .15
232 Jose Lind .05 .15
233 Shawn Green .10 .30
234 Rafael Belliard .05 .15
235 Randy Myers .05 .15
236 Frank Thomas CE .20 .50
237 Darren Daulton CE .05 .15
238 Sammy Sosa CE .20 .50
239 Cal Ripken CE .50 1.25
240 Jeff Bagwell CE .10 .30
241 Ken Griffey Jr. .50 1.25
242 Brett Butler .10 .30
243 Derrick May .05 .15
244 Pat Listach .05 .15
245 Mike Bordick .05 .15
246 Mark Langston .05 .15
247 Randy Velarde .05 .15
248 Julio Franco .10 .30
249 Chuck Knoblauch .10 .30
250 Bill Gullickson .05 .15
251 Dave Henderson .05 .15
252 Bret Boone .10 .30
253 Al Martin .05 .15
254 Armando Benitez .05 .15
255 Wil Cordero .05 .15
256 Al Leiter .10 .30
257 Luis Gonzalez .10 .30
258 Charlie O'Brien .05 .15
259 Tim Wallach .05 .15
260 Scott Sanders .05 .15
261 Tom Henke .05 .15
262 Otis Nixon .05 .15
263 Darren Daulton .10 .30
264 Manny Ramirez .20 .50
265 Bret Barberie .05 .15
266 Mel Rojas .05 .15
267 John Burkett .05 .15
268 Brady Anderson .10 .30
269 John Roper .05 .15
270 Shane Reynolds .05 .15
271 Barry Bonds .75 2.00
272 Alex Fernandez .05 .15
273 Brian McRae .05 .15
274 Todd Zeile .05 .15
275 Greg Swindell .05 .15
276 Johnny Ruffin .05 .15
277 Troy Neel .05 .15
278 Eric Karros .10 .30
279 John Hudek .05 .15
280 Thomas Howard .05 .15
281 Joe Carter .10 .30
282 Mike Devereaux .05 .15
283 Butch Henry .05 .15
284 Reggie Jefferson .05 .15
285 Mark Lemke .05 .15
286 Jeff Montgomery .05 .15
287 Ryan Thompson .05 .15
288 Paul Shuey .05 .15
289 Mark McGwire .75 2.00
290 Bernie Williams .20 .50
291 Mickey Morandini .05 .15
292 Scott Leius .05 .15
293 David Hulse .05 .15
294 Greg Gagne .05 .15
295 Moises Alou .10 .30
296 Geronimo Berroa .05 .15
297 Eddie Zambrano .05 .15
298 Alan Trammell .10 .30
299 Don Slaught .05 .15
300 Jose Rijo .05 .15
301 Joe Ausanio .05 .15
302 Tim Raines .10 .30
303 Melido Perez .05 .15
304 Kent Mercker .05 .15
305 James Mouton .05 .15
306 Luis Lopez .05 .15
307 Mike Kingery .05 .15
308 Willie Greene .05 .15
309 Cecil Fielder .10 .30
310 Scott Kamieniecki .05 .15
311 Mike Greenwell BES .05 .15
312 Bobby Bonilla BES .05 .15
313 A.Galarraga BES .05 .15
314 Cal Ripken BES .50 1.25
315 Matt Williams BES .05 .15
316 Tom Pagnozzi BES .05 .15
317 Len Dykstra BES .05 .15
318 Frank Thomas BES .20 .50
319 Kirby Puckett BES .30 .75
320 Mike Piazza BES .30 .75
321 Jason Jacome .05 .15
322 Brian Hunter .05 .15
323 Brent Gates .05 .15
324 Jim Converse .05 .15
325 Damion Easley .05 .15
326 Dante Bichette .10 .30
327 Kurt Abbott .05 .15
328 Scott Cooper .05 .15
329 Mike Henneman .05 .15
330 Orlando Miller .05 .15
331 John Kruk .10 .30
332 Jose Oliva .05 .15
333 Reggie Sanders .10 .30
334 Omar Vizquel .20 .50
335 Devon White .10 .30
336 Mike Morgan .05 .15
337 J.R. Phillips .05 .15
338 Gary DiSarcina .05 .15
339 Joey Hamilton .05 .15
340 Randy Johnson .30 .75
341 Jim Leyritz .05 .15
342 Bobby Jones .05 .15
343 Jaime Navarro .05 .15
344 Bip Roberts .05 .15
345 Steve Karsay .05 .15
346 Kevin Stocker .05 .15
347 Jose Canseco .20 .50
348 Bill Wegman .05 .15
349 Rondell White .10 .30
350 Mo Vaughn .10 .30
351 Joe Orsulak .05 .15
352 Pat Meares .05 .15
353 Albie Lopez .05 .15
354 Edgar Martinez .20 .50
355 Brian Jordan .10 .30
356 Tommy Greene .05 .15
357 Chuck Carr .05 .15
358 Pedro Astacio .05 .15
359 Russ Davis .05 .15
360 Chris Hammond .05 .15
361 Gregg Jefferies .05 .15
362 Shane Mack .05 .15
363 Fred McGriff .20 .50
364 Pat Rapp .05 .15
365 Bill Swift .05 .15
366 Checklist .05 .15
367 Robin Ventura .10 .30
368 Bobby Witt .05 .15
369 Karl Rhodes .05 .15
370 Eddie Williams .05 .15
371 John Jaha .05 .15
372 Steve Howe .05 .15
373 Leo Gomez .05 .15
374 Hector Fajardo .05 .15
375 Jeff Bagwell .20 .50
376 Mark Acre .05 .15
377 Wayne Kirby .05 .15
378 Mark Portugal .05 .15
379 Jesus Tavarez .05 .15
380 Jim Lindeman .05 .15
381 Don Mattingly .75 2.00
382 Trevor Hoffman .10 .30
383 Chris Gomez .05 .15
384 Garret Anderson .10 .30
385 Bobby Munoz .05 .15
386 Jon Lieber .05 .15
387 Rick Helling .05 .15
388 Marvin Freeman .05 .15
389 Juan Castillo .05 .15
390 Jeff Cirillo .05 .15
391 Sean Berry .05 .15
392 Hector Carrasco .05 .15
393 Mark Grace .20 .50
394 Pat Kelly .05 .15
395 Tim Naehring .05 .15
396 Greg Pirkl .05 .15
397 John Smoltz .20 .50
398 Robby Thompson .05 .15
399 Rick White .05 .15
400 Frank Thomas .30 .75
401 Jeff Conine CS .05 .15
402 Jose Valentin CS .05 .15
403 Carlos Baerga CS .05 .15
404 Rick Aguilera CS .05 .15
405 Wilson Alvarez CS .05 .15
406 Juan Gonzalez CS .05 .15
407 Barry Larkin CS .10 .30
408 Ken Hill CS .05 .15
409 Chuck Carr CS .05 .15
410 Tim Raines CS .05 .15
411 Bryan Eversgerd .05 .15
412 Phil Plantier .05 .15
413 Josias Manzanillo .05 .15
414 Roberto Kelly .05 .15
415 Rickey Henderson .30 .75
416 John Smiley .05 .15
417 Kevin Brown .10 .30
418 Jimmy Key .10 .30
419 Wally Joyner .10 .30
420 Roberto Hernandez .05 .15
421 Felix Fermin .05 .15
422 Checklist .05 .15
423 Greg Vaughn .05 .15
424 Ray Lankford .10 .30
425 Greg Maddux .50 1.25
426 Mike Mussina .20 .50
427 Geronimo Pena .05 .15
428 David Nied .05 .15
429 Scott Erickson .05 .15
430 Kevin Mitchell .05 .15
431 Mike Lansing .05 .15
432 Brian Anderson .05 .15
433 Jeff King .05 .15
434 Ramon Martinez .05 .15
435 Kevin Seitzer .05 .15
436 Salomon Torres .05 .15
437 Brian L.Hunter .05 .15
438 Melvin Nieves .05 .15
439 Mike Kelly .05 .15
440 Marquis Grissom .10 .30
441 Chuck Finley .10 .30
442 Len Dykstra .10 .30
443 Ellis Burks .10 .30
444 Harold Baines .10 .30
445 Kevin Appier .10 .30
446 David Justice .10 .30
447 Darryl Kile .10 .30
448 John Olerud .10 .30
449 Greg McMichael .05 .15
450 Kirby Puckett .30 .75
451 Jose Valentin .05 .15
452 Rick Wilkins .05 .15
453 Arthur Rhodes .05 .15
454 Pat Hentgen .05 .15
455 Tom Gordon .05 .15
456 Tom Candiotti .05 .15
457 Jason Bere .05 .15
458 Wes Chamberlain .05 .15
459 Greg Colbrunn .05 .15
460 John Doherty .05 .15
461 Kevin Foster .05 .15
462 Mark Whiten .05 .15
463 Terry Steinbach .05 .15
464 Aaron Sele .05 .15
465 Kirt Manwaring .05 .15
466 Darren Hall .05 .15
467 Delino DeShields .05 .15
468 Andujar Cedeno .05 .15
469 Billy Ashley .05 .15
470 Kenny Lofton .10 .30
471 Pedro Munoz .05 .15
472 John Wetteland .10 .30
473 Tim Salmon .20 .50
474 Denny Neagle .10 .30
475 Tony Gwynn .40 1.00
476 Vinny Castilla .10 .30
477 Steve Dreyer .05 .15
478 Jeff Shaw .05 .15
479 Chad Ogea .05 .15
480 Scott Ruffcorn .05 .15
481 Lou Whitaker .10 .30
482 J.T. Snow .10 .30
483 Rich Rowland .05 .15
484 Denny Martinez .10 .30
485 Pedro Martinez .20 .50
486 Rusty Greer .10 .30
487 Dave Fleming .05 .15
488 John Dettmer .05 .15
489 Albert Belle .10 .30
490 Ravelo Manzanillo .05 .15
491 Henry Rodriguez .05 .15
492 Andrew Lorraine .05 .15
493 Dwayne Hosey .05 .15
494 Mike Blowers .05 .15
495 Turner Ward .05 .15
496 Fred McGriff EC .10 .30
497 Sammy Sosa EC .20 .50
498 Barry Larkin EC .10 .30
499 Andres Galarraga EC .05 .15
500 Gary Sheffield EC .05 .15
501 Jeff Bagwell EC .10 .30
502 Mike Piazza EC .30 .75
503 Moises Alou EC .05 .15
504 Bobby Bonilla EC .05 .15
505 Darren Daulton EC .05 .15
506 Jeff King EC .05 .15
507 Ray Lankford EC .05 .15
508 Tony Gwynn EC .20 .50
509 Barry Bonds EC .40 1.00
510 Cal Ripken EC .50 1.25
511 Mo Vaughn EC .05 .15
512 Tim Salmon EC .10 .30
513 Frank Thomas EC .20 .50
514 Albert Belle EC .05 .15
515 Cecil Fielder EC .05 .15
516 Kevin Appier EC .05 .15
517 Greg Vaughn EC .05 .15
518 Kirby Puckett EC .20 .50
519 Paul O'Neill EC .10 .30
520 Ruben Sierra EC .05 .15
521 Ken Griffey Jr. EC .30 .75
522 Will Clark EC .10 .30
523 Joe Carter EC .05 .15
524 Antonio Osuna .05 .15
525 Glenallen Hill .05 .15
526 Alex Gonzalez .05 .15
527 Dave Stewart .10 .30
528 Ron Gant .10 .30
529 Jason Bates .05 .15
530 Mike Macfarlane .05 .15
531 Esteban Loaiza .05 .15
532 Joe Randa .10 .30
533 Dave Winfield .10 .30
534 Danny Darwin .05 .15
535 Pete Harnisch .05 .15
536 Joey Cora .05 .15
537 Jaime Navarro .05 .15
538 Marty Cordova .05 .15
539 Andujar Cedeno .05 .15
540 Mickey Tettleton .05 .15
541 Andy Van Slyke .20 .50
542 Carlos Perez RC .15 .40
543 Chipper Jones .30 .75
544 Tony Fernandez .05 .15
545 Tom Henke .05 .15
546 Pat Borders .05 .15
547 Chad Curtis .05 .15
548 Ray Durham .10 .30
549 Joe Oliver .05 .15
550 Jose Mesa .05 .15
551 Steve Finley .10 .30
552 Otis Nixon .05 .15
553 Jacob Brumfield .05 .15
554 Bill Swift .05 .15
555 Quilvio Veras .05 .15
556 Hideo Nomo RC UER 1.00 2.50
Wins and IP totals reversed
557 Joe Vitiello .05 .15
558 Mike Perez .05 .15
559 Charlie Hayes .05 .15
560 Brad Radke RC .30 .75
561 Darren Bragg .05 .15
562 Orel Hershiser .10 .30
563 Edgardo Alfonzo .05 .15
564 Doug Jones .05 .15
565 Andy Pettitte .20 .50
566 Benito Santiago .10 .30
567 John Burkett .05 .15
568 Brad Clontz .05 .15
569 Jim Abbott .20 .50
570 Joe Rosselli .05 .15
571 Mark Grudzielanek RC .30 .75
572 Dustin Hermanson .05 .15
573 Benji Gil .05 .15
574 Mark Whiten .05 .15
575 Mike Ignasiak .05 .15
576 Kevin Ritz .05 .15
577 Paul Quantrill .05 .15
578 Andre Dawson .10 .30
579 Jerald Clark .05 .15
580 Frank Rodriguez .05 .15
581 Mark Kiefer .05 .15
582 Trevor Wilson .05 .15
583 Gary Wilson RC .05 .15
584 Andy Stankiewicz .05 .15
585 Felipe Lira .05 .15
586 Mike Mimbs RC .05 .15
587 Jon Nunnally .05 .15
588 Tomas Perez RC .05 .15
589 Chad Fonville .05 .15
590 Todd Hollandsworth .05 .15
591 Roberto Petagine .05 .15
592 Mariano Rivera .75 2.00
593 Mark McLemore .05 .15
594 Bobby Witt .05 .15
595 Jose Offerman .05 .15
596 J.Christiansen RC .05 .15
597 Jeff Manto .05 .15
598 Jim Dougherty RC .05 .15
599 Juan Acevedo RC .05 .15
600 Troy O'Leary .05 .15
601 Ron Villone .05 .15
602 Tripp Cromer .05 .15
603 Steve Scarsone .05 .15
604 Lance Parrish .10 .30
605 Ozzie Timmons .05 .15
606 Ray Holbert .05 .15
607 Tony Phillips .05 .15
608 Phil Plantier .05 .15
609 Shane Andrews .05 .15
610 Heathcliff Slocumb .05 .15
611 Bobby Higginson RC .30 .75
612 Bob Tewksbury .05 .15
613 Terry Pendleton .10 .30
614 Scott Cooper TA .05 .15
615 John Wetteland TA .05 .15
616 Ken Hill TA .05 .15
617 Marquis Grissom TA .05 .15
618 Larry Walker TA .05 .15
619 Derek Bell TA .05 .15
620 David Cone TA .05 .15
621 Ken Caminiti TA .05 .15
622 Jack McDowell TA .05 .15
623 Vaughn Eshelman TA .05 .15
624 Brian McRae TA .05 .15
625 Gregg Jefferies TA .05 .15
626 Kevin Brown TA .05 .15
627 Lee Smith TA .05 .15
628 Tony Tarasco TA .05 .15
629 Brett Butler TA .05 .15
630 Jose Canseco TA .10 .30

1995 Stadium Club First Day Issue

Parallel to the basic first series Stadium Club issue, these cards, were primarily inserted in second series Topps packs. They were also inserted at a rate of ten per Topps factory set. Nine double printed cards were issued in both first and second series Topps packs. Those cards are as follows: 29, 39, 79, 96, 131, 149, 153, 168 and 197. Limited instances of duplicitous parties transferring the FDI foil logos from "common" players to the fronts of "star" players were chronicled shortly after release - thus it's recommended for collectors to take a close look at the logo on front before purchasing these cards.

COMPLETE SET (270) 125.00 250.00
COMMON CARD (1-270) .75 2.00
*STARS: 5X TO 12X BASIC CARDS
*ROOKIES: 3X TO 8X BASIC CARDS
*DP STARS: 1.25X TO 3X BASIC CARDS
TEN PER TOPPS FACTORY SET
DPs INSERTED IN TOPPS SER.1 & 2 PACKS

1995 Stadium Club Members Only Parallel

This set is a parallel to the regular 1995 Stadium Club set.These cards are identical to their regular issue counterparts except for the distinctive "Members Only" logo. According to Topps, only 4,000 factory sets were issued through the Topps Stadium Club at a price of $200 each. A certificate of authenicity carrying the serial number accompanied each set. In addition to the 630 regular cards, the factory set includes Members Only versions of the following inserts: Crystal Ball, Clear Cut, Power Zone, Ring Leaders, Super Skills, Virtual Extremists and Virtual Reality (listed separately). Only the insert cards are listed below. Please use the multipliers for values on the basic cards.

COMP.SET w/o VR (755) 27.50 250.00
*MEM.ONLY 1-630: 1.5X TO 4X BASIC CARDS
CB1 Chipper Jones 3.00 8.00
CB2 Dustin Hermanson .30 .75
CB3 Ray Durham .60 1.50
CB4 Phil Nevin .30 .75
CB5 Billy Ashley .08 .25
CB6 Shawn Green .75 2.00
CB7 Jason Bates .08 .25
CB8 Benji Gil .08 .25
CB9 Marty Cordova .08 .25
CB10 Quilvio Veras .30 .75
CB11 Mark Grudzielanek .30 .75
CB12 Ruben Rivera .08 .25
CB13 Bill Pulsipher .08 .25
CB14 Derek Jeter 6.00 15.00
CB15 LaTroy Hawkins .08 .25
CC1 Mike Piazza 3.00 8.00
CC2 Ruben Sierra .08 .25
CC3 Tony Gwynn 3.00 8.00
CC4 Frank Thomas 2.50 6.00
CC5 Fred McGriff .60 1.50
CC6 Rafael Palmeiro .75 2.00
CC7 Bobby Bonilla .08 .25
CC8 Chili Davis .30 .75
CC9 Hal Morris .08 .25
CC10 Jose Canseco 1.25 3.00
CC11 Jay Bell .30 .75
CC12 Kirby Puckett 2.50 6.00
CC13 Gary Sheffield .75 2.00
CC14 Bob Hamelin .08 .25
CC15 Jeff Bagwell 1.25 3.00
CC16 Albert Belle .30 .75
CC17 Sammy Sosa 3.00 8.00
CC18 Ken Griffey Jr. 5.00 12.00
CC19 Todd Zeile .30 .75
CC20 Mo Vaughn .30 .75
CC21 Moises Alou .30 .75
CC22 Paul O'Neill .30 .75
CC23 Andres Galarraga .75 2.00
CC24 Greg Vaughn .30 .75
CC25 Len Dykstra .30 .75
CC26 Joe Carter .30 .75
CC27 Barry Bonds 3.00 8.00
CC28 Cecil Fielder .30 .75
PZ1 Jeff Bagwell 1.25 3.00
PZ2 Albert Belle .30 .75
PZ3 Barry Bonds 3.00 8.00
PZ4 Joe Carter .30 .75
PZ5 Cecil Fielder .30 .75
PZ6 Andres Galarraga .75 2.00
PZ7 Ken Griffey Jr. 5.00 12.00
PZ8 Paul Molitor .75 2.00
PZ9 Fred McGriff .60 1.50
PZ10 Rafael Palmeiro .75 2.00
PZ11 Frank Thomas 2.50 6.00
PZ12 Matt Williams .60 1.50
RL1 Jeff Bagwell 1.25 3.00
RL2 Mark McGwire 5.00 12.00
RL3 Ozzie Smith 2.50 6.00
RL4 Paul Molitor .75 2.00
RL5 Darryl Strawberry .08 .25
RL6 Eddie Murray .75 2.00
RL7 Tony Gwynn 3.00 8.00
RL8 Jose Canseco 1.25 3.00
RL9 Howard Johnson .08 .25
RL10 Andre Dawson .60 1.50
RL11 Matt Williams .60 1.50
RL12 Tim Raines .30 .75
RL13 Fred McGriff .60 1.50
RL14 Ken Griffey Jr. 5.00 12.00
RL15 Gary Sheffield .75 2.00
RL16 Dennis Eckersley .30 .75
RL17 Kevin Mitchell .08 .25
RL18 Will Clark .75 2.00
RL19 Darren Daulton .30 .75
RL20 Paul O'Neill .75 2.00
RL21 Julio Franco .08 .25
RL22 Albert Belle .30 .75
RL23 Juan Gonzalez 1.25 3.00
RL24 Kirby Puckett 2.50 6.00
RL25 Joe Carter .30 .75
RL26 Frank Thomas 2.50 6.00
RL27 Cal Ripken 6.00 15.00
RL28 John Olerud .30 .75
RL29 Ruben Sierra .30 .75
RL30 Barry Bonds 3.00 8.00
RL31 Cecil Fielder .30 .75
RL32 Roger Clemens 3.00 8.00
RL33 Don Mattingly 3.00 8.00
RL34 Terry Pendleton .08 .25
RL35 Rickey Henderson 1.25 3.00
RL36 Dave Winfield 1.25 3.00
RL37 Edgar Martinez .60 1.50
RL38 Wade Boggs 1.25 3.00
RL39 Willie McGee .30 .75
RL40 Andres Galarraga .75 2.00
SS1 Roberto Alomar .75 2.00
SS2 Barry Bonds 3.00 8.00
SS3 Jay Buhner .30 .75
SS4 Chuck Carr .08 .25
SS5 Don Mattingly 3.00 8.00
SS6 Raul Mondesi .60 1.50
SS7 Tim Salmon .75 2.00
SS8 Deion Sanders .30 .75
SS9 Devon White .08 .25
SS10 Mark Whiten .08 .25
SS11 Ken Griffey Jr. 5.00 12.00
SS12 Marquis Grissom .08 .25
SS13 Paul O'Neill .30 .75
SS14 Kenny Lofton .08 .25
SS15 Larry Walker .75 2.00
SS16 Scott Cooper .08 .25
SS17 Barry Larkin .75 2.00
SS18 Matt Williams .60 1.50
SS19 John Wetteland .30 .75
SS20 Randy Johnson 1.25 3.00
VRE1 Barry Bonds 3.00 8.00
VRE2 Ken Griffey Jr. 5.00 12.00
VRE3 Jeff Bagwell 1.25 3.00
VRE4 Albert Belle .30 .75
VRE5 Frank Thomas 2.50 6.00
VRE6 Tony Gwynn 3.00 8.00
VRE7 Kenny Lofton .30 .75
VRE8 Deion Sanders .75 2.00
VRE9 Ken Hill .08 .25
VRE10 Jimmy Key .30 .75

1995 Stadium Club Super Team Division Winners

Each of these six team sets was available exclusively by mailing in the corresponding winning 1994 Super Team card. Each team set was distributed in a clear plastic sealed wrapper and included ten player cards and a Super Team card (of which was stamped "REDEEMED" on back). The card design and numbering for the player cards parallels regular issue 1995 Stadium Club cards. In fact, the only way to tell these cards apart is by the gold foil "Division Winner" logo on each card front. The cards are listed below alphabetically by team; the prefixes B, D, I, M, R and RS have been added to denote Braves, Dodgers,

Indians, Mariners, Reds and Red Sox.

COMP.BRAVES SET (11) 3.00 8.00
COMP.DODGERS (11) 3.00 8.00
COMP.INDIANS SET (11) 2.50 6.00
COMP.MARINERS (11) 3.00 8.00
COMP.REDS SET (11) 1.25 3.00
COMP.RED SOX SET (11) 2.50 6.00
COMMON SUPER TEAM .40 1.00
B1T Braves DW .40 1.00
Super Team
Jeff Blauser
Terry Pendleton
B19 Ryan Klesko .25 .60
B126 Mark Wohlers .10 .30
B151 Steve Avery .10 .30
B183 Tom Glavine .40 1.00
B200 Javy Lopez .25 .60
B393 Fred McGriff .40 1.00
B397 John Smoltz .40 1.00
B425 Greg Maddux 1.00 2.50
B446 Dave Justice .25 .60
B543 Chipper Jones .60 1.50
D7T Dodgers DW .40 1.00
Super Team
Mike Piazza
D57 Raul Mondesi .25 .60
D149 Mike Piazza 1.00 2.50
D161 Ismael Valdes .10 .30
D242 Brett Butler .25 .60
D259 Tim Wallach .10 .30
D278 Eric Karros .25 .60
D434 Ramon Martinez .10 .30
D456 Tom Candiotti .10 .30
D467 Delino Deshields .10 .30
D556 Hideo Nomo 2.00 5.00
I19T Indians DW .40 1.00
Super Team
Carlos Baerga
Albert Belle
Kenny Lofton
I36 Carlos Baerga .10 .30
I147 Jim Thome .40 1.00
I186 Eddie Murray .60 1.50
I264 Manny Ramirez .40 1.00
I334 Omar Vizquel .40 1.00
I470 Kenny Lofton .25 .60
I484 Dennis Martinez .25 .60
I489 Albert Belle .25 .60
I550 Jose Mesa .10 .30
I562 Orel Hershiser .25 .60
M26T Mariners DW .40 1.00
Super Team
Mike Blowers
Jay Buhner
M73 Jay Buhner .25 .60
M92 Chris Bosio .10 .30
M152 Dan Wilson .10 .30
M227 Tino Martinez .40 1.00
M241 Ken Griffey Jr. 1.00 2.50
M340 Randy Johnson .60 1.50
M354 Edgar Martinez .40 1.00
M421 Felix Fermin .10 .30
M494 Mike Blowers .10 .30
M536 Joey Cora .10 .30
RE3T Reds DW
Super Team
Barry Larkin
Reggie Sanders
RE35 Barry Larkin .40 1.00
RE231 Hal Morris .10 .30
RE252 Bret Boone .25 .60
RE280 Thomas Howard .10 .30
RE300 Jose Rijo .10 .30
RE333 Reggie Sanders .25 .60
RE392 Hector Carrasco .10 .30
RE416 John Smiley .10 .30
RE528 Ron Gant .25 .60
RE566 Benito Santiago .25 .60
RS1T Red Sox DW .40 1.00
Super Team
Luis Rivera
John Valentin
RS10 Roger Clemens 1.25 3.00
RS62 John Valentin .10 .30
RS121 Mike Greenwell .10 .30
RS160 Lee Tinsley .10 .30
RS347 Jose Canseco .40 1.00
RS350 Mo Vaughn .25 .60
RS395 Tim Naehring .10 .30
RS464 Aaron Sele .10 .30
RS530 Mike Macfarlane .10 .30
RS600 Troy O'Leary .10 .30

1995 Stadium Club Super Team Master Photos

This 20-card set was distributed in two separate 10-card sealed team bags. The cards were available exclusively by mailing in a Braves or Indians 1994 Super Team card. These oversized cards (5" by 7") feature a reproduction of the player's standard 1995 Stadium Club card enframed around a shining blue background. Unlike the standard issue cards they parallel, these are numbered X of 20.

COMP.BRAVES SET (10) 4.00 10.00
COMP.INDIANS SET (10) 3.00 8.00
1 Steve Avery .15 .40
2 Tom Glavine .50 1.25
3 Chipper Jones .75 2.00
4 Dave Justice .30 .75
5 Ryan Klesko .30 .75
6 Javy Lopez .30 .75
7 Greg Maddux 1.25 3.00
8 Fred McGriff .50 1.25
9 John Smoltz .50 1.25
10 Mark Wohlers .15 .40
11 Carlos Baerga .15 .40
12 Albert Belle .30 .75
13 Orel Hershiser .30 .75
14 Kenny Lofton .30 .75
15 Dennis Martinez .30 .75
16 Jose Mesa .15 .40
17 Eddie Murray .75 2.00
18 Manny Ramirez .50 1.25
19 Jim Thome .50 1.25
20 Omar Vizquel .50 1.25

1995 Stadium Club Super Team World Series

Because of the strike-interrupted season, the 1994 Stadium Club Super Team insert program had to be finished up with the 1995 product. Collectors who

redeemed the 1994 Atlanta Braves Super Team card received: 1) a complete 630-card 1995 Stadium Club parallel set stamped with a special gold foil World Series logo (of which was mailed in two separate series of 585 and 45 cards) 2) a Division Winner parallel Braves team set along with the winner card stamped "redeemed" on its back 3) a jumbo-sized (3" by 5") parallel Master Photo Braves team set. Collectors who redeemed the 1994 Cleveland Indians Super Team card got parallel Indians Division Winner and Master Photo team sets. Collectors who redeemed the 1994 Super Team card of a division winner (Dodgers, Mariners, Red Sox and Reds) received a Division Winner parallel team set of the respective team that they sent in. All of these winner cards parallel the 1995 Stadium Club regular series cards.

COMP.WS SET (585) 50.00 120.00
COMP.EC/TA SET (45) 6.00 15.00
*STARS: .6X TO 1.5X BASIC CARDS
*ROOKIES: .6X TO 1.5X BASIC CARDS

1995 Stadium Club Virtual Reality

This 270-card standard-size set parallels a selection of cards from the regular 1995 Stadium Club set. Differences include the words "Virtual Reality" printed above the player's name and the numbering on the back. These cards were inserted in the first two Stadium Club series on a one per pack, two per rack pack basis.

COMPLETE SET (270) 40.00 100.00
COMP.SERIES 1 (135) 20.00 50.00
COMP.SERIES 2 (135) 20.00 50.00
*STARS: .75X TO 2X BASIC CARDS

1995 Stadium Club Virtual Reality Members Only

These cards parallel the regular 1995 Stadium Club Stadium Club Virtual Reality cards. The only difference is that they all have a Stadium Club Members Only logo imprinted on the front. These cards were distributed as part of the package of material that members of the "Stadium Club Members Only" club received when they ordered the 1995 parallel master set.

COMP.FACT.SET (270) 40.00 100.00
*MEMBERS ONLY: 2X BASIC VIRTUAL REALITY

1995 Stadium Club Clear Cut

Randomly inserted at a rate of one in 24 hobby and retail packs, this 28-card set features a full color action photo of the player against a clear acetate background with the player's name printed vertically.

COMPLETE SET (28) 30.00 80.00
COMPLETE SERIES 1 (14) 15.00 40.00
COMP.SERIES 2 (14) 15.00 40.00
STATED ODDS 1:24 HOB/RET,1:10 RACK
CC1 Mike Piazza 4.00 10.00
CC2 Ruben Sierra 1.00 2.50
CC3 Tony Gwynn 3.00 8.00
CC4 Frank Thomas 2.50 6.00
CC5 Fred McGriff 1.50 4.00
CC6 Rafael Palmeiro 1.50 4.00
CC7 Bobby Bonilla 1.00 2.50
CC8 Chili Davis 1.00 2.50
CC9 Hal Morris .50 1.25
CC10 Jose Canseco 1.50 4.00
CC11 Jay Bell 1.00 2.50
CC12 Kirby Puckett 2.50 6.00
CC13 Gary Sheffield 1.00 2.50
CC14 Bob Hamelin .50 1.25
CC15 Jeff Bagwell 1.50 4.00
CC16 Albert Belle 1.00 2.50
CC17 Sammy Sosa 2.50 6.00
CC18 Ken Griffey Jr. 4.00 10.00
CC19 Todd Zeile .50 1.25
CC20 Mo Vaughn 1.00 2.50
CC21 Moises Alou 1.00 2.50
CC22 Paul O'Neill 1.50 4.00
CC23 Andres Galarraga 1.00 2.50
CC24 Greg Vaughn .50 1.25
CC25 Len Dykstra 1.00 2.50
CC26 Joe Carter 1.00 2.50
CC27 Barry Bonds 6.00 15.00
CC28 Cecil Fielder 1.00 2.50

1995 Stadium Club Crunch Time

This 20-card standard-size set features home run hitters and was randomly inserted in first series rack packs. The cards are numbered as "X" of 20 in the upper right corner.

COMPLETE SET (20) 20.00 50.00
1 Jeff Bagwell .75 2.00
2 Kirby Puckett 1.25 3.00
3 Frank Thomas 1.25 3.00
4 Albert Belle .50 1.25
5 Julio Franco .50 1.25
6 Jose Canseco .75 2.00
7 Paul Molitor .50 1.25
8 Joe Carter .50 1.25
9 Ken Griffey Jr. 2.00 5.00
10 Larry Walker .50 1.25
11 Dante Bichette .50 1.25
12 Carlos Baerga .25 .60
13 Fred McGriff .75 2.00
14 Ruben Sierra .50 1.25
15 Will Clark .75 2.00
16 Moises Alou .50 1.25
17 Rafael Palmeiro .75 2.00
18 Travis Fryman .50 1.25
19 Barry Bonds 3.00 8.00
20 Cal Ripken 4.00 10.00

1995 Stadium Club Crystal Ball

This 15-card standard-size set was inserted into series three packs at a rate of one in 24. Fifteen leading 1995 rookies and prospects were featured in this set. The player is identified on the top and the cards are numbered with a "CB" prefix in the upper left corner.

COMPLETE SET (15) 50.00 80.00
SER.3 STATED ODDS 1:24
CB1 Chipper Jones 4.00 10.00
CB2 Dustin Hermanson .75 2.00
CB3 Ray Durham 1.50 4.00
CB4 Phil Nevin 1.50 4.00
CB5 Billy Ashley .75 2.00
CB6 Shawn Green 1.50 4.00
CB7 Jason Bates .75 2.00
CB8 Benji Gil .75 2.00
CB9 Marty Cordova .75 2.00
CB10 Quilvio Veras .75 2.00
CB11 Mark Grudzielanek 2.50 6.00
CB12 Ruben Rivera .75 2.00
CB13 Bill Pulsipher .75 2.00
CB14 Derek Jeter 8.00 20.00
CB15 LaTroy Hawkins .75 2.00

1995 Stadium Club Phone Cards

These phone cards were randomly inserted into packs. The prizes for these cards were as follows. The Gold Winner card was redeemable for the ring depicted on the front of the card. The silver winner card was redeemable for a set of all 39 phone cards. The regular winner card was redeemable for a Ring Leaders set. The fronts feature a photo of a specific ring while the backs have game information. If the card was not a winner for any of the prizes, it was still good for three minutes of time. The phone cards expired on January 1, 1996. If the PIN number is revealed the value is a percentage of an untouched card.

COMP.REGULAR (13) 10.00 20.00
COMMON REGULAR 1.00 2.00
COMP.SILVER SET (13) 15.00 30.00
COMMON SILVER CARD 2.00 4.00
COMP.GOLD SET (13) 30.00 75.00
COMMON GOLD CARD 4.00 8.00
*PIN NUMBER REVEALED: .25X to .50X BASIC CARDS

1995 Stadium Club Power Zone

This 12-card standard-size set was inserted into series three packs at a rate of one in 24. The cards are numbered in the upper right corner with a "PZ" prefix.

COMPLETE SET (12) 20.00 50.00
SER.3 STATED ODDS 1:24
PZ1 Jeff Bagwell 1.50 4.00
PZ2 Albert Belle 1.00 2.50
PZ3 Barry Bonds 6.00 15.00
PZ4 Joe Carter 1.00 2.50
PZ5 Cecil Fielder 1.00 2.50
PZ6 Andres Galarraga 1.00 2.50
PZ7 Ken Griffey Jr. 4.00 10.00
PZ8 Paul Molitor 1.00 2.50
PZ9 Fred McGriff 1.50 4.00
PZ10 Rafael Palmeiro 1.50 4.00
PZ11 Frank Thomas 2.50 6.00
PZ12 Matt Williams 1.00 2.50

1995 Stadium Club Ring Leaders

Randomly inserted in packs, this set features players who have won various awards or titles. This set was also redeemable as a prize with winning regular phone cards. This set features Stadium Club's "Power Matrix Technology," which makes the cards shine and glow. The horizontal fronts feature a player photo, rings in both upper corners as well as other designs that make for a very busy front. The backs have information on how the player earned his rings, along with a player photo and some other pertinent information.

COMPLETE SET (40) 40.00 100.00
COMPLETE SERIES 1 (20) 20.00 50.00
COMP.SERIES 2 (20) 20.00 50.00
STATED ODDS 1:24 HOB/RET,1:10 RACK
ONE SET VIA MAIL PER PHONE WINNER
RL1 Jeff Bagwell 2.00 5.00
RL2 Mark McGwire 8.00 20.00
RL3 Ozzie Smith 5.00 12.00
RL4 Paul Molitor 1.25 3.00
RL5 Darryl Strawberry .60 1.50
RL6 Eddie Murray 3.00 8.00
RL7 Tony Gwynn 4.00 10.00
RL8 Jose Canseco 2.00 5.00
RL9 Howard Johnson .60 1.50
RL10 Andre Dawson 1.25 3.00
RL11 Matt Williams 1.25 3.00
RL12 Tim Raines 1.25 3.00
RL13 Fred McGriff 2.00 5.00
RL14 Ken Griffey Jr. 5.00 12.00
RL15 Gary Sheffield 1.25 3.00
RL16 Dennis Eckersley 1.25 3.00
RL17 Kevin Mitchell .60 1.50
RL18 Will Clark 2.00 5.00
RL19 Darren Daulton 1.25 3.00
RL20 Paul O'Neill 2.00 5.00
RL21 Julio Franco 1.25 3.00
RL22 Albert Belle 1.25 3.00
RL23 Juan Gonzalez 1.25 3.00
RL24 Kirby Puckett 3.00 8.00
RL25 Joe Carter 1.25 3.00
RL26 Frank Thomas 3.00 8.00
RL27 Cal Ripken 10.00 25.00
RL28 John Olerud 1.25 3.00
RL29 Ruben Sierra 1.25 3.00
RL30 Barry Bonds 8.00 20.00
RL31 Cecil Fielder 1.25 3.00
RL32 Roger Clemens 6.00 15.00
RL33 Don Mattingly 8.00 20.00
RL34 Terry Pendleton 1.25 3.00
RL35 Rickey Henderson 3.00 8.00
RL36 Dave Winfield 1.25 3.00
RL37 Edgar Martinez 2.00 5.00
RL38 Wade Boggs 2.00 5.00
RL39 Willie McGee 1.25 3.00
RL40 Andres Galarraga 1.25 3.00

1995 Stadium Club Super Skills

This 20-card set was randomly inserted into hobby packs. The cards are numbered in the upper left as "X" of 9.

COMPLETE SET (20) 30.00 70.00
COMPLETE SERIES 1 (9) 12.50 30.00
COMP.SERIES 2 (11) 15.00 40.00
STATED ODDS 1:24 HOBBY
SS1 Roberto Alomar 1.50 4.00
SS2 Barry Bonds 6.00 15.00
SS3 Jay Buhner 1.00 2.50
SS4 Chuck Carr .50 1.25
SS5 Don Mattingly 6.00 15.00
SS6 Raul Mondesi 1.00 2.50
SS7 Tim Salmon 1.50 4.00
SS8 Deion Sanders 1.50 4.00
SS9 Devon White 1.00 2.50
SS10 Mark Whiten .50 1.25
SS11 Ken Griffey Jr. 4.00 10.00
SS12 Marquis Grissom 1.00 2.50
SS13 Paul O'Neill 1.50 4.00
SS14 Kenny Lofton 1.00 2.50
SS15 Larry Walker 1.00 2.50
SS16 Scott Cooper .50 1.25
SS17 Barry Larkin 1.50 4.00
SS18 Matt Williams 1.00 2.50
SS19 John Wetteland 1.00 2.50
SS20 Randy Johnson 2.50 6.00

1995 Stadium Club Virtual Extremists

This 10-card set was inserted randomly into second series rack packs. The fronts feature a player photo against a baseball backdrop. The words "VR Extremist" are spelled vertically down the right side while the player name is in silver foil on the bottom. All of this is surrounded by blue and purple borders. The horizontal backs feature projected full-season 1994 stats. The cards are numbered with a "VRE" prefix in the upper right corner.

COMPLETE SET (10) 30.00 80.00
SER.2 STATED ODDS 1:10 RACK
VRE1 Barry Bonds 10.00 25.00
VRE2 Ken Griffey Jr. 6.00 15.00
VRE3 Jeff Bagwell 2.50 6.00
VRE4 Albert Belle 1.50 4.00
VRE5 Frank Thomas 4.00 10.00
VRE6 Tony Gwynn 5.00 12.00
VRE7 Kenny Lofton 1.50 4.00
VRE8 Deion Sanders 2.50 6.00
VRE9 Ken Hill .75 2.00
VRE10 Jimmy Key 1.50 4.00

1995 Stadium Club Members Only 50

Topps produced a 50-card boxed set for each of the four major sports. With their club membership, members received one set of their choice and had the option of purchasing additional sets for $10.00 each. Player section was based on 1994 leaders from both leagues in various statistical categories. The five Finest cards (46-50) represent Topps' selection of the top rookies of 1994. The color action photos on the fronts have brightly-colored backgrounds and carry the distinctive Topps Stadium Club Members Only gold foil seal. The backs present a second color photo and player profile.

COMP. FACT SET (50) 8.00 20.00
1 Moises Alou .08 .25
2 Jeff Bagwell .40 1.00
3 Albert Belle .08 .25
4 Andy Benes .02 .10
5 Dante Bichette .08 .25
6 Craig Biggio .20 .50
7 Wade Boggs .40 1.00
8 Barry Bonds .60 1.50
9 Brett Butler .08 .25
10 Jose Canseco .40 1.00
11 Joe Carter .08 .25
12 Vince Coleman .02 .10
13 Jeff Conine .02 .10
14 Cecil Fielder .08 .25
15 John Franco .08 .25
16 Julio Franco .08 .25
17 Travis Fryman .08 .25
18 Andres Galarraga .30 .75
19 Ken Griffey Jr. 1.00 2.50
20 Marquis Grissom .02 .10
21 Tony Gwynn .75 2.00
22 Ken Hill .02 .10
23 Randy Johnson .50 1.25
24 Lance Johnson .02 .10
25 Jimmy Key .08 .25
26 Chuck Knoblauch .20 .50
27 Ray Lankford .08 .25
28 Darren Lewis .02 .10
29 Kenny Lofton .20 .50
30 Greg Maddux 1.00 2.50
31 Fred McGriff .20 .50
32 Kevin Mitchell .02 .10
33 Paul Molitor .40 1.00
34 Hal Morris .02 .10
35 Paul O'Neill .08 .25
36 Rafael Palmeiro .30 .75
37 Tony Phillips .02 .10
38 Mike Piazza 1.00 2.50
39 Kirby Puckett .50 1.25
40 Cal Ripken 1.50 4.00
41 Deion Sanders .30 .75
42 Lee Smith .08 .25
43 Frank Thomas .50 1.25
44 Larry Walker .30 .75
45 Matt Williams .20 .50
46 Manny Ramirez .40 1.00
47 Joey Hamilton .02 .10
48 Raul Mondesi .20 .50
49 Bob Hamelin .02 .10
50 Ryan Klesko .20 .50

1995 Stadium Club Members Only Finest Bronze

As a special bonus along with the complete 1995 Stadium Club Members Only factory set, members received these four cards featuring the 1994 Rookie of the Year and Cy Young Award Winners. The first shipment included series 1 and 2 cards as well as two of the Finest Bronze cards. The second shipment included series 3 cards and the remaining two Finest Bronze cards. The cards feature chromium metallized graphics, mounted on bronze and factory sealed in clear resin. Also, collectors got one of thsese cards if they only ordered one series. Bob Hamelin (series 1), Greg Maddux (Series 2) and David Cone (series 3). Mondesi was only available if one bought a complete set.

COMPLETE SET (4) 20.00 50.00
1 Bob Hamelin 1.25 3.00
2 Greg Maddux 15.00 40.00
3 David Cone 2.00 5.00
4 Raul Mondesi 2.00 5.00

1996 Stadium Club

The 1996 Stadium Club set consists of 450 cards with cards 1-225 in first series packs and 226-450 in second series packs. The product was primarily distributed in first and second series foil-wrapped packs.There was also a factory set, which included the Mantle insert cards, packaged in mini-cereal box type cartons and made available through retail outlets. The set includes a Team TSC subset (181-270). These subset cards were slightly shortprinted in comparison to the other cards in the set. Though not confirmed by the manufacturer, it is believed that card number 22 (Roberto Hernandez) is a short-print.

COMPLETE SET (450) 40.00 80.00
COMP.CEREAL SET (454) 40.00 80.00
COMP.SERIES 1 (225) 20.00 40.00
COMP.SERIES 2 (225) 20.00 40.00
COMMON (1-180/271-450) .10 .30
COMMON SP (181-270) .20 .50
1 Hideo Nomo .30 .75
2 Paul Molitor .10 .30
3 Garret Anderson .10 .30
4 Jose Mesa .10 .30
5 Vinny Castilla .10 .30
6 Mike Mussina .20 .50
7 Ray Durham .10 .30
8 Jack McDowell .10 .30
9 Juan Gonzalez .10 .30
10 Chipper Jones .30 .75
11 Deion Sanders .20 .50
12 Rondell White .10 .30
13 Tom Henke .10 .30
14 Derek Bell .10 .30
15 Randy Myers .10 .30
16 Randy Johnson .30 .75
17 Len Dykstra .10 .30
18 Bill Pulsipher .10 .30
19 Greg Colbrunn .10 .30
20 David Wells .10 .30
21 Chad Curtis .10 .30
22 Roberto Hernandez SP 2.00 5.00
23 Kirby Puckett .30 .75
24 Joe Vitiello .10 .30
25 Roger Clemens .60 1.50
26 Al Martin .10 .30
27 Chad Ogea .10 .30
28 David Segui .10 .30
29 Joey Hamilton .10 .30
30 Dan Wilson .10 .30
31 Chad Fonville .10 .30
32 Bernard Gilkey .10 .30
33 Kevin Seitzer .10 .30
34 Shawn Green .10 .30
35 Rick Aguilera .10 .30
36 Gary DiSarcina .10 .30
37 Jaime Navarro .10 .30
38 Doug Jones .10 .30
39 Brent Gates .10 .30
40 Dean Palmer .10 .30
41 Pat Rapp .10 .30
42 Tony Clark .10 .30
43 Bill Swift .10 .30
44 Randy Velarde .10 .30
45 Matt Williams .10 .30
46 John Mabry .10 .30
47 Mike Fetters .10 .30
48 Orlando Miller .10 .30
49 Tom Glavine .20 .50
50 Delino DeShields .10 .30
51 Scott Erickson .10 .30
52 Andy Van Slyke .20 .50
53 Jim Bullinger .10 .30
54 Lyle Mouton .10 .30
55 Bret Saberhagen .10 .30
56 Benito Santiago .10 .30
57 Dan Miceli .10 .30
58 Carl Everett .10 .30
59 Rod Beck .10 .30
60 Phil Nevin .10 .30
61 Jason Giambi .10 .30
62 Paul Menhart .10 .30
63 Eric Karros .10 .30
64 Allen Watson .10 .30
65 Jeff Cirillo .10 .30
66 Lee Smith .10 .30
67 Sean Berry .10 .30
68 Luis Sojo .10 .30
69 Jeff Montgomery .10 .30
70 Todd Hundley .10 .30
71 John Burkett .10 .30
72 Mark Gubicza .10 .30
73 Don Mattingly .75 2.00
74 Jeff Brantley .10 .30
75 Matt Walbeck .10 .30
76 Steve Parris .10 .30
77 Ken Caminiti .10 .30
78 Kirt Manwaring .10 .30
79 Greg Vaughn .10 .30
80 Pedro Martinez .20 .50
81 Benji Gil .10 .30
82 Heathcliff Slocumb .10 .30
83 Joe Girardi .10 .30
84 Sean Bergman .10 .30
85 Matt Karchner .10 .30
86 Butch Huskey .10 .30
87 Mike Morgan .10 .30
88 Todd Worrell .10 .30
89 Mike Bordick .10 .30
90 Bip Roberts .10 .30
91 Mike Hampton .10 .30
92 Troy O'Leary .10 .30
93 Wally Joyner .10 .30
94 Dave Stevens .10 .30
95 Cecil Fielder .10 .30
96 Wade Boggs .20 .50
97 Hal Morris .10 .30
98 Mickey Tettleton .10 .30
99 Jeff Kent .10 .30
100 Denny Martinez .10 .30
101 Luis Gonzalez .10 .30
102 John Jaha .10 .30
103 Javier Lopez .10 .30
104 Mark McGwire .75 2.00
105 Ken Griffey Jr. .50 1.25
106 Darren Daulton .10 .30
107 Bryan Rekar .10 .30
108 Mike Macfarlane .10 .30
109 Gary Gaetti .10 .30
110 Shane Reynolds .10 .30
111 Pat Meares .10 .30
112 Jason Schmidt .20 .50
113 Otis Nixon .10 .30
114 John Franco .10 .30
115 Marc Newfield .10 .30
116 Andy Benes .10 .30
117 Ozzie Guillen .10 .30
118 Brian Jordan .10 .30
119 Terry Pendleton .10 .30
120 Chuck Finley .10 .30
121 Scott Stahoviak .10 .30
122 Sid Fernandez .10 .30
123 Derek Jeter .75 2.00
124 John Smiley .10 .30
125 David Bell .10 .30
126 Brett Butler .10 .30
127 Doug Drabek .10 .30
128 J.T. Snow .10 .30
129 Joe Carter .10 .30
130 Dennis Eckersley .10 .30
131 Marty Cordova .10 .30
132 Greg Maddux .50 1.25
133 Tom Goodwin .10 .30
134 Andy Ashby .10 .30
135 Paul Sorrento .10 .30
136 Ricky Bones .10 .30
137 Shawon Dunston .10 .30
138 Moises Alou .10 .30
139 Mickey Morandini .10 .30
140 Ramon Martinez .10 .30
141 Royce Clayton .10 .30
142 Brad Ausmus .10 .30
143 Kenny Rogers .10 .30
144 Tim Naehring .10 .30
145 Chris Gomez .10 .30
146 Bobby Bonilla .10 .30
147 Wilson Alvarez .10 .30
148 Johnny Damon .20 .50
149 Pat Hentgen .10 .30
150 Andres Galarraga .10 .30
151 David Cone .10 .30
152 Lance Johnson .10 .30
153 Carlos Garcia .10 .30
154 Doug Johns .10 .30
155 Midre Cummings .10 .30
156 Steve Sparks .10 .30
157 Sandy Martinez .10 .30
158 Wm. Van Landingham .10 .30
159 David Justice .10 .30
160 Mark Grace .20 .50
161 Robb Nen .10 .30
162 Mike Greenwell .10 .30
163 Brad Radke .10 .30
164 Edgardo Alfonzo .10 .30
165 Mark Leiter .10 .30
166 Walt Weiss .10 .30
167 Mel Rojas .10 .30
168 Bret Boone .10 .30
169 Ricky Bottalico .10 .30
170 Bobby Higginson .10 .30
171 Trevor Hoffman .10 .30
172 Jay Bell .10 .30
173 Gabe White .10 .30
174 Curtis Goodwin .10 .30
175 Tyler Green .10 .30
176 Roberto Alomar .20 .50
177 Sterling Hitchcock .10 .30
178 Ryan Klesko .10 .30
179 Donne Wall .10 .30
180 Brian McRae .10 .30
181 Will Clark TSC SP .30 .75
182 F.Thomas TSC SP .40 1.00
183 Jeff Bagwell TSC SP .20 .50
184 Mo Vaughn TSC SP .20 .50
185 Tino Martinez TSC SP .30 .75
186 Craig Biggio TSC SP .30 .75
187 C. Knoblauch TSC SP .20 .50
188 Carlos Baerga TSC SP .20 .50
189 Quilvio Veras TSC SP .20 .50
190 Luis Alicea TSC SP .20 .50
191 Jim Thome TSC SP .30 .75
192 Mike Blowers TSC SP .20 .50
193 R.Ventura TSC SP .20 .50
194 Jeff King TSC SP .20 .50
195 Tony Phillips TSC SP .20 .50
196 John Valentin TSC SP .20 .50
197 Barry Larkin TSC SP .30 .75
198 Cal Ripken TSC SP 1.25 3.00
199 Omar Vizquel TSC SP .30 .75
200 Kurt Abbott TSC SP .20 .50
201 Albert Belle TSC SP .20 .50
202 Barry Bonds TSC SP 1.00 2.50
203 Ron Gant TSC SP .20 .50
204 D.Bichette TSC SP .20 .50
205 Jeff Conine TSC SP .20 .50
206 Jim Edmonds TSC .20 .50
SP UER
Greg Myers pictured on front
207 Stan Javier TSC SP .20 .50
208 Kenny Lofton TSC SP .20 .50
209 Ray Lankford TSC SP .20 .50
210 B.Williams TSC SP .30 .75
211 Jay Buhner TSC SP .20 .50
212 Paul O'Neill TSC SP .30 .75
213 Tim Salmon TSC SP .30 .75
214 R.Sanders TSC SP .20 .50
215 M.Ramirez TSC SP .30 .75
216 Mike Piazza TSC SP .60 1.50
217 Mike Stanley TSC SP .20 .50
218 Tony Eusebio TSC SP .20 .50
219 Chris Hoiles TSC SP .20 .50
220 R.Karkovice TSC SP .20 .50
221 E.Martinez TSC SP .30 .75
222 Chili Davis TSC SP .20 .50
223 Jose Canseco TSC SP .20 .50
224 Eddie Murray TSC SP .40 1.00
225 G.Berroa TSC SP .20 .50
226 C.Jones TSC SP .40 1.00
227 G.Anderson TSC SP .20 .50
228 M.Cordova TSC SP .20 .50
229 Jon Nunnally TSC SP .20 .50
230 Brian L.Hunter TSC SP .20 .50
231 Shawn Green TSC SP .20 .50
232 Ray Durham TSC SP .20 .50
233 Alex Gonzalez TSC SP .20 .50
234 B.Higginson TSC SP .20 .50
235 R.Johnson TSC SP .40 1.00
236 Al Leiter TSC SP .20 .50
237 Tom Glavine TSC SP .30 .75
238 Kenny Rogers TSC SP .20 .50
239 M.Hampton TSC SP .20 .50
240 David Wells TSC SP .20 .50
241 Jim Abbott TSC SP .30 .75
242 Denny Neagle TSC SP .20 .50
243 W.Alvarez TSC SP .20 .50
244 John Smiley TSC SP .20 .50
245 Greg Maddux TSC SP .30 .75
246 Andy Ashby TSC SP .20 .50
247 Hideo Nomo TSC SP .40 1.00
248 Pat Rapp TSC SP .20 .50
249 T.Wakefield TSC SP .20 .50
250 John Smoltz TSC SP .30 .75
251 J.Hamilton TSC SP .20 .50
252 Frank Castillo TSC SP .20 .50
253 D.Martinez TSC SP .20 .50
254 J.Navarro TSC SP .20 .50
255 Karim Garcia TSC SP .20 .50
256 Bob Abreu TSC SP .40 1.00
257 Butch Huskey TSC SP .20 .50
258 Ruben Rivera TSC SP .20 .50
259 J.Damon TSC SP .30 .75
260 Derek Jeter TSC SP 1.00 2.50
261 D. Eckersley TSC SP .20 .50
262 Jose Mesa TSC SP .20 .50
263 Tom Henke TSC SP .20 .50
264 Rick Aguilera TSC SP .20 .50
265 Randy Myers TSC SP .20 .50
266 John Franco TSC SP .20 .50
267 Jeff Brantley TSC SP .20 .50
268 J.Wetteland TSC SP .20 .50
269 Mark Wohlers TSC SP .20 .50
270 Rod Beck TSC SP .20 .50
271 Barry Larkin .20 .50
272 Paul O'Neill .20 .50
273 Bobby Jones .10 .30
274 Will Clark .20 .50
275 Steve Avery .10 .30
276 Jim Edmonds .10 .30
277 John Olerud .10 .30
278 Carlos Perez .10 .30
279 Chris Hoiles .10 .30
280 Jeff Conine .10 .30
281 Jim Eisenreich .10 .30
282 Jason Jacome .10 .30
283 Ray Lankford .10 .30
284 John Wasdin .10 .30
285 Frank Thomas .30 .75
286 Jason Isringhausen .10 .30
287 Glenallen Hill .10 .30
288 Esteban Loaiza .10 .30
289 Bernie Williams .20 .50
290 Curtis Leskanic .10 .30
291 Scott Cooper .10 .30
292 Curt Schilling .10 .30
293 Eddie Murray .30 .75
294 Rick Krivda .10 .30
295 Domingo Cedeno .10 .30
296 Jeff Fassero .10 .30
297 Albert Belle .10 .30

298 Craig Biggio .20 .50
299 Fernando Vina .10 .30
300 Edgar Martinez .20 .50
301 Tony Gwynn .40 1.00
302 Felipe Lira .10 .30
303 Mo Vaughn .10 .30
304 Alex Fernandez .10 .30
305 Keith Lockhart .10 .30
306 Roger Pavlik .10 .30
307 Lee Tinsley .10 .30
308 Omar Vizquel .20 .50
309 Scott Servais .10 .30
310 Danny Tartabull .10 .30
311 Chili Davis .10 .30
312 Cal Eldred .10 .30
313 Roger Cedeno .10 .30
314 Chris Hammond .10 .30
315 Rusty Greer .10 .30
316 Brady Anderson .10 .30
317 Ron Villone .10 .30
318 Mark Carreon .10 .30
319 Larry Walker .10 .30
320 Pete Harnisch .10 .30
321 Robin Ventura .10 .30
322 Tim Belcher .10 .30
323 Tony Tarasco .10 .30
324 Juan Guzman .10 .30
325 Kenny Lofton .10 .30
326 Kevin Foster .10 .30
327 Wil Cordero .10 .30
328 Troy Percival .10 .30
329 Turk Wendell .10 .30
330 Thomas Howard .10 .30
331 Carlos Baerga .10 .30
332 B.J. Surhoff .10 .30
333 Jay Buhner .10 .30
334 Andujar Cedeno .10 .30
335 Jeff King .10 .30
336 Dante Bichette .10 .30
337 Alan Trammell .10 .30
338 Scott Leius .10 .30
339 Chris Snopek .10 .30
340 Roger Bailey .10 .30
341 Jacob Brumfield .10 .30
342 Jose Canseco .20 .50
343 Rafael Palmeiro .20 .50
344 Quilvio Veras .10 .30
345 Darrin Fletcher .10 .30
346 Carlos Delgado .10 .30
347 Tony Eusebio .10 .30
348 Ismael Valdes .10 .30
349 Terry Steinbach .10 .30
350 Orel Hershiser .10 .30
351 Kurt Abbott .10 .30
352 Jody Reed .10 .30
353 David Howard .10 .30
354 Ruben Sierra .10 .30
355 John Ericks .10 .30
356 Buck Showalter MG .10 .30
357 Jim Thome .20 .50
358 Geronimo Berroa .10 .30
359 Robby Thompson .10 .30
360 Jose Vizcaino .10 .30
361 Jeff Frye .10 .30
362 Kevin Appier .10 .30
363 Pat Kelly .10 .30
364 Ron Gant .10 .30
365 Luis Alicea .10 .30
366 Armando Benitez .10 .30
367 Rico Brogna .10 .30
368 Manny Ramirez .20 .50
369 Mike Lansing .10 .30
370 Sammy Sosa .30 .75
371 Don Wengert .10 .30
372 Dave Nilsson .10 .30
373 Sandy Alomar Jr. .10 .30
374 Joey Cora .10 .30
375 Larry Thomas .10 .30
376 John Valentin .10 .30
377 Kevin Ritz .10 .30
378 Steve Finley .10 .30
379 Frank Rodriguez .10 .30
380 Ivan Rodriguez .20 .50
381 Alex Ochoa .10 .30
382 Mark Lemke .10 .30
383 Scott Brosius .10 .30
384 James Mouton .10 .30
385 Mark Langston .10 .30
386 Ed Sprague .10 .30
387 Joe Oliver .10 .30
388 Steve Ontiveros .10 .30
389 Rey Sanchez .10 .30
390 Mike Henneman .10 .30
391 Jose Valentin .10 .30
392 Tom Candiotti .10 .30
393 Damon Buford .10 .30
394 Erik Hanson .10 .30
395 Mark Smith .10 .30
396 Pete Schourek .10 .30
397 John Flaherty .10 .30
398 Dave Martinez .10 .30
399 Tommy Greene .10 .30
400 Gary Sheffield .10 .30
401 Glenn Dishman .10 .30
402 Barry Bonds .75 2.00
403 Tom Pagnozzi .10 .30
404 Todd Stottlemyre .10 .30
405 Tim Salmon .20 .50
406 John Hudek .10 .30
407 Fred McGriff .20 .50
408 Orlando Merced .10 .30
409 Brian Barber .10 .30
410 Ryan Thompson .10 .30
411 Mariano Rivera .60 1.50
412 Eric Young .10 .30
413 Chris Bosio .10 .30
414 Chuck Knoblauch .10 .30
415 Jamie Moyer .10 .30
416 Chan Ho Park .10 .30
417 Mark Portugal .10 .30
418 Tim Raines .10 .30
419 Antonio Osuna .10 .30
420 Todd Zeile .10 .30
421 Steve Wojciechowski .10 .30
422 Marquis Grissom .10 .30
423 Norm Charlton .10 .30
424 Cal Ripken 1.00 2.50
425 Gregg Jefferies .10 .30
426 Mike Stanton .10 .30
427 Tony Fernandez .10 .30
428 Jose Rijo .10 .30
429 Jeff Bagwell .20 .50
430 Raul Mondesi .10 .30
431 Travis Fryman .10 .30
432 Ron Karkovice .10 .30
433 Alan Benes .10 .30
434 Tony Phillips .10 .30
435 Reggie Sanders .10 .30
436 Andy Pettitte .20 .50
437 Matt Lawton RC .10 .30
438 Jeff Blauser .10 .30
439 Michael Tucker .10 .30
440 Mark Loretta .10 .30
441 Charlie Hayes .10 .30
442 Mike Piazza .50 1.25
443 Shane Andrews .10 .30
444 Jeff Suppan .10 .30
445 Steve Rodriguez .10 .30
446 Mike Matheny .10 .30
447 Trenidad Hubbard .10 .30
448 Denny Hocking .10 .30
449 Mark Grudzielanek .10 .30
450 Joe Randa .10 .30
NNO Roger Clemens 2.00 5.00
Extreme Gold PROMO

1996 Stadium Club Members Only Parallel

This set, of which only 750 were produced is a parallel to the regular 1996 Stadium Club set. The cards are embossed with a "Members Only" logo and were available only to members of Topps' Stadium Club. The set includes a parallel of the complete 450-card basic set plus the following inserts: Bash and Burn, Mickey Mantle Heroes, Megaheroes, Metalists, Midsummer Matchups, Power Packed, Power Streak, Prime Cuts and TSC Awards. Only the inserts cards are priced below. Please refer to the multiplier for value on parallels to the basic issue cards.

COMP.SET W/INSERTS (555) 200.00 500.00
COMP.BASE SET (450) 80.00 200.00
COMMON CARD (1-450) .10 .25
COMMON (M1-M19) 2.00 5.00
*MEMBERS ONLY: 6X BASIC CARDS
M1 Jeff Bagwell 1.50 4.00
M2 Barry Bonds 4.00 10.00
M3 Jose Canseco 1.50 4.00
M4 Roger Clemens 4.00 10.00
M5 Dennis Eckersley .60 1.50
M6 Greg Maddux 5.00 12.00
M7 Cal Ripken 8.00 20.00
M8 Frank Thomas 3.00 8.00
BB1 Sammy Sosa 4.00 10.00
BB2 Barry Bonds 4.00 10.00
BB3 Reggie Sanders .40 1.00
BB4 Craig Biggio .75 2.00
BB5 Raul Mondesi .75 2.00
BB6 Ron Gant .40 1.00
BB7 Ray Lankford .60 1.50
BB8 Glenallen Hill .40 1.00
BB9 Chad Curtis .40 1.00
BB10 John Valentin .60 1.50
MH1 Frank Thomas 3.00 8.00
MH2 Ken Griffey Jr. 6.00 15.00
MH3 Hideo Nomo 1.50 4.00
MH4 Ozzie Smith 1.50 4.00
MH5 Will Clark 1.25 3.00
MH6 Jack McDowell .40 1.00
MH7 Andres Galarraga 1.25 3.00
MH8 Roger Clemens 4.00 10.00
MH9 Deion Sanders .60 1.50
MH10 Mo Vaughn .60 1.50
MM1 Hideo Nomo 2.00 5.00
Randy Johnson
MM2 Mike Piazza 5.00 12.00
Ivan Rodriguez
MM3 Fred McGriff 3.00 8.00
Frank Thomas
MM4 Craig Biggio .75 2.00
Carlos Baerga
MM5 Vinny Castilla 1.50 4.00
Wade Boggs
MM6 Barry Larkin 8.00 20.00
Cal Ripken
MM7 Barry Bonds 3.00 8.00
Albert Belle
MM8 Len Dykstra .60 1.50
Kenny Lofton
MM9 Tony Gwynn 4.00 10.00
Kirby Puckett
MM10 Ron Gant .75 2.00
Edgar Martinez
PC1 Albert Belle .60 1.50
PC2 Barry Bonds 1.50 4.00
PC3 Ken Griffey Jr. 6.00 15.00
PC4 Tony Gwynn 4.00 10.00
PC5 Edgar Martinez .75 2.00
PC6 Rafael Palmeiro 1.25 3.00
PC7 Mike Piazza 4.00 10.00
PC8 Frank Thomas 3.00 8.00
PP1 Albert Belle .60 1.50
PP2 Mark McGwire 6.00 15.00
PP3 Jose Canseco 1.50 4.00
PP4 Mike Piazza 4.00 10.00
PP5 Ron Gant .60 1.50
PP6 Ken Griffey Jr. 6.00 15.00
PP7 Mo Vaughn .60 1.50
PP8 Cecil Fielder .60 1.50
PP9 Tim Salmon 1.25 3.00
PP10 Frank Thomas 3.00 8.00
PP11 Juan Gonzalez 1.50 4.00
PP12 Andres Galarraga 1.25 3.00
PP13 Fred McGriff .75 2.00
PP14 Jay Buhner .60 1.50
PP15 Dante Bichette .60 1.50
PS1 Randy Johnson 1.50 4.00
PS2 Hideo Nomo 2.00 5.00
PS3 Albert Belle .60 1.50
PS4 Dante Bichette .60 1.50
PS5 Jay Buhner .60 1.50
PS6 Frank Thomas 3.00 8.00
PS7 Mark McGwire 6.00 15.00
PS8 Rafael Palmeiro 1.25 3.00
PS9 Mo Vaughn .60 1.50
PS10 Sammy Sosa 4.00 10.00
PS11 Larry Walker 1.25 3.00
PS12 Gary Gaetti .60 1.50
PS13 Tim Salmon 1.25 3.00
PS14 Barry Bonds 4.00 10.00
PS15 Jim Edmonds 1.25 3.00
TSCA1 Cal Ripken 8.00 20.00
TSCA2 Albert Belle .60 1.50
TSCA3 Tom Glavine 1.25 3.00
TSCA4 Jeff Conine .40 1.00
TSCA5 Ken Griffey Jr. 6.00 15.00
TSCA6 Hideo Nomo 1.50 4.00
TSCA7 Greg Maddux 4.00 10.00
TSCA8 Chipper Jones 4.00 10.00
TSCA9 Randy Johnson 1.50 4.00
TSCA10 Jose Mesa .40 1.00

1996 Stadium Club Bash and Burn

Randomly inserted in packs at a rate of one in 24 (retail) and one in 48 (hobby), this ten card set features power/speed players.

COMPLETE SET (10) 15.00 40.00
SER.2 STATED ODDS 1:48 HOB, 1:24 RET
BB1 Sammy Sosa 4.00 10.00
BB2 Barry Bonds 10.00 25.00
BB3 Reggie Sanders 1.50 4.00
BB4 Craig Biggio 2.50 6.00
BB5 Raul Mondesi 1.50 4.00
BB6 Ron Gant 1.50 4.00
BB7 Ray Lankford 1.50 4.00
BB8 Glenallen Hill 1.50 4.00
BB9 Chad Curtis 1.50 4.00
BB10 John Valentin 1.50 4.00

1996 Stadium Club Extreme Players Bronze

One hundred and seventy nine different players were featured on Extreme Player game cards randomly issued in 1996 Stadium Club first and second series packs. Each player has three versions: Bronze, Silver and Gold. All of these cards parallel their corresponding regular issue card except for the Bronze foil "Extreme Players" logo on each card front and the "EP" suffix on the card number, thus creating a skip-numbered set. The Bronze cards listed below were seeded at a rate of 1:12 packs. At the conclusion of the 1996 regular season, an Extreme Player from each of ten positions was identified as a winner based on scores calculated from their actual playing statistics. The 10 winning players are noted with a "W" below. Prior to the December 31st, 1996 deadline, each of the ten winning Extreme Players Bronze cards was redeemable for a 10-card set of Extreme Winners Bronze. Unredeemed winners are now in much shorter supply than other cards in this set and carry premium values.

COMP.BRONZE SET (180) 100.00 240.00
COMP.BRONZE SER.1 (90) 50.00 120.00
COMP.BRONZE SER.2 (90) 50.00 120.00
*BRONZE: 2X TO 5X BASE CARD HI
BRONZE STATED ODDS 1:12
*SILVER SINGLES: .6X TO 1.5X BRONZE
*SILVER WIN: .6X TO 1.5X BRONZE WIN
SILVER STATED ODDS 1:24
*GOLD SINGLES: 1.25X TO 3X BRONZE
*GOLD WIN: 1.25X TO 3X BRONZE WIN
GOLD STATED ODDS 1:48
SKIP-NUMBERED 179-CARD SET
77 Ken Caminiti W 1.50 4.00
88 Todd Worrell W .60 1.50
105 Ken Griffey Jr. W 5.00 12.00
132 Greg Maddux W 5.00 12.00
150 Andres Galarraga W 1.50 4.00
271 Barry Larkin W 1.50 4.00
400 Gary Sheffield W 2.00 5.00
402 Barry Bonds W 8.00 20.00
414 Chuck Knoblauch W 1.25 3.00
442 Mike Piazza W 5.00 12.00

1996 Stadium Club Extreme Winners Bronze

This 10-card skip-numbered set was only available to collectors who redeemed one of the ten winning Bronze Extreme Players cards before the December 31st, 1996 deadline. The cards parallel the Extreme Players cards inserted in Stadium Club packs except for their distinctive diffraction foil fronts.

COMPLETE SET (10) 10.00 25.00
*SILVER: 1.25X TO 3X BRONZE WINNERS
ONE SILV.SET VIA MAIL PER SILV.WINNER
*GOLD: 5X TO 12X BRONZE WINNERS
ONE GOLD CARD VIA MAIL PER GOLD WNR.
EW1 Greg Maddux 1.50 4.00
EW2 Mike Piazza 1.50 4.00
EW3 Andres Galarraga .40 1.00
EW4 Chuck Knoblauch .40 1.00
EW5 Ken Caminiti .40 1.00
EW6 Barry Larkin .60 1.50
EW7 Barry Bonds 2.50 6.00
EW8 Ken Griffey Jr. 1.50 4.00
EW9 Gary Sheffield .40 1.00
EW10 Todd Worrell .40 1.00

1996 Stadium Club Mantle

Randomly inserted at a rate of one card in every 24 packs in series one, one in 12 packs in series two, this 19-card retrospective set chronicles Mantle's career with classic photography, celebrity quotes and highlights from each year. The cards are double foil-stamped. The series one cards feature black-and-white photos, series two color photos. Mantle's name is printed across a silver foil facade of Yankee Stadium on each card top. Cereal Box factory sets include these cards with gold foil. They are valued the same as the pack inserts.

COMPLETE SET (19) 50.00 120.00
COMPLETE SERIES 1 (9) 30.00 80.00
COMMON (MM1-MM9) 4.00 10.00
COMMON (MM10-MM19) 2.50 6.00
SER.1 STATED ODDS 1:24
SER.2 STATED ODDS 1:12

1996 Stadium Club Megaheroes

Randomly inserted at a rate of one in every 48 hobby and 24 retail packs, this 10-card set features super-heroic players matched with a comic book-style illustration depicting their nicknames.

COMPLETE SET (10) 15.00 40.00
SER.1 STATED ODDS 1:48 HOB, 1:24 RET
MH1 Frank Thomas 2.00 5.00
MH2 Ken Griffey Jr. 3.00 8.00
MH3 Hideo Nomo 2.00 5.00
MH4 Ozzie Smith 2.00 5.00
MH5 Will Clark 1.25 3.00
MH6 Jack McDowell .75 2.00
MH7 Andres Galarraga .75 2.00
MH8 Roger Clemens 4.00 10.00
MH9 Deion Sanders 1.25 3.00
MH10 Mo Vaughn .75 2.00

1996 Stadium Club Metalists

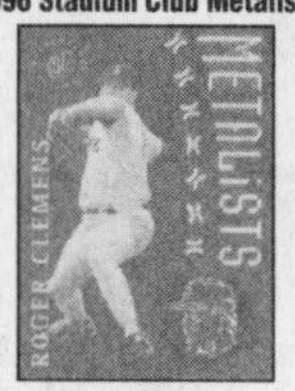

Randomly inserted in packs at a rate of one in 96 (retail) and one in 48 (hobby), this eight-card set features players with two or more MLB awards and is printed on laser-cut foil board.

COMPLETE SET (8) 15.00 40.00
SER.2 STATED ODDS 1:48 HOB, 1:96 RET
M1 Jeff Bagwell 1.00 2.50
M2 Barry Bonds 4.00 10.00
M3 Jose Canseco 1.00 2.50
M4 Roger Clemens 3.00 8.00
M5 Dennis Eckersley .60 1.50
M6 Greg Maddux 2.50 6.00
M7 Cal Ripken 5.00 12.00
M8 Frank Thomas 1.50 4.00

1996 Stadium Club Midsummer Matchups

Randomly inserted at a rate of one in every 48 hobby and 24 retail packs, this 10-card set salutes 1995 National League and American League All-Stars as they are matched back-to-back by position on these two-sided etched foil cards.

COMPLETE SET (10) 25.00 60.00
SER.1 STATED ODDS 1:48 HOB, 1:24 RET
M1 Hideo Nomo 2.00 5.00
Randy Johnson
M2 Mike Piazza 3.00 8.00
Ivan Rodriguez
M3 Fred McGriff 2.00 5.00
Frank Thomas
M4 Craig Biggio 1.25 3.00
Carlos Baerga
M5 Vinny Castilla 1.25 3.00
Wade Boggs
M6 Barry Larkin 6.00 15.00
Cal Ripken
M7 Barry Bonds 5.00 12.00
Albert Belle
M8 Len Dykstra .75 2.00
Kenny Lofton
M9 Tony Gwynn 2.50 6.00
Kirby Puckett
M10 Ron Gant 1.25 3.00
Edgar Martinez

1996 Stadium Club Power Packed

Randomly inserted in packs at a rate of one in 48, this 15-card set features the biggest, most powerful hitters in the League. Printed on Power Matrix, the cards carry diagrams showing where the players hit the ball over the fence and how far.

COMPLETE SET (15) 25.00 60.00
SER.2 STATED ODDS 1:48 RETAIL
PP1 Albert Belle 1.00 2.50
PP2 Mark McGwire 6.00 15.00
PP3 Jose Canseco 1.50 4.00
PP4 Mike Piazza 4.00 10.00
PP5 Ron Gant 1.00 2.50
PP6 Ken Griffey Jr. 4.00 10.00
PP7 Mo Vaughn 1.00 2.50
PP8 Cecil Fielder 1.00 2.50
PP9 Tim Salmon 1.50 4.00
PP10 Frank Thomas 2.50 6.00
PP11 Juan Gonzalez 1.00 2.50
PP12 Andres Galarraga 1.00 2.50
PP13 Fred McGriff 1.50 4.00
PP14 Jay Buhner 1.00 2.50
PP15 Dante Bichette 1.00 2.50

1996 Stadium Club Power Streak

Randomly inserted at a rate of one in every 24 hobby packs and 48 retail packs, this 15-card set spotlights baseball's most awesome power hitters and strikeout artists.

COMPLETE SET (15) 25.00 60.00
SER.1 STATED ODDS 1:24 HOB, 1:48 RET
PS1 Randy Johnson 2.50 6.00
PS2 Hideo Nomo 2.50 6.00
PS3 Albert Belle 1.00 2.50
PS4 Dante Bichette 1.00 2.50
PS5 Jay Buhner 1.00 2.50
PS6 Frank Thomas 2.50 6.00
PS7 Mark McGwire 6.00 15.00
PS8 Rafael Palmeiro 1.50 4.00
PS9 Mo Vaughn 1.00 2.50
PS10 Sammy Sosa 2.50 6.00
PS11 Larry Walker 1.00 2.50
PS12 Gary Gaetti 1.00 2.50
PS13 Tim Salmon 1.50 4.00
PS14 Barry Bonds 6.00 15.00
PS15 Jim Edmonds 1.00 2.50

1996 Stadium Club Prime Cuts

Randomly inserted at a rate of one in every 36 hobby and 72 retail packs, this eight card set this set highlights hitters with the purest swings. The cards are numbered on the back with a "PC" prefix.

COMPLETE SET (8) 20.00 50.00
SER.1 STATED ODDS 1:36 HOB, 1:72 RET
PC1 Albert Belle .75 2.00
PC2 Barry Bonds 5.00 12.00
PC3 Ken Griffey Jr. 3.00 8.00
PC4 Tony Gwynn 2.50 6.00
PC5 Edgar Martinez 1.25 3.00
PC6 Rafael Palmeiro 1.25 3.00
PC7 Mike Piazza 3.00 8.00
PC8 Frank Thomas 2.00 5.00

1996 Stadium Club TSC Awards

Randomly inserted in packs at a rate of one in 24 (retail) and one in 48 (hobby), this ten-card set features players whom TSC baseball experts voted to win various awards and is printed on diffraction foil.

COMPLETE SET (10) 15.00 40.00
SER.2 STATED ODDS 1:48 HOB, 1:24 RET
1 Cal Ripken 5.00 12.00
2 Albert Belle .60 1.50
3 Tom Glavine 1.00 2.50
4 Jeff Conine .60 1.50
5 Ken Griffey Jr. 2.50 6.00
6 Hideo Nomo 1.50 4.00
7 Greg Maddux 2.50 6.00
8 Chipper Jones 1.50 4.00
9 Randy Johnson 1.50 4.00
10 Jose Mesa .60 1.50

1996 Stadium Club Members Only 50

This 50-card set features color player photos of Topps' selection of 45 (numbers 1-45) of the top 1995 American and National League players. The set includes five Finest Cards (numbers 46-50) which represent Topps' selection of the top rookies from 1995. The backs carry information about the player.

COMP. FACT SET (50) 8.00 20.00
1 Carlos Baerga .02 .10
2 Derek Bell .02 .10
3 Albert Belle .08 .25
4 Dante Bichette .08 .25
5 Craig Biggio .15 .40
6 Wade Boggs .30 .75
7 Barry Bonds .50 1.25
8 Jay Buhner .08 .25
9 Vinny Castilla .08 .25
10 Jeff Conine .02 .10
11 Jim Edmonds .25 .60
12 Steve Finley .08 .25
13 Andres Galarraga .25 .60
14 Mark Grace .15 .40
15 Tony Gwynn .60 1.50
16 Lance Johnson .02 .10
17 Randy Johnson .30 .75
18 Eric Karros .08 .25
19 Chuck Knoblauch .15 .40
20 Barry Larkin .25 .60
21 Kenny Lofton .15 .40
22 Greg Maddux .75 2.00
23 Edgar Martinez .15 .40
24 Tino Martinez .08 .25
25 Mark McGwire .60 1.50
26 Brian McRae .02 .10
27 Jose Mesa .02 .10
28 Eddie Murray .30 .75
29 Mike Mussina .25 .60
30 Randy Myers .02 .10
31 Hideo Nomo .30 .75
32 Rafael Palmeiro .30 .75
33 Tony Phillips .02 .10
34 Mike Piazza .75 2.00
35 Kirby Puckett .40 1.00
36 Manny Ramirez .30 .75
37 Tim Salmon .15 .40
38 Reggie Sanders .02 .10
39 Sammy Sosa .50 1.25
40 Frank Thomas .30 .75
41 Jim Thome .30 .75
42 John Valentin .02 .10
43 Mo Vaughn .08 .25
44 Quilvio Veras .02 .10
45 Larry Walker .30 .75
46 Hideo Nomo FIN .60 1.50
47 Marty Cordova FIN .08 .25
48 Chipper Jones FIN 1.25 3.00
49 Garret Anderson FIN .40 1.00
50 Andy Pettitte FIN .25 .60

1997 Stadium Club

Cards from this 390 card set were distributed in eight-card hobby and retail packs (SRP $3) and 13-card hobby collector packs (SRP $5). Card fronts feature color action player photos printed on 20 pt. card stock with Topps Super Color processing, Hi-gloss laminating, embossing and double foil stamping. The backs carry player information and statistics. In addition to the standard selection of major leaguers, the set contains a 15-card TSC 2000 subset (181-195) featuring a selection of top young prospects. These subset cards were inserted one in every two eight-card first series packs and one per 13-card first series pack. First series cards were released in February, 1997. The 195-card Series two set was issued in six-card retail packs with a suggested retail price of $2 and in nine-card hobby packs with a suggested retail price of $3. The second series set features a 15-card Stadium Sluggers subset (376-390) with an insertion rate of one in every two hobby and three retail Series 2 packs. Second series cards were released in April, 1997. Please note that cards 361 and 374 do not exist. Due to an error at the manufacturer both Mike Sweeney and Tom Pagnozzi had their cards numbered as 274. In addition, Jermaine Dye and Brant Brown both had their cards numbered as 351. These numbering errors were never corrected and no premiums in value are associated.

COMPLETE SET (390) 30.00 80.00
COMP.SERIES 1 (195) 15.00 40.00
COMP.SERIES 2 (195) 15.00 40.00
COMMON (1-180/196-375) .10 .30
COM.SP (181-195/376-390) .30 .75
1 Chipper Jones .30 .75
2 Gary Sheffield .10 .30
3 Kenny Lofton .10 .30
4 Brian Jordan .10 .30
5 Mark McGwire .75 2.00
6 Charles Nagy .10 .30
7 Tim Salmon .20 .50
8 Cal Ripken 1.00 2.50
9 Jeff Conine .10 .30
10 Paul Molitor .10 .30
11 Mariano Rivera .30 .75
12 Pedro Martinez .20 .50
13 Jeff Bagwell .20 .50
14 Bobby Bonilla .10 .30
15 Barry Bonds .75 2.00
16 Ryan Klesko .10 .30
17 Barry Larkin .20 .50
18 Jim Thome .20 .50
19 Jay Buhner .10 .30
20 Juan Gonzalez .10 .30
21 Mike Mussina .20 .50
22 Kevin Appier .10 .30
23 Eric Karros .10 .30
24 Steve Finley .10 .30
25 Ed Sprague .10 .30
26 Bernard Gilkey .10 .30
27 Tony Phillips .10 .30
28 Henry Rodriguez .10 .30
29 John Smoltz .20 .50
30 Dante Bichette .10 .30
31 Mike Piazza .50 1.25
32 Paul O'Neill .20 .50
33 Billy Wagner .10 .30
34 Reggie Sanders .10 .30
35 John Jaha .10 .30
36 Eddie Murray .30 .75
37 Eric Young .10 .30
38 Roberto Hernandez .10 .30
39 Pat Hentgen .10 .30
40 Sammy Sosa .30 .75
41 Todd Hundley .10 .30
42 Mo Vaughn .10 .30
43 Robin Ventura .10 .30
44 Mark Grudzielanek .10 .30
45 Shane Reynolds .10 .30
46 Andy Pettitte .20 .50
47 Fred McGriff .20 .50
48 Rey Ordonez .10 .30
49 Will Clark .20 .50
50 Ken Griffey Jr. .50 1.25
51 Todd Worrell .10 .30
52 Rusty Greer .10 .30
53 Mark Grace .20 .50
54 Tom Glavine .20 .50
55 Derek Jeter .75 2.00
56 Rafael Palmeiro .20 .50
57 Bernie Williams .20 .50
58 Marty Cordova .10 .30
59 Andres Galarraga .10 .30
60 Ken Caminiti .10 .30
61 Garret Anderson .10 .30
62 Denny Martinez .10 .30
63 Mike Greenwell .10 .30
64 David Segui .10 .30
65 Julio Franco .10 .30
66 Rickey Henderson .30 .75
67 Ozzie Guillen .10 .30
68 Pete Harnisch .10 .30
69 Chan Ho Park .10 .30
70 Harold Baines .10 .30
71 Mark Clark .10 .30
72 Steve Avery .10 .30
73 Brian Hunter .10 .30
74 Pedro Astacio .10 .30
75 Jack McDowell .10 .30
76 Gregg Jefferies .10 .30
77 Jason Kendall .10 .30
78 Todd Walker .10 .30
79 B.J. Surhoff .10 .30
80 Moises Alou .10 .30
81 Fernando Vina .10 .30
82 Darryl Strawberry .10 .30
83 Jose Rosado .10 .30
84 Chris Gomez .10 .30
85 Chili Davis .10 .30
86 Alan Benes .10 .30
87 Todd Hollandsworth .10 .30
88 Jose Vizcaino .10 .30
89 Edgardo Alfonzo .10 .30
90 Ruben Rivera .10 .30
91 Donovan Osborne .10 .30
92 Doug Glanville .10 .30
93 Gary DiSarcina .10 .30
94 Brooks Kieschnick .10 .30
95 Bobby Jones .10 .30
96 Raul Casanova .10 .30
97 Jermaine Allensworth .10 .30
98 Kenny Rogers .10 .30
99 Mark McLemore .10 .30
100 Jeff Fassero .10 .30
101 Sandy Alomar Jr. .10 .30
102 Chuck Finley .10 .30
103 Eric Owens .10 .30
104 Billy McMillon .10 .30
105 Dwight Gooden .10 .30
106 Sterling Hitchcock .10 .30
107 Doug Drabek .10 .30
108 Paul Wilson .10 .30
109 Chris Snopek .10 .30
110 Al Leiter .10 .30
111 Bob Tewksbury .10 .30
112 Todd Greene .10 .30
113 Jose Valentin .10 .30
114 Delino DeShields .10 .30
115 Mike Bordick .10 .30
116 Pat Meares .10 .30
117 Mariano Duncan .10 .30
118 Steve Trachsel .10 .30
119 Luis Castillo .10 .30
120 Andy Benes .10 .30
121 Donne Wall .10 .30
122 Alex Gonzalez .10 .30
123 Dan Wilson .10 .30
124 Omar Vizquel .20 .50
125 Devon White .10 .30
126 Darryl Hamilton .10 .30
127 Orlando Merced .10 .30
128 Royce Clayton .10 .30
129 W.VanLandingham .10 .30
130 Terry Steinbach .10 .30
131 Jeff Blauser .10 .30
132 Jeff Cirillo .10 .30
133 Roger Pavlik .10 .30
134 Danny Tartabull .10 .30
135 Jeff Montgomery .10 .30
136 Bobby Higginson .10 .30
137 Mike Grace .10 .30
138 Kevin Elster .10 .30
139 Brian Giles RC .60 1.50
140 Rod Beck .10 .30
141 Ismael Valdes .10 .30
142 Scott Brosius .10 .30
143 Mike Fetters .10 .30
144 Gary Gaetti .10 .30
145 Mike Lansing .10 .30
146 Glenallen Hill .10 .30
147 Shawn Green .10 .30
148 Mel Rojas .10 .30
149 Joey Cora .10 .30
150 John Smiley .10 .30
151 Marvin Benard .10 .30
152 Curt Schilling .10 .30
153 Dave Nilsson .10 .30
154 Edgar Renteria .10 .30
155 Joey Hamilton .10 .30
156 Carlos Garcia .10 .30
157 Nomar Garciaparra .50 1.25
158 Kevin Ritz .10 .30
159 Keith Lockhart .10 .30
160 Justin Thompson .10 .30
161 Terry Adams .10 .30
162 Jamey Wright .10 .30
163 Otis Nixon .10 .30
164 Michael Tucker .10 .30
165 Mike Stanley .10 .30
166 Ben McDonald .10 .30
167 John Mabry .10 .30
168 Troy O'Leary .10 .30
169 Mel Nieves .10 .30
170 Bret Boone .10 .30

171 Mike Timlin .10 .30
172 Scott Rolen .20 .50
173 Reggie Jefferson .10 .30
174 Neifi Perez .10 .30
175 Brian McRae .10 .30
176 Tom Goodwin .10 .30
177 Aaron Sele .10 .30
178 Benito Santiago .10 .30
179 Frank Rodriguez .10 .30
180 Eric Davis .10 .30
181 A.Jones 2000 SP .30 .75
182 Todd Walker 2000 SP .30 .75
183 Wes Helms 2000 SP .30 .75
184 Nelson Figueroa 2000 SP RC .30 .75
185 V. Guerrero 2000 SP .50 1.25
186 B.McMillon 2000 SP .30 .75
187 Todd Helton 2000 SP .50 1.25
188 Nomar Garciaparra 2000 SP 1.00 2.50
189 K. Maeda 2000 SP .30 .75
190 R.Branyan 2000 SP .30 .75
191 G.Rusch 2000 SP .30 .75
192 B.Colon 2000 SP .30 .75
193 Scott Rolen 2000 SP .30 .75
194 A. Echevarria 2000 SP .30 .75
195 Bob Abreu 2000 SP .30 .75
196 Greg Maddux .50 1.25
197 Joe Carter .10 .30
198 Alex Ochoa .10 .30
199 Ellis Burks .10 .30
200 Ivan Rodriguez .20 .50
201 Marquis Grissom .10 .30
202 Trevor Hoffman .10 .30
203 Matt Williams .10 .30
204 Carlos Delgado .10 .30
205 Ramon Martinez .10 .30
206 Chuck Knoblauch .10 .30
207 Juan Guzman .10 .30
208 Derek Bell .10 .30
209 Roger Clemens .60 1.50
210 Vladimir Guerrero .30 .75
211 Cecil Fielder .10 .30
212 Hideo Nomo .30 .75
213 Frank Thomas .30 .75
214 Greg Vaughn .10 .30
215 Javy Lopez .10 .30
216 Raul Mondesi .10 .30
217 Wade Boggs .20 .50
218 Carlos Baerga .10 .30
219 Tony Gwynn .40 1.00
220 Tino Martinez .20 .50
221 Vinny Castilla .10 .30
222 Lance Johnson .10 .30
223 David Justice .10 .30
224 Rondell White .10 .30
225 Dean Palmer .10 .30
226 Jim Edmonds .10 .30
227 Albert Belle .10 .30
228 Alex Fernandez .10 .30
229 Ryne Sandberg .50 1.25
230 Jose Mesa .10 .30
231 David Cone .10 .30
232 Troy Percival .10 .30
233 Edgar Martinez .20 .50
234 Jose Canseco .20 .50
235 Kevin Brown .10 .30
236 Ray Lankford .10 .30
237 Karim Garcia .10 .30
238 J.T. Snow .10 .30
239 Dennis Eckersley .10 .30
240 Roberto Alomar .20 .50
241 John Valentin .10 .30
242 Ron Gant .10 .30
243 Geronimo Berroa .10 .30
244 Manny Ramirez .20 .50
245 Travis Fryman .10 .30
246 Denny Neagle .10 .30
247 Randy Johnson .30 .75
248 Darin Erstad .10 .30
249 Mark Wohlers .10 .30
250 Ken Hill .10 .30
251 Larry Walker .10 .30
252 Craig Biggio .20 .50
253 Brady Anderson .10 .30
254 John Wetteland .10 .30
255 Andruw Jones .20 .50
256 Turk Wendell .10 .30
257 Jason Isringhausen .10 .30
258 Jaime Navarro .10 .30
259 Sean Berry .10 .30
260 Albie Lopez .10 .30
261 Jay Bell .10 .30
262 Bobby Witt .10 .30
263 Tony Clark .10 .30
264 Tim Wakefield .10 .30
265 Brad Radke .10 .30
266 Tim Belcher .10 .30
267 Nerio Rodriguez RC .10 .30
268 Roger Cedeno .10 .30
269 Tim Naehring .10 .30
270 Kevin Tapani .10 .30
271 Joe Randa .10 .30
272 Randy Myers .10 .30
273 Dave Burba .10 .30
274 Mike Sweeney .10 .30
275 Danny Graves .10 .30
276 Chad Mottola .10 .30
277 Ruben Sierra .10 .30
278 Norm Charlton .10 .30
279 Scott Servais .10 .30
280 Jacob Cruz .10 .30
281 Mike Macfarlane .10 .30
282 Rich Becker .10 .30
283 Shannon Stewart .10 .30
284 Gerald Williams .10 .30
285 Jody Reed .10 .30
286 Jeff D'Amico .10 .30
287 Walt Weiss .10 .30
288 Jim Leyritz .10 .30
289 Francisco Cordova .10 .30
290 F.P. Santangelo .10 .30
291 Scott Erickson .10 .30
292 Hal Morris .10 .30
293 Ray Durham .10 .30
294 Andy Ashby .10 .30
295 Darryl Kile .10 .30
296 Jose Paniagua .10 .30
297 Mickey Tettleton .10 .30
298 Joe Girardi .10 .30
299 Rocky Coppinger .10 .30
300 Bob Abreu .20 .50
301 John Olerud .10 .30
302 Paul Shuey .10 .30
303 Jeff Brantley .10 .30
304 Bob Wells .10 .30
305 Kevin Seitzer .10 .30
306 Shawon Dunston .10 .30
307 Jose Herrera .10 .30
308 Butch Huskey .10 .30
309 Jose Offerman .10 .30
310 Rick Aguilera .10 .30
311 Greg Gagne .10 .30
312 John Burkett .10 .30
313 Mark Thompson .10 .30
314 Alvaro Espinoza .10 .30
315 Todd Stottlemyre .10 .30
316 Al Martin .10 .30
317 James Baldwin .10 .30
318 Cal Eldred .10 .30
319 Sid Fernandez .10 .30
320 Mickey Morandini .10 .30
321 Robb Nen .10 .30
322 Mark Lemke .10 .30
323 Pete Schourek .10 .30
324 Marcus Jensen .10 .30
325 Rich Aurilia .10 .30
326 Jeff King .10 .30
327 Scott Stahoviak .10 .30
328 Ricky Otero .10 .30
329 Antonio Osuna .10 .30
330 Chris Hoiles .10 .30
331 Luis Gonzalez .10 .30
332 Wil Cordero .10 .30
333 Johnny Damon .20 .50
334 Mark Langston .10 .30
335 Orlando Miller .10 .30
336 Jason Giambi .10 .30
337 Damian Jackson .10 .30
338 David Wells .10 .30
339 Bip Roberts .10 .30
340 Matt Ruebel .10 .30
341 Tom Candiotti .10 .30
342 Wally Joyner .10 .30
343 Jimmy Key .10 .30
344 Tony Batista .10 .30
345 Paul Sorrento .10 .30
346 Ron Karkovice .10 .30
347 Wilson Alvarez .10 .30
348 John Flaherty .10 .30
349 Rey Sanchez .10 .30
350 John Vander Wal .10 .30
351 Jermaine Dye .10 .30
352 Mike Hampton .10 .30
353 Greg Colbrunn .10 .30
354 Heathcliff Slocumb .10 .30
355 Ricky Bottalico .10 .30
356 Marty Janzen .10 .30
357 Orel Hershiser .10 .30
358 Rex Hudler .10 .30
359 Amaury Telemaco .10 .30
360 Darrin Fletcher .10 .30
361 Brant Brown UER .10 .30
Card numbered 351
362 Russ Davis .10 .30
363 Allen Watson .10 .30
364 Mike Lieberthal .10 .30
365 Dave Stevens .10 .30
366 Jay Powell .10 .30
367 Tony Fossas .10 .30
368 Bob Wolcott .10 .30
369 Mark Loretta .10 .30
370 Shawn Estes .10 .30
371 Sandy Martinez .10 .30
372 Wendell Magee Jr. .10 .30
373 John Franco .10 .30
374 Tom Pagnozzi UER .10 .30
misnumbered as 274
375 Willie Adams .10 .30
376 Chipper Jones SS SP .50 1.25
377 Mo Vaughn SS SP .30 .75
378 Frank Thomas SS SP .50 1.25
379 Albert Belle SS SP .30 .75
380 A.Galarraga SS SP .30 .75
381 Gary Sheffield SS SP .30 .75
382 Jeff Bagwell SS SP .30 .75
383 Mike Piazza SS SP 1.00 2.50
384 Mark McGwire SS SP 1.50 4.00
385 Ken Griffey Jr. SS SP 1.00 2.50
386 Barry Bonds SS SP 1.50 4.00
387 Juan Gonzalez SS SP .30 .75
388 B.Anderson SS SP .30 .75
389 Ken Caminiti SS SP .30 .75
390 Jay Buhner SS SP .30 .75

1997 Stadium Club Matrix

Randomly inserted in first and second series eight-card packs at a rate of one in 12 and in 13-card packs at a rate of one in six, this 120-card set is parallel to the first 60 cards of both the series one and series two of the regular set. Each Matrix card was reproduced with Power Matrix technology, giving the card fronts a glittering effect.

*STARS: 4X TO 10X BASIC CARDS
STATED ODDS 1:12 H/R, 1:18 ANCO, 1:6 HCP

1997 Stadium Club Members Only Parallel

These cards are a parallel issue to the 1997 Stadium Club Series one and Series two sets and the following insert sets: Millennium, Instavision, Firebrand, and Pure Gold. No first series Co-Signers insert cards are in this set, but it does contain the second series Patent Leather insert set. The only difference between the regular issue cards and these parallels are the words "TSC Members Only" printed lightly in the background. The cards all come together in factory set form and one must be a member of Topps Stadium Club to order these cards.

COMP.FACT SET (497) 160.00 400.00
COMP.SERIES 1 (235) 80.00 200.00
COMP.SERIES 2 (242) 80.00 200.00
COMMON CARD (1-390) .10 .25
*MEMBERS ONLY: 6X BASIC CARDS
I1 Eddie Murray 1.50 4.00
I2 Paul Molitor 1.50 4.00
I3 Todd Hundley .75 2.00
I4 Roger Clemens 4.00 10.00
I5 Barry Bonds 2.00 5.00
I6 Mark McGwire 10.00 25.00
I7 Brady Anderson .75 2.00
I8 Barry Larkin 1.50 4.00
I9 Ken Caminiti 1.25 3.00
I10 Hideo Nomo 1.50 4.00
I11 Bernie Williams 1.50 4.00
I12 Juan Gonzalez 1.50 4.00
I13 Andy Pettitte 1.25 3.00
I14 Albert Belle .75 2.00
I15 John Smoltz .75 2.00
I16 Brian Jordan .40 1.00
I17 Derek Jeter 10.00 25.00
I18 Ken Caminiti .75 2.00
I19 John Wetteland .75 2.00
I20 Brady Anderson .75 2.00
I21 Andruw Jones 2.00 5.00
I22 Jim Leyritz .40 1.00
M1 Derek Jeter 10.00 25.00
M2 Mark Grudzielanek .75 2.00
M3 Jacob Cruz .40 1.00
M4 Ray Durham 1.25 3.00
M5 Tony Clark .75 2.00
M6 Chipper Jones 5.00 12.00
M7 Luis Castillo .75 2.00
M8 Carlos Delgado 2.00 5.00
M9 Brant Brown .40 1.00
M10 Jason Kendall 1.25 3.00
M11 Alan Benes .40 1.00
M12 Rey Ordonez .40 1.00
M13 Justin Thompson .40 1.00
M14 J.Allensworth .40 1.00
M15 Brian L. Hunter .40 1.00
M16 Marty Cordova .40 1.00
M17 Edgar Renteria .40 1.00
M18 Karim Garcia .40 1.00
M19 Todd Greene .40 1.00
M20 Paul Wilson .40 1.00
M21 Andruw Jones 2.00 5.00
M22 Todd Walker .40 1.00
M23 Alex Ochoa .40 1.00
M24 Bartolo Colon 1.50 4.00
M25 Wendell Magee Jr. .40 1.00
M26 Jose Rosado .40 1.00
M27 Katsuhiro Maeda .40 1.00
M28 Bob Abreu 1.50 4.00
M29 Brooks Kieschnick .40 1.00
M30 Derrick Gibson .40 1.00
M31 Mike Sweeney 2.00 5.00
M32 Jeff D'Amico .40 1.00
M33 Chad Mottola .40 1.00
M34 Chris Snopek .40 1.00
M35 Jaime Bluma .40 1.00
M36 Vladimir Guerrero 3.00 8.00
M37 Nomar Garciaparra 6.00 15.00
M38 Scott Rolen 1.50 4.00
M39 Dmitri Young .75 2.00
M40 Neifi Perez .40 1.00
FB1 Jeff Bagwell 2.00 5.00
FB2 Albert Belle .75 2.00
FB3 Barry Bonds 5.00 12.00
FB4 Andres Galarraga 1.50 4.00
FB5 Ken Griffey Jr. 8.00 20.00
FB6 Brady Anderson .75 2.00
FB7 Mark McGwire 8.00 20.00
FB8 Chipper Jones 5.00 12.00
FB9 Frank Thomas 3.00 8.00
FB10 Mike Piazza 6.00 15.00
FB11 Mo Vaughn .75 2.00
FB12 Juan Gonzalez 2.00 5.00
PG1 Brady Anderson .75 2.00
PG2 Albert Belle .75 2.00
PG3 Dante Bichette .75 2.00
PG4 Barry Bonds 5.00 12.00
PG5 Jay Buhner .75 2.00
PG6 Tony Gwynn 5.00 12.00
PG7 Chipper Jones 5.00 12.00
PG8 Mark McGwire 8.00 20.00
PG9 Gary Sheffield 1.50 4.00
PG10 Frank Thomas 4.00 10.00
PG11 Juan Gonzalez 2.00 5.00
PG12 Ken Caminiti .75 2.00
PG13 Kenny Lofton .75 2.00
PG14 Jeff Bagwell 2.00 5.00
PG15 Ken Griffey Jr. 8.00 20.00
PG16 Cal Ripken 10.00 25.00
PG17 Mo Vaughn .75 2.00
PG18 Mike Piazza 5.00 12.00
PG19 Derek Jeter 10.00 25.00
PG20 Andres Galarraga 1.50 4.00
PL1 Ivan Rodriguez 2.00 5.00
PL2 Ken Caminiti .75 2.00
PL3 Barry Bonds 5.00 12.00
PL4 Ken Griffey Jr. 8.00 20.00
PL5 Greg Maddux 6.00 15.00
PL6 Craig Biggio 1.25 3.00
PL7 Andres Galarraga 1.50 4.00
PL8 Kenny Lofton .75 2.00
PL9 Barry Larkin 1.50 4.00
PL10 Mark Grace 1.50 4.00
PL11 Rey Ordonez .40 1.00
PL12 Roberto Alomar 1.50 4.00
PL13 Derek Jeter 10.00 25.00

1997 Stadium Club Co-Signers

Randomly inserted in first series eight-card hobby packs at a rate of one in 168 and first series 13-card hobby collector packs at a rate of one in 96, cards (CO1-CO5) from this dual-sided, dual-player set feature color action player photos printed on 20pt. card stock with authentic signatures of two major league stand-outs per card. The last five cards (CO6-CO10) were randomly inserted in second series 10-card hobby packs with a rate of one in 168 and inserted with a rate of one in 96 Hobby Collector packs.

STATED ODDS 1:168 HOBBY, 1:36 HCP
CO1 Andy Pettitte 125.00 250.00
Derek Jeter
CO2 Paul Wilson 6.00 15.00
Todd Hundley
CO3 Jermaine Dye 6.00 15.00
Mark Wohlers
CO4 Scott Rolen 8.00 20.00
Gregg Jefferies
CO5 Todd Hollandsworth 6.00 15.00
Jason Kendall
CO6 Alan Benes 6.00 15.00
Robin Ventura
CO7 Eric Karros 6.00 15.00
Raul Mondesi
CO8 Rey Ordonez 40.00 80.00
Nomar Garciaparra
CO9 Rondell White 6.00 15.00
Marty Cordova
CO10 Tony Gwynn 12.50 30.00
Karim Garcia

1997 Stadium Club Firebrand Redemption

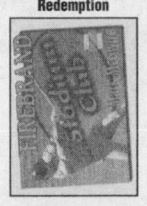

Randomly inserted exclusively into first series eight-card retail packs at a rate of one in 36, these redemption cards feature a selection of the leagues top sluggers. Due to circumstances beyond the manufacturers control, they were not able to insert the actual etched-wood cards into packs and had to resort to these redemption cards.

SER.1 STAT.ODDS 1:24 HOB/RET, 1:36 ANCO
*WOOD: 5X TO 1.2X BASIC FIREBRAND
ONE WOOD CARD VIA MAIL PER EXCH.CARD
F1 Jeff Bagwell 1.50 4.00
F2 Albert Belle 1.00 2.50
F3 Barry Bonds 6.00 15.00
F4 Andres Galarraga 1.00 2.50
F5 Ken Griffey Jr. 4.00 10.00
F6 Brady Anderson 1.00 2.50
F7 Mark McGwire 6.00 15.00
F8 Chipper Jones 2.50 6.00
F9 Frank Thomas 2.50 6.00
F10 Mike Piazza 4.00 10.00
F11 Mo Vaughn 1.00 2.50
F12 Juan Gonzalez 1.00 2.50

1997 Stadium Club Instavision

The first ten cards of this 22-card set were randomly inserted in first series eight-card packs at a rate of one in 24 and first series 13-card packs at a rate of 1:12. The last 12 cards were inserted in series two packs at the rate of one in 24 and one in 12 in hobby collector packs. The set highlights some of the 1996 season's most exciting moments through exclusive holographic video action.

COMPLETE SET (22) 20.00 50.00
COMPLETE SERIES 1 (10) 10.00 25.00
COMPLETE SERIES 2 (12) 10.00 25.00
STATED ODDS 1:24 HOB/RET, 1:36 ANCO
I1 Eddie Murray 1.50 4.00
I2 Paul Molitor .60 1.50
I3 Todd Hundley .60 1.50
I4 Roger Clemens 3.00 8.00
I5 Barry Bonds 4.00 10.00
I6 Mark McGwire 4.00 10.00
I7 Brady Anderson .60 1.50
I8 Barry Larkin 1.00 2.50
I9 Ken Caminiti .60 1.50
I10 Hideo Nomo 1.50 4.00
I11 Bernie Williams 1.00 2.50
I12 Juan Gonzalez .60 1.50
I13 Andy Pettitte 1.00 2.50
I14 Albert Belle .60 1.50
I15 John Smoltz 1.00 2.50
I16 Brian Jordan .60 1.50
I17 Derek Jeter 4.00 10.00
I18 Ken Caminiti .60 1.50
I19 John Wetteland .60 1.50
I20 Brady Anderson .60 1.50
I21 Andruw Jones 1.00 2.50
I22 Jim Leyritz .60 1.50

1997 Stadium Club Millennium

Randomly inserted in first and second series eight-card packs at a rate of one in 24 and 13-card packs at a rate of 1:12, this 40-card set features color player photos of breakthrough stars of Major League Baseball reproduced using state-of-the-art advanced embossed holographic technology.

COMPLETE SET (40) 50.00 130.00
COMPLETE SERIES 1 (20) 20.00 50.00
COMPLETE SERIES 2 (20) 30.00 80.00
STATED ODDS 1:24H/R, 1:36ANCO, 1:12HCP
M1 Derek Jeter 8.00 20.00
M2 Mark Grudzielanek .60 1.50
M3 Jacob Cruz .60 1.50
M4 Ray Durham 1.00 2.50
M5 Tony Clark .60 1.50
M6 Chipper Jones 2.50 6.00
M7 Luis Castillo .60 1.50
M8 Carlos Delgado 1.00 2.50
M9 Brant Brown .60 1.50
M10 Jason Kendall 1.00 2.50
M11 Alan Benes .60 1.50
M12 Rey Ordonez .60 1.50
M13 Justin Thompson .60 1.50
M14 J.Allensworth .60 1.50
M15 Brian Hunter .60 1.50
M16 Marty Cordova .60 1.50
M17 Edgar Renteria 1.00 2.50
M18 Karim Garcia .60 1.50
M19 Todd Greene .60 1.50
M20 Paul Wilson .60 1.50
M21 Andruw Jones 1.50 4.00
M22 Todd Walker .60 1.50
M23 Alex Ochoa .60 1.50
M24 Bartolo Colon 1.00 2.50
M25 Wendell Magee Jr. .60 1.50
M26 Jose Rosado .60 1.50
M27 Katsuhiro Maeda .60 1.50
M28 Bob Abreu .60 1.50
M29 Brooks Kieschnick .60 1.50
M30 Derrick Gibson .60 1.50
M31 Mike Sweeney 1.00 2.50
M32 Jeff D'Amico .60 1.50
M33 Chad Mottola .60 1.50
M34 Chris Snopek .60 1.50
M35 Jaime Bluma .60 1.50
M36 Vladimir Guerrero 2.50 6.00
M37 Nomar Garciaparra 5.00 12.00
M38 Scott Rolen 1.50 4.00
M39 Dmitri Young 1.00 2.50
M40 Neifi Perez .60 1.50

1997 Stadium Club Patent Leather

Randomly inserted in second series retail packs only at a rate of one in 36, this 13-card set features action player images standing in a baseball glove and with an inner die-cut glove background printed on leather card stock.

COMPLETE SET (13) 50.00 120.00
SER.2 STATED ODDS 1:36 RETAIL
PL1 Ivan Rodriguez 2.50 6.00
PL2 Ken Caminiti 1.50 4.00
PL3 Barry Bonds 10.00 25.00
PL4 Ken Griffey Jr. 6.00 15.00
PL5 Greg Maddux 6.00 15.00
PL6 Craig Biggio 2.50 6.00
PL7 Andres Galarraga 1.50 4.00
PL8 Kenny Lofton 1.50 4.00
PL9 Barry Larkin 2.50 6.00
PL10 Mark Grace 2.50 6.00
PL11 Rey Ordonez 1.50 4.00
PL12 Roberto Alomar 2.50 6.00
PL13 Derek Jeter 10.00 25.00

1997 Stadium Club Pure Gold

Randomly inserted in first and second series eight-card packs at a rate of one in 72 and 13-card packs at a rate of one in 36, this 20-card set features color action star player photos reproduced on 20 pt. embossed gold mirror foilboard.

COMPLETE SET (20) 80.00 200.00
COMPLETE SERIES 1 (10) 50.00 120.00
COMPLETE SERIES 2 (10) 80.00 200.00
STATED ODDS 1:72H/R, 1:108ANCO, 1:36HCP
PG1 Brady Anderson 1.25 3.00
PG2 Albert Belle 1.25 3.00
PG3 Dante Bichette 1.25 3.00
PG4 Barry Bonds 8.00 20.00
PG5 Jay Buhner 1.25 3.00
PG6 Tony Gwynn 4.00 10.00
PG7 Chipper Jones 3.00 8.00
PG8 Mark McGwire 8.00 20.00
PG9 Gary Sheffield 1.25 3.00
PG10 Frank Thomas 3.00 8.00
PG11 Juan Gonzalez 1.25 3.00
PG12 Ken Caminiti 1.25 3.00
PG13 Kenny Lofton 1.25 3.00
PG14 Jeff Bagwell 2.00 5.00
PG15 Ken Griffey Jr. 5.00 12.00
PG16 Cal Ripken 10.00 25.00
PG17 Mo Vaughn 1.25 3.00
PG18 Mike Piazza 5.00 12.00
PG19 Derek Jeter 8.00 20.00
PG20 Andres Galarraga 1.25 3.00

1998 Stadium Club

The 1998 Stadium Club set was issued in two separate 200-card series and distributed in six-card retail packs for $2, nine-card hobby packs for $3, and 15-card Home Team Advantage packs for $5. The card fronts feature action color player photos with player information displayed on the backs. The series one set included odd numbered cards only and series two included even numbered cards only. The set contains the topical subsets: Future Stars (odd-numbered 361-379), Draft Picks (odd-numbered 381-399) and Traded (even-numbered 356-400). Two separate Cal Ripken Sound Chip cards were distributed as chiptoppers in Home Team Advantage boxes. The second series features a 23-card Transaction subset (356-400). Second series cards were released in April, 1998. Rookie Cards include Jack Cust, Kevin Millwood and Magglio Ordonez.

COMPLETE SET (400) 30.00 80.00
COMP.SERIES 1 (200) 15.00 40.00
COMP.SERIES 2 (200) 15.00 40.00
1 Chipper Jones .30 .75
2 Frank Thomas .30 .75
3 Vladimir Guerrero .30 .75
4 Ellis Burks .10 .30
5 John Franco .10 .30
6 Paul Molitor .10 .30
7 Rusty Greer .10 .30
8 Todd Hundley .10 .30
9 Brett Tomko .10 .30
10 Eric Karros .10 .30
11 Mike Cameron .10 .30
12 Jim Edmonds .10 .30
13 Bernie Williams .20 .50
14 Denny Neagle .10 .30
15 Jason Dickson .10 .30
16 Sammy Sosa .30 .75
17 Brian Jordan .10 .30
18 Jose Vidro .10 .30
19 Scott Spiezio .10 .30
20 Jay Buhner .10 .30
21 Jim Thome .20 .50
22 Sandy Alomar Jr. .10 .30
23 Livan Hernandez .10 .30
24 Roberto Alomar .20 .50
25 Chris Gomez .10 .30
26 John Wetteland .10 .30
27 Willie Greene .10 .30
28 Gregg Jefferies .10 .30
29 Johnny Damon .20 .50
30 Barry Larkin .20 .50
31 Chuck Knoblauch .10 .30
32 Mo Vaughn .10 .30
33 Tony Clark .10 .30
34 Marty Cordova .10 .30
35 Vinny Castilla .10 .30
36 Jeff King .10 .30
37 Reggie Jefferson .10 .30
38 Mariano Rivera .30 .75
39 Jermaine Allensworth .10 .30
40 Livan Hernandez .10 .30
41 Heathcliff Slocumb .10 .30
42 Jacob Cruz .10 .30
43 Barry Bonds .75 2.00
44 Dave Magadan .10 .30
45 Chan Ho Park .10 .30
46 Jeremi Gonzalez .10 .30
47 Jeff Cirillo .10 .30
48 Delino DeShields .10 .30
49 Craig Biggio .20 .50
50 Benito Santiago .10 .30
51 Mark Clark .10 .30
52 Fernando Vina .10 .30
53 F.P. Santangelo .10 .30
54 Pep Harris .10 .30
55 Edgar Renteria .10 .30
56 Jeff Bagwell .20 .50
57 Jimmy Key .10 .30
58 Bartolo Colon .10 .30
59 Curt Schilling .10 .30
60 Steve Finley .10 .30
61 Andy Ashby .10 .30
62 John Burkett .10 .30
63 Orel Hershiser .10 .30
64 Pokey Reese .10 .30
65 Scott Servais .10 .30
66 Todd Jones .10 .30
67 Javy Lopez .10 .30
68 Robin Ventura .10 .30
69 Miguel Tejada .30 .75
70 Raul Casanova .10 .30
71 Reggie Sanders .10 .30
72 Edgardo Alfonzo .10 .30
73 Dean Palmer .10 .30
74 Todd Stottlemyre .10 .30
75 David Wells .10 .30
76 Troy Percival .10 .30
77 Albert Belle .10 .30
78 Pat Hentgen .10 .30
79 Brian Hunter .10 .30
80 Richard Hidalgo .10 .30
81 Darren Oliver .10 .30
82 Mark Wohlers .10 .30
83 Cal Ripken 1.00 2.50
84 Hideo Nomo .30 .75
85 Derrek Lee .20 .50
86 Stan Javier .10 .30
87 Rey Ordonez .10 .30
88 Randy Johnson .30 .75
89 Jeff Kent .10 .30
90 Brian McRae .10 .30
91 Manny Ramirez .20 .50
92 Trevor Hoffman .10 .30
93 Doug Glanville .10 .30
94 Todd Walker .10 .30
95 Andy Benes .10 .30
96 Jason Schmidt .10 .30
97 Mike Matheny .10 .30
98 Tim Naehring .10 .30
99 Keith Lockhart .10 .30
100 Jose Rosado .10 .30
101 Roger Clemens .60 1.50
102 Pedro Astacio .10 .30
103 Mark Bellhorn .10 .30
104 Paul O'Neill .20 .50
105 Darin Erstad .10 .30
106 Mike Lieberthal .10 .30
107 Wilson Alvarez .10 .30
108 Mike Mussina .20 .50
109 George Williams .10 .30
110 Cliff Floyd .10 .30
111 Shawn Estes .10 .30
112 Mark Grudzielanek .10 .30
113 Tony Gwynn .40 1.00
114 Alan Benes .10 .30
115 Terry Steinbach .10 .30
116 Greg Maddux .50 1.25
117 Andy Pettitte .20 .50
118 Dave Nilsson .10 .30
119 Deivi Cruz .10 .30
120 Carlos Delgado .10 .30
121 Scott Hatteberg .10 .30
122 John Olerud .10 .30
123 Todd Dunwoody .10 .30
124 Garret Anderson .10 .30
125 Royce Clayton .10 .30
126 Dante Powell .10 .30
127 Tom Glavine .20 .50
128 Gary DiSarcina .10 .30
129 Terry Adams .10 .30
130 Raul Mondesi .10 .30
131 Dan Wilson .10 .30
132 Al Martin .10 .30
133 Mickey Morandini .10 .30
134 Rafael Palmeiro .20 .50
135 Juan Encarnacion .10 .30
136 Jim Pittsley .10 .30
137 Magglio Ordonez RC 1.25 3.00
138 Will Clark .20 .50
139 Todd Helton .20 .50
140 Kelvim Escobar .10 .30
141 Esteban Loaiza .10 .30
142 John Jaha .10 .30
143 Jeff Fassero .10 .30
144 Harold Baines .10 .30
145 Butch Huskey .10 .30
146 Pat Meares .10 .30
147 Brian Giles .10 .30
148 Ramiro Mendoza .10 .30
149 John Smoltz .20 .50
150 Felix Martinez .10 .30
151 Jose Valentin .10 .30
152 Brad Rigby .10 .30
153 Ed Sprague .10 .30
154 Mike Hampton .10 .30
155 Carlos Perez .10 .30
156 Ray Lankford .10 .30
157 Bobby Bonilla .10 .30
158 Bill Mueller .10 .30
159 Jeffrey Hammonds .10 .30
160 Charles Nagy .10 .30
161 Rich Loiselle RC .10 .30
162 Al Leiter .10 .30
163 Larry Walker .10 .30
164 Chris Hoiles .10 .30
165 Jeff Montgomery .10 .30
166 Francisco Cordova .10 .30
167 James Baldwin .10 .30
168 Mark McLemore .10 .30
169 Kevin Appier .10 .30
170 Jamey Wright .10 .30
171 Nomar Garciaparra .50 1.25
172 Matt Franco .10 .30
173 Armando Benitez .10 .30
174 Jeromy Burnitz .10 .30
175 Ismael Valdes .10 .30
176 Lance Johnson .10 .30
177 Paul Sorrento .10 .30
178 Rondell White .10 .30
179 Kevin Elster .10 .30
180 Jason Giambi .10 .30
181 Carlos Baerga .10 .30
182 Russ Davis .10 .30
183 Ryan McGuire .10 .30
184 Eric Young .10 .30
185 Ron Gant .10 .30
186 Manny Alexander .10 .30
187 Scott Karl .10 .30
188 Brady Anderson .10 .30
189 Randall Simon .10 .30
190 Tim Belcher .10 .30
191 Jaret Wright .10 .30
192 Dante Bichette .10 .30
193 John Valentin .10 .30
194 Darren Bragg .10 .30
195 Mike Sweeney .10 .30
196 Craig Counsell .10 .30
197 Jaime Navarro .10 .30
198 Todd Dunn .10 .30
199 Ken Griffey Jr. .50 1.25
200 Juan Gonzalez .10 .30
201 Billy Wagner .10 .30
202 Tino Martinez .20 .50
203 Mark McGwire .75 2.00
204 Jeff D'Amico .10 .30
205 Rico Brogna .10 .30
206 Todd Hollandsworth .10 .30
207 Chad Curtis .10 .30
208 Tom Goodwin .10 .30
209 Neifi Perez .10 .30
210 Derek Bell .10 .30
211 Quilvio Veras .10 .30
212 Greg Vaughn .10 .30
213 Kirk Rueter .10 .30
214 Arthur Rhodes .10 .30
215 Cal Eldred .10 .30
216 Bill Taylor .10 .30
217 Todd Greene .10 .30
218 Mario Valdez .10 .30
219 Ricky Bottalico .10 .30
220 Frank Rodriguez .10 .30
221 Rich Becker .10 .30
222 Roberto Duran RC .10 .30
223 Ivan Rodriguez .20 .50
224 Mike Jackson .10 .30
225 Deion Sanders .20 .50
226 Tony Womack .10 .30
227 Mark Kotsay .10 .30
228 Steve Trachsel .10 .30
229 Ryan Klesko .10 .30
230 Ken Cloude .10 .30
231 Luis Gonzalez .10 .30
232 Gary Gaetti .10 .30
233 Michael Tucker .10 .30
234 Shawn Green .10 .30
235 Ariel Prieto .10 .30
236 Kirt Manwaring .10 .30
237 Omar Vizquel .20 .50
238 Matt Beech .10 .30
239 Justin Thompson .10 .30
240 Bret Boone .10 .30
241 Derek Jeter .75 2.00
242 Ken Caminiti .10 .30
243 Jose Offerman .10 .30
244 Kevin Tapani .10 .30
245 Jason Kendall .10 .30
246 Jose Guillen .10 .30
247 Mike Bordick .10 .30
248 Dustin Hermanson .10 .30
249 Darrin Fletcher .10 .30
250 Dave Hollins .10 .30
251 Ramon Martinez .10 .30
252 Hideki Irabu .10 .30
253 Mark Grace .20 .50
254 Jason Isringhausen .10 .30

255 Jose Cruz Jr. .10 .30
256 Brian Johnson .10 .30
257 Brad Ausmus .10 .30
258 Andruw Jones .20 .50
259 Doug Jones .10 .30
260 Jeff Shaw .10 .30
261 Chuck Finley .10 .30
262 Gary Sheffield .10 .30
263 David Segui .10 .30
264 John Smiley .10 .30
265 Tim Salmon .20 .50
266 J.T. Snow .10 .30
267 Alex Fernandez .10 .30
268 Matt Stairs .10 .30
269 B.J. Surhoff .10 .30
270 Keith Foulke .10 .30
271 Edgar Martinez .20 .50
272 Shannon Stewart .10 .30
273 Eduardo Perez .10 .30
274 Wally Joyner .10 .30
275 Kevin Young .10 .30
276 Eli Marrero .10 .30
277 Brad Radke .10 .30
278 Jamie Moyer .10 .30
279 Joe Girardi .10 .30
280 Troy O'Leary .10 .30
281 Jeff Frye .10 .30
282 Jose Offerman .10 .30
283 Scott Erickson .10 .30
284 Sean Berry .10 .30
285 Shigetoshi Hasegawa .10 .30
286 Felix Heredia .10 .30
287 Willie McGee .10 .30
288 Alex Rodriguez .50 1.25
289 Ugueth Urbina .10 .30
290 Jon Lieber .10 .30
291 Fernando Tatis .10 .30
292 Chris Stynes .10 .30
293 Bernard Gilkey .10 .30
294 Joey Hamilton .10 .30
295 Matt Karchner .10 .30
296 Paul Wilson .10 .30
297 Damion Easley .10 .30
298 Kevin Millwood RC .40 1.00
299 Ellis Burks .10 .30
300 Jerry DiPoto .10 .30
301 Jermaine Dye .10 .30
302 Travis Lee .10 .30
303 Ron Coomer .10 .30
304 Matt Williams .10 .30
305 Bobby Higginson .10 .30
306 Jorge Fabregas .10 .30
307 Jon Nunnally .10 .30
308 Jay Bell .10 .30
309 Jason Schmidt .10 .30
310 Andy Benes .10 .30
311 Sterling Hitchcock .10 .30
312 Jeff Suppan .10 .30
313 Shane Reynolds .10 .30
314 Willie Blair .10 .30
315 Scott Rolen .20 .50
316 Wilson Alvarez .10 .30
317 David Justice .10 .30
318 Fred McGriff .20 .50
319 Bobby Jones .10 .30
320 Wade Boggs .20 .50
321 Tim Wakefield .10 .30
322 Tony Saunders .10 .30
323 David Cone .10 .30
324 Roberto Hernandez .10 .30
325 Jose Canseco .20 .50
326 Kevin Stocker .10 .30
327 Gerald Williams .10 .30
328 Quinton McCracken .10 .30
329 Mark Gardner .10 .30
330 Ben Grieve .10 .30
331 Kevin Brown .20 .50
332 Mike Lowell RC .60 1.50
333 Jed Hansen .10 .30
334 Abraham Nunez .10 .30
335 John Thomson .10 .30
336 Masato Yoshii RC .15 .40
337 Mike Piazza .50 1.25
338 Brad Fullmer .10 .30
339 Ray Durham .10 .30
340 Kerry Wood .15 .40
341 Kevin Polcovich .10 .30
342 Russ Johnson .10 .30
343 Darryl Hamilton .10 .30
344 David Ortiz .40 1.00
345 Kevin Orie .10 .30
346 Mike Caruso .10 .30
347 Juan Guzman .10 .30
348 Ruben Rivera .10 .30
349 Rick Aguilera .10 .30
350 Bobby Estalella .10 .30
351 Bobby Witt .10 .30
352 Paul Konerko .10 .30
353 Matt Morris .10 .30
354 Carl Pavano .10 .30
355 Todd Zeile .10 .30
356 Kevin Brown TR .20 .50
357 Alex Gonzalez .10 .30
358 Chuck Knoblauch TR .10 .30
359 Joey Cora .10 .30
360 Mike Lansing TR .10 .30
361 Adrian Beltre .10 .30
362 Dennis Eckersley TR .10 .30
363 A.J. Hinch .10 .30
364 Kenny Lofton TR .10 .30
365 Alex Gonzalez .10 .30
366 Henry Rodriguez TR .10 .30
367 Mike Stoner RC .10 .30
368 Darryl Kile TR .10 .30
369 Kevin McGlinchy .10 .30
370 Walt Weiss TR .10 .30
371 Kris Benson .10 .30
372 Cecil Fielder TR .10 .30
373 Dermal Brown .10 .30
374 Rod Beck TR .10 .30
375 Eric Milton .10 .30
376 Travis Fryman TR .10 .30
377 Preston Wilson .10 .30
378 Chili Davis TR .10 .30
379 Travis Lee .10 .30
380 Jim Leyritz TR .10 .30
381 Vernon Wells .10 .30
382 Joe Carter TR .10 .30
383 J.J. Davis .10 .30
384 Marquis Grissom TR .10 .30
385 Mike Cuddyer RC .40 1.00
386 Rickey Henderson TR .30 .75
387 Chris Enochs RC .10 .30
388 Andres Galarraga TR .10 .30
389 Jason Dellaero .10 .30
390 Robb Nen TR .10 .30
391 Mark Mangum .10 .30
392 Jeff Blauser TR .10 .30
393 Adam Kennedy .10 .30
394 Bob Abreu TR .10 .30
395 Jack Cust RC .75 2.00
396 Jose Vizcaino TR .10 .30
397 Jon Garland .10 .30
398 Pedro Martinez TR .20 .50
399 Aaron Akin .10 .30
400 Jeff Conine TR .10 .30
NNO Cal Ripken Sound Chip 1 6.00 15.00
NNO Cal Ripken Sound Chip 2 6.00 15.00

1998 Stadium Club First Day Issue

Randomly inserted in first series retail packs at the rate of one in 42 and second series retail packs at the rate of one in 47, this 400-card set parallels the 1998 Stadium Club base set and features a "First Day Issue" foil stamp on the front. Each card is serial numbered out of 200 on back.

*STARS: 6X TO 15X BASIC CARDS
*ROOKIES: 6X TO 15X BASIC CARDS
SER.1 STATED ODDS 1:42 RETAIL PACKS
SER.2 STATED ODDS 1:47 RETAIL PACKS

1998 Stadium Club One Of A Kind

Randomly inserted in first and second series hobby and Home Team Advantage packs this 400-card set parallels the 1998 Stadium Club base set. First series cards were seeded at 1:21 hobby and 1:13 HTA packs. Series 2 cards were seeded at 1:24 hobby and 1:14 HTA packs. Each card front features a special metalized foil treatment coupled with a "One of a Kind" logo. In addition, each card is serial numbered out of 150 on back.

*STARS: 8X TO 20X BASIC CARDS
*ROOKIES: 8X TO 20X BASIC CARDS
SER.1 STATED ODDS 1:21 HOB, 1:13 HTA
SER.2 STATED ODDS 1:24 HOB, 1:14 HTA

1998 Stadium Club Printing Plates

Randomly inserted at a rate of one in every 95 first series and one in every 86 second series Home Team Advantage packs, this set features the actual press plates used to create the fronts of the cards in the 1998 Stadium Club base set. Each card had four different colors produced (Black, Cyan, Magenta and Yellow). Only fronts of the regular issue cards were used. Printing Plates were not issued for insert cards nor card backs. Pricing is unavailable due to scarcity.

SER.1 STATED ODDS 1:95 HTA
SER.2 STATED ODDS 1:86 HTA

1998 Stadium Club Co-Signers

Randomly inserted exclusively in first and second series hobby and Home Team Advantage packs, this 36-card set features color photos of two top players on each card along with their autographs. These cards were released in three different levels of scarcity: A, B and C. Seeding rates are as follows: Series 1 Group A 1:4372 hobby and 1:2623 HTA, Series 1 Group B 1:1457 hobby and 1:874 HTA, Series 1 Group C 1:121 hobby and 1:73 HTA, Series 2 Group A 1:4702 hobby and 1:2821 HTA, Series 2 Group B 1:1567 hobby and 1:940 HTA and Series 2 Group C 1:131 hobby and 1:78 HTA. The scarce group A cards (rumored to be only 25 of each made) are the most difficult to obtain.

SER.1 A ODDS 1:4372 HOB, 1:2623 HTA
SER.2 A ODDS 1:4702 HOB, 1:2821 HTA
SER.1 B ODDS 1:1457 HOB, 1:874 HTA
SER.2 B ODDS 1:1567 HOB, 1:940 HTA
SER.1 C ODDS 1:121 HOB, 1:73 HTA
SER.2 C ODDS 1:131 HOB, 1:78 HTA
CS1 Nomar Garciaparra A 60.00 120.00
Scott Rolen
CS2 Nomar Garciaparra B 175.00 300.00
Derek Jeter
CS3 Nomar Garciaparra C 15.00 40.00
Eric Karros
CS4 Scott Rolen C 75.00 150.00
Derek Jeter
CS5 Scott Rolen B 20.00 50.00
Eric Karros
CS6 Derek Jeter A 75.00 150.00
Eric Karros
CS7 Travis Lee B 6.00 15.00
Jose Cruz Jr.
CS8 Travis Lee C 6.00 15.00
Mark Kotsay
CS9 Travis Lee A 40.00 80.00
Paul Konerko
CS10 Jose Cruz Jr. A 20.00 50.00
Mark Kotsay
CS11 Jose Cruz Jr. C 15.00 40.00
Paul Konerko
CS12 Mark Kotsay B 20.00 50.00
Paul Konerko
CS13 Tony Gwynn A 150.00 300.00
Larry Walker
CS14 Tony Gwynn C 10.00 25.00
Mark Grudzielanek
CS15 Tony Gwynn B 60.00 120.00
Andres Galarraga
CS16 Larry Walker B 40.00 80.00
Mark Grudzielanek
CS17 Larry Walker C 30.00 60.00
Andres Galarraga
CS18 Mark Grudzielanek A 20.00 50.00
Andres Galarraga
CS19 Sandy Alomar A 15.00 40.00
Roberto Alomar
CS20 Sandy Alomar C 15.00 40.00
Andy Pettitte
CS21 Sandy Alomar B 30.00 60.00
Tino Martinez
CS22 Roberto Alomar B 30.00 60.00
Andy Pettitte
CS23 Roberto Alomar C 20.00 50.00
Tino Martinez
CS24 Andy Pettitte A 60.00 120.00
Tino Martinez
CS25 Tony Clark A 20.00 50.00
Todd Hundley
CS26 Tony Clark B 20.00 50.00
Tim Salmon
CS27 Tony Clark C 10.00 25.00
Robin Ventura
CS28 Todd Hundley C 6.00 15.00
Tim Salmon
CS29 Todd Hundley B 15.00 40.00
Robin Ventura
CS30 Tim Salmon A 40.00 80.00
Robin Ventura
CS31 Roger Clemens B 100.00 200.00
Randy Johnson
CS32 Roger Clemens A 75.00 150.00
Jaret Wright
CS33 Roger Clemens C 50.00 100.00
Matt Morris
CS34 Randy Johnson C 10.00 25.00
Jaret Wright
CS35 Randy Johnson A 60.00 120.00
Matt Morris
CS36 Jaret Wright B 15.00 40.00
Matt Morris

1998 Stadium Club In The Wings

Randomly inserted in first series hobby and retail packs at the rate of one in 36 and first series Home Team Advantage packs at a rate of one in 12, this 15-card set features color photos of some of the top young players in the league.

COMPLETE SET (15) 15.00 40.00
SER.1 STATED ODDS 1:36 H/R, 1:12 HTA
W1 Juan Encarnacion 1.50 4.00
W2 Brad Fullmer 1.50 4.00
W3 Ben Grieve 1.50 4.00
W4 Todd Helton 2.50 6.00
W5 Richard Hidalgo 1.50 4.00
W6 Russ Johnson 1.50 4.00
W7 Paul Konerko 1.50 4.00
W8 Mark Kotsay 1.50 4.00
W9 Derrek Lee 2.50 6.00
W10 Travis Lee 1.50 4.00
W11 Eli Marrero 1.50 4.00
W12 David Ortiz 5.00 12.00
W13 Randall Simon 1.50 4.00
W14 Shannon Stewart 1.50 4.00
W15 Fernando Tatis 1.50 4.00

1998 Stadium Club Never Compromise

Randomly inserted in first series hobby and retail packs at the rate of one in 12 and first series HTA packs at the rate of one in four, this 20-card set features color photos of top players who never compromise in their game play.

COMPLETE SET (20) 30.00 80.00
SER.1 STATED ODDS 1:12 H/R, 1:4 HTA
NC1 Cal Ripken 4.00 10.00
NC2 Ivan Rodriguez .75 2.00
NC3 Ken Griffey Jr. 2.00 5.00
NC4 Frank Thomas 1.25 3.00
NC5 Tony Gwynn 1.50 4.00
NC6 Mike Piazza 2.00 5.00
NC7 Randy Johnson 1.25 3.00
NC8 Greg Maddux 2.00 5.00
NC9 Roger Clemens 2.50 6.00
NC10 Derek Jeter 3.00 8.00
NC11 Chipper Jones 1.25 3.00
NC12 Barry Bonds 3.00 8.00
NC13 Larry Walker .50 1.25
NC14 Jeff Bagwell .75 2.00
NC15 Barry Larkin .75 2.00
NC16 Ken Caminiti .50 1.25
NC17 Mark McGwire 3.00 8.00
NC18 Manny Ramirez .75 2.00
NC19 Tim Salmon .75 2.00
NC20 Paul Molitor .50 1.25

1998 Stadium Club Playing With Passion

Randomly seeded into second series hobby and retail packs at a rate of one in 12 and second series Home Team Advantage packs at a rate of one in four, cards from this 10-card set feature a selection of players who've got true fire in their hearts and the burning desire to win.

COMPLETE SET (10) 10.00 25.00
SER.2 STATED ODDS 1:12 H/R, 1:4 HTA
P1 Bernie Williams .60 1.50
P2 Jim Edmonds .40 1.00
P3 Chipper Jones 1.00 2.50
P4 Cal Ripken 3.00 8.00
P5 Craig Biggio .60 1.50
P6 Juan Gonzalez .40 1.00
P7 Alex Rodriguez 1.50 4.00
P8 Tino Martinez .60 1.50
P9 Mike Piazza 1.50 4.00
P10 Ken Griffey Jr. 1.50 4.00

1998 Stadium Club Royal Court

Randomly seeded into second series hobby and retail packs at a rate of one in 36 and second series Home Team Advantage packs at a rate of one in 12, cards from this 15-card set feature a selection of players that have proven their talent and dedication that they've got what it takes to achieve royalty. Players are broken into groups of ten Kings (veterans) and five Princes (rookies). Each card features a special Uniluster technology on front.

COMPLETE SET (15) 50.00 120.00
SER.2 STATED ODDS 1:36 H/R, 1:12 HTA
RC1 Ken Griffey Jr. 5.00 12.00
RC2 Frank Thomas 3.00 8.00
RC3 Mike Piazza 5.00 12.00
RC4 Chipper Jones 3.00 8.00
RC5 Mark McGwire 8.00 20.00
RC6 Cal Ripken 10.00 25.00
RC7 Jeff Bagwell 2.00 5.00
RC8 Barry Bonds 8.00 20.00
RC9 Juan Gonzalez 1.25 3.00
RC10 Alex Rodriguez 5.00 12.00
RC11 Travis Lee 1.25 3.00
RC12 Paul Konerko 1.25 3.00
RC13 Todd Helton 2.00 5.00
RC14 Ben Grieve 1.25 3.00
RC15 Mark Kotsay 1.25 3.00

1998 Stadium Club Triumvirate Luminous

Randomly inserted in first and second series retail packs at the rate of one in 48, the cards of this 54-card set feature color photos of three teammates that can be fused together to make one big card. These laser cut cards use Luminous technology.

STATED ODDS 1:48 RETAIL
*LUMINESCENT: 1.25X TO 3X LUMINOUS
LUMINESCENT STATED ODDS 1:192 RETAIL
*ILLUMINATOR: 2X TO 5X LUMINOUS
ILLUMINATOR STATED ODDS 1:384 RETAIL
T1A Chipper Jones 2.50 6.00
T1B Andruw Jones 1.50 4.00
T1C Kenny Lofton 1.00 2.50
T2A Derek Jeter 6.00 15.00
T2B Bernie Williams 1.50 4.00
T2C Tino Martinez 1.50 4.00
T3A Jay Buhner 1.00 2.50
T3B Edgar Martinez 1.50 4.00
T3C Ken Griffey Jr. 4.00 10.00
T4A Albert Belle 1.00 2.50
T4B Robin Ventura 1.00 2.50
T4C Frank Thomas 2.50 6.00
T5A Brady Anderson 1.00 2.50
T5B Cal Ripken 8.00 20.00
T5C Rafael Palmeiro 1.50 4.00
T6A Mike Piazza 4.00 10.00
T6B Raul Mondesi 1.00 2.50
T6C Eric Karros 1.00 2.50
T7A Vinny Castilla 1.00 2.50
T7B Andres Galarraga 1.00 2.50
T7C Larry Walker 1.00 2.50
T8A Jim Thome 1.50 4.00
T8B Manny Ramirez 1.50 4.00
T8C David Justice 1.00 2.50
T9A Mike Mussina 1.50 4.00
T9B Greg Maddux 4.00 10.00
T9C Randy Johnson 2.50 6.00
T10A Mike Piazza 4.00 10.00
T10B Sandy Alomar Jr. 1.00 2.50
T10C Ivan Rodriguez 1.50 4.00
T11A Mark McGwire 6.00 15.00
T11B Tino Martinez 1.50 4.00
T11C Frank Thomas 2.50 6.00
T12A Roberto Alomar 1.50 4.00
T12B Chuck Knoblauch 1.00 2.50
T12C Craig Biggio 1.50 4.00
T13A Cal Ripken 8.00 20.00
T13B Chipper Jones 2.50 6.00
T13C Ken Caminiti 1.00 2.50
T14A Derek Jeter 6.00 15.00
T14B Nomar Garciaparra 4.00 10.00
T14C Alex Rodriguez 4.00 10.00
T15A Barry Bonds 6.00 15.00
T15B David Justice 1.00 2.50
T15C Albert Belle 1.00 2.50
T16A Bernie Williams 1.50 4.00
T16B Ken Griffey Jr. 4.00 10.00
T16C Ray Lankford 1.00 2.50
T17A Tim Salmon 1.50 4.00
T17B Larry Walker 1.00 2.50
T17C Tony Gwynn 3.00 8.00
T18A Paul Molitor 1.00 2.50
T18B Edgar Martinez 1.50 4.00
T18C Juan Gonzalez 1.00 2.50

1999 Stadium Club

This 355-card set of 1999 Stadium Club cards was distributed in two separate series of 170 and 185 cards respectively. Six-card hobby and six-card retail packs each carried a suggested retail price of $2. 15-card Home Team Advantage packs (SRP of $5) were also distributed. All pack types contained a trifold/checklist info card. The card fronts feature color action player photos printed on 20 pt. card stock. The backs carry player information and career statistics. Draft Pick and Future Stars cards 141-160 and 336-355 were shortprinted at the following rates: 1:3 hobby/retail packs, one per HTA pack. Key Rookie Cards include Pat Burrell, Nick Johnson and Austin Kearns.

COMPLETE SET (355) 40.00 100.00
COMP.SERIES 1 (170) 20.00 50.00
COMP.SER.1 w/o SP's (150) 10.00 25.00
COMP.SERIES 2 (185) 20.00 50.00
COMP.SER.2 w/o SP's (165) 10.00 25.00
COMMON (1-140/161-170) .10 .30
COMMON (171-335) .10 .30
COMMON (141-160/336-355) .75 2.00
1 Alex Rodriguez .50 1.25
2 Chipper Jones .30 .75
3 Rusty Greer .10 .30
4 Jim Edmonds .10 .30
5 Ron Gant .10 .30
6 Kevin Polcovich .10 .30
7 Darryl Strawberry .10 .30
8 Bill Mueller .10 .30
9 Vinny Castilla .10 .30
10 Wade Boggs .20 .50
11 Jose Lima .10 .30
12 Darren Dreifort .10 .30
13 Jay Bell .10 .30
14 Ben Grieve .10 .30
15 Shawn Green .10 .30
16 Andres Galarraga .10 .30
17 Bartolo Colon .10 .30
18 Francisco Cordova .10 .30
19 Paul O'Neill .20 .50
20 Trevor Hoffman .10 .30
21 Darren Oliver .10 .30
22 John Franco .10 .30
23 Eli Marrero .10 .30
24 Roberto Hernandez .10 .30
25 Craig Biggio .20 .50
26 Brad Fullmer .10 .30
27 Scott Erickson .10 .30
28 Tom Gordon .10 .30
29 Brian Hunter .10 .30
30 Raul Mondesi .10 .30
31 Rick Reed .10 .30
32 Jose Canseco .20 .50
33 Robb Nen .10 .30
34 Turner Ward .10 .30
35 Orlando Hernandez .10 .30
36 Jeff Shaw .10 .30
37 Matt Lawton .10 .30
38 David Wells .10 .30
39 Bob Abreu .10 .30
40 Jeromy Burnitz .10 .30
41 Deivi Cruz .10 .30
42 Derek Bell .10 .30
43 Rico Brogna .10 .30
44 Dmitri Young .10 .30
45 Chuck Knoblauch .10 .30
46 Johnny Damon .20 .50
47 Brian Meadows .10 .30
48 Jeremi Gonzalez .10 .30
49 Gary DiSarcina .10 .30
50 Frank Thomas .30 .75
51 F.P. Santangelo .10 .30
52 Tom Candiotti .10 .30
53 Shane Reynolds .10 .30
54 Rod Beck .10 .30
55 Rey Ordonez .10 .30
56 Todd Helton .20 .50
57 Mickey Morandini .10 .30
58 Jorge Posada .20 .50
59 Mike Mussina .20 .50
60 Al Leiter .10 .30
61 David Segui .10 .30
62 Brian McRae .10 .30
63 Fred McGriff .20 .50
64 Brett Tomko .10 .30
65 Derek Jeter .75 2.00
66 Sammy Sosa .30 .75
67 Kenny Rogers .10 .30
68 Dave Nilsson .10 .30
69 Eric Young .10 .30
70 Mark McGwire .75 2.00
71 Kenny Lofton .10 .30
72 Tom Glavine .20 .50
73 Joey Hamilton .10 .30
74 John Valentin .10 .30
75 Mariano Rivera .30 .75
76 Ray Durham .10 .30
77 Tony Clark .10 .30
78 Livan Hernandez .10 .30
79 Rickey Henderson .30 .75
80 Vladimir Guerrero .30 .75
81 J.T. Snow .10 .30
82 Juan Guzman .10 .30
83 Darryl Hamilton .10 .30
84 Matt Anderson .10 .30
85 Travis Lee .10 .30
86 Joe Randa .10 .30
87 Dave Dellucci .10 .30
88 Moises Alou .10 .30
89 Alex Gonzalez .10 .30
90 Tony Womack .10 .30
91 Neifi Perez .10 .30
92 Travis Fryman .10 .30
93 Masato Yoshii .10 .30
94 Woody Williams .10 .30
95 Ray Lankford .10 .30
96 Roger Clemens .60 1.50
97 Dustin Hermanson .10 .30
98 Joe Carter .10 .30
99 Jason Schmidt .10 .30
100 Greg Maddux .50 1.25
101 Kevin Tapani .10 .30
102 Charles Johnson .10 .30
103 Derrek Lee .20 .50
104 Pete Harnisch .10 .30
105 Dante Bichette .10 .30
106 Scott Brosius .10 .30
107 Mike Caruso .10 .30
108 Eddie Taubensee .10 .30
109 Jeff Fassero .10 .30
110 Marquis Grissom .10 .30
111 Jose Hernandez .10 .30
112 Chan Ho Park .10 .30
113 Wally Joyner .10 .30
114 Bobby Estalella .10 .30
115 Pedro Martinez .20 .50
116 Shawn Estes .10 .30
117 Walt Weiss .10 .30
118 John Mabry .10 .30
119 Brian Johnson .10 .30
120 Jim Thome .20 .50
121 Bill Spiers .10 .30
122 John Olerud .10 .30
123 Jeff King .10 .30
124 Tim Belcher .10 .30
125 John Wetteland .10 .30
126 Tony Gwynn .40 1.00
127 Brady Anderson .10 .30
128 Randy Winn .10 .30
129 Andy Fox .10 .30
130 Eric Karros .10 .30
131 Kevin Millwood .10 .30
132 Andy Benes .10 .30
133 Andy Ashby .10 .30
134 Ron Coomer .10 .30
135 Juan Gonzalez .10 .30
136 Randy Johnson .30 .75
137 Aaron Sele .10 .30
138 Edgardo Alfonzo .10 .30
139 B.J. Surhoff .10 .30
140 Jose Vizcaino .10 .30
141 Chad Moeller SP RC .75 2.00
142 Mike Zywica SP RC .75 2.00
143 Angel Pena SP .75 2.00
144 Nick Johnson SP RC 1.00 2.50
145 G. Chiaramonte SP RC .75 2.00
146 Kit Pellow SP RC .75 2.00
147 C.Andrews SP RC .75 2.00
148 Jerry Hairston Jr. SP .75 2.00
149 Jason Tyner SP RC .75 2.00
150 Chip Ambres SP RC .75 2.00
151 Pat Burrell SP RC 1.50 4.00
152 Josh McKinley SP RC .75 2.00
153 Choo Freeman SP RC .75 2.00
154 Rick Elder SP RC .75 2.00
155 Eric Valent SP RC .75 2.00
156 J.Winchester SP RC .75 2.00
157 Mike Nannini SP RC .75 2.00
158 Mamon Tucker SP RC .75 2.00
159 Nate Bump SP RC .75 2.00
160 Andy Brown SP RC .75 2.00
161 Troy Glaus .20 .50
162 Adrian Beltre .10 .30
163 Mitch Meluskey .10 .30
164 Alex Gonzalez .10 .30
165 George Lombard .10 .30
166 Eric Chavez .10 .30
167 Ruben Mateo .10 .30
168 Calvin Pickering .10 .30
169 Gabe Kapler .10 .30
170 Bruce Chen .10 .30
171 Darin Erstad .10 .30
172 Sandy Alomar Jr. .10 .30
173 Miguel Cairo .10 .30
174 Jason Kendall .10 .30
175 Cal Ripken 1.00 2.50
176 Darryl Kile .10 .30
177 David Cone .10 .30
178 Mike Sweeney .10 .30
179 Royce Clayton .10 .30
180 Curt Schilling .10 .30
181 Barry Larkin .20 .50
182 Eric Milton .10 .30
183 Ellis Burks .10 .30
184 A.J. Hinch .10 .30
185 Garret Anderson .10 .30
186 Sean Bergman .10 .30
187 Shannon Stewart .10 .30
188 Bernard Gilkey .10 .30
189 Jeff Blauser .10 .30
190 Andruw Jones .20 .50
191 Omar Daal .10 .30
192 Jeff Kent .10 .30
193 Mark Kotsay .10 .30
194 Dave Burba .10 .30
195 Bobby Higginson .10 .30
196 Hideki Irabu .10 .30
197 Jamie Moyer .10 .30
198 Doug Glanville .10 .30
199 Quinton McCracken .10 .30
200 Ken Griffey Jr. .50 1.25
201 Mike Lieberthal .10 .30
202 Carl Everett .10 .30
203 Omar Vizquel .20 .50
204 Mike Lansing .10 .30
205 Manny Ramirez .20 .50
206 Ryan Klesko .10 .30
207 Jeff Montgomery .10 .30
208 Chad Curtis .10 .30
209 Rick Helling .10 .30
210 Justin Thompson .10 .30
211 Tom Goodwin .10 .30
212 Todd Dunwoody .10 .30
213 Kevin Young .10 .30
214 Tony Saunders .10 .30
215 Gary Sheffield .10 .30
216 Jaret Wright .10 .30
217 Quilvio Veras .10 .30
218 Marty Cordova .10 .30
219 Tino Martinez .20 .50
220 Scott Rolen .20 .50
221 Fernando Tatis .10 .30
222 Damion Easley .10 .30
223 Aramis Ramirez .10 .30
224 Brad Radke .10 .30
225 Nomar Garciaparra .50 1.25
226 Magglio Ordonez .10 .30
227 Andy Pettitte .20 .50
228 David Ortiz .30 .75
229 Todd Jones .10 .30
230 Larry Walker .10 .30
231 Tim Wakefield .10 .30
232 Jose Guillen .10 .30
233 Gregg Olson .10 .30
234 Ricky Gutierrez .10 .30
235 Todd Walker .10 .30
236 Abraham Nunez .10 .30
237 Sean Casey .10 .30
238 Greg Norton .10 .30
239 Bret Saberhagen .10 .30
240 Bernie Williams .20 .50
241 Tim Salmon .20 .50
242 Jason Giambi .10 .30
243 Fernando Vina .10 .30
244 Darrin Fletcher .10 .30
245 Mike Bordick .10 .30
246 Dennis Reyes .10 .30
247 Hideo Nomo .30 .75
248 Kevin Stocker .10 .30
249 Mike Hampton .10 .30
250 Kerry Wood .10 .30
251 Ismael Valdes .10 .30
252 Pat Hentgen .10 .30
253 Scott Spiezio .10 .30
254 Chuck Finley .10 .30
255 Troy Glaus .20 .50
256 Bobby Jones .10 .30
257 Wayne Gomes .10 .30
258 Rondell White .10 .30
259 Todd Zeile .10 .30
260 Matt Williams .10 .30
261 Henry Rodriguez .10 .30
262 Matt Stairs .10 .30
263 Jose Valentin .10 .30
264 David Justice .10 .30
265 Javy Lopez .10 .30
266 Matt Morris .10 .30
267 Steve Trachsel .10 .30
268 Edgar Martinez .20 .50
269 Al Martin .10 .30
270 Ivan Rodriguez .20 .50
271 Carlos Delgado .10 .30
272 Mark Grace .20 .50
273 Ugueth Urbina .10 .30
274 Jay Buhner .10 .30
275 Mike Piazza .50 1.25
276 Rick Aguilera .10 .30
277 Javier Valentin .10 .30
278 Brian Anderson .10 .30
279 Cliff Floyd .10 .30
280 Barry Bonds .75 2.00
281 Troy O'Leary .10 .30
282 Seth Greisinger .10 .30
283 Mark Grudzielanek .10 .30
284 Jose Cruz Jr. .10 .30
285 Jeff Bagwell .20 .50
286 John Smoltz .20 .50
287 Jeff Cirillo .10 .30
288 Richie Sexson .10 .30
289 Charles Nagy .10 .30
290 Pedro Martinez .20 .50
291 Juan Encarnacion .10 .30
292 Phil Nevin .10 .30
293 Terry Steinbach .10 .30
294 Miguel Tejada .10 .30
295 Dan Wilson .10 .30
296 Chris Peters .10 .30
297 Brian Moehler .10 .30
298 Jason Christiansen .10 .30
299 Kelly Stinnett .10 .30
300 Dwight Gooden .10 .30
301 Randy Velarde .10 .30
302 Kirt Manwaring .10 .30
303 Jeff Abbott .10 .30
304 Dave Hollins .10 .30
305 Kerry Ligtenberg .10 .30
306 Aaron Boone .10 .30
307 Carlos Hernandez .10 .30
308 Mike Difelice .10 .30
309 Brian Meadows .10 .30
310 Tim Bogar .10 .30
311 Greg Vaughn TR .10 .30
312 Brant Brown TR .10 .30
313 Steve Finley TR .10 .30
314 Bret Boone TR .10 .30
315 Albert Belle TR .10 .30
316 Robin Ventura TR .10 .30
317 Eric Davis TR .10 .30
318 Todd Hundley TR .10 .30
319 Roger Clemens TR .60 1.50
320 Kevin Brown TR .10 .30
321 Jose Offerman TR .10 .30

322 Brian Jordan TR .10 .30
323 Mike Cameron TR .10 .30
324 Bobby Bonilla TR .10 .30
325 Roberto Alomar TR .20 .50
326 Ken Caminiti TR .10 .30
327 Todd Stottlemyre TR .10 .30
328 Randy Johnson TR .30 .75
329 Luis Gonzalez TR .10 .30
330 Rafael Palmeiro TR .20 .50
331 Devon White TR .10 .30
332 Will Clark TR .20 .50
333 Dean Palmer TR .10 .30
334 Gregg Jefferies TR .10 .30
335 Mo Vaughn TR .10 .30
336 Brad Lidge SP RC 1.50 4.00
337 Chris George SP RC .75 2.00
338 Austin Kearns SP RC 1.50 4.00
339 Matt Belisle SP RC .75 2.00
340 Nate Cornejo SP RC .75 2.00
341 Matt Holliday SP RC 3.00 8.00
342 J.M. Gold SP RC .75 2.00
343 Matt Roney SP RC .75 2.00
344 Seth Etherton SP RC .75 2.00
345 Adam Everett SP RC .75 2.00
346 Marlon Anderson SP .75 2.00
347 Ron Belliard SP .75 2.00
348 F.Seguignol SP .75 2.00
349 Michael Barrett SP .75 2.00
350 Dernell Stenson SP .75 2.00
351 Ryan Anderson SP .75 2.00
352 Ramon Hernandez SP .75 2.00
353 Jeremy Giambi SP .75 2.00
354 Ricky Ledee SP .75 2.00
355 Carlos Lee SP .75 2.00

1999 Stadium Club First Day Issue

Randomly inserted in retail packs only at the rate of 1:75 series one packs and 1:60 series two packs, this 355-card set is parallel to Stadium Club Series one base set. Only 170 serially numbered series one sets were produced and 200 serial numbered series two sets were produced.

*STARS: 6X TO 15X BASIC CARDS
*SP 141-160/336-355: 2X TO 5X BASIC SP
SER.1 STATED ODDS 1:75 RETAIL
SER.2 STATED ODDS 1:60 RETAIL

1999 Stadium Club One of a Kind

This set is a parallel version of the regular issue printed on mirrorboard and sequentially numbered to 150. The cards were randomly inserted packs at the rate of 1:53 first series hobby packs, 1:21 first series HTA packs, 1:48 second series retail packs and 1:19 second series HTA packs.

*STARS: 6X TO 15X BASIC CARDS
*SP'S 141-160/336-355: 2X TO 5X BASIC
SER.1 STATED ODDS 1:53 HOBBY, 1:21 HTA
SER.2 STATED ODDS 1:48 HOBBY, 1:19 HTA

1999 Stadium Club Printing Plates

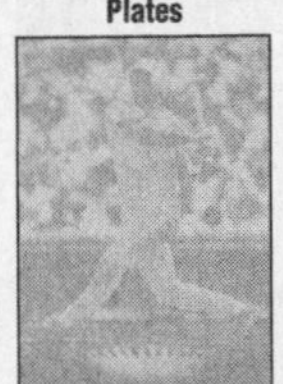

Randomly inserted in Home Team Advantage packs only at the rate of 1:190 first series and 1:175 second series, this 355-card set is a metal-plated parallel version of the Stadium Club base set. Each player has one plate for each of the four printing colors: Cyan, Magenta, Yellow, and Black. No pricing is available due to the scarcity of these cards.

SER.1 STATED ODDS 1:190 HTA
SER.2 STATED ODDS 1:175 HTA

1999 Stadium Club Autographs

This 10-card set features color player photos with the pictured player's autograph and a gold-foil Topps Certified Autograph Issue stamp on the card front. They were inserted exclusively into retail packs as follows: series 1 1:1107, series 2 1:877.

SER.1 STATED ODDS 1:1107 RETAIL
SER.2 STATED ODDS 1:877 RETAIL
CARDS 1-5 IN SER.1, 6-10 IN SER.2
SCA1 Alex Rodriguez 60.00 120.00
SCA2 Chipper Jones 20.00 50.00
SCA3 Barry Bonds 100.00 175.00
SCA4 Tino Martinez 10.00 25.00
SCA5 Ben Grieve 6.00 15.00
SCA6 Juan Gonzalez 10.00 25.00
SCA7 Vladimir Guerrero 15.00 40.00
SCA8 Albert Belle 6.00 15.00
SCA9 Kerry Wood 10.00 25.00
SCA10 Todd Helton 10.00 25.00

1999 Stadium Club Chrome

Randomly inserted in packs at the rate of one in 24 hobby and retail packs and one in six HTA packs, this 40-card set features color player photos printed using chromium technology which gives the cards the shimmering metallic light of fresh steel.

COMPLETE SET (40) 60.00 120.00
COMPLETE SERIES 1 (20) 30.00 60.00
COMPLETE SERIES 2 (20) 30.00 60.00
STATED ODDS 1:24 HOB/RET, 1:6 HTA
*REFRACTORS: 1X TO 2.5X BASIC CHROME
REFRACTOR ODDS 1:96 HOB/RET, 1:24 HTA
SCC1 Nomar Garciaparra 2.50 6.00
SCC2 Kerry Wood .60 1.50
SCC3 Jeff Bagwell 1.00 2.50
SCC4 Ivan Rodriguez 1.00 2.50
SCC5 Albert Belle .60 1.50
SCC6 Gary Sheffield .60 1.50
SCC7 Andruw Jones 1.00 2.50
SCC8 Kevin Brown .60 1.50
SCC9 David Cone .60 1.50
SCC10 Darin Erstad .60 1.50
SCC11 Manny Ramirez 1.00 2.50
SCC12 Larry Walker .60 1.50
SCC13 Mike Piazza 2.50 6.00
SCC14 Cal Ripken 5.00 12.00
SCC15 Pedro Martinez 1.00 2.50
SCC16 Greg Vaughn .60 1.50
SCC17 Barry Bonds 4.00 10.00
SCC18 Mo Vaughn .60 1.50
SCC19 Bernie Williams 1.00 2.50
SCC20 Ken Griffey Jr. 2.50 6.00
SCC21 Alex Rodriguez 2.50 6.00
SCC22 Chipper Jones 1.50 4.00
SCC23 Ben Grieve .60 1.50
SCC24 Frank Thomas 1.50 4.00
SCC25 Derek Jeter 4.00 10.00
SCC26 Sammy Sosa 1.50 4.00
SCC27 Mark McGwire 4.00 10.00
SCC28 Vladimir Guerrero 1.50 4.00
SCC29 Greg Maddux 2.50 6.00
SCC30 Juan Gonzalez .60 1.50
SCC31 Troy Glaus 1.00 2.50
SCC32 Adrian Beltre .60 1.50
SCC33 Mitch Meluskey .60 1.50
SCC34 Alex Gonzalez .60 1.50
SCC35 George Lombard .60 1.50
SCC36 Eric Chavez .60 1.50
SCC37 Ruben Mateo .60 1.50
SCC38 Calvin Pickering .60 1.50
SCC39 Gabe Kapler .60 1.50
SCC40 Bruce Chen .60 1.50

1999 Stadium Club Co-Signers

Randomly inserted in hobby packs only, this 42-card set features color player photos with their autographs and Topps "Certified Autograph Issue" stamp. Cards 1-21 were seeded in first series packs and 22-42 in second series. The cards are divided into four groups. Group A was signed by all four players appearing on the cards. Groups B-D are dual player cards featuring two autographs. Series 1 hobby pack insertion rates are as follows: Group A 1:45,213, Group B 1:3617, Group C 1:1006, and Group D 1:102. Series 2 hobby pack insertion rates are as follows: Group A 1:43,369, Group B 1:8984, Group C 1:2975 and Group D 1:251. Series 2 HTA pack insertion rates are as follows: Group A 1:18,171, Group B 1:3533, Group C 1:1189 and Group D 1:100. Pricing is available for all cards where possible.

SER.1 A ODDS 1:45213 HOB, 1:18085 HTA
SER.2 A ODDS 1:43639 HOB, 1:18171 HTA
SER.1 B ODDS 1:9043 HOB, 1:3617 HTA
SER.2 B ODDS 1:8984 HOB, 1:3533 HTA
SER.1 C ODDS 1:3104 HOB, 1:1006 HTA
SER.2 C ODDS 1:2975 HOB, 1:1189 HTA
SER.1 D ODDS 1:254 HOB, 1:102 HTA
SER.2 D ODDS 1:251 HOB, 1:100 HTA
CS1 Ben Grieve 8.00 20.00
Richie Sexson D
CS2 Todd Helton 30.00 60.00
Troy Glaus D
CS3 Alex Rodriguez 60.00 120.00
Scott Rolen D
CS4 Derek Jeter 150.00 300.00
Chipper Jones D
CS5 Cliff Floyd 8.00 20.00
Eli Marrero D
CS6 Jay Buhner 8.00 20.00
Kevin Young D
CS7 Ben Grieve 15.00 40.00
Troy Glaus C
CS8 Todd Helton 15.00 40.00
Richie Sexson C
CS9 Alex Rodriguez 90.00 150.00
Chipper Jones C
CS10 Derek Jeter 125.00 250.00
Scott Rolen C
CS11 Cliff Floyd 8.00 20.00
Kevin Young C
CS12 Jay Buhner 8.00 20.00
Eli Marrero B
CS13 Ben Grieve 30.00 60.00
Todd Helton B
CS14 Richie Sexson 30.00 60.00
Troy Glaus B
CS15 Alex Rodriguez 250.00 500.00
Derek Jeter B
CS16 Chipper Jones 60.00 120.00
Scott Rolen B
CS17 Cliff Floyd 15.00 40.00
Jay Buhner B
CS18 Eli Marrero 8.00 20.00
Kevin Young B
CS19 Ben Grieve
Todd Helton
Richie Sexson
Troy Glaus A
CS20 Alex Rodriguez
Derek Jeter
Chipper Jones
Scott Rolen A
CS21 Cliff Floyd
Jay Buhner
Eli Marrero
Kevin Young A
CS22 Edgardo Alfonzo 8.00 20.00
Jose Guillen D
CS23 Mike Lowell 8.00 20.00
Ricardo Rincon D
CS24 Juan Gonzalez 8.00 20.00
Vinny Castilla D
CS25 Moises Alou 20.00 50.00
Roger Clemens D
CS26 Scott Spiezio 6.00 15.00
Tony Womack D
CS27 Fernando Vina 6.00 15.00
Quilvio Veras D
CS28 Edgardo Alfonzo 8.00 20.00
Ricardo Rincon C
CS29 Jose Guillen 8.00 20.00
Mike Lowell C
CS30 Juan Gonzalez 8.00 20.00
Moises Alou C
CS31 Roger Clemens 30.00 60.00
Vinny Castilla C
CS32 Scott Spiezio 6.00 15.00
Fernando Vina C
CS33 Tony Womack 8.00 20.00
Quilvio Veras B
CS34 Edgardo Alfonzo 15.00 40.00
Mike Lowell B
CS35 Jose Guillen 15.00 40.00
Ricardo Rincon B
CS36 Juan Gonzalez 150.00 250.00
Roger Clemens B
CS37 Moises Alou 30.00 60.00
Vinny Castilla B
CS38 Scott Spiezio 8.00 20.00
Quilvio Veras B
CS39 Tony Womack 8.00 20.00
Fernando Vina B
CS40 Edgardo Alfonzo
Jose Guillen
Mike Lowell
Ricardo Rincon A
CS41 Juan Gonzalez
Moises Alou
Roger Clemens
Vinny Castilla A
CS42 Scott Spiezio
Tony Womack
Fernando Vina
Quilvio Veras A

1999 Stadium Club Never Compromise

Randomly inserted in packs at the rate of one in 12 hobby and retail packs and one in four HTA packs, this 10-card set features color action photos of top players.

COMPLETE SET (20) 25.00 50.00
COMPLETE SERIES 1 (10) 15.00 30.00
COMPLETE SERIES 2 (10) 10.00 20.00
STATED ODDS 1:12 HOB/RET, 1:4 HTA
NC1 Mark McGwire 2.00 5.00
NC2 Sammy Sosa .75 2.00
NC3 Ken Griffey Jr. 1.25 3.00
NC4 Greg Maddux 1.25 3.00
NC5 Barry Bonds 2.00 5.00
NC6 Alex Rodriguez 1.25 3.00
NC7 Darin Erstad .30 .75
NC8 Roger Clemens 1.50 4.00
NC9 Nomar Garciaparra 1.25 3.00
NC10 Derek Jeter 2.00 5.00
NC11 Cal Ripken 2.50 6.00
NC12 Mike Piazza 1.25 3.00
NC13 Kerry Wood .30 .75
NC14 Andres Galarraga .30 .75
NC15 Vinny Castilla .30 .75
NC16 Jeff Bagwell .50 1.25
NC17 Chipper Jones .75 2.00
NC18 Eric Chavez .30 .75
NC19 Orlando Hernandez .30 .75
NC20 Troy Glaus .50 1.25

1999 Stadium Club Triumvirate Luminous

Randomly inserted in hobby packs at the rate of one in 36 and in retail packs at the rate of one in 48, this 24-card set features color player photos printed on cards made to fit together to form eight different long cards.

COMPLETE SET (48) 135.00 270.00
COMPLETE SERIES 1 (24) 60.00 120.00
COMPLETE SERIES 2 (24) 75.00 150.00
STATED ODDS 1:36 H, 1:48 R, 1:18 HTA
*ILLUMINATOR: 2X TO 5X LUMINOUS
ILLUM.ODDS 1:288 H, 1:384 R, 1:144 HTA
*LUMINESCENT: 1X TO 2.5X LUMINOUS
L'SCENT.ODDS 1:144 H, 1:192 R, 1:72 HTA
T1A Greg Vaughn .75 2.00
T1B Ken Caminiti .75 2.00
T1C Tony Gwynn 2.50 6.00
T2A Andruw Jones 1.25 3.00
T2B Chipper Jones 2.00 5.00
T2C Andres Galarraga .75 2.00
T3A Jay Buhner .75 2.00
T3B Ken Griffey Jr. 3.00 8.00
T3C Alex Rodriguez 3.00 8.00
T4A Derek Jeter 5.00 12.00
T4B Tino Martinez 1.25 3.00
T4C Bernie Williams 1.25 3.00
T5A Brian Jordan .75 2.00
T5B Ray Lankford .75 2.00
T5C Mark McGwire 5.00 12.00
T6A Jeff Bagwell 1.25 3.00
T6B Craig Biggio 1.25 3.00
T6C Randy Johnson 2.00 5.00
T7A Nomar Garciaparra 3.00 8.00
T7B Pedro Martinez 1.25 3.00
T7C Mo Vaughn .75 2.00
T8A Sammy Sosa 2.00 5.00
T8B Mark Grace 1.25 3.00
T8C Kerry Wood .75 2.00
T9A Alex Rodriguez 3.00 8.00
T9B Nomar Garciaparra 3.00 8.00
T9C Derek Jeter 5.00 12.00
T10A Todd Helton 1.25 3.00
T10B Travis Lee .75 2.00
T10C Pat Burrell 1.25 3.00
T11A Greg Maddux 3.00 8.00
T11B Kerry Wood .75 2.00
T11C Tom Glavine 1.25 3.00
T12A Chipper Jones 2.00 5.00
T12B Vinny Castilla .75 2.00
T12C Scott Rolen 1.25 3.00
T13A Juan Gonzalez .75 2.00
T13B Ken Griffey Jr. 3.00 8.00
T13C Ben Grieve .75 2.00
T14A Sammy Sosa 2.00 5.00
T14B Vladimir Guerrero 2.00 5.00
T14C Barry Bonds 5.00 12.00
T15A Frank Thomas 2.00 5.00
T15B Jim Thome 1.25 3.00
T15C Tino Martinez 1.25 3.00
T16A Mark McGwire 5.00 12.00
T16B Andres Galarraga .75 2.00
T16C Jeff Bagwell 1.25 3.00

1999 Stadium Club Video Replay

Randomly inserted in Series two hobby and retail packs at the rate of one in 12 and HTA packs at the rate of one in four, this five-card set features live-action video images of top players on lenticular cards.

COMPLETE SET (5) 5.00 12.00
SER.2 STATED ODDS 1:12 HOB/RET, 1:4 HTA
VR1 Mark McGwire 1.50 4.00
VR2 Sammy Sosa .60 1.50
VR3 Ken Griffey Jr. 1.00 2.50
VR4 Kerry Wood .25 .60
VR5 Alex Rodriguez 1.00 2.50

2000 Stadium Club

This 250-card single series set was released in February, 2000. Six-card hobby and retail packs carried an SRP of $2.00. There was also a HTC (Home Team Collector) fourteen card pack issued with a SRP of $5.00. The last 50 cards were printed in shorter supply the first 200 cards. These cards were inserted one in five packs and one per HTC pack. This was the first time the Stadium Club set was issued in a single series. Notable Rookie Cards include Rick Asadoorian and Bobby Bradley.

COMPLETE SET (250) 50.00 120.00
COMP.SET w/o SP'S (200) 12.50 30.00
COMMON CARD (1-200) .10 .30
COMMON SP (201-250) 1.25 3.00
1 Nomar Garciaparra .50 1.25
2 Brian Jordan .10 .30
3 Mark Grace .20 .50
4 Jeromy Burnitz .10 .30
5 Shane Reynolds .10 .30
6 Alex Gonzalez .10 .30
7 Jose Offerman .10 .30
8 Orlando Hernandez .10 .30
9 Mike Caruso .10 .30
10 Tony Clark .10 .30
11 Sean Casey .10 .30
12 Johnny Damon .20 .50
13 Dante Bichette .10 .30
14 Kevin Young .10 .30
15 Juan Gonzalez .10 .30
16 Chipper Jones .30 .75
17 Quilvio Veras .10 .30
18 Trevor Hoffman .10 .30
19 Roger Cedeno .10 .30
20 Ellis Burks .10 .30
21 Richie Sexson .10 .30
22 Gary Sheffield .10 .30
23 Delino DeShields .10 .30
24 Wade Boggs .20 .50
25 Ray Lankford .10 .30
26 Kevin Appier .10 .30
27 Roy Halladay .10 .30
28 Harold Baines .10 .30
29 Todd Zeile .10 .30
30 Barry Larkin .20 .50
31 Ron Coomer .10 .30
32 Jorge Posada .20 .50
33 Magglio Ordonez .10 .30
34 Brian Giles .10 .30
35 Jeff Kent .10 .30
36 Henry Rodriguez .10 .30
37 Fred McGriff .20 .50
38 Shawn Green .10 .30
39 Derek Bell .10 .30
40 Ben Grieve .10 .30
41 Dave Nilsson .10 .30
42 Mo Vaughn .10 .30
43 Rondell White .10 .30
44 Doug Glanville .10 .30
45 Paul O'Neill .20 .50
46 Carlos Lee .10 .30
47 Vinny Castilla .10 .30
48 Mike Sweeney .10 .30
49 Rico Brogna .10 .30
50 Alex Rodriguez .50 1.25
51 Luis Castillo .10 .30
52 Kevin Brown .20 .50
53 Jose Vidro .10 .30
54 John Smoltz .20 .50
55 Garret Anderson .10 .30
56 Matt Stairs .10 .30
57 Omar Vizquel .20 .50
58 Tom Goodwin .10 .30
59 Scott Brosius .10 .30
60 Robin Ventura .20 .50
61 B.J. Surhoff .10 .30
62 Andy Ashby .10 .30
63 Chris Widger .10 .30
64 Tim Hudson .10 .30
65 Javy Lopez .10 .30
66 Tim Salmon .20 .50
67 Warren Morris .10 .30
68 John Wetteland .10 .30
69 Gabe Kapler .10 .30
70 Bernie Williams .20 .50
71 Rickey Henderson .30 .75
72 Andruw Jones .20 .50
73 Eric Young .10 .30
74 Bob Abreu .10 .30
75 David Cone .10 .30
76 Rusty Greer .10 .30
77 Ron Belliard .10 .30
78 Troy Glaus .10 .30
79 Mike Hampton .10 .30
80 Miguel Tejada .10 .30
81 Jeff Cirillo .10 .30
82 Todd Hundley .10 .30
83 Roberto Alomar .20 .50
84 Charles Johnson .10 .30
85 Rafael Palmeiro .20 .50
86 Doug Mientkiewicz .10 .30
87 Mariano Rivera .30 .75
88 Neifi Perez .10 .30
89 Jermaine Dye .10 .30
90 Ivan Rodriguez .20 .50
91 Jay Buhner .10 .30
92 Pokey Reese .10 .30
93 John Olerud .10 .30
94 Brady Anderson .10 .30
95 Manny Ramirez .20 .50
96 Keith Osik RC .10 .30
97 Mickey Morandini .10 .30
98 Matt Williams .10 .30
99 Eric Karros .10 .30
100 Ken Griffey Jr. .50 1.25
101 Bret Boone .10 .30
102 Ryan Klesko .10 .30
103 Craig Biggio .10 .30
104 John Jaha .10 .30
105 Vladimir Guerrero .30 .75
106 Devon White .10 .30
107 Tony Womack .10 .30
108 Marvin Benard .10 .30
109 Kenny Lofton .10 .30
110 Preston Wilson .10 .30
111 Al Leiter .10 .30
112 Reggie Sanders .10 .30
113 Scott Williamson .10 .30
114 Deivi Cruz .10 .30
115 Carlos Beltran .10 .30
116 Ray Durham .10 .30
117 Ricky Ledee .10 .30
118 Torii Hunter .10 .30
119 John Valentin .10 .30
120 Scott Rolen .20 .50
121 Jason Kendall .10 .30
122 Dave Martinez .10 .30
123 Jim Thome .20 .50
124 David Bell .10 .30
125 Jose Canseco .20 .50
126 Jose Lima .10 .30
127 Carl Everett .10 .30
128 Kevin Millwood .10 .30
129 Bill Spiers .10 .30
130 Omar Daal .10 .30
131 Miguel Cairo .10 .30
132 Mark Grudzielanek .10 .30
133 David Justice .10 .30
134 Russ Ortiz .10 .30
135 Mike Piazza .50 1.25
136 Brian Meadows .10 .30
137 Tony Gwynn .40 1.00
138 Cal Ripken 1.00 2.50
139 Kris Benson .10 .30
140 Larry Walker .10 .30
141 Cristian Guzman .10 .30
142 Tino Martinez .20 .50
143 Chris Singleton .10 .30
144 Lee Stevens .10 .30
145 Rey Ordonez .10 .30
146 Russ Davis .10 .30
147 J.T. Snow .10 .30
148 Luis Gonzalez .10 .30
149 Marquis Grissom .10 .30
150 Greg Maddux .50 1.25
151 Fernando Tatis .10 .30
152 Jason Giambi .10 .30
153 Carlos Delgado .10 .30
154 Joe McEwing .10 .30
155 Raul Mondesi .10 .30
156 Rich Aurilia .10 .30
157 Alex Fernandez .10 .30
158 Albert Belle .10 .30
159 Pat Meares .10 .30
160 Mike Lieberthal .10 .30
161 Mike Cameron .10 .30
162 Juan Encarnacion .10 .30
163 Chuck Knoblauch .10 .30
164 Pedro Martinez .20 .50
165 Randy Johnson .30 .75
166 Shannon Stewart .10 .30
167 Jeff Bagwell .20 .50
168 Edgar Renteria .10 .30
169 Barry Bonds .75 2.00
170 Steve Finley .10 .30
171 Brian Hunter .10 .30
172 Tom Glavine .20 .50
173 Mark Kotsay .10 .30
174 Tony Fernandez .10 .30
175 Sammy Sosa .30 .75
176 Geoff Jenkins .10 .30
177 Adrian Beltre .10 .30
178 Jay Bell .10 .30
179 Mike Bordick .10 .30
180 Ed Sprague .10 .30
181 Dave Roberts .10 .30
182 Greg Vaughn .10 .30
183 Brian Daubach .10 .30
184 Damion Easley .10 .30
185 Carlos Febles .10 .30
186 Kevin Tapani .10 .30
187 Frank Thomas .30 .75
188 Roger Clemens .60 1.50
189 Mike Benjamin .10 .30
190 Curt Schilling .10 .30
191 Edgardo Alfonzo .10 .30
192 Mike Mussina .20 .50
193 Todd Helton .20 .50
194 Todd Jones .10 .30
195 Dean Palmer .10 .30
196 John Flaherty .10 .30
197 Derek Jeter .75 2.00
198 Todd Walker .10 .30
199 Brad Ausmus .10 .30
200 Mark McGwire .75 2.00
201 Erubiel Durazo SP 1.25 3.00
202 Nick Johnson SP 1.25 3.00
203 Ruben Mateo SP 1.25 3.00
204 Lance Berkman SP 1.25 3.00
205 Pat Burrell SP 1.25 3.00
206 Pablo Ozuna SP 1.25 3.00
207 Roosevelt Brown SP 1.25 3.00
208 Alfonso Soriano SP 1.50 4.00
209 A.J. Burnett SP 1.25 3.00
210 Rafael Furcal SP 1.25 3.00
211 Scott Morgan SP 1.25 3.00
212 Adam Piatt SP 1.25 3.00
213 Dee Brown SP 1.25 3.00
214 Corey Patterson SP 1.25 3.00
215 Mickey Lopez SP 1.25 3.00
216 Rob Ryan SP 1.25 3.00
217 Sean Burroughs SP 1.25 3.00
218 Jack Cust SP 1.25 3.00
219 John Patterson SP 1.25 3.00
220 Kit Pellow SP 1.25 3.00
221 Chad Hermansen SP 1.25 3.00
222 Daryle Ward SP 1.25 3.00
223 Jayson Werth SP 1.25 3.00
224 Jason Standridge SP 1.25 3.00
225 Mark Mulder SP 1.25 3.00
226 Peter Bergeron SP 1.25 3.00
227 Willi Mo Pena SP 1.25 3.00
228 Aramis Ramirez SP 1.25 3.00
229 John Sneed SP RC 1.25 3.00
230 Wilton Veras SP 1.25 3.00
231 Josh Hamilton SP 3.00 8.00
232 Eric Munson SP 1.25 3.00
233 Bobby Bradley SP RC 1.25 3.00
234 Larry Bigbie SP RC 1.50 4.00
235 B.J. Garbe SP RC 1.25 3.00
236 Brett Myers SP RC 1.50 4.00
237 Jason Stumm SP RC 1.25 3.00
238 Corey Myers SP RC 1.25 3.00
239 R.Christianson SP RC 1.25 3.00
240 David Walling SP 1.25 3.00
241 Josh Girdley SP 1.25 3.00
242 Omar Ortiz SP 1.25 3.00
243 Jason Jennings SP 1.25 3.00
244 Kyle Snyder SP 1.25 3.00
245 Jay Gehrke SP 1.25 3.00
246 Mike Paradis SP 1.25 3.00
247 Chance Caple SP RC 1.25 3.00
248 B.Christensen SP RC 1.25 3.00
249 Brad Baker SP RC 1.25 3.00
250 R.Asadoorian SP RC 1.25 3.00

2000 Stadium Club First Day Issue

This parallel to the Stadium Club set was inserted at a rate of one in 36 retail packs and were serial numbered to 150. These cards can be identified by the first day issue stamp on the front.

*STARS: 10X TO 25X BASIC CARDS
*SP'S 201-250: 1X TO 2.5X BASIC
*SP RC'S 201-250: 1.25X TO 3X BASIC

2000 Stadium Club One of a Kind

This parallel set was issued at a rate of one in 27 hobby and one in 11 HTC packs. The cards are serial numbered to 150 as well. These cards are differentiated from the regular cards by the mirrorboard technology.

*STARS 1-250: 10X TO 25X BASIC CARDS
*SP'S 201-250: 1X TO 2.5X BASIC
*SP RC'S 201-250: 1.25X TO 3X BASIC

2000 Stadium Club Bats of Brilliance

Issued at a rate of one in 12 hobby packs, one in 15 retail packs and one in six HTC packs these 10 cards feature some of the best clutch hitters in the game.

COMPLETE SET (10) 8.00 20.00
*DIE CUTS: 1.25X TO 3X BASIC BATS
DIE CUT ODDS 1:60 HOB, 1:75 RET, 1:30 HTC
BB1 Mark McGwire 1.50 4.00
BB2 Sammy Sosa .60 1.50
BB3 Jose Canseco .40 1.00
BB4 Jeff Bagwell .40 1.00
BB5 Ken Griffey Jr. 1.00 2.50
BB6 Nomar Garciaparra 1.00 2.50
BB7 Mike Piazza 1.00 2.50
BB8 Alex Rodriguez 1.00 2.50
BB9 Vladimir Guerrero .60 1.50
BB10 Chipper Jones .60 1.50

2000 Stadium Club Capture the Action

Inserted one in 12 hobby and retail packs and one in six HTC packs, these 20 cards feature players who continually hustle when on the field. This set is broken up into three groups: Rookies (CA1 through CA5); Stars (CA6 through CA14) and Legends (CA15 through CA20).

COMPLETE SET (20) 25.00 60.00
*GAME VIEW 1-5: 5X TO 12X BASIC CAPT
*GAME VIEW: 5X TO 12X BASIC CAPTURE
GAME VIEW ODDS 1:508 HOB, 1:203 HTC
GAME VIEW PRINT RUN 100 SERIAL #'d SETS
CA1 Josh Hamilton 1.25 3.00
CA2 Pat Burrell .40 1.00
CA3 Erubiel Durazo .40 1.00
CA4 Alfonso Soriano .50 1.25
CA5 A.J. Burnett .40 1.00
CA6 Alex Rodriguez 1.50 4.00
CA7 Sean Casey .40 1.00
CA8 Derek Jeter 2.50 6.00
CA9 Vladimir Guerrero 1.00 2.50
CA10 Nomar Garciaparra 1.50 4.00
CA11 Mike Piazza 1.50 4.00
CA12 Ken Griffey Jr. 1.50 4.00
CA13 Sammy Sosa 1.00 2.50
CA14 Juan Gonzalez .40 1.00
CA15 Mark McGwire 2.50 6.00
CA16 Ivan Rodriguez .60 1.50
CA17 Barry Bonds 2.50 6.00
CA18 Wade Boggs .60 1.50
CA19 Tony Gwynn 1.25 3.00
CA20 Cal Ripken 3.00 8.00

2000 Stadium Club Chrome Preview

Inserted at a rate of one in 24 for hobby and retail and one in 12 HTC packs, these 20 cards preview the "Chrome" set. These cards carry a "SCC" prefix.

COMPLETE SET (20) 50.00 100.00
*REFRACTOR: 1.25X TO 3X BASIC CHR.PREV.
REFRACTOR ODDS 1:120 HOB/RET, 1:60 HTC
SCC1 Nomar Garciaparra 2.50 6.00
SCC2 Juan Gonzalez 1.50 4.00
SCC3 Chipper Jones 1.50 4.00
SCC4 Alex Rodriguez 2.50 6.00
SCC5 Ivan Rodriguez 1.00 2.50
SCC6 Manny Ramirez 1.00 2.50
SCC7 Ken Griffey Jr. 2.50 6.00
SCC8 Vladimir Guerrero 1.50 4.00
SCC9 Mike Piazza 2.50 6.00
SCC10 Pedro Martinez 1.00 2.50
SCC11 Jeff Bagwell 1.00 2.50
SCC12 Barry Bonds 4.00 10.00
SCC13 Sammy Sosa 1.50 4.00
SCC14 Derek Jeter 4.00 10.00
SCC15 Mark McGwire 4.00 10.00
SCC16 Erubiel Durazo .60 1.50
SCC17 Nick Johnson .60 1.50
SCC18 Pat Burrell .60 1.50
SCC19 Alfonso Soriano 1.50 4.00
SCC20 Adam Piatt .60 1.50

2000 Stadium Club Co-Signers

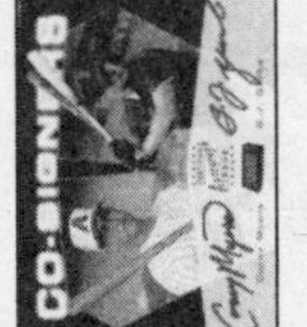

Inserted in hobby packs only at different rates, these 15 cards feature a pair of players who have signed these cards. The odds are broken down like this: Group A was issued one every 10,184 hobby packs and one every 4060 HTC packs. Group B was issued one every 5092 hobby packs and one every 2032 HTC packs. Group C was issued one every 508 hobby packs and one every 203 HTC packs.

CO1 Alex Rodriguez 600.00 1000.00
Derek Jeter A
CO2 Derek Jeter 125.00 200.00
Omar Vizquel B
CO3 Alex Rodriguez 90.00 150.00
Rey Ordonez B
CO4 Derek Jeter 100.00 175.00
Rey Ordonez B
CO5 Omar Vizquel 90.00 150.00
Alex Rodriguez B

CO6 Rey Ordonez 15.00 40.00
Omar Vizquel C
CO7 Wade Boggs 15.00 40.00
Robin Ventura C
CO8 Randy Johnson 75.00 150.00
Mike Mussina C
CO9 Pat Burrell 10.00 25.00
Magglio Ordonez C
CO10 Chad Hermansen 6.00 15.00
Pat Burrell C
CO11 Magglio Ordonez 10.00 25.00
Chad Hermansen C
CO12 Josh Hamilton 15.00 40.00
Corey Myers C
CO13 B.J.Garbe 12.50 30.00
Josh Hamilton C
CO14 Corey Myers 6.00 15.00
B.J. Garbe C
CO15 Tino Martinez 20.00 50.00
Fred McGriff C

2000 Stadium Club Lone Star Signatures

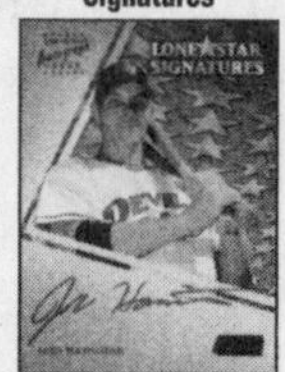

Issued at different rates throughout the various packaging, these 16 cards feature signed cards of various stars. The cards were inserted at these rates: Group 1 was inserted at a rate of one in 1981 retail packs, one in 1979 hobby packs and one in 792 HTC packs. Group 2 was inserted at a rate of one in 2421 retail packs, one in 2374 hobby packs and one in 946 HTC packs. Group 3 was issued at the same rate as Group 1 (1:1979 hobby, 1:1981 retail; 1:792 HTC packs). Group 4 were issued at a rate of one in 424 hobby packs, one in 423 retail packs and one in 169 HTC packs. These cards are authenticated with a "Topps Certified Autograph" stamp as well as a "Topps3M" sticker.

LS1 Derek Jeter G1 75.00 150.00
LS2 Alex Rodriguez G1 90.00 150.00
LS3 Wade Boggs G1 15.00 40.00
LS4 Robin Ventura G1 6.00 15.00
LS5 Randy Johnson G2 40.00 80.00
LS6 Mike Mussina G2 10.00 25.00
LS7 Tino Martinez G3 20.00 50.00
LS8 Fred McGriff G3 20.00 50.00
LS9 Omar Vizquel G4 10.00 25.00
LS10 Rey Ordonez G4 4.00 10.00
LS11 Pat Burrell G4 6.00 15.00
LS12 Chad Hermansen G4 4.00 10.00
LS13 Magglio Ordonez G4 6.00 15.00
LS14 Josh Hamilton G4 20.00 50.00
LS15 Corey Myers G4 4.00 10.00
LS16 B.J. Garbe G4 4.00 10.00

2000 Stadium Club Onyx Extreme

Inserted at a rate of one in 12 hobby, one in 15 retail and one in six HTC packs, these 10 cards feature 10 cards printed using black styrene technology with silver foil stamping.

COMPLETE SET (10) 10.00 25.00
*DIE CUTS: 1.25X TO 3X BASIC ONYX
DIE CUT ODDS 1:60 HOB, 1:75 RET, 1:30 HTC
OE1 Ken Griffey Jr. 1.00 2.50
OE2 Derek Jeter 1.50 4.00
OE3 Vladimir Guerrero .60 1.50
OE4 Nomar Garciaparra 1.00 2.50
OE5 Barry Bonds 1.50 4.00
OE6 Alex Rodriguez 1.00 2.50
OE7 Sammy Sosa .60 1.50
OE8 Ivan Rodriguez .40 1.00
OE9 Larry Walker .25 .60
OE10 Andruw Jones .40 1.00

2000 Stadium Club Scenes

Inserted as a box-topper in hobby and HTC boxes, these eight cards which measure 2 1/2" by 4 11/16" feature superstar players in a special "widevision" format.

COMPLETE SET (8) 10.00 25.00
SCS1 Mark McGwire 2.00 5.00
SCS2 Alex Rodriguez 1.25 3.00
SCS3 Cal Ripken 2.50 6.00
SCS4 Sammy Sosa .75 2.00
SCS5 Derek Jeter 2.00 5.00
SCS6 Ken Griffey Jr. 1.25 3.00
SCS7 Nomar Garciaparra 1.25 3.00
SCS8 Chipper Jones .75 2.00

2000 Stadium Club Souvenir

Inserted exclusively into hobby packs at a rate of one in 339 hobby packs and one in 136 HTC packs, these cards feature die-cut technology which incorporates an actual piece of a game-used uniform.

S1 Wade Boggs 10.00 25.00
S2 Edgardo Alfonzo 4.00 10.00
S3 Robin Ventura 6.00 15.00

2000 Stadium Club 3 X 3 Luminous

Inserted at a rate of one in 18 hobby, one in 24 retail and one in nine HTC packs, these 30 cards can be fused together to form one very oversized card. The luminous variety is the most common of the three forms used (Luminous, Luminescent and Illuminator).

COMPLETE SET (30) 60.00 120.00
*ILLUMINATOR: 1.5X TO 4X LUMINOUS
ILLUM ODDS 1:144 HOB, 1:192 RET, 1:72 HTC
*L'SCENT: .75X TO 2X LUMINOUS
L'SCENT ODDS 1:72 HOB, 1:96 RET, 1:36 HTC
1A Randy Johnson 1.50 4.00
1B Pedro Martinez 1.00 2.50
1C Greg Maddux 2.50 6.00
2A Mike Piazza 2.50 6.00
2B Ivan Rodriguez 1.00 2.50
2C Mike Lieberthal .60 1.50
3A Mark McGwire 4.00 10.00
3B Jeff Bagwell 1.00 2.50
3C Sean Casey .60 1.50
4A Craig Biggio 1.00 2.50
4B Roberto Alomar 1.00 2.50
4C Jay Bell .60 1.50
5A Chipper Jones 1.50 4.00
5B Matt Williams .60 1.50
5C Robin Ventura 1.00 2.50
6A Alex Rodriguez 2.50 6.00
6B Derek Jeter 4.00 10.00
6C Nomar Garciaparra 2.50 6.00
7A Barry Bonds 4.00 10.00
7B Luis Gonzalez .60 1.50
7C Dante Bichette .60 1.50
8A Ken Griffey Jr. 2.50 6.00
8B Bernie Williams 1.00 2.50
8C Andruw Jones 1.00 2.50
9A Manny Ramirez 1.00 2.50
9B Sammy Sosa 1.50 4.00
9C Juan Gonzalez .60 1.50
10A Jose Canseco 1.00 2.50
10B Frank Thomas 1.50 4.00
10C Rafael Palmeiro 1.00 2.50

2001 Stadium Club

The 2001 Stadium Club product was released in late December, 2000 and features a 200-card base set. The set is broken into tiers as follows: 175 Base Veterans and 25 Prospects (1:6). Each pack contained seven cards and carried a suggested retail price of $1.99.

COMPLETE SET (200) 50.00 120.00
COMP.SET w/o SP's (175) 10.00 25.00
COMMON CARD (1-150) .10 .30
COMMON SP (151-200) 1.25 3.00
1 Nomar Garciaparra .50 1.25
2 Chipper Jones .30 .75
3 Jeff Bagwell .20 .50
4 Chad Kreuter .10 .30
5 Randy Johnson .30 .75
6 Mike Hampton .10 .30
7 Barry Larkin .20 .50
8 Bernie Williams .20 .50
9 Chris Singleton .10 .30
10 Larry Walker .10 .30
11 Brad Ausmus .10 .30
12 Ron Coomer .10 .30
13 Edgardo Alfonzo .10 .30
14 Delino DeShields .10 .30
15 Tony Gwynn .40 1.00
16 Andruw Jones .20 .50
17 Raul Mondesi .10 .30
18 Troy Glaus .10 .30
19 Ben Grieve .10 .30
20 Sammy Sosa .30 .75
21 Fernando Vina .10 .30
22 Jeromy Burnitz .10 .30
23 Jay Bell .10 .30
24 Pete Harnisch .10 .30
25 Barry Bonds .75 2.00
26 Eric Karros .10 .30
27 Alex Gonzalez .10 .30
28 Mike Lieberthal .10 .30
29 Juan Encarnacion .10 .30
30 Derek Jeter .75 2.00
31 Luis Sojo .10 .30
32 Eric Milton .10 .30
33 Aaron Boone .10 .30
34 Roberto Alomar .20 .50
35 John Olerud .10 .30
36 Orlando Cabrera .10 .30
37 Shawn Green .10 .30
38 Roger Cedeno .10 .30
39 Garret Anderson .10 .30
40 Jim Thome .20 .50
41 Gabe Kapler .10 .30
42 Mo Vaughn .10 .30
43 Sean Casey .10 .30
44 Preston Wilson .10 .30
45 Javy Lopez .10 .30
46 Ryan Klesko .10 .30
47 Ray Durham .10 .30
48 Dean Palmer .10 .30
49 Jorge Posada .20 .50
50 Alex Rodriguez .50 1.25
51 Tom Glavine .20 .50
52 Ray Lankford .10 .30
53 Jose Canseco .20 .50
54 Tim Salmon .20 .50
55 Cal Ripken 1.00 2.50
56 Bob Abreu .10 .30
57 Robin Ventura .10 .30
58 Damion Easley .10 .30
59 Paul O'Neill .20 .50
60 Ivan Rodriguez .20 .50
61 Carl Everett .10 .30
62 Doug Glanville .10 .30
63 Jeff Kent .10 .30
64 Jay Buhner .10 .30
65 Cliff Floyd .10 .30
66 Rick Ankiel .10 .30
67 Mark Grace .20 .50
68 Brian Jordan .10 .30
69 Craig Biggio .20 .50
70 Carlos Delgado .10 .30
71 Brad Radke .10 .30
72 Greg Maddux .50 1.25
73 Al Leiter .10 .30
74 Pokey Reese .10 .30
75 Todd Helton .20 .50
76 Mariano Rivera .30 .75
77 Shane Spencer .10 .30
78 Jason Kendall .10 .30
79 Chuck Knoblauch .10 .30
80 Scott Rolen .20 .50
81 Jose Offerman .10 .30
82 J.T. Snow .10 .30
83 Pat Meares .10 .30
84 Quilvio Veras .10 .30
85 Edgar Renteria .10 .30
86 Luis Matos .10 .30
87 Adrian Beltre .10 .30
88 Luis Gonzalez .10 .30
89 Rickey Henderson .30 .75
90 Brian Giles .10 .30
91 Carlos Febles .10 .30
92 Tino Martinez .20 .50
93 Magglio Ordonez .10 .30
94 Rafael Furcal .10 .30
95 Mike Mussina .20 .50
96 Gary Sheffield .10 .30
97 Kenny Lofton .10 .30
98 Fred McGriff .20 .50
99 Ken Caminiti .10 .30
100 Mark McGwire .75 2.00
101 Tom Goodwin .10 .30
102 Mark Grudzielanek .10 .30
103 Derek Bell .10 .30
104 Mike Lowell .10 .30
105 Jeff Cirillo .10 .30
106 Orlando Hernandez .10 .30
107 Jose Valentin .10 .30
108 Warren Morris .10 .30
109 Mike Williams .10 .30
110 Greg Zaun .10 .30
111 Jose Vidro .10 .30
112 Omar Vizquel .20 .50
113 Vinny Castilla .10 .30
114 Gregg Jefferies .10 .30
115 Kevin Brown .10 .30
116 Shannon Stewart .10 .30
117 Marquis Grissom .10 .30
118 Manny Ramirez .20 .50
119 Albert Belle .10 .30
120 Bret Boone .10 .30
121 Johnny Damon .20 .50
122 Juan Gonzalez .10 .30
123 David Justice .10 .30
124 Jeffrey Hammonds .10 .30
125 Ken Griffey Jr. .50 1.25
126 Mike Sweeney .10 .30
127 Tony Clark .10 .30
128 Todd Zeile .10 .30
129 Mark Johnson .10 .30
130 Matt Williams .10 .30
131 Geoff Jenkins .10 .30
132 Jason Giambi .10 .30
133 Steve Finley .10 .30
134 Derrek Lee .20 .50
135 Royce Clayton .10 .30
136 Joe Randa .10 .30
137 Rafael Palmeiro .20 .50
138 Kevin Young .10 .30
139 Mike Redmond .10 .30
140 Vladimir Guerrero .30 .75
141 Greg Vaughn .10 .30
142 Jermaine Dye .10 .30
143 Roger Clemens .60 1.50
144 Denny Hocking .10 .30
145 Frank Thomas .30 .75
146 Carlos Beltran .10 .30
147 Eric Young .10 .30
148 Pat Burrell .10 .30
149 Pedro Martinez .20 .50
150 Mike Piazza .50 1.25
151 Adrian Gonzalez 1.25 3.00
152 Adam Johnson .20 .50
153 Luis Montanez SP RC 1.25 3.00
154 Mike Stodolka .20 .50
155 Phil Dumatrait .20 .50
156 Sean Burnett SP 1.25 3.00
157 Dominic Rich SP RC 1.25 3.00
158 Adam Wainwright .40 1.00
159 Scott Thorman .20 .50
160 Scott Heard SP 1.25 3.00
161 Chad Petty SP RC 1.25 3.00
162 Matt Wheatland .20 .50
163 Bryan Digby .20 .50
164 Rocco Baldelli .20 .50
165 Grady Sizemore .75 2.00
166 Brian Sellier SP RC 1.25 3.00
167 Rick Brosseau SP RC 1.25 3.00
168 Shawn Fagan SP RC 1.25 3.00
169 Sean Smith SP 1.25 3.00
170 Chris Bass SP RC 1.25 3.00
171 Corey Patterson .20 .50
172 Sean Burroughs .20 .50
173 Ben Petrick .20 .50
174 Mike Glendenning .20 .50
175 Barry Zito .30 .75
176 Milton Bradley .20 .50
177 Bobby Bradley .20 .50
178 Jason Hart .20 .50
179 Ryan Anderson .20 .50
180 Ben Sheets .30 .75
181 Adam Everett .20 .50
182 Alfonso Soriano .20 .50
183 Josh Hamilton .40 1.00
184 Eric Munson .20 .50
185 Chin-Feng Chen .20 .50
186 Tim Christman SP RC 1.25 3.00
187 J.R. House SP 1.25 3.00
188 B.Parker SP RC 1.25 3.00
189 Sean Fesh SP RC 1.25 3.00
190 Joel Pineiro SP 1.25 3.00
191 Oscar Ramirez SP RC 1.25 3.00
192 Alex Santos SP RC 1.25 3.00
193 Eddy Reyes SP RC 1.25 3.00
194 Mike Jacobs SP RC 6.00 15.00
195 Erick Almonte SP RC 1.25 3.00
196 B.Claussen SP RC 1.25 3.00
197 Kris Keller SP RC 1.25 3.00
198 Wilson Betemit SP RC 3.00 8.00
199 Andy Phillips SP RC 6.00 15.00
200 A.Pettyjohn SP RC 1.25 3.00

2001 Stadium Club Beam Team

Randomly inserted into packs at one in 175 Hobby, and one in 68 HTA, this 30-card die-cut insert set features players who possess unparalleled style to accompany their world-class talent. Please note that these cards are individually serial numbered to 500, and that the card backs carry a "BT" prefix.

BT1 Sammy Sosa 5.00 12.00
BT2 Mark McGwire 12.50 30.00
BT3 Vladimir Guerrero 5.00 12.00
BT4 Chipper Jones 5.00 12.00
BT5 Manny Ramirez 3.00 8.00
BT6 Derek Jeter 12.50 30.00
BT7 Alex Rodriguez 8.00 20.00
BT8 Cal Ripken 15.00 40.00
BT9 Ken Griffey Jr. 8.00 20.00
BT10 Greg Maddux 8.00 20.00
BT11 Barry Bonds 12.50 30.00
BT12 Pedro Martinez 3.00 8.00
BT13 Nomar Garciaparra 8.00 20.00
BT14 Randy Johnson 5.00 12.00
BT15 Frank Thomas 5.00 12.00
BT16 Ivan Rodriguez 3.00 8.00
BT17 Jeff Bagwell 3.00 8.00
BT18 Mike Piazza 8.00 20.00
BT19 Todd Helton 3.00 8.00
BT20 Shawn Green 2.00 5.00
BT21 Juan Gonzalez 2.00 5.00
BT22 Larry Walker 2.00 5.00
BT23 Tony Gwynn 8.00 20.00
BT24 Pat Burrell 2.00 5.00
BT25 Rafael Furcal 2.00 5.00
BT26 Corey Patterson 2.00 5.00
BT27 Chin-Feng Chen 2.00 5.00
BT28 Sean Burroughs 2.00 5.00
BT29 Ryan Anderson 2.00 5.00
BT30 Josh Hamilton 4.00 10.00

2001 Stadium Club Capture the Action

Randomly inserted into packs at one in eight HOB/RET and one in two HTA, this 15-card insert features transformer technology that open up to enlarged action photos of ballplayers at the top of their game. Card backs carry a "CA" prefix.

COMPLETE SET (15) 12.50 30.00
*GAME VIEW: 10X TO 25X BASIC CAPTURE
GAME VIEW ODDS 1:577 HOBBY, 1:224 HTA
GAME VIEW PRINT RUN 100 SERIAL #'d SETS
CA1 Cal Ripken 1.50 4.00
CA2 Alex Rodriguez .75 2.00
CA3 Mike Piazza .75 2.00
CA4 Mark McGwire 1.25 3.00
CA5 Greg Maddux .75 2.00
CA6 Derek Jeter 1.25 3.00
CA7 Chipper Jones .50 1.25
CA8 Pedro Martinez .40 1.00
CA9 Ken Griffey Jr. .75 2.00
CA10 Nomar Garciaparra .75 2.00
CA11 Randy Johnson .50 1.25
CA12 Sammy Sosa .50 1.25
CA13 Vladimir Guerrero .50 1.25
CA14 Barry Bonds 1.25 3.00
CA15 Ivan Rodriguez .40 1.00

2001 Stadium Club Co-Signers

Randomly inserted into packs at one in 962 Hobby and one in 374 HTA packs, this nine-card insert features authenticated autographs of two players on the same card. Please note that the Chipper Jones/Troy Glaus and the Corey Patterson/Nick Johnson cards packed out as exchange cards, and must be redeemed by 11/30/01.

CO1 Nomar Garciaparra 300.00 500.00
Derek Jeter
CO2 Roberto Alomar 20.00 50.00
Edgardo Alfonzo
CO3 Rick Ankiel 15.00 40.00
Kevin Millwood
CO4 Chipper Jones 40.00 80.00
Troy Glaus
CO5 Magglio Ordonez 15.00 40.00
Bob Abreu
CO6 Adam Piatt 10.00 25.00
Sean Burroughs
CO7 Corey Patterson 15.00 40.00
Nick Johnson
CO8 Adrian Gonzalez 20.00 50.00
Rocco Baldelli
CO9 Adam Johnson 10.00 25.00
Mike Stodolka

2001 Stadium Club Diamond Pearls

Randomly inserted into packs at one in eight HOB/RET packs, and one in 3 HTA packs; this 20-card insert features players that are the most sought after treasures in the game today. Card backs carry a "DP" prefix.

COMPLETE SET (20) 20.00 50.00
DP1 Ken Griffey Jr. 1.25 3.00
DP2 Alex Rodriguez 1.25 3.00
DP3 Derek Jeter 2.00 5.00
DP4 Chipper Jones .75 2.00
DP5 Nomar Garciaparra 1.25 3.00

DP6 Vladimir Guerrero .75 2.00
DP7 Jeff Bagwell .60 1.50
DP8 Cal Ripken 2.50 6.00
DP9 Sammy Sosa .75 2.00
DP10 Mark McGwire 2.00 5.00
DP11 Frank Thomas .75 2.00
DP12 Pedro Martinez .60 1.50
DP13 Manny Ramirez .60 1.50
DP14 Randy Johnson .75 2.00
DP15 Barry Bonds 2.00 5.00
DP16 Ivan Rodriguez .60 1.50
DP17 Greg Maddux 1.25 3.00
DP18 Mike Piazza 1.25 3.00
DP19 Todd Helton .60 1.50
DP20 Shawn Green .60 1.50

2001 Stadium Club King of the Hill Dirt Relic

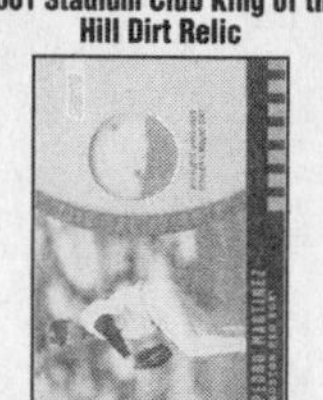

Randomly inserted into packs at one in 20 HTA, this five-card insert features game-used dirt cards from the pitchers mound of today's top pitchers. The Topps Company announced that the ten exchange subjects from Stadium Club Play at the Plate, King of the Hill, and Souvenirs contain the wrong card back stating that they were autographed. None of these cards are actually autographed. Also note that these cards were inserted into packs with a white "waxpaper" covering to protect the cards. Card backs carry a "KH" prefix. Please note that Greg Maddux and Rick Ankiel both packed out as exchange cards and must be returned to Topps by 11/30/01.

KH1 Pedro Martinez 4.00 10.00
KH2 Randy Johnson 4.00 10.00
KH3 G.Maddux ERR 4.00 10.00
KH4 R.Ankiel ERR 3.00 8.00
KH5 Kevin Brown 3.00 8.00

2001 Stadium Club Lone Star Signatures

Randomly inserted into packs, this 18-card inserrt features authentic autographs from some of the Major Leagues most prolific players. Please note that this insert was broken into four tiers as follows: Group A (1:937 HOB/RET, 1:364 HTA), Group B (1:1010 HOB/RET, 1:392 HTA), Group C (1:1541 HOB/RET, 1:600 HTA), and Group D (1:354 HOB/RET, 1:138 HTA). The overall odds for pulling an autograph was one in 181 HOB/RET and one in 70 HTA.

GROUP A ODDS 1:937 H/R 1:364 HTA
GROUP B ODDS 1:1010 H/R 1:392 HTA
GROUP C ODDS 1:1541 H/R 1:600 HTA
GROUP D ODDS 1:354 H/R 1:138 HTA
LS1 Nomar Garciaparra A 50.00 100.00
LS2 Derek Jeter A 100.00 200.00
LS3 Edgardo Alfonzo A 10.00 25.00
LS4 Roberto Alomar A 30.00 60.00
LS5 Magglio Ordonez A 10.00 25.00
LS6 Bobby Abreu A 15.00 40.00
LS7 Chipper Jones A 20.00 50.00
LS8 Troy Glaus A 15.00 40.00
LS9 Nick Johnson B 6.00 15.00
LS10 Adam Piatt B 6.00 15.00
LS11 Sean Burroughs B 4.00 10.00
LS12 Corey Patterson B 4.00 10.00
LS13 Rick Ankiel C 10.00 25.00
LS14 Kevin Millwood C 6.00 15.00
LS15 Adrian Gonzalez D 20.00 50.00
LS16 Adam Johnson D 4.00 10.00
LS17 Rocco Baldelli D 6.00 15.00
LS18 Mike Stodolka D 4.00 10.00

2001 Stadium Club Play at the Plate Dirt Relic

Randomly inserted into packs at one in 10 HTA, this nine-card insert features game-used dirt from the batter's box in which these top players played in. The Topps Company announced that the ten exchange subjects from Stadium Club Play at the Plate, King of the Hill, and Souvenirs contain the wrong card back stating that they were autographed. None of these cards are actually autographed. Please note that both Chipper Jones and Jeff Bagwell are number PP6. Also note that these cards were inserted into packs with a white "waxpaper" covering to protect the cards. The exchange deadline for these cards was 11/30/01.

PP1 Mark McGwire 15.00 40.00
ERR
PP2 S.Sosa ERR 4.00 10.00
PP3 Vladimir Guerrero 4.00 10.00
PP4 Ken Griffey Jr. 6.00 15.00
ERR
PP5 Mike Piazza 4.00 10.00
PP6 J.Bagwell ERR 4.00 10.00
PP6 C.Jones ERR 4.00 10.00
PP7 Barry Bonds 10.00 25.00
PP8 Alex Rodriguez 6.00 15.00
PP10 Nomar Garciaparra 6.00 15.00
ERR

2001 Stadium Club Prospect Performance

Randomly inserted into packs at one in 262 HOB/RET and one in 102 HTA, this 20-card insert features game-used jersey cards from some of the hottest young players in the Major Leagues. Card backs carry a "PRP" prefix.

PRP1 Chin-Feng Chen 40.00 80.00
PRP2 Bobby Bradley 3.00 8.00
PRP3 Tomokazu Ohka 4.00 10.00
PRP4 Kurt Ainsworth 3.00 8.00
PRP5 Craig Anderson 3.00 8.00
PRP6 Josh Hamilton 6.00 15.00
PRP7 Felipe Lopez 4.00 10.00
PRP8 Ryan Anderson 3.00 8.00
PRP9 Alex Escobar 3.00 8.00
PRP10 Ben Sheets 6.00 15.00
PRP11 Ntema Ndungidi 3.00 8.00
PRP12 Eric Munson 3.00 8.00
PRP13 Aaron Myette 3.00 8.00
PRP14 Jack Cust 3.00 8.00
PRP15 Julio Zuleta 3.00 8.00
PRP16 Corey Patterson 3.00 8.00
PRP17 Carlos Pena 3.00 8.00
PRP18 Marcus Giles 4.00 10.00
PRP19 Travis Wilson 3.00 8.00
PRP20 Barry Zito 6.00 15.00

2001 Stadium Club Souvenirs

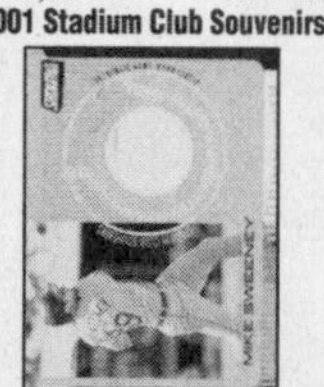

Randomly inserted into HTA packs, this eight-card insert features game-used bat cards and game-used jersey cards of modern superstars. Card backs carry a "SCS" prefix. Please note that the Topps Company announced that the ten exchange subjects from Stadium Club Play at the Plate, King of the Hill, and Souvenirs contain the wrong card back stating that they were autographed. None of these cards are actually autographed. Also note that cards of Scott Rolen, Matt Lawton, Jose Vidro, and Pat Burrell all packed out as exchange cards. These cards needed to have been returned to Topps by 11/30/01.

GROUP A BAT ODDS 1:849 H/R, 1:330 HTA
GROUP B BAT ODDS 1:2164 H/R, 1:847 HTA
SCS1 Scott Rolen 6.00 15.00
Bat A ERR
SCS2 Larry Walker Bat B 6.00 15.00
SCS3 Rafael Furcal Bat A 6.00 15.00
SCS4 Darin Erstad Bat A 6.00 15.00
SCS5 Mike Sweeney Jsy 4.00 10.00
SCS6 Matt Lawton 4.00 10.00
Jsy ERR
SCS7 Jose Vidro 4.00 10.00
Jsy ERR
SCS8 Pat Burrell 4.00 10.00
Jsy ERR

2002 Stadium Club

This 125 card set was issued in late 2001. The set was issued in either six card regular packs or 15 card HTA packs. Cards numbered 101-125 were short printed and are serial numbered to 2999.

COMP.SET w/o SP's (100) 12.50 30.00
COMMON CARD (1-100) .10 .30
COMMON (101-125) 10.00 25.00
1 Pedro Martinez .20 .50
2 Derek Jeter .75 2.00
3 Chipper Jones .30 .75
4 Roberto Alomar .20 .50
5 Albert Pujols 5.00 12.00
6 Bret Boone .10 .30
7 Alex Rodriguez .50 1.25
8 Jose Cruz Jr. .10 .30
9 Mike Hampton .10 .30
10 Vladimir Guerrero .30 .75
11 Jim Edmonds .10 .30
12 Luis Gonzalez .10 .30
13 Jeff Kent .10 .30
14 Mike Piazza .50 1.25
15 Ben Sheets .10 .30
16 Tsuyoshi Shinjo .10 .30
17 Pat Burrell UER .10 .30
Card has a photo of Scott Rolen
18 Jermaine Dye .10 .30
19 Rafael Furcal .10 .30
20 Randy Johnson .30 .75
21 Carlos Delgado .10 .30
22 Roger Clemens .60 1.50
23 Eric Chavez .10 .30
24 Nomar Garciaparra .50 1.25
25 Ivan Rodriguez .20 .50
26 Juan Gonzalez .10 .30
27 Reggie Sanders .10 .30
28 Jeff Bagwell .20 .50
29 Kazuhiro Sasaki .10 .30
30 Larry Walker .10 .30
31 Ben Grieve .10 .30
32 David Justice .10 .30
33 David Wells .10 .30
34 Kevin Brown .10 .30
35 Miguel Tejada .10 .30
36 Jorge Posada .20 .50
37 Javy Lopez .10 .30
38 Cliff Floyd .10 .30
39 Carlos Lee .10 .30
40 Manny Ramirez .20 .50
41 Jim Thome .20 .50
42 Pokey Reese .10 .30
43 Scott Rolen .20 .50
44 Richie Sexson .10 .30
45 Dean Palmer .10 .30
46 Rafael Palmeiro .20 .50
47 Alfonso Soriano .10 .30
48 Craig Biggio .20 .50
49 Troy Glaus .10 .30
50 Andruw Jones .20 .50
51 Ichiro Suzuki .60 1.50
52 Kenny Lofton .10 .30
53 Hideo Nomo .30 .75
54 Magglio Ordonez .10 .30
55 Brad Penny .10 .30
56 Omar Vizquel .20 .50
57 Mike Sweeney .10 .30
58 Gary Sheffield .10 .30
59 Ken Griffey Jr. .50 1.25
60 Curt Schilling .10 .30
61 Bobby Higginson .10 .30
62 Terrence Long .10 .30
63 Moises Alou .10 .30
64 Sandy Alomar Jr. .10 .30
65 Cristian Guzman .10 .30
66 Sammy Sosa .30 .75
67 Jose Vidro .10 .30
68 Edgar Martinez .20 .50
69 Jason Giambi .10 .30
70 Mark McGwire .75 2.00
71 Barry Bonds .75 2.00
72 Greg Vaughn .10 .30
73 Phil Nevin .10 .30
74 Jason Kendall .10 .30
75 Greg Maddux .50 1.25
76 Jeromy Burnitz .10 .30
77 Mike Mussina .20 .50
78 Johnny Damon .20 .50
79 Shawn Green .10 .30
80 Jimmy Rollins .10 .30
81 Edgardo Alfonzo .10 .30
82 Barry Larkin .20 .50
83 Raul Mondesi .10 .30
84 Preston Wilson .10 .30
85 Mike Lieberthal .10 .30
86 J.D. Drew .10 .30
87 Ryan Klesko .10 .30
88 David Segui .10 .30
89 Derek Bell .10 .30
90 Bernie Williams .20 .50
91 Doug Mientkiewicz .10 .30
92 Rich Aurilia .10 .30
93 Ellis Burks .10 .30
94 Placido Polanco .10 .30
95 Darin Erstad .10 .30
96 Brian Giles .10 .30
97 Geoff Jenkins .10 .30
98 Kerry Wood .10 .30
99 Mariano Rivera .30 .75
100 Todd Helton .20 .50
101 Adam Dunn FS 10.00 25.00
102 Grant Balfour FS 10.00 25.00
103 Jae Seo FS 10.00 25.00
104 Hank Blalock FS 10.00 25.00
105 Chris George FS 10.00 25.00
106 Jack Cust FS 10.00 25.00
107 Juan Cruz FS 10.00 25.00
108 Adrian Gonzalez FS 10.00 25.00
109 Nick Johnson FS 10.00 25.00
110 Jeff DaVanon FS 10.00 25.00
111 Juan Diaz FS 10.00 25.00
112 B. Duckworth FS 10.00 25.00
113 Jason Lane FS 10.00 25.00
114 Seung Song FS 10.00 25.00
115 Morgan Ensberg FS 10.00 25.00
116 Marlyn Tisdale FY RC 10.00 25.00
117 Jason Botts FY RC 6.00 15.00
118 Henry Pichardo FY RC 10.00 25.00
119 J. Rodriguez FY RC 10.00 25.00
120 Mike Peeples FY RC 10.00 25.00
121 Rob Bowen EFY RC 10.00 25.00
122 Jeremy Affeldt EFY 10.00 25.00
123 Jorge Buret EFY RC 10.00 25.00
124 Manny Ravelo EFY RC 10.00 25.00
125 Eudy Lajara EFY RC 10.00 25.00
NNO B.Bonds AU Ball 50.00 100.00

2002 Stadium Club All-Star Relics

Randomly inserted in packs, these 28 cards feature relics of players who participated in the All-Star game. Depending on which group the player belonged to there could be between 400 and 4800 of each card printed.

GROUP 1 ODDS 1:477 H, 1:548 R, 1:80 HTA
GROUP 1 PRINT RUN 400 SERIAL #'d SETS
GROUP 2 ODDS 1:795 H, 1:915 R, 1:133 HTA
GROUP 2 PRINT RUN 800 SERIAL #'d SETS

GROUP 3 ODDS 1:199 H, 1:247 R, 1:33 HTA
GROUP 3 PRINT RUN 1200 SERIAL #'d SETS
GROUP 4 ODDS 1:199 H, 1:247 R, 1:33 HTA
GROUP 4 PRINT RUN 2400 SERIAL #'d SETS
GROUP 5 ODDS 1:265 H, 1:305 R, 1:44 HTA
GROUP 5 PRINT RUN 3600 SERIAL #'d SETS
GROUP 6 ODDS 1:397 H, 1:457 R, 1:67 HTA
GROUP 6 PRINT RUN 4800 SERIAL #'d SETS
SCASAP Albert Pujols Bat/800 G2 10.00 25.00
SCASBB Barry Bonds Uni/4800 G6 12.50 30.00
SCASBG Brian Giles Bat/800 G2 4.00 10.00
SCASCF Cliff Floyd Bat/400 G1 4.00 10.00
SCASCG C.Guzman Bat/400 G1 4.00 10.00
SCASCJ Chipper Jones Jsy/1200 G3 6.00 15.00
SCASEM Edgar Martinez Jsy/1200 G3 6.00 15.00
SCASIR Ivan Rodriguez Uni/2400 G4 6.00 15.00
SCASJG Juan Gonzalez Bat/400 G1 4.00 10.00
SCASJK Jeff Kent Bat/400 G1 4.00 10.00
SCASJO John Olerud Jsy/1200 G3 4.00 10.00
SCASJP Jorge Posada Bat/400 G1 6.00 15.00
SCASKS Kaz Sasaki Jsy/1200 G3 4.00 10.00
SCASLW Larry Walker Jsy/2400 G4 4.00 10.00
SCASMA Moises Alou Bat/400 G1 4.00 10.00
SCASMC Mike Cameron Bat/400 G1 4.00 10.00
SCASMO M. Ordonez Bat/400 G1 4.00 10.00
SCASMP Mike Piazza Uni/1200 G3 15.00 40.00
SCASMR Manny Ramirez Uni/3600 G5 6.00 15.00
SCASMS Mike Sweeney Bat/400 G1 4.00 10.00
SCASRA Roberto Alomar Uni/3600 G5 6.00 15.00
SCASRJ Randy Johnson Jsy/2400 G4 6.00 15.00
SCASRK Ryan Klesko Jsy/1200 G3 4.00 10.00
SCASSC Sean Casey Bat/400 G1 4.00 10.00
SCASTG Tony Gwynn Jsy/2400 G4 8.00 20.00
SCASTH Todd Helton Jsy/1200 G3 6.00 15.00
SCASBRB Bret Boone Bat/1200 G3 4.00 10.00
SCASLGJ Luis Gonzalez Bat/800 G2 4.00 10.00

2002 Stadium Club Chasing 500-500

Randomly inserted in packs, these three cards feature memorabilia from Barry Bonds as he chases becoming the first member of the 500 homer, 500 stolen base club.

C55BB1 Barry Bonds Dual 20.00 50.00
C55BB2 Barry Bonds Jsy/600 15.00 40.00
C55BB3 Barry Bonds Multiple/200 50.00 100.00

2002 Stadium Club Passport to the Majors

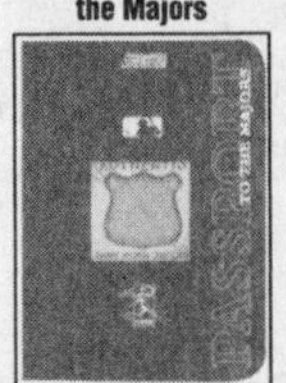

Randomly inserted in packs, these cards feature foreign players as well as a game-used relic. The jersey relics are serial numbered to 1200 while the bats are printed to differing amounts. The specific print information is notated in our checklist.

PTMAG Andres Galarraga Jsy/1200 4.00 10.00
PTMAJ Andruw Jones Jsy/1200 6.00 15.00
PTMAP Albert Pujols Bat/450 20.00 50.00
PTMAS Alfonso Soriano Bat/400 4.00 10.00
PTMBA Bob Abreu Bat/450 4.00 10.00
PTMBC Bartolo Colon Uni/1200 4.00 10.00
PTMCL Carlos Lee Jsy/1200 4.00 10.00
PTMCP Chan Ho Park Jsy/1200 4.00 10.00
PTMEA Edgardo Alfonzo Jsy/1200 4.00 10.00
PTMIR Ivan Rodriguez Uni/1200 6.00 15.00
PTMJG Juan Gonzalez Jsy/1200 4.00 10.00
PTMJL Javier Lopez Jsy/1200 4.00 10.00
PTMKS Kazuhiro Sasaki Jsy/1200 4.00 10.00
PTMLW Larry Walker Jsy/1200 4.00 10.00
PTMMO Magglio Ordonez Jsy/1200 4.00 10.00
PTMMR Manny Ramirez Jsy/1200 6.00 15.00
PTMMT Miguel Tejada Bat/375 4.00 10.00
PTMPM Pedro Martinez Jsy/1200 6.00 15.00
PTMRA Roberto Alomar Uni/1200 6.00 15.00
PTMRF Rafael Furcal Jsy/1200 4.00 10.00
PTMRM Raul Mondesi Jsy/1200 4.00 10.00
PTMRP Rafael Palmeiro Jsy/1200 6.00 15.00
PTMSH Shig Hasegawa Jsy/1200 4.00 10.00
PTMTS Tsuyoshi Shinjo Bat/400 4.00 10.00
PTMWB Wilson Betemit Bat/325 4.00 10.00

2002 Stadium Club Reel Time

Inserted at a rate of one in eight hobby/retail packs and one in four HTA packs this 20 card set features players who constantly make the highlight reel.

COMPLETE SET (20) 30.00 60.00
RT1 Luis Gonzalez .75 2.00
RT2 Derek Jeter 2.50 6.00
RT3 Ken Griffey Jr. 1.50 4.00
RT4 Alex Rodriguez 1.50 4.00
RT5 Barry Bonds 2.50 6.00
RT6 Ichiro Suzuki 2.00 5.00
RT7 Carlos Delgado .75 2.00
RT8 Manny Ramirez .75 2.00
RT9 Mike Piazza 1.50 4.00
RT10 Mark McGwire 2.50 6.00
RT11 Todd Helton .75 2.00
RT12 Vladimir Guerrero 1.00 2.50
RT13 Jim Thome .75 2.00
RT14 Rich Aurilia .75 2.00
RT15 Bret Boone .75 2.00
RT16 Roberto Alomar .75 2.00
RT17 Jason Giambi .75 2.00
RT18 Chipper Jones 1.00 2.50
RT19 Albert Pujols 2.00 5.00
RT20 Sammy Sosa 1.00 2.50

2002 Stadium Club Stadium Shots

Inserted at a rate of one in 12 hobby/retail packs and one in six HTA packs, these 10 cards feature 10 sluggers known for their long homers.

COMPLETE SET (10) 10.00 25.00
SS1 Sammy Sosa 1.00 2.50
SS2 Manny Ramirez 1.00 2.50
SS3 Jason Giambi 1.00 2.50
SS4 Mike Piazza 1.50 4.00
SS5 Barry Bonds 2.50 6.00
SS6 Ken Griffey Jr. 1.50 4.00
SS7 Juan Gonzalez 1.00 2.50
SS8 Jeff Bagwell 1.00 2.50
SS9 Jim Thome 1.00 2.50
SS10 Mark McGwire 2.50 6.00

2002 Stadium Club Stadium Slices Barrel Relics

These five cards were inserted in packs and feature bat slices cut from the barrel of the bat. Each card is printed to a different amount and that information is notated in our checklist.

GROUP A ODDS 1:4289 HOBBY, 1:1700 HTA
GROUP B ODDS 1:6768 HOBBY, 1:2680 HTA
GROUP C ODDS 1:6465 HOBBY, 1:2581 HTA
GROUP D ODDS 1:5101 HOBBY, 1:2489 HTA
SCSSAP Albert Pujols B/95 50.00 100.00
SCSSBB Barry Bonds C/100 50.00 100.00
SCSSBW Bern Williams A/100 12.50 30.00
SCSSIR Ivan Rodriguez D/105 12.50 30.00
SCSSLG Luis Gonzalez A/75 12.50 30.00

2002 Stadium Club Stadium Slices Handle Relics

These five cards were inserted in packs and feature bat slices cut from the handle of the bat. Each card is printed to a different amount and that information is notated in our checklist.

GROUP A ODDS 1:3671 HOBBY, 1:1483 HTA
GROUP B ODDS 1:3580 HOBBY, 1:1422 HTA
GROUP C ODDS 1:3384 HOBBY, 1:1366 HTA
GROUP D ODDS 1:3209 HOBBY, 1:1290 HTA
GROUP E ODDS 1:3050 HOBBY, 1:1222 HTA
SCSSAP Albert Pujols C/190 30.00 60.00
SCSSBB Barry Bonds A/175 25.00 60.00
SCSSBW Bernie Williams E/210 8.00 20.00
SCSSIR Ivan Rodriguez B/180 8.00 20.00
SCSSLG Luis Gonzalez D/200 8.00 20.00

2002 Stadium Club Stadium Slices Trademark Relics

These five cards were inserted in packs and feature bat slices cut from the middle of the bat. Each card is printed to a different amount and that information is notated in our checklist.

GROUP A ODDS 1:6101 HOBBY, 1:2489 HTA
GROUP B ODDS 1:5853 HOBBY, 1:2323 HTA
GROUP C ODDS 1:4922 HOBBY, 1:1991 HTA
GROUP D ODDS 1:4559 HOBBY, 1:1834 HTA
GROUP E ODDS 1:3800 HOBBY, 1:1515 HTA
SCSSAP Albert Pujols C/130 40.00 80.00
SCSSBB Barry Bonds A/105 40.00 80.00
SCSSBW Bernie Williams B/110 10.00 25.00
SCSSIR Ivan Rodriguez E/170 10.00 25.00
SCSSLG Luis Gonzalez D/140 10.00 25.00

2002 Stadium Club World Champion Relics

Inserted at different odds depending on what type of relic, these 69 cards feature game-used relics from World Series ring holders. The Rickey Henderson card was short printed and we have notated this information in our checklist.

BAT ODDS 1:94 H, 1:108 R, 1:16 HTA
JERSEY ODDS 1:106 H, 1:122 R, 1:18 HTA
PANTS ODDS 1:795 H, 1:1022 R, 1:133 HTA
SPIKES 1:38,400 H, 1:51,696 R, 1:6335 HTA
WCAB Al Bumbry Bat 4.00 10.00
WCAL Al Leiter Jsy 6.00 15.00
WCAT Alan Trammell Bat 6.00 15.00
WCBB Bert Blyleven Jsy 6.00 15.00
WCBD Bucky Dent Bat 6.00 15.00
WCBM Bill Madlock Bat 6.00 15.00
WCBW B.Williams Bat 8.00 20.00
WCBRB Bob Boone Jsy 6.00 15.00
WCCC C.Chambliss Bat 6.00 15.00
WCCJ Chipper Jones Bat 10.00 25.00
WCCK C.Knoblauch Bat 6.00 15.00
WCDB Don Baylor Bat 6.00 15.00
WCDC D.Concepcion Bat 6.00 15.00
WCDJ David Justice Bat 6.00 15.00
WCDL Dave Lopes Bat 6.00 15.00
WCDP Dave Parker Bat 6.00 15.00
WCDW Dave Winfield Bat 6.00 15.00
WCED Eric Davis Bat 6.00 15.00
WCES Ed Sprague Jsy 4.00 10.00
WCEM1 Eddie Murray Bat 10.00 25.00
WCEM2 Ed. Murray Jsy 10.00 25.00
WCFM Fred McGriff Jsy 8.00 20.00
WCFV F. Valenzuela Bat 6.00 15.00
WCGB George Brett Bat 20.00 50.00
WCGF George Foster Bat 6.00 15.00
WCGH G. Hendrick Bat 6.00 15.00
WCGL Greg Luzinski Bat 6.00 15.00
WCGM Greg Maddux Jsy 15.00 40.00
WCGC1 Gary Carter Bat 6.00 15.00
WCGC2 Gary Carter Jsy 6.00 15.00
WCHM Hal McRae Bat 6.00 15.00
WCJB Johnny Bench Bat 10.00 25.00
WCJC Joe Carter Jsy 6.00 15.00
WCJL Javy Lopez Bat 6.00 15.00
WCJO John Olerud Jsy 6.00 15.00
WCJP Jorge Posada Bat 8.00 20.00
WCJS John Smoltz Jsy 8.00 20.00
WCJV Jose Vizcaino Bat 4.00 10.00
WCJC1 Jose Canseco Yankees Bat 8.00 20.00
WCJC2 Jose Canseco A's Bat 8.00 20.00
WCKG Ken Griffey Sr. Bat 8.00 20.00
WCKH K. Hernandez Bat 6.00 15.00
WCKP Kirby Puckett Bat 10.00 25.00
WCKG1 Kirk Gibson Bat 6.00 15.00
WCKG2 Kirk Gibson Jsy 6.00 15.00
WCLW Lou Whitaker Bat 6.00 15.00
WCLP Lou Piniella Bat 6.00 15.00
WCMA Moises Alou Bat 6.00 15.00
WCMS Mike Scioscia Bat 6.00 15.00
WCMW M. Wilson Bat 6.00 15.00
WCMJS M. Schmidt Bat 20.00 50.00
WCOH Orel Hershiser Jsy 6.00 15.00
WCOS Ozzie Smith Bat 15.00 40.00
WCPG Phil Garner Bat 6.00 15.00
WCPM Paul Molitor Bat 6.00 15.00
WCPO Paul O'Neill Pants 8.00 20.00
WCRA R. Alomar Pants 8.00 20.00
WCRC Ron Cey Bat 6.00 15.00
WCRH R.Henderson Spikes SP/50 *
WCRJ R. Jackson Bat 8.00 20.00
WCSB Scott Brosius Bat 6.00 15.00
WCTG Tom Glavine Jsy 8.00 20.00
WCTM T. Munson Bat 30.00 60.00
WCTP Tony Perez Bat 6.00 15.00
WCTLM T. Martinez Bat 8.00 20.00
WCWB Wade Boggs Bat 8.00 20.00
WCWH W. Hernandez Jsy 6.00 15.00
WCWR W. Randolph Bat 6.00 15.00
WCWS Willie Stargell Bat 8.00 20.00

2003 Stadium Club

This 125 card set was released in November, 2002. This set marked the conclusion of the 13 year run of Stadium Club product being released as a baseball brand by Topps. This set was issued in either 10 card packs or 20 card HTA packs. The 10-card packs were issued 10 cards to a pack with 24 packs to a box and 12 boxes to a case with an SRP of $3 per pack. The 20-card HTA packs were issued 10 packs to a box and eight boxes to a case with an SRP of $10 per pack. Cards numbered from 101 through 113 featured future stars while cards numbered 114 through 125 feature players in their first year on a Stadium Club card. Cards numbered 101 through 125 were issued with different photos depending on whether or not they came from hobby or retail packs. These cards have two different varieties in all the parallel sets as well. Sets are considered complete at 125 cards - with one copy of either the hobby or retail versions of cards 101-125.

COMP.MASTER SET (150) 30.00 60.00
COMPLETE SET (125) 20.00 40.00
COMMON CARD (1-100) .10 .30
COMMON CARD (101-115) .20 .50
COMMON CARD (116-125) .40 1.00
1 Rafael Furcal .10 .30
2 Randy Winn .10 .30
3 Eric Chavez .10 .30
4 Fernando Vina .10 .30
5 Pat Burrell .10 .30
6 Derek Jeter .75 2.00
7 Ivan Rodriguez .20 .50
8 Eric Hinske .10 .30
9 Roberto Alomar .20 .50
10 Tony Batista .10 .30
11 Jacque Jones .10 .30
12 Alfonso Soriano .10 .30
13 Omar Vizquel .20 .50
14 Paul Konerko .10 .30
15 Shawn Green .10 .30
16 Garret Anderson .10 .30
17 Darin Erstad .10 .30
18 Johnny Damon .20 .50
19 Juan Gonzalez .10 .30
20 Luis Gonzalez .10 .30
21 Sean Burroughs .10 .30
22 Mark Prior .20 .50
23 Javier Vazquez .10 .30
24 Shannon Stewart .10 .30
25 Jay Gibbons .10 .30
26 A.J. Pierzynski .10 .30
27 Vladimir Guerrero .30 .75
28 Austin Kearns .10 .30
29 Shea Hillenbrand .10 .30
30 Magglio Ordonez .10 .30
31 Mike Cameron .10 .30
32 Tim Salmon .20 .50
33 Brian Jordan .10 .30
34 Moises Alou .10 .30
35 Rich Aurilia .10 .30
36 Nick Johnson .10 .30
37 Junior Spivey .10 .30
38 Curt Schilling .10 .30
39 Jose Vidro .10 .30
40 Orlando Cabrera .10 .30
41 Jeff Bagwell .20 .50
42 Mo Vaughn .10 .30
43 Luis Castillo .10 .30
44 Vicente Padilla .10 .30
45 Pedro Martinez .20 .50
46 John Olerud .10 .30
47 Tom Glavine .20 .50
48 Torii Hunter .10 .30
49 J.D. Drew .10 .30
50 Alex Rodriguez .50 1.25
51 Randy Johnson .30 .75
52 Richie Sexson .10 .30
53 Jimmy Rollins .10 .30
54 Cristian Guzman .10 .30
55 Tim Hudson .10 .30
56 Mark Buehrle .10 .30
57 Paul Lo Duca .10 .30
58 Aramis Ramirez .10 .30
59 Todd Helton .20 .50
60 Lance Berkman .10 .30
61 Josh Beckett .10 .30
62 Bret Boone .10 .30
63 Miguel Tejada .10 .30
64 Nomar Garciaparra .50 1.25
65 Albert Pujols .60 1.50
66 Chipper Jones .30 .75
67 Scott Rolen .20 .50
68 Kerry Wood .10 .30
69 Jorge Posada .20 .50
70 Ichiro Suzuki .60 1.50
71 Jeff Kent .10 .30
72 David Eckstein .10 .30
73 Phil Nevin .10 .30
74 Brian Giles .10 .30
75 Barry Zito .10 .30
76 Andruw Jones .20 .50
77 Jim Thome .20 .50
78 Robert Fick .10 .30
79 Rafael Palmeiro .20 .50
80 Barry Bonds .75 2.00
81 Gary Sheffield .10 .30
82 Jim Edmonds .10 .30
83 Kazuhisa Ishii .10 .30
84 Jose Hernandez .10 .30
85 Jason Giambi .10 .30
86 Mark Mulder .10 .30
87 Roger Clemens .60 1.50
88 Troy Glaus .10 .30
89 Carlos Delgado .10 .30
90 Mike Sweeney .10 .30
91 Ken Griffey Jr. .50 1.25
92 Manny Ramirez .20 .50
93 Ryan Klesko .10 .30
94 Larry Walker .10 .30
95 Adam Dunn .10 .30
96 Raul Ibanez .10 .30
97 Preston Wilson .10 .30
98 Roy Oswalt .10 .30
99 Sammy Sosa .30 .75
100 Mike Piazza .50 1.25
101H Jose Reyes FS .30 .75
101R Jose Reyes FS .30 .75
102H Ed Rogers FS .20 .50
102R Ed Rogers FS .20 .50
103H Hank Blalock FS .30 .75
103R Hank Blalock FS .30 .75
104H Mark Teixeira FS .40 1.00
104R Mark Teixeira FS .40 1.00
105H Orlando Hudson FS .20 .50
105R Orlando Hudson FS .20 .50
106H Drew Henson FS .20 .50
106R Drew Henson FS .20 .50
107H Joe Mauer FS .60 1.50
107R Joe Mauer FS .60 1.50
108H Carl Crawford FS .30 .75
108R Carl Crawford FS .30 .75
109H Marlon Byrd FS .20 .50
109R Marlon Byrd FS .20 .50
110H Jason Stokes FS .20 .50
110R Jason Stokes FS .20 .50
111H Miguel Cabrera FS .60 1.50
111R Miguel Cabrera FS .60 1.50
112H Wilson Betemit FS .20 .50
112R Wilson Betemit FS .20 .50
113H Jerome Williams FS .20 .50
113R Jerome Williams FS .20 .50
114H Walter Young FYP .40 1.00
114R Walter Young FYP .40 1.00
115H Juan Camacho FYP RC .40 1.00
115R Juan Camacho FYP RC .40 1.00
116H Chris Duncan FYP RC 2.00 5.00
116R Chris Duncan FYP RC 2.00 5.00
117H F.Gutierrez FYP RC .75 2.00
117R F.Gutierrez FYP RC .75 2.00
118H Adam LaRoche FYP .40 1.00
118R Adam LaRoche FYP .40 1.00
119H M.Ramirez FYP RC .60 1.50
119R M.Ramirez FYP RC .60 1.50
120H Il Kim FYP RC .40 1.00
120R Il Kim FYP RC .40 1.00
121H Wayne Lydon FYP RC .40 1.00
121R Wayne Lydon FYP RC .40 1.00
122H Daryl Clark FYP RC .40 1.00
122R Daryl Clark FYP RC .40 1.00
123H Sean Pierce FYP .40 1.00
123R Sean Pierce FYP .40 1.00
124H Andy Marte FYP RC 1.50 4.00
124R Andy Marte FYP RC 1.50 4.00
125H Mat.Peterson FYP RC .40 1.00
125R Mat.Peterson FYP RC .40 1.00

2003 Stadium Club Photographer's Proof

Randomly inserted into packs:, this is a parallel to the Stadium Club set. These cards were issued to a stated print run of 299 serial numbered sets.

*PROOF 1-100: 4X TO 10X BASIC
*PROOF 101-115: 2X TO 5X BASIC
*PROOF 116-125: 1.5X TO 4X BASIC
1-100 ODDS 1:39 H, 1:23 HTA, 1:34 R
101-125 ODDS 1:61 H, 1:17 HTA, 1:92 R

2003 Stadium Club Royal Gold

Inserted one per pack, this is a parallel to the Stadium Club set. These cards can be differentiated by their thickness compared to the regular cards. Photo variations were created for cards 101-125 whereby hobby and retail packs each had exclusive distribution on one image per player.

*GOLD 1-100: 1X TO 2.5X BASIC
*GOLD 101-115: 1X TO 2.5X BASIC
*GOLD 116-125: .75X TO 2X BASIC

2003 Stadium Club Beam Team

Inserted into packs at a stated rate of one in 12 hobby, one in 12 retail and one in two HTA, these 20 cards feature some of the hottest talents in baseball.

BT1 Lance Berkman .75 2.00
BT2 Barry Bonds 3.00 8.00
BT3 Carlos Delgado .75 2.00
BT4 Adam Dunn .75 2.00
BT5 Nomar Garciaparra 2.00 5.00
BT6 Jason Giambi .75 2.00
BT7 Brian Giles .75 2.00
BT8 Shawn Green .75 2.00
BT9 Vladimir Guerrero 1.25 3.00
BT10 Todd Helton 1.25 3.00
BT11 Derek Jeter 3.00 8.00
BT12 Chipper Jones 1.25 3.00
BT13 Jeff Kent .75 2.00
BT14 Mike Piazza 2.00 5.00
BT15 Alex Rodriguez 2.00 5.00
BT16 Ivan Rodriguez 1.25 3.00
BT17 Sammy Sosa 1.25 3.00
BT18 Ichiro Suzuki 2.50 6.00
BT19 Miguel Tejada .75 2.00
BT20 Larry Walker .75 2.00

2003 Stadium Club Born in the USA Relics

Inserted into packs at different odds depending on what type of game-used memorabilia piece was used, these 50 cards feature those memorabilia pieces cut into the shape of the player's home state.

BAT ODDS 1:76 H, 1:23 HTA, 1:89 R
JERSEY ODDS 1:52 H, 1:15 HTA, 1:61 R
UNIFORM ODDS 1:413 H, 1:126 HTA, 1:484 R
AB A.J. Burnett Jsy 4.00 10.00
AD Adam Dunn Bat 4.00 10.00
AR Alex Rodriguez Bat 10.00 25.00
BB Bret Boone Jsy 4.00 10.00
BF Brad Fullmer Bat 4.00 10.00
BL Barry Larkin Jsy 6.00 15.00
CB Craig Biggio Jsy 6.00 15.00
CF Cliff Floyd Bat 4.00 10.00
CJ Chipper Jones Jsy 6.00 15.00
CP Corey Patterson Bat 4.00 10.00
CE Eric Chavez Uni 4.00 10.00
EM Eric Milton Jsy 4.00 10.00
FT Frank Thomas Bat 6.00 15.00
GM Greg Maddux Jsy 6.00 15.00
GS Gary Sheffield Bat 4.00 10.00
JB Jeff Bagwell Jsy 6.00 15.00
JD Johnny Damon Bat 6.00 15.00
JDD J.D. Drew Bat 4.00 10.00
JE Jim Edmonds Jsy 4.00 10.00
JH Josh Hamilton Bat 8.00 20.00
JNB Jeromy Burnitz Bat 4.00 10.00
JO John Olerud Jsy 4.00 10.00
JS John Smoltz Jsy 6.00 15.00
JT Jim Thome Jsy 6.00 15.00
KW Kerry Wood Bat 4.00 10.00
LG Luis Gonzalez Bat 4.00 10.00
MG Mark Grace Jsy 6.00 15.00
MP Mike Piazza Jsy 6.00 15.00
MV Mo Vaughn Bat 4.00 10.00
MW Matt Williams Bat 4.00 10.00
NG Nomar Garciaparra Bat 10.00 25.00
PB Pat Burrell Bat 4.00 10.00
PK Paul Konerko Bat 4.00 10.00
PW Preston Wilson Jsy 4.00 10.00
RA Rich Aurilia Jsy 4.00 10.00
RH Rickey Henderson Bat 6.00 15.00
RJ Randy Johnson Bat 6.00 15.00
RK Ryan Klesko Bat 4.00 10.00
RS Richie Sexson Bat 4.00 10.00
RV Robin Ventura Bat 4.00 10.00
SB Sean Burroughs Bat 4.00 10.00
SG Shawn Green Bat 4.00 10.00
SR Scott Rolen Bat 6.00 15.00
TC Tony Clark Bat 4.00 10.00
TH Todd Helton Bat 6.00 15.00
TJH Toby Hall Bat 4.00 10.00
TL Terrence Long Uni 4.00 10.00
TM Tino Martinez Bat 6.00 15.00
TRL Travis Lee Bat 4.00 10.00
WM Willie Mays Bat 30.00 60.00

2003 Stadium Club Clubhouse Exclusive

Inserted into packs at a different rate depending on how many memorabilia pieces are used, these four cards feature game-worn memorabilia pieces of Cardinals star Albert Pujols.

JSY ODDS 1:488 H, 1:178 HTA
BAT-JSY ODDS 1:2073 H, 1:758 HTA
BAT-JSY-SPK ODDS 1:2750 H, 1:1016 HTA
BAT-HAT-JSY-SPK ODDS 1:1016 HTA
CE1 Albert Pujols Jsy 8.00 20.00
CE2 Albert Pujols Bat-Jsy 15.00 40.00
CE3 Albert Pujols Bat-Jsy-Spike 50.00 100.00
CE4 Albert Pujols Bat-Hat-Jsy-Spike

2003 Stadium Club Co-Signers

Randomly inserted into packs, these two cards feature a pair of important baseball players who each signed cards for this set. This set features the first Masanori Murakami (the first Japanese player to play in the majors) certified signed cards. Murakami, to honor his heritage, signed an equivalent amount of cards in English and Japanese.

GROUP A STATED ODDS 1:339 HTA
GROUP B STATED ODDS 1:1016 HTA
AM Hank Aaron Willie Mays A 300.00 500.00
MI Masanori Murakami Kazuhisa Ishii B 175.00 300.00

2003 Stadium Club License to Drive Bat Relics

Inserted into packs at a stated rate of one in 98 hobby, one in 114 retail and one in 29 HTA, these 25 cards feature game-used bat relics of players who have driven in 100 runs in a season.

AB Adrian Beltre 4.00 10.00
AD Adam Dunn 4.00 10.00
AJ Andruw Jones 6.00 15.00
ANR Aramis Ramirez 4.00 10.00
AP Albert Pujols 8.00 20.00
AR Alex Rodriguez 10.00 25.00
BW Bernie Williams 6.00 15.00
CJ Chipper Jones 6.00 15.00
EC Eric Chavez 4.00 10.00
FT Frank Thomas 6.00 15.00
GS Gary Sheffield 4.00 10.00
IR Ivan Rodriguez 6.00 15.00
JG Juan Gonzalez 4.00 10.00
LB Lance Berkman 4.00 10.00
LG Luis Gonzalez 4.00 10.00
LW Larry Walker 4.00 10.00
MA Moises Alou 4.00 10.00
MP Mike Piazza 10.00 25.00
NG Nomar Garciaparra 10.00 25.00
RA Roberto Alomar 6.00 15.00
RP Rafael Palmeiro 6.00 15.00
SG Shawn Green 4.00 10.00
SR Scott Rolen 6.00 15.00
TH Todd Helton 6.00 15.00
TM Tino Martinez 6.00 15.00

2003 Stadium Club MLB Match-Up Dual Relics

Inserted into hobby packs at a stated rate of one in 485, one in 570 retail and HTA packs at one in 148, these five cards feature both a game-worn jersey swatch as well as a game-used bat relic of the featured players.

AJ Andruw Jones 10.00 25.00
AP Albert Pujols 15.00 40.00
BB Bret Boone 8.00 20.00
GM Greg Maddux 12.50 30.00
TH Todd Helton 10.00 25.00

2003 Stadium Club Shots

Inserted into hobby packs at a stated rate of one in 24, retail packs at one in 24 and HTA packs at a stated rate of one in four, these 10 cards feature players who are known for their long distance slugging.

SS1 Lance Berkman .75 2.00
SS2 Barry Bonds 3.00 8.00
SS3 Jason Giambi .75 2.00
SS4 Shawn Green .75 2.00
SS5 Miguel Tejada .75 2.00
SS6 Paul Konerko .75 2.00
SS7 Mike Piazza 2.00 5.00
SS8 Alex Rodriguez 2.00 5.00
SS9 Sammy Sosa 1.25 3.00
SS10 Gary Sheffield .75 2.00

2003 Stadium Club Stadium Slices Barrel Relics

Inserted into hobby packs at a stated rate of one in 550 and HTA packs at a stated rate of one in 204, these 10 cards feature game-used bat pieces taken from the barrel.

AJ Andruw Jones 15.00 40.00

AP Albert Pujols 20.00 50.00
AR Alex Rodriguez 30.00 60.00
CD Carlos Delgado 10.00 25.00
GS Gary Sheffield 10.00 25.00
MP Mike Piazza 30.00 60.00
NG Nomar Garciaparra 40.00 80.00
RA Roberto Alomar 15.00 40.00
RP Rafael Palmeiro 15.00 40.00
TH Todd Helton 15.00 40.00

2003 Stadium Club Stadium Slices Handle Relics

Inserted into hobby packs at a stated rate of one in 237 and HTA packs at a stated rate of one in 86, these 10 cards feature game-used bat pieces taken from the handle.

AJ Andruw Jones 8.00 20.00
AP Albert Pujols 10.00 25.00
AR Alex Rodriguez 12.50 30.00
CD Carlos Delgado 5.00 12.00
GS Gary Sheffield 5.00 12.00
MP Mike Piazza 12.50 30.00
NG Nomar Garciaparra 15.00 40.00
RA Roberto Alomar 8.00 20.00
RP Rafael Palmeiro 8.00 20.00
TH Todd Helton 8.00 20.00

2003 Stadium Club Stadium Slices Trademark Relics

Inserted into hobby packs at a stated rate of one in 415 and HTA packs at a stated rate of one in 151, these 10 cards feature game-used bat pieces taken from the middle of the bat.

AJ Andruw Jones 10.00 25.00
AP Albert Pujols 12.50 30.00
AR Alex Rodriguez 15.00 40.00
CD Carlos Delgado 6.00 15.00
GS Gary Sheffield 6.00 15.00
MP Mike Piazza 15.00 40.00
NG Nomar Garciaparra 20.00 50.00
RA Roberto Alomar 10.00 25.00
RP Rafael Palmeiro 10.00 25.00
TH Todd Helton 10.00 25.00

2003 Stadium Club World Stage Relics

Inserted into packs at a different rate depending on whether or not it is a bat or a jersey, these 10 cards feature game-used memorabilia pieces of players born outside the continental U.S.

BAT ODDS 1:809 H, 1:246 HTA, 1:950 R
JSY ODDS 1:118 H, 1:36 HTA, 1:138 R
AB Adrian Beltre Jsy 3.00 8.00
AP Albert Pujols Jsy 8.00 20.00
AS Alfonso Soriano Bat 4.00 10.00
BK Byung-Hyun Kim Jsy 4.00 10.00
HN Hideo Nomo Bat 10.00 25.00
IR Ivan Rodriguez Jsy 4.00 10.00
KI Kazuhisa Ishii Jsy 3.00 8.00
KS Kazuhiro Sasaki Jsy 3.00 8.00
MT Miguel Tejada Jsy 3.00 8.00
TS Tsuyoshi Shinjo Bat 4.00 10.00

2008 Stadium Club

This set was released on November 5, 2008.

COMMON CARD(1-100) .40 1.00
COMMON 999 (1-100) .75 2.00
COMMON RC (1-150) .40 1.00
COMMON RC 999 (1-150) .60 1.50
COMMON AU RC (151-185) 4.00 10.00
AU RC A ODDS 1:3
AU RC B ODDS 1:8
EXCHANGE DEADLINE 10/31/2010
PRINTING PLATE ODDS 1:85 HOBBY
PRINT.PLATE AUTO ODDS 1:198 HOBBY
PLATE PRINT RUN 1 SET PER COLOR
BLACK-CYAN-MAGENTA-YELLOW ISSUED
NO PLATE PRICING DUE TO SCARCITY
1 Chase Utley 1.00 2.50
2 Tim Lincecum 1.50 4.00
3 Ryan Zimmerman/999 1.00 2.50
4 Todd Helton .60 1.50
5 Russell Martin .40 1.00
6 Curtis Granderson/999 1.00 2.50
7 Torii Hunter .40 1.00
8 Mark Teixeira 1.00 2.50
9 Alfonso Soriano/999 1.00 2.50
10 C.C. Sabathia .60 1.50
11 David Ortiz .60 1.50
12 Miguel Tejada/999 1.00 2.50
13 Alex Rodriguez 1.50 4.00
14 Prince Fielder .60 1.50
15 Alex Gordon/999 1.00 2.50
16 Jake Peavy .40 1.00
17 B.J. Upton .60 1.50
18 Michael Young/999 1.00 2.50
19 Jason Bay .60 1.50
20 Jorge Posada .60 1.50
21 Jacoby Ellsbury/999 2.50 6.00
22 Nick Markakis 1.00 2.50
23 Tom Glavine .60 1.50
24 Justin Upton/999 1.00 2.50
25 Edinson Volquez .40 1.00
26 Miguel Cabrera 1.00 2.50
27 Carlos Lee/999 .60 1.50
28 Ryan Church .40 1.00
29 Delmon Young .60 1.50
30 Carlos Quentin/999 .60 1.50
31 Carl Crawford .60 1.50
32 Roy Halladay 1.00 2.50
33 Brandon Webb/999 1.00 2.50
34 Brian Roberts .40 1.00
35 Ken Griffey Jr. 1.50 4.00
36 Troy Tulowitzki/999 1.50 4.00
37 Hanley Ramirez 1.00 2.50
38 Hunter Pence 1.00 2.50
39 Johnny Damon/999 1.00 2.50
40 Eric Chavez .40 1.00
41 Adrian Gonzalez .60 1.50
42 Carlos Pena/999 1.00 2.50
43 Felix Hernandez 1.00 2.50
44 Magglio Ordonez .60 1.50
45 Josh Beckett/999 1.00 2.50
46 Fausto Carmona .40 1.00
47 Chris Young .40 1.00
48 John Lackey/999 .60 1.50
49 John Smoltz 1.00 2.50
50 David Wright 1.25 3.00
51 Ichiro Suzuki/999 2.50 6.00
52 Vernon Wells .40 1.00
53 Josh Hamilton 1.00 2.50
54 Albert Pujols/999 4.00 10.00
55 Dustin Pedroia 1.25 3.00
56 Garrett Atkins .40 1.00
57 Roy Oswalt/999 1.00 2.50
58 Jose Reyes .60 1.50
59 Derek Jeter 2.50 6.00
60 Scott Kazmir/999 1.00 2.50
61 Vladimir Guerrero 1.00 2.50
62 Joba Chamberlain .60 1.50
63 Kevin Youkilis/999 1.00 2.50
64 Victor Martinez .60 1.50
65 Nick Swisher 1.00 2.50
66 Carlos Beltran/999 .60 1.50
67 Joe Mauer 1.00 2.50
68 Gary Sheffield .40 1.00
69 Cole Hamels/999 1.50 4.00
70 Brian McCann .60 1.50
71 Grady Sizemore .60 1.50
72 Robinson Cano/999 1.50 4.00
73 Greg Maddux 1.25 3.00
74 Rich Harden .40 1.00
75 Ryan Howard/999 2.00 5.00
76 Johan Santana 1.00 2.50
77 Dan Uggla .60 1.50
78 Justin Verlander/999 2.00 5.00
79 Derrek Lee .40 1.00
80 Ryan Braun 1.25 3.00
81 Lance Berkman/999 1.00 2.50
82 Manny Ramirez 1.00 2.50
83 Chipper Jones 1.00 2.50
84 Daisuke Matsuzaka/999 1.50 4.00
85 Matt Holliday 1.00 2.50
86 Justin Morneau 1.00 2.50
87 Jimmy Rollins/999 1.00 2.50
88 Hideki Matsui 1.00 2.50
89 Pedro Martinez .60 1.50
90 Carlos Zambrano/999 1.00 2.50
91 Jackie Robinson 1.00 2.50
92 Mickey Mantle 3.00 8.00
93 Ty Cobb/999 2.50 6.00
94 Joe DiMaggio
Cut Out
95 Honus Wagner 1.00 2.50
96 Babe Ruth/999 4.00 10.00
97 Nolan Ryan 3.00 8.00
98 Roberto Clemente 2.00 5.00
99 Ted Williams/999 4.00 10.00
100 Tom Seaver .60 1.50
101a Luke Hochevar RC .60 1.50
101b Luke Hochevar VAR/999 1.00 2.50
Pitching
102a Daric Barton/999 (RC) .60 1.50
102b Daric Barton VAR/999 (RC) .60 1.50
Swinging away hit down the 3rd base line
103a Nick Adenhart (RC) .40 1.00
103b Nick Adenhart VAR/999 .60 1.50
(Photoday shot in the dugout
104a Gregor Blanco (RC) .40 1.00
104b Gregor Blanco VAR/999 .60 1.50
Hitting
105a Chris Carter/999 (RC) 1.00 2.50
105b Chris Carter VAR/999 (RC) 1.00 2.50
Hitting
106a Eric Hurley (RC) .40 1.00
106b Eric Hurley VAR/999 .60 1.50
Starting his windup
107a Clayton Kershaw RC 2.00 5.00
107b Clayton Kershaw VAR/999 3.00 8.00
Throwing fastball to home
108a Evan Longoria/999 RC 2.50 6.00
108b Evan Longoria VAR/999 RC 2.50 6.00
Photoday shot
109a Garrett Mock (RC) .40 1.00
109b Garrett Mock VAR/999 .60 1.50
In mid windup
110a David Purcey (RC) .40 1.00
110b David Purcey VAR/999 .60 1.50
Ready to release a pitch
111a Ryan Tucker/999 (RC) .60 1.50
111b Ryan Tucker VAR/999 (RC) .60 1.50
Photoday shot throwing up baseball
112a Joey Votto (RC) 1.50 4.00
112b Joey Votto VAR/999 2.50 6.00
Flipping ball to pitcher for an out
113a Jeff Clement (RC) .60 1.50
113b Jeff Clement VAR/999 1.00 2.50
Running back to homeplate
114a Michael Aubrey/999 RC 1.00 2.50
114b Michael Aubrey VAR RC/999 1.00 2.50
Just got a basehit
115a Brandon Boggs (RC) .60 1.50
115b Brandon Boggs VAR/999 1.00 2.50
Throwing someone out in the outfield
116a Johnny Cueto RC .60 1.50
116b Johnny Cueto VAR/999 1.00 2.50
Delivering a pitch
117a Hernan Iribarren/999 (RC) 1.00 2.50
117b Hernan Iribarren VAR/999 (RC) 1.00 2.50
Throwing in the outfield
118a Masahide Kobayashi RC .60 1.50
118b Masahide Kobayashi VAR/999 1.00 2.50
Photoday shot
119a Jed Lowrie (RC) 1.00 2.50
119b Jed Lowrie VAR/999 1.50 4.00
Tagging someone out at 3rd base
120a Greg Reynolds/999 RC 1.00 2.50
120b Greg Reynolds VAR/999 RC 1.00 2.50
Delivering a pitch towards home
121a Matt Tolbert RC .60 1.50
121b Matt Tolbert VAR/999 1.00 2.50
Turning a double play
122a Jonathan Herrera RC .60 1.50
122b Jonathan Herrera VAR/999 1.00 2.50
Safe at home
123a J.R. Towles/999 RC 1.00 2.50
123b J.R. Towles VAR/999 RC 1.00 2.50
Single up the middle
124a Armando Galarraga RC .60 1.50
124b Armando Galarraga VAR/999 1.00 2.50
Delivering a pitch
125a Josh Banks (RC) .40 1.00
125b Josh Banks VAR/999 .60 1.50
Delivering a pitch
126a Mitch Boggs/999 (RC) .60 1.50
126b Mitch Boggs VAR/999 (RC) .60 1.50
Delivering a pitch
127a Blake DeWitt (RC) 1.00 2.50
127b Blake DeWitt VAR/999 1.50 4.00
Getting ready for a pitch
128a Carlos Gonzalez (RC) 1.00 2.50
128b Carlos Gonzalez VAR/999 1.50 4.00
Walking to home with bat in hand
129a Elliot Johnson/999 (RC) .60 1.50
129b Elliot Johnson VAR/999 (RC) .60 1.50
Throwing to first base
130a Brian Barton RC .60 1.50
130b Brian Barton VAR/999 1.00 2.50
Getting ready to crush a pitch
131a Sean Rodriguez (RC) .40 1.00
131b Sean Rodriguez VAR/999 .60 1.50
Making a sweet double play
132a Kosuke Fukudome/999 RC 2.00 5.00
132b Kosuke Fukudome VAR/999 RC 2.00 5.00
Throwing someone out in the outfield
133a Chin-Lung Hu (RC) .60 1.50
133b Chin-Lung Hu VAR/999 1.00 2.50
Catching the ball at second base
134a Wladimir Balentien (RC) .40 1.00
134b Wladimir Balentien VAR/999 .60 1.50
Safe at home!
135a Jeff Niemann/999 (RC) .60 1.50
135b Jeff Niemann VAR/999 (RC) .60 1.50
Warming up in the bullpen
136a Jay Bruce (RC) 1.50 4.00
136b Jay Bruce VAR/999 2.50 6.00
Taking a massive cut
137a Brandon Jones RC 1.00 2.50
137b Brandon Jones VAR/999 1.50 4.00
Ready for the pitch
138a Justin Masterson/999 RC 1.50 4.00
138b Justin Masterson VAR/999 RC 1.50 4.00
3/4 body shot pitching
139a Jayson Nix (RC) .40 1.00
139b Jayson Nix VAR/999 .60 1.50
Throwing to home
140a Max Scherzer RC 1.25 3.00
140b Max Scherzer VAR/999 2.00 5.00
Unloading a pitch to home
141a Mike Aviles/999 RC 1.00 2.50
141b Mike Aviles VAR/999 RC 1.00 2.50
Connecting on a fastball
142a Greg Smith RC .40 1.00
142b Greg Smith VAR/999 .60 1.50
Delivering a pitch
143a Nick Blackburn RC .60 1.50
143b Nick Blackburn VAR/999 1.00 2.50
Warming up on the mound
144a Justin Ruggiano/999 RC 1.00 2.50
144b Justin Ruggiano VAR/999 RC 1.00 2.50
Relaxing before taking another cut
145a Clay Buchholz 1.00 2.50
145b Clay Buchholz VAR/999 (RC) 1.50 4.00
Throwing a nasty breaking ball
146a German Duran RC .60 1.50
146b German Duran VAR/999 1.00 2.50
Turning a sweet double play
147a Radhames Liz/999 RC 1.00 2.50
147b Radhames Liz VAR/999 RC 1.00 2.50
Throwing a pitch to home
148a Chris Perez RC .60 1.50
148b Chris Perez VAR/999 1.00 2.50
Delivering a pitch
149a Hiroki Kuroda RC .60 1.50
149b Hiroki Kuroda VAR/999 1.00 2.50
Delivering an unorthodox pitch to home
150a Gregorio Petit RC .60 1.50
150b Gregorio Petit VAR/999 1.00 2.50
Getting ready to field one in the hole
151 Emmanuel Burriss AU RC EXCH A 4.00 10.00
152 Elliot Johnson AU A 4.00 10.00
153 Jonathan Van Every AU RC A 4.00 10.00
154 Darren O'Day AU RC A 4.00 10.00
155 Matt Joyce AU RC A 8.00 20.00
156 Burke Badenhop AU RC A 4.00 10.00
157 Brent Lillibridge AU (RC) A 4.00 10.00
158 Johnny Cueto AU A 5.00 12.00
159 Jeff Niemann AU A 4.00 10.00
160 John Bowker AU (RC) A 4.00 10.00
161 Brandon Boggs AU A 4.00 10.00
162 Justin Masterson AU A 12.50 30.00
163 Masahide Kobayashi AU A 5.00 12.00
164 Nick Adenhart AU A 8.00 20.00
165 Chris Perez AU EXCH A 4.00 10.00
166 Gregor Blanco AU A 4.00 10.00
167 Travis Denker AU RC A 4.00 10.00
168 Jeff Clement AU EXCH A 4.00 10.00
169 Evan Longoria AU A 30.00 60.00
170 Greg Smith AU A 4.00 10.00
171 Jay Bruce AU B 10.00 25.00
172 Brian Barton AU B 6.00 15.00
173 Max Scherzer AU B 6.00 15.00
174 Blake DeWitt AU B 6.00 15.00
175 Jed Lowrie AU EXCH B 6.00 15.00
176 Clayton Kershaw AU B 15.00 40.00
177 Jonathan Albaladejo AU RC B 4.00 10.00
178 Josh Banks AU B 4.00 10.00
179 Brian Horwitz AU RC B 4.00 10.00
180 Micah Hoffpauir AU RC B 8.00 20.00
181 Robinzon Diaz AU (RC) B 4.00 10.00
182 Nick Evans AU RC B 6.00 15.00
183 Joe Mather AU RC EXCH B 5.00 12.00
184 Danny Herrera AU RC B 4.00 10.00
185 Eugenio Velez AU RC B 4.00 10.00

2008 Stadium Club First Day Issue

*1ST DAY VET 1-100: .6X TO 1.5X BASIC
*1ST DAY RC 101-150: .6X TO 1.5X BASIC
APPX. ODDS TEN PER HOBBY BOX
STATED PRINT RUN 599 SER.#'d SETS

2008 Stadium Club First Day Issue Unnumbered

*1ST DAY UNUM VET 1-100: .5X TO 1.2X BASIC
*1ST DAY UNUM RC 101-150: .5X TO 1.2X BASIC
RANDOM INSERTS IN RETAIL BACKS

2008 Stadium Club Photographer's Proof Blue

*BLUE VET 1-100: 1X TO 2.5X BASIC
*BLUE 999 1-100: .6X TO 1.5X BASIC
*BLUE RC 101-150: 1X TO 2.5X BASIC
*BLUE 999 101-150: .6X TO 1.5X BASIC
NON-AU BLUE ODDS 1:5 HOBBY
*BLUE AU: .5X TO 1.2X BASIC
AU BLUE ODDS 1:29 HOBBY
BLUE PRINT RUN 99 SER.#'d SETS
162 Justin Masterson AU 40.00 80.00

2008 Stadium Club Photographer's Proof Gold

*GLD VET 1-100: 1.2X TO 3X BASIC
*GLD 999 1-100: .75X TO 2X BASIC
*GLD RC 101-150: 1.2X TO 3X BASIC
*GLD 999 101-150: .75X TO 2X BASIC
NON-AU GOLD ODDS 1:9 HOBBY
*GLD AU: .6X TO 1.5X BASIC
AU GOLD ODDS 1:62 HOBBY
GOLD PRINT RUN 50 SER.#'d SETS

2008 Stadium Club Photographer's Proof Platinum

STATED ODDS 1:340 HOBBY
STATED AUTO ODDS 1:1970 HOBBY
STATED PRINT RUN 1 SER.#'d SET
NO PRICING DUE TO SCARCITY

2008 Stadium Club Beam Team Autographs

GROUP A ODDS 1:13 HOBBY
GROUP B ODDS 1:6 HOBBY
GROUP C ODDS 1:11 HOBBY
PRINTING PLATE ODDS 1:198 HOBBY
PLATE PRINT RUN 1 SET PER COLOR
BLACK-CYAN-MAGENTA-YELLOW ISSUED
NO PLATE PRICING DUE TO SCARCITY
EXCHANGE DEADLINE 10/31/2010
AG Adrian Gonzalez C 10.00 25.00
BH Brad Hawpe C 4.00 10.00
BP Brandon Phillips B 5.00 12.00
BT Brad Thompson C 8.00 20.00
CC Carl Crawford C 6.00 15.00
CCR Callix Crabbe C 4.00 10.00
CD Carlos Delgado C 8.00 20.00
CF Chone Figgins B 4.00 10.00
CM Carlos Marmol C 8.00 20.00
CMO Craig Monroe B 4.00 10.00
CP Carlos Pena C 6.00 15.00
CV Claudio Vargas C 4.00 10.00
CVI Carlos Villanueva B 4.00 10.00
CW C.J. Wilson B 8.00 20.00
DH Dan Haren C 4.00 10.00
DS Darryl Strawberry B 6.00 15.00
DY Delwyn Young A 4.00 10.00
ER Edwar Ramirez C 4.00 10.00
FL Francisco Liriano C 5.00 12.00
FP Felix Pie B 4.00 10.00
FS Freddy Sanchez C 4.00 10.00
GC Gary Carter C 6.00 15.00
GD German Duran B 4.00 10.00
GP Glen Perkins B 4.00 10.00
GS Gary Sheffield C 6.00 15.00
GSM Greg Smith C 4.00 10.00
JB Jason Bartlett C 4.00 10.00
JC Jack Cust C 5.00 12.00
JCR Jesse Crain A 4.00 10.00
JGA Joey Gathright C 4.00 10.00
JGU Jeremy Guthrie C 4.00 10.00
JH Josh Hamilton B 15.00 40.00
JJ Jair Jurrjens C 10.00 25.00
JL John Lackey B 5.00 12.00
JN Jayson Nix A 4.00 10.00
JP Jonathan Papelbon C 8.00 20.00
JPO Johnny Podres B 5.00 12.00
JR Jose Reyes C 12.50 30.00
JS Jeff Salazar B 4.00 10.00
KS Kevin Slowey B 5.00 12.00
LM Lastings Milledge B 4.00 10.00
ME Mark Ellis C 4.00 10.00
MK Mark Kotsay C 4.00 10.00
MN Mike Napoli C 8.00 20.00
MT Marcus Thames C 4.00 10.00
MTO Matt Tolbert A 4.00 10.00
NR Nate Robertson B 4.00 10.00
RC Robinson Cano B 12.50 30.00
RP Ronny Paulino B 4.00 10.00
TG Tom Gorzelanny C 4.00 10.00
TJ Todd Jones B 4.00 10.00
YP Yusmeiro Petit A 4.00 10.00

2008 Stadium Club Beam Team Autographs Black and White

*B AND W: .5X TO 1.2X BASIC
STATED ODDS 1:19 HOBBY
STATED PRINT RUN 99 SER.#'d SETS
EXCHANGE DEADLINE 10/31/2010

2008 Stadium Club Beam Team Autographs Gold

*GOLD: .5X TO 1.2X BASIC
STATED ODDS 1:40 HOBBY
STATED PRINT RUN 50 SER.#'d SETS
EXCHANGE DEADLINE 10/31/2010

2008 Stadium Club Beam Team Autographs Platinum

STATED ODDS 1:1327 HOBBY
STATED PRINT RUN 1 SER.#'d SET
NO PRICING DUE TO SCARCITY
EXCHANGE DEADLINE 10/31/2010

2008 Stadium Club Ceremonial Cuts

STATED ODDS 1:34 HOBBY
STATED PRINT RUN 199 SER.#'d SETS
BR Babe Ruth 15.00 40.00
GB George Bush 10.00 25.00
JF Jimmie Foxx 8.00 20.00
JR Jackie Robinson 12.50 30.00
LG Lou Gehrig 15.00 40.00
MO Mel Ott 8.00 20.00
RH Rogers Hornsby 8.00 20.00
TC Ty Cobb 12.50 30.00
TW Ted Williams 12.50 30.00

2008 Stadium Club Ceremonial Cuts Photographer's Proof Blue

*BLUE: .5X TO 1.2X BASIC
STATED ODDS 1:28 HOBBY
STATED PRINT RUN 99 SER.#'d SETS

2008 Stadium Club Ceremonial Cuts Photographer's Proof Platinum

STATED ODDS 1:2710 HOBBY
STATED PRINT RUN 1 SER.#'d SET
NO PRICING DUE TO SCARCITY

2008 Stadium Club Stadium Slices

STATED ODDS 1:23 HOBBY
PRINT RUNS B/WN 89-428 COPIES PER
AP Albert Pujols/428 10.00 25.00
AR Alex Rodriguez/89 30.00 60.00
DM Daisuke Matsuzaka/428 10.00 25.00
DO David Ortiz/428 4.00 10.00
GG Goose Gossage/89 15.00 40.00
HM Hideki Matsui/428 12.50 30.00
IS Ichiro Suzuki/428 10.00 25.00
JT Joe Torre/89 15.00 40.00
LP Lou Piniella/89 8.00 20.00
MM Mickey Mantle/89 40.00 80.00
MR Mariano Rivera/428 12.50 30.00
RJ Reggie Jackson/89 15.00 40.00
TM Thurman Munson/89 30.00 60.00
WF Whitey Ford/89 20.00 50.00
YB Yogi Berra/89 20.00 50.00

2008 Stadium Club Stadium Slices Photographer's Proof Blue

*BLUE: .5X TO 1.2X BASIC
STATED ODDS 1:28 HOBBY
PRINT RUNS B/WN 25-99 SER.#'d SETS
NO PRICING ON QTY 25 OR LESS

2008 Stadium Club Stadium Slices Photographer's Proof Gold

*GOLD: .5X TO 1.2X BASIC
STATED ODDS 1:55 HOBBY
PRINT RUNS B/WN 5-50 SER.#'d SETS
NO PRICING ON QTY 5 OR LESS

2008 Stadium Club Stadium Slices Photographer's Proof Platinum

STATED ODDS 1:2710 HOBBY
STATED PRINT RUN 1 SER.#'d SET
NO PRICING DUE TO SCARCITY

2008 Stadium Club Triumvirate Memorabilia Autographs

STATED ODDS 1:26 HOBBY
PRINT RUNS B/WN 49-99 SER.#'d SETS
EXCHANGE DEADLINE 10/31/2010
AD Adam Dunn 10.00 25.00
AP Albert Pujols 100.00 200.00
AR Aramis Ramirez 12.50 30.00
ARI Alex Rios 12.50 30.00
AS Alfonso Soriano 15.00 40.00
BU B.J. Upton 10.00 25.00
CC Carl Crawford 12.50 30.00
CL Carlos Lee 6.00 15.00
CW Chien-Ming Wang 60.00 120.00
DL Derrek Lee 12.50 30.00
DO David Ortiz 30.00 60.00
HR Hanley Ramirez 20.00 50.00
JF Jeff Francoeur 10.00 25.00
JM Justin Morneau 15.00 40.00
JP Jake Peavy 15.00 40.00
JPA Jonathan Papelbon 15.00 40.00
JU Justin Upton 12.50 30.00
MH Matt Holliday 15.00 40.00
MO Magglio Ordonez/49 6.00 15.00
MR Mariano Rivera 60.00 120.00
MT Miguel Tejada 6.00 15.00
RM Russ Martin 8.00 20.00
SK Scott Kazmir 15.00 40.00
TH Torii Hunter 12.50 30.00
TLH Todd Helton 10.00 25.00
TT Troy Tulowitzki 8.00 20.00
VG Vladimir Guerrero 20.00 50.00
VW Vernon Wells 10.00 25.00

2008 Stadium Club Triumvirate Memorabilia Autographs Black

STATED ODDS 1:2501 HOBBY
STATED PRINT RUN 1 SER.#'d SET
NO PRICING DUE TO SCARCITY
EXCHANGE DEADLINE 10/31/2010

2000 Stadium Club Chrome

The 2000 Stadium Club Chrome set was released in May, 2000 as a 250-card set. The set features 200 Player cards, 30 Future Star cards, and 20 Draft Pick cards. Each pack contained five cards and carried a suggested retail price of $4.00. Notable Rookie Cards include Rick Asadoorian and Bobby Bradley.

COMPLETE SET (250) 20.00 50.00
COMMON CARD (1-250) .20 .50
COMMON RC .30 .75
1 Nomar Garciaparra .75 2.00
2 Brian Jordan .20 .50
3 Mark Grace .30 .75
4 Jeromy Burnitz .20 .50
5 Shane Reynolds .20 .50
6 Alex Gonzalez .20 .50
7 Jose Offerman .20 .50
8 Orlando Hernandez .20 .50
9 Mike Caruso .20 .50
10 Tony Clark .20 .50
11 Sean Casey .20 .50
12 Johnny Damon .30 .75
13 Dante Bichette .20 .50
14 Kevin Young .20 .50
15 Juan Gonzalez .20 .50
16 Chipper Jones .50 1.25
17 Quilvio Veras .20 .50
18 Trevor Hoffman .20 .50
19 Roger Cedeno .20 .50
20 Ellis Burks .20 .50
21 Richie Sexson .20 .50
22 Gary Sheffield .20 .50
23 Delino DeShields .20 .50
24 Wade Boggs .30 .75
25 Ray Lankford .20 .50
26 Kevin Appier .20 .50
27 Roy Halladay .20 .50
28 Harold Baines .20 .50
29 Todd Zeile .20 .50
30 Barry Larkin .30 .75
31 Ron Coomer .20 .50
32 Jorge Posada .30 .75
33 Magglio Ordonez .20 .50
34 Brian Giles .20 .50
35 Jeff Kent .20 .50
36 Henry Rodriguez .20 .50
37 Fred McGriff .30 .75
38 Shawn Green .20 .50
39 Derek Bell .20 .50
40 Ben Grieve .20 .50
41 Dave Nilsson .20 .50
42 Mo Vaughn .20 .50
43 Rondell White .20 .50
44 Doug Glanville .20 .50
45 Paul O'Neill .30 .75
46 Carlos Lee .20 .50
47 Vinny Castilla .20 .50
48 Mike Sweeney .20 .50
49 Rico Brogna .20 .50
50 Alex Rodriguez .75 2.00
51 Luis Castillo .20 .50
52 Kevin Brown .30 .75
53 Jose Vidro .20 .50
54 John Smoltz .30 .75
55 Garret Anderson .20 .50
56 Matt Stairs .20 .50
57 Omar Vizquel .30 .75
58 Tom Goodwin .20 .50
59 Scott Brosius .20 .50
60 Robin Ventura .30 .75
61 B.J. Surhoff .20 .50
62 Andy Ashby .20 .50
63 Chris Widger .20 .50
64 Tim Hudson .20 .50
65 Javy Lopez .20 .50
66 Tim Salmon .30 .75
67 Warren Morris .20 .50
68 John Wetteland .20 .50
69 Gabe Kapler .20 .50
70 Bernie Williams .30 .75
71 Rickey Henderson .50 1.25
72 Andruw Jones .30 .75
73 Eric Young .20 .50
74 Bob Abreu .20 .50
75 David Cone .20 .50
76 Rusty Greer .20 .50
77 Ron Belliard .20 .50
78 Troy Glaus .20 .50
79 Mike Hampton .20 .50
80 Miguel Tejada .20 .50
81 Jeff Cirillo .20 .50
82 Todd Hundley .20 .50
83 Roberto Alomar .30 .75
84 Charles Johnson .20 .50
85 Rafael Palmeiro .30 .75
86 Doug Mientkiewicz .20 .50
87 Mariano Rivera .50 1.25
88 Neifi Perez .20 .50
89 Jermaine Dye .20 .50
90 Ivan Rodriguez .30 .75
91 Jay Buhner .20 .50
92 Pokey Reese .20 .50
93 John Olerud .20 .50
94 Brady Anderson .20 .50
95 Manny Ramirez .30 .75
96 Keith Osik RC .30 .75
97 Mickey Morandini .20 .50
98 Matt Williams .20 .50
99 Eric Karros .20 .50
100 Ken Griffey Jr. .75 2.00
101 Bret Boone .20 .50
102 Ryan Klesko .20 .50
103 Craig Biggio .30 .75
104 John Jaha .20 .50
105 Vladimir Guerrero .50 1.25
106 Devon White .20 .50
107 Tony Womack .20 .50
108 Marvin Benard .20 .50
109 Kenny Lofton .20 .50
110 Preston Wilson .20 .50
111 Al Leiter .20 .50
112 Reggie Sanders .20 .50
113 Scott Williamson .20 .50
114 Deivi Cruz .20 .50
115 Carlos Beltran .20 .50
116 Ray Durham .20 .50
117 Ricky Ledee .20 .50
118 Torii Hunter .20 .50
119 John Valentin .20 .50
120 Scott Rolen .30 .75
121 Jason Kendall .20 .50
122 Dave Martinez .20 .50
123 Jim Thome .30 .75
124 David Bell .20 .50
125 Jose Canseco .30 .75
126 Jose Lima .20 .50
127 Carl Everett .20 .50
128 Kevin Millwood .20 .50
129 Bill Spiers .20 .50
130 Omar Daal .20 .50
131 Miguel Cairo .20 .50
132 Mark Grudzielanek .20 .50
133 David Justice .20 .50
134 Russ Ortiz .20 .50
135 Mike Piazza .75 2.00
136 Brian Meadows .20 .50
137 Tony Gwynn .60 1.50
138 Cal Ripken 1.50 4.00
139 Kris Benson .20 .50
140 Larry Walker .20 .50
141 Cristian Guzman .20 .50
142 Tino Martinez .30 .75
143 Chris Singleton .20 .50
144 Lee Stevens .20 .50
145 Rey Ordonez .20 .50
146 Russ Davis .20 .50
147 J.T. Snow .20 .50
148 Luis Gonzalez .20 .50
149 Marquis Grissom .20 .50
150 Greg Maddux .75 2.00
151 Fernando Tatis .20 .50
152 Jason Giambi .20 .50
153 Carlos Delgado .20 .50
154 Joe McEwing .20 .50
155 Raul Mondesi .20 .50
156 Rich Aurilia .20 .50
157 Alex Fernandez .20 .50
158 Albert Belle .20 .50
159 Pat Meares .20 .50
160 Mike Lieberthal .20 .50
161 Mike Cameron .20 .50
162 Juan Encarnacion .20 .50
163 Chuck Knoblauch .20 .50
164 Pedro Martinez .30 .75
165 Randy Johnson .50 1.25
166 Shannon Stewart .20 .50
167 Jeff Bagwell .30 .75
168 Edgar Renteria .20 .50
169 Barry Bonds 1.25 3.00
170 Steve Finley .20 .50
171 Brian Hunter .20 .50
172 Tom Glavine .30 .75
173 Mark Kotsay .20 .50
174 Tony Fernandez .20 .50
175 Sammy Sosa .50 1.25
176 Geoff Jenkins .20 .50
177 Adrian Beltre .20 .50
178 Jay Bell .20 .50

179 Mike Bordick .20 .50
180 Ed Sprague .20 .50
181 Dave Roberts .20 .50
182 Greg Vaughn .20 .50
183 Brian Daubach .20 .50
184 Damion Easley .20 .50
185 Carlos Febles .20 .50
186 Kevin Tapani .20 .50
187 Frank Thomas .50 1.25
188 Roger Clemens 1.00 2.50
189 Mike Benjamin .20 .50
190 Curt Schilling .20 .50
191 Edgardo Alfonzo .20 .50
192 Mike Mussina .30 .75
193 Todd Helton .30 .75
194 Todd Jones .20 .50
195 Dean Palmer .20 .50
196 John Flaherty .20 .50
197 Derek Jeter 1.25 3.00
198 Todd Walker .20 .50
199 Brad Ausmus .20 .50
200 Mark McGwire 1.25 3.00
201 Erubiel Durazo .20 .50
202 Nick Johnson .20 .50
203 Ruben Mateo .20 .50
204 Lance Berkman .20 .50
205 Pat Burrell .20 .50
206 Pablo Ozuna .20 .50
207 Roosevelt Brown .20 .50
208 Alfonso Soriano .50 1.25
209 A.J. Burnett .20 .50
210 Rafael Furcal .20 .50
211 Scott Morgan .20 .50
212 Adam Piatt .20 .50
213 Dee Brown .20 .50
214 Corey Patterson .20 .50
215 Mickey Lopez .20 .50
216 Rob Ryan .20 .50
217 Sean Burroughs .20 .50
218 Jack Cust .20 .50
219 John Patterson .20 .50
220 Kit Pellow .20 .50
221 Chad Hermansen .20 .50
222 Daryle Ward .20 .50
223 Jayson Werth .20 .50
224 Jason Standridge .20 .50
225 Mark Mulder .20 .50
226 Peter Bergeron .20 .50
227 Willi Mo Pena .20 .50
228 Aramis Ramirez .20 .50
229 John Sneed RC .30 .75
230 Wilton Veras .20 .50
231 Josh Hamilton .75 2.00
232 Eric Munson .20 .50
233 Bobby Bradley RC .30 .75
234 Larry Bigbie RC .50 1.25
235 B.J. Garbe RC .30 .75
236 Brett Myers RC 1.00 2.50
237 Jason Stumm RC .30 .75
238 Corey Myers RC .30 .75
239 Ryan Christianson RC .30 .75
240 David Walling .20 .50
241 Josh Girdley .20 .50
242 Omar Ortiz .20 .50
243 Jason Jennings .20 .50
244 Kyle Snyder .20 .50
245 Jay Gehrke .20 .50
246 Mike Paradis .20 .50
247 Chance Caple RC .30 .75
248 Ben Christensen RC .30 .75
249 Brad Baker RC .30 .75
250 Rick Asadoorian RC .30 .75

2000 Stadium Club Chrome First Day Issue

Randomly inserted into packs at one in 33, this 250-card insert is a complete parallel of the Stadium Club Chrome base set. Each card is individually serial numbered to 100.

*STARS: 6X TO 15X BASIC CARDS
*ROOKIES: 2.5X TO 6X BASIC CARDS

2000 Stadium Club Chrome First Day Issue Refractors

Randomly inserted into packs at one in 131, this 250-card insert is a complete parallel of the Stadium Club Chrome base set. Each card features Topps' "refractor" technology. Each card is also individually serial numbered to 25.

*STARS: 15X TO 40X BASIC CARDS

2000 Stadium Club Chrome Refractors

Randomly inserted into packs at one in 12, this 250-card insert is a complete parallel of the Stadium Club Chrome base set. Each card features Topps' "refractor" technology.

*STARS: 4X TO 10X BASIC CARDS
*ROOKIES: 1.5X TO 4X BASIC CARDS

2000 Stadium Club Chrome Capture the Action

Randomly inserted into packs at one in 18, this 20-card insert features some of the major league's top prospects and veteran players. Card backs carry a "CA" prefix.

COMPLETE SET (20) 75.00 150.00
*REFRACTORS: 1X TO 2.5X BASIC CAPTURE
REFRACTOR STATED ODDS 1:90
CA1 Josh Hamilton 1.25 3.00
CA2 Pat Burrell .50 1.25
CA3 Erubiel Durazo .50 1.25
CA4 Alfonso Soriano 1.25 3.00
CA5 A.J. Burnett .50 1.25
CA6 Alex Rodriguez 2.00 5.00
CA7 Sean Casey .50 1.25
CA8 Derek Jeter 3.00 8.00
CA9 Vladimir Guerrero 1.25 3.00
CA10 Nomar Garciaparra 2.00 5.00
CA11 Mike Piazza 2.00 5.00
CA12 Ken Griffey Jr. 2.00 5.00
CA13 Sammy Sosa 1.25 3.00
CA14 Juan Gonzalez .50 1.25
CA15 Mark McGwire 3.00 8.00
CA16 Ivan Rodriguez .75 2.00
CA17 Barry Bonds 3.00 8.00
CA18 Wade Boggs .75 2.00
CA19 Tony Gwynn 1.50 4.00
CA20 Cal Ripken 4.00 10.00

2000 Stadium Club Chrome Clear Shots

Randomly inserted into packs at one in 24, this insert features ten of the major leagues most famous stars from both front and back angles at the same time. Card backs carry a "CS" prefix.

COMPLETE SET (10) 12.50 30.00
*REFRACTORS: 1X TO 2.5X BASIC CLEAR
REFRACTOR ODDS 1:120
CS1 Derek Jeter 2.50 6.00
CS2 Bernie Williams .60 1.50
CS3 Roger Clemens 2.00 5.00
CS4 Chipper Jones 1.00 2.50
CS5 Greg Maddux 1.50 4.00
CS6 Andruw Jones .60 1.50
CS7 Juan Gonzalez .40 1.00
CS8 Manny Ramirez .60 1.50
CS9 Ken Griffey Jr. 1.50 4.00
CS10 Josh Hamilton 1.25 3.00

2000 Stadium Club Chrome Eyes of the Game

Randomly inserted into packs at one in 16, this 10-card insert features players who have an "eye" for the game. Card backs carry an "EG" prefix.

COMPLETE SET (10) 12.50 30.00
*REFRACTORS: 1X TO 2.5X BASIC EYES
REFRACTOR ODDS 1:80
EG1 Randy Johnson .75 2.00
EG2 Mike Piazza 1.25 3.00
EG3 Nomar Garciaparra 1.25 3.00
EG4 Mark McGwire 2.00 5.00
EG5 Alex Rodriguez 1.25 3.00
EG6 Derek Jeter 2.00 5.00
EG7 Tony Gwynn 1.00 2.50
EG8 Sammy Sosa .75 2.00
EG9 Larry Walker .30 .75
EG10 Ken Griffey Jr. 1.25 3.00

2000 Stadium Club Chrome True Colors

Randomly inserted into packs at one in 32, this 10-card insert features players that rise to the occasion when the game's on the line. Card backs carry a "TC" prefix.

COMPLETE SET (10) 20.00 50.00
*REFRACTORS: 1X TO 2.5X BASIC TRUE
REFRACTOR ODDS 1:160
TC1 Sammy Sosa 1.25 3.00
TC2 Nomar Garciaparra 2.00 5.00
TC3 Alex Rodriguez 2.00 5.00
TC4 Derek Jeter 3.00 8.00
TC5 Mark McGwire 3.00 8.00
TC6 Chipper Jones 1.25 3.00
TC7 Mike Piazza 2.00 5.00
TC8 Ken Griffey Jr. 2.00 5.00
TC9 Manny Ramirez .75 2.00
TC10 Vladimir Guerrero 1.25 3.00

2000 Stadium Club Chrome Visionaries

Randomly inserted into packs at one in 18, this 20-card insert features some of the major league's most talented prospects. Card backs carry a "V" prefix.

COMPLETE SET (20) 25.00 60.00
*REF: .75X TO 2X BASIC VISIONARIES
REFRACTOR ODDS 1:90
V1 Alfonso Soriano 1.25 3.00
V2 Josh Hamilton 1.25 3.00
V3 A.J. Burnett .50 1.25
V4 Pat Burrell .50 1.25
V5 Ruben Salazar .50 1.25
V6 Aaron Rowand 1.50 4.00
V7 Adam Piatt .50 1.25
V8 Nick Johnson .50 1.25
V9 Brett Myers 1.25 3.00
V10 Jack Cust .50 1.25
V11 Corey Patterson .50 1.25
V12 Sean Burroughs .50 1.25
V13 Pablo Ozuna .50 1.25
V14 Dee Brown .50 1.25
V15 John Patterson .50 1.25
V16 Willi Mo Pena .50 1.25
V17 Mark Mulder .50 1.25
V18 Eric Munson .50 1.25
V19 Alex Escobar 1.25 3.00
V20 Rick Asadoorian .50 1.25

1996 Stadum Club Porcelain

These six cards were available through the Topps catalog at an issue price of $79. The six players in the set each represent a key player from each year of the Stadium Club brand history. A special display which cost an additional $19.95 was also available for this set.

1 Ken Griffey Jr 10.00 25.00
2 Frank Thomas 10.00 25.00
3 Kenny Lofton 8.00 20.00
4 Barry Bonds 12.50 30.00
5 Paul Molitor 8.00 20.00
6 Randy Johnson 10.00 25.00

2001 Studio

This 200 card set was issued in six-card packs with 18 packs per box. Cards numbered 151-200 were shorter printed than cards 1-150. Each of the cards from 151-200 were serial numbered to 700.

COMP.SET w/o SP's (150) 15.00 40.00
COMMON CARD (1-150) .20 .50
COMMON (151-200) 3.00 8.00
1 Alex Rodriguez .75 2.00
2 Barry Bonds 1.25 3.00
3 Cal Ripken 1.50 4.00
4 Chipper Jones .50 1.25
5 Derek Jeter 1.25 3.00
6 Troy Glaus .20 .50
7 Frank Thomas .50 1.25
8 Greg Maddux .75 2.00
9 Ivan Rodriguez .30 .75
10 Jeff Bagwell .30 .75
11 Mark Quinn .20 .50
12 Todd Helton .30 .75
13 Ken Griffey Jr. .75 2.00
14 Manny Ramirez Sox .30 .75
15 Mark McGwire 1.25 3.00
16 Mike Piazza .75 2.00
17 Nomar Garciaparra .75 2.00
18 Robin Ventura .20 .50
19 Aramis Ramirez .20 .50
20 J.T. Snow .20 .50
21 Pat Burrell .20 .50
22 Curt Schilling .20 .50
23 Carlos Delgado .20 .50
24 J.D. Drew .20 .50
25 Cliff Floyd .20 .50
26 Brian Jordan .20 .50
27 Roberto Alomar .30 .75
28 Barry Zito .30 .75
29 Harold Baines .20 .50
30 Brad Penny .20 .50
31 Jose Cruz Jr. .20 .50
32 Andy Pettitte .30 .75
33 Jim Edmonds .20 .50
34 Darin Erstad .20 .50
35 Jason Giambi .20 .50
36 Tom Glavine .30 .75
37 Juan Gonzalez .20 .50
38 Mark Grace .30 .75
39 Shawn Green .20 .50
40 Tim Hudson .20 .50
41 Andruw Jones .30 .75
42 Jeff Kent .20 .50
43 Barry Larkin .30 .75
44 Rafael Furcal .20 .50
45 Mike Mussina .30 .75
46 Hideo Nomo .50 1.25
47 Rafael Palmeiro .30 .75
48 Scott Rolen .30 .75
49 Gary Sheffield .20 .50
50 Bernie Williams .30 .75
51 Bob Abreu .20 .50
52 Edgardo Alfonzo .20 .50
53 Edgar Martinez .30 .75
54 Magglio Ordonez .20 .50
55 Kerry Wood .20 .50
56 Matt Morris .20 .50
57 Lance Berkman .20 .50
58 Kevin Brown .20 .50
59 Sean Casey .20 .50
60 Eric Chavez .20 .50
61 Bartolo Colon .20 .50
62 Johnny Damon .30 .75
63 Jermaine Dye .20 .50
64 Juan Encarnacion .20 .50
65 Carl Everett .20 .50
66 Brian Giles .20 .50
67 Mike Hampton .20 .50
68 Richard Hidalgo .20 .50
69 Geoff Jenkins .20 .50
70 Jacque Jones .20 .50
71 Jason Kendall .20 .50
72 Ryan Klesko .20 .50
73 Chan Ho Park .20 .50
74 Richie Sexson .20 .50
75 Mike Sweeney .20 .50
76 Fernando Tatis .20 .50
77 Miguel Tejada .20 .50
78 Jose Vidro .20 .50
79 Larry Walker .75 2.00
80 Preston Wilson .20 .50
81 Craig Biggio .30 .75
82 Fred McGriff .30 .75
83 Jim Thome .30 .75
84 Garret Anderson .20 .50
85 Mark Mulder .20 .50
86 Tony Batista .20 .50
87 Terrence Long .20 .50
88 Brad Fullmer .20 .50
89 Rusty Greer .20 .50
90 Orlando Hernandez .20 .50
91 Gabe Kapler .20 .50
92 Paul Konerko .20 .50
93 Carlos Lee .20 .50
94 Kenny Lofton .20 .50
95 Raul Mondesi .20 .50
96 Jorge Posada .30 .75
97 Tim Salmon .30 .75
98 Greg Vaughn .20 .50
99 Mo Vaughn .20 .50
100 Omar Vizquel .30 .75
101 Ben Grieve .20 .50
102 Luis Gonzalez .20 .50
103 Ray Durham .20 .50
104 Ryan Dempster .20 .50
105 Eric Karros .20 .50
106 David Justice .20 .50
107 Pedro Martinez .30 .75
108 Randy Johnson .50 1.25
109 Rick Ankiel .20 .50
110 Rickey Henderson .50 1.25
111 Roger Clemens 1.00 2.50
112 Sammy Sosa .50 1.25
113 Tony Gwynn .60 1.50
114 Vladimir Guerrero .50 1.25
115 Kazuhiro Sasaki .20 .50
116 Phil Nevin .20 .50
117 Ruben Mateo .20 .50
118 Shannon Stewart .20 .50
119 Matt Williams .20 .50
120 Tino Martinez .30 .75
121 Ken Caminiti .20 .50
122 Edgar Renteria .20 .50
123 Charles Johnson .20 .50
124 Aaron Sele .20 .50
125 Javy Lopez .20 .50
126 Mariano Rivera .50 1.25
127 Shea Hillenbrand .20 .50
128 Jeff D'Amico .20 .50
129 Brady Anderson .20 .50
130 Kevin Millwood .20 .50
131 Trot Nixon .20 .50
132 Mike Lieberthal .20 .50
133 Juan Pierre .20 .50
134 Russ Ortiz .20 .50
135 Jose Macias .20 .50
136 John Smoltz .30 .75
137 Jason Varitek .50 1.25
138 Dean Palmer .20 .50
139 Jeff Cirillo .20 .50
140 Paul O'Neill .30 .75
141 Andres Galarraga .20 .50
142 David Wells .20 .50
143 Brad Radke .20 .50
144 Wade Miller .20 .50
145 John Olerud .20 .50
146 Moises Alou .20 .50
147 Carlos Beltran .20 .50
148 Jeromy Burnitz .20 .50
149 Steve Finley .20 .50
150 Joe Mays .20 .50
151 Alex Escobar ROO 3.00 8.00
152 J. Estrada ROO RC 4.00 10.00
153 Pedro Feliz ROO 3.00 8.00
154 Nate Frese ROO RC 3.00 8.00
155 Dee Brown ROO 3.00 8.00
156 B. Larson ROO RC 3.00 8.00
157 A. Gomez ROO RC 3.00 8.00
158 Jason Hart ROO 3.00 8.00
159 C.C. Sabathia ROO 3.00 8.00
160 Josh Towers ROO RC 4.00 10.00
161 C. Parker ROO RC 3.00 8.00
162 J. Melian ROO RC 3.00 8.00
163 Joe Kennedy ROO RC 4.00 10.00
164 A. Hernandez ROO RC 3.00 8.00
165 Jimmy Rollins ROO 3.00 8.00
166 Jose Mieses ROO RC 3.00 8.00
167 Roy Oswalt ROO 4.00 10.00
168 Eric Munson ROO 3.00 8.00
169 Xavier Nady ROO 3.00 8.00
170 H. Ramirez ROO RC 4.00 10.00
171 Abraham Nunez ROO 3.00 8.00
172 Jose Ortiz ROO 3.00 8.00
173 Jeremy Owens ROO RC UER 3.00 8.00
Eric Owens pictured on front
174 C. Vargas ROO RC 3.00 8.00
175 Corey Patterson ROO 3.00 8.00
176 Carlos Pena ROO 3.00 8.00
177 Bud Smith ROO RC 3.00 8.00
178 Adam Dunn ROO 4.00 10.00
179 A. Pettyjohn ROO RC 3.00 8.00
180 E. Guzman ROO RC 3.00 8.00
181 Jay Gibbons ROO RC 4.00 10.00
182 Wilkin Ruan ROO RC 3.00 8.00
183 T. Shinjo ROO RC 4.00 10.00
184 Alfonso Soriano ROO 4.00 10.00
185 Marcus Giles ROO 3.00 8.00
186 Ichiro Suzuki ROO RC 40.00 80.00
187 Juan Uribe ROO RC 4.00 10.00
188 D. Williams ROO RC 3.00 8.00
189 Carlos Valderrama ROO RC 3.00 8.00
190 Matt White ROO RC 3.00 8.00
191 Albert Pujols ROO RC 150.00 225.00
192 D. Mendez ROO RC 3.00 8.00
193 C. Aldridge ROO RC 3.00 8.00
194 Endy Chavez ROO RC 3.00 8.00
195 Josh Beckett ROO 4.00 10.00
196 W. Betemit ROO RC 4.00 10.00
197 Ben Sheets ROO 4.00 10.00
198 A. Torres ROO RC 3.00 8.00
199 Aubrey Huff ROO 3.00 8.00
200 Jack Wilson ROO RC 4.00 10.00

2001 Studio Diamond Collection

Randomly inserted in packs, these 47 cards feature each of these players along with a game-worn jersey swatch. Cards numbered 24, 35 and 44 were not printed for this set.

DC1 Vladimir Guerrero 6.00 15.00
DC2 Barry Bonds 10.00 25.00
DC3 Cal Ripken 15.00 40.00
DC4 Nomar Garciaparra 6.00 15.00
DC5 Greg Maddux 6.00 15.00
DC6 Frank Thomas 6.00 15.00
DC7 Roger Clemens 10.00 25.00
DC8 Luis Gonzalez SP 6.00 15.00
DC9 Tony Gwynn 6.00 15.00
DC10 Carlos Lee SP 6.00 15.00
DC11 Troy Glaus 4.00 10.00
DC12 Randy Johnson 6.00 15.00
DC13 Manny Ramirez SP 10.00 25.00
DC14 Pedro Martinez 6.00 15.00
DC15 Todd Helton 6.00 15.00
DC16 Jeff Bagwell 6.00 15.00
DC17 Rickey Henderson 6.00 15.00
DC18 Kazuhiro Sasaki 4.00 10.00
DC19 Albert Pujols SP 30.00 60.00
DC20 Ivan Rodriguez 6.00 15.00
DC21 Darin Erstad 4.00 10.00
DC22 Andruw Jones 6.00 15.00
DC23 Roberto Alomar 6.00 15.00
DC25 Juan Gonzalez 4.00 10.00
DC26 Shawn Green 4.00 10.00
DC27 Lance Berkman 4.00 10.00
DC28 Scott Rolen 6.00 15.00
DC29 Rafael Palmeiro 6.00 15.00
DC30 J.D. Drew 4.00 10.00
DC31 Kerry Wood 4.00 10.00
DC32 Jim Edmonds 4.00 10.00
DC33 Tom Glavine SP 10.00 25.00
DC34 Hideo Nomo SP 10.00 25.00
DC36 Tim Hudson 4.00 10.00
DC37 Miguel Tejada 4.00 10.00
DC38 Chipper Jones 6.00 15.00
DC39 Edgar Martinez SP 10.00 25.00
DC40 Chan Ho Park 4.00 10.00
DC41 Magglio Ordonez 4.00 10.00
DC42 Sean Casey 4.00 10.00
DC43 Larry Walker 4.00 10.00
DC45 Cliff Floyd 4.00 10.00
DC46 Mike Sweeney 4.00 10.00
DC47 Kevin Brown 4.00 10.00
DC48 Richie Sexson 4.00 10.00
DC49 Jermaine Dye 4.00 10.00
DC50 Craig Biggio 6.00 15.00

2001 Studio Diamond Cut Collection

This parallel to the Diamond Cut insert set was randomly inserted in packs. Each card was serial numbered to 75 and features an upgraded patch swatch of fabric (as averse to the standard jersey swatch used for the more readily available Diamond Collection inserts). Six player signed 25 of their cards, thus creating an Autograph parallel set. Please note, the six players have been tagged as "SP/50" in our checklist for this set.

1/8/19/26-28 PRINT RUN 50 #'d OF EACH

2001 Studio Leather and Lumber

Randomly inserted in packs, these 47 cards feature player cards along with one swatch of a game-used bat. A few players were printed in lesser quantity and we have notated those players with an SP. Also, cards numbered 4,22 and 39 do not exist.

COMBOS PRINT RUN 25 #'d SETS
NO COMBO PRICING DUE TO SCARCITY
LL1 Barry Bonds 10.00 25.00
LL2 Cal Ripken 15.00 40.00
LL3 Miguel Tejada 4.00 10.00
LL5 Frank Thomas 6.00 15.00
LL6 Greg Maddux 6.00 15.00
LL7 Ivan Rodriguez 6.00 15.00
LL8 Jeff Bagwell SP 10.00 25.00
LL9 Sean Casey SP 6.00 15.00
LL10 Todd Helton 6.00 15.00
LL11 Cliff Floyd 4.00 10.00
LL12 Hideo Nomo 6.00 15.00
LL13 Chipper Jones 6.00 15.00
LL14 Rickey Henderson 6.00 15.00
LL15 Richard Hidalgo 4.00 10.00
LL16 Mike Piazza 6.00 15.00
LL17 Larry Walker 4.00 10.00
LL18 Tony Gwynn 6.00 15.00
LL19 Vladimir Guerrero 6.00 15.00
LL20 Rafael Furcal 4.00 10.00
LL21 Roberto Alomar SP 10.00 25.00
LL23 Albert Pujols 30.00 60.00
LL24 Raul Mondesi 4.00 10.00
LL25 J.D. Drew 4.00 10.00
LL26 Jim Edmonds 4.00 10.00
LL27 Darin Erstad SP 6.00 15.00
LL28 Craig Biggio 6.00 15.00
LL29 Kenny Lofton 4.00 10.00
LL30 Juan Gonzalez 4.00 10.00
LL31 John Olerud 4.00 10.00
LL32 Shawn Green 4.00 10.00
LL33 Andruw Jones SP 10.00 25.00
LL34 Moises Alou 4.00 10.00
LL35 Jeff Kent 4.00 10.00
LL36 Ryan Klesko 4.00 10.00
LL37 Luis Gonzalez 4.00 10.00
LL38 Rafael Palmeiro 6.00 15.00
LL40 Scott Rolen 6.00 15.00
LL41 Carlos Lee 4.00 10.00
LL42 Bob Abreu 4.00 10.00
LL43 Edgardo Alfonzo 4.00 10.00
LL44 Bernie Williams 6.00 15.00
LL45 Brian Giles 4.00 10.00
LL46 Jermaine Dye 4.00 10.00
LL47 Lance Berkman 4.00 10.00
LL48 Edgar Martinez 6.00 15.00
LL49 Richie Sexson 4.00 10.00
LL50 Magglio Ordonez 4.00 10.00

2001 Studio Masterstrokes

Randomly inserted in packs, these 30 cards feature the player along with both a swatch of game-used bat and a game-used jersey. These cards are serial numbered to 200 and cards numbered 13 and 15 were not issued.

MS1 Tony Gwynn 10.00 25.00
MS2 Ivan Rodriguez 10.00 25.00
MS3 J.D. Drew 6.00 15.00
MS4 Cal Ripken 30.00 60.00
MS5 Hideo Nomo 10.00 25.00
MS6 Darin Erstad 6.00 15.00
MS7 Frank Thomas 10.00 25.00
MS8 Andruw Jones 10.00 25.00
MS9 Roberto Alomar 10.00 25.00
MS10 Larry Walker 6.00 15.00
MS11 Vladimir Guerrero 10.00 25.00
MS12 Barry Bonds 20.00 50.00
MS14 Luis Gonzalez 6.00 15.00
MS16 Juan Gonzalez 6.00 15.00
MS17 Todd Helton 10.00 25.00
MS18 Jeff Bagwell 10.00 25.00
MS19 Albert Pujols 75.00 150.00

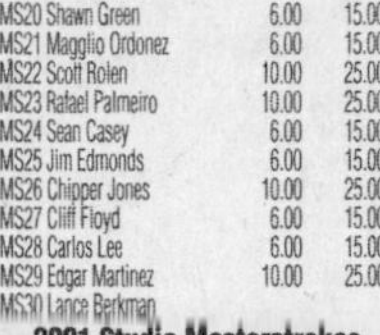

MS20 Shawn Green 6.00 15.00
MS21 Magglio Ordonez 6.00 15.00
MS22 Scott Rolen 10.00 25.00
MS23 Rafael Palmeiro 10.00 25.00
MS24 Sean Casey 6.00 15.00
MS25 Jim Edmonds 6.00 15.00
MS26 Chipper Jones 10.00 25.00
MS27 Cliff Floyd 6.00 15.00
MS28 Carlos Lee 6.00 15.00
MS29 Edgar Martinez 10.00 25.00
MS30 Lance Berkman

2001 Studio Masterstrokes Artist's Proofs

This parallel to the Studio Masterstroke set was issued to a print run of 25 sets. A few of the players signed their cards for inclusion in the set.

2/11/14/19-20/24 ARE AUTO CARDS

2001 Studio Private Signings 5 x 7

Issued one per sealed box, these cards measure 5" by 7" and were signed by the players. A few cards were issued in shorter supply and we have notated them with an SP and print run information supplied by Donruss/Playoff.

1 Bob Abreu 6.00 15.00
2 Roberto Alomar SP/200 10.00 25.00
3 Rick Ankiel 10.00 25.00
4 Josh Beckett 10.00 25.00
5 Lance Berkman 6.00 15.00
6 Wilson Betemit 10.00 25.00
7 Barry Bonds SP/95 100.00 175.00
8 Sean Casey 6.00 15.00
9 Roger Clemens SP/200 60.00 120.00
10 Adam Dunn 10.00 25.00
11 Darin Erstad SP/25
12 Alex Escobar 4.00 10.00
13 Cliff Floyd 6.00 15.00
14 Jason Giambi SP/250 6.00 15.00
15 Brian Giles 6.00 15.00
16 Troy Glaus 10.00 25.00
17 Tom Glavine 15.00 40.00
18 Luis Gonzalez 6.00 15.00
19 Shawn Green SP/190 10.00 25.00
20 Vladimir Guerrero 6.00 15.00
21 Tony Gwynn SP/190 50.00 100.00
22 Todd Helton SP/125 10.00 25.00
23 Andruw Jones SP/250 10.00 25.00
24 Gabe Kapler 6.00 15.00
25 Ryan Klesko 6.00 15.00
26 Carlos Lee 6.00 15.00
27 Greg Maddux SP/200 50.00 100.00
28 Edgar Martinez 15.00 40.00
29 Mike Mussina SP/144 15.00 40.00
30 Magglio Ordonez 6.00 15.00
31 R. Palmeiro SP/250 20.00 50.00
32 Corey Patterson 4.00 10.00
33 Brad Penny 4.00 10.00
34 Albert Pujols SP/50 800.00 1200.00
35 Manny Ramirez Sox SP/115 12.50 30.00
36 Cal Ripken SP/50 150.00 250.00
37 Alex Rodriguez 50.00 100.00
38 Ivan Rodriguez SP/150 15.00 40.00
39 Scott Rolen 10.00 25.00
40 C.C. Sabathia 6.00 15.00
41 Curt Schilling 8.00 20.00
42 Ben Sheets 10.00 25.00
43 Alfonso Soriano 10.00 25.00
44 Mike Sweeney 6.00 15.00
45 Miguel Tejada 10.00 25.00
46 Frank Thomas 15.00 40.00
47 Kerry Wood 10.00 25.00
48 Barry Zito 6.00 15.00

2001 Studio Warning Track

Randomly inserted in packs, these 35 cards feature the player along with a swatch from an outfield-wall. Card number 26 does not exist in this set.

OFF THE WALL 25 SERIAL #'D SETS
OFF THE WALL: NO PRICING DUE TO SCARCITY
WT1 Andruw Jones 4.00 10.00
WT2 Rafael Palmeiro 4.00 10.00
WT3 Gary Sheffield 3.00 8.00
WT4 Larry Walker 3.00 8.00
WT5 Shawn Green 3.00 8.00
WT6 Mike Piazza 6.00 15.00
WT7 Barry Bonds 10.00 25.00
WT8 J.D. Drew 3.00 8.00
WT9 Magglio Ordonez 3.00 8.00
WT10 Todd Helton 4.00 10.00
WT11 Juan Gonzalez 3.00 8.00
WT12 Pat Burrell 3.00 8.00
WT13 Mark McGwire 12.50 30.00
WT14 Frank Robinson 4.00 10.00
WT15 Manny Ramirez 4.00 10.00
WT16 Lance Berkman 3.00 8.00
WT17 Kirby Puckett 4.00 10.00
WT18 Johnny Bench 4.00 10.00
WT19 Chipper Jones 4.00 10.00
WT20 Mike Schmidt 8.00 20.00
WT21 Vladimir Guerrero 4.00 10.00
WT22 Sammy Sosa 4.00 10.00
WT23 Cal Ripken 12.50 30.00
WT24 Roberto Alomar 4.00 10.00
WT25 Willie Stargell 4.00 10.00
WT27 Scott Rolen 4.00 10.00
WT28 R. Clemente SP 30.00 60.00
WT29 Tony Gwynn 6.00 15.00
WT30 Ivan Rodriguez 4.00 10.00
WT31 Sean Casey 3.00 8.00
WT32 Frank Thomas 4.00 10.00
WT33 Jeff Bagwell 4.00 10.00
WT34 Jeff Kent 3.00 8.00
WT35 Reggie Jackson 4.00 10.00

2001-02 Studio Chicago Collection

These cards were among the first in a project in which Donruss/Playoff unveiled a show-exclusive program. At the March 2002 Chicago Sun-Times Show, if a collector opened a box at the Donruss/Playoff booth -- they received a card from what Donruss/Playoff called the "Chicago Collection". Donruss/Playoff created a limited amount of singles from selected products and sequentially numbered each card to 5. The cards were distributed on a strict product-specific basis. For example, collectors who opened 2001 Donruss packs or boxes in front of a Donruss representative were be rewarded with the appropriate number of 2001

NO PRICING DUE TO SCARCITY

2002 Studio Samples

This 200 card set, which previewed the veteran players from the Studio set, was issued one per Beckett Baseball Card Monthly issue number 210. These cards are valued at a multiple of the regular Studio cards. These cards can be differentiated from the regular cards with the "Sample" verbiage in the back.

*SAMPLES: 1.5X TO 4X BASIC CARDS
ONE PER ICHIRO BBCM 210
*GOLD: 1.5X TO 4X BASIC SAMPLES
GOLD: ISSUED IN 10% OF TOTAL RUN

2002 Studio

This 275 card set was issued in two separate series. The Studio product, containing cards 1-250, was released in July, 2002. The product was issued in five card packs which came 18 packs to a box and 16 boxes to a case. Cards numbered 1 through 200 feature veterans while cards 201 through 250 feature rookies and prospects and have a stated print run of 1500 serial numbered sets. Cards 251-275 were distributed in 2002 Donruss the Rookies packs in mid-December 2002. Like cards 201-250, these update cards featured a selection of prospects and were each serial-numbered to 1500 copies.

COMP.LOW SET w/o SP's (200) 20.00 50.00
COMMON CARD (1-200) .20 .50
COMMON ROOKIE (1-200) .20 .50
COMMON CARD (201-275) 1.50 4.00
1 Vladimir Guerrero .50 1.25
2 Chipper Jones .50 1.25
3 Bob Abreu .20 .50
4 Barry Zito .20 .50
5 Larry Walker .20 .50
6 Miguel Tejada .20 .50
7 Mike Sweeney .20 .50
8 Shannon Stewart .20 .50
9 Sammy Sosa .50 1.25
10 Bud Smith .20 .50
11 Wilson Betemit .20 .50
12 Kevin Brown .20 .50
13 Ellis Burks .20 .50
14 Pat Burrell .20 .50
15 Cliff Floyd .20 .50
16 Marcus Giles .20 .50
17 Troy Glaus .20 .50
18 Barry Larkin .30 .75
19 Carlos Lee .20 .50
20 Brian Lawrence .20 .50
21 Paul Lo Duca .20 .50
22 Ben Grieve .20 .50
23 Shawn Green .20 .50
24 Mike Cameron .20 .50
25 Roger Clemens 1.00 2.50
26 Joe Crede .20 .50
27 Jose Cruz Jr. .20 .50
28 Jeremy Affeldt .20 .50
29 Adrian Beltre .20 .50
30 Josh Beckett .20 .50
31 Roberto Alomar .30 .75
32 Toby Hall .20 .50
33 Mike Hampton .20 .50
34 Eric Milton .20 .50
35 Eric Munson .20 .50
36 Trot Nixon .20 .50
37 Roy Oswalt .20 .50
38 Chan Ho Park .20 .50
39 Charles Johnson .20 .50
40 Nick Johnson .20 .50
41 Tim Hudson .20 .50
42 Cristian Guzman .20 .50
43 Drew Henson .20 .50
44 Mark Grace .30 .75
45 Luis Gonzalez .20 .50
46 Pedro Martinez .30 .75
47 Joe Mays .20 .50
48 Jorge Posada .30 .75
49 Aramis Ramirez .20 .50

Card	Low	High
50 Kip Wells	.20	.50
51 Moises Alou	.20	.50
52 Omar Vizquel	.30	.75
53 Ichiro Suzuki	1.00	2.50
54 Jimmy Rollins	.20	.50
55 Freddy Garcia	.20	.50
56 Steve Green	.20	.50
57 Brian Jordan	.20	.50
58 Paul Konerko	.20	.50
59 Jack Cust	.20	.50
60 Sean Casey	.20	.50
61 Bret Boone	.20	.50
62 Hideo Nomo	.50	1.25
63 Magglio Ordonez	.20	.50
64 Frank Thomas	.50	1.25
65 Josh Towers	.20	.50
66 Javier Vazquez	.20	.50
67 Robin Ventura	.20	.50
68 Aubrey Huff	.20	.50
69 Richard Hidalgo	.20	.50
70 Brandon Claussen	.20	.50
71 Bartolo Colon	.20	.50
72 John Buck	.20	.50
73 Dee Brown	.20	.50
74 Barry Bonds	1.25	3.00
75 Jason Giambi	.20	.50
76 Erick Almonte	.20	.50
77 Ryan Dempster	.20	.50
78 Jim Edmonds	.20	.50
79 Jay Gibbons	.20	.50
80 Shigetoshi Hasegawa	.20	.50
81 Todd Helton	.30	.75
82 Erik Bedard	.20	.50
83 Carlos Beltran	.20	.50
84 Rafael Soriano	.20	.50
85 Gary Sheffield	.20	.50
86 Richie Sexson	.20	.50
87 Mike Rivera	.20	.50
88 Jose Ortiz	.20	.50
89 Abraham Nunez	.20	.50
90 Dave Williams	.20	.50
91 Preston Wilson	.20	.50
92 Jason Jennings	.20	.50
93 Juan Diaz	.20	.50
94 Steve Smyth	.20	.50
95 Phil Nevin	.20	.50
96 John Olerud	.20	.50
97 Brad Penny	.20	.50
98 Andy Pettitte	.30	.75
99 Juan Pierre	.20	.50
100 Manny Ramirez	.30	.75
101 Edgardo Alfonzo	.20	.50
102 Michael Cuddyer	.20	.50
103 Johnny Damon Sox	.30	.75
104 Carlos Zambrano	.20	.50
105 Jose Vidro	.20	.50
106 Tsuyoshi Shinjo	.20	.50
107 Ed Rogers	.20	.50
108 Scott Rolen	.30	.75
109 Mariano Rivera	.50	1.25
110 Tim Redding	.20	.50
111 Josh Phelps	.20	.50
112 Gabe Kapler	.20	.50
113 Edgar Martinez	.30	.75
114 Fred McGriff	.30	.75
115 Raul Mondesi	.20	.50
116 Wade Miller	.20	.50
117 Mike Mussina	.30	.75
118 Rafael Palmeiro	.30	.75
119 Adam Johnson	.20	.50
120 Rickey Henderson	.50	1.25
121 Bill Hall	.20	.50
122 Ken Griffey Jr.	.75	2.00
123 Geronimo Gil	.20	.50
124 Robert Fick	.20	.50
125 Darin Erstad	.20	.50
126 Brandon Duckworth	.20	.50
127 Garret Anderson	.20	.50
128 Pedro Feliz	.20	.50
129 Jeff Cirillo	.20	.50
130 Brian Giles	.20	.50
131 Craig Biggio	.30	.75
132 Willie Harris	.20	.50
133 Doug Davis	.20	.50
134 Jeff Kent	.20	.50
135 Terrence Long	.20	.50
136 Carlos Delgado	.20	.50
137 Tino Martinez	.30	.75
138 Donaldo Mendez	.20	.50
139 Sean Douglass	.20	.50
140 Eric Chavez	.20	.50
141 Rick Ankiel	.20	.50
142 Jeremy Giambi	.20	.50
143 Juan Pena	.20	.50
144 Bernie Williams	.30	.75
145 Craig Wilson	.20	.50
146 Ricardo Rodriguez	.20	.50
147 Albert Pujols	1.00	2.50
148 Antonio Perez	.20	.50
149 Russ Ortiz	.20	.50
150 Corky Miller	.20	.50
151 Rich Aurilia	.20	.50
152 Kerry Wood	.20	.50
153 Joe Thurston	.20	.50
154 Jeff Deardorff	.20	.50
155 Jermaine Dye	.20	.50
156 Andruw Jones	.30	.75
157 Victor Martinez	.50	1.25
158 Nick Neugebauer	.20	.50
159 Matt Morris	.20	.50
160 Casey Fossum	.20	.50
161 J.D. Drew	.20	.50
162 Matt Childers	.20	.50
163 Mark Buehrle	.20	.50
164 Jeff Bagwell	.30	.75
165 Kazuhiro Sasaki	.20	.50
166 Ben Sheets	.20	.50
167 Alex Rodriguez	.75	2.00
168 Adam Pettyjohn	.20	.50
169 Chris Snelling RC	.50	1.25
170 Robert Person	.20	.50
171 Juan Uribe	.20	.50
172 Mo Vaughn	.20	.50
173 Alfredo Amezaga	.20	.50
174 Ryan Drese	.20	.50
175 Corey Thurman RC	.20	.50
176 Jim Thome	.30	.75
177 Orlando Cabrera	.20	.50
178 Eric Cyr	.20	.50
179 Greg Maddux	.75	2.00
180 Earl Snyder RC	.20	.50
181 C.C. Sabathia	.20	.50
182 Mark Mulder	.20	.50
183 Jose Mieses	.20	.50
184 Joe Kennedy	.20	.50
185 Randy Johnson	.50	1.25
186 Tom Glavine	.30	.75
187 Eric Junge RC	.20	.50
188 Mike Piazza	.75	2.00
189 Corey Patterson	.20	.50
190 Carlos Pena	.20	.50
191 Curt Schilling	.20	.50
192 Nomar Garciaparra	.75	2.00
193 Lance Berkman	.20	.50
194 Ryan Klesko	.20	.50
195 Ivan Rodriguez	.30	.75
196 Alfonso Soriano	.20	.50
197 Derek Jeter	1.25	3.00
198 David Justice	.20	.50
199 Juan Gonzalez	.20	.50
200 Adam Dunn	.20	.50
201 Victor Alvarez ROO RC	1.50	4.00
202 Miguel Asencio ROO RC	1.50	4.00
203 Brandon Backe ROO RC	2.00	5.00
204 Chris Baker ROO RC	1.50	4.00
205 Steve Bechler ROO RC	1.50	4.00
206 Francis Beltran ROO RC	1.50	4.00
207 Angel Berroa ROO	1.50	4.00
208 Hank Blalock ROO	2.00	5.00
209 Dewon Brazelton ROO	1.50	4.00
210 Sean Burroughs ROO	1.50	4.00
211 Marlon Byrd ROO	1.50	4.00
212 Raul Chavez ROO RC	1.50	4.00
213 Juan Cruz ROO	1.50	4.00
214 J.De La Rosa ROO RC	1.50	4.00
215 Doug Devore ROO RC	1.50	4.00
216 John Ennis ROO RC	1.50	4.00
217 Felix Escalona ROO RC	1.50	4.00
218 Morgan Ensberg ROO	1.50	4.00
219 Cam Esslinger ROO RC	1.50	4.00
220 Kevin Frederick ROO RC	1.50	4.00
221 Fr.German ROO RC	1.50	4.00
222 Eric Hinske ROO	1.50	4.00
223 Ben Howard ROO RC	1.50	4.00
224 Orlando Hudson ROO	1.50	4.00
225 Travis Hughes ROO RC	1.50	4.00
226 Kazuhisa Ishii ROO RC	2.00	5.00
227 Ryan Jamison ROO	1.50	4.00
228 Reed Johnson ROO RC	2.00	5.00
229 Kyle Kane ROO RC	1.50	4.00
230 Austin Kearns ROO	1.50	4.00
231 Sat.Komiyama ROO RC	1.50	4.00
232 Jason Lane ROO	1.50	4.00
233 Jeremy Lambert ROO RC	1.50	4.00
234 And. Machado ROO RC	1.50	4.00
235 Brian Mallette ROO RC	1.50	4.00
236 Tak. Nomura ROO RC	1.50	4.00
237 Jorge Padilla ROO RC	1.50	4.00
238 Luis Ugueto ROO RC	1.50	4.00
239 Mark Prior ROO	2.00	5.00
240 Rene Reyes ROO RC	1.50	4.00
241 Deivis Santos ROO	1.50	4.00
242 Elio Serrano ROO RC	1.50	4.00
243 Tom Shearn ROO RC	1.50	4.00
244 Allan Simpson ROO RC	1.50	4.00
245 So Taguchi ROO RC	2.00	5.00
246 Dennis Tankersley ROO	1.50	4.00
247 Mark Teixeira ROO	2.00	5.00
248 Matt Thornton ROO RC	1.50	4.00
249 Bobby Hill ROO	1.50	4.00
250 Ramon Vazquez ROO	1.50	4.00
251 Freddy Sanchez ROO RC	2.00	5.00
252 Josh Bard ROO RC	1.50	4.00
253 Trey Hodges ROO RC	1.50	4.00
254 Jorge Sosa ROO RC	2.00	5.00
255 Ben Kozlowski ROO RC	1.50	4.00
256 Eric Good ROO RC	1.50	4.00
257 Brian Tallet ROO RC	1.50	4.00
258 P.J. Bevis ROO RC	1.50	4.00
259 Rodrigo Rosario ROO RC	1.50	4.00
260 Kirk Saarloos ROO RC	1.50	4.00
261 Run. Hernandez ROO RC	1.50	4.00
262 Josh Hancock ROO RC	2.00	5.00
263 Tim Kalita ROO RC	1.50	4.00
264 J.Simontacchi ROO RC	1.50	4.00
265 Clay Condrey ROO RC	1.50	4.00
266 Cliff Lee ROO RC	5.00	12.00
267 Aaron Guiel ROO RC	1.50	4.00
268 Andy Pratt ROO RC	1.50	4.00
269 Wilson Valdez ROO RC	1.50	4.00
270 Oliver Perez ROO RC	2.00	5.00
271 Joe Borchard ROO	1.50	4.00
272 J.Robertson ROO RC	1.50	4.00
273 Aaron Cook ROO RC	1.50	4.00
274 Kevin Cash ROO RC	1.50	4.00
275 Chone Figgins ROO RC	2.00	5.00

2002 Studio Private Signings

Randomly inserted in packs of Studio and Donruss the Rookies, these 210 cards partially parallel the 2002 Studio set. Since these cards are signed to a variable amount of cards, we have listed the print run next to the player's name. Those players who signed 25 or fewer cards are not priced due to market scarcity.

Card	Low	High
1 Vladimir Guerrero/25		
2 Chipper Jones/15		
3 Bob Abreu/50	10.00	25.00
4 Barry Zito/25		
6 Miguel Tejada/50	15.00	40.00
7 Mike Sweeney/50	10.00	25.00
8 Shannon Stewart/50	10.00	25.00
10 Bud Smith/100	6.00	15.00
11 Wilson Betemit/250	4.00	10.00
12 Kevin Brown/25		
15 Cliff Floyd/50	10.00	25.00
16 Marcus Giles/250	6.00	15.00
17 Troy Glaus/50	15.00	40.00
18 Barry Larkin/25		
19 Carlos Lee/25		
20 Brian Lawrence/250	4.00	10.00
21 Paul Lo Duca/50	10.00	25.00
25 Roger Clemens/15		
26 Joe Crede/250	6.00	15.00
28 Jeremy Affeldt/250	4.00	10.00
29 Adrian Beltre/25		
30 Josh Beckett/25		
31 Roberto Alomar/25		
32 Toby Hall/250	4.00	10.00
35 Eric Munson/25		
37 Roy Oswalt/50	10.00	25.00
40 Nick Johnson/250	6.00	15.00
41 Tim Hudson/25		
43 Drew Henson/150	4.00	10.00
45 Luis Gonzalez/15		
46 Pedro Martinez/15		
47 Joe Mays/100	6.00	15.00
49 Aramis Ramirez/50	10.00	25.00
50 Kip Wells/250	4.00	10.00
51 Moises Alou/15		
55 Freddy Garcia/50	10.00	25.00
56 Steve Green/250	4.00	10.00
59 Jack Cust/250	4.00	10.00
60 Sean Casey/50	10.00	25.00
63 Magglio Ordonez/15		
64 Frank Thomas/15		
65 Josh Towers/250	4.00	10.00
66 Javier Vazquez/100	8.00	20.00
68 Aubrey Huff/250	6.00	15.00
69 Richard Hidalgo/25		
70 Brandon Claussen/250	4.00	10.00
72 John Buck/250	4.00	10.00
73 Dee Brown/250	4.00	10.00
75 Jason Giambi/25		
76 Erick Almonte/250	4.00	10.00
79 Jay Gibbons/250	4.00	10.00
81 Todd Helton/15		
82 Erik Bedard/250	6.00	15.00
83 Carlos Beltran/15		
84 Rafael Soriano/250	4.00	10.00
85 Gary Sheffield/15		
86 Richie Sexson/50	10.00	25.00
87 Mike Rivera/250	4.00	10.00
88 Jose Ortiz/250	4.00	10.00
89 Abraham Nunez/250	4.00	10.00
90 Dave Williams/250	4.00	10.00
92 Jason Jennings/250	4.00	10.00
93 Juan Diaz/250	4.00	10.00
94 Steve Smyth/250	4.00	10.00
97 Brad Penny/80	6.00	15.00
99 Juan Pierre/100	8.00	20.00
100 Manny Ramirez/15		
102 Michael Cuddyer/250	4.00	10.00
104 Carlos Zambrano/250	10.00	25.00
105 Jose Vidro/100	6.00	15.00
107 Ed Rogers/250	4.00	10.00
108 Scott Rolen/15		
110 Tim Redding/250	4.00	10.00
111 Josh Phelps/250	4.00	10.00
112 Gabe Kapler/100	8.00	20.00
113 Edgar Martinez/50	20.00	50.00
116 Wade Miller/250	4.00	10.00
117 Mike Mussina/15		
118 Rafael Palmeiro/25		
120 Rickey Henderson/15		
121 Bill Hall/250	6.00	15.00
123 Geronimo Gil/250	4.00	10.00
124 Robert Fick/150	4.00	10.00
125 Darin Erstad/15		
126 Brandon Duckworth/250	4.00	10.00
128 Pedro Feliz/250	4.00	10.00
130 Brian Giles/15		
131 Craig Biggio/15		
132 Willie Harris/250	4.00	10.00
133 Doug Davis/250	4.00	10.00
135 Terrence Long/50	10.00	25.00
138 Donaldo Mendez/250	4.00	10.00
139 Sean Douglass/250	4.00	10.00
140 Eric Chavez/15		
141 Rick Ankiel/250	12.50	30.00
142 Jeremy Giambi/100	6.00	15.00
143 Juan Pena/250	4.00	10.00
144 Bernie Williams/15		
145 Craig Wilson/250	4.00	10.00
146 Ricardo Rodriguez/250	4.00	10.00
147 Albert Pujols/25		
148 Antonio Perez/250	4.00	10.00
150 Corky Miller/250	4.00	10.00
151 Rich Aurilia/25		
152 Kerry Wood/25		
153 Joe Thurston/250	4.00	10.00
154 Jeff Deardorff/250	4.00	10.00
155 Jermaine Dye/15		
156 Andruw Jones/15		
157 Victor Martinez/250	10.00	25.00
158 Nick Neugebauer/150	4.00	10.00
160 Casey Fossum/250	4.00	10.00
161 J.D. Drew/25		
162 Matt Childers/250	4.00	10.00
163 Mark Buehrle/150	12.50	30.00
164 Jeff Bagwell/15		
166 Ben Sheets/100	8.00	20.00
167 Alex Rodriguez/15		
168 Adam Pettyjohn/250	4.00	10.00
169 Chris Snelling/250	5.00	12.00
170 Robert Person/250	4.00	10.00
171 Juan Uribe/250	4.00	10.00
173 Alfredo Amezaga/250	4.00	10.00
175 Corey Thurman/250	4.00	10.00
176 Jim Thome/15		
178 Eric Cyr/250	4.00	10.00
179 Greg Maddux/15		
180 Earl Snyder/250	4.00	10.00
181 C.C. Sabathia/50	10.00	25.00
182 Mark Mulder/50	10.00	25.00
183 Jose Mieses/250	4.00	10.00
184 Joe Kennedy/250	4.00	10.00
186 Tom Glavine/15		
187 Eric Junge/250	4.00	10.00
189 Corey Patterson/205	4.00	10.00
190 Carlos Pena/200	4.00	10.00
191 Curt Schilling/15		
192 Nomar Garciaparra/15		
193 Lance Berkman/15		
194 Ryan Klesko/15		
195 Ivan Rodriguez/15		
196 Alfonso Soriano/50	15.00	40.00
198 David Justice/15		
199 Juan Gonzalez/15		
200 Adam Dunn/25		
201 Victor Alvarez ROO/250	4.00	10.00
203 Brandon Backe ROO/250	6.00	15.00
204 Chris Baker ROO/250	4.00	10.00
205 Steve Bechler ROO/250	4.00	10.00
206 Francis Beltran ROO/250	4.00	10.00
207 Angel Berroa ROO/250	4.00	10.00
208 Hank Blalock ROO/100	8.00	20.00
209 Dewon Brazelton ROO/200	4.00	10.00
210 Sean Burroughs ROO/50	10.00	25.00
211 Marlon Byrd ROO/200	4.00	10.00
212 Raul Chavez ROO/250	4.00	10.00
213 Juan Cruz ROO/50	10.00	25.00
214 Jorge De La Rosa ROO/250	4.00	10.00
215 Doug Devore ROO/250	4.00	10.00
216 John Ennis ROO/250	4.00	10.00
217 Felix Escalona ROO/250	4.00	10.00
218 Morgan Ensberg ROO/250	6.00	15.00
219 Cam Esslinger ROO/250	4.00	10.00
220 Kevin Frederick ROO/250	4.00	10.00
221 Franklyn German ROO/250	4.00	10.00
222 Eric Hinske ROO/250	4.00	10.00
223 Ben Howard ROO/250	4.00	10.00
224 Orlando Hudson ROO/250	4.00	10.00
225 Travis Hughes ROO/250	4.00	10.00
226 Kazuhisa Ishii ROO/50	15.00	40.00
227 Ryan Jamison ROO/250	4.00	10.00
228 Reed Johnson ROO/250	6.00	15.00
229 Kyle Kane ROO/250	4.00	10.00
230 Austin Kearns ROO/250	4.00	10.00
231 Satoru Komiyama ROO/50	15.00	40.00
232 Jason Lane ROO/200	6.00	15.00
233 Jeremy Lambert ROO/250	4.00	10.00
234 And Machado ROO/200	4.00	10.00
235 Brian Mallette ROO/250	4.00	10.00
236 Takahito Nomura ROO/100	10.00	25.00
237 Jorge Padilla ROO/200	4.00	10.00
238 Luis Ugueto ROO/250	4.00	10.00
239 Mark Prior ROO/100	8.00	20.00
240 Rene Reyes ROO/250	4.00	10.00
241 Deivis Santos ROO/250	4.00	10.00
242 Elio Serrano ROO/250	4.00	10.00
243 Tom Shearn ROO/250	4.00	10.00
244 Allan Simpson ROO/250	4.00	10.00
245 So Taguchi ROO/100	10.00	25.00
246 Dennis Tankersley ROO/100	6.00	15.00
247 Mark Teixeira ROO/50	20.00	50.00
248 Matt Thornton ROO/250	4.00	10.00
249 Bobby Hill ROO/100	6.00	15.00
250 Ramon Vazquez ROO/250	4.00	10.00
252 Josh Bard ROO/100	4.00	10.00
253 Trey Hodges ROO/250	4.00	10.00
255 Ben Kozlowski ROO/200	4.00	10.00
256 Eric Good ROO/200	4.00	10.00
257 Brian Tallet ROO/100	4.00	10.00
258 P.J. Bevis ROO/50	10.00	25.00
259 Rodrigo Rosario ROO/250	4.00	10.00
260 Kirk Saarloos ROO/100	4.00	10.00
263 Tim Kalita ROO/50	6.00	15.00
266 Cliff Lee ROO/100	50.00	100.00
268 Andy Pratt ROO/250	4.00	10.00
269 Wilson Valdez ROO/200	4.00	10.00
270 Oliver Perez ROO/25		
271 Joe Borchard ROO/100	6.00	15.00
274 Kevin Cash ROO/100	4.00	10.00
275 Chone Figgins ROO/100	10.00	25.00

2002 Studio Proofs

Randomly issued in Studio and Donruss the Rookies packs, this is a complete parallel of the 2002 Studio set. Cards 1-250 were distributed in Studio packs and 251-275 in Donruss the Rookies. These cards were printed to a stated print run of 100 serial numbered sets.

*PROOFS 1-200: 4X TO 10X BASIC
*PROOFS RC'S 1-200: 3X TO 8X BASIC
*PROOFS 201-275: .75X TO 2X BASIC

Card	Low	High
201 Victor Alvarez ROO	3.00	8.00
202 Miguel Asencio ROO	3.00	8.00
203 Brandon Backe ROO	4.00	10.00
204 Chris Baker ROO	3.00	8.00
205 Steve Bechler ROO	3.00	8.00
206 Francis Beltran ROO	3.00	8.00
207 Angel Berroa ROO	3.00	8.00
208 Hank Blalock ROO	4.00	10.00
209 Dewon Brazelton ROO	3.00	8.00
210 Sean Burroughs ROO	3.00	8.00
211 Marlon Byrd ROO	3.00	8.00
212 Raul Chavez ROO	3.00	8.00
213 Juan Cruz ROO	3.00	8.00
214 Jorge De La Rosa ROO	3.00	8.00
215 Doug Devore ROO	3.00	8.00
216 John Ennis ROO	3.00	8.00
217 Felix Escalona ROO	3.00	8.00
218 Morgan Ensberg ROO	3.00	8.00
219 Cam Esslinger ROO	3.00	8.00
220 Kevin Frederick ROO	3.00	8.00
221 Franklyn German ROO	3.00	8.00
222 Eric Hinske ROO	3.00	8.00
223 Ben Howard ROO	3.00	8.00
224 Orlando Hudson ROO	3.00	8.00
225 Travis Hughes ROO	3.00	8.00
226 Kazuhisa Ishii ROO	4.00	10.00
227 Ryan Jamison ROO	3.00	8.00
228 Reed Johnson ROO	4.00	10.00
229 Kyle Kane ROO	3.00	8.00
230 Austin Kearns ROO	3.00	8.00
231 Satoru Komiyama ROO	3.00	8.00
232 Jason Lane ROO	3.00	8.00
233 Jeremy Lambert ROO	3.00	8.00
234 Anderson Machado ROO	3.00	8.00
235 Brian Mallette ROO	3.00	8.00
236 Takahito Nomura ROO	3.00	8.00
237 Jorge Padilla ROO	3.00	8.00
238 Luis Ugueto ROO	3.00	8.00
239 Mark Prior ROO	4.00	10.00
240 Rene Reyes ROO	3.00	8.00
241 Deivis Santos ROO	3.00	8.00
242 Elio Serrano ROO	3.00	8.00
243 Tom Shearn ROO	3.00	8.00
244 Allan Simpson ROO	3.00	8.00
245 So Taguchi ROO	4.00	10.00
246 Dennis Tankersley ROO	3.00	8.00
247 Mark Teixeira ROO	4.00	10.00
248 Matt Thornton ROO	3.00	8.00
249 Bobby Hill ROO	3.00	8.00
250 Ramon Vazquez ROO	3.00	8.00
251 Freddy Sanchez ROO	4.00	10.00
252 Josh Bard ROO	3.00	8.00
253 Trey Hodges ROO	3.00	8.00
254 Jorge Sosa ROO	4.00	10.00
255 Ben Kozlowski ROO	3.00	8.00
256 Eric Good ROO	3.00	8.00
257 Brian Tallet ROO	3.00	8.00
258 P.J. Bevis ROO	3.00	8.00
259 Rodrigo Rosario ROO	3.00	8.00
260 Kirk Saarloos ROO	3.00	8.00
261 Runelvys Hernandez ROO	3.00	8.00
262 Josh Hancock ROO	4.00	10.00
263 Tim Kalita ROO	3.00	8.00
264 Jason Simontacchi ROO	3.00	8.00
265 Clay Condrey ROO	3.00	8.00
266 Cliff Lee ROO	8.00	20.00
267 Aaron Guiel ROO	3.00	8.00
268 Andy Pratt ROO	3.00	8.00
269 Wilson Valdez ROO	3.00	8.00
270 Oliver Perez ROO	4.00	10.00
271 Joe Borchard ROO	3.00	8.00
272 Jeriome Robertson ROO	3.00	8.00
273 Aaron Cook ROO	3.00	8.00
274 Kevin Cash ROO	3.00	8.00
275 Chone Figgins ROO	4.00	10.00

2002 Studio Classic

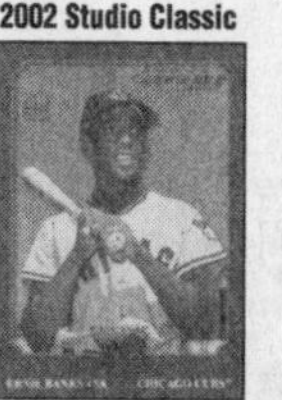

Randomly inserted in packs, these 25 card feature players elected to the Hall of Fame on the first ballot and have a stated print run of 1,000 serial numbered sets.

Card	Low	High
COMPLETE SET (25)	75.00	150.00
*1ST BALLOT: 2X TO 5X BASIC CLASSIC		
1ST BALLOT PRINT RUN BASED ON HOF YR		
1 Kirby Puckett	3.00	8.00
2 George Brett	5.00	12.00
3 Nolan Ryan	6.00	15.00
4 Mike Schmidt	5.00	12.00
5 Steve Carlton	2.00	5.00
6 Reggie Jackson	2.00	5.00
7 Tom Seaver	2.00	5.00
8 Joe Morgan	2.00	5.00
9 Jim Palmer	2.00	5.00
10 Johnny Bench	3.00	8.00
11 Willie McCovey	2.00	5.00
12 Brooks Robinson	2.00	5.00
13 Al Kaline	3.00	8.00
14 Stan Musial	4.00	10.00
15 Ozzie Smith	4.00	10.00
16 Dave Winfield	2.00	5.00
17 Robin Yount	3.00	8.00
18 Rod Carew	2.00	5.00
19 Willie Stargell	2.00	5.00
20 Lou Brock	2.00	5.00
21 Ernie Banks	3.00	8.00
22 Ted Williams	5.00	12.00
23 Jackie Robinson	3.00	8.00
24 Roberto Clemente	6.00	15.00
25 Lou Gehrig	6.00	15.00

2002 Studio Diamond Collection

Inserted in packs at stated odds of one in 17, these 25 cards feature some of the most popular players in baseball.

Card	Low	High
COMPLETE SET (25)	60.00	120.00
1 Todd Helton	1.50	4.00
2 Chipper Jones	1.50	4.00
3 Lance Berkman	1.50	4.00
4 Derek Jeter	4.00	10.00
5 Hideo Nomo	1.50	4.00
6 Kazuhisa Ishii	1.50	4.00
7 Barry Bonds	4.00	10.00
8 Alex Rodriguez	2.50	6.00
9 Ichiro Suzuki	3.00	8.00
10 Mike Piazza	2.50	6.00
11 Jim Thome	1.50	4.00
12 Greg Maddux	2.50	6.00
13 Jeff Bagwell	1.50	4.00
14 Vladimir Guerrero	1.50	4.00
15 Ken Griffey Jr.	2.50	6.00
16 Jason Giambi	1.50	4.00
17 Nomar Garciaparra	2.50	6.00
18 Albert Pujols	3.00	8.00
19 Manny Ramirez	1.50	4.00
20 Pedro Martinez	1.50	4.00
21 Roger Clemens	3.00	8.00
22 Randy Johnson	1.50	4.00
23 Mark Prior	1.50	4.00
24 So Taguchi	1.50	4.00
25 Sammy Sosa	1.50	4.00

2002 Studio Diamond Collection Artist's Proofs

Randomly inserted in packs, these cards partially parallel the Diamond Collection insert set. Each card features a memorabilia piece and we have notated both the information as to what type of piece along with the

stated print run next to the player's name in our checklist.

Card	Low	High
1 Todd Helton Jsy/200	6.00	15.00
2 Chipper Jones Jsy/150	6.00	15.00
3 Lance Berkman Jsy/200	4.00	10.00
4 Derek Jeter Base/200	10.00	25.00
5 Hideo Nomo Jsy/150	30.00	80.00
6 Kazuhisa Ishii Jsy/150	6.00	15.00
7 Barry Bonds Base/200	10.00	25.00
8 Alex Rodriguez Jsy/150	8.00	20.00
9 Ichiro Suzuki Base/200	10.00	25.00
10 Mike Piazza Jsy/150	6.00	15.00
11 Jim Thome Jsy/150	6.00	15.00
12 Greg Maddux Jsy/150	6.00	15.00
13 Jeff Bagwell Jsy/150	6.00	15.00
14 Vladimir Guerrero Jsy/200	6.00	15.00
15 Ken Griffey Jr. Base/200	6.00	15.00
16 Jason Giambi Base/200	4.00	10.00
17 Nomar Garciaparra Jsy/150	8.00	20.00
18 Albert Pujols Base/200	6.00	15.00
19 Manny Ramirez Jsy/150	6.00	15.00
20 Pedro Martinez Jsy/150	6.00	15.00
21 Roger Clemens Jsy/150	10.00	25.00
22 Randy Johnson Jsy/150	6.00	15.00
24 So Taguchi Jsy/200	6.00	15.00
25 Sammy Sosa Base/200	6.00	15.00

2002 Studio Heroes Icons Texans

Randomly inserted in packs, these four cards honor that Texas sports legend, Nolan Ryan. There are four stated print runs with the highlight being an autograph card numbered to a stated print run of 32 serial numbered cards.

Card	Low	High
HIT2 Nolan Ryan	4.00	10.00
HIT2 Nolan Ryan/500	6.00	15.00
HIT2 Nolan Ryan/100	20.00	50.00
HIT2 Nolan Ryan AU/32	150.00	250.00

2002 Studio Leather and Lumber

Randomly inserted in packs, these 25 cards feature some of the game's most dominating batsmen. Each card contains one game-used bat piece. And since there are different print runs, we have put that information next to the player's name in our checklist.

Card	Low	High
COMPLETE SET (25)	4.00	10.00
1 Nomar Garciaparra/200	10.00	25.00
2 Jeff Bagwell/150	6.00	15.00
3 Alex Rodriguez/200	8.00	20.00
4 Vladimir Guerrero/100	8.00	20.00
5 Luis Gonzalez/200	4.00	10.00
6 Chipper Jones/200	6.00	15.00
7 Shawn Green/200	4.00	10.00
8 Kirby Puckett/100	8.00	20.00
9 Juan Gonzalez/200	4.00	10.00
10 Troy Glaus/200	4.00	10.00
11 Don Mattingly/100	15.00	40.00
12 Todd Helton/200	6.00	15.00
13 Jim Thome/200	6.00	15.00
14 Rickey Henderson/200	6.00	15.00
15 Mike Schmidt/100	15.00	40.00
16 Adam Dunn/100	6.00	15.00
17 Ivan Rodriguez/200	6.00	15.00
18 Manny Ramirez/150	6.00	15.00
19 Tsuyoshi Shinjo/200	4.00	10.00
20 Andruw Jones/150	6.00	15.00
21 Roberto Alomar/200	6.00	15.00
22 Lance Berkman/200	4.00	10.00
23 Derek Jeter Ball/50	30.00	80.00
24 Ichiro Suzuki Ball/50	30.00	80.00
25 Mike Piazza/200	6.00	15.00

2002 Studio Leather and Lumber Artist's Proofs

Randomly inserted in packs, these cards parallel the Leather and Lumber insert set. These cards have a stated print run of 50 serial numbered sets which included a combination of a bat chip and a ball swatch. Of note, the cards for Derek Jeter and Ichiro feature two ball swatches.

5 Luis Gonzalez SP/25

2002 Studio Masterstrokes

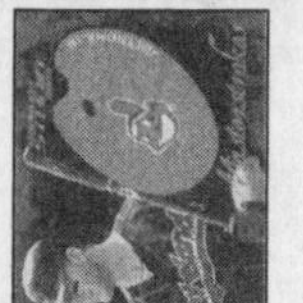

Inserted in packs at stated odds of one in 17, these 25 cards feature baseball's most skilled hitters.

Card	Low	High
COMPLETE SET (25)	50.00	100.00
1 Vladimir Guerrero	1.50	4.00
2 Frank Thomas	1.50	4.00
3 Alex Rodriguez	2.50	6.00
4 Manny Ramirez	1.50	4.00
5 Jeff Bagwell	1.50	4.00
6 Jim Thome	1.50	4.00
7 Ichiro Suzuki	3.00	8.00
8 Andruw Jones	1.50	4.00
9 Troy Glaus	1.50	4.00
10 Chipper Jones	1.50	4.00
11 Juan Gonzalez	1.50	4.00
12 Lance Berkman	1.50	4.00
13 Mike Piazza	2.50	6.00
14 Darin Erstad	1.50	4.00
15 Albert Pujols	3.00	8.00
16 Kazuhisa Ishii	1.50	4.00
17 Shawn Green	1.50	4.00
18 Rafael Palmeiro	1.50	4.00
19 Todd Helton	1.50	4.00
20 Carlos Delgado	1.50	4.00
21 Ivan Rodriguez	1.50	4.00
22 Luis Gonzalez	1.50	4.00
23 Derek Jeter	4.00	10.00
24 Nomar Garciaparra	2.50	6.00
25 J.D. Drew	1.50	4.00

2002 Studio Masterstrokes Artist's Proofs

Randomly inserted in packs, these 25 cards are a parallel to the Masterstrokes insert set and most of them feature a bat-jersey combo. The Ichiro Suzuki, Derek Jeter and J.D. Drew cards feature a ball-base combo.

Card	Low	High
1 Vladimir Guerrero/200	8.00	20.00
2 Frank Thomas/200	8.00	20.00
3 Alex Rodriguez/100	15.00	40.00
4 Manny Ramirez/200	8.00	20.00
5 Jeff Bagwell/150	8.00	20.00
6 Jim Thome/200	8.00	20.00
7 Ichiro Suzuki/100	30.00	60.00
8 Andruw Jones/200	8.00	20.00
9 Troy Glaus/200	6.00	15.00
10 Chipper Jones/200	8.00	20.00
11 Juan Gonzalez/200	6.00	15.00
12 Lance Berkman/200	6.00	15.00
13 Mike Piazza/200	15.00	40.00
14 Darin Erstad/200	6.00	15.00
15 Albert Pujols/100	15.00	40.00
16 Kazuhisa Ishii/150	8.00	20.00
17 Shawn Green/200	6.00	15.00
18 Rafael Palmeiro/200	8.00	20.00
19 Todd Helton/200	8.00	20.00
20 Carlos Delgado/200	6.00	15.00
21 Ivan Rodriguez/200	8.00	20.00
22 Luis Gonzalez/200	6.00	15.00
23 Derek Jeter/100	25.00	60.00
24 Nomar Garciaparra/150	15.00	40.00
25 J.D. Drew/150	6.00	15.00

2002 Studio Spirit of the Game

Inserted in packs at a stated odds of one in nine, these 50 cards highlight players who play the game with a real passion.

Card	Low	High
COMPLETE SET (50)	60.00	120.00
1 Alex Rodriguez	2.50	6.00
2 Curt Schilling	1.00	2.50
3 Hideo Nomo	1.50	4.00
4 Derek Jeter	4.00	10.00
5 Mike Sweeney	1.00	2.50
6 Mike Piazza	2.50	6.00
7 Roger Clemens	3.00	8.00
8 Shawn Green	1.00	2.50
9 Vladimir Guerrero	1.50	4.00
10 Carlos Lee	1.00	2.50
11 Edgar Martinez	1.00	2.50
12 Albert Pujols	3.00	8.00
13 Mark Prior	1.00	2.50
14 Mark Buehrle	1.00	2.50
15 Chipper Jones	1.50	4.00
16 Paul Lo Duca	1.00	2.50
17 Frank Thomas	1.50	4.00
18 Randy Johnson	1.50	4.00
19 Cliff Floyd	1.00	2.50

20 Todd Helton 1.00 2.50
21 Luis Gonzalez 1.00 2.50
22 Brandon Duckworth 1.00 2.50
23 Jason Giambi 1.00 2.50
24 Juan Uribe 1.00 2.50
25 Dewon Brazelton 1.00 2.50
26 J.D. Drew 1.00 2.50
27 Troy Glaus 1.00 2.50
28 Wade Miller 1.00 2.50
29 Darin Erstad 1.00 2.50
30 Brian Giles 1.00 2.50
31 Lance Berkman 1.00 2.50
32 Shannon Stewart 1.00 2.50
33 Kazuhisa Ishii 1.00 2.50
34 Corey Patterson 1.00 2.50
35 Rafael Palmeiro 1.00 2.50
36 Roy Oswalt 1.00 2.50
37 Jason Lane 1.00 2.50
38 Andruw Jones 1.00 2.50
39 Brad Penny 1.00 2.50
40 Bud Smith 1.00 2.50
41 Carlos Beltran 1.00 2.50
42 Magglio Ordonez 1.00 2.50
43 Craig Biggio 1.00 2.50
44 Hank Blalock 1.00 2.50
45 Jeff Bagwell 1.00 2.50
46 Josh Beckett 1.00 2.50
47 Juan Cruz 1.00 2.50
48 Kerry Wood 1.00 2.50
49 Brandon Berger 1.00 2.50
50 Juan Pierre 1.00 2.50

2002 Studio Spirit of the Game Hats Off

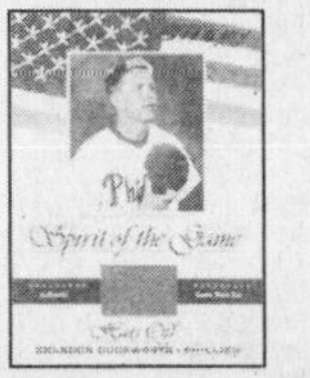

Randomly inserted in packs, these 24 cards form a partial parallel to the Spirit of the Game insert set. These cards feature pieces of game-used hats and most are serial numbered to 100. The Kazuishi Ishii card has a stated print run of 50 serial numbered sets.

MLB LOGO PRINT RUN 1 SERIAL #'d SET
NO MLB LOGO PRICING DUE TO SCARCITY
USA FLAG PRINT RUN 1 SERIAL #'d SET
NO USA FLAG PRICING DUE TO SCARCITY
10 Carlos Lee 10.00 25.00
14 Mark Buehrle 10.00 25.00
16 Paul Lo Duca 10.00 25.00
22 Brandon Duckworth 6.00 15.00
26 J.D. Drew 10.00 25.00
28 Wade Miller 6.00 15.00
30 Brian Giles 10.00 25.00
31 Lance Berkman 10.00 25.00
32 Shannon Stewart 10.00 25.00
33 Kazuhisa Ishii SP/50 10.00 25.00
35 Rafael Palmeiro 15.00 40.00
36 Roy Oswalt 10.00 25.00
37 Jason Lane 10.00 25.00
38 Andruw Jones 15.00 40.00
39 Brad Penny 6.00 15.00
40 Bud Smith 6.00 15.00
41 Carlos Beltran 10.00 25.00
42 Magglio Ordonez 10.00 25.00
43 Craig Biggio 15.00 40.00
45 Jeff Bagwell 15.00 40.00
47 Juan Cruz 6.00 15.00
48 Kerry Wood 10.00 25.00
49 Brandon Berger 6.00 15.00
50 Juan Pierre 6.00 15.00

2002 Studio Stars

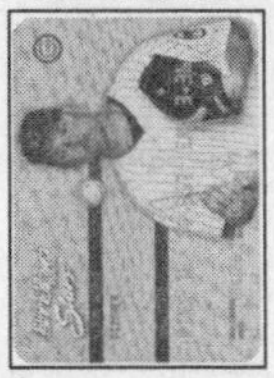

Randomly inserted in packs, these 50 cards feature leading players in a credit charge design. These cards have some key statistics for the players listed across the front of their cards.

COMPLETE SET (50) 50.00 100.00
1 Mike Piazza 1.50 4.00
2 Ivan Rodriguez .75 2.00
3 Albert Pujols 2.00 5.00
4 Scott Rolen .75 2.00
5 Alex Rodriguez 1.50 4.00
6 Curt Schilling .75 2.00
7 Vladimir Guerrero .75 2.00
8 Jim Thome .75 2.00
9 Derek Jeter 2.50 6.00
10 C.C. Sabathia .75 2.00
11 Sammy Sosa .75 2.00
12 Adam Dunn .75 2.00
13 Bernie Williams .75 2.00
14 Ichiro Suzuki 2.00 5.00
15 Barry Bonds 2.50 6.00
16 Rickey Henderson .75 2.00
17 Ken Griffey Jr. 1.50 4.00
18 Kazuhisa Ishii .75 2.00
19 Kerry Wood .75 2.00
20 Todd Helton .75 2.00
21 Hideo Nomo .75 2.00
22 Frank Thomas .75 2.00
23 Manny Ramirez .75 2.00
24 Luis Gonzalez .75 2.00
25 Rafael Palmeiro .75 2.00
26 Mike Mussina .75 2.00
27 Roy Oswalt .75 2.00
28 Darin Erstad .75 2.00
29 Barry Larkin .75 2.00
30 Randy Johnson .75 2.00
31 Tom Glavine .75 2.00
32 Lance Berkman .75 2.00
33 Juan Gonzalez .75 2.00
34 Shawn Green .75 2.00
35 Nomar Garciaparra 1.50 4.00
36 Troy Glaus .75 2.00
37 Tim Hudson .75 2.00
38 Carlos Delgado .75 2.00
39 Jason Giambi .75 2.00
40 Andruw Jones .75 2.00
41 Roberto Alomar .75 2.00
42 Greg Maddux 1.50 4.00
43 Pedro Martinez .75 2.00
44 Tony Gwynn 1.25 3.00
45 Alfonso Soriano .75 2.00
46 Chipper Jones .75 2.00
47 J.D. Drew .75 2.00
48 Roger Clemens 2.00 5.00
49 Barry Zito .75 2.00
50 Jeff Bagwell .75 2.00

2003 Studio

This 210-card set was issued in two separate series. The primary Studio product - containing cards 1-200 from the basic set - was released in June, 2003. The set was issued in six card packs with an $4 SRP which came packed 20 packs to a box and 16 boxes to a case. The first 190 cards feature just one player while the final 10 cards portray two teammates. Cards 201-211 were randomly seeded into packs of DLP Rookies and Traded of which was distributed in December, 2003. Each of these update cards featured a top prospect and was serial numbered to 1500 copies.

COMP.LO SET (200) 20.00 50.00
COMMON CARD (1-190) .20 .50
COMMON RC (1-190) .15 .40
COMMON CARD (191-200) .40 1.00
COMMON CARD (201-211) 1.50 4.00
1 Darin Erstad .20 .50
2 David Eckstein .20 .50
3 Garret Anderson .20 .50
4 Jarrod Washburn .20 .50
5 Tim Salmon .30 .75
6 Troy Glaus .20 .50
7 Jay Gibbons .20 .50
8 Melvin Mora .20 .50
9 Rodrigo Lopez .20 .50
10 Tony Batista .20 .50
11 Freddy Sanchez .20 .50
12 Derek Lowe .20 .50
13 Johnny Damon .30 .75
14 Manny Ramirez .30 .75
15 Nomar Garciaparra .75 2.00
16 Pedro Martinez .30 .75
17 Rickey Henderson .50 1.25
18 Shea Hillenbrand .20 .50
19 Carlos Lee .20 .50
20 Frank Thomas .50 1.25
21 Magglio Ordonez .20 .50
22 Bartolo Colon .20 .50
23 Paul Konerko .20 .50
24 Josh Stewart RC .15 .40
25 C.C. Sabathia .20 .50
26 Jeremy Guthrie .20 .50
27 Ellis Burks .20 .50
28 Omar Vizquel .30 .75
29 Victor Martinez .30 .75
30 Cliff Lee .75 2.00
31 Jhonny Peralta .50 1.25
32 Brian Tallet .20 .50
33 Bobby Higginson .20 .50
34 Carlos Pena .20 .50
35 Nook Logan RC .20 .50
36 Steve Sparks .20 .50
37 Travis Chapman .20 .50
38 Carlos Beltran .20 .50
39 Joe Randa .20 .50
40 Mike Sweeney .20 .50
41 Jimmy Gobble .20 .50
42 Michael Tucker .20 .50
43 Runelvys Hernandez .20 .50
44 Brad Radke .20 .50
45 Corey Koskie .20 .50
46 Cristian Guzman .20 .50
47 J.C. Romero .20 .50
48 Doug Mientkiewicz .20 .50
49 Lew Ford RC .20 .50
50 Jacque Jones .20 .50
51 Torii Hunter .20 .50
52 Alfonso Soriano .20 .50
53 Nick Johnson .20 .50
54 Bernie Williams .30 .75
55 Jose Contreras RC .30 .75
56 Derek Jeter 1.25 3.00
57 Jason Giambi .20 .50
58 Brandon Claussen .20 .50
59 Jorge Posada .30 .75
60 Mike Mussina .30 .75
61 Roger Clemens 1.00 2.50
62 Hideki Matsui RC 2.00 5.00
63 Barry Zito .20 .50
64 Adam Morrissey .20 .50
65 Eric Chavez .20 .50
66 Jermaine Dye .20 .50
67 Mark Mulder .20 .50
68 Miguel Tejada .20 .50
69 Joe Valentine RC .15 .40
70 Tim Hudson .20 .50
71 Bret Boone .20 .50
72 Chris Snelling .20 .50
73 Edgar Martinez .30 .75
74 Freddy Garcia .20 .50
75 Ichiro Suzuki 1.00 2.50
76 Jamie Moyer .20 .50
77 John Olerud .20 .50
78 Kazuhiro Sasaki .20 .50
79 Aubrey Huff .20 .50
80 Joe Kennedy .20 .50
81 Dewon Brazelton .20 .50
82 Pete LaForest RC .15 .40
83 Alex Rodriguez .75 2.00
84 Chan Ho Park .20 .50
85 Hank Blalock .20 .50
86 Juan Gonzalez .20 .50
87 Kevin Mench .20 .50
88 Rafael Palmeiro .30 .75
89 Carlos Delgado .20 .50
90 Eric Hinske .20 .50
91 Josh Phelps .20 .50
92 Roy Halladay .20 .50
93 Shannon Stewart .20 .50
94 Vernon Wells .20 .50
95 Vinny Chulk .20 .50
96 Curt Schilling .20 .50
97 Junior Spivey .20 .50
98 Luis Gonzalez .20 .50
99 Mark Grace .30 .75
100 Randy Johnson .50 1.25
101 Andruw Jones .30 .75
102 Chipper Jones .50 1.25
103 Gary Sheffield .20 .50
104 Greg Maddux .75 2.00
105 John Smoltz .30 .75
106 Mike Hampton .20 .50
107 Adam LaRoche .20 .50
108 Michael Hessman RC .15 .40
109 Corey Patterson .20 .50
110 Kerry Wood .20 .50
111 Mark Prior .30 .75
112 Moises Alou .20 .50
113 Sammy Sosa .50 1.25
114 Adam Dunn .20 .50
115 Austin Kearns .20 .50
116 Barry Larkin .30 .75
117 Ken Griffey Jr. .75 2.00
118 Sean Casey .20 .50
119 Jason Jennings .20 .50
120 Jay Payton .20 .50
121 Larry Walker .20 .50
122 Todd Helton .30 .75
123 Jeff Baker .20 .50
124 Clint Barmes RC .40 1.00
125 Ivan Rodriguez .30 .75
126 Josh Beckett .20 .50
127 Juan Encarnacion .20 .50
128 Mike Lowell .20 .50
129 Craig Biggio .30 .75
130 Jason Lane .20 .50
131 Jeff Bagwell .30 .75
132 Lance Berkman .20 .50
133 Roy Oswalt .20 .50
134 Jeff Kent .20 .50
135 Hideo Nomo .50 1.25
136 Kazuhisa Ishii .20 .50
137 Kevin Brown .20 .50
138 Odalis Perez .20 .50
139 Paul Lo Duca .20 .50
140 Shawn Green .20 .50
141 Adrian Beltre .20 .50
142 Ben Sheets .20 .50
143 Bill Hall .20 .50
144 Jeffrey Hammonds .20 .50
145 Richie Sexson .20 .50
146 Termel Sledge RC .15 .40
147 Brad Wilkerson .20 .50
148 Javier Vazquez .20 .50
149 Jose Vidro .20 .50
150 Michael Barrett .20 .50
151 Vladimir Guerrero .50 1.25
152 Al Leiter .20 .50
153 Mike Piazza .75 2.00
154 Mo Vaughn .20 .50
155 Cliff Floyd .20 .50
156 Roberto Alomar .30 .75
157 Roger Cedeno .20 .50
158 Tom Glavine .30 .75
159 Prentice Redman RC .15 .40
160 Bobby Abreu .20 .50
161 Jimmy Rollins .20 .50
162 Mike Lieberthal .20 .50
163 Pat Burrell .20 .50
164 Vicente Padilla .20 .50
165 Jim Thome .30 .75
166 Kevin Millwood .20 .50
167 Aramis Ramirez .20 .50
168 Brian Giles .20 .50
169 Jason Kendall .20 .50
170 Josh Fogg .20 .50
171 Kip Wells .20 .50
172 Jose Castillo .20 .50
173 Mark Kotsay .20 .50
174 Oliver Perez .20 .50
175 Phil Nevin .20 .50
176 Ryan Klesko .20 .50
177 Sean Burroughs .20 .50
178 Brian Lawrence .20 .50
179 Shane Victorino RC .40 1.00
180 Barry Bonds 1.25 3.00
181 Benito Santiago .20 .50
182 Ray Durham .20 .50
183 Rich Aurilla .20 .50
184 Damian Moss .20 .50
185 Albert Pujols 1.00 2.50
186 J.D. Drew .20 .50
187 Jim Edmonds .20 .50
188 Matt Morris .20 .50
189 Tino Martinez .30 .75
190 Scott Rolen .30 .75
191 Troy Glaus .60 1.50
Tim Salmon
192 Barry Zito .40 1.00
Tim Hudson
193 Carlos Lee .60 1.50
Frank Thomas
194 Lance Berkman .40 1.00
Jeff Kent
195 Jose Contreras .60 1.50
Mariano Rivera
196 Alex Rodriguez .60 1.50
Juan Gonzalez
197 Andy Pettitte .60 1.50
David Wells
198 Shawn Green .40 1.00
Dave Roberts
199 Mike Lieberthal .40 1.00
Jimmy Rollins
200 Mike Mussina .75 2.00
Hideki Matsui
201 Adam Loewen ROO RC 2.00 5.00
202 Jeremy Bonderman ROO RC 4.00 10.00
203 Brandon Webb ROO RC 4.00 10.00
204 Chien-Ming Wang ROO RC 4.00 10.00
205 Chad Gaudin ROO RC 1.50 4.00
206 Ryan Wagner ROO RC 1.50 4.00
207 Hong-Chih Kuo ROO RC 4.00 10.00
208 Dan Haren ROO RC 2.00 5.00
209 Rickie Weeks ROO RC 2.50 6.00
210 Ramon Nivar ROO RC 1.50 4.00
211 Delmon Young ROO RC 4.00 10.00

2003 Studio Private Signings

PRINT RUNS B/WN 5-200 COPIES PER
NO PRICING ON QTY OF 35 OR LESS
1 Darin Erstad/5
6 Troy Glaus/15
7 Jay Gibbons/100 6.00 15.00
11 Freddy Sanchez/150 6.00 15.00
16 Pedro Martinez/5
17 Rickey Henderson/10
19 Carlos Lee/25
20 Frank Thomas/5
22 Mark Buehrle/50
24 Josh Stewart/200 4.00 10.00
25 C.C. Sabathia/10
26 Jeremy Guthrie/125 4.00 10.00
29 Victor Martinez/200 10.00 25.00
30 Cliff Lee/150 15.00 40.00
31 Jhonny Peralta/200 6.00 15.00
32 Brian Tallet/35
35 Nook Logan/100 6.00 15.00
37 Travis Chapman/150 4.00 10.00
38 Carlos Beltran/25
40 Mike Sweeney/25
41 Jimmy Gobble/200 4.00 10.00
47 J.C. Romero/200 4.00 10.00
49 Lew Ford/200 6.00 15.00
51 Torii Hunter/50 10.00 25.00
52 Alfonso Soriano/5
53 Nick Johnson/100 8.00 20.00
54 Bernie Williams/5
55 Jose Contreras/100 12.50 30.00
58 Brandon Claussen/200 4.00 10.00
60 Mike Mussina/5
61 Roger Clemens/10
63 Barry Zito/25
64 Adam Morrissey/100
66 Jermaine Dye/25
67 Mark Mulder/15
69 Joe Valentine/200 4.00 10.00
70 Tim Hudson/15
72 Chris Snelling/25
73 Edgar Martinez/15
74 Freddy Garcia/5
79 Aubrey Huff/50 10.00 25.00
80 Joe Kennedy/25
81 Dewon Brazelton/75 6.00 15.00
82 Pete LaForest/200 4.00 10.00
83 Alex Rodriguez/5
85 Hank Blalock/50 10.00 25.00
87 Kevin Mench/200 6.00 15.00
90 Eric Hinske/125 4.00 10.00
95 Vinny Chulk/100 6.00 15.00
97 Junior Spivey/50 6.00 15.00
98 Luis Gonzalez/5
101 Andruw Jones/15
102 Chipper Jones/5
103 Gary Sheffield/10
104 Greg Maddux/10
107 Adam LaRoche/200 4.00 10.00
108 Michael Hessman/200 4.00 10.00
109 Corey Patterson/20
110 Kerry Wood/15
111 Mark Prior/50 15.00 40.00
114 Adam Dunn/25
115 Austin Kearns/25
116 Barry Larkin/15
119 Jason Jennings/50 6.00 15.00
123 Jeff Baker/75 6.00 15.00
124 Clint Barmes/200 6.00 15.00
125 Ivan Rodriguez/5
126 Josh Beckett/10
129 Craig Biggio/10
130 Jason Lane/100 8.00 20.00
132 Lance Berkman/10
133 Roy Oswalt/25
136 Kazuhisa Ishii/10
139 Paul Lo Duca/75 8.00 20.00
140 Shawn Green/5
143 Bill Hall/50 6.00 15.00
145 Richie Sexson/15
146 Termel Sledge/125 4.00 10.00
148 Javier Vazquez/25
149 Jose Vidro/50 6.00 15.00
151 Vladimir Guerrero/15
156 Roberto Alomar/20
158 Tom Glavine/15
159 Prentice Redman/200 4.00 10.00
160 Bobby Abreu/50 10.00 25.00
163 Pat Burrell/10
165 Jim Thome/10
167 Aramis Ramirez/15
168 Brian Giles/25
171 Kip Wells/100 6.00 15.00
172 Jose Castillo/175 4.00 10.00
176 Ryan Klesko/20
178 Brian Lawrence/100 6.00 15.00
179 Shane Victorino/200 12.50 30.00
185 Albert Pujols/15
187 Jim Edmonds/5
201 Adam Loewen ROO/100 10.00 25.00
202 Jeremy Bonderman ROO/50 30.00 60.00
203 Brandon Webb ROO/100 10.00 25.00
204 C.Wang ROO/50 60.00 120.00
205 Chad Gaudin ROO/25
206 Ryan Wagner ROO/100 4.00 10.00
207 Hong-Chih Kuo ROO/25
208 Dan Haren ROO/100 5.00 12.00
209 Rickie Weeks ROO/10
210 Ramon Nivar ROO/100 4.00 10.00
211 Delmon Young ROO/25

2003 Studio Proofs

*PROOFS 1-190: 4X TO 10X BASIC
*PROOFS RC's 1-190: 2X TO 5X BASIC
*PROOFS 191-200: 1.5X TO 4X BASIC
*PROOFS 201-211: .6X TO 1.5X BASIC
STATED PRINT RUN 100 SERIAL #'d SETS
204 Chien-Ming Wang ROO 12.50 30.00
207 Hong-Chih Kuo ROO 20.00 50.00

2003 Studio Big League Challenge

STATED PRINT RUN 400 SERIAL #'d SETS
*PROOFS: 1.5X TO 4X BASIC BLC
PROOFS PRINT RUN 25 SERIAL #'d SETS
NO PROOFS PRICING DUE TO SCARCITY
1 Jose Canseco 00 WIN 3.00 8.00
2 Magglio Ordonez 03 WIN 2.00 5.00
3 Alex Rodriguez 03 4.00 10.00
4 Lance Berkman 03 2.00 5.00
5 Rafael Palmeiro 03 3.00 8.00
6 Nomar Garciaparra 00 4.00 10.00
7 Nomar Garciaparra 00 4.00 10.00
8 Nomar Garciaparra 00 4.00 10.00
9 Troy Glaus 02 WIN 2.00 5.00
10 Mark McGwire 00 6.00 15.00
11 Mark McGwire 00 6.00 15.00
12 Mark McGwire 00 6.00 15.00
13 Jim Thome 02 3.00 8.00
14 Chipper Jones 00 3.00 8.00
15 Shawn Green 02 2.00 5.00
16 Alex Rodriguez 00 4.00 10.00
17 Alex Rodriguez 00 4.00 10.00
18 Alex Rodriguez 00 4.00 10.00
19 Alex Rodriguez 00 4.00 10.00
20 Jason Giambi 01 2.00 5.00
21 Pat Burrell 03 2.00 5.00
22 Mike Piazza 01 4.00 10.00
23 Mike Piazza 01 4.00 10.00
24 Mike Piazza 01 4.00 10.00
25 Frank Thomas 01 3.00 8.00
26 Rafael Palmeiro 01 WIN 3.00 8.00
27 Todd Helton 01 3.00 8.00
28 Jose Canseco 01 3.00 8.00
29 Albert Pujols 03 4.00 10.00
30 Troy Glaus 01 2.00 5.00
31 Barry Bonds 01 4.00 10.00
32 Barry Bonds 01 4.00 10.00
33 Barry Bonds 01 4.00 10.00
34 Todd Helton 02 3.00 8.00
35 Rafael Palmeiro 02 3.00 8.00
36 Jim Thome 02 3.00 8.00
37 Ozzie Smith 02 6.00 15.00
38 Troy Glaus 02 WIN 2.00 5.00
39 Shawn Green 02 2.00 5.00
40 Barry Bonds 02 4.00 10.00
41 Barry Bonds 02 4.00 10.00
42 Barry Bonds 02 4.00 10.00
43 Magglio Ordonez 03 WIN 2.00 5.00
44 Alex Rodriguez 03 4.00 10.00
45 Alex Rodriguez 03 4.00 10.00
46 Alex Rodriguez 03 4.00 10.00
47 Lance Berkman 03 2.00 5.00
48 Rafael Palmeiro 03 3.00 8.00
49 Pat Burrell 03 2.00 5.00
50 Albert Pujols 03 4.00 10.00

2003 Studio Big League Challenge Materials

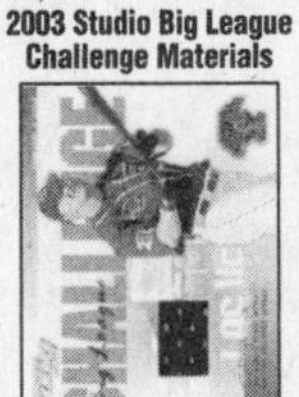

STATED ODDS 1:20
*PRIME 100: 1X TO 2.5X BASIC MATERIAL
*PRIME 50: 1.5X TO 4X BASIC MATERIAL
PRIME PRINT RUN B/WN 50-100 COPIES PER
2 Magglio Ordonez 03 BP Jsy 3.00 8.00
3 Alex Rodriguez 03 BP Jsy 6.00 15.00
4 Lance Berkman 03 Jsy 3.00 8.00
15 Shawn Green 02 BP Jsy 3.00 8.00
29 Albert Pujols 03 Jsy 10.00 25.00
36 Jim Thome 02 BP Jsy 3.00 8.00
39 Shawn Green 02 Pants 3.00 8.00
40 Barry Bonds 02 Base 6.00 15.00
41 Barry Bonds 02 Base 6.00 15.00
42 Barry Bonds 02 Plate 6.00 15.00
43 Magglio Ordonez 03 Jsy 3.00 8.00
45 Alex Rodriguez 03 Jsy 6.00 15.00
46 Alex Rodriguez 03 Pants 6.00 15.00
47 Lance Berkman 03 BP Jsy 3.00 8.00
48 Rafael Palmeiro 03 BP Jsy 3.00 8.00
50 Albert Pujols 03 Pants 6.00 15.00

2003 Studio Enshrinement

STATED PRINT RUN 750 SERIAL #'d SETS
PROOFS PRINT RUN B/WN 20-21 COPIES PER
NO PROOFS PRICING DUE TO SCARCITY
1 Gary Carter 2.00 5.00
2 Ozzie Smith 4.00 10.00
3 Kirby Puckett 3.00 8.00
4 Carlton Fisk 3.00 8.00
5 Tony Perez 2.00 5.00
6 Nolan Ryan 6.00 15.00
7 George Brett 5.00 12.00
8 Robin Yount 3.00 8.00
9 Orlando Cepeda 2.00 5.00
10 Phil Niekro 2.00 5.00
11 Mike Schmidt 5.00 12.00
12 Richie Ashburn 3.00 8.00
13 Steve Carlton 2.00 5.00
14 Phil Rizzuto 3.00 8.00
15 Reggie Jackson 3.00 8.00
16 Tom Seaver 3.00 8.00
17 Rollie Fingers 2.00 5.00
18 Rod Carew 3.00 8.00
19 Gaylord Perry 2.00 5.00
20 Fergie Jenkins 2.00 5.00
21 Jim Palmer 2.00 5.00
22 Joe Morgan 2.00 5.00
23 Johnny Bench 3.00 8.00
24 Willie Stargell 3.00 8.00
25 Billy Williams 2.00 5.00
26 Catfish Hunter 3.00 8.00
27 Willie McCovey 2.00 5.00
28 Bobby Doerr 2.00 5.00
29 Lou Brock 3.00 8.00
30 Enos Slaughter 2.00 5.00
31 Hoyt Wilhelm 2.00 5.00
32 Harmon Killebrew 3.00 8.00
33 Pee Wee Reese 3.00 8.00
34 Luis Aparicio 2.00 5.00
35 Brooks Robinson 3.00 8.00
36 Juan Marichal 2.00 5.00
37 Frank Robinson 3.00 8.00
38 Bob Gibson 3.00 8.00
39 Al Kaline 3.00 8.00
40 Duke Snider 3.00 8.00
41 Eddie Mathews 3.00 8.00
42 Robin Roberts 2.00 5.00
43 Ralph Kiner 2.00 5.00
44 Whitey Ford 3.00 8.00
45 Roberto Clemente 5.00 12.00
46 Warren Spahn 3.00 8.00
47 Yogi Berra 3.00 8.00
48 Early Wynn 2.00 5.00
49 Stan Musial 4.00 10.00
50 Bob Feller 2.00 5.00

2003 Studio Enshrinement Autographs

Randomly inserted into packs, this is a partial parallel to the Enshriement insert set. Each of these cards is signed to beween one and 100 copies and we have notated the print run in our checklist. If a card was printed to 25 or fewer copies there is no pricing available due to market scarcity.

1 Gary Carter/50 12.50 30.00
2 Ozzie Smith/5
3 Kirby Puckett/5
4 Carlton Fisk/5
5 Tony Perez/50 20.00 50.00
6 Nolan Ryan/5
7 George Brett/5
8 Robin Yount/5
9 Orlando Cepeda/50 12.50 30.00
10 Phil Niekro/50 12.50 30.00
11 Mike Schmidt/5
13 Steve Carlton/50 12.50 30.00
14 Phil Rizzuto/15
15 Reggie Jackson/5
16 Tom Seaver/5
20 Fergie Jenkins/50 12.50 30.00
21 Jim Palmer/25
22 Joe Morgan/10
23 Johnny Bench/10
27 Willie McCovey/10
28 Bobby Doerr/100 10.00 25.00
29 Lou Brock/25
31 Hoyt Wilhelm/50 20.00 50.00
32 Harmon Killebrew/10
34 Luis Aparicio/100 10.00 25.00
35 Brooks Robinson/25
37 Frank Robinson/25
39 Al Kaline/25
40 Duke Snider/10
43 Ralph Kiner/25
46 Warren Spahn/1
47 Yogi Berra/10
49 Stan Musial/5
50 Bob Feller/100 10.00 25.00

2003 Studio Leather and Lumber

COMMON CARD p/r 300-400 3.00 8.00
PRINT RUNS B/WN 100-400 COPIES PER
1 Adam Dunn Bat/400 3.00 8.00
2 Alex Rodriguez Bat/250 8.00 20.00
3 Alfonso Soriano Bat/250 4.00 10.00
4 Andruw Jones Bat/400 4.00 10.00

5 Austin Kearns Bat/400 3.00 8.00
6 Chipper Jones Bat/400 4.00 10.00
7 Derek Jeter Ball/100 15.00 40.00
8 Don Mattingly Bat/100 15.00 40.00
9 Edgar Martinez Bat/400 4.00 10.00
10 Frank Thomas Bat/400 4.00 10.00
11 Fred McGriff Bat/400 4.00 10.00
12 Garret Anderson Bat/400
13 Greg Maddux Bat/150 6.00 15.00
14 Hideki Matsui Ball/100 15.00 40.00
15 Hideo Nomo Bat/150 8.00 20.00
16 Ichiro Suzuki Ball/100 15.00 40.00
17 Ivan Rodriguez Bat/250 6.00 15.00
18 Jason Giambi Bat/400 3.00 8.00
19 Jeff Bagwell Bat/400 4.00 10.00
20 Jim Edmonds Bat/150 4.00 10.00
21 Jim Thome Bat/400 4.00 10.00
22 Juan Gonzalez Bat/400 3.00 8.00
23 Kerry Wood Bat/250 4.00 10.00
24 Kirby Puckett Bat/100 10.00 25.00
25 Lance Berkman Bat/400 3.00 8.00
26 Magglio Ordonez Bat/400 3.00 8.00
27 Manny Ramirez Bat/250 6.00 15.00
28 Mark Prior Bat/400 4.00 10.00
29 Miguel Tejada Bat/200 4.00 10.00
30 Mike Piazza Bat/400 4.00 10.00
31 Mike Schmidt Bat/200 15.00 40.00
32 Nomar Garciaparra Bat/400 6.00 15.00
33 Pat Burrell Bat/400 3.00 8.00
34 Pedro Martinez Bat/150 6.00 15.00
35 Rafael Palmeiro Bat/400
36 Randy Johnson Bat/250 6.00 15.00
37 Rickey Henderson Bat/175 6.00 15.00
38 Sammy Sosa Bat/300 4.00 10.00
39 Shawn Green Bat/400 3.00 8.00
40 Vladimir Guerrero Bat/400 4.00 10.00

2003 Studio Leather and Lumber Combos

PRINT RUNS B/WN 25-50 COPIES PER
NO PRICING ON QTY OF 25 OR LESS
1 Adam Dunn Bat-Btg Glv/50 10.00 25.00
2 Alex Rodriguez Bat-Fld Glv/50 20.00 50.00
3 Alfonso Soriano Bat-Ball/25
4 Andruw Jones Bat-Fld Glv/50 15.00 40.00
5 Austin Kearns Bat-Shoe/50 10.00 25.00
6 Chipper Jones Bat-Ball/25
7 Derek Jeter Ball-Ball/25
8 Don Mattingly Bat-Btg Glv/25
9 Edgar Martinez Bat-Ball/25
10 Frank Thomas Bat-Btg Glv/50 15.00 40.00
11 Fred McGriff Bat-Ball/25
12 Garret Anderson Bat-Ball/25
13 Greg Maddux Bat-Shoe/50 15.00 40.00
14 Hideki Matsui Ball-Ball/25
15 Hideo Nomo Bat-Ball/25
16 Ichiro Suzuki Ball-Ball/25
17 Ivan Rodriguez Bat-Btg Glv/50 15.00 40.00
18 Jason Giambi Bat-Ball/25
19 Jeff Bagwell Bat-Ball/25
20 Jim Edmonds Bat-Shoe/50 10.00 25.00
21 Jim Thome Bat-Ball/25
22 Juan Gonzalez Bat-Ball/25
23 Kerry Wood Bat-Fld Glv/50 10.00 25.00
24 Kirby Puckett Bat-Btg Glv/25
25 Lance Berkman Bat-Fld Glv/50 10.00 25.00
26 Magglio Ordonez Bat-Shoe/25
27 Manny Ramirez Bat-Ball/25
28 Mark Prior Bat-Shoe/25
29 Miguel Tejada Bat-Ball/25
30 Mike Piazza Bat-Shoe/25
31 Mike Schmidt Bat-Btg Glv/25
32 Nomar Garciaparra Bat-Ball/25
33 Pat Burrell Bat-Ball/25
34 Pedro Martinez Bat-Ball/25
35 Rafael Palmeiro Bat-Fld Glv/25
36 Randy Johnson Bat-Ball/25
37 Rickey Henderson Bat-Ball/25
38 Sammy Sosa Bat-Shoe/25
39 Shawn Green Bat-Ball/25
40 Vladimir Guerrero Bat-Ball/25

2003 Studio Masterstrokes

STATED PRINT RUN 1000 SERIAL #'d SETS
1 Adam Dunn 1.25 3.00
2 Albert Pujols 4.00 10.00
3 Alex Rodriguez 3.00 8.00
4 Alfonso Soriano 1.25 3.00
5 Andruw Jones 2.00 5.00
6 Chipper Jones 2.00 5.00
7 Derek Jeter 5.00 12.00
8 Greg Maddux 3.00 8.00
9 Hideki Matsui 4.00 10.00

10 Hideo Nomo 2.00 5.00
11 Ivan Rodriguez 2.00 5.00
12 Jason Giambi 1.25 3.00
13 Jeff Bagwell 2.00 5.00
14 Juan Gonzalez 1.25 3.00
15 Ken Griffey Jr. 3.00 8.00
16 Lance Berkman 1.25 3.00
17 Magglio Ordonez 1.25 3.00
18 Manny Ramirez 2.00 5.00
19 Mark Prior 2.00 5.00
20 Miguel Tejada 1.25 3.00
21 Mike Piazza 3.00 8.00
22 Nomar Garciaparra 3.00 8.00
23 Pat Burrell 1.25 3.00
24 Sammy Sosa 2.00 5.00
25 Vladimir Guerrero 2.00 5.00

2003 Studio Masterstrokes Proofs

STATED PRINT RUN 50 SERIAL #'d SETS
1 Adam Dunn Bat-Jsy 8.00 20.00
2 Albert Pujols Bat-Jsy 25.00 60.00
3 Alex Rodriguez Bat-Jsy 25.00 60.00
4 Alfonso Soriano Bat-Jsy 8.00 20.00
5 Andruw Jones Bat-Jsy 12.50 30.00
6 Chipper Jones Bat-Jsy 12.50 30.00
7 Derek Jeter Base-Ball 30.00 80.00
8 Greg Maddux Bat-Jsy 15.00 40.00
9 Hideki Matsui Base-Ball 40.00 80.00
10 Hideo Nomo Bat-Jsy 60.00 120.00
11 Ivan Rodriguez Bat-Jsy 12.50 30.00
12 Jason Giambi Bat-Jsy 8.00 20.00
13 Jeff Bagwell Bat-Jsy 12.50 30.00
14 Juan Gonzalez Bat-Jsy 8.00 20.00
15 Ken Griffey Jr. Base-Base 20.00 50.00
16 Lance Berkman Bat-Jsy 8.00 20.00
17 Magglio Ordonez Bat-Jsy 8.00 20.00
18 Manny Ramirez Bat-Jsy 12.50 30.00
19 Mark Prior Bat-Jsy 12.50 30.00
20 Miguel Tejada Bat-Jsy 8.00 20.00
21 Mike Piazza Bat-Jsy 15.00 40.00
22 Nomar Garciaparra Bat-Jsy 20.00 50.00
23 Pat Burrell Bat-Jsy 8.00 20.00
24 Sammy Sosa Bat-Jsy 12.50 30.00
25 Vladimir Guerrero Bat-Jsy 12.50 30.00

2003 Studio Recollection Autographs 5 x 7

Inserted at a stated rate of one per sealed hobby case, these 27 cards feature authentic autographs of the featured players. Please note that these cards are alll 2001 Studio buybacks and we have put the stated print run next to the player's name in our checklist. In addition, if a card has a print run of 25 or fewer copies, there is no pricing due to market scarcity.

1 Josh Beckett/3
2 Lance Berkman/13
3 Sean Casey/125 8.00 20.00
4 Adam Dunn/12
5 Troy Glaus/82 12.50 30.00
6 Tom Glavine/3
7 Shawn Green/3
8 Vladimir Guerrero/125 15.00 40.00
9 Tony Gwynn/13
10 Todd Helton/55 15.00 40.00
11 Andruw Jones/3
12 Ryan Klesko/75 8.00 20.00
13 Greg Maddux/25
14 Edgar Martinez/11
15 Magglio Ordonez/6
16 Cal Ripken/4
17 Alex Rodriguez/3
18 Ivan Rodriguez/50 20.00 50.00
19 C.C. Sabathia/50 10.00 25.00
20 Curt Schilling/75 20.00 50.00
21 Ben Sheets/1
22 Alfonso Soriano/8
23 Mike Sweeney/42 10.00 25.00
24 Miguel Tejada/44 15.00 40.00
25 Frank Thomas/11
26 Kerry Wood/200 10.00 25.00
27 Barry Zito/200 10.00 25.00

2003 Studio Spirit of the Game

STATED PRINT RUN 1250 SERIAL #'d SETS
1 Garret Anderson 1.00 2.50
2 Nomar Garciaparra 2.50 6.00
3 Pedro Martinez 1.50 4.00
4 Rickey Henderson 1.50 4.00
5 Magglio Ordonez 1.00 2.50
6 Torii Hunter 1.00 2.50
7 Alfonso Soriano 1.00 2.50
8 Jose Contreras 1.50 4.00
9 Derek Jeter 4.00 10.00
10 Jason Giambi 1.00 2.50
11 Roger Clemens 3.00 8.00
12 Hideki Matsui 3.00 8.00
13 Barry Zito 1.00 2.50
14 Ichiro Suzuki 3.00 8.00
15 Alex Rodriguez 2.50 6.00
16 Curt Schilling 1.00 2.50
17 Randy Johnson 1.50 4.00
18 Andruw Jones 1.50 4.00
19 Chipper Jones 1.50 4.00
20 Greg Maddux 2.50 6.00
21 Sammy Sosa 1.50 4.00
22 Adam Dunn 1.00 2.50
23 Ken Griffey Jr. 2.50 6.00
24 Todd Helton 1.50 4.00
25 Ivan Rodriguez 1.50 4.00
26 Lance Berkman 1.00 2.50
27 Hideo Nomo 1.50 4.00
28 Shawn Green 1.00 2.50
29 Vladimir Guerrero 1.50 4.00
30 Mike Piazza 2.50 6.00
31 Roberto Alomar 1.50 4.00
32 Jim Thome 1.50 4.00
33 Barry Bonds 4.00 10.00
34 Albert Pujols 3.00 8.00
35 Scott Rolen 1.50 4.00

2003 Studio Spirit of MLB

STATED PRINT RUN 1 SERIAL #'d SET

2003 Studio Stars

STATED ODDS 1:5
*GOLD: 1X TO 2.5X BASIC STARS
GOLD PRINT RUN 100 SERIAL #'d SETS
PLATINUM PRINT RUN 25 SERIAL #'d SETS
NO PLATINUM PRICING DUE TO SCARCITY
1 Troy Glaus .75 2.00
2 Manny Ramirez .75 2.00
3 Nomar Garciaparra 2.00 5.00
4 Pedro Martinez .75 2.00
5 Rickey Henderson 1.25 3.00
6 Torii Hunter .75 2.00
7 Frank Thomas 1.25 3.00
8 Magglio Ordonez .75 2.00
9 Alfonso Soriano .75 2.00
10 Jose Contreras 1.25 3.00
11 Derek Jeter 3.00 8.00
12 Jason Giambi .75 2.00
13 Roger Clemens 2.50 6.00
14 Mike Mussina .75 2.00
15 Barry Zito .75 2.00
16 Miguel Tejada .75 2.00
17 Ichiro Suzuki 2.50 6.00
18 Alex Rodriguez 2.00 5.00
19 Juan Gonzalez .75 2.00
20 Rafael Palmeiro .75 2.00
21 Hank Blalock .75 2.00
22 Curt Schilling .75 2.00
23 Randy Johnson 1.25 3.00
24 Junior Spivey .75 2.00
25 Andruw Jones .75 2.00
26 Chipper Jones 1.25 3.00
27 Greg Maddux 2.00 5.00
28 Kerry Wood .75 2.00
29 Mark Prior .75 2.00
30 Sammy Sosa 1.25 3.00
31 Adam Dunn .75 2.00
32 Ken Griffey Jr. 2.00 5.00
33 Austin Kearns .75 2.00
34 Larry Walker .75 2.00
35 Todd Helton .75 2.00
36 Ivan Rodriguez .75 2.00
37 Jeff Bagwell .75 2.00
38 Lance Berkman .75 2.00
39 Craig Biggio .75 2.00
40 Hideo Nomo 1.25 3.00
41 Shawn Green .75 2.00
42 Vladimir Guerrero 1.25 3.00
43 Mike Piazza 2.00 5.00
44 Tom Glavine .75 2.00
45 Roberto Alomar .75 2.00
46 Pat Burrell .75 2.00
47 Jim Thome .75 2.00
48 Barry Bonds 3.00 8.00
49 Albert Pujols 2.50 6.00
50 Scott Rolen .75 2.00

2004 Studio

This 275 card was actually issued twice during the 2004 year. The first 225 cards of this set were relased in June. Those cards were issued in six-card packs with an $3 SRP which came 24 packs to a box and 12 boxes to a case. Cards numbered 201-225 featured signed Rookie Cards issued to varying print runs. Cards numbered 226-275 were issued as part of the 2005 Donruss released and those cards were issued at a stated rate of one in 23. Please note that cards 220 and 222-225 were not issued.

COMP.SET w/o SP's (200) 20.00 50.00
COMMON ACTIVE (1-200) .15 .40
COMMON RETIRED (1-200) .15 .40
COMMON RC (1-200) .15 .40
COMMON AU p/r 766-800 3.00 8.00
COMMON AU p/r 400-550 4.00 10.00
AU'S RANDOM INSERTS IN PACKS
AU PRINT RUNS B/WN 400-800 COPIES PER
COMMON CARD (226-241) .40 1.00
COMMON CARD (242-275) 1.50 4.00
226-275 ODDS 1:23 '05 DONRUSS
CARDS 220/222-225 DO NOT EXIST
1 Bartolo Colon .15 .40
2 Garret Anderson .15 .40
3 Tim Salmon .15 .40
4 Troy Glaus .15 .40
5 Vladimir Guerrero .40 1.00
6 Brandon Webb .15 .40
7 Brian Bruney .15 .40
8 Casey Fossum .15 .40
9 Luis Gonzalez .15 .40
10 Randy Johnson .40 1.00
11 Richie Sexson .15 .40
12 Robby Hammock .15 .40
13 Roberto Alomar .25 .60
14 Shea Hillenbrand .15 .40
15 Steve Finley .15 .40
16 Adam LaRoche .15 .40
17 Andruw Jones .15 .40
18 Bubba Nelson .15 .40
19 Chipper Jones .40 1.00
20 Dale Murphy .25 .60
21 J.D. Drew .15 .40
22 Marcus Giles .15 .40
23 Michael Hessman .15 .40
24 Rafael Furcal .15 .40
25 Warren Spahn .25 .60
26 Adam Loewen .15 .40
27 Cal Ripken 1.50 4.00
28 Javy Lopez .15 .40
29 Jay Gibbons .15 .40
30 Luis Matos .15 .40
31 Miguel Tejada .25 .60
32 Rafael Palmeiro .25 .60
33 Curt Schilling .25 .60
34 Jason Varitek .40 1.00
35 Kevin Youkilis .25 .60
36 Manny Ramirez .40 1.00
37 Nomar Garciaparra .40 1.00
38 Pedro Martinez .25 .60
39 Trot Nixon .15 .40
40 Aramis Ramirez .15 .40
41 Brendan Harris .15 .40
42 Derrek Lee .15 .40
43 Ernie Banks .40 1.00
44 Greg Maddux .60 1.50
45 Kerry Wood .15 .40
46 Mark Prior .25 .60
47 Ryne Sandberg .75 2.00
48 Sammy Sosa .40 1.00
49 Todd Wellemeyer .15 .40
50 Carlos Lee .15 .40
51 Edwin Almonte .15 .40
52 Frank Thomas .40 1.00
53 Joe Borchard .15 .40
54 Joe Crede .15 .40
55 Magglio Ordonez .25 .60
56 Adam Dunn .25 .60
57 Austin Kearns .15 .40
58 Barry Larkin .25 .60
59 Brandon Larson .15 .40
60 Ken Griffey Jr. .60 1.50
61 Ryan Wagner .15 .40
62 Sean Casey .15 .40
63 Brian Tallet .15 .40
64 C.C. Sabathia .25 .60
65 Jeremy Guthrie .15 .40
66 Jody Gerut .15 .40
67 Travis Hafner .15 .40
68 Clint Barmes .25 .60
69 Jeff Baker .15 .40
70 Joe Kennedy .15 .40
71 Larry Walker .25 .60
72 Preston Wilson .15 .40
73 Todd Helton .25 .60
74 Dmitri Young .15 .40
75 Ivan Rodriguez .25 .60
76 Jeremy Bonderman .15 .40
77 Preston Larrison .15 .40
78 Dontrelle Willis .15 .40
79 Josh Beckett .25 .60
80 Juan Pierre .15 .40
81 Luis Castillo .15 .40
82 Miguel Cabrera .40 1.00
83 Mike Lowell .15 .40
84 Andy Pettitte .25 .60
85 Chris Burke .15 .40
86 Craig Biggio .25 .60
87 Jeff Bagwell .25 .60
88 Jeff Kent .15 .40
89 Lance Berkman .25 .60
90 Morgan Ensberg .15 .40
91 Richard Hidalgo .15 .40
92 Roger Clemens .50 1.25
93 Roy Oswalt .25 .60
94 Wade Miller .15 .40
95 Angel Berroa .15 .40
96 Byron Gettis .15 .40
97 Carlos Beltran .15 .40
98 Juan Gonzalez .15 .40
99 Mike Sweeney .15 .40
100 Duke Snider .25 .60
101 Edwin Jackson .15 .40
102 Eric Gagne .15 .40
103 Hideo Nomo .40 1.00
104 Hong-Chih Kuo .15 .40
105 Kazuhisa Ishii .15 .40
106 Paul Lo Duca .15 .40
107 Robin Ventura .15 .40
108 Shawn Green .15 .40
109 Junior Spivey .15 .40
110 Lyle Overbay .15 .40
111 Rickie Weeks .15 .40
112 Scott Podsednik .15 .40
113 J.D. Durbin .15 .40
114 Jacque Jones .15 .40
115 Jason Kubel .15 .40
116 Johan Santana .40 1.00
117 Shannon Stewart .15 .40
118 Torii Hunter .15 .40
119 Brad Wilkerson .15 .40
120 Jose Vidro .15 .40
121 Nick Johnson .15 .40
122 Orlando Cabrera .15 .40
123 Zach Day .15 .40
124 Gary Carter .15 .40
125 Jae Weong Seo .15 .40
126 Kazuo Matsui RC .25 .60
127 Mike Piazza .40 1.00
128 Tom Glavine .25 .60
129 Alex Rodriguez Yanks .60 1.50
130 Bernie Williams .25 .60
131 Chien-Ming Wang .75 2.00
132 Derek Jeter 1.00 2.50
133 Don Mattingly .75 2.00
134 Gary Sheffield .15 .40
135 Hideki Matsui .60 1.50
136 Jason Giambi .15 .40
137 Javier Vazquez .15 .40
138 Jorge Posada .25 .60
139 Jose Contreras .15 .40
140 Kevin Brown .15 .40
141 Mariano Rivera .40 1.00
142 Mike Mussina .25 .60
143 Whitey Ford .25 .60
144 Barry Zito .15 .40
145 Eric Chavez .15 .40
146 Mark Mulder .15 .40
147 Rich Harden .15 .40
148 Tim Hudson .25 .60
149 Bobby Abreu .15 .40
150 Jim Thome .25 .60
151 Kevin Millwood .15 .40
152 Marlon Byrd .15 .40
153 Mike Schmidt .60 1.50
154 Ryan Howard .50 1.25
155 Jack Wilson .15 .40
156 Jason Kendall .15 .40
157 Akinori Otsuka RC .15 .40
158 Brian Giles .15 .40
159 David Wells .15 .40
160 Jay Payton .15 .40
161 Phil Nevin .15 .40
162 Ryan Klesko .15 .40
163 Sean Burroughs .15 .40
164 A.J. Pierzynski .15 .40
165 J.T. Snow .15 .40
166 Jason Schmidt .15 .40
167 Jerome Williams .15 .40
168 Merkin Valdez RC .15 .40
169 Will Clark .25 .60
170 Bret Boone .15 .40
171 Chris Snelling .15 .40
172 Edgar Martinez .25 .60
173 Ichiro Suzuki .60 1.50
174 Jamie Moyer .15 .40
175 Randy Winn .15 .40
176 Rich Aurilia .15 .40
177 Shigetoshi Hasegawa .15 .40
178 Albert Pujols 1.00 2.50
179 Dan Haren .15 .40
180 Edgar Renteria .15 .40
181 Jim Edmonds .25 .60
182 Matt Morris .15 .40
183 Scott Rolen .25 .60
184 Stan Musial .60 1.50
185 Aubrey Huff .15 .40
186 Chad Gaudin .15 .40
187 Delmon Young .25 .60
188 Fred McGriff .15 .40
189 Rocco Baldelli .15 .40
190 Alfonso Soriano .15 .40
191 Hank Blalock .15 .40
192 Mark Teixeira .40 1.00
193 Nolan Ryan 1.25 3.00
194 Alexis Rios .25 .60
195 Carlos Delgado .15 .40
196 Dustin McGowan .15 .40
197 Guillermo Quiroz .15 .40
198 Josh Phelps .15 .40
199 Roy Halladay .40 1.00
200 Vernon Wells .15 .40
201 Mike Gosling AU/400 RC 4.00 10.00
202 Ronny Cedeno AU/766 RC 6.00 15.00
203 Ron Belisario AU/400 RC 4.00 10.00
204 Justin Hampson AU/800 RC 3.00 8.00
205 Carlos Vasquez AU/800 RC 3.00 8.00
206 Linc.Holdzkom AU/800 RC 3.00 8.00
207 Casey Daigle AU/550 RC 4.00 10.00
208 Jason Bartlett AU/800 RC 4.00 10.00
209 Mariano Gomez AU/800 RC 3.00 8.00
210 Mike Rouse AU/800 RC 3.00 8.00
211 Chris Shelton AU/800 RC 3.00 8.00
212 Dennis Sarfate AU/800 RC 3.00 8.00
213 Shingo Takatsu AU/400 RC 6.00 15.00
214 Justin Leone AU/800 RC 4.00 10.00
215 Cory Sullivan AU/800 RC 3.00 8.00
216 Michael Wuertz AU/800 RC 4.00 10.00
217 Tim Bausher AU/800 RC 3.00 8.00
218 Jesse Harper AU/800 RC 3.00 8.00
219 Ryan Meaux AU/800 RC 3.00 8.00
221 Kevin Cave AU/800 RC 3.00 8.00
226 Abe Alvarez XRC .40 1.00
227 Carlos Hines XRC .40 1.00
228 Charles Thomas XRC .40 1.00
229 Frankie Francisco XRC .40 1.00
230 Greg Dobbs XRC .40 1.00
231 Hector Gimenez XRC .40 1.00
232 Jesse Crain XRC .40 1.00
233 Joey Gathright XRC .40 1.00
234 Justin Knoedler XRC .40 1.00
235 Kazuhito Tadano XRC .40 1.00
236 Lance Cormier XRC .40 1.00
237 Scott Proctor XRC .40 1.00
238 Tim Bittner XRC .40 1.00
239 Travis Blackley XRC .40 1.00
240 Mike Johnston XRC .40 1.00
241 Yadier Molina XRC 2.50 6.00
242 B.J. Upton 2.50 6.00
243 Ben Sheets 1.50 4.00
244 Bobby Crosby 1.50 4.00
245 Brad Penny 1.50 4.00
246 Carl Crawford 2.50 6.00
247 Carlos Beltran 1.50 4.00
248 Carlos Guillen 1.50 4.00
249 Carlos Zambrano 2.50 6.00
250 Casey Kotchman 1.50 4.00
251 Chase Utley 4.00 10.00
252 Craig Wilson 1.50 4.00
253 Danny Graves 1.50 4.00
254 Danny Kolb 1.50 4.00
255 David Wright 6.00 15.00
256 Eric Milton 1.50 4.00
257 Esteban Loaiza 1.50 4.00
258 Francisco Cordero 1.50 4.00
259 Francisco Rodriguez 2.50 6.00
260 Jake Peavy 1.50 4.00
261 Jason Bay 2.50 6.00
262 Jermaine Dye 1.50 4.00
263 Joe Nathan 1.50 4.00
264 John Lackey 1.50 4.00
265 Ken Harvey 1.50 4.00
266 Khalil Greene 2.50 6.00
267 Lew Ford 1.50 4.00
268 Livan Hernandez 1.50 4.00
269 Milton Bradley 1.50 4.00
270 Nomar Garciaparra 4.00 10.00
271 Orlando Cabrera Sox 1.50 4.00
272 Paul Lo Duca 1.50 4.00
273 Richard Hidalgo 1.50 4.00
274 Steve Finley 1.50 4.00
275 Victor Martinez 2.50 6.00

2004 Studio Proofs Gold

*GOLD 1-200: 5X TO 12X BASIC ACTIVE
*GOLD 1-200: 5X TO 12X BASIC RETIRED
*GOLD 1-200: 5X TO 12X BASIC RC'S
COMMON CARD (201-221) 2.00 5.00
SEMISTARS 3.00 8.00
UNLISTED STARS 5.00 12.00
COMMON (220/222-225) 2.00 5.00
SEMIS 220/222-225 3.00 8.00
UNLISTED 220/222-225 5.00 12.00
1-225 RANDOM INSERTS IN PACKS
220/222-225 EXIST ONLY IN PARALLEL SET
*GOLD 226-241: 2X TO 5X BASIC
*GOLD 242-275: .6X TO 1.5X BASIC
226-275 RANDOM IN '05 DONRUSS
STATED PRINT RUN 50 SERIAL #'d SETS
201 Mike Gosling 2.00 5.00
202 Ronny Cedeno 2.00 5.00
203 Ronald Belisario 2.00 5.00
204 Justin Hampson 2.00 5.00
205 Carlos Vasquez 2.00 5.00
206 Lincoln Holdzkom 2.00 5.00
207 Casey Daigle 2.00 5.00
208 Jason Bartlett 6.00 15.00
209 Mariano Gomez 2.00 5.00
210 Mike Rouse 2.00 5.00
211 Chris Shelton 2.00 5.00
212 Dennis Sarfate 2.00 5.00
213 Shingo Takatsu 2.00 5.00
214 Justin Leone 2.00 5.00
215 Cory Sullivan 2.00 5.00
216 Michael Wuertz 2.00 5.00
217 Tim Bausher 2.00 5.00
218 Jesse Harper 2.00 5.00
219 Ryan Meaux 2.00 5.00
220 David Aardsma 2.00 5.00
221 Kevin Cave 2.00 5.00
222 Mike Johnston 2.00 5.00
223 Jason Szuminski 2.00 5.00
224 Shawn Camp 2.00 5.00
225 Colby Miller 2.00 5.00

2004 Studio Proofs Platinum

226-275 RANDOM IN '05 DONRUSS
STATED PRINT RUN 10 SERIAL #'d SETS
NO PRICING DUE TO SCARCITY

2004 Studio Proofs Silver

*SILVER 1-200: 3X TO 8X BASIC ACTIVE
*SILVER 1-200: 3X TO 8X BASIC RETIRED
*SILVER 1-200: 3X TO 8X BASIC RC'S
COMMON CARD (201-221) 1.25 3.00
SEMISTARS 2.00 5.00
UNLISTED STARS 3.00 8.00
COMMON (220/222-225) 1.25 3.00
SEMIS 220/222-225 2.00 5.00
UNLISTED 220/222-225 3.00 8.00
1-225 RANDOM INSERTS IN PACKS
*SILVER 226-241: 1.25X TO 3X BASIC
*SILVER 242-275: .5X TO 1.2X BASIC
226-275 RANDOM IN '05 DONRUSS
STATED PRINT RUN 100 SERIAL #'d SETS
220/222-225 EXIST ONLY IN PARALLEL SET
201 Mike Gosling 1.25 3.00
202 Ronny Cedeno 1.25 3.00
203 Ronald Belisario 1.25 3.00
204 Justin Hampson 1.25 3.00
205 Carlos Vasquez 1.25 3.00
206 Lincoln Holdzkom 1.25 3.00
207 Casey Daigle 1.25 3.00
208 Jason Bartlett 4.00 10.00
209 Mariano Gomez 1.25 3.00
210 Mike Rouse 1.25 3.00
211 Chris Shelton 1.25 3.00
212 Dennis Sarfate 1.25 3.00
213 Shingo Takatsu 1.25 3.00
214 Justin Leone 1.25 3.00
215 Cory Sullivan 1.25 3.00
216 Michael Wuertz 1.25 3.00
217 Tim Bausher 1.25 3.00
218 Jesse Harper 1.25 3.00
219 Ryan Meaux 1.25 3.00
220 David Aardsma 1.25 3.00
222 Mike Johnston 1.25 3.00
223 Jason Szuminski 1.25 3.00
224 Shawn Camp 1.25 3.00
225 Colby Miller 1.25 3.00

2004 Studio Private Signings Gold

PRINT RUNS B/WN 1-100 COPIES PER
NO PRICING ON QTY OF 12 OR LESS
NO RC YR PRICING ON QTY OF 25 OR LESS
2 Garret Anderson/16 15.00 40.00
5 Vladimir Guerrero/10
6 Brandon Webb/55 6.00 15.00
7 Brian Bruney/100 4.00 10.00
8 Casey Fossum/5
10 Randy Johnson/5
11 Richie Sexson/5
12 Robby Hammock/7
14 Shea Hillenbrand/28 10.00 25.00
15 Steve Finley/12
16 Adam LaRoche/25 8.00 20.00
17 Andruw Jones/5
18 Bubba Nelson/100 4.00 10.00
19 Chipper Jones/10
20 Dale Murphy/5
21 J.D. Drew/7
22 Marcus Giles/25 12.50 30.00
23 Michael Hessman/25 8.00 20.00
24 Rafael Furcal/1
25 Warren Spahn/5
26 Adam Loewen/1
27 Cal Ripken/10
29 Jay Gibbons/25 8.00 20.00
30 Luis Matos/100 4.00 10.00
32 Rafael Palmeiro/5
33 Curt Schilling/5
34 Jason Varitek/33 30.00 60.00
35 Kevin Youkilis/100 4.00 10.00
36 Manny Ramirez/1
39 Trot Nixon/7
40 Aramis Ramirez/16 15.00 40.00
41 Brendan Harris/75 4.00 10.00
43 Ernie Banks/5
45 Kerry Wood/5
46 Mark Prior/22 15.00 40.00
47 Ryne Sandberg/1
48 Sammy Sosa/10
49 Todd Wellemeyer/50 5.00 12.00
50 Carlos Lee/45 8.00 20.00
51 Edwin Almonte/56 5.00 12.00
52 Frank Thomas/5
53 Joe Borchard/25 8.00 20.00
54 Joe Crede/24 12.50 30.00
55 Magglio Ordonez/10
57 Austin Kearns/28 6.00 15.00
58 Barry Larkin/11
59 Brandon Larson/16 10.00 25.00
61 Ryan Wagner/38 5.00 12.00
63 Brian Tallet/50 5.00 12.00
65 Jeremy Guthrie/67 4.00 10.00
66 Jody Gerut/25 8.00 20.00
67 Travis Hafner/34 10.00 25.00
68 Clint Barmes/36 8.00 20.00
69 Jeff Baker/62 4.00 10.00
70 Joe Kennedy/37 5.00 12.00
72 Preston Wilson/10
73 Todd Helton/17 30.00 60.00
77 Preston Larrison/56 5.00 12.00
78 Dontrelle Willis/35 15.00 40.00
79 Josh Beckett/1
81 Luis Castillo/1
82 Miguel Cabrera/24 20.00 50.00
84 Andy Pettitte/5
85 Chris Burke/46 8.00 20.00
86 Craig Biggio/7
87 Jeff Bagwell/5
89 Lance Berkman/17 30.00 60.00
90 Morgan Ensberg/25 12.50 30.00
93 Roy Oswalt/5
94 Wade Miller/10
95 Angel Berroa/4
96 Byron Gettis/100 4.00 10.00
97 Carlos Beltran/25 12.50 30.00
98 Juan Gonzalez/22 12.50 30.00
100 Duke Snider/25 20.00 50.00
101 Edwin Jackson/50 5.00 12.00
103 Hideo Nomo/1
104 Hong-Chih Kuo/100 20.00 50.00
105 Kazuhisa Ishii/17 15.00 40.00
106 Paul Lo Duca/16 15.00 40.00
107 Robin Ventura/25 20.00 50.00
108 Shawn Green/15 30.00 60.00
109 Junior Spivey/37 5.00 12.00
110 Lyle Overbay/10
111 Rickie Weeks/1
112 Scott Podsednik/20 20.00 50.00
113 J.D. Durbin/31 6.00 15.00
114 Jacque Jones/25 12.50 30.00
116 Johan Santana/57 12.50 30.00
117 Shannon Stewart/23 8.00 20.00
118 Torii Hunter/10
120 Jose Vidro/3
121 Nick Johnson/21 12.50 30.00
122 Orlando Cabrera/18 15.00 40.00
123 Zach Day/1
124 Gary Carter/25 12.50 30.00
125 Jae Weong Seo/25 12.50 30.00
127 Mike Piazza/1
128 Tom Glavine/1
129 Alex Rodriguez Yanks/3
130 Bernie Williams/1
131 Chien-Ming Wang/100 75.00 150.00
133 Don Mattingly/5
134 Gary Sheffield/11
137 Javier Vazquez/5
138 Jorge Posada/10
139 Jose Contreras/5
142 Mike Mussina/1
143 Whitey Ford/5
144 Barry Zito/1
146 Mark Mulder/10
147 Rich Harden/53 8.00 20.00
148 Tim Hudson/5
149 Bobby Abreu/5
152 Marlon Byrd/29 6.00 15.00
153 Mike Schmidt/5
154 Ryan Howard/100 40.00 80.00
157 Akinori Otsuka/16
160 Jay Payton/17 10.00 25.00
165 J.T. Snow/10
167 Jerome Williams/50 5.00 12.00
168 Merkin Valdez/100 4.00 10.00
169 Will Clark/10
171 Chris Snelling/32 6.00 15.00
172 Edgar Martinez/11
174 Jamie Moyer/1
176 Rich Aurilia/10
177 Shigetoshi Hasegawa/17 60.00 120.00
178 Albert Pujols/5
179 Dan Haren/100 4.00 10.00
181 Jim Edmonds/10
183 Scott Rolen/10
184 Stan Musial/25 40.00 80.00
185 Aubrey Huff/19 15.00 40.00
186 Chad Gaudin/100 4.00 10.00
187 Delmon Young/73 10.00 25.00
188 Fred McGriff/5
189 Rocco Baldelli/5
191 Hank Blalock/5
192 Mark Teixeira/25 20.00 50.00
193 Nolan Ryan/10
194 Alexis Rios/50 8.00 20.00
196 Dustin McGowan/50 5.00 12.00
197 Guillermo Quiroz/12
198 Josh Phelps/17 10.00 25.00
199 Roy Halladay/5
226 Abe Alvarez/50 6.00 15.00
227 Carlos Hines/50 4.00 10.00
228 Charles Thomas/50 5.00 12.00
229 Frankie Francisco/50 4.00 10.00
231 Hector Gimenez/50 4.00 10.00
232 Jesse Crain/50 8.00 20.00
233 Joey Gathright/50 6.00 15.00
234 Justin Knoedler/50 4.00 10.00
236 Lance Cormier/50 4.00 10.00
237 Scott Proctor/50 6.00 15.00
238 Tim Bittner/50 4.00 10.00
239 Travis Blackley/50 4.00 10.00
240 Mike Johnston/50 4.00 10.00
241 Yadier Molina/50 12.50 30.00
244 Bobby Crosby/5
245 Brad Penny/5
246 Carl Crawford/5
247 Carlos Beltran/5
252 Craig Wilson/5
255 David Wright/5
257 Esteban Loaiza/5
260 Jake Peavy/5
261 Jason Bay/5
262 Jermaine Dye/5
263 Joe Nathan/5
264 John Lackey/5
265 Ken Harvey/5
267 Lew Ford/5
269 Milton Bradley/5
271 Orlando Cabrera/5
272 Paul Lo Duca/5
275 Victor Martinez/5

2004 Studio Private Signings Platinum

PRINT RUNS B/WN 1-10 COPIES PER
NO PRICING DUE TO SCARCITY

2004 Studio Private Signings Silver

PRINT RUNS B/WN 1-250 COPIES PER
NO PRICING ON QTY OF 10 OR LESS
NO RC YR PRICING ON QTY OF 25 OR LESS
2 Garret Anderson/25 12.50 30.00
5 Vladimir Guerrero/5
6 Brandon Webb/25 10.00 25.00
7 Brian Bruney/200 4.00 10.00
8 Casey Fossum/63 4.00 10.00
10 Randy Johnson/5
11 Richie Sexson/5
13 Roberto Alomar/5
14 Shea Hillenbrand/25 12.50 30.00

15 Steve Finley/10
16 Adam LaRoche/26 6.00 15.00
17 Andruw Jones/10
18 Bubba Nelson/250 4.00 10.00
19 Chipper Jones/1
21 J.D. Drew/1
22 Marcus Giles/25 12.50 30.00
23 Michael Hessman/95 4.00 10.00
24 Rafael Furcal/25 12.50 30.00
25 Warren Spahn/10
26 Adam Loewen/25 8.00 20.00
27 Cal Ripken/10
29 Jay Gibbons/50 5.00 12.00
30 Luis Matos/250 4.00 10.00
32 Rafael Palmeiro/5
33 Curt Schilling/5
34 Jason Varitek/10
35 Kevin Youkilis/250 4.00 10.00
36 Manny Ramirez/1
39 Trot Nixon/25 12.50 30.00
40 Aramis Ramirez/25 12.50 30.00
41 Brendan Harris/100 4.00 10.00
43 Ernie Banks/25 40.00 80.00
45 Kerry Wood/5
46 Mark Prior/10
48 Sammy Sosa/21 50.00 100.00
49 Todd Wellemeyer/92 4.00 10.00
50 Carlos Lee/25 12.50 30.00
51 Edwin Almonte/227 4.00 10.00
52 Frank Thomas/5
53 Joe Borchard/100 4.00 10.00
54 Joe Crede/10
55 Magglio Ordonez/10
57 Austin Kearns/10
58 Barry Larkin/5
59 Brandon Larson/100 4.00 10.00
61 Ryan Wagner/50 5.00 12.00
63 Brian Tallet/250 4.00 10.00
65 Jeremy Guthrie/89 4.00 10.00
66 Jody Gerut/100 4.00 10.00
67 Travis Hafner/100 6.00 15.00
68 Clint Barmes/100 6.00 15.00
69 Jeff Baker/50 5.00 12.00
70 Joe Kennedy/100 4.00 10.00
72 Preston Wilson/25 12.50 30.00
73 Todd Helton/5
77 Preston Larrison/100 4.00 10.00
78 Dontrelle Willis/10
79 Josh Beckett/1
81 Luis Castillo/25 8.00 20.00
82 Miguel Cabrera/25 20.00 50.00
84 Andy Pettitte/5
85 Chris Burke/100 4.00 10.00
86 Craig Biggio/5
87 Jeff Bagwell/5
89 Lance Berkman/10
90 Morgan Ensberg/50 8.00 20.00
93 Roy Oswalt/10
94 Wade Miller/10
95 Angel Berroa/10
96 Byron Gettis/250 4.00 10.00
97 Carlos Beltran/50 8.00 20.00
98 Juan Gonzalez/10
100 Duke Snider/50 12.50 30.00
101 Edwin Jackson/100 4.00 10.00
103 Hideo Nomo/1
104 Hong-Chih Kuo/250 20.00 50.00
105 Kazuhisa Ishii/5
106 Paul Lo Duca/25 12.50 30.00
107 Robin Ventura/25 20.00 50.00
108 Shawn Green/1
109 Junior Spivey/50 5.00 12.00
111 Rickie Weeks/1
112 Scott Podsednik/100 10.00 25.00
113 J.D. Durbin/250 4.00 10.00
114 Jacque Jones/50 8.00 20.00
115 Jason Kubel/100 4.00 10.00
116 Johan Santana/25 20.00 50.00
117 Shannon Stewart/25 8.00 20.00
118 Torii Hunter/10
120 Jose Vidro/15 10.00 25.00
121 Nick Johnson/5
122 Orlando Cabrera/15 15.00 40.00
123 Zach Day/6
124 Gary Carter/50 8.00 20.00
127 Mike Piazza/1
128 Tom Glavine/1
129 Alex Rodriguez Yanks/3
130 Bernie Williams/1
131 Chien-Ming Wang/243 60.00 120.00
133 Don Mattingly/25 50.00 100.00
134 Gary Sheffield/25 20.00 50.00
137 Javier Vazquez/5
138 Jorge Posada/10
139 Jose Contreras/5
143 Whitey Ford/5
144 Barry Zito/5
146 Mark Mulder/5
147 Rich Harden/200 6.00 15.00
148 Tim Hudson/5
149 Bobby Abreu/5
152 Marlon Byrd/10
153 Mike Schmidt/10
154 Ryan Howard/250 30.00 60.00
157 Akinori Otsuka/25
160 Jay Payton/50 5.00 12.00
165 J.T. Snow/10
167 Jerome Williams/57 5.00 12.00
168 Merkin Valdez/250 3.00 8.00
169 Will Clark/25 60.00 120.00
171 Chris Snelling/200 4.00 10.00
172 Edgar Martinez/7
176 Rich Aurilia/8
177 Shigetoshi Hasegawa/25 60.00 120.00
178 Albert Pujols/5
179 Dan Haren/250 4.00 10.00
181 Jim Edmonds/5
183 Scott Rolen/10
184 Stan Musial/25 40.00 80.00
185 Aubrey Huff/250 6.00 15.00
186 Chad Gaudin/100 4.00 10.00
187 Delmon Young/25 20.00 50.00
188 Fred McGriff/5
189 Rocco Baldelli/10
191 Hank Blalock/5
192 Mark Teixeira/23 20.00 50.00
193 Nolan Ryan/34 60.00 120.00
194 Alexis Rios/250 6.00 15.00
196 Dustin McGowan/115 4.00 10.00
197 Guillermo Quiroz/120 4.00 10.00
198 Josh Phelps/10
199 Roy Halladay/5
226 Abe Alvarez/100 5.00 12.00
227 Carlos Hines/100 3.00 8.00
228 Charles Thomas/100 4.00 10.00
229 Frankie Francisco/100 3.00 8.00
230 Greg Dobbs/40 3.00 8.00
231 Hector Gimenez/100 3.00 8.00
232 Jesse Crain/100 6.00 15.00
233 Joey Gathright/100 5.00 12.00
234 Justin Knoedler/100 3.00 8.00
236 Lance Cormier/100 3.00 8.00
237 Scott Proctor/100 5.00 12.00
238 Tim Bittner/100 3.00 8.00
239 Travis Blackley/100 3.00 8.00
240 Mike Johnston/100 3.00 8.00
241 Yadier Molina/100 20.00 50.00
244 Bobby Crosby/10
245 Brad Penny/10
246 Carl Crawford/10
247 Carlos Beltran/10
252 Craig Wilson/10
255 David Wright/10
257 Esteban Loaiza/10
260 Jake Peavy/10
261 Jason Bay/10
262 Jermaine Dye/10
263 Joe Nathan/10
264 John Lackey/10
265 Ken Harvey/10
267 Lew Ford/10
269 Milton Bradley/10
271 Orlando Cabrera/10
272 Paul Lo Duca/10
275 Victor Martinez/10

2004 Studio Big League Challenge

STATED PRINT RUN 999 SERIAL #'d SETS
*DIE CUT: .6X TO 1.5X BASIC
DIE CUT PRINT RUN 500 SERIAL #'d SETS
*GOLD: .6X TO 1.5X BASIC
GOLD PRINT RUN 499 SERIAL #'d SETS
1 Albert Pujols Left 3.00 8.00
2 Albert Pujols Right 3.00 8.00
3 Alex Rodriguez Rgr Left 2.00 5.00
4 Alex Rodriguez Rgr Right 2.00 5.00
5 Magglio Ordonez .75 2.00
6 Rafael Palmeiro .75 2.00
7 Troy Glaus Follow .50 1.25
8 Troy Glaus Start .50 1.25
9 Albert Pujols Bat Up 3.00 8.00
10 Alex Rodriguez Rgr Bat Up 2.00 5.00

2004 Studio Big League Challenge Material

STATED PRINT RUN 100 SERIAL #'d SETS
*COMBO: .75X TO 2X BASIC
COMBO PRINT RUN 50 SERIAL #'d SETS
RANDOM INSERTS IN PACKS
1 Albert Pujols Jsy 6.00 15.00
2 Albert Pujols Pants 6.00 15.00
3 Alex Rodriguez Rgr Jsy 4.00 10.00
4 Alex Rodriguez Rgr Pants 4.00 10.00
5 Magglio Ordonez Jsy 3.00 8.00
6 Rafael Palmeiro Jsy 4.00 10.00
7 Troy Glaus Jsy 3.00 8.00
8 Troy Glaus Pants 3.00 8.00
9 Albert Pujols Hat 8.00 20.00
10 Alex Rodriguez Rgr Hat 6.00 15.00

2004 Studio Diamond Cuts Material Bat

RANDOM INSERTS IN PACKS
PRINT RUNS B/WN 100-200 COPIES PER
1 Derek Jeter/100 10.00 25.00
2 Greg Maddux/100 5.00 12.00
3 Nomar Garciaparra/200 4.00 10.00
4 Miguel Cabrera/200 3.00 8.00
5 Mark Mulder/200 2.00 5.00
6 Rafael Furcal/200 2.00 5.00
7 Mark Prior/200 3.00 8.00
8 Roy Oswalt/200 2.00 5.00
9 Dontrelle Willis/100 4.00 10.00
10 Jay Gibbons/200 2.00 5.00
11 Josh Beckett/200 2.00 5.00
12 Angel Berroa/200 2.00 5.00
13 Adam Dunn/200 2.00 5.00
14 Hank Blalock/200 2.00 5.00
15 Carlos Beltran/200 2.00 5.00
16 Shannon Stewart/200 2.00 5.00
17 Aubrey Huff/200 2.00 5.00
18 Jeff Bagwell/200 3.00 8.00
19 Trot Nixon/200 2.00 5.00
21 Tony Gwynn/200 5.00 12.00
22 Andre Dawson/200 3.00 8.00
23 Don Mattingly/200 6.00 15.00
24 Dale Murphy/200 4.00 10.00
25 Gary Carter/200 3.00 8.00

2004 Studio Diamond Cuts Material Jersey

PRINT RUNS B/WN 200-250 COPIES PER
PRIME PRINT RUN B/WN 5-10 COPIES PER
NO PRIME PRICING DUE TO SCARCITY
1 Derek Jeter/250 8.00 20.00
2 Greg Maddux/250 4.00 10.00
3 Nomar Garciaparra/200 4.00 10.00
4 Miguel Cabrera/250 3.00 8.00
5 Mark Mulder/250 2.00 5.00
6 Rafael Furcal/250 2.00 5.00
7 Mark Prior/250 3.00 8.00
8 Roy Oswalt/250 2.00 5.00
9 Dontrelle Willis/250 3.00 8.00
10 Jay Gibbons/250 2.00 5.00
11 Josh Beckett/250 2.00 5.00
12 Angel Berroa/250 2.00 5.00
13 Adam Dunn/250 2.00 5.00
14 Hank Blalock/250 2.00 5.00
15 Carlos Beltran/250 2.00 5.00
16 Shannon Stewart/250 2.00 5.00
17 Aubrey Huff/250 2.00 5.00
18 Jeff Bagwell/250 3.00 8.00
19 Trot Nixon/250 2.00 5.00
20 Nolan Ryan Jacket/250 10.00 25.00
21 Tony Gwynn/250 6.00 15.00
22 Andre Dawson/250 3.00 8.00
23 Don Mattingly Jacket/250 6.00 15.00
24 Dale Murphy/250 4.00 10.00
25 Gary Carter/250 3.00 8.00

2004 Studio Diamond Cuts Combo Material

PRINT RUNS B/WN 25-50 COPIES PER
PRIME PRINT RUN 5 SERIAL #'d SETS
NO PRIME PRICING DUE TO SCARCITY
RANDOM INSERTS IN PACKS
1 Derek Jeter Bat-Jsy/50 20.00 50.00
2 Greg Maddux Bat-Jsy/50 12.50 30.00
3 N.Garciaparra Bat-Jsy/25
4 Miguel Cabrera Bat-Jsy/50 8.00 20.00
5 Mark Mulder Bat-Jsy/50 5.00 12.00
6 Rafael Furcal Bat-Jsy/50 5.00 12.00
7 Mark Prior Bat-Jsy/50 8.00 20.00
8 Roy Oswalt Bat-Jsy/50 5.00 12.00
9 Dontrelle Willis Bat-Jsy/25
10 Jay Gibbons Bat-Jsy/50 5.00 12.00
11 Josh Beckett Bat-Jsy/50 5.00 12.00
12 Angel Berroa Bat-Jsy/50 5.00 12.00
13 Adam Dunn Bat-Jsy/50 5.00 12.00
14 Hank Blalock Bat-Jsy/50 5.00 12.00
15 Carlos Beltran Bat-Jsy/50 5.00 12.00
16 Shannon Stewart Bat-Jsy/50 5.00 12.00
17 Aubrey Huff Bat-Jsy/50 5.00 12.00
18 Jeff Bagwell Bat-Jsy/50 8.00 20.00
19 Trot Nixon Bat-Jsy/50 5.00 12.00
20 Nolan Ryan Jacket-Jsy/50 15.00 40.00
21 Tony Gwynn Bat-Jsy/50 15.00 40.00
22 Andre Dawson Bat-Jsy/50 6.00 15.00
23 D.Mattingly Bat-Jacket/50 20.00 50.00
24 Dale Murphy Bat-Jsy/50 10.00 25.00
25 Gary Carter Bat-Jsy/50 6.00 15.00

2004 Studio Diamond Cuts Combo Material Signature

PRINT RUNS B/WN 1-5 COPIES PER
PRIME PRINT RUNS B/WN 1-5 COPIES PER
RANDOM INSERTS IN PACKS
NO PRICING DUE TO SCARCITY

2004 Studio Fans of the Game

216 Regis Philbin 1.50 4.00
217 Denis Leary 1.25 3.00
218 Bode Miller 1.50 4.00
219 Steve Schirripa .75 2.00
220 Adam Mesh .75 2.00

2004 Studio Fans of the Game Autographs

RANDOM INSERTS IN PACKS
SP PRINT RUNS PROVIDED BY DONRUSS
SP'S ARE NOT SERIAL-NUMBERED
216 Regis Philbin 20.00 50.00
217 Denis Leary 20.00 50.00
218 Bode Miller SP/250 15.00 40.00
219 Steve Schirripa 6.00 15.00
220 Adam Mesh SP/300 10.00 25.00

2004 Studio Game Day Souvenirs

These cards were distributed by the MLB Player's Association and MLB Properties for a sepcial promotion. Donruss-Playoff printed the cards and provided them to the league's after packout and distribution for the standard 2004 Studio product. These promotional cards can be easily differentiated from the Number and Position Game Day memorabilia cards issued in '04 Studio packs by the home plate shaped cut out housing the jersey fabric coupled with the lack of any serial-numbering. Of note, representatives at D/P have confirmed that all 80 cards from this promotional set were issued in equal quantity.

*SOUV: .4X TO 1X NUMBER p/r 150-300
*SOUV: .25X TO .6X NUMBER p/r 75-100
*SOUV: .2X TO .5X NUMBER p/r 50
*SOUV: .12X TO .3X NUMBER p/r 25
DISTRIBUTED BY MLBPA AND PROPERTIES

2004 Studio Game Day Souvenirs Number

PRINT RUNS B/WN 25-300 COPIES PER
*POSITION: .4X TO 1X BASIC
POSITION PRINT B/WN 25-300 COPIES PER
1 Garret Anderson Jsy/300 2.00 5.00
2 Troy Glaus Jsy/300 2.00 5.00
3 Vladimir Guerrero Jsy/300 3.00 8.00
4 Steve Finley Jsy/250 2.00 5.00
5 Luis Gonzalez Jsy/25 6.00 15.00
6 Richie Sexson Jsy/250 2.00 5.00
7 Andruw Jones Jsy/300 3.00 8.00
8 Chipper Jones Jsy/250 3.00 8.00
9 Rafael Furcal Jsy/250 2.00 5.00
13 Curt Schilling Jsy/300 3.00 8.00
14 Pedro Martinez Jsy/300 3.00 8.00
15 David Ortiz Jsy/300 3.00 8.00
16 Sammy Sosa Jsy/300 3.00 8.00
17 Corey Patterson Jsy/250 2.00 5.00
18 Moises Alou Jsy/300 2.00 5.00
19 Magglio Ordonez Jsy/250 2.00 5.00
20 Paul Konerko Jsy/300 2.00 5.00
21 Frank Thomas Jsy/300 3.00 8.00
22 Austin Kearns Jsy/50 4.00 10.00
23 Sean Casey Jsy/200 2.00 5.00
24 Adam Dunn Jsy/300 2.00 5.00
25 Omar Vizquel Jsy/250 3.00 8.00
26 C.C. Sabathia Jsy/300 2.00 5.00
27 Jody Gerut Jsy/250 2.00 5.00
28 Todd Helton Jsy/300 3.00 8.00
29 Vinny Castilla Jsy/300 2.00 5.00
30 Jeromy Burnitz Jsy/300 2.00 5.00
31 Fernando Vina Jsy/250 2.00 5.00
32 Ivan Rodriguez Jsy/300 3.00 8.00
33 Jeremy Bonderman Jsy/300 2.00 5.00
34 Mike Lowell Jsy/225 2.00 5.00
35 Luis Castillo Jsy/250 2.00 5.00
36 Miguel Cabrera Jsy/250 3.00 8.00
37 Roger Clemens Jsy/300 4.00 10.00
38 Andy Pettitte Jsy/300 3.00 8.00
39 Jeff Bagwell Jsy/300 3.00 8.00
40 Mike Sweeney Jsy/150 2.00 5.00
41 Carlos Beltran Jsy/200 2.00 5.00
42 Angel Berroa Jsy/250 2.00 5.00
43 Paul Lo Duca Jsy/75 3.00 8.00
44 Shawn Green Jsy/300 2.00 5.00
45 Adrian Beltre Jsy/150 2.00 5.00
46 Ben Sheets Jsy/300 2.00 5.00
47 Geoff Jenkins Jsy/250 2.00 5.00
48 Junior Spivey Jsy/300 2.00 5.00
49 Doug Mientkiewicz Jsy/100 3.00 8.00
50 Shannon Stewart Jsy/300 2.00 5.00
51 Torii Hunter Jsy/300 2.00 5.00
52 Livan Hernandez Jsy/300 2.00 5.00
53 Jose Vidro Jsy/200 2.00 5.00
54 Orlando Cabrera Jsy/300 2.00 5.00
55 Mike Piazza Jsy/250 3.00 8.00
56 Mike Cameron Jsy/250 2.00 5.00
57 Kazuo Matsui Jsy/200 3.00 8.00
58 Derek Jeter Jsy/50 10.00 25.00
59 Jason Giambi Jsy/50 4.00 10.00
61 Barry Zito Jsy/200 2.00 5.00
62 Eric Chavez Jsy/150 2.00 5.00
63 Eric Byrnes Jsy/150 2.00 5.00
65 Jim Thome Jsy/300 3.00 8.00
66 Jimmy Rollins Jsy/250 2.00 5.00
67 Jason Kendall Jsy/250 2.00 5.00
68 Craig Wilson Jsy/250 2.00 5.00
69 Jack Wilson Jsy/250 2.00 5.00
70 Ryan Klesko Jsy/300 2.00 5.00
71 Brian Giles Jsy/300 2.00 5.00
72 Sean Burroughs Jsy/300 2.00 5.00
73 A.J. Pierzynski Jsy/300 2.00 5.00
74 J.T. Snow Jsy/300 2.00 5.00
75 Michael Tucker Jsy/300 2.00 5.00
77 Edgar Martinez Jsy/50 6.00 15.00
79 Scott Rolen Jsy/300 3.00 8.00
80 Albert Pujols Jsy/300 6.00 15.00
81 Jim Edmonds Jsy/300 2.00 5.00
82 Aubrey Huff Jsy/100 3.00 8.00
83 Tino Martinez Jsy/100 5.00 12.00
84 Rocco Baldelli Jsy/100 2.00 5.00
85 Alfonso Soriano Jsy/200 2.00 5.00
86 Michael Young Jsy/250 2.00 5.00
87 Hank Blalock Jsy/300 2.00 5.00
88 Eric Hinske Jsy/200 2.00 5.00
89 Carlos Delgado Jsy/300 2.00 5.00
90 Vernon Wells Jsy/250 2.00 5.00

2004 Studio Game Day Souvenirs Signature Number

STATED PRINT RUN 5 SERIAL #'d SETS
POSITION PRINT RUN 5 SERIAL #'d SETS
RANDOM INSERTS IN PACKS
NO PRICING DUE TO SCARCITY

2004 Studio Heritage

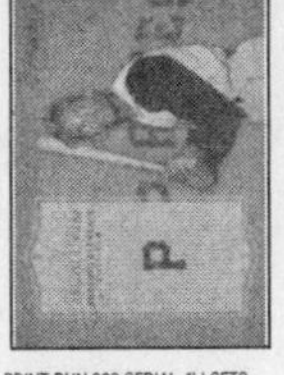

STATED PRINT RUN 999 SERIAL #'d SETS
*DIE CUT: 1.25X TO 3X BASIC
DIE CUT PRINT RUN 100 SERIAL #'d SETS
*GOLD: .6X TO 1.5X BASIC
GOLD PRINT RUN 499 SERIAL #'d SETS
1 George Brett 2.50 6.00
2 Nolan Ryan 4.00 10.00
3 Cal Ripken 5.00 12.00
4 Mike Schmidt 2.00 5.00
5 Roberto Clemente 3.00 8.00
6 Don Mattingly 2.50 6.00
7 Dale Murphy .75 2.00
8 Ryne Sandberg 2.50 6.00
9 Harmon Killebrew 1.25 3.00
10 Stan Musial 2.00 5.00

2004 Studio Heritage Material Bat

STATED PRINT RUN 50 SERIAL #'d SETS
1 George Brett 10.00 25.00
3 Cal Ripken 30.00 60.00
4 Mike Schmidt 10.00 25.00
5 Roberto Clemente 50.00 100.00
6 Don Mattingly 10.00 25.00
7 Dale Murphy 8.00 20.00
8 Ryne Sandberg 15.00 40.00
9 Harmon Killebrew 8.00 20.00
10 Stan Musial 15.00 40.00

2004 Studio Heritage Material Jersey

PRINT RUNS B/WN 50-200 COPIES PER
PRIME PRINT RUN B/WN 3-10 COPIES PER
NO PRIME PRICING DUE TO SCARCITY
RANDOM INSERTS IN PACKS
1 George Brett/200 6.00 15.00
2 Nolan Ryan Jacket/200 10.00 25.00
3 Cal Ripken/200 15.00 40.00
4 Mike Schmidt Pants/200 6.00 15.00
5 Roberto Clemente/50 50.00 100.00
6 Don Mattingly Jacket/200 6.00 15.00
7 Dale Murphy/200 4.00 10.00
8 Ryne Sandberg/200 10.00 25.00
9 Harmon Killebrew Pants/200 6.00 15.00
10 Stan Musial/100 10.00 25.00

2004 Studio Heritage Material Signature Jersey

STATED PRINT RUN 5 SERIAL #'d SETS
NO PRICING DUE TO SCARCITY

2004 Studio Heroes of the Hall

STATED PRINT RUN 999 SERIAL #'d SETS
*DIE CUT: .6X TO 1.5X BASIC
DIE CUT PRINT RUN 500 SERIAL #'d SETS
*GOLD: .6X TO 1.5X BASIC
GOLD PRINT RUN 499 SERIAL #'d SETS
1 Fergie Jenkins .50 1.25
2 Gary Carter .50 1.25
3 Gaylord Perry .50 1.25
4 George Brett 2.50 6.00
5 Jim Palmer .50 1.25
6 Nolan Ryan 4.00 10.00
7 Paul Molitor 1.25 3.00
8 Rod Carew .75 2.00
9 Steve Carlton .50 1.25
10 Robin Yount 1.25 3.00

2004 Studio Heroes of the Hall Material Bat

STATED PRINT RUN 100 SERIAL #'d SETS
2 Gary Carter 3.00 8.00
4 George Brett 10.00 25.00
7 Paul Molitor 3.00 8.00
8 Rod Carew 4.00 10.00
9 Steve Carlton 3.00 8.00
10 Robin Yount 4.00 10.00

2004 Studio Heroes of the Hall Material Jersey

STATED PRINT RUN 200 SERIAL #'d SETS
PRIME PRINT RUN 10 SERIAL #'d SETS
NO PRIME PRICING DUE TO SCARCITY
1 Fergie Jenkins Pants/200 3.00 8.00
2 Gary Carter/200 3.00 8.00
3 Gaylord Perry/100 3.00 8.00
4 George Brett/200 6.00 15.00
5 Jim Palmer/200 3.00 8.00
6 Nolan Ryan/200 10.00 25.00
7 Paul Molitor/200 3.00 8.00
8 Rod Carew/200 4.00 10.00
9 Steve Carlton/200 3.00 8.00
10 Robin Yount/200 4.00 10.00

2004 Studio Heroes of the Hall Material Signature Jersey

PRINT RUNS B/WN 1-10 COPIES PER
NO PRICING DUE TO SCARCITY

2004 Studio Masterstrokes Material Bat

STATED PRINT RUN 200 SERIAL #'d SETS
1 Todd Helton 3.00 8.00
2 Jose Vidro .75 2.00
3 Edgar Renteria 2.00 5.00
4 Mike Lowell 2.00 5.00
5 Gary Sheffield 2.00 5.00
6 Albert Pujols 6.00 15.00
7 Javy Lopez 2.00 5.00
8 Carlos Delgado 2.00 5.00
9 Bret Boone 2.00 5.00
10 Alex Rodriguez Rgr 4.00 10.00
11 Vernon Wells 2.00 5.00
12 Manny Ramirez 3.00 8.00
13 Jorge Posada 3.00 8.00
14 Edgar Martinez 3.00 8.00
15 Bernie Williams 3.00 8.00
16 Magglio Ordonez 2.00 5.00
17 Garret Anderson 2.00 5.00
18 Eric Chavez 2.00 5.00
19 Alfonso Soriano 2.00 5.00
20 Jason Giambi 2.00 5.00
21 Jeff Kent 2.00 5.00
22 Scott Rolen 3.00 8.00
23 Vladimir Guerrero 3.00 8.00
24 Sammy Sosa 3.00 8.00
25 Mike Piazza 4.00 10.00

2004 Studio Masterstrokes Material Jersey

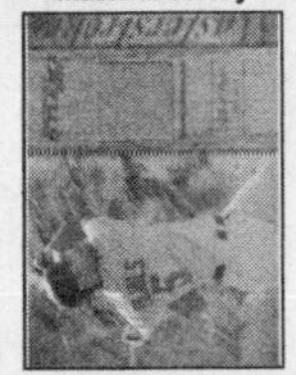

PRINT RUNS B/WN 150-250 COPIES PER
PRIME PRINT RUN 5 SERIAL #'d SETS
NO PRIME PRICING DUE TO SCARCITY
RANDOM INSERTS IN PACKS
1 Todd Helton/250 3.00 8.00
2 Jose Vidro/250 2.00 5.00
3 Edgar Renteria/250 2.00 5.00
4 Mike Lowell/250 2.00 5.00
5 Gary Sheffield/250 2.00 5.00
6 Albert Pujols/250 6.00 15.00
7 Javy Lopez/250 2.00 5.00
8 Carlos Delgado/250 2.00 5.00
9 Bret Boone/250 2.00 5.00
10 Alex Rodriguez Rgr/250 4.00 10.00
11 Vernon Wells/250 2.00 5.00
12 Manny Ramirez/250 3.00 8.00
13 Jorge Posada/250 3.00 8.00
14 Edgar Martinez/250 3.00 8.00
15 Bernie Williams/250 3.00 8.00
16 Magglio Ordonez/250 2.00 5.00
17 Garret Anderson/250 2.00 5.00
18 Eric Chavez/250 2.00 5.00
19 Alfonso Soriano/150 2.00 5.00
20 Jason Giambi/250 2.00 5.00
21 Jeff Kent/250 2.00 5.00
22 Scott Rolen/250 3.00 8.00
23 Vladimir Guerrero/250 3.00 8.00
24 Sammy Sosa/250 3.00 8.00
25 Mike Piazza/250 4.00 10.00

2004 Studio Masterstrokes Combo Material

STATED PRINT RUN 50 SERIAL #'d SETS
PRIME PRINT RUN 5 SERIAL #'d SETS
NO PRIME PRICING DUE TO SCARCITY
RANDOM INSERTS IN PACKS
1 Todd Helton Bat-Jsy/50 8.00 20.00
2 Jose Vidro Bat-Jsy/50 5.00 12.00
3 Edgar Renteria Bat-Jsy/50 5.00 12.00
4 Mike Lowell Bat-Jsy/50 5.00 12.00
5 Gary Sheffield Bat-Jsy/50 5.00 12.00
6 Albert Pujols Bat-Jsy/50 15.00 40.00
7 Javy Lopez Bat-Jsy/50 5.00 12.00
8 Carlos Delgado Bat-Jsy/50 5.00 12.00
9 Bret Boone Bat-Jsy/50 5.00 12.00
10 A.Rodriguez Rgr Bat-Jsy/50 10.00 25.00
11 Vernon Wells Bat-Jsy/50 5.00 12.00
12 Manny Ramirez Bat-Jsy/50 8.00 20.00
13 Jorge Posada Bat-Jsy/50 8.00 20.00
14 Edgar Martinez Bat-Jsy/50 8.00 20.00
15 Bernie Williams Bat-Jsy/50 8.00 20.00
16 Magglio Ordonez Bat-Jsy/50 5.00 12.00
17 Garret Anderson Bat-Jsy/50 5.00 12.00
18 Eric Chavez Bat-Jsy/50 5.00 12.00
19 Alfonso Soriano Bat-Jsy/50 5.00 12.00
20 Jason Giambi Bat-Jsy/50 5.00 12.00
21 Jeff Kent Bat-Jsy/50
22 Scott Rolen Bat-Jsy/50 8.00 20.00
23 Vladimir Guerrero Bat-Jsy/50 8.00 20.00
24 Sammy Sosa Bat-Jsy/50 8.00 20.00
25 Mike Piazza Bat-Jsy/50 12.50 30.00

2004 Studio Masterstrokes Combo Material Signature

PRINT RUNS B/WN 1-10 COPIES PER
PRIME PRINT RUNS B/WN 1-5 COPIES PER
RANDOM INSERTS IN PACKS
NO PRICING DUE TO SCARCITY

2004 Studio Players Collection Jersey

*STUDIO PC: .4X TO 1X PRESTIGE PC
STATED PRINT RUN 150 SERIAL #'d SETS
*STUDIO PC PLAT: .75X TO 2X PRESTIGE PC
PLATINUM PRINT RUN 50 SERIAL #'d SETS
RANDOM INSERTS IN PACKS

2004 Studio Rally Caps

STATED PRINT RUN 999 SERIAL #'d SETS
*DIE CUT: .6X TO 1.5X BASIC
DIE CUT PRINT RUN 500 SERIAL #'d SETS
*GOLD: .6X TO 1.5X BASIC
GOLD PRINT RUN 499 SERIAL #'d SETS
1 Adam Dunn .75 2.00
2 Adrian Beltre .50 1.25
3 Albert Pujols 3.00 8.00
4 Alex Rodriguez 2.00 5.00
5 Andruw Jones .50 1.25
6 Angel Berroa .50 1.25
7 Aubrey Huff .50 1.25
8 Austin Kearns .50 1.25
9 Ben Sheets .50 1.25
10 Brad Penny .50 1.25
11 Carlos Beltran .50 1.25
12 Carlos Lee .50 1.25
13 Casey Fossum .50 1.25
14 Eric Hinske .50 1.25
15 Geoff Jenkins .50 1.25
16 Jack Wilson .50 1.25
17 Jason Jennings .50 1.25
18 Joe Kennedy .50 1.25
19 Lance Berkman .75 2.00
20 Magglio Ordonez .75 2.00
21 Kerry Wood .50 1.25
22 Mark Buehrle .75 2.00
23 Mark Prior .75 2.00
24 Mark Teixeira 1.25 3.00
25 Michael Cuddyer .50 1.25
26 Jeff Conine .50 1.25
27 Mike Mussina .75 2.00
28 Mike Piazza 1.25 3.00
29 Jose Reyes .75 2.00
30 Paul Lo Duca .50 1.25
31 Pedro Martinez .75 2.00
32 Roy Oswalt .75 2.00
33 Ryan Klesko .50 1.25
34 Sammy Sosa 1.25 3.00
35 Tim Hudson .75 2.00
36 Todd Helton .75 2.00
37 Torii Hunter .50 1.25
38 Vernon Wells .50 1.25
39 Craig Wilson .50 1.25
40 Edgar Renteria .50 1.25

2004 Studio Spirit of the Game

STATED PRINT RUN 999 SERIAL #'d SETS
*DIE CUT: .6X TO 1.5X BASIC
DIE CUT PRINT RUN 500 SERIAL #'d SETS
RANDOM INSERTS IN PACKS
1 Sammy Sosa 1.25 3.00
2 Alex Rodriguez Rgr 2.00 5.00
3 Nomar Garciaparra 1.25 3.00
4 Derek Jeter 3.00 8.00
5 Albert Pujols 3.00 8.00
6 Roger Clemens 1.50 4.00
7 Mark Prior .75 2.00
8 Randy Johnson 1.25 3.00
9 Pedro Martinez .75 2.00
10 Vladimir Guerrero 1.25 3.00
11 Todd Helton .75 2.00
12 Jeff Bagwell .75 2.00
13 Mike Mussina .75 2.00
14 Josh Beckett .75 2.00
15 Hideo Nomo 1.25 3.00
16 Mike Piazza 1.25 3.00
17 Don Mattingly 2.50 6.00
18 George Brett 2.50 6.00
19 Nolan Ryan 4.00 10.00
20 Cal Ripken 5.00 12.00

2004 Studio Spirit of the Game Material Bat

RANDOM INSERTS IN PACKS
PRINT RUNS B/WN 10-100 COPIES PER
NO PRICING ON QTY OF 10 OR LESS
1 Sammy Sosa/100 4.00 10.00
2 Alex Rodriguez Rgr/100 5.00 12.00
3 Nomar Garciaparra/100 5.00 12.00

4 Derek Jeter/100 10.00 25.00
5 Albert Pujols/100 8.00 20.00
6 Roger Clemens/50 10.00 25.00
7 Mark Prior/100 4.00 10.00
8 Randy Johnson/100 4.00 10.00
9 Pedro Martinez/100
10 Vladimir Guerrero/100 4.00 10.00
11 Todd Helton/100 4.00 10.00
12 Jeff Bagwell/100 4.00 10.00
13 Mike Mussina/50 4.00 10.00
14 Josh Beckett/100 3.00 8.00
15 Hideo Nomo/100 4.00 10.00
16 Mike Piazza/100 5.00 12.00
17 Don Mattingly/100 10.00 25.00
18 George Brett/100 10.00 25.00
19 Nolan Ryan/10
20 Cal Ripken/50 30.00 60.00

2004 Studio Spirit of the Game Material Jersey

PRINT RUNS B/WN 100-200 COPIES PER
PRIME PRINT RUNS B/WN 1-5 COPIES PER
NO PRIME PRICING DUE TO SCARCITY
1 Sammy Sosa/200 3.00 8.00
2 Alex Rodriguez Rgr/200 4.00 10.00
3 Nomar Garciaparra/100 5.00 12.00
4 Derek Jeter/200 8.00 20.00
5 Albert Pujols/100 8.00 20.00
7 Mark Prior/200 3.00 8.00
8 Randy Johnson/100 4.00 10.00
9 Pedro Martinez/200 3.00 8.00
11 Todd Helton/100 4.00 10.00
12 Jeff Bagwell/200 3.00 8.00
13 Mike Mussina/200 3.00 8.00
14 Josh Beckett/200 2.00 5.00
15 Hideo Nomo/200 3.00 8.00
16 Mike Piazza/200 4.00 10.00
17 Don Mattingly Jacket/200 6.00 15.00
18 George Brett/200 6.00 15.00
19 Nolan Ryan/100 15.00 40.00
20 Cal Ripken/100 20.00 50.00

2004 Studio Spirit of the Game Material Signature Jersey

PRINT RUNS B/WN 1-5 COPIES PER
NO PRICING DUE TO SCARCITY

2004 Studio Stars

STATED ODDS 1:5
*GOLD: 1.25X TO 3X BASIC
GOLD PRINT RUN 100 SERIAL #'d SETS
*PLAT: 2.5X TO 6X BASIC
PLATINUM PRINT RUN 25 SERIAL #'d SETS
GOLD/PLATINUM RANDOM IN PACKS
1 Albert Pujols 2.50 6.00
2 Alex Rodriguez Yanks 1.50 4.00
3 Alfonso Soriano .40 1.00
4 Andy Pettitte .60 1.50
5 Angel Berroa .40 1.00
6 Aubrey Huff .40 1.00
7 Austin Kearns .40 1.00
8 Barry Zito .40 1.00
9 Brian Giles .40 1.00
10 Carlos Delgado .40 1.00
11 Chipper Jones 1.00 2.50
12 Craig Biggio .60 1.50
13 Curt Schilling .60 1.50
14 Derek Jeter 2.50 6.00
15 Edgar Martinez .60 1.50
16 Eric Gagne .40 1.00
17 Frank Thomas 1.00 2.50
18 Hank Blalock .40 1.00
19 Hideki Matsui 1.50 4.00
20 Hideo Nomo 1.00 2.50
21 Ichiro Suzuki 1.50 4.00
22 Ivan Rodriguez .60 1.50
23 Jason Kendall .40 1.00
24 Jason Schmidt .40 1.00
25 Jeff Bagwell .60 1.50
26 Jim Edmonds .60 1.50
27 Jim Thome .60 1.50
28 Josh Beckett .60 1.50
29 Kazuo Matsui .60 1.50
30 Ken Griffey Jr. 1.50 4.00
31 Larry Walker .60 1.50
32 Magglio Ordonez .60 1.50
33 Manny Ramirez 1.00 2.50
34 Mark Mulder .40 1.00
35 Mark Prior .60 1.50
36 Mark Teixeira 1.00 2.50
37 Miguel Tejada .60 1.50
38 Mike Mussina .60 1.50
39 Mike Piazza 1.00 2.50
40 Pedro Martinez .60 1.50
41 Randy Johnson 1.00 2.50
42 Roger Clemens 1.25 3.00
43 Roy Halladay 1.00 2.50
44 Russ Ortiz .40 1.00
45 Sammy Sosa 1.00 2.50
46 Scott Podsednik .40 1.00
47 Tim Hudson .60 1.50
48 Todd Helton .60 1.50
49 Vernon Wells .40 1.00
50 Vladimir Guerrero 1.00 2.50

2005 Studio

This 300-card set was released in June, 2005. The set was issued in six-card packs with an $4 SRP which came 24 packs in a box and 12 boxes in a case.

COMPLETE SET (300) 30.00 60.00
COMMON CARD (1-300) .15 .40
COMMON RC .15 .40
1 Casey Kotchman .15 .40
2 Chone Figgins .15 .40
3 Dallas McPherson .15 .40
4 Darin Erstad .15 .40
5 Ervin Santana .15 .40
6 Garret Anderson .15 .40
7 Norihiro Nakamura RC .15 .40
8 John Lackey .15 .40
9 Orlando Cabrera .15 .40
10 Robb Quinlan .15 .40
11 Steve Finley .15 .40
12 Tim Salmon .15 .40
13 Vladimir Guerrero .40 1.00
14 Brandon Webb .25 .60
15 Craig Counsell .15 .40
16 Javier Vazquez .15 .40
17 Luis Gonzalez .15 .40
18 Tony Pena RC .15 .40
19 Russ Ortiz .15 .40
20 Scott Hairston .15 .40
21 Shawn Green .15 .40
22 Jose Cruz Jr. .15 .40
23 Troy Glaus .15 .40
24 Adam LaRoche .15 .40
25 Andruw Jones .15 .40
26 Chipper Jones .40 1.00
27 Danny Kolb .15 .40
28 John Smoltz .40 1.00
29 Johnny Estrada .15 .40
30 Marcus Giles .15 .40
31 Nick Green .15 .40
32 Rafael Furcal .15 .40
33 Tim Hudson .25 .60
34 Brian Roberts .15 .40
35 Javy Lopez .15 .40
36 Jay Gibbons .15 .40
37 Melvin Mora .15 .40
38 Miguel Tejada .25 .60
39 Rafael Palmeiro .25 .60
40 Rodrigo Lopez .15 .40
41 Sidney Ponson .15 .40
42 Abe Alvarez .15 .40
43 Bill Mueller .15 .40
44 Curt Schilling .25 .60
45 David Ortiz .40 1.00
46 David Wells .15 .40
47 Edgar Renteria .15 .40
48 Jason Varitek .40 1.00
49 Jay Payton .15 .40
50 Johnny Damon .25 .60
51 Juan Cedeno .15 .40
52 Manny Ramirez .40 1.00
53 Matt Clement .15 .40
54 Trot Nixon .15 .40
55 Wade Miller .15 .40
56 Aramis Ramirez .15 .40
57 Carlos Zambrano .25 .60
58 Corey Patterson .15 .40
59 Derrek Lee .15 .40
60 Greg Maddux .60 1.50
61 Kerry Wood .15 .40
62 Mark Prior .25 .60
63 Nomar Garciaparra .40 1.00
64 Sammy Sosa .40 1.00
65 Todd Walker .15 .40
66 A.J. Pierzynski .15 .40
67 Aaron Rowand .15 .40
68 Frank Thomas .40 1.00
69 Freddy Garcia .15 .40
70 Jermaine Dye .15 .40
71 Mark Buehrle .25 .60
72 Paul Konerko .25 .60
73 Tadahito Iguchi RC .25 .60
74 Pedro Lopez RC .15 .40
75 Scott Podsednik .15 .40
76 Shingo Takatsu .15 .40
77 Adam Dunn .25 .60
78 Austin Kearns .15 .40
79 Barry Larkin .25 .60
80 Bubba Nelson .15 .40
81 Danny Graves .15 .40
82 Eric Milton .15 .40
83 Ken Griffey Jr. .60 1.50
84 Ryan Wagner .15 .40
85 Sean Casey .15 .40
86 C.C. Sabathia .25 .60
87 Cliff Lee .25 .60
88 Fausto Carmona .15 .40
89 Grady Sizemore .25 .60
90 Jake Westbrook .15 .40
91 Jody Gerut .15 .40
92 Juan Gonzalez .15 .40
93 Kazuhito Tadano .15 .40
94 Travis Hafner .15 .40
95 Victor Martinez .25 .60
96 Charles Johnson .15 .40
97 Clint Barmes .15 .40
98 Cory Sullivan .15 .40
99 Jeff Baker .15 .40
100 Jeff Francis .15 .40
101 Jeff Salazar .15 .40
102 Jeromy Burnitz .15 .40
103 Joe Kennedy .15 .40
104 Matt Holliday .40 1.00
105 Preston Wilson .15 .40
106 Todd Helton .25 .60
107 Ubaldo Jimenez RC .50 1.25
108 Brandon Inge .15 .40
109 Carlos Guillen .15 .40
110 Carlos Pena .25 .60
111 Craig Monroe .15 .40
112 Ivan Rodriguez .25 .60
113 Jeremy Bonderman .15 .40
114 Justin Verlander RC 3.00 8.00
115 Magglio Ordonez .25 .60
116 Troy Percival .15 .40
117 Vance Wilson .15 .40
118 A.J. Burnett .25 .60
119 Al Leiter .15 .40
120 Dontrelle Willis .15 .40
121 Josh Beckett .25 .60
122 Juan Pierre .15 .40
123 Miguel Cabrera .40 1.00
124 Mike Lowell .15 .40
125 Paul Lo Duca .15 .40
126 Randy Messenger RC .15 .40
127 Yorman Bazardo RC .15 .40
128 Andy Pettitte .25 .60
129 Brad Lidge .15 .40
130 Chris Burke .15 .40
131 Craig Biggio .25 .60
132 Fernando Nieve .15 .40
133 Jason Lane .15 .40
134 Jeff Bagwell .25 .60
135 Lance Berkman .25 .60
136 Morgan Ensberg .15 .40
137 Roger Clemens .50 1.25
138 Roy Oswalt .25 .60
139 Ambiorix Burgos RC .15 .40
140 David DeJesus .15 .40
141 Jeremy Affeldt .15 .40
142 Jose Lima .15 .40
143 Ken Harvey .15 .40
144 Mike MacDougal .15 .40
145 Mike Sweeney .15 .40
146 Terrence Long .15 .40
147 Zack Greinke .25 .60
148 Brad Penny .15 .40
149 Derek Lowe .15 .40
150 Dioner Navarro .15 .40
151 Edwin Jackson .15 .40
152 Eric Gagne .15 .40
153 Hee Seop Choi .15 .40
154 Hideo Nomo .40 1.00
155 J.D. Drew .15 .40
156 Jeff Kent .15 .40
157 Jeff Weaver .15 .40
158 Milton Bradley .15 .40
159 Yhency Brazoban .15 .40
160 Ben Sheets .15 .40
161 Bill Hall .15 .40
162 Carlos Lee .15 .40
163 Gustavo Chacin .15 .40
164 Geoff Jenkins .15 .40
165 Jose Capellan .15 .40
166 Lyle Overbay .15 .40
167 Rickie Weeks .25 .60
168 Jacque Jones .15 .40
169 Joe Mauer .40 1.00
170 Joe Nathan .15 .40
171 Johan Santana .40 1.00
172 Justin Morneau .40 1.00
173 Lew Ford .15 .40
174 Michael Cuddyer .15 .40
175 Shannon Stewart .15 .40
176 Torii Hunter .15 .40
177 Brad Radke .15 .40
178 Ambiorix Concepcion RC .15 .40
179 Carlos Beltran .25 .60
180 David Wright .60 1.50
181 Jose Reyes .25 .60
182 Kazuo Matsui .15 .40
183 Kris Benson .15 .40
184 Mike Piazza .40 1.00
185 Pedro Martinez .25 .60
186 Phil Humber RC .40 1.00
187 Tom Glavine .25 .60
188 Alex Rodriguez .60 1.50
189 Carl Pavano .15 .40
190 Derek Jeter 1.00 2.50
191 Yuniesky Betancourt RC .60 1.50
192 Hideki Matsui .60 1.50
193 Jorge Posada .25 .60
194 Kevin Brown .15 .40
195 Mariano Rivera .40 1.00
196 Mike Mussina .25 .60
197 Randy Johnson .40 1.00
198 Scott Proctor .15 .40
199 Tom Gordon .15 .40
200 Barry Zito .15 .40
201 Bobby Crosby .15 .40
202 Dan Haren .15 .40
203 Eric Chavez .15 .40
204 Keiichi Yabu RC .15 .40
205 Jason Kendall .15 .40
206 Joe Blanton .15 .40
207 Mark Kotsay .15 .40
208 Nick Swisher .40 1.00
209 Octavio Dotel .15 .40
210 Rich Harden .15 .40
211 Billy Wagner .15 .40
212 Bobby Abreu .15 .40
213 Chase Utley .25 .60
214 Gavin Floyd .15 .40
215 Jim Thome .25 .60
216 Jimmy Rollins .25 .60
217 Jon Lieber UER .15 .40
Name misspelled in text in Back
218 Kenny Lofton .15 .40
219 Mike Lieberthal .15 .40
220 Pat Burrell .15 .40
221 Randy Wolf .15 .40
222 Craig Wilson .15 .40
223 Jack Wilson .15 .40
224 Jason Bay .15 .40
225 John Van Benschoten .15 .40
226 Jose Castillo .15 .40
227 Kip Wells .15 .40
228 Matt Lawton .15 .40
229 Akinori Otsuka .15 .40
230 Brian Giles .15 .40
231 Freddy Guzman .15 .40
232 Jake Peavy .15 .40
233 Khalil Greene .15 .40
234 Mark Loretta .15 .40
235 Sean Burroughs .15 .40
236 Trevor Hoffman .25 .60
237 Woody Williams .15 .40
238 Armando Benitez .15 .40
239 Edgardo Alfonzo .15 .40
240 Erick Threets RC .15 .40
241 Jason Schmidt .15 .40
242 Marquis Grissom .15 .40
243 Merkin Valdez .15 .40
244 Michael Tucker .15 .40
245 Moises Alou .15 .40
246 Omar Vizquel .25 .60
247 Adrian Beltre .15 .40
248 Bret Boone .15 .40
249 Bucky Jacobsen .15 .40
250 Clint Nageotte .15 .40
251 Ichiro Suzuki .60 1.50
252 J.J. Putz .15 .40
253 Jeremy Reed .15 .40
254 Miguel Olivo .15 .40
255 Mike Morse RC .40 1.00
256 Richie Sexson .15 .40
257 Wladimir Balentien RC .25 .60
258 Albert Pujols 1.00 2.50
259 Jason Isringhausen .15 .40
260 Jeff Suppan .15 .40
261 Jim Edmonds .25 .60
262 Larry Walker .25 .60
263 Mark Mulder .15 .40
264 Rick Ankiel .15 .40
265 Scott Rolen .25 .60
266 Yadier Molina .25 .60
267 Aubrey Huff .15 .40
268 B.J. Upton .25 .60
269 Carl Crawford .25 .60
270 Chris Seddon RC .15 .40
271 Delmon Young .40 1.00
272 Dewon Brazelton .15 .40
273 Jeff Niemann RC .40 1.00
274 Rocco Baldelli .15 .40
275 Scott Kazmir .40 1.00
276 Adrian Gonzalez .25 .60
277 Alfonso Soriano .25 .60
278 Francisco Cordero .15 .40
279 Hank Blalock .15 .40
280 Kameron Loe .15 .40
281 Kenny Rogers .15 .40
282 Laynce Nix .15 .40
283 Mark Teixeira .40 1.00
284 Michael Young .25 .60
285 Corey Koskie .15 .40
286 Dave Bush .15 .40
287 Frank Catalanotto .15 .40
288 Gabe Gross .15 .40
289 Raul Tablado RC .15 .40
290 Roy Halladay .40 1.00
291 Shea Hillenbrand .15 .40
292 Vernon Wells .15 .40
293 Chad Cordero .15 .40
294 Cristian Guzman .15 .40
295 Jose Guillen .15 .40
296 Jose Vidro .15 .40
297 Josh Karp .15 .40
298 Livan Hernandez .15 .40
299 Nick Johnson .15 .40
300 Vinny Castilla .15 .40

2005 Studio Proofs Gold

*GOLD: 6X TO 15X BASIC
OVERALL INSERT ODDS 1:1 HOBBY
STATED PRINT RUN 25 SERIAL #'d SETS
NO RC YR PRICING DUE TO SCARCITY

2005 Studio Proofs Platinum

OVERALL INSERT ODDS 1:1 HOBBY
STATED PRINT RUN 10 SERIAL #'d SETS
NO PRICING DUE TO SCARCITY

2005 Studio Proofs Silver

*SILVER: 2.5X TO 6X BASIC
*SILVER: 2X TO 5X BASIC RC's
OVERALL INSERT ODDS 1:1 HOBBY
STATED PRINT RUN 100 SERIAL #'d SETS

2005 Studio Autographs

OVERALL AU-GU ODDS 1:8 HOBBY
NO SP PRICING DUE TO SCARCITY
CARDS LACK PRIVATE SIGNINGS LOGO
1 Casey Kotchman 4.00 10.00
3 Dallas McPherson 4.00 10.00
5 Ervin Santana 4.00 10.00
8 John Lackey 4.00 10.00
18 Tony Pena 4.00 10.00
31 Nick Green 4.00 10.00
51 Juan Cedeno 4.00 10.00
80 Bubba Nelson 4.00 10.00
88 Fausto Carmona 6.00 15.00
93 Kazuhito Tadano 6.00 15.00
101 Jeff Salazar 4.00 10.00
103 Joe Kennedy 4.00 10.00
108 Brandon Inge 4.00 10.00
111 Craig Monroe 4.00 10.00
113 Jeremy Bonderman 6.00 15.00
117 Vance Wilson 4.00 10.00
126 Randy Messenger 4.00 10.00
127 Yorman Bazardo 4.00 10.00
150 Dioner Navarro 4.00 10.00
159 Yhency Brazoban 4.00 10.00
161 Bill Hall 4.00 10.00
170 Joe Nathan 6.00 15.00
178 Ambiorix Concepcion 4.00 10.00
191 Yuniesky Betancourt 15.00 30.00
198 Scott Proctor 4.00 10.00
223 Jack Wilson 6.00 15.00
226 Jose Castillo 4.00 10.00
231 Freddy Guzman 4.00 10.00
240 Erick Threets SP
250 Clint Nageotte 4.00 10.00
252 J.J. Putz 4.00 10.00
254 Miguel Olivo SP
257 Wladimir Balentien 6.00 15.00
260 Jeff Suppan 6.00 15.00
266 Yadier Molina SP
276 Adrian Gonzalez 10.00 25.00
280 Kameron Loe 4.00 10.00
282 Laynce Nix 4.00 10.00
293 Chad Cordero SP
297 Josh Karp 4.00 10.00

2005 Studio Private Signings Gold

*GOLD: .5X TO 1.2X SILVER
*GOLD RC YR: .5X TO 1.2X SILVER RC YR
OVERALL AU-GU ODDS 1:8 HOBBY
STATED PRINT RUN 50 SERIAL #'d SETS
6 Garret Anderson 8.00 20.00
10 Robb Quinlan 5.00 12.00
11 Steve Finley 8.00 20.00
14 Brandon Webb 5.00 12.00
29 Johnny Estrada 5.00 12.00
32 Rafael Furcal 8.00 20.00
40 Rodrigo Lopez 5.00 12.00
47 Edgar Renteria 8.00 20.00
53 Matt Clement 8.00 20.00
54 Trot Nixon 8.00 20.00
59 Derrek Lee 20.00 50.00
71 Mark Buehrle 15.00 40.00
72 Paul Konerko 12.50 30.00
76 Shingo Takatsu 8.00 20.00
78 Austin Kearns 5.00 12.00
93 Kazuhito Tadano 8.00 20.00
116 Troy Percival 8.00 20.00
123 Miguel Cabrera 12.50 30.00
148 Brad Penny 5.00 12.00
168 Jacque Jones 8.00 20.00
175 Shannon Stewart 8.00 20.00
199 Tom Gordon 5.00 12.00
229 Akinori Otsuka 8.00 20.00
235 Sean Burroughs 5.00 12.00
243 Merkin Valdez 5.00 12.00
246 Omar Vizquel 12.50 30.00
249 Bucky Jacobsen 5.00 12.00
254 Miguel Olivo 5.00 12.00
266 Yadier Molina 5.00 12.00
267 Aubrey Huff 8.00 20.00
268 B.J. Upton 8.00 20.00
269 Carl Crawford 8.00 20.00
271 Delmon Young 12.50 30.00
272 Dewon Brazelton 5.00 12.00
284 Michael Young 8.00 20.00
299 Nick Johnson 8.00 20.00

2005 Studio Private Signings Platinum

OVERALL AU-GU ODDS 1:8 HOBBY
STATED PRINT RUN 10 SERIAL #'d SETS
NO PRICING DUE TO SCARCITY

2005 Studio Private Signings Silver

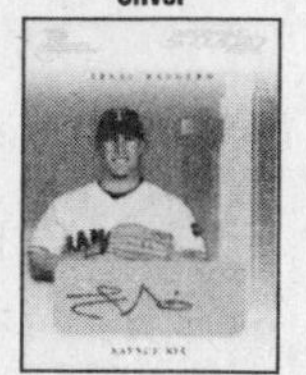

OVERALL AU-GU ODDS 1:8 HOBBY
STATED PRINT RUN 100 SERIAL #'d SETS
1 Casey Kotchman 6.00 15.00
2 Chone Figgins 4.00 10.00
5 Ervin Santana 4.00 10.00
9 Orlando Cabrera 6.00 15.00
12 Tim Salmon 10.00 25.00
18 Tony Pena 4.00 10.00
19 Russ Ortiz 4.00 10.00
24 Adam LaRoche 4.00 10.00
27 Danny Kolb 4.00 10.00
31 Nick Green 6.00 15.00
34 Brian Roberts 6.00 15.00
36 Jay Gibbons 4.00 10.00
49 Jay Payton 4.00 10.00
51 Juan Cedeno 4.00 10.00
55 Wade Miller 4.00 10.00
57 Carlos Zambrano 10.00 25.00
65 Todd Walker 6.00 15.00
70 Jermaine Dye 6.00 15.00
80 Bubba Nelson 4.00 10.00
81 Danny Graves 4.00 10.00
84 Ryan Wagner 4.00 10.00
87 Cliff Lee 10.00 25.00
88 Fausto Carmona 10.00 25.00
91 Jody Gerut 4.00 10.00
94 Travis Hafner 6.00 15.00
98 Cory Sullivan 4.00 10.00
101 Jeff Salazar 4.00 10.00
103 Joe Kennedy 4.00 10.00
108 Brandon Inge 6.00 15.00
111 Craig Monroe 4.00 10.00
113 Jeremy Bonderman 6.00 15.00
117 Vance Wilson 4.00 10.00
127 Yorman Bazardo 4.00 10.00
133 Jason Lane 6.00 15.00
136 Morgan Ensberg 6.00 15.00
141 Jeremy Affeldt 4.00 10.00
143 Ken Harvey 4.00 10.00
150 Dioner Navarro 6.00 15.00
151 Edwin Jackson 4.00 10.00
158 Milton Bradley 6.00 15.00
159 Yhency Brazoban 4.00 10.00
161 Bill Hall 4.00 10.00
162 Carlos Lee 6.00 15.00
166 Lyle Overbay 4.00 10.00
170 Joe Nathan 6.00 15.00
173 Lew Ford 4.00 10.00
191 Yuniesky Betancourt 20.00 40.00
198 Scott Proctor 4.00 10.00
201 Bobby Crosby 6.00 15.00
202 Dan Haren 4.00 10.00
209 Octavio Dotel 4.00 10.00
210 Rich Harden 6.00 15.00
219 Mike Lieberthal 6.00 15.00
221 Randy Wolf 4.00 10.00
222 Craig Wilson 4.00 10.00
223 Jack Wilson 6.00 15.00
224 Jason Bay 6.00 15.00
226 Jose Castillo 4.00 10.00
231 Freddy Guzman 4.00 10.00
232 Jake Peavy 10.00 25.00
234 Mark Loretta 4.00 10.00
250 Clint Nageotte 4.00 10.00
252 J.J. Putz 4.00 10.00
260 Jeff Suppan 6.00 15.00
276 Adrian Gonzalez 4.00 10.00
278 Francisco Cordero 6.00 15.00
280 Kameron Loe 4.00 10.00
282 Laynce Nix 4.00 10.00
291 Shea Hillenbrand 4.00 10.00
293 Chad Cordero 6.00 15.00
295 Jose Guillen 6.00 15.00
297 Josh Karp 4.00 10.00
298 Livan Hernandez 10.00 25.00

2005 Studio Diamond Cuts

STATED PRINT RUN 1250 SERIAL #'d SETS
*DIE CUT: .6X TO 1.5X BASIC
DIE CUT PRINT RUN 250 #'d SETS
*DC GOLD: 1X TO 2.5X BASIC
DC GOLD PRINT RUN 75 #'d SETS
OVERALL INSERT ODDS 1:1 HOBBY
1 Roger Clemens 1.50 4.00
2 Manny Ramirez 1.25 3.00

3 Francisco Rodriguez .75 2.00
4 Brian Roberts .50 1.25
5 Javy Lopez .50 1.25
6 Vernon Wells .50 1.25
7 Johan Santana 1.25 3.00
8 Torii Hunter .50 1.25
9 Mike Mussina .75 2.00
10 Sammy Sosa 1.25 3.00
11 Ryan Wagner .50 1.25
12 Jack Wilson .50 1.25
13 Ichiro Suzuki 2.00 5.00
14 Greg Maddux 2.00 5.00
15 Albert Pujols 3.00 8.00
16 Jeremy Bonderman .50 1.25
17 Johnny Estrada .50 1.25
18 Mark Buehrle .75 2.00
19 Jorge Posada .75 2.00
20 Carl Crawford .75 2.00
21 Paul Konerko .75 2.00
22 Victor Martinez .75 2.00
23 Jose Vidro .50 1.25
24 Jim Thome .75 2.00
25 Andruw Jones .50 1.25

2005 Studio Diamond Cuts Bat

*BAT p/r 200-300: .4X TO 1X JSY p/r 175-250
*BAT p/r 200-300: .15X TO .4X JSY p/r 15
*BAT p/r 50: .6X TO 1.5X JSY p/r 175-250
*BAT p/r 50: .5X TO 1.2X JSY p/r 125
*BAT p/r 25: .75X TO 2X JSY p/r 175-250
OVERALL AU-GU ODDS 1:8 HOBBY
PRINT RUNS B/WN 5-300 COPIES PER
NO PRICING ON QTY OF 10 OR LESS

2005 Studio Diamond Cuts Jersey

PRINT RUNS B/WN 15-250 COPIES PER
PRIME PRINT RUNS B/WN 5-10 COPIES PER
NO PRIME PRICING DUE TO SCARCITY
OVERALL AU-GU ODDS 1:8 HOBBY
1 Roger Clemens/125 5.00 12.00
2 Manny Ramirez/250 2.50 6.00
3 Francisco Rodriguez/250 2.00 5.00
4 Brian Roberts/250 2.00 5.00
5 Javy Lopez/250 2.00 5.00
6 Vernon Wells/250 2.00 5.00
7 Johan Santana/175 3.00 8.00
8 Torii Hunter/250 2.00 5.00
9 Mike Mussina/250 2.50 6.00
10 Sammy Sosa/250 3.00 8.00
11 Ryan Wagner/250 2.00 5.00
12 Jack Wilson/15 5.00 12.00
14 Greg Maddux/250 4.00 10.00
15 Albert Pujols/250 6.00 15.00
16 Jeremy Bonderman/250 2.00 5.00
17 Johnny Estrada/250 2.00 5.00
18 Mark Buehrle/250 2.00 5.00
19 Jorge Posada/250 2.50 6.00
20 Carl Crawford/250 2.00 5.00
21 Paul Konerko/250 2.00 5.00
22 Victor Martinez/250 2.00 5.00
23 Jose Vidro/175 2.00 5.00
24 Jim Thome/250 2.50 6.00
25 Andruw Jones/250 2.50 6.00

2005 Studio Diamond Cuts Combo

*COMBO p/r 50: .75X TO 2X JSY p/r 175-250
*COMBO p/r 50: .6X TO 1.5X JSY p/r 125
*COMBO p/r 50: .3X TO .8X JSY p/r 15
PRINT RUNS B/WN 5-50 COPIES PER
PRIME PRINT RUN 10 SERIAL #'d SETS
NO PRIME PRICING DUE TO SCARCITY
OVERALL AU-GU ODDS 1:8 HOBBY

2005 Studio Diamond Cuts Signature Combo

PRINT RUNS B/WN 25-50 COPIES PER
PRIME PRINT 10 SERIAL #'d SETS
NO PRIME PRICING DUE TO SCARCITY
OVERALL AU-GU ODDS 1:8 HOBBY

3 F.Rodriguez Jsy-Jsy/25 20.00 50.00
6 Vernon Wells Jsy-Jsy/25 12.50 30.00
8 Torii Hunter Bat-Jsy/25 10.00 25.00
11 Ryan Wagner Jsy-Jsy/50 6.00 15.00
12 Jack Wilson Bat-Jsy/50 10.00 25.00
16 J.Bonderman Jsy-Jsy/50 10.00 25.00
17 J.Estrada Fld Glv-Jsy/50 6.00 15.00
21 Paul Konerko Jsy-Jsy/25 20.00 50.00

2005 Studio Heritage

STATED PRINT RUN 1000 SERIAL #'d SETS
*DIE CUT: .6X TO 1.5X BASIC
DIE CUT PRINT RUN 200 #'d SETS
*DC GOLD: 1.25X TO 3X BASIC
DC GOLD PRINT RUN 50 #'d SETS
OVERALL INSERT ODDS 1:1 HOBBY
1 Rickey Henderson .75 2.00
2 Jeff Bagwell .75 2.00
3 Steve Garvey .50 1.25
4 Albert Pujols 3.00 8.00
5 Don Mattingly 2.50 6.00
6 Frank Thomas 1.25 3.00
7 Tony Gwynn 1.50 4.00
8 Gary Sheffield .50 1.25
9 Dale Murphy .50 1.25
10 Kerry Wood .50 1.25
11 Cal Ripken 5.00 12.00
12 Miguel Cabrera 1.25 3.00
13 Dwight Gooden .50 1.25
14 Barry Zito .50 1.25
15 Darryl Strawberry .50 1.25

2005 Studio Heritage Bat

*BAT: .4X TO 1X JSY p/r 250
*BAT: .25X TO .6X JSY p/r 50
OVERALL AU-GU ODDS 1:8 HOBBY
STATED PRINT RUN 150 SERIAL #'d SETS
8 Gary Sheffield 2.00 5.00

2005 Studio Heritage Jersey

PRINT RUNS B/WN 50-250 COPIES PER
PRIME PRINT RUN 10 SERIAL #'d SETS
NO PRIME PRICING DUE TO SCARCITY
OVERALL AU-GU ODDS 1:8 HOBBY
1 Rickey Henderson/250 4.00 10.00
2 Jeff Bagwell/250 2.50 6.00
3 Steve Garvey/250 2.50 6.00
4 Albert Pujols/250 6.00 15.00
5 Don Mattingly/250 5.00 12.00
6 Frank Thomas/250 3.00 8.00
7 Tony Gwynn/250 4.00 10.00
9 Dale Murphy/250 3.00 8.00
10 Kerry Wood/250 2.00 5.00
11 Cal Ripken/250 10.00 25.00
12 Miguel Cabrera/50 4.00 10.00
13 Dwight Gooden/250 2.50 6.00
14 Barry Zito/250 2.00 5.00
15 Darryl Strawberry/250 2.50 6.00

2005 Studio Heritage Combo

*COMBO p/r 50: .75X TO 2X JSY p/r 250
*COMBO p/r 50: .5X TO 1.2X JSY p/r 50
*COMBO p/r 25: 1X TO 2.5X JSY p/r 250
PRINT RUNS B/WN 10-50 COPIES PER
NO PRICING ON QTY OF 10
PRIME PRINT RUN 10 SERIAL #'d SETS
NO PRIME PRICING DUE TO SCARCITY
OVERALL AU-GU ODDS 1:8 HOBBY
8 Gary Sheffield Bat-Jsy/50 4.00 10.00

2005 Studio Heritage Signature Combo

PRINT RUNS B/WN 10-50 COPIES PER
NO PRICING ON QTY OF 10
PRIME PRINT RUNS B/WN 5-10 COPIES PER
NO PRIME PRICING DUE TO SCARCITY
OVERALL AU-GU ODDS 1:8 HOBBY
3 Steve Garvey Bat-Jsy/50 10.00 25.00
5 Don Mattingly Bat-Jsy/25 40.00 80.00
6 Frank Thomas Bat-Jsy/10
7 Tony Gwynn Bat-Jsy/15 50.00 100.00
9 Dale Murphy Bat-Jsy/25 20.00 50.00
11 Cal Ripken Bat-Jsy/50 100.00 175.00
12 Miguel Cabrera Bat-Jsy/25 20.00 50.00
13 Dwight Gooden Bat-Jsy/25 12.50 30.00
15 D.Strawberry Bat-Jsy/25 12.50 30.00

2005 Studio Heroes of the Hall

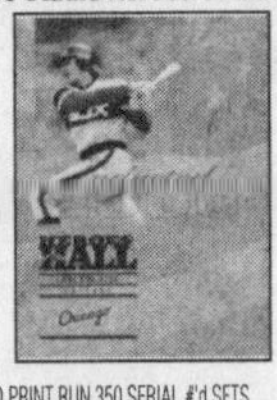

STATED PRINT RUN 350 SERIAL #'d SETS
*DIE CUT: .6X TO 1.5X BASIC
DIE CUT PRINT RUN 75 #'d SETS
*DC GOLD: 1.25X TO 3X BASIC
DC GOLD PRINT RUN 25 #'d SETS
OVERALL INSERT ODDS 1:1 HOBBY
1 Luis Aparicio .75 2.00
2 Dennis Eckersley .75 2.00
3 Brooks Robinson 1.25 3.00
4 Carlton Fisk 1.25 3.00
5 Tom Seaver 1.25 3.00
6 Paul Molitor 2.00 5.00
7 Rod Carew 1.25 3.00
8 George Brett 4.00 10.00
9 Nolan Ryan 5.00 12.00
10 Mike Schmidt 4.00 10.00
11 Willie Mays 4.00 10.00
12 Gary Carter .75 2.00
13 Lou Brock 1.25 3.00
14 Steve Carlton .75 2.00
15 Harmon Killebrew 2.00 5.00

2005 Studio Heroes of the Hall Bat

*BAT p/r 150: .4X TO 1X JSY p/r 150
*BAT p/r 150: .25X TO .6X JSY p/r 50
*BAT p/r 100-125: .5X TO 1.2X JSY p/r 150
*BAT p/r 100-125: .4X TO 1X JSY p/r 100
*BAT p/r 100-125: .3X TO .8X JSY p/r 50
OVERALL AU-GU ODDS 1:8 HOBBY
PRINT RUNS B/WN 100-150 COPIES PER
13 Lou Brock/150 3.00 8.00

2005 Studio Heroes of the Hall Jersey

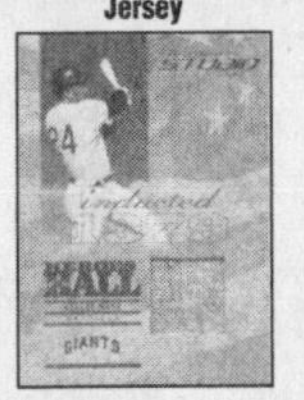

PRINT RUNS B/WN 50-150 COPIES PER
PRIME PRINT RUNS B/WN 5-10 COPIES PER
NO PRIME PRICING DUE TO SCARCITY
OVERALL AU-GU ODDS 1:8 HOBBY
1 Luis Aparicio/150 2.50 6.00
2 Dennis Eckersley/150 2.50 6.00
3 Brooks Robinson/150 5.00 12.00
4 Carlton Fisk/150 3.00 8.00
5 Tom Seaver/150 3.00 8.00
6 Paul Molitor/150 2.50 6.00
7 Rod Carew/150 3.00 8.00
8 George Brett/150 5.00 12.00
9 Nolan Ryan/100 8.00 20.00
10 Mike Schmidt/100 6.00 15.00
11 Willie Mays/50 20.00 50.00
12 Gary Carter/150 2.50 6.00
14 Steve Carlton/150 2.50 6.00
15 Harmon Killebrew/150 4.00 10.00

2005 Studio Heroes of the Hall Combo

*COMBO p/r 50: .75X TO 2X JSY p/r 150
*COMBO p/r 50: .6X TO 1.5X JSY p/r 100
*COMBO p/r 25: .6X TO 1.5X JSY p/r 50
PRINT RUNS B/WN 25-50 COPIES PER
PRIME PRINT RUNS B/WN 5-10 COPIES PER
NO PRIME PRICING DUE TO SCARCITY
OVERALL AU-GU ODDS 1:8 HOBBY
13 Lou Brock Bat-Jkt/50 6.00 15.00

2005 Studio Heroes of the Hall Signature Combo

PRINT RUNS B/WN 5-50 COPIES PER
NO PRICING ON QTY OF 10 OR LESS
PRIME PRINT RUNS B/WN 5-10 COPIES PER
NO PRIME PRICING DUE TO SCARCITY
OVERALL AU-GU ODDS 1:8 HOBBY
1 Luis Aparicio Bat-Jsy/50 10.00 25.00
2 D.Eckersley Jsy-Pants/25 12.50 30.00
3 B.Robinson Bat-Jsy/10
4 Carlton Fisk Bat-Jsy/25 20.00 50.00
5 Tom Seaver Jsy-Pants/15 40.00 80.00
6 Paul Molitor Bat-Jsy/25 12.50 30.00
11 Willie Mays Bat-Jsy/5
12 Gary Carter Jsy-Pants/15 15.00 40.00
14 Steve Carlton Bat-Jsy/25 12.50 30.00
15 H.Killebrew Bat-Jsy/25 40.00 80.00

2005 Studio Masterstrokes

STATED PRINT RUN 750 SERIAL #'d SETS
*DIE CUT: .6X TO 1.5X BASIC
DIE CUT PRINT RUN 150 #'d SETS
*DC GOLD: 1X TO 2.5X BASIC
DC GOLD PRINT RUN 50 #'d SETS
OVERALL INSERT ODDS 1:1 HOBBY
1 Hideki Matsui 2.50 6.00
2 David Ortiz 1.50 4.00
3 Aramis Ramirez .60 1.50
4 Lance Berkman 1.00 2.50
5 Ichiro Suzuki 2.50 6.00
6 Mike Piazza 1.50 4.00
7 Ivan Rodriguez 1.00 2.50
8 Hideo Nomo 1.50 4.00
9 Jeff Bagwell 1.00 2.50
10 Travis Hafner .60 1.50
11 Casey Kotchman .60 1.50
12 Jim Edmonds 1.00 2.50
13 Michael Young 1.00 2.50
14 Lyle Overbay .60 1.50
15 Eric Chavez .60 1.50
16 Jason Bay .60 1.50
17 Hank Blalock .60 1.50
18 Frank Thomas 1.50 4.00
19 Craig Biggio 1.00 2.50
20 Miguel Cabrera 1.50 4.00
21 Vladimir Guerrero 1.50 4.00
22 Sammy Sosa 1.50 4.00
23 Chipper Jones 1.50 4.00
24 Rafael Palmeiro 1.00 2.50
25 Adam Dunn 1.00 2.50

2005 Studio Masterstrokes Bat

*BAT p/r 200-250: .4X TO 1X JSY p/r 150-250
*BAT p/r 200-250: .25X TO .6X JSY p/r 40-50
*BAT p/r 100: .5X TO 1.2X JSY p/r 150-250
*BAT p/r 50: .6X TO 1.5X JSY p/r 150-250
*BAT p/r 25: .75X TO 2X JSY p/r 150-250
OVERALL AU-GU ODDS 1:8 HOBBY
PRINT RUNS B/WN 25-250 COPIES PER

2005 Studio Masterstrokes Jersey

PRINT RUNS B/WN 40-250 COPIES PER
PRIME PRINT RUN 10 SERIAL #'d SETS
NO PRIME PRICING DUE TO SCARCITY
OVERALL AU-GU ODDS 1:8 HOBBY
1 Hideki Matsui/250 10.00 25.00
2 David Ortiz/250 2.50 6.00
3 Aramis Ramirez/250 2.00 5.00
4 Lance Berkman/250 2.00 5.00
6 Mike Piazza/250 3.00 8.00
7 Ivan Rodriguez/250 2.50 6.00
8 Hideo Nomo/250 3.00 8.00
9 Jeff Bagwell/250 2.50 6.00
10 Travis Hafner/200 2.00 5.00
11 Casey Kotchman/250 2.00 5.00
12 Jim Edmonds/250 2.00 5.00
13 Michael Young/150 2.00 5.00
14 Lyle Overbay/250 2.00 5.00
15 Eric Chavez/250 2.00 5.00
16 Jason Bay/150 2.00 5.00
17 Hank Blalock/250 2.00 5.00
18 Frank Thomas/250 3.00 8.00
19 Craig Biggio/250 2.50 6.00
20 Miguel Cabrera/250 2.50 6.00
21 Vladimir Guerrero/50 5.00 12.00
22 Sammy Sosa/250 3.00 8.00
23 Chipper Jones/250 3.00 8.00
24 Rafael Palmeiro/40 4.00 10.00
25 Adam Dunn/250 2.00 5.00

2005 Studio Masterstrokes Combo

*COMBO p/r 50: .75X TO 2X JSY p/r 150-250
*COMBO p/r 50: .5X TO 1.2X JSY p/r 40-50
*COMBO p/r 15: 1.25X TO 3X JSY p/r 150-250
PRINT RUNS B/WN 15-50 COPIES PER
PRIME PRINT RUN 10 SERIAL #'d SETS
NO PRIME PRICING DUE TO SCARCITY
OVERALL AU-GU ODDS 1:8 HOBBY

2005 Studio Masterstrokes Signature Combo

PRINT RUNS B/WN 5-50 COPIES PER
NO PRICING ON QTY OF 10 OR LESS
PRIME PRINT RUNS B/WN 5-10 COPIES PER
NO PRIME PRICING DUE TO SCARCITY
OVERALL AU-GU ODDS 1:8 HOBBY
10 Travis Hafner Bat-Jsy/50 10.00 25.00
11 C.Kotchman Bat-Jsy/50 10.00 25.00
12 Jim Edmonds Jsy-Jsy/5
13 Michael Young Bat-Jsy/10
14 Lyle Overbay Bat-Jsy/50 6.00 15.00
15 Eric Chavez Bat-Jsy/25 12.50 30.00
16 Jason Bay Bat-Jsy/50 10.00 25.00
17 Hank Blalock Jsy-Jsy/25 12.50 30.00
18 Frank Thomas Bat-Jsy/10
20 Miguel Cabrera Bat-Jsy/25 20.00 50.00
23 Chipper Jones Bat-Jsy/5
25 Adam Dunn Bat-Jsy/10

2005 Studio Portraits Zenith White

STATED PRINT RUN 70 SERIAL #'d SETS
*PARALLEL #'d OF 50-60: .4X TO 1X
*PARALLEL #'d OF 40-45: .5X TO 1.2X
*PARALLEL #'d OF 30-35: .6X TO 1.5X
*PARALLEL #'d OF 20-25: .75X TO 2X
*PARALLEL #'d OF 15: 1X TO 2.5X
PARALLELS #'d FROM 5-60 COPIES PER
NO PRICING ON QTY OF 10 OR LESS
OVERALL PORTRAITS ODDS 1:3 HOBBY
1 Ozzie Smith 2.50 6.00
2 Derek Jeter 4.00 10.00
3 Eric Chavez .60 1.50
4 Duke Snider 1.00 2.50
5 Albert Pujols 4.00 10.00
6 Stan Musial 2.50 6.00
7 Ivan Rodriguez 1.00 2.50
8 Cal Ripken 6.00 15.00
9 Hank Blalock .60 1.50
10 Chipper Jones 1.50 4.00
11 Gary Sheffield .60 1.50
12 Alfonso Soriano 1.00 2.50
13 Carl Crawford 1.00 2.50
14 Lou Brock 1.00 2.50
15 Jim Edmonds 1.00 2.50
16 Bo Jackson 1.50 4.00
17 Todd Helton 1.00 2.50
18 Javy Lopez .60 1.50
19 Tony Gwynn 2.00 5.00
20 Mark Mulder .60 1.50
21 Sammy Sosa 1.50 4.00
22 Roger Clemens 2.00 5.00
23 Don Mattingly 3.00 8.00
24 Willie Mays 3.00 8.00
25 Andruw Jones .60 1.50
26 Steve Garvey .60 1.50
27 Scott Rolen 1.00 2.50
28 George Brett 3.00 8.00
29 Rod Carew 1.00 2.50
30 Ken Griffey Jr. 2.50 6.00
31 Mike Piazza 1.50 4.00
32 Steve Carlton 1.00 2.50
33 Larry Walker 1.00 2.50
34 Kerry Wood .60 1.50
35 Frank Thomas 1.50 4.00
36 Lance Berkman 1.00 2.50
37 Nomar Garciaparra 1.50 4.00
38 Curt Schilling 1.00 2.50
39 Carl Yastrzemski 2.00 5.00
40 Mark Grace 1.00 2.50
41 Tom Seaver 1.00 2.50
42 Mariano Rivera 1.50 4.00
43 Carlos Beltran 1.00 2.50
44 Reggie Jackson 1.50 4.00
45 Pedro Martinez 1.00 2.50
46 Richie Sexson .60 1.50
47 Tom Glavine 1.00 2.50
48 Torii Hunter .60 1.50
49 Ron Guidry .60 1.50
50 Michael Young .60 1.50
51 Ichiro Suzuki 2.50 6.00
52 C.C. Sabathia 1.00 2.50
53 Johnny Bench 1.50 4.00
54 Mark Teixeira 1.50 4.00
55 Hideki Matsui 2.50 6.00
56 Mike Mussina 1.00 2.50
57 Johan Santana 1.50 4.00
58 Fergie Jenkins .60 1.50
59 Hideo Nomo 1.50 4.00
60 Nolan Ryan 4.00 10.00
61 Whitey Ford 1.00 2.50
62 Jim Thome 1.00 2.50
63 Gary Carter .60 1.50
64 Randy Johnson 1.50 4.00
65 Vladimir Guerrero 1.50 4.00
66 Harmon Killebrew 1.50 4.00
67 Tim Hudson 1.00 2.50
68 Josh Beckett 1.00 2.50
69 Eddie Murray 1.50 4.00
70 Greg Maddux 2.50 6.00
71 J.D. Drew .60 1.50
72 Bob Feller .60 1.50
73 Adrian Beltre .60 1.50
74 Wade Boggs 1.00 2.50
75 Barry Zito .60 1.50
76 David Ortiz 1.50 4.00
77 Mike Schmidt 3.00 8.00
78 Miguel Cabrera 1.50 4.00
79 Carlos Delgado .60 1.50
80 Andre Dawson 1.00 2.50
81 Garret Anderson .60 1.50
82 Rickey Henderson 1.00 2.50
83 Shawn Green .60 1.50
84 Dale Murphy .60 1.50
85 Alex Rodriguez 2.50 6.00
86 Mark Prior 1.00 2.50
87 Paul Molitor 1.50 4.00
88 Jeff Bagwell 1.00 2.50
89 Eric Gagne .60 1.50
90 Troy Glaus .60 1.50
91 Robin Yount 1.50 4.00
92 Miguel Tejada 1.00 2.50
93 Kirk Gibson .60 1.50
94 Manny Ramirez 1.50 4.00
95 Rafael Palmeiro 1.00 2.50
96 Maury Wills .60 1.50
97 Craig Biggio 1.00 2.50
98 Jim Palmer .60 1.50
99 Adam Dunn 1.00 2.50
100 Carlton Fisk 1.00 2.50

2005 Studio Spirit of the Game

STATED PRINT RUN 600 SERIAL #'d SETS
*DIE CUT: .6X TO 1.5X BASIC
DIE CUT PRINT RUN 125 #'d SETS
*DC GOLD: 1.5X TO 4X BASIC
DC GOLD PRINT RUN 25 #'d SETS
OVERALL INSERT ODDS 1:1 HOBBY
1 Mark Prior 1.25 3.00
2 Sean Casey .75 2.00
3 Ichiro Suzuki 3.00 8.00
4 Andruw Jones .75 2.00
5 Francisco Cordero .75 2.00
6 Ben Sheets .75 2.00
7 Rocco Baldelli .75 2.00
8 Rafael Furcal .75 2.00
9 Angel Berroa .75 2.00
10 Roy Oswalt 1.25 3.00
11 Jose Reyes 1.25 3.00
12 Shannon Stewart .75 2.00
13 Greg Maddux 3.00 8.00
14 Alfonso Soriano 1.25 3.00
15 Curt Schilling 1.25 3.00
16 Jody Gerut .75 2.00
17 Brandon Webb 1.25 3.00
18 Josh Beckett 1.25 3.00
19 Laynce Nix .75 2.00
20 Scott Rolen 1.25 3.00

2005 Studio Spirit of the Game Bat

*BAT p/r 225-300: .4X TO 1X JSY p/r 250
*BAT p/r 225-300: .3X TO .8X JSY p/r 125
*BAT p/r 75: .5X TO 1.2X JSY p/r 250
OVERALL AU-GU ODDS 1:8 HOBBY
PRINT RUNS B/WN 75-300 COPIES PER

2005 Studio Spirit of the Game Jersey

PRINT RUNS B/WN 125-250 COPIES PER
PRIME PRINT RUN 10 SERIAL #'d SETS
NO PRIME PRICING DUE TO SCARCITY
OVERALL AU-GU ODDS 1:8 HOBBY
1 Mark Prior/250 2.50 6.00
2 Sean Casey/250 2.00 5.00
4 Andruw Jones/250 2.50 6.00
5 Francisco Cordero/250 2.50 6.00
6 Ben Sheets/250 2.00 5.00
7 Rocco Baldelli/250 2.00 5.00
8 Rafael Furcal/250 2.00 5.00
10 Roy Oswalt/250 2.00 5.00
11 Jose Reyes/250 2.00 5.00
12 Shannon Stewart/250 2.00 5.00
13 Greg Maddux/250 4.00 10.00
14 Alfonso Soriano/250 2.00 5.00
15 Curt Schilling/250 2.50 6.00
16 Jody Gerut/125 2.50 6.00
18 Josh Beckett/250 2.00 5.00
19 Laynce Nix/250 2.00 5.00
20 Scott Rolen/250 2.50 6.00

2005 Studio Spirit of the Game Combo

*COMBO: .75X TO 2X JSY p/r 250
*COMBO: .6X TO 1.5X JSY p/r 125
STATED PRINT RUN 50 SERIAL #'d SETS
PRIME PRINT RUN 10 SERIAL #'d SETS
NO PRIME PRICING DUE TO SCARCITY
OVERALL AU-GU ODDS 1:8 HOBBY

2005 Studio Spirit of the Game Signature Combo

PRINT RUNS B/WN 10-25 COPIES PER
NO PRICING ON QTY OF 10
PRIME PRINT RUNS B/WN 5-10 COPIES PER
NO PRIME PRICING DUE TO SCARCITY
OVERALL AU-GU ODDS 1:8 HOBBY
1 Mark Prior Bat-Jsy/15 20.00 50.00
2 Sean Casey Jsy-Jsy/25 12.50 30.00
6 Ben Sheets Bat-Jsy/10
8 Rafael Furcal Bat-Jsy/25 12.50 30.00
12 S.Stewart Jsy-Jsy/25 12.50 30.00
14 A.Soriano Jsy-Jsy/15 15.00 40.00
16 Jody Gerut Bat-Jsy/25 8.00 20.00
19 Laynce Nix Bat-Jsy/25 8.00 20.00
20 Scott Rolen Jsy-Jsy/10

2005 Studio Stars

STATED ODDS 1:6
*GOLD: .75X TO 2X BASIC
GOLD PRINT RUN 500 #'d SETS
*PLATINUM: 1.5X TO 4X BASIC
PLATINUM PRINT RUN 50 #'d SETS
OVERALL INSERT ODDS 1:1 HOBBY
1 Carlos Beltran .40 1.00
2 Sean Casey .40 1.00
3 Ichiro Suzuki 1.50 4.00
4 Vladimir Guerrero 1.00 2.50
5 Tim Hudson .60 1.50
6 Alex Rodriguez 1.50 4.00
7 Miguel Tejada .60 1.50
8 Curt Schilling .60 1.50
9 Roger Clemens 1.25 3.00
10 Ben Sheets .40 1.00
11 Todd Helton .60 1.50
12 Mark Mulder .40 1.00
13 Scott Podsednik .40 1.00
14 Victor Martinez .60 1.50
15 Mark Prior .60 1.50
16 Ivan Rodriguez .60 1.50
17 Dontrelle Willis .40 1.00
18 Andy Pettitte .60 1.50
19 Khalil Greene .40 1.00
20 Jeff Kent .40 1.00
21 Paul Konerko .60 1.50
22 Joe Mauer 1.00 2.50
23 Bobby Crosby .40 1.00
24 Pedro Martinez .60 1.50
25 John Smoltz 1.00 2.50
26 Derek Jeter 2.50 6.00
27 Moises Alou .40 1.00
28 Rich Harden .40 1.00
29 Jim Thome .60 1.50
30 Jason Bay .40 1.00
31 Aramis Ramirez .40 1.00
32 Carlos Lee .40 1.00
33 B.J. Upton .60 1.50
34 Nomar Garciaparra 1.00 2.50
35 Ken Griffey Jr. 1.50 4.00
36 Darin Erstad .40 1.00
37 Larry Walker .60 1.50
38 Jose Vidro .40 1.00
39 Zack Greinke .60 1.50
40 Michael Young .60 1.50
41 David Wright 1.50 4.00
42 Albert Pujols 2.50 6.00
43 Vernon Wells .40 1.00
44 Mark Teixeira 1.00 2.50
45 Jacque Jones .40 1.00
46 Brian Giles .40 1.00
47 Austin Kearns .40 1.00
48 Omar Vizquel .60 1.50
49 Randy Johnson 1.00 2.50
50 Jason Varitek 1.00 2.50

2001 Sweet Spot

COMP.UPDATE w/o SP's (30) 4.00 10.00
COMMON CARD (1-60) .15 .40
COMMON CARD (61-90) 4.00 10.00
COMMON CARD (91-120) .25 .60
COMMON (121-150) 2.00 5.00
1 Troy Glaus .15 .40
2 Darin Erstad .15 .40
3 Jason Giambi .15 .40

Card	Low	High
4 Tim Hudson	.15	.40
5 Ben Grieve	.15	.40
6 Carlos Delgado	.15	.40
7 David Wells	.15	.40
8 Greg Vaughn	.15	.40
9 Roberto Alomar	.25	.60
10 Jim Thome	.25	.60
11 John Olerud	.15	.40
12 Edgar Martinez	.25	.60
13 Cal Ripken	1.25	3.00
14 Albert Belle	.15	.40
15 Ivan Rodriguez	.25	.60
16 Alex Rodriguez Rangers	1.25	3.00
17 Pedro Martinez	.25	.60
18 Nomar Garciaparra	.60	1.50
19 Manny Ramirez	.25	.60
20 Jermaine Dye	.15	.40
21 Juan Gonzalez	.15	.40
22 Dean Palmer	.15	.40
23 Matt Lawton	.15	.40
24 Eric Milton	.15	.40
25 Frank Thomas	.40	1.00
26 Magglio Ordonez	.15	.40
27 Derek Jeter	1.00	2.50
28 Bernie Williams	.25	.60
29 Roger Clemens	.75	2.00
30 Jeff Bagwell	.25	.60
31 Richard Hidalgo	.15	.40
32 Chipper Jones	.40	1.00
33 Greg Maddux	.60	1.50
34 Richie Sexson	.15	.40
35 Jeromy Burnitz	.15	.40
36 Mark McGwire	1.00	2.50
37 Jim Edmonds	.15	.40
38 Sammy Sosa	.40	1.00
39 Randy Johnson	.40	1.00
40 Steve Finley	.15	.40
41 Gary Sheffield	.15	.40
42 Shawn Green	.15	.40
43 Vladimir Guerrero	.40	1.00
44 Jose Vidro	.15	.40
45 Barry Bonds	1.00	2.50
46 Jeff Kent	.15	.40
47 Preston Wilson	.15	.40
48 Luis Castillo	.15	.40
49 Mike Piazza	.60	1.50
50 Edgardo Alfonzo	.15	.40
51 Tony Gwynn	.50	1.25
52 Ryan Klesko	.15	.40
53 Scott Rolen	.25	.60
54 Bob Abreu	.15	.40
55 Jason Kendall	.15	.40
56 Brian Giles	.15	.40
57 Ken Griffey Jr.	.60	1.50
58 Barry Larkin	.25	.60
59 Todd Helton	.25	.60
60 Mike Hampton	.15	.40
Card back has batting header lines UER		
61 Corey Patterson SB	4.00	10.00
62 Ichiro Suzuki SB RC	125.00	200.00
63 Jason Grilli SB	4.00	10.00
64 Brian Cole SB	4.00	10.00
65 Juan Pierre SB	4.00	10.00
66 Matt Ginter SB	4.00	10.00
67 Jimmy Rollins SB	4.00	10.00
68 Jason Smith SB RC	4.00	10.00
69 Israel Alcantara SB	4.00	10.00
70 Adam Pettyjohn SB RC	4.00	10.00
71 Luke Prokopec SB	4.00	10.00
72 Barry Zito SB	5.00	12.00
73 Keith Ginter SB	4.00	10.00
74 Sun Woo Kim SB	4.00	10.00
75 Ross Gload SB	4.00	10.00
76 Matt Wise SB	4.00	10.00
77 Aubrey Huff SB	4.00	10.00
78 Ryan Franklin SB	4.00	10.00
79 Brandon Inge SB	4.00	10.00
80 Wes Helms SB	4.00	10.00
81 Junior Spivey SB RC	5.00	12.00
82 Ryan Vogelsong SB	4.00	10.00
83 John Parrish SB	4.00	10.00
84 Joe Crede SB	5.00	12.00
85 Damian Rolls SB	4.00	10.00
86 Esix Snead SB RC	4.00	10.00
87 Rocky Biddle SB	4.00	10.00
88 Brady Clark SB	4.00	10.00
89 Timo Perez SB	4.00	10.00
90 Jay Spurgeon SB	4.00	10.00
91 Garret Anderson	.25	.60
92 Jermaine Dye	.25	.60
93 Shannon Stewart	.25	.60
94 Ben Grieve	.25	.60
95 Juan Gonzalez	.25	.60
96 Brett Boone	.25	.60
97 Tony Batista	.25	.60
98 Rafael Palmeiro	.40	1.00
99 Carl Everett	.25	.60
100 Mike Sweeney	.25	.60
101 Tony Clark	.25	.60
102 Doug Mientkiewicz	.25	.60
103 Jose Canseco	.40	1.00
104 Mike Mussina	.40	1.00
105 Lance Berkman	.25	.60
106 Andruw Jones	.40	1.00
107 Geoff Jenkins	.25	.60
108 Matt Morris	.25	.60
109 Fred McGriff	.40	1.00
110 Luis Gonzalez	.25	.60
111 Kevin Brown	.25	.60
112 Tony Armas Jr.	.25	.60
113 John Vander Wal	.25	.60
114 Cliff Floyd	.25	.60
115 Matt Lawton	.25	.60
116 Phil Nevin	.25	.60
117 Pat Burrell	.25	.60
118 Aramis Ramirez	.25	.60
119 Sean Casey	.25	.60
120 Larry Walker	.25	.60
121 Albert Pujols SB RC	100.00	200.00
122 J.Estrada SB RC	2.00	5.00
123 Wilson Betemit SB RC	3.00	8.00
124 A.Hernandez SB RC	2.00	5.00
125 M.Ensberg SB RC	3.00	8.00
126 H.Ramirez SB RC	2.00	5.00
127 Josh Towers SB RC	2.00	5.00
128 Juan Uribe SB RC	2.00	5.00
129 Wilken Ruan SB RC	2.00	5.00
130 Andres Torres SB RC	2.00	5.00
131 B.Lawrence SB RC	2.00	5.00
132 Ryan Freel SB RC	2.00	5.00
133 B.Duckworth SB RC	2.00	5.00
134 Juan Diaz SB RC	2.00	5.00
135 Rafael Soriano SB RC	2.00	5.00
136 R.Rodriguez SB RC	2.00	5.00
137 Bud Smith SB RC	2.00	5.00
138 Mark Teixeira SB RC	15.00	40.00
139 Mark Prior SB RC	5.00	12.00
140 J.Melian SB RC	2.00	5.00
141 D.Brazelton SB RC	2.00	5.00
142 Greg Miller SB RC	2.00	5.00
143 Billy Sylvester SB RC	2.00	5.00
144 E.Guzman SB RC	2.00	5.00
145 Jack Wilson SB RC	2.00	5.00
146 Jose Mieses SB RC	2.00	5.00
147 Brandon Lyon SB RC	2.00	5.00
148 T.Shinjo SB RC	2.00	5.00
149 Juan Cruz SB RC	2.00	5.00
150 Jay Gibbons SB RC	2.00	5.00

2001 Sweet Spot Big League Challenge

Randomly inserted into packs at one in six, this 20-card insert features the top power-hitting players in the league. Card backs carry a "BL" prefix.

Card	Low	High
COMPLETE SET (20)	30.00	60.00
BL1 Mark McGwire	3.00	8.00
BL2 Richard Hidalgo	.75	2.00
BL3 Alex Rodriguez	2.00	5.00
BL4 Shawn Green	.75	2.00
BL5 Frank Thomas	1.25	3.00
BL6 Chipper Jones	1.25	3.00
BL7 Rafael Palmeiro	.75	2.00
BL8 Troy Glaus	.75	2.00
BL9 Mike Piazza	2.00	5.00
BL10 Andruw Jones	.75	2.00
BL11 Todd Helton	.75	2.00
BL12 Jason Giambi	.75	2.00
BL13 Sammy Sosa	1.25	3.00
BL14 Carlos Delgado	.75	2.00
BL15 Barry Bonds	3.00	8.00
BL16 Jose Canseco	.75	2.00
BL17 Jim Edmonds	.75	2.00
BL18 Manny Ramirez	.75	2.00
BL19 Gary Sheffield	.75	2.00
BL20 Nomar Garciaparra	2.00	5.00

2001 Sweet Spot Game Base Duos

Randomly inserted into packs at one in 18, this 16-card insert set features dual-player cards with a swatch of an actual game-used base. Card backs carry a "B1" prefix followed by the player's initials.

Card	Low	High
B1BD Jeff Bagwell	6.00	15.00
Jermaine Dye		
B1BH Barry Bonds	10.00	25.00
Todd Helton		
B1CP Roger Clemens	6.00	15.00
Mike Piazza		
B1GD Vladimir Guerrero	6.00	15.00
Carlos Delgado		
B1HG Jeffrey Hammonds	4.00	10.00
Troy Glaus		
B1JG Chipper Jones	6.00	15.00
Nomar Garciaparra		
B1JP Mike Piazza	15.00	40.00
Derek Jeter		
B1MG Mark McGwire	30.00	60.00
Ken Griffey Jr.		
B1MP Mark McGwire	20.00	50.00
Timo Perez		
B1RJ Alex Rodriguez	15.00	40.00
Derek Jeter		
B1RR Scott Rolen	10.00	25.00
Cal Ripken		
B1SR Gary Sheffield	6.00	15.00
Alex Rodriguez		
B1ST Sammy Sosa	6.00	15.00
Frank Thomas		
B1GRA Ken Griffey Jr.	6.00	15.00
Manny Ramirez		
B1GRO Tony Gwynn	4.00	10.00
Ivan Rodriguez		
B1JGI Randy Johnson	6.00	15.00
Jason Giambi		

2001 Sweet Spot Game Base Trios

Randomly inserted into packs, this 13-card insert set features three players on one card with a swatch of an actual game-used base. Card backs carry a "B2" prefix followed by the player's initials. Please note that there were only 50 serial numbered sets produced.

Card	Low	High
BDH Jef Bagwell	15.00	40.00
Jermaine Dye		
Richard Hidalgo		
BHK Barry Bonds	40.00	80.00
Todd Helton		
Jeff Kent		
GDM V. Guerrero	15.00	40.00
Carlos Delgado		
Raul Mondesi		
GRP Tony Gwynn	15.00	40.00
Ivan Rodriguez		
Rafael Palmeiro		
GRT Ken Griffey Jr.	15.00	40.00
Manny Ramirez		
Jim Thome		
HGH Jeffrey Hammonds	15.00	40.00
Troy Glaus		
Todd Helton		
JGC Randy Johnson	15.00	40.00
Jason Giambi		
Eric Chavez		
JGJ Chipper Jones	20.00	50.00
Nomar Garciaparra		
Andruw Jones		
MGE Mark McGwire	50.00	100.00
Ken Griffey Jr.		
Jim Edmonds		
PJW Mike Piazza	40.00	80.00
Derek Jeter		
Bernie Williams		
RRB Scott Rolen	30.00	60.00
Cal Ripken		
Albert Belle		
SRM Gary Sheffield	15.00	40.00
Alex Rodriguez		
Edgar Martinez		
STO Sammy Sosa	15.00	40.00
Frank Thomas		
Magglio Ordonez		

2001 Sweet Spot Game Bat

Randomly inserted into packs at one in 18, this 19-card insert set features a swatch of actual game-used bat. Card backs carry a "B" prefix followed by the player's initials.

Card	Low	High
BAJ Andruw Jones	6.00	15.00
BAR Alex Rodriguez	6.00	15.00
BBB Barry Bonds	10.00	25.00
BCR Cal Ripken	15.00	40.00
BFT Frank Thomas	6.00	15.00
BGS Gary Sheffield	4.00	10.00
BHA Hank Aaron	15.00	40.00
BIR Ivan Rodriguez	6.00	15.00
BJC Jose Canseco	6.00	15.00
BJD Joe DiMaggio	30.00	60.00
BKG Ken Griffey Jr.	6.00	15.00
BMM Mickey Mantle	50.00	100.00
BNR Nolan Ryan	15.00	40.00
BRA Rick Ankiel	6.00	15.00
BRJ Reggie Jackson	6.00	15.00
BSM Stan Musial	15.00	40.00
BSS Sammy Sosa	6.00	15.00
BTC Ty Cobb	75.00	150.00
BWM Willie Mays	30.00	60.00

2001 Sweet Spot Game Jersey

Randomly inserted into packs at one in 18, this 20-card insert set features a swatch from an actual game-used jersey. Card backs carry a "J" prefix followed by the player's initials. The Ichiro jersey actually was not major league regular-season game worn, but was worn in an spring training game in 1999.

Card	Low	High
JAJ Andruw Jones	6.00	15.00
JAR Alex Rodriguez	6.00	15.00
JBB Barry Bonds	10.00	25.00
JCJ Chipper Jones	6.00	15.00
JCR Cal Ripken	15.00	40.00
JDS Duke Snider	6.00	15.00
JFT Frank Thomas	6.00	15.00
JIR Ivan Rodriguez	6.00	15.00
JIS Ichiro Suzuki	50.00	100.00
JJC Jose Canseco	6.00	15.00
JJD Joe DiMaggio	40.00	80.00
JKG Ken Griffey Jr.	6.00	15.00
JMM Mickey Mantle	40.00	80.00
JNR Nolan Ryan	15.00	40.00
JRC Roberto Clemente	40.00	80.00
JRC Roger Clemens	6.00	15.00
JRJ Randy Johnson	6.00	15.00
JSM Stan Musial	20.00	50.00
JSS Sammy Sosa	6.00	15.00
JWM Willie Mays	20.00	50.00

2001 Sweet Spot Players Party

Inserted at a rate of one in 12 packs, these 10 cards feature some of Baseball's leading players. These cards have a "PP" prefix.

Card	Low	High
COMPLETE SET (10)	25.00	50.00
PP1 Derek Jeter	3.00	8.00
PP2 Randy Johnson	1.25	3.00
PP3 Frank Thomas	1.25	3.00
PP4 Nomar Garciaparra	2.00	5.00
PP5 Ken Griffey Jr.	2.00	5.00
PP6 Carlos Delgado	.75	2.00
PP7 Mike Piazza	2.00	5.00
PP8 Barry Bonds	3.00	8.00
PP9 Sammy Sosa	1.25	3.00
PP10 Pedro Martinez	.75	2.00

2001 Sweet Spot Signatures

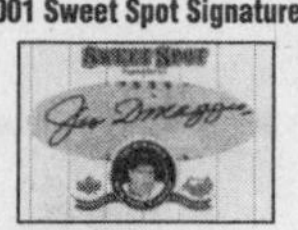

This 52-card insert set features authentic autographs from some of the Major League's top active and retired players. These cards incorporate the leather sweet spots from actual baseballs, whereby the featured athlete signed the leather swatch. The stunning design of these cards made them one of the most popular autograph inserts of the modern era. One in every eighteen packs of Sweet Spot contained either a Game Base insert or one of these Signatures inserts. Please note the following players packed out as exchange cards with a redemption deadline of November 8th, 2001: Roger Clemens and Willie Mays. In addition, the following players packed out as 50% exchange cards and 50% actual signed cards: Albert Belle, Pat Burrell and Rafael Furcal. Though the cards lack actual serial-numbering, representatives at Upper Deck publicly announced specific print runs on several short-printed cards within this set. That information is listed within our checklist. Forty of the 150 serial numbered Joe DiMaggio cards were actually inscribed by DiMaggio as "Joe DiMaggio - Yankee Clipper". Card backs carry a "S" prefix followed by the player's initials.

NO PRICING ON QTY OF 10 OR LESS

Card	Low	High
SAB Albert Belle	15.00	40.00
SAH Art Howe	10.00	25.00
SAJ Andruw Jones	30.00	60.00
SAR A. Rodriguez SP/154	100.00	200.00
SAT Alan Trammell	15.00	40.00
SBB Buddy Bell	10.00	25.00
SBM Bill Madlock	10.00	25.00
SBR Babe Ruth SP/1		
SBV Bobby Valentine	15.00	40.00
SCB Chris Chambliss	15.00	40.00
SCD Carlos Delgado	15.00	40.00
SCJ Chipper Jones	30.00	60.00
SDB Dusty Baker	10.00	25.00
SDB Don Baylor	15.00	40.00
SDE Darin Erstad	10.00	25.00
SDJ Davey Johnson	15.00	40.00
SDL Davey Lopes	10.00	25.00
SFT Frank Thomas	50.00	100.00
SGS Gary Sheffield	10.00	25.00
SHM Hal McRae	15.00	40.00
SIR I. Rodriguez SP/150	60.00	120.00
SJB Jeff Bagwell SP/214	90.00	150.00
SJC Jose Canseco	30.00	60.00
SJD J.DiMaggio SP/110	450.00	600.00
SJDa DiMag Clipper SP/40	600.00	1000.00
SJG Joe Garagiola	40.00	80.00
SJG Jason Giambi	15.00	40.00
SJR Jim Rice	15.00	40.00
SKG Ken Griffey Jr. SP/100	200.00	300.00
SLP Lou Piniella	15.00	40.00
SMB Milton Bradley	15.00	40.00
SML Mike Lamb	10.00	25.00
SMM Mickey Mantle SP/10		
SMW Matt Williams	30.00	60.00
SNR Nolan Ryan	90.00	150.00
SPB Pat Burrell	10.00	25.00
SPO Paul O'Neill	30.00	60.00
SRAI Roberto Alomar	12.50	30.00
SRAN Rick Ankiel	10.00	25.00
SRC R. Clemens EXCH	30.00	60.00
SRF Rafael Furcal	15.00	40.00
SRJ Randy Johnson	60.00	120.00
SRV Robin Ventura	10.00	25.00
SSG Shawn Green	30.00	60.00
SSM Stan Musial	90.00	150.00
SSS S. Sosa SP/148	90.00	150.00
STC Ty Cobb SP/1		
STGL Troy Glaus	10.00	25.00
STGW Tony Gwynn	50.00	100.00
STH Tim Hudson	30.00	60.00
STL Tony LaRussa	15.00	40.00
SWM Willie Mays	150.00	250.00

2002 Sweet Spot

This 175 card set was released in October, 2002. The four card packs were issued 12 packs to a box and 16 boxes to a case with an $10 SRP per pack. Cards numbered 1 through 90 feature veterans while cards numbered 91 through 145 feature rookies and cards numbered 146-175 feature veterans as part of the "Game Face" subset. Cards numbered 91 through 130 were issued to a stated print run of 1300 serial numbered sets while cards 131 through 145 were issued to either a stated print run of 750 or 100 serial numbered sets. Cards numbered 146 through 175 were issued at stated odds of one in 24. Also randomly inserted in packs were redemptions for Mark McGwire autographs which had an exchange deadline of September 12, 2003. These McGwire exchange cards entitled the bearer to send in a item for McGwire to sign.

Card	Low	High
COMP.SET w/o SP's (90)	8.00	20.00
COMMON CARD (1-90)	.15	.40
COMMON CARD (91-130)	1.50	4.00
COMMON TIER 1 AU (131-145)	6.00	15.00
COMMON TIER 2 AU (131-145)	10.00	25.00
COMMON CARD (146-175)	4.00	10.00
1 Troy Glaus	.15	.40
2 Darin Erstad	.15	.40
3 Tim Hudson	.15	.40
4 Eric Chavez	.15	.40
5 Barry Zito	.15	.40
6 Miguel Tejada	.15	.40
7 Carlos Delgado	.15	.40
8 Eric Hinske	.15	.40
9 Ben Grieve	.15	.40
10 Jim Thome	.25	.60
11 C.C. Sabathia	.15	.40
12 Omar Vizquel	.25	.60
13 Ichiro Suzuki	.75	2.00
14 Edgar Martinez	.25	.60
15 Bret Boone	.15	.40
16 Freddy Garcia	.15	.40
17 Tony Batista	.15	.40
18 Geronimo Gil	.15	.40
19 Alex Rodriguez	.60	1.50
20 Rafael Palmeiro	.25	.60
21 Ivan Rodriguez	.25	.60
22 Hank Blalock	.25	.60
23 Juan Gonzalez	.15	.40
24 Nomar Garciaparra	.60	1.50
25 Pedro Martinez	.25	.60
26 Manny Ramirez	.25	.60
27 Mike Sweeney	.15	.40
28 Carlos Beltran	.15	.40
29 Dmitri Young	.15	.40
30 Torii Hunter	.15	.40
31 Eric Milton	.15	.40
32 Corey Koskie	.15	.40
33 Frank Thomas	.40	1.00
34 Mark Buehrle	.15	.40
35 Magglio Ordonez	.15	.40
36 Roger Clemens	.75	2.00
37 Derek Jeter	1.00	2.50
38 Jason Giambi	.15	.40
39 Alfonso Soriano	.15	.40
40 Bernie Williams	.25	.60
41 Jeff Bagwell	.25	.60
42 Roy Oswalt	.15	.40
43 Lance Berkman	.15	.40
44 Greg Maddux	.60	1.50
45 Chipper Jones	.40	1.00
46 Gary Sheffield	.15	.40
47 Andruw Jones	.25	.60
48 Richie Sexson	.15	.40
49 Ben Sheets	.15	.40
50 Albert Pujols	.75	2.00
51 Matt Morris	.15	.40
52 J.D. Drew	.15	.40
53 Sammy Sosa	.40	1.00
54 Kerry Wood	.15	.40
55 Mark Prior	.25	.60
56 Moises Alou	.15	.40
57 Corey Patterson	.15	.40
58 Randy Johnson	.40	1.00
59 Luis Gonzalez	.15	.40
60 Curt Schilling	.15	.40
61 Shawn Green	.15	.40
62 Kevin Brown	.15	.40
63 Paul Lo Duca	.15	.40
64 Adrian Beltre	.15	.40
65 Vladimir Guerrero	.40	1.00
66 Jose Vidro	.15	.40
67 Javier Vazquez	.15	.40
68 Barry Bonds	1.00	2.50
69 Jeff Kent	.15	.40
70 Rich Aurilia	.15	.40
71 Mike Lowell	.15	.40
72 Josh Beckett	.15	.40
73 Brad Penny	.15	.40
74 Roberto Alomar	.25	.60
75 Mike Piazza	.60	1.50
76 Jeromy Burnitz	.15	.40
77 Mo Vaughn	.15	.40
78 Phil Nevin	.15	.40
79 Sean Burroughs	.15	.40
80 Jeremy Giambi	.15	.40
81 Bobby Abreu	.15	.40
82 Jimmy Rollins	.15	.40
83 Pat Burrell	.15	.40
84 Brian Giles	.15	.40
85 Aramis Ramirez	.15	.40
86 Ken Griffey Jr.	.60	1.50
87 Adam Dunn	.15	.40
88 Austin Kearns	.15	.40
89 Todd Helton	.25	.60
90 Larry Walker	.15	.40
91 Earl Snyder SB RC	1.50	4.00
92 Jorge Padilla SB RC	1.50	4.00
93 Felix Escalona SB RC	1.50	4.00
94 John Foster SB RC	1.50	4.00
95 Brandon Puffer SB RC	1.50	4.00
96 Steve Bechler SB RC	1.50	4.00
97 Hansel Izquierdo SB RC	1.50	4.00
98 Chris Baker SB RC	1.50	4.00
99 Jeremy Ward SB RC	1.50	4.00
100 Kevin Frederick SB RC	1.50	4.00
101 Josh Hancock SB RC	2.00	5.00
102 Allan Simpson SB RC	1.50	4.00
103 Mitch Wylie SB RC	1.50	4.00
104 Mark Corey SB RC	1.50	4.00
105 Victor Alvarez SB RC	1.50	4.00
106 Todd Donovan SB RC	1.50	4.00
107 Nelson Castro SB RC	1.50	4.00
108 Chris Booker SB RC	1.50	4.00
109 Corey Thurman SB RC	1.50	4.00
110 Kirk Saarloos SB RC	1.50	4.00
111 Michael Crudale SB RC	1.50	4.00
112 J.Simontacchi SB RC	1.50	4.00
113 Ron Calloway SB RC	1.50	4.00
114 Brandon Backe SB RC	2.00	5.00
115 Tom Shearn SB RC	1.50	4.00
116 Oliver Perez SB RC	2.00	5.00
117 Kyle Kane SB RC	1.50	4.00
118 Francis Beltran SB RC	1.50	4.00
119 So Taguchi SB RC	2.00	5.00
120 Doug Devore SB RC	1.50	4.00
121 Juan Brito SB RC	1.50	4.00
122 Cliff Bartosh SB RC	1.50	4.00
123 Eric Junge SB RC	1.50	4.00
124 Joe Orloski SB RC	1.50	4.00
125 Scotty Layfield SB RC	1.50	4.00
126 Jorge Sosa SB RC	2.00	5.00
127 Satoru Komiyama SB RC	1.50	4.00
128 Edwin Almonte SB RC	1.50	4.00
129 Takahito Nomura SB RC	1.50	4.00
130 John Ennis SB RC	1.50	4.00
131 Kazuhisa Ishii T2 AU RC	40.00	80.00
132 Ben Howard T2 AU RC	10.00	25.00
133 Aaron Cook T1 AU RC	8.00	20.00
134 Andy Machado T1 AU RC	6.00	15.00
135 Luis Ugueto T1 AU RC	6.00	15.00
136 Tyler Yates T1 AU RC	6.00	15.00
137 Rod. Rosario T1 AU RC	6.00	15.00
138 Jaime Cerda T1 AU RC	6.00	15.00
139 Luis Martinez T1 AU RC	6.00	15.00
140 Rene Reyes T1 AU RC	6.00	15.00
141 Eric Good T1 AU RC	6.00	15.00
142 Matt Thornton T2 AU RC	10.00	25.00
143 Steve Kent T1 AU RC	6.00	15.00
144 Jose Valverde T1 AU RC	6.00	15.00
145 A.Burnside T1 AU RC	6.00	15.00
146 Barry Bonds GF	10.00	25.00
147 Ken Griffey Jr. GF	6.00	15.00
148 Alex Rodriguez GF	6.00	15.00
149 Jason Giambi GF	1.50	4.00
150 Chipper Jones GF	4.00	10.00
151 Nomar Garciaparra GF	6.00	15.00
152 Mike Piazza GF	6.00	15.00
153 Sammy Sosa GF	4.00	10.00
154 Derek Jeter GF	10.00	25.00
155 Jeff Bagwell GF	4.00	10.00
156 Albert Pujols GF	6.00	15.00
157 Ichiro Suzuki GF	6.00	15.00
158 Randy Johnson GF	4.00	10.00
159 Frank Thomas GF	4.00	10.00
160 Greg Maddux GF	6.00	15.00
161 Jim Thome GF	4.00	10.00
162 Scott Rolen GF	4.00	10.00
163 Shawn Green GF	4.00	10.00
164 Vladimir Guerrero GF	4.00	10.00
165 Troy Glaus GF	4.00	10.00
166 Carlos Delgado GF	4.00	10.00
167 Luis Gonzalez GF	4.00	10.00
168 Roger Clemens GF	8.00	20.00
169 Todd Helton GF	4.00	10.00
170 Eric Chavez GF	4.00	10.00
171 Rafael Palmeiro GF	4.00	10.00
172 Pedro Martinez GF	4.00	10.00
173 Lance Berkman GF	4.00	10.00
174 Josh Beckett GF	4.00	10.00
175 Sean Burroughs GF	4.00	10.00

2002 Sweet Spot Game Face Blue Portraits

Randomly inserted in packs, this is a parallel to the Game Face subset. These cards can be differentiated from the regular card by their "blue" tint and were issued to a stated print run of 100 serial numbered sets.

*GAME FACE: .6X TO 1.5X BASIC CARDS

2002 Sweet Spot Legendary Signatures

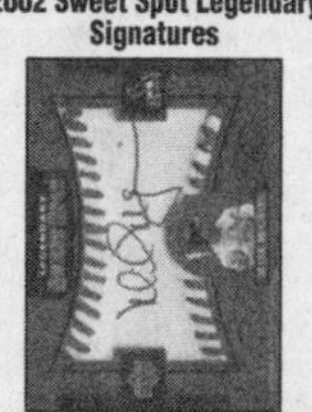

Inserted at stated odds of one in 72, these 16 cards feature signatures of retired greats. Since each player signed a different amount of cards we have notated that stated print run information next to their name in our checklist.

PRINT RUN INFO PROVIDED BY UD

Card	Low	High
AK Al Kaline/835 *	15.00	40.00
AT Alan Trammell/843 *	10.00	25.00
BP Boog Powell/944 *	12.50	30.00
BR Brooks Robinson	12.50	30.00
CR Cal Ripken/194 *	75.00	150.00
FJ Ferguson Jenkins/857 *	10.00	25.00
FL Fred Lynn/853 *	10.00	25.00
GP Gaylord Perry/921 *	10.00	25.00
JD Joe DiMaggio/50 *	500.00	800.00
KH Keith Hernandez/906 *	10.00	25.00
LA Luis Aparicio/485 *	10.00	25.00
MM Mark McGwire/90 *	300.00	500.00
PM Paul Molitor/852 *	10.00	25.00
RF Rollie Fingers/866 *	10.00	25.00
SG Steve Garvey/871 *	10.00	25.00
SK Sandy Koufax/485 *	175.00	300.00

2002 Sweet Spot Signatures

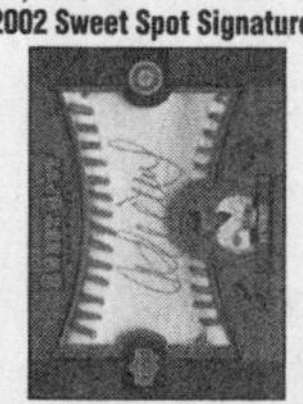

Inserted at stated odds of one in 72, these 25 cards feature signatures of some of today's leading players. Since each player signed a different amount of cards we have notated that stated print run information next to their name in our checklist. The Barry Bonds cards were not returned in time for inclusion in packs and those cards could be redeemed until October 23rd, 2005.

Card	Low	High
AD Adam Dunn/291	15.00	40.00
AJ Andruw Jones/291	15.00	40.00
AR Alex Rodriguez/291	100.00	175.00
BB Barry Bonds/380	100.00	200.00
BG Brian Giles/291	10.00	25.00
BZ Barry Zito/291	15.00	40.00
CD Carlos Delgado/291	10.00	25.00
FG Freddy Garcia/145	10.00	25.00
FT Frank Thomas/291	40.00	80.00
HB Hank Blalock/291	10.00	25.00
IS Ichiro Suzuki/145	400.00	500.00
JB Jeromy Burnitz/291	10.00	25.00
JG Jason Giambi/291	10.00	25.00
JT Jim Thome/291	20.00	50.00
KG Ken Griffey Jr./291	75.00	150.00
LB Lance Berkman/291	15.00	40.00
LG Luis Gonzalez/291	10.00	25.00
MPr Mark Prior/291	10.00	25.00
MS Mike Sweeney/291	10.00	25.00
RC Roger Clemens/194	100.00	175.00
RO Roy Oswalt/291	10.00	25.00
SB Sean Burroughs/291	10.00	25.00
SR Scott Rolen/291	15.00	40.00
SS Sammy Sosa/145	50.00	100.00
TG Tom Glavine/291	20.00	50.00

2002 Sweet Spot Swatches

Inserted at stated odds of one in 12, these 25 cards feature game-used swatches of the featured players.

Card	Low	High
AR Alex Rodriguez	6.00	15.00
BG Brian Giles	4.00	10.00
BW Bernie Williams	4.00	10.00
CJ Chipper Jones	4.00	10.00
DE Darin Erstad	4.00	10.00
EC Eric Chavez	4.00	10.00
FT Frank Thomas	4.00	10.00
GM Greg Maddux	6.00	15.00
IR Ivan Rodriguez	4.00	10.00
IS Ichiro Suzuki	20.00	50.00
JBa Jeff Bagwell	4.00	10.00
JBe Josh Beckett	4.00	10.00
JE Jim Edmonds	4.00	10.00
JGI Jason Giambi	4.00	10.00
JGo Juan Gonzalez	4.00	10.00
KG Ken Griffey Jr.	6.00	15.00
KI Kazuhisa Ishii	4.00	10.00
LG Luis Gonzalez	4.00	10.00
MP Mike Piazza	6.00	15.00
OV Omar Vizquel	4.00	10.00
PM Pedro Martinez	4.00	10.00
SB Sean Burroughs	4.00	10.00
SG Shawn Green	4.00	10.00
SR Scott Rolen	4.00	10.00
SS Sammy Sosa	4.00	10.00

2002 Sweet Spot USA Jerseys

Issued at a stated rate of one in 12, these 17 cards feature jersey swatches from players who represented the USA team in International competition.

Card	Low	High
AE Adam Everett	3.00	8.00
AK Adam Kennedy	3.00	8.00
BA Brent Abernathy	3.00	8.00
DB Dewon Brazelton	3.00	8.00
DG Danny Graves	3.00	8.00
DM Doug Mientkiewicz	3.00	8.00
EM Eric Munson	3.00	8.00
JG Jake Gautreau	3.00	8.00
JK Josh Karp	3.00	8.00
JM Joe Mauer	10.00	25.00
JR Jon Rauch	3.00	8.00
JW Justin Wayne	3.00	8.00
MP Mark Prior	4.00	10.00
MT Mark Teixeira	4.00	10.00
RO Roy Oswalt	3.00	8.00
TB Tagg Bozied	4.00	10.00
XN Xavier Nady	3.00	8.00

2003 Sweet Spot

This 231 card set was released in September, 2003. The set was issued in four card packs with an $10 SRP which were issued in 12 pack boxes which came 16 boxes to a case. Thirty of the first 130 cards were issued at a stated rate of one in four packs and we have notated those cards with an SP in our checklist. Cards number 131 through 190 are part of the Sweet Beginning subset and those cards were issued at a stated rate of one in three. Cards numbered 191 through 232 were issued at an overall stated rate of one in nine and those cards were issued in three different tiers. Card number 217 was not issued.

Card	Low	High
COMP.SET w/o SP's (100)	8.00	20.00
COMP.SET w/SP's (130)	60.00	120.00
COMMON CARD (1-130)	.20	.50
COMMON SP (1-130)	1.25	3.00
COMMON CARD (131-190)	1.25	3.00
131-190 PRINT RUN 2003 SERIAL #'d SETS		
COMMON P1 (191-232)	1.50	4.00
P1 191-232 PRINT RUN 500 SERIAL #'d SETS		
COMMON P2-P3 (191-232)	1.25	3.00
P2 191-232 PRINT RUN 1200 SERIAL #'d SETS		
P3 191-232 PRINT RUN 1430 SERIAL #'d SETS		
1 Darin Erstad	.20	.50
2 Garret Anderson	.20	.50

3 Tim Salmon .30 .75
4 Troy Glaus .20 .50
5 Luis Gonzalez .20 .50
6 Randy Johnson .50 1.25
7 Curt Schilling .20 .50
8 Lyle Overbay .20 .50
9 Andruw Jones SP 1.50 4.00
10 Gary Sheffield SP 1.25 3.00
11 Rafael Furcal SP 1.25 3.00
12 Greg Maddux SP 2.50 6.00
13 Chipper Jones SP 1.50 4.00
14 Tony Batista .20 .50
15 Rodrigo Lopez .20 .50
16 Jay Gibbons .20 .50
17 Jason Johnson .20 .50
18 Byung-Hyun Kim SP 1.25 3.00
19 Johnny Damon SP 1.50 4.00
20 Derek Lowe SP 1.25 3.00
21 Nomar Garciaparra SP 2.50 6.00
22 Pedro Martinez SP 1.50 4.00
23 Manny Ramirez SP 1.50 4.00
24 Mark Prior .30 .75
25 Kerry Wood .20 .50
26 Corey Patterson .20 .50
27 Sammy Sosa .50 1.25
28 Moises Alou .20 .50
29 Magglio Ordonez .20 .50
30 Frank Thomas .50 1.25
31 Paul Konerko .20 .50
32 Roberto Alomar .30 .75
33 Adam Dunn .20 .50
34 Austin Kearns .20 .50
35 Ryan Wagner RC .20 .50
36 Ken Griffey Jr. .75 2.00
37 Sean Casey .20 .50
38 Omar Vizquel .30 .75
39 C.C. Sabathia .20 .50
40 Jason Davis .20 .50
41 Travis Hafner .20 .50
42 Brandon Phillips .20 .50
43 Larry Walker .20 .50
44 Preston Wilson .20 .50
45 Jay Payton .20 .50
46 Todd Helton .30 .75
47 Carlos Pena .20 .50
48 Eric Munson .20 .50
49 Ivan Rodriguez .30 .75
50 Josh Beckett .20 .50
51 Alex Gonzalez .20 .50
52 Roy Oswalt .20 .50
53 Craig Biggio .30 .75
54 Jeff Bagwell .30 .75
55 Lance Berkman .20 .50
56 Mike Sweeney .20 .50
57 Carlos Beltran .20 .50
58 Brent Mayne .20 .50
59 Mike MacDougal .20 .50
60 Hideo Nomo .50 1.25
61 Dave Roberts .20 .50
62 Adrian Beltre .20 .50
63 Shawn Green .20 .50
64 Kazuhisa Ishii .20 .50
65 Rickey Henderson .50 1.25
66 Richie Sexson .20 .50
67 Torii Hunter .20 .50
68 Jacque Jones .20 .50
69 Joe Mays .20 .50
70 Corey Koskie .20 .50
71 A.J. Pierzynski .20 .50
72 Jose Vidro .20 .50
73 Vladimir Guerrero .50 1.25
74 Tom Glavine .30 .75
75 Mike Piazza .75 2.00
76 Jose Reyes .20 .50
77 Jae Weong Seo .20 .50
78 Jorge Posada SP 1.50 4.00
79 Mike Mussina SP 1.50 4.00
80 Robin Ventura SP 1.25 3.00
81 Mariano Rivera SP 1.50 4.00
82 Roger Clemens SP 3.00 8.00
83 Jason Giambi SP 1.25 3.00
84 Bernie Williams SP 1.50 4.00
85 Alfonso Soriano SP 1.25 3.00
86 Derek Jeter 1.25 3.00
87 Miguel Tejada .20 .50
88 Eric Chavez .20 .50
89 Tim Hudson .20 .50
90 Barry Zito .20 .50
91 Mark Mulder .20 .50
92 Erubiel Durazo .20 .50
93 Pat Burrell .20 .50
94 Jim Thome .30 .75
95 Bobby Abreu .20 .50
96 Brian Giles .20 .50
97 Reggie Sanders .20 .50
98 Jose Hernandez .20 .50
99 Ryan Klesko .20 .50
100 Sean Burroughs .20 .50
101 Edgardo Alfonzo SP 1.25 3.00
102 Rich Aurilia SP 1.25 3.00
103 Jose Cruz Jr. SP 1.25 3.00
104 Barry Bonds SP 4.00 10.00
105 Andres Galarraga SP 1.25 3.00
106 Mike Cameron .20 .50
107 Kazuhiro Sasaki .20 .50
108 Bret Boone .20 .50
109 Ichiro Suzuki 1.00 2.50
110 John Olerud .20 .50
111 J.D. Drew SP 1.25 3.00
112 Jim Edmonds SP 1.25 3.00
113 Scott Rolen SP 1.50 4.00
114 Matt Morris SP 1.25 3.00
115 Tino Martinez SP 1.50 4.00
116 Albert Pujols SP 3.00 8.00
117 Jared Sandberg .20 .50
118 Carl Crawford .20 .50
119 Rafael Palmeiro .30 .75
120 Hank Blalock .20 .50
121 Alex Rodriguez SP 2.50 6.00
122 Kevin Mench .20 .50
123 Juan Gonzalez .20 .50
124 Mark Teixeira .30 .75
125 Shannon Stewart .20 .50
126 Vernon Wells .20 .50
127 Josh Phelps .20 .50
128 Eric Hinske .20 .50
129 Orlando Hudson .20 .50
130 Carlos Delgado .20 .50
131 Juan Shiell SB RC 1.25 3.00
132 Kevin Tolar SB RC 1.25 3.00
133 Nathan Bland SB RC 1.25 3.00
134 Brent Hoard SB RC 1.25 3.00
135 Jon Pridie SB RC 1.25 3.00
136 Mike Ryan SB RC 1.25 3.00
137 Francisco Rosario SB RC 1.25 3.00
138 Runelvys Hernandez SB 1.25 3.00
139 Guillermo Quiroz SB RC 1.25 3.00
140 Chin-Hui Tsao SB 1.25 3.00
141 Rett Johnson SB RC 1.25 3.00
142 Colin Porter SB RC 1.25 3.00
143 Jose Castillo SB 1.25 3.00
144 Chris Waters SB RC 1.25 3.00
145 Jeremy Guthrie SB 1.25 3.00
146 Pedro Liriano SB 1.25 3.00
147 Joe Borowski SB 1.25 3.00
148 Felix Sanchez SB RC 1.25 3.00
149 Todd Wellemeyer SB RC 1.25 3.00
150 Gerald Laird SB 1.25 3.00
151 Brandon Webb SB RC 3.00 8.00
152 Tommy Whiteman SB 1.25 3.00
153 Carlos Rivera SB 1.25 3.00
154 Rick Roberts SB RC 1.25 3.00
155 Termel Sledge SB RC 1.25 3.00
156 Jeff Duncan SB RC 1.25 3.00
157 Craig Brazell SB RC 1.25 3.00
158 Bernie Castro SB RC 1.25 3.00
159 Cory Stewart SB RC 1.25 3.00
160 Brandon Villafuerte SB 1.25 3.00
161 Tommy Phelps SB 1.25 3.00
162 Josh Hall SB RC 1.25 3.00
163 Ryan Cameron SB RC 1.25 3.00
164 Garret Atkins SB 1.25 3.00
165 Brian Stokes SB RC 1.25 3.00
166 Rafael Betancourt SB RC 1.50 4.00
167 Jaime Cerda SB 1.25 3.00
168 D.J. Carrasco SB RC 1.25 3.00
169 Ian Ferguson SB RC 1.25 3.00
170 Jorge Cordova SB RC 1.25 3.00
171 Eric Munson SB 1.25 3.00
172 Nook Logan SB RC 1.50 4.00
173 Jeremy Bonderman SB RC 5.00 12.00
174 Kyle Snyder SB 1.25 3.00
175 Rich Harden SB 1.50 4.00
176 Kevin Ohme SB RC 1.25 3.00
177 Roger Deago SB RC 1.25 3.00
178 Marlon Byrd SB 1.25 3.00
179 Dontrelle Willis SB 1.50 4.00
180 Bobby Hill SB 1.25 3.00
181 Jesse Foppert SB 1.25 3.00
182 Andrew Good SB 1.25 3.00
183 Chase Utley SB 1.50 4.00
184 Bo Hart SB RC 1.25 3.00
185 Dan Haren SB RC 1.50 4.00
186 Tim Olson SB RC 1.25 3.00
187 Joe Thurston SB 1.25 3.00
188 Jason Anderson SB 1.25 3.00
189 Jason Gilfillan SB RC 1.25 3.00
190 Rickie Weeks SB RC 3.00 8.00
191 Hideki Matsui SB P1 RC 10.00 25.00
192 J.Contreras SB P3 RC 1.50 4.00
193 Willie Eyre SB P3 RC 1.25 3.00
194 Matt Bruback SB P3 RC 1.25 3.00
195 Heath Bell SB P3 RC 1.25 3.00
196 Lew Ford SB P3 RC 1.50 4.00
197 J.Griffiths SB P3 RC 1.25 3.00
198 O.Villarreal SB P1 RC 1.50 4.00
199 Fr. Cruceta SB P3 RC 1.50 4.00
200 Fern Cabrera SB P3 RC 1.25 3.00
201 Jhonny Peralta SB P3 1.50 4.00
202 Shane Bazzell SB P3 RC 1.25 3.00
203 B.Madritsch SB P1 RC 1.50 4.00
204 Phil Seibel SB P3 RC 1.25 3.00
205 J.Willingham SB P3 RC 2.00 5.00
206 Rob Hammock SB P1 RC 1.50 4.00
207 Al. Machado SB P3 RC 1.25 3.00
208 David Sanders SB P3 RC 1.25 3.00
209 Mike Neu SB P1 RC 1.50 4.00
210 Andrew Brown SB P3 RC 1.25 3.00
211 N. Robertson SB P3 RC 2.00 5.00
212 Miguel Ojeda SB P3 RC 1.25 3.00
213 Beau Kemp SB P3 RC 1.25 3.00
214 Aaron Looper SB P3 RC 1.25 3.00
215 Alf.Gonzalez SB P3 RC 1.25 3.00
216 Rich Fischer SB P1 RC 1.50 4.00
218 Jeremy Wedel SB P3 RC 1.25 3.00
219 Pr.Redman SB P3 RC 1.25 3.00
220 Mi.Hernandez SB P3 RC 1.25 3.00
221 Rocco Baldelli SB P1 1.50 4.00
222 Luis Ayala SB P3 RC 1.25 3.00
223 Arnaldo Munoz SB P3 RC 1.25 3.00
224 Wil.Ledezma SB P3 RC 1.25 3.00
225 Chris Capuano SB P3 RC 1.50 4.00
226 Aquilino Lopez SB P3 RC 1.25 3.00
227 Joe Valentine SB P1 RC 1.50 4.00
228 Matt Kata SB P2 RC 1.25 3.00
229 D.Markwell SB P2 RC 1.25 3.00
230 Clint Barmes SB P2 RC 1.25 3.00
231 Mike Nicolas SB P1 RC 1.50 4.00
232 Jon Leicester SB P2 RC 1.25 3.00

2003 Sweet Spot Sweet Beginnings 75

*SB 75: .6X TO 1.5X BASIC P1
*SB 75 MATSUI: .75X TO 1.5X BASIC MATSUI
*SB 75: .75X TO 2X BASIC P2-P3
STATED PRINT RUN 75 SERIAL #'d SETS
CARDS ARE NOT GAME-USED MATERIAL

2003 Sweet Spot Sweet Beginnings Game Used 25

STATED PRINT RUN 25 SERIAL #'d SETS
NO PRICING DUE TO SCARCITY
191 Hideki Matsui
193 Willie Eyre
194 Matt Bruback
195 Heath Bell
197 Jeremy Griffiths

2003 Sweet Spot Sweet Beginnings Game Used 10

STATED PRINT RUN 10 SERIAL #'d SETS
NO PRICING DUE TO SCARCITY
191 Hideki Matsui
202 Shane Bazzell
203 Bobby Madritsch
204 Phil Seibel
206 Robby Hammock
207 Alejandro Machado

2003 Sweet Spot Bat Barrels

STATED ODDS 1:6000
NO PRICING DUE TO SCARCITY

2003 Sweet Spot Instant Win Redemptions

Randomly inserted into packs, these cards enabled a lucky collector to receive a prize from the Upper Deck Company.

ONE OR MORE CARDS PER CASE
PRINT RUNS B/WN 1-350 COPIES PER
NO PRICING ON QTY OF 28 OR LESS
EXCHANGE DEADLINE 09/16/06

2003 Sweet Spot Patches

*PATCH 75: 1X TO 2.5X BASIC
PATCH 75 PRINT RUN 75 SERIAL #'d SETS
CUMULATIVE PATCHES ODDS 1:8
CARDS ARE NOT GAME-USED MATERIAL
AD1 Adam Dunn 3.00 8.00
AJ1 Andruw Jones 4.00 10.00
AP1 Albert Pujols 6.00 15.00
AR1 Alex Rodriguez 6.00 15.00
AS1 Alfonso Soriano 3.00 8.00
BB1 Barry Bonds 8.00 20.00
BW1 Bernie Williams 4.00 10.00
BZ1 Barry Zito 3.00 8.00
CD1 Carlos Delgado 3.00 8.00
CJ1 Chipper Jones 4.00 10.00
CP1 Corey Patterson 3.00 8.00
CS1 Curt Schilling 3.00 8.00
DE1 Darin Erstad 3.00 8.00
DJ1 Derek Jeter 8.00 20.00
GM1 Greg Maddux 6.00 15.00
GS1 Gary Sheffield 3.00 8.00
HN1 Hideo Nomo 4.00 10.00
IS1 Ichiro Suzuki 6.00 15.00
JB1 Jeff Bagwell 3.00 8.00
JE1 Jim Edmonds 3.00 8.00
JG1 Jason Giambi 3.00 8.00
JK1 Jeff Kent 3.00 8.00
JT1 Jim Thome 4.00 10.00
KG1 Ken Griffey Jr. 6.00 15.00
KI1 Kazuhisa Ishii 3.00 8.00
LB1 Lance Berkman 3.00 8.00
LG1 Luis Gonzalez 3.00 8.00
MA1 Mark Prior 4.00 10.00
MO1 Magglio Ordonez 3.00 8.00
MP1 Mike Piazza 6.00 15.00
MT1 Miguel Tejada 3.00 8.00
NG1 Nomar Garciaparra 6.00 15.00
PB1 Pat Burrell 3.00 8.00
PM1 Pedro Martinez 4.00 10.00
RC1 Roger Clemens 6.00 15.00
RJ1 Randy Johnson 4.00 10.00
SG1 Shawn Green 3.00 8.00
SS1 Sammy Sosa 4.00 10.00
TG1 Troy Glaus 3.00 8.00
TH1 Torii Hunter 3.00 8.00
TO1 Tom Glavine 4.00 10.00
VG1 Vladimir Guerrero 4.00 10.00

2003 Sweet Spot Patches Game Used 25

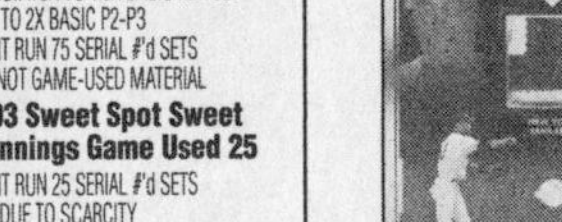

STATED PRINT RUN 25 SERIAL #'d SETS
NO PRICING DUE TO SCARCITY

2003 Sweet Spot Patches Game Used 10

STATED PRINT RUN 10 SERIAL #'d SETS
NO PRICING DUE TO SCARCITY

2003 Sweet Spot Signatures Black Ink

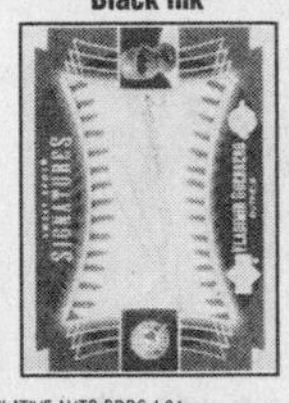

CUMULATIVE AUTO ODDS 1:24
SP PRINT RUNS PROVIDED BY UPPER DECK
SP'S ARE NOT SERIAL-NUMBERED
AD Adam Dunn 15.00 40.00
AK Austin Kearns 6.00 15.00
BH Bo Hart 6.00 15.00
BP Brandon Phillips 6.00 15.00
BW Brandon Webb 12.50 30.00
CR Cal Ripken SP/122 125.00 200.00
CS Curt Schilling 20.00 50.00
DH Drew Henson 6.00 15.00
DW Dontrelle Willis 10.00 25.00
GL Tom Glavine 20.00 50.00
GS Gary Sheffield 15.00 40.00
HA Travis Hafner 10.00 25.00
HB Hank Blalock 10.00 25.00
HM Hideki Matsui SP/147 175.00 300.00
JC Jose Contreras 15.00 40.00
JG Jason Giambi SP 20.00 50.00
JR Jose Reyes 10.00 25.00
JT Jim Thome 20.00 50.00
JW Jerome Williams 6.00 15.00
KGJ Ken Griffey Jr. 50.00 100.00
KGS Ken Griffey Sr. 10.00 25.00
KI Kazuhisa Ishii SP 20.00 50.00
LO Lyle Overbay 6.00 15.00
MP Mark Prior 12.50 30.00
MT Mark Teixeira 15.00 40.00
NG Nomar Garciaparra 50.00 100.00
NR Nolan Ryan SP 50.00 100.00
PB Pat Burrell 10.00 25.00
RC Roger Clemens SP/73 40.00 80.00
RO Roy Oswalt 10.00 25.00
TH Todd Helton SP/45 40.00 80.00
TR Troy Glaus 15.00 40.00
TS Tim Salmon 15.00 40.00
VG Vladimir Guerrero 30.00 60.00

2003 Sweet Spot Signatures Black Ink Holo-Foil

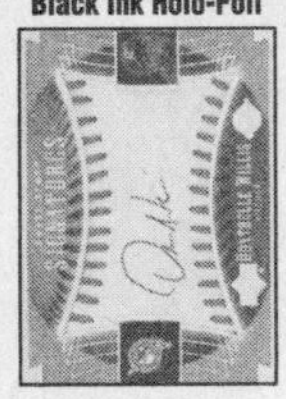

CUMULATIVE AUTO ODDS 1:24
STATED PRINT RUN 25 SERIAL #'d SETS
SOSA PRINT RUN 7 SERIAL #'d CARDS
NO PRICING DUE TO SCARCITY

2003 Sweet Spot Signatures Blue Ink

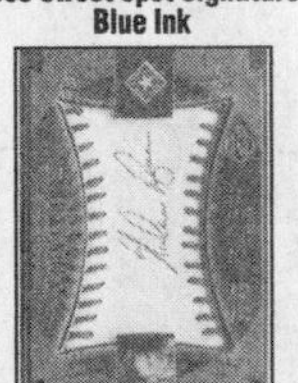

Rickie Weeks did not return his cards in time for inclusion in this product. Those cards were issued as exchange cards and were redeemable until September 16, 2006.

CUMULATIVE AUTO ODDS 1:24
STATED PRINT RUN 40 SERIAL #'d SETS
T.GWYNN CARD NOT SERIAL-NUMBERED
T.GWYNN AU IN FAR GREATER SUPPLY
AD Adam Dunn 30.00 60.00
AK Austin Kearns 10.00 25.00
BH Bo Hart 10.00 25.00
BP Brandon Phillips 10.00 25.00
BW Brandon Webb 15.00 40.00
CR Cal Ripken 150.00 250.00
CS Curt Schilling 40.00 80.00
DH Drew Henson 10.00 25.00
DW Dontrelle Willis 15.00 40.00
GL Tom Glavine 40.00 80.00
GS Gary Sheffield 30.00 60.00
HA Travis Hafner 15.00 40.00
HB Hank Blalock 15.00 40.00
HM Hideki Matsui 250.00 400.00
IS Ichiro Suzuki 400.00 600.00
JC Jose Contreras 20.00 50.00
JG Jason Giambi 15.00 40.00
JR Jose Reyes 15.00 40.00
JT Jim Thome 40.00 80.00
JW Jerome Williams 10.00 25.00
KGJ Ken Griffey Jr. 75.00 150.00
KGS Ken Griffey Sr. 15.00 40.00
KI Kazuhisa Ishii 15.00 40.00
LO Lyle Overbay 10.00 25.00
MM Mickey Mantle/7
MP Mark Prior 20.00 50.00
MT Mark Teixeira 30.00 60.00
NG Nomar Garciaparra 60.00 120.00
NR Nolan Ryan 60.00 120.00
PB Pat Burrell 15.00 40.00
RC Roger Clemens 125.00 200.00
RO Roy Oswalt 15.00 40.00
RW Rickie Weeks/100 40.00 80.00
SS Sammy Sosa 50.00 120.00
TG Tony Gwynn NNO 20.00 50.00
TH Todd Helton 30.00 60.00
TR Troy Glaus 30.00 60.00
TS Tim Salmon 15.00 40.00
TW Ted Williams/9
VG Vladimir Guerrero 40.00 80.00

2003 Sweet Spot Signatures Red Ink

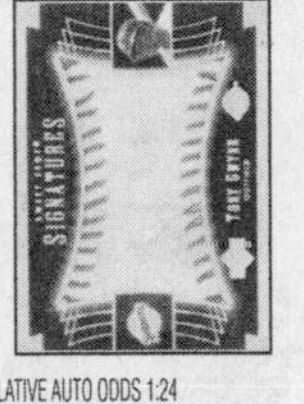

CUMULATIVE AUTO ODDS 1:24
PRINT RUNS B/WN 9-35 COPIES PER
GWYNN CARD NOT SERIAL-NUMBERED
NO PRICING ON QTY OF 10 OR LESS

2003 Sweet Spot Signatures Barrel

CUMULATIVE AUTO ODDS 1:24
PRINT RUNS B/WN 49-445 COPIES PER
CARDS ARE NOT GAME-USED MATERIAL
AD Adam Dunn/345 15.00 40.00
CR Cal Ripken/149 125.00 200.00
HB Hank Blalock/420 15.00 40.00
HM Hideki Matsui/124 250.00 400.00
JT Jim Thome/345 30.00 60.00
KG Ken Griffey Jr./295 60.00 120.00
NR Nolan Ryan/445 75.00 150.00
PB Pat Burrell/345 15.00 40.00
RC Roger Clemens/49 150.00 250.00
TG Tom Glavine/345 30.00 60.00
TR Troy Glaus/345 20.00 50.00

2003 Sweet Spot Swatches

SP INFO PROVIDED BY UPPER DECK
SP'S ARE NOT SERIAL-NUMBERED
*SWATCH 75: .6X TO 1.5X BASIC
*SWATCH 75: .5X TO 1.2X BASIC SP
*SWATCH 75: .4X TO 1X BASIC SP p/r 75-100
*SWATCH 75: .5X TO 1.2X BASIC
SWATCH 75 PRINT RUN 75 #'d SETS
CUMULATIVE SWATCHES ODDS 1:20
AJ Andruw Jones 3.00 8.00
AK Austin Kearns 2.00 5.00
AP Albert Pujols 8.00 20.00
AR Alex Rodriguez 4.00 10.00
AS Alfonso Soriano SP/81 4.00 10.00
BW Bernie Williams SP 6.00 15.00
BZ Barry Zito SP 4.00 10.00
CJ Chipper Jones 4.00 10.00
CS Curt Schilling 2.00 5.00
FT Frank Thomas 3.00 8.00
GM Greg Maddux 4.00 10.00
GS Gary Sheffield SP 4.00 10.00
HM Hideki Matsui SP/150 15.00 40.00
IS Ichiro Suzuki 10.00 25.00
JG Jason Giambi 2.00 5.00
JT Jim Thome 3.00 8.00
KG Ken Griffey Jr. 6.00 15.00
LG Luis Gonzalez 2.00 5.00
MM M.Mantle Pants UER SP/100 75.00 150.00
Card erroneously states Game Used Jersey
MP Mike Piazza 4.00 10.00
MP Mark Prior SP 6.00 15.00
MT Miguel Tejada 2.00 5.00
NG Nomar Garciaparra SP/75
PB Pat Burrell 2.00 5.00
RA Roberto Alomar SP 6.00 15.00
RC Roger Clemens 6.00 15.00
RJ Randy Johnson SP 6.00 15.00
RO Roy Oswalt 2.00 5.00
SS Sammy Sosa 3.00 8.00
TG Troy Glaus 2.00 5.00
TG Tom Glavine SP 6.00 15.00
TH Torii Hunter 2.00 5.00
TW Ted Williams Pants SP/100 50.00 100.00
VG Vladimir Guerrero 3.00 8.00

2004 Sweet Spot

This 262 card set was released in October, 2004. The set was issued in three card packs with an $10 SRP which came 12 packs to a box and 10 boxes to a case. The first 90 cards in this set feature veterans while cards 91 through 170 and 261-262 feature Rookie Cards. Those cards were issued at a stated rate of one in two. Cards numbered 91 through 170 and 261-262 were issued to a stated print run of 799 serial numnbered sets. Cards numbered 171 through 205 comprise a swinging for the fences subset and cards numbered 206 through 230 are season leader subset cards. Those cards were issued to a stated print run of 399 serial numbered sets. Cards numbered 231 through 250 is a pennant drive subset and those cards were issued to a stated print run of 299 serial numbered sets. Cards numbered 251 through 260 comprise a diamond duo subset and those cards were issued to a stated print run of 199 serial numbered sets.

COMP.SET w/o SP's (90) 8.00 20.00
COMMON CARD (1-90) .20 .50
COMMON (91-170/261-262) .60 1.50
91-170/261-262 STATED ODDS 1:12
91-170/261-262 PRINT RUN 799 #'d SETS
COMMON CARD (171-230) .75 2.00
171-230 PRINT RUN 399 SERIAL #'d SETS
COMMON CARD (231-250) .75 2.00
231-250 PRINT RUN 299 SERIAL #'d SETS
COMMON CARD (251-260) 1.00 2.50
251-260 PRINT RUN 199 SERIAL #'d SETS
171-260/Ltd 10/W99 OVERALL ODDS 1:12
OVERALL PLATES ODDS 1:360 HOBBY
PLATES PRINT RUN 1 SET PER COLOR
BLACK-CYAN-MAGENTA-YELLOW ISSUED
NO PLATES PRICING DUE TO SCARCITY
1 Albert Pujols 1.25 3.00
2 Alex Rodriguez .75 2.00
3 Alfonso Soriano .20 .50
4 Andruw Jones .20 .50
5 Andy Pettitte .30 .75
6 Aubrey Huff .20 .50
7 Austin Kearns .20 .50
8 Barry Zito .20 .50
9 Bobby Abreu .20 .50
10 Brandon Webb .20 .50
11 Bret Boone .20 .50
12 Brian Giles .20 .50
13 C.C. Sabathia .30 .75
14 Carlos Beltran .20 .50
15 Carlos Delgado .20 .50
16 Chipper Jones .50 1.25
17 Cliff Floyd .20 .50
18 Curt Schilling .30 .75
19 Delmon Young .30 .75
20 Derek Jeter 1.25 3.00
21 Dontrelle Willis .20 .50
22 Edgar Martinez .30 .75
23 Edgar Renteria .20 .50
24 Eric Chavez .20 .50
25 Eric Gagne .20 .50
26 Frank Thomas .50 1.25
27 Garret Anderson .20 .50
28 Gary Sheffield .20 .50
29 Geoff Jenkins .20 .50
30 Greg Maddux .75 2.00
31 Hank Blalock .20 .50
32 Hideo Nomo .50 1.25
33 Ichiro Suzuki .75 2.00
34 Ivan Rodriguez .30 .75
35 Jacque Jones .20 .50
36 Jason Giambi .20 .50
37 Jason Schmidt .20 .50
38 Javier Vazquez .20 .50
39 Javy Lopez .20 .50
40 Jeff Bagwell .30 .75
41 Jim Edmonds .30 .75
42 Jim Thome .30 .75
43 Joe Mauer .50 1.25
44 John Smoltz .50 1.25
45 Jose Cruz Jr. .20 .50
46 Jose Reyes .30 .75
47 Jose Vidro .20 .50
48 Josh Beckett .20 .50
49 Ken Griffey Jr. .75 2.00
50 Kerry Wood .20 .50
51 Kevin Brown .20 .50
52 Larry Walker .30 .75
53 Magglio Ordonez .30 .75
54 Manny Ramirez .50 1.25
55 Mark Mulder .20 .50
56 Mark Prior .30 .75
57 Mark Teixeira .50 1.25
58 Miguel Cabrera .50 1.25
59 Miguel Tejada .30 .75
60 Mike Lowell .20 .50
61 Mike Mussina .30 .75
62 Mike Piazza .50 1.25
63 Nomar Garciaparra .50 1.25
64 Orlando Cabrera .20 .50
65 Pat Burrell .20 .50
66 Pedro Martinez .30 .75
67 Phil Nevin .20 .50
68 Preston Wilson .20 .50
69 Rafael Furcal .20 .50
70 Rafael Palmeiro .30 .75
71 Randy Johnson .50 1.25
72 Craig Wilson .20 .50
73 Rich Harden .20 .50
74 Richie Sexson .20 .50
75 Rickie Weeks .20 .50
76 Rocco Baldelli .20 .50
77 Roger Clemens .60 1.50
78 Roy Halladay .50 1.25
79 Roy Oswalt .30 .75
80 Ryan Klesko .20 .50
81 Sammy Sosa .50 1.25
82 Scott Podsednik .20 .50
83 Scott Rolen .30 .75
84 Shawn Green .20 .50
85 Tim Hudson .30 .75
86 Todd Helton .30 .75
87 Torii Hunter .20 .50
88 Troy Glaus .20 .50
89 Vernon Wells .20 .50
90 Vladimir Guerrero .50 1.25
91 Aarom Baldiris SB RC .75 2.00
92 Akinori Otsuka SB RC .75 2.00
93 Andres Blanco SB RC .75 2.00
94 Angel Chavez SB RC .75 2.00
95 Brian Dallimore SB RC .75 2.00
96 Carlos Hines SB RC .75 2.00
97 Carlos Vasquez SB RC .75 2.00
98 Casey Daigle SB RC .75 2.00
99 Chad Bentz SB RC .75 2.00
100 Chris Aguila SB RC .75 2.00
101 Chris Oxspring SB RC .75 2.00
102 Chris Saenz SB RC .75 2.00
103 Chris Shelton SB RC .75 2.00
104 Colby Miller SB RC .75 2.00
105 Dave Crouthers SB RC .75 2.00
106 David Aardsma SB RC .75 2.00
107 Dennis Sarfate SB RC .75 2.00
108 Donnie Kelly SB RC 1.25 3.00
109 Eddy Rodriguez SB RC .75 2.00
110 Eduardo Villacis SB RC .75 2.00
111 Edwin Moreno SB RC .75 2.00
112 Enemencio Pacheco SB RC .75 2.00
113 Fernando Nieve SB RC .75 2.00
114 Franklyn Gracesqui SB RC .75 2.00
115 Freddy Guzman SB RC .75 2.00
116 Greg Dobbs SB RC .75 2.00
117 Hector Gimenez SB RC .75 2.00
118 Ian Snell SB RC .75 2.00
119 Ivan Ochoa SB RC .75 2.00
120 Jake Woods SB RC .75 2.00
121 Jamie Brown SB RC .75 2.00
122 Jason Bartlett SB RC 2.50 6.00
123 Jason Frasor SB RC .75 2.00
124 Jeff Bennett SB RC .75 2.00
125 Jerome Gamble SB RC .75 2.00
126 Jerry Gil SB RC .75 2.00
127 Brandon Medders SB RC .75 2.00
128 Ryan Meaux SB RC .75 2.00
129 John Gall SB RC .75 2.00
130 Jorge Sequea SB RC .75 2.00
131 Jorge Vasquez SB RC .75 2.00
132 Jose Capellan SB RC .75 2.00
133 Josh Labandeira SB RC .75 2.00
134 Justin Germano SB RC .75 2.00
135 Justin Hampson SB RC .75 2.00
136 Justin Huisman SB RC .75 2.00
137 Justin Knoedler SB RC .75 2.00
138 Justin Leone SB RC .75 2.00
139 Kazuhito Tadano SB RC .75 2.00
140 Kazuo Matsui SB RC 1.25 3.00
141 Kevin Cave SB RC .75 2.00
142 Lincoln Holdzkom SB RC .75 2.00
143 Lino Urdaneta SB RC .75 2.00
144 Luis A. Gonzalez SB RC .75 2.00
145 Mariano Gomez SB RC .75 2.00
146 Merkin Valdez SB RC .75 2.00
147 Michael Vento SB RC .75 2.00
148 Michael Wuertz SB RC .75 2.00
149 Mike Gosling SB RC .75 2.00
150 Mike Johnston SB RC .75 2.00
151 Mike Rouse SB RC .75 2.00
152 Nick Regilio SB RC .75 2.00
153 Onil Joseph SB RC .75 2.00
154 Orlando Rodriguez SB RC .75 2.00
155 Ramon Ramirez SB RC .75 2.00
156 Renyel Pinto SB RC .75 2.00
157 Roberto Novoa SB RC .75 2.00
158 Roman Colon SB RC .75 2.00
159 Ronald Belisario SB RC .75 2.00
160 Ronny Cedeno SB RC .75 2.00
161 Rusty Tucker SB RC .75 2.00
162 Ryan Wing SB RC .75 2.00
163 Scott Dohmann SB RC .75 2.00
164 Scott Proctor SB RC .75 2.00
165 Sean Henn SB RC .75 2.00
166 Shawn Camp SB RC .75 2.00
167 Shawn Hill SB RC .75 2.00
168 Shingo Takatsu SB RC .75 2.00
169 Tim Hamulack SB RC .75 2.00
170 William Bergolla SB RC .75 2.00
171 Adam Dunn SF 1.25 3.00
172 Albert Pujols SF 5.00 12.00
173 Alex Rodriguez SF 3.00 8.00
174 Alfonso Soriano SF .75 2.00
175 Andruw Jones SF .75 2.00
176 Bret Boone SF .75 2.00
177 Brian Giles SF .75 2.00
178 Carlos Delgado SF .75 2.00
179 Derrek Lee SF .75 2.00
180 Eric Chavez SF .75 2.00
181 Frank Thomas SF 2.00 5.00
182 Garret Anderson SF .75 2.00
183 Gary Sheffield SF .75 2.00
184 Hank Blalock SF .75 2.00
185 Jason Giambi SF .75 2.00
186 Javy Lopez SF .75 2.00
187 Jeff Bagwell SF 1.25 3.00
188 Jim Edmonds SF 1.25 3.00
189 Jim Thome SF 1.25 3.00
190 Ken Griffey Jr. SF 3.00 8.00
191 Lance Berkman SF 1.25 3.00
192 Magglio Ordonez SF 1.25 3.00
193 Manny Ramirez SF 2.00 5.00
194 Mike Lowell SF .75 2.00
195 Mike Piazza SF 2.00 5.00
196 Preston Wilson SF .75 2.00
197 Rafael Palmeiro SF 1.25 3.00
198 Richie Sexson SF .75 2.00
199 Sammy Sosa SF 2.00 5.00
200 Scott Rolen SF 1.25 3.00
201 Shawn Green SF .75 2.00
202 Todd Helton SF 1.25 3.00
203 Troy Glaus SF .75 2.00
204 Vernon Wells SF .75 2.00
205 Vladimir Guerrero SF 2.00 5.00
206 Garret Anderson 2.00 5.00
Vladimir Guerrero SL
207 Luis Gonzalez .75 2.00
Richie Sexson SL
208 Andruw Jones .75 2.00
Chipper Jones SL
209 Javy Lopez 1.25 3.00

Miguel Tejada SL
210 Manny Ramirez 2.00 5.00
David Ortiz SL
211 Derrek Lee 2.00 5.00
Sammy Sosa SL
212 Frank Thomas 1.25 3.00
Magglio Ordonez SL
213 Austin Kearns 3.00 8.00
Ken Griffey Jr. SL
214 Preston Wilson 1.25 3.00
Todd Helton SL
215 Dmitri Young 1.25 3.00
Ivan Rodriguez SL
216 Miguel Cabrera 2.00 5.00
Mike Lowell SL
217 Jeff Bagwell 1.25 3.00
Lance Berkman SL
218 Lyle Overbay .75 2.00
Geoff Jenkins SL
219 Adrian Beltre .75 2.00
Shawn Green SL
220 Jacque Jones .75 2.00
Torii Hunter SL
221 Jose Vidro .75 2.00
Nick Johnson SL
222 Kazuo Matsui 2.00 5.00
Mike Piazza SL
223 Alex Rodriguez 3.00 8.00
Jason Giambi SL
224 Eric Chavez .75 2.00
Jermaine Dye SL
225 Jim Thome 1.25 3.00
Pat Burrell SL
226 Brian Giles .75 2.00
Phil Nevin SL
227 Bret Boone 3.00 8.00
Ichiro Suzuki SL
228 Albert Pujols 5.00 12.00
Scott Rolen SL
229 Hank Blalock 2.00 5.00
Mark Teixeira SL
230 Carlos Delgado .75 2.00
Vernon Wells SL
231 Albert Pujols PD 5.00 12.00
232 Alex Rodriguez PD 3.00 8.00
233 Chipper Jones PD 2.00 5.00
234 Craig Biggio PD 1.25 3.00
235 Curt Schilling PD 1.25 3.00
236 Derek Jeter PD 5.00 12.00
237 Ivan Rodriguez PD 1.25 3.00
238 Jeff Bagwell PD 1.25 3.00
239 Jim Edmonds PD 1.25 3.00
240 Jim Thome PD 1.25 3.00
241 Josh Beckett PD 1.25 3.00
242 Kerry Wood PD .75 2.00
243 Kevin Brown PD .75 2.00
244 Mark Prior PD 1.25 3.00
245 Miguel Tejada PD 1.25 3.00
246 Mike Mussina PD 1.25 3.00
247 Nomar Garciaparra PD 2.00 5.00
248 Pedro Martinez PD 1.25 3.00
249 Randy Johnson PD 2.00 5.00
250 Roger Clemens PD 2.50 6.00
251 Alex Rodriguez 6.00 15.00
Derek Jeter DD
252 Alfonso Soriano 1.00 2.50
Hank Blalock DD
253 Bobby Abreu 1.00 2.50
Pat Burrell DD
254 Edgar Renteria 1.50 4.00
Scott Rolen DD
255 Garret Anderson 2.50 6.00
Vladimir Guerrero DD
256 Jeff Bagwell 1.50 4.00
Jeff Kent DD
257 Jose Reyes 1.50 4.00
Kazuo Matsui DD
258 Khalil Greene 1.50 4.00
Sean Burroughs DD
259 Marcus Giles 1.00 2.50
Rafael Furcal DD
260 Manny Ramirez 2.50 6.00
Johnny Damon DD
261 Tim Bausher SB RC .60 1.50
262 Tim Bittner SB RC .60 1.50

2004 Sweet Spot Limited

Basic 171-260/Ltd 10/Wood 99 ODDS 1:12
STATED PRINT RUN 10 SERIAL #'d SETS
NO PRICING DUE TO SCARCITY

2004 Sweet Spot Wood

*WOOD 91-170/261-262: .6X TO 1.5X BASIC
*WOOD 171-230: .6X TO 1.5X BASIC
*WOOD 231-250: .6X TO 1.5X BASIC
*WOOD 251-260: .5X TO 1.2X BASIC
Wood 99/Basic 171-260/Ltd 10 ODDS 1:12
STATED PRINT RUN 99 SERIAL #'d SETS
OVERALL PLATES ODDS 1:360 HOBBY
PLATES PRINT RUN 1 SET PER COLOR
BLACK-CYAN-MAGENTA-YELLOW ISSUED
NO PLATES PRICING DUE TO SCARCITY

2004 Sweet Spot Diamond Champs Jersey

STATED PRINT RUN 150 SERIAL #'d SETS
PATCH PRINT RUN 10 SERIAL #'d SETS
A-ROD PATCH PRINT RUN 1 #'d CARD
NO PATCH PRICING DUE TO SCARCITY
OVERALL GAME-USED ODDS 1:6
AP Albert Pujols 8.00 20.00
AR Alex Rodriguez Yanks 6.00 15.00
BZ Barry Zito 3.00 8.00
CJ Chipper Jones 4.00 10.00
CS Curt Schilling 6.00 15.00
DJ Derek Jeter 10.00 25.00
EG Eric Gagne 3.00 8.00
GA Garret Anderson 3.00 8.00
GM Greg Maddux 6.00 15.00
IR Ivan Rodriguez 4.00 10.00
IS Ichiro Suzuki 12.50 30.00
JB Josh Beckett 3.00 8.00
KG Ken Griffey Jr. 6.00 15.00
MP Mike Piazza 6.00 15.00
MT Miguel Tejada 3.00 8.00
PE Andy Pettitte 4.00 10.00
PM Pedro Martinez 4.00 10.00
RC Roger Clemens 6.00 15.00
RH Roy Halladay 3.00 8.00
RJ Randy Johnson 4.00 10.00

2004 Sweet Spot Home Run Heroes Jersey

STATED PRINT RUN 199 SERIAL #'d SETS
*1-2 COLOR PATCH: .75X TO 2X BASIC
*3-4 COLOR PATCH: 1.25X TO 3X BASIC
PATCH PRINT RUN 55 SERIAL #'d SETS
A-ROD PATCH PRINT RUN 10 #'d CARDS
NO A-ROD PATCH PRICING AVAILABLE
OVERALL GAME-USED ODDS 1:6
AB Adrian Beltre 3.00 8.00
AD Adam Dunn 3.00 8.00
AJ Andruw Jones 4.00 10.00
AP Albert Pujols 8.00 20.00
AR A.Rod Yanks Bat Up 6.00 15.00
AR1 A.Rod Yanks Swing 6.00 15.00
AS Alfonso Soriano 3.00 8.00
BB Bret Boone 3.00 8.00
BG Brian Giles 3.00 8.00
BW Bernie Williams 4.00 10.00
CB Carlos Beltran 3.00 8.00
CD Carlos Delgado 3.00 8.00
CJ Chipper Jones 4.00 10.00
DJ Derek Jeter 10.00 25.00
DL Derrek Lee 4.00 10.00
DO David Ortiz 4.00 10.00
EC Eric Chavez 3.00 8.00
FM Fred McGriff 4.00 10.00
FT Frank Thomas 4.00 10.00
GA Garret Anderson 3.00 8.00
GS Gary Sheffield 3.00 8.00
HA Travis Hafner 3.00 8.00
HB Hank Blalock 3.00 8.00
HM Hideki Matsui 12.50 30.00
IR Ivan Rodriguez 4.00 10.00
JB Jeff Bagwell 4.00 10.00
JD J.D. Drew 3.00 8.00
JE Jim Edmonds 3.00 8.00
JG Jason Giambi 3.00 8.00
JK Jeff Kent 3.00 8.00
JM Joe Mauer 4.00 10.00
JP Jorge Posada 4.00 10.00
JT Jim Thome 4.00 10.00
KG Ken Griffey Jr. 6.00 15.00
KG1 Ken Griffey Jr. 6.00 15.00
LB Lance Berkman 3.00 8.00
LG Luis Gonzalez 3.00 8.00
MC Miguel Cabrera 4.00 10.00
ML Mike Lowell 3.00 8.00
MO Magglio Ordonez 3.00 8.00
MP Mike Piazza 6.00 15.00
MR Manny Ramirez 4.00 10.00
MT Mark Teixeira 4.00 10.00
PB Pat Burrell 3.00 8.00
PW Preston Wilson 3.00 8.00
RP Rafael Palmeiro 4.00 10.00
RS Richie Sexson 3.00 8.00
SG Shawn Green 3.00 8.00
SR Scott Rolen 4.00 10.00
SS Sammy Sosa 4.00 10.00
TE Miguel Tejada 3.00 8.00
TG Troy Glaus 3.00 8.00
TH Todd Helton 4.00 10.00
VG Vladimir Guerrero 4.00 10.00
VW Vernon Wells 3.00 8.00

2004 Sweet Spot Marquee Attractions Jersey

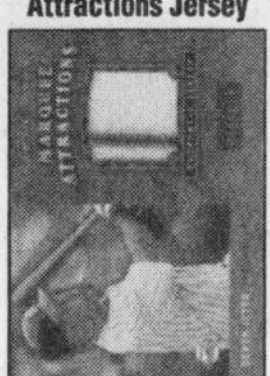

STATED PRINT RUN 199 SERIAL #'d SETS
*1-2 COLOR PATCH: 1X TO 2.5X BASIC
*3-4 COLOR PATCH: 1.5X TO 4X BASIC
*5+ COLOR PATCH: 2X TO 5X BASIC
PATCH PRINT RUN 35 SERIAL #'d SETS
A-ROD PATCH PRINT RUN 5 #'d CARDS
NO A-ROD PATCH PRICING AVAILABLE
OVERALL GAME-USED ODDS 1:6
AJ Andruw Jones 4.00 10.00
AP Albert Pujols 8.00 20.00
AR Alex Rodriguez Yanks 6.00 15.00
BG Brian Giles 3.00 8.00
BS Ben Sheets 3.00 8.00
CD Carlos Delgado 3.00 8.00
CS Curt Schilling 4.00 10.00
DJ Derek Jeter 10.00 25.00
EC Eric Chavez 3.00 8.00
EG Eric Gagne 3.00 8.00
FT Frank Thomas 4.00 10.00
HB Hank Blalock 3.00 8.00
HU Torii Hunter 3.00 8.00
IR Ivan Rodriguez 4.00 10.00
IS Ichiro Suzuki 12.50 30.00
JS Jason Schmidt 3.00 8.00
JT Jim Thome 4.00 10.00
KG Ken Griffey Jr. 6.00 15.00
MC Miguel Cabrera 4.00 10.00
MP Mark Prior 4.00 10.00
MS Mike Sweeney 3.00 8.00
MT Miguel Tejada 3.00 8.00
PI Mike Piazza 6.00 15.00
RC Roger Clemens 6.00 15.00
RJ Randy Johnson 4.00 10.00
TH Todd Helton 4.00 10.00
VG Vladimir Guerrero 4.00 10.00

2004 Sweet Spot Signatures

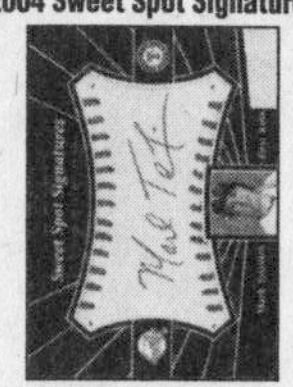

TIER 4 PRINT RUNS 201 COPIES AND UP
TIER 3 PRINT RUNS B/WN 101-200 PER
TIER 2 PRINT RUNS B/WN 51-100 PER
TIER 1 PRINT RUNS B/WN 27-34 PER
TIER 1 PRINT RUNS PROVIDED BY UD
OVERALL AU ODDS 1:12
TIER INFO PROVIDED BY UPPER DECK
CARDS ARE NOT SERIAL-NUMBERED
BASIC SIGNATURES FEATURE RED STITCH
EXCHANGE DEADLINE 11/22/07
AB Angel Berroa T4 6.00 15.00
AD Adam Dunn T4 6.00 15.00
AK Austin Kearns T4 6.00 15.00
AP Albert Pujols T3 150.00 250.00
AR Alex Rodriguez T1/27 *
BB Bret Boone T4 10.00 25.00
BE Josh Beckett T3 15.00 40.00
BG Brian Giles T4 6.00 15.00
BS Ben Sheets T4 6.00 15.00
BW Brandon Webb T4 6.00 15.00
CB Carlos Beltran T3 10.00 25.00
CL Carlos Lee T4 6.00 15.00
CZ Carlos Zambrano T3 15.00 40.00
DJ Derek Jeter T2 125.00 200.00
DL Derrek Lee T4 10.00 25.00
DM Don Mattingly T4 30.00 60.00
DW Dontrelle Willis T4 10.00 25.00
DY Delmon Young T4 10.00 25.00
EC Eric Chavez T4 6.00 15.00
EL Esteban Loaiza T4 6.00 15.00
EM Edgar Martinez T3 12.50 30.00
FT Frank Thomas T3 30.00 60.00
GA Garret Anderson T4 6.00 15.00
GJ Geoff Jenkins T4 6.00 15.00
GL Tom Glavine T2 20.00 50.00
GS Gary Sheffield T4 15.00 40.00
HA Roy Halladay T3 50.00 100.00
HB Hank Blalock T4 6.00 15.00
HI Richard Hidalgo T4 6.00 15.00
HO Trevor Hoffman T4 6.00 15.00
HU Torii Hunter T4 6.00 15.00
IS Ichiro Suzuki T4 200.00 400.00
JD J.D. Drew T3 10.00 25.00
JG Juan Gonzalez T2 12.50 30.00
JJ Jacque Jones T4 6.00 15.00
JM Joe Mauer T4 30.00 60.00
JR Jose Reyes T4 12.50 30.00
JS Jason Schmidt T4 6.00 15.00
JV Javier Vazquez T4 6.00 15.00
KG Ken Griffey Jr. T4 40.00 80.00
KW Kerry Wood T4 6.00 15.00
LG Luis Gonzalez T2 12.50 30.00
LO Mike Lowell T3 10.00 25.00
MA Mike Marshall T1/34 *
MC Miguel Cabrera T4 10.00 25.00
MG Marcus Giles T4 6.00 15.00
ML Mike Lieberthal T4 6.00 15.00
MM Mike Mussina T3 15.00 40.00
MP Mark Prior T3 15.00 40.00
MR Manny Ramirez T2 40.00 80.00
MT Mark Teixeira T4 20.00 50.00
MU Mark Mulder T4 6.00 15.00
NG Nomar Garciaparra T4 30.00 60.00
OP Odalis Perez T4 6.00 15.00
PB Pat Burrell T2 12.50 30.00
PI Mike Piazza T2 60.00 120.00
RB Rocco Baldelli T2 12.50 30.00
RC Roger Clemens T2 75.00 150.00
RH Rich Harden T4 6.00 15.00
RK Ryan Klesko T4 6.00 15.00
RO Roy Oswalt T4 12.50 30.00
RS Ryne Sandberg T2 40.00 80.00
RW Randy Wolf T4 6.00 15.00
SA Johan Santana T4 12.50 30.00
SB Sean Burroughs T4 6.00 15.00
SM John Smoltz T3 30.00 60.00
SP Scott Podsednik T4 10.00 25.00
SR Scott Rolen T4 20.00 50.00
TE Miguel Tejada T3 15.00 40.00
TG Tony Gwynn T3 30.00 60.00
TH Todd Helton T2 20.00 50.00
TI Tim Hudson T2 20.00 50.00
TS Tom Seaver T3 30.00 60.00
VG Vladimir Guerrero T2 30.00 60.00
VW Vernon Wells T1/30 *
WA Billy Wagner T4 10.00 25.00
WC Will Clark T4 10.00 25.00
WE Rickie Weeks T4 6.00 15.00

2004 Sweet Spot Signatures Black Stitch

BLK/RED-BLUE/DUAL/HIST AU ODDS 1:180
STATED PRINT RUN 1 SERIAL #'d SET
NO PRICING DUE TO SCARCITY
EXCHANGE DEADLINE 11/22/07

2004 Sweet Spot Signatures Red-Blue Stitch

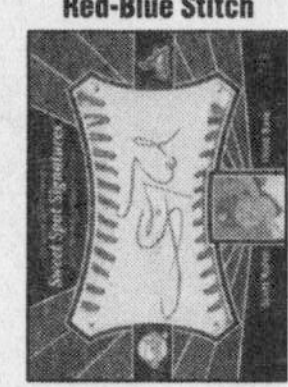

*R/B p/r 40-55: .6X TO 1.5X TIER 4
*R/B p/r 40-55: .5X TO 1.2X TIER 3
*R/B p/r 40-55: .5X TO 1.2X TIER 2
*R/B p/r 20-35: .6X TO 1.5X TIER 3
*R/B p/r 20-35: .6X TO 1.5X TIER 2
*R/B p/r 15: .75X TO 2X TIER 4
BLK/RED-BLUE/DUAL/HIST AU ODDS 1:180
PRINT RUNS B/WN 10-55 COPIES PER
NO PRICING ON QTY OF 10 OR LESS
EXCHANGE DEADLINE 11/22/07
AP Albert Pujols/45 200.00 300.00
CR Cal Ripken/35* 175.00 300.00
DJ Derek Jeter/35 200.00 350.00
IS Ichiro Suzuki/25 400.00 600.00
NR Nolan Ryan/40 125.00 200.00
PI Mike Piazza/20 150.00 250.00
RC Roger Clemens/30 * 125.00 200.00

2004 Sweet Spot Signatures Barrel

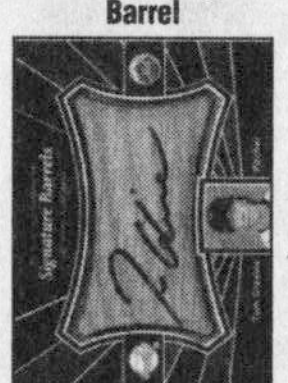

OVERALL AU ODDS 1:12
PRINT RUNS B/WN 13-74 COPIES PER
CARDS ARE NOT SERIAL-NUMBERED
PRINT RUNS PROVIDED BY UPPER DECK
NO PRICING ON QTY OF 14 OR LESS
EXCHANGE DEADLINE 11/22/07
AB Angel Berroa/64 * 12.50 30.00
AD Adam Dunn/74 * 20.00 50.00
AK Austin Kearns/64 * 12.50 30.00
AP Albert Pujols/64 * 200.00 300.00
AR Alex Rodriguez/28 * 150.00 300.00
BB Bret Boone/64 * 20.00 50.00
BE Josh Beckett/65 * 20.00 50.00
BG Brian Giles/64 * 15.00 40.00
BS Ben Sheets/64 * 15.00 40.00
BW Brandon Webb/64 * 12.50 30.00
CB Carlos Beltran/55 * 15.00 40.00
CL Carlos Lee/64 * 15.00 40.00
CR Cal Ripken/38 * 150.00 250.00
CZ Carlos Zambrano/38 * 30.00 60.00
DJ Derek Jeter/53 * 175.00 300.00
DL Derrek Lee/64 * 20.00 50.00
DM Don Mattingly/38 * 75.00 150.00
DW Dontrelle Willis/64 * 20.00 50.00
DY Delmon Young/74 * 20.00 50.00
EC Eric Chavez/74 * 15.00 40.00
EL Esteban Loaiza/64 * 12.50 30.00
EM Edgar Martinez/64 * 40.00 80.00
FT Frank Thomas/13 *
GA Garret Anderson/74 * 15.00 40.00
GJ Geoff Jenkins/64 * 15.00 40.00
GL Tom Glavine/64 * 20.00 50.00
GS Gary Sheffield/38 * 40.00 80.00
HA Roy Halladay/64 * 15.00 40.00
HB Hank Blalock/74 * 15.00 40.00
HI Richard Hidalgo/64 * 12.50 30.00
HO Trevor Hoffman/68 * 15.00 40.00
HU Torii Hunter/64 * 15.00 40.00
IR Ivan Rodriguez/64 * 40.00 80.00
IS Ichiro Suzuki/64 * 400.00 600.00
JD J.D. Drew/13 *
JG Juan Gonzalez/13 *
JJ Jacque Jones/64 * 15.00 40.00
JM Joe Mauer/72 * 75.00 150.00
JR Jose Reyes/49 * 20.00 50.00
JS Jason Schmidt/64 * 15.00 40.00
JV Javier Vazquez/64 * 15.00 40.00
KG Ken Griffey Jr./64 * 75.00 150.00
KW Kerry Wood/64 * 20.00 50.00
LG Luis Gonzalez/13 *
LO Mike Lowell/64 * 15.00 40.00
MA Mike Marshall/13 *
MC Miguel Cabrera/64 * 20.00 50.00
MG Marcus Giles/64 * 15.00 40.00
ML Mike Lieberthal/64 * 15.00 40.00
MM Mike Mussina/64 * 30.00 60.00
MP Mark Prior/64 * 15.00 40.00
MR Manny Ramirez/63 * 40.00 80.00
MT Mark Teixeira/64 * 20.00 50.00
MU Mark Mulder/64 * 15.00 40.00
NG Nomar Garciaparra/38 * 50.00 100.00
NR Nolan Ryan/38 * 125.00 200.00
OP Odalis Perez/64 * 12.50 30.00
PB Pat Burrell/13 *
PI Mike Piazza/38 * 100.00 175.00
RB Rocco Baldelli/19 * 30.00 60.00
RH Rich Harden/64 * 15.00 40.00
RK Ryan Klesko/64 * 15.00 40.00
RO Roy Oswalt/64 * 15.00 40.00
RS Ryne Sandberg/14 *
RW Randy Wolf/64 * 12.50 30.00
SA Johan Santana/64 * 30.00 60.00
SB Sean Burroughs/64 * 12.50 30.00
SM John Smoltz/13 *
SP Scott Podsednik/64 * 20.00 50.00
TE Miguel Tejada/64 * 20.00 50.00
TG Tony Gwynn/15 *
TH Todd Helton/38 * 30.00 60.00
TI Tim Hudson/64 * 20.00 50.00
TS Tom Seaver/38 * 40.00 80.00
VG Vladimir Guerrero/38 * 40.00 80.00
VW Vernon Wells/33 * 20.00 50.00
WA Billy Wagner/64 * 20.00 50.00
WC Will Clark/13 *
WE Rickie Weeks/64 * 15.00 40.00

2004 Sweet Spot Signatures Glove

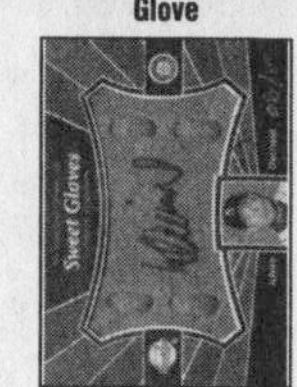

OVERALL AU ODDS 1:12
PRINT RUNS B/WN 5-25 #'d COPIES PER
NO PRICING ON QTY OF 5 OR LESS
EXCHANGE DEADLINE 11/22/07
AB Angel Berroa/25 20.00 50.00
AD Adam Dunn/25 40.00 80.00
AK Austin Kearns/25 20.00 50.00
AP Albert Pujols/25 250.00 400.00
AR Alex Rodriguez/5
BB Bret Boone/25 40.00 80.00
BE Josh Beckett/25 40.00 80.00
BG Brian Giles/25 30.00 60.00
BS Ben Sheets/25 30.00 60.00
BW Brandon Webb/25 20.00 50.00
CB Carlos Beltran/25 30.00 60.00
CL Carlos Lee/25 30.00 60.00
CR Cal Ripken/25 225.00 350.00
CZ Carlos Zambrano/15 50.00 100.00
DJ Derek Jeter/5
DL Derrek Lee/25 40.00 80.00
DM Don Mattingly/25 125.00 200.00
DW Dontrelle Willis/25 40.00 80.00
DY Delmon Young/25 40.00 80.00
EC Eric Chavez/25 30.00 60.00
EL Esteban Loaiza/25 20.00 50.00
EM Edgar Martinez/25 60.00 120.00
FT Frank Thomas/15 75.00 150.00
GA Garret Anderson/25 30.00 60.00
GJ Geoff Jenkins/25 30.00 60.00
GL Tom Glavine/25 40.00 80.00
GS Gary Sheffield/20 50.00 100.00
HA Roy Halladay/24 50.00 100.00
HB Hank Blalock/25 30.00 60.00
HI Richard Hidalgo/15 30.00 60.00
HO Trevor Hoffman/15 40.00 80.00
HU Torii Hunter/25 30.00 60.00
IS Ichiro Suzuki/15
JD J.D. Drew/5
JG Juan Gonzalez/25 30.00 60.00
JJ Jacque Jones/25 30.00 60.00
JM Joe Mauer/25 50.00 100.00
JR Jose Reyes/25 30.00 60.00
JS Jason Schmidt/25 30.00 60.00
JV Javier Vazquez/25 30.00 60.00
KG Ken Griffey Jr./25 150.00 250.00
KW Kerry Wood/25 40.00 80.00
LG Luis Gonzalez/25 30.00 60.00
LO Mike Lowell/5
MA Mike Marshall/25 40.00 80.00
MC Miguel Cabrera/25 40.00 80.00
MG Marcus Giles/25 30.00 60.00
ML Mike Lieberthal/25 30.00 60.00
MM Mike Mussina/25 50.00 100.00
MP Mark Prior/25 30.00 60.00
MR Manny Ramirez/25 60.00 120.00
MT Mark Teixeira/25 40.00 80.00
MU Mark Mulder/25 30.00 60.00
NG Nomar Garciaparra/25 75.00 150.00
NR Nolan Ryan/25 175.00 300.00
OP Odalis Perez/25 20.00 50.00
PB Pat Burrell/15 40.00 80.00
PI Mike Piazza/5
RB Rocco Baldelli/25 30.00 60.00
RH Rich Harden/25 30.00 60.00
RK Ryan Klesko/15 40.00 80.00
RO Roy Oswalt/25 30.00 60.00
RS Ryne Sandberg/20 75.00 150.00
RW Randy Wolf/15 30.00 60.00
SA Johan Santana/25 60.00 120.00
SB Sean Burroughs/25 20.00 50.00
SM John Smoltz/5
SP Scott Podsednik/25 40.00 80.00
TE Miguel Tejada/25 40.00 80.00
TG Tony Gwynn/25 60.00 120.00
TH Todd Helton/25 30.00 60.00
TI Tim Hudson/25 40.00 80.00
TS Tom Seaver/15 60.00 120.00
VG Vladimir Guerrero/25 60.00 120.00
VW Vernon Wells/5
WA Billy Wagner/25 40.00 80.00
WC Will Clark/25 75.00 150.00
WE Rickie Weeks/25 30.00 60.00

2004 Sweet Spot Signatures Dual

BLK/RED-BLUE/DUAL/HIST AU ODDS 1:180
STATED PRINT RUN 10 SERIAL #'d SETS
NO PRICING DUE TO SCARCITY
EXCHANGE DEADLINE 11/22/07

2004 Sweet Spot Signatures Historical Ball

BLK/RED-BLUE/DUAL/HIST AU ODDS 1:180
STATED PRINT RUN 1 SERIAL #'d SET
NO PRICING DUE TO SCARCITY

2004 Sweet Spot Sweet Sticks

OVERALL GAME-USED ODDS 1:6
STATED PRINT RUN 199 SERIAL #'d SETS
AB Adrian Beltre 3.00 8.00
AD Adam Dunn 3.00 8.00
AJ Andruw Jones 4.00 10.00
AP Albert Pujols 8.00 20.00
AR Alex Rodriguez 6.00 15.00
AS Alfonso Soriano 3.00 8.00
BA Bobby Abreu 3.00 8.00
BB Bret Boone 3.00 8.00
BE Carlos Beltran 3.00 8.00
BG Brian Giles 3.00 8.00
CB Craig Biggio 4.00 10.00
CD Carlos Delgado 3.00 8.00
CJ Chipper Jones 4.00 10.00
CR Cal Ripken 12.50 30.00
CS Curt Schilling 4.00 10.00
DJ Derek Jeter 10.00 25.00
DL Derrek Lee 4.00 10.00
EC Eric Chavez 3.00 8.00
ER Edgar Renteria 3.00 8.00
FT Frank Thomas 4.00 10.00
GA Garret Anderson 3.00 8.00
GL Tom Glavine 4.00 10.00
GM Greg Maddux 6.00 15.00
GS Gary Sheffield 3.00 8.00
HB Hank Blalock 3.00 8.00
HM Hideki Matsui 12.50 30.00
IR Ivan Rodriguez 4.00 10.00
IS Ichiro Suzuki 12.50 30.00
JB Jeff Bagwell 4.00 10.00
JD J.D. Drew 3.00 8.00
JE Jim Edmonds 3.00 8.00
JG Jason Giambi 3.00 8.00
JK Jeff Kent 3.00 8.00
JR Jose Reyes 3.00 8.00
JT Jim Thome 4.00 10.00
KG Ken Griffey Jr. 6.00 15.00
KM Kazuo Matsui 3.00 8.00
LB Lance Berkman 4.00 10.00
LG Luis Gonzalez 3.00 8.00
LW Larry Walker Cards 4.00 10.00
MA Moises Alou 3.00 8.00
MC Miguel Cabrera 4.00 10.00
MG Marcus Giles 3.00 8.00
ML Mike Lowell 3.00 8.00
MO Magglio Ordonez 3.00 8.00
MP Mike Piazza 6.00 15.00
MR Manny Ramirez 4.00 10.00
MT Mark Teixeira 4.00 10.00
NG Nomar Garciaparra 6.00 15.00
PB Pat Burrell 3.00 8.00
PR Mark Prior 4.00 10.00
PW Preston Wilson 3.00 8.00
RC Roger Clemens 6.00 15.00
RF Rafael Furcal 3.00 8.00
RJ Randy Johnson 4.00 10.00
RP Rafael Palmeiro 4.00 10.00
RS Richie Sexson 3.00 8.00
SG Shawn Green 3.00 8.00
SR Scott Rolen 4.00 10.00
SS Sammy Sosa 4.00 10.00
TE Miguel Tejada 3.00 8.00
TG Troy Glaus 3.00 8.00
TH Todd Helton 4.00 10.00
TW Ted Williams 20.00 50.00
VG Vladimir Guerrero 4.00 10.00

2004 Sweet Spot Sweet Sticks Dual

OVERALL GAME-USED ODDS 1:6
STATED PRINT RUN 100 SERIAL #'d SETS
BT Hank Blalock 6.00 15.00
Mark Teixeira
CL Miguel Cabrera 6.00 15.00
Mike Lowell
JC Randy Johnson 12.50 30.00
Roger Clemens
JG Derek Jeter 15.00 40.00
Nomar Garciaparra
JM Jose Reyes 6.00 15.00
Kazuo Matsui
MM Hideki Matsui 30.00 60.00
Kazuo Matsui
PR Albert Pujols 15.00 40.00
Scott Rolen
RG Manny Ramirez 6.00 15.00
Nomar Garciaparra
RJ Alex Rodriguez 30.00 60.00
Derek Jeter
RP Ivan Rodriguez 6.00 15.00
Mike Piazza
TB Jim Thome 6.00 15.00
Pat Burrell
WP Kerry Wood 6.00 15.00
Mark Prior

2004 Sweet Spot Sweet Sticks Triple

OVERALL GAME-USED ODDS 1:6
STATED PRINT RUN 50 SERIAL #'d SETS
GPS Ken Griffey Jr. 20.00 50.00
Rafael Palmeiro
Sammy Sosa
JJD Andruw Jones 12.50 30.00
Chipper Jones
J.D. Drew
JSG Derek Jeter 75.00 150.00
Ichiro Suzuki
Ken Griffey Jr.
MWP Greg Maddux 20.00 50.00
Kerry Wood
Mark Prior
RJG Alex Rodriguez 40.00 80.00
Derek Jeter
Jason Giambi

2004 Sweet Spot Sweet Sticks Quad

OVERALL GAME-USED ODDS 1:6
STATED PRINT RUN 25 SERIAL #'d SETS
PRSG Albert Pujols 100.00 200.00
Alex Rodriguez
Ichiro Suzuki
Ken Griffey Jr.
RGDM Babe Ruth 600.00 1000.00
Lou Gehrig
Joe DiMaggio
Mickey Mantle

2004 Sweet Spot Sweet Threads

*1-2 COLOR PATCH: .75X TO 2X BASIC
*3-4 COLOR PATCH: 1.25X TO 3X BASIC
*1-2 COLOR PATCH: .6X TO 1.5X BASIC SP
*3-4 COLOR PATCH: 1X TO 2.5X BASIC SP
PATCH PRINT RUN 85 SERIAL #'d SETS
MAUER PATCH PRINT RUN 70 #'d CARDS
OVERALL GAME-USED ODDS 1:6
PLATES PRINT RUN 4 SERIAL #'d SETS
BLACK-CYAN-MAGENTA-YELLOW EXIST
NO PLATES PRICING DUE TO SCARCITY
AS Alfonso Soriano 2.00 5.00
BB Bret Boone 2.00 5.00
BC Bartolo Colon 2.00 5.00
BG Brian Giles 2.00 5.00
CB Carlos Beltran 2.00 5.00
CD Carlos Delgado 2.00 5.00
DW Dontrelle Willis 3.00 8.00
DY Delmon Young 3.00 8.00
EC Eric Chavez 2.00 5.00
EM Edgar Martinez 3.00 8.00
FT Frank Thomas 3.00 8.00
GS Gary Sheffield 2.00 5.00
HB Hank Blalock 2.00 5.00
HE Todd Helton 3.00 8.00
HN Hideo Nomo 3.00 8.00
JB Jeff Bagwell 3.00 8.00
JG Jason Giambi 2.00 5.00
JM Joe Mauer 3.00 8.00
JR Jose Reyes 2.00 5.00
JS Jason Schmidt 2.00 5.00
JT Jim Thome 3.00 8.00
KM Kazuo Matsui SP 4.00 10.00
KW Kerry Wood 2.00 5.00
LB Lance Berkman 2.00 5.00
MC Miguel Cabrera 3.00 8.00
ML Mike Lowell 2.00 5.00
MM Mark Mulder 2.00 5.00
MO Magglio Ordonez 2.00 5.00
MP Mark Prior 3.00 8.00
MR Manny Ramirez 3.00 8.00
MT Mark Teixeira 3.00 8.00
PW Preston Wilson 2.00 5.00
RH Rich Harden 2.00 5.00
RO Roy Oswalt 2.00 5.00
RS Richie Sexson 2.00 5.00
RW Rickie Weeks 2.00 5.00
SG Shawn Green 2.00 5.00
SS Sammy Sosa 3.00 8.00
TG Troy Glaus 2.00 5.00

TH Tim Hudson 2.00 5.00
VG Vladimir Guerrero 3.00 8.00
VW Vernon Wells 2.00 5.00

2004 Sweet Spot Sweet Threads Dual

OVERALL GAME-USED ODDS 1:6
STATED PRINT RUN 150 SERIAL #'d SETS
BP Angel Berroa 4.00 10.00
Scott Podsednik
BT Hank Blalock 6.00 15.00
Mark Teixeira
CK Curt Schilling 6.00 15.00
Kevin Brown
CS Roger Clemens 8.00 20.00
Sammy Sosa
DT Carlos Delgado 6.00 15.00
Jim Thome
GH Eric Gagne 4.00 10.00
Roy Halladay
HG Tim Hudson 4.00 10.00
Vladimir Guerrero
JC Randy Johnson 10.00 25.00
Roger Clemens
JH Andruw Jones 6.00 15.00
Torii Hunter
JJ Andruw Jones 6.00 15.00
Chipper Jones
MM Hideki Matsui 20.00 50.00
Kazuo Matsui
MP Joe Mauer 6.00 15.00
Mark Prior
PC Andy Pettitte 8.00 20.00
Roger Clemens
PP Jorge Posada 6.00 15.00
Mike Piazza
PS Albert Pujols 20.00 50.00
Ichiro Suzuki
PW Albert Pujols 8.00 20.00
Kerry Wood
RJ Alex Rodriguez 20.00 50.00
Derek Jeter
RM Jose Reyes 6.00 15.00
Kazuo Matsui
SB Alfonso Soriano 4.00 10.00
Bret Boone
SM Gary Sheffield 6.00 15.00
Pedro Martinez
WP Kerry Wood 6.00 15.00
Mark Prior
YW Delmon Young 6.00 15.00
Rickie Weeks

2004 Sweet Spot Sweet Threads Dual Patch

*PATCHES: 1X TO 2.5X BASIC
OVERALL GAME-USED ODDS 1:6
STATED PRINT RUN 60 SERIAL #'d SETS
A.ROD-JETER PRINT RUN 10 #'d CARDS
NO A.ROD-JETER PRICING AVAILABLE
MM Hideki Matsui 75.00 150.00
Kazuo Matsui
PS Albert Pujols 100.00 175.00
Ichiro Suzuki

2004 Sweet Spot Sweet Threads Triple

OVERALL GAME-USED ODDS 1:6
STATED PRINT RUN 99 SERIAL #'d SETS
AGG Garret Anderson 10.00 25.00
Troy Glaus
Vladimir Guerrero
BKE Jeff Bagwell 6.00 15.00
Jeff Kent
Morgan Ensberg
BLR Adrian Beltre 6.00 15.00
Mike Lowell
Scott Rolen
BMS Bret Boone 30.00 60.00
Edgar Martinez
Ichiro Suzuki
BWC Josh Beckett 12.50 30.00
Kerry Wood
Roger Clemens
CMM Bobby Crosby 10.00 25.00
Joe Mauer
Kazuo Matsui
DHW Carlos Delgado 6.00 15.00
Roy Halladay
Vernon Wells
DKG Adam Dunn 10.00 25.00
Austin Kearns
Ken Griffey Jr.
DMJ Joe DiMaggio 175.00 300.00
Mickey Mantle
Derek Jeter
DMW Joe DiMaggio 200.00 350.00
Mickey Mantle
Ted Williams
DRN Johnny Damon 20.00 50.00
Manny Ramirez
Trot Nixon
FRP Keith Foulke 10.00 25.00
Mariano Rivera
Troy Percival
GPS Ken Griffey Jr. 15.00 40.00
Rafael Palmeiro
Sammy Sosa
JJD Andruw Jones 10.00 25.00
Chipper Jones
J.D. Drew
JTG Derek Jeter 12.50 30.00
Miguel Tejada
Nomar Garciaparra
JWH Edwin Jackson 6.00 15.00
Jerome Williams
Rich Harden
KVG Jeff Kent 6.00 15.00
Jose Vidro
Marcus Giles
LTO Carlos Lee 10.00 25.00
Frank Thomas
Magglio Ordonez
LTP Javy Lopez 6.00 15.00
Miguel Tejada
Rafael Palmeiro
MCF Kazuo Matsui 10.00 25.00
Orlando Cabrera
Rafael Furcal
MMH Mike Mussina 10.00 25.00
Pedro Martinez
Tim Hudson
MSH Joe Mauer 15.00 40.00
Johan Santana
Torii Hunter
MWP Greg Maddux 15.00 40.00
Kerry Wood
Mark Prior
PAS Corey Patterson 10.00 25.00
Moises Alou
Sammy Sosa
PCO Andy Pettitte 12.50 30.00
Roger Clemens
Roy Oswalt
PRR Albert Pujols 15.00 40.00
Edgar Renteria
Scott Rolen
PTH Albert Pujols 12.50 30.00
Jim Thome
Todd Helton
RCB Alex Rodriguez 10.00 25.00
Eric Chavez
Hank Blalock
RGJ Alex Rodriguez 15.00 40.00
Ken Griffey Jr.
Randy Johnson
RGW Jose Reyes 10.00 25.00
Khalil Greene
Rickie Weeks
RJG Alex Rodriguez 30.00 60.00
Derek Jeter
Jason Giambi
RMP Jose Reyes 15.00 40.00
Kazuo Matsui
Mike Piazza
SBK Alfonso Soriano 6.00 15.00
Bret Boone
Adam Kennedy
SBP Jason Schmidt 10.00 25.00
Josh Beckett
Mark Prior
SBT Alfonso Soriano 10.00 25.00
Hank Blalock
Mark Teixeira
SLM Curt Schilling 20.00 50.00
Derek Lowe
Pedro Martinez
VBM Javier Vazquez 6.00 15.00
Kevin Brown
Mike Mussina
WBP Brandon Webb 10.00 25.00
Josh Beckett
Mark Prior
WGS Billy Wagner 10.00 25.00
Eric Gagne
John Smoltz
WRC Kerry Wood 40.00 80.00
Nolan Ryan
Roger Clemens
YCW Delmon Young 10.00 25.00
Miguel Cabrera
Rickie Weeks
ZMH Barry Zito 6.00 15.00
Mark Mulder
Tim Hudson

2004 Sweet Spot Sweet Threads Triple Patch

*PATCH p/r 20-25: 1.5X TO 3X BASIC
OVERALL GAME-USED ODDS 1:6
PRINT RUNS B/WN 5-25 COPIES PER
NO PRICING ON QTY OF 5 OR LESS
FRP Keith Foulke 30.00 60.00
Mariano Rivera
Troy Percival/25
GPS Ken Griffey Jr. 40.00 80.00
Rafael Palmeiro
Sammy Sosa/25
JTG Derek Jeter 40.00 80.00
Miguel Tejada
Nomar Garciaparra/25
MSH Joe Mauer 40.00 80.00
Johan Santana
Torii Hunter/20
WRC Kerry Wood 100.00 200.00
Nolan Ryan
Roger Clemens/25

2004 Sweet Spot Sweet Threads Quad

OVERALL GAME-USED ODDS 1:6
STATED PRINT RUN 99 SERIAL #'d SETS
BADH Carlos Beltran 15.00 40.00
Garret Anderson
Johnny Damon
Torii Hunter
BBGS Angel Berroa 10.00 25.00
Carlos Beltran
Juan Gonzalez
Mike Sweeney
BPJC Josh Beckett 20.00 50.00
Mark Prior
Randy Johnson
Roger Clemens
BWRC Josh Beckett 40.00 80.00
Kerry Wood
Nolan Ryan
Roger Clemens
CAGG Bartolo Colon 15.00 40.00
Garret Anderson
Troy Glaus
Vladimir Guerrero
DHHW Carlos Delgado 10.00 25.00
Eric Hinske
Roy Halladay
Vernon Wells
DOGP Carlos Delgado 15.00 40.00
David Ortiz
Jason Giambi
Rafael Palmeiro
GNKB Brian Giles 10.00 25.00
Phil Nevin
Ryan Klesko
Sean Burroughs
GNLG Eric Gagne 15.00 40.00
Hideo Nomo
Paul LoDuca
Shawn Green
JBGB Chipper Jones 10.00 25.00
Lance Berkman
Luis Gonzalez
Pat Burrell
JEGW Andruw Jones 15.00 40.00
Jim Edmonds
Ken Griffey Jr.
Preston Wilson
JJDF Andruw Jones 15.00 40.00
Chipper Jones
J.D. Drew
Rafael Furcal
JMSH Jacque Jones 12.50 30.00
Joe Mauer
Shannon Stewart
Torii Hunter
JRMT Derek Jeter 20.00 50.00
Edgar Renteria
Kazuo Matsui
Miguel Tejada
KGCS Austin Kearns 15.00 40.00
Brian Giles
Miguel Cabrera
Sammy Sosa
LMRS Carlos Lee 30.00 60.00
Hideki Matsui
Manny Ramirez
Shannon Stewart
LTOK Carlos Lee 15.00 40.00
Frank Thomas
Magglio Ordonez
Paul Konerko
LTPP Javy Lopez 15.00 40.00
Miguel Tejada
Rafael Palmeiro
Sidney Ponson
MMMH Mark Mulder 10.00 25.00
Mike Mussina
Pedro Martinez
Roy Halladay
MTTS Edgar Martinez 15.00 40.00
Frank Thomas
Mark Teixeira
Mike Sweeney
NSGH Phil Nevin 10.00 25.00
Richie Sexson
Shawn Green
Todd Helton
PBBC Andy Pettitte 20.00 50.00
Craig Biggio
Jeff Bagwell
Roger Clemens
PLBT Albert Pujols 15.00 40.00
Derrek Lee
Jeff Bagwell
Jim Thome
PRER Albert Pujols 40.00 80.00
Edgar Renteria
Jim Edmonds
Scott Rolen
PWPS Corey Patterson 15.00 40.00
Kerry Wood
Mark Prior
Sammy Sosa
RCBG Alex Rodriguez 15.00 40.00
Eric Chavez
Hank Blalock
Troy Glaus
RDRW Alex Rodriguez 100.00 200.00
Joe DiMaggio
Manny Ramirez
Ted Williams
RJDM Alex Rodriguez 250.00 400.00
Derek Jeter
Joe DiMaggio
Mickey Mantle
RJGP Alex Rodriguez 50.00 100.00
Derek Jeter
Jason Giambi
Jorge Posada
RLPM Ivan Rodriguez 15.00 40.00
Javy Lopez
Jorge Posada
Joe Mauer
RMPG Jose Reyes 15.00 40.00
Kazuo Matsui
Mike Piazza
Tom Glavine
SBKV Alfonso Soriano 10.00 25.00
Bret Boone
Jeff Kent
Jose Vidro
SBMM Curt Schilling 15.00 40.00
Kevin Brown
Mike Mussina
Pedro Martinez
SDRM Curt Schilling 50.00 100.00
Johnny Damon
Manny Ramirez
Pedro Martinez
SSOG Gary Sheffield 30.00 60.00
Ichiro Suzuki
Magglio Ordonez
Vladimir Guerrero
VCBM Javier Vazquez 10.00 25.00
Jose Contreras
Kevin Brown
Mike Mussina
WATM Billy Wagner 15.00 40.00
Bobby Abreu
Jim Thome
Kevin Millwood
WBCL Dontrelle Willis 15.00 40.00
Josh Beckett
Miguel Cabrera
Mike Lowell
WGJS Brandon Webb 10.00 25.00
Luis Gonzalez
Randy Johnson
Richie Sexson
ZMHH Barry Zito 15.00 40.00
Mark Mulder
Rich Harden
Tim Hudson

2004 Sweet Spot Sweet Threads Quad Patch

*PATCH: 1.5X TO 3X BASIC
OVERALL GAME-USED ODDS 1:6
PRINT RUNS B/WN 1-15 #'d COPIES PER
NO PRICING ON QTY OF 10 OR LESS
BWRC Josh Beckett 250.00 400.00
Kerry Wood
Nolan Ryan
Roger Clemens/15
LMRS Carlos Lee 125.00 200.00
Hideki Matsui
Manny Ramirez
Shannon Stewart/15
PRER Albert Pujols 125.00 200.00
Edgar Renteria
Jim Edmonds
Scott Rolen/15
PWPS Corey Patterson 60.00 120.00
Kerry Wood
Mark Prior
Sammy Sosa/15
SBMM Curt Schilling 40.00 80.00
Kevin Brown
Mike Mussina
Pedro Martinez/15
SDRM Curt Schilling 175.00 300.00
Johnny Damon
Manny Ramirez
Pedro Martinez/15

2005 Sweet Spot

This product was released in September, 2005. The product was issued in five-card packs with an $10 SRP which came 12 packs to a box and 16 boxes to a case. Of note, cards 1-90 from the basic set were issued in standard '05 Sweet Spot packs. Cards 91-174 were distributed within packs of '05 Upper Deck Update in February, 2006. Each 5-card pack of UD Update contained one Sweet Spot card.

COMP.BASIC SET (90) 8.00 20.00
COMP.UPDATE SET (84) 10.00 25.00
COMMON CARD (1-90) .20 .50
COMMON RC 1-90 .20 .50
COMMON CARD (91-174) .20 .50
91-174 ONE PER '05 UD UPDATE PACK
1 Magglio Ordonez .30 .75
2 Craig Biggio .30 .75
3 Hank Blalock .20 .50
4 Nomar Garciaparra .50 1.25
5 Ken Griffey Jr. .75 2.00
6 Khalil Greene .20 .50
7 Andruw Jones .20 .50
8 Ichiro Suzuki .75 2.00
9 Philip Humber RC .50 1.25
10 Vladimir Guerrero .50 1.25
11 Carlos Delgado .20 .50
12 Jeff Niemann RC .50 1.25
13 Chipper Jones .50 1.25
14 Jose Vidro .20 .50
15 Miguel Cabrera .50 1.25
16 Albert Pujols 1.25 3.00
17 Tadahito Iguchi RC .30 .75
18 Norihiro Nakamura RC .20 .50
19 Jeff Bagwell .30 .75
20 Troy Glaus .20 .50
21 Scott Rolen .30 .75
22 Derek Lowe .20 .50
23 Mark Prior .30 .75
24 Bobby Abreu .20 .50
25 David Wright .75 2.00
26 Barry Zito .20 .50
27 Livan Hernandez .20 .50
28 Mark Teixeira .50 1.25
29 Manny Ramirez .50 1.25
30 Paul Konerko .30 .75
31 Victor Martinez .30 .75
32 Greg Maddux .75 2.00
33 Jim Thome .30 .75
34 Miguel Tejada .30 .75
35 Ivan Rodriguez .30 .75
36 Carlos Beltran .20 .50
37 Steve Finley .20 .50
38 Torii Hunter .20 .50
39 Bobby Crosby .20 .50
40 Jorge Posada .30 .75
41 Ben Sheets .20 .50
42 Mike Piazza .50 1.25
43 Luis Gonzalez .20 .50
44 Joe Mauer .50 1.25
45 Shawn Green .20 .50
46 Eric Gagne .20 .50
47 Kerry Wood .20 .50
48 Derek Jeter 1.25 3.00
49 Josh Beckett .30 .75
50 Alex Rodriguez .75 2.00
51 Aubrey Huff .20 .50
52 Eric Chavez .20 .50
53 Sammy Sosa .50 1.25
54 Roger Clemens .60 1.50
55 Mike Mussina .30 .75
56 Mike Sweeney .20 .50
57 Oliver Perez .20 .50
58 Tim Hudson .30 .75
59 Justin Verlander RC 4.00 10.00
60 Johan Santana .50 1.25
61 Hideki Matsui .75 2.00
62 Mark Mulder .20 .50
63 Jake Peavy .20 .50
64 Adam Dunn .30 .75
65 Dallas McPherson .20 .50
66 Jeff Kent .20 .50
67 Pedro Martinez .30 .75
68 J.D. Drew .20 .50
69 Frank Thomas .50 1.25
70 Kazuo Matsui .20 .50
71 Travis Hafner .20 .50
72 John Smoltz .50 1.25
73 Jason Schmidt .20 .50
74 Carlos Lee .20 .50
75 Todd Helton .30 .75
76 David Ortiz .50 1.25
77 Roy Oswalt .30 .75
78 Brian Giles .20 .50
79 Gary Sheffield .20 .50
80 Jason Bay .20 .50
81 Alfonso Soriano .30 .75
82 Randy Johnson .50 1.25
83 Tom Glavine .30 .75
84 Richie Sexson .20 .50
85 Curt Schilling .30 .75
86 Adrian Beltre .20 .50
87 Jim Edmonds .30 .75
88 Roy Halladay .50 1.25
89 Johnny Damon .30 .75
90 Lance Berkman .30 .75
91 Adam Shabala SB RC .20 .50
92 Ambiorix Burgos SB RC .20 .50
93 Ambiorix Concepcion SB RC .20 .50
94 Anibal Sanchez SB RC 1.00 2.50
95 Bill McCarthy SB RC .20 .50
96 Brandon McCarthy SB RC .30 .75
97 Brian Burres SB RC .20 .50
98 Carlos Ruiz SB RC .20 .50
99 Casey Rogowski SB RC .30 .75
100 Chad Orvella SB RC .20 .50
101 Chris Resop SB RC .20 .50
102 Chris Roberson SB RC .20 .50
103 Chris Seddon SB RC .20 .50
104 Colter Bean SB RC .20 .50
105 Dae-Sung Koo SB RC .20 .50
106 Ryan Zimmerman SB RC 1.50 4.00
107 Dave Gassner SB RC .20 .50
108 Brian Anderson SB RC .30 .75
109 D.J. Houlton SB RC .20 .50
110 Derek Wathan SB RC .20 .50
111 Devon Lowery SB RC .20 .50
112 Enrique Gonzalez SB RC .20 .50
113 Chris Denorfia SB RC .20 .50
114 Eude Brito SB RC .20 .50
115 Francisco Butto SB RC .20 .50
116 Franquelis Osoria SB RC .20 .50
117 Garrett Jones SB RC .30 .75
118 Geovany Soto SB RC 1.00 2.50
119 Hayden Penn SB RC .20 .50
120 Ismael Ramirez SB RC .20 .50
121 Jared Gothreaux SB RC .20 .50
122 Jason Hammel SB RC .20 .50
123 Dana Eveland SB RC .20 .50
124 Jeff Miller SB RC .20 .50
125 Jermaine Van Buren SB .20 .50
126 Joel Peralta SB RC .20 .50
127 John Hattig SB RC .20 .50
128 Jorge Campillo SB RC .20 .50
129 Juan Morillo SB RC .20 .50
130 Ryan Garko SB RC .20 .50
131 Keiichi Yabu SB RC .20 .50
132 Kendry Morales SB RC .50 1.25
133 Luis Hernandez SB RC .20 .50
134 Mark McLemore SB RC .20 .50
135 Luis Pena SB RC .20 .50
136 Luis O.Rodriguez SB RC .20 .50
137 Luke Scott SB RC .50 1.25
138 Marcos Carvajal SB RC .20 .50
139 Mark Woodyard SB RC .20 .50
140 Matt A.Smith SB RC .20 .50
141 Matthew Lindstrom SB RC .20 .50
142 Miguel Negron SB RC .30 .75
143 Mike Morse SB RC .50 1.25
144 Nate McLouth SB RC .30 .75
145 Nelson Cruz SB RC .75 2.00
146 Nick Masset SB RC .20 .50
147 Ryan Spilborghs SB RC .50 1.25
148 Oscar Robles SB RC .20 .50
149 Paulino Reynoso SB RC .20 .50
150 Pedro Lopez SB RC .20 .50
151 Pete Orr SB RC .30 .75
152 Prince Fielder SB RC 1.00 2.50
153 Randy Messenger SB RC .20 .50
154 Randy Williams SB RC .20 .50
155 Raul Tablado SB RC .20 .50
156 Ronny Paulino SB RC .30 .75
157 Russ Rohlicek SB RC .20 .50
158 Russell Martin SB RC .75 2.00
159 Scott Baker SB RC .30 .75
160 Scott Munter SB RC .20 .50
161 Sean Thompson SB RC .20 .50
162 Sean Tracey SB RC .20 .50
163 Shane Costa SB RC .20 .50
164 Stephen Drew SB RC 1.00 2.50
165 Steve Schmoll SB RC .20 .50
166 Ryan Speier SB RC .20 .50
167 Tadahito Iguchi SB .30 .75
168 Tony Giarratano SB RC .20 .50
169 Tony Pena SB RC .20 .50
170 Travis Bowyer SB RC .20 .50
171 Ubaldo Jimenez SB RC .60 1.50
172 Wladimir Balentien SB RC .30 .75
173 Yorman Bazardo SB RC .20 .50
174 Yuniesky Betancourt SB RC .75 2.00

2005 Sweet Spot Gold

*GOLD 1-90: 1.25X TO 3X BASIC
*GOLD 1-90: 1X TO 2.5X BASIC RC
1-90 OVERALL PARALLEL ODDS 1:6
1-90 PRINT RUN 599 SERIAL #'d SETS
*GOLD 91-174: 1X TO 2.5X BASIC
91-174 ISSUED IN '05 UD UPDATE PACKS
91-174 ONE #'d CARD OR AU PER PACK
91-174 PRINT RUN 399 SERIAL #'d SETS

2005 Sweet Spot Platinum

*PLATINUM 1-90: 2X TO 5X BASIC
*PLATINUM 1-90: 1.25X TO 3X BASIC RC
1-90 OVERALL PARALLEL ODDS 1:6
*PLATINUM 91-174: 1.5X TO 4X BASIC
91-174 ISSUED IN '05 UD UPDATE PACKS
91-174 ONE #'d CARD OR AU PER PACK
STATED PRINT RUN 99 SERIAL #'d SETS

2005 Sweet Spot Plutonium

1-90 OVERALL PARALLEL ODDS 1:6
91-174 ISSUED IN '05 UD UPDATE PACKS
91-174 ONE #'d CARD OR AU PER PACK
STATED PRINT RUN 1 SERIAL #'d SET
NO PRICING DUE TO SCARCITY

2005 Sweet Spot Majestic Materials

*GOLD: .6X TO 1.5X BASIC
GOLD PRINT RUN 75 SERIAL #'d SETS
PLATINUM PRINT RUN 10 SERIAL #'d SETS
NO PLATINUM PRICING DUE TO SCARCITY
PLUTONIUM PRINT RUN 1 SERIAL #'d SET
NO PLUTONIUM PRICING DUE TO SCARCITY
OVERALL 1-PIECE GU ODDS 1:6
*PATCH: 1.5X TO 4X BASIC
OVERALL PATCH ODDS 1:96
PATCH PRINT RUN 35 SERIAL #'d SETS
PRICES ARE FOR 2-3 COLOR PATCHES
REDUCE 20% FOR 1-COLOR PATCH
ADD 20% FOR 4-COLOR PATCH
ADD 50% FOR 5-COLOR+ PATCH
AD Adam Dunn 2.00 5.00
AJ Andruw Jones 3.00 8.00
AP Andy Pettitte 3.00 8.00
BA Bobby Abreu 2.00 5.00
BB Bret Boone 2.00 5.00
BC Bobby Crosby 2.00 5.00
BE Josh Beckett 2.00 5.00
BG Brian Giles 2.00 5.00
BS Ben Sheets 2.00 5.00
BU B.J. Upton 2.00 5.00
BZ Barry Zito 2.00 5.00
CB Craig Biggio 3.00 8.00
CD Carlos Delgado 2.00 5.00
DM Dallas McPherson 2.00 5.00
DW David Wright 4.00 10.00
ER Edgar Renteria 2.00 5.00
GS Gary Sheffield 2.00 5.00
HA Travis Hafner 2.00 5.00
HU Torii Hunter 2.00 5.00
JB Jason Bay 2.00 5.00
JD J.D. Drew 2.00 5.00
JE Jim Edmonds 2.00 5.00
JG Jason Giambi 2.00 5.00
JK Jeff Kent 2.00 5.00
JM Joe Mauer 3.00 8.00
JP Jake Peavy 2.00 5.00
JR Jose Reyes 2.00 5.00
JS Jason Schmidt 2.00 5.00
JV Jose Vidro 2.00 5.00
KG Khalil Greene 3.00 8.00
KM Kazuo Matsui 2.00 5.00
LB Lance Berkman 2.00 5.00
LG Luis Gonzalez 2.00 5.00
MA Moises Alou 2.00 5.00
MM Mark Mulder 2.00 5.00
MO Magglio Ordonez 2.00 5.00
MU Mike Mussina 3.00 8.00
OP Oliver Perez 2.00 5.00
PO Jorge Posada 3.00 8.00
RH Roy Halladay 2.00 5.00
RO Roy Oswalt 2.00 5.00
RS Richie Sexson 2.00 5.00
SG Shawn Green 2.00 5.00
SK Scott Kazmir 2.00 5.00
ST Shingo Takatsu 2.00 5.00
TG Troy Glaus 2.00 5.00
TH Tim Hudson 2.00 5.00
TI Tadahito Iguchi 6.00 15.00
VM Victor Martinez 2.00 5.00
VW Vernon Wells 2.00 5.00

2005 Sweet Spot Majestic Materials Dual

STATED PRINT RUN 25 SERIAL #'d SETS
GOLD PRINT RUN 5 SERIAL #'d SETS
NO GOLD PRICING DUE TO SCARCITY
PLUTONIUM PRINT RUN 1 SERIAL #'d SET
NO PLUTONIUM PRICING DUE TO SCARCITY
OVERALL COMBO GU ODDS 1:192
OVERALL PATCH ODDS 1:96
PATCH PRINT RUN 5 SERIAL #'d SETS
NO PATCH PRICING DUE TO SCARCITY
BB Craig Biggio 8.00 20.00
Jeff Bagwell
BP Jason Bay 6.00 15.00
Oliver Perez
BS Adrian Beltre 6.00 15.00
Richie Sexson
BT Hank Blalock 8.00 20.00
Mark Teixeira
CC Bobby Crosby 6.00 15.00
Eric Chavez
DG Adam Dunn 15.00 40.00
Ken Griffey Jr.
DK J.D. Drew 6.00 15.00
Jeff Kent
DR Johnny Damon 8.00 20.00
Manny Ramirez
GG Shawn Green 6.00 15.00
Troy Glaus
GR Eric Gagne 10.00 25.00
Mariano Rivera
HM Travis Hafner 6.00 15.00
Victor Martinez
JJ Andruw Jones 10.00 25.00
Chipper Jones
MC Don Mattingly 15.00 40.00
Will Clark
MW Dallas McPherson 10.00 25.00
David Wright
PC Albert Pujols 15.00 40.00
Miguel Cabrera
PG Jake Peavy 8.00 20.00
Khalil Greene
PL Albert Pujols 15.00 40.00
Derrek Lee
RM Jose Reyes 6.00 15.00
Kazuo Matsui
RO Ivan Rodriguez 8.00 20.00
Magglio Ordonez
RT Brian Roberts 6.00 15.00
Miguel Tejada
SH John Smoltz 8.00 20.00
Tim Hudson
SM Joe Mauer 8.00 20.00
Johan Santana
TI Shingo Takatsu 12.50 30.00
Tadahito Iguchi
UK B.J. Upton 6.00 15.00
Scott Kazmir
WC David Wright 12.50 30.00
Miguel Cabrera

2005 Sweet Spot Majestic Materials Triple

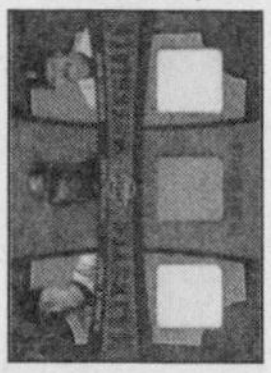

STATED PRINT RUN 25 SERIAL #'d SETS
GOLD PRINT RUN 5 SERIAL #'d SETS
NO GOLD PRICING DUE TO SCARCITY
PLUTONIUM PRINT RUN 1 SERIAL #'d SET
NO PLUTONIUM PRICING DUE TO SCARCITY
OVERALL COMBO GU ODDS 1:192
OVERALL PATCH ODDS 1:96
PATCH PRINT RUN 5 SERIAL #'d SETS
NO PATCH PRICING DUE TO SCARCITY

BPO Josh Beckett 10.00 25.00
Mark Prior
Roy Oswalt
BSB George Brett 30.00 60.00
Mike Schmidt
Wade Boggs
BTH Jeff Bagwell 10.00 25.00
Jim Thome
Todd Helton
HRG Torii Hunter 10.00 25.00
Manny Ramirez
Vladimir Guerrero
JCG Andruw Jones 10.00 25.00
Miguel Cabrera
Vladimir Guerrero
JRT Derek Jeter 15.00 40.00
Edgar Renteria
Miguel Tejada
MMP Greg Maddux 15.00 40.00
Pedro Martinez
Jake Peavy
MSG Greg Maddux 30.00 60.00
John Smoltz
Tom Glavine
OGP David Ortiz 10.00 25.00
Jason Giambi
Rafael Palmeiro
PBC Albert Pujols 15.00 40.00
Carlos Beltran
Miguel Cabrera
RBW Nolan Ryan 30.00 60.00
Josh Beckett
Kerry Wood
RGB Cal Ripken 40.00 80.00
Tony Gwynn
Wade Boggs
SSJ Curt Schilling 10.00 25.00
Johan Santana
Randy Johnson
VPP Jason Varitek 10.00 25.00
Jorge Posada
Mike Piazza
WRG David Wright 12.50 30.00
Scott Rolen
Troy Glaus

2005 Sweet Spot Majestic Materials Quad

STATED PRINT RUN 25 SERIAL #'d SETS
GOLD PRINT RUN 5 SERIAL #'d SETS
NO GOLD PRICING DUE TO SCARCITY
PLUTONIUM PRINT RUN 1 SERIAL #'d SET
NO PLUTONIUM PRICING DUE TO SCARCITY
OVERALL COMBO GU ODDS 1:192
OVERALL PATCH ODDS 1:96
PATCH PRINT RUN 5 SERIAL #'d SETS
NO PATCH PRICING DUE TO SCARCITY

JJSH Andruw Jones 20.00 50.00
Chipper Jones
John Smoltz
Tim Hudson
JSJP Derek Jeter 50.00 100.00
Gary Sheffield
Randy Johnson
Jorge Posada
OVDR David Ortiz 30.00 60.00
Jason Varitek
Johnny Damon
Manny Ramirez
PEWR Albert Pujols 40.00 80.00
Jim Edmonds
Larry Walker
Scott Rolen
ZMWP Carlos Zambrano 20.00 50.00
Greg Maddux
Kerry Wood
Mark Prior

2005 Sweet Spot Signatures Black Stitch Black Ink

OVERALL AU ODDS 1:12
STATED PRINT RUN 1 SERIAL #'d SET
NO PRICING DUE TO SCARCITY

2005 Sweet Spot Signatures Black Stitch Blue Ink

OVERALL AU ODDS 1:12
STATED PRINT RUN 1 SERIAL #'d SET
NO PRICING DUE TO SCARCITY

2005 Sweet Spot Signatures Black Stitch Red Ink

OVERALL AU ODDS 1:12
STATED PRINT RUN 1 SERIAL #'d SET
NO PRICING DUE TO SCARCITY

2005 Sweet Spot Signatures Red Stitch Black Ink

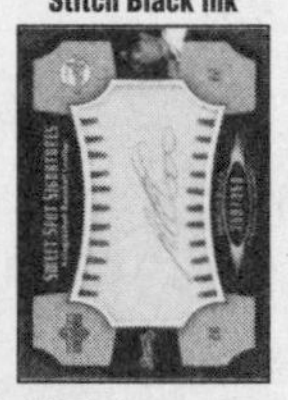

OVERALL AU ODDS 1:12
PRINT RUNS B/WN 58-350 COPIES PER
EXCHANGE DEADLINE 09/15/08

AD Adam Dunn/175 12.50 30.00
AH Aubrey Huff/350 6.00 15.00
AJ Andruw Jones/175 20.00 50.00
AP Albert Pujols/175 150.00 250.00
AR Aramis Ramirez/350 6.00 15.00
BC Bobby Crosby/350 6.00 15.00
BJ Bo Jackson/175 30.00 60.00
BL Barry Larkin/175 12.50 30.00
BU B.J. Upton/350 8.00 20.00
CA Miguel Cabrera/175 12.50 30.00
CC Carl Crawford/350 6.00 15.00
CR Cal Ripken/175 75.00 125.00
CZ Carlos Zambrano/350 10.00 25.00
DA Andre Dawson/175 8.00 20.00
DJ Derek Jeter/175 110.00 175.00
DW David Wright/350 30.00 60.00
EM Edgar Martinez/175 12.50 30.00
GF Gavin Floyd/350 6.00 15.00
GR Khalil Greene/350 10.00 25.00
HB Hank Blalock/175 8.00 20.00
HO Ryan Howard/350 30.00 60.00
JB Jason Bay/350 6.00 15.00
JN Jeff Niemann/350 8.00 20.00
JP Jake Peavy/350 10.00 25.00
JV Justin Verlander/350 30.00 60.00
KG Ken Griffey Jr./175 50.00 100.00
KH Keith Hernandez/350 6.00 15.00
LO Lyle Overbay/350 6.00 15.00
MA Don Mattingly/175 40.00 80.00
MG Marcus Giles/350 6.00 15.00
MM Mark Mulder/350 6.00 15.00
MO Justin Morneau/350 8.00 20.00
MP Mark Prior/175 12.50 30.00
MS Mike Schmidt/175 30.00 60.00
MT Mark Teixeira/175 12.50 30.00
NG Nomar Garciaparra/175 40.00 80.00
NR Nolan Ryan/175 50.00 100.00
PH Philip Humber/350 8.00 20.00
PI Mike Piazza/175 50.00 100.00
PM Paul Molitor/175 8.00 20.00
RC Roger Clemens/175 60.00 120.00
RH Rich Harden/350 6.00 15.00
RJ Randy Johnson/175 50.00 100.00
RO Roy Oswalt/350 6.00 15.00
RS Ryne Sandberg/175 30.00 60.00
RY Robin Yount/175 20.00 50.00
SC Steve Carlton/58 10.00 25.00
SE Sean Casey/350 6.00 15.00
SK Scott Kazmir/350 8.00 20.00
WB Wade Boggs/175 12.50 30.00
WC Will Clark/175 12.50 30.00

2005 Sweet Spot Signatures Red Stitch Blue Ink

*BLUE p/r 135: .5X TO 1.2X BLK p/r 350
*BLUEp/r135: .5X TO 1.2X BLK RC YRp/r350
*BLUE p/r 75: .5X TO 1.2X BLK p/r 175
*BLUE p/r 75: .4X TO 1X BLK p/r 58
OVERALL AU ODDS 1:12
PRINT RUNS B/WN 75-135 COPIES PER
EXCHANGE DEADLINE 09/15/08

AP Albert Pujols/75 150.00 250.00
CP Corey Patterson/135 8.00 20.00
CR Cal Ripken/75 90.00 150.00
DJ Derek Jeter/75 125.00 200.00
GL Tom Glavine/135 12.50 30.00
HA Travis Hafner/135 8.00 20.00
NR Nolan Ryan/75 50.00 100.00
PI Mike Piazza/75 60.00 120.00
RC Roger Clemens/75 75.00 150.00

2005 Sweet Spot Signatures Red Stitch Red Ink

*RED p/r 35: .75X TO 2X BLK p/r 350
*RED p/r 35: .75X TO 2X BLK RC YR p/r 350
*RED p/r 15: .75X TO 2X BLK p/r 175
*RED p/r 15: .6X TO 1.5X BLK p/r 58
OVERALL AU ODDS 1:12
PRINT RUNS B/WN 15-35 COPIES PER
EXCHANGE DEADLINE 09/15/08

AP Albert Pujols/15 175.00 300.00
CP Corey Patterson/35 12.50 30.00
CR Cal Ripken/15 150.00 250.00
DJ Derek Jeter/15 250.00 400.00
GL Tom Glavine/35 20.00 50.00
HA Travis Hafner/35 12.50 30.00
NR Nolan Ryan/15 90.00 150.00
PI Mike Piazza/15 110.00 175.00
RC Roger Clemens/15 100.00 200.00

2005 Sweet Spot Signatures Red-Blue Stitch Black Ink

*BLK p/r 50: .6X TO 1.5X BLK p/r 350
*BLK p/r 50: .6X TO 1.5X BLK RC YR p/r 350
*BLK p/r 25: .6X TO 1.5X BLK p/r 175
*BLK p/r 25: .5X TO 1.2X BLK p/r 58
OVERALL AU ODDS 1:12
PRINT RUNS B/WN 25-50 COPIES PER
EXCHANGE DEADLINE 09/15/08

AP Albert Pujols/25 150.00 250.00
CR Cal Ripken/25 125.00 200.00
DJ Derek Jeter/25 175.00 300.00
JS Johan Santana/25 40.00 80.00
NR Nolan Ryan/25 75.00 125.00
PI Mike Piazza/25 90.00 150.00
RC Roger Clemens/25 90.00 150.00

2005 Sweet Spot Signatures Red-Blue Stitch Blue Ink

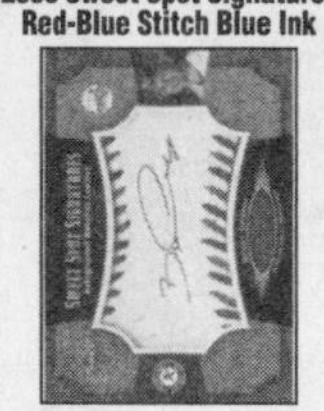

*BLUE p/r 30: .75X TO 2X BLK p/r 350
*BLUE p/r 30: .75X TO 2X BLK RC YR p/r 350
*BLUE p/r 15: .75X TO 2X BLK p/r 175
*BLUE p/r 15: .6X TO 1.5X BLK p/r 58
OVERALL AU ODDS 1:12
PRINT RUNS B/WN 15-30 COPIES PER
EXCHANGE DEADLINE 09/15/08

AP Albert Pujols/15 250.00 400.00
CR Cal Ripken/15 150.00 250.00
GL Tom Glavine/30 20.00 50.00
HA Travis Hafner/30 12.50 30.00
JS Johan Santana/15 40.00 80.00
NR Nolan Ryan/15 90.00 150.00
RC Roger Clemens/15 100.00 200.00

2005 Sweet Spot Signatures Red-Blue Stitch Red Ink

OVERALL AU ODDS 1:12
PRINT RUNS B/WN 5-10 SERIAL #'d SETS
NO PRICING DUE TO SCARCITY
EXCHANGE DEADLINE 09/15/08

2005 Sweet Spot Signatures Barrel Black Ink

*BLK p/r 50: .6X TO 1.5X BLK p/r 350
*BLK p/r 50: .6X TO 1.5X BLK RC YR p/r 350
*BLK p/r 25: .6X TO 1.5X BLK p/r 175
*BLK p/r 25: .5X TO 1.2X BLK p/r 58
OVERALL AU ODDS 1:12
PRINT RUNS B/WN 25-50 COPIES PER
EXCHANGE DEADLINE 09/15/08

AP Albert Pujols/25 150.00 250.00
DJ Derek Jeter/25 200.00 400.00
GL Tom Glavine/50 15.00 40.00
HA Travis Hafner/50 10.00 25.00

2005 Sweet Spot Signatures Barrel Blue Ink

*BLUE p/r 30: .75X TO 2X BLK p/r 350
*BLUE p/r 30: .75X TO 2X BLK RC YR p/r 350
*BLUE p/r 15: .75X TO 2X BLK p/r 175
*BLUE p/r 15: .6X TO 1.5X BLK p/r 58
OVERALL AU ODDS 1:12
PRINT RUNS B/WN 15-30 COPIES PER
EXCHANGE DEADLINE 09/15/08

AP Albert Pujols/15 175.00 300.00
CP Corey Patterson/30 12.50 30.00
CR Cal Ripken/15 150.00 250.00
DJ Derek Jeter/15 300.00 500.00
GL Tom Glavine/30 20.00 50.00
HA Travis Hafner/30 12.50 30.00
NR Nolan Ryan/15 90.00 150.00
PH Philip Humber/30 20.00 50.00
PI Mike Piazza/15 110.00 175.00
RC Roger Clemens/15 125.00 200.00

2005 Sweet Spot Signatures Barrel Red Ink

OVERALL AU ODDS 1:12
PRINT RUNS B/WN 5-10 COPIES PER
NO PRICING DUE TO SCARCITY
EXCHANGE DEADLINE 09/15/08

2005 Sweet Spot Signatures Glove Black Ink

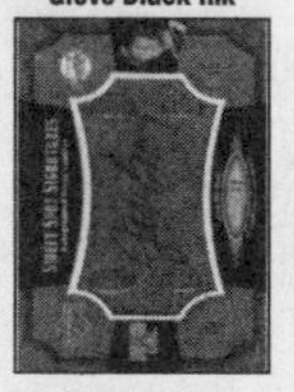

*BLK p/r 30: 1X TO 2.5X BLK p/r 350
*BLK p/r 30: 1X TO 2.5X BLK RC YR p/r 350
*BLK p/r 15: 1X TO 2.5X BLK p/r 175
*BLK p/r 15: .75X TO 2X BLK p/r 58
OVERALL AU ODDS 1:12
PRINT RUNS B/WN 15-30 COPIES PER
EXCHANGE DEADLINE 09/15/08

AP Albert Pujols/15 250.00 400.00
BJ Bo Jackson/15 125.00 200.00
CP Corey Patterson/30 15.00 40.00
CR Cal Ripken/15 175.00 300.00
DJ Derek Jeter/15 300.00 500.00
GL Tom Glavine/30 25.00 60.00
HA Travis Hafner/30 15.00 40.00
NR Nolan Ryan/15 125.00 200.00
PI Mike Piazza/15 150.00 250.00

2005 Sweet Spot Signatures Glove Blue Ink

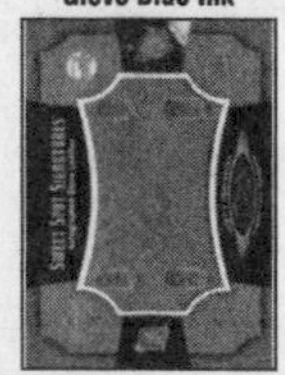

OVERALL AU ODDS 1:12
PRINT RUNS B/WN 5-10 COPIES PER
NO PRICING DUE TO SCARCITY

2005 Sweet Spot Signatures Glove Red Ink

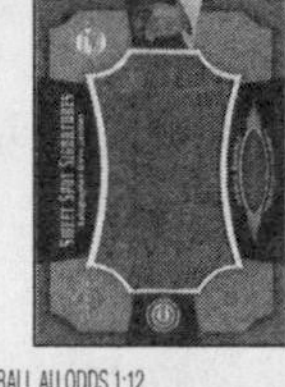

OVERALL AU ODDS 1:12
PRINT RUNS B/WN 2-5 COPIES PER
NO PRICING DUE TO SCARCITY

2005 Sweet Spot Signatures Dual Black Stitch

OVERALL AU ODDS 1:12
STATED PRINT RUN 1 SERIAL #'d SET
NO PRICING DUE TO SCARCITY

2005 Sweet Spot Signatures Dual Red Stitch

OVERALL DUAL AU ODDS 1:196
STATED PRINT RUN 25 SERIAL #'d SETS
EXCHANGE DEADLINE 09/15/08

BJ Bobby Crosby 30.00 60.00
Jason Bay
DC Adam Dunn 30.00 60.00
Sean Casey
GL Khalil Greene 40.00 80.00
Mark Loretta
NH Jeff Niemann 30.00 60.00
Philip Humber
PB Jason Bay 30.00 60.00
Oliver Perez
PC Albert Pujols 250.00 400.00
Miguel Cabrera
PO Jake Peavy 30.00 60.00
Roy Oswalt
SB Ryne Sandberg 60.00 120.00
Wade Boggs
SG Nomar Garciaparra 125.00 200.00
Ryne Sandberg
SP Ben Sheets 30.00 60.00
Jake Peavy
WC David Wright 90.00 150.00
Miguel Cabrera
WR David Wright 150.00 250.00
Jose Reyes

2005 Sweet Spot Signatures Dual Red-Blue Stitch

OVERALL DUAL AU ODDS 1:196
STATED PRINT RUN 15 SERIAL #'d SETS
NO PRICING DUE TO SCARCITY
EXCHANGE DEADLINE 09/15/08

2005 Sweet Spot Signatures Dual Barrel

OVERALL DUAL AU ODDS 1:196
STATED PRINT RUN 15 SERIAL #'d SETS
NO PRICING DUE TO SCARCITY
EXCHANGE DEADLINE 09/15/08

2005 Sweet Spot Signatures Dual Glove

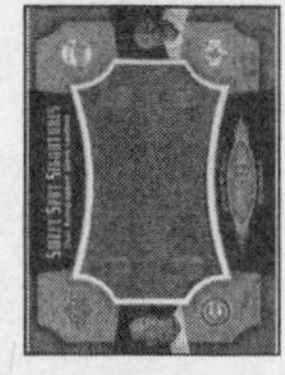

OVERALL DUAL AU ODDS 1:196
STATED PRINT RUN 10 SERIAL #'d SETS
NO PRICING DUE TO SCARCITY
EXCHANGE DEADLINE 09/15/08

2005 Sweet Spot Signatures Game Used Ball

OVERALL AU ODDS 1:12
STATED PRINT RUN 1 SERIAL #'d SET
NO PRICING DUE TO SCARCITY
EXCHANGE DEADLINE 09/15/08

2005 Sweet Spot Signatures Game Used Barrel

OVERALL AU ODDS 1:12
PRINT RUNS B/WN 1-10 COPIES PER
NO PRICING DUE TO SCARCITY

2005 Sweet Spot Signatures Game Used Fielding Glove

OVERALL AU ODDS 1:12
PRINT RUNS B/WN 9-10 COPIES PER
NO PRICING DUE TO SCARCITY

2005 Sweet Spot Sweet Threads

*GOLD: .6X TO 1.5X BASIC
GOLD PRINT RUN 75 SERIAL #'d SETS
PLATINUM PRINT RUN 10 SERIAL #'d SETS
NO PLATINUM PRICING DUE TO SCARCITY
PLUTONIUM PRINT RUN 1 SERIAL #'d SET
NO PLUTONIUM PRICING DUE TO SCARCITY
OVERALL 1-PIECE GU ODDS 1:6
*PATCH: 1.5X TO 4X BASIC
OVERALL PATCH ODDS 1:96
PATCH PRINT RUN 35 SERIAL #'d SETS
PRICES ARE FOR 2-3 COLOR PATCHES
REDUCE 20% FOR 1-COLOR PATCH
ADD 20% FOR 4-COLOR PATCH
ADD 50% FOR 5-COLOR+ PATCH

AB Adrian Beltre 2.00 5.00
AP Albert Pujols 6.00 15.00
AS Alfonso Soriano 2.00 5.00
BC Bartolo Colon 2.00 5.00
BJ Bo Jackson 4.00 10.00
BW Bernie Williams 3.00 8.00
CB Carlos Beltran 2.00 5.00
CJ Chipper Jones 4.00 10.00
CL Carlos Lee 2.00 5.00
CR Cal Ripken 8.00 20.00
CS Curt Schilling 3.00 8.00
DJ Derek Jeter 10.00 25.00
DM Don Mattingly 5.00 12.00
DO David Ortiz 4.00 10.00
EC Eric Chavez 2.00 5.00
EG Eric Gagne 2.00 5.00
FT Frank Thomas 4.00 10.00
GB George Brett 5.00 12.00
GM Greg Maddux 4.00 10.00
GW Tony Gwynn 4.00 10.00
HB Hank Blalock 2.00 5.00
HO Trevor Hoffman 2.00 5.00
IR Ivan Rodriguez 3.00 8.00
JB Jeff Bagwell 3.00 8.00
JD Johnny Damon 3.00 8.00
JS Johan Santana 4.00 10.00
JT Jim Thome 3.00 8.00
JV Jason Varitek 6.00 15.00
KG Ken Griffey Jr. 6.00 15.00
KW Kerry Wood 2.00 5.00
MC Miguel Cabrera 3.00 8.00
MP Mark Prior 3.00 8.00
MR Manny Ramirez 3.00 8.00
MS Mike Schmidt 5.00 12.00
MT Mark Teixeira 3.00 8.00
NR Nolan Ryan 6.00 15.00
PI Mike Piazza 4.00 10.00
PM Pedro Martinez 3.00 8.00
RJ Randy Johnson 4.00 10.00
RP Rafael Palmeiro 3.00 8.00
RS Ryne Sandberg 5.00 12.00
SM John Smoltz 3.00 8.00
SR Scott Rolen 3.00 8.00
SS Sammy Sosa 4.00 10.00
TE Miguel Tejada 2.00 5.00
TG Tom Glavine 3.00 8.00
TH Todd Helton 3.00 8.00
VG Vladimir Guerrero 4.00 10.00
WB Wade Boggs 3.00 8.00
WC Will Clark 3.00 8.00

2005 Sweet Spot Sweet Threads Dual

STATED PRINT RUN 25 SERIAL #'d SETS
GOLD PRINT RUN 5 SERIAL #'d SETS
NO GOLD PRICING DUE TO SCARCITY
PLUTONIUM PRINT RUN 1 SERIAL #'d SET
NO PLUTONIUM PRICING DUE TO SCARCITY
OVERALL COMBO GU ODDS 1:192
OVERALL PATCH ODDS 1:96
PATCH PRINT RUN 5 SERIAL #'d SETS
NO PATCH PRICING DUE TO SCARCITY

BG Carlos Beltran 15.00 40.00
Ken Griffey Jr.
BM Carlos Beltran 8.00 20.00
Pedro Martinez
DC Carlos Delgado 8.00 20.00
Miguel Cabrera
GC Ken Griffey Jr. 15.00 40.00
Miguel Cabrera
GM Dallas McPherson 10.00 25.00
Vladimir Guerrero
JB Bo Jackson 15.00 40.00
George Brett
JJ Randy Johnson 20.00 50.00
Derek Jeter
JM Derek Jeter 30.00 60.00
Don Mattingly
JS Jim Thome 15.00 40.00
Mike Schmidt
MG Greg Maddux 15.00 40.00
Tom Glavine
MJ Mike Mussina 10.00 25.00
Randy Johnson
MP Greg Maddux 15.00 40.00
Mark Prior
OR David Ortiz 8.00 20.00
Manny Ramirez
PO Andy Pettitte 8.00 20.00
Roy Oswalt
PR Pedro Martinez 10.00 25.00
Randy Johnson
PS Rafael Palmeiro 10.00 25.00
Sammy Sosa
PW David Wright 15.00 40.00
Mike Piazza
RJ Cal Ripken 40.00 80.00
Derek Jeter
RP Albert Pujols 15.00 40.00
Scott Rolen
RT Cal Ripken 30.00 60.00
Miguel Tejada
SB Ryne Sandberg 15.00 40.00
Wade Boggs
SJ Curt Schilling 10.00 25.00
Randy Johnson
SV Curt Schilling 10.00 25.00
Jason Varitek
WP Kerry Wood 8.00 20.00
Mark Prior

2005 Sweet Spot Sweet Threads Triple

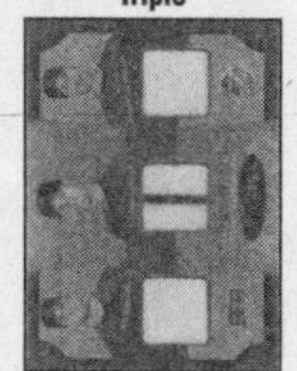

STATED PRINT RUN 25 SERIAL #'d SETS
GOLD PRINT RUN 5 SERIAL #'d SETS
NO GOLD PRICING DUE TO SCARCITY
PLUTONIUM PRINT RUN 1 SERIAL #'d SET
NO PLUTONIUM PRICING DUE TO SCARCITY
OVERALL COMBO GU ODDS 1:192
OVERALL PATCH ODDS 1:96
PATCH PRINT RUN 5 SERIAL #'d SETS
NO PATCH PRICING DUE TO SCARCITY

BBB Craig Biggio 10.00 25.00
Jeff Bagwell
Lance Berkman
BWP Carlos Beltran 15.00 40.00
David Wright
Mike Piazza
GGG Luis Gonzalez 8.00 20.00
Shawn Green
Troy Glaus
JMB Randy Johnson 10.00 25.00
Mike Mussina
Kevin Brown
JWS Derek Jeter 30.00 60.00
Bernie Williams
Gary Sheffield
KGD Austin Kearns 15.00 40.00
Ken Griffey Jr.
Adam Dunn
LOP Brad Lidge 10.00 25.00
Roy Oswalt
Andy Pettitte
ODR David Ortiz 10.00 25.00
Johnny Damon
Manny Ramirez
PER Albert Pujols 15.00 40.00
Jim Edmonds
Scott Rolen
PWM Mark Prior 15.00 40.00
Kerry Wood
Greg Maddux
RDN Manny Ramirez 15.00 40.00
Johnny Damon
Trot Nixon
SBT Alfonso Soriano 10.00 25.00
Hank Blalock
Mark Teixeira
SMJ Curt Schilling 10.00 25.00
Pedro Martinez
Randy Johnson
TPS Miguel Tejada 10.00 25.00
Rafael Palmeiro
Sammy Sosa

2005 Sweet Spot Sweet Threads Quad

STATED PRINT RUN 25 SERIAL #'d SETS
GOLD PRINT RUN 5 SERIAL #'d SETS
NO GOLD PRICING DUE TO SCARCITY
PLUTONIUM PRINT RUN 1 SERIAL #'d SET
NO PLUTONIUM PRICING DUE TO SCARCITY

OVERALL COMBO GU ODDS 1:192
OVERALL PATCH ODDS 1:96
PATCH PRINT RUN 5 SERIAL #'d SETS
NO PATCH PRICING DUE TO SCARCITY

Card	Low	High
BMCB Adrian Beltre	15.00	40.00
Dallas McPherson		
Eric Chavez		
Hank Blalock		
BRGG Carlos Beltran	30.00	60.00
Manny Ramirez		
Ken Griffey Jr.		
Vladimir Guerrero		
POTH Albert Pujols	30.00	60.00
David Ortiz		
Jim Thome		
Todd Helton		
RBGB Cal Ripken	60.00	120.00
George Brett		
Tony Gwynn		
Wade Boggs		
RVMP Ivan Rodriguez	20.00	50.00
Jason Varitek		
Joe Mauer		
Jorge Posada		

2006 Sweet Spot

This 183-card set was released in June, 2006. The set was issued in five-card hobby packs with an $10 SRP and those packs were issued 12 packs per box and 12 boxes per case. Cards numbered 1-100 feature veterans while cards 101-184 were all signed. These cards were issued to stated print runs between 86 and 275 copies. A few players did not return their signatures in time for pack out and those cards could be redeemed until May 25, 2008.

Card	Low	High
COMP.SET w/o AU's (100)	10.00	25.00
COMMON CARD (1-100)	.20	.50

OVERALL AU ODDS 1:12
AU PRINT RUNS B/WN 45-275 PER
EXCHANGE DEADLINE 05/25/08
ASTERISK = PARTIAL EXCHANGE

Card	Low	High
1 Bartolo Colon	.20	.50
2 Garret Anderson	.20	.50
3 Francisco Rodriguez	.30	.75
4 Dallas McPherson	.20	.50
5 Andy Pettitte	.30	.75
6 Lance Berkman	.30	.75
7 Willy Taveras	.20	.50
8 Bobby Crosby	.20	.50
9 Dan Haren	.20	.50
10 Nick Swisher	.50	1.25
11 Vernon Wells	.20	.50
12 Orlando Hudson	.20	.50
13 Roy Halladay	.50	1.25
14 Andruw Jones	.20	.50
15 Chipper Jones	.50	1.25
16 Jeff Francoeur	.50	1.25
17 John Smoltz	.50	1.25
18 Carlos Lee	.20	.50
19 Rickie Weeks	.30	.75
20 Bill Hall	.20	.50
21 Jim Edmonds	.30	.75
22 David Eckstein	.20	.50
23 Mark Mulder	.20	.50
24 Aramis Ramirez	.20	.50
25 Greg Maddux	.75	2.00
26 Nomar Garciaparra	.50	1.25
27 Carlos Zambrano	.30	.75
28 Scott Kazmir	.30	.75
29 Jorge Cantu	.20	.50
30 Carl Crawford	.30	.75
31 Luis Gonzalez	.20	.50
32 Troy Glaus	.20	.50
33 Shawn Green	.20	.50
34 Jeff Kent	.20	.50
35 Milton Bradley	.20	.50
36 Cesar Izturis	.20	.50
37 Omar Vizquel	.30	.75
38 Moises Alou	.20	.50
39 Randy Winn	.20	.50
40 Jason Schmidt	.20	.50
41 Coco Crisp	.20	.50
42 C.C. Sabathia	.30	.75
43 Cliff Lee	.30	.75
44 Ichiro Suzuki	.75	2.00
45 Richie Sexson	.20	.50
46 Jeremy Reed	.20	.50
47 Carlos Delgado	.20	.50
48 Miguel Cabrera	.50	1.25
49 Luis Castillo	.20	.50
50 Carlos Beltran	.20	.50
51 Tom Glavine	.30	.75
52 David Wright	.75	2.00
53 Cliff Floyd	.20	.50
54 Chad Cordero	.20	.50
55 Jose Vidro	.20	.50
56 Jose Guillen	.20	.50
57 Nick Johnson	.20	.50
58 Miguel Tejada	.30	.75
59 Melvin Mora	.20	.50
60 Javy Lopez	.20	.50
61 Khalil Greene	.20	.50
62 Brian Giles	.20	.50
63 Trevor Hoffman	.30	.75
64 Bobby Abreu	.20	.50
65 Jimmy Rollins	.30	.75
66 Pat Burrell	.20	.50
67 Billy Wagner	.20	.50
68 Jack Wilson	.20	.50
69 Zach Duke	.20	.50
70 Craig Wilson	.20	.50
71 Mark Teixeira	.50	1.25
72 Hank Blalock	.20	.50
73 David Dellucci	.20	.50
74 Manny Ramirez	.50	1.25
75 Johnny Damon	.30	.75
76 Jason Varitek	.50	1.25
77 Trot Nixon	.20	.50
78 Adam Dunn	.30	.75
79 Felipe Lopez	.20	.50
80 Brandon Claussen	.20	.50
81 Sean Casey	.20	.50
82 Todd Helton	.30	.75
83 Clint Barmes	.20	.50
84 Matt Holliday	.50	1.25
85 Mike Sweeney	.20	.50
86 Zack Greinke	.30	.75
87 David DeJesus	.20	.50
88 Ivan Rodriguez	.30	.75
89 Jeremy Bonderman	.20	.50
90 Magglio Ordonez	.30	.75
91 Torii Hunter	.20	.50
92 Joe Nathan	.20	.50
93 Michael Cuddyer	.20	.50
94 Paul Konerko	.30	.75
95 Jermaine Dye	.20	.50
96 Jon Garland	.20	.50
97 Alex Rodriguez	.75	2.00
98 Hideki Matsui	.50	1.25
99 Jason Giambi	.20	.50
100 Mariano Rivera	.50	1.25
101 Adrian Beltre AU/99	15.00	40.00
102 Matt Cain AU/275 (RC)	8.00	20.00
103 Craig Biggio AU/99	30.00	60.00
104 Eric Chavez AU/99	12.50	30.00
105 J.D. Drew AU/99	12.50	30.00
106 Eric Gagne AU/99	20.00	50.00
107 Tim Hudson AU/99	15.00	40.00
108 Tom Glavine AU/275	20.00	50.00
109 David Ortiz AU/99	40.00	80.00
110 Scott Rolen AU/275	15.00	40.00
111 Johan Santana AU/99	20.00	50.00
112 Curt Schilling AU/96	40.00	80.00
113 John Smoltz AU/99	30.00	60.00
114 Alfonso Soriano AU/99	30.00	60.00
115 Kerry Wood AU/99	12.50	30.00
116 Edwin Jackson AU/99	8.00	20.00
117 Felix Hernandez AU/125	20.00	50.00
118 Prince Fielder AU/99 (RC)	30.00	60.00
119 Vladimir Guerrero AU/86	30.00	60.00
120 Roger Clemens AU/99	30.00	60.00
121 Albert Pujols AU/45	175.00	300.00
122 Chris Carpenter AU/99	20.00	50.00
123 Derrek Lee AU/99	15.00	40.00
124 Dontrelle Willis AU/99	12.50	30.00
125 Roy Oswalt AU/99	15.00	40.00
126 Ryan Garko AU/275 (RC)	10.00	25.00
127 Tadahito Iguchi AU/275	20.00	50.00
128 Mark Loretta AU/275	10.00	25.00
129 Joe Mauer AU/275	40.00	80.00
130 Victor Martinez AU/275	8.00	20.00
131 Wily Mo Pena AU/275	10.00	25.00
132 Oliver Perez AU/274	6.00	15.00
134 Ben Sheets AU/275	10.00	25.00
135 Michael Young AU/275	10.00	25.00
136 Jonny Gomes AU/275	6.00	15.00
137 Derek Jeter AU/99	125.00	200.00
139 Ryan Zimmerman AU/275 (RC)	10.00	25.00
140 Scott Baker AU/275 (RC)	6.00	15.00
141 Huston Street AU/275	10.00	25.00
143 Ryan Howard AU/275	40.00	80.00
145 Travis Hafner AU/275	10.00	25.00
146 Brian Myrow AU/275 RC	6.00	15.00
147 Scott Podsednik AU/275	10.00	25.00
148 Brian Roberts AU/275	10.00	25.00
149 Grady Sizemore AU/135	15.00	40.00
150 Chris Demaria AU/275 RC	6.00	15.00
151 Jonah Bayliss AU/275 RC	6.00	15.00
152 Geovany Soto AU/275 (RC)	15.00	40.00
153 Lyle Overbay AU/275	6.00	15.00
154 Joey Devine AU/275 RC	6.00	15.00
155 Alejandro Freire AU/275 RC	6.00	15.00
156 Conor Jackson AU/275 (RC)	10.00	25.00
157 Danny Sandoval AU/275 RC	6.00	15.00
158 Chase Utley AU/275	20.00	50.00
159 Jeff Harris AU/275 RC	6.00	15.00
160 Ron Flores AU/275 RC	6.00	15.00
161 Scott Feldman AU/275 RC	6.00	15.00
162 Yadier Molina AU/275	15.00	40.00
163 Tim Corcoran AU/275 RC	6.00	15.00
164 Craig Hansen AU/275 RC	15.00	40.00
165 Jason Bergmann AU/275 RC	6.00	15.00
166 Craig Breslow AU/275 RC	6.00	15.00
167 Jhonny Peralta AU/275	6.00	15.00
168 Jeremy Hermida AU/275 (RC)	10.00	25.00
169 Scott Kazmir AU/275	10.00	25.00
170 Bobby Crosby AU/99	12.50	30.00
171 Rich Harden AU/275	6.00	15.00
172 Casey Kotchman AU/275	6.00	15.00
173 Tim Hamulack AU/275 (RC)	6.00	15.00
174 Justin Morneau AU/275	12.50	30.00
175 Jake Peavy AU/275	10.00	25.00
176 Yuniesky Betancourt AU/275	10.00	25.00
177 Jeremy Accardo AU/275 RC	6.00	15.00
178 Jorge Cantu AU/200	10.00	25.00
179 Marlon Byrd AU/275	6.00	15.00
180 Ryan Jorgensen AU/275 RC	6.00	15.00
181 Chris Denorfia AU/275 (RC)	6.00	15.00
182 Steve Stemle AU/275 RC	6.00	15.00
183 Robert Andino AU/275 RC	6.00	15.00
184 Chris Heintz AU/275 RC	6.00	15.00

2006 Sweet Spot Signatures Red Stitch Blue Ink

*RS BLUE p/r 114-150: .4X TO 1X p/r 125-275
*RS BLUE p/r 114-150: .3X TO .8X p/r 99
*RS BLUE p/r 75-100: .5X TO 1.2X p/r 125-275
*RS BLUE p/r 40: .6X TO 1.5X p/r 125-275
OVERALL AUTO ODDS 1:12
PRINT RUNS B/WN 15-150 COPIES PER
NO PRICING ON QTY OF 25 OR LESS
EXCHANGE DEADLINE 05/25/08

Card	Low	High
144 Mike Piazza/100	50.00	100.00

2006 Sweet Spot Signatures Black Stitch Black Ink

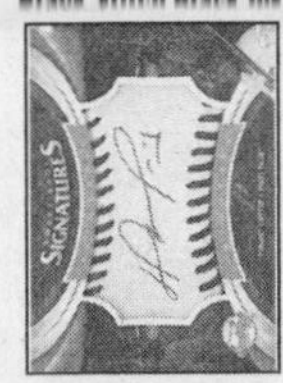

OVERALL AUTO ODDS 1:12
STATED PRINT RUN 1 SERIAL #'d SET
NO PRICING DUE TO SCARCITY
EXCHANGE DEADLINE 05/25/08

2006 Sweet Spot Signatures Black Stitch Blue Ink

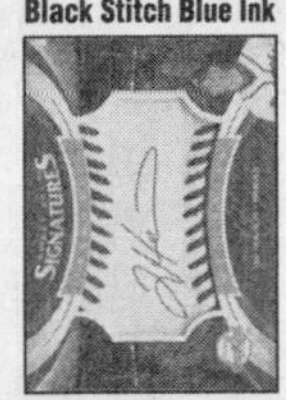

OVERALL AUTO ODDS 1:12
STATED PRINT RUN 1 SERIAL #'d SET
NO PRICING DUE TO SCARCITY
EXCHANGE DEADLINE 05/25/08

2006 Sweet Spot Signatures Red-Blue Stitch Black Ink

*RBS BLK p/r 50-99: .5X TO 1.2X p/r 125-275
*RBS BLACK p/r 50-99: .4X TO 1X p/r 86-99
*RBS BLACK p/r 45-49: .5X TO 1.2X p/r 86-99
OVERALL AUTO ODDS 1:12
PRINT RUNS B/WN 25-99 COPIES PER
NO PRICING ON QTY OF 25 OR LESS
EXCHANGE DEADLINE 05/25/08

2006 Sweet Spot Signatures Red-Blue Stitch Blue Ink

*RBS BLUE p/r 50: .5X TO 1.2X p/r 125-275
*RBS BLUE p/r 50: .4X TO 1X p/r 86-99
*RBS BLUE p/r 30-49: .6X TO 1.5X p/r 125-275
OVERALL AUTO ODDS 1:12
PRINT RUNS B/WN 5-50 COPIES PER
NO PRICING ON QTY OF 25 OR LESS
EXCHANGE DEADLINE 05/25/08

Card	Low	High
144 Mike Piazza/50	60.00	120.00

2006 Sweet Spot Signatures Bat Barrel Black Ink

OVERALL AU ODDS 1:12
PRINT RUNS B/WN 13-25 COPIES PER
NO PRICING DUE TO SCARCITY
EXCHANGE DEADLINE 05/25/08

2006 Sweet Spot Signatures Bat Barrel Blue Ink

OVERALL AU ODDS 1:12
STATED PRINT RUN 5 SERIAL #'d SETS
FELDMAN PRINT RUN 3 SER. #'d SETS
NO PRICING DUE TO SCARCITY
EXCHANGE DEADLINE 05/25/08

2006 Sweet Spot Signatures Glove Leather Black Ink

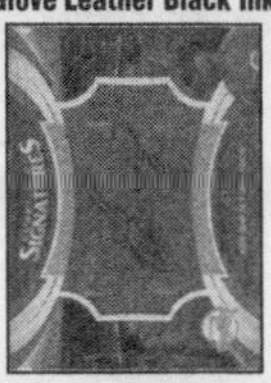

OVERALL AU ODDS 1:12
PRINT RUNS B/WN 5-15 COPIES PER
NO PRICING DUE TO SCARCITY
EXCHANGE DEADLINE 05/25/08

2006 Sweet Spot Signatures Glove Leather Blue Ink

OVERALL AU ODDS 1:12
STATED PRINT RUN 5 SERIAL #'d SETS
HARDEN PRINT RUN 4 SER. #'d SETS
NO PRICING DUE TO SCARCITY
EXCHANGE DEADLINE 05/25/08

2006 Sweet Spot Super Sweet Swatch

OVERALL GU ODDS 1:12
PRINT RUNS B/WN 5-299 COPIES PER
NO PRICING ON QTY OF 9 OR LESS

Card	Low	High
AD Adam Dunn Jsy/299	4.00	10.00
AE Adam Eaton Jsy/299	3.00	8.00
AJ Andruw Jones Jsy/299	5.00	12.00
AN Andy Pettitte Jsy/299	5.00	12.00
AP Albert Pujols Jsy/299	10.00	25.00
AT Garrett Atkins Jsy/299	3.00	8.00
BA Bobby Abreu Jsy/299	4.00	10.00
BC Brandon Claussen Jsy/299	3.00	8.00
BE Josh Beckett Jsy/299	4.00	10.00
BG Brian Giles Jsy/299	3.00	8.00
BS Ben Sheets Jsy/299	4.00	10.00
BW Bernie Williams Bat/299	5.00	12.00
BZ Barry Zito Jsy/299	4.00	10.00
CB Craig Biggio Jsy/299	4.00	10.00
CD Carlos Delgado Bat/299	5.00	12.00
CJ Chipper Jones Jsy/299	6.00	15.00
CR Bobby Crosby Bat/136	4.00	10.00
CS Curt Schilling Jsy/299	5.00	12.00
DJ Derek Jeter Bat/299	15.00	40.00
DL Derrek Lee Jsy/299	4.00	10.00
DO David Ortiz Jsy/299	6.00	15.00
DW Dontrelle Willis Jsy/299	4.00	10.00
DY Jermaine Dye Jsy/299	4.00	10.00
EC Eric Chavez Jsy/299	4.00	10.00
ED Jim Edmonds Bat/257	5.00	12.00
EG Eric Gagne Jsy/299	4.00	10.00
FG Freddy Garcia Jsy/299	3.00	8.00
FH Felix Hernandez Jsy/299	4.00	10.00
FR Jeff Francoeur Jsy/299	10.00	25.00
FT Frank Thomas Jsy/299	6.00	15.00
GA Garret Anderson Jsy/299	4.00	10.00
GL Tom Glavine Jsy/299	5.00	12.00
GR Grady Sizemore Jsy/299	5.00	12.00
GS Gary Sheffield Bat/189	4.00	10.00
HA Travis Hafner Jsy/299	4.00	10.00
HB Hank Blalock Jsy/299	4.00	10.00
HE Ramon Hernandez Bat/272	3.00	8.00
HO Trevor Hoffman Jsy/299	4.00	10.00
HU Torii Hunter Bat/287	4.00	10.00
HY Roy Halladay Jsy/299	4.00	10.00
IR Ivan Rodriguez Jsy/299	5.00	12.00
JA Jay Payton Bat/193	3.00	8.00
JB Jason Bay Jsy/299	4.00	10.00
JE Johnny Estrada Jsy/299	3.00	8.00
JG Jason Giambi Jsy/299	6.00	15.00
JJ Jacque Jones Jsy/299	4.00	10.00
JL Jeff Bagwell Jsy/299	5.00	12.00
JM Joe Mauer Jsy/299	5.00	12.00
JO John Smoltz Jsy/299	5.00	12.00
JP Jorge Posada Jsy/299	8.00	20.00
JR Jose Reyes Jsy/299	4.00	10.00
JS Jason Schmidt Jsy/299	4.00	10.00
JU Justin Morneau Jsy/299	4.00	10.00
JV Jason Varitek Jsy/299	6.00	15.00
JW Jack Wilson Jsy/299	3.00	8.00
KG Ken Griffey Jr. Jsy/299	15.00	40.00
KO Paul Konerko Jsy/299	4.00	10.00
KW Kerry Wood Jsy/299	4.00	10.00
LB Lance Berkman Bat/299	4.00	10.00
MA Matt Cain Jsy/299	5.00	12.00
MC Matt Clement Jsy/299	4.00	10.00
MG Marcus Giles Jsy/299	3.00	8.00
MI Miguel Cabrera Jsy/299	5.00	12.00
ML Mark Loretta Bat/267	3.00	8.00
MM Mark Mulder Jsy/299	4.00	10.00
MO Maggio Ordonez Bat/9		
MP Mark Prior Jsy/299	4.00	10.00
MR Manny Ramirez Jsy/299	5.00	12.00
MS Mike Sweeney Jsy/299	3.00	8.00
MT Miguel Tejada Jsy/299	4.00	10.00
MY Michael Young Bat/221	4.00	10.00
NJ Nick Johnson Jsy/299	3.00	8.00
NL Noah Lowry Jsy/299	3.00	8.00
NS Nick Swisher Jsy/299	4.00	10.00
PE Jake Peavy Jsy/299	4.00	10.00
PF Prince Fielder Jsy/299	8.00	20.00
PI Mike Piazza Jsy/299	6.00	15.00
PM Pedro Martinez Jsy/299	5.00	12.00
RB Rocco Baldelli Jsy/299	3.00	8.00
RH Ryan Howard Jsy/299	12.50	30.00
RK Ryan Klesko Jsy/299	3.00	8.00
RO Roy Oswalt Jsy/299	4.00	10.00
RS Richie Sexson Jsy/299	3.00	8.00
RW Rickie Weeks Jsy/299	4.00	10.00
RZ Ryan Zimmerman Jsy/299	10.00	25.00
SA Johan Santana Jsy/299	5.00	12.00
SF Steve Finley Bat/5		
SK Scott Kazmir Jsy/299	4.00	10.00
SR Scott Rolen Jsy/299	5.00	12.00
ST Huston Street Jsy/299	4.00	10.00
TG Troy Glaus Bat/160	4.00	10.00
TH Tim Hudson Jsy/299	4.00	10.00
TN Trot Nixon Jsy/299	5.00	12.00
TO Todd Helton Bat/232	5.00	12.00
TX Mark Teixeira Jsy/299	4.00	10.00
VG Vladimir Guerrero Jsy/299	6.00	15.00
VM Victor Martinez Jsy/299	4.00	10.00
VW Vernon Wells Jsy/299	4.00	10.00
WE David Wells Jsy/299	3.00	8.00
ZD Zach Duke Jsy/299	3.00	8.00

2006 Sweet Spot Super Sweet Swatch Gold

*GOLD: .5X TO 1.2X BASIC
OVERALL GU ODDS 1:12
STATED PRINT RUN 75 SERIAL #'d SETS

Card	Low	High
MO Magglio Ordonez Bat	5.00	12.00
SF Steve Finley Bat	5.00	12.00

2006 Sweet Spot Super Sweet Swatch Platinum

*PLATINUM: .6X TO 1.5X BASIC
OVERALL GU ODDS 1:12
STATED PRINT RUN 45 SERIAL #'d SETS

Card	Low	High
MO Magglio Ordonez Bat	6.00	15.00
SF Steve Finley Bat	6.00	15.00

2007 Sweet Spot

Card	Low	High
COMMON CARD (1-100)	.75	2.00

STATED PRINT RUN 850 SER.#'d SETS
TWO BASE CARDS PER TIN

Card	Low	High
COMMON AU RC (101-142)	3.00	8.00

OVERALL AU ODDS ONE PER TIN
EXCHANGE DEADLINE 11/9/2009

Card	Low	High
1 Adam Dunn	1.25	3.00
2 Adrian Beltre	.75	2.00
3 Albert Pujols	5.00	12.00
4 Alex Rios	1.25	3.00
5 Alex Rodriguez	3.00	8.00
6 Alfonso Soriano	1.25	3.00
7 Andruw Jones	.75	2.00
8 Aramis Ramirez	.75	2.00
9 B.J. Upton	.75	2.00
10 Barry Zito	.75	2.00
11 Bartolo Colon	.75	2.00
12 Ben Sheets	.75	2.00
13 Bill Hall	.75	2.00
14 Brad Penny	.75	2.00
15 Brandon Webb	1.25	3.00
16 C.C. Sabathia	1.25	3.00
17 Carl Crawford	1.25	3.00
18 Carlos Beltran	.75	2.00
19 Carlos Guillen	.75	2.00
20 Carlos Lee	.75	2.00
21 Chase Utley	2.00	5.00
22 Chien-Ming Wang	1.25	3.00
23 Chipper Jones	2.00	5.00
24 Chris Carpenter	2.00	5.00
25 Cole Hamels	2.00	5.00
26 Craig Biggio	1.25	3.00
27 Curt Schilling	1.25	3.00
28 Dan Haren	.75	2.00
29 David Ortiz	1.25	3.00
30 David Wright	3.00	8.00
31 Delmon Young	1.25	3.00
32 Derek Jeter	5.00	12.00
33 Derrek Lee	.75	2.00
34 Dontrelle Willis	.75	2.00
35 Felix Hernandez	2.00	5.00
36 Frank Thomas	2.00	5.00
37 Gil Meche	.75	2.00
38 Grady Sizemore	1.25	3.00
39 Greg Maddux	3.00	8.00
40 Ian Kinsler	1.25	3.00
41 Ichiro Suzuki	3.00	8.00
42 Ivan Rodriguez	1.25	3.00
43 Jake Peavy	.75	2.00
44 Jason Bay	1.25	3.00
45 Jason Varitek	2.00	5.00
46 Jeff Kent	.75	2.00
47 Jermaine Dye	.75	2.00
48 Jim Edmonds	1.25	3.00
49 Jim Thome	1.25	3.00
50 Jimmy Rollins	1.25	3.00
51 Joe Mauer	2.00	5.00
52 Johan Santana	2.00	5.00
53 John Smoltz	2.00	5.00
54 Jonathan Papelbon	2.00	5.00
55 Jorge Posada	1.25	3.00
56 Jose Reyes	1.25	3.00
57 Josh Beckett	1.25	3.00
58 Justin Morneau	2.00	5.00
59 Justin Verlander	2.50	6.00
60 Ken Griffey Jr.	3.00	8.00
61 Kenji Johjima	2.00	5.00
62 Lance Berkman	1.25	3.00
63 Magglio Ordonez	1.25	3.00
64 Manny Ramirez	2.00	5.00
65 Mariano Rivera	2.00	5.00
66 Mark Buehrle	1.25	3.00
67 Mark Teixeira	2.00	5.00
68 Matt Holliday	2.00	5.00
69 Matt Morris	.75	2.00
70 Melvin Mora	.75	2.00
71 Michael Young	1.25	3.00
72 Miguel Cabrera	2.00	5.00
73 Miguel Tejada	1.25	3.00
74 Mike Lowell	.75	2.00
75 Mike Mussina	1.25	3.00
76 Mike Piazza	2.00	5.00
77 Nick Swisher	2.00	5.00
78 Orlando Hudson	.75	2.00
79 Paul Konerko	1.25	3.00
80 Paul Lo Duca	.75	2.00
81 Pedro Martinez	1.25	3.00
82 Prince Fielder	1.25	3.00
83 Randy Johnson	2.00	5.00
84 Rickie Weeks	1.25	3.00
85 Roger Clemens	2.50	6.00
86 Roy Halladay	2.00	5.00
87 Roy Oswalt	1.25	3.00
88 Russell Martin	.75	2.00
89 Ryan Howard	3.00	8.00
90 Ryan Zimmerman	1.25	3.00
91 Sammy Sosa	2.00	5.00
92 Scott Rolen	1.25	3.00
93 Shawn Green	.75	2.00
94 Todd Helton	1.25	3.00
95 Tom Glavine	1.25	3.00
96 Torii Hunter	.75	2.00
97 Travis Hafner	.75	2.00
98 Vernon Wells	.75	2.00
99 Victor Martinez	1.25	3.00
100 Vladimir Guerrero	2.00	5.00
101 Adam Lind AU (RC)	3.00	8.00
102 Akinori Iwamura AU SP RC	10.00	25.00
103 Alex Gordon AU RC	8.00	20.00
104 Alexi Casilla AU RC	6.00	15.00
105 Andy LaRoche AU (RC)	6.00	15.00
106 Billy Butler AU (RC)	6.00	15.00
107 Ryan Rowland-Smith AU RC	3.00	8.00
108 Brandon Wood AU (RC)	6.00	15.00
109 Brian Burres AU (RC)	3.00	8.00
110 Chase Wright AU RC	4.00	10.00
111 Chris Stewart AU RC	3.00	8.00
112 Daisuke Matsuzaka AU SP RC	60.00	120.00
113 Delmon Young AU SP (RC)	6.00	15.00
114 Andy Sonnanstine AU RC	6.00	15.00
115 Andrew Miller AU RC		
116 Fred Lewis AU (RC)	4.00	10.00
117 Glen Perkins AU SP (RC)	10.00	25.00
118 David Murphy AU (RC)	3.00	8.00
119 Hunter Pence AU (RC)	12.50	30.00
120 Jarrod Saltalamacchia AU (RC)	6.00	15.00
121 Jeff Baker AU SP (RC)	4.00	10.00
122 Jesus Flores AU SP RC	10.00	25.00
123 Joakim Soria AU SP RC	10.00	25.00
124 Joe Smith AU RC	4.00	10.00
125 Jon Knott AU (RC)	3.00	8.00
126 Josh Hamilton AU (RC)	20.00	50.00
127 Justin Hampson AU (RC)	3.00	8.00
128 Kei Igawa AU SP RC	10.00	25.00
129 Kevin Cameron AU RC	3.00	8.00
130 Matt Chico AU (RC)	4.00	10.00
131 Matt DeSalvo AU (RC)	4.00	10.00
132 Micah Owings AU SP (RC)	10.00	25.00
133 Michael Bourn AU (RC)	4.00	10.00
134 Miguel Montero AU (RC)	3.00	8.00
135 Phil Hughes AU SP (RC)	20.00	50.00
136 Rick Vanden Hurk AU RC	3.00	8.00
137 Ryan Sweeney AU SP (RC)		
138 Tim Lincecum AU RC		
139 Travis Buck AU (RC)	4.00	10.00
140 Troy Tulowitzki AU SP (RC)	12.50	30.00
141 Sean Henn AU (RC)	4.00	10.00
142 Zack Segovia AU (RC)	4.00	10.00
NNO Michael Buysner	15.00	40.00

2007 Sweet Spot Sweet Swatch Memorabilia

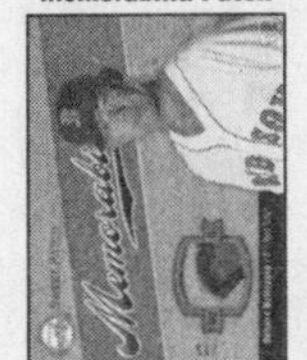

OVERALL MEM ODDS TWO PER TIN

Card	Low	High
AD Adam Dunn	3.00	8.00
AJ Andruw Jones	3.00	8.00
AP Albert Pujols	6.00	15.00
AS Alfonso Soriano	3.00	8.00
AT Garrett Atkins	3.00	8.00
BA Bobby Abreu	3.00	8.00
BE Josh Beckett	4.00	10.00
BG Brian Giles	3.00	8.00
BI Craig Biggio	3.00	8.00
BO Jeremy Bonderman	3.00	8.00
BR Brian Roberts	3.00	8.00
BU B.J. Upton	3.00	8.00
BW Billy Wagner	3.00	8.00
CA Chris Carpenter	3.00	8.00
CB Carlos Beltran	3.00	8.00
CC Carl Crawford	3.00	8.00
CD Carlos Delgado	3.00	8.00
CH Cole Hamels	3.00	8.00
CJ Chipper Jones	4.00	10.00
CL Carlos Lee	3.00	8.00
CS Curt Schilling	4.00	10.00
CU Chase Utley	4.00	10.00
DA Johnny Damon		
DJ Derek Jeter	8.00	20.00
DM Daisuke Matsuzaka	6.00	15.00
DO David Ortiz	5.00	12.00
DW Dontrelle Willis	3.00	8.00
EB Erik Bedard	3.00	8.00
EC Eric Chavez	3.00	8.00
FG Freddy Garcia	3.00	8.00
FH Felix Hernandez	3.00	8.00
FL Francisco Liriano	3.00	8.00
FT Frank Thomas	5.00	12.00
GA Garret Anderson	3.00	8.00
GM Greg Maddux	5.00	12.00
GR Khalil Greene	3.00	8.00
GS Grady Sizemore	3.00	8.00
HA Roy Halladay	3.00	8.00
HB Hank Blalock	3.00	8.00
HE Todd Helton	3.00	8.00
HO Trevor Hoffman	3.00	8.00
HR Hanley Ramirez	3.00	8.00
HS Huston Street	3.00	8.00
HU Torii Hunter	3.00	8.00
IK Ian Kinsler	3.00	8.00
IR Ivan Rodriguez	3.00	8.00
JB Jason Bay	3.00	8.00
JD Jermaine Dye	3.00	8.00
JE Jim Edmonds	4.00	10.00
JF Jeff Francoeur	4.00	10.00
JG Jason Giambi	3.00	8.00
JK Jeff Kent	3.00	8.00
JM Joe Mauer	3.00	8.00
JN Joe Nathan	3.00	8.00
JP Jake Peavy	3.00	8.00
JR Jimmy Rollins	3.00	8.00
JS Jason Schmidt	3.00	8.00
JT Jim Thome	3.00	8.00
JV Jason Varitek	5.00	12.00
JW Jered Weaver	3.00	8.00
JZ Joel Zumaya	3.00	8.00
KG Ken Griffey Jr.	6.00	15.00
KM Kendry Morales	3.00	8.00
LB Lance Berkman	3.00	8.00
LG Luis Gonzalez	3.00	8.00
MC Miguel Cabrera	3.00	8.00
MM Mike Mussina	3.00	8.00
MO Justin Morneau	3.00	8.00
MR Manny Ramirez	4.00	10.00
MT Mark Teixeira	3.00	8.00
MY Michael Young	3.00	8.00
OR Magglio Ordonez	3.00	8.00
OS Roy Oswalt	3.00	8.00
PA Jonathan Papelbon	5.00	12.00
PB Pat Burrell	3.00	8.00
PE Jhonny Peralta	3.00	8.00
PF Prince Fielder	3.00	8.00
PM Pedro Martinez	3.00	8.00
PO Jorge Posada	3.00	8.00
RC Robinson Cano	4.00	10.00
RE Jose Reyes	5.00	12.00
RH Rich Harden	3.00	8.00
RI Mariano Rivera	3.00	8.00
RJ Randy Johnson	3.00	8.00
RO Roger Clemens	6.00	15.00
RW Rickie Weeks	3.00	8.00
RZ Ryan Zimmerman	5.00	12.00
SA Johan Santana	3.00	8.00
SD Stephen Drew	3.00	8.00
SK Scott Kazmir	3.00	8.00
SM John Smoltz	4.00	10.00
SR Scott Rolen	3.00	8.00
TE Miguel Tejada	3.00	8.00
TG Tom Glavine	3.00	8.00
TH Tim Hudson	3.00	8.00
TR Travis Hafner	3.00	8.00
VE Justin Verlander	4.00	10.00
VG Vladimir Guerrero	3.00	8.00
VM Victor Martinez	3.00	8.00
VW Vernon Wells	3.00	8.00

2007 Sweet Spot Sweet Swatch Memorabilia Patch

OVERALL MEM ODDS TWO PER TIN
STATED PRINT RUN 25 SER.#'d SETS
NO PRICING DUE TO SCARCITY

2007 Sweet Spot Signatures Red Stitch Blue Ink

OVERALL AU ODDS ONE PER TIN
PRINT RUNS B/WN 99-350 COPIES PER
EXCHANGE DEADLINE 11/9/2009

Card	Low	High
AD Adam Dunn/99	12.50	30.00
AG Adrian Gonzalez/350	8.00	20.00
AI Akinori Iwamura/99	15.00	40.00
AK Austin Kearns/299	4.00	10.00

AL Adam LaRoche/350 4.00 10.00
AM Andrew Miller/99 15.00 40.00
AX Alex Gordon/99 12.50 30.00
BB Boof Bonser/299 4.00 10.00
BP Brandon Phillips/99 10.00 25.00
BR Brian Bruney/299 4.00 10.00
BW Brandon Wood/350 6.00 15.00
CA Carl Crawford/99 6.00 15.00
CB Chad Billingsley/299 4.00 10.00
CC Chris Capuano/299 4.00 10.00
CH Cole Hamels/99 15.00 40.00
CJ Conor Jackson/299 4.00 10.00
CK Casey Kotchman/99 6.00 15.00
CL Cliff Lee/299 30.00 60.00
CQ Carlos Quentin/299 5.00 12.00
CY Chris Young/350 4.00 10.00
DC Daniel Cabrera/299 4.00 10.00
DH Dan Haren/299 6.00 15.00
DR Darrel Rasner/299 4.00 10.00
DY Delmon Young/99 10.00 25.00
EA Erick Aybar/299 4.00 10.00
FH Felix Hernandez/99 15.00 40.00
FP Felix Pie/99 10.00 25.00
GP Glen Perkins/350 4.00 10.00
HA Travis Hafner/99 6.00 15.00
HK Howie Kendrick/350 4.00 10.00
HP Hunter Pence/350 20.00 50.00
HS Huston Street/99 6.00 15.00
JH Josh Hamilton/350 12.50 30.00
JK Jason Kubel/299 4.00 10.00
JL Jon Lester/99 10.00 25.00
JN Joe Nathan/299 4.00 10.00
JP Jonathan Papelbon/99 20.00 50.00
JS Jeremy Sowers/99 6.00 15.00
JV Jason Varitek/99 20.00 50.00
JW Josh Willingham/299 4.00 10.00
KA Jeff Karstens/299 4.00 10.00
KS Kurt Suzuki/299 4.00 10.00
LI Adam Lind/299 4.00 10.00
LO Lyle Overbay/299 4.00 10.00
MC Matt Cain/299 6.00 15.00
MM Melvin Mora/99 6.00 15.00
NS Nick Swisher/299 6.00 15.00
PH Phil Hughes/99 12.50 30.00
PK Paul Konerko/99 10.00 25.00
RC Roger Clemens/99 50.00 100.00
RH Rich Hill/299 6.00 15.00
RI Rich Harden/99 6.00 15.00
RW Rickie Weeks/99 6.00 15.00
RZ Ryan Zimmerman/99 12.50 30.00
SE Sergio Mitre/299 4.00 10.00
SK Scott Kazmir/99 10.00 25.00
TB Travis Buck/299 6.00 15.00
TG Tom Glavine/99 10.00 25.00
TL Tim Lincecum/99 75.00 150.00
VE Justin Verlander/99 20.00 50.00
VM Victor Martinez/99 6.00 15.00
YG Chris B. Young/299 6.00 15.00
NNO 756 Asterisk

2007 Sweet Spot Signatures Red-Blue Stitch Red Ink

OVERALL AU ODDS ONE PER TIN
PRINT RUNS B/WN 5-15 COPIES PER
NO PRICING DUE TO SCARCITY
EXCHANGE DEADLINE 11/9/2009

2007 Sweet Spot Signatures Black Stitch Black Ink

OVERALL AU ODDS ONE PER TIN
STATED PRINT RUN 1 SER.#'d SET
NO PRICING DUE TO SCARCITY
EXCHANGE DEADLINE 11/9/2009

2007 Sweet Spot Signatures Black-Silver Stitch Silver Ink

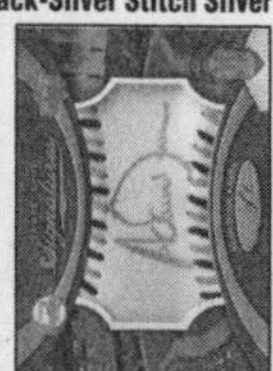

OVERALL AU ODDS ONE PER TIN
STATED PRINT RUN 1 SER.#'d SET
NO PRICING DUE TO SCARCITY
EXCHANGE DEADLINE 11/9/2009

2007 Sweet Spot Signatures Gold Stitch Gold Ink

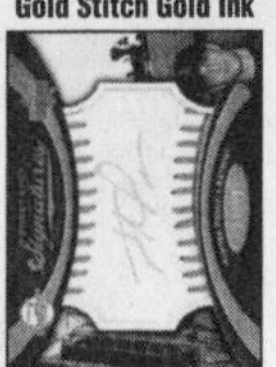

OVERALL AU ODDS ONE PER TIN
PRINT RUNS B/WN 25-99 COPIES PER
NO PRICING ON QTY 25 OR LESS
EXCHANGE DEADLINE 11/9/2009
AD Adam Dunn/25
AG Adrian Gonzalez/99 12.50 30.00
AI Akinori Iwamura/25
AK Austin Kearns/99 6.00 15.00
AL Adam LaRoche/99 6.00 15.00
AM Andrew Miller/25
AX Alex Gordon/25
BB Boof Bonser/99 6.00 15.00
BP Brandon Phillips/25
BR Brian Bruney/99 6.00 15.00
BW Brandon Wood/99 10.00 25.00
CA Carl Crawford/25
CB Chad Billingsley/99 10.00 25.00
CC Chris Capuano/99 6.00 15.00
CH Cole Hamels/25
CJ Conor Jackson/99 6.00 15.00
CK Casey Kotchman/25
CL Cliff Lee/99 40.00 80.00
CQ Carlos Quentin/99 8.00 20.00
CY Chris Young/99 6.00 15.00
DC Daniel Cabrera/99 6.00 15.00
DH Dan Haren/99 6.00 15.00
DR Darrel Rasner/99 6.00 15.00
DY Delmon Young/25
EA Erick Aybar/99 6.00 15.00
FH Felix Hernandez/25
FP Felix Pie/25
GP Glen Perkins/99 6.00 15.00
HA Travis Hafner/25
HK Howie Kendrick/99 6.00 15.00
HP Hunter Pence/99 40.00 80.00
HS Huston Street/25
JH Josh Hamilton/99 30.00 60.00
JK Jason Kubel/99 6.00 15.00
JL Jon Lester/25
JN Joe Nathan/99 6.00 15.00
JP Jonathan Papelbon/25
JS Jeremy Sowers/25
JV Jason Varitek/25
JW Josh Willingham/99 6.00 15.00
KA Jeff Karstens/99 6.00 15.00
KS Kurt Suzuki/99 6.00 15.00
LI Adam Lind/99 6.00 15.00
LO Lyle Overbay/99 6.00 15.00
MC Matt Cain/99 15.00 40.00
MH Matt Holliday/25
MM Melvin Mora/25
NS Nick Swisher/99 10.00 25.00
PH Phil Hughes/25
PK Paul Konerko/25
RC Roger Clemens/25
RH Rich Hill/99 10.00 25.00
RI Rich Harden/25
RW Rickie Weeks/25
RZ Ryan Zimmerman/25
SE Sergio Mitre/99 6.00 15.00
SK Scott Kazmir/25
TB Travis Buck/99 10.00 25.00
TG Tom Glavine/25
TH Torii Hunter/25
TL Tim Lincecum/25
VE Justin Verlander/25
VM Victor Martinez/25
YG Chris B. Young/99 10.00 25.00

2007 Sweet Spot Signatures Silver Stitch Silver Ink

OVERALL AU ODDS ONE PER TIN
PRINT RUNS B/WN 1-99 COPIES PER
NO PRICING ON QTY 25 OR LESS
EXCHANGE DEADLINE 11/9/2009
AD Adam Dunn/44 15.00 40.00
AG Adrian Gonzalez/23
AI Akinori Iwamura/1
AK Austin Kearns/25
AL Adam LaRoche/25
AM Andrew Miller/48 20.00 50.00
AX Alex Gordon/7
BB Boof Bonser/26 8.00 20.00
BP Brandon Phillips/99 10.00 25.00
BR Brian Bruney/99 6.00 15.00
BW Brandon Wood/3
CA Carl Crawford/13
CB Chad Billingsley/58 10.00 25.00
CC Chris Capuano/39 8.00 20.00
CH Cole Hamels/35 20.00 50.00
CJ Conor Jackson/16
CK Casey Kotchman/99 6.00 15.00
CL Cliff Lee/31 30.00 60.00
CQ Carlos Quentin/7
CY Chris Young/32 8.00 20.00
DC Daniel Cabrera/35 8.00 20.00
DH Dan Haren/15
DJ Derek Jeter/2
DJ2 Derek Jeter/2
DR Darrel Rasner/27 8.00 20.00
DY Delmon Young/26 12.50 30.00
EA Erick Aybar/32 8.00 20.00
FH Felix Hernandez/34 20.00 50.00
FP Felix Pie/99 10.00 25.00
GP Glen Perkins/60 6.00 15.00
HA Travis Hafner/48 8.00 20.00
HK Howie Kendrick/47 8.00 20.00
HP Hunter Pence/9
HS Huston Street/20
JH Josh Hamilton/33 20.00 50.00
JK Jason Kubel/16
JL Jon Lester/31 12.50 30.00
JN Joe Nathan/36 8.00 20.00
JP Jonathan Papelbon/58 20.00 50.00
JS Jeremy Sowers/45 8.00 20.00
JV Jason Varitek/33 30.00 60.00
JW Josh Willingham/14
KG Ken Griffey Jr./3
KG2 Ken Griffey Jr./3
KS Kurt Suzuki/99 6.00 15.00
LI Adam Lind/99 6.00 15.00
LO Lyle Overbay/17
MC Matt Cain/18
MH Matt Holliday/5
MM Melvin Mora/6
NS Nick Swisher/33 12.50 30.00
PH Phil Hughes/65 12.50 30.00
PK Paul Konerko/99 10.00 25.00
RC Roger Clemens/22
RH Rich Hill/51 10.00 25.00
RI Rich Harden/40 8.00 20.00
RW Rickie Weeks/23
RZ Ryan Zimmerman/11
SE Sergio Mitre/99 6.00 15.00
SK Scott Kazmir/19
TB Travis Buck/6
TG Tom Glavine/47 20.00 50.00
TH Torii Hunter/48 8.00 20.00
TL Tim Lincecum/55 100.00 175.00
VE Justin Verlander/35 30.00 60.00
VM Victor Martinez/41 8.00 20.00
YG Chris B. Young/24

2007 Sweet Spot Signatures Bat Barrel Blue Ink

OVERALL AU ODDS ONE PER TIN
PRINT RUNS B/WN 1-99 COPIES PER
NO PRICING ON QTY 25 OR LESS
EXCHANGE DEADLINE 11/9/2009
AD Adam Dunn/44 15.00 40.00
AG Adrian Gonzalez/23
AI Akinori Iwamura/1
AK Austin Kearns/25
AL Adam LaRoche/25
AM Andrew Miller/48 20.00 50.00
AX Alex Gordon/7
BB Boof Bonser/26 8.00 20.00
BP Brandon Phillips/99 10.00 25.00
BR Brian Bruney/99 6.00 15.00
BW Brandon Wood/3
CA Carl Crawford/13
CB Chad Billingsley/58 10.00 25.00
CC Chris Capuano/39 8.00 20.00
CH Cole Hamels/35 10.00 25.00
CJ Conor Jackson/16
CK Casey Kotchman/99 6.00 15.00
CL Cliff Lee/31 30.00 60.00
CQ Carlos Quentin/7
CY Chris Young/32 8.00 20.00
DC Daniel Cabrera/35 8.00 20.00
DH Dan Haren/15
DJ Derek Jeter/2
DJ2 Derek Jeter/2
DR Darrel Rasner/27 8.00 20.00
DY Delmon Young/26 12.50 30.00
EA Erick Aybar/23
FH Felix Hernandez/34 20.00 50.00
FP Felix Pie/99 10.00 25.00
GP Glen Perkins/60 6.00 15.00
HA Travis Hafner/48 8.00 20.00
HK Howie Kendrick/47 8.00 20.00
HP Hunter Pence/9
HS Huston Street/20
JH Josh Hamilton/33 30.00 60.00
JK Jason Kubel/16
JL Jon Lester/31 20.00 50.00
JN Joe Nathan/36 8.00 20.00
JP Jonathan Papelbon/58 20.00 50.00
JS Jeremy Sowers/45 8.00 20.00
JV Jason Varitek/33 30.00 60.00
JW Josh Willingham/14
KA Jeff Karstens/17
KS Kurt Suzuki/99 6.00 15.00
LI Adam Lind/99 6.00 15.00
LO Lyle Overbay/17
MC Matt Cain/18
MH Matt Holliday/5
MM Melvin Mora/6
NS Nick Swisher/33 12.50 30.00
PH Phil Hughes/65 12.50 30.00
PK Paul Konerko/99 10.00 25.00
RC Roger Clemens/22
RH Rich Hill/53 10.00 25.00
RW Rickie Weeks/23
RZ Ryan Zimmerman/11
SE Sergio Mitre/99 6.00 15.00
SK Scott Kazmir/19
TB Travis Buck/6
TG Tom Glavine/47 20.00 50.00
TL Tim Lincecum/55 100.00 175.00
VE Justin Verlander/35 30.00 60.00
VM Victor Martinez/41 8.00 20.00
YG Chris B. Young/24

2007 Sweet Spot Signatures Bat Barrel Gold Ink

OVERALL AU ODDS ONE PER TIN
STATED PRINT RUN 1 SER.#'d SET
NO PRICING DUE TO SCARCITY
EXCHANGE DEADLINE 11/9/2009

2007 Sweet Spot Signatures Bat Barrel Red Ink

OVERALL AU ODDS ONE PER TIN
STATED PRINT RUN 5 SER.#'d SETS
NO PRICING DUE TO SCARCITY
EXCHANGE DEADLINE 11/9/2009

2007 Sweet Spot Signatures Bat Barrel Silver Ink

OVERALL AU ODDS ONE PER TIN
PRINT RUNS B/WN 5-25 COPIES PER
NO PRICING DUE TO SCARCITY
EXCHANGE DEADLINE 11/9/2009

2007 Sweet Spot Signatures Black Bat Barrel Gold Ink

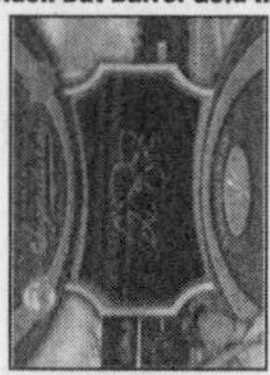

OVERALL AU ODDS ONE PER TIN
STATED PRINT RUN 1 SER.#'d SET
NO PRICING DUE TO SCARCITY
EXCHANGE DEADLINE 11/9/2009

2007 Sweet Spot Signatures Black Bat Barrel Red Ink

OVERALL AU ODDS ONE PER TIN
STATED PRINT RUN 5 SER.#'d SETS
NO PRICING DUE TO SCARCITY
EXCHANGE DEADLINE 11/9/2009

2007 Sweet Spot Signatures Black Bat Barrel Silver Ink

OVERALL AU ODDS ONE PER TIN
PRINT RUNS B/WN 5-15 COPIES PER
NO PRICING DUE TO SCARCITY
EXCHANGE DEADLINE 11/9/2009

2007 Sweet Spot Signatures Glove Leather Black Ink

OVERALL AU ODDS ONE PER TIN
PRINT RUNS B/WN 25-75 COPIES PER
NO PRICING DUE TO SCARCITY
EXCHANGE DEADLINE 11/9/2009
AD Adam Dunn/25
AG Adrian Gonzalez/75 12.50 30.00
AI Akinori Iwamura/25
AK Austin Kearns/75 6.00 15.00
AL Adam LaRoche/75 6.00 15.00
AM Andrew Miller/25
AX Alex Gordon/25
BB Boof Bonser/75 6.00 15.00
BP Brandon Phillips/25
BR Brian Bruney/75 6.00 15.00
BW Brandon Wood/75 10.00 25.00
CA Carl Crawford/25
CB Chad Billingsley/75 10.00 25.00
CC Chris Capuano/75 6.00 15.00
CH Cole Hamels/25
CJ Conor Jackson/75 6.00 15.00
CK Casey Kotchman/25
CL Cliff Lee/75 20.00 50.00
CQ Carlos Quentin/75 8.00 20.00
CY Chris Young/75 6.00 15.00
DC Daniel Cabrera/75 6.00 15.00
DH Dan Haren/75 6.00 15.00
DR Darrel Rasner/75 6.00 15.00
DY Delmon Young/25
EA Erick Aybar/75 6.00 15.00
FH Felix Hernandez/25
FP Felix Pie/25
GP Glen Perkins/75 6.00 15.00
HA Travis Hafner/25
HK Howie Kendrick/75 6.00 15.00
HP Hunter Pence/75 40.00 80.00
HS Huston Street/25
JB Jeff Baker/75
JH Josh Hamilton/75 40.00 80.00
JK Jason Kubel/75 6.00 15.00
JL Jon Lester/25
JN Joe Nathan/75 6.00 15.00
JP Jonathan Papelbon/25
JS Jeremy Sowers/25
JV Jason Varitek/25
KA Jeff Karstens/75 6.00 15.00
KS Kurt Suzuki/75 6.00 15.00
LO Lyle Overbay/75 6.00 15.00
MC Matt Cain/75 10.00 25.00
MM Melvin Mora/25
NS Nick Swisher/75 10.00 25.00
PH Phil Hughes/25
PK Paul Konerko/25
RC Roger Clemens/25
RH Rich Hill/75 10.00 25.00
RI Rich Harden/25
RM Russell Martin/75 15.00 40.00
RW Rickie Weeks/25
RZ Ryan Zimmerman/25
SE Sergio Mitre/75 6.00 15.00
SK Scott Kazmir/25
TB Travis Buck/75 10.00 25.00
TG Tom Glavine/25
TL Tim Lincecum/25
VE Justin Verlander/25
VM Victor Martinez/25
YG Chris B. Young/75 10.00 25.00

2007 Sweet Spot Signatures Glove Leather Green Ink

OVERALL AU ODDS ONE PER TIN
STATED PRINT RUN 1 SER.#'d SET
NO PRICING DUE TO SCARCITY
EXCHANGE DEADLINE 11/9/2009

2007 Sweet Spot Signatures Glove Leather Silver Ink

OVERALL AU ODDS ONE PER TIN
PRINT RUNS B/WN 5-25 COPIES PER
NO PRICING DUE TO SCARCITY
EXCHANGE DEADLINE 11/9/2009

2007 Sweet Spot Signatures Black Glove Leather Gold Ink

OVERALL AU ODDS ONE PER TIN
STATED PRINT RUN 5 SER.#'d SETS
NO PRICING DUE TO SCARCITY
EXCHANGE DEADLINE 11/9/2009

2007 Sweet Spot Signatures Black Glove Leather Metallic Blue Ink

OVERALL AU ODDS ONE PER TIN
STATED PRINT RUN 1 SER.#'d SET
NO PRICING DUE TO SCARCITY
EXCHANGE DEADLINE 11/9/2009

2007 Sweet Spot Signatures Black Glove Leather Silver Ink

OVERALL AU ODDS ONE PER TIN
PRINT RUNS B/WN 5-25 COPIES PER
NO PRICING DUE TO SCARCITY
EXCHANGE DEADLINE 11/9/2009

2007 Sweet Spot Dual Signatures Red Stitch Blue Ink

OVERALL AU ODDS ONE PER TIN
PRINT RUNS B/WN 5-15 COPIES PER
NO PRICING DUE TO SCARCITY
EXCHANGE DEADLINE 11/9/2009

2007 Sweet Spot Dual Signatures Black Stitch Black Ink

OVERALL AU ODDS ONE PER TIN
STATED PRINT RUN 1 SER.#'d SET
NO PRICING DUE TO SCARCITY
EXCHANGE DEADLINE 11/9/2009

2007 Sweet Spot Dual Signatures Gold Stitch Gold Ink

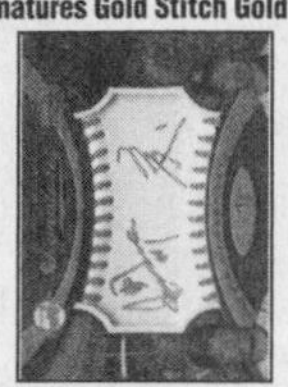

OVERALL AU ODDS ONE PER TIN
PRINT RUNS B/WN 5-10 COPIES PER
NO PRICING DUE TO SCARCITY
EXCHANGE DEADLINE 11/9/2009

2007 Sweet Spot Dual Signatures Silver Stitch Silver Ink

OVERALL AU ODDS ONE PER TIN
STATED PRINT RUN 5 SER.#'d SETS
NO PRICING DUE TO SCARCITY
EXCHANGE DEADLINE 11/9/2009

2007 Sweet Spot Dual Signatures Glove Leather Black Ink

OVERALL AU ODDS ONE PER TIN
PRINT RUNS B/WN 5-15 COPIES PER
NO PRICING DUE TO SCARCITY
EXCHANGE DEADLINE 11/9/2009

2007 Sweet Spot Dual Signatures Glove Leather Silver Ink

OVERALL AU ODDS ONE PER TIN
STATED PRINT RUN 1 SER.#'d SET
NO PRICING DUE TO SCARCITY
EXCHANGE DEADLINE 11/9/2009

2007 Sweet Spot Dual Signatures Black Glove Leather Gold Ink

OVERALL AU ODDS ONE PER TIN
PRINT RUNS B/WN 5-10 COPIES PER
NO PRICING DUE TO SCARCITY
EXCHANGE DEADLINE 11/9/2009

2007 Sweet Spot Dual Signatures Black Glove Leather Silver Ink

OVERALL AU ODDS ONE PER TIN
STATED PRINT RUN 1 SER.#'d SET
NO PRICING DUE TO SCARCITY
EXCHANGE DEADLINE 11/9/2009

2008 Sweet Spot

This set was released on December 23, 2008. The base set consists of 150 cards.

COMMON CARD (1-100) .40 1.00
COMMON AUTO (101-150) 3.00 8.00
AU PRINT RUNS B/WN 199-699 COPIES PER
OVERALL AUTO ODDS 1:3 PACKS
EXCH DEADLINE 11/10/2010
1 Aaron Harang .40 1.00
2 Aaron Rowand .40 1.00
3 Adam Dunn .60 1.50
4 Albert Pujols 2.50 6.00
5 Alex Gordon .60 1.50
6 Alex Rios .60 1.50
7 Alex Rodriguez 1.50 4.00
8 Alfonso Soriano .60 1.50
9 Andruw Jones .40 1.00
10 Aramis Ramirez .40 1.00
11 B.J. Upton .60 1.50
12 Barry Zito .40 1.00
13 Billy Butler .40 1.00
14 Brandon Phillips .40 1.00
15 Brandon Webb .60 1.50
16 Brian McCann .60 1.50
17 Brian Roberts .40 1.00
18 CC Sabathia .60 1.50
19 Carl Crawford .60 1.50
20 Carlos Beltran .40 1.00
21 Carlos Lee .40 1.00
22 Carlos Pena .60 1.50
23 Carlos Zambrano .60 1.50
24 Chase Utley 1.00 2.50
25 Chipper Jones 1.00 2.50
26 Chris B. Young .40 1.00
27 Chris Carpenter 1.00 2.50
28 Cole Hamels 1.00 2.50
29 Daisuke Matsuzaka 1.00 2.50
30 Dan Haren .40 1.00
31 Dan Uggla .60 1.50
32 David Ortiz .60 1.50
33 David Wright 1.25 3.00
34 Derek Jeter 2.50 6.00
35 Dontrelle Willis .40 1.00
36 Dustin Pedroia 1.25 3.00
37 Erik Bedard .40 1.00
38 Felix Hernandez 1.00 2.50
39 Frank Thomas 1.00 2.50
40 Freddy Sanchez .40 1.00
41 Gary Sheffield .40 1.00
42 Grady Sizemore .60 1.50
43 Greg Maddux 1.25 3.00
44 Hanley Ramirez 1.00 2.50
45 Hideki Matsui 1.00 2.50
46 Hunter Pence 1.00 2.50
47 Ichiro Suzuki 1.50 4.00
48 Ivan Rodriguez .60 1.50
49 Jake Peavy .40 1.00
50 Jason Bay .60 1.50
51 Jeff Francoeur .60 1.50
52 Jeff Kent .40 1.00
53 Jim Thome .60 1.50
54 Jimmy Rollins .60 1.50
55 Joba Chamberlain .60 1.50
56 Joe Blanton .40 1.00
57 Joe Mauer 1.00 2.50
58 Johan Santana 1.00 2.50
59 John Smoltz 1.00 2.50
60 Jonathan Papelbon .60 1.50
61 Jose Reyes .60 1.50
62 Josh Beckett .60 1.50
63 Josh Hamilton 1.00 2.50
64 Justin Morneau 1.00 2.50
65 Justin Verlander 1.25 3.00
66 Ken Griffey Jr. 1.50 4.00
67 Lance Berkman .60 1.50
68 Lastings Milledge .40 1.00
69 Magglio Ordonez .60 1.50
70 Manny Ramirez 1.00 2.50
71 Mariano Rivera 1.00 2.50
72 Mark Teixeira 1.00 2.50
73 Matt Holliday 1.00 2.50
74 Michael Young .60 1.50
75 Miguel Cabrera 1.00 2.50
76 Miguel Tejada .60 1.50
77 Mike Lowell .40 1.00
78 Nick Markakis 1.00 2.50
79 Nick Swisher 1.00 2.50
80 Paul Konerko .60 1.50
81 Pedro Martinez .60 1.50
82 Phil Hughes 1.00 2.50
83 Prince Fielder .60 1.50
84 Randy Johnson 1.00 2.50
85 Rich Harden .40 1.00
86 Robinson Cano 1.00 2.50
87 Roy Oswalt .60 1.50
88 Russell Martin .40 1.00
89 Ryan Braun 1.25 3.00
90 Ryan Howard 1.25 3.00
91 Ryan Zimmerman .60 1.50
92 Scott Rolen .60 1.50
93 Tom Glavine .60 1.50
94 Torii Hunter .40 1.00
95 Travis Hafner .40 1.00
96 Trevor Hoffman .60 1.50
97 Troy Tulowitzki 1.00 2.50
98 Vernon Wells .40 1.00
99 Victor Martinez .60 1.50
100 Vladimir Guerrero 1.00 2.50
101 Alex Romero AU/499 (RC) 3.00 8.00
102 Alexei Ramirez AU/399 RC 20.00 50.00
103 Bobby Korecky AU/399 RC 3.00 8.00
104 Bobby Wilson AU/499 RC 3.00 8.00
105 Brad Harman AU/699 RC 3.00 8.00
106 Brandon Boggs AU/699 (RC) 3.00 8.00
107 Brent Lillibridge AU/399 (RC) 4.00 10.00
108 Brian Barton AU/699 RC 3.00 8.00
109 Brian Bass AU/699 (RC) 3.00 8.00
110 Brian Bixler AU/699 (RC) 3.00 8.00
111 Brian Bocock AU/399 RC 3.00 8.00
112 Burke Badenhop AU/699 RC 3.00 8.00
113 Chin-Lung Hu AU/199 (RC) 12.50 30.00
114 Clay Buchholz AU/199 (RC) 12.50 30.00
115 Clay Timpner AU/699 (RC) 3.00 8.00
116 Cory Wade AU/699 (RC) 3.00 8.00
117 Daric Barton AU/399 (RC) 3.00 8.00
118 Eider Torres AU/699 (RC) 3.00 8.00
119 Jonathan Van Every AU/399 RC 3.00 8.00
120 Emmanuel Burriss AU/399 RC 3.00 8.00
121 Evan Longoria AU/249 RC 60.00 120.00
122 Felipe Paulino AU/499 RC 3.00 8.00
123 Fernando Hernandez AU/499 RC 3.00 8.00
124 German Duran AU/499 RC 3.00 8.00
125 Greg Smith AU/399 RC 3.00 8.00
126 Hernan Iribarren AU/699 (RC) EXCH 3.00 8.00
127 Ian Kennedy AU/249 RC 8.00 20.00
128 Jed Lowrie AU/349 (RC) 10.00 25.00
129 Jeff Clement AU/199 (RC) 15.00 40.00
130 Jesse Carlson AU/649 RC 3.00 8.00
131 Johnny Cueto AU/249 RC 6.00 15.00
132 Jonathan Albaladejo AU/399 RC
133 Clayton Kershaw AU/199 RC 15.00 40.00
134 Josh Newman AU/699 RC 3.00 8.00
135 Justin Masterson AU/399 RC 12.50 30.00
136 Kevin Hart AU/399 (RC) 3.00 8.00
137 Luke Hochevar AU/199 RC 6.00 15.00
138 Jay Bruce AU/399 (RC) 8.00 20.00
139 Max Scherzer AU/299 RC 10.00 25.00
140 Nick Adenhart AU/399 (RC) 8.00 20.00
141 Nick Blackburn AU/399 RC 4.00 10.00
142 Nyjer Morgan AU/399 (RC) 4.00 10.00
143 Ramon Troncoso AU/699 RC 3.00 8.00
144 Randor Bierd AU/499 RC 3.00 8.00
145 Rich Thompson AU/399 RC 3.00 8.00
146 Robinzon Diaz AU/699 (RC) 3.00 8.00
147 Ross Ohlendorf AU/399 RC 3.00 8.00
148 Steve Holm AU/699 RC 3.00 8.00
149 Wesley Wright AU/499 RC 3.00 8.00
150 Wladimir Balentien AU/399 (RC) 3.00 8.00

2008 Sweet Spot Rookie Signatures 50

OVERALL AU ODDS 1:3 PACKS
STATED PRINT RUN 50 SER.#'d SETS
EXCH DEADLINE 11/10/2010
101 Alex Romero AU 5.00 12.00
102 Alexei Ramirez AU 50.00 100.00
103 Bobby Korecky AU 5.00 12.00
104 Bobby Wilson AU 5.00 12.00
105 Brad Harman AU 5.00 12.00
106 Brandon Boggs AU 5.00 12.00
107 Brent Lillibridge AU 6.00 15.00
108 Brian Barton AU 5.00 12.00
109 Brian Bass AU 5.00 12.00
110 Brian Bixler AU 5.00 12.00
111 Brian Bocock AU 5.00 12.00
112 Burke Badenhop AU 5.00 12.00
113 Chin-Lung Hu AU 20.00 50.00
114 Clay Buchholz AU 20.00 50.00
115 Clay Timpner AU 5.00 12.00
116 Cory Wade AU 5.00 12.00
117 Daric Barton AU 5.00 12.00
118 Eider Torres AU 5.00 12.00
119 Jonathan Van Every AU 5.00 12.00
120 Emmanuel Burriss AU 5.00 12.00
121 Evan Longoria AU 75.00 150.00
122 Felipe Paulino AU 5.00 12.00
123 Fernando Hernandez AU 5.00 12.00
124 German Duran AU 5.00 12.00
125 Greg Smith AU 5.00 12.00
126 Hernan Iribarren AU 5.00 12.00
127 Ian Kennedy AU 12.50 30.00

128 Jed Lowrie AU 15.00 40.00
129 Jeff Clement AU 30.00 60.00
130 Jesse Carlson AU 5.00 12.00
131 Johnny Cueto AU 10.00 25.00
132 Jonathan Albaladejo AU
133 Clayton Kershaw AU 20.00 50.00
134 Josh Newman AU 5.00 12.00
135 Justin Masterson AU 20.00 50.00
136 Kevin Hart AU 5.00 12.00
137 Luke Hochevar AU 10.00 25.00
138 Jay Bruce AU 20.00 50.00
139 Max Scherzer AU 15.00 40.00
140 Nick Adenhart AU 12.50 30.00
141 Nick Blackburn AU 6.00 15.00
142 Nyjer Morgan AU 6.00 15.00
143 Ramon Troncoso AU 5.00 12.00
144 Randor Bierd AU 5.00 12.00
145 Rich Thompson AU 5.00 12.00
146 Robinzon Diaz AU 5.00 12.00
147 Ross Ohlendorf AU 5.00 12.00
148 Steve Holm AU 5.00 12.00
149 Wesley Wright AU 5.00 12.00
150 Wladimir Balentien AU 5.00 12.00

2008 Sweet Spot Signatures Bat Barrel Black Ink
OVERALL AU ODDS 1:3 PACKS
PRINT RUNS B/WN 1-51 COPIES PER
NO PRICING ON QTY 25 OR LESS
EXCH DEADLINE 11/10/2010
JR Jose Reyes/51 20.00 50.00

2008 Sweet Spot Signatures Bat Barrel Blue Ink
OVERALL AU ODDS 1:3 PACKS
PRINT RUNS B/WN 1-75 COPIES PER
NO PRICING ON QTY 25 OR LESS
EXCH DEADLINE 11/10/2010
JR Jose Reyes/30 30.00 60.00
RC Roger Clemens/28 50.00 100.00
TG Tony Gwynn/75 20.00 50.00

2008 Sweet Spot Signatures Bat Barrel Gold Ink
OVERALL AU ODDS 1:3 PACKS
STATED PRINT RUN 1 SER.#'d SET
NO PRICING DUE TO SCARCITY
EXCH DEADLINE 11/10/2010

2008 Sweet Spot Signatures Bat Barrel Red Ink
OVERALL AU ODDS 1:3 PACKS
PRINT RUNS B/WN 4-10 COPIES PER
NO PRICING DUE TO SCARCITY
EXCH DEADLINE 11/10/2010

2008 Sweet Spot Signatures Bat Barrel Silver Ink
OVERALL AU ODDS 1:3 PACKS
PRINT RUNS B/WN 1-50 COPIES PER
NO PRICING ON QTY 10 OR LESS
EXCH DEADLINE 11/10/2010
TG Tony Gwynn/50 30.00 60.00

2008 Sweet Spot Signatures Black Glove Leather Silver Ink
OVERALL AU ODDS 1:3 PACKS
PRINT RUNS B/WN 3-250 COPIES PER
NO PRICING ON QTY 16 OR LESS
EXCH DEADLINE 11/10/2010
BD Bucky Dent/250 10.00 25.00
BG Bob Gibson/150 20.00 50.00
BH Bill Hall/250 5.00 12.00
BO Bobby Richardson/250 12.50 30.00
CB Chad Billingsley/246 8.00 20.00
CW Chien-Ming Wang/250 50.00 100.00
DB Don Baylor/100 6.00 15.00
DL Don Larsen/150 15.00 40.00
JH Josh Hamilton/150 15.00 40.00
KG Ken Griffey Jr./3
LB Lance Berkman/99 20.00 50.00
MA Daisuke Matsuzaka/16
MK Matt Kemp/245 15.00 40.00
SK Bill Skowron/250 8.00 20.00

2008 Sweet Spot Signatures Brown Glove Leather
OVERALL AU ODDS 1:3 PACKS
PRINT RUNS B/WN 10-150 COPIES PER
NO PRICING ON QTY 15 OR LESS
EXCH DEADLINE 11/10/2010
BG Bob Gibson/100 20.00 50.00
DB Don Baylor Blk Leather/150 6.00 15.00

2008 Sweet Spot Signatures Brown Glove Leather Black Ink
OVERALL AU ODDS 1:3 PACKS
PRINT RUNS B/WN 7-100 COPIES PER
NO PRICING ON QTY 20 OR LESS
EXCH DEADLINE 11/10/2010
AB Adrian Beltre/10
AE Andre Ethier/20
CH Cole Hamels/20
EE Edwin Encarnacion/100 6.00 15.00
FL Francisco Liriano/7
GR Ken Griffey Jr./20
JR Jose Reyes/38 30.00 60.00
JS John Smoltz/10
JV Justin Verlander/20
KG Ken Griffey Jr./20
KJ Kelly Johnson/100 6.00 15.00
SR2 Scott Rolen/15
TS Takashi Saito/20
VM Victor Martinez/20

2008 Sweet Spot Signatures Brown Glove Leather Silver Ink
OVERALL AU ODDS 1:3 PACKS
PRINT RUNS B/WN 1-150 COPIES PER
NO PRICING ON QTY 4 OR LESS
EXCH DEADLINE 11/10/2010
AE Andre Ethier/1
CH Cole Hamels/1
EE Edwin Encarnacion/150 6.00 15.00
FL Francisco Liriano/1
JK Jason Kubel/4
JP Jonathan Papelbon/1
KJ Kelly Johnson/150 6.00 15.00
TG Tony Gwynn/50 30.00 60.00
TS Takashi Saito/1

2008 Sweet Spot Signatures Ken Griffey Jr.
OVERALL AU ODDS 1:3 PACKS
PRINT RUNS B/WN 15-30 COPIES PER
NO PRICING ON QTY 15 OR LESS
EXCH DEADLINE 11/10/2010
KG1 Ken Griffey Jr. Bat/230 40.00 80.00
KG2 Ken Griffey Jr. Bat/230 40.00 80.00
KG3 Ken Griffey Jr. Bat/230 40.00 80.00
KG4 Ken Griffey Jr. Bat/230 40.00 80.00
KG5 Ken Griffey Jr. Bat/243 40.00 80.00
KG6 Ken Griffey Jr. 1997 AL MVP/300 40.00 80.00
KG7 Ken Griffey Jr. 1992 ASG MVP/135 50.00 100.00
KG8 Ken Griffey Jr. Gold Glove/15

2008 Sweet Spot Signatures Red Stitch Black Ink

OVERALL AU ODDS 1:3 PACKS
PRINT RUNS B/WN 1-366 COPIES PER
NO PRICING ON QTY 25 OR LESS
EXCH DEADLINE 11/10/2010
AB Adrian Beltre/84 6.00 15.00
BD Bucky Dent/145 8.00 20.00
BG Bob Gibson/250 15.00 40.00
BH Bill Hall/125 6.00 15.00
BM Bobby Murcer/250
BO Bobby Richardson/250 12.50 30.00
BPA Brandon Phillips/299 6.00 15.00
BPB Brandon Phillips/200 6.00 15.00
CB Craig Biggio/56
CB Chad Billingsley/250 8.00 20.00
CW Chien-Ming Wang/95 100.00 175.00
DB Don Baylor/250 5.00 12.00
DO David Ortiz/56 30.00 60.00
EC Eric Chavez/59 10.00 25.00
EE Edwin Encarnacion/250 5.00 12.00
EG Eric Gagne/59 5.00 12.00
JD J.D. Drew/45 20.00 50.00
JH Josh Hamilton/250 15.00 40.00
JR Jim Rice/99 15.00 40.00
JR Jose Reyes/27 30.00 60.00
JS John Smoltz/59 30.00 60.00
JS Johan Santana/32 30.00 60.00
JT Jim Thome/358 20.00 50.00
JV Justin Verlander/15
KJ Kelly Johnson/248 5.00 12.00
KW Kerry Wood/58 10.00 25.00
LO Lyle Overbay/366 5.00 12.00
MA Daisuke Matsuzaka/250 50.00 100.00
MK Matt Kemp/250 15.00 40.00
MM Mark Mulder/1
MY Michael Young/38 15.00 40.00
NR Nolan Ryan/12
OP Oliver Perez/43 12.50 30.00
RS Ryne Sandberg/226 20.00 50.00
RS2 Ryne Sandberg/265 20.00 50.00
SK Bill Skowron/250 8.00 20.00
SR Scott Rolen/207 5.00 12.00
TG Tony Gwynn/25
TG Tom Glavine/222 15.00 40.00
TH Tim Hudson/57 10.00 25.00
TH Travis Hafner/171 6.00 15.00
VM Victor Martinez/15

2008 Sweet Spot Signatures Red Stitch Blue Ink

OVERALL AU ODDS 1:3 PACKS
PRINT RUNS B/WN 1-315 COPIES PER
NO PRICING ON QTY 15 OR LESS
EXCH DEADLINE 11/10/2010
AB Adrian Beltre/74 8.00 20.00
AE Andre Ethier/250 10.00 25.00
AP Albert Pujols/45 150.00 250.00
AW Adam Wainwright/135 12.50 30.00
BB Boof Bonser/300 5.00 12.00
BR Brian Roberts/290 5.00 12.00
BR Brooks Robinson/48 20.00 50.00
CB Craig Biggio/49
CH Cole Hamels/300 12.50 30.00
CQ Carlos Quentin/315 12.50 30.00
CR Cal Ripken Jr./275 40.00 80.00
CR Cal Ripken Jr./275 40.00 80.00
CR3 Cal Ripken Jr./258 40.00 80.00
CY Carl Yastrzemski/50 20.00 50.00
DL Don Larsen/250 12.50 30.00
DO David Ortiz/49 30.00 60.00
DW Dontrelle Willis/174 5.00 12.00
EC Eric Chavez/49 12.50 30.00
EG Eric Gagne/49 6.00 15.00
FL Francisco Liriano/190 6.00 15.00
HK Hong-Chih Kuo/300 12.50 30.00
HK Harmon Killebrew/229 30.00 60.00
HR Hanley Ramirez/300 12.50 30.00
HS Huston Street/225 5.00 12.00
IK Ian Kinsler/150 12.50 30.00
JD J.D. Drew/49 20.00 50.00
JJ Josh Johnson/180 8.00 20.00
JK Jason Kubel/300 5.00 12.00
JM Joe Mauer/1
JN Joe Nathan/225 6.00 15.00
JS Johan Santana/38 30.00 60.00
JT Jim Thome/5
JV Justin Verlander/299 20.00 50.00
KG Ken Griffey Jr./2
KW Kerry Wood/73 10.00 25.00
MM Mark Mulder/124 6.00 15.00
MS Mike Schmidt/1
PM Paul Molitor/250 12.50 30.00
RS Ryne Sandberg/60 30.00 60.00
RY Robin Yount/1
SR Scott Rolen/1
TG Tony Gwynn/105 15.00 40.00
TH Tim Hudson/49 10.00 25.00
TS Takashi Saito/300 12.50 30.00
VM Victor Martinez/15
WC Will Clark/200 15.00 40.00

2008 Sweet Spot Signatures Red Stitch Red Ink
OVERALL AU ODDS 1:3 PACKS
PRINT RUNS B/WN 1-35 COPIES PER
NO PRICING ON QTY 25 OR LESS
EXCH DEADLINE 11/10/2010
JR Jose Reyes/35 30.00 60.00

2008 Sweet Spot Signatures Red-Blue Stitch Black Ink
OVERALL AU ODDS 1:3 PACKS
PRINT RUNS B/WN 1-126 COPIES PER
NO PRICING ON QTY 25 OR LESS
EXCH DEADLINE 11/10/2010
CQ Carlos Quentin/15
EC Eric Chavez/1
JR Jim Rice/25
OS Ozzie Smith/25
TG Tony Gwynn/25
TH Travis Hafner/126 6.00 15.00

2008 Sweet Spot Signatures Red-Blue Stitch Blue Ink
OVERALL AU ODDS 1:3 PACKS
PRINT RUNS B/WN 3-100 COPIES PER
NO PRICING ON QTY 25 OR LESS
EXCH DEADLINE 11/10/2010
AB Adrian Beltre/19
CB Craig Biggio/4
CQ Carlos Quentin/35 15.00 40.00
CU Chase Utley/100 75.00 150.00
DO David Ortiz/3
EC Eric Chavez/5
JD J.D. Drew/4
JR Jim Rice/15
JR Jose Reyes/25
JS John Smoltz/4
JS Johan Santana/15
KW Kerry Wood/6
OS Ozzie Smith/15
TG Tony Gwynn/15
TH Tim Hudson/4
VM Victor Martinez/15

2008 Sweet Spot Signatures Red-Blue Stitch Red Ink
OVERALL AU ODDS 1:3 PACKS
PRINT RUNS B/WN 5-304 COPIES PER
NO PRICING ON QTY 18 OR LESS
EXCH DEADLINE 11/10/2010
AB Adrian Beltre/18
AE Andre Ethier/50 30.00 60.00
AW Adam Wainwright/50 15.00 40.00
BB Boof Bonser/50 6.00 15.00
BR Brian Roberts/199 6.00 15.00
CB Craig Biggio/5
DO David Ortiz/5
DW Dontrelle Willis/73 6.00 15.00
EC Eric Chavez/5
EG Eric Gagne/5
FC Fausto Carmona/50
FL Francisco Liriano/48 10.00 25.00
HK Hong-Chih Kuo/50 30.00 60.00
HR Hanley Ramirez/50 15.00 40.00
HS Huston Street/199 5.00 12.00
JD J.D. Drew/5
JK Jason Kubel/50 6.00 15.00
JL Jon Lester/90 30.00 60.00
JM Joe Mauer/10
JN Joe Nathan/202 6.00 15.00
JP Jonathan Papelbon/304 12.50 30.00
JR Jose Reyes/10
JR Jim Rice/5
JS John Smoltz/291 20.00 50.00
JT Jim Thome/50 15.00 40.00
JV Justin Verlander/125 20.00 50.00
KG Ken Griffey Jr./5
KW Kerry Wood/5
MM Mark Mulder/13
MY Michael Young/9
OP Oliver Perez/10
OS Ozzie Smith/5
SR Scott Rolen/10
TG Tony Gwynn/5
TH Tim Hudson/5

2008 Sweet Spot Swatches
OVERALL MEM ODDS 2:3 PACKS
SAP Albert Pujols 5.00 12.00
SAS Alfonso Soriano 3.00 8.00
SBU B.J. Upton 3.00 8.00
SCA Miguel Cabrera 3.00 8.00
SCF Carlton Fisk 3.00 8.00
SCJ Chipper Jones 3.00 8.00
SCM Chien-Ming Wang 4.00 10.00
SCR Cal Ripken Jr. 8.00 20.00
SCU Chase Utley 6.00 15.00
SCY Carl Yastrzemski 4.00 10.00
SCZ Carlos Zambrano 3.00 8.00
SDH Dan Haren 3.00 8.00
SDJ Derek Jeter 8.00 20.00
SDM Daisuke Matsuzaka 4.00 10.00
SDO David Ortiz 3.00 8.00
SDW Dontrelle Willis 3.00 8.00
SEM Eddie Murray 3.00 8.00
SFH Felix Hernandez 3.00 8.00
SFL Francisco Liriano 3.00 8.00
SFT Frank Thomas 4.00 10.00
SGS Grady Sizemore 3.00 8.00
SHR Hanley Ramirez 3.00 8.00
SIR Ivan Rodriguez 3.00 8.00
SJB Jeremy Bonderman 3.00 8.00
SJM Joe Mauer 3.00 8.00
SJP Jake Peavy 3.00 8.00
SJS Johan Santana 3.00 8.00
SJT Jim Thome 3.00 8.00
SMA Don Mattingly 6.00 15.00
SMO Joe Morgan 3.00 8.00
SMR Manny Ramirez 4.00 10.00
SMS Mike Schmidt 5.00 12.00
SMT Mark Teixeira 3.00 8.00
SNM Nick Markakis 3.00 8.00
SNR Nolan Ryan 8.00 20.00
SOS Ozzie Smith 6.00 15.00
SPF Prince Fielder 0.00 0.00
SPM Pedro Martinez 3.00 8.00
SRA Roberto Alomar 3.00 8.00
SRG Ron Guidry 4.00 10.00
SRJ Reggie Jackson 3.00 8.00
SRS Ryne Sandberg 5.00 12.00
SRY Robin Yount 5.00 12.00
SSM John Smoltz 3.00 8.00
STG Tony Gwynn 4.00 10.00
STH Travis Hafner 3.00 8.00
STR Tim Raines 3.00 8.00
SVG Vladimir Guerrero 3.00 8.00
SWB Wade Boggs 4.00 10.00
SWI Dave Winfield 3.00 8.00

2008 Sweet Spot Swatches Patch
OVERALL MEM ODDS 2:3 PACKS
STATED PRINT RUN 25 SER.#'d SETS
NO PRICING DUE TO SCARCITY

2008 Sweet Spot Swatches Dual

OVERALL MEM ODDS 2:3 PACKS
DBM Josh Beckett 6.00 15.00
Daisuke Matsuzaka
DBT Lance Berkman 4.00 10.00
Mark Teixeira
DCW Miguel Cabrera 4.00 10.00
Dontrelle Willis
DDR Andre Dawson 5.00 12.00
Tim Raines
DFB Prince Fielder 6.00 15.00
Ryan Braun
DGS Ken Griffey Jr. 6.00 15.00
Grady Sizemore
DHM Travis Hafner 4.00 10.00
Justin Morneau
DJH Derek Jeter 8.00 20.00
Hanley Ramirez
DJR Nolan Ryan 8.00 20.00
Randy Johnson
DJZ Chipper Jones 5.00 12.00
Ryan Zimmerman
DLP Albert Pujols 5.00 12.00
Derrek Lee
DMJ Don Mattingly 10.00 25.00
Derek Jeter
DMM Joe Mauer 5.00 12.00
Justin Morneau
DMS Johan Santana 4.00 10.00
Pedro Martinez
DMW Dave Winfield 10.00 25.00
Don Mattingly
DOZ Roy Oswalt 4.00 10.00
Carlos Zambrano
DPL Jake Peavy 5.00 12.00
Tim Lincecum
DRC Robinson Cano 4.00 10.00
Brian Roberts
DRM Cal Ripken Jr. 15.00 40.00
Eddie Murray
DRO Manny Ramirez 4.00 10.00
David Ortiz
DRP Jonathan Papelbon 4.00 10.00
Mariano Rivera
DSH Alfonso Soriano 4.00 10.00
Matt Holliday
DUH Chase Utley 6.00 15.00
Cole Hamels
DVH Felix Hernandez 4.00 10.00
Justin Verlander
DWM Chien-Ming Wang 5.00 12.00
Daisuke Matsuzaka

2008 Sweet Spot Swatches Triple
OVERALL MEM ODDS 2:3 PACKS
TBOP Lance Berkman 4.00 10.00
Roy Oswalt
Hunter Pence
TFPB Ryan Braun 4.00 10.00
Hunter Pence
Jeff Francoeur
TGBY Tony Gwynn 15.00 40.00
Wade Boggs
Robin Yount
TGOO Vladimir Guerrero 4.00 10.00
David Ortiz
Magglio Ordonez
TJMH Pedro Martinez 5.00 12.00
Trevor Hoffman
Randy Johnson
TJMJ Reggie Jackson 15.00 40.00
Don Mattingly
Derek Jeter
TLHW Felix Hernandez 4.00 10.00
Jered Weaver
Francisco Liriano
TLPF Albert Pujols 6.00 15.00
Prince Fielder
Derrek Lee
TMCH Greg Maddux 6.00 15.00
Chris Carpenter
Roy Halladay
TPMM Joe Mauer 5.00 12.00
Russell Martin
Jorge Posada
TSPM Daisuke Matsuzaka 8.00 20.00
Curt Schilling
Jonathan Papelbon
TSRJ Ozzie Smith 20.00 50.00
Cal Ripken Jr.
Derek Jeter
TSSP Jake Peavy 6.00 15.00
Johan Santana
John Smoltz
TTGT Miguel Tejada 4.00 10.00
Troy Tulowitzki
Khalil Greene
TWIO Grady Sizemore 1.00 10.00
Torii Hunter
Vernon Wells

2008 Sweet Spot Swatches Quad
OVERALL MEM ODDS 2:3 PACKS
QBSPS Johan Santana 5.00 12.00
Jake Peavy
CC Sabathia
Josh Beckett
QGLPC Albert Pujols 6.00 15.00
Vladimir Guerrero
Miguel Cabrera
Carlos Lee
QGTTR Ken Griffey Jr. 12.50 30.00
Frank Thomas
Jim Thome
Manny Ramirez
QJYRR Hanley Ramirez 8.00 20.00
Jimmy Rollins
Derek Jeter
Michael Young
QLRSZ Alfonso Soriano 6.00 15.00
Aramis Ramirez
Derrek Lee
Carlos Zambrano
QMJJC Don Mattingly 20.00 50.00
Reggie Jackson
Derek Jeter
Robinson Cano
QOCGV Miguel Cabrera 5.00 12.00
Justin Verlander
Magglio Ordonez
Curtis Granderson
QRSOM David Ortiz 6.00 15.00
Manny Ramirez
Daisuke Matsuzaka
Curt Schilling
QSCSS Mike Schmidt 20.00 50.00
Ozzie Smith
Ryne Sandberg
Will Clark
QTGHO David Ortiz 5.00 12.00
Travis Hafner
Jim Thome
Jason Giambi

2008 Sweet Spot USA Signatures Black Glove Leather
OVERALL AU ODDS 1:3 PACKS
PRINT RUNS B/WN 29-32 COPIES PER
EXCH DEADLINE 11/10/2010
AG A.J. Griffin/32 6.00 15.00
AO Andrew Oliver/32 10.00 25.00
BS Blake Smith/30 8.00 20.00
CC Christian Colon/32 40.00 80.00
CH Chris Hernandez/30 6.00 15.00
DD Derek Dietrich/32
HM Hunter Morris/32
KD Kentrail Davis/29
KG Kyle Gibson/32 30.00 60.00
KR Kevin Rhoderick/32 6.00 15.00
KV Kendal Volz/32 10.00 25.00
MD Matt den Dekker/32
MG Micah Gibbs/32
ML Mike Leake/32 40.00 80.00
MM Mike Minor/32 20.00 50.00
RJ Ryan Jackson/32 6.00 15.00
SS Stephen Strasburg/32 400.00 800.00
TL Tyler Lyons/30

2008 Sweet Spot USA Signatures Black Stitch Red Ink
OVERALL AU ODDS 1:3 PACKS
PRINT RUNS B/WN 140-260 COPIES PER
EXCH DEADLINE 11/10/2010
AG A.J. Griffin Blk Glv/230 4.00 10.00
AO Andrew Oliver Blk Glv/220 6.00 15.00
BS Blake Smith/219 4.00 10.00
CC Christian Colon/230 8.00 20.00
CH Chris Hernandez/220 6.00 15.00
DD Derek Dietrich/200 6.00 15.00
HM Hunter Morris Blk Glv/219 6.00 15.00
JF Josh Fellhauer/230 4.00 10.00
KD Kentrail Davis/200 15.00 40.00
KG Kyle Gibson/198 20.00 50.00
KR Kevin Rhoderick/200 6.00 15.00
KV Kendal Volz/140 6.00 15.00
MD Matt den Dekker/200 4.00 10.00
MG Micah Gibbs/200 5.00 12.00
ML Mike Leake/189 15.00 40.00
MM Mike Minor/219 8.00 20.00
RJ Ryan Jackson/222 5.00 12.00
RL Ryan Lipkin/218 5.00 12.00
SS Stephen Strasburg/260 175.00 350.00
TL Tyler Lyons/215 4.00 10.00

2008 Sweet Spot USA Signatures Red-Blue Stitch Black Ink
OVERALL AU ODDS 1:3 PACKS
PRINT RUNS B/WN 16-40 COPIES PER
NO PRICING ON QTY 16
EXCH DEADLINE 11/10/2010
AG A.J. Griffin/37 8.00 20.00
AO Andrew Oliver/37 10.00 25.00
BS Blake Smith/37 12.50 30.00
CC Christian Colon/33
CH Chris Hernandez/37
DD Derek Dietrich/37 12.50 30.00
HM Hunter Morris/37
JF Josh Fellhauer/36
KD Kentrail Davis/38
KR Kevin Rhoderick/37 6.00 15.00
KV Kendal Volz/40 6.00 15.00
MD Matt den Dekker/37
MG Micah Gibbs/37
ML Mike Leake/37 40.00 80.00
MM Mike Minor/16
RJ Ryan Jackson/37 8.00 20.00
RL Ryan Lipkin/35
SS Stephen Strasburg/37 300.00 600.00
TL Tyler Lyons/37 12.50 30.00

2009 Sweet Spot

COMP.SET w/o AU's (100) 12.50 30.00
COMMON CARD (1-100) .25 .60
COMMON AU RC (101-130) 3.00 8.00
OVERALL AUTO ODDS 1:3 HOBBY
AU PRINT RUN B/WN 99-699 COPIES PER
EXCHANGE DEADLINE 10/7/2011
1 A.J. Burnett .40 1.00
2 Adam Dunn .40 1.00
3 Adam Jones .40 1.00
4 Adrian Gonzalez .40 1.00
5 Albert Pujols 1.50 4.00
6 Alex Rodriguez 1.00 2.50
7 Alfonso Soriano .40 1.00
8 B.J. Upton .40 1.00
9 Brian McCann .40 1.00
10 Brian Roberts .25 .60
11 Carl Crawford .40 1.00
12 Carlos Beltran .25 .60
13 Carlos Quentin .40 1.00
14 Carlos Zambrano .40 1.00
15 CC Sabathia .40 1.00
16 Chad Billingsley .25 .60
17 Chase Utley .60 1.50
18 Chien-Ming Wang .40 1.00
19 Chipper Jones .60 1.50
20 Chris Carpenter .60 1.50
21 Clayton Kershaw .60 1.50
22 Cliff Lee .40 1.00
23 Cole Hamels .60 1.50
24 Curtis Granderson .40 1.00
25 Daisuke Matsuzaka .60 1.50
26 David Ortiz .40 1.00
27 David Wright .75 2.00
28 Derek Jeter 1.50 4.00
29 Dustin Pedroia .75 2.00
30 Evan Longoria .75 2.00
31 Felix Hernandez .60 1.50
32 Francisco Rodriguez .40 1.00
33 Freddy Sanchez .25 .60
34 Geovany Soto .40 1.00
35 Grady Sizemore .40 1.00
36 Hanley Ramirez .60 1.50
37 Hideki Matsui .60 1.50
38 Hideki Okajima .25 .60
39 Hiroki Kuroda .25 .60
40 Hunter Pence .40 1.00
41 Ian Kinsler .40 1.00
42 Ichiro Suzuki 1.00 2.50
43 Jake Peavy .25 .60
44 Pedro Martinez .40 1.00
45 Jason Varitek .60 1.50
46 Javier Vazquez .25 .60
47 Jay Bruce .40 1.00
48 Jeff Samardzija .40 1.00
49 Jermaine Dye .25 .60
50 Jim Thome .40 1.00
51 Jimmy Rollins .40 1.00
52 Joba Chamberlain .40 1.00
53 Joe Mauer .60 1.50
54 Joey Votto .60 1.50
55 Johan Santana .60 1.50
56 Shin-Soo Choo .40 1.00
57 Johnny Cueto .25 .60
58 Johnny Damon .40 1.00
59 Jon Lester .60 1.50
60 Jose Reyes .40 1.00
61 Josh Beckett .40 1.00
62 Josh Hamilton .60 1.50
63 Josh Johnson .40 1.00
64 Justin Morneau .60 1.50
65 Justin Upton .40 1.00
66 Justin Verlander .75 2.00
67 Ken Griffey Jr. 1.00 2.50
68 Kevin Youkilis .40 1.00
69 Kosuke Fukudome .60 1.50
70 Lance Berkman .40 1.00
71 Manny Ramirez .60 1.50
72 Mariano Rivera .60 1.50
73 Mark Teixeira .60 1.50
74 Matt Holliday .60 1.50
75 Matt Kemp .40 1.00
76 Max Scherzer .40 1.00
77 Michael Young .40 1.00
78 Miguel Cabrera .60 1.50
79 Miguel Tejada .40 1.00
80 Nate McLouth .25 .60
81 Nick Markakis .60 1.50
82 Nomar Garciaparra .60 1.50
83 Prince Fielder .40 1.00
84 Randy Johnson .40 1.00
85 Raul Ibanez .40 1.00
86 Roy Halladay .60 1.50
87 Roy Oswalt .40 1.00
88 Russell Martin .25 .60
89 Ryan Braun .75 2.00
90 Ryan Howard .75 2.00
91 Ryan Ludwick .40 1.00
92 Ryan Zimmerman .40 1.00
93 Stephen Drew .25 .60
94 Tim Lincecum 1.00 2.50
95 Todd Helton .40 1.00
96 Troy Tulowitzki .60 1.50
97 Victor Martinez .40 1.00
98 Vladimir Guerrero .60 1.50
99 Yovani Gallardo .25 .60
100 Zack Greinke .40 1.00
101 Bobby Parnell AU/699 RC 6.00 15.00
102 Brett Anderson AU/650 RC 5.00 12.00
103 Brett Gardner AU/699 15.00 40.00
104 Colby Rasmus AU/350 (RC) 12.50 30.00
105 David Price AU/299 RC 10.00 25.00
106 Dexter Fowler AU/699 (RC) 8.00 20.00
107 Donald Veal AU/650 RC 4.00 10.00
108 Elvis Andrus AU/350 RC 12.50 30.00
109 Everth Cabrera AU/699 RC 4.00 10.00
110 Fernando Martinez AU/300 RC 6.00 15.00
111 Gordon Beckham AU/99 RC 40.00 80.00
112 James McDonald AU/699 RC 3.00 8.00
113 James Parr AU/699 (RC) 3.00 8.00
114 Jason Motte AU/699 (RC) 6.00 15.00
115 Jordan Schafer AU/350 (RC) 4.00 10.00
116 Jordan Zimmermann AU/699 RC 4.00 10.00
117 Kenshin Kawakami AU/350 RC 20.00 50.00
118 Kevin Jepsen AU/699 (RC) 3.00 8.00
119 Koji Uehara AU/300 RC 20.00 50.00
120 Luis Perdomo AU/699 RC 3.00 8.00
121 Matt Tuiasosopo AU/699 (RC) 3.00 8.00
122 Matt Wieters AU/350 RC 20.00 50.00
123 Pablo Sandoval AU/550 20.00 50.00
124 Phil Coke AU/699 RC 4.00 10.00
125 Rick Porcello AU/550 RC 12.50 30.00
126 Ryan Perry AU/199 RC 8.00 20.00
127 Shairon Martis AU/699 RC 3.00 8.00
128 Tommy Hanson AU/199 RC 20.00 50.00
129 Travis Snider AU/300 RC 10.00 25.00
130 Trevor Cahill AU/499 RC 4.00 10.00

2009 Sweet Spot Rookie Signatures Silver
OVERALL AUTO ODDS 1:3 HOBBY
STATED PRINT RUN 65 SER.#'d SETS
EXCHANGE DEADLINE 10/7/2011
101 Bobby Parnell AU 4.00 10.00
102 Brett Anderson AU 6.00 15.00
103 Brett Gardner AU 20.00 50.00
104 Colby Rasmus AU 12.50 30.00
105 David Price AU 50.00 100.00
106 Dexter Fowler AU 10.00 25.00
107 Donald Veal AU 5.00 12.00
108 Elvis Andrus AU 15.00 40.00
109 Everth Cabrera AU 10.00 25.00
110 Fernando Martinez AU 10.00 25.00
111 Gordon Beckham AU 60.00 120.00
112 James McDonald AU 4.00 10.00
113 James Parr AU 4.00 10.00
114 Jason Motte AU 10.00 25.00
115 Jordan Schafer AU 5.00 12.00
116 Jordan Zimmermann AU 8.00 20.00
117 Kenshin Kawakami AU 30.00 60.00
118 Kevin Jepsen AU 4.00 10.00
119 Koji Uehara AU 20.00 50.00
120 Luis Perdomo AU 4.00 10.00
121 Matt Tuiasosopo AU 8.00 20.00
122 Matt Wieters AU 40.00 80.00
123 Pablo Sandoval AU 40.00 80.00
124 Phil Coke AU 8.00 20.00
125 Rick Porcello AU 30.00 60.00
126 Ryan Perry AU 10.00 25.00
127 Shairon Martis AU 4.00 10.00
128 Tommy Hanson AU 30.00 60.00
129 Travis Snider AU 10.00 25.00
130 Trevor Cahill AU 6.00 15.00

2009 Sweet Spot Classic Patches
OVERALL MEM ODDS 2:3 HOBBY
PRINT RUNS B/WN 9-52 COPIES PER
NO PRICING ON QTY 22 OR LESS
BD Bucky Dent/20
BJ Bo Jackson/48 75.00 150.00
BW Billy Williams/52 75.00 150.00
CH Catfish Hunter/27 60.00 120.00
EM Eddie Mathews/41 200.00 300.00
JP Jim Palmer/22
MA Edgar Martinez/44 100.00 200.00
OC Orlando Cepeda/30
RC Rod Carew/49 60.00 120.00
RF Rollie Fingers/47 90.00 150.00
RJ Reggie Jackson/44 200.00 300.00
RS Ryne Sandberg/50 125.00 250.00
SA Sparky Anderson/46 90.00 150.00
TW Ted Williams/9

2009 Sweet Spot Classic Signatures Bat Barrel Black Ink
OVERALL AUTO ODDS 1:3 HOBBY
PRINT RUNS B/WN 1-40 COPIES PER
NO PRICING ON QTY 25 OR LESS
EXCHANGE DEADLINE 10/7/2011
EM Edgar Martinez/40 20.00 50.00

2009 Sweet Spot Classic Signatures Black Baseball Black Stitch Silver Ink
OVERALL AUTO ODDS 1:3 HOBBY
PRINT RUNS B/WN 1-34 COPIES PER
NO PRICING ON QTY 23 OR LESS
EXCHANGE DEADLINE 10/7/2011
BO Bo Jackson/16
DA Dick Allen/15
DE Bucky Dent/20
GP Gaylord Perry/1
KG Ken Griffey Sr./30
KH Kent Hrbek/14
MJ Michael Jordan/23
NR Nolan Ryan/34 75.00 150.00
OC Dennis Boyd/23
TR Tim Raines/30 10.00 25.00

2009 Sweet Spot Classic Signatures Black Bat Barrel Silver Ink
OVERALL AUTO ODDS 1:3 HOBBY
PRINT RUNS B/WN 5-50 COPIES PER
NO PRICING ON QTY 25 OR LESS
EXCHANGE DEADLINE 10/7/2011
KG Ken Griffey Sr./50 8.00 20.00

2009 Sweet Spot Classic Signatures Red-Blue Stitch Blue Ink
OVERALL AUTO ODDS 1:3 HOBBY
STATED PRINT RUN 40 SER.#'d SETS
EXCHANGE DEADLINE 10/7/2011
RY Robin Yount/40 20.00 50.00

2009 Sweet Spot Classic Signatures Red Stitch Black Ink
OVERALL AUTO ODDS 1:3 HOBBY
PRINT RUNS B/WN 5-250 COPIES PER
NO PRICING ON QTY 25 OR LESS
EXCHANGE DEADLINE 10/7/2011
KG Ken Griffey Sr./250 6.00 15.00
KH Kent Hrbek/50 10.00 25.00
OC Dennis Boyd/99 10.00 25.00
TR Tim Raines/10

2009 Sweet Spot Classic Signatures Red Stitch Blue Ink
OVERALL AUTO ODDS 1:3 HOBBY
PRINT RUNS B/WN 1-199 COPIES PER

NO PRICING ON QTY 25 OR LESS
EXCHANGE DEADLINE 10/7/2011
AK Al Kaline/99 15.00 40.00
BD Bobby Doerr/15
BO Bo Jackson/25
BW Billy Williams/50 20.00 50.00
CR Cal Ripken Jr./199 50.00 100.00
CY Carl Yastrzemski/25
DA Dick Allen/50 12.50 30.00
DE Bucky Dent/25
GP Gaylord Perry/50 10.00 25.00
JP Jim Palmer/49 10.00 25.00
KG Ken Griffey Sr./1
KH Kent Hrbek/99 10.00 25.00
LA Luis Aparicio/16
RY Robin Yount/50 20.00 50.00
TR Tim Raines/99 10.00 25.00

2009 Sweet Spot Classic Signatures Red Stitch Green Ink

OVERALL AUTO ODDS 1:3 HOBBY
ANNOUNCED PRINT RUNS LISTED
PRINT RUN INFO PROVIDED BY UD
EXCHANGE DEADLINE 10/7/2011
AK Al Kaline/100 * 20.00 50.00
BD Bucky Dent/13 *
BJ Bo Jackson/26 * 90.00 150.00
BR Brooks Robinson/58 * 30.00 60.00
CF Carlton Fisk/81 * 20.00 50.00
CR Cal Ripken Jr./55 * 90.00 150.00
EM Edgar Martinez/46 * 20.00 50.00
MJ Michael Jordan/25 *
NR Nolan Ryan/61 * 90.00 150.00
RY Robin Yount/14 *

2009 Sweet Spot Classic Signatures Red Stitch Red Ink

OVERALL AUTO ODDS 1:3 HOBBY
PRINT RUNS B/WN 1-47 COPIES PER
NO PRICING ON QTY 25 OR LESS
EXCHANGE DEADLINE 10/7/2011
BR Brooks Robinson/47 40.00 80.00
JP Jim Palmer/47 10.00 25.00

2009 Sweet Spot Immortal Signatures

OVERALL AUTO ODDS 1:3 HOBBY
PRINT RUNS B/WN 1-32 COPIES PER
NO PRICING ON QTY 19 OR LESS
EXCHANGE DEADLINE 10/7/2011
DC Dolph Camilli/26 90.00 150.00
HS Hank Sauer/31 50.00 100.00

2009 Sweet Spot Signatures Bat Barrel Black Ink

OVERALL AUTO ODDS 1:3 HOBBY
PRINT RUNS B/WN 1-50 COPIES PER
NO PRICING ON QTY 25 OR LESS
EXCHANGE DEADLINE 10/7/2011
DJ Derek Jeter/50 150.00 300.00
ML Mark Loretta/35 6.00 15.00

2009 Sweet Spot Signatures Bat Barrel Blue Ink

OVERALL AUTO ODDS 1:3 HOBBY
PRINT RUNS B/WN 1-199 COPIES PER
NO PRICING ON QTY 25 OR LESS
EXCHANGE DEADLINE 10/7/2011
JR Ken Griffey Jr./199 50.00 100.00

2009 Sweet Spot Signatures Bat Barrel Red Ink

OVERALL AUTO ODDS 1:3 HOBBY
PRINT RUNS B/WN 1-25 COPIES PER
NO PRICING DUE TO SCARCITY
EXCHANGE DEADLINE 10/7/2011

2009 Sweet Spot Signatures Bat Barrel Silver Ink

OVERALL AUTO ODDS 1:3 HOBBY
STATED PRINT RUN 10 SER.#'d SETS
NO PRICING DUE TO SCARCITY
EXCHANGE DEADLINE 10/7/2011
BU B.J. Upton/10
GS Grady Sizemore/10

2009 Sweet Spot Signatures Black Baseball Black Stitch Silver Ink

OVERALL AUTO ODDS 1:3 HOBBY
PRINT RUNS B/WN 1-60 COPIES PER
NO PRICING ON QTY 25 OR LESS
EXCHANGE DEADLINE 10/7/2011
BU B.J. Upton/2
CB Chad Billingsley/58 6.00 15.00
CJ Chipper Jones/10
CL Carlos Lee/45 8.00 20.00
CW Chien-Ming Wang/1
DJ Derek Jeter/2
DP David Price/14
EL Evan Longoria/3
FH Felix Hernandez/34 40.00 80.00
GP Glen Perkins/15
JB Jay Bruce/32 30.00 60.00
JM John Maine/33
JN Joe Nathan/36 10.00 25.00
JR Ken Griffey Jr./24
JW Josh Willingham/16
KU Koji Uehara/19
KY Kevin Youkilis/20
MC Matt Cain/18
MK Matt Kemp/27 30.00 60.00
MN Nick Markakis/21
MU David Murphy/7
PK Paul Konerko/14
RJ Randy Johnson/1
TC Trevor Cahill/60 6.00 15.00
ZG Zack Greinke/23

2009 Sweet Spot Signatures Black Bat Barrel Silver Ink

OVERALL AUTO ODDS 1:3 HOBBY
PRINT RUN B/WN 5-60 COPIES PER
NO PRICING ON QTY 25 OR LESS
EXCHANGE DEADLINE 10/7/2011
BU B.J. Upton/15
CB Chad Billingsley/50 6.00 15.00
CJ Chipper Jones/25
CL Carlos Lee/25
CW Chien-Ming Wang/25
DJ Derek Jeter/50 200.00 300.00
DP David Price/10
EL Evan Longoria/25
FH Felix Hernandez/10
GP Glen Perkins/50 5.00 12.00
JB Jay Bruce/50 15.00 40.00
JN Joe Nathan/50 8.00 20.00
JR Ken Griffey Jr./60 100.00 175.00
JW Josh Willingham/50 8.00 20.00
KU Koji Uehara/10
KY Kevin Youkilis/25
MC Matt Cain/50 12.50 30.00
MK Matt Kemp/50 10.00 25.00
MN Nick Markakis/50 10.00 25.00
MU David Murphy/25
PK Paul Konerko/10
RJ Randy Johnson/5
TC Trevor Cahill/10
ZG Zack Greinke/25

2009 Sweet Spot Signatures Black Glove Leather Silver Ink

OVERALL AUTO ODDS 1:3 HOBBY
PRINT RUNS B/WN 1-30 COPIES PER
NO PRICING ON QTY 25 OR LESS
EXCHANGE DEADLINE 10/7/2011
BU B.J. Upton/10
CB Chad Billingsley/30 10.00 25.00
CJ Chipper Jones/15
CL Carlos Lee/15
CW Chien-Ming Wang/15
DJ Derek Jeter/30 250.00 500.00
DP David Price/5
EL Evan Longoria/10
FH Felix Hernandez/5
GP Glen Perkins/1
JB Jay Bruce/30 40.00 80.00
JM John Maine/15
JN Joe Nathan/30 8.00 20.00
JR Ken Griffey Jr./30 150.00 250.00
JW Josh Willingham/30
KU Koji Uehara/5
KY Kevin Youkilis/15
MC Matt Cain/30 15.00 40.00
MK Matt Kemp/30
MN Nick Markakis/30 20.00 50.00
MU David Murphy/15
PK Paul Konerko/5
RJ Randy Johnson/5
TC Trevor Cahill/5
TS Travis Snider/5
ZG Zack Greinke/25

2009 Sweet Spot Signatures Glove Leather Black Ink

OVERALL AUTO ODDS 1:3 HOBBY
PRINT RUNS B/WN 10-30 COPIES PER
NO PRICING ON QTY 15 OR LESS
EXCHANGE DEADLINE 10/7/2011
GS Grady Sizemore/15
TG Tom Glavine/10
YM Yadier Molina/30 15.00 40.00

2009 Sweet Spot Signatures Red-Blue Stitch Blue Ink

OVERALL AUTO ODDS 1:3 HOBBY
PRINT RUNS B/WN 10-50 COPIES PER
NO PRICING ON QTY 25 OR LESS
EXCHANGE DEADLINE 10/7/2011
HR Hanley Ramirez/50 15.00 40.00
MR Manny Ramirez/25
RJ Randy Johnson/10
TG Tom Glavine/15

2009 Sweet Spot Signatures Red-Blue Stitch Red Ink

OVERALL AUTO ODDS 1:3 HOBBY
PRINT RUNS B/WN 5-50 COPIES PER
NO PRICING ON QTY 5 OR LESS
EXCHANGE DEADLINE 10/7/2011
CR Cody Ross/50 15.00 40.00
DU Dan Uggla/50 5.00 12.00
JP James Shields/50 10.00 25.00
KS Kelly Shoppach/50 5.00 12.00
NM Nate McLouth/50 5.00 12.00
RJ Randy Johnson/5
SM Sean Marshall/49 8.00 20.00

2009 Sweet Spot Signatures Red Stitch Black Ink

OVERALL AUTO ODDS 1:3 HOBBY
PRINT RUNS B/WN 1-120 COPIES PER
NO PRICING ON QTY 25 OR LESS
EXCHANGE DEADLINE 10/7/2011
BU B.J. Upton/10
CB Chad Billingsley/50 6.00 15.00
CC Carl Crawford/1
CJ Chipper Jones/10
CL Carlos Lee/25
CW Chien-Ming Wang/10
CZ Carlos Zambrano/15
DJ Derek Jeter/150 150.00 300.00
DP David Price/50 20.00 50.00
EL Evan Longoria/5
FH Felix Hernandez/10
GP Glen Perkins/99 6.00 15.00
GS Grady Sizemore/75 12.50 30.00
JB Jay Bruce/150 12.50 30.00
JD J.D. Drew/11
JN Joe Nathan/50 5.00 12.00
JR Ken Griffey Jr./199 50.00 100.00
JW Josh Willingham/99 5.00 12.00
KU Koji Uehara/10
KY Kevin Youkilis/25
MB Marlon Byrd/350 4.00 10.00
MC Matt Cain/1
MK Matt Kemp/99 20.00 50.00
MN Nick Markakis/99 12.50 30.00
MU David Murphy/99 4.00 10.00
PK Paul Konerko/50 15.00 40.00
RJ Randy Johnson/10
TC Trevor Cahill/50 6.00 15.00
TG Tom Glavine/50 15.00 40.00
TS Travis Snider/25
TT Troy Tulowitzki/199 20.00 50.00
VM Victor Martinez/120 6.00 15.00
YM Yadier Molina/37 15.00 40.00
ZG Zack Greinke/25

2009 Sweet Spot Signatures Red Stitch Blue Ink

OVERALL AUTO ODDS 1:3 HOBBY
PRINT RUNS B/WN 2-199 COPIES PER
NO PRICING ON QTY 25 OR LESS
EXCHANGE DEADLINE 10/7/2011
BU B.J. Upton/50 8.00 20.00
CB Chad Billingsley/199 8.00 20.00
CC Carl Crawford/4
CJ Chipper Jones/50 60.00 120.00
CL Carlos Lee/199
CR Cody Ross/299 10.00 25.00
CW Chien-Ming Wang/25
DJ Derek Jeter/299 100.00 200.00
DP David Price/99 15.00 40.00
DU Dan Uggla/35 12.50 30.00
EJ Edwin Jackson/350 10.00 25.00
EL Evan Longoria/10
FC Fausto Carmona/300 5.00 12.00
FH Felix Hernandez/50 30.00 60.00
GP Glen Perkins/199 5.00 12.00
HR Hanley Ramirez/300 10.00 25.00
IK Ian Kinsler/150 10.00 25.00
JB Jay Bruce/299 10.00 25.00
JD J.D. Drew/21
JN Joe Nathan/299 5.00 12.00
JP James Shields/300 8.00 20.00
JW Josh Willingham/199 5.00 12.00
JW Jered Weaver/100 12.50 30.00
KB Kobe Bryant/10
KS Kelly Shoppach/300 5.00 12.00
KU Koji Uehara/50 30.00 60.00
LJ LeBron James/15
MB Marlon Byrd/2
MJ Mike Jacobs/199 5.00 12.00
MK Matt Kemp/199 20.00 50.00
MN Nick Markakis/199 12.50 30.00
MU David Murphy/199 10.00 25.00
NM Nate McLouth/300 5.00 12.00
PK Paul Konerko/99 12.50 30.00
PM Paul Maholm/200 5.00 12.00
RB Rocco Baldelli/99 12.50 30.00
RJ Randy Johnson/5
SM Sean Marshall/250 6.00 15.00
TC Trevor Cahill/99 12.50 30.00
TS Travis Snider/50 15.00 40.00
TT Troy Tulowitzki/99 10.00 25.00
VW Vernon Wells/63 10.00 25.00
ZG Zack Greinke/50 15.00 40.00

2009 Sweet Spot Signatures Red Stitch Green Ink

OVERALL AUTO ODDS 1:3 HOBBY
ANNOUNCED PRINT RUNS LISTED
PRINT RUN INFO PROVIDED BY UD
EXCHANGE DEADLINE 10/7/2011
BU B.J. Upton/96 * 10.00 25.00
CJ Chipper Jones/96 * 60.00 120.00
CL Carlos Lee/98 * 8.00 20.00
CW Chien-Ming Wang/49 * 90.00 150.00
EL Evan Longoria/77 * 60.00 120.00
LJ LeBron James/25 *
RJ Randy Johnson/13 *
VM Victor Martinez/98 * 20.00 50.00

2009 Sweet Spot Signatures Red Stitch Red Ink

OVERALL AUTO ODDS 1:3 HOBBY
PRINT RUNS B/WN 1-100 COPIES PER
NO PRICING ON QTY 25 OR LESS
EXCHANGE DEADLINE 10/7/2011
BU B.J. Upton/1
CB Chad Billingsley/5
CL Carlos Lee/10
CW Chien-Ming Wang/1
DJ Derek Jeter/50 200.00 300.00
DP David Price/25
EL Evan Longoria/1
FH Felix Hernandez/5
GP Glen Perkins/25
JB Jay Bruce/50 15.00 40.00
JM John Maine/25
JN Joe Nathan/5
JP James Shields/5
JW Josh Willingham/25
KU Koji Uehara/5
KY Kevin Youkilis/10
MB Marlon Byrd/10
MC Matt Cain/100 10.00 25.00
MK Matt Kemp/25
ML Mark Loretta/35 10.00 25.00
MN Nick Markakis/25
MU David Murphy/25
MY Michael Young/56 10.00 25.00
PK Paul Konerko/5
PM Paul Maholm/50 6.00 15.00
RB Rocco Baldelli/10
RJ Randy Johnson/1
TC Trevor Cahill/25
TS Travis Snider/5
YM Yadier Molina/35 15.00 40.00
ZG Zack Greinke/10

2009 Sweet Spot Swatch Patches

OVERALL MEM ODDS 2:3 HOBBY
PRINT RUNS B/WN 10-30 COPIES PER
NO PRICING ON QTY 25 OR LESS
AJ Adam Jones/30
AP Albert Pujols/30 15.00 40.00
AR Aramis Ramirez/25
BB Billy Butler/10
CB Clay Buchholz/25
CD Carlos Delgado/30 6.00 15.00
CG Curtis Granderson/30
CL Carlos Lee/30 6.00 15.00
CY Carl Yastrzemski/30
DO David Ortiz/30 6.00 15.00
DW Dave Winfield/30
FS Freddy Sanchez/30 6.00 15.00
GS Grady Sizemore/30 10.00 25.00
HK Howie Kendrick/25
IK Ian Kinsler/30 6.00 15.00
JB Jason Bay/25
JH Josh Hamilton/25
JP Jake Peavy/25
JW Jered Weaver/25
KW Kerry Wood/25
LE Cliff Lee/25
NM Nick Markakis/25
RG Ryan Garko/25
RH Roy Halladay/25
RP Rick Porcello/25
SC Steve Carlton/25
SH Shin-Soo Choo/25
TH Trevor Hoffman/25
VW Vernon Wells/25
ZG Zack Greinke/25

2009 Sweet Spot Swatches

OVERALL MEM ODDS 2:3 HOBBY
AJ Adam Jones 3.00 8.00
AP Albert Pujols 5.00 12.00
AR Aramis Ramirez 3.00 8.00
BB Billy Butler 3.00 8.00
CB Clay Buchholz 3.00 8.00
CD Carlos Delgado 3.00 8.00
CG Curtis Granderson 3.00 8.00
CL Carlos Lee 3.00 8.00
CY Carl Yastrzemski 3.00 8.00
DO David Ortiz 3.00 8.00
DW Dave Winfield 3.00 8.00
FS Freddy Sanchez
GS Grady Sizemore 3.00 8.00
HK Howie Kendrick 3.00 8.00
IK Ian Kinsler 3.00 8.00
JB Jason Bay 3.00 8.00
JH Josh Hamilton 3.00 8.00
JP Jake Peavy 3.00 8.00
JW Jered Weaver 3.00 8.00
KW Kerry Wood 3.00 8.00
LE Cliff Lee 3.00 8.00
NM Nick Markakis 3.00 8.00
RG Ryan Garko 3.00 8.00
RH Roy Halladay 3.00 8.00
RP Rick Porcello 3.00 8.00
SC Steve Carlton 3.00 8.00
SH Shin-Soo Choo 3.00 8.00
TH Trevor Hoffman 3.00 8.00
VW Vernon Wells 3.00 8.00
ZG Zack Greinke 3.00 8.00

2009 Sweet Spot Swatches Dual

OVERALL MEM ODDS 2:3 HOBBY
BB Johnny Bench 10.00 25.00
Yogi Berra
BM Josh Beckett 4.00 10.00
Daisuke Matsuzaka
BS Red Schoendienst 10.00 25.00
Lou Brock
BV Jay Bruce 12.50 30.00
Joey Votto
GJ Ken Griffey Jr. 10.00 25.00
Derek Jeter
HP Josh Hamilton 8.00 20.00
Albert Pujols
JP Derek Jeter 12.50 30.00
Jorge Posada
MJ Kenji Johjima 4.00 10.00
Daisuke Matsuzaka
MM Joe Mauer 6.00 15.00
Justin Morneau
MW Daisuke Matsuzaka 4.00 10.00
Chien-Ming Wang
PV Jake Peavy 4.00 10.00
Justin Verlander
RH Josh Hamilton 12.50 30.00
Nolan Ryan
SP Albert Pujols 12.50 30.00
Ozzie Smith
SR Ozzie Smith 10.00 25.00
Jose Reyes
SW Ryne Sandberg 8.00 20.00
Billy Williams
UW Justin Upton 4.00 10.00
Brandon Webb
VO David Ortiz 4.00 10.00
Jason Varitek
WL Tim Lincecum 4.00 10.00
Brandon Webb
YC Carl Yastrzemski 4.00 10.00
Orlando Cepeda
YJ Fergie Jenkins 6.00 15.00
Carl Yastrzemski

2009 Sweet Spot Swatches Quad

OVERALL MEM ODDS 2:3 HOBBY
CNR Mike Schmidt 10.00 25.00
Prince Fielder
Chipper Jones
Eddie Murray
CST Daisuke Matsuzaka 12.50 30.00
Fergie Jenkins
Tim Lincecum
Gaylord Perry
GNY Tim Lincecum 8.00 20.00
Adam Jones
Jose Reyes
Cole Hamels
NYC Reggie Jackson 50.00 100.00
Joe DiMaggio
Yogi Berra
Derek Jeter
PHI Cole Hamels 12.50 30.00
Steve Carlton
Chase Utley
Mike Schmidt
TOP Josh Hamilton 15.00 40.00
Albert Pujols
Derek Jeter
Ken Griffey Jr.
VEN Felix Hernandez 5.00 12.00
Johan Santana
Magglio Ordonez
Miguel Cabrera
VET Billy Wagner 5.00 12.00
Roy Halladay
Tom Glavine
Josh Beckett

2009 Sweet Spot Swatches Triple

OVERALL MEM ODDS 2:3 HOBBY
ATL Tom Glavine 4.00 10.00
Tim Hudson
Phil Niekro
BPL Josh Beckett 4.00 10.00
Tim Lincecum
Jake Peavy
FMM Brian McCann 4.00 10.00
Carlton Fisk
Joe Mauer
JPN Kosuke Fukudome 5.00 12.00
Kenji Johjima
Daisuke Matsuzaka
LMR Jose Reyes 5.00 12.00
Brian McCann
Jon Lester
MIL Bill Hall 4.00 10.00
Prince Fielder
Ryan Braun
MIN Francisco Liriano 4.00 10.00
Joe Mauer
Justin Morneau
NYC Johnny Damon 10.00 25.00
Derek Jeter
Reggie Jackson
NYY Derek Jeter 50.00 100.00
Yogi Berra
Joe DiMaggio
ODF David Ortiz 4.00 10.00
Carlos Delgado
Prince Fielder
SFG Juan Marichal 10.00 25.00
Tim Lincecum
Willie McCovey
SSC Orlando Cepeda 12.50 30.00
Ryne Sandberg
Mike Schmidt

2002 Sweet Spot Classics

This 90 card set was issued in February, 2002. These cards were issued in four card packs which came 12 packs to a box and eight boxes to a case.

COMPLETE SET (90) 15.00 40.00
1 Mickey Mantle 2.50 6.00
2 Joe DiMaggio 1.25 3.00
3 Babe Ruth 2.00 5.00
4 Ty Cobb 1.00 2.50
5 Nolan Ryan 1.50 4.00
6 Sandy Koufax 1.25 3.00
7 Cy Young .60 1.50
8 Roberto Clemente 1.50 4.00
9 Lefty Grove .40 1.00
10 Lou Gehrig 1.25 3.00
11 Walter Johnson .60 1.50
12 Honus Wagner .75 2.00
13 Christy Mathewson .60 1.50
14 Jackie Robinson .60 1.50
15 Joe Morgan .40 1.00
16 Reggie Jackson .40 1.00
17 Eddie Collins .40 1.00
18 Cal Ripken 2.00 5.00
19 Hank Greenberg .60 1.50
20 Harmon Killebrew .60 1.50
21 Johnny Bench .60 1.50
22 Ernie Banks .60 1.50
23 Willie McCovey .40 1.00
24 Mel Ott .60 1.50
25 Tom Seaver .40 1.00
26 Tony Gwynn .75 2.00
27 Dave Winfield .40 1.00
28 Willie Stargell .40 1.00
29 Mark McGwire 1.50 4.00
30 Al Kaline .60 1.50
31 Jimmie Foxx .60 1.50
32 Satchel Paige .60 1.50
33 Eddie Murray .60 1.50
34 Lou Boudreau .40 1.00
35 Joe Jackson 1.25 3.00
36 Luke Appling .40 1.00
37 Ralph Kiner .40 1.00
38 Robin Yount .60 1.50
39 Paul Molitor .40 1.00
40 Juan Marichal .40 1.00
41 Brooks Robinson .40 1.00
42 Wade Boggs .40 1.00
43 Kirby Puckett .60 1.50
44 Yogi Berra .60 1.50
45 George Sisler .40 1.00
46 Buck Leonard .40 1.00
47 Billy Williams .40 1.00
48 Duke Snider .40 1.00
49 Don Drysdale .40 1.00
50 Bill Mazeroski .40 1.00
51 Tony Oliva .40 1.00
52 Luis Aparicio .40 1.00
53 Carlton Fisk .40 1.00
54 Kirk Gibson .40 1.00
55 Catfish Hunter .40 1.00
56 Joe Carter .40 1.00
57 Gaylord Perry .40 1.00
58 Don Mattingly 1.25 3.00
59 Eddie Mathews .60 1.50
60 Fergie Jenkins .40 1.00
61 Roy Campanella .60 1.50
62 Orlando Cepeda .40 1.00
63 Tony Perez .40 1.00
64 Dave Parker .40 1.00
65 Richie Ashburn .40 1.00
66 Andre Dawson .40 1.00
67 Dwight Evans .40 1.00
68 Rollie Fingers .40 1.00
69 Dale Murphy .40 1.00
70 Ron Santo .40 1.00
71 Steve Garvey .40 1.00
72 Monte Irvin .40 1.00
73 Alan Trammell .40 1.00
74 Ryne Sandberg 1.00 2.50
75 Gary Carter .40 1.00
76 Fred Lynn .40 1.00
77 Maury Wills .40 1.00
78 Ozzie Smith 1.00 2.50
79 Bobby Bonds .40 1.00
80 Mickey Cochrane .40 1.00
81 Dizzy Dean .60 1.50
82 Graig Nettles .40 1.00
83 Keith Hernandez .40 1.00
84 Boog Powell .40 1.00
85 Jack Clark .40 1.00
86 Dave Stewart .40 1.00
87 Tommy Lasorda .40 1.00
88 Dennis Eckersley .40 1.00
89 Ken Griffey Sr. .40 1.00
90 Bucky Dent .40 1.00

2002 Sweet Spot Classics Game Bat

Inserted at stated odds of one in eight, these cards feature the most notable tools of the trade. Please note that if the player has a DP next to their name than that card is perceived to be in larger supply. Also note that some player have shorter print runs and that information is notated in our checklist along with a stated print run from the company.

GOLD PRINT RUN 25 SERIAL #'d SETS
GOLD NO PRICING DUE TO SCARCITY
BAK Al Kaline 6.00 15.00
BBBO Bob Boone 4.00 10.00
BBBU Bill Buckner 4.00 10.00
BBD Bucky Dent 4.00 10.00
BBM Bill Madlock 4.00 10.00
BBR Brooks Robinson 6.00 15.00
BBW Billy Williams 4.00 10.00
BCR Cal Ripken DP 10.00 25.00
BDE Dwight Evans 6.00 15.00
BDM Don Mattingly 10.00 25.00
BDP Dave Parker 4.00 10.00
BDW Dave Winfield DP 4.00 10.00
BFJ Fergie Jenkins 4.00 10.00
BFL Fred Lynn 4.00 10.00
BGC Gary Carter 4.00 10.00
BGN Graig Nettles 4.00 10.00
BHG Hank Greenberg SP 30.00 60.00
BJB Johnny Bench 6.00 15.00
BJD Joe DiMaggio SP/40 *
BKG Ken Griffey Sr. DP 4.00 10.00
BKP Kirby Puckett DP 6.00 15.00
BNR Nolan Ryan 15.00 40.00
BPM Paul Molitor 4.00 10.00
BRC Roberto Clemente 30.00 60.00
BRJ Reggie Jackson 6.00 15.00
BSG Steve Garvey 4.00 10.00
BTG Tony Gwynn DP 6.00 15.00
BTM Thurman Munson 15.00 40.00
BWB Wade Boggs DP 6.00 15.00
BYB Yogi Berra 6.00 15.00

2002 Sweet Spot Classics Game Jersey

Inserted at stated odds of one in eight, these cards feature memorabilia from the featured player. Please note that if the player has a DP next to their name than that card is perceived to be in larger supply. Also note that some player have shorter print runs and that information is notated in our checklist along with a stated print run from the company if available.

GOLD PRINT RUN 25 SERIAL #'d SETS
GOLD NO PRICING DUE TO SCARCITY
JBM Bill Madlock 4.00 10.00
JBW Billy Williams 4.00 10.00
JCR Cal Ripken DP 10.00 25.00
JDM Don Mattingly DP 10.00 25.00
JDP Dave Parker 4.00 10.00
JDSN Duke Snider SP/53 * 50.00 100.00
JDST Dave Stewart 4.00 10.00
JEM Eddie Murray 6.00 15.00
JGC Gary Carter 4.00 10.00
JGN Graig Nettles 4.00 10.00
JJC Joe Carter 4.00 10.00
JJD Joe DiMaggio SP/53 * 100.00 200.00
JJMA Juan Marichal 4.00 10.00
JMM Mickey Mantle SP/53 * 150.00 250.00
JNR Nolan Ryan DP 15.00 40.00
JOS Ozzie Smith 6.00 15.00
JPM Paul Molitor DP 4.00 10.00
JRF Rollie Fingers 4.00 10.00
JRJ Reggie Jackson 6.00 15.00
JRS Ryne Sandberg 6.00 15.00
JRY Robin Yount DP 6.00 15.00
JSG Steve Garvey 4.00 10.00
JSK Sandy Koufax SP 75.00 150.00
JTG Tony Gwynn DP 6.00 15.00
JTS Tom Seaver 6.00 15.00
JWB Wade Boggs 6.00 15.00
JWS Willie Stargell 6.00 15.00

2002 Sweet Spot Classics Signatures

Inserted at stated odds of one in 24, these cards feature the top stars of yesterday with their signature on a "sweet spot". Though UD refused to comment on the matter, it's believed that Don Mattingly's card is in larger supply than others from this set. Also note that some players, as verified by UD, have shorter print runs and that information is notated in our checklist along with a stated print run from the company. Though not stated as SP's by Upper Deck, our own research provided solid evidence that Reggie Jackson, Sandy Koufax and Willie McCovey were also seeded in shorter supply than the typical allotment for this set. These cards have been tagged with an "SP *" in our checklist below. Finally, the Kirk Gibson card was detailed as an SP by Upper Deck, but a specific print run for the card was not divulged. That card is simpl tagged as an SP (bereft of the asterisk - indicating it's verified status by Upper Deck).

GOLD PRINT RUN 25 SERIAL #'d SETS
GOLD NO PRICING DUE TO SCARCITY
SAD Andre Dawson SP/100 * 30.00 60.00
SAK Al Kaline 15.00 40.00
SAT Alan Trammell 10.00 25.00
SBD Bucky Dent 10.00 25.00
SBM Bill Mazeroski 20.00 50.00
SBP Boog Powell 12.50 30.00
SBR Brooks Robinson 15.00 40.00
SCF Carlton Fisk SP/100 * 75.00 150.00
SCR Cal Ripken 50.00 100.00
SDAM Dale Murphy 10.00 25.00
SDAS Dave Stewart 10.00 25.00
SDEE Dennis Eckersley 10.00 25.00
SDOM Don Mattingly DP 30.00 60.00
SDW Dave Winfield SP/70 * 60.00 120.00
SEB Ernie Banks 40.00 80.00
SFJ Fergie Jenkins 10.00 25.00
SFL Fred Lynn 10.00 25.00
SGP Gaylord Perry 10.00 25.00
SJB Johnny Bench 40.00 80.00
SJM Joe Morgan 10.00 25.00
SKG Kirk Gibson/SP 12.50 30.00
SKH Keith Hernandez 10.00 25.00
SKP Kirby Puckett SP/74 * 75.00 150.00
SNR Nolan Ryan SP/74 * 225.00 350.00
SOS Ozzie Smith SP/137 * 75.00 150.00
SPM Paul Molitor 10.00 25.00
SRF Rollie Fingers 10.00 25.00
SRJ Reggie Jackson SP * 40.00 80.00
SSG Steve Garvey 10.00 25.00
SSK Sandy Koufax SP * 200.00 350.00
STL Tommy Lasorda 40.00 80.00
STS Tom Seaver 30.00 60.00
SWM Willie McCovey SP * 50.00 100.00
SYB Yogi Berra SP/100 * 100.00 175.00

2003 Sweet Spot Classics

This 150 card set was issued in March, 2003. It was issued in five-card packs with an $10 SRP. The packs were issued in 12 pack boxes which came 16 boxes to a case. The following subsets are included: Ted Williams Ball Game (91-120) and Yankee Heritage (121-150). The Williams's cards were printed to a stated print run of 1941 and the Yankee Heritage cards were printed to a stated print run of 1500 serial numbered sets. While this set features mainly retired players, a special Hideki Matsui card (75) was issued. That card was issued to a stated print run of 1999 serial numbered sets. Originally that card was supposed to be Rod Carew and a few Carew cards made it through the production process. However, at this time no pricing information is available on the Carew card which was supposed to be card number 75 originally.

COMP.SET w/o SP's (89) 15.00 40.00
COMMON (1-74/76-90) .30 .75
COMMON CARD (91-120) 3.00 8.00
COMMON CARD (121-150) 2.00 5.00
1 Al Hrabosky .30 .75
2 Al Lopez .30 .75
3 Andre Dawson .30 .75
4 Bill Buckner .30 .75
5 Billy Williams .30 .75
6 Bob Feller .30 .75
7 Bob Lemon .30 .75
8 Bobby Doerr .30 .75
9 Cecil Cooper .30 .75
10 Cal Ripken 2.50 6.00
11 Carlton Fisk .50 1.25
12 Catfish Hunter .50 1.25
13 Chris Chambliss .30 .75
14 Dale Murphy .50 1.25
15 Gaylord Perry .30 .75
16 Dave Kingman .30 .75
17 Dave Parker .30 .75
18 Dave Stewart .30 .75
19 David Cone .30 .75
20 Dennis Eckersley .30 .75
21 Don Baylor .30 .75
22 Don Sutton .30 .75
23 Duke Snider .50 1.25
24 Dwight Evans .50 1.25
25 Dwight Gooden .30 .75
26 Earl Weaver MG .30 .75
27 Early Wynn .30 .75
28 Eddie Mathews .75 2.00
29 Enos Slaughter .30 .75
30 Ernie Banks .75 2.00
31 Fred Lynn .30 .75
32 Fred Stanley .30 .75
33 Gary Carter .30 .75
34 George Foster .30 .75
35 Hal Newhouser .30 .75
36 George Kell .30 .75
37 Harmon Killebrew .75 2.00
38 Hoyt Wilhelm .30 .75
39 Jack Morris .30 .75
40 Jim Bunning .30 .75
41 Jim Gilliam .30 .75
42 Jim Leyritz .30 .75
43 Jimmy Key .30 .75
44 Joe Carter .30 .75
45 Joe Morgan .30 .75
46 John Montefusco .30 .75
47 Johnny Bench .75 2.00
48 Johnny Podres .30 .75
49 Jose Canseco .50 1.25
50 Juan Marichal .30 .75
51 Keith Hernandez .30 .75
52 Ken Griffey Sr. .30 .75
53 Kirby Puckett .75 2.00
54 Kirk Gibson .30 .75
55 Larry Doby .30 .75
56 Lee May .30 .75
57 Lee Mazzilli .30 .75

58 Lou Boudreau .30 .75
59 Mark McGwire 2.00 5.00
60 Maury Wills .30 .75
61 Mike Pagliarulo .30 .75
62 Monte Irvin .30 .75
63 Nolan Ryan 2.00 5.00
64 Orlando Cepeda .30 .75
65 Ozzie Smith 1.25 3.00
66 Paul O'Neill .50 1.25
67 Pee Wee Reese .50 1.25
68 Phil Niekro .30 .75
69 Ralph Kiner .30 .75
70 Red Schoendienst .30 .75
71 Richie Ashburn .50 1.25
72 Rick Ferrell .30 .75
73 Robin Roberts .30 .75
74 Robin Yount .75 2.00
75 Hideki Matsui/1999 XRC 6.00 15.00
75B Rod Carew ERR
Not Intended for Public Release
76 Rollie Fingers .30 .75
77 Ron Cey .30 .75
78 Tom Seaver .50 1.25
79 Sparky Anderson MG .30 .75
80 Stan Musial 1.25 3.00
81 Steve Garvey .30 .75
82 Ted Williams 1.50 4.00
83 Tommy Lasorda .30 .75
84 Tony Gwynn 1.00 2.50
85 Tony Perez .30 .75
86 Vida Blue .30 .75
87 Warren Spahn .50 1.25
88 Bob Gibson .50 1.25
89 Willie McCovey .30 .75
90 Willie Stargell .50 1.25
91 Ted Williams TB 3.00 8.00
92 Ted Williams TB 3.00 8.00
93 Ted Williams TB 3.00 8.00
94 Ted Williams TB 3.00 8.00
95 Ted Williams TB 3.00 8.00
96 Ted Williams TB 3.00 8.00
97 Ted Williams TB 3.00 8.00
98 Ted Williams TB 3.00 8.00
99 Ted Williams TB 3.00 8.00
100 Ted Williams TB 3.00 8.00
101 Ted Williams TB 3.00 8.00
102 Ted Williams TB 3.00 8.00
103 Ted Williams TB 3.00 8.00
104 Ted Williams TB 3.00 8.00
105 Ted Williams TB 3.00 8.00
106 Ted Williams TB 3.00 8.00
106B Ted Williams TB UER 116 3.00 8.00
107 Ted Williams TB 3.00 8.00
108 Ted Williams TB 3.00 8.00
109 Ted Williams TB 3.00 8.00
110 Ted Williams TB 3.00 8.00
111 Ted Williams TB 3.00 8.00
112 Ted Williams TB 3.00 8.00
113 Ted Williams TB 3.00 8.00
114 Ted Williams TB 3.00 8.00
115 Ted Williams TB 3.00 8.00
117 Ted Williams TB 3.00 8.00
118 Ted Williams TB 3.00 8.00
119 Ted Williams TB 3.00 8.00
120 Ted Williams TB 3.00 8.00
121 Babe Ruth YH 6.00 15.00
122 Bucky Dent YH 2.00 5.00
123 Casey Stengel YH 2.00 5.00
124 Dave Righetti YH 2.00 5.00
125 Dave Winfield YH 2.00 5.00
126 Dick Tidrow YH 2.00 5.00
127 Dock Ellis YH 2.00 5.00
128 Don Mattingly YH 5.00 12.00
129 Hank Bauer YH 2.00 5.00
130 Jim Bouton YH 2.00 5.00
131 Jim Kaat YH 2.00 5.00
132 Joe DiMaggio YH 4.00 10.00
133 Joe Torre YH 2.00 5.00
134 Lou Piniella YH 2.00 5.00
135 Mel Stottlemyre YH 2.00 5.00
136 Mickey Mantle YH 8.00 20.00
137 Mickey Rivers YH 2.00 5.00
138 Phil Rizzuto YH 2.00 5.00
139 Ralph Branca YH 2.00 5.00
140 Ralph Houk YH 2.00 5.00
141 Roger Maris YH 3.00 8.00
142 Ron Guidry YH 2.00 5.00
143 Ruben Amaro Sr. YH 2.00 5.00
144 Sparky Lyle YH 2.00 5.00
145 Thurman Munson YH 3.00 8.00
146 Tommy Henrich YH 2.00 5.00
147 Tommy John YH 2.00 5.00
148 Tony Kubek YH 2.00 5.00
149 Whitey Ford YH 2.00 5.00
150 Yogi Berra YH 3.00 8.00

2003 Sweet Spot Classics Matsui Parallel

Randomly inserted into packs, these cards parallel the Hideki Matsui base card. There are three different versions of this card and they were all issued to different stated print runs. Please note the silver version (75C) was issued to a stated print run of 25 serial numbered sets and there is no pricing due to market scarcity.

75A Hideki Matsui Red/500 6.00 15.00
75B Hideki Matsui Blue/250 8.00 20.00
75C Hideki Matsui Silver/25

2003 Sweet Spot Classics Autographs Black Ink

Randomly inserted into packs, these cards feature the players signing in black ink. These autograph cards were in packs at overall rate of one in 24. Each card was printed to a different amount and we have noted that information next to the player's name in our checklist. All the Mark McGwire autos are inscribed "Maris '61"

AD Andre Dawson/75 20.00 50.00
AH Al Hrabosky/100 15.00 40.00
AT Alan Trammell/173 15.00 40.00
BB Bill Buckner/85 15.00 40.00
BW Billy Williams/173 15.00 40.00
CR Cal Ripken/38
DB Don Baylor/50 20.00 50.00
DE Dwight Evans/100 40.00 80.00
DP Dave Parker/113 15.00 40.00
DS Don Sutton/123 15.00 40.00
EB Ernie Banks/73 60.00 120.00
GC Gary Carter/173 15.00 40.00
GF George Foster/173 15.00 40.00
GI Kirk Gibson/173 15.00 40.00
HK Harmon Killebrew/73 30.00 60.00
JB Johnny Bench/73 75.00 150.00
JC Joe Carter/123 15.00 40.00
JM Joe Morgan/169 15.00 40.00
JM Jack Morris/123 15.00 40.00
JP Johnny Podres/173 15.00 40.00
KG Ken Griffey Sr./100 20.00 50.00
KH Keith Hernandez/173 15.00 40.00
KP Kirby Puckett/174 75.00 150.00
MM Mark McGwire/73 300.00 500.00
MW Maury Wills/173 15.00 40.00
OC Orlando Cepeda/34
PN Phil Niekro/173 15.00 40.00
RF Rollie Fingers/73 20.00 50.00
RR Robin Roberts/173 20.00 50.00
RY Robin Yount/73 75.00 150.00
SG Steve Garvey/173 15.00 40.00
SN Duke Snider/100 40.00 80.00
TG Tony Gwynn/101 40.00 80.00
TP Tony Perez/51 40.00 80.00
TS Tom Seaver/74 40.00 80.00

2003 Sweet Spot Classics Autographs Blue Ink

Randomly inserted in packs, these cards feature the players signing their cards in black ink. A few players were issued in shorter quantity and we have notated that information with an SP next to their name in our checklist. In addition, Upper Deck purchased nine Ted Williams cuts and issued nine of these cards to match his uniform number.

AD Andre Dawson 10.00 25.00
AH Al Hrabosky SP 10.00 25.00
BB Bill Buckner SP 10.00 25.00
CF Carlton Fisk 30.00 60.00
CR Cal Ripken 100.00 200.00
DB Don Baylor SP 10.00 25.00
DE Dennis Eckersley 10.00 25.00
DE Dwight Evans * 15.00 40.00
DM Dale Murphy 12.50 30.00
DS Dave Stewart 10.00 25.00
KG Ken Griffey Sr. 10.00 25.00
KP Kirby Puckett 75.00 150.00
OC Orlando Cepeda * 10.00 25.00
SN Duke Snider 15.00 40.00
TG Tony Gwynn 20.00 50.00
TW Ted Williams/9

2003 Sweet Spot Classics Autographs Yankee Greats Black Ink

Randomly inserted in packs, these cards feature former New York Yankees who signed their card in black ink. We have notated the stated print run information next to the player's name in our checklist. Please note that the Hideki Matsui card was issued as an exchange card and has an exchange deadline of March 13, 2006.

CC Chris Chambliss/101 30.00 60.00
DC David Cone/74 40.00 80.00
DE Dock Ellis/174 15.00 40.00
DG Dwight Gooden/74 30.00 60.00
DK Dave Kingman/100 30.00 60.00
DM Don Mattingly/74 75.00 150.00
DR Dave Righetti/173 30.00 60.00
DT Dick Tidrow/101 15.00 40.00
DW Dave Winfield/25
FS Fred Stanley/101 15.00 40.00
GU Ron Guidry/100 40.00 80.00
HB Hank Bauer/75 30.00 60.00
HM Hideki Matsui/25
JB Jim Bouton/100 15.00 40.00
JC Jose Canseco/73 40.00 80.00
JD Joe DiMaggio/5
JK Jim Kaat/100 15.00 40.00
JK Jimmy Key/100 15.00 40.00
JL Jim Leyritz/100 15.00 40.00
JM John Montefusco/100 15.00 40.00
JT Joe Torre/73 40.00 80.00
LM Lee Mazzilli/100 15.00 40.00
LP Lou Piniella/100 15.00 40.00
MP Mike Pagliarulo/99 15.00 40.00
MR Mickey Rivers/73 30.00 60.00
MS Mel Stottlemyre/73 30.00 60.00
PO Paul O'Neill/100 40.00 80.00
PR Phil Rizzuto/173 40.00 80.00
RA Ruben Amaro Sr./100 15.00 40.00
RB Ralph Branca/100 15.00 40.00
RH Ralph Houk/100 15.00 40.00
SL Sparky Lyle/100 15.00 40.00
TH Tommy Henrich/100 15.00 40.00
TJ Tommy John/100 15.00 40.00
TK Tony Kubek/123 20.00 50.00
YB Yogi Berra/73 60.00 120.00

2003 Sweet Spot Classics Autographs Yankee Greats Blue Ink

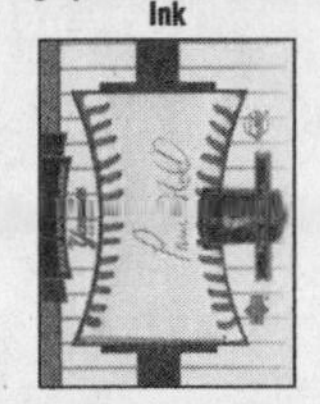

Randomly inserted in packs, these cards feature former New York Yankees who signed their card in blue ink. A few cards were issued in lesser quantity and we have notated those cards with an SP in our checklist. In addition, the Bucky Dent card seems to be in larger supply and we have notated that with an asterisk in our checklist. Also, Upper Deck purchased seven Mickey Mantle autographs and used those as scarce cuts in this product.

BD Bucky Dent * 10.00 25.00
CC Chris Chambliss SP 15.00 40.00
DK Dave Kingman 15.00 40.00
DT Dick Tidrow 10.00 25.00
FS Fred Stanley 10.00 25.00
GU Ron Guidry 20.00 50.00
HB Hank Bauer SP 15.00 40.00
JB Jim Bouton 10.00 25.00
JK Jim Kaat 10.00 25.00
JK Jimmy Key 15.00 40.00
JL Jim Leyritz 10.00 25.00
JM John Montefusco 10.00 25.00
LM Lee Mazzilli 10.00 25.00
LP Lou Piniella SP 15.00 40.00
MM Mickey Mantle/7
MP Mike Pagliarulo 10.00 25.00
PO Paul O'Neill 20.00 50.00
RA Ruben Amaro Sr. 10.00 25.00
RB Ralph Branca 10.00 25.00
RH Ralph Houk 10.00 25.00
SL Sparky Lyle SP 15.00 40.00
TH Tommy Henrich SP 15.00 40.00
TJ Tommy John 10.00 25.00

2003 Sweet Spot Classics Game Jersey

Issued at a stated rate of one in 16, these 30 cards feature game-worn jersey swatches on the card. A few cards were issued in smaller quantities and we have notated those cards with an SP in our checklist.

AD Andre Dawson SP 4.00 10.00
CC Cecil Cooper 4.00 10.00
CF Carlton Fisk 6.00 15.00
CR Cal Ripken 10.00 25.00
DM Dale Murphy 6.00 15.00
DP0 Dave Parker Pants 4.00 10.00
DS Duke Snider SP 6.00 15.00
EB Ernie Banks SP 6.00 15.00
FL Fred Lynn 4.00 10.00
GC Gary Carter SP 4.00 10.00
GF George Foster 4.00 10.00
HK Harmon Killebrew 6.00 15.00
JB Johnny Bench 6.00 15.00
JC Jose Canseco 6.00 15.00
JG Jim Gilliam 4.00 10.00
JM0 Joe Morgan Pants 4.00 10.00
JP Johnny Podres 4.00 10.00
KP Kirby Puckett 6.00 15.00
LM Lee May 4.00 10.00
MM Mark McGwire 20.00 50.00
NR Nolan Ryan 15.00 40.00
OS Ozzie Smith 6.00 15.00
RC Ron Cey 4.00 10.00
RF Rollie Fingers 4.00 10.00
RY Robin Yount 6.00 15.00
SG Steve Garvey 4.00 10.00
SM Stan Musial SP 15.00 40.00
TG Tony Gwynn 6.00 15.00
TW Ted Williams SP 50.00 100.00
WS Willie Stargell SP 6.00 15.00

2003 Sweet Spot Classics Patch Cards

Inserted at a stated rate of one in six, these 83 cards feature special patch-type pieces. These cards honor different highlights in many player's career and we have notated that information next to their name in our checklist.

BR1 Babe Ruth Red Sox/350 15.00 40.00
BR2 Babe Ruth Yankees 12.50 30.00
BR3 Babe Ruth 27 WS/150 20.00 50.00
BW1 Billy Williams 4.00 10.00
CF1 Carlton Fisk Red Sox 6.00 15.00
CF2 Carlton Fisk White Sox/150 10.00 25.00
CH1 Catfish Hunter A's/350 6.00 15.00
CH2 Catfish Hunter Yankees 6.00 15.00
CH3 Catfish Hunter A's GU/39 30.00 60.00
CH4 Catfish Hunter 72 WS/50 15.00 40.00
CR1 Cal Ripken 10.00 25.00
CR2 Cal Ripken GU/75 75.00 150.00
CR3 Cal Ripken 83 WS/150 30.00 60.00
DS1 Duke Snider 6.00 15.00
DS2 Duke Snider LA/150 10.00 25.00
DS3 Duke Snider Mets/350 6.00 15.00
DS4 Duke Snider Dodgers GU/25
DS5 Duke Snider Brooklyn/150 10.00 25.00
DS6 Duke Snider 59 WS/150 10.00 25.00
EB1 Ernie Banks 6.00 15.00
FL1 Fred Lynn Red Sox 4.00 10.00
FL2 Fred Lynn Angels/350 4.00 10.00
FL3 Fred Lynn O's/150 6.00 15.00
FL4 Fred Lynn Tigers/50 10.00 25.00
GF1 George Foster Mets/350 4.00 10.00
GF2 George Foster Reds 4.00 10.00
HM1 Hideki Matsui 10.00 25.00
JB1 Johnny Bench 6.00 15.00
JB2 Johnny Bench GU/150 30.00 60.00
JB3 Johnny Bench 76 WS/150 15.00 40.00
JD1 Joe DiMaggio 6.00 15.00
JD2 Joe DiMaggio 47 WS/50 50.00 100.00
JD3 Joe DiMaggio 37 WS/350 12.50 30.00
JD4 Joe DiMaggio 39 WS/150 15.00 40.00
JM1 Joe Morgan Reds 4.00 10.00
JM2 Joe Morgan Astros/350 4.00 10.00
JM3 Joe Morgan Giants/150 6.00 15.00
JM4 Joe Morgan Reds GU/150 15.00 40.00
JM5 Joe Morgan 76 WS/100 6.00 15.00
KG1 Kirk Gibson Dodgers 4.00 10.00
KG2 Kirk Gibson Tigers/350 4.00 10.00
KP1 Kirby Puckett 6.00 15.00
KP2 Kirby Puckett GU/40 50.00 100.00
MC1 Mark McGwire A's 10.00 25.00
MC2 Mark McGwire Cards/350 20.00 50.00
MC3 Mark McGwire Cards GU/9
MM1 Mickey Mantle 15.00 40.00
MM2 M.Mantle 52 WS/150 60.00 120.00
MM3 M.Mantle 56 WS/150 60.00 120.00
MM4 M.Mantle 60 WS/150 60.00 120.00
MM5 Mickey Mantle Logo/7
NR1 Nolan Ryan Astros 10.00 25.00
NR2 Nolan Ryan Rangers/350 20.00 50.00
NR3 Nolan Ryan Angels/150 30.00 60.00
NR4 N.Ryan Astros GU/105 60.00 120.00
OS1 Ozzie Smith Cards 6.00 15.00
OS2 Ozzie Smith Padres/350 10.00 25.00
OS3 Ozzie Smith Cards GU/150 30.00 60.00
OS4 Ozzie Smith 82 WS/100 15.00 40.00
OS5 Ozzie Smith 85 WS/100 15.00 40.00
RM1 Roger Maris Yankees 10.00 25.00
RM2 Roger Maris Cards/350 10.00 25.00
RM3 Roger Maris 62 WS/150 15.00 40.00
RM4 Roger Maris 67 WS/50 20.00 50.00
RY1 Robin Yount 6.00 15.00
RY2 Robin Yount GU/150 15.00 40.00
RY3 Robin Yount 82 WS/350 10.00 25.00
SG1 Steve Garvey Dodgers 4.00 10.00
SG2 Steve Garvey Padres/350 4.00 10.00
SG3 S.Garvey Dodgers GU/150 15.00 40.00
SG4 Steve Garvey 77 WS/50 10.00 25.00
SG5 Steve Garvey 81 WS/50 10.00 25.00
TG1 Tony Gwynn 6.00 15.00
TG2 Tony Gwynn GU/150 40.00 80.00
TG3 Tony Gwynn 84 WS/350 10.00 25.00
TW1 Ted Williams 8.00 20.00
TW2 Ted Williams 46 WS/350 15.00 40.00
WS1 Willie Stargell 6.00 15.00
WS2 Willie Stargell GU/137 20.00 50.00
WS3 Willie Stargell 71 WS/150 10.00 25.00
WS4 Willie Stargell 79 WS/50 15.00 40.00
YB1 Yogi Berra 6.00 15.00
YB2 Yogi Berra 53 WS/350 10.00 25.00
YB3 Yogi Berra 56 WS/150 15.00 40.00

2003 Sweet Spot Classics Pinstripes

Inserted at a stated rate of one in 40, these 12 cards feature authentic game-used pieces of New York Yankee uniforms. Please note that a few cards were issued in shorter supply and we have notated that information with an SP notation in our checklist.

BR0 Babe Ruth Pants SP 150.00 250.00
CS Casey Stengel 6.00 15.00
DE Bucky Dent 4.00 10.00
DG0 Dwight Gooden Pants 4.00 10.00
DM0 Don Mattingly Pants 15.00 40.00
DR Dave Righetti 4.00 10.00
JB Jim Bouton 4.00 10.00
JD Joe DiMaggio SP 60.00 120.00
MM Mickey Mantle SP 50.00 100.00
PR Phil Rizzuto 6.00 15.00
TM Thurman Munson SP 15.00 40.00
YB Yogi Berra 8.00 20.00

2004 Sweet Spot Classic

This 159 card standard-size set was released in February, 2004. The set was issued in four card packs which came 12 packs to a box and 8 boxes to a case. Cards numbered 1-90 were issued in higher quantity than cards 91-161. The cards 91 through 161 feature "famous firsts" in players careers. Each of these cards are numbered to that year in issue. Cards numbered 143 and 148 which were supposed to feature Roger Clemens were removed from the set when Clemens came out of a very short retirement to sign with the Houston Astros.

COMP.SET w/o SP'S (90) 15.00 40.00
COMMON CARD (1-90) .30 .75
COMMON CARD (91-161) 1.25 3.00
91-161 STATED ODDS 1:3
91-161 PRINTS B/WN 1910-1999 COPIES PER
CARDS 143 AND 148 DO NOT EXIST
1 Al Kaline .75 2.00
2 Andre Dawson .50 1.25
3 Bert Blyleven .30 .75
4 Bill Dickey .30 .75
5 Bill Mazeroski .50 1.25
6 Billy Martin .50 1.25
7 Bob Feller .30 .75
8 Bob Gibson .50 1.25
9 Bob Lemon .30 .75
10 George Kell .30 .75
11 Bobby Doerr .30 .75
12 Brooks Robinson .50 1.25
13 Cal Ripken 3.00 8.00
14 Carl Hubbell .30 .75
15 Carl Yastrzemski .75 2.00
16 Charlie Keller .30 .75
17 Chuck Dressen .30 .75
18 Cy Young .50 1.25
19 Dave Winfield .30 .75
20 Dizzy Dean .50 1.25
21 Don Drysdale .50 1.25
22 Don Larsen .30 .75
23 Don Mattingly 1.50 4.00
24 Don Newcombe .30 .75
25 Duke Snider .50 1.25
26 Early Wynn .30 .75
27 Eddie Mathews .75 2.00
28 Elston Howard .30 .75
29 Frank Robinson .50 1.25
30 Gary Carter .30 .75
31 Gil Hodges .50 1.25
32 Gil McDougald .30 .75
33 Hank Greenberg .75 2.00
34 Harmon Killebrew .75 2.00
35 Harry Caray .50 1.25
36 Honus Wagner .75 2.00
37 Hoyt Wilhelm .30 .75
38 Jackie Robinson .75 2.00
39 Jim Bunning .30 .75
40 Jim Palmer .30 .75
41 Jimmie Foxx .75 2.00
42 Jimmy Wynn .30 .75
43 Joe DiMaggio 2.00 5.00
44 Joe Torre .50 1.25
45 Johnny Mize .30 .75
46 Juan Marichal .30 .75
47 Larry Doby .30 .75
48 Lefty Gomez .30 .75
49 Lefty Grove .30 .75
50 Leo Durocher .30 .75
51 Lou Boudreau .30 .75
52 Lou Brock .50 1.25
53 Lou Gehrig 1.50 4.00
54 Luis Aparicio .30 .75
55 Maury Wills .30 .75
56 Mel Allen .30 .75
57 Mel Ott .75 2.00
58 Mickey Cochrane .30 .75
59 Mickey Mantle 2.50 6.00
60 Mike Schmidt 1.25 3.00
61 Monte Irvin .30 .75
62 Nolan Ryan 2.50 6.00
63 Pee Wee Reese .50 1.25
64 Phil Rizzuto .50 1.25
65 Ralph Kiner .50 1.25
66 Richie Ashburn .50 1.25
67 Rick Ferrell .30 .75
68 Roberto Clemente 2.00 5.00
69 Robin Roberts .30 .75
70 Robin Yount .75 2.00
71 Rogers Hornsby .50 1.25
72 Rollie Fingers .30 .75
73 Roy Campanella .75 2.00
74 Ryne Sandberg 1.50 4.00
75 Tony Gwynn .75 2.00
76 Satchel Paige .75 2.00
77 Shoeless Joe Jackson 1.25 3.00
78 Stan Musial 1.25 3.00
79 Ted Williams 2.00 5.00
80 Thurman Munson .75 2.00
81 Tom Seaver .50 1.25
82 Tommy Henrich .30 .75
83 Tony Perez .30 .75
84 Tris Speaker .50 1.25
85 Vida Blue .30 .75
86 Wade Boggs .50 1.25
87 Walter Johnson .50 1.25
88 Warren Spahn .50 1.25
89 Whitey Ford .50 1.25
90 Willie McCovey .50 1.25
91 Andre Dawson FF/1987 2.00 5.00
92 Andre Dawson FF/1990 2.00 5.00
93 Ernie Banks FF/1958 3.00 8.00
94 Bob Lemon FF/1948 1.25 3.00
95 Cal Ripken FF/1982 6.00 15.00
96 Cal Ripken FF/1995 6.00 15.00
97 Carl Yastrzemski FF/1979 3.00 8.00
98 Carlton Fisk FF/1972 2.00 5.00
99 Cy Young FF/1910 2.00 5.00
100 Don Larsen FF/1956 1.25 3.00
101 Don Newcombe FF/1949 1.25 3.00
102 Don Newcombe FF/1956 1.25 3.00
103 Dwight Evans FF/1986 1.25 3.00
104 Elston Howard FF/1955 1.25 3.00
105 Frank Robinson FF/1956 2.00 5.00
106 Frank Robinson FF/1966 2.00 5.00
107 Frank Robinson FF/1973 2.00 5.00
108 Gil McDougald FF/1951 1.25 3.00
109 Hank Greenberg FF/1941 3.00 8.00
110 Harmon Killebrew FF/1964 3.00 8.00
111 Hoyt Wilhelm FF/1952 1.25 3.00
112 Hoyt Wilhelm FF/1958 1.25 3.00
113 Jackie Robinson FF/1946 3.00 8.00
114 J.Robinson FF Black/1947 3.00 8.00
115 J.Robinson FF ROY/1947 3.00 8.00
116 Jackie Robinson FF/1997 3.00 8.00
117 Jim Bunning FF/1964 1.25 3.00
118 J.DiMaggio FF Bench/1950 4.00 10.00
119 Joe Morgan FF/1976 1.25 3.00
120 Johnny Mize FF/1939 1.25 3.00
121 Johnny Mize FF/1947 1.25 3.00
122 Juan Marichal FF/1968 1.25 3.00
123 Ken Griffey Sr. FF/1990 1.25 3.00
124 Larry Doby FF/1947 1.25 3.00
125 Lefty Gomez FF/1933 1.25 3.00
126 Lou Boudreau FF/1946 1.25 3.00
127 Lou Gehrig FF Lineup/1939 4.00 10.00
128 Lou Gehrig FF Number/1939 4.00 10.00
129 Mark McGwire FF/1989 4.00 10.00
130 Mark McGwire FF/1998 4.00 10.00
131 Maury Wills FF/1962 1.25 3.00
132 Mel Ott FF/1946 3.00 8.00
133 Mike Schmidt FF/1980 4.00 10.00
134 Nolan Ryan FF/1973 5.00 12.00
135 Nolan Ryan FF/1989 5.00 12.00
136 Pee Wee Reese FF/1955 2.00 5.00
137 Nolan Ryan FF/1979 5.00 12.00
138 Richie Ashburn FF/1962 2.00 5.00
139 Roberto Clemente FF/1971 5.00 12.00
140 Roberto Clemente FF/1973 5.00 12.00
141 Robin Roberts FF/1956 1.25 3.00
142 Robin Yount FF/1982 3.00 8.00
144 Rollie Fingers FF/1975 1.25 3.00
145 Rollie Fingers FF/1981 1.25 3.00
146 Roy Campanella FF/1953 3.00 8.00
147 Ryne Sandberg FF/1990 3.00 8.00
149 Satchel Paige FF/1948 3.00 8.00
150 Stan Musial FF/1952 3.00 8.00
151 Stan Musial FF/1954 3.00 8.00
152 Stan Musial FF/1963 3.00 8.00
153 Ted Williams FF/1947 4.00 10.00
154 Ted Williams FF/1957 4.00 10.00
155 Tom Seaver FF/1970 2.00 5.00
156 Tom Seaver FF/1975 2.00 5.00
157 Wade Boggs FF/1999 2.00 5.00
158 Warren Spahn FF/1957 2.00 5.00
159 Warren Spahn FF/1958 2.00 5.00
160 Joe DiMaggio FF AS/1950 4.00 10.00
161 Yogi Berra FF/1947 3.00 8.00

2004 Sweet Spot Classic Barrel Signatures

Lou Brock did not return his cards in time for inclusion in this product. Those cards could be redeemed until January 27, 2004. A few cards have been seen on the secondary market with Duke Snider's photo used on Wade Boggs' card.

OVERALL AUTO ODDS 1:24
PRINT RUNS B/WN 24-203 COPIES PER
NO PRICING ON QTY OF 25 OR LESS
BM Bill Mazeroski/24
BW Billy Williams/200 20.00 50.00
CR Cal Ripken/25
HB Harold Baines/200 20.00 50.00
JB Johnny Bench/50
NR Nolan Ryan/25
RS Ron Santo/203 30.00 60.00
SM Stan Musial/25
TS Tom Seaver/25
WB Wade Boggs/200 40.00 80.00

2004 Sweet Spot Classic Game Used Memorabilia

OVERALL GU MEMORABILIA ODDS 1:24
STATED PRINT RUN 275 SERIAL #'d SETS
AD Andre Dawson Expos Jsy 4.00 10.00
AD1 Andre Dawson Cubs Jsy 4.00 10.00
BB Bert Blyleven Jsy 4.00 10.00
BM Billy Martin Pants 6.00 15.00
CD Chuck Dressen Pants 4.00 10.00
CK Charlie Keller Jsy 4.00 10.00
CR Cal Ripken Jsy 15.00 40.00
CY Carl Yastrzemski Jsy 10.00 25.00
DM Don Mattingly Jsy 10.00 25.00
EH Elston Howard Jsy 6.00 15.00
EM Eddie Mathews Jsy 6.00 15.00
FR Frank Robinson Jsy 4.00 10.00
GC Gary Carter Pants 4.00 10.00
GM Gil McDougald Jsy 6.00 15.00
JB Jim Bunning Pants 6.00 15.00
JD Joe DiMaggio Pants 40.00 80.00
JM Juan Marichal Pants 4.00 10.00
JO Johnny Mize Pants 6.00 15.00
JP Jim Palmer Jsy 4.00 10.00
JR Jackie Robinson Pants 15.00 40.00
JT Joe Torre Jsy 6.00 15.00
KG Ken Griffey Sr. Jsy 4.00 10.00
ML Mickey Lolich Jsy 4.00 10.00
MM Mickey Mantle Pants 60.00 120.00
MW Maury Wills Pants 4.00 10.00
NR Nolan Ryan Jsy 15.00 40.00
OS Ozzie Smith Jsy 6.00 15.00
PR Phil Rizzuto Pants 6.00 15.00
RB Ron Blomberg Jsy 4.00 10.00
RC Roberto Clemente Pants 40.00 80.00
RM Roger Maris Pants 30.00 60.00
RY Robin Yount Jsy 6.00 15.00
SA Sparky Anderson Jsy 4.00 10.00
SB Sal Bando Jsy 4.00 10.00
SM Stan Musial Pants 15.00 40.00
TG Tony Gwynn Pants 6.00 15.00
TM Thurman Munson Jsy 12.50 30.00
TS Tom Seaver Pants 6.00 15.00
TW Ted Williams Pants 30.00 60.00
WB Wade Boggs Sox Pants 6.00 15.00
WB1 Wade Boggs Yanks Pants 6.00 15.00

2004 Sweet Spot Classic Game Used Memorabilia Silver Rainbow

*SILVER RBW: .75X TO 2X BASIC SWATCH
OVERALL GU MEMORABILIA ODDS 1:24
STATED PRINT RUN 50 SERIAL #'d SETS
JD Joe DiMaggio Pants 50.00 100.00
MM Mickey Mantle Pants 125.00 200.00
RC Roberto Clemente Pants 50.00 100.00
TW Ted Williams Pants 40.00 80.00

2004 Sweet Spot Classic Game Used Patch

PRINT RUNS B/WN 17-176 COPIES PER
NO PRICING ON QTY OF 23 OR LESS
SILVER RAINBOW PRINT RUN 10 #'d SETS
NO SILV.RAIN.PRICING DUE TO SCARCITY
RANDOM INSERTS IN PACKS
AD Andre Dawson/100 10.00 25.00
BB Bert Blyleven/113 10.00 25.00
CK Charlie Keller/55 15.00 40.00
CR Cal Ripken/17
CY Carl Yastrzemski/20
DM Don Mattingly/176 30.00 60.00
EH Elston Howard/23
FR Frank Robinson/50 15.00 40.00
GM Gil McDougald/31 20.00 50.00
ML Mickey Lolich/115 10.00 25.00
MW Maury Wills/78 10.00 25.00
NR Nolan Ryan/96 50.00 100.00
RY Robin Yount/100 20.00 50.00
TG Tony Gwynn/100 30.00 60.00
TM Thurman Munson/100 30.00 60.00
TS Tom Seaver/94 15.00 40.00
WB Wade Boggs/90 15.00 40.00

2004 Sweet Spot Classic Patch 300

STATED PRINT RUN 300 SERIAL #'d SETS
*PATCH 230: .4X TO 1X BASIC
PATCH 230 PRINT RUN 230 SERIAL #'d SETS
*PATCH 200: .4X TO 1X BASIC
PATCH 200 PRINT RUN 200 SERIAL #'d SETS
*PATCH 150: .5X TO 1.2X BASIC
PATCH 150 PRINT RUN 150 SERIAL #'d SETS
*PATCH 125: .5X TO 1.2X BASIC
PATCH 125 PRINT RUN 125 SERIAL #'d SETS
*PATCH 75: .6X TO 1.5X BASIC
PATCH 75 PRINT RUN 75 SERIAL #'d SETS
*PATCH 50: .75X TO 2X BASIC
PATCH 50 PRINT RUN 50 SERIAL #'d SETS
PATCH 25 PRINT RUN 25 SERIAL #'d SETS
NO PATCH 25 PRICING DUE TO SCARCITY
PATCH 10 PRINT RUN 10 SERIAL #'d SETS
NO PATCH 10 PRICING DUE TO SCARCITY
OVERALL PATCH ODDS 1:3
AD Andre Dawson Cubs 4.00 10.00
AK Al Kaline Tigers 8.00 20.00
AL Mel Allen Yanks 4.00 10.00
BD Bill Dickey Yanks 6.00 15.00
BF Bob Feller Indians 4.00 10.00
BG Bob Gibson Cards 6.00 15.00
BL Bob Lemon Indians 4.00 10.00
BM Billy Martin Yanks 6.00 15.00
BR Lou Brock Cards 6.00 15.00
CA Roy Campanella Dodgers 6.00 15.00
CG Charlie Gehringer Tigers 4.00 10.00
CH Carl Hubbell Giants 6.00 15.00
CM Christy Mathewson Giants 6.00 15.00
CO Mickey Cochrane Tigers 4.00 10.00
CR Cal Ripken AS 15.00 40.00
CY Cy Young Indians 6.00 15.00
DD Dizzy Dean Cards 6.00 15.00
DL Don Larsen Yanks 4.00 10.00
DM Don Mattingly Yanks 10.00 25.00
DN Don Newcombe Dodgers 4.00 10.00
DO Bobby Doerr Red Sox 4.00 10.00
DR Don Drysdale Dodgers 6.00 15.00
DS Duke Snider AS 6.00 15.00
DU Leo Durocher Dodgers 4.00 10.00
DW Dave Winfield Yanks 4.00 10.00
EM Eddie Mathews Braves 6.00 15.00
ES Enos Slaughter Cards 4.00 10.00
EW Early Wynn Indians 4.00 10.00
FF Frankie Frisch Cards 4.00 10.00
FI Rollie Fingers A's 4.00 10.00
FJ Ferguson Jenkins Cubs 4.00 10.00
FR Frank Robinson Reds 4.00 10.00
GC Gary Carter Mets 4.00 10.00
GE Lou Gehrig Yanks 12.50 30.00
GH Gil Hodges Dodgers 6.00 15.00
GP Gaylord Perry Giants 4.00 10.00
GR Lefty Grove A's 6.00 15.00

HC Harry Caray Cubs 4.00 10.00
HG Hank Greenberg Tigers 6.00 15.00
HK Harmon Killebrew Twins 8.00 20.00
HW Honus Wagner Pirates 6.00 15.00
IR Monte Irvin Giants 4.00 10.00
JB Jim Bunning Phils 6.00 15.00
JD Joe DiMaggio AS 8.00 20.00
JF Jimmie Foxx A's 6.00 15.00
JJ Shoeless Joe Jackson Sox 8.00 20.00
JM Johnny Mize Cards 4.00 10.00
JP Jim Palmer O's 4.00 10.00
JR Jackie Robinson Dodgers 6.00 15.00
JT Joe Torre Braves 4.00 10.00
LA Luis Aparicio White Sox 4.00 10.00
LB Lou Boudreau Indians 4.00 10.00
LD Larry Doby Indians 4.00 10.00
LG Lefty Gomez Yanks 6.00 15.00
MA Juan Marichal Giants 4.00 10.00
MI Mickey Mantle AS 20.00 50.00
ML Mickey Lolich Tigers 4.00 10.00
MO Mel Ott Giants 6.00 15.00
MS Mike Schmidt Phils 10.00 25.00
MW Maury Wills Dodgers 4.00 10.00
NR Nolan Ryan Mets 12.50 30.00
PR Pee Wee Reese Dodgers 6.00 15.00
RA Richie Ashburn Phils 6.00 15.00
RC Roberto Clemente Pirates 12.50 30.00
RF Rick Ferrell Red Sox 4.00 10.00
RH Rogers Hornsby Cards 6.00 15.00
RI Phil Rizzuto Yanks 6.00 15.00
RK Ralph Kiner Pirates 4.00 10.00
RO Brooks Robinson O's 6.00 15.00
RR Robin Roberts Phils 4.00 10.00
RS Ryne Sandberg Cubs 10.00 25.00
RU Babe Ruth AS 12.50 30.00
SK Bill Skowron Yanks 4.00 10.00
SM Stan Musial Cards 8.00 20.00
SP Satchel Paige Indians 6.00 15.00
TC Ty Cobb Tigers 8.00 20.00
TH Tommy Henrich Yanks 4.00 10.00
TL Tommy Lasorda Dodgers 4.00 10.00
TM Thurman Munson Yanks 6.00 15.00
TP Tony Perez Reds 4.00 10.00
TR Tris Speaker Red Sox 6.00 15.00
TS Tom Seaver Mets 6.00 15.00
TW Ted Williams AS 10.00 25.00
WB Wade Boggs Red Sox 6.00 15.00
WF Whitey Ford Yanks 6.00 15.00
WI Hoyt Wilhelm White Sox 4.00 10.00
WJ Walter Johnson Senators 6.00 15.00
WM Willie McCovey Giants 4.00 10.00
WS Warren Spahn Braves 6.00 15.00
YA Carl Yastrzemski Red Sox 10.00 25.00

2004 Sweet Spot Classic Signatures Black

Randomly inserted in packs, these cards feature signatures from the noted personages in black ink. Several people including long-time Phillies announcer Harry Kalas and one time NL consecutive-games played leader Gus Suhr have their 1st certified autograph card in this set. Please note that several people did not return their cards in time for inclusion in pack out and those cards could be redeemed until January 27, 2004. Please note that for players with 25 or fewer signatures that no pricing is provided due to market scarcity.

OVERALL AUTO ODDS 1:24
PRINT RUNS B/WN 25-275 COPIES PER
2 Preacher Roe/225 15.00 40.00
4 Bob Feller/65 20.00 50.00
5 Bob Gibson/50 40.00 80.00
6 Harry Kalas/100 75.00 150.00
7 Bobby Doerr/100 15.00 40.00
8 Cal Ripken/50 100.00 175.00
9 Carl Yastrzemski/35
10 Carlton Fisk/100 30.00 60.00
11 Chuck Tanner/150 10.00 25.00
12 Cito Gaston/150 10.00 25.00
13 Danny Ozark/150 10.00 25.00
14 Dave Winfield/80 40.00 80.00
15 Davey Johnson/175 15.00 40.00
16 Ernie Harwell/100 40.00 80.00
17 Dick Williams/150 10.00 25.00
18 Don Mattingly/40
19 Don Newcombe/40 20.00 50.00
20 Duke Snider/35 40.00 80.00
21 Steve Carlton/150 15.00 40.00
22 Felipe Alou/175 10.00 25.00
23 Frank Robinson/65 40.00 80.00
24 Gary Carter/100 15.00 40.00
25 Gene Mauch/225 10.00 25.00
26 George Bamberger/225 10.00 25.00
28 Gus Suhr/100 15.00 40.00
30 Harmon Killebrew/50 60.00 120.00
31 Jack McKeon/225 15.00 40.00
32 Jim Bunning/100 40.00 80.00
33 Jimmy Piersall/212 15.00 40.00
35 Johnny Bench/50 50.00 100.00
36 Juan Marichal/50 20.00 50.00
38 George Kell/40 20.00 50.00
39 Maury Wills/40 20.00 50.00
42 Nolan Ryan/50
43 Ozzie Smith/65 50.00 100.00
44 Eddie Mayo/140 10.00 25.00
45 Phil Rizzuto/50 40.00 80.00
47 Lonny Frey/114 10.00 25.00
48 Bill Mazeroski/50 40.00 80.00
49 Robin Roberts/40 40.00 80.00
50 Robin Yount/40 50.00 100.00
52 Roger Craig/175 15.00 40.00
55 Tony Perez/40 20.00 50.00
56 Sparky Anderson/175 15.00 40.00
57 Stan Musial/40
58 Ted Radcliffe/225 40.00 80.00
60 Tom Seaver/25
61 Tony Gwynn/65
62 Tony LaRussa/275 10.00 25.00
63 Tony Oliva/150 15.00 40.00
64 Tony Pena/150 10.00 25.00
66 Whitey Ford/45 40.00 80.00
67 Yogi Berra/65 50.00 100.00

2004 Sweet Spot Classic Signatures Black Holo-Foil

For those people who did not return their cards in time for inclusion in this product, those exchange cards could be returned until January 27, 2007.

OVERALL AUTO ODDS 1:24
PRINT RUNS B/WN 10-100 COPIES PER
NO PRICING ON QTY OF 25 OR LESS
MOST CARDS FEATURE INSCRIPTIONS
11 Chuck Tanner/100 10.00 25.00
12 Cito Gaston/100 10.00 25.00
13 Danny Ozark/100 10.00 25.00
15 Davey Johnson/50 20.00 50.00
17 Dick Williams/100 10.00 25.00
22 Felipe Alou/50 12.50 30.00
24 Gary Carter/50 20.00 50.00
52 Roger Craig/50 20.00 50.00
56 Sparky Anderson/50 20.00 50.00
62 Tony LaRussa/50 12.50 30.00
63 Tony Oliva/100 15.00 40.00
64 Tony Pena/100 10.00 25.00

2004 Sweet Spot Classic Signatures Blue

A few people did not return their cards in time for inclusion in packs, those signed cards could be redeemed until January 27, 2004.

OVERALL AUTO ODDS 1:24
PRINT RUNS B/WN 15-150 COPIES PER
NO PRICING ON QTY OF 25 OR LESS
2 Preacher Roe/150 15.00 40.00
4 Bob Feller/50 20.00 50.00
5 Bob Gibson/25
6 Harry Kalas/50 60.00 120.00
7 Bobby Doerr/50 20.00 50.00
8 Cal Ripken/25
9 Carl Yastrzemski/15
10 Carlton Fisk/50 40.00 80.00
11 Chuck Tanner/125 10.00 25.00
12 Cito Gaston/125 10.00 25.00
13 Danny Ozark/125 10.00 25.00
14 Dave Winfield/35 40.00 80.00
15 Davey Johnson/150 15.00 40.00
17 Dick Williams/125 10.00 25.00
18 Don Mattingly/25
19 Don Newcombe/25
20 Duke Snider/25
21 Steve Carlton/100 15.00 40.00
22 Felipe Alou/150 10.00 25.00
23 Frank Robinson/50 40.00 80.00
24 Gary Carter/75 20.00 50.00
25 Gene Mauch/150 10.00 25.00
26 George Bamberger/150 10.00 25.00
28 Gus Suhr/85 20.00 50.00
30 Harmon Killebrew/25
31 Jack McKeon/150 15.00 40.00
32 Jim Bunning/65 50.00 100.00
33 Jimmy Piersall/150 15.00 40.00
35 Johnny Bench/20
36 Juan Marichal/25
38 George Kell/25
39 Maury Wills/25
42 Nolan Ryan/25
43 Ozzie Smith/50 50.00 100.00
44 Eddie Mayo/50 12.50 30.00
45 Phil Rizzuto/25
47 Lonny Frey/75 12.50 30.00
48 Bill Mazeroski/25
49 Robin Roberts/25
50 Robin Yount/25
52 Roger Craig/150 15.00 40.00
55 Tony Perez/25
56 Sparky Anderson/150 15.00 40.00
57 Stan Musial/25
58 Ted Radcliffe/150 40.00 80.00
60 Tom Seaver/15
61 Tony Gwynn/25
62 Tony LaRussa/145 10.00 25.00
63 Tony Oliva/125 15.00 40.00
64 Tony Pena/115 10.00 25.00
66 Whitey Ford/20
67 Yogi Berra/50 50.00 100.00

2004 Sweet Spot Classic Signatures Red

Ernie Harwell, Lou Brock, Mike Schmidt and Ralph Kiner did not return their cards in time for inclusion in packs. Redemption cards with an expiration date of January 27th, 2007 were seeded into packs for these aforementioned athletes. The Joe DiMaggio and Ted Williams cards from this set feature blue ink signed leather baseball patches (as averse to the red ink featured on the other cards). Representatives at Upper Deck have confirmed that they estimate approximately 25% of the Joe DiMaggio cards actually feature the added notation "Yankee Clipper".

OVERALL AUTO ODDS 1:24
PRINT RUNS B/WN 2-86 COPIES PER
NO PRICING ON QTY OF 25 OR LESS
34 Joe DiMaggio/86 500.00 800.00

2005 Sweet Spot Classic

COMPLETE SET (100) 15.00 40.00
COMMON CARD (1-100) .30 .75
1 Al Kaline .75 2.00
2 Al Rosen .30 .75
3 Babe Ruth 2.00 5.00
4 Bill Mazeroski .50 1.25
5 Billy Williams .30 .75
6 Bob Feller .30 .75
7 Bob Gibson .50 1.25
8 Bobby Doerr .30 .75
9 Brooks Robinson .50 1.25
10 Cal Ripken 3.00 8.00
11 Carl Yastrzemski 1.00 2.50
12 Carlton Fisk .50 1.25
13 Casey Stengel .30 .75
14 Christy Mathewson .75 2.00
15 Cy Young .50 1.25
16 Dale Murphy .30 .75
17 Dave Winfield .30 .75
18 Dennis Eckersley .30 .75
19 Dizzy Dean .50 1.25
20 Don Drysdale .50 1.25
21 Don Mattingly 1.50 4.00
22 Don Newcombe .30 .75
23 Don Sutton .30 .75
24 Duke Snider .50 1.25
25 Dwight Evans .50 1.25
26 Eddie Mathews .50 1.25
27 Eddie Murray .75 2.00
28 Enos Slaughter .30 .75
29 Ernie Banks .75 2.00
30 Frank Howard .30 .75
31 Frank Robinson .50 1.25
32 Gary Carter .30 .75
33 Gaylord Perry .30 .75
34 George Brett 1.50 4.00
35 George Kell .30 .75
36 George Sisler .30 .75
37 Larry Doby .30 .75
38 Harmon Killebrew .75 2.00
39 Honus Wagner .50 1.25
40 Jackie Robinson .50 1.25
41 Jim Bunning .30 .75
42 Jim Palmer .30 .75
43 Jim Rice .30 .75
44 Jimmie Foxx .50 1.25
45 Joe DiMaggio 2.00 5.00
46 Joe Morgan .30 .75
47 Johnny Bench .75 2.00
48 Johnny Mize .50 1.25
49 Johnny Podres .30 .75
50 Juan Marichal .30 .75
51 Keith Hernandez .30 .75
52 Kirby Puckett .75 2.00
53 Lefty Grove .30 .75
54 Lou Brock .50 1.25
55 Lou Gehrig 1.50 4.00
56 Luis Aparicio .30 .75
57 Fergie Jenkins .30 .75
58 Maury Wills .30 .75
59 Mel Ott .75 2.00
60 Mickey Cochrane .30 .75
61 Mickey Mantle 2.50 6.00
62 Mike Schmidt 1.50 4.00
63 Monte Irvin .30 .75
64 Nolan Ryan UER 2.00 5.00
Ryan led his league in strikeouts 11 times; not 12
65 Orlando Cepeda .30 .75
66 Ozzie Smith 1.25 3.00
67 Paul Molitor .75 2.00
68 Pee Wee Reese .50 1.25
69 Phil Niekro .30 .75
70 Phil Rizzuto .50 1.25
71 Ralph Kiner .30 .75
72 Richie Ashburn .50 1.25
73 Roberto Clemente 2.00 5.00
74 Robin Roberts .30 .75
75 Robin Yount .75 2.00
76 Rocky Colavito .50 1.25
77 Rod Carew .50 1.25
78 Rogers Hornsby .30 .75
79 Rollie Fingers .30 .75
80 Roy Campanella .50 1.25
81 Bob Lemon .30 .75
82 Red Schoendienst .30 .75
83 Satchel Paige .75 2.00
84 Stan Musial 1.25 3.00
85 Steve Carlton .30 .75
86 Ted Williams 1.50 4.00
87 Thurman Munson .50 1.25
88 Tom Seaver .50 1.25
89 Tony Gwynn 1.00 2.50
90 Tony Perez .30 .75
91 Ty Cobb 1.25 3.00
92 Wade Boggs .50 1.25
93 Walter Johnson .50 1.25
94 Warren Spahn .50 1.25
95 Whitey Ford .50 1.25
96 Will Clark .50 1.25
97 Catfish Hunter .30 .75
98 Willie McCovey .50 1.25
99 Willie Stargell .50 1.25
100 Yogi Berra .75 2.00

2005 Sweet Spot Classic Gold

*GOLD: 2.5X TO 6X BASIC
STATED ODDS 1:120 HOBBY
STATED PRINT RUN 50 SERIAL #'d SETS

2005 Sweet Spot Classic Silver

*SILVER: X TO X BASIC
STATED PRINT RUN 100 SERIAL #'d SETS

2005 Sweet Spot Classic Materials

OVERALL GAME-USED ODDS 1:6
SP INFO PROVIDED BY UPPER DECK
STARGELL PRINT RUN PROVIDED BY UD
NO STARGELL PRICING DUE TO SCARCITY
AD Andre Dawson Jsy 3.00 8.00
AK Al Kaline Jsy 6.00 15.00
BE Johnny Bench Jsy 6.00 15.00
BF Bob Feller Jsy 4.00 10.00
BG Bob Gibson Jsy 4.00 10.00
BM Bill Mazeroski Jsy 4.00 10.00
BR Babe Ruth Pants SP 175.00 300.00
CA Rod Carew Jsy 4.00 10.00
CF Carlton Fisk Jsy 4.00 10.00
CH Catfish Hunter Pants 4.00 10.00
CO Rocky Colavito Jsy 10.00 25.00
CP Roy Campanella Pants 6.00 15.00
CR C.Ripken Hitting Jsy 8.00 20.00
CR1 C.Ripken Fielding Pants 8.00 20.00
CY Carl Yastrzemski Jsy 6.00 15.00
DC David Cone Jsy 3.00 8.00
DD Don Drysdale Pants 6.00 15.00
DM D.Mattingly Pose Jsy 6.00 15.00
DM1 D.Mattingly Hitting Jsy 6.00 15.00
DS Don Sutton Dgr Jsy 3.00 8.00
DS1 Don Sutton Astros Jsy 3.00 8.00
DW D.Winfield Yanks Jsy 3.00 8.00
DW1 D.Winfield Padres Jsy 3.00 8.00
ED Eddie Murray O's Jsy 6.00 15.00
ED1 Eddie Murray Dgr Jsy 6.00 15.00
EM Eddie Mathews Pants 6.00 15.00
EW Early Wynn Pants 4.00 10.00
FJ Fergie Jenkins Jsy 3.00 8.00
FR Frank Robinson Jsy 4.00 10.00
FV Fernando Valenzuela Jsy 4.00 10.00
GB G.Brett Sunglass Jsy 6.00 15.00
GB1 G.Brett Hitting Jsy 6.00 15.00
GC Gary Carter Expos Jsy 3.00 8.00
GP Gaylord Perry Jsy 3.00 8.00
HK Harmon Killebrew Jsy 6.00 15.00
JB Jim Bunning Jsy 4.00 10.00
JD Joe DiMaggio Jsy 20.00 50.00
JM Joe Morgan Reds Pants 3.00 8.00
JM1 Joe Morgan Astros Jsy 3.00 8.00
JP Jim Palmer Jsy 3.00 8.00
JR Jackie Robinson Jsy 15.00 40.00
LB Lou Brock Jsy 4.00 10.00
LG Lou Gehrig Pants SP 100.00 175.00
MA Juan Marichal Jsy 3.00 8.00
MG Mark Grace Jsy 4.00 10.00
MM Mickey Mantle Jsy SP 75.00 150.00
MS M.Schmidt Hitting Jsy 6.00 15.00
MS1 M.Schmidt Running Jsy 6.00 15.00
MU Dale Murphy Jsy 4.00 10.00
MW Maury Wills Dgr Jsy 3.00 8.00
MW1 Maury Wills Pirates Jsy 3.00 8.00
NR Nolan Ryan Astros Jsy 12.50 30.00
NR1 Nolan Ryan Rgr Jsy 12.50 30.00
OC Orlando Cepeda Jsy 3.00 8.00
OS Ozzie Smith Jsy SP 10.00 25.00
PM Paul Molitor Brewers Jsy 3.00 8.00
PN Phil Niekro Jsy 3.00 8.00
PR Phil Rizzuto Pants 4.00 10.00
RC Roberto Clemente Pants 30.00 60.00
RE Pee Wee Reese Jsy SP 6.00 15.00
RG Ron Guidry Jsy 3.00 8.00
RI Jim Rice Jsy 3.00 8.00
RO Brooks Robinson Jsy 6.00 15.00
RR Robin Roberts Pants 4.00 10.00
RY Robin Yount Jsy 6.00 15.00
SC Steve Carlton Pants 3.00 8.00
SD Red Schoendienst Jsy 3.00 8.00
SM Stan Musial Pants SP 10.00 25.00
SN Duke Snider Pants 6.00 15.00
SP Satchel Paige Pants 30.00 60.00
ST Willie Stargell Jsy SP/18
TC Ty Cobb Pants SP 300.00 600.00
TG Tony Gwynn Jsy 6.00 15.00
TM Thurman Munson Jsy SP 10.00 25.00
TP Tony Perez Jsy 4.00 10.00
TS Tom Seaver Reds Jsy 4.00 10.00
TW Ted Williams Jsy SP 40.00 80.00
WB Wade Boggs Jsy 4.00 10.00
WC Will Clark Giants Jsy 4.00 10.00
WC1 Will Clark Rgr Jsy 4.00 10.00
WI Willie McCovey Jsy 4.00 10.00
WS Warren Spahn Jsy 6.00 15.00
YB Yogi Berra Pants 6.00 15.00

2005 Sweet Spot Classic Patches

OVERALL GAME-USED ODDS 1:6
PRINT RUNS B/WN 1-50 COPIES PER
NO PRICING ON QTY OF 19 OR LESS
LISTED PRICES ARE 2-3 COLOR PATCH
*1-COLOR PATCH: DROP 20-50% DISCOUNT

*4-5-COLOR PATCH: ADD 20-50% PREMIUM
LOGO PATCHES TOO VOLATILE TO PRICE
AD Andre Dawson/7
BE Johnny Bench/32 250.00 500.00
BG Bob Gibson/1
BS Bruce Sutter/50 75.00 150.00
CF1 Carlton Fisk/50 125.00 250.00
CR C.Ripken Hitting/34 400.00 800.00
CR1 C.Ripken Fielding/34 400.00 800.00
CY Carl Yastrzemski/35 200.00 400.00
DC David Cone/39 100.00 175.00
DM D.Mattingly Pose/9
DM1 D.Mattingly Hitting/9
DS Don Sutton Dgr/34 40.00 80.00
DS1 Don Sutton Astros/50 40.00 80.00
DW D.Winfield Yanks/3
DW1 D.Winfield Padres/50 100.00 175.00
ED Eddie Murray O's/34 100.00 175.00
ED1 Eddie Murray Dgr/50 100.00 175.00
FH Frank Howard/34 200.00 400.00
FJ Fergie Jenkins/34 100.00 175.00
FR Frank Robinson/34 125.00 250.00
GB G.Brett Pose/38 175.00 350.00
GB1 G.Brett Action/50 175.00 350.00
GC Gary Carter Expos/47 75.00 150.00
GC1 Gary Carter Mets/34 75.00 150.00
GP Gaylord Perry/34 75.00 150.00
JD Joe DiMaggio/38 400.00 800.00
JM Joe Morgan Reds/50 125.00 250.00
JR Jackie Robinson/12
LA Luis Aparicio/19
LB Lou Brock/34 100.00 175.00
MM Mickey Mantle/19
MS M.Schmidt Hitting/6
MS1 M.Schmidt Running/5
MU Dale Murphy/34 100.00 175.00
MW Maury Wills Dgr/50 100.00 175.00
MW1 Maury Wills Pirates/47 100.00 175.00
NR Nolan Ryan Astros/16
NR1 Nolan Ryan Rgr/3
NR2 Nolan Ryan Angels/15
OC Orlando Cepeda/40 75.00 150.00
OS Ozzie Smith/34 125.00 250.00
PM Paul Molitor Brewers/13
PM1 Paul Molitor Twins/12
PN Phil Niekro/44 75.00 150.00
PO Johnny Podres/50 100.00 175.00
RE Pee Wee Reese/10
RG Ron Guidry/30 75.00 150.00
RI Jim Rice/34 100.00 175.00
RO B.Robinson Color/50 175.00 350.00
RO1 B.Robinson B/W/43 175.00 350.00
RY R.Yount Bat Back/34 125.00 250.00
RY1 R.Yount Bat Out/19
SC Steve Carlton/50 100.00 175.00
SD Red Schoendienst/42 75.00 150.00
SM Stan Musial/3
ST Willie Stargell/50 100.00 175.00
TG T.Gwynn Blue Uni/34 125.00 250.00
TG1 T.Gwynn Camo Uni/30 125.00 250.00
TP Tony Perez/34 125.00 250.00
TS Tom Seaver Reds/50 100.00 175.00
TS1 Tom Seaver Mets/50 100.00 175.00
WB Wade Boggs Sox/25 100.00 175.00
WB1 Wade Boggs Yanks/34 100.00 175.00
WI Willie McCovey/50 100.00 175.00

2005 Sweet Spot Classic Signatures

OVERALL AUTO ODDS 1:12
TIER 1 PRINT RUNS B/WN 25-99 PER
TIER 2 PRINT RUNS B/WN 125-230 PER
TIER 3 PRINT RUNS 250 OR MORE PER
CARDS ARE NOT SERIAL-NUMBERED
TIER 1-3 INFO PROVIDED BY UPPER DECK
NO DIMAGGIO PRICING DUE TO SCARCITY
EXCHANGE DEADLINE 01/28/08
AD Andre Dawson T3 10.00 25.00
AK Al Kaline T3 20.00 50.00
AR Al Rosen T3 10.00 25.00
BD Bobby Doerr T3 10.00 25.00
BE Johnny Bench T2 30.00 60.00
BF Bob Feller T3 15.00 40.00
BG Bob Gibson T3 20.00 50.00
BJ Bo Jackson T2 50.00 100.00
BM Bill Mazeroski T3 20.00 50.00
BR Brooks Robinson T3 15.00 40.00
BW Billy Williams T3 10.00 25.00
CA Rod Carew T2 20.00 50.00
CF Carlton Fisk T2 20.00 50.00
CR Cal Ripken T2 100.00 175.00
CY Carl Yastrzemski T2 30.00 60.00
DC David Cone T3 10.00 25.00
DE Dennis Eckersley T3 10.00 25.00
DJ Dave Justice T3 10.00 25.00
DM Don Mattingly T2 40.00 80.00
DN Don Newcombe T2 12.50 30.00
DS Don Sutton T2 12.50 30.00
EB Ernie Banks T2 30.00 60.00
EV Dwight Evans T3 15.00 40.00
FH Frank Howard T3 10.00 25.00
FR Frank Robinson T2 12.50 30.00
FV Fernando Valenzuela T3 15.00 40.00
GB George Brett T2 75.00 150.00
GC Gary Carter T3 10.00 25.00
GK George Kell T3 12.50 30.00
GP Gaylord Perry T3 10.00 25.00
HB Harold Baines T3 6.00 15.00
HK Harmon Killebrew T3 30.00 60.00
JB Jim Bunning T3 10.00 25.00
JC Jose Canseco T2 30.00 60.00
JD Joe DiMaggio T1/25
JM Joe Morgan T1/99 15.00 40.00
JP Jim Palmer T3 10.00 25.00
JR Jim Rice T3 10.00 25.00
KA Harry Kalas T3 60.00 120.00
KH Keith Hernandez T3 10.00 25.00
LA Luis Aparicio T3 10.00 25.00
LT Luis Tiant T3 6.00 15.00
MA Juan Marichal T3 15.00 40.00
MC Willie McCovey T1/99 30.00 60.00
MG Mark Grace T3 20.00 50.00
MI Monte Irvin T3 10.00 25.00
MS Mike Schmidt T2 50.00 100.00
MU Dale Murphy T3 10.00 25.00
MW Matt Williams T3 15.00 40.00
NR Nolan Ryan T2 75.00 150.00
OC Orlando Cepeda T3 10.00 25.00
OS Ozzie Smith T2 30.00 60.00
PM Paul Molitor T3 10.00 25.00
PN Phil Niekro T2 12.50 30.00
PO Johnny Podres T3 10.00 25.00
PR Phil Rizzuto T2 20.00 50.00
RE Red Schoendienst T2 12.50 30.00
RF Rollie Fingers T3 10.00 25.00
RK Ralph Kiner T1/99 10.00 25.00
RR Robin Roberts T2 12.50 30.00
RS Ron Santo T3 15.00 40.00
SC Steve Carlton T2 12.50 30.00
SM Stan Musial T2 50.00 100.00
SN Duke Snider T2 10.00 25.00
ST Rusty Staub T3 10.00 25.00
SU Bruce Sutter T3 15.00 40.00
TG Tony Gwynn T2 20.00 50.00
TP Tony Perez T2 12.50 30.00
TS Tom Seaver T2 30.00 60.00
WB Wade Boggs T2 20.00 50.00
WC Will Clark T3 15.00 40.00
WF Whitey Ford T2 20.00 50.00
WI Maury Wills T3 10.00 25.00
YB Yogi Berra T1/99 30.00 60.00

2005 Sweet Spot Classic Signatures Black Stitch

OVERALL AUTO ODDS 1:12
STATED PRINT RUN 1 SERIAL #'d SET
NO PRICING DUE TO SCARCITY
EXCHANGE DEADLINE 01/28/08

2005 Sweet Spot Classic Signatures Red-Blue Stitch

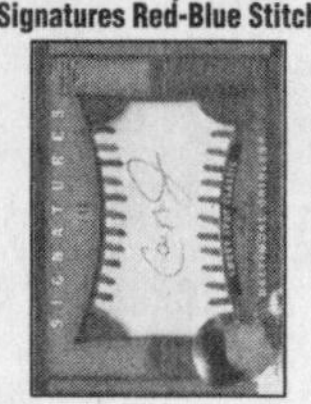

*R/B: .6X TO 1.5X TIER 3
*R/B: .5X TO 1.2X TIER 2
*R/B: .5X TO 1.2X TIER 1 p/r 99
*R/B: .4X TO 1X TIER 1 p/r 50-56
OVERALL AUTO ODDS 1:12
STATED PRINT RUN 40 SERIAL #'d SETS
BO JACKSON PRINT RUN 36 #'d CARDS
EXCHANGE DEADLINE 01/28/08
BJ Bo Jackson/36 75.00 150.00
CR Cal Ripken 100.00 200.00
DM Don Mattingly 60.00 120.00
GB George Brett 60.00 120.00
HB Harold Baines 15.00 40.00
JC Jose Canseco 30.00 80.00
JD Joe DiMaggio
LT Luis Tiant 15.00 40.00
MS Mike Schmidt 60.00 120.00
MU Dale Murphy 25.00 60.00
NR Nolan Ryan 90.00 180.00
SM Stan Musial 60.00 120.00
ST Rusty Staub 15.00 40.00
SU Bruce Sutter 25.00 60.00

2005 Sweet Spot Classic Signature Sticks

*STICKS: .75X TO 2X TIER 3
*STICKS: .6X TO 1.5X TIER 2
*STICKS: .6X TO 1.5X TIER 1 p/r 99
*STICKS: .5X TO 1.2X TIER 1 p/r 50-56
OVERALL AUTO ODDS 1:12
STATED PRINT RUN 35 SERIAL #'d SETS
BJ Bo Jackson 90.00 180.00
CR Cal Ripken 175.00 300.00
DA Darryl Strawberry
DM Don Mattingly 75.00 150.00
GB George Brett 75.00 150.00
HB Harold Baines 20.00 50.00
JC Jose Canseco 40.00 100.00
LT Luis Tiant 20.00 50.00
MS Mike Schmidt 75.00 150.00
MU Dale Murphy 30.00 80.00
NR Nolan Ryan 100.00 200.00
RC Rocky Colavito 75.00 150.00
SM Stan Musial 75.00 150.00
ST Rusty Staub 20.00 50.00
SU Bruce Sutter 30.00 80.00

2005 Sweet Spot Classic Signatures Sweet Leather

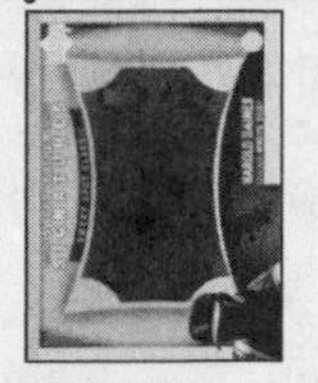

*LEATHER: 1.25X TO 2.5X TIER 3
*LEATHER: 1X TO 2X TIER 2
*LEATHER: 1X TO 2X TIER 1 p/r 99
*LEATHER: .75X TO 1.5X TIER 1 p/r 50-56
OVERALL AUTO ODDS 1:12
STATED PRINT RUN 25 SERIAL #'d SETS
EXCHANGE DEADLINE 01/28/08
BJ Bo Jackson 100.00 200.00
CR Cal Ripken 200.00 350.00
DA Darryl Strawberry
DM Don Mattingly 90.00 180.00
GB George Brett 90.00 180.00
HB Harold Baines 30.00 60.00
JC Jose Canseco 60.00 120.00
LT Luis Tiant 30.00 60.00
MS Mike Schmidt 90.00 180.00
MU Dale Murphy 50.00 100.00
NR Nolan Ryan 150.00 250.00
SM Stan Musial 90.00 180.00
ST Rusty Staub 30.00 60.00
SU Bruce Sutter 50.00 100.00

2005 Sweet Spot Classic Signatures Dual

OVERALL AUTO ODDS 1:12
STATED PRINT RUN 15 SERIAL #'d SETS
CARLTON/SCHMIDT PRINT 14 #'d CARDS
NO PRICING DUE TO SCARCITY
EXCHANGE DEADLINE 01/28/08

2005 Sweet Spot Classic Wingfield Classics Collection

ONE PER SEALED HOBBY BOX
1 Al Kaline 4.00 10.00
2 Pee Wee Reese 2.50 6.00
3 Stan Musial 8.00 20.00
Ted Williams
4 Bill Dickey 1.50 4.00
5 Frank Robinson 2.50 6.00
6 Billy Martin 2.50 6.00
7 Joe DiMaggio 10.00 25.00
Casey Stengel
8 Dwight D. Eisenhower 1.50 4.00
Bob Feller
9 Duke Snider 2.50 6.00
10 Carl Yastrzemski 5.00 12.00
11 Honus Wagner 2.50 6.00
12 Clark Griffith 1.50 4.00
Dwight D. Eisenhower
13 Mickey Mantle 10.00 25.00
Joe DiMaggio
14 Don Drysdale 2.50 6.00
15 Ted Williams 8.00 20.00
16 Mickey Mantle 12.00 30.00
Al Kaline
17 Ernie Banks 4.00 10.00
18 Lou Boudreau 1.50 4.00
19 George Sisler 4.00 10.00
Harmon Killebrew
20 Gil Hodges 2.50 6.00
21 Rogers Hornsby 1.50 4.00
22 Luis Aparicio 1.50 4.00
23 Jackie Robinson 2.50 6.00
24 Joe Morgan 1.50 4.00
25 Enos Slaughter 1.50 4.00
26 Joe DiMaggio 10.00 25.00
27 Mickey Mantle 2.50 6.00
Ted Kluszewski
28 John F. Kennedy 4.00 10.00
29 Johnny Bench 4.00 10.00
30 Juan Marichal 1.50 4.00
31 Larry Doby 1.50 4.00
32 Don Newcombe 1.50 4.00
Elston Howard
33 Dwight D. Eisenhower 4.00 10.00
Harmon Killebrew
34 Roger Maris 12.00 30.00
Mickey Mantle
35 Stan Musial 12.00 30.00
Mickey Mantle
36 Ted Williams 12.00 30.00

Yogi Berra
Mickey Mantle
37 Nellie Fox 2.50 6.00
38 Richie Ashburn 2.50 6.00
39 Roberto Clemente 10.00 25.00
40 Stan Musial 6.00 15.00
Robin Roberts
41 Joe DiMaggio 10.00 25.00
Tommy Henrich
42 Roy Campanella 2.50 6.00
43 Rocky Colavito 2.50 6.00
Harmon Killebrew
44 Steve Carlton 1.50 4.00
45 Thurman Munson 2.50 6.00
46 Ernie Banks 4.00 10.00
Luis Aparicio
47 Dwight D. Eisenhower 4.00 10.00
Gil Hodges
Yogi Berra
48 Whitey Ford 2.50 6.00
49 Yogi Berra 10.00 25.00
Mickey Mantle
Joe DiMaggio
50 Yogi Berra 4.00 10.00

2007 Sweet Spot Classic

This 197-card set was released in August, 2007. The set was issued in five-card "tins" which came 20 tins to a box. All cards in this set were issued to a stated print run of 575 serial numbered cards. Cards numbered 35, 75 and 164 were never issued.

COMMON CARD .60 1.50
STATED PRINT RUN 575 SER.#'d SETS
1 Phil Niekro .60 1.50
2 Fred McGriff 1.00 2.50
3 Bob Horner .60 1.50
4 Earl Weaver .60 1.50
5 Boog Powell .60 1.50
6 Eddie Murray 1.50 4.00
7 Fred Lynn .60 1.50
8 Dwight Evans .60 1.50
9 Jim Rice .60 1.50
10 Carlton Fisk 1.00 2.50
11 Luis Tiant .60 1.50
12 Robin Yount 1.50 4.00
13 Bobby Doerr .60 1.50
14 Ryne Sandberg 3.00 8.00
15 Billy Williams .60 1.50
16 Andre Dawson 1.00 2.50
17 Mark Grace 1.00 2.50
18 Ron Santo 1.00 2.50
19 Shawon Dunston .60 1.50
20 Harold Baines .60 1.50
21 Carlton Fisk 1.00 2.50
22 Sparky Anderson .60 1.50
23 George Foster .60 1.50
24 Dave Parker .60 1.50
25 Ken Griffey Sr. .60 1.50
26 Dave Concepcion .60 1.50
27 Rafael Palmeiro 1.00 2.50
28 Al Rosen .60 1.50
29 Kirk Gibson .60 1.50
30 Alan Trammell .60 1.50
31 Jack Morris .60 1.50
32 Willie Horton .60 1.50
33 JR Richard .60 1.50
34 Jose Cruz .60 1.50
36 Willie Wilson .60 1.50
37 Bo Jackson 1.50 4.00
38 Nolan Ryan 4.00 10.00
39 Don Baylor .60 1.50
40 Maury Wills .60 1.50
41 Tommy John .60 1.50
42 Ron Cey .60 1.50
43 Davey Lopes .60 1.50
44 Tommy Lasorda .60 1.50
45 Burt Hooton .60 1.50
46 Reggie Smith .60 1.50
47 Rollie Fingers .60 1.50
48 Cecil Cooper .60 1.50
49 Paul Molitor 1.50 4.00
50 Vern Stephens .60 1.50
51 Tony Oliva .60 1.50
52 Andres Galarraga .60 1.50
53 Tim Raines .60 1.50
54 Dennis Martinez .60 1.50
55 Lee Mazzilli .60 1.50
56 Rusty Staub .60 1.50
57 David Cone .60 1.50
58 Reggie Jackson 1.00 2.50
59 Ron Guidry .60 1.50
60 Tino Martinez .60 1.50
61 Don Mattingly 3.00 8.00
62 Chris Chambliss .60 1.50
63 Sparky Lyle .60 1.50
64 Goose Gossage .60 1.50
65 Dave Righetti .60 1.50
66 Phil Garner .60 1.50
67 Bill Madlock .60 1.50
68 Kent Hrbek .60 1.50
69 Al Oliver .60 1.50
70 John Kruk .60 1.50
71 Greg Luzinski .60 1.50
72 Dick Allen .60 1.50
73 Richie Ashburn 1.00 2.50
74 Gary Matthews .60 1.50
76 Mike Schmidt 2.50 6.00
77 Waite Hoyt .60 1.50
78 Bruce Sutter .60 1.50
79 Roger Maris 1.50 4.00
80 Joe Torre 1.00 2.50
81 Kevin Mitchell .60 1.50
82 John Montefusco .60 1.50
83 Rick Reuschel .60 1.50
84 Will Clark 1.00 2.50
85 Jack Clark .60 1.50
86 Matt Williams .60 1.50
87 Steve Garvey .60 1.50
88 Dave Winfield .60 1.50
89 Jay Buhner .60 1.50
90 Edgar Martinez 1.00 2.50
91 Carney Lansford .60 1.50
92 Sal Bando .60 1.50
93 Dave Stewart .60 1.50
94 Dennis Eckersley .60 1.50
95 Jose Canseco 1.00 2.50
96 Dennis Eckersley .60 1.50
97 Roberto Alomar 1.00 2.50
98 George Bell .60 1.50
99 Joe Carter .60 1.50
100 Frank Howard .60 1.50
101 Brooks Robinson 1.00 2.50
102 Frank Robinson .60 1.50
103 Jim Palmer .60 1.50
104 Cal Ripken Jr. 6.00 15.00
105 Warren Spahn 1.00 2.50
106 Cy Young 1.50 4.00
107 Waite Hoyt .60 1.50
108 Carl Yastrzemski 2.50 6.00
109 Johnny Pesky .60 1.50
110 Wade Boggs 1.00 2.50
111 Jackie Robinson 1.50 4.00
112 Roy Campanella 1.50 4.00
113 Pee Wee Reese 1.00 2.50
114 Don Newcombe .60 1.50
115 Rod Carew 1.00 2.50
116 Ernie Banks 1.50 4.00
117 Fergie Jenkins .60 1.50
118 Al Lopez .60 1.50
119 Luis Aparicio .60 1.50
120 Toby Harrah .60 1.50
121 Joe Morgan .60 1.50
122 Johnny Bench 1.50 4.00
123 Tony Perez .60 1.50
124 Ted Kluszewski 1.00 2.50
125 Bob Feller .60 1.50
126 Bob Lemon .60 1.50
127 Larry Doby .60 1.50
128 Lou Boudreau .60 1.50
129 George Kell .60 1.50
130 Hal Newhouser .60 1.50
131 Al Kaline 1.50 4.00
132 Ty Cobb 2.50 6.00
133 Denny McLain .60 1.50
134 Buck Leonard .60 1.50
135 Dean Chance .60 1.50
136 Don Drysdale 1.00 2.50
137 Don Sutton .60 1.50
138 Eddie Mathews 1.50 4.00
139 Paul Molitor 1.50 4.00
140 Kirby Puckett 1.50 4.00
141 Rod Carew 1.00 2.50
142 Harmon Killebrew 1.50 4.00
143 Monte Irvin .60 1.50
144 Mel Ott .60 1.50
145 Christy Mathewson 1.50 4.00
146 Hoyt Wilhelm .60 1.50
147 Tom Seaver 1.00 2.50
148 Joe McCarthy .60 1.50
149 Joe DiMaggio 4.00 10.00
150 Lou Gehrig 3.00 8.00
151 Babe Ruth 4.00 10.00
152 Casey Stengel .60 1.50
153 Phil Rizzuto 1.00 2.50
154 Thurman Munson 1.50 4.00
155 Johnny Mize .60 1.50
156 Yogi Berra 1.50 4.00
157 Roger Maris 1.50 4.00
158 Don Larsen .60 1.50
159 Bill Skowron .60 1.50
160 Lou Piniella .60 1.50
161 Joe Pepitone .60 1.50
162 Ray Dandridge .60 1.50
163 Rollie Fingers .60 1.50
165 Reggie Jackson 1.00 2.50
166 Mickey Cochrane .60 1.50
167 Jimmie Foxx 1.50 4.00
168 Lefty Grove .60 1.50
169 Gus Zernial .60 1.50
170 Jim Bunning .60 1.50
171 Steve Carlton .60 1.50
172 Robin Roberts .60 1.50
173 Ralph Kiner 1.00 2.50
174 Willie Stargell 1.00 2.50
175 Roberto Clemente 5.00 12.00
176 Bill Mazeroski 1.00 2.50
177 Honus Wagner 1.50 4.00
178 Pie Traynor .60 1.50
179 Elroy Face .60 1.50
180 Dick Groat .60 1.50
181 Tony Gwynn 1.50 4.00
182 Willie McCovey 1.00 2.50
183 Gaylord Perry .60 1.50
184 Juan Marichal .60 1.50
185 Orlando Cepeda .60 1.50
186 Satchel Paige 1.50 4.00
187 George Sisler .60 1.50
188 Rogers Hornsby 1.00 2.50
189 Stan Musial 2.50 6.00
190 Dizzy Dean 1.00 2.50
191 Bob Gibson 1.00 2.50
192 Red Schoendienst .60 1.50
193 Lou Brock 1.00 2.50
194 Enos Slaughter .60 1.50
195 Nolan Ryan 4.00 10.00
196 Mickey Vernon .60 1.50
197 Walter Johnson 1.50 4.00
198 Rick Ferrell .60 1.50
199 Roy Sievers .60 1.50
200 Judy Johnson .60 1.50

2007 Sweet Spot Classic Cal Ripken Immortal Membership

RANDOM INSERTS IN TINS
STATED PRINT RUN 1 SER.#'d SET
NO PRICING DUE TO SCARCITY
IM1 Cal Ripken Jr.
Lou Gehrig
IM2 Cal Ripken Jr.
Pee Wee Reese
IM3 Cal Ripken Jr.
Lou Boudreau
IM4 Cal Ripken Jr.
Charlie Gehringer
IM5 Cal Ripken Jr.
Joe DiMaggio

2007 Sweet Spot Classic Classic Cuts

RANDOM INSERTS IN TINS
PRINT RUNS B/WN 1-103
NO PRICING ON MOST DUE TO SCARCITY
CARDS LISTED ALPHABETICALLY
CHECKLIST MAY BE INCOMPLETE
MYSTERY EXCHANGE RANDOMLY INSERTED
EXCHANGE DEADLINE 8/3/2009
AC Agatha Christie/1
AC Art Carney/34 150.00 250.00
AH Alex Haley/108 20.00 50.00
GF Gerald Ford/61 200.00 400.00
PB Pappy Boyington/52 100.00 200.00

2007 Sweet Spot Classic Classic Memorabilia

RANDOM INSERTS IN TINS
AD Andre Dawson Pants 3.00 8.00
AK Al Kaline 4.00 10.00
AO Al Oliver 3.00 8.00
BE Johnny Bench Pants 5.00 12.00
BJ Bo Jackson 5.00 12.00
BM Bill Madlock Bat 3.00 8.00
BO Wade Boggs Yanks 4.00 10.00
BR Babe Ruth Bat 300.00 400.00
BS Bruce Sutter Cubs Pants 3.00 8.00
CF1 Carlton Fisk Red Sox 4.00 10.00
CF2 Carlton Fisk ChiSox 4.00 10.00
CL Roberto Clemente 15.00 40.00
CM Christy Mathewson Pants 70.00 100.00
CR Cal Ripken Jr. 6.00 15.00
CS Casey Stengel 6.00 15.00
CY Carl Yastrzemski 4.00 10.00
DD Dizzy Dean 12.50 30.00
DE Dennis Eckersley 3.00 8.00
DM Don Mattingly 5.00 12.00
DP Dave Parker Reds 3.00 8.00
DR Don Drysdale Pants 4.00 10.00
DS Don Sutton 3.00 8.00
DW Dave Winfield 3.00 8.00
ED Eddie Murray Pants 3.00 8.00
EM Eddie Mathews Pants 5.00 12.00
EV Dwight Evans 3.00 8.00
EW Early Wynn Pants 4.00 10.00
FG Fred McGriff Jsy 3.00 8.00
FI Rollie Fingers Mil 3.00 8.00
FR Frank Robinson Cle Jsy 6.00 15.00
FR1 Frank Robinson Giants Pants 6.00 15.00
GF George Foster 3.00 8.00
GG Goose Gossage 3.00 8.00
GI Kirk Gibson 3.00 8.00
GP Gaylord Perry 3.00 8.00
GW Tony Gwynn 5.00 12.00
HB Harold Baines Bat 3.00 8.00
HK Harmon Killebrew 15.00 40.00
JB Jim Bunning Pants 3.00 8.00
JD Joe DiMaggio Pants 15.00 40.00
JI Jim Rice Bat 3.00 8.00
JM Jack Morris 3.00 8.00
JP Jim Palmer 3.00 8.00
JU Juan Marichal 5.00 12.00
KG Ken Griffey Sr. 3.00 8.00
KH Kent Hrbek 3.00 8.00
KP Kirby Puckett 5.00 12.00
LA Luis Aparicio 3.00 8.00
LB Lou Brock 4.00 10.00
LG Lou Gehrig Pants 50.00 100.00
MA Don Mattingly Pants 5.00 12.00
ME Eddie Murray Pants 3.00 8.00
MG Mark Grace 3.00 8.00
MI1 Johnny Mize NYG Pants 4.00 10.00
MI2 Johnny Mize Yanks Bat 4.00 10.00
MO1 Mel Ott 40.00 80.00
MO2 Mel Ott Bat
MP Paul Molitor Mil 3.00 8.00
MR Edgar Martinez 3.00 8.00
MS Mike Schmidt 5.00 12.00
MW Maury Wills Pants 3.00 8.00
NR Nolan Ryan Hou 8.00 20.00
PA Dave Parker Brewers 3.00 8.00
PE Tony Perez Sox 3.00 8.00
PM Paul Molitor Twins Pants 3.00 8.00
PN Phil Niekro 3.00 8.00
PR Pee Wee Reese Bat 5.00 12.00
RC1 Rod Carew Twins 3.00 8.00
RC2 Rod Carew Angels Pants 3.00 8.00
RF Rollie Fingers Oak 3.00 8.00
RG Ron Guidry Pants 10.00 25.00
RH Rogers Hornsby Pants 10.00 25.00
RJ1 Reggie Jackson Oak 4.00 10.00
RJ2 Reggie Jackson Cal 4.00 10.00
RJ3 Reggie Jackson 4.00 10.00
RK Ralph Kiner Bat 4.00 10.00
RM Roger Maris Pants 12.50 30.00
RO Roy Campanella Pants 6.00 15.00
RS Ron Santo Bat 8.00 20.00
RY Nolan Ryan Tex 8.00 20.00
SC Red Schoendienst Bat 3.00 8.00
SG Steve Garvey 3.00 8.00
ST Steve Carlton Bat 3.00 8.00
SU Bruce Sutter Cards 3.00 8.00
TG Tony Gwynn Bat 4.00 10.00
TM Thurman Munson Pants 6.00 15.00
TO Tony Oliva 3.00 8.00
TP Tony Perez Reds 3.00 8.00
TR Tim Raines 3.00 8.00
WB Wade Boggs Sox 4.00 10.00
WC1 Will Clark Bat 3.00 8.00
WM Willie McCovey Pants 4.00 10.00
WS Willie Stargell Bat 4.00 10.00
YO Robin Yount Bat 4.00 10.00
WC2 Will Clark Jsy 4.00 10.00

2007 Sweet Spot Classic Classic Memorabilia Patch

RANDOM INSERTS IN TINS
STATED PRINT RUNS B/WN 10-55 COPIES PER
NO PRICING ON QTY UNDER 28
PRICING FOR NON-PREMIUM PATCHES
AD Andre Dawson/55 12.50 30.00
AK Al Kaline/55 20.00 50.00
AO Al Oliver/55 5.00 12.00
BE Johnny Bench/55 30.00 60.00
BJ Bo Jackson/55 10.00 25.00
BM Bill Madlock/55 5.00 12.00
BO Wade Boggs/55 15.00 40.00
BS Bruce Sutter/55 8.00 20.00
CF1 Carlton Fisk/55 8.00 20.00
CF2 Carlton Fisk/55 8.00 20.00
CL Roberto Clemente/55 100.00 200.00
CR Cal Ripken Jr./55 30.00 60.00
CS Casey Stengel/55 20.00 50.00
CY Carl Yastrzemski/55 12.50 30.00
DE Dennis Eckersley/55 5.00 12.00
DM Don Mattingly/55 12.50 30.00
DP Dave Parker/55 5.00 12.00
DR Don Drysdale/55 40.00 80.00
DS Don Sutton/55 6.00 15.00
DW Dave Winfield/55 10.00 25.00
ED Eddie Murray/55 6.00 15.00
EV Dwight Evans/55 8.00 20.00
FI Rollie Fingers/55 8.00 20.00
FR Frank Robinson/28 15.00 40.00
FR1 Frank Robinson/28 15.00 40.00
GF George Foster/55 5.00 12.00
GG Goose Gossage/55 5.00 12.00
GI Kirk Gibson/55 8.00 20.00
GP Gaylord Perry/55 5.00 12.00
GW Tony Gwynn/55 10.00 25.00
HB Harold Baines/55 6.00 15.00
JI Jim Rice/55 20.00 50.00
JM Jack Morris/55 6.00 15.00
JP Jim Palmer/55 6.00 15.00
JU Juan Marichal/15
KG Ken Griffey Sr./55 5.00 12.00
KP Kirby Puckett/55 15.00 40.00
LA Luis Aparicio/55 12.50 30.00
LB Lou Brock/55 10.00 25.00
MA Don Mattingly/55 30.00 60.00
ME Eddie Murray/55 6.00 15.00
MG Mark Grace/55 10.00 25.00
MP Paul Molitor/55 15.00 40.00
MS Mike Schmidt/55 10.00 25.00
MW Maury Wills/55 6.00 15.00
PA Dave Parker/55 5.00 12.00
PE Tony Perez/55 10.00 25.00
PM Paul Molitor/55 15.00 40.00
PN Phil Niekro/55 20.00 50.00
PR Pee Wee Reese/55 40.00 80.00
RA Roberto Alomar/55 6.00 15.00
RC1 Rod Carew/55 5.00 12.00
RC2 Rod Carew/55 5.00 12.00
RF Rollie Fingers/55 8.00 20.00
RG Ron Guidry/55 15.00 40.00
RI Cal Ripken Jr./25
RJ1 Reggie Jackson/55 50.00 100.00
RJ2 Reggie Jackson/55 8.00 20.00
RJ3 Reggie Jackson/55 12.50 30.00
RM Roger Maris/55 40.00 80.00
RY Nolan Ryan/55 30.00 60.00
SC Red Schoendienst/55 20.00 50.00
SG Steve Garvey/55 6.00 15.00
SU Bruce Sutter/55 8.00 20.00
TG Tony Gwynn/55 10.00 25.00
TO Tony Oliva/55 6.00 15.00
TP Tony Perez/55 10.00 25.00
TR Tim Raines/55 8.00 20.00
WC Will Clark/55 8.00 20.00
WI Dave Winfield/55 10.00 25.00
WM Willie McCovey/55 40.00 80.00
WS Willie Stargell/10
YO Robin Yount/55 12.50 30.00

2007 Sweet Spot Classic Dual Signatures Red Stitch Blue Ink

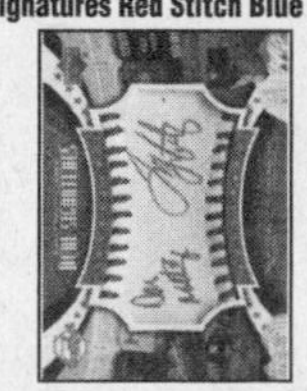

RANDOM INSERTS IN TINS
STATED PRINT RUN 50 SER.#'d SETS
EXCHANGE DEADLINE 8/3/2009
AG Luis Aparicio 30.00 60.00
Ozzie Guillen
BC Brooks Robinson 100.00 150.00
Cal Ripken Jr.
BF Carlton Fisk 15.00 40.00
Johnny Bench
BG Harold Baines 20.00 50.00
Ozzie Guillen
BR Jim Bunning 30.00 60.00
Robin Roberts
CO Rod Carew 30.00 60.00
Tony Oliva
FE Rollie Fingers 30.00 60.00
Dennis Eckersley
FG Elroy Face 20.00 50.00
Dick Groat
FM Frank Robinson 40.00 80.00
Mike Schmidt
FR Carlton Fisk 40.00 80.00
Jim Rice
GR Bob Gibson 10.00 25.00
JR Richard
GS Steve Garvey 20.00 50.00
Reggie Smith
GW Tony Gwynn 40.00 80.00
Dave Winfield
HK Willie Horton 40.00 80.00
Al Kaline
KM Ralph Kiner 40.00 80.00
Bill Mazeroski
MC Willie McCovey 40.00 80.00
Jack Clark
MG Juan Marichal 30.00 60.00
Bob Gibson
MK Stan Musial 40.00 80.00
Al Kaline
MM Don Mattingly 50.00 100.00
Tino Martinez
OH Tony Oliva 20.00 50.00
Kent Hrbek
RR JR Richard 60.00 120.00
Nolan Ryan
SC Mike Schmidt 30.00 60.00
Steve Carlton
SD Ryne Sandberg 50.00 100.00
Shawon Dunston
SV Roy Sievers 20.00 50.00
Mickey Vernon

2007 Sweet Spot Classic Dual Signatures Black Stitch Red Ink

RANDOM INSERTS IN TINS
STATED PRINT RUN 1 SER.#'d SET
NO PRICING DUE TO SCARCITY
EXCHANGE DEADLINE 8/3/2009

2007 Sweet Spot Classic Dual Signatures Gold Stitch Black Ink

RANDOM INSERTS IN TINS
STATED PRINT RUN 15 SER.#'d SETS
NO PRICING DUE TO SCARCITY
EXCHANGE DEADLINE 8/3/2009

2007 Sweet Spot Classic Immortal Signatures

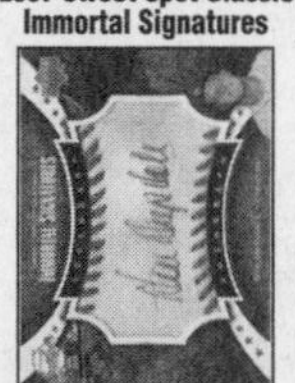

RANDOM INSERTS IN TINS
PRINT RUNS B/WN 1-126 COPIES PER
NO PRICING ON QTY 25 OR LESS
EXCHANGE DEADLINE 8/3/2009
AB Al Barlick/43 15.00 40.00
AL Al Lopez/9
AR Allie Reynolds/1
BB Bo Belinsky/6
BD Bill Dickey/10
BH Billy Herman/49 60.00 100.00
BL Bob Lemon/58 60.00 100.00
BM Billy Martin/1
BO Buck O'Neil/126 30.00 60.00
BR Babe Ruth/1
CG Charlie Gehringer/7
CH Carl Hubbell/1
DC Dolph Camilli/13
DD Don Drysdale/18
DI Joe DiMaggio/2
DU Leo Durocher/4
EM Eddie Mathews/35 150.00 200.00
ES Enos Slaughter/80 60.00 100.00
EW Early Wynn/26 75.00 120.00
HC Happy Chandler/29 60.00 100.00
HN Hal Newhouser/33 60.00 100.00
HW Hoyt Wilhelm/33 60.00 100.00
JA Joe Adcock/6
JD Joe DiMaggio/2
JM Johnny Mize/48 60.00 100.00
JO Johnny Oates/1
JS Joe Sewell/23
JV Johnny Vander Meer/49 75.00 120.00
LA Luke Appling/31 75.00 120.00
LB Lou Boudreau/47 75.00 120.00
LD Larry Doby/7
MH Mel Harder/37 30.00 60.00
PR Pee Wee Reese/37 150.00 200.00
RA Richie Ashburn/29 100.00 150.00
RD Ray Dandridge/20
RF Rick Ferrell/52 60.00 100.00
ST Willie Stargell/30 150.00 200.00
TA Tommie Agee/2
WS Warren Spahn/102 30.00 60.00

2007 Sweet Spot Classic Legendary Lettermen

E.BANKS p/r 25 30.00 60.00
E.BANKS TWO p/r 15 20.00 50.00
J.BENCH p/r 25 30.00 60.00
R.CAMPANELLA p/r 10 30.00 60.00
T.COBB p/r 25 20.00 50.00
T.COBB PEACH p/r 5 30.00 60.00
D.DEAN p/r 25 30.00 60.00
D.DRYSDALE p/r 25 15.00 40.00
C.FISK p/r 20 30.00 60.00
J.FOXX p/r 25 30.00 60.00
L.GEHRIG p/r 15 100.00 150.00
B.GIBSON p/r 25 15.00 40.00
T.GWYNN p/r 25 15.00 40.00
R.HORNSBY p/r 25 30.00 60.00
R.JACKSON p/r 25 20.00 50.00
B.JACKSON p/r 25 20.00 50.00
B.JACKSON KNOWS p/r 15 20.00 50.00
W.JOHNSON p/r 15 15.00 40.00
W.JOHNSON TRAIN p/r 10 20.00 50.00
A.KALINE p/r 25 15.00 40.00
S.KOUFAX p/r 25 225.00 300.00
C.MATHEWSON p/r 10 30.00 60.00
D.MATTINGLY p/r 15 30.00 60.00
B.MAZEROSKI p/r 15 10.00 25.00
T.MUNSON p/r 25 30.00 60.00
T.MUNSON CAPTAIN p/r 10 40.00 80.00
S.MUSIAL p/r 25 20.00 50.00
S.MUSIAL MAN p/r 25 20.00 50.00
M.OTT p/r 25 15.00 40.00
S.PAIGE p/r 25 30.00 60.00
C.RIPKEN p/r 25 20.00 50.00
C.RIPKEN IRON p/r 25 20.00 50.00
J.ROBINSON p/r 10 15.00 40.00
J.ROBINSON PIONEER p/r 10 15.00 40.00
B.RUTH p/r 25 30.00 60.00
B.RUTH SULTAN p/r 15 100.00 200.00
N.RYAN p/r 20 30.00 60.00
N.RYAN EXPRESS p/r 15 30.00 60.00
R.SANDBERG p/r 25 75.00 150.00
M.SCHMIDT p/r 25 30.00 60.00
H.WAGNER p/r 25 20.00 50.00
C.YASTRZEMSKI p/r 15 30.00 60.00
RANDOM INSERTS IN TINS
PRINT RUNS B/WN 5-25 COPIES PER
LL1H Babe Ruth H/25 30.00 60.00
LL1R Babe Ruth R/25 30.00 60.00
LL1T Babe Ruth T/25 30.00 60.00
LL1U Babe Ruth U/25 30.00 60.00
LL2B Ty Cobb B/25 20.00 50.00
LL2B Ty Cobb B/25 20.00 50.00
LL2C Ty Cobb C/25 20.00 50.00
LL2O Ty Cobb O/25 20.00 50.00
LL3A Christy Mathewson A/10 30.00 60.00
LL3E Christy Mathewson E/10 30.00 60.00
LL3H Christy Mathewson H/10 30.00 60.00
LL3M Christy Mathewson M/10 30.00 60.00
LL3N Christy Mathewson N/10 30.00 60.00
LL3O Christy Mathewson O/10 30.00 60.00
LL3S Christy Mathewson S/10 30.00 60.00
LL3T Christy Mathewson T/10 30.00 60.00
LL3W Christy Mathewson W/10 30.00 60.00
LL4B Jackie Robinson B/10 15.00 40.00
LL4I Jackie Robinson I/10 15.00 40.00
LL4N Jackie Robinson N/10 15.00 40.00
LL4N Jackie Robinson N/10 15.00 40.00
LL4O Jackie Robinson O/10 15.00 40.00
LL4O Jackie Robinson O/10 15.00 40.00
LL4R Jackie Robinson R/10 15.00 40.00
LL4S Jackie Robinson S/10 15.00 40.00
LL5A Roy Campanella A/10 30.00 60.00
LL5A Roy Campanella A/10 30.00 60.00
LL5A Roy Campanella A/10 30.00 60.00
LL5C Roy Campanella C/10 30.00 60.00
LL5E Roy Campanella E/10 30.00 60.00
LL5L Roy Campanella L/10 30.00 60.00
LL5L Roy Campanella L/10 30.00 60.00
LL5M Roy Campanella M/10 30.00 60.00
LL5N Roy Campanella N/10 30.00 60.00
LL5P Roy Campanella P/10 30.00 60.00
LL6E Lou Gehrig E/15 100.00 150.00
LL6G Lou Gehrig G/15 100.00 150.00
LL6G Lou Gehrig G/15 100.00 150.00
LL6H Lou Gehrig H/15 100.00 150.00
LL6I Lou Gehrig I/15 100.00 150.00
LL6R Lou Gehrig R/15 100.00 150.00
LL7O Mel Ott O/25 15.00 40.00
LL7T Mel Ott T/25 15.00 40.00
LL7T Mel Ott T/25 15.00 40.00
LL8F Jimmie Foxx F/25 30.00 60.00
LL8O Jimmie Foxx O/25 30.00 60.00
LL8X Jimmie Foxx X/25 30.00 60.00
LL8X Jimmie Foxx X/25 30.00 60.00
LL9A Satchel Paige A/25 30.00 60.00
LL9E Satchel Paige E/25 30.00 60.00
LL9G Satchel Paige G/25 30.00 60.00
LL9I Satchel Paige I/25 30.00 60.00
LL9P Satchel Paige P/25 30.00 60.00
LL10A Don Drysdale A/25 15.00 40.00
LL10D Don Drysdale D/25 15.00 40.00
LL10D Don Drysdale D/25 15.00 40.00
LL10E Don Drysdale E/25 15.00 40.00
LL10L Don Drysdale L/25 15.00 40.00
LL10R Don Drysdale R/25 15.00 40.00
LL10S Don Drysdale S/25 15.00 40.00
LL10Y Don Drysdale Y/25 15.00 40.00
LL11B Rogers Hornsby B/25 30.00 60.00
LL11H Rogers Hornsby H/25 30.00 60.00
LL11N Rogers Hornsby N/25 30.00 60.00
LL11O Rogers Hornsby O/25 30.00 60.00
LL11R Rogers Hornsby R/25 30.00 60.00
LL11S Rogers Hornsby S/25 30.00 60.00
LL11Y Rogers Hornsby Y/25 30.00 60.00
LL12A Honus Wagner A/25 20.00 50.00
LL12E Honus Wagner E/25 20.00 50.00
LL12G Honus Wagner G/25 20.00 50.00
LL12N Honus Wagner N/25 20.00 50.00
LL12R Honus Wagner R/25 20.00 50.00
LL12W Honus Wagner W/25 20.00 50.00
LL13A Babe Ruth A/15 100.00 200.00
LL13B Babe Ruth B/15 100.00 200.00
LL13B Babe Ruth B/15 100.00 200.00
LL13I Babe Ruth I/15 100.00 200.00
LL13M Babe Ruth M/15 100.00 200.00
LL13N Babe Ruth N/15 100.00 200.00
LL13O Babe Ruth O/15 100.00 200.00
LL14A Dizzy Dean A/25 30.00 60.00
LL14D Dizzy Dean D/25 30.00 60.00
LL14E Dizzy Dean E/25 30.00 60.00
LL14N Dizzy Dean N/25 30.00 60.00
LL15A Ty Cobb A/5 30.00 60.00
LL15A Ty Cobb A/5 30.00 60.00
LL15C Ty Cobb C/5 30.00 60.00
LL15E Ty Cobb E/5 30.00 60.00
LL15E Ty Cobb E/5 30.00 60.00
LL15G Ty Cobb G/5 30.00 60.00
LL15G Ty Cobb G/5 30.00 60.00
LL15H Ty Cobb H/5 30.00 60.00
LL15I Ty Cobb I/5 30.00 60.00
LL15O Ty Cobb O/5 30.00 60.00
LL15P Ty Cobb P/5 30.00 60.00
LL15R Ty Cobb R/5 30.00 60.00
LL16H Walter Johnson H/15 15.00 40.00
LL16J Walter Johnson J/15 15.00 40.00
LL16N Walter Johnson N/15 15.00 40.00
LL16N Walter Johnson N/15 15.00 40.00
LL16O Walter Johnson O/15 15.00 40.00
LL16O Walter Johnson O/15 15.00 40.00
LL16S Walter Johnson S/15 15.00 40.00
LL17A Walter Johnson A/10 20.00 50.00
LL17B Walter Johnson B/10 20.00 50.00
LL17G Walter Johnson G/10 20.00 50.00
LL17I Walter Johnson I/10 20.00 50.00
LL17I Walter Johnson I/10 20.00 50.00
LL17N Walter Johnson N/10 20.00 50.00
LL17R Walter Johnson R/10 20.00 50.00
LL17T Walter Johnson T/10 20.00 50.00
LL18E Cal Ripken Jr. E/25 20.00 50.00
LL18I Cal Ripken Jr. I/25 20.00 50.00
LL18K Cal Ripken Jr. K/25 20.00 50.00
LL18N Cal Ripken Jr. N/25 20.00 50.00
LL18P Cal Ripken Jr. P/25 20.00 50.00
LL18R Cal Ripken Jr. R/25 20.00 50.00
LL19A Sandy Koufax A/25 225.00 300.00
LL19F Sandy Koufax F/25 225.00 300.00
LL19K Sandy Koufax K/25 225.00 300.00
LL19O Sandy Koufax O/25 225.00 300.00
LL19U Sandy Koufax U/25 225.00 300.00
LL19X Sandy Koufax X/25 225.00 300.00
LL20M Thurman Munson M/25 30.00 60.00
LL20N Thurman Munson N/25 30.00 60.00
LL20N Thurman Munson N/25 30.00 60.00
LL20O Thurman Munson O/25 30.00 60.00
LL20S Thurman Munson S/25 30.00 60.00
LL20U Thurman Munson U/25 30.00 60.00
LL21A Thurman Munson A/10 40.00 80.00
LL21A Thurman Munson A/10 40.00 80.00
LL21C Thurman Munson C/10 40.00 80.00
LL21I Thurman Munson I/10 40.00 80.00
LL21N Thurman Munson N/10 40.00 80.00
LL21P Thurman Munson P/10 40.00 80.00
LL21T Thurman Munson T/10 40.00 80.00
LL22A Cal Ripken Jr. A/25 20.00 50.00
LL22I Cal Ripken Jr. I/25 20.00 50.00
LL22M Cal Ripken Jr. M/25 20.00 50.00
LL22N Cal Ripken Jr. N/25 20.00 50.00
LL22N Cal Ripken Jr. N/25 20.00 50.00
LL22O Cal Ripken Jr. O/25 20.00 50.00
LL22R Cal Ripken Jr. R/25 20.00 50.00
LL23G Tony Gwynn G/25 15.00 40.00
LL23N Tony Gwynn N/25 15.00 40.00
LL23N Tony Gwynn N/25 15.00 40.00
LL23W Tony Gwynn W/25 15.00 40.00
LL23Y Tony Gwynn Y/25 15.00 40.00
LL24A Nolan Ryan A/20 30.00 60.00
LL24N Nolan Ryan N/20 30.00 60.00
LL24R Nolan Ryan R/20 30.00 60.00
LL24Y Nolan Ryan Y/20 30.00 60.00
LL25A Nolan Ryan A/15 30.00 60.00
LL25E Nolan Ryan E/15 30.00 60.00
LL25E Nolan Ryan E/15 30.00 60.00
LL25N Nolan Ryan N/15 30.00 60.00
LL25P Nolan Ryan P/15 30.00 60.00
LL25R Nolan Ryan R/15 30.00 60.00
LL25R Nolan Ryan R/15 30.00 60.00
LL25S Nolan Ryan S/15 30.00 60.00
LL25S Nolan Ryan S/15 30.00 60.00
LL25X Nolan Ryan X/15 30.00 60.00
LL25Y Nolan Ryan Y/15 30.00 60.00
LL26E Jackie Robinson E/10 15.00 40.00
LL26E Jackie Robinson E/10 15.00 40.00
LL26I Jackie Robinson I/10 15.00 40.00
LL26N Jackie Robinson N/10 15.00 40.00
LL26O Jackie Robinson O/10 15.00 40.00
LL26P Jackie Robinson P/10 15.00 40.00
LL26R Jackie Robinson R/10 15.00 40.00
LL27F Carlton Fisk F/20 30.00 60.00
LL27I Carlton Fisk I/20 30.00 60.00
LL27K Carlton Fisk K/20 30.00 60.00
LL27S Carlton Fisk S/20 30.00 60.00
LL28A Carl Yastrzemski A/15 20.00 50.00
LL28E Carl Yastrzemski E/15 20.00 50.00
LL28I Carl Yastrzemski I/15 20.00 50.00
LL28K Carl Yastrzemski K/15 20.00 50.00
LL28M Carl Yastrzemski M/15 20.00 50.00
LL28R Carl Yastrzemski R/15 20.00 50.00
LL28S Carl Yastrzemski S/15 20.00 50.00
LL28S Carl Yastrzemski S/15 20.00 50.00
LL28T Carl Yastrzemski T/15 20.00 50.00
LL28Y Carl Yastrzemski Y/15 20.00 50.00
LL28Z Carl Yastrzemski Z/15 20.00 50.00
LL29B Johnny Bench B/25 30.00 60.00
LL29C Johnny Bench C/25 30.00 60.00
LL29E Johnny Bench E/25 30.00 60.00
LL29H Johnny Bench H/25 30.00 60.00
LL29N Johnny Bench N/25 30.00 60.00
LL30A Ryne Sandberg A/25 75.00 150.00
LL30B Ryne Sandberg B/25 75.00 150.00
LL30D Ryne Sandberg D/25 75.00 150.00
LL30E Ryne Sandberg E/25 75.00 150.00
LL30G Ryne Sandberg G/25 75.00 150.00
LL30N Ryne Sandberg N/25 75.00 150.00
LL30R Ryne Sandberg R/25 75.00 150.00
LL30S Ryne Sandberg S/25 75.00 150.00
LL31A Don Mattingly A/15 50.00 100.00
LL31G Don Mattingly G/15 50.00 100.00
LL31I Don Mattingly I/15 50.00 100.00
LL31L Don Mattingly L/15 50.00 100.00
LL31M Don Mattingly M/15 50.00 100.00
LL31N Don Mattingly N/15 50.00 100.00
LL31T Don Mattingly T/15 50.00 100.00
LL31T Don Mattingly T/15 50.00 100.00
LL31Y Don Mattingly Y/15 50.00 100.00
LL32A Ernie Banks A/25 30.00 60.00
LL32B Ernie Banks B/25 30.00 60.00
LL32K Ernie Banks K/25 30.00 60.00
LL32N Ernie Banks N/25 30.00 60.00
LL32S Ernie Banks S/25 30.00 60.00
LL33A Bill Mazeroski A/15 10.00 25.00
LL33E Bill Mazeroski E/15 10.00 25.00
LL33I Bill Mazeroski I/15 10.00 25.00
LL33K Bill Mazeroski K/15 10.00 25.00
LL33M Bill Mazeroski M/15 10.00 25.00
LL33O Bill Mazeroski O/15 10.00 25.00
LL33R Bill Mazeroski R/15 10.00 25.00
LL33S Bill Mazeroski S/15 10.00 25.00
LL33Z Bill Mazeroski Z/15 10.00 25.00
LL34A Ernie Banks A/15 20.00 50.00
LL34E Ernie Banks E/15 20.00 50.00
LL34L Ernie Banks L/15 20.00 50.00
LL34L Ernie Banks L/15 20.00 50.00

LL34O Ernie Banks O/15 20.00 50.00
LL34P Ernie Banks P/15 20.00 50.00
LL34S Ernie Banks S/15 20.00 50.00
LL34T Ernie Banks T/15 20.00 50.00
LL34T Ernie Banks T/15 20.00 50.00
LL34W Ernie Banks W/15 20.00 50.00
LL34Y Ernie Banks Y/15 20.00 50.00
LL35B Bob Gibson B/25 15.00 40.00
LL35G Bob Gibson G/25 15.00 40.00
LL35I Bob Gibson I/25 15.00 40.00
LL35N Bob Gibson N/25 15.00 40.00
LL35O Bob Gibson O/25 15.00 40.00
LL35S Bob Gibson S/25 15.00 40.00
LL36C Mike Schmidt C/25 30.00 60.00
LL36D Mike Schmidt D/25 30.00 60.00
LL36H Mike Schmidt H/25 30.00 60.00
LL36I Mike Schmidt I/25 30.00 60.00
LL36M Mike Schmidt M/25 30.00 60.00
LL36S Mike Schmidt S/25 30.00 60.00
LL36T Mike Schmidt T/25 30.00 60.00
LL37A Al Kaline A/25 12.50 30.00
LL37E Al Kaline E/25 12.50 30.00
LL37I Al Kaline I/25 12.50 30.00
LL37K Al Kaline K/25 12.50 30.00
LL37L Al Kaline L/25 12.50 30.00
LL37N Al Kaline N/25 12.50 30.00
LL38A Reggie Jackson A/25 20.00 50.00
LL38C Reggie Jackson C/25 20.00 50.00
LL38J Reggie Jackson J/25 20.00 50.00
LL38K Reggie Jackson K/25 20.00 50.00
LL38N Reggie Jackson N/25 20.00 50.00
LL38O Reggie Jackson O/25 20.00 50.00
LL38S Reggie Jackson S/25 20.00 50.00
LL39A Stan Musial A/25 20.00 50.00
LL39I Stan Musial I/25 20.00 50.00
LL39L Stan Musial L/25 20.00 50.00
LL39M Stan Musial M/25 20.00 50.00
LL39S Stan Musial S/25 20.00 50.00
LL39U Stan Musial U/25 20.00 50.00
LL40A Bo Jackson A/25 20.00 50.00
LL40C Bo Jackson C/25 20.00 50.00
LL40J Bo Jackson J/25 20.00 50.00
LL40K Bo Jackson K/25 20.00 50.00
LL40N Bo Jackson N/25 20.00 50.00
LL40O Bo Jackson O/25 20.00 50.00
LL40S Bo Jackson S/25 20.00 50.00
LL41B Bo Jackson B/15 20.00 50.00
LL41K Bo Jackson K/15 20.00 50.00
LL41N Bo Jackson N/15 20.00 50.00
LL41O Bo Jackson O/15 20.00 50.00
LL41O Bo Jackson O/15 20.00 50.00
LL41S Bo Jackson S/15 20.00 50.00
LL41W Bo Jackson W/15 20.00 50.00
LL42A Stan Musial A/25 20.00 50.00
LL42E Stan Musial E/25 20.00 50.00
LL42H Stan Musial H/25 20.00 50.00
LL42M Stan Musial M/25 20.00 50.00
LL42N Stan Musial N/25 20.00 50.00
LL42T Stan Musial T/25 20.00 50.00

2007 Sweet Spot Classic Signatures Red Stitch Black Ink

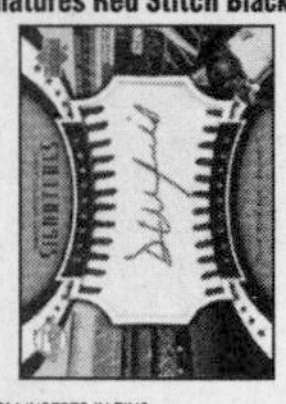

RANDOM INSERTS IN TINS
PRINT RUNS B/WN 35-175 COPIES PER
EXCHANGE DEADLINE 8/3/2009
AG Andres Galarraga/175 6.00 15.00
AK Al Kaline/175 12.50 30.00
AO Al Oliver/175 6.00 15.00
BJ Bo Jackson/175 20.00 50.00
BM Bill Mazeroski/175 15.00 40.00
BO Wade Boggs/75 15.00 40.00
BR Brooks Robinson/175 10.00 25.00
BS Bruce Sutter/75 12.50 30.00
BW Billy Williams/175 6.00 15.00
CF Carlton Fisk/75 15.00 40.00
CL Carney Lansford/175 6.00 15.00
CO Dave Concepcion/175 10.00 25.00
CY Carl Yastrzemski/75 30.00 60.00
DA Dick Allen/175 6.00 15.00
DG Dick Groat/175 10.00 25.00
DL Don Larsen/175 10.00 25.00
DM Don Mattingly/75 30.00 60.00
DS Don Sutton/175 6.00 15.00
DW Dave Winfield/75 15.00 40.00
EB Ernie Banks/75 30.00 60.00
EC Dennis Eckersley/175 10.00 25.00
EF Elroy Face/175 6.00 15.00
EM Edgar Martinez/175 12.50 30.00
EV Dwight Evans/175 6.00 15.00
FL Fred Lynn/175 6.00 15.00
FM Fred McGriff/175 10.00 25.00
FR Frank Robinson Blue/75 15.00 40.00
GI Bob Gibson/175 12.50 30.00
GP Gaylord Perry/175 6.00 15.00
HB Harold Baines/175 6.00 15.00
JB Johnny Bench/75 20.00 50.00
JI Jim Bunning/175 6.00 15.00
JK John Kruk/175 6.00 15.00
JP Johnny Pesky/175 10.00 25.00
JR Jim Rice/175 6.00 15.00
KG Ken Griffey Sr./175 6.00 15.00
LA Luis Aparicio/175 6.00 15.00
LB Lou Brock/75 15.00 40.00
MA Juan Marichal/175 10.00 25.00
MG Mark Grace/175 12.50 30.00
MO Jack Morris/175 10.00 25.00
MS Mike Schmidt/75 30.00 60.00
MU Stan Musial/75 40.00 80.00
MV Mickey Vernon/75 12.50 30.00
NR Nolan Ryan/75 50.00 100.00
OG Ozzie Guillen/175 6.00 15.00
OS Ozzie Smith/75 20.00 50.00
PN Phil Niekro/175 6.00 15.00
RA Roberto Alomar/175 10.00 25.00
RC Rod Carew/75 12.50 30.00
RF Rollie Fingers/175 6.00 15.00
RI Jim Rice/175 6.00 15.00
RJ Reggie Jackson/75 30.00 60.00
RK Ralph Kiner/75 15.00 40.00
RR Robin Roberts/175 10.00 25.00
RS Ryne Sandberg/75 20.00 50.00
RY Robin Yount/75 15.00 40.00
SA Ron Santo/75 12.50 30.00
SC Steve Carlton/175 10.00 25.00
SD Shawon Dunston/175 6.00 15.00
SG Steve Garvey/175 6.00 15.00
SK Bill Skowron/175 6.00 15.00
SM Reggie Smith/175 6.00 15.00
TG Tony Gwynn/75 30.00 60.00
TH Toby Harrah/175 6.00 15.00
TM Tino Martinez/175 10.00 25.00
TO Tony Oliva/175 6.00 15.00
TP Tony Perez/175 10.00 25.00
TR Tim Raines/175 6.00 15.00
WB Wade Boggs/75 15.00 40.00
WD Willie Davis/75 10.00 25.00
WH Willie Horton/175 6.00 15.00
WM Willie McCovey/75 15.00 40.00
YB Yogi Berra/75 40.00 80.00

2007 Sweet Spot Classic Signatures Red Stitch Blue Ink

*BLUE p/r 75-125: .5X TO 1.2X BLK p/r 175
*BLUE p/r 75-125: .4X TO 1X BLK p/r 75
*BLUE p/r 35: .6X TO 1.5X BLK p/r 175
*BLUE p/r 35: .5X TO 1.2X BLK p/r 75
RANDOM INSERTS IN TINS
PRINT RUNS B/WN 35-125 COPIES PER
EXCHANGE DEADLINE 8/3/2009

2007 Sweet Spot Classic Signatures Black Stitch Blue Ink

RANDOM INSERTS IN TINS
STATED PRINT RUN 1 SER.#'d SET
NO PRICING DUE TO SCARCITY
EXCHANGE DEADLINE 8/3/2009

2007 Sweet Spot Classic Signatures Black Stitch Red Ink

RANDOM INSERTS IN TINS
STATED PRINT RUN 1 SER.#'d SET
NO PRICING DUE TO SCARCITY
EXCHANGE DEADLINE 8/3/2009

2007 Sweet Spot Classic Signatures Gold Stitch Black Ink

RANDOM INSERTS IN TINS
PRINT RUNS B/WN 25-99 COPIES PER
NO PRICING ON QTY 25 OR LESS
EXCHANGE DEADLINE 8/3/2009
N.RYAN/25 SIGNED IN GOLD INK
AG Andres Galarraga/99 6.00 15.00
AK Al Kaline/99 10.00 25.00
AO Al Oliver/99 6.00 15.00
BJ Bo Jackson/99 30.00 60.00
BM Bill Mazeroski/99 15.00 40.00
BR Brooks Robinson/99 10.00 25.00
BW Billy Williams/99 10.00 25.00
CL Carney Lansford/99 6.00 15.00
CO Dave Concepcion/99 10.00 25.00
DA Dick Allen/99 10.00 25.00
DG Dick Groat/99 10.00 25.00
DL Don Larsen/99 10.00 25.00
DS Don Sutton/99 10.00 25.00
EB Ernie Banks/99 40.00 80.00
EC Dennis Eckersley/99 10.00 25.00
EF Elroy Face/99 10.00 25.00
EM Edgar Martinez/99 15.00 40.00
EV Dwight Evans/99 6.00 15.00
FL Fred Lynn/99 6.00 15.00
FM Fred McGriff/99 15.00 40.00
GI Bob Gibson/99 20.00 50.00
GP Gaylord Perry/99 6.00 15.00
HB Harold Baines/99 6.00 15.00
JI Jim Bunning/99 10.00 25.00
JK John Kruk/99 6.00 15.00
JP Johnny Pesky/99 10.00 25.00
JR Jim Rice/99 10.00 25.00
KG Ken Griffey Sr./99 6.00 15.00
LA Luis Aparicio/99 10.00 25.00
MA Juan Marichal/99 10.00 25.00
MG Mark Grace/99 15.00 40.00
MO Jack Morris/99 10.00 25.00
MV Mickey Vernon/99 10.00 25.00
OG Ozzie Guillen/99 10.00 25.00
PN Phil Niekro/99 10.00 25.00
RA Roberto Alomar/99 15.00 40.00
RF Rollie Fingers/99 10.00 25.00
RI Jim Rice/99 10.00 25.00
RR Robin Roberts/99 15.00 40.00
SA Ron Santo/99 30.00 60.00
SC Steve Carlton/99 15.00 40.00
SD Shawon Dunston/99 10.00 25.00
SG Steve Garvey/99 10.00 25.00
SK Bill Skowron/99 6.00 15.00
SM Reggie Smith/99 6.00 15.00
TH Toby Harrah/99 6.00 15.00
TM Tino Martinez/99 15.00 40.00
TO Tony Oliva/99 8.00 20.00
TP Tony Perez/99 10.00 25.00
TR Tim Raines/99 10.00 25.00
WH Willie Horton/99 10.00 25.00

2007 Sweet Spot Classic Signatures Gold Stitch Blue Ink

*BLUE: .5X TO 1.2X BLACK INK
RANDOM INSERTS IN TINS
PRINT RUNS B/WN 15-50 COPIES PER
NO PRICING ON QTY 25 OR LESS
EXCHANGE DEADLINE 8/3/2009
CY Carl Yastrzemski/50 30.00 60.00
DW Dave Winfield/50 12.50 30.00
MU Stan Musial/50 40.00 80.00
RY Robin Yount/50 20.00 50.00

2007 Sweet Spot Classic Signatures Sepia Black Ink

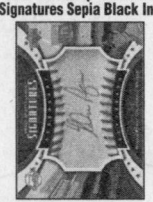

RANDOM INSERTS IN TINS
PRINT RUNS B/WN 16-199 COPIES PER
NO PRICING ON QTY 25 OR LESS
EXCHANGE DEADLINE 8/3/2009
CF Carlton Fisk/124 12.50 30.00
CY Carl Yastrzemski/124 20.00 50.00
DM Don Mattingly/124 20.00 50.00
DS Duke Snider/30 30.00 60.00
JM Juan Marichal/124 10.00 25.00
JR Jim Rice/85 10.00 25.00
KH Keith Hernandez/16
MU Dale Murphy/183 12.50 30.00
NR Nolan Ryan/123 50.00 100.00
OS Ozzie Smith/183 20.00 50.00
RS Ryne Sandberg/199 20.00 50.00
TG Tony Gwynn/199 20.00 50.00
TS Tom Seaver/16

2007 Sweet Spot Classic Signatures Sepia Blue Ink

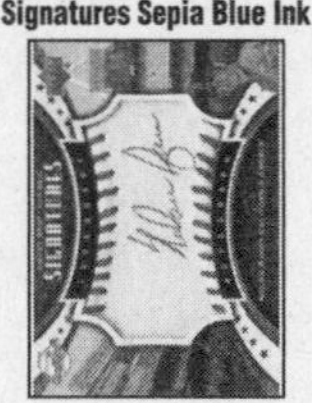

RANDOM INSERTS IN TINS
PRINT RUNS B/WN 15-200 COPIES PER
NO PRICING ON QTY 25 OR LESS
EXCHANGE DEADLINE 8/3/2009
AK Al Kaline/199 10.00 25.00
BR Brooks Robinson/200 10.00 25.00
BW Billy Williams/199 10.00 25.00
CF Carlton Fisk/78 15.00 40.00
CR Cal Ripken Jr./199 60.00 100.00
CY Carl Yastrzemski/90 30.00 60.00
DE Dennis Eckersley/15
DM Don Mattingly/78 30.00 60.00
DS Duke Snider/199 12.50 30.00
EM Edgar Martinez/74 30.00 60.00
JM Juan Marichal/84 12.50 30.00
JP Jim Palmer/200 10.00 25.00
JR Jim Rice/75 10.00 25.00
LM Lee Mazzilli/199 10.00 25.00
MU Dale Murphy/75 15.00 40.00
NR Nolan Ryan/80 60.00 120.00
OS Ozzie Smith/75 30.00 60.00
RC Rocky Colavito/199 30.00 60.00
RY Robin Yount/35 30.00 60.00
TG Tony Gwynn/199 20.00 50.00
WC Will Clark/199 12.50 30.00
WF Whitey Ford/15

2007 Sweet Spot Classic Signatures Sepia Red Ink

RANDOM INSERTS IN TINS
STATED PRINT RUN 15 SER.#'d SETS
NO PRICING DUE TO SCARCITY
EXCHANGE DEADLINE 8/3/2009

2007 Sweet Spot Classic Signatures Silver Stitch Black Ink

RANDOM INSERTS IN TINS
PRINT RUNS B/WN 15-25 COPIES PER
NO PRICING DUE TO SCARCITY
EXCHANGE DEADLINE 8/3/2009

2007 Sweet Spot Classic Signatures Silver Stitch Blue Ink

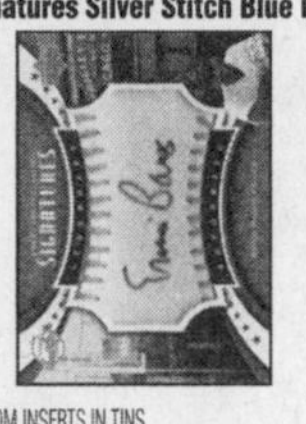

RANDOM INSERTS IN TINS
PRINT RUNS B/WN 16-199 COPIES PER
NO PRICING ON QTY 25 OR LESS
EXCHANGE DEADLINE 8/3/2009
AG Andres Galarraga/14
AK Al Kaline/6
AO Al Oliver/16
BJ Bo Jackson/16
BM Bill Mazeroski/9
BO Wade Boggs/12
BR Brooks Robinson/5
BW Billy Williams/26 12.50 30.00
CF Carlton Fisk/15
CL Carney Lansford/4
CO Dave Concepcion/13
CY Carl Yastrzemski/8
DA Dick Allen/15
DG Dick Groat/24
DL Don Larsen/18
DM Don Mattingly/23
DS Don Sutton/20
DW Dave Winfield/31 30.00 60.00
EB Ernie Banks/14
EC Dennis Eckersley/43 10.00 25.00
EF Elroy Face/25
EM Edgar Martinez/11
EV Dwight Evans/24
FL Fred Lynn/19
FM Fred McGriff/27 30.00 60.00
FR Frank Robinson/20
GI Bob Gibson/45 30.00 60.00
GP Gaylord Perry/36 12.50 30.00
HB Harold Baines/3
JB Johnny Bench/5
JI Jim Bunning/14
JK John Kruk/29 12.50 30.00
JP Johnny Pesky/6
JR Jim Rice/14
KG Ken Griffey Sr./30 12.50 30.00
KO Sandy Koufax/32
LA Luis Aparicio/11
LB Lou Brock/5
MA Juan Marichal/27 12.50 30.00
MG Mark Grace/17
MO Jack Morris/47 10.00 25.00
MS Mike Schmidt/20
MU Stan Musial/6
MV Mickey Vernon/3
NR Nolan Ryan/30 60.00 150.00
OG Ozzie Guillen/13
OS Ozzie Smith/1
PN Phil Niekro/35 12.50 30.00
RA Roberto Alomar/12
RC Rod Carew/29 12.50 30.00
RF Rollie Fingers/34 10.00 25.00
RI Jim Rice/14
RJ Reggie Jackson/44 30.00 60.00
RK Ralph Kiner/4
RR Robin Roberts/36 20.00 50.00
RS Ryne Sandberg/23
RY Robin Yount/19
SA Ron Santo/11
SC Steve Carlton/32 12.50 30.00
SD Shawon Dunston/12
SG Steve Garvey/6
SK Bill Skowron/14
SM Reggie Smith/8
TG Tony Gwynn/19
TH Toby Harrah/11
TM Tino Martinez/24
TO Tony Oliva/6
TP Tony Perez/24
TR Tim Raines/30 40.00 80.00
WB Wade Boggs/26 20.00 50.00
WD Willie Davis/3
WH Willie Horton/23
WM Willie McCovey/44 30.00 60.00
YB Yogi Berra/8

2007 Sweet Spot Classic Signatures Barrel Black Ink

*BLUE: .5X TO 1.2X BLACK INK
RANDOM INSERTS IN TINS
STATED PRINT RUN B/WN 15-50 PER
NO BLUE PRICING ON QTY 25 OR LESS
EXCHANGE DEADLINE 8/3/2009
RR Robin Roberts Blue/50 20.00 50.00

2007 Sweet Spot Classic Signatures Barrel Blue Ink

RANDOM INSERTS IN TINS
PRINT RUNS B/WN 25-75 COPIES PER
NO PRICING ON QTY 25 OR LESS
*BLUE: .5X TO 1.2X BLACK INK
BLUE RANDOMLY INSERTED IN TINS
BLUE PRINT RUN B/WN 15-50 PER
NO BLUE PRICING ON QTY 25 OR LESS
EXCHANGE DEADLINE 8/3/2009
AG Andres Galarraga/75 6.00 15.00
AK Al Kaline/75 15.00 40.00
AO Al Oliver/75 8.00 20.00
BJ Bo Jackson/75 30.00 60.00
BM Bill Mazeroski/75 20.00 50.00
BR Brooks Robinson/75 30.00 60.00
BW Billy Williams/75 12.50 30.00
CL Carney Lansford/75 8.00 20.00
DA Dick Allen/75 10.00 25.00
DG Dick Groat/75 10.00 25.00
DL Don Larsen/75 10.00 25.00
DS Don Sutton/75 10.00 25.00
EC Dennis Eckersley/75 10.00 25.00
EF Elroy Face/75 12.50 30.00
EM Edgar Martinez/75 10.00 25.00
EV Dwight Evans/75 10.00 25.00
FL Fred Lynn/75 8.00 20.00
FM Fred McGriff/75 8.00 20.00
GP Gaylord Perry/75 10.00 25.00
HB Harold Baines/75 10.00 25.00
JI Jim Bunning/75 10.00 25.00
JK John Kruk/75 8.00 20.00
JP Johnny Pesky/75 12.50 30.00
KG Ken Griffey Sr./75 10.00 25.00
LA Luis Aparicio/75 10.00 25.00
MA Juan Marichal/75 15.00 40.00
MG Mark Grace/75 15.00 40.00
MO Jack Morris/75 8.00 20.00
MV Mickey Vernon/75 12.50 30.00
OG Ozzie Guillen/75 10.00 25.00
PN Phil Niekro/75 10.00 25.00
RA Roberto Alomar/75 30.00 60.00
RF Rollie Fingers/75 8.00 20.00
RI Jim Rice/75 10.00 25.00
RR Robin Roberts/50 20.00 50.00
SA Ron Santo/75 20.00 50.00
SC Steve Carlton/75 20.00 50.00
SD Shawon Dunston/75 10.00 25.00
SG Steve Garvey/75 10.00 25.00
SK Bill Skowron/75 10.00 25.00
SM Reggie Smith/75 6.00 15.00
TH Toby Harrah/75 6.00 15.00
TM Tino Martinez/75 12.50 30.00
TO Tony Oliva/75 10.00 25.00
TP Tony Perez/75 12.50 30.00
TR Tim Raines/75 10.00 25.00
WH Willie Horton/75 10.00 25.00

2007 Sweet Spot Classic Signatures Black Barrel Gold Ink

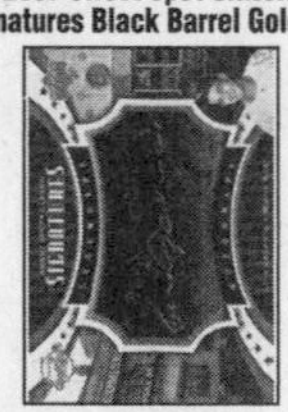

RANDOM INSERTS IN TINS
STATED PRINT RUN 1 SER.#'d SET
NO PRICING DUE TO SCARCITY
EXCHANGE DEADLINE 8/3/2009

2007 Sweet Spot Classic Signatures Black Barrel Silver Ink

RANDOM INSERTS IN TINS
PRINT RUNS B/WN 1-47 COPIES PER
NO PRICING ON QTY 25 OR LESS
EXCHANGE DEADLINE 8/3/2009
BW Billy Williams/26 20.00 50.00
EC Dennis Eckersley/43 12.50 30.00
EF Elroy Face/26 20.00 50.00
FM Fred McGriff/27 30.00 60.00
GP Gaylord Perry/36 10.00 25.00
JK John Kruk/29 12.50 30.00
KG Ken Griffey Sr./30 15.00 40.00
MA Juan Marichal/27 10.00 25.00
MO Jack Morris/47 10.00 25.00
PN Phil Niekro/35 15.00 40.00
RF Rollie Fingers/34 10.00 25.00
RR Robin Roberts/36 20.00 50.00
SC Steve Carlton/32 20.00 50.00
TR Tim Raines/30 30.00 60.00

2007 Sweet Spot Classic Signatures Black Leather Green Ink

RANDOM INSERTS IN TINS
STATED PRINT RUN 1 SER.#'d SET
NO PRICING DUE TO SCARCITY
EXCHANGE DEADLINE 8/3/2009

2007 Sweet Spot Classic Signatures Black Leather Silver Ink

RANDOM INSERTS IN TINS
PRINT RUNS B/WN 1-47 COPIES PER
NO PRICING ON QTY 25 OR LESS
EXCHANGE DEADLINE 8/3/2009
BS Bruce Sutter/42 12.50 30.00
BW Billy Williams/26 20.00 50.00
CF Carlton Fisk/27 20.00 50.00
DW Dave Winfield/31 20.00 50.00
EC Dennis Eckersley/43 12.50 30.00
EF Elroy Face/26 20.00 50.00
FM Fred McGriff/27 30.00 60.00
GI Bob Gibson/45 40.00 80.00
GP Gaylord Perry/36 10.00 25.00
JK John Kruk/29 12.50 30.00
KG Ken Griffey Sr./30 15.00 40.00
MA Juan Marichal/27 30.00 60.00
MO Jack Morris/47 10.00 25.00
NR Nolan Ryan/30 60.00 120.00
PN Phil Niekro/35 15.00 40.00
RC Rod Carew/29 20.00 50.00
RF Rollie Fingers/34 12.50 30.00
RJ Reggie Jackson/44 30.00 60.00
RR Robin Roberts/36 20.00 50.00
SC Steve Carlton/32 40.00 80.00
TR Tim Raines/30 30.00 60.00
WB Wade Boggs/26 30.00 60.00
WM Willie McCovey/44 30.00 60.00

2007 Sweet Spot Classic Signatures Leather Blue Ink

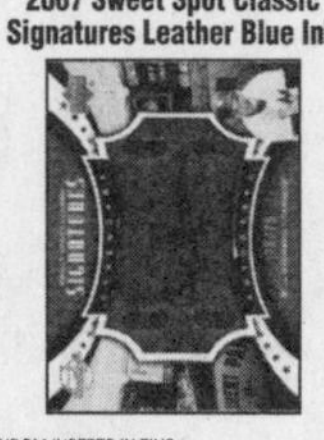

RANDOM INSERTS IN TINS
PRINT RUNS B/WN 25-75 COPIES PER
NO PRICING ON QTY 25 OR LESS
EXCHANGE DEADLINE 8/3/2009
AG Andres Galarraga/75 6.00 15.00
AK Al Kaline/75 15.00 40.00
AO Al Oliver/75 8.00 20.00
BJ Bo Jackson/75 30.00 60.00
BM Bill Mazeroski/75 20.00 50.00
BR Brooks Robinson/75 15.00 40.00
BW Billy Williams/75 12.50 30.00
CL Carney Lansford/75 8.00 20.00
DA Dick Allen/75 10.00 25.00
DG Dick Groat/75 10.00 25.00
DL Don Larsen/75 12.50 30.00
EC Dennis Eckersley/75 10.00 25.00
EF Elroy Face/75 12.50 30.00
EM Edgar Martinez/75 20.00 50.00
EV Dwight Evans/75 10.00 25.00
FL Fred Lynn/75 8.00 20.00
FM Fred McGriff/75 15.00 40.00
GP Gaylord Perry/75 10.00 25.00
HB Harold Baines/75 10.00 25.00
JI Jim Bunning/75 10.00 25.00
JK John Kruk/75 8.00 20.00
JP Johnny Pesky/75 12.50 30.00
KG Ken Griffey Sr./75 10.00 25.00
LA Luis Aparicio/75 10.00 25.00
LB Lou Brock/75 15.00 40.00
MA Juan Marichal/75 15.00 40.00
MG Mark Grace/75 15.00 40.00
MO Jack Morris/75 8.00 20.00
MV Mickey Vernon/75 12.50 30.00
OG Ozzie Guillen/75 10.00 25.00
RA Roberto Alomar/75 30.00 60.00
RC Rod Carew/75 12.50 30.00
RF Rollie Fingers/75 8.00 20.00
RI Jim Rice/75 10.00 25.00
RR Robin Roberts/75 15.00 40.00
RS Ryne Sandberg/75 20.00 50.00
SA Ron Santo/75 30.00 60.00
SC Steve Carlton/75 20.00 50.00
SD Shawon Dunston/75 10.00 25.00
SG Steve Garvey/75 10.00 25.00
SK Bill Skowron/75 10.00 25.00
SM Reggie Smith/75 6.00 15.00
TH Toby Harrah/75 6.00 15.00
TM Tino Martinez/75 12.50 30.00
TO Tony Oliva/75 10.00 25.00
TP Tony Perez/75 12.50 30.00
TR Tim Raines/75 10.00 25.00
WH Willie Horton/75 10.00 25.00

2007 Sweet Spot Classic Signatures Leather Gold Ink

*GOLD: .5X TO 1.2X BLUE INK
GOLD RANDOMLY INSERTED IN TINS
GOLD PRINT RUN B/WN 15-50 PER
NO GOLD PRICING ON QTY 25 OR LESS
EXCHANGE DEADLINE 8/3/2009
PN Phil Niekro/50 12.50 30.00

2006 Sweet Spot Update

This 182-card set was released in December, 2006. The set was issued in five-card packs with an $9.99 SRP and those packs came 12 to a box and 16 boxes to a case. Cards numbered 1-100 feature veteran players while cards 101-182 feature signed cards of 2006 rookies. Those cards, which were issued to a stated print run range between 98 and 499 serial numbered copies, were inserted at a stated rate of one in six. A few players did not return their signatures in time for pack out and those cards could be redeemed until December 19, 2009.

COMP.SET w/o AU's (100) 10.00 25.00
COMMON CARD (1-100) .20 .50
COMMON AU p/r 399-499 3.00 8.00
COMMON AU p/r 150-240 4.00 10.00
COMMON AU p/r 98-125 4.00 10.00
OVERALL AU ODDS 1:6
AU PRINT RUNS B/WN 98-499 PER
EXCHANGE DEADLINE 12/19/09
1 Luis Gonzalez .20 .50
2 Chad Tracy .20 .50
3 Brandon Webb .30 .75
4 Andruw Jones .20 .50
5 Chipper Jones .50 1.25
6 John Smoltz .50 1.25
7 Tim Hudson .30 .75
8 Miguel Tejada .30 .75
9 Brian Roberts .20 .50
10 Ramon Hernandez .20 .50
11 Curt Schilling .30 .75
12 David Ortiz .30 .75
13 Manny Ramirez .50 1.25
14 Jason Varitek .50 1.25
15 Josh Beckett .30 .75
16 Greg Maddux .75 2.00
17 Derrek Lee .20 .50
18 Mark Prior .20 .50
19 Aramis Ramirez .20 .50
20 Jim Thome .30 .75
21 Paul Konerko .30 .75
22 Scott Podsednik .20 .50
23 Jose Contreras .20 .50
24 Ken Griffey Jr. .75 2.00
25 Adam Dunn .30 .75
26 Felipe Lopez .20 .50
27 Travis Hafner .20 .50
28 Victor Martinez .30 .75
29 Grady Sizemore .30 .75
30 Jhonny Peralta .30 .75
31 Todd Helton .30 .75
32 Garrett Atkins .20 .50
33 Clint Barmes .20 .50
34 Ivan Rodriguez .30 .75
35 Chris Shelton .20 .50
36 Jeremy Bonderman .20 .50
37 Miguel Cabrera .50 1.25
38 Dontrelle Willis .20 .50
39 Lance Berkman .30 .75
40 Morgan Ensberg .20 .50
41 Roy Oswalt .30 .75
42 Reggie Sanders .20 .50
43 Mike Sweeney .20 .50
44 Vladimir Guerrero .50 1.25
45 Bartolo Colon .20 .50
46 Chone Figgins .20 .50
47 Nomar Garciaparra .50 1.25
48 Jeff Kent .20 .50
49 J.D. Drew .20 .50
50 Carlos Lee .20 .50
51 Ben Sheets .20 .50
52 Rickie Weeks .20 .50
53 Johan Santana .50 1.25
54 Torii Hunter .20 .50
55 Joe Mauer .50 1.25
56 Pedro Martinez .30 .75
57 David Wright .75 2.00
58 Carlos Beltran .20 .50
59 Carlos Delgado .20 .50
60 Jose Reyes .30 .75
61 Derek Jeter 1.25 3.00
62 Alex Rodriguez .75 2.00
63 Randy Johnson .50 1.25
64 Hideki Matsui .50 1.25
65 Gary Sheffield .20 .50
66 Rich Harden .20 .50
67 Eric Chavez .20 .50
68 Huston Street .20 .50
69 Bobby Crosby .20 .50
70 Bobby Abreu .20 .50
71 Ryan Howard .75 2.00
72 Chase Utley .50 1.25
73 Pat Burrell .20 .50
74 Jason Bay .20 .50
75 Sean Casey .20 .50
76 Mike Piazza .50 1.25
77 Jake Peavy .20 .50
78 Brian Giles .20 .50
79 Milton Bradley .20 .50
80 Omar Vizquel .30 .75
81 Jason Schmidt .20 .50
82 Ichiro Suzuki .75 2.00
83 Felix Hernandez .50 1.25
84 Kenji Johjima RC .50 1.25
85 Albert Pujols 1.25 3.00
86 Chris Carpenter .50 1.25
87 Scott Rolen .30 .75
88 Jim Edmonds .30 .75
89 Carl Crawford .30 .75
90 Johnny Gomes .20 .50
91 Scott Kazmir .30 .75
92 Mark Teixeira .50 1.25
93 Michael Young .30 .75
94 Phil Nevin .20 .50
95 Vernon Wells .20 .50
96 Roy Halladay .50 1.25
97 Troy Glaus .20 .50

98 Alfonso Soriano .30 .75
99 Nick Johnson .20 .50
100 Jose Vidro .20 .50
101 Adam Wainwright AU/100 (RC) 15.00 40.00
103 Andre Ethier AU/150 (RC) 30.00 60.00
105 Ben Johnson AU/400 (RC) 3.00 8.00
106 Boof Bonser AU/100 (RC) 6.00 15.00
107 Boone Logan AU/200 RC 4.00 10.00
108 Brian Anderson AU/200 (RC) 4.00 10.00
109 Brian Bannister AU/100 (RC) 8.00 20.00
110 Chris Denorfia AU/100 (RC) 4.00 10.00
111 Agustin Montero AU/100 (RC) 6.00 15.00
112 Cody Ross AU/100 (RC) 20.00 50.00
113 Cole Hamels AU/399 (RC) 20.00 50.00
114 Conor Jackson AU/400 (RC) 4.00 10.00
115 Dan Uggla AU/125 (RC) 12.50 30.00
116 Dave Gassner AU/100 (RC) 4.00 10.00
117 C.J. Wilson AU/150 (RC) 12.50 30.00
118 Eric Reed AU/150 (RC) 4.00 10.00
119 Fausto Carmona AU/99 (RC) 10.00 25.00
120 Fernando Nieve AU/100 (RC) 4.00 10.00
121 Francisco Liriano AU/499 (RC) 6.00 15.00
122 Freddie Bynum AU/100 (RC) 4.00 10.00
123 Hanley Ramirez AU/100 (RC) 15.00 40.00
124 Hong-Chih Kuo AU/100 (RC) 75.00 150.00
125 Ian Kinsler AU/100 (RC) 12.50 30.00
126 Carlos Marmol AU/100 RC 6.00 15.00
127 Bobby Keppel AU/200 (RC) 4.00 10.00
128 Jason Kubel AU/100 (RC) 6.00 15.00
129 Jeff Harris AU/100 RC 4.00 10.00
130 Alay Soler AU/100 RC 6.00 15.00
131 Jered Weaver AU/100 (RC) 10.00 25.00
132 Carlos Quentin AU/100 (RC) 12.50 30.00
133 Jeremy Hermida AU/100 (RC) 6.00 15.00
134 Joel Zumaya AU/100 (RC) 20.00 50.00
135 Joey Devine AU/100 RC 6.00 15.00
136 John Koronka AU/98 (RC) 4.00 10.00
137 Jonathan Papelbon AU/399 (RC) 15.00 40.00
138 Jose Capellan AU/240 (RC) 4.00 10.00
139 Josh Johnson AU/100 (RC) 12.50 30.00
141 Josh Willingham AU/100 (RC) 4.00 10.00
143 Justin Verlander AU/100 (RC) 20.00 50.00
144 Kelly Shoppach AU/100 (RC) 6.00 15.00
146 Kevin Thompson AU/100 (RC) 4.00 10.00
147 Macay McBride AU/100 (RC) 4.00 10.00
150 Clay Hensley AU/100 (RC) 4.00 10.00
151 Ty Taubenheim AU/100 RC 10.00 25.00
152 Mike Jacobs AU/200 (RC) 4.00 10.00
153 Saul Rivera AU/100 (RC) 4.00 10.00
154 Mike Thompson AU/100 RC 4.00 10.00
155 Nate McLouth AU/100 (RC) 10.00 25.00
156 Mike Vento AU/100 (RC) 4.00 10.00
157 Paul Maholm AU/200 (RC) 4.00 10.00
159 Reggie Abercrombie AU/100 (RC) 4.00 10.00
160 Mike Rouse AU/100 (RC) 4.00 10.00
161 Ken Ray AU/100 (RC) 4.00 10.00
162 Ron Flores AU/100 RC 4.00 10.00
163 Ryan Zimmerman AU/100 (RC) 30.00 60.00
164 Erick Aybar AU/100 (RC) 6.00 15.00
165 Sean Marshall AU/150 (RC) 8.00 20.00
167 Taylor Buchholz AU/100 (RC) 4.00 10.00
168 Matt Murton AU/100 (RC) 12.50 30.00
170 Wil Nieves AU/100 (RC) 6.00 15.00
171 James Shields AU/100 RC 8.00 20.00
172 Jon Lester AU/399 RC 20.00 50.00
174 Aaron Rakers AU/100 (RC) 4.00 10.00
175 Bobby Livingston AU/100 (RC) 6.00 15.00
176 Brendan Harris AU/100 (RC) 4.00 10.00
177 Zach Jackson AU/100 (RC) 6.00 15.00
178 Chris Britton AU/100 RC 4.00 10.00
179 Howie Kendrick AU/399 (RC) 8.00 20.00
180 Zach Miner AU/100 (RC) 6.00 15.00
181 Kevin Frandsen AU/100 (RC) 4.00 10.00
182 Matt Capps AU/100 (RC) 4.00 10.00
183 Peter Moylan AU/100 RC 4.00 10.00

2006 Sweet Spot Update Rookie Signatures Black Stitch Black Ink

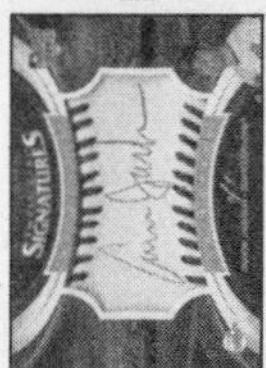

OVERALL AUTO ODDS 1:6
STATED PRINT RUN 1 SERIAL #'d SET
NO PRICING DUE TO SCARCITY
EXCHANGE DEADLINE 12/19/09

2006 Sweet Spot Update Rookie Signatures Red-Blue Stitch Red Ink

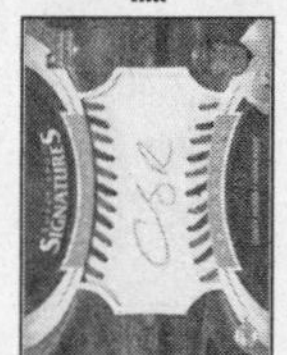

*RB p/r 175-225:.5X TO 1.2X RC p/r 399-499
*RB p/r 100: .6X TO 1.5X RC p/r 399-499
*RB p/r 100: .5X TO 1.2X RC p/r 150-240
*RB p/r 100: .4X TO 1X RC p/r 98-125
*RB p/r 50: .6X TO 1.5X RC p/r 150-240
*RB p/r 50: .5X TO 1.2X RC p/r 98-125
OVERALL AUTO ODDS 1:6
PRINT RUNS B/WN 50-225 COPIES PER
EXCHANGE DEADLINE 12/19/09
ASTERISK = PARTIAL EXCHANGE
124 Hong-Chih Kuo/50 150.00 250.00
164 Erick Aybar/50 10.00 25.00

2006 Sweet Spot Update Rookie Signatures Bat Barrel Black Ink

*BLK p/r 34-35:1X TO 2.5X RC p/r 399-499
*BLK p/r 70: .5X TO 1.2X RC p/r 150-240
*BLK p/r 34-35: .75X TO 2X RC p/r 150-240
*BLK p/r 70: .6X TO 1.5X RC p/r 399-499
*BLK p/r 34-35: .6X TO 1.5X RC p/r 98-125
OVERALL AUTO ODDS 1:6
PRINT RUNS B/WN 34-70 COPIES PER
EXCHANGE DEADLINE 12/19/09
101 Adam Wainwright/35 20.00 50.00
119 Fausto Carmona/35 20.00 50.00
124 Hong-Chih Kuo/35 200.00 250.00
137 Jonathan Papelbon/70 30.00 60.00

2006 Sweet Spot Update Rookie Signatures Bat Barrel Blue Ink

OVERALL AUTO ODDS 1:6
PRINT RUNS B/WN 9-20 PER
NO PRICING DUE TO SCARCITY
EXCHANGE DEADLINE 12/19/09

2006 Sweet Spot Update Rookie Signatures Bat Barrel Silver Ink

OVERALL AUTO ODDS 1:6
STATED PRINT RUN 1 SERIAL #'d SET
NO PRICING DUE TO SCARCITY
EXCHANGE DEADLINE 12/19/09

2006 Sweet Spot Update Rookie Signatures Glove Leather Black Ink

OVERALL AUTO ODDS 1:6
PRINT RUNS B/WN 20-40 PER
NO PRICING ON QTY OF 25 OR LESS
EXCHANGE DEADLINE 12/19/09
ASTERISK = PARTIAL EXCHANGE
121 Francisco Liriano/40 15.00 40.00
137 Jonathan Papelbon/40 40.00 80.00
172 Jon Lester/40 50.00 100.00
179 Howie Kendrick/40 15.00 40.00

2006 Sweet Spot Update Rookie Signatures Glove Leather Blue Ink

OVERALL AUTO ODDS 1:6
PRINT RUNS B/WN 5-10 PER
NO PRICING DUE TO SCARCITY
EXCHANGE DEADLINE 12/19/09

2006 Sweet Spot Update Rookie Signatures Glove Leather Silver Ink

OVERALL AUTO ODDS 1:6
STATED PRINT RUN 1 SERIAL #'d SET
NO PRICING DUE TO SCARCITY
EXCHANGE DEADLINE 12/19/09

2006 Sweet Spot Update Announcer Signatures

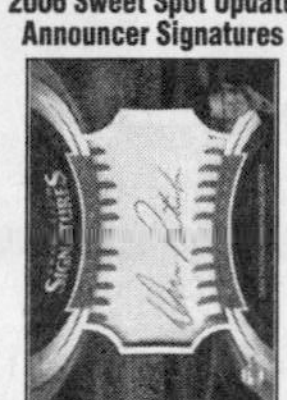

OVERALL AUTO ODDS 1:6
PRINT RUNS B/WN 25-50 PER
CB Chris Berman/50 20.00 50.00
DP Dan Patrick/50 30.00 60.00
LC Linda Cohn/50 15.00 40.00
PG Peter Gammons/25 30.00 60.00
SS Stuart Scott/50 15.00 40.00

2006 Sweet Spot Update Dual Signatures

OVERALL AUTO ODDS 1:6
PRINT RUNS B/WN 1-55 PER
NO PRICING ON QTY OF 25 OR LESS
EXCHANGE DEADLINE 12/19/09
BN Taylor Buchholz 15.00 40.00
Fernando Nieve/55
CK Carl Crawford 15.00 40.00
Scott Kazmir/50
CV Roger Clemens
Justin Verlander/5
EG Andre Ethier 20.00 50.00
Tony Gwynn Jr./35
GJ Ken Griffey Jr.
Michael Jordan/1
HJ Howie Kendrick
Jered Weaver/25
HK Jason Kubel 15.00 40.00
Jeremy Hermida/55
HL Francisco Liriano
Cole Hamels/15
HM Travis Hafner
Victor Martinez/35
HS Cole Hamels
Jeremy Sowers/35
HW Josh Willingham 15.00 40.00
Jeremy Hermida/55
IU Tadahito Iguchi
Chase Utley/35
JB Derek Jeter
Reggie Bush/5
JG Ken Griffey Jr.
Derek Jeter/5
KL Ken Griffey Jr.
LeBron James/5
KR Howie Kendrick
Brian Roberts/35
KU Scott Kazmir 15.00 40.00
B.J. Upton/55
KW Scott Kazmir 15.00 40.00
Dontrelle Willis/35
LN Francisco Liriano 40.00 80.00
Joe Nathan/35
ML Joe Mauer
Francisco Liriano/15
MM Justin Morneau 100.00 200.00
Joe Mauer/35
PZ Jonathan Papelbon 50.00 100.00
Joel Zumaya/35
SN Huston Street 15.00 40.00
Joe Nathan/35
UH Chase Utley 125.00 250.00
Cole Hamels/35
UU Chase Utley 40.00 80.00
Dan Uggla/35
WL Jered Weaver
Francisco Liriano/10

2006 Sweet Spot Update Spokesmen Signatures

OVERALL AUTO ODDS 1:6
UNPRICED AU PRINT RUN 5-20
2 Derek Jeter/15
4 Michael Jordan/20
5 Michael Jordan
Derek Jeter/5
6 Ken Griffey Jr.
Michael Jordan/5
7 Ken Griffey Jr.
Derek Jeter/5
8 Derek Jeter
LeBron James/5
10 Michael Jordan
LeBron James/5
11 LeBron James
Reggie Bush/5
SP1 Ken Griffey Jr./20

2006 Sweet Spot Update Sweet Beginnings Swatches

OVERALL GU ODDS 1:12
NO SP PRICING DUE TO SCARCITY
AB Adrian Beltre 3.00 8.00
AE Andre Ethier SP
AI Akinori Iwamura 12.50 30.00
AJ Andruw Jones 4.00 10.00
AP Ariel Pestano 3.00 8.00
AR Alex Rios 3.00 8.00
AS Alfonso Soriano 3.00 8.00
BA Bobby Abreu 4.00 10.00
BB Brian Bannister 3.00 8.00
BI Chad Billingsley 4.00 10.00
BW Bernie Williams 4.00 10.00
CA Miguel Cabrera 6.00 15.00
CB Carlos Beltran 4.00 10.00
CD Carlos Delgado 3.00 8.00
CH Chin-Lung Hu 20.00 50.00
CJ Conor Jackson 4.00 10.00
CL Carlos Lee 3.00 8.00
CM Matt Cain 4.00 10.00
CR Craig Hansen SP
CU Chris Duncan 4.00 10.00
CZ Carlos Zambrano 3.00 8.00
DL Derrek Lee 3.00 8.00
DO David Ortiz 6.00 15.00
DU Dan Uggla SP
EB Erik Bedard 3.00 8.00
EP Eduardo Paret 3.00 8.00
FA Fausto Carmona 3.00 8.00
FC Frederich Cepeda 3.00 8.00
FL Francisco Liriano SP
GY Guogang Yang 3.00 8.00
HA Cole Hamels 6.00 15.00
HC Hee Seop Choi 3.00 8.00
HK Hong-Chih Kuo SP
HR Hanley Ramirez SP
HT Hitoshi Tamura 12.50 30.00
IK Ian Kinsler 6.00 15.00
IR Ivan Rodriguez 6.00 15.00
IS Ichiro Suzuki 100.00 200.00
JB Jason Bay 6.00 15.00
JD Johnny Damon 4.00 10.00
JF Jeff Francis 3.00 8.00
JH Jeremy Hermida 3.00 8.00
JJ Josh Johnson SP
JK Jason Kubel SP
JL Jong Beom Lee 3.00 8.00
JM Justin Morneau 6.00 15.00
JO Josh Barfield SP
JP Jin Man Park 3.00 8.00
JS Johan Santana 6.00 15.00
JV Jason Varitek 10.00 25.00
JZ Joel Zumaya 10.00 25.00
KE Matt Kemp 4.00 10.00
KG Ken Griffey Jr. 10.00 25.00
KJ Kenji Johjima SP
KM Kendry Morales SP
KU Koji Uehara 12.50 30.00
LE Jon Lester SP
LM Lastings Milledge SP
LO Javy Lopez 3.00 8.00
MA Moises Alou 3.00 8.00
MC Michael Collins 4.00 10.00
ME Michel Enriquez 3.00 8.00
MF Maikel Folch 3.00 8.00
MJ Mike Jacobs 3.00 8.00
MK Munenori Kawasaki 20.00 50.00
MN Mike Napoli 4.00 10.00
MO Michihiro Ogasawara 12.50 30.00
MP Mike Piazza 8.00 20.00
MS Min Han Son 4.00 10.00
MT Miguel Tejada 3.00 8.00
NI Nick Markakis SP
NM Nobuhiko Matsunaka 12.50 30.00
NS Naoyuki Shimizu 12.50 30.00
OU Osmany Urrutia 3.00 8.00
PA Jonathan Papelbon SP
PE Mike Pelfrey SP
PF Prince Fielder SP
PL Pedro Luis Lazo 3.00 8.00
PU Albert Pujols 12.50 30.00
RM Russell Martin SP
RN Ricky Nolasco SP
RO Alex Rodriguez 8.00 20.00
RZ Ryan Zimmerman SP
SH James Shields 3.00 8.00
SW Shunsuke Watanabe 12.50 30.00
TN Tsuyoshi Nishioka 15.00 40.00
TW Tsuyoshi Wada 15.00 40.00
VE Justin Verlander 6.00 15.00
VM Victor Martinez 6.00 15.00
VO Vicyohandry Odelin 3.00 8.00
WE Jered Weaver SP
WI Josh Willingham 3.00 8.00
WL Wei-Chu Lin 30.00 60.00
YG Yulieski Gourriel 6.00 15.00
YM Yunieski Maya 3.00 8.00

2006 Sweet Spot Update Sweet Beginnings Patches

OVERALL GU ODDS 1:12
PRICING FOR NON-LOGO PATCHES
NO SP PRICING DUE TO SCARCITY
AB Adrian Beltre 30.00 60.00
AE Andre Ethier 20.00 50.00
AI Akinori Iwamura SP
AJ Andruw Jones 20.00 50.00
AP Ariel Pestano 20.00 50.00
AR Alex Rios SP
AS Alfonso Soriano 60.00 120.00
BA Bobby Abreu 30.00 60.00
BB Brian Bannister 20.00 50.00
BI Chad Billingsley 20.00 50.00
BW Bernie Williams 60.00 120.00
CA Miguel Cabrera 30.00 60.00
CB Carlos Beltran 30.00 60.00
CD Carlos Delgado 40.00 80.00
CJ Conor Jackson 30.00 60.00
CL Carlos Lee 20.00 50.00
CM Matt Cain 40.00 80.00
CU Chris Duncan 20.00 50.00
CZ Carlos Zambrano 40.00 80.00
DL Derrek Lee 40.00 80.00
DO David Ortiz 40.00 80.00
DU Dan Uggla 20.00 50.00
EB Erik Bedard 30.00 60.00
EP Eduardo Paret 20.00 50.00
FA Fausto Carmona 10.00 25.00
FC Frederich Cepeda 20.00 50.00
FL Francisco Liriano 20.00 50.00
GY Guogan Yang SP
HA Cole Hamels 20.00 50.00
HK Hong-Chih Kuo 175.00 300.00
HT Hitoshi Tamura
IK Ian Kinsler
IR Ivan Rodriguez SP
IS Ichiro Suzuki
JB Jason Bay 20.00 50.00
JD Johnny Damon 20.00 50.00
JF Jeff Francis 20.00 50.00
JH Jeremy Hermida 20.00 50.00
JJ Josh Johnson 20.00 50.00
JL Jong Beom Lee SP
JM Justin Morneau
JO Josh Barfield 20.00 50.00
JP Jin Man Park SP
JS Johan Santana 50.00 100.00
JV Jason Varitek 20.00 50.00
JZ Joel Zumaya 30.00 60.00
KE Matt Kemp 20.00 50.00
KG Ken Griffey Jr. SP
KJ Kenji Johjima 125.00 250.00
KU Koji Uehara
LE Jon Lester 30.00 60.00
LM Lastings Milledge SP
LO Javy Lopez 20.00 50.00
MA Moises Alou SP
MC Michael Collins 20.00 50.00
ME Michel Enriquez 20.00 50.00
MF Maikel Folch 20.00 50.00
MJ Mike Jacobs 20.00 50.00
MK Munenori Kawasaki 200.00 300.00
MN Mike Napoli 20.00 50.00
MO Michihiro Ogasawara 150.00 250.00
MP Mike Piazza 60.00 120.00
MS Min Han Son SP
MT Miguel Tejada
NI Nick Markakis 30.00 60.00
NM Nobuhiko Matsunaka 40.00 80.00
NS Naoyuki Shimizu
OU Osmany Urrutia 30.00 60.00
PA Jonathan Papelbon 50.00 100.00
PE Mike Pelfrey 50.00 100.00
PF Prince Fielder SP
PL Pedro Luis Lazo 30.00 60.00
PU Albert Pujols
RM Russell Martin 30.00 60.00
RN Ricky Nolasco 20.00 50.00
RZ Ryan Zimmerman 50.00 100.00
SW Shunsuke Watanabe
TN Tsuyoshi Nishioka
TW Tsuyoshi Wada 150.00 300.00
VE Justin Verlander 30.00 60.00
VM Victor Martinez 30.00 60.00
VO Vicyohandry Odelin 20.00 50.00
WE Jered Weaver 20.00 50.00
WI Josh Willingham 20.00 50.00
WL Wei-Chu Lin SP
YG Yulieski Gourriel 50.00 100.00
YM Yunieski Maya 20.00 50.00

2006 Sweet Spot Update Veteran Signatures Red Stitch Blue Ink

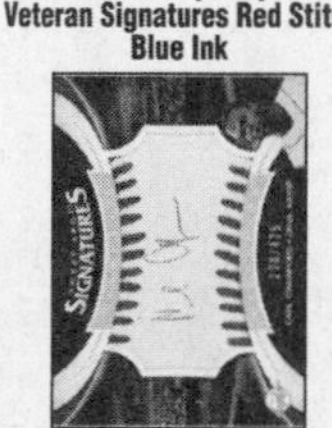

OVERALL AUTO ODDS 1:6
PRINT RUNS B/WN 30-525 COPIES PER
EXCHANGE DEADLINE 12/19/09
ASTERISK = PARTIAL EXCHANGE
AG Tony Gwynn Jr./425 6.00 15.00
AH Aaron Harang/425 5.00 12.00
AP Albert Pujols/30 175.00 300.00
AZ Aramis Ramirez/225 6.00 15.00
BJ B.J. Upton/193 10.00 25.00
BR Brian Roberts/300 6.00 15.00
CC Carl Crawford/425 10.00 25.00
CU Chase Utley/425 30.00 60.00
DJ Derek Jeter/75 125.00 250.00
DW Dontrelle Willis/125 8.00 20.00
HS Huston Street/200 6.00 15.00
JB Jason Bay/425 8.00 20.00
JN Joe Nathan/200 6.00 15.00
JS Jeremy Sowers/425 6.00 15.00
JT Jim Thome/75 30.00 60.00
KG Ken Griffey Jr./50 60.00 120.00
KY Kevin Youkilis/425 8.00 20.00
MC Miguel Cabrera/525 10.00 25.00
MO Justin Morneau/425 10.00 25.00
RC Roger Clemens/30 75.00 150.00
SD Stephen Drew/525 10.00 25.00
SK Scott Kazmir/522 8.00 20.00
SP Scott Podsednik/247 5.00 12.00
SS Mark Mulder/300 5.00 12.00
TH Travis Hafner/525 6.00 15.00
TI Tadahito Iguchi/425 12.50 30.00

2006 Sweet Spot Update Veteran Signatures Red-Blue Stitch Red Ink

*RBS: .5X TO 1.2X RED STITCH AU
OVERALL AUTO ODDS 1:6
PRINT RUNS B/WN 5-299 COPIES PER
NO PRICING ON QTY OF 25 OR LESS
EXCHANGE DEADLINE 12/19/09
ASTERISK = PARTIAL EXCHANGE
KG Ken Griffey Jr./38 50.00 100.00
KG2 Ken Griffey Jr./37 50.00 100.00

2006 Sweet Spot Update Veteran Signatures Black and White

APPX. ODDS 1 PER CASE
NO PRICING DUE TO SCARCITY
EXCHANGE DEADLINE 12/19/09

2006 Sweet Spot Update Veteran Signatures Black Stitch Black Ink

OVERALL AUTO ODDS 1:6
STATED PRINT RUN 1 SERIAL #'d SET
NO PRICING DUE TO SCARCITY
EXCHANGE DEADLINE 12/19/09

2006 Sweet Spot Update Veteran Signatures Bat Barrel Black Ink

COMMON CARD 12.50 30.00
OVERALL AUTO ODDS 1:6
PRINT RUNS B/WN 10-35 COPIES PER
NO PRICING ON QTY OF 25 OR LESS
EXCHANGE DEADLINE 12/19/09
BJ B.J. Upton/35 20.00 50.00
CU Chase Utley/35 60.00 120.00
KG Ken Griffey Jr./28 50.00 100.00
KY Kevin Youkilis/35 20.00 50.00
MC Miguel Cabrera/35 20.00 50.00
SD Stephen Drew/35 30.00 60.00
SM John Smoltz/35 20.00 50.00
TH Travis Hafner/35 20.00 50.00
TI Tadahito Iguchi/35 30.00 60.00

1911 T205 Gold Border

The cards in this 218-card set measure approximately 1 1/2" by 2 5/8". The T205 set (catalog designation), also known as the "Gold Border" set, was issued in 1911 in packages of the following cigarette brands: American Beauty, Broadleaf, Cycle, Drum, Hassan, Honest Long Cut, Piedmont, Polar Bear, Sovereign and Sweet Caporal. All the above were products of the American Tobacco Company, and the ads for the various brands appear below the biographical section on the back of each card. There are pose variations noted in the checklist (which is alphabetized and numbered for reference) and there are 12 minor league cards of a more ornate design which are somewhat scarce. The numbers below correspond to alphabetical order within category, i.e., major leaguers and minor leaguers are alphabetized separately. The gold borders of T205 cards chip easily and they are hard to find in "Mint" or even "Near Mint" condition, due to this there is a high premium on these high condition cards. Listed pricing for raw cards references "EX" condition.

COMPLETE SET (218) 25000.00 50000.00
COMMON (1-186) 90.00 150.00
COMMON (187-198) 150.00 300.00
1 Ed Abbaticchio 60.00 100.00
2 Doc Adkins 125.00 200.00
3 Red Ames 60.00 100.00
4 Jimmy Archer 60.00 100.00
5 Jimmy Austin 60.00 100.00
6 Bill Bailey 60.00 100.00
7 Home Run Baker 175.00 300.00
8 Neal Ball 60.00 100.00
9 Cy Barger 60.00 100.00
(Full B)
10 Cy Barger 250.00 400.00
Part B
11 Jack Barry 60.00 100.00
12 Emil Batch 125.00 200.00
13 Johnny Bates 60.00 100.00
14 Fred Beck 60.00 100.00
15 Beals Becker 60.00 100.00
16 George Bell 60.00 100.00
17 Chief Bender 175.00 [illegible]
18 Bill Bergen 60.00 100.00
19 Bob Bescher 60.00 100.00
20 Joe Birmingham 60.00 100.00
21 Russ Blackburne 60.00 100.00
22 Kitty Bransfield 60.00 100.00
23 Roger Bresnahan 175.00 300.00
(Mouth closed)
24 Roger Bresnahan 300.00 500.00
(Mouth open)
25 Al Bridwell 60.00 100.00
26 Mordecai Brown 175.00 300.00
27 Bobby Byrne 60.00 100.00
28 Hick Cady 150.00 250.00
29 Howie Camnitz 60.00 100.00
30 Bill Carrigan 60.00 100.00
31 Frank Chance 175.00 300.00
32A Hal Chase Both Ears 125.00 200.00
Border Ends at Shoulders
32B Hal Chase Both Ears 125.00 200.00
Border Extends Beyond Shoulders
33 Hal Chase Left Ear 300.00 500.00
34 Eddie Cicotte 250.00 400.00
35 Fred Clarke 150.00 250.00
36 Ty Cobb 2500.00 4000.00
37 Edward T. Collins 175.00 300.00
(Mouth closed)
38 Edward T. Collins 350.00 600.00
(Mouth open)
39 Jimmy Collins 250.00 400.00
40 Frank Corridon 60.00 100.00
41A Otis Crandall 150.00 250.00
T Crossed in name
41B Otis Crandall 90.00 150.00
T Not Crossed in Name
42 Lou Criger 60.00 100.00
43 Bill Dahlen 250.00 400.00
44 Jake Daubert 60.00 100.00
45 Jim Delahanty 60.00 100.00
46 Art Devlin 60.00 100.00
47 Josh Devore 60.00 100.00
48 Walt Dickson 60.00 100.00
49 Jiggs Donahue UER 250.00 400.00
(Misspelled Donohue on card)
50 Red Dooin 60.00 100.00
51 Mickey Doolan 60.00 100.00
52A Patsy Dougherty 150.00 250.00
(Red stocking)
52B Patsy Dougherty 150.00 250.00
(White stocking)
53 Tom Downey 60.00 100.00
54 Larry Doyle 60.00 100.00
55 Hugh Duffy 175.00 300.00
56 Jack Dunn 175.00 300.00
57 Jimmy Dygert 60.00 100.00
58 Dick Egan 60.00 100.00
59 Kid Elberfeld 60.00 100.00
60 Clyde Engle 60.00 100.00
61 Steve Evans 60.00 100.00
62 Johnny Evers 300.00 500.00
63 Bob Ewing 60.00 100.00
64 George Ferguson 60.00 100.00
65 Ray Fisher 175.00 300.00
66 Art Fletcher 60.00 100.00
67 John Flynn 60.00 100.00
68 Russell Ford 60.00 100.00
(Dark cap)
69 Russell Ford 250.00 400.00
(Light cap)
70 Bill Foxen 60.00 100.00
71 James Frick 150.00 250.00
72 Art Fromme 60.00 100.00
73 Earl Gardner 60.00 100.00
74 Harry Gaspar 60.00 100.00
75 George Gibson 60.00 100.00
76 William Goode 60.00 100.00
UER (Sic Good)
77 George F. Graham 250.00 400.00
(Chicago Cubs)
78 George F. Graham 60.00 100.00
(Boston Rustlers)
79 Eddie Grant 250.00 400.00
80A Dolly Gray 150.00 250.00
No stats on back
80B Dolly Gray 600.00 1000.00
Stats on back
81 Clark Griffith 175.00 300.00
82 Bob Groom 60.00 100.00
83 Charles Hanford 150.00 250.00
84 Robert Harmon 60.00 100.00
(Both ears)
85 Robert Harmon 250.00 400.00
(Left ear only)
86 Topsy Hartsel 60.00 100.00
87 Arnold Hauser 60.00 100.00
88 Charlie Hemphill 60.00 100.00
89 Buck Herzog 60.00 100.00
90A Dick Hoblitzell 7000.00 12000.00
No Stats
90B Dick Hoblitzell 90.00 150.00
CIN after second 1908
90C Dick Hoblitzell 350.00 600.00
sic.Hoblitzel
90D Dick Hoblitzell 350.00 600.00
No CIN after second 1908
91 Danny Hoffman 60.00 100.00
92 Miller Huggins 175.00 300.00
93 John Hummell 60.00 100.00
94 Fred Jacklitsch 60.00 100.00
95 Hughie Jennings MG 175.00 300.00
96 Walter Johnson 1000.00 1800.00
97 Davy Jones 60.00 100.00
98 Tom Jones 60.00 100.00
99 Addie Joss 900.00 1500.00
100 Ed Karger 250.00 400.00
101 Ed Killian 60.00 100.00
102 Red Kleinow 250.00 400.00
103 John Kling 60.00 100.00
104 John Knight 60.00 100.00
105 Ed Konetchy 60.00 100.00

106 Harry Krause	60.00	100.00
107 Rube Kroh	60.00	100.00
108 Frank Lang	60.00	100.00
109 Frank LaPorte	60.00	100.00
110A Arlie Latham	125.00	200.00
A. Latham on back		
110B Arlie Latham	250.00	400.00
Back says W.A. Latham		
111 Tommy Leach	60.00	100.00
112 Wyatt Lee	90.00	150.00
113 Sam Leever	60.00	100.00
114A Lefty Leifield	150.00	250.00
A.Leifield on front		
114B Lefty Leifield	250.00	400.00
A.P.Leifield on front		
115 Ed Lennox	60.00	100.00
116 Paddy Livingston	60.00	100.00
117 Hans Lobert	60.00	100.00
118 Bris Lord	60.00	100.00
119 Harry Lord	60.00	100.00
120 John Lush	60.00	100.00
121 Nick Maddox	60.00	100.00
122 Sherry Magee	60.00	100.00
123 Rube Marquard	175.00	300.00
124 Christy Mathewson	1000.00	1800.00
125 Al Mattern	60.00	100.00
126 Lewis McAllister	90.00	150.00
127 George McBride	60.00	100.00
128 Amby McConnell	60.00	100.00
129 Pryor McElveen	60.00	100.00
130 John McGraw	175.00	300.00
131 Harry McIntire	60.00	100.00
132 Matty McIntyre	60.00	100.00
133 Larry McLean	60.00	100.00
134 Fred Merkle	60.00	100.00
135 George Merritt	150.00	250.00
136 Chief Meyers	60.00	100.00
137 Clyde Milan	60.00	100.00
138 Dots Miller	60.00	100.00
139 Mike Mitchell	60.00	100.00
140A Pat Moran	900.00	1500.00
Stray Line Under Stats		
140B Pat Moran	60.00	100.00
No Stray Line		
141 George Moriarity	60.00	100.00
142 George Mullin	60.00	100.00
143 Danny Murphy	60.00	100.00
144 Jack Murray	60.00	100.00
145 John Nee	150.00	250.00
146 Tom Needham	60.00	100.00
147 Rebel Oakes	60.00	100.00
148 Rube Oldring	60.00	100.00
149 Charley O'Leary	60.00	100.00
150 Fred Olmstead	60.00	100.00
151 Orval Overall	60.00	100.00
152 Freddy Parent	60.00	100.00
153 Dode Paskert	60.00	100.00
154 Fred Payne	60.00	100.00
155 Barney Pelty	60.00	100.00
156 Jack Pfiester	60.00	100.00
157 James Phelan	150.00	250.00
158 Ed Phelps	60.00	100.00
159 Decon Phillippe	60.00	100.00
160 Jack Quinn	60.00	100.00
161 Bugs Raymond	250.00	400.00
162 Ed Reulbach	60.00	100.00
163 Lewis Richie	60.00	100.00
164 Jack Rowan	175.00	300.00
165 George Rucker	60.00	100.00
166 W.D. Scanlan	250.00	400.00
167 Germany Schaefer	60.00	100.00
168 Admiral Schlei	60.00	100.00
169 Boss Schmidt	60.00	100.00
170 F.M. Schulte	60.00	100.00
171 Jim Scott	60.00	100.00
172 Bayard Sharpe	60.00	100.00
173 David Shean	175.00	300.00
(Chicago Cubs)		
174 David Shean	60.00	100.00
(Boston Rustlers)		
175 Jimmy Sheckard	60.00	100.00
176 Hack Simmons	60.00	100.00
177 Tony Smith	60.00	100.00
178 Fred Snodgrass	60.00	100.00
179 Tris Speaker	500.00	800.00
180 Jake Stahl	60.00	100.00
181 Oscar Stanage	60.00	100.00
182 Harry Steinfeldt	60.00	100.00
183 George Stone	60.00	100.00
184 George Stovall	60.00	100.00
185 Gabby Street	60.00	100.00
186 George Suggs	250.00	400.00
187 Ed Summers	60.00	100.00
188 Jeff Sweeney	250.00	400.00
189 Lee Tannehill	60.00	100.00
190 Ira Thomas	60.00	100.00
191 Joe Tinker	175.00	300.00
192 John Titus	60.00	100.00
193 Terry Turner	250.00	400.00
194 Hippo Vaughn	300.00	500.00
195 Heinie Wagner	175.00	300.00
196 Bobby Wallace	150.00	250.00
(With cap)		
197A Bobby Wallace	1200.00	2000.00
no cap 1 line/1910		
197B Bobby Wallace	700.00	1200.00
no cap 2 lines/1910		
198 Ed Walsh	500.00	800.00
199 Zach Wheat	175.00	300.00
200 Doc White	60.00	100.00
201 Kirby White	250.00	400.00
202A Irvin K. Wilhelm	350.00	600.00
202B Irvin K. Wilhelm	175.00	300.00
Suffe ed in Bio		
203 Ed Willett	60.00	100.00
204 Owen Wilson	60.00	100.00
205 Hooks Wiltse	60.00	100.00
(Both ears)		
206 Hooks Wiltse	250.00	400.00
(Right ear only)		
207 Harry Wolter	60.00	100.00
208 Cy Young	1000.00	1800.00

1909-11 T206

The T206 set was and is the most popular of all the tobacco issues. The set was issued from 1909 to 1911 with sixteen different brands of cigarettes: American Beauty, Broadleaf, Cycle, Carolina Brights, Drum, El Principe de Gales, Hindu, Lenox, Old Mill, Piedmont, Polar Bear, Sovereign, Sweet Caporal, Tolstoi, and Uzit. There was also an extremely rare Ty Cobb back version for the Ty Cobb Red Portrait that it's believed was issued as a promotional card. Pricing for the Cobb back card is unavailable and it's typically not considered part of the complete 524-card set. The minor league cards are supposedly slightly more difficult to obtain than the cards of the major leaguers, with the Southern League player cards being definitively more difficult. Minor League players were obtained from the American Association and the Eastern league. Southern League players were obtained from a variety of leagues including the following: South Atlantic League, Southern League, Texas League, and Virginia League. Series 150 (notated as such on the card backs) was issued between February 1909 thru the end of May, 1909. Series 350 was issued from the end of May, 1909 thru April, 1910. The last series 350 to 460 was issued in late December 1910 through early 1911. The set price below does not include ultra-expensive Wagner, Plank, Magie error, or Doyle variation. The Wagner card is one of the most sought after cards in the hobby. This card was pulled from circulation almost immediately after being issued. Estimates of how many Wagners are in existence generally settle on around 50 to 60 copies. The backs vary in scarcity as follows: Exceedingly Rare: Ty Cobb; Rare: Drum, Uzit, Lenox, Broadleaf 460 and Hindu; Scarce: Broadleaf 350, Carolina brights, Hindu Red; Less Common: American Beauty, Cycle and Tolstoi; Readily Available: El Principe de Gales, Old Mill, Polar Bear and Sovereign and Common: Piedmont and Sweet Caporal. Listed prices refer to the Piedmont and Sweet caporal backs in raw "EX" condition. Of note, the O'Hara St. Louis and Demmitt St. Louis cards were only issued with Polar Bear backs and are are priced as such. Pricing is unavailable for the unbelieveably rare Joe Doyle Nat'l variation (perhaps a dozen or fewer copies exist) in addition to the Bud Shappe and Fred nodgrass printing variaitons. Finally, unlike the other cards in this set, listed raw pricing for the famed Honus Wagner references "Good" condition insetad of "EX".

COMPLETE SET (520)	30000.00	55000.00
COMMON (1-389)	50.00	100.00
COMMON (390-475)	50.00	100.00
COMMON (476-523)	125.00	250.00
CARDS PRICED IN EXMT CONDITION		
HONUS WAGNER PRICED IN GOOD CONDITION		
1 Ed Abbaticchio	85.00	135.00
Blue Sleeves		
2 Ed Abbaticchio	85.00	135.00
Brown Sleeves		
3 Fred Abbott ML	60.00	100.00
4 Bill Abstein	60.00	100.00
5 Doc Adkins ML	125.00	200.00
6 Whitey Alperman	60.00	100.00
7 Red Ames	150.00	250.00
Hands at Chest		
8 Red Ames	60.00	100.00
Hands over Head		
9 Red Ames	60.00	100.00
Portrait		
10 John Anderson ML	60.00	100.00
11 Frank Arellanes	60.00	100.00
12 Herman Armbruster ML	60.00	100.00
13 Harry Arndt ML	70.00	120.00
14 Jake Atz	60.00	100.00
15 Home Run Baker	250.00	400.00
16 Neal Ball	60.00	100.00
Cleveland		
17 Neal Ball	60.00	100.00
New York		
18 Jap Barbeau	60.00	100.00
19 Cy Barger ML	60.00	100.00
20 Jack Barry	60.00	100.00
21 Shad Barry ML	60.00	100.00
22 Jack Bastian SL	175.00	300.00
23 Emil Batch ML	60.00	100.00
24 Johnny Bates	60.00	100.00
25 Harry Bay SL	175.00	300.00
26 Ginger Beaumont	60.00	100.00
27 Fred Beck	60.00	100.00
28 Beals Becker	60.00	100.00
29 Jake Beckley ML	175.00	300.00
30 George Bell	60.00	100.00
Follow Through		
31 George Bell	60.00	100.00
Hands above Head		
32 Chief Bender	250.00	400.00
Pitching No Trees		
33 Chief Bender	250.00	400.00
Pitching Trees in Back		
34 Chief Bender	300.00	500.00
Portrait		
35 Bill Bergen	60.00	100.00
Batting		
36 Bill Bergen	60.00	100.00
Catching		
37 Heinie Berger	60.00	100.00
38 Bill Bernhard SL	175.00	300.00
39 Bob Bescher	60.00	100.00
Hands in Air		
40 Bob Bescher	60.00	100.00
Portrait		
41 Joe Birmingham	90.00	150.00
Horizontal		
42 Lena Blackburne ML	60.00	100.00
43 Jack Bliss	60.00	100.00
44 Frank Bowerman	60.00	100.00
45 Bill Bradley	60.00	100.00
with Bat		
46 Bill Bradley	60.00	100.00
Portrait		
47 Dave Brain ML	60.00	100.00
48 Kitty Bransfield	60.00	100.00
49 Roy Brashear ML	60.00	100.00
50 Ted Breitenstein SL	175.00	300.00
51 Roger Bresnahan	175.00	300.00
Portrait		
52 Roger Bresnahan	175.00	300.00
with Bat		
53 Al Bridwell	60.00	100.00
No Cap		
54 Al Bridwell	60.00	100.00
with Cap		
55 George Brown	125.00	200.00
Chicago		
56 George Brown	300.00	500.00
Washington		
57 Mordecai Brown	200.00	350.00
Chicago Shirt		
58 Mordecai Brown	350.00	600.00
Cubs Shirt		
59 Mordecai Brown	300.00	500.00
Portrait		
60 Al Burch	125.00	200.00
Batting		
61 Al Burch	60.00	100.00
Fielding		
62 Fred Burchell ML	60.00	100.00
63 Jimmy Burke ML	60.00	100.00
64 Bill Burns	60.00	100.00
65 Donie Bush	60.00	100.00
66 John Butler ML	60.00	100.00
67 Bobby Byrne	60.00	100.00
68 Howie Camnitz	60.00	100.00
Arm at Side		
69 Howie Camnitz	60.00	100.00
Arms Folded		
70 Howie Camnitz	60.00	100.00
Hands above Head		
71 Billy Campbell	60.00	100.00
72 Scoops Carey SL	175.00	300.00
73 Charley Carr ML	60.00	100.00
74 Bill Carrigan	60.00	100.00
75 Doc Casey ML	60.00	100.00
76 Peter Cassidy ML	60.00	100.00
77 Frank Chance	250.00	400.00
Batting		
78 Frank Chance	300.00	500.00
Portrait Red		
79 Frank Chance	250.00	400.00
Portrait Yellow		
80 Bill Chappelle ML	60.00	100.00
81 Chappie Charles	60.00	100.00
82 Hal Chase	90.00	150.00
Throwing Dark Cap		
83 Hal Chase	150.00	250.00
Holding Trophy		
84 Hal Chase	90.00	150.00
Portrait Blue		
85 Hal Chase	250.00	400.00
Portrait Pink		
86 Hal Chase	125.00	200.00
Throwing White Cap		
87 Jack Chesbro	250.00	400.00
88 Ed Cicotte	175.00	300.00
89 Bill Clancy (Clancey) ML	60.00	100.00
90 Fred Clarke	250.00	400.00
Holding Bat		
91 Fred Clarke	250.00	400.00
Portrait		
92 Josh Clark (Clarke) ML	60.00	100.00
93 J.J. (Nig) Clarke	60.00	100.00
94 Bill Clymer ML	60.00	100.00
95 Ty Cobb	1500.00	2500.00
Bat off Shoulder		
96 Ty Cobb	1500.00	2500.00
Bat on Shoulder		
97 Ty Cobb	3500.00	5000.00
Portrait Green		
98 Ty Cobb	1200.00	2000.00
Portrait Red		
99 Cad Coles	175.00	300.00
100 Eddie Collins	200.00	350.00
Philadelphia		
101 Jimmy Collins	175.00	300.00
Minneapolis ML		
102 Bunk Congalton ML	60.00	100.00
103 Wid Conroy	60.00	100.00
Fielding		
104 Wid Conroy	60.00	100.00
with Bat		
105 Harry Covaleski (Coveleski)	60.00	100.00
106 Doc Crandall	60.00	100.00
No Cap		
107 Doc Crandall	60.00	100.00
with Cap		
108 Bill Cranston SL	175.00	300.00
109 Gavvy Cravath ML	60.00	100.00
110 Sam Crawford	250.00	400.00
Throwing		
111 Sam Crawford	250.00	400.00
with Bat		
112 Birdie Cree	60.00	100.00
113 Lou Criger	60.00	100.00
114 Dode Criss UER	60.00	100.00
115 Monte Cross	60.00	100.00
116 Bill Dahlen	90.00	150.00
Boston		
117 Bill Dahlen	300.00	500.00
Brooklyn		
118 Paul Davidson ML	60.00	100.00
119 George Davis	175.00	300.00
120 Harry Davis	60.00	100.00
Davis on Front		
121 Harry Davis	60.00	100.00
H.Davis on Front		
122 Frank Delehanty	60.00	100.00
(Delahanty) ML		
123 Jim Delehanty	60.00	100.00
124 Ray Demmitt	70.00	120.00
New York		
125 Ray Demmitt	6000.00	10000.00
St. Louis		
126 Rube Dessau ML	85.00	135.00
127 Art Devlin	60.00	100.00
128 Josh Devore	60.00	100.00
129 Bill Dineen	60.00	100.00
130 Mike Donlin	125.00	200.00
Fielding		
131 Mike Donlin	60.00	100.00
Seated		
132 Mike Donlin	60.00	100.00
with Bat		
133 Jiggs Donahue (Donohue)	60.00	100.00
134 Wild Bill Donovan	60.00	100.00
Portrait		
135 Wild Bill Donovan	60.00	100.00
Throwing		
136 Red Dooin	60.00	100.00
137 Mickey Doolan	60.00	100.00
Batting		
138 Mickey Doolan	60.00	100.00
Fielding		
139 Mickey Doolin	60.00	100.00
Portrait (Doolan)		
140 Gus Dorner ML	60.00	100.00
141 Gus Dorner		
Card Spelled Dopner on Back		
142 Patsy Dougherty	60.00	100.00
Arm in Air		
143 Patsy Dougherty	60.00	100.00
Portrait		
144 Tom Downey	60.00	100.00
Batting		
145 Tom Downey	60.00	100.00
Fielding		
146 Jerry Downs ML	60.00	100.00
147 Joe Doyle	350.00	600.00
Hands Above Head		
148 Joe Doyle		
Hands Above Head Nat'l		
149 Larry Doyle Portrait	60.00	100.00
150 Larry Doyle	60.00	100.00
Throwing		
151 Larry Doyle	60.00	100.00
with Bat		
152 Jean Dubuc	60.00	100.00
153 Hugh Duffy	175.00	300.00
154 Jack Dunn	60.00	100.00
Baltimore ML		
155 Joe Dunn	60.00	100.00
Brooklyn		
156 Bull Durham	60.00	100.00
157 Jimmy Dygert	60.00	100.00
158 Ted Easterly	60.00	100.00
159 Dick Egan	90.00	150.00
160 Kid Elberfeld	60.00	100.00
Fielding		
161 Kid Elberfeld	60.00	100.00
Portrait New York		
162 Kid Elberfeld	1800.00	3000.00
Portrait Washington		
163 Roy Ellam SL	175.00	300.00
164 Clyde Engle	60.00	100.00
165 Steve Evans	60.00	100.00
166 Johnny Evers	350.00	600.00
Portrait		
167 Johnny Evers	250.00	400.00
with Bat Chicago Shirt		
168 Johnny Evers	500.00	800.00
with Bat Cubs Shirt		
169 Bob Ewing	60.00	100.00
170 Cecil Ferguson	60.00	100.00
171 Hobe Ferris	60.00	100.00
172 Lou Fiene	60.00	100.00
Portrait		
173 Lou Fiene	60.00	100.00
Throwing		
174 Steamer Flanagan ML	60.00	100.00
175 Art Fletcher	60.00	100.00
176 Elmer Flick	175.00	300.00
177 Russ Ford	60.00	100.00
178 Ed Foster SL	175.00	300.00
179 Jerry Freeman ML	60.00	100.00
180 John Frill	60.00	100.00
181 Charlie Fritz SL	175.00	300.00
182 Art Fromme	60.00	100.00
183 Chick Gandil	175.00	300.00
184 Bob Ganley	60.00	100.00
185 John Ganzel ML	60.00	100.00
186 Harry Gasper (Gaspar)	60.00	100.00
187 Rube Geyer	60.00	100.00
188 George Gibson	60.00	100.00
189 Billy Gilbert	60.00	100.00
190 Wilbur Goode (Good)	60.00	100.00
191 Bill Graham	60.00	100.00
St. Louis		
192 Peaches Graham	70.00	120.00
Boston		
193 Dolly Gray	60.00	100.00
194 Ed Greminger SL	175.00	300.00
195 Clark Griffith	175.00	300.00
Batting		
196 Clark Griffith	175.00	300.00
Portrait		
197 Moose Grimshaw ML	60.00	100.00
198 Bob Groom	60.00	100.00
199 Tom Guiheen SL	175.00	300.00
200 Ed Hahn	60.00	100.00
201 Bob Hall ML	60.00	100.00
202 Bill Hallman ML	60.00	100.00
203 Jack Hannifan	60.00	100.00
(Hannifin) ML		
204 Bill Hart	175.00	300.00
Little Rock SL		
205 Jimmy Hart	175.00	300.00
Montgomery SL		
206 Topsy Hartsel	60.00	100.00
207 Jack Hayden ML	60.00	100.00
208 J.Ross Helm SL	175.00	300.00
209 Charlie Hemphill	60.00	100.00
210 Buck Herzog	60.00	100.00
Boston		
211 Buck Herzog	60.00	100.00
New York		
212 Gordon Hickman SL	175.00	300.00
213 Bill Hinchman	60.00	100.00
Cleveland		
214 Harry Hinchman	60.00	100.00
Toledo ML		
215 Doc Hoblitzell	60.00	100.00
216 Danny Hoffman	60.00	100.00
St. Louis		
217 Izzy Hoffman	60.00	100.00
Providence ML		
218 Solly Hofman	60.00	100.00
219 Bock Hooker SL	175.00	300.00
220 Del Howard	60.00	100.00
Chicago		
221 Ernie Howard	175.00	300.00
Savannah SL		
222 Harry Howell	60.00	100.00
Hand at Waist		
223 Harry Howell	60.00	100.00
Portrait		
224 Miller Huggins	175.00	300.00
Hands at Mouth		
225 Miller Huggins	175.00	300.00
Portrait		
226 Rudy Hulswitt	60.00	100.00
227 John Hummel	60.00	100.00
228 George Hunter	60.00	100.00
229 Frank Isbell	60.00	100.00
230 Fred Jacklitsch	60.00	100.00
231 Jimmy Jackson ML	60.00	100.00
232 Hughie Jennings	175.00	300.00
Both Hands Showing		
233 Hughie Jennings	175.00	300.00
One Hand Showing		
234 Hughie Jennings	175.00	300.00
Portrait		
235 Walter Johnson	700.00	1200.00
Hands at Chest		
236 Walter Johnson	1000.00	1800.00
Portrait		
237 Davy Jones	60.00	100.00
Detroit		
238 Fielder Jones	60.00	100.00
Hands at Hips		
239 Fielder Jones	60.00	100.00
Portrait		
240 Tom Jones	60.00	100.00
St. Louis		
241 Dutch Jordan	175.00	300.00
Atlanta SL		
242 Tim Jordan	60.00	100.00
Brooklyn Batting		
243 Tim Jordan	60.00	100.00
Brooklyn Portrait		
244 Addie Joss	175.00	300.00
Pitching		
245 Addie Joss	250.00	400.00
Portrait		
246 Ed Karger	60.00	100.00
247 Willie Keeler	350.00	600.00
Portrait		
248 Willie Keeler	350.00	600.00
with Bat		
249 Joe Kelley ML	150.00	250.00
250 J.F. Kiernan SL	300.00	500.00
251 Ed Killian	60.00	100.00
Pitching		
252 Ed Killian	60.00	100.00
Portrait		
253 Frank King SL	175.00	300.00
254 Rube Kisinger	60.00	100.00
(Kissinger) ML		
255 Red Kleinow	300.00	500.00
Boston		
256 Red Kleinow	60.00	100.00
New York Catching		
257 Red Kleinow	60.00	100.00
New York with Bat		
258 Johnny Kling	60.00	100.00
259 Otto Knabe	60.00	100.00
260 Jack Knight	60.00	100.00
Portrait		
261 Jack Knight	60.00	100.00
with Bat		
262 Ed Konetchy	60.00	100.00
Glove Near Ground		
263 Ed Konetchy	60.00	100.00
Glove Above Head		
264 Harry Krause	60.00	100.00
Pitching		
265 Harry Krause	60.00	100.00
Portrait		
266 Rube Kroh	60.00	100.00
267 Otto Kruger	60.00	100.00
(Krueger) ML		
268 James LaFitte SL	175.00	300.00
269 Nap Lajoie	500.00	800.00
Portrait		
270 Nap Lajoie	400.00	700.00
Throwing		
271 Nap Lajoie	400.00	700.00
with Bat		
272 Joe Lake	60.00	100.00
New York		
273 Joe Lake	60.00	100.00
St. Louis No Ball		
274 Joe Lake	60.00	100.00
St. Louis with Ball		
275 Frank LaPorte	60.00	100.00
276 Arlie Latham	60.00	100.00
277 Bill Lattimore ML	60.00	100.00
278 Jimmy Lavender ML	60.00	100.00
279 Tommy Leach	60.00	100.00
Bending Over		
280 Tommy Leach	60.00	100.00
Portrait		
281 Lefty Leifield	60.00	100.00
Batting		
282 Lefty Leifield	60.00	100.00
Pitching		
283 Ed Lennox	60.00	100.00
284 Harry Lentz	250.00	400.00
(Sentz) SL		
285 Glenn Liebhardt	60.00	100.00
286 Vive Lindaman	60.00	100.00
287 Perry Lipe SL	175.00	300.00
288 Paddy Livingstone	60.00	100.00
(Livingston)		
289 Hans Lobert	60.00	100.00
290 Harry Lord	60.00	100.00
291 Harry Lumley	60.00	100.00
292 Carl Lundgren	500.00	800.00
Chicago		
293 Carl Lundgren	125.00	200.00
Kansas City ML		
294 Nick Maddox	60.00	100.00
294 Sherry Magie	15000.00	25000.00
Portrait ERR (Magee)		
295 Sherry Magee	60.00	100.00
with Bat		
296 Sherry Magee	150.00	250.00
Portrait		
298 Bill Malarkey ML	60.00	100.00
299 Billy Maloney ML	60.00	100.00
300 George Manion SL	175.00	300.00
301 Rube Manning	60.00	100.00
Batting		
302 Rube Manning	60.00	100.00
Pitching		
303 Rube Marquard	175.00	300.00
Follow Through		
304 Rube Marquard	175.00	300.00
Hands at Thighs		
305 Rube Marquard	200.00	350.00
Portrait		
306 Doc Marshall	60.00	100.00
307 Christy Mathewson	700.00	1200.00
Dark Cap		
308 Christy Mathewson	900.00	1500.00
Portrait		
309 Christy Mathewson	900.00	1500.00
White Cap		
310 Al Mattern	60.00	100.00
311 John McAleese	60.00	100.00
312 George McBride	60.00	100.00
313 Pat McCauley SL	175.00	300.00
314 Moose McCormick	60.00	100.00
315 Pryor McElveen	60.00	100.00
316 Dan McGann ML	60.00	100.00
317 Jim McGinley ML	60.00	100.00
318 Iron Man McGinnity ML	175.00	300.00
319 Stoney McGlynn ML	60.00	100.00
320 John McGraw	250.00	400.00
Finger in Air		
321 John McGraw	250.00	400.00
Glove at Hip		
322 John McGraw	250.00	400.00
Portrait No Cap		
323 John McGraw	250.00	400.00
Portrait with Cap		
324 Harry McIntyre	60.00	100.00
Brooklyn		
325 Harry McIntyre	60.00	100.00
Brooklyn-Chicago		
326 Matty McIntyre	60.00	100.00
Detroit		
327 Larry McLean	60.00	100.00
328 George McQuillan	60.00	100.00
Ball in Hand		
329 George McQuillan	60.00	100.00
with Bat		
330 Fred Merkle Portrait	70.00	120.00
331 Fred Merkle Throwing	90.00	150.00
332 George Merritt ML	60.00	100.00
333 Chief Meyers	60.00	100.00
334 Chief Myers	70.00	120.00
Batting (Meyers)		
335 Chief Myers	60.00	100.00
Fielding (Meyers)		
336 Clyde Milan	60.00	100.00
337 Molly Miller	175.00	300.00
Dallas SL		
338 Dots Miller	60.00	100.00
Pittsburgh		
339 Bill Milligan ML	60.00	100.00
340 Fred Mitchell	60.00	100.00
Toronto ML		
341 Mike Mitchell	60.00	100.00
Cincinnati		
342 Dan Moeller ML	60.00	100.00
343 Carleton Molesworth SL	175.00	300.00
344 Herbie Moran	60.00	100.00
Providence ML		
345 Pat Moran	60.00	100.00
Chicago		
346 George Moriarty	60.00	100.00
347 Mike Mowrey	60.00	100.00
348 Dom Mullaney SL	175.00	300.00
349 George Mullen	60.00	100.00
(Mullin)		
350 George Mullin	60.00	100.00
with Bat		
351 George Mullin	60.00	100.00
Throwing Horizontal		
352 Danny Murphy	60.00	100.00
Batting		
353 Danny Murphy	60.00	100.00
Throwing		
354 Red Murray	60.00	100.00
Batting		
355 Red Murray	60.00	100.00
Portrait		
356 Billy Nattress ML	60.00	100.00
357 Tom Needham	60.00	100.00
358 Simon Nicholls	60.00	100.00
Hands on Knees		
359 Simon Nichols	60.00	100.00
Batting (Nicholls)		
360 Harry Niles	60.00	100.00
361 Rebel Oakes	60.00	100.00
362 Frank Oberlin ML	60.00	100.00
363 Peter O'Brien ML	60.00	100.00
364 Bill O'Hara	60.00	100.00
New York		
365 Bill O'Hara	6000.00	10000.00
St. Louis		
366 Rube Oldring	60.00	100.00
Batting		
367 Rube Oldring	60.00	100.00
Fielding		
368 Charley O'Leary	60.00	100.00
Hands on Knees		
369 Charley O'Leary	60.00	100.00
Portrait		
370 William O'Neil ML	150.00	250.00
371 Al Orth SL	175.00	300.00
372 William Otey SL	175.00	300.00
373 Orval Overall	60.00	100.00
Hand at Face		
374 Orval Overall	60.00	100.00
Hands at Waist		
375 Orval Overall	60.00	100.00
Portrait		
376 Frank Owen (Owens)	60.00	100.00
377 George Paige SL	175.00	300.00
378 Freddy Parent	60.00	100.00
379 Dode Paskert	60.00	100.00
380 Jim Pastorius	60.00	100.00
381 Harry Pattee	60.00	100.00
382 Fred Payne	60.00	100.00
383 Barney Pelty	60.00	100.00
Horizontal		
384 Barney Pelty	60.00	100.00
Vertical		
385 Hub Perdue SL	175.00	300.00
386 George Perring	60.00	100.00
387 Arch Persons SL	175.00	300.00
388 Jeff Pfeffer	60.00	100.00
389 Jake Pfeister	60.00	100.00
Seated (Pfiester)		
390 Jake Pfeister	60.00	100.00
Throwing (Pfiester)		
391 Jimmy Phelan ML	60.00	100.00
392 Ed Phelps	60.00	100.00
393 Deacon Phillippe.	60.00	100.00
394 Ollie Pickering ML	60.00	100.00
395 Eddie Plank	45000.00	60000.00
396 Phil Poland ML	60.00	100.00
397 Jack Powell	60.00	100.00
Horizontal		
398 Mike Powers	60.00	100.00
399 Billy Purtell	60.00	100.00
400 Ambrose Puttman	85.00	135.00
(Puttmann) ML		
401 Lee Quillen	60.00	100.00
(Quillin) ML		
402 Jack Quinn	60.00	100.00
403 Newt Randall ML	60.00	100.00
404 Bugs Raymond	60.00	100.00
405 Ed Reagan SL	175.00	300.00
406 Ed Reulbach	60.00	100.00
Glove Showing		
407 Ed Reulbach	70.00	120.00
No Glove		
408 Dutch Revelle SL	175.00	300.00
409 Bob Rhoades	60.00	100.00
Hands at Chest		
410 Bob Rhoades	60.00	100.00
Right Arm Out		
411 Charlie Rhodes	60.00	100.00
412 Claude Ritchey	60.00	100.00
413 Lou Ritter ML	60.00	100.00
414 Ike Rockenfeld SL	175.00	300.00
415 Claude Rossman	60.00	100.00
416 Nap Rucker	60.00	100.00
Portrait		
417 Nap Rucker	60.00	100.00
Throwing		
418 Dick Rudolph ML	60.00	100.00
419 Ray Ryan SL	175.00	300.00
420 Germany Schaefer	60.00	100.00
Detroit		
421 Germany Schaefer	60.00	100.00
Washington		
422 George Schirm ML	85.00	135.00
423 Larry Schlafly ML	60.00	100.00
424 Admiral Schlei	60.00	100.00
Batting		
425 Admiral Schlei	60.00	100.00
Catching		
426 Admiral Schlei	60.00	100.00
Portrait		
427 Boss Schmidt	60.00	100.00
Portrait		
428 Boss Schmidt	60.00	100.00
Throwing		
429 Ossee Schreck	70.00	120.00
(Schreckengost) ML		
430 Wildfire Schulte	60.00	100.00
Back View		
431 Wildfire Schulte	175.00	300.00
Front View		
432 Jim Scott	60.00	100.00
433 Charles Seitz SL	175.00	300.00
434 Cy Seymour	60.00	100.00
Batting		
435 Cy Seymour	60.00	100.00
Portrait		
436 Cy Seymour	60.00	100.00
Throwing		
437 Spike Shannon ML	60.00	100.00
438 Bud Sharpe ML	60.00	100.00
439 Bud Shappe ERR		
(Sharpe) ML		
440 Frank Shaughnessy SL	175.00	300.00
441 Al Shaw	60.00	100.00
St. Louis		
442 Hunky Shaw	60.00	100.00
Providence ML		
443 Jimmy Sheckard	60.00	100.00
Glove Showing		
444 Jimmy Sheckard	60.00	100.00
No Glove		
445 Bill Shipke	60.00	100.00
446 Jimmy Slagle ML	60.00	100.00
447 Carlos Smith	175.00	300.00
Shreveport SL		
448 Frank Smith	350.00	600.00
Chicago-Boston		
449 Frank Smith	60.00	100.00
Chicago		
Listed as F.Smith		
450 Frank Smith	60.00	100.00
Chicago		
Listed as Smith		
White Cap		
451 Heinie Smith	60.00	100.00
Buffalo ML		
452 Happy Smith	60.00	100.00
Brooklyn		
453 Sid Smith	175.00	300.00
Atlanta SL		
454 Fred Snodgrass	60.00	100.00
Batting		
455 Fred nodgrass		
Batting ERR (MIssing S)		
456 Fred Snodgrass	60.00	100.00
Catching		
457 Bob Spade	60.00	100.00
458 Tris Speaker	600.00	1000.00
459 Tubby Spencer	60.00	100.00
460 Jake Stahl	85.00	135.00
Glove Shows		
461 Jake Stahl	60.00	100.00
No Glove Shows		
462 Oscar Stanage	60.00	100.00
463 Dolly Stark SL	175.00	300.00
464 Charlie Starr	60.00	100.00
465 Harry Steinfeldt	60.00	100.00
with Bat		
466 Harry Steinfeldt	60.00	100.00
Portrait		
467 Jim Stephens	60.00	100.00
468 George Stone	60.00	100.00
469 George Stovall	60.00	100.00
Batting		
470 George Stovall	60.00	100.00
Portrait		
471 Sam Strang ML	60.00	100.00
472 Gabby Street	60.00	100.00
Catching		
473 Gabby Street	60.00	100.00
Portrait		
474 Billy Sullivan	60.00	100.00
475 Ed Summers	60.00	100.00
476 Bill Sweeney	60.00	100.00
Boston		

477 Jeff Sweeney 60.00 100.00
New York
478 Jesse Tannehill 60.00 100.00
Washington
479 Lee Tannehill 60.00 100.00
Chicago L.Tannehill
480 Lee Tannehill 60.00 100.00
Chicago Tannehill
481 Dummy Taylor ML 60.00 100.00
482 Fred Tenney 60.00 100.00
483 Tony Thebo SL 175.00 300.00
484 Jake Thielman ML 90.00 150.00
485 Ira Thomas 60.00 100.00
486 Woodie Thornton SL 175.00 300.00
487 Joe Tinker 250.00 400.00
Bat off Shoulder
488 Joe Tinker 400.00 400.00
Bat on Shoulder
489 Joe Tinker 350.00 600.00
Hands on Knees
490 Joe Tinker 350.00 600.00
Portrait
491 John Titus 60.00 100.00
492 Terry Turner 60.00 100.00
493 Bob Unglaub 60.00 100.00
494 Juan Violat (Viola) SL 175.00 300.00
495 Rube Waddell 250.00 400.00
Portrait
496 Rube Waddell 250.00 400.00
Throwing
497 Heinie Wagner 60.00 100.00
Bat on Left Shoulder
498 Heinie Wagner 60.00 100.00
Bat on Right Shoulder
499 Honus Wagner 250000.00 350000.00
500 Bobby Wallace 175.00 300.00
501 Ed Walsh 250.00 400.00
502 Jack Warhop 60.00 100.00
503 Jake Weimer 60.00 100.00
504 James Westlake SL 175.00 300.00
505 Zack Wheat 200.00 350.00
506 Doc White 60.00 100.00
Chicago Pitching
507 Doc White 60.00 100.00
Chicago Portrait
508 Foley White 175.00 300.00
Houston SL
509 Jack White 60.00 100.00
Buffalo ML
510 Kaiser Wilhelm 60.00 100.00
Hands at Chest
511 Kaiser Wilhelm 60.00 100.00
with Bat
512 Ed Willett 60.00 100.00
with Bat
513 Ed Willetts 60.00 100.00
Throwing (Willett)
514 Jimmy Williams 60.00 100.00
515 Vic Willis 200.00 350.00
Pittsburgh Portrait
516 Vic Willis 175.00 300.00
St. Louis Throwing
517 Vic Willis 175.00 300.00
St. Louis with Bat
518 Owen Wilson 60.00 100.00
519 Hooks Wiltse 60.00 100.00
Pitching
520 Hooks Wiltse 60.00 100.00
Portrait No Cap
521 Hooks Wiltse 60.00 100.00
Portrait with Cap
522 Lucky Wright ML 60.00 100.00
523 Cy Young 700.00 1200.00
Bare Hand Shows
524 Cy Young 700.00 1200.00
Glove Shows
525 Cy Young 1000.00 1800.00
Portrait
526 Irv Young 70.00 120.00
Minneapolis ML
527 Heinie Zimmerman: 60.00 100.00

1951 Topps Blue Backs

The cards in this 52-card set measure approximately 2" by 2 5/8". The 1951 Topps series of blue-backed baseball cards could be used to play a baseball game by shuffling the cards and drawing them from a pile. These cards (packaged two adjoined in a penny pack) were marketed with a piece of caramel candy, which often melted or was squashed in such a way as to damage the card and wrapper (despite the fact that a paper shield was inserted between candy and card). Blue Backs are more difficult to obtain than the similarly styled Red Backs. The set is denoted on the cards as "Set B" and the Red Back set is correspondingly Set A. The only notable Rookie Card in the set is Billy Pierce.

COMPLETE SET (52) 1000.00 1700.00
WRAPPER (1-CENT) 150.00 200.00
1 Eddie Yost 35.00 60.00
2 Hank Majeski 15.00 30.00
3 Richie Ashburn 125.00 200.00
4 Del Ennis 15.00 30.00
5 Johnny Pesky 15.00 30.00
6 Red Schoendienst 60.00 100.00
7 Gerry Staley RC 15.00 30.00
8 Dick Sisler 15.00 30.00
9 Johnny Sain 30.00 50.00
10 Joe Page 30.00 50.00
11 Johnny Groth 15.00 30.00
12 Sam Jethroe 20.00 40.00
13 Mickey Vernon 15.00 30.00
14 George Munger 15.00 30.00
15 Eddie Joost 15.00 30.00
16 Murry Dickson 15.00 30.00
17 Roy Smalley 15.00 30.00
18 Ned Garver 15.00 30.00
19 Phil Masi 15.00 30.00
20 Ralph Branca 30.00 50.00
21 Billy Johnson 15.00 30.00
22 Bob Kuzava 15.00 30.00
23 Dizzy Trout 20.00 40.00
24 Sherman Lollar 15.00 30.00
25 Sam Mele 15.00 30.00
26 Chico Carrasquel RC 20.00 40.00
27 Andy Pafko 15.00 30.00
28 Harry Brecheen 15.00 30.00
29 Granville Hamner 15.00 30.00
30 Enos Slaughter 60.00 100.00
31 Lou Brissie 15.00 30.00
32 Bob Elliott 20.00 40.00
33 Don Lenhardt RC 15.00 30.00
34 Earl Torgeson 15.00 30.00
35 Tommy Byrne RC 15.00 30.00
36 Cliff Fannin 15.00 30.00
37 Bobby Doerr 60.00 100.00
38 Irv Noren 15.00 30.00
39 Ed Lopat 30.00 50.00
40 Vic Wertz 15.00 30.00
41 Johnny Schmitz 15.00 30.00
42 Bruce Edwards 15.00 30.00
43 Willie Jones 15.00 30.00
44 Johnny Wyrostek 15.00 30.00
45 Billy Pierce RC 30.00 50.00
46 Gerry Priddy 15.00 30.00
47 Herman Wehmeier 15.00 30.00
48 Billy Cox 20.00 40.00
49 Hank Sauer 20.00 40.00
50 Johnny Mize 60.00 100.00
51 Eddie Waitkus 20.00 40.00
52 Sam Chapman 30.00 50.00

1951 Topps Red Backs

The cards in this 52-card set measure approximately 2" by 2 5/8". The 1951 Topps Red Back set is identical in style to the Blue Back set of the same year. The cards have rounded corners and were designed to be used as a baseball game. Zernial, number 36, is listed with either the White Sox or Athletics, and Holmes, number 52, with either the Braves or Hartford. The set is denoted on the cards as "Set A" and the Blue Back set is correspondingly Set B. The cards were packaged as two connected cards along with a piece of caramel in a penny pack. There were 120 penny packs in a box. The most notable Rookie Card in the set is Monte Irvin.

COMPLETE SET (54) 500.00 800.00
WRAPPER (1-CENT) 4.00 5.00
1 Yogi Berra 75.00 125.00
2 Sid Gordon 5.00 10.00
3 Ferris Fain 6.00 12.00
4 Vern Stephens 6.00 12.00
5 Phil Rizzuto 35.00 60.00
6 Allie Reynolds 10.00 20.00
7 Howie Pollet 5.00 10.00
8 Early Wynn 12.50 25.00
9 Roy Sievers 7.50 15.00
10 Mel Parnell 6.00 12.00
11 Gene Hermanski 6.00 12.00
12 Jim Hegan 6.00 12.00
13 Dale Mitchell 6.00 12.00
14 Wayne Terwilliger 5.00 10.00
15 Ralph Kiner 12.50 25.00
16 Preacher Roe 7.50 15.00
17 Gus Bell RC 7.50 15.00
18 Jerry Coleman 7.50 15.00
19 Dick Kokos 5.00 10.00
20 Dom DiMaggio 10.00 20.00
21 Larry Jansen 6.00 12.00
22 Bob Feller 35.00 60.00
23 Ray Boone RC 7.50 15.00
24 Hank Bauer 10.00 20.00
25 Cliff Chambers 5.00 10.00
26 Luke Easter RC 7.50 15.00
27 Wally Westlake 6.00 12.00
28 Elmer Valo 5.00 10.00
29 Bob Kennedy RC 6.00 12.00
30 Warren Spahn 35.00 60.00
31 Gil Hodges 30.00 50.00
32 Henry Thompson 6.00 12.00
33 William Werle 5.00 10.00
34 Grady Hatton 5.00 10.00
35 Al Rosen 7.50 15.00
36A Gus Zernial 20.00 40.00
(Chicago)
36B Gus Zernial 10.00 20.00
(Philadelphia)
37 Wes Westrum RC 6.00 12.00
38 Duke Snider 35.00 60.00
39 Ted Kluszewski 12.50 25.00
40 Mike Garcia 7.50 15.00
41 Whitey Lockman 6.00 12.00
42 Ray Scarborough 5.00 10.00
43 Maurice McDermott 5.00 10.00
44 Sid Hudson 5.00 10.00
45 Andy Seminick 6.00 12.00
46 Billy Goodman 6.00 12.00
47 Tommy Glaviano RC 5.00 10.00
48 Eddie Stanky 6.00 12.00
49 Al Zarilla 5.00 10.00
50 Monte Irvin RC 20.00 40.00
51 Eddie Robinson 5.00 10.00
52A Tommy Holmes 20.00 40.00
(Boston)
52B Tommy Holmes 12.50 25.00
(Hartford)

1951 Topps Connie Mack's All-Stars

The cards in this 11-card set measure approximately 2 1/16" by 5 1/4". The series of die-cut cards which comprise the set entitled Connie Mack All-Stars was one of Topps' most distinctive and fragile card designs. Printed on thin cardboard, these elegant cards were protected in the wrapper by panels of accompanying Red Backs, but once removed were easily damaged (after all, they were intended to be folded and used as

toy figures). Cards without tops have a value less than one-half of that listed below. The cards are unnumbered and are listed below in alphabetical order.

COMPLETE SET (11) 4200.00 7000.00
WRAPPER (1-CENT) 300.00 350.00
1 Grover C. Alexander 250.00 400.00
2 Mickey Cochrane 175.00 300.00
3 Eddie Collins 90.00 150.00
4 Jimmy Collins 90.00 150.00
5 Lou Gehrig 1200.00 2000.00
6 Walter Johnson 450.00 700.00
7 Connie Mack 175.00 300.00
8 Christy Mathewson 300.00 500.00
9 Babe Ruth 1500.00 2500.00
10 Tris Speaker 150.00 250.00
11 Honus Wagner 250.00 400.00

1951 Topps Major League All-Stars

The cards in this 11-card set measure approximately 2 1/16" by 5 1/4". The 1951 Topps Current All-Star series is probably the rarest of all legitimate, nationally issued, post war baseball issues. The set price listed below does not include the prices for the cards of Konstanty, Roberts and Stanky, which likely never were released to the public in gum packs. These three cards (SP in the checklist below) were probably obtained directly from the company and exist in extremely limited numbers. As with the Connie Mack set, cards without the die-cut background are worth half of the value listed below. The cards are unnumbered and are listed below in alphabetical order. These cards were issued in two card packs (one being a Current AS the other being a Topps Team card).

COMPLETE SET (8) 2700.00 4500.00
WRAPPER (1-CENT) 400.00 500.00
1 Yogi Berra 1000.00 1500.00
2 Larry Doby 250.00 400.00
3 Walt Dropo 150.00 250.00
4 Hoot Evers 150.00 250.00
5 George Kell 350.00 600.00
6 Ralph Kiner 450.00 750.00
7 Jim Konstanty SP 7500.00 12500.00
8 Bob Lemon 350.00 600.00
9 Phil Rizzuto 500.00 800.00
10 Robin Roberts SP 9000.00 15000.00
11 Eddie Stanky SP 7500.00 12500.00

1951 Topps Teams

The cards in this nine-card set measure approximately 2 1/16" by 5 1/4". These unnumbered team cards issued by Topps in 1951 carry black and white photographs framed by a yellow border. These cards were issued in the same five-cent wrapper as the Connie Mack and Current All Stars. They have been assigned reference numbers in the checklist alphabetically by team city and name. They are found with or without "1950" printed in the name panel before the team name. Although the dated variations are slightly more difficult to find, there is usually no difference in value.

COMPLETE SET (9) 1500.00 3000.00
1 Boston Red Sox 250.00 500.00
2 Brooklyn Dodgers 250.00 500.00
3 Chicago White Sox 150.00 300.00
4 Cincinnati Reds 150.00 300.00
5 New York Giants 200.00 400.00
6 Philadelphia Athletics 150.00 300.00
7 Philadelphia Phillies 150.00 300.00
8 St. Louis Cardinals 250.00 500.00
9 Washington Senators 150.00 300.00

1952 Topps

The cards in this 407-card set measure approximately 2 5/8" by 3 3/4". The 1952 Topps set is Topps' first truly major set. Card numbers 1 to 80 were issued with red or black backs, both of which are less plentiful than card numbers 81 to 250. In fact, the first series is considered the most difficult with respect to finding perfect condition cards. Card number 48 (Joe Page) and number 49 (Johnny Sain) can be found with each other's write-up on their back. However, many dealers today believe that all cards numbered 1-250 were produced in the same quantities. Card numbers 251 to 310 are somewhat scarce and numbers 311 to 407 are quite scarce. Cards 281-300 were single printed compared to the other cards in the next to last series. Cards 311-313 were double printed on the last high number printing sheet. The key card in the set is Mickey Mantle, number 311, which was Mickey's first of many Topps cards. A minor variation on cards from 311 through 313 is that they exist with the stitching on the number circle in the back pointing right or left. There seems to be no print run difference between the two versions. Card number 307, Frank Campos, can be found in a scarce version with with one red star and one black star next to the words "Topps Baseball" on the back. In the early 1980's, Topps issued a standard-size reprint set of the 52 Topps set. These cards were issued only as a factory set. Five people portrayed in the regular set: Billy Loes (number 20), Dom DiMaggio (number 22), Saul Rogovin (number 159), Solly Hemus (number 190) and Tommy Holmes (number 289) are not in the reprint set. Although rarely seen, salesman sample panels of three cards containing the fronts of regular cards with ad information on the back do exist.

COMP.MASTER SET (487) 40000.00 80000.00
COMPLETE SET (407) 40000.00 65000.00
COMMON CARD (1-80) 35.00 60.00
COMMON CARD (81-250) 20.00 40.00
COMMON (251-310) 30.00 50.00
COMMON (311-407) 150.00 250.00
WRAPPER (1-CENT) 200.00 250.00
WRAPPER (5-CENT) 75.00 100.00
1 Andy Pafko 3000.00 5000.00
1A Andy Pafko Black 1800.00 3000.00
2 Pete Runnels RC 150.00 250.00
2A Pete Runnels Black 150.00 250.00
3 Hank Thompson 40.00 70.00
3A Hank Thompson Black 40.00 70.00
4 Don Lenhardt 35.00 60.00
4A Don Lenhardt Black 35.00 60.00
5 Larry Jansen 40.00 70.00
5A Larry Jansen Black 40.00 70.00
6 Grady Hatton 35.00 60.00
6A Grady Hatton Black 35.00 60.00
7 Wayne Terwilliger 35.00 60.00
7A W. Terwilliger Black 35.00 60.00
8 Fred Marsh RC 35.00 60.00
8A Fred Marsh Black 35.00 60.00
9 Robert Hogue RC 35.00 60.00
9A Robert Hogue Black 35.00 60.00
10 Al Rosen 40.00 70.00
10A Al Rosen Black 40.00 70.00
11 Phil Rizzuto 250.00 400.00
11A Phil Rizzuto Black 200.00 350.00
12 Monty Basgall RC 35.00 60.00
12A Monty Basgall Black 35.00 60.00
13 Johnny Wyrostek 35.00 60.00
13A J. Wyrostek Black 35.00 60.00
14 Bob Elliott 40.00 70.00
14A Bob Elliott Black 40.00 70.00
15 Johnny Pesky 40.00 70.00
15A Johnny Pesky Black 40.00 70.00
16 Gene Hermanski 35.00 60.00
16A G. Hermanski Black 35.00 60.00
17 Jim Hegan 40.00 70.00
17A Jim Hegan Black 40.00 70.00
18 Merrill Combs RC 35.00 60.00
18A Merrill Combs Black 35.00 60.00
19 Johnny Bucha RC 35.00 60.00
19A Johnny Bucha Black 35.00 60.00
20 Billy Loes SP RC 90.00 150.00
20A Billy Loes Black 90.00 150.00
21 Ferris Fain 40.00 70.00
21A Ferris Fain Black 40.00 70.00
22 Dom DiMaggio 75.00 125.00
22A Dom DiMaggio Black 60.00 100.00
23 Billy Goodman 40.00 70.00
23A Billy Goodman Black 40.00 70.00
24 Luke Easter 50.00 80.00
24A Luke Easter Black 50.00 80.00
25 Johnny Groth 35.00 60.00
25A Johnny Groth Black 35.00 60.00
26 Monte Irvin 90.00 150.00
26A Monte Irvin Black 90.00 150.00
27 Sam Jethroe 40.00 70.00
27A Sam Jethroe Black 40.00 70.00
28 Jerry Priddy 35.00 60.00
28A Jerry Priddy Black 35.00 60.00
29 Ted Kluszewski 75.00 125.00
29A Ted Kluszewski Black 75.00 125.00
30 Mel Parnell 40.00 70.00
30A Mel Parnell Black 40.00 70.00
31 Gus Zernial 50.00 80.00
Posed with six baseballs
31A Gus Zernial Black 50.00 80.00
Posed with six baseballs
32 Eddie Robinson 35.00 60.00
32A Eddie Robinson Black 35.00 60.00
33 Warren Spahn 175.00 300.00
33A Warren Spahn Black 175.00 300.00
34 Elmer Valo 35.00 60.00
34A Elmer Valo Black 35.00 60.00
35 Hank Sauer 40.00 70.00
35A Hank Sauer Black 40.00 70.00
36 Gil Hodges 175.00 300.00
36A Gil Hodges Black 175.00 300.00
37 Duke Snider 300.00 500.00
37A Duke Snider Black 300.00 500.00
38 Wally Westlake 35.00 60.00
38A Wally Westlake Black 35.00 60.00
39 Dizzy Trout 40.00 70.00
39A Dizzy Trout Black 40.00 70.00
40 Irv Noren 40.00 70.00
40A Irv Noren Black 40.00 70.00
41 Bob Wellman RC 35.00 60.00
41A Bob Wellman Black 35.00 60.00
42 Lou Kretlow RC 35.00 60.00
42A Lou Kretlow Black 35.00 60.00
43 Ray Scarborough 35.00 60.00
43A R. Scarbourough Black 35.00 60.00
44 Con Dempsey RC 35.00 60.00
44A Con Dempsey Black 35.00 60.00
45 Eddie Joost 35.00 60.00
45A Eddie Joost Black 35.00 60.00
46 Gordon Goldsberry RC 35.00 60.00
46A Gordon Goldsberry Black 35.00 60.00
47 Willie Jones 40.00 70.00
47A Willie Jones Black 40.00 70.00
48A Joe Page ERR 250.00 400.00
Bio for Sain
Black Back
48B Joe Page COR 75.00 125.00
Black Back
48C Joe Page COR 75.00 125.00
Red Back
49A John Sain ERR 250.00 400.00
Bio for Page
Black Back
49B John Sain COR 75.00 125.00
Black Back
49C John Sain COR 75.00 125.00
Red Back
50 Marv Rickert RC 35.00 60.00
50A Marv Rickert Black 35.00 60.00
51 Jim Russell 35.00 60.00
51A Jim Russell Black 35.00 60.00
52 Don Mueller 40.00 70.00
52A Don Mueller Black 40.00 70.00
53 Chris Van Cuyk RC 35.00 60.00
53A Chris Van Cuyk Black 35.00 60.00
54 Leo Kiely RC 35.00 60.00
54A Leo Kiely Black 35.00 60.00
55 Ray Boone 50.00 80.00
55A Ray Boone Black 50.00 80.00
56 Tommy Glaviano 35.00 60.00
56A T. Glaviano Black 35.00 60.00
57 Ed Lopat 60.00 100.00
57A Ed Lopat Black 60.00 100.00
58 Bob Mahoney RC 35.00 60.00
58A Bob Mahoney Black 35.00 60.00
59 Robin Roberts 100.00 175.00
59A Robin Roberts Black 100.00 175.00
60 Sid Hudson 35.00 60.00
60A Sid Hudson Black 35.00 60.00
61 Tookie Gilbert 35.00 60.00
61A Tookie Gilbert Black 35.00 60.00
62 Chuck Stobbs RC 35.00 60.00
62A Chuck Stobbs Black 35.00 60.00
63 Howie Pollet 35.00 60.00
63A Howie Pollet Black 35.00 60.00
64 Roy Sievers 40.00 70.00
64A Roy Sievers Black 40.00 70.00
65 Enos Slaughter 100.00 175.00
65A Enos Slaughter Black 100.00 175.00
66 Preacher Roe 60.00 100.00
66A Preacher Roe Black 60.00 100.00
67 Allie Reynolds 75.00 125.00
67A Allie Reynolds Black 75.00 125.00
68 Cliff Chambers 35.00 60.00
68A Cliff Chambers Black 35.00 60.00
69 Virgil Stallcup 35.00 60.00
69A Virgil Stallcup Black 35.00 60.00
70 Al Zarilla 35.00 60.00
70A Al Zarilla Black 35.00 60.00
71 Tom Upton RC 35.00 60.00
71A Tom Upton Black 35.00 60.00
72 Karl Olson RC 35.00 60.00
72A Karl Olson Black 35.00 60.00
73 Bill Werle 35.00 60.00
73A Bill Werle Black 35.00 60.00
74 Andy Hansen RC 35.00 60.00
74A Andy Hansen Black 35.00 60.00
75 Wes Westrum 40.00 70.00
75A Wes Westrum Black 40.00 70.00
76 Eddie Stanky 40.00 70.00
76A Eddie Stanky Black 40.00 70.00
77 Bob Kennedy 40.00 70.00
77A Bob Kennedy Black 40.00 70.00
78 Ellis Kinder 35.00 60.00
78A Ellis Kinder Black 35.00 60.00
79 Gerry Staley 35.00 60.00
79A Gerry Staley Black 35.00 60.00
80 Herman Wehmeier 50.00 80.00
80A H. Wehmeier Black 50.00 80.00
81 Vernon Law 50.00 80.00
82 Duane Pillette 20.00 40.00
83 Billy Johnson 20.00 40.00
84 Vern Stephens 30.00 50.00
85 Bob Kuzava 30.00 50.00
86 Ted Gray 20.00 40.00
87 Dale Coogan 20.00 40.00
88 Bob Feller 150.00 250.00
89 Johnny Lipon 20.00 40.00
90 Mickey Grasso 20.00 40.00
91 Red Schoendienst 90.00 150.00
92 Dale Mitchell 30.00 50.00
93 Al Sima RC 20.00 40.00
94 Sam Mele 20.00 40.00
95 Ken Holcombe 20.00 40.00
96 Willard Marshall 20.00 40.00
97 Earl Torgeson 20.00 40.00
98 Billy Pierce 30.00 50.00
99 Gene Woodling 35.00 60.00
100 Del Rice 20.00 40.00
101 Max Lanier 20.00 40.00
102 Bill Kennedy 20.00 40.00
103 Cliff Mapes 20.00 40.00
104 Don Kolloway 20.00 40.00
105 Johnny Pramesa 20.00 40.00
106 Mickey Vernon 35.00 60.00
107 Connie Ryan 20.00 40.00
108 Jim Konstanty 35.00 60.00
109 Ted Wilks 20.00 40.00
110 Dutch Leonard 20.00 40.00
111 Peanuts Lowrey 20.00 40.00
112 Hank Majeski 20.00 40.00
113 Dick Sisler 30.00 50.00
114 Willard Ramsdell 20.00 40.00
115 George Munger 20.00 40.00
116 Carl Scheib 20.00 40.00
117 Sherm Lollar 30.00 50.00
118 Ken Raffensberger 20.00 40.00
119 Mickey McDermott 20.00 40.00
120 Bob Chakales RC 20.00 40.00
121 Gus Niarhos 20.00 40.00
122 Jackie Jensen 50.00 80.00
123 Eddie Yost 30.00 50.00
124 Monte Kennedy 20.00 40.00
125 Bill Rigney 20.00 40.00
126 Fred Hutchinson 30.00 50.00
127 Paul Minner RC 20.00 40.00
128 Don Bollweg RC 20.00 40.00
129 Johnny Mize 90.00 150.00
130 Sheldon Jones 20.00 40.00
131 Morrie Martin RC 20.00 40.00
132 Clyde Kluttz RC 20.00 40.00
133 Al Widmar 20.00 40.00
134 Joe Tipton 20.00 40.00
135 Dixie Howell 20.00 40.00
136 Johnny Schmitz 20.00 40.00
137 Roy McMillan RC 30.00 50.00
138 Bill MacDonald 20.00 40.00
139 Ken Wood 20.00 40.00
140 Johnny Antonelli 35.00 60.00
141 Clint Hartung 20.00 40.00
142 Harry Perkowski RC 20.00 40.00
143 Les Moss 20.00 40.00
144 Ed Blake RC 20.00 40.00
145 Joe Haynes 20.00 40.00
146 Frank House RC 20.00 40.00
147 Bob Young RC 20.00 40.00
148 Johnny Klippstein 20.00 40.00
149 Dick Kryhoski 20.00 40.00
150 Ted Beard 20.00 40.00
151 Wally Post RC 30.00 50.00
152 Al Evans 20.00 40.00
153 Bob Rush 20.00 40.00
154 Joe Muir RC 20.00 40.00
155 Frank Overmire 20.00 40.00
156 Frank Hiller RC 20.00 40.00
157 Bob Usher 20.00 40.00
158 Eddie Waitkus 20.00 40.00
159 Saul Rogovin RC 20.00 40.00
160 Owen Friend 20.00 40.00
161 Bud Byerly RC 20.00 40.00
162 Del Crandall 30.00 50.00
163 Stan Rojek 20.00 40.00
164 Walt Dubiel 20.00 40.00
165 Eddie Kazak 20.00 40.00
166 Paul LaPalme RC 20.00 40.00
167 Bill Howerton 20.00 40.00
168 Charlie Silvera RC 35.00 60.00
169 Howie Judson 20.00 40.00
170 Gus Bell 30.00 50.00
171 Ed Erautt RC 20.00 40.00
172 Eddie Miksis 20.00 40.00
173 Roy Smalley 20.00 40.00
174 Clarence Marshall RC 35.00 60.00
175 Billy Martin RC 300.00 500.00
176 Hank Edwards 20.00 40.00
177 Bill Wight 20.00 40.00
178 Cass Michaels 20.00 40.00
179 Frank Smith RC 20.00 40.00
180 Charlie Maxwell RC 30.00 50.00
181 Bob Swift 20.00 40.00
182 Billy Hitchcock 20.00 40.00
183 Erv Dusak 20.00 40.00
184 Bob Ramazzotti 20.00 40.00
185 Bill Nicholson 30.00 50.00
186 Walt Masterson 20.00 40.00
187 Bob Miller 20.00 40.00
188 Clarence Podbielan RC 20.00 40.00
189 Pete Reiser 35.00 60.00
190 Don Johnson RC 20.00 40.00
191 Yogi Berra 500.00 800.00
192 Myron Ginsberg RC 20.00 40.00
193 Harry Simpson RC 30.00 50.00
194 Joe Hatton 20.00 40.00
195 Minnie Minoso RC 90.00 150.00
196 Solly Hemus RC 35.00 60.00
197 George Strickland RC 20.00 40.00
198 Phil Haugstad RC 20.00 40.00
199 George Zuverink RC 20.00 40.00
200 Ralph Houk RC 50.00 80.00
201 Alex Kellner 20.00 40.00
202 Joe Collins RC 35.00 60.00
203 Curt Simmons 35.00 60.00
204 Ron Northey 20.00 40.00
205 Clyde King 35.00 60.00
206 Joe Ostrowski RC 20.00 40.00
207 Mickey Harris 20.00 40.00
208 Marlin Stuart RC 20.00 40.00
209 Howie Fox 20.00 40.00
210 Dick Fowler 20.00 40.00
211 Ray Coleman 20.00 40.00
212 Ned Garver 20.00 40.00
213 Nippy Jones 20.00 40.00
214 Johnny Hopp 30.00 50.00
215 Hank Bauer 60.00 100.00
216 Richie Ashburn 150.00 250.00
217 Snuffy Stirnweiss 30.00 50.00
218 Clyde McCullough 20.00 40.00
219 Bobby Shantz 35.00 60.00
220 Joe Presko RC 20.00 40.00
221 Granny Hamner 20.00 40.00
222 Hoot Evers 20.00 40.00
223 Del Ennis 30.00 50.00
224 Bruce Edwards 20.00 40.00
225 Frank Baumholtz 20.00 40.00
226 Dave Philley 20.00 40.00
227 Joe Garagiola 50.00 80.00
228 Al Brazle 20.00 40.00
229 Gene Bearden UER 20.00 40.00
(Misspelled Beardon)
230 Matt Batts 20.00 40.00
231 Sam Zoldak 20.00 40.00
232 Billy Cox 30.00 50.00
233 Bob Friend RC 50.00 80.00
234 Steve Souchock RC 20.00 40.00
235 Walt Dropo 20.00 40.00
236 Ed Fitzgerald 20.00 40.00
237 Jerry Coleman 35.00 60.00
238 Art Houtteman 20.00 40.00
239 Rocky Bridges RC 30.00 50.00
240 Jack Phillips RC 20.00 40.00
241 Tommy Byrne 20.00 40.00
242 Tom Poholsky RC 20.00 40.00
243 Larry Doby 50.00 80.00
244 Vic Wertz 20.00 40.00
245 Sherry Robertson 20.00 40.00
246 George Kell 50.00 80.00
247 Randy Gumpert 20.00 40.00
248 Frank Shea 20.00 40.00
249 Bobby Adams 20.00 40.00
250 Carl Erskine 60.00 100.00
251 Chico Carrasquel 30.00 50.00
252 Vern Bickford 30.00 50.00
253 Johnny Berardino 60.00 100.00
254 Joe Dobson 30.00 50.00
255 Clyde Vollmer 30.00 50.00
256 Pete Suder 30.00 50.00
257 Bobby Avila 35.00 60.00
258 Steve Gromek 35.00 60.00
259 Bob Addis RC 30.00 50.00
260 Pete Castiglione 30.00 50.00
261 Willie Mays 2000.00 3000.00
262 Virgil Trucks 35.00 60.00
263 Harry Brecheen 35.00 60.00
264 Roy Hartsfield 30.00 50.00
265 Chuck Diering 30.00 50.00
266 Murry Dickson 30.00 50.00
267 Sid Gordon 35.00 60.00
268 Bob Lemon 90.00 150.00
269 Willard Nixon 30.00 50.00
270 Lou Brissie 30.00 50.00
271 Jim Delsing 35.00 60.00
272 Mike Garcia 50.00 80.00
273 Erv Palica 30.00 50.00
274 Ralph Branca 75.00 125.00
275 Pat Mullin 30.00 50.00
276 Jim Wilson RC 30.00 50.00
277 Early Wynn 100.00 175.00
278 Allie Clark 30.00 50.00
279 Eddie Stewart 30.00 50.00
280 Cloyd Boyer 50.00 80.00
281 Tommy Brown SP 50.00 80.00
282 Birdie Tebbetts SP 50.00 80.00
283 Phil Masi SP 35.00 60.00
284 Hank Arft SP 35.00 60.00
285 Cliff Fannin SP 35.00 60.00
286 Joe DeMaestri SP RC 35.00 60.00
287 Steve Bilko SP 35.00 60.00
288 Chet Nichols SP RC 50.00 80.00
289 Tommy Holmes SP 60.00 100.00
290 Joe Astroth SP 35.00 60.00
291 Gil Coan SP 35.00 60.00
292 Floyd Baker SP 35.00 60.00
293 Sibby Sisti SP 35.00 60.00
294 Walker Cooper SP 35.00 60.00
295 Phil Cavarretta SP 50.00 80.00
296 Red Rolfe MG SP 35.00 60.00
297 Andy Seminick SP 35.00 60.00
298 Bob Ross SP RC 35.00 60.00
299 Ray Murray SP RC 50.00 80.00
300 Barney McCosky SP 50.00 80.00
301 Bob Porterfield 30.00 50.00
302 Max Surkont RC 30.00 50.00
303 Harry Dorish 30.00 50.00
304 Sam Dente 30.00 50.00
305 Paul Richards MG 35.00 60.00
306 Lou Sleater RC 30.00 50.00
307 Frank Campos RC 30.00 50.00
Two red stars on back in copyright line
307A Frank Campos RC
One red/one black star on back in copyright line
308 Luis Aloma 30.00 50.00
309 Jim Busby 35.00 60.00
310 George Metkovich 60.00 100.00
311 Mickey Mantle DP 18000.00 30000.00
Rough marquee along top edge on front,
Last E on facsimile autograph curls upward
Stitching on back number circle points left
311B Mickey Mantle DP 18000.00 30000.00
Clean marquee along top edge on front,
Last E on facsimile autograph stops at bottom
Stitching on back number circle points right
312 Jackie Robinson DP 1500.00 2500.00
Stitching on back number circle points left,
Seven stars and white circle on left side of marquee
312B Jackie Robinson DP 1500.00 2500.00
Stitching on back number circle points right
Seven stars only on left side of marquee
313 Bobby Thomson DP 200.00 350.00
Stitching on back number circle points left
Marquee is clean along top and right edges
313B Bobby Thomson DP 200.00 350.00
Stitching on back number circle points right
Marquee is rough along top and right edges
314 Roy Campanella 1500.00 2500.00
315 Leo Durocher MG 350.00 600.00
316 Dave Williams RC 175.00 300.00
317 Conrado Marrero 175.00 300.00
318 Harold Gregg RC 175.00 300.00
319 Rube Walker RC 150.00 250.00
320 John Rutherford RC 175.00 300.00
321 Joe Black RC 350.00 500.00
322 Randy Jackson RC 175.00 300.00
323 Bubba Church 150.00 250.00
324 Warren Hacker 150.00 250.00
325 Bill Serena 175.00 300.00
326 George Shuba RC 350.00 500.00
327 Al Wilson RC 150.00 250.00
328 Bob Borkowski RC 175.00 300.00
329 Ike Delock RC 175.00 300.00
330 Turk Lown RC 175.00 300.00
331 Tom Morgan RC 175.00 300.00
332 Tony Bartirome RC 175.00 300.00
333 Pee Wee Reese 1000.00 1800.00
334 Wilmer Mizell RC 175.00 300.00
335 Ted Lepcio RC 150.00 250.00
336 Dave Koslo 150.00 250.00
337 Jim Hearn 175.00 300.00
338 Sal Yvars RC 175.00 300.00
339 Russ Meyer 175.00 300.00
340 Bob Hooper 175.00 300.00
341 Hal Jeffcoat 175.00 300.00
342 Clem Labine RC 350.00 500.00
343 Dick Gernert RC 150.00 250.00
344 Ewell Blackwell 175.00 300.00
345 Sammy White RC 150.00 250.00
346 George Spencer RC 150.00 250.00
347 Joe Adcock 250.00 400.00
348 Robert Kelly RC 150.00 250.00
349 Bob Cain 175.00 300.00
350 Cal Abrams 175.00 300.00
351 Alvin Dark 175.00 300.00
352 Karl Drews 175.00 300.00
353 Bobby Del Greco RC 175.00 300.00
354 Fred Hatfield RC 175.00 300.00
355 Bobby Morgan 175.00 300.00
356 Toby Atwell RC 175.00 300.00
357 Smoky Burgess 175.00 300.00
358 John Kucab RC 175.00 300.00
359 Dee Fondy RC 150.00 250.00
360 George Crowe RC 175.00 300.00
361 Bill Posedel CO 150.00 250.00
362 Ken Heintzelman 175.00 300.00
363 Dick Rozek RC 175.00 300.00
364 Clyde Sukeforth CO RC 175.00 300.00
365 Cookie Lavagetto CO 250.00 400.00
366 Dave Madison RC 150.00 250.00
367 Ben Thorpe RC 175.00 300.00
368 Ed Wright RC 175.00 300.00
369 Dick Groat RC 350.00 500.00
370 Billy Hoeft RC 175.00 300.00
371 Bobby Hofman 150.00 250.00
372 Gil McDougald RC 300.00 500.00
373 Jim Turner CO RC 250.00 400.00
374 Al Benton RC 150.00 250.00
375 John Merson RC 150.00 250.00
376 Faye Throneberry RC 150.00 250.00
377 Chuck Dressen MG 250.00 400.00
378 Leroy Fusselman RC 175.00 300.00
379 Joe Rossi RC 150.00 250.00
380 Clem Koshorek RC 150.00 250.00
381 Milton Stock CO RC 175.00 300.00
382 Sam Jones RC 200.00 350.00
383 Del Wilber RC 150.00 250.00
384 Frank Crosetti CO 300.00 500.00
385 H.Franks CO RC 150.00 250.00
386 Ed Yuhas RC 175.00 300.00
387 Billy Meyer MG 150.00 250.00

388 Bob Chipman 150.00 250.00
389 Ben Wade RC 175.00 300.00
390 Rocky Nelson RC 175.00 300.00
391 Ben Chapman UER CO 150.00 250.00
Photo actually
Sam Chapman
392 Hoyt Wilhelm RC 600.00 1000.00
393 Ebba St.Claire RC 175.00 300.00
394 Billy Herman CO 350.00 600.00
395 Jake Pitler CO 175.00 300.00
396 Dick Williams RC 300.00 500.00
397 Forrest Main RC 150.00 250.00
398 Hal Rice 150.00 250.00
399 Jim Fridley RC 150.00 250.00
400 Bill Dickey CO 1000.00 1800.00
401 Bob Schultz RC 175.00 300.00
402 Earl Harrist RC 175.00 300.00
403 Bill Miller RC 175.00 300.00
404 Dick Brodowski RC 175.00 300.00
405 Eddie Pellagrini 175.00 300.00
406 Joe Nuxhall RC 250.00 400.00
407 Eddie Mathews RC 6000.00 10000.00

1953 Topps

The cards in this 274-card set measure 2 5/8" by 3 3/4". Card number 69, Dick Brodowski, features the first known drawing of a player during a night game. Although the last card is numbered 280, there are only 274 cards in the set since numbers 253, 261, 267, 268, 271, and 275 were never issued. The 1953 Topps series contains line drawings of players in full color. The name and team panel at the card base is easily damaged, making it very difficult to complete a mint set. The high number series, 221 to 280, was produced in shorter supply late in the year and hence is more difficult to complete than the lower numbers. The key cards in the set are Mickey Mantle (82) and Willie Mays (244). The key Rookie Cards in this set are Roy Face, Jim Gilliam, and Johnny Podres, all from the last series. There are a number of double-printed cards (actually not double but 50 percent more of each of these numbers were printed compared to the other cards in the series) indicated by DP in the checklist below. There were five players (10 Smoky Burgess, 44 Ellis Kinder, 61 Early Wynn, 72 Fred Hutchinson, and 81 Joe Black) held out of the first run of 1-85 (but printed in with numbers 86-165), who are each marked by SP in the checklist below. In addition, there are five numbers which were printed with the more plentiful series 166-220; these cards (94, 107, 131, 145, and 156) are also indicated by DP in the checklist below. All these aforementioned cards from 86 through 165 and the five short prints come with the biographical information on the back in either white or black lettering. These seem to be printed in equal quantities and no price differential is given for either variety. The cards were issued in one-card penny packs or six-card nickel packs. The nickel packs were issued 24 to a box. There were some three-card advertising panels produced by Topps, the players include Johnny Mize/Clem Koshorek/Toby Atwell; Jim Hearn/Johnny Groth/Sherman Lollar and Mickey Mantle/Johnny Wyrostek/

COMPLETE SET (274) 9000.00 15000.00
COMMON CARD (1-165) 15.00 30.00
COMMON DP (1-165) 7.50 15.00
COMMON (166-220) 12.50 25.00
COMMON (221-280) 50.00 100.00
NOT ISSUED (253/261/267)
NOT ISSUED (268/271/275)
WRAP.(1-CENT, DATED) 150.00 200.00
WRAP.(1-CENT, UNDATED) 250.00 300.00
WRAP.(5-CENT, DATED) 300.00 400.00
WRAP.(5-CENT, UNDATED) 275.00 350.00
1 Jackie Robinson DP 500.00 800.00
2 Luke Easter DP 10.00 20.00
3 George Crowe 25.00 40.00
4 Ben Wade 15.00 30.00
5 Joe Dobson 15.00 30.00
6 Sam Jones 25.00 40.00
7 Bob Borkowski DP 7.50 15.00
8 Clem Koshorek DP 7.50 15.00
9 Joe Collins 35.00 60.00
10 Smoky Burgess SP 50.00 80.00
11 Sal Yvars 15.00 30.00
12 Howie Judson DP 7.50 15.00
13 Conrado Marrero DP 7.50 15.00
14 Clem Labine DP 10.00 20.00
15 Bobo Newsom DP RC 10.00 20.00
16 Peanuts Lowrey DP 7.50 15.00
17 Billy Hitchcock 15.00 30.00
18 Ted Lepcio DP 7.50 15.00
19 Mel Parnell DP 10.00 20.00
20 Hank Thompson 25.00 40.00
21 Billy Johnson 15.00 30.00
22 Howie Fox 15.00 30.00
23 Toby Atwell DP 7.50 15.00
24 Ferris Fain 25.00 40.00
25 Ray Boone 25.00 40.00
26 Dale Mitchell DP 10.00 20.00
27 Roy Campanella DP 175.00 300.00
28 Eddie Pellagrini 15.00 30.00
29 Hal Jeffcoat 15.00 30.00
30 Willard Nixon 15.00 30.00
31 Ewell Blackwell 35.00 60.00
32 Clyde Vollmer 15.00 30.00
33 Bob Kennedy DP 7.50 15.00
34 George Shuba 25.00 40.00
35 Irv Noren DP 7.50 15.00
36 Johnny Groth DP 7.50 15.00
37 Eddie Mathews DP 150.00 250.00
38 Jim Hearn DP 7.50 15.00
39 Eddie Miksis 15.00 30.00
40 John Lipon 15.00 30.00
41 Enos Slaughter 50.00 80.00
42 Gus Zernial DP 10.00 20.00
43 Gil McDougald 35.00 60.00
44 Ellis Kinder SP 35.00 60.00
45 Grady Hatton DP 7.50 15.00
46 Johnny Klippstein DP 7.50 15.00
47 Bubba Church DP 7.50 15.00
48 Bob Del Greco DP 7.50 15.00
49 Faye Throneberry DP 7.50 15.00
50 Chuck Dressen MG DP 10.00 20.00
51 Frank Campos DP 7.50 15.00
52 Ted Gray DP 7.50 15.00
53 Sherm Lollar DP 10.00 20.00
54 Bob Feller DP 90.00 150.00
55 Maurice McDermott DP 7.50 15.00
56 Gerry Staley DP 7.50 15.00
57 Carl Scheib 15.00 30.00
58 George Metkovich 15.00 30.00
59 Karl Drews DP 7.50 15.00
60 Cloyd Boyer DP 7.50 15.00
61 Early Wynn SP 75.00 125.00
62 Monte Irvin DP 25.00 40.00
63 Gus Niarhos DP 7.50 15.00
64 Dave Philley 15.00 30.00
65 Earl Harrist 15.00 30.00
66 Minnie Minoso 35.00 60.00
67 Roy Sievers DP 10.00 20.00
68 Del Rice 15.00 30.00
69 Dick Brodowski 15.00 30.00
70 Ed Yuhas 15.00 30.00
71 Tony Bartirome 15.00 30.00
72 F.Hutchinson MG SP 35.00 60.00
73 Eddie Robinson 15.00 30.00
74 Joe Rossi 15.00 30.00
75 Mike Garcia 25.00 40.00
76 Pee Wee Reese 100.00 175.00
77 Johnny Mize DP 50.00 80.00
78 Red Schoendienst 50.00 80.00
79 Johnny Wyrostek 15.00 30.00
80 Jim Hegan 25.00 40.00
81 Joe Black SP 50.00 80.00
82 Mickey Mantle 2000.00 3000.00
83 Howie Pollet 15.00 30.00
84 Bob Hooper DP 7.50 15.00
85 Bobby Morgan DP 7.50 15.00
86 Billy Martin 75.00 125.00
87 Ed Lopat 35.00 60.00
88 Willie Jones DP 7.50 15.00
89 Chuck Stobbs DP 7.50 15.00
90 Hank Edwards DP 7.50 15.00
91 Ebba St.Claire DP 7.50 15.00
92 Paul Minner DP 7.50 15.00
93 Hal Rice DP 7.50 15.00
94 Bill Kennedy DP 7.50 15.00
95 Willard Marshall DP 7.50 15.00
96 Virgil Trucks 25.00 40.00
97 Don Kolloway DP 7.50 15.00
98 Cal Abrams DP 7.50 15.00
99 Dave Madison 15.00 30.00
100 Bill Miller 15.00 30.00
101 Ted Wilks 15.00 30.00
102 Connie Ryan DP 7.50 15.00
103 Joe Astroth DP 7.50 15.00
104 Yogi Berra 250.00 400.00
105 Joe Nuxhall DP 10.00 20.00
106 Johnny Antonelli 25.00 40.00
107 Danny O'Connell DP 7.50 15.00
108 Bob Porterfield DP 7.50 15.00
109 Alvin Dark 35.00 60.00
110 Herman Wehmeier DP 7.50 15.00
111 Hank Sauer DP 7.50 15.00
112 Ned Garver DP 7.50 15.00
113 Jerry Priddy 15.00 30.00
114 Phil Rizzuto 150.00 250.00
115 George Spencer 15.00 30.00
116 Frank Smith DP 7.50 15.00
117 Sid Gordon DP 7.50 15.00
118 Gus Bell DP 10.00 20.00
119 Johnny Sain SP 35.00 60.00
120 Davey Williams 25.00 40.00
121 Walt Dropo 25.00 40.00
122 Elmer Valo 15.00 30.00
123 Tommy Byrne DP 7.50 15.00
124 Sibby Sisti DP 7.50 15.00
125 Dick Williams DP 10.00 20.00
126 Bill Connelly DP RC 7.50 15.00
127 Clint Courtney DP RC 7.50 15.00
128 Wilmer Mizell DP 10.00 20.00
(Inconsistent design,
logo on front with
black birds)
129 Keith Thomas RC 15.00 30.00
130 Turk Lown DP 7.50 15.00
131 Harry Byrd DP RC 7.50 15.00
132 Tom Morgan 15.00 30.00
133 Gil Coan 15.00 30.00
134 Rube Walker 25.00 40.00
135 Al Rosen DP 10.00 20.00
136 Ken Heintzelman DP 7.50 15.00
137 John Rutherford DP 7.50 15.00
138 George Kell 50.00 80.00
139 Sammy White 15.00 30.00
140 Tommy Glaviano 15.00 30.00
141 Allie Reynolds DP 25.00 40.00
142 Vic Wertz 25.00 40.00
143 Billy Pierce 35.00 60.00
144 Bob Schultz DP 7.50 15.00
145 Harry Dorish DP 7.50 15.00
146 Granny Hamner 15.00 30.00
147 Warren Spahn 100.00 175.00
148 Mickey Grasso 15.00 30.00
149 Dom DiMaggio DP 25.00 40.00
150 Harry Simpson DP 7.50 15.00
151 Hoyt Wilhelm 60.00 100.00
152 Bob Adams DP 7.50 15.00
153 Andy Seminick DP 7.50 15.00
154 Dick Groat 25.00 40.00
155 Dutch Leonard 15.00 30.00
156 Jim Rivera DP RC 10.00 20.00
157 Bob Addis DP 7.50 15.00
158 Johnny Logan RC 25.00 40.00
159 Wayne Terwilliger DP 7.50 15.00
160 Bob Young 15.00 30.00
161 Vern Bickford DP 7.50 15.00
162 Ted Kluszewski 35.00 60.00
163 Fred Hatfield DP 7.50 15.00
164 Frank Shea DP 7.50 15.00
165 Billy Hoeft 15.00 30.00
166 Billy Hunter RC 12.50 25.00
167 Art Schult RC 12.50 25.00
168 Willard Schmidt RC 12.50 25.00
169 Dizzy Trout 15.00 30.00
170 Bill Werle 12.50 25.00
171 Bill Glynn RC 12.50 25.00
172 Rip Repulski RC 12.50 25.00
173 Preston Ward 12.50 25.00
174 Billy Loes 15.00 30.00
175 Ron Kline RC 12.50 25.00
176 Don Hoak RC 25.00 40.00
177 Jim Dyck RC 12.50 25.00
178 Jim Waugh RC 12.50 25.00
179 Gene Hermanski 12.50 25.00
180 Virgil Stallcup 12.50 25.00
181 Al Zarilla 12.50 25.00
182 Bobby Hofman 12.50 25.00
183 Stu Miller RC 25.00 40.00
184 Hal Brown RC 25.00 40.00
185 Jim Pendleton RC 12.50 25.00
186 Charlie Bishop RC 12.50 25.00
187 Jim Fridley 12.50 25.00
188 Andy Carey RC 25.00 40.00
189 Ray Jablonski RC 12.50 25.00
190 Dixie Walker CO 15.00 30.00
191 Ralph Kiner 50.00 80.00
192 Wally Westlake 12.50 25.00
193 Mike Clark RC 12.50 25.00
194 Eddie Kazak 12.50 25.00
195 Ed McGhee RC 12.50 25.00
196 Bob Keegan RC 12.50 25.00
197 Del Crandall 25.00 40.00
198 Forrest Main 12.50 25.00
199 Marion Fricano RC 12.50 25.00
200 Gordon Goldsberry 12.50 25.00
201 Paul LaPalme 12.50 25.00
202 Carl Sawatski RC 12.50 25.00
203 Cliff Fannin 12.50 25.00
204 Dick Bokelman RC 12.50 25.00
205 Vern Benson RC 12.50 25.00
206 Ed Bailey RC 15.00 30.00
207 Whitey Ford 175.00 300.00
208 Jim Wilson 12.50 25.00
209 Jim Greengrass RC 12.50 25.00
210 Bob Cerv RC 25.00 40.00
211 J.W. Porter RC 12.50 25.00
212 Jack Dittmer RC 12.50 25.00
213 Ray Scarborough 12.50 25.00
214 Bill Bruton RC 25.00 40.00
215 Gene Conley RC 15.00 30.00
216 Jim Hughes RC 12.50 25.00
217 Murray Wall RC 12.50 25.00
218 Les Fusselman 12.50 25.00
219 Pete Runnels UER 15.00 30.00
(Photo actually
Don Johnson)
220 Satchel Paige UER 350.00 600.00
(Misspelled Satchell
on card front)
221 Bob Milliken RC 50.00 100.00
222 Vic Janowicz DP RC 25.00 50.00
223 Johnny O'Brien DP RC 25.00 50.00
224 Lou Sleater DP 25.00 50.00
225 Bobby Shantz 75.00 125.00
226 Ed Erautt 50.00 100.00
227 Morrie Martin 50.00 100.00
228 Hal Newhouser 90.00 150.00
229 Rocky Krsnich RC 50.00 100.00
230 Johnny Lindell DP 25.00 50.00
231 Solly Hemus DP 25.00 50.00
232 Dick Kokos 50.00 100.00
233 Al Aber RC 50.00 100.00
234 Ray Murray DP 25.00 50.00
235 John Hetki DP RC 25.00 50.00
236 Harry Perkowski DP 25.00 50.00
237 Bud Podbielan DP 25.00 50.00
238 Cal Hogue DP RC 25.00 50.00
239 Jim Delsing 50.00 100.00
240 Fred Marsh 50.00 100.00
241 Al Sima DP 25.00 50.00
242 Charlie Silvera 75.00 125.00
243 Carlos Bernier DP RC 25.00 50.00
244 Willie Mays 1500.00 2500.00
245 Bill Norman CO 50.00 100.00
246 Roy Face DP RC 50.00 80.00
247 Mike Sandlock DP RC 25.00 50.00
248 Gene Stephens DP RC 25.00 50.00
249 Eddie O'Brien RC 50.00 100.00
250 Bob Wilson RC 50.00 100.00
251 Sid Hudson 50.00 100.00
252 Hank Foiles RC 50.00 100.00
253 Does Not Exist
254 Preacher Roe DP 50.00 80.00
255 Dixie Howell 50.00 100.00
256 Les Peden RC 50.00 100.00
257 Bob Boyd RC 50.00 100.00
258 Jim Gilliam RC 250.00 400.00
259 Roy McMillan DP 25.00 50.00
260 Sam Calderone RC 50.00 100.00
261 Does Not Exist
262 Bob Oldis RC 50.00 100.00
263 Johnny Podres RC 175.00 300.00
264 Gene Woodling DP 30.00 60.00
265 Jackie Jensen 75.00 125.00
266 Bob Cain 50.00 100.00
267 Does Not Exist
268 Does Not Exist
269 Duane Pillette 50.00 100.00
270 Vern Stephens 75.00 125.00
271 Does Not Exist
272 Bill Antonello RC 50.00 100.00
273 Harvey Haddix RC 90.00 150.00
274 John Riddle CO 50.00 100.00
275 Does Not Exist
276 Ken Raffensberger 50.00 100.00
277 Don Lund RC 50.00 100.00
278 Willie Miranda RC 50.00 100.00
279 Joe Coleman DP 25.00 50.00
280 Milt Bolling RC 200.00 350.00

1954 Topps

The cards in this 250-card set measure approximately 2 5/8" by 3 3/4". Each of the cards in the 1954 Topps set contains a large "head" shot of the player in color plus a smaller full-length photo in black and white set against a color background. The cards were issued in one-card penny packs or five-card nickel packs. Fifteen-card cello packs have also been seen. The penny packs came 120 to a box while the nickel packs came 24 to a box. The nickel boxes had a drawing of Ted Williams along with his name printed on the box to indicate that Williams was part of this product. This set contains the Rookie Cards of Hank Aaron, Ernie Banks, and Al Kaline and two separate cards of Ted Williams (number 1 and number 250). Conspicuous by his absence is Mickey Mantle who apparently was the exclusive property of Bowman during 1954 (and 1955). The first two issues of Sports Illustrated magazine contained "card" inserts on regular paper stock. The first issue showed actual cards in the set in color, while the second issue showed some created cards of New York Yankees players in black and white, including Mickey Mantle. There was also a Canadian printing of the first 50 cards. These cards can be easily discerned as they have "grey" backs rather than the white backs of the American printed cards. To celebrate this set as the first Topps set to feature Ted Williams, his visage is also featured on the five cent box. The Canadian cards came four cards to a pack and 36 packs to a box and cost five cents when issued.

COMPLETE SET (250) 5000.00 8000.00
COMMON (1-50/76-250) 7.50 15.00
COMMON CARD (51-75) 12.50 25.00
WRAP.(1-CENT, DATED) 150.00 200.00
WRAP.(1-CENT, UNDATED) 100.00 150.00
WRAP.(5-CENT, DATED) 250.00 300.00
WRAP.(5-CENT, UNDATED) 200.00 250.00
1 Ted Williams 500.00 800.00
2 Gus Zernial 12.50 25.00
3 Monte Irvin 25.00 50.00
4 Hank Sauer 12.50 25.00
5 Ed Lopat 12.50 25.00
6 Pete Runnels 12.50 25.00
7 Ted Kluszewski 25.00 50.00
8 Bob Young 7.50 15.00
9 Harvey Haddix 12.50 25.00
10 Jackie Robinson 250.00 400.00
11 Paul Leslie Smith RC 7.50 15.00
12 Del Crandall 12.50 25.00
13 Billy Martin 60.00 100.00
14 Preacher Roe UER 12.50 25.00
February is misspelled
15 Al Rosen 12.50 25.00
16 Vic Janowicz 12.50 25.00
17 Phil Rizzuto 75.00 125.00
18 Walt Dropo 12.50 25.00
19 Johnny Lipon 7.50 15.00
Orioles Team Name on Front
White Sox team on Back
Wearing a Red Sox cap
20 Warren Spahn 75.00 125.00
21 Bobby Shantz 12.50 25.00
22 Jim Greengrass 7.50 15.00
23 Luke Easter 12.50 25.00
24 Granny Hamner 7.50 15.00
25 Harvey Kuenn RC 20.00 40.00
26 Ray Jablonski 7.50 15.00
27 Ferris Fain 12.50 25.00
28 Paul Minner 7.50 15.00
29 Jim Hegan 12.50 25.00
30 Eddie Mathews 60.00 100.00
31 Johnny Klippstein 7.50 15.00
32 Duke Snider 125.00 200.00
33 Johnny Schmitz 7.50 15.00
34 Jim Rivera 12.50 25.00
35 Junior Gilliam 25.00 50.00
36 Hoyt Wilhelm 25.00 50.00
37 Whitey Ford 125.00 200.00
38 Eddie Stanky MG 12.50 25.00
39 Sherm Lollar 12.50 25.00
40 Mel Parnell 12.50 25.00
41 Willie Jones 7.50 15.00
42 Don Mueller 12.50 25.00
43 Dick Groat 12.50 25.00
44 Ned Garver 7.50 15.00
45 Richie Ashburn 50.00 80.00
46 Ken Raffensberger 7.50 15.00
47 Ellis Kinder 7.50 15.00
48 Billy Hunter 12.50 25.00
49 Ray Murray 7.50 15.00
50 Yogi Berra 175.00 300.00
51 Johnny Lindell 12.50 25.00
52 Vic Power RC 15.00 30.00
53 Jack Dittmer 12.50 25.00
54 Vern Stephens 15.00 30.00
55 Phil Cavarretta MG 15.00 30.00
56 Willie Miranda 12.50 25.00
57 Luis Aloma 12.50 25.00
58 Bob Wilson 12.50 25.00
59 Gene Conley 15.00 30.00
60 Frank Baumholtz 12.50 25.00
61 Bob Cain 12.50 25.00
62 Eddie Robinson 12.50 25.00
63 Johnny Pesky 15.00 30.00
64 Hank Thompson 15.00 30.00
65 Bob Swift CO 12.50 25.00
66 Ted Lepcio 12.50 25.00
67 Jim Willis RC 12.50 25.00
68 Sam Calderone 12.50 25.00
69 Bud Podbielan 12.50 25.00
70 Larry Doby 30.00 60.00
71 Frank Smith 12.50 25.00
72 Preston Ward 12.50 25.00
73 Wayne Terwilliger 12.50 25.00
74 Bill Taylor RC 12.50 25.00
75 Fred Haney MG RC 12.50 25.00
76 Bob Scheffing CO 7.50 15.00
77 Ray Boone 12.50 25.00
78 Ted Kazanski RC 7.50 15.00
79 Andy Pafko 12.50 25.00
80 Jackie Jensen 12.50 25.00
81 Dave Hoskins RC 7.50 15.00
82 Milt Bolling 7.50 15.00
83 Joe Collins 12.50 25.00
84 Dick Cole RC 7.50 15.00
85 Bob Turley RC 20.00 40.00
86 Billy Herman CO 12.50 25.00
87 Roy Face 12.50 25.00
88 Matt Batts 7.50 15.00
89 Howie Pollet 7.50 15.00
90 Willie Mays 500.00 800.00
91 Bob Oldis 7.50 15.00
92 Wally Westlake 7.50 15.00
93 Sid Hudson 7.50 15.00
94 Ernie Banks RC 900.00 1500.00
95 Hal Rice 7.50 15.00
96 Charlie Silvera 12.50 25.00
97 Jerald Hal Lane RC 7.50 15.00
98 Joe Black 20.00 40.00
99 Bobby Hofman 7.50 15.00
100 Bob Keegan 7.50 15.00
101 Gene Woodling 12.50 25.00
102 Gil Hodges 50.00 80.00
103 Jim Lemon RC 7.50 15.00
104 Mike Sandlock 7.50 15.00
105 Andy Carey 12.50 25.00
106 Dick Kokos 7.50 15.00
107 Duane Pillette 7.50 15.00
108 Thornton Kipper RC 7.50 15.00
109 Bill Bruton 12.50 25.00
110 Harry Dorish 7.50 15.00
111 Jim Delsing 7.50 15.00
112 Bill Renna RC 7.50 15.00
113 Bob Boyd 7.50 15.00
114 Dean Stone RC 7.50 15.00
115 Rip Repulski 7.50 15.00
116 Steve Bilko 7.50 15.00
117 Solly Hemus 7.50 15.00
118 Carl Scheib 7.50 15.00
119 Johnny Antonelli 12.50 25.00
120 Roy McMillan 12.50 25.00
121 Clem Labine 12.50 25.00
122 Johnny Logan 12.50 25.00
123 Bobby Adams 7.50 15.00
124 Marion Fricano 7.50 15.00
125 Harry Perkowski 7.50 15.00
126 Ben Wade 7.50 15.00
127 Steve O'Neill MG 7.50 15.00
128 Hank Aaron RC 1000.00 1800.00
129 Forrest Jacobs RC 7.50 15.00
130 Hank Bauer 12.50 25.00
131 Reno Bertoia RC 12.50 25.00
132 Tommy Lasorda RC 150.00 250.00
133 Del Baker CO 7.50 15.00
134 Cal Hogue 7.50 15.00
135 Joe Presko 7.50 15.00
136 Connie Ryan 7.50 15.00
137 Wally Moon RC 20.00 40.00
138 Bob Borkowski 7.50 15.00
139 The O'Briens 25.00 50.00
Johnny O'Brien
Eddie O'Brien
140 Tom Wright 7.50 15.00
141 Joey Jay RC 12.50 25.00
142 Tom Poholsky 7.50 15.00
143 Rollie Hemsley CO 7.50 15.00
144 Bill Werle 7.50 15.00
145 Elmer Valo 7.50 15.00
146 Don Johnson 7.50 15.00
147 Johnny Riddle CO 7.50 15.00
148 Bob Trice RC 7.50 15.00
149 Al Robertson 7.50 15.00
150 Dick Kryhoski 7.50 15.00
151 Alex Grammas RC 7.50 15.00
152 Michael Blyzka RC 7.50 15.00
153 Al Walker 12.50 25.00
154 Mike Fornieles RC 7.50 15.00
155 Bob Kennedy 12.50 25.00
156 Joe Coleman 7.50 15.00
157 Don Lenhardt 7.50 15.00
158 Peanuts Lowrey 7.50 15.00
159 Dave Philley 7.50 15.00
160 Ralph Kress CO 7.50 15.00
161 John Hetki 7.50 15.00
162 Herman Wehmeier 7.50 15.00
163 Frank House 7.50 15.00
164 Stu Miller 12.50 25.00
165 Jim Pendleton 7.50 15.00
166 Johnny Podres 20.00 40.00
167 Don Lund 7.50 15.00
168 Morrie Martin 12.50 25.00
169 Jim Hughes 20.00 40.00
170 Dusty Rhodes RC 12.50 25.00
171 Leo Kiely 7.50 15.00
172 Harold Brown RC 7.50 15.00
173 Jack Harshman RC 7.50 15.00
174 Tom Qualters RC 7.50 15.00
175 Frank Leja RC 12.50 25.00
176 Robert Keely CO 7.50 15.00
177 Bob Milliken 7.50 15.00
178 Bill Glynn UER 7.50 15.00
Spelled Gylnn on the front
179 Gair Allie RC 7.50 15.00
180 Wes Westrum 12.50 25.00
181 Mel Roach RC 7.50 15.00
182 Chuck Harmon RC 7.50 15.00
183 Earle Combs CO 12.50 25.00
184 Ed Bailey 7.50 15.00
185 Chuck Stobbs 7.50 15.00
186 Karl Olson 7.50 15.00
187 Heinie Manush CO 12.50 25.00
188 Dave Jolly RC 7.50 15.00
189 Bob Ross 7.50 15.00
190 Ray Herbert RC 7.50 15.00
191 John Schofield RC 12.50 25.00
192 Ellis Deal CO 7.50 15.00
193 Johnny Hopp CO 12.50 25.00
194 Bill Sarni RC 7.50 15.00
195 Billy Consolo RC 7.50 15.00
196 Stan Jok RC 7.50 15.00
197 Lynwood Rowe CO 12.50 25.00
(Schoolboy)
198 Carl Sawatski 7.50 15.00
199 Glenn (Rocky) Nelson 7.50 15.00
200 Larry Jansen 12.50 25.00
201 Al Kaline RC 400.00 700.00
202 Bob Purkey RC 12.50 25.00
203 Harry Brecheen CO 12.50 25.00
204 Angel Scull RC 7.50 15.00
205 Johnny Sain 20.00 40.00
206 Ray Crone RC 7.50 15.00
207 Tom Oliver CO RC 7.50 15.00
208 Grady Hatton 7.50 15.00
209 Chuck Thompson RC 7.50 15.00
210 Bob Buhl RC 12.50 25.00
211 Don Hoak 12.50 25.00
212 Bob Micelotta RC 7.50 15.00
213 Johnny Fitzpatrick CO RC 7.50 15.00
214 Arnie Portocarrero RC 7.50 15.00
215 Ed McGhee 7.50 15.00
216 Al Sima 7.50 15.00
217 Paul Schreiber CO RC 7.50 15.00
218 Fred Marsh 7.50 15.00
219 Chuck Kress RC 7.50 15.00
220 Ruben Gomez RC 12.50 25.00
221 Dick Brodowski 7.50 15.00
222 Bill Wilson RC 7.50 15.00
223 Joe Haynes CO 7.50 15.00
224 Dick Weik RC 7.50 15.00
225 Don Liddle RC 7.50 15.00
226 Jehosie Heard RC 12.50 25.00
227 Buster Mills CO RC 7.50 15.00
228 Gene Hermanski 7.50 15.00
229 Bob Talbot RC 7.50 15.00
230 Bob Kuzava 12.50 25.00
231 Roy Smalley 7.50 15.00
232 Lou Limmer RC 7.50 15.00
233 Augie Galan CO 7.50 15.00
234 Jerry Lynch RC 7.50 15.00
235 Vern Law 12.50 25.00
236 Paul Penson RC 7.50 15.00
237 Mike Ryba CO RC 7.50 15.00
238 Al Aber 7.50 15.00
239 Bill Skowron RC 60.00 100.00
240 Sam Mele 12.50 25.00
241 Robert Miller RC 7.50 15.00
242 Curt Roberts RC 7.50 15.00
243 Ray Blades CO RC 7.50 15.00
244 Leroy Wheat RC 7.50 15.00
245 Roy Sievers 12.50 25.00
246 Howie Fox 7.50 15.00
247 Ed Mayo CO 7.50 15.00
248 Al Smith RC 12.50 25.00
249 Wilmer Mizell 12.50 25.00
250 Ted Williams 500.00 1000.00

1955 Topps

The cards in this 206-card set measure approximately 2 5/8" by 3 3/4". Both the large "head" shot and the smaller full-length photos used on each card of the 1955 Topps set are in color. The card fronts were designed horizontally for the first time in Topps' history. The first card features Dusty Rhodes, hitting star and MVP in the New York Giants' 1954 World Series sweep over the Cleveland Indians. A "high" series, 161 to 210, is more difficult to find than cards 1 to 160. Numbers 175, 186, 203, and 209 were never issued. To fill in for the four cards not issued in the high number series, Topps double printed four players, those appearing on cards 170, 172, 184, and 188. Cards were issued in one-card penny packs or six-card nickel packs (which came 36 packs to a box) and 15-card cello packs (rarely seen). Although rarely seen, there exist salesman sample panels of three cards containing the fronts of regular cards with ad information for the 1955 Topps regular and the 1955 Topps Doubleheaders on the back. One panel depicts (from top to bottom) Danny Schell, Jake Thies, and Howie Pollet. Another Panel consists of Jackie Robinson, Bill Taylor and Curt Roberts. The key Rookie Cards in this set are Ken Boyer, Roberto Clemente, Harmon Killebrew, and Sandy Koufax. The Frank Sullivan card has a very noticable print dot which appears on some of the cards but not all of the cards. We are not listing that card as a variation at this point, but we will continue to monitor information about that card.

COMPLETE SET (206) 5000.00 8000.00
COMMON CARD (1-150) 6.00 12.00
COMMON (151-160) 10.00 20.00
COMMON (161-210) 15.00 30.00
NOT ISSUED (175/186/203/209)
WRAP.(1-CENT, DATED) 100.00 150.00
WRAP.(1-CENT, UNDATED) 40.00 50.00
WRAP.(5-CENT, DATED) 100.00 150.00
WRAP.(5-CENT, UNDATED) 75.00 100.00
1 Dusty Rhodes 15.00 25.00
2 Ted Williams 400.00 700.00
3 Art Fowler RC 7.50 15.00
4 Al Kaline 90.00 150.00
5 Jim Gilliam 20.00 40.00
6 Stan Hack MG RC 12.50 25.00
7 Jim Hegan 7.50 15.00
8 Harold Smith RC 6.00 12.00
9 Robert Miller 6.00 12.00
10 Bob Keegan 6.00 12.00
11 Ferris Fain 7.50 15.00
12 Vernon (Jake) Thies RC 6.00 12.00
13 Fred Marsh 6.00 12.00
14 Jim Finigan RC 6.00 12.00
15 Jim Pendleton 6.00 12.00
16 Roy Sievers 7.50 15.00
17 Bobby Hofman 6.00 12.00
18 Russ Kemmerer RC 6.00 12.00
19 Billy Herman CO 7.50 15.00
20 Andy Carey 7.50 15.00
21 Alex Grammas 6.00 12.00
22 Bill Skowron 20.00 40.00
23 Jack Parks RC 6.00 12.00
24 Hal Newhouser 20.00 40.00
25 Johnny Podres 12.50 25.00
26 Dick Groat 7.50 15.00
27 Billy Gardner RC 7.50 15.00
28 Ernie Banks 125.00 200.00
29 Herman Wehmeier 6.00 12.00
30 Vic Power 7.50 15.00
31 Warren Spahn 60.00 100.00
32 Warren McGhee RC 6.00 12.00
33 Tom Qualters 6.00 12.00
34 Wayne Terwilliger 6.00 12.00
35 Dave Jolly 6.00 12.00
36 Leo Kiely 6.00 12.00
37 Joe Cunningham RC 7.50 15.00
38 Bob Turley 7.50 15.00
39 Bill Glynn 6.00 12.00
40 Don Hoak 7.50 15.00
41 Chuck Stobbs 6.00 12.00
42 John (Windy) McCall RC 6.00 12.00
43 Harvey Haddix 7.50 15.00
44 Harold Valentine RC 6.00 12.00
45 Hank Sauer 7.50 15.00
46 Ted Kazanski 6.00 12.00
47 Hank Aaron 250.00 400.00
48 Bob Kennedy 7.50 15.00
49 J.W. Porter 6.00 12.00
50 Jackie Robinson 300.00 500.00
51 Jim Hughes 7.50 15.00
52 Bill Tremel RC 6.00 12.00
53 Bill Taylor 6.00 12.00
54 Lou Limmer 6.00 12.00
55 Rip Repulski 6.00 12.00
56 Ray Jablonski 6.00 12.00
57 Billy O'Dell RC 6.00 12.00
58 Jim Rivera 6.00 12.00
59 Gair Allie 6.00 12.00
60 Dean Stone 6.00 12.00
61 Forrest Jacobs 6.00 12.00
62 Thornton Kipper 6.00 12.00
63 Joe Collins 7.50 15.00
64 Gus Triandos RC 7.50 15.00
65 Ray Boone 7.50 15.00
66 Ron Jackson RC 6.00 12.00
67 Wally Moon 7.50 15.00
68 Jim Davis RC 6.00 12.00
69 Ed Bailey 7.50 15.00
70 Al Rosen 7.50 15.00
71 Ruben Gomez 6.00 12.00
72 Karl Olson 6.00 12.00
73 Jack Shepard RC 6.00 12.00
74 Bob Borkowski 6.00 12.00
75 Sandy Amoros RC 20.00 40.00
76 Howie Pollet 6.00 12.00
77 Arnie Portocarrero 6.00 12.00
78 Gordon Jones RC 6.00 12.00
79 Clyde (Danny) Schell RC 6.00 12.00
80 Bob Grim RC 7.50 15.00
81 Gene Conley 7.50 15.00
82 Chuck Harmon 6.00 12.00
83 Tom Brewer RC 6.00 12.00
84 Camilo Pascual RC 7.50 15.00
85 Don Mossi RC 12.50 25.00
86 Bill Wilson 6.00 12.00
87 Frank House 6.00 12.00
88 Bob Skinner RC 7.50 15.00
89 Joe Frazier RC 7.50 15.00
90 Karl Spooner RC 7.50 15.00
91 Milt Bolling 6.00 12.00
92 Don Zimmer RC 12.50 25.00
93 Steve Bilko 6.00 12.00
94 Reno Bertoia 6.00 12.00
95 Preston Ward 6.00 12.00
96 Chuck Bishop 6.00 12.00
97 Carlos Paula RC 6.00 12.00
98 John Riddle CO 6.00 12.00
99 Frank Leja 6.00 12.00
100 Monte Irvin 20.00 40.00
101 Johnny Gray RC 6.00 12.00
102 Wally Westlake 6.00 12.00
103 Chuck White RC 6.00 12.00
104 Jack Harshman 6.00 12.00
105 Chuck Diering 6.00 12.00
106 Frank Sullivan RC 6.00 12.00
107 Curt Roberts 6.00 12.00
108 Rube Walker 7.50 15.00
109 Ed Lopat 7.50 15.00
110 Gus Zernial 7.50 15.00
111 Bob Milliken 7.50 15.00
112 Nelson King RC 6.00 12.00
113 Harry Brecheen CO 7.50 15.00
114 Louis Ortiz RC 6.00 12.00
115 Ellis Kinder 6.00 12.00
116 Tom Hurd RC 6.00 12.00
117 Mel Roach 6.00 12.00
118 Bob Purkey 6.00 12.00
119 Bob Lennon RC 6.00 12.00
120 Ted Kluszewski 50.00 80.00
121 Bill Renna 6.00 12.00
122 Carl Sawatski 6.00 12.00
123 Sandy Koufax RC 700.00 1200.00
124 Harmon Killebrew RC 150.00 250.00
125 Ken Boyer RC 50.00 80.00
126 Dick Hall RC 6.00 12.00
127 Dale Long RC 7.50 15.00
128 Ted Lepcio 6.00 12.00
129 Elvin Tappe 7.50 15.00
130 Mayo Smith MG RC 6.00 12.00
131 Grady Hatton 6.00 12.00
132 Bob Trice 6.00 12.00
133 Dave Hoskins 6.00 12.00
134 Joey Jay 7.50 15.00
135 Johnny O'Brien 7.50 15.00
136 Veston (Bunky) Stewart RC 6.00 12.00
137 Harry Elliott RC 6.00 12.00
138 Ray Herbert 6.00 12.00
139 Steve Kraly RC 6.00 12.00
140 Mel Parnell 7.50 15.00
141 Tom Wright 6.00 12.00
142 Jerry Lynch 6.00 12.00
143 John Schofield 7.50 15.00
144 Joe Amalfitano RC 6.00 12.00
145 Elmer Valo 6.00 12.00
146 Dick Donovan RC 6.00 12.00
147 Hugh Pepper RC 6.00 12.00
148 Hal Brown 6.00 12.00
149 Ray Crone 6.00 12.00
150 Mike Higgins MG 6.00 12.00
151 Ralph Kress CO 10.00 20.00
152 Harry Agganis RC 60.00 100.00
153 Bud Podbielan 12.50 25.00
154 Willie Miranda 10.00 20.00
155 Eddie Mathews 125.00 200.00
156 Joe Black 30.00 50.00
157 Robert Miller 10.00 20.00
158 Tommy Carroll RC 12.50 25.00
159 Johnny Schmitz 10.00 20.00
160 Ray Narleski RC 10.00 20.00
161 Chuck Tanner RC 20.00 40.00
162 Joe Coleman 15.00 30.00
163 Faye Throneberry 15.00 30.00
164 Roberto Clemente RC 1400.00 2200.00
165 Don Johnson 15.00 30.00
166 Hank Bauer 50.00 80.00
167 Tom Casagrande RC 15.00 30.00
168 Duane Pillette 15.00 30.00
169 Bob Oldis 20.00 40.00
170 Jim Pearce DP RC 7.50 15.00
171 Dick Brodowski 15.00 30.00
172 Frank Baumholtz DP 7.50 15.00
173 Bob Kline RC 15.00 30.00
174 Rudy Minarcin RC 15.00 30.00
175 Does Not Exist
176 Norm Zauchin RC 15.00 30.00
177 Al Robertson 15.00 30.00
178 Bobby Adams 15.00 30.00
179 Jim Bolger RC 15.00 30.00
180 Clem Labine 30.00 60.00

181 Roy McMillan	20.00	40.00
182 Humberto Robinson RC	15.00	30.00
183 Anthony Jacobs RC	15.00	30.00
184 Harry Perkowski DP	7.50	15.00
185 Don Ferrarese RC	15.00	30.00
186 Does Not Exist		
187 Gil Hodges	100.00	175.00
188 Charlie Silvera DP	7.50	15.00
189 Phil Rizzuto	100.00	175.00
190 Gene Woodling	20.00	40.00
191 Eddie Stanky MG	20.00	40.00
192 Jim Delsing	20.00	40.00
193 Johnny Sain	30.00	60.00
194 Willie Mays	350.00	600.00
195 Ed Roebuck RC	30.00	60.00
196 Gale Wade RC	15.00	30.00
197 Al Smith	30.00	60.00
198 Yogi Berra	175.00	300.00
199 Bert Hamric RC	20.00	40.00
200 Jackie Jensen	30.00	60.00
201 Sherman Lollar	20.00	40.00
202 Jim Owens RC	15.00	30.00
203 Does Not Exist		
204 Frank Smith	15.00	30.00
205 Gene Freese RC	20.00	40.00
206 Pete Daley RC	15.00	30.00
207 Billy Consolo	15.00	30.00
208 Ray Moore RC	20.00	40.00
209 Does Not Exist		
210 Duke Snider	350.00	600.00

1955 Topps Double Header

The cards in this 66-card set measure approximately 2 1/16" by 4 7/8". Borrowing a design from the T201 Mecca series, Topps issued a 132-player "Double Header" set in a separate wrapper in 1955. Each player is numbered in the biographical section on the reverse. When open, with perforated flap up, one player is revealed; when the flap is lowered, or closed, the player design on top incorporates a portion of the inside player artwork. When the cards are placed side by side, a continuous ballpark background is formed. Some cards have been found without perforations, and all players pictured appear in the low series of the 1955 regular issue. The cards were issued in one-card penny packs which came 120 packs to a box with a piece of bubble gum.

COMPLETE SET (66)	2500.00	4000.00
WRAPPER (1-CENT)	150.00	200.00
1 Al Rosen and 2 Chuck Diering	30.00	50.00
3 Monte Irvin and 4 Russ Kemmerer	35.00	60.00
5 Ted Kazanski and 6 Gordon Jones	25.00	40.00
7 Bill Taylor and 8 Billy O'Dell	25.00	40.00
9 J.W. Porter and 10 Thornton Kipper	25.00	40.00
11 Curt Roberts and 12 Arnie Portocarrero	25.00	40.00
13 Wally Westlake and 14 Frank House	30.00	50.00
15 Rube Walker and 16 Lou Limmer	30.00	50.00
17 Dean Stone and 18 Charlie White	25.00	40.00
19 Karl Spooner and 20 Jim Hughes	30.00	50.00
21 Bill Skowron and 22 Frank Sullivan	35.00	60.00
23 Jack Shepard and 24 Stan Hack MG	25.00	40.00
25 Jackie Robinson and 26 Don Hoak	150.00	250.00
27 Dusty Rhodes and 28 Jim Davis	30.00	50.00
29 Vic Power and 30 Ed Bailey	25.00	40.00
31 Howie Pollet and 32 Ernie Banks	125.00	200.00
33 Jim Pendleton and 34 Gene Conley	25.00	40.00
35 Karl Olson and 36 Andy Carey	25.00	40.00
37 Wally Moon and 38 Joe Cunningham	30.00	50.00
39 Freddie Marsh and 40 Vernon Thies	25.00	40.00
41 Eddie Lopat and 42 Harvey Haddix	35.00	60.00
43 Leo Kiely and 44 Chuck Stobbs	25.00	40.00
45 Al Kaline and 46 Harold Valentine	125.00	200.00
47 Forrest Jacobs and 48 Johnny Gray	25.00	40.00
49 Ron Jackson and 50 Jim Finigan	25.00	40.00
51 Ray Jablonski and 52 Bob Keegan	25.00	40.00
53 Billy Herman CO and 54 Sandy Amoros	50.00	80.00
55 Chuck Harmon and 56 Bob Skinner	25.00	40.00
57 Dick Hall and 58 Bob Grim	25.00	40.00
59 Billy Glynn and 60 Bob Miller	30.00	50.00
61 Billy Gardner and 62 John Hetki	25.00	40.00
63 Bob Borkowski and 64 Bob Turley	25.00	40.00
65 Joe Collins and 66 Jack Harshman	25.00	40.00
67 Jim Hegan and 68 Jack Parks	25.00	40.00
69 Ted Williams and 70 Mayo Smith MG	250.00	400.00
71 Gair Allie and 72 Grady Hatton	25.00	40.00
73 Jerry Lynch and 74 Harry Brecheen CO	25.00	40.00
75 Tom Wright and 76 Vernon Stewart	25.00	40.00
77 Dave Hoskins and 78 Warren McGhee	25.00	40.00
79 Roy Sievers and 80 Art Fowler	30.00	50.00
81 Danny Schell and 82 Gus Triandos	25.00	40.00
83 Joe Frazier and 84 Don Mossi	25.00	40.00
85 Elmer Valo and 86 Hector Brown	25.00	40.00
87 Bob Kennedy and 88 Windy McCall	30.00	50.00
89 Ruben Gomez and 90 Jim Rivera	25.00	40.00
91 Louis Ortiz and 92 Milt Bolling	25.00	40.00
93 Carl Sawatski and 94 El Tappe	25.00	40.00
95 Dave Jolly and 96 Bobby Hofman	25.00	40.00
97 Preston Ward and 98 Don Zimmer	35.00	60.00
99 Bill Renna and 100 Dick Groat	30.00	50.00
101 Bill Wilson and 102 Bill Tremel	25.00	40.00
103 Hank Sauer and 104 Camilo Pascual	30.00	50.00
105 Hank Aaron and 106 Ray Herbert	300.00	500.00
107 Alex Grammas and 108 Tom Qualters	25.00	40.00
109 Hal Newhouser and 110 Chuck Bishop	35.00	60.00
111 Harmon Killebrew and 112 John Podres	125.00	200.00
113 Ray Boone and 114 Bob Purkey	25.00	40.00
115 Dale Long and 116 Ferris Fain	30.00	50.00
117 Steve Bilko and 118 Bob Milliken	25.00	40.00
119 Mel Parnell and 120 Tom Hurd	30.00	50.00
121 Ted Kluszewski and 122 Jim Owens	50.00	80.00
123 Gus Zernial and 124 Bob Trice	25.00	40.00
125 Rip Repulski and 126 Ted Lepcio	25.00	40.00
127 Warren Spahn and 128 Tom Brewer	90.00	150.00
129 Jim Gilliam and 130 Ellis Kinder	50.00	80.00
131 Herm Wehmeier and 132 Wayne Terwilliger	25.00	40.00

1956 Topps

The cards in this 340-card set measure approximately 2 5/8" by 3 3/4". Following up with another horizontally oriented card in 1956, Topps improved the format by layering the color "head" shot onto an actual action sequence involving the player. Cards 1 to 180 come with either white or gray backs: in the 1 to 100 sequence, gray backs are less common (worth about 10 percent more) and in the 101 to 180 sequence, white backs are less common (worth 30 percent more). The team cards, used for the first time in a regular set by Topps, are found dated 1955, or undated, with the team name appearing on either side. The dated team cards in the first series were not printed on the gray stock. The two unnumbered checklist cards are highly prized (must be unmarked to qualify as excellent or mint). The complete set price below does not include the unnumbered checklist cards or any of the variations. The set was issued in one-card penny packs or six-card nickel packs. The six card nickel packs came 24 to a box with 24 boxes in a case while the once cent packs came 120 to a box. Both types of packs included a piece of bubble gum. Promotional three card strips were issued for this set. Among those strips were one featuring Johnny O'Brien/Harvey Haddix and Frank House. The key Rookie Cards in this set are Walt Alston, Luis Aparicio, and Roger Craig. There are ten double-printed cards in the first series as evidenced by the discovery of an uncut sheet of 110 cards (10 by 11); these DP's are listed below.

COMPLETE SET (340)	5000.00	8000.00
COMMON CARD (1-100)	5.00	10.00
COMMON (101-180)	6.00	12.00
COMMON (261-340)	6.00	12.00
COMMON (181-260)	7.50	15.00
WRAPPER (1-CENT)	200.00	250.00
WRAP.(1-CENT, REPEAT)	75.00	100.00
WRAPPER (5-CENT)	150.00	200.00
1 Will Harridge PRES	75.00	125.00
2 Warren Giles PRES DP	30.00	50.00
3 Elmer Valo	7.50	15.00
4 Carlos Paula	7.50	15.00
5 Ted Williams	300.00	500.00
6 Ray Boone	15.00	25.00
7 Ron Negray RC	5.00	10.00
8 Walter Alston MG RC	25.00	40.00
9 Ruben Gomez DP	5.00	10.00
10 Warren Spahn	70.00	120.00
11A Chicago Cubs TC (Centered)	15.00	30.00
11B Chicago Cubs TC (Dated 1955)	50.00	80.00
11C Chicago Cubs TC (Name at far left)	15.00	30.00
12 Andy Carey	7.50	15.00
13 Roy Face	7.50	15.00
14 Ken Boyer DP	7.50	15.00
15 Ernie Banks DP	60.00	100.00
16 Hector Lopez RC	7.50	15.00
17 Gene Conley	7.50	15.00
18 Dick Donovan	5.00	10.00
19 Chuck Diering DP	5.00	10.00
20 Al Kaline	75.00	125.00
21 Joe Collins DP	7.50	15.00
22 Jim Finigan	5.00	10.00
23 Fred Marsh	5.00	10.00
24 Dick Groat	7.50	15.00
25 Ted Kluszewski	50.00	80.00
26 Grady Hatton	5.00	10.00
27 Nelson Burbrink DP RC	5.00	10.00
28 Bobby Hofman	5.00	10.00
29 Jack Harshman	5.00	10.00
30 Jackie Robinson DP	150.00	250.00
31 Hank Aaron UER DP (Small photo actually Willie Mays)	200.00	350.00
32 Frank House	5.00	10.00
33 Roberto Clemente	250.00	400.00
34 Tom Brewer DP	5.00	10.00
35 Al Rosen	7.50	15.00
36 Rudy Minarcin	7.50	15.00
37 Alex Grammas	5.00	10.00
38 Bob Kennedy	7.50	15.00
39 Don Mossi	7.50	15.00
40 Bob Turley	7.50	15.00
41 Hank Sauer	7.50	15.00
42 Sandy Amoros	15.00	25.00
43 Ray Moore	5.00	10.00
44 Windy McCall	5.00	10.00
45 Gus Zernial	7.50	15.00
46 Gene Freese DP	5.00	10.00
47 Art Fowler	5.00	10.00
48 Jim Hegan	7.50	15.00
49 Pedro Ramos RC	5.00	10.00
50 Dusty Rhodes DP	7.50	15.00
51 Ernie Oravetz RC	5.00	10.00
52 Bob Grim DP	7.50	15.00
53 Arnie Portocarrero	5.00	10.00
54 Bob Keegan	5.00	10.00
55 Wally Moon	7.50	15.00
56 Dale Long	7.50	15.00
57 Duke Maas RC	5.00	10.00
58 Ed Roebuck	15.00	25.00
59 Jose Santiago RC	5.00	10.00
60 Mayo Smith MG DP	5.00	10.00
61 Bill Skowron	15.00	25.00
62 Hal Smith	7.50	15.00
63 Roger Craig RC	25.00	40.00
64 Luis Arroyo RC	5.00	10.00
65 Johnny O'Brien	7.50	15.00
66 Bob Speake DP RC	5.00	10.00
67 Vic Power	7.50	15.00
68 Chuck Stobbs	5.00	10.00
69 Chuck Tanner	7.50	15.00
70 Jim Rivera	5.00	10.00
71 Frank Sullivan	5.00	10.00
72A Philadelphia Phillies TC (Centered)	15.00	30.00
72B Philadelphia Phillies TC (Dated 1955)	50.00	80.00
72C Philadelphia Phillies TC (Name at far left) DP	15.00	30.00
73 Wayne Terwilliger	5.00	10.00
74 Jim King RC	5.00	10.00
75 Roy Sievers DP	7.50	15.00
76 Ray Crone	5.00	10.00
77 Harvey Haddix	7.50	15.00
78 Herman Wehmeier	5.00	10.00
79 Sandy Koufax	200.00	350.00
80 Gus Triandos DP	5.00	10.00
81 Wally Westlake	5.00	10.00
82 Bill Renna DP	5.00	10.00
83 Karl Spooner	7.50	15.00
84 Babe Birrer RC	5.00	10.00
85A Cleveland Indians TC (Centered)	15.00	30.00
85B Cleveland Indians TC (Dated 1955)	50.00	80.00
85C Cleveland Indians TC (Name at far left)	15.00	30.00
86 Ray Jablonski DP	5.00	10.00
87 Dean Stone	5.00	10.00
88 Johnny Kucks RC	7.50	15.00
89 Norm Zauchin	5.00	10.00
90A Cincinnati Redleg TC (Centered)	15.00	30.00
90B Cincinnati Reds TC (Dated 1955)	50.00	80.00
90C Cincinnati Reds TC (Name at far left)	15.00	30.00
91 Gail Harris RC	5.00	10.00
92 Bob (Red) Wilson	5.00	10.00
93 George Susce	5.00	10.00
94 Ron Kline UER Facimile auto is J.Robert Klein	5.00	10.00
95A Milwaukee Braves TC (Centered)	20.00	40.00
95B Milwaukee Braves TC (Dated 1955)	50.00	80.00
95C Milwaukee Braves TC (Name at far left)	20.00	40.00
96 Bill Tremel	5.00	10.00
97 Jerry Lynch	7.50	15.00
98 Camilo Pascual	7.50	15.00
99 Don Zimmer	15.00	25.00
100A Baltimore Orioles TC (Centered)	20.00	40.00
100B Baltimore Orioles TC (Dated 1955)	50.00	80.00
100C Baltimore Orioles TC (Name at far left)	20.00	40.00
101 Roy Campanella	90.00	150.00
102 Jim Davis	6.00	12.00
103 Willie Miranda	6.00	12.00
104 Bob Lennon	6.00	12.00
105 Al Smith	6.00	12.00
106 Joe Astroth	6.00	12.00
107 Eddie Mathews	60.00	100.00
108 Laurin Pepper	6.00	12.00
109 Enos Slaughter	25.00	40.00
110 Yogi Berra	100.00	175.00
111 Boston Red Sox TC	20.00	40.00
112 Dee Fondy	6.00	12.00
113 Phil Rizzuto	90.00	150.00
114 Jim Owens	7.50	15.00
115 Jackie Jensen	7.50	15.00
116 Eddie O'Brien	6.00	12.00
117 Virgil Trucks	7.50	15.00
118 Nellie Fox	50.00	80.00
119 Larry Jackson RC	7.50	15.00
120 Richie Ashburn	35.00	60.00
121 Pittsburgh Pirates TC	20.00	40.00
122 Willard Nixon	6.00	12.00
123 Roy McMillan	7.50	15.00
124 Don Kaiser	6.00	12.00
125 Minnie Minoso	25.00	40.00
126 Jim Brady RC	6.00	12.00
127 Willie Jones	7.50	15.00
128 Eddie Yost	7.50	15.00
129 Jake Martin RC	6.00	12.00
130 Willie Mays	175.00	300.00
131 Bob Roselli RC	6.00	12.00
132 Bobby Avila	6.00	12.00
133 Ray Narleski	6.00	12.00
134 St. Louis Cardinals TC	20.00	40.00
135 Mickey Mantle	900.00	1500.00
136 Johnny Logan	7.50	15.00
137 Al Silvera RC	6.00	12.00
138 Johnny Antonelli	7.50	15.00
139 Tommy Carroll	7.50	15.00
140 Herb Score RC	35.00	60.00
141 Joe Frazier	6.00	12.00
142 Gene Baker	6.00	12.00
143 Jim Piersall	7.50	15.00
144 Leroy Powell RC	6.00	12.00
145 Gil Hodges	35.00	60.00
146 Washington Nationals TC	20.00	40.00
147 Earl Torgeson	6.00	12.00
148 Alvin Dark	7.50	15.00
149 Dixie Howell	6.00	12.00
150 Duke Snider	75.00	125.00
151 Spook Jacobs	7.50	15.00
152 Billy Hoeft	7.50	15.00
153 Frank Thomas	7.50	15.00
154 Dave Pope	6.00	12.00
155 Harvey Kuenn	7.50	15.00
156 Wes Westrum	7.50	15.00
157 Dick Brodowski	6.00	12.00
158 Wally Post	7.50	15.00
159 Clint Courtney	6.00	12.00
160 Billy Pierce	7.50	15.00
161 Joe DeMaestri	6.00	12.00
162 Dave (Gus) Bell	7.50	15.00
163 Gene Woodling	7.50	15.00
164 Harmon Killebrew	60.00	100.00
165 Red Schoendienst	25.00	40.00
166 Brooklyn Dodgers TC	125.00	200.00
167 Harry Dorish	6.00	12.00
168 Sammy White	6.00	12.00
169 Bob Nelson RC	6.00	12.00
170 Bill Virdon	7.50	15.00
171 Jim Wilson	6.00	12.00
172 Frank Torre RC	7.50	15.00
173 Johnny Podres	15.00	25.00
174 Glen Gorbous RC	6.00	12.00
175 Del Crandall	7.50	15.00
176 Alex Kellner	6.00	12.00
177 Hank Bauer	15.00	25.00
178 Joe Black	7.50	15.00
179 Harry Chiti	6.00	12.00
180 Robin Roberts	30.00	50.00
181 Billy Martin	75.00	125.00
182 Paul Minner	7.50	15.00
183 Stan Lopata	10.00	20.00
184 Don Bessent RC	10.00	20.00
185 Bill Bruton	10.00	20.00
186 Ron Jackson	7.50	15.00
187 Early Wynn	30.00	50.00
188 Chicago White Sox TC	30.00	50.00
189 Ned Garver	7.50	15.00
190 Carl Furillo	18.00	30.00
191 Frank Lary	10.00	20.00
192 Smoky Burgess	10.00	20.00
193 Wilmer Mizell	10.00	20.00
194 Monte Irvin	18.00	30.00
195 George Kell	18.00	30.00
196 Tom Poholsky	7.50	15.00
197 Granny Hamner	7.50	15.00
198 Ed Fitzgerald	7.50	15.00
199 Hank Thompson	10.00	20.00
200 Bob Feller	75.00	125.00
201 Rip Repulski	7.50	15.00
202 Jim Hearn	7.50	15.00
203 Bill Tuttle	7.50	15.00
204 Art Swanson RC	7.50	15.00
205 Whitey Lockman	10.00	20.00
206 Erv Palica	7.50	15.00
207 Jim Small RC	7.50	15.00
208 Elston Howard	35.00	60.00
209 Max Surkont	7.50	15.00
210 Mike Garcia	10.00	20.00
211 Murry Dickson	7.50	15.00
212 Johnny Temple	7.50	15.00
213 Detroit Tigers TC	35.00	60.00
214 Bob Rush	7.50	15.00
215 Tommy Byrne	10.00	20.00
216 Jerry Schoonmaker RC	7.50	15.00
217 Billy Klaus	7.50	15.00
218 Joe Nuxhall UER (Misspelled Nuxall)	10.00	20.00
219 Lew Burdette	10.00	20.00
220 Del Ennis	10.00	20.00
221 Bob Friend	10.00	20.00
222 Dave Philley	7.50	15.00
223 Randy Jackson	7.50	15.00
224 Bud Podbielan	7.50	15.00
225 Gil McDougald	30.00	50.00
226 New York Giants TC	50.00	80.00
227 Russ Meyer	7.50	15.00
228 Mickey Vernon	10.00	20.00
229 Harry Brecheen CO	10.00	20.00
230 Chico Carrasquel	7.50	15.00
231 Bob Hale RC	7.50	15.00
232 Toby Atwell	7.50	15.00
233 Carl Erskine	18.00	30.00
234 Pete Runnels	7.50	15.00
235 Don Newcombe	30.00	50.00
236 Kansas City Athletics TC	20.00	40.00
237 Jose Valdivielso RC	7.50	15.00
238 Walt Dropo	10.00	20.00
239 Harry Simpson	7.50	15.00
240 Whitey Ford	75.00	125.00
241 Don Mueller UER (6-inch Tall)	10.00	20.00
242 Hershell Freeman	7.50	15.00
243 Sherm Lollar	10.00	20.00
244 Bob Buhl	18.00	30.00
245 Billy Goodman	10.00	20.00
246 Tom Gorman	7.50	15.00
247 Bill Sarni	7.50	15.00
248 Bob Porterfield	7.50	15.00
249 Johnny Klippstein	7.50	15.00
250 Larry Doby	18.00	30.00
251 New York Yankees TC UER Larsen misspelled as Larson on front)	150.00	250.00
252 Vern Law	10.00	20.00
253 Irv Noren	10.00	20.00
254 George Crowe	7.50	15.00
255 Bob Lemon	30.00	50.00
256 Tom Hurd	7.50	15.00
257 Bobby Thomson	18.00	30.00
258 Art Ditmar	7.50	15.00
259 Sam Jones	10.00	20.00
260 Pee Wee Reese	90.00	150.00
261 Bobby Shantz	7.50	15.00
262 Howie Pollet	6.00	12.00
263 Bob Miller	6.00	12.00
264 Ray Monzant RC	6.00	12.00
265 Sandy Consuegra	6.00	12.00
266 Don Ferrarese	6.00	12.00
267 Bob Nieman	6.00	12.00
268 Dale Mitchell	7.50	15.00
269 Jack Meyer RC	6.00	12.00
270 Billy Loes	7.50	15.00
271 Foster Castleman RC	6.00	12.00
272 Danny O'Connell	6.00	12.00
273 Walker Cooper	6.00	12.00
274 Frank Baumholtz	6.00	12.00
275 Jim Greengrass	6.00	12.00
276 George Zuverink	6.00	12.00
277 Daryl Spencer	6.00	12.00
278 Chet Nichols	6.00	12.00
279 Johnny Groth	6.00	12.00
280 Jim Gilliam	25.00	40.00
281 Art Houtteman	6.00	12.00
282 Warren Hacker	6.00	12.00
283 Hal Smith RC UER Wrong Facsimile Autograph, belongs to Hal W. Smith	7.50	15.00
284 Ike Delock	6.00	12.00
285 Eddie Miksis	6.00	12.00
286 Bill Wight	6.00	12.00
287 Bobby Adams	6.00	12.00
288 Bob Cerv	25.00	40.00
289 Hal Jeffcoat	6.00	12.00
290 Curt Simmons	7.50	15.00
291 Frank Kellert RC	6.00	12.00
292 Luis Aparicio RC	90.00	150.00
293 Stu Miller	15.00	25.00
294 Ernie Johnson	7.50	15.00
295 Clem Labine	7.50	15.00
296 Andy Seminick	6.00	12.00
297 Bob Skinner	7.50	15.00
298 Johnny Schmitz	6.00	12.00
299 Charlie Neal	25.00	40.00
300 Vic Wertz	7.50	15.00
301 Marv Grissom	6.00	12.00
302 Eddie Robinson	6.00	12.00
303 Jim Dyck	6.00	12.00
304 Frank Malzone	7.50	15.00
305 Brooks Lawrence	6.00	12.00
306 Curt Roberts	6.00	12.00
307 Hoyt Wilhelm	25.00	40.00
308 Chuck Harmon	6.00	12.00
309 Don Blasingame RC	7.50	15.00
310 Steve Gromek	6.00	12.00
311 Hal Naragon	6.00	12.00
312 Andy Pafko	7.50	15.00
313 Gene Stephens	6.00	12.00
314 Hobie Landrith	6.00	12.00
315 Milt Bolling	6.00	12.00
316 Jerry Coleman	7.50	15.00
317 Al Aber	6.00	12.00
318 Fred Hatfield	6.00	12.00
319 Jack Crimian RC	6.00	12.00
320 Joe Adcock	7.50	15.00
321 Jim Konstanty	7.50	15.00
322 Karl Olson	6.00	12.00
323 Willard Schmidt	6.00	12.00
324 Rocky Bridges	7.50	15.00
325 Don Liddle	6.00	12.00
326 Connie Johnson RC	6.00	12.00
327 Bob Wiesler RC	6.00	12.00
328 Preston Ward	6.00	12.00
329 Lou Berberet RC	6.00	12.00
330 Jim Busby	7.50	15.00
331 Dick Hall	6.00	12.00
332 Don Larsen	35.00	60.00
333 Rube Walker	6.00	12.00
334 Bob Miller	7.50	15.00
335 Don Hoak	7.50	15.00
336 Ellis Kinder	6.00	12.00
337 Bobby Morgan	6.00	12.00
338 Jim Delsing	6.00	12.00
339 Rance Pless RC	6.00	12.00
340 Mickey McDermott	35.00	60.00
CL1 Checklist 1/3	175.00	300.00
CL2 Checklist 2/4	175.00	300.00

1957 Topps

The cards in this 407-card set measure 2 1/2" by 3 1/2". In 1957, Topps returned to the vertical obverse, adopted what we now call the standard card size, and used a large, uncluttered color photo for the first time since 1952. Cards in the series 265 to 352 and the unnumbered checklist cards are scarcer than other cards in the set. However within this scarce series (265-352) there are 22 cards which were printed in double the quantity of the other cards in the series; these 22 double prints are indicated by DP in the checklist below. The first star combination cards, cards 400 and 407, are quite popular with collectors. They feature the big stars of the previous season's World Series teams, the Dodgers (Furillo, Hodges, Campanella, and Snider) and Yankees (Berra and Mantle). The complete set price below does not include the unnumbered checklist cards. Confirmed packaging includes one-cent penny packs and six-card nickel packs. Cello packs are definately known to exist and some collectors remember buying rack packs of 57's as well. The key Rookie Cards in this set are Jim Bunning, Rocky Colavito, Don Drysdale, Whitey Herzog, Tony Kubek, Bill Mazeroski, Bobby Richardson, Brooks Robinson, and Frank Robinson.

COMPLETE SET (407)	7000.00	10000.00
COMMON CARD (1-88)	5.00	10.00
COMMON CARD (89-176)	4.00	8.00
COMMON (177-264)	4.00	8.00
COMMON (265-352)	10.00	20.00
COMMON (353-407)	4.00	8.00
COMMON DP (265-352)	6.00	12.00
WRAPPER (1-CENT)	250.00	300.00
WRAPPER (5-CENT)	150.00	200.00
1 Ted Williams	350.00	600.00
2 Yogi Berra	125.00	200.00
3 Dale Long	10.00	20.00
4 Johnny Logan	10.00	20.00
5 Sal Maglie	10.00	20.00
6 Hector Lopez	7.50	15.00
7 Luis Aparicio	15.00	30.00
8 Don Mossi	7.50	15.00
9 Johnny Temple	7.50	15.00
10 Willie Mays	250.00	400.00
11 George Zuverink	5.00	10.00
12 Dick Groat	10.00	20.00
13 Wally Burnette RC	5.00	10.00
14 Bob Nieman	5.00	10.00
15 Robin Roberts	15.00	30.00
16 Walt Moryn	5.00	10.00
17 Billy Gardner	5.00	10.00
18 Don Drysdale RC	150.00	250.00
19 Bob Wilson	5.00	10.00
20 Hank Aaron UER (Reverse negative photo on front)	175.00	300.00
21 Frank Sullivan	5.00	10.00
22 Jerry Snyder UER Photo actually Ed Fitzgerald	5.00	10.00
23 Sherm Lollar	7.50	15.00
24 Bill Mazeroski RC	50.00	80.00
25 Whitey Ford	100.00	175.00
26 Bob Boyd	5.00	10.00
27 Ted Kazanski	5.00	10.00
28 Gene Conley	7.50	15.00
29 Whitey Herzog RC	15.00	30.00
30 Pee Wee Reese	50.00	80.00
31 Ron Northey	5.00	10.00
32 Hershell Freeman	5.00	10.00
33 Jim Small	5.00	10.00
34 Tom Sturdivant RC	7.50	15.00
35 Frank Robinson RC	175.00	300.00
36 Bob Grim	5.00	10.00
37 Frank Torre	7.50	15.00
38 Nellie Fox	30.00	50.00
39 Al Worthington RC	5.00	10.00
40 Early Wynn	15.00	30.00
41 Hal W. Smith	5.00	10.00
42 Dee Fondy	5.00	10.00
43 Connie Johnson	5.00	10.00
44 Joe DeMaestri	5.00	10.00
45 Carl Furillo	15.00	30.00
46 Robert J. Miller	5.00	10.00
47 Don Blasingame	5.00	10.00
48 Bill Bruton	7.50	15.00
49 Daryl Spencer	5.00	10.00
50 Herb Score	15.00	30.00
51 Clint Courtney	5.00	10.00
52 Lee Walls	5.00	10.00
53 Clem Labine	10.00	20.00
54 Elmer Valo	5.00	10.00
55 Ernie Banks	75.00	125.00
56 Dave Sisler RC	5.00	10.00
57 Jim Lemon	7.50	15.00
58 Ruben Gomez	5.00	10.00
59 Dick Williams	7.50	15.00
60 Billy Hoeft	7.50	15.00
61 Dusty Rhodes	7.50	15.00
62 Billy Martin	35.00	60.00
63 Ike Delock	5.00	10.00
64 Pete Runnels	7.50	15.00
65 Wally Moon	7.50	15.00
66 Brooks Lawrence	5.00	10.00
67 Chico Carrasquel	5.00	10.00
68 Ray Crone	5.00	10.00
69 Roy McMillan	7.50	15.00
70 Richie Ashburn	30.00	50.00
71 Murry Dickson	5.00	10.00
72 Bill Tuttle	5.00	10.00
73 George Crowe	5.00	10.00
74 Vito Valentinetti RC	5.00	10.00
75 Jimmy Piersall	7.50	15.00
76 Roberto Clemente	175.00	300.00
77 Paul Foytack RC	5.00	10.00
78 Vic Wertz	7.50	15.00
79 Lindy McDaniel RC	7.50	15.00
80 Gil Hodges	30.00	50.00
81 Herman Wehmeier	5.00	10.00
82 Elston Howard	15.00	30.00
83 Lou Skizas RC	5.00	10.00
84 Moe Drabowsky RC	7.50	15.00
85 Larry Doby	15.00	30.00
86 Bill Sarni	5.00	10.00
87 Tom Gorman	5.00	10.00
88 Harvey Kuenn	7.50	15.00
89 Roy Sievers	7.50	15.00
90 Warren Spahn	50.00	80.00
91 Mack Burk RC	4.00	8.00
92 Mickey Vernon	7.50	15.00
93 Hal Jeffcoat	4.00	8.00
94 Bobby Del Greco	4.00	8.00
95 Mickey Mantle	700.00	1200.00
96 Hank Aguirre RC	4.00	8.00
97 New York Yankees TC	60.00	100.00
98 Alvin Dark	7.50	15.00
99 Bob Keegan	4.00	8.00
100 Warren Giles PRES Will Harridge PRES	7.50	15.00
101 Chuck Stobbs	4.00	8.00
102 Ray Boone	7.50	15.00
103 Joe Nuxhall	7.50	15.00
104 Hank Foiles	4.00	8.00
105 Johnny Antonelli	7.50	15.00
106 Ray Moore	4.00	8.00
107 Jim Rivera	4.00	8.00
108 Tommy Byrne	7.50	15.00
109 Hank Thompson	4.00	8.00
110 Bill Virdon	7.50	15.00
111 Hal R. Smith	4.00	8.00
112 Tom Brewer	4.00	8.00
113 Wilmer Mizell	7.50	15.00
114 Milwaukee Braves TC	10.00	20.00
115 Jim Gilliam	7.50	15.00
116 Mike Fornieles	4.00	8.00
117 Joe Adcock	10.00	20.00
118 Bob Porterfield	4.00	8.00
119 Stan Lopata	4.00	8.00
120 Bob Lemon	15.00	30.00
121 Clete Boyer RC	15.00	30.00
122 Ken Boyer	10.00	20.00
123 Steve Ridzik	4.00	8.00
124 Dave Philley	4.00	8.00
125 Al Kaline	60.00	100.00
126 Bob Wiesler	4.00	8.00
127 Bob Buhl	7.50	15.00
128 Ed Bailey	7.50	15.00
129 Saul Rogovin	4.00	8.00
130 Don Newcombe	10.00	20.00
131 Milt Bolling	4.00	8.00
132 Art Ditmar	7.50	15.00
133 Del Crandall	7.50	15.00
134 Don Kaiser	4.00	8.00
135 Bill Skowron	10.00	20.00
136 Jim Hegan	7.50	15.00
137 Bob Rush	4.00	8.00
138 Minnie Minoso	10.00	20.00
139 Lou Kretlow	4.00	8.00
140 Frank Thomas	7.50	15.00
141 Al Aber	4.00	8.00
142 Charley Thompson	4.00	8.00
143 Andy Pafko	7.50	15.00
144 Ray Narleski	4.00	8.00
145 Al Smith	4.00	8.00
146 Don Ferrarese	4.00	8.00
147 Al Walker	4.00	8.00
148 Don Mueller	7.50	15.00
149 Bob Kennedy	7.50	15.00
150 Bob Friend	7.50	15.00
151 Willie Miranda	4.00	8.00
152 Jack Harshman	4.00	8.00
153 Karl Olson	4.00	8.00
154 Red Schoendienst	15.00	30.00
155 Jim Brosnan	7.50	15.00
156 Gus Triandos	7.50	15.00
157 Wally Post	7.50	15.00
158 Curt Simmons	7.50	15.00
159 Solly Drake RC	4.00	8.00
160 Billy Pierce	7.50	15.00
161 Pittsburgh Pirates TC	7.50	15.00
162 Jack Meyer	4.00	8.00
163 Sammy White	4.00	8.00
164 Tommy Carroll	4.00	8.00
165 Ted Kluszewski	60.00	100.00
166 Roy Face	7.50	15.00
167 Vic Power	7.50	15.00
168 Frank Lary	7.50	15.00
169 Herb Plews RC	4.00	8.00
170 Duke Snider	75.00	125.00
171 Boston Red Sox TC	7.50	15.00
172 Gene Woodling	7.50	15.00
173 Roger Craig	7.50	15.00
174 Willie Jones	4.00	8.00
175 Don Larsen	15.00	30.00
176A Gene Baker ERR (Misspelled Bakep on card back)	200.00	350.00
176B Gene Baker COR	7.50	15.00
177 Eddie Yost	7.50	15.00
178 Don Bessent	4.00	8.00
179 Ernie Oravetz	4.00	8.00
180 Gus Bell	7.50	15.00
181 Dick Donovan	4.00	8.00
182 Hobie Landrith	4.00	8.00
183 Chicago Cubs TC	7.50	15.00
184 Tito Francona RC	4.00	8.00
185 Johnny Kucks	7.50	15.00
186 Jim King	7.50	15.00
187 Virgil Trucks	7.50	15.00
188 Felix Mantilla RC	7.50	15.00
189 Willard Nixon	4.00	8.00
190 Randy Jackson	4.00	8.00
191 Joe Margoneri RC	4.00	8.00
192 Jerry Coleman	7.50	15.00
193 Del Rice	4.00	8.00
194 Hal Brown	4.00	8.00
195 Bobby Avila	4.00	8.00
196 Larry Jackson	7.50	15.00
197 Hank Sauer	7.50	15.00
198 Detroit Tigers TC	7.50	15.00
199 Vern Law	7.50	15.00
200 Gil McDougald	7.50	15.00
201 Sandy Amoros	7.50	15.00
202 Dick Gernert	4.00	8.00
203 Hoyt Wilhelm	15.00	30.00
204 Kansas City Athletics TC	7.50	15.00
205 Charlie Maxwell	7.50	15.00
206 Willard Schmidt	4.00	8.00
207 Gordon (Billy) Hunter	4.00	8.00
208 Lou Burdette	7.50	15.00
209 Bob Skinner	7.50	15.00
210 Roy Campanella	90.00	150.00
211 Camilo Pascual	7.50	15.00
212 Rocky Colavito RC	75.00	125.00
213 Les Moss	4.00	8.00
214 Philadelphia Phillies TC	7.50	15.00
215 Enos Slaughter	15.00	30.00
216 Marv Grissom	4.00	8.00
217 Gene Stephens	4.00	8.00
218 Ray Jablonski	4.00	8.00
219 Tom Acker RC	4.00	8.00
220 Jackie Jensen	10.00	20.00
221 Dixie Howell	4.00	8.00
222 Alex Grammas	4.00	8.00
223 Frank House	4.00	8.00
224 Marv Blaylock	4.00	8.00
225 Harry Simpson	4.00	8.00
226 Preston Ward	4.00	8.00
227 Gerry Staley	4.00	8.00
228 Smoky Burgess UER (Misspelled Smokey on card back)	7.50	15.00
229 George Susce	4.00	8.00
230 George Kell	15.00	30.00
231 Solly Hemus	4.00	8.00
232 Whitey Lockman	7.50	15.00
233 Art Fowler	4.00	8.00
234 Dick Cole	4.00	8.00

1957 Topps

235 Tom Poholsky 4.00 8.00
236 Joe Ginsberg 4.00 8.00
237 Foster Castleman 4.00 8.00
238 Eddie Robinson 4.00 8.00
239 Tom Morgan 4.00 8.00
240 Hank Bauer 7.50 15.00
241 Joe Lonnett RC 4.00 8.00
242 Charlie Neal 7.50 15.00
243 St. Louis Cardinals TC 7.50 15.00
244 Billy Loes 7.50 15.00
245 Rip Repulski 4.00 8.00
246 Jose Valdivielso 4.00 8.00
247 Turk Lown 4.00 8.00
248 Jim Finigan 4.00 8.00
249 Dave Pope 4.00 8.00
250 Eddie Mathews 30.00 50.00
251 Baltimore Orioles TC 7.50 15.00
252 Carl Erskine 7.50 15.00
253 Gus Zernial 7.50 15.00
254 Ron Negray 4.00 8.00
255 Charlie Silvera 7.50 15.00
256 Ron Kline 4.00 8.00
257 Walt Dropo 4.00 8.00
258 Steve Gromek 4.00 8.00
259 Eddie O'Brien 4.00 8.00
260 Del Ennis 7.50 15.00
261 Bob Chakales 4.00 8.00
262 Bobby Thomson 7.50 15.00
263 George Strickland 4.00 8.00
264 Bob Turley 7.50 15.00
265 Harvey Haddix DP 6.00 12.00
266 Ken Kuhn DP RC 6.00 12.00
267 Danny Kravitz RC 10.00 20.00
268 Jack Collum 10.00 20.00
269 Bob Cerv 15.00 30.00
270 Washington Senators TC 35.00 60.00
271 Danny O'Connell DP 6.00 12.00
272 Bobby Shantz 15.00 30.00
273 Jim Davis 10.00 20.00
274 Don Hoak 7.50 15.00
275 Cleveland Indians TC 35.00 60.00
UER Text on back credits Tribe
with winning AL title in '28.
The Yankees won that year.)
276 Jim Pyburn RC 10.00 20.00
277 Johnny Podres DP 20.00 40.00
278 Fred Hatfield DP 6.00 12.00
279 Bob Thurman RC 10.00 20.00
280 Alex Kellner 10.00 20.00
281 Gail Harris 10.00 20.00
282 Jack Dittmer DP 6.00 12.00
283 Wes Covington DP RC 6.00 12.00
284 Don Zimmer 20.00 40.00
285 Ned Garver 10.00 20.00
286 Bobby Richardson RC 75.00 125.00
287 Sam Jones 10.00 20.00
288 Ted Lepcio 10.00 20.00
289 Jim Bolger DP 6.00 12.00
290 Andy Carey DP 20.00 40.00
291 Windy McCall 10.00 20.00
292 Billy Klaus 10.00 20.00
293 Ted Abernathy RC 10.00 20.00
294 Rocky Bridges DP 6.00 12.00
295 Joe Collins DP 20.00 40.00
296 Johnny Klippstein 10.00 20.00
297 Jack Crimian 10.00 20.00
298 Irv Noren DP 6.00 12.00
299 Chuck Harmon 10.00 20.00
300 Mike Garcia 15.00 30.00
301 Sammy Esposito DP RC 10.00 20.00
302 Sandy Koufax DP 200.00 350.00
303 Billy Goodman 15.00 30.00
304 Joe Cunningham 15.00 30.00
305 Chico Fernandez 10.00 20.00
306 Darrell Johnson DP RC 6.00 12.00
307 Jack D. Phillips DP 6.00 12.00
308 Dick Hall 10.00 20.00
309 Jim Busby DP 6.00 12.00
310 Max Surkont DP 6.00 12.00
311 Al Pilarcik DP RC 6.00 12.00
312 Tony Kubek DP RC 60.00 100.00
313 Mel Parnell 7.50 15.00
314 Ed Bouchee DP RC 6.00 12.00
315 Lou Berberet DP 6.00 12.00
316 Billy O'Dell 10.00 20.00
317 New York Giants TC 50.00 80.00
318 Mickey McDermott 10.00 20.00
319 Gino Cimoli RC 10.00 20.00
320 Neil Chrisley RC 10.00 20.00
321 John (Red) Murff RC 10.00 20.00
322 Cincinnati Reds TC 50.00 80.00
323 Wes Westrum 15.00 30.00
324 Brooklyn Dodgers TC 90.00 150.00
325 Frank Bolling 10.00 20.00
326 Pedro Ramos 10.00 20.00
327 Jim Pendleton 10.00 20.00
328 Brooks Robinson RC 250.00 400.00
329 Chicago White Sox TC 35.00 60.00
330 Jim Wilson 10.00 20.00
331 Ray Katt 10.00 20.00
332 Bob Bowman RC 10.00 20.00
333 Ernie Johnson 10.00 20.00
334 Jerry Schoonmaker 10.00 20.00
335 Granny Hamner 10.00 20.00
336 Haywood Sullivan RC 20.00 40.00
337 Rene Valdes RC 12.50 25.00
338 Jim Bunning RC 90.00 150.00
339 Bob Speake 10.00 20.00
340 Bill Wight 10.00 20.00
341 Don Gross RC 10.00 20.00
342 Gene Mauch 15.00 30.00
343 Taylor Phillips RC 7.50 15.00
344 Paul LaPalme 10.00 20.00
345 Paul Smith 10.00 20.00
346 Dick Littlefield 10.00 20.00
347 Hal Naragon 10.00 20.00
348 Jim Hearn 10.00 20.00
349 Nellie King 10.00 20.00
350 Eddie Miksis 10.00 20.00
351 Dave Hillman RC 10.00 20.00
352 Ellis Kinder 10.00 20.00
353 Cal Neeman RC 4.00 8.00
354 Rip Coleman RC 4.00 8.00
355 Frank Malzone 7.50 15.00
356 Faye Throneberry 4.00 8.00
357 Earl Torgeson 4.00 8.00
358 Jerry Lynch 7.50 15.00
359 Tom Cheney RC 4.00 8.00
360 Johnny Groth 4.00 8.00
361 Curt Barclay RC 4.00 8.00
362 Roman Mejias RC 7.50 15.00
363 Eddie Kasko RC 4.00 8.00
364 Cal McLish RC 7.50 15.00
365 Ozzie Virgil RC 4.00 8.00
366 Ken Lehman 4.00 8.00
367 Ed Fitzgerald 4.00 8.00
368 Bob Purkey 4.00 8.00
369 Milt Graff RC 4.00 8.00
370 Warren Hacker 4.00 8.00
371 Bob Lennon 4.00 8.00
372 Norm Zauchin 4.00 8.00
373 Pete Whisenant RC 4.00 8.00
374 Don Cardwell RC 4.00 8.00
375 Jim Landis RC 7.50 15.00
376 Don Elston RC 4.00 8.00
377 Andre Rodgers RC 4.00 8.00
378 Elmer Singleton 4.00 8.00
379 Don Lee RC 4.00 8.00
380 Walker Cooper 4.00 8.00
381 Dean Stone 4.00 8.00
382 Jim Brideweser 4.00 8.00
383 Juan Pizarro RC 4.00 8.00
384 Bobby G. Smith RC 4.00 8.00
385 Art Houtteman 4.00 8.00
386 Lyle Luttrell RC 4.00 8.00
387 Jack Sanford RC 7.50 15.00
388 Pete Daley 4.00 8.00
389 Dave Jolly 4.00 8.00
390 Reno Bertoia 4.00 8.00
391 Ralph Terry RC 7.50 15.00
392 Chuck Tanner 7.50 15.00
393 Raul Sanchez RC 4.00 8.00
394 Luis Arroyo 7.50 15.00
395 Bubba Phillips 4.00 8.00
396 Casey Wise RC 4.00 8.00
397 Roy Smalley 4.00 8.00
398 Al Cicotte RC 7.50 15.00
399 Billy Consolo 4.00 8.00
400 Dodgers Sluggers 150.00 250.00
Carl Furillo
Gil Hodges
Roy Campanella
Duke Snider
401 Earl Battey RC 7.50 15.00
402 Jim Pisoni RC 4.00 8.00
403 Dick Hyde RC 4.00 8.00
404 Harry Anderson RC 4.00 8.00
405 Duke Maas 4.00 8.00
406 Bob Hale 4.00 8.00
407 Yankees Power Hitters 350.00 600.00
Mickey Mantle
Yogi Berra
CC1 Contest Card 60.00 100.00
Saturday, May 4th
Boston Red Sox
vs. Cleveland Indians
Cincinnati Redlegs
vs. New York Giants
CC2 Contest Card 60.00 100.00
Saturday, May 25th
Detroit Tigers
vs. Kansas City Athletics
Pittsburgh Pirates
vs. Philadelphia Phillies
CC3 Contest Card 75.00 125.00
Saturday, June 22nd
Brooklyn Dodgers
vs. St. Louis Cardinals
Chicago White Sox
vs. New York Yankees
CC4 Contest Card 75.00 125.00
Saturday, July 19th
Milwaukee Braves
vs. New York Giants
Baltimore Orioles
vs. Kansas City Athletics
NNO Checklist 1/2 150.00 250.00
Bazooka Back
NNO Checklist 1/2 150.00 250.00
Blony Back
NNO Checklist 2/3 250.00 400.00
Bazooka Back
NNO Checklist 2/3 250.00 400.00
Blony Back
NNO Checklist 3/4 500.00 800.00
(Bazooka Back
NNO Checklist 3/4 350.00 600.00
Blony Back
NNO Checklist 4/5 600.00 1000.00
Bazooka Back
NNO Checklist 4/5 500.00 800.00
Blony Back
NNO Lucky Penny Charm 60.00 100.00
and Key Chain
offer card

1958 Topps

This is a 494-card standard-size set. Card number 145, which was supposedly to be Ed Bouchee, was not issued. The 1958 Topps set contains the first Sport Magazine All-Star Selection series (475-495) and expanded use of combination cards. For the first time team cards carried series checklists on back (Milwaukee, Detroit, Baltimore, and Cincinnati are also found with players listed alphabetically). In the first series some cards were issued with yellow name (YN) or team (YT) lettering, as opposed to the common white lettering. They are explicity noted below. Cards were issued in one-card penny packs or six-card nickel packs. In the last series, All-Star cards of Stan Musial and Mickey Mantle were triple printed; the cards they replaced (443, 446, 450, and 462) on the printing sheet were hence printed in shorter supply than other cards in the last series and are marked with an SP in the list below. The All-Star card of Musial marked his first appearance on a Topps card. Technically the New York Giants team card (19) is an error as the Giants had already moved to San Francisco. The key Rookie Cards in this set are Orlando Cepeda, Curt Flood, Roger Maris, and Vada Pinson. These cards were issued in varying formats, including one cent packs which were issued 120 to a box.

COMP. MASTER (534) 8000.00 12000.00
COMPLETE SET (494) 4000.00 6000.00
COMMON CARD (1-110) 6.00 12.00
COMMON (111-495) 4.00 8.00
WRAPPER (1-CENT) 75.00 100.00
WRAPPER (5-CENT) 100.00 125.00
1 Ted Williams 350.00 600.00
2A Bob Lemon 15.00 30.00
2B Bob Lemon YT 35.00 60.00
3 Alex Kellner 6.00 12.00
4 Hank Foiles 6.00 12.00
5 Willie Mays 175.00 300.00
6 George Zuverink 6.00 12.00
7 Dale Long 7.50 15.00
8A Eddie Kasko 6.00 12.00
8B Eddie Kasko YN 20.00 40.00
9 Hank Bauer 10.00 20.00
10 Lou Burdette 10.00 20.00
11A Jim Rivera 6.00 12.00
11B Jim Rivera YT 20.00 40.00
12 George Crowe 6.00 12.00
13A Billy Hoeft 6.00 12.00
13B Billy Hoeft YN 20.00 40.00
14 Rip Repulski 6.00 12.00
15 Jim Lemon 7.50 15.00
16 Charlie Neal 7.50 15.00
17 Felix Mantilla 6.00 12.00
18 Frank Sullivan 6.00 12.00
19 San Francisco Giants TC 20.00 40.00
20A Gil McDougald 10.00 20.00
20B Gil McDougald YN 35.00 60.00
21 Curt Barclay 6.00 12.00
22 Hal Naragon 6.00 12.00
23A Bill Tuttle 6.00 12.00
23B Bill Tuttle YN 20.00 40.00
24A Hobie Landrith 6.00 12.00
24B Hobie Landrith YN 20.00 40.00
25 Don Drysdale 60.00 100.00
26 Ron Jackson 6.00 12.00
27 Bud Freeman 6.00 12.00
28 Jim Busby 6.00 12.00
29 Ted Lepcio 6.00 12.00
30A Hank Aaron 125.00 200.00
30B Hank Aaron YN 350.00 600.00
31 Tex Clevenger RC 6.00 12.00
32A J.W. Porter 6.00 12.00
32B J.W. Porter YN 20.00 40.00
33A Cal Neeman 6.00 12.00
33B Cal Neeman YT 20.00 40.00
34 Bob Thurman 6.00 12.00
35A Don Mossi 7.50 15.00
35B Don Mossi YT 20.00 40.00
36 Ted Kazanski 6.00 12.00
37 Mike McCormick RC 7.50 15.00
UER Photo actually
Ray Monzant
38 Dick Gernert 6.00 12.00
39 Bob Martyn RC 6.00 12.00
40 George Kell 15.00 30.00
41 Dave Hillman 6.00 12.00
42 John Roseboro RC 15.00 30.00
43 Sal Maglie 7.50 15.00
44 Washington Senators TC 10.00 20.00
45 Dick Groat 7.50 15.00
46A Lou Sleater 6.00 12.00
46B Lou Sleater YN 20.00 40.00
47 Roger Maris RC 300.00 500.00
48 Chuck Harmon 6.00 12.00
49 Smoky Burgess 7.50 15.00
50A Billy Pierce 7.50 15.00
50B Billy Pierce YT 20.00 40.00
51 Del Rice 6.00 12.00
52A Roberto Clemente 175.00 300.00
52B Roberto Clemente YT 300.00 500.00
53A Morrie Martin 6.00 12.00
53B Morrie Martin YN 20.00 40.00
54 Norm Siebern RC 10.00 20.00
55 Chico Carrasquel 6.00 12.00
56 Bill Fischer RC 6.00 12.00
57A Tim Thompson 6.00 12.00
57B Tim Thompson YN 20.00 40.00
58A Art Schult 6.00 12.00
58B Art Schult YT 20.00 40.00
59 Dave Sisler 6.00 12.00
60A Del Ennis 7.50 15.00
60B Del Ennis YN 20.00 40.00
61A Darrell Johnson 6.00 12.00
61B Darrell Johnson YN 20.00 40.00
62 Joe DeMaestri 6.00 12.00
63 Joe Nuxhall 7.50 15.00
64 Joe Lonnett 6.00 12.00
65A Von McDaniel RC 6.00 12.00
65B Von McDaniel YN 20.00 40.00
66 Lee Walls 6.00 12.00
67 Joe Ginsberg 6.00 12.00
68 Daryl Spencer 6.00 12.00
69 Wally Burnette 6.00 12.00
70A Al Kaline 60.00 100.00
70B Al Kaline YN 150.00 250.00
71 Los Angeles Dodgers TC 35.00 60.00
72 Bud Byerly UER 6.00 12.00
Photo is Hal Griggs
73 Pete Daley 6.00 12.00
74 Roy Face 7.50 15.00
75 Gus Bell 7.50 15.00
76A Dick Farrell RC 6.00 12.00
76B Dick Farrell YT 20.00 40.00
77A Don Zimmer 7.50 15.00
77B Don Zimmer YT 20.00 40.00
78A Ernie Johnson 7.50 15.00
78B Ernie Johnson YN 20.00 40.00
79A Dick Williams 7.50 15.00
79B Dick Williams YT 20.00 40.00
80 Dick Drott RC 6.00 12.00
81A Steve Boros RC 6.00 12.00
81B Steve Boros YT 20.00 40.00
82 Ron Kline 6.00 12.00
83 Bob Hazle RC 6.00 12.00
84 Billy O'Dell 6.00 12.00
85A Luis Aparicio 15.00 30.00
85B Luis Aparicio YT 50.00 80.00
86 Valmy Thomas RC 6.00 12.00
87 Johnny Kucks 6.00 12.00
88 Duke Snider 50.00 80.00
89 Billy Klaus 6.00 12.00
90 Robin Roberts 15.00 30.00
91 Chuck Tanner 7.50 15.00
92A Clint Courtney 6.00 12.00
92B Clint Courtney YN 20.00 40.00
93 Sandy Amoros 7.50 15.00
94 Bob Skinner 7.50 15.00
95 Frank Bolling 6.00 12.00
96 Joe Durham RC 6.00 12.00
97A Larry Jackson 6.00 12.00
97B Larry Jackson YN 20.00 40.00
98A Billy Hunter 6.00 12.00
98B Billy Hunter YN 20.00 40.00
99 Bobby Adams 6.00 12.00
100A Early Wynn 15.00 30.00
100B Early Wynn YT 50.00 80.00
101A Bobby Richardson 15.00 30.00
101B B.Richardson YN 35.00 60.00
102 George Strickland 6.00 12.00
103 Jerry Lynch 7.50 15.00
104 Jim Pendleton 6.00 12.00
105 Billy Gardner 6.00 12.00
106 Dick Schofield 7.50 15.00
107 Ossie Virgil 6.00 12.00
108A Jim Landis 6.00 12.00
108B Jim Landis YT 20.00 40.00
109 Herb Plews 6.00 12.00
110 Johnny Logan 7.50 15.00
111 Stu Miller 5.00 10.00
112 Gus Zernial 5.00 10.00
113 Jerry Walker RC 5.00 10.00
114 Irv Noren 5.00 10.00
115 Jim Bunning 15.00 30.00
116 Dave Philley 4.00 8.00
117 Frank Torre 5.00 10.00
118 Harvey Haddix 5.00 10.00
119 Harry Chiti 4.00 8.00
120 Johnny Podres 5.00 10.00
121 Eddie Miksis 4.00 8.00
122 Walt Moryn 4.00 8.00
123 Dick Tomanek RC 4.00 8.00
124 Bobby Usher 4.00 8.00
125 Alvin Dark 5.00 10.00
126 Stan Palys RC 4.00 8.00
127 Tom Sturdivant 5.00 10.00
128 Willie Kirkland RC 4.00 8.00
129 Jim Derrington RC 4.00 8.00
130 Jackie Jensen 5.00 10.00
131 Bob Henrich RC 4.00 8.00
132 Vern Law 5.00 10.00
133 Russ Nixon RC 4.00 8.00
134 Philadelphia Phillies TC 7.50 15.00
135 Mike (Moe) Drabowsky 5.00 10.00
136 Jim Finigan 4.00 8.00
137 Russ Kemmerer 4.00 8.00
138 Earl Torgeson 4.00 8.00
139 George Brunet RC 4.00 8.00
140 Wes Covington 5.00 10.00
141 Ken Lehman 4.00 8.00
142 Enos Slaughter 12.50 25.00
143 Billy Muffett RC 4.00 8.00
144 Bobby Morgan 4.00 8.00
145 Never issued
146 Dick Gray RC 4.00 8.00
147 Don McMahon RC 4.00 8.00
148 Billy Consolo 4.00 8.00
149 Tom Acker 4.00 8.00
150 Mickey Mantle 600.00 1000.00
151 Buddy Pritchard RC 4.00 8.00
152 Johnny Antonelli 5.00 10.00
153 Les Moss 4.00 8.00
154 Harry Byrd 4.00 8.00
155 Hector Lopez 5.00 10.00
156 Dick Hyde 4.00 8.00
157 Dee Fondy 4.00 8.00
158 Cleveland Indians TC 7.50 15.00
159 Taylor Phillips 4.00 8.00
160 Don Hoak 5.00 10.00
161 Don Larsen 7.50 15.00
162 Gil Hodges 20.00 40.00
163 Jim Wilson 4.00 8.00
164 Bob Taylor RC 4.00 8.00
165 Bob Nieman 4.00 8.00
166 Danny O'Connell 4.00 8.00
167 Frank Baumann RC 4.00 8.00
168 Joe Cunningham 4.00 8.00
169 Ralph Terry 5.00 10.00
170 Vic Wertz 5.00 10.00
171 Harry Anderson 4.00 8.00
172 Don Gross 4.00 8.00
173 Eddie Yost 5.00 10.00
174 Kansas City Athletics TC 7.50 15.00
175 Marv Throneberry RC 7.50 15.00
176 Bob Buhl 5.00 10.00
177 Al Smith 4.00 8.00
178 Ted Kluszewski 12.50 25.00
179 Willie Miranda 4.00 8.00
180 Lindy McDaniel 5.00 10.00
181 Willie Jones 4.00 8.00
182 Joe Caffie RC 4.00 8.00
183 Dave Jolly 4.00 8.00
184 Elvin Tappe 4.00 8.00
185 Ray Boone 5.00 10.00
186 Jack Meyer 4.00 8.00
187 Sandy Koufax 150.00 250.00
188 Milt Bolling UER 4.00 8.00
(Photo actually
Lou Berberet)
189 George Susce 4.00 8.00
190 Red Schoendienst 12.50 25.00
191 Art Ceccarelli RC 4.00 8.00
192 Milt Graff 4.00 8.00
193 Jerry Lumpe RC 4.00 8.00
194 Roger Craig 5.00 10.00
195 Whitey Lockman 5.00 10.00
196 Mike Garcia 5.00 10.00
197 Haywood Sullivan 5.00 10.00
198 Bill Virdon 5.00 10.00
199 Don Blasingame 4.00 8.00
200 Bob Keegan 4.00 8.00
201 Jim Bolger 4.00 8.00
202 Woody Held RC 4.00 8.00
203 Al Walker 4.00 8.00
204 Leo Kiely 4.00 8.00
205 Johnny Temple 5.00 10.00
206 Bob Shaw RC 4.00 8.00
207 Solly Hemus 4.00 8.00
208 Cal McLish 4.00 8.00
209 Bob Anderson RC 4.00 8.00
210 Wally Moon 5.00 10.00
211 Pete Burnside RC 4.00 8.00
212 Bubba Phillips 4.00 8.00
213 Red Wilson 4.00 8.00
214 Willard Schmidt 4.00 8.00
215 Jim Gilliam 7.50 15.00
216 St. Louis Cardinals TC 7.50 15.00
217 Jack Harshman 4.00 8.00
218 Dick Rand RC 4.00 8.00
219 Camilo Pascual 5.00 10.00
220 Tom Brewer 4.00 8.00
221 Jerry Kindall RC 4.00 8.00
222 Bud Daley RC 4.00 8.00
223 Andy Pafko 5.00 10.00
224 Bob Grim 5.00 10.00
225 Billy Goodman 5.00 10.00
226 Bob Smith RC 4.00 8.00
227 Gene Stephens 4.00 8.00
228 Duke Maas 4.00 8.00
229 Frank Zupo RC 4.00 8.00
230 Richie Ashburn 20.00 40.00
231 Lloyd Merritt RC 4.00 8.00
232 Reno Bertoia 4.00 8.00
233 Mickey Vernon 5.00 10.00
234 Carl Sawatski 4.00 8.00
235 Tom Gorman 4.00 8.00
236 Ed Fitzgerald 4.00 8.00
237 Bill Wight 4.00 8.00
238 Bill Mazeroski 15.00 30.00
239 Chuck Stobbs 4.00 8.00
240 Bill Skowron 12.50 25.00
241 Dick Littlefield 4.00 8.00
242 Johnny Klippstein 4.00 8.00
243 Larry Raines RC 4.00 8.00
244 Don Demeter RC 4.00 8.00
245 Frank Lary 5.00 10.00
246 New York Yankees TC 60.00 100.00
247 Casey Wise 4.00 8.00
248 Herman Wehmeier 4.00 8.00
249 Ray Moore 4.00 8.00
250 Roy Sievers 5.00 10.00
251 Warren Hacker 4.00 8.00
252 Bob Trowbridge RC 4.00 8.00
253 Don Mueller 5.00 10.00
254 Alex Grammas 4.00 8.00
255 Bob Turley 5.00 10.00
256 Chicago White Sox TC 7.50 15.00
257 Hal Smith 4.00 8.00
258 Carl Erskine 7.50 15.00
259 Al Pilarcik 4.00 8.00
260 Frank Malzone 5.00 10.00
261 Turk Lown 4.00 8.00
262 Johnny Groth 4.00 8.00
263 Eddie Bressoud RC 5.00 10.00
264 Jack Sanford 5.00 10.00
265 Pete Runnels 5.00 10.00
266 Connie Johnson 4.00 8.00
267 Sherm Lollar 5.00 10.00
268 Granny Hamner 4.00 8.00
269 Paul Smith 4.00 8.00
270 Warren Spahn 35.00 60.00
271 Billy Martin 20.00 40.00
272 Ray Crone 4.00 8.00
273 Hal Smith 4.00 8.00
274 Rocky Bridges 4.00 8.00
275 Elston Howard 7.50 15.00
276 Bobby Avila 4.00 8.00
277 Virgil Trucks 5.00 10.00
278 Mack Burk 4.00 8.00
279 Bob Boyd 4.00 8.00
280 Jim Piersall 5.00 10.00
281 Sammy Taylor RC 4.00 8.00
282 Paul Foytack 4.00 8.00
283 Ray Shearer RC 4.00 8.00
284 Ray Katt 4.00 8.00
285 Frank Robinson 60.00 100.00
286 Gino Cimoli 4.00 8.00
287 Sam Jones 5.00 10.00
288 Harmon Killebrew 60.00 100.00
289 Series Hurling Rivals 5.00 10.00
Lou Burdette
Bobby Shantz
290 Dick Donovan 4.00 8.00
291 Don Landrum RC 4.00 8.00
292 Ned Garver 4.00 8.00
293 Gene Freese 4.00 8.00
294 Hal Jeffcoat 4.00 8.00
295 Minnie Minoso 12.50 25.00
296 Ryne Duren RC 7.50 15.00
297 Don Buddin RC 4.00 8.00
298 Jim Hearn 4.00 8.00
299 Harry Simpson 4.00 8.00
300 League Presidents 7.50 15.00
Will Harridge
Warren Giles
301 Randy Jackson 4.00 8.00
302 Mike Baxes RC 4.00 8.00
303 Neil Chrisley 4.00 8.00
304 Tigers Big Bats 12.50 25.00
Harvey Kuenn
Al Kaline
305 Clem Labine 5.00 10.00
306 Whammy Douglas RC 4.00 8.00
307 Brooks Robinson 60.00 100.00
308 Paul Giel 5.00 10.00
309 Gail Harris 4.00 8.00
310 Ernie Banks 60.00 100.00
311 Bob Purkey 4.00 8.00
312 Boston Red Sox TC 7.50 15.00
313 Bob Rush 4.00 8.00
314 Dodgers Boss and Power 30.00 50.00
Duke Snider
Walt Alston MG
315 Bob Friend 5.00 10.00
316 Tito Francona 5.00 10.00
317 Albie Pearson RC 5.00 10.00
318 Frank House 4.00 8.00
319 Lou Skizas 4.00 8.00
320 Whitey Ford 35.00 60.00
321 Sluggers Supreme 60.00 100.00
Ted Kluszewski
Ted Williams
322 Harding Peterson RC 5.00 10.00
323 Elmer Valo 5.00 10.00
324 Hoyt Wilhelm 12.50 25.00
325 Joe Adcock 5.00 10.00
326 Bob Miller 4.00 8.00
327 Chicago Cubs TC 7.50 15.00
328 Ike Delock 4.00 8.00
329 Bob Cerv 5.00 10.00
330 Ed Bailey 5.00 10.00
331 Pedro Ramos 4.00 8.00
332 Jim King 4.00 8.00
333 Andy Carey 5.00 10.00
334 Mound Aces 5.00 10.00
Bob Friend
Billy Pierce
335 Ruben Gomez 4.00 8.00
336 Bert Hamric 4.00 8.00
337 Hank Aguirre 4.00 8.00
338 Walt Dropo 5.00 10.00
339 Fred Hatfield 4.00 8.00
340 Don Newcombe 7.50 15.00
341 Pittsburgh Pirates TC 7.50 15.00
342 Jim Brosnan 5.00 10.00
343 Orlando Cepeda RC 60.00 100.00
344 Bob Porterfield 4.00 8.00
345 Jim Hegan 5.00 10.00
346 Steve Bilko 4.00 8.00
347 Don Rudolph RC 4.00 8.00
348 Chico Fernandez 4.00 8.00
349 Murry Dickson 4.00 8.00
350 Ken Boyer 12.50 25.00
351 Braves Fence Busters 20.00 40.00
Del Crandall
Eddie Mathews
Hank Aaron
Joe Adcock
352 Herb Score 7.50 15.00
353 Stan Lopata 4.00 8.00
354 Art Ditmar 5.00 10.00
355 Bill Bruton 5.00 10.00
356 Bob Malkmus RC 4.00 8.00
357 Danny McDevitt RC 4.00 8.00
358 Gene Baker 4.00 8.00
359 Billy Loes 5.00 10.00
360 Roy McMillan 5.00 10.00
361 Mike Fornieles 4.00 8.00
362 Ray Jablonski 4.00 8.00
363 Don Elston 4.00 8.00
364 Earl Battey 4.00 8.00
365 Tom Morgan 4.00 8.00
366 Gene Green RC 4.00 8.00
367 Jack Urban RC 4.00 8.00
368 Rocky Colavito 30.00 50.00
369 Ralph Lumenti RC 4.00 8.00
370 Yogi Berra 60.00 100.00
371 Marty Keough RC 4.00 8.00
372 Don Cardwell 4.00 8.00
373 Joe Pignatano RC 4.00 8.00
374 Brooks Lawrence 4.00 8.00
375 Pee Wee Reese 50.00 80.00
376 Charley Rabe RC 4.00 8.00
377A Milwaukee Braves TC 7.50 15.00
Alphabetical
377B Milwaukee Braves TC 60.00 100.00
Numerical
378 Hank Sauer 5.00 10.00
379 Ray Herbert 4.00 8.00
380 Charlie Maxwell 5.00 10.00
381 Hal Brown 4.00 8.00
382 Al Cicotte 4.00 8.00
383 Lou Berberet 4.00 8.00
384 John Goryl RC 4.00 8.00
385 Wilmer Mizell 5.00 10.00
386 Birds Young Sluggers 7.50 15.00
Ed Bailey
Birdie Tebbetts MG
Frank Robinson
387 Wally Post 5.00 10.00
388 Billy Moran RC 4.00 8.00
389 Bill Taylor 4.00 8.00
390 Del Crandall 5.00 10.00
391 Dave Melton RC 4.00 8.00
392 Bennie Daniels RC 4.00 8.00
393 Tony Kubek 15.00 30.00
394 Jim Grant RC 4.00 8.00
395 Willard Nixon 4.00 8.00
396 Dutch Dotterer RC 4.00 8.00
397A Detroit Tigers TC 7.50 15.00
Alphabetical
397B Detroit Tigers TC 60.00 100.00
Numerical
398 Gene Woodling 5.00 10.00
399 Marv Grissom 4.00 8.00
400 Nellie Fox 20.00 40.00
401 Don Bessent 4.00 8.00
402 Bobby Gene Smith 4.00 8.00
403 Steve Korcheck RC 4.00 8.00
404 Curt Simmons 5.00 10.00
405 Ken Aspromonte RC 4.00 8.00
406 Vic Power 5.00 10.00
407 Carlton Willey RC 5.00 10.00
408A Baltimore Orioles TC 7.50 15.00
Alphabetical
408B Baltimore Orioles TC 60.00 100.00
Numerical
409 Frank Thomas 5.00 10.00
410 Murray Wall 4.00 8.00
411 Tony Taylor RC 5.00 10.00
412 Gerry Staley 4.00 8.00
413 Jim Davenport RC 5.00 10.00
414 Sammy White 4.00 8.00
415 Bob Bowman 4.00 8.00
416 Foster Castleman 4.00 8.00
417 Carl Furillo 7.50 15.00
418 World Series Batting Foes 250.00 400.00
Mickey Mantle
Hank Aaron
419 Bobby Shantz 5.00 10.00
420 Vada Pinson RC 20.00 40.00
421 Dixie Howell 4.00 8.00
422 Norm Zauchin 4.00 8.00
423 Phil Clark RC 4.00 8.00
424 Larry Doby UER 12.50 25.00
Spelled Lary on the back
425 Sammy Esposito 4.00 8.00
426 Johnny O'Brien 5.00 10.00
427 Al Worthington 4.00 8.00
428A Cincinnati Reds TC 7.50 15.00
Alphabetical
428B Cincinnati Reds TC 60.00 100.00
Numerical
429 Gus Triandos 5.00 10.00
430 Bobby Thomson 5.00 10.00
431 Gene Conley 5.00 10.00
432 John Powers RC 4.00 8.00
433A Pancho Herrera COR RC 5.00 10.00
433B Pancho Herrer ERR 350.00 600.00
(most or all of the last A
missing from player's name on front)
433C Pancho Herre ERR
(most or all of the last RA
missing from player's name on front)
433D Pancho Herr ERR
(most or all of the last ERA
missing from player's name on front)
434 Harvey Kuenn 5.00 10.00
435 Ed Roebuck 5.00 10.00
436 Rival Fence Busters 60.00 100.00
Willie Mays
Duke Snider
437 Bob Speake 4.00 8.00
438 Whitey Herzog 5.00 10.00
439 Ray Narleski 4.00 8.00
440 Eddie Mathews 50.00 80.00
441 Jim Marshall RC 5.00 10.00
442 Phil Paine RC 4.00 8.00
443 Billy Harrell SP RC 10.00 20.00
444 Danny Kravitz 4.00 8.00
445 Bob Smith RC 4.00 8.00
446 Carroll Hardy SP RC 10.00 20.00
447 Ray Monzant 4.00 8.00
448 Charlie Lau RC 5.00 10.00
449 Gene Fodge RC 4.00 8.00
450 Preston Ward SP 10.00 20.00
451 Joe Taylor RC 4.00 8.00
452 Roman Mejias 4.00 8.00
453 Tom Qualters 4.00 8.00
454 Harry Hanebrink RC 4.00 8.00
455 Hal Griggs RC 4.00 8.00
456 Dick Brown RC 4.00 8.00
457 Milt Pappas RC 5.00 10.00
458 Julio Becquer RC 4.00 8.00
459 Ron Blackburn RC 4.00 8.00
460 Chuck Essegian RC 4.00 8.00
461 Ed Mayer RC 4.00 8.00
462 Gary Geiger SP RC 10.00 20.00
463 Vito Valentinetti 4.00 8.00
464 Curt Flood RC 15.00 30.00
465 Arnie Portocarrero 4.00 8.00
466 Pete Whisenant 4.00 8.00
467 Glen Hobbie RC 4.00 8.00
468 Bob Schmidt RC 4.00 8.00
469 Don Ferrarese 4.00 8.00
470 R.C. Stevens RC 4.00 8.00
471 Lenny Green RC 4.00 8.00
472 Joey Jay 5.00 10.00
473 Bill Renna 4.00 8.00
474 Roman Semproch RC 4.00 8.00
475 All-Star Managers 12.50 25.00
Fred Haney
Casey Stengel
476 Stan Musial AS TP 30.00 50.00
477 Bill Skowron AS 5.00 10.00
478 Johnny Temple AS UER 4.00 8.00
Card says record vs American League
Temple was NL AS
479 Nellie Fox AS 7.50 15.00
480 Eddie Mathews AS 15.00 30.00
481 Frank Malzone AS 4.00 8.00
482 Ernie Banks AS 20.00 40.00
483 Luis Aparicio AS 7.50 15.00
484 Frank Robinson AS 20.00 40.00
485 Ted Williams AS 90.00 150.00
486 Willie Mays AS 35.00 60.00
487 Mickey Mantle AS TP 125.00 200.00
488 Hank Aaron AS 35.00 60.00
489 Jackie Jensen AS 5.00 10.00
490 Ed Bailey AS 4.00 8.00
491 Sherm Lollar AS 4.00 8.00
492 Bob Friend AS 4.00 8.00
493 Bob Turley AS 5.00 10.00
494 Warren Spahn AS 12.50 25.00
495 Herb Score AS 7.50 15.00
NNO Contest Cards 20.00 40.00
NNO Felt Emblem Insert

1959 Topps

The cards in this 572-card set measure 2 1/2" by 3 1/2". The 1959 Topps set contains bust pictures of the players in a colored circle. Card numbers 551 to 572 are Sporting News All-Star Selections. High numbers 507 to 572 have the card number in a black background on the reverse rather than a green background as in the lower numbers. The high numbers are more difficult to obtain. Several cards in the 300s exist with or without an extra traded or option line on the back of the card. Cards 199 to 286 exist with either white or gray backs. There is no price differential for either colored back. Cards 461 to 470 contain "Highlights" while cards 116 to 146 give an alphabetically ordered listing of "Rookie Prospects." These Rookie Prospects (RP) were Topps' first organized inclusion of untested "Rookie" cards. Card 440 features Lew Burdette erroneously posing as a left-handed pitcher. Cards were issued in one-card penny packs or six-card nickel packs. There were some three-card advertising panels produced by Topps; the players included are from the first series. Panels which had Ted Kluszewski's card back on the back included Don McMahon/Red Wilson/Bob Boyd; Joe Pignatano/Sam Jones/Jack Urban also with Kluszewski's card back on back. Strips with Nellie Fox on the back included Billy Hunter/Chuck Stobbs/Carl Sawatski; Vito Valentinetti/Ken Lehman/Ed Bouchee; Mel Roach/Brooks Lawrence/Warren Spahn. Other panels include Harvey Kuenn/Alex Grammas/Bob Cerv; and Bob Cerv/Jim Bolger/Mickey Mantle. When separated, these advertising cards are distinguished by the non-standard card back, i.e., part of an advertisement for the 1959 Topps set instead of the typical statistics and biographical information about the player pictured. The key Rookie Cards in this set are Felipe Alou, Sparky Anderson (called George on the card), Norm Cash, Bob Gibson, and Bill White.

COMPLETE SET (572) 5000.00 8000.00
COMMON CARD (1-110) 3.00 6.00
COMMON (111-506) 2.00 4.00
COMMON (507-572) 7.50 15.00
WRAPPER (1-CENT) 100.00 125.00
WRAPPER (5-CENT) 75.00 100.00
1 Ford Frick COMM 35.00 60.00
2 Eddie Yost 4.00 8.00
3 Don McMahon 4.00 8.00
4 Albie Pearson 4.00 8.00
5 Dick Donovan 4.00 8.00
6 Alex Grammas 3.00 6.00
7 Al Pilarcik 3.00 6.00
8 Philadelphia Phillies CL 50.00 80.00
9 Paul Giel 4.00 8.00
10 Mickey Mantle 600.00 1000.00
11 Billy Hunter 4.00 8.00
12 Vern Law 4.00 8.00
13 Dick Gernert 3.00 6.00
14 Pete Whisenant 3.00 6.00
15 Dick Drott 3.00 6.00
16 Joe Pignatano 3.00 6.00
17 Danny's All-Stars 4.00 8.00

Frank Thomas
Danny Murtaugh MG
Ted Kluszewski
18 Jack Urban 3.00 6.00
19 Eddie Bressoud 3.00 6.00
20 Duke Snider 35.00 60.00
21 Connie Johnson 3.00 6.00
22 Al Smith 4.00 8.00
23 Murry Dickson 4.00 8.00
24 Red Wilson 3.00 6.00
25 Don Hoak 4.00 8.00
26 Chuck Stobbs 3.00 6.00
27 Andy Pafko 4.00 8.00
28 Al Worthington 3.00 6.00
29 Jim Bolger 3.00 6.00
30 Nellie Fox 15.00 30.00
31 Ken Lehman 3.00 6.00
32 Don Buddin 3.00 6.00
33 Ed Fitzgerald 3.00 6.00
34 Pitchers Beware 10.00 20.00
Al Kaline
Charley Maxwell
35 Ted Kluszewski 6.00 12.00
36 Hank Aguirre 3.00 6.00
37 Gene Green 3.00 6.00
38 Morrie Martin 3.00 6.00
39 Ed Bouchee 3.00 6.00
40A Warren Spahn ERR 50.00 80.00
(Born 1931)
40B Warren Spahn ERR 60.00 100.00
(Born 1931, but three
is partially obscured)
40C Warren Spahn COR 35.00 60.00
(Born 1921)
41 Bob Martyn 3.00 6.00
42 Murray Wall 3.00 6.00
43 Steve Bilko 3.00 6.00
44 Vito Valentinetti 3.00 6.00
45 Andy Carey 4.00 8.00
46 Bill R. Henry 3.00 6.00
47 Jim Finigan 3.00 6.00
48 Baltimore Orioles CL 12.50 25.00
49 Bill Hall RC 3.00 6.00
50 Willie Mays 100.00 175.00
51 Rip Coleman 3.00 6.00
52 Coot Veal RC 3.00 6.00
53 Stan Williams RC 4.00 8.00
54 Mel Roach 3.00 6.00
55 Tom Brewer 3.00 6.00
56 Carl Sawatski 3.00 6.00
57 Al Cicotte 3.00 6.00
58 Eddie Miksis 3.00 6.00
59 Irv Noren 4.00 8.00
60 Bob Turley 4.00 8.00
61 Dick Brown 3.00 6.00
62 Tony Taylor 4.00 8.00
63 Jim Hearn 3.00 6.00
64 Joe DeMaestri 3.00 6.00
65 Frank Torre 4.00 8.00
66 Joe Ginsberg 3.00 6.00
67 Brooks Lawrence 3.00 6.00
68 Dick Schofield 4.00 8.00
69 San Francisco Giants CL 12.50 25.00
70 Harvey Kuenn 4.00 8.00
71 Don Bessent 3.00 6.00
72 Bill Renna 3.00 6.00
73 Ron Jackson 4.00 8.00
74 Directing the Power 4.00 8.00
Jim Lemon
Cookie Lavagetto MG
Roy Sievers
75 Sam Jones 4.00 8.00
76 Bobby Richardson 10.00 20.00
77 John Goryl 3.00 6.00
78 Pedro Ramos 3.00 6.00
79 Harry Chiti 3.00 6.00
80 Minnie Minoso 6.00 12.00
81 Hal Jeffcoat 3.00 6.00
82 Bob Boyd 3.00 6.00
83 Bob Smith 3.00 6.00
84 Reno Bertoia 3.00 6.00
85 Harry Anderson 3.00 6.00
86 Bob Keegan 4.00 8.00
87 Danny O'Connell 3.00 6.00
88 Herb Score 6.00 12.00
89 Billy Gardner 3.00 6.00
90 Bill Skowron 6.00 12.00
91 Herb Moford RC 3.00 6.00
92 Dave Philley 3.00 6.00
93 Julio Becquer 3.00 6.00
94 Chicago White Sox CL 20.00 40.00
95 Carl Willey 3.00 6.00
96 Lou Berberet 3.00 6.00
97 Jerry Lynch 4.00 8.00
98 Arnie Portocarrero 3.00 6.00
99 Ted Kazanski 3.00 6.00
100 Bob Cerv 4.00 8.00
101 Alex Kellner 3.00 6.00
102 Felipe Alou RC 15.00 30.00
103 Billy Goodman 4.00 8.00
104 Del Rice 4.00 8.00
105 Lee Walls 3.00 6.00
106 Hal Woodeshick RC 3.00 6.00
107 Norm Larker RC 4.00 8.00
108 Zack Monroe RC 4.00 8.00
109 Bob Schmidt 3.00 6.00
110 George Witt RC 4.00 8.00
111 Cincinnati Redlegs CL 7.50 15.00
112 Billy Consolo 2.00 4.00
113 Taylor Phillips 2.00 4.00
114 Earl Battey 4.00 8.00
115 Mickey Vernon 4.00 8.00
116 Bob Allison RS RC 6.00 12.00
117 John Blanchard RS RC 6.00 12.00
118 John Buzhardt RS RC 2.50 5.00
119 Johnny Callison RS RC 6.00 12.00
120 Chuck Coles RS RC 2.50 5.00
121 Bob Conley RS RC 2.50 5.00
122 Bennie Daniels RS 2.50 5.00
123 Don Dillard RS RC 2.50 5.00
124 Dan Dobbek RS RC 2.50 5.00
125 Ron Fairly RS RC 6.00 12.00
126 Eddie Haas RS RC 2.50 5.00
127 Kent Hadley RS RC 2.50 5.00
128 Bob Hartman RS RC 2.50 5.00
129 Frank Herrera RS 2.50 5.00
130 Lou Jackson RS RC 2.50 5.00
131 Deron Johnson RS RC 6.00 12.00
132 Don Lee RS 2.50 5.00
133 Bob Lillis RS RC 2.50 5.00
134 Jim McDaniel RS RC 2.50 5.00
135 Gene Oliver RS RC 2.50 5.00
136 Jim O'Toole RS RC 2.50 5.00
137 Dick Ricketts RS RC 2.50 5.00
138 John Romano RS RC 2.50 5.00
139 Ed Sadowski RS RC 2.50 5.00
140 Charlie Secrest RS RC 2.50 5.00
141 Joe Shipley RS RC 2.50 5.00
142 Dick Stigman RS RC 2.50 5.00
143 Willie Tasby RS RC 2.50 5.00
144 Jerry Walker RS 2.50 5.00
145 Dom Zanni RS RC 2.50 5.00
146 Jerry Zimmerman RS RC 2.50 5.00
147 Cubs Clubbers 15.00 30.00
Dale Long
Ernie Banks
Walt Moryn
148 Mike McCormick 4.00 8.00
149 Jim Bunning 10.00 20.00
150 Stan Musial 60.00 120.00
151 Bob Malkmus 2.00 4.00
152 Johnny Klippstein 2.00 4.00
153 Jim Marshall 2.00 4.00
154 Ray Herbert 2.00 4.00
155 Enos Slaughter 10.00 20.00
156 Ace Hurlers 6.00 12.00
Billy Pierce
Robin Roberts
157 Felix Mantilla 2.00 4.00
158 Walt Dropo 2.00 4.00
159 Bob Shaw 4.00 8.00
160 Dick Groat 4.00 8.00
161 Frank Baumann 2.00 4.00
162 Bobby G. Smith 2.00 4.00
163 Sandy Koufax 90.00 150.00
164 Johnny Groth 2.00 4.00
165 Bill Bruton 2.00 4.00
166 Destruction Crew 15.00 30.00
Minnie Minoso
Rocky Colavito UER
(Misspelled Colovito
on card back)
Larry Doby
167 Duke Maas 2.00 4.00
168 Carroll Hardy 2.00 4.00
169 Ted Abernathy 2.00 4.00
170 Gene Woodling 4.00 8.00
171 Willard Schmidt 2.00 4.00
172 Kansas City Athletics CL 7.50 15.00
173 Bill Monbouquette RC 4.00 8.00
174 Jim Pendleton 2.00 4.00
175 Dick Farrell 4.00 8.00
176 Preston Ward 2.00 4.00
177 John Briggs RC 2.00 4.00
178 Ruben Amaro RC 6.00 12.00
179 Don Rudolph 2.00 4.00
180 Yogi Berra 50.00 80.00
181 Bob Porterfield 2.00 4.00
182 Milt Graff 2.00 4.00
183 Stu Miller 4.00 8.00
184 Harvey Haddix 4.00 8.00
185 Jim Busby 2.00 4.00
186 Mudcat Grant 4.00 8.00
187 Bubba Phillips 4.00 8.00
188 Juan Pizarro 2.00 4.00
189 Neil Chrisley 2.00 4.00
190 Bill Virdon 4.00 8.00
191 Russ Kemmerer 2.00 4.00
192 Charlie Beamon RC 2.00 4.00
193 Sammy Taylor 2.00 4.00
194 Jim Brosnan 4.00 8.00
195 Rip Repulski 2.00 4.00
196 Billy Moran 2.00 4.00
197 Ray Semproch 2.00 4.00
198 Jim Davenport 4.00 8.00
199 Leo Kiely 2.00 4.00
200 Warren Giles NL PRES 4.00 8.00
201 Tom Acker 2.00 4.00
202 Roger Maris 75.00 125.00
203 Ossie Virgil 2.00 4.00
204 Casey Wise 2.00 4.00
205 Don Larsen 4.00 8.00
206 Carl Furillo 6.00 12.00
207 George Strickland 2.00 4.00
208 Willie Jones 2.00 4.00
209 Lenny Green 2.00 4.00
210 Ed Bailey 2.00 4.00
211 Bob Blaylock RC 2.00 4.00
212 Fence Busters 50.00 80.00
Hank Aaron
Eddie Mathews
213 Jim Rivera 4.00 8.00
214 Marcelino Solis RC 2.00 4.00
215 Jim Lemon 4.00 8.00
216 Andre Rodgers 2.00 4.00
217 Carl Erskine 6.00 12.00
218 Roman Mejias 2.00 4.00
219 George Zuverink 2.00 4.00
220 Frank Malzone 4.00 8.00
221 Bob Bowman 2.00 4.00
222 Bobby Shantz 4.00 8.00
223 St. Louis Cardinals CL 7.50 15.00
224 Claude Osteen RC 4.00 8.00
225 Johnny Logan 4.00 8.00
226 Art Ceccarelli 2.00 4.00
227 Hal W. Smith 2.00 4.00
228 Don Gross 2.00 4.00
229 Vic Power 4.00 8.00
230 Bill Fischer 2.00 4.00
231 Ellis Burton RC 2.00 4.00
232 Eddie Kasko 2.00 4.00
233 Paul Foytack 2.00 4.00
234 Chuck Tanner 4.00 8.00
235 Valmy Thomas 2.00 4.00
236 Ted Bowsfield RC 2.00 4.00
237 Run Preventers 6.00 12.00
Gil McDougald
Bob Turley
Bobby Richardson
238 Gene Baker 2.00 4.00
239 Bob Trowbridge 2.00 4.00
240 Hank Bauer 6.00 12.00
241 Billy Muffett 2.00 4.00
242 Ron Samford RC 2.00 4.00
243 Marv Grissom 2.00 4.00
244 Ted Gray 2.00 4.00
245 Ned Garver 2.00 4.00
246 J.W. Porter 2.00 4.00
247 Don Ferrarese 2.00 4.00
248 Boston Red Sox CL 7.50 15.00
249 Bobby Adams 2.00 4.00
250 Billy O'Dell 2.00 4.00
251 Clete Boyer 6.00 12.00
252 Ray Boone 4.00 8.00
253 Seth Morehead RC 2.00 4.00
254 Zeke Bella RC 2.00 4.00
255 Del Ennis 4.00 8.00
256 Jerry Davie RC 2.00 4.00
257 Leon Wagner RC 4.00 8.00
258 Fred Kipp RC 2.00 4.00
259 Jim Pisoni 2.00 4.00
260 Early Wynn UER 10.00 20.00
1957 Cleveland
261 Gene Stephens 2.00 4.00
262 Hitters Foes 6.00 12.00
Johnny Podres
Clem Labine
Don Drysdale
263 Bud Daley 2.00 4.00
264 Chico Carrasquel 2.00 4.00
265 Ron Kline 2.00 4.00
266 Woody Held 2.00 4.00
267 John Romonosky RC 2.00 4.00
268 Tito Francona 4.00 8.00
269 Jack Meyer 2.00 4.00
270 Gil Hodges 15.00 30.00
271 Orlando Pena RC 2.00 4.00
272 Jerry Lumpe 2.00 4.00
273 Joey Jay 4.00 8.00
274 Jerry Kindall 4.00 8.00
275 Jack Sanford 4.00 8.00
276 Pete Daley 2.00 4.00
277 Turk Lown 4.00 8.00
278 Chuck Essegian 2.00 4.00
279 Ernie Johnson 2.00 4.00
280 Frank Bolling 2.00 4.00
281 Walt Craddock RC 2.00 4.00
282 R.C. Stevens 2.00 4.00
283 Russ Heman RC 2.00 4.00
284 Steve Korcheck 2.00 4.00
285 Joe Cunningham 2.00 4.00
286 Dean Stone 2.00 4.00
287 Don Zimmer 6.00 12.00
288 Dutch Dotterer 2.00 4.00
289 Johnny Kucks 4.00 8.00
290 Wes Covington 2.00 4.00
291 Pitching Parrtners 2.00 4.00
Pedro Ramos
Camilo Pascual
292 Dick Williams 4.00 8.00
293 Ray Moore 2.00 4.00
294 Hank Foiles 2.00 4.00
295 Billy Martin 15.00 30.00
296 Ernie Broglio RC 2.00 4.00
297 Jackie Brandt RC 2.00 4.00
298 Tex Clevenger 2.00 4.00
299 Billy Klaus 2.00 4.00
300 Richie Ashburn 15.00 30.00
301 Earl Averill Jr. RC 2.00 4.00
302 Don Mossi 4.00 8.00
303 Marty Keough 2.00 4.00
304 Chicago Cubs CL 7.50 15.00
305 Curt Raydon RC 2.00 4.00
306 Jim Gilliam 4.00 8.00
307 Curt Barclay 2.00 4.00
308 Norm Siebern 2.00 4.00
309 Sal Maglie 4.00 8.00
310 Luis Aparicio 10.00 20.00
311 Norm Zauchin 2.00 4.00
312 Don Newcombe 4.00 8.00
313 Frank House 2.00 4.00
314 Don Cardwell 2.00 4.00
315 Joe Adcock 4.00 8.00
316A Ralph Lumenti UER 2.00 4.00
(Option)
(Photo actually
Camilo Pascual)
316B Ralph Lumenti UER 50.00 80.00
(No option)
(Photo actually
Camilo Pascual)
317 NL Hitting Kings 50.00 80.00
Willie Mays
Richie Ashburn
318 Rocky Bridges 2.00 4.00
319 Dave Hillman 2.00 4.00
320 Bob Skinner 4.00 8.00
321A Bob Giallombardo RC 4.00 8.00
(With Option line)
321B Bob Giallombardo ERR 50.00 80.00
(No option)
322A Harry Hanebrink 4.00 8.00
(Traded)
322B Harry Hanebrink 50.00 80.00
(No trade)
323 Frank Sullivan 2.00 4.00
324 Don Demeter 2.00 4.00
325 Ken Boyer 6.00 12.00
326 Marv Throneberry 4.00 8.00
327 Gary Bell RC 2.00 4.00
328 Lou Skizas 2.00 4.00
329 Detroit Tigers CL 7.50 15.00
330 Gus Triandos 4.00 8.00
331 Steve Boros 2.00 4.00
332 Ray Monzant 2.00 4.00
333 Harry Simpson 2.00 4.00
334 Glen Hobbie 2.00 4.00
335 Johnny Temple 4.00 8.00
336A Billy Loes 4.00 8.00
(With traded line)
336B Billy Loes 50.00 80.00
(No trade)
337 George Crowe 2.00 4.00
338 Sparky Anderson RC 35.00 60.00
339 Roy Face 4.00 8.00
340 Roy Sievers 4.00 8.00
341 Tom Qualters 2.00 4.00
342 Ray Jablonski 2.00 4.00
343 Billy Hoeft 2.00 4.00
344 Russ Nixon 2.00 4.00
345 Gil McDougald 6.00 12.00
346 Batter Bafflers 2.00 4.00
Dave Sisler
Tom Brewer
347 Bob Buhl 2.00 4.00
348 Ted Lepcio 2.00 4.00
349 Hoyt Wilhelm 10.00 20.00
350 Ernie Banks 50.00 80.00
351 Earl Torgeson 2.00 4.00
352 Robin Roberts 10.00 20.00
353 Curt Flood 4.00 8.00
354 Pete Burnside 2.00 4.00
355 Jimmy Piersall 4.00 8.00
356 Bob Mabe RC 2.00 4.00
357 Dick Stuart RC 4.00 8.00
358 Ralph Terry 4.00 8.00
359 Bill White RC 10.00 20.00
360 Al Kaline 35.00 60.00
361 Willard Nixon 2.00 4.00
362A Dolan Nichols RC 2.00 4.00
(With option line)
362B Dolan Nichols 50.00 80.00
(No option)
363 Bobby Avila 2.00 4.00
364 Danny McDevitt 2.00 4.00
365 Gus Bell 4.00 8.00
366 Humberto Robinson 2.00 4.00
367 Cal Neeman 2.00 4.00
368 Don Mueller 4.00 8.00
369 Dick Tomanek 2.00 4.00
370 Pete Runnels 4.00 8.00
371 Dick Brodowski 2.00 4.00
372 Jim Hegan 4.00 8.00
373 Herb Plews 2.00 4.00
374 Art Ditmar 4.00 8.00
375 Bob Nieman 2.00 4.00
376 Hal Naragon 2.00 4.00
377 John Antonelli 4.00 8.00
378 Gail Harris 2.00 4.00
379 Bob Miller 2.00 4.00
380 Hank Aaron 90.00 150.00
381 Mike Baxes 2.00 4.00
382 Curt Simmons 4.00 8.00
383 Words of Wisdom 6.00 12.00
Don Larsen
Casey Stengel MG
384 Dave Sisler 2.00 4.00
385 Sherm Lollar 4.00 8.00
386 Jim Delsing 2.00 4.00
387 Don Drysdale 30.00 50.00
388 Bob Will RC 2.00 4.00
389 Joe Nuxhall 4.00 8.00
390 Orlando Cepeda 10.00 20.00
391 Milt Pappas 4.00 8.00
392 Whitey Herzog 4.00 8.00
393 Frank Lary 4.00 8.00
394 Randy Jackson 2.00 4.00
395 Elston Howard 6.00 12.00
396 Bob Rush 2.00 4.00
397 Washington Senators CL 7.50 15.00
398 Wally Post 4.00 8.00
399 Larry Jackson 2.00 4.00
400 Jackie Jensen 4.00 8.00
401 Ron Blackburn 2.00 4.00
402 Hector Lopez 4.00 8.00
403 Clem Labine 4.00 8.00
404 Hank Sauer 4.00 8.00
405 Roy McMillan 4.00 8.00
406 Solly Drake 2.00 4.00
407 Moe Drabowsky 4.00 8.00
408 Keystone Combo 20.00 40.00
Nellie Fox
Luis Aparicio
409 Gus Zernial 4.00 8.00
410 Billy Pierce 4.00 8.00
411 Whitey Lockman 4.00 8.00
412 Stan Lopata 2.00 4.00
413 Camilo Pascual UER 4.00 8.00
(Listed as Camillo
on front and Pasqual
on back)
414 Dale Long 4.00 8.00
415 Bill Mazeroski 6.00 12.00
416 Haywood Sullivan 4.00 8.00
417 Virgil Trucks 4.00 8.00
418 Gino Cimoli 2.00 4.00
419 Milwaukee Braves CL 7.50 15.00
420 Rocky Colavito 15.00 30.00
421 Herman Wehmeier 2.00 4.00
422 Hobie Landrith 2.00 4.00
423 Bob Grim 4.00 8.00
424 Ken Aspromonte 2.00 4.00
425 Del Crandall 4.00 8.00
426 Gerry Staley 4.00 8.00
427 Charlie Neal 4.00 8.00
428 Buc Hill Aces 2.00 4.00
Ron Kline
Bob Friend
Vernon Law
Roy Face
429 Bobby Thomson 4.00 8.00
430 Whitey Ford 35.00 60.00
431 Whammy Douglas 2.00 4.00
432 Smoky Burgess 4.00 8.00
433 Billy Harrell 2.00 4.00
434 Hal Griggs 2.00 4.00
435 Frank Robinson 30.00 50.00
436 Granny Hamner 2.00 4.00
437 Ike Delock 2.00 4.00
438 Sammy Esposito 2.00 4.00
439 Brooks Robinson 30.00 50.00
440 Lou Burdette 4.00 8.00
(Posing as if
lefthanded)
441 John Roseboro 4.00 8.00
442 Ray Narleski 2.00 4.00
443 Daryl Spencer 2.00 4.00
444 Ron Hansen RC 4.00 8.00
445 Cal McLish 2.00 4.00
446 Rocky Nelson 2.00 4.00
447 Bob Anderson 2.00 4.00
448 Vada Pinson UER 6.00 12.00
(Born: 8/8/38
should be 8/11/38)
449 Tom Gorman 2.00 4.00
450 Eddie Mathews 20.00 40.00
451 Jimmy Constable RC 2.00 4.00
452 Chico Fernandez 2.00 4.00
453 Les Moss 2.00 4.00
454 Phil Clark 2.00 4.00
455 Larry Doby 6.00 12.00
456 Jerry Casale RC 2.00 4.00
457 Los Angeles Dodgers CL 15.00 30.00
458 Gordon Jones 2.00 4.00
459 Bill Tuttle 2.00 4.00
460 Bob Friend 4.00 8.00
461 Mickey Mantle BT 75.00 125.00
42nd Homer
462 Rocky Colavito BT 6.00 12.00
Great Catch
463 Al Kaline BT 15.00 30.00
Bat Champ
464 Willie Mays BT 20.00 40.00
Catch
465 Roy Sievers BT 4.00 8.00
Homer Mark
466 Billy Pierce BT 4.00 8.00
AS Starter
467 Hank Aaron BT 20.00 40.00
WS Homer
468 Duke Snider BT 10.00 20.00
LA Victory
469 Ernie Banks BT 10.00 20.00
MVP Award
470 Stan Musial BT 15.00 30.00
3000 Hits
471 Tom Sturdivant 2.00 4.00
472 Gene Freese 2.00 4.00
473 Mike Fornieles 2.00 4.00
474 Moe Thacker RC 2.00 4.00
475 Jack Harshman 2.00 4.00
476 Cleveland Indians CL 7.50 15.00
477 Barry Latman RC 2.00 4.00
478 Roberto Clemente UER 100.00 175.00
The words the best run together
479 Lindy McDaniel 4.00 8.00
480 Red Schoendienst 6.00 12.00
481 Charlie Maxwell 4.00 8.00
482 Russ Meyer 2.00 4.00
483 Clint Courtney 2.00 4.00
484 Willie Kirkland 2.00 4.00
485 Ryne Duren 4.00 8.00
486 Sammy White 2.00 4.00
487 Hal Brown 2.00 4.00
488 Walt Moryn 2.00 4.00
489 John Powers 2.00 4.00
490 Frank Thomas 4.00 8.00
491 Don Blasingame 2.00 4.00
492 Gene Conley 4.00 8.00
493 Jim Landis 4.00 8.00
494 Don Pavletich RC 2.00 4.00
495 Johnny Podres 6.00 12.00
496 W.Terwilliger UER 2.00 4.00
Athlftics on front
497 Hal R. Smith 2.00 4.00
498 Dick Hyde 2.00 4.00
499 Johnny O'Brien 4.00 8.00
500 Vic Wertz 4.00 8.00
501 Bob Tiefenauer RC 2.00 4.00
502 Alvin Dark 4.00 8.00
503 Jim Owens 2.00 4.00
504 Ossie Alvarez RC 2.00 4.00
505 Tony Kubek 6.00 12.00
506 Bob Purkey 2.00 4.00
507 Bob Hale 7.50 15.00
508 Art Fowler 7.50 15.00
509 Norm Cash RC 50.00 80.00
510 New York Yankees CL 75.00 125.00
511 George Susce 7.50 15.00
512 George Altman RC 7.50 15.00
513 Tommy Carroll 7.50 15.00
514 Bob Gibson RC 175.00 300.00
515 Harmon Killebrew 75.00 125.00
516 Mike Garcia 10.00 20.00
517 Joe Koppe RC 7.50 15.00
518 Mike Cueller UER RC 18.00 30.00
Sic, Cuellar
519 Infield Power 10.00 20.00
Pete Runnels
Dick Gernert
Frank Malzone
520 Don Elston 7.50 15.00
521 Gary Geiger 7.50 15.00
522 Gene Snyder RC 7.50 15.00
523 Harry Bright RC 7.50 15.00
524 Larry Osborne RC 7.50 15.00
525 Jim Coates RC 10.00 20.00
526 Bob Speake 7.50 15.00
527 Solly Hemus 7.50 15.00
528 Pittsburgh Pirates CL 50.00 80.00
529 G.Bamberger RC 10.00 20.00
530 Wally Moon 10.00 20.00
531 Ray Webster RC 7.50 15.00
532 Mark Freeman RC 7.50 15.00
533 Darrell Johnson 10.00 20.00
534 Faye Throneberry 7.50 15.00
535 Ruben Gomez 7.50 15.00
536 Danny Kravitz 7.50 15.00
537 Rudolph Arias RC 7.50 15.00
538 Chick King 7.50 15.00
539 Gary Blaylock RC 7.50 15.00
540 Willie Miranda 7.50 15.00
541 Bob Thurman 7.50 15.00
542 Jim Perry RC 18.00 30.00
543 Corsair Trio 75.00 125.00
Bob Skinner
Bill Virdon
Roberto Clemente
544 Lee Tate RC 7.50 15.00
545 Tom Morgan 7.50 15.00
546 Al Schroll 7.50 15.00
547 Jim Baxes RC 7.50 15.00
548 Elmer Singleton 7.50 15.00
549 Howie Nunn RC 7.50 15.00
550 Roy Campanella 90.00 150.00
(Symbol of Courage)
551 Fred Haney AS MG 7.50 15.00
552 Casey Stengel AS MG 18.00 30.00
553 Orlando Cepeda AS 18.00 30.00
554 Bill Skowron AS 10.00 20.00
555 Bill Mazeroski AS 18.00 30.00
556 Nellie Fox AS 20.00 40.00
557 Ken Boyer AS 18.00 30.00
558 Frank Malzone AS 7.50 15.00
559 Ernie Banks AS 35.00 60.00
560 Luis Aparicio AS 25.00 40.00
561 Hank Aaron AS 75.00 125.00
562 Al Kaline AS 35.00 60.00
563 Willie Mays AS 75.00 125.00
564 Mickey Mantle AS 175.00 300.00
565 Wes Covington AS 10.00 20.00
566 Roy Sievers AS 7.50 15.00
567 Del Crandall AS 7.50 15.00
568 Gus Triandos AS 7.50 15.00
569 Bob Friend AS 7.50 15.00
570 Bob Turley AS 7.50 15.00
571 Warren Spahn AS 30.00 50.00
572 Billy Pierce AS 25.00 40.00

1960 Topps

The cards in this 572-card set measure 2 1/2" by 3 1/2". The 1960 Topps set is the first Topps standard size issue to use a horizontally oriented front. World Series cards appeared for the first time (385 to 391), and there is a Rookie Prospect (RP) series (117-148), the most famous of which is Carl Yastrzemski, and a Sport Magazine All-Star Selection (AS) series (553-572). There are 16 manager cards listed alphabetically from 212 through 227. The 1959 Topps All-Rookie team is featured on cards 316-325. This was the first time the Topps All-Rookie team was ever selected and the only time that all of the cards were placed together in a subset. The coaching staff of each team was also afforded their own card in a 16-card subset (455-470). There is no price differential for either color back. The high series (507-572) were printed on a more limited basis than the rest of the set. The team cards have series checklists on the reverse. Cards were issued in one-card penny packs, six-card nickel packs (which came 24 to a box), 10 cent cello packs (which came 36 packs to a box) and 36-card rack packs which cost 29 cents . Three card ad-sheets have been seen. One such sheet features Wayne Terwilliger, Kent Hadley and Faye Throneberry on the front with Gene Woodling and an Ad on the back. Another sheet featured Hank Foiles/Hobie Landrith and Hal Smith on the front. The key Rookie Cards in this set are Jim Kaat, Willie McCovey and Carl Yastrzemski. Recently, a Kent Hadley was discovered with a Kansas City A's logo on the front, while this card was rumoured to exist for years, this is the first known spotting of the card. According the published reports at the time, seven copies of the Hadley card, along with the Gino Cimoli and the Faye Throneberry cards were produced. Each series of this set had different card backs. Cards numbered 1-110 had cream colored white back, cards numbered 111-198 had grey backs, cards numbered 119-286 had cream colored white backs, cards numbered 287-

COMPLETE SET (572) 2500.00 5000.00
COMMON CARD (1-440) 1.50 4.00
COMMON (441-506) 3.00 8.00
COMMON (507-572) 6.00 15.00
WRAPPER (1-CENT) 500.00 1000.00
WRAP. (1-CENT REPEAT) 250.00 500.00
WRAPPER (5-CENT) 15.00 40.00
1 Early Wynn 15.00 40.00
2 Roman Mejias 1.50 4.00
3 Joe Adcock 2.50 6.00
4 Bob Purkey 1.50 4.00
5 Wally Moon 2.50 6.00
6 Lou Berberet 1.50 4.00
7 Master and Mentor 10.00 25.00
Willie Mays
Bill Rigney MG
8 Bud Daley 1.50 4.00
9 Faye Throneberry 1.50 4.00
9A Faye Throneberry
Yankees logo on Card
10 Ernie Banks 20.00 50.00
11 Norm Siebern 1.50 4.00
12 Milt Pappas 2.50 6.00
13 Wally Post 2.50 6.00
14 Jim Grant 2.50 6.00
15 Pete Runnels 2.50 6.00
16 Ernie Broglio 2.50 6.00
17 Johnny Callison 2.50 6.00
18 Los Angeles Dodgers CL 20.00 50.00
19 Felix Mantilla 1.50 4.00
20 Roy Face 2.50 6.00
21 Dutch Dotterer 1.50 4.00
22 Rocky Bridges 1.50 4.00
23 Eddie Fisher RC 1.50 4.00
24 Dick Gray 1.50 4.00
25 Roy Sievers 2.50 6.00
26 Wayne Terwilliger 1.50 4.00
27 Dick Drott 1.50 4.00
28 Brooks Robinson 20.00 50.00
29 Clem Labine 2.50 6.00
30 Tito Francona 1.50 4.00
31 Sammy Esposito 1.50 4.00
32 Sophomore Stalwarts 1.50 4.00
Jim O'Toole
Vada Pinson
33 Tom Morgan 1.50 4.00
34 Sparky Anderson 6.00 15.00
35 Whitey Ford 20.00 50.00
36 Russ Nixon 1.50 4.00
37 Bill Bruton 1.50 4.00
38 Jerry Casale 1.50 4.00
39 Earl Averill Jr. 1.50 4.00
40 Joe Cunningham 1.50 4.00
41 Barry Latman 1.50 4.00
42 Hobie Landrith 1.50 4.00
43 Washington Senators CL 4.00 10.00
44 Bobby Locke RC 1.50 4.00
45 Roy McMillan 2.50 6.00
46 Jack Fisher RC 1.50 4.00
47 Don Zimmer 2.50 6.00
48 Hal W. Smith 1.50 4.00
49 Curt Raydon 1.50 4.00
50 Al Kaline 20.00 50.00
51 Jim Coates 2.50 6.00
52 Dave Philley 1.50 4.00
53 Jackie Brandt 1.50 4.00
54 Mike Fornieles 1.50 4.00
55 Bill Mazeroski 6.00 15.00
56 Steve Korcheck 1.50 4.00
57 Win Savers 1.50 4.00
Turk Lown
Gerry Staley
58 Gino Cimoli 1.50 4.00
58A Gino Cimoli
Cardinals Team Logo
Final Date on Back is July 24
59 Juan Pizarro 1.50 4.00
60 Gus Triandos 2.50 6.00
61 Eddie Kasko 1.50 4.00
62 Roger Craig 2.50 6.00
63 George Strickland 1.50 4.00
64 Jack Meyer 1.50 4.00
65 Elston Howard 2.50 6.00
66 Bob Trowbridge 1.50 4.00
67 Jose Pagan RC 1.50 4.00
68 Dave Hillman 1.50 4.00
69 Billy Goodman 2.50 6.00
70 Lew Burdette UER 2.50 6.00
Card spelled as Lou on front and back
71 Marty Keough 1.50 4.00
72 Detroit Tigers CL 10.00 25.00
73 Bob Gibson 20.00 50.00
74 Walt Moryn 1.50 4.00
75 Vic Power 2.50 6.00
76 Bill Fischer 1.50 4.00
77 Hank Foiles 1.50 4.00
78 Bob Grim 1.50 4.00
79 Walt Dropo 1.50 4.00
80 Johnny Antonelli 2.50 6.00
81 Russ Snyder RC 1.50 4.00
82 Ruben Gomez 1.50 4.00
83 Tony Kubek 6.00 15.00
84 Hal R. Smith 1.50 4.00
85 Frank Lary 2.50 6.00
86 Dick Gernert 1.50 4.00
87 John Romonosky 1.50 4.00
88 John Roseboro 2.50 6.00
89 Hal Brown 1.50 4.00
90 Bobby Avila 1.50 4.00
91 Bennie Daniels 1.50 4.00
92 Whitey Herzog 2.50 6.00
93 Art Schult 1.50 4.00
94 Leo Kiely 1.50 4.00
95 Frank Thomas 2.50 6.00
96 Ralph Terry 2.50 6.00
97 Ted Lepcio 1.50 4.00
98 Gordon Jones 1.50 4.00
99 Lenny Green 1.50 4.00
100 Nellie Fox 8.00 20.00
101 Bob Miller RC 1.50 4.00
102 Kent Hadley 1.50 4.00
102A Kent Hadley
Athletics Team Logo
103 Dick Farrell 2.50 6.00
104 Dick Schofield 2.50 6.00
105 Larry Sherry RC 2.50 6.00
106 Billy Gardner 1.50 4.00
107 Carlton Willey 1.50 4.00
108 Pete Daley 1.50 4.00
109 Clete Boyer 6.00 15.00
110 Cal McLish 1.50 4.00
111 Vic Wertz 2.50 6.00
112 Jack Harshman 1.50 4.00
113 Bob Skinner 1.50 4.00
114 Ken Aspromonte 1.50 4.00
115 Fork and Knuckler 2.50 6.00
Roy Face
Hoyt Wilhelm
116 Jim Rivera 1.50 4.00
117 Tom Borland RS 1.50 4.00
118 Bob Bruce RS RC 1.50 4.00
119 Chico Cardenas RS RC 2.50 6.00
120 Duke Carmel RS RC 1.50 4.00
121 Camilo Carreon RS RC 1.50 4.00
122 Don Dillard RS 1.50 4.00
123 Dan Dobbek RS 1.50 4.00
124 Jim Donohue RS RC 1.50 4.00
125 Dick Ellsworth RS RC 2.50 6.00
126 Chuck Estrada RS RC 1.50 4.00
127 Ron Hansen RS 2.50 6.00
128 Bill Harris RS RC 1.50 4.00
129 Bob Hartman RS 1.50 4.00
130 Frank Herrera RS 1.50 4.00
131 Ed Hobaugh RS RC 1.50 4.00
132 Frank Howard RS RC 10.00 25.00
133 Manuel Javier RS RC 2.50 6.00
(Sic, Julian)
134 Deron Johnson RS 2.50 6.00
135 Ken Johnson RS RC 1.50 4.00
136 Jim Kaat RS RC 15.00 40.00
137 Lou Klimchock RS RC 1.50 4.00
138 Art Mahaffey RS RC 2.50 6.00
139 Carl Mathias RS RC 1.50 4.00
140 Julio Navarro RS RC 1.50 4.00
141 Jim Proctor RS RC 1.50 4.00
142 Bill Short RS RC 1.50 4.00
143 Al Spangler RS RC 1.50 4.00
144 Al Stieglitz RS RC 1.50 4.00
145 Jim Umbricht RS RC 1.50 4.00
146 Ted Wieand RS RC 1.50 4.00
147 Bob Will RS 1.50 4.00
148 Carl Yastrzemski RS RC 100.00 200.00
149 Bob Nieman 1.50 4.00
150 Billy Pierce 2.50 6.00
151 San Francisco Giants CL 4.00 10.00
152 Gail Harris 1.50 4.00
153 Bobby Thomson 2.50 6.00
154 Jim Davenport 2.50 6.00
155 Charlie Neal 2.50 6.00
156 Art Ceccarelli 1.50 4.00
157 Rocky Nelson 2.50 6.00
158 Wes Covington 2.50 6.00
159 Jim Piersall 2.50 6.00
160 Rival All-Stars 60.00 120.00
Mickey Mantle
Ken Boyer
161 Ray Narleski 1.50 4.00
162 Sammy Taylor 1.50 4.00
163 Hector Lopez 2.50 6.00
164 Cincinnati Reds CL 4.00 10.00
165 Jack Sanford 2.50 6.00
166 Chuck Essegian 1.50 4.00
167 Valmy Thomas 1.50 4.00
168 Alex Grammas 1.50 4.00
169 Jake Striker RC 1.50 4.00
170 Del Crandall 2.50 6.00
171 Johnny Groth 1.50 4.00
172 Willie Kirkland 1.50 4.00
173 Billy Martin 8.00 20.00
174 Cleveland Indians CL 4.00 10.00
175 Pedro Ramos 1.50 4.00
176 Vada Pinson 2.50 6.00
177 Johnny Kucks 1.50 4.00
178 Woody Held 1.50 4.00
179 Rip Coleman 1.50 4.00
180 Harry Simpson 1.50 4.00
181 Billy Loes 2.50 6.00
182 Glen Hobbie 1.50 4.00
183 Eli Grba RC 1.50 4.00
184 Gary Geiger 1.50 4.00
185 Jim Owens 1.50 4.00
186 Dave Sisler 1.50 4.00
187 Jay Hook RC 1.50 4.00
188 Dick Williams 2.50 6.00

189 Don McMahon 1.50 4.00
190 Gene Woodling 2.50 6.00
191 Johnny Klippstein 1.50 4.00
192 Danny O'Connell 1.50 4.00
193 Dick Hyde 1.50 4.00
194 Bobby Gene Smith 1.50 4.00
195 Lindy McDaniel 2.50 6.00
196 Andy Carey 2.50 6.00
197 Ron Kline 1.50 4.00
198 Jerry Lynch 2.50 6.00
199 Dick Donovan 2.50 6.00
200 Willie Mays 60.00 120.00
201 Larry Osborne 1.50 4.00
202 Fred Kipp 1.50 4.00
203 Sammy White 1.50 4.00
204 Ryne Duren 2.50 6.00
205 Johnny Logan 2.50 6.00
206 Claude Osteen 2.50 6.00
207 Bob Boyd 1.50 4.00
208 Chicago White Sox CL 4.00 10.00
209 Ron Blackburn 1.50 4.00
210 Harmon Killebrew 15.00 40.00
211 Taylor Phillips 1.50 4.00
212 Walter Alston MG 4.00 10.00
213 Chuck Dressen MG 2.50 6.00
214 Jimmy Dykes MG 2.50 6.00
215 Bob Elliott MG 2.50 6.00
216 Joe Gordon MG 2.50 6.00
217 Charlie Grimm MG 2.50 6.00
218 Solly Hemus MG 1.50 4.00
219 Fred Hutchinson MG 2.50 6.00
220 Billy Jurges MG 1.50 4.00
221 Cookie Lavagetto MG 1.50 4.00
222 Al Lopez MG 4.00 10.00
223 Danny Murtaugh MG 2.50 6.00
224 Paul Richards MG 2.50 6.00
225 Bill Rigney MG 1.50 4.00
226 Eddie Sawyer MG 1.50 4.00
227 Casey Stengel MG 6.00 15.00
228 Ernie Johnson 2.50 6.00
229 Joe M. Morgan RC 1.50 4.00
230 Mound Magicians 4.00 10.00
Lou Burdette
Warren Spahn
Bob Buhl
231 Hal Naragon 1.50 4.00
232 Jim Busby 1.50 4.00
233 Don Elston 1.50 4.00
234 Don Demeter 1.50 4.00
235 Gus Bell 2.50 6.00
236 Dick Ricketts 1.50 4.00
237 Elmer Valo 1.50 4.00
238 Danny Kravitz 1.50 4.00
239 Joe Shipley 1.50 4.00
240 Luis Aparicio 6.00 15.00
241 Albie Pearson 2.50 6.00
242 St. Louis Cardinals CL 4.00 10.00
243 Bubba Phillips 1.50 4.00
244 Hal Griggs 1.50 4.00
245 Eddie Yost 2.50 6.00
246 Lee Maye RC 2.50 6.00
247 Gil McDougald 4.00 10.00
248 Del Rice 1.50 4.00
249 Earl Wilson RC 2.50 6.00
250 Stan Musial 50.00 100.00
251 Bob Malkmus 1.50 4.00
252 Ray Herbert 1.50 4.00
253 Eddie Bressoud 1.50 4.00
254 Arnie Portocarrero 1.50 4.00
255 Jim Gilliam 2.50 6.00
256 Dick Brown 1.50 4.00
257 Gordy Coleman RC 1.50 4.00
258 Dick Groat 2.50 6.00
259 George Altman 1.50 4.00
260 Power Plus 6.00 15.00
Rocky Colavito
Tito Francona
261 Pete Burnside 1.50 4.00
262 Hank Bauer 2.50 6.00
263 Darrell Johnson 1.50 4.00
264 Robin Roberts 6.00 15.00
265 Rip Repulski 1.50 4.00
266 Joey Jay 2.50 6.00
267 Jim Marshall 1.50 4.00
268 Al Worthington 1.50 4.00
269 Gene Green 1.50 4.00
270 Bob Turley 2.50 6.00
271 Julio Becquer 1.50 4.00
272 Fred Green RC 2.50 6.00
273 Neil Chrisley 1.50 4.00
274 Tom Acker 1.50 4.00
275 Curt Flood 2.50 6.00
276 Ken McBride RC 1.50 4.00
277 Harry Bright 1.50 4.00
278 Stan Williams 2.50 6.00
279 Chuck Tanner 2.50 6.00
280 Frank Sullivan 1.50 4.00
281 Ray Boone 2.50 6.00
282 Joe Nuxhall 2.50 6.00
283 John Blanchard 2.50 6.00
284 Don Gross 1.50 4.00
285 Harry Anderson 1.50 4.00
286 Ray Semproch 1.50 4.00
287 Felipe Alou 2.50 6.00
288 Bob Mabe 1.50 4.00
289 Willie Jones 1.50 4.00
290 Jerry Lumpe 1.50 4.00
291 Bob Keegan 1.50 4.00
292 Dodger Backstops 2.50 6.00
Joe Pignatano
John Roseboro
293 Gene Conley 2.50 6.00
294 Tony Taylor 2.50 6.00
295 Gil Hodges 10.00 25.00
296 Nelson Chittum RC 1.50 4.00
297 Reno Bertoia 1.50 4.00
298 George Witt 1.50 4.00
299 Earl Torgeson 1.50 4.00
300 Hank Aaron 60.00 120.00
301 Jerry Davie 1.50 4.00
302 Philadelphia Phillies CL 4.00 10.00
303 Billy O'Dell 1.50 4.00
304 Joe Ginsberg 1.50 4.00
305 Richie Ashburn 8.00 20.00
306 Frank Baumann 1.50 4.00
307 Gene Oliver 1.50 4.00
308 Dick Hall 1.50 4.00
309 Bob Hale 1.50 4.00
310 Frank Malzone 2.50 6.00
311 Raul Sanchez 1.50 4.00
312 Charley Lau 2.50 6.00
313 Turk Lown 1.50 4.00
314 Chico Fernandez 1.50 4.00
315 Bobby Shantz 4.00 10.00
316 Willie McCovey ASR RC 60.00 120.00
317 Pumpsie Green ASR 2.50 6.00
318 Jim Baxes ASR 2.50 6.00
319 Joe Koppe ASR 2.50 6.00
320 Bob Allison ASR 2.50 6.00
321 Ron Fairly ASR 2.50 6.00
322 Willie Tasby ASR 2.50 6.00
323 John Romano ASR 2.50 6.00
324 Jim Perry ASR 2.50 6.00
325 Jim O'Toole ASR 2.50 6.00
326 Roberto Clemente 100.00 200.00
327 Ray Sadecki RC 1.50 4.00
328 Earl Battey 1.50 4.00
329 Zack Monroe 1.50 4.00
330 Harvey Kuenn 2.50 6.00
331 Henry Mason RC 1.50 4.00
332 New York Yankees CL 40.00 80.00
333 Danny McDevitt 1.50 4.00
334 Ted Abernathy 1.50 4.00
335 Red Schoendienst 6.00 15.00
336 Ike Delock 1.50 4.00
337 Cal Neeman 1.50 4.00
338 Ray Monzant 1.50 4.00
339 Harry Chiti 1.50 4.00
340 Harvey Haddix 2.50 6.00
341 Carroll Hardy 1.50 4.00
342 Casey Wise 1.50 4.00
343 Sandy Koufax 60.00 120.00
344 Clint Courtney 1.50 4.00
345 Don Newcombe 2.50 6.00
346 J.C. Martin UER RC 2.50 6.00
(Face actually
Gary Peters)
347 Ed Bouchee 1.50 4.00
348 Barry Shetrone RC 1.50 4.00
349 Moe Drabowsky 2.50 6.00
350 Mickey Mantle 300.00 600.00
351 Don Nottebart RC 1.50 4.00
352 Cincy Clouters 4.00 10.00
Gus Bell
Frank Robinson
Jerry Lynch
353 Don Larsen 2.50 6.00
354 Bob Lillis 1.50 4.00
355 Bill White 2.50 6.00
356 Joe Amalfitano 1.50 4.00
357 Al Schroll 1.50 4.00
358 Joe DeMaestri 1.50 4.00
359 Buddy Gilbert RC 1.50 4.00
360 Herb Score 2.50 6.00
361 Bob Oldis 2.50 6.00
362 Russ Kemmerer 1.50 4.00
363 Gene Stephens 1.50 4.00
364 Paul Foytack 1.50 4.00
365 Minnie Minoso 4.00 10.00
366 Dallas Green RC 4.00 10.00
367 Bill Tuttle 1.50 4.00
368 Daryl Spencer 1.50 4.00
369 Billy Hoeft 1.50 4.00
370 Bill Skowron 4.00 10.00
371 Bud Byerly 1.50 4.00
372 Frank House 1.50 4.00
373 Don Hoak 2.50 6.00
374 Bob Buhl 2.50 6.00
375 Dale Long 4.00 10.00
376 John Briggs 1.50 4.00
377 Roger Maris 50.00 100.00
378 Stu Miller 2.50 6.00
379 Red Wilson 1.50 4.00
380 Bob Shaw 1.50 4.00
381 Milwaukee Braves CL 4.00 10.00
382 Ted Bowsfield 1.50 4.00
383 Leon Wagner 1.50 4.00
384 Don Cardwell 1.50 4.00
385 World Series Game 1 3.00 8.00
Charlie Neal
Steals Second
386 World Series Game 2 3.00 8.00
Charlie Neal
Belts Second Homer
387 World Series Game 3 3.00 8.00
Carl Furillo
Breaks Game
388 World Series Game 4 4.00 10.00
Gil Hodges
Winning Homer
389 World Series Game 5 4.00 10.00
Aparicio Steals Base
w/Maury Wills
390 World Series Game 6 3.00 8.00
Scrambling After Ball
391 World Series Summary 3.00 8.00
The Champs Celebrate
392 Tex Clevenger 1.50 4.00
393 Smoky Burgess 2.50 6.00
394 Norm Larker 2.50 6.00
395 Hoyt Wilhelm 6.00 15.00
396 Steve Bilko 1.50 4.00
397 Don Blasingame 1.50 4.00
398 Mike Cuellar 2.50 6.00
399 Young Hill Stars 2.50 6.00
Milt Pappas
Jack Fisher
Jerry Walker
400 Rocky Colavito 8.00 20.00
401 Bob Duliba RC 1.50 4.00
402 Dick Stuart 6.00 15.00
403 Ed Sadowski 1.50 4.00
404 Bob Rush 1.50 4.00
405 Bobby Richardson 6.00 15.00
406 Billy Klaus 1.50 4.00
407 Gary Peters RC UER 2.50 6.00
(Face actually
J.C. Martin)
408 Carl Furillo 4.00 10.00
409 Ron Samford 1.50 4.00
410 Sam Jones 2.50 6.00
411 Ed Bailey 1.50 4.00
412 Bob Anderson 1.50 4.00
413 Kansas City Athletics CL 4.00 10.00
414 Don Williams RC 1.50 4.00
415 Bob Cerv 1.50 4.00
416 Humberto Robinson 1.50 4.00
417 Chuck Cottier RC 1.50 4.00
418 Don Mossi 2.50 6.00
419 George Crowe 1.50 4.00
420 Eddie Mathews 15.00 40.00
421 Duke Maas 1.50 4.00
422 John Powers 1.50 4.00
423 Ed Fitzgerald 1.50 4.00
424 Pete Whisenant 1.50 4.00
425 Johnny Podres 2.50 6.00
426 Ron Jackson 1.50 4.00
427 Al Grunwald RC 1.50 4.00
428 Al Smith 1.50 4.00
429 American League Kings 4.00 10.00
Nellie Fox
Harvey Kuenn
430 Art Ditmar 1.50 4.00
431 Andre Rodgers 1.50 4.00
432 Chuck Stobbs 1.50 4.00
433 Irv Noren 1.50 4.00
434 Brooks Lawrence 2.50 6.00
435 Gene Freese 1.50 4.00
436 Marv Throneberry 2.50 6.00
437 Bob Friend 2.50 6.00
438 Jim Coker RC 1.50 4.00
439 Tom Brewer 1.50 4.00
440 Jim Lemon 2.50 6.00
441 Gary Bell 4.00 10.00
442 Joe Pignatano 3.00 8.00
443 Charlie Maxwell 3.00 8.00
444 Jerry Kindall 3.00 8.00
445 Warren Spahn 20.00 50.00
446 Ellis Burton 3.00 8.00
447 Ray Moore 3.00 8.00
448 Jim Gentile RC 6.00 15.00
449 Jim Brosnan 3.00 8.00
450 Orlando Cepeda 10.00 25.00
451 Curt Simmons 3.00 8.00
452 Ray Webster 3.00 8.00
453 Vern Law 10.00 25.00
454 Hal Woodeshick 3.00 8.00
455 Baltimore Coaches 3.00 8.00
Eddie Robinson
Harry Brecheen
Luman Harris
456 Red Sox Coaches 4.00 10.00
Rudy York
Billy Herman
Sal Maglie
Del Baker
457 Cubs Coaches 3.00 8.00
Charlie Root
Lou Klein
Elvin Tappe
458 White Sox Coaches 3.00 8.00
Johnny Cooney
Don Gutteridge
Tony Cuccinello
Ray Berres
459 Reds Coaches 3.00 8.00
Reggie Otero
Cot Deal
Wally Moses
460 Indians Coaches 6.00 15.00
Mel Harder
Jo Jo White
Bob Lemon
Ralph (Red) Kress
461 Tigers Coaches 4.00 10.00
Tom Ferrick
Luke Appling
Billy Hitchcock
462 Athletics Coaches 3.00 8.00
Fred Fitzsimmons
Don Heffner
Walker Cooper
463 Dodgers Coaches 3.00 8.00
Bobby Bragan
Pete Reiser
Joe Becker
Greg Mulleavy
464 Braves Coaches 3.00 8.00
Bob Scheffing
Whitlow Wyatt
Andy Pafko
George Myatt
465 Yankees Coaches 10.00 25.00
Bill Dickey
Ralph Houk
Frank Crosetti
Ed Lopat
466 Phillies Coaches 3.00 8.00
Ken Silvestri
Dick Carter
Andy Cohen
467 Pirates Coaches 3.00 8.00
Mickey Vernon
Frank Oceak
Sam Narron
Bill Burwell
468 Cardinals Coaches 3.00 8.00
Johnny Keane
Howie Pollet
Ray Katt
Harry Walker
469 Giants Coaches 3.00 8.00
Wes Westrum
Salty Parker
Bill Posedel
470 Senators Coaches 3.00 8.00
Bob Swift
Ellis Clary
Sam Mele
471 Ned Garver 3.00 8.00
472 Alvin Dark 3.00 8.00
473 Al Cicotte 3.00 8.00
474 Haywood Sullivan 3.00 8.00
475 Don Drysdale 15.00 40.00
476 Lou Johnson RC 3.00 8.00
477 Don Ferrarese 3.00 8.00
478 Frank Torre 3.00 8.00
479 Georges Maranda RC 3.00 8.00
480 Yogi Berra 40.00 80.00
481 Wes Stock RC 3.00 8.00
482 Frank Bolling 3.00 8.00
483 Camilo Pascual 3.00 8.00
484 Pittsburgh Pirates CL 15.00 40.00
485 Ken Boyer 6.00 15.00
486 Bobby Del Greco 3.00 8.00
487 Tom Sturdivant 3.00 8.00
488 Norm Cash 10.00 25.00
Shown with Indians Cap but listed as a Tiger
489 Steve Ridzik 3.00 8.00
490 Frank Robinson 20.00 50.00
491 Mel Roach 3.00 8.00
492 Larry Jackson 3.00 8.00
493 Duke Snider 20.00 50.00
494 Baltimore Orioles CL 10.00 25.00
495 Sherm Lollar 3.00 8.00
496 Bill Virdon 4.00 10.00
497 John Tsitouris 3.00 8.00
498 Al Pilarcik 3.00 8.00
499 Johnny James RC 4.00 10.00
500 Johnny Temple 3.00 8.00
501 Bob Schmidt 3.00 8.00
502 Jim Bunning 10.00 25.00
503 Don Lee 3.00 8.00
504 Seth Morehead 3.00 8.00
505 Ted Kluszewski 10.00 25.00
506 Lee Walls 3.00 8.00
507 Dick Stigman 6.00 15.00
508 Billy Consolo 6.00 15.00
509 Tommy Davis RC 10.00 25.00
510 Gerry Staley 6.00 15.00
511 Ken Walters RC 6.00 15.00
512 Joe Gibbon RC 6.00 15.00
513 Chicago Cubs CL 12.50 30.00
514 Steve Barber RC 6.00 15.00
515 Stan Lopata 6.00 15.00
516 Marty Kutyna RC 6.00 15.00
517 Charlie James RC 10.00 25.00
518 Tony Gonzalez RC 6.00 15.00
519 Ed Roebuck 6.00 15.00
520 Don Buddin 6.00 15.00
521 Mike Lee RC 6.00 15.00
522 Ken Hunt RC 12.50 30.00
523 Clay Dalrymple RC 6.00 15.00
524 Bill Henry 6.00 15.00
525 Marv Breeding RC 6.00 15.00
526 Paul Giel 10.00 25.00
527 Jose Valdivielso 10.00 25.00
528 Ben Johnson RC 6.00 15.00
529 Norm Sherry RC 8.00 20.00
530 Mike McCormick 6.00 15.00
531 Sandy Amoros 8.00 20.00
532 Mike Garcia 8.00 20.00
533 Lu Clinton RC 6.00 15.00
534 Ken MacKenzie RC 6.00 15.00
535 Whitey Lockman 6.00 15.00
536 Wynn Hawkins RC 6.00 15.00
537 Boston Red Sox CL 12.50 30.00
538 Frank Barnes RC 6.00 15.00
539 Gene Baker 6.00 15.00
540 Jerry Walker 6.00 15.00
541 Tony Curry RC 6.00 15.00
542 Ken Hamlin RC 6.00 15.00
543 Elio Chacon RC 6.00 15.00
544 Bill Monbouquette 8.00 20.00
545 Carl Sawatski 6.00 15.00
546 Hank Aguirre 6.00 15.00
547 Bob Aspromonte RC 8.00 20.00
548 Don Mincher RC 8.00 20.00
549 John Buzhardt 6.00 15.00
550 Jim Landis 6.00 15.00
551 Ed Rakow RC 6.00 15.00
552 Walt Bond RC 6.00 15.00
553 Bill Skowron AS 8.00 20.00
554 Willie McCovey AS 15.00 40.00
555 Nellie Fox AS 12.50 30.00
556 Charlie Neal AS 6.00 15.00
557 Frank Malzone AS 6.00 15.00
558 Eddie Mathews AS 15.00 40.00
559 Luis Aparicio AS 12.50 30.00
560 Ernie Banks AS 30.00 60.00
561 Al Kaline AS 30.00 60.00
562 Joe Cunningham AS 6.00 15.00
563 Mickey Mantle AS 125.00 250.00
564 Willie Mays AS 50.00 100.00
565 Roger Maris AS 50.00 100.00
566 Hank Aaron AS 50.00 100.00
567 Sherm Lollar AS 6.00 15.00
568 Del Crandall AS 6.00 15.00
569 Camilo Pascual AS 6.00 15.00
570 Don Drysdale AS 15.00 40.00
571 Billy Pierce AS 6.00 15.00
572 Johnny Antonelli AS 12.50 30.00
NNO Iron-On Team Transfer

1961 Topps

The cards in this 587-card set measure 2 1/2" by 3 1/2". In 1961, Topps returned to the vertical obverse format. Introduced for the first time were "League Leaders" (41-50) and separate, numbered checklist cards. Two number 463s exist: the Braves team card carrying that number was meant to be number 426. There are three versions of the second series checklist card number 98; the variations are distinguished by the color of the "CHECKLIST" headline on the front of the card, the color of the printing of the card number on the bottom of the reverse, and the presence of the copyright notice running vertically on the card back. There are two groups of managers (131-139/219-226) as well as separate subsets of World Series cards (306-313), Baseball Thrills (401-410), MVP's of the 1950's (AL 471-478/NL 479-486) and Sporting News All-Stars (566-589). The usual last series scarcity (523-589) exists. Some collectors believe that 61 high numbers are the toughest of all the Topps hi series numbers. The set actually totals 587 cards since numbers 587 and 588 were never issued. These card advertising promos have been seen: Dan Dobbek/Russ Nixon/60 NL Pitching Leaders on the front along with an ad and Roger Maris on the back.Other strips feature Jack Kralick/Dick Stigman/Joe Christopher; Ed Roebuck/Bob Schmidt/Zoilo Versalles; Lindy (McDaniel) Shows Larry (Jackson)/John Blanchard/Johnny Kucks. Cards were issued in one-card penny packs, five-card nickel packs, 10 cent cello packs (which came 36 to a box) and 36-card rack packs which cost 29 cents. The one card packs came 120 to a box. The key Rookie Cards in this set are Juan Marichal, Ron Santo and Billy Williams.

COMPLETE SET (587) 3500.00 7000.00
COMMON CARD (1-370) 1.25 3.00
COMMON (371-446) 1.50 4.00
COMMON (447-522) 3.00 8.00
COMMON (523-589) 12.50 30.00
NOT ISSUED (587/588)
WRAPPER (1-CENT) 100.00 200.00
WRAP (1-CENT, REPEAT) 50.00 100.00
WRAPPER (5-CENT) 15.00 40.00
1 Dick Groat 12.50 30.00
2 Roger Maris 125.00 250.00
3 John Buzhardt 1.25 3.00
4 Lenny Green 1.25 3.00
5 John Romano 1.25 3.00
6 Ed Roebuck 1.25 3.00
7 Chicago White Sox TC 3.00 8.00
8 Dick Williams UER 2.50 6.00
Blurb states career high in RBI, however his career high in RBI was in 1959
9 Bob Purkey 1.25 3.00
10 Brooks Robinson 20.00 50.00
11 Curt Simmons 2.50 6.00
12 Moe Thacker 1.25 3.00
13 Chuck Cottier 1.25 3.00
14 Don Mossi 2.50 6.00
15 Willie Kirkland 1.25 3.00
16 Billy Muffett 1.25 3.00
17 Checklist 1 4.00 10.00
18 Jim Grant 2.50 6.00
19 Clete Boyer 3.00 8.00
20 Robin Roberts 6.00 15.00
21 Zorro Versalles 3.00 8.00
UER RC
First name should
be Zoilo
22 Clem Labine 2.50 6.00
23 Don Demeter 1.25 3.00
24 Ken Johnson 2.50 6.00
25 Reds Heavy Artillery 3.00 8.00
Vada Pinson
Gus Bell
Frank Robinson
26 Wes Stock 1.25 3.00
27 Jerry Kindall 1.25 3.00
28 Hector Lopez 2.50 6.00
29 Don Nottebart 1.25 3.00
30 Nellie Fox 6.00 15.00
31 Bob Schmidt 1.25 3.00
32 Ray Sadecki 1.25 3.00
33 Gary Geiger 1.25 3.00
34 Wynn Hawkins 1.25 3.00
35 Ron Santo RC 15.00 40.00
36 Jack Kralick RC 1.25 3.00
37 Charley Maxwell 2.50 6.00
38 Bob Lillis 1.25 3.00
39 Leo Posada RC 1.25 3.00
40 Bob Turley 2.50 6.00
41 NL Batting Leaders 15.00 40.00
Dick Groat
Norm Larker
Willie Mays
Roberto Clemente
42 AL Batting Leaders 3.00 8.00
Pete Runnels
Al Smith
Minnie Minoso
Bill Skowron
43 NL Home Run Leaders 12.50 30.00
Ernie Banks
Hank Aaron
Ed Mathews
Ken Boyer
44 AL Home Run Leaders 40.00 80.00
Mickey Mantle
Roger Maris
Jim Lemon
Rocky Colavito
45 NL ERA Leaders 3.00 8.00
Mike McCormick
Ernie Broglio
Don Drysdale
Bob Friend
Stan Williams
46 AL ERA Leaders 3.00 8.00
Frank Baumann
Jim Bunning
Art Ditmar
Hal Brown
47 NL Pitching Leaders 3.00 8.00
Ernie Broglio
Warren Spahn
Vern Law
Lou Burdette
48 AL Pitching Leaders 3.00 8.00
Chuck Estrada
Jim Perry UER
(Listed as an Oriole)
Bud Daley
Art Ditmar
Frank Lary
Milt Pappas
49 NL Strikeout Leaders 8.00 20.00
Don Drysdale
Sandy Koufax
Sam Jones
Ernie Broglio
50 AL Strikeout Leaders 3.00 8.00
Jim Bunning
Pedro Ramos
Early Wynn
Frank Lary
51 Detroit Tigers TC 3.00 8.00
52 George Crowe 1.25 3.00
53 Russ Nixon 1.25 3.00
54 Earl Francis RC 1.25 3.00
55 Jim Davenport 2.50 6.00
56 Russ Kemmerer 1.25 3.00
57 Marv Throneberry 2.50 6.00
58 Joe Schaffernoth RC 1.25 3.00
59 Jim Woods 1.25 3.00
60 Woody Held 1.25 3.00
61 Ron Piche RC 1.25 3.00
62 Al Pilarcik 1.25 3.00
63 Jim Kaat 3.00 8.00
64 Alex Grammas 1.25 3.00
65 Ted Kluszewski 3.00 8.00
66 Bill Henry 1.25 3.00
67 Ossie Virgil 1.25 3.00
68 Deron Johnson 2.50 6.00
69 Earl Wilson 2.50 6.00
70 Bill Virdon 2.50 6.00
71 Jerry Adair 1.25 3.00
72 Stu Miller 2.50 6.00
73 Al Spangler 1.25 3.00
74 Joe Pignatano 1.25 3.00
75 Lindy Shows Larry 2.50 6.00
Lindy McDaniel
Larry Jackson
76 Harry Anderson 1.25 3.00
77 Dick Stigman 1.25 3.00
78 Lee Walls 2.50 6.00
79 Joe Ginsberg 1.25 3.00
80 Harmon Killebrew 8.00 20.00
81 Tracy Stallard RC 1.25 3.00
82 Joe Christopher RC 1.25 3.00
83 Bob Bruce 1.25 3.00
84 Lee Maye 1.25 3.00
85 Jerry Walker 1.25 3.00
86 Los Angeles Dodgers TC 3.00 8.00
87 Joe Amalfitano 1.25 3.00
88 Richie Ashburn 6.00 15.00
89 Billy Martin 6.00 15.00
90 Gerry Staley 1.25 3.00
91 Walt Moryn 1.25 3.00
92 Hal Naragon 1.25 3.00
93 Tony Gonzalez 1.25 3.00
94 Johnny Kucks 1.25 3.00
95 Norm Cash 3.00 8.00
96 Billy O'Dell 1.25 3.00
97 Jerry Lynch 2.50 6.00
98A Checklist 2 4.00 10.00
(Red Checklist
98 black on white)
98B Checklist 2 4.00 10.00
(Yellow Checklist
98 black on white)
98C Checklist 2 4.00 10.00
(Yellow Checklist
98 white on black
no copyright)
99 Don Buddin UER 1.25 3.00
(66 HR's)
100 Harvey Haddix 2.50 6.00
101 Bubba Phillips 1.25 3.00
102 Gene Stephens 1.25 3.00
103 Ruben Amaro 1.25 3.00
104 John Blanchard 3.00 8.00
105 Carl Willey 1.25 3.00
106 Whitey Herzog 1.25 3.00
107 Seth Morehead 1.25 3.00
108 Dan Dobbek 1.25 3.00
109 Johnny Podres 3.00 8.00
110 Vada Pinson 3.00 8.00
111 Jack Meyer 1.25 3.00
112 Chico Fernandez 1.25 3.00
113 Mike Fornieles 1.25 3.00
114 Hobie Landrith 1.25 3.00
115 Johnny Antonelli 2.50 6.00
116 Joe DeMaestri 1.25 3.00
117 Dale Long 2.50 6.00
118 Chris Cannizzaro RC 1.25 3.00
119 A's Big Armor 2.50 6.00
Norm Siebern
Hank Bauer
Jerry Lumpe
120 Eddie Mathews 12.50 30.00
121 Eli Grba 2.50 6.00
122 Chicago Cubs TC 3.00 8.00
123 Billy Gardner 1.25 3.00
124 J.C. Martin 1.25 3.00
125 Steve Barber 1.25 3.00
126 Dick Stuart 2.50 6.00
127 Ron Kline 1.25 3.00
128 Rip Repulski 1.25 3.00
129 Ed Hobaugh 1.25 3.00
130 Norm Larker 1.25 3.00
131 Paul Richards MG 2.50 6.00
132 Al Lopez MG 3.00 8.00
133 Ralph Houk MG 2.50 6.00
134 Mickey Vernon MG 2.50 6.00
135 Fred Hutchinson MG 2.50 6.00
136 Walter Alston MG 3.00 8.00
137 Chuck Dressen MG 2.50 6.00
138 Danny Murtaugh MG 2.50 6.00
139 Solly Hemus MG 2.50 6.00
140 Gus Triandos 2.50 6.00
141 Billy Williams RC 30.00 60.00
142 Luis Arroyo 2.50 6.00
143 Russ Snyder 1.25 3.00
144 Jim Coker 1.25 3.00
145 Bob Buhl 2.50 6.00
146 Marty Keough 1.25 3.00
147 Ed Rakow 1.25 3.00
148 Julian Javier 2.50 6.00
149 Bob Oldis 1.25 3.00
150 Willie Mays 50.00 100.00
151 Jim Donohue 1.25 3.00
152 Earl Torgeson 1.25 3.00
153 Don Lee 1.25 3.00
154 Bobby Del Greco 1.25 3.00
155 Johnny Temple 2.50 6.00
156 Ken Hunt 2.50 6.00
157 Cal McLish 1.25 3.00
158 Pete Daley 1.25 3.00
159 Baltimore Orioles TC 3.00 8.00
160 Whitey Ford UER 20.00 50.00
Incorrectly listed
as 5'0 tall
161 Sherman Jones UER RC 1.25 3.00
(Photo actually
Eddie Fisher)
162 Jay Hook 1.25 3.00
163 Ed Sadowski 1.25 3.00
164 Felix Mantilla 1.25 3.00
165 Gino Cimoli 1.25 3.00
166 Danny Kravitz 1.25 3.00
167 San Francisco Giants TC 3.00 8.00
168 Tommy Davis 3.00 8.00
169 Don Elston 1.25 3.00
170 Al Smith 1.25 3.00
171 Paul Foytack 1.25 3.00
172 Don Dillard 1.25 3.00
173 Beantown Bombers 2.50 6.00
Frank Malzone
Vic Wertz
Jackie Jensen
174 Ray Semproch 1.25 3.00
175 Gene Freese 1.25 3.00
176 Ken Aspromonte 1.25 3.00
177 Don Larsen 2.50 6.00
178 Bob Nieman 1.25 3.00
179 Joe Koppe 1.25 3.00
180 Bobby Richardson 5.00 12.00
181 Fred Green 2.50 6.00
182 Dave Nicholson RC 1.25 3.00
183 Andre Rodgers 1.25 3.00
184 Steve Bilko 2.50 6.00
185 Herb Score 2.50 6.00
186 Elmer Valo 2.50 6.00
187 Billy Klaus 1.25 3.00
188 Jim Marshall 1.25 3.00
189A Checklist 3 4.00 10.00
(Copyright symbol
almost adjacent to
263 Ken Hamlin)
189B Checklist 3 4.00 10.00
(Copyright symbol
adjacent to
264 Glen Hobbie)
190 Stan Williams 2.50 6.00
191 Mike de la Hoz RC 1.25 3.00
192 Dick Brown 1.25 3.00
193 Gene Conley 2.50 6.00
194 Gordy Coleman 2.50 6.00
195 Jerry Casale 1.25 3.00
196 Ed Bouchee 1.25 3.00
197 Dick Hall 1.25 3.00
198 Carl Sawatski 1.25 3.00
199 Bob Boyd 1.25 3.00
200 Warren Spahn 15.00 40.00
201 Pete Whisenant 1.25 3.00
202 Al Neiger RC 1.25 3.00
203 Eddie Bressoud 1.25 3.00
204 Bob Skinner 2.50 6.00
205 Billy Pierce 2.50 6.00
206 Gene Green 1.25 3.00
207 Dodger Southpaws 12.50 30.00
Sandy Koufax
Johnny Podres
208 Larry Osborne 1.25 3.00
209 Ken McBride 1.25 3.00
210 Pete Runnels 2.50 6.00
211 Bob Gibson 15.00 40.00
212 Haywood Sullivan 2.50 6.00
213 Bill Stafford RC 1.25 3.00
214 Danny Murphy RC 2.50 6.00
215 Gus Bell 2.50 6.00
216 Ted Bowsfield 1.25 3.00
217 Mel Roach 1.25 3.00
218 Hal Brown 1.25 3.00
219 Gene Mauch MG 2.50 6.00
220 Alvin Dark MG 2.50 6.00
221 Mike Higgins MG 2.50 6.00
222 Jimmy Dykes MG 2.50 6.00
223 Bob Scheffing MG 2.50 6.00
224 Joe Gordon MG 2.50 6.00
225 Bill Rigney MG 2.50 6.00
226 Cookie Lavagetto MG 2.50 6.00
227 Juan Pizarro 1.25 3.00
228 New York Yankees TC 30.00 60.00
229 Rudy Hernandez RC 1.25 3.00
230 Don Hoak 2.50 6.00
231 Dick Drott 1.25 3.00
232 Bill White 2.50 6.00
233 Joey Jay 2.50 6.00
234 Ted Lepcio 1.25 3.00
235 Camilo Pascual 2.50 6.00
236 Don Gile RC 1.25 3.00
237 Billy Loes 2.50 6.00
238 Jim Gilliam 2.50 6.00
239 Dave Sisler 1.25 3.00
240 Ron Hansen 1.25 3.00
241 Al Cicotte 1.25 3.00
242 Hal Smith 1.25 3.00
243 Frank Lary 2.50 6.00
244 Chico Cardenas 2.50 6.00
245 Joe Adcock 2.50 6.00
246 Bob Davis RC 1.25 3.00
247 Billy Goodman 2.50 6.00
248 Ed Keegan RC 1.25 3.00
249 Cincinnati Reds TC 3.00 8.00
250 Buc Hill Aces 2.50 6.00
Vern Law
Roy Face
251 Bill Bruton 1.25 3.00
252 Bill Short 1.25 3.00
253 Sammy Taylor 1.25 3.00
254 Ted Sadowski RC 2.50 6.00
255 Vic Power 2.50 6.00
256 Billy Hoeft 1.25 3.00
257 Carroll Hardy 2.50 6.00
258 Jack Sanford 2.50 6.00
259 John Schaive RC 1.25 3.00
260 Don Drysdale 12.50 30.00
261 Charlie Lau 2.50 6.00
262 Tony Curry 1.25 3.00
263 Ken Hamlin 1.25 3.00
264 Glen Hobbie 1.25 3.00
265 Tony Kubek 5.00 12.00
266 Lindy McDaniel 2.50 6.00
267 Norm Siebern 1.25 3.00
268 Ike Delock 1.25 3.00
269 Harry Chiti 1.25 3.00
270 Bob Friend 2.50 6.00
271 Jim Landis 1.25 3.00
272 Tom Morgan 1.25 3.00
273A Checklist 4 6.00 15.00
(Copyright symbol
adjacent to
336 Don Mincher)
273B Checklist 4 4.00 10.00
(Copyright symbol
adjacent to
339 Gene Baker)
274 Gary Bell 1.25 3.00
275 Gene Woodling 2.50 6.00
276 Ray Rippelmeyer RC 1.25 3.00
277 Hank Foiles 1.25 3.00
278 Don McMahon 1.25 3.00
279 Jose Pagan 1.25 3.00
280 Frank Howard 3.00 8.00
281 Frank Sullivan 1.25 3.00
282 Faye Throneberry 1.25 3.00
283 Bob Anderson 1.25 3.00
284 Dick Gernert 1.25 3.00
285 Sherm Lollar 2.50 6.00
286 George Witt 1.25 3.00
287 Carl Yastrzemski 20.00 50.00
288 Albie Pearson 2.50 6.00
289 Ray Moore 1.25 3.00
290 Stan Musial 50.00 100.00
291 Tex Clevenger 1.25 3.00
292 Jim Baumer RC 1.25 3.00
293 Tom Sturdivant 1.25 3.00
294 Don Blasingame 1.25 3.00
295 Milt Pappas 2.50 6.00

296 Wes Covington 2.50 6.00
297 Kansas City Athletics TC 3.00 8.00
298 Jim Golden RC 1.25 3.00
299 Clay Dalrymple 1.25 3.00
300 Mickey Mantle 300.00 600.00
301 Chet Nichols 1.25 3.00
302 Al Heist RC 1.25 3.00
303 Gary Peters 2.50 6.00
304 Rocky Nelson 1.25 3.00
305 Mike McCormick 2.50 6.00
306 World Series Game 1 4.00 10.00
Bill Virdon
307 World Series Game 2 40.00 80.00
Mickey Mantle
308 World Series Game 3 5.00 12.00
Bobby Richardson
309 World Series Game 4 4.00 10.00
Gino Cimoli
310 World Series Game 5 4.00 10.00
Roy Face
311 World Series Game 6 6.00 15.00
Whitey Ford
312 World Series Game 7 8.00 20.00
Bill Mazeroski
313 World Series Summary 6.00 15.00
Winners Celebrate
314 Bob Miller 1.25 3.00
315 Earl Battey 2.50 6.00
316 Bobby Gene Smith 1.25 3.00
317 Jim Brewer RC 1.25 3.00
318 Danny O'Connell 1.25 3.00
319 Valmy Thomas 1.25 3.00
320 Lou Burdette 2.50 6.00
321 Marv Breeding 1.25 3.00
322 Bill Kunkel RC 2.50 6.00
323 Sammy Esposito 1.25 3.00
324 Hank Aguirre 1.25 3.00
325 Wally Moon 2.50 6.00
326 Dave Hillman 1.25 3.00
327 Matty Alou RC 5.00 12.00
328 Jim O'Toole 2.50 6.00
329 Julio Bocquer 1.25 3.00
330 Rocky Colavito 8.00 20.00
331 Ned Garver 1.25 3.00
332 Dutch Dotterer UER 1.25 3.00
(Photo actually
Tommy Dotterer
Dutch's brother)
333 Fritz Brickell RC 1.25 3.00
334 Walt Bond 1.25 3.00
335 Frank Bolling 1.25 3.00
336 Don Mincher 2.50 6.00
337 Al's Aces 3.00 8.00
Early Wynn
Al Lopez
Herb Score
338 Don Landrum 1.25 3.00
339 Gene Baker 1.25 3.00
340 Vic Wertz 2.50 6.00
341 Jim Owens 1.25 3.00
342 Clint Courtney 1.25 3.00
343 Earl Robinson RC 1.25 3.00
344 Sandy Koufax 50.00 100.00
345 Jimmy Piersall 3.00 8.00
346 Howie Nunn 1.25 3.00
347 St. Louis Cardinals TC 3.00 8.00
348 Steve Boros 1.25 3.00
349 Danny McDevitt 1.25 3.00
350 Ernie Banks 15.00 40.00
351 Jim King 1.25 3.00
352 Bob Shaw 1.25 3.00
353 Howie Bedell RC 1.25 3.00
354 Billy Harrell 2.50 6.00
355 Bob Allison 3.00 8.00
356 Ryne Duren 1.25 3.00
357 Daryl Spencer 1.25 3.00
358 Earl Averill Jr. 2.50 6.00
359 Dallas Green 1.25 3.00
360 Frank Robinson 15.00 40.00
361A Checklist 5 6.00 15.00
(No ad on back)
361B Checklist 5 6.00 15.00
(Special Feature
ad on back)
362 Frank Funk RC 1.25 3.00
363 John Roseboro 2.50 6.00
364 Moe Drabowsky 2.50 6.00
365 Jerry Lumpe 1.25 3.00
366 Eddie Fisher 1.25 3.00
367 Jim Rivera 1.25 3.00
368 Bennie Daniels 1.25 3.00
369 Dave Philley 1.25 3.00
370 Roy Face 2.50 6.00
371 Bill Skowron SP 20.00 50.00
372 Bob Hendley RC 1.50 4.00
373 Boston Red Sox TC 3.00 8.00
374 Paul Giel 1.50 4.00
375 Ken Boyer 5.00 12.00
376 Mike Roarke RC 2.50 6.00
377 Ruben Gomez 1.50 4.00
378 Wally Post 2.50 6.00
379 Bobby Shantz 1.50 4.00
380 Minnie Minoso 3.00 8.00
381 Dave Wickersham RC 1.50 4.00
382 Frank Thomas 2.50 6.00
383 Frisco First Liners 2.50 6.00
Mike McCormick
Jack Sanford
Billy O'Dell
384 Chuck Essegian 1.50 4.00
385 Jim Perry 2.50 6.00
386 Joe Hicks 1.50 4.00
387 Duke Maas 1.50 4.00
388 Roberto Clemente 60.00 120.00
389 Ralph Terry 2.50 6.00
390 Del Crandall 3.00 8.00
391 Winston Brown RC 1.50 4.00
392 Reno Bertoia 1.50 4.00
393 Batter Bafflers 1.50 4.00
Don Cardwell
Glen Hobbie
394 Ken Walters 1.50 4.00
395 Chuck Estrada 2.50 6.00
396 Bob Aspromonte 1.50 4.00
397 Hal Woodeshick 1.50 4.00
398 Hank Bauer 2.50 6.00
399 Cliff Cook RC 1.50 4.00
400 Vern Law 2.50 6.00
401 Babe Ruth 60th HR 30.00 60.00
402 Don Larsen Perfect SP 10.00 25.00
403 26 Inning Tire 3.00 8.00
Joe OeschgerL
Leon Cadore
404 Rogers Hornsby .424 5.00 12.00
405 Lou Gehrig Streak 40.00 80.00
406 Mickey Mantle 565 HR 50.00 100.00
407 Jack Chesbro Wins 41 3.00 8.00
408 Christy Mathewson K's SP 8.00 20.00
409 Walter Johnson Shutout 5.00 12.00
410 Harvey Haddix 12 Perfect 3.00 8.00
411 Tony Taylor 2.50 6.00
412 Larry Sherry 2.50 6.00
413 Eddie Yost 2.50 6.00
414 Dick Donovan 2.50 6.00
415 Hank Aaron 60.00 120.00
416 Dick Howser RC 3.00 8.00
417 Juan Marichal SP RC 50.00 100.00
418 Ed Bailey 2.50 6.00
419 Tom Borland 1.50 4.00
420 Ernie Broglio 2.50 6.00
421 Ty Cline SP RC 8.00 20.00
422 Bud Daley 1.50 4.00
423 Charlie Neal SP 8.00 20.00
424 Turk Lown 1.50 4.00
425 Yogi Berra 40.00 80.00
426 Milwaukee Braves TC 5.00 12.00
(Back numbered 463)
427 Dick Ellsworth 2.50 6.00
428 Ray Barker SP RC 8.00 20.00
429 Al Kaline 20.00 50.00
430 Bill Mazeroski SP 20.00 50.00
431 Chuck Stobbs 1.50 4.00
432 Coot Veal 2.50 6.00
433 Art Mahaffey 1.50 4.00
434 Tom Brewer 1.50 4.00
435 Orlando Cepeda UER 5.00 12.00
(San Francis on
card front)
436 Jim Maloney SP RC 8.00 20.00
437A Checklist 6 6.00 15.00
440 Louis Aparicio
437B Checklist 6 6.00 15.00
440 Luis Aparicio
438 Curt Flood 3.00 8.00
439 Phil Regan RC 2.50 6.00
440 Luis Aparicio 5.00 12.00
441 Dick Bertell RC 1.50 4.00
442 Gordon Jones 1.50 4.00
443 Duke Snider 20.00 50.00
444 Joe Nuxhall 2.50 6.00
445 Frank Malzone 2.50 6.00
446 Bob Taylor 1.50 4.00
447 Harry Bright 3.00 8.00
448 Del Rice 6.00 15.00
449 Bob Bolin RC 3.00 8.00
450 Jim Lemon 3.00 8.00
451 Power for Ernie 3.00 8.00
Daryl Spencer
Bill White
Ernie Broglio
452 Bob Allen RC 3.00 8.00
453 Dick Schofield 3.00 8.00
454 Pumpsie Green 3.00 8.00
455 Early Wynn 6.00 15.00
456 Hal Bevan 3.00 8.00
457 Johnny James 3.00 8.00
(Listed as Angel,
but wearing Yankee
uniform and cap)
458 Willie Tasby 3.00 8.00
459 Terry Fox RC 4.00 10.00
460 Gil Hodges 10.00 25.00
461 Smoky Burgess 6.00 15.00
462 Lou Klimchock 3.00 8.00
463 Jack Fisher 3.00 8.00
(See also 426)
464 Lee Thomas RC 4.00 10.00
(Pictured with Yankee
cap but listed as
Los Angeles Angel)
465 Roy McMillan 6.00 15.00
466 Ron Moeller RC 3.00 8.00
467 Cleveland Indians TC 5.00 12.00
468 John Callison 4.00 10.00
469 Ralph Lumenti 3.00 8.00
470 Roy Sievers 4.00 10.00
471 Phil Rizzuto MVP 10.00 25.00
472 Yogi Berra MVP 20.00 50.00
473 Bob Shantz MVP 3.00 8.00
474 Al Rosen MVP 4.00 10.00
475 Mickey Mantle MVP 100.00 200.00
476 Jackie Jensen MVP 4.00 10.00
477 Nellie Fox MVP 6.00 15.00
478 Roger Maris MVP 30.00 60.00
479 Jim Konstanty MVP 3.00 8.00
480 Roy Campanella MVP 15.00 40.00
481 Hank Sauer MVP 3.00 8.00
482 Willie Mays MVP 20.00 50.00
483 Don Newcombe MVP 4.00 10.00
484 Hank Aaron MVP 20.00 50.00
485 Ernie Banks MVP 15.00 40.00
486 Dick Groat MVP 4.00 10.00
487 Gene Oliver 3.00 8.00
488 Joe McClain RC 4.00 10.00
489 Walt Dropo 3.00 8.00
490 Jim Bunning 10.00 25.00
491 Philadelphia Phillies TC 5.00 12.00
492A Ron Fairly 4.00 10.00
Area below bottom stitch of baseball is white
492B Ron Fairly 8.00 20.00
Area below bottom stitch of baseball is green
493 Don Zimmer UER 4.00 10.00
(Brooklyn A.L.)
494 Tom Cheney 4.00 10.00
495 Elston Howard 6.00 15.00
496 Ken MacKenzie 3.00 8.00
497 Willie Jones 3.00 8.00
498 Ray Herbert 3.00 8.00
499 Chuck Schilling RC 3.00 8.00
500 Harvey Kuenn 4.00 10.00
501 John DeMerit RC 3.00 8.00
502 Choo Choo Coleman RC 4.00 10.00
503 Tito Francona 3.00 8.00
504 Billy Consolo 3.00 8.00
505 Red Schoendienst 6.00 15.00
506 Willie Davis RC 6.00 15.00
507 Pete Burnside 3.00 8.00
508 Rocky Bridges 3.00 8.00
509 Camilo Carreon 3.00 8.00
510 Art Ditmar 3.00 8.00
511 Joe M. Morgan 3.00 8.00
512 Bob Will 3.00 8.00
513 Jim Brosnan 3.00 8.00
514 Jake Wood RC 3.00 8.00
515 Jackie Brandt 3.00 8.00
516 Checklist 7 6.00 15.00
517 Willie McCovey 15.00 40.00
518 Andy Carey 3.00 8.00
519 Jim Pagliaroni RC 3.00 8.00
520 Joe Cunningham 3.00 8.00
521 Brother Battery 3.00 8.00
Norm Sherry
Larry Sherry
522 Dick Farrell UER 6.00 15.00
(Phillies cap but
listed on Dodgers)
523 Joe Gibbon 12.50 30.00
524 Johnny Logan 12.50 30.00
525 Ron Perranoski RC 30.00 60.00
526 R.C. Stevens 12.50 30.00
527 Gene Leek RC 12.50 30.00
528 Pedro Ramos 12.50 30.00
529 Bob Roselli 12.50 30.00
530 Bob Malkmus 12.50 30.00
531 Jim Coates 20.00 50.00
532 Bob Hale 12.50 30.00
533 Jack Curtis RC 12.50 30.00
534 Eddie Kasko 15.00 40.00
535 Larry Jackson 12.50 30.00
536 Bill Tuttle 12.50 30.00
537 Bobby Locke 12.50 30.00
538 Chuck Hiller RC 12.50 30.00
539 Johnny Klippstein 12.50 30.00
540 Jackie Jensen 15.00 40.00
541 Roland Sheldon RC 20.00 50.00
542 Minnesota Twins TC 30.00 60.00
543 Roger Craig 15.00 40.00
544 George Thomas RC 20.00 50.00
545 Hoyt Wilhelm 30.00 60.00
546 Marty Kutyna 12.50 30.00
547 Leon Wagner 12.50 30.00
548 Ted Wills 12.50 30.00
549 Hal R. Smith 12.50 30.00
550 Frank Baumann 12.50 30.00
551 George Altman 15.00 40.00
552 Jim Archer RC 12.50 30.00
553 Bill Fischer 12.50 30.00
554 Pittsburgh Pirates TC 40.00 80.00
555 Sam Jones 12.50 30.00
556 Ken R. Hunt RC 12.50 30.00
557 Jose Valdivielso 12.50 30.00
558 Don Ferrarese 12.50 30.00
559 Jim Gentile 30.00 60.00
560 Barry Latman 15.00 40.00
561 Charley James 12.50 30.00
562 Bill Monbouquette 12.50 30.00
563 Bob Cerv 30.00 60.00
564 Don Cardwell 12.50 30.00
565 Felipe Alou 20.00 50.00
566 Paul Richards AS MG 12.50 30.00
567 Danny Murtaugh AS MG 12.50 30.00
568 Bill Skowron AS 20.00 50.00
569 Frank Herrera AS 15.00 40.00
570 Nellie Fox AS 30.00 60.00
571 Bill Mazeroski AS 30.00 60.00
572 Brooks Robinson AS 40.00 80.00
573 Ken Boyer AS 20.00 50.00
574 Luis Aparicio AS 30.00 60.00
575 Ernie Banks AS 40.00 80.00
576 Roger Maris AS 100.00 200.00
577 Hank Aaron AS 75.00 150.00
578 Mickey Mantle AS 250.00 500.00
579 Willie Mays AS 75.00 150.00
580 Al Kaline AS 40.00 80.00
581 Frank Robinson AS 40.00 80.00
582 Earl Battey AS 12.50 30.00
583 Del Crandall AS 12.50 30.00
584 Jim Perry AS 12.50 30.00
585 Bob Friend AS 12.50 30.00
586 Whitey Ford AS 50.00 100.00
589 Warren Spahn AS 50.00 100.00

1961 Topps Magic Rub-Offs

There are 36 "Magic Rub-Offs" in this set of inserts also marketed in packages of 1961 Topps baseball cards. Each rub off measures 2 1/16" by 3 1/16". Of this number, 18 are team designs (numbered 1-18 below), while the remaining 18 depict players (numbered 19-36 below). The latter, one from each team, were apparently selected for their unusual nicknames. Note: The Duke Maas insert is misspelled "Mass".

COMPLETE SET (36) 150.00 300.00
COMMON RUB-OFF (1-18) .75 2.00
COMMON CARD (19-36) 2.00 5.00
1 Detroit Tigers 2.00 5.00
2 New York Yankees 2.50 6.00
3 Minnesota Twins 1.25 3.00
4 Washington Senators 1.25 3.00
5 Boston Red Sox 2.00 5.00
6 Los Angeles Angels 1.25 3.00
7 Kansas City A's 1.25 3.00
8 Baltimore Orioles 1.25 3.00
9 Chicago White Sox 1.25 3.00
10 Cleveland Indians 1.25 3.00
11 Pittsburgh Pirates 1.25 3.00
12 San Francisco Giants 1.25 3.00
13 Los Angeles Dodgers 2.50 6.00
14 Philadelphia Phillies 1.25 3.00
15 Cincinnati Redlegs 1.25 3.00
16 St. Louis Cardinals 1.25 3.00
17 Chicago Cubs 1.25 3.00
18 Milwaukee Braves 1.25 3.00
19 John Romano 4.00 10.00
20 Ray Moore 4.00 10.00
21 Ernie Banks 20.00 50.00
22 Charlie Maxwell 4.00 10.00
23 Yogi Berra 20.00 50.00
24 Henry Dutch Dotterer 4.00 10.00
25 Jim Brosnan 4.00 10.00
26 Billy Martin 8.00 20.00
27 Jackie Brandt 4.00 10.00
28 Duke Maas 5.00 12.00
sic, Mass
29 Pete Runnels 5.00 12.00
30 Joe Gordon MG 5.00 12.00
31 Sam Jones 4.00 10.00
32 Walt Moryn 4.00 10.00
33 Harvey Haddix 5.00 12.00
34 Frank Howard 6.00 15.00
35 Turk Lown 4.00 10.00
36 Frank Herrera 4.00 10.00

1961 Topps Stamps

There are 207 different baseball players depicted in this stamp series, which was issued as an insert in packages of the regular Topps cards of 1961. The set is actually comprised of 208 stamps: 104 players are pictured on brown stamps and 104 players appear on green stamps, with Kaline found in both colors. The stamps were issued in attached pairs and an album was sold separately (10 cents) at retail outlets. Each stamp measures 1 3/8" by 1 3/16". Stamps are unnumbered but are presented here in alphabetical order by team, Chicago Cubs (1-12), Cincinnati Reds (13-24), Los Angeles Dodgers (25-36), Milwaukee Braves (37-48), Philadelphia Phillies (49-60), Pittsburgh Pirates (61-72), San Francisco Giants (73-84), St. Louis Cardinals (85-96), Baltimore Orioles AL (97-107), Boston Red Sox (108-119), Chicago White Sox (120-131), Cleveland Indians (132-143), Detroit Tigers (144-155), Kansas City A's (156-168), Los Angeles Angels (169-175), Minnesota Twins (176-187), New York Yankees (188-200) and Washington Senators (201-207).

COMPLETE SET (207) 300.00 600.00
1 George Altman .75 2.00
2 Bob Anderson .75 2.00
brown
3 Richie Ashburn 2.00 5.00
4 Ernie Banks 3.00 8.00
5 Ed Bouchee .75 2.00
6 Jim Brewer .75 2.00
7 Dick Ellsworth .75 2.00
8 Don Elston .75 2.00
9 Ron Santo 2.00 5.00
10 Sammy Taylor .75 2.00
11 Bob Will .75 2.00
12 Billy Williams 2.00 5.00
13 Ed Bailey .75 2.00
14 Gus Bell .75 2.00
15 Jim Brosnan .75 2.00
brown
16 Chico Cardenas .75 2.00
17 Gene Freese .75 2.00
18 Eddie Kasko .75 2.00
19 Jerry Lynch .75 2.00
20 Billy Martin 2.00 5.00
21 Jim O'Toole .75 2.00
22 Vada Pinson 1.25 3.00
23 Wally Post .75 2.00
brown
24 Frank Robinson 3.00 8.00
25 Tommy Davis 1.25 3.00
26 Don Drysdale 2.00 5.00
27 Frank Howard 1.25 3.00
brown
28 Norm Larker .75 2.00
29 Wally Moon .75 2.00
brown
30 Charlie Neal .75 2.00
31 Johnny Podres 1.25 3.00
32 Ed Roebuck .75 2.00
33 Johnny Roseboro .75 2.00
34 Larry Sherry .75 2.00
35 Duke Snider 3.00 8.00
36 Stan Williams .75 2.00
37 Hank Aaron 10.00 25.00
38 Joe Adcock .75 2.00
39 Bill Bruton .75 2.00
40 Bob Buhl .75 2.00
41 Wes Covington .75 2.00
brown
42 Del Crandall .75 2.00
43 Joey Jay .75 2.00
44 Felix Mantilla .75 2.00
45 Eddie Mathews 3.00 8.00
46 Roy McMillan .75 2.00
47 Warren Spahn 3.00 8.00
48 Carlton Willey .75 2.00
brown
49 John Buzhardt .75 2.00
50 Johnny Callison .75 2.00
51 Tony Curry .75 2.00
52 Clay Dalrymple .75 2.00
brown
53 Bobby Del Greco .75 2.00
brown
54 Dick Farrell .75 2.00
brown
55 Tony Gonzalez .75 2.00
56 Pancho Herrera .75 2.00
57 Art Mahaffey .75 2.00
58 Robin Roberts 1.25 3.00
brown
59 Tony Taylor .75 2.00
60 Lee Walls .75 2.00
61 Smoky Burgess .75 2.00
62 Roy Face (brown) .75 2.00
63 Bob Friend .75 2.00
64 Dick Groat 1.25 3.00
65 Don Hoak .75 2.00
66 Vern Law .75 2.00
67 Bill Mazeroski 1.25 3.00
68 Rocky Nelson .75 2.00
69 Bob Skinner .75 2.00
70 Hal Smith .75 2.00
71 Dick Stuart .75 2.00
72 Bill Virdon .75 2.00
73 Don Blasingame .75 2.00
74 Eddie Bressoud .75 2.00
brown
75 Orlando Cepeda 1.25 3.00
76 Jim Davenport .75 2.00
77 Harvey Kuenn 1.25 3.00
brown
78 Hobie Landrith .75 2.00
79 Juan Marichal 2.00 5.00
80 Willie Mays 10.00 25.00
81 Mike McCormick .75 2.00
82 Willie McCovey 3.00 8.00
83 Billy O'Dell .75 2.00
84 Jack Sanford .75 2.00
85 Ken Boyer 1.25 3.00
86 Curt Flood 1.25 3.00
87 Alex Grammas .75 2.00
brown
88 Larry Jackson .75 2.00
89 Julian Javier .75 2.00
90 Ron Kline .75 2.00
brown
91 Lindy McDaniel .75 2.00
92 Stan Musial 6.00 15.00
93 Curt Simmons .75 2.00
brown
94 Hal Smith .75 2.00
95 Daryl Spencer .75 2.00
96 Bill White .75 2.00
brown
97 Steve Barber .75 2.00
98 Jackie Brandt .75 2.00
brown
99 Marv Breeding .75 2.00
100 Chuck Estrada .75 2.00
101 Jim Gentile .75 2.00
102 Ron Hansen .75 2.00
103 Milt Pappas .75 2.00
104 Brooks Robinson 3.00 8.00
105 Gene Stephens .75 2.00
106 Gus Triandos .75 2.00
107 Hoyt Wilhelm 1.25 3.00
108 Tom Brewer .75 2.00
109 Gene Conley .75 2.00
brown
110 Ike Delock .75 2.00
brown
111 Gary Geiger .75 2.00
112 Jackie Jensen 1.25 3.00
113 Frank Malzone .75 2.00
114 Bill Monbouquette .75 2.00
115 Russ Nixon .75 2.00
116 Pete Runnels .75 2.00
117 Willie Tasby .75 2.00
118 Vic Wertz .75 2.00
brown
119 Carl Yastrzemski 6.00 15.00
120 Luis Aparicio 1.25 3.00
121 Russ Kemmerer .75 2.00
brown
122 Jim Landis .75 2.00
123 Sherman Lollar .75 2.00
124 J.C. Martin .75 2.00
125 Minnie Minoso 1.25 3.00
126 Billy Pierce .75 2.00
127 Bob Shaw .75 2.00
128 Roy Sievers .75 2.00
129 Al Smith .75 2.00
130 Gerry Staley .75 2.00
brown
131 Early Wynn 1.25 3.00
132 Johnny Antonelli .75 2.00
brown
133 Ken Aspromonte .75 2.00
134 Tito Francona .75 2.00
135 Jim Grant .75 2.00
136 Woody Held .75 2.00
137 Barry Latman .75 2.00
138 Jim Perry .75 2.00
139 Jimmy Piersall 1.25 3.00
140 Bubba Phillips .75 2.00
141 Vic Power .75 2.00
142 John Romano .75 2.00
143 Johnny Temple .75 2.00
144 Hank Aguirre .75 2.00
brown
145 Frank Bolling .75 2.00
146 Steve Boros .75 2.00
brown
147 Jim Bunning 1.25 3.00
brown
148 Norm Cash 1.25 3.00
149 Harry Chiti .75 2.00
150 Chico Fernandez .75 2.00
151 Dick Gernert .75 2.00
152A Al Kaline (green) 3.00 8.00
152B Al Kaline (brown) 3.00 8.00
153 Frank Lary .75 2.00
154 Charlie Maxwell .75 2.00
155 Dave Sisler .75 2.00
156 Hank Bauer .75 2.00
157 Bob Boyd (brown) .75 2.00
158 Andy Carey .75 2.00
159 Bud Daley .75 2.00
160 Dick Hall .75 2.00
161 J.C. Hartman .75 2.00
162 Ray Herbert .75 2.00
163 Whitey Herzog 1.25 3.00
164 Jerry Lumpe .75 2.00
brown
165 Norm Siebern .75 2.00
166 Marv Throneberry .75 2.00
167 Bill Tuttle .75 2.00
168 Dick Williams .75 2.00
169 Jerry Casale .75 2.00
brown
170 Bob Cerv .75 2.00
171 Ned Garver .75 2.00
172 Ken Hunt .75 2.00
173 Ted Kluszewski 2.00 5.00
174 Ed Sadowski .75 2.00
brown
175 Eddie Yost .75 2.00
176 Bob Allison .75 2.00
177 Earl Battey .75 2.00
brown
178 Reno Bertoia .75 2.00
179 Billy Gardner .75 2.00
180 Jim Kaat 1.25 3.00
181 Harmon Killebrew 3.00 8.00
182 Jim Lemon .75 2.00
183 Camilo Pascual .75 2.00
184 Pedro Ramos .75 2.00
185 Chuck Stobbs .75 2.00
186 Zoilo Versalles .75 2.00
187 Pete Whisenant .75 2.00
188 Luis Arroyo .75 2.00
brown
189 Yogi Berra 5.00 12.00
190 John Blanchard .75 2.00
191 Clete Boyer .75 2.00
192 Art Ditmar .75 2.00
193 Whitey Ford 5.00 12.00
194 Elston Howard 2.00 5.00
195 Tony Kubek 2.00 5.00
196 Mickey Mantle 50.00 100.00
197 Roger Maris 10.00 25.00
198 Bobby Shantz .75 2.00
199 Bill Stafford .75 2.00
200 Bob Turley .75 2.00
201 Bud Daley .75 2.00
brown
202 Dick Donovan .75 2.00
203 Bobby Klaus .75 2.00
204 Johnny Klippstein .75 2.00
205 Dale Long .75 2.00
206 Ray Semproch .75 2.00
207 Gene Woodling .75 2.00
XX Stamp Album 8.00 20.00

1962 Topps

The cards in this 598-card set measure 2 1/2" by 3 1/2". The 1962 Topps set contains a mini-series spotlighting Babe Ruth (135-144). Other subsets in the set include League Leaders (51-60), World Series cards (232-237), In Action cards (311-319), NL All Stars (390-399), AL All Stars (466-475), and Rookie Prospects (591-598). The All-Star selections were again provided by Sport Magazine, as in 1958 and 1960. The second series had two distinct printings which are distinguishable by numerous color and pose variations. Those cards with a distinctive "green tint" are valued at a slight premuim as they are basically the result of a flawed printing process occurring early in the second series run. Card number 139 exists as A: Babe Ruth Special card, B: Hal Reniff with arms over head, or C: Hal Reniff in the same pose as card number 159. In addition, two poses exist for these cards: 129, 132, 134, 147, 174, 176, and 190. The high number series, 523 to 598, is somewhat more difficult to obtain than other cards in the set. Within the last series (523-598) there are 43 cards which were printed in lesser quantities; these are marked SP in the checklist below. In particular, the Rookie Parade subset (591-598) of this last series is even more difficult. This was the first year Topps produced multi-player Rookie Cards. The set price listed does not include the pose variations (see checklist below for individual values). A three card ad sheet has been seen. The players on the front include AL HR leaders, Barney Schultz and Carl Sawatski, while the back features an ad and a Roger Maris card. Cards were issued in one-card penny packs as well as five-card nickel packs. The five card packs came 24 to a box. The key Rookie Cards in this set are Lou Brock, Tim McCarver, Gaylord Perry, and Bob Uecker.

COMP. MASTER (688) 5000.00 10000.00
COMPLETE SET (598) 4000.00 8000.00
COMMON CARD (1-370) 2.00 5.00
COMMON (371-446) 2.50 6.00
COMMON (447-522) 5.00 12.00
COMMON (523-598) 8.00 20.00
WRAPPER (1-CENT) 50.00 100.00
WRAPPER (5-CENT) 12.50 30.00
1 Roger Maris 250.00 500.00
2 Jim Brosnan 2.00 5.00
3 Pete Runnels 2.00 5.00
4 John DeMerit 3.00 8.00
5 Sandy Koufax UER 75.00 150.00
Struck ou 18
6 Marv Breeding 2.00 5.00
7 Frank Thomas 4.00 10.00
8 Ray Herbert 2.00 5.00
9 Jim Davenport 3.00 8.00
10 Roberto Clemente 100.00 200.00
11 Tom Morgan 2.00 5.00
12 Harry Craft MG 3.00 8.00
13 Dick Howser 3.00 8.00
14 Bill White 3.00 8.00
15 Dick Donovan 2.00 5.00
16 Darrell Johnson 2.00 5.00
17 Johnny Callison 3.00 8.00
18 Managers Dream 100.00 200.00
Mickey Mantle
Willie Mays
19 Ray Washburn RC 2.00 5.00
20 Rocky Colavito 6.00 15.00
21 Jim Kaat 3.00 8.00
22A Checklist 1 ERR 5.00 12.00
(121-176 on back)
22B Checklist 1 COR 5.00 12.00
33-88 on back)
23 Norm Larker 2.00 5.00
24 Detroit Tigers TC 4.00 10.00
25 Ernie Banks 20.00 50.00
26 Chris Cannizzaro 3.00 8.00
27 Chuck Cottier 2.00 5.00
28 Minnie Minoso 4.00 10.00
29 Casey Stengel MG 8.00 20.00
30 Eddie Mathews 15.00 40.00
31 Tom Tresh RC 6.00 15.00
32 John Roseboro 3.00 8.00
33 Don Larsen 3.00 8.00
34 Johnny Temple 3.00 8.00
35 Don Schwall RC 4.00 10.00
36 Don Leppert RC 2.00 5.00
37 Tribe Hill Trio 2.00 5.00
Barry Latman
Dick Stigman
Jim Perry
38 Gene Stephens 2.00 5.00
39 Joe Koppe 2.00 5.00
40 Orlando Cepeda 6.00 15.00
41 Cliff Cook 2.00 5.00
42 Jim King 2.00 5.00
43 Los Angeles Dodgers TC 4.00 10.00
44 Don Taussig RC 2.00 5.00
45 Brooks Robinson 20.00 50.00
46 Jack Baldschun RC 2.00 5.00
47 Bob Will 2.00 5.00
48 Ralph Terry 3.00 8.00
49 Hal Jones RC 2.00 5.00
50 Stan Musial 50.00 100.00
51 AL Batting Leaders 3.00 8.00
Norm Cash
Jim Piersall
Al Kaline
Elston Howard
52 NL Batting Leaders 8.00 20.00
Roberto Clemente
Vada Pinson
Ken Boyer
Wally Moon
53 AL Home Run Leaders 50.00 100.00
Roger Maris
Mickey Mantle
Jim Gentile
Harmon Killebrew
54 NL Home Run Leaders 8.00 20.00
Orlando Cepeda
Willie Mays
Frank Robinson
55 AL ERA Leaders 3.00 8.00
Dick Donovan
Bill Stafford
Don Mossi
Milt Pappas
56 NL ERA Leaders 3.00 8.00
Warren Spahn
Jim O'Toole
Curt Simmons
Mike McCormick
57 AL Win Leaders 3.00 8.00
Whitey Ford
Frank Lary
Steve Barber
Jim Bunning
58 NL Win Leaders 3.00 8.00
Warren Spahn
Joe Jay
Jim O'Toole
59 AL Strikout Leaders 3.00 8.00
Camilo Pascual
Whitey Ford
Jim Bunning
Juan Pizzaro
60 NL Strikeout Leaders 8.00 20.00
Sandy Koufax
Stan Williams
Don Drysdale
Jim O'Toole
61 St. Louis Cardinals TC 4.00 10.00
62 Steve Boros 2.00 5.00
63 Tony Cloninger RC 3.00 8.00
64 Russ Snyder 2.00 5.00
65 Bobby Richardson 4.00 10.00
66 Cuno Barragan RC 2.00 5.00
67 Harvey Haddix 3.00 8.00
68 Ken Hunt 2.00 5.00
69 Phil Ortega RC 2.00 5.00
70 Harmon Killebrew 10.00 25.00
71 Dick LeMay RC 2.00 5.00
72 Bob's Pupils 2.00 5.00
Steve Boros
Bob Scheffing MG
Jake Wood
73 Nellie Fox 8.00 20.00
74 Bob Lillis 3.00 8.00
75 Milt Pappas 3.00 8.00
76 Howie Bedell 2.00 5.00
77 Tony Taylor 3.00 8.00
78 Gene Green 2.00 5.00
79 Ed Hobaugh 2.00 5.00
80 Vada Pinson 3.00 8.00
81 Jim Pagliaroni 2.00 5.00
82 Deron Johnson 3.00 8.00
83 Larry Jackson 2.00 5.00
84 Lenny Green 2.00 5.00
85 Gil Hodges 8.00 20.00
86 Donn Clendenon RC 3.00 8.00
87 Mike Roarke 2.00 5.00
88 Ralph Houk MG 3.00 8.00
(Berra in background)
89 Barney Schultz RC 2.00 5.00
90 Jimmy Piersall 3.00 8.00
91 J.C. Martin 2.00 5.00
92 Sam Jones 2.00 5.00
93 John Blanchard 3.00 8.00
94 Jay Hook 3.00 8.00
95 Don Hoak 3.00 8.00
96 Eli Grba 2.00 5.00
97 Tito Francona 2.00 5.00
98 Checklist 2 5.00 12.00
99 John (Boog) Powell RC 12.50 30.00
100 Warren Spahn 15.00 40.00
101 Carroll Hardy 2.00 5.00
102 Al Schroll 2.00 5.00
103 Don Blasingame 2.00 5.00
104 Ted Savage RC 2.00 5.00
105 Don Mossi 3.00 8.00
106 Carl Sawatski 2.00 5.00
107 Mike McCormick 3.00 8.00
108 Willie Davis 3.00 8.00
109 Bob Shaw 2.00 5.00
110 Bill Skowron 3.00 8.00
110A Bill Skowron 3.00 8.00
Green Tint
111 Dallas Green 3.00 8.00
111A Dallas Green 3.00 8.00
Green Tint
112 Hank Foiles 2.00 5.00
112A Hank Foiles 2.00 5.00
Green Tint
113 Chicago White Sox TC 4.00 10.00
113A Chicago White Sox TC 4.00 10.00
Green Tint
114 Howie Koplitz RC 2.00 5.00
114A Howie Koplitz 2.00 5.00
Green Tint
115 Bob Skinner 3.00 8.00

115A Bob Skinner	3.00	8.00
Green Tint		
116 Herb Score	3.00	8.00
116A Herb Score	3.00	8.00
Green Tint		
117 Gary Geiger	3.00	8.00
117A Gary Geiger	3.00	8.00
Green Tint		
118 Julian Javier	3.00	8.00
118A Julian Javier	3.00	8.00
Green Tint		
119 Danny Murphy	2.00	5.00
119A Danny Murphy	2.00	5.00
Green Tint		
120 Bob Purkey	2.00	5.00
120A Bob Purkey	2.00	5.00
Green Tint		
121 Billy Hitchcock MG	2.00	5.00
121A Billy Hitchcock	2.00	5.00
Green Tint		
122 Norm Bass RC	2.00	5.00
122A Norm Bass	2.00	5.00
Green Tint		
123 Mike de la Hoz	2.00	5.00
123A Mike de la Hoz	2.00	5.00
Green Tint		
124 Bill Pleis RC	2.00	5.00
124A Bill Pleis	2.00	5.00
Green Tint		
125 Gene Woodling	3.00	8.00
125A Gene Woodling	3.00	8.00
Green Tint		
126 Al Cicotte	2.00	5.00
126A Al Cicotte	2.00	5.00
Green Tint		
127 Pride of A's	2.00	5.00
Norm Siebern		
Hank Bauer MG		
Jerry Lumpe		
127A Pride of A's	2.00	5.00
Norm Siebern		
Hank Bauer MG		
Jerry Lumpe		
Green Tint		
128 Art Fowler	2.00	5.00
128A Art Fowler	2.00	5.00
Green Tint		
129A Lee Walls	2.00	5.00
Plain Jersey, facing right		
129B Lee Walls	12.50	30.00
Pinstriped Jersey, facing left#(Card has a Green Tint		
130 Frank Bolling	2.00	5.00
130A Frank Bolling	2.00	5.00
Green Tint		
131 Pete Richert RC	2.00	5.00
131A Pete Richert	2.00	5.00
Green Tint		
132A Los Angeles Angels TC	4.00	10.00
(No Inset Photos)		
132B Los Angeles Angels TC	12.50	30.00
(With Inset Photos)		
133 Felipe Alou	3.00	8.00
133A Felipe Alou	3.00	8.00
Green Tint		
134A Billy Hoeft	2.00	5.00
Blue Sky		
134B Billy Hoeft	12.50	30.00
Green Sky		
135 Babe Ruth Special 1	8.00	20.00
Babe as a Boy		
135A Babe Ruth Special 1	8.00	20.00
Babe as a Boy		
Green Tint		
136 Babe Ruth Special 2	8.00	20.00
Babe Joins Yanks		
Pictured Owner with Jacob Ruppert		
136A Babe Ruth Special 2	8.00	20.00
Babe Joins Yanks		
Pictured Owner with Jacob Ruppert		
GReen Tint		
137 Babe Ruth Special 3	8.00	20.00
Babe with Mgr. Huggins		
137A Babe Ruth Special 3	8.00	20.00
Babe with Mgr. Huggins		
Green Tint		
138 Babe Ruth Special 4	8.00	20.00
The Famous Slugger		
138A Babe Ruth Special 4	8.00	20.00
The Famous Slugger		
Green Tint		
139A1 Babe Ruth Special 5	12.50	30.00
Babe Hits 60 (Pole)		
139A2 Babe Ruth Special 5	12.50	30.00
Babe Hits 60 (No Pole)		
139B Hal Reniff Portrait	6.00	15.00
139C Hal Reniff Pitching	30.00	60.00
140 Babe Ruth Special 6	30.00	60.00
Gehrig and Ruth		
140A Babe Ruth Special 6	30.00	60.00
Gehrig and Ruth		
Green Tint		
141 Babe Ruth Special 7	8.00	20.00
Twilight Years		
141A Babe Ruth Special 7	8.00	20.00
Twilight Years		
Green Tint		
142 Babe Ruth Special 8	8.00	20.00
Coaching the Dodgers		
142A Babe Ruth Special 8	8.00	20.00
Coaching the Dodgers		
Green Tint		
143 Babe Ruth Special 9	8.00	20.00
Greatest Sports Hero		
143A Babe Ruth Special 9	8.00	20.00
Greatest Sports Hero		
Green Tint		
144 Babe Ruth Special 10	8.00	20.00
Farewell Speech		
144A Babe Ruth Special 10	8.00	20.00
Farewell Speech		
Green Tint		
145 Barry Latman	2.00	5.00
145A Barry Latman	2.00	5.00
Green Tint		
146 Don Demeter	2.00	5.00
146A Don Demeter	2.00	5.00
Green Tint		
147A Bill Kunkel Portrait	2.00	5.00
147B Bill Kunkel Pitching	12.50	30.00
148 Wally Post	2.00	5.00
148A Wally Post	2.00	5.00
Green Tint		
149 Bob Duliba	2.00	5.00
149A Bob Duliba	2.00	5.00
Green Tint		
150 Al Kaline	20.00	50.00
150A Al Kaline	20.00	50.00
Green Tint		
151 Johnny Klippstein	2.00	5.00
151A Johnny Klippstein	2.00	5.00
Green Tint		
152 Mickey Vernon MG	3.00	8.00
152A Mickey Vernon MG	3.00	8.00
Green Tint		
153 Pumpsie Green	2.50	6.00
153A Pumpsie Green	2.50	6.00
Green Tint		
154 Lee Thomas	2.50	6.00
154A Lee Thomas	2.50	6.00
Green Tint		
155 Stu Miller	2.50	6.00
155A Stu Miller	2.50	6.00
Green Tint		
156 Merritt Ranew RC	2.00	5.00
156A Merritt Ranew	2.00	5.00
Green Tint		
157 Wes Covington	3.00	8.00
157A Wes Covington	3.00	8.00
Green Tint		
158 Milwaukee Braves TC	4.00	10.00
158A Milwaukee Braves TC	6.00	15.00
Green Tint		
159 Hal Reniff RC	3.00	8.00
160 Dick Stuart	3.00	8.00
160A Dick Stuart	3.00	8.00
Green Tint		
161 Frank Baumann	2.00	5.00
161A Frank Baumann	2.00	5.00
Green Tint		
162 Sammy Drake RC	2.00	5.00
162A Sammy Drake	2.00	5.00
Green Tint		
163 Hot Corner Guard	3.00	8.00
Billy Gardner		
Cletis Boyer		
163A Hot Corner Guard	3.00	8.00
Billy Gardner		
Cletis Boyer		
Green Tint		
164 Hal Naragon	2.00	5.00
164A Hal Naragon	2.00	5.00
Green Tint		
165 Jackie Brandt	2.00	5.00
165A Jackie Brandt	2.00	5.00
Green Tint		
166 Don Lee	2.00	5.00
166A Don Lee	2.00	5.00
Green Tint		
167 Tim McCarver RC	12.50	30.00
167A Tim McCarver	12.50	30.00
Green Tint		
168 Leo Posada	2.00	5.00
168A Leo Posada	2.00	5.00
Green Tint		
169 Bob Cerv	4.00	10.00
169A Bob Cerv	4.00	10.00
Green Tint		
170 Ron Santo	6.00	15.00
170A Ron Santo	6.00	15.00
Green Tint		
171 Dave Sisler	2.00	5.00
171A Dave Sisler	2.00	5.00
Green Tint		
172 Fred Hutchinson MG	3.00	8.00
172A Fred Hutchinson MG	3.00	8.00
Green Tint		
173 Chico Fernandez	2.00	5.00
173A Chico Fernandez	2.00	5.00
Green Tint		
174A Carl Willey w/o Cap	2.00	5.00
174B Carl Willey w/Cap	12.50	30.00
175 Frank Howard	4.00	10.00
175A Frank Howard	4.00	10.00
Green Tint		
176A Eddie Yost Portrait	2.00	5.00
176B Eddie Yost Batting	12.50	30.00
177 Bobby Shantz	3.00	8.00
177A Bobby Shantz	3.00	8.00
Green Tint		
178 Camilo Carreon	2.00	5.00
178A Camilo Carreon	2.00	5.00
Green Tint		
179 Tom Sturdivant	2.00	5.00
179A Tom Sturdivant	2.00	5.00
Green Tint		
180 Bob Allison	4.00	10.00
180A Bob Allison	4.00	10.00
Green Tint		
181 Paul Brown RC	2.00	5.00
181A Paul Brown	2.00	5.00
Green Tint		
182 Bob Nieman	2.00	5.00
182A Bob Nieman	2.00	5.00
Green Tint		
183 Roger Craig	3.00	8.00
183A Roger Craig	3.00	8.00
Green Tint		
184 Haywood Sullivan	3.00	8.00
184A Haywood Sullivan	3.00	8.00
Green Tint		
185 Roland Sheldon	4.00	10.00
185A Roland Sheldon	4.00	10.00
Green Tint		
186 Mack Jones RC	2.00	5.00
186A Mack Jones	2.00	5.00
Green Tint		
187 Gene Conley	2.00	5.00
187A Gene Conley	2.00	5.00
Green Tint		
188 Chuck Hiller	2.00	5.00
188A Chuck Hiller	2.00	5.00
Green Tint		
189 Dick Hall	2.00	5.00
189A Dick Hall	2.00	5.00
Green Tint		
190A Wally Moon No Cap	3.00	8.00
190B Wally Moon With Cap	12.50	30.00
191 Jim Brewer	2.00	5.00
191A Jim Brewer	2.00	5.00
Green Tint		
192A Checklist 3 w/o Comma	5.00	12.00
192B Checklist 3 w/Comma	6.00	15.00
193 Eddie Kasko	2.00	5.00
193A Eddie Kasko	2.00	5.00
Green Tint		
194 Dean Chance RC	3.00	8.00
194A Dean Chance	3.00	8.00
Green Tint		
195 Joe Cunningham	2.00	5.00
195A Joe Cunningham	2.00	5.00
Green Tint		
196 Terry Fox	2.00	5.00
196A Terry Fox	2.00	5.00
Green Tint		
197 Daryl Spencer	2.00	5.00
198 Johnny Keane MG	2.00	5.00
199 Gaylord Perry RC	40.00	80.00
200 Mickey Mantle	300.00	600.00
201 Ike Delock	2.00	5.00
202 Carl Warwick RC	2.00	5.00
203 Jack Fisher	2.00	5.00
204 Johnny Weekly RC	2.00	5.00
205 Gene Freese	2.00	5.00
206 Washington Senators TC	4.00	10.00
207 Pete Burnside	2.00	5.00
208 Billy Martin	8.00	20.00
209 Jim Fregosi RC	6.00	15.00
210 Roy Face	3.00	8.00
211 Midway Masters	2.00	5.00
Frank Bolling		
Roy McMillan		
212 Jim Owens	2.00	5.00
213 Richie Ashburn	8.00	20.00
214 Dom Zanni	2.00	5.00
215 Woody Held	2.00	5.00
216 Ron Kline	2.00	5.00
217 Walter Alston MG	4.00	10.00
218 Joe Torre RC	15.00	40.00
219 Al Downing RC	3.00	8.00
220 Roy Sievers	3.00	8.00
221 Bill Short	2.00	5.00
222 Jerry Zimmerman	2.00	5.00
223 Alex Grammas	2.00	5.00
224 Don Rudolph	2.00	5.00
225 Frank Malzone	3.00	8.00
226 San Francisco Giants TC	4.00	10.00
227 Bob Tiefenauer	2.00	5.00
228 Dale Long	4.00	10.00
229 Jesus McFarlane RC	2.00	5.00
230 Camilo Pascual	3.00	8.00
231 Ernie Bowman RC	2.00	5.00
232 World Series Game 1	4.00	10.00
Yanks Win Opener		
233 World Series Game 2	4.00	10.00
Joey Jay		
234 World Series Game 3	10.00	25.00
Roger Maris		
235 World Series Game 4	6.00	15.00
Whitey Ford		
236 World Series Game 5	4.00	10.00
Yanks Crush Reds		
237 World Series Summary	4.00	10.00
Yanks Celebrate		
238 Norm Sherry	2.00	5.00
239 Cecil Butler RC	2.00	5.00
240 George Altman	2.00	5.00
241 Johnny Kucks	2.00	5.00
242 Mel McGaha MG RC	2.00	5.00
243 Robin Roberts	6.00	15.00
244 Don Gile	2.00	5.00
245 Ron Hansen	2.00	5.00
246 Art Ditmar	2.00	5.00
247 Joe Pignatano	2.00	5.00
248 Bob Aspromonte	3.00	8.00
249 Ed Keegan	2.00	5.00
250 Norm Cash	4.00	10.00
251 New York Yankees TC	20.00	50.00
252 Earl Francis	2.00	5.00
253 Harry Chiti CO	2.00	5.00
254 Gordon Windhorn RC	2.00	5.00
255 Juan Pizarro	2.00	5.00
256 Elio Chacon	3.00	8.00
257 Jack Spring RC	2.00	5.00
258 Marty Keough	2.00	5.00
259 Lou Klimchock	2.00	5.00
260 Billy Pierce	3.00	8.00
261 George Alusik RC	2.00	5.00
262 Bob Schmidt	2.00	5.00
263 The Right Pitch	2.00	5.00
Bob Purkey		
Jim Turner CO		
Joe Jay		
264 Dick Ellsworth	3.00	8.00
265 Joe Adcock	3.00	8.00
266 John Anderson RC	2.00	5.00
267 Dan Dobbek	2.00	5.00
268 Ken McBride	2.00	5.00
269 Bob Oldis	2.00	5.00
270 Dick Groat	3.00	8.00
271 Ray Rippelmeyer	2.00	5.00
272 Earl Robinson	2.00	5.00
273 Gary Bell	2.00	5.00
274 Sammy Taylor	2.00	5.00
275 Norm Siebern	2.00	5.00
276 Hal Kolstad RC	2.00	5.00
277 Checklist 4	6.00	15.00
278 Ken Johnson	3.00	8.00
279 Hobie Landrith UER	3.00	8.00
(Wrong birthdate)		
280 Johnny Podres	3.00	8.00
281 Jake Gibbs RC	4.00	10.00
282 Dave Hillman	2.00	5.00
283 Charlie Smith RC	2.00	5.00
284 Ruben Amaro	2.00	5.00
285 Curt Simmons	3.00	8.00
286 Al Lopez MG	4.00	10.00
287 George Witt	2.00	5.00
288 Billy Williams	12.50	30.00
289 Mike Krsnich RC	2.00	5.00
290 Jim Gentile	3.00	8.00
291 Hal Stowe RC	2.00	5.00
292 Jerry Kindall	2.00	5.00
293 Bob Miller	3.00	8.00
294 Philadelphia Phillies TC	4.00	10.00
295 Vern Law	3.00	8.00
296 Ken Hamlin	2.00	5.00
297 Ron Perranoski	3.00	8.00
298 Bill Tuttle	2.00	5.00
299 Don Wert RC	2.00	5.00
300 Willie Mays	125.00	250.00
301 Galen Cisco RC	2.00	5.00
302 Johnny Edwards RC	2.00	5.00
303 Frank Torre	3.00	8.00
304 Dick Farrell	3.00	8.00
305 Jerry Lumpe	2.00	5.00
306 Redbird Rippers	2.00	5.00
Lindy McDaniel		
Larry Jackson		
307 Jim Grant	3.00	8.00
308 Neil Chrisley	3.00	8.00
309 Moe Morhardt RC	2.00	5.00
310 Whitey Ford	20.00	50.00
311 Tony Kubek IA	3.00	8.00
312 Warren Spahn IA	6.00	15.00
313 Roger Maris IA	40.00	80.00
314 Rocky Colavito IA	3.00	8.00
315 Whitey Ford IA	6.00	15.00
316 Harmon Killebrew IA	6.00	15.00
317 Stan Musial IA	8.00	20.00
318 Mickey Mantle IA	75.00	150.00
319 Mike McCormick IA	2.00	5.00
320 Hank Aaron	75.00	150.00
321 Lee Stange RC	2.00	5.00
322 Alvin Dark MG	3.00	8.00
323 Don Landrum	2.00	5.00
324 Joe McClain	2.00	5.00
325 Luis Aparicio	6.00	15.00
326 Tom Parsons RC	2.00	5.00
327 Ozzie Virgil	2.00	5.00
328 Ken Walters	2.00	5.00
329 Bob Bolin	2.00	5.00
330 John Romano	2.00	5.00
331 Moe Drabowsky	3.00	8.00
332 Don Buddin	2.00	5.00
333 Frank Cipriani RC	2.00	5.00
334 Boston Red Sox TC	4.00	10.00
335 Bill Bruton	2.00	5.00
336 Billy Muffett	2.00	5.00
337 Jim Marshall	3.00	8.00
338 Billy Gardner	2.00	5.00
339 Jose Valdivielso	2.00	5.00
340 Don Drysdale	20.00	50.00
341 Mike Hershberger RC	2.00	5.00
342 Ed Rakow	2.00	5.00
343 Albie Pearson	3.00	8.00
344 Ed Bauta RC	2.00	5.00
345 Chuck Schilling	2.00	5.00
346 Jack Kralick	2.00	5.00
347 Chuck Hinton RC	2.00	5.00
348 Larry Burright RC	3.00	8.00
349 Paul Foytack	2.00	5.00
350 Frank Robinson	20.00	50.00
351 Braves Backstops	3.00	8.00
Joe Torre		
Del Crandall		
352 Frank Sullivan	2.00	5.00
353 Bill Mazeroski	6.00	15.00
354 Roman Mejias	3.00	8.00
355 Steve Barber	2.00	5.00
356 Tom Haller RC	2.00	5.00
357 Jerry Walker	2.00	5.00
358 Tommy Davis	3.00	8.00
359 Bobby Locke	2.00	5.00
360 Yogi Berra	40.00	80.00
361 Bob Hendley	2.00	5.00
362 Ty Cline	2.00	5.00
363 Bob Roselli	2.00	5.00
364 Ken Hunt	2.00	5.00
365 Charlie Neal	3.00	8.00
366 Phil Regan	3.00	8.00
367 Checklist 5	6.00	15.00
368 Bob Tillman RC	2.00	5.00
369 Ted Bowsfield	2.00	5.00
370 Ken Boyer	4.00	10.00
371 Earl Battey	2.50	6.00
372 Jack Curtis	2.50	6.00
373 Al Heist	2.50	6.00
374 Gene Mauch MG	4.00	10.00
375 Ron Fairly	4.00	10.00
376 Bud Daley	3.00	8.00
377 John Orsino RC	2.50	6.00
378 Bennie Daniels	2.50	6.00
379 Chuck Essegian	2.50	6.00
380 Lou Burdette	4.00	10.00
381 Chico Cardenas	4.00	10.00
382 Dick Williams	3.00	8.00
383 Ray Sadecki	2.50	6.00
384 Kansas City Athletics TC	4.00	10.00
385 Early Wynn	6.00	15.00
386 Don Mincher	3.00	8.00
387 Lou Brock RC	60.00	120.00
388 Ryne Duren	3.00	8.00
389 Smoky Burgess	4.00	10.00
390 Orlando Cepeda AS	4.00	10.00
391 Bill Mazeroski AS	4.00	10.00
392 Ken Boyer AS UER	3.00	8.00
Batting Average mistakenly listed as .392		
393 Roy McMillan AS	2.50	6.00
394 Hank Aaron AS	20.00	50.00
395 Willie Mays AS	20.00	50.00
396 Frank Robinson AS	6.00	15.00
397 John Roseboro AS	2.50	6.00
398 Don Drysdale AS	6.00	15.00
399 Warren Spahn AS	6.00	15.00
400 Elston Howard	4.00	10.00
401 AL and NL Homer Kings	30.00	60.00
Roger Maris		
Orlando Cepeda		
402 Gino Cimoli	2.50	6.00
403 Chet Nichols	2.50	6.00
404 Tim Harkness RC	3.00	8.00
405 Jim Perry	3.00	8.00
406 Bob Taylor	2.50	6.00
407 Hank Aguirre	2.50	6.00
408 Gus Bell	3.00	8.00
409 Pittsburgh Pirates TC	4.00	10.00
410 Al Smith	2.50	6.00
411 Danny O'Connell	2.50	6.00
412 Charlie James	2.50	6.00
413 Matty Alou	4.00	10.00
414 Joe Gaines RC	2.50	6.00
415 Bill Virdon	4.00	10.00
416 Bob Scheffing MG	2.50	6.00
417 Joe Azcue RC	2.50	6.00
418 Andy Carey	2.50	6.00
419 Bob Bruce	3.00	8.00
420 Gus Triandos	3.00	8.00
421 Ken MacKenzie	3.00	8.00
422 Steve Bilko	2.50	6.00
423 Rival League Relief Aces	4.00	10.00
Roy Face		
Hoyt Wilhelm		
424 Al McBean RC	2.50	6.00
425 Carl Yastrzemski	60.00	120.00
426 Bob Farley RC	2.50	6.00
427 Jake Wood	2.50	6.00
428 Joe Hicks	2.50	6.00
429 Billy O'Dell	2.50	6.00
430 Tony Kubek	6.00	15.00
431 Bob (Buck) Rodgers RC	3.00	8.00
432 Jim Pendleton	2.50	6.00
433 Jim Archer	2.50	6.00
434 Clay Dalrymple	2.50	6.00
435 Larry Sherry	3.00	8.00
436 Felix Mantilla	3.00	8.00
437 Ray Moore	2.50	6.00
438 Dick Brown	2.50	6.00
439 Jerry Buchek RC	2.50	6.00
440 Joey Jay	2.50	6.00
441 Checklist 6	6.00	15.00
442 Wes Stock	2.50	6.00
443 Del Crandall	3.00	8.00
444 Ted Wills	2.50	6.00
445 Vic Power	3.00	8.00
446 Don Elston	2.50	6.00
447 Willie Kirkland	5.00	12.00
448 Joe Gibbon	5.00	12.00
449 Jerry Adair	5.00	12.00
450 Jim O'Toole	6.00	15.00
451 Jose Tartabull RC	6.00	15.00
452 Earl Averill Jr.	5.00	12.00
453 Cal McLish	5.00	12.00
454 Floyd Robinson RC	5.00	12.00
455 Luis Arroyo	6.00	15.00
456 Joe Amalfitano	6.00	15.00
457 Lou Clinton	5.00	12.00
458A Bob Buhl M on Cap	6.00	15.00
458B Bob Buhl Plain Cap	20.00	50.00
459 Ed Bailey	5.00	12.00
460 Jim Bunning	8.00	20.00
461 Ken Hubbs RC	12.50	30.00
462A Willie Tasby W on Cap	5.00	12.00
462B Willie Tasby Plain Cap	20.00	50.00
463 Hank Bauer MG	6.00	15.00
464 Al Jackson RC	5.00	12.00
465 Cincinnati Reds TC	8.00	20.00
466 Norm Cash AS	6.00	15.00
467 Chuck Schilling AS	5.00	12.00
468 Brooks Robinson AS	10.00	25.00
469 Luis Aparicio AS	6.00	15.00
470 Al Kaline AS	10.00	25.00
471 Mickey Mantle AS	100.00	200.00
472 Rocky Colavito AS	6.00	15.00
473 Elston Howard AS	6.00	15.00
474 Frank Lary AS	5.00	12.00
475 Whitey Ford AS	8.00	20.00
476 Baltimore Orioles TC	8.00	20.00
477 Andre Rodgers	5.00	12.00
478 Don Zimmer	8.00	20.00
479 Joel Horlen RC	5.00	12.00
480 Harvey Kuenn	6.00	15.00
481 Vic Wertz	6.00	15.00
482 Sam Mele MG	5.00	12.00
483 Don McMahon	5.00	12.00
484 Dick Schofield	5.00	12.00
485 Pedro Ramos	5.00	12.00
486 Jim Gilliam	6.00	15.00
487 Jerry Lynch	5.00	12.00
488 Hal Brown	5.00	12.00
489 Julio Gotay RC	5.00	12.00
490 Clete Boyer UER	6.00	15.00
Reversed Negative		
491 Leon Wagner	5.00	12.00
492 Hal W. Smith	6.00	15.00
493 Danny McDevitt	5.00	12.00
494 Sammy White	5.00	12.00
495 Don Cardwell	5.00	12.00
496 Wayne Causey RC	5.00	12.00
497 Ed Bouchee	6.00	15.00
498 Jim Donohue	5.00	12.00
499 Zoilo Versalles	6.00	15.00
500 Duke Snider	30.00	60.00
501 Claude Osteen	6.00	15.00
502 Hector Lopez	6.00	15.00
503 Danny Murtaugh MG	6.00	15.00
504 Eddie Bressoud	5.00	12.00
505 Juan Marichal	15.00	40.00
506 Charlie Maxwell	6.00	15.00
507 Ernie Broglio	6.00	15.00
508 Gordy Coleman	6.00	15.00
509 Dave Giusti RC	6.00	15.00
510 Jim Lemon	5.00	12.00
511 Bubba Phillips	5.00	12.00
512 Mike Fornieles	5.00	12.00
513 Whitey Herzog	6.00	15.00
514 Sherm Lollar	6.00	15.00
515 Stan Williams	6.00	15.00
516A Checklist 7	6.00	15.00
White Boxes		
516B Checklist 7	6.00	15.00
Yellow Boxes		
517 Dave Wickersham	5.00	12.00
518 Lee Maye	5.00	12.00
519 Bob Johnson RC	5.00	12.00
520 Bob Friend	6.00	15.00
521 Jacke Davis UER RC	5.00	12.00
(Listed as OF on		
front and P on back)		
522 Lindy McDaniel	6.00	15.00
523 Russ Nixon SP	12.50	30.00
524 Howie Nunn SP	12.50	30.00
525 George Thomas	8.00	20.00
526 Hal Woodeshick SP	12.50	30.00
527 Dick McAuliffe RC	12.50	30.00
528 Turk Lown	8.00	20.00
529 John Schaive SP	12.50	30.00
530 Bob Gibson SP	60.00	120.00
531 Bobby G. Smith	8.00	20.00
532 Dick Stigman	8.00	20.00
533 Charley Lau SP	12.50	30.00
534 Tony Gonzalez SP	12.50	30.00
535 Ed Roebuck	8.00	20.00
536 Dick Gernert	8.00	20.00
537 Cleveland Indians TC	20.00	50.00
538 Jack Sanford	8.00	20.00
539 Billy Moran	8.00	20.00
540 Jim Landis SP	12.50	30.00
541 Don Nottebart SP	12.50	30.00
542 Dave Philley	8.00	20.00
543 Bob Allen SP	12.50	30.00
544 Willie McCovey SP	60.00	120.00
545 Hoyt Wilhelm SP	20.00	50.00
546 Moe Thacker SP	12.50	30.00
547 Don Ferrarese	8.00	20.00
548 Bobby Del Greco	8.00	20.00
549 Bill Rigney MG SP	12.50	30.00
550 Art Mahaffey SP	12.50	30.00
551 Harry Bright	8.00	20.00
552 Chicago Cubs TC SP	20.00	50.00
553 Jim Coates	12.50	30.00
554 Bubba Morton SP RC	12.50	30.00
555 John Buzhardt SP	12.50	30.00
556 Al Spangler	8.00	20.00
557 Bob Anderson SP	12.50	30.00
558 John Goryl	8.00	20.00
559 Mike Higgins MG	8.00	20.00
560 Chuck Estrada SP	12.50	30.00
561 Gene Oliver SP	12.50	30.00
562 Bill Henry	8.00	20.00
563 Ken Aspromonte	8.00	20.00
564 Bob Grim	8.00	20.00
565 Jose Pagan	8.00	20.00
566 Marty Kutyna SP	12.50	30.00
567 Tracy Stallard SP	12.50	30.00
568 Jim Golden	8.00	20.00
569 Ed Sadowski SP	12.50	30.00
570 Bill Stafford SP	12.50	30.00
571 Billy Klaus SP	12.50	30.00
572 Bob G. Miller SP	12.50	30.00
573 Johnny Logan	8.00	20.00
574 Dean Stone	8.00	20.00
575 Red Schoendienst SP	20.00	50.00
576 Russ Kemmerer SP	12.50	30.00
577 Dave Nicholson SP	12.50	30.00
578 Jim Duffalo RC	8.00	20.00
579 Jim Schaffer SP RC	12.50	30.00
580 Bill Monbouquette	8.00	20.00
581 Mel Roach	8.00	20.00
582 Ron Piche	8.00	20.00
583 Larry Osborne	8.00	20.00
584 Minnesota Twins TC SP	30.00	60.00
585 Glen Hobbie SP	12.50	30.00
586 Sammy Esposito SP	12.50	30.00
587 Frank Funk SP	12.50	30.00
588 Birdie Tebbetts MG	8.00	20.00
589 Bob Turley	12.50	30.00
590 Curt Flood	12.50	30.00
591 Rookie Parade	40.00	80.00
Sam McDowell RC		
Ron Taylor RC		
Ron Nischwitz RC		
Art Quirk RC		
Dick Radatz RC SP		
592 Rookie Parade	40.00	80.00
Dan Pfister RC		
Bo Belinsky RC		
Dave Stenhous RCe		
Jim Bouton RC		
Joe Bonikowski RC SP		
593 Rookie Parade	20.00	50.00
Jack Lamabe RC		
Craig Anderson RC		
Jack Hamilton RC		
Bob Moorhead RC		
Bob Veale RC SP		
594 Rookie Parade	40.00	80.00
Doc Edwards RC		
Ken Retzer RC		
Bob Uecker RC		
Doug Camilli RC		
Don Pavletich SP		
595 Rookie Parade	20.00	50.00
Bob Sadowski RC		
Felix Torres RC		
Marlan Coughtry RC		
Ed Charles RC SP		
596 Rookie Parade	40.00	80.00
Bernie Allen RC		
Joe Pepitone RC		
Phil Linz RC		
Rich Rollins RC SP		
597 Rookie Parade	20.00	50.00
Jim McKnight RC		
Rod Kanehl RC		
Amado Samuel RC		
Denis Menke RC SP		
598 Rookie Parade	40.00	80.00
Al Luplow RC		
Manny Jimenez RC		
Howie Goss RC		
Jim Hickman RC		
Ed Olivares RC SP		

1962 Topps Bucks

There are 96 "Baseball Bucks" in this unusual set released in its own one-cent package in 1962. Each "buck" measures 1 3/4" by 4 1/8". Each depicts a player with accompanying biography and facsimile autograph to the left. To the right is found a drawing of the player's home stadium. His team and position are listed under the ribbon design containing his name. The team affiliation and league are also indicated within circles on the reverse.

COMPLETE SET (96)	600.00	1200.00
WRAPPER (1-CENT)	20.00	50.00
1 Hank Aaron	30.00	60.00
2 Joe Adcock	2.50	6.00
3 George Altman	2.00	5.00
4 Jim Archer	2.00	5.00
5 Richie Ashburn	10.00	25.00
6 Ernie Banks	15.00	40.00
7 Earl Battey	2.00	5.00
8 Gus Bell	2.00	5.00
9 Yogi Berra	15.00	40.00
10 Ken Boyer	3.00	8.00
11 Jackie Brandt	2.00	5.00
12 Jim Bunning	10.00	25.00
13 Lew Burdette	2.50	6.00
14 Don Cardwell	2.00	5.00
15 Norm Cash	3.00	8.00
16 Orlando Cepeda	8.00	20.00
17 Roberto Clemente	100.00	200.00
18 Rocky Colavito	6.00	15.00
19 Chuck Cottier	2.00	5.00
20 Roger Craig	2.50	6.00
21 Bennie Daniels	2.00	5.00
22 Don Demeter	2.00	5.00
23 Don Drysdale	12.50	30.00
24 Chuck Estrada	2.00	5.00
25 Dick Farrell	2.00	5.00
26 Whitey Ford	15.00	40.00
27 Nellie Fox	10.00	25.00
28 Tito Francona	2.00	5.00
29 Bob Friend	2.00	5.00
30 Jim Gentile	2.50	6.00
31 Dick Gernert	2.00	5.00
32 Lenny Green	2.00	5.00
33 Dick Groat	2.50	6.00
34 Woodie Held	2.00	5.00
35 Don Hoak	2.00	5.00
36 Gil Hodges	10.00	25.00
37 Elston Howard	6.00	15.00
38 Frank Howard	3.00	8.00
39 Dick Howser	2.50	6.00
40 Ken Hunt	2.00	5.00
41 Larry Jackson	2.00	5.00
42 Joey Jay	2.00	5.00
43 Al Kaline	15.00	40.00
44 Harmon Killebrew	10.00	25.00
45 Sandy Koufax	40.00	80.00
46 Harvey Kuenn	2.50	6.00
47 Jim Landis	2.00	5.00
48 Norm Larker	2.00	5.00
49 Frank Lary	2.00	5.00
50 Jerry Lumpe	2.00	5.00
51 Art Mahaffey	2.00	5.00
52 Frank Malzone	2.00	5.00
53 Felix Mantilla	2.00	5.00
54 Mickey Mantle	100.00	200.00
55 Roger Maris	20.00	50.00
56 Eddie Mathews	10.00	25.00
57 Willie Mays	30.00	60.00
58 Ken McBride	2.00	5.00
59 Mike McCormick	2.00	5.00
60 Stu Miller	2.00	5.00
61 Minnie Minoso	3.00	8.00
62 Wally Moon	2.50	6.00
63 Stan Musial	30.00	60.00
64 Danny O'Connell	2.00	5.00
65 Jim O'Toole	2.00	5.00
66 Camilo Pascual	2.00	5.00
67 Jim Perry	2.50	6.00
68 Jimmy Piersall	2.50	6.00
69 Vada Pinson	3.00	8.00
70 Juan Pizarro	2.00	5.00
71 Johnny Podres	2.50	6.00
72 Vic Power	2.00	5.00
73 Bob Purkey	2.00	5.00
74 Pedro Ramos	2.00	5.00
75 Brooks Robinson	15.00	40.00
76 Floyd Robinson	2.00	5.00
77 Frank Robinson	15.00	40.00
78 John Romano	2.00	5.00
79 Pete Runnels	2.00	5.00
80 Don Schwall	2.00	5.00
81 Bobby Shantz	2.00	5.00
82 Norm Siebern	2.00	5.00
83 Roy Sievers	2.00	5.00
84 Hal Smith	2.00	5.00
85 Warren Spahn	10.00	25.00
86 Dick Stuart	2.50	6.00
87 Tony Taylor	2.00	5.00
88 Lee Thomas	2.50	6.00
89 Gus Triandos	2.00	5.00
90 Leon Wagner	2.00	5.00
91 Jerry Walker	2.00	5.00
92 Bill White	3.00	8.00
93 Billy Williams	10.00	25.00
94 Gene Woodling	2.50	6.00
95 Early Wynn	10.00	25.00
96 Carl Yastrzemski	15.00	40.00

1962 Topps Stamps

The 201 baseball player stamps inserted into the Topps regular issue of 1962 are color photos set upon red or yellow backgrounds (100 players for each color). They came in two-stamp panels with a small additional strip which contained advertising for an album. Roy Sievers appears with Kansas City or Philadelphia; the set price includes both versions. Each stamp measures 1 3/8" by 1 7/8". Stamps are unnumbered but are presented here in alphabetical order by team, Baltimore Orioles AL (1-10), Boston Red Sox (11-20), Chicago White Sox (21-30), Cleveland Indians (31-40), Detroit Tigers (41-50), Kansas City A's (51-61), Los Angeles Angels (62-71), Minnesota Twins (72-81), New York Yankees (82-91), Washington Senators (92-101), Chicago Cubs NL (102-111), Cincinnati Reds (112-121), Houston Colt .45's (122-131), Los Angeles Dodgers (132-141), Milwaukee Braves (142-151), New York Mets (152-161), Philadelphia Phillies (162-171), Pittsburgh Pirates (172-181), St. Louis Cardinals (182-191) and San Francisco Giants (192-201). For some time there has been the rumored existence of a Roy Sievers stamp wearing an A's cap but it has yet to be confirmed.

COMPLETE SET (201)	200.00	400.00
1 Baltimore Emblem	.40	1.00
2 Jerry Adair	.40	1.00
3 Jackie Brandt	.40	1.00
4 Chuck Estrada	.40	1.00
5 Jim Gentile	.60	1.50
6 Ron Hansen	.40	1.00
7 Milt Pappas	.60	1.50
8 Brooks Robinson	3.00	8.00
9 Gus Triandos	.60	1.50
10 Hoyt Wilhelm	1.00	2.50
11 Boston Emblem	.40	1.00
12 Mike Fornieles	.40	1.00
13 Gary Geiger	.40	1.00
14 Frank Malzone	.60	1.50
15 Bill Monbouquette	.40	1.00
16 Russ Nixon	.40	1.00
17 Pete Runnels	.60	1.50
18 Chuck Schilling	.40	1.00
19 Don Schwall	.40	1.00
20 Carl Yastrzemski	5.00	12.00
21 Chicago Emblem	.40	1.00
22 Luis Aparicio	1.00	2.50
23 Camilo Carreon	.40	1.00
24 Nellie Fox	1.50	4.00
25 Ray Herbert	.40	1.00
26 Jim Landis	.40	1.00
27 J.C. Martin	.40	1.00
28 Juan Pizzaro	.40	1.00

29 Floyd Robinson .40 1.00
30 Early Wynn 1.00 2.50
31 Cleveland Emblem .40 1.00
32 Ty Cline .40 1.00
33 Dick Donovan .40 1.00
34 Tito Francona .40 1.00
35 Woody Held .40 1.00
36 Barry Latman .40 1.00
37 Jim Perry .60 1.50
38 Bubba Phillips .40 1.00
39 Vic Power .40 1.00
40 Johnny Romano .40 1.00
41 Detroit Emblem .40 1.00
42 Steve Boros .40 1.00
43 Bill Bruton .40 1.00
44 Jim Bunning 1.00 2.50
45 Norm Cash 1.00 2.50
46 Rocky Colavito 1.00 2.50
47 Al Kaline 3.00 8.00
48 Frank Lary .60 1.50
49 Don Mossi .60 1.50
50 Jake Wood .40 1.00
51 Kansas City Emblem .40 1.00
52 Jim Archer .40 1.00
53 Dick Howser 1.00 2.50
54 Jerry Lumpe .40 1.00
55 Leo Posada .40 1.00
56 Bob Shaw .40 1.00
57 Norm Siebern .40 1.00
59 Gene Stephens .40 1.00
60 Haywood Sullivan .40 1.00
61 Jerry Walker .40 1.00
62 Los Angeles Emblem .40 1.00
63 Steve Bilko .40 1.00
64 Ted Bowsfield .40 1.00
65 Ken Hunt .40 1.00
66 Ken McBride .40 1.00
67 Albie Pearson .40 1.00
68 Bob Rodgers .60 1.50
69 George Thomas .40 1.00
70 Lee Thomas .60 1.50
71 Leon Wagner .40 1.00
72 Minnesota Emblem .40 1.00
73 Bob Allison .60 1.50
74 Earl Battey .40 1.00
75 Lenny Green .40 1.00
76 Harmon Killebrew 2.50 6.00
77 Jack Kralick .40 1.00
78 Camilo Pascual .60 1.50
79 Pedro Ramos .40 1.00
80 Bill Tuttle .40 1.00
81 Zoilo Versalles .40 1.00
82 New York Emblem .60 1.50
83 Yogi Berra 5.00 12.00
84 Clete Boyer 1.00 2.50
85 Whitey Ford 4.00 10.00
86 Elston Howard 1.50 4.00
87 Tony Kubek 1.00 2.50
88 Mickey Mantle 30.00 60.00
89 Roger Maris 8.00 20.00
90 Bobby Richardson 1.00 2.50
91 Bill Skowron 1.00 2.50
92 Washington Emblem .40 1.00
93 Chuck Cottier .40 1.00
94 Pete Daley .40 1.00
95 Bennie Daniels .40 1.00
96 Chuck Hinton .40 1.00
97 Bob Johnson .40 1.00
98 Joe McClain .40 1.00
99 Danny O'Connell .40 1.00
100 Jimmy Piersall 1.00 2.50
101 Gene Woodling .60 1.50
102 Chicago Emblem .40 1.00
103 George Altman .40 1.00
104 Ernie Banks 3.00 8.00
105 Dick Bertell .40 1.00
106 Don Cardwell .40 1.00
107 Dick Ellsworth .40 1.00
108 Glen Hobbie .40 1.00
109 Ron Santo 1.00 2.50
110 Barney Schultz .40 1.00
111 Billy Williams 1.00 2.50
112 Cincinnati Emblem .40 1.00
113 Gordon Coleman .40 1.00
114 Johnny Edwards .40 1.00
115 Gene Freese .40 1.00
116 Joey Jay .40 1.00
117 Eddie Kasko .40 1.00
118 Jim O'Toole .40 1.00
119 Vada Pinson 1.00 2.50
120 Bob Purkey .40 1.00
121 Frank Robinson 3.00 8.00
122 Houston Emblem .40 1.00
123 Joe Amalfitano .40 1.00
124 Bob Aspromonte .40 1.00
125 Dick Farrell .40 1.00
126 Al Heist .40 1.00
127 Sam Jones .40 1.00
128 Bobby Shantz .60 1.50
129 Hal W. Smith .40 1.00
130 Al Spangler .40 1.00
131 Bob Tiefenauer .40 1.00
132 Los Angeles Emblem .40 1.00
133 Don Drysdale 2.50 6.00
134 Ron Fairly .60 1.50
135 Frank Howard 1.00 2.50
136 Sandy Koufax 6.00 15.00
137 Wally Moon .60 1.50
138 Johnny Podres 1.00 2.50
139 John Roseboro .60 1.50
140 Duke Snider 4.00 10.00
141 Daryl Spencer .40 1.00
142 Milwaukee Emblem .40 1.00
143 Hank Aaron 6.00 15.00
144 Joe Adcock .60 1.50
145 Frank Bolling .40 1.00
146 Lou Burdette 1.00 2.50
147 Del Crandall .40 1.00
148 Eddie Mathews 2.50 6.00
149 Roy McMillan .40 1.00
150 Warren Spahn 3.00 8.00
151 Joe Torre 2.00 5.00
152 New York Emblem .60 1.50
153 Gus Bell .60 1.50
154 Roger Craig 1.00 2.50
155 Gil Hodges 2.50 6.00
156 Jay Hook .60 1.50
157 Hobie Landrith .60 1.50
158 Felix Mantilla .60 1.50
159 Bob L. Miller .60 1.50
160 Lee Walls .60 1.50
161 Don Zimmer 1.00 2.50
162 Philadelphia Emblem .40 1.00
163 Ruben Amaro .40 1.00
164 Jack Baldschun .40 1.00
165 Johnny Callison UER .60 1.50
Name spelled Callizon
166 Clay Dalrymple .40 1.00
167 Don Demeter .40 1.00
168 Tony Gonzalez .40 1.00
169 Roy Sievers 1.00 2.50
Phils, see also 58
170 Tony Taylor .60 1.50
171 Art Mahaffey .40 1.00
172 Pittsburgh Emblem .40 1.00
173 Smoky Burgess .60 1.50
174 Roberto Clemente 15.00 40.00
175 Roy Face 1.00 2.50
176 Bob Friend .60 1.50
177 Dick Groat 1.00 2.50
178 Don Hoak .40 1.00
179 Bill Mazeroski 1.50 4.00
180 Dick Stuart .60 1.50
181 Bill Virdon 1.00 2.50
182 St. Louis Emblem .40 1.00
183 Ken Boyer 1.00 2.50
184 Larry Jackson .40 1.00
185 Julio Javier .40 1.00
186 Tim McCarver 1.50 4.00
187 Lindy McDaniel .40 1.00
188 Minnie Minoso 1.00 2.50
189 Stan Musial 6.00 15.00
190 Ray Sadecki .40 1.00
191 Bill White 1.00 2.50
192 S.F. Emblem .40 1.00
193 Felipe Alou 1.00 2.50
194 Ed Bailey .40 1.00
195 Orlando Cepeda 1.00 2.50
196 Jim Davenport .40 1.00
197 Harvey Kuenn 1.00 2.50
198 Juan Marichal 1.50 4.00
199 Willie Mays 8.00 20.00
200 Mike McCormick .60 1.50
201 Stu Miller .40 1.00
NNO Stamp Album 8.00 20.00

1963 Topps

The cards in this 576-card set measure 2 1/2" by 3 1/2". The sharp color photographs of the 1963 set are a vivid contrast to the drab pictures of 1962. In addition to the "League Leaders" series (1-10) and World Series cards (142-148), the seventh and last series of cards (523-576) contains seven rookie cards (each depicting four players). Cards were issued, among other ways, in one-card penny packs and five-card nickel packs. There were some three-card advertising panels produced by Topps; the players included are from the first series; one panel shows Hoyt Wilhelm, Don Lock, and Bob Duliba on the front with a Stan Musial ad/endorsement on one of the backs. Key Rookie Cards in this set are Bill Freehan, Tony Oliva, Pete Rose, Willie Stargell and Rusty Staub.

COMPLETE SET (576) 3000.00 6000.00
COMMON CARD (1-196) 1.50 4.00
COMMON (197-283) 2.00 5.00
COMMON (284-370) 2.00 5.00
COMMON (371-446) 2.00 5.00
COMMON (447-522) 10.00 25.00
COMMON (523-576) 6.00 15.00
WRAPPER (1-CENT) 15.00 40.00
WRAPPER (5-CENT) 12.50 30.00
1 NL Batting Leaders 15.00 40.00
Tommy Davis
Frank Robinson
Stan Musial
Hank Aaron
Bill White
2 AL Batting Leaders 20.00 50.00
Pete Runnels
Mickey Mantle
Floyd Robinson
Norm Siebern
Chuck Hinton
3 NL Home Run Leaders 15.00 40.00
Willie Mays
Hank Aaron
Frank Robinson
Orlando Cepeda
Ernie Banks
4 AL Home Run Leaders 8.00 20.00
Harmon Killebrew
Norm Cash
Rocky Colavito
Roger Maris
Jim Gentile
Leon Wagner
5 NL ERA Leaders 10.00 25.00
Sandy Koufax
Bob Shaw
Bob Purkey
Bob Gibson
Don Drysdale
6 AL ERA Leaders 4.00 10.00
Hank Aguirre
Robin Roberts
Whitey Ford
Eddie Fisher
Dean Chance
7 NL Pitching Leaders 4.00 10.00
Don Drysdale
Jack Sanford
Bob Purkey
Billy O'Dell
Art Mahaffey
Joe Jay
8 AL Pitching Leaders 3.00 8.00
Ralph Terry
Dick Donovan
Ray Herbert
Jim Bunning
Camilo Pascual
9 NL Strikeout Leaders 12.50 30.00
Don Drysdale
Sandy Koufax
Bob Gibson
Billy O'Dell
Dick Farrell
10 AL Strikeout Leaders 3.00 8.00
Camilo Pascual
Jim Bunning
Ralph Terry
Juan Pizarro
Jim Kaat
11 Lee Walls 1.50 4.00
12 Steve Barber 1.50 4.00
13 Philadelphia Phillies TC 3.00 8.00
14 Pedro Ramos 1.50 4.00
15 Ken Hubbs UER 4.00 10.00
(No position listed
on front of card)
16 Al Smith 1.50 4.00
17 Ryne Duren 3.00 8.00
18 Buc Blasters 40.00 80.00
Smoky Burgess
Dick Stuart
Bob Clemente
Bob Skinner
19 Pete Burnside 1.50 4.00
20 Tony Kubek 4.00 10.00
21 Marty Keough 1.50 4.00
22 Curt Simmons 3.00 8.00
23 Ed Lopat MG 3.00 8.00
24 Bob Bruce 1.50 4.00
25 Al Kaline 20.00 50.00
26 Ray Moore 1.50 4.00
27 Choo Choo Coleman 3.00 8.00
28 Mike Fornieles 1.50 4.00
29A Rookie Stars 1962 4.00 10.00
Sammy Ellis
Ray Culp
John Boozer
Jesse Gonder
29B Rookie Stars 1963 1.50 4.00
Sammy Ellis RC
Ray Culp
John Boozer RC
Jesse Gonder RC
30 Harvey Kuenn 3.00 8.00
31 Cal Koonce RC 1.50 4.00
32 Tony Gonzalez 1.50 4.00
33 Bo Belinsky 3.00 8.00
34 Dick Schofield 1.50 4.00
35 John Buzhardt 1.50 4.00
36 Jerry Kindall 1.50 4.00
37 Jerry Lynch 1.50 4.00
38 Bud Daley 3.00 8.00
39 Los Angeles Angels TC 3.00 8.00
40 Vic Power 3.00 8.00
41 Charley Lau 3.00 8.00
42 Stan Williams 3.00 8.00
(Listed as a Yankee, but wearing an LA cap)
43 Veteran Masters 3.00 8.00
Casey Stengel
Gene Woodling
44 Terry Fox 1.50 4.00
45 Bob Aspromonte 1.50 4.00
46 Tommie Aaron RC 3.00 8.00
47 Don Lock RC 1.50 4.00
48 Birdie Tebbetts MG 3.00 8.00
49 Dal Maxvill RC 3.00 8.00
50 Billy Pierce 3.00 8.00
51 George Alusik 1.50 4.00
52 Chuck Schilling 1.50 4.00
53 Joe Moeller RC 3.00 8.00
54A Rookie Stars 1962 6.00 15.00
Nelson Mathews
Harry Fanok
Jack Cullen
Dave DeBusschere RC
54B Rookie Stars 1963 3.00 8.00
Nelson Mathews RC
Harry Fanok RC
Jack Cullen RC
Dave DeBusschere RC
55 Bill Virdon 3.00 8.00
56 Dennis Bennett RC 1.50 4.00
57 Billy Moran 1.50 4.00
58 Bob Will 1.50 4.00
59 Craig Anderson 1.50 4.00
60 Elston Howard 3.00 8.00
61 Ernie Bowman 1.50 4.00
62 Bob Hendley 1.50 4.00
63 Cincinnati Reds TC 3.00 8.00
64 Dick McAuliffe 3.00 8.00
65 Jackie Brandt 1.50 4.00
66 Mike Joyce RC 1.50 4.00
67 Ed Charles 1.50 4.00
68 Friendly Foes 10.00 25.00
Duke Snider
Gil Hodges
69 Bud Zipfel RC 1.50 4.00
70 Jim O'Toole 3.00 8.00
71 Bobby Wine RC 3.00 8.00
72 Johnny Romano 1.50 4.00
73 Bobby Bragan MG RC 3.00 8.00
74 Denny Lemaster RC 1.50 4.00
75 Bob Allison 3.00 8.00
76 Earl Wilson 3.00 8.00
77 Al Spangler 1.50 4.00
78 Marv Throneberry 3.00 8.00
79 Checklist 1 5.00 12.00
80 Jim Gilliam 3.00 8.00
81 Jim Schaffer 1.50 4.00
82 Ed Rakow 1.50 4.00
83 Charley James 1.50 4.00
84 Ron Kline 1.50 4.00
85 Tom Haller 3.00 8.00
86 Charley Maxwell 3.00 8.00
87 Bob Veale 3.00 8.00
88 Ron Hansen 1.50 4.00
89 Dick Stigman 1.50 4.00
90 Gordy Coleman 3.00 8.00
91 Dallas Green 3.00 8.00
92 Hector Lopez 3.00 8.00
93 Galen Cisco 1.50 4.00
94 Bob Schmidt 1.50 4.00
95 Larry Jackson 1.50 4.00
96 Lou Clinton 1.50 4.00
97 Bob Duliba 1.50 4.00
98 George Thomas 1.50 4.00
99 Jim Umbricht 1.50 4.00
100 Joe Cunningham 1.50 4.00
101 Joe Gibbon 1.50 4.00
102A Checklist 2 Red/Yellow 5.00 12.00
102B Checklist 2 White/Red 5.00 12.00
103 Chuck Essegian 1.50 4.00
104 Lew Krausse RC 1.50 4.00
105 Ron Fairly 3.00 8.00
106 Bobby Bolin 1.50 4.00
107 Jim Hickman 3.00 8.00
108 Hoyt Wilhelm 4.00 10.00
109 Lee Maye 1.50 4.00
110 Rich Rollins 3.00 8.00
111 Al Jackson 1.50 4.00
112 Dick Brown 1.50 4.00
113 Don Landrum UER 1.50 4.00
(Photo actually
Ron Santo)
114 Dan Osinski RC 1.50 4.00
115 Carl Yastrzemski 15.00 40.00
116 Jim Brosnan 1.50 4.00
117 Jacke Davis 1.50 4.00
118 Sherm Lollar 1.50 4.00
119 Bob Lillis 1.50 4.00
120 Roger Maris 40.00 80.00
121 Jim Hannan RC 1.50 4.00
122 Julio Gotay 1.50 4.00
123 Frank Howard 3.00 8.00
124 Dick Howser 1.50 4.00
125 Robin Roberts 6.00 15.00
126 Bob Uecker 6.00 15.00
127 Bill Tuttle 1.50 4.00
128 Matty Alou 1.50 4.00
129 Gary Bell 1.50 4.00
130 Dick Groat 3.00 8.00
131 Washington Senators TC 3.00 8.00
132 Jack Hamilton 1.50 4.00
133 Gene Freese 1.50 4.00
134 Bob Scheffing MG 1.50 4.00
135 Richie Ashburn 8.00 20.00
136 Ike Delock 1.50 4.00
137 Mack Jones 1.50 4.00
138 Pride of NL 40.00 80.00
Willie Mays
Stan Musial
139 Earl Averill Jr. 1.50 4.00
140 Frank Lary 3.00 8.00
141 Manny Mota RC 3.00 8.00
142 World Series Game 1 4.00 10.00
Whitey Ford
143 World Series Game 2 3.00 8.00
Jack Sanford
144 World Series Game 3 6.00 15.00
Roger Maris
145 World Series Game 4 3.00 8.00
Chuck Hiller
146 World Series Game 5 3.00 8.00
Tom Tresh
147 World Series Game 6 3.00 8.00
Billy Pierce
148 World Series Game 7 3.00 8.00
Yanks Celebrate
Ralph Terry
149 Marv Breeding 1.50 4.00
150 Johnny Podres 3.00 8.00
151 Pittsburgh Pirates TC 3.00 8.00
152 Ron Nischwitz 1.50 4.00
153 Hal Smith 1.50 4.00
154 Walter Alston MG 3.00 8.00
155 Bill Stafford 1.50 4.00
156 Roy McMillan 3.00 8.00
157 Diego Segui RC 3.00 8.00
158 Rookie Stars 3.00 8.00
Rogelio Alvares RC
Dave Roberts RC
Tommy Harper RC
Bob Saverine RC
159 Jim Pagliaroni 1.50 4.00
160 Juan Pizarro 1.50 4.00
161 Frank Torre 3.00 8.00
162 Minnesota Twins TC 3.00 8.00
163 Don Larsen 3.00 8.00
164 Bubba Morton 1.50 4.00
165 Jim Kaat 3.00 8.00
166 Johnny Keane MG 1.50 4.00
167 Jim Fregosi 3.00 8.00
168 Russ Nixon 1.50 4.00
169 Rookie Stars 10.00 25.00
Dick Egan RC
Julio Navarro
Tommie Sisk RC
Gaylord Perry
170 Joe Adcock 3.00 8.00
171 Steve Hamilton RC 1.50 4.00
172 Gene Oliver 1.50 4.00
173 Bomber's Best 75.00 150.00
Tom Tresh
Mickey Mantle
Bobby Richardson
174 Larry Burright 1.50 4.00
175 Bob Buhl 3.00 8.00
176 Jim King 1.50 4.00
177 Bubba Phillips 1.50 4.00
178 Johnny Edwards 1.50 4.00
179 Ron Piche 1.50 4.00
180 Bill Skowron 3.00 8.00
181 Sammy Esposito 1.50 4.00
182 Albie Pearson 3.00 8.00
183 Joe Pepitone 3.00 8.00
184 Vern Law 3.00 8.00
185 Chuck Hiller 1.50 4.00
186 Jerry Zimmerman 1.50 4.00
187 Willie Kirkland 1.50 4.00
188 Eddie Bressoud 1.50 4.00
189 Dave Giusti 3.00 8.00
190 Minnie Minoso 3.00 8.00
191 Checklist 3 5.00 12.00
192 Clay Dalrymple 1.50 4.00
193 Andre Rodgers 1.50 4.00
194 Joe Nuxhall 3.00 8.00
195 Manny Jimenez 1.50 4.00
196 Doug Camilli 1.50 4.00
197 Roger Craig 3.00 8.00
198 Lenny Green 2.00 5.00
199 Joe Amalfitano 2.00 5.00
200 Mickey Mantle 300.00 600.00
201 Cecil Butler 2.00 5.00
202 Boston Red Sox TC 3.00 8.00
203 Chico Cardenas 3.00 8.00
204 Don Nottebart 2.00 5.00
205 Luis Aparicio 6.00 15.00
206 Ray Washburn 2.00 5.00
207 Ken Hunt 2.00 5.00
208 Rookie Stars 2.00 5.00
Ron Herbel RC
John Miller RC
Wally Wolf RC
Ron Taylor
209 Hobie Landrith 2.00 5.00
210 Sandy Koufax 75.00 150.00
211 Fred Whitfield RC 2.00 5.00
212 Glen Hobbie 2.00 5.00
213 Billy Hitchcock MG 2.00 5.00
214 Orlando Pena 2.00 5.00
215 Bob Skinner 3.00 8.00
216 Gene Conley 3.00 8.00
217 Joe Christopher 2.00 5.00
218 Tiger Twirlers 3.00 8.00
Frank Lary
Don Mossi
Jim Bunning
219 Chuck Cottier 2.00 5.00
220 Camilo Pascual 3.00 8.00
221 Cookie Rojas RC 3.00 8.00
222 Chicago Cubs TC 3.00 8.00
223 Eddie Fisher 2.00 5.00
224 Mike Roarke 2.00 5.00
225 Joey Jay 2.00 5.00
226 Julian Javier 3.00 8.00
227 Jim Grant 3.00 8.00
228 Rookie Stars 20.00 50.00
Max Alvis RC
Bob Bailey RC
Tony Oliva RC
(Listed as Pedro)
Ed Kranepool RC
229 Willie Davis 3.00 8.00
230 Pete Runnels 3.00 8.00
231 Eli Grba UER 2.00 5.00
(Large photo is
Ryne Duren)
232 Frank Malzone 3.00 8.00
233 Casey Stengel MG 8.00 20.00
234 Dave Nicholson 2.00 5.00
235 Billy O'Dell 2.00 5.00
236 Bill Bryan RC 2.00 5.00
237 Jim Coates 3.00 8.00
238 Lou Johnson 2.00 5.00
239 Harvey Haddix 3.00 8.00
240 Rocky Colavito 6.00 15.00
241 Billy Smith RC 2.00 5.00
242 Power Plus 30.00 60.00
Ernie Banks
Hank Aaron
243 Don Leppert 2.00 5.00
244 John Tsitouris 2.00 5.00
245 Gil Hodges 8.00 20.00
246 Lee Stange 2.00 5.00
247 New York Yankees TC 20.00 50.00
248 Tito Francona 2.00 5.00
249 Leo Burke RC 2.00 5.00
250 Stan Musial 50.00 100.00
251 Jack Lamabe 2.00 5.00
252 Ron Santo 4.00 10.00
253 Rookie Stars 2.00 5.00
Len Gabrielson RC
Pete Jernigan RC
John Wojcik RC
Deacon Jones RC
254 Mike Hershberger 2.00 5.00
255 Bob Shaw 2.00 5.00
256 Jerry Lumpe 2.00 5.00
257 Hank Aguirre 2.00 5.00
258 Alvin Dark MG 3.00 8.00
259 Johnny Logan 3.00 8.00
260 Jim Gentile 3.00 8.00
261 Bob Miller 2.00 5.00
262 Ellis Burton 2.00 5.00
263 Dave Stenhouse 2.00 5.00
264 Phil Linz 2.00 5.00
265 Vada Pinson 3.00 8.00
266 Bob Allen 2.00 5.00
267 Carl Sawatski 2.00 5.00
268 Don Demeter 2.00 5.00
269 Don Mincher 2.00 5.00
270 Felipe Alou 3.00 8.00
271 Dean Stone 2.00 5.00
272 Danny Murphy 2.00 5.00
273 Sammy Taylor 2.00 5.00
274 Checklist 4 5.00 12.00
275 Eddie Mathews 12.50 30.00
276 Barry Shetrone 2.00 5.00
277 Dick Farrell 2.00 5.00
278 Chico Fernandez 2.00 5.00
279 Wally Moon 3.00 8.00
280 Bob (Buck) Rodgers 2.00 5.00
281 Tom Sturdivant 2.00 5.00
282 Bobby Del Greco 2.00 5.00
283 Roy Sievers 3.00 8.00
284 Dave Sisler 2.00 5.00
285 Dick Stuart 3.00 8.00
286 Stu Miller 3.00 8.00
287 Dick Bertell 2.00 5.00
288 Chicago White Sox TC 4.00 10.00
289 Hal Brown 2.00 5.00
290 Bill White 3.00 8.00
291 Don Rudolph 2.00 5.00
292 Pumpsie Green 3.00 8.00
293 Bill Pleis 2.00 5.00
294 Bill Rigney MG 2.00 5.00
295 Ed Roebuck 2.00 5.00
296 Doc Edwards 2.00 5.00
297 Jim Golden 2.00 5.00
298 Don Dillard 2.00 5.00
299 Rookie Stars 3.00 8.00
Dave Morehead RC
Bob Dustal RC
Tom Butters RC
Dan Schneider RC
300 Willie Mays 75.00 150.00
301 Bill Fischer 2.00 5.00
302 Whitey Herzog 3.00 8.00
303 Earl Francis 2.00 5.00
304 Harry Bright 2.00 5.00
305 Don Hoak 2.00 5.00
306 Star Receivers 4.00 10.00
Earl Battey
Elston Howard
307 Chet Nichols 2.00 5.00
308 Camilo Carreon 2.00 5.00
309 Jim Brewer 2.00 5.00
310 Tommy Davis 3.00 8.00
311 Joe McClain 2.00 5.00
312 Houston Colts TC 10.00 25.00
313 Ernie Broglio 2.00 5.00
314 John Goryl 2.00 5.00
315 Ralph Terry 3.00 8.00
316 Norm Sherry 3.00 8.00
317 Sam McDowell 3.00 8.00
318 Gene Mauch MG 3.00 8.00
319 Joe Gaines 2.00 5.00
320 Warren Spahn 30.00 60.00
321 Gino Cimoli 2.00 5.00
322 Bob Turley 3.00 8.00
323 Bill Mazeroski 6.00 15.00
324 Rookie Stars 3.00 8.00
George Williams RC
Pete Ward RC
Phil Roof RC
Vic Davalillo RC
325 Jack Sanford 2.00 5.00
326 Hank Foiles 2.00 5.00
327 Paul Foytack 2.00 5.00
328 Dick Williams 3.00 8.00
329 Lindy McDaniel 3.00 8.00
330 Chuck Hinton 2.00 5.00
331 Series Foes 3.00 8.00
Bill Stafford
Bill Pierce
332 Joel Horlen 3.00 8.00
333 Carl Warwick 2.00 5.00
334 Wynn Hawkins 2.00 5.00
335 Leon Wagner 2.00 5.00
336 Ed Bauta 2.00 5.00
337 Los Angeles Dodgers TC 10.00 25.00
338 Russ Kemmerer 2.00 5.00
339 Ted Bowsfield 2.00 5.00
340 Yogi Berra P/CO 50.00 100.00
341 Jack Baldschun 2.00 5.00
342 Gene Woodling 3.00 8.00
343 Johnny Pesky MG 3.00 8.00
344 Don Schwall 2.00 5.00
345 Brooks Robinson 30.00 60.00
346 Billy Hoeft 2.00 5.00
347 Joe Torre 6.00 15.00
348 Vic Wertz 3.00 8.00
349 Zoilo Versalles 3.00 8.00
350 Bob Purkey 2.00 5.00
351 Al Luplow 2.00 5.00
352 Ken Johnson 2.00 5.00
353 Billy Williams 12.50 30.00
354 Dom Zanni 2.00 5.00
355 Dean Chance 3.00 8.00
356 John Schaive 2.00 5.00
357 George Altman 2.00 5.00
358 Milt Pappas 3.00 8.00
359 Haywood Sullivan 3.00 8.00
360 Don Drysdale 30.00 60.00
361 Clete Boyer 4.00 10.00
362 Checklist 5 5.00 12.00
363 Dick Radatz 3.00 8.00
364 Howie Goss 2.00 5.00
365 Jim Bunning 8.00 20.00
366 Tony Taylor 3.00 8.00
367 Tony Cloninger 2.00 5.00
368 Ed Bailey 2.00 5.00
369 Jim Lemon 2.00 5.00
370 Dick Donovan 2.00 5.00
371 Rod Kanehl 3.00 8.00
372 Don Lee 2.00 5.00
373 Jim Campbell RC 2.00 5.00
374 Claude Osteen 3.00 8.00
375 Ken Boyer 6.00 15.00
376 John Wyatt RC 2.00 5.00
377 Baltimore Orioles TC 4.00 10.00
378 Bill Henry 2.00 5.00
379 Bob Anderson 2.00 5.00
380 Ernie Banks UER 50.00 100.00
(Back has career Major
and Minor, but he
never played in Minors)
381 Frank Baumann 2.00 5.00
382 Ralph Houk MG 4.00 10.00
383 Pete Richert 2.00 5.00
384 Bob Tillman 2.00 5.00
385 Art Mahaffey 2.00 5.00
386 Rookie Stars 2.00 5.00
Ed Kirkpatrick RC
John Bateman RC
Larry Bearnarth RC
Garry Roggenburk RC
387 Al McBean 2.00 5.00
388 Jim Davenport 3.00 8.00
389 Frank Sullivan 2.00 5.00
390 Hank Aaron 100.00 200.00
391 Bill Dailey RC 2.00 5.00
392 Tribe Thumpers 2.00 5.00
Johnny Romano
Tito Francona
393 Ken MacKenzie 3.00 8.00
394 Tim McCarver 6.00 15.00
395 Don McMahon 2.00 5.00
396 Joe Koppe 2.00 5.00
397 Kansas City Athletics TC 4.00 10.00
398 Boog Powell 10.00 25.00
399 Dick Ellsworth 2.00 5.00
400 Frank Robinson 30.00 60.00
401 Jim Bouton 6.00 15.00
402 Mickey Vernon MG 3.00 8.00
403 Ron Perranoski 3.00 8.00
404 Bob Oldis 2.00 5.00
405 Floyd Robinson 2.00 5.00
406 Howie Koplitz 2.00 5.00
407 Rookie Stars 3.00 8.00
Frank Kostro RC
Chico Ruiz RC
Larry Elliot RC
Dick Simpson RC
408 Billy Gardner 2.00 5.00
409 Roy Face 3.00 8.00
410 Earl Battey 2.00 5.00
411 Jim Constable 2.00 5.00
412 Dodgers Big Three 20.00 50.00
Johnny Podres
Don Drysdale
Sandy Koufax
413 Jerry Walker 2.00 5.00
414 Ty Cline 2.00 5.00
415 Bob Gibson 30.00 60.00
416 Alex Grammas 2.00 5.00
417 San Francisco Giants TC 4.00 10.00
418 John Orsino 2.00 5.00
419 Tracy Stallard 2.00 5.00
420 Bobby Richardson 6.00 15.00
421 Tom Morgan 2.00 5.00
422 Fred Hutchinson MG 3.00 8.00
423 Ed Hobaugh 2.00 5.00
424 Charlie Smith 2.00 5.00
425 Smoky Burgess 3.00 8.00
426 Barry Latman 2.00 5.00
427 Bernie Allen 2.00 5.00
428 Carl Boles RC 2.00 5.00
429 Lou Burdette 3.00 8.00
430 Norm Siebern 2.00 5.00
431A Checklist 6 White/Red 5.00 12.00
431B Checklist 6 Black/Orange 12.50 30.00
432 Roman Mejias 2.00 5.00
433 Denis Menke 2.00 5.00
434 John Callison 3.00 8.00
435 Woody Held 2.00 5.00
436 Tim Harkness 3.00 8.00
437 Bill Bruton 2.00 5.00
438 Wes Stock 2.00 5.00
439 Don Zimmer 3.00 8.00
440 Juan Marichal 12.50 30.00
441 Lee Thomas 3.00 8.00
442 J.C. Hartman RC 2.00 5.00
443 Jimmy Piersall 3.00 8.00
444 Jim Maloney 3.00 8.00
445 Norm Cash 4.00 10.00
446 Whitey Ford 30.00 60.00
447 Felix Mantilla 10.00 25.00
448 Jack Kralick 10.00 25.00
449 Jose Tartabull 10.00 25.00
450 Bob Friend 12.50 30.00
451 Cleveland Indians TC 15.00 40.00
452 Barney Schultz 10.00 25.00
453 Jake Wood 10.00 25.00
454A Art Fowler 10.00 25.00
(Card number on
white background)
454B Art Fowler 12.50 30.00
(Card number on
orange background)
455 Ruben Amaro 10.00 25.00
456 Jim Coker 10.00 25.00
457 Tex Clevenger 10.00 25.00
458 Al Lopez MG 12.50 30.00
459 Dick LeMay 10.00 25.00
460 Del Crandall 12.50 30.00
461 Norm Bass 10.00 25.00
462 Wally Post 10.00 25.00
463 Joe Schaffernoth 10.00 25.00
464 Ken Aspromonte 10.00 25.00
465 Chuck Estrada 10.00 25.00
466 Rookie Stars 30.00 60.00
Nate Oliver RC
Tony Martinez RC
Bill Freehan RC
Jerry Robinson RC SP
467 Phil Ortega 10.00 25.00
468 Carroll Hardy 12.50 30.00
469 Jay Hook 12.50 30.00
470 Tom Tresh SP 30.00 60.00
471 Ken Retzer 10.00 25.00
472 Lou Brock 40.00 80.00
473 New York Mets TC 50.00 100.00
474 Jack Fisher 10.00 25.00
475 Gus Triandos 12.50 30.00
476 Frank Funk 10.00 25.00
477 Donn Clendenon 12.50 30.00
478 Paul Brown 10.00 25.00
479 Ed Brinkman RC 10.00 25.00
480 Bill Monbouquette 10.00 25.00
481 Bob Taylor 10.00 25.00
482 Felix Torres 10.00 25.00
483 Jim Owens UER 10.00 25.00
(Stat column for Wins
has an R instead)
484 Dale Long SP 12.50 30.00
485 Jim Landis 10.00 25.00
486 Ray Sadecki 10.00 25.00
487 John Roseboro 12.50 30.00
488 Jerry Adair 10.00 25.00
489 Paul Toth RC 10.00 25.00
490 Willie McCovey 50.00 100.00
491 Harry Craft MG 10.00 25.00
492 Dave Wickersham 10.00 25.00
493 Walt Bond 10.00 25.00
494 Phil Regan 10.00 25.00
495 Frank Thomas SP 12.50 30.00
496 Rookie Stars 12.50 30.00
Steve Dalkowski RC
Fred Newman RC
Jack Smith RC
Carl Bouldin RC
497 Bennie Daniels 10.00 25.00
498 Eddie Kasko 10.00 25.00
499 J.C. Martin 10.00 25.00
500 Harmon Killebrew SP 75.00 150.00
501 Joe Azcue 10.00 25.00
502 Daryl Spencer 10.00 25.00
503 Milwaukee Braves TC 15.00 40.00
504 Bob Johnson 10.00 25.00
505 Curt Flood 15.00 40.00
506 Gene Green 10.00 25.00
507 Roland Sheldon 12.50 30.00
508 Ted Savage 10.00 25.00
509A Checklist 7 Centered 12.50 30.00
509B Checklist 7 Right 12.50 30.00
510 Ken McBride 10.00 25.00
511 Charlie Neal 12.50 30.00
512 Cal McLish 10.00 25.00
513 Gary Geiger 10.00 25.00
514 Larry Osborne 10.00 25.00
515 Don Elston 10.00 25.00
516 Purnell Goldy RC 10.00 25.00
517 Hal Woodeshick 10.00 25.00
518 Don Blasingame 10.00 25.00
519 Claude Raymond RC 10.00 25.00
520 Orlando Cepeda 15.00 40.00
521 Dan Pfister 10.00 25.00
522 Rookie Stars 12.50 30.00
Mel Nelson RC
Gary Peters
Jim Roland RC
Art Quirk
523 Bill Kunkel 6.00 15.00
524 St. Louis Cardinals TC 12.50 30.00
525 Nellie Fox 20.00 50.00
526 Dick Hall 6.00 15.00
527 Ed Sadowski 6.00 15.00
528 Carl Willey 6.00 15.00
529 Wes Covington 6.00 15.00

Card	Low	High
530 Don Mossi	8.00	20.00
531 Sam Mele MG	6.00	15.00
532 Steve Boros	6.00	15.00
533 Bobby Shantz	8.00	20.00
534 Ken Walters	6.00	15.00
535 Jim Perry	8.00	20.00
536 Norm Larker	6.00	15.00
537 Rookie Stars	500.00	1000.00
Pedro Gonzalez RC		
Ken McMullen RC		
Al Weis RC		
Pete Rose RC		
538 George Brunet	6.00	15.00
539 Wayne Causey	6.00	15.00
540 Roberto Clemente	125.00	250.00
541 Ron Moeller	6.00	15.00
542 Lou Klimchock	6.00	15.00
543 Russ Snyder	6.00	15.00
544 Rookie Stars	20.00	50.00
Duke Carmel		
Bill Haas RC		
Rusty Staub RC		
Dick Phillips RC		
545 Jose Pagan	6.00	15.00
546 Hal Reniff	8.00	20.00
547 Gus Bell	6.00	15.00
548 Tom Satriano RC	6.00	15.00
549 Rookie Stars	6.00	15.00
Marcelino Lopez RC		
Pete Lovrich RC		
Paul Ratliff RC		
Elmo Plaskett RC		
550 Duke Snider	40.00	80.00
551 Billy Klaus	6.00	15.00
552 Detroit Tigers TC	20.00	50.00
553 Rookie Stars	60.00	120.00
Brock Davis RC		
Jim Gosger RC		
Willie Stargell RC		
John Herrnstein RC		
554 Hank Fischer RC	6.00	15.00
555 John Blanchard	8.00	20.00
556 Al Worthington	6.00	15.00
557 Cuno Barragan	6.00	15.00
558 Rookie Stars	8.00	20.00
Bill Faul RC		
Ron Hunt RC		
Al Moran RC		
Bob Lipski RC		
559 Danny Murtaugh MG	6.00	15.00
560 Ray Herbert	6.00	15.00
561 Mike De La Hoz	6.00	15.00
562 Rookie Stars	12.50	30.00
Randy Cardinal RC		
Dave McNally RC		
Ken Rowe RC		
Don Rowe RC		
563 Mike McCormick	6.00	15.00
564 George Banks RC	6.00	15.00
565 Larry Sherry	6.00	15.00
566 Cliff Cook	6.00	15.00
567 Jim Duffalo	6.00	15.00
568 Bob Sadowski	6.00	15.00
569 Luis Arroyo	8.00	20.00
570 Frank Bolling	6.00	15.00
571 Johnny Klippstein	6.00	15.00
572 Jack Spring	6.00	15.00
573 Coot Veal	6.00	15.00
574 Hal Kolstad	6.00	15.00
575 Don Cardwell	6.00	15.00
576 Johnny Temple	12.50	30.00

1963 Topps Peel-Offs

Stick-on inserts were found in several series of the 1963 Topps cards. Each sticker measures 1 1/4" by 2 3/4". They are found either with blank backs or with instructions on the reverse. Stick-ons with the instruction backs are a little tougher to find. The player photo is in color inside an oval with name, team and postion below. Since these inserts were unnumbered, they are ordered below alphabetically.

Card	Low	High
COMPLETE SET (46)	300.00	600.00
1 Hank Aaron	15.00	40.00
2 Luis Aparicio	5.00	12.00
3 Richie Ashburn	6.00	15.00
4 Bob Aspromonte	1.50	4.00
5 Ernie Banks	8.00	20.00
6 Ken Boyer	2.50	6.00
7 Jim Bunning	60.00	120.00
8 Johnny Callison	1.50	4.00
9 Roberto Clemente	30.00	60.00
10 Orlando Cepeda	5.00	12.00
11 Rocky Colavito	4.00	10.00
12 Tommy Davis	2.00	5.00
13 Dick Donovan	1.50	4.00
14 Don Drysdale	6.00	15.00
15 Dick Farrell	1.50	4.00
16 Jim Gentile	2.00	5.00
17 Ray Herbert	1.50	4.00
18 Chuck Hinton	1.50	4.00
19 Ken Hubbs	2.50	6.00
20 Al Jackson	1.50	4.00
21 Al Kaline	8.00	20.00
22 Harmon Killebrew	5.00	12.00
23 Sandy Koufax	12.50	30.00
24 Jerry Lumpe	1.50	4.00
25 Art Mahaffey	1.50	4.00
26 Mickey Mantle	50.00	100.00
27 Willie Mays	20.00	50.00
28 Bill Mazeroski	4.00	10.00
29 Bill Monbouquette	1.50	4.00
30 Stan Musial	12.50	30.00
31 Camilo Pascual	1.50	4.00
32 Bob Purkey	1.50	4.00
33 Bobby Richardson	2.50	6.00
34 Brooks Robinson	8.00	20.00
35 Floyd Robinson	1.50	4.00
36 Frank Robinson	8.00	20.00
37 Bob Rodgers	1.50	4.00
38 Johnny Romano	1.50	4.00
39 Jack Sanford	1.50	4.00
40 Norm Siebern	1.50	4.00
41 Warren Spahn	5.00	12.00
42 Dave Stenhouse	1.50	4.00
43 Ralph Terry	1.50	4.00
44 Lee Thomas	2.00	5.00
45 Bill White	2.00	5.00
46 Carl Yastrzemski	10.00	25.00

1964 Topps

The cards in this 587-card set measure 2 1/2" by 3 1/2". Players in the 1964 Topps baseball series were easy to sort by team due to the giant block lettering found at the top of each card. The name and position of the player are found underneath the picture, and the card is numbered in a ball design on the orange-colored back. The usual last series scarcity holds for this set (523 to 587). Subsets within this set include League Leaders (1-12) and World Series cards (136-140). Among other vehicles, cards were issued in one-card penny packs as well as five-card nickel packs. There were some three-card advertising panels produced by Topps; the players included are from the first series; Panels with Mickey Mantle card backs include Walt Alston/Bill Henry/Vada Pinson; Carl Willey/White Sox Rookies/Bob Friend; and Jimmie Hall/Ernie Broglio/A.L. ERA Leaders on the front with a Mickey Mantle card back on one of the backs. The key Rookie Cards in this set are Richie Allen, Tony Conigliaro, Tommy John, Tony LaRussa, Phil Niekro and Lou Piniella.

Card	Low	High
COMPLETE SET (587)	2750.00	3500.00
COMMON CARD (1-196)	1.25	3.00
COMMON (197-370)	1.50	4.00
COMMON (371-522)	3.00	8.00
COMMON (523-587)	6.00	15.00
WRAPPER (1-CENT)	50.00	100.00
WRAP. (1-CENT, REPEAT)	60.00	120.00
WRAPPER (5-CENT)	12.50	30.00
WRAP.(5-CENT, COIN)	15.00	40.00
1 NL ERA Leaders	12.50	30.00
Sandy Koufax		
Dick Ellsworth		
Bob Friend		
2 AL ERA Leaders	3.00	8.00
Gary Peters		
Juan Pizarro		
Camilo Pascual		
3 NL Pitching Leaders	8.00	20.00
Sandy Koufax		
Juan Marichal		
Warren Spahn		
Jim Maloney		
4 AL Pitching Leaders	3.00	8.00
Whitey Ford		
Camilo Pascual		
Jim Bouton		
5 NL Strikeout Leaders	6.00	15.00
Sandy Koufax		
Jim Maloney		
Don Drysdale		
6 AL Strikeout Leaders	3.00	8.00
Camilo Pascual		
Jim Bunning		
Dick Stigman		
7 NL Batting Leaders	8.00	20.00
Tommy Davis		
Roberto Clemente		
Dick Groat		
Hank Aaron		
8 AL Batting Leaders	6.00	15.00
Carl Yastrzemski		
Al Kaline		
Rich Rollins		
9 NL Home Run Leaders	12.50	30.00
Hank Aaron		
Willie McCovey		
Willie Mays		
Orlando Cepeda		
10 AL Home Run Leaders	3.00	8.00
Harmon Killebrew		
Dick Stuart		
Bob Allison		
11 NL RBI Leaders	6.00	15.00
Hank Aaron		
Ken Boyer		
Bill White		
12 AL RBI Leaders	3.00	8.00
Dick Stuart		
Al Kaline		
Harmon Killebrew		
13 Hoyt Wilhelm	5.00	12.00
14 Rookie Stars	1.25	3.00
Dick Nen RC		
Nick Willhite RC		
15 Zoilo Versalles	2.50	6.00
16 John Boozer	1.25	3.00
17 Willie Kirkland	1.25	3.00
18 Billy O'Dell	1.25	3.00
19 Don Wert	1.25	3.00
20 Bob Friend	2.50	6.00
21 Yogi Berra MG	15.00	40.00
22 Jerry Adair	1.25	3.00
23 Chris Zachary RC	1.25	3.00
24 Carl Sawatski	1.25	3.00
25 Bill Monbouquette	1.25	3.00
26 Gino Cimoli	1.25	3.00
27 New York Mets TC	3.00	8.00
28 Claude Osteen	2.50	6.00
29 Lou Brock	15.00	40.00
30 Ron Perranoski	2.50	6.00
31 Dave Nicholson	1.25	3.00
32 Dean Chance	2.50	6.00
33 Rookie Stars	2.50	6.00
Sammy Ellis		
Mel Queen		
34 Jim Perry	2.50	6.00
35 Eddie Mathews	8.00	20.00
36 Hal Reniff	1.25	3.00
37 Smoky Burgess	2.50	6.00
38 Jim Wynn RC	3.00	8.00
39 Hank Aguirre	1.25	3.00
40 Dick Groat	2.50	6.00
41 Friendly Foes	3.00	8.00
Willie McCovey		
Leon Wagner		
42 Moe Drabowsky	2.50	6.00
43 Roy Sievers	2.50	6.00
44 Duke Carmel	1.25	3.00
45 Milt Pappas	2.50	6.00
46 Ed Brinkman	1.25	3.00
47 Rookie Stars	2.50	6.00
Jesus Alou RC		
Ron Herbel		
48 Bob Perry RC	1.25	3.00
49 Bill Henry	1.25	3.00
50 Mickey Mantle	250.00	500.00
51 Pete Richert	1.25	3.00
52 Chuck Hinton	1.25	3.00
53 Denis Menke	1.25	3.00
54 Sam Mele MG	1.25	3.00
55 Ernie Banks	15.00	40.00
56 Hal Brown	1.25	3.00
57 Tim Harkness	2.50	6.00
58 Don Demeter	2.50	6.00
59 Ernie Broglio	1.25	3.00
60 Frank Malzone	2.50	6.00
61 Angel Backstops	2.50	6.00
Bob Rodgers		
Ed Sadowski		
62 Ted Savage	1.25	3.00
63 John Orsino	1.25	3.00
64 Ted Abernathy	1.25	3.00
65 Felipe Alou	2.50	6.00
66 Eddie Fisher	1.25	3.00
67 Detroit Tigers TC	2.50	6.00
68 Willie Davis	2.50	6.00
69 Clete Boyer	2.50	6.00
70 Joe Torre	3.00	8.00
71 Jack Spring	1.25	3.00
72 Chico Cardenas	2.50	6.00
73 Jimmie Hall RC	3.00	8.00
74 Rookie Stars	1.25	3.00
Bob Priddy RC		
Tom Butters		
75 Wayne Causey	1.25	3.00
76 Checklist 1	4.00	10.00
77 Jerry Walker	1.25	3.00
78 Merritt Ranew	1.25	3.00
79 Bob Heffner RC	1.25	3.00
80 Vada Pinson	3.00	8.00
81 All-Star Vets	5.00	12.00
Nellie Fox		
Harmon Killebrew		
82 Jim Davenport	2.50	6.00
83 Gus Triandos	2.50	6.00
84 Carl Willey	1.25	3.00
85 Pete Ward	1.25	3.00
86 Al Downing	2.50	6.00
87 St. Louis Cardinals TC	2.50	6.00
88 John Roseboro	2.50	6.00
89 Boog Powell	2.50	6.00
90 Earl Battey	1.25	3.00
91 Bob Bailey	2.50	6.00
92 Steve Ridzik	1.25	3.00
93 Gary Geiger	1.25	3.00
94 Rookie Stars	1.25	3.00
Jim Britton RC		
Larry Maxie RC		
95 George Altman	1.25	3.00
96 Bob Buhl	2.50	6.00
97 Jim Fregosi	2.50	6.00
98 Bill Bruton	1.25	3.00
99 Al Stanek RC	1.25	3.00
100 Elston Howard	2.50	6.00
101 Walt Alston MG	3.00	8.00
102 Checklist 2	4.00	10.00
103 Curt Flood	2.50	6.00
104 Art Mahaffey	2.50	6.00
105 Woody Held	1.25	3.00
106 Joe Nuxhall	2.50	6.00
107 Rookie Stars	1.25	3.00
Bruce Howard RC		
Frank Kreutzer RC		
108 John Wyatt	1.25	3.00
109 Rusty Staub	2.50	6.00
110 Albie Pearson	2.50	6.00
111 Don Elston	1.25	3.00
112 Bob Tillman	1.25	3.00
113 Grover Powell RC	2.50	6.00
114 Don Lock	1.25	3.00
115 Frank Bolling	1.25	3.00
116 Rookie Stars	5.00	12.00
Jay Ward RC		
Tony Oliva		
117 Earl Francis	1.25	3.00
118 John Blanchard	2.50	6.00
119 Gary Kolb RC	1.25	3.00
120 Don Drysdale	8.00	20.00
121 Pete Runnels	2.50	6.00
122 Don McMahon	1.25	3.00
123 Jose Pagan	1.25	3.00
124 Orlando Pena	1.25	3.00
125 Pete Rose UER	125.00	250.00
Born in 1942		
126 Russ Snyder	1.25	3.00
127 Rookie Stars	1.25	3.00
Aubrey Gatewood RC		
Dick Simpson		
128 Mickey Lolich RC	8.00	20.00
129 Amado Samuel	1.25	3.00
130 Gary Peters	2.50	6.00
131 Steve Boros	1.25	3.00
132 Milwaukee Braves TC	2.50	6.00
133 Jim Grant	2.50	6.00
134 Don Zimmer	2.50	6.00
135 Johnny Callison	2.50	6.00
136 World Series Game 1	8.00	20.00
Sandy Koufax		
137 World Series Game 2	3.00	8.00
Willie Davis		
138 World Series Game 3	3.00	8.00
Ron Fairly		
139 World Series Game 4	3.00	8.00
Frank Howard		
140 World Series Summary	3.00	8.00
Dodgers Celebrate		
141 Danny Murtaugh MG	2.50	6.00
142 John Bateman	1.25	3.00
143 Bubba Phillips	1.25	3.00
144 Al Worthington	1.25	3.00
145 Norm Siebern	1.25	3.00
146 Rookie Stars	12.50	30.00
Tommy John RC		
Bob Chance RC		
147 Ray Sadecki	1.25	3.00
148 J.C. Martin	1.25	3.00
149 Paul Foytack	1.25	3.00
150 Willie Mays	60.00	120.00
151 Kansas City Athletics TC	2.50	6.00
152 Denny Lemaster	1.25	3.00
153 Dick Williams	2.50	6.00
154 Dick Tracewski RC	2.50	6.00
155 Duke Snider	12.50	30.00
156 Bill Dailey	1.25	3.00
157 Gene Mauch MG	2.50	6.00
158 Ken Johnson	1.25	3.00
159 Charlie Dees RC	1.25	3.00
160 Ken Boyer	2.50	6.00
161 Dave McNally	2.50	6.00
162 Hitting Area	2.50	6.00
Dick Sisler CO		
Vada Pinson		
163 Donn Clendenon	2.50	6.00
164 Bud Daley	1.25	3.00
165 Jerry Lumpe	1.25	3.00
166 Marty Keough	1.25	3.00
167 Rookie Stars	12.50	30.00
Mike Brumley RC		
Lou Piniella RC		
168 Al Weis	1.25	3.00
169 Del Crandall	2.50	6.00
170 Dick Radatz	2.50	6.00
171 Ty Cline	1.25	3.00
172 Cleveland Indians TC	2.50	6.00
173 Ryne Duren	2.50	6.00
174 Doc Edwards	1.25	3.00
175 Billy Williams	5.00	12.00
176 Tracy Stallard	1.25	3.00
177 Harmon Killebrew	8.00	20.00
178 Hank Bauer MG	2.50	6.00
179 Carl Warwick	1.25	3.00
180 Tommy Davis	2.50	6.00
181 Dave Wickersham	1.25	3.00
182 Sox Sockers	6.00	15.00
Carl Yastrzemski		
Chuck Schilling		
183 Ron Taylor	1.25	3.00
184 Al Luplow	1.25	3.00
185 Jim O'Toole	2.50	6.00
186 Roman Mejias	1.25	3.00
187 Ed Roebuck	1.25	3.00
188 Checklist 3	4.00	10.00
189 Bob Hendley	1.25	3.00
190 Bobby Richardson	3.00	8.00
191 Clay Dalrymple	2.50	6.00
192 Rookie Stars	1.25	3.00
John Boccabella RC		
Billy Cowan RC		
193 Jerry Lynch	1.25	3.00
194 John Goryl	1.25	3.00
195 Floyd Robinson	1.25	3.00
196 Jim Gentile	1.25	3.00
197 Frank Lary	2.50	6.00
198 Len Gabrielson	1.50	4.00
199 Joe Azcue	1.50	4.00
200 Sandy Koufax	60.00	120.00
201 Rookie Stars	2.50	6.00
Sam Bowens RC		
Wally Bunker RC		
202 Galen Cisco	2.50	6.00
203 John Kennedy RC	2.50	6.00
204 Matty Alou	2.50	6.00
205 Nellie Fox	5.00	12.00
206 Steve Hamilton	2.50	6.00
207 Fred Hutchinson MG	2.50	6.00
208 Wes Covington	2.50	6.00
209 Bob Allen	1.50	4.00
210 Carl Yastrzemski	15.00	40.00
211 Jim Coker	1.50	4.00
212 Pete Lovrich	1.50	4.00
213 Los Angeles Angels TC	2.50	6.00
214 Ken McMullen	2.50	6.00
215 Ray Herbert	1.50	4.00
216 Mike de la Hoz	1.50	4.00
217 Jim King	1.50	4.00
218 Hank Fischer	1.50	4.00
219 Young Aces	2.50	6.00
Al Downing		
Jim Bouton		
220 Dick Ellsworth	2.50	6.00
221 Bob Saverine	1.50	4.00
222 Billy Pierce	2.50	6.00
223 George Banks	1.50	4.00
224 Tommie Sisk	1.50	4.00
225 Roger Maris	30.00	60.00
226 Rookie Stars	2.50	6.00
Jerry Grote RC		
Larry Yellen RC		
227 Barry Latman	1.50	4.00
228 Felix Mantilla	1.50	4.00
229 Charley Lau	2.50	6.00
230 Brooks Robinson	15.00	40.00
231 Dick Calmus RC	1.50	4.00
232 Al Lopez MG	3.00	8.00
233 Hal Smith	1.50	4.00
234 Gary Bell	1.50	4.00
235 Ron Hunt	1.50	4.00
236 Bill Faul	1.50	4.00
237 Chicago Cubs TC	2.50	6.00
238 Roy McMillan	2.50	6.00
239 Herm Starrette RC	1.50	4.00
240 Bill White	2.50	6.00
241 Jim Owens	1.50	4.00
242 Harvey Kuenn	2.50	6.00
243 Rookie Stars	12.50	30.00
Richie Allen RC		
John Herrnstein		
244 Tony LaRussa RC	12.50	30.00
245 Dick Stigman	1.50	4.00
246 Manny Mota	2.50	6.00
247 Dave DeBusschere	2.50	6.00
248 Johnny Pesky MG	2.50	6.00
249 Doug Camilli	1.50	4.00
250 Al Kaline	15.00	40.00
251 Choo Choo Coleman	2.50	6.00
252 Ken Aspromonte	1.50	4.00
253 Wally Post	2.50	6.00
254 Don Hoak	2.50	6.00
255 Lee Thomas	2.50	6.00
256 Johnny Weekly	1.50	4.00
257 San Francisco Giants TC	2.50	6.00
258 Garry Roggenburk	1.50	4.00
259 Harry Bright	1.50	4.00
260 Frank Robinson	15.00	40.00
261 Jim Hannan	1.50	4.00
262 Rookie Stars	3.00	8.00
Mike Shannon RC		
Harry Fanok		
263 Chuck Estrada	1.50	4.00
264 Jim Landis	1.50	4.00
265 Jim Bunning	5.00	12.00
266 Gene Freese	1.50	4.00
267 Wilbur Wood RC	2.50	6.00
268 Bill's Got It	2.50	6.00
Danny Murtaugh MG		
Bill Virdon		
269 Ellis Burton	1.50	4.00
270 Rich Rollins	2.50	6.00
271 Bob Sadowski	1.50	4.00
272 Jake Wood	1.50	4.00
273 Mel Nelson	1.50	4.00
274 Checklist 4	4.00	10.00
275 John Tsitouris	1.50	4.00
276 Jose Tartabull	2.50	6.00
277 Ken Retzer	1.50	4.00
278 Bobby Shantz	2.50	6.00
279 Joe Koppe	1.50	4.00
280 Juan Marichal	6.00	15.00
281 Rookie Stars	2.50	6.00
Jake Gibbs		
Tom Metcalf RC		
282 Bob Bruce	1.50	4.00
283 Tom McCraw RC	1.50	4.00
284 Dick Schofield	1.50	4.00
285 Robin Roberts	6.00	15.00
286 Don Landrum	1.50	4.00
287 Rookie Stars	20.00	50.00
Tony Conigliaro RC		
Bill Spanswick RC		
288 Al Moran	1.50	4.00
289 Frank Funk	1.50	4.00
290 Bob Allison	2.50	6.00
291 Phil Ortega	1.50	4.00
292 Mike Roarke	1.50	4.00
293 Philadelphia Phillies TC	2.50	6.00
294 Ken L. Hunt	1.50	4.00
295 Roger Craig	2.50	6.00
296 Ed Kirkpatrick	1.50	4.00
297 Ken MacKenzie	1.50	4.00
298 Harry Craft MG	1.50	4.00
299 Bill Stafford	1.50	4.00
300 Hank Aaron	50.00	100.00
301 Larry Brown RC	1.50	4.00
302 Dan Pfister	1.50	4.00
303 Jim Campbell	1.50	4.00
304 Bob Johnson	1.50	4.00
305 Jack Lamabe	1.50	4.00
306 Giant Gunners	15.00	40.00
Willie Mays		
Orlando Cepeda		
307 Joe Gibbon	1.50	4.00
308 Gene Stephens	1.50	4.00
309 Paul Toth	1.50	4.00
310 Jim Gilliam	2.50	6.00
311 Tom W. Brown RC	2.50	6.00
312 Rookie Stars	1.50	4.00
Fritz Fisher RC		
Fred Gladding RC		
313 Chuck Hiller	1.50	4.00
314 Jerry Buchek	1.50	4.00
315 Bo Belinsky	2.50	6.00
316 Gene Oliver	1.50	4.00
317 Al Smith	1.50	4.00
318 Minnesota Twins TC	2.50	6.00
319 Paul Brown	1.50	4.00
320 Rocky Colavito	5.00	12.00
321 Bob Lillis	1.50	4.00
322 George Brunet	1.50	4.00
323 John Buzhardt	1.50	4.00
324 Casey Stengel MG	6.00	15.00
325 Hector Lopez	2.50	6.00
326 Ron Brand RC	1.50	4.00
327 Don Blasingame	1.50	4.00
328 Bob Shaw	1.50	4.00
329 Russ Nixon	1.50	4.00
330 Tommy Harper	2.50	6.00
331 AL Bombers	75.00	150.00
Roger Maris		
Norm Cash		
Mickey Mantle		
Al Kaline		
332 Ray Washburn	1.50	4.00
333 Billy Moran	1.50	4.00
334 Lew Krausse	1.50	4.00
335 Don Mossi	2.50	6.00
336 Andre Rodgers	1.50	4.00
337 Rookie Stars	2.50	6.00
Al Ferrara RC		
Jeff Torborg RC		
338 Jack Kralick	1.50	4.00
339 Walt Bond	1.50	4.00
340 Joe Cunningham	1.50	4.00
341 Jim Roland	1.50	4.00
342 Willie Stargell	12.50	30.00
343 Washington Senators TC	2.50	6.00
344 Phil Linz	2.50	6.00
345 Frank Thomas	3.00	8.00
346 Joey Jay	1.50	4.00
347 Bobby Wine	2.50	6.00
348 Ed Lopat MG	2.50	6.00
349 Art Fowler	1.50	4.00
350 Willie McCovey	10.00	25.00
351 Dan Schneider	1.50	4.00
352 Eddie Bressoud	1.50	4.00
353 Wally Moon	2.50	6.00
354 Dave Giusti	1.50	4.00
355 Vic Power	2.50	6.00
356 Rookie Stars	2.50	6.00
Bill McCool RC		
Chico Ruiz		
357 Charley James	1.50	4.00
358 Ron Kline	1.50	4.00
359 Jim Schaffer	1.50	4.00
360 Joe Pepitone	5.00	12.00
361 Jay Hook	1.50	4.00
362 Checklist 5	4.00	10.00
363 Dick McAuliffe	2.50	6.00
364 Joe Gaines	1.50	4.00
365 Cal McLish	2.50	6.00
366 Nelson Mathews	1.50	4.00
367 Fred Whitfield	1.50	4.00
368 Rookie Stars	2.50	6.00
Fritz Ackley RC		
Don Buford RC		
369 Jerry Zimmerman	1.50	4.00
370 Hal Woodeshick	1.50	4.00
371 Frank Howard	3.00	8.00
372 Howie Koplitz	3.00	8.00
373 Pittsburgh Pirates TC	5.00	12.00
374 Bobby Bolin	3.00	8.00
375 Ron Santo	4.00	10.00
376 Dave Morehead	3.00	8.00
377 Bob Skinner	3.00	8.00
378 Rookie Stars	4.00	10.00
Woody Woodward RC		
Jack Smith		
379 Tony Gonzalez	3.00	8.00
380 Whitey Ford	15.00	40.00
381 Bob Taylor	3.00	8.00
382 Wes Stock	3.00	8.00
383 Bill Rigney MG	3.00	8.00
384 Ron Hansen	3.00	8.00
385 Curt Simmons	4.00	10.00
386 Lenny Green	3.00	8.00
387 Terry Fox	3.00	8.00
388 Rookie Stars	4.00	10.00
John O'Donoghue RC		
George Williams		
389 Jim Umbricht	4.00	10.00
390 Orlando Cepeda	10.00	25.00
391 Sam McDowell	4.00	10.00
392 Jim Pagliaroni	3.00	8.00
393 Casey Teaches	6.00	15.00
Casey Stengel MG		
Ed Kranepool		
394 Bob Miller	3.00	8.00
395 Tom Tresh	4.00	10.00
396 Dennis Bennett	3.00	8.00
397 Chuck Cottier	3.00	8.00
398 Rookie Stars	4.00	10.00
Bill Haas		
Dick Smith		
399 Jackie Brandt	3.00	8.00
400 Warren Spahn	15.00	40.00
401 Charlie Maxwell	3.00	8.00
402 Tom Sturdivant	3.00	8.00
403 Cincinnati Reds TC	5.00	12.00
404 Tony Martinez	3.00	8.00
405 Ken McBride	3.00	8.00
406 Al Spangler	3.00	8.00
407 Bill Freehan	4.00	10.00
408 Rookie Stars	3.00	8.00
Jim Stewart RC		
Fred Burdette RC		
409 Bill Fischer	3.00	8.00
410 Dick Stuart	4.00	10.00
411 Lee Walls	3.00	8.00
412 Ray Culp	4.00	10.00
413 Johnny Keane MG	3.00	8.00
414 Jack Sanford	3.00	8.00
415 Tony Kubek	6.00	15.00
416 Lee Maye	3.00	8.00
417 Don Cardwell	3.00	8.00
418 Rookie Stars	4.00	10.00
Darold Knowles RC		
Buster Narum RC		
419 Ken Harrelson RC	6.00	15.00
420 Jim Maloney	4.00	10.00
421 Camilo Carreon	3.00	8.00
422 Jack Fisher	3.00	8.00
423 Tops in NL	60.00	120.00
Hank Aaron		
Willie Mays		
424 Dick Bertell	3.00	8.00
425 Norm Cash	4.00	10.00
426 Bob Rodgers	3.00	8.00
427 Don Rudolph	3.00	8.00
428 Rookie Stars	3.00	8.00
Archie Skeen RC		
Pete Smith RC		
429 Tim McCarver	4.00	10.00
430 Juan Pizarro	3.00	8.00
431 George Alusik	3.00	8.00
432 Ruben Amaro	4.00	10.00
433 New York Yankees TC	15.00	40.00
434 Don Nottebart	3.00	8.00
435 Vic Davalillo	3.00	8.00
436 Charlie Neal	4.00	10.00
437 Ed Bailey	3.00	8.00
438 Checklist 6	6.00	15.00
439 Harvey Haddix	4.00	10.00
440 R.Clemente UER	100.00	200.00
1960 Pittsburth		
441 Bob Duliba	3.00	8.00
442 Pumpsie Green	4.00	10.00
443 Chuck Dressen MG	4.00	10.00
444 Larry Jackson	3.00	8.00
445 Bill Skowron	4.00	10.00
446 Julian Javier	6.00	15.00
447 Ted Bowsfield	3.00	8.00
448 Cookie Rojas	4.00	10.00
449 Deron Johnson	4.00	10.00
450 Steve Barber	3.00	8.00
451 Joe Amalfitano	3.00	8.00
452 Rookie Stars	4.00	10.00
Gil Garrido RC		
Jim Ray Hart RC		
453 Frank Baumann	3.00	8.00
454 Tommie Aaron	4.00	10.00
455 Bernie Allen	3.00	8.00
456 Rookie Stars	4.00	10.00
Wes Parker RC		
John Werhas RC		
457 Jesse Gonder	3.00	8.00
458 Ralph Terry	4.00	10.00
459 Rookie Stars	3.00	8.00
Pete Charton RC		
Dalton Jones RC		
460 Bob Gibson	15.00	40.00
461 George Thomas	3.00	8.00
462 Birdie Tebbetts MG	3.00	8.00
463 Don Leppert	3.00	8.00
464 Dallas Green	6.00	15.00
465 Mike Hershberger	3.00	8.00
466 Rookie Stars	4.00	10.00
Dick Green RC		
Aurelio Monteagudo RC		
467 Bob Aspromonte	3.00	8.00
468 Gaylord Perry	15.00	40.00
469 Rookie Stars	4.00	10.00
Fred Norman RC		
Sterling Slaughter RC		
470 Jim Bouton	4.00	10.00
471 Gates Brown RC	4.00	10.00
472 Vern Law	4.00	10.00
473 Baltimore Orioles TC	5.00	12.00
474 Larry Sherry	4.00	10.00
475 Ed Charles	3.00	8.00
476 Rookie Stars	6.00	15.00
Rico Carty RC		
Dick Kelley RC		
477 Mike Joyce	3.00	8.00
478 Dick Howser	4.00	10.00
479 Rookie Stars	3.00	8.00
Dave Bakenhaster RC		
Johnny Lewis RC		
480 Bob Purkey	3.00	8.00
481 Chuck Schilling	3.00	8.00
482 Rookie Stars	4.00	10.00
John Briggs RC		
Danny Cater RC		
483 Fred Valentine RC	3.00	8.00
484 Bill Pleis	3.00	8.00
485 Tom Haller	3.00	8.00
486 Bob Kennedy MG	3.00	8.00
487 Mike McCormick	4.00	10.00
488 Rookie Stars	6.00	15.00
Pete Mikkelsen RC		
Bob Meyer RC		
489 Julio Navarro	3.00	8.00
490 Ron Fairly	4.00	10.00
491 Ed Rakow	3.00	8.00
492 Rookie Stars	3.00	8.00
Jim Beauchamp RC		
Mike White RC		
493 Don Lee	3.00	8.00
494 Al Jackson	3.00	8.00
495 Bill Virdon	4.00	10.00
496 Chicago White Sox TC	5.00	12.00
497 Jeoff Long RC	3.00	8.00
498 Dave Stenhouse	3.00	8.00
499 Rookie Stars	3.00	8.00
Chico Salmon RC		
Gordon Seyfried RC		
500 Camilo Pascual	4.00	10.00
501 Bob Veale	4.00	10.00
502 Rookie Stars	3.00	8.00
Bobby Knoop RC		
Bob Lee RC		
503 Earl Wilson	3.00	8.00
504 Claude Raymond	3.00	8.00
505 Stan Williams	3.00	8.00
506 Bobby Bragan MG	3.00	8.00
507 Johnny Edwards	3.00	8.00
508 Diego Segui	3.00	8.00
509 Rookie Stars	4.00	10.00
Gene Alley RC		
Orlando McFarlane RC		
510 Lindy McDaniel	4.00	10.00
511 Lou Jackson	4.00	10.00
512 Rookie Stars	6.00	15.00
Willie Horton RC		
Joe Sparma RC		
513 Don Larsen	4.00	10.00
514 Jim Hickman	4.00	10.00
515 Johnny Romano	3.00	8.00
516 Rookie Stars	3.00	8.00
Jerry Arrigo RC		
Dwight Siebler RC		
517A Checklist 7 ERR	10.00	25.00
(Incorrect numbering sequence on back)		
517B Checklist 7 COR	6.00	15.00
(Correct numbering on back)		
518 Carl Bouldin	3.00	8.00
519 Charlie Smith	3.00	8.00
520 Jack Baldschun	4.00	10.00
521 Tom Satriano	3.00	8.00
522 Bob Tiefenauer	3.00	8.00
523 Lou Burdette UER	8.00	20.00
(Pitching lefty)		
524 Rookie Stars	6.00	15.00
Jim Dickson RC		
Bobby Klaus RC		
525 Al McBean	6.00	15.00
526 Lou Clinton	6.00	15.00
527 Larry Bearnarth	6.00	15.00
528 Rookie Stars	8.00	20.00
Dave Duncan RC		
Tommie Reynolds RC		
529 Alvin Dark MG	8.00	20.00
530 Leon Wagner	6.00	15.00
531 Los Angeles Dodgers TC	10.00	25.00
532 Rookie Stars	6.00	15.00
Bud Bloomfield UER RC		
(Photo is Jay Ward)		
Joe Nossek RC		
533 Johnny Klippstein	6.00	15.00
534 Gus Bell	6.00	15.00
535 Phil Regan	6.00	15.00
536 Rookie Stars	6.00	15.00
Larry Elliot		
John Stephenson RC		
537 Dan Osinski	6.00	15.00
538 Minnie Minoso	8.00	20.00
539 Roy Face	8.00	20.00
540 Luis Aparicio	15.00	40.00
541 Rookie Stars	40.00	80.00
Phil Roof		
Phil Niekro RC		
542 Don Mincher	6.00	15.00
543 Bob Uecker	15.00	40.00
544 Rookie Stars	6.00	15.00
Steve Hertz RC		
Joe Hoerner RC		
545 Max Alvis	6.00	15.00
546 Joe Christopher	6.00	15.00
547 Gil Hodges MG	12.50	30.00
548 Rookie Stars	8.00	20.00
Wayne Schurr RC		
Paul Speckenbach RC		
549 Joe Moeller	6.00	15.00
550 Ken Hubbs	15.00	40.00
In Memoriam		
551 Billy Hoeft	6.00	15.00
552 Rookie Stars	6.00	15.00
Tom Kelley RC		
Sonny Siebert RC		
553 Jim Brewer	6.00	15.00

Card	Low	High
554 Hank Foiles	6.00	15.00
555 Lee Stange	6.00	15.00
556 Rookie Stars	6.00	15.00
Steve Dillon RC		
Ron Locke RC		
557 Leo Burke	6.00	15.00
558 Don Schwall	6.00	15.00
559 Dick Phillips	6.00	15.00
560 Dick Farrell	6.00	15.00
561 Rookie Stars	8.00	20.00
Dave Bennett UER RC		
(19 ... is 18)		
Rick Wise RC		
562 Pedro Ramos	6.00	15.00
563 Dal Maxvill	8.00	20.00
564 Rookie Stars	8.00	20.00
Joe McCabe RC		
Jerry McNertney RC		
565 Stu Miller	6.00	15.00
566 Ed Kranepool	8.00	20.00
567 Jim Kaat	8.00	20.00
568 Rookie Stars	6.00	15.00
Phil Gagliano RC		
Cap Peterson RC		
569 Fred Newman	6.00	15.00
570 Bill Mazeroski	15.00	40.00
571 Gene Conley	6.00	15.00
572 Rookie Stars	6.00	15.00
Dave Gray RC		
Dick Egan		
573 Jim Duffalo	6.00	15.00
574 Manny Jimenez	6.00	15.00
575 Tony Cloninger	6.00	15.00
576 Rookie Stars	6.00	15.00
Jerry Hinsley RC		
Bill Wakefield RC		
577 Gordy Coleman	6.00	15.00
578 Glen Hobbie	6.00	15.00
579 Boston Red Sox TC	10.00	25.00
580 Johnny Podres	8.00	20.00
581 Rookie Stars	8.00	20.00
Pedro Gonzalez		
Archie Moore RC		
582 Rod Kanehl	8.00	20.00
583 Tito Francona	6.00	15.00
584 Joel Horlen	6.00	15.00
585 Tony Taylor	8.00	20.00
586 Jimmy Piersall	8.00	20.00
587 Bennie Daniels	8.00	20.00

1964 Topps Coins

This set of 164 unnumbered coins issued in 1964 is sometimes divided into two sets -- the regular series (1-120) and the all-star series (121-164). Each metal coin is approximately 1 1/2" in diameter. The regular series features gold and silver coins with a full color photo of the player, including the background of the photo. The player's name, team and position are delineated on the coin front. The back includes the line "Collect the entire set of 120 all-stars". The all-star series (denoted AS in the checklist below) contains a full color cutout photo of the player on a solid background. The fronts feature the line "1964 All-stars" along with the name only of the player. The backs contain the line "Collect all 44 special stars". Mantle, Causey and Hinton appear in two variations each. The complete set price below includes all variations. Some dealers believe the following coins are short printed: Callison, Tresh, Rollins, Santo, Pappas, Freehan, Hendley, Staub, Bateman and O'Dell.

Card	Low	High
COMPLETE SET (167)	500.00	1000.00
1 Don Zimmer	2.50	6.00
2 Jim Wynn	2.00	5.00
3 Johnny Orsino	1.50	4.00
4 Jim Bouton	2.00	5.00
5 Dick Groat	2.00	5.00
6 Leon Wagner	1.50	4.00
7 Frank Malzone	1.50	4.00
8 Steve Barber	1.50	4.00
9 Johnny Romano	1.50	4.00
10 Tom Tresh	2.50	6.00
11 Felipe Alou	2.00	5.00
12 Dick Stuart	2.00	5.00
13 Claude Osteen	1.50	4.00
14 Juan Pizarro	1.50	4.00
15 Donn Clendenon	1.50	4.00
16 Jimmie Hall	1.50	4.00
17 Al Jackson	1.50	4.00
18 Brooks Robinson	10.00	25.00
19 Bob Allison	2.00	5.00
20 Ed Roebuck	1.50	4.00
21 Pete Ward	1.50	4.00
22 Willie McCovey	4.00	10.00
23 Elston Howard	4.00	10.00
24 Diego Segui	1.50	4.00
25 Ken Boyer	2.50	6.00
26 Carl Yastrzemski	10.00	25.00
27 Bill Mazeroski	4.00	10.00
28 Jerry Lumpe	1.50	4.00
29 Woody Held	1.50	4.00
30 Dick Radatz	1.50	4.00
31 Luis Aparicio	2.50	6.00
32 Dave Nicholson	1.50	4.00
33 Eddie Mathews	10.00	25.00
34 Don Drysdale	8.00	20.00
35 Ray Culp	1.50	4.00
36 Juan Marichal	4.00	10.00
37 Frank Robinson	10.00	25.00
38 Chuck Hinton	1.50	4.00
39 Floyd Robinson	1.50	4.00
40 Tommy Harper	2.00	5.00
41 Ron Hansen	1.50	4.00
42 Ernie Banks	10.00	25.00
43 Jesse Gonder	1.50	4.00
44 Billy Williams	2.50	6.00
45 Vada Pinson	2.00	5.00
46 Rocky Colavito	5.00	12.00
47 Bill Monbouquette	1.50	4.00
48 Max Alvis	1.50	4.00
49 Norm Siebern	1.50	4.00
50 Johnny Callison	2.00	5.00
51 Rich Rollins	1.50	4.00
52 Ken McBride	1.50	4.00
53 Don Lock	1.50	4.00
54 Ron Fairly	2.00	5.00
55 Roberto Clemente	40.00	80.00
56 Dick Ellsworth	1.50	4.00
57 Tommy Davis	2.00	5.00
58 Tony Gonzalez	1.50	4.00
59 Bob Gibson	8.00	20.00
60 Jim Maloney	2.00	5.00
61 Frank Howard	2.00	5.00
62 Jim Pagliaroni	1.50	4.00
63 Orlando Cepeda	2.50	6.00
64 Ron Perranoski	1.50	4.00
65 Curt Flood	2.50	6.00
66 Alvin McBean	1.50	4.00
67 Dean Chance	1.50	4.00
68 Ron Santo	2.50	6.00
69 Jack Baldschun	1.50	4.00
70 Milt Pappas	2.00	5.00
71 Gary Peters	1.50	4.00
72 Bobby Richardson	2.50	6.00
73 Frank Thomas	1.50	4.00
74 Hank Aguirre	1.50	4.00
75 Carlton Willey	1.50	4.00
76 Camilo Pascual	2.00	5.00
77 Bob Friend	2.00	5.00
78 Bill White	2.00	5.00
79 Norm Cash	2.50	6.00
80 Willie Mays	30.00	60.00
81 Leon Carmel	1.50	4.00
82 Pete Rose	40.00	80.00
83 Hank Aaron	15.00	40.00
84 Bob Aspromonte	1.50	4.00
85 Jim O'Toole	1.50	4.00
86 Vic Davalillo	2.00	5.00
87 Bill Freehan	2.00	5.00
88 Warren Spahn	4.00	10.00
89 Ken Hunt	1.50	4.00
90 Denis Menke	1.50	4.00
91 Dick Farrell	1.50	4.00
92 Jim Hickman	2.00	5.00
93 Jim Bunning	2.50	6.00
94 Bob Hendley	1.50	4.00
95 Ernie Broglio	1.50	4.00
96 Rusty Staub	2.00	5.00
97 Lou Brock	4.00	10.00
98 Jim Fregosi	2.00	5.00
99 Jim Grant	1.50	4.00
100 Al Kaline	8.00	20.00
101 Earl Battey	2.00	5.00
102 Wayne Causey	1.50	4.00
103 Chuck Schilling	1.50	4.00
104 Boog Powell	2.50	6.00
105 Dave Wickersham	1.50	4.00
106 Sandy Koufax	10.00	25.00
107 John Bateman	2.00	5.00
108 Ed Brinkman	1.50	4.00
109 Al Downing	1.50	4.00
110 Joe Azcue	1.50	4.00
111 Albie Pearson	1.50	4.00
112 Harmon Killebrew	8.00	20.00
113 Tony Taylor	2.00	5.00
114 Larry Jackson	1.50	4.00
115 Billy O'Dell	2.00	5.00
116 Don Demeter	2.00	5.00
117 Ed Charles	1.50	4.00
118 Joe Torre	4.00	10.00
119 Don Nottebart	1.50	4.00
120 Mickey Mantle	50.00	100.00
121 Joe Pepitone AS	2.00	5.00
122 Dick Stuart AS	2.00	5.00
123 Bobby Richardson AS	2.50	6.00
124 Jerry Lumpe AS	1.50	4.00
125 Brooks Robinson AS	8.00	20.00
126 Frank Malzone AS	1.50	4.00
127 Luis Aparicio AS	2.50	6.00
128 Jim Fregosi AS	2.00	5.00
129 Al Kaline AS	6.00	15.00
130 Leon Wagner AS	1.50	4.00
131A Mickey Mantle AS	20.00	50.00
Right Handed)		
131B Mickey Mantle AS	20.00	50.00
Left Handed)		
132 Albie Pearson AS	1.50	4.00
133 Harmon Killebrew AS	6.00	15.00
134 Carl Yastrzemski AS	10.00	25.00
135 Elston Howard AS	2.50	6.00
136 Earl Battey AS	1.50	4.00
137 Camilo Pascual AS	1.50	4.00
138 Jim Bouton AS	2.00	5.00
139 Whitey Ford AS	8.00	20.00
140 Gary Peters AS	1.50	4.00
141 Bill White AS	2.00	5.00
142 Orlando Cepeda AS	2.50	6.00
143 Bill Mazeroski AS	4.00	10.00
144 Tony Taylor AS	1.50	4.00
145 Ken Boyer AS	2.50	6.00
146 Ron Santo AS	2.50	6.00
147 Dick Groat AS	2.00	5.00
148 Roy McMillan AS	1.50	4.00
149 Hank Aaron AS	10.00	25.00
150 Roberto Clemente AS	12.50	30.00
151 Willie Mays AS	12.50	30.00
152 Vada Pinson AS	2.00	5.00
153 Tommy Davis AS	2.00	5.00
154 Frank Robinson AS	8.00	20.00
155 Joe Torre AS	4.00	10.00
156 Tim McCarver AS	2.00	5.00
157 Juan Marichal AS	4.00	10.00
158 Jim Maloney AS	2.00	5.00
159 Sandy Koufax AS	10.00	25.00
160 Warren Spahn AS	4.00	10.00
161A Wayne Causey AS	6.00	15.00
National League		
161B Wayne Causey AS	2.00	5.00
American League		
162A Chuck Hinton AS	8.00	20.00
National League		
162B Chuck Hinton AS	2.00	5.00
American League		
163 Bob Aspromonte AS	1.50	4.00
164 Ron Hunt AS	1.50	4.00

1964 Topps Giants

The cards in this 60-card set measure approximately 3 1/8" by 5 1/4". The 1964 Topps Giants are postcard size cards containing color player photographs. They are numbered on the backs, which also contain biographical information presented in a newspaper format. These "giant size" cards were distributed in both cellophane and waxed gum packs apart from the Topps regular issue of 1964. The gum packs contain three cards. The Cards 3, 28, 42, 45, 47, 51 and 60 are more difficult to find and are indicated by SP in the checklist below.

Card	Low	High
COMPLETE SET (60)	150.00	300.00
COMMON CARD (1-60)	.60	1.50
COMMON SP'S	4.00	10.00
WRAPPER (5-CENT)	15.00	40.00
1 Gary Peters	.75	2.00
2 Ken Johnson	.60	1.50
3 Sandy Koufax SP	15.00	40.00
4 Bob Bailey	.60	1.50
5 Milt Pappas	.75	2.00
6 Ron Hunt	.60	1.50
7 Whitey Ford	2.00	5.00
8 Roy McMillan	.60	1.50
9 Rocky Colavito	2.00	5.00
10 Jim Bunning	1.25	3.00
11 Roberto Clemente	12.50	30.00
12 Al Kaline	2.00	5.00
13 Nellie Fox	2.00	5.00
14 Tony Gonzalez	.60	1.50
15 Jim Gentile	.75	2.00
16 Dean Chance	.75	2.00
17 Dick Ellsworth	.75	2.00
18 Jim Fregosi	.75	2.00
19 Dick Groat	.75	2.00
20 Chuck Hinton	.60	1.50
21 Elston Howard	.75	2.00
22 Dick Farrell	.60	1.50
23 Albie Pearson	.60	1.50
24 Frank Howard	.75	2.00
25 Mickey Mantle	20.00	50.00
26 Joe Torre	2.00	5.00
27 Eddie Brinkman	.60	1.50
28 Bob Friend SP	4.00	10.00
29 Frank Robinson	2.00	5.00
30 Bill Freehan	.75	2.00
31 Warren Spahn	2.00	5.00
32 Camilo Pascual	.75	2.00
33 Pete Ward	.60	1.50
34 Jim Maloney	.75	2.00
35 Dave Wickersham	.60	1.50
36 Johnny Callison	.75	2.00
37 Juan Marichal	1.25	3.00
38 Harmon Killebrew	2.00	5.00
39 Luis Aparicio	1.25	3.00
40 Dick Radatz	.60	1.50
41 Bob Gibson	2.00	5.00
42 Dick Stuart SP	4.00	10.00
43 Tommy Davis	.75	2.00
44 Tony Oliva	1.25	3.00
45 Wayne Causey SP	4.00	10.00
46 Max Alvis	.60	1.50
47 Galen Cisco SP	4.00	10.00
48 Carl Yastrzemski	2.00	5.00
49 Hank Aaron	4.00	10.00
50 Brooks Robinson	2.00	5.00
51 Willie Mays SP	20.00	50.00
52 Billy Williams	1.25	3.00
53 Juan Pizarro	.60	1.50
54 Leon Wagner	.60	1.50
55 Orlando Cepeda	1.25	3.00
56 Vada Pinson	.75	2.00
57 Ken Boyer	1.25	3.00
58 Ron Santo	1.25	3.00
59 John Romano	.60	1.50
60 Bill Skowron SP	6.00	15.00

1964 Topps Stand-Ups

In 1964 Topps produced a die-cut "Stand-Up" card design for the first time since their Connie Mack and Current All Stars of 1951. These cards were issued in both one cent and five cent packs. The cards have full-length, color player photos set against a green and yellow background. Of the 77 cards in the set, 22 were single printed and these are marked in the checklist below with an SP. These unnumbered cards are standard-size (2 1/2" by 3 1/2"), blank backed, and have been numbered here for reference in alphabetical order of players. Interestingly there were four different wrapper designs used for this set. All the design variations are valued at the same price.

Card	Low	High
COMPLETE SET (77)	2500.00	4000.00
COMMON CARD (1-77)	4.00	10.00
COMMON CARD SP	15.00	40.00
WRAPPER (1-CENT)	75.00	150.00
WRAPPER (5-CENT)	175.00	350.00
1 Hank Aaron	100.00	200.00
2 Hank Aguirre	5.00	12.00
3 George Altman	8.00	20.00
4 Max Alvis	5.00	12.00
5 Bob Aspromonte	5.00	12.00
6 Jack Baldschun SP	20.00	50.00
7 Ernie Banks	50.00	100.00
8 Steve Barber	5.00	12.00
9 Earl Battey	5.00	12.00
10 Ken Boyer	10.00	25.00
11 Ernie Broglio	5.00	12.00
12 John Callison	8.00	20.00
13 Norm Cash SP	40.00	80.00
14 Wayne Causey	5.00	12.00
15 Orlando Cepeda	10.00	25.00
16 Ed Charles	8.00	20.00
17 Roberto Clemente	125.00	250.00
18 Donn Clendenon SP	20.00	50.00
19 Rocky Colavito	15.00	40.00
20 Ray Culp SP	30.00	60.00
21 Tommy Davis	8.00	20.00
22 Don Drysdale SP	75.00	150.00
23 Dick Ellsworth	5.00	12.00
24 Dick Farrell	5.00	12.00
25 Jim Fregosi	8.00	20.00
26 Bob Friend	5.00	12.00
27 Jim Gentile	8.00	20.00
28 Jesse Gonder SP	20.00	50.00
29 Tony Gonzalez SP	20.00	50.00
30 Dick Groat	10.00	25.00
31 Woody Held	5.00	12.00
32 Chuck Hinton	5.00	12.00
33 Elston Howard	10.00	25.00
34 Frank Howard SP	40.00	80.00
35 Ron Hunt	8.00	20.00
36 Al Jackson	5.00	12.00
37 Ken Johnson	5.00	12.00
38 Al Kaline	50.00	100.00
39 Harmon Killebrew	50.00	100.00
40 Sandy Koufax	100.00	200.00
41 Don Lock SP	20.00	50.00
42 Jerry Lumpe SP	20.00	50.00
43 Jim Maloney	8.00	20.00
44 Frank Malzone	5.00	12.00
45 Mickey Mantle	300.00	600.00
46 Juan Marichal SP	60.00	120.00
47 Eddie Mathews SP	75.00	150.00
48 Willie Mays	150.00	300.00
49 Bill Mazeroski	15.00	40.00
50 Ken McBride	5.00	12.00
51 Willie McCovey SP	60.00	120.00
52 Claude Osteen	8.00	20.00
53 Jim O'Toole	5.00	12.00
54 Camilo Pascual	8.00	20.00
55 Albie Pearson SP	30.00	60.00
56 Gary Peters	5.00	12.00
57 Vada Pinson	8.00	20.00
58 Juan Pizarro	5.00	12.00
59 Boog Powell	10.00	25.00
60 Bobby Richardson	10.00	25.00
61 Brooks Robinson	50.00	100.00
62 Floyd Robinson	5.00	12.00
63 Frank Robinson	50.00	100.00
64 Ed Roebuck SP	20.00	50.00
65 Rich Rollins	5.00	12.00
66 John Romano	5.00	12.00
67 Ron Santo SP	40.00	80.00
68 Norm Siebern	5.00	12.00
69 Warren Spahn SP	75.00	150.00
70 Dick Stuart SP	30.00	60.00
71 Lee Thomas	5.00	12.00
72 Joe Torre	10.00	25.00
73 Pete Ward	5.00	12.00
74 Bill White SP	30.00	60.00
75 Billy Williams SP	60.00	120.00
76 Hal Woodeshick SP	20.00	50.00
77 Carl Yastrzemski SP	250.00	500.00

1964 Topps Tattoos Inserts

These tattoos measure 1 9/16" by 3 1/2" and are printed in color on very thin paper. One side gives instructions for applying the tattoo. The picture side gives either the team logo and name (on tattoos numbered 1-20 below) or the player's face, name and team (21-75 below). The tattoos are unnumbered and are presented below in alphabetical order within type for convenience. This set was issued in one cent packs which came 120 to a box. The boxes had photos of Whitey Ford on them.

Card	Low	High
COMPLETE SET (75)	600.00	1200.00
COMMON TATOO (1-20)	1.50	4.00
COMMON TATTOO (21-75)	3.00	8.00
8 Detroit Tigers	2.00	5.00
11 Los Angeles Dodgers	5.00	12.00
14 New York Mets	2.00	5.00
15 New York Yankees	5.00	12.00
21 Hank Aaron	60.00	120.00
22 Max Alvis	3.00	8.00
23 Hank Aguirre	3.00	8.00
24 Ernie Banks	30.00	60.00
25 Steve Barber	3.00	8.00
26 Ken Boyer	5.00	12.00
27 John Callison	3.00	8.00
28 Norm Cash	4.00	10.00
29 Wayne Causey	3.00	8.00
30 Orlando Cepeda	8.00	20.00
31 Rocky Colavito	8.00	20.00
32 Ray Culp	3.00	8.00
33 Vic Davalillo	3.00	8.00
34 Moe Drabowsky	3.00	8.00
35 Dick Ellsworth	3.00	8.00
36 Curt Flood	5.00	12.00
37 Bill Freehan	4.00	10.00
38 Jim Fregosi	4.00	10.00
39 Bob Friend	3.00	8.00
40 Dick Groat	5.00	12.00
41 Woody Held	3.00	8.00
42 Frank Howard	5.00	12.00
43 Al Jackson	3.00	8.00
44 Larry Jackson	3.00	8.00
45 Ken Johnson	3.00	8.00
46 Al Kaline	30.00	60.00
47 Harmon Killebrew	15.00	40.00
48 Sandy Koufax	60.00	120.00
49 Don Lock	3.00	8.00
50 Frank Malzone	4.00	10.00
51 Mickey Mantle	150.00	300.00
52 Eddie Mathews	20.00	50.00
53 Willie Mays	60.00	120.00
54 Bill Mazeroski	6.00	15.00
55 Ken McBride	3.00	8.00
56 Bill Monbouquette	3.00	8.00
57 Dave Nicholson	3.00	8.00
58 Claude Osteen	3.00	8.00
59 Milt Pappas	4.00	10.00
60 Camilo Pascual	3.00	8.00
61 Albie Pearson	3.00	8.00
62 Ron Perranoski	3.00	8.00
63 Gary Peters	3.00	8.00
64 Boog Powell	5.00	12.00
65 Frank Robinson	20.00	50.00
66 Johnny Romano	3.00	8.00
67 Norm Siebern	3.00	8.00
68 Warren Spahn	20.00	50.00
69 Dick Stuart	4.00	10.00
70 Lee Thomas	3.00	8.00
71 Joe Torre	6.00	15.00
72 Pete Ward	3.00	8.00
73 Carlton Willey	3.00	8.00
74 Billy Williams	15.00	40.00
75 Carl Yastrzemski	30.00	60.00

1965 Topps

The cards in this 598-card set measure 2 1/2" by 3 1/2". The cards comprising the 1965 Topps set have team names located within a distinctive pennant design below the picture. The cards have blue borders on the reverse and were issued by series. Within this last series (523-598) there are 44 cards that were printed in lesser quantities than the other cards in that series; these shorter-printed cards are marked by SP in the checklist below. Featured subsets within this set include League Leaders (1-12) and World Series cards (132-139). This was the last year Topps issued one-card penny packs. Card were also issued in five-card nickel packs. The key Rookie Cards in this set are Steve Carlton, Jim "Catfish" Hunter, Joe Morgan, Mansori Murakami and Tony Perez.

Card	Low	High
COMPLETE SET (598)	2500.00	5000.00
COMMON CARD (1-196)	.75	2.00
COMMON (197-283)	1.00	2.50
COMMON (284-370)	1.50	4.00
COMMON (371-598)	3.00	8.00
WRAPPER (1-CENT)	60.00	120.00
WRAPPER (5-CENT)	50.00	100.00
1 AL Batting Leaders	8.00	20.00
Tony Oliva		
Elston Howard		
Brooks Robinson		
2 NL Batting Leaders	10.00	25.00
Roberto Clemente		
Hank Aaron		
Rico Carty		
3 AL Home Run Leaders	20.00	50.00
Harmon Killebrew		
Mickey Mantle		
Boog Powell		
4 NL Home Run Leaders	6.00	15.00
Willie Mays		
Billy Williams		
Jim Ray Hart		
Orlando Cepeda		
Johnny Callison		
5 AL RBI Leaders	15.00	40.00
Brooks Robinson		
Harmon Killebrew		
Mickey Mantle		
Dick Stuart		
6 NL RBI Leaders	5.00	12.00
Ken Boyer		
Willie Mays		
Ron Santo		
7 AL ERA Leaders	2.00	5.00
Dean Chance		
Joel Horlen		
8 NL ERA Leaders	8.00	20.00
Sandy Koufax		
Don Drysdale		
9 AL Pitching Leaders	2.00	5.00
Dean Chance		
Gary Peters		
Dave Wickersham		
Juan Pizarro		
Wally Bunker		
10 NL Pitching Leaders	2.00	5.00
Larry Jackson		
Ray Sadecki		
Juan Marichal		
11 AL Strikeout Leaders	2.00	5.00
Al Downing		
Dean Chance		
Camilo Pascual		
12 NL Strikeout Leaders	4.00	10.00
Bob Veale		
Don Drysdale		
Bob Gibson		
13 Pedro Ramos	1.50	4.00
14 Len Gabrielson	.75	2.00
15 Robin Roberts	4.00	10.00
16 Rookie Stars	30.00	60.00
Joe Morgan RC		
Sonny Jackson RC DP		
17 Johnny Romano	.75	2.00
18 Bill McCool	.75	2.00
19 Gates Brown	1.50	4.00
20 Jim Bunning	4.00	10.00
21 Don Blasingame	.75	2.00
22 Charlie Smith	.75	2.00
23 Bob Tiefenauer	.75	2.00
24 Minnesota Twins TC	2.50	6.00
25 Al McBean	.75	2.00
26 Bobby Knoop	.75	2.00
27 Dick Bertell	.75	2.00
28 Barney Schultz	.75	2.00
29 Felix Mantilla	.75	2.00
30 Jim Bouton	2.50	6.00
31 Mike White	.75	2.00
32 Herman Franks MG	.75	2.00
33 Jackie Brandt	.75	2.00
34 Cal Koonce	.75	2.00
35 Ed Charles	.75	2.00
36 Bobby Wine	.75	2.00
37 Fred Gladding	.75	2.00
38 Jim King	.75	2.00
39 Gerry Arrigo	.75	2.00
40 Frank Howard	2.50	6.00
41 Rookie Stars	.75	2.00
Bruce Howard		
Marv Staehle RC		
42 Earl Wilson	1.50	4.00
43 Mike Shannon	1.50	4.00
(Name in red, other		
Cardinals in yellow)		
44 Wade Blasingame RC	.75	2.00
45 Roy McMillan	1.50	4.00
46 Bob Lee	.75	2.00
47 Tommy Harper	1.50	4.00
48 Claude Raymond	1.50	4.00
49 Rookie Stars	1.50	4.00
Curt Blefary RC		
John Miller		
50 Juan Marichal	4.00	10.00
51 Bill Bryan	.75	2.00
52 Ed Roebuck	.75	2.00
53 Dick McAuliffe	1.50	4.00
54 Joe Gibbon	.75	2.00
55 Tony Conigliaro	6.00	15.00
56 Ron Kline	.75	2.00
57 St. Louis Cardinals TC	2.50	6.00
58 Fred Talbot RC	.75	2.00
59 Nate Oliver	.75	2.00
60 Jim O'Toole	1.50	4.00
61 Chris Cannizzaro	.75	2.00
62 Jim Kaat UER DP	2.50	6.00
(Misspelled Katt)		
63 Ty Cline	.75	2.00
64 Lou Burdette	1.50	4.00
65 Tony Kubek	4.00	10.00
66 Bill Rigney MG	.75	2.00
67 Harvey Haddix	1.50	4.00
68 Del Crandall	1.50	4.00
69 Bill Virdon	1.50	4.00
70 Bill Skowron	2.50	6.00
71 John O'Donoghue	.75	2.00
72 Tony Gonzalez	.75	2.00
73 Dennis Ribant RC	.75	2.00
74 Rookie Stars	4.00	10.00
Rico Petrocelli RC		
Jerry Stephenson RC		
75 Deron Johnson	1.50	4.00
76 Sam McDowell	2.50	6.00
77 Doug Camilli	.75	2.00
78 Dal Maxvill	.75	2.00
79A Checklist 1	4.00	10.00
(61 Cannizzaro)		
79B Checklist 1	4.00	10.00
(61 C.Cannizzaro)		
80 Turk Farrell	.75	2.00
81 Don Buford	1.50	4.00
82 Rookie Stars	2.50	6.00
Santos Alomar RC		
John Braun RC		
83 George Thomas	.75	2.00
84 Ron Herbel	.75	2.00
85 Willie Smith RC	.75	2.00
86 Buster Narum	.75	2.00
87 Nelson Mathews	.75	2.00
88 Jack Lamabe	.75	2.00
89 Mike Hershberger	.75	2.00
90 Rich Rollins	1.50	4.00
91 Chicago Cubs TC	2.50	6.00
92 Dick Howser	1.50	4.00
93 Jack Fisher	.75	2.00
94 Charlie Lau	1.50	4.00
95 Bill Mazeroski DP	2.50	6.00
96 Sonny Siebert	1.50	4.00
97 Pedro Gonzalez	.75	2.00
98 Bob Miller	.75	2.00
99 Gil Hodges MG	2.50	6.00
100 Ken Boyer	4.00	10.00
101 Fred Newman	.75	2.00
102 Steve Boros	.75	2.00
103 Harvey Kuenn	1.50	4.00
104 Checklist 2	4.00	10.00
105 Chico Salmon	.75	2.00
106 Gene Oliver	.75	2.00
107 Rookie Stars	1.50	4.00
Pat Corrales RC		
Costen Shockley RC		
108 Don Mincher	.75	2.00
109 Walt Bond	.75	2.00
110 Ron Santo	2.50	6.00
111 Lee Thomas	1.50	4.00
112 Derrell Griffith RC	.75	2.00
113 Steve Barber	.75	2.00
114 Jim Hickman	1.50	4.00
115 Bobby Richardson	4.00	10.00
116 Rookie Stars	1.50	4.00
Dave Dowling RC		
Bob Tolan RC		
117 Wes Stock	.75	2.00
118 Hal Lanier RC	1.50	4.00
119 John Kennedy	.75	2.00
120 Frank Robinson	15.00	40.00
121 Gene Alley	1.50	4.00
122 Bill Pleis	.75	2.00
123 Frank Thomas	1.50	4.00
124 Tom Satriano	.75	2.00
125 Juan Pizarro	.75	2.00
126 Los Angeles Dodgers TC	2.50	6.00
127 Frank Lary	.75	2.00
128 Vic Davalillo	.75	2.00
129 Bennie Daniels	.75	2.00
130 Al Kaline	15.00	40.00
131 Johnny Keane MG	.75	2.00
132 World Series Game 1	4.00	10.00
Cards Take Opener		
133 World Series Game 2	2.50	6.00
Mel Stottlemyre		
134 World Series Game 3	40.00	80.00
Mickey Mantle		
135 World Series Game 4	4.00	10.00
Ken Boyer		
136 World Series Game 5	2.50	6.00
Tim McCarver		
137 World Series Game 6	2.50	6.00
Jim Bouton		
138 World Series Game 7	5.00	12.00
Bob Gibson		
139 World Series Summary	2.50	6.00
Cards Celebrate		
140 Dean Chance	1.50	4.00
141 Charlie James	.75	2.00
142 Bill Monbouquette	.75	2.00
143 Rookie Stars	.75	2.00
John Gelnar RC		
Jerry May RC		
144 Ed Kranepool	1.50	4.00
145 Luis Tiant RC	4.00	10.00
146 Ron Hansen	.75	2.00
147 Dennis Bennett	.75	2.00
148 Willie Kirkland	.75	2.00
149 Wayne Schurr	.75	2.00
150 Brooks Robinson	15.00	40.00
151 Kansas City Athletics TC	2.50	6.00
152 Phil Ortega	.75	2.00
153 Norm Cash	2.50	6.00
154 Bob Humphreys RC	.75	2.00
155 Roger Maris	30.00	60.00
156 Bob Sadowski	.75	2.00
157 Zoilo Versalles	1.50	4.00
158 Dick Sisler	.75	2.00
159 Jim Duffalo	.75	2.00
160 R.Clemente UER	100.00	200.00
1960 Pittsburfh		
161 Frank Baumann	.75	2.00
162 Russ Nixon	.75	2.00
163 Johnny Briggs	.75	2.00
164 Al Spangler	.75	2.00
165 Dick Ellsworth	.75	2.00
166 Rookie Stars	1.50	4.00
George Culver RC		
Tommie Agee RC		
167 Bill Wakefield	.75	2.00
168 Dick Green	.75	2.00
169 Dave Vineyard RC	.75	2.00
170 Hank Aaron	75.00	150.00
171 Jim Roland	.75	2.00
172 Jimmy Piersall	2.50	6.00
173 Detroit Tigers TC	2.50	6.00
174 Joey Jay	.75	2.00
175 Bob Aspromonte	.75	2.00
176 Willie McCovey	8.00	20.00
177 Pete Mikkelsen	.75	2.00
178 Dalton Jones	.75	2.00
179 Hal Woodeshick	.75	2.00
180 Bob Allison	1.50	4.00
181 Rookie Stars	.75	2.00
Don Loun RC		
Joe McCabe		
182 Mike de la Hoz	.75	2.00
183 Dave Nicholson	.75	2.00
184 John Boozer	.75	2.00
185 Max Alvis	.75	2.00
186 Billy Cowan	.75	2.00
187 Casey Stengel MG	6.00	15.00
188 Sam Bowens	.75	2.00
189 Checklist 3	4.00	10.00
190 Bill White	2.50	6.00
191 Phil Regan	1.50	4.00
192 Jim Coker	.75	2.00
193 Gaylord Perry	6.00	15.00
194 Rookie Stars	.75	2.00
Bill Kelso RC		
Rick Reichardt RC		
195 Bob Veale	1.50	4.00
196 Ron Fairly	1.50	4.00
197 Diego Segui	1.00	2.50
198 Smoky Burgess	1.50	4.00
199 Bob Heffner	1.00	2.50
200 Joe Torre	2.50	6.00
201 Rookie Stars	1.50	4.00
Sandy Valdespino RC		
Cesar Tovar RC		
202 Leo Burke	1.00	2.50
203 Dallas Green	1.50	4.00
204 Russ Snyder	1.00	2.50
205 Warren Spahn	12.50	30.00
206 Willie Horton	1.50	4.00
207 Pete Rose	100.00	200.00
208 Tommy John	2.50	6.00
209 Pittsburgh Pirates TC	2.50	6.00
210 Jim Fregosi	1.50	4.00
211 Steve Ridzik	1.00	2.50
212 Ron Brand	1.00	2.50
213 Jim Davenport	1.00	2.50
214 Bob Purkey	1.00	2.50
215 Pete Ward	1.00	2.50
216 Al Worthington	1.00	2.50
217 Walter Alston MG	2.50	6.00
218 Dick Schofield	1.00	2.50
219 Bob Meyer	1.00	2.50
220 Billy Williams	4.00	10.00
221 John Tsitouris	1.00	2.50
222 Bob Tillman	1.00	2.50
223 Dan Osinski	1.00	2.50
224 Bob Chance	1.00	2.50
225 Bo Belinsky	1.50	4.00
226 Rookie Stars	2.50	6.00
Elvio Jimenez RC		
Jake Gibbs		
227 Bobby Klaus	1.00	2.50
228 Jack Sanford	1.00	2.50
229 Lou Clinton	1.00	2.50
230 Ray Sadecki	1.00	2.50
231 Jerry Adair	1.00	2.50
232 Steve Blass RC	1.50	4.00
233 Don Zimmer	1.50	4.00
234 Chicago White Sox TC	2.50	6.00
235 Chuck Hinton	1.00	2.50
236 Denny McLain RC	10.00	25.00
237 Bernie Allen	1.00	2.50
238 Joe Moeller	1.00	2.50
239 Doc Edwards	1.00	2.50
240 Bob Bruce	1.00	2.50
241 Mack Jones	1.00	2.50
242 George Brunet	1.00	2.50
243 Rookie Stars	1.50	4.00
Ted Davidson RC		
Tommy Helms RC		
244 Lindy McDaniel	1.50	4.00
245 Joe Pepitone	2.50	6.00
246 Tom Butters	1.50	4.00
247 Wally Moon	1.50	4.00
248 Gus Triandos	1.50	4.00
249 Dave McNally	1.50	4.00
250 Willie Mays	75.00	150.00
251 Billy Herman MG	1.50	4.00
252 Pete Richert	1.00	2.50
253 Danny Cater	1.00	2.50
254 Roland Sheldon	1.00	2.50
255 Camilo Pascual	1.50	4.00
256 Tito Francona	1.00	2.50
257 Jim Wynn	1.50	4.00
258 Larry Bearnarth	1.00	2.50
259 Rookie Stars	2.50	6.00
Jim Northrup RC		
Ray Oyler RC		
260 Don Drysdale	8.00	20.00
261 Duke Carmel	1.00	2.50
262 Bud Daley	1.00	2.50
263 Marty Keough	1.00	2.50
264 Bob Buhl	1.50	4.00
265 Jim Pagliaroni	1.00	2.50
266 Bert Campaneris RC	4.00	10.00
267 Washington Senators TC	2.50	6.00
268 Ken McBride	1.00	2.50
269 Frank Bolling	1.00	2.50
270 Milt Pappas	1.50	4.00
271 Don Wert	1.50	4.00
272 Chuck Schilling	1.00	2.50
273 Checklist 4	4.00	10.00
274 Lum Harris MG RC	1.00	2.50
275 Dick Groat	2.50	6.00
276 Hoyt Wilhelm	4.00	10.00
277 Johnny Lewis	1.00	2.50
278 Ken Retzer	1.00	2.50
279 Dick Tracewski	1.00	2.50
280 Dick Stuart	1.50	4.00
281 Bill Stafford	1.00	2.50
282 Rookie Stars	15.00	40.00
Dick Estelle RC		
Masanori Murakami RC		
283 Fred Whitfield	1.00	2.50
284 Nick Willhite	1.50	4.00
285 Ron Hunt	1.50	4.00
286 Rookie Stars	1.50	4.00
Jim Dickson		
Aurelio Monteagudo		
287 Gary Kolb	1.50	4.00
288 Jack Hamilton	1.50	4.00
289 Gordy Coleman	2.50	6.00
290 Wally Bunker	2.50	6.00
291 Jerry Lynch	1.50	4.00
292 Larry Yellen	1.50	4.00
293 Los Angeles Angels TC	2.50	6.00
294 Tim McCarver	4.00	10.00
295 Dick Radatz	2.50	6.00
296 Tony Taylor	2.50	6.00
297 Dave DeBusschere	4.00	10.00
298 Jim Stewart	1.50	4.00
299 Jerry Zimmerman	1.50	4.00
300 Sandy Koufax	50.00	100.00

Card	Low	High
301 Birdie Tebbetts MG	2.50	6.00
302 Al Stanek	1.50	4.00
303 John Orsino	1.50	4.00
304 Dave Stenhouse	1.50	4.00
305 Rico Carty	2.50	6.00
306 Bubba Phillips	1.50	4.00
307 Barry Latman	1.50	4.00
308 Rookie Stars	2.50	6.00
Cleon Jones RC		
Tom Parsons		
309 Steve Hamilton	2.50	6.00
310 Johnny Callison	2.50	6.00
311 Orlando Pena	1.50	4.00
312 Joe Nuxhall	1.50	4.00
313 Jim Schaffer	1.50	4.00
314 Sterling Slaughter	1.50	4.00
315 Frank Malzone	2.50	6.00
316 Cincinnati Reds TC	2.50	6.00
317 Don McMahon	1.50	4.00
318 Matty Alou	2.50	6.00
319 Ken McMullen	1.50	4.00
320 Bob Gibson	20.00	50.00
321 Rusty Staub	4.00	10.00
322 Rick Wise	2.50	6.00
323 Hank Bauer MG	2.50	6.00
324 Bobby Locke	1.50	4.00
325 Donn Clendenon	2.50	6.00
326 Dwight Siebler	1.50	4.00
327 Denis Menke	1.50	4.00
328 Eddie Fisher	1.50	4.00
329 Hawk Taylor RC	1.50	4.00
330 Whitey Ford	15.00	40.00
331 Rookie Stars	2.50	6.00
Al Ferrara		
John Purdin RC		
332 Ted Abernathy	1.50	4.00
333 Tom Reynolds	1.50	4.00
334 Vic Roznovsky RC	1.50	4.00
335 Mickey Lolich	2.50	6.00
336 Woody Held	1.50	4.00
337 Mike Cuellar	2.50	6.00
338 Philadelphia Phillies TC	2.50	6.00
339 Ryne Duren	2.50	6.00
340 Tony Oliva	8.00	20.00
341 Bob Bolin	1.50	4.00
342 Bob Rodgers	2.50	6.00
343 Mike McCormick	2.50	6.00
344 Wes Parker	2.50	6.00
345 Floyd Robinson	1.50	4.00
346 Bobby Bragan MG	1.50	4.00
347 Roy Face	2.50	6.00
348 George Banks	1.50	4.00
349 Larry Miller RC	1.50	4.00
350 Mickey Mantle	300.00	600.00
351 Jim Perry	2.50	6.00
352 Alex Johnson RC	2.50	6.00
353 Jerry Lumpe	1.50	4.00
354 Rookie Stars	1.50	4.00
Billy Ott RC		
Jack Warner RC		
355 Vada Pinson	4.00	10.00
356 Bill Spanswick	1.50	4.00
357 Carl Warwick	1.50	4.00
358 Albie Pearson	2.50	6.00
359 Ken Johnson	1.50	4.00
360 Orlando Cepeda	6.00	15.00
361 Checklist 5	5.00	12.00
362 Don Schwall	1.50	4.00
363 Bob Johnson	1.50	4.00
364 Galen Cisco	1.50	4.00
365 Jim Gentile	2.50	6.00
366 Dan Schneider	1.50	4.00
367 Leon Wagner	1.50	4.00
368 Rookie Stars	2.50	6.00
Ken Berry RC		
Joel Gibson RC		
369 Phil Linz	2.50	6.00
370 Tommy Davis	2.50	6.00
371 Frank Kreutzer	3.00	8.00
372 Clay Dalrymple	3.00	8.00
373 Curt Simmons	3.00	8.00
374 Rookie Stars	3.00	8.00
Jose Cardenal RC		
Dick Simpson		
375 Dave Wickersham	3.00	8.00
376 Jim Landis	3.00	8.00
377 Willie Stargell	10.00	25.00
378 Chuck Estrada	3.00	8.00
379 San Francisco Giants TC	3.00	8.00
380 Rocky Colavito	10.00	25.00
381 Al Jackson	3.00	8.00
382 J.C. Martin	3.00	8.00
383 Felipe Alou	6.00	15.00
384 Johnny Klippstein	3.00	8.00
385 Carl Yastrzemski	30.00	60.00
386 Rookie Stars	3.00	8.00
Paul Jaeckel RC		
Fred Norman		
387 Johnny Podres	6.00	15.00
388 John Blanchard	6.00	15.00
389 Don Larsen	6.00	15.00
390 Bill Freehan	6.00	15.00
391 Mel McGaha MG	3.00	8.00
392 Bob Friend	6.00	15.00
393 Ed Kirkpatrick	3.00	8.00
394 Jim Hannan	3.00	8.00
395 Jim Ray Hart	3.00	8.00
396 Frank Bertaina RC	3.00	8.00
397 Jerry Buchek	3.00	8.00
398 Rookie Stars	6.00	15.00
Dan Neville RC		
Art Shamsky RC		
399 Ray Herbert	3.00	8.00
400 Harmon Killebrew	20.00	50.00
401 Carl Willey	3.00	8.00
402 Joe Amalfitano	3.00	8.00
403 Boston Red Sox TC	3.00	8.00
404 Stan Williams	3.00	8.00
(Listed as Indian		
but Yankee cap)		
405 John Roseboro	8.00	20.00
406 Ralph Terry	6.00	15.00
407 Lee Maye	3.00	8.00
408 Larry Sherry	3.00	8.00
409 Rookie Stars	6.00	15.00
Jim Beauchamp		
Larry Dierker RC		
410 Luis Aparicio	10.00	25.00
411 Roger Craig	6.00	15.00
412 Bob Bailey	3.00	8.00
413 Hal Reniff	3.00	8.00
414 Al Lopez MG	6.00	15.00
415 Curt Flood	6.00	15.00
416 Jim Brewer	3.00	8.00
417 Ed Brinkman	3.00	8.00
418 Johnny Edwards	3.00	8.00
419 Ruben Amaro	3.00	8.00
420 Larry Jackson	3.00	8.00
421 Rookie Stars	3.00	8.00
Gary Dotter RC		
Jay Ward		
422 Aubrey Gatewood	3.00	8.00
423 Jesse Gonder	3.00	8.00
424 Gary Bell	3.00	8.00
425 Wayne Causey	3.00	8.00
426 Milwaukee Braves TC	3.00	8.00
427 Bob Saverine	3.00	8.00
428 Bob Shaw	3.00	8.00
429 Don Demeter	3.00	8.00
430 Gary Peters	3.00	8.00
431 Rookie Stars	6.00	15.00
Nelson Briles RC		
Wayne Spiezio RC		
432 Jim Grant	6.00	15.00
433 John Bateman	3.00	8.00
434 Dave Morehead	3.00	8.00
435 Willie Davis	6.00	15.00
436 Don Elston	3.00	8.00
437 Chico Cardenas	6.00	15.00
438 Harry Walker MG	3.00	8.00
439 Moe Drabowsky	6.00	15.00
440 Tom Tresh	6.00	15.00
441 Denny Lemaster	3.00	8.00
442 Vic Power	3.00	8.00
443 Checklist 6	5.00	12.00
444 Bob Hendley	3.00	8.00
445 Don Lock	3.00	8.00
446 Art Mahaffey	3.00	8.00
447 Julian Javier	6.00	15.00
448 Lee Stange	3.00	8.00
449 Rookie Stars	6.00	15.00
Jerry Hinsley		
Gary Kroll RC		
450 Elston Howard	6.00	15.00
451 Jim Owens	3.00	8.00
452 Gary Geiger	3.00	8.00
453 Rookie Stars	6.00	15.00
Willie Crawford RC		
John Werhas		
454 Ed Rakow	3.00	8.00
455 Norm Siebern	3.00	8.00
456 Bill Henry	3.00	8.00
457 Bob Kennedy MG	6.00	15.00
458 John Buzhardt	3.00	8.00
459 Frank Kostro	3.00	8.00
460 Richie Allen	15.00	40.00
461 Rookie Stars	20.00	50.00
Clay Carroll RC		
Phil Niekro		
462 Lew Krausse UER	3.00	8.00
(Photo actually		
Pete Lovrich)		
463 Manny Mota	6.00	15.00
464 Ron Piche	3.00	8.00
465 Tom Haller	6.00	15.00
466 Rookie Stars	3.00	8.00
Pete Craig RC		
Dick Nen		
467 Ray Washburn	3.00	8.00
468 Larry Brown	3.00	8.00
469 Don Nottebart	3.00	8.00
470 Yogi Berra P/CO	20.00	50.00
471 Billy Hoeft	3.00	8.00
472 Don Pavletich UER	3.00	8.00
Listed as a pitcher		
473 Rookie Stars	6.00	15.00
Paul Blair RC		
Davey Johnson RC		
474 Cookie Rojas	6.00	15.00
475 Clete Boyer	6.00	15.00
476 Billy O'Dell	3.00	8.00
477 Rookie Stars	100.00	200.00
Fritz Ackley		
Steve Carlton RC		
478 Wilbur Wood	6.00	15.00
479 Ken Harrelson	6.00	15.00
480 Joel Horlen	3.00	8.00
481 Cleveland Indians TC	4.00	10.00
482 Bob Priddy	3.00	8.00
483 George Smith RC	3.00	8.00
484 Ron Perranoski	8.00	20.00
485 Nellie Fox P/CO	10.00	25.00
486 Rookie Stars	3.00	8.00
Tom Egan RC		
Pat Rogan RC		
487 Woody Woodward	6.00	15.00
488 Ted Wills	3.00	8.00
489 Gene Mauch MG	6.00	15.00
490 Earl Battey	3.00	8.00
491 Tracy Stallard	3.00	8.00
492 Gene Freese	3.00	8.00
493 Rookie Stars	3.00	8.00
Bill Roman RC		
Bruce Brubaker RC		
494 Jay Ritchie RC	3.00	8.00
495 Joe Christopher	3.00	8.00
496 Joe Cunningham	3.00	8.00
497 Rookie Stars	6.00	15.00
Ken Henderson RC		
Jack Hiatt RC		
498 Gene Stephens	3.00	8.00
499 Stu Miller	6.00	15.00
500 Eddie Mathews	15.00	40.00
501 Rookie Stars	3.00	8.00
Ralph Gagliano RC		
Jim Rittwage RC		
502 Don Cardwell	3.00	8.00
503 Phil Gagliano	3.00	8.00
504 Jerry Grote	6.00	15.00
505 Ray Culp	3.00	8.00
506 Sam Mele MG	3.00	8.00
507 Sammy Ellis	3.00	8.00
508 Checklist 7	5.00	12.00
509 Rookie Stars	3.00	8.00
Bob Guindon RC		
Gerry Vezendy RC		
510 Ernie Banks	40.00	80.00
511 Ron Locke	3.00	8.00
512 Cap Peterson	3.00	8.00
513 New York Yankees TC	15.00	40.00
514 Joe Azcue	3.00	8.00
515 Vern Law	6.00	15.00
516 Al Weis	3.00	8.00
517 Rookie Stars	6.00	15.00
Paul Schaal RC		
Jack Warner		
518 Ken Rowe	3.00	8.00
519 Bob Uecker UER	12.50	30.00
(Posing as a left-		
handed batter)		
520 Tony Cloninger	3.00	8.00
521 Rookie Stars	3.00	8.00
Dave Bennett		
Morrie Stevens RC		
522 Hank Aguirre	3.00	8.00
523 Mike Brumley SP	5.00	12.00
524 Dave Giusti SP	5.00	12.00
525 Eddie Bressoud	3.00	8.00
526 Rookie Stars	40.00	80.00
Rene Lachemann RC		
Johnny Odom RC		
Jim Hunter RC		
(UER Tim on back)		
Skip Lockwood RC SP		
527 Jeff Torborg SP	5.00	12.00
528 George Altman	3.00	8.00
529 Jerry Fosnow SP RC	5.00	12.00
530 Jim Maloney	6.00	15.00
531 Chuck Hiller	3.00	8.00
532 Hector Lopez	6.00	15.00
533 Rookie Stars	10.00	25.00
Dan Napoleon RC		
Ron Swoboda RC		
Tug McGraw RC		
Jim Bethke RC SP		
534 John Herrnstein	3.00	8.00
535 Jack Kralick SP	5.00	12.00
536 Andre Rodgers SP	5.00	12.00
537 Rookie Stars	3.00	8.00
Marcelino Lopez		
Phil Roof		
Rudy May RC		
538 Chuck Dressen MG SP	5.00	12.00
539 Herm Starrette	3.00	8.00
540 Lou Brock SP	20.00	50.00
541 Rookie Stars	3.00	8.00
Greg Bollo RC		
Bob Locker RC		
542 Lou Klimchock	3.00	8.00
543 Ed Connolly SP RC	5.00	12.00
544 Howie Reed RC	3.00	8.00
545 Jesus Alou SP	6.00	15.00
546 Rookie Stars	3.00	8.00
Bill Davis RC		
Mike Hedlund RC		
Ray Barker		
Floyd Weaver RC		
547 Jake Wood SP	5.00	12.00
548 Dick Stigman	3.00	8.00
549 Rookie Stars	8.00	20.00
Roberto Pena RC		
Glenn Beckert RC		
550 Mel Stottlemyre SP RC	12.50	30.00
551 New York Mets TC SP	12.50	30.00
552 Julio Gotay	3.00	8.00
553 Rookie Stars	3.00	8.00
Dan Coombs RC		
Gene Ratliff RC		
Jack McClure RC		
554 Chico Ruiz SP	5.00	12.00
555 Jack Baldschun SP	5.00	12.00
556 Red Schoendienst MG SP	10.00	25.00
557 Jose Santiago RC	3.00	8.00
558 Tommie Sisk	3.00	8.00
559 Ed Bailey SP	5.00	12.00
560 Boog Powell SP	10.00	25.00
561 Rookie Stars	6.00	15.00
Dennis Daboll RC		
Mike Kekich RC		
Hector Valle RC		
Jim Lefebvre RC		
562 Billy Moran	3.00	8.00
563 Julio Navarro	3.00	8.00
564 Mel Nelson	3.00	8.00
565 Ernie Broglio SP	5.00	12.00
566 Rookie Stars	5.00	12.00
Gil Blanco RC		
Ross Moschitto RC		
Art Lopez RC SP		
567 Tommie Aaron	3.00	8.00
568 Ron Taylor SP	5.00	12.00
569 Gino Cimoli SP	5.00	12.00
570 Claude Osteen SP	6.00	15.00
571 Ossie Virgil SP	5.00	12.00
572 Baltimore Orioles TC SP	10.00	25.00
573 Rookie Stars	10.00	25.00
Jim Lonborg RC		
Gerry Moses RC		
Bill Schlesinger RC		
Mike Ryan RC SP		
574 Roy Sievers	6.00	15.00
575 Jose Pagan	3.00	8.00
576 Terry Fox SP	5.00	12.00
577 Rookie Stars	5.00	12.00
Darold Knowles		
Don Buschhorn RC		
Richie Scheinblum RC SP		
578 Camilo Carreon SP	5.00	12.00
579 Dick Smith SP	5.00	12.00
580 Jimmie Hall SP	5.00	12.00
581 Rookie Stars	40.00	80.00
Tony Perez RC		
Dave Ricketts RC		
Kevin Collins RC SP		
582 Bob Schmidt SP	5.00	12.00
583 Wes Covington SP	5.00	12.00
584 Harry Bright	6.00	15.00
585 Hank Fischer	3.00	8.00
586 Tom McCraw SP UER	5.00	12.00
Name is spelled McGraw on the back		
587 Joe Sparma	3.00	8.00
588 Lenny Green	3.00	8.00
589 Rookie Stars	5.00	12.00
Frank Linzy RC		
Bob Schroder RC SP		
590 John Wyatt	3.00	8.00
591 Bob Skinner SP	5.00	12.00
592 Frank Bork SP RC	5.00	12.00
593 Rookie Stars	5.00	12.00
Jackie Moore RC		
John Sullivan RC SP		
594 Joe Gaines	3.00	8.00
595 Don Lee	3.00	8.00
596 Don Landrum SP	5.00	12.00
597 Rookie Stars	3.00	8.00
Joe Nossek		
John Sevcik RC		
Dick Reese RC		
598 Al Downing SP	10.00	25.00

1965 Topps Embossed

The cards in this 72-card set measure approximately 2 1/8" by 3 1/2". The 1965 Topps Embossed set contains gold foil cameo player portraits. Each league had 36 representatives set on blue backgrounds for the AL and red backgrounds for the NL. The Topps embossed set was distributed as inserts in packages of the regular 1965 baseball series.

Card	Low	High
COMPLETE SET (72)	150.00	300.00
1 Carl Yastrzemski	4.00	10.00
2 Ron Fairly	.75	2.00
3 Max Alvis	.75	2.00
4 Jim Ray Hart	.75	2.00
5 Bill Skowron	1.25	3.00
6 Ed Kranepool	.75	2.00
7 Tim McCarver	1.25	3.00
8 Sandy Koufax	8.00	20.00
9 Donn Clendenon	.75	2.00
10 John Romano	.75	2.00
11 Mickey Mantle	50.00	100.00
12 Joe Torre	2.00	5.00
13 Al Kaline	4.00	10.00
14 Al McBean	.75	2.00
15 Don Drysdale	2.00	5.00
16 Brooks Robinson	4.00	10.00
17 Jim Bunning	1.25	3.00
18 Gary Peters	.75	2.00
19 Roberto Clemente	20.00	50.00
20 Milt Pappas	.75	2.00
21 Wayne Causey	.75	2.00
22 Frank Robinson	2.00	5.00
23 Bill Mazeroski	2.00	5.00
24 Diego Segui	.75	2.00
25 Jim Bouton	1.25	3.00
26 Eddie Mathews	2.50	6.00
27 Willie Mays	10.00	25.00
28 Ron Santo	1.25	3.00
29 Boog Powell	1.25	3.00
30 Ken McBride	.75	2.00
31 Leon Wagner	.75	2.00
32 Johnny Callison	.75	2.00
33 Zoilo Versalles	.75	2.00
34 Jack Baldschun	.75	2.00
35 Ron Hunt	.75	2.00
36 Richie Allen	2.00	5.00
37 Frank Malzone	.75	2.00
38 Bob Allison	.75	2.00
39 Jim Fregosi	1.25	3.00
40 Billy Williams	1.25	3.00
41 Bill Freehan	1.25	3.00
42 Vada Pinson	1.25	3.00
43 Bill White	1.25	3.00
44 Roy McMillan	.75	2.00
45 Orlando Cepeda	1.25	3.00
46 Rocky Colavito	2.00	5.00
47 Ken Boyer	1.25	3.00
48 Dick Radatz	.75	2.00
49 Tommy Davis	1.25	3.00
50 Walt Bond	.75	2.00
51 John Orsino	.75	2.00
52 Joe Christopher	.75	2.00
53 Al Spangler	.75	2.00
54 Jim King	.75	2.00
55 Mickey Lolich	1.25	3.00
56 Harmon Killebrew	2.50	6.00
57 Bob Shaw	.75	2.00
58 Ernie Banks	4.00	10.00
59 Hank Aaron	10.00	25.00
60 Chuck Hinton	.75	2.00
61 Bob Aspromonte	.75	2.00
62 Lee Maye	.75	2.00
63 Joe Cunningham	.75	2.00
64 Pete Ward	.75	2.00
65 Bobby Richardson	1.25	3.00
66 Dean Chance	.75	2.00
67 Dick Ellsworth	.75	2.00
68 Jim Maloney	.75	2.00
69 Bob Gibson	2.00	5.00
70 Earl Battey	.75	2.00
71 Tony Kubek	1.25	3.00
72 Jack Kralick	.75	2.00

1965 Topps Transfers Inserts

The 1965 Topps transfers (2" by 3") were issued in series of 24 each as inserts in three of the regular 1965 Topps cards series. Thirty-six of the transfers feature blue bands at the top and bottom while 36 feature red bands at the top and bottom. The team name and position are listed in the top band while the player's name is listed in the bottom band. Transfers 1-36 have blue panels whereas 37-72 have red panels. These unnumbered transfers are ordered below alphabetically by player's name within each color group. Transfers of Bob Veale and Carl Yastrzemski are supposedly tougher to find than the others in the set; they are marked below by SP.

Card	Low	High
COMPLETE SET (72)	200.00	400.00
1 Bob Allison	1.00	2.50
2 Max Alvis	1.00	2.50
3 Luis Aparicio	2.50	6.00
4 Walt Bond	1.00	2.50
5 Jim Bouton	1.50	4.00
6 Jim Bunning	2.50	6.00
7 Rico Carty	1.50	4.00
8 Wayne Causey	1.00	2.50
9 Orlando Cepeda	2.50	6.00
10 Dean Chance	1.00	2.50
11 Tony Conigliaro	1.50	4.00
12 Bill Freehan	1.50	4.00
13 Jim Fregosi	1.50	4.00
14 Bob Gibson	4.00	10.00
15 Dick Groat	1.50	4.00
16 Tom Haller	1.00	2.50
17 Al Jackson	1.00	2.50
18 Bobby Knoop	1.00	2.50
19 Jim Maloney	1.50	4.00
20 Juan Marichal	2.50	6.00
21 Lee Maye	1.00	2.50
22 Jim O'Toole	1.00	2.50
23 Camilo Pascual	1.00	2.50
24 Vada Pinson	1.50	4.00
25 Juan Pizarro	1.00	2.50
26 Bobby Richardson	2.50	6.00
27 Bob Rodgers	1.00	2.50
28 John Roseboro	1.00	2.50
29 Dick Stuart	1.50	4.00
30 Luis Tiant	1.50	4.00
31 Joe Torre	2.50	6.00
32 Bob Veale SP	5.00	12.00
33 Leon Wagner	1.00	2.50
34 Dave Wickersham	1.00	2.50
35 Billy Williams	2.50	6.00
36 Carl Yastrzemski SP	20.00	50.00
37 Hank Aaron	15.00	40.00
38 Richie Allen	4.00	10.00
39 Bob Aspromonte	1.00	2.50
40 Ken Boyer	2.50	6.00
41 Johnny Callison	1.50	4.00
42 Dean Chance	1.00	2.50
43 Joe Christopher	1.00	2.50
44 Roberto Clemente	30.00	60.00
45 Rocky Colavito	4.00	10.00
46 Tommy Davis	1.50	4.00
47 Don Drysdale	4.00	10.00
48 Chuck Hinton	1.00	2.50
49 Elston Howard	2.50	6.00
50 Ron Hunt	1.00	2.50
51 Al Kaline	8.00	20.00
52 Harmon Killebrew	5.00	12.00
53 Jim King	1.00	2.50
54 Ron Kline	1.00	2.50
55 Sandy Koufax	15.00	40.00
56 Ed Kranepool	1.00	2.50
57 Mickey Mantle	60.00	120.00
58 Willie Mays	15.00	40.00
59 Bill Mazeroski	4.00	10.00
60 Tony Oliva	2.50	6.00
61 Milt Pappas	1.00	2.50
62 Gary Peters	1.00	2.50
63 Boog Powell	2.50	6.00
64 Dick Radatz	1.00	2.50
65 Brooks Robinson	8.00	20.00
66 Frank Robinson	4.00	10.00
67 Ron Santo	2.50	6.00
68 Diego Segui	1.00	2.50
69 Bill Skowron	1.50	4.00
70 Al Spangler	1.00	2.50
71 Pete Ward	1.00	2.50
72 Bill White	1.50	4.00

1966 Topps

The cards in this 598-card set measure 2 1/2" by 3 1/2". There are the same number of cards as in the 1965 set. Once again, the seventh series cards (523 to 598) are considered more difficult to obtain than the cards of any other series in the set. Within this last series there are 43 cards that were printed in lesser quantities than the other cards in that series; these shorter-printed cards are marked by SP in the checklist below. Among other ways, cards were issued in five-card nickel wax packs, 12-card dime cello packs which came 36 packs to a box and 12 boxes to a case. These cards were also issued in 36-card rack packs which cost 29 cents. These rack packs were issued 48 to a case. The only featured subset within this set is League Leaders (215-226). Noteworthy Rookie Cards in the set include Jim Palmer (126), Ferguson Jenkins (254), and Don Sutton (288). Jim Palmer is described in the bio (on his card back) as a left-hander.

Card	Low	High
COMPLETE SET (598)	2500.00	4000.00
COMMON CARD (1-109)	.60	1.50
COMMON (110-283)	.75	2.00
COMMON (284-370)	1.25	3.00
COMMON (371-446)	2.00	5.00
COMMON (447-522)	4.00	10.00
COMMON (523-598)	6.00	15.00
COMMON SP (523-598)	12.50	30.00
WRAPPER (5-CENT)	10.00	25.00
1 Willie Mays	125.00	250.00
2 Ted Abernathy	.60	1.50
3 Sam Mele MG	.60	1.50
4 Ray Culp	.60	1.50
5 Jim Fregosi	.75	2.00
6 Chuck Schilling	.60	1.50
7 Tracy Stallard	.60	1.50
8 Floyd Robinson	.60	1.50
9 Clete Boyer	.75	2.00
10 Tony Cloninger	.60	1.50
11 Rookie Stars	.60	1.50
Brant Alyea RC		
Pete Craig		
12 John Tsitouris	.60	1.50
13 Lou Johnson	.75	2.00
14 Norm Siebern	.60	1.50
15 Vern Law	.75	2.00
16 Larry Brown	.60	1.50
17 John Stephenson	.60	1.50
18 Roland Sheldon	.60	1.50
19 San Francisco Giants TC	2.00	5.00
20 Willie Horton	.75	2.00
21 Don Nottebart	.60	1.50
22 Joe Nossek	.60	1.50
23 Jack Sanford	.60	1.50
24 Don Kessinger RC	1.50	4.00
25 Pete Ward	.60	1.50
26 Ray Sadecki	.60	1.50
27 Rookie Stars	.60	1.50
Darold Knowles		
Andy Etchebarren RC		
28 Phil Niekro	8.00	20.00
29 Mike Brumley	.60	1.50
30 Pete Rose DP UER	50.00	100.00
1963 Hit total is wrong		
31 Jack Cullen	.75	2.00
32 Adolfo Phillips RC	.60	1.50
33 Jim Pagliaroni	.60	1.50
34 Checklist 1	3.00	8.00
35 Ron Swoboda	1.50	4.00
36 Jim Hunter DP	8.00	20.00
UER Stats say 1963 and 1964		
should be 1964 and 1965		
37 Billy Herman MG	.75	2.00
38 Ron Nischwitz	.60	1.50
39 Ken Henderson	.60	1.50
40 Jim Grant	.60	1.50
41 Don LeJohn RC	.60	1.50
42 Aubrey Gatewood	.60	1.50
43A Don Landrum	.75	2.00
(Dark button on pants		
showing)		
43B Don Landrum	8.00	20.00
(Button on pants		
partially airbrushed)		
43C Don Landrum	.75	2.00
(Button on pants		
not showing)		
44 Rookie Stars	.60	1.50
Bill Davis		
Tom Kelley		
45 Jim Gentile	.75	2.00
46 Howie Koplitz	.60	1.50
47 J.C. Martin	.60	1.50
48 Paul Blair	.75	2.00
49 Woody Woodward	.75	2.00
50 Mickey Mantle DP	175.00	350.00
51 Gordon Richardson RC	.60	1.50
52 Power Plus	1.50	4.00
Wes Covington		
Johnny Callison		
53 Bob Duliba	.60	1.50
54 Jose Pagan	.60	1.50
55 Ken Harrelson	.75	2.00
56 Sandy Valdespino	.60	1.50
57 Jim Lefebvre	.75	2.00
58 Dave Wickersham	.60	1.50
59 Cincinnati Reds TC	2.00	5.00
60 Curt Flood	1.50	4.00
61 Bob Bolin	.60	1.50
62A Merritt Ranew	.75	2.00
(With sold line)		
62B Merritt Ranew	12.50	30.00
(Without sold line)		
63 Jim Stewart	.60	1.50
64 Bob Bruce	.60	1.50
65 Leon Wagner	.60	1.50
66 Al Weis	.60	1.50
67 Rookie Stars	1.50	4.00
Cleon Jones		
Dick Selma RC		
68 Hal Reniff	.60	1.50
69 Ken Hamlin	.60	1.50
70 Carl Yastrzemski	12.50	30.00
71 Frank Carpin RC	.60	1.50
72 Tony Perez	10.00	25.00
73 Jerry Zimmerman	.60	1.50
74 Don Mossi	.75	2.00
75 Tommy Davis	.75	2.00
76 Red Schoendienst MG	1.50	4.00
77 John Orsino	.60	1.50
78 Frank Linzy	.60	1.50
79 Joe Pepitone	1.50	4.00
80 Richie Allen	2.50	6.00
81 Ray Oyler	.60	1.50
82 Bob Hendley	.60	1.50
83 Albie Pearson	.75	2.00
84 Rookie Stars	.60	1.50
Jim Beauchamp		
Dick Kelley		
85 Eddie Fisher	.60	1.50
86 John Bateman	.60	1.50
87 Dan Napoleon	.60	1.50
88 Fred Whitfield	.60	1.50
89 Ted Davidson	.60	1.50
90 Luis Aparicio	3.00	8.00
91A Bob Uecker TR	4.00	10.00
91B Bob Uecker NTR	15.00	40.00
92 New York Yankees TC	6.00	15.00
93 Jim Lonborg DP	.75	2.00
94 Matty Alou	.75	2.00
95 Pete Richert	.60	1.50
96 Felipe Alou	1.50	4.00
97 Jim Merritt RC	.60	1.50
98 Don Demeter	.60	1.50
99 Buc Belters	2.50	6.00
Willie Stargell		
Donn Clendenon		
100 Sandy Koufax	50.00	100.00
101A Checklist 2	6.00	15.00
(115 W. Spahn) ERR		
101B Checklist 2	4.00	10.00
(115 Bill Henry) COR		
102 Ed Kirkpatrick	.60	1.50
103A Dick Groat TR	.75	2.00
103B Dick Groat NTR	15.00	40.00
104A Alex Johnson TR	.75	2.00
104B Alex Johnson NTR	12.50	30.00
105 Milt Pappas	.75	2.00
106 Rusty Staub	1.50	4.00
107 Rookie Stars	.60	1.50
Larry Stahl RC		
Ron Tompkins RC		
108 Bobby Klaus	.60	1.50
109 Ralph Terry	.75	2.00
110 Ernie Banks	12.50	30.00
111 Gary Peters	.75	2.00
112 Manny Mota	1.50	4.00
113 Hank Aguirre	.75	2.00
114 Jim Gosger	.75	2.00
115 Bill Henry	.75	2.00
116 Walter Alston MG	2.50	6.00
117 Jake Gibbs	.75	2.00
118 Mike McCormick	.75	2.00
119 Art Shamsky	.75	2.00
120 Harmon Killebrew	6.00	15.00
121 Ray Herbert	.75	2.00
122 Joe Gaines	.75	2.00
123 Rookie Stars	.75	2.00
Frank Bork		
Jerry May		
124 Tug McGraw	1.50	4.00
125 Lou Brock	8.00	20.00
126 Jim Palmer RC	50.00	100.00
UER Described as		
lefthander on		
card back		
127 Ken Berry	.75	2.00
128 Jim Landis	.75	2.00
129 Jack Kralick	.75	2.00
130 Joe Torre	2.50	6.00
131 California Angels TC	2.00	5.00
132 Orlando Cepeda	3.00	8.00
133 Don McMahon	.75	2.00
134 Wes Parker	1.50	4.00
135 Dave Morehead	.75	2.00
136 Woody Held	.75	2.00
137 Pat Corrales	.75	2.00
138 Roger Repoz RC	.75	2.00
139 Rookie Stars	.75	2.00
Byron Browne RC		
Don Young RC		
140 Jim Maloney	1.50	4.00
141 Tom McCraw	.75	2.00
142 Don Dennis RC	.75	2.00
143 Jose Tartabull	1.50	4.00
144 Don Schwall	.75	2.00
145 Bill Freehan	1.50	4.00
146 George Altman	.75	2.00
147 Lum Harris MG	.75	2.00
148 Bob Johnson	.75	2.00
149 Dick Nen	.75	2.00
150 Rocky Colavito	3.00	8.00
151 Gary Wagner RC	.75	2.00
152 Frank Malzone	1.50	4.00
153 Rico Carty	1.50	4.00
154 Chuck Hiller	.75	2.00
155 Marcelino Lopez	.75	2.00
156 DP Combo	.75	2.00
Dick Schofield		
Hal Lanier		
157 Rene Lachemann	.75	2.00
158 Jim Brewer	.75	2.00
159 Chico Ruiz	.75	2.00
160 Whitey Ford	12.50	30.00
161 Jerry Lumpe	.75	2.00
162 Lee Maye	.75	2.00
163 Tito Francona	.75	2.00
164 Rookie Stars	1.50	4.00
Tommie Agee		
Marv Staehle		
165 Don Lock	.75	2.00
166 Chris Krug RC	.75	2.00
167 Boog Powell	2.50	6.00
168 Dan Osinski	.75	2.00
169 Duke Sims RC	.75	2.00
170 Cookie Rojas	1.50	4.00
171 Nick Willhite	.75	2.00
172 New York Mets TC	2.00	5.00
173 Al Spangler	.75	2.00
174 Ron Taylor	.75	2.00
175 Bert Campaneris	1.50	4.00
176 Jim Davenport	.75	2.00
177 Hector Lopez	.75	2.00
178 Bob Tillman	.75	2.00
179 Rookie Stars	1.50	4.00
Dennis Aust RC		
Bob Tolan		
180 Vada Pinson	1.50	4.00
181 Al Worthington	.75	2.00
182 Jerry Lynch	.75	2.00
183A Checklist 3	3.00	8.00
(Large print		
on front)		
183B Checklist 3	3.00	8.00
(Small print		
on front)		
184 Denis Menke	.75	2.00
185 Bob Buhl	1.50	4.00
186 Ruben Amaro	.75	2.00
187 Chuck Dressen MG	1.50	4.00
188 Al Luplow	.75	2.00
189 John Roseboro	1.50	4.00
190 Jimmie Hall	.75	2.00
191 Darrell Sutherland RC	.75	2.00
192 Vic Power	1.50	4.00
193 Dave McNally	1.50	4.00
194 Washington Senators TC	2.00	5.00
195 Joe Morgan	6.00	15.00
196 Don Pavletich	.75	2.00
197 Sonny Siebert	.75	2.00
198 Mickey Stanley RC	2.50	6.00
199 ChiSox Clubbers	1.50	4.00
Bill Skowron		
Johnny Romano		
Floyd Robinson		
200 Eddie Mathews	6.00	15.00
201 Jim Dickson	.75	2.00
202 Clay Dalrymple	.75	2.00
203 Jose Santiago	.75	2.00
204 Chicago Cubs TC	2.00	5.00
205 Tom Tresh	1.50	4.00
206 Al Jackson	.75	2.00
207 Frank Quilici RC	.75	2.00
208 Bob Miller	.75	2.00
209 Rookie Stars	1.50	4.00
Fritz Fisher		
John Hiller RC		
210 Bill Mazeroski	3.00	8.00
211 Frank Kreutzer	.75	2.00
212 Ed Kranepool	1.50	4.00
213 Fred Newman	.75	2.00
214 Tommy Harper	1.50	4.00
215 NL Batting Leaders	20.00	50.00
Bob Clemente		
Hank Aaron		
Willie Mays		
216 AL Batting Leaders	2.00	5.00
Tony Oliva		
Carl Yastrzemski		
Vic Davalillo		
217 NL Home Run Leaders	8.00	20.00
Willie Mays		
Willie McCovey		
Billy Williams		
218 AL Home Run Leaders	2.00	5.00
Tony Conigliaro		
Norm Cash		
Willie Horton		
219 NL RBI Leaders	5.00	12.00
Deron Johnson		
Frank Robinson		
Willie Mays		

220 AL RBI Leaders 2.00 5.00
Rocky Colavito
Willie Horton
Tony Oliva
221 NL ERA Leaders 5.00 12.00
Sandy Koufax
Juan Marichal
Vern Law
222 AL ERA Leaders 2.00 5.00
Sam McDowell
Eddie Fisher
Sonny Siebert
223 NL Pitching Leaders 5.00 12.00
Sandy Koufax
Tony Cloninger
Don Drysdale
224 AL Pitching Leaders 2.00 5.00
Jim Grant
Mel Stottlemyre
Jim Kaat
225 NL Strikeout Leaders 5.00 12.00
Sandy Koufax
Bob Veale
Bob Gibson
226 AL Strikeout Leaders 2.00 5.00
Sam McDowell
Mickey Lolich
Dennis McLain
Sonny Siebert
227 Russ Nixon .75 2.00
228 Larry Dierker 1.50 4.00
229 Hank Bauer MG 1.50 4.00
230 Johnny Callison 1.50 4.00
231 Floyd Weaver .75 2.00
232 Glenn Beckert 1.50 4.00
233 Dom Zanni .75 2.00
234 Rookie Stars 3.00 8.00
Rich Beck RC
Roy White RC
235 Don Cardwell .75 2.00
236 Mike Hershberger .75 2.00
237 Billy O'Dell .75 2.00
238 Los Angeles Dodgers TC 2.00 5.00
239 Orlando Pena .75 2.00
240 Earl Battey .75 2.00
241 Dennis Ribant .75 2.00
242 Jesus Alou .75 2.00
243 Nelson Briles 1.50 4.00
244 Rookie Stars .75 2.00
Chuck Harrison RC
Sonny Jackson
245 John Buzhardt .75 2.00
246 Ed Bailey .75 2.00
247 Carl Warwick .75 2.00
248 Pete Mikkelsen .75 2.00
249 Bill Rigney MG .75 2.00
250 Sammy Ellis .75 2.00
251 Ed Brinkman .75 2.00
252 Denny Lemaster .75 2.00
253 Don Wert .75 2.00
254 Rookie Stars 30.00 60.00
Fergie Jenkins RC
Bill Sorrell RC
255 Willie Stargell 8.00 20.00
256 Lew Krausse .75 2.00
257 Jeff Torborg 1.50 4.00
258 Dave Giusti .75 2.00
259 Boston Red Sox TC 2.00 5.00
260 Bob Shaw .75 2.00
261 Ron Hansen .75 2.00
262 Jack Hamilton .75 2.00
263 Tom Egan .75 2.00
264 Rookie Stars .75 2.00
Andy Kosco RC
Ted Uhlaender RC
265 Stu Miller 1.50 4.00
266 Pedro Gonzalez UER .75 2.00
(Misspelled Gonzales
on card back)
267 Joe Sparma .75 2.00
268 John Blanchard .75 2.00
269 Don Heffner MG .75 2.00
270 Claude Osteen 1.50 4.00
271 Hal Lanier .75 2.00
272 Jack Baldschun .75 2.00
273 Astro Aces 1.50 4.00
Bob Aspromonte
Rusty Staub
274 Buster Narum .75 2.00
275 Tim McCarver 1.50 4.00
276 Jim Bouton 1.50 4.00
277 George Thomas .75 2.00
278 Cal Koonce .75 2.00
279A Checklist 4 3.00 8.00
(Player's cap black)
279B Checklist 4 3.00 8.00
(Player's cap red)
280 Bobby Knoop .75 2.00
281 Bruce Howard .75 2.00
282 Johnny Lewis .75 2.00
283 Jim Perry 1.50 4.00
284 Bobby Wine 1.25 3.00
285 Luis Tiant 2.00 5.00
286 Gary Geiger 1.25 3.00
287 Jack Aker RC 1.25 3.00
288 Rookie Stars 30.00 60.00
Bill Singer RC
Don Sutton RC
289 Larry Sherry 1.25 3.00
290 Ron Santo 2.00 5.00
291 Moe Drabowsky 2.00 5.00
292 Jim Coker 1.25 3.00
293 Mike Shannon 2.00 5.00
294 Steve Ridzik 1.25 3.00
295 Jim Ray Hart 2.00 5.00
296 Johnny Keane MG 2.00 5.00
297 Jim Owens 1.25 3.00
298 Rico Petrocelli 2.00 5.00
299 Lou Burdette 2.00 5.00
300 Bob Clemente 75.00 150.00
301 Greg Bollo 1.25 3.00
302 Ernie Bowman 1.25 3.00
303 Cleveland Indians TC 2.00 5.00
304 John Hermstein 1.25 3.00
305 Camilo Pascual 2.00 5.00
306 Ty Cline 1.25 3.00
307 Clay Carroll 2.00 5.00
308 Tom Haller 2.00 5.00
309 Diego Segui 1.25 3.00
310 Frank Robinson 15.00 40.00
311 Rookie Stars 2.00 5.00
Tommy Helms
Dick Simpson
312 Bob Saverine 1.25 3.00
313 Chris Zachary 1.25 3.00
314 Hector Valle 1.25 3.00
315 Norm Cash 2.00 5.00
316 Jack Fisher 1.25 3.00
317 Dalton Jones 1.25 3.00
318 Harry Walker MG 1.25 3.00
319 Gene Freese 1.25 3.00
320 Bob Gibson 10.00 25.00
321 Rick Reichardt 1.25 3.00
322 Bill Faul 1.25 3.00
323 Ray Barker 1.25 3.00
324 John Boozer UER 1.25 3.00
1965 Record is incorrect
325 Vic Davalillo 1.25 3.00
326 Atlanta Braves TC 2.00 5.00
327 Bernie Allen 1.25 3.00
328 Jerry Grote 2.00 5.00
329 Pete Charton 1.25 3.00
330 Ron Fairly 2.00 5.00
331 Ron Herbel 1.25 3.00
332 Bill Bryan 1.25 3.00
333 Rookie Stars 1.25 3.00
Joe Coleman RC
Jim French RC
334 Marty Keough 1.25 3.00
335 Juan Pizarro 1.25 3.00
336 Gene Alley 2.00 5.00
337 Fred Gladding 1.25 3.00
338 Dal Maxvill 1.25 3.00
339 Del Crandall 2.00 5.00
340 Dean Chance 2.00 5.00
341 Wes Westrum MG 2.00 5.00
342 Bob Humphreys 1.25 3.00
343 Joe Christopher 1.25 3.00
344 Steve Blass 2.00 5.00
345 Bob Allison 2.00 5.00
346 Mike de la Hoz 1.25 3.00
347 Phil Regan 2.00 5.00
348 Baltimore Orioles TC 3.00 8.00
349 Cap Peterson 1.25 3.00
350 Mel Stottlemyre 3.00 8.00
351 Fred Valentine 1.25 3.00
352 Bob Aspromonte 1.25 3.00
353 Al McBean 1.25 3.00
354 Smoky Burgess 2.00 5.00
355 Wade Blasingame 1.25 3.00
356 Rookie Stars 1.25 3.00
Owen Johnson RC
Ken Sanders RC
357 Gerry Arrigo 1.25 3.00
358 Charlie Smith 1.25 3.00
359 Johnny Briggs 1.25 3.00
360 Ron Hunt 1.25 3.00
361 Tom Satriano 1.25 3.00
362 Gates Brown 2.00 5.00
363 Checklist 5 4.00 10.00
364 Nate Oliver 1.25 3.00
365 Roger Maris UER 20.00 50.00
Wrong birth year listed on card
366 Wayne Causey 1.25 3.00
367 Mel Nelson 1.25 3.00
368 Charlie Lau 2.00 5.00
369 Jim King 1.25 3.00
370 Chico Cardenas 1.25 3.00
371 Lee Stange 2.00 5.00
372 Harvey Kuenn 3.00 8.00
373 Rookie Stars 3.00 8.00
Jack Hiatt
Dick Estelle
374 Bob Locker 2.00 5.00
375 Donn Clendenon 3.00 8.00
376 Paul Schaal 2.00 5.00
377 Turk Farrell 2.00 5.00
378 Dick Tracewski 2.00 5.00
379 St. Louis Cardinals TC 4.00 10.00
380 Tony Conigliaro 4.00 10.00
381 Hank Fischer 2.00 5.00
382 Phil Roof 2.00 5.00
383 Jackie Brandt 2.00 5.00
384 Al Downing 3.00 8.00
385 Ken Boyer 4.00 10.00
386 Gil Hodges MG 3.00 8.00
387 Howie Reed 2.00 5.00
388 Don Mincher 2.00 5.00
389 Jim O'Toole 3.00 8.00
390 Brooks Robinson 20.00 50.00
391 Chuck Hinton 2.00 5.00
392 Rookie Stars 3.00 8.00
Bill Hands RC
Randy Hundley RC
393 George Brunet 2.00 5.00
394 Ron Brand 2.00 5.00
395 Len Gabrielson 2.00 5.00
396 Jerry Stephenson 2.00 5.00
397 Bill White 3.00 8.00
398 Danny Cater 2.00 5.00
399 Ray Washburn 2.00 5.00
400 Zoilo Versalles 3.00 8.00
401 Ken McMullen 2.00 5.00
402 Jim Hickman 2.00 5.00
403 Fred Talbot 2.00 5.00
404 Pittsburgh Pirates TC 4.00 10.00
405 Elston Howard 3.00 8.00
406 Joey Jay 2.00 5.00
407 John Kennedy 2.00 5.00
408 Lee Thomas 3.00 8.00
409 Billy Hoeft 2.00 5.00
410 Al Kaline 15.00 40.00
411 Gene Mauch MG 2.00 5.00
412 Sam Bowens 2.00 5.00
413 Johnny Romano 2.00 5.00
414 Dan Coombs 2.00 5.00
415 Max Alvis 2.00 5.00
416 Phil Ortega 2.00 5.00
417 Rookie Stars 2.00 5.00
Jim McGlothlin RC
Ed Sukla RC
418 Phil Gagliano 2.00 5.00
419 Mike Ryan 2.00 5.00
420 Juan Marichal 6.00 15.00
421 Roy McMillan 3.00 8.00
422 Ed Charles 2.00 5.00
423 Ernie Broglio 2.00 5.00
424 Rookie Stars 4.00 10.00
Lee May RC
Darrell Osteen RC
425 Bob Veale 3.00 8.00
426 Chicago White Sox TC 4.00 10.00
427 John Miller 2.00 5.00
428 Sandy Alomar 2.00 5.00
429 Bill Monbouquette 2.00 5.00
430 Don Drysdale 8.00 20.00
431 Walt Bond 2.00 5.00
432 Bob Heffner 2.00 5.00
433 Alvin Dark MG 3.00 8.00
434 Willie Kirkland 2.00 5.00
435 Jim Bunning 6.00 15.00
436 Julian Javier 3.00 8.00
437 Al Stanek 2.00 5.00
438 Willie Smith 2.00 5.00
439 Pedro Ramos 2.00 5.00
440 Deron Johnson 3.00 8.00
441 Tommie Sisk 2.00 5.00
442 Rookie Stars 2.00 5.00
Ed Barnowski RC
Eddie Watt RC
443 Bill Wakefield 1.25 3.00
444 Checklist 6 4.00 10.00
445 Jim Kaat 4.00 10.00
446 Mack Jones 2.00 5.00
447 Dick Ellsworth UER 6.00 15.00
(Photo actually
Ken Hubbs)
448 Eddie Stanky MG 4.00 10.00
449 Joe Moeller 4.00 10.00
450 Tony Oliva 6.00 15.00
451 Barry Latman 4.00 10.00
452 Joe Azcue 4.00 10.00
453 Ron Kline 4.00 10.00
454 Jerry Buchek 4.00 10.00
455 Mickey Lolich 6.00 15.00
456 Rookie Stars 4.00 10.00
Darrell Brandon RC
Joe Foy RC
457 Joe Gibbon 4.00 10.00
458 Manny Jiminez 4.00 10.00
459 Bill McCool 4.00 10.00
460 Curt Blefary 4.00 10.00
461 Roy Face 6.00 15.00
462 Bob Rodgers 4.00 10.00
463 Philadelphia Phillies TC 6.00 15.00
464 Larry Bearnarth 4.00 10.00
465 Don Buford 4.00 10.00
466 Ken Johnson 4.00 10.00
467 Vic Roznovsky 4.00 10.00
468 Johnny Podres 6.00 15.00
469 Rookie Stars 12.50 30.00
Bobby Murcer RC
Dooley Womack RC
470 Sam McDowell 6.00 15.00
471 Bob Skinner 4.00 10.00
472 Terry Fox 4.00 10.00
473 Rich Rollins 4.00 10.00
474 Dick Schofield 4.00 10.00
475 Dick Radatz 4.00 10.00
476 Bobby Bragan MG 4.00 10.00
477 Steve Barber 4.00 10.00
478 Tony Gonzalez 4.00 10.00
479 Jim Hannan 4.00 10.00
480 Dick Stuart 4.00 10.00
481 Bob Lee 4.00 10.00
482 Rookie Stars 4.00 10.00
John Boccabella
Dave Dowling
483 Joe Nuxhall 4.00 10.00
484 Wes Covington 4.00 10.00
485 Bob Bailey 4.00 10.00
486 Tommy John 6.00 15.00
487 Al Ferrara 4.00 10.00
488 George Banks 4.00 10.00
489 Curt Simmons 4.00 10.00
490 Bobby Richardson 10.00 25.00
491 Dennis Bennett 4.00 10.00
492 Kansas City Athletics TC 6.00 15.00
493 Johnny Klippstein 4.00 10.00
494 Gordy Coleman 4.00 10.00
495 Dick McAuliffe 6.00 15.00
496 Lindy McDaniel 4.00 10.00
497 Chris Cannizzaro 4.00 10.00
498 Rookie Stars 4.00 10.00
Luke Walker RC
Woody Fryman RC
499 Wally Bunker 4.00 10.00
500 Hank Aaron 60.00 120.00
501 John O'Donoghue 4.00 10.00
502 Lenny Green UER 4.00 10.00
Born: aJn. 6, 1933
503 Steve Hamilton 6.00 15.00
504 Grady Hatton MG 4.00 10.00
505 Jose Cardenal 4.00 10.00
506 Bo Belinsky 6.00 15.00
507 Johnny Edwards 4.00 10.00
508 Steve Hargan RC 6.00 15.00
509 Jake Wood 4.00 10.00
510 Hoyt Wilhelm 10.00 25.00
511 Rookie Stars 4.00 10.00
Bob Barton RC
Tito Fuentes RC
512 Dick Stigman 4.00 10.00
513 Camilo Carreon 4.00 10.00
514 Hal Woodeshick 4.00 10.00
515 Frank Howard 6.00 15.00
516 Eddie Bressoud 4.00 10.00
517A Checklist 7 6.00 15.00
529 White Sox Rookies
544 Cardinals Rookies
517B Checklist 7 6.00 15.00
529 W. Sox Rookies
544 Cards Rookies
518 Rookie Stars 4.00 10.00
Herb Hippauf RC
Arnie Umbach RC
519 Bob Friend 6.00 15.00
520 Jim Wynn 6.00 15.00
521 John Wyatt 4.00 10.00
522 Phil Linz 4.00 10.00
523 Bob Sadowski 4.00 10.00
524 Rookie Stars 12.50 30.00
Ollie Brown RC
Don Mason RC SP
525 Gary Bell SP 12.50 30.00
526 Minnesota Twins TC SP 50.00 100.00
527 Julio Navarro 6.00 15.00
528 Jesse Gonder SP 12.50 30.00
529 Rookie Stars 6.00 15.00
Lee Elia RC
Dennis Higgins RC
Bill Voss RC
530 Robin Roberts 20.00 50.00
531 Joe Cunningham 6.00 15.00
532 A.Monteagudo SP 12.50 30.00
533 Jerry Adair SP 12.50 30.00
534 Rookie Stars 6.00 15.00
Dave Eilers RC
Rob Gardner RC
535 Willie Davis SP 15.00 40.00
536 Dick Egan 6.00 15.00
537 Herman Franks MG 6.00 15.00
538 Bob Allen SP 12.50 30.00
539 Rookie Stars 10.00 25.00
Bill Heath RC
Carroll Sembera RC
540 Denny McLain SP 30.00 60.00
541 Gene Oliver SP 12.50 30.00
542 George Smith 6.00 15.00
543 Roger Craig SP 12.50 30.00
544 Rookie Stars 12.50 30.00
Joe Hoerner
George Kernek RC
Jimy Williams RC SP
(UER Misspelled Jimmy
on card)
545 Dick Green SP 12.50 30.00
546 Dwight Siebler 10.00 25.00
547 Horace Clarke SP RC 15.00 40.00
548 Gary Kroll SP 12.50 30.00
549 Rookie Stars 6.00 15.00
Al Closter RC
Casey Cox RC
550 Willie McCovey SP 50.00 100.00
551 Bob Purkey SP 12.50 30.00
552 B.Tebbetts MG SP 12.50 30.00
553 Rookie Stars 6.00 15.00
Pat Garrett RC
Jackie Warner
554 Jim Northrup SP 12.50 30.00
555 Ron Perranoski SP 12.50 30.00
556 Mel Queen SP 12.50 30.00
557 Felix Mantilla SP 12.50 30.00
558 Rookie Stars 8.00 20.00
Guido Grilli RC
Pete Magrini RC
George Scott RC
559 Roberto Pena SP 12.50 30.00
560 Joel Horlen 6.00 15.00
561 Choo Choo Coleman SP 12.50 30.00
562 Russ Snyder 10.00 25.00
563 Rookie Stars 6.00 15.00
Pete Cimino RC
Cesar Tovar RC
564 Bob Chance SP 12.50 30.00
565 Jimmy Piersall SP 15.00 40.00
566 Mike Cuellar SP 12.50 30.00
567 Dick Howser SP 15.00 40.00
568 Rookie Stars 6.00 15.00
Paul Lindblad RC
Ron Stone RC
569 Orlando McFarlane SP 12.50 30.00
570 Art Mahaffey SP 12.50 30.00
571 Dave Roberts SP 12.50 30.00
572 Bob Priddy 6.00 15.00
573 Derrell Griffith 6.00 15.00
574 Rookie Stars 6.00 15.00
Bill Hepler RC
Bill Murphy RC
575 Earl Wilson 6.00 15.00
576 Dave Nicholson SP 12.50 30.00
577 Jack Lamabe SP 12.50 30.00
578 Chi Chi Olivo SP RC 12.50 30.00
579 Rookie Stars 8.00 20.00
Frank Bertaina
Gene Brabender RC
Dave Johnson
580 Billy Williams SP 30.00 60.00
581 Tony Martinez 6.00 15.00
582 Garry Roggenburk 6.00 15.00
583 Detroit Tigers TC SP 60.00 120.00
UER Text on back states Tigers
finished third in 1965 instead
of fourth
584 Rookie Stars 6.00 15.00
Frank Fernandez RC
Fritz Peterson RC
585 Tony Taylor 10.00 25.00
586 Claude Raymond SP 12.50 30.00
587 Dick Bertell 6.00 15.00
588 Rookie Stars 6.00 15.00
Chuck Dobson RC
Ken Suarez RC
589 Lou Klimchock SP 12.50 30.00
590 Bill Skowron SP 15.00 40.00
591 Rookie Stars 15.00 40.00
Bart Shirley RC
Grant Jackson RC SP
592 Andre Rodgers 6.00 15.00
593 Doug Camilli SP 12.50 30.00
594 Chico Salmon 6.00 15.00
595 Larry Jackson 6.00 15.00
596 Rookie Stars 12.50 30.00
Nate Colbert RC
Greg Sims RC SP
597 John Sullivan 6.00 15.00
598 Gaylord Perry SP 100.00 200.00

1966 Topps Rub-Offs

There are 120 "rub-offs" in the Topps insert set of 1966, of which 100 depict players and the remaining 20 show team pennants. Each rub off measures 2 1/16" by 3". The color player photos are vertical while the team pennants are horizontal; both types of transfer have a large black printer's mark. These rub-offs were originally printed in rolls of 20 and are frequently still found this way. These rub-offs were issued one per wax pack and three per rack pack. Since these rub-offs are unnumbered, they are ordered below alphabetically within type, players (1-100) and team pennants (101-120).

COMPLETE SET (120) 200.00 400.00
COMMON (1-100) .60 1.50
COMMON (101-120) .40 1.00
1 Hank Aaron 10.00 25.00
2 Jerry Adair .60 1.50
3 Richie Allen .75 2.00
4 Jesus Alou .75 2.00
5 Max Alvis .60 1.50
6 Bob Aspromonte .60 1.50
7 Ernie Banks 4.00 10.00
8 Earl Battey .60 1.50
9 Curt Blefary .60 1.50
10 Ken Boyer 1.25 3.00
11 Bob Bruce .60 1.50
12 Jim Bunning 1.25 3.00
13 Johnny Callison .75 2.00
14 Bert Campaneris .75 2.00
15 Jose Cardenal .60 1.50
16 Dean Chance .75 2.00
17 Ed Charles .60 1.50
18 Roberto Clemente 30.00 60.00
19 Tony Cloninger .60 1.50
20 Rocky Colavito 2.00 5.00
21 Tony Conigliaro .75 2.00
22 Vic Davalillo .60 1.50
23 Willie Davis .75 2.00
24 Don Drysdale 2.00 5.00
25 Sammy Ellis .60 1.50
26 Dick Ellsworth .60 1.50
27 Ron Fairly .75 2.00
28 Dick Farrell .60 1.50
29 Eddie Fisher .60 1.50
30 Jack Fisher .60 1.50
31 Curt Flood .75 2.00
32 Whitey Ford 2.00 5.00
33 Bill Freehan .75 2.00
34 Jim Fregosi .75 2.00
35 Bob Gibson 2.00 5.00
36 Jim Grant .60 1.50
37 Jimmie Hall .60 1.50
38 Ken Harrelson .75 2.00
39 Jim Ray Hart .60 1.50
40 Joel Horlen .60 1.50
41 Willie Horton .75 2.00
42 Frank Howard .75 2.00
43 Deron Johnson .60 1.50
44 Al Kaline 4.00 10.00
45 Harmon Killebrew 3.00 8.00
46 Bobby Knoop .60 1.50
47 Sandy Koufax 8.00 20.00
48 Ed Kranepool .60 1.50
49 Gary Kroll .60 1.50
50 Don Landrum .60 1.50
51 Vern Law .75 2.00
52 Johnny Lewis .60 1.50
53 Don Lock .60 1.50
54 Mickey Lolich .75 2.00
55 Jim Maloney .75 2.00
56 Felix Mantilla .60 1.50
57 Mickey Mantle 30.00 60.00
58 Juan Marichal 2.00 5.00
59 Eddie Mathews 3.00 8.00
60 Willie Mays 10.00 25.00
61 Bill Mazeroski 2.00 5.00
62 Dick McAuliffe .60 1.50
63 Tim McCarver .75 2.00
64 Willie McCovey 2.00 5.00
65 Sam McDowell .60 1.50
66 Ken McMullen .60 1.50
67 Denis Menke .60 1.50
68 Bill Monbouquette .60 1.50
69 Joe Morgan 2.00 5.00
70 Fred Newman .60 1.50
71 John O'Donoghue .60 1.50
72 Tony Oliva 1.25 3.00
73 Johnny Orsino .60 1.50
74 Phil Ortega .60 1.50
75 Milt Pappas .75 2.00
76 Dick Radatz .75 2.00
77 Bobby Richardson 1.25 3.00
78 Pete Richert .60 1.50
79 Brooks Robinson 4.00 10.00
80 Floyd Robinson .60 1.50
81 Frank Robinson 2.00 5.00
82 Cookie Rojas .60 1.50
83 Pete Rose 12.50 30.00
84 John Roseboro .75 2.00
85 Ron Santo 1.25 3.00
86 Bill Skowron .75 2.00
87 Willie Stargell 2.00 5.00
88 Mel Stottlemyre .75 2.00
89 Dick Stuart .60 1.50
90 Ron Swoboda .75 2.00
91 Fred Talbot .60 1.50
92 Ralph Terry .60 1.50
93 Joe Torre 2.00 5.00
94 Tom Tresh 1.25 3.00
95 Bob Veale .60 1.50
96 Pete Ward .60 1.50
97 Bill White .75 2.00
98 Billy Williams 1.25 3.00
99 Jim Wynn .75 2.00
100 Carl Yastrzemski 5.00 12.00
101 Baltimore Orioles 1.00 2.50
102 Boston Red Sox 1.00 2.50
103 California Angels .40 1.00
104 Chicago Cubs .40 1.00
105 Chicago White Sox .40 1.00
106 Cincinnati Reds .40 1.00
107 Cleveland Indians .40 1.00
108 Detroit Tigers 1.00 2.50
109 Houston Astros .40 1.00
110 Kansas City Athletics .40 1.00
111 Los Angeles Dodgers 1.00 2.50
112 Atlanta Braves .40 1.00
113 Minnesota Twins .40 1.00
114 New York Mets 1.00 2.50
115 New York Yankees 1.50 4.00
116 Philadelphia Phillies .40 1.00
117 Pittsburgh Pirates .40 1.00
118 San Francisco Giants .40 1.00
119 St. Louis Cardinals .40 1.00
120 Washington Senators 1.00 2.50

1967 Topps

The cards in this 609-card set measure 2 1/2" by 3 1/2". The 1967 Topps series is considered by some collectors to be one of the company's finest accomplishments in baseball card production. Excellent color photographs are combined with easy-to-read backs. Cards 458 to 533 are slightly harder to find than numbers 1 to 457, and the inevitable high series (534 to 609) exists. Each checklist card features a small circular picture of a popular player included in that series. Printing discrepancies resulted in some high series cards being in shorter supply. The checklist below identifies (by DP) 22 double-printed high numbers; of the 76 cards in the last series, 54 cards were short printed and the other 22 cards are much more plentiful. Featured subsets within this set include World Series cards (151-155) and League Leaders (233-244). A limited number of "proof" Roger Maris cards were produced. These cards are blank backed and Maris is listed as a New York Yankee on it. Some Bob Bolin cards: (number 252) have a white smear in between his names. Another tough variation that has been recently discovered involves card number 58 Paul Schaal. The tough version has a green bat above his name. The key Rookie Cards in the set are high number cards of Rod Carew and Tom Seaver. Confirmed methods of selling these cards include five-card nickel wax packs. Although rarely seen, there exists a salesman's sample panel of three cards that pictures Earl Battey, Manny Mota, and Gene Brabender with ad information on the back about the "new" Topps cards.

COMPLETE SET (609) 2500.00 5000.00
COMMON CARD (1-109) .60 1.50
COMMON (110-283) .75 2.00
COMMON (284-370) 1.00 2.50
COMMON (371-457) 1.50 4.00
COMMON (458-533) 2.50 6.00
COMMON (534-609) 6.00 15.00
COMMON DP (534-609) 3.00 8.00
WRAPPER (5-CENT) 10.00 25.00
1 The Champs 10.00 25.00
Frank Robinson
Hank Bauer MG
Brooks Robinson DP
2 Jack Hamilton .60 1.50
3 Duke Sims .60 1.50
4 Hal Lanier .60 1.50
5 Whitey Ford UER 8.00 20.00
(1953 listed as
1933 in stats on back)
6 Dick Simpson .60 1.50
7 Don McMahon .60 1.50
8 Chuck Harrison .60 1.50
9 Ron Hansen .60 1.50
10 Matty Alou 1.50 4.00
11 Barry Moore RC .60 1.50
12 Rookie Stars 1.50 4.00
Jim Campanis RC
Bill Singer
13 Joe Sparma .60 1.50
14 Phil Linz 1.50 4.00
15 Earl Battey .60 1.50
16 Bill Hands .60 1.50
17 Jim Gosger .60 1.50
18 Gene Oliver .60 1.50
19 Jim McGlothlin .60 1.50
20 Orlando Cepeda 3.00 8.00
21 Dave Bristol MG RC .60 1.50
22 Gene Brabender .60 1.50
23 Larry Elliot .60 1.50
24 Bob Allen .60 1.50
25 Elston Howard 1.50 4.00
26A Bob Priddy NTR 12.50 30.00
26B Bob Priddy TR 1.50 4.00
27 Bob Saverine .60 1.50
28 Barry Latman .60 1.50
29 Tom McCraw .60 1.50
30 Al Kaline DP 8.00 20.00
31 Jim Brewer .60 1.50
32 Bob Bailey 1.50 4.00
33 Rookie Stars 2.50 6.00
Sal Bando RC
Randy Schwartz RC
34 Pete Cimino .60 1.50
35 Rico Carty 1.50 4.00
36 Bob Tillman .60 1.50
37 Rick Wise 1.50 4.00
38 Bob Johnson .60 1.50
39 Curt Simmons 1.50 4.00
40 Rick Reichardt .60 1.50
41 Joe Hoerner .60 1.50
42 New York Mets TC 4.00 10.00
43 Chico Salmon .60 1.50
44 Joe Nuxhall 1.50 4.00
45 Roger Maris 20.00 50.00
45A Roger Maris 900.00 1500.00
Yankees listed as team
Blank Back
46 Lindy McDaniel 1.50 4.00
47 Ken McMullen .60 1.50
48 Bill Freehan 1.50 4.00
49 Roy Face 1.50 4.00
50 Tony Oliva 2.50 6.00
51 Rookie Stars .60 1.50
Dave Adlesh RC
Wes Bales RC
52 Dennis Higgins .60 1.50
53 Clay Dalrymple .60 1.50
54 Dick Green .60 1.50
55 Don Drysdale 6.00 15.00
56 Jose Tartabull 1.50 4.00
57 Pat Jarvis RC 1.50 4.00
58A Paul Schaal 8.00 20.00
Green Bat
58B Paul Schaal .60 1.50
Normal Colored Bat
59 Ralph Terry 1.50 4.00
60 Luis Aparicio 3.00 8.00
61 Gordy Coleman .60 1.50
62 Frank Robinson CL1 3.00 8.00
63 Cards Clubbers 3.00 8.00
Lou Brock
Curt Flood
64 Fred Valentine .60 1.50
65 Tom Haller 1.50 4.00
66 Manny Mota 1.50 4.00
67 Ken Berry .60 1.50
68 Bob Buhl 1.50 4.00
69 Vic Davalillo .60 1.50
70 Ron Santo 2.50 6.00
71 Camilo Pascual 1.50 4.00
72 Rookie Stars .60 1.50
George Korince RC
(UER Photo is
James Murray Brown)
John (Tom) Matchick RC
73 Rusty Staub [illegible] [illegible]
74 Wes Stock .60 1.50
75 George Scott 1.50 4.00
76 Jim Barbieri RC .60 1.50
77 Dooley Womack 1.50 4.00
78 Pat Corrales .60 1.50
79 Bubba Morton .60 1.50
80 Jim Maloney 1.50 4.00
81 Eddie Stanky MG 1.50 4.00
82 Steve Barber .60 1.50
83 Ollie Brown .60 1.50
84 Tommie Sisk .60 1.50
85 Johnny Callison 1.50 4.00
86A Mike McCormick NTR 12.50 30.00
(Senators on front
and Senators on back)
86B Mike McCormick TR 1.50 4.00
(Traded line
at end of bio;
Senators on front,
but Giants on back)
87 George Altman .60 1.50
88 Mickey Lolich 1.50 4.00
89 Felix Millan RC 1.50 4.00
90 Jim Nash RC .60 1.50
91 Johnny Lewis .60 1.50
92 Ray Washburn .60 1.50
93 Rookie Stars 1.50 4.00
Stan Bahnsen RC
Bobby Murcer
94 Ron Fairly .60 1.50
95 Sonny Siebert .60 1.50
96 Art Shamsky .60 1.50
97 Mike Cuellar 1.50 4.00
98 Rich Rollins .60 1.50
99 Lee Stange .60 1.50
100 Frank Robinson DP 6.00 15.00
101 Ken Johnson .60 1.50
102 Philadelphia Phillies TC 1.50 4.00
103A Mickey Mantle CL2 DP 8.00 20.00
170 is D McAuliffe
103B Mickey Mantle CL2 DP
170 is D McAuliffe
104 Minnie Rojas RC .60 1.50
105 Ken Boyer 2.50 6.00
106 Randy Hundley 1.50 4.00
107 Joel Horlen .60 1.50
108 Alex Johnson 1.50 4.00
109 Tribe Thumpers 2.50 6.00
Rocky Colavito
Leon Wagner
110 Jack Aker 1.50 4.00
111 John Kennedy .75 2.00
112 Dave Wickersham .75 2.00
113 Dave Nicholson .75 2.00
114 Jack Baldschun .75 2.00
115 Paul Casanova RC .75 2.00
116 Herman Franks MG .75 2.00
117 Darrell Brandon .75 2.00
118 Bernie Allen .75 2.00
119 Wade Blasingame .75 2.00
120 Floyd Robinson .75 2.00
121 Eddie Bressoud .75 2.00
122 George Brunet .75 2.00
123 Rookie Stars 1.50 4.00
Jim Price RC
Luke Walker
124 Jim Stewart .75 2.00
125 Moe Drabowsky 1.50 4.00
126 Tony Taylor .75 2.00
127 John O'Donoghue .75 2.00
128 Ed Spiezio RC .75 2.00
129 Phil Roof .75 2.00
130 Phil Regan 1.50 4.00
131 New York Yankees TC 4.00 10.00
132 Ozzie Virgil .75 2.00
133 Ron Kline .75 2.00
134 Gates Brown 2.50 6.00
135 Deron Johnson 1.50 4.00
136 Carroll Sembera .75 2.00
137 Rookie Stars .75 2.00
Ron Clark RC
Jim Ollum
138 Dick Kelley .75 2.00
139 Dalton Jones 1.50 4.00
140 Willie Stargell 8.00 20.00
141 John Miller .75 2.00
142 Jackie Brandt .75 2.00
143 Sox Sockers .75 2.00
Pete Ward
Don Buford
144 Bill Hepler .75 2.00
145 Larry Brown .75 2.00
146 Steve Carlton 20.00 50.00
147 Tom Egan .75 2.00
148 Adolfo Phillips .75 2.00
149 Joe Moeller .75 2.00
150 Mickey Mantle 175.00 350.00
151 World Series Game 1 2.00 5.00
Moe Drabowsky
152 World Series Game 2 3.00 8.00
Jim Palmer
153 World Series Game 3 2.00 5.00
Paul Blair
154 World Series Game 4 2.00 5.00
Robinson/McNally
155 World Series Summary 2.00 5.00
Winners Celebrate
156 Ron Herbel .75 2.00
157 Danny Cater .75 2.00
158 Jimmie Coker .75 2.00
159 Bruce Howard .75 2.00
160 Willie Davis 1.50 4.00
161 Dick Williams MG 1.50 4.00
162 Billy O'Dell .75 2.00
163 Vic Roznovsky .75 2.00
164 Dwight Siebler UER .75 2.00
(Last line of stats
shows 1960 Minnesota)

165 Cleon Jones 1.50 4.00
166 Eddie Mathews 6.00 15.00
167 Rookie Stars .75 2.00
Joe Coleman RC
Tim Cullen RC
168 Ray Culp .75 2.00
169 Horace Clarke 1.50 4.00
170 Dick McAuliffe 1.50 4.00
171 Cal Koonce .75 2.00
172 Bill Heath .75 2.00
173 St. Louis Cardinals TC 1.50 4.00
174 Dick Radatz 1.50 4.00
175 Bobby Knoop .75 2.00
176 Sammy Ellis .75 2.00
177 Tito Fuentes .60 1.50
178 John Buzhardt .75 2.00
179 Rookie Stars 1.50 4.00
Charles Vaughan RC
Cecil Upshaw RC
180 Curt Blefary .75 2.00
181 Terry Fox .75 2.00
182 Ed Charles .75 2.00
183 Jim Pagliaroni .75 2.00
184 George Thomas .75 2.00
185 Ken Holtzman RC 1.50 4.00
186 Mets Maulers 1.50 4.00
Ed Kranepool
Ron Swoboda
187 Pedro Ramos .75 2.00
188 Ken Harrelson 1.50 4.00
189 Chuck Hinton .75 2.00
190 Turk Farrell .75 2.00
191A Willie Mays CL3 4.00 10.00
214 Tom Kelley
191B Willie Mays CL3 5.00 12.00
214 Dick Kelley
192 Fred Gladding .75 2.00
193 Jose Cardenal 1.50 4.00
194 Bob Allison 1.50 4.00
195 Al Jackson .75 2.00
196 Johnny Romano .75 2.00
197 Ron Perranoski 1.50 4.00
198 Chuck Hiller .75 2.00
199 Billy Hitchcock MG .75 2.00
200 Willie Mays UER 50.00 100.00
('63 Sna Francisco
on card back stats)
201 Hal Reniff 1.50 4.00
202 Johnny Edwards .75 2.00
203 Al McBean .75 2.00
204 Rookie Stars 2.50 6.00
Mike Epstein RC
Tom Phoebus RC
205 Dick Groat 1.50 4.00
206 Dennis Bennett .75 2.00
207 John Orsino .75 2.00
208 Jack Lamabe .75 2.00
209 Joe Nossek .75 2.00
210 Bob Gibson 8.00 20.00
211 Minnesota Twins TC 1.50 4.00
212 Chris Zachary .75 2.00
213 Jay Johnstone RC 1.50 4.00
214 Tom Kelley .75 2.00
215 Ernie Banks 8.00 20.00
216 Bengal Belters 3.00 8.00
Norm Cash
Al Kaline
217 Rob Gardner .75 2.00
218 Wes Parker 1.50 4.00
219 Clay Carroll 1.50 4.00
220 Jim Ray Hart 1.50 4.00
221 Woody Fryman 1.50 4.00
222 Rookie Stars 1.50 4.00
Darrell Osteen
Lee May
223 Mike Ryan 1.50 4.00
224 Walt Bond .75 2.00
225 Mel Stottlemyre 2.50 6.00
226 Julian Javier 1.50 4.00
227 Paul Lindblad .75 2.00
228 Gil Hodges MG 2.50 6.00
229 Larry Jackson .75 2.00
230 Boog Powell 2.50 6.00
231 John Bateman .75 2.00
232 Don Buford .75 2.00
233 AL ERA Leaders 1.50 4.00
Gary Peters
Joel Horlen
Steve Hargan
234 NL ERA Leaders 6.00 15.00
Sandy Koufax
Mike Cuellar
Juan Marichal
235 AL Pitching Leaders 2.50 6.00
Jim Kaat
Denny McLain
Earl Wilson
236 NL Pitching Leaders 10.00 25.00
Sandy Koufax
Juan Marichal
Bob Gibson
Gaylord Perry
237 AL Strikeout Leaders 2.50 6.00
Sam McDowell
Jim Kaat
Earl Wilson
238 NL Strikeout Leaders 5.00 12.00
Sandy Koufax
Jim Bunning
Bob Veale
239 AL Batting Leaders 4.00 10.00
Frank Robinson
Tony Oliva
Al Kaline
240 NL Batting Leaders 2.50 6.00
Matty Alou
Felipe Alou
Rico Carty
241 AL RBI Leaders 4.00 10.00
Frank Robinson
Harmon Killebrew
Boog Powell
242 NL RBI Leaders 10.00 25.00
Hank Aaron
Bob Clemente
Richie Allen
243 AL Home Run Leaders 4.00 10.00
Frank Robinson
Harmon Killebrew
Boog Powell
244 NL Home Run Leaders 8.00 20.00
Hank Aaron
Richie Allen
Willie Mays
245 Curt Flood 2.50 6.00
246 Jim Perry 1.50 4.00
247 Jerry Lumpe .75 2.00
248 Gene Mauch MG 1.50 4.00
249 Nick Willhite .75 2.00
250 Hank Aaron UER 40.00 80.00
(Second 1961 in stats
should be 1962)
251 Woody Held .75 2.00
252 Bob Bolin .75 2.00
253 Rookie Stars .75 2.00
Bill Davis
Gus Gil RC
254 Milt Pappas 1.50 4.00
(No facsimile auto-
graph on card front)
255 Frank Howard 1.50 4.00
256 Bob Hendley .75 2.00
257 Charlie Smith .75 2.00
258 Lee Maye .75 2.00
259 Don Dennis .75 2.00
260 Jim Lefebvre 1.50 4.00
261 John Wyatt .75 2.00
262 Kansas City Athletics TC 1.50 4.00
263 Hank Aguirre .75 2.00
264 Ron Swoboda 1.50 4.00
265 Lou Burdette 1.50 4.00
266 Pitt Power 1.50 4.00
Willie Stargell
Donn Clendenon
267 Don Schwall .75 2.00
268 Johnny Briggs .75 2.00
269 Don Nottebart .75 2.00
270 Zoilo Versalles .75 2.00
271 Eddie Watt .75 2.00
272 Rookie Stars 1.50 4.00
Bill Connors RC
Dave Dowling
273 Dick Lines RC .75 2.00
274 Bob Aspromonte .75 2.00
275 Fred Whitfield .75 2.00
276 Bruce Brubaker .75 2.00
277 Steve Whitaker RC 2.50 6.00
278 Jim Kaat CL4 3.00 8.00
279 Frank Linzy .75 2.00
280 Tony Conigliaro 3.00 8.00
281 Bob Rodgers .75 2.00
282 John Odom .75 2.00
283 Gene Alley 1.50 4.00
284 Johnny Podres 1.50 4.00
285 Lou Brock 8.00 20.00
286 Wayne Causey 1.00 2.50
287 Rookie Stars 1.00 2.50
Greg Goosen RC
Bart Shirley
288 Denny Lemaster 1.00 2.50
289 Tom Tresh 2.00 5.00
290 Bill White 2.00 5.00
291 Jim Hannan 1.00 2.50
292 Don Pavletich 1.00 2.50
293 Ed Kirkpatrick 1.00 2.50
294 Walter Alston MG 3.00 8.00
295 Sam McDowell 2.00 5.00
296 Glenn Beckert 2.00 5.00
297 Dave Morehead 2.00 5.00
298 Ron Davis RC 1.00 2.50
299 Norm Siebern 1.00 2.50
300 Jim Kaat 2.00 5.00
301 Jesse Gonder 1.00 2.50
302 Baltimore Orioles TC 3.00 8.00
303 Gil Blanco 1.00 2.50
304 Phil Gagliano 1.00 2.50
305 Earl Wilson 2.00 5.00
306 Bud Harrelson RC 2.00 5.00
307 Jim Beauchamp 1.00 2.50
308 Al Downing 2.00 5.00
309 Hurlers Beware 2.00 5.00
Johnny Callison
Richie Allen
310 Gary Peters 1.00 2.50
311 Ed Brinkman 1.00 2.50
312 Don Mincher 1.00 2.50
313 Bob Lee 1.00 2.50
314 Rookie Stars 3.00 8.00
Mike Andrews RC
Reggie Smith RC
315 Billy Williams 6.00 15.00
316 Jack Kralick 1.00 2.50
317 Cesar Tovar 1.00 2.50
318 Dave Giusti 1.00 2.50
319 Paul Blair 2.00 5.00
320 Gaylord Perry 6.00 15.00
321 Mayo Smith MG 1.00 2.50
322 Jose Pagan 1.00 2.50
323 Mike Hershberger 1.00 2.50
324 Hal Woodeshick 1.00 2.50
325 Chico Cardenas 2.00 5.00
326 Bob Uecker 4.00 10.00
327 California Angels TC 3.00 8.00
328 Clete Boyer UER 2.00 5.00
(Stats only go up
through 1965)
329 Charlie Lau 2.00 5.00
330 Claude Osteen 2.00 5.00
331 Joe Foy 2.00 5.00
332 Jesus Alou 1.00 2.50
333 Fergie Jenkins 8.00 20.00
334 Twin Terrors 4.00 10.00
Bob Allison
Harmon Killebrew
335 Bob Veale 2.00 5.00
336 Joe Azcue 1.00 2.50
337 Joe Morgan 6.00 15.00
338 Bob Locker 1.00 2.50
339 Chico Ruiz 1.00 2.50
340 Joe Pepitone 3.00 8.00
341 Rookie Stars 1.00 2.50
Dick Dietz RC
Bill Sorrell
342 Hank Fischer 1.00 2.50
343 Tom Satriano 1.00 2.50
344 Ossie Chavarria RC 1.00 2.50
345 Stu Miller 2.00 5.00
346 Jim Hickman 1.00 2.50
347 Grady Hatton MG 1.00 2.50
348 Tug McGraw 2.00 5.00
349 Bob Chance 1.00 2.50
350 Joe Torre 3.00 8.00
351 Vern Law 2.00 5.00
352 Ray Oyler 1.00 2.50
353 Bill McCool 1.00 2.50
354 Chicago Cubs TC 3.00 8.00
355 Carl Yastrzemski 30.00 60.00
356 Larry Jaster RC 1.00 2.50
357 Bill Skowron 2.00 5.00
358 Ruben Amaro 1.00 2.50
359 Dick Ellsworth 1.00 2.50
360 Leon Wagner 1.00 2.50
361 Roberto Clemente CL5 6.00 15.00
362 Darold Knowles 1.00 2.50
363 Davey Johnson 2.00 5.00
364 Claude Raymond 1.00 2.50
365 John Roseboro 2.00 5.00
366 Andy Kosco 1.00 2.50
367 Rookie Stars 1.00 2.50
Bill Kelso
Don Wallace RC
368 Jack Hiatt 1.00 2.50
369 Jim Hunter 6.00 15.00
370 Tommy Davis 2.00 5.00
371 Jim Lonborg 3.00 8.00
372 Mike de la Hoz 1.50 4.00
373 Rookie Stars 1.50 4.00
Duane Josephson RC
Fred Klages RC DP
374A Mel Queen ERR 8.00 20.00
(Incomplete stat
line on back)
374B Mel Queen COR DP 1.50 4.00
(Complete stat
line on back)
375 Jake Gibbs 3.00 8.00
376 Don Lock DP 1.50 4.00
377 Luis Tiant 3.00 8.00
378 Detroit Tigers TC 3.00 8.00
(UER Willie Horton with
262 RBI's in 1966)
379 Jerry May DP 1.50 4.00
380 Dean Chance DP 1.50 4.00
381 Dick Schofield DP 1.50 4.00
382 Dave McNally 3.00 8.00
383 Ken Henderson DP 1.50 4.00
384 Rookie Stars 1.50 4.00
Jim Cosman RC
Dick Hughes RC
385 Jim Fregosi 3.00 8.00
(Batting wrong)
386 Dick Selma DP 1.50 4.00
387 Cap Peterson DP 1.50 4.00
388 Arnold Earley DP 1.50 4.00
389 Alvin Dark MG DP 1.50 4.00
390 Jim Wynn DP 3.00 8.00
391 Wilbur Wood DP 3.00 8.00
392 Tommy Harper DP 3.00 8.00
393 Jim Bouton DP 3.00 8.00
394 Jake Wood DP 1.50 4.00
395 Chris Short RC 3.00 8.00
396 Atlanta Aces 1.50 4.00
Denis Menke
Tony Cloninger
397 Willie Smith DP 1.50 4.00
398 Jeff Torborg 3.00 8.00
399 Al Worthington DP 1.50 4.00
400 Bob Clemente DP 60.00 120.00
401 Jim Coates 1.50 4.00
402A Rookie Stars 8.00 20.00
Grant Jackson
Billy Wilson
Incomplete stat line
402B Rookie Stars 3.00 8.00
Grant Jackson
Billy Wilson RC DP
403 Dick Nen 1.50 4.00
404 Nelson Briles 3.00 8.00
405 Russ Snyder 1.50 4.00
406 Lee Elia DP 1.50 4.00
407 Cincinnati Reds TC 3.00 8.00
408 Jim Northrup DP 3.00 8.00
409 Ray Sadecki 1.50 4.00
410 Lou Johnson DP 1.50 4.00
411 Dick Howser DP 1.50 4.00
412 Rookie Stars 3.00 8.00
Norm Miller RC
Doug Rader RC
413 Jerry Grote 1.50 4.00
414 Casey Cox 1.50 4.00
415 Sonny Jackson 1.50 4.00
416 Roger Repoz 1.50 4.00
417A Bob Bruce ERR 12.50 30.00
(RBAVES on back)
417B Bob Bruce COR DP 1.50 4.00
418 Sam Mele MG 1.50 4.00
419 Don Kessinger DP 4.00 8.00
420 Denny McLain 5.00 12.00
421 Dal Maxvill DP 1.50 4.00
422 Hoyt Wilhelm 6.00 15.00
423 Fence Busters 10.00 25.00
Willie Mays
Willie McCovey DP
424 Pedro Gonzalez 1.50 4.00
425 Pete Mikkelsen 1.50 4.00
426 Lou Clinton 1.50 4.00
427A Ruben Gomez ERR 8.00 20.00
Incomplete stat
line on back
427B R.Gomez COR DP 1.50 4.00
Complete stat
line on back
428 Rookie Stars 3.00 8.00
Tom Hutton RC
Gene Michael RCDP
429 Gary Roggenburk DP 1.50 4.00
430 Pete Rose 50.00 100.00
431 Ted Uhlaender 1.50 4.00
432 Jimmie Hall DP 1.50 4.00
433 Al Luplow DP 1.50 4.00
434 Eddie Fisher DP 1.50 4.00
435 Mack Jones DP 1.50 4.00
436 Pete Ward 1.50 4.00
437 Washington Senators TC 3.00 8.00
438 Chuck Dobson 1.50 4.00
439 Byron Browne 1.50 4.00
440 Steve Hargan 1.50 4.00
441 Jim Davenport 1.50 4.00
442 Rookie Stars 3.00 8.00
Bill Robinson RC
Joe Verbanic RC DP
443 Tito Francona DP 1.50 4.00
444 George Smith 1.50 4.00
445 Don Sutton 10.00 25.00
446 Russ Nixon DP 1.50 4.00
447A Bo Belinsky ERR DP 1.50 4.00
(Incomplete stat
line on back)
447B Bo Belinsky COR 3.00 8.00
(Complete stat
line on back)
448 Harry Walker MG DP 1.50 4.00
449 Orlando Pena 1.50 4.00
450 Richie Allen 3.00 8.00
451 Fred Newman DP 1.50 4.00
452 Ed Kranepool 3.00 8.00
453 A.Monteagudo DP 1.50 4.00
454A Juan Marichal CL6 DP 5.00 12.00
Missing left ear
454B Juan Marichal CL6 5.00 12.00
left ear showing
455 Tommie Agee 3.00 8.00
456 Phil Niekro UER 6.00 15.00
(ERA incorrect as .288)
457 Andy Etchebarren DP 3.00 8.00
458 Lee Thomas 2.50 6.00
459 Rookie Stars 2.50 6.00
Dick Bosman RC
Pete Craig
460 Harmon Killebrew 30.00 60.00
461 Bob Miller 5.00 12.00
462 Bob Barton 2.50 6.00
463 Hill Aces 5.00 12.00
Sam McDowell
Sonny Siebert
464 Dan Coombs 2.50 6.00
465 Willie Horton 5.00 12.00
466 Bobby Wine 2.50 6.00
467 Jim O'Toole 2.50 6.00
468 Ralph Houk MG 2.50 6.00
469 Len Gabrielson 2.50 6.00
470 Bob Shaw 2.50 6.00
471 Rene Lachemann 2.50 6.00
472 Rookie Stars 2.50 6.00
John Gelnar
George Spriggs RC
473 Jose Santiago 2.50 6.00
474 Bob Tolan 2.50 6.00
475 Jim Palmer 40.00 80.00
476 Tony Perez SP 30.00 60.00
477 Atlanta Braves TC 6.00 15.00
478 Bob Humphreys 2.50 6.00
479 Gary Bell 2.50 6.00
480 Willie McCovey 15.00 40.00
481 Leo Durocher MG 8.00 20.00
482 Bill Monbouquette 2.50 6.00
483 Jim Landis 2.50 6.00
484 Jerry Adair 2.50 6.00
485 Tim McCarver 10.00 25.00
486 Rookie Stars 2.50 6.00
Rich Reese RC
Bill Whitby RC
487 Tommie Reynolds 2.50 6.00
488 Gerry Arrigo 2.50 6.00
489 Doug Clemens RC 2.50 6.00
490 Tony Cloninger 2.50 6.00
491 Sam Bowens 2.50 6.00
492 Pittsburgh Pirates TC 6.00 15.00
493 Phil Ortega 2.50 6.00
494 Bill Rigney MG 2.50 6.00
495 Fritz Peterson 2.50 6.00
496 Orlando McFarlane 2.50 6.00
497 Ron Campbell RC 2.50 6.00
498 Larry Dierker 5.00 12.00
499 Rookie Stars 2.50 6.00
George Culver
Jose Vidal RC
500 Juan Marichal 10.00 25.00
501 Jerry Zimmerman 2.50 6.00
502 Derrell Griffith 2.50 6.00
503 Los Angeles Dodgers TC 8.00 20.00
504 Orlando Martinez RC 2.50 6.00
505 Tommy Helms 5.00 12.00
506 Smoky Burgess 5.00 12.00
507 Rookie Stars 2.50 6.00
Ed Barnowski
Larry Haney RC
508 Dick Hall 2.50 6.00
509 Jim King 2.50 6.00
510 Bill Mazeroski 10.00 25.00
511 Don Wert 2.50 6.00
512 Red Schoendienst MG 10.00 25.00
513 Marcelino Lopez 2.50 6.00
514 John Werhas 2.50 6.00
515 Bert Campaneris 5.00 12.00
516 San Francisco Giants TC 6.00 15.00
517 Fred Talbot 5.00 12.00
518 Denis Menke 2.50 6.00
519 Ted Davidson 2.50 6.00
520 Max Alvis 2.50 6.00
521 Bird Bombers 5.00 12.00
Boog Powell
Curt Blefary
522 John Stephenson 2.50 6.00
523 Jim Merritt 2.50 6.00
524 Felix Mantilla 2.50 6.00
525 Ron Hunt 2.50 6.00
526 Rookie Stars 2.50 6.00
Pat Dobson RC
George Korince RC
(See 67T card 72 ERR)
527 Dennis Ribant 2.50 6.00
528 Rico Petrocelli 8.00 20.00
529 Gary Wagner 2.50 6.00
530 Felipe Alou 5.00 12.00
531 Brooks Robinson CL7 DP 6.00 15.00
532 Jim Hicks RC 2.50 6.00
533 Jack Fisher 2.50 6.00
534 Hank Bauer MG DP 3.00 8.00
535 Donn Clendenon 10.00 25.00
536 Rookie Stars 20.00 50.00
Joe Niekro RC
Paul Popovich RC
537 Chuck Estrada DP 3.00 8.00
538 J.C. Martin 6.00 15.00
539 Dick Egan DP 3.00 8.00
540 Norm Cash 20.00 50.00
541 Joe Gibbon 6.00 15.00
542 Rookie Stars 6.00 15.00
Rick Monday RC
Tony Pierce RC DP
543 Dan Schneider 6.00 15.00
544 Cleveland Indians TC 12.50 30.00
545 Jim Grant 10.00 25.00
546 Woody Woodward 10.00 25.00
547 Rookie Stars 3.00 8.00
Russ Gibson RC
Bill Rohr RC DP
548 Tony Gonzalez DP 3.00 8.00
549 Jack Sanford 6.00 15.00
550 Vada Pinson DP 4.00 10.00
551 Doug Camilli DP 3.00 8.00
552 Ted Savage 10.00 25.00
553 Rookie Stars 15.00 40.00
Mike Hegan RC
Thad Tillotson
554 Andre Rodgers DP 3.00 8.00
555 Don Cardwell 10.00 25.00
556 Al Weis DP 3.00 8.00
557 Al Ferrara 10.00 25.00
558 Rookie Stars 20.00 50.00
Mark Belanger RC
Bill Dillman RC
559 Dick Tracewski DP 3.00 8.00
560 Jim Bunning 30.00 60.00
561 Sandy Alomar 15.00 40.00
562 Steve Blass DP 3.00 8.00
563 Joe Adcock 15.00 40.00
564 Rookie Stars 3.00 8.00
Alonzo Harris RC
Aaron Pointer RC DP
565 Lew Krausse 10.00 25.00
566 Gary Geiger DP 3.00 8.00
567 Steve Hamilton 15.00 40.00
568 John Sullivan 15.00 40.00
569 Rookie Stars 150.00 300.00
Rod Carew RC
Hank Allen RC DP
570 Maury Wills 40.00 80.00
571 Larry Sherry 10.00 25.00
572 Don Demeter 10.00 25.00
573 Chicago White Sox TC 12.50 30.00
574 Jerry Buchek 10.00 25.00
575 Dave Boswell RC 6.00 15.00
576 Rookie Stars 15.00 40.00
Ramon Hernandez RC
Norm Gigon RC
577 Bill Short 6.00 15.00
578 John Boccabella 6.00 15.00
579 Bill Henry 6.00 15.00
580 Rocky Colavito 75.00 150.00
581 Rookie Stars 300.00 600.00
Bill Denehy RC
Tom Seaver RC
582 Jim Owens DP 3.00 8.00
583 Ray Barker 15.00 40.00
584 Jimmy Piersall 15.00 40.00
585 Wally Bunker 10.00 25.00
586 Manny Jimenez 6.00 15.00
587 Rookie Stars 15.00 40.00
Don Shaw RC
Gary Sutherland RC
588 Johnny Klippstein DP 3.00 8.00
589 Dave Ricketts DP 3.00 8.00
590 Pete Richert 6.00 15.00
591 Ty Cline 10.00 25.00
592 Rookie Stars 10.00 25.00
Jim Shellenback RC
Ron Willis RC
593 Wes Westrum MG 20.00 50.00
594 Dan Osinski 15.00 40.00
595 Cookie Rojas 10.00 25.00
596 Galen Cisco DP 3.00 8.00
597 Ted Abernathy 6.00 15.00
598 Rookie Stars 10.00 25.00
Walt Williams RC
Ed Stroud RC
599 Bob Duliba DP 3.00 8.00
600 Brooks Robinson 125.00 250.00
601 Bill Bryan DP 3.00 8.00
602 Juan Pizarro 15.00 40.00
603 Rookie Stars 10.00 25.00
Tim Talton RC
Ramon Webster RC
604 Boston Red Sox TC 60.00 120.00
605 Mike Shannon 20.00 50.00
606 Ron Taylor 10.00 25.00
607 Mickey Stanley 20.00 50.00
608 Rookie Stars 3.00 8.00
Rich Nye RC
John Upham RC DP
609 Tommy John 40.00 80.00

1967 Topps Posters Inserts

The wrappers of the 1967 Topps cards have this 32-card set advertised as follows: 'Extra -- All Star Pin-Up Inside." Printed on (5" by 7") paper in full color, these "All-Star" inserts have fold lines which are generally not very noticeable when stored carefully. They are numbered, blank-backed, and carry a facsimile autograph.

COMPLETE SET (32) 50.00 100.00
1 Boog Powell 1.00 2.50
2 Bert Campaneris .75 2.00
3 Brooks Robinson 1.50 4.00
4 Tommie Agee .50 1.25
5 Carl Yastrzemski 2.00 5.00
6 Mickey Mantle 8.00 20.00
7 Frank Howard .75 2.00
8 Sam McDowell .75 2.00
9 Orlando Cepeda 1.25 3.00
10 Chico Cardenas .50 1.25
11 Roberto Clemente 4.00 10.00
12 Willie Mays 3.00 8.00
13 Cleon Jones .50 1.25
14 Johnny Callison .75 2.00
15 Hank Aaron 2.50 6.00
16 Don Drysdale 1.25 3.00
17 Bobby Knoop .50 1.25
18 Tony Oliva 1.00 2.50
19 Frank Robinson 1.25 3.00
20 Denny McLain 1.00 2.50
21 Al Kaline 1.50 4.00
22 Joe Pepitone .75 2.00
23 Harmon Killebrew 1.50 4.00
24 Leon Wagner .50 1.25
25 Joe Morgan 1.25 3.00
26 Ron Santo 1.00 2.50
27 Joe Torre 1.00 2.50
28 Juan Marichal 1.00 2.50
29 Matty Alou .50 1.25
30 Felipe Alou .75 2.00
31 Ron Hunt .50 1.25
32 Willie McCovey 1.25 3.00

1968 Topps

The cards in this 598-card set measure 2 1/2" by 3 1/2". The 1968 Topps set includes Sporting News All-Star Selections as card numbers 361 to 380. Other subsets in the set include League Leaders (1-12) and World Series cards (151-158). The front of each checklist card features a picture of a popular player inside a circle. Higher numbers 458 to 598 are slightly more difficult to obtain. The first series looks different from the other series, as it has a lighter, wider mesh background on the card front. The later series all had a much darker, finer mesh pattern. Among other fashions, cards were issued in five-card nickel packs. Those five cent packs were issued 24 packs to a box. Thirty-six card rack packs with an SRP of 29 cents were also issued. The key Rookie Cards in the set are Johnny Bench and Nolan Ryan. Lastly, some cards were also issued along with the "Win-A-Card" board game from Milton Bradley that included cards from the 1965 Topps Hot Rods and 1967 Topps football card sets. This version of these cards is somewhat difficult to distinguish, but are often found with a slight touch of the 1967 football set white border on the front top or bottom edge as well as a brighter yellow card back instead of the darker yellow or gold color. The known cards from this product include card numbers 16, 20, 34, 45, 108, and 149.

COMPLETE SET (598) 1500.00 3000.00
COMMON CARD (1-457) .75 2.00
COMMON (458-598) 1.50 4.00
WRAPPER (5-CENT) 10.00 25.00
1 NL Batting Leaders 12.50 30.00
Roberto Clemente
Tony Gonzalez
Matty Alou
2 AL Batting Leaders 6.00 15.00
Carl Yastrzemski
Frank Robinson
Al Kaline
3 NL RBI Leaders 8.00 20.00
Orlando Cepeda
Roberto Clemente
Hank Aaron
4 AL RBI Leaders 6.00 15.00
Carl Yastrzemski
Harmon Killebrew
Frank Robinson
5 NL Home Run Leaders 3.00 8.00
Hank Aaron
Jim Wynn
Ron Santo
Willie McCovey
6 AL Home Run Leaders 3.00 8.00
Carl Yastrzemski
Harmon Killebrew
Frank Howard
7 NL ERA Leaders 1.50 4.00
Phil Niekro
Jim Bunning
Chris Short
8 AL ERA Leaders 1.50 4.00
Joel Horlen
Gary Peters
Sonny Siebert
9 NL Pitching Leaders 1.50 4.00
Mike McCormick
Ferguson Jenkins
Jim Bunning
Claude Osteen
10A AL Pitching Leaders 1.50 4.00
Jim Lonborg ERR
(Misspelled Lonberg
on card back)
Earl Wilson
Dean Chance
10B AL Pitching Leaders 1.50 4.00
Jim Lonborg COR
Earl Wilson
Dean Chance
11 NL Strikeout Leaders 2.50 6.00
Jim Bunning
Ferguson Jenkins
Gaylord Perry
12 AL Strikeout Leaders 1.50 4.00
Jim Lonborg UER
(Misspelled Longberg
on card back)
Sam McDowell
Dean Chance
13 Chuck Hartenstein RC .75 2.00
14 Jerry McNertney .75 2.00
15 Ron Hunt .75 2.00
16 Rookie Stars 2.50 6.00
Lou Piniella
Richie Scheinblum
17 Dick Hall .75 2.00
18 Mike Hershberger .75 2.00
19 Juan Pizarro .75 2.00
20 Brooks Robinson 10.00 25.00
21 Ron Davis .75 2.00
22 Pat Dobson 1.50 4.00
23 Chico Cardenas 1.50 4.00
24 Bobby Locke .75 2.00
25 Julian Javier 1.50 4.00
26 Darrell Brandon .75 2.00
27 Gil Hodges MG 3.00 8.00
28 Ted Uhlaender .75 2.00
29 Joe Verbanic .75 2.00
30 Joe Torre 2.50 6.00
31 Ed Stroud .75 2.00
32 Joe Gibbon .75 2.00
33 Pete Ward .75 2.00
34 Al Ferrara .75 2.00
35 Steve Hargan .75 2.00
36 Rookie Stars 1.50 4.00
Bob Moose RC
Bob Robertson RC
37 Billy Williams 3.00 8.00
38 Tony Pierce .75 2.00
39 Cookie Rojas .75 2.00
40 Denny McLain 3.00 8.00
41 Julio Gotay .75 2.00
42 Larry Haney .75 2.00
43 Gary Bell .75 2.00
44 Frank Kostro .75 2.00
45 Tom Seaver 20.00 50.00
46 Dave Ricketts .75 2.00
47 Ralph Houk MG 1.50 4.00
48 Ted Davidson .75 2.00
49A Eddie Brinkman .75 2.00
(White team name)
49B Eddie Brinkman 20.00 50.00
(Yellow team name)
50 Willie Mays 30.00 60.00
51 Bob Locker .75 2.00
52 Hawk Taylor .75 2.00
53 Gene Alley 1.50 4.00
54 Stan Williams .75 2.00
55 Felipe Alou 1.50 4.00
56 Rookie Stars .75 2.00
Dave Leonhard RC
Dave May RC
57 Dan Schneider .75 2.00
58 Eddie Mathews 6.00 15.00
59 Don Lock .75 2.00
60 Ken Holtzman 1.50 4.00
61 Reggie Smith 1.50 4.00
62 Chuck Dobson .75 2.00
63 Dick Kenworthy RC .75 2.00
64 Jim Merritt .75 2.00
65 John Roseboro 1.50 4.00
66A Casey Cox .75 2.00
(White team name)
66B Casey Cox 50.00 100.00
(Yellow team name)
67 Checklist 1 2.50 6.00
Jim Kaat
68 Ron Willis .75 2.00
69 Tom Tresh 1.50 4.00
70 Bob Veale 1.50 4.00
71 Vern Fuller RC .75 2.00
72 Tommy John 2.50 6.00
73 Jim Ray Hart 1.50 4.00
74 Milt Pappas 1.50 4.00
75 Don Mincher .75 2.00
76 Rookie Stars 1.50 4.00
Jim Britton
Ron Reed RC
77 Don Wilson RC 1.50 4.00
78 Jim Northrup 2.50 6.00
79 Ted Kubiak RC .75 2.00
80 Rod Carew 20.00 50.00
81 Larry Jackson .75 2.00
82 Sam Bowens .75 2.00
83 John Stephenson .75 2.00
84 Bob Tolan .75 2.00
85 Gaylord Perry 3.00 8.00
86 Willie Stargell 3.00 8.00
87 Dick Williams MG 1.50 4.00
88 Phil Regan 1.50 4.00
89 Jake Gibbs 1.50 4.00
90 Vada Pinson 1.50 4.00
91 Jim Ollom RC .75 2.00
92 Ed Kranepool 1.50 4.00
93 Tony Cloninger .75 2.00
94 Lee Maye .75 2.00
95 Bob Aspromonte .75 2.00
96 Rookie Stars .75 2.00
Frank Coggins RC
Dick Nold
97 Tom Phoebus .75 2.00
98 Gary Sutherland .75 2.00
99 Rocky Colavito 3.00 8.00
100 Bob Gibson 10.00 25.00
101 Glenn Beckert 1.50 4.00
102 Jose Cardenal 1.50 4.00
103 Don Sutton 3.00 8.00
104 Dick Dietz .75 2.00
105 Al Downing 1.50 4.00
106 Dalton Jones .75 2.00
107A Checklist 2 2.50 6.00
Juan Marichal
(Tan wide mesh)
107B Checklist 2 2.50 6.00
Juan Marichal
(Brown fine mesh)
108 Don Pavletich .75 2.00
109 Bert Campaneris 1.50 4.00
110 Hank Aaron 30.00 60.00
111 Rich Reese .75 2.00
112 Woody Fryman .75 2.00
113 Rookie Stars 1.50 4.00
Tom Matchick
Daryl Patterson RC
114 Ron Swoboda 1.50 4.00
115 Sam McDowell 1.50 4.00
116 Ken McMullen .75 2.00
117 Larry Jaster .75 2.00
118 Mark Belanger 1.50 4.00
119 Ted Savage .75 2.00
120 Mel Stottlemyre 1.50 4.00

121 Jimmie Hall .75 2.00
122 Gene Mauch MG 1.50 4.00
123 Jose Santiago .75 2.00
124 Nate Oliver .75 2.00
125 Joel Horlen .75 2.00
126 Bobby Etheridge RC .75 2.00
127 Paul Lindblad .75 2.00
128 Rookie Stars .75 2.00
Tom Dukes RC
Alonzo Harris
129 Mickey Stanley 2.00 6.00
130 Tony Perez 3.00 8.00
131 Frank Bertaina .75 2.00
132 Bud Harrelson 1.50 4.00
133 Fred Whitfield .75 2.00
134 Pat Jarvis .75 2.00
135 Paul Blair 1.50 4.00
136 Randy Hundley 1.50 4.00
137 Minnesota Twins TC 1.50 4.00
138 Ruben Amaro .75 2.00
139 Chris Short .75 2.00
140 Tony Conigliaro 3.00 8.00
141 Dal Maxvill .75 2.00
142 Rookie Stars .75 2.00
Buddy Bradford RC
Bill Voss
143 Pete Cimino .75 2.00
144 Joe Morgan 5.00 12.00
145 Don Drysdale 5.00 12.00
146 Sal Bando 1.50 4.00
147 Frank Linzy .75 2.00
148 Dave Bristol MG .75 2.00
149 Bob Saverine .75 2.00
150 Roberto Clemente 40.00 80.00
151 World Series Game 1 4.00 10.00
Lou Brock
152 World Series Game 2 4.00 10.00
Carl Yastrzemski
153 World Series Game 3 2.00 5.00
Nelson Briles
154 World Series Game 4 4.00 10.00
Bob Gibson
155 World Series Game 5 2.00 5.00
Jim Lonborg
156 World Series Game 6 2.00 5.00
Rico Petrocelli
157 World Series Game 7 2.00 5.00
St. Louis wins it
Red Schoendienst, Bob Gibson and Bobby Tolan among those visible
158 WS Summary 2.00 5.00
Cardinals Celebrate
Tim McCarver and Joe Schultz very visible in photo
159 Don Kessinger 1.50 4.00
160 Earl Wilson 1.50 4.00
161 Norm Miller .75 2.00
162 Rookie Stars 1.50 4.00
Hal Gilson RC
Mike Torrez RC
163 Gene Brabender .75 2.00
164 Ramon Webster .75 2.00
165 Tony Oliva 2.50 6.00
166 Claude Raymond .75 2.00
167 Elston Howard 2.50 6.00
168 Los Angeles Dodgers TC 1.50 4.00
169 Bob Bolin .75 2.00
170 Jim Fregosi 1.50 4.00
171 Don Nottebart .75 2.00
172 Walt Williams .75 2.00
173 John Boozer .75 2.00
174 Bob Tillman .75 2.00
175 Maury Wills 2.50 6.00
176 Bob Allen .75 2.00
177 Rookie Stars 250.00 500.00
Jerry Koosman RC
Nolan Ryan RC
UER Sensational
is spelled incorrectly
178 Don Wert 1.50 4.00
179 Bill Stoneman RC .75 2.00
180 Curt Flood 2.50 6.00
181 Jerry Zimmerman .75 2.00
182 Dave Giusti .75 2.00
183 Bob Kennedy MG 1.50 4.00
184 Lou Johnson .75 2.00
185 Tom Haller .75 2.00
186 Eddie Watt .75 2.00
187 Sonny Jackson .75 2.00
188 Cap Peterson .75 2.00
189 Bill Landis RC .75 2.00
190 Bill White 1.50 4.00
191 Dan Frisella RC .75 2.00
192A Checklist 3 3.00 8.00
Carl Yastrzemski
(Special Baseball
192B Checklist 3 3.00 8.00
Carl Yastrzemski
(Special Baseball
Playing Card Game
193 Jack Hamilton .75 2.00
194 Don Buford .75 2.00
195 Joe Pepitone 1.50 4.00
196 Gary Nolan RC 1.50 4.00
197 Larry Brown .75 2.00
198 Roy Face 1.50 4.00
199 Rookie Stars .75 2.00
Roberto Rodriquez RC
Darrell Osteen
200 Orlando Cepeda 3.00 8.00
201 Mike Marshall RC 1.50 4.00
202 Adolfo Phillips .75 2.00
203 Dick Kelley .75 2.00
204 Andy Etchebarren .75 2.00
205 Juan Marichal 3.00 8.00
206 Cal Ermer MG RC .75 2.00
207 Carroll Sembera .75 2.00
208 Willie Davis 1.50 4.00
209 Tim Cullen .75 2.00
210 Gary Peters .75 2.00
211 J.C. Martin .75 2.00
212 Dave Morehead .75 2.00
213 Chico Ruiz .75 2.00
214 Rookie Stars 1.50 4.00
Stan Bahnsen
Frank Fernandez
215 Jim Bunning 3.00 8.00
216 Bubba Morton .75 2.00
217 Dick Farrell .75 2.00
218 Ken Suarez .75 2.00
219 Rob Gardner .75 2.00
220 Harmon Killebrew 6.00 15.00
221 Atlanta Braves TC 1.50 4.00
222 Jim Hardin RC .75 2.00
223 Ollie Brown .75 2.00
224 Jack Aker .75 2.00
225 Richie Allen 2.50 6.00
226 Jimmie Price .75 2.00
227 Joe Hoerner .75 2.00
228 Rookie Stars 1.50 4.00
Jack Billingham RC
Jim Fairey RC
229 Fred Klages .75 2.00
230 Pete Rose 30.00 60.00
231 Dave Baldwin RC .75 2.00
232 Denis Menke .75 2.00
233 George Scott 1.50 4.00
234 Bill Monbouquette .75 2.00
235 Ron Santo 3.00 8.00
236 Tug McGraw 2.50 6.00
237 Alvin Dark MG 1.50 4.00
238 Tom Satriano .75 2.00
239 Bill Henry .75 2.00
240 Al Kaline 15.00 40.00
241 Felix Millan .75 2.00
242 Moe Drabowsky 1.50 4.00
243 Rich Rollins .75 2.00
244 John Donaldson RC .75 2.00
245 Tony Gonzalez .75 2.00
246 Fritz Peterson 1.50 4.00
247 Rookie Stars 60.00 120.00
Johnny Bench RC
Ron Tompkins UER (the is Misspelled in First Line)
248 Fred Valentine .75 2.00
249 Bill Singer .75 2.00
250 Carl Yastrzemski 12.50 30.00
251 Manny Sanguillen RC 2.50 6.00
252 California Angels TC 1.50 4.00
253 Dick Hughes .75 2.00
254 Cleon Jones 1.50 4.00
255 Dean Chance 1.50 4.00
256 Norm Cash 2.50 6.00
257 Phil Niekro 3.00 8.00
258 Rookie Stars .75 2.00
Jose Arcia RC
Bill Schlesinger
259 Ken Boyer 2.50 6.00
260 Jim Wynn 1.50 4.00
261 Dave Duncan 1.50 4.00
262 Rick Wise 1.50 4.00
263 Horace Clarke 1.50 4.00
264 Ted Abernathy .75 2.00
265 Tommy Davis 1.50 4.00
266 Paul Popovich .75 2.00
267 Herman Franks MG .75 2.00
268 Bob Humphreys .75 2.00
269 Bob Tiefenauer .75 2.00
270 Matty Alou 1.50 4.00
271 Bobby Knoop .75 2.00
272 Ray Culp .75 2.00
273 Dave Johnson 1.50 4.00
274 Mike Cuellar 1.50 4.00
275 Tim McCarver 2.50 6.00
276 Jim Roland .75 2.00
277 Jerry Buchek .75 2.00
278 Checklist 4 2.50 6.00
Orlando Cepeda
279 Bill Hands .75 2.00
280 Mickey Mantle 175.00 350.00
281 Jim Campanis .75 2.00
282 Rick Monday 1.50 4.00
283 Mel Queen .75 2.00
284 Johnny Briggs .75 2.00
285 Dick McAuliffe 2.50 6.00
286 Cecil Upshaw .75 2.00
287 Rookie Stars .75 2.00
Mickey Abarbanel RC
Cisco Carlos RC
288 Dave Wickersham .75 2.00
289 Woody Held .75 2.00
290 Willie McCovey 5.00 12.00
291 Dick Lines .75 2.00
292 Art Shamsky .75 2.00
293 Bruce Howard .75 2.00
294 Red Schoendienst MG 2.50 6.00
295 Sonny Siebert .75 2.00
296 Byron Browne .75 2.00
297 Russ Gibson .75 2.00
298 Jim Brewer .75 2.00
299 Gene Michael 1.50 4.00
300 Rusty Staub 1.50 4.00
301 Rookie Stars .75 2.00
George Mitterwald RC
Rick Renick RC
302 Gerry Arrigo .75 2.00
303 Dick Green 1.50 4.00
304 Sandy Valdespino .75 2.00
305 Minnie Rojas .75 2.00
306 Mike Ryan .75 2.00
307 John Hiller 1.50 4.00
308 Pittsburgh Pirates TC 1.50 4.00
309 Ken Henderson .75 2.00
310 Luis Aparicio 3.00 8.00
311 Jack Lamabe .75 2.00
312 Curt Blefary .75 2.00
313 Al Weis .75 2.00
314 Rookie Stars .75 2.00
Bill Rohr
George Spriggs
315 Zoilo Versalles .75 2.00
316 Steve Barber .75 2.00
317 Ron Brand .75 2.00
318 Chico Salmon .75 2.00
319 George Culver .75 2.00
320 Frank Howard 1.50 4.00
321 Leo Durocher MG 2.50 6.00
322 Dave Boswell .75 2.00
323 Deron Johnson 1.50 4.00
324 Jim Nash .75 2.00
325 Manny Mota 1.50 4.00
326 Dennis Ribant .75 2.00
327 Tony Taylor 1.50 4.00
328 Rookie Stars .75 2.00
Chuck Vinson RC
Jim Weaver RC
329 Duane Josephson .75 2.00
330 Roger Maris 20.00 50.00
331 Dan Osinski .75 2.00
332 Doug Rader 1.50 4.00
333 Ron Herbel .75 2.00
334 Baltimore Orioles TC 1.50 4.00
335 Bob Allison 1.50 4.00
336 John Purdin .75 2.00
337 Bill Robinson 1.50 4.00
338 Bob Johnson .75 2.00
339 Rich Nye .75 2.00
340 Max Alvis .75 2.00
341 Jim Lemon MG .75 2.00
342 Ken Johnson .75 2.00
343 Jim Gosger .75 2.00
344 Donn Clendenon 1.50 4.00
345 Bob Hendley .75 2.00
346 Jerry Adair .75 2.00
347 George Brunet .75 2.00
348 Rookie Stars .75 2.00
Larry Colton RC
Dick Thoenen RC
349 Ed Spiezio 1.50 4.00
350 Hoyt Wilhelm 3.00 8.00
351 Bob Barton .75 2.00
352 Jackie Hernandez RC .75 2.00
353 Mack Jones .75 2.00
354 Pete Richert .75 2.00
355 Ernie Banks 10.00 25.00
356A Checklist 5 2.50 6.00
Ken Holtzman
(Head centered
within circle
356B Checklist 5 2.50 6.00
Ken Holtzman
Head shifted right
within circle
357 Len Gabrielson .75 2.00
358 Mike Epstein .75 2.00
359 Joe Moeller .75 2.00
360 Willie Horton 2.50 6.00
361 Harmon Killebrew AS 3.00 8.00
362 Orlando Cepeda AS 2.50 6.00
363 Rod Carew AS 3.00 8.00
364 Joe Morgan AS 3.00 8.00
365 Brooks Robinson AS 3.00 8.00
366 Ron Santo AS 2.50 6.00
367 Jim Fregosi AS 1.50 4.00
368 Gene Alley AS 1.50 4.00
369 Carl Yastrzemski AS 4.00 10.00
370 Hank Aaron AS 8.00 20.00
371 Tony Oliva AS 2.50 6.00
372 Lou Brock AS 3.00 8.00
373 Frank Robinson AS 3.00 8.00
374 Bob Clemente AS 12.50 30.00
375 Bill Freehan AS 1.50 4.00
376 Tim McCarver AS 1.50 4.00
377 Joel Horlen AS 1.50 4.00
378 Bob Gibson AS 3.00 8.00
379 Gary Peters AS 1.50 4.00
380 Ken Holtzman AS 1.50 4.00
381 Boog Powell 1.50 4.00
382 Ramon Hernandez .75 2.00
383 Steve Whitaker .75 2.00
384 Rookie Stars 2.50 6.00
Bill Henry
Hal McRae RC
385 Jim Hunter 4.00 10.00
386 Greg Goossen .75 2.00
387 Joe Foy .75 2.00
388 Ray Washburn .75 2.00
389 Jay Johnstone 1.50 4.00
390 Bill Mazeroski 3.00 8.00
391 Bob Priddy .75 2.00
392 Grady Hatton MG .75 2.00
393 Jim Perry 1.50 4.00
394 Tommie Aaron 2.50 6.00
395 Camilo Pascual 1.50 4.00
396 Bobby Wine .75 2.00
397 Vic Davalillo .75 2.00
398 Jim Grant .75 2.00
399 Ray Oyler 1.50 4.00
400A Mike McCormick 1.50 4.00
(Yellow letters)
400B Mike McCormick 75.00 150.00
(Team name in
white letters)
401 Mets Team 1.50 4.00
402 Mike Hegan 1.50 4.00
403 John Buzhardt .75 2.00
404 Floyd Robinson .75 2.00
405 Tommy Helms 1.50 4.00
406 Dick Ellsworth .75 2.00
407 Gary Kolb .75 2.00
408 Steve Carlton 12.50 30.00
409 Rookie Stars .75 2.00
Frank Peters RC
Ron Stone
410 Ferguson Jenkins 4.00 10.00
411 Ron Hansen .75 2.00
412 Clay Carroll 1.50 4.00
413 Tom McCraw .75 2.00
414 Mickey Lolich 3.00 8.00
415 Johnny Callison 1.50 4.00
416 Bill Rigney MG .75 2.00
417 Willie Crawford .75 2.00
418 Eddie Fisher .75 2.00
419 Jack Hiatt .75 2.00
420 Cesar Tovar .75 2.00
421 Ron Taylor .75 2.00
422 Rene Lachemann .75 2.00
423 Fred Gladding .75 2.00
424 Chicago White Sox TC 1.50 4.00
425 Jim Maloney 1.50 4.00
426 Hank Allen .75 2.00
427 Dick Calmus .75 2.00
428 Vic Roznovsky .75 2.00
429 Tommie Sisk .75 2.00
430 Rico Petrocelli 1.50 4.00
431 Dooley Womack .75 2.00
432 Rookie Stars .75 2.00
Bill Davis
Jose Vidal
433 Bob Rodgers .75 2.00
434 Ricardo Joseph RC .75 2.00
435 Ron Perranoski 1.50 4.00
436 Hal Lanier .75 2.00
437 Don Cardwell .75 2.00
438 Lee Thomas 1.50 4.00
439 Lum Harris MG .75 2.00
440 Claude Osteen 1.50 4.00
441 Alex Johnson 1.50 4.00
442 Dick Bosman .75 2.00
443 Joe Azcue .75 2.00
444 Jack Fisher .75 2.00
445 Mike Shannon 1.50 4.00
446 Ron Kline .75 2.00
447 Rookie Stars 1.50 4.00
George Korince
Fred Lasher RC
448 Gary Wagner .75 2.00
449 Gene Oliver .75 2.00
450 Jim Kaat 2.50 6.00
451 Al Spangler .75 2.00
452 Jesus Alou .75 2.00
453 Sammy Ellis .75 2.00
454A Checklist 6 3.00 8.00
Frank Robinson
(Cap complete
within circle
454B Checklist 6 3.00 8.00
Frank Robinson CL
Cap partially within circle
455 Rico Carty 1.50 4.00
456 John O'Donoghue .75 2.00
457 Jim Lefebvre 1.50 4.00
458 Lew Krausse 2.50 6.00
459 Dick Simpson 1.50 4.00
460 Jim Lonborg 2.50 6.00
461 Chuck Hiller 1.50 4.00
462 Barry Moore 1.50 4.00
463 Jim Schaffer 1.50 4.00
464 Don McMahon 1.50 4.00
465 Tommie Agee 4.00 10.00
466 Bill Dillman 1.50 4.00
467 Dick Howser 4.00 10.00
468 Larry Sherry 1.50 4.00
469 Ty Cline 1.50 4.00
470 Bill Freehan 4.00 10.00
471 Orlando Pena 1.50 4.00
472 Walter Alston MG 2.50 6.00
473 Al Worthington 1.50 4.00
474 Paul Schaal 1.50 4.00
475 Joe Niekro 2.50 6.00
476 Woody Woodward 1.50 4.00
477 Philadelphia Phillies TC 3.00 8.00
478 Dave McNally 2.50 6.00
479 Phil Gagliano 2.50 6.00
480 Manager's Dream 40.00 80.00
Tony Oliva
Chico Cardenas
Bob Clemente
481 John Wyatt 1.50 4.00
482 Jose Pagan 1.50 4.00
483 Darold Knowles 1.50 4.00
484 Phil Roof 1.50 4.00
485 Ken Berry 2.50 6.00
486 Cal Koonce 1.50 4.00
487 Lee May 4.00 10.00
488 Dick Tracewski 2.50 6.00
489 Wally Bunker 1.50 4.00
490 Super Stars 75.00 150.00
Harmon Killebrew
Willie Mays
Mickey Mantle
491 Denny Lemaster 1.50 4.00
492 Jeff Torborg 2.50 6.00
493 Jim McGlothlin 1.50 4.00
494 Ray Sadecki 1.50 4.00
495 Leon Wagner 1.50 4.00
496 Steve Hamilton 2.50 6.00
497 St. Louis Cardinals TC 3.00 8.00
498 Bill Bryan 2.50 6.00
499 Steve Blass 2.50 6.00
500 Frank Robinson 12.50 30.00
501 John Odom 2.50 6.00
502 Mike Andrews 1.50 4.00
503 Al Jackson 2.50 6.00
504 Russ Snyder 1.50 4.00
505 Joe Sparma 4.00 10.00
506 Clarence Jones RC 1.50 4.00
507 Wade Blasingame 1.50 4.00
508 Duke Sims 1.50 4.00
509 Dennis Higgins 1.50 4.00
510 Ron Fairly 4.00 10.00
511 Bill Kelso 1.50 4.00
512 Grant Jackson 1.50 4.00
513 Hank Bauer MG 2.50 6.00
514 Al McBean 1.50 4.00
515 Russ Nixon 1.50 4.00
516 Pete Mikkelsen 1.50 4.00
517 Diego Segui 2.50 6.00
518A Checklist 7 ERR 5.00 12.00
(539 AL Rookies)
(Clete Boyer)
518B Checklist 7 COR 5.00 12.00
(539 ML Rookies)
(Clete Boyer)
519 Jerry Stephenson 1.50 4.00
520 Lou Brock 10.00 25.00
521 Don Shaw 1.50 4.00
522 Wayne Causey 1.50 4.00
523 John Tsitouris 1.50 4.00
524 Andy Kosco 2.50 6.00
525 Jim Davenport 1.50 4.00
526 Bill Denehy 1.50 4.00
527 Tito Francona 1.50 4.00
528 Detroit Tigers TC 30.00 60.00
529 Bruce Von Hoff RC 1.50 4.00
530 Bird Belters 15.00 40.00
Brooks Robinson
Frank Robinson
531 Chuck Hinton 1.50 4.00
532 Luis Tiant 2.50 6.00
533 Wes Parker 2.50 6.00
534 Bob Miller 2.50 6.00
535 Danny Cater 2.50 6.00
536 Bill Short 1.50 4.00
537 Norm Siebern 2.50 6.00
538 Manny Jimenez 2.50 6.00
539 Rookie Stars 1.50 4.00
Jim Ray RC
Mike Ferraro RC
540 Nelson Briles 2.50 6.00
541 Sandy Alomar 2.50 6.00
542 John Boccabella 1.50 4.00
543 Bob Lee 1.50 4.00
544 Mayo Smith MG 5.00 12.00
545 Lindy McDaniel 2.50 6.00
546 Roy White 2.50 6.00
547 Dan Coombs 1.50 4.00
548 Bernie Allen 1.50 4.00
549 Rookie Stars 1.50 4.00
Curt Motton RC
Roger Nelson RC
550 Clete Boyer 2.50 6.00
551 Darrell Sutherland 1.50 4.00
552 Ed Kirkpatrick 1.50 4.00
553 Hank Aguirre 1.50 4.00
554 Oakland Athletics TC 4.00 10.00
555 Jose Tartabull 2.50 6.00
556 Dick Selma 1.50 4.00
557 Frank Quilici 2.50 6.00
558 Johnny Edwards 1.50 4.00
559 Rookie Stars 1.50 4.00
Carl Taylor RC
Luke Walker
560 Paul Casanova 1.50 4.00
561 Lee Elia 1.50 4.00
562 Jim Bouton 2.50 6.00
563 Ed Charles 1.50 4.00
564 Eddie Stanky MG 2.50 6.00
565 Larry Dierker 2.50 6.00
566 Ken Harrelson 2.50 6.00
567 Clay Dalrymple 1.50 4.00
568 Willie Smith 1.50 4.00
569 Rookie Stars 1.50 4.00
Ivan Murrell RC
Les Rohr RC
570 Rick Reichardt 1.50 4.00
571 Tony LaRussa 5.00 12.00
572 Don Bosch RC 1.50 4.00
573 Joe Coleman 1.50 4.00
574 Cincinnati Reds TC 4.00 10.00
575 Jim Palmer 15.00 40.00
576 Dave Adlesh 1.50 4.00
577 Fred Talbot 1.50 4.00
578 Orlando Martinez 1.50 4.00
579 Rookie Stars 4.00 10.00
Larry Hisle RC
Mike Lum RC
580 Bob Bailey 1.50 4.00
581 Garry Roggenburk 1.50 4.00
582 Jerry Grote 4.00 10.00
583 Gates Brown 4.00 10.00
584 Larry Shepard MG RC 1.50 4.00
585 Wilbur Wood 2.50 6.00
586 Jim Pagliaroni 2.50 6.00
587 Roger Repoz 1.50 4.00
588 Dick Schofield 1.50 4.00
589 Rookie Stars 1.50 4.00
Ron Clark
Moe Ogier RC
590 Tommy Harper 2.50 6.00
591 Dick Nen 1.50 4.00
592 John Bateman 1.50 4.00
593 Lee Stange 1.50 4.00
594 Phil Linz 2.50 6.00
595 Phil Ortega 1.50 4.00
596 Charlie Smith 1.50 4.00
597 Bill McCool 1.50 4.00
598 Jerry May 2.50 6.00

1968 Topps Game

The cards in this 33-card set measure approximately 2 1/4" by 3 1/4". This "Game" card set of players, issued as inserts with the regular third series 1968 Topps baseball cards, was patterned directly after the Red Back and Blue Back sets of 1951. Each card has a color player photo set upon a pure white background, with a facsimile autograph underneath the picture. The cards have blue backs, and were also sold in boxed sets, which had an original cost of 15 cents on a limited basis.

COMPLETE SET (33) 60.00 120.00
COMP.FACT SET (33) 60.00 120.00
1 Matty Alou 1.00 2.50
2 Mickey Mantle 15.00 40.00
3 Carl Yastrzemski 3.00 8.00
4 Hank Aaron 6.00 15.00
5 Harmon Killebrew 3.00 8.00
6 Roberto Clemente 10.00 25.00
7 Frank Robinson 2.00 5.00
8 Willie Mays 6.00 15.00
9 Brooks Robinson 3.00 8.00
10 Tommy Davis .75 2.00
11 Bill Freehan 1.00 2.50
12 Claude Osteen .75 2.00
13 Gary Peters .75 2.00
14 Jim Lonborg .75 2.00
15 Steve Hargan .75 2.00
16 Dean Chance .75 2.00
17 Mike McCormick .75 2.00
18 Tim McCarver 1.00 2.50
19 Ron Santo 1.25 3.00
20 Tony Gonzalez .75 2.00
21 Frank Howard 1.00 2.50
22 George Scott .75 2.00
23 Richie Allen 1.25 3.00
24 Jim Wynn 1.00 2.50
25 Gene Alley .75 2.00
26 Rick Monday .75 2.00
27 Al Kaline 3.00 8.00
28 Rusty Staub 1.00 2.50
29 Rod Carew 2.00 5.00
30 Pete Rose 6.00 15.00
31 Joe Torre 1.25 3.00
32 Orlando Cepeda 1.25 3.00
33 Jim Fregosi 1.00 2.50

1969 Topps

The cards in this 664-card set measure 2 1/2" by 3 1/2". The 1969 Topps set includes Sporting News All-Star Selections as card numbers 416 to 435. Other popular subsets within this set include League Leaders (1-12) and World Series cards (162-169). The fifth series contains several variations; the more difficult variety consists of cards with the player's first name, last name, and/or position in white letters instead of lettering in some other color. These are designated in the checklist below by WL (white letters). Each checklist card features a different popular player's picture inside a circle on the front of the checklist card. Two different team identifications of Clay Dalrymple and Donn Clendenon exist, as indicated in the checklist. The key Rookie Cards in this set are Rollie Fingers, Reggie Jackson, and Graig Nettles. This was the last year that Topps issued multi-player special star cards, ending a 13-year tradition, which they had begun in 1957. There were cropping differences in checklist cards 57, 214, and 412, due to their each being printed with two different series. The differences are difficult to explain and have not been greatly sought by collectors; hence they are not listed explicitly in the list below. The All-Star cards 426-435, when turned over and placed together, form a puzzle back of Pete Rose. This would turn out to be the final year that Topps issued cards in five-card nickel wax packs. Cards were also issued in thirty-six card rack packs which were sold for 29 cents.

COMP. MASTER (695) 2500.00 5000.00
COMPLETE SET (664) 1500.00 3000.00
COMMON (1-218/328-512) .60 1.50
COMMON (219-327) 1.00 2.50
COMMON (513-588) .75 2.00
COMMON (589-664) 1.25 3.00
WRAPPER (5-CENT) 8.00 20.00
1 AL Batting Leaders 6.00 15.00
Carl Yastrzemski
Danny Cater
Tony Oliva
2 NL Batting Leaders 3.00 8.00
Pete Rose
Matty Alou
Felipe Alou
3 AL RBI Leaders 1.50 4.00
Ken Harrelson
Frank Howard
Jim Northrup
4 NL RBI Leaders 2.50 6.00
Willie McCovey
Ron Santo
Billy Williams
5 AL Home Run Leaders 1.50 4.00
Frank Howard
Willie Horton
Ken Harrelson
6 NL Home Run Leaders 2.50 6.00
Willie McCovey
Richie Allen
Ernie Banks
7 AL ERA Leaders 1.50 4.00
Luis Tiant
Sam McDowell
Dave McNally
8 NL ERA Leaders 2.50 6.00
Bob Gibson
Bobby Bolin
Bob Veale
9 AL Pitching Leaders 1.50 4.00
Denny McLain
Dave McNally
Luis Tiant
Mel Stottlemyre
10 NL Pitching Leaders 3.00 8.00
Juan Marichal
Bob Gibson
Fergie Jenkins
11 AL Strikeout Leaders 1.50 4.00
Sam McDowell
Denny McLain
Luis Tiant
12 NL Strikeout Leaders 1.50 4.00
Bob Gibson
Fergie Jenkins
Bill Singer
13 Mickey Stanley 1.00 2.50
14 Al McBean .60 1.50
15 Boog Powell 1.50 4.00
16 Rookie Stars .60 1.50
Cesar Gutierrez RC
Rich Robertson RC
17 Mike Marshall 1.00 2.50
18 Dick Schofield .60 1.50
19 Ken Suarez .60 1.50
20 Ernie Banks 8.00 20.00
21 Jose Santiago .60 1.50
22 Jesus Alou 1.00 2.50
23 Lew Krausse .60 1.50
24 Walt Alston MG 1.50 4.00
25 Roy White 1.00 2.50
26 Clay Carroll 1.00 2.50
27 Bernie Allen .60 1.50
28 Mike Ryan .60 1.50
29 Dave Morehead .60 1.50
30 Bob Allison 1.00 2.50
31 Rookie Stars 1.00 2.50
Gary Gentry RC
Amos Otis RC
32 Sammy Ellis .60 1.50
33 Wayne Causey .60 1.50
34 Gary Peters .60 1.50
35 Joe Morgan 4.00 10.00
36 Luke Walker .60 1.50
37 Curt Motton .60 1.50
38 Zoilo Versalles 1.00 2.50
39 Dick Hughes .60 1.50
40 Mayo Smith MG .60 1.50
41 Bob Barton .60 1.50
42 Tommy Harper 1.00 2.50
43 Joe Niekro 1.00 2.50
44 Danny Cater .60 1.50
45 Maury Wills 1.00 2.50
46 Fritz Peterson 1.00 2.50
47A Paul Popovich 1.00 2.50
No helmet emblem, thick airbrushing
47B Paul Popovich 1.00 2.50
No helmet emblem, light airbrushing
47C Paul Popovich 10.00 25.00
(C emblem on helmet)
48 Brant Alyea .60 1.50
49A Rookie Stars 10.00 25.00
Steve Jones
E. Rodriquez ERR
49B Rookie Stars .60 1.50
Steve Jones RC
Ellie Rodriguez RC COR
50 Roberto Clemente 30.00 60.00
UER Bats Right listed twice
51 Woody Fryman 1.00 2.50
52 Mike Andrews .60 1.50
53 Sonny Jackson .60 1.50
54 Cisco Carlos .60 1.50
55 Jerry Grote 1.00 2.50
56 Rich Reese .60 1.50
57 Checklist 1 2.50 6.00
Denny McLain
58 Fred Gladding .60 1.50
59 Jay Johnstone 1.00 2.50
60 Nelson Briles 1.00 2.50
61 Jimmie Hall .60 1.50
62 Chico Salmon .60 1.50
63 Jim Hickman 1.00 2.50
64 Bill Monbouquette .60 1.50
65 Willie Davis 1.00 2.50
66 Rookie Stars .60 1.50
Mike Adamson RC
Merv Rettenmund RC
67 Bill Stoneman 1.00 2.50
68 Dave Duncan 1.00 2.50
69 Steve Hamilton 1.00 2.50
70 Tommy Helms 1.00 2.50
71 Steve Whitaker 1.00 2.50
72 Ron Taylor .60 1.50
73 Johnny Briggs .60 1.50
74 Preston Gomez MG RC 1.00 2.50
75 Luis Aparicio 2.50 6.00
76 Norm Miller .60 1.50
77A Ron Perranoski 1.00 2.50
(No emblem on cap)
77B Ron Perranoski 10.00 25.00
(LA on cap)
78 Tom Satriano .60 1.50
79 Milt Pappas 1.00 2.50
80 Norm Cash 1.00 2.50
81 Mel Queen .60 1.50
82 Rookie Stars 3.00 8.00
Rich Hebner RC
Al Oliver RC
83 Mike Ferraro 1.00 2.50
84 Bob Humphreys .60 1.50
85 Lou Brock 8.00 20.00
86 Pete Richert .60 1.50
87 Horace Clarke 1.00 2.50
88 Rich Nye .60 1.50
89 Russ Gibson .60 1.50
90 Jerry Koosman 1.00 2.50
91 Alvin Dark MG 1.00 2.50
92 Jack Billingham 1.00 2.50
93 Joe Foy 1.00 2.50
94 Hank Aguirre .60 1.50
95 Johnny Bench 20.00 50.00
96 Denny Lemaster .60 1.50
97 Buddy Bradford .60 1.50
98 Dave Giusti .60 1.50
99A Rookie Stars 6.00 15.00
Danny Morris RC
Graig Nettles RC
(No loop)
99B Rookie Stars 6.00 15.00
Danny Morris
Graig Nettles
(Errant loop in
upper left corner
of obverse)

100 Hank Aaron 20.00 50.00
101 Daryl Patterson .60 1.50
102 Jim Davenport .60 1.50
103 Roger Repoz .60 1.50
104 Steve Blass .60 1.50
105 Rick Monday 1.00 2.50
106 Jim Hannan .60 1.50
107A Checklist 2 ERR 2.50 6.00
Bob Gibson
161 Jim Purdin
107B Checklist 2 COR 3.00 8.00
Bob Gibson
161 John Purdin
108 Tony Taylor 1.00 2.50
109 Jim Lonborg 1.00 2.50
110 Mike Shannon 1.00 2.50
111 John Morris RC .60 1.50
112 J.C. Martin 1.00 2.50
113 Dave May .60 1.50
114 Rookie Stars 1.00 2.50
Alan Closter
John Cumberland RC
115 Bill Hands .60 1.50
116 Chuck Harrison .60 1.50
117 Jim Fairey 1.00 2.50
118 Stan Williams .60 1.50
119 Doug Rader 1.00 2.50
120 Pete Rose 20.00 50.00
121 Joe Grzenda RC .60 1.50
122 Ron Fairly 1.00 2.50
123 Wilbur Wood 1.00 2.50
124 Hank Bauer MG 1.00 2.50
125 Ray Sadecki .60 1.50
126 Dick Tracewski .60 1.50
127 Kevin Collins 1.00 2.50
128 Tommie Aaron 1.00 2.50
129 Bill McCool .60 1.50
130 Carl Yastrzemski 8.00 20.00
131 Chris Cannizzaro .60 1.50
132 Dave Baldwin .60 1.50
133 Johnny Callison 1.00 2.50
134 Jim Weaver .60 1.50
135 Tommy Davis 1.00 2.50
136 Rookie Stars .60 1.50
Steve Huntz RC
Mike Torrez
137 Wally Bunker .60 1.50
138 John Bateman .60 1.50
139 Andy Kosco .60 1.50
140 Jim Lefebvre 1.00 2.50
141 Bill Dillman .60 1.50
142 Woody Woodward .60 1.50
143 Joe Nossek .60 1.50
144 Bob Hendley 1.00 2.50
145 Max Alvis .60 1.50
146 Jim Perry 1.00 2.50
147 Leo Durocher MG 1.50 4.00
148 Lee Stange .60 1.50
149 Ollie Brown 1.00 2.50
150 Denny McLain 1.50 4.00
151A Clay Dalrymple .60 1.50
Portrait, Orioles
151B Clay Dalrymple 6.00 15.00
Catching, Phillies
152 Tommie Sisk .60 1.50
153 Ed Brinkman .60 1.50
154 Jim Britton .60 1.50
155 Pete Ward .60 1.50
156 Rookie Stars .60 1.50
Hal Gilson
Leon McFadden RC
157 Bob Rodgers 1.00 2.50
158 Joe Gibbon .60 1.50
159 Jerry Adair .60 1.50
160 Vada Pinson 1.00 2.50
161 John Purdin .60 1.50
162 World Series Game 1 3.00 8.00
Bob Gibson
163 World Series Game 2 2.50 6.00
Willie Horton
164 World Series Game 3 5.00 12.00
Tim McCarver
w/Maris
165 World Series Game 4 3.00 8.00
Lou Brock
166 World Series Game 5 3.00 8.00
Al Kaline
167 World Series Game 6 2.50 6.00
Jim Northrup
168 World Series Game 7 3.00 8.00
Mickey Lolich
Bob Gibson
169 World Series Summary 2.50 6.00
Tigers Celebrate
Dick McAuliffe
Denny McLain
Willie Horton
170 Frank Howard 1.00 2.50
171 Glenn Beckert 1.00 2.50
172 Jerry Stephenson .60 1.50
173 Rookie Stars .60 1.50
Bob Christian RC
Gerry Nyman RC
174 Grant Jackson .60 1.50
175 Jim Bunning 2.50 6.00
176 Joe Azcue .60 1.50
177 Ron Reed .60 1.50
178 Ray Oyler 1.00 2.50
179 Don Pavletich .60 1.50
180 Willie Horton 1.00 2.50
181 Mel Nelson .60 1.50
182 Bill Rigney MG .60 1.50
183 Don Shaw 1.00 2.50
184 Roberto Pena .60 1.50
185 Tom Phoebus .60 1.50
186 Johnny Edwards .60 1.50
187 Leon Wagner .60 1.50
188 Rick Wise 1.00 2.50
189 Rookie Stars .60 1.50
Joe Lahoud RC
John Thibodeau RC
190 Willie Mays 40.00 80.00
191 Lindy McDaniel 1.00 2.50
192 Jose Pagan .60 1.50
193 Don Cardwell 1.00 2.50
194 Ted Uhlaender .60 1.50
195 John Odom .60 1.50
196 Lum Harris MG .60 1.50
197 Dick Selma .60 1.50
198 Willie Smith .60 1.50
199 Jim French .60 1.50
200 Bob Gibson 5.00 12.00
201 Russ Snyder .60 1.50
202 Don Wilson 1.00 2.50
203 Dave Johnson 1.00 2.50
204 Jack Hiatt .60 1.50
205 Rick Reichardt .60 1.50
206 Rookie Stars 1.00 2.50
Larry Hisle
Barry Lersch RC
207 Roy Face 1.00 2.50
208A Donn Clendenon 1.00 2.50
Houston
208B Donn Clendenon 6.00 15.00
Expos
209 Larry Haney UER .60 1.50
(Reverse negative)
210 Felix Millan .60 1.50
211 Galen Cisco .60 1.50
212 Tom Tresh 1.00 2.50
213 Gerry Arrigo .60 1.50
214 Checklist 3 2.50 6.00
With 69T deckle CL
on back (no player)
215 Rico Petrocelli 1.00 2.50
216 Don Sutton 2.50 6.00
217 John Donaldson .60 1.50
218 John Roseboro 1.00 2.50
219 Freddie Patek RC 1.50 4.00
220 Sam McDowell 1.50 4.00
221 Art Shamsky 1.50 4.00
222 Duane Josephson 1.00 2.50
223 Tom Dukes 1.50 4.00
224 Rookie Stars 1.00 2.50
Bill Harrelson RC
Steve Kealey RC
225 Don Kessinger 1.50 4.00
226 Bruce Howard 1.00 2.50
227 Frank Johnson RC 1.00 2.50
228 Dave Leonhard 1.00 2.50
229 Don Lock 1.00 2.50
230 Rusty Staub UER 1.50 4.00
For 1966 stats, Houston spelled Huston
231 Pat Dobson 1.50 4.00
232 Dave Ricketts 1.00 2.50
233 Steve Barber 1.50 4.00
234 Dave Bristol MG 1.00 2.50
235 Jim Hunter 4.00 10.00
236 Manny Mota 1.50 4.00
237 Bobby Cox RC 8.00 20.00
238 Ken Johnson 1.00 2.50
239 Bob Taylor 1.50 4.00
240 Ken Harrelson 1.50 4.00
241 Jim Brewer 1.00 2.50
242 Frank Kostro 1.00 2.50
243 Ron Kline 1.00 2.50
244 Rookie Stars 1.50 4.00
Ray Fosse RC
George Woodson RC
245 Ed Charles 1.50 4.00
246 Joe Coleman 1.00 2.50
247 Gene Oliver 1.00 2.50
248 Bob Priddy 1.00 2.50
249 Ed Spiezio 1.50 4.00
250 Frank Robinson 8.00 20.00
251 Ron Herbel 1.00 2.50
252 Chuck Cottier 1.00 2.50
253 Jerry Johnson RC 1.00 2.50
254 Joe Schultz MG RC 1.50 4.00
255 Steve Carlton 12.50 30.00
256 Gates Brown 1.50 4.00
257 Jim Ray 1.00 2.50
258 Jackie Hernandez 1.50 4.00
259 Bill Short 1.00 2.50
260 Reggie Jackson RC 150.00 300.00
261 Bob Johnson 1.00 2.50
262 Mike Kekich 1.50 4.00
263 Jerry May 1.00 2.50
264 Bill Landis 1.00 2.50
265 Chico Cardenas 1.50 4.00
266 Rookie Stars 1.50 4.00
Tom Hutton
Alan Foster RC
267 Vicente Romo RC 1.00 2.50
268 Al Spangler 1.00 2.50
269 Al Weis 1.50 4.00
270 Mickey Lolich 1.50 4.00
271 Larry Stahl 1.50 4.00
272 Ed Stroud 1.00 2.50
273 Ron Willis 1.00 2.50
274 Clyde King MG 1.00 2.50
275 Vic Davalillo 1.00 2.50
276 Gary Wagner 1.00 2.50
277 Elrod Hendricks RC 1.00 2.50
278 Gary Geiger UER 1.00 2.50
(Batting wrong)
279 Roger Nelson 1.50 4.00
280 Alex Johnson 1.50 4.00
281 Ted Kubiak 1.00 2.50
282 Pat Jarvis 1.00 2.50
283 Sandy Alomar 1.50 4.00
284 Rookie Stars 1.50 4.00
Jerry Robertson RC
Mike Wegener RC
285 Don Mincher 1.50 4.00
286 Dock Ellis RC 1.50 4.00
287 Jose Tartabull 1.50 4.00
288 Ken Holtzman 1.50 4.00
289 Bart Shirley 1.00 2.50
290 Jim Kaat 1.50 4.00
291 Vern Fuller 1.00 2.50
292 Al Downing 1.50 4.00
293 Dick Dietz 1.00 2.50
294 Jim Lemon MG 1.00 2.50
295 Tony Perez 5.00 12.00
296 Andy Messersmith RC 1.50 4.00
297 Deron Johnson 1.00 2.50
298 Dave Nicholson 1.50 4.00
299 Mark Belanger 1.50 4.00
300 Felipe Alou 1.50 4.00
301 Darrell Brandon 1.50 4.00
302 Jim Pagliaroni 1.00 2.50
303 Cal Koonce 1.50 4.00
304 Rookie Stars 2.50 6.00
Bill Davis
Clarence Gaston RC
305 Dick McAuliffe 1.50 4.00
306 Jim Grant 1.50 4.00
307 Gary Kolb 1.00 2.50
308 Wade Blasingame 1.00 2.50
309 Walt Williams 1.00 2.50
310 Tom Haller 1.00 2.50
311 Sparky Lyle RC 4.00 10.00
312 Lee Elia 1.00 2.50
313 Bill Robinson 1.50 4.00
314 Checklist 4 2.50 6.00
Don Drysdale
315 Eddie Fisher 1.00 2.50
316 Hal Lanier 1.00 2.50
317 Bruce Look RC 1.00 2.50
318 Jack Fisher 1.00 2.50
319 Ken McMullen UER 1.00 2.50
(Headings on back
are for a pitcher)
320 Dal Maxvill 1.00 2.50
321 Jim McAndrew RC 1.50 4.00
322 Jose Vidal 1.50 4.00
323 Larry Miller 1.00 2.50
324 Rookie Stars 1.50 4.00
Les Cain RC
Dave Campbell RC
325 Jose Cardenal 1.50 4.00
326 Gary Sutherland 1.50 4.00
327 Willie Crawford 1.00 2.50
328 Joel Horlen .60 1.50
329 Rick Joseph .60 1.50
330 Tony Conigliaro 1.50 4.00
331 Rookie Stars 1.00 2.50
Gil Garrido
Tom House RC
332 Fred Talbot .60 1.50
333 Ivan Murrell .60 1.50
334 Phil Roof .60 1.50
335 Bill Mazeroski 2.50 6.00
336 Jim Roland .60 1.50
337 Marty Martinez RC .60 1.50
338 Del Unser RC .60 1.50
339 Rookie Stars .60 1.50
Steve Mingori RC
Jose Pena RC
340 Dave McNally 1.00 2.50
341 Dave Adlesh .60 1.50
342 Bubba Morton .60 1.50
343 Dan Frisella .60 1.50
344 Tom Matchick .60 1.50
345 Frank Linzy .60 1.50
346 Wayne Comer RC .60 1.50
347 Randy Hundley 1.00 2.50
348 Steve Hargan .60 1.50
349 Dick Williams MG 1.00 2.50
350 Richie Allen 1.50 4.00
351 Carroll Sembera .60 1.50
352 Paul Schaal 1.00 2.50
353 Jeff Torborg 1.00 2.50
354 Nate Oliver .60 1.50
355 Phil Niekro 2.50 6.00
356 Frank Quilici .60 1.50
357 Carl Taylor .60 1.50
358 Rookie Stars .60 1.50
George Lauzerique RC
Roberto Rodriquez
359 Dick Kelley .60 1.50
360 Jim Wynn 1.00 2.50
361 Gary Holman RC .60 1.50
362 Jim Maloney 1.00 2.50
363 Russ Nixon .60 1.50
364 Tommie Agee 1.50 4.00
365 Jim Fregosi 1.00 2.50
366 Bo Belinsky 1.00 2.50
367 Lou Johnson 1.00 2.50
368 Vic Roznovsky .60 1.50
369 Bob Skinner MG 1.00 2.50
370 Juan Marichal 3.00 8.00
371 Sal Bando 1.00 2.50
372 Adolfo Phillips .60 1.50
373 Fred Lasher .60 1.50
374 Bob Tillman .60 1.50
375 Harmon Killebrew 6.00 15.00
376 Rookie Stars .60 1.50
Mike Fiore RC
Jim Rooker RC
377 Gary Bell .60 1.50
378 Jose Herrera RC .60 1.50
379 Ken Boyer 1.00 2.50
380 Stan Bahnsen 1.00 2.50
381 Ed Kranepool 1.00 2.50
382 Pat Corrales 1.00 2.50
383 Casey Cox .60 1.50
384 Larry Shepard MG .60 1.50
385 Orlando Cepeda 2.50 6.00
386 Jim McGlothlin .60 1.50
387 Bobby Klaus .60 1.50
388 Tom McCraw .60 1.50
389 Dan Coombs .60 1.50
390 Bill Freehan 1.00 2.50
391 Ray Culp .60 1.50
392 Bob Burda RC .60 1.50
393 Gene Brabender 1.00 2.50
394 Rookie Stars 2.50 6.00
Lou Piniella
Marv Staehle
395 Chris Short .60 1.50
396 Jim Campanis .60 1.50
397 Chuck Dobson .60 1.50
398 Tito Francona .60 1.50
399 Bob Bailey 1.00 2.50
400 Don Drysdale 6.00 15.00
401 Jake Gibbs 1.00 2.50
402 Ken Boswell RC 1.00 2.50
403 Bob Miller .60 1.50
404 Rookie Stars 1.00 2.50
Vic LaRose RC
Gary Ross RC
405 Lee May 1.00 2.50
406 Phil Ortega .60 1.50
407 Tom Egan .60 1.50
408 Nate Colbert .60 1.50
409 Bob Moose .60 1.50
410 Al Kaline 10.00 25.00
411 Larry Dierker 1.00 2.50
412 Checklist 5 6.00 15.00
Mickey Mantle DP
413 Roland Sheldon 1.00 2.50
414 Duke Sims .60 1.50
415 Ray Washburn .60 1.50
416 Willie McCovey AS 3.00 8.00
417 Ken Harrelson AS 1.25 3.00
418 Tommy Helms AS 1.25 3.00
419 Rod Carew AS 4.00 10.00
420 Ron Santo AS 1.50 4.00
421 Brooks Robinson AS 3.00 8.00
422 Don Kessinger AS 1.25 3.00
423 Bert Campaneris AS 1.50 4.00
424 Pete Rose AS 6.00 15.00
425 Carl Yastrzemski AS 4.00 10.00
426 Curt Flood AS 1.50 4.00
427 Tony Oliva AS 1.50 4.00
428 Lou Brock AS 2.50 6.00
429 Willie Horton AS 1.25 3.00
430 Johnny Bench AS 4.00 10.00
431 Bill Freehan AS 1.50 4.00
432 Bob Gibson AS 2.50 6.00
433 Denny McLain AS 1.25 3.00
434 Jerry Koosman AS 1.25 3.00
435 Sam McDowell AS 1.25 3.00
436 Gene Alley 1.00 2.50
437 Luis Alcaraz RC .60 1.50
438 Gary Waslewski RC .60 1.50
439 Rookie Stars .60 1.50
Ed Herrmann RC
Dan Lazar RC
440A Willie McCovey 6.00 15.00
440B Willie McCovey WL 50.00 100.00
(McCovey white)
441A Dennis Higgins .60 1.50
441B Dennis Higgins WL 10.00 25.00
(Higgins white)
442 Ty Cline .60 1.50
443 Don Wert .60 1.50
444A Joe Moeller .60 1.50
444B Joe Moeller WL 10.00 25.00
(Moeller white)
445 Bobby Knoop .60 1.50
446 Claude Raymond .60 1.50
447A Ralph Houk MG 1.00 2.50
447B Ralph Houk MG WL 10.00 25.00
(Houk white)
448 Bob Tolan 1.00 2.50
449 Paul Lindblad .60 1.50
450 Billy Williams 3.00 8.00
451A Rich Rollins 1.00 2.50
451B Rich Rollins WL 10.00 25.00
(Rich and 3B white)
452A Al Ferrara .60 1.50
452B Al Ferrara WL 10.00 25.00
(Al and OF white)
453 Mike Cuellar 1.00 2.50
454A Rookie Stars 1.00 2.50
Larry Colton
Don Money RC
454B Rookie Stars 10.00 25.00
Larry Colton
Don Money
(Names in white) WL
455 Sonny Siebert .60 1.50
456 Bud Harrelson 1.00 2.50
457 Dalton Jones .60 1.50
458 Curt Blefary .60 1.50
459 Dave Boswell .60 1.50
460 Joe Torre 1.50 4.00
461A Mike Epstein .60 1.50
461B Mike Epstein WL 10.00 25.00
(Epstein white)
462 R.Schoendienst MG 1.00 2.50
463 Dennis Ribant .60 1.50
464A Dave Marshall RC .60 1.50
464B Dave Marshall WL 10.00 25.00
(Marshall white)
465 Tommy John 1.50 4.00
466 John Boccabella 1.00 2.50
467 Tommie Reynolds .60 1.50
468A Rookie Stars .60 1.50
Bruce Dal Canton RC
Bob Robertson
468B Rookie Stars 10.00 25.00
Bruce Dal Canton
Bob Robertson
(Names in white) WL
469 Chico Ruiz .60 1.50
470A Mel Stottlemyre 1.00 2.50
470B Mel Stottlemyre WL 12.50 30.00
(Stottlemyre white)
471A Ted Savage .60 1.50
471B Ted Savage WL 10.00 25.00
(Savage white)
472 Jim Price .60 1.50
473A Jose Arcia .60 1.50
473B Jose Arcia WL 10.00 25.00
(Jose and 2B white)
474 Tom Murphy RC .60 1.50
475 Tim McCarver 1.50 4.00
476A Rookie Stars 1.00 2.50
Ken Brett RC
Gerry Moses
476B Rookie Stars 12.50 30.00
Ken Brett
Gerry Moses
(Names in white) WL
477 Jeff James RC .60 1.50
478 Don Buford .60 1.50
479 Richie Scheinblum .60 1.50
480 Tom Seaver 40.00 80.00
481 Bill Melton RC 1.00 2.50
482A Jim Gosger .60 1.50
482B Jim Gosger WL 10.00 25.00
(Jim and OF white)
483 Ted Abernathy .60 1.50
484 Joe Gordon MG 1.00 2.50
485A Gaylord Perry 4.00 10.00
485B Gaylord Perry WL 40.00 80.00
(Perry white)
486A Paul Casanova .60 1.50
486B Paul Casanova WL 10.00 25.00
(Casanova white)
487 Denis Menke .60 1.50
488 Joe Sparma .60 1.50
489 Clete Boyer 1.00 2.50
490 Matty Alou 1.00 2.50
491A Rookie Stars .60 1.50
Jerry Crider RC
George Mitterwald
491B Rookie Stars 10.00 25.00
Jerry Crider
George Mitterwald
(Names in white) WL
492 Tony Cloninger .60 1.50
493A Wes Parker 1.00 2.50
493B Wes Parker WL 10.00 25.00
(Parker white)
494 Ken Berry .60 1.50
495 Bert Campaneris 1.00 2.50
496 Larry Jaster .60 1.50
497 Julian Javier 1.00 2.50
498 Juan Pizarro 1.00 2.50
499 Rookie Stars .60 1.50
Don Bryant RC
Steve Shea RC
500A Mickey Mantle UER 175.00 350.00
(No Topps copy-
right on card back)
500B Mickey Mantle WL 1000.00 2000.00
(Mantle in white;
no Topps copyright
on card back) UER
501A Tony Gonzalez 1.00 2.50
501B Tony Gonzalez WL 10.00 25.00
(Tony and OF white)
502 Minnie Rojas .60 1.50
503 Larry Brown .60 1.50
504 Checklist 6 3.00 8.00
Brooks Robinson
505A Bobby Bolin .60 1.50
505B Bobby Bolin WL 10.00 25.00
(Bolin white)
506 Paul Blair 1.00 2.50
507 Cookie Rojas 1.00 2.50
508 Moe Drabowsky 1.00 2.50
509 Manny Sanguillen 1.00 2.50
510 Rod Carew 15.00 40.00
511A Diego Segui 1.00 2.50
511B Diego Segui WL 10.00 25.00
(Diego and P white)
512 Cleon Jones 1.00 2.50
513 Camilo Pascual 1.25 3.00
514 Mike Lum .75 2.00
515 Dick Green .75 2.00
516 Earl Weaver MG RC 8.00 20.00
517 Mike McCormick 1.25 3.00
518 Fred Whitfield .75 2.00
519 Rookie Stars .75 2.00
Jerry Kenney RC
Len Boehmer RC
520 Bob Veale 1.25 3.00
521 George Thomas .75 2.00
522 Joe Hoerner .75 2.00
523 Bob Chance .75 2.00
524 Rookie Stars 1.25 3.00
Jose Laboy RC
Floyd Wicker RC
525 Earl Wilson 1.25 3.00
526 Hector Torres RC .75 2.00
527 Al Lopez MG 2.00 5.00
528 Claude Osteen 1.25 3.00
529 Ed Kirkpatrick 1.25 3.00
530 Cesar Tovar .75 2.00
531 Dick Farrell .75 2.00
532 Bird Hill Aces 1.25 3.00
Tom Phoebus
Jim Hardin
Dave McNally
Mike Cuellar
533 Nolan Ryan 100.00 200.00
534 Jerry McNertney 1.25 3.00
535 Phil Regan 1.25 3.00
536 Rookie Stars .75 2.00
Danny Breeden RC
Dave Roberts RC
537 Mike Paul RC .75 2.00
538 Charlie Smith .75 2.00
539 Ted Shows How 5.00 12.00
Mike Epstein
Ted Williams MG
540 Curt Flood 1.25 3.00
541 Joe Verbanic .75 2.00
542 Bob Aspromonte .75 2.00
543 Fred Newman .75 2.00
544 Rookie Stars .75 2.00
Mike Kilkenny RC
Ron Woods RC
545 Willie Stargell 5.00 12.00
546 Jim Nash .75 2.00
547 Billy Martin MG 2.00 5.00
548 Bob Locker .75 2.00
549 Ron Brand .75 2.00
550 Brooks Robinson 12.50 30.00
551 Wayne Granger RC .75 2.00
552 Rookie Stars 1.25 3.00
Ted Sizemore RC
Bill Sudakis RC
553 Ron Davis .75 2.00
554 Frank Bertaina .75 2.00
555 Jim Ray Hart 1.25 3.00
556 A's Stars 1.25 3.00
Sal Bando
Bert Campaneris
Danny Cater
557 Frank Fernandez .75 2.00
558 Tom Burgmeier RC 1.25 3.00
559 Rookie Stars .75 2.00
Joe Hague RC
Jim Hicks
560 Luis Tiant 1.25 3.00
561 Ron Clark .75 2.00
562 Bob Watson RC 3.00 8.00
563 Marty Pattin RC 1.25 3.00
564 Gil Hodges MG 4.00 10.00
565 Hoyt Wilhelm 3.00 8.00
566 Ron Hansen .75 2.00
567 Rookie Stars .75 2.00
Elvio Jimenez
Jim Shellenback
568 Cecil Upshaw .75 2.00
569 Billy Harris .60 1.50
570 Ron Santo 3.00 8.00
571 Cap Peterson .75 2.00
572 Giants Heroes 6.00 15.00
Willie McCovey
Juan Marichal
573 Jim Palmer 12.50 30.00
574 George Scott 1.25 3.00
575 Bill Singer 1.25 3.00
576 Rookie Stars .75 2.00
Ron Stone
Bill Wilson
577 Mike Hegan 1.25 3.00
578 Don Bosch .75 2.00
579 Dave Nelson RC .75 2.00
580 Jim Northrup 1.25 3.00
581 Gary Nolan 1.25 3.00
582A Checklist 7 2.50 6.00
Tony Oliva
White circle on back
582B Checklist 7 3.00 8.00
Tony Oliva
Red circle on back
583 Clyde Wright RC .75 2.00
584 Don Mason .75 2.00
585 Ron Swoboda 1.25 3.00
586 Tim Cullen .75 2.00
587 Joe Rudi RC 3.00 8.00
588 Bill White 1.25 3.00
589 Joe Pepitone 2.00 5.00
590 Rico Carty 2.00 5.00
591 Mike Hedlund 1.25 3.00
592 Rookie Stars 2.00 5.00
Rafael Robles RC
Al Santorini RC
593 Don Nottebart 1.25 3.00
594 Dooley Womack 1.25 3.00
595 Lee Maye 1.25 3.00
596 Chuck Hartenstein 1.25 3.00
597 Rookie Stars 15.00 40.00
Bob Floyd RC
Larry Burchart RC
Rollie Fingers RC
598 Ruben Amaro 1.25 3.00
599 John Boozer 1.25 3.00
600 Tony Oliva 3.00 8.00
601 Tug McGraw 3.00 8.00
602 Rookie Stars 2.00 5.00
Alec Distaso RC
Don Young
Jim Qualls RC
603 Joe Keough RC 1.25 3.00
604 Bobby Etheridge 1.25 3.00
605 Dick Ellsworth 1.25 3.00
606 Gene Mauch MG 2.00 5.00
607 Dick Bosman 1.25 3.00
608 Dick Simpson 1.25 3.00
609 Phil Gagliano 1.25 3.00
610 Jim Hardin 1.25 3.00
611 Rookie Stars 2.00 5.00
Bob Didier RC
Walt Hriniak RC
Gary Neibauer RC
612 Jack Aker 2.00 5.00
613 Jim Beauchamp 1.25 3.00
614 Rookie Stars 1.25 3.00
Tom Griffin RC
Skip Guinn RC
615 Len Gabrielson 1.25 3.00
616 Don McMahon 1.25 3.00
617 Jesse Gonder 1.25 3.00
618 Ramon Webster 1.25 3.00
619 Rookie Stars 2.00 5.00
Bill Butler RC
Pat Kelly RC
Juan Rios RC
620 Dean Chance 2.00 5.00
621 Bill Voss 1.25 3.00
622 Dan Osinski 1.25 3.00
623 Hank Allen 1.25 3.00
624 Rookie Stars 2.00 5.00
Darrel Chaney RC
Duffy Dyer RC
Terry Harmon RC
625 Mack Jones UER 2.00 5.00
(Batting wrong)
626 Gene Michael 2.00 5.00
627 George Stone RC 1.25 3.00
628 Rookie Stars 2.00 5.00
Bill Conigliaro RC
Syd O'Brien RC
Fred Wenz RC
629 Jack Hamilton 1.25 3.00
630 Bobby Bonds RC 12.50 30.00
631 John Kennedy 2.00 5.00
632 Jon Warden RC 1.25 3.00
633 Harry Walker MG 1.25 3.00
634 Andy Etchebarren 1.25 3.00
635 George Culver 1.25 3.00
636 Woody Held 1.25 3.00
637 Rookie Stars 2.00 5.00
Jerry DaVanon RC
Frank Reberger RC
Clay Kirby RC
638 Ed Sprague RC 1.25 3.00
639 Barry Moore 1.25 3.00
640 Ferguson Jenkins 8.00 20.00
641 Rookie Stars 2.00 5.00
Bobby Darwin RC
John Miller
Tommy Dean RC
642 John Hiller 1.25 3.00
643 Billy Cowan 1.25 3.00
644 Chuck Hinton 1.25 3.00
645 George Brunet 1.25 3.00
646 Rookie Stars 2.00 5.00
Dan McGinn RC
Carl Morton RC
647 Dave Wickersham 1.25 3.00
648 Bobby Wine 2.00 5.00
649 Al Jackson 1.25 3.00
650 Ted Williams MG 8.00 20.00
651 Gus Gil 2.00 5.00
652 Eddie Watt 1.25 3.00
653 Aurelio Rodriguez RC 2.00 5.00
UER Photo is
Angels batboy Leonard Garcia
654 Rookie Stars 2.00 5.00
Carlos May RC
Don Secrist RC
Rich Morales RC
655 Mike Hershberger 1.25 3.00
656 Dan Schneider 1.25 3.00
657 Bobby Murcer 3.00 8.00
658 Rookie Stars 1.25 3.00
Tom Hall RC
Bill Burbach RC
Jim Miles RC
659 Johnny Podres 2.00 5.00
660 Reggie Smith 2.00 5.00
661 Jim Merritt 1.25 3.00
662 Rookie Stars 2.00 5.00
Dick Drago RC
George Spriggs
Bob Oliver RC
663 Dick Radatz 2.00 5.00
664 Ron Hunt 2.00 5.00

1969 Topps Decals

The 1969 Topps Decal Inserts are a set of 48 unnumbered decals issued as inserts in packages of 1969 Topps regular issue cards. Each decal is approximately 1" by 1 1/2" although including the plain backing the measurement is 1 3/4" by 2 1/8". The decals appear to be miniature versions of the Topps regular issue of that year. The copyright notice on the side indicates that these decals were produced in the United Kingdom. Most of the players on the decals are stars.

COMPLETE SET (48) 250.00 500.00
1 Hank Aaron 20.00 50.00
2 Richie Allen 3.00 8.00
3 Felipe Alou 2.00 5.00
4 Matty Alou 2.00 5.00
5 Luis Aparicio 3.00 8.00
6 Roberto Clemente 30.00 60.00
7 Donn Clendenon 1.50 4.00
8 Tommy Davis 2.00 5.00
9 Don Drysdale 4.00 10.00
10 Joe Foy 1.50 4.00
11 Jim Fregosi 2.00 5.00
12 Bob Gibson 4.00 10.00
13 Tony Gonzalez 1.50 4.00
14 Tom Haller 1.50 4.00
15 Ken Harrelson 2.00 5.00
16 Tommy Helms 1.50 4.00
17 Willie Horton 2.00 5.00
18 Frank Howard 2.00 5.00
19 Reggie Jackson 20.00 50.00
20 Ferguson Jenkins 3.00 8.00
21 Harmon Killebrew 6.00 15.00
22 Jerry Koosman 2.00 5.00
23 Mickey Mantle 50.00 100.00
24 Willie Mays 20.00 50.00
25 Tim McCarver 2.00 5.00
26 Willie McCovey 4.00 10.00
27 Sam McDowell 2.00 5.00
28 Denny McLain 2.00 5.00
29 Dave McNally 2.00 5.00
30 Don Mincher 1.50 4.00
31 Rick Monday 2.00 5.00
32 Tony Oliva 3.00 8.00
33 Camilo Pascual 1.50 4.00
34 Rick Reichardt 1.50 4.00
35 Frank Robinson 4.00 10.00
36 Pete Rose 20.00 50.00

37 Ron Santo 3.00 8.00
38 Tom Seaver 12.50 30.00
39 Dick Selma 1.50 4.00
40 Chris Short 1.50 4.00
41 Rusty Staub 3.00 8.00
42 Mel Stottlemyre 2.00 5.00
43 Luis Tiant 2.00 5.00
44 Pete Ward 1.50 4.00
45 Hoyt Wilhelm 3.00 8.00
46 Maury Wills 3.00 8.00
47 Jim Wynn 2.00 5.00
48 Carl Yastrzemski 8.00 20.00

1969 Topps Deckle Edge

The cards in this 33-card set measure approximately 2 1/4" by 3 1/4". This unusual black and white insert set derives its name from the serrated border, or edge, of the cards. The cards were included as inserts in the regularly issued Topps baseball third series of 1969. Card number 11 is found with either Hoyt Wilhelm or Jim Wynn, and number 22 with either Rusty Staub or Joe Foy. The set price below does include all variations. The set numbering is arranged in team order by league except for cards 11 and 22.

COMPLETE SET (35) 50.00 100.00
1 Brooks Robinson 2.50 6.00
2 Boog Powell 1.25 3.00
3 Ken Harrelson .60 1.50
4 Carl Yastrzemski 3.00 8.00
5 Jim Fregosi .75 2.00
6 Luis Aparicio 1.25 3.00
7 Luis Tiant .75 2.00
8 Denny McLain 1.25 3.00
9 Willie Horton .75 2.00
10 Bill Freehan .75 2.00
11A Hoyt Wilhelm 3.00 8.00
11B Jim Wynn 6.00 15.00
12 Rod Carew 1.50 4.00
13 Mel Stottlemyre .75 2.00
14 Rick Monday .60 1.50
15 Tommy Davis .75 2.00
16 Frank Howard .75 2.00
17 Felipe Alou .75 2.00
18 Don Kessinger .60 1.50
19 Ron Santo 1.25 3.00
20 Tommy Helms .60 1.50
21 Pete Rose 5.00 12.00
22A Rusty Staub .75 2.00
22B Joe Foy 10.00 25.00
23 Tom Haller .60 1.50
24 Maury Wills 1.25 3.00
25 Jerry Koosman .75 2.00
26 Richie Allen 1.50 4.00
27 Roberto Clemente 8.00 20.00
28 Curt Flood 1.25 3.00
29 Bob Gibson 1.50 4.00
30 Al Ferrara .60 1.50
31 Willie McCovey 1.50 4.00
32 Juan Marichal 1.25 3.00
33 Willie Mays 5.00 12.00

1970 Topps

The cards in this 720-card set measure 2 1/2" by 3 1/2". The Topps set for 1970 has color photos surrounded by white frame lines and gray borders. The backs have a blue biographical section and a yellow record section. All-Star selections are featured on cards 450 to 469. Other topical subsets within this set include League Leaders (61-72), Playoffs cards (195-202), and World Series cards (305-310). There are graduations of scarcity, terminating in the high series (634-720), which are outlined in the value summary. Cards were issued in ten-card dime packs as well as thirty-three card cello packs which sold for a quarter and were encased in a small Topps box, and in 54-card rack packs which sold for 39 cents. The key Rookie Card in this set is Thurman Munson.

COMPLETE SET (720) 1000.00 2000.00
COMMON CARD (1-132) .30 .75
COMMON (373-459) .40 1.00
COMMON CARD (373-459) .60 1.50
COMMON (460-546) .75 2.00
COMMON (547-633) 1.50 4.00
COMMON (634-720) 4.00 10.00
WRAPPER (10-CENT) 8.00 20.00
1 New York Mets TC 12.50 30.00
2 Diego Segui .40 1.00
3 Darrel Chaney .30 .75
4 Tom Egan .30 .75
5 Wes Parker .40 1.00
6 Grant Jackson .30 .75
7 Rookie Stars .30 .75
Gary Boyd RC
Russ Nagelson RC
8 Jose Martinez RC .30 .75
9 Checklist 1 5.00 12.00
10 Carl Yastrzemski 8.00 20.00
11 Nate Colbert .30 .75
12 John Hiller .30 .75
13 Jack Hiatt .30 .75
14 Hank Allen .30 .75
15 Larry Dierker .30 .75
16 Charlie Metro MG RC .30 .75
17 Hoyt Wilhelm 1.50 4.00
18 Carlos May .40 1.00
19 John Boccabella .30 .75
20 Dave McNally .40 1.00
21 Rookie Stars 1.50 4.00
Vida Blue RC
Gene Tenace RC
22 Ray Washburn .30 .75
23 Bill Robinson .40 1.00
24 Dick Selma .30 .75
25 Cesar Tovar .30 .75
26 Tug McGraw .75 2.00
27 Chuck Hinton .30 .75
28 Billy Wilson .30 .75
29 Sandy Alomar .40 1.00
30 Matty Alou .40 1.00
31 Marty Pattin .40 1.00
32 Harry Walker MG .30 .75
33 Don Wert .30 .75
34 Willie Crawford .30 .75
35 Joel Horlen .30 .75
36 Rookie Stars .40 1.00
Danny Breeden
Bernie Carbo RC
37 Dick Drago .30 .75
38 Mack Jones .30 .75
39 Mike Nagy RC .30 .75
40 Rich Allen .75 2.00
41 George Lauzerique .30 .75
42 Tito Fuentes .30 .75
43 Jack Aker .30 .75
44 Roberto Pena .30 .75
45 Dave Johnson .40 1.00
46 Ken Rudolph RC .30 .75
47 Bob Miller .30 .75
48 Gil Garrido .30 .75
49 Tim Cullen .30 .75
50 Tommie Agee .40 1.00
51 Bob Christian .30 .75
52 Bruce Dal Canton .30 .75
53 John Kennedy .30 .75
54 Jeff Torborg .40 1.00
55 John Odom .30 .75
56 Rookie Stars .30 .75
Joe Lis RC
Scott Reid RC
57 Pat Kelly .30 .75
58 Dave Marshall .30 .75
59 Dick Ellsworth .30 .75
60 Jim Wynn .40 1.00
61 NL Batting Leaders 5.00 12.00
Pete Rose
Bob Clemente
Cleon Jones
62 AL Batting Leaders .75 2.00
Rod Carew
Reggie Smith
Tony Oliva
63 NL RBI Leaders .75 2.00
Willie McCovey
Ron Santo
Tony Perez
64 AL RBI Leaders 1.50 4.00
Harmon Killebrew
Boog Powell
Reggie Jackson
65 NL Home Run Leaders 1.50 4.00
Willie McCovey
Hank Aaron
Lee May
66 AL Home Run Leaders 1.50 4.00
Harmon Killebrew
Frank Howard
Reggie Jackson
67 NL ERA Leaders 1.50 4.00
Juan Marichal
Steve Carlton
Bob Gibson
68 AL ERA Leaders .40 1.00
Dick Bosman
Jim Palmer
Mike Cuellar
69 NL Pitching Leaders 1.50 4.00
Tom Seaver
Phil Niekro
Fergie Jenkins
Juan Marichal
70 AL Pitching Leaders .40 1.00
Dennis McLain
Mike Cuellar
Dave Boswell
Dave McNally
Jim Perry
Mel Stottlemyre
71 NL Strikeout Leaders .75 2.00
Fergie Jenkins
Bob Gibson
Bill Singer
72 AL Strikeout Leaders .40 1.00
Sam McDowell
Mickey Lolich
Andy Messersmith
73 Wayne Granger .30 .75
74 Rookie Stars .30 .75
Greg Washburn RC
Wally Wolf
75 Jim Kaat .40 1.00
76 Carl Taylor UER .30 .75
Collecting is spelled incorrectly in the cartoon
77 Frank Linzy .30 .75
78 Joe Lahoud .30 .75
79 Clay Kirby .30 .75
80 Don Kessinger .40 1.00
81 Dave May .30 .75
82 Frank Fernandez .30 .75
83 Don Cardwell .30 .75
84 Paul Casanova .30 .75
85 Max Alvis .30 .75
86 Lum Harris MG .30 .75
87 Steve Renko RC .30 .75
88 Rookie Stars .40 1.00
Miguel Fuentes RC
Dick Baney RC
89 Juan Rios .30 .75
90 Tim McCarver .40 1.00
91 Rich Morales .30 .75
92 George Culver .30 .75
93 Rick Renick .30 .75
94 Freddie Patek .40 1.00
95 Earl Wilson .40 1.00
96 Rookie Stars .40 1.00
Leron Lee RC
Jerry Reuss RC
97 Joe Moeller .30 .75
98 Gates Brown .40 1.00
99 Bobby Pfeil RC .30 .75
100 Mel Stottlemyre .40 1.00
101 Bobby Floyd .30 .75
102 Joe Rudi .40 1.00
103 Frank Reberger .30 .75
104 Gerry Moses .30 .75
105 Tony Gonzalez .30 .75
106 Darold Knowles .30 .75
107 Bobby Etheridge .30 .75
108 Tom Burgmeier .30 .75
109 Rookie Stars .30 .75
Garry Jestadt RC
Carl Morton
110 Bob Moose .30 .75
111 Mike Hegan .40 1.00
112 Dave Nelson .30 .75
113 Jim Ray .30 .75
114 Gene Michael .40 1.00
115 Alex Johnson .40 1.00
116 Sparky Lyle .40 1.00
117 Don Young .30 .75
118 George Mitterwald .30 .75
119 Chuck Taylor RC .30 .75
120 Sal Bando .40 1.00
121 Rookie Stars .30 .75
Fred Beene RC
Terry Crowley RC
122 George Stone .30 .75
123 Don Gutteridge MG RC .30 .75
124 Larry Jaster .30 .75
125 Deron Johnson .30 .75
126 Marty Martinez .30 .75
127 Joe Coleman .30 .75
128A Checklist 2 ERR 2.50 6.00
(226 R Perranoski)
128B Checklist 2 COR 2.50 6.00
(226 R. Perranoski)
129 Jimmie Price .30 .75
130 Ollie Brown .30 .75
131 Rookie Stars .30 .75
Ray Lamb RC
Bob Stinson RC
132 Jim McGlothlin .30 .75
133 Clay Carroll .40 1.00
134 Danny Walton RC .40 1.00
135 Dick Dietz .40 1.00
136 Steve Hargan .40 1.00
137 Art Shamsky .40 1.00
138 Joe Foy .40 1.00
139 Rich Nye .40 1.00
140 Reggie Jackson 20.00 50.00
141 Rookie Stars .60 1.50
Dave Cash RC
Johnny Jeter RC
142 Fritz Peterson .40 1.00
143 Phil Gagliano .40 1.00
144 Ray Culp .40 1.00
145 Rico Carty .60 1.50
146 Danny Murphy .40 1.00
147 Angel Hermoso RC .40 1.00
148 Earl Weaver MG 1.25 3.00
149 Billy Champion RC .40 1.00
150 Harmon Killebrew 3.00 8.00
151 Dave Roberts .40 1.00
152 Ike Brown RC .40 1.00
153 Gary Gentry .40 1.00
154 Rookie Stars .40 1.00
Jim Miles
Jan Dukes RC
155 Denis Menke .40 1.00
156 Eddie Fisher .40 1.00
157 Manny Mota .60 1.50
158 Jerry McNertney .60 1.50
159 Tommy Helms .60 1.50
160 Phil Niekro 2.00 5.00
161 Richie Scheinblum .40 1.00
162 Jerry Johnson .40 1.00
163 Syd O'Brien .40 1.00
164 Ty Cline .40 1.00
165 Ed Kirkpatrick .40 1.00
166 Al Oliver 1.25 3.00
167 Bill Burbach .40 1.00
168 Dave Watkins RC .40 1.00
169 Tom Hall .40 1.00
170 Billy Williams 2.00 5.00
171 Jim Nash .40 1.00
172 Rookie Stars .60 1.50
Garry Hill RC
Ralph Garr RC
173 Jim Hicks .40 1.00
174 Ted Sizemore .60 1.50
175 Dick Bosman .40 1.00
176 Jim Ray Hart .60 1.50
177 Jim Northrup .60 1.50
178 Denny Lemaster .40 1.00
179 Ivan Murrell .40 1.00
180 Tommy John .60 1.50
181 Sparky Anderson MG 2.00 5.00
182 Dick Hall .40 1.00
183 Jerry Grote .60 1.50
184 Ray Fosse .40 1.00
185 Don Mincher .60 1.50
186 Rick Joseph .40 1.00
187 Mike Hedlund .40 1.00
188 Manny Sanguillen .60 1.50
189 Rookie Stars 50.00 100.00
Thurman Munson RC
Dave McDonald RC
190 Joe Torre 1.25 3.00
191 Vicente Romo .40 1.00
192 Jim Qualls .40 1.00
193 Mike Wegener .40 1.00
194 Chuck Manuel RC 1.00 2.50
195 NL Playoff Game 1 6.00 15.00
Tom Seaver
196 NL Playoff Game 2 .75 2.00
Ken Boswell
197 NL Playoff Game 3 12.50 30.00
Nolan Ryan
198 NL Playoff Summary 6.00 15.00
Mets Celebrate
(w/Nolan Ryan
199 AL Playoff Game 1 .75 2.00
Mike Cuellar
200 AL Playoff Game 2 1.25 3.00
Boog Powell
Scoring over George Mitterwald
201 AL Playoff Game 3 .75 2.00
Boog Powell
Andy Etchebarren
202 AL Playoff Summary .75 2.00
Orioles Celebrate
203 Rudy May .40 1.00
204 Len Gabrielson .40 1.00
205 Bert Campaneris .60 1.50
206 Clete Boyer .60 1.50
207 Rookie Stars .40 1.00
Norman McRae RC
Bob Reed RC
208 Fred Gladding .40 1.00
209 Ken Suarez .40 1.00
210 Juan Marichal 2.00 5.00
211 Ted Williams MG UER 6.00 15.00
Throwing information on back incorrect
212 Al Santorini .40 1.00
213 Andy Etchebarren .40 1.00
214 Ken Boswell .40 1.00
215 Reggie Smith .60 1.50
216 Chuck Hartenstein .40 1.00
217 Ron Hansen .40 1.00
218 Ron Stone .40 1.00
219 Jerry Kenney .40 1.00
220 Steve Carlton 6.00 15.00
221 Ron Brand .40 1.00
222 Jim Rooker .40 1.00
223 Nate Oliver .40 1.00
224 Steve Barber .60 1.50
225 Lee May .60 1.50
226 Ron Perranoski .40 1.00
227 Rookie Stars .60 1.50
John Mayberry RC
Bob Watkins RC
228 Aurelio Rodriguez .40 1.00
229 Rich Robertson .40 1.00
230 Brooks Robinson 6.00 15.00
231 Luis Tiant .60 1.50
232 Bob Didier .40 1.00
233 Lew Krausse .40 1.00
234 Tommy Dean .40 1.00
235 Mike Epstein .40 1.00
236 Bob Veale .40 1.00
237 Russ Gibson .40 1.00
238 Jose Laboy .40 1.00
239 Ken Berry .40 1.00
240 Ferguson Jenkins 2.00 5.00
241 Rookie Stars .40 1.00
Al Fitzmorris RC
Scott Northey RC
242 Walter Alston MG 1.25 3.00
243 Joe Sparma .40 1.00
244A Checklist 3 2.50 6.00
(Red bat on front)
244B Checklist 3 2.50 6.00
(Brown bat on front)
245 Leo Cardenas .40 1.00
246 Jim McAndrew .40 1.00
247 Lou Klimchock .40 1.00
248 Jesus Alou .40 1.00
249 Bob Locker .40 1.00
250 Willie McCovey UER 4.00 10.00
(1963 San Francisci)
251 Dick Schofield .40 1.00
252 Lowell Palmer RC .40 1.00
253 Ron Woods .40 1.00
254 Camilo Pascual .40 1.00
255 Jim Spencer RC .40 1.00
256 Vic Davalillo .40 1.00
257 Dennis Higgins .40 1.00
258 Paul Popovich .40 1.00
259 Tommie Reynolds .40 1.00
260 Claude Osteen .40 1.00
261 Curt Motton .40 1.00
262 Rookie Stars .40 1.00
Jerry Morales RC
Jim Williams RC
263 Duane Josephson .40 1.00
264 Rich Hebner .40 1.00
265 Randy Hundley .40 1.00
266 Wally Bunker .40 1.00
267 Rookie Stars .40 1.00
Herman Hill RC
Paul Ratliff
268 Claude Raymond .40 1.00
269 Cesar Gutierrez .40 1.00
270 Chris Short .40 1.00
271 Greg Goossen .60 1.50
272 Hector Torres .40 1.00
273 Ralph Houk MG .60 1.50
274 Gerry Arrigo .40 1.00
275 Duke Sims .40 1.00
276 Ron Hunt .40 1.00
277 Paul Doyle RC .40 1.00
278 Tommie Aaron .40 1.00
279 Bill Lee RC .60 1.50
280 Donn Clendenon .60 1.50
281 Casey Cox .40 1.00
282 Steve Huntz .40 1.00
283 Angel Bravo RC .40 1.00
284 Jack Baldschun .40 1.00
285 Paul Blair .60 1.50
286 Rookie Stars 2.00 5.00
Jack Jenkins RC
Bill Buckner RC
287 Fred Talbot .40 1.00
288 Larry Hisle .60 1.50
289 Gene Brabender .40 1.00
290 Rod Carew 6.00 15.00
291 Leo Durocher MG 1.25 3.00
292 Eddie Leon RC .40 1.00
293 Bob Bailey .60 1.50
294 Jose Azcue .40 1.00
295 Cecil Upshaw .40 1.00
296 Woody Woodward .40 1.00
297 Curt Blefary .40 1.00
298 Ken Henderson .40 1.00
299 Buddy Bradford .40 1.00
300 Tom Seaver 12.50 30.00
301 Chico Salmon .40 1.00
302 Jeff James .40 1.00
303 Brant Alyea .40 1.00
304 Bill Russell RC 2.00 5.00
305 World Series Game 1 1.50 4.00
Don Buford
306 World Series Game 2 1.50 4.00
Donn Clendenon
307 World Series Game 3 1.50 4.00
Tommie Agee
308 World Series Game 4 1.50 4.00
J.C. Martin
309 World Series Game 5 1.50 4.00
Jerry Koosman
310 World Series Summary 2.00 5.00
Mets Whoop it Up
311 Dick Green .40 1.00
312 Mike Torrez .40 1.00
313 Mayo Smith MG .40 1.00
314 Bill McCool .40 1.00
315 Luis Aparicio 2.00 5.00
316 Skip Guinn .40 1.00
317 Rookie Stars .60 1.50
Billy Conigliaro
Luis Alvarado RC
318 Willie Smith .40 1.00
319 Clay Dalrymple .40 1.00
320 Jim Maloney .60 1.50
321 Lou Piniella .60 1.50
322 Luke Walker .40 1.00
323 Wayne Comer .40 1.00
324 Tony Taylor .60 1.50
325 Dave Boswell .40 1.00
326 Bill Voss .40 1.00
327 Hal King RC .40 1.00
328 George Brunet .40 1.00
329 Chris Cannizzaro .40 1.00
330 Lou Brock 4.00 10.00
331 Chuck Dobson .40 1.00
332 Bobby Wine .40 1.00
333 Bobby Murcer .60 1.50
334 Phil Regan .40 1.00
335 Bill Freehan .60 1.50
336 Del Unser .40 1.00
337 Mike McCormick .60 1.50
338 Paul Schaal .40 1.00
339 Johnny Edwards .40 1.00
340 Tony Conigliaro 1.25 3.00
341 Bill Sudakis .40 1.00
342 Wilbur Wood .60 1.50
343A Checklist 4 2.50 6.00
(Red bat on front)
343B Checklist 4 2.50 6.00
(Brown bat on front)
344 Marcelino Lopez .40 1.00
345 Al Ferrara .40 1.00
346 Red Schoendienst MG .60 1.50
347 Russ Snyder .40 1.00
348 Rookie Stars .60 1.50
Mike Jorgensen RC
Jesse Hudson RC
349 Steve Hamilton .40 1.00
350 Roberto Clemente 30.00 60.00
351 Tom Murphy .40 1.00
352 Bob Barton .40 1.00
353 Stan Williams .40 1.00
354 Amos Otis .60 1.50
355 Doug Rader .40 1.00
356 Fred Lasher .40 1.00
357 Bob Burda .40 1.00
358 Pedro Borbon RC .60 1.50
359 Phil Roof .40 1.00
360 Curt Flood .60 1.50
361 Ray Jarvis .40 1.00
362 Joe Hague .40 1.00
363 Tom Shopay RC .40 1.00
364 Dan McGinn .40 1.00
365 Zoilo Versalles .40 1.00
366 Barry Moore .40 1.00
367 Mike Lum .40 1.00
368 Ed Herrmann .40 1.00
369 Alan Foster .40 1.00
370 Tommy Harper .60 1.50
371 Rod Gaspar RC .40 1.00
372 Dave Giusti .40 1.00
373 Roy White .75 2.00
374 Tommie Sisk .60 1.50
375 Johnny Callison .75 2.00
376 Lefty Phillips MG RC .60 1.50
377 Bill Butler .60 1.50
378 Jim Davenport .60 1.50
379 Tom Tischinski RC .60 1.50
380 Tony Perez 2.50 6.00
381 Rookie Stars .60 1.50
Bobby Brooks RC
Mike Olivo RC
382 Jack DiLauro RC .60 1.50
383 Mickey Stanley .75 2.00
384 Gary Neibauer .60 1.50
385 George Scott .75 2.00
386 Bill Dillman .60 1.50
387 Baltimore Orioles TC 1.25 3.00
388 Byron Browne .60 1.50
389 Jim Shellenback .60 1.50
390 Willie Davis .75 2.00
391 Larry Brown .60 1.50
392 Walt Hriniak .75 2.00
393 John Gelnar .60 1.50
394 Gil Hodges MG 1.50 4.00
395 Walt Williams .60 1.50
396 Steve Blass .75 2.00
397 Roger Repoz .60 1.50
398 Bill Stoneman .60 1.50
399 New York Yankees TC 1.25 3.00
400 Denny McLain 1.50 4.00
401 Rookie Stars .60 1.50
John Harrell RC
Bernie Williams RC
402 Ellie Rodriguez .60 1.50
403 Jim Bunning 2.50 6.00
404 Rich Reese .60 1.50
405 Bill Hands .60 1.50
406 Mike Andrews .60 1.50
407 Bob Watson .75 2.00
408 Paul Lindblad .60 1.50
409 Bob Tolan .60 1.50
410 Boog Powell 1.50 4.00
411 Los Angeles Dodgers TC 1.25 3.00
412 Larry Burchart .60 1.50
413 Sonny Jackson .60 1.50
414 Paul Edmondson RC .60 1.50
415 Julian Javier .75 2.00
416 Joe Verbanic .60 1.50
417 John Bateman .60 1.50
418 John Donaldson .60 1.50
419 Ron Taylor .60 1.50
420 Ken McMullen .75 2.00
421 Pat Dobson .75 2.00
422 Kansas City Royals TC 1.25 3.00
423 Jerry May .60 1.50
424 Mike Kilkenny .60 1.50
(Inconsistent design
card number in
white circle)
425 Bobby Bonds 2.50 6.00
426 Bill Rigney MG .60 1.50
427 Fred Norman .60 1.50
428 Don Buford .60 1.50
429 Rookie Stars .60 1.50
Randy Bobb RC
Jim Cosman
430 Andy Messersmith .75 2.00
431 Ron Swoboda .75 2.00
432A Checklist 5 2.50 6.00
(Baseball in
yellow letters)
432B Checklist 5 2.50 6.00
(Baseball in
white letters)
433 Ron Bryant RC .60 1.50
434 Felipe Alou .75 2.00
435 Nelson Briles .75 2.00
436 Philadelphia Phillies TC 1.25 3.00
437 Danny Cater .60 1.50
438 Pat Jarvis .60 1.50
439 Lee Maye .60 1.50
440 Bill Mazeroski 2.50 6.00
441 John O'Donoghue .60 1.50
442 Gene Mauch MG .75 2.00
443 Al Jackson .60 1.50
444 Rookie Stars .60 1.50
Billy Farmer RC
John Matias RC
445 Vada Pinson .75 2.00
446 Billy Grabarkewitz RC .60 1.50
447 Lee Stange .60 1.50
448 Houston Astros TC 1.25 3.00
449 Jim Palmer 5.00 12.00
450 Willie McCovey AS 2.50 6.00
451 Boog Powell AS 1.50 4.00
452 Felix Millan AS .75 2.00
453 Rod Carew AS 2.50 6.00
454 Ron Santo AS 1.50 4.00
455 Brooks Robinson AS 2.50 6.00
456 Don Kessinger AS .75 2.00
457 Rico Petrocelli AS 1.50 4.00
458 Pete Rose AS 6.00 15.00
459 Reggie Jackson AS 5.00 12.00
460 Matty Alou AS 1.25 3.00
461 Carl Yastrzemski AS 4.00 10.00
462 Hank Aaron AS 6.00 15.00
463 Frank Robinson AS 3.00 8.00
464 Johnny Bench AS 6.00 15.00
465 Bill Freehan AS 1.25 3.00
466 Juan Marichal AS 2.00 5.00
467 Denny McLain AS 1.25 3.00
468 Jerry Koosman AS 1.25 3.00
469 Sam McDowell AS 1.25 3.00
470 Willie Stargell 4.00 10.00
471 Chris Zachary .75 2.00
472 Atlanta Braves TC 1.50 4.00
473 Don Bryant .75 2.00
474 Dick Kelley .75 2.00
475 Dick McAuliffe 1.25 3.00
476 Don Shaw .75 2.00
477 Rookie Stars .75 2.00
Al Severinsen RC
Roger Freed RC
478 Bobby Heise RC .75 2.00
479 Dick Woodson RC .75 2.00
480 Glenn Beckert 1.25 3.00
481 Jose Tartabull .75 2.00
482 Tom Hilgendorf RC .75 2.00
483 Gail Hopkins RC .75 2.00
484 Gary Nolan 1.25 3.00
485 Jay Johnstone 1.25 3.00
486 Terry Harmon .75 2.00
487 Cisco Carlos .75 2.00
488 J.C. Martin .75 2.00
489 Eddie Kasko MG .75 2.00
490 Bill Singer 1.25 3.00
491 Graig Nettles 2.00 5.00
492 Rookie Stars .75 2.00
Keith Lampard RC
Scipio Spinks RC
493 Lindy McDaniel 1.25 3.00
494 Larry Stahl .75 2.00
495 Dave Morehead .75 2.00
496 Steve Whitaker .75 2.00
497 Eddie Watt .75 2.00
498 Al Weis .75 2.00
499 Skip Lockwood 1.25 3.00
500 Hank Aaron 20.00 50.00
501 Chicago White Sox TC 1.50 4.00
502 Rollie Fingers 4.00 10.00
503 Dal Maxvill .75 2.00
504 Don Pavletich .75 2.00
505 Ken Holtzman 1.25 3.00
506 Ed Stroud .75 2.00
507 Pat Corrales .75 2.00
508 Joe Niekro 1.25 3.00
509 Montreal Expos TC 1.50 4.00
510 Tony Oliva 2.00 5.00
511 Joe Hoerner .75 2.00
512 Billy Harris .75 2.00
513 Preston Gomez MG .75 2.00
514 Steve Hovley RC .75 2.00
515 Don Wilson 1.25 3.00
516 Rookie Stars .75 2.00
John Ellis RC
Jim Lyttle RC
517 Joe Gibbon .75 2.00
518 Bill Melton .75 2.00
519 Don McMahon .75 2.00
520 Willie Horton 1.25 3.00
521 Cal Koonce .75 2.00
522 California Angels TC 1.50 4.00
523 Jose Pena .75 2.00
524 Alvin Dark MG 1.25 3.00
525 Jerry Adair .75 2.00
526 Ron Herbel .75 2.00
527 Don Bosch .75 2.00
528 Elrod Hendricks .75 2.00
529 Bob Aspromonte .75 2.00
530 Bob Gibson 6.00 15.00
531 Ron Clark .75 2.00
532 Danny Murtaugh MG 1.25 3.00
533 Buzz Stephen RC .75 2.00
534 Minnesota Twins TC 1.50 4.00
535 Andy Kosco .75 2.00
536 Mike Kekich .75 2.00
537 Joe Morgan 4.00 10.00
538 Bob Humphreys .75 2.00
539 Rookie Stars 3.00 8.00
Denny Doyle RC
Larry Bowa RC
540 Gary Peters .75 2.00
541 Bill Heath .75 2.00
542A Checklist 6 2.50 6.00
Brown Bat on Front
542B Checklist 6 2.50 6.00
Gray Bat on Front
543 Clyde Wright .75 2.00
544 Cincinnati Reds TC 1.50 4.00
545 Ken Harrelson 1.25 3.00
546 Ron Reed .75 2.00
547 Rick Monday 2.50 6.00
548 Howie Reed 1.50 4.00
549 St. Louis Cardinals TC 2.50 6.00
550 Frank Howard 2.50 6.00
551 Dock Ellis 2.50 6.00
552 Rookie Stars 1.50 4.00
Don O'Riley RC
Dennis Paepke RC
Fred Rico RC
553 Jim Lefebvre 2.50 6.00
554 Tom Timmermann RC 1.50 4.00
555 Orlando Cepeda 5.00 12.00
556 Dave Bristol MG 2.50 6.00
557 Ed Kranepool 2.50 6.00
558 Vern Fuller 1.50 4.00
559 Tommy Davis 2.50 6.00
560 Gaylord Perry 5.00 12.00
561 Tom McCraw 1.50 4.00
562 Ted Abernathy 1.50 4.00
563 Boston Red Sox TC 2.50 6.00
564 Johnny Briggs 1.50 4.00
565 Jim Hunter 5.00 12.00
566 Gene Alley 2.50 6.00
567 Bob Oliver 1.50 4.00
568 Stan Bahnsen 2.50 6.00
569 Cookie Rojas 2.50 6.00
570 Jim Fregosi 2.50 6.00
White Chevy Pick-Up in Background
571 Jim Brewer 1.50 4.00
572 Frank Quilici 1.50 4.00
573 Rookie Stars 1.50 4.00
Mike Corkins RC
Rafael Robles
Ron Slocum RC
574 Bobby Bolin 2.50 6.00
575 Cleon Jones 2.50 6.00
576 Milt Pappas 2.50 6.00
577 Bernie Allen 1.50 4.00
578 Tom Griffin 1.50 4.00
579 Detroit Tigers TC 2.50 6.00
580 Pete Rose 30.00 60.00
581 Tom Satriano 1.50 4.00
582 Mike Paul 1.50 4.00

583 Hal Lanier 1.50 4.00
584 Al Downing 2.50 6.00
585 Rusty Staub 3.00 8.00
586 Rickey Clark RC 1.50 4.00
587 Jose Arcia 1.50 4.00
588A Checklist 7 ERR 3.00 8.00
(666 Adolfo)
588B Checklist 7 COR 2.50 6.00
(666 Adolpho)
589 Joe Keough 1.50 4.00
590 Mike Cuellar 2.50 6.00
591 Mike Ryan UER 1.50 4.00
(Pitching Record
header on card back)
592 Daryl Patterson 1.50 4.00
593 Chicago Cubs TC 3.00 8.00
594 Jake Gibbs 1.50 4.00
595 Maury Wills 3.00 8.00
596 Mike Hershberger 2.50 6.00
597 Sonny Siebert 1.50 4.00
598 Joe Pepitone 2.50 6.00
599 Rookie Stars 1.50 4.00
Dick Stelmaszek RC
Gene Martin RC
Dick Such RC
600 Willie Mays 40.00 80.00
601 Pete Richert 1.50 4.00
602 Ted Savage 1.50 4.00
603 Ray Oyler 1.50 4.00
604 Clarence Gaston 2.50 6.00
605 Rick Wise 2.50 6.00
606 Chico Ruiz 1.50 4.00
607 Gary Waslewski 1.50 4.00
608 Pittsburgh Pirates TC 2.50 6.00
609 Buck Martinez RC 2.50 6.00
(Inconsistent design
card number in
white circle)
610 Jerry Koosman 3.00 8.00
611 Norm Cash 2.50 6.00
612 Jim Hickman 2.50 6.00
613 Dave Baldwin 2.50 6.00
614 Mike Shannon 2.50 6.00
615 Mark Belanger 2.50 6.00
616 Jim Merritt 1.50 4.00
617 Jim French 1.50 4.00
618 Billy Wynne RC 1.50 4.00
619 Norm Miller 1.50 4.00
620 Jim Perry 2.50 6.00
621 Rookie Stars 5.00 12.00
Mike McQueen RC
Darrell Evans RC
Rick Kester RC
622 Don Sutton 5.00 12.00
623 Horace Clarke 2.50 6.00
624 Clyde King MG 1.50 4.00
625 Dean Chance 1.50 4.00
626 Dave Ricketts 1.50 4.00
627 Gary Wagner 1.50 4.00
628 Wayne Garrett RC 1.50 4.00
629 Merv Rettenmund 1.50 4.00
630 Ernie Banks 20.00 50.00
631 Oakland Athletics TC 2.50 6.00
632 Gary Sutherland 1.50 4.00
633 Roger Nelson 1.50 4.00
634 Bud Harrelson 6.00 15.00
635 Bob Allison 6.00 15.00
636 Jim Stewart 4.00 10.00
637 Cleveland Indians TC 5.00 12.00
638 Frank Bertaina 4.00 10.00
639 Dave Campbell 6.00 15.00
640 Al Kaline 20.00 50.00
641 Al McBean 4.00 10.00
642 Rookie Stars 4.00 10.00
Greg Garrett RC
Gordon Lund RC
Jarvis Tatum RC
643 Jose Pagan 4.00 10.00
644 Gerry Nyman 4.00 10.00
645 Don Money 6.00 15.00
646 Jim Britton 4.00 10.00
647 Tom Matchick 4.00 10.00
648 Larry Haney 4.00 10.00
649 Jimmie Hall 4.00 10.00
650 Sam McDowell 6.00 15.00
651 Jim Gosger 4.00 10.00
652 Rich Rollins 6.00 15.00
653 Moe Drabowsky 4.00 10.00
654 Rookie Stars 6.00 15.00
Oscar Gamble RC
Boots Day RC
Angel Mangual RC
655 John Roseboro 6.00 15.00
656 Jim Hardin 4.00 10.00
657 San Diego Padres TC 5.00 12.00
658 Ken Tatum RC 4.00 10.00
659 Pete Ward 4.00 10.00
660 Johnny Bench 40.00 80.00
661 Jerry Robertson 4.00 10.00
662 Frank Lucchesi MG RC 4.00 10.00
663 Tito Francona 4.00 10.00
664 Bob Robertson 4.00 10.00
665 Jim Lonborg 6.00 15.00
666 Adolpho Phillips 4.00 10.00
667 Bob Meyer 6.00 15.00
668 Bob Tillman 4.00 10.00
669 Rookie Stars 4.00 10.00
Bart Johnson RC
Dan Lazar
Mickey Scott RC
670 Ron Santo 6.00 15.00
671 Jim Campanis 4.00 10.00
672 Leon McFadden 4.00 10.00
673 Ted Uhlaender 4.00 10.00
674 Dave Leonhard 4.00 10.00
675 Jose Cardenal 6.00 15.00
676 Washington Senators TC 5.00 12.00
677 Woodie Fryman 4.00 10.00
678 Dave Duncan 6.00 15.00
679 Ray Sadecki 4.00 10.00
680 Rico Petrocelli 6.00 15.00
681 Bob Garibaldi RC 4.00 10.00
682 Dalton Jones 4.00 10.00
683 Rookie Stars 6.00 15.00
Vern Geishert RC
Hal McRae
Wayne Simpson RC
684 Jack Fisher 4.00 10.00
685 Tom Haller 4.00 10.00
686 Jackie Hernandez 4.00 10.00
687 Bob Priddy 4.00 10.00
688 Ted Kubiak 6.00 15.00
689 Frank Tepedino RC 6.00 15.00
690 Ron Fairly 6.00 15.00
691 Joe Grzenda 4.00 10.00
692 Duffy Dyer 4.00 10.00
693 Bob Johnson 4.00 10.00
694 Gary Ross 4.00 10.00
695 Bobby Knoop 4.00 10.00
696 San Francisco Giants TC 5.00 12.00
697 Jim Hannan 4.00 10.00
698 Tom Tresh 6.00 15.00
699 Hank Aguirre 4.00 10.00
700 Frank Robinson 20.00 50.00
701 Jack Billingham 4.00 10.00
702 Rookie Stars 4.00 10.00
Bob Johnson
Ron Klimkowski RC
Bill Zepp RC
703 Lou Marone RC 4.00 10.00
704 Frank Baker RC 4.00 10.00
705 Tony Cloninger UER 4.00 10.00
(Batter headings
on card back)
706 John McNamara MG RC 4.00 10.00
707 Kevin Collins 4.00 10.00
708 Jose Santiago 4.00 10.00
709 Mike Fiore 4.00 10.00
710 Felix Millan 4.00 10.00
711 Ed Brinkman 4.00 10.00
712 Nolan Ryan 100.00 200.00
713 Seattle Pilots TC 10.00 25.00
714 Al Spangler 4.00 10.00
715 Mickey Lolich 6.00 15.00
716 Rookie Stars 6.00 15.00
Sal Campisi RC
Reggie Cleveland RC
Santiago Guzman RC
717 Tom Phoebus 4.00 10.00
718 Ed Spiezio 4.00 10.00
719 Jim Roland 4.00 10.00
720 Rick Reichardt 6.00 15.00

1970 Topps Booklets

Inserted into packages of the 1970 Topps (and O-Pee-Chee) regular issue of cards, there are 24 miniature biographies of ballplayers in the set. Each numbered paper booklet, which features one player per team, contains six pages of comic book style story and a checklist of the booklet is available on the back page. These little booklets measure approximately 2 1/2" by 3 7/16".

COMPLETE SET (24) 15.00 40.00
COMMON CARD (1-16) .40 1.00
COMMON CARD (17-24) .40 1.00
1 Mike Cuellar .40 1.00
2 Rico Petrocelli .40 1.00
3 Jay Johnstone .40 1.00
4 Walt Williams .40 1.00
5 Vada Pinson .40 1.00
6 Bill Freehan .40 1.00
7 Wally Bunker .40 1.00
8 Tony Oliva .60 1.50
9 Bobby Murcer .40 1.00
10 Reggie Jackson 2.50 6.00
11 Tommy Harper .40 1.00
12 Mike Epstein .40 1.00
13 Orlando Cepeda .60 1.50
14 Ernie Banks 1.50 4.00
15 Pete Rose 2.50 6.00
16 Denis Menke .40 1.00
17 Bill Singer .40 1.00
18 Rusty Staub .60 1.50
19 Cleon Jones .40 1.00
20 Deron Johnson .40 1.00
21 Bob Moose .40 1.00
22 Bob Gibson 1.00 2.50
23 Al Ferrara .40 1.00
24 Willie Mays 3.00 8.00

1970 Topps Posters Inserts

In 1970 Topps raised its price per package of cards to ten cents, and a series of 24 color posters was included as a bonus to the collector. Each thin-paper poster is numbered and features a large portrait and a smaller black and white action pose. It was folded five times to fit in the packaging. Each poster measures 8 11/16" by 9 5/8".

COMPLETE SET (24) 30.00 60.00
1 Joe Horlen .60 1.50
2 Phil Niekro .75 2.00
3 Willie Davis .60 1.50
4 Lou Brock 2.00 5.00
5 Ron Santo 1.25 3.00
6 Ken Harrelson .60 1.50
7 Willie McCovey 2.00 5.00
8 Rick Wise .60 1.50
9 Andy Messersmith .60 1.50
10 Ron Fairly .60 1.50
11 Johnny Bench 4.00 10.00
12 Frank Robinson 2.00 5.00
13 Tommie Agee .60 1.50
14 Roy White .60 1.50
15 Larry Dierker .60 1.50
16 Rod Carew 2.00 5.00
17 Don Mincher .60 1.50
18 Ollie Brown .60 1.50
19 Ed Kirkpatrick .60 1.50
20 Reggie Smith .75 2.00
21 Roberto Clemente 8.00 20.00
22 Frank Howard .75 2.00
23 Bert Campaneris .75 2.00
24 Denny McLain .75 2.00

1970 Topps Scratchoffs

The 1970 Topps Scratch-off inserts are heavy cardboard, folded inserts issued with the regular card series of those years. Unfolded, they form a game board upon which a baseball game is played by means of rubbing off black ink from the playing squares to reveal moves. Inserts with white centers were issued in 1970 and inserts with red centers in 1971. Unfolded, these inserts measure 3 3/8" by 5". Obviously, a card which has been scratched off can be considered to be in no better than vg condition.

COMPLETE SET (24) 20.00 50.00
COMMON CARD (1-24) .40 1.00
1 Hank Aaron 3.00 8.00
2 Rich Allen .60 1.50
3 Luis Aparicio 1.00 2.50
4 Sal Bando .60 1.50
5 Glenn Beckert .40 1.00
6 Dick Bosman .40 1.00
7 Nate Colbert .40 1.00
8 Mike Hegan .40 1.00
9 Mack Jones .40 1.00
10 Al Kaline 2.00 5.00
11 Harmon Killebrew 2.00 5.00
12 Juan Marichal 1.00 2.50
13 Tim McCarver .60 1.50
14 Sam McDowell .60 1.50
15 Claude Osteen .40 1.00
16 Tony Perez 1.00 2.50
17 Lou Piniella .60 1.50
18 Boog Powell 1.00 2.50
19 Tom Seaver 2.00 5.00
20 Jim Spencer .40 1.00
21 Willie Stargell 1.50 4.00
22 Mel Stottlemyre .60 1.50
23 Jim Wynn .60 1.50
24 Carl Yastrzemski 2.50 6.00

1971 Topps

The cards in this 752-card set measure 2 1/2" by 3 1/2". The 1971 Topps set is a challenge to complete in strict mint condition because the black obverse border is easily scratched and damaged. An unusual feature of this set is that the player is also pictured in black and white on the back of the card. Featured subsets within this set include League Leaders (61-72), Playoffs cards (195-202), and World Series cards (327-332). Cards 524-643 and the last series (644-752) are somewhat scarce. The last series was printed in two sheets of 132. On the printing sheets 44 cards were printed in 50 percent greater quantity than the other 66 cards. These 66 (slightly) shorter-printed numbers are identified in the checklist below by SP. The key Rookie Cards in this set are the multi-player Rookie Card of Dusty Baker and Don Baylor and the individual cards of Bert Blyleven, Dave Concepcion, Steve Garvey, and Ted Simmons. The Jim Northrup and Jim Nash cards have been seen with our without printing "blotches" on the card. There is still debate on whether those two cards are just printing issues or legitimate variations. Among the ways these cards were issued were in 54-card rack packs which retailed for 39 cents.

COMPLETE SET (752) 1250.00 2500.00
COMMON CARD (1-393) .60 1.50
COMMON (394-523) 1.00 2.50
COMMON (524-643) 1.50 4.00
COMMON (644-752) 3.00 8.00
COMMON SP (644-752) 5.00 12.00
WRAPPER (10-CENT) 6.00 15.00
1 Baltimore Orioles TC 8.00 20.00
2 Dock Ellis .60 1.50
3 Dick McAuliffe .75 2.00
4 Vic Davalillo .60 1.50
5 Thurman Munson 60.00 120.00
6 Ed Spiezio .60 1.50
7 Jim Holt RC .60 1.50
8 Mike McQueen .60 1.50
9 George Scott .75 2.00
10 Claude Osteen .75 2.00
11 Elliott Maddox RC .60 1.50
12 Johnny Callison .75 2.00
13 Rookie Stars .60 1.50
Charlie Brinkman RC
Dick Moloney RC
14 Dave Concepcion RC 6.00 15.00
15 Andy Messersmith .75 2.00
16 Ken Singleton RC 1.50 4.00
17 Billy Sorrell .60 1.50
18 Norm Miller .60 1.50
19 Skip Pitlock RC .60 1.50
20 Reggie Jackson 20.00 50.00
21 Dan McGinn .60 1.50
22 Phil Roof .60 1.50
23 Oscar Gamble .60 1.50
24 Rich Hand RC .60 1.50
25 Clarence Gaston .75 2.00
26 Bert Blyleven RC 8.00 20.00
27 Rookie Stars .60 1.50
Fred Cambria RC
Gene Clines RC
28 Ron Klimkowski .60 1.50
29 Don Buford .60 1.50
30 Phil Niekro 2.50 6.00
31 Eddie Kasko MG .60 1.50
32 Jerry DaVanon .60 1.50
33 Del Unser .60 1.50
34 Sandy Vance RC .60 1.50
35 Lou Piniella .75 2.00
36 Dean Chance .75 2.00
37 Rich McKinney RC .60 1.50
38 Jim Colborn RC .60 1.50
39 Rookie Stars .75 2.00
Lerrin LaGrow RC
Gene Lamont RC
40 Lee May .75 2.00
41 Rick Austin RC .60 1.50
42 Boots Day .60 1.50
43 Steve Kealey .60 1.50
44 Johnny Edwards .60 1.50
45 Jim Hunter 2.50 6.00
46 Dave Campbell .75 2.00
47 Johnny Jeter .60 1.50
48 Dave Baldwin .60 1.50
49 Don Money .60 1.50
50 Willie McCovey 4.00 10.00
51 Steve Kline RC .60 1.50
52 Rookie Stars .60 1.50
Oscar Brown RC
Earl Williams RC
53 Paul Blair .75 2.00
54 Checklist 1 4.00 10.00
55 Steve Carlton 8.00 20.00
56 Duane Josephson .60 1.50
57 Von Joshua RC .60 1.50
58 Bill Lee .75 2.00
59 Gene Mauch MG .75 2.00
60 Dick Bosman .60 1.50
61 AL Batting Leaders 1.50 4.00
Alex Johnson
Carl Yastrzemski
Tony Oliva
62 NL Batting Leaders .75 2.00
Rico Carty
Joe Torre
Manny Sanguillen
63 AL RBI Leaders 1.50 4.00
Frank Howard
Tony Conigliaro
Boog Powell
64 NL RBI Leaders 2.50 6.00
Johnny Bench
Tony Perez
Billy Williams
65 AL Home Run Leaders 1.50 4.00
Frank Howard
Harmon Killebrew
Carl Yastrzemski
66 NL Home Run Leaders 2.50 6.00
Johnny Bench
Billy Williams
Tony Perez
67 AL ERA Leaders 1.50 4.00
Diego Segui
Jim Palmer
Clyde Wright
68 NL ERA Leaders 1.50 4.00
Tom Seaver
Wayne Simpson
Luke Walker
69 AL Pitching Leaders .75 2.00
Mike Cuellar
Dave McNally
Jim Perry
70 NL Pitching Leaders 2.50 6.00
Bob Gibson
Gaylord Perry
Fergie Jenkins
71 AL Strikeout Leaders .75 2.00
Sam McDowell
Mickey Lolich
Bob Johnson
72 NL Strikeout Leaders 2.50 6.00
Tom Seaver
Bob Gibson
Fergie Jenkins
73 George Brunet .60 1.50
74 Rookie Stars .60 1.50
Pete Hamm RC
Jim Nettles RC
75 Gary Nolan .75 2.00
76 Ted Savage .60 1.50
77 Mike Compton RC .60 1.50
78 Jim Spencer .60 1.50
79 Wade Blasingame .60 1.50
80 Bill Melton .60 1.50
81 Felix Millan .60 1.50
82 Casey Cox .60 1.50
83 Rookie Stars .75 2.00
Tim Foli RC
Randy Bobb
84 Marcel Lachemann RC .60 1.50
85 Billy Grabarkewitz .60 1.50
86 Mike Kilkenny .60 1.50
87 Jack Heidemann RC .60 1.50
88 Hal King .60 1.50
89 Ken Brett .60 1.50
90 Joe Pepitone .75 2.00
91 Bob Lemon MG .75 2.00
92 Fred Wenz .60 1.50
93 Rookie Stars .60 1.50
Norm McRae
Denny Riddleberger
94 Don Hahn RC .60 1.50
95 Luis Tiant .75 2.00
96 Joe Hague .60 1.50
97 Floyd Wicker .60 1.50
98 Joe Decker RC .60 1.50
99 Mark Belanger .75 2.00
100 Pete Rose 40.00 80.00
101 Les Cain .60 1.50
102 Rookie Stars .75 2.00
Ken Forsch RC
Larry Howard RC
103 Rich Severson RC .60 1.50
104 Dan Frisella .60 1.50
105 Tony Conigliaro .75 2.00
106 Tom Dukes .60 1.50
107 Roy Foster RC .60 1.50
108 John Cumberland .60 1.50
109 Steve Hovley .60 1.50
110 Bill Mazeroski 2.50 6.00
111 Rookie Stars .60 1.50
Loyd Colson RC
Bobby Mitchell RC
112 Manny Mota .75 2.00
113 Jerry Crider .60 1.50
114 Billy Conigliaro .75 2.00
115 Donn Clendenon .75 2.00
116 Ken Sanders .60 1.50
117 Ted Simmons RC 3.00 8.00
118 Cookie Rojas .75 2.00
119 Frank Lucchesi MG .60 1.50
120 Willie Horton .75 2.00
121 Rookie Stars .60 1.50
Jim Dunegan RC
Roe Skidmore RC
122 Eddie Watt .60 1.50
123A Checklist 2 4.00 10.00
(Card number
at bottom right)
123B Checklist 2 4.00 10.00
(Card number
centered)
124 Don Gullett RC .75 2.00
125 Ray Fosse .60 1.50
126 Danny Coombs .60 1.50
127 Danny Thompson RC .75 2.00
128 Frank Johnson .60 1.50
129 Aurelio Monteagudo .60 1.50
130 Denis Menke .60 1.50
131 Curt Blefary .60 1.50
132 Jose Laboy .60 1.50
133 Mickey Lolich .75 2.00
134 Jose Arcia .60 1.50
135 Rick Monday .75 2.00
136 Duffy Dyer .60 1.50
137 Marcelino Lopez .60 1.50
138 Rookie Stars .75 2.00
Joe Lis
Willie Montanez RC
139 Paul Casanova .60 1.50
140 Gaylord Perry 2.50 6.00
141 Frank Quilici .60 1.50
142 Mack Jones .60 1.50
143 Steve Blass .75 2.00
144 Jackie Hernandez .60 1.50
145 Bill Singer .75 2.00
146 Ralph Houk MG .75 2.00
147 Bob Priddy .60 1.50
148 John Mayberry .75 2.00
149 Mike Hershberger .60 1.50
150 Sam McDowell .75 2.00
151 Tommy Davis .75 2.00
152 Rookie Stars .60 1.50
Lloyd Allen RC
Winston Llenas RC
153 Gary Ross .60 1.50
154 Cesar Gutierrez .60 1.50
155 Ken Henderson .60 1.50
156 Bart Johnson .60 1.50
157 Bob Bailey .75 2.00
158 Jerry Reuss .75 2.00
159 Jarvis Tatum .60 1.50
160 Tom Seaver 12.50 30.00
161 Coin Checklist 4.00 10.00
162 Jack Billingham .75 2.00
163 Buck Martinez .75 2.00
164 Rookie Stars .75 2.00
Frank Duffy RC
Milt Wilcox RC
165 Cesar Tovar .60 1.50
166 Joe Hoerner .60 1.50
167 Tom Grieve RC .75 2.00
168 Bruce Dal Canton .60 1.50
169 Ed Herrmann .60 1.50
170 Mike Cuellar .75 2.00
171 Bobby Wine .60 1.50
172 Duke Sims .60 1.50
173 Gil Garrido .60 1.50
174 Dave LaRoche RC .60 1.50
175 Jim Hickman .60 1.50
176 Rookie Stars .75 2.00
Bob Montgomery RC
Doug Griffin RC
177 Hal McRae .75 2.00
178 Dave Duncan .75 2.00
179 Mike Corkins .60 1.50
180 Al Kaline UER 8.00 20.00
(Home instead
of Birth)
181 Hal Lanier .60 1.50
182 Al Downing .75 2.00
183 Gil Hodges MG 1.50 4.00
184 Stan Bahnsen .60 1.50
185 Julian Javier .60 1.50
186 Bob Spence RC .60 1.50
187 Ted Abernathy .60 1.50
188 Rookie Stars 2.50 6.00
Bob Valentine RC
Mike Strahler RC
189 George Mitterwald .60 1.50
190 Bob Tolan .60 1.50
191 Mike Andrews .60 1.50
192 Billy Wilson .60 1.50
193 Bob Grich RC 1.50 4.00
194 Mike Lum .60 1.50
195 AL Playoff Game 1 .75 2.00
Boog Powell
196 AL Playoff Game 2 .75 2.00
Dave McNally
197 AL Playoff Game 3 1.50 4.00
Jim Palmer
198 AL Playoff Summary .75 2.00
Orioles Celebrate
199 NL Playoff Game 1 .75 2.00
Ty Cline
200 NL Playoff Game 2 .75 2.00
Bobby Tolan
201 NL Playoff Game 3 .75 2.00
Ty Cline
202 NL Playoff Summary .75 2.00
Reds Celebrate
203 Larry Gura RC .75 2.00
204 Rookie Stars .60 1.50
Bernie Smith RC
George Kopacz RC
205 Gerry Moses .60 1.50
206 Checklist 3 4.00 10.00
207 Alan Foster .60 1.50
208 Billy Martin MG 1.50 4.00
209 Steve Renko .60 1.50
210 Rod Carew 6.00 15.00
211 Phil Hennigan RC .60 1.50
212 Rich Hebner .75 2.00
213 Frank Baker RC .60 1.50
214 Al Ferrara .60 1.50
215 Diego Segui .60 1.50
216 Rookie Stars .60 1.50
Reggie Cleveland
Luis Melendez RC
217 Ed Stroud .60 1.50
218 Tony Cloninger .60 1.50
219 Elrod Hendricks .60 1.50
220 Ron Santo 1.50 4.00
221 Dave Morehead .60 1.50
222 Bob Watson .75 2.00
223 Cecil Upshaw .60 1.50
224 Alan Gallagher RC .60 1.50
225 Gary Peters .60 1.50
226 Bill Russell .75 2.00
227 Floyd Weaver .60 1.50
228 Wayne Garrett .60 1.50
229 Jim Hannan .60 1.50
230 Willie Stargell 6.00 15.00
231 Rookie Stars .75 2.00
Vince Colbert RC
John Lowenstein RC
232 John Strohmayer RC .60 1.50
233 Larry Bowa .75 2.00
234 Jim Lyttle .60 1.50
235 Nate Colbert .60 1.50
236 Bob Humphreys .60 1.50
237 Cesar Cedeno RC .75 2.00
238 Chuck Dobson .60 1.50
239 Red Schoendienst MG .75 2.00
240 Clyde Wright .60 1.50
241 Dave Nelson .60 1.50
242 Jim Ray .60 1.50
243 Carlos May .60 1.50
244 Bob Tillman .60 1.50
245 Jim Kaat .75 2.00
246 Tony Taylor .60 1.50
247 Rookie Stars .75 2.00
Jerry Cram RC
Paul Splittorff RC
248 Hoyt Wilhelm 2.50 6.00
249 Chico Salmon .60 1.50
250 Johnny Bench 20.00 50.00
251 Frank Reberger .60 1.50
252 Eddie Leon .60 1.50
253 Bill Sudakis .60 1.50
254 Cal Koonce .60 1.50
255 Bob Robertson .75 2.00
256 Tony Gonzalez .60 1.50
257 Nelson Briles .75 2.00
258 Dick Green .60 1.50
259 Dave Marshall .60 1.50
260 Tommy Harper .75 2.00
261 Darold Knowles .60 1.50
262 Rookie Stars .60 1.50
Jim Williams
Dave Robinson RC
263 John Ellis .60 1.50
264 Joe Morgan 3.00 8.00
265 Jim Northrup .75 2.00
266 Bill Stoneman .60 1.50
267 Rich Morales .60 1.50
268 Philadelphia Phillies TC 1.50 4.00
269 Gail Hopkins .60 1.50
270 Rico Carty .75 2.00
271 Bill Zepp .60 1.50
272 Tommy Helms .75 2.00
273 Pete Richert .60 1.50
274 Ron Slocum .60 1.50
275 Vada Pinson .75 2.00
276 Rookie Stars 3.00 8.00
Mike Davison RC
George Foster RC
277 Gary Waslewski .60 1.50
278 Jerry Grote .75 2.00
279 Lefty Phillips MG .60 1.50
280 Ferguson Jenkins 2.50 6.00
281 Danny Walton .60 1.50
282 Jose Pagan .60 1.50
283 Dick Such .60 1.50
284 Jim Gosger .60 1.50
285 Sal Bando .75 2.00
286 Jerry McNertney .60 1.50
287 Mike Fiore .60 1.50
288 Joe Moeller .60 1.50
289 Chicago White Sox TC 1.50 4.00
290 Tony Oliva 1.50 4.00
291 George Culver .60 1.50
292 Jay Johnstone .75 2.00
293 Pat Corrales .75 2.00
294 Steve Dunning RC .60 1.50
295 Bobby Bonds 1.50 4.00
296 Tom Timmermann .60 1.50
297 Johnny Briggs .60 1.50
298 Jim Nelson RC .60 1.50
299 Ed Kirkpatrick .60 1.50
300 Brooks Robinson 8.00 20.00
301 Earl Wilson .60 1.50
302 Phil Gagliano .60 1.50
303 Lindy McDaniel .75 2.00
304 Ron Brand .60 1.50
305 Reggie Smith .75 2.00
306 Jim Nash .60 1.50
307 Don Wert .60 1.50
308 St. Louis Cardinals TC 1.50 4.00
309 Dick Ellsworth .60 1.50
310 Tommie Agee .75 2.00
311 Lee Stange .60 1.50
312 Harry Walker MG .60 1.50
313 Tom Hall .60 1.50
314 Jeff Torborg .75 2.00
315 Ron Fairly .75 2.00
316 Fred Scherman RC .60 1.50
317 Rookie Stars .60 1.50
Jim Driscoll RC
Angel Mangual
318 Rudy May .60 1.50
319 Ty Cline .60 1.50
320 Dave McNally .75 2.00
321 Tom Matchick .60 1.50
322 Jim Beauchamp .60 1.50
323 Billy Champion .60 1.50
324 Graig Nettles .75 2.00
325 Juan Marichal 3.00 8.00
326 Richie Scheinblum .60 1.50
327 World Series Game 1 .75 2.00
Boog Powell
328 World Series Game 2 .75 2.00
Don Buford
329 World Series Game 3 1.50 4.00
Frank Robinson
330 World Series Game 4 .75 2.00
Reds Stay Alive
331 World Series Game 5 2.50 6.00
Brooks Robinson
332 World Series Summary .75 2.00
Orioles Celebrate
333 Clay Kirby .60 1.50
334 Roberto Pena .60 1.50
335 Jerry Koosman .75 2.00
336 Detroit Tigers TC 1.50 4.00
337 Jesus Alou .60 1.50
338 Gene Tenace .75 2.00
339 Wayne Simpson .60 1.50
340 Rico Petrocelli .75 2.00
341 Steve Garvey RC 12.50 30.00
342 Frank Tepedino .75 2.00
343 Rookie Stars .75 2.00
Ed Acosta RC
Milt May RC
344 Ellie Rodriguez .60 1.50
345 Joel Horlen .60 1.50
346 Lum Harris MG .60 1.50
347 Ted Uhlaender .60 1.50
348 Fred Norman .60 1.50
349 Rich Reese .60 1.50
350 Billy Williams 2.50 6.00
351 Jim Shellenback .60 1.50
352 Denny Doyle .60 1.50
353 Carl Taylor .60 1.50
354 Don McMahon .60 1.50
355 Bud Harrelson 1.50 4.00
(Nolan Ryan in photo)
356 Bob Locker .60 1.50
357 Cincinnati Reds TC 1.50 4.00
358 Danny Cater .60 1.50
359 Ron Reed .60 1.50
360 Jim Fregosi .75 2.00
361 Don Sutton 2.50 6.00
362 Rookie Stars .60 1.50
Mike Adamson
Roger Freed
363 Mike Nagy .60 1.50
364 Tommy Dean .60 1.50
365 Bob Johnson .60 1.50
366 Ron Stone .60 1.50
367 Dalton Jones .60 1.50
368 Bob Veale .75 2.00
369 Checklist 4 4.00 10.00
370 Joe Torre 1.50 4.00
371 Jack Hiatt .60 1.50
372 Lew Krausse .60 1.50
373 Tom McCraw .60 1.50
374 Clete Boyer .75 2.00
375 Steve Hargan .60 1.50
376 Rookie Stars .60 1.50
Clyde Mashore RC
Ernie McAnally RC
377 Greg Garrett .60 1.50
378 Tito Fuentes .60 1.50
379 Wayne Granger .60 1.50
380 Ted Williams MG 5.00 12.00
381 Fred Gladding .60 1.50
382 Jake Gibbs .60 1.50
383 Rod Gaspar .60 1.50
384 Rollie Fingers 2.50 6.00

385 Maury Wills 1.50 4.00
386 Boston Red Sox TC .75 2.00
387 Ron Herbel .60 1.50
388 Al Oliver 1.50 4.00
389 Ed Brinkman .60 1.50
390 Glenn Beckert .75 2.00
391 Rookie Stars .75 2.00
Steve Brye RC
Cotton Nash RC
392 Grant Jackson .60 1.50
393 Merv Rettenmund .75 2.00
394 Clay Carroll 1.00 2.50
395 Roy White 1.50 4.00
396 Dick Schofield 1.00 2.50
397 Alvin Dark MG 1.50 4.00
398 Howie Reed 1.00 2.50
399 Jim French 1.00 2.50
400 Hank Aaron 30.00 60.00
401 Tom Murphy 1.00 2.50
402 Los Angeles Dodgers TC 2.50 6.00
403 Joe Coleman 1.00 2.50
404 Rookie Stars 1.00 2.50
Buddy Harris RC
Roger Metzger RC
405 Leo Cardenas 1.00 2.50
406 Ray Sadecki 1.00 2.50
407 Joe Rudi 1.50 4.00
408 Rafael Robles 1.00 2.50
409 Don Pavletich 1.00 2.50
410 Ken Holtzman 1.50 4.00
411 George Spriggs 1.00 2.50
412 Jerry Johnson 1.00 2.50
413 Pat Kelly 1.00 2.50
414 Woodie Fryman 1.00 2.50
415 Mike Hegan 1.00 2.50
416 Gene Alley 1.00 2.50
417 Dick Hall 1.00 2.50
418 Adolfo Phillips 1.00 2.50
419 Ron Hansen 1.00 2.50
420 Jim Merritt 1.00 2.50
421 John Stephenson 1.00 2.50
422 Frank Bertaina 1.00 2.50
423 Rookie Stars 1.00 2.50
Dennis Saunders RC
Tim Marting RC
424 Roberto Rodriquez 1.00 2.50
425 Doug Rader 1.50 4.00
426 Chris Cannizzaro 1.00 2.50
427 Bernie Allen 1.00 2.50
428 Jim McAndrew 1.00 2.50
429 Chuck Hinton 1.00 2.50
430 Wes Parker 1.50 4.00
431 Tom Burgmeier 1.00 2.50
432 Bob Didier 1.00 2.50
433 Skip Lockwood 1.00 2.50
434 Gary Sutherland 1.00 2.50
435 Jose Cardenal 1.50 4.00
436 Wilbur Wood 1.50 4.00
437 Danny Murtaugh MG 1.50 4.00
438 Mike McCormick 1.50 4.00
439 Rookie Stars 2.50 6.00
Greg Luzinski RC
Scott Reid
440 Bert Campaneris 1.50 4.00
441 Milt Pappas 1.50 4.00
442 California Angels TC 1.50 4.00
443 Rich Robertson 1.00 2.50
444 Jimmie Price 1.00 2.50
445 Art Shamsky 1.00 2.50
446 Bobby Bolin 1.00 2.50
447 Cesar Geronimo RC 1.50 4.00
448 Dave Roberts 1.00 2.50
449 Brant Alyea 1.00 2.50
450 Bob Gibson 6.00 15.00
451 Joe Keough 1.00 2.50
452 John Boccabella 1.00 2.50
453 Terry Crowley 1.00 2.50
454 Mike Paul 1.00 2.50
455 Don Kessinger 1.50 4.00
456 Bob Meyer 1.00 2.50
457 Willie Smith 1.00 2.50
458 Rookie Stars 1.00 2.50
Ron Lolich RC
Dave Lemonds RC
459 Jim Lefebvre 1.00 2.50
460 Fritz Peterson 1.00 2.50
461 Jim Ray Hart 1.00 2.50
462 Washington Senators TC 2.50 6.00
463 Tom Kelley 1.00 2.50
464 Aurelio Rodriguez 1.00 2.50
465 Tim McCarver 2.50 6.00
466 Ken Berry 1.00 2.50
467 Al Santorini 1.00 2.50
468 Frank Fernandez 1.00 2.50
469 Bob Aspromonte 1.00 2.50
470 Bob Oliver 1.00 2.50
471 Tom Griffin 1.00 2.50
472 Ken Rudolph 1.00 2.50
473 Gary Wagner 1.00 2.50
474 Jim Fairey 1.00 2.50
475 Ron Perranoski 1.00 2.50
476 Dal Maxvill 1.00 2.50
477 Earl Weaver MG 2.50 6.00
478 Bernie Carbo 1.00 2.50
479 Dennis Higgins 1.00 2.50
480 Manny Sanguillen 1.50 4.00
481 Daryl Patterson 1.00 2.50
482 San Diego Padres TC 2.50 6.00
483 Gene Michael 1.00 2.50
484 Don Wilson 1.00 2.50
485 Ken McMullen 1.00 2.50
486 Steve Huntz 1.00 2.50
487 Paul Schaal 1.00 2.50
488 Jerry Stephenson 1.00 2.50
489 Luis Alvarado 1.00 2.50
490 Deron Johnson 1.00 2.50
491 Jim Hardin 1.00 2.50
492 Ken Boswell 1.00 2.50
493 Dave May 1.00 2.50
494 Rookie Stars 1.50 4.00
Ralph Garr
Rick Kester
495 Felipe Alou 1.50 4.00
496 Woody Woodward 1.00 2.50
497 Horacio Pina RC 1.00 2.50
498 John Kennedy 1.00 2.50
499 Checklist 5 4.00 10.00
500 Jim Perry 1.50 4.00
501 Andy Etchebarren 1.00 2.50
502 Chicago Cubs TC 2.50 6.00
503 Gates Brown 1.00 2.50
504 Ken Wright RC 1.00 2.50
505 Ollie Brown 1.00 2.50
506 Bobby Knoop 1.00 2.50
507 George Stone 1.00 2.50
508 Roger Repoz 1.00 2.50
509 Jim Grant 1.00 2.50
510 Ken Harrelson 1.50 4.00
511 Chris Short 1.50 4.00
(Pete Rose leading off second)
512 Rookie Stars 1.00 2.50
Dick Mills RC
Mike Garman RC
513 Nolan Ryan 75.00 150.00
514 Ron Woods 1.00 2.50
515 Carl Morton 1.00 2.50
516 Ted Kubiak 1.00 2.50
517 Charlie Fox MG RC 1.00 2.50
518 Joe Grzenda 1.00 2.50
519 Willie Crawford 1.00 2.50
520 Tommy John 2.50 6.00
521 Leron Lee 1.00 2.50
522 Minnesota Twins TC 2.50 6.00
523 John Odom 1.00 2.50
524 Mickey Stanley 2.50 6.00
525 Ernie Banks 20.00 50.00
526 Ray Jarvis 1.50 4.00
527 Cleon Jones 2.50 6.00
528 Wally Bunker 1.50 4.00
529 Rookie Stars 2.50 6.00
Enzo Hernandez RC
Bill Buckner
Marty Perez RC
530 Carl Yastrzemski 12.50 30.00
531 Mike Torrez 1.50 4.00
532 Bill Rigney MG 1.50 4.00
533 Mike Ryan 1.50 4.00
534 Luke Walker 1.50 4.00
535 Curt Flood 2.50 6.00
536 Claude Raymond 1.50 4.00
537 Tom Egan 1.50 4.00
538 Angel Bravo 1.50 4.00
539 Larry Brown 1.50 4.00
540 Larry Dierker 2.50 6.00
541 Bob Burda 1.50 4.00
542 Bob Miller 1.50 4.00
543 New York Yankees TC 4.00 10.00
544 Vida Blue 2.50 6.00
545 Dick Dietz 1.50 4.00
546 John Matias 1.50 4.00
547 Pat Dobson 2.50 6.00
548 Don Mason 1.50 4.00
549 Jim Brewer 2.50 6.00
550 Harmon Killebrew 10.00 25.00
551 Frank Linzy 1.50 4.00
552 Buddy Bradford 1.50 4.00
553 Kevin Collins 1.50 4.00
554 Lowell Palmer 1.50 4.00
555 Walt Williams 1.50 4.00
556 Jim McGlothlin 1.50 4.00
557 Tom Satriano 1.50 4.00
558 Hector Torres 1.50 4.00
559 Rookie Stars 1.50 4.00
Terry Cox RC
Bill Gogolewski RC
Gary Jones RC
560 Rusty Staub 2.50 6.00
561 Syd O'Brien 1.50 4.00
562 Dave Giusti 1.50 4.00
563 San Francisco Giants TC 3.00 8.00
564 Al Fitzmorris 1.50 4.00
565 Jim Wynn 2.50 6.00
566 Tim Cullen 1.50 4.00
567 Walt Alston MG 3.00 8.00
568 Sal Campisi 1.50 4.00
569 Ivan Murrell 1.50 4.00
570 Jim Palmer 12.50 30.00
571 Ted Sizemore 1.50 4.00
572 Jerry Kenney 1.50 4.00
573 Ed Kranepool 2.50 6.00
574 Jim Bunning 3.00 8.00
575 Bill Freehan 2.50 6.00
576 Rookie Stars 1.50 4.00
Adrian Garrett RC
Brock Davis
Garry Jestadt
577 Jim Lonborg 2.50 6.00
578 Ron Hunt 1.50 4.00
579 Marty Pattin 1.50 4.00
580 Tony Perez 8.00 20.00
581 Roger Nelson 1.50 4.00
582 Dave Cash 2.50 6.00
583 Ron Cook RC 1.50 4.00
584 Cleveland Indians TC 3.00 8.00
585 Willie Davis 2.50 6.00
586 Dick Woodson 1.50 4.00
587 Sonny Jackson 1.50 4.00
588 Tom Bradley RC 1.50 4.00
589 Bob Barton 1.50 4.00
590 Alex Johnson 2.50 6.00
591 Jackie Brown RC 1.50 4.00
592 Randy Hundley 2.50 6.00
593 Jack Aker 1.50 4.00
594 Rookie Stars 2.50 6.00
Bob Chlupsa RC
Bob Stinson
Al Hrabosky RC
595 Dave Johnson 2.50 6.00
596 Mike Jorgensen 1.50 4.00
597 Ken Suarez 1.50 4.00
598 Rick Wise 2.50 6.00
599 Norm Cash 2.50 6.00
600 Willie Mays 50.00 100.00
601 Ken Tatum 1.50 4.00
602 Marty Martinez 1.50 4.00
603 Pittsburgh Pirates TC 3.00 8.00
604 John Gelnar 1.50 4.00
605 Orlando Cepeda 3.00 8.00
606 Chuck Taylor 1.50 4.00
607 Paul Ratliff 1.50 4.00
608 Mike Wegener 1.50 4.00
609 Leo Durocher MG 3.00 8.00
610 Amos Otis 2.50 6.00
611 Tom Phoebus 1.50 4.00
612 Rookie Stars 1.50 4.00
Lou Camilli RC
Ted Ford RC
Steve Mingori
613 Pedro Borbon 1.50 4.00
614 Billy Cowan 1.50 4.00
615 Mel Stottlemyre 2.50 6.00
616 Larry Hisle 2.50 6.00
617 Clay Dalrymple 1.50 4.00
618 Tug McGraw 2.50 6.00
619A Checklist 6 ERR 4.00 10.00
(No copyright)
619B Checklist 6 COR 2.50 6.00
(Copyright on back)
620 Frank Howard 2.50 6.00
621 Ron Bryant 1.50 4.00
622 Joe Lahoud 1.50 4.00
623 Pat Jarvis 1.50 4.00
624 Oakland Athletics TC 3.00 8.00
625 Lou Brock 12.50 30.00
626 Freddie Patek 2.50 6.00
627 Steve Hamilton 1.50 4.00
628 John Bateman 1.50 4.00
629 John Hiller 2.50 6.00
630 Roberto Clemente 75.00 150.00
631 Eddie Fisher 1.50 4.00
632 Darrel Chaney 1.50 4.00
633 Rookie Stars 1.50 4.00
Bobby Brooks
Pete Koegel RC
Scott Northey
634 Phil Regan 1.50 4.00
635 Bobby Murcer 2.50 6.00
636 Denny Lemaster 1.50 4.00
637 Dave Bristol MG 1.50 4.00
638 Stan Williams 1.50 4.00
639 Tom Haller 1.50 4.00
640 Frank Robinson 12.50 40.00
641 New York Mets TC 6.00 15.00
642 Jim Roland 1.50 4.00
643 Rick Reichardt 1.50 4.00
644 Jim Stewart SP 5.00 12.00
645 Jim Maloney SP 6.00 15.00
646 Bobby Floyd SP 5.00 12.00
647 Juan Pizarro 3.00 8.00
648 Rookie Stars 10.00 25.00
Rich Folkers RC
Ted Martinez RC
John Matlack RC SP
649 Sparky Lyle SP 6.00 15.00
650 Rich Allen SP 12.50 30.00
651 Jerry Robertson SP 5.00 12.00
652 Atlanta Braves TC 5.00 12.00
653 Russ Snyder SP 5.00 12.00
654 Don Shaw SP 5.00 12.00
655 Mike Epstein SP 5.00 12.00
656 Gerry Nyman SP 5.00 12.00
657 Jose Azcue 3.00 8.00
658 Paul Lindblad SP 5.00 12.00
659 Byron Browne SP 5.00 12.00
660 Ray Culp 3.00 8.00
661 Chuck Tanner MG SP 6.00 15.00
662 Mike Hedlund SP 5.00 12.00
663 Marv Staehle 3.00 8.00
664 Rookie Stars 5.00 12.00
Archie Reynolds RC
Bob Reynolds RC
Ken Reynolds RC SP
665 Ron Swoboda SP 6.00 15.00
666 Gene Brabender SP 5.00 12.00
667 Pete Ward 3.00 8.00
668 Gary Neibauer 3.00 8.00
669 Ike Brown SP 5.00 12.00
670 Bill Hands 3.00 8.00
671 Bill Voss SP 5.00 12.00
672 Ed Crosby SP RC 5.00 12.00
673 Gerry Janeski SP RC 5.00 12.00
674 Montreal Expos TC 5.00 12.00
675 Dave Boswell 3.00 8.00
676 Tommie Reynolds 3.00 8.00
677 Jack DiLauro SP 5.00 12.00
678 George Thomas 3.00 8.00
679 Don O'Riley 3.00 8.00
680 Don Mincher SP 5.00 12.00
681 Bill Butler 3.00 8.00
682 Terry Harmon 3.00 8.00
683 Bill Burbach SP 5.00 12.00
684 Curt Motton 3.00 8.00
685 Moe Drabowsky 3.00 8.00
686 Chico Ruiz SP 5.00 12.00
687 Ron Taylor SP 5.00 12.00
688 Sparky Anderson MG SP 12.50 30.00
689 Frank Baker 3.00 8.00
690 Bob Moose 3.00 8.00
691 Bobby Heise 3.00 8.00
692 Rookie Stars 5.00 12.00
Hal Haydel RC
Rogelio Moret RC
Wayne Twitchell RC SP
693 Jose Pena SP 5.00 12.00
694 Rick Renick SP 5.00 12.00
695 Joe Niekro 5.00 12.00
696 Jerry Morales 3.00 8.00
697 Rickey Clark SP 5.00 12.00
698 Milwaukee Brewers TC SP 8.00 20.00
699 Jim Britton 3.00 8.00
700 Boog Powell SP 10.00 25.00
701 Bob Garibaldi 3.00 8.00
702 Milt Ramirez RC 3.00 8.00
703 Mike Kekich 3.00 8.00
704 J.C. Martin SP 5.00 12.00
705 Dick Selma SP 5.00 12.00
706 Joe Foy SP 5.00 12.00
707 Fred Lasher 3.00 8.00
708 Russ Nagelson SP 5.00 12.00
709 Rookie Stars 40.00 80.00
Dusty Baker RC
Don Baylor RC
Tom Paciorek RC SP
710 Sonny Siebert 3.00 8.00
711 Larry Stahl SP 5.00 12.00
712 Jose Martinez 3.00 8.00
713 Mike Marshall SP 6.00 15.00
714 Dick Williams MG SP 6.00 15.00
715 Horace Clarke SP 6.00 15.00
716 Dave Leonhard 3.00 8.00
717 Tommie Aaron SP 5.00 12.00
718 Billy Wynne 3.00 8.00
719 Jerry May SP 5.00 12.00
720 Matty Alou 5.00 12.00
721 John Morris 3.00 8.00
722 Houston Astros TC SP 8.00 20.00
723 Vicente Romo SP 5.00 12.00
724 Tom Tischinski SP 5.00 12.00
725 Gary Gentry SP 5.00 12.00
726 Paul Popovich 3.00 8.00
727 Ray Lamb SP 5.00 12.00
728 Rookie Stars 3.00 8.00
Wayne Redmond RC
Keith Lampard
Bernie Williams
729 Dick Billings RC 3.00 8.00
730 Jim Rooker 3.00 8.00
731 Jim Qualls SP 5.00 12.00
732 Bob Reed 3.00 8.00
733 Lee Maye SP 5.00 12.00
734 Rob Gardner SP 5.00 12.00
735 Mike Shannon SP 6.00 15.00
736 Mel Queen SP 5.00 12.00
737 Preston Gomez MG SP 5.00 12.00
738 Russ Gibson SP 5.00 12.00
739 Barry Lersch SP 5.00 12.00
740 Luis Aparicio UER SP 12.50 30.00
(Led AL in steals
from 1965 to 1964,
should be 1956 to 1964)
741 Skip Guinn 3.00 8.00
742 Kansas City Royals TC 5.00 12.00
743 John O'Donoghue SP 5.00 12.00
744 Chuck Manuel SP 5.00 12.00
745 Sandy Alomar SP 5.00 12.00
746 Andy Kosco 3.00 8.00
747 Rookie Stars 3.00 8.00
Al Severinsen
Scipio Spinks
Balor Moore RC
748 John Purdin SP 5.00 12.00
749 Ken Szotkiewicz RC 3.00 8.00
750 Denny McLain SP 10.00 25.00
751 Al Weis SP 6.00 15.00
752 Dick Drago 5.00 12.00

1971 Topps Coins

This full-color set of 153 coins, which were inserted into packs, contains the photo of the player surrounded by a colored band, which contains the player's name, his team, his position and several stars. The backs contain the coin number, short biographical data and the line "Collect the entire set of 153 coins." The set was evidently produced in three groups of 51 as coins 1-51 have brass backs, coins 52-102 have chrome backs and coins 103-153 have blue backs. In fact it has been verified that the coins were printed in three sheets of 51 coins comprised of three rows of 17 coins. Each coin measures approximately 1 1/2" in diameter.

COMPLETE SET (153) 200.00 400.00
1 Clarence Gaston 1.00 2.50
2 Dave Johnson 1.00 2.50
3 Jim Bunning 2.00 5.00
4 Jim Spencer .75 2.00
5 Felix Millan .75 2.00
6 Gerry Moses .75 2.00
7 Ferguson Jenkins 2.00 5.00
8 Felipe Alou 1.00 2.50
9 Jim McGlothlin .75 2.00
10 Dick McAuliffe .75 2.00
11 Joe Torre 2.00 5.00
12 Jim Perry 1.00 2.50
13 Bobby Bonds 1.25 3.00
14 Danny Cater .75 2.00
15 Bill Mazeroski 2.00 5.00
16 Luis Aparicio 2.00 5.00
17 Doug Rader .75 2.00
18 Vada Pinson 1.25 3.00
19 John Bateman .75 2.00
20 Lew Krausse .75 2.00
21 Billy Grabarkewitz 1.00 2.50
22 Frank Howard 1.25 3.00
23 Jerry Koosman 1.25 3.00
24 Rod Carew 2.00 5.00
25 Al Ferrara .75 2.00
26 Dave McNally 1.00 2.50
27 Jim Hickman .75 2.00
28 Sandy Alomar 1.00 2.50
29 Lee May 1.00 2.50
30 Rico Petrocelli 1.00 2.50
31 Don Money .75 2.00
32 Jim Rooker .75 2.00
33 Dick Dietz .75 2.00
34 Roy White 1.00 2.50
35 Carl Morton .75 2.00
36 Walt Williams .75 2.00
37 Phil Niekro 2.00 5.00
38 Bill Freehan 1.00 2.50
39 Julian Javier .75 2.00
40 Rick Monday 1.00 2.50
41 Don Wilson .75 2.00
42 Ray Fosse 1.00 2.50
43 Art Shamsky .75 2.00
44 Ted Savage .75 2.00
45 Claude Osteen .75 2.00
46 Ed Brinkman .75 2.00
47 Matty Alou 1.00 2.50
48 Bob Oliver .75 2.00
49 Danny Coombs .75 2.00
50 Frank Robinson 2.00 5.00
51 Randy Hundley .75 2.00
52 Cesar Tovar 1.00 2.50
53 Wayne Simpson .75 2.00
54 Bobby Murcer 1.25 3.00
55 Carl Taylor .75 2.00
56 Tommy John 1.00 2.50
57 Willie McCovey 2.00 5.00
58 Carl Yastrzemski 5.00 12.00
59 Bob Bailey .75 2.00
60 Clyde Wright .75 2.00
61 Orlando Cepeda 2.00 5.00
62 Al Kaline 4.00 10.00
63 Bob Gibson 2.00 5.00
64 Bert Campaneris .75 2.00
65 Ted Sizemore .75 2.00
66 Duke Sims .75 2.00
67 Bud Harrelson 1.25 3.00
68 Gerald McNertney .75 2.00
69 Jim Wynn 1.00 2.50
70 Dick Bosman 1.00 2.50
71 Roberto Clemente 12.50 30.00
72 Rich Reese .75 2.00
73 Gaylord Perry 2.00 5.00
74 Boog Powell 1.00 2.50
75 Billy Williams 2.00 5.00
76 Bill Melton .75 2.00
77 Nate Colbert .75 2.00
78 Reggie Smith 1.00 2.50
79 Deron Johnson .75 2.00
80 Jim Hunter 2.00 5.00
81 Bobby Tolan 1.00 2.50
82 Jim Northrup .75 2.00
83 Ron Fairly 1.00 2.50
84 Alex Johnson .75 2.00
85 Pat Jarvis .75 2.00
86 Sam McDowell 1.00 2.50
87 Lou Brock 2.00 5.00
88 Danny Walton .75 2.00
89 Denis Menke .75 2.00
90 Jim Palmer 2.00 5.00
91 Tommy Agee 1.00 2.50
92 Duane Josephson .75 2.00
93 Willie Davis 1.00 2.50
94 Mel Stottlemyre 1.00 2.50
95 Ron Santo 1.00 2.50
96 Amos Otis 1.00 2.50
97 Ken Henderson .75 2.00
98 George Scott 1.00 2.50
99 Dock Ellis 1.00 2.50
100 Harmon Killebrew 4.00 10.00
101 Pete Rose 8.00 20.00
102 Rick Reichardt .75 2.00
103 Cleon Jones .75 2.00
104 Ron Perranoski .75 2.00
105 Tony Perez 2.00 5.00
106 Mickey Lolich 1.00 2.50
107 Tim McCarver 1.00 2.50
108 Reggie Jackson 6.00 15.00
109 Chris Cannizzaro .75 2.00
110 Steve Hargan .75 2.00
111 Rusty Staub 1.00 2.50
112 Andy Messersmith 1.00 2.50
113 Rico Carty 1.00 2.50
114 Brooks Robinson 4.00 10.00
115 Steve Carlton 2.00 5.00
116 Mike Hegan .75 2.00
117 Joe Morgan 2.00 5.00
118 Thurman Munson 5.00 12.00
119 Don Kessinger .75 2.00
120 Joel Horlen .75 2.00
121 Wes Parker 1.00 2.50
122 Sonny Siebert .75 2.00
123 Willie Stargell 2.00 5.00
124 Ellie Rodriguez .75 2.00
125 Juan Marichal 2.00 5.00
126 Mike Epstein .75 2.00
127 Tom Seaver 5.00 12.00
128 Tony Oliva 1.00 2.50
129 Jim Merritt .75 2.00
130 Willie Horton 1.00 2.50
131 Rick Wise .75 2.00
132 Sal Bando 1.00 2.50
133 Ollie Brown .75 2.00
134 Ken Harrelson 1.00 2.50
135 Mack Jones .75 2.00
136 Jim Fregosi 1.00 2.50
137 Hank Aaron 8.00 20.00
138 Fritz Peterson .75 2.00
139 Joe Hague .75 2.00
140 Tommy Harper .75 2.00
141 Larry Dierker .75 2.00
142 Tony Conigliaro 1.00 2.50
143 Glenn Beckert .75 2.00
144 Carlos May .75 2.00
145 Don Sutton 2.00 5.00
146 Paul Casanova .75 2.00
147 Bob Moose .75 2.00
148 Chico Cardenas .75 2.00
149 Johnny Bench 6.00 15.00
150 Mike Cuellar 1.00 2.50
151 Donn Clendenon .75 2.00
152 Lou Piniella 1.00 2.50
153 Willie Mays 10.00 25.00

1971 Topps Scratchoffs

These pack inserts featured the same players are the 1970 Topps Scratchoffs. However, the only difference is that the center of the game is red rather than black.

COMPLETE SET (24) 15.00 40.00
1 Hank Aaron 3.00 8.00
2 Rich Allen .60 1.50
3 Luis Aparicio 1.50 4.00
4 Sal Bando .40 1.00
5 Glenn Beckert .40 1.00
6 Dick Bosman .40 1.00
7 Nate Colbert .40 1.00
8 Mike Hegan .40 1.00
9 Mack Jones .40 1.00
10 Al Kaline 2.00 5.00
11 Harmon Killebrew 2.00 5.00
12 Juan Marichal 1.50 4.00
13 Tim McCarver .75 2.00
14 Sam McDowell .50 1.25
15 Claude Osteen .40 1.00
16 Tony Perez 1.25 3.00
17 Lou Piniella .60 1.50
18 Boog Powell .60 1.50
19 Tom Seaver 2.50 6.00
20 Jim Spencer .40 1.00
21 Willie Stargell 2.00 5.00
22 Mel Stottlemyre .50 1.25
23 Jim Wynn .50 1.25
24 Carl Yastrzemski 2.00 5.00

1971 Topps Greatest Moments

The cards in this 55-card set measure 2 1/2" by 4 3/4". The 1971 Topps Greatest Moments set contains numbered cards depicting specific career highlights of current players. The obverses are black bordered and contain a small cameo picture of the left side; a deckle-bordered black and white action photo dominates the rest of the card. The backs are designed in newspaper style. Sometimes found in uncut sheets, this test set was retailed in gum packs on a very limited basis. Double prints (DP) are listed in our checklist; there were 22 double prints and 33 single prints.

COMPLETE SET (55) 750.00 1500.00
COMMON CARD (1-55) 8.00 20.00
COMMON DP 3.00 8.00
1 Thurman Munson DP 12.50 40.00
2 Hoyt Wilhelm 10.00 25.00
3 Rico Carty 8.00 20.00
4 Carl Morton DP 3.00 8.00
5 Sal Bando DP 4.00 10.00
6 Bert Campaneris DP 4.00 10.00
7 Jim Kaat 10.00 25.00
8 Harmon Killebrew 40.00 80.00
9 Brooks Robinson 40.00 80.00
10 Jim Perry 8.00 20.00
11 Tony Oliva 12.50 30.00
12 Vada Pinson 10.00 25.00
13 Johnny Bench 60.00 120.00
14 Tony Perez 12.50 30.00
15 Pete Rose DP 40.00 80.00
16 Jim Fregosi DP 4.00 10.00
17 Alex Johnson DP 3.00 8.00
18 Clyde Wright DP 3.00 8.00
19 Al Kaline DP 12.50 40.00
20 Denny McLain 12.50 30.00
21 Jim Northrup 8.00 20.00
22 Bill Freehan 8.00 20.00
23 Mickey Lolich 10.00 25.00
24 Bob Gibson DP 12.50 30.00
25 Tim McCarver DP 3.00 8.00
26 Orlando Cepeda DP 8.00 20.00
27 Lou Brock DP 12.50 30.00
28 Nate Colbert DP 3.00 8.00
29 Maury Wills 12.50 30.00
30 Wes Parker 8.00 20.00
31 Jim Wynn 10.00 25.00
32 Larry Dierker 10.00 25.00
33 Bill Melton 8.00 20.00
34 Joe Morgan 12.50 30.00
35 Rusty Staub 10.00 25.00
36 Ernie Banks DP 12.50 40.00
37 Billy Williams 12.50 30.00
38 Lou Piniella 10.00 25.00
39 Rico Petrocelli DP 4.00 10.00
40 Carl Yastrzemski DP 20.00 50.00
41 Willie Mays DP 50.00 100.00
42 Tommy Harper 8.00 20.00
43 Jim Bunning DP 4.00 10.00
44 Fritz Peterson 10.00 25.00
45 Roy White 10.00 25.00
46 Bobby Murcer 12.50 30.00
47 Reggie Jackson 100.00 200.00
48 Frank Howard 10.00 25.00
49 Dick Bosman 8.00 20.00
50 Sam McDowell DP 4.00 10.00
51 Luis Aparicio DP 4.00 10.00
52 Willie McCovey DP 12.50 30.00
53 Joe Pepitone 10.00 25.00
54 Jerry Grote 10.00 25.00
55 Bud Harrelson 8.00 20.00

1972 Topps

The cards in this 787-card set measure 2 1/2" by 3 1/2". The 1972 Topps set contained the most cards ever for a Topps set to that point in time. Features appearing for the first time were "Boyhood Photos" (341-348/491-498), Awards and Trophy cards (621-626), "In Action" (distributed throughout the set), and "Traded Cards" (751-757). Other subsets included League Leaders (85-96), Playoffs cards (221-222), and World Series cards (223-230). The curved lines of the color picture are a departure from the rectangular designs of other years. There is a series of intermediate scarcity (526-656) and the usual high numbers (657-787). The backs of cards 692, 694, 696, 700, 706 and 710 form a picture back of Tom Seaver. The backs of cards 698, 702, 704, 708, 712, 714 form a picture back of Tony Oliva. As in previous years, cards were issued in a variety of ways including ten-card wax packs which cost a dime, 28-card cello packs which cost a quarter and 54-card rack packs which cost 39 cents. The 10 cents wax packs were issued 24 packs to a box while the cello packs were also issued 24 packs to a box. Rookie Cards in this set include Ron Cey and Carlton Fisk.

COMPLETE SET (787) 750.00 1500.00
COMMON CARD (1-132) .25 .60
COMMON (133-263) .40 1.00
COMMON (264-394) .50 1.25
COMMON (395-525) .60 1.50
COMMON (526-656) 1.50 4.00
COMMON (657-787) 5.00 12.00
WRAPPER (10-CENT) 6.00 15.00
1 Pittsburgh Pirates TC 3.00 8.00
2 Ray Culp .25 .60
3 Bob Tolan .25 .60
4 Checklist 1-132 2.50 6.00
5 John Bateman .25 .60
6 Fred Scherman .25 .60
7 Enzo Hernandez .25 .60
8 Ron Swoboda .50 1.25
9 Stan Williams .25 .60
10 Amos Otis .50 1.25
11 Bobby Valentine .50 1.25
12 Jose Cardenal .25 .60
13 Joe Grzenda .25 .60
14 Rookie Stars .25 .60
Pete Koegel
Mike Anderson RC
Wayne Twitchell
15 Walt Williams .25 .60
16 Mike Jorgensen .25 .60
17 Dave Duncan .50 1.25
18A Juan Pizarro .25 .60
(Yellow underline
C and S of Cubs)
18B Juan Pizarro 2.00 5.00
(Green underline
C and S of Cubs)
19 Billy Cowan .25 .60
20 Don Wilson .25 .60
21 Atlanta Braves TC .60 1.50
22 Rob Gardner .25 .60
23 Ted Kubiak .25 .60
24 Ted Ford .25 .60
25 Bill Singer .25 .60
26 Andy Etchebarren .25 .60
27 Bob Johnson .25 .60
28 Rookie Stars .25 .60
Bob Gebhard RC
Steve Brye
Hal Haydel
29A Bill Bonham RC .25 .60
(Yellow underline
C and S of Cubs)
29B Bill Bonham 2.00 5.00
(Green underline
C and S of Cubs)
30 Rico Petrocelli .50 1.25
31 Cleon Jones .50 1.25
32 Cleon Jones IA .25 .60
33 Billy Martin MG 1.50 4.00
34 Billy Martin IA 1.00 2.50
35 Jerry Johnson .25 .60
36 Jerry Johnson IA .25 .60
37 Carl Yastrzemski 4.00 10.00
38 Carl Yastrzemski IA 3.00 8.00
39 Bob Barton .25 .60
40 Bob Barton IA .25 .60
41 Tommy Davis .50 1.25
42 Tommy Davis IA .25 .60
43 Rick Wise .50 1.25
44 Rick Wise IA .25 .60
45A Glenn Beckert .50 1.25
(Yellow underline
C and S of Cubs)
45B Glenn Beckert 2.00 5.00
(Green underline
C and S of Cubs)
46 Glenn Beckert IA .25 .60
47 John Ellis .25 .60
48 John Ellis IA .25 .60
49 Willie Mays 12.50 40.00
50 Willie Mays IA 8.00 20.00
51 Harmon Killebrew 3.00 8.00
52 Harmon Killebrew IA 1.50 4.00
53 Bud Harrelson .50 1.25

54 Bud Harrelson IA	.25	.60
55 Clyde Wright	.25	.60
56 Rich Chiles RC	.25	.60
57 Bob Oliver	.25	.60
58 Ernie McAnally	.25	.60
59 Fred Stanley RC	.25	.60
60 Manny Sanguillen	.50	1.25
61 Rookie Stars	.50	1.25
Burt Hooton RC		
Gene Hiser RC		
Earl Stephenson RC		
62 Angel Mangual	.25	.60
63 Duke Sims	.25	.60
64 Pete Broberg RC	.25	.60
65 Cesar Cedeno	.50	1.25
66 Ray Corbin RC	.25	.60
67 Red Schoendienst MG	1.00	2.50
68 Jim York RC	.25	.60
69 Roger Freed	.25	.60
70 Mike Cuellar	.50	1.25
71 California Angels TC	.60	1.50
72 Bruce Kison RC	.25	.60
73 Steve Huntz	.25	.60
74 Cecil Upshaw	.25	.60
75 Bert Campaneris	.50	1.25
76 Don Carrithers RC	.25	.60
77 Ron Theobald RC	.25	.60
78 Steve Arlin RC	.25	.60
79 Rookie Stars	20.00	50.00
Mike Garman		
Cecil Cooper RC		
Carlton Fisk RC		
80 Tony Perez	1.50	4.00
81 Mike Hedlund	.25	.60
82 Ron Woods	.25	.60
83 Dalton Jones	.25	.60
84 Vince Colbert	.25	.60
85 NL Batting Leaders	1.00	2.50
Joe Torre		
Ralph Garr		
Glenn Beckert		
86 AL Batting Leaders	1.00	2.50
Tony Oliva		
Bobby Murcer		
Merv Rettenmund		
87 NL RBI Leaders	1.50	4.00
Joe Torre		
Willie Stargell		
Hank Aaron		
88 AL RBI Leaders	1.50	4.00
Harmon Killebrew		
Frank Robinson		
Reggie Smith		
89 NL Home Run Leaders	1.00	2.50
Willie Stargell		
Hank Aaron		
Lee May		
90 AL Home Run Leaders	1.00	2.50
Bill Melton		
Norm Cash		
Reggie Jackson		
91 NL ERA Leaders	1.00	2.50
Tom Seaver		
Dave Roberts UER		
(Photo actually		
Danny Coombs)		
Don Wilson		
92 AL ERA Leaders	1.00	2.50
Vida Blue		
Wilbur Wood		
Jim Palmer		
93 NL Pitching Leaders	1.50	4.00
Fergie Jenkins		
Steve Carlton		
Al Downing		
Tom Seaver		
94 AL Pitching Leaders	1.00	2.50
Mickey Lolich		
Vida Blue		
Wilbur Wood		
95 NL Strikeout Leaders	1.50	4.00
Tom Seaver		
Fergie Jenkins		
Bill Stoneman		
96 AL Strikeout Leaders	1.00	2.50
Mickey Lolich		
Vida Blue		
Joe Coleman		
97 Tom Kelley	.25	.60
98 Chuck Tanner MG	.50	1.25
99 Ross Grimsley RC	.25	.60
100 Frank Robinson	3.00	8.00
101 Rookie Stars	1.00	2.50
Bill Greif RC		
J.R. Richard RC		
Ray Busse RC		
102 Lloyd Allen	.25	.60
103 Checklist 133-263	2.50	6.00
104 Toby Harrah RC	.50	1.25
105 Gary Gentry	.25	.60
106 Milwaukee Brewers TC	.60	1.50
107 Jose Cruz RC	.50	1.25
108 Gary Waslewski	.25	.60
109 Jerry May	.25	.60
110 Ron Hunt	.25	.60
111 Jim Grant	.25	.60
112 Greg Luzinski	.50	1.25
113 Rogelio Moret	.25	.60
114 Bill Buckner	.50	1.25
115 Jim Fregosi	.50	1.25
116 Ed Farmer RC	.25	.60
117A Cleo James RC	.25	.60
(Yellow underline		
C and S of Cubs)		
117B Cleo James	2.00	5.00
(Green underline		
C and S of Cubs)		
118 Skip Lockwood	.25	.60
119 Marty Perez	.25	.60
120 Bill Freehan	.50	1.25
121 Ed Sprague	.25	.60
122 Larry Biittner RC	.25	.60
123 Ed Acosta	.25	.60
124 Rookie Stars	.25	.60
Alan Closter		
Rusty Torres RC		
Roger Hambright RC		
125 Dave Cash	.50	1.25
126 Bart Johnson	.25	.60
127 Duffy Dyer	.25	.60
128 Eddie Watt	.25	.60
129 Charlie Fox MG	.25	.60
130 Bob Gibson	3.00	8.00
131 Jim Nettles	.25	.60
132 Joe Morgan	2.50	6.00
133 Joe Keough	.40	1.00
134 Carl Morton	.40	1.00
135 Vada Pinson	.75	2.00
136 Darrel Chaney	.40	1.00
137 Dick Williams MG	.75	2.00
138 Mike Kekich	.40	1.00
139 Tim McCarver	.75	2.00
140 Pat Dobson	.75	2.00
141 Rookie Stars	.75	2.00
Buzz Capra RC		
Lee Stanton RC		
Jon Matlack		
142 Chris Chambliss RC	1.50	4.00
143 Garry Jestadt	.40	1.00
144 Marty Pattin	.40	1.00
145 Don Kessinger	.75	2.00
146 Steve Kealey	.40	1.00
147 Dave Kingman RC	2.50	6.00
148 Dick Billings	.40	1.00
149 Gary Neibauer	.40	1.00
150 Norm Cash	.75	2.00
151 Jim Brewer	.40	1.00
152 Gene Clines	.40	1.00
153 Rick Auerbach RC	.40	1.00
154 Ted Simmons	1.50	4.00
155 Larry Dierker	.40	1.00
156 Minnesota Twins TC	.75	2.00
157 Don Gullett	.40	1.00
158 Jerry Kenney	.40	1.00
159 John Boccabella	.40	1.00
160 Andy Messersmith	.75	2.00
161 Brock Davis	.40	1.00
162 Rookie Stars	.75	2.00
Jerry Bell RC		
Darrell Porter RC		
Bob Reynolds UER		
(Porter and Bell		
photos switched)		
163 Tug McGraw	1.50	4.00
164 Tug McGraw IA	.75	2.00
165 Chris Speier RC	.75	2.00
166 Chris Speier IA	.40	1.00
167 Deron Johnson	.40	1.00
168 Deron Johnson IA	.40	1.00
169 Vida Blue	1.50	4.00
170 Vida Blue IA	.75	2.00
171 Darrell Evans	1.50	4.00
172 Darrell Evans IA	.75	2.00
173 Clay Kirby	.40	1.00
174 Clay Kirby IA	.40	1.00
175 Tom Haller	.40	1.00
176 Tom Haller IA	.40	1.00
177 Paul Schaal	.40	1.00
178 Paul Schaal IA	.40	1.00
179 Dock Ellis	.40	1.00
180 Dock Ellis IA	.40	1.00
181 Ed Kranepool	.75	2.00
182 Ed Kranepool IA	.40	1.00
183 Bill Melton	.40	1.00
184 Bill Melton IA	.40	1.00
185 Ron Bryant	.40	1.00
186 Ron Bryant IA	.40	1.00
187 Gates Brown	.40	1.00
188 Frank Lucchesi MG	.40	1.00
189 Gene Tenace	.75	2.00
190 Dave Giusti	.40	1.00
191 Jeff Burroughs RC	1.50	4.00
192 Chicago Cubs TC	.75	2.00
193 Kurt Bevacqua RC	.40	1.00
194 Fred Norman	.40	1.00
195 Orlando Cepeda	2.50	6.00
196 Mel Queen	.40	1.00
197 Johnny Briggs	.40	1.00
198 Rookie Stars	2.50	6.00
Charlie Hough RC		
Bob O'Brien RC		
Mike Strahler		
199 Mike Fiore	.40	1.00
200 Lou Brock	3.00	8.00
201 Phil Roof	.40	1.00
202 Scipio Spinks	.40	1.00
203 Ron Blomberg RC	.40	1.00
204 Tommy Helms	.40	1.00
205 Dick Drago	.40	1.00
206 Dal Maxvill	.40	1.00
207 Tom Egan	.40	1.00
208 Milt Pappas	.75	2.00
209 Joe Rudi	.75	2.00
210 Denny McLain	.75	2.00
211 Gary Sutherland	.40	1.00
212 Grant Jackson	.40	1.00
213 Rookie Stars	.40	1.00
Billy Parker RC		
Art Kusnyer RC		
Tom Silverio RC		
214 Mike McQueen	.40	1.00
215 Alex Johnson	.75	2.00
216 Joe Niekro	.75	2.00
217 Roger Metzger	.40	1.00
218 Eddie Kasko MG	.40	1.00
219 Rennie Stennett RC	.75	2.00
220 Jim Perry	.75	2.00
221 NL Playoffs	.75	2.00
Bucs Champs		
222 AL Playoffs	1.50	4.00
Orioles Champs		
Brooks Robinson		
223 World Series Game 1	.75	2.00
Dave McNally		
224 World Series Game 2	.75	2.00
Dave Johnson		
Mark Belanger		
225 World Series Game 3	.75	2.00
Manny Sanguillen		
226 World Series Game 4	3.00	8.00
Roberto Clemente		
227 World Series Game 5	.75	2.00
Nellie Briles		
228 World Series Game 6	.75	2.00
Frank Robinson		
Manny Sanguillen		
229 World Series Game 7	.75	2.00
Steve Blass		
230 World Series Summary	.75	2.00
Pirates Celebrate		
231 Casey Cox	.40	1.00
232 Rookie Stars	.40	1.00
Chris Arnold RC		
Jim Barr RC		
Dave Rader RC		
233 Jay Johnstone	.75	2.00
234 Ron Taylor	.40	1.00
235 Merv Rettenmund	.40	1.00
236 Jim McGlothlin	.40	1.00
237 New York Yankees TC	.75	2.00
238 Leron Lee	.40	1.00
239 Tom Timmermann	.40	1.00
240 Rich Allen	.75	2.00
241 Rollie Fingers	2.50	6.00
242 Don Mincher	.40	1.00
243 Frank Linzy	.40	1.00
244 Steve Braun RC	.40	1.00
245 Tommie Agee	.75	2.00
246 Tom Burgmeier	.40	1.00
247 Milt May	.40	1.00
248 Tom Bradley	.40	1.00
249 Harry Walker MG	.40	1.00
250 Boog Powell	.75	2.00
251 Checklist 264-394	2.50	6.00
252 Ken Reynolds	.40	1.00
253 Sandy Alomar	.75	2.00
254 Boots Day	.40	1.00
255 Jim Lonborg	.75	2.00
256 George Foster	.75	2.00
257 Rookie Stars	.40	1.00
Jim Foor RC		
Tim Hosley RC		
Paul Jata RC		
258 Randy Hundley	.40	1.00
259 Sparky Lyle	.75	2.00
260 Ralph Garr	.75	2.00
261 Steve Mingori	.40	1.00
262 San Diego Padres TC	.75	2.00
263 Felipe Alou	.75	2.00
264 Tommy John	.75	2.00
265 Wes Parker	.75	2.00
266 Bobby Bolin	.50	1.25
267 Dave Concepcion	1.50	4.00
268 Rookie Stars	.50	1.25
Dwain Anderson RC		
Chris Floethe RC		
269 Don Hahn	.50	1.25
270 Jim Palmer	3.00	8.00
271 Ken Rudolph	.50	1.25
272 Mickey Rivers RC	.75	2.00
273 Bobby Floyd	.50	1.25
274 Al Severinsen	.50	1.25
275 Cesar Tovar	.50	1.25
276 Gene Mauch MG	.75	2.00
277 Elliott Maddox	.50	1.25
278 Dennis Higgins	.50	1.25
279 Larry Brown	.50	1.25
280 Willie McCovey	2.50	6.00
281 Bill Parsons RC	.50	1.25
282 Houston Astros TC	.75	2.00
283 Darrell Brandon	.50	1.25
284 Ike Brown	.50	1.25
285 Gaylord Perry	2.50	6.00
286 Gene Alley	.50	1.25
287 Jim Hardin	.50	1.25
288 Johnny Jeter	.50	1.25
289 Syd O'Brien	.50	1.25
290 Sonny Siebert	.50	1.25
291 Hal McRae	.75	2.00
292 Hal McRae IA	.50	1.25
293 Dan Frisella	.50	1.25
294 Dan Frisella IA	.50	1.25
295 Dick Dietz	.50	1.25
296 Dick Dietz IA	.50	1.25
297 Claude Osteen	.75	2.00
298 Claude Osteen IA	.50	1.25
299 Hank Aaron	12.50	40.00
300 Hank Aaron IA	8.00	20.00
301 George Mitterwald	.50	1.25
302 George Mitterwald IA	.50	1.25
303 Joe Pepitone	.75	2.00
304 Joe Pepitone IA	.50	1.25
305 Ken Boswell	.50	1.25
306 Ken Boswell IA	.50	1.25
307 Steve Renko	.50	1.25
308 Steve Renko IA	.50	1.25
309 Roberto Clemente	20.00	50.00
310 Roberto Clemente IA	10.00	25.00
311 Clay Carroll	.50	1.25
312 Clay Carroll IA	.50	1.25
313 Luis Aparicio	2.50	6.00
314 Luis Aparicio IA	.75	2.00
315 Paul Splittorff	.50	1.25
316 Rookie Stars	.75	2.00
Jim Bibby RC		
Jorge Roque RC		
Santiago Guzman		
317 Rich Hand	.50	1.25
318 Sonny Jackson	.50	1.25
319 Aurelio Rodriguez	.50	1.25
320 Steve Blass	.75	2.00
321 Joe Lahoud	.50	1.25
322 Jose Pena	.50	1.25
323 Earl Weaver MG	1.50	4.00
324 Mike Ryan	.50	1.25
325 Mel Stottlemyre	.75	2.00
326 Pat Kelly	.50	1.25
327 Steve Stone RC	.75	2.00
328 Boston Red Sox TC	.75	2.00
329 Roy Foster	.50	1.25
330 Jim Hunter	2.50	6.00
331 Stan Swanson RC	.50	1.25
332 Buck Martinez	.50	1.25
333 Steve Barber	.50	1.25
334 Rookie Stars	.50	1.25
Bill Fahey RC		
Jim Mason RC		
Tom Ragland RC		
335 Bill Hands	.50	1.25
336 Marty Martinez	.50	1.25
337 Mike Kilkenny	.50	1.25
338 Bob Grich	.75	2.00
339 Ron Cook	.50	1.25
340 Roy White	.75	2.00
341 Joe Torre KP	.50	1.25
342 Wilbur Wood KP	.50	1.25
343 Willie Stargell KP	.75	2.00
344 Dave McNally KP	.50	1.25
345 Rick Wise KP	.50	1.25
346 Jim Fregosi KP	.50	1.25
347 Tom Seaver KP	1.50	4.00
348 Sal Bando KP	.50	1.25
349 Al Fitzmorris	.50	1.25
350 Frank Howard	.75	2.00
351 Rookie Stars	.75	2.00
Tom House		
Rick Kester		
Jimmy Britton		
352 Dave LaRoche	.50	1.25
353 Art Shamsky	.50	1.25
354 Tom Murphy	.50	1.25
355 Bob Watson	.75	2.00
356 Gerry Moses	.50	1.25
357 Woody Fryman	.50	1.25
358 Sparky Anderson MG	1.50	4.00
359 Don Pavletich	.50	1.25
360 Dave Roberts	.50	1.25
361 Mike Andrews	.50	1.25
362 New York Mets TC	.75	2.00
363 Ron Klimkowski	.50	1.25
364 Johnny Callison	.75	2.00
365 Dick Bosman	.75	2.00
366 Jimmy Rosario RC	.50	1.25
367 Ron Perranoski	.50	1.25
368 Danny Thompson	.50	1.25
369 Jim Lefebvre	.75	2.00
370 Don Buford	.50	1.25
371 Denny Lemaster	.50	1.25
372 Rookie Stars	.50	1.25
Lance Clemons RC		
Monty Montgomery RC		
373 John Mayberry	.75	2.00
374 Jack Heidemann	.50	1.25
375 Reggie Cleveland	.50	1.25
376 Andy Kosco	.50	1.25
377 Terry Harmon	.50	1.25
378 Checklist 395-525	2.50	6.00
379 Ken Berry	.50	1.25
380 Earl Williams	.50	1.25
381 Chicago White Sox TC	.75	2.00
382 Joe Gibbon	.50	1.25
383 Brant Alyea	.50	1.25
384 Dave Campbell	.75	2.00
385 Mickey Stanley	.75	2.00
386 Jim Colborn	.50	1.25
387 Horace Clarke	.75	2.00
388 Charlie Williams RC	.50	1.25
389 Bill Rigney MG	.50	1.25
390 Willie Davis	.75	2.00
391 Ken Sanders	.50	1.25
392 Rookie Stars	.75	2.00
Fred Cambria		
Richie Zisk RC		
393 Curt Motton	.50	1.25
394 Ken Forsch	.75	2.00
395 Matty Alou	.75	2.00
396 Paul Lindblad	.60	1.50
397 Philadelphia Phillies TC	.75	2.00
398 Larry Hisle	.75	2.00
399 Milt Wilcox	.75	2.00
400 Tony Oliva	1.50	4.00
401 Jim Nash	.60	1.50
402 Bobby Heise	.60	1.50
403 John Cumberland	.60	1.50
404 Jeff Torborg	.75	2.00
405 Ron Fairly	.75	2.00
406 George Hendrick RC	.75	2.00
407 Chuck Taylor	.60	1.50
408 Jim Northrup	.75	2.00
409 Frank Baker	.60	1.50
410 Ferguson Jenkins	2.50	6.00
411 Bob Montgomery	.60	1.50
412 Dick Kelley	.60	1.50
413 Rookie Stars	.60	1.50
Don Eddy RC		
Dave Lemonds		
414 Bob Miller	.60	1.50
415 Cookie Rojas	.75	2.00
416 Johnny Edwards	.60	1.50
417 Tom Hall	.60	1.50
418 Tom Shopay	.60	1.50
419 Jim Spencer	.60	1.50
420 Steve Carlton	8.00	20.00
421 Ellie Rodriguez	.60	1.50
422 Ray Lamb	.60	1.50
423 Oscar Gamble	.75	2.00
424 Bill Gogolewski	.60	1.50
425 Ken Singleton	.75	2.00
426 Ken Singleton IA	.60	1.50
427 Tito Fuentes	.60	1.50
428 Tito Fuentes IA	.60	1.50
429 Bob Robertson	.60	1.50
430 Bob Robertson IA	.60	1.50
431 Clarence Gaston	.75	2.00
432 Clarence Gaston IA	.75	2.00
433 Johnny Bench	10.00	25.00
434 Johnny Bench IA	6.00	15.00
435 Reggie Jackson	12.50	30.00
436 Reggie Jackson IA	5.00	12.00
437 Maury Wills	.75	2.00
438 Maury Wills IA	.75	2.00
439 Billy Williams	2.50	6.00
440 Billy Williams IA	1.50	4.00
441 Thurman Munson	6.00	15.00
442 Thurman Munson IA	3.00	8.00
443 Ken Henderson	.60	1.50
444 Ken Henderson IA	.60	1.50
445 Tom Seaver	12.50	30.00
446 Tom Seaver IA	6.00	15.00
447 Willie Stargell	3.00	8.00
448 Willie Stargell IA	1.50	4.00
449 Bob Lemon MG	.75	2.00
450 Mickey Lolich	.75	2.00
451 Tony LaRussa	1.50	4.00
452 Ed Herrmann	.60	1.50
453 Barry Lersch	.60	1.50
454 Oakland Athletics TC	.75	2.00
455 Tommy Harper	.75	2.00
456 Mark Belanger	.75	2.00
457 Rookie Stars	.60	1.50
Darcy Fast RC		
Derrel Thomas RC		
Mike Ivie RC		
458 Aurelio Monteagudo	.60	1.50
459 Rick Renick	.60	1.50
460 Al Downing	.60	1.50
461 Tim Cullen	.60	1.50
462 Rickey Clark	.60	1.50
463 Bernie Carbo	.60	1.50
464 Jim Roland	.60	1.50
465 Gil Hodges MG	1.50	4.00
466 Norm Miller	.60	1.50
467 Steve Kline	.60	1.50
468 Richie Scheinblum	.60	1.50
469 Ron Herbel	.60	1.50
470 Ray Fosse	.60	1.50
471 Luke Walker	.60	1.50
472 Phil Gagliano	.60	1.50
473 Dan McGinn	.60	1.50
474 Rookie Stars	6.00	15.00
Don Baylor		
Roric Harrison RC		
Johnny Oates RC		
475 Gary Nolan	.75	2.00
476 Lee Richard RC	.60	1.50
477 Tom Phoebus	.60	1.50
478 Checklist 526-656	2.50	6.00
479 Don Shaw	.60	1.50
480 Lee May	.75	2.00
481 Billy Conigliaro	.75	2.00
482 Joe Hoerner	.60	1.50
483 Ken Suarez	.60	1.50
484 Lum Harris MG	.60	1.50
485 Phil Regan	.75	2.00
486 John Lowenstein	.60	1.50
487 Detroit Tigers TC	.75	2.00
488 Mike Nagy	.60	1.50
489 Rookie Stars	.60	1.50
Terry Humphrey RC		
Keith Lampard		
490 Dave McNally	.75	2.00
491 Lou Piniella KP	.75	2.00
492 Mel Stottlemyre KP	.75	2.00
493 Bob Bailey KP	.75	2.00
494 Willie Horton KP	.75	2.00
495 Bill Melton KP	.75	2.00
496 Bud Harrelson KP	.75	2.00
497 Jim Perry KP	.75	2.00
498 Brooks Robinson KP	1.50	4.00
499 Vicente Romo	.60	1.50
500 Joe Torre	1.50	4.00
501 Pete Hamm	.60	1.50
502 Jackie Hernandez	.60	1.50
503 Gary Peters	.60	1.50
504 Ed Spiezio	.60	1.50
505 Mike Marshall	.75	2.00
506 Rookie Stars	.60	1.50
Terry Ley RC		
Jim Moyer RC		
Dick Tidrow RC		
507 Fred Gladding	.60	1.50
508 Elrod Hendricks	.60	1.50
509 Don McMahon	.60	1.50
510 Ted Williams MG	5.00	12.00
511 Tony Taylor	.75	2.00
512 Paul Popovich	.60	1.50
513 Lindy McDaniel	.75	2.00
514 Ted Sizemore	.75	2.00
515 Bert Blyleven	1.50	4.00
516 Oscar Brown	.60	1.50
517 Ken Brett	.60	1.50
518 Wayne Garrett	.60	1.50
519 Ted Abernathy	.60	1.50
520 Larry Bowa	.75	2.00
521 Alan Foster	.60	1.50
522 Los Angeles Dodgers TC	.75	2.00
523 Chuck Dobson	.60	1.50
524 Rookie Stars	.60	1.50
Ed Armbrister RC		
Mel Behney RC		
525 Carlos May	.75	2.00
526 Bob Bailey	2.50	6.00
527 Dave Leonhard	1.50	4.00
528 Ron Stone	1.50	4.00
529 Dave Nelson	2.50	6.00
530 Don Sutton	5.00	12.00
531 Freddie Patek	2.50	6.00
532 Fred Kendall RC	1.50	4.00
533 Ralph Houk MG	2.50	6.00
534 Jim Hickman	2.50	6.00
535 Ed Brinkman	1.50	4.00
536 Doug Rader	2.50	6.00
537 Bob Locker	1.50	4.00
538 Charlie Sands RC	1.50	4.00
539 Terry Forster RC	2.50	6.00
540 Felix Millan	1.50	4.00
541 Roger Repoz	1.50	4.00
542 Jack Billingham	1.50	4.00
543 Duane Josephson	1.50	4.00
544 Ted Martinez	1.50	4.00
545 Wayne Granger	1.50	4.00
546 Joe Hague	1.50	4.00
547 Cleveland Indians TC	3.00	8.00
548 Frank Reberger	1.50	4.00
549 Dave May	1.50	4.00
550 Brooks Robinson	10.00	25.00
551 Ollie Brown	1.50	4.00
552 Ollie Brown IA	1.50	4.00
553 Wilbur Wood	2.50	6.00
554 Wilbur Wood IA	1.50	4.00
555 Ron Santo	3.00	8.00
556 Ron Santo IA	2.50	6.00
557 John Odom	1.50	4.00
558 John Odom IA	1.50	4.00
559 Pete Rose	20.00	50.00
560 Pete Rose IA	10.00	25.00
561 Leo Cardenas	1.50	4.00
562 Leo Cardenas IA	1.50	4.00
563 Ray Sadecki	1.50	4.00
564 Ray Sadecki IA	1.50	4.00
565 Reggie Smith	2.50	6.00
566 Reggie Smith IA	1.50	4.00
567 Juan Marichal	5.00	12.00
568 Juan Marichal IA	2.50	6.00
569 Ed Kirkpatrick	1.50	4.00
570 Ed Kirkpatrick IA	1.50	4.00
571 Nate Colbert	1.50	4.00
572 Nate Colbert IA	1.50	4.00
573 Fritz Peterson	1.50	4.00
574 Fritz Peterson IA	1.50	4.00
575 Al Oliver	3.00	8.00
576 Leo Durocher MG	2.50	6.00
577 Mike Paul	2.50	6.00
578 Billy Grabarkewitz	1.50	4.00
579 Doyle Alexander RC	2.50	6.00
580 Lou Piniella	2.50	6.00
581 Wade Blasingame	1.50	4.00
582 Montreal Expos TC	3.00	8.00
583 Darold Knowles	1.50	4.00
584 Jerry McNertney	1.50	4.00
585 George Scott	2.50	6.00
586 Denis Menke	1.50	4.00
587 Billy Wilson	1.50	4.00
588 Jim Holt	1.50	4.00
589 Hal Lanier	1.50	4.00
590 Graig Nettles	3.00	8.00
591 Paul Casanova	1.50	4.00
592 Lew Krausse	1.50	4.00
593 Rich Morales	1.50	4.00
594 Jim Beauchamp	1.50	4.00
595 Nolan Ryan	50.00	100.00
596 Manny Mota	2.50	6.00
597 Jim Magnuson RC	1.50	4.00
598 Hal King	2.50	6.00
599 Billy Champion	1.50	4.00
600 Al Kaline	10.00	25.00
601 George Stone	1.50	4.00
602 Dave Bristol MG	1.50	4.00
603 Jim Ray	1.50	4.00
604A Checklist 657-787	5.00	12.00
(Copyright on back		
bottom right)		
604B Checklist 657-787	5.00	12.00
(Copyright on back		
bottom left)		
605 Nelson Briles	2.50	6.00
606 Luis Melendez	1.50	4.00
607 Frank Duffy	1.50	4.00
608 Mike Corkins	1.50	4.00
609 Tom Grieve	2.50	6.00
610 Bill Stoneman	2.50	6.00
611 Rich Reese	1.50	4.00
612 Joe Decker	1.50	4.00
613 Mike Ferraro	1.50	4.00
614 Ted Uhlaender	1.50	4.00
615 Steve Hargan	1.50	4.00
616 Joe Ferguson RC	2.50	6.00
617 Kansas City Royals TC	3.00	8.00
618 Rich Robertson	1.50	4.00
619 Rich McKinney	1.50	4.00
620 Phil Niekro	5.00	12.00
621 Comm. Award	3.00	8.00
622 MVP Award	3.00	8.00
623 Cy Young Award	3.00	8.00
624 Minor League Player	3.00	8.00
of the Year Award		
625 Rookie of the Year	3.00	8.00
626 Babe Ruth Award	3.00	8.00
627 Moe Drabowsky	1.50	4.00
628 Terry Crowley	1.50	4.00
629 Paul Doyle	1.50	4.00
630 Rich Hebner	2.50	6.00
631 John Strohmayer	1.50	4.00
632 Mike Hegan	1.50	4.00
633 Jack Hiatt	1.50	4.00
634 Dick Woodson	1.50	4.00
635 Don Money	2.50	6.00
636 Bill Lee	2.50	6.00
637 Preston Gomez MG	1.50	4.00
638 Ken Wright	1.50	4.00
639 J.C. Martin	1.50	4.00
640 Joe Coleman	1.50	4.00
641 Mike Lum	1.50	4.00
642 Dennis Riddleberger RC	1.50	4.00
643 Russ Gibson	1.50	4.00
644 Bernie Allen	1.50	4.00
645 Jim Maloney	2.50	6.00
646 Chico Salmon	1.50	4.00
647 Bob Moose	1.50	4.00
648 Jim Lyttle	1.50	4.00
649 Pete Richert	1.50	4.00
650 Sal Bando	2.50	6.00
651 Cincinnati Reds TC	3.00	8.00
652 Marcelino Lopez	1.50	4.00
653 Jim Fairey	1.50	4.00
654 Horacio Pina	2.50	6.00
655 Jerry Grote	1.50	4.00
656 Rudy May	1.50	4.00
657 Bobby Wine	5.00	12.00
658 Steve Dunning	5.00	12.00
659 Bob Aspromonte	5.00	12.00
660 Paul Blair	6.00	15.00
661 Bill Virdon MG	5.00	12.00
662 Stan Bahnsen	5.00	12.00
663 Fran Healy RC	6.00	15.00
664 Bobby Knoop	5.00	12.00
665 Chris Short	5.00	12.00
666 Hector Torres	5.00	12.00
667 Ray Newman RC	5.00	12.00
668 Texas Rangers TC	12.50	30.00
669 Willie Crawford	5.00	12.00
670 Ken Holtzman	6.00	15.00
671 Donn Clendenon	6.00	15.00
672 Archie Reynolds	5.00	12.00
673 Dave Marshall	5.00	12.00
674 John Kennedy	5.00	12.00
675 Pat Jarvis	5.00	12.00
676 Danny Cater	5.00	12.00
677 Ivan Murrell	5.00	12.00
678 Steve Luebber RC	5.00	12.00
679 Rookie Stars	5.00	12.00
Bob Fenwick RC		
Bob Stinson		
680 Dave Johnson	6.00	15.00
681 Bobby Pfeil	5.00	12.00
682 Mike McCormick	6.00	15.00
683 Steve Hovley	5.00	12.00
684 Hal Breeden RC	5.00	12.00
685 Joel Horlen	5.00	12.00
686 Steve Garvey	12.50	40.00
687 Del Unser	5.00	12.00
688 St. Louis Cardinals TC	8.00	20.00
689 Eddie Fisher	5.00	12.00
690 Willie Montanez	6.00	15.00
691 Curt Blefary	5.00	12.00
692 Curt Blefary IA	5.00	12.00
693 Alan Gallagher	5.00	12.00
694 Alan Gallagher IA	5.00	12.00
695 Rod Carew	20.00	50.00
696 Rod Carew IA	12.50	30.00
697 Jerry Koosman	6.00	15.00
698 Jerry Koosman IA	6.00	15.00
699 Bobby Murcer	6.00	15.00
700 Bobby Murcer IA	6.00	15.00
701 Jose Pagan	5.00	12.00
702 Jose Pagan IA	5.00	12.00
703 Doug Griffin	5.00	12.00
704 Doug Griffin IA	5.00	12.00
705 Pat Corrales	6.00	15.00
706 Pat Corrales IA	5.00	12.00
707 Tim Foli	5.00	12.00
708 Tim Foli IA	5.00	12.00
709 Jim Kaat	6.00	15.00
710 Jim Kaat IA	6.00	15.00
711 Bobby Bonds	8.00	20.00
712 Bobby Bonds IA	6.00	15.00
713 Gene Michael	8.00	20.00
714 Gene Michael IA	6.00	15.00
715 Mike Epstein	5.00	12.00
716 Jesus Alou	5.00	12.00
717 Bruce Dal Canton	5.00	12.00
718 Del Rice MG	5.00	12.00
719 Cesar Geronimo	5.00	12.00
720 Sam McDowell	6.00	15.00
721 Eddie Leon	5.00	12.00
722 Bill Sudakis	5.00	12.00
723 Al Santorini	5.00	12.00
724 Rookie Stars	5.00	12.00
John Curtis RC		
Rich Hinton RC		
Mickey Scott		
725 Dick McAuliffe	6.00	15.00
726 Dick Selma	5.00	12.00
727 Jose Laboy	5.00	12.00
728 Gail Hopkins	5.00	12.00
729 Bob Veale	6.00	15.00
730 Rick Monday	6.00	15.00
731 Baltimore Orioles TC	8.00	20.00
732 George Culver	5.00	12.00
733 Jim Ray Hart	6.00	15.00
734 Bob Burda	5.00	12.00
735 Diego Segui	5.00	12.00
736 Bill Russell	6.00	15.00
737 Len Randle RC	6.00	15.00
738 Jim Merritt	5.00	12.00
739 Don Mason	5.00	12.00
740 Rico Carty	6.00	15.00
741 Rookie Stars	6.00	15.00
Tom Hutton		
John Milner RC		
Rick Miller RC		
742 Jim Rooker	5.00	12.00
743 Cesar Gutierrez	5.00	12.00
744 Jim Slaton RC	5.00	12.00
745 Julian Javier	6.00	15.00
746 Lowell Palmer	5.00	12.00
747 Jim Stewart	5.00	12.00
748 Phil Hennigan	5.00	12.00
749 Walter Alston MG	8.00	20.00
750 Willie Horton	6.00	15.00
751 Steve Carlton TR	12.50	40.00
752 Joe Morgan TR	12.50	40.00
753 Denny McLain TR	8.00	20.00
754 Frank Robinson TR	12.50	40.00
755 Jim Fregosi TR	6.00	15.00
756 Rick Wise TR	6.00	15.00
757 Jose Cardenal TR	6.00	15.00
758 Gil Garrido	5.00	12.00
759 Chris Cannizzaro	5.00	12.00
760 Bill Mazeroski	10.00	25.00

761 Rookie Stars 10.00 25.00
Ben Oglivie RC
Ron Cey RC
Bernie Williams
762 Wayne Simpson 5.00 12.00
763 Ron Hansen 5.00 12.00
764 Dusty Baker 8.00 20.00
765 Ken McMullen 5.00 12.00
766 Steve Hamilton 5.00 12.00
767 Tom McCraw 6.00 15.00
768 Denny Doyle 5.00 12.00
769 Jack Aker 5.00 12.00
770 Jim Wynn 6.00 15.00
771 San Francisco Giants TC 8.00 20.00
772 Ken Tatum 5.00 12.00
773 Ron Brand 5.00 12.00
774 Luis Alvarado 5.00 12.00
775 Jerry Reuss 6.00 15.00
776 Bill Voss 5.00 12.00
777 Hoyt Wilhelm 10.00 25.00
778 Rookie Stars 8.00 20.00
Vic Albury RC
Rick Dempsey RC
Jim Strickland RC
779 Tony Cloninger 5.00 12.00
780 Dick Green 5.00 12.00
781 Jim McAndrew 5.00 12.00
782 Larry Stahl 5.00 12.00
783 Les Cain 5.00 12.00
784 Ken Aspromonte 5.00 12.00
785 Vic Davalillo 5.00 12.00
786 Chuck Brinkman 5.00 12.00
787 Ron Reed 6.00 15.00

1973 Topps

The cards in this 660-card set measure 2 1/2" by 3 1/2". The 1973 Topps set marked the last year in which Topps marketed baseball cards in consecutive series. The last series (529-660) is more difficult to obtain. In some parts of the country, however, all five series were distributed together. Beginning in 1974, all Topps cards were printed at the same time, thus eliminating the "high number" factor. The set features team leader cards with small individual pictures of the coaching staff members and a larger picture of the manager. The "background" variations below with respect to these leader cards are subtle and are best understood after a side-by-side comparison of the two varieties. An "All-Time Leaders" series (471-478) appeared for the first time in this set. Kid Pictures appeared again for the second year in a row (341-346). Other topical subsets within the set included League Leaders (61-68), Playoffs cards (201-202), World Series cards (203-210), and Rookie Prospects (601-616). For the fourth and final time, cards were issued in ten-card dime packs which were issued 24 packs to a box, in addition, these cards were also released in 54-card rack packs which cost 39 cents upon release. The key Rookie Cards in this set are all in the Rookie Prospect series: Bob Boone, Dwight Evans, and Mike Schmidt.

COMPLETE SET (660) 350.00 700.00
COMMON CARD (1-264) .20 .50
COMMON (265-396) .30 .75
COMMON (397-528) .50 1.25
COMMON (529-660) 1.25 3.00
WRAP. (10-CENT, BAT) 6.00 15.00
WRAPPER (10-CENT) 6.00 15.00
1 Babe Ruth 714 12.50 40.00
Hank Aaron 673
Willie Mays 654
All-Time Home Run Leaders
2 Rich Hebner .60 1.50
3 Jim Lonborg .60 1.50
4 John Milner .20 .50
5 Ed Brinkman .20 .50
6 Mac Scarce RC .20 .50
7 Texas Rangers TC .75 2.00
8 Tom Hall .20 .50
9 Johnny Oates .60 1.50
10 Don Sutton 1.50 4.00
11 Chris Chambliss UER .60 1.50
His Home town is spelled incorrectly
12A Don Zimmer MG 1.25 3.00
Dave Garcia CO
Johnny Podres CO
Bob Skinner CO
Whitey Wietelmann CO
(Podres no right ear)
12B Don Zimmer MG .30 .75
Dave Garcia CO
Johnny Podres CO
Bob Skinner CO
Whitey Wietelmann CO
(Podres has right ear)
13 George Hendrick .60 1.50
14 Sonny Siebert .20 .50
15 Ralph Garr .60 1.50
16 Steve Braun .20 .50
17 Fred Gladding .20 .50
18 Leroy Stanton .20 .50
19 Tim Foli .20 .50
20 Stan Bahnsen .20 .50
21 Randy Hundley .60 1.50
22 Ted Abernathy .20 .50
23 Dave Kingman .60 1.50
24 Al Santorini .20 .50
25 Roy White .60 1.50
26 Pittsburgh Pirates TC .75 2.00
27 Bill Gogolewski .20 .50
28 Hal McRae .60 1.50
29 Tony Taylor .60 1.50
30 Tug McGraw .60 1.50
31 Buddy Bell RC 1.00 2.50
32 Fred Norman .20 .50
33 Jim Breazeale RC .20 .50
34 Pat Dobson .20 .50
35 Willie Davis .60 1.50
36 Steve Barber .20 .50
37 Bill Robinson .60 1.50
38 Mike Epstein .20 .50
39 Dave Roberts .20 .50
40 Reggie Smith .60 1.50
41 Tom Walker RC .20 .50
42 Mike Andrews .20 .50
43 Randy Moffitt RC .20 .50
44 Rick Monday .60 1.50
45 Ellie Rodriguez UER .20 .50
(Photo is either John Felske or Paul Ratliff)
46 Lindy McDaniel .60 1.50
47 Luis Melendez .20 .50
48 Paul Splittorff .20 .50
49A Frank Quilici MG 1.25 3.00
Vern Morgan CO
Bob Rodgers CO
Ralph Rowe CO
Al Worthington CO
(Solid backgrounds)
49B Frank Quilici MG .30 .75
Vern Morgan CO
Bob Rodgers CO
Ralph Rowe CO
Al Worthington CO
(Natural backgrounds)
50 Roberto Clemente 12.50 40.00
51 Chuck Seelbach RC .20 .50
52 Denis Menke .20 .50
53 Steve Dunning .20 .50
54 Checklist 1-132 1.25 3.00
55 Jon Matlack .60 1.50
56 Merv Rettenmund .20 .50
57 Derrel Thomas .20 .50
58 Mike Paul .20 .50
59 Steve Yeager RC .60 1.50
60 Ken Holtzman .60 1.50
61 Batting Leaders 1.00 2.50
Billy Williams
Rod Carew
62 Home Run Leaders 1.00 2.50
Johnny Bench
Dick Allen
63 RBI Leaders 1.00 2.50
Johnny Bench
Dick Allen
64 Stolen Base Leaders .60 1.50
Lou Brock
Bert Campaneris
65 ERA Leaders .60 1.50
Steve Carlton
Luis Tiant
66 Victory Leaders .60 1.50
Steve Carlton
Gaylord Perry
Wilbur Wood
67 Strikeout Leaders 10.00 25.00
Steve Carlton
Nolan Ryan
68 Leading Firemen .60 1.50
Clay Carroll
Sparky Lyle
69 Phil Gagliano .20 .50
70 Milt Pappas .60 1.50
71 Johnny Briggs .20 .50
72 Ron Reed .20 .50
73 Ed Herrmann .20 .50
74 Billy Champion .20 .50
75 Vada Pinson .60 1.50
76 Doug Rader .20 .50
77 Mike Torrez .60 1.50
78 Richie Scheinblum .20 .50
79 Jim Willoughby RC .20 .50
80 Tony Oliva UER 1.00 2.50
(Minnseota on front)
81A Whitey Lockman MG .60 1.50
Hank Aguirre CO
Ernie Banks CO
Larry Jansen CO
Pete Reiser CO
(Solid backgrounds)
81B Whitey Lockman MG .60 1.50
Hank Aguirre CO
Ernie Banks CO
Larry Jansen CO
Pete Reiser CO
(Natural backgrounds)
82 Fritz Peterson .20 .50
83 Leron Lee .20 .50
84 Rollie Fingers 1.50 4.00
85 Ted Simmons .60 1.50
86 Tom McCraw .20 .50
87 Ken Boswell .20 .50
88 Mickey Stanley .60 1.50
89 Jack Billingham .20 .50
90 Brooks Robinson 3.00 8.00
91 Los Angeles Dodgers TC .75 2.00
92 Jerry Bell .20 .50
93 Jesus Alou .20 .50
94 Dick Billings .20 .50
95 Steve Blass .60 1.50
96 Doug Griffin .20 .50
97 Willie Montanez .60 1.50
98 Dick Woodson .20 .50
99 Carl Taylor .20 .50
100 Hank Aaron 12.50 40.00
101 Ken Henderson .20 .50
102 Rudy May .20 .50
103 Celerino Sanchez RC .20 .50
104 Reggie Cleveland .20 .50
105 Carlos May .20 .50
106 Terry Humphrey .20 .50
107 Phil Hennigan .20 .50
108 Bill Russell .60 1.50
109 Doyle Alexander .60 1.50
110 Bob Watson .60 1.50
111 Dave Nelson .20 .50
112 Gary Ross .20 .50
113 Jerry Grote .60 1.50
114 Lynn McGlothen RC .20 .50
115 Ron Santo .60 1.50
116A Ralph Houk MG 1.25 3.00
Jim Hegan CO
Elston Howard CO
Dick Howser CO
Jim Turner CO
(Solid backgrounds)
116B Ralph Houk MG .30 .75
Jim Hegan CO
Elston Howard CO
Dick Howser CO
Jim Turner CO
(Natural backgrounds)
117 Ramon Hernandez .20 .50
118 John Mayberry .60 1.50
119 Larry Bowa .60 1.50
120 Joe Coleman .20 .50
121 Dave Rader .20 .50
122 Jim Strickland .20 .50
123 Sandy Alomar .60 1.50
124 Jim Hardin .20 .50
125 Ron Fairly .60 1.50
126 Jim Brewer .20 .50
127 Milwaukee Brewers TC .75 2.00
128 Ted Sizemore .20 .50
129 Terry Forster .60 1.50
130 Pete Rose 12.50 30.00
131A Eddie Kasko MG 1.25 3.00
Doug Camilli CO
Don Lenhardt CO
Eddie Popowski CO
(No right ear)
Lee Stange CO
131B Eddie Kasko MG .60 1.50
Doug Camilli CO
Don Lenhardt CO
Eddie Popowski CO
(Right ear showing)
Lee Stange CO
132 Matty Alou .60 1.50
133 Dave Roberts RC .20 .50
134 Milt Wilcox .20 .50
135 Lee May UER .60 1.50
(Career average .000)
136A Earl Weaver MG .60 1.50
George Bamberger CO
Jim Frey CO
Billy Hunter CO
George Staller CO
(Orange background)
136B Earl Weaver MG 1.25 3.00
George Bamberger CO
Jim Frey CO
Billy Hunter CO
George Staller CO
(Dark Pale background)
137 Jim Beauchamp .20 .50
138 Horacio Pina .20 .50
139 Carmen Fanzone RC .20 .50
140 Lou Piniella 1.00 2.50
141 Bruce Kison .20 .50
142 Thurman Munson 3.00 8.00
143 John Curtis .20 .50
144 Marty Perez .20 .50
145 Bobby Bonds 1.00 2.50
146 Woodie Fryman .20 .50
147 Mike Anderson .20 .50
148 Dave Goltz .20 .50
149 Ron Hunt .20 .50
150 Wilbur Wood .60 1.50
151 Wes Parker .60 1.50
152 Dave May .20 .50
153 Al Hrabosky .60 1.50
154 Jeff Torborg .60 1.50
155 Sal Bando .60 1.50
156 Cesar Geronimo .20 .50
157 Denny Riddleberger .20 .50
158 Houston Astros TC .75 2.00
159 Clarence Gaston .60 1.50
160 Jim Palmer 2.50 6.00
161 Ted Martinez .20 .50
162 Pete Broberg .20 .50
163 Vic Davalillo .20 .50
164 Monty Montgomery .20 .50
165 Luis Aparicio 1.50 4.00
166 Terry Harmon .20 .50
167 Steve Stone .60 1.50
168 Jim Northrup .60 1.50
169 Ron Schueler RC .60 1.50
170 Harmon Killebrew 2.00 5.00
171 Bernie Carbo .20 .50
172 Steve Kline .20 .50
173 Hal Breeden .20 .50
174 Goose Gossage RC 12.50 30.00
175 Frank Robinson 2.50 6.00
176 Chuck Taylor .20 .50
177 Bill Plummer RC .20 .50
178 Don Rose RC .20 .50
179A Dick Williams MG 1.50 4.00
Jerry Adair CO
Vern Hoscheit CO
Irv Noren CO
Wes Stock CO
(Hoscheit left ear
showing)
179B Dick Williams MG .60 1.50
Jerry Adair CO
Vern Hoscheit CO
Irv Noren CO
Wes Stock CO
(Hoscheit left ear
not showing)
180 Ferguson Jenkins 1.50 4.00
181 Jack Brohamer RC .20 .50
182 Mike Caldwell RC .60 1.50
183 Don Buford .20 .50
184 Jerry Koosman .60 1.50
185 Jim Wynn .60 1.50
186 Bill Fahey .20 .50
187 Luke Walker .20 .50
188 Cookie Rojas .60 1.50
189 Greg Luzinski 1.00 2.50
190 Bob Gibson 3.00 8.00
191 Detroit Tigers TC 1.00 2.50
192 Pat Jarvis .20 .50
193 Carlton Fisk 4.00 10.00
194 Jorge Orta RC .20 .50
195 Clay Carroll .20 .50
196 Ken McMullen .20 .50
197 Ed Goodson RC .20 .50
198 Horace Clarke .20 .50
199 Bert Blyleven 1.00 2.50
200 Billy Williams 1.50 4.00
201 AL Playoffs .60 1.50
George Hendrick
202 NL Playoff .60 1.50
George Foster
203 World Series Game 1 .60 1.50
Gene Tenace
204 World Series Game 2 .60 1.50
A's Two Straight
205 World Series Game 3 1.00 2.50
Tony Perez
206 World Series Game 4 .60 1.50
Gene Tenace
207 World Series Game 5 .60 1.50
Blue Moon Odom
208 World Series Game 6 2.00 5.00
Johnny Bench
209 World Series Game 7 .60 1.50
Bert Campaneris
210 World Series Summary .20 .50
World Champions
A's Win
211 Balor Moore .20 .50
212 Joe Lahoud .20 .50
213 Steve Garvey 2.00 5.00
214 Dave Hamilton RC .20 .50
215 Dusty Baker 1.00 2.50
216 Toby Harrah .60 1.50
217 Don Wilson .20 .50
218 Aurelio Rodriguez .20 .50
219 St. Louis Cardinals TC 1.00 2.50
220 Nolan Ryan 20.00 50.00
221 Fred Kendall .20 .50
222 Rob Gardner .20 .50
223 Bud Harrelson .60 1.50
224 Bill Lee .60 1.50
225 Al Oliver .60 1.50
226 Ray Fosse .20 .50
227 Wayne Twitchell .20 .50
228 Bobby Darwin .20 .50
229 Roric Harrison .20 .50
230 Joe Morgan 2.50 6.00
231 Bill Parsons .20 .50
232 Ken Singleton .60 1.50
233 Ed Kirkpatrick .20 .50
234 Bill North RC .20 .50
235 Jim Hunter 1.50 4.00
236 Tito Fuentes .20 .50
237A Eddie Mathews MG .60 1.50
Lew Burdette CO
Jim Busby CO
Roy Hartsfield CO
Ken Silvestri CO
(Burdette right ear
showing)
237B Eddie Mathews MG 1.25 3.00
Lew Burdette CO
Jim Busby CO
Roy Hartsfield CO
Ken Silvestri CO
(Burdette right ear
not showing)
238 Tony Muser RC .20 .50
239 Pete Richert .20 .50
240 Bobby Murcer .60 1.50
241 Dwain Anderson .20 .50
242 George Culver .20 .50
243 California Angels TC 1.00 2.50
244 Ed Acosta .20 .50
245 Carl Yastrzemski 4.00 10.00
246 Ken Sanders .20 .50
247 Del Unser .20 .50
248 Jerry Johnson .20 .50
249 Larry Biittner .20 .50
250 Manny Sanguillen .60 1.50
251 Roger Nelson .20 .50
252A Charlie Fox MG 1.50 4.00
Joe Amalfitano CO
Andy Gilbert CO
Don McMahon CO
John McNamara CO
(Orange background)
252B Charlie Fox MG .60 1.50
Joe Amalfitano CO
Andy Gilbert CO
Don McMahon CO
John McNamara CO
(Dark Pale background)
253 Mark Belanger .60 1.50
254 Bill Stoneman .20 .50
255 Reggie Jackson 6.00 15.00
256 Chris Zachary .20 .50
257A Yogi Berra MG 1.25 3.00
Roy McMillan CO
Joe Pignatano CO
Rube Walker CO
Eddie Yost CO
(Orange background)
257B Yogi Berra MG 2.00 5.00
Roy McMillan CO
Joe Pignatano CO
Rube Walker CO
Eddie Yost CO
(Dark Pale Orange background)
258 Tommy John .60 1.50
259 Jim Holt .20 .50
260 Gary Nolan .60 1.50
261 Pat Kelly .20 .50
262 Jack Aker .20 .50
263 George Scott .60 1.50
264 Checklist 133-264 1.25 3.00
265 Gene Michael .60 1.50
266 Mike Lum .30 .75
267 Lloyd Allen .30 .75
268 Jerry Morales .30 .75
269 Tim McCarver .60 1.50
270 Luis Tiant .60 1.50
271 Tom Hutton .30 .75
272 Ed Farmer .30 .75
273 Chris Speier .30 .75
274 Darold Knowles .30 .75
275 Tony Perez 1.50 4.00
276 Joe Lovitto RC .30 .75
277 Bob Miller .30 .75
278 Baltimore Orioles TC .60 1.50
279 Mike Strahler .30 .75
280 Al Kaline 3.00 8.00
281 Mike Jorgensen .30 .75
282 Steve Hovley .30 .75
283 Ray Sadecki .30 .75
284 Glenn Borgmann RC .30 .75
285 Don Kessinger .60 1.50
286 Frank Linzy .30 .75
287 Eddie Leon .30 .75
288 Gary Gentry .30 .75
289 Bob Oliver .30 .75
290 Cesar Cedeno .60 1.50
291 Rogelio Moret .30 .75
292 Jose Cruz .60 1.50
293 Bernie Allen .30 .75
294 Steve Arlin .30 .75
295 Bert Campaneris .60 1.50
296 Sparky Anderson MG 1.00 2.50
Alex Grammas CO
Ted Kluszewski CO
George Scherger CO
Larry Shepard CO
297 Walt Williams .30 .75
298 Ron Bryant .30 .75
299 Ted Ford .30 .75
300 Steve Carlton 4.00 10.00
301 Billy Grabarkewitz .30 .75
302 Terry Crowley .30 .75
303 Nelson Briles .30 .75
304 Duke Sims .30 .75
305 Willie Mays 12.50 40.00
306 Tom Burgmeier .30 .75
307 Boots Day .30 .75
308 Skip Lockwood .30 .75
309 Paul Popovich .30 .75
310 Dick Allen .60 1.50
311 Joe Decker .30 .75
312 Oscar Brown .30 .75
313 Jim Ray .30 .75
314 Ron Swoboda .60 1.50
315 John Odom .30 .75
316 San Diego Padres TC .60 1.50
317 Danny Cater .30 .75
318 Jim McGlothlin .30 .75
319 Jim Spencer .30 .75
320 Lou Brock 3.00 8.00
321 Rich Hinton .30 .75
322 Garry Maddox RC .60 1.50
323 Billy Martin MG .60 1.50
Art Fowler CO
Charlie Silvera CO
Dick Tracewski CO
Joe Schultz CO UER
Schult's name not printed on card
324 Al Downing .30 .75
325 Boog Powell .60 1.50
326 Darrell Brandon .30 .75
327 John Lowenstein .30 .75
328 Bill Bonham .30 .75
329 Ed Kranepool .60 1.50
330 Rod Carew 3.00 8.00
331 Carl Morton .30 .75
332 John Felske RC .30 .75
333 Gene Clines .30 .75
334 Freddie Patek .30 .75
335 Bob Tolan .30 .75
336 Tom Bradley .30 .75
337 Dave Duncan .60 1.50
338 Checklist 265-396 1.25 3.00
339 Dick Tidrow .30 .75
340 Nate Colbert .30 .75
341 Jim Palmer KP 1.00 2.50
342 Sam McDowell KP .30 .75
343 Bobby Murcer KP .30 .75
344 Jim Hunter KP 1.00 2.50
345 Chris Speier KP .30 .75
346 Gaylord Perry KP .60 1.50
347 Kansas City Royals TC .60 1.50
348 Rennie Stennett .30 .75
349 Dick McAuliffe .30 .75
350 Tom Seaver 5.00 12.00
351 Jimmy Stewart .30 .75
352 Don Stanhouse RC .30 .75
353 Steve Brye .30 .75
354 Billy Parker .30 .75
355 Mike Marshall .60 1.50
356 Chuck Tanner MG 1.50 4.00
Joe Lonnett CO
Jim Mahoney CO
Al Monchak CO
Johnny Sain CO
357 Ross Grimsley .30 .75
358 Jim Nettles .30 .75
359 Cecil Upshaw .30 .75
360 Joe Rudi UER .60 1.50
(Photo actually
Gene Tenace)
361 Fran Healy .30 .75
362 Eddie Watt .30 .75
363 Jackie Hernandez .30 .75
364 Rick Wise .30 .75
365 Rico Petrocelli .60 1.50
366 Brock Davis .30 .75
367 Burt Hooton .60 1.50
368 Bill Buckner .60 1.50
369 Lerrin LaGrow .30 .75
370 Willie Stargell 2.00 5.00
371 Mike Kekich .30 .75
372 Oscar Gamble .30 .75
373 Clyde Wright .30 .75
374 Darrell Evans .60 1.50
375 Larry Dierker .60 1.50
376 Frank Duffy .30 .75
377 Gene Mauch MG 1.50 4.00
Dave Bristol CO
Larry Doby CO
Cal McLish CO
Jerry Zimmerman CO
378 Len Randle .30 .75
379 Cy Acosta RC .30 .75
380 Johnny Bench 5.00 12.00
381 Vicente Romo .30 .75
382 Mike Hegan .30 .75
383 Diego Segui .30 .75
384 Don Baylor 1.50 4.00
385 Jim Perry .60 1.50
386 Don Money .30 .75
387 Jim Barr .30 .75
388 Ben Oglivie .60 1.50
389 New York Mets TC 1.50 4.00
390 Mickey Lolich .60 1.50
391 Lee Lacy RC .60 1.50
392 Dick Drago .30 .75
393 Jose Cardenal .30 .75
394 Sparky Lyle .60 1.50
395 Roger Metzger .30 .75
396 Grant Jackson .30 .75
397 Dave Cash .50 1.25
398 Rich Hand .50 1.25
399 George Foster .75 2.00
400 Gaylord Perry 2.00 5.00
401 Clyde Mashore .50 1.25
402 Jack Hiatt .50 1.25
403 Sonny Jackson .50 1.25
404 Chuck Brinkman .50 1.25
405 Cesar Tovar .50 1.25
406 Paul Lindblad .50 1.25
407 Felix Millan .50 1.25
408 Jim Colborn .50 1.25
409 Ivan Murrell .50 1.25
410 Willie McCovey 2.50 6.00
(Bench behind plate)
411 Ray Corbin .50 1.25
412 Manny Mota .75 2.00
413 Tom Timmermann .50 1.25
414 Ken Rudolph .50 1.25
415 Marty Pattin .50 1.25
416 Paul Schaal .50 1.25
417 Scipio Spinks .50 1.25
418 Bob Grich .75 2.00
419 Casey Cox .50 1.25
420 Tommie Agee .50 1.25
421A Bobby Winkles MG RC .60 1.50
Tom Morgan CO
Salty Parker CO
Jimmie Reese CO
John Roseboro CO
(Orange background)
421B Bobby Winkles MG 1.25 3.00
Tom Morgan CO
Salty Parker CO
Jimmie Reese CO
John Roseboro CO
(Dark Pale background)
422 Bob Robertson .50 1.25
423 Johnny Jeter .50 1.25
424 Denny Doyle .50 1.25
425 Alex Johnson .50 1.25
426 Dave LaRoche .50 1.25
427 Rick Auerbach .50 1.25
428 Wayne Simpson .50 1.25
429 Jim Fairey .50 1.25
430 Vida Blue .75 2.00
431 Gerry Moses .50 1.25
432 Dan Frisella .50 1.25
433 Willie Horton .75 2.00
434 San Francisco Giants TC 1.25 3.00
435 Rico Carty .75 2.00
436 Jim McAndrew .50 1.25
437 John Kennedy .50 1.25
438 Enzo Hernandez .50 1.25
439 Eddie Fisher .50 1.25
440 Glenn Beckert .50 1.25
441 Gail Hopkins .50 1.25
442 Dick Dietz .50 1.25
443 Danny Thompson .50 1.25
444 Ken Brett .50 1.25
445 Ken Berry .50 1.25
446 Jerry Reuss .75 2.00
447 Joe Hague .50 1.25
448 John Hiller .50 1.25
449A Ken Aspromonte MG 1.50 4.00
Rocky Colavito CO
Joe Lutz CO
Warren Spahn CO
(Spahn's right
ear pointed)
449B Ken Aspromonte MG 1.50 4.00
Rocky Colavito CO
Joe Lutz CO
Warren Spahn CO
(Spahn's right
ear round)
450 Joe Torre 1.25 3.00
451 John Vukovich RC .50 1.25
452 Paul Casanova .50 1.25
453 Checklist 397-528 1.25 3.00
454 Tom Haller .50 1.25
455 Bill Melton .50 1.25
456 Dick Green .50 1.25
457 John Strohmayer .50 1.25
458 Jim Mason .50 1.25
459 Jimmy Howarth RC .50 1.25
460 Bill Freehan .75 2.00
461 Mike Corkins .50 1.25
462 Ron Blomberg .50 1.25
463 Ken Tatum .50 1.25
464 Chicago Cubs TC 1.25 3.00
465 Dave Giusti .50 1.25
466 Jose Arcia .50 1.25
467 Mike Ryan .50 1.25
468 Tom Griffin .50 1.25
469 Dan Monzon RC .50 1.25
470 Mike Cuellar .75 2.00
471 Ty Cobb 4.00 10.00
All-Time Hit Leader
472 Lou Gehrig 6.00 15.00
All-Time Grand Slam Leader
473 Hank Aaron 4.00 10.00
All-Time Total Base Leader
474 Babe Ruth 8.00 20.00
All-Time RBI Leader
475 Ty Cobb 3.00 8.00
All-Time Batting Leader
476 Walter Johnson 1.25 3.00
All-Time Shutout Leader
477 Cy Young 1.25 3.00
All-Time Victory Leader
478 Walter Johnson 1.25 3.00
All-Time Strikeout Leader
479 Hal Lanier .50 1.25
480 Juan Marichal 2.00 5.00
481 Chicago White Sox TC 1.25 3.00
482 Rick Reuschel RC 1.25 3.00
483 Dal Maxvill .50 1.25
484 Ernie McAnally .50 1.25
485 Norm Cash .75 2.00
486A Danny Ozark MG RC .60 1.50
Carroll Beringer CO
Billy DeMars CO
Ray Rippelmeyer CO
Bobby Wine CO
(Orange background)
486B Danny Ozark MG 1.25 3.00
Carroll Beringer CO
Billy DeMars CO
Ray Rippelmeyer CO
Bobby Wine CO
(Dark Pale background)
487 Bruce Dal Canton .50 1.25
488 Dave Campbell .75 2.00
489 Jeff Burroughs .75 2.00
490 Claude Osteen .75 2.00
491 Bob Montgomery .50 1.25
492 Pedro Borbon .50 1.25
493 Duffy Dyer .50 1.25
494 Rich Morales .50 1.25
495 Tommy Helms .50 1.25
496 Ray Lamb .50 1.25
497A Red Schoendienst MG .75 2.00
Vern Benson CO
George Kissell CO
Barney Schultz CO
(Orange background)
497B Red Schoendienst MG 1.25 3.00
Vern Benson CO
George Kissell CO
Barney Schultz CO
(Dark Pale background)
498 Graig Nettles 1.25 3.00
499 Bob Moose .50 1.25
500 Oakland Athletics TC 1.25 3.00
501 Larry Gura .50 1.25
502 Bobby Valentine 1.25 3.00
503 Phil Niekro 2.00 5.00
504 Earl Williams .50 1.25
505 Bob Bailey .50 1.25
506 Bart Johnson .50 1.25
507 Darrel Chaney .50 1.25
508 Gates Brown .50 1.25
509 Jim Nash .50 1.25
510 Amos Otis .75 2.00
511 Sam McDowell .75 2.00
512 Dalton Jones .50 1.25
513 Dave Marshall .50 1.25
514 Jerry Kenney .50 1.25
515 Andy Messersmith .75 2.00
516 Danny Walton .50 1.25
517A Bill Virdon MG .60 1.50
Don Leppert CO
Bill Mazeroski CO
Dave Ricketts CO
Mel Wright CO
(Mazeroski has
no right ear)
517B Bill Virdon MG 1.25 3.00
Don Leppert CO
Bill Mazeroski CO
Dave Ricketts CO
Mel Wright CO
(Mazeroski has
right ear)
518 Bob Veale .50 1.25
519 Johnny Edwards .50 1.25
520 Mel Stottlemyre .75 2.00
521 Atlanta Braves TC 1.25 3.00
522 Leo Cardenas .50 1.25
523 Wayne Granger .50 1.25
524 Gene Tenace .75 2.00
525 Jim Fregosi .75 2.00
526 Ollie Brown .50 1.25

527 Dan McGinn .50 1.25
528 Paul Blair .50 1.25
529 Milt May 1.25 3.00
530 Jim Kaat 2.00 5.00
531 Ron Woods 1.25 3.00
532 Steve Mingori 1.25 3.00
533 Larry Stahl 1.25 3.00
534 Dave Lemonds 1.25 3.00
535 Johnny Callison 2.00 5.00
536 Philadelphia Phillies TC 2.50 6.00
537 Bill Slayback RC 1.25 3.00
538 Jim Ray Hart 2.00 5.00
539 Tom Murphy 1.25 3.00
540 Cleon Jones 2.00 5.00
541 Bob Bolin 1.25 3.00
542 Pat Corrales 2.00 5.00
543 Alan Foster 1.25 3.00
544 Von Joshua 1.25 3.00
545 Orlando Cepeda 3.00 8.00
546 Jim York 1.25 3.00
547 Bobby Heise 1.25 3.00
548 Don Durham RC 1.25 3.00
549 Whitey Herzog MG 2.00 5.00
Chuck Estrada CO
Chuck Hiller CO
Jackie Moore CO
550 Dave Johnson 2.00 5.00
551 Mike Kilkenny 1.25 3.00
552 J.C. Martin 1.25 3.00
553 Mickey Scott 1.25 3.00
554 Dave Concepcion 2.00 5.00
555 Bill Hands 1.25 3.00
556 New York Yankees TC 3.00 8.00
557 Bernie Williams 1.25 3.00
558 Jerry May 1.25 3.00
559 Barry Lersch 1.25 3.00
560 Frank Howard 2.00 5.00
561 Jim Geddes RC 1.25 3.00
562 Wayne Garrett 1.25 3.00
563 Larry Haney 1.25 3.00
564 Mike Thompson RC 1.25 3.00
565 Jim Hickman 1.25 3.00
566 Lew Krausse 1.25 3.00
567 Bob Fenwick 1.25 3.00
568 Ray Newman 1.25 3.00
569 Walt Alston MG 3.00 8.00
Red Adams CO
Monty Basgall CO
Jim Gilliam CO
Tom Lasorda CO
570 Bill Singer 2.00 5.00
571 Rusty Torres 1.25 3.00
572 Gary Sutherland 1.25 3.00
573 Fred Beene 1.25 3.00
574 Bob Didier 1.25 3.00
575 Dock Ellis 1.25 3.00
576 Montreal Expos TC 2.50 6.00
577 Eric Soderholm RC 1.25 3.00
578 Ken Wright 1.25 3.00
579 Tom Grieve 2.00 5.00
580 Joe Pepitone 2.00 5.00
581 Steve Kealey 1.25 3.00
582 Darrell Porter 2.00 5.00
583 Bill Greif 1.25 3.00
584 Chris Arnold 1.25 3.00
585 Joe Niekro 2.00 5.00
586 Bill Sudakis 1.25 3.00
587 Rich McKinney 1.25 3.00
588 Checklist 529-660 8.00 20.00
589 Ken Forsch 1.25 3.00
590 Deron Johnson 1.25 3.00
591 Mike Hedlund 1.25 3.00
592 John Boccabella 1.25 3.00
593 Jack McKeon MG RC 1.50 4.00
Galen Cisco CO
Harry Dunlop CO
Charlie Lau CO
594 Vic Harris RC 1.25 3.00
595 Don Gullett 2.00 5.00
596 Boston Red Sox TC 2.50 6.00
597 Mickey Rivers 2.00 5.00
598 Phil Roof 1.25 3.00
599 Ed Crosby 1.25 3.00
600 Dave McNally 2.00 5.00
601 Rookie Catchers 2.00 5.00
Sergio Robles RC
George Pena RC
Rick Stelmaszek
602 Rookie Pitchers 2.00 5.00
Mel Behney
Ralph Garcia RC
Doug Rau RC
603 Rookie Third Basemen 2.00 5.00
Terry Hughes RC
Bill McNulty RC
Ken Reitz RC
604 Rookie Pitchers 2.00 5.00
Jesse Jefferson RC
Dennis O'Toole RC
Bob Strampe RC
605 Rookie First Baseman 2.00 5.00
Enos Cabell RC
Pat Bourque RC
Gonzalo Marquez RC
606 Rookie Outfielders 2.00 5.00
Gary Matthews RC
Tom Paciorek
Jorge Roque
607 Rookie Shortstops 2.00 5.00
Pepe Frias RC
Ray Busse
Mario Guerrero RC
608 Rookie Pitchers 2.00 5.00
Steve Busby RC
Dick Colpaert RC
George Medich RC
609 Rookie Second Basemen 2.00 5.00
Larvell Blanks RC
Pedro Garcia RC
Dave Lopes RC
610 Rookie Pitchers 2.00 5.00
Jimmy Freeman
Charlie Hough
Hank Webb RC
611 Rookie Outfielders 2.00 5.00
Rich Coggins RC
Jim Wohlford RC
Richie Zisk
612 Rookie Pitchers 2.00 5.00
Steve Lawson RC
Bob Reynolds
Brent Strom RC
613 Rookie Catchers 6.00 15.00
Bob Boone RC
Skip Jutze RC
Mike Ivie
614 Rookie Outfielders 8.00 20.00
Al Bumbry RC
Dwight Evans RC
Charlie Spikes RC
615 Rookie Third Basemen 75.00 150.00
Ron Cey
John Hilton RC
Mike Schmidt RC
616 Rookie Pitchers 2.00 5.00
Norm Angelini RC
Steve Blateric
Mike Garman
617 Rich Chiles 1.25 3.00
618 Andy Etchebarren 1.25 3.00
619 Billy Wilson 1.25 3.00
620 Tommy Harper 2.00 5.00
621 Joe Ferguson 2.00 5.00
622 Larry Hisle 2.00 5.00
623 Steve Renko 1.25 3.00
624 Leo Durocher MG 2.00 5.00
Preston Gomez CO
Grady Hatton CO
Hub Kittle CO
Jim Owens CO
625 Angel Mangual 1.25 3.00
626 Bob Barton 1.25 3.00
627 Luis Alvarado 1.25 3.00
628 Jim Slaton 1.25 3.00
629 Cleveland Indians TC 2.50 6.00
630 Denny McLain 3.00 8.00
631 Tom Matchick 1.25 3.00
632 Dick Selma 1.25 3.00
633 Ike Brown 1.25 3.00
634 Alan Closter 1.25 3.00
635 Gene Alley 2.00 5.00
636 Rickey Clark 1.25 3.00
637 Norm Miller 1.25 3.00
638 Ken Reynolds 1.25 3.00
639 Willie Crawford 1.25 3.00
640 Dick Bosman 1.25 3.00
641 Cincinnati Reds TC 2.50 6.00
642 Jose Laboy 1.25 3.00
643 Al Fitzmorris 1.25 3.00
644 Jack Heidemann 1.25 3.00
645 Bob Locker 1.25 3.00
646 Del Crandall MG 1.50 4.00
Harvey Kuenn CO
Joe Nossek CO
Bob Shaw CO
Jim Walton CO
647 George Stone 1.25 3.00
648 Tom Egan 1.25 3.00
649 Rich Folkers 1.25 3.00
650 Felipe Alou 2.00 5.00
651 Don Carrithers 1.25 3.00
652 Ted Kubiak 1.25 3.00
653 Joe Hoerner 1.25 3.00
654 Minnesota Twins TC 2.50 6.00
655 Clay Kirby 1.25 3.00
656 John Ellis 1.25 3.00
657 Bob Johnson 1.25 3.00
658 Elliott Maddox 1.25 3.00
659 Jose Pagan 1.25 3.00
660 Fred Scherman 2.00 5.00

1974 Topps

The cards in this 660-card set measure 2 1/2" by 3 1/2". This year marked the first time Topps issued all the cards of its baseball set at the same time rather than in series. Among other methods, cards were issued in eight-card fifteem-cent wax packs and 42 card rack packs. The ten cent packs were issued 36 to a box. For the first time, factory sets were issued through the JC Penny's catalog. Sales were probably disappointing for it would be several years before factory sets were issued again. Some interesting variations were created by the rumored move of the San Diego Padres to Washington. Fifteen cards (13 players, the team card, and the rookie card (599) of the Padres were printed either as "San Diego" (SD) or "Washington." The latter are the scarcer variety and are denoted in the checklist below by WAS. Each team's manager and his coaches again have a combined card with small pictures of each coach below the larger photo of the team's manager. The first six cards in the set (1-6) feature Hank Aaron and his illustrious career. Other topical subsets included in the set are League.Leaders (201-208), All-Star selections (331-339), Playoffs cards (470-471), World Series cards (472-479), and Rookie Prospects (596-608). The card backs for the All-Stars (331-339) have no statistics, but form a picture puzzle of Bobby Bonds, the 1973 All-Star Game MVP. The key Rookie Cards in this set are Ken Griffey Sr., Dave Parker and Dave Winfield.

COMPLETE SET (660) 200.00 400.00
COMP.FACT.SET (660) 300.00 600.00
WRAPPERS (10-CENTS) 4.00 10.00
1 Hank Aaron 715 20.00 50.00
2 Hank Aaron 54-57 3.00 8.00
3 Hank Aaron 58-61 3.00 8.00
4 Hank Aaron 62-65 3.00 8.00
5 Hank Aaron 66-69 3.00 8.00
6 Hank Aaron 70-73 3.00 8.00
7 Jim Hunter 1.50 4.00
8 George Theodore RC .20 .50
9 Mickey Lolich .40 1.00
10 Johnny Bench 6.00 15.00
11 Jim Bibby .20 .50
12 Dave May .20 .50
13 Tom Hilgendorf .20 .50
14 Paul Popovich .20 .50
15 Joe Torre .75 2.00
16 Baltimore Orioles TC .40 1.00
17 Doug Bird RC .20 .50
18 Gary Thomasson RC .20 .50
19 Gerry Moses .20 .50
20 Nolan Ryan 12.50 40.00
21 Bob Gallagher RC .20 .50
22 Cy Acosta .20 .50
23 Craig Robinson RC .20 .50
24 John Hiller .40 1.00
25 Ken Singleton .40 1.00
26 Bill Campbell RC .20 .50
27 George Scott .40 1.00
28 Manny Sanguillen .40 1.00
29 Phil Niekro 1.25 3.00
30 Bobby Bonds .75 2.00
31 Preston Gomez MG .40 1.00
Roger Craig CO
Hub Kittle CO
Grady Hatton CO
Bob Lillis CO
32A Johnny Grubb SD RC .40 1.00
32B Johnny Grubb WASH 1.50 4.00
33 Don Newhauser RC .20 .50
34 Andy Kosco .20 .50
35 Gaylord Perry 1.25 3.00
36 St. Louis Cardinals TC .40 1.00
37 Dave Sells RC .20 .50
38 Don Kessinger .40 1.00
39 Ken Suarez .20 .50
40 Jim Palmer 3.00 8.00
41 Bobby Floyd .20 .50
42 Claude Osteen .40 1.00
43 Jim Wynn .40 1.00
44 Mel Stottlemyre .40 1.00
45 Dave Johnson .40 1.00
46 Pat Kelly .20 .50
47 Dick Ruthven RC .20 .50
48 Dick Sharon RC .20 .50
49 Steve Renko .20 .50
50 Rod Carew 3.00 8.00
51 Bobby Heise .20 .50
52 Al Oliver .40 1.00
53A Fred Kendall SD .40 1.00
53B Fred Kendall WASH 1.50 4.00
54 Elias Sosa RC .20 .50
55 Frank Robinson 3.00 8.00
56 New York Mets TC .40 1.00
57 Darold Knowles .20 .50
58 Charlie Spikes .20 .50
59 Ross Grimsley .20 .50
60 Lou Brock 2.50 6.00
61 Luis Aparicio 1.25 3.00
62 Bob Locker .20 .50
63 Bill Sudakis .20 .50
64 Doug Rau .20 .50
65 Amos Otis .40 1.00
66 Sparky Lyle .40 1.00
67 Tommy Helms .20 .50
68 Grant Jackson .20 .50
69 Del Unser .20 .50
70 Dick Allen .75 2.00
71 Dan Frisella .20 .50
72 Aurelio Rodriguez .20 .50
73 Mike Marshall .75 2.00
74 Minnesota Twins TC .40 1.00
75 Jim Colborn .20 .50
76 Mickey Rivers .40 1.00
77A Rich Troedson SD RC .40 1.00
77B Rich Troedson WASH 1.50 4.00
78 Charlie Fox MG .40 1.00
John McNamara CO
Joe Amalfitano CO
Andy Gilbert CO
Don McMahon CO
79 Gene Tenace .40 1.00
80 Tom Seaver 5.00 12.00
81 Frank Duffy .20 .50
82 Dave Giusti .20 .50
83 Orlando Cepeda 1.25 3.00
84 Rick Wise .20 .50
85 Joe Morgan 3.00 8.00
86 Joe Ferguson .40 1.00
87 Fergie Jenkins 1.25 3.00
88 Freddie Patek .40 1.00
89 Jackie Brown .20 .50
90 Bobby Murcer .40 1.00
91 Ken Forsch .20 .50
92 Paul Blair .40 1.00
93 Rod Gilbreath RC .20 .50
94 Detroit Tigers TC .40 1.00
95 Steve Carlton 3.00 8.00
96 Jerry Hairston RC .20 .50
97 Bob Bailey .20 .50
98 Bert Blyleven .75 2.00
99 Del Crandall MG .40 1.00
Harvey Kuenn CO
Joe Nossek CO
Jim Walton CO
Al Widmar CO
100 Willie Stargell 2.50 6.00
101 Bobby Valentine .40 1.00
102A Bill Greif SD .40 1.00
102B Bill Greif WASH 1.50 4.00
103 Sal Bando .40 1.00
104 Ron Bryant .20 .50
105 Carlton Fisk 5.00 12.00
106 Harry Parker RC .20 .50
107 Alex Johnson .20 .50
108 Al Hrabosky .40 1.00
109 Bob Grich .40 1.00
110 Billy Williams 1.25 3.00
111 Clay Carroll .20 .50
112 Dave Lopes .75 2.00
113 Dick Drago .20 .50
114 California Angels TC .40 1.00
115 Willie Horton .40 1.00
116 Jerry Reuss .40 1.00
117 Ron Blomberg .20 .50
118 Bill Lee .40 1.00
119 Danny Ozark MG .40 1.00
Ray Ripplemeyer CO
Bobby Wine CO
Carroll Beringer CO
Billy DeMars CO
120 Wilbur Wood .20 .50
121 Larry Lintz RC .20 .50
122 Jim Holt .20 .50
123 Nelson Briles .40 1.00
124 Bobby Coluccio RC .20 .50
125A Nate Colbert SD .40 1.00
125B Nate Colbert WASH 1.50 4.00
126 Checklist 1-132 1.25 3.00
127 Tom Paciorek .40 1.00
128 John Ellis .20 .50
129 Chris Speier .20 .50
130 Reggie Jackson 6.00 15.00
131 Bob Boone .75 2.00
132 Felix Millan .20 .50
133 David Clyde RC .40 1.00
134 Denis Menke .20 .50
135 Roy White .40 1.00
136 Rick Reuschel .40 1.00
137 Al Bumbry .40 1.00
138 Eddie Brinkman .20 .50
139 Aurelio Monteagudo .20 .50
140 Darrell Evans .75 2.00
141 Pat Bourque .20 .50
142 Pedro Garcia .20 .50
143 Dick Woodson .20 .50
144 Walter Alston MG 1.25 3.00
Tom Lasorda CO
Jim Gilliam CO
Red Adams CO
Monty Basgall CO
145 Dock Ellis .20 .50
146 Ron Fairly .40 1.00
147 Bart Johnson .20 .50
148A Dave Hilton SD .40 1.00
148B Dave Hilton WASH 1.50 4.00
149 Mac Scarce .20 .50
150 John Mayberry .40 1.00
151 Diego Segui .20 .50
152 Oscar Gamble .40 1.00
153 Jon Matlack .40 1.00
154 Houston Astros TC .40 1.00
155 Bert Campaneris .40 1.00
156 Randy Moffitt .20 .50
157 Vic Harris .20 .50
158 Jack Billingham .20 .50
159 Jim Ray Hart .20 .50
160 Brooks Robinson 3.00 8.00
161 Ray Burris RC .40 1.00
(UER Card number is
printed sideways)
162 Bill Freehan .40 1.00
163 Ken Berry .20 .50
164 Tom House .20 .50
165 Willie Davis .40 1.00
166 Jack McKeon MG .40 1.00
Charlie Lau CO
Harry Dunlop CO
Galen Cisco CO
167 Luis Tiant .75 2.00
168 Danny Thompson .20 .50
169 Steve Rogers RC .75 2.00
170 Bill Melton .20 .50
171 Eduardo Rodriguez RC .20 .50
172 Gene Clines .20 .50
173A Randy Jones SD RC .75 2.00
173B Randy Jones WASH 2.00 5.00
174 Bill Robinson .40 1.00
175 Reggie Cleveland .20 .50
176 John Lowenstein .20 .50
177 Dave Roberts .20 .50
178 Garry Maddox .40 1.00
179 Yogi Berra MG 2.00 5.00
Rube Walker CO
Eddie Yost CO
Roy McMillan CO
Joe Pignatano CO
180 Ken Holtzman .40 1.00
181 Cesar Geronimo .20 .50
182 Lindy McDaniel .40 1.00
183 Johnny Oates .40 1.00
184 Texas Rangers TC .40 1.00
185 Jose Cardenal .20 .50
186 Fred Scherman .20 .50
187 Don Baylor .75 2.00
188 Rudy Meoli RC .20 .50
189 Jim Brewer .20 .50
190 Tony Oliva .75 2.00
191 Al Fitzmorris .20 .50
192 Mario Guerrero .20 .50
193 Tom Walker .20 .50
194 Darrell Porter .40 1.00
195 Carlos May .20 .50
196 Jim Fregosi .40 1.00
197A Vicente Romo SD .40 1.00
197B V.Romo WASH 1.50 4.00
198 Dave Cash .20 .50
199 Mike Kekich .20 .50
200 Cesar Cedeno .40 1.00
201 Batting Leaders 2.50 6.00
Rod Carew
Pete Rose
202 Home Run Leaders 2.00 5.00
Reggie Jackson
Willie Stargell
203 RBI Leaders 2.00 5.00
Reggie Jackson
Willie Stargell
204 Stolen Base Leaders .75 2.00
Tommy Harper
Lou Brock
205 Victory Leaders .40 1.00
Wilbur Wood
Ron Bryant
206 ERA Leaders 2.00 5.00
Jim Palmer
Tom Seaver
207 Strikeout Leaders 5.00 12.00
Nolan Ryan
Tom Seaver
208 Leading Firemen .40 1.00
John Hiller
Mike Marshall
209 Ted Sizemore .20 .50
210 Bill Singer .20 .50
211 Chicago Cubs TC .40 1.00
212 Rollie Fingers 1.25 3.00
213 Dave Rader .20 .50
214 Billy Grabarkewitz .20 .50
215 Al Kaline UER 4.00 10.00
(No copyright on back)
216 Ray Sadecki .20 .50
217 Tim Foli .20 .50
218 Johnny Briggs .20 .50
219 Doug Griffin .20 .50
220 Don Sutton 1.25 3.00
221 Chuck Tanner MG .40 1.00
Jim Mahoney CO
Alex Monchak CO
Johnny Sain CO
Joe Lonnett CO
222 Ramon Hernandez .20 .50
223 Jeff Burroughs .75 2.00
224 Roger Metzger .20 .50
225 Paul Splittorff .20 .50
226A San Diego Padres TC SD .75 2.00
226B San Diego Padres TC 3.00 8.00
Washington Variation
227 Mike Lum .20 .50
228 Ted Kubiak .20 .50
229 Fritz Peterson .20 .50
230 Tony Perez 1.50 4.00
231 Dick Tidrow .20 .50
232 Steve Brye .20 .50
233 Jim Barr .20 .50
234 John Milner .20 .50
235 Dave McNally .40 1.00
236 Red Schoendienst MG 1.25 3.00
Barney Schultz CO
George Kissell CO
Johnny Lewis CO
Vern Benson CO
237 Ken Brett .20 .50
238 Fran Healy .20 .50
(Munson sliding
in background)
239 Bill Russell .40 1.00
240 Joe Coleman .20 .50
241A Glenn Beckert SD .40 1.00
241B Glenn Beckert WASH 1.50 4.00
242 Bill Gogolewski .20 .50
243 Bob Oliver .20 .50
244 Carl Morton .20 .50
245 Cleon Jones .20 .50
246 Oakland Athletics TC .75 2.00
247 Rick Miller .20 .50
248 Tom Hall .20 .50
249 George Mitterwald .20 .50
250A Willie McCovey SD 3.00 8.00
250B W.McCovey WASH 10.00 25.00
251 Graig Nettles .75 2.00
252 Dave Parker RC 4.00 10.00
253 John Boccabella .20 .50
254 Stan Bahnsen .20 .50
255 Larry Bowa .40 1.00
256 Tom Griffin .20 .50
257 Buddy Bell .75 2.00
258 Jerry Morales .20 .50
259 Bob Reynolds .20 .50
260 Ted Simmons .75 2.00
261 Jerry Bell .20 .50
262 Ed Kirkpatrick .20 .50
263 Checklist 133-264 1.25 3.00
264 Joe Rudi .40 1.00
265 Tug McGraw .75 2.00
266 Jim Northrup .40 1.00
267 Andy Messersmith .40 1.00
268 Tom Grieve .40 1.00
269 Bob Johnson .20 .50
270 Ron Santo .75 2.00
271 Bill Hands .20 .50
272 Paul Casanova .20 .50
273 Checklist 265-396 1.25 3.00
274 Fred Beene .20 .50
275 Ron Hunt .20 .50
276 Bobby Winkles MG .40 1.00
John Roseboro CO
Tom Morgan CO
Jimmie Reese CO
Salty Parker CO
277 Gary Nolan .40 1.00
278 Cookie Rojas .40 1.00
279 Jim Crawford RC .20 .50
280 Carl Yastrzemski 5.00 12.00
281 San Francisco Giants TC .40 1.00
282 Doyle Alexander .40 1.00
283 Mike Schmidt 8.00 20.00
284 Dave Duncan .40 1.00
285 Reggie Smith .40 1.00
286 Tony Muser .20 .50
287 Clay Kirby .20 .50
288 Gorman Thomas RC .75 2.00
289 Rick Auerbach .20 .50
290 Vida Blue .40 1.00
291 Don Hahn .20 .50
292 Chuck Seelbach .20 .50
293 Milt May .20 .50
294 Steve Foucault RC .20 .50
295 Rick Monday .40 1.00
296 Ray Corbin .20 .50
297 Hal Breeden .20 .50
298 Roric Harrison .20 .50
299 Gene Michael .20 .50
300 Pete Rose 10.00 25.00
301 Bob Montgomery .20 .50
302 Rudy May .20 .50
303 George Hendrick .40 1.00
304 Don Wilson .20 .50
305 Tito Fuentes .20 .50
306 Earl Weaver MG 1.25 3.00
Jim Frey CO
George Bamberger CO
Billy Hunter CO
George Staller CO
307 Luis Melendez .20 .50
308 Bruce Dal Canton .20 .50
309A Dave Roberts SD .40 1.00
309B Dave Roberts WASH 2.50 6.00
310 Terry Forster .40 1.00
311 Jerry Grote .40 1.00
312 Deron Johnson .20 .50
313 Barry Lersch .20 .50
314 Milwaukee Brewers TC .40 1.00
315 Ron Cey .75 2.00
316 Jim Perry .40 1.00
317 Richie Zisk .40 1.00
318 Jim Merritt .20 .50
319 Randy Hundley .20 .50
320 Dusty Baker .75 2.00
321 Steve Braun .20 .50
322 Ernie McAnally .20 .50
323 Richie Scheinblum .20 .50
324 Steve Kline .20 .50
325 Tommy Harper .40 1.00
326 Sparky Anderson MG 1.25 3.00
Larry Shepard CO
George Scherger CO
Alex Grammas CO
Ted Kluszewski CO
327 Tom Timmermann .20 .50
328 Skip Jutze .20 .50
329 Mark Belanger .40 1.00
330 Juan Marichal 2.00 5.00
331 Carlton Fisk 2.00 5.00
Johnny Bench AS
332 Dick Allen 3.00 8.00
Hank Aaron AS
333 Rod Carew 1.50 4.00
Joe Morgan AS
334 Brooks Robinson .75 2.00
Ron Santo AS
335 Bert Campaneris .40 1.00
Chris Speier AS
336 Bobby Murcer 2.00 5.00
Pete Rose AS
337 Amos Otis .40 1.00
Cesar Cedeno AS
338 Reggie Jackson 2.00 5.00
Billy Williams AS
339 Jim Hunter 1.25 3.00
Rick Wise AS
340 Thurman Munson 3.00 8.00
341 Dan Driessen RC .40 1.00
342 Jim Lonborg .40 1.00
343 Kansas City Royals TC .40 1.00
344 Mike Caldwell .20 .50
345 Bill North .20 .50
346 Ron Reed .20 .50
347 Sandy Alomar .40 1.00
348 Pete Richert .20 .50
349 John Vukovich .20 .50
350 Bob Gibson 3.00 8.00
351 Dwight Evans 1.25 3.00
352 Bill Stoneman .20 .50
353 Rich Coggins .20 .50
354 Whitey Lockman MG .40 1.00
J.C. Martin CO
Hank Aguirre CO
Al Spangler CO
Jim Marshall CO
355 Dave Nelson .20 .50
356 Jerry Koosman .40 1.00
357 Buddy Bradford .20 .50
358 Dal Maxvill .20 .50
359 Brent Strom .20 .50
360 Greg Luzinski .75 2.00
361 Don Carrithers .20 .50
362 Hal King .20 .50
363 New York Yankees TC .75 2.00
364A Cito Gaston SD .75 2.00
364B Cito Gaston WASH 3.00 8.00
365 Steve Busby .40 1.00
366 Larry Hisle .40 1.00
367 Norm Cash .75 2.00
368 Manny Mota .40 1.00
369 Paul Lindblad .20 .50
370 Bob Watson .40 1.00
371 Jim Slaton .20 .50
372 Ken Reitz .20 .50
373 John Curtis .20 .50
374 Marty Perez .20 .50
375 Earl Williams .20 .50
376 Jorge Orta .20 .50
377 Ron Woods .20 .50
378 Burt Hooton .40 1.00
379 Billy Martin MG .75 2.00
Frank Lucchesi CO
Art Fowler CO
Charlie Silvera CO
Jackie Moore CO
380 Bud Harrelson .40 1.00
381 Charlie Sands .20 .50
382 Bob Moose .20 .50
383 Philadelphia Phillies TC .40 1.00
384 Chris Chambliss .40 1.00
385 Don Gullett .40 1.00
386 Gary Matthews .75 2.00
387A Rich Morales SD .40 1.00
387B Rich Morales WASH 2.50 6.00
388 Phil Roof .20 .50
389 Gates Brown .20 .50
390 Lou Piniella .75 2.00
391 Billy Champion .20 .50
392 Dick Green .20 .50
393 Orlando Pena .20 .50
394 Ken Henderson .20 .50
395 Doug Rader .20 .50
396 Tommy Davis .40 1.00
397 George Stone .20 .50
398 Duke Sims .20 .50
399 Mike Paul .20 .50
400 Harmon Killebrew 2.50 6.00
401 Elliott Maddox .20 .50
402 Jim Rooker .20 .50
403 Darrell Johnson MG .40 1.00
Eddie Popowski CO
Lee Stange CO
Don Zimmer CO
Don Bryant CO
404 Jim Howarth .20 .50
405 Ellie Rodriguez .20 .50
406 Steve Arlin .20 .50
407 Jim Wohlford .20 .50
408 Charlie Hough .40 1.00
409 Ike Brown .20 .50
410 Pedro Borbon .20 .50
411 Frank Baker .20 .50
412 Chuck Taylor .20 .50
413 Don Money .40 1.00
414 Checklist 397-528 1.25 3.00
415 Gary Gentry .20 .50
416 Chicago White Sox TC .40 1.00
417 Rich Folkers .20 .50
418 Walt Williams .20 .50
419 Wayne Twitchell .20 .50
420 Ray Fosse .20 .50
421 Dan Fife RC .20 .50
422 Gonzalo Marquez .20 .50
423 Fred Stanley .20 .50
424 Jim Beauchamp .20 .50
425 Pete Broberg .20 .50
426 Rennie Stennett .20 .50
427 Bobby Bolin .20 .50
428 Gary Sutherland .20 .50
429 Dick Lange RC .20 .50
430 Matty Alou .40 1.00
431 Gene Garber RC .40 1.00
432 Chris Arnold .20 .50
433 Lerrin LaGrow .20 .50
434 Ken McMullen .20 .50
435 Dave Concepcion .75 2.00
436 Don Hood RC .20 .50
437 Jim Lyttle .20 .50
438 Ed Herrmann .20 .50
439 Norm Miller .20 .50
440 Jim Kaat .75 2.00
441 Tom Ragland .20 .50
442 Alan Foster .20 .50
443 Tom Hutton .20 .50
444 Vic Davalillo .20 .50
445 George Medich .20 .50
446 Len Randle .20 .50
447 Frank Quilici MG .40 1.00
Ralph Rowe CO
Bob Rodgers CO
Vern Morgan CO
448 Ron Hodges RC .20 .50
449 Tom McCraw .20 .50
450 Rich Hebner .40 1.00
451 Tommy John .75 2.00
452 Gene Hiser .20 .50
453 Balor Moore .20 .50
454 Kurt Bevacqua .20 .50
455 Tom Bradley .20 .50
456 Dave Winfield RC 20.00 50.00
457 Chuck Goggin RC .20 .50
458 Jim Ray .20 .50
459 Cincinnati Reds TC .75 2.00
460 Boog Powell .75 2.00
461 John Odom .20 .50
462 Luis Alvarado .20 .50
463 Pat Dobson .20 .50
464 Jose Cruz .75 2.00
465 Dick Bosman .20 .50
466 Dick Billings .20 .50
467 Winston Llenas .20 .50
468 Pepe Frias .20 .50
469 Joe Decker .20 .50
470 AL Playoffs 2.00 5.00
Reggie Jackson
471 NL Playoffs .40 1.00
Jon Matlack
472 World Series Game 1 .40 1.00
Darold Knowles
473 World Series Game 2 3.00 8.00
Willie Mays
474 World Series Game 3 .40 1.00
Bert Campaneris
475 World Series Game 4 .40 1.00
Rusty Staub
476 World Series Game 5 .40 1.00
Cleon Jones
477 World Series Game 6 2.00 5.00
Reggie Jackson
478 World Series Game 7 .40 1.00

Bert Campaneris
479 World Series Summary .40 1.00
A's Celebrate
480 Willie Crawford .20 .50
481 Jerry Terrell RC .20 .50
482 Bob Didier .20 .50
483 Atlanta Braves TC .40 1.00
484 Carmen Fanzone .20 .50
485 Felipe Alou .75 2.00
486 Steve Stone .40 1.00
487 Ted Martinez .20 .50
488 Andy Etchebarren .20 .50
489 Danny Murtaugh MG .40 1.00
Don Osborn CO
Don Leppert CO
Bill Mazeroski CO
Bob Skinner CO
490 Vada Pinson .75 2.00
491 Roger Nelson .20 .50
492 Mike Rogodzinski RC .20 .50
493 Joe Hoerner .20 .50
494 Ed Goodson .20 .50
495 Dick McAuliffe .40 1.00
496 Tom Murphy .20 .50
497 Bobby Mitchell .20 .50
498 Pat Corrales .20 .50
499 Rusty Torres .20 .50
500 Lee May .40 1.00
501 Eddie Leon .20 .50
502 Dave LaRoche .20 .50
503 Eric Soderholm .20 .50
504 Joe Niekro .40 1.00
505 Bill Buckner .40 1.00
506 Ed Farmer .20 .50
507 Larry Stahl .20 .50
508 Montreal Expos TC .40 1.00
509 Jesse Jefferson .20 .50
510 Wayne Garrett .20 .50
511 Toby Harrah .40 1.00
512 Joe Lahoud .20 .50
513 Jim Campanis .20 .50
514 Paul Schaal .20 .50
515 Willie Montanez .20 .50
516 Horacio Pina .20 .50
517 Mike Hegan .20 .50
518 Derrel Thomas .20 .50
519 Bill Sharp RC .20 .50
520 Tim McCarver .75 2.00
521 Ken Aspromonte MG .40 1.00
Clay Bryant CO
Tony Pacheco CO
522 J.R. Richard .75 2.00
523 Cecil Cooper .75 2.00
524 Bill Plummer .20 .50
525 Clyde Wright .20 .50
526 Frank Tepedino .40 1.00
527 Bobby Darwin .20 .50
528 Bill Bonham .20 .50
529 Horace Clarke .40 1.00
530 Mickey Stanley .40 1.00
531 Gene Mauch MG .40 1.00
Dave Bristol CO
Cal McLish CO
Larry Doby CO
Jerry Zimmerman CO
532 Skip Lockwood .20 .50
533 Mike Phillips RC .20 .50
534 Eddie Watt .20 .50
535 Bob Tolan .20 .50
536 Duffy Dyer .20 .50
537 Steve Mingori .20 .50
538 Cesar Tovar .20 .50
539 Lloyd Allen .20 .50
540 Bob Robertson .20 .50
541 Cleveland Indians TC .40 1.00
542 Goose Gossage .75 2.00
543 Danny Cater .20 .50
544 Ron Schueler .20 .50
545 Billy Conigliaro .40 1.00
546 Mike Corkins .20 .50
547 Glenn Borgmann .20 .50
548 Sonny Siebert .20 .50
549 Mike Jorgensen .20 .50
550 Sam McDowell .40 1.00
551 Von Joshua .20 .50
552 Denny Doyle .20 .50
553 Jim Willoughby .20 .50
554 Tim Johnson RC .20 .50
555 Woodie Fryman .20 .50
556 Dave Campbell .40 1.00
557 Jim McGlothlin .20 .50
558 Bill Fahey .20 .50
559 Darrel Chaney .20 .50
560 Mike Cuellar .40 1.00
561 Ed Kranepool .40 1.00
562 Jack Aker .20 .50
563 Hal McRae .40 1.00
564 Mike Ryan .20 .50
565 Milt Wilcox .20 .50
566 Jackie Hernandez .20 .50
567 Boston Red Sox TC .40 1.00
568 Mike Torrez .40 1.00
569 Rick Dempsey .40 1.00
570 Ralph Garr .40 1.00
571 Rich Hand .20 .50
572 Enzo Hernandez .20 .50
573 Mike Adams RC .20 .50
574 Bill Parsons .20 .50
575 Steve Garvey 1.25 3.00
576 Scipio Spinks .20 .50
577 Mike Sadek RC .20 .50
578 Ralph Houk MG .40 1.00
579 Cecil Upshaw .20 .50
580 Jim Spencer .20 .50
581 Fred Norman .20 .50
582 Bucky Dent RC 2.00 5.00
583 Marty Pattin .20 .50
584 Ken Rudolph .20 .50
585 Merv Rettenmund .20 .50
586 Jack Brohamer .20 .50
587 Larry Christenson RC .20 .50
588 Hal Lanier .20 .50
589 Boots Day .20 .50
590 Roger Moret .20 .50
591 Sonny Jackson .20 .50
592 Ed Bane RC .20 .50
593 Steve Yeager .40 1.00
594 Leroy Stanton .20 .50
595 Steve Blass .40 1.00
596 Rookie Pitchers .20 .50
Wayne Garland RC
Fred Holdsworth RC
Mark Littell RC
Dick Pole RC
597 Rookie Infielders .40 1.00
Dave Chalk RC
John Gamble RC
Pete MacKanin RC
Manny Trillo RC
598 Rookie Outfielders 5.00 12.00
Dave Augustine RC
Ken Griffey RC
Steve Ontiveros RC
Jim Tyrone RC
599A Rookie Pitchers .75 2.00
Ron Diorio RC
Dave Freisleben RC
Frank Riccelli RC
Greg Shanahan RC (Washington)
599B Rookie Pitchers 6.00 15.00
Ron Diorio
Dave Freisleben
Frank Riccelli
Greg Shanahan (San Diego - in Large Print)
599C Rookie Pitchers 2.50 6.00
Ron Diorio
Dave Freisleben
Frank Riccelli
Greg Shanahan (San Diego - in Small Print)
600 Rookie Infielders 2.00 5.00
Ron Cash RC
Jim Cox RC
Bill Madlock RC
Reggie Sanders RC
601 Rookie Outfielders 1.25 3.00
Ed Armbrister
Rich Bladt RC
Brian Downing RC
Bake McBride RC
602 Rookie Pitchers .40 1.00
Glen Abbott RC
Rick Henninger RC
Craig Swan RC
Dan Vossler RC
603 Rookie Catchers .40 1.00
Barry Foote RC
Tom Lundstedt RC
Charlie Moore RC
Sergio Robles
604 Rookie Infielders 2.00 5.00
Terry Hughes
John Knox RC
Andre Thornton RC
Frank White RC
605 Rookie Pitchers 1.50 4.00
Vic Albury
Ken Frailing RC
Kevin Kobel RC
Frank Tanana RC
606 Rookie Outfielders .40 1.00
Jim Fuller RC
Wilbur Howard RC
Tommy Smith RC
Otto Velez RC
607 Rookie Shortstops .40 1.00
Leo Foster RC
Tom Heintzelman RC
Dave Rosello RC
Frank Taveras RC
608A Rookie Pitchers .75 2.00
Bob Apodaco ERR (Apodaca)
Dick Baney
John D'Acquisto
Mike Wallace
608B Rookie Pitchers .40 1.00
Bob Apodaca COR RC
Dick Baney
John D'Acquisto RC
Mike Wallace RC
609 Rico Petrocelli .40 1.00
610 Dave Kingman .75 2.00
611 Rich Stelmaszek .20 .50
612 Luke Walker .20 .50
613 Dan Monzon .20 .50
614 Adrian Devine RC .20 .50
615 Johnny Jeter UER .20 .50
(Misspelled Johnnie
on card back)
616 Larry Gura .20 .50
617 Ted Ford .20 .50
618 Jim Mason .20 .50
619 Mike Anderson .20 .50
620 Al Downing .20 .50
621 Bernie Carbo .20 .50
622 Phil Gagliano .20 .50
623 Celerino Sanchez .20 .50
624 Bob Miller .20 .50
625 Ollie Brown .20 .50
626 Pittsburgh Pirates TC .40 1.00
627 Carl Taylor .20 .50
628 Ivan Murrell .20 .50
629 Rusty Staub .75 2.00
630 Tommie Agee .40 1.00
631 Steve Barber .20 .50
632 George Culver .20 .50
633 Dave Hamilton .20 .50
634 Eddie Mathews MG 1.25 3.00
Herm Starrette CO
Connie Ryan CO
Jim Busby CO
Ken Silvestri CO
635 Johnny Edwards .20 .50
636 Dave Goltz .20 .50
637 Checklist 529-660 1.25 3.00
638 Ken Sanders .20 .50
639 Joe Lovitto .20 .50
640 Milt Pappas .40 1.00
641 Chuck Brinkman .20 .50
642 Terry Harmon .20 .50
643 Los Angeles Dodgers TC .40 1.00
644 Wayne Granger .20 .50
645 Ken Boswell .20 .50
646 George Foster .75 2.00
647 Juan Beniquez RC .20 .50
648 Terry Crowley .20 .50
649 Fernando Gonzalez RC .20 .50
650 Mike Epstein .20 .50
651 Leron Lee .20 .50
652 Gail Hopkins .20 .50
653 Bob Stinson .20 .50
654A Jesus Alou ERR 1.50 4.00
(No Position)
654B Jesus Alou COR .40 1.00
(Outfield)
655 Mike Tyson RC .20 .50
656 Adrian Garrett .20 .50
657 Jim Shellenback .20 .50
658 Lee Lacy .20 .50
659 Joe Lis .20 .50
660 Larry Dierker .75 2.00

1974 Topps Traded

The cards in this 44-card set measure 2 1/2" by 3 1/2". The 1974 Topps Traded set contains 43 player cards and one unnumbered checklist card. The fronts have the word "traded" in block letters and the backs are designed in newspaper style. Card numbers are the same as in the regular set except they are followed by a "T." No known scarcities exist for this set. The cards were inserted in all packs toward the end of the production run. They were produced in large enough quantity that they are no scarcer than the regular Topps cards.

COMPLETE SET (44) 8.00 20.00
23T Craig Robinson .20 .50
42T Claude Osteen .30 .75
43T Jim Wynn .30 .75
51T Bobby Heise .20 .50
59T Ross Grimsley .20 .50
62T Bob Locker .20 .50
63T Bill Sudakis .20 .50
73T Mike Marshall .30 .75
123T Nelson Briles .30 .75
139T Aurelio Monteagudo .20 .50
151T Diego Segui .20 .50
165T Willie Davis .30 .75
175T Reggie Cleveland .20 .50
182T Lindy McDaniel .30 .75
186T Fred Scherman .20 .50
249T George Mitterwald .20 .50
262T Ed Kirkpatrick .20 .50
269T Bob Johnson .20 .50
270T Ron Santo .40 1.00
313T Barry Lersch .20 .50
319T Randy Hundley .30 .75
330T Juan Marichal .75 2.00
348T Pete Richert .20 .50
373T John Curtis .20 .50
390T Lou Piniella .40 1.00
428T Gary Sutherland .20 .50
454T Kurt Bevacqua .20 .50
458T Jim Ray .20 .50
485T Felipe Alou .40 1.00
486T Steve Stone .30 .75
496T Tom Murphy .20 .50
516T Horacio Pina .20 .50
534T Eddie Watt .20 .50
538T Cesar Tovar .20 .50
544T Ron Schueler .20 .50
579T Cecil Upshaw .20 .50
585T Merv Rettenmund .20 .50
612T Luke Walker .20 .50
616T Larry Gura .30 .75
618T Jim Mason .20 .50
630T Tommie Agee .30 .75
648T Terry Crowley .20 .50
649T Fernando Gonzalez .20 .50
NNO Traded Checklist .60 1.50

1975 Topps

The 1975 Topps set consists of 660 standard size cards. The design was radically different in appearance from sets of the preceding years. The most prominent change was the use of a two-color frame surrounding the picture area rather than a single, subdued color. A facsimile autograph appears on the picture, and the backs are printed in red and green on gray. Cards were released in ten-card wax packs, 18-card cello packs with a 25 cent SRP and were packaged 24 to a box and 15 boxes to a case, as well as in 42-card rack packs which cost 49 cents upon release. The cello packs were issued 24 to a box. Cards 189-212 depict the MVP's of both leagues from 1951 through 1974. The first seven cards (1-7) feature players (listed in alphabetical order) breaking records or achieving milestones during the previous season. Cards 306-313 picture league leaders in various statistical categories. Cards 459-466 depict the results of post-season action. Team cards feature a checklist back for players on that team and show a small inset photo of the manager on the front. The following players' regular issue cards are explicitly denoted as All-Stars, 1, 50, 80, 140, 170, 180, 260, 320, 350, 390, 400, 420, 440, 470, 530, 570, and 600. This set is quite popular with collectors, at least in part due to the fact that the Rookie Cards of George Brett, Gary Carter, Keith Hernandez, Fred Lynn, Jim Rice and Robin Yount are all in the set.

COMPLETE SET (660) 300.00 600.00
WRAPPER (15-CENT) 3.00 8.00
1 Hank Aaron HL 12.50 30.00
Sets Homer Mark
2 Lou Brock HL 1.25 3.00
118 Stolen Bases
3 Bob Gibson HL 1.25 3.00
3000th Strikeout
4 Al Kaline HL 2.50 6.00
3000 Hit Club
5 Nolan Ryan HL 6.00 15.00
Fans 300 for
3rd Year in a Row
6 Mike Marshall HL .40 1.00
Hurls 106 Games
7 Steve Busby HL 3.00 8.00
Dick Bosman
Nolan Ryan
8 Rogelio Moret .20 .50
9 Frank Tepedino .40 1.00
10 Willie Davis .40 1.00
11 Bill Melton .20 .50
12 David Clyde .20 .50
13 Gene Locklear RC .40 1.00
14 Milt Wilcox .20 .50
15 Jose Cardenal .40 1.00
16 Frank Tanana .75 2.00
17 Dave Concepcion .75 2.00
18 Detroit Tigers CL .75 2.00
Ralph Houk MG
19 Jerry Koosman .40 1.00
20 Thurman Munson 3.00 8.00
21 Rollie Fingers 1.25 3.00
22 Dave Cash .20 .50
23 Bill Russell .40 1.00
24 Al Fitzmorris .20 .50
25 Lee May .40 1.00
26 Dave McNally .40 1.00
27 Ken Reitz .20 .50
28 Tom Murphy .20 .50
29 Dave Parker 1.25 3.00
30 Bert Blyleven .75 2.00
31 Dave Rader .20 .50
32 Reggie Cleveland .20 .50
33 Dusty Baker .75 2.00
34 Steve Renko .20 .50
35 Ron Santo .40 1.00
36 Joe Lovitto .20 .50
37 Dave Freisleben .20 .50
38 Buddy Bell .75 2.00
39 Andre Thornton .40 1.00
40 Bill Singer .20 .50
41 Cesar Geronimo .40 1.00
42 Joe Coleman .20 .50
43 Cleon Jones .40 1.00
44 Pat Dobson .20 .50
45 Joe Rudi .40 1.00
46 Philadelphia Phillies CL .75 2.00
Danny Ozark MG UER
Terry Harmon listed as 339
instead of 399
47 Tommy John .75 2.00
48 Freddie Patek .40 1.00
49 Larry Dierker .40 1.00
50 Brooks Robinson 3.00 8.00
51 Bob Forsch RC .40 1.00
52 Darrell Porter .40 1.00
53 Dave Giusti .20 .50
54 Eric Soderholm .20 .50
55 Bobby Bonds .75 2.00
56 Rick Wise .40 1.00
57 Dave Johnson .40 1.00
58 Chuck Taylor .20 .50
59 Ken Henderson .20 .50
60 Fergie Jenkins 1.25 3.00
61 Dave Winfield 6.00 15.00
62 Fritz Peterson .20 .50
63 Steve Swisher RC .20 .50
64 Dave Chalk .20 .50
65 Don Gullett .40 1.00
66 Willie Horton .40 1.00
67 Tug McGraw .40 1.00
68 Ron Blomberg .20 .50
69 John Odom .20 .50
70 Mike Schmidt 8.00 20.00
71 Charlie Hough .40 1.00
72 Kansas City Royals CL .75 2.00
Jack McKeon MG
73 J.R. Richard .40 1.00
74 Mark Belanger .40 1.00
75 Ted Simmons .75 2.00
76 Ed Sprague .20 .50
77 Richie Zisk .40 1.00
78 Ray Corbin .20 .50
79 Gary Matthews .40 1.00
80 Carlton Fisk 3.00 8.00
81 Ron Reed .20 .50
82 Pat Kelly .20 .50
83 Jim Merritt .20 .50
84 Enzo Hernandez .20 .50
85 Bill Bonham .20 .50
86 Joe Lis .20 .50
87 George Foster .75 2.00
88 Tom Egan .20 .50
89 Jim Ray .20 .50
90 Rusty Staub .75 2.00
91 Dick Green .20 .50
92 Cecil Upshaw .20 .50
93 Dave Lopes .75 2.00
94 Jim Lonborg .40 1.00
95 John Mayberry .40 1.00
96 Mike Cosgrove RC .20 .50
97 Earl Williams .20 .50
98 Rich Folkers .20 .50
99 Mike Hegan .20 .50
100 Willie Stargell 1.50 4.00
101 Montreal Expos CL .75 2.00
Gene Mauch MG
102 Joe Decker .20 .50
103 Rick Miller .20 .50
104 Bill Madlock .75 2.00
105 Buzz Capra .20 .50
106 Mike Hargrove RC 1.25 3.00
UER Gastonia At-Bats are wrong
107 Jim Barr .20 .50
108 Tom Hall .20 .50
109 George Hendrick .40 1.00
110 Wilbur Wood .20 .50
111 Wayne Garrett .20 .50
112 Larry Hardy RC .20 .50
113 Elliott Maddox .20 .50
114 Dick Lange .20 .50
115 Joe Ferguson .20 .50
116 Lerrin LaGrow .20 .50
117 Baltimore Orioles CL 1.25 3.00
Earl Weaver MG
118 Mike Anderson .20 .50
119 Tommy Helms .20 .50
120 Steve Busby UER .40 1.00
(Photo actually
Fran Healy)
121 Bill North .20 .50
122 Al Hrabosky .40 1.00
123 Johnny Briggs .20 .50
124 Jerry Reuss .40 1.00
125 Ken Singleton .40 1.00
126 Checklist 1-132 1.25 3.00
127 Glenn Borgmann .20 .50
128 Bill Lee .40 1.00
129 Rick Monday .40 1.00
130 Phil Niekro 1.25 3.00
131 Toby Harrah .40 1.00
132 Randy Moffitt .20 .50
133 Dan Driessen .40 1.00
134 Ron Hodges .20 .50
135 Charlie Spikes .20 .50
136 Jim Mason .20 .50
137 Terry Forster .40 1.00
138 Del Unser .20 .50
139 Horacio Pina .20 .50
140 Steve Garvey 1.25 3.00
141 Mickey Stanley .40 1.00
142 Bob Reynolds .20 .50
143 Cliff Johnson RC .40 1.00
144 Jim Wohlford .20 .50
145 Ken Holtzman .40 1.00
146 San Diego Padres CL .75 2.00
John McNamara MG
147 Pedro Garcia .20 .50
148 Jim Rooker .20 .50
149 Tim Foli .20 .50
150 Bob Gibson 2.50 6.00
151 Steve Brye .20 .50
152 Mario Guerrero .20 .50
153 Rick Reuschel .40 1.00
154 Mike Lum .20 .50
155 Jim Bibby .20 .50
156 Dave Kingman .75 2.00
157 Pedro Borbon .40 1.00
158 Jerry Grote .20 .50
159 Steve Arlin .20 .50
160 Graig Nettles .75 2.00
161 Stan Bahnsen .20 .50
162 Willie Montanez .20 .50
163 Jim Brewer .20 .50
164 Mickey Rivers .40 1.00
165 Doug Rader .40 1.00
166 Woodie Fryman .20 .50
167 Rich Coggins .20 .50
168 Bill Greif .20 .50
169 Cookie Rojas .20 .50
170 Bert Campaneris .40 1.00
171 Ed Kirkpatrick .20 .50
172 Boston Red Sox CL 1.25 3.00
Darrell Johnson MG
173 Steve Rogers .40 1.00
174 Bake McBride .40 1.00
175 Don Money .40 1.00
176 Burt Hooton .40 1.00
177 Vic Correll RC .20 .50
178 Cesar Tovar .20 .50
179 Tom Bradley .20 .50
180 Joe Morgan 2.50 6.00
181 Fred Beene .20 .50
182 Don Hahn .20 .50
183 Mel Stottlemyre .40 1.00
184 Jorge Orta .20 .50
185 Steve Carlton 3.00 8.00
186 Willie Crawford .20 .50
187 Denny Doyle .20 .50
188 Tom Griffin .20 .50
189 Yogi Berra 1.50 4.00
Roy Campanella MVP
Campanella card never issued
190 Bobby Shantz .75 2.00
Hank Sauer MVP
191 Al Rosen .75 2.00
Roy Campanella MVP
192 Yogi Berra 1.50 4.00
Willie Mays MVP
193 Yogi Berra 1.25 3.00
Roy Campanella MVP
Campanella card never issued
he is pictured with LA cap
194 Mickey Mantle 4.00 10.00
Don Newcombe MVP
195 Mickey Mantle 5.00 12.00
Hank Aaron MVP
196 Jackie Jensen 1.25 3.00
Ernie Banks MVP
197 Nellie Fox .75 2.00
Ernie Banks MVP
198 Roger Maris .75 2.00
Dick Groat MVP
199 Roger Maris 1.25 3.00
Frank Robinson MVP
200 Mickey Mantle 4.00 10.00
Maury Wills MVP
(Wills card never issued)
201 Elston Howard .75 2.00
Sandy Koufax MVP
202 Brooks Robinson .40 1.00
Ken Boyer MVP
203 Zoilo Versalles .75 2.00
Willie Mays MVP
204 Frank Robinson 2.50 6.00
Bob Clemente MVP
205 Carl Yastrzemski .75 2.00
Orlando Cepeda MVP
206 Denny McLain UER .75 2.00
Bob Gibson MVP
On the back McLain is spelled McClain
207 Harmon Killebrew .40 1.00
Willie McCovey MVP
208 Boog Powell .75 2.00
Johnny Bench MVP
209 Vida Blue .75 2.00
Joe Torre MVP
210 Rich Allen .75 2.00
Johnny Bench MVP
211 Reggie Jackson 2.00 5.00
Pete Rose MVP
212 Jeff Burroughs .75 2.00
Steve Garvey MVP
213 Oscar Gamble .40 1.00
214 Harry Parker .20 .50
215 Bobby Valentine .40 1.00
216 San Francisco Giants CL .75 2.00
Wes Westrum MG
217 Lou Piniella .75 2.00
218 Jerry Johnson .20 .50
219 Ed Herrmann .20 .50
220 Don Sutton 1.25 3.00
221 Aurelio Rodriguez .20 .50
222 Dan Spillner RC .20 .50
223 Robin Yount RC 20.00 50.00
224 Ramon Hernandez .20 .50
225 Bob Grich .40 1.00
226 Bill Campbell .20 .50
227 Bob Watson .40 1.00
228 George Brett RC 40.00 80.00
229 Barry Foote .20 .50
230 Jim Hunter 1.50 4.00
231 Mike Tyson .20 .50
232 Diego Segui .20 .50
233 Billy Grabarkewitz .20 .50
234 Tom Grieve .40 1.00
235 Jack Billingham .40 1.00
236 California Angels CL .75 2.00
Dick Williams MG
237 Carl Morton .40 1.00
238 Dave Duncan .40 1.00
239 George Stone .20 .50
240 Garry Maddox .40 1.00
241 Dick Tidrow .20 .50
242 Jay Johnstone .40 1.00
243 Jim Kaat .75 2.00
244 Bill Buckner .40 1.00
245 Mickey Lolich .75 2.00
246 St. Louis Cardinals CL .75 2.00
Red Schoendienst MG
247 Enos Cabell .20 .50
248 Randy Jones .75 2.00
249 Danny Thompson .20 .50
250 Ken Brett .20 .50
251 Fran Healy .20 .50
252 Fred Scherman .20 .50
253 Jesus Alou .20 .50
254 Mike Torrez .40 1.00
255 Dwight Evans .75 2.00
256 Billy Champion .20 .50
257 Checklist: 133-264 1.25 3.00
258 Dave LaRoche .20 .50
259 Len Randle .20 .50
260 Johnny Bench 6.00 15.00
261 Andy Hassler RC .20 .50
262 Rowland Office RC .20 .50
263 Jim Perry .40 1.00
264 John Milner .20 .50
265 Ron Bryant .20 .50
266 Sandy Alomar .40 1.00
267 Dick Ruthven .20 .50
268 Hal McRae .40 1.00
269 Doug Rau .20 .50
270 Ron Fairly .40 1.00
271 Gerry Moses .20 .50
272 Lynn McGlothen .20 .50
273 Steve Braun .20 .50
274 Vicente Romo .20 .50
275 Paul Blair .40 1.00
276 Chicago White Sox CL .75 2.00
Chuck Tanner MG
277 Frank Taveras .20 .50
278 Paul Lindblad .20 .50
279 Milt May .20 .50
280 Carl Yastrzemski 5.00 12.00
281 Jim Slaton .20 .50
282 Jerry Morales .20 .50
283 Steve Foucault .20 .50
284 Ken Griffey 1.50 4.00
285 Ellie Rodriguez .20 .50
286 Mike Jorgensen .20 .50
287 Roric Harrison .20 .50
288 Bruce Ellingsen RC .20 .50
289 Ken Rudolph .20 .50
290 Jon Matlack .20 .50
291 Bill Sudakis .20 .50
292 Ron Schueler .20 .50
293 Dick Sharon .20 .50
294 Geoff Zahn RC .20 .50
295 Vada Pinson .75 2.00
296 Alan Foster .20 .50
297 Craig Kusick RC .20 .50
298 Johnny Grubb .20 .50
299 Bucky Dent .75 2.00
300 Reggie Jackson 6.00 15.00
301 Dave Roberts .20 .50
302 Rick Burleson RC .40 1.00
303 Grant Jackson .20 .50
304 Pittsburgh Pirates CL .75 2.00
Danny Murtaugh MG
305 Jim Colborn .20 .50
306 Batting Leaders .75 2.00
Rod Carew
Ralph Garr
307 Home Run Leaders 1.50 4.00
Dick Allen
Mike Schmidt
308 RBI Leaders .75 2.00
Jeff Burroughs
Johnny Bench
309 Stolen Base Leaders .75 2.00
Bill North
Lou Brock
310 Victory Leaders .75 2.00
Jim Hunter
Fergie Jenkins
Andy Messersmith
Phil Niekro
311 ERA Leaders .75 2.00
Jim Hunter
Buzz Capra
312 Strikeout Leaders 5.00 12.00
Nolan Ryan
Steve Carlton
313 Leading Firemen .40 1.00
Terry Forster
Mike Marshall
314 Buck Martinez .20 .50
315 Don Kessinger .40 1.00
316 Jackie Brown .20 .50
317 Joe Lahoud .20 .50
318 Ernie McAnally .20 .50
319 Johnny Oates .40 1.00
320 Pete Rose 12.50 30.00
321 Rudy May .20 .50
322 Ed Goodson .20 .50
323 Fred Holdsworth .20 .50
324 Ed Kranepool .40 1.00
325 Tony Oliva .75 2.00
326 Wayne Twitchell .20 .50
327 Jerry Hairston .20 .50
328 Sonny Siebert .20 .50
329 Ted Kubiak .20 .50
330 Mike Marshall .40 1.00
331 Cleveland Indians CL .75 2.00
Frank Robinson MG
332 Fred Kendall .20 .50
333 Dick Drago .20 .50
334 Greg Gross RC .20 .50
335 Jim Palmer 2.50 6.00
336 Rennie Stennett .20 .50
337 Kevin Kobel .20 .50
338 Rich Stelmaszek .20 .50
339 Jim Fregosi .40 1.00
340 Paul Splittorff .20 .50
341 Hal Breeden .20 .50
342 Leroy Stanton .20 .50
343 Danny Frisella .20 .50
344 Ben Oglivie .40 1.00
345 Clay Carroll .40 1.00
346 Bobby Darwin .20 .50
347 Mike Caldwell .20 .50
348 Tony Muser .20 .50
349 Ray Sadecki .20 .50
350 Bobby Murcer .40 1.00
351 Bob Boone .75 2.00
352 Darold Knowles .20 .50
353 Luis Melendez .20 .50
354 Dick Bosman .20 .50
355 Chris Cannizzaro .20 .50
356 Rico Petrocelli .40 1.00
357 Ken Forsch UER .20 .50
Forsch is misspelled in blurb
358 Al Bumbry .40 1.00
359 Paul Popovich .20 .50
360 George Scott .40 1.00
361 Los Angeles Dodgers CL .75 2.00
Walter Alston MG
362 Steve Hargan .20 .50
363 Carmen Fanzone .20 .50
364 Doug Bird .20 .50
365 Bob Bailey .20 .50
366 Ken Sanders .20 .50
367 Craig Robinson .20 .50
368 Vic Albury .20 .50
369 Merv Rettenmund .20 .50
370 Tom Seaver 5.00 12.00
371 Gates Brown .20 .50
372 John D'Acquisto .20 .50
373 Bill Sharp .20 .50
374 Eddie Watt .20 .50
375 Roy White .40 1.00
376 Steve Yeager .40 1.00
377 Tom Hilgendorf .20 .50
378 Derrel Thomas .20 .50
379 Bernie Carbo .20 .50

380 Sal Bando .40 1.00
381 John Curtis .20 .50
382 Don Baylor .75 2.00
383 Jim York .20 .50
384 Milwaukee Brewers CL .75 2.00
Del Crandall MG
385 Dock Ellis .20 .50
386 Checklist: 265-396 UER 1.25 3.00
Dick Sharon's name is misspelled
387 Jim Spencer .20 .50
388 Steve Stone .40 1.00
389 Tony Solaita RC .20 .50
390 Ron Cey .75 2.00
391 Don DeMola RC .20 .50
392 Bruce Bochte RC .40 1.00
393 Gary Gentry .20 .50
394 Larvell Blanks .20 .50
395 Bud Harrelson .40 1.00
396 Fred Norman .40 1.00
397 Bill Freehan .40 1.00
398 Elias Sosa .20 .50
399 Terry Harmon .20 .50
400 Dick Allen .75 2.00
401 Mike Wallace .20 .50
402 Bob Tolan .20 .50
403 Tom Buskey RC .20 .50
404 Ted Sizemore .20 .50
405 John Montague RC .20 .50
406 Bob Gallagher .20 .50
407 Herb Washington RC .75 2.00
408 Clyde Wright UER .20 .50
Listed with wrong 1974 team
409 Bob Robertson .20 .50
410 Mike Cueller UER .40 1.00
Sic, Cuellar
411 George Mitterwald .20 .50
412 Bill Hands .20 .50
413 Marty Pattin .20 .50
414 Manny Mota .40 1.00
415 John Hiller .40 1.00
416 Larry Lintz .20 .50
417 Skip Lockwood .20 .50
418 Leo Foster .20 .50
419 Dave Goltz .20 .50
420 Larry Bowa .75 2.00
421 New York Mets CL 1.25 3.00
Yogi Berra MG
422 Brian Downing .40 1.00
423 Clay Kirby .20 .50
424 John Lowenstein .20 .50
425 Tito Fuentes .20 .50
426 George Medich .20 .50
427 Clarence Gaston .40 1.00
428 Dave Hamilton .20 .50
429 Jim Dwyer RC .20 .50
430 Luis Tiant .75 2.00
431 Rod Gilbreath .20 .50
432 Ken Berry .20 .50
433 Larry Demery RC .20 .50
434 Bob Locker .20 .50
435 Dave Nelson .20 .50
436 Ken Frailing .20 .50
437 Al Cowens RC .40 1.00
438 Don Carrithers .20 .50
439 Ed Brinkman .20 .50
440 Andy Messersmith .40 1.00
441 Bobby Heise .20 .50
442 Maximino Leon RC .20 .50
443 Minnesota Twins CL .75 2.00
Frank Quilici MG
444 Gene Garber .40 1.00
445 Felix Millan .20 .50
446 Bart Johnson .20 .50
447 Terry Crowley .20 .50
448 Frank Duffy .20 .50
449 Charlie Williams .20 .50
450 Willie McCovey 2.50 6.00
451 Rick Dempsey .40 1.00
452 Angel Mangual .20 .50
453 Claude Osteen .40 1.00
454 Doug Griffin .20 .50
455 Don Wilson .20 .50
456 Bob Coluccio .20 .50
457 Mario Mendoza RC .20 .50
458 Ross Grimsley .20 .50
459 1974 AL Championships .40 1.00
Brooks Robinson
A's 2nd Baseman
460 1974 NL Championships .75 2.00
Steve Garvey
Frank Taveras
461 World Series Game 1 2.00 5.00
Reggie Jackson
462 World Series Game 2 .40 1.00
Walter Alston
Joe Ferguson
463 World Series Game 3 .75 2.00
Rollie Fingers
464 World Series Game 4 .40 1.00
A's Batter
465 World Series Game 5 .40 1.00
Joe Rudi
466 World Series Summary .75 2.00
A's Do it Again
467 Ed Halicki RC .20 .50
468 Bobby Mitchell .20 .50
469 Tom Dettore RC .20 .50
470 Jeff Burroughs .40 1.00
471 Bob Stinson .20 .50
472 Bruce Dal Canton .20 .50
473 Ken McMullen .20 .50
474 Luke Walker .20 .50
475 Darrell Evans .40 1.00
476 Ed Figueroa RC .20 .50
477 Tom Hutton .20 .50
478 Tom Burgmeier .20 .50
479 Ken Boswell .20 .50
480 Carlos May .20 .50
481 Will McEnaney RC .40 1.00
482 Tom McCraw .20 .50
483 Steve Ontiveros .20 .50
484 Glenn Beckert .40 1.00
485 Sparky Lyle .40 1.00
486 Ray Fosse .20 .50
487 Houston Astros CL .75 2.00
Preston Gomez MG
488 Bill Travers RC .20 .50
489 Cecil Cooper .75 2.00
490 Reggie Smith .40 1.00
491 Doyle Alexander. .40 1.00
492 Rich Hebner .40 1.00
493 Don Stanhouse .20 .50
494 Pete LaCock RC .20 .50
495 Nelson Briles .40 1.00
496 Pepe Frias .20 .50
497 Jim Nettles .20 .50
498 Al Downing .20 .50
499 Marty Perez .20 .50
500 Nolan Ryan 20.00 50.00
501 Bill Robinson .40 1.00
502 Pat Bourque .20 .50
503 Fred Stanley .20 .50
504 Buddy Bradford .20 .50
505 Chris Speier .20 .50
506 Leron Lee .20 .50
507 Tom Carroll RC .20 .50
508 Bob Hansen RC .20 .50
509 Dave Hilton .20 .50
510 Vida Blue .40 1.00
511 Texas Rangers CL .75 2.00
Billy Martin MG
512 Larry Milbourne RC .20 .50
513 Dick Pole .20 .50
514 Jose Cruz .75 2.00
515 Manny Sanguillen .40 1.00
516 Don Hood .20 .50
517 Checklist: 397-528 1.25 3.00
518 Leo Cardenas .20 .50
519 Jim Todd RC .20 .50
520 Amos Otis .40 1.00
521 Dennis Blair RC .20 .50
522 Gary Sutherland .20 .50
523 Tom Paciorek .40 1.00
524 John Doherty RC .20 .50
525 Tom House .20 .50
526 Larry Hisle .40 1.00
527 Mac Scarce .20 .50
528 Eddie Leon .20 .50
529 Gary Thomasson .20 .50
530 Gaylord Perry 1.25 3.00
531 Cincinnati Reds CL 2.00 5.00
Sparky Anderson MG
532 Gorman Thomas .40 1.00
533 Rudy Meoli .20 .50
534 Alex Johnson .20 .50
535 Gene Tenace .40 1.00
536 Bob Moose .20 .50
537 Tommy Harper .40 1.00
538 Duffy Dyer .20 .50
539 Jesse Jefferson .20 .50
540 Lou Brock 2.50 6.00
541 Roger Metzger .20 .50
542 Pete Broberg .20 .50
543 Larry Biittner .20 .50
544 Steve Mingori .20 .50
545 Billy Williams 1.25 3.00
546 John Knox .20 .50
547 Von Joshua .20 .50
548 Charlie Sands .20 .50
549 Bill Butler .20 .50
550 Ralph Garr .40 1.00
551 Larry Christenson .20 .50
552 Jack Brohamer .20 .50
553 John Boccabella .20 .50
554 Goose Gossage .75 2.00
555 Al Oliver .40 1.00
556 Tim Johnson .20 .50
557 Larry Gura .20 .50
558 Dave Roberts .20 .50
559 Bob Montgomery .20 .50
560 Tony Perez 1.50 4.00
561 Oakland Athletics CL .75 2.00
Alvin Dark MG
562 Gary Nolan .40 1.00
563 Wilbur Howard .20 .50
564 Tommy Davis .40 1.00
565 Joe Torre .75 2.00
566 Ray Burris .20 .50
567 Jim Sundberg RC .75 2.00
568 Dale Murray RC .20 .50
569 Frank White .40 1.00
570 Jim Wynn .40 1.00
571 Dave Lemanczyk RC .20 .50
572 Roger Nelson .20 .50
573 Orlando Pena .20 .50
574 Tony Taylor .20 .50
575 Gene Clines .20 .50
576 Phil Roof .20 .50
577 John Morris .20 .50
578 Dave Tomlin RC .20 .50
579 Skip Pitlock .20 .50
580 Frank Robinson 2.50 6.00
581 Darrel Chaney .20 .50
582 Eduardo Rodriguez .20 .50
583 Andy Etchebarren .20 .50
584 Mike Garman .20 .50
585 Chris Chambliss .40 1.00
586 Tim McCarver .75 2.00
587 Chris Ward RC .20 .50
588 Rick Auerbach .20 .50
589 Atlanta Braves CL .75 2.00
Clyde King MG
590 Cesar Cedeno .40 1.00
591 Glenn Abbott .20 .50
592 Balor Moore .20 .50
593 Gene Lamont .20 .50
594 Jim Fuller .20 .50
595 Joe Niekro .40 1.00
596 Ollie Brown .20 .50
597 Winston Llenas .20 .50
598 Bruce Kison .20 .50
599 Nate Colbert .20 .50
600 Rod Carew 3.00 8.00
601 Juan Beniquez .20 .50
602 John Vukovich .20 .50
603 Lew Krausse .20 .50
604 Oscar Zamora RC .20 .50
605 John Ellis .20 .50
606 Bruce Miller RC .20 .50
607 Jim Holt .20 .50
608 Gene Michael .20 .50
609 Elrod Hendricks .20 .50
610 Ron Hunt .20 .50
611 New York Yankees CL .75 2.00
Bill Virdon MG
612 Terry Hughes .20 .50
613 Bill Parsons .20 .50
614 Rookie Pitchers .40 1.00
Jack Kucek RC
Dyar Miller RC
Vern Ruhle RC
Paul Siebert RC
615 Rookie Pitchers .75 2.00
Pat Darcy RC
Dennis Leonard RC
Tom Underwood RC
Hank Webb
616 Rookie Outfielders 10.00 25.00
Dave Augustine
Pepe Mangual RC
Jim Rice RC
John Scott RC
617 Rookie Infielders .75 2.00
Mike Cubbage RC
Doug DeCinces RC
Reggie Sanders
Manny Trillo
618 Rookie Pitchers .40 1.00
Jamie Easterly RC
Tom Johnson RC
Scott McGregor RC
Rick Rhoden RC
619 Rookie Outfielders .40 1.00
Benny Ayala RC
Nyls Nyman RC
Tommy Smith
Jerry Turner RC
620 Rookie Catchers and Outfielders 6.00 15.00
Gary Carter RC
Marc Hill RC
Danny Meyer RC
Leon Roberts RC
621 Rookie Pitchers .75 2.00
John Denny RC
Rawly Eastwick RC
Jim Kern RC
Juan Veintidos RC
622 Rookie Outfielders 3.00 8.00
Ed Armbrister RC
Fred Lynn RC
Tom Poquette RC
Terry Whitfield RC
(UER Listed as Ney York)
623 Rookie Infielders 4.00 10.00
Phil Garner RC
Keith Hernandez RC
(UER Sic, bats right)
Bob Sheldon RC
Tom Veryzer RC
624 Rookie Pitchers .40 1.00
Doug Konieczny RC
Gary Lavelle RC
Jim Otten RC
Eddie Solomon RC
625 Boog Powell .75 2.00
626 Larry Haney UER .20 .50
Photo actually
Dave Duncan
627 Tom Walker .20 .50
628 Ron LeFlore RC .40 1.00
629 Joe Hoerner .20 .50
630 Greg Luzinski .75 2.00
631 Lee Lacy .20 .50
632 Morris Nettles RC .20 .50
633 Paul Casanova .20 .50
634 Cy Acosta .20 .50
635 Chuck Dobson .20 .50
636 Charlie Moore .20 .50
637 Ted Martinez .20 .50
638 Chicago Cubs CL .75 2.00
Jim Marshall MG
639 Steve Kline .20 .50
640 Harmon Killebrew 2.50 6.00
641 Jim Northrup .40 1.00
642 Mike Phillips .20 .50
643 Brent Strom .20 .50
644 Bill Fahey .20 .50
645 Danny Cater .20 .50
646 Checklist: 529-660 1.25 3.00
647 Cl. Washington RC .75 2.00
648 Dave Pagan RC .20 .50
649 Jack Heidemann .20 .50
650 Dave May .20 .50
651 John Morlan RC .20 .50
652 Lindy McDaniel .40 1.00
653 Lee Richard UER .20 .50
(Listed as Richards
on card front)
654 Jerry Terrell .20 .50
655 Rico Carty .40 1.00
656 Bill Plummer .20 .50
657 Bob Oliver .20 .50
658 Vic Harris .20 .50
659 Bob Apodaca .20 .50
660 Hank Aaron 12.50 30.00

1975 Topps Mini

This set is a parallel to the regular 1975 Topps set. Each card measures 2 1/4" by 3 1/8" and the set was regionally issued. Michigan and California were among the two areas to receive this issue. These cards were also sporadically distributed in other areas as collectors have recalled getting them in their local areas other than those mentioned above. The cards are currently valued the same as the regular 75 Topps cards and have proven not to have remained as popular as the regular 1975 issue. These cards were issued in 10 card packs which cost 15 cents on issue and were packed 36 to a box.

COMPLETE SET (660) 300.00 600.00
*MINI STARS: .75X TO 1.5X BASIC CARDS
*MINI RC'S: .5X TO 1X BASIC ROOKIE CARDS

1975 Topps Team Checklist Sheet

This uncut sheet of the 24 1975 Topps team checklists measures 10 1/2" by 20 1/8". The sheet was obtained by sending 40 cents plus one wrapper to Topps. When cut, each card measures the standard size.

1 Topps Team CL Sheet 20.00 50.00

1976 Topps

The 1976 Topps set of 660 standard-size cards is known for its sharp color photographs and interesting presentation of subjects. Cards were issued in ten-card wax packs which cost 15 cents upon release, 42-card rack packs as well as cello packs and other options. Team cards feature a checklist back for players on that team and show a small inset photo of the manager on the front. A "Father and Son" series (66-70) spotlights five Major Leaguers whose fathers also made the "Big Show." Other subseries include "All Time All Stars" (341-350), "Record Breakers" from the previous season (1-6), League Leaders (191-205), Post-season cards (461-462), and Rookie Prospects (589-599). The following players' regular issue cards are explicitly denoted as All-Stars, 10, 48, 60, 140, 150, 165, 169, 240, 300, 370, 380, 395, 400, 420, 475, 500, 580, and 650. The key Rookie Cards in this set are Dennis Eckersley, Ron Guidry, and Willie Randolph. We've heard recent reports that this set was also issued in seven-card wax packs which cost a dime. Confirmation of that information would be appreciated.

COMPLETE SET (660) 125.00 250.00
1 Hank Aaron RB 6.00 15.00
2 Bobby Bonds RB .60 1.50
3 Mickey Lolich RB .30 .75
4 Dave Lopes RB .30 .75
5 Tom Seaver RB 2.00 5.00
6 Rennie Stennett RB .30 .75
7 Jim Umbarger RC .15 .40
8 Tito Fuentes .15 .40
9 Paul Lindblad .15 .40
10 Lou Brock 2.00 5.00
11 Jim Hughes .15 .40
12 Richie Zisk .30 .75
13 John Wockenfuss RC .15 .40
14 Gene Garber .30 .75
15 George Scott .30 .75
16 Bob Apodaca .15 .40
17 New York Yankees CL .60 1.50
Billy Martin MG
18 Dale Murray .15 .40
19 George Brett 12.50 30.00
20 Bob Watson .30 .75
21 Dave LaRoche .15 .40
22 Bill Russell .30 .75
23 Brian Downing .15 .40
24 Cesar Geronimo .30 .75
25 Mike Torrez .30 .75
26 Andre Thornton .30 .75
27 Ed Figueroa .15 .40
28 Dusty Baker .60 1.50
29 Rick Burleson .30 .75
30 John Montefusco RC .30 .75
31 Len Randle .15 .40
32 Danny Frisella .15 .40
33 Bill North .15 .40
34 Mike Garman .15 .40
35 Tony Oliva .60 1.50
36 Frank Taveras .15 .40
37 John Hiller .30 .75
38 Garry Maddox .30 .75
39 Pete Broberg .15 .40
40 Dave Kingman .60 1.50
41 Tippy Martinez RC .30 .75
42 Barry Foote .15 .40
43 Paul Splittorff .15 .40
44 Doug Rader .30 .75
45 Boog Powell .60 1.50
46 Los Angeles Dodgers CL .60 1.50
Walter Alston MG
47 Jesse Jefferson .15 .40
48 Dave Concepcion .60 1.50
49 Dave Duncan .30 .75
50 Fred Lynn .60 1.50
51 Ray Burris .15 .40
52 Dave Chalk .15 .40
53 Mike Beard RC .15 .40
54 Dave Rader .15 .40
55 Gaylord Perry 1.00 2.50
56 Bob Tolan .15 .40
57 Phil Garner .30 .75
58 Ron Reed .15 .40
59 Larry Hisle .30 .75
60 Jerry Reuss .30 .75
61 Ron LeFlore .30 .75
62 Johnny Oates .30 .75
63 Bobby Darwin .15 .40
64 Jerry Koosman .30 .75
65 Chris Chambliss .30 .75
66 Gus Bell FS .30 .75
Buddy Bell
67 Ray Boone FS .30 .75
Bob Boone
68 Joe Coleman FS .15 .40
Joe Coleman Jr.
69 Jim Hegan FS .15 .40
Mike Hegan
70 Roy Smalley FS .30 .75
Roy Smalley Jr.
71 Steve Rogers .30 .75
72 Hal McRae .30 .75
73 Baltimore Orioles CL .60 1.50
Earl Weaver MG
74 Oscar Gamble .30 .75
75 Larry Dierker .30 .75
76 Willie Crawford .15 .40
77 Pedro Borbon .30 .75
78 Cecil Cooper .30 .75
79 Jerry Morales .15 .40
80 Jim Kaat .60 1.50
81 Darrell Evans .30 .75
82 Von Joshua .15 .40
83 Jim Spencer .15 .40
84 Brent Strom .15 .40
85 Mickey Rivers .30 .75
86 Mike Tyson .15 .40
87 Tom Burgmeier .15 .40
88 Duffy Dyer .15 .40
89 Vern Ruhle .15 .40
90 Sal Bando .30 .75
91 Tom Hutton .15 .40
92 Eduardo Rodriguez .15 .40
93 Mike Phillips .15 .40
94 Jim Dwyer .15 .40
95 Brooks Robinson 2.50 6.00
96 Doug Bird .15 .40
97 Wilbur Howard .15 .40
98 Dennis Eckersley RC 12.50 30.00
99 Lee Lacy .15 .40
100 Jim Hunter 1.25 3.00
101 Pete LaCock .15 .40
102 Jim Willoughby .15 .40
103 Biff Pocoroba RC .15 .40
104 Cincinnati Reds CL 1.00 2.50
Sparky Anderson MG
105 Gary Lavelle .15 .40
106 Tom Grieve .30 .75
107 Dave Roberts .15 .40
108 Don Kirkwood RC .15 .40
109 Larry Lintz .15 .40
110 Carlos May .15 .40
111 Danny Thompson .15 .40
112 Kent Tekulve RC .60 1.50
113 Gary Sutherland .15 .40
114 Jay Johnstone .30 .75
115 Ken Holtzman .30 .75
116 Charlie Moore .15 .40
117 Mike Jorgensen .15 .40
118 Boston Red Sox CL .60 1.50
Darrell Johnson MG
119 Checklist 1-132 .60 1.50
120 Rusty Staub .30 .75
121 Tony Solaita .15 .40
122 Mike Cosgrove .15 .40
123 Walt Williams .15 .40
124 Doug Rau .15 .40
125 Don Baylor .60 1.50
126 Tom Dettore .15 .40
127 Larvell Blanks .15 .40
128 Ken Griffey Sr. 1.00 2.50
129 Andy Etchebarren .15 .40
130 Luis Tiant .60 1.50
131 Bill Stein RC .15 .40
132 Don Hood .15 .40
133 Gary Matthews .30 .75
134 Mike Ivie .15 .40
135 Bake McBride .30 .75
136 Dave Goltz .15 .40
137 Bill Robinson .30 .75
138 Lerrin LaGrow .15 .40
139 Gorman Thomas .30 .75
140 Vida Blue .30 .75
141 Larry Parrish RC .60 1.50
142 Dick Drago .15 .40
143 Jerry Grote .15 .40
144 Al Fitzmorris .15 .40
145 Larry Bowa .30 .75
146 George Medich .15 .40
147 Houston Astros CL .60 1.50
Bill Virdon MG
148 Stan Thomas RC .15 .40
149 Tommy Davis .30 .75
150 Steve Garvey 1.00 2.50
151 Bill Bonham .15 .40
152 Leroy Stanton .15 .40
153 Buzz Capra .15 .40
154 Bucky Dent .30 .75
155 Jack Billingham .30 .75
156 Rico Carty .30 .75
157 Mike Caldwell .15 .40
158 Ken Reitz .15 .40
159 Jerry Terrell .15 .40
160 Dave Winfield 4.00 10.00
161 Bruce Kison .15 .40
162 Jack Pierce RC .15 .40
163 Jim Slaton .15 .40
164 Pepe Mangual .15 .40
165 Gene Tenace .30 .75
166 Skip Lockwood .15 .40
167 Freddie Patek .30 .75
168 Tom Hilgendorf .15 .40
169 Graig Nettles .60 1.50
170 Rick Wise .15 .40
171 Greg Gross .15 .40
172 Texas Rangers CL .60 1.50
Frank Lucchesi MG
173 Steve Swisher .15 .40
174 Charlie Hough .30 .75
175 Ken Singleton .30 .75
176 Dick Lange .15 .40
177 Marty Perez .15 .40
178 Tom Buskey .15 .40
179 George Foster .60 1.50
180 Goose Gossage .60 1.50
181 Willie Montanez .15 .40
182 Harry Rasmussen .15 .40
183 Steve Braun .15 .40
184 Bill Greif .15 .40
185 Dave Parker .60 1.50
186 Tom Walker .15 .40
187 Pedro Garcia .15 .40
188 Fred Scherman .15 .40
189 Claudell Washington .30 .75
190 Jon Matlack .15 .40
191 NL Batting Leaders .30 .75
Bill Madlock
Ted Simmons
Manny Sanguillen
192 AL Batting Leaders 1.00 2.50
Rod Carew
Fred Lynn
Thurman Munson
193 NL Home Run Leaders 1.25 3.00
Mike Schmidt
Dave Kingman
Greg Luzinski
194 AL Home Run Leaders 1.25 3.00
Reggie Jackson
George Scott
John Mayberry
195 NL RBI Leaders .60 1.50
Greg Luzinski
Johnny Bench
Tony Perez
196 AL RBI Leaders .30 .75
George Scott
John Mayberry
Fred Lynn
197 NL Stolen Base Leaders .60 1.50
Dave Lopes
Joe Morgan
Lou Brock
198 AL Stolen Base Leaders .30 .75
Mickey Rivers
Claudell Washington
Amos Otis
199 NL Victory Leaders 1.00 2.50
Tom Seaver
Randy Jones
Andy Messersmith
200 AL Victory Leaders .60 1.50
Jim Hunter
Jim Palmer
Vida Blue
201 NL ERA Leaders .60 1.50
Randy Jones
Andy Messersmith
Tom Seaver
202 AL ERA Leaders 1.25 3.00
Jim Palmer
Jim Hunter
Dennis Eckersley
203 NL Strikeout Leaders 1.00 2.50
Tom Seaver
John Montefusco
Andy Messersmith
204 AL Strikeout Leaders .30 .75
Frank Tanana
Bert Blyleven
Gaylord Perry
205 NL/AL Leading Firemen .30 .75
Al Hrabosky
Rich Gossage
206 Manny Trillo .15 .40
207 Andy Hassler .15 .40
208 Mike Lum .15 .40
209 Alan Ashby RC .15 .40
210 Lee May .30 .75
211 Clay Carroll .15 .40
212 Pat Kelly .15 .40
213 Dave Heaverlo RC .15 .40
214 Eric Soderholm .15 .40
215 Reggie Smith .30 .75
216 Montreal Expos CL .60 1.50
Karl Kuehl MG
217 Dave Freisleben .15 .40
218 John Knox .15 .40
219 Tom Murphy .15 .40
220 Manny Sanguillen .30 .75
221 Jim Todd .15 .40
222 Wayne Garrett .15 .40
223 Ollie Brown .15 .40
224 Jim York .15 .40
225 Roy White .30 .75
226 Jim Sundberg .30 .75
227 Oscar Zamora .15 .40
228 John Hale RC .15 .40
229 Jerry Remy RC .15 .40
230 Carl Yastrzemski 4.00 10.00
231 Tom House .15 .40
232 Frank Duffy .15 .40
233 Grant Jackson .15 .40
234 Mike Sadek .15 .40
235 Bert Blyleven .60 1.50
236 Kansas City Royals CL .60 1.50
Whitey Herzog MG
237 Dave Hamilton .15 .40
238 Larry Biittner .15 .40
239 John Curtis .15 .40
240 Pete Rose 10.00 25.00
241 Hector Torres .15 .40
242 Dan Meyer .15 .40
243 Jim Rooker .15 .40
244 Bill Sharp .15 .40
245 Felix Millan .15 .40
246 Cesar Tovar .15 .40
247 Terry Harmon .15 .40
248 Dick Tidrow .15 .40
249 Cliff Johnson .30 .75
250 Fergie Jenkins 1.00 2.50
251 Rick Monday .30 .75
252 Tim Nordbrook RC .15 .40
253 Bill Buckner .30 .75
254 Rudy Meoli .15 .40
255 Fritz Peterson .15 .40
256 Rowland Office .15 .40
257 Ross Grimsley .15 .40
258 Nyls Nyman .15 .40
259 Darrel Chaney .15 .40
260 Steve Busby .15 .40
261 Gary Thomasson .15 .40
262 Checklist 133-264 .60 1.50
263 Lyman Bostock RC .60 1.50
264 Steve Renko .15 .40
265 Willie Davis .30 .75
266 Alan Foster .15 .40
267 Aurelio Rodriguez .15 .40
268 Del Unser .15 .40
269 Rick Austin .15 .40
270 Willie Stargell 1.25 3.00
271 Jim Lonborg .30 .75
272 Rick Dempsey .30 .75
273 Joe Niekro .30 .75
274 Tommy Harper .30 .75
275 Rick Manning RC .15 .40
276 Mickey Scott .15 .40
277 Chicago Cubs CL .60 1.50
Jim Marshall MG
278 Bernie Carbo .15 .40
279 Roy Howell RC .15 .40
280 Burt Hooton .30 .75
281 Dave May .15 .40
282 Dan Osborn RC .15 .40
283 Merv Rettenmund .15 .40
284 Steve Ontiveros .15 .40
285 Mike Cuellar .30 .75
286 Jim Wohlford .15 .40
287 Pete Mackanin .15 .40
288 Bill Campbell .15 .40
289 Enzo Hernandez .15 .40
290 Ted Simmons .30 .75
291 Ken Sanders .15 .40
292 Leon Roberts .15 .40
293 Bill Castro RC .15 .40
294 Ed Kirkpatrick .15 .40
295 Dave Cash .15 .40
296 Pat Dobson .15 .40
297 Roger Metzger .15 .40
298 Dick Bosman .15 .40
299 Champ Summers RC .15 .40
300 Johnny Bench 5.00 12.00
301 Jackie Brown .15 .40
302 Rick Miller .15 .40
303 Steve Foucault .15 .40
304 California Angels CL .60 1.50
Dick Williams MG
305 Andy Messersmith .30 .75
306 Rod Gilbreath .15 .40
307 Al Bumbry .30 .75
308 Jim Barr .15 .40
309 Bill Melton .15 .40
310 Randy Jones .30 .75
311 Cookie Rojas .15 .40
312 Don Carrithers .15 .40
313 Dan Ford RC .15 .40
314 Ed Kranepool .15 .40
315 Al Hrabosky .30 .75
316 Robin Yount 6.00 15.00
317 John Candelaria RC .60 1.50
318 Bob Boone .60 1.50
319 Larry Gura .15 .40
320 Willie Horton .30 .75
321 Jose Cruz .60 1.50
322 Glenn Abbott .15 .40
323 Rob Sperring RC .15 .40
324 Jim Bibby .15 .40
325 Tony Perez 1.25 3.00
326 Dick Pole .15 .40
327 Dave Moates RC .15 .40
328 Carl Morton .15 .40
329 Joe Ferguson .15 .40
330 Nolan Ryan 10.00 25.00
331 San Diego Padres CL .60 1.50
John McNamara MG
332 Charlie Williams .15 .40
333 Bob Coluccio .15 .40
334 Dennis Leonard .30 .75
335 Bob Grich .30 .75
336 Vic Albury .15 .40
337 Bud Harrelson .30 .75
338 Bob Bailey .15 .40
339 John Denny .30 .75
340 Jim Rice 1.50 4.00
341 Lou Gehrig ATG 5.00 12.00
342 Rogers Hornsby ATG 1.25 3.00
343 Pie Traynor ATG .60 1.50
344 Honus Wagner ATG 2.00 5.00
345 Babe Ruth ATG 6.00 15.00
346 Ty Cobb ATG 5.00 12.00

347 Ted Williams ATG 5.00 12.00
348 Mickey Cochrane ATG .60 1.50
349 Walter Johnson ATG 2.00 5.00
350 Lefty Grove ATG .60 1.50
351 Randy Hundley .30 .75
352 Dave Giusti .15 .40
353 Sixto Lezcano RC .30 .75
354 Ron Blomberg .15 .40
355 Steve Carlton 2.50 6.00
356 Ted Martinez .15 .40
357 Ken Forsch .15 .40
358 Buddy Bell .30 .75
359 Rick Reuschel .30 .75
360 Jeff Burroughs .30 .75
361 Detroit Tigers CL .60 1.50
Ralph Houk MG
362 Will McEnaney .30 .75
363 Dave Collins RC .30 .75
364 Elias Sosa .15 .40
365 Carlton Fisk 2.50 6.00
366 Bobby Valentine .30 .75
367 Bruce Miller .15 .40
368 Wilbur Wood .15 .40
369 Frank White .30 .75
370 Ron Cey .30 .75
371 Elrod Hendricks .15 .40
372 Rick Baldwin RC .15 .40
373 Johnny Briggs .15 .40
374 Dan Warthen RC .15 .40
375 Ron Fairly .30 .75
376 Rich Hebner .30 .75
377 Mike Hegan .15 .40
378 Steve Stone .30 .75
379 Ken Boswell .15 .40
380 Bobby Bonds .60 1.50
381 Denny Doyle .15 .40
382 Matt Alexander RC .15 .40
383 John Ellis .15 .40
384 Philadelphia Phillies CL .60 1.50
Danny Ozark MG
385 Mickey Lolich .30 .75
386 Ed Goodson .15 .40
387 Mike Miley RC .15 .40
388 Stan Perzanowski RC .15 .40
389 Glenn Adams RC .15 .40
390 Don Gullett .30 .75
391 Jerry Hairston .15 .40
392 Checklist 265-396 .60 1.50
393 Paul Mitchell RC .15 .40
394 Fran Healy .15 .40
395 Jim Wynn .30 .75
396 Bill Lee .15 .40
397 Tim Foli .15 .40
398 Dave Tomlin .15 .40
399 Luis Melendez .15 .40
400 Rod Carew 2.50 6.00
401 Ken Brett .15 .40
402 Don Money .30 .75
403 Geoff Zahn .15 .40
404 Enos Cabell .15 .40
405 Rollie Fingers 1.00 2.50
406 Ed Herrmann .15 .40
407 Tom Underwood .15 .40
408 Charlie Spikes .15 .40
409 Dave Lemanczyk .15 .40
410 Ralph Garr .30 .75
411 Bill Singer .15 .40
412 Toby Harrah .30 .75
413 Pete Varney RC .15 .40
414 Wayne Garland .15 .40
415 Vada Pinson .60 1.50
416 Tommy John .60 1.50
417 Gene Clines .15 .40
418 Jose Morales RC .15 .40
419 Reggie Cleveland .15 .40
420 Joe Morgan 2.00 5.00
421 Oakland Athletics CL .60 1.50
(No Manager on front)
422 Johnny Grubb .15 .40
423 Ed Halicki .15 .40
424 Phil Roof .15 .40
425 Rennie Stennett .15 .40
426 Bob Forsch .15 .40
427 Kurt Bevacqua .15 .40
428 Jim Crawford .15 .40
429 Fred Stanley .15 .40
430 Jose Cardenal .30 .75
431 Dick Ruthven .15 .40
432 Tom Veryzer .15 .40
433 Rick Waits RC .15 .40
434 Morris Nettles .15 .40
435 Phil Niekro 1.00 2.50
436 Bill Fahey .15 .40
437 Terry Forster .15 .40
438 Doug DeCinces .30 .75
439 Rick Rhoden .30 .75
440 John Mayberry .30 .75
441 Gary Carter 1.50 4.00
442 Hank Webb .15 .40
443 San Francisco Giants CL .60 1.50
(No Manager on front
444 Gary Nolan .30 .75
445 Rico Petrocelli .30 .75
446 Larry Haney .15 .40
447 Gene Locklear .30 .75
448 Tom Johnson .15 .40
449 Bob Robertson .15 .40
450 Jim Palmer 2.00 5.00
451 Buddy Bradford .15 .40
452 Tom Hausman RC .15 .40
453 Lou Piniella .60 1.50
454 Tom Griffin .15 .40
455 Dick Allen .60 1.50
456 Joe Coleman .15 .40
457 Ed Crosby .15 .40
458 Earl Williams .15 .40
459 Jim Brewer .15 .40
460 Cesar Cedeno .30 .75
461 NL and AL Championships .30 .75
Bench/Gullett/Perez
Luis Tiant
462 1975 World Series .30 .75
Reds Champs
463 Steve Hargan .15 .40
464 Ken Henderson .15 .40
465 Mike Marshall .30 .75
466 Bob Stinson .15 .40
467 Woodie Fryman .15 .40
468 Jesus Alou .15 .40
469 Rawly Eastwick .30 .75
470 Bobby Murcer .30 .75
471 Jim Burton .15 .40
472 Bob Davis RC .30 .75
473 Paul Blair .30 .75
474 Ray Corbin .15 .40
475 Joe Rudi .30 .75
476 Bob Moose .15 .40
477 Cleveland Indians CL .60 1.50
Frank Robinson MG
478 Lynn McGlothen .15 .40
479 Bobby Mitchell .15 .40
480 Mike Schmidt 6.00 15.00
481 Rudy May .15 .40
482 Tim Hosley .15 .40
483 Mickey Stanley .15 .40
484 Eric Raich RC .15 .40
485 Mike Hargrove .30 .75
486 Bruce Dal Canton .15 .40
487 Leron Lee .15 .40
488 Claude Osteen .30 .75
489 Skip Jutze .15 .40
490 Frank Tanana .30 .75
491 Terry Crowley .15 .40
492 Marty Pattin .15 .40
493 Derrel Thomas .15 .40
494 Craig Swan .30 .75
495 Nate Colbert .15 .40
496 Juan Beniquez .15 .40
497 Joe McIntosh RC .15 .40
498 Glenn Borgmann .15 .40
499 Mario Guerrero .15 .40
500 Reggie Jackson 5.00 12.00
501 Billy Champion .15 .40
502 Tim McCarver .60 1.50
503 Elliott Maddox .15 .40
504 Pittsburgh Pirates CL .60 1.50
Danny Murtaugh MG
505 Mark Belanger .30 .75
506 George Mitterwald .15 .40
507 Ray Bare RC .15 .40
508 Duane Kuiper RC .15 .40
509 Bill Hands .15 .40
510 Amos Otis .30 .75
511 Jamie Easterley .15 .40
512 Ellie Rodriguez .15 .40
513 Bart Johnson .15 .40
514 Dan Driessen .15 .40
515 Steve Yeager .30 .75
516 Wayne Granger .15 .40
517 John Milner .15 .40
518 Doug Flynn RC .15 .40
519 Steve Brye .15 .40
520 Willie McCovey 2.00 5.00
521 Jim Colborn .15 .40
522 Ted Sizemore .15 .40
523 Bob Montgomery .15 .40
524 Pete Falcone RC .15 .40
525 Billy Williams 1.00 2.50
526 Checklist 397-528 .60 1.50
527 Mike Anderson .15 .40
528 Dock Ellis .15 .40
529 Deron Johnson .15 .40
530 Don Sutton 1.00 2.50
531 New York Mets CL .60 1.50
Joe Frazier MG
532 Milt May .15 .40
533 Lee Richard .15 .40
534 Stan Bahnsen .15 .40
535 Dave Nelson .15 .40
536 Mike Thompson .15 .40
537 Tony Muser .15 .40
538 Pat Darcy .15 .40
539 John Balaz RC .15 .40
540 Bill Freehan .30 .75
541 Steve Mingori .15 .40
542 Keith Hernandez .30 .75
543 Wayne Twitchell .15 .40
544 Pepe Frias .15 .40
545 Sparky Lyle .30 .75
546 Dave Rosello .15 .40
547 Roric Harrison .15 .40
548 Manny Mota .30 .75
549 Randy Tate RC .15 .40
550 Hank Aaron 10.00 25.00
551 Jerry DaVanon .15 .40
552 Terry Humphrey .15 .40
553 Randy Moffitt .15 .40
554 Ray Fosse .15 .40
555 Dyar Miller .15 .40
556 Minnesota Twins CL .60 1.50
Gene Mauch MG
557 Dan Spillner .15 .40
558 Clarence Gaston .30 .75
559 Clyde Wright .15 .40
560 Jorge Orta .15 .40
561 Tom Carroll .15 .40
562 Adrian Garrett .15 .40
563 Larry Demery .15 .40
564 Kurt Bevacqua .60 1.50
Bubble Gum Champ
565 Tug McGraw .30 .75
566 Ken McMullen .15 .40
567 George Stone .15 .40
568 Rob Andrews RC .15 .40
569 Nelson Briles .15 .40
570 George Hendrick .30 .75
571 Don DeMola .15 .40
572 Rich Coggins .15 .40
573 Bill Travers .15 .40
574 Don Kessinger .30 .75
575 Dwight Evans .60 1.50
576 Maximino Leon .15 .40
577 Marc Hill .15 .40
578 Ted Kubiak .15 .40
579 Clay Kirby .15 .40
580 Bert Campaneris .30 .75
581 St. Louis Cardinals CL .60 1.50
Red Schoendienst MG
582 Mike Kekich .15 .40
583 Tommy Helms .15 .40
584 Stan Wall RC .15 .40
585 Joe Torre .60 1.50
586 Ron Schueler .15 .40
587 Leo Cardenas .15 .40
588 Kevin Kobel .15 .40
589 Rookie Pitchers .60 1.50
Santo Alcala RC
Mike Flanagan RC
Joe Pactwa RC
Pablo Torrealba RC
590 Rookie Outfielders .30 .75
Henry Cruz RC
Chet Lemon RC
Ellis Valentine RC
Terry Whitfield
591 Rookie Pitchers .30 .75
Steve Grilli RC
Craig Mitchell RC
Jose Sosa RC
George Throop RC
592 Rookie Infielders 2.00 5.00
Willie Randolph RC
Dave McKay RC
Jerry Royster RC
Roy Staiger RC
593 Rookie Pitchers .30 .75
Larry Anderson RC
Ken Crosby RC
Mark Littell
Butch Metzger RC
594 Rookie Catchers and Outfielders .30 .75
Andy Merchant RC
Ed Ott RC
Royle Stillman RC
Jerry White RC
595 Rookie Pitchers .30 .75
Art DeFillipis RC
Randy Lerch RC
Sid Monge RC
Steve Barr RC
596 Rookie Infielders .30 .75
Craig Reynolds RC
Lamar Johnson RC
Johnnie LeMaster RC
Jerry Manuel RC
597 Rookie Pitchers .30 .75
Don Aase RC
Jack Kucek
Frank LaCorte RC
Mike Pazik RC
598 Rookie Outfielders .30 .75
Hector Cruz RC
Jamie Quirk RC
Jerry Turner
Joe Wallis RC
599 Rookie Pitchers 3.00 8.00
Rob Dressler RC
Ron Guidry RC
Bob McClure RC
Pat Zachry RC
600 Tom Seaver 4.00 10.00
601 Ken Rudolph .15 .40
602 Doug Konieczny .15 .40
603 Jim Holt .15 .40
604 Joe Lovitto .15 .40
605 Al Downing .15 .40
606 Milwaukee Brewers CL .60 1.50
Alex Grammas MG
607 Rich Hinton .15 .40
608 Vic Correll .15 .40
609 Fred Norman .15 .40
610 Greg Luzinski .60 1.50
611 Rich Folkers .15 .40
612 Joe Lahoud .15 .40
613 Tim Johnson .15 .40
614 Fernando Arroyo RC .15 .40
615 Mike Cubbage .15 .40
616 Buck Martinez .15 .40
617 Darold Knowles .15 .40
618 Jack Brohamer .15 .40
619 Bill Butler .15 .40
620 Al Oliver .30 .75
621 Tom Hall .15 .40
622 Rick Auerbach .15 .40
623 Bob Allietta RC .15 .40
624 Tony Taylor .15 .40
625 J.R. Richard .30 .75
626 Bob Sheldon .15 .40
627 Bill Plummer .15 .40
628 John D'Acquisto .15 .40
629 Sandy Alomar .30 .75
630 Chris Speier .15 .40
631 Atlanta Braves CL .60 1.50
Dave Bristol MG
632 Rogelio Moret .15 .40
633 John Stearns RC .30 .75
634 Larry Christenson .15 .40
635 Jim Fregosi .30 .75
636 Joe Decker .15 .40
637 Bruce Bochte .15 .40
638 Doyle Alexander .30 .75
639 Fred Kendall .15 .40
640 Bill Madlock .60 1.50
641 Tom Paciorek .30 .75
642 Dennis Blair .15 .40
643 Checklist 529-660 .60 1.50
644 Tom Bradley .15 .40
645 Darrell Porter .30 .75
646 John Lowenstein .15 .40
647 Ramon Hernandez .15 .40
648 Al Cowens .30 .75
649 Dave Roberts .15 .40
650 Thurman Munson 2.50 6.00
651 John Odom .15 .40
652 Ed Armbrister .15 .40
653 Mike Norris RC .30 .75
654 Doug Griffin .15 .40
655 Mike Vail RC .15 .40
656 Chicago White Sox CL .60 1.50
Chuck Tanner MG
657 Roy Smalley RC .30 .75
658 Jerry Johnson .15 .40
659 Ben Oglivie .30 .75
660 Dave Lopes .60 1.50

1976 Topps Traded

The cards in this 44-card set measure 2 1/2" by 3 1/2". The 1976 Topps Traded set contains 43 players and one unnumbered checklist card. The individuals pictured were traded after the Topps regular set was printed. A "Sports Extra" heading design is found on each picture and is also used to introduce the biographical section of the reverse. Each card is numbered according to the player's regular 1976 card with the addition of "T" to indicate his new status. As in 1974, the cards were inserted in all packs toward the end of the production run. According to published reports at the time, they were not released until April, 1976. Because they were produced in large quantities, they are no scarcer than the basic cards. Reports at the time indicated that a dealer could make approximately 35 sets from a vending case. The vending cases included both regular and traded cards.

COMPLETE SET (44) 12.50 30.00
27T Ed Figueroa .15 .40
28T Dusty Baker .60 1.50
44T Doug Rader .30 .75
58T Ron Reed .15 .40
74T Oscar Gamble .60 1.50
80T Jim Kaat .60 1.50
83T Jim Spencer .15 .40
85T Mickey Rivers .30 .75
99T Lee Lacy .15 .40
120T Rusty Staub .30 .75
127T Larvell Blanks .15 .40
146T George Medich .15 .40
158T Ken Reitz .15 .40
208T Mike Lum .15 .40
211T Clay Carroll .15 .40
231T Tom House .15 .40
250T Fergie Jenkins 1.25 3.00
259T Darrel Chaney .15 .40
292T Leon Roberts .15 .40
296T Pat Dobson .15 .40
309T Bill Melton .15 .40
338T Bob Bailey .15 .40
380T Bobby Bonds .60 1.50
383T John Ellis .15 .40
385T Mickey Lolich .30 .75
401T Ken Brett .15 .40
410T Ralph Garr .15 .40
411T Bill Singer .15 .40
428T Jim Crawford .15 .40
434T Morris Nettles .15 .40
464T Ken Henderson .15 .40
497T Joe McIntosh .15 .40
524T Pete Falcone .15 .40
527T Mike Anderson .15 .40
528T Dock Ellis .15 .40
532T Milt May .15 .40
554T Ray Fosse .15 .40
579T Clay Kirby .15 .40
583T Tommy Helms .15 .40
592T Willie Randolph 2.00 5.00
618T Jack Brohamer .15 .40
632T Rogelio Moret .15 .40
649T Dave Roberts .15 .40
NNO Traded Checklist .75 2.00

1977 Topps

In 1977 for the fifth consecutive year, Topps produced a 660-card standard-size baseball set. Among other fashions, this set was released in 10-card wax packs as well as thirty-nine card rack packs. The player's name, team affiliation, and his position are compactly arranged over the picture area and a facsimile autograph appears on the photo. Team cards feature a checklist of that team's players in the set and a small picture of the manager on the front of the card. Appearing for the first time are the series "Brothers" (631-634) and "Turn Back the Clock" (433-437). Other subseries in the set are League Leaders (1-8), Record Breakers (231-234), Playoffs cards (276-277), World Series cards (411-413), and Rookie Prospects (472-479/487-494). The following players' regular issue cards are explicitly denoted as All-Stars, 30, 70, 100, 120, 170, 210, 240, 265, 301, 347, 400, 420, 450, 500, 521, 550, 560, and 580. The key Rookie Cards in the set are Jack Clark, Andre Dawson, Mark "The Bird" Fidrych, Dennis Martinez and Dale Murphy. Cards numbered 23 or lower, that feature Yankees and do not follow the numbering checklisted below, are not necessarily error cards. Those cards were issued in the NY area and distributed by Burger King. There was an aluminum version of the Dale Murphy rookie card number 476 produced (legally) in the early '80s; proceeds from the sales originally priced at 10.00) of this "card" went to the Huntington's Disease Foundation.

COMPLETE SET (660) 125.00 250.00
1 Batting Leaders 3.00 8.00
George Brett
Bill Madlock
2 Home Run Leaders 1.00 2.50
Graig Nettles
Mike Schmidt
3 RBI Leaders .60 1.50
Lee May
George Foster
4 Stolen Base Leaders .30 .75
Bill North
Dave Lopes
5 Victory Leaders .60 1.50
Jim Palmer
Randy Jones
6 Strikeout Leaders 6.00 15.00
Nolan Ryan
Tom Seaver
7 ERA Leaders .30 .75
Mark Fidrych
John Denny
8 Leading Firemen .30 .75
Bill Campbell
Rawly Eastwick
9 Doug Rader .12 .30
10 Reggie Jackson 4.00 10.00
11 Rob Dressler .12 .30
12 Larry Haney .12 .30
13 Luis Gomez RC .12 .30
14 Tommy Smith .12 .30
15 Don Gullett .30 .75
16 Bob Jones RC .12 .30
17 Steve Stone .30 .75
18 Cleveland Indians CL .60 1.50
Frank Robinson MG
19 John D'Acquisto .12 .30
20 Graig Nettles .60 1.50
21 Ken Forsch .12 .30
22 Bill Freehan .30 .75
23 Dan Driessen .12 .30
24 Carl Morton .12 .30
25 Dwight Evans .60 1.50
26 Ray Sadecki .12 .30
27 Bill Buckner .30 .75
28 Woodie Fryman .12 .30
29 Bucky Dent .30 .75
30 Greg Luzinski .60 1.50
31 Jim Todd .12 .30
32 Checklist 1-132 .60 1.50
33 Wayne Garland .12 .30
34 California Angels CL .60 1.50
Norm Sherry MG
35 Rennie Stennett .12 .30
36 John Ellis .12 .30
37 Steve Hargan .12 .30
38 Craig Kusick .12 .30
39 Tom Griffin .12 .30
40 Bobby Murcer .30 .75
41 Jim Kern .12 .30
42 Jose Cruz .30 .75
43 Ray Bare .12 .30
44 Bud Harrelson .30 .75
45 Rawly Eastwick .12 .30
46 Buck Martinez .12 .30
47 Lynn McGlothen .12 .30
48 Tom Paciorek .30 .75
49 Grant Jackson .12 .30
50 Ron Cey .30 .75
51 Milwaukee Brewers CL .60 1.50
Alex Grammas MG
52 Ellis Valentine .12 .30
53 Paul Mitchell .12 .30
54 Sandy Alomar .12 .30
55 Jeff Burroughs .30 .75
56 Rudy May .12 .30
57 Marc Hill .12 .30
58 Chet Lemon .30 .75
59 Larry Christenson .12 .30
60 Jim Rice 1.00 2.50
61 Manny Sanguillen .30 .75
62 Eric Raich .12 .30
63 Tito Fuentes .12 .30
64 Larry Biittner .12 .30
65 Skip Lockwood .12 .30
66 Roy Smalley .30 .75
67 Joaquin Andujar RC .30 .75
68 Bruce Bochte .12 .30
69 Jim Crawford .12 .30
70 Johnny Bench 4.00 10.00
71 Dock Ellis .12 .30
72 Mike Anderson .12 .30
73 Charlie Williams .12 .30
74 Oakland Athletics CL .60 1.50
Jack McKeon MG
75 Dennis Leonard .30 .75
76 Tim Foli .12 .30
77 Dyar Miller .12 .30
78 Bob Davis .12 .30
79 Don Money .30 .75
80 Andy Messersmith .30 .75
81 Juan Beniquez .12 .30
82 Jim Rooker .12 .30
83 Kevin Bell RC .12 .30
84 Ollie Brown .12 .30
85 Duane Kuiper .12 .30
86 Pat Zachry .12 .30
87 Glenn Borgmann .12 .30
88 Stan Wall .12 .30
89 Butch Hobson RC .30 .75
90 Cesar Cedeno .30 .75
91 John Verhoeven RC .12 .30
92 Dave Rosello .12 .30
93 Tom Poquette .12 .30
94 Craig Swan .12 .30
95 Keith Hernandez .30 .75
96 Lou Piniella .30 .75
97 Dave Heaverlo .12 .30
98 Milt May .12 .30
99 Tom Hausman .12 .30
100 Joe Morgan 1.50 4.00
101 Dick Bosman .12 .30
102 Jose Morales .12 .30
103 Mike Bacsik RC .12 .30
104 Omar Moreno RC .30 .75
105 Steve Yeager .30 .75
106 Mike Flanagan .30 .75
107 Bill Melton .12 .30
108 Alan Foster .12 .30
109 Jorge Orta .12 .30
110 Steve Carlton 2.00 5.00
111 Rico Petrocelli .30 .75
112 Bill Greif .12 .30
113 Blue Jays Leaders .60 1.50
Roy Hartsfield MG
Don Leppert CO
Bob Miller CO
Jackie Moore CO
Harry Warner CO
114 Bruce Dal Canton .12 .30
115 Rick Manning .12 .30
116 Joe Niekro .30 .75
117 Frank White .30 .75
118 Rick Jones RC .12 .30
119 John Stearns .12 .30
120 Rod Carew 2.00 5.00
121 Gary Nolan .12 .30
122 Ben Oglivie .30 .75
123 Fred Stanley .12 .30
124 George Mitterwald .12 .30
125 Bill Travers .12 .30
126 Rod Gilbreath .12 .30
127 Ron Fairly .30 .75
128 Tommy John .60 1.50
129 Mike Sadek .12 .30
130 Al Oliver .30 .75
131 Orlando Ramirez RC .12 .30
132 Chip Lang RC .12 .30
133 Ralph Garr .30 .75
134 San Diego Padres CL .60 1.50
John McNamara MG
135 Mark Belanger .30 .75
136 Jerry Mumphrey RC .30 .75
137 Jeff Terpko RC .12 .30
138 Bob Stinson .12 .30
139 Fred Norman .12 .30
140 Mike Schmidt 5.00 12.00
141 Mark Littell .12 .30
142 Steve Dillard RC .12 .30
143 Ed Herrmann .12 .30
144 Bruce Sutter RC 6.00 15.00
145 Tom Veryzer .12 .30
146 Dusty Baker .60 1.50
147 Jackie Brown .12 .30
148 Fran Healy .12 .30
149 Mike Cubbage .12 .30
150 Tom Seaver 3.00 8.00
151 Johnny LeMaster .12 .30
152 Gaylord Perry 1.00 2.50
153 Ron Jackson RC .12 .30
154 Dave Giusti .12 .30
155 Joe Rudi .30 .75
156 Pete Mackanin .12 .30
157 Ken Brett .12 .30
158 Ted Kubiak .12 .30
159 Bernie Carbo .12 .30
160 Will McEnaney .12 .30
161 Garry Templeton RC .60 1.50
162 Mike Cuellar .30 .75
163 Dave Hilton .12 .30
164 Tug McGraw .30 .75
165 Jim Wynn .30 .75
166 Bill Campbell .12 .30
167 Rich Hebner .30 .75
168 Charlie Spikes .12 .30
169 Darold Knowles .12 .30
170 Thurman Munson 2.00 5.00
171 Ken Sanders .12 .30
172 John Milner .12 .30
173 Chuck Scrivener RC .12 .30
174 Nelson Briles .30 .75
175 Butch Wynegar RC .30 .75
176 Bob Robertson .12 .30
177 Bart Johnson .12 .30
178 Bombo Rivera RC .12 .30
179 Paul Hartzell RC .12 .30
180 Dave Lopes .30 .75
181 Ken McMullen .12 .30
182 Dan Spillner .12 .30
183 St. Louis Cardinals CL .60 1.50
Vern Rapp MG
184 Bo McLaughlin RC .12 .30
185 Sixto Lezcano .12 .30
186 Doug Flynn .12 .30
187 Dick Pole .12 .30
188 Bob Tolan .12 .30
189 Rick Dempsey .30 .75
190 Ray Burris .12 .30
191 Doug Griffin .12 .30
192 Clarence Gaston .30 .75
193 Larry Gura .12 .30
194 Gary Matthews .30 .75
195 Ed Figueroa .12 .30
196 Len Randle .12 .30
197 Ed Ott .12 .30
198 Wilbur Wood .12 .30
199 Pepe Frias .12 .30
200 Frank Tanana .30 .75
201 Ed Kranepool .12 .30
202 Tom Johnson .12 .30
203 Ed Armbrister .12 .30
204 Jeff Newman RC .12 .30
205 Pete Falcone .12 .30
206 Boog Powell .60 1.50
207 Glenn Abbott .12 .30
208 Checklist 133-264 .60 1.50
209 Rob Andrews .12 .30
210 Fred Lynn .30 .75
211 San Francisco Giants CL .60 1.50
Joe Altobelli MG
212 Jim Mason .12 .30
213 Maximino Leon .12 .30
214 Darrell Porter .30 .75
215 Butch Metzger .12 .30
216 Doug DeCinces .30 .75
217 Tom Underwood .12 .30
218 John Wathan RC .30 .75
219 Joe Coleman .12 .30
220 Chris Chambliss .30 .75
221 Bob Bailey .12 .30
222 Francisco Barrios RC .12 .30
223 Earl Williams .12 .30
224 Rusty Torres .12 .30
225 Bob Apodaca .12 .30
226 Leroy Stanton .30 .75
227 Joe Sambito RC .12 .30
228 Minnesota Twins CL .60 1.50
Gene Mauch MG
229 Don Kessinger .30 .75
230 Vida Blue .30 .75
231 George Brett RB 3.00 8.00
232 Minnie Minoso RB .30 .75
233 Jose Morales RB .12 .30
234 Nolan Ryan RB 6.00 15.00
235 Cecil Cooper .30 .75
236 Tom Buskey .12 .30
237 Gene Clines .12 .30
238 Tippy Martinez .12 .30
239 Bill Plummer .12 .30
240 Ron LeFlore .30 .75
241 Dave Tomlin .12 .30
242 Ken Henderson .12 .30
243 Ron Reed .12 .30
244 John Mayberry .30 .75
(Cartoon mentions
T206 Wagner)
245 Rick Rhoden .30 .75
246 Mike Vail .12 .30
247 Chris Knapp RC .12 .30
248 Wilbur Howard .12 .30
249 Pete Redfern RC .12 .30
250 Bill Madlock .30 .75
251 Tony Muser .12 .30
252 Dale Murray .12 .30
253 John Hale .12 .30
254 Doyle Alexander .12 .30
255 George Scott .30 .75
256 Joe Hoerner .12 .30
257 Mike Miley .12 .30
258 Luis Tiant .30 .75
259 New York Mets CL .60 1.50
Joe Frazier MG
260 J.R. Richard .30 .75
261 Phil Garner .30 .75
262 Al Cowens .30 .75
263 Mike Marshall .30 .75
264 Tom Hutton .12 .30
265 Mark Fidrych RC 1.25 3.00
266 Derrel Thomas .12 .30
267 Ray Fosse .12 .30
268 Rick Sawyer RC .12 .30
269 Joe Lis .12 .30
270 Dave Parker .60 1.50
271 Terry Forster .12 .30
272 Lee Lacy .12 .30
273 Eric Soderholm .12 .30
274 Don Stanhouse .12 .30
275 Mike Hargrove .30 .75
276 AL Championship .60 1.50
Chris Chambliss
277 NL Championship 2.00 5.00
Pete Rose
278 Danny Frisella .12 .30
279 Joe Wallis .12 .30
280 Jim Hunter 1.00 2.50
281 Roy Staiger .12 .30
282 Sid Monge .12 .30
283 Jerry DaVanon .12 .30
284 Mike Norris .12 .30
285 Brooks Robinson 2.00 5.00
286 Johnny Grubb .12 .30
287 Cincinnati Reds CL .60 1.50
Sparky Anderson MG
288 Bob Montgomery .12 .30
289 Gene Garber .12 .30
290 Amos Otis .30 .75
291 Jason Thompson RC .30 .75
292 Rogelio Moret .12 .30
293 Jack Brohamer .12 .30
294 George Medich .12 .30
295 Gary Carter 1.00 2.50
296 Don Hood .12 .30
297 Ken Reitz .12 .30
298 Charlie Hough .30 .75
299 Otto Velez .30 .75
300 Jerry Koosman .30 .75
301 Toby Harrah .30 .75
302 Mike Garman .12 .30
303 Gene Tenace .30 .75
304 Jim Hughes .12 .30
305 Mickey Rivers .30 .75
306 Rick Waits .12 .30
307 Gary Sutherland .12 .30

308 Gene Pentz RC .12 .30
309 Boston Red Sox CL .60 1.50
Don Zimmer MG
310 Larry Bowa .30 .75
311 Vern Ruhle .12 .30
312 Rob Belloir RC .12 .30
313 Paul Blair .30 .75
314 Steve Mingori .12 .30
315 Dave Chalk .12 .30
316 Steve Rogers .12 .30
317 Kurt Bevacqua .12 .30
318 Duffy Dyer .12 .30
319 Goose Gossage .60 1.50
320 Ken Griffey Sr. .60 1.50
321 Dave Goltz .12 .30
322 Bill Russell .30 .75
323 Larry Lintz .12 .30
324 John Curtis .12 .30
325 Mike Ivie .12 .30
326 Jesse Jefferson .12 .30
327 Houston Astros CL .60 1.50
Bill Virdon MG
328 Tommy Boggs RC .12 .30
329 Ron Hodges .12 .30
330 George Hendrick .30 .75
331 Jim Colborn .12 .30
332 Elliott Maddox .12 .30
333 Paul Reuschel RC .12 .30
334 Bill Stein .12 .30
335 Bill Robinson .30 .75
336 Denny Doyle .12 .30
337 Ron Schueler .12 .30
338 Dave Duncan .30 .75
339 Adrian Devine .12 .30
340 Hal McRae .30 .75
341 Joe Kerrigan RC .12 .30
342 Jerry Remy .12 .30
343 Ed Halicki .12 .30
344 Brian Downing .30 .75
345 Reggie Smith .30 .75
346 Bill Singer .12 .30
347 George Foster .60 1.50
348 Brent Strom .12 .30
349 Jim Holt .12 .30
350 Larry Dierker .30 .75
351 Jim Sundberg .30 .75
352 Mike Phillips .12 .30
353 Stan Thomas .12 .30
354 Pittsburgh Pirates CL .60 1.50
Chuck Tanner MG
355 Lou Brock 1.50 4.00
356 Checklist 265-396 .60 1.50
357 Tim McCarver .60 1.50
358 Tom House .12 .30
359 Willie Randolph .60 1.50
360 Rick Monday .30 .75
361 Eduardo Rodriguez .12 .30
362 Tommy Davis .30 .75
363 Dave Roberts .12 .30
364 Vic Correll .12 .30
365 Mike Torrez .30 .75
366 Ted Sizemore .12 .30
367 Dave Hamilton .12 .30
368 Mike Jorgensen .12 .30
369 Terry Humphrey .12 .30
370 John Montefusco .12 .30
371 Kansas City Royals CL .60 1.50
Whitey Herzog MG
372 Rich Folkers .12 .30
373 Bert Campaneris .30 .75
374 Kent Tekulve .30 .75
375 Larry Hisle .30 .75
376 Nino Espinosa RC .12 .30
377 Dave McKay .12 .30
378 Jim Umbarger .12 .30
379 Larry Cox RC .12 .30
380 Lee May .30 .75
381 Bob Forsch .12 .30
382 Charlie Moore .12 .30
383 Stan Bahnsen .12 .30
384 Darrel Chaney .12 .30
385 Dave LaRoche .12 .30
386 Manny Mota .30 .75
387 New York Yankees CL 1.00 2.50
Billy Martin MG
388 Terry Harmon .12 .30
389 Ken Kravec RC .12 .30
390 Dave Winfield 2.50 6.00
391 Dan Warthen .12 .30
392 Phil Roof .12 .30
393 John Lowenstein .12 .30
394 Bill Laxton RC .12 .30
395 Manny Trillo .12 .30
396 Tom Murphy .12 .30
397 Larry Herndon RC .30 .75
398 Tom Burgmeier .12 .30
399 Bruce Boisclair RC .12 .30
400 Steve Garvey 1.00 2.50
401 Mickey Scott .12 .30
402 Tommy Helms .12 .30
403 Tom Grieve .30 .75
404 Eric Rasmussen RC .12 .30
405 Claudell Washington .30 .75
406 Tim Johnson .12 .30
407 Dave Freisleben .12 .30
408 Cesar Tovar .12 .30
409 Pete Broberg .12 .30
410 Willie Montanez .12 .30
411 World Series 1.00 2.50
Joe Morgan
Johnny Bench
412 World Series 1.00 2.50
Johnny Bench
413 World Series .30 .75
Cincy Wins
414 Tommy Harper .30 .75
415 Jay Johnstone .30 .75
416 Chuck Hartenstein .12 .30
417 Wayne Garrett .12 .30
418 Chicago White Sox CL .60 1.50
Bob Lemon MG
419 Steve Swisher .12 .30
420 Rusty Staub .60 1.50
421 Doug Rau .12 .30
422 Freddie Patek .30 .75
423 Gary Lavelle .12 .30
424 Steve Brye .12 .30
425 Joe Torre .60 1.50
426 Dick Drago .12 .30
427 Dave Rader .12 .30
428 Texas Rangers CL .60 1.50
Frank Lucchesi
429 Ken Boswell .12 .30
430 Fergie Jenkins 1.00 2.50
431 Dave Collins UER .30 .75
(Photo actually
Bobby Jones)
432 Buzz Capra .12 .30
433 Nate Colbert TBC .12 .30
434 Carl Yastrzemski TBC .60 1.50
435 Maury Wills TBC .30 .75
436 Bob Keegan TBC .12 .30
437 Ralph Kiner TBC .60 1.50
438 Marty Perez .12 .30
439 Gorman Thomas .30 .75
440 Jon Matlack .12 .30
441 Larvell Blanks .12 .30
442 Atlanta Braves CL .60 1.50
Dave Bristol MG
443 Lamar Johnson .12 .30
444 Wayne Twitchell .12 .30
445 Ken Singleton .30 .75
446 Bill Bonham .12 .30
447 Jerry Turner .12 .30
448 Ellie Rodriguez .12 .30
449 Al Fitzmorris .12 .30
450 Pete Rose 8.00 20.00
451 Checklist 397-528 .60 1.50
452 Mike Caldwell .12 .30
453 Pedro Garcia .12 .30
454 Andy Etchebarren .12 .30
455 Rick Wise .12 .30
456 Leon Roberts .12 .30
457 Steve Luebber .12 .30
458 Leo Foster .12 .30
459 Steve Foucault .12 .30
460 Willie Stargell 1.00 2.50
461 Dick Tidrow .12 .30
462 Don Baylor .60 1.50
463 Jamie Quirk .12 .30
464 Randy Moffitt .12 .30
465 Rico Carty .30 .75
466 Fred Holdsworth .12 .30
467 Philadelphia Phillies CL .60 1.50
Danny Ozark MG
468 Ramon Hernandez .12 .30
469 Pat Kelly .12 .30
470 Ted Simmons .30 .75
471 Del Unser .12 .30
472 Rookie Pitchers .12 .30
Don Aase
Bob McClure
Gil Patterson RC
Dave Wehrmeister RC
UER Sheldon Gill pictured
instead of Gil Patterson
473 Rookie Outfielders 8.00 20.00
Andre Dawson RC
Gene Richards RC
John Scott
Denny Walling RC
474 Rookie Shortstops .30 .75
Bob Bailor RC
Kiko Garcia RC
Craig Reynolds
Alex Taveras RC
475 Rookie Pitchers .30 .75
Chris Batton RC
Rick Camp RC
Scott McGregor
Manny Sarmiento RC
476 Rookie Catchers 6.00 15.00
Gary Alexander RC
Rick Cerone RC
Dale Murphy RC
Kevin Pasley RC
477 Rookie Infielders .30 .75
Doug Ault RC
Rich Dauer RC
Orlando Gonzalez RC
Phil Mankowski RC
478 Rookie Pitchers .30 .75
Jim Gideon RC
Leon Hooten RC
Dave Johnson RC
Mark Lemongello RC
479 Rookie Outfielders .30 .75
Brian Asselstine RC
Wayne Gross RC
Sam Mejias RC
Alvis Woods RC
480 Carl Yastrzemski 3.00 8.00
481 Roger Metzger .12 .30
482 Tony Solaita .12 .30
483 Richie Zisk .12 .30
484 Burt Hooton .30 .75
485 Roy White .30 .75
486 Ed Bane .12 .30
487 Rookie Pitchers .30 .75
Larry Anderson
Ed Glynn RC
Joe Henderson RC
Greg Terlecky RC
488 Rookie Outfielders 1.25 3.00
Jack Clark RC
Ruppert Jones RC
Lee Mazzilli RC
Dan Thomas RC
489 Rookie Pitchers .30 .75
Len Barker RC
Randy Lerch
Greg Minton RC
Mike Overy RC
490 Rookie Shortstops .30 .75
Billy Almon RC
Mickey Klutts RC
Tommy McMillan RC
Mark Wagner RC
491 Rookie Pitchers 1.25 3.00
Mike Dupree RC
Dennis Martinez RC
Craig Mitchell
Bob Sykes RC
492 Rookie Outfielders .30 .75
Tony Armas RC
Steve Kemp RC
Carlos Lopez RC
Gary Woods RC
493 Rookie Pitchers .30 .75
Mike Krukow RC
Jim Otten
Gary Wheelock RC
Mike Willis RC
494 Rookie Infielders .60 1.50
Juan Bernhardt RC
Mike Champion RC
Jim Gantner RC
Bump Wills RC
495 Al Hrabosky .30 .75
496 Gary Thomasson .12 .30
497 Clay Carroll .12 .30
498 Sal Bando .30 .75
499 Pablo Torrealba .12 .30
500 Dave Kingman .60 1.50
501 Jim Bibby .12 .30
502 Randy Hundley .12 .30
503 Bill Lee .12 .30
504 Los Angeles Dodgers CL .60 1.50
Tom Lasorda MG
505 Oscar Gamble .30 .75
506 Steve Grilli .12 .30
507 Mike Hegan .12 .30
508 Dave Pagan .12 .30
509 Cookie Rojas .30 .75
510 John Candelaria .12 .30
511 Bill Fahey .12 .30
512 Jack Billingham .12 .30
513 Jerry Terrell .12 .30
514 Cliff Johnson .12 .30
515 Chris Speier .12 .30
516 Bake McBride .30 .75
517 Pete Vuckovich RC .30 .75
518 Chicago Cubs CL .60 1.50
Herman Franks MG
519 Don Kirkwood .12 .30
520 Garry Maddox .12 .30
521 Bob Grich .30 .75
Only card in set with no date of birth
522 Enzo Hernandez .12 .30
523 Rollie Fingers 1.00 2.50
524 Rowland Office .12 .30
525 Dennis Eckersley 2.00 5.00
526 Larry Parrish .30 .75
527 Dan Meyer .30 .75
528 Bill Castro .12 .30
529 Jim Essian RC .12 .30
530 Rick Reuschel .30 .75
531 Lyman Bostock .30 .75
532 Jim Willoughby .12 .30
533 Mickey Stanley .12 .30
534 Paul Splittorff .12 .30
535 Cesar Geronimo .12 .30
536 Vic Albury .12 .30
537 Dave Roberts .12 .30
538 Frank Taveras .12 .30
539 Mike Wallace .12 .30
540 Bob Watson .30 .75
541 John Denny .30 .75
542 Frank Duffy .12 .30
543 Ron Blomberg .12 .30
544 Gary Ross .10 .30
545 Bob Boone .30 .75
546 Baltimore Orioles CL .60 1.50
Earl Weaver MG
547 Willie McCovey 1.50 4.00
548 Joel Youngblood RC .12 .30
549 Jerry Royster .12 .30
550 Randy Jones .12 .30
551 Bill North .12 .30
552 Pepe Mangual .12 .30
553 Jack Heidemann .12 .30
554 Bruce Kimm RC .12 .30
555 Dan Ford .12 .30
556 Doug Bird .12 .30
557 Jerry White .12 .30
558 Elias Sosa .12 .30
559 Alan Bannister RC .12 .30
560 Dave Concepcion .60 1.50
561 Pete LaCock .12 .30
562 Checklist 529-660 .60 1.50
563 Bruce Kison .12 .30
564 Alan Ashby .12 .30
565 Mickey Lolich .30 .75
566 Rick Miller .12 .30
567 Enos Cabell .12 .30
568 Carlos May .12 .30
569 Jim Lonborg .30 .75
570 Bobby Bonds .60 1.50
571 Darrell Evans .30 .75
572 Ross Grimsley .12 .30
573 Joe Ferguson .12 .30
574 Aurelio Rodriguez .12 .30
575 Dick Ruthven .12 .30
576 Fred Kendall .12 .30
577 Jerry Augustine RC .12 .30
578 Bob Randall RC .12 .30
579 Don Carrithers .12 .30
580 George Brett 6.00 15.00
581 Pedro Borbon .12 .30
582 Ed Kirkpatrick .12 .30
583 Paul Lindblad .12 .30
584 Ed Goodson .12 .30
585 Rick Burleson .30 .75
586 Steve Renko .12 .30
587 Rick Baldwin .12 .30
588 Dave Moates .12 .30
589 Mike Cosgrove .12 .30
590 Buddy Bell .30 .75
591 Chris Arnold .12 .30
592 Dan Briggs RC .12 .30
593 Dennis Blair .12 .30
594 Biff Pocoroba .12 .30
595 John Hiller .12 .30
596 Jerry Martin RC .12 .30
597 Mariners Leaders CL .60 1.50
Darrell Johnson MG
Don Bryant CO
Jim Busby CO
Vada Pinson CO
Wes Stock CO
598 Sparky Lyle .30 .75
599 Mike Tyson .12 .30
600 Jim Palmer 1.50 4.00
601 Mike Lum .12 .30
602 Andy Hassler .12 .30
603 Willie Davis .30 .75
604 Jim Slaton .12 .30
605 Felix Millan .12 .30
606 Steve Braun .12 .30
607 Larry Demery .12 .30
608 Roy Howell .12 .30
609 Jim Barr .12 .30
610 Jose Cardenal .30 .75
611 Dave Lemanczyk .12 .30
612 Barry Foote .12 .30
613 Reggie Cleveland .12 .30
614 Greg Gross .12 .30
615 Phil Niekro 1.00 2.50
616 Tommy Sandt RC .12 .30
617 Bobby Darwin .12 .30
618 Pat Dobson .12 .30
619 Johnny Oates .30 .75
620 Don Sutton 1.00 2.50
621 Detroit Tigers CL .60 1.50
Ralph Houk MG
622 Jim Wohlford .12 .30
623 Jack Kucek .12 .30
624 Hector Cruz .12 .30
625 Ken Holtzman .30 .75
626 Al Bumbry .30 .75
627 Bob Myrick RC .12 .30
628 Mario Guerrero .12 .30
629 Bobby Valentine .30 .75
630 Bert Blyleven .60 1.50
631 Brothers 2.50 6.00
George Brett
Ken Brett
632 Brothers .30 .75
Bob Forsch
Ken Forsch
633 Brothers .30 .75
Lee May
Carlos May
634 Brothers .30 .75
Paul Reuschel
Rick Reuschel UER
(Photos switched)
635 Robin Yount 3.00 8.00
636 Santo Alcala .12 .30
637 Alex Johnson .12 .30
638 Jim Kaat .60 1.50
639 Jerry Morales .12 .30
640 Carlton Fisk 2.00 5.00
641 Dan Larson RC .12 .30
642 Willie Crawford .12 .30
643 Mike Pazik .12 .30
644 Matt Alexander .12 .30
645 Jerry Reuss .30 .75
646 Andres Mora RC .12 .30
647 Montreal Expos CL .60 1.50
Dick Williams MG
648 Jim Spencer .12 .30
649 Dave Cash .12 .30
650 Nolan Ryan 12.50 30.00
651 Von Joshua .12 .30
652 Tom Walker .12 .30
653 Diego Segui .30 .75
654 Ron Pruitt RC .12 .30
655 Tony Perez 1.00 2.50
656 Ron Guidry .60 1.50
657 Mick Kelleher RC .12 .30
658 Marty Pattin .12 .30
659 Merv Rettenmund .12 .30
660 Willie Horton .60 1.50

1978 Topps

The cards in this 726-card set measure 2 1/2" by 3 1/2". As in previous years, this set was issued in many different ways: some of them include 14-card wax packs, 30-card supermarket packs which came 48 to a case and had an SRP of 20 cents and 39-card rack packs. The 1978 Topps set experienced an increase in number of cards from the previous five regular issue sets of 660. Card numbers 1 through 7 feature Record Breakers (RB) of the 1977 season. Other subsets within this set include League Leaders (201-208), Post-season cards (411-413), and Rookie Prospects (701-711). The key Rookie Cards in this set are the multi-player Rookie Card of Paul Molitor and Alan Trammell, Jack Morris, Eddie Murray, Lance Parrish, and Lou Whitaker. Many of the Molitor/Trammell cards are found with black printing smudges. The manager cards in the set feature a "then and now" format on the card front showing the manager as he looked during his playing days. While no scarcities exist, 66 of the cards are more abundant in supply, as they were "double printed." These 66 double-printed cards are noted in the checklist by DP. Team cards again feature a checklist of that team's players in the set on the back. Cards numbered 23 or lower, that feature Astros, Rangers, Tigers, or Yankees and do not follow the numbering checklisted below, are not hecessarily error cards. They are undoubtedly Burger King cards, separate sets with their own pricing and mass distribution. The Bump Wills card has been seen with either no black mark or a major black mark on the front of the card. We will continue to investigate this card and see whether or not it should be considered a variation.

COMPLETE SET (726) 100.00 200.00
COMMON CARD (1-726) .10 .25
COMMON CARD DP .08 .20
1 Lou Brock RB 1.25 3.00
2 Sparky Lyle RB .25 .60
3 Willie McCovey RB 1.00 2.50
4 Brooks Robinson RB .50 1.25
5 Pete Rose RB 3.00 8.00
6 Nolan Ryan RB 6.00 15.00
7 Reggie Jackson RB 1.50 4.00
8 Mike Sadek .10 .25
9 Doug DeCinces .25 .60
10 Phil Niekro 1.00 2.50
11 Rick Manning .10 .25
12 Don Aase .10 .25
13 Art Howe RC .25 .60
14 Lerrin LaGrow .10 .25
15 Tony Perez DP .50 1.25
16 Roy White .25 .60
17 Mike Krukow .10 .25
18 Bob Grich .25 .60
19 Darrell Porter .25 .60
20 Pete Rose DP 5.00 12.00
21 Steve Kemp .10 .25
22 Charlie Hough .25 .60
23 Bump Wills .10 .25
24 Don Money DP .08 .20
25 Jon Matlack .10 .25
26 Rich Hebner .25 .60
27 Geoff Zahn .10 .25
28 Ed Ott .10 .25
29 Bob Lacey RC .10 .25
30 George Hendrick .25 .60
31 Glenn Abbott .10 .25
32 Garry Templeton .25 .60
33 Dave Lemanczyk .10 .25
34 Willie McCovey 1.25 3.00
35 Sparky Lyle .25 .60
36 Eddie Murray RC 40.00 80.00
37 Rick Waits .10 .25
38 Willie Montanez .10 .25
39 Floyd Bannister RC .10 .25
40 Carl Yastrzemski 2.50 6.00
41 Burt Hooton .25 .60
42 Jorge Orta .10 .25
43 Bill Atkinson RC .10 .25
44 Toby Harrah .25 .60
45 Mark Fidrych 1.00 2.50
46 Al Cowens .25 .60
47 Jack Billingham .10 .25
48 Don Baylor .50 1.25
49 Ed Kranepool .25 .60
50 Rick Reuschel .25 .60
51 Charlie Moore DP .08 .20
52 Jim Lonborg .25 .60
53 Phil Garner DP .10 .25
54 Tom Johnson .10 .25
55 Mitchell Page RC .10 .25
56 Randy Jones .10 .25
57 Dan Meyer .10 .25
58 Bob Forsch .10 .25
59 Otto Velez .10 .25
60 Thurman Munson 1.50 4.00
61 Larvell Blanks .10 .25
62 Jim Barr .10 .25
63 Don Zimmer MG .25 .60
64 Gene Pentz .10 .25
65 Ken Singleton .25 .60
66 Chicago White Sox CL .50 1.25
67 Claudell Washington .25 .60
68 Steve Foucault DP .08 .20
69 Mike Vail .10 .25
70 Goose Gossage .50 1.25
71 Terry Humphrey .10 .25
72 Andre Dawson 1.50 4.00
73 Andy Hassler .10 .25
74 Checklist 1-121 .50 1.25
75 Dick Ruthven .10 .25
76 Steve Ontiveros .10 .25
77 Ed Kirkpatrick .10 .25
78 Pablo Torrealba .10 .25
79 Darrell Johnson MG DP .08 .20
80 Ken Griffey Sr. .50 1.25
81 Pete Redfern .10 .25
82 San Francisco Giants CL .50 1.25
83 Bob Montgomery .10 .25
84 Kent Tekulve .25 .60
85 Ron Fairly .25 .60
86 Dave Tomlin .10 .25
87 John Lowenstein .10 .25
88 Mike Phillips .10 .25
89 Ken Clay RC .10 .25
90 Larry Bowa .50 1.25
91 Oscar Zamora .10 .25
92 Adrian Devine .10 .25
93 Bobby Cox DP .08 .20
94 Chuck Scrivener .10 .25
95 Jamie Quirk .10 .25
96 Baltimore Orioles CL .50 1.25
97 Stan Bahnsen .10 .25
98 Jim Essian .25 .60
99 Willie Hernandez RC .50 1.25
100 George Brett 6.00 15.00
101 Sid Monge .10 .25
102 Matt Alexander .10 .25
103 Tom Murphy .10 .25
104 Lee Lacy .10 .25
105 Reggie Cleveland .10 .25
106 Bill Plummer .10 .25
107 Ed Halicki .10 .25
108 Von Joshua .10 .25
109 Joe Torre MG .25 .60
110 Richie Zisk .10 .25
111 Mike Tyson .10 .25
112 Houston Astros CL .50 1.25
113 Don Carrithers .10 .25
114 Paul Blair .25 .60
115 Gary Nolan .10 .25
116 Tucker Ashford RC .10 .25
117 John Montague .10 .25
118 Terry Harmon .10 .25
119 Dennis Martinez 1.00 2.50
120 Gary Carter 1.00 2.50
121 Alvis Woods .10 .25
122 Dennis Eckersley 1.25 3.00
123 Manny Trillo .10 .25
124 Dave Rozema RC .10 .25
125 George Scott .25 .60
126 Paul Moskau RC .10 .25
127 Chet Lemon .25 .60
128 Bill Russell .25 .60
129 Jim Colborn .10 .25
130 Jeff Burroughs .25 .60
131 Bert Blyleven .50 1.25
132 Enos Cabell .10 .25
133 Jerry Augustine .10 .25
134 Steve Henderson RC .10 .25
135 Ron Guidry DP .50 1.25
136 Ted Sizemore .10 .25
137 Craig Kusick .10 .25
138 Larry Demery .10 .25
139 Wayne Gross .10 .25
140 Rollie Fingers 1.00 2.50
141 Ruppert Jones .10 .25
142 John Montefusco .10 .25
143 Keith Hernandez .25 .60
144 Jesse Jefferson .10 .25
145 Rick Monday .25 .60
146 Doyle Alexander .25 .60
147 Lee Mazzilli .10 .25
148 Andre Thornton .25 .60
149 Dale Murray .10 .25
150 Bobby Bonds .50 1.25
151 Milt Wilcox .10 .25
152 Ivan DeJesus RC .10 .25
153 Steve Stone .25 .60
154 Cecil Cooper DP .10 .25
155 Butch Hobson .10 .25
156 Andy Messersmith .25 .60
157 Pete LaCock DP .08 .20
158 Joaquin Andujar .25 .60
159 Lou Piniella .25 .60
160 Jim Palmer 1.25 3.00
161 Bob Boone .50 1.25
162 Paul Thormodsgard RC .10 .25
163 Bill North .10 .25
164 Bob Owchinko RC .10 .25
165 Rennie Stennett .10 .25
166 Carlos Lopez .10 .25
167 Tim Foli .10 .25
168 Reggie Smith .25 .60
169 Jerry Johnson .10 .25
170 Lou Brock 1.25 3.00
171 Pat Zachry .10 .25
172 Mike Hargrove .25 .60
173 Robin Yount UER 2.00 5.00
(Played for Newark
in 1973, not 1971)
174 Wayne Garland .10 .25
175 Jerry Morales .10 .25
176 Milt May .10 .25
177 Gene Garber DP .10 .25
178 Dave Chalk .10 .25
179 Dick Tidrow .10 .25
180 Dave Concepcion .50 1.25
181 Ken Forsch .10 .25
182 Jim Spencer .10 .25
183 Doug Bird .10 .25
184 Checklist 122-242 .50 1.25
185 Ellis Valentine .10 .25
186 Bob Stanley DP RC .08 .20
187 Jerry Royster DP .08 .20
188 Al Bumbry .25 .60
189 Tom Lasorda MG DP 1.00 2.50
190 John Candelaria .25 .60
191 Rodney Scott RC .10 .25
192 San Diego Padres CL .50 1.25
193 Rich Chiles .10 .25
194 Derrel Thomas .10 .25
195 Larry Dierker .25 .60
196 Bob Bailor .10 .25
197 Nino Espinosa .10 .25
198 Ron Pruitt .10 .25
199 Craig Reynolds .10 .25
200 Reggie Jackson 3.00 8.00
201 Batting Leaders .50 1.25
Dave Parker
Rod Carew
202 Home Run Leaders DP .25 .60
George Foster
Jim Rice
203 RBI Leaders .25 .60
George Foster
Larry Hisle
204 Stolen Base Leaders DP .10 .25
Frank Taveras
Freddie Patek
205 Victory Leaders 1.00 2.50
Steve Carlton
Dave Goltz
Dennis Leonard
Jim Palmer
206 Strikeout Leaders DP 2.50 6.00
Phil Niekro
Nolan Ryan
207 ERA Leaders DP .25 .60
John Candelaria
Frank Tanana
208 Leading Firemen .50 1.25
Rollie Fingers
Bill Campbell
209 Dock Ellis .10 .25
210 Jose Cardenal .10 .25
211 Earl Weaver MG DP .50 1.25
212 Mike Caldwell .10 .25
213 Alan Bannister .10 .25
214 California Angels CL .50 1.25
215 Darrell Evans .25 .60
216 Mike Paxton RC .10 .25
217 Rod Gilbreath .10 .25
218 Marty Pattin .10 .25
219 Mike Cubbage .10 .25
220 Pedro Borbon .10 .25
221 Chris Speier .10 .25
222 Jerry Martin .10 .25
223 Bruce Kison .10 .25
224 Jerry Tabb RC .10 .25
225 Don Gullett DP .10 .25
226 Joe Ferguson .10 .25
227 Al Fitzmorris .10 .25
228 Manny Mota DP .10 .25
229 Leo Foster .10 .25
230 Al Hrabosky .25 .60
231 Wayne Nordhagen RC .10 .25
232 Mickey Stanley .10 .25
233 Dick Pole .10 .25
234 Herman Franks MG .10 .25
235 Tim McCarver .25 .60
236 Terry Whitfield .10 .25
237 Rich Dauer .10 .25
238 Juan Beniquez .10 .25
239 Dyar Miller .10 .25
240 Gene Tenace .25 .60
241 Pete Vuckovich .25 .60
242 Barry Bonnell DP RC .08 .20
243 Bob McClure .10 .25
244 Montreal Expos CL DP .25 .60
245 Rick Burleson .25 .60
246 Dan Driessen .10 .25
247 Larry Christenson .10 .25
248 Frank White DP .25 .60
249 Dave Goltz DP .08 .20
250 Graig Nettles DP .25 .60
251 Don Kirkwood .10 .25
252 Steve Swisher DP .08 .20
253 Jim Kern .10 .25
254 Dave Collins .25 .60
255 Jerry Reuss .25 .60
256 Joe Altobelli MG RC .10 .25
257 Hector Cruz .10 .25
258 John Hiller .10 .25
259 Los Angeles Dodgers CL .50 1.25
260 Bert Campaneris .25 .60
261 Tim Hosley .10 .25
262 Rudy May .10 .25
263 Danny Walton .10 .25
264 Jamie Easterly .10 .25
265 Sal Bando DP .25 .60
266 Bob Shirley RC .10 .25
267 Doug Ault .10 .25
268 Gil Flores RC .10 .25
269 Wayne Twitchell .10 .25
270 Carlton Fisk 1.50 4.00
271 Randy Lerch DP .08 .20
272 Royle Stillman .10 .25
273 Fred Norman .10 .25
274 Freddie Patek .25 .60
275 Dan Ford .10 .25
276 Bill Bonham DP .08 .20
277 Bruce Boisclair .10 .25
278 Enrique Romo RC .10 .25
279 Bill Virdon MG .10 .25
280 Buddy Bell .25 .60
281 Eric Rasmussen DP .08 .20
282 New York Yankees CL 1.00 2.50
283 Omar Moreno .10 .25
284 Randy Moffitt .10 .25
285 Steve Yeager DP .25 .60
286 Ben Oglivie .25 .60
287 Kiko Garcia .10 .25
288 Dave Hamilton .10 .25
289 Checklist 243-363 .50 1.25
290 Willie Horton .25 .60
291 Gary Ross .10 .25
292 Gene Richards .10 .25
293 Mike Willis .10 .25
294 Larry Parrish .25 .60
295 Bill Lee .10 .25
296 Biff Pocoroba .10 .25
297 Warren Brusstar DP RC .08 .20
298 Tony Armas .25 .60
299 Whitey Herzog MG .25 .60
300 Joe Morgan 1.25 3.00
301 Buddy Schultz RC .10 .25
302 Chicago Cubs CL .50 1.25
303 Sam Hinds RC .10 .25
304 John Milner .10 .25
305 Rico Carty .25 .60
306 Joe Niekro .25 .60
307 Glenn Borgmann .10 .25
308 Jim Rooker .10 .25
309 Cliff Johnson .10 .25
310 Don Sutton 1.00 2.50
311 Jose Baez DP RC .08 .20
312 Greg Minton .10 .25
313 Andy Etchebarren .10 .25
314 Paul Lindblad .10 .25

315 Mark Belanger .25 .60
316 Henry Cruz DP .08 .20
317 Dave Johnson .10 .25
318 Tom Griffin .10 .25
319 Alan Ashby .10 .25
320 Fred Lynn .25 .60
321 Santo Alcala .10 .25
322 Tom Paciorek .25 .60
323 Jim Fregosi DP .10 .25
324 Vern Rapp MG RC .10 .25
325 Bruce Sutter 1.25 3.00
326 Mike Lum DP .08 .20
327 Rick Langford DP RC .08 .20
328 Milwaukee Brewers CL .50 1.25
329 John Verhoeven .10 .25
330 Bob Watson .25 .60
331 Mark Littell .10 .25
332 Duane Kuiper .10 .25
333 Jim Todd .10 .25
334 John Stearns .10 .25
335 Bucky Dent .25 .60
336 Steve Busby .10 .25
337 Tom Grieve .25 .60
338 Dave Heaverlo .10 .25
339 Mario Guerrero .10 .25
340 Bake McBride .25 .60
341 Mike Flanagan .25 .60
342 Aurelio Rodriguez .10 .25
343 John Wathan DP .08 .20
344 Sam Ewing RC .10 .25
345 Luis Tiant .25 .60
346 Larry Biittner .10 .25
347 Terry Forster .10 .25
348 Del Unser .10 .25
349 Rick Camp DP .08 .20
350 Steve Garvey 1.00 2.50
351 Jeff Torborg .25 .60
352 Tony Scott RC .10 .25
353 Doug Bair RC .10 .25
354 Cesar Geronimo .10 .25
355 Bill Travers .10 .25
356 New York Mets CL .50 1.25
357 Tom Poquette .10 .25
358 Mark Lemongello .10 .25
359 Marc Hill .10 .25
360 Mike Schmidt 4.00 10.00
361 Chris Knapp .10 .25
362 Dave May .10 .25
363 Bob Randall .10 .25
364 Jerry Turner .10 .25
365 Ed Figueroa .10 .25
366 Larry Milbourne DP .08 .20
367 Rick Dempsey .25 .60
368 Balor Moore .10 .25
369 Tim Nordbrook .10 .25
370 Rusty Staub .50 1.25
371 Ray Burris .10 .25
372 Brian Asselstine .10 .25
373 Jim Willoughby .10 .25
374 Jose Morales .10 .25
375 Tommy John .50 1.25
376 Jim Wohlford .10 .25
377 Manny Sarmiento .10 .25
378 Bobby Winkles MG .10 .25
379 Skip Lockwood .10 .25
380 Ted Simmons .25 .60
381 Philadelphia Phillies CL .50 1.25
382 Joe Lahoud .10 .25
383 Mario Mendoza .10 .25
384 Jack Clark .50 1.25
385 Tito Fuentes .10 .25
386 Bob Gorinski RC .10 .25
387 Ken Holtzman .25 .60
388 Bill Fahey DP .08 .20
389 Julio Gonzalez RC .10 .25
390 Oscar Gamble .25 .60
391 Larry Haney .10 .25
392 Billy Almon .10 .25
393 Tippy Martinez .25 .60
394 Roy Howell DP .08 .20
395 Jim Hughes .10 .25
396 Bob Stinson DP .08 .20
397 Greg Gross .10 .25
398 Don Hood .10 .25
399 Pete Mackanin .10 .25
400 Nolan Ryan 10.00 25.00
401 Sparky Anderson MG .25 .60
402 Dave Campbell .10 .25
403 Bud Harrelson .25 .60
404 Detroit Tigers CL .50 1.25
405 Rawly Eastwick .10 .25
406 Mike Jorgensen .10 .25
407 Odell Jones RC .10 .25
408 Joe Zdeb RC .10 .25
409 Ron Schueler .10 .25
410 Bill Madlock .25 .60
411 AL Championships .25 .60
Mickey Rivers
412 NL Championships .25 .60
Davey Lopes
413 World Series 1.50 4.00
Reggie Jackson
414 Darold Knowles DP .08 .20
415 Ray Fosse .10 .25
416 Jack Brohamer .10 .25
417 Mike Garman DP .08 .20
418 Tony Muser .10 .25
419 Jerry Garvin RC .10 .25
420 Greg Luzinski .50 1.25
421 Junior Moore RC .10 .25
422 Steve Braun .10 .25
423 Dave Rosello .10 .25
424 Boston Red Sox CL .50 1.25
425 Steve Rogers DP .10 .25
426 Fred Kendall .10 .25
427 Mario Soto RC .25 .60
428 Joel Youngblood .10 .25
429 Mike Barlow RC .10 .25
430 Al Oliver .25 .60
431 Butch Metzger .10 .25
432 Terry Bulling RC .10 .25
433 Fernando Gonzalez .10 .25
434 Mike Norris .10 .25
435 Checklist 364-484 .50 1.25
436 Vic Harris DP .08 .20
437 Bo McLaughlin .10 .25
438 John Ellis .10 .25
439 Ken Kravec .10 .25
440 Dave Lopes .25 .60
441 Larry Gura .10 .25
442 Elliott Maddox .10 .25
443 Darrel Chaney .10 .25
444 Roy Hartsfield MG .10 .25
445 Mike Ivie .10 .25
446 Tug McGraw .25 .60
447 Leroy Stanton .10 .25
448 Bill Castro .10 .25
449 Tim Blackwell DP RC .08 .20
450 Tom Seaver 2.50 6.00
451 Minnesota Twins CL .50 1.25
452 Jerry Mumphrey .10 .25
453 Doug Flynn .10 .25
454 Dave LaRoche .10 .25
455 Bill Robinson .25 .60
456 Vern Ruhle .10 .25
457 Bob Bailey .10 .25
458 Jeff Newman .10 .25
459 Charlie Spikes .10 .25
460 Jim Hunter 1.00 2.50
461 Rob Andrews DP .08 .20
462 Rogelio Moret .10 .25
463 Kevin Bell .10 .25
464 Jerry Grote .10 .25
465 Hal McRae .25 .60
466 Dennis Blair .10 .25
467 Alvin Dark MG .25 .60
468 Warren Cromartie RC .25 .60
469 Rick Cerone .25 .60
470 J.R. Richard .25 .60
471 Roy Smalley .25 .60
472 Ron Reed .10 .25
473 Bill Buckner .25 .60
474 Jim Slaton .10 .25
475 Gary Matthews .25 .60
476 Bill Stein .10 .25
477 Doug Capilla RC .10 .25
478 Jerry Remy .10 .25
479 St. Louis Cardinals CL .50 1.25
480 Ron LeFlore .25 .60
481 Jackson Todd RC .10 .25
482 Rick Miller .10 .25
483 Ken Macha RC .10 .25
484 Jim Norris RC .10 .25
485 Chris Chambliss .25 .60
486 John Curtis .10 .25
487 Jim Tyrone .10 .25
488 Dan Spillner .10 .25
489 Rudy Meoli .10 .25
490 Amos Otis .25 .60
491 Scott McGregor .25 .60
492 Jim Sundberg .25 .60
493 Steve Renko .10 .25
494 Chuck Tanner MG .25 .60
495 Dave Cash .10 .25
496 Jim Clancy DP RC .08 .20
497 Glenn Adams .10 .25
498 Joe Sambito .10 .25
499 Seattle Mariners CL .50 1.25
500 George Foster .50 1.25
501 Dave Roberts .10 .25
502 Pat Rockett RC .10 .25
503 Ike Hampton RC .10 .25
504 Roger Freed .10 .25
505 Felix Millan .10 .25
506 Ron Blomberg .10 .25
507 Willie Crawford .10 .25
508 Johnny Oates .25 .60
509 Brent Strom .10 .25
510 Willie Stargell 1.00 2.50
511 Frank Duffy .10 .25
512 Larry Herndon .10 .25
513 Barry Foote .10 .25
514 Rob Sperring .10 .25
515 Tim Corcoran RC .10 .25
516 Gary Beare RC .10 .25
517 Andres Mora .10 .25
518 Tommy Boggs DP .08 .20
519 Brian Downing .25 .60
520 Larry Hisle .10 .25
521 Steve Staggs RC .10 .25
522 Dick Williams MG .25 .60
523 Donnie Moore RC .10 .25
524 Bernie Carbo .10 .25
525 Jerry Terrell .10 .25
526 Cincinnati Reds CL .50 1.25
527 Vic Correll .10 .25
528 Rob Picciolo RC .10 .25
529 Paul Hartzell .10 .25
530 Dave Winfield 1.50 4.00
531 Tom Underwood .10 .25
532 Skip Jutze .10 .25
533 Sandy Alomar .25 .60
534 Wilbur Howard .10 .25
535 Checklist 485-605 .50 1.25
536 Roric Harrison .10 .25
537 Bruce Bochte .10 .25
538 Johnny LeMaster .10 .25
539 Vic Davalillo DP .08 .20
540 Steve Carlton 1.50 4.00
541 Larry Cox .10 .25
542 Tim Johnson .10 .25
543 Larry Harlow DP RC .08 .20
544 Len Randle DP .08 .20
545 Bill Campbell .10 .25
546 Ted Martinez .10 .25
547 John Scott .10 .25
548 Billy Hunter MG DP .08 .20
549 Joe Kerrigan .10 .25
550 John Mayberry .25 .60
551 Atlanta Braves CL .50 1.25
552 Francisco Barrios .10 .25
553 Terry Puhl RC .25 .60
554 Joe Coleman .10 .25
555 Butch Wynegar .10 .25
556 Ed Armbrister .10 .25
557 Tony Solaita .10 .25
558 Paul Mitchell .10 .25
559 Phil Mankowski .10 .25
560 Dave Parker .50 1.25
561 Charlie Williams .10 .25
562 Glenn Burke RC .10 .25
563 Dave Rader .10 .25
564 Mick Kelleher .10 .25
565 Jerry Koosman .25 .60
566 Merv Rettenmund .10 .25
567 Dick Drago .10 .25
568 Tom Hutton .10 .25
569 Lary Sorensen RC .10 .25
570 Dave Kingman .50 1.25
571 Buck Martinez .10 .25
572 Rick Wise .10 .25
573 Luis Gomez .10 .25
574 Bob Lemon MG .50 1.25
575 Pat Dobson .10 .25
576 Sam Mejias .10 .25
577 Oakland Athletics CL .50 1.25
578 Buzz Capra .10 .25
579 Rance Mulliniks RC .10 .25
580 Rod Carew 1.50 4.00
581 Lynn McGlothen .10 .25
582 Fran Healy .10 .25
583 George Medich .10 .25
584 John Hale .10 .25
585 Woodie Fryman DP .08 .20
586 Ed Goodson .10 .25
587 John Urrea RC .10 .25
588 Jim Mason .10 .25
589 Bob Knepper RC .10 .25
590 Bobby Murcer .25 .60
591 George Zeber RC .10 .25
592 Bob Apodaca .10 .25
593 Dave Skaggs RC .10 .25
594 Dave Freisleben .10 .25
595 Sixto Lezcano .10 .25
596 Gary Wheelock .10 .25
597 Steve Dillard .10 .25
598 Eddie Solomon .10 .25
599 Gary Woods .10 .25
600 Frank Tanana .25 .60
601 Gene Mauch MG .25 .60
602 Eric Soderholm .10 .25
603 Will McEnaney .10 .25
604 Earl Williams .10 .25
605 Rick Rhoden .25 .60
606 Pittsburgh Pirates CL .50 1.25
607 Fernando Arroyo .10 .25
608 Johnny Grubb .10 .25
609 John Denny .10 .25
610 Garry Maddox .25 .60
611 Pat Scanlon RC .10 .25
612 Ken Henderson .10 .25
613 Marty Perez .10 .25
614 Joe Wallis .10 .25
615 Clay Carroll .10 .25
616 Pat Kelly .10 .25
617 Joe Nolan RC .10 .25
618 Tommy Helms .10 .25
619 Thad Bosley DP RC .08 .20
620 Willie Randolph .50 1.25
621 Craig Swan DP .08 .20
622 Champ Summers .10 .25
623 Eduardo Rodriguez .10 .25
624 Gary Alexander DP .08 .20
625 Jose Cruz .25 .60
626 Toronto Blue Jays CL DP .50 1.25
627 David Johnson .10 .25
628 Ralph Garr .25 .60
629 Don Stanhouse .10 .25
630 Ron Cey .50 1.25
631 Danny Ozark MG .10 .25
632 Rowland Office .10 .25
633 Tom Veryzer .10 .25
634 Len Barker .10 .25
635 Joe Rudi .25 .60
636 Jim Bibby .10 .25
637 Duffy Dyer .10 .25
638 Paul Splittorff .10 .25
639 Gene Clines .10 .25
640 Lee May DP .10 .25
641 Doug Rau .10 .25
642 Denny Doyle .10 .25
643 Tom House .10 .25
644 Jim Dwyer .10 .25
645 Mike Torrez .25 .60
646 Rick Auerbach DP .08 .20
647 Steve Dunning .10 .25
648 Gary Thomasson .10 .25
649 Moose Haas RC .10 .25
650 Cesar Cedeno .25 .60
651 Doug Rader .10 .25
652 Checklist 606-726 .50 1.25
653 Ron Hodges DP .08 .20
654 Pepe Frias .10 .25
655 Lyman Bostock .25 .60
656 Dave Garcia MG RC .10 .25
657 Bombo Rivera .10 .25
658 Manny Sanguillen .25 .60
659 Texas Rangers CL .50 1.25
660 Jason Thompson .25 .60
661 Grant Jackson .10 .25
662 Paul Dade RC .10 .25
663 Paul Reuschel .10 .25
664 Fred Stanley .10 .25
665 Dennis Leonard .25 .60
666 Billy Smith RC .10 .25
667 Jeff Byrd RC .10 .25
668 Dusty Baker .50 1.25
669 Pete Falcone .10 .25
670 Jim Rice .50 1.25
671 Gary Lavelle .10 .25
672 Don Kessinger .25 .60
673 Steve Brye .10 .25
674 Ray Knight RC 1.00 2.50
675 Jay Johnstone .25 .60
676 Bob Myrick .10 .25
677 Ed Herrmann .10 .25
678 Tom Burgmeier .10 .25
679 Wayne Garrett .10 .25
680 Vida Blue .25 .60
681 Bob Bailor .10 .25
682 Ken Brett .10 .25
683 Mike Champion .10 .25
684 Ralph Houk MG .25 .60
685 Frank Taveras .10 .25
686 Gaylord Perry 1.00 2.50
687 Julio Cruz RC .10 .25
688 George Mitterwald .10 .25
689 Cleveland Indians CL .50 1.25
690 Mickey Rivers .25 .60
691 Ross Grimsley .10 .25
692 Ken Reitz .10 .25
693 Lamar Johnson .10 .25
694 Elias Sosa .10 .25
695 Dwight Evans .50 1.25
696 Steve Mingori .10 .25
697 Roger Metzger .10 .25
698 Juan Bernhardt .10 .25
699 Jackie Brown .10 .25
700 Johnny Bench 3.00 8.00
701 Rookie Pitchers .25 .60
Tom Hume RC
Larry Landreth RC
Steve McCatty RC
Bruce Taylor
702 Rookie Catchers .25 .60
Bill Nahorodny RC
Kevin Pasley
Rick Sweet RC
Don Werner RC
703 Rookie Pitchers 2.00 5.00
Larry Andersen RC
Tim Jones RC
Mickey Mahler RC
Jack Morris RC DP
704 Rookie 2nd Basemen 3.00 8.00
Garth Iorg RC
Dave Oliver RC
Sam Perlozzo RC
Lou Whitaker RC
705 Rookie Outfielders .50 1.25
Dave Bergman RC
Miguel Dilone RC
Clint Hurdle RC
Willie Norwood RC
706 Rookie 1st Basemen .25 .60
Wayne Cage RC
Ted Cox RC
Pat Putnam RC
Dave Revering RC
707 Rookie Shortstops 20.00 50.00
Mickey Klutts
Paul Molitor RC
Alan Trammell RC
U.L. Washington RC
708 Rookie Catchers 1.50 4.00
Bo Diaz RC
Dale Murphy
Lance Parrish RC
Ernie Whitt RC
709 Rookie Pitchers .25 .60
Steve Burke RC
Matt Keough RC
Lance Rautzhan RC
Dan Schatzeder RC
710 Rookie Outfielders .50 1.25
Dell Alston RC
Rick Bosetti RC
Mike Easler RC
Keith Smith RC
711 Rookie Pitchers .10 .25
Cardell Campe RCr
Dennis Lamp RC
Craig Mitchell
Roy Thomas RC DP
712 Bobby Valentine .25 .60
713 Bob Davis .10 .25
714 Mike Anderson .10 .25
715 Jim Kaat .50 1.25
716 Clarence Gaston .25 .60
717 Nelson Briles .10 .25
718 Ron Jackson .10 .25
719 Randy Elliott RC .10 .25
720 Fergie Jenkins 1.00 2.50
721 Billy Martin MG .50 1.25
722 Pete Broberg .10 .25
723 John Wockenfuss .10 .25
724 Kansas City Royals CL .50 1.25
725 Kurt Bevacqua .10 .25
726 Wilbur Wood .50 1.25

1979 Topps

The cards in this 726-card set measure 2 1/2" by 3 1/2". Topps continued with the same number of cards as in 1978. As in previous years, this set was released in many different formats, among them are 12-card wax packs and 39-card rack packs which cost 59 cents upon release. Those rack packs came 24 packs to a box and three boxes to a case. Various series spotlight League Leaders (1-8), "Season and Career Record Holders" (411-418), "Record Breakers" (201-206), and one "Prospects" card for each team (701-726). Team cards feature a checklist on back of that team's players in the set and a small picture of the manager on the front of the card. There are 66 cards that were double printed and these are noted in the checklist by the abbreviation DP. Bump Wills (369) was initially depicted in a Ranger uniform but with a Blue Jays affiliation; later printings correctly labeled him with Texas. The set price includes either Wills card. The key Rookie Cards in this set are Pedro Guerrero, Carney Lansford, Ozzie Smith, Bob Welch and Willie Wilson. Cards numbered 23 or lower, which feature Phillies or Yankees and do not follow the numbering checklisted below, are not necessarily error cards. They are undoubtedly Burger King cards, separate sets for each team with their own pricing and mass distribution.

COMPLETE SET (726) 100.00 200.00
COMMON CARD (1-726) .10 .25
COMMON CARD DP .08 .20
1 Batting Leaders 1.00 2.50
Rod Carew
Dave Parker
2 Home Run Leaders .60 1.50
Jim Rice
George Foster
3 RBI Leaders .60 1.50
Jim Rice
George Foster
4 Stolen Base Leaders .30 .75
Ron LeFlore
Omar Moreno
5 Victory Leaders .30 .75
Ron Guidry
Gaylord Perry
6 Strikeout Leaders 2.00 5.00
Nolan Ryan
J.R. Richard
7 ERA Leaders .30 .75
Ron Guidry
Craig Swan
8 Leading Firemen .60 1.50
Rich Gossage
Rollie Fingers
9 Dave Campbell .10 .25
10 Lee May .30 .75
11 Marc Hill .10 .25
12 Dick Drago .10 .25
13 Paul Dade .10 .25
14 Rafael Landestoy RC .10 .25
15 Ross Grimsley .10 .25
16 Fred Stanley .10 .25
17 Donnie Moore .10 .25
18 Tony Solaita .10 .25
19 Larry Gura DP .08 .20
20 Joe Morgan DP 1.00 2.50
21 Kevin Kobel .10 .25
22 Mike Jorgensen .10 .25
23 Terry Forster .10 .25
24 Paul Molitor 4.00 10.00
25 Steve Carlton 1.25 3.00
26 Jamie Quirk .10 .25
27 Dave Goltz .10 .25
28 Steve Brye .10 .25
29 Rick Langford .10 .25
30 Dave Winfield 1.50 4.00
31 Tom House DP .08 .20
32 Jerry Mumphrey .10 .25
33 Dave Rozema .10 .25
34 Rob Andrews .10 .25
35 Ed Figueroa .10 .25
36 Alan Ashby .10 .25
37 Joe Kerrigan DP .08 .20
38 Bernie Carbo .10 .25
39 Dale Murphy 1.25 3.00
40 Dennis Eckersley 1.00 2.50
41 Minnesota Twins CL .60 1.50
Gene Mauch MG
42 Ron Blomberg .10 .25
43 Wayne Twitchell .10 .25
44 Kurt Bevacqua .10 .25
45 Al Hrabosky .30 .75
46 Ron Hodges .10 .25
47 Fred Norman .10 .25
48 Merv Rettenmund .10 .25
49 Vern Ruhle .10 .25
50 Steve Garvey DP .60 1.50
51 Ray Fosse DP .08 .20
52 Randy Lerch .10 .25
53 Mick Kelleher .10 .25
54 Dell Alston DP .08 .20
55 Willie Stargell 1.00 2.50
56 John Hale .10 .25
57 Eric Rasmussen .10 .25
58 Bob Randall DP .08 .20
59 John Denny DP .10 .25
60 Mickey Rivers .30 .75
61 Bo Diaz .10 .25
62 Randy Moffitt .10 .25
63 Jack Brohamer .10 .25
64 Tom Underwood .10 .25
65 Mark Belanger .30 .75
66 Detroit Tigers CL .60 1.50
Les Moss MG
67 Jim Mason DP .08 .20
68 Joe Niekro DP .10 .25
69 Elliott Maddox .10 .25
70 John Candelaria .30 .75
71 Brian Downing .30 .75
72 Steve Mingori .10 .25
73 Ken Henderson .10 .25
74 Shane Rawley RC .10 .25
75 Steve Yeager .30 .75
76 Warren Cromartie .30 .75
77 Dan Briggs DP .08 .20
78 Elias Sosa .10 .25
79 Ted Cox .10 .25
80 Jason Thompson .30 .75
81 Roger Erickson RC .10 .25
82 New York Mets CL .60 1.50
Joe Torre MG
83 Fred Kendall .10 .25
84 Greg Minton .10 .25
85 Gary Matthews .30 .75
86 Rodney Scott .10 .25
87 Pete Falcone .10 .25
88 Bob Molinaro RC .10 .25
89 Dick Tidrow .10 .25
90 Bob Boone .60 1.50
91 Terry Crowley .10 .25
92 Jim Bibby .10 .25
93 Phil Mankowski .10 .25
94 Len Barker .10 .25
95 Robin Yount 2.00 5.00
96 Cleveland Indians CL .60 1.50
Jeff Torborg
97 Sam Mejias .10 .25
98 Ray Burris .10 .25
99 John Wathan .30 .75
100 Tom Seaver DP 1.50 4.00
101 Roy Howell .10 .25
102 Mike Anderson .10 .25
103 Jim Todd .10 .25
104 Johnny Oates DP .10 .25
105 Rick Camp DP .08 .20
106 Frank Duffy .10 .25
107 Jesus Alou DP .08 .20
108 Eduardo Rodriguez .10 .25
109 Joel Youngblood .10 .25
110 Vida Blue .30 .75
111 Roger Freed .10 .25
112 Phillies Team .60 1.50
Danny Ozark MG
113 Pete Redfern .10 .25
114 Cliff Johnson .10 .25
115 Nolan Ryan 8.00 20.00
116 Ozzie Smith RC 30.00 60.00
117 Grant Jackson .10 .25
118 Bud Harrelson .30 .75
119 Don Stanhouse .10 .25
120 Jim Sundberg .30 .75
121 Checklist 1-121 DP .30 .75
122 Mike Paxton .10 .25
123 Lou Whitaker 1.00 2.50
124 Dan Schatzeder .10 .25
125 Rick Burleson .10 .25
126 Doug Bair .10 .25
127 Thad Bosley .10 .25
128 Ted Martinez .10 .25
129 Marty Pattin DP .08 .20
130 Bob Watson DP .10 .25
131 Jim Clancy .10 .25
132 Rowland Office .10 .25
133 Bill Castro .10 .25
134 Alan Bannister .10 .25
135 Bobby Murcer .30 .75
136 Jim Kaat .30 .75
137 Larry Wolfe DP RC .08 .20
138 Mark Lee RC .10 .25
139 Luis Pujols RC .10 .25
140 Don Gullett .30 .75
141 Tom Paciorek .30 .75
142 Charlie Williams .10 .25
143 Tony Scott .10 .25
144 Sandy Alomar .10 .25
145 Rick Rhoden .10 .25
146 Duane Kuiper .10 .25
147 Dave Hamilton .10 .25
148 Bruce Boisclair .10 .25
149 Manny Sarmiento .10 .25
150 Wayne Cage .10 .25
151 John Hiller .10 .25
152 Rick Cerone .10 .25
153 Dennis Lamp .10 .25
154 Jim Gantner DP .10 .25
155 Dwight Evans .60 1.50
156 Buddy Solomon RC .10 .25
157 U.L. Washington UER .10 .25
(Sic, bats left,
should be right)
158 Joe Sambito .10 .25
159 Roy White .30 .75
160 Mike Flanagan .60 1.50
161 Barry Foote .10 .25
162 Tom Johnson .10 .25
163 Glenn Burke .10 .25
164 Mickey Lolich .30 .75
165 Frank Taveras .10 .25
166 Leon Roberts .10 .25
167 Roger Metzger DP .08 .20
168 Dave Freisleben .10 .25
169 Bill Nahorodny .10 .25
170 Don Sutton 1.00 2.50
171 Gene Clines .10 .25
172 Mike Bruhert RC .10 .25
173 John Lowenstein .10 .25
174 Rick Auerbach .10 .25
175 George Hendrick .60 1.50
176 Aurelio Rodriguez .10 .25
177 Ron Reed .10 .25
178 Alvis Woods .10 .25
179 Jim Beattie DP RC .08 .20
180 Larry Hisle .10 .25
181 Mike Garman .10 .25
182 Tim Johnson .10 .25
183 Paul Splittorff .10 .25
184 Darrel Chaney .10 .25
185 Mike Torrez .30 .75
186 Eric Soderholm .10 .25
187 Mark Lemongello .10 .25
188 Pat Kelly .10 .25
189 Eddie Whitson RC .10 .25
190 Ron Cey .30 .75
191 Mike Norris .10 .25
192 St. Louis Cardinals CL .60 1.50
Ken Boyer MG
193 Glenn Adams .10 .25
194 Randy Jones .10 .25
195 Bill Madlock .30 .75
196 Steve Kemp DP .10 .25
197 Bob Apodaca .10 .25
198 Johnny Grubb .10 .25
199 Larry Milbourne .10 .25
200 Johnny Bench DP 2.00 5.00
201 Mike Edwards RB .10 .25
202 Ron Guidry RB .30 .75
203 J.R. Richard RB .10 .25
204 Pete Rose RB 2.00 5.00
205 John Stearns RB .10 .25
206 Sammy Stewart RB .10 .25
207 Dave Lemanczyk .10 .25
208 Clarence Gaston .10 .25
209 Reggie Cleveland .10 .25
210 Larry Bowa .30 .75
211 Denny Martinez 1.00 2.50
212 Carney Lansford RC .60 1.50
213 Bill Travers .10 .25
214 Boston Red Sox CL .60 1.50
Don Zimmer MG
215 Willie McCovey 1.00 2.50
216 Wilbur Wood .10 .25
217 Steve Dillard .10 .25
218 Dennis Leonard .30 .75
219 Roy Smalley .30 .75
220 Cesar Geronimo .10 .25
221 Jesse Jefferson .10 .25
222 Bob Beall RC .10 .25
223 Kent Tekulve .30 .75
224 Dave Revering .10 .25
225 Goose Gossage .60 1.50
226 Ron Pruitt .10 .25
227 Steve Stone .30 .75
228 Vic Davalillo .10 .25
229 Doug Flynn .10 .25
230 Bob Forsch .10 .25
231 John Wockenfuss .10 .25
232 Jimmy Sexton RC .10 .25
233 Paul Mitchell .10 .25
234 Toby Harrah .30 .75
235 Steve Rogers .10 .25
236 Jim Dwyer .10 .25
237 Billy Smith .10 .25
238 Balor Moore .10 .25
239 Willie Horton .30 .75
240 Rick Reuschel .30 .75
241 Checklist 122-242 DP .30 .75
242 Pablo Torrealba .10 .25
243 Buck Martinez DP .08 .20
244 Pittsburgh Pirates CL .60 1.50
Chuck Tanner MG
245 Jeff Burroughs .30 .75
246 Darrell Jackson RC .10 .25
247 Tucker Ashford DP .08 .20
248 Pete LaCock .10 .25
249 Paul Thormodsgard .10 .25
250 Willie Randolph .30 .75
251 Jack Morris 1.00 2.50
252 Bob Stinson .10 .25
253 Rick Wise .10 .25
254 Luis Gomez .10 .25
255 Tommy John .60 1.50
256 Mike Sadek .10 .25
257 Adrian Devine .10 .25
258 Mike Phillips .10 .25
259 Cincinnati Reds CL .60 1.50
Sparky Anderson MG
260 Richie Zisk .10 .25
261 Mario Guerrero .10 .25
262 Nelson Briles .10 .25
263 Oscar Gamble .30 .75
264 Don Robinson RC .10 .25
265 Don Money .10 .25
266 Jim Willoughby .10 .25
267 Joe Rudi .30 .75
268 Julio Gonzalez .10 .25
269 Woodie Fryman .10 .25
270 Butch Hobson .30 .75
271 Rawly Eastwick .10 .25
272 Tim Corcoran .10 .25
273 Jerry Terrell .10 .25
274 Willie Norwood .10 .25
275 Junior Moore .10 .25
276 Jim Colborn .10 .25
277 Tom Grieve .30 .75
278 Andy Messersmith .30 .75
279 Jerry Grote DP .08 .20
280 Andre Thornton .30 .75
281 Vic Correll DP .08 .20
282 Toronto Blue Jays CL .30 .75
Roy Hartsfield MG
283 Ken Kravec .10 .25
284 Johnnie LeMaster .10 .25
285 Bobby Bonds .60 1.50
286 Duffy Dyer .10 .25
287 Andres Mora .10 .25
288 Milt Wilcox .10 .25
289 Jose Cruz .60 1.50
290 Dave Lopes .30 .75
291 Tom Griffin .10 .25
292 Don Reynolds RC .10 .25
293 Jerry Garvin .10 .25
294 Pepe Frias .10 .25
295 Mitchell Page .10 .25
296 Preston Hanna RC .10 .25
297 Ted Sizemore .10 .25
298 Rich Gale RC .10 .25
299 Steve Ontiveros .10 .25
300 Rod Carew 1.25 3.00
301 Tom Hume .10 .25
302 Atlanta Braves CL .60 1.50
Bobby Cox MG
303 Lary Sorensen DP .08 .20
304 Steve Swisher .10 .25
305 Willie Montanez .10 .25
306 Floyd Bannister .10 .25
307 Larvell Blanks .10 .25

308 Bert Blyleven	.60	1.50
309 Ralph Garr	.30	.75
310 Thurman Munson	1.25	3.00
311 Gary Lavelle	.10	.25
312 Bob Robertson	.10	.25
313 Dyar Miller	.10	.25
314 Larry Harlow	.10	.25
315 Jon Matlack	.10	.25
316 Milt May	.10	.25
317 Jose Cardenal	.30	.75
318 Bob Welch RC	1.00	2.50
319 Wayne Garrett	.10	.25
320 Carl Yastrzemski	2.00	5.00
321 Gaylord Perry	1.00	2.50
322 Danny Goodwin RC	.10	.25
323 Lynn McGlothen	.10	.25
324 Mike Tyson	.10	.25
325 Cecil Cooper	.30	.75
326 Pedro Borbon	.10	.25
327 Art Howe DP	.10	.25
328 Oakland Athletics CL	.60	1.50
Jack McKeon MG		
329 Joe Coleman	.10	.25
330 George Brett	4.00	10.00
331 Mickey Mahler	.10	.25
332 Gary Alexander	.10	.25
333 Chet Lemon	.30	.75
334 Craig Swan	.10	.25
335 Chris Chambliss	.30	.75
336 Bobby Thompson RC	.10	.25
337 John Montague	.10	.25
338 Vic Harris	.10	.25
339 Ron Jackson	.10	.25
340 Jim Palmer	1.00	2.50
341 Willie Upshaw RC	.30	.75
342 Dave Roberts	.10	.25
343 Ed Glynn	.10	.25
344 Jerry Royster	.10	.25
345 Tug McGraw	.30	.75
346 Bill Buckner	.30	.75
347 Doug Rau	.10	.25
348 Andre Dawson	1.25	3.00
349 Jim Wright RC	.10	.25
350 Garry Templeton	.30	.75
351 Wayne Nordhagen DP	.08	.20
352 Steve Renko	.10	.25
353 Checklist 243-363	.60	1.50
354 Bill Bonham	.10	.25
355 Lee Mazzilli	.10	.25
356 San Francisco Giants CL	.60	1.50
Joe Altobelli MG		
357 Jerry Augustine	.10	.25
358 Alan Trammell	1.25	3.00
359 Dan Spillner DP	.08	.20
360 Amos Otis	.30	.75
361 Tom Dixon RC	.10	.25
362 Mike Cubbage	.10	.25
363 Craig Skok RC	.10	.25
364 Gene Richards	.10	.25
365 Sparky Lyle	.30	.75
366 Juan Bernhardt	.10	.25
367 Dave Skaggs	.10	.25
368 Don Aase	.10	.25
369A Bump Wills ERR	1.25	3.00
(Blue Jays)		
369B Bump Wills COR	.75	2.00
(Rangers)		
370 Dave Kingman	.60	1.50
371 Jeff Holly RC	.10	.25
372 Lamar Johnson	.10	.25
373 Lance Rautzhan	.10	.25
374 Ed Herrmann	.10	.25
375 Bill Campbell	.10	.25
376 Gorman Thomas	.30	.75
377 Paul Moskau	.10	.25
378 Rob Picciolo DP	.08	.20
379 Dale Murray	.10	.25
380 John Mayberry	.30	.75
381 Houston Astros CL	.60	1.50
Bill Virdon MG		
382 Jerry Martin	.10	.25
383 Phil Garner	.30	.75
384 Tommy Boggs	.10	.25
385 Dan Ford	.10	.25
386 Francisco Barrios	.10	.25
387 Gary Thomasson	.10	.25
388 Jack Billingham	.10	.25
389 Joe Zdeb	.10	.25
390 Rollie Fingers	1.00	2.50
391 Al Oliver	.30	.75
392 Doug Ault	.10	.25
393 Scott McGregor	.30	.75
394 Randy Stein RC	.10	.25
395 Dave Cash	.10	.25
396 Bill Plummer	.10	.25
397 Sergio Ferrer RC	.10	.25
398 Ivan DeJesus	.10	.25
399 David Clyde	.10	.25
400 Jim Rice	.60	1.50
401 Ray Knight	.30	.75
402 Paul Hartzell	.10	.25
403 Tim Foli	.10	.25
404 Chicago White Sox CL	.60	1.50
Don Kessinger MG		
405 Butch Wynegar DP	.08	.20
406 Joe Wallis DP	.08	.20
407 Pete Vuckovich	.30	.75
408 Charlie Moore DP	.08	.20
409 Willie Wilson RC	.60	1.50
410 Darrell Evans	.60	1.50
411 George Sisler ATL	1.00	2.50
Ty Cobb		
412 Hack Wilson ATL	1.00	2.50
Hank Aaron		
413 Roger Maris ATL	1.50	4.00
Hank Aaron		
414 Rogers Hornsby ATL	1.00	2.50
Ty Cobb		
415 Lou Brock ATL	.60	1.50
Lou Brock		
416 Jack Chesbro ATL	.30	.75
Cy Young		
417 Nolan Ryan ATL DP	2.00	5.00
Walter Johnson		
418 Dutch Leonard ATL DP	.10	.25
Walter Johnson		
419 Dick Ruthven	.10	.25
420 Ken Griffey Sr.	.30	.75
421 Doug DeCinces	.30	.75
422 Ruppert Jones	.10	.25
423 Bob Montgomery	.10	.25
424 California Angels CL	.60	1.50
Jim Fregosi MG		
425 Rick Manning	.10	.25
426 Chris Speier	.10	.25
427 Andy Replogle RC	.10	.25
428 Bobby Valentine	.30	.75
429 John Urrea DP	.08	.20
430 Dave Parker	.30	.75
431 Glenn Borgmann	.10	.25
432 Dave Heaverlo	.10	.25
433 Larry Biittner	.10	.25
434 Ken Clay	.10	.25
435 Gene Tenace	.30	.75
436 Hector Cruz	.10	.25
437 Rick Williams RC	.10	.25
438 Horace Speed RC	.10	.25
439 Frank White	.30	.75
440 Rusty Staub	.60	1.50
441 Lee Lacy	.10	.25
442 Doyle Alexander	.10	.25
443 Bruce Bochte	.10	.25
444 Aurelio Lopez RC	.10	.25
445 Steve Henderson	.10	.25
446 Jim Lonborg	.30	.75
447 Manny Sanguillen	.30	.75
448 Moose Haas	.10	.25
449 Bombo Rivera	.10	.25
450 Dave Concepcion	.60	1.50
451 Kansas City Royals CL	.60	1.50
Whitey Herzog MG		
452 Jerry Morales	.10	.25
453 Chris Knapp	.10	.25
454 Len Randle	.10	.25
455 Bill Lee DP	.08	.20
456 Chuck Baker RC	.10	.25
457 Bruce Sutter	1.00	2.50
458 Jim Essian	.10	.25
459 Sid Monge	.10	.25
460 Graig Nettles	.60	1.50
461 Jim Barr DP	.08	.20
462 Otto Velez	.10	.25
463 Steve Comer RC	.10	.25
464 Joe Nolan	.10	.25
465 Reggie Smith	.30	.75
466 Mark Littell	.10	.25
467 Don Kessinger DP	.10	.25
468 Stan Bahnsen DP	.08	.20
469 Lance Parrish	.60	1.50
470 Garry Maddox DP	.10	.25
471 Joaquin Andujar	.30	.75
472 Craig Kusick	.10	.25
473 Dave Roberts	.10	.25
474 Dick Davis RC	.10	.25
475 Dan Driessen	.10	.25
476 Tom Poquette	.10	.25
477 Bob Grich	.30	.75
478 Juan Beniquez	.10	.25
479 San Diego Padres CL	.60	1.50
Roger Craig MG		
480 Fred Lynn	.30	.75
481 Skip Lockwood	.10	.25
482 Craig Reynolds	.10	.25
483 Checklist 364-484 DP	.30	.75
484 Rick Waits	.10	.25
485 Bucky Dent	.30	.75
486 Bob Knepper	.10	.25
487 Miguel Dilone	.10	.25
488 Bob Owchinko	.10	.25
489 Larry Cox UER	.10	.25
(Photo actually		
Dave Rader)		
490 Al Cowens	.30	.75
491 Tippy Martinez	.10	.25
492 Bob Bailor	.10	.25
493 Larry Christenson	.10	.25
494 Jerry White	.10	.25
495 Tony Perez	1.00	2.50
496 Barry Bonnell DP	.08	.20
497 Glenn Abbott	.10	.25
498 Rich Chiles	.10	.25
499 Texas Rangers CL	.60	1.50
Pat Corrales MG		
500 Ron Guidry	.30	.75
501 Junior Kennedy RC	.10	.25
502 Steve Braun	.10	.25
503 Terry Humphrey	.10	.25
504 Larry McWilliams RC	.10	.25
505 Ed Kranepool	.10	.25
506 John D'Acquisto	.10	.25
507 Tony Armas	.30	.75
508 Charlie Hough	.30	.75
509 Mario Mendoza UER	.10	.25
(Career BA .278,		
should say .204)		
510 Ted Simmons	.60	1.50
511 Paul Reuschel DP	.08	.20
512 Jack Clark	.30	.75
513 Dave Johnson	.30	.75
514 Mike Proly RC	.10	.25
515 Enos Cabell	.10	.25
516 Champ Summers DP	.08	.20
517 Al Bumbry	.30	.75
518 Jim Umbarger	.10	.25
519 Ben Oglivie	.30	.75
520 Gary Carter	.60	1.50
521 Sam Ewing	.10	.25
522 Ken Holtzman	.30	.75
523 John Milner	.10	.25
524 Tom Burgmeier	.10	.25
525 Freddie Patek	.10	.25
526 Los Angeles Dodgers CL	.60	1.50
Tom Lasorda MG		
527 Lerrin LaGrow	.10	.25
528 Wayne Gross DP	.08	.20
529 Brian Asselstine	.10	.25
530 Frank Tanana	.30	.75
531 Fernando Gonzalez	.10	.25
532 Buddy Schultz	.10	.25
533 Leroy Stanton	.10	.25
534 Ken Forsch	.10	.25
535 Ellis Valentine	.10	.25
536 Jerry Reuss	.30	.75
537 Tom Veryzer	.10	.25
538 Mike Ivie DP	.08	.20
539 John Ellis	.10	.25
540 Greg Luzinski	.30	.75
541 Jim Slaton	.10	.25
542 Rick Bosetti	.10	.25
543 Kiko Garcia	.10	.25
544 Fergie Jenkins	1.00	2.50
545 John Stearns	.10	.25
546 Bill Russell	.30	.75
547 Clint Hurdle	.10	.25
548 Enrique Romo	.10	.25
549 Bob Bailey	.10	.25
550 Sal Bando	.30	.75
551 Chicago Cubs CL	.60	1.50
Herman Franks MG		
552 Jose Morales	.10	.25
553 Denny Walling	.10	.25
554 Matt Keough	.10	.25
555 Biff Pocoroba	.10	.25
556 Mike Lum	.10	.25
557 Ken Brett	.10	.25
558 Jay Johnstone	.30	.75
559 Greg Pryor RC	.10	.25
560 John Montefusco	.10	.25
561 Ed Ott	.10	.25
562 Dusty Baker	.60	1.50
563 Roy Thomas	.10	.25
564 Jerry Turner	.10	.25
565 Rico Carty	.30	.75
566 Nino Espinosa	.10	.25
567 Richie Hebner	.30	.75
568 Carlos Lopez	.10	.25
569 Bob Sykes	.10	.25
570 Cesar Cedeno	.30	.75
571 Darrell Porter	.30	.75
572 Rod Gilbreath	.10	.25
573 Jim Kern	.10	.25
574 Claudell Washington	.30	.75
575 Luis Tiant	.30	.75
576 Mike Parrott RC	.10	.25
577 Milwaukee Brewers CL	.60	1.50
George Bamberger MG		
578 Pete Broberg	.10	.25
579 Greg Gross	.10	.25
580 Ron Fairly	.30	.75
581 Darold Knowles	.10	.25
582 Paul Blair	.30	.75
583 Julio Cruz	.10	.25
584 Jim Rooker	.10	.25
585 Hal McRae	.60	1.50
586 Bob Horner RC	.60	1.50
587 Ken Reitz	.10	.25
588 Tom Murphy	.10	.25
589 Terry Whitfield	.10	.25
590 J.R. Richard	.30	.75
591 Mike Hargrove	.30	.75
592 Mike Krukow	.10	.25
593 Rick Dempsey	.30	.75
594 Bob Shirley	.10	.25
595 Phil Niekro	1.00	2.50
596 Jim Wohlford	.10	.25
597 Bob Stanley	.10	.25
598 Mark Wagner	.10	.25
599 Jim Spencer	.10	.25
600 George Foster	.30	.75
601 Dave LaRoche	.10	.25
602 Checklist 485-605	.60	1.50
603 Rudy May	.10	.25
604 Jeff Newman	.10	.25
605 Rick Monday DP	.10	.25
606 Montreal Expos CL	.60	1.50
Dick Williams MG		
607 Omar Moreno	.10	.25
608 Dave McKay	.10	.25
609 Silvio Martinez RC	.10	.25
610 Mike Schmidt	3.00	8.00
611 Jim Norris	.10	.25
612 Rick Honeycutt RC	.30	.75
613 Mike Edwards RC	.10	.25
614 Willie Hernandez	.30	.75
615 Ken Singleton	.30	.75
616 Billy Almon	.10	.25
617 Terry Puhl	.10	.25
618 Jerry Remy	.10	.25
619 Ken Landreaux RC	.30	.75
620 Bert Campaneris	.30	.75
621 Pat Zachry	.10	.25
622 Dave Collins	.30	.75
623 Bob McClure	.10	.25
624 Larry Herndon	.10	.25
625 Mark Fidrych	1.00	2.50
626 New York Yankees CL	.60	1.50
Bob Lemon MG		
627 Gary Serum RC	.10	.25
628 Del Unser	.10	.25
629 Gene Garber	.30	.75
630 Bake McBride	.30	.75
631 Jorge Orta	.10	.25
632 Don Kirkwood	.10	.25
633 Rob Wilfong DP RC	.08	.20
634 Paul Lindblad	.10	.25
635 Don Baylor	.60	1.50
636 Wayne Garland	.10	.25
637 Bill Robinson	.30	.75
638 Al Fitzmorris	.10	.25
639 Manny Trillo	.10	.25
640 Eddie Murray	5.00	12.00
641 Bobby Castillo RC	.10	.25
642 Wilbur Howard DP	.08	.20
643 Tom Hausman	.10	.25
644 Manny Mota	.30	.75
645 George Scott DP	.10	.25
646 Rick Sweet	.10	.25
647 Bob Lacey	.10	.25
648 Lou Piniella	.30	.75
649 John Curtis	.10	.25
650 Pete Rose	5.00	12.00
651 Mike Caldwell	.10	.25
652 Stan Papi RC	.10	.25
653 Warren Brusstar DP	.08	.20
654 Rick Miller	.10	.25
655 Jerry Koosman	.30	.75
656 Hosken Powell RC	.10	.25
657 George Medich	.10	.25
658 Taylor Duncan RC	.10	.25
659 Seattle Mariners CL	.60	1.50
Darrell Johnson MG		
660 Ron LeFlore DP	.10	.25
661 Bruce Kison	.10	.25
662 Kevin Bell	.10	.25
663 Mike Vail	.10	.25
664 Doug Bird	.10	.25
665 Lou Brock	1.00	2.50
666 Rich Dauer	.10	.25
667 Don Hood	.10	.25
668 Bill North	.10	.25
669 Checklist 606-726	.60	1.50
670 Jim Hunter DP	.60	1.50
671 Joe Ferguson DP	.08	.20
672 Ed Halicki	.10	.25
673 Tom Hutton	.10	.25
674 Dave Tomlin	.10	.25
675 Tim McCarver	.60	1.50
676 Johnny Sutton RC	.10	.25
677 Larry Parrish	.30	.75
678 Geoff Zahn	.10	.25
679 Derrel Thomas	.10	.25
680 Carlton Fisk	1.25	3.00
681 John Henry Johnson RC	.10	.25
682 Dave Chalk	.10	.25
683 Dan Meyer DP	.08	.20
684 Jamie Easterly DP	.08	.20
685 Sixto Lezcano	.10	.25
686 Ron Schueler DP	.08	.20
687 Rennie Stennett	.10	.25
688 Mike Willis	.10	.25
689 Baltimore Orioles CL	.60	1.50
Earl Weaver MG		
690 Buddy Bell DP	.10	.25
691 Dock Ellis DP	.08	.20
692 Mickey Stanley	.10	.25
693 Dave Rader	.10	.25
694 Burt Hooton	.30	.75
695 Keith Hernandez	.30	.75
696 Andy Hassler	.10	.25
697 Dave Bergman	.10	.25
698 Bill Stein	.10	.25
699 Hal Dues RC	.10	.25
700 Reggie Jackson DP	2.00	5.00
701 Mark Corey RC	.30	.75
John Flinn RC		
Sammy Stewart RC		
702 Joel Finch RC	.30	.75
Garry Hancock RC		
Allen Ripley RC		
703 Jim Anderson RC	.30	.75
Dave Frost RC		
Bob Slater RC		
704 Ross Baumgarten RC	.30	.75
Mike Colbern RC		
Mike Squires RC		
705 Alfredo Griffin RC	.60	1.50
Tim Norrid RC		
Dave Oliver		
706 Dave Stegman RC	.30	.75
Dave Tobik RC		
Kip Young RC		
707 Randy Bass RC	.60	1.50
Jim Gaudet RC		
Randy McGilberry RC		
708 Kevin Bass RC	.60	1.50
Eddie Romero RC		
Ned Yost RC		
709 Sam Perlozzo	.30	.75
Rick Sofield RC		
Kevin Stanfield RC		
710 Brian Doyle RC	.30	.75
Mike Heath RC		
Dave Rajsich RC		
711 Dwayne Murphy RC	.60	1.50
Bruce Robinson RC		
Alan Wirth RC		
712 Bud Anderson RC	.30	.75
Greg Biercevicz RC		
Byron McLaughlin RC		
713 Danny Darwin RC	.60	1.50
Pat Putnam		
Billy Sample RC		
714 Victor Cruz RC	.30	.75
Pat Kelly		
Ernie Whitt		
715 Bruce Benedict RC	.60	1.50
Glenn Hubbard RC		
Larry Whisenton RC		
716 Dave Geisel RC	.30	.75
Karl Pagel RC		
Scot Thompson RC		
717 Mike LaCoss RC	.30	.75
Ron Oester RC		
Harry Spilman RC		
718 Bruce Bochy RC	.30	.75
Mike Fischlin RC		
Don Pisker RC		
719 Pedro Guerrero RC	.60	1.50
Rudy Law RC		
Joe Simpson RC		
720 Jerry Fry RC	.60	1.50
Jerry Pirtle RC		
Scott Sanderson RC		
721 Juan Berenguer RC	.30	.75
Dwight Bernard RC		
Dan Norman RC		
722 Jim Morrison RC	.60	1.50
Lonnie Smith RC		
Jim Wright RC		
723 Dale Berra RC	.30	.75
Eugenio Cotes RC		
Ben Wiltbank RC		
724 Tom Bruno RC	.60	1.50
George Frazier RC		
Terry Kennedy RC		
725 Jim Beswick RC	.30	.75
Steve Mura RC		
Broderick Perkins RC		
726 Greg Johnston RC	.30	.75
Joe Strain RC		
John Tamargo RC		

1980 Topps

The cards in this 726-card set measure the standard size. In 1980 Topps released another set of the same size and number of cards as the previous two years. Distribution for these cards included 15-card wax packs as well as 42-card rack packs. The 15-card wax packs had an 25 cent SRP and came 36 packs to a box and 20 boxes to a case. A special experiment in 1980 was the issuance of a 28-card cello pack with a 59 cent SRP which had a three-pack of gum at the bottom so no cards would be damaged. As with those sets, Topps again produced 66 double-printed cards in the set; they are noted by DP in the checklist below. The player's name appears over the picture and his position and team are found in pennant design. Every card carries a facsimile autograph. Team cards feature a team checklist of players in the set on the back and the manager's name on the front. Cards 1-6 show Highlights (HL) of the 1979 season, cards 201-207 are League Leaders, and cards 661-686 feature American and National League rookie "Future Stars," one card for each team showing three young prospects. The key Rookie Card in this set is Rickey Henderson; other Rookie Cards included in this set are Dan Quisenberry, Dave Stieb and Rick Sutcliffe.

COMPLETE SET (726)	70.00	120.00
COMMON CARD (1-726)	.10	.25
COMMON DP	.08	.25
1 Lou Brock HL	1.00	2.50
Carl Yastrzemski		
2 Willie McCovey HL	.30	.75
3 Manny Mota HL	.10	.25
4 Pete Rose HL	1.25	3.00
5 Garry Templeton HL	.10	.25
6 Del Unser HL	.10	.25
7 Mike Lum	.10	.25
8 Craig Swan	.10	.25
9 Steve Braun	.10	.25
10 Dennis Martinez	.30	.75
11 Jimmy Sexton	.10	.25
12 John Curtis DP	.10	.25
13 Ron Pruitt	.10	.25
14 Dave Cash	.30	.75
15 Bill Campbell	.10	.25
16 Jerry Narron RC	.10	.25
17 Bruce Sutter	.60	1.50
18 Ron Jackson	.10	.25
19 Balor Moore	.10	.25
20 Dan Ford	.10	.25
21 Manny Sarmiento	.10	.25
22 Pat Putnam	.10	.25
23 Derrel Thomas	.10	.25
24 Jim Slaton	.10	.25
25 Lee Mazzilli	.30	.75
26 Marty Pattin	.10	.25
27 Del Unser	.10	.25
28 Bruce Kison	.10	.25
29 Mark Wagner	.10	.25
30 Vida Blue	.30	.75
31 Jay Johnstone	.10	.25
32 Julio Cruz DP	.10	.25
33 Tony Scott	.10	.25
34 Jeff Newman DP	.10	.25
35 Luis Tiant	.30	.75
36 Rusty Torres	.10	.25
37 Kiko Garcia	.10	.25
38 Dan Spillner DP	.10	.25
39 Rowland Office	.10	.25
40 Carlton Fisk	1.00	2.50
41 Texas Rangers CL	.30	.75
Pat Corrales MG		
42 David Palmer RC	.10	.25
43 Bombo Rivera	.10	.25
44 Bill Fahey	.10	.25
45 Frank White	.30	.75
46 Rico Carty	.30	.75
47 Bill Bonham DP	.10	.25
48 Rick Miller	.10	.25
49 Mario Guerrero	.10	.25
50 J.R. Richard	.30	.75
51 Joe Ferguson DP	.10	.25
52 Warren Brusstar	.10	.25
53 Ben Oglivie	.30	.75
54 Dennis Lamp	.10	.25
55 Bill Madlock	.30	.75
56 Bobby Valentine	.30	.75
57 Pete Vuckovich	.10	.25
58 Doug Flynn	.10	.25
59 Eddy Putman RC	.10	.25
60 Bucky Dent	.30	.75
61 Gary Serum	.10	.25
62 Mike Ivie	.10	.25
63 Bob Stanley	.10	.25
64 Joe Nolan	.10	.25
65 Al Bumbry	.30	.75
66 Kansas City Royals CL	.30	.75
Jim Frey MG		
67 Doyle Alexander	.10	.25
68 Larry Harlow	.10	.25
69 Rick Williams	.10	.25
70 Gary Carter	.60	1.50
71 John Milner DP	.10	.25
72 Fred Howard DP RC	.10	.25
73 Dave Collins	.10	.25
74 Sid Monge	.10	.25
75 Bill Russell	.30	.75
76 John Stearns	.10	.25
77 Dave Stieb RC	.60	1.50
78 Ruppert Jones	.10	.25
79 Bob Owchinko	.10	.25
80 Ron LeFlore	.30	.75
81 Ted Sizemore	.10	.25
82 Houston Astros CL	.30	.75
Bill Virdon MG		
83 Steve Trout RC	.10	.25
84 Gary Lavelle	.10	.25
85 Ted Simmons	.30	.75
86 Dave Hamilton	.10	.25
87 Pepe Frias	.10	.25
88 Ken Landreaux	.10	.25
89 Don Hood	.10	.25
90 Manny Trillo	.30	.75
91 Rick Dempsey	.30	.75
92 Rick Rhoden	.10	.25
93 Dave Roberts DP	.10	.25
94 Neil Allen RC	.10	.25
95 Cecil Cooper	.30	.75
96 Oakland Athletics CL	.30	.75
Jim Marshall MG		
97 Bill Lee	.30	.75
98 Jerry Terrell	.10	.25
99 Victor Cruz	.10	.25
100 Johnny Bench	1.25	3.00
101 Aurelio Lopez	.10	.25
102 Rich Dauer	.10	.25
103 Bill Caudill RC	.10	.25
104 Manny Mota	.30	.75
105 Frank Tanana	.30	.75
106 Jeff Leonard RC	.60	1.50
107 Francisco Barrios	.10	.25
108 Bob Horner	.30	.75
109 Bill Travers	.10	.25
110 Fred Lynn DP	.20	.50
111 Bob Knepper	.10	.25
112 Chicago White Sox CL	.30	.75
Tony LaRussa MG		
113 Geoff Zahn	.10	.25
114 Juan Beniquez	.10	.25
115 Sparky Lyle	.30	.75
116 Larry Cox	.10	.25
117 Dock Ellis	.30	.75
118 Phil Garner	.30	.75
119 Sammy Stewart	.10	.25
120 Greg Luzinski	.30	.75
121 Checklist 1-121	.30	.75
122 Dave Rosello DP	.10	.25
123 Lynn Jones RC	.10	.25
124 Dave Lemanczyk	.10	.25
125 Tony Perez	.30	.75
126 Dave Tomlin	.10	.25
127 Gary Thomasson	.10	.25
128 Tom Burgmeier	.10	.25
129 Craig Reynolds	.10	.25
130 Amos Otis	.30	.75
131 Paul Mitchell	.10	.25
132 Biff Pocoroba	.10	.25
133 Jerry Turner	.10	.25
134 Matt Keough	.10	.25
135 Bill Buckner	.30	.75
136 Dick Ruthven	.10	.25
137 John Castino RC	.10	.25
138 Ross Baumgarten	.10	.25
139 Dane Iorg RC	.10	.25
140 Rich Gossage	.30	.75
141 Gary Alexander	.10	.25
142 Phil Huffman RC		
143 Bruce Bochte DP	.10	.25
144 Steve Comer	.10	.25
145 Darrell Evans	.30	.75
146 Bob Welch	.30	.75
147 Terry Puhl	.10	.25
148 Manny Sanguillen	.30	.75
149 Tom Hume	.10	.25
150 Jason Thompson	.10	.25
151 Tom Hausman DP	.10	.25
152 John Fulgham RC	.10	.25
153 Tim Blackwell	.10	.25
154 Lary Sorensen	.10	.25
155 Jerry Remy	.10	.25
156 Tony Brizzolara RC	.10	.25
157 Willie Wilson DP	.20	.50
158 Rob Picciolo DP	.10	.25
159 Ken Clay	.10	.25
160 Eddie Murray	2.00	5.00
161 Larry Christenson	.10	.25
162 Bob Randall	.10	.25
163 Steve Swisher	.10	.25
164 Greg Pryor	.10	.25
165 Omar Moreno	.10	.25
166 Glenn Abbott	.10	.25
167 Jack Clark	.30	.75
168 Rick Waits	.10	.25
169 Luis Gomez	.10	.25
170 Burt Hooton	.30	.75
171 Fernando Gonzalez	.10	.25
172 Ron Hodges	.10	.25
173 John Henry Johnson	.10	.25
174 Ray Knight	.30	.75
175 Rick Reuschel	.30	.75
176 Champ Summers	.10	.25
177 Dave Heaverlo	.10	.25
178 Tim McCarver	.30	.75
179 Ron Davis RC	.10	.25
180 Warren Cromartie	.10	.25
181 Moose Haas	.10	.25
182 Ken Reitz	.10	.25
183 Jim Anderson DP	.10	.25
184 Steve Renko DP	.10	.25
185 Hal McRae	.30	.75
186 Junior Moore	.10	.25
187 Alan Ashby	.10	.25
188 Terry Crowley	.10	.25
189 Kevin Kobel	.10	.25
190 Buddy Bell	.30	.75
191 Ted Martinez	.10	.25
192 Atlanta Braves CL	.30	.75
Bobby Cox MG		
193 Dave Goltz	.10	.25
194 Mike Easler	.10	.25
195 John Montefusco	.30	.75
196 Lance Parrish	.30	.75
197 Byron McLaughlin	.10	.25
198 Dell Alston DP	.10	.25
199 Mike LaCoss	.10	.25
200 Jim Rice	.30	.75
201 Batting Leaders	.30	.75
Keith Hernandez		
Fred Lynn		
202 Home Run Leaders	.60	1.50
Dave Kingman		
Gorman Thomas		
203 RBI Leaders	.60	1.50
Dave Winfield		
Don Baylor		
204 Stolen Base Leaders	.30	.75
Omar Moreno		
Willie Wilson		
205 Victory Leaders	.30	.75
Joe Niekro		
Phil Niekro		
Mike Flanagan		
206 Strikeout Leaders	2.00	5.00
J.R. Richard		
Nolan Ryan		
207 ERA Leaders	.30	.75
J.R. Richard		
Ron Guidry		
208 Wayne Cage	.10	.25
209 Von Joshua	.10	.25
210 Steve Carlton	.60	1.50
211 Dave Skaggs DP	.10	.25
212 Dave Roberts	.10	.25
213 Mike Jorgensen DP	.10	.25
214 California Angels CL	.30	.75
Jim Fregosi MG		
215 Sixto Lezcano	.10	.25
216 Phil Mankowski	.10	.25
217 Ed Halicki	.10	.25
218 Jose Morales	.10	.25
219 Steve Mingori	.10	.25
220 Dave Concepcion	.30	.75
221 Joe Cannon RC	.10	.25
222 Ron Hassey RC	.10	.25
223 Bob Sykes	.10	.25
224 Willie Montanez	.10	.25
225 Lou Piniella	.30	.75
226 Bill Stein	.10	.25
227 Len Barker	.30	.75
228 Johnny Oates	.30	.75
229 Jim Bibby	.10	.25
230 Dave Winfield	.60	1.50
231 Steve McCatty	.10	.25
232 Alan Trammell	.60	1.50
233 LaRue Washington RC	.10	.25
234 Vern Ruhle	.10	.25
235 Andre Dawson	.60	1.50
236 Marc Hill	.10	.25
237 Scott McGregor	.30	.75
238 Rob Wilfong	.10	.25
239 Don Aase	.10	.25
240 Dave Kingman	.30	.75
241 Checklist 122-242	.30	.75
242 Lamar Johnson	.10	.25
243 Jerry Augustine	.10	.25
244 St. Louis Cardinals CL	.30	.75
Ken Boyer MG		
245 Phil Niekro	.30	.75
246 Tim Foli DP	.10	.25
247 Frank Riccelli	.10	.25
248 Jamie Quirk	.10	.25
249 Jim Clancy	.10	.25
250 Jim Kaat	.30	.75
251 Kip Young	.10	.25
252 Ted Cox	.10	.25
253 John Montague	.10	.25
254 Paul Dade DP	.10	.25
255 Dusty Baker DP	.20	.50
256 Roger Erickson	.10	.25
257 Larry Herndon	.10	.25
258 Paul Moskau	.10	.25
259 New York Mets CL	.60	1.50
Joe Torre MG		
260 Al Oliver	.30	.75
261 Dave Chalk	.10	.25
262 Benny Ayala	.10	.25
263 Dave LaRoche DP	.10	.25
264 Bill Robinson	.10	.25
265 Robin Yount	1.25	3.00
266 Bernie Carbo	.10	.25
267 Dan Schatzeder	.10	.25
268 Rafael Landestoy	.10	.25
269 Dave Tobik	.10	.25
270 Mike Schmidt DP	1.25	3.00

271 Dick Drago DP .10 .25
272 Ralph Garr .30 .75
273 Eduardo Rodriguez .10 .25
274 Dale Murphy 1.00 2.50
275 Jerry Koosman .30 .75
276 Tom Veryzer .10 .25
277 Rick Bosetti .10 .25
278 Jim Spencer .10 .25
279 Rob Andrews .10 .25
280 Gaylord Perry .30 .75
281 Paul Blair .30 .75
282 Seattle Mariners CL .30 .75
Darrell Johnson MG
283 John Ellis .10 .25
284 Larry Murray DP RC .10 .25
285 Don Baylor .30 .75
286 Darold Knowles DP .10 .25
287 John Lowenstein .10 .25
288 Dave Rozema .10 .25
289 Bruce Bochy .10 .25
290 Steve Garvey .60 1.50
291 Randy Scarberry RC .10 .25
292 Dale Berra .10 .25
293 Elias Sosa .10 .25
294 Charlie Spikes .10 .25
295 Larry Gura .10 .25
296 Dave Rader .10 .25
297 Tim Johnson .10 .25
298 Ken Holtzman .30 .75
299 Steve Henderson .10 .25
300 Ron Guidry .30 .75
301 Mike Edwards .10 .25
302 Los Angeles Dodgers CL .60 1.50
Tom Lasorda MG
303 Bill Castro .10 .25
304 Butch Wynegar .10 .25
305 Randy Jones .30 .75
306 Denny Walling .10 .25
307 Rick Honeycutt .10 .25
308 Mike Hargrove .30 .75
309 Larry McWilliams .10 .25
310 Dave Parker .30 .75
311 Roger Metzger .10 .25
312 Mike Barlow .10 .25
313 Johnny Grubb .10 .25
314 Tim Stoddard RC .10 .25
315 Steve Kemp .30 .75
316 Bob Lacey .10 .25
317 Mike Anderson DP .10 .25
318 Jerry Reuss .30 .75
319 Chris Speier .10 .25
320 Dennis Eckersley .60 1.50
321 Keith Hernandez .30 .75
322 Claudell Washington .10 .25
323 Mick Kelleher .10 .25
324 Tom Underwood .10 .25
325 Dan Driessen .10 .25
326 Bo McLaughlin .10 .25
327 Ray Fosse DP .20 .50
328 Minnesota Twins CL .30 .75
Gene Mauch MG
329 Bert Roberge RC .10 .25
330 Al Cowens .30 .75
331 Richie Hebner .10 .25
332 Enrique Romo .10 .25
333 Jim Norris DP .10 .25
334 Jim Beattie .10 .25
335 Willie McCovey .60 1.50
336 George Medich .10 .25
337 Carney Lansford .30 .75
338 John Wockenfuss .10 .25
339 John D'Acquisto .10 .25
340 Ken Singleton .30 .75
341 Jim Essian .10 .25
342 Odell Jones .10 .25
343 Mike Vail .10 .25
344 Randy Lerch .10 .25
345 Larry Parrish .30 .75
346 Buddy Solomon .10 .25
347 Harry Chappas RC .10 .25
348 Checklist 243-363 .30 .75
349 Jack Brohamer .10 .25
350 George Hendrick .30 .75
351 Bob Davis .10 .25
352 Dan Briggs .10 .25
353 Andy Hassler .10 .25
354 Rick Auerbach .10 .25
355 Gary Matthews .30 .75
356 San Diego Padres CL .30 .75
Jerry Coleman MG
357 Bob McClure .10 .25
358 Lou Whitaker .30 .75
359 Randy Moffitt .10 .25
360 Darrell Porter DP .20 .50
361 Wayne Garland .10 .25
362 Danny Goodwin .10 .25
363 Wayne Gross .10 .25
364 Ray Burris .10 .25
365 Bobby Murcer .30 .75
366 Rob Dressler .10 .25
367 Billy Smith .10 .25
368 Willie Aikens RC .10 .25
369 Jim Kern .10 .25
370 Cesar Cedeno .30 .75
371 Jack Morris .30 .75
372 Joel Youngblood .10 .25
373 Dan Petry DP RC .30 .75
374 Jim Gantner .30 .75
375 Ross Grimsley .10 .25
376 Gary Allenson RC .10 .25
377 Junior Kennedy .10 .25
378 Jerry Mumphrey .10 .25
379 Kevin Bell .10 .25
380 Garry Maddox .10 .25
381 Chicago Cubs CL .30 .75
Preston Gomez MG
382 Dave Freisleben .10 .25
383 Ed Ott .10 .25
384 Joey McLaughlin RC .10 .25
385 Enos Cabell .10 .25
386 Darrell Jackson .10 .25
387A Fred Stanley .75 2.00
Yellow Name on Front
387B Fred Stanley .10 .25
(Red name on front)
388 Mike Paxton .10 .25
389 Pete LaCock .10 .25
390 Fergie Jenkins .30 .75
391 Tony Armas DP .20 .50
392 Milt Wilcox .10 .25
393 Ozzie Smith 4.00 10.00
394 Reggie Cleveland .10 .25
395 Ellis Valentine .10 .25
396 Dan Meyer .10 .25
397 Roy Thomas DP .10 .25
398 Barry Foote .10 .25
399 Mike Proly DP .10 .25
400 George Foster .30 .75
401 Pete Falcone .10 .25
402 Merv Rettenmund .10 .25
403 Pete Redfern DP .10 .25
404 Baltimore Orioles CL .30 .75
Earl Weaver MG
405 Dwight Evans .60 1.50
406 Paul Molitor 1.50 4.00
407 Tony Solaita .10 .25
408 Bill North .10 .25
409 Paul Splittorff .10 .25
410 Bobby Bonds .30 .75
411 Frank LaCorte .10 .25
412 Thad Bosley .10 .25
413 Allen Ripley .10 .25
414 George Scott .30 .75
415 Bill Atkinson .10 .25
416 Tom Brookens RC .10 .25
417 Craig Chamberlain DP RC .10 .25
418 Roger Freed DP .10 .25
419 Vic Correll .10 .25
420 Butch Hobson .10 .25
421 Doug Bird .10 .25
422 Larry Milbourne .10 .25
423 Dave Frost .10 .25
424 New York Yankees CL .30 .75
Dick Howser MG
424A New York Yankees CL
Billy Martin MG
Card is believed to be a Pre-Production issue
425 Mark Belanger .30 .75
426 Grant Jackson .10 .25
427 Tom Hutton DP .10 .25
428 Pat Zachry .10 .25
429 Duane Kuiper .10 .25
430 Larry Hisle DP .10 .25
431 Mike Krukow .10 .25
432 Willie Norwood .10 .25
433 Rich Gale .10 .25
434 Johnnie LeMaster .10 .25
435 Don Gullett .30 .75
436 Billy Almon .10 .25
437 Joe Niekro .30 .75
438 Dave Revering .10 .25
439 Mike Phillips .10 .25
440 Don Sutton .30 .75
441 Eric Soderholm .10 .25
442 Jorge Orta .10 .25
443 Mike Parrott .10 .25
444 Alvis Woods .10 .25
445 Mark Fidrych .30 .75
446 Duffy Dyer .10 .25
447 Nino Espinosa .10 .25
448 Jim Wohlford .10 .25
449 Doug Bair .10 .25
450 George Brett 3.00 8.00
451 Cleveland Indians CL .30 .75
Dave Garcia MG
452 Steve Dillard .10 .25
453 Mike Bacsik .10 .25
454 Tom Donohue RC .10 .25
455 Mike Torrez .30 .75
456 Frank Taveras .10 .25
457 Bert Blyleven .30 .75
458 Billy Sample .10 .25
459 Mickey Lolich DP .20 .50
460 Willie Randolph .30 .75
461 Dwayne Murphy .10 .25
462 Mike Sadek DP .10 .25
463 Jerry Royster .10 .25
464 John Denny .30 .75
465 Rick Monday .30 .75
466 Mike Squires .10 .25
467 Jesse Jefferson .10 .25
468 Aurelio Rodriguez .10 .25
469 Randy Niemann DP RC .10 .25
470 Bob Boone .30 .75
471 Hosken Powell DP .10 .25
472 Willie Hernandez .30 .75
473 Bump Wills .10 .25
474 Steve Busby .10 .25
475 Cesar Geronimo .30 .75
476 Bob Shirley .10 .25
477 Buck Martinez .10 .25
478 Gil Flores .10 .25
479 Montreal Expos CL .30 .75
Dick Williams MG
480 Bob Watson .30 .75
481 Tom Paciorek .30 .75
482 Rickey Henderson RC 25.00 60.00
UER 7 steals at
Modesto should be Fresno
483 Bo Diaz .10 .25
484 Checklist 364-484 .30 .75
485 Mickey Rivers .30 .75
486 Mike Tyson DP .10 .25
487 Wayne Nordhagen .10 .25
488 Roy Howell .10 .25
489 Preston Hanna DP .10 .25
490 Lee May .30 .75
491 Steve Mura DP .10 .25
492 Todd Cruz RC .10 .25
493 Jerry Martin .10 .25
494 Craig Minetto RC .10 .25
495 Bake McBride .30 .75
496 Silvio Martinez .10 .25
497 Jim Mason .10 .25
498 Danny Darwin .10 .25
499 San Francisco Giants CL .30 .75
Dave Bristol MG
500 Tom Seaver 1.25 3.00
501 Rennie Stennett .10 .25
502 Rich Wortham DP RC .10 .25
503 Mike Cubbage .10 .25
504 Gene Garber .10 .25
505 Bert Campaneris .30 .75
506 Tom Buskey .10 .25
507 Leon Roberts .10 .25
508 U.L. Washington .10 .25
509 Ed Glynn .10 .25
510 Ron Cey .30 .75
511 Eric Wilkins RC .10 .25
512 Jose Cardenal .10 .25
513 Tom Dixon DP .10 .25
514 Steve Ontiveros .10 .25
515 Mike Caldwell UER .10 .25
1979 loss total reads
96 instead of 6
516 Hector Cruz .10 .25
517 Don Stanhouse .10 .25
518 Nelson Norman RC .10 .25
519 Steve Nicosia RC .10 .25
520 Steve Rogers .30 .75
521 Ken Brett .10 .25
522 Jim Morrison .10 .25
523 Ken Henderson .10 .25
524 Jim Wright DP .10 .25
525 Clint Hurdle .10 .25
526 Philadelphia Phillies CL .30 .75
Dallas Green MG
527 Doug Rau DP .10 .25
528 Adrian Devine .10 .25
529 Jim Barr .10 .25
530 Jim Sundberg DP .20 .50
531 Eric Rasmussen .10 .25
532 Willie Horton .30 .75
533 Checklist 485-605 .30 .75
534 Andre Thornton .30 .75
535 Bob Forsch .10 .25
536 Lee Lacy .10 .25
537 Alex Trevino RC .10 .25
538 Joe Strain .10 .25
539 Rudy May .10 .25
540 Pete Rose 3.00 8.00
541 Miguel Dilone .10 .25
542 Joe Coleman .10 .25
543 Pat Kelly .10 .25
544 Rick Sutcliffe RC .60 1.50
545 Jeff Burroughs .30 .75
546 Rick Langford .10 .25
547 John Wathan .10 .25
548 Dave Rajsich .10 .25
549 Larry Wolfe .10 .25
550 Ken Griffey Sr. .30 .75
551 Pittsburgh Pirates CL .30 .75
Chuck Tanner MG
552 Bill Nahorodny .10 .25
553 Dick Davis .10 .25
554 Art Howe .30 .75
555 Ed Figueroa .10 .25
556 Joe Rudi .30 .75
557 Mark Lee .10 .25
558 Alfredo Griffin .10 .25
559 Dale Murray .10 .25
560 Dave Lopes .30 .75
561 Eddie Whitson .10 .25
562 Joe Wallis .10 .25
563 Will McEnaney .10 .25
564 Rick Manning .10 .25
565 Dennis Leonard .10 .25
566 Bud Harrelson .30 .75
567 Skip Lockwood .10 .25
568 Gary Roenicke RC .10 .25
569 Terry Kennedy .10 .25
570 Roy Smalley .30 .75
571 Joe Sambito .10 .25
572 Jerry Morales DP .10 .25
573 Kent Tekulve .30 .75
574 Scot Thompson .10 .25
575 Ken Kravec .10 .25
576 Jim Dwyer .10 .25
577 Toronto Blue Jays CL .30 .75
Bobby Mattick MG
578 Scott Sanderson .10 .25
579 Charlie Moore .10 .25
580 Nolan Ryan 6.00 15.00
581 Bob Bailor .10 .25
582 Brian Doyle .10 .25
583 Bob Stinson .10 .25
584 Kurt Bevacqua .10 .25
585 Al Hrabosky .30 .75
586 Mitchell Page .10 .25
587 Garry Templeton .30 .75
588 Greg Minton .10 .25
589 Chet Lemon .30 .75
590 Jim Palmer .60 1.50
591 Rick Cerone .10 .25
592 Jon Matlack .30 .75
593 Jesus Alou .10 .25
594 Dick Tidrow .10 .25
595 Don Money .10 .25
596 Rick Matula RC .10 .25
597 Tom Poquette .10 .25
598 Fred Kendall DP .10 .25
599 Mike Norris .10 .25
600 Reggie Jackson 1.25 3.00
601 Buddy Schultz .10 .25
602 Brian Downing .30 .75
603 Jack Billingham DP .10 .25
604 Glenn Adams .10 .25
605 Terry Forster .30 .75
606 Cincinnati Reds CL .30 .75
John McNamara MG
607 Woodie Fryman .10 .25
608 Alan Bannister .10 .25
609 Ron Reed .10 .25
610 Willie Stargell .60 1.50
611 Jerry Garvin DP .10 .25
612 Cliff Johnson .10 .25
613 Randy Stein .10 .25
614 John Hiller .10 .25
615 Doug DeCinces .30 .75
616 Gene Richards .10 .25
617 Joaquin Andujar .30 .75
618 Bob Montgomery DP .10 .25
619 Sergio Ferrer .10 .25
620 Richie Zisk .30 .75
621 Bob Grich .30 .75
622 Mario Soto .30 .75
623 Gorman Thomas .30 .75
624 Lerrin LaGrow .10 .25
625 Chris Chambliss .30 .75
626 Detroit Tigers CL .30 .75
Sparky Anderson MG
627 Pedro Borbon .10 .25
628 Doug Capilla .10 .25
629 Jim Todd .10 .25
630 Larry Bowa .30 .75
631 Mark Littell .10 .25
632 Barry Bonnell .10 .25
633 Bob Apodaca .10 .25
634 Glenn Borgmann DP .10 .25
635 John Candelaria .30 .75
636 Toby Harrah .30 .75
637 Joe Simpson .10 .25
638 Mark Clear RC .10 .25
639 Larry Biittner .10 .25
640 Mike Flanagan .30 .75
641 Ed Kranepool .30 .75
642 Ken Forsch DP .10 .25
643 John Mayberry .30 .75
644 Charlie Hough .30 .75
645 Rick Burleson .30 .75
646 Checklist 606-726 .30 .75
647 Milt May .10 .25
648 Roy White .30 .75
649 Tom Griffin .10 .25
650 Joe Morgan .60 1.50
651 Rollie Fingers .30 .75
652 Mario Mendoza .10 .25
653 Stan Bahnsen .10 .25
654 Bruce Boisclair DP .10 .25
655 Tug McGraw .30 .75
656 Larvell Blanks .10 .25
657 Dave Edwards RC .10 .25
658 Chris Knapp .10 .25
659 Milwaukee Brewers CL .30 .75
George Bamberger MG
660 Rusty Staub .30 .75
661 Mark Corey .10 .25
Dave Ford
Wayne Krenchicki RC
662 Joel Finch .10 .25
Mike O'Berry RC
Chuck Rainey RC
663 Ralph Botting RC .30 .75
Bob Clark RC
Dickie Thon RC
664 Mike Colbern .10 .25
Guy Hoffman RC
Dewey Robinson RC
665 Larry Andersen .10 .25
Bobby Cuellar RC
Sandy Wihtol RC
666 Mike Chris RC .10 .25
Al Greene RC
Bruce Robbins RC
667 Renie Martin RC .30 .75
Bill Paschall RC
Dan Quisenberry RC
668 Danny Boitano RC .10 .25
Willie Mueller RC
Lenn Sakata RC
669 Dan Graham RC .30 .75
Rick Sofield
Gary Ward RC
670 Bobby Brown RC .10 .25
Brad Gulden RC
Darryl Jones RC
671 Derek Bryant RC .30 .75
Brian Kingman RC
Mike Morgan RC
672 Charlie Beamon RC .10 .25
Rodney Craig RC
Rafael Vasquez RC
673 Brian Allard RC .10 .25
Jerry Don Gleaton RC
Greg Mahlberg RC
674 Butch Edge RC .10 .25
Pat Kelly
Ted Wilborn RC
675 Bruce Benedict .10 .25
Larry Bradford RC
Eddie Miller
676 Dave Geisel .10 .25
Steve Macko RC
Karl Pagel
677 Art DeFreites RC .10 .25
Frank Pastore RC
Harry Spilman
678 Reggie Baldwin RC .10 .25
Alan Knicely RC
Pete Ladd RC
679 Joe Beckwith RC .30 .75
Mickey Hatcher RC
Dave Patterson RC
680 Tony Bernazard RC .10 .25
Randy Miller RC
John Tamargo
681 Dan Norman .60 1.50
Jesse Orosco RC
Mike Scott RC
682 Ramon Aviles RC .10 .25
Dickie Noles RC
Kevin Saucier RC
683 Dorian Boyland RC .10 .25
Alberto Lois RC
Harry Saferight RC
684 George Frazier .30 .75
Tom Herr RC
Dan O'Brien RC
685 Tim Flannery RC .10 .25
Brian Greer RC
Jim Wilhelm RC
686 Greg Johnston .10 .25
Dennis Littlejohn RC
Phil Nastu RC
687 Mike Heath DP .10 .25
688 Steve Stone .30 .75
689 Boston Red Sox CL .30 .75
Don Zimmer MG
690 Tommy John .30 .75
691 Ivan DeJesus .10 .25
692 Rawly Eastwick DP .20 .50
693 Craig Kusick .10 .25
694 Jim Rooker .10 .25
695 Reggie Smith .30 .75
696 Julio Gonzalez .10 .25
697 David Clyde .10 .25
698 Oscar Gamble .30 .75
699 Floyd Bannister .10 .25
700 Rod Carew DP .30 .75
701 Ken Oberkfell RC .10 .25
702 Ed Farmer .10 .25
703 Otto Velez .10 .25
704 Gene Tenace .30 .75
705 Freddie Patek .10 .25
706 Tippy Martinez .10 .25
707 Elliott Maddox .10 .25
708 Bob Tolan .10 .25
709 Pat Underwood RC .10 .25
710 Graig Nettles .30 .75
711 Bob Galasso RC .10 .25
712 Rodney Scott .10 .25
713 Terry Whitfield .10 .25
714 Fred Norman .10 .25
715 Sal Bando .30 .75
716 Lynn McGlothen .10 .25
717 Mickey Klutts DP .10 .25
718 Greg Gross .10 .25
719 Don Robinson .30 .75
720 Carl Yastrzemski DP .75 2.00
721 Paul Hartzell .10 .25
722 Jose Cruz .30 .75
723 Shane Rawley .10 .25
724 Jerry White .10 .25
725 Rick Wise .10 .25
726 Steve Yeager .30 .75

1981 Topps

The cards in this 726-card set measure the standard size. This set was issued primarily in 15-card wax packs and 50-card rack packs. League Leaders (1-8), Record Breakers (201-208), and Post-season cards (401-404) are the topical subsets. The team cards are all grouped together (661-686) and feature team checklist backs and a very small photo of the team's manager in the upper right corner of the obverse. The obverses carry the player's position and team in a baseball cap design, and the company name is printed in a small baseball. The backs are red and gray. The 66 double-printed cards are noted in the checklist by DP. Notable Rookie Cards in the set include Harold Baines, Kirk Gibson, Tim Raines, Jeff Reardon, and Fernando Valenzuela. During 1981, a promotion existed where collectors could order complete set in sheet form from Topps for $24.

COMPLETE SET (726) 30.00 60.00
COMMON CARD (1-726) .05 .15
COMMON CARD DP .05 .15
1 George Brett 1.25 3.00
Bill Buckner LL
2 Reggie Jackson .60 1.50
Ben Oglivie
Mike Schmidt LL
3 Cecil Cooper .60 1.50
Mike Schmidt LL
4 Rickey Henderson 1.25 3.00
Ron LeFlore LL
5 Steve Stone .15 .40
Steve Carlton LL
6 Len Barker .15 .40
Steve Carlton LL
7 Rudy May .15 .40
Don Sutton LL
8 Dan Quisenberry .15 .40
Rollie Fingers
Tom Hume LL
9 Pete LaCock DP .05 .15
10 Mike Flanagan .05 .15
11 Jim Wohlford DP .05 .15
12 Mark Clear .05 .15
13 Joe Charboneau RC .60 1.50
14 John Tudor RC .60 1.50
15 Larry Parrish .05 .15
16 Ron Davis .05 .15
17 Cliff Johnson .05 .15
18 Glenn Adams .05 .15
19 Jim Clancy .05 .15
20 Jeff Burroughs .15 .40
21 Ron Oester .05 .15
22 Danny Darwin .05 .15
23 Alex Trevino .05 .15
24 Don Stanhouse .05 .15
25 Sixto Lezcano .05 .15
26 U.L. Washington .05 .15
27 Champ Summers DP .05 .15
28 Enrique Romo .05 .15
29 Gene Tenace .15 .40
30 Jack Clark .15 .40
31 Checklist 1-121 DP .08 .25
32 Ken Oberkfell .05 .15
33 Rick Honeycutt .05 .15
34 Aurelio Rodriguez .05 .15
35 Mitchell Page .05 .15
36 Ed Farmer .05 .15
37 Gary Roenicke .05 .15
38 Win Remmerswaal RC .05 .15
39 Tom Veryzer .05 .15
40 Tug McGraw .15 .40
41 Bob Babcock RC .08 .25
John Butcher RC
Jerry Don Gleaton
42 Jerry White DP .05 .15
43 Jose Morales .05 .15
44 Larry McWilliams .05 .15
45 Enos Cabell .05 .15
46 Rick Bosetti .05 .15
47 Ken Brett .05 .15
48 Dave Skaggs .05 .15
49 Bob Shirley .05 .15
50 Dave Lopes .15 .40
51 Bill Robinson DP .05 .15
52 Hector Cruz .05 .15
53 Kevin Saucier .05 .15
54 Ivan DeJesus .05 .15
55 Mike Norris .05 .15
56 Buck Martinez .05 .15
57 Dave Roberts .05 .15
58 Joel Youngblood .05 .15
59 Dan Petry .05 .15
60 Willie Randolph .15 .40
61 Butch Wynegar .05 .15
62 Joe Pettini RC .05 .15
63 Steve Renko DP .05 .15
64 Brian Asselstine .05 .15
65 Scott McGregor .05 .15
66 Manny Castillo RC .08 .25
Tim Ireland RC
Mike Jones RC
67 Ken Kravec .05 .15
68 Matt Alexander DP .05 .15
69 Ed Halicki .05 .15
70 Al Oliver DP .08 .25
71 Hal Dues .05 .15
72 Barry Evans DP RC .05 .15
73 Doug Bair .05 .15
74 Mike Hargrove .05 .15
75 Reggie Smith .15 .40
76 Mario Mendoza .05 .15
77 Mike Barlow .05 .15
78 Steve Dillard .05 .15
79 Bruce Robbins .05 .15
80 Rusty Staub .15 .40
81 Dave Stapleton RC .05 .15
82 Danny Heep RC .08 .25
Alan Knicely
Bobby Sprowl RC
83 Mike Proly .05 .15
84 Johnnie LeMaster .05 .15
85 Mike Caldwell .05 .15
86 Wayne Gross .05 .15
87 Rick Camp .05 .15
88 Joe Lefebvre RC .05 .15
89 Darrell Jackson .05 .15
90 Bake McBride .15 .40
91 Tim Stoddard DP .05 .15
92 Mike Easler .05 .15
93 Ed Glynn DP .05 .15
94 Harry Spilman DP .05 .15
95 Jim Sundberg .15 .40
96 Dave Beard RC .08 .25
Ernie Camacho RC
Pat Dempsey RC
97 Chris Speier .05 .15
98 Clint Hurdle .05 .15
99 Eric Wilkins .05 .15
100 Rod Carew .30 .75
101 Benny Ayala .05 .15
102 Dave Tobik .05 .15
103 Jerry Martin .05 .15
104 Terry Forster .15 .40
105 Jose Cruz .15 .40
106 Don Money .05 .15
107 Rich Wortham .05 .15
108 Bruce Benedict .05 .15
109 Mike Scott .15 .40
110 Carl Yastrzemski 1.00 2.50
111 Greg Minton .05 .15
112 Rusty Kuntz RC .08 .25
Fran Mullins RC
Leo Sutherland RC
113 Mike Phillips .05 .15
114 Tom Underwood .05 .15
115 Roy Smalley .15 .40
116 Joe Simpson .05 .15
117 Pete Falcone .05 .15
118 Kurt Bevacqua .05 .15
119 Tippy Martinez .05 .15
120 Larry Bowa .15 .40
121 Larry Harlow .05 .15
122 John Denny .05 .15
123 Al Cowens .05 .15
124 Jerry Garvin .05 .15
125 Andre Dawson .30 .75
126 Charlie Leibrandt RC .30 .75
127 Rudy Law .05 .15
128 Gary Allenson DP .05 .15
129 Art Howe .05 .15
130 Larry Gura .05 .15
131 Keith Moreland RC .05 .15
132 Tommy Boggs .05 .15
133 Jeff Cox RC .05 .15
134 Steve Mura .05 .15
135 Gorman Thomas .15 .40
136 Doug Capilla .05 .15
137 Hosken Powell .05 .15
138 Rich Dotson DP RC .05 .15
139 Oscar Gamble .05 .15
140 Bob Forsch .05 .15
141 Miguel Dilone .05 .15
142 Jackson Todd .05 .15
143 Dan Meyer .05 .15
144 Allen Ripley .05 .15
145 Mickey Rivers .05 .15
146 Bobby Castillo .05 .15
147 Dale Berra .05 .15
148 Randy Niemann .05 .15
149 Joe Nolan RC .05 .15
150 Mark Fidrych .15 .40
151 Claudell Washington .05 .15
152 John Urrea .05 .15
153 Tom Poquette .05 .15
154 Rick Langford .05 .15
155 Chris Chambliss .15 .40
156 Bob McClure .05 .15
157 John Wathan .05 .15
158 Fergie Jenkins .15 .40
159 Brian Doyle .05 .15
160 Garry Maddox .05 .15
161 Dan Graham .05 .15
162 Doug Corbett RC .05 .15
163 Bill Almon .05 .15
164 LaMarr Hoyt RC .30 .75
165 Tony Scott .05 .15
166 Floyd Bannister .05 .15
167 Terry Whitfield .05 .15
168 Don Robinson DP .05 .15
169 John Mayberry .05 .15
170 Ross Grimsley .05 .15
171 Gene Richards .05 .15
172 Gary Woods .05 .15
173 Bump Wills .05 .15
174 Doug Rau .05 .15
175 Dave Collins .05 .15
176 Mike Krukow .05 .15
177 Rick Peters RC .05 .15
178 Jim Essian DP .05 .15
179 Rudy May .05 .15
180 Pete Rose 2.00 5.00
181 Elias Sosa .05 .15
182 Bob Grich .15 .40
183 Dick Davis DP .05 .15
184 Jim Dwyer .05 .15
185 Dennis Leonard .05 .15
186 Wayne Nordhagen .05 .15
187 Mike Parrott .05 .15
188 Doug DeCinces .05 .15
189 Craig Swan .05 .15
190 Cesar Cedeno .15 .40
191 Rick Sutcliffe .15 .40
192 Terry Harper RC .08 .25
Ed Miller RC
Rafael Ramirez RC
193 Pete Vuckovich .05 .15
194 Rod Scurry RC .05 .15
195 Rich Murray RC .05 .15
196 Duffy Dyer .05 .15
197 Jim Kern .05 .15
198 Jerry Dybzinski RC .05 .15
199 Chuck Rainey .05 .15
200 George Foster .15 .40
201 Johnny Bench RB .30 .75
202 Steve Carlton RB .15 .40
203 Bill Gullickson RB .15 .40
204 Ron LeFlore RB .15 .40
Rodney Scott
205 Pete Rose RB .60 1.50
206 Mike Schmidt RB .60 1.50
207 Ozzie Smith RB .75 2.00
208 Willie Wilson RB .15 .40
209 Dickie Thon DP .05 .15
210 Jim Palmer .30 .75
211 Derrel Thomas .05 .15
212 Steve Nicosia .05 .15
213 Al Holland RC .05 .15
214 Ralph Botting .08 .25
Jim Dorsey RC
John Harris RC
215 Larry Hisle .05 .15
216 John Henry Johnson .05 .15
217 Rich Hebner .05 .15
218 Paul Splittorff .05 .15
219 Ken Landreaux .05 .15
220 Tom Seaver .60 1.50
221 Bob Davis .05 .15
222 Jorge Orta .05 .15
223 Roy Lee Jackson RC .05 .15
224 Pat Zachry .05 .15
225 Ruppert Jones .05 .15
226 Manny Sanguillen DP .08 .25
227 Fred Martinez RC .05 .15
228 Tom Paciorek .05 .15
229 Rollie Fingers .15 .40
230 George Hendrick .15 .40
231 Joe Beckwith .05 .15
232 Mickey Klutts .05 .15
233 Skip Lockwood .05 .15
234 Lou Whitaker .30 .75
235 Scott Sanderson .05 .15
236 Mike Ivie .05 .15
237 Charlie Moore .05 .15
238 Willie Hernandez .05 .15
239 Rick Miller DP .05 .15
240 Nolan Ryan 3.00 8.00
241 Checklist 122-242 DP .08 .25
242 Chet Lemon .15 .40
243 Sal Butera RC .05 .15
244 Tito Landrum RC .08 .25
Al Olmsted RC

Andy Rincon RC
245 Ed Figueroa .05 .15
246 Ed Ott DP .05 .15
247 Glenn Hubbard DP .05 .15
248 Joey McLaughlin .05 .15
249 Larry Cox .05 .15
250 Ron Guidry .15 .40
251 Tom Brookens .05 .15
252 Victor Cruz .05 .15
253 Dave Bergman .05 .15
254 Ozzie Smith 2.00 5.00
255 Mark Littell .05 .15
256 Bombo Rivera .05 .15
257 Rennie Stennett .05 .15
258 Joe Price RC .05 .15
259 Juan Berenguer 2.00 5.00
Hubie Brooks RC
Mookie Wilson RC
260 Ron Cey .15 .40
261 Rickey Henderson 4.00 10.00
262 Sammy Stewart .05 .15
263 Brian Downing .15 .40
264 Jim Norris .05 .15
265 John Candelaria .15 .40
266 Tom Herr .05 .15
267 Stan Bahnsen .05 .15
268 Jerry Royster .05 .15
269 Ken Forsch .05 .15
270 Greg Luzinski .15 .40
271 Bill Castro .05 .15
272 Bruce Kimm .05 .15
273 Stan Papi .05 .15
274 Craig Chamberlain .05 .15
275 Dwight Evans .30 .75
276 Dan Spillner .05 .15
277 Alfredo Griffin .05 .15
278 Rick Sofield .05 .15
279 Bob Knepper .05 .15
280 Ken Griffey .15 .40
281 Fred Stanley .05 .15
282 Rick Anderson RC .08 .25
Greg Biercevicz
Rodney Craig
283 Billy Sample .05 .15
284 Brian Kingman .05 .15
285 Jerry Turner .05 .15
286 Dave Frost .05 .15
287 Lenn Sakata .05 .15
288 Bob Clark .05 .15
289 Mickey Hatcher .05 .15
290 Bob Boone DP .08 .25
291 Aurelio Lopez .05 .15
292 Mike Squires .05 .15
293 Charlie Lea RC .05 .15
294 Mike Tyson DP .05 .15
295 Hal McRae .15 .40
296 Bill Nahorodny DP .05 .15
297 Bob Bailor .05 .15
298 Buddy Solomon .05 .15
299 Elliott Maddox .05 .15
300 Paul Molitor .60 1.50
301 Matt Keough .05 .15
302 Jack Perconte RC 3.00 8.00
Mike Scioscia RC
Fernando Valenzuela RC
303 Johnny Oates .15 .40
304 John Castino .05 .15
305 Ken Clay .05 .15
306 Juan Beniquez DP .05 .15
307 Gene Garber .05 .15
308 Rick Manning .05 .15
309 Luis Salazar RC .30 .75
310 Vida Blue DP .08 .25
311 Freddie Patek .05 .15
312 Rick Rhoden .05 .15
313 Luis Pujols .05 .15
314 Rich Dauer .05 .15
315 Kirk Gibson RC 3.00 8.00
316 Craig Minetto .05 .15
317 Lonnie Smith .15 .40
318 Steve Yeager .15 .40
319 Rowland Office .05 .15
320 Tom Burgmeier .05 .15
321 Leon Durham RC .30 .75
322 Neil Allen .05 .15
323 Jim Morrison DP .05 .15
324 Mike Willis .05 .15
325 Ray Knight .15 .40
326 Biff Pocoroba .05 .15
327 Moose Haas .05 .15
328 Dave Engle RC .08 .25
Greg Johnston
Gary Ward
329 Joaquin Andujar .15 .40
330 Frank White .15 .40
331 Dennis Lamp .05 .15
332 Lee Lacy DP .05 .15
333 Sid Monge .05 .15
334 Dane Iorg .05 .15
335 Rick Cerone .05 .15
336 Eddie Whitson .05 .15
337 Lynn Jones .05 .15
338 Checklist 243-363 .15 .40
339 John Ellis .05 .15
340 Bruce Kison .05 .15
341 Dwayne Murphy .05 .15
342 Eric Rasmussen DP .05 .15
343 Frank Taveras .05 .15
344 Byron McLaughlin .05 .15
345 Warren Cromartie .05 .15
346 Larry Christenson DP .05 .15
347 Harold Baines RC 1.25 3.00
348 Bob Sykes .05 .15
349 Glenn Hoffman RC .05 .15
350 J.R. Richard .15 .40
351 Otto Velez .05 .15
352 Dick Tidrow DP .05 .15
353 Terry Kennedy .05 .15
354 Mario Soto .15 .40
355 Bob Horner .15 .40
356 George Stablein RC .08 .25
Craig Stimac RC
Tom Tellmann RC
357 Jim Slaton .05 .15
358 Mark Wagner .05 .15
359 Tom Hausman .05 .15
360 Willie Wilson .15 .40
361 Joe Strain .05 .15
362 Bo Diaz .05 .15
363 Geoff Zahn .05 .15
364 Mike Davis RC .08 .25
365 Graig Nettles DP .08 .25
366 Mike Ramsey RC .08 .25
367 Dennis Martinez .15 .40
368 Leon Roberts .05 .15
369 Frank Tanana .15 .40
370 Dave Winfield .30 .75
371 Charlie Hough .15 .40
372 Jay Johnstone .05 .15
373 Pat Underwood .05 .15
374 Tommy Hutton .05 .15
375 Dave Concepcion .15 .40
376 Ron Reed .05 .15
377 Jerry Morales .05 .15
378 Dave Rader .05 .15
379 Lary Sorensen .05 .15
380 Willie Stargell .30 .75
381 Carlos Lezcano RC .08 .25
Steve Macko
Randy Martz RC
382 Paul Mirabella RC .05 .15
383 Eric Soderholm DP .05 .15
384 Mike Sadek .05 .15
385 Joe Sambito .05 .15
386 Dave Edwards .05 .15
387 Phil Niekro .15 .40
388 Andre Thornton .15 .40
389 Marty Pattin .05 .15
390 Cesar Geronimo .05 .15
391 Dave Lemanczyk DP .05 .15
392 Lance Parrish .15 .40
393 Broderick Perkins .05 .15
394 Woodie Fryman .05 .15
395 Scot Thompson .05 .15
396 Bill Campbell .05 .15
397 Julio Cruz .05 .15
398 Ross Baumgarten .05 .15
399 Mike Boddicker RC .30 .75
Mark Corey
Floyd Rayford RC
400 Reggie Jackson .60 1.50
401 George Brett ALCS 1.00 2.50
402 NL Champs .30 .75
Phillies squeak
past Astros
(Phillies celebrating)
403 Larry Bowa WS .30 .75
404 Tug McGraw WS .30 .75
405 Nino Espinosa .05 .15
406 Dickie Noles .05 .15
407 Ernie Whitt .05 .15
408 Fernando Arroyo .05 .15
409 Larry Herndon .05 .15
410 Bert Campaneris .15 .40
411 Terry Puhl .05 .15
412 Britt Burns RC .05 .15
413 Tony Bernazard .05 .15
414 John Pacella DP RC .05 .15
415 Ben Oglivie .15 .40
416 Gary Alexander .05 .15
417 Dan Schatzeder .05 .15
418 Bobby Brown .05 .15
419 Tom Hume .05 .15
420 Keith Hernandez .15 .40
421 Bob Stanley .05 .15
422 Dan Ford .05 .15
423 Shane Rawley .05 .15
424 Tim Lollar RC .08 .25
Bruce Robinson
Dennis Werth RC
425 Al Bumbry .05 .15
426 Warren Brusstar .05 .15
427 John D'Acquisto .05 .15
428 John Stearns .05 .15
429 Mick Kelleher .05 .15
430 Jim Bibby .05 .15
431 Dave Roberts .05 .15
432 Len Barker .15 .40
433 Rance Mulliniks .05 .15
434 Roger Erickson .05 .15
435 Jim Spencer .05 .15
436 Gary Lucas RC .05 .15
437 Mike Heath DP .05 .15
438 John Montefusco .05 .15
439 Denny Walling .05 .15
440 Jerry Reuss .05 .15
441 Ken Reitz .05 .15
442 Ron Pruitt .05 .15
443 Jim Beattie DP .05 .15
444 Garth Iorg .05 .15
445 Ellis Valentine .05 .15
446 Checklist 364-484 .15 .40
447 Junior Kennedy DP .05 .15
448 Tim Corcoran .05 .15
449 Paul Mitchell .05 .15
450 Dave Kingman DP .08 .25
451 Chris Bando RC .08 .25
Tom Brennan RC
Sandy Wihtol
452 Renie Martin .05 .15
453 Rob Wilfong DP .05 .15
454 Andy Hassler .05 .15
455 Rick Burleson .05 .15
456 Jeff Reardon RC .60 1.50
457 Mike Lum .05 .15
458 Randy Jones .15 .40
459 Greg Gross .05 .15
460 Rich Gossage .15 .40
461 Dave McKay RC .05 .15
462 Jack Brohamer .05 .15
463 Milt May .05 .15
464 Adrian Devine .05 .15
465 Bill Russell .15 .40
466 Bob Molinaro .05 .15
467 Dave Stieb .15 .40
468 John Wockenfuss .05 .15
469 Jeff Leonard .15 .40
470 Manny Trillo .05 .15
471 Mike Vail .05 .15
472 Dyar Miller DP .05 .15
473 Jose Cardenal .05 .15
474 Mike LaCoss .05 .15
475 Buddy Bell .15 .40
476 Jerry Koosman .15 .40
477 Luis Gomez .05 .15
478 Juan Eichelberger RC .05 .15
479 Tim Raines RC 1.50 4.00
Roberto Ramos RC
Bobby Pate RC
480 Carlton Fisk .30 .75
481 Bob Lacey DP .05 .15
482 Jim Gantner .05 .15
483 Mike Griffin RC .08 .25
484 Max Venable DP RC .05 .15
485 Garry Templeton .15 .40
486 Marc Hill .05 .15
487 Dewey Robinson .05 .15
488 Damaso Garcia RC .05 .15
489 John Littlefield RC .05 .15
Photo on card believed to be Mark Riggins
490 Eddie Murray 1.00 2.50
491 Gordy Pladson RC .05 .15
492 Barry Foote .05 .15
493 Dan Quisenberry .05 .15
494 Bob Walk RC .30 .75
495 Dusty Baker .15 .40
496 Paul Dade .05 .15
497 Fred Norman .05 .15
498 Pat Putnam .05 .15
499 Frank Pastore .05 .15
500 Jim Rice .15 .40
501 Tim Foli DP .05 .15
502 Chris Bourjos RC .08 .25
Al Hargesheimer RC
Mike Rowland RC
503 Steve McCatty .05 .15
504 Dale Murphy .30 .75
505 Jason Thompson .05 .15
506 Phil Huffman .05 .15
507 Jamie Quirk .05 .15
508 Rob Dressler .05 .15
509 Pete Mackanin .05 .15
510 Lee Mazzilli .15 .40
511 Wayne Garland .05 .15
512 Gary Thomasson .05 .15
513 Frank LaCorte .05 .15
514 George Riley RC .05 .15
515 Robin Yount 1.00 2.50
516 Doug Bird .05 .15
517 Richie Zisk .05 .15
518 Grant Jackson .05 .15
519 John Tamargo DP .05 .15
520 Steve Stone .05 .15
521 Sam Mejias .05 .15
522 Mike Colbern .05 .15
523 John Fulgham .05 .15
524 Willie Aikens .05 .15
525 Mike Torrez .05 .15
526 Marty Bystrom RC .08 .25
Jay Loviglio RC
Jim Wright
527 Danny Goodwin .05 .15
528 Gary Matthews .15 .40
529 Dave LaRoche .05 .15
530 Steve Garvey .30 .75
531 John Curtis .05 .15
532 Bill Stein .05 .15
533 Jesus Figueroa RC .05 .15
534 Dave Smith RC .30 .75
535 Omar Moreno .05 .15
536 Bob Owchinko DP .05 .15
537 Ron Hodges .05 .15
538 Tom Griffin .05 .15
539 Rodney Scott .05 .15
540 Mike Schmidt DP .75 2.00
541 Steve Swisher .05 .15
542 Larry Bradford DP .05 .15
543 Terry Crowley .05 .15
544 Rich Gale .05 .15
545 Johnny Grubb .05 .15
546 Paul Moskau .05 .15
547 Mario Guerrero .05 .15
548 Dave Goltz .05 .15
549 Jerry Remy .05 .15
550 Tommy John .15 .40
551 Vance Law RC .30 .75
Tony Pena RC
Pascual Perez RC
552 Steve Trout .05 .15
553 Tim Blackwell .05 .15
554 Bert Blyleven UER .15 .40
(1 is missing from
1980 on card back)
555 Cecil Cooper .15 .40
556 Jerry Mumphrey .05 .15
557 Chris Knapp .05 .15
558 Barry Bonnell .05 .15
559 Willie Montanez .05 .15
560 Joe Morgan .30 .75
561 Dennis Littlejohn .05 .15
562 Checklist 485-605 .15 .40
563 Jim Kaat .15 .40
564 Ron Hassey DP .05 .15
565 Burt Hooton .05 .15
566 Del Unser .05 .15
567 Mark Bomback RC .05 .15
568 Dave Revering .05 .15
569 Al Williams DP RC .05 .15
570 Ken Singleton .15 .40
571 Todd Cruz .05 .15
572 Jack Morris .30 .75
573 Phil Garner .15 .40
574 Bill Caudill .05 .15
575 Tony Perez .30 .75
576 Reggie Cleveland .05 .15
577 Luis Leal RC .08 .25
Brian Milner RC
Ken Schrom RC
578 Bill Gullickson RC .30 .75
579 Tim Flannery .05 .15
580 Don Baylor .15 .40
581 Roy Howell .05 .15
582 Gaylord Perry .15 .40
583 Larry Milbourne .05 .15
584 Randy Lerch .05 .15
585 Amos Otis .15 .40
586 Silvio Martinez .05 .15
587 Jeff Newman .05 .15
588 Gary Lavelle .05 .15
589 Lamar Johnson .05 .15
590 Bruce Sutter .30 .75
591 John Lowenstein .05 .15
592 Steve Comer .05 .15
593 Steve Kemp .05 .15
594 Preston Hanna DP .05 .15
595 Butch Hobson .05 .15
596 Jerry Augustine .05 .15
597 Rafael Landestoy .05 .15
598 George Vukovich DP RC .05 .15
599 Dennis Kinney RC .05 .15
600 Johnny Bench .60 1.50
601 Don Aase .05 .15
602 Bobby Murcer .15 .40
603 John Verhoeven .05 .15
604 Rob Picciolo .05 .15
605 Don Sutton .15 .40
606 Bruce Berenyi RC .08 .25
Geoff Combe RC
Paul Householder RC DP
607 David Palmer .05 .15
608 Greg Pryor .05 .15
609 Lynn McGlothen .05 .15
610 Darrell Porter .05 .15
611 Rick Matula DP .05 .15
612 Duane Kuiper .05 .15
613 Jim Anderson .05 .15
614 Dave Rozema .05 .15
615 Rick Dempsey .05 .15
616 Rick Wise .05 .15
617 Craig Reynolds .05 .15
618 John Milner .05 .15
619 Steve Henderson .05 .15
620 Dennis Eckersley .30 .75
621 Tom Donohue .05 .15
622 Randy Moffitt .05 .15
623 Sal Bando .15 .40
624 Bob Welch .15 .40
625 Bill Buckner .15 .40
626 Dave Steffen RC .08 .25
Jerry Ujdur RC
Roger Weaver RC
627 Luis Tiant .15 .40
628 Vic Correll .05 .15
629 Tony Armas .15 .40
630 Steve Carlton .30 .75
631 Ron Jackson .05 .15
632 Alan Bannister .05 .15
633 Bill Lee .15 .40
634 Doug Flynn .05 .15
635 Bobby Bonds .15 .40
636 Al Hrabosky .15 .40
637 Jerry Narron .05 .15
638 Checklist 606-726 .15 .40
639 Carney Lansford .15 .40
640 Dave Parker .15 .40
641 Mark Belanger .05 .15
642 Vern Ruhle .05 .15
643 Lloyd Moseby RC .30 .75
644 Ramon Aviles DP .05 .15
645 Rick Reuschel .15 .40
646 Marvis Foley RC .05 .15
647 Dick Drago .05 .15
648 Darrell Evans .15 .40
649 Manny Sarmiento .05 .15
650 Bucky Dent .15 .40
651 Pedro Guerrero .15 .40
652 John Montague .05 .15
653 Bill Fahey .05 .15
654 Ray Burris .05 .15
655 Dan Driessen .05 .15
656 Jon Matlack .05 .15
657 Mike Cubbage DP .05 .15
658 Milt Wilcox .05 .15
659 John Flinn .30 .75
Ed Romero
Ned Yost
660 Gary Carter .30 .75
661 Orioles Team CL .15 .40
Earl Weaver MG
662 Red Sox Team CL .15 .40
Ralph Houk MG
663 Angels Team CL .15 .40
Jim Fregosi MG
664 White Sox CL .15 .40
Tony LaRussa MG
665 Indians Team CL .15 .40
Dave Garcia MG
666 Tigers Team CL .15 .40
Sparky Anderson MG
667 Royals Team CL .15 .40
Jim Frey MG
668 Brewers Team CL .15 .40
Bob Rodgers MG
669 Twins Team CL. .15 .40
John Goryl MG
670 Yankees Team CL .15 .40
Gene Michael MG
671 A's Team CL .30 .75
Billy Martin MG
672 Mariners Team CL .15 .40
Maury Wills MG
673 Rangers Team CL .15 .40
Don Zimmer MG
674 Blue Jays Team CL .15 .40
Bobby Mattick MG
675 Braves Team CL .15 .40
Bobby Cox MG
676 Cubs Team CL .15 .40
Joe Amalfitano MG
677 Reds Team CL .15 .40
John McNamara MG
678 Astros Team CL .15 .40
Bill Virdon MG
679 Dodgers Team CL .30 .75
Tom Lasorda MG
680 Expos Team CL .15 .40
Dick Williams MG
681 Mets Team CL .30 .75
Joe Torre MG
682 Phillies Team CL .15 .40
Dallas Green MG
683 Pirates Team CL .15 .40
Chuck Tanner MG
684 Cardinals Team CL .15 .40
Whitey Herzog MG
685 Padres Team CL .15 .40
Frank Howard MG
686 Giants Team CL .15 .40
Dave Bristol MG
687 Jeff Jones RC .05 .15
688 Kiko Garcia .05 .15
689 Bruce Hurst RC .30 .75
Keith MacWhorter RC
Reid Nichols RC
690 Bob Watson .05 .15
691 Dick Ruthven .05 .15
692 Lenny Randle .05 .15
693 Steve Howe RC .08 .25
694 Bud Harrelson DP .08 .25
695 Kent Tekulve .05 .15
696 Alan Ashby .05 .15
697 Rick Waits .05 .15
698 Mike Jorgensen .05 .15
699 Glenn Abbott .05 .15
700 George Brett 1.50 4.00
701 Joe Rudi .15 .40
702 George Medich .05 .15
703 Alvis Woods .05 .15
704 Bill Travers DP .05 .15
705 Ted Simmons .15 .40
706 Dave Ford .05 .15
707 Dave Cash .05 .15
708 Doyle Alexander .05 .15
709 Alan Trammell DP .20 .50
710 Ron LeFlore DP .08 .25
711 Joe Ferguson .05 .15
712 Bill Bonham .05 .15
713 Bill North .05 .15
714 Pete Redfern .05 .15
715 Bill Madlock .15 .40
716 Glenn Borgmann .05 .15
717 Jim Barr DP .05 .15
718 Larry Biittner .05 .15
719 Sparky Lyle .15 .40
720 Fred Lynn .15 .40
721 Toby Harrah .15 .40
722 Joe Niekro .05 .15
723 Bruce Bochte .05 .15
724 Lou Piniella .15 .40
725 Steve Rogers .15 .40
726 Rick Monday .15 .40

1981 Topps Traded

For the first time since 1976, Topps issued a 132-card factory boxed "traded" set in 1981, issued exclusively through hobby dealers. This set was sequentially numbered, alphabetically, from 727 to 858 and carries the same design as the regular issue 1981 Topps set. There are no key Rookie Cards in this set although Hubie Brooks, Tim Raines, Jeff Reardon, and Fernando Valenzuela are depicted in their rookie year for cards. The key extended Rookie Card in the set is Danny Ainge. According to reports at the time, dealers were required to order a minimum of two cases, which cost them $4.50 per set.

COMP.FACT.SET (132) 10.00 25.00
727 Danny Ainge XRC 2.00 5.00
728 Doyle Alexander .08 .25
729 Gary Alexander .08 .25
730 Bill Almon .08 .25
731 Joaquin Andujar .40 1.00
732 Bob Bailor .08 .25
733 Juan Beniquez .08 .25
734 Dave Bergman .08 .25
735 Tony Bernazard .08 .25
736 Larry Biittner .08 .25
737 Doug Bird .08 .25
738 Bert Blyleven .40 1.00
739 Mark Bomback .08 .25
740 Bobby Bonds .40 1.00
741 Rick Bosetti .08 .25
742 Hubie Brooks .75 2.00
743 Rick Burleson .08 .25
744 Ray Burris .08 .25
745 Jeff Burroughs .40 1.00
746 Enos Cabell .08 .25
747 Ken Clay .08 .25
748 Mark Clear .08 .25
749 Larry Cox .08 .25
750 Hector Cruz .08 .25
751 Victor Cruz .08 .25
752 Mike Cubbage .08 .25
753 Dick Davis .08 .25
754 Brian Doyle .08 .25
755 Dick Drago .08 .25
756 Leon Durham .40 1.00
757 Jim Dwyer .08 .25
758 Dave Edwards UER .08 .25
No birthdate on card
759 Jim Essian .08 .25
760 Bill Fahey .08 .25
761 Rollie Fingers .40 1.00
762 Carlton Fisk .75 2.00
763 Barry Foote .08 .25
764 Ken Forsch .08 .25
765 Kiko Garcia .08 .25
766 Cesar Geronimo .08 .25
767 Gary Gray XRC .08 .25
768 Mickey Hatcher .08 .25
769 Steve Henderson .08 .25
770 Marc Hill .08 .25
771 Butch Hobson .08 .25
772 Rick Honeycutt .08 .25
773 Roy Howell .08 .25
774 Mike Ivie .08 .25
775 Roy Lee Jackson .08 .25
776 Cliff Johnson .08 .25
777 Randy Jones .40 1.00
778 Ruppert Jones .08 .25
779 Mick Kelleher .08 .25
780 Terry Kennedy .08 .25
781 Dave Kingman .40 1.00
782 Bob Knepper .08 .25
783 Ken Kravec .08 .25
784 Bob Lacey .08 .25
785 Dennis Lamp .08 .25
786 Rafael Landestoy .08 .25
787 Ken Landreaux .08 .25
788 Carney Lansford .40 1.00
789 Dave LaRoche .08 .25
790 Joe Lefebvre .08 .25
791 Ron LeFlore .40 1.00
792 Randy Lerch .08 .25
793 Sixto Lezcano .08 .25
794 John Littlefield .08 .25
795 Mike Lum .08 .25
796 Greg Luzinski .40 1.00
797 Fred Lynn .40 1.00
798 Jerry Martin .08 .25
799 Buck Martinez .08 .25
800 Gary Matthews .40 1.00
801 Mario Mendoza .08 .25
802 Larry Milbourne .08 .25
803 Rick Miller .08 .25
804 John Montefusco .08 .25
805 Jerry Morales .08 .25
806 Jose Morales .08 .25
807 Joe Morgan .75 2.00
808 Jerry Mumphrey .08 .25
809 Gene Nelson XRC .08 .25
810 Ed Ott .08 .25
811 Bob Owchinko .08 .25
812 Gaylord Perry .40 1.00
813 Mike Phillips .08 .25
814 Darrell Porter .08 .25
815 Mike Proly .08 .25
816 Tim Raines 2.00 5.00
817 Lenny Randle .08 .25
818 Doug Rau .08 .25
819 Jeff Reardon .75 2.00
820 Ken Reitz .08 .25
821 Steve Renko .08 .25
822 Rick Reuschel .40 1.00
823 Dave Revering .08 .25
824 Dave Roberts .08 .25
825 Leon Roberts .08 .25
826 Joe Rudi .40 1.00
827 Kevin Saucier .08 .25
828 Tony Scott .08 .25
829 Bob Shirley .08 .25
830 Ted Simmons .40 1.00
831 Lary Sorensen .08 .25
832 Jim Spencer .08 .25
833 Harry Spilman .08 .25
834 Fred Stanley .08 .25
835 Rusty Staub .40 1.00
836 Bill Stein .08 .25
837 Joe Strain .08 .25
838 Bruce Sutter .75 2.00
839 Don Sutton .40 1.00
840 Steve Swisher .08 .25
841 Frank Tanana .40 1.00
842 Gene Tenace .40 1.00
843 Jason Thompson .08 .25
844 Dickie Thon .08 .25
845 Bill Travers .08 .25
846 Tom Underwood .08 .25
847 John Urrea .08 .25
848 Mike Vail .08 .25
849 Ellis Valentine .08 .25
850 Fernando Valenzuela 4.00 10.00
851 Pete Vuckovich .08 .25
852 Mark Wagner .08 .25
853 Bob Walk .40 1.00
854 Claudell Washington .08 .25
855 Dave Winfield .75 2.00
856 Geoff Zahn .08 .25
857 Richie Zisk .08 .25
858 Checklist 727-858 .08 .25

1982 Topps

The cards in this 792-card set measure the standard size. Cards were primarily distributed in 15-card wax packs and 51-card rack packs. The 1982 baseball series was the first of the largest sets Topps issued at one printing. The 66-card increase from the previous year's total eliminated the "double print" practice, that had occurred in every regular issue since 1978. Cards 1-6 depict Highlights of the strike-shortened 1981 season, cards 161-168 picture League Leaders, and there are subsets of AL (547-557) and NL (337-347) All-Stars (AS). The abbreviation "IA" in the checklist is given for the 40 "In Action" cards introduced in this set. The team cards are actually Team Leader (TL) cards picturing the batting average and ERA leader for that team with a checklist back. All 26 of these cards were available from Topps on a perforated sheet through an offer on wax pack wrappers. Notable Rookie Cards include Brett Butler, Chili Davis, Cal Ripken Jr., Lee Smith, and Dave Stewart. Be careful when purchasing blank-back Cal Ripken Jr. Rookie Cards. Those cards are extremely likely to be counterfeit.

COMPLETE SET (792) 40.00 80.00
1 Steve Carlton HL .10 .30
2 Ron Davis HL .05 .15
3 Tim Raines HL .10 .30
4 Pete Rose HL .25 .60
5 Nolan Ryan HL 1.25 3.00
6 Fernando Valenzuela HL .25 .60
7 Scott Sanderson .05 .15
8 Rich Dauer .05 .15
9 Ron Guidry .10 .30
10 Ron Guidry IA .05 .15
11 Gary Alexander .05 .15
12 Moose Haas .05 .15
13 Lamar Johnson .05 .15
14 Steve Howe .05 .15
15 Ellis Valentine .05 .15
16 Steve Comer .05 .15
17 Darrell Evans .10 .30
18 Fernando Arroyo .05 .15
19 Ernie Whitt .05 .15
20 Garry Maddox .05 .15
21 Bob Bonner RC 15.00 40.00
Cal Ripken RC
Jeff Schneider RC
Birthdate for Jeff Scheider is wrong
22 Jim Beattie .05 .15
23 Willie Hernandez .05 .15
24 Dave Frost .05 .15
25 Jerry Remy .05 .15
26 Jorge Orta .05 .15
27 Tom Herr .05 .15
28 John Urrea .05 .15
29 Dwayne Murphy .05 .15
30 Tom Seaver .50 1.25
31 Tom Seaver IA .10 .30
32 Gene Garber .05 .15
33 Jerry Morales .05 .15
34 Joe Sambito .05 .15
35 Willie Aikens .05 .15
36 Al Oliver .25 .60
Doc Medich TL
37 Dan Graham .05 .15
38 Charlie Lea .05 .15
39 Lou Whitaker .10 .30
40 Dave Parker .10 .30
41 Dave Parker IA .05 .15
42 Rick Sofield .05 .15
43 Mike Cubbage .05 .15
44 Britt Burns .05 .15
45 Rick Cerone .05 .15
46 Jerry Augustine .05 .15
47 Jeff Leonard .05 .15
48 Bobby Castillo .05 .15
49 Alvis Woods .05 .15
50 Buddy Bell .10 .30
51 Jay Howell RC .30 .75
Carlos Lezcano
Ty Waller RC
52 Larry Andersen .05 .15
53 Greg Gross .05 .15
54 Ron Hassey .05 .15
55 Rick Burleson .05 .15
56 Mark Littell .05 .15
57 Craig Reynolds .05 .15
58 John D'Acquisto .05 .15
59 Rich Gedman .30 .75
60 Tony Armas .10 .30
61 Tommy Boggs .05 .15
62 Mike Tyson .05 .15
63 Mario Soto .10 .30
64 Lynn Jones .05 .15
65 Terry Kennedy .05 .15
66 Art Howe .75 2.00
Nolan Ryan TL
67 Rich Gale .05 .15
68 Roy Howell .05 .15
69 Al Williams .05 .15
70 Tim Raines .25 .60
71 Roy Lee Jackson .05 .15
72 Rick Auerbach .05 .15
73 Buddy Solomon .05 .15
74 Bob Clark .05 .15
75 Tommy John .10 .30
76 Greg Pryor .05 .15
77 Miguel Dilone .05 .15
78 George Medich .05 .15
79 Bob Bailor .05 .15
80 Jim Palmer .10 .30
81 Jim Palmer IA .05 .15

82 Bob Welch .10 .30
83 Steve Balboni RC .30 .75
Andy McGaffigan RC
Andre Robertson RC
84 Rennie Stennett .05 .15
85 Lynn McGlothen .05 .15
86 Dane Iorg .05 .15
87 Matt Keough .05 .15
88 Biff Pocoroba .05 .15
89 Steve Henderson .05 .15
90 Nolan Ryan 2.50 6.00
91 Carney Lansford .10 .30
92 Brad Havens .05 .15
93 Larry Hisle .05 .15
94 Andy Hassler .05 .15
95 Ozzie Smith 1.00 2.50
96 George Brett .50 1.25
Larry Gura TL
97 Paul Moskau .05 .15
98 Terry Bulling .05 .15
99 Barry Bonnell .05 .15
100 Mike Schmidt 1.25 3.00
101 Mike Schmidt IA .50 1.25
102 Dan Briggs .05 .15
103 Bob Lacey .05 .15
104 Rance Mulliniks .05 .15
105 Kirk Gibson .50 1.25
106 Enrique Romo .05 .15
107 Wayne Krenchicki .05 .15
108 Bob Sykes .05 .15
109 Dave Revering .05 .15
110 Carlton Fisk .25 .60
111 Carlton Fisk IA .10 .30
112 Billy Sample .05 .15
113 Steve McCatty .05 .15
114 Ken Landreaux .05 .15
115 Gaylord Perry .10 .30
116 Jim Wohlford .05 .15
117 Rawly Eastwick .10 .30
118 Terry Francona RC 2.00 5.00
Brad Mills RC
Bryn Smith RC
119 Joe Pittman .05 .15
120 Gary Lucas .05 .15
121 Ed Lynch .05 .15
122 Jamie Easterly UER .05 .15
(Photo actually
Reggie Cleveland)
123 Danny Goodwin .05 .15
124 Reid Nichols .05 .15
125 Danny Ainge .10 .30
126 Claudell Washington .25 .60
Rick Mahler TL
127 Lonnie Smith .05 .15
128 Frank Pastore .05 .15
129 Checklist 1-132 .10 .30
130 Julio Cruz .05 .15
131 Stan Bahnsen .05 .15
132 Lee May .05 .15
133 Pat Underwood .05 .15
134 Dan Ford .05 .15
135 Andy Rincon .05 .15
136 Lenn Sakata .05 .15
137 George Cappuzzello .05 .15
138 Tony Pena .10 .30
139 Jeff Jones .05 .15
140 Ron LeFlore .10 .30
141 Chris Bando .30 .75
Tom Brennan
Von Hayes RC
142 Dave LaRoche .05 .15
143 Mookie Wilson .10 .30
144 Fred Breining .05 .15
145 Bob Horner .10 .30
146 Mike Griffin .05 .15
147 Denny Walling .05 .15
148 Mickey Klutts .05 .15
149 Pat Putnam .05 .15
150 Ted Simmons .10 .30
151 Dave Edwards .05 .15
152 Ramon Aviles .05 .15
153 Roger Erickson .05 .15
154 Dennis Werth .05 .15
155 Otto Velez .05 .15
156 Rickey Henderson .50 1.25
Steve McCatty TL
157 Steve Crawford .05 .15
158 Brian Downing .10 .30
159 Larry Biittner .05 .15
160 Luis Tiant .10 .30
161 Bill Madlock .10 .30
Carney Lansford LL
162 Mike Schmidt .50 1.25
Tony Armas
Dwight Evans
Bobby Grich
Eddie Murray LL
163 Mike Schmidt .50 1.25
Eddie Murray LL
164 Tim Raines .50 1.25
Rickey Henderson LL
165 Tom Seaver .10 .30
Denny Martinez
Steve McCatty
Jack Morris
Pete Vuckovich LL
166 Fernando Valenzuela .10 .30
Len Barker LL
167 Nolan Ryan .75 2.00
Steve McCatty LL
168 Bruce Sutter .10 .30
Rollie Fingers LL
169 Charlie Leibrandt .05 .15
170 Jim Bibby .05 .15
171 Bob Brenly RC .60 1.50
Chili Davis RC
Bob Tufts RC
172 Bill Gullickson .05 .15
173 Jamie Quirk .05 .15
174 Dave Ford .05 .15
175 Jerry Mumphrey .05 .15
176 Dewey Robinson .05 .15
177 John Ellis .05 .15
178 Dyar Miller .05 .15
179 Steve Garvey .10 .30
180 Steve Garvey IA .05 .15
181 Silvio Martinez .05 .15
182 Larry Herndon .05 .15
183 Mike Proly .05 .15
184 Mick Kelleher .05 .15
185 Phil Niekro .10 .30
186 Keith Hernandez .10 .30
Bob Forsch TL
187 Jeff Newman .05 .15
188 Randy Martz .05 .15
189 Glenn Hoffman .05 .15
190 J.R. Richard .10 .30
191 Tim Wallach RC .60 1.50
192 Broderick Perkins .05 .15
193 Darrell Jackson .05 .15
194 Mike Vail .05 .15
195 Paul Molitor .10 .30
196 Willie Upshaw .30 .75
197 Shane Rawley .05 .15
198 Chris Speier .05 .15
199 Don Aase .05 .15
200 George Brett 1.25 3.00
201 George Brett IA .60 1.50
202 Rick Manning .05 .15
203 Jesse Barfield RC .60 1.50
Brian Milner
Boomer Wells RC
204 Gary Roenicke .05 .15
205 Neil Allen .05 .15
206 Tony Bernazard .05 .15
207 Rod Scurry .05 .15
208 Bobby Murcer .10 .30
209 Gary Lavelle .05 .15
210 Keith Hernandez .10 .30
211 Dan Petry .05 .15
212 Mario Mendoza .05 .15
213 Dave Stewart RC 1.00 2.50
214 Brian Asselstine .05 .15
215 Mike Krukow .05 .15
216 Chet Lemon .25 .60
Dennis Lamp TL
217 Bo McLaughlin .05 .15
218 Dave Roberts .05 .15
219 John Curtis .05 .15
220 Manny Trillo .05 .15
221 Jim Slaton .05 .15
222 Butch Wynegar .05 .15
223 Lloyd Moseby .05 .15
224 Bruce Bochte .05 .15
225 Mike Torrez .05 .15
226 Checklist 133-264 .25 .60
227 Ray Burris .05 .15
228 Sam Mejias .05 .15
229 Geoff Zahn .05 .15
230 Willie Wilson .10 .30
231 Mark Davis RC .30 .75
Bob Dernier RC
Ozzie Virgil RC
232 Terry Crowley .05 .15
233 Duane Kuiper .05 .15
234 Ron Hodges .05 .15
235 Mike Easler .05 .15
236 John Martin RC .08 .25
237 Rusty Kuntz .05 .15
238 Kevin Saucier .05 .15
239 Jon Matlack .05 .15
240 Bucky Dent .10 .30
241 Bucky Dent IA .05 .15
242 Milt May .05 .15
243 Bob Owchinko .05 .15
244 Rufino Linares .05 .15
245 Ken Reitz .05 .15
246 Hubie Brooks .25 .60
Mike Scott TL
247 Pedro Guerrero .10 .30
248 Frank LaCorte .05 .15
249 Tim Flannery .05 .15
250 Tug McGraw .10 .30
251 Fred Lynn .10 .30
252 Fred Lynn IA .05 .15
253 Chuck Baker .05 .15
254 Jorge Bell RC .60 1.50
255 Tony Perez .25 .60
256 Tony Perez IA .10 .30
257 Larry Harlow .05 .15
258 Bo Diaz .05 .15
259 Rodney Scott .05 .15
260 Bruce Sutter .25 .60
261 Howard Bailey RC .05 .15
Marty Castillo RC
Dave Rucker RC
(UER Rucker photo
is Roger Weaver)
262 Doug Bair .05 .15
263 Victor Cruz .05 .15
264 Dan Quisenberry .05 .15
265 Al Bumbry .05 .15
266 Rick Leach .05 .15
267 Kurt Bevacqua .05 .15
268 Rickey Keeton .05 .15
269 Jim Essian .05 .15
270 Rusty Staub .10 .30
271 Larry Bradford .05 .15
272 Bump Wills .05 .15
273 Doug Bird .05 .15
274 Bob Ojeda RC .30 .75
275 Bob Watson .05 .15
276 Rod Carew .25 .60
Ken Forsch TL
277 Terry Puhl .05 .15
278 John Littlefield .05 .15
279 Bill Russell .10 .30
280 Ben Oglivie .10 .30
281 John Verhoeven .05 .15
282 Ken Macha .05 .15
283 Brian Allard .05 .15
284 Bobby Grich .10 .30
285 Sparky Lyle .10 .30
286 Bill Fahey .05 .15
287 Alan Bannister .05 .15
288 Garry Templeton .10 .30
289 Bob Stanley .05 .15
290 Ken Singleton .10 .30
291 Vance Law .10 .30
Bob Long
Johnny Ray RC
292 David Palmer .05 .15
293 Rob Picciolo .05 .15
294 Mike LaCoss .05 .15
295 Jason Thompson .05 .15
296 Bob Walk .05 .15
297 Clint Hurdle .05 .15
298 Danny Darwin .05 .15
299 Steve Trout .05 .15
300 Reggie Jackson .25 .60
301 Reggie Jackson IA .10 .30
302 Doug Flynn .05 .15
303 Bill Caudill .05 .15
304 Johnnie LeMaster .05 .15
305 Don Sutton .10 .30
306 Don Sutton IA .05 .15
307 Randy Bass .30 .75
308 Charlie Moore .05 .15
309 Pete Redfern .05 .15
310 Mike Hargrove .05 .15
311 Dusty Baker .10 .30
Burt Hooton TL
312 Lenny Randle .05 .15
313 John Harris .05 .15
314 Buck Martinez .05 .15
315 Burt Hooton .05 .15
316 Steve Braun .05 .15
317 Dick Ruthven .05 .15
318 Mike Heath .05 .15
319 Dave Rozema .05 .15
320 Chris Chambliss .10 .30
321 Chris Chambliss IA .05 .15
322 Garry Hancock .05 .15
323 Bill Lee .10 .30
324 Steve Dillard .05 .15
325 Jose Cruz .10 .30
326 Pete Falcone .05 .15
327 Joe Nolan .05 .15
328 Ed Farmer .05 .15
329 U.L. Washington .05 .15
330 Rick Wise .05 .15
331 Benny Ayala .05 .15
332 Don Robinson .05 .15
333 Frank DiPino RC .05 .15
Marshall Edwards RC
Chuck Porter RC
334 Aurelio Rodriguez .05 .15
335 Jim Sundberg .10 .30
336 Tom Paciorek .25 .60
Glenn Abbott TL
337 Pete Rose AS .25 .60
338 Dave Lopes AS .05 .15
339 Mike Schmidt AS .50 1.25
340 Dave Concepcion AS .05 .15
341 Andre Dawson AS .05 .15
342A George Foster AS w/Auto .10 .30
342B George Foster AS .50 1.25
(W/o autograph)
343 Dave Parker AS .05 .15
344 Gary Carter AS .05 .15
345 F. Valenzuela AS .25 .60
346 Tom Seaver AS ERR .10 .30
('ed')
346B Tom Seaver AS COR .10 .30
347 Bruce Sutter AS .10 .30
348 Derrel Thomas .05 .15
349 George Frazier .05 .15
350 Thad Bosley .05 .15
351 Scott Brown RC .05 .15
Geoff Combe
Paul Householder
352 Dick Davis .05 .15
353 Jack O'Connor .05 .15
354 Roberto Ramos .05 .15
355 Dwight Evans .25 .60
356 Denny Lewallyn .05 .15
357 Butch Hobson .05 .15
358 Mike Parrott .05 .15
359 Jim Dwyer .05 .15
360 Len Barker .05 .15
361 Rafael Landestoy .05 .15
362 Jim Wright UER .05 .15
(Wrong Jim Wright
pictured)
363 Bob Molinaro .05 .15
364 Doyle Alexander .05 .15
365 Bill Madlock .10 .30
366 Luis Salazar .25 .60
Juan Eichelberger TL
367 Jim Kaat .10 .30
368 Alex Trevino .05 .15
369 Champ Summers .05 .15
370 Mike Norris .05 .15
371 Jerry Don Gleaton .05 .15
372 Luis Gomez .05 .15
373 Gene Nelson .05 .15
374 Tim Blackwell .05 .15
375 Dusty Baker .10 .30
376 Chris Welsh .05 .15
377 Kiko Garcia .05 .15
378 Mike Caldwell .05 .15
379 Rob Wilfong .05 .15
380 Dave Stieb .10 .30
381 Bruce Hurst .05 .15
Dave Schmidt RC
Julio Valdez RC
382 Joe Simpson .05 .15
383A Pascual Perez ERR 15.00 40.00
(No position
on front)
383B Pascual Perez COR .10 .30
384 Keith Moreland .05 .15
385 Ken Forsch .05 .15
386 Jerry White .05 .15
387 Tom Veryzer .05 .15
388 Joe Rudi .10 .30
389 George Vukovich .05 .15
390 Eddie Murray .50 1.25
391 Dave Tobik .05 .15
392 Rick Bosetti .05 .15
393 Al Hrabosky .05 .15
394 Checklist 265-396 .25 .60
395 Omar Moreno .05 .15
396 John Castino .25 .60
Fernando Arroyo TL
397 Ken Brett .05 .15
398 Mike Squires .05 .15
399 Pat Zachry .05 .15
400 Johnny Bench .50 1.25
401 Johnny Bench IA .25 .60
402 Bill Stein .05 .15
403 Jim Tracy .10 .30
404 Dickie Thon .05 .15
405 Rick Reuschel .10 .30
406 Al Holland .05 .15
407 Danny Boone .05 .15
408 Ed Romero .05 .15
409 Don Cooper .05 .15
410 Ron Cey .10 .30
411 Ron Cey IA .05 .15
412 Luis Leal .05 .15
413 Dan Meyer .05 .15
414 Elias Sosa .05 .15
415 Don Baylor .10 .30
416 Marty Bystrom .05 .15
417 Pat Kelly .05 .15
418 John Butcher .05 .15
Bobby Johnson RC
Dave Schmidt RC
419 Steve Stone .05 .15
420 George Hendrick .10 .30
421 Mark Clear .05 .15
422 Cliff Johnson .05 .15
423 Stan Papi .05 .15
424 Bruce Benedict .05 .15
425 John Candelaria .05 .15
426 Eddie Murray .25 .60
Sammy Stewart
427 Ron Oester .05 .15
428 LaMarr Hoyt .05 .15
429 John Wathan .05 .15
430 Vida Blue .10 .30
431 Vida Blue IA .05 .15
432 Mike Scott .10 .30
433 Alan Ashby .05 .15
434 Joe Lefebvre .05 .15
435 Robin Yount .75 2.00
436 Joe Strain .05 .15
437 Juan Berenguer .05 .15
438 Pete Mackanin .05 .15
439 Dave Righetti RC 1.00 2.50
440 Jeff Burroughs .05 .15
441 Danny Heep .05 .15
Billy Smith RC
Bobby Sprowl
442 Bruce Kison .05 .15
443 Mark Wagner .05 .15
444 Terry Forster .10 .30
445 Larry Parrish .05 .15
446 Wayne Garland .05 .15
447 Darrell Porter .05 .15
448 Darrell Porter IA .05 .15
449 Luis Aguayo .05 .15
450 Jack Morris .10 .30
451 Ed Miller .05 .15
452 Lee Smith RC 1.25 3.00
453 Art Howe .05 .15
454 Rick Langford .05 .15
455 Tom Burgmeier .05 .15
456 Bill Buckner .10 .30
Randy Martz TL
457 Tim Stoddard .05 .15
458 Willie Montanez .05 .15
459 Bruce Berenyi .05 .15
460 Jack Clark .10 .30
461 Rich Dotson .05 .15
462 Dave Chalk .05 .15
463 Jim Kern .05 .15
464 Juan Bonilla RC .08 .25
465 Lee Mazzilli .10 .30
466 Randy Lerch .05 .15
467 Mickey Hatcher .05 .15
468 Floyd Bannister .05 .15
469 Ed Ott .05 .15
470 John Mayberry .05 .15
471 Atlee Hammaker RC .05 .15
Mike Jones
Darryl Motley RC
472 Oscar Gamble .05 .15
473 Mike Stanton .05 .15
474 Ken Oberkfell .05 .15
475 Alan Trammell .10 .30
476 Brian Kingman .05 .15
477 Steve Yeager .10 .30
478 Ray Searage .05 .15
479 Rowland Office .05 .15
480 Steve Carlton .25 .60
481 Steve Carlton IA .10 .30
482 Glenn Hubbard .05 .15
483 Gary Woods .05 .15
484 Ivan DeJesus .05 .15
485 Kent Tekulve .05 .15
486 Jerry Mumphrey .10 .30
Tommy John TL
487 Bob McClure .05 .15
488 Ron Jackson .05 .15
489 Rick Dempsey .05 .15
490 Dennis Eckersley .25 .60
491 Checklist 397-528 .25 .60
492 Joe Price .05 .15
493 Chet Lemon .10 .30
494 Hubie Brooks .05 .15
495 Dennis Leonard .05 .15
496 Johnny Grubb .05 .15
497 Jim Anderson .05 .15
498 Dave Bergman .05 .15
499 Paul Mirabella .05 .15
500 Rod Carew .25 .60
501 Rod Carew IA .10 .30
502 Steve Bedrosian RC UER .60 1.50
(Photo actually Larry Owen)
Brett Butler RC
Larry Owen
503 Julio Gonzalez .05 .15
504 Rick Peters .05 .15
505 Graig Nettles .10 .30
506 Graig Nettles IA .05 .15
507 Terry Harper .05 .15
508 Jody Davis .05 .15
509 Harry Spilman .05 .15
510 Fernando Valenzuela .50 1.25
511 Ruppert Jones .05 .15
512 Jerry Dybzinski .05 .15
513 Rick Rhoden .05 .15
514 Joe Ferguson .05 .15
515 Larry Bowa .10 .30
516 Larry Bowa IA .05 .15
517 Mark Brouhard .05 .15
518 Garth Iorg .05 .15
519 Glenn Adams .05 .15
520 Mike Flanagan .05 .15
521 Bill Almon .05 .15
522 Chuck Rainey .05 .15
523 Gary Gray .05 .15
524 Tom Hausman .05 .15
525 Ray Knight .10 .30
526 Warren Cromartie .25 .60
Bill Gullickson TL
527 John Henry Johnson .05 .15
528 Matt Alexander .05 .15
529 Allen Ripley .05 .15
530 Dickie Noles .05 .15
531 Rich Bordi RC .05 .15
Mark Budaska RC
Kelvin Moore RC
532 Toby Harrah .10 .30
533 Joaquin Andujar .10 .30
534 Dave McKay .05 .15
535 Lance Parrish .10 .30
536 Rafael Ramirez .05 .15
537 Doug Capilla .05 .15
538 Lou Piniella .10 .30
539 Vern Ruhle .05 .15
540 Andre Dawson .10 .30
541 Barry Evans .05 .15
542 Ned Yost .05 .15
543 Bill Robinson .05 .15
544 Larry Christenson .05 .15
545 Reggie Smith .10 .30
546 Reggie Smith IA .05 .15
547 Rod Carew AS .10 .30
548 Willie Randolph AS .05 .15
549 George Brett AS .60 1.50
550 Bucky Dent AS .05 .15
551 Reggie Jackson AS .10 .30
552 Ken Singleton AS .05 .15
553 Dave Winfield AS .05 .15
554 Carlton Fisk AS .10 .30
555 Scott McGregor AS .05 .15
556 Jack Morris AS .05 .15
557 Rich Gossage AS .05 .15
558 John Tudor .10 .30
559 Mike Hargrove .10 .30
Bert Blyleven TL
560 Doug Corbett .05 .15
561 Glenn Brummer RC .05 .15
Luis DeLeon RC
Gene Roof RC
562 Mike O'Berry .05 .15
563 Ross Baumgarten .05 .15
564 Doug DeCinces .05 .15
565 Jackson Todd .05 .15
566 Mike Jorgensen .05 .15
567 Bob Babcock .05 .15
568 Joe Pettini .05 .15
569 Willie Randolph .10 .30
570 Willie Randolph IA .05 .15
571 Glenn Abbott .05 .15
572 Juan Beniquez .05 .15
573 Rick Waits .05 .15
574 Mike Ramsey .05 .15
575 Al Cowens .05 .15
576 Milt May .25 .60
Vida Blue TL
577 Rick Monday .10 .30
578 Shooty Babitt .05 .15
579 Rick Mahler .05 .15
580 Bobby Bonds .10 .30
581 Ron Reed .05 .15
582 Luis Pujols .05 .15
583 Tippy Martinez .05 .15
584 Hosken Powell .05 .15
585 Rollie Fingers .10 .30
586 Rollie Fingers IA .05 .15
587 Tim Lollar .05 .15
588 Dale Berra .05 .15
589 Dave Stapleton .05 .15
590 Al Oliver .10 .30
591 Al Oliver IA .05 .15
592 Craig Swan .05 .15
593 Billy Smith .05 .15
594 Renie Martin .05 .15
595 Dave Collins .05 .15
596 Damaso Garcia .05 .15
597 Wayne Nordhagen .05 .15
598 Bob Galasso .05 .15
599 Jay Loviglio .05 .15
Reggie Patterson RC
Leo Sutherland
600 Dave Winfield .10 .30
601 Sid Monge .05 .15
602 Freddie Patek .05 .15
603 Rich Hebner .05 .15
604 Orlando Sanchez .05 .15
605 Steve Rogers .10 .30
606 John Mayberry .10 .30
Dave Stieb TL
607 Leon Durham .05 .15
608 Jerry Royster .05 .15
609 Rick Sutcliffe .10 .30
610 Rickey Henderson 1.50 4.00
611 Joe Niekro .05 .15
612 Gary Ward .05 .15
613 Jim Gantner .05 .15
614 Juan Eichelberger .05 .15
615 Bob Boone .10 .30
616 Bob Boone IA .05 .15
617 Scott McGregor .05 .15
618 Tim Foli .05 .15
619 Bill Campbell .05 .15
620 Ken Griffey .10 .30
621 Ken Griffey IA .05 .15
622 Dennis Lamp .05 .15
623 Ron Gardenhire RC .30 .75
Terry Leach RC
Tim Leary RC
624 Fergie Jenkins .10 .30
625 Hal McRae .10 .30
626 Randy Jones .05 .15
627 Enos Cabell .05 .15
628 Bill Travers .05 .15
629 John Wockenfuss .05 .15
630 Joe Charboneau .10 .30
631 Gene Tenace .10 .30
632 Bryan Clark RC .08 .25
633 Mitchell Page .05 .15
634 Checklist 529-660 .25 .60
635 Ron Davis .05 .15
636 Pete Rose .50 1.25
Steve Carlton TL
637 Rick Camp .05 .15
638 John Milner .05 .15
639 Ken Kravec .05 .15
640 Cesar Cedeno .10 .30
641 Steve Mura .05 .15
642 Mike Scioscia .10 .30
643 Pete Vuckovich .05 .15
644 John Castino .05 .15
645 Frank White .10 .30
646 Frank White IA .05 .15
647 Warren Brusstar .05 .15
648 Jose Morales .05 .15
649 Ken Clay .05 .15
650 Carl Yastrzemski .75 2.00
651 Carl Yastrzemski IA .50 1.25
652 Steve Nicosia .05 .15
653 Tom Brunansky RC .60 1.50
Luis Sanchez RC
Daryl Sconiers RC
654 Jim Morrison .05 .15
655 Joel Youngblood .05 .15
656 Eddie Whitson .05 .15
657 Tom Poquette .05 .15
658 Tito Landrum .05 .15
659 Fred Martinez .05 .15
660 Dave Concepcion .10 .30
661 Dave Concepcion IA .05 .15
662 Luis Salazar .05 .15
663 Hector Cruz .05 .15
664 Dan Spillner .05 .15
665 Jim Clancy .05 .15
666 Steve Kemp .25 .60
Dan Petry TL
667 Jeff Reardon .10 .30
668 Dale Murphy .25 .60
669 Larry Milbourne .05 .15
670 Steve Kemp .05 .15
671 Mike Davis .05 .15
672 Bob Knepper .05 .15
673 Keith Drumwright .05 .15
674 Dave Goltz .05 .15
675 Cecil Cooper .10 .30
676 Sal Butera .05 .15
677 Alfredo Griffin .05 .15
678 Tom Paciorek .05 .15
679 Sammy Stewart .05 .15
680 Gary Matthews .10 .30
681 Mike Marshall RC .60 1.50
Ron Roenicke RC
Steve Sax RC
682 Jesse Jefferson .05 .15
683 Phil Garner .10 .30
684 Harold Baines .10 .30
685 Bert Blyleven .10 .30
686 Gary Allenson .05 .15
687 Greg Minton .05 .15
688 Leon Roberts .05 .15
689 Lary Sorensen .05 .15
690 Dave Kingman .10 .30
691 Dan Schatzeder .05 .15
692 Wayne Gross .05 .15
693 Cesar Geronimo .05 .15
694 Dave Wehrmeister .05 .15
695 Warren Cromartie .05 .15
696 Bill Madlock .25 .60
Eddie Solomon TL
697 John Montefusco .05 .15
698 Tony Scott .05 .15
699 Dick Tidrow .05 .15
700 George Foster .10 .30
701 George Foster IA .05 .15
702 Steve Renko .05 .15
703 Cecil Cooper .25 .60
Pete Vuckovich TL
704 Mickey Rivers .05 .15
705 Mickey Rivers IA .05 .15
706 Barry Foote .05 .15
707 Mark Bomback .05 .15
708 Gene Richards .05 .15
709 Don Money .05 .15
710 Jerry Reuss .05 .15
711 Dave Edler .30 .75
Dave Henderson RC
Reggie Walton RC
712 Dennis Martinez .10 .30
713 Del Unser .05 .15
714 Jerry Koosman .10 .30
715 Willie Stargell .25 .60
716 Willie Stargell IA .10 .30
717 Rick Miller .05 .15
718 Charlie Hough .10 .30
719 Jerry Narron .05 .15
720 Greg Luzinski .10 .30
721 Greg Luzinski IA .05 .15
722 Jerry Martin .05 .15
723 Junior Kennedy .05 .15
724 Dave Rosello .05 .15
725 Amos Otis .10 .30
726 Amos Otis IA .05 .15
727 Sixto Lezcano .05 .15
728 Aurelio Lopez .05 .15
729 Jim Spencer .05 .15
730 Gary Carter .10 .30
731 Mike Armstrong .05 .15
Doug Gwosdz RC
Fred Kuhaulua
732 Mike Lum .05 .15
733 Larry McWilliams .05 .15
734 Mike Ivie .05 .15
735 Rudy May .05 .15
736 Jerry Turner .05 .15
737 Reggie Cleveland .05 .15
738 Dave Engle .05 .15
739 Joey McLaughlin .05 .15
740 Dave Lopes .10 .30
741 Dave Lopes IA .05 .15
742 Dick Drago .05 .15
743 John Stearns .05 .15
744 Mike Witt .30 .75
745 Bake McBride .10 .30
746 Andre Thornton .05 .15
747 John Lowenstein .05 .15
748 Marc Hill .05 .15
749 Bob Shirley .05 .15
750 Jim Rice .10 .30
751 Rick Honeycutt .05 .15
752 Lee Lacy .05 .15
753 Tom Brookens .05 .15
754 Joe Morgan .10 .30
755 Joe Morgan IA .05 .15
756 Ken Griffey .10 .30
Tom Seaver TL
757 Tom Underwood .05 .15
758 Claudell Washington .05 .15
759 Paul Splittorff .05 .15
760 Bill Buckner .10 .30
761 Dave Smith .05 .15
762 Mike Phillips .05 .15
763 Tom Hume .05 .15
764 Steve Swisher .05 .15
765 Gorman Thomas .05 .15
766 Lenny Faedo RC .60 1.50
Kent Hrbek RC
Tim Laudner RC
767 Roy Smalley .05 .15
768 Jerry Garvin .05 .15
769 Richie Zisk .05 .15
770 Rich Gossage .10 .30
771 Rich Gossage IA .05 .15
772 Bert Campaneris .10 .30
773 John Denny .05 .15
774 Jay Johnstone .05 .15
775 Bob Forsch .05 .15
776 Mark Belanger .05 .15
777 Tom Griffin .05 .15
778 Kevin Hickey RC .08 .25
779 Grant Jackson .05 .15
780 Pete Rose 1.50 4.00
781 Pete Rose IA .50 1.25
782 Frank Taveras .05 .15
783 Greg Harris RC .08 .25
784 Milt Wilcox .05 .15
785 Dan Driessen .05 .15
786 Carney Lansford .25 .60
Mike Torrez TL
787 Fred Stanley .05 .15
788 Woodie Fryman .05 .15
789 Checklist 661-792 .25 .60
790 Larry Gura .05 .15
791 Bobby Brown .05 .15
792 Frank Tanana .10 .30

1982 Topps Traded

The cards in this 132-card set measure the standard size. These sets were shipped to hobby dealers in 100-ct cases. The 1982 Topps Traded or extended series is distinguished by a "T" printed after the number (located on the reverse). This was the first time Topps began a tradition of newly numbering (and alphabetizing) their traded series from 1T to 132T. All 131 player photos used in the set are completely new. Of this total, 112 individuals are seen in the uniform of their new team, 11 youngsters have been elevated to single card status from multi-player "Future Stars" cards, and eight more are entirely new to the 1982 Topps lineup. The backs are almost completely red in color with black print. There are no key Rookie Cards in this set. Although the Cal Ripken card is this set's most valuable card, it is not his Rookie Card since he had already been included in the 1982 regular set, albeit on a multi-player card.

Card	Low	High
COMP.FACT.SET (132)	90.00	150.00
1T Doyle Alexander	.20	.50
2T Jesse Barfield	1.25	3.00
3T Ross Baumgarten	.20	.50
4T Steve Bedrosian	.60	1.50
5T Mark Belanger	.20	.50
6T Kurt Bevacqua	.20	.50
7T Tim Blackwell	.20	.50
8T Vida Blue	.40	1.00
9T Bob Boone	.40	1.00
10T Larry Bowa	.40	1.00
11T Dan Briggs	.20	.50
12T Bobby Brown	.20	.50
13T Tom Brunansky	1.25	3.00
14T Jeff Burroughs	.20	.50
15T Enos Cabell	.20	.50
16T Bill Campbell	.20	.50
17T Bobby Castillo	.20	.50
18T Bill Caudill	.20	.50
19T Cesar Cedeno	.40	1.00
20T Dave Collins	.20	.50
21T Doug Corbett	.20	.50
22T Al Cowens	.20	.50
23T Chili Davis	1.25	3.00
24T Dick Davis	.20	.50
25T Ron Davis	.20	.50
26T Doug DeCinces	.20	.50
27T Ivan DeJesus	.20	.50
28T Bob Dernier	.20	.50
29T Bo Diaz	.20	.50
30T Roger Erickson	.20	.50
31T Jim Essian	.20	.50
32T Ed Farmer	.20	.50
33T Doug Flynn	.20	.50
34T Tim Foli	.20	.50
35T Dan Ford	.20	.50
36T George Foster	.40	1.00
37T Dave Frost	.20	.50
38T Rich Gale	.20	.50
39T Ron Gardenhire	.60	1.50
40T Ken Griffey	.40	1.00
41T Greg Harris	.20	.50
42T Von Hayes	.60	1.50
43T Larry Herndon	.20	.50
44T Kent Hrbek	1.25	3.00
45T Mike Ivie	.20	.50
46T Grant Jackson	.20	.50
47T Reggie Jackson	.75	2.00
48T Ron Jackson	.20	.50
49T Fergie Jenkins	.40	1.00
50T Lamar Johnson	.20	.50
51T Randy Johnson	.20	.50
52T Jay Johnstone	.20	.50
53T Mick Kelleher	.20	.50
54T Steve Kemp	.20	.50
55T Junior Kennedy	.20	.50
56T Jim Kern	.20	.50
57T Ray Knight	.40	1.00
58T Wayne Krenchicki	.20	.50
59T Mike Krukow	.20	.50
60T Duane Kuiper	.20	.50
61T Mike LaCoss	.20	.50
62T Chet Lemon	.40	1.00
63T Sixto Lezcano	.20	.50
64T Dave Lopes	.40	1.00
65T Jerry Martin	.20	.50
66T Renie Martin	.20	.50
67T John Mayberry	.20	.50
68T Lee Mazzilli	.40	1.00
69T Bake McBride	.40	1.00
70T Dan Meyer	.20	.50
71T Larry Milbourne	.20	.50
72T Eddie Milner	.20	.50
73T Sid Monge	.20	.50
74T John Montefusco	.20	.50
75T Jose Morales	.20	.50
76T Keith Moreland	.20	.50
77T Jim Morrison	.20	.50
78T Rance Mulliniks	.20	.50
79T Steve Mura	.20	.50
80T Gene Nelson	.20	.50
81T Joe Nolan	.20	.50
82T Dickie Noles	.20	.50
83T Al Oliver	.40	1.00
84T Jorge Orta	.20	.50
85T Tom Paciorek	.20	.50
86T Larry Parrish	.20	.50
87T Jack Perconte	.20	.50
88T Gaylord Perry	.40	1.00
89T Rob Picciolo	.20	.50
90T Joe Pittman	.20	.50
91T Hosken Powell	.20	.50
92T Mike Proly	.20	.50
93T Greg Pryor	.20	.50
94T Charlie Puleo	.20	.50
95T Shane Rawley	.20	.50
96T Johnny Ray	.60	1.50
97T Dave Revering	.20	.50
98T Cal Ripken	90.00	150.00
99T Allen Ripley	.20	.50
100T Bill Robinson	.20	.50
101T Aurelio Rodriguez	.20	.50
102T Joe Rudi	.40	1.00
103T Steve Sax	1.25	3.00
104T Dan Schatzeder	.20	.50
105T Bob Shirley	.20	.50
106T Eric Show XRC	.60	1.50
107T Roy Smalley	.20	.50
108T Lonnie Smith	.20	.50
109T Ozzie Smith	6.00	15.00
110T Reggie Smith	.40	1.00
111T Lary Sorensen	.20	.50
112T Elias Sosa	.20	.50
113T Mike Stanton	.20	.50
114T Steve Stroughter	.20	.50
115T Champ Summers	.20	.50
116T Rick Sutcliffe	.40	1.00
117T Frank Tanana	.40	1.00
118T Frank Taveras	.20	.50
119T Garry Templeton	.40	1.00
120T Alex Trevino	.20	.50
121T Jerry Turner	.20	.50
122T Ed VandeBerg	.20	.50
123T Tom Veryzer	.20	.50
124T Ron Washington XRC	.40	1.00
125T Bob Watson	.20	.50
126T Dennis Werth	.20	.50
127T Eddie Whitson	.20	.50
128T Rob Wilfong	.20	.50
129T Bump Wills	.20	.50
130T Gary Woods	.20	.50
131T Butch Wynegar	.20	.50
132T Checklist: 1-132	.20	.50

1983 Topps

The cards in this 792-card set measure the standard size. Cards were primarily issued in 15-card wax packs and 51-card rack packs. The wax packs had 15 cards in each pack with an 30 cent SRP and were packed 36 packs to a box and 20 boxes to a case. Each player card front features a large action shot with a small cameo portrait at bottom right. There are special series for AL and NL All Stars (386-407), League Leaders (701-708), and Record Breakers (1-6). In addition, there are 34 "Super Veteran" (SV) cards and six numbered checklist cards. The Super Veteran cards are oriented horizontally and show two pictures of the featured player, a recent picture and a picture showing the player as a rookie. The team cards are actually Team Leader (TL) cards picturing the batting and pitching leader for that team with a checklist back. Notable Rookie Cards include Wade Boggs, Tony Gwynn and Ryne Sandberg. In each wax pack a game card was included which included prizes all the way up to a trip and tickets to the World Series. Card prizes possible from these cards included the 1983 Topps League Leaders sheet as well as with enough run accumulation, ordering of a part of the 1983 Topps Mail-Away glossy set. The factory sets were available in JC Penney's Christmas Catalog for $15.99.

Card	Low	High
COMPLETE SET (792)	40.00	80.00
1 Tony Armas RB	.10	.30
2 Rickey Henderson RB	.50	1.25
3 Greg Minton RB	.05	.15
4 Lance Parrish RB	.05	.15
5 Manny Trillo RB	.05	.15
6 John Wathan RB	.05	.15
7 Gene Richards	.05	.15
8 Steve Balboni	.05	.15
9 Joey McLaughlin	.05	.15
10 Gorman Thomas	.10	.30
11 Billy Gardner MG	.05	.15
12 Paul Mirabella	.05	.15
13 Larry Herndon	.05	.15
14 Frank LaCorte	.05	.15
15 Ron Cey	.10	.30
16 George Vukovich	.05	.15
17 Kent Tekulve	.05	.15
18 Kent Tekulve SV	.05	.15
19 Oscar Gamble	.05	.15
20 Carlton Fisk	.25	.60
21 Eddie Murray	.25	.60
Jim Palmer TL		
22 Randy Martz	.05	.15
23 Mike Heath	.05	.15
24 Steve Mura	.05	.15
25 Hal McRae	.10	.30
26 Jerry Royster	.05	.15
27 Doug Corbett	.05	.15
28 Bruce Bochte	.05	.15
29 Randy Jones	.05	.15
30 Jim Rice	.10	.30
31 Bill Gullickson	.05	.15
32 Dave Bergman	.05	.15
33 Jack O'Connor	.05	.15
34 Paul Householder	.05	.15
35 Rollie Fingers	.10	.30
36 Rollie Fingers SV	.05	.15
37 Darrell Johnson MG	.05	.15
38 Tim Flannery	.05	.15
39 Terry Puhl	.05	.15
40 Fernando Valenzuela	.10	.30
41 Jerry Turner	.05	.15
42 Dale Murray	.05	.15
43 Bob Dernier	.05	.15
44 Don Robinson	.05	.15
45 John Mayberry	.05	.15
46 Richard Dotson	.05	.15
47 Dave McKay	.05	.15
48 Lary Sorensen	.05	.15
49 Willie McGee RC	1.00	2.50
50 Bob Horner UER	.10	.30
('82 RBI total 7)		
51 Leon Durham	.05	.15
Fergie Jenkins TL		
52 Onix Concepcion	.05	.15
53 Mike Witt	.05	.15
54 Jim Maler	.05	.15
55 Mookie Wilson	.10	.30
56 Chuck Rainey	.05	.15
57 Tim Blackwell	.05	.15
58 Al Holland	.05	.15
59 Benny Ayala	.05	.15
60 Johnny Bench	.50	1.25
61 Johnny Bench SV	.25	.60
62 Bob McClure	.05	.15
63 Rick Monday	.10	.30
64 Bill Stein	.05	.15
65 Jack Morris	.10	.30
66 Bob Lillis MG	.05	.15
67 Sal Butera	.05	.15
68 Eric Show RC	.30	.75
69 Lee Lacy	.05	.15
70 Steve Carlton	.25	.60
71 Steve Carlton SV	.10	.30
72 Tom Paciorek	.05	.15
73 Allen Ripley	.05	.15
74 Julio Gonzalez	.05	.15
75 Amos Otis	.10	.30
76 Rick Mahler	.05	.15
77 Hosken Powell	.05	.15
78 Bill Caudill	.05	.15
79 Mick Kelleher	.05	.15
80 George Foster	.10	.30
81 Jerry Mumphrey	.10	.30
Dave Righetti TL		
82 Bruce Hurst	.05	.15
83 Ryne Sandberg RC	8.00	20.00
84 Milt May	.05	.15
85 Ken Singleton	.10	.30
86 Tom Hume	.05	.15
87 Joe Rudi	.10	.30
88 Jim Gantner	.05	.15
89 Leon Roberts	.05	.15
90 Jerry Reuss	.05	.15
91 Larry Milbourne	.05	.15
92 Mike LaCoss	.05	.15
93 John Castino	.05	.15
94 Dave Edwards	.05	.15
95 Alan Trammell	.10	.30
96 Dick Howser MG	.05	.15
97 Ross Baumgarten	.05	.15
98 Vance Law	.05	.15
99 Dickie Noles	.05	.15
100 Pete Rose	1.50	4.00
101 Pete Rose SV	.50	1.25
102 Dave Beard	.05	.15
103 Darrell Porter	.05	.15
104 Bob Walk	.05	.15
105 Don Baylor	.10	.30
106 Gene Nelson	.05	.15
107 Mike Jorgensen	.05	.15
108 Glenn Hoffman	.05	.15
109 Luis Leal	.05	.15
110 Ken Griffey	.10	.30
111 Al Oliver	.10	.30
Steve Rogers TL		
112 Bob Shirley	.05	.15
113 Ron Roenicke	.05	.15
114 Jim Slaton	.05	.15
115 Chili Davis	.10	.30
116 Dave Schmidt	.05	.15
117 Alan Knicely	.05	.15
118 Chris Welsh	.05	.15
119 Tom Brookens	.05	.15
120 Len Barker	.05	.15
121 Mickey Hatcher	.05	.15
122 Jimmy Smith	.05	.15
123 George Frazier	.05	.15
124 Marc Hill	.05	.15
125 Leon Durham	.05	.15
126 Joe Torre MG	.10	.30
127 Preston Hanna	.05	.15
128 Mike Ramsey	.05	.15
129 Checklist: 1-132	.10	.30
130 Dave Stieb	.10	.30
131 Ed Ott	.05	.15
132 Todd Cruz	.05	.15
133 Jim Barr	.05	.15
134 Hubie Brooks	.05	.15
135 Dwight Evans	.25	.60
136 Willie Aikens	.05	.15
137 Woodie Fryman	.05	.15
138 Rick Dempsey	.05	.15
139 Bruce Berenyi	.05	.15
140 Willie Randolph	.10	.30
141 Toby Harrah	.10	.30
Rick Sutcliffe TL		
142 Mike Caldwell	.05	.15
143 Joe Pettini	.05	.15
144 Mark Wagner	.05	.15
145 Don Sutton	.10	.30
146 Don Sutton SV	.05	.15
147 Rick Leach	.05	.15
148 Dave Roberts	.05	.15
149 Johnny Ray	.05	.15
150 Bruce Sutter	.25	.60
151 Bruce Sutter SV	.10	.30
152 Jay Johnstone	.05	.15
153 Jerry Koosman	.10	.30
154 Johnnie LeMaster	.05	.15
155 Dan Quisenberry	.05	.15
156 Billy Martin MG	.25	.60
157 Steve Bedrosian	.05	.15
158 Rob Wilfong	.05	.15
159 Mike Stanton	.05	.15
160 Dave Kingman	.10	.30
161 Dave Kingman SV	.05	.15
162 Mark Clear	.05	.15
163 Cal Ripken	4.00	10.00
164 David Palmer	.05	.15
165 Dan Driessen	.05	.15
166 John Pacella	.05	.15
167 Mark Brouhard	.05	.15
168 Juan Eichelberger	.05	.15
169 Doug Flynn	.05	.15
170 Steve Howe	.05	.15
171 Joe Morgan	.10	.30
Bill Laskey TL		
172 Vern Ruhle	.05	.15
173 Jim Morrison	.05	.15
174 Jerry Ujdur	.05	.15
175 Bo Diaz	.05	.15
176 Dave Righetti	.10	.30
177 Harold Baines	.10	.30
178 Luis Tiant	.10	.30
179 Luis Tiant SV	.05	.15
180 Rickey Henderson	1.00	2.50
181 Terry Felton	.05	.15
182 Mike Fischlin	.05	.15
183 Ed VandeBerg	.05	.15
184 Bob Clark	.05	.15
185 Tim Lollar	.05	.15
186 Whitey Herzog MG	.10	.30
187 Terry Leach	.05	.15
188 Rick Miller	.05	.15
189 Dan Schatzeder	.05	.15
190 Cecil Cooper	.10	.30
191 Joe Price	.05	.15
192 Floyd Rayford	.05	.15
193 Harry Spilman	.05	.15
194 Cesar Geronimo	.05	.15
195 Bob Stoddard	.05	.15
196 Bill Fahey	.05	.15
197 Jim Eisenreich RC	.30	.75
198 Kiko Garcia	.05	.15
199 Marty Bystrom	.05	.15
200 Rod Carew	.25	.60
201 Rod Carew SV	.10	.30
202 Damaso Garcia	.10	.30
Dave Stieb TL		
203 Mike Morgan	.05	.15
204 Junior Kennedy	.05	.15
205 Dave Parker	.10	.30
206 Ken Oberkfell	.05	.15
207 Rick Camp	.05	.15
208 Dan Meyer	.05	.15
209 Mike Moore RC	.30	.75
210 Jack Clark	.10	.30
211 John Denny	.05	.15
212 John Stearns	.05	.15
213 Tom Burgmeier	.05	.15
214 Jerry White	.05	.15
215 Mario Soto	.10	.30
216 Tony LaRussa MG	.10	.30
217 Tim Stoddard	.05	.15
218 Roy Howell	.05	.15
219 Mike Armstrong	.05	.15
220 Dusty Baker	.10	.30
221 Joe Niekro	.05	.15
222 Damaso Garcia	.05	.15
223 John Montefusco	.05	.15
224 Mickey Rivers	.05	.15
225 Enos Cabell	.05	.15
226 Enrique Romo	.05	.15
227 Chris Bando	.05	.15
228 Joaquin Andujar	.10	.30
229 Bo Diaz	.05	.15
Steve Carlton TL		
230 Fergie Jenkins	.10	.30
231 Fergie Jenkins SV	.05	.15
232 Tom Brunansky	.10	.30
233 Wayne Gross	.05	.15
234 Larry Andersen	.05	.15
235 Claudell Washington	.05	.15
236 Steve Renko	.05	.15
237 Dan Norman	.05	.15
238 Bud Black RC	.30	.75
239 Dave Stapleton	.05	.15
240 Rich Gossage	.10	.30
241 Rich Gossage SV	.05	.15
242 Joe Nolan	.05	.15
243 Duane Walker	.05	.15
244 Dwight Bernard	.05	.15
245 Steve Sax	.10	.30
246 G.Bamberger MG	.05	.15
247 Dave Smith	.05	.15
248 Bake McBride	.10	.30
249 Checklist: 133-264	.10	.30
250 Bill Buckner	.10	.30
251 Alan Wiggins	.05	.15
252 Luis Aguayo	.05	.15
253 Larry McWilliams	.05	.15
254 Rick Cerone	.05	.15
255 Gene Garber	.05	.15
256 Gene Garber SV	.05	.15
257 Jesse Barfield	.10	.30
258 Manny Castillo	.05	.15
259 Jeff Jones	.05	.15
260 Steve Kemp	.05	.15
261 Larry Herndon	.10	.30
Dan Petry TL		
262 Ron Jackson	.05	.15
263 Renie Martin	.05	.15
264 Jamie Quirk	.05	.15
265 Joel Youngblood	.05	.15
266 Paul Boris	.05	.15
267 Terry Francona	.10	.30
268 Storm Davis RC	.30	.75
269 Ron Oester	.05	.15
270 Dennis Eckersley	.25	.60
271 Ed Romero	.05	.15
272 Frank Tanana	.10	.30
273 Mark Belanger	.05	.15
274 Terry Kennedy	.05	.15
275 Ray Knight	.10	.30
276 Gene Mauch MG	.05	.15
277 Rance Mulliniks	.05	.15
278 Kevin Hickey	.05	.15
279 Greg Gross	.05	.15
280 Bert Blyleven	.10	.30
281 Andre Robertson	.05	.15
282 Reggie Smith	.50	1.25
(Ryne Sandberg		
ducking back)		
283 Reggie Smith SV	.05	.15
284 Jeff Lahti	.05	.15
285 Lance Parrish	.10	.30
286 Rick Langford	.05	.15
287 Bobby Brown	.05	.15
288 Joe Cowley	.05	.15
289 Jerry Dybzinski	.05	.15
290 Jeff Reardon	.10	.30
291 Bill Madlock	.10	.30
John Candelaria TL		
292 Craig Swan	.05	.15
293 Glenn Gulliver	.05	.15
294 Dave Engle	.05	.15
295 Jerry Remy	.05	.15
296 Greg Harris	.05	.15
297 Ned Yost	.05	.15
298 Floyd Chiffer	.05	.15
299 George Wright RC	.30	.75
300 Mike Schmidt	1.25	3.00
301 Mike Schmidt SV	.50	1.25
302 Ernie Whitt	.05	.15
303 Miguel Dilone	.05	.15
304 Dave Rucker	.05	.15
305 Larry Bowa	.10	.30
306 Tom Lasorda MG	.25	.60
307 Lou Piniella	.10	.30
308 Jesus Vega	.05	.15
309 Jeff Leonard	.05	.15
310 Greg Luzinski	.10	.30
311 Glenn Brummer	.05	.15
312 Brian Kingman	.05	.15
313 Gary Gray	.05	.15
314 Ken Dayley	.05	.15
315 Rick Burleson	.05	.15
316 Paul Splittorff	.05	.15
317 Gary Rajsich	.05	.15
318 John Tudor	.10	.30
319 Lenn Sakata	.05	.15
320 Steve Rogers	.10	.30
321 Robin Yount	.50	1.25
Pete Vuckovich TL		
322 Dave Van Gorder	.05	.15
323 Luis DeLeon	.05	.15
324 Mike Marshall	.05	.15
325 Von Hayes	.05	.15
326 Garth Iorg	.05	.15
327 Bobby Castillo	.05	.15
328 Craig Reynolds	.05	.15
329 Randy Niemann	.05	.15
330 Buddy Bell	.10	.30
331 Mike Krukow	.05	.15
332 Glenn Wilson	.30	.75
333 Dave LaRoche	.05	.15
334 Dave LaRoche SV	.05	.15
335 Steve Henderson	.05	.15
336 Rene Lachemann MG	.05	.15
337 Tito Landrum	.05	.15
338 Bob Owchinko	.05	.15
339 Terry Harper	.05	.15
340 Larry Gura	.05	.15
341 Doug DeCinces	.05	.15
342 Atlee Hammaker	.05	.15
343 Bob Bailor	.05	.15
344 Roger LaFrancois	.05	.15
345 Jim Clancy	.05	.15
346 Joe Pittman	.05	.15
347 Sammy Stewart	.05	.15
348 Alan Bannister	.05	.15
349 Checklist: 265-396	.10	.30
350 Robin Yount	.75	2.00
351 Cesar Cedeno	.10	.30
Mario Soto TL		
352 Mike Scioscia	.10	.30
353 Steve Comer	.05	.15
354 Randy Johnson	.05	.15
355 Jim Bibby	.05	.15
356 Gary Woods	.05	.15
357 Len Matuszek	.05	.15
358 Jerry Garvin	.05	.15
359 Dave Collins	.05	.15
360 Nolan Ryan	2.50	6.00
361 Nolan Ryan SV	1.25	3.00
362 Bill Almon	.05	.15
363 John Stuper	.05	.15
364 Brett Butler	.10	.30
365 Dave Lopes	.10	.30
366 Dick Williams MG	.05	.15
367 Bud Anderson	.05	.15
368 Richie Zisk	.05	.15
369 Jesse Orosco	.05	.15
370 Gary Carter	.10	.30
371 Mike Richardt	.05	.15
372 Terry Crowley	.05	.15
373 Kevin Saucier	.05	.15
374 Wayne Krenchicki	.05	.15
375 Pete Vuckovich	.05	.15
376 Ken Landreaux	.05	.15
377 Lee May	.05	.15
378 Lee May SV	.05	.15
379 Guy Sularz	.05	.15
380 Ron Davis	.05	.15
381 Jim Rice	.10	.30
Bob Stanley TL		
382 Bob Knepper	.05	.15
383 Ozzie Virgil	.05	.15
384 Dave Dravecky RC	.60	1.50
385 Mike Easler	.05	.15
386 Rod Carew AS	.10	.30
387 Bob Grich AS	.05	.15
388 George Brett AS	.60	1.50
389 Robin Yount AS	.50	1.25
390 Reggie Jackson AS	.10	.30
391 Rickey Henderson AS	.50	1.25
392 Fred Lynn AS	.05	.15
393 Carlton Fisk AS	.10	.30
394 Pete Vuckovich AS	.05	.15
395 Larry Gura AS	.05	.15
396 Dan Quisenberry AS	.05	.15
397 Pete Rose AS	.25	.60
398 Manny Trillo AS	.05	.15
399 Mike Schmidt AS	.50	1.25
400 Dave Concepcion AS	.05	.15
401 Dale Murphy AS	.10	.30
402 Andre Dawson AS	.05	.15
403 Tim Raines AS	.05	.15
404 Gary Carter AS	.05	.15
405 Steve Rogers AS	.05	.15
406 Steve Carlton AS	.10	.30
407 Bruce Sutter AS	.10	.30
408 Rudy May	.05	.15
409 Marvis Foley	.05	.15
410 Phil Niekro	.10	.30
411 Phil Niekro SV	.05	.15
412 Buddy Bell	.10	.30
Charlie Hough TL		
413 Matt Keough	.05	.15
414 Julio Cruz	.05	.15
415 Bob Forsch	.05	.15
416 Joe Ferguson	.05	.15
417 Tom Hausman	.05	.15
418 Greg Pryor	.05	.15
419 Steve Crawford	.05	.15
420 Al Oliver	.10	.30
421 Al Oliver SV	.05	.15
422 George Cappuzzello	.05	.15
423 Tom Lawless	.05	.15
424 Jerry Augustine	.05	.15
425 Pedro Guerrero	.10	.30
426 Earl Weaver MG	.10	.30
427 Roy Lee Jackson	.05	.15
428 Champ Summers	.05	.15
429 Eddie Whitson	.05	.15
430 Kirk Gibson	.10	.30
431 Gary Gaetti RC	.60	1.50
432 Porfirio Altamirano	.05	.15
433 Dale Berra	.05	.15
434 Dennis Lamp	.05	.15
435 Tony Armas	.10	.30
436 Bill Campbell	.05	.15
437 Rick Sweet	.05	.15
438 Dave LaPoint	.05	.15
439 Rafael Ramirez	.05	.15
440 Ron Guidry	.10	.30
441 Ray Knight	.10	.30
Joe Niekro TL		
442 Brian Downing	.10	.30
443 Don Hood	.05	.15
444 Wally Backman	.05	.15
445 Mike Flanagan	.05	.15
446 Reid Nichols	.05	.15
447 Bryn Smith	.05	.15
448 Darrell Evans	.10	.30
449 Eddie Milner	.05	.15
450 Ted Simmons	.10	.30
451 Ted Simmons SV	.05	.15
452 Lloyd Moseby	.05	.15
453 Lamar Johnson	.05	.15
454 Bob Welch	.10	.30
455 Sixto Lezcano	.05	.15
456 Lee Elia MG	.05	.15
457 Milt Wilcox	.05	.15
458 Ron Washington RC	.10	.25
459 Ed Farmer	.05	.15
460 Roy Smalley	.05	.15
461 Steve Trout	.05	.15
462 Steve Nicosia	.05	.15
463 Gaylord Perry	.10	.30
464 Gaylord Perry SV	.05	.15
465 Lonnie Smith	.05	.15
466 Tom Underwood	.05	.15
467 Rufino Linares	.05	.15
468 Dave Goltz	.05	.15
469 Ron Gardenhire	.05	.15
470 Greg Minton	.05	.15
471 Willie Wilson	.10	.30
Vida Blue TL		
472 Gary Allenson	.05	.15
473 John Lowenstein	.05	.15
474 Ray Burris	.05	.15
475 Cesar Cedeno	.10	.30
476 Rob Picciolo	.05	.15
477 Tom Niedenfuer	.05	.15
478 Phil Garner	.10	.30
479 Charlie Hough	.10	.30
480 Toby Harrah	.10	.30
481 Scot Thompson	.05	.15
482 Tony Gwynn UER RC	10.00	25.00
No Topps logo under		
card number on back		
483 Lynn Jones	.05	.15
484 Dick Ruthven	.05	.15
485 Omar Moreno	.05	.15
486 Clyde King MG	.05	.15
487 Jerry Hairston	.05	.15
488 Alfredo Griffin	.05	.15
489 Tom Herr	.05	.15
490 Jim Palmer	.10	.30
491 Jim Palmer SV	.05	.15
492 Paul Serna	.05	.15
493 Steve McCatty	.05	.15
494 Bob Brenly	.05	.15
495 Warren Cromartie	.05	.15
496 Tom Veryzer	.05	.15
497 Rick Sutcliffe	.10	.30
498 Wade Boggs RC	6.00	15.00
499 Jeff Little	.05	.15
500 Reggie Jackson	.25	.60
501 Reggie Jackson SV	.10	.30
502 Dale Murphy	.25	.60
Phil Niekro TL		
503 Moose Haas	.05	.15
504 Don Werner	.05	.15
505 Garry Templeton	.10	.30
506 Jim Gott RC	.30	.75
507 Tony Scott	.05	.15
508 Tom Filer	.05	.15
509 Lou Whitaker	.10	.30
510 Tug McGraw	.10	.30
511 Tug McGraw SV	.05	.15
512 Doyle Alexander	.05	.15
513 Fred Stanley	.05	.15
514 Rudy Law	.05	.15
515 Gene Tenace	.10	.30
516 Bill Virdon MG	.05	.15
517 Gary Ward	.05	.15
518 Bill Laskey	.05	.15
519 Terry Bulling	.05	.15
520 Fred Lynn	.10	.30
521 Bruce Benedict	.05	.15
522 Pat Zachry	.05	.15
523 Carney Lansford	.10	.30
524 Tom Brennan	.05	.15
525 Frank White	.10	.30
526 Checklist: 397-528	.10	.30
527 Larry Biittner	.05	.15
528 Jamie Easterly	.05	.15
529 Tim Laudner	.05	.15
530 Eddie Murray	.50	1.25
531 Rickey Henderson	.50	1.25
Rick Langford TL		
532 Dave Stewart	.10	.30
533 Luis Salazar	.05	.15
534 John Butcher	.05	.15
535 Manny Trillo	.05	.15
536 John Wockenfuss	.05	.15
537 Rod Scurry	.05	.15
538 Danny Heep	.05	.15
539 Roger Erickson	.05	.15
540 Ozzie Smith	.75	2.00
541 Britt Burns	.05	.15
542 Jody Davis	.05	.15
543 Alan Fowlkes	.05	.15
544 Larry Whisenton	.05	.15
545 Floyd Bannister	.05	.15
546 Dave Garcia MG	.05	.15
547 Geoff Zahn	.05	.15
548 Brian Giles	.05	.15
549 Charlie Puleo	.05	.15
550 Carl Yastrzemski	.75	2.00
551 Carl Yastrzemski SV	.50	1.25
552 Tim Wallach	.10	.30
553 Dennis Martinez	.10	.30
554 Mike Vail	.05	.15
555 Steve Yeager	.10	.30
556 Willie Upshaw	.05	.15
557 Rick Honeycutt	.05	.15
558 Dickie Thon	.05	.15
559 Pete Redfern	.05	.15
560 Ron LeFlore	.10	.30
561 Lonnie Smith	.10	.30
Joaquin Andujar TL		
562 Dave Rozema	.05	.15
563 Juan Bonilla	.05	.15
564 Sid Monge	.05	.15
565 Bucky Dent	.10	.30
566 Manny Sarmiento	.05	.15
567 Joe Simpson	.05	.15
568 Willie Hernandez	.05	.15
569 Jack Perconte	.05	.15
570 Vida Blue	.10	.30
571 Mickey Klutts	.05	.15
572 Bob Watson	.05	.15
573 Andy Hassler	.05	.15
574 Glenn Adams	.05	.15
575 Neil Allen	.05	.15
576 Frank Robinson MG	.25	.60
577 Luis Aponte	.05	.15
578 David Green RC	.30	.75
579 Rich Dauer	.05	.15
580 Tom Seaver	.50	1.25
581 Tom Seaver SV	.10	.30
582 Marshall Edwards	.05	.15
583 Terry Forster	.10	.30
584 Dave Hostetler	.05	.15
585 Jose Cruz	.10	.30
586 Frank Viola RC	1.00	2.50
587 Ivan DeJesus	.05	.15
588 Pat Underwood	.05	.15
589 Alvis Woods	.05	.15
590 Tony Pena	.05	.15
591 Greg Luzinski	.10	.30
LaMarr Hoyt TL		
592 Shane Rawley	.05	.15
593 Broderick Perkins	.05	.15
594 Eric Rasmussen	.05	.15
595 Tim Raines	.10	.30
596 Randy Johnson	.05	.15
597 Mike Proly	.05	.15
598 Dwayne Murphy	.05	.15
599 Don Aase	.05	.15
600 George Brett	1.25	3.00
601 Ed Lynch	.05	.15
602 Rich Gedman	.05	.15
603 Joe Morgan	.10	.30
604 Joe Morgan SV	.05	.15
605 Gary Roenicke	.05	.15
606 Bobby Cox MG	.10	.30
607 Charlie Leibrandt	.05	.15
608 Don Money	.05	.15
609 Danny Darwin	.05	.15
610 Steve Garvey	.10	.30
611 Bert Roberge	.05	.15
612 Steve Swisher	.05	.15
613 Mike Ivie	.05	.15
614 Ed Glynn	.05	.15
615 Garry Maddox	.05	.15
616 Bill Nahorodny	.05	.15
617 Butch Wynegar	.05	.15
618 LaMarr Hoyt	.05	.15
619 Keith Moreland	.05	.15
620 Mike Norris	.05	.15
621 Mookie Wilson	.10	.30
Craig Swan TL		
622 Dave Edler	.05	.15
623 Luis Sanchez	.05	.15
624 Glenn Hubbard	.05	.15
625 Ken Forsch	.05	.15
626 Jerry Martin	.05	.15
627 Doug Bair	.05	.15
628 Julio Valdez	.05	.15
629 Charlie Lea	.05	.15
630 Paul Molitor	.10	.30
631 Tippy Martinez	.05	.15
632 Alex Trevino	.05	.15
633 Vicente Romo	.05	.15
634 Max Venable	.05	.15

635 Graig Nettles .10 .30
636 Graig Nettles SV .05 .15
637 Pat Corrales MG .05 .15
638 Dan Petry .05 .15
639 Art Howe .05 .15
640 Andre Thornton .05 .15
641 Billy Sample .05 .15
642 Checklist: 529-660 .10 .30
643 Bump Wills .05 .15
644 Joe Lefebvre .05 .15
645 Bill Madlock .10 .30
646 Jim Essian .05 .15
647 Bobby Mitchell .05 .15
648 Jeff Burroughs .05 .15
649 Tommy Boggs .05 .15
650 George Hendrick .10 .30
651 Rod Carew .10 .30
Mike Witt TL
652 Butch Hobson .05 .15
653 Ellis Valentine .05 .15
654 Bob Ojeda .05 .15
655 Al Bumbry .05 .15
656 Dave Frost .05 .15
657 Mike Gates .05 .15
658 Frank Pastore .05 .15
659 Charlie Moore .05 .15
660 Mike Hargrove .05 .15
661 Bill Russell .10 .30
662 Joe Sambito .05 .15
663 Tom O'Malley .05 .15
664 Bob Molinaro .05 .15
665 Jim Sundberg .10 .30
666 Sparky Anderson MG .10 .30
667 Dick Davis .05 .15
668 Larry Christenson .05 .15
669 Mike Squires .05 .15
670 Jerry Mumphrey .05 .15
671 Lenny Faedo .05 .15
672 Jim Kaat .10 .30
673 Jim Kaat SV .05 .15
674 Kurt Bevacqua .05 .15
675 Jim Beattie .05 .15
676 Biff Pocoroba .05 .15
677 Dave Revering .05 .15
678 Juan Beniquez .05 .15
679 Mike Scott .10 .30
680 Andre Dawson .10 .30
681 Pedro Guerrero .10 .30
Fernando Valenzuela TL
682 Bob Stanley .05 .15
683 Dan Ford .05 .15
684 Rafael Landestoy .05 .15
685 Lee Mazzilli .10 .30
686 Randy Lerch .05 .15
687 U.L. Washington .05 .15
688 Jim Wohlford .05 .15
689 Ron Hassey .05 .15
690 Kent Hrbek .10 .30
691 Dave Tobik .05 .15
692 Denny Walling .05 .15
693 Sparky Lyle .10 .30
694 Sparky Lyle SV .05 .15
695 Ruppert Jones .05 .15
696 Chuck Tanner MG .05 .15
697 Barry Foote .05 .15
698 Tony Bernazard .05 .15
699 Lee Smith .25 .60
700 Keith Hernandez .10 .30
701 Willie Wilson .10 .30
Al Oliver LL
702 Reggie Jackson .10 .30
Gorman Thomas
Dave Kingman LL
703 Hal McRae .25 .60
Dale Murphy
Al Oliver LL
704 Rickey Henderson .50 1.25
Tim Raines LL
705 LaMarr Hoyt .10 .30
Steve Carlton LL
706 Floyd Bannister .10 .30
Steve Carlton LL
707 Rick Sutcliffe .10 .30
Steve Rogers LL
708 Dan Quisenberry .10 .30
Bruce Sutter LL
709 Jimmy Sexton .05 .15
710 Willie Wilson .10 .30
711 Bruce Bochte .10 .30
Jim Beattie TL
712 Bruce Kison .05 .15
713 Ron Hodges .05 .15
714 Wayne Nordhagen .05 .15
715 Tony Perez .25 .60
716 Tony Perez SV .10 .30
717 Scott Sanderson .05 .15
718 Jim Dwyer .05 .15
719 Rich Gale .05 .15
720 Dave Concepcion .10 .30
721 John Martin .05 .15
722 Jorge Orta .05 .15
723 Randy Moffitt .05 .15
724 Johnny Grubb .05 .15
725 Dan Spillner .05 .15
726 Harvey Kuenn MG .05 .15
727 Chet Lemon .10 .30
728 Ron Reed .05 .15
729 Jerry Morales .05 .15
730 Jason Thompson .05 .15
731 Al Williams .05 .15
732 Dave Henderson .05 .15
733 Buck Martinez .05 .15
734 Steve Braun .05 .15
735 Tommy John .10 .30
736 Tommy John SV .05 .15
737 Mitchell Page .05 .15
738 Tim Foli .05 .15
739 Rick Ownbey .05 .15
740 Rusty Staub .10 .30
741 Rusty Staub SV .05 .15
742 Terry Kennedy .10 .30
Tim Lollar
743 Mike Torrez .05 .15
744 Brad Mills .05 .15
745 Scott McGregor .05 .15
746 John Wathan .05 .15
747 Fred Breining .05 .15
748 Derrel Thomas .05 .15
749 Jon Matlack .05 .15
750 Ben Oglivie .10 .30
751 Brad Havens .05 .15
752 Luis Pujols .05 .15
753 Elias Sosa .05 .15
754 Bill Robinson .05 .15
755 John Candelaria .05 .15
756 Russ Nixon MG .05 .15
757 Rick Manning .05 .15
758 Aurelio Rodriguez .05 .15
759 Doug Bird .05 .15
760 Dale Murphy .25 .60
761 Gary Lucas .05 .15
762 Cliff Johnson .05 .15
763 Al Cowens .05 .15
764 Pete Falcone .05 .15
765 Bob Boone .10 .30
766 Barry Bonnell .05 .15
767 Duane Kuiper .05 .15
768 Chris Speier .05 .15
769 Checklist: 661-792 .10 .30
770 Dave Winfield .10 .30
771 Kent Hrbek .10 .30
Bobby Castillo TL
772 Jim Kern .05 .15
773 Larry Hisle .05 .15
774 Alan Ashby .05 .15
775 Burt Hooton .05 .15
776 Larry Parrish .05 .15
777 John Curtis .05 .15
778 Rich Hebner .05 .15
779 Rick Waits .05 .15
780 Gary Matthews .10 .30
781 Rick Rhoden .05 .15
782 Bobby Murcer .10 .30
783 Bobby Murcer SV .05 .15
784 Jeff Newman .05 .15
785 Dennis Leonard .05 .15
786 Ralph Houk MG .05 .15
787 Dick Tidrow .05 .15
788 Dane Iorg .05 .15
789 Bryan Clark .05 .15
790 Bob Grich .10 .30
791 Gary Lavelle .05 .15
792 Chris Chambliss .10 .30
XX Game Insert Card .02 .10

1983 Topps Glossy Send-Ins

The cards in this 40-card set measure the standard size. The 1983 Topps "Collector's Edition" or "All-Star Set" (popularly known as "Glossies") consists of color ballplayer picture cards with shiny, glazed surfaces. The player's name appears in small print outside the frame line at bottom left. The backs contain no biography or record and list only the set titles, the player's name, team, position, and the card number.

COMPLETE SET (40) 6.00 15.00
1 Carl Yastrzemski .40 1.25
2 Mookie Wilson .07 .20
3 Andre Thornton .02 .10
4 Keith Hernandez .07 .20
5 Robin Yount .40 1.25
6 Terry Kennedy .02 .10
7 Dave Winfield .40 1.25
8 Mike Schmidt .60 1.50
9 Buddy Bell .07 .20
10 Fernando Valenzuela .10 .30
11 Rich Gossage .07 .20
12 Bob Horner .02 .10
13 Toby Harrah .02 .10
14 Pete Rose .60 1.50
15 Cecil Cooper .07 .20
16 Dale Murphy .20 .50
17 Carlton Fisk .40 1.25
18 Ray Knight .02 .10
19 Jim Palmer .30 1.00
20 Gary Carter .12 1.00
21 Richie Zisk .02 .10
22 Dusty Baker .07 .20
23 Willie Wilson .02 .10
24 Bill Buckner .07 .20
25 Dave Stieb .02 .10
26 Bill Madlock .02 .10
27 Lance Parrish .07 .20
28 Nolan Ryan 2.00 5.00
29 Rod Carew .40 1.00
30 Al Oliver .07 .20
31 George Brett 1.00 2.50
32 Jack Clark .02 .10
33 Rickey Henderson .75 2.00
34 Dave Concepcion .07 .20
35 Kent Hrbek .07 .20
36 Steve Carlton .30 1.00
37 Eddie Murray .50 1.25
38 Ruppert Jones .02 .10
39 Reggie Jackson .40 1.25
40 Bruce Sutter .30 .75

1983 Topps Traded

For the third year in a row, Topps issued a 132-card standard-size Traded (or extended) set featuring some of the year's top rookies and players who had changed teams during the year. The cards were available through hobby dealers only in factory set form and were printed in Ireland by the Topps affiliate in that country. The set is numbered alphabetically by player. The Darryl Strawberry card number 108 can be found with either one or two asterisks (in the lower left corner of the reverse). There is no difference in value for either version. The key (extended) Rookie Cards in this set include Julio Franco, Tony Phillips and Darryl Strawberry.

COMP.FACT.SET (132) 15.00 40.00
1T Neil Allen .08 .25
2T Bill Almon .08 .25
3T Joe Altobelli MG .08 .25
4T Tony Armas .40 1.00
5T Doug Bair .08 .25
6T Steve Baker .08 .25
7T Floyd Bannister .08 .25
8T Don Baylor .40 1.00
9T Tony Bernazard .08 .25
10T Larry Biittner .08 .25
11T Dann Bilardello .08 .25
12T Doug Bird .08 .25
13T Steve Boros MG .08 .25
14T Greg Brock .08 .25
15T Mike C. Brown .08 .25
16T Tom Burgmeier .08 .25
17T Randy Bush .08 .25
18T Bert Campaneris .40 1.00
19T Ron Cey .40 1.00
20T Chris Codiroli .08 .25
21T Dave Collins .08 .25
22T Terry Crowley .08 .25
23T Julio Cruz .08 .25
24T Mike Davis .08 .25
25T Frank DiPino .08 .25
26T Bill Doran XRC .40 1.00
27T Jerry Dybzinski .08 .25
28T Jamie Easterly .08 .25
29T Juan Eichelberger .08 .25
30T Jim Essian .08 .25
31T Pete Falcone .08 .25
32T Mike Ferraro MG .08 .25
33T Terry Forster .40 1.00
34T Julio Franco XRC 3.00 8.00
35T Rich Gale .08 .25
36T Kiko Garcia .08 .25
37T Steve Garvey .40 1.00
38T Johnny Grubb .08 .25
39T Mel Hall XRC .40 1.00
40T Von Hayes .08 .25
41T Danny Heep .08 .25
42T Steve Henderson .08 .25
43T Keith Hernandez .40 1.00
44T Leo Hernandez .08 .25
45T Willie Hernandez .08 .25
46T Al Holland .08 .25
47T Frank Howard MG .40 1.00
48T Bobby Johnson .08 .25
49T Cliff Johnson .08 .25
50T Odell Jones .08 .25
51T Mike Jorgensen .08 .25
52T Bob Kearney .08 .25
53T Steve Kemp .08 .25
54T Matt Keough .08 .25
55T Ron Kittle XRC .75 2.00
56T Mickey Klutts .08 .25
57T Alan Knicely .08 .25
58T Mike Krukow .08 .25
59T Rafael Landestoy .08 .25
60T Carney Lansford .40 1.00
61T Joe Lefebvre .08 .25
62T Bryan Little .08 .25
63T Aurelio Lopez .08 .25
64T Mike Madden .08 .25
65T Rick Manning .08 .25
66T Billy Martin MG .75 2.00
67T Lee Mazzilli .40 1.00
68T Andy McGaffigan .08 .25
69T Craig McMurtry .08 .25
70T John McNamara MG .08 .25
71T Orlando Mercado .08 .25
72T Larry Milbourne .08 .25
73T Randy Moffitt .08 .25
74T Sid Monge .08 .25
75T Jose Morales .08 .25
76T Omar Moreno .08 .25
77T Joe Morgan .40 1.00
78T Mike Morgan .08 .25
79T Dale Murray .08 .25
80T Jeff Newman .08 .25
81T Pete O'Brien XRC .40 1.00
82T Jorge Orta .08 .25
83T Alejandro Pena XRC .75 2.00
84T Pascual Perez .75 2.00
85T Tony Perez .75 2.00
86T Broderick Perkins .08 .25
87T Tony Phillips XRC .75 2.00
88T Charlie Puleo .08 .25
89T Pat Putnam .08 .25
90T Jamie Quirk .08 .25
91T Doug Rader MG .08 .25
92T Chuck Rainey .08 .25
93T Bobby Ramos .08 .25
94T Gary Redus XRC .40 1.00
95T Steve Renko .08 .25
96T Leon Roberts .08 .25
97T Aurelio Rodriguez .08 .25
98T Dick Ruthven .08 .25
99T Daryl Sconiers .08 .25
100T Mike Scott .40 1.00
101T Tom Seaver .75 2.00
102T John Shelby .08 .25
103T Bob Shirley .08 .25
104T Joe Simpson .08 .25
105T Doug Sisk .08 .25
106T Mike Smithson .08 .25
107T Elias Sosa .08 .25
108T D.Strawberry XRC 6.00 15.00
109T Tom Tellmann .08 .25
110T Gene Tenace .40 1.00
111T Gorman Thomas .40 1.00
112T Dick Tidrow .08 .25
113T Dave Tobik .08 .25
114T Wayne Tolleson .08 .25
115T Mike Torrez .08 .25
116T Manny Trillo .08 .25
117T Steve Trout .08 .25
118T Lee Tunnell .08 .25
119T Mike Vail .08 .25
120T Ellis Valentine .08 .25
121T Tom Veryzer .08 .25
122T George Vukovich .08 .25
123T Rick Waits .08 .25
124T Greg Walker .40 1.00
125T Chris Welsh .08 .25
126T Len Whitehouse .08 .25
127T Eddie Whitson .08 .25
128T Jim Wohlford .08 .25
129T Matt Young XRC .40 1.00
130T Joel Youngblood .08 .25
131T Pat Zachry .08 .25
132T Checklist 1T-132T .08 .25

1984 Topps

The cards in this 792-card set measure the standard size. Cards were primarily distributed in 15-card wax packs and 54-card rack packs. For the second year in a row, Topps utilized a dual picture on the front of the card. A portrait is shown in a square insert and an action shot is featured in the main photo. Card numbers 1-6 feature 1983 Highlights (HL), cards 131-138 depict League Leaders, card numbers 386-407 feature All-Stars, and card numbers 701-718 feature active Major League career leaders in various statistical categories. Each team leader (TL) card features the team's leading hitter and pitcher pictured on the front with a team checklist back. There are six numerical checklist cards in the set. The player cards feature team logos in the upper right corner of the reverse. The key Rookie Cards in this set are Don Mattingly and Darryl Strawberry. Topps tested a special send-in offer in Michigan and a few other states whereby collectors could obtain direct from Topps ten cards of their choice. Needless to say most people ordered the key (most valuable) players necessitating the printing of a special sheet to keep up with the demand. The special sheet had five cards of Darryl Strawberry, three cards of Don Mattingly, etc. The test was apparently a failure in Topps' eyes as they have never tried it again.

COMPLETE SET (792) 20.00 50.00
1 Steve Carlton HL .08 .25
2 Rickey Henderson HL .25 .60
3 Dan Quisenberry HL .05 .15
4 Nolan Ryan HL .40 1.00
Steve Carlton
Gaylord Perry
5 Dave Righetti HL .08 .25
Bob Forsch
Mike Warren
6 Johnny Bench HL .15 .40
Gaylord Perry
Carl Yastrzemski
7 Gary Lucas .05 .15
8 Don Mattingly RC 6.00 15.00
9 Jim Gott .05 .15
10 Robin Yount .40 1.00
11 Kent Hrbek .08 .25
Ken Schrom TL
12 Billy Sample .05 .15
13 Scott Holman .05 .15
14 Tom Brookens .08 .25
15 Burt Hooton .05 .15
16 Omar Moreno .05 .15
17 John Denny .05 .15
18 Dale Berra .05 .15
19 Ray Fontenot .05 .15
20 Greg Luzinski .08 .25
21 Joe Altobelli MG .05 .15
22 Bryan Clark .05 .15
23 Keith Moreland .05 .15
24 John Martin .05 .15
25 Glenn Hubbard .05 .15
26 Bud Black .05 .15
27 Daryl Sconiers .05 .15
28 Frank Viola .15 .40
29 Danny Heep .05 .15
30 Wade Boggs .60 1.50
31 Andy McGaffigan .05 .15
32 Bobby Ramos .05 .15
33 Tom Burgmeier .05 .15
34 Eddie Milner .05 .15
35 Don Sutton .08 .25
36 Denny Walling .05 .15
37 Buddy Bell .08 .25
Rick Honeycutt TL
38 Luis DeLeon .05 .15
39 Garth Iorg .05 .15
40 Dusty Baker .08 .25
41 Tony Bernazard .05 .15
42 Johnny Grubb .05 .15
43 Ron Reed .05 .15
44 Jim Morrison .05 .15
45 Jerry Mumphrey .05 .15
46 Ray Smith .05 .15
47 Rudy Law .05 .15
48 Julio Franco .08 .25
49 John Stuper .05 .15
50 Chris Chambliss .08 .25
51 Jim Frey MG .05 .15
52 Paul Splittorff .05 .15
53 Juan Beniquez .05 .15
54 Jesse Orosco .05 .15
55 Dave Concepcion .08 .25
56 Gary Allenson .05 .15
57 Dan Schatzeder .05 .15
58 Max Venable .05 .15
59 Sammy Stewart .05 .15
60 Paul Molitor UER .08 .25
('83 stats .272, 613, 167; should be .270, 608, 164)
61 Chris Codiroli .05 .15
62 Dave Hostetler .05 .15
63 Ed VandeBerg .05 .15
64 Mike Scioscia .08 .25
65 Kirk Gibson .25 .60
66 Jose Cruz .40 1.00
Nolan Ryan TL
67 Gary Ward .05 .15
68 Luis Salazar .05 .15
69 Rod Scurry .05 .15
70 Gary Matthews .08 .25
71 Leo Hernandez .05 .15
72 Mike Squires .05 .15
73 Jody Davis .05 .15
74 Jerry Martin .05 .15
75 Bob Forsch .05 .15
76 Alfredo Griffin .05 .15
77 Brett Butler .08 .25
78 Mike Torrez .05 .15
79 Rob Wilfong .05 .15
80 Steve Rogers .08 .25
81 Billy Martin MG .15 .40
82 Doug Bird .05 .15
83 Richie Zisk .05 .15
84 Lenny Faedo .05 .15
85 Atlee Hammaker .05 .15
86 John Shelby .05 .15
87 Frank Pastore .05 .15
88 Rob Picciolo .05 .15
89 Mike Smithson .05 .15
90 Pedro Guerrero .08 .25
91 Dan Spillner .05 .15
92 Lloyd Moseby .05 .15
93 Bob Knepper .05 .15
94 Mario Ramirez .05 .15
95 Aurelio Lopez .08 .25
96 Hal McRae .08 .25
Larry Gura TL
97 LaMarr Hoyt .05 .15
98 Steve Nicosia .05 .15
99 Craig Lefferts RC .05 .15
100 Reggie Jackson .15 .40
101 Porfirio Altamirano .05 .15
102 Ken Oberkfell .05 .15
103 Dwayne Murphy .05 .15
104 Ken Dayley .05 .15
105 Tony Armas .08 .25
106 Tim Stoddard .05 .15
107 Ned Yost .05 .15
108 Randy Moffitt .05 .15
109 Brad Wellman .05 .15
110 Ron Guidry .08 .25
111 Bill Virdon MG .05 .15
112 Tom Niedenfuer .05 .15
113 Kelly Paris .05 .15
114 Checklist 1-132 .08 .25
115 Andre Thornton .05 .15
116 George Bjorkman .05 .15
117 Tom Veryzer .05 .15
118 Charlie Hough .08 .25
119 John Wockenfuss .05 .15
120 Keith Hernandez .08 .25
121 Pat Sheridan .05 .15
122 Cecilio Guante .05 .15
123 Butch Wynegar .05 .15
124 Damaso Garcia .05 .15
125 Britt Burns .05 .15
126 Dale Murphy .15 .40
Craig McMurtry TL
127 Mike Madden .05 .15
128 Rick Manning .05 .15
129 Bill Laskey .05 .15
130 Ozzie Smith .40 1.00
131 Bill Madlock .25 .60
Wade Boggs LL
132 Mike Schmidt .25 .60
Jim Rice LL
133 Dale Murphy .15 .40
Cecil Cooper
Jim Rice LL
134 Tim Raines .25 .60
Rickey Henderson LL
135 John Denny .25 .60
LaMarr Hoyt LL
136 Steve Carlton .08 .25
Jack Morris LL
137 Atlee Hammaker .08 .25
Rick Honeycutt LL
138 Al Holland .08 .25
Dan Quisenberry LL
139 Bert Campaneris .08 .25
140 Storm Davis .05 .15
141 Pat Corrales MG .05 .15
142 Rich Gale .05 .15
143 Jose Morales .05 .15
144 Brian Harper RC .15 .40
145 Gary Lavelle .05 .15
146 Ed Romero .05 .15
147 Dan Petry .08 .25
148 Joe Lefebvre .05 .15
149 Jon Matlack .05 .15
150 Dale Murphy .15 .40
151 Steve Trout .05 .15
152 Glenn Brummer .05 .15
153 Dick Tidrow .05 .15
154 Dave Henderson .08 .25
155 Frank White .08 .25
156 Rickey Henderson .25 .60
Tim Conroy TL
157 Gary Gaetti .15 .40
158 John Curtis .05 .15
159 Darryl Cias .05 .15
160 Mario Soto .08 .25
161 Junior Ortiz .05 .15
162 Bob Ojeda .05 .15
163 Lorenzo Gray .05 .15
164 Scott Sanderson .05 .15
165 Ken Singleton .08 .25
166 Jamie Nelson .05 .15
167 Marshall Edwards .05 .15
168 Juan Bonilla .05 .15
169 Larry Parrish .05 .15
170 Jerry Reuss .05 .15
171 Frank Robinson MG .15 .40
172 Frank DiPino .05 .15
173 Marvell Wynne .15 .40
174 Juan Berenguer .05 .15
175 Graig Nettles .08 .25
176 Lee Smith .08 .25
177 Jerry Hairston .05 .15
178 Bill Krueger RC .05 .15
179 Buck Martinez .05 .15
180 Manny Trillo .05 .15
181 Roy Thomas .05 .15
182 Darryl Strawberry RC 1.25 3.00
183 Al Williams .05 .15
184 Mike O'Berry .05 .15
185 Sixto Lezcano .05 .15
186 Lonnie Smith .08 .25
John Stuper TL
187 Luis Aponte .05 .15
188 Bryan Little .05 .15
189 Tim Conroy .05 .15
190 Ben Oglivie .08 .25
191 Mike Boddicker .05 .15
192 Nick Esasky .05 .15
193 Darrell Brown .05 .15
194 Domingo Ramos .05 .15
195 Jack Morris .08 .25
196 Don Slaught .08 .25
197 Garry Hancock .05 .15
198 Bill Doran RC .15 .40
199 Willie Hernandez .05 .15
200 Andre Dawson .08 .25
201 Bruce Kison .05 .15
202 Bobby Cox MG .08 .25
203 Matt Keough .05 .15
204 Bobby Meacham .05 .15
205 Greg Minton .05 .15
206 Andy Van Slyke RC .60 1.50
207 Donnie Moore .05 .15
208 Jose Oquendo RC .15 .40
209 Manny Sarmiento .05 .15
210 Joe Morgan .08 .25
211 Rick Sweet .05 .15
212 Broderick Perkins .05 .15
213 Bruce Hurst .05 .15
214 Paul Householder .05 .15
215 Tippy Martinez .05 .15
216 Carlton Fisk .08 .25
Richard Dotson TL
217 Alan Ashby .05 .15
218 Rick Waits .05 .15
219 Joe Simpson .05 .15
220 Fernando Valenzuela .08 .25
221 Cliff Johnson .05 .15
222 Rick Honeycutt .05 .15
223 Wayne Krenchicki .05 .15
224 Sid Monge .05 .15
225 Lee Mazzilli .08 .25
226 Juan Eichelberger .05 .15
227 Steve Braun .05 .15
228 John Rabb .05 .15
229 Paul Owens MG .05 .15
230 Rickey Henderson .40 1.00
231 Gary Woods .05 .15
232 Tim Wallach .05 .15
233 Checklist 133-264 .08 .25
234 Rafael Ramirez .05 .15
235 Matt Young RC .15 .40
236 Ellis Valentine .05 .15
237 John Castino .05 .15
238 Reid Nichols .05 .15
239 Jay Howell .05 .15
240 Eddie Murray .25 .60
241 Bill Almon .05 .15
242 Alex Trevino .05 .15
243 Pete Ladd .05 .15
244 Candy Maldonado .05 .15
245 Rick Sutcliffe .08 .25
246 Mookie Wilson .08 .25
Tom Seaver TL
247 Onix Concepcion .05 .15
248 Bill Dawley .05 .15
249 Jay Johnstone .05 .15
250 Bill Madlock .08 .25
251 Tony Gwynn 1.00 2.50
252 Larry Christenson .05 .15
253 Jim Wohlford .05 .15
254 Shane Rawley .05 .15
255 Bruce Benedict .05 .15
256 Dave Geisel .05 .15
257 Julio Cruz .05 .15
258 Luis Sanchez .05 .15
259 Sparky Anderson MG .08 .25
260 Scott McGregor .05 .15
261 Bobby Brown .05 .15
262 Tom Candiotti RC .30 .75
263 Jack Fimple .05 .15
264 Doug Frobel RC .05 .15
265 Donnie Hill .05 .15
266 Steve Lubratich .05 .15
267 Carmelo Martinez .05 .15
268 Jack O'Connor .05 .15
269 Aurelio Rodriguez .05 .15
270 Jeff Russell RC .15 .40
271 Moose Haas .05 .15
272 Rick Dempsey .05 .15
273 Charlie Puleo .05 .15
274 Rick Monday .08 .25
275 Len Matuszek .05 .15
276 Rod Carew .08 .25
Geoff Zahn TL
277 Eddie Whitson .05 .15
278 Jorge Bell .08 .25
279 Ivan DeJesus .05 .15
280 Floyd Bannister .05 .15
281 Larry Milbourne .05 .15
282 Jim Barr .05 .15
283 Larry Biittner .05 .15
284 Howard Bailey .05 .15
285 Darrell Porter .05 .15
286 Lary Sorensen .05 .15
287 Warren Cromartie .05 .15
288 Jim Beattie .05 .15
289 Randy Johnson .05 .15
290 Dave Dravecky .05 .15
291 Chuck Tanner MG .05 .15
292 Tony Scott .05 .15
293 Ed Lynch .05 .15
294 U.L. Washington .05 .15
295 Mike Flanagan .05 .15
296 Jeff Newman .05 .15
297 Bruce Berenyi .05 .15
298 Jim Gantner .05 .15
299 John Butcher .05 .15
300 Pete Rose .75 2.00
301 Frank LaCorte .05 .15
302 Barry Bonnell .05 .15
303 Marty Castillo .05 .15
304 Warren Brusstar .05 .15
305 Roy Smalley .05 .15
306 Pedro Guerrero .08 .25
Bob Welch TL
307 Bobby Mitchell .05 .15
308 Ron Hassey .05 .15
309 Tony Phillips RC .30 .75
310 Willie McGee .08 .25
311 Jerry Koosman .08 .25
312 Jorge Orta .05 .15
313 Mike Jorgensen .05 .15
314 Orlando Mercado .05 .15
315 Bobby Grich .08 .25
316 Mark Bradley .05 .15
317 Greg Pryor .05 .15
318 Bill Gullickson .05 .15
319 Al Bumbry .05 .15
320 Bob Stanley .05 .15
321 Harvey Kuenn MG .05 .15
322 Ken Schrom .05 .15
323 Alan Knicely .05 .15
324 Alejandro Pena RC .30 .75
325 Darrell Evans .08 .25
326 Bob Kearney .05 .15
327 Ruppert Jones .05 .15
328 Vern Ruhle .05 .15
329 Pat Tabler .05 .15
330 John Candelaria .05 .15
331 Bucky Dent .08 .25
332 Kevin Gross RC .15 .40
333 Larry Herndon .08 .25
334 Chuck Rainey .05 .15
335 Don Baylor .08 .25
336 Pat Putnam .08 .25
Matt Young TL
337 Kevin Hagen .05 .15
338 Mike Warren .05 .15
339 Roy Lee Jackson .05 .15
340 Hal McRae .08 .25
341 Dave Tobik .05 .15
342 Tim Foli .05 .15
343 Mark Davis .05 .15
344 Rick Miller .05 .15
345 Kent Hrbek .08 .25
346 Kurt Bevacqua .05 .15
347 Allan Ramirez .05 .15
348 Toby Harrah .08 .25
349 Bob L. Gibson RC .05 .15
350 George Foster .08 .25
351 Russ Nixon MG .05 .15
352 Dave Stewart .08 .25
353 Jim Anderson .05 .15
354 Jeff Burroughs .05 .15
355 Jason Thompson .05 .15
356 Glenn Abbott .05 .15
357 Ron Cey .08 .25
358 Bob Dernier .05 .15
359 Jim Acker .05 .15
360 Willie Randolph .08 .25
361 Dave Smith .05 .15
362 David Green .05 .15
363 Tim Laudner .05 .15
364 Scott Fletcher .05 .15
365 Steve Bedrosian .05 .15
366 Terry Kennedy .08 .25

Dave Dravecky TL
367 Jamie Easterly .05 .15
368 Hubie Brooks .05 .15
369 Steve McCatty .05 .15
370 Tim Raines .08 .25
371 Dave Gumpert .05 .15
372 Gary Roenicke .05 .15
373 Bill Scherrer .05 .15
374 Don Money .05 .15
375 Dennis Leonard .05 .15
376 Dave Anderson RC .05 .15
377 Danny Darwin .05 .15
378 Bob Brenly .05 .15
379 Checklist 265-396 .08 .25
380 Steve Garvey .08 .25
381 Ralph Houk MG .05 .15
382 Chris Nyman .05 .15
383 Terry Puhl .05 .15
384 Lee Tunnell .05 .15
385 Tony Perez .15 .40
386 George Hendrick AS .05 .15
387 Johnny Ray AS .05 .15
388 Mike Schmidt AS .25 .60
389 Ozzie Smith AS .25 .60
390 Tim Raines AS .05 .15
391 Dale Murphy AS .08 .25
392 Andre Dawson AS .05 .15
393 Gary Carter AS .05 .15
394 Steve Rogers AS .05 .15
395 Steve Carlton AS .08 .25
396 Jesse Orosco AS .05 .15
397 Eddie Murray AS .15 .40
398 Lou Whitaker AS .05 .15
399 George Brett AS .25 .60
400 Cal Ripken AS .75 2.00
401 Jim Rice AS .05 .15
402 Dave Winfield AS .05 .15
403 Lloyd Moseby AS .05 .15
404 Ted Simmons AS .05 .15
405 LaMarr Hoyt AS .05 .15
406 Ron Guidry AS .05 .15
407 Dan Quisenberry AS .05 .15
408 Lou Piniella .08 .25
409 Juan Agosto .05 .15
410 Claudell Washington .05 .15
411 Houston Jimenez .05 .15
412 Doug Rader MG .05 .15
413 Spike Owen RC .15 .40
414 Mitchell Page .05 .15
415 Tommy John .08 .25
416 Dane Iorg .05 .15
417 Mike Armstrong .05 .15
418 Ron Hodges .05 .15
419 John Henry Johnson .05 .15
420 Cecil Cooper .08 .25
421 Charlie Lea .05 .15
422 Jose Cruz .08 .25
423 Mike Morgan .05 .15
424 Dann Bilardello .05 .15
425 Steve Howe .05 .15
426 Cal Ripken .60 1.50
Mike Boddicker TL
427 Rick Leach .05 .15
428 Fred Breining .05 .15
429 Randy Bush .05 .15
430 Rusty Staub .08 .25
431 Chris Bando .05 .15
432 Charles Hudson .05 .15
433 Rich Hebner .05 .15
434 Harold Baines .08 .25
435 Neil Allen .05 .15
436 Rick Peters .05 .15
437 Mike Proly .05 .15
438 Biff Pocoroba .05 .15
439 Bob Stoddard .05 .15
440 Steve Kemp .05 .15
441 Bob Lillis MG .05 .15
442 Byron McLaughlin .05 .15
443 Benny Ayala .05 .15
444 Steve Renko .05 .15
445 Jerry Remy .05 .15
446 Luis Pujols .05 .15
447 Tom Brunansky .05 .15
448 Ben Hayes .05 .15
449 Joe Pettini .05 .15
450 Gary Carter .08 .25
451 Bob Jones .05 .15
452 Chuck Porter .05 .15
453 Willie Upshaw .05 .15
454 Joe Beckwith .05 .15
455 Terry Kennedy .05 .15
456 Keith Moreland .05 .15
Fergie Jenkins TL
457 Dave Rozema .05 .15
458 Kiko Garcia .05 .15
459 Kevin Hickey .05 .15
460 Dave Winfield .08 .25
461 Jim Maler .05 .15
462 Lee Lacy .05 .15
463 Dave Engle .05 .15
464 Jeff A. Jones .05 .15
465 Mookie Wilson .08 .25
466 Gene Garber .05 .15
467 Mike Ramsey .05 .15
468 Geoff Zahn .05 .15
469 Tom O'Malley .05 .15
470 Nolan Ryan 1.25 3.00
471 Dick Howser MG .05 .15
472 Mike G. Brown RC .05 .15
473 Jim Dwyer .05 .15
474 Greg Bargar .05 .15
475 Gary Redus RC .15 .40
476 Tom Tellmann .05 .15
477 Rafael Landestoy .05 .15
478 Alan Bannister .05 .15
479 Frank Tanana .08 .25
480 Ron Kittle .05 .15
481 Mark Thurmond .05 .15
482 Enos Cabell .05 .15
483 Fergie Jenkins .08 .25
484 Ozzie Virgil .05 .15
485 Rick Rhoden .05 .15
486 Don Baylor .08 .25
Ron Guidry TL
487 Ricky Adams .05 .15
488 Jesse Barfield .08 .25
489 Dave Von Ohlen .05 .15
490 Cal Ripken 1.50 4.00
491 Bobby Castillo .05 .15
492 Tucker Ashford .05 .15
493 Mike Norris .05 .15
494 Chili Davis .08 .25
495 Rollie Fingers .08 .25
496 Terry Francona .08 .25
497 Bud Anderson .05 .15
498 Rich Gedman .05 .15
499 Mike Witt .05 .15
500 George Brett .60 1.50
501 Steve Henderson .05 .15
502 Joe Torre MG .08 .25
503 Elias Sosa .05 .15
504 Mickey Rivers .05 .15
505 Pete Vuckovich .05 .15
506 Ernie Whitt .05 .15
507 Mike LaCoss .05 .15
508 Mel Hall .08 .25
509 Brad Havens .05 .15
510 Alan Trammell .08 .25
511 Marty Bystrom .05 .15
512 Oscar Gamble .05 .15
513 Dave Beard .05 .15
514 Floyd Rayford .05 .15
515 Gorman Thomas .08 .25
516 Al Oliver .08 .25
Charlie Lea TL
517 John Moses .05 .15
518 Greg Walker .15 .40
519 Ron Davis .05 .15
520 Bob Boone .08 .25
521 Pete Falcone .05 .15
522 Dave Bergman .05 .15
523 Glenn Hoffman .05 .15
524 Carlos Diaz .05 .15
525 Willie Wilson .08 .25
526 Ron Oester .05 .15
527 Checklist 397-528 .08 .25
528 Mark Brouhard .05 .15
529 Keith Atherton .05 .15
530 Dan Ford .05 .15
531 Steve Boros MG .05 .15
532 Eric Show .05 .15
533 Ken Landreaux .05 .15
534 Pete O'Brien RC .15 .40
535 Bo Diaz .05 .15
536 Doug Bair .05 .15
537 Johnny Ray .05 .15
538 Kevin Bass .05 .15
539 George Frazier .05 .15
540 George Hendrick .05 .15
541 Dennis Lamp .05 .15
542 Duane Kuiper .05 .15
543 Craig McMurtry .05 .15
544 Cesar Geronimo .05 .15
545 Bill Buckner .08 .25
546 Mike Hargrove .08 .25
Lary Sorensen TL
547 Mike Moore .05 .15
548 Ron Jackson .05 .15
549 Walt Terrell .05 .15
550 Jim Rice .08 .25
551 Scott Ullger .05 .15
552 Ray Burris .05 .15
553 Joe Nolan .05 .15
554 Ted Power .05 .15
555 Greg Brock .05 .15
556 Joey McLaughlin .05 .15
557 Wayne Tolleson .05 .15
558 Mike Davis .05 .15
559 Mike Scott .08 .25
560 Carlton Fisk .15 .40
561 Whitey Herzog MG .08 .25
562 Manny Castillo .05 .15
563 Glenn Wilson .08 .25
564 Al Holland .05 .15
565 Leon Durham .05 .15
566 Jim Bibby .05 .15
567 Mike Heath .05 .15
568 Pete Filson .05 .15
569 Bake McBride .08 .25
570 Dan Quisenberry .05 .15
571 Bruce Bochy .05 .15
572 Jerry Royster .05 .15
573 Dave Kingman .08 .25
574 Brian Downing .08 .25
575 Jim Clancy .05 .15
576 Jeff Leonard .08 .25
Atlee Hammaker TL
577 Mark Clear .05 .15
578 Lenn Sakata .05 .15
579 Bob James .05 .15
580 Lonnie Smith .05 .15
581 Jose DeLeon RC .15 .40
582 Bob McClure .05 .15
583 Derrel Thomas .05 .15
584 Dave Schmidt .05 .15
585 Dan Driessen .05 .15
586 Joe Niekro .05 .15
587 Von Hayes .05 .15
588 Milt Wilcox .05 .15
589 Mike Easler .05 .15
590 Dave Stieb .08 .25
591 Tony LaRussa MG .08 .25
592 Andre Robertson .05 .15
593 Jeff Lahti .05 .15
594 Gene Richards .05 .15
595 Jeff Reardon .08 .25
596 Ryne Sandberg 1.00 2.50
597 Rick Camp .05 .15
598 Rusty Kuntz .05 .15
599 Doug Sisk .05 .15
600 Rod Carew .15 .40
601 John Tudor .08 .25
602 John Wathan .05 .15
603 Renie Martin .05 .15
604 John Lowenstein .05 .15
605 Mike Caldwell .05 .15
606 Lloyd Moseby .08 .25
Dave Stieb TL
607 Tom Hume .05 .15
608 Bobby Johnson .05 .15
609 Dan Meyer .05 .15
610 Steve Sax .05 .15
611 Chet Lemon .08 .25
612 Harry Spilman .05 .15
613 Greg Gross .05 .15
614 Len Barker .05 .15
615 Garry Templeton .08 .25
616 Don Robinson .05 .15
617 Rick Cerone .05 .15
618 Dickie Noles .05 .15
619 Jerry Dybzinski .05 .15
620 Al Oliver .08 .25
621 Frank Howard MG .08 .25
622 Al Cowens .05 .15
623 Ron Washington .05 .15
624 Terry Harper .05 .15
625 Larry Gura .05 .15
626 Bob Clark .05 .15
627 Dave LaPoint .05 .15
628 Ed Jurak .05 .15
629 Rick Langford .05 .15
630 Ted Simmons .08 .25
631 Dennis Martinez .08 .25
632 Tom Foley .05 .15
633 Mike Krukow .05 .15
634 Mike Marshall .05 .15
635 Dave Righetti .08 .25
636 Pat Putnam .05 .15
637 Gary Matthews .08 .25
John Denny TL
638 George Vukovich .05 .15
639 Rick Lysander .05 .15
640 Lance Parrish .15 .40
641 Mike Richardt .05 .15
642 Tom Underwood .05 .15
643 Mike C. Brown .05 .15
644 Tim Lollar .05 .15
645 Tony Pena .05 .15
646 Checklist 529-660 .08 .25
647 Ron Roenicke .05 .15
648 Len Whitehouse .05 .15
649 Tom Herr .05 .15
650 Phil Niekro .08 .25
651 John McNamara MG .05 .15
652 Rudy May .05 .15
653 Dave Stapleton .05 .15
654 Bob Bailor .05 .15
655 Amos Otis .08 .25
656 Bryn Smith .05 .15
657 Thad Bosley .05 .15
658 Jerry Augustine .05 .15
659 Duane Walker .05 .15
660 Ray Knight .08 .25
661 Steve Yeager .08 .25
662 Tom Brennan .05 .15
663 Johnnie LeMaster .05 .15
664 Dave Stegman .05 .15
665 Buddy Bell .08 .25
666 Lou Whitaker .08 .25
Jack Morris TL
667 Vance Law .05 .15
668 Larry McWilliams .05 .15
669 Dave Lopes .08 .25
670 Rich Gossage .08 .25
671 Jamie Quirk .05 .15
672 Ricky Nelson .05 .15
673 Mike Walters .05 .15
674 Tim Flannery .05 .15
675 Pascual Perez .05 .15
676 Brian Giles .05 .15
677 Doyle Alexander .05 .15
678 Chris Speier .05 .15
679 Art Howe .05 .15
680 Fred Lynn .08 .25
681 Tom Lasorda MG .15 .40
682 Dan Morogiello .05 .15
683 Marty Barrett RC .15 .40
684 Bob Shirley .05 .15
685 Willie Aikens .05 .15
686 Joe Price .05 .15
687 Roy Howell .05 .15
688 George Wright .05 .15
689 Mike Fischlin .05 .15
690 Jack Clark .08 .25
691 Steve Lake .05 .15
692 Dickie Thon .05 .15
693 Alan Wiggins .05 .15
694 Mike Stanton .05 .15
695 Lou Whitaker .08 .25
696 Bill Madlock .08 .25
Rick Rhoden TL
697 Dale Murray .05 .15
698 Marc Hill .05 .15
699 Dave Rucker .05 .15
700 Mike Schmidt .60 1.50
701 Bill Madlock .25 .60
Pete Rose
Dave Parker LL
702 Pete Rose .25 .60
Rusty Staub
Tony Perez LL
703 Mike Schmidt .25 .60
Tony Perez
Dave Kingman LL
704 Tony Perez .08 .25
Rusty Staub
Al Oliver LL
705 Joe Morgan .15 .40
Cesar Cedeno
Larry Bowa LL
706 Steve Carlton .08 .25
Fergie Jenkins
Tom Seaver LL
707 Steve Carlton .60 1.50
Nolan Ryan
Tom Seaver LL
708 Tom Seaver .08 .25
Steve Carlton
Steve Rogers LL
709 Bruce Sutter .08 .25
Tug McGraw
Gene Garber LL
710 Rod Carew .15 .40
George Brett
Cecil Cooper LL
711 Rod Carew .08 .25
Bert Campaneris
Reggie Jackson LL
712 Reggie Jackson .08 .25
Graig Nettles
Greg Luzinski LL
713 Reggie Jackson .08 .25
Ted Simmons
Graig Nettles LL
714 Bert Campaneris .08 .25
Dave Lopes
Omar Moreno LL
715 Jim Palmer .08 .25
Don Sutton
Tommy John LL
716 Don Sutton .15 .40
Bert Blyleven
Jerry Koosman LL
717 Jim Palmer .08 .25
Rollie Fingers
Ron Guidry LL
718 Rollie Fingers .08 .25
Rich Gossage
Dan Quisenberry LL
719 Andy Hassler .05 .15
720 Dwight Evans .15 .40
721 Del Crandall MG .05 .15
722 Bob Welch .08 .25
723 Rich Dauer .05 .15
724 Eric Rasmussen .05 .15
725 Cesar Cedeno .08 .25
726 Ted Simmons .08 .25
Moose Haas TL
727 Joel Youngblood .05 .15
728 Tug McGraw .08 .25
729 Gene Tenace .08 .25
730 Bruce Sutter .15 .40
731 Lynn Jones .05 .15
732 Terry Crowley .05 .15
733 Dave Collins .05 .15
734 Odell Jones .05 .15
735 Rick Burleson .05 .15
736 Dick Ruthven .05 .15
737 Jim Essian .05 .15
738 Bill Schroeder .05 .15
739 Bob Watson .05 .15
740 Tom Seaver .25 .60
741 Wayne Gross .05 .15
742 Dick Williams MG .05 .15
743 Don Hood .05 .15
744 Jamie Allen .05 .15
745 Dennis Eckersley .15 .40
746 Mickey Hatcher .05 .15
747 Pat Zachry .05 .15
748 Jeff Leonard .05 .15
749 Doug Flynn .05 .15
750 Jim Palmer .08 .25
751 Charlie Moore .05 .15
752 Phil Garner .08 .25
753 Doug Gwosdz .05 .15
754 Kent Tekulve .05 .15
755 Garry Maddox .05 .15
756 Ron Oester .08 .25
Mario Soto TL
757 Larry Bowa .08 .25
758 Bill Stein .05 .15
759 Richard Dotson .05 .15
760 Bob Horner .08 .25
761 John Montefusco .05 .15
762 Rance Mulliniks .05 .15
763 Craig Swan .05 .15
764 Mike Hargrove .05 .15
765 Ken Forsch .05 .15
766 Mike Vail .05 .15
767 Carney Lansford .08 .25
768 Champ Summers .05 .15
769 Bill Caudill .05 .15
770 Ken Griffey .08 .25
771 Billy Gardner MG .05 .15
772 Jim Slaton .05 .15
773 Todd Cruz .05 .15
774 Tom Gorman .05 .15
775 Dave Parker .08 .25
776 Craig Reynolds .05 .15
777 Tom Paciorek .05 .15
778 Andy Hawkins .05 .15
779 Jim Sundberg .08 .25
780 Steve Carlton .15 .40
781 Checklist 661-792 .08 .25
782 Steve Balboni .05 .15
783 Luis Leal .05 .15
784 Leon Roberts .05 .15
785 Joaquin Andujar .08 .25
786 Wade Boggs .15 .40
Bob Ojeda TL
787 Bill Campbell .05 .15
788 Milt May .05 .15
789 Bert Blyleven .08 .25
790 Doug DeCinces .05 .15
791 Terry Forster .08 .25
792 Bill Russell .08 .25

1984 Topps Tiffany

This 792 card standard-size set was issued by Topps as a parallel to their regular issue. Printed in their Ireland facility, these cards are differentiated from the regular cards by the glossy fronts and pure white stock. These sets were available only through Topps' dealer network and sold only in factory set form. According to information from the time of issue, 10,000 of these sets were produced.

COMP.FACT.SET (792) 90.00 150.00
*STARS: 3X TO 8X BASIC CARDS
*ROOKIES: 2.5X TO 6X BASIC CARDS
DISTRIBUTED ONLY IN FACTORY SET FORM
FACTORY SET PRICE IS FOR SEALED SETS

1984 Topps Glossy All-Stars

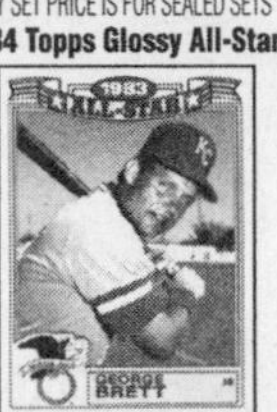

The cards in this 22-card set measure the standard size. Unlike the 1983 Topps Glossy set which was not distributed with its regular baseball cards, the 1984 Topps Glossy set was distributed as inserts in Topps Rak-Paks. The set features the nine American and National League All-Stars who started in the 1983 All Star game in Chicago. The managers and team captains (Yastrzemski and Bench) complete the set. The cards are numbered on the back and are ordered by position within league (AL: 1-11 and NL: 12-22).

COMPLETE SET (22) 2.00 5.00
1 Harvey Kuenn MG .01 .05
2 Rod Carew .20 .50
3 Manny Trillo .01 .05
4 George Brett .40 1.00
5 Robin Yount .20 .50
6 Jim Rice .02 .10
7 Fred Lynn .02 .10
8 Dave Winfield .20 .50
9 Ted Simmons .02 .10
10 Dave Stieb .01 .05
11 Carl Yastrzemski CAPT .20 .50
12 Whitey Herzog MG .01 .05
13 Al Oliver .02 .10
14 Steve Sax .02 .10
15 Mike Schmidt .30 .75
16 Ozzie Smith .40 1.00
17 Tim Raines .05 .15
18 Andre Dawson .08 .25
19 Dale Murphy .08 .25
20 Gary Carter .15 .40
21 Mario Soto .01 .05
22 Johnny Bench CAPT .20 .50

1984 Topps Glossy Send-Ins

The cards in this 40-card set measure the standard size. Similar to last year's glossy set, this set was issued as a bonus prize to Topps All-Star Baseball Game cards found in wax packs. Twenty-five bonus runs from the game cards were necessary to obtain a five card subset of the series. There were eight different subsets of five cards. The cards are numbered and the set contains 20 stars from each league.

COMPLETE SET (40) 4.80 12.00
1 Pete Rose .50 1.25
2 Lance Parrish .07 .20
3 Steve Rogers .02 .10
4 Eddie Murray .40 1.00
5 Johnny Ray .02 .10
6 Rickey Henderson .75 2.00
7 Atlee Hammaker .02 .10
8 Wade Boggs .60 1.50
9 Gary Carter .50 1.25
10 Jack Morris .07 .20
11 Darrell Evans .07 .20
12 George Brett 1.00 2.50
13 Bob Horner .02 .10
14 Ron Guidry .07 .20
15 Nolan Ryan 2.00 5.00
16 Dave Winfield .40 1.00
17 Ozzie Smith .75 2.00
18 Ted Simmons .07 .20
19 Bill Madlock .02 .10
20 Tony Armas .02 .10
21 Al Oliver .07 .20
22 Jim Rice .07 .20
23 George Hendrick .02 .10
24 Dave Stieb .02 .10
25 Pedro Guerrero .07 .20
26 Rod Carew .40 1.00
27 Steve Carlton .40 1.00
28 Dave Righetti .07 .20
29 Darryl Strawberry .20 .50
30 Lou Whitaker .07 .20
31 Dale Murphy .10 .30
32 LaMarr Hoyt .02 .10
33 Jesse Orosco .07 .20
34 Cecil Cooper .07 .20
35 Andre Dawson .20 .50
36 Robin Yount .50 1.25
37 Tim Raines .10 .30
38 Dan Quisenberry .02 .10
39 Mike Schmidt .75 2.00
40 Carlton Fisk .60 1.50

1984 Topps Traded

In what was now standard procedure, Topps issued its standard-size Traded (or extended) set for the fourth year in a row. Several of 1984's top rookies not contained in the regular set are pictured in the Traded set. Extended Rookie Cards in this set include Dwight Gooden, Jimmy Key, Mark Langston, Jose Rijo, and Bret Saberhagen. Again this year, the Topps affiliate in Ireland printed the cards, and the cards were available through hobby channels only in factory set form. The set numbering is in alphabetical order by player's name. The 132-card sets were shipped to dealers in 100-ct set cases. A few cards have been seen with a "grey" logo for Topps, these cards draw a significant multiplier of the regular Topps Traded cards, but are not yet known in sufficient quantity to price in our checklist.

COMP.FACT.SET (132) 15.00 30.00
1T Willie Aikens .15 .40
2T Luis Aponte .15 .40
3T Mike Armstrong .15 .40
4T Bob Bailor .15 .40
5T Dusty Baker .25 .60
6T Steve Balboni .15 .40
7T Alan Bannister .15 .40
8T Dave Beard .15 .40
9T Joe Beckwith .15 .40
10T Bruce Berenyi .15 .40
11T Dave Bergman .15 .40
12T Tony Bernazard .15 .40
13T Yogi Berra MG .60 1.50
14T Barry Bonnell .15 .40
15T Phil Bradley .40 1.00
16T Fred Breining .15 .40
17T Bill Buckner .25 .60
18T Ray Burris .15 .40
19T John Butcher .15 .40
20T Brett Butler .25 .60
21T Enos Cabell .15 .40
22T Bill Campbell .15 .40
23T Bill Caudill .15 .40
24T Bob Clark .15 .40
25T Bryan Clark .15 .40
26T Jaime Cocanower .15 .40
27T Ron Darling XRC .75 2.00
28T Alvin Davis XRC .40 1.00
29T Ken Dayley .15 .40
30T Jeff Dedmon .15 .40
31T Bob Dernier .15 .40
32T Carlos Diaz .15 .40
33T Mike Easler .15 .40
34T Dennis Eckersley .40 1.00
35T Jim Essian .15 .40
36T Darrell Evans .25 .60
37T Mike Fitzgerald .15 .40
38T Tim Foli .15 .40
39T George Frazier .15 .40
40T Rich Gale .15 .40
41T Barbaro Garbey .15 .40
42T Dwight Gooden XRC 4.00 10.00
43T Rich Gossage .25 .60
44T Wayne Gross .15 .40
45T Mark Gubicza XRC .40 1.00
46T Jackie Gutierrez .15 .40
47T Mel Hall .25 .60
48T Toby Harrah .25 .60
49T Ron Hassey .15 .40
50T Rich Hebner .15 .40
51T Willie Hernandez .15 .40
52T Ricky Horton .15 .40
53T Art Howe .15 .40
54T Dane Iorg .15 .40
55T Brook Jacoby .40 1.00
56T Mike Jeffcoat XRC .20 .50
57T Dave Johnson MG .15 .40
58T Lynn Jones .15 .40
59T Ruppert Jones .15 .40
60T Mike Jorgensen .15 .40
61T Bob Kearney .15 .40
62T Jimmy Key XRC .75 2.00
63T Dave Kingman .25 .60
64T Jerry Koosman .25 .60
65T Wayne Krenchicki .15 .40
66T Rusty Kuntz .15 .40
67T Rene Lachemann MG .15 .40
68T Frank LaCorte .15 .40
69T Dennis Lamp .15 .40
70T Mark Langston XRC .75 2.00
71T Rick Leach .15 .40
72T Craig Lefferts .20 .50
73T Gary Lucas .15 .40
74T Jerry Martin .15 .40
75T Carmelo Martinez .15 .40
76T Mike Mason XRC .20 .50
77T Gary Matthews .25 .60
78T Andy McGaffigan .15 .40
79T Larry Milbourne .15 .40
80T Sid Monge .15 .40
81T Jackie Moore MG .15 .40
82T Joe Morgan .25 .60
83T Graig Nettles .25 .60
84T Phil Niekro .25 .60
85T Ken Oberkfell .15 .40
86T Mike O'Berry .15 .40
87T Al Oliver .25 .60
88T Jorge Orta .15 .40
89T Amos Otis .25 .60
90T Dave Parker .25 .60
91T Tony Perez .40 1.00
92T Gerald Perry .40 1.00
93T Gary Pettis .15 .40
94T Rob Picciolo .15 .40
95T Vern Rapp MG .15 .40
96T Floyd Rayford .15 .40
97T Randy Ready XRC .40 1.00
98T Ron Reed .15 .40
99T Gene Richards .15 .40
100T Jose Rijo XRC .75 2.00
101T Jeff D. Robinson .15 .40
102T Ron Romanick .15 .40
103T Pete Rose 2.00 5.00
104T Bret Saberhagen XRC 1.50 4.00
105T Juan Samuel XRC .75 2.00
106T Scott Sanderson .15 .40
107T Dick Schofield XRC .40 1.00
108T Tom Seaver .60 1.50
109T Jim Slaton .15 .40
110T Mike Smithson .15 .40
111T Lary Sorensen .15 .40
112T Tim Stoddard .15 .40
113T Champ Summers .15 .40
114T Jim Sundberg .25 .60
115T Rick Sutcliffe .25 .60
116T Craig Swan .15 .40
117T Tim Teufel XRC .40 1.00
118T Derrel Thomas .15 .40
119T Gorman Thomas .25 .60
120T Alex Trevino .15 .40
121T Manny Trillo .15 .40
122T John Tudor .25 .60
123T Tom Underwood .15 .40
124T Mike Vail .15 .40
125T Tom Waddell .15 .40
126T Gary Ward .15 .40
127T Curtis Wilkerson .15 .40
128T Frank Williams .15 .40
129T Glenn Wilson .25 .60
130T John Wockenfuss .15 .40
131T Ned Yost .15 .40
132T Checklist 1T-132T .15 .40

1984 Topps Traded Tiffany

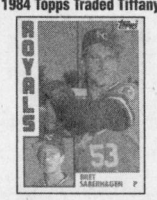

This 132-card standard-size set was issued by Topps as a premium parallel to their regular issue. This set was printed in the Topps Ireland factory and are differentiated from the regular cards by their glossy sheen and clean backs. These sets were only available through the Topps hobby distribution system. Topps issued these sets only if a dealer ordered the regular Tiffany sets, therefore approximately 10,000 of these sets were produced as well.

COMP.FACT.SET (132) 30.00 60.00
*STARS: .6X TO 1.5X BASIC CARDS
*ROOKIES: 1X TO 2.5X BASIC CARDS
DISTRIBUTED ONLY IN FACTORY SET FORM
FACTORY SET PRICE IS FOR SEALED SETS

1985 Topps

The 1985 Topps set contains 792 standard-size full-color cards. Cards were primarily distributed in 15-card wax packs, 51-card rack packs and factory (usually available through retail catalogs) sets. The wax packs were issued with an 35 cent SRP and were packaged 36 packs to a box and 20 boxes to a case. Manager cards feature the team checklist on the reverse. Full color card fronts feature both the Topps and team logos along with the team name, player's name, and his position. The first ten cards (1-10) are Record Breakers, cards 131-143 are Father and Sons, and cards 701 to 722 portray All-Star selections. Cards 271-282 represent "First Draft Picks" still active in professional baseball and cards 389-404 feature selected members of the 1984 U.S. Olympic Baseball Team. Rookie Cards include Roger Clemens, Eric Davis, Shawon Dunston, Dwight Gooden, Orel Hershiser, Jimmy Key, Mark Langston, Mark McGwire, Terry Pendleton, Kirby Puckett and Bret Saberhagen.

COMPLETE SET (792) 30.00 60.00
COMP.FACT.SET (792) 100.00 175.00
1 Carlton Fisk RB .08 .25
2 Steve Garvey RB .05 .15
3 Dwight Gooden RB .25 .60
4 Cliff Johnson RB .05 .15
5 Joe Morgan RB .05 .15

6 Pete Rose RB .15 .40
7 Nolan Ryan RB .60 1.50
8 Juan Samuel RB .05 .15
9 Bruce Sutter RB .05 .15
10 Don Sutton RB .05 .15
11 Ralph Houk MG .05 .15
12 Dave Lopes .08 .25
13 Tim Lollar .05 .15
14 Chris Bando .05 .15
15 Jerry Koosman .08 .25
16 Bobby Meacham .05 .15
17 Mike Scott .08 .25
18 Mickey Hatcher .05 .15
19 George Frazier .05 .15
20 Chet Lemon .08 .25
21 Lee Tunnell .05 .15
22 Duane Kuiper .05 .15
23 Bret Saberhagen RC .40 1.00
24 Jesse Barfield .08 .25
25 Steve Bedrosian .05 .15
26 Roy Smalley .05 .15
27 Bruce Berenyi .05 .15
28 Dann Bilardello .05 .15
29 Odell Jones .05 .15
30 Cal Ripken 1.00 2.50
31 Terry Whitfield .05 .15
32 Chuck Porter .05 .15
33 Tito Landrum .05 .15
34 Ed Nunez .05 .15
35 Graig Nettles .08 .25
36 Fred Breining .05 .15
37 Reid Nichols .05 .15
38 Jackie Moore MG .05 .15
39 John Wockenfuss .05 .15
40 Phil Niekro .08 .25
41 Mike Fischlin .05 .15
42 Luis Sanchez .05 .15
43 Andre David .05 .15
44 Dickie Thon .05 .15
45 Greg Minton .05 .15
46 Gary Woods .05 .15
47 Dave Rozema .05 .15
48 Tony Fernandez .08 .25
49 Butch Davis .05 .15
50 John Candelaria .05 .15
51 Bob Watson .05 .15
52 Jerry Dybzinski .05 .15
53 Tom Gorman .05 .15
54 Cesar Cedeno .08 .25
55 Frank Tanana .08 .25
56 Jim Dwyer .05 .15
57 Pat Zachry .05 .15
58 Orlando Mercado .05 .15
59 Rick Waits .05 .15
60 George Hendrick .08 .25
61 Curt Kaufman .05 .15
62 Mike Ramsey .05 .15
63 Steve McCatty .05 .15
64 Mark Bailey .05 .15
65 Bill Buckner .08 .25
66 Dick Williams MG .05 .15
67 Rafael Santana .05 .15
68 Von Hayes .05 .15
69 Jim Winn .05 .15
70 Don Baylor .08 .25
71 Tim Laudner .05 .15
72 Rick Sutcliffe .08 .25
73 Rusty Kuntz .05 .15
74 Mike Krukow .05 .15
75 Willie Upshaw .05 .15
76 Alan Bannister .05 .15
77 Joe Beckwith .05 .15
78 Scott Fletcher .05 .15
79 Rick Mahler .05 .15
80 Keith Hernandez .08 .25
81 Lenn Sakata .05 .15
82 Joe Price .05 .15
83 Charlie Moore .05 .15
84 Spike Owen .05 .15
85 Mike Marshall .05 .15
86 Don Aase .05 .15
87 David Green .05 .15
88 Bryn Smith .05 .15
89 Jackie Gutierrez .05 .15
90 Rich Gossage .08 .25
91 Jeff Burroughs .05 .15
92 Paul Owens MG .05 .15
93 Don Schulze .05 .15
94 Toby Harrah .08 .25
95 Jose Cruz .08 .25
96 Johnny Ray .05 .15
97 Pete Filson .05 .15
98 Steve Lake .05 .15
99 Milt Wilcox .05 .15
100 George Brett .60 1.50
101 Jim Acker .05 .15
102 Tommy Dunbar .05 .15
103 Randy Lerch .05 .15
104 Mike Fitzgerald .05 .15
105 Ron Kittle .05 .15
106 Pascual Perez .05 .15
107 Tom Foley .05 .15
108 Darnell Coles .05 .15
109 Gary Roenicke .05 .15
110 Alejandro Pena .05 .15
111 Doug DeCinces .05 .15
112 Tom Tellmann .05 .15
113 Tom Herr .05 .15
114 Bob James .05 .15
115 Rickey Henderson .30 .75
116 Dennis Boyd .05 .15
117 Greg Gross .05 .15
118 Eric Show .05 .15
119 Pat Corrales MG .05 .15
120 Steve Kemp .05 .15
121 Checklist: 1-132 .05 .15
122 Tom Brunansky .05 .15
123 Dave Smith .05 .15
124 Rich Hebner .05 .15
125 Kent Tekulve .05 .15
126 Ruppert Jones .05 .15
127 Mark Gubicza RC* .15 .40
128 Ernie Whitt .05 .15
129 Gene Garber .05 .15
130 Al Oliver .08 .25
131 Buddy Bell FS .08 .25
Gus Bell
132 Dale Berra FS .25 .60
Yogi Berra
133 Bob Boone FS .05 .15
Ray Boone
134 Terry Francona FS .08 .25
Tito Francona
135 Terry Kennedy FS .05 .15
Bob Kennedy
136 Jeff Kunkel FS .05 .15
Bill Kunkel
137 Vance Law FS .08 .25
Vern Law
138 Dick Schofield FS .05 .15
Dick Schofield
139 Joel Skinner FS .05 .15
Bob Skinner
140 Roy Smalley Jr. FS .05 .15
Roy Smalley
141 Mike Stenhouse FS .05 .15
Dave Stenhouse
142 Steve Trout FS .05 .15
Dizzy Trout
143 Ozzie Virgil FS .05 .15
Ossie Virgil
144 Ron Gardenhire .05 .15
145 Alvin Davis RC* .15 .40
146 Gary Redus .05 .15
147 Bill Swaggerty .05 .15
148 Steve Yeager .08 .25
149 Dickie Noles .05 .15
150 Jim Rice .08 .25
151 Moose Haas .05 .15
152 Steve Braun .05 .15
153 Frank LaCorte .05 .15
154 Angel Salazar .05 .15
155 Yogi Berra MG .25 .60
156 Craig Reynolds .05 .15
157 Tug McGraw .08 .25
158 Pat Tabler .05 .15
159 Carlos Diaz .05 .15
160 Lance Parrish .08 .25
161 Ken Schrom .05 .15
162 Benny Distefano .05 .15
163 Dennis Eckersley .15 .40
164 Jorge Orta .05 .15
165 Dusty Baker .08 .25
166 Keith Atherton .05 .15
167 Rufino Linares .05 .15
168 Garth Iorg .05 .15
169 Dan Spillner .05 .15
170 George Foster .08 .25
171 Bill Stein .05 .15
172 Jack Perconte .05 .15
173 Mike Young .05 .15
174 Rick Honeycutt .05 .15
175 Dave Parker .08 .25
176 Bill Schroeder .05 .15
177 Dave Von Ohlen .05 .15
178 Miguel Dilone .05 .15
179 Tommy John .08 .25
180 Dave Winfield .08 .25
181 Roger Clemens RC 6.00 15.00
182 Tim Flannery .05 .15
183 Larry McWilliams .05 .15
184 Carmen Castillo .05 .15
185 Al Holland .05 .15
186 Bob Lillis MG .05 .15
187 Mike Walters .05 .15
188 Greg Pryor .05 .15
189 Warren Brusstar .05 .15
190 Rusty Staub .08 .25
191 Steve Nicosia .05 .15
192 Howard Johnson .08 .25
193 Jimmy Key RC .30 .75
194 Dave Stegman .05 .15
195 Glenn Hubbard .05 .15
196 Pete O'Brien .05 .15
197 Mike Warren .05 .15
198 Eddie Milner .05 .15
199 Dennis Martinez .08 .25
200 Reggie Jackson .15 .40
201 Burt Hooton .05 .15
202 Gorman Thomas .08 .25
203 Bob McClure .05 .15
204 Art Howe .05 .15
205 Steve Rogers .08 .25
206 Phil Garner .08 .25
207 Mark Clear .05 .15
208 Champ Summers .05 .15
209 Bill Campbell .05 .15
210 Gary Matthews .08 .25
211 Clay Christiansen .05 .15
212 George Vukovich .05 .15
213 Billy Gardner MG .05 .15
214 John Tudor .08 .25
215 Bob Brenly .05 .15
216 Jerry Don Gleaton .05 .15
217 Leon Roberts .05 .15
218 Doyle Alexander .05 .15
219 Gerald Perry .05 .15
220 Fred Lynn .08 .25
221 Ron Reed .05 .15
222 Hubie Brooks .05 .15
223 Tom Hume .05 .15
224 Al Cowens .05 .15
225 Mike Boddicker .05 .15
226 Juan Beniquez .05 .15
227 Danny Darwin .05 .15
228 Dion James .05 .15
229 Dave LaPoint .05 .15
230 Gary Carter .08 .25
231 Dwayne Murphy .05 .15
232 Dave Beard .05 .15
233 Ed Jurak .05 .15
234 Jerry Narron .05 .15
235 Garry Maddox .05 .15
236 Mark Thurmond .05 .15
237 Julio Franco .08 .25
238 Jose Rijo RC .30 .75
239 Tim Teufel .05 .15
240 Dave Stieb .08 .25
241 Jim Frey MG .05 .15
242 Greg Harris .05 .15
243 Barbaro Garbey .05 .15
244 Mike Jones .05 .15
245 Chili Davis .08 .25
246 Mike Norris .05 .15
247 Wayne Tolleson .05 .15
248 Terry Forster .08 .25
249 Harold Baines .08 .25
250 Jesse Orosco .05 .15
251 Brad Gulden .05 .15
252 Dan Ford .05 .15
253 Sid Bream RC .15 .40
254 Pete Vuckovich .05 .15
255 Lonnie Smith .05 .15
256 Mike Stanton .05 .15
257 Bryan Little UER .05 .15
Name spelled Brian on front
258 Mike C. Brown .05 .15
259 Gary Allenson .05 .15
260 Dave Righetti .08 .25
261 Checklist: 133-264 .05 .15
262 Greg Booker .05 .15
263 Mel Hall .05 .15
264 Joe Sambito .05 .15
265 Juan Samuel .05 .15
266 Frank Viola .08 .25
267 Henry Cotto RC .05 .15
268 Chuck Tanner MG .05 .15
269 Doug Baker .05 .15
270 Dan Quisenberry .05 .15
271 Tim Foli FDP .05 .15
272 Jeff Burroughs FDP .05 .15
273 Bill Almon FDP .05 .15
274 F.Bannister FDP76 .05 .15
275 Harold Baines FDP77 .05 .15
276 Bob Horner FDP .05 .15
277 Al Chambers FDP .05 .15
278 Darryl Strawberry .15 .40
FDP80
279 Mike Moore FDP .05 .15
280 S.Dunston FDP82 RC .30 .75
281 T.Belcher RC FDP83 .15 .40
282 Shawn Abner FDP RC .05 .15
283 Fran Mullins .05 .15
284 Marty Bystrom .05 .15
285 Dan Driessen .05 .15
286 Rudy Law .05 .15
287 Walt Terrell .05 .15
288 Jeff Kunkel .05 .15
289 Tom Underwood .05 .15
290 Cecil Cooper .08 .25
291 Bob Welch .08 .25
292 Brad Komminsk .05 .15
293 Curt Young .05 .15
294 Tom Nieto .05 .15
295 Joe Niekro .05 .15
296 Ricky Nelson .05 .15
297 Gary Lucas .05 .15
298 Marty Barrett .05 .15
299 Andy Hawkins .05 .15
300 Rod Carew .15 .40
301 John Montefusco .05 .15
302 Tim Corcoran .05 .15
303 Mike Jeffcoat .05 .15
304 Gary Gaetti .08 .25
305 Dale Berra .05 .15
306 Rick Reuschel .08 .25
307 Sparky Anderson MG .08 .25
308 John Wathan .05 .15
309 Mike Witt .05 .15
310 Manny Trillo .05 .15
311 Jim Gott .05 .15
312 Marc Hill .05 .15
313 Dave Schmidt .05 .15
314 Ron Oester .05 .15
315 Doug Sisk .05 .15
316 John Lowenstein .05 .15
317 Jack Lazorko .05 .15
318 Ted Simmons .08 .25
319 Jeff Jones .05 .15
320 Dale Murphy .15 .40
321 Ricky Horton .05 .15
322 Dave Stapleton .05 .15
323 Andy McGaffigan .05 .15
324 Bruce Bochy .05 .15
325 John Denny .05 .15
326 Kevin Bass .05 .15
327 Brook Jacoby .05 .15
328 Bob Shirley .05 .15
329 Ron Washington .05 .15
330 Leon Durham .05 .15
331 Bill Laskey .05 .15
332 Brian Harper .05 .15
333 Willie Hernandez .05 .15
334 Dick Howser MG .05 .15
335 Bruce Benedict .05 .15
336 Rance Mulliniks .05 .15
337 Billy Sample .05 .15
338 Britt Burns .05 .15
339 Danny Heep .05 .15
340 Robin Yount .40 1.00
341 Floyd Rayford .05 .15
342 Ted Power .05 .15
343 Bill Russell .08 .25
344 Dave Henderson .05 .15
345 Charlie Lea .05 .15
346 Terry Pendleton RC .30 .75
347 Rick Langford .05 .15
348 Bob Boone .08 .25
349 Domingo Ramos .05 .15
350 Wade Boggs .25 .60
351 Juan Agosto .05 .15
352 Joe Morgan .08 .25
353 Julio Solano .05 .15
354 Andre Robertson .05 .15
355 Bert Blyleven .08 .25
356 Dave Meier .05 .15
357 Rich Bordi .05 .15
358 Tony Pena .05 .15
359 Pat Sheridan .05 .15
360 Steve Carlton .08 .25
361 Alfredo Griffin .05 .15
362 Craig McMurtry .05 .15
363 Ron Hodges .05 .15
364 Richard Dotson .05 .15
365 Danny Ozark MG .05 .15
366 Todd Cruz .05 .15
367 Keefe Cato .05 .15
368 Dave Bergman .05 .15
369 R.J. Reynolds .05 .15
370 Bruce Sutter .08 .25
371 Mickey Rivers .05 .15
372 Roy Howell .05 .15
373 Mike Moore .05 .15
374 Brian Downing .08 .25
375 Jeff Reardon .08 .25
376 Jeff Newman .05 .15
377 Checklist: 265-396 .05 .15
378 Alan Wiggins .05 .15
379 Charles Hudson .05 .15
380 Ken Griffey .08 .25
381 Roy Smith .05 .15
382 Denny Walling .05 .15
383 Rick Lysander .05 .15
384 Jody Davis .05 .15
385 Jose DeLeon .05 .15
386 Dan Gladden RC .15 .40
387 Buddy Biancalana .05 .15
388 Bert Roberge .05 .15
389 Rod Dedeaux OLY CO RC .08 .25
390 Sid Akins OLY RC .05 .15
391 Flavio Alfaro OLY RC .05 .15
392 Don August OLY RC .05 .15
393 S.Bankhead RC OLY .05 .15
394 Bob Caffrey OLY RC .05 .15
395 Mike Dunne OLY RC .05 .15
396 Gary Green OLY RC .05 .15
397 John Hoover OLY RC .05 .15
398 Shane Mack RC OLY .15 .40
399 John Marzano OLY RC .05 .15
400 O.McDowell RC OLY .15 .40
401 Mark McGwire OLY RC 8.00 20.00
402 Pat Pacillo OLY RC .05 .15
403 Cory Snyder OLY RC .30 .75
404 Billy Swift OLY RC .15 .40
405 Tom Veryzer .05 .15
406 Len Whitehouse .05 .15
407 Bobby Ramos .05 .15
408 Sid Monge .05 .15
409 Brad Wellman .05 .15
410 Bob Horner .08 .25
411 Bobby Cox MG .08 .25
412 Bud Black .05 .15
413 Vance Law .05 .15
414 Gary Ward .05 .15
415 Ron Darling UER .08 .25
(No trivia answer)
416 Wayne Gross .05 .15
417 John Franco RC .30 .75
418 Ken Landreaux .05 .15
419 Mike Caldwell .05 .15
420 Andre Dawson .08 .25
421 Dave Rucker .05 .15
422 Carney Lansford .08 .25
423 Barry Bonnell .05 .15
424 Al Nipper .05 .15
425 Mike Hargrove .05 .15
426 Vern Ruhle .05 .15
427 Mario Ramirez .05 .15
428 Larry Andersen .05 .15
429 Rick Cerone .05 .15
430 Ron Davis .05 .15
431 U.L. Washington .05 .15
432 Thad Bosley .05 .15
433 Jim Morrison .05 .15
434 Gene Richards .05 .15
435 Dan Petry .05 .15
436 Willie Aikens .05 .15
437 Al Jones .05 .15
438 Joe Torre MG .08 .25
439 Junior Ortiz .05 .15
440 Fernando Valenzuela .08 .25
441 Duane Walker .05 .15
442 Ken Forsch .05 .15
443 George Wright .05 .15
444 Tony Phillips .05 .15
445 Tippy Martinez .05 .15
446 Jim Sundberg .08 .25
447 Jeff Lahti .05 .15
448 Derrel Thomas .05 .15
449 Phil Bradley .15 .40
450 Steve Garvey .08 .25
451 Bruce Hurst .05 .15
452 John Castino .05 .15
453 Tom Waddell .05 .15
454 Glenn Wilson .05 .15
455 Bob Knepper .05 .15
456 Tim Foli .05 .15
457 Cecilio Guante .05 .15
458 Randy Johnson .05 .15
459 Charlie Leibrandt .05 .15
460 Ryne Sandberg .50 1.25
461 Marty Castillo .05 .15
462 Gary Lavelle .05 .15
463 Dave Collins .05 .15
464 Mike Mason RC .05 .15
465 Bobby Grich .08 .25
466 Tony LaRussa MG .08 .25
467 Ed Lynch .05 .15
468 Wayne Krenchicki .05 .15
469 Sammy Stewart .05 .15
470 Steve Sax .05 .15
471 Pete Ladd .05 .15
472 Jim Essian .05 .15
473 Tim Wallach .05 .15
474 Kurt Kepshire .05 .15
475 Andre Thornton .05 .15
476 Jeff Stone RC .05 .15
477 Bob Ojeda .05 .15
478 Kurt Bevacqua .05 .15
479 Mike Madden .05 .15
480 Lou Whitaker .08 .25
481 Dale Murray .05 .15
482 Harry Spilman .05 .15
483 Mike Smithson .05 .15
484 Larry Bowa .08 .25
485 Matt Young .05 .15
486 Steve Balboni .05 .15
487 Frank Williams .05 .15
488 Joel Skinner .05 .15
489 Bryan Clark .05 .15
490 Jason Thompson .05 .15
491 Rick Camp .05 .15
492 Dave Johnson MG .05 .15
493 Orel Hershiser RC .75 2.00
494 Rich Dauer .05 .15
495 Mario Soto .08 .25
496 Donnie Scott .05 .15
497 Gary Pettis UER .05 .15
(Photo actually
Gary's little
brother Lynn)
498 Ed Romero .05 .15
499 Danny Cox .05 .15
500 Mike Schmidt .60 1.50
501 Dan Schatzeder .05 .15
502 Rick Miller .05 .15
503 Tim Conroy .05 .15
504 Jerry Willard .05 .15
505 Jim Beattie .05 .15
506 Franklin Stubbs .05 .15
507 Ray Fontenot .05 .15
508 John Shelby .05 .15
509 Milt May .05 .15
510 Kent Hrbek .08 .25
511 Lee Smith .08 .25
512 Tom Brookens .05 .15
513 Lynn Jones .05 .15
514 Jeff Cornell .05 .15
515 Dave Concepcion .08 .25
516 Roy Lee Jackson .05 .15
517 Jerry Martin .05 .15
518 Chris Chambliss .08 .25
519 Doug Rader MG .05 .15
520 LaMarr Hoyt .05 .15
521 Rick Dempsey .05 .15
522 Paul Molitor .08 .25
523 Candy Maldonado .05 .15
524 Rob Wilfong .05 .15
525 Darrell Porter .05 .15
526 David Palmer .05 .15
527 Checklist: 397-528 .05 .15
528 Bill Krueger .05 .15
529 Rich Gedman .05 .15
530 Dave Dravecky .05 .15
531 Joe Lefebvre .05 .15
532 Frank DiPino .05 .15
533 Tony Bernazard .05 .15
534 Brian Dayett .05 .15
535 Pat Putnam .05 .15
536 Kirby Puckett RC 5.00 12.00
537 Don Robinson .05 .15
538 Keith Moreland .05 .15
539 Aurelio Lopez .05 .15
540 Claudell Washington .05 .15
541 Mark Davis .05 .15
542 Don Slaught .05 .15
543 Mike Squires .05 .15
544 Bruce Kison .05 .15
545 Lloyd Moseby .05 .15
546 Brent Gaff .05 .15
547 Pete Rose MG .15 .40
548 Larry Parrish .05 .15
549 Mike Scioscia .08 .25
550 Scott McGregor .05 .15
551 Andy Van Slyke .15 .40
552 Chris Codiroli .05 .15
553 Bob Clark .05 .15
554 Doug Flynn .05 .15
555 Bob Stanley .05 .15
556 Sixto Lezcano .05 .15
557 Len Barker .05 .15
558 Carmelo Martinez .05 .15
559 Jay Howell .05 .15
560 Bill Madlock .08 .25
561 Darryl Motley .05 .15
562 Houston Jimenez .05 .15
563 Dick Ruthven .05 .15
564 Alan Ashby .05 .15
565 Kirk Gibson .08 .25
566 Ed VandeBerg .05 .15
567 Joel Youngblood .05 .15
568 Cliff Johnson .05 .15
569 Ken Oberkfell .05 .15
570 Darryl Strawberry .25 .60
571 Charlie Hough .08 .25
572 Tom Paciorek .05 .15
573 Jay Tibbs .05 .15
574 Joe Altobelli MG .05 .15
575 Pedro Guerrero .08 .25
576 Jaime Cocanower .05 .15
577 Chris Speier .05 .15
578 Terry Francona .08 .25
579 Ron Romanick .05 .15
580 Dwight Evans .15 .40
581 Mark Wagner .05 .15
582 Ken Phelps .05 .15
583 Bobby Brown .05 .15
584 Kevin Gross .05 .15
585 Butch Wynegar .05 .15
586 Bill Scherrer .05 .15
587 Doug Frobel .05 .15
588 Bobby Castillo .05 .15
589 Bob Dernier .05 .15
590 Ray Knight .08 .25
591 Larry Herndon .05 .15
592 Jeff D. Robinson .05 .15
593 Rick Leach .05 .15
594 Curt Wilkerson .05 .15
595 Larry Gura .05 .15
596 Jerry Hairston .05 .15
597 Brad Lesley .05 .15
598 Jose Oquendo .05 .15
599 Storm Davis .05 .15
600 Pete Rose .60 1.50
601 Tom Lasorda MG .15 .40
602 Jeff Dedmon .05 .15
603 Rick Manning .05 .15
604 Daryl Sconiers .05 .15
605 Ozzie Smith .40 1.00
606 Rich Gale .05 .15
607 Bill Almon .05 .15
608 Craig Lefferts .05 .15
609 Broderick Perkins .05 .15
610 Jack Morris .08 .25
611 Ozzie Virgil .05 .15
612 Mike Armstrong .05 .15
613 Terry Puhl .05 .15
614 Al Williams .05 .15
615 Marvell Wynne .05 .15
616 Scott Sanderson .05 .15
617 Willie Wilson .08 .25
618 Pete Falcone .05 .15
619 Jeff Leonard .05 .15
620 Dwight Gooden RC .75 2.00
621 Marvis Foley .05 .15
622 Luis Leal .05 .15
623 Greg Walker .05 .15
624 Benny Ayala .05 .15
625 Mark Langston RC .30 .75
626 German Rivera .05 .15
627 Eric Davis RC .75 2.00
628 Rene Lachemann MG .05 .15
629 Dick Schofield .05 .15
630 Tim Raines .08 .25
631 Bob Forsch .05 .15
632 Bruce Bochte .05 .15
633 Glenn Hoffman .05 .15
634 Bill Dawley .05 .15
635 Terry Kennedy .05 .15
636 Shane Rawley .05 .15
637 Brett Butler .08 .25
638 Mike Pagliarulo .05 .15
639 Ed Hodge .05 .15
640 Steve Henderson .05 .15
641 Rod Scurry .05 .15
642 Dave Owen .05 .15
643 Johnny Grubb .05 .15
644 Mark Huismann .05 .15
645 Damaso Garcia .05 .15
646 Scot Thompson .05 .15
647 Rafael Ramirez .05 .15
648 Bob Jones .05 .15
649 Sid Fernandez .08 .25
650 Greg Luzinski .08 .25
651 Jeff Russell .05 .15
652 Joe Nolan .05 .15
653 Mark Brouhard .05 .15
654 Dave Anderson .05 .15
655 Joaquin Andujar .08 .25
656 Chuck Cottier MG .05 .15
657 Jim Slaton .05 .15
658 Mike Stenhouse .05 .15
659 Checklist: 529-660 .05 .15
660 Tony Gwynn .50 1.25
661 Steve Crawford .05 .15
662 Mike Heath .05 .15
663 Luis Aguayo .05 .15
664 Steve Farr RC .15 .40
665 Don Mattingly 1.00 2.50
666 Mike LaCoss .05 .15
667 Dave Engle .05 .15
668 Steve Trout .05 .15
669 Lee Lacy .05 .15
670 Tom Seaver .15 .40
671 Dane Iorg .05 .15
672 Juan Berenguer .05 .15
673 Buck Martinez .05 .15
674 Atlee Hammaker .05 .15
675 Tony Perez .15 .40
676 Albert Hall .05 .15
677 Wally Backman .05 .15
678 Joey McLaughlin .05 .15
679 Bob Kearney .05 .15
680 Jerry Reuss .05 .15
681 Ben Oglivie .08 .25
682 Doug Corbett .05 .15
683 Whitey Herzog MG .08 .25
684 Bill Doran .05 .15
685 Bill Caudill .05 .15
686 Mike Easler .05 .15
687 Bill Gullickson .05 .15
688 Len Matuszek .05 .15
689 Luis DeLeon .05 .15
690 Alan Trammell .08 .25
691 Dennis Rasmussen .05 .15
692 Randy Bush .05 .15
693 Tim Stoddard .05 .15
694 Joe Carter .25 .60
695 Rick Rhoden .05 .15
696 John Rabb .05 .15
697 Onix Concepcion .05 .15
698 Jorge Bell .08 .25
699 Donnie Moore .05 .15
700 Eddie Murray .25 .60
701 Eddie Murray AS .15 .40
702 Damaso Garcia AS .05 .15
703 George Brett AS .25 .60
704 Cal Ripken AS .60 1.50
705 Dave Winfield AS .05 .15
706 Rickey Henderson AS .15 .40
707 Tony Armas AS .05 .15
708 Lance Parrish AS .05 .15
709 Mike Boddicker AS .05 .15
710 Frank Viola AS .05 .15
711 Dan Quisenberry AS .05 .15
712 Keith Hernandez AS .05 .15
713 Ryne Sandberg AS .25 .60
714 Mike Schmidt AS .25 .60
715 Ozzie Smith AS .25 .60
716 Dale Murphy AS .08 .25
717 Tony Gwynn AS .40 1.00
718 Jeff Leonard AS .05 .15
719 Gary Carter AS .05 .15
720 Rick Sutcliffe AS .05 .15
721 Bob Knepper AS .05 .15
722 Bruce Sutter AS .05 .15
723 Dave Stewart .08 .25
724 Oscar Gamble .05 .15
725 Floyd Bannister .05 .15
726 Al Bumbry .05 .15
727 Frank Pastore .05 .15
728 Bob Bailor .05 .15
729 Don Sutton .08 .25
730 Dave Kingman .08 .25
731 Neil Allen .05 .15
732 John McNamara MG .05 .15
733 Tony Scott .05 .15
734 John Henry Johnson .05 .15
735 Garry Templeton .08 .25
736 Jerry Mumphrey .05 .15
737 Bo Diaz .05 .15
738 Omar Moreno .05 .15
739 Ernie Camacho .05 .15
740 Jack Clark .08 .25
741 John Butcher .05 .15
742 Ron Hassey .05 .15
743 Frank White .08 .25
744 Doug Bair .05 .15
745 Buddy Bell .08 .25
746 Jim Clancy .05 .15
747 Alex Trevino .05 .15
748 Lee Mazzilli .08 .25
749 Julio Cruz .05 .15
750 Rollie Fingers .08 .25
751 Kelvin Chapman .05 .15
752 Bob Owchinko .05 .15
753 Greg Brock .05 .15
754 Larry Milbourne .05 .15
755 Ken Singleton .08 .25
756 Rob Picciolo .05 .15
757 Willie McGee .08 .25
758 Ray Burris .05 .15
759 Jim Fanning MG .05 .15
760 Nolan Ryan 1.25 3.00
761 Jerry Remy .05 .15
762 Eddie Whitson .05 .15
763 Kiko Garcia .05 .15
764 Jamie Easterly .05 .15
765 Willie Randolph .08 .25
766 Paul Mirabella .05 .15
767 Darrell Brown .05 .15
768 Ron Cey .08 .25
769 Joe Cowley .05 .15
770 Carlton Fisk .15 .40
771 Geoff Zahn .05 .15
772 Johnnie LeMaster .05 .15
773 Hal McRae .08 .25
774 Dennis Lamp .05 .15
775 Mookie Wilson .08 .25
776 Jerry Royster .05 .15
777 Ned Yost .05 .15
778 Mike Davis .05 .15
779 Nick Esasky .05 .15
780 Mike Flanagan .05 .15
781 Jim Gantner .05 .15
782 Tom Niedenfuer .05 .15
783 Mike Jorgensen .05 .15
784 Checklist: 661-792 .05 .15
785 Tony Armas .08 .25
786 Enos Cabell .05 .15
787 Jim Wohlford .05 .15
788 Steve Comer .05 .15
789 Luis Salazar .05 .15
790 Ron Guidry .08 .25
791 Ivan DeJesus .05 .15
792 Darrell Evans .08 .25

1985 Topps Tiffany

For the second year, Topps issued a special glossy set through their hobby dealers. This set is a direct parallel to the regular Topps issue. These 792 cards are differentiated from the regular issue by their glossy fronts and very clear backs. These sets were only available through Topps' hobby dealers. According to original reports in 1985, only 5,000 of these sets were produced.

COMP.FACT.SET (792) 350.00 600.00
*STARS: 3X TO 8X BASIC CARDS
*ROOKIES: 2.5X TO 6X BASIC CARDS
DISTRIBUTED ONLY IN FACTORY SET FORM
FACTORY SET PRICE IS FOR SEALED SETS

1985 Topps Glossy All-Stars

The cards in this 22-card set the standard size. Similar in design, both front and back, to last year's Glossy set, this edition features the managers, starting nine players and honorary captains of the National and American League teams in the 1984 All-Star game. The set is numbered on the reverse with players essentially ordered by position within league, NL: 1-11 and AL: 12-22.

COMPLETE SET (22)	2.00	5.00
1 Paul Owens MG	.01	.05
2 Steve Garvey	.05	.15
3 Ryne Sandberg	.40	1.00
4 Mike Schmidt	.30	.75
5 Ozzie Smith	.40	1.00
6 Tony Gwynn	.50	1.25
7 Dale Murphy	.07	.20
8 Darryl Strawberry	.02	.10
9 Gary Carter	.20	.50
10 Charlie Lea	.01	.05
11 Willie McCovey CAPT	.02	.10
12 Joe Altobelli MG	.01	.05
13 Rod Carew	.20	.50
14 Lou Whitaker	.02	.10
15 George Brett	.40	1.00
16 Cal Ripken	.75	2.00
17 Dave Winfield	.20	.50
18 Chet Lemon	.01	.05
19 Reggie Jackson	.20	.50
20 Lance Parrish	.01	.05
21 Dave Stieb	.01	.05
22 Hank Greenberg CAPT	.02	.10

1985 Topps Glossy Send-Ins

The cards in this 40-card set measure the standard size. Similar to last year's glossy set, this set was issued as a bonus prize to Topps All-Star Baseball Game cards found in wax packs. The set could be obtained by sending in the "Bonus Runs" from the "Winning Pitch" game insert cards. For 25 runs and 75 cents, a collector could send in for one of the eight different five card series plus automatically be entered in the Grand Prize Sweepstakes for a chance at a free trip to the All-Star game. The cards are numbered and contain 20 stars from each league.

COMPLETE SET (40)	4.00	10.00
1 Dale Murphy	.10	.30
2 Jesse Orosco	.07	.20
3 Bob Brenly	.02	.10
4 Mike Boddicker	.02	.10
5 Dave Kingman	.07	.20
6 Jim Rice	.07	.20
7 Frank Viola	.07	.20
8 Alvin Davis	.02	.10
9 Rick Sutcliffe	.02	.10
10 Pete Rose	.50	1.25
11 Leon Durham	.02	.10
12 Joaquin Andujar	.02	.10
13 Keith Hernandez	.07	.20
14 Dave Winfield	.30	.75
15 Reggie Jackson	.30	.75
16 Alan Trammell	.10	.30
17 Bert Blyleven	.07	.20
18 Tony Armas	.02	.10
19 Rich Gossage	.07	.20
20 Jose Cruz	.07	.20
21 Ryne Sandberg	.75	2.00
22 Bruce Sutter	.30	.75
23 Mike Schmidt	.50	1.25
24 Cal Ripken	2.00	5.00
25 Dan Petry	.02	.10
26 Jack Morris	.07	.20
27 Don Mattingly	1.00	2.50
28 Eddie Murray	.40	1.00
29 Tony Gwynn	1.00	2.50
30 Charlie Lea	.02	.10
31 Juan Samuel	.02	.10
32 Phil Niekro	.30	.75
33 Alejandro Pena	.02	.10
34 Harold Baines	.07	.20
35 Dan Quisenberry	.02	.10
36 Gary Carter	.30	.75
37 Mario Soto	.02	.10
38 Dwight Gooden	.20	.50
39 Tom Brunansky	.02	.10
40 Dave Stieb	.02	.10

1985 Topps Traded

In its now standard procedure, Topps issued its standard-size Traded (or extended) set for the fifth year in a row. In addition to the typical factory set hobby distribution, Topps tested the limited issuance of these Traded cards in wax packs. Card design is identical to the regular-issue 1985 Topps set except for whiter card stock and T-suffixed numbering on back. The set numbering is in alphabetical order by player's name. The key extended Rookie Cards in this set include Vince Coleman, Ozzie Guillen, and Mickey Tettleton.

COMP.FACT.SET (132)	3.00	8.00
1T Don Aase	.05	.15
2T Bill Almon	.05	.15
3T Benny Ayala	.05	.15
4T Dusty Baker	.15	.40
5T George Bamberger MG	.05	.15
6T Dale Berra	.05	.15
7T Rich Bordi	.05	.15
8T Daryl Boston XRC	.08	.25
9T Hubie Brooks	.05	.15
10T Chris Brown XRC	.08	.25
11T Tom Browning XRC	.20	.50
12T Al Bumbry	.05	.15
13T Ray Burris	.05	.15
14T Jeff Burroughs	.05	.15
15T Bill Campbell	.05	.15
16T Don Carman	.05	.15
17T Gary Carter	.15	.40
18T Bobby Castillo	.05	.15
19T Bill Caudill	.05	.15
20T Rick Cerone	.05	.15
21T Bryan Clark	.05	.15
22T Jack Clark	.15	.40
23T Pat Clements	.05	.15
24T Vince Coleman XRC	.40	1.00
25T Dave Collins	.05	.15
26T Danny Darwin	.05	.15
27T Jim Davenport MG	.05	.15
28T Jerry Davis	.05	.15
29T Brian Dayett	.05	.15
30T Ivan DeJesus	.05	.15
31T Ken Dixon	.05	.15
32T Mariano Duncan XRC	.20	.50
33T John Felske MG	.05	.15
34T Mike Fitzgerald	.05	.15
35T Ray Fontenot	.05	.15
36T Greg Gagne XRC	.20	.50
37T Oscar Gamble	.05	.15
38T Scott Garrelts	.05	.15
39T Bob L. Gibson	.05	.15
40T Jim Gott	.05	.15
41T David Green	.05	.15
42T Alfredo Griffin	.05	.15
43T Ozzie Guillen XRC	2.00	5.00
44T Eddie Haas MG	.05	.15
45T Terry Harper	.05	.15
46T Toby Harrah	.15	.40
47T Greg Harris	.05	.15
48T Ron Hassey	.05	.15
49T Rickey Henderson	1.00	2.50
50T Steve Henderson	.05	.15
51T George Hendrick	.15	.40
52T Joe Hesketh	.05	.15
53T Teddy Higuera XRC	.20	.50
54T Donnie Hill	.05	.15
55T Al Holland	.05	.15
56T Burt Hooton	.05	.15
57T Jay Howell	.05	.15
58T Ken Howell	.05	.15
59T LaMarr Hoyt	.05	.15
60T Tim Hulett XRC	.08	.25
61T Bob James	.05	.15
62T Steve Jeltz XRC	.08	.25
63T Cliff Johnson	.05	.15
64T Howard Johnson	.15	.40
65T Ruppert Jones	.05	.15
66T Steve Kemp	.05	.15
67T Bruce Kison	.05	.15
68T Alan Knicely	.05	.15
69T Mike LaCoss	.05	.15
70T Lee Lacy	.05	.15
71T Dave LaPoint	.05	.15
72T Gary Lavelle	.05	.15
73T Vance Law	.05	.15
74T Johnnie LeMaster	.05	.15
75T Sixto Lezcano	.05	.15
76T Tim Lollar	.05	.15
77T Fred Lynn	.15	.40
78T Billy Martin MG	.30	.75
79T Ron Mathis	.05	.15
80T Len Matuszek	.05	.15
81T Gene Mauch MG	.05	.15
82T Oddibe McDowell	.20	.50
83T Roger McDowell XRC	.20	.50
84T John McNamara MG	.05	.15
85T Donnie Moore	.05	.15
86T Gene Nelson	.05	.15
87T Steve Nicosia	.05	.15
88T Al Oliver	.15	.40
89T Joe Orsulak XRC	.20	.50
90T Rob Picciolo	.05	.15
91T Chris Pittaro	.05	.15
92T Jim Presley	.20	.50
93T Rick Reuschel	.15	.40
94T Bert Roberge	.05	.15
95T Bob Rodgers MG	.05	.15
96T Jerry Royster	.05	.15
97T Dave Rozema	.05	.15
98T Dave Rucker	.05	.15
99T Vern Ruhle	.05	.15
100T Paul Runge XRC	.08	.25
101T Mark Salas	.05	.15
102T Luis Salazar	.05	.15
103T Joe Sambito	.05	.15
104T Rick Schu	.05	.15
105T Donnie Scott	.05	.15
106T Larry Sheets XRC	.08	.25
107T Don Slaught	.05	.15
108T Roy Smalley	.05	.15
109T Lonnie Smith	.05	.15
110T Nate Snell UER	.05	.15
(Headings on back for a batter)		
111T Chris Speier	.05	.15
112T Mike Stenhouse	.05	.15
113T Tim Stoddard	.05	.15
114T Jim Sundberg	.15	.40
115T Bruce Sutter	.15	.40
116T Don Sutton	.15	.40
117T Kent Tekulve	.05	.15
118T Tom Tellmann	.05	.15
119T Walt Terrell	.05	.15
120T M.Tettleton XRC	.20	.50
121T Derrel Thomas	.05	.15
122T Rich Thompson	.05	.15
123T Alex Trevino	.05	.15
124T John Tudor	.15	.40
125T Jose Uribe	.05	.15
126T Bobby Valentine MG	.15	.40
127T Dave Von Ohlen	.05	.15
128T U.L. Washington	.05	.15
129T Earl Weaver MG	.15	.40
130T Eddie Whitson	.05	.15
131T Herm Winningham	.05	.15
132T Checklist 1-132	.05	.15

1985 Topps Traded Tiffany

Just as in 1984, Topps issued an glossy update set. The 132-card standard-size set is a parallel to the Topps update issue. These sets were issued to the hobby through Topps dealer network and were printed in Ireland. Again -- similar to the regular Tiffany issue -- it is believed that 5,000 of these sets were produced.

COMP.FACT.SET (132)	20.00	50.00

*STARS: 1.5X TO 4X BASIC CARDS
*ROOKIES: 1.5X TO 4X BASIC CARDS
DISTRIBUTED ONLY IN FACTORY SET FORM
FACTORY SET PRICE IS FOR SEALED SETS

1986 Topps

This set consists of 792 standard-size cards. Cards were primarily distributed in 15-card wax packs, 48-card rack packs and factory sets. This was also the first year Topps offered a factory set to hobby dealers. Standard card fronts feature a black and white split border framing a color photo with team name on top and player name on bottom. Subsets include Pete Rose tribute (1-7), Record Breakers (201-207), Turn Back the Clock (401-405), All-Stars (701-722) and Team Leaders (seeded throughout the set). Manager cards feature the team checklist on the reverse. There are two uncorrected errors involving misnumbered cards; see card numbers 51, 57, 141, and 171 in the checklist below. The key Rookie Cards in this set are Darren Daulton, Len Dykstra, Cecil Fielder, and Mickey Tettleton.

COMPLETE SET (792)	10.00	25.00
COMP.X-MAS.SET (792)	75.00	150.00
1 Pete Rose	.75	2.00
2 Pete Rose 63-66	.08	.25
3 Pete Rose 67-70	.08	.25
4 Pete Rose 71-74	.08	.25
5 Pete Rose 75-78	.08	.25
6 Pete Rose 79-82	.08	.25
7 Pete Rose 83-85	.08	.25
8 Dwayne Murphy	.02	.10
9 Roy Smith	.02	.10
10 Tony Gwynn	.25	.60
11 Bob Ojeda	.02	.10
12 Jose Uribe	.02	.10
13 Bob Kearney	.02	.10
14 Julio Cruz	.02	.10
15 Eddie Whitson	.02	.10
16 Rick Schu	.02	.10
17 Mike Stenhouse	.02	.10
18 Brent Gaff	.02	.10
19 Rich Hebner	.02	.10
20 Lou Whitaker	.05	.15
21 George Bamberger MG	.02	.10
22 Duane Walker	.02	.10
23 Manny Lee RC	.02	.10
24 Len Barker	.02	.10
25 Willie Wilson	.05	.15
26 Frank DiPino	.02	.10
27 Ray Knight	.05	.15
28 Eric Davis	.15	.40
29 Tony Phillips	.02	.10
30 Eddie Murray	.15	.40
31 Jamie Easterly	.02	.10
32 Steve Yeager	.05	.15
33 Jeff Lahti	.02	.10
34 Ken Phelps	.02	.10
35 Jeff Reardon	.05	.15
36 Lance Parrish TL	.05	.15
37 Mark Thurmond	.02	.10
38 Glenn Hoffman	.02	.10
39 Dave Rucker	.02	.10
40 Ken Griffey	.05	.15
41 Brad Wellman	.02	.10
42 Geoff Zahn	.02	.10
43 Dave Engle	.02	.10
44 Lance McCullers	.02	.10
45 Damaso Garcia	.02	.10
46 Billy Hatcher	.02	.10
47 Juan Berenguer	.02	.10
48 Bill Almon	.02	.10
49 Rick Manning	.02	.10
50 Dan Quisenberry	.02	.10
51 Bobby Wine MG ERR	.02	.10
Number of card on back is actually 57)		
52 Chris Welsh	.02	.10
53 Len Dykstra RC	.30	.75
54 John Franco	.05	.15
55 Fred Lynn	.05	.15
56 Tom Niedenfuer	.02	.10
57 Bill Doran	.02	.10
(See also 51)		
58 Bill Krueger	.02	.10
59 Andre Thornton	.02	.10
60 Dwight Evans	.08	.25
61 Karl Best	.02	.10
62 Bob Boone	.05	.15
63 Ron Roenicke	.02	.10
64 Floyd Bannister	.02	.10
65 Dan Driessen	.02	.10
66 Bob Forsch TL	.02	.10
67 Carmelo Martinez	.02	.10
68 Ed Lynch	.02	.10
69 Luis Aguayo	.02	.10
70 Dave Winfield	.05	.15
71 Ken Schrom	.02	.10
72 Shawon Dunston	.05	.15
73 Randy O'Neal	.02	.10
74 Rance Mulliniks	.02	.10
75 Jose DeLeon	.02	.10
76 Dion James	.02	.10
77 Charlie Leibrandt	.02	.10
78 Bruce Benedict	.02	.10
79 Dave Schmidt	.02	.10
80 Darryl Strawberry	.08	.25
81 Gene Mauch MG	.02	.10
82 Tippy Martinez	.02	.10
83 Phil Garner	.05	.15
84 Curt Young	.02	.10
85 Tony Perez	.05	.15
(Eric Davis also shown on card)		
86 Tom Waddell	.02	.10
87 Candy Maldonado	.02	.10
88 Tom Nieto	.02	.10
89 Randy St.Claire	.02	.10
90 Garry Templeton	.05	.15
91 Steve Crawford	.02	.10
92 Al Cowens	.02	.10
93 Scot Thompson	.02	.10
94 Rich Bordi	.02	.10
95 Ozzie Virgil	.02	.10
96 Jim Clancy TL	.02	.10
97 Gary Gaetti	.05	.15
98 Dick Ruthven	.02	.10
99 Buddy Biancalana	.02	.10
100 Nolan Ryan	.75	2.00
101 Dave Bergman	.02	.10
102 Joe Orsulak RC	.08	.25
103 Luis Salazar	.02	.10
104 Sid Fernandez	.02	.10
105 Gary Ward	.02	.10
106 Ray Burris	.02	.10
107 Rafael Ramirez	.02	.10
108 Ted Power	.02	.10
109 Len Matuszek	.02	.10
110 Scott McGregor	.02	.10
111 Roger Craig MG	.05	.15
112 Bill Campbell	.02	.10
113 U.L. Washington	.02	.10
114 Mike C. Brown	.02	.10
115 Jay Howell	.02	.10
116 Brook Jacoby	.02	.10
117 Bruce Kison	.02	.10
118 Jerry Royster	.02	.10
119 Barry Bonnell	.02	.10
120 Steve Carlton	.05	.15
121 Nelson Simmons	.02	.10
122 Pete Filson	.02	.10
123 Greg Walker	.02	.10
124 Luis Sanchez	.02	.10
125 Dave Lopes	.05	.15
126 Mookie Wilson TL	.02	.10
127 Jack Howell	.02	.10
128 John Wathan	.02	.10
129 Jeff Dedmon	.02	.10
130 Alan Trammell	.05	.15
131 Checklist: 1-132	.02	.10
132 Razor Shines	.02	.10
133 Andy McGaffigan	.02	.10
134 Carney Lansford	.05	.15
135 Joe Niekro	.02	.10
136 Mike Hargrove	.02	.10
137 Charlie Moore	.02	.10
138 Mark Davis	.02	.10
139 Daryl Boston	.02	.10
140 John Candelaria	.02	.10
141 Chuck Cottier MG	.02	.10
See also 171		
142 Bob Jones	.02	.10
143 Dave Van Gorder	.02	.10
144 Doug Sisk	.02	.10
145 Pedro Guerrero	.05	.15
146 Jack Perconte	.02	.10
147 Larry Sheets	.02	.10
148 Mike Heath	.02	.10
149 Brett Butler	.05	.15
150 Joaquin Andujar	.05	.15
151 Dave Stapleton	.02	.10
152 Mike Morgan	.02	.10
153 Ricky Adams	.02	.10
154 Bert Roberge	.02	.10
155 Bobby Grich	.05	.15
156 Richard Dotson TL	.02	.10
157 Ron Hassey	.02	.10
158 Derrel Thomas	.02	.10
159 Orel Hershiser UER	.15	.40
(82 Alburquerque)		
160 Chet Lemon	.05	.15
161 Lee Tunnell	.02	.10
162 Greg Gagne	.05	.15
163 Pete Ladd	.02	.10
164 Steve Balboni	.02	.10
165 Mike Davis	.02	.10
166 Dickie Thon	.02	.10
167 Zane Smith	.05	.15
168 Jeff Burroughs	.02	.10
169 George Wright	.02	.10
170 Gary Carter	.05	.15
171 Bob Rodgers MG ERR	.02	.10
Number of card on back actually 141)		
172 Jerry Reed	.02	.10
173 Wayne Gross	.02	.10
174 Brian Snyder	.02	.10
175 Steve Sax	.02	.10
176 Jay Tibbs	.02	.10
177 Joel Youngblood	.02	.10
178 Ivan DeJesus	.02	.10
179 Stu Cliburn	.02	.10
180 Don Mattingly	.50	1.25
181 Al Nipper	.02	.10
182 Bobby Brown	.02	.10
183 Larry Andersen	.02	.10
184 Tim Laudner	.02	.10
185 Rollie Fingers	.05	.15
186 Jose Cruz TL	.02	.10
187 Scott Fletcher	.02	.10
188 Bob Dernier	.02	.10
189 Mike Mason	.02	.10
190 George Hendrick	.05	.15
191 Wally Backman	.02	.10
192 Milt Wilcox	.02	.10
193 Daryl Sconiers	.02	.10
194 Craig McMurtry	.02	.10
195 Dave Concepcion	.05	.15
196 Doyle Alexander	.02	.10
197 Enos Cabell	.02	.10
198 Ken Dixon	.02	.10
199 Dick Howser MG	.02	.10
200 Mike Schmidt	.40	1.00
201 Vince Coleman RB	.05	.15
202 Dwight Gooden RB	.08	.25
203 Keith Hernandez RB	.02	.10
204 Phil Niekro RB	.05	.15
205 Tony Perez RB	.05	.15
206 Pete Rose RB	.15	.40
207 F. Valenzuela RB	.02	.10
208 Ramon Romero	.02	.10
209 Randy Ready	.02	.10
210 Calvin Schiraldi	.02	.10
211 Ed Wojna	.02	.10
212 Chris Speier	.02	.10
213 Bob Shirley	.02	.10
214 Randy Bush	.02	.10
215 Frank White	.05	.15
216 Dwayne Murphy TL	.02	.10
217 Bill Scherrer	.02	.10
218 Randy Hunt	.02	.10
219 Dennis Lamp	.02	.10
220 Bob Horner	.05	.15
221 Dave Henderson	.02	.10
222 Craig Gerber	.02	.10
223 Atlee Hammaker	.02	.10
224 Cesar Cedeno	.05	.15
225 Ron Darling	.05	.15
226 Lee Lacy	.02	.10
227 Al Jones	.02	.10
228 Tom Lawless	.02	.10
229 Bill Gullickson	.02	.10
230 Terry Kennedy	.02	.10
231 Jim Frey MG	.02	.10
232 Rick Rhoden	.02	.10
233 Steve Lyons	.02	.10
234 Doug Corbett	.02	.10
235 Butch Wynegar	.02	.10
236 Frank Eufemia	.02	.10
237 Ted Simmons	.05	.15
238 Larry Parrish	.02	.10
239 Joel Skinner	.02	.10
240 Tommy John	.05	.15
241 Tony Fernandez	.05	.15
242 Rich Thompson	.02	.10
243 Johnny Grubb	.02	.10
244 Craig Lefferts	.02	.10
245 Jim Sundberg	.05	.15
246 Steve Carlton TL	.05	.15
247 Terry Harper	.02	.10
248 Spike Owen	.02	.10
249 Rob Deer	.02	.10
250 Dwight Gooden	.15	.40
251 Rich Dauer	.02	.10
252 Bobby Castillo	.02	.10
253 Dann Bilardello	.02	.10
254 Ozzie Guillen RC	.60	1.50
255 Tony Armas	.02	.10
256 Kurt Kepshire	.02	.10
257 Doug DeCinces	.02	.10
258 Tim Burke	.02	.10
259 Dan Pasqua	.02	.10
260 Tony Pena	.02	.10
261 Bobby Valentine MG	.05	.15
262 Mario Ramirez	.02	.10
263 Checklist: 133-264	.05	.15
264 Darren Daulton RC	.20	.50
265 Ron Davis	.02	.10
266 Keith Moreland	.02	.10
267 Paul Molitor	.05	.15
268 Mike Scott	.02	.10
269 Dane Iorg	.02	.10
270 Jack Morris	.05	.15
271 Dave Collins	.05	.15
272 Tim Tolman	.02	.10
273 Jerry Willard	.02	.10
274 Ron Gardenhire	.02	.10
275 Charlie Hough	.05	.15
276 Willie Randolph TL	.05	.15
277 Jaime Cocanower	.02	.10
278 Sixto Lezcano	.02	.10
279 Al Pardo	.02	.10
280 Tim Raines	.05	.15
281 Steve Mura	.02	.10
282 Jerry Mumphrey	.02	.10
283 Mike Fischlin	.02	.10
284 Brian Dayett	.02	.10
285 Buddy Bell	.05	.15
286 Luis DeLeon	.02	.10
287 John Christensen	.02	.10
288 Don Aase	.02	.10
289 Johnnie LeMaster	.02	.10
290 Carlton Fisk	.08	.25
291 Tom Lasorda MG	.08	.25
292 Chuck Porter	.02	.10
293 Chris Chambliss	.05	.15
294 Danny Cox	.02	.10
295 Kirk Gibson	.05	.15
296 Geno Petralli	.02	.10
297 Tim Lollar	.02	.10
298 Craig Reynolds	.02	.10
299 Bryn Smith	.02	.10
300 George Brett	.40	1.00
301 Dennis Rasmussen	.02	.10
302 Greg Gross	.02	.10
303 Curt Wardle	.02	.10
304 Mike Gallego RC	.02	.10
305 Phil Bradley	.02	.10
306 Terry Kennedy TL	.02	.10
307 Dave Sax	.02	.10
308 Ray Fontenot	.02	.10
309 John Shelby	.02	.10
310 Greg Minton	.02	.10
311 Dick Schofield	.02	.10
312 Tom Filer	.02	.10
313 Joe DeSa	.02	.10
314 Frank Pastore	.02	.10
315 Mookie Wilson	.05	.15
316 Sammy Khalifa	.02	.10
317 Ed Romero	.02	.10
318 Terry Whitfield	.02	.10
319 Rick Camp	.02	.10
320 Jim Rice	.05	.15
321 Earl Weaver MG	.05	.15
322 Bob Forsch	.02	.10
323 Jerry Davis	.02	.10
324 Dan Schatzeder	.02	.10
325 Juan Beniquez	.02	.10
326 Kent Tekulve	.02	.10
327 Mike Pagliarulo	.02	.10
328 Pete O'Brien	.02	.10
329 Kirby Puckett	.40	1.00
330 Rick Sutcliffe	.05	.15
331 Alan Ashby	.02	.10
332 Darryl Motley	.02	.10
333 Tom Henke	.05	.15
334 Ken Oberkfell	.02	.10
335 Don Sutton	.05	.15
336 Andre Thornton TL	.05	.15
337 Darnell Coles	.02	.10
338 Jorge Bell	.05	.15
339 Bruce Berenyi	.02	.10
340 Cal Ripken	.60	1.50
341 Frank Williams	.02	.10
342 Gary Redus	.02	.10
343 Carlos Diaz	.02	.10
344 Jim Wohlford	.02	.10
345 Donnie Moore	.02	.10
346 Bryan Little	.02	.10
347 Teddy Higuera RC	.08	.25
348 Cliff Johnson	.02	.10
349 Mark Clear	.02	.10
350 Jack Clark	.05	.15
351 Chuck Tanner MG	.02	.10
352 Harry Spilman	.02	.10
353 Keith Atherton	.02	.10
354 Tony Bernazard	.02	.10
355 Lee Smith	.05	.15
356 Mickey Hatcher	.02	.10
357 Ed VandeBerg	.02	.10
358 Rick Dempsey	.02	.10
359 Mike LaCoss	.02	.10
360 Lloyd Moseby	.02	.10
361 Shane Rawley	.02	.10
362 Tom Paciorek	.02	.10
363 Terry Forster	.05	.15
364 Reid Nichols	.02	.10
365 Mike Flanagan	.02	.10
366 Dave Concepcion TL	.05	.15
367 Aurelio Lopez	.02	.10
368 Greg Brock	.02	.10
369 Al Holland	.02	.10
370 Vince Coleman RC	.20	.50
371 Bill Stein	.02	.10
372 Ben Oglivie	.05	.15
373 Urbano Lugo	.02	.10
374 Terry Francona	.05	.15
375 Rich Gedman	.02	.10
376 Bill Dawley	.02	.10
377 Joe Carter	.05	.15
378 Bruce Bochte	.02	.10
379 Bobby Meacham	.02	.10
380 LaMarr Hoyt	.02	.10
381 Ray Miller MG	.02	.10
382 Ivan Calderon RC	.08	.25
383 Chris Brown RC	.05	.15
384 Steve Trout	.02	.10
385 Cecil Cooper	.05	.15
386 Cecil Fielder RC	.40	1.00
387 Steve Kemp	.02	.10
388 Dickie Noles	.02	.10
389 Glenn Davis	.02	.10
390 Tom Seaver	.08	.25
391 Julio Franco	.05	.15
392 John Russell	.02	.10
393 Chris Pittaro	.02	.10
394 Checklist: 265-396	.05	.15
395 Scott Garrelts	.02	.10
396 Dwight Evans TL	.08	.25
397 Steve Buechele RC	.08	.25
398 Earnie Riles	.02	.10
399 Bill Swift	.02	.10
400 Rod Carew	.08	.25
401 Fernando Valenzuela TBC '81	.02	.10
402 Tom Seaver TBC '76	.05	.15
403 Willie Mays TBC '71	.15	.40
404 Frank Robinson TBC '66	.05	.15
405 Roger Maris TBC '61	.15	.40
406 Scott Sanderson	.02	.10
407 Sal Butera	.02	.10
408 Dave Smith	.02	.10
409 Paul Runge RC	.02	.10
410 Dave Kingman	.05	.15
411 Sparky Anderson MG	.05	.15
412 Jim Clancy	.02	.10
413 Tim Flannery	.02	.10
414 Tom Gorman	.02	.10
415 Hal McRae	.05	.15
416 Dennis Martinez	.05	.15
417 R.J. Reynolds	.02	.10
418 Alan Knicely	.02	.10
419 Frank Wills	.02	.10
420 Von Hayes	.02	.10
421 David Palmer	.02	.10
422 Mike Jorgensen	.02	.10
423 Dan Spillner	.02	.10
424 Rick Miller	.02	.10
425 Larry McWilliams	.02	.10
426 Charlie Moore TL	.02	.10
427 Joe Cowley	.02	.10
428 Max Venable	.02	.10
429 Greg Booker	.02	.10
430 Kent Hrbek	.05	.15
431 George Frazier	.02	.10
432 Mark Bailey	.02	.10
433 Chris Codiroli	.02	.10
434 Curt Wilkerson	.02	.10
435 Bill Caudill	.02	.10
436 Doug Flynn	.02	.10
437 Rick Mahler	.02	.10
438 Clint Hurdle	.02	.10
439 Rick Honeycutt	.02	.10
440 Alvin Davis	.02	.10
441 Whitey Herzog MG	.08	.25
442 Ron Robinson	.02	.10
443 Bill Buckner	.05	.15
444 Alex Trevino	.02	.10
445 Bert Blyleven	.05	.15
446 Lenn Sakata	.02	.10
447 Jerry Don Gleaton	.02	.10
448 Herm Winningham	.02	.10
449 Rod Scurry	.02	.10
450 Graig Nettles	.05	.15
451 Mark Brown	.02	.10
452 Bob Clark	.02	.10
453 Steve Jeltz	.02	.10
454 Burt Hooton	.02	.10
455 Willie Randolph	.05	.15
456 Dale Murphy TL	.08	.25
457 Mickey Tettleton RC	.08	.25
458 Kevin Bass	.02	.10
459 Luis Leal	.02	.10
460 Leon Durham	.02	.10
461 Walt Terrell	.02	.10
462 Domingo Ramos	.02	.10
463 Jim Gott	.02	.10
464 Ruppert Jones	.02	.10
465 Jesse Orosco	.02	.10
466 Tom Foley	.02	.10
467 Bob James	.02	.10
468 Mike Scioscia	.05	.15
469 Storm Davis	.02	.10
470 Bill Madlock	.05	.15
471 Bobby Cox MG	.05	.15
472 Joe Hesketh	.02	.10
473 Mark Brouhard	.02	.10
474 John Tudor	.05	.15
475 Juan Samuel	.02	.10
476 Ron Mathis	.02	.10
477 Mike Easler	.02	.10
478 Andy Hawkins	.02	.10
479 Bob Melvin	.02	.10
480 Oddibe McDowell	.02	.10
481 Scott Bradley	.02	.10
482 Rick Lysander	.02	.10
483 George Vukovich	.02	.10
484 Donnie Hill	.02	.10
485 Gary Matthews	.05	.15
486 Bobby Grich TL	.05	.15
487 Bret Saberhagen	.05	.15
488 Lou Thornton	.02	.10
489 Jim Winn	.02	.10
490 Jeff Leonard	.02	.10
491 Pascual Perez	.02	.10
492 Kelvin Chapman	.02	.10
493 Gene Nelson	.02	.10
494 Gary Roenicke	.02	.10
495 Mark Langston	.05	.15
496 Jay Johnstone	.02	.10
497 John Stuper	.02	.10
498 Tito Landrum	.02	.10
499 Bob L. Gibson	.02	.10
500 Rickey Henderson	.15	.40
501 Dave Johnson MG	.02	.10
502 Glen Cook	.02	.10
503 Mike Fitzgerald	.02	.10
504 Denny Walling	.02	.10
505 Jerry Koosman	.05	.15
506 Bill Russell	.05	.15
507 Steve Ontiveros RC	.02	.10
508 Alan Wiggins	.02	.10
509 Ernie Camacho	.02	.10
510 Wade Boggs	.08	.25
511 Ed Nunez	.02	.10
512 Thad Bosley	.02	.10
513 Ron Washington	.02	.10
514 Mike Jones	.02	.10
515 Darrell Evans	.05	.15
516 Greg Minton TL	.02	.10
517 Milt Thompson RC	.08	.25
518 Buck Martinez	.02	.10
519 Danny Darwin	.02	.10
520 Keith Hernandez	.05	.15
521 Nate Snell	.02	.10
522 Bob Bailor	.02	.10
523 Joe Price	.02	.10
524 Darrell Miller	.02	.10
525 Marvell Wynne	.02	.10
526 Charlie Lea	.02	.10
527 Checklist: 397-528	.05	.15
528 Terry Pendleton	.05	.15
529 Marc Sullivan	.02	.10

530 Rich Gossage .05 .15
531 Tony LaRussa MG .05 .15
532 Don Carman .02 .10
533 Billy Sample .02 .10
534 Jeff Calhoun .02 .10
535 Toby Harrah .05 .15
536 Jose Rijo .05 .15
537 Mark Salas .02 .10
538 Dennis Eckersley .08 .25
539 Glenn Hubbard .02 .10
540 Dan Petry .02 .10
541 Jorge Orta .02 .10
542 Don Schulze .02 .10
543 Jerry Narron .02 .10
544 Eddie Milner .02 .10
545 Jimmy Key .05 .15
546 Dave Henderson TL .02 .10
547 Roger McDowell RC .08 .25
548 Mike Young .02 .10
549 Bob Welch .05 .15
550 Tom Herr .02 .10
551 Dave LaPoint .02 .10
552 Marc Hill .02 .10
553 Jim Morrison .02 .10
554 Paul Householder .02 .10
555 Hubie Brooks .02 .10
556 John Denny .02 .10
557 Gerald Perry .02 .10
558 Tim Stoddard .02 .10
559 Tommy Dunbar .02 .10
560 Dave Righetti .05 .15
561 Bob Lillis MG .02 .10
562 Joe Beckwith .02 .10
563 Alejandro Sanchez .02 .10
564 Warren Brusstar .02 .10
565 Tom Brunansky .02 .10
566 Alfredo Griffin .02 .10
567 Jeff Barkley .02 .10
568 Donnie Scott .02 .10
569 Jim Acker .02 .10
570 Rusty Staub .05 .15
571 Mike Jeffcoat .02 .10
572 Paul Zuvella .02 .10
573 Tom Hume .02 .10
574 Ron Kittle .02 .10
575 Mike Boddicker .02 .10
576 Andre Dawson TL .02 .10
577 Jerry Reuss .02 .10
578 Lee Mazzilli .05 .15
579 Jim Slaton .02 .10
580 Willie McGee .05 .15
581 Bruce Hurst .02 .10
582 Jim Gantner .02 .10
583 Al Bumbry .02 .10
584 Brian Fisher RC .02 .10
585 Garry Maddox .02 .10
586 Greg Harris .02 .10
587 Rafael Santana .02 .10
588 Steve Lake .02 .10
589 Sid Bream .02 .10
590 Bob Knepper .02 .10
591 Jackie Moore MG .02 .10
592 Frank Tanana .05 .15
593 Jesse Barfield .05 .15
594 Chris Bando .02 .10
595 Dave Parker .05 .15
596 Onix Concepcion .02 .10
597 Sammy Stewart .02 .10
598 Jim Presley .02 .10
599 Rick Aguilera RC .08 .25
600 Dale Murphy .08 .25
601 Gary Lucas .02 .10
602 Mariano Duncan RC .08 .25
603 Bill Laskey .02 .10
604 Gary Pettis .02 .10
605 Dennis Boyd .02 .10
606 Hal McRae TL .05 .15
607 Ken Dayley .02 .10
608 Bruce Bochy .02 .10
609 Barbaro Garbey .02 .10
610 Ron Guidry .05 .15
611 Gary Woods .02 .10
612 Richard Dotson .02 .10
613 Roy Smalley .02 .10
614 Rick Waits .02 .10
615 Johnny Ray .02 .10
616 Glenn Brummer .02 .10
617 Lonnie Smith .02 .10
618 Jim Pankovits .02 .10
619 Danny Heep .02 .10
620 Bruce Sutter .05 .15
621 John Felske MG .02 .10
622 Gary Lavelle .02 .10
623 Floyd Rayford .02 .10
624 Steve McCatty .02 .10
625 Bob Brenly .02 .10
626 Roy Thomas .02 .10
627 Ron Oester .02 .10
628 Kirk McCaskill RC .08 .25
629 Mitch Webster .02 .10
630 Fernando Valenzuela .05 .15
631 Steve Braun .02 .10
632 Dave Von Ohlen .02 .10
633 Jackie Gutierrez .02 .10
634 Roy Lee Jackson .02 .10
635 Jason Thompson .02 .10
636 Lee Smith TL .02 .10
637 Rudy Law .02 .10
638 John Butcher .02 .10
639 Bo Diaz .02 .10
640 Jose Cruz .05 .15
641 Wayne Tolleson .02 .10
642 Ray Searage .02 .10
643 Tom Brookens .02 .10
644 Mark Gubicza .02 .10
645 Dusty Baker .05 .15
646 Mike Moore .02 .10
647 Mel Hall .02 .10
648 Steve Bedrosian .02 .10
649 Ronn Reynolds .02 .10
650 Dave Stieb .05 .15
651 Billy Martin MG .08 .25
652 Tom Browning .02 .10
653 Jim Dwyer .02 .10
654 Ken Howell .02 .10
655 Manny Trillo .02 .10
656 Brian Harper .02 .10
657 Juan Agosto .02 .10
658 Rob Wilfong .02 .10
659 Checklist: 529-660 .05 .15
660 Steve Garvey .05 .15
661 Roger Clemens 1.50 4.00
662 Bill Schroeder .02 .10
663 Neil Allen .02 .10
664 Tim Corcoran .02 .10
665 Alejandro Pena .02 .10
666 Charlie Hough TL .05 .15
667 Tim Teufel .02 .10
668 Cecilio Guante .02 .10
669 Ron Cey .05 .15
670 Willie Hernandez .02 .10
671 Lynn Jones .02 .10
672 Rob Picciolo .02 .10
673 Ernie Whitt .02 .10
674 Pat Tabler .02 .10
675 Claudell Washington .02 .10
676 Matt Young .02 .10
677 Nick Esasky .02 .10
678 Dan Gladden .02 .10
679 Britt Burns .02 .10
680 George Foster .05 .15
681 Dick Williams MG .02 .10
682 Junior Ortiz .02 .10
683 Andy Van Slyke .08 .25
684 Bob McClure .02 .10
685 Tim Wallach .02 .10
686 Jeff Stone .02 .10
687 Mike Trujillo .02 .10
688 Larry Herndon .02 .10
689 Dave Stewart .05 .15
690 Ryne Sandberg UER .30 .75
(No Topps logo
on front)
691 Mike Madden .02 .10
692 Dale Berra .02 .10
693 Tom Tellmann .02 .10
694 Garth Iorg .02 .10
695 Mike Smithson .02 .10
696 Bill Russell TL .05 .15
697 Bud Black .02 .10
698 Brad Komminsk .02 .10
699 Pat Corrales MG .02 .10
700 Reggie Jackson .08 .25
701 Keith Hernandez AS .02 .10
702 Tom Herr AS .02 .10
703 Tim Wallach AS .02 .10
704 Ozzie Smith AS .15 .40
705 Dale Murphy AS .05 .15
706 Pedro Guerrero AS .02 .10
707 Willie McGee AS .02 .10
708 Gary Carter AS .02 .10
709 Dwight Gooden AS .08 .25
710 John Tudor AS .02 .10
711 Jeff Reardon AS .02 .10
712 Don Mattingly AS .25 .60
713 Damaso Garcia AS .02 .10
714 George Brett AS .15 .40
715 Cal Ripken AS .15 .40
716 Rickey Henderson AS .08 .25
717 Dave Winfield AS .02 .10
718 George Bell AS .02 .10
719 Carlton Fisk AS .05 .15
720 Bret Saberhagen AS .02 .10
721 Ron Guidry AS .02 .10
722 Dan Quisenberry AS .02 .10
723 Marty Bystrom .02 .10
724 Tim Hulett .02 .10
725 Mario Soto .05 .15
726 Rick Dempsey TL .05 .15
727 David Green .02 .10
728 Mike Marshall .02 .10
729 Jim Beattie .02 .10
730 Ozzie Smith .25 .60
731 Don Robinson .02 .10
732 Floyd Youmans .02 .10
733 Ron Romanick .02 .10
734 Marty Barrett .02 .10
735 Dave Dravecky .02 .10
736 Glenn Wilson .02 .10
737 Pete Vuckovich .02 .10
738 Andre Robertson .02 .10
739 Dave Rozema .02 .10
740 Lance Parrish .05 .15
741 Pete Rose MG .15 .40
742 Frank Viola .05 .15
743 Pat Sheridan .02 .10
744 Lary Sorensen .02 .10
745 Willie Upshaw .02 .10
746 Denny Gonzalez .02 .10
747 Rick Cerone .02 .10
748 Steve Henderson .02 .10
749 Ed Jurak .02 .10
750 Gorman Thomas .05 .15
751 Howard Johnson .05 .15
752 Mike Krukow .02 .10
753 Dan Ford .02 .10
754 Pat Clements .02 .10
755 Harold Baines .05 .15
756 Rick Rhoden TL .02 .10
757 Darrell Porter .02 .10
758 Dave Anderson .02 .10
759 Moose Haas .02 .10
760 Andre Dawson .05 .15
761 Don Slaught .02 .10
762 Eric Show .02 .10
763 Terry Puhl .02 .10
764 Kevin Gross .02 .10
765 Don Baylor .05 .15
766 Rick Langford .02 .10
767 Jody Davis .02 .10
768 Vern Ruhle .02 .10
769 Harold Reynolds RC .30 .75
770 Vida Blue .05 .15
771 John McNamara MG .02 .10
772 Brian Downing .05 .15
773 Greg Pryor .02 .10
774 Terry Leach .02 .10
775 Al Oliver .05 .15
776 Gene Garber .02 .10
777 Wayne Krenchicki .02 .10
778 Jerry Hairston .02 .10
779 Rick Reuschel .05 .15
780 Robin Yount .25 .60
781 Joe Nolan .02 .10
782 Ken Landreaux .02 .10
783 Ricky Horton .02 .10
784 Alan Bannister .02 .10
785 Bob Stanley .02 .10
786 Mickey Hatcher TL .02 .10
787 Vance Law .02 .10
788 Marty Castillo .02 .10
789 Kurt Bevacqua .02 .10
790 Phil Niekro .05 .15
791 Checklist: 661-792 .05 .15
792 Charles Hudson .02 .10

1986 Topps Tiffany

These 792 cards form a parallel to the regular Topps set. These cards, available only through the Topps dealer network were issued in factory sealed boxes. Each case contained six sets. These cards have a "glossy" front and a very clear back. These cards were printed in the Topps Ireland plant. Reports within the hobby indicate that it is believed that 5,000 of these sets were produced.

COMP.FACT.SET (792) 75.00 150.00
*STARS: 5X TO 12X BASIC CARDS
*ROOKIES: 5X TO 12X BASIC CARDS
DISTRIBUTED ONLY IN FACTORY SET FORM
FACTORY SET PRICE IS FOR SEALED SETS

1986 Topps Glossy All-Stars

This 22-card standard-size set was distributed as an insert, one card per rak pack. The players featured are the starting lineups of the 1985 All-Star Game played in Minnesota. The cards are very colorful and have a high gloss finish.

COMPLETE SET (22) 2.00 5.00
1 Sparky Anderson MG .01 .05
2 Eddie Murray .20 .50
3 Lou Whitaker .02 .10
4 George Brett .40 1.00
5 Cal Ripken .75 2.00
6 Jim Rice .02 .10
7 Rickey Henderson .20 .50
8 Dave Winfield .20 .50
9 Carlton Fisk .15 .40
10 Jack Morris .02 .10
11 AL Team Photo .01 .05
12 Dick Williams MG .01 .05
13 Steve Garvey .02 .10
14 Tom Herr .01 .05
15 Graig Nettles .02 .10
16 Ozzie Smith .40 1.00
17 Tony Gwynn .40 1.00
18 Dale Murphy .07 .20
19 Darryl Strawberry .02 .10
20 Terry Kennedy .01 .05
21 LaMarr Hoyt .01 .05
22 NL Team Photo .01 .05

1986 Topps Glossy Send-Ins

This 60-card glossy standard-size set was produced by Topps and distributed ten cards at a time based on the offer found on the wax packs. Each series of ten cards was available by sending in 1.00 plus six "special offer" cards inserted one per wax pack. The card backs are printed in red and blue on white card stock. The card fronts feature a white border and a green frame surrounding a full-color photo of the player.

COMPLETE SET (60) 4.80 12.00
1 Oddibe McDowell .02 .10
2 Reggie Jackson .30 .75
3 Fernando Valenzuela .07 .20
4 Jack Clark .02 .10
5 Rickey Henderson .40 1.25
6 Steve Balboni .02 .10
7 Keith Hernandez .07 .20
8 Lance Parrish .07 .20
9 Willie McGee .07 .20
10 Chris Brown .02 .10
11 Darryl Strawberry .07 .20
12 Ron Guidry .07 .20
13 Dave Parker .07 .20
14 Cal Ripken 1.50 4.00
15 Tim Raines .07 .20
16 Rod Carew .30 .75
17 Mike Schmidt .40 1.00
18 George Brett .75 2.00
19 Joe Hesketh .02 .10
20 Dan Pasqua .02 .10
21 Vince Coleman .07 .20
22 Tom Seaver .30 .75
23 Gary Carter .30 .75
24 Orel Hershiser .07 .20
25 Pedro Guerrero .02 .10
26 Wade Boggs .30 .75
27 Bret Saberhagen .07 .20
28 Carlton Fisk .30 .75
29 Kirk Gibson .07 .20
30 Brian Fisher .02 .10
31 Don Mattingly .75 2.00
32 Tom Herr .02 .10
33 Eddie Murray .30 .75
34 Ryne Sandberg .60 1.50
35 Dan Quisenberry .02 .10
36 Jim Rice .07 .20
37 Dale Murphy .10 .30
38 Steve Garvey .07 .20
39 Roger McDowell .02 .10
40 Earnie Riles .02 .10
41 Dwight Gooden .07 .20
42 Dave Winfield .30 .75
43 Dave Stieb .02 .10
44 Bob Horner .02 .10
45 Nolan Ryan 1.50 4.00
46 Ozzie Smith .75 2.00
47 George Bell .02 .10
48 Gorman Thomas .02 .10
49 Tom Browning .02 .10
50 Larry Sheets .02 .10
51 Pete Rose .40 1.00
52 Brett Butler .07 .20
53 John Tudor .02 .10
54 Phil Bradley .02 .10
55 Jeff Reardon .07 .20
56 Rich Gossage .07 .20
57 Tony Gwynn .75 2.00
58 Ozzie Guillen .20 .50
59 Glenn Davis .02 .10
60 Darrell Evans .02 .10

1986 Topps Wax Box Cards

Topps printed cards (each measuring the standard 2 1/2" by 3 1/2") on the bottoms of their wax pack boxes for their regular issue cards; there are four different boxes, each with four cards. These sixteen cards ("numbered" A through P) are listed below; they are not considered an integral part of the regular set but are considered a separate set. The order of the set is alphabetical by player's name. These wax box cards are styled almost exactly like the 1986 Topps regular issue cards. Complete boxes would be worth an additional 25 percent premium over the prices below. The card lettering is sequenced in alphabetical order.

COMPLETE SET (16) 3.20 8.00
A George Bell .07 .20
B Wade Boggs .40 1.00
C George Brett .75 2.00
D Vince Coleman .15 .40
E Carlton Fisk .40 1.00
F Dwight Gooden .15 .40
G Pedro Guerrero .15 .40
H Ron Guidry .15 .40
I Reggie Jackson .40 1.00
J Don Mattingly .75 2.00
K Oddibe McDowell .07 .20
L Willie McGee .15 .40
M Dale Murphy .30 .75
N Pete Rose .50 1.25
O Bret Saberhagen .15 .40
P Fernando Valenzuela .15 .40

1986 Topps Traded

This 132-card standard-size Traded set was distributed in factory set form, which were packed 100 to a case, in a red and white box through hobby dealers. The cards are identical in style to regular-issue 1986 Topps cards except for whiter stock and t-suffixed numbering. The key extended Rookie Cards in this set are Barry Bonds, Bobby Bonilla, Jose Canseco, Will Clark, Andres Galarraga, Bo Jackson, Wally Joyner, John Kruk, and Kevin Mitchell.

COMP.FACT.SET (132) 15.00 40.00
1T Andy Allanson XRC .02 .10
2T Neil Allen .02 .10
3T Joaquin Andujar .05 .15
4T Paul Assenmacher .15 .40
5T Scott Bailes .02 .10
6T Don Baylor .05 .15
7T Steve Bedrosian .02 .10
8T Juan Beniquez .02 .10
9T Juan Berenguer .02 .10
10T Mike Bielecki .02 .10
11T Barry Bonds XRC 6.00 15.00
12T Bobby Bonilla XRC .30 .75
13T Juan Bonilla .02 .10
14T Rich Bordi .02 .10
15T Steve Boros MG .02 .10
16T Rick Burleson .02 .10
17T Bill Campbell .02 .10
18T Tom Candiotti .02 .10
19T John Cangelosi .02 .10
20T Jose Canseco XRC 1.50 4.00
21T Carmen Castillo .02 .10
22T Rick Cerone .02 .10
23T John Cerutti .02 .10
24T Will Clark XRC .60 1.50
25T Mark Clear .02 .10
26T Darnell Coles .02 .10
27T Dave Collins .02 .10
28T Tim Conroy .02 .10
29T Joe Cowley .02 .10
30T Joel Davis .02 .10
31T Rob Deer .02 .10
32T John Denny .02 .10
33T Mike Easler .02 .10
34T Mark Eichhorn .02 .10
35T Steve Farr .02 .10
36T Scott Fletcher .02 .10
37T Terry Forster .05 .15
38T Terry Francona .05 .15
39T Jim Fregosi MG .02 .10
40T Andres Galarraga XRC .40 1.00
41T Ken Griffey .05 .15
42T Bill Gullickson .02 .10
43T Jose Guzman XRC .02 .10
44T Moose Haas .02 .10
45T Billy Hatcher .02 .10
46T Mike Heath .02 .10
47T Tom Hume .02 .10
48T Pete Incaviglia XRC .15 .40
49T Dane Iorg .02 .10
50T Bo Jackson XRC 2.00 5.00
51T Wally Joyner XRC .30 .75
52T Charlie Kerfeld .02 .10
53T Eric King .02 .10
54T Bob Kipper .02 .10
55T Wayne Krenchicki .02 .10
56T John Kruk XRC .40 1.00
57T Mike LaCoss .02 .10
58T Pete Ladd .02 .10
59T Mike Laga .02 .10
60T Hal Lanier MG .02 .10
61T Dave LaPoint .02 .10
62T Rudy Law .02 .10
63T Rick Leach .02 .10
64T Tim Leary .02 .10
65T Dennis Leonard .02 .10
66T Jim Leyland MG XRC .20 .50
67T Steve Lyons .02 .10
68T Mickey Mahler .02 .10
69T Candy Maldonado .02 .10
70T Roger Mason XRC .02 .10
71T Bob McClure .02 .10
72T Andy McGaffigan .02 .10
73T Gene Michael MG .02 .10
74T Kevin Mitchell XRC .30 .75
75T Omar Moreno .02 .10
76T Jerry Mumphrey .02 .10
77T Phil Niekro .05 .15
78T Randy Niemann .02 .10
79T Juan Nieves .02 .10
80T Otis Nixon XRC .30 .75
81T Bob Ojeda .02 .10
82T Jose Oquendo .02 .10
83T Tom Paciorek .02 .10
84T David Palmer .02 .10
85T Frank Pastore .02 .10
86T Lou Piniella MG .05 .15
87T Dan Plesac .15 .40
88T Darrell Porter .02 .10
89T Rey Quinones .02 .10
90T Gary Redus .02 .10
91T Bip Roberts XRC .15 .40
92T Billy Joe Robidoux XRC .02 .10
93T Jeff D. Robinson .02 .10
94T Gary Roenicke .02 .10
95T Ed Romero .02 .10
96T Angel Salazar .02 .10
97T Joe Sambito .02 .10
98T Billy Sample .02 .10
99T Dave Schmidt .02 .10
100T Ken Schrom .02 .10
101T Tom Seaver .08 .25
102T Ted Simmons .05 .15
103T Sammy Stewart .02 .10
104T Kurt Stillwell .02 .10
105T Franklin Stubbs .02 .10
106T Dale Sveum .02 .10
107T Chuck Tanner MG .02 .10
108T Danny Tartabull .05 .15
109T Tim Teufel .02 .10
110T Bob Tewksbury XRC .15 .40
111T Andres Thomas .02 .10
112T Milt Thompson .15 .40
113T R.Thompson XRC .15 .40
114T Jay Tibbs .02 .10
115T Wayne Tolleson .02 .10
116T Alex Trevino .02 .10
117T Manny Trillo .02 .10
118T Ed VandeBerg .02 .10
119T Ozzie Virgil .02 .10
120T Bob Walk .02 .10
121T Gene Walter .02 .10
122T Claudell Washington .02 .10
123T Bill Wegman XRC .02 .10
124T Dick Williams MG .02 .10
125T Mitch Williams XRC .15 .40
126T Bobby Witt XRC .15 .40
127T Todd Worrell XRC .15 .40
128T George Wright .02 .10
129T Ricky Wright .02 .10
130T Steve Yeager .05 .15
131T Paul Zuvella .02 .10
132T Checklist 1T-132T .02 .10

1986 Topps Traded Tiffany

For the third consecutive season, Topps issued a Tiffany Update issue to go with their regular issue. These 132 cards feature the same players as in the regular set but have a "glossy" front and very clear back. These cards, released through Topps hobby dealers, were sent out only if the dealer ordered the regular Tiffany set. These cards were printed in Topps' Ireland plant. Again, similar to the regular set, it is believed that 5,000 of these sets were produced.

COMP.FACT.SET (132) 300.00 500.00
*STARS: 5X TO 12X BASIC CARDS
*ROOKIES: 4X TO 10X BASIC CARDS
DISTRIBUTED ONLY IN FACTORY SET FORM
FACTORY SET PRICE IS FOR SEALED SETS
OPENED SETS SELL FOR 50-60% OF SEALED

1987 Topps

This set consists of 792 standard-size cards. Cards were primarily issued in 17-card wax packs, 50-card rack packs and factory sets. Card fronts feature wood grain borders encasing a color photo (reminiscent of Topps' classic 1962 baseball set). Subsets include Record Breakers (1-7), Turn Back the Clock (311-315), All-Star selections (595-616) and Team Leaders (scattered throughout the set). The manager cards contain a team checklist on back. The key Rookie Cards in this set are Barry Bonds, Bobby Bonilla, Will Clark, Bo Jackson, Wally Joyner, John Kruk, Barry Larkin, Rafael Palmiero, Ruben Sierra, and Devon White.

COMPLETE SET (792) 10.00 25.00
COMP.FACT SET (792) 15.00 40.00
COMP.HOBBY SET (792) 15.00 40.00
COMP.X-MAS.SET (792) 15.00 40.00
1 Roger Clemens RB .40 1.00
2 Jim Deshaies RB .01 .05
3 Dwight Evans RB .05 .15
4 Davey Lopes RB .01 .05
5 Dave Righetti RB .01 .05
6 Ruben Sierra RB .08 .25
7 Todd Worrell RB .01 .05
8 Terry Pendleton .02 .10
9 Jay Tibbs .01 .05
10 Cecil Cooper .02 .10
11 Indians Team .01 .05
(Mound conference)
12 Jeff Sellers .01 .05
13 Nick Esasky .01 .05
14 Dave Stewart .02 .10
15 Claudell Washington .01 .05
16 Pat Clements .01 .05
17 Pete O'Brien .01 .05
18 Dick Howser MG .01 .05
19 Matt Young .01 .05
20 Gary Carter .02 .10
21 Mark Davis .01 .05
22 Doug DeCinces .01 .05
23 Lee Smith .02 .10
24 Tony Walker .01 .05
25 Bert Blyleven .02 .10
26 Greg Brock .01 .05
27 Joe Cowley .01 .05
28 Rick Dempsey .01 .05
29 Jimmy Key .02 .10
30 Tim Raines .02 .10
31 Braves Team .01 .05
(Glenn Hubbard and
Rafael Ramirez)
32 Tim Leary .01 .05
33 Andy Van Slyke .05 .15
34 Jose Rijo .02 .10
35 Sid Bream .01 .05
36 Eric King .01 .05
37 Marvell Wynne .01 .05
38 Dennis Leonard .01 .05
39 Marty Barrett .01 .05
40 Dave Righetti .02 .10
41 Bo Diaz .01 .05
42 Gary Redus .01 .05
43 Gene Michael MG .01 .05
44 Greg Harris .01 .05
45 Jim Presley .01 .05
46 Dan Gladden .01 .05
47 Dennis Powell .01 .05
48 Wally Backman .01 .05
49 Terry Harper .01 .05
50 Dave Smith .01 .05
51 Mel Hall .01 .05
52 Keith Atherton .01 .05
53 Ruppert Jones .01 .05
54 Bill Dawley .01 .05
55 Tim Wallach .01 .05
56 Brewers Team .02 .10
(Mound conference)
57 Scott Nielsen .01 .05
58 Thad Bosley .01 .05
59 Ken Dayley .01 .05
60 Tony Pena .01 .05
61 Bobby Thigpen RC .08 .25
62 Bobby Meacham .01 .05
63 Fred Toliver .01 .05
64 Harry Spilman .01 .05
65 Tom Browning .01 .05
66 Marc Sullivan .01 .05
67 Bill Swift .01 .05
68 Tony LaRussa MG .02 .10
69 Lonnie Smith .01 .05
70 Charlie Hough .02 .10
71 Mike Aldrete .01 .05
72 Walt Terrell .01 .05
73 Dave Anderson .01 .05
74 Dan Pasqua .01 .05
75 Ron Darling .02 .10
76 Rafael Ramirez .01 .05
77 Bryan Oelkers .01 .05
78 Tom Foley .01 .05
79 Juan Nieves .01 .05
80 Wally Joyner RC .15 .40
81 Padres Team .01 .05
(Andy Hawkins and
Terry Kennedy)
82 Rob Murphy .01 .05
83 Mike Davis .01 .05
84 Steve Lake .01 .05
85 Kevin Bass .01 .05
86 Nate Snell .01 .05
87 Mark Salas .01 .05
88 Ed Wojna .01 .05
89 Ozzie Guillen .05 .15
90 Dave Stieb .02 .10
91 Harold Reynolds .02 .10
92A Urbano Lugo .05 .15
ERR (no trademark)
92B Urbano Lugo COR .01 .05
93 Jim Leyland MG/TC RC .08 .25
94 Calvin Schiraldi .01 .05
95 Oddibe McDowell .01 .05
96 Frank Williams .01 .05
97 Glenn Wilson .01 .05
98 Bill Scherrer .01 .05
99 Darryl Motley .01 .05
(Now with Braves
on card front)
100 Steve Garvey .02 .10
101 Carl Willis RC .02 .10
102 Paul Zuvella .01 .05
103 Rick Aguilera .01 .05
104 Billy Sample .01 .05
105 Floyd Youmans .01 .05
106 Blue Jays Team .01 .05
(George Bell and
Jesse Barfield)
107 John Butcher .01 .05
108 Jim Gantner UER .01 .05
(Brewers logo
reversed)
109 R.J. Reynolds .01 .05
110 John Tudor .02 .10
111 Alfredo Griffin .01 .05
112 Alan Ashby .01 .05
113 Neil Allen .01 .05
114 Billy Beane .02 .10
115 Donnie Moore .01 .05
116 Bill Russell .02 .10
117 Jim Beattie .01 .05
118 Bobby Valentine MG .02 .10
119 Ron Robinson .01 .05
120 Eddie Murray .08 .25
121 Kevin Romine .01 .05
122 Jim Clancy .01 .05
123 John Kruk RC .20 .50
124 Ray Fontenot .01 .05
125 Bob Brenly .01 .05
126 Mike Loynd RC .02 .10
127 Vance Law .01 .05
128 Checklist 1-132 .01 .05
129 Rick Cerone .01 .05
130 Dwight Gooden .05 .15
131 Pirates Team .01 .05
(Sid Bream and
Tony Pena)
132 Paul Assenmacher .08 .25
133 Jose Oquendo .01 .05
134 Rich Yett .01 .05
135 Mike Easler .01 .05
136 Ron Romanick .01 .05
137 Jerry Willard .01 .05
138 Roy Lee Jackson .01 .05
139 Devon White RC .15 .40
140 Bret Saberhagen .02 .10
141 Herm Winningham .01 .05
142 Rick Sutcliffe .02 .10
143 Steve Boros MG .01 .05
144 Mike Scioscia .02 .10
145 Charlie Kerfeld .01 .05
146 Tracy Jones .01 .05
147 Randy Niemann .01 .05
148 Dave Collins .01 .05
149 Ray Searage .01 .05
150 Wade Boggs .05 .15
151 Mike LaCoss .01 .05
152 Toby Harrah .02 .10
153 Duane Ward RC .08 .25
154 Tom O'Malley .01 .05
155 Eddie Whitson .01 .05
156 Mariners Team .01 .05
(Mound conference)

157 Danny Darwin .01 .05
158 Tim Teufel .01 .05
159 Ed Olwine .01 .05
160 Julio Franco .02 .10
161 Steve Ontiveros .01 .05
162 Mike LaValliere RC .08 .25
163 Kevin Gross .01 .05
164 Sammy Khalifa .01 .05
165 Jeff Reardon .02 .10
166 Bob Boone .02 .10
167 Jim Deshaies RC .02 .10
168 Lou Piniella MG .02 .10
169 Ron Washington .01 .05
170 Bo Jackson RC 1.25 3.00
171 Chuck Cary .01 .05
172 Ron Oester .01 .05
173 Alex Trevino .01 .05
174 Henry Cotto .01 .05
175 Bob Stanley .01 .05
176 Steve Buechele .01 .05
177 Keith Moreland .01 .05
178 Cecil Fielder .02 .10
179 Bill Wegman .01 .05
180 Chris Brown .01 .05
181 Cardinals Team .01 .05
(Mound conference)
182 Lee Lacy .01 .05
183 Andy Hawkins .01 .05
184 Bobby Bonilla RC .15 .40
185 Roger McDowell .01 .05
186 Bruce Benedict .01 .05
187 Mark Huismann .01 .05
188 Tony Phillips .01 .05
189 Joe Hesketh .01 .05
190 Jim Sundberg .02 .10
191 Charles Hudson .01 .05
192 Cory Snyder .01 .05
193 Roger Craig MG .02 .10
194 Kirk McCaskill .01 .05
195 Mike Pagliarulo .01 .05
196 Randy O'Neal UER .01 .05
(Wrong ML career
W-L totals)
197 Mark Bailey .01 .05
198 Lee Mazzilli .02 .10
199 Mariano Duncan .01 .05
200 Pete Rose .25 .60
201 John Cangelosi .01 .05
202 Ricky Wright .01 .05
203 Mike Kingery RC .02 .10
204 Sammy Stewart .01 .05
205 Graig Nettles .02 .10
206 Twins Team .01 .05
(Frank Viola and
Tim Laudner)
207 George Frazier .01 .05
208 John Shelby .01 .05
209 Rick Schu .01 .05
210 Lloyd Moseby .01 .05
211 John Morris .01 .05
212 Mike Fitzgerald .01 .05
213 Randy Myers RC .15 .40
214 Omar Moreno .01 .05
215 Mark Langston .01 .05
216 B.J. Surhoff RC .15 .40
217 Chris Codiroli .01 .05
218 Sparky Anderson MG .02 .10
219 Cecilio Guante .01 .05
220 Joe Carter .02 .10
221 Vern Ruhle .01 .05
222 Denny Walling .01 .05
223 Charlie Leibrandt .01 .05
224 Wayne Tolleson .01 .05
225 Mike Smithson .01 .05
226 Max Venable .01 .05
227 Jamie Moyer RC .20 .50
228 Curt Wilkerson .01 .05
229 Mike Birkbeck .02 .10
230 Don Baylor .02 .10
231 Giants Team .01 .05
(Bob Brenly and
Jim Gott)
232 Reggie Williams .01 .05
233 Russ Morman .01 .05
234 Pat Sheridan .01 .05
235 Alvin Davis .01 .05
236 Tommy John .02 .10
237 Jim Morrison .01 .05
238 Bill Krueger .01 .05
239 Juan Espino .01 .05
240 Steve Balboni .01 .05
241 Danny Heep .01 .05
242 Rick Mahler .01 .05
243 Whitey Herzog MG .02 .10
244 Dickie Noles .01 .05
245 Willie Upshaw .01 .05
246 Jim Dwyer .01 .05
247 Jeff Reed .01 .05
248 Gene Walter .01 .05
249 Jim Pankovits .01 .05
250 Teddy Higuera .01 .05
251 Rob Wilfong .01 .05
252 Dennis Martinez .02 .10
253 Eddie Milner .01 .05
254 Bob Tewksbury RC .08 .25
255 Juan Samuel .01 .05
256 Royals Team .05 .15
(George Brett and
Frank White)
257 Bob Forsch .01 .05
258 Steve Yeager .02 .10
259 Mike Greenwell RC .08 .25
260 Vida Blue .02 .10
261 Ruben Sierra RC .20 .50
262 Jim Winn .01 .05
263 Stan Javier .01 .05
264 Checklist 133-264 .01 .05
265 Darrell Evans .02 .10
266 Jeff Hamilton .01 .05
267 Howard Johnson .02 .10
268 Pat Corrales MG .01 .05
269 Cliff Speck .01 .05
270 Jody Davis .01 .05
271 Mike G. Brown .01 .05
272 Andres Galarraga .02 .10
273 Gene Nelson .01 .05
274 Jeff Hearron UER .01 .05
(Duplicate 1986
stat line on back)
275 LaMarr Hoyt .01 .05
276 Jackie Gutierrez .01 .05
277 Juan Agosto .01 .05
278 Gary Pettis .01 .05
279 Dan Plesac .01 .05
280 Jeff Leonard .01 .05
281 Reds Team .08 .25
Pete Rose, Bo Diaz
and Bill Gullickson
282 Jeff Calhoun .01 .05
283 Doug Drabek RC .15 .40
284 John Moses .01 .05
285 Dennis Boyd .01 .05
286 Mike Woodard .01 .05
287 Dave Von Ohlen .01 .05
288 Tito Landrum .01 .05
289 Bob Kipper .01 .05
290 Leon Durham .01 .05
291 Mitch Williams RC .08 .25
292 Franklin Stubbs .01 .05
293 Bob Rodgers MG .01 .05
294 Steve Jeltz .01 .05
295 Len Dykstra .02 .10
296 Andres Thomas .01 .05
297 Don Schulze .01 .05
298 Larry Herndon .01 .05
299 Joel Davis .01 .05
300 Reggie Jackson .05 .15
301 Luis Aquino UER .01 .05
(No trademark
never corrected)
302 Bill Schroeder .01 .05
303 Juan Berenguer .01 .05
304 Phil Garner .02 .10
305 John Franco .02 .10
306 Red Sox Team .02 .10
(Tom Seaver,
John McNamara MG,
and Rich Gedman)
307 Lee Guetterman .01 .05
308 Don Slaught .01 .05
309 Mike Young .01 .05
310 Frank Viola .02 .10
311 Rickey Henderson .05 .15
TBC '82
312 Reggie Jackson .02 .10
TBC '77
313 Roberto Clemente .08 .25
TBC '72
314 Carl Yastrzemski UER .08 .25
TBC '67 (Sic, 112
RBI's on back)
315 Maury Wills TBC '62 .02 .10
316 Brian Fisher .01 .05
317 Clint Hurdle .01 .05
318 Jim Fregosi MG .01 .05
319 Greg Swindell RC .08 .25
320 Barry Bonds RC 3.00 8.00
321 Mike Laga .01 .05
322 Chris Bando .01 .05
323 Al Newman RC .01 .05
324 David Palmer .01 .05
325 Garry Templeton .02 .10
326 Mark Gubicza .01 .05
327 Dale Sveum .01 .05
328 Bob Welch .02 .10
329 Ron Roenicke .01 .05
330 Mike Scott .02 .10
331 Mets Team .02 .10
(Gary Carter and
Darryl Strawberry)
332 Joe Price .01 .05
333 Ken Phelps .01 .05
334 Ed Correa .01 .05
335 Candy Maldonado .01 .05
336 Allan Anderson RC .01 .05
337 Darrell Miller .01 .05
338 Tim Conroy .01 .05
339 Donnie Hill .01 .05
340 Roger Clemens .60 1.50
341 Mike C. Brown .01 .05
342 Bob James .01 .05
343 Hal Lanier MG .01 .05
344A Joe Niekro .01 .05
(Copyright inside
righthand border)
344B Joe Niekro .01 .05
(Copyright outside
righthand border)
345 Andre Dawson .02 .10
346 Shawon Dunston .01 .05
347 Mickey Brantley .01 .05
348 Carmelo Martinez .01 .05
349 Storm Davis .01 .05
350 Keith Hernandez .02 .10
351 Gene Garber .01 .05
352 Mike Felder .01 .05
353 Ernie Camacho .01 .05
354 Jamie Quirk .01 .05
355 Don Carman .01 .05
356 White Sox Team .01 .05
(Mound conference)
357 Steve Fireovid .01 .05
358 Sal Butera .01 .05
359 Doug Corbett .01 .05
360 Pedro Guerrero .02 .10
361 Mark Thurmond .01 .05
362 Luis Quinones .01 .05
363 Jose Guzman .01 .05
364 Randy Bush .01 .05
365 Rick Rhoden .01 .05
366 Mark McGwire 1.50 4.00
367 Jeff Lahti .01 .05
368 John McNamara MG .01 .05
369 Brian Dayett .01 .05
370 Fred Lynn .02 .10
371 Mark Eichhorn .01 .05
372 Jerry Mumphrey .01 .05
373 Jeff Dedmon .01 .05
374 Glenn Hoffman .01 .05
375 Ron Guidry .02 .10
376 Scott Bradley .01 .05
377 John Henry Johnson .01 .05
378 Rafael Santana .01 .05
379 John Russell .01 .05
380 Rich Gossage .02 .10
381 Expos Team .01 .05
(Mound conference)
382 Rudy Law .01 .05
383 Ron Davis .01 .05
384 Johnny Grubb .01 .05
385 Orel Hershiser .05 .15
386 Dickie Thon .01 .05
387 T.R. Bryden .01 .05
388 Geno Petralli .01 .05
389 Jeff D. Robinson .01 .05
390 Gary Matthews .02 .10
391 Jay Howell .01 .05
392 Checklist 265-396 .01 .05
393 Pete Rose MG .05 .15
394 Mike Bielecki .01 .05
395 Damaso Garcia .01 .05
396 Tim Lollar .01 .05
397 Greg Walker .01 .05
398 Brad Havens .01 .05
399 Curt Ford .01 .05
400 George Brett .25 .60
401 Billy Joe Robidoux .01 .05
402 Mike Trujillo .01 .05
403 Jerry Royster .01 .05
404 Doug Sisk .01 .05
405 Brook Jacoby .01 .05
406 Yankees Team .20 .50
(Rickey Henderson and
Don Mattingly)
407 Jim Acker .01 .05
408 John Mizerock .01 .05
409 Milt Thompson .01 .05
410 Fernando Valenzuela .02 .10
411 Darnell Coles .01 .05
412 Eric Davis .05 .15
413 Moose Haas .01 .05
414 Joe Orsulak .01 .05
415 Bobby Witt RC .08 .25
416 Tom Nieto .01 .05
417 Pat Perry .01 .05
418 Dick Williams MG .01 .05
419 Mark Portugal RC .08 .25
420 Will Clark RC .40 1.00
421 Jose DeLeon .01 .05
422 Jack Howell .01 .05
423 Jaime Cocanower .01 .05
424 Chris Speier .01 .05
425 Tom Seaver UER .05 .15
Earned Runs amount is wrong
For 86 Red Sox and Career
Also the ERA is wrong for 86 and career
426 Floyd Rayford .01 .05
427 Edwin Nunez .01 .05
428 Bruce Bochy .01 .05
429 Tim Pyznarski .01 .05
430 Mike Schmidt .20 .50
431 Dodgers Team .01 .05
(Mound conference)
432 Jim Slaton .01 .05
433 Ed Hearn RC .01 .05
434 Mike Fischlin .01 .05
435 Bruce Sutter .02 .10
436 Andy Allanson RC .01 .05
437 Ted Power .01 .05
438 Kelly Downs RC .02 .10
439 Karl Best .01 .05
440 Willie McGee .02 .10
441 Dave Leiper .01 .05
442 Mitch Webster .01 .05
443 John Felske MG .01 .05
444 Jeff Russell .01 .05
445 Dave Lopes .02 .10
446 Chuck Finley RC .15 .40
447 Bill Almon .01 .05
448 Chris Bosio RC .08 .25
449 Pat Dodson .02 .10
450 Kirby Puckett .20 .50
451 Joe Sambito .01 .05
452 Dave Henderson .01 .05
453 Scott Terry RC .02 .10
454 Luis Salazar .01 .05
455 Mike Boddicker .01 .05
456 A's Team .01 .05
(Mound conference)
457 Len Matuszek .01 .05
458 Kelly Gruber .01 .05
459 Dennis Eckersley .05 .15
460 Darryl Strawberry .02 .10
461 Craig McMurtry .01 .05
462 Scott Fletcher .01 .05
463 Tom Candiotti .01 .05
464 Butch Wynegar .01 .05
465 Todd Worrell .01 .05
466 Kal Daniels .01 .05
467 Randy St.Claire .01 .05
468 G.Bamberger MG .01 .05
469 Mike Diaz .01 .05
470 Dave Dravecky .01 .05
471 Ronn Reynolds .01 .05
472 Bill Doran .01 .05
473 Steve Farr .01 .05
474 Jerry Narron .01 .05
475 Scott Garrelts .01 .05
476 Danny Tartabull .01 .05
477 Ken Howell .01 .05
478 Tim Laudner .01 .05
479 Bob Sebra .01 .05
480 Jim Rice .02 .10
481 Phillies Team .01 .05
(Glenn Wilson
Juan Samuel and
Von Hayes)
482 Daryl Boston .01 .05
483 Dwight Lowry .01 .05
484 Jim Traber .01 .05
485 Tony Fernandez .01 .05
486 Otis Nixon .01 .05
487 Dave Gumpert .01 .05
488 Ray Knight .02 .10
489 Bill Gullickson .01 .05
490 Dale Murphy .05 .15
491 Ron Karkovice RC .08 .25
492 Mike Heath .01 .05
493 Tom Lasorda MG .05 .15
494 Barry Jones .01 .05
495 Gorman Thomas .02 .10
496 Bruce Bochte .01 .05
497 Dale Mohorcic .01 .05
498 Bob Kearney .01 .05
499 Bruce Ruffin RC .02 .10
500 Don Mattingly .25 .60
501 Craig Lefferts .01 .05
502 Dick Schofield .01 .05
503 Larry Andersen .01 .05
504 Mickey Hatcher .01 .05
505 Bryn Smith .01 .05
506 Orioles Team .01 .05
(Mound conference)
507 Dave L. Stapleton .01 .05
508 Scott Bankhead .01 .05
509 Enos Cabell .01 .05
510 Tom Henke .01 .05
511 Steve Lyons .01 .05
512 Dave Magadan RC .08 .25
513 Carmen Castillo .01 .05
514 Orlando Mercado .01 .05
515 Willie Hernandez .01 .05
516 Ted Simmons .02 .10
517 Mario Soto .02 .10
518 Gene Mauch MG .01 .05
519 Curt Young .01 .05
520 Jack Clark .02 .10
521 Rick Reuschel .02 .10
522 Checklist 397-528 .01 .05
523 Earnie Riles .01 .05
524 Bob Shirley .01 .05
525 Phil Bradley .01 .05
526 Roger Mason .01 .05
527 Jim Wohlford .01 .05
528 Ken Dixon .01 .05
529 Alvaro Espinoza RC .02 .10
530 Tony Gwynn .10 .30
531 Astros Team .02 .10
(Yogi Berra conference)
532 Jeff Stone .01 .05
533 Angel Salazar .01 .05
534 Scott Sanderson .01 .05
535 Tony Armas .02 .10
536 Terry Mulholland RC .08 .25
537 Rance Mulliniks .01 .05
538 Tom Niedenfuer .01 .05
539 Reid Nichols .01 .05
540 Terry Kennedy .01 .05
541 Rafael Belliard RC .08 .25
542 Ricky Horton .01 .05
543 Dave Johnson MG .01 .05
544 Zane Smith .01 .05
545 Buddy Bell .02 .10
546 Mike Morgan .01 .05
547 Rob Deer .01 .05
548 Bill Mooneyham .01 .05
549 Bob Melvin .01 .05
550 Pete Incaviglia RC .08 .25
551 Frank Wills .01 .05
552 Larry Sheets .01 .05
553 Mike Maddux RC .01 .05
554 Buddy Biancalana .01 .05
555 Dennis Rasmussen .01 .05
556 Angels Team .01 .05
(Rene Lachemann CO,
Mike Witt, and
Bob Boone)
557 John Cerutti .01 .05
558 Greg Gagne .01 .05
559 Lance McCullers .01 .05
560 Glenn Davis .01 .05
561 Rey Quinones .01 .05
562 Bryan Clutterbuck .01 .05
563 John Stefero .01 .05
564 Larry McWilliams .01 .05
565 Dusty Baker .02 .10
566 Tim Hulett .01 .05
567 Greg Mathews .01 .05
568 Earl Weaver MG .02 .10
569 Wade Rowdon .01 .05
570 Sid Fernandez .01 .05
571 Ozzie Virgil .01 .05
572 Pete Ladd .01 .05
573 Hal McRae .02 .10
574 Manny Lee .01 .05
575 Pat Tabler .01 .05
576 Frank Pastore .01 .05
577 Dann Bilardello .01 .05
578 Billy Hatcher .01 .05
579 Rick Burleson .01 .05
580 Mike Krukow .01 .05
581 Cubs Team .01 .05
(Ron Cey and
Steve Trout)
582 Bruce Berenyi .01 .05
583 Junior Ortiz .01 .05
584 Ron Kittle .01 .05
585 Scott Bailes .01 .05
586 Ben Oglivie .02 .10
587 Eric Plunk .01 .05
588 Wallace Johnson .01 .05
589 Steve Crawford .01 .05
590 Vince Coleman .01 .05
591 Spike Owen .01 .05
592 Chris Welsh .01 .05
593 Chuck Tanner MG .01 .05
594 Rick Anderson .01 .05
595 Keith Hernandez AS .01 .05
596 Steve Sax AS .01 .05
597 Mike Schmidt AS .08 .25
598 Ozzie Smith AS .08 .25
599 Tony Gwynn AS .05 .15
600 Dave Parker AS .01 .05
601 Darryl Strawberry AS .01 .05
602 Gary Carter AS .01 .05
603A D.Gooden AS .02 .10
ERR no trademark
603B D.Gooden AS COR .02 .10
604 Fernando Valenzuela AS .01 .05
605 Todd Worrell AS .01 .05
606 Don Mattingly AS COR .10 .30
606A Don Mattingly AS .40 1.00
ERR (no trademark)
607 Tony Bernazard AS .01 .05
608 Wade Boggs AS .02 .10
609 Cal Ripken AS .08 .25
610 Jim Rice AS .01 .05
611 Kirby Puckett AS .08 .25
612 George Bell AS .01 .05
613 Lance Parrish AS UER .01 .05
(Pitcher heading
on back)
614 Roger Clemens AS .40 1.00
615 Teddy Higuera AS .01 .05
616 Dave Righetti AS .01 .05
617 Al Nipper .01 .05
618 Tom Kelly MG .01 .05
619 Jerry Reed .01 .05
620 Jose Canseco .40 1.00
621 Danny Cox .01 .05
622 Glenn Braggs RC .02 .10
623 Kurt Stillwell .01 .05
624 Tim Burke .01 .05
625 Mookie Wilson .02 .10
626 Joel Skinner .01 .05
627 Ken Oberkfell .01 .05
628 Bob Walk .01 .05
629 Larry Parrish .01 .05
630 John Candelaria .01 .05
631 Tigers Team .01 .05
(Mound conference)
632 Rob Woodward .01 .05
633 Jose Uribe .01 .05
634 Rafael Palmeiro RC .60 1.50
635 Ken Schrom .01 .05
636 Darren Daulton .02 .10
637 Bip Roberts RC .08 .25
638 Rich Bordi .01 .05
639 Gerald Perry .01 .05
640 Mark Clear .01 .05
641 Domingo Ramos .01 .05
642 Al Pulido .01 .05
643 Ron Shepherd .01 .05
644 John Denny .01 .05
645 Dwight Evans .05 .15
646 Mike Mason .01 .05
647 Tom Lawless .01 .05
648 Barry Larkin RC .40 1.00
649 Mickey Tettleton .01 .05
650 Hubie Brooks .01 .05
651 Benny Distefano .01 .05
652 Terry Forster .02 .10
653 Kevin Mitchell RC .15 .40
654 Checklist 529-660 .02 .10
655 Jesse Barfield .02 .10
656 Rangers Team .01 .05
(Bobby Valentine MG
and Ricky Wright)
657 Tom Waddell .01 .05
658 Robby Thompson RC .08 .25
659 Aurelio Lopez .01 .05
660 Bob Horner .02 .10
661 Lou Whitaker .02 .10
662 Frank DiPino .01 .05
663 Cliff Johnson .01 .05
664 Mike Marshall .01 .05
665 Rod Scurry .01 .05
666 Von Hayes .01 .05
667 Ron Hassey .01 .05
668 Juan Bonilla .01 .05
669 Bud Black .01 .05
670 Jose Cruz .02 .10
671A Ray Soff ERR .01 .05
(No D* before
copyright line)
671B Ray Soff COR .01 .05
(D* before
copyright line)
672 Chili Davis .02 .10
673 Don Sutton .02 .10
674 Bill Campbell .01 .05
675 Ed Romero .01 .05
676 Charlie Moore .01 .05
677 Bob Grich .02 .10
678 Carney Lansford .02 .10
679 Kent Hrbek .02 .10
680 Ryne Sandberg .15 .40
681 George Bell .02 .10
682 Jerry Reuss .01 .05
683 Gary Roenicke .01 .05
684 Kent Tekulve .01 .05
685 Jerry Hairston .01 .05
686 Doyle Alexander .01 .05
687 Alan Trammell .02 .10
688 Juan Beniquez .01 .05
689 Darrell Porter .01 .05
690 Dane Iorg .01 .05
691 Dave Parker .02 .10
692 Frank White .02 .10
693 Terry Puhl .01 .05
694 Phil Niekro .02 .10
695 Chico Walker .01 .05
696 Gary Lucas .01 .05
697 Ed Lynch .01 .05
698 Ernie Whitt .01 .05
699 Ken Landreaux .01 .05
700 Dave Bergman .01 .05
701 Willie Randolph .02 .10
702 Greg Gross .01 .05
703 Dave Schmidt .01 .05
704 Jesse Orosco .01 .05
705 Bruce Hurst .01 .05
706 Rick Manning .01 .05
707 Bob McClure .01 .05
708 Scott McGregor .01 .05
709 Dave Kingman .02 .10
710 Gary Gaetti .02 .10
711 Ken Griffey .02 .10
712 Don Robinson .01 .05
713 Tom Brookens .01 .05
714 Dan Quisenberry .01 .05
715 Bob Dernier .01 .05
716 Rick Leach .01 .05
717 Ed VandeBerg .01 .05
718 Steve Carlton .02 .10
719 Tom Hume .01 .05
720 Richard Dotson .01 .05
721 Tom Herr .01 .05
722 Bob Knepper .01 .05
723 Brett Butler .02 .10
724 Greg Minton .01 .05
725 George Hendrick .02 .10
726 Frank Tanana .02 .10
727 Mike Moore .01 .05
728 Tippy Martinez .01 .05
729 Tom Paciorek .01 .05
730 Eric Show .01 .05
731 Dave Concepcion .02 .10
732 Manny Trillo .01 .05
733 Bill Caudill .01 .05
734 Bill Madlock .02 .10
735 Rickey Henderson .08 .25
736 Steve Bedrosian .01 .05
737 Floyd Bannister .01 .05
738 Jorge Orta .01 .05
739 Chet Lemon .02 .10
740 Rich Gedman .01 .05
741 Paul Molitor .02 .10
742 Andy McGaffigan .01 .05
743 Dwayne Murphy .01 .05
744 Roy Smalley .01 .05
745 Glenn Hubbard .01 .05
746 Bob Ojeda .01 .05
747 Johnny Ray .01 .05
748 Mike Flanagan .01 .05
749 Ozzie Smith .15 .40
750 Steve Trout .01 .05
751 Garth Iorg .01 .05
752 Dan Petry .01 .05
753 Rick Honeycutt .01 .05
754 Dave LaPoint .01 .05
755 Luis Aguayo .01 .05
756 Carlton Fisk .05 .15
757 Nolan Ryan .40 1.00
758 Tony Bernazard .01 .05
759 Joel Youngblood .01 .05
760 Mike Witt .01 .05
761 Greg Pryor .01 .05
762 Gary Ward .01 .05
763 Tim Flannery .01 .05
764 Bill Buckner .02 .10
765 Kirk Gibson .02 .10
766 Don Aase .01 .05
767 Ron Cey .02 .10
768 Dennis Lamp .01 .05
769 Steve Sax .01 .05
770 Dave Winfield .02 .10
771 Shane Rawley .01 .05
772 Harold Baines .02 .10
773 Robin Yount .15 .40
774 Wayne Krenchicki .01 .05
775 Joaquin Andujar .02 .10
776 Tom Brunansky .01 .05
777 Chris Chambliss .02 .10
778 Jack Morris .02 .10
779 Craig Reynolds .01 .05
780 Andre Thornton .01 .05
781 Atlee Hammaker .01 .05
782 Brian Downing .02 .10
783 Willie Wilson .02 .10
784 Cal Ripken .30 .75
785 Terry Francona .02 .10
786 Jimy Williams MG .01 .05
787 Alejandro Pena .01 .05
788 Tim Stoddard .01 .05
789 Dan Schatzeder .01 .05
790 Julio Cruz .01 .05
791 Lance Parrish .02 .10
792 Checklist 661-792 .01 .05

1987 Topps Tiffany

These 792 standard-size cards were a parallel to the regular Topps issue. These cards feature "glossy" fronts and easy to read backs. These cards are in the same style as the regular Topps issue. This set was printed in Ireland and was issued only in factory set form. Unlike previous years, a significantly higher amount of these cards were produced. Therefore, the values of these cards are a much lower mulitplier to the regular cards than previous years. It is believed that as many as 30,000 of these sets were produced. This increase was probably in response to increased dealer interest.

COMP.FACT.SET (792) 60.00 120.00
*STARS: 2.5X TO 6X BASIC CARDS
*ROOKIES: 2.5X TO 6X BASIC CARDS
DISTRIBUTED ONLY IN FACTORY SET FORM
FACTORY SET PRICE IS FOR SEALED SETS

1987 Topps Glossy All-Stars

This set of 22 glossy cards was inserted one per rack pack. Players selected for the set are the starting players (plus manager and two pitchers) in the 1986 All-Star Game in Houston. Cards measure the standard size and the backs feature red and blue printing on a white card stock.

COMPLETE SET (22) 2.00 5.00
1 Whitey Herzog MG .02 .10
2 Keith Hernandez .02 .10
3 Ryne Sandberg .40 1.00
4 Mike Schmidt .20 .50
5 Ozzie Smith .40 1.00
6 Tony Gwynn .40 1.00
7 Dale Murphy .07 .20
8 Darryl Strawberry .02 .10
9 Gary Carter .20 .50
10 Dwight Gooden .05 .15
11 Fernando Valenzuela .02 .10
12 Dick Howser MG .01 .05
13 Wally Joyner .02 .10
14 Lou Whitaker .02 .10
15 Wade Boggs .20 .50
16 Cal Ripken .75 2.00
17 Dave Winfield .20 .50
18 Rickey Henderson .25 .60
19 Kirby Puckett .30 .75
20 Lance Parrish .02 .10
21 Roger Clemens .40 1.00
22 Teddy Higuera .01 .05

1987 Topps Glossy Send-Ins

Topps issued this set through a mail-in offer explained and advertised on the wax packs. This 60-card set features glossy fronts with each card measuring the standard size. The offer provided your choice of any one of the six 10-card subsets (1-10, 11-20, etc.) for 1.00 plus six of the Special Offer ("Spring Fever Baseball") insert cards, which were found one per wax pack. The last two players (numerically) in each ten-card subset are actually "Hot Prospects." This set is highlighted by an early Barry Bonds card.

COMPLETE SET (60) 10.00 25.00
DISTRIBUTED VIA MAIL EXCH.PROGRAM
1 Don Mattingly .75 2.00
2 Tony Gwynn .40 1.00
3 Gary Gaetti .10 .30
4 Glenn Davis .07 .20
5 Roger Clemens 1.25 3.00
6 Dale Murphy .20 .50
7 Lou Whitaker .10 .30
8 Roger McDowell .07 .20
9 Cory Snyder .07 .20
10 Todd Worrell .10 .30
11 Gary Carter .10 .30
12 Eddie Murray .30 .75
13 Bob Knepper .07 .20
14 Harold Baines .10 .30
15 Jeff Reardon .10 .30
16 Joe Carter .10 .30
17 Dave Parker .10 .30
18 Wade Boggs .20 .50
19 Danny Tartabull .07 .20
20 Jim Deshaies .07 .20
21 Rickey Henderson .30 .75
22 Rob Deer .07 .20
23 Ozzie Smith .50 1.25
24 Dave Righetti .10 .30
25 Kent Hrbek .10 .30
26 Keith Hernandez .10 .30
27 Don Baylor .10 .30
28 Mike Schmidt .60 1.50
29 Pete Incaviglia .10 .30
30 Barry Bonds 4.00 10.00
31 George Brett .75 2.00
32 Darryl Strawberry .10 .30
33 Mike Witt .07 .20
34 Kevin Bass .07 .20
35 Jesse Barfield .07 .20
36 Bob Ojeda .07 .20
37 Cal Ripken 1.00 2.50
38 Vince Coleman .07 .20
39 Wally Joyner .20 .50
40 Robby Thompson .10 .30

41 Pete Rose .75 2.00
42 Jim Rice .10 .30
43 Tony Bernazard .07 .20
44 Eric Davis .20 .50
45 George Bell .07 .20
46 Hubie Brooks .07 .20
47 Jack Morris .10 .30
48 Tim Raines .10 .30
49 Mark Eichhorn .07 .20
50 Kevin Mitchell .10 .30
51 Dwight Gooden .20 .50
52 Doug DeCinces .07 .20
53 Fernando Valenzuela .10 .30
54 Reggie Jackson .20 .50
55 Johnny Ray .07 .20
56 Mike Pagliarulo .07 .20
57 Kirby Puckett .40 1.00
58 Lance Parrish .10 .30
59 Jose Canseco .60 1.50
60 Greg Mathews .07 .20

1987 Topps Rookies

Inserted in each supermarket jumbo pack is a card from this series of 22 of 1986's best rookies as determined by Topps. Jumbo packs consisted of 100 (regular issue 1987 Topps baseball) cards with a stick of gum plus the insert "Rookie" card. The card fronts are in full color and measure the standard size. The card backs are printed in red and blue on white card stock and are numbered at the bottom essentially by alphabetical order.

COMPLETE SET (22) 6.00 12.00
ONE PER RETAIL JUMBO PACK
1 Andy Allanson .08 .25
2 John Cangelosi .08 .25
3 Jose Canseco .75 2.00
4 Will Clark 1.00 2.50
5 Mark Eichhorn .08 .25
6 Pete Incaviglia .20 .50
7 Wally Joyner .30 .75
8 Eric King .08 .25
9 Dave Magadan .20 .50
10 John Morris .08 .25
11 Juan Nieves .08 .25
12 Rafael Palmeiro 2.00 5.00
13 Billy Joe Robidoux .08 .25
14 Bruce Ruffin .08 .25
15 Ruben Sierra .40 1.00
16 Cory Snyder .08 .25
17 Kurt Stillwell .08 .25
18 Dale Sveum .08 .25
19 Danny Tartabull .08 .25
20 Andres Thomas .08 .25
21 Robby Thompson .20 .50
22 Todd Worrell .20 .50

1987 Topps Wax Box Cards

This set of eight cards is really four different sets of two smaller (approximately 2 1/8" by 3") cards which were printed on the side of the wax pack box; these eight cards are lettered A through H and are very similar in design to the Topps regular issue cards. The order of the set is alphabetical by player's name. Complete boxes would be worth an additional 25 percent premium over the prices below. The card backs are done in a newspaper headline style describing something about that player that happened the previous season. The card backs feature blue and yellow ink on gray card stock.

COMPLETE SET (8) 1.20 3.00
A Don Baylor .08 .25
B Steve Carlton .30 .75
C Ron Cey .08 .25
D Cecil Cooper .02 .10
E Rickey Henderson .30 .75
F Jim Rice .08 .25
G Don Sutton .30 .75
H Dave Winfield .30 .75

1987 Topps Traded

This 132-card standard-size Traded set was distributed exclusively in factory set form in a special green and white box through hobby dealers. The card fronts are identical in style to the Topps regular issue except for whiter stock and t-suffixed numbering on back. The cards are ordered alphabetically by player's last name. The key extended Rookie Cards in this set are Ellis Burks, David Cone, Greg Maddux, Fred McGriff and Matt Williams.

COMP.FACT.SET (132) 3.00 8.00
1T Bill Almon .01 .05
2T Scott Bankhead .01 .05
3T Eric Bell .02 .10
4T Juan Beniquez .01 .05
5T Juan Berenguer .01 .05
6T Greg Booker .01 .05
7T Thad Bosley .01 .05
8T Larry Bowa MG .02 .10
9T Greg Brock .01 .05
10T Bob Brower .01 .05
11T Jerry Browne .02 .10
12T Ralph Bryant .01 .05
13T DeWayne Buice .01 .05
14T Ellis Burks XRC .20 .50
15T Ivan Calderon .01 .05
16T Jeff Calhoun .01 .05
17T Casey Candaele .01 .05
18T John Cangelosi .01 .05
19T Steve Carlton .02 .10
20T Juan Castillo .02 .10
21T Rick Cerone .01 .05
22T Ron Cey .02 .10
23T John Christensen .01 .05
24T David Cone XRC .30 .75
25T Chuck Crim .01 .05
26T Storm Davis .01 .05
27T Andre Dawson .02 .10
28T Rick Dempsey .01 .05
29T Doug Drabek .20 .50
30T Mike Dunne .01 .05
31T Dennis Eckersley .05 .15
32T Lee Elia MG .01 .05
33T Brian Fisher .01 .05
34T Terry Francona .02 .10
35T Willie Fraser .02 .10
36T Billy Gardner MG .01 .05
37T Ken Gerhart .01 .05
38T Dan Gladden .01 .05
39T Jim Gott .01 .05
40T Cecilio Guante .01 .05
41T Albert Hall .01 .05
42T Terry Harper .01 .05
43T Mickey Hatcher .01 .05
44T Brad Havens .01 .05
45T Neal Heaton .01 .05
46T Mike Henneman XRC .08 .25
47T Donnie Hill .01 .05
48T Guy Hoffman .01 .05
49T Brian Holton .01 .05
50T Charles Hudson .01 .05
51T Danny Jackson .01 .05
52T Reggie Jackson .05 .15
53T Chris James XRC .02 .10
54T Dion James .01 .05
55T Stan Jefferson .01 .05
56T Joe Johnson .01 .05
57T Terry Kennedy .01 .05
58T Mike Kingery .02 .10
59T Ray Knight .02 .10
60T Gene Larkin XRC .08 .25
61T Mike LaValliere .08 .25
62T Jack Lazorko .01 .05
63T Terry Leach .01 .05
64T Tim Leary .01 .05
65T Jim Lindeman .02 .10
66T Steve Lombardozzi .01 .05
67T Bill Long .01 .05
68T Barry Lyons .01 .05
69T Shane Mack .01 .05
70T Greg Maddux XRC 2.00 5.00
71T Bill Madlock .02 .10
72T Joe Magrane XRC .02 .10
73T Dave Martinez XRC .08 .25
74T Fred McGriff .25 .60
75T Mark McLemore .02 .10
76T Kevin McReynolds .02 .10
77T Dave Meads .01 .05
78T Eddie Milner .01 .05
79T Greg Minton .01 .05
80T John Mitchell XRC .02 .10
81T Kevin Mitchell .05 .15
82T Charlie Moore .01 .05
83T Jeff Musselman .01 .05
84T Gene Nelson .01 .05
85T Graig Nettles .02 .10
86T Al Newman .01 .05
87T Reid Nichols .01 .05
88T Tom Niedenfuer .01 .05
89T Joe Niekro .01 .05
90T Tom Nieto .01 .05
91T Matt Nokes XRC .08 .25
92T Dickie Noles .01 .05
93T Pat Pacillo .01 .05
94T Lance Parrish .02 .10
95T Tony Pena .01 .05
96T Luis Polonia XRC .08 .25
97T Randy Ready .01 .05
98T Jeff Reardon .02 .10
99T Gary Redus .01 .05
100T Jeff Reed .01 .05
101T Rick Rhoden .01 .05
102T Cal Ripken Sr. MG .01 .05
103T Wally Ritchie .01 .05
104T Jeff M. Robinson .01 .05
105T Gary Roenicke .01 .05
106T Jerry Royster .01 .05
107T Mark Salas .01 .05
108T Luis Salazar .01 .05
109T Benny Santiago .02 .10
110T Dave Schmidt .01 .05
111T Kevin Seitzer XRC .08 .25
112T John Shelby .01 .05
113T Steve Shields .01 .05
114T John Smiley XRC .08 .25
115T Chris Speier .01 .05
116T Mike Stanley XRC .08 .25
117T Terry Steinbach XRC .20 .50
118T Les Straker .01 .05
119T Jim Sundberg .02 .10
120T Danny Tartabull .01 .05
121T Tom Trebelhorn MG .01 .05
122T Dave Valle XRC .02 .10
123T Ed VandeBerg .01 .05
124T Andy Van Slyke .05 .15
125T Gary Ward .01 .05
126T Alan Wiggins .01 .05
127T Bill Wilkinson .01 .05
128T Frank Williams .01 .05
129T Matt Williams XRC .40 1.00
130T Jim Winn .01 .05
131T Matt Young .01 .05
132T Checklist 1T-132T .01 .05

1987 Topps Traded Tiffany

Since the update Tiffany cards were issued in the same quantities as the regular cards, again these cards are not valued as high as a multiplier as the previous years. These 132 standard-size cards parallel the regular cards but have glossy fronts and easy to read backs. These cards were issued in factory set form only. These sets, believed to be issued in the range of 30,000, are among the easiest of the Tiffany sets to find in the secondary market.

COMP.FACT.SET (132) 15.00 40.00
*STARS: 2X TO 5X BASIC CARDS
*ROOKIES: 2X TO 5X BASIC CARDS
DISTRIBUTED ONLY IN FACTORY SET FORM
FACTORY SET PRICE IS FOR SEALED SETS

1988 Topps

This set consists of 792 standard-size cards. The cards were primarily issued in 15-card wax packs, 42-card rack packs and factory sets. Card fronts feature white borders encasing a color photo with team name running across the top and player name diagonally across the bottom. Subsets include Record Breakers (1-7), All-Stars (386-407), Turn Back the Clock (661-665), and Team Leaders (scattered throughout the set). The manager cards contain a team checklist on back. The key Rookie Cards in this set are Ellis Burks, Ken Caminiti, Tom Glavine, and Matt Williams.

COMPLETE SET (792) 6.00 15.00
COMP.FACT SET (792) 6.00 15.00
COMP.X-MAS.SET (792) 15.00 40.00
1 Vince Coleman RB .01 .05
2 Don Mattingly RB .10 .30
3 Mark McGwire RB .30 .75
Rookie Homer Record
(No white spot)
3A Mark McGwire RB .30 .75
Rookie Homer Record
(White spot behind
left foot)
4 Eddie Murray RB .05 .15
Switch Home Runs,
Two Straight Games
(No caption on front)
4A Eddie Murray RB .20 .50
Switch Home Runs,
Two Straight Games
(Caption in box
on card front)
5 Phil Niekro .02 .10
Joe Niekro RB
6 Nolan Ryan RB .15 .40
7 Benito Santiago RB .01 .05
8 Kevin Elster .01 .05
9 Andy Hawkins .01 .05
10 Ryne Sandberg .15 .40
11 Mike Young .01 .05
12 Bill Schroeder .01 .05
13 Andres Thomas .01 .05
14 Sparky Anderson MG .02 .10
15 Chili Davis .02 .10
16 Kirk McCaskill .01 .05
17 Ron Oester .01 .05
18A Al Leiter ERR .20 .50
(Photo actually
Steve George,
right ear visible)
18B Al Leiter RC .20 .50
(COR Left ear visible)
19 Mark Davidson .01 .05
20 Kevin Gross .01 .05
21 Wade Boggs .02 .10
Spike Owen TL
22 Greg Swindell .01 .05
23 Ken Landreaux .01 .05
24 Jim Deshaies .01 .05
25 Andres Galarraga .02 .10
26 Mitch Williams .01 .05
27 R.J. Reynolds .01 .05
28 Jose Nunez .01 .05
29 Angel Salazar .01 .05
30 Sid Fernandez .01 .05
31 Bruce Bochy .01 .05
32 Mike Morgan .01 .05
33 Rob Deer .01 .05
34 Ricky Horton .01 .05
35 Harold Baines .02 .10
36 Jamie Moyer .02 .10
37 Ed Romero .01 .05
38 Jeff Calhoun .01 .05
39 Gerald Perry .01 .05
40 Orel Hershiser .02 .10
41 Bob Melvin .01 .05
42 Bill Landrum .01 .05
43 Dick Schofield .01 .05
44 Lou Piniella MG .02 .10
45 Kent Hrbek .02 .10
46 Darnell Coles .01 .05
47 Joaquin Andujar .02 .10
48 Alan Ashby .01 .05
49 Dave Clark .01 .05
50 Hubie Brooks .01 .05
51 Eddie Murray .15 .40
Cal Ripken TL
52 Don Robinson .01 .05
53 Curt Wilkerson .01 .05
54 Jim Clancy .01 .05
55 Phil Bradley .01 .05
56 Ed Hearn .01 .05
57 Tim Crews RC .08 .25
58 Dave Magadan .01 .05
59 Danny Cox .01 .05
60 Rickey Henderson .07 .20
61 Mark Knudson .01 .05
62 Jeff Hamilton .01 .05
63 Jimmy Jones .01 .05
64 Ken Caminiti RC .75 2.00
65 Leon Durham .01 .05
66 Shane Rawley .01 .05
67 Ken Oberkfell .01 .05
68 Dave Dravecky .01 .05
69 Mike Hart .01 .05
70 Roger Clemens .40 1.00
71 Gary Pettis .01 .05
72 Dennis Eckersley .05 .15
73 Randy Bush .01 .05
74 Tom Lasorda MG .05 .15
75 Joe Carter .02 .10
76 Dennis Martinez .02 .10
77 Tom O'Malley .01 .05
78 Dan Petry .01 .05
79 Ernie Whitt .01 .05
80 Mark Langston .01 .05
81 Ron Robinson .01 .05
John Franco TL
82 Darrel Akerfelds .01 .05
83 Jose Oquendo .01 .05
84 Cecilio Guante .01 .05
85 Howard Johnson .02 .10
86 Ron Karkovice .01 .05
87 Mike Mason .01 .05
88 Earnie Riles .01 .05
89 Gary Thurman .01 .05
90 Dale Murphy .05 .15
91 Joey Cora RC .08 .25
92 Len Matuszek .01 .05
93 Bob Sebra .01 .05
94 Chuck Jackson .01 .05
95 Lance Parrish .02 .10
96 Todd Benzinger RC .08 .25
97 Scott Garrelts .01 .05
98 Rene Gonzales RC .02 .10
99 Chuck Finley .02 .10
100 Jack Clark .02 .10
101 Allan Anderson .01 .05
102 Barry Larkin .05 .15
103 Curt Young .01 .05
104 Dick Williams MG .01 .05
105 Jesse Orosco .01 .05
106 Jim Walewander .01 .05
107 Scott Bailes .01 .05
108 Steve Lyons .01 .05
109 Joel Skinner .01 .05
110 Teddy Higuera .01 .05
111 Hubie Brooks .01 .05
Vance Law TL
112 Les Lancaster .01 .05
113 Kelly Gruber .01 .05
114 Jeff Russell .01 .05
115 Johnny Ray .01 .05
116 Jerry Don Gleaton .01 .05
117 James Steels .01 .05
118 Bob Welch .02 .10
119 Robbie Wine .01 .05
120 Kirby Puckett .07 .20
121 Checklist 1-132 .01 .05
122 Tony Bernazard .01 .05
123 Tom Candiotti .01 .05
124 Ray Knight .02 .10
125 Bruce Hurst .01 .05
126 Steve Jeltz .01 .05
127 Jim Gott .01 .05
128 Johnny Grubb .01 .05
129 Greg Minton .01 .05
130 Buddy Bell .02 .10
131 Don Schulze .01 .05
132 Donnie Hill .01 .05
133 Greg Mathews .01 .05
134 Chuck Tanner MG .01 .05
135 Dennis Rasmussen .01 .05
136 Brian Dayett .01 .05
137 Chris Bosio .01 .05
138 Mitch Webster .01 .05
139 Jerry Browne .01 .05
140 Jesse Barfield .02 .10
141 George Brett .07 .20
Bret Saberhagen TL
142 Andy Van Slyke .05 .15
143 Mickey Tettleton .01 .05
144 Don Gordon .01 .05
145 Bill Madlock .02 .10
146 Donell Nixon .01 .05
147 Bill Buckner .02 .10
148 Carmelo Martinez .01 .05
149 Ken Howell .01 .05
150 Eric Davis .02 .10
151 Bob Knepper .01 .05
152 Jody Reed RC .08 .25
153 John Habyan .01 .05
154 Jeff Stone .01 .05
155 Bruce Sutter .02 .10
156 Gary Matthews .02 .10
157 Atlee Hammaker .01 .05
158 Tim Hulett .01 .05
159 Brad Arnsberg .01 .05
160 Willie McGee .02 .10
161 Bryn Smith .01 .05
162 Mark McLemore .01 .05
163 Dale Mohorcic .01 .05
164 Dave Johnson MG .01 .05
165 Robin Yount .10 .30
166 Rick Rodriquez .01 .05
167 Rance Mulliniks .01 .05
168 Barry Jones .01 .05
169 Ross Jones .01 .05
170 Rich Gossage .02 .10
171 Shawon Dunston .01 .05
Manny Trillo TL
172 Lloyd McClendon RC .08 .25
173 Eric Plunk .01 .05
174 Phil Garner .02 .10
175 Kevin Bass .01 .05
176 Jeff Reed .01 .05
177 Frank Tanana .02 .10
178 Dwayne Henry .01 .05
179 Charlie Puleo .01 .05
180 Terry Kennedy .01 .05
181 David Cone .02 .10
182 Ken Phelps .01 .05
183 Tom Lawless .01 .05
184 Ivan Calderon .01 .05
185 Rick Rhoden .01 .05
186 Rafael Palmeiro .15 .40
187 Steve Kiefer .01 .05
188 John Russell .01 .05
189 Wes Gardner .01 .05
190 Candy Maldonado .01 .05
191 John Cerutti .01 .05
192 Devon White .02 .10
193 Brian Fisher .01 .05
194 Tom Kelly MG .01 .05
195 Dan Quisenberry .01 .05
196 Dave Engle .01 .05
197 Lance McCullers .01 .05
198 Franklin Stubbs .01 .05
199 Dave Meads .01 .05
200 Wade Boggs .05 .15
201 Bobby Valentine MG .01 .05
Pete O'Brien
Pete Incaviglia
Steve Buechele TL
202 Glenn Hoffman .01 .05
203 Fred Toliver .01 .05
204 Paul O'Neill .05 .15
205 Nelson Liriano .01 .05
206 Domingo Ramos .01 .05
207 John Mitchell RC .02 .10
208 Steve Lake .01 .05
209 Richard Dotson .01 .05
210 Willie Randolph .02 .10
211 Frank DiPino .01 .05
212 Greg Brock .01 .05
213 Albert Hall .01 .05
214 Dave Schmidt .01 .05
215 Von Hayes .01 .05
216 Jerry Reuss .01 .05
217 Harry Spilman .01 .05
218 Dan Schatzeder .01 .05
219 Mike Stanley .01 .05
220 Tom Henke .01 .05
221 Rafael Belliard .01 .05
222 Steve Farr .01 .05
223 Stan Jefferson .01 .05
224 Tom Trebelhorn MG .01 .05
225 Mike Scioscia .02 .10
226 Dave Lopes .02 .10
227 Ed Correa .01 .05
228 Wallace Johnson .01 .05
229 Jeff Musselman .01 .05
230 Pat Tabler .01 .05
231 Barry Bonds .40 1.00
Bobby Bonilla TL
232 Bob James .01 .05
233 Rafael Santana .01 .05
234 Ken Dayley .01 .05
235 Gary Ward .01 .05
236 Ted Power .01 .05
237 Mike Heath .01 .05
238 Luis Polonia RC .08 .25
239 Roy Smalley .01 .05
240 Lee Smith .02 .10
241 Damaso Garcia .01 .05
242 Tom Niedenfuer .01 .05
243 Mark Ryal .01 .05
244 Jeff D. Robinson .01 .05
245 Rich Gedman .01 .05
246 Mike Campbell .01 .05
247 Thad Bosley .01 .05
248 Storm Davis .01 .05
249 Mike Marshall .01 .05
250 Nolan Ryan .40 1.00
251 Tom Foley .01 .05
252 Bob Brower .01 .05
253 Checklist 133-264 .01 .05
254 Lee Elia MG .01 .05
255 Mookie Wilson .02 .10
256 Ken Schrom .01 .05
257 Jerry Royster .01 .05
258 Ed Nunez .01 .05
259 Ron Kittle .01 .05
260 Vince Coleman .01 .05
261 Giants TL .01 .05
(Five players)
262 Drew Hall .01 .05
263 Glenn Braggs .01 .05
264 Les Straker .01 .05
265 Bo Diaz .01 .05
266 Paul Assenmacher .01 .05
267 Billy Bean RC .02 .10
268 Bruce Ruffin .01 .05
269 Ellis Burks RC .15 .40
270 Mike Witt .01 .05
271 Ken Gerhart .01 .05
272 Steve Ontiveros .01 .05
273 Garth Iorg .01 .05
274 Junior Ortiz .01 .05
275 Kevin Seitzer .01 .05
276 Luis Salazar .01 .05
277 Alejandro Pena .01 .05
278 Jose Cruz .02 .10
279 Randy St.Claire .01 .05
280 Pete Incaviglia .01 .05
281 Jerry Hairston .01 .05
282 Pat Perry .01 .05
283 Phil Lombardi .01 .05
284 Larry Bowa MG .02 .10
285 Jim Presley .01 .05
286 Chuck Crim .01 .05
287 Manny Trillo .01 .05
288 Pat Pacillo .01 .05
289 Dave Bergman .01 .05
290 Tony Fernandez .01 .05
291 Billy Hatcher .01 .05
Kevin Bass TL
292 Carney Lansford .02 .10
293 Doug Jones RC .08 .25
294 Al Pedrique .01 .05
295 Bert Blyleven .02 .10
296 Floyd Rayford .01 .05
297 Zane Smith .01 .05
298 Milt Thompson .01 .05
299 Steve Crawford .01 .05
300 Don Mattingly .25 .60
301 Bud Black .01 .05
302 Jose Uribe .01 .05
303 Eric Show .01 .05
304 George Hendrick .02 .10
305 Steve Sax .01 .05
306 Billy Hatcher .01 .05
307 Mike Trujillo .01 .05
308 Lee Mazzilli .02 .10
309 Bill Long .01 .05
310 Tom Herr .01 .05
311 Scott Sanderson .01 .05
312 Joey Meyer .01 .05
313 Bob McClure .01 .05
314 Jimy Williams MG .01 .05
315 Dave Parker .02 .10
316 Jose Rijo .02 .10
317 Tom Nieto .01 .05
318 Mel Hall .01 .05
319 Mike Loynd .01 .05
320 Alan Trammell .02 .10
321 Harold Baines .02 .10
Carlton Fisk TL
322 Vicente Palacios .01 .05
323 Rick Leach .01 .05
324 Danny Jackson .01 .05
325 Glenn Hubbard .01 .05
326 Al Nipper .01 .05
327 Larry Sheets .01 .05
328 Greg Cadaret .01 .05
329 Chris Speier .01 .05
330 Eddie Whitson .01 .05
331 Brian Downing .02 .10
332 Jerry Reed .01 .05
333 Wally Backman .01 .05
334 Dave LaPoint .01 .05
335 Claudell Washington .01 .05
336 Ed Lynch .01 .05
337 Jim Gantner .01 .05
338 Brian Holton UER .01 .05
1987 ERA .389,
should be 3.89
339 Kurt Stillwell .01 .05
340 Jack Morris .02 .10
341 Carmen Castillo .01 .05
342 Larry Andersen .01 .05
343 Greg Gagne .01 .05
344 Tony LaRussa MG .02 .10
345 Scott Fletcher .01 .05
346 Vance Law .01 .05
347 Joe Johnson .01 .05
348 Jim Eisenreich .01 .05
349 Bob Walk .01 .05
350 Will Clark .07 .20
351 Red Schoendienst CO .02 .10
Tony Pena TL
352 Bill Ripken RC .01 .05
353 Ed Olwine .01 .05
354 Marc Sullivan .01 .05
355 Roger McDowell .01 .05
356 Luis Aguayo .01 .05
357 Floyd Bannister .01 .05
358 Rey Quinones .01 .05
359 Tim Stoddard .01 .05
360 Tony Gwynn .10 .30
361 Greg Maddux .40 1.00
362 Juan Castillo .01 .05
363 Willie Fraser .01 .05
364 Nick Esasky .01 .05
365 Floyd Youmans .01 .05
366 Chet Lemon .02 .10
367 Tim Leary .01 .05
368 Gerald Young .01 .05
369 Greg Harris .01 .05
370 Jose Canseco .20 .50
371 Joe Hesketh .01 .05
372 Matt Williams RC .30 .75
373 Checklist 265-396 .01 .05
374 Doc Edwards MG .01 .05
375 Tom Brunansky .01 .05
376 Bill Wilkinson .01 .05
377 Sam Horn RC .02 .10
378 Todd Frohwirth .01 .05
379 Rafael Ramirez .01 .05
380 Joe Magrane RC .01 .05
381 Wally Joyner .02 .10
Jack Howell TL
382 Keith A. Miller RC .08 .25
383 Eric Bell .01 .05
384 Neil Allen .01 .05
385 Carlton Fisk .05 .15
386 Don Mattingly AS .10 .30
387 Willie Randolph AS .01 .05
388 Wade Boggs AS .02 .10
389 Alan Trammell AS .01 .05
390 George Bell AS .01 .05
391 Kirby Puckett AS .05 .15
392 Dave Winfield AS .01 .05
393 Matt Nokes AS .01 .05
394 Roger Clemens AS .20 .50
395 Jimmy Key AS .01 .05
396 Tom Henke AS .01 .05
397 Jack Clark AS .01 .05
398 Juan Samuel AS .01 .05
399 Tim Wallach AS .01 .05
400 Ozzie Smith AS .07 .20
401 Andre Dawson AS .01 .05
402 Tony Gwynn AS .05 .15
403 Tim Raines AS .01 .05
404 Benny Santiago AS .01 .05
405 Dwight Gooden AS .01 .05
406 Shane Rawley AS .01 .05
407 Steve Bedrosian AS .01 .05
408 Dion James .01 .05
409 Joel McKeon .01 .05
410 Tony Pena .01 .05
411 Wayne Tolleson .01 .05
412 Randy Myers .02 .10
413 John Christensen .01 .05
414 John McNamara MG .01 .05
415 Don Carman .01 .05
416 Keith Moreland .01 .05
417 Mark Ciardi .01 .05
418 Joel Youngblood .01 .05
419 Scott McGregor .01 .05
420 Wally Joyner .02 .10
421 Ed VandeBerg .01 .05
422 Dave Concepcion .02 .10
423 John Smiley RC .08 .25
424 Dwayne Murphy .01 .05
425 Jeff Reardon .02 .10
426 Randy Ready .01 .05
427 Paul Kilgus .01 .05
428 John Shelby .01 .05
429 Alan Trammell .02 .10
Kirk Gibson TL
430 Glenn Davis .01 .05
431 Casey Candaele .01 .05
432 Mike Moore .01 .05
433 Bill Pecota RC .01 .05
434 Rick Aguilera .01 .05
435 Mike Pagliarulo .01 .05
436 Mike Bielecki .01 .05
437 Fred Manrique .01 .05
438 Rob Ducey .01 .05
439 Dave Martinez .01 .05
440 Steve Bedrosian .01 .05
441 Rick Manning .01 .05
442 Tom Bolton .01 .05
443 Ken Griffey .02 .10
444 C.Ripken Sr. MG UER .01 .05
two copyrights
445 Mike Krukow .01 .05
446 Doug DeCinces .01 .05
(Now with Cardinals
on card front)
447 Jeff Montgomery RC .08 .25
448 Mike Davis .01 .05
449 Jeff M. Robinson .01 .05
450 Barry Bonds .75 2.00
451 Keith Atherton .01 .05
452 Willie Wilson .02 .10
453 Dennis Powell .01 .05
454 Marvell Wynne .01 .05
455 Shawn Hillegas .01 .05
456 Dave Anderson .01 .05
457 Terry Leach .01 .05
458 Ron Hassey .01 .05
459 Dave Winfield .01 .05
Willie Randolph TL
460 Ozzie Smith .10 .30
461 Danny Darwin .01 .05
462 Don Slaught .01 .05
463 Fred McGriff .07 .20
464 Jay Tibbs .01 .05
465 Paul Molitor .02 .10
466 Jerry Mumphrey .01 .05
467 Don Aase .01 .05
468 Darren Daulton .02 .10
469 Jeff Dedmon .01 .05
470 Dwight Evans .05 .15
471 Donnie Moore .01 .05
472 Robby Thompson .01 .05
473 Joe Niekro .01 .05
474 Tom Brookens .01 .05
475 Pete Rose MG .20 .50
476 Dave Stewart .02 .10
477 Jamie Quirk .01 .05
478 Sid Bream .01 .05
479 Brett Butler .02 .10
480 Dwight Gooden .02 .10
481 Mariano Duncan .01 .05
482 Mark Davis .01 .05
483 Rod Booker .01 .05
484 Pat Clements .01 .05
485 Harold Reynolds .02 .10
486 Pat Keedy .01 .05
487 Jim Pankovits .01 .05
488 Andy McGaffigan .01 .05
489 Pedro Guerrero .01 .05
Fernando Valenzuela TL
490 Larry Parrish .01 .05
491 B.J. Surhoff .02 .10
492 Doyle Alexander .01 .05
493 Mike Greenwell .01 .05

494 Wally Ritchie .01 .05
495 Eddie Murray .07 .20
496 Guy Hoffman .01 .05
497 Kevin Mitchell .02 .10
498 Bob Boone .02 .10
499 Eric King .01 .05
500 Andre Dawson .02 .10
501 Tim Birtsas .01 .05
502 Dan Gladden .01 .05
503 Junior Noboa .01 .05
504 Bob Rodgers MG .01 .05
505 Willie Upshaw .01 .05
506 John Cangelosi .01 .05
507 Mark Gubicza .01 .05
508 Tim Teufel .01 .05
509 Bill Dawley .01 .05
510 Dave Winfield .02 .10
511 Joel Davis .01 .05
512 Alex Trevino .01 .05
513 Tim Flannery .01 .05
514 Pat Sheridan .01 .05
515 Juan Nieves .01 .05
516 Jim Sundberg .02 .10
517 Ron Robinson .01 .05
518 Greg Gross .01 .05
519 Harold Reynolds .01 .05
Phil Bradley TL
520 Dave Smith .01 .05
521 Jim Dwyer .01 .05
522 Bob Patterson .01 .05
523 Gary Roenicke .01 .05
524 Gary Lucas .01 .05
525 Marty Barrett .01 .05
526 Juan Berenguer .01 .05
527 Steve Henderson .01 .05
528A Checklist 397-528 .05 .15
ERR (455 S. Carlton)
528B Checklist 397-528 .02 .10
COR (455 S. Hillegas)
529 Tim Burke .01 .05
530 Gary Carter .02 .10
531 Rich Yett .01 .05
532 Mike Kingery .01 .05
533 John Farrell RC .02 .10
534 John Wathan MG .01 .05
535 Ron Guidry .02 .10
536 John Morris .01 .05
537 Steve Buechele .01 .05
538 Bill Wegman .01 .05
539 Mike LaValliere .01 .05
540 Bret Saberhagen .02 .10
541 Juan Beniquez .01 .05
542 Paul Noce .01 .05
543 Kent Tekulve .01 .05
544 Jim Traber .01 .05
545 Don Baylor .02 .10
546 John Candelaria .01 .05
547 Felix Fermin .01 .05
548 Shane Mack .01 .05
549 Albert Hall .02 .10
Dale Murphy
Ken Griffey
Dion James TL
550 Pedro Guerrero .02 .10
551 Terry Steinbach .02 .10
552 Mark Thurmond .01 .05
553 Tracy Jones .01 .05
554 Mike Smithson .01 .05
555 Brook Jacoby .01 .05
556 Stan Clarke .01 .05
557 Craig Reynolds .01 .05
558 Bob Ojeda .01 .05
559 Ken Williams RC .01 .05
560 Tim Wallach .01 .05
561 Rick Cerone .01 .05
562 Jim Lindeman .01 .05
563 Jose Guzman .01 .05
564 Frank Lucchesi MG .01 .05
565 Lloyd Moseby .01 .05
566 Charlie O'Brien .01 .05
567 Mike Diaz .01 .05
568 Chris Brown .01 .05
569 Charlie Leibrandt .01 .05
570 Jeffrey Leonard .01 .05
571 Mark Williamson .01 .05
572 Chris James .01 .05
573 Bob Stanley .01 .05
574 Graig Nettles .02 .10
575 Don Sutton .02 .10
576 Tommy Hinzo .01 .05
577 Tom Browning .01 .05
578 Gary Gaetti .02 .10
579 Gary Carter .01 .05
Kevin McReynolds TL
580 Mark McGwire .60 1.50
581 Tito Landrum .01 .05
582 Mike Henneman RC .08 .25
583 Dave Valle .01 .05
584 Steve Trout .01 .05
585 Ozzie Guillen .02 .10
586 Bob Forsch .01 .05
587 Terry Puhl .01 .05
588 Jeff Parrett .01 .05
589 Geno Petralli .01 .05
590 George Bell .02 .10
591 Doug Drabek .01 .05
592 Dale Sveum .01 .05
593 Bob Tewksbury .01 .05
594 Bobby Valentine MG .02 .10
595 Frank White .02 .10
596 John Kruk .02 .10
597 Gene Garber .01 .05
598 Lee Lacy .01 .05
599 Calvin Schiraldi .01 .05
600 Mike Schmidt .20 .50
601 Jack Lazorko .01 .05
602 Mike Aldrete .01 .05
603 Rob Murphy .01 .05
604 Chris Bando .01 .05
605 Kirk Gibson .07 .20
606 Moose Haas .01 .05
607 Mickey Hatcher .01 .05
608 Charlie Kerfeld .01 .05
609 Gary Gaetti .02 .10
Kent Hrbek TL
610 Keith Hernandez .02 .10
611 Tommy John .02 .10
612 Curt Ford .01 .05
613 Bobby Thigpen .01 .05
614 Herm Winningham .01 .05
615 Jody Davis .01 .05
616 Jay Aldrich .01 .05
617 Oddibe McDowell .01 .05
618 Cecil Fielder .02 .10
619 Mike Dunne .01 .05
Inconsistent design;
black name on front
620 Cory Snyder .01 .05
621 Gene Nelson .01 .05
622 Kal Daniels .01 .05
623 Mike Flanagan .01 .05
624 Jim Leyland MG .02 .10
625 Frank Viola .02 .10
626 Glenn Wilson .01 .05
627 Joe Boever .01 .05
628 Dave Henderson .01 .05
629 Kelly Downs .01 .05
630 Darrell Evans .02 .10
631 Jack Howell .01 .05
632 Steve Shields .01 .05
633 Barry Lyons .01 .05
634 Jose DeLeon .01 .05
635 Terry Pendleton .02 .10
636 Charles Hudson .01 .05
637 Jay Bell RC .15 .40
638 Steve Balboni .01 .05
639 Glenn Braggs .01 .05
Tony Muser CO TL
640 Garry Templeton .02 .10
(Inconsistent design,
green border)
641 Rick Honeycutt .01 .05
642 Bob Dernier .01 .05
643 Rocky Childress .01 .05
644 Terry McGriff .01 .05
645 Matt Nokes RC .08 .25
646 Checklist 529-660 .01 .05
647 Pascual Perez .01 .05
648 Al Newman .01 .05
649 DeWayne Buice .01 .05
650 Cal Ripken .30 .75
651 Mike Jackson RC .08 .25
652 Bruce Benedict .01 .05
653 Jeff Sellers .01 .05
654 Roger Craig MG .02 .10
655 Len Dykstra .02 .10
656 Lee Guetterman .01 .05
657 Gary Redus .01 .05
658 Tim Conroy .01 .05
(Inconsistent design,
name in white)
659 Bobby Meacham .01 .05
660 Rick Reuschel .02 .10
661 Nolan Ryan TBC '83 .20 .50
662 Jim Rice TBC .02 .10
663 Ron Blomberg TBC .01 .05
664 Bob Gibson TBC '68 .08 .25
665 Stan Musial TBC '63 .07 .20
666 Mario Soto .02 .10
667 Luis Quinones .01 .05
668 Walt Terrell .01 .05
669 Lance Parrish .01 .05
Mike Ryan CO TL
670 Dan Plesac .01 .05
671 Tim Laudner .01 .05
672 John Davis .01 .05
673 Tony Phillips .01 .05
674 Mike Fitzgerald .01 .05
675 Jim Rice .02 .10
676 Ken Dixon .01 .05
677 Eddie Milner .01 .05
678 Jim Acker .01 .05
679 Darrell Miller .01 .05
680 Charlie Hough .02 .10
681 Bobby Bonilla .02 .10
682 Jimmy Key .02 .10
683 Julio Franco .02 .10
684 Hal Lanier MG .01 .05
685 Ron Darling .02 .10
686 Terry Francona .02 .10
687 Mickey Brantley .01 .05
688 Jim Winn .01 .05
689 Tom Pagnozzi RC .02 .10
690 Jay Howell .01 .05
691 Dan Pasqua .01 .05
692 Mike Birkbeck .01 .05
693 Benito Santiago .02 .10
694 Eric Nolte .01 .05
695 Shawon Dunston .01 .05
696 Duane Ward .01 .05
697 Steve Lombardozzi .01 .05
698 Brad Havens .01 .05
699 Benito Santiago .02 .10
Tony Gwynn TL
700 George Brett .20 .50
701 Sammy Stewart .01 .05
702 Mike Gallego .01 .05
703 Bob Brenly .01 .05
704 Dennis Boyd .01 .05
705 Juan Samuel .01 .05
706 Rick Mahler .01 .05
707 Fred Lynn .02 .10
708 Gus Polidor .01 .05
709 George Frazier .01 .05
710 Darryl Strawberry .02 .10
711 Bill Gullickson .01 .05
712 John Moses .01 .05
713 Willie Hernandez .01 .05
714 Jim Fregosi MG .01 .05
715 Todd Worrell .01 .05
716 Lenn Sakata .01 .05
717 Jay Baller .01 .05
718 Mike Felder .01 .05
719 Denny Walling .01 .05
720 Tim Raines .02 .10
721 Pete O'Brien .01 .05
722 Manny Lee .01 .05
723 Bob Kipper .01 .05
724 Danny Tartabull .01 .05
725 Mike Boddicker .01 .05
726 Alfredo Griffin .01 .05
727 Greg Booker .01 .05
728 Andy Allanson .01 .05
729 George Bell .02 .10
Fred McGriff TL
730 John Franco .02 .10
731 Rick Schu .01 .05
732 David Palmer .01 .05
733 Spike Owen .01 .05
734 Craig Lefferts .01 .05
735 Kevin McReynolds .01 .05
736 Matt Young .01 .05
737 Butch Wynegar .01 .05
738 Scott Bankhead .01 .05
739 Daryl Boston .01 .05
740 Rick Sutcliffe .02 .10
741 Mike Easler .01 .05
742 Mark Clear .01 .05
743 Larry Herndon .01 .05
744 Whitey Herzog MG .02 .10
745 Bill Doran .01 .05
746 Gene Larkin RC .08 .25
747 Bobby Witt .01 .05
748 Reid Nichols .01 .05
749 Mark Eichhorn .01 .05
750 Bo Jackson .07 .20
751 Jim Morrison .01 .05
752 Mark Grant .01 .05
753 Danny Heep .01 .05
754 Mike LaCoss .01 .05
755 Ozzie Virgil .01 .05
756 Mike Maddux .01 .05
757 John Marzano .01 .05
758 Eddie Williams RC .02 .10
759 Mark McGwire .40 1.00
Jose Canseco TL UER
(two copyrights)
760 Mike Scott .02 .10
761 Tony Armas .02 .10
762 Scott Bradley .01 .05
763 Doug Sisk .01 .05
764 Greg Walker .01 .05
765 Neal Heaton .01 .05
766 Henry Cotto .01 .05
767 Jose Lind RC .08 .25
768 Dickie Noles .01 .05
(Now with Tigers
on card front)
769 Cecil Cooper .02 .10
770 Lou Whitaker .02 .10
771 Ruben Sierra .02 .10
772 Sal Butera .01 .05
773 Frank Williams .01 .05
774 Gene Mauch MG .01 .05
775 Dave Stieb .02 .10
776 Checklist 661-792 .01 .05
777 Lonnie Smith .01 .05
778A Keith Comstock ERR .75 2.00
(White Padres)
778B Keith Comstock COR .01 .05
(Blue Padres)
779 Tom Glavine RC 1.00 2.50
780 Fernando Valenzuela .02 .10
781 Keith Hughes .01 .05
782 Jeff Ballard .01 .05
783 Ron Roenicke .01 .05
784 Joe Sambito .01 .05
785 Alvin Davis .01 .05
786 Joe Price .01 .05
Inconsistent design,
orange team name
787 Bill Almon .01 .05
788 Ray Searage .01 .05
789 Joe Carter .01 .05
Cory Snyder TL
790 Dave Righetti .02 .10
791 Ted Simmons .02 .10
792 John Tudor .02 .10

1988 Topps Tiffany

This was the fifth year that Topps issued a "Tiffany" set. These 792 standard-size cards parallel the regular Topps cards. These cards were issued in factory set form only, produced in Topps Irish facility, and only available through Topps hobby dealers. These cards were again produced in relatively large quantities and the mulitplier value is reduced compared to pre-1987 levels. It is believed that as many as 25,000 of these sets were produced.

COMP.FACT.SET (792) 40.00 80.00
*STARS: 4X TO 10X BASIC CARDS
*ROOKIES: 3X TO 8X BASIC CARDS
DISTRIBUTED ONLY IN FACTORY SET FORM
FACTORY SET PRICE IS FOR SEALED SETS

1988 Topps Glossy All-Stars

This set of 22 glossy cards was inserted one per rack pack. Players selected for the set are the starting players (plus manager and honorary captain) in the 1987 All-Star Game in Oakland. Cards measure the standard size and the backs feature red and blue printing on a white card stock.

COMPLETE SET (22) 1.60 4.00
1 John McNamara MG .01 .05
2 Don Mattingly .40 1.00
3 Willie Randolph .02 .10
4 Wade Boggs .20 .50
5 Cal Ripken .75 2.00
6 George Bell .01 .05
7 Rickey Henderson .30 .75
8 Dave Winfield .15 .40
9 Terry Kennedy .01 .05
10 Bret Saberhagen .02 .10
11 Jim Hunter CAPT .08 .25
12 Dave Johnson MG .02 .10
13 Jack Clark .02 .10
14 Ryne Sandberg .40 1.00
15 Mike Schmidt .20 .50
16 Ozzie Smith .40 1.00
17 Eric Davis .02 .10
18 Andre Dawson .07 .20
19 Darryl Strawberry .02 .10
20 Gary Carter .15 .40
21 Mike Scott .01 .05
22 Billy Williams CAPT .08 .25

1988 Topps Glossy Send-Ins

Topps issued this set through a mail-in offer explained and advertised on the wax packs. This 60-card set features glossy fronts with each card measuring the standard size. The offer provided your choice of any one of the six 10-card subsets (1-10, 11-20, etc.) for 1.25 plus six of the Special Offer ("Spring Fever Baseball") insert cards, which were found one per wax pack. One complete set was obtainable by sending 7.50 plus 18 special offer cards. The last two players (numerically) in each ten-card subset are actually "Hot Prospects."

COMPLETE SET (60) 4.00 10.00
1 Andre Dawson .15 .40
2 Jesse Barfield .02 .10
3 Mike Schmidt .40 1.00
4 Ruben Sierra .07 .20
5 Mike Scott .02 .10
6 Cal Ripken 1.50 4.00
7 Gary Carter .30 .75
8 Kent Hrbek .07 .20
9 Kevin Seitzer .02 .10
10 Mike Henneman .07 .20
11 Don Mattingly .75 2.00
12 Tim Raines .07 .20
13 Roger Clemens .75 2.00
14 Ryne Sandberg .60 1.50
15 Tony Fernandez .07 .20
16 Eric Davis .07 .20
17 Jack Morris .07 .20
18 Tim Wallach .02 .10
19 Mike Dunne .02 .10
20 Mike Greenwell .07 .20
21 Dwight Evans .07 .20
22 Darryl Strawberry .07 .20
23 Cory Snyder .02 .10
24 Pedro Guerrero .02 .10
25 Rickey Henderson .40 1.25
26 Dale Murphy .15 .40
27 Kirby Puckett .40 1.00
28 Steve Bedrosian .02 .10
29 Devon White .07 .20
30 Benito Santiago .07 .20
31 George Bell .02 .10
32 Keith Hernandez .07 .20
33 Dave Stewart .07 .20
34 Dave Parker .07 .20
35 Tom Henke .02 .10
36 Willie McGee .07 .20
37 Alan Trammell .10 .30
38 Tony Gwynn .75 2.00
39 Mark McGwire .75 2.00
40 Joe Magrane .02 .10
41 Jack Clark .07 .20
42 Willie Randolph .07 .20
43 Juan Samuel .02 .10
44 Joe Carter .10 .30
45 Shane Rawley .02 .10
46 Dave Winfield .20 .50
47 Ozzie Smith .75 2.00
48 Wally Joyner .07 .20
49 B.J. Surhoff .07 .20
50 Ellis Burks .30 .75
51 Wade Boggs .30 .75
52 Howard Johnson .02 .10
53 George Brett .75 2.00
54 Dwight Gooden .07 .20
55 Jose Canseco .40 1.00
56 Lee Smith .07 .20
57 Paul Molitor .30 .75
58 Andres Galarraga .15 .40
59 Matt Nokes .02 .10
60 Casey Candaele .02 .10

1988 Topps Rookies

Inserted in each supermarket jumbo pack is a card from this series of 22 of 1987's best rookies as determined by Topps. Jumbo packs consisted of 100 (regular issue 1988 Topps baseball) cards with a stick of gum plus the insert "Rookie" card.

The card fronts are in full color and measure the standard size. The card backs are printed in red and blue on white card stock and are numbered at the bottom.

COMPLETE SET (22) 12.50 25.00
ONE PER RETAIL JUMBO PACK
1 Bill Ripken .08 .25
2 Ellis Burks .40 1.00
3 Mike Greenwell .08 .25
4 DeWayne Buice .08 .25
5 Devon White .20 .50
6 Fred Manrique .08 .25
7 Mike Henneman .20 .50
8 Matt Nokes .08 .25
9 Kevin Seitzer .20 .50
10 B.J. Surhoff .20 .50
11 Casey Candaele .08 .25
12 Randy Myers .30 .75
13 Mark McGwire 6.00 15.00
14 Luis Polonia .08 .25
15 Terry Steinbach .20 .50
16 Mike Dunne .08 .25
17 Al Pedrique .08 .25
18 Benito Santiago .20 .50
19 Kelly Downs .08 .25
20 Joe Magrane .08 .25
21 Jerry Browne .08 .25
22 Jeff Musselman .08 .25

1988 Topps Wax Box Cards

The cards in this 16-card set measure the standard size. Cards have essentially the same design as the 1988 Topps regular issue set. The cards were printed on the bottoms of the regular issue wax pack boxes. These 16 cards, "lettered" A through P, are considered a separate set in their own right and are not typically included in a complete set of the regular issue 1988 Topps cards. The value of the panels uncut is slightly greater, perhaps by 25 percent greater, than the value of the individual cards cut up carefully. The card lettering is sequenced alphabetically by player's name.

COMPLETE SET (16) 2.00 5.00
A Don Baylor .07 .20
B Steve Bedrosian .02 .10
C Juan Beniquez .02 .10
D Bob Boone .07 .20
E Darrell Evans .07 .20
F Tony Gwynn .50 1.25
G John Kruk .07 .20
H Marvell Wynne .02 .10
I Joe Carter .15 .40
J Eric Davis .07 .20
K Howard Johnson .07 .20
L Darryl Strawberry .07 .20
M Rickey Henderson .40 1.00
N Nolan Ryan 1.00 2.50
O Mike Schmidt .30 .75
P Kent Tekulve .02 .10

1988 Topps Traded

This standard-size 132-card Traded set was distributed exclusively in factory set form in blue and white taped boxes through hobby dealers. The cards are identical in style to the Topps regular issue except for whiter stock and t-suffixed numbering on back. Cards are ordered alphabetically by player's last name. This set generated additional interest upon release due to the inclusion of members of the 1988 U.S. Olympic baseball team. These Olympians are indicated in the checklist below by OLY. The key extended Rookie Cards in this set are Jim Abbott, Roberto Alomar, Brady Anderson, Andy Benes, Jay Buhner, Ron Gant, Mark Grace, Tino Martinez, Charles Nagy, Robin Ventura and Walt Weiss.

COMP.FACT.SET (132) 3.00 8.00
1T Jim Abbott OLY XRC .75 2.00
2T Juan Agosto .02 .10
3T Luis Alicea XRC .20 .50
4T Roberto Alomar XRC .75 2.00
5T Brady Anderson XRC .30 .75
6T Jack Armstrong XRC .20 .50
7T Don August .02 .10
8T Floyd Bannister .02 .10
9T Bret Barberie OLY XRC .08 .25
10T Jose Bautista XRC .08 .25
11T Don Baylor .07 .20
12T Tim Belcher .02 .10
13T Buddy Bell .07 .20
14T Andy Benes OLY XRC .30 .75
15T Damon Berryhill XRC .20 .50
16T Bud Black .02 .10
17T Pat Borders XRC .20 .50
18T Phil Bradley .02 .10
19T Jeff Branson OLY XRC .20 .50
20T Tom Brunansky .02 .10
21T Jay Buhner XRC .40 1.00
22T Brett Butler .07 .20
23T Jim Campanis OLY XRC .02 .10
24T Sil Campusano .02 .10
25T John Candelaria .02 .10
26T Jose Cecena .02 .10
27T Rick Cerone .02 .10
28T Jack Clark .07 .20
29T Kevin Coffman .02 .10
30T Pat Combs OLY XRC .08 .25
31T Henry Cotto .02 .10
32T Chili Davis .07 .20
33T Mike Davis .02 .10
34T Jose DeLeon .02 .10
35T Richard Dotson .02 .10
36T Cecil Espy XRC .02 .10
37T Tom Filer .02 .10
38T Mike Fiore OLY .02 .10
39T Ron Gant XRC .30 .75
40T Kirk Gibson .20 .50
41T Rich Gossage .07 .20
42T Mark Grace XRC .75 2.00
43T Alfredo Griffin .02 .10
44T Ty Griffin OLY .02 .10
45T Bryan Harvey XRC .20 .50
46T Ron Hassey .02 .10
47T Ray Hayward .02 .10
48T Dave Henderson .02 .10
49T Tom Herr .02 .10
50T Bob Horner .07 .20
51T Ricky Horton .02 .10
52T Jay Howell .02 .10
53T Glenn Hubbard .02 .10
54T Jeff Innis .02 .10
55T Danny Jackson .02 .10
56T Darrin Jackson XRC .08 .25
57T Roberto Kelly XRC .20 .50
58T Ron Kittle .02 .10
59T Ray Knight .07 .20
60T Vance Law .02 .10
61T Jeffrey Leonard .02 .10
62T Mike Macfarlane XRC .20 .50
63T Scott Madison .02 .10
64T Kirt Manwaring .02 .10
65T M.Marquess OLY CO .02 .10
66T Tino Martinez OLY XRC 1.25 3.00
67T Billy Masse OLY XRC .08 .25
68T Jack McDowell XRC .30 .75
69T Jack McKeon MG .07 .20
70T Larry McWilliams .02 .10
71T Mickey Morandini OLY XRC .20 .50
72T Keith Moreland .02 .10
73T Mike Morgan .02 .10
74T Charles Nagy OLY XRC .20 .50
75T Al Nipper .02 .10
76T Russ Nixon MG .02 .10
77T Jesse Orosco .02 .10
78T Joe Orsulak .02 .10
79T Dave Palmer .02 .10
80T Mark Parent .02 .10
81T Dave Parker .07 .20
82T Dan Pasqua .02 .10
83T Melido Perez XRC .20 .50
84T Steve Peters .02 .10
85T Dan Petry .02 .10
86T Gary Pettis .02 .10
87T Jeff Pico .02 .10
88T Jim Poole OLY XRC .08 .25
89T Ted Power .02 .10
90T Rafael Ramirez .02 .10
91T Dennis Rasmussen .02 .10
92T Jose Rijo .07 .20
93T Ernie Riles .02 .10
94T Luis Rivera .02 .10
95T Doug Robbins OLY XRC .08 .25
96T Frank Robinson MG .10 .30
97T Cookie Rojas MG .02 .10
98T Chris Sabo XRC .30 .75
99T Mark Salas .02 .10
100T Luis Salazar .02 .10
101T Rafael Santana .02 .10
102T Nelson Santovenia .02 .10
103T Mackey Sasser XRC .20 .50
104T Calvin Schiraldi .02 .10
105T Mike Schooler .02 .10
106T Scott Servais OLY XRC .20 .50
107T Dave Silvestri OLY XRC .08 .25
108T Don Slaught .02 .10
109T Jeff Slusarski OLY XRC .08 .25
110T Lee Smith .07 .20
111T Pete Smith XRC .08 .25
112T Jim Snyder MG .02 .10
113T Ed Sprague OLY XRC .20 .50
114T Pete Stanicek .02 .10
115T Kurt Stillwell .02 .10
116T Todd Stottlemyre XRC .20 .50
117T Bill Swift .02 .10
118T Pat Tabler .02 .10
119T Scott Terry .02 .10
120T Mickey Tettleton .02 .10
121T Dickie Thon .02 .10
122T Jeff Treadway XRC .20 .50
123T Willie Upshaw .02 .10
124T Robin Ventura OLY XRC .60 1.50
125T Ron Washington .02 .10
126T Walt Weiss XRC .30 .75
127T Bob Welch .07 .20
128T David Wells XRC .60 1.50
129T Glenn Wilson .02 .10
130T Ted Wood OLY XRC .08 .25
131T Don Zimmer MG .07 .20
132T Checklist 1T-132T .02 .10

1988 Topps Traded Tiffany

As a bonus for those dealers who ordered the regular Tiffany sets, they received an equivalent number of Tiffany update sets. These 132 standard-size cards parallel the regular traded issue. Again issued in the Topps Irish facility, these cards feature glossy fronts and easy to read backs. These sets were only issued in complete factory form.

COMP.FACT.SET (132) 15.00 40.00
*STARS: 1.5X TO 4X BASIC CARDS
*ROOKIES: 2.5X TO 6X BASIC CARDS
DISTRIBUTED ONLY IN FACTORY SET FORM
FACTORY SET PRICE IS FOR SEALED SETS
66T Tino Martinez OLY 4.00 10.00

1989 Topps

This set consists of 792 standard-size cards. Cards were primarily issued in 15-card wax packs, 42-card rack packs and factory sets. Subsets in the set include Record Breakers (1-7), Turn Back the Clock (661-665), All-Star selections (386-407) and First Draft Picks, Future Stars and Team Leaders (all scattered throughout the set). The manager cards contain a team checklist on back. The key Rookie Cards in this set are Jim Abbott, Sandy Alomar Jr., Brady Anderson, Steve Avery, Andy Benes, Dante Bichette, Craig Biggio, Randy Johnson, Ramon Martinez, Gary Sheffield, John Smoltz, and Robin Ventura.

COMPLETE SET (792) 8.00 20.00
COMP.FACT.SET (792) 10.00 25.00
COMP.X-MAS.SET (792) 10.00 25.00
FS SUBSET VARIATIONS EXIST
FS PHOTOS ARE PLACED HIGHER/LOWER
1 George Bell RB .01 .05
Slams 3 HR on
Opening Day
2 Wade Boggs RB .02 .10
3 Gary Carter RB .01 .05
Sets Record for
Career Putouts
4 Andre Dawson RB .01 .05
Logs Double Figures
in HR and SB
5 Orel Hershiser RB .01 .05
Pitches 59
Scoreless Innings
6 Doug Jones RB UER .01 .05
Earns His 15th
Straight Save

Photo actually Chris Codiroli
7 Kevin McReynolds RB .01 .05
Steals 21 Without
Being Caught
8 Dave Eiland .01 .05
9 Tim Teufel .01 .05
10 Andre Dawson .02 .10
11 Bruce Sutter .02 .10
12 Dale Sveum .01 .05
13 Doug Sisk .01 .05
14 Tom Kelly MG .01 .05
15 Robby Thompson .01 .05
16 Ron Robinson .01 .05
17 Brian Downing .02 .10
18 Rick Rhoden .01 .05
19 Greg Gagne .01 .05
20 Steve Bedrosian .01 .05
21 Greg Walker TL .01 .05
22 Tim Crews .01 .05
23 Mike Fitzgerald .01 .05
24 Larry Andersen .01 .05
25 Frank White .02 .10
26 Dale Mohorcic .01 .05
27A Orestes Destrade .02 .10
(F* next to copyright) RC
27B Orestes Destrade .02 .10
(E*F* next to
copyright) VAR
28 Mike Moore .01 .05
29 Kelly Gruber .01 .05
30 Dwight Gooden .02 .10
31 Terry Francona .02 .10
32 Dennis Rasmussen .01 .05
33 B.J. Surhoff .02 .10
34 Ken Williams .01 .05
35 John Tudor UER .02 .10
(With Red Sox in '84,should be Pirates)
36 Mitch Webster .01 .05
37 Bob Stanley .01 .05

38 Paul Runge .01 .05
39 Mike Maddux .01 .05
40 Steve Sax .01 .05
41 Terry Mulholland .01 .05
42 Jim Eppard .01 .05
43 Guillermo Hernandez .01 .05
44 Jim Snyder MG .01 .05
45 Kal Daniels .01 .05
46 Mark Portugal .01 .05
47 Carney Lansford .02 .10
48 Tim Burke .01 .05
49 Craig Biggio RC 1.25 3.00
50 George Bell .02 .10
51 Mark McLemore TL .01 .05
52 Bob Brenly .01 .05
53 Ruben Sierra .02 .10
54 Steve Trout .01 .05
55 Julio Franco .02 .10
56 Pat Tabler .01 .05
57 Alejandro Pena .01 .05
58 Lee Mazzilli .02 .10
59 Mark Davis .01 .05
60 Tom Brunansky .01 .05
61 Neil Allen .01 .05
62 Alfredo Griffin .01 .05
63 Mark Clear .01 .05
64 Alex Trevino .01 .05
65 Rick Reuschel .02 .10
66 Manny Trillo .01 .05
67 Dave Palmer .01 .05
68 Darrell Miller .01 .05
69 Jeff Ballard .01 .05
70 Mark McGwire .40 1.00
71 Mike Boddicker .01 .05
72 John Moses .01 .05
73 Pascual Perez .01 .05
74 Nick Leyva MG .01 .05
75 Tom Henke .01 .05
76 Terry Blocker .01 .05
77 Doyle Alexander .01 .05
78 Jim Sundberg .02 .10
79 Scott Bankhead .01 .05
80 Cory Snyder .01 .05
81 Tim Raines TL .01 .05
82 Dave Leiper .01 .05
83 Jeff Blauser .01 .05
84 Bill Bene FDP .01 .05
85 Kevin McReynolds .01 .05
86 Al Nipper .01 .05
87 Larry Owen .01 .05
88 Darryl Hamilton RC .08 .25
89 Dave LaPoint .01 .05
90 Vince Coleman UER .01 .05
(Wrong birth year)
91 Floyd Youmans .01 .05
92 Jeff Kunkel .01 .05
93 Ken Howell .01 .05
94 Chris Speier .01 .05
95 Gerald Young .01 .05
96 Rick Cerone .01 .05
97 Greg Mathews .01 .05
98 Larry Sheets .01 .05
99 Sherman Corbett .01 .05
100 Mike Schmidt .20 .50
101 Les Straker .01 .05
102 Mike Gallego .01 .05
103 Tim Birtsas .01 .05
104 Dallas Green MG .01 .05
105 Ron Darling .02 .10
106 Willie Upshaw .01 .05
107 Jose DeLeon .01 .05
108 Fred Manrique .01 .05
109 Hipolito Pena .01 .05
110 Paul Molitor .02 .10
111 Eric Davis TL .01 .05
112 Jim Presley .01 .05
113 Lloyd Moseby .01 .05
114 Bob Kipper .01 .05
115 Jody Davis .01 .05
116 Jeff Montgomery .01 .05
117 Dave Anderson .01 .05
118 Checklist 1-132 .01 .05
119 Terry Puhl .01 .05
120 Frank Viola .02 .10
121 Garry Templeton .02 .10
122 Lance Johnson .01 .05
123 Spike Owen .01 .05
124 Jim Traber .01 .05
125 Mike Krukow .01 .05
126 Sid Bream .01 .05
127 Walt Terrell .01 .05
128 Milt Thompson .01 .05
129 Terry Clark .01 .05
130 Gerald Perry .01 .05
131 Dave Otto .01 .05
132 Curt Ford .01 .05
133 Bill Long .01 .05
134 Don Zimmer MG .02 .10
135 Jose Rijo .02 .10
136 Joey Meyer .01 .05
137 Geno Petralli .01 .05
138 Wallace Johnson .01 .05
139 Mike Flanagan .01 .05
140 Shawon Dunston .01 .05
141 Brook Jacoby TL .01 .05
142 Mike Diaz .01 .05
143 Mike Campbell .01 .05
144 Jay Bell .02 .10
145 Dave Stewart .02 .10
146 Gary Pettis .01 .05
147 DeWayne Buice .01 .05
148 Bill Pecota .01 .05
149 Doug Dascenzo .01 .05
150 Fernando Valenzuela .02 .10
151 Terry McGriff .01 .05
152 Mark Thurmond .01 .05
153 Jim Pankovits .01 .05
154 Don Carman .01 .05
155 Marty Barrett .01 .05
156 Dave Gallagher .01 .05
157 Tom Glavine .08 .25
158 Mike Aldrete .01 .05
159 Pat Clements .01 .05
160 Jeffrey Leonard .01 .05
161 G. Olson RC FDP UER .08 .25
Born Scribner, NE,
should be Omaha, NE
162 John Davis .01 .05
163 Bob Forsch .01 .05
164 Hal Lanier MG .01 .05
165 Mike Dunne .01 .05
166 Doug Jennings .01 .05
167 Steve Searcy FS .01 .05
168 Willie Wilson .02 .10
169 Mike Jackson .01 .05
170 Tony Fernandez .01 .05
171 Andres Thomas TL .01 .05
172 Frank Williams .01 .05
173 Mel Hall .01 .05
174 Todd Burns .01 .05
175 John Shelby .01 .05
176 Jeff Parrett .01 .05
177 Monty Fariss FDP .01 .05
178 Mark Grant .01 .05
179 Ozzie Virgil .01 .05
180 Mike Scott .02 .10
181 Craig Worthington .01 .05
182 Bob McClure .01 .05
183 Oddibe McDowell .01 .05
184 John Costello .01 .05
185 Claudell Washington .01 .05
186 Pat Perry .01 .05
187 Darren Daulton .02 .10
188 Dennis Lamp .01 .05
189 Kevin Mitchell .02 .10
190 Mike Witt .01 .05
191 Sil Campusano .01 .05
192 Paul Mirabella .01 .05
193 Sparky Anderson MG .02 .10
UER (553 Salazer)
194 Greg W. Harris RC .02 .10
195 Ozzie Guillen .02 .10
196 Denny Walling .01 .05
197 Neal Heaton .01 .05
198 Danny Heep .01 .05
199 Mike Schooler RC .02 .10
200 George Brett .25 .60
201 Kelly Gruber TL .01 .05
202 Brad Moore .01 .05
203 Rob Ducey .01 .05
204 Brad Havens .01 .05
205 Dwight Evans .05 .15
206 Roberto Alomar .08 .25
207 Terry Leach .01 .05
208 Tom Pagnozzi .01 .05
209 Jeff Bittiger .01 .05
210 Dale Murphy .05 .15
211 Mike Pagliarulo .01 .05
212 Scott Sanderson .01 .05
213 Rene Gonzales .01 .05
214 Charlie O'Brien .01 .05
215 Kevin Gross .01 .05
216 Jack Howell .01 .05
217 Joe Price .01 .05
218 Mike LaValliere .01 .05
219 Jim Clancy .01 .05
220 Gary Gaetti .02 .10
221 Cecil Espy .01 .05
222 Mark Lewis FDP RC .08 .25
223 Jay Buhner .02 .10
224 Tony LaRussa MG .02 .10
225 Ramon Martinez RC .08 .25
226 Bill Doran .01 .05
227 John Farrell .01 .05
228 Nelson Santovenia .01 .05
229 Jimmy Key .02 .10
230 Ozzie Smith .15 .40
231 Roberto Alomar TL .08 .25
(Gary Carter at plate)
232 Ricky Horton .01 .05
233 Gregg Jefferies FS .01 .05
234 Tom Browning .01 .05
235 John Kruk .02 .10
236 Charles Hudson .01 .05
237 Glenn Hubbard .01 .05
238 Eric King .01 .05
239 Tim Laudner .01 .05
240 Greg Maddux .20 .50
241 Brett Butler .02 .10
242 Ed VandeBerg .01 .05
243 Bob Boone .02 .10
244 Jim Acker .01 .05
245 Jim Rice .02 .10
246 Rey Quinones .01 .05
247 Shawn Hillegas .01 .05
248 Tony Phillips .01 .05
249 Tim Leary .01 .05
250 Cal Ripken .30 .75
251 John Dopson .01 .05
252 Billy Hatcher .01 .05
253 Jose Alvarez RC .02 .10
254 Tom Lasorda MG .05 .15
255 Ron Guidry .02 .10
256 Benny Santiago .02 .10
257 Rick Aguilera .01 .05
258 Checklist 133-264 .01 .05
259 Larry McWilliams .01 .05
260 Dave Winfield .02 .10
261 Tom Brunansky .01 .05
Luis Alicea TL
262 Jeff Pico .01 .05
263 Mike Felder .01 .05
264 Rob Dibble RC .15 .40
265 Kent Hrbek .02 .10
266 Luis Aquino .01 .05
267 Jeff M. Robinson .01 .05
268 Keith Miller RC .08 .25
269 Tom Bolton .01 .05
270 Wally Joyner .02 .10
271 Jay Tibbs .01 .05
272 Ron Hassey .01 .05
273 Jose Lind .01 .05
274 Mark Eichhorn .01 .05
275 Danny Tartabull UER .01 .05
(Born San Juan, PR
should be Miami, FL)
276 Paul Kilgus .01 .05
277 Mike Davis .01 .05
278 Andy McGaffigan .01 .05
279 Scott Bradley .01 .05
280 Bob Knepper .01 .05
281 Gary Redus .01 .05
282 Cris Carpenter RC .02 .10
283 Andy Allanson .01 .05
284 Jim Leyland MG .02 .10
285 John Candelaria .01 .05
286 Darrin Jackson .02 .10
287 Juan Nieves .01 .05
288 Pat Sheridan .01 .05
289 Ernie Whitt .01 .05
290 John Franco .02 .10
291 Darryl Strawberry .01 .05
Keith Hernandez
Kevin McReynolds TL
292 Jim Corsi .01 .05
293 Glenn Wilson .01 .05
294 Juan Berenguer .01 .05
295 Scott Fletcher .01 .05
296 Ron Gant .02 .10
297 Oswald Peraza .01 .05
298 Chris James .01 .05
299 Steve Ellsworth .01 .05
300 Darryl Strawberry .02 .10
301 Charlie Leibrandt .01 .05
302 Gary Ward .01 .05
303 Felix Fermin .01 .05
304 Joel Youngblood .01 .05
305 Dave Smith .01 .05
306 Tracy Woodson .01 .05
307 Lance McCullers .01 .05
308 Ron Karkovice .01 .05
309 Mario Diaz .01 .05
310 Rafael Palmeiro .08 .25
311 Chris Bosio .01 .05
312 Tom Lawless .01 .05
313 Dennis Martinez .02 .10
314 Bobby Valentine MG .02 .10
315 Greg Swindell .01 .05
316 Walt Weiss .01 .05
317 Jack Armstrong RC .08 .25
318 Gene Larkin .01 .05
319 Greg Booker .01 .05
320 Lou Whitaker .02 .10
321 Jody Reed TL .01 .05
322 John Smiley .01 .05
323 Gary Thurman .01 .05
324 Bob Milacki .01 .05
325 Jesse Barfield .02 .10
326 Dennis Boyd .01 .05
327 Mark Lemke RC .15 .40
328 Rick Honeycutt .01 .05
329 Bob Melvin .01 .05
330 Eric Davis .02 .10
331 Curt Wilkerson .01 .05
332 Tony Armas .02 .10
333 Bob Ojeda .01 .05
334 Steve Lyons .01 .05
335 Dave Righetti .02 .10
336 Steve Balboni .01 .05
337 Calvin Schiraldi .01 .05
338 Jim Adduci .01 .05
339 Scott Bailes .01 .05
340 Kirk Gibson .02 .10
341 Jim Deshaies .01 .05
342 Tom Brookens .01 .05
343 Gary Sheffield FS RC .60 1.50
344 Tom Trebelhorn MG .01 .05
345 Charlie Hough .02 .10
346 Rex Hudler .01 .05
347 John Cerutti .01 .05
348 Ed Hearn .01 .05
349 Ron Jones .02 .10
350 Andy Van Slyke .05 .15
351 Bob Melvin .01 .05
Bill Fahey CO TL
352 Rick Schu .01 .05
353 Marvell Wynne .01 .05
354 Larry Parrish .01 .05
355 Mark Langston .01 .05
356 Kevin Elster .01 .05
357 Jerry Reuss .01 .05
358 Ricky Jordan RC .08 .25
359 Tommy John .02 .10
360 Ryne Sandberg .15 .40
361 Kelly Downs .01 .05
362 Jack Lazorko .01 .05
363 Rich Yett .01 .05
364 Rob Deer .01 .05
365 Mike Henneman .01 .05
366 Herm Winningham .01 .05
367 Johnny Paredes .01 .05
368 Brian Holton .01 .05
369 Ken Caminiti .05 .15
370 Dennis Eckersley .05 .15
371 Manny Lee .01 .05
372 Craig Lefferts .01 .05
373 Tracy Jones .01 .05
374 John Wathan MG .01 .05
375 Terry Pendleton .02 .10
376 Steve Lombardozzi .01 .05
377 Mike Smithson .01 .05
378 Checklist 265-396 .01 .05
379 Tim Flannery .01 .05
380 Rickey Henderson .08 .25
381 Larry Sheets TL .01 .05
382 John Smoltz RC .60 1.50
383 Howard Johnson .02 .10
384 Mark Salas .01 .05
385 Von Hayes .01 .05
386 Andres Galarraga AS .01 .05
387 Ryne Sandberg AS .08 .25
388 Bobby Bonilla AS .01 .05
389 Ozzie Smith AS .08 .25
390 Darryl Strawberry AS .01 .05
391 Andre Dawson AS .01 .05
392 Andy Van Slyke AS .02 .10
393 Gary Carter AS .01 .05
394 Orel Hershiser AS .01 .05
395 Danny Jackson AS .01 .05
396 Kirk Gibson AS .02 .10
397 Don Mattingly AS .10 .30
398 Julio Franco AS .01 .05
399 Wade Boggs AS .02 .10
400 Alan Trammell AS .01 .05
401 Jose Canseco AS .05 .15
402 Mike Greenwell AS .01 .05
403 Kirby Puckett AS .05 .15
404 Bob Boone AS .01 .05
405 Roger Clemens AS .20 .50
406 Frank Viola AS .01 .05
407 Dave Winfield AS .01 .05
408 Greg Walker .01 .05
409 Ken Dayley .01 .05
410 Jack Clark .02 .10
411 Mitch Williams .01 .05
412 Barry Lyons .01 .05
413 Mike Kingery .01 .05
414 Jim Fregosi MG .01 .05
415 Rich Gossage .02 .10
416 Fred Lynn .02 .10
417 Mike LaCoss .01 .05
418 Bob Dernier .01 .05
419 Tom Filer .01 .05
420 Joe Carter .02 .10
421 Kirk McCaskill .01 .05
422 Bo Diaz .01 .05
423 Brian Fisher .01 .05
424 Luis Polonia UER .01 .05
(Wrong birthdate)
425 Jay Howell .01 .05
426 Dan Gladden .01 .05
427 Eric Show .01 .05
428 Craig Reynolds .01 .05
429 Greg Gagne TL .01 .05
430 Mark Gubicza .01 .05
431 Luis Rivera .01 .05
432 Chad Kreuter RC .08 .25
433 Albert Hall .01 .05
434 Ken Patterson .01 .05
435 Len Dykstra .02 .10
436 Bobby Meacham .01 .05
437 Andy Benes FDP RC .15 .40
438 Greg Gross .01 .05
439 Frank DiPino .01 .05
440 Bobby Bonilla .02 .10
441 Jerry Reed .01 .05
442 Jose Oquendo .01 .05
443 Rod Nichols .01 .05
444 Moose Stubing MG .01 .05
445 Matt Nokes .01 .05
446 Rob Murphy .01 .05
447 Donell Nixon .01 .05
448 Eric Plunk .01 .05
449 Carmelo Martinez .01 .05
450 Roger Clemens .40 1.00
451 Mark Davidson .01 .05
452 Israel Sanchez .01 .05
453 Tom Prince .01 .05
454 Paul Assenmacher .01 .05
455 Johnny Ray .01 .05
456 Tim Belcher .01 .05
457 Mackey Sasser .01 .05
458 Donn Pall .01 .05
459 Dave Valle TL .01 .05
460 Dave Stieb .02 .10
461 Buddy Bell .02 .10
462 Jose Guzman .01 .05
463 Steve Lake .01 .05
464 Bryn Smith .01 .05
465 Mark Grace .08 .25
466 Chuck Crim .01 .05
467 Jim Walewander .01 .05
468 Henry Cotto .01 .05
469 Jose Bautista RC .02 .10
470 Lance Parrish .02 .10
471 Steve Curry .01 .05
472 Brian Harper .01 .05
473 Don Robinson .01 .05
474 Bob Rodgers MG .01 .05
475 Dave Parker .02 .10
476 Jon Perlman .01 .05
477 Dick Schofield .01 .05
478 Doug Drabek .01 .05
479 Mike Macfarlane RC .08 .25
480 Keith Hernandez .02 .10
481 Chris Brown .01 .05
482 Steve Peters .01 .05
483 Mickey Hatcher .01 .05
484 Steve Shields .01 .05
485 Hubie Brooks .01 .05
486 Jack McDowell .02 .10
487 Scott Lusader .01 .05
488 Kevin Coffman .01 .05
Now with Cubs
489 Mike Schmidt TL .05 .15
490 Chris Sabo RC .15 .40
491 Mike Birkbeck .01 .05
492 Alan Ashby .01 .05
493 Todd Benzinger .01 .05
494 Shane Rawley .01 .05
495 Candy Maldonado .01 .05
496 Dwayne Henry .01 .05
497 Pete Stanicek .01 .05
498 Dave Valle .01 .05
499 Don Heinkel .01 .05
500 Jose Canseco .08 .25
501 Vance Law .01 .05
502 Duane Ward .01 .05
503 Al Newman .01 .05
504 Bob Walk .01 .05
505 Pete Rose MG .20 .50
506 Kirt Manwaring .01 .05
507 Steve Farr .01 .05
508 Wally Backman .01 .05
509 Bud Black .01 .05
510 Bob Horner .02 .10
511 Richard Dotson .01 .05
512 Donnie Hill .01 .05
513 Jesse Orosco .01 .05
514 Chet Lemon .02 .10
515 Barry Larkin .05 .15
516 Eddie Whitson .01 .05
517 Greg Brock .01 .05
518 Bruce Ruffin .01 .05
519 Willie Randolph TL .01 .05
520 Rick Sutcliffe .02 .10
521 Mickey Tettleton .01 .05
522 Randy Kramer .01 .05
523 Andres Thomas .01 .05
524 Checklist 397-528 .01 .05
525 Chili Davis .02 .10
526 Wes Gardner .01 .05
527 Dave Henderson .01 .05
528 Luis Medina .01 .05
(Lower left front
has white triangle)
529 Tom Foley .01 .05
530 Nolan Ryan .40 1.00
531 Dave Hengel .01 .05
532 Jerry Browne .01 .05
533 Andy Hawkins .01 .05
534 Doc Edwards MG .01 .05
535 Todd Worrell UER .01 .05
(4 wins in '88,
should be 5)
536 Joel Skinner .01 .05
537 Pete Smith .01 .05
538 Juan Castillo .01 .05
539 Barry Jones .01 .05
540 Bo Jackson .08 .25
541 Cecil Fielder .02 .10
542 Todd Frohwirth .01 .05
543 Damon Berryhill .01 .05
544 Jeff Sellers .01 .05
545 Mookie Wilson .02 .10
546 Mark Williamson .01 .05
547 Mark McLemore .01 .05
548 Bobby Witt .01 .05
549 Jamie Moyer TL .01 .05
550 Orel Hershiser .02 .10
551 Randy Ready .01 .05
552 Greg Cadaret .01 .05
553 Luis Salazar .01 .05
554 Nick Esasky .01 .05
555 Bert Blyleven .02 .10
556 Bruce Fields .01 .05
557 Keith A. Miller .01 .05
558 Dan Pasqua .01 .05
559 Juan Agosto .01 .05
560 Tim Raines .02 .10
561 Luis Aguayo .01 .05
562 Danny Cox .01 .05
563 Bill Schroeder .01 .05
564 Russ Nixon MG .01 .05
565 Jeff Russell .01 .05
566 Al Pedrique .01 .05
567 David Wells UER .02 .10
(Complete Pitching
Recor)
568 Mickey Brantley .01 .05
569 German Jimenez .01 .05
570 Tony Gwynn UER .10 .30
('88 average should
be italicized as
league leader)
571 Billy Ripken .01 .05
572 Atlee Hammaker .01 .05
573 Jim Abbott FDP RC .40 1.00
574 Dave Clark .01 .05
575 Juan Samuel .01 .05
576 Greg Minton .01 .05
577 Randy Bush .01 .05
578 John Morris .01 .05
579 Glenn Davis TL .01 .05
580 Harold Reynolds .02 .10
581 Gene Nelson .01 .05
582 Mike Marshall .01 .05
583 Paul Gibson .01 .05
584 Randy Velarde UER .01 .05
(Signed 1935,
should be 1985)
585 Harold Baines .02 .10
586 Joe Boever .01 .05
587 Mike Stanley .01 .05
588 Luis Alicea RC .08 .25
589 Dave Meads .01 .05
590 Andres Galarraga .02 .10
591 Jeff Musselman .01 .05
592 John Cangelosi .01 .05
593 Drew Hall .01 .05
594 Jimy Williams MG .01 .05
595 Teddy Higuera .01 .05
596 Kurt Stillwell .01 .05
597 Terry Taylor RC .02 .10
598 Ken Gerhart .01 .05
599 Tom Candiotti .01 .05
600 Wade Boggs .05 .15
601 Dave Dravecky .01 .05
602 Devon White .02 .10
603 Frank Tanana .02 .10
604 Paul O'Neill .05 .15
605A Bob Welch ERR 4.00 10.00
(Missing line on back
Complete M.L. Pitching Record
605B Bob Welch COR .02 .10
606 Rick Dempsey .01 .05
607 Willie Ansley FDP RC .02 .10
608 Phil Bradley .01 .05
609 Frank Tanana .01 .05
Alan Trammell
Mike Heath TL
610 Randy Myers .02 .10
611 Don Slaught .01 .05
612 Dan Quisenberry .01 .05
613 Gary Varsho .01 .05
614 Joe Hesketh .01 .05
615 Robin Yount .15 .40
616 Steve Rosenberg .01 .05
617 Mark Parent .01 .05
618 Rance Mulliniks .02 .10
619 Checklist 529-660 .01 .05
620 Barry Bonds .60 1.50
621 Rick Mahler .01 .05
622 Stan Javier .01 .05
623 Fred Toliver .01 .05
624 Jack McKeon MG .02 .10
625 Eddie Murray .08 .25
626 Jeff Reed .01 .05
627 Greg A. Harris .01 .05
628 Matt Williams .08 .25
629 Pete O'Brien .01 .05
630 Mike Greenwell .01 .05
631 Dave Bergman .01 .05
632 Bryan Harvey RC .08 .25
633 Daryl Boston .01 .05
634 Marvin Freeman .01 .05
635 Willie Randolph .02 .10
636 Bill Wilkinson .01 .05
637 Carmen Castillo .01 .05
638 Floyd Bannister .01 .05
639 Walt Weiss TL .01 .05
640 Willie McGee .02 .10
641 Curt Young .01 .05
642 Angel Salazar .01 .05
643 Louie Meadows .01 .05
644 Lloyd McClendon .01 .05
645 Jack Morris .02 .10
646 Kevin Bass .01 .05
647 Randy Johnson RC .75 2.00
648 Sandy Alomar FS RC .15 .40
649 Stu Cliburn .01 .05
650 Kirby Puckett .08 .25
651 Tom Niedenfuer .01 .05
652 Rich Gedman .01 .05
653 Tommy Barrett .01 .05
654 Whitey Herzog MG .02 .10
655 Dave Magadan .01 .05
656 Ivan Calderon .01 .05
657 Joe Magrane .01 .05
658 R.J. Reynolds .01 .05
659 Al Leiter .08 .25
660 Will Clark .05 .15
661 D.Gooden TBC84 .01 .05
662 Lou Brock TBC79 .02 .10
663 Hank Aaron TBC74 .08 .25
664 Gil Hodges TBC 69 .02 .10
665A Tony Oliva TBC64
ERR (fabricated card
is enlarged version
of Oliva's 64T card;
Topps copyright
missing)
665B Tony Oliva TBC 64 .02 .10
COR (fabricated
card)
666 Randy St.Claire .01 .05
667 Dwayne Murphy .01 .05
668 Mike Bielecki .01 .05
669 Orel Hershiser .02 .10
Mike Scioscia TL
670 Kevin Seitzer .01 .05
671 Jim Gantner .01 .05
672 Allan Anderson .01 .05
673 Don Baylor .02 .10
674 Otis Nixon .01 .05
675 Bruce Hurst .01 .05
676 Ernie Riles .01 .05
677 Dave Schmidt .01 .05
678 Dion James .01 .05
679 Willie Fraser .01 .05
680 Gary Carter .02 .10
681 Jeff D. Robinson .01 .05
682 Rick Leach .01 .05
683 Jose Cecena .01 .05
684 Dave Johnson MG .01 .05
685 Jeff Treadway .01 .05
686 Scott Terry .01 .05
687 Alvin Davis .01 .05
688 Zane Smith .01 .05
689A Stan Jefferson 4.00 10.00
(Pink triangle on
front bottom left)
689B Stan Jefferson .01 .05
(Violet triangle on
front bottom left)
690 Doug Jones .01 .05
691 Roberto Kelly UER .01 .05
(83 Oneonita)
692 Steve Ontiveros .01 .05
693 Pat Borders RC .08 .25
694 Les Lancaster .01 .05
695 Carlton Fisk .05 .15
696 Don August .01 .05
697A Franklin Stubbs ERR 4.00 10.00
(Team name on front
in white)
697B Franklin Stubbs .01 .05
(Team name on front
in gray)
698 Keith Atherton .01 .05
699 Al Pedrique TL .01 .05
Tony Gwynn sliding
700 Don Mattingly .25 .60
701 Storm Davis .01 .05
702 Jamie Quirk .01 .05
703 Scott Garrelts .01 .05
704 Carlos Quintana RC .02 .10
705 Terry Kennedy .01 .05
706 Pete Incaviglia .01 .05
707 Steve Jeltz .01 .05
708 Chuck Finley .02 .10
709 Tom Herr .01 .05
710 David Cone .02 .10
711 Candy Sierra .01 .05
712 Bill Swift .01 .05
713 Ty Griffin FDP .01 .05
714 Joe Morgan MG .02 .10
715 Tony Pena .01 .05
716 Wayne Tolleson .01 .05
717 Jamie Moyer .02 .10
718 Glenn Braggs .01 .05
719 Danny Darwin .01 .05
720 Tim Wallach .01 .05
721 Ron Tingley .01 .05
722 Todd Stottlemyre .01 .05
723 Rafael Belliard .01 .05
724 Jerry Don Gleaton .01 .05
725 Terry Steinbach .02 .10
726 Dickie Thon .01 .05
727 Joe Orsulak .01 .05
728 Charlie Puleo .01 .05
729 Steve Buechele TL .01 .05
(Inconsistent design,
team name on front
surrounded by black,
should be white)
730 Danny Jackson .01 .05
731 Mike Young .01 .05
732 Steve Buechele .01 .05
733 Randy Bockus .01 .05
734 Jody Reed .01 .05
735 Roger McDowell .01 .05
736 Jeff Hamilton .01 .05
737 Norm Charlton RC .08 .25
738 Darnell Coles .01 .05
739 Brook Jacoby .01 .05
740 Dan Plesac .01 .05
741 Ken Phelps .01 .05
742 Mike Harkey FS RC .02 .10
743 Mike Heath .01 .05
744 Roger Craig MG .02 .10
745 Fred McGriff .05 .15
746 G.Gonzalez UER .01 .05
Wrong birthdate
747 Wil Tejada .01 .05
748 Jimmy Jones .01 .05
749 Rafael Ramirez .01 .05
750 Bret Saberhagen .02 .10
751 Ken Oberkfell .01 .05
752 Jim Gott .01 .05
753 Jose Uribe .01 .05
754 Bob Brower .01 .05
755 Mike Scioscia .02 .10
756 Scott Medvin .01 .05
757 Brady Anderson RC .15 .40
758 Gene Walter .01 .05
759 Rob Deer TL .01 .05
760 Lee Smith .02 .10
761 Dante Bichette RC .15 .40
762 Bobby Thigpen .01 .05
763 Dave Martinez .01 .05
764 Robin Ventura FDP RC .30 .75
765 Glenn Davis .01 .05
766 Cecilio Guante .01 .05
767 Mike Capel .01 .05
768 Bill Wegman .01 .05
769 Junior Ortiz .01 .05
770 Alan Trammell .02 .10
771 Ron Kittle .01 .05
772 Ron Oester .01 .05
773 Keith Moreland .01 .05
774 Frank Robinson MG .05 .15
775 Jeff Reardon .02 .10
776 Nelson Liriano .01 .05
777 Ted Power .01 .05
778 Bruce Benedict .01 .05
779 Craig McMurtry .01 .05
780 Pedro Guerrero .02 .10
781 Greg Briley .02 .10
782 Checklist 661-792 .01 .05
783 Trevor Wilson RC .02 .10
784 Steve Avery FDP RC .08 .25
785 Ellis Burks .02 .10
786 Melido Perez .01 .05
787 Dave West RC .02 .10
788 Mike Morgan .01 .05
789 Bo Jackson TL .08 .25
790 Sid Fernandez .01 .05
791 Jim Lindeman .01 .05
792 Rafael Santana .01 .05

1989 Topps Tiffany

Again, Topps issed a standard-size "Glossy" parallel to their regular set. These cards, printed in the Topps Irish facility, have 792 standard-size cards and were issued in complete set form only. These cards have a "shiny" front as well as an easy to read back. These cards were issued only through Topps hobby dealers. With the "glut" of the previous two years Tiffany sets in the marketplace, it seems that approximately 15,000 of these sets were produced in 1989.

COMP.FACT.SET (792) 60.00 120.00
*STARS: 5X TO 12X BASIC CARDS
*ROOKIES: 5X TO 12X BASIC CARDS
DISTRIBUTED ONLY IN FACTORY SET FORM
FACTORY SET PRICE IS FOR SEALED SETS

1989 Topps Batting Leaders

The 1989 Topps Batting Leaders set contains 22 standard-size glossy cards. The fronts are bright red. The set depicts the 22 veterans with the highest lifetime batting averages. The cards were distributed one per Topps blister pack. These blister packs were sold exclusively through K-Mart stores. The cards in the set were numbered by K-Mart essentially in order of highest active career batting average entering the 1989 season.

COMPLETE SET (22)	40.00	100.00
1 Wade Boggs	4.00	10.00
2 Tony Gwynn	8.00	20.00
3 Don Mattingly	8.00	20.00
4 Kirby Puckett	6.00	15.00
5 George Brett	8.00	20.00
6 Pedro Guerrero	.20	.50
7 Tim Raines	.40	1.00
8 Keith Hernandez	.40	1.00
9 Jim Rice	.40	1.00
10 Paul Molitor	3.00	8.00
11 Eddie Murray	3.00	8.00
12 Willie McGee	.40	1.00
13 Dave Parker	.40	1.00
14 Julio Franco	.40	1.00
15 Rickey Henderson	5.00	12.00
16 Kent Hrbek	.40	1.00
17 Willie Wilson	.20	.50
18 Johnny Ray	.20	.50
19 Pat Tabler	.20	.50
20 Carney Lansford	.20	.50
21 Robin Yount	3.00	8.00
22 Alan Trammell	.75	2.00
23 Roger Clemens	.60	1.50
24 Bobby Bonilla	.07	.20
25 Alan Trammell	.10	.30
26 Kevin McReynolds	.02	.10
27 George Bell	.02	.10
28 Bruce Hurst	.02	.10
29 Mark Grace	.30	.75
30 Tim Belcher	.02	.10
31 Mike Greenwell	.02	.10
32 Glenn Davis	.02	.10
33 Gary Gaetti	.07	.20
34 Ryne Sandberg	.60	1.50
35 Rickey Henderson	.30	1.00
36 Dwight Evans	.07	.20
37 Dwight Gooden	.07	.20
38 Robin Yount	.25	.60
39 Damon Berryhill	.02	.10
40 Chris Sabo	.02	.10
41 Mark McGwire	.60	1.50
42 Ozzie Smith	.60	1.50
43 Paul Molitor	.25	.60
44 Andres Galarraga	.15	.40
45 Dave Stewart	.07	.20
46 Tom Browning	.02	.10
47 Cal Ripken	1.25	3.00
48 Orel Hershiser	.07	.20
49 Dave Gallagher	.02	.10
50 Walt Weiss	.02	.10
51 Don Mattingly	.60	1.50
52 Tony Fernandez	.02	.10
53 Tim Raines	.07	.20
54 Jeff Reardon	.07	.20
55 Kirk Gibson	.07	.20
56 Jack Clark	.02	.10
57 Danny Jackson	.02	.10
58 Tony Gwynn	.60	1.50
59 Cecil Espy	.02	.10
60 Jody Reed	.02	.10

1989 Topps Glossy All-Stars

These glossy cards were inserted with Topps rack packs and honor the starting line-ups, managers, and honorary captains of the 1988 National and American League All-Star teams. The standard size cards are very similar in design to what Topps has used since 1984. The backs are printed in red and blue on white card stock.

COMPLETE SET (22)	1.20	3.00
1 Tom Kelly MG	.01	.05
2 Mark McGwire	.30	.75
3 Paul Molitor	.15	.40
4 Wade Boggs	.10	.30
5 Cal Ripken	.60	1.50
6 Jose Canseco	.08	.25
7 Rickey Henderson	.25	.60
8 Dave Winfield	.15	.40
9 Terry Steinbach	.01	.05
10 Frank Viola	.01	.05
11 Bobby Doerr CAPT	.08	.25
12 Whitey Herzog MG	.01	.05
13 Will Clark	.07	.20
14 Ryne Sandberg	.20	.50
15 Bobby Bonilla	.02	.10
16 Ozzie Smith	.20	.50
17 Vince Coleman	.01	.05
18 Andre Dawson	.07	.20
19 Darryl Strawberry	.02	.10
20 Gary Carter	.15	.40
21 Dwight Gooden	.02	.10
22 Willie Stargell CAPT	.08	.25

1989 Topps Glossy Send-Ins

The 1989 Topps Glossy Send-In set contains 60 standard-size cards. The fronts have color photos with white borders; the backs are light blue. The cards were distributed through the mail by Topps in six groups of ten cards. The last two cards out of each group of ten are young players or prospects.

COMPLETE SET (60)	4.00	10.00
1 Kirby Puckett	.40	1.00
2 Eric Davis	.07	.20
3 Joe Carter	.07	.20
4 Andy Van Slyke	.02	.10
5 Wade Boggs	.25	.60
6 David Cone	.07	.20
7 Kent Hrbek	.07	.20
8 Darryl Strawberry	.07	.20
9 Jay Buhner	.07	.20
10 Ron Gant	.07	.20
11 Will Clark	.15	.40
12 Jose Canseco	.30	.75
13 Juan Samuel	.02	.10
14 George Brett	.60	1.50
15 Benito Santiago	.07	.20
16 Dennis Eckersley	.25	.60
17 Gary Carter	.25	.60
18 Frank Viola	.02	.10
19 Roberto Alomar	.60	1.50
20 Paul Gibson	.02	.10
21 Dave Winfield	.25	.60
22 Howard Johnson	.02	.10

1989 Topps Rookies

Inserted in each supermarket jumbo pack is a card from this series of 22 of 1988's best rookies as determined by Topps. Jumbo packs consisted of 100 (regular issue 1989 Topps baseball) cards with a stick of gum plus the insert "Rookie" card. The card fronts are in full color and measure the standard size. The card backs are printed in red and blue on white card stock and are numbered at the bottom. The order of the set is alphabetical by player's name.

COMPLETE SET (22)	6.00	12.00
1 Roberto Alomar	1.00	2.50
2 Brady Anderson	.30	.75
3 Tim Belcher	.08	.25
4 Damon Berryhill	.08	.25
5 Jay Buhner	.40	1.00
6 Kevin Elster	.08	.25
7 Cecil Espy	.08	.25
8 Dave Gallagher	.08	.25
9 Ron Gant	.40	1.00
10 Paul Gibson	.08	.25
11 Mark Grace	.75	2.00
12 Darrin Jackson	.08	.25
13 Gregg Jefferies	.20	.50
14 Ricky Jordan	.08	.25
15 Al Leiter	.40	1.00
16 Melido Perez	.08	.25
17 Chris Sabo	.08	.25
18 Nelson Santovenia	.08	.25
19 Mackey Sasser	.08	.25
20 Gary Sheffield	1.25	3.00
21 Walt Weiss	.08	.25
22 David Wells	.75	2.00

1989 Topps Wax Box Cards

The cards in this 16-card set measure the standard size. Cards have essentially the same design as the 1989 Topps regular issue set. The cards were printed on the bottoms of the regular issue wax pack boxes. These 16 cards, "lettered" A through P, are considered a separate set in their own right and are not typically included in a complete set of the regular issue 1989 Topps cards. The order of the set is alphabetical by player's name. The value of the panels uncut is slightly greater, perhaps by 25 percent greater, than the value of the individual cards cut up carefully. The sixteen cards in this set honor players (and one manager) who reached career milestones during the 1988 season.

COMPLETE SET (16)	3.20	8.00
A George Brett	.40	1.00
B Bill Buckner	.07	.20
C Darrell Evans	.07	.20
D Rich Gossage	.07	.20
E Greg Gross	.02	.10
F Rickey Henderson	.30	.75
G Keith Hernandez	.07	.20
H Tom Lasorda MG	.15	.40
I Jim Rice	.07	.20
J Cal Ripken	.75	2.00
K Nolan Ryan	.75	2.00
L Mike Schmidt	.30	.75
M Bruce Sutter	.20	.50
N Don Sutton	.20	.50
O Kent Tekulve	.02	.10
P Dave Winfield	.30	.75

1989 Topps Traded

The 1989 Topps Traded set contains 132 standard-size cards. The cards were distributed exclusively in factory set form in red and white taped boxes through hobby dealers. The cards are identical to the 1989 Topps regular issue cards except for whiter stock and t-suffixed numbering on back. Rookie Cards in this set include Ken Griffey Jr., Kenny Rogers, Deion Sanders and Omar Vizquel.

COMP.FACT.SET (132)	4.00	10.00
1T Don Aase	.01	.05
2T Jim Abbott	.20	.50
3T Kent Anderson	.01	.05
4T Keith Atherton	.01	.05
5T Wally Backman	.01	.05
6T Steve Balboni	.01	.05
7T Jesse Barfield	.02	.10
8T Steve Bedrosian	.01	.05
9T Todd Benzinger	.01	.05
10T Geronimo Berroa	.01	.05
11T Bert Blyleven	.02	.10
12T Bob Boone	.02	.10
13T Phil Bradley	.01	.05
14T Jeff Brantley RC	.08	.25
15T Kevin Brown	.08	.25
16T Jerry Browne	.01	.05
17T Chuck Cary	.01	.05
18T Carmen Castillo	.01	.05
19T Jim Clancy	.01	.05
20T Jack Clark	.02	.10
21T Bryan Clutterbuck	.01	.05
22T Jody Davis	.01	.05
23T Mike Devereaux	.01	.05
24T Frank DiPino	.01	.05
25T Benny Distefano	.01	.05
26T John Dopson	.01	.05
27T Len Dykstra	.02	.10
28T Jim Eisenreich	.01	.05
29T Nick Esasky	.01	.05
30T Alvaro Espinoza	.01	.05
31T Darrell Evans UER (Stat headings on back are for a pitcher)	.02	.10
32T Junior Felix RC	.02	.10
33T Felix Fermin	.01	.05
34T Julio Franco	.02	.10
35T Terry Francona	.02	.10
36T Cito Gaston MG	.01	.05
37T Bob Geren UER RC	.01	.05
38T Tom Gordon RC	.20	.50
39T Tommy Gregg	.01	.05
40T Ken Griffey Sr.	.02	.10
41T Ken Griffey Jr. RC	3.00	8.00
42T Kevin Gross	.01	.05
43T Lee Guetterman	.01	.05
44T Mel Hall	.01	.05
45T Erik Hanson RC	.08	.25
46T Gene Harris RC	.02	.10
47T Andy Hawkins	.01	.05
48T Rickey Henderson	.08	.25
49T Tom Herr	.01	.05
50T Ken Hill RC	.08	.25
51T Brian Holman RC	.02	.10
52T Brian Holton	.01	.05
53T Art Howe MG	.01	.05
54T Ken Howell	.01	.05
55T Bruce Hurst	.01	.05
56T Chris James	.01	.05
57T Randy Johnson	.60	1.50
58T Jimmy Jones	.01	.05
59T Terry Kennedy	.01	.05
60T Paul Kilgus	.01	.05
61T Eric King	.01	.05
62T Ron Kittle	.01	.05
63T John Kruk	.02	.10
64T Randy Kutcher	.01	.05
65T Steve Lake	.01	.05
66T Mark Langston	.01	.05
67T Dave LaPoint	.01	.05
68T Rick Leach	.01	.05
69T Terry Leach	.01	.05
70T Jim Lefebvre MG	.01	.05
71T Al Leiter	.08	.25
72T Jeffrey Leonard	.01	.05
73T Derek Lilliquist RC	.02	.10
74T Rick Mahler	.01	.05
75T Tom McCarthy	.01	.05
76T Lloyd McClendon	.01	.05
77T Lance McCullers	.01	.05
78T Oddibe McDowell	.01	.05
79T Roger McDowell	.01	.05
80T Larry McWilliams	.01	.05
81T Randy Milligan	.01	.05
82T Mike Moore	.01	.05
83T Keith Moreland	.01	.05
84T Mike Morgan	.01	.05
85T Jamie Moyer	.02	.10
86T Rob Murphy	.01	.05
87T Eddie Murray	.08	.25
88T Pete O'Brien	.01	.05
89T Gregg Olson	.08	.25
90T Steve Ontiveros	.01	.05
91T Jesse Orosco	.01	.05
92T Spike Owen	.01	.05
93T Rafael Palmeiro	.08	.25
94T Clay Parker	.01	.05
95T Jeff Parrett	.01	.05
96T Lance Parrish	.02	.10
97T Dennis Powell	.01	.05
98T Rey Quinones	.01	.05
99T Doug Rader MG	.01	.05
100T Willie Randolph	.02	.10
101T Shane Rawley	.01	.05
102T Randy Ready	.01	.05
103T Bip Roberts	.01	.05
104T Kenny Rogers RC	.75	2.00
105T Ed Romero	.01	.05
106T Nolan Ryan	.60	1.50
107T Luis Salazar	.01	.05
108T Juan Samuel	.01	.05
109T Alex Sanchez RC	.01	.05
110T Deion Sanders RC	.60	1.50
111T Steve Sax	.01	.05
112T Rick Schu	.01	.05
113T Dwight Smith RC	.08	.25
114T Lonnie Smith	.01	.05
115T Billy Spiers RC	.08	.25
116T Kent Tekulve	.01	.05
117T Walt Terrell	.01	.05
118T Milt Thompson	.01	.05
119T Dickie Thon	.01	.05
120T Jeff Torborg MG	.01	.05
121T Jeff Treadway	.01	.05
122T Omar Vizquel RC	.40	1.00
123T Jerome Walton RC	.08	.25
124T Gary Ward	.01	.05
125T Claudell Washington	.01	.05
126T Curt Wilkerson	.01	.05
127T Eddie Williams	.01	.05
128T Frank Williams	.01	.05
129T Ken Williams	.01	.05
130T Mitch Williams	.01	.05
131T Steve Wilson RC	.02	.10
132T Checklist 1T-132T	.01	.05

1989 Topps Traded Tiffany

For each set of regular Tiffany cards ordered, dealers received an update set. These 132 standard-size cards update the regular Topps issue. Again, these cards feature "glossy" fronts as well as easy to read backs. This set was issued only in complete form from the company. Again, the Topps Ireland printing facility produced these cards. Again, approximately 15,000 of these sets were produced.

COMP.FACT.SET (132)	60.00	120.00

*STARS: 4X TO 10X BASIC CARDS
*ROOKIES: 4X TO 10X BASIC CARDS
DISTRIBUTED ONLY IN FACTORY SET FORM
FACTORY SET PRICE IS FOR SEALED SETS

1990 Topps

The 1990 Topps set contains 792 standard-size cards. Cards were issued primarily in wax packs, rack packs and hobby and retail Christmas factory sets. Card fronts feature various colored borders with the player's name at the bottom and team name at top. Subsets include All-Stars (385-407), Turn Back the Clock (661-665) and Draft Picks (scattered throughout the set). The key Rookie Cards in this set are Juan Gonzalez, Marquis Grissom, Sammy Sosa, Frank Thomas, Larry Walker and Bernie Williams. The Frank Thomas card (#414A) was printed without his name on the front, as well as portions of the black borders being omitted, creating a scarce variation. Several additional cards in the set were subsequently discovered missing portions of the black borders or missing some of the black printing in the backgrounds of the photos that occured in the same printing that created the Thomas error. These cards are rarely seen and the Thomas card, for a newer issue, has experienced unprecedented growth as far as value. Be careful when purchasing the Frank Thomas NNOF version as counterfeits have been produced. A very few cards of President George Bush made their ways into packs. While these cards were supposed to have never been issued, a few collectors did receive these cards when opening packs.

COMPLETE SET (792)	8.00	20.00
COMP.FACT.SET (792)	10.00	25.00
COMP.X-MAS.SET (792)	15.00	40.00
1 Nolan Ryan	.40	1.00
2 Nolan Ryan Mets	.20	.50
3 Nolan Ryan Angels	.20	.50
4 Nolan Ryan Astros	.20	.50
5 N.Ryan Rangers UER (Says Texas Stadium rather than Arlington Stadium)	.20	.50
6 Vince Coleman RB	.01	.05
7 Rickey Henderson RB	.05	.15
8 Cal Ripken RB	.08	.25
9 Eric Plunk	.01	.05
10 Barry Larkin	.05	.15
11 Paul Gibson	.01	.05
12 Joe Girardi	.05	.15
13 Mark Williamson	.01	.05
14 Mike Fetters RC	.08	.25
15 Teddy Higuera	.01	.05
16 Kent Anderson	.01	.05
17 Kelly Downs	.01	.05
18 Carlos Quintana	.01	.05
19 Al Newman	.01	.05
20 Mark Gubicza	.01	.05
21 Jeff Torborg MG	.01	.05
22 Bruce Ruffin	.01	.05
23 Randy Velarde	.01	.05
24 Joe Hesketh	.01	.05
25 Willie Randolph	.02	.10
26 Don Slaught	.01	.05
27 Rick Leach	.01	.05
28 Duane Ward	.01	.05
29 John Cangelosi	.01	.05
30 David Cone	.02	.10
31 Henry Cotto	.01	.05
32 John Farrell	.01	.05
33 Greg Walker	.01	.05
34 Tony Fossas RC	.01	.05
35 Benito Santiago	.02	.10
36 John Costello	.01	.05
37 Domingo Ramos	.01	.05
38 Wes Gardner	.01	.05
39 Curt Ford	.01	.05
40 Jay Howell	.01	.05
41 Matt Williams	.02	.10
42 Jeff M. Robinson	.01	.05
43 Dante Bichette	.02	.10
44 Roger Salkeld FDP RC	.02	.10
45 Dave Parker UER (Born in Jackson, not Calhoun)	.02	.10
46 Rob Dibble	.02	.10
47 Brian Harper	.01	.05
48 Zane Smith	.01	.05
49 Tom Lawless	.01	.05
50 Glenn Davis	.01	.05
51 Doug Rader MG	.01	.05
52 Jack Daugherty RC	.01	.05
53 Mike LaCoss	.01	.05
54 Joel Skinner	.01	.05
55 Darrell Evans UER (HR total should be 414, not 424)	.02	.10
56 Franklin Stubbs	.01	.05
57 Greg Vaughn	.01	.05
58 Keith Miller	.01	.05
59 Ted Power	.01	.05
60 George Brett	.25	.60
61 Deion Sanders	.08	.25
62 Ramon Martinez	.01	.05
63 Mike Pagliarulo	.01	.05
64 Danny Darwin	.01	.05
65 Devon White	.02	.10
66 Greg Litton	.01	.05
67 Scott Sanderson	.01	.05
68 Dave Henderson	.01	.05
69 Todd Frohwirth	.01	.05
70 Mike Greenwell	.01	.05
71 Allan Anderson	.01	.05
72 Jeff Huson RC	.02	.10
73 Bob Milacki	.01	.05
74 Jeff Jackson FDP RC	.02	.10
75 Doug Jones	.01	.05
76 Dave Valle	.01	.05
77 Dave Bergman	.01	.05
78 Mike Flanagan	.01	.05
79 Ron Kittle	.01	.05
80 Jeff Russell	.01	.05
81 Bob Rodgers MG	.01	.05
82 Scott Terry	.01	.05
83 Hensley Meulens	.01	.05
84 Ray Searage	.01	.05
85 Juan Samuel	.01	.05
86 Paul Kilgus	.01	.05
87 Rick Luecken RC	.01	.05
88 Glenn Braggs	.01	.05
89 Clint Zavaras RC	.01	.05
90 Jack Clark	.02	.10
91 Steve Frey RC	.01	.05
92 Mike Stanley	.01	.05
93 Shawn Hillegas	.01	.05
94 Herm Winningham	.01	.05
95 Todd Worrell	.01	.05
96 Jody Reed	.01	.05
97 Curt Schilling	.40	1.00
98 Jose Gonzalez	.01	.05
99 Rich Monteleone	.01	.05
100 Will Clark	.05	.15
101 Shane Rawley	.01	.05
102 Stan Javier	.01	.05
103 Marvin Freeman	.01	.05
104 Bob Knepper	.01	.05
105 Randy Myers	.02	.10
106 Charlie O'Brien	.01	.05
107 Fred Lynn	.01	.05
108 Rod Nichols	.01	.05
109 Roberto Kelly	.01	.05
110 Tommy Helms MG	.01	.05
111 Ed Whited RC	.01	.05
112 Glenn Wilson	.01	.05
113 Manny Lee	.01	.05
114 Mike Bielecki	.01	.05
115 Tony Pena	.01	.05
116 Floyd Bannister	.01	.05
117 Mike Sharperson	.01	.05
118 Erik Hanson	.01	.05
119 Billy Hatcher	.01	.05
120 John Franco	.02	.10
121 Robin Ventura	.08	.25
122 Shawn Abner	.01	.05
123 Rich Gedman	.01	.05
124 Dave Dravecky	.02	.10
125 Kent Hrbek	.02	.10
126 Randy Kramer	.01	.05
127 Mike Devereaux	.01	.05
128 Checklist 1	.01	.05
129 Ron Jones	.01	.05
130 Bert Blyleven	.02	.10
131 Matt Nokes	.01	.05
132 Lance Blankenship	.01	.05
133 Ricky Horton	.01	.05
134 Earl Cunningham FDP RC	.02	.10
135 Dave Magadan	.01	.05
136 Kevin Brown	.02	.10
137 Marty Pevey RC	.01	.05
138 Al Leiter	.08	.25
139 Greg Brock	.01	.05
140 Andre Dawson	.02	.10
141A John Hart MG ERR BL		
141B John Hart MG RC	.01	.05
142 Jeff Wetherby RC	.01	.05
143 Rafael Belliard	.01	.05
144 Bud Black	.01	.05
145 Terry Steinbach	.01	.05
146 Rob Richie RC	.01	.05
147 Chuck Finley	.02	.10
148 Edgar Martinez	.05	.15
149 Steve Farr	.01	.05
150 Kirk Gibson	.02	.10
151 Rick Mahler	.01	.05
152 Lonnie Smith	.01	.05
153 Randy Milligan	.01	.05
154 Mike Maddux	.01	.05
155 Ellis Burks	.05	.15
156 Ken Patterson	.01	.05
157 Craig Biggio	.08	.25
158 Craig Lefferts	.01	.05
159 Mike Felder	.01	.05
160 Dave Righetti	.01	.05
161 Harold Reynolds	.02	.10
162 Todd Zeile	.02	.10
163 Phil Bradley	.01	.05
164 Jeff Juden FDP RC	.02	.10
165 Walt Weiss	.01	.05
166 Bobby Witt	.01	.05
167 Kevin Appier	.02	.10
168 Jose Lind	.01	.05
169 Richard Dotson	.01	.05
170 George Bell	.01	.05
171 Russ Nixon MG	.01	.05
172 Tom Lampkin	.01	.05
173 Tim Belcher	.01	.05
174 Jeff Kunkel	.01	.05
175 Mike Moore	.01	.05
176 Luis Quinones	.01	.05
177 Mike Henneman	.01	.05
178 Chris James	.01	.05
179 Brian Holton	.01	.05
180 Tim Raines	.02	.10
181 Juan Agosto	.01	.05
182 Mookie Wilson	.02	.10
183 Steve Lake	.01	.05
184 Danny Cox	.01	.05
185 Ruben Sierra	.02	.10
186 Dave LaPoint	.01	.05
187 Rick Wrona	.01	.05
188 Mike Smithson	.01	.05
189 Dick Schofield	.01	.05
190 Rick Reuschel	.01	.05
191 Pat Borders	.01	.05
192 Don August	.01	.05
193 Andy Benes	.02	.10
194 Glenallen Hill	.01	.05
195 Tim Burke	.01	.05
196 Gerald Young	.01	.05
197 Doug Drabek	.01	.05
198 Mike Marshall	.01	.05
199 Sergio Valdez RC	.01	.05
200 Don Mattingly	.25	.60
201 Cito Gaston MG	.01	.05
202 Mike Macfarlane	.01	.05
203 Mike Roesler RC	.01	.05
204 Bob Dernier	.01	.05
205 Mark Davis	.01	.05
206 Nick Esasky	.01	.05
207 Bob Ojeda	.01	.05
208 Brook Jacoby	.01	.05
209 Greg Mathews	.01	.05
210 Ryne Sandberg	.15	.40
211 John Cerutti	.01	.05
212 Joe Orsulak	.01	.05
213 Scott Bankhead	.01	.05
214 Terry Francona	.02	.10
215 Kirk McCaskill	.01	.05
216 Ricky Jordan	.01	.05
217 Don Robinson	.01	.05
218 Wally Backman	.01	.05
219 Donn Pall	.01	.05
220 Barry Bonds	.40	1.00
221 Gary Mielke RC	.01	.05
222 Kurt Stillwell UER (Graduate misspelled as gradute)	.01	.05
223 Tommy Gregg	.01	.05
224 Delino DeShields RC	.08	.25
225 Jim Deshaies	.01	.05
226 Mickey Hatcher	.01	.05
227A Kevin Tapani ERR BL		
227B Kevin Tapani RC	.08	.25
228 Dave Martinez	.01	.05
229 David Wells	.02	.10
230 Keith Hernandez	.02	.10
231 Jack McKeon MG	.01	.05
232 Darnell Coles	.01	.05
233 Ken Hill	.02	.10
234 Mariano Duncan	.01	.05
235 Jeff Reardon	.02	.10
236 Hal Morris	.01	.05
237 Kevin Ritz RC	.01	.05
238 Felix Jose	.01	.05
239 Eric Show	.01	.05
240 Mark Grace	.05	.15
241 Mike Krukow	.01	.05
242 Fred Manrique	.01	.05
243 Barry Jones	.01	.05
244 Bill Schroeder	.01	.05
245 Roger Clemens	.40	1.00
246 Jim Eisenreich	.01	.05
247 Jerry Reed	.01	.05
248 Dave Anderson	.01	.05
249 Mike (Texas) Smith RC	.01	.05
250 Jose Canseco	.05	.15
251 Jeff Blauser	.01	.05
252 Otis Nixon	.01	.05
253 Mark Portugal	.01	.05
254 Francisco Cabrera	.01	.05
255 Bobby Thigpen	.01	.05
256 Marvell Wynne	.01	.05
257 Jose DeLeon	.01	.05
258 Barry Lyons	.01	.05
259 Lance McCullers	.01	.05
260 Eric Davis	.02	.10
261 Whitey Herzog MG	.02	.10
262 Checklist 2	.01	.05
263 Mel Stottlemyre Jr.	.01	.05
264 Bryan Clutterbuck	.01	.05
265 Pete O'Brien	.01	.05
266 German Gonzalez	.01	.05
267 Mark Davidson	.01	.05
268 Rob Murphy	.01	.05
269 Dickie Thon	.01	.05
270 Dave Stewart	.02	.10
271 Chet Lemon	.01	.05
272 Bryan Harvey	.01	.05
273 Bobby Bonilla	.02	.10
274 Mauro Gozzo RC	.01	.05
275 Mickey Tettleton	.01	.05
276 Gary Thurman	.01	.05
277 Lenny Harris	.01	.05
278 Pascual Perez	.01	.05
279 Steve Buechele	.01	.05
280 Lou Whitaker	.02	.10
281 Kevin Bass	.01	.05
282 Derek Lilliquist	.01	.05
283 Joey Belle	.08	.25
284 Mark Gardner RC	.02	.10
285 Willie McGee	.02	.10
286 Lee Guetterman	.01	.05
287 Vance Law	.01	.05
288 Greg Briley	.01	.05
289 Norm Charlton	.01	.05
290 Robin Yount	.15	.40
291 Dave Johnson MG	.02	.10
292 Jim Gott	.01	.05
293 Mike Gallego	.01	.05
294 Craig McMurtry	.01	.05
295 Fred McGriff	.08	.25
296 Jeff Ballard	.01	.05
297 Tommy Herr	.01	.05
298 Dan Gladden	.01	.05
299 Adam Peterson	.01	.05
300 Bo Jackson	.08	.25
301 Don Aase	.01	.05
302A Marcus Lawton ERR BL		
302B Marcus Lawton RC	.01	.05
303 Rick Cerone	.01	.05
304 Marty Clary	.01	.05
305 Eddie Murray	.08	.25
306 Tom Niedenfuer	.01	.05
307 Bip Roberts	.01	.05
308 Jose Guzman	.01	.05
309 Eric Yelding RC	.01	.05
310 Steve Bedrosian	.01	.05
311 Dwight Smith	.01	.05
312 Dan Quisenberry	.01	.05
313 Gus Polidor	.01	.05
314 Donald Harris FDP RC	.01	.05
315 Bruce Hurst	.01	.05
316 Carney Lansford	.02	.10
317 Mark Guthrie RC	.01	.05
318 Wallace Johnson	.01	.05
319 Dion James	.01	.05
320 Dave Stieb	.02	.10
321 Joe Morgan MG	.01	.05
322 Junior Ortiz	.01	.05
323 Willie Wilson	.01	.05
324 Pete Harnisch	.01	.05
325 Robby Thompson	.01	.05
326 Tom McCarthy	.01	.05
327 Ken Williams	.01	.05
328 Curt Young	.01	.05
329 Oddibe McDowell	.01	.05
330 Ron Darling	.01	.05
331 Juan Gonzalez RC	.40	1.00
332 Paul O'Neill	.05	.15
333 Bill Wegman	.01	.05
334 Johnny Ray	.01	.05
335 Andy Hawkins	.01	.05
336 Ken Griffey Jr.	.30	.75
337 Lloyd McClendon	.01	.05
338 Dennis Lamp	.01	.05
339 Dave Clark	.01	.05
340 Fernando Valenzuela	.02	.10
341 Tom Foley	.01	.05
342 Alex Trevino	.01	.05
343 Frank Tanana	.01	.05
344 George Canale RC	.01	.05
345 Harold Baines	.02	.10
346 Jim Presley	.01	.05
347 Junior Felix	.01	.05
348 Gary Wayne	.01	.05
349 Steve Finley	.02	.10
350 Bret Saberhagen	.02	.10
351 Roger Craig MG	.01	.05
352 Bryn Smith	.01	.05
353 Sandy Alomar Jr. (Not listed as Jr. on card front)	.02	.10
354 Stan Belinda RC	.02	.10
355 Marty Barrett	.01	.05
356 Randy Ready	.01	.05
357 Dave West	.01	.05
358 Andres Thomas	.01	.05
359 Jimmy Jones	.01	.05

360 Paul Molitor .02 .10
361 Randy McCament RC .01 .05
362 Damon Berryhill .01 .05
363 Dan Petry .01 .05
364 Rolando Roomes .01 .05
365 Ozzie Guillen .02 .10
366 Mike Heath .01 .05
367 Mike Morgan .01 .05
368 Bill Doran .01 .05
369 Todd Burns .01 .05
370 Tim Wallach .01 .05
371 Jimmy Key .02 .10
372 Terry Kennedy .01 .05
373 Alvin Davis .01 .05
374 Steve Cummings RC .01 .05
375 Dwight Evans .05 .15
376 Checklist 3 UER .01 .05
(Higuera misalphabet-
ized in Brewer list)
377 Mickey Weston RC .01 .05
378 Luis Salazar .01 .05
379 Steve Rosenberg .01 .05
380 Dave Winfield .02 .10
381 Frank Robinson MG .05 .15
382 Jeff Musselman .01 .05
383A John Morris ERR BL
383B John Morris .01 .05
384 Pat Combs .01 .05
385A Fred McGriff AS ERR BL
385B Fred McGriff AS .02 .10
386A Julio Franco AS ERR BL
386B Julio Franco AS .01 .05
387 Wade Boggs AS .02 .10
388 Cal Ripken AS .15 .40
389 Robin Yount AS .08 .25
390 Ruben Sierra AS .01 .05
391 Kirby Puckett AS .05 .15
392A Carlton Fisk AS ERR BL
392B Carlton Fisk AS .02 .10
393 Bret Saberhagen AS .01 .05
394 Jeff Ballard AS .01 .05
395A Jeff Russell AS ERR BL
395B Jeff Russell AS .01 .05
396 A.Bartlett Giamatti .08 .25
COMM MEM
397 Will Clark AS .02 .10
398 Ryne Sandberg AS .08 .25
399 Howard Johnson AS .01 .05
400 Ozzie Smith AS .08 .25
401 Kevin Mitchell AS .01 .05
402 Eric Davis AS .01 .05
403 Tony Gwynn AS .05 .15
404A Craig Biggio AS ERR BL
404B Craig Biggio AS .08 .25
405 Mike Scott AS .01 .05
406A Joe Magrane AS ERR BL
406B Joe Magrane AS .01 .05
407 Mark Davis AS .01 .05
408 Trevor Wilson .01 .05
409 Tom Brunansky .01 .05
410 Joe Boever .01 .05
411 Ken Phelps .01 .05
412 Jamie Moyer .02 .10
413 Brian DuBois RC .01 .05
414A Frank Thomas ERR NNOF 400.00 700.00
(Name missing on card front)
414B Frank Thomas RC .75 2.00
415 Shawon Dunston .01 .05
416 Dave Wayne Johnson RC .01 .05
417 Jim Gantner .01 .05
418 Tom Browning .01 .05
419 Beau Allred RC .01 .05
420 Carlton Fisk .05 .15
421 Greg Minton .01 .05
422 Pat Sheridan .01 .05
423 Fred Toliver .01 .05
424 Jerry Reuss .01 .05
425 Bill Landrum .01 .05
426 Jeff Hamilton UER .01 .05
(Stats say he fanned
197 times in 1987, but
he only had 147 at bats)
427 Carmen Castillo .01 .05
428 Steve Davis RC .01 .05
429 Tom Kelly MG .01 .05
430 Pete Incaviglia .01 .05
431 Randy Johnson .20 .50
432 Damaso Garcia .01 .05
433 Steve Olin RC .08 .25
434 Mark Carreon .01 .05
435 Kevin Seitzer .01 .05
436 Mel Hall .01 .05
437 Les Lancaster .01 .05
438 Greg Myers .01 .05
439 Jeff Parrett .01 .05
440 Alan Trammell .02 .10
441 Bob Kipper .01 .05
442 Jerry Browne .01 .05
443 Cris Carpenter .01 .05
444 Kyle Abbott FDP RC .01 .05
445 Danny Jackson .01 .05
446 Dan Pasqua .01 .05
447 Atlee Hammaker .01 .05
448 Greg Gagne .01 .05
449 Dennis Rasmussen .01 .05
450 Rickey Henderson .08 .25
451 Mark Lemke .01 .05
452 Luis DeLosSantos .01 .05
453 Jody Davis .01 .05
454 Jeff King .01 .05
455 Jeffrey Leonard .01 .05
456 Chris Gwynn .01 .05
457 Gregg Jefferies .02 .10
458 Bob McClure .01 .05
459 Jim Lefebvre MG .01 .05
460 Mike Scott .01 .05
461 Carlos Martinez .01 .05
462 Denny Walling .01 .05
463 Drew Hall .01 .05
464 Jerome Walton .01 .05
465 Kevin Gross .01 .05
466 Rance Mulliniks .01 .05
467 Juan Nieves .01 .05
468 Bill Ripken .01 .05
469 John Kruk .02 .10
470 Frank Viola .01 .05
471 Mike Brumley .01 .05
472 Jose Uribe .01 .05
473 Joe Price .01 .05
474 Rich Thompson .01 .05
475 Bob Welch .01 .05
476 Brad Komminsk .01 .05
477 Willie Fraser .01 .05
478 Mike LaValliere .01 .05
479 Frank White .02 .10
480 Sid Fernandez .01 .05
481 Garry Templeton .01 .05
482 Steve Carter .01 .05
483 Alejandro Pena .01 .05
484 Mike Fitzgerald .01 .05
485 John Candelaria .01 .05
486 Jeff Treadway .01 .05
487 Steve Searcy .01 .05
488 Ken Oberkfell .01 .05
489 Nick Leyva MG .01 .05
490 Dan Plesac .01 .05
491 Dave Cochrane RC .01 .05
492 Ron Oester .01 .05
493 Jason Grimsley RC .02 .10
494 Terry Puhl .01 .05
495 Lee Smith .02 .10
496 Cecil Espy UER .01 .05
('88 stats have 3
SB's, should be 33)
497 Dave Schmidt .01 .05
498 Rick Schu .01 .05
499 Bill Long .01 .05
500 Kevin Mitchell .01 .05
501 Matt Young .01 .05
502 Mitch Webster .01 .05
503 Randy St.Claire .01 .05
504 Tom O'Malley .01 .05
505 Kelly Gruber .01 .05
506 Tom Glavine .05 .15
507 Gary Redus .01 .05
508 Terry Leach .01 .05
509 Tom Pagnozzi .01 .05
510 Dwight Gooden .02 .10
511 Clay Parker .01 .05
512 Gary Pettis .01 .05
513 Mark Eichhorn .01 .05
514 Andy Allanson .01 .05
515 Len Dykstra .02 .10
516 Tim Leary .01 .05
517 Roberto Alomar .05 .15
518 Bill Krueger .01 .05
519 Bucky Dent MG .01 .05
520 Mitch Williams .01 .05
521 Craig Worthington .01 .05
522 Mike Dunne .01 .05
523 Jay Bell .02 .10
524 Daryl Boston .01 .05
525 Wally Joyner .02 .10
526 Checklist 4 .01 .05
527 Ron Hassey .01 .05
528 Kevin Wickander UER .01 .05
(Monthly scoreboard
strikeout total was 2.2,
that was his innings
pitched total)
529 Greg A. Harris .01 .05
530 Mark Langston .01 .05
531 Ken Caminiti .02 .10
532 Cecilio Guante .01 .05
533 Tim Jones .01 .05
534 Louie Meadows .01 .05
535 John Smoltz .08 .25
536 Bob Geren .01 .05
537 Mark Grant .01 .05
538 Bill Spiers UER .01 .05
(Photo actually
George Canale)
539 Neal Heaton .01 .05
540 Danny Tartabull .01 .05
541 Pat Perry .01 .05
542 Darren Daulton .02 .10
543 Nelson Liriano .01 .05
544 Dennis Boyd .01 .05
545 Kevin McReynolds .01 .05
546 Kevin Hickey .01 .05
547 Jack Howell .01 .05
548 Pat Clements .01 .05
549 Don Zimmer MG .01 .05
550 Julio Franco .02 .10
551 Tim Crews .01 .05
552 Mike (Miss.) Smith RC .01 .05
553 Scott Scudder UER .01 .05
(Cedar Rap1ds)
554 Jay Buhner .02 .10
555 Jack Morris .02 .10
556 Gene Larkin .01 .05
557 Jeff Innis RC .01 .05
558 Rafael Ramirez .01 .05
559 Andy McGaffigan .01 .05
560 Steve Sax .01 .05
561 Ken Dayley .01 .05
562 Chad Kreuter .01 .05
563 Alex Sanchez .01 .05
564 Tyler Houston FDP RC .08 .25
565 Scott Fletcher .01 .05
566 Mark Knudson .01 .05
567 Ron Gant .02 .10
568 John Smiley .01 .05
569 Ivan Calderon .01 .05
570 Cal Ripken .30 .75
571 Brett Butler .02 .10
572 Greg W. Harris .01 .05
573 Danny Heep .01 .05
574 Bill Swift .01 .05
575 Lance Parrish .01 .05
576 Mike Dyer RC .01 .05
577 Charlie Hayes .01 .05
578 Joe Magrane .01 .05
579 Art Howe MG .01 .05
580 Joe Carter .02 .10
581 Ken Griffey Sr. .02 .10
582 Rick Honeycutt .01 .05
583 Bruce Benedict .01 .05
584 Phil Stephenson .01 .05
585 Kal Daniels .01 .05
586 Edwin Nunez .01 .05
587 Lance Johnson .01 .05
588 Rick Rhoden .01 .05
589 Mike Aldrete .01 .05
590 Ozzie Smith .15 .40
591 Todd Stottlemyre .02 .10
592 R.J. Reynolds .01 .05
593 Scott Bradley .01 .05
594 Luis Sojo RC .01 .05
595 Greg Swindell .01 .05
596 Jose DeJesus .01 .05
597 Chris Bosio .01 .05
598 Brady Anderson .02 .10
599 Frank Williams .01 .05
600 Darryl Strawberry .02 .10
601 Luis Rivera .01 .05
602 Scott Garrelts .01 .05
603 Tony Armas .01 .05
604 Ron Robinson .01 .05
605 Mike Scioscia .01 .05
606 Storm Davis .01 .05
607 Steve Jeltz .01 .05
608 Eric Anthony RC .02 .10
609 Sparky Anderson MG .02 .10
610 Pedro Guerrero .01 .05
611 Walt Terrell .01 .05
612 Dave Gallagher .01 .05
613 Jeff Pico .01 .05
614 Nelson Santovenia .01 .05
615 Rob Deer .01 .05
616 Brian Holman .01 .05
617 Geronimo Berroa .01 .05
618 Ed Whitson .01 .05
619 Rob Ducey .01 .05
620 Tony Castillo .01 .05
621 Melido Perez .01 .05
622 Sid Bream .01 .05
623 Jim Corsi .01 .05
624A Darrin Jackson ERR BL
624B Darrin Jackson .01 .05
625 Roger McDowell .01 .05
626 Bob Melvin .01 .05
627 Jose Rijo .01 .05
628 Candy Maldonado .01 .05
629 Eric Hetzel .01 .05
630 Gary Gaetti .02 .10
631 John Wetteland .08 .25
632 Scott Lusader .01 .05
633 Dennis Cook .01 .05
634 Luis Polonia .01 .05
635 Brian Downing .01 .05
636 Jesse Orosco .01 .05
637 Craig Reynolds .01 .05
638 Jeff Montgomery .02 .10
639 Tony LaRussa MG .02 .10
640 Rick Sutcliffe .02 .10
641 Doug Strange RC .01 .05
642 Jack Armstrong .01 .05
643 Alfredo Griffin .01 .05
644 Paul Assenmacher .01 .05
645 Jose Oquendo .01 .05
646 Checklist 5 .01 .05
647 Rex Hudler .01 .05
648 Jim Clancy .01 .05
649 Dan Murphy RC .02 .10
650 Mike Witt .01 .05
651 Rafael Santana .01 .05
652 Mike Boddicker .01 .05
653 John Moses .01 .05
654 Paul Coleman FDP RC .02 .10
655 Gregg Olson .02 .10
656 Mackey Sasser .01 .05
657 Terry Mulholland .01 .05
658 Donell Nixon .01 .05
659 Greg Cadaret .01 .05
660 Vince Coleman .01 .05
661 Dick Howser TBC'85 .01 .05
UER (Seaver's 300th
on 7/11/85, should
be 8/4/85)
662 Mike Schmidt TBC'80 .08 .25
663 Fred Lynn TBC'75 .01 .05
664 Johnny Bench TBC'70 .05 .15
665 Sandy Koufax TBC'65 .20 .50
666 Brian Fisher .01 .05
667 Curt Wilkerson .01 .05
668 Joe Oliver .01 .05
669 Tom Lasorda MG .08 .25
670 Dennis Eckersley .02 .10
671 Bob Boone .02 .10
672 Roy Smith .01 .05
673 Joey Meyer .01 .05
674 Spike Owen .01 .05
675 Jim Abbott .05 .15
676 Randy Kutcher .01 .05
677 Jay Tibbs .01 .05
678 Kirt Manwaring UER .01 .05
('88 Phoenix stats
repeated)
679 Gary Ward .01 .05
680 Howard Johnson .01 .05
681 Mike Schooler .01 .05
682 Dann Bilardello .01 .05
683 Kenny Rogers .02 .10
684 Julio Machado RC .01 .05
685 Tony Fernandez .01 .05
686 Carmelo Martinez .01 .05
687 Tim Birtsas .01 .05
688 Milt Thompson .01 .05
689 Rich Yett .01 .05
690 Mark McGwire .25 .60
691 Chuck Cary .01 .05
692 Sammy Sosa RC 1.00 2.50
693 Calvin Schiraldi .01 .05
694 Mike Stanton RC .08 .25
695 Tom Henke .01 .05
696 B.J. Surhoff .02 .10
697 Mike Davis .01 .05
698 Omar Vizquel .08 .25
699 Jim Leyland MG .01 .05
700 Kirby Puckett .08 .25
701 Bernie Williams RC .60 1.50
702 Tony Phillips .01 .05
703 Jeff Brantley .01 .05
704 Chip Hale RC .01 .05
705 Claudell Washington .01 .05
706 Geno Petralli .01 .05
707 Luis Aquino .01 .05
708 Larry Sheets .01 .05
709 Juan Berenguer .01 .05
710 Von Hayes .01 .05
711 Rick Aguilera .02 .10
712 Todd Benzinger .01 .05
713 Tim Drummond RC .01 .05
714 Marquis Grissom RC .15 .40
715 Greg Maddux .15 .40
716 Steve Balboni .01 .05
717 Ron Karkovice .01 .05
718 Gary Sheffield .08 .25
719 Wally Whitehurst .01 .05
720 Andres Galarraga .02 .10
721 Lee Mazzilli .01 .05
722 Felix Fermin .01 .05
723 Jeff D. Robinson .01 .05
724 Juan Bell .01 .05
725 Terry Pendleton .02 .10
726 Gene Nelson .01 .05
727 Pat Tabler .01 .05
728A Jim Acker ERR BL
728B Jim Acker .01 .05
729 Bobby Valentine MG .01 .05
730 Tony Gwynn .10 .30
731 Don Carman .01 .05
732 Ernest Riles .01 .05
733 John Dopson .01 .05
734 Kevin Elster .01 .05
735 Charlie Hough .02 .10
736 Rick Dempsey .01 .05
737 Chris Sabo .01 .05
738 Gene Harris .01 .05
739 Dale Sveum .01 .05
740 Jesse Barfield .01 .05
741 Steve Wilson .01 .05
742 Ernie Whitt .01 .05
743 Tom Candiotti .01 .05
744 Kelly Mann RC .01 .05
745 Hubie Brooks .01 .05
746 Dave Smith .01 .05
747 Randy Bush .01 .05
748 Doyle Alexander .01 .05
749 Mark Parent UER .01 .05
('87 BA .80,
should be .080)
750 Dale Murphy .05 .15
751 Steve Lyons .01 .05
752 Tom Gordon .02 .10
753 Chris Speier .01 .05
754 Bob Walk .01 .05
755 Rafael Palmeiro .05 .15
756 Ken Howell .01 .05
757 Larry Walker RC .40 1.00
758 Mark Thurmond .01 .05
759 Tom Trebelhorn MG .01 .05
760 Wade Boggs .05 .15
761 Mike Jackson .01 .05
762 Doug Dascenzo .01 .05
763 Dennis Martinez .02 .10
764 Tim Teufel .01 .05
765 Chili Davis .02 .10
766 Brian Meyer .01 .05
767 Tracy Jones .01 .05
768 Chuck Crim .01 .05
769 Greg Hibbard RC .02 .10
770 Cory Snyder .01 .05
771 Pete Smith .01 .05
772 Jeff Reed .01 .05
773 Dave Leiper .01 .05
774 Ben McDonald RC .08 .25
775 Andy Van Slyke .05 .15
776 Charlie Leibrandt .01 .05
777 Tim Laudner .01 .05
778 Mike Jeffcoat .01 .05
779 Lloyd Moseby .01 .05
780 Orel Hershiser .02 .10
781 Mario Diaz .01 .05
782 Jose Alvarez .01 .05
783 Checklist 6 .01 .05
784 Scott Bailes .01 .05
785 Jim Rice .02 .10
786 Eric King .01 .05
787 Rene Gonzales .01 .05
788 Frank DiPino .01 .05
789 John Wathan MG .01 .05
790 Gary Carter .02 .10
791 Alvaro Espinoza .01 .05
792 Gerald Perry .01 .05
NNO George Bush PRES

1990 Topps Tiffany

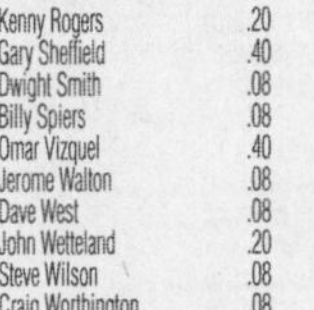

For the seventh year, Topps issued through its hobby dealer network a special "Tiffany" set. These sets which parallel the regular cards consist of 792 standard-size cards. These cards were only issued in complete set form. Since the number of cards produced is similar to the 1989 issue, it is believed that approximately 15,000 of these sets were produced.

COMP.FACT.SET (792) 30.00 60.00
*STARS: 6X TO 15X BASIC CARDS
*ROOKIES: 4X TO 10X BASIC CARDS
414 Frank Thomas FDP 8.00 20.00

1990 Topps Batting Leaders

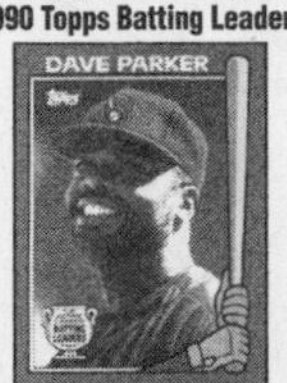

The 1990 Topps Batting Leaders set contains 22 standard-size cards. The front borders are emerald green, and the backs are white, blue and evergreen. This set, like the 1989 set of the same name, depicts the 22 major leaguers with the highest lifetime batting averages (minimum 765 games). The card numbers correspond to the player's rank in terms of career batting average. Many of the photos are the same as those from the 1989 set. The cards were distributed one per special 100-card Topps blister pack available only at K-Mart stores and were produced by Topps. The K-Mart logo does not appear anywhere on the cards themselves, although there is a Topps logo on the front and back of each card.

COMPLETE SET (22) 40.00 100.00
1 Wade Boggs 4.00 10.00
2 Tony Gwynn 8.00 20.00
3 Kirby Puckett 6.00 15.00
4 Don Mattingly 8.00 20.00
5 George Brett 8.00 20.00
6 Pedro Guerrero .20 .50
7 Tim Raines .40 1.00
8 Paul Molitor 3.00 8.00
9 Jim Rice .40 1.00
10 Keith Hernandez .40 1.00
11 Julio Franco .40 1.00
12 Carney Lansford .40 1.00
13 Dave Parker .40 1.00
14 Willie McGee .40 1.00
15 Robin Yount 3.00 8.00
16 Tony Fernandez .40 1.00
17 Eddie Murray 3.00 8.00
18 Johnny Ray .20 .50
19 Lonnie Smith .20 .50
20 Phil Bradley .20 .50
21 Rickey Henderson 5.00 12.00
22 Kent Hrbek .40 1.00

1990 Topps Glossy All-Stars

The 1990 Topps Glossy All-Star set contains 22 standard-size glossy cards. The front and back borders are white, and other design elements are red, blue and yellow. This set is almost identical to previous year sets of the same name. One card was included in each 1990 Topps rack pack. The players selected for the set were the starters, managers, and honorary captains in the previous year's All-Star Game.

COMPLETE SET (22) 1.20 3.00
1 Tom Lasorda MG .07 .20
2 Will Clark .07 .20
3 Ryne Sandberg .20 .50
4 Howard Johnson .01 .05
5 Ozzie Smith .25 .60
6 Kevin Mitchell .01 .05
7 Eric Davis .02 .10
8 Tony Gwynn .30 .75
9 Benito Santiago .02 .10
10 Rick Reuschel .01 .05
11 Don Drysdale CAPT .08 .25
12 Tony LaRussa MG .02 .10
13 Mark McGwire .30 .75
14 Julio Franco .02 .10
15 Wade Boggs .15 .40
16 Cal Ripken .60 1.50
17 Bo Jackson .08 .25
18 Kirby Puckett .15 .40
19 Ruben Sierra .02 .10
20 Terry Steinbach .01 .05
21 Dave Stewart .02 .10
22 Carl Yastrzemski CAPT .10 .30

1990 Topps Glossy Send-Ins

The 1990 Topps Glossy 60 set was issued as a mailaway by Topps for the eighth straight year. This standard-size, 60-card set features two young players among every ten players as Topps again broke down these cards into six series of ten cards each.

COMPLETE SET (60) 4.80 12.00
1 Ryne Sandberg .60 1.50

2 Nolan Ryan 2.00 5.00
3 Glenn Davis .02 .10
4 Dave Stewart .07 .20
5 Barry Larkin .15 .40
6 Carney Lansford .07 .20
7 Darryl Strawberry .07 .20
8 Steve Sax .02 .10
9 Carlos Martinez .02 .10
10 Gary Sheffield .30 .75
11 Don Mattingly 1.00 2.50
12 Mark Grace .40 1.00
13 Bret Saberhagen .07 .20
14 Mike Scott .02 .10
15 Robin Yount .20 .50
16 Ozzie Smith .60 1.50
17 Jeff Ballard .02 .10
18 Rick Reuschel .02 .10
19 Greg Briley .02 .10
20 Ken Griffey Jr. 1.00 2.50
21 Kevin Mitchell .02 .10
22 Wade Boggs .30 .75
23 Dwight Gooden .07 .20
24 George Bell .02 .10
25 Eric Davis .07 .20
26 Ruben Sierra .07 .20
27 Roberto Alomar .30 .75
28 Gary Gaetti .07 .20
29 Gregg Olson .02 .10
30 Tom Gordon .10 .30
31 Jose Canseco .30 .75
32 Pedro Guerrero .07 .20
33 Joe Carter .07 .20
34 Mike Scioscia .07 .20
35 Julio Franco .07 .20
36 Joe Magrane .07 .20
37 Rickey Henderson .40 1.00
38 Tim Raines .07 .20
39 Jerome Walton .02 .10
40 Bob Geren .02 .10
41 Andre Dawson .15 .40
42 Mark McGwire 1.00 2.50
43 Howard Johnson .02 .10
44 Bo Jackson .20 .50
45 Shawon Dunston .02 .10
46 Carlton Fisk .20 .50
47 Mitch Williams .02 .10
48 Kirby Puckett .40 1.00
49 Craig Worthington .02 .10
50 Jim Abbott .20 .50
51 Cal Ripken 2.00 5.00
52 Will Clark .15 .40
53 Dennis Eckersley .20 .50
54 Craig Biggio .10 .30
55 Fred McGriff .15 .40
56 Tony Gwynn .75 2.00
57 Mickey Tettleton .07 .20
58 Mark Davis .02 .10
59 Omar Vizquel .15 .40
60 Gregg Jefferies .02 .10

1990 Topps Rookies

The 1990 Topps Jumbo Rookies set contains 33 standard-size glossy cards. The front and back borders are white, and other design elements are red, blue and yellow. This set is almost identical to previous year sets of the same name except that it contains 33 cards rather than only 22. One card was included in each 1990 Topps "jumbo" pack. The cards are numbered in alphabetical order. Sets of these cards were issued and stamped with various colors so Topps could test for colors of foil stamping.

COMPLETE SET (33) 12.50 25.00
1 Jim Abbott .30 .75
2 Albert Belle .40 1.00
3 Andy Benes .20 .50
4 Greg Briley .08 .25
5 Kevin Brown .20 .50
6 Mark Carreon .08 .25
7 Mike Devereaux .08 .25
8 Junior Felix .08 .25
9 Bob Geren .08 .25
10 Tom Gordon .20 .50
11 Ken Griffey Jr. 2.00 5.00
12 Pete Harnisch .08 .25
13 Greg W. Harris .08 .25
14 Greg Hibbard .08 .25
15 Ken Hill .08 .25
16 Gregg Jefferies .08 .25
17 Jeff King .08 .25
18 Derek Lilliquist .08 .25
19 Carlos Martinez .08 .25
20 Ramon Martinez .08 .25
21 Bob Milacki .08 .25
22 Gregg Olson .08 .25
23 Donn Pall .08 .25
24 Kenny Rogers .20 .50
25 Gary Sheffield .40 1.00
26 Dwight Smith .08 .25
27 Billy Spiers .08 .25
28 Omar Vizquel .40 1.00
29 Jerome Walton .08 .25
30 Dave West .08 .25
31 John Wetteland .20 .50
32 Steve Wilson .08 .25
33 Craig Worthington .08 .25

1990 Topps Wax Box Cards

The 1990 Topps wax box cards comprise four different box bottoms with four cards each, for a total of 16 standard-size cards. The front borders are green. The vertically oriented backs are yellowish green. The cards depict various career milestones achieved during the 1989 season. The card numbers are actually the letters A through P. The card ordering is alphabetical by player's name.

COMPLETE SET (16) 3.20 8.00
A Wade Boggs .20 .50
B George Brett .40 1.00
C Andre Dawson .15 .40
D Darrell Evans .07 .20
E Dwight Gooden .07 .20
F Rickey Henderson .30 .75
G Tom Lasorda MG .10 .30
H Fred Lynn .02 .10
I Mark McGwire .50 1.25
J Dave Parker .07 .20
K Jeff Reardon .07 .20
L Rick Reuschel .02 .10
M Jim Rice .07 .20
N Cal Ripken 1.00 2.50
O Nolan Ryan 1.00 2.50
P Ryne Sandberg .20 .50

1990 Topps Traded

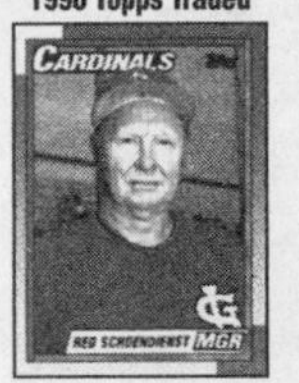

The 1990 Topps Traded Set was the tenth consecutive year Topps issued a 132-card standard-size set at the end of the year. For the first time, Topps not only issued the set in factory set form but also distributed (on a significant basis) the set via seven-card wax packs. Unlike the factory set cards (which feature the whiter paper stock typical of the previous years Traded sets), the wax pack cards feature gray paper stock. Gray and white stock cards are equally valued. This set was arranged alphabetically by player and includes a mix of traded players and rookies for whom Topps did not include a card in the regular set. The key Rookie Cards in this set are Travis Fryman, Todd Hundley and Dave Justice.

COMPLETE SET (132) 1.25 3.00
COMP.FACT.SET (132) 1.25 3.00
1T Darrel Akerfelds .01 .05
2T Sandy Alomar Jr. .02 .10
3T Brad Arnsberg .01 .05
4T Steve Avery .01 .05
5T Wally Backman .01 .05
6T Carlos Baerga RC .08 .25
7T Kevin Bass .01 .05
8T Willie Blair RC .02 .10
9T Mike Blowers RC .08 .25
10T Shawn Boskie RC .02 .10
11T Daryl Boston .01 .05
12T Dennis Boyd .01 .05
13T Glenn Braggs .01 .05
14T Hubie Brooks .01 .05
15T Tom Brunansky .01 .05
16T John Burkett .01 .05
17T Casey Candaele .01 .05
18T John Candelaria .01 .05
19T Gary Carter .02 .10
20T Joe Carter .02 .10
21T Rick Cerone .01 .05
22T Scott Coolbaugh RC .01 .05
23T Bobby Cox MG .02 .10
24T Mark Davis .01 .05
25T Storm Davis .01 .05
26T Edgar Diaz RC .01 .05
27T Wayne Edwards RC .01 .05
28T Mark Eichhorn .01 .05
29T Scott Erickson RC .08 .25
30T Nick Esasky .01 .05
31T Cecil Fielder .02 .10
32T John Franco .02 .10
33T Travis Fryman RC .15 .40
34T Bill Gullickson .01 .05
35T Darryl Hamilton .01 .05
36T Mike Harkey .01 .05
37T Bud Harrelson MG .01 .05
38T Billy Hatcher .01 .05
39T Keith Hernandez .02 .10
40T Joe Hesketh .01 .05
41T Dave Hollins RC .08 .25

42T Sam Horn .01 .05
43T Steve Howard RC .01 .05
44T Todd Hundley RC .08 .25
45T Jeff Huson .01 .05
46T Chris James .01 .05
47T Stan Javier .01 .05
48T Dave Justice RC .20 .50
49T Jeff Kaiser .01 .05
50T Dana Kiecker RC .01 .05
51T Joe Klink RC .01 .05
52T Brent Knackert RC .02 .10
53T Brad Komminsk .01 .05
54T Mark Langston .01 .05
55T Tim Layana RC .01 .05
56T Rick Leach .01 .05
57T Terry Leach .01 .05
58T Tim Leary .01 .05
59T Craig Lefferts .01 .05
60T Charlie Leibrandt .01 .05
61T Jim Leyritz RC .08 .25
62T Fred Lynn .01 .05
63T Kevin Maas RC .08 .25
64T Shane Mack .01 .05
65T Candy Maldonado .01 .05
66T Fred Manrique .01 .05
67T Mike Marshall .01 .05
68T Carmelo Martinez .01 .05
69T John Marzano .01 .05
70T Ben McDonald .01 .05
71T Jack McDowell .01 .05
72T John McNamara MG .01 .05
73T Orlando Mercado .01 .05
74T Stump Merrill MG RC .01 .05
75T Alan Mills RC .02 .10
76T Hal Morris .01 .05
77T Lloyd Moseby .01 .05
78T Randy Myers .02 .10
79T Tim Naehring RC .02 .10
80T Junior Noboa .01 .05
81T Matt Nokes .01 .05
82T Pete O'Brien .01 .05
83T John Olerud RC .20 .50
84T Greg Olson (C) RC .02 .10
85T Junior Ortiz .01 .05
86T Dave Parker .02 .10
87T Rick Parker RC .01 .05
88T Bob Patterson .01 .05
89T Alejandro Pena .01 .05
90T Tony Pena .01 .05
91T Pascual Perez .01 .05
92T Gerald Perry .01 .05
93T Dan Petry .01 .05
94T Gary Pettis .01 .05
95T Tony Phillips .01 .05
96T Lou Piniella MG .02 .10
97T Luis Polonia .01 .05
98T Jim Presley .01 .05
99T Scott Radinsky RC .02 .10
100T Willie Randolph .02 .10
101T Jeff Reardon .02 .10
102T Greg Riddoch MG RC .01 .05
103T Jeff Robinson .01 .05
104T Ron Robinson .01 .05
105T Kevin Romine .01 .05
106T Scott Ruskin RC .01 .05
107T John Russell .01 .05
108T Bill Sampen RC .01 .05
109T Juan Samuel .01 .05
110T Scott Sanderson .01 .05
111T Jack Savage .01 .05
112T Dave Schmidt .01 .05
113T R.Schoendienst MG .08 .25
114T Terry Shumpert RC .01 .05
115T Matt Sinatro .01 .05
116T Don Slaught .01 .05
117T Bryn Smith .01 .05
118T Lee Smith .02 .10
119T Paul Sorrento RC .08 .25
120T Franklin Stubbs UER .01 .05
('84 says '99 and has the same stats as '89, '83 stats are missing)
121T Russ Swan RC .02 .10
122T Bob Tewksbury .01 .05
123T Wayne Tolleson .01 .05
124T John Tudor .01 .05
125T Randy Veres .01 .05
126T Hector Villanueva RC .02 .10
127T Mitch Webster .01 .05
128T Ernie Whitt .01 .05
129T Frank Wills .01 .05
130T Dave Winfield .02 .10
131T Matt Young .01 .05
132T Checklist 1T-132T .01 .05

1990 Topps Traded Tiffany

Again, one of these sets were issued for each regular Tiffany set produced. These 132 standard-size cards parallel the regular Traded issue and feature Glossy fronts and clearer backs. These cards were issued in complete set form only and were distributed through Topps hobby network. Similar to the regular Topps Tiffany set, it is believed that 15,000 of these sets were produced.

COMP.FACT.SET (132) 12.50 30.00
*STARS: 6X TO 15X BASIC CARDS
*ROOKIES: 6X TO 15X BASIC CARDS

1991 Topps

This set marks Topps tenth consecutive year of issuing a 792-card standard-size set. Cards were primarily issued in wax packs, rack packs and factory sets. The fronts feature a full color player photo with a white border. Topps also commemorated their fortieth anniversary by including a "Topps 40" logo on the front and back of each card. Virtually all of the cards have been discovered without the 40th logo on the back. Subsets include Record Breakers (2-8) and All-Stars (386-407). In addition, First Draft Picks and Future Stars subset cards are scattered throughout the set. The key Rookie Cards include Chipper Jones and Brian McRae. As a special promotion Topps inserted (randomly) into their wax packs one of every previous card they ever issued.

COMPLETE SET (792) 8.00 20.00
COMP.FACT.SET (792) 10.00 25.00
1 Nolan Ryan .60 1.50
2 George Brett RB .10 .30
3 Carlton Fisk RB .02 .10
4 Kevin Maas RB .01 .05
5 Cal Ripken RB .15 .40
6 Nolan Ryan RB .20 .50
7 Ryne Sandberg RB .08 .25
8 Bobby Thigpen RB .01 .05
9 Darrin Fletcher .01 .05
10 Gregg Olson .01 .05
11 Roberto Kelly .01 .05
12 Paul Assenmacher .01 .05
13 Mariano Duncan .01 .05
14 Dennis Lamp .01 .05
15 Von Hayes .01 .05
16 Mike Heath .01 .05
17 Jeff Brantley .01 .05
18 Nelson Liriano .01 .05
19 Jeff D. Robinson .01 .05
20 Pedro Guerrero .02 .10
21 Joe Morgan MG .01 .05
22 Storm Davis .01 .05
23 Jim Gantner .01 .05
24 Dave Martinez .01 .05
25 Tim Belcher .01 .05
26 Luis Sojo UER .01 .05
(Born in Barquisimento, not Carquis)
27 Bobby Witt .01 .05
28 Alvaro Espinoza .01 .05
29 Bob Walk .01 .05
30 Gregg Jefferies .01 .05
31 Colby Ward RC .01 .05
32 Mike Simms RC .01 .05
33 Barry Jones .01 .05
34 Atlee Hammaker .01 .05
35 Greg Maddux .15 .40
36 Donnie Hill .01 .05
37 Tom Bolton .01 .05
38 Scott Bradley .01 .05
39 Jim Neidlinger RC .01 .05
40 Kevin Mitchell .01 .05
41 Ken Dayley .01 .05
42 Chris Hoiles .01 .05
43 Roger McDowell .01 .05
44 Mike Felder .01 .05
45 Chris Sabo .01 .05
46 Tim Drummond .01 .05
47 Brook Jacoby .01 .05
48 Dennis Boyd .01 .05
49A Pat Borders ERR .08 .25
(40 steals at Kinston in '86)
49B Pat Borders COR .01 .05
(0 steals at Kinston in '86)
50 Bob Welch .01 .05
51 Art Howe MG .01 .05
52 Francisco Oliveras .01 .05
53 Mike Sharperson UER .01 .05
(Born in 1961, not 1960)
54 Gary Mielke .01 .05
55 Jeffrey Leonard .01 .05
56 Jeff Parrett .01 .05
57 Jack Howell .01 .05
58 Mel Stottlemyre Jr. .01 .05
59 Eric Yelding .01 .05
60 Frank Viola .02 .10
61 Stan Javier .01 .05
62 Lee Guetterman .01 .05
63 Milt Thompson .01 .05
64 Tom Herr .01 .05
65 Bruce Hurst .01 .05
66 Terry Kennedy .01 .05
67 Rick Honeycutt .01 .05
68 Gary Sheffield .02 .10
69 Steve Wilson .01 .05
70 Ellis Burks .02 .10
71 Jim Acker .01 .05
72 Junior Ortiz .01 .05
73 Craig Worthington .01 .05
74 Shane Andrews RC .08 .25
75 Jack Morris .02 .10
76 Jerry Browne .01 .05
77 Drew Hall .01 .05
78 Geno Petralli .01 .05
79 Frank Thomas .08 .25
80A Fernando Valenzuela .15 .40
ERR (104 earned runs in '90 tied for league lead)
80B Fernando Valenzuela .02 .10
COR (104 earned runs in '90 led league, 20 CG's in 1986 now italicized)
81 Cito Gaston MG .01 .05
82 Tom Glavine .05 .15
83 Daryl Boston .01 .05
84 Bob McClure .01 .05
85 Jesse Barfield .01 .05
86 Les Lancaster .01 .05
87 Tracy Jones .01 .05
88 Bob Tewksbury .01 .05
89 Darren Daulton .02 .10
90 Danny Tartabull .01 .05
91 Greg Colbrunn RC .08 .25
92 Danny Jackson .01 .05
93 Ivan Calderon .01 .05
94 John Dopson .01 .05
95 Paul Molitor .02 .10
96 Trevor Wilson .01 .05
97A Brady Anderson ERR .15 .40
(September, 2 RBI and 3 hits, should be 3 RBI and 14 hits
97B Brady Anderson COR .02 .10
98 Sergio Valdez .01 .05
99 Chris Gwynn .01 .05
100 Don Mattingly COR .25 .60
(101 hits in 1990)
100A Don Mattingly ERR .75 2.00
(10 hits in 1990)
101 Rob Ducey .01 .05
102 Gene Larkin .01 .05
103 Tim Costo RC .01 .05
104 Don Robinson .01 .05
105 Kevin McReynolds .01 .05
106 Ed Nunez .01 .05
107 Luis Polonia .01 .05
108 Matt Young .01 .05
109 Greg Riddoch MG .01 .05
110 Tom Henke .01 .05
111 Andres Thomas .01 .05
112 Frank DiPino .01 .05
113 Carl Everett RC .20 .50
114 Lance Dickson RC .02 .10
115 Hubie Brooks .01 .05
116 Mark Davis .01 .05
117 Dion James .01 .05
118 Tom Edens RC .01 .05
119 Carl Nichols .01 .05
120 Joe Carter .02 .10
121 Eric King .01 .05
122 Paul O'Neill .05 .15
123 Greg A. Harris .01 .05
124 Randy Bush .01 .05
125 Steve Bedrosian .01 .05
126 Bernard Gilkey .01 .05
127 Joe Price .01 .05
128 Travis Fryman .02 .10
(Front has SS back has SS-3B)
129 Mark Eichhorn .01 .05
130 Ozzie Smith .15 .40
131A Checklist 1 ERR .08 .25
727 Phil Bradley
131B Checklist 1 COR .01 .05
717 Phil Bradley
132 Jamie Quirk .01 .05
133 Greg Briley .01 .05
134 Kevin Elster .01 .05
135 Jerome Walton .01 .05
136 Dave Schmidt .01 .05
137 Randy Ready .01 .05
138 Jamie Moyer .02 .10
139 Jeff Treadway .01 .05
140 Fred McGriff .05 .15
141 Nick Leyva MG .01 .05
142 Curt Wilkerson .01 .05
143 John Smiley .01 .05
144 Dave Henderson .01 .05
145 Lou Whitaker .02 .10
146 Dan Plesac .01 .05
147 Carlos Baerga .01 .05
148 Rey Palacios .01 .05
149 Al Osuna UER RC .02 .10
(Shown throwing right, but bio says lefty)
150 Cal Ripken .30 .75
151 Tom Browning .01 .05
152 Mickey Hatcher .01 .05
153 Bryan Harvey .01 .05
154 Jay Buhner .02 .10
155A Dwight Evans ERR .20 .50
(Led league with 162 games in '82)
155B Dwight Evans COR .05 .15
(Tied for lead with 162 games in '82)
156 Carlos Martinez .01 .05
157 John Smoltz .05 .15
158 Jose Uribe .01 .05
159 Joe Boever .01 .05
160 Vince Coleman UER .01 .05
(Wrong birth year, born 9/22/60)
161 Tim Leary .01 .05
162 Ozzie Canseco .01 .05
163 Dave Johnson .01 .05
164 Edgar Diaz .01 .05
165 Sandy Alomar Jr. .01 .05
166 Harold Baines .02 .10
167A R.Tomlin ERR .08 .25
Harriburg
167B R.Tomlin RC COR .02 .10
Harrisburg
168 John Olerud .02 .10
169 Luis Aquino .01 .05
170 Carlton Fisk .05 .15
171 Tony LaRussa MG .02 .10
172 Pete Incaviglia .01 .05
173 Jason Grimsley .01 .05
174 Ken Caminiti .02 .10
175 Jack Armstrong .01 .05
176 John Orton .01 .05
177 Reggie Harris .01 .05
178 Dave Valle .01 .05
179 Pete Harnisch .01 .05
180 Tony Gwynn .10 .30
181 Duane Ward .01 .05
182 Junior Noboa .01 .05
183 Clay Parker .01 .05
184 Gary Green .01 .05
185 Joe Magrane .01 .05
186 Rod Booker .01 .05
187 Greg Cadaret .01 .05
188 Damon Berryhill .01 .05
189 Daryl Irvine RC .01 .05
190 Matt Williams .02 .10
191 Willie Blair .01 .05
192 Rob Deer .01 .05
193 Felix Fermin .01 .05
194 Xavier Hernandez .01 .05
195 Wally Joyner .02 .10
196 Jim Vatcher RC .01 .05
197 Chris Nabholz .01 .05
198 R.J. Reynolds .01 .05
199 Mike Hartley .01 .05
200 Darryl Strawberry .02 .10
201 Tom Kelly MG .01 .05
202 Jim Leyritz .01 .05
203 Gene Harris .01 .05
204 Herm Winningham .01 .05
205 Mike Perez RC .02 .10
206 Carlos Quintana .01 .05
207 Gary Wayne .01 .05
208 Willie Wilson .01 .05
209 Ken Howell .01 .05
210 Lance Parrish .02 .10
211 Brian Barnes RC .01 .05
212 Steve Finley .02 .10
213 Frank Wills .01 .05
214 Joe Girardi .01 .05
215 Dave Smith .01 .05
216 Greg Gagne .01 .05
217 Chris Bosio .01 .05
218 Rick Parker .01 .05
219 Jack McDowell .01 .05
220 Tim Wallach .01 .05
221 Don Slaught .01 .05
222 Brian McRae RC .08 .25
223 Allan Anderson .01 .05
224 Juan Gonzalez .08 .25
225 Randy Johnson .10 .30
226 Alfredo Griffin .01 .05
227 Steve Avery UER .01 .05
(Pitched 13 games for Durham in 1989, not 2)
228 Rex Hudler .01 .05
229 Rance Mulliniks .01 .05
230 Sid Fernandez .01 .05
231 Doug Rader MG .01 .05
232 Jose DeJesus .01 .05
233 Al Leiter .02 .10
234 Scott Erickson .01 .05
235 Dave Parker .02 .10
236A Frank Tanana ERR .08 .25
(Tied for lead with 269 K's in '75)
236B Frank Tanana COR .01 .05
(Led league with 269 K's in '75)
237 Rick Cerone .01 .05
238 Mike Dunne .01 .05
239 Darren Lewis .01 .05
240 Mike Scott .01 .05
241 Dave Clark UER .01 .05
(Career totals 19 HR and 5 3B, should be 22 and 3)
242 Mike LaCoss .01 .05
243 Lance Johnson .01 .05
244 Mike Jeffcoat .01 .05
245 Kal Daniels .01 .05
246 Kevin Wickander .01 .05
247 Jody Reed .01 .05
248 Tom Gordon .01 .05
249 Bob Melvin .01 .05
250 Dennis Eckersley .02 .10
251 Mark Lemke .01 .05
252 Mel Rojas .01 .05
253 Garry Templeton .01 .05
254 Shawn Boskie .01 .05
255 Brian Downing .01 .05
256 Greg Hibbard .01 .05
257 Tom O'Malley .01 .05
258 Chris Hammond .01 .05
259 Hensley Meulens .01 .05
260 Harold Reynolds .02 .10
261 Bud Harrelson MG .01 .05
262 Tim Jones .01 .05
263 Checklist 2 .01 .05
264 Dave Hollins .01 .05
265 Mark Gubicza .01 .05
266 Carmelo Castillo .01 .05
267 Mark Knudson .01 .05
268 Tom Brookens .01 .05
269 Joe Hesketh .01 .05
270 Mark McGwire COR .30 .75
(1987 Slugging Pctg. listed as .618)
270A Mark McGwire ERR .75 2.00
(1987 Slugging Pctg. listed as 618)
271 Omar Olivares RC .02 .10
272 Jeff King .01 .05
273 Johnny Ray .01 .05
274 Ken Williams .01 .05
275 Alan Trammell .02 .10
276 Bill Swift .01 .05
277 Scott Coolbaugh .01 .05
278 Alex Fernandez UER .01 .05
(No '90 White Sox stats)
279A Jose Gonzalez ERR .08 .25
(Photo actually Billy Bean)
279B Jose Gonzalez COR .01 .05
280 Bret Saberhagen .02 .10
281 Larry Sheets .01 .05
282 Don Carman .01 .05
283 Marquis Grissom .02 .10
284 Billy Spiers .01 .05
285 Jim Abbott .05 .15
286 Ken Oberkfell .01 .05
287 Mark Grant .01 .05
288 Derrick May .01 .05
289 Tim Birtsas .01 .05
290 Steve Sax .01 .05
291 John Wathan MG .01 .05
292 Bud Black .01 .05
293 Jay Bell .02 .10
294 Mike Moore .01 .05
295 Rafael Palmeiro .05 .15
296 Mark Williamson .01 .05
297 Manny Lee .01 .05
298 Omar Vizquel .05 .15
299 Scott Radinsky .01 .05
300 Kirby Puckett .08 .25
301 Steve Farr .01 .05
302 Tim Teufel .01 .05
303 Mike Boddicker .01 .05
304 Kevin Reimer .01 .05
305 Mike Scioscia .01 .05
306A Lonnie Smith ERR .15 .40
(136 games in '90)
306B Lonnie Smith COR .01 .05
(135 games in '90)
307 Andy Benes .01 .05
308 Tom Pagnozzi .01 .05
309 Norm Charlton .01 .05
310 Gary Carter .02 .10
311 Jeff Pico .01 .05
312 Charlie Hayes .01 .05
313 Ron Robinson .01 .05
314 Gary Pettis .01 .05
315 Roberto Alomar .05 .15
316 Gene Nelson .01 .05
317 Mike Fitzgerald .01 .05
318 Rick Aguilera .02 .10
319 Jeff McKnight .01 .05
320 Tony Fernandez .01 .05
321 Bob Rodgers MG .01 .05
322 Terry Shumpert .01 .05
323 Cory Snyder .01 .05
324A Ron Kittle ERR .15 .40
(Set another standard ...)
324B Ron Kittle COR .01 .05
(Tied another standard ...)
325 Brett Butler .02 .10
326 Ken Patterson .01 .05
327 Ron Hassey .01 .05
328 Walt Terrell .01 .05
329 Dave Justice UER .02 .10
(Drafted third round on card, should say fourth pick)
330 Dwight Gooden .02 .10
331 Eric Anthony .01 .05
332 Kenny Rogers .02 .10
333 C.Jones FDP RC 1.50 4.00
334 Todd Benzinger .01 .05
335 Mitch Williams .01 .05
336 Matt Nokes .01 .05
337A Keith Comstock ERR .08 .25
(Cubs logo on front)
337B Keith Comstock COR .01 .05
(Mariners logo on front)
338 Luis Rivera .01 .05
339 Larry Walker .08 .25
340 Ramon Martinez .01 .05
341 John Moses .01 .05
342 Mickey Morandini .01 .05
343 Jose Oquendo .01 .05
344 Jeff Russell .01 .05
345 Len Dykstra .02 .10
346 Jesse Orosco .01 .05
347 Greg Vaughn .01 .05
348 Todd Stottlemyre .01 .05
349 Dave Gallagher .01 .05
350 Glenn Davis .01 .05
351 Joe Torre MG .02 .10
352 Frank White .02 .10
353 Tony Castillo .01 .05
354 Sid Bream .01 .05
355 Chili Davis .02 .10
356 Mike Marshall .01 .05
357 Jack Savage .01 .05
358 Mark Parent .01 .05
359 Chuck Cary .01 .05
360 Tim Raines .02 .10
361 Scott Garrelts .01 .05
362 Hector Villenueva .01 .05
363 Rick Mahler .01 .05
364 Dan Pasqua .01 .05
365 Mike Schooler .01 .05
366A Checklist 3 ERR .08 .25
19 Carl Nichols
366B Checklist 3 COR .01 .05
119 Carl Nichols
367 Dave Walsh RC .01 .05
368 Felix Jose .01 .05
369 Steve Searcy .01 .05
370 Kelly Gruber .01 .05
371 Jeff Montgomery .01 .05
372 Spike Owen .01 .05
373 Darrin Jackson .01 .05
374 Larry Casian RC .01 .05
375 Tony Pena .01 .05
376 Mike Harkey .01 .05
377 Rene Gonzales .01 .05
378A Wilson Alvarez ERR .08 .25
('89 Port Charlotte and '90 Birmingham stat lines omitted)
378B Wilson Alvarez COR .01 .05
Text still says 143 K's in 1988, whereas stats say 134
379 Randy Velarde .01 .05
380 Willie McGee .02 .10
381 Jim Leyland MG .01 .05
382 Mackey Sasser .01 .05
383 Pete Smith .01 .05
384 Gerald Perry .01 .05
385 Mickey Tettleton .01 .05
386 Cecil Fielder AS .01 .05
387 Julio Franco AS .01 .05
388 Kelly Gruber AS .01 .05
389 Alan Trammell AS .02 .10
390 Jose Canseco AS .02 .10
391 Rickey Henderson AS .05 .15
392 Ken Griffey Jr. AS .15 .40
393 Carlton Fisk AS .02 .10
394 Bob Welch AS .01 .05
395 Chuck Finley AS .01 .05
396 Bobby Thigpen AS .01 .05
397 Eddie Murray AS .05 .15
398 Ryne Sandberg AS .08 .25
399 Matt Williams AS .01 .05
400 Barry Larkin AS .02 .10
401 Barry Bonds AS .20 .50
402 Darryl Strawberry AS .01 .05
403 Bobby Bonilla AS .01 .05
404 Mike Scioscia AS .01 .05
405 Doug Drabek AS .01 .05
406 Frank Viola AS .01 .05
407 John Franco AS .01 .05
408 Earnest Riles .01 .05
409 Mike Stanley .01 .05
410 Dave Righetti .02 .10
411 Lance Blankenship .01 .05
412 Dave Bergman .01 .05
413 Terry Mulholland .01 .05
414 Sammy Sosa .08 .25
415 Rick Sutcliffe .02 .10
416 Randy Milligan .01 .05
417 Bill Krueger .01 .05
418 Nick Esasky .01 .05
419 Jeff Reed .01 .05
420 Bobby Thigpen .01 .05
421 Alex Cole .01 .05
422 Rick Reuschel .01 .05
423 Rafael Ramirez UER .01 .05
(Born 1959, not 1958)
424 Calvin Schiraldi .01 .05
425 Andy Van Slyke .05 .15
426 Joe Grahe RC .02 .10
427 Rick Dempsey .01 .05
428 John Barfield .01 .05
429 Stump Merrill MG .01 .05
430 Gary Gaetti .02 .10
431 Paul Gibson .01 .05
432 Delino DeShields .02 .10
433 Pat Tabler .01 .05
434 Julio Machado .01 .05
435 Kevin Maas .01 .05
436 Scott Bankhead .01 .05
437 Doug Dascenzo .01 .05
438 Vicente Palacios .01 .05
439 Dickie Thon .01 .05
440 George Bell .01 .05
441 Zane Smith .01 .05
442 Charlie O'Brien .01 .05
443 Jeff Innis .01 .05
444 Glenn Braggs .01 .05
445 Greg Swindell .01 .05
446 Craig Grebeck .01 .05
447 John Burkett .01 .05
448 Craig Lefferts .01 .05
449 Juan Berenguer .01 .05
450 Wade Boggs .05 .15
451 Neal Heaton .01 .05
452 Bill Schroeder .01 .05
453 Lenny Harris .01 .05
454A Kevin Appier ERR .15 .40
('90 Omaha stat line omitted)
454B Kevin Appier COR .02 .10
455 Walt Weiss .01 .05
456 Charlie Leibrandt .01 .05
457 Todd Hundley .01 .05
458 Brian Holman .01 .05
459 T.Trebelhorn MG UER .01 .05
Pitching and batting columns switched
460 Dave Stieb .01 .05
461 Robin Ventura .02 .10
462 Steve Frey .01 .05
463 Dwight Smith .01 .05
464 Steve Buechele .01 .05
465 Ken Griffey Sr. .02 .10
466 Charles Nagy .01 .05
467 Dennis Cook .01 .05
468 Tim Hulett .01 .05
469 Chet Lemon .01 .05
470 Howard Johnson .01 .05
471 Mike Lieberthal RC .15 .40
472 Kirt Manwaring .01 .05
473 Curt Young .01 .05
474 Phil Plantier RC .02 .10
475 Ted Higuera .01 .05
476 Glenn Wilson .01 .05
477 Mike Fetters .01 .05
478 Kurt Stillwell .01 .05
479 Bob Patterson UER .01 .05
(Has a decimal point between 7 and 9)
480 Dave Magadan .01 .05
481 Eddie Whitson .01 .05
482 Tino Martinez .08 .25
483 Mike Aldrete .01 .05
484 Dave LaPoint .01 .05
485 Terry Pendleton .02 .10
486 Tommy Greene .01 .05
487 Rafael Belliard .01 .05
488 Jeff Manto .01 .05
489 Bobby Valentine MG .01 .05
490 Kirk Gibson .02 .10
491 Kurt Miller RC .01 .05
492 Ernie Whitt .01 .05
493 Jose Rijo .01 .05
494 Chris James .01 .05
495 Charlie Hough .02 .10
496 Marty Barrett .01 .05
497 Ben McDonald .01 .05
498 Mark Salas .01 .05
499 Melido Perez .01 .05
500 Will Clark .05 .15
501 Mike Bielecki .01 .05
502 Carney Lansford .02 .10
503 Roy Smith .01 .05
504 Julio Valera .01 .05
505 Chuck Finley .02 .10
506 Darnell Coles .01 .05
507 Steve Jeltz .01 .05
508 Mike York RC .01 .05
509 Glenallen Hill .01 .05
510 John Franco .02 .10
511 Steve Balboni .01 .05
512 Jose Mesa .01 .05
513 Jerald Clark .01 .05
514 Mike Stanton .01 .05
515 Alvin Davis .01 .05
516 Karl Rhodes .01 .05
517 Joe Oliver .01 .05
518 Cris Carpenter .01 .05
519 Sparky Anderson MG .02 .10
520 Mark Grace .05 .15
521 Joe Orsulak .01 .05
522 Stan Belinda .01 .05
523 Rodney McCray RC .01 .05
524 Darrel Akerfelds .01 .05
525 Willie Randolph .02 .10
526A Moises Alou ERR .15 .40
(37 runs in 2 games for '90 Pirates)
526B Moises Alou COR .02 .10
(0 runs in 2 games for '90 Pirates)
527A Checklist 4 ERR .08 .25
105 Keith Miller
719 Kevin McReynolds
527B Checklist 4 COR .01 .05
105 Kevin McReynolds
719 Keith Miller
528 Dennis Martinez .02 .10
529 Marc Newfield RC .02 .10
530 Roger Clemens .30 .75
531 Dave Rohde .01 .05
532 Kirk McCaskill .01 .05
533 Oddibe McDowell .01 .05
534 Mike Jackson .01 .05
535 Ruben Sierra UER .02 .10
(Back reads 100 Runs amd 100 RBI's)
536 Mike Witt .01 .05
537 Jose Lind .01 .05
538 Bip Roberts .01 .05
539 Scott Terry .01 .05
540 George Brett .25 .60
541 Domingo Ramos .01 .05
542 Rob Murphy .01 .05
543 Junior Felix .01 .05
544 Alejandro Pena .01 .05
545 Dale Murphy .05 .15
546 Jeff Ballard .01 .05
547 Mike Pagliarulo .01 .05
548 Jaime Navarro .01 .05
549 John McNamara MG .01 .05
550 Eric Davis .02 .10
551 Bob Kipper .01 .05
552 Jeff Hamilton .01 .05
553 Joe Klink .01 .05
554 Brian Harper .01 .05
555 Turner Ward RC .02 .10
556 Gary Ward .01 .05
557 Wally Whitehurst .01 .05
558 Otis Nixon .01 .05
559 Adam Peterson .01 .05
560 Greg Smith .01 .05
561 Tim McIntosh .01 .05
562 Jeff Kunkel .01 .05
563 Brent Knackert .01 .05
564 Dante Bichette .02 .10
565 Craig Biggio .05 .15
566 Craig Wilson RC .01 .05
567 Dwayne Henry .01 .05
568 Ron Karkovice .01 .05
569 Curt Schilling .08 .25
570 Barry Bonds .40 1.00
571 Pat Combs .01 .05
572 Dave Anderson .01 .05
573 Rich Rodriguez UER RC .01 .05
(Stats say drafted 4th, but bio says 9th round)
574 John Marzano .01 .05
575 Robin Yount .15 .40
576 Jeff Kaiser .01 .05
577 Bill Doran .01 .05
578 Dave West .01 .05
579 Roger Craig MG .01 .05
580 Dave Stewart .02 .10
581 Luis Quinones .01 .05
582 Marty Clary .01 .05
583 Tony Phillips .01 .05

584 Kevin Brown .02 .10
585 Pete O'Brien .01 .05
586 Fred Lynn .01 .05
587 Jose Offerman UER .01 .05
(Text says he signed 7/24/86, but bio says 1988)
588 Mark Whiten .01 .05
589 Scott Ruskin .01 .05
590 Eddie Murray .08 .25
591 Ken Hill .01 .05
592 B.J. Surhoff .02 .10
593A Mike Walker ERR .08 .25
('90 Canton-Akron stat line omitted)
593B Mike Walker COR .01 .05
594 Rich Garces RC .02 .10
595 Bill Landrum .01 .05
596 Ronnie Walden RC .02 .10
597 Jerry Don Gleaton .01 .05
598 Sam Horn .01 .05
599A Greg Myers ERR .08 .25
('90 Syracuse stat line omitted)
599B Greg Myers COR .01 .05
600 Bo Jackson .08 .25
601 Bob Ojeda .01 .05
602 Casey Candaele .01 .05
603A W.Chamberlain RC ERR .15 .40
Photo actually Louie Meadows
603B Wes Chamberlain COR RC .02 .10
604 Billy Hatcher .01 .05
605 Jeff Reardon .02 .10
606 Jim Gott .01 .05
607 Edgar Martinez .05 .15
608 Todd Burns .01 .05
609 Jeff Torborg MG .01 .05
610 Andres Galarraga .02 .10
611 Dave Eiland .01 .05
612 Steve Lyons .01 .05
613 Eric Show .01 .05
614 Luis Salazar .01 .05
615 Bert Blyleven .02 .10
616 Todd Zeile .01 .05
617 Bill Wegman .01 .05
618 Sil Campusano .01 .05
619 David Wells .02 .10
620 Ozzie Guillen .02 .10
621 Ted Power .01 .05
622 Jack Daugherty .01 .05
623 Jeff Blauser .01 .05
624 Tom Candiotti .01 .05
625 Terry Steinbach .01 .05
626 Gerald Young .01 .05
627 Tim Layana .01 .05
628 Greg Litton .01 .05
629 Wes Gardner .01 .05
630 Dave Winfield .02 .10
631 Mike Morgan .01 .05
632 Lloyd Moseby .01 .05
633 Kevin Tapani .01 .05
634 Henry Cotto .01 .05
635 Andy Hawkins .01 .05
636 Geronimo Pena .01 .05
637 Bruce Ruffin .01 .05
638 Mike Macfarlane .01 .05
639 Frank Robinson MG .05 .15
640 Andre Dawson .02 .10
641 Mike Henneman .01 .05
642 Hal Morris .01 .05
643 Jim Presley .01 .05
644 Chuck Crim .01 .05
645 Juan Samuel .01 .05
646 Andujar Cedeno .01 .05
647 Mark Portugal .01 .05
648 Lee Stevens .01 .05
649 Bill Sampen .01 .05
650 Jack Clark .02 .10
651 Alan Mills .01 .05
652 Kevin Romine .01 .05
653 Anthony Telford RC .01 .05
654 Paul Sorrento .01 .05
655 Erik Hanson .01 .05
656A Checklist 5 ERR .08 .25
348 Vicente Palacios
381 Jose Lind
537 Mike LaValliere
665 Jim Leyland
656B Checklist 5 ERR .08 .25
433 Vicente Palacios
(Palacios should be 438)
537 Jose Lind
665 Mike LaValliere
381 Jim Leyland
656C Checklist 5 COR .01 .05
438 Vicente Palacios
537 Jose Lind
665 Mike LaValliere
381 Jim Leyland
657 Mike Kingery .01 .05
658 Scott Aldred .01 .05
659 Oscar Azocar .01 .05
660 Lee Smith .02 .10
661 Steve Lake .01 .05
662 Ron Dibble .02 .10
663 Greg Brock .01 .05
664 John Farrell .01 .05
665 Mike LaValliere .01 .05
666 Danny Darwin .01 .05
667 Kent Anderson .01 .05
668 Bill Long .01 .05
669 Lou Piniella MG .02 .10
670 Rickey Henderson .08 .25
671 Andy McGaffigan .01 .05
672 Shane Mack .01 .05
673 Greg Olson UER .01 .05
(6 RBI in '88 at Tidewater and 2 RBI in '87, should be 48 and 15)
674A Kevin Gross ERR .08 .25
(89 BB with Phillies in '88 tied for league lead)
674B Kevin Gross COR .01 .05
(89 BB with Phillies in '88 led league)
675 Tom Brunansky .01 .05
676 Scott Chiamparino .01 .05
677 Billy Ripken .01 .05
678 Mark Davidson .01 .05
679 Bill Bathe .01 .05
680 David Cone .02 .10
681 Jeff Schaefer .01 .05
682 Ray Lankford .02 .10
683 Derek Lilliquist .01 .05
684 Milt Cuyler .01 .05
685 Doug Drabek .01 .05
686 Mike Gallego .01 .05
687A John Cerutti ERR .08 .25
(4.46 ERA in '90)
687B John Cerutti COR .01 .05
(4.76 ERA in '90)
688 Rosario Rodriguez RC .01 .05
689 John Kruk .02 .10
690 Orel Hershiser .02 .10
691 Mike Blowers .01 .05
692A Efrain Valdez ERR .08 .25
(Born 6/11/66)
692B Efrain Valdez COR RC .01 .05
(Born 7/11/66 and two lines of text added)
693 Francisco Cabrera .01 .05
694 Randy Veres .01 .05
695 Kevin Seitzer .01 .05
696 Steve Olin .01 .05
697 Shawn Abner .01 .05
698 Mark Guthrie .01 .05
699 Jim Lefebvre MG .01 .05
700 Jose Canseco .05 .15
701 Pascual Perez .01 .05
702 Tim Naehring .01 .05
703 Juan Agosto .01 .05
704 Devon White .02 .10
705 Robby Thompson .01 .05
706A Brad Arnsberg ERR .08 .25
(68.2 IP in '90)
706B Brad Arnsberg COR .01 .05
(62.2 IP in '90)
707 Jim Eisenreich .01 .05
708 John Mitchell .01 .05
709 Matt Sinatro .01 .05
710 Kent Hrbek .02 .10
711 Jose DeLeon .01 .05
712 Ricky Jordan .01 .05
713 Scott Scudder .01 .05
714 Marvell Wynne .01 .05
715 Tim Burke .01 .05
716 Bob Geren .01 .05
717 Phil Bradley .01 .05
718 Steve Crawford .01 .05
719 Keith Miller .01 .05
720 Cecil Fielder .02 .10
721 Mark Lee RC .01 .05
722 Wally Backman .01 .05
723 Candy Maldonado .01 .05
724 David Segui .01 .05
725 Ron Gant .02 .10
726 Phil Stephenson .01 .05
727 Mookie Wilson .02 .10
728 Scott Sanderson .01 .05
729 Don Zimmer MG .02 .10
730 Barry Larkin .05 .15
731 Jeff Gray RC .01 .05
732 Franklin Stubbs .01 .05
733 Kelly Downs .01 .05
734 John Russell .01 .05
735 Ron Darling .01 .05
736 Dick Schofield .01 .05
737 Tim Crews .01 .05
738 Mel Hall .01 .05
739 Russ Swan .01 .05
740 Ryne Sandberg .15 .40
741 Jimmy Key .02 .10
742 Tommy Gregg .01 .05
743 Bryn Smith .01 .05
744 Nelson Santovenia .01 .05
745 Doug Jones .01 .05
746 John Shelby .01 .05
747 Tony Fossas .01 .05
748 Al Newman .01 .05
749 Greg W. Harris .01 .05
750 Bobby Bonilla .02 .10
751 Wayne Edwards .01 .05
752 Kevin Bass .01 .05
753 Paul Marak UER RC .01 .05
(Stats say drafted in Jan. but bio says May)
754 Bill Pecota .01 .05
755 Mark Langston .01 .05
756 Jeff Huson .01 .05
757 Mark Gardner .01 .05
758 Mike Devereaux .01 .05
759 Bobby Cox MG .01 .05
760 Benny Santiago .02 .10
761 Larry Andersen .01 .05
762 Mitch Webster .01 .05
763 Dana Kiecker .01 .05
764 Mark Carreon .01 .05
765 Shawon Dunston .01 .05
766 Jeff Robinson .01 .05
767 Dan Wilson RC .08 .25
768 Don Pall .01 .05
769 Tim Sherrill .01 .05
770 Jay Howell .01 .05
771 Gary Redus UER .01 .05
(Born in Tanner, should say Athens)
772 Kent Mercker UER .01 .05
(Born in Indianapolis, should say Dublin, Ohio)
773 Tom Foley .01 .05
774 Dennis Rasmussen .01 .05
775 Julio Franco .02 .10
776 Brent Mayne .01 .05
777 John Candelaria .01 .05
778 Dan Gladden .01 .05
779 Carmelo Martinez .01 .05
780A Randy Myers ERR .15 .40
(15 career losses)
780B Randy Myers COR .01 .05
(10 career losses)
781 Darryl Hamilton .01 .05
782 Jim Deshaies .01 .05
783 Joel Skinner .01 .05
784 Willie Fraser .01 .05
785 Scott Fletcher .01 .05
786 Eric Plunk .01 .05
787 Checklist 6 .01 .05
788 Bob Milacki .01 .05
789 Tom Lasorda MG .08 .25
790 Ken Griffey Jr. .30 .75
791 Mike Benjamin .01 .05
792 Mike Greenwell .01 .05

1991 Topps Desert Shield

These 792 standard-size cards are parallel to the regular Topps issue. These cards were issued in special packs available only to service people serving in the Desert Shield (later to be Desert Storm) campaign. The cards are differentiated by a "Desert Shield" gold foil logo in the upper right corner. There were many different types of forgeries created for these cards so some caution is urged in purchasing any expensive cards from the set.

*STARS: 40X TO 100X BASIC CARDS
*ROOKIES: 15X TO 40X BASIC CARDS
333 Chipper Jones FDP 100.00 200.00

1991 Topps Micro

This 792 card set parallels the regular Topps issue. The cards are significantly smaller (slightly larger than a postage stamp) than the regular Topps cards and are valued at a percentage of the regular 1991 Topps cards.

COMP.FACT.SET (792) 8.00 20.00
*STARS: .4X to 1X BASIC CARDS

1991 Topps Tiffany

This 792 standard-size set proved to be the final time Topps issued their Tiffany sets. These cards again parallel the regular issue and have "glossy" fronts and easy to read backs. These cards were issued in complete set form only. Since a limited amount of these sets were produced, the multiplier is one of the highest for any of these Topps sets. While no production number is guessed at for these sets, it is perceived in the hobby to be among the shortest printed Tiffany sets.

COMP.FACT.SET (792) 100.00 200.00
*STARS: 12.5X TO 30X BASIC CARDS
*ROOKIES: 6X TO 15X BASIC CARDS

1991 Topps Rookies

This set contains 33 standard-size cards and were distributed at a rate of one per retail jumbo pack. The front and back borders are white and other design elements are red, blue, and yellow. This set is identical to the previous year's set. Topps also commemorated its 40th anniversary by including a "Topps 40" logo on the front. The cards are unnumbered and checklisted below in alphabetical order.

COMPLETE SET (33) 10.00 20.00
1 Sandy Alomar .20 .50
2 Kevin Appier .20 .50
3 Steve Avery .08 .25
4 Carlos Baerga .20 .50
5 John Burkett .08 .25
6 Alex Cole .08 .25
7 Pat Combs .08 .25
8 Delino DeShields .20 .50
9 Travis Fryman .20 .50
10 Marquis Grissom .40 1.00
11 Mike Harkey .08 .25
12 Glenallen Hill .08 .25
13 Jeff Huson .08 .25
14 Felix Jose .08 .25
15 Dave Justice .60 1.50
16 Jim Leyritz .08 .25
17 Kevin Maas .08 .25
18 Ben McDonald .08 .25
19 Kent Mercker .08 .25
20 Hal Morris .08 .25
21 Chris Nabholz .08 .25
22 Tim Naehring .08 .25
23 Jose Offerman .08 .25
24 John Olerud .75 2.00
25 Scott Radinsky .08 .25
26 Scott Ruskin .08 .25
27 Kevin Tapani .08 .25
28 Frank Thomas 3.00 8.00
29 Randy Tomlin .08 .25
30 Greg Vaughn .20 .50
31 Robin Ventura .40 1.00
32 Larry Walker .60 1.50
33 Todd Zeile .20 .50

1991 Topps Wax Box Cards

Topps again in 1991 issued cards on the bottom of their wax pack boxes. There are four different boxes, each with four cards and a checklist on the side. These standard-size cards have yellow borders rather than the white borders of the regular issue cards, and they have different photos of the players. The backs are printed in pink and blue on gray cardboard stock and feature outstanding achievements of the players. The cards are numbered by letter on the back. The cards have the typical Topps 1991 design on the front of the card. The set was ordered in alphabetical order and lettered A-P.

COMPLETE SET (16) 2.40 6.00
A Bert Blyleven .07 .20
B George Brett .40 1.00
C Brett Butler .02 .10
D Andre Dawson .20 .50
E Dwight Evans .07 .20
F Carlton Fisk .25 .60
G Alfredo Griffin .02 .10
H Rickey Henderson .25 .60
I Willie McGee .07 .20
J Dale Murphy .20 .50
K Eddie Murray .25 .60
L Dave Parker .07 .20
M Jeff Reardon .07 .20
N Nolan Ryan 1.00 2.50
O Juan Samuel .02 .10
P Robin Yount .25 .60

1991 Topps Traded

The 1991 Topps Traded set contains 132 standard-size cards. The cards were issued primarily in factory set form through hobby dealers but were also made available on a limited basis in wax packs. The cards in the wax packs (gray backs) and collated factory sets (white backs) are from different card stock. Both versions are valued equally. The card design is identical to the regular issue 1991 Topps cards except for the whiter stock (for factory set cards) and T-suffixed numbering. The set is numbered in alphabetical order. The set includes a Team U.S.A. subset, featuring 25 of America's top collegiate players. The key Rookie Cards in this set are Jeff Bagwell, Jason Giambi, Luis Gonzalez, Charles Johnson and Ivan Rodriguez.

COMPLETE SET (132) 4.00 10.00
COMP.FACT.SET (132) 4.00 10.00
1T Juan Agosto .01 .05
2T Roberto Alomar .05 .15
3T Wally Backman .01 .05
4T Jeff Bagwell RC .60 1.50
5T Skeeter Barnes .01 .05
6T Steve Bedrosian .01 .05
7T Derek Bell .02 .10
8T George Bell .01 .05
9T Rafael Belliard .01 .05
10T Dante Bichette .02 .10
11T Bud Black .01 .05
12T Mike Boddicker .01 .05
13T Sid Bream .01 .05
14T Hubie Brooks .01 .05
15T Brett Butler .02 .10
16T Ivan Calderon .01 .05
17T John Candelaria .01 .05
18T Tom Candiotti .01 .05
19T Gary Carter .02 .10
20T Joe Carter .02 .10
21T Rick Cerone .01 .05
22T Jack Clark .02 .10
23T Vince Coleman .01 .05
24T Scott Coolbaugh .01 .05
25T Danny Cox .01 .05
26T Danny Darwin .01 .05
27T Chili Davis .02 .10
28T Glenn Davis .01 .05
29T Steve Decker RC .01 .05
30T Rob Deer .01 .05
31T Rich DeLucia RC .01 .05
32T John Dettmer USA RC .08 .25
33T Brian Downing .01 .05
34T D.Dreifort USA RC .08 .25
35T K.Dressendorfer RC .01 .05
36T Jim Essian MG .01 .05
37T Dwight Evans .05 .15
38T Steve Farr .01 .05
39T Jeff Fassero RC .08 .25
40T Junior Felix .01 .05
41T Tony Fernandez .01 .05
42T Steve Finley .02 .10
43T Jim Fregosi MG .01 .05
44T Gary Gaetti .02 .10
45T Jason Giambi USA RC 2.00 5.00
46T Kirk Gibson .02 .10
47T Leo Gomez .01 .05
48T Luis Gonzalez RC .20 .50
49T Jeff Granger USA RC .08 .25
50T Todd Greene USA RC .20 .50
51T J.Hammonds USA RC .20 .50
52T Mike Hargrove MG .01 .05
53T Pete Harnisch .01 .05
54T R.Helling USA UER RC .20 .50
Misspelled Hellings on card back)
55T Glenallen Hill .01 .05
56T Charlie Hough .02 .10
57T Pete Incaviglia .01 .05
58T Bo Jackson .08 .25
59T Danny Jackson .01 .05
60T Reggie Jefferson .01 .05
61T C.Johnson USA RC .30 .75
62T Jeff Johnson RC .01 .05
63T Todd Johnson USA RC .08 .25
64T Barry Jones .01 .05
65T Chris Jones RC .02 .10
66T Scott Kamieniecki RC .02 .10
67T Pat Kelly RC .02 .10
68T Darryl Kile .02 .10
69T Chuck Knoblauch .02 .10
70T Bill Krueger .01 .05
71T Scott Leius .01 .05
72T Donnie Leshnock USA RC .08 .25
73T Mark Lewis .01 .05
74T Candy Maldonado .01 .05
75T Jason McDonald USA RC .08 .25
76T Willie McGee .02 .10
77T Fred McGriff .05 .15
78T Billy McMillon USA RC .08 .25
79T Hal McRae MG .02 .10
80T Dan Melendez USA RC .08 .25
81T Orlando Merced RC .02 .10
82T Jack Morris .02 .10
83T Phil Nevin USA RC .30 .75
84T Otis Nixon .01 .05
85T Johnny Oates MG .01 .05
86T Bob Ojeda .01 .05
87T Mike Pagliarulo .01 .05
88T Dean Palmer .02 .10
89T Dave Parker .02 .10
90T Terry Pendleton .02 .10
91T Tony Phillips (P) USA RC .08 .25
92T Doug Piatt RC .01 .05
93T Ron Polk USA CO .08 .25
94T Tim Raines .02 .10
95T Willie Randolph .02 .10
96T Dave Righetti .02 .10
97T Ernie Riles .01 .05
98T Chris Roberts USA RC .08 .25
99T Jeff D. Robinson .01 .05
100T Jeff M. Robinson .01 .05
101T Ivan Rodriguez RC 1.25 3.00
102T Steve Rodriguez USA RC .08 .25
103T Tom Runnells MG .01 .05
104T Scott Sanderson .01 .05
105T Bob Scanlan RC .01 .05
106T Pete Schourek RC .02 .10
107T Gary Scott RC .01 .05
108T Paul Shuey USA RC .20 .50
109T Doug Simons RC .01 .05
110T Dave Smith .01 .05
111T Cory Snyder .01 .05
112T Luis Sojo .01 .05
113T Kennie Steenstra USA RC .08 .25
114T Darryl Strawberry .02 .10
115T Franklin Stubbs .01 .05
116T Todd Taylor USA RC .08 .25
117T Wade Taylor RC .01 .05
118T Garry Templeton .01 .05
119T Mickey Tettleton .01 .05
120T Tim Teufel .01 .05
121T Mike Timlin RC .08 .25
122T David Tuttle USA RC .08 .25
123T Mo Vaughn .02 .10
124T Jeff Ware USA RC .08 .25
125T Devon White .02 .10
126T Mark Whiten .01 .05
127T Mitch Williams .01 .05
128T Craig Wilson USA RC .08 .25
129T Willie Wilson .01 .05
130T Chris Wimmer USA RC .08 .25
131T Ivan Zweig USA RC .08 .25
132T Checklist 1T-132T .01 .05

1991 Topps Traded Tiffany

In the final Tiffany relase, this 132-card standard-size set was released as a parallel issue to the regular Topps Traded issue. These cards were released in very limited quantities and the multiplier for these cards is higher than many previous Tiffany issues. These cards were issued in complete factory set form only. The set is considered to be among the shortest print of the Tiffany run and these cards are rarely seen in the secondary market.

COMP.FACT.SET (132) 90.00 150.00
*STARS: 12.5X TO 30X BASIC CARDS
*ROOKIES: 10X TO 25X BASIC CARDS
*USA ROOKIES: 6X TO 15X BASIC CARDS

1992 Topps

The 1992 Topps set contains 792 standard-size cards. Cards were distributed in plastic wrap packs, jumbo packs, rack packs and factory sets. The fronts have either posed or action color player

photos on a white card face. Different color stripes frame the pictures, and the player's name and team name appear in two short color stripes respectively at the bottom. Special subsets included are Record Breakers (2-5), Prospects (58, 126, 179, 473, 551, 591, 618, 656, 676), and All-Stars (386-407). The key Rookie Cards in this set are Shawn Green and Manny Ramirez.

COMPLETE SET (792) 10.00 25.00
COMP.FACT.SET (802) 10.00 25.00
COMP.HOLIDAY (811) 15.00 40.00
1 Nolan Ryan .40 1.00
2 Rickey Henderson RB .05 .15
Most career SB's
(Some cards have print marks that show 1.991 on the front)
3 Jeff Reardon RB .01 .05
4 Nolan Ryan RB .20 .50
5 Dave Winfield RB .01 .05
6 Brien Taylor RC .08 .25
7 Jim Olander .01 .05
8 Bryan Hickerson RC .02 .10
9 Jon Farrell RC .02 .10
10 Wade Boggs .05 .15
11 Jack McDowell .01 .05
12 Luis Gonzalez .02 .10
13 Mike Scioscia .01 .05
14 Wes Chamberlain .01 .05
15 Dennis Martinez .02 .10
16 Jeff Montgomery .01 .05
17 Randy Milligan .01 .05
18 Greg Cadaret .01 .05
19 Jamie Quirk .01 .05
20 Bip Roberts .01 .05
21 Buck Rodgers MG .01 .05
22 Bill Wegman .01 .05
23 Chuck Knoblauch .02 .10
24 Randy Myers .01 .05
25 Ron Gant .02 .10
26 Mike Bielecki .01 .05
27 Juan Gonzalez .05 .15
28 Mike Schooler .01 .05
29 Mickey Tettleton .01 .05
30 John Kruk .02 .10
31 Bryn Smith .01 .05
32 Chris Nabholz .01 .05
33 Carlos Baerga .01 .05
34 Jeff Juden .01 .05
35 Dave Righetti .02 .10
36 Scott Ruffcorn RC .02 .10
37 Luis Polonia .01 .05
38 Tom Candiotti .01 .05
39 Greg Olson .01 .05
40 Cal Ripken .75 2.00
41 Craig Lefferts .01 .05
42 Mike Macfarlane .01 .05
43 Jose Lind .01 .05
44 Rick Aguilera .02 .10
45 Gary Carter .02 .10
46 Steve Farr .01 .05
47 Rex Hudler .01 .05
48 Scott Scudder .01 .05
49 Damon Berryhill .01 .05
50 Ken Griffey Jr. .15 .40
51 Tom Runnells MG .01 .05
52 Juan Bell .01 .05
53 Tommy Gregg .01 .05
54 David Wells .02 .10
55 Rafael Palmeiro .05 .15
56 Charlie O'Brien .01 .05
57 Donn Pall .01 .05
58 Brad Ausmus RC .60 1.50
Jim Campanis Jr.
Dave Nilsson
Doug Robbins
59 Mo Vaughn .02 .10
60 Tony Fernandez .01 .05
61 Paul O'Neill .05 .15
62 Gene Nelson .01 .05
63 Randy Ready .01 .05
64 Bob Kipper .01 .05
65 Willie McGee .02 .10
66 Scott Stahoviak RC .01 .05
67 Luis Salazar .01 .05
68 Marvin Freeman .01 .05
69 Kenny Lofton .05 .15
70 Gary Gaetti .02 .10
71 Erik Hanson .01 .05
72 Eddie Zosky .01 .05
73 Brian Barnes .01 .05
74 Scott Leius .01 .05
75 Bret Saberhagen .02 .10
76 Mike Gallego .01 .05
77 Jack Armstrong .01 .05
78 Ivan Rodriguez .08 .25
79 Jesse Orosco .01 .05
80 David Justice .02 .10
81 Ced Landrum .01 .05
82 Doug Simons .01 .05
83 Tommy Greene .01 .05
84 Leo Gomez .01 .05
85 Jose DeLeon .01 .05
86 Steve Finley .02 .10
87 Bob MacDonald .01 .05
88 Darrin Jackson .01 .05
89 Neal Heaton .01 .05
90 Robin Yount .15 .40
91 Jeff Reed .01 .05
92 Lenny Harris .01 .05
93 Reggie Jefferson .01 .05
94 Sammy Sosa .08 .25
95 Scott Bailes .01 .05
96 Tom McKinnon RC .02 .10
97 Luis Rivera .01 .05
98 Mike Harkey .01 .05
99 Jeff Treadway .01 .05
100 Jose Canseco .05 .15
101 Omar Vizquel .05 .15
102 Scott Kamieniecki .01 .05
103 Ricky Jordan .01 .05
104 Jeff Ballard .01 .05
105 Felix Jose .01 .05
106 Mike Boddicker .01 .05
107 Dan Pasqua .01 .05
108 Mike Timlin .01 .05
109 Roger Craig MG .01 .05
110 Ryne Sandberg .15 .40
111 Mark Carreon .01 .05
112 Oscar Azocar .01 .05
113 Mike Greenwell .01 .05
114 Mark Portugal .01 .05
115 Terry Pendleton .02 .10
116 Willie Randolph .02 .10
117 Scott Terry .01 .05
118 Chili Davis .02 .10
119 Mark Gardner .01 .05
120 Alan Trammell .02 .10
121 Derek Bell .02 .10
122 Gary Varsho .01 .05
123 Bob Ojeda .01 .05
124 Shawn Livsey RC .02 .10
125 Chris Hoiles .01 .05
126 Ryan Klesko .08 .25
John Jaha RC
Rico Brogna
Dave Staton
127 Carlos Quintana .01 .05
128 Kurt Stillwell .01 .05
129 Melido Perez .01 .05
130 Alvin Davis .01 .05
131 Checklist 1-132 .01 .05
132 Eric Show .01 .05
133 Rance Mulliniks .01 .05
134 Darryl Kile .02 .10
135 Von Hayes .01 .05
136 Bill Doran .01 .05
137 Jeff D. Robinson .01 .05
138 Monty Fariss .01 .05
139 Jeff Innis .01 .05
140 Mark Grace UER .05 .15
Home Calie., should be Calif.
141 Jim Leyland MG UER .02 .10
(No closed parenthesis after East in 1991)
142 Todd Van Poppel .01 .05
143 Paul Gibson .01 .05
144 Bill Swift .01 .05
145 Danny Tartabull .01 .05
146 Al Newman .01 .05
147 Cris Carpenter .01 .05
148 Anthony Young .01 .05
149 Brian Bohanon .01 .05
150 Roger Clemens UER .20 .50
(League leading ERA in 1990 not italicized)
151 Jeff Hamilton .01 .05
152 Charlie Leibrandt .01 .05
153 Ron Karkovice .01 .05
154 Hensley Meulens .01 .05
155 Scott Bankhead .01 .05
156 Manny Ramirez RC 2.00 5.00
157 Keith Miller .01 .05
158 Todd Frohwirth .01 .05
159 Darrin Fletcher .01 .05
160 Bobby Bonilla .02 .10
161 Casey Candaele .01 .05
162 Paul Faries .01 .05
163 Dana Kiecker .01 .05
164 Shane Mack .01 .05
165 Mark Langston .01 .05
166 Geronimo Pena .01 .05
167 Andy Allanson .01 .05
168 Dwight Smith .01 .05
169 Chuck Crim .01 .05
170 Alex Cole .01 .05
171 Bill Plummer MG .01 .05
172 Juan Berenguer .01 .05
173 Brian Downing .01 .05
174 Steve Frey .01 .05
175 Orel Hershiser .02 .10
176 Ramon Garcia .01 .05
177 Dan Gladden .01 .05
178 Jim Acker .01 .05
179 Bobby DeJardin .01 .05
Cesar Bernhardt
Armando Moreno
Andy Stankiewicz
180 Kevin Mitchell .01 .05
181 Hector Villanueva .01 .05
182 Jeff Reardon .02 .10
183 Brent Mayne .01 .05
184 Jimmy Jones .01 .05
185 Benito Santiago .02 .10
186 Cliff Floyd RC .30 .75
187 Ernie Riles .01 .05
188 Jose Guzman .01 .05
189 Junior Felix .01 .05
190 Glenn Davis .01 .05
191 Charlie Hough .02 .10
192 Dave Fleming .01 .05
193 Omar Olivares .01 .05
194 Eric Karros .02 .10
195 David Cone .02 .10
196 Frank Castillo .01 .05
197 Glenn Braggs .01 .05

198 Scott Aldred .01 .05
199 Jeff Blauser .01 .05
200 Len Dykstra .02 .10
201 Buck Showalter MG RC .08 .25
202 Rick Honeycutt .01 .05
203 Greg Myers .01 .05
204 Trevor Wilson .01 .05
205 Jay Howell .01 .05
206 Luis Sojo .01 .05
207 Jack Clark .02 .10
208 Julio Machado .01 .05
209 Lloyd McClendon .01 .05
210 Ozzie Guillen .02 .10
211 Jeremy Hernandez RC .02 .10
212 Randy Velarde .01 .05
213 Les Lancaster .01 .05
214 Andy Mota .01 .05
215 Rich Gossage .02 .10
216 Brent Gates RC .02 .10
217 Brian Harper .01 .05
218 Mike Flanagan .01 .05
219 Jerry Browne .01 .05
220 Jose Rijo .01 .05
221 Skeeter Barnes .01 .05
222 Jaime Navarro .01 .05
223 Mel Hall .01 .05
224 Bret Barberie .01 .05
225 Roberto Alomar .05 .15
226 Pete Smith .01 .05
227 Daryl Boston .01 .05
228 Eddie Whitson .01 .05
229 Shawn Boskie .01 .05
230 Dick Schofield .01 .05
231 Brian Drahman .01 .05
232 John Smiley .01 .05
233 Mitch Webster .01 .05
234 Terry Steinbach .01 .05
235 Jack Morris .02 .10
236 Bill Pecota .01 .05
237 Jose Hernandez RC .08 .25
238 Greg Litton .01 .05
239 Brian Holman .01 .05
240 Andres Galarraga .02 .10
241 Gerald Young .01 .05
242 Mike Mussina .08 .25
243 Alvaro Espinoza .01 .05
244 Darren Daulton .02 .10
245 John Smoltz .05 .15
246 Jason Pruitt RC .02 .10
247 Chuck Finley .02 .10
248 Jim Gantner .01 .05
249 Tony Fossas .01 .05
250 Ken Griffey Sr. .02 .10
251 Kevin Elster .01 .05
252 Dennis Rasmussen .01 .05
253 Terry Kennedy .01 .05
254 Ryan Bowen .01 .05
255 Robin Ventura .02 .10
256 Mike Aldrete .01 .05
257 Jeff Russell .01 .05
258 Jim Lindeman .01 .05
259 Ron Darling .01 .05
260 Devon White .02 .10
261 Tom Lasorda MG .02 .10
262 Terry Lee .01 .05
263 Bob Patterson .01 .05
264 Checklist 133-264 .01 .05
265 Teddy Higuera .01 .05
266 Roberto Kelly .01 .05
267 Steve Bedrosian .01 .05
268 Brady Anderson .02 .10
269 Ruben Amaro .01 .05
270 Tony Gwynn .10 .30
271 Tracy Jones .01 .05
272 Jerry Don Gleaton .01 .05
273 Craig Grebeck .01 .05
274 Bob Scanlan .01 .05
275 Todd Zeile .01 .05
276 Shawn Green RC .40 1.00
277 Scott Chiamparino .01 .05
278 Darryl Hamilton .01 .05
279 Jim Clancy .01 .05
280 Carlos Martinez .01 .05
281 Kevin Appier .02 .10
282 John Wehner .01 .05
283 Reggie Sanders .02 .10
284 Gene Larkin .01 .05
285 Bob Welch .01 .05
286 Gilberto Reyes .01 .05
287 Pete Schourek .01 .05
288 Andujar Cedeno .01 .05
289 Mike Morgan .01 .05
290 Bo Jackson .08 .25
291 Phil Garner MG .02 .10
292 Ray Lankford .02 .10
293 Mike Henneman .01 .05
294 Dave Valle .01 .05
295 Alonzo Powell .01 .05
296 Tom Brunansky .01 .05
297 Kevin Brown .02 .10
298 Kelly Gruber .01 .05
299 Charles Nagy .01 .05
300 Don Mattingly .25 .60
301 Kirk McCaskill .01 .05
302 Joey Cora .01 .05
303 Dan Plesac .01 .05
304 Joe Oliver .01 .05
305 Tom Glavine .05 .15
306 Al Shirley RC .02 .10
307 Bruce Ruffin .01 .05
308 Craig Shipley .01 .05
309 Dave Martinez .01 .05
310 Jose Mesa .01 .05
311 Henry Cotto .01 .05
312 Mike LaValliere .01 .05
313 Kevin Tapani .01 .05
314 Jeff Huson .01 .05
315 Juan Samuel .01 .05
316 Curt Schilling .05 .15
317 Mike Bordick .01 .05
318 Steve Howe .01 .05
319 Tony Phillips .01 .05
320 George Bell .01 .05
321 Lou Piniella MG .02 .10
322 Tim Burke .01 .05
323 Milt Thompson .01 .05
324 Danny Darwin .01 .05
325 Joe Orsulak .01 .05
326 Eric King .01 .05
327 Jay Buhner .02 .10
328 Joel Johnston .01 .05
329 Franklin Stubbs .01 .05
330 Will Clark .05 .15
331 Steve Lake .01 .05
332 Chris Jones .01 .05
333 Pat Tabler .01 .05
334 Kevin Gross .01 .05
335 Dave Henderson .01 .05
336 Greg Anthony RC .02 .10
337 Alejandro Pena .01 .05
338 Shawn Abner .01 .05
339 Tom Browning .01 .05
340 Otis Nixon .01 .05
341 Bob Geren .01 .05
342 Tim Spehr .01 .05
343 John Vander Wal .01 .05
344 Jack Daugherty .01 .05
345 Zane Smith .01 .05
346 Rheal Cormier .01 .05
347 Kent Hrbek .02 .10
348 Rick Wilkins .01 .05
349 Steve Lyons .01 .05
350 Gregg Olson .01 .05
351 Greg Riddoch MG .01 .05
352 Ed Nunez .01 .05
353 Braulio Castillo .01 .05
354 Dave Bergman .01 .05
355 Warren Newson .01 .05
356 Luis Quinones .01 .05
357 Mike Witt .01 .05
358 Ted Wood .01 .05
359 Mike Moore .01 .05
360 Lance Parrish .02 .10
361 Barry Jones .01 .05
362 Javier Ortiz .01 .05
363 John Candelaria .01 .05
364 Glenallen Hill .01 .05
365 Duane Ward .01 .05
366 Checklist 265-396 .01 .05
367 Rafael Belliard .01 .05
368 Bill Krueger .01 .05
369 Steve Whitaker RC .02 .10
370 Shawon Dunston .01 .05
371 Dante Bichette .02 .10
372 Kip Gross .01 .05
373 Don Robinson .01 .05
374 Bernie Williams .05 .15
375 Bert Blyleven .02 .10
376 Chris Donnels .01 .05
377 Bob Zupcic RC .02 .10
378 Joel Skinner .01 .05
379 Steve Chitren .01 .05
380 Barry Bonds .40 1.00
381 Sparky Anderson MG .02 .10
382 Sid Fernandez .01 .05
383 Dave Hollins .01 .05
384 Mark Lee .01 .05
385 Tim Wallach .01 .05
386 Will Clark AS .02 .10
387 Ryne Sandberg AS .08 .25
388 Howard Johnson AS .01 .05
389 Barry Larkin AS .02 .10
390 Barry Bonds AS .20 .50
391 Ron Gant AS .01 .05
392 Bobby Bonilla AS .01 .05
393 Craig Biggio AS .02 .10
394 Dennis Martinez AS .01 .05
395 Tom Glavine AS .02 .10
396 Lee Smith AS .01 .05
397 Cecil Fielder AS .01 .05
398 Julio Franco AS .01 .05
399 Wade Boggs AS .02 .10
400 Cal Ripken AS .15 .40
401 Jose Canseco AS .05 .15
402 Joe Carter AS .01 .05
403 Ruben Sierra AS .01 .05
404 Matt Nokes AS .01 .05
405 Roger Clemens AS .08 .25
406 Jim Abbott AS .02 .10
407 Bryan Harvey AS .01 .05
408 Bob Milacki .01 .05
409 Geno Petralli .01 .05
410 Dave Stewart .02 .10
411 Mike Jackson .01 .05
412 Luis Aquino .01 .05
413 Tim Teufel .01 .05
414 Jeff Ware .01 .05
415 Jim Deshaies .01 .05
416 Ellis Burks .02 .10
417 Allan Anderson .01 .05
418 Alfredo Griffin .01 .05
419 Wally Whitehurst .01 .05
420 Sandy Alomar Jr. .01 .05
421 Juan Agosto .01 .05
422 Sam Horn .01 .05
423 Jeff Fassero .01 .05
424 Paul McClellan .01 .05
425 Cecil Fielder .02 .10
426 Tim Raines .02 .10
427 Eddie Taubensee RC .08 .25
428 Dennis Boyd .01 .05
429 Tony LaRussa MG .02 .10
430 Steve Sax .01 .05
431 Tom Gordon .01 .05
432 Billy Hatcher .01 .05
433 Cal Eldred .01 .05
434 Wally Backman .01 .05
435 Mark Eichhorn .01 .05
436 Mookie Wilson .02 .10
437 Scott Servais .01 .05
438 Mike Maddux .01 .05
439 Chico Walker .01 .05
440 Doug Drabek .01 .05
441 Rob Deer .01 .05
442 Dave West .01 .05
443 Spike Owen .01 .05
444 Tyrone Hill RC .02 .10
445 Matt Williams .02 .10
446 Mark Lewis .01 .05
447 David Segui .01 .05
448 Tom Pagnozzi .01 .05
449 Jeff Johnson .01 .05
450 Mark McGwire .25 .60
451 Tom Henke .01 .05
452 Wilson Alvarez .01 .05
453 Gary Redus .01 .05
454 Darren Holmes .01 .05
455 Pete O'Brien .01 .05
456 Pat Combs .01 .05
457 Hubie Brooks .01 .05
458 Frank Tanana .01 .05
459 Tom Kelly MG .01 .05
460 Andre Dawson .02 .10
461 Doug Jones .01 .05
462 Rich Rodriguez .01 .05
463 Mike Simms .01 .05
464 Mike Jeffcoat .01 .05
465 Barry Larkin .05 .15
466 Stan Belinda .01 .05
467 Lonnie Smith .01 .05
468 Greg Harris .01 .05
469 Jim Eisenreich .01 .05
470 Pedro Guerrero .02 .10
471 Jose DeJesus .01 .05
472 Rich Rowland RC .02 .10
473 Frank Bolick .01 .05
Craig Paquette
Tom Redington
Paul Russo UER
(Line around top border)
474 Mike Rossiter RC .02 .10
475 Robby Thompson .01 .05
476 Randy Bush .01 .05
477 Greg Hibbard .01 .05
478 Dale Sveum .01 .05
479 Chito Martinez .01 .05
480 Scott Sanderson .01 .05
481 Tino Martinez .05 .15
482 Jimmy Key .02 .10
483 Terry Shumpert .01 .05
484 Mike Hartley .01 .05
485 Chris Sabo .01 .05
486 Bob Walk .01 .05
487 John Cerutti .01 .05
488 Scott Cooper .01 .05
489 Bobby Cox MG .02 .10
490 Julio Franco .02 .10
491 Jeff Brantley .01 .05
492 Mike Devereaux .01 .05
493 Jose Offerman .01 .05
494 Gary Thurman .01 .05
495 Carney Lansford .02 .10
496 Joe Grahe .01 .05
497 Andy Ashby .01 .05
498 Gerald Perry .01 .05
499 Dave Otto .01 .05
500 Vince Coleman .01 .05
501 Rob Mallicoat .01 .05
502 Greg Briley .01 .05
503 Pascual Perez .01 .05
504 Aaron Sele RC .08 .25
505 Bobby Thigpen .01 .05
506 Todd Benzinger .01 .05
507 Candy Maldonado .01 .05
508 Bill Gullickson .01 .05
509 Doug Dascenzo .01 .05
510 Frank Viola .02 .10
511 Kenny Rogers .02 .10
512 Mike Heath .01 .05
513 Kevin Bass .01 .05
514 Kim Batiste .01 .05
515 Delino DeShields .01 .05
516 Ed Sprague .01 .05
517 Jim Gott .01 .05
518 Jose Melendez .01 .05
519 Hal McRae MG .02 .10
520 Jeff Bagwell .08 .25
521 Joe Hesketh .01 .05
522 Milt Cuyler .01 .05
523 Shawn Hillegas .01 .05
524 Don Slaught .01 .05
525 Randy Johnson .08 .25
526 Doug Platt .01 .05
527 Checklist 397-528 .01 .05
528 Steve Foster .01 .05
529 Joe Girardi .01 .05
530 Jim Abbott .05 .15
531 Larry Walker .05 .15
532 Mike Huff .01 .05
533 Mackey Sasser .01 .05
534 Benji Gil RC .08 .25
535 Dave Stieb .01 .05
536 Willie Wilson .01 .05
537 Mark Leiter .01 .05
538 Jose Uribe .01 .05
539 Thomas Howard .01 .05
540 Ben McDonald .01 .05
541 Jose Tolentino .01 .05
542 Keith Mitchell .01 .05
543 Jerome Walton .01 .05
544 Cliff Brantley .01 .05
545 Andy Van Slyke .05 .15
546 Paul Sorrento .01 .05
547 Herm Winningham .01 .05
548 Mark Guthrie .01 .05
549 Joe Torre MG .02 .10
550 Darryl Strawberry .02 .10
551 Wilfredo Cordero .08 .25
Chipper Jones
Manny Alexander
Alex Arias UER
(No line around
top border)
552 Dave Gallagher .01 .05
553 Edgar Martinez .05 .15
554 Donald Harris .01 .05
555 Frank Thomas .08 .25
556 Storm Davis .01 .05
557 Dickie Thon .01 .05
558 Scott Garrelts .01 .05
559 Steve Olin .01 .05
560 Rickey Henderson .08 .25
561 Jose Vizcaino .01 .05
562 Wade Taylor .01 .05
563 Pat Borders .01 .05
564 Jimmy Gonzalez RC .02 .10
565 Lee Smith .02 .10
566 Bill Sampen .01 .05
567 Dean Palmer .02 .10
568 Bryan Harvey .01 .05
569 Tony Pena .01 .05
570 Lou Whitaker .02 .10
571 Randy Tomlin .01 .05
572 Greg Vaughn .01 .05
573 Kelly Downs .01 .05
574 Steve Avery UER .01 .05
(Should be 13 games
for Durham in 1989)
575 Kirby Puckett .08 .25
576 Heathcliff Slocumb .01 .05
577 Kevin Seitzer .01 .05
578 Lee Guetterman .01 .05
579 Johnny Oates MG .01 .05
580 Greg Maddux .15 .40
581 Stan Javier .01 .05
582 Vicente Palacios .01 .05
583 Mel Rojas .01 .05
584 Wayne Rosenthal RC .02 .10
585 Lenny Webster .01 .05
586 Rod Nichols .01 .05
587 Mickey Morandini .01 .05
588 Russ Swan .01 .05
589 Mariano Duncan .01 .05
590 Howard Johnson .01 .05
591 Jeromy Burnitz .02 .10
Jacob Brumfield
Alan Cockrell
D.J. Dozier
592 Denny Neagle .02 .10
593 Steve Decker .01 .05
594 Brian Barber RC .02 .10
595 Bruce Hurst .01 .05
596 Kent Mercker .01 .05
597 Mike Magnante RC .02 .10
598 Jody Reed .01 .05
599 Steve Searcy .01 .05
600 Paul Molitor .02 .10
601 Dave Smith .01 .05
602 Mike Fetters .01 .05
603 Luis Mercedes .01 .05
604 Chris Gwynn .01 .05
605 Scott Erickson .01 .05
606 Brook Jacoby .01 .05
607 Todd Stottlemyre .01 .05
608 Scott Bradley .01 .05
609 Mike Hargrove MG .01 .05
610 Eric Davis .02 .10
611 Brian Hunter .01 .05
612 Pat Kelly .01 .05
613 Pedro Munoz .01 .05
614 Al Osuna .01 .05
615 Matt Merullo .01 .05
616 Larry Andersen .01 .05
617 Junior Ortiz .01 .05
618 Cesar Hernandez .01 .05
Steve Hosey
Jeff McNeely
Dan Peltier
619 Danny Jackson .01 .05
620 George Brett .25 .60
621 Dan Gakeler .01 .05
622 Steve Buechele .01 .05
623 Bob Tewksbury .01 .05
624 Shawn Estes RC .08 .25
625 Kevin McReynolds .01 .05
626 Chris Haney .01 .05
627 Mike Sharperson .01 .05
628 Mark Williamson .01 .05
629 Wally Joyner .02 .10
630 Carlton Fisk .05 .15
631 Armando Reynoso RC .08 .25
632 Felix Fermin .01 .05
633 Mitch Williams .01 .05
634 Manuel Lee .01 .05
635 Harold Baines .02 .10
636 Greg Harris .01 .05
637 Orlando Merced .01 .05
638 Chris Bosio .01 .05
639 Wayne Housie .01 .05
640 Xavier Hernandez .01 .05
641 David Howard .01 .05
642 Tim Crews .01 .05
643 Rick Cerone .01 .05
644 Terry Leach .01 .05
645 Deion Sanders .05 .15
646 Craig Wilson .01 .05
647 Marquis Grissom .02 .10
648 Scott Fletcher .01 .05
649 Norm Charlton .01 .05
650 Jesse Barfield .01 .05
651 Joe Slusarski .01 .05
652 Bobby Rose .01 .05
653 Dennis Lamp .01 .05
654 Allen Watson RC .02 .10
655 Brett Butler .02 .10
656 Rudy Pemberton .02 .10
Henry Rodriguez
Lee Tinsley RC
Gerald Williams
657 Dave Johnson .01 .05
658 Checklist 529-660 .01 .05
659 Brian McRae .01 .05
660 Fred McGriff .05 .15
661 Bill Landrum .01 .05
662 Juan Guzman .01 .05
663 Greg Gagne .01 .05
664 Ken Hill .01 .05
665 Dave Haas .01 .05
666 Tom Foley .01 .05
667 Roberto Hernandez .01 .05
668 Dwayne Henry .01 .05
669 Jim Fregosi MG .01 .05
670 Harold Reynolds .02 .10
671 Mark Whiten .01 .05
672 Eric Plunk .01 .05
673 Todd Hundley .01 .05
674 Mo Sanford .01 .05
675 Bobby Witt .01 .05
676 Sam Militello .08 .25
Pat Mahomes RC
Turk Wendell
Roger Salkeld
677 John Marzano .01 .05
678 Joe Klink .01 .05
679 Pete Incaviglia .01 .05
680 Dale Murphy .05 .15
681 Rene Gonzales .01 .05
682 Andy Benes .01 .05
683 Jim Poole .01 .05
684 Trever Miller RC .02 .10
685 Scott Livingstone .01 .05
686 Rich DeLucia .01 .05
687 Harvey Pulliam .01 .05
688 Tim Belcher .01 .05
689 Mark Lemke .01 .05
690 John Franco .02 .10
691 Walt Weiss .01 .05
692 Scott Ruskin .01 .05
693 Jeff King .01 .05
694 Mike Gardiner .01 .05
695 Gary Sheffield .02 .10
696 Joe Boever .01 .05
697 Mike Felder .01 .05
698 John Habyan .01 .05
699 Cito Gaston MG .01 .05
700 Ruben Sierra .02 .10
701 Scott Radinsky .01 .05
702 Lee Stevens .01 .05
703 Mark Wohlers .01 .05
704 Curt Young .01 .05
705 Dwight Evans .05 .15
706 Rob Murphy .01 .05
707 Gregg Jefferies .01 .05
708 Tom Bolton .01 .05
709 Chris James .01 .05
710 Kevin Maas .01 .05
711 Ricky Bones .01 .05
712 Curt Wilkerson .01 .05
713 Roger McDowell .01 .05
714 Pokey Reese RC .08 .25
715 Craig Biggio .05 .15
716 Kirk Dressendorfer .01 .05
717 Ken Dayley .01 .05
718 B.J. Surhoff .02 .10
719 Terry Mulholland .01 .05
720 Kirk Gibson .02 .10
721 Mike Pagliarulo .01 .05
722 Walt Terrell .01 .05
723 Jose Oquendo .01 .05
724 Kevin Morton .01 .05
725 Dwight Gooden .02 .10
726 Kirt Manwaring .01 .05
727 Chuck McElroy .01 .05
728 Dave Burba .01 .05
729 Art Howe MG .01 .05
730 Ramon Martinez .01 .05
731 Donnie Hill .01 .05
732 Nelson Santovenia .01 .05
733 Bob Melvin .01 .05
734 Scott Hatteberg RC .08 .25
735 Greg Swindell .01 .05
736 Lance Johnson .01 .05
737 Kevin Reimer .01 .05
738 Dennis Eckersley .02 .10
739 Rob Ducey .01 .05
740 Ken Caminiti .02 .10
741 Mark Gubicza .01 .05
742 Bill Spiers .01 .05
743 Darren Lewis .01 .05
744 Chris Hammond .01 .05
745 Dave Magadan .01 .05
746 Bernard Gilkey .01 .05
747 Willie Banks .01 .05
748 Matt Nokes .01 .05
749 Jerald Clark .01 .05
750 Travis Fryman .02 .10
751 Steve Wilson .01 .05
752 Billy Ripken .01 .05
753 Paul Assenmacher .01 .05
754 Charlie Hayes .01 .05
755 Alex Fernandez .01 .05
756 Gary Pettis .01 .05
757 Rob Dibble .02 .10
758 Tim Naehring .01 .05
759 Jeff Torborg MG .01 .05
760 Ozzie Smith .15 .40
761 Mike Fitzgerald .01 .05
762 John Burkett .01 .05
763 Kyle Abbott .01 .05
764 Tyler Green RC .02 .10
765 Pete Harnisch .01 .05
766 Mark Davis .01 .05
767 Kal Daniels .01 .05
768 Jim Thome .08 .25
769 Jack Howell .01 .05
770 Sid Bream .01 .05
771 Arthur Rhodes .01 .05
772 Garry Templeton UER .01 .05
(Stat heading in for pitchers)
773 Hal Morris .01 .05
774 Bud Black .01 .05
775 Ivan Calderon .01 .05
776 Doug Henry RC .02 .10
777 John Olerud .02 .10
778 Tim Leary .01 .05
779 Jay Bell .02 .10
780 Eddie Murray .08 .25
781 Paul Abbott .01 .05
782 Phil Plantier .01 .05
783 Joe Magrane .01 .05
784 Ken Patterson .01 .05
785 Albert Belle .02 .10
786 Royce Clayton .01 .05
787 Checklist 661-792 .01 .05
788 Mike Stanton .01 .05
789 Bobby Valentine MG .01 .05
790 Joe Carter .02 .10
791 Danny Cox .01 .05
792 Dave Winfield .02 .10

1992 Topps Gold

Topps produced a 792-card Topps Gold factory set packaged in a foil display box. Only this factory set contained an additional card of Brien Taylor, numbered 793 and hand signed by him. The production run was 12,000 sets. The Topps Gold cards were also available in regular series packs. According to Topps, on average collectors would find one Topps Gold card in every 36 wax packs, one in every 18 cello packs, one in every 12 rak packs, five per Vending box, one in every six jumbo packs, and ten per regular factory set. The checklist cards in the regular set were replaced with six individual Rookie player cards (131, 264, 366, 527, 658, 787) in the gold set. There were a number of uncorrected errors in the Gold set. Steve Finley (86) has gold band indicating he is Mark Davidson of the Astros. Andujar Cedeno (288) is listed as a member of the New York Yankees. Mike Huff (532) is listed as a member of the Boston Red Sox. Barry Larkin (465) is listed as a member of the Houston Astros but is correctly listed as a member of the Cincinnati Reds on his Gold Winners cards. Typically the individual cards are sold at a multiple of the player's respective value in the regular set.

COMPLETE SET (792) 30.00 80.00
COMP.FACT.SET (793) 30.00 80.00
*STARS: 6X TO 15X BASIC CARDS
*ROOKIES: 4X TO 10X BASIC CARDS
RANDOM INSERTS IN PACKS
131 Terry Mathews .30 .75
264 Rod Beck .30 .75
366 Tony Perezchica .30 .75
527 Terry McDaniel .30 .75
658 John Ramos .30 .75
787 Brian Williams .30 .75
793 Brien Taylor AU/12000 6.00 15.00

1992 Topps Gold Winners

The 1992 Topps baseball card packs featured "Match-the-Stats" game cards in which the consumer could save "Runs". For 2.00 and every 100 Runs saved in this game, the consumer could receive through a mail-in offer ten Topps Gold cards. These particular Topps Gold cards carry the word "Winner" in gold foil on the card front. The checklist cards in the regular set were replaced with six individual Rookie player cards (131, 264, 366, 527, 658, 787) in the gold set. Typically the individual cards are sold at a multiple of the player's respective value in the regular set. The Gold winner promotion was very popular and the cards are in noticably larger supply than the basic Gold parallels. It did not hurt the supply of Winnner cards collectors could hold their cards up to the light to see which were the correct answers. Later printing of 1992 game cards were fixed so collectors could not cheat to get the answers.

COMPLETE SET (792) 20.00 40.00
*STARS: 1.25X TO 3X BASIC CARDS
*ROOKIES: 1.25X TO 3X BASIC CARDS
131 Terry Mathews .05 .15
264 Rod Beck .05 .15
366 Tony Perezchica .05 .15
527 Terry McDaniel .05 .15
658 John Ramos .05 .15
787 Brian Williams .05 .15

1992 Topps Micro

This 804 card parallel set was issued in factory set form only. The set is an exact replica of the regular issue 1992 Topps set (not including the Traded set).The cards, however, measure considerably smaller (1" by 1 3/8") than the regular cards. The set also includes 12 special gold foil parallel mini cards which are listed below. Please refer to the multipliers provided for values on the other singles.

COMP. FACT.SET (804) 12.00 30.00
COMMON GOLD INSERT .04 .10
*STARS: .4X TO 1X BASIC CARDS
G1 Nolan Ryan RB 1.00 2.50
G2 Rickey Henderson RB .20 .50
G10 Wade Boggs .20 .50
G50 Ken Griffey Jr. 1.00 2.50
G100 Jose Canseco .20 .50
G270 Tony Gwynn .50 1.25
G300 Don Mattingly .50 1.25
G380 Barry Bonds .20 .50
G397 Cecil Fielder AS .02 .10
G403 Ruben Sierra AS .02 .10
G460 Andre Dawson .15 .40
G725 Dwight Gooden .07 .20

1992 Topps Traded

The 1992 Topps Traded set comprises 132 standard-size cards. The set was distributed exclusively in factory set form through hobby dealers. As in past editions, the set focuses on promising rookies, new managers, and players who changed teams. The set also includes a Team U.S.A. subset, featuring 25 of America's top college players and the Team U.S.A. coach. Card design is identical to the regular issue 1992 Topps cards except for the T-suffixed numbering. The cards are arranged in alphabetical order by player's last name. The key Rookie Cards in this set are Nomar Garciaparra, Brian Jordan and Jason Varitek.

COMP.FACT.SET (132) 20.00 50.00
1T Willie Adams USA RC .08 .25
2T Jeff Alkire USA RC .08 .25
3T Felipe Alou MG .07 .20
4T Moises Alou .07 .20
5T Ruben Amaro .02 .10
6T Jack Armstrong .02 .10
7T Scott Bankhead .02 .10
8T Tim Belcher .02 .10
9T George Bell .02 .10
10T Freddie Benavides .02 .10
11T Todd Benzinger .02 .10
12T Joe Boever .02 .10
13T Ricky Bones .02 .10
14T Bobby Bonilla .07 .20
15T Hubie Brooks .02 .10
16T Jerry Browne .02 .10
17T Jim Bullinger .02 .10
18T Dave Burba .02 .10
19T Kevin Campbell .02 .10
20T Tom Candiotti .02 .10
21T Mark Carreon .02 .10
22T Gary Carter .07 .20
23T Archi Cianfrocco RC .02 .10
24T Phil Clark .02 .10
25T Chad Curtis RC .15 .40
26T Eric Davis .07 .20
27T Tim Davis USA RC .08 .25
28T Gary DiSarcina .02 .10
29T Darren Dreifort USA .02 .10
30T Mariano Duncan .02 .10
31T Mike Fitzgerald .02 .10
32T John Flaherty .02 .10
33T Darrin Fletcher .02 .10
34T Scott Fletcher .02 .10
35T Ron Fraser USA CO RC .08 .25
36T Andres Galarraga .07 .20
37T Dave Gallagher .02 .10
38T Mike Gallego .02 .10
39T Nomar Garciaparra USA RC 6.00 15.00
40T Jason Giambi USA .40 1.00
41T Danny Gladden .02 .10
42T Rene Gonzales .02 .10
43T Jeff Granger USA .02 .10
44T Rick Greene USA RC .08 .25
45T J.Hammonds USA .07 .20
46T Charlie Hayes .02 .10
47T Von Hayes .02 .10
48T Rick Helling USA .02 .10
49T Butch Henry RC .02 .10
50T Carlos Hernandez .02 .10
51T Ken Hill .02 .10
52T Butch Hobson .02 .10
53T Vince Horsman .02 .10
54T Pete Incaviglia .02 .10
55T Gregg Jefferies .02 .10
56T Charles Johnson USA .07 .20
57T Doug Jones .02 .10
58T Brian Jordan RC .30 .75
59T Wally Joyner .07 .20
60T D.Kirkreit USA RC .08 .25
61T Bill Krueger .02 .10
62T Gene Lamont MG .02 .10
63T Jim Lefebvre MG .02 .10
64T Danny Leon .02 .10
65T Pat Listach RC .15 .40
66T Kenny Lofton .10 .30
67T Dave Martinez .02 .10
68T Derrick May .02 .10
69T Kirk McCaskill .02 .10
70T Chad McConnell USA RC .08 .25
71T Kevin McReynolds .02 .10
72T Rusty Meacham .02 .10
73T Keith Miller .02 .10
74T Kevin Mitchell .02 .10
75T Jason Moler USA RC .08 .25
76T Mike Morgan .02 .10
77T Jack Morris .07 .20
78T Calvin Murray USA RC .30 .75
79T Eddie Murray .20 .50
80T Randy Myers .07 .20
81T Denny Neagle .07 .20
82T Phil Nevin USA .07 .20
83T Dave Nilsson .02 .10
84T Junior Ortiz .02 .10
85T Donovan Osborne .02 .10
86T Bill Pecota .02 .10

87T Melido Perez .02 .10
88T Mike Perez .02 .10
89T Hipolito Pichardo RC .02 .10
90T Willie Randolph .07 .20
91T Darren Reed .02 .10
92T Bip Roberts .02 .10
93T Chris Roberts USA .02 .10
94T Steve Rodriguez USA .02 .10
95T Bruce Ruffin .02 .10
96T Scott Ruskin .02 .10
97T Bret Saberhagen .07 .20
98T Rey Sanchez RC .15 .40
99T Steve Sax .02 .10
100T Curt Schilling .10 .30
101T Dick Schofield .02 .10
102T Gary Scott .02 .10
103T Kevin Seitzer .02 .10
104T Frank Seminara RC .02 .10
105T Gary Sheffield .07 .20
106T John Smiley .02 .10
107T Cory Snyder .02 .10
108T Paul Sorrento .02 .10
109T Sammy Sosa .60 1.50
110T Matt Stairs RC .20 .50
111T Andy Stankiewicz .02 .10
112T Kurt Stillwell .02 .10
113T Rick Sutcliffe .07 .20
114T Bill Swift .02 .10
115T Jeff Tackett .02 .10
116T Danny Tartabull .02 .10
117T Eddie Taubensee .07 .20
118T Dickie Thon .02 .10
119T Michael Tucker USA RC .30 .75
120T Scooter Tucker .02 .10
121T Marc Valdes USA RC .08 .25
122T Julio Valera .02 .10
123T Jason Varitek USA RC 5.00 12.00
124T Ron Villone USA RC .08 .25
125T Frank Viola .07 .20
126T B.J. Wallace USA RC .08 .25
127T Dan Walters .02 .10
128T Craig Wilson USA .02 .10
129T Chris Wimmer USA .02 .10
130T Dave Winfield .07 .20
131T Herm Winningham .02 .10
132T Checklist 1T-132T .02 .10

1992 Topps Traded Gold

This 132 card standard-size set parallels the regular 1992 Topps Traded set. It was only issued through the Topps dealer network. Six thousand of these sets were produced and the only player difference is that Kerry Woodson replaces the checklist card

COMP.FACT.SET (132) 40.00 80.00
*GOLD STARS: 1.5X TO 4X BASIC CARDS
*GOLD RC's: .75X TO 2X BASIC CARDS

1993 Topps

The 1993 Topps baseball set consists of two series, respectively, of 396 and 429 standard-size cards. A Topps Gold card was inserted in every 15-card pack. In addition, hobby and retail factory sets were produced. The fronts feature color action player photos with white borders. The player's name appears in a stripe at the bottom of the picture, and this stripe and two short diagonal stripes at the bottom corners of the picture are team color-coded. The backs are colorful and carry a color head shot, biography, complete statistical information, with a career highlight if space permitted. Cards 401-411 comprise an All-Star subset. Rookie Cards in this set include Jim Edmonds, Derek Jeter and Jason Kendall.

COMPLETE SET (825) 30.00 60.00
COMP.HOBBY.SET (847) 30.00 60.00
COMP.RETAIL.SET (838) 30.00 60.00
COMP. SERIES 1 (396) 10.00 25.00
COMP.SERIES 2 (429) 10.00 25.00
1 Robin Yount .30 .75
2 Barry Bonds .60 1.50
3 Ryne Sandberg .30 .75
4 Roger Clemens .40 1.00
5 Tony Gwynn .25 .60
6 Jeff Tackett .02 .10
7 Pete Incaviglia .02 .10
8 Mark Wohlers .02 .10
9 Kent Hrbek .07 .20
10 Will Clark .10 .30
11 Eric Karros .07 .20
12 Lee Smith .07 .20
13 Esteban Beltre .02 .10
14 Greg Briley .02 .10
15 Marquis Grissom .07 .20
16 Dan Plesac .02 .10
17 Dave Hollins .02 .10
18 Terry Steinbach .02 .10
19 Ed Nunez .02 .10
20 Tim Salmon .10 .30
21 Luis Salazar .02 .10
22 Jim Eisenreich .02 .10
23 Todd Stottlemyre .02 .10
24 Tim Naehring .02 .10
25 John Franco .07 .20
26 Skeeter Barnes .02 .10
27 Carlos Garcia .02 .10
28 Joe Orsulak .02 .10
29 Dwayne Henry .02 .10
30 Fred McGriff .10 .30
31 Derek Lilliquist .02 .10
32 Don Mattingly .50 1.25
33 B.J. Wallace .02 .10
34 Juan Gonzalez .07 .20
35 John Smoltz .10 .30
36 Scott Servais .02 .10
37 Lenny Webster .02 .10
38 Chris James .02 .10
39 Roger McDowell .02 .10
40 Ozzie Smith .30 .75
41 Alex Fernandez .02 .10
42 Spike Owen .02 .10
43 Ruben Amaro .02 .10
44 Kevin Seitzer .02 .10
45 Dave Fleming .02 .10
46 Eric Fox .02 .10
47 Bob Scanlan .02 .10
48 Bert Blyleven .07 .20
49 Brian McRae .02 .10
50 Roberto Alomar .10 .30
51 Mo Vaughn .07 .20
52 Bobby Bonilla .07 .20
53 Frank Tanana .02 .10
54 Mike LaValliere .02 .10
55 Mark McLemore .02 .10
56 Chad Mottola RC .02 .10
57 Norm Charlton .02 .10
58 Jose Melendez .02 .10
59 Carlos Martinez .02 .10
60 Roberto Kelly .02 .10
61 Gene Larkin .02 .10
62 Rafael Belliard .02 .10
63 Al Osuna .02 .10
64 Scott Chiamparino .02 .10
65 Brett Butler .07 .20
66 John Burkett .02 .10
67 Felix Jose .02 .10
68 Omar Vizquel .10 .30
69 John Vander Wal .02 .10
70 Roberto Hernandez .02 .10
71 Ricky Bones .02 .10
72 Jeff Grotewold .02 .10
73 Mike Moore .02 .10
74 Steve Buechele .02 .10
75 Juan Guzman .02 .10
76 Kevin Appier .07 .20
77 Junior Felix .02 .10
78 Greg W. Harris .02 .10
79 Dick Schofield .02 .10
80 Cecil Fielder .07 .20
81 Lloyd McClendon .02 .10
82 David Segui .02 .10
83 Reggie Sanders .07 .20
84 Kurt Stillwell .02 .10
85 Sandy Alomar Jr. .02 .10
86 John Habyan .02 .10
87 Kevin Reimer .02 .10
88 Mike Stanton .02 .10
89 Eric Anthony .02 .10
90 Scott Erickson .02 .10
91 Craig Colbert .02 .10
92 Tom Pagnozzi .02 .10
93 Pedro Astacio .02 .10
94 Lance Johnson .02 .10
95 Larry Walker .07 .20
96 Russ Swan .02 .10
97 Scott Fletcher .02 .10
98 Derek Jeter RC 8.00 20.00
99 Mike Williams .02 .10
100 Mark McGwire .50 1.25
101 Jim Bullinger .02 .10
102 Brian Hunter .02 .10
103 Jody Reed .02 .10
104 Mike Butcher .02 .10
105 Gregg Jefferies .02 .10
106 Howard Johnson .02 .10
107 John Kiely .02 .10
108 Jose Lind .02 .10
109 Sam Horn .02 .10
110 Barry Larkin .10 .30
111 Bruce Hurst .02 .10
112 Brian Barnes .02 .10
113 Thomas Howard .02 .10
114 Mel Hall .02 .10
115 Robby Thompson .02 .10
116 Mark Lemke .02 .10
117 Eddie Taubensee .02 .10
118 David Hulse RC .02 .10
119 Pedro Munoz .02 .10
120 Ramon Martinez .02 .10
121 Todd Worrell .02 .10
122 Joey Cora .02 .10
123 Moises Alou .07 .20
124 Franklin Stubbs .02 .10
125 Pete O'Brien .02 .10
126 Bob Ayrault .02 .10
127 Carney Lansford .07 .20
128 Kal Daniels .02 .10
129 Joe Grahe .02 .10
130 Jeff Montgomery .02 .10
131 Dave Winfield .07 .20
132 Preston Wilson RC .30 .75
133 Steve Wilson .02 .10
134 Lee Guetterman .02 .10
135 Mickey Tettleton .02 .10
136 Jeff King .02 .10
137 Alan Mills .02 .10
138 Joe Oliver .02 .10
139 Gary Gaetti .07 .20
140 Gary Sheffield .07 .20
141 Dennis Cook .02 .10
142 Charlie Hayes .02 .10
143 Jeff Huson .02 .10
144 Kent Mercker .02 .10
145 Eric Young .02 .10
146 Scott Leius .02 .10
147 Bryan Hickerson .02 .10
148 Steve Finley .07 .20
149 Rheal Cormier .02 .10
150 Frank Thomas UER .20 .50
(Categories leading
league are italicized
but not printed in red)
151 Archi Cianfrocco .02 .10
152 Rich DeLucia .02 .10
153 Greg Vaughn .02 .10
154 Wes Chamberlain .02 .10
155 Dennis Eckersley .07 .20
156 Sammy Sosa .20 .50
157 Gary DiSarcina .02 .10
158 Kevin Koslofski .02 .10
159 Doug Linton .02 .10
160 Lou Whitaker .07 .20
161 Chad McDonnell .02 .10
162 Joe Hesketh .02 .10
163 Tim Wakefield .20 .50
164 Leo Gomez .02 .10
165 Jose Rijo .02 .10
166 Tim Scott .02 .10
167 Steve Olin UER .02 .10
(Born 10/4/65
should say 10/10/65)
168 Kevin Maas .02 .10
169 Kenny Rogers .07 .20
170 David Justice .07 .20
171 Doug Jones .02 .10
172 Jeff Reboulet .02 .10
173 Andres Galarraga .07 .20
174 Randy Velarde .02 .10
175 Kirk McCaskill .02 .10
176 Darren Lewis .02 .10
177 Lenny Harris .02 .10
178 Jeff Fassero .02 .10
179 Ken Griffey Jr. .30 .75
180 Darren Daulton .07 .20
181 John Jaha .02 .10
182 Ron Darling .02 .10
183 Greg Maddux .30 .75
184 Damion Easley .02 .10
185 Jack Morris .07 .20
186 Mike Magnante .02 .10
187 John Dopson .02 .10
188 Sid Fernandez .02 .10
189 Tony Phillips .02 .10
190 Doug Drabek .02 .10
191 Sean Lowe RC .02 .10
192 Bob Milacki .02 .10
193 Steve Foster .02 .10
194 Jerald Clark .02 .10
195 Pete Harnisch .02 .10
196 Pat Kelly .02 .10
197 Jeff Frye .02 .10
198 Alejandro Pena .02 .10
199 Junior Ortiz .02 .10
200 Kirby Puckett .20 .50
201 Jose Uribe .02 .10
202 Mike Scioscia .02 .10
203 Bernard Gilkey .02 .10
204 Dan Pasqua .02 .10
205 Gary Carter .07 .20
206 Henry Cotto .02 .10
207 Paul Molitor .07 .20
208 Mike Hartley .02 .10
209 Jeff Parrett .02 .10
210 Mark Langston .02 .10
211 Doug Dascenzo .02 .10
212 Rick Reed .02 .10
213 Candy Maldonado .02 .10
214 Danny Darwin .02 .10
215 Pat Howell .02 .10
216 Mark Leiter .02 .10
217 Kevin Mitchell .02 .10
218 Ben McDonald .02 .10
219 Bip Roberts .02 .10
220 Benny Santiago .07 .20
221 Carlos Baerga .02 .10
222 Bernie Williams .10 .30
223 Roger Pavlik .02 .10
224 Sid Bream .02 .10
225 Matt Williams .07 .20
226 Willie Banks .02 .10
227 Jeff Bagwell .10 .30
228 Tom Goodwin .02 .10
229 Mike Perez .02 .10
230 Carlton Fisk .10 .30
231 John Wetteland .07 .20
232 Tino Martinez .10 .30
233 Rick Greene .02 .10
234 Tim McIntosh .02 .10
235 Mitch Williams .02 .10
236 Kevin Campbell .02 .10
237 Jose Vizcaino .02 .10
238 Chris Donnels .02 .10
239 Mike Boddicker .02 .10
240 John Olerud .07 .20
241 Mike Gardiner .02 .10
242 Charlie O'Brien .02 .10
243 Rob Deer .02 .10
244 Denny Neagle .07 .20
245 Chris Sabo .02 .10
246 Gregg Olson .02 .10
247 Frank Seminara UER .02 .10
(Acquired 12/3/98)
248 Scott Scudder .02 .10
249 Tim Burke .02 .10
250 Chuck Knoblauch .07 .20
251 Mike Bielecki .02 .10
252 Xavier Hernandez .02 .10
253 Jose Guzman .02 .10
254 Cory Snyder .02 .10
255 Orel Hershiser .07 .20
256 Wil Cordero .02 .10
257 Luis Alicea .02 .10
258 Mike Schooler .02 .10
259 Craig Grebeck .02 .10
260 Duane Ward .02 .10
261 Bill Wegman .02 .10
262 Mickey Morandini .02 .10
263 Vince Horsman .02 .10
264 Paul Sorrento .02 .10
265 Andre Dawson .07 .20
266 Rene Gonzales .02 .10
267 Keith Miller .02 .10
268 Derek Bell .02 .10
269 Todd Steverson RC .02 .10
270 Frank Viola .07 .20
271 Wally Whitehurst .02 .10
272 Kurt Knudsen .02 .10
273 Dan Walters .02 .10
274 Rick Sutcliffe .07 .20
275 Andy Van Slyke .10 .30
276 Paul O'Neill .10 .30
277 Mark Whiten .02 .10
278 Chris Nabholz .02 .10
279 Todd Burns .02 .10
280 Tom Glavine .10 .30
281 Butch Henry .02 .10
282 Shane Mack .02 .10
283 Mike Jackson .02 .10
284 Henry Rodriguez .02 .10
285 Bob Tewksbury .02 .10
286 Ron Karkovice .02 .10
287 Mike Gallego .02 .10
288 Dave Cochrane .02 .10
289 Jesse Orosco .02 .10
290 Dave Stewart .07 .20
291 Tommy Greene .02 .10
292 Rey Sanchez .02 .10
293 Rob Ducey .02 .10
294 Brent Mayne .02 .10
295 Dave Stieb .02 .10
296 Luis Rivera .02 .10
297 Jeff Innis .02 .10
298 Scott Livingstone .02 .10
299 Bob Patterson .02 .10
300 Cal Ripken .60 1.50
301 Cesar Hernandez .02 .10
302 Randy Myers .02 .10
303 Brook Jacoby .02 .10
304 Melido Perez .02 .10
305 Rafael Palmeiro .10 .30
306 Damon Berryhill .02 .10
307 Dan Serafini RC .02 .10
308 Darryl Kile .07 .20
309 J.T. Bruett .02 .10
310 Dave Righetti .07 .20
311 Jay Howell .02 .10
312 Geronimo Pena .02 .10
313 Greg Hibbard .02 .10
314 Mark Gardner .02 .10
315 Edgar Martinez .10 .30
316 Dave Nilsson .02 .10
317 Kyle Abbott .02 .10
318 Willie Wilson .02 .10
319 Paul Assenmacher .02 .10
320 Tim Fortugno .02 .10
321 Rusty Meacham .02 .10
322 Pat Borders .02 .10
323 Mike Greenwell .02 .10
324 Willie Randolph .07 .20
325 Bill Gullickson .02 .10
326 Gary Varsho .02 .10
327 Tim Hulett .02 .10
328 Scott Ruskin .02 .10
329 Mike Maddux .02 .10
330 Danny Tartabull .02 .10
331 Kenny Lofton .07 .20
332 Geno Petralli .02 .10
333 Otis Nixon .02 .10
334 Jason Kendall RC .40 1.00
335 Mark Portugal .02 .10
336 Mike Pagliarulo .02 .10
337 Kirt Manwaring .02 .10
338 Bob Ojeda .02 .10
339 Mark Clark .02 .10
340 John Kruk .07 .20
341 Mel Rojas .02 .10
342 Erik Hanson .02 .10
343 Doug Henry .02 .10
344 Jack McDowell .02 .10
345 Harold Baines .07 .20
346 Chuck McElroy .02 .10
347 Luis Sojo .02 .10
348 Andy Stankiewicz .02 .10
349 Hipolito Pichardo .02 .10
350 Joe Carter .07 .20
351 Ellis Burks .07 .20
352 Pete Schourek .02 .10
353 Buddy Groom .02 .10
354 Jay Bell .07 .20
355 Brady Anderson .07 .20
356 Freddie Benavides .02 .10
357 Phil Stephenson .02 .10
358 Kevin Wickander .02 .10
359 Mike Stanley .02 .10
360 Ivan Rodriguez .10 .30
361 Scott Bankhead .02 .10
362 Luis Gonzalez .07 .20
363 John Smiley .02 .10
364 Trevor Wilson .02 .10
365 Tom Candiotti .02 .10
366 Craig Wilson .02 .10
367 Steve Sax .02 .10
368 Delino DeShields .02 .10
369 Jaime Navarro .02 .10
370 Dave Valle .02 .10
371 Mariano Duncan .02 .10
372 Rod Nichols .02 .10
373 Mike Morgan .02 .10
374 Julio Valera .02 .10
375 Wally Joyner .07 .20
376 Tom Henke .02 .10
377 Herm Winningham .02 .10
378 Orlando Merced .02 .10
379 Mike Munoz .02 .10
380 Todd Hundley .02 .10
381 Mike Flanagan .02 .10
382 Tim Belcher .02 .10
383 Jerry Browne .02 .10
384 Mike Benjamin .02 .10
385 Jim Leyritz .07 .20
386 Ray Lankford .07 .20
387 Devon White .07 .20
388 Jeremy Hernandez .02 .10
389 Brian Harper .02 .10
390 Wade Boggs .10 .30
391 Derrick May .02 .10
392 Travis Fryman .07 .20
393 Ron Gant .07 .20
394 Checklist 1-132 .02 .10
395 CL 133-264 UER .02 .10
Eckersley
396 Checklist 265-396 .02 .10
397 George Brett .50 1.25
398 Bobby Witt .02 .10
399 Daryl Boston .02 .10
400 Bo Jackson .20 .50
401 Fred McGriff .10 .30
Frank Thomas AS
402 Ryne Sandberg .20 .50
Carlos Baerga AS
403 Gary Sheffield .07 .20
Edgar Martinez AS
404 Barry Larkin .07 .20
Travis Fryman AS
405 Andy Van Slyke .20 .50
Ken Griffey Jr. AS
406 Larry Walker .10 .30
Kirby Puckett AS
407 Barry Bonds .30 .75
Joe Carter AS
408 Darren Daulton .07 .20
Brian Harper AS
409 Greg Maddux .20 .50
Roger Clemens AS
410 Tom Glavine .07 .20
Dave Fleming AS
411 Lee Smith .07 .20
Dennis Eckersley AS
412 Jamie McAndrew .02 .10
413 Pete Smith .02 .10
414 Juan Guerrero .02 .10
415 Todd Frohwirth .02 .10
416 Randy Tomlin .02 .10
417 B.J. Surhoff .07 .20
418 Jim Gott .02 .10
419 Mark Thompson RC .02 .10
420 Kevin Tapani .02 .10
421 Curt Schilling .07 .20
422 J.T. Snow RC .20 .50
423 Ryan Klesko .07 .20
Ivan Cruz
Bubba Smith
Larry Sutton RC
424 John Valentin .02 .10
425 Joe Girardi .02 .10
426 Nigel Wilson .02 .10
427 Bob MacDonald .02 .10
428 Todd Zeile .02 .10
429 Milt Cuyler .02 .10
430 Eddie Murray .20 .50
431 Rich Amaral .02 .10
432 Pete Young .02 .10
433 Roger Bailey RC .02 .10
Tom Schmidt
434 Jack Armstrong .02 .10
435 Willie McGee .07 .20
436 Greg W. Harris .02 .10
437 Chris Hammond .02 .10
438 Ritchie Moody RC .02 .10
439 Bryan Harvey .02 .10
440 Ruben Sierra .07 .20
441 Don Lemon .02 .10
Todd Pridy RC
442 Kevin McReynolds .02 .10
443 Terry Leach .02 .10
444 David Nied .02 .10
445 Dale Murphy .10 .30
446 Luis Mercedes .02 .10
447 Keith Shepherd RC .02 .10
448 Ken Caminiti .07 .20
449 Jim Austin .02 .10
450 Darryl Strawberry .07 .20
451 Ramon Caraballo .08 .25
Jon Shave RC
Brent Gates
Quinton McCracken
452 Bob Wickman .02 .10
453 Victor Cole .02 .10
454 John Johnstone RC .02 .10
455 Chili Davis .07 .20
456 Scott Taylor .02 .10
457 Tracy Woodson .02 .10
458 David Wells .07 .20
459 Derek Wallace RC .02 .10
460 Randy Johnson .20 .50
461 Steve Reed RC .02 .10
462 Felix Fermin .02 .10
463 Scott Aldred .02 .10
464 Greg Colbrunn .02 .10
465 Tony Fernandez .02 .10
466 Mike Felder .02 .10
467 Lee Stevens .02 .10
468 Matt Whiteside RC .02 .10
469 Dave Hansen .02 .10
470 Rob Dibble .07 .20
471 Dave Gallagher .02 .10
472 Chris Gwynn .02 .10
473 Dave Henderson .02 .10
474 Ozzie Guillen .07 .20
475 Jeff Reardon .07 .20
476 Mark Voisard .02 .10
Will Scalzitti RC
477 Jimmy Jones .02 .10
478 Greg Cadaret .02 .10
479 Todd Pratt RC .02 .10
480 Pat Listach .02 .10
481 Ryan Luzinski RC .02 .10
482 Darren Reed .02 .10
483 Brian Griffiths RC .02 .10
484 John Wehner .02 .10
485 Glenn Davis .02 .10
486 Eric Wedge RC .02 .10
487 Jesse Hollins .02 .10
488 Manuel Lee .02 .10
489 Scott Fredrickson RC .02 .10
490 Omar Olivares .02 .10
491 Shawn Hare .02 .10
492 Tom Lampkin .02 .10
493 Jeff Nelson .02 .10
494 Kevin Young .02 .10
Adell Davenport
Eduardo Perez
Lou Lucca RC
495 Ken Hill .02 .10
496 Reggie Jefferson .02 .10
497 Matt Petersen .02 .10
Willie Brown RC
498 Bud Black .02 .10
499 Chuck Crim .02 .10
500 Jose Canseco .10 .30
501 Johnny Oates MG .07 .20
Bobby Cox MG
502 Butch Hobson MG .02 .10
Jim Lefebvre MG
503 Buck Rodgers MG .07 .20
Tony Perez MG
504 Gene Lamont MG .07 .20
Don Baylor MG
505 Mike Hargrove MG .07 .20
Rene Lachemann MG
506 Sparky Anderson MG .07 .20
Art Howe MG
507 Hal McRae MG .07 .20
Tom Lasorda MG
508 Phil Garner MG .07 .20
Felipe Alou MG
509 Tom Kelly MG .02 .10
Jeff Torborg MG
510 Buck Showalter MG .07 .20
Jim Fregosi MG
511 Tony LaRussa MG .07 .20
Jim Leyland MG
512 Lou Piniella MG .07 .20
Joe Torre MG
513 Kevin Kennedy MG .02 .10
Jim Riggleman MG
514 Cito Gaston MG .07 .20
Dusty Baker MG
515 Greg Swindell .02 .10
516 Alex Arias .02 .10
517 Bill Pecota .02 .10
518 Benji Grigsby RC UER .02 .10
(Misspelled Bengi
on card front)
519 David Howard .02 .10
520 Charlie Hough .07 .20
521 Kevin Flora .02 .10
522 Shane Reynolds .02 .10
523 Doug Bochtler RC .02 .10
524 Chris Hoiles .02 .10
525 Scott Sanderson .02 .10
526 Mike Sharperson .02 .10
527 Mike Fetters .02 .10
528 Paul Quantrill .02 .10
529 Dave Silvestri .20 .50
Chipper Jones
Benji Gil
Jeff Patzke
530 Sterling Hitchcock RC .08 .25
531 Joe Millette .02 .10
532 Tom Brunansky .02 .10
533 Frank Castillo .02 .10
534 Randy Knorr .02 .10
535 Jose Oquendo .02 .10
536 Dave Haas .02 .10
537 Jason Hutchins RC .02 .10
Ryan Turner
538 Jimmy Baron RC .02 .10
539 Kerry Woodson .02 .10
540 Ivan Calderon .02 .10
541 Denis Boucher .02 .10
542 Royce Clayton .02 .10
543 Reggie Williams .02 .10
544 Steve Decker .02 .10
545 Dean Palmer .07 .20
546 Hal Morris .02 .10
547 Ryan Thompson .02 .10
548 Lance Blankenship .02 .10
549 Hensley Meulens .02 .10
550 Scott Radinsky .02 .10
551 Eric Young .02 .10
552 Jeff Blauser .02 .10
553 Andujar Cedeno .02 .10
554 Arthur Rhodes .02 .10
555 Terry Mulholland .02 .10
556 Darryl Hamilton .02 .10
557 Pedro Martinez .40 1.00
558 Ryan Whitman RC .02 .10
Mark Skeels
559 Jamie Arnold RC .02 .10
560 Zane Smith .02 .10
561 Matt Nokes .02 .10
562 Bob Zupcic .02 .10
563 Shawn Boskie .02 .10
564 Mike Timlin .02 .10
565 Jerald Clark .02 .10
566 Rod Brewer .02 .10
567 Mark Carreon .02 .10
568 Andy Benes .02 .10
569 Shawn Barton RC .02 .10
570 Tim Wallach .02 .10
571 Dave Mlicki .02 .10
572 Trevor Hoffman .20 .50
573 John Patterson .02 .10
574 De Shawn Warren RC .02 .10
575 Monty Fariss .02 .10
576 Darrell Sherman .07 .20
Damon Buford
Cliff Floyd
Michael Moore
577 Tim Costo .02 .10
578 Dave Magadan .02 .10
579 Neil Garrett .02 .10
Jason Bates RC
580 Walt Weiss .02 .10
581 Chris Haney .02 .10
582 Shawn Abner .02 .10
583 Marvin Freeman .02 .10
584 Casey Candaele .02 .10
585 Ricky Jordan .02 .10
586 Jeff Tabaka RC .02 .10
587 Manny Alexander .02 .10
588 Mike Trombley .02 .10
589 Carlos Hernandez .02 .10
590 Cal Eldred .02 .10
591 Alex Cole .02 .10
592 Phil Plantier .02 .10
593 Brett Merriman RC .02 .10
594 Jerry Nielsen .02 .10
595 Shawon Dunston .02 .10
596 Jimmy Key .07 .20
597 Gerald Perry .02 .10
598 Rico Brogna .02 .10
599 Clemente Nunez .02 .10
Daniel Robinson
600 Bret Saberhagen .07 .20
601 Craig Shipley .02 .10
602 Henry Mercedes .02 .10
603 Jim Thome .10 .30
604 Rod Beck .02 .10
605 Chuck Finley .07 .20
606 Jayhawk Owens RC .02 .10
607 Dan Smith .02 .10
608 Bill Doran .02 .10
609 Lance Parrish .07 .20
610 Dennis Martinez .07 .20
611 Tom Gordon .02 .10
612 Byron Mathews RC .02 .10
613 Joel Adamson RC .02 .10
614 Brian Williams .02 .10
615 Steve Avery .02 .10
616 Matt Mieske .02 .10
Tracy Sanders
Midre Cummings RC
Ryan Freeburg
617 Craig Lefferts .02 .10
618 Tony Pena .02 .10
619 Billy Spiers .02 .10
620 Todd Benzinger .02 .10
621 Mike Kotarski .02 .10
Greg Boyd RC
622 Ben Rivera .02 .10
623 Al Martin .02 .10
624 Sam Militello UER .02 .10
(Profile says drafted
in 1988, bio says
drafted in 1990)
625 Rick Aguilera .02 .10
626 Dan Gladden .02 .10
627 Andres Berumen RC .02 .10
628 Kelly Gruber .02 .10
629 Cris Carpenter .02 .10
630 Mark Grace .10 .30
631 Jeff Brantley .02 .10
632 Chris Widger RC .08 .25
633 Three Russians UER .02 .10
Rudolf Razjigaev
Eugenyi Puchkov
Ilya Bogatyrev
Bogatyrev is a shortstop,
card has pitching header
634 Mo Sanford .02 .10
635 Albert Belle .07 .20
636 Tim Teufel .02 .10
637 Greg Myers .02 .10
638 Brian Bohanon .02 .10
639 Mike Bordick .02 .10
640 Dwight Gooden .07 .20
641 Pat Leahy .02 .10
Gavin Baugh RC
642 Milt Hill .02 .10
643 Luis Aquino .02 .10
644 Dante Bichette .07 .20
645 Bobby Thigpen .02 .10
646 Rich Scheid RC .02 .10
647 Brian Sackinsky RC .02 .10
648 Ryan Hawblitzel .02 .10
649 Tom Marsh .02 .10
650 Terry Pendleton .07 .20
651 Rafael Bournigal .02 .10
652 Dave West .02 .10
653 Steve Hosey .02 .10
654 Gerald Williams .02 .10
655 Scott Cooper .02 .10
656 Gary Scott .02 .10
657 Mike Harkey .02 .10
658 Jeromy Burnitz .07 .20
Melvin Nieves
Rich Becker
Shon Walker RC
659 Ed Sprague .02 .10
660 Alan Trammell .07 .20
661 Garvin Alston RC .02 .10
Michael Case
662 Donovan Osborne .02 .10
663 Jeff Gardner .02 .10
664 Calvin Jones .02 .10
665 Darrin Fletcher .02 .10
666 Glenallen Hill .02 .10
667 Jim Rosenbohm RC .02 .10
668 Scott Lewis .02 .10
669 Kip Yaughn RC .02 .10
670 Julio Franco .07 .20
671 Dave Martinez .02 .10
672 Kevin Bass .02 .10
673 Todd Van Poppel .02 .10
674 Mark Gubicza .02 .10
675 Tim Raines .07 .20

676 Rudy Seanez .02 .10
677 Charlie Leibrandt .02 .10
678 Randy Milligan .02 .10
679 Kim Batiste .02 .10
680 Craig Biggio .10 .30
681 Darren Holmes .02 .10
682 John Candelaria .02 .10
683 Jerry Stafford .02 .10
Eddie Christian RC
684 Pat Mahomes .02 .10
685 Bob Walk .02 .10
686 Russ Springer .02 .10
687 Tony Sheffield RC .02 .10
688 Dwight Smith .02 .10
689 Eddie Zosky .02 .10
690 Bien Figueroa .02 .10
691 Jim Tatum RC .02 .10
692 Chad Kreuter .02 .10
693 Rich Rodriguez .02 .10
694 Shane Turner .02 .10
695 Kent Bottenfield .02 .10
696 Jose Mesa .02 .10
697 Darrell Whitmore RC .02 .10
698 Ted Wood .02 .10
699 Chad Curtis .02 .10
700 Nolan Ryan .75 2.00
701 Mike Piazza 1.50 4.00
Brook Fordyce
Carlos Delgado
Donnie Leshnock
702 Tim Pugh RC .02 .10
703 Jeff Kent .20 .50
704 Jon Goodrich .02 .10
Danny Figueroa RC
705 Bob Welch .02 .10
706 S.Clinkscales RC .02 .10
707 Donn Pall .02 .10
708 Greg Olson .02 .10
709 Jeff Juden .02 .10
710 Mike Mussina .10 .30
711 Scott Chiamparino .02 .10
712 Stan Javier .02 .10
713 John Doherty .02 .10
714 Kevin Gross .02 .10
715 Greg Gagne .02 .10
716 Steve Cooke .02 .10
717 Steve Farr .02 .10
718 Jay Buhner .07 .20
719 Butch Henry .02 .10
720 David Cone .07 .20
721 Rick Wilkins .02 .10
722 Chuck Carr .02 .10
723 Kenny Felder RC .02 .10
724 Guillermo Velasquez .02 .10
725 Billy Hatcher .02 .10
726 Mike Veneziale RC .02 .10
Ken Kendrena
727 Jonathan Hurst .02 .10
728 Steve Frey .02 .10
729 Mark Leonard .02 .10
730 Charles Nagy .02 .10
731 Donald Harris .02 .10
732 Travis Buckley RC .02 .10
733 Tom Browning .02 .10
734 Anthony Young .02 .10
735 Steve Shifflett .02 .10
736 Jeff Russell .02 .10
737 Wilson Alvarez .02 .10
738 Lance Painter RC .02 .10
739 Dave Weathers .02 .10
740 Len Dykstra .07 .20
741 Mike Devereaux .02 .10
742 Rene Arocha .08 .25
Alan Embree
Brien Taylor
Tim Crabtree
743 Dave Landaker RC .02 .10
744 Chris George .02 .10
745 Eric Davis .07 .20
746 Mark Strittmatter .02 .10
Lamarr Rogers RC
747 Carl Willis .02 .10
748 Stan Belinda .02 .10
749 Scott Kamieniecki .02 .10
750 Rickey Henderson .20 .50
751 Eric Hillman .02 .10
752 Pat Hentgen .02 .10
753 Jim Corsi .02 .10
754 Brian Jordan .07 .20
755 Bill Swift .02 .10
756 Mike Henneman .02 .10
757 Harold Reynolds .07 .20
758 Sean Berry .02 .10
759 Charlie Hayes .02 .10
760 Luis Polonia .02 .10
761 Darrin Jackson .02 .10
762 Mark Lewis .02 .10
763 Rob Maurer .02 .10
764 Willie Greene .02 .10
765 Vince Coleman .02 .10
766 Todd Revenig .02 .10
767 Rich Ireland RC .02 .10
768 Mike Macfarlane .02 .10
769 Francisco Cabrera .02 .10
770 Robin Ventura .07 .20
771 Kevin Ritz .02 .10
772 Chito Martinez .02 .10
773 Cliff Brantley .02 .10
774 Curt Leskanic RC .08 .25
775 Chris Bosio .02 .10
776 Jose Offerman .02 .10
777 Mark Guthrie .02 .10
778 Don Slaught .02 .10
779 Rich Monteleone .02 .10
780 Jim Abbott .10 .30
781 Jack Clark .07 .20
782 Reynol Mendoza .02 .10
Dan Roman RC
783 Heathcliff Slocumb .02 .10
784 Jeff Branson .02 .10
785 Kevin Brown .07 .20
786 Mike Christopher .02 .10
Ken Ryan
Aaron Taylor
Gus Gandarillas RC
787 Mike Matthews RC .02 .10
788 Mackey Sasser .02 .10
789 Jeff Conine UER .07 .20
No inclusion of 1990
RBI stats in career total
790 George Bell .02 .10
791 Pat Rapp .02 .10
792 Joe Boever .02 .10
793 Jim Poole .02 .10
794 Andy Ashby .02 .10
795 Deion Sanders .10 .30
796 Scott Brosius .07 .20
797 Brad Pennington .02 .10
798 Greg Blosser .02 .10
799 Jim Edmonds RC .75 2.00
800 Shawn Jeter .02 .10
801 Jesse Levis .02 .10
802 Phil Clark UER .02 .10
(Word a is missing in sentence beginning with In 1992 ...)
803 Ed Pierce RC .02 .10
804 Jose Valentin RC .08 .25
805 Terry Jorgensen .02 .10
806 Mark Hutton .02 .10
807 Troy Neel .02 .10
808 Bret Boone .07 .20
809 Cris Colon .02 .10
810 Domingo Martinez RC .02 .10
811 Javier Lopez .10 .30
812 Matt Walbeck RC .02 .10
813 Dan Wilson .07 .20
814 Scooter Tucker .02 .10
815 Billy Ashley .02 .10
816 Tim Laker RC .02 .10
817 Bobby Jones .07 .20
818 Brad Brink .02 .10
819 William Pennyfeather .02 .10
820 Stan Royer .02 .10
821 Doug Brocail .02 .10
822 Kevin Rogers .02 .10
823 Checklist 397-540 .02 .10
824 Checklist 541-691 .02 .10
825 Checklist 692-825 .02 .10

1993 Topps Gold

Several insertion schemes were devised for these 825 standard-size cards. Gold cards were inserted one per wax pack, three per rack pack, five per jumbo pack, and ten per factory set. The cards are identical to the regular-issue 1993 Topps baseball cards except that the gold-foil Topps Gold logo appears in an upper corner, and the team color-coded stripe at the bottom of the front, which carried the player's name, has been replaced with an embossed gold-foil stripe. The checklist cards (394-396, 823-825) have been replaced by player cards.

*STARS: 1X TO 2.5X BASIC CARDS
*ROOKIES: 1.25X TO 3X BASIC CARDS
394 Bernardo Brito .08 .25
395 Jim McNamara .08 .25
396 Rich Sauveur .08 .25
823 Keith Brown .08 .25
824 Russ McGinnis .08 .25
825 Mike Walker UER .08 .25
(Card has 1993 Mariner stats, should be 1992)

1993 Topps Inaugural Marlins

These 825-card standard-size sets were issued by Topps to commemorate the debut seasons of the Colorado Rockies and Florida Marlins. Gold foil Marlins or Rockies logos distinguish these from regular issue cards. These cards were only issued in factory set form. 5,000 Rockies sets and 4,000 Marlins sets were initially printed, but each team had the option of receiving a maximum of 10,000 sets. The Rockies sets were distributed through the four team-owned stores and at Mile High Stadium. The Marlins sets were distributed through FMI and Joe Robbie Stadium.

COMP.FACT.SET (825) 40.00 100.00
*STARS: 2.5X TO 6X BASIC CARDS
*ROOKIES: 2.5X TO 6X BASIC CARDS

1993 Topps Inaugural Rockies

Similar to the Marlins set. This was a 1993 set with the Rockies logo imprinted on the card. They were only issued in factory set form. They were distributed through four Rockie owned stores and at Mile High Stadium. They are valued slightly less than the Marlins card as 1,000 more sets of Rockies were produced

COMP.FACT.SET (825) 40.00 100.00
*STARS: 2.5X TO 6X BASIC CARDS
*ROOKIES: 2.5X TO 6X BASIC CARDS

1993 Topps Micro

This set was only issued in factory set form. It was issued as a 837 card set with the regular 825 card as well as a special 12 card prism insert set. The cards measure 1" by 1 3/8" which is approximately 40 percent of the regular card size. Only the Prism inserts are listed below. Please refer to the multiplier for values on the other other cards. This was the final year Topps issued the Micro factory set.

COMP. FACT. SET (837) 15.00 40.00
COMMON PRISM INSERT .04 .10
*MICRO: .25X TO .6X BASIC CARDS
98 Derek Jeter 12.50 30.00
P1 Robin Yount .20 .50
P20 Tim Salmon .15 .40
P32 Don Mattingly .50 1.25
P50 Roberto Alomar .15 .40
P150 Frank Thomas .40 1.00
P155 Dennis Eckersley .07 .20
P179 Ken Griffey Jr. 1.00 2.50
P200 Kirby Puckett .40 1.00
P397 George Brett .40 1.00
P426 Nigel Wilson .02 .10
P444 David Nied .02 .10
P700 Nolan Ryan 1.00 2.50

1993 Topps Black Gold

Topps Black Gold cards 1-22 were randomly inserted in series I packs while card numbers 23-44 were featured in series II packs. They were also inserted three per factory set. In the packs, the cards were inserted one every 72 hobby or retail packs; one every 12 jumbo packs and one every 24 rack packs. Hobbyists could obtain the set by collecting individual random insert cards or receive 11, 22, or 44 Black Gold cards by mail when they sent in special "You've Just Won" cards, which were randomly inserted in packs. Series I packs featured three different "You've Just Won" cards, entitling the holder to receive Group A (cards 1-11), Group B (cards 12-22), or Groups A and B (Cards 1-22). In a similar fashion, four "You've Just Won" cards were inserted in series II packs and entitled the holder to receive Group C (23-33), Group D (34-44), Groups C and D (23-44), or Groups A-D (1-44). By returning the "You've Just Won" card with 1.50 for postage and handling, the collector received not only the Black Gold cards won but also a special "You've Just Won" card and a congratulatory letter informing the collector that his/her name has been entered into a drawing for one of 500 uncut sheets of all 44 Topps Black Gold cards in a leatherette frame. These standard-size cards feature different color player photos than either the 1993 Topps regular issue or the Topps Gold issue. The player pictures are cut out and superimposed on a black gloss background. Inside white borders, gold refractory foil edges the top and bottom of the card face. On a black-and-gray pinstripe pattern inside white borders, the horizontal backs have a a second cut out player photo and a player profile on a blue panel. The player's name appears in gold foil lettering on a blue-and-gray geometric shape. The first 22 cards are National Leaguers while the second 22 cards are American Leaguers. Winner cards C and D were both originally produced erroneously and later corrected; the error versions show the players from Winner A and B on the respective fronts of Winner cards Cand D. There is no value difference in the variations at this time. The winner cards were redeemable until January 31, 1994.

COMPLETE SET (44) 4.00 10.00
COMPLETE SERIES 1 (22) 1.50 4.00
COMPLETE SERIES 2 (22) 2.50 6.00
STATED ODDS 1:72 H/R, 1:12 J, 1:24 RACK
STATED ODDS 1:35 34CT JUM, 1:37 18CT JUM
THREE PER FACTORY SET
1 Barry Bonds 1.00 2.50
2 Will Clark .20 .50
3 Darren Daulton .10 .30
4 Andre Dawson .10 .30
5 Delino DeShields .05 .15
6 Tom Glavine .20 .50
7 Marquis Grissom .10 .30
8 Tony Gwynn .40 1.00
9 Eric Karros .10 .30
10 Ray Lankford .10 .30
11 Barry Larkin .20 .50
12 Greg Maddux .50 1.25
13 Fred McGriff .20 .50
14 Joe Oliver .05 .15
15 Terry Pendleton .10 .30
16 Bip Roberts .05 .15
17 Ryne Sandberg .50 1.25
18 Gary Sheffield .10 .30
19 Lee Smith .10 .30
20 Ozzie Smith .50 1.25
21 Andy Van Slyke .20 .50
22 Larry Walker .10 .30
23 Roberto Alomar .20 .50
24 Brady Anderson .10 .30
25 Carlos Baerga .05 .15
26 Joe Carter .10 .30
27 Roger Clemens .60 1.50
28 Mike Devereaux .05 .15
29 Dennis Eckersley .10 .30
30 Cecil Fielder .10 .30
31 Travis Fryman .10 .30
32 Juan Gonzalez UER .10 .30
(No copyright or licensing on card)
33 Ken Griffey Jr. .50 1.25
34 Brian Harper .05 .15
35 Pat Listach .05 .15
36 Kenny Lofton .10 .30
37 Edgar Martinez .20 .50
38 Jack McDowell .05 .15
39 Mark McGwire .75 2.00
40 Kirby Puckett .30 .75
41 Mickey Tettleton .05 .15
42 Frank Thomas UER .30 .75
(No copyright or licensing on card)
43 Robin Ventura .10 .30
44 Dave Winfield .10 .30

1993 Topps Traded

This 132-card standard-size set focuses on promising rookies, new managers, free agents, and players who changed teams. The set also includes 22 members of Team USA. The set has the same design on the front as the regular 1993 Topps issue. The backs are also the same design and carry a head shot, biography, stats, and career highlights. Rookie Cards in this set include Todd Helton.

COMP.FACT.SET (132) 10.00 25.00
1T Barry Bonds .60 1.50
2T Rich Renteria .02 .10
3T Aaron Sele .02 .10
4T C.Loewer USA RC .08 .25
5T Erik Pappas .02 .10
6T Greg McMichael RC .08 .25
7T Freddie Benavides .02 .10
8T Kirk Gibson .07 .20
9T Tony Fernandez .02 .10
10T Jay Gainer RC .08 .25
11T Orestes Destrade .02 .10
12T A.J. Hinch USA RC .20 .50
13T Bobby Munoz .02 .10
14T Tom Henke .02 .10
15T Rob Butler .02 .10
16T Gary Wayne .02 .10
17T David McCarty .02 .10
18T Walt Weiss .02 .10
19T Todd Helton USA RC 4.00 10.00
20T Mark Whiten .02 .10
21T Ricky Gutierrez .02 .10
22T D.Hermanson USA RC .40 1.00
23T Sherman Obando RC .08 .25
24T Mike Piazza 1.25 3.00
25T Jeff Russell .02 .10
26T Jason Bere .02 .10
27T Jack Voigt RC .08 .25
28T Chris Bosio .02 .10
29T Phil Hiatt .02 .10
30T M.Beaumont USA RC .08 .25
31T Andres Galarraga .07 .20
32T Greg Swindell .02 .10
33T Vinny Castilla .20 .50
34T P.Clougherty RC USA .08 .25
35T Greg Briley .02 .10
36T Dallas Green MG .02 .10
Davey Johnson MG
37T Tyler Green .02 .10
38T Craig Paquette .02 .10
39T Danny Sheaffer RC .08 .25
40T Jim Converse RC .08 .25
41T Terry Harvey USA RC .08 .25
42T Phil Plantier .02 .10
43T Doug Saunders RC .08 .25
44T Benny Santiago .07 .20
45T Dante Powell USA RC .08 .25
46T Jeff Parrett .02 .10
47T Wade Boggs .10 .30
48T Paul Molitor .07 .20
49T Turk Wendell .02 .10
50T David Wells .07 .20
51T Gary Sheffield .07 .20
52T Kevin Young .07 .20
53T Nelson Liriano .02 .10
54T Greg Maddux .30 .75
55T Derek Bell .02 .10
56T Matt Turner RC .08 .25
57T C.Nelson RC USA .08 .25
58T Mike Hampton .07 .20
59T Troy O'Leary RC .08 .25
60T Benji Gil .02 .10
61T Mitch Lyden RC .08 .25
62T J.T. Snow .07 .20
63T Damon Buford .02 .10
64T Gene Harris .02 .10
65T Randy Myers .02 .10
66T Felix Jose .02 .10
67T Todd Dunn USA RC .08 .25
68T Jimmy Key .07 .20
69T Pedro Castellano .02 .10
70T Mark Merila USA RC .08 .25
71T Rich Rodriguez .02 .10
72T Matt Mieske .02 .10
73T Pete Incaviglia .02 .10
74T Carl Everett .07 .20
75T Jim Abbott .10 .30
76T Luis Aquino .02 .10
77T Rene Arocha .07 .20
78T Jon Shave .02 .10
79T Todd Walker USA RC .40 1.00
80T Jack Armstrong .02 .10
81T Jeff Richardson .02 .10
82T Blas Minor .02 .10
83T Dave Winfield .07 .20
84T Paul O'Neill .10 .30
85T Steve Reich USA RC .08 .25
86T Chris Hammond .02 .10
87T Hilly Hathaway RC .08 .25
88T Fred McGriff .10 .30
89T Dave Telgheder RC .08 .25
90T Richie Lewis RC .08 .25
91T Brent Gates .02 .10
92T Andre Dawson .07 .20
93T Andy Barkett USA RC .08 .25
94T Doug Drabek .02 .10
95T Joe Klink .02 .10
96T Willie Blair .02 .10
97T D.Graves USA RC .20 .50
98T Pat Meares RC .20 .50
99T Mike Lansing RC .20 .50
100T Marcos Armas RC .08 .25
101T D.Grass RC USA .08 .25
102T Chris Jones .02 .10
103T Ken Ryan RC .08 .25
104T Ellis Burks .07 .20
105T Roberto Kelly .02 .10
106T Dave Magadan .02 .10
107T Paul Wilson USA RC .20 .50
108T Rob Natal .02 .10
109T Paul Wagner .02 .10
110T Jeromy Burnitz .07 .20
111T Monty Fariss .02 .10
112T Kevin Mitchell .02 .10
113T Scott Pose RC .08 .25
114T Dave Stewart .07 .20
115T R.Johnson USA RC .08 .25
116T Armando Reynoso .02 .10
117T Geronimo Berroa .02 .10
118T Woody Williams RC .40 1.00
119T Tim Bogar RC .08 .25
120T Bob Scafa USA RC .08 .25
121T Henry Cotto .02 .10
122T Gregg Jefferies .02 .10
123T Norm Charlton .02 .10
124T B.Wagner USA RC .08 .25
125T David Cone .07 .20
126T Daryl Boston .02 .10
127T Tim Wallach .02 .10
128T Mike Martin USA RC .08 .25
129T John Cummings RC .08 .25
130T Ryan Bowen .02 .10
131T John Powell USA RC .08 .25
132T Checklist 1-132 .02 .10

1994 Topps

These 792 standard-size cards were issued in two series of 396. Two types of factory sets were also issued. One features the 792 basic cards, ten Topps Gold, three Black Gold and three Finest Pre-Production cards for a total of 808. The other factory set (Bakers Dozen) includes the 792 basic cards, ten Topps Gold, three Black Gold, nine 1995 Topps Pre-Production cards and a sample pack of three special Topps cards for a total of 817. The standard cards feature glossy color player photos with white borders on the fronts. The player's name is in white cursive lettering at the bottom left, with the team name and player's position printed on a team color-coded bar. There is an inner multicolored border along the left side that extends obliquely across the bottom. The horizontal backs carry an action shot of the player with biography, statistics and highlights. Subsets include Draft Picks (201-210/739-762), All-Stars (384-394) and Stat Twins (601-609). Rookie Cards include Billy Wagner.

COMPLETE SET (792) 20.00 50.00
COMP.FACT.SET (808) 40.00 80.00
COMP.BAKER SET (817) 40.00 80.00
COMP. SERIES 1 (396) 10.00 25.00
COMP. SERIES 2 (396) 10.00 25.00
1 Mike Piazza .40 1.00
2 Bernie Williams .10 .30
3 Kevin Rogers .02 .10
4 Paul Carey .02 .10
5 Ozzie Guillen .07 .20
6 Derrick May .02 .10
7 Jose Mesa .02 .10
8 Todd Hundley .02 .10
9 Chris Haney .02 .10
10 John Olerud .07 .20
11 Andujar Cedeno .02 .10
12 John Smiley .02 .10
13 Phil Plantier .02 .10
14 Willie Banks .02 .10
15 Jay Bell .07 .20
16 Doug Henry .02 .10
17 Lance Blankenship .02 .10
18 Greg W. Harris .02 .10
19 Scott Livingstone .02 .10
20 Bryan Harvey .02 .10
21 Wil Cordero .02 .10
22 Roger Pavlik .02 .10
23 Mark Lemke .02 .10
24 Jeff Nelson .02 .10
25 Todd Zeile .02 .10
26 Billy Hatcher .02 .10
27 Joe Magrane .02 .10
28 Tony Longmire .02 .10
29 Omar Daal .02 .10
30 Kirt Manwaring .02 .10
31 Melido Perez .02 .10
32 Tim Hulett .02 .10
33 Jeff Schwarz .02 .10
34 Nolan Ryan .75 2.00
35 Jose Guzman .02 .10
36 Felix Fermin .02 .10
37 Jeff Innis .02 .10
38 Brett Mayne .02 .10
39 Huck Flener RC .02 .10
40 Jeff Bagwell .10 .30
41 Kevin Wickander .02 .10
42 Ricky Gutierrez .02 .10
43 Pat Mahomes .02 .10
44 Jeff King .02 .10
45 Cal Eldred .02 .10
46 Craig Paquette .02 .10
47 Richie Lewis .02 .10
48 Tony Phillips .02 .10
49 Armando Reynoso .02 .10
50 Moises Alou .07 .20
51 Manuel Lee .02 .10
52 Otis Nixon .02 .10
53 Billy Ashley .02 .10
54 Mark Whiten .02 .10
55 Jeff Russell .02 .10
56 Chad Curtis .02 .10
57 Kevin Stocker .02 .10
58 Mike Jackson .02 .10
59 Matt Nokes .02 .10
60 Chris Bosio .02 .10
61 Damon Buford .02 .10
62 Tim Belcher .02 .10
63 Glenallen Hill .02 .10
64 Bill Wertz .02 .10
65 Eddie Murray .20 .50
66 Tom Gordon .02 .10
67 Alex Gonzalez .02 .10
68 Eddie Taubensee .02 .10
69 Jacob Brumfield .02 .10
70 Andy Benes .02 .10
71 Rich Becker .02 .10
72 Steve Cooke .02 .10
73 Billy Spiers .02 .10
74 Scott Brosius .07 .20
75 Alan Trammell .07 .20
76 Luis Aquino .02 .10
77 Jerald Clark .02 .10
78 Mel Rojas .02 .10
79 Billy Masse .02 .10
Stanton Cameron
Tim Clark
Craig McClure RC
80 Jose Canseco .10 .30
81 Greg McMichael .02 .10
82 Brian Turang RC .02 .10
83 Tom Urbani .02 .10
84 Garret Anderson .20 .50
85 Tony Pena .02 .10
86 Ricky Jordan .02 .10
87 Jim Gott .02 .10
88 Pat Kelly .02 .10
89 Bud Black .02 .10
90 Robin Ventura .07 .20
91 Rick Sutcliffe .07 .20
92 Jose Bautista .02 .10
93 Bob Ojeda .02 .10
94 Phil Hiatt .02 .10
95 Tim Pugh .02 .10
96 Randy Knorr .02 .10
97 Todd Jones .02 .10
98 Ryan Thompson .02 .10
99 Tim Mauser .02 .10
100 Kirby Puckett .20 .50
101 Mark Dewey .02 .10
102 B.J. Surhoff .07 .20
103 Sterling Hitchcock .02 .10
104 Alex Arias .02 .10
105 David Wells .07 .20
106 Daryl Boston .02 .10
107 Mike Stanton .02 .10
108 Gary Redus .02 .10
109 Delino DeShields .02 .10
110 Lee Smith .07 .20
111 Greg Litton .02 .10
112 Frankie Rodriguez .02 .10
113 Russ Springer .02 .10
114 Mitch Williams .02 .10
115 Eric Karros .07 .20
116 Jeff Brantley .02 .10
117 Jack Voigt .02 .10
118 Jason Bere .02 .10
119 Kevin Roberson .02 .10
120 Jimmy Key .07 .20
121 Reggie Jefferson .02 .10
122 Jeromy Burnitz .07 .20
123 Billy Brewer .02 .10
124 Willie Canate .02 .10
125 Greg Swindell .02 .10
126 Hal Morris .02 .10
127 Brad Ausmus .10 .30
128 George Tsamis .02 .10
129 Denny Neagle .07 .20
130 Pat Listach .02 .10
131 Steve Karsay .02 .10
132 Bret Barberie .02 .10
133 Mark Leiter .02 .10
134 Greg Colbrunn .02 .10
135 David Nied .02 .10
136 Dean Palmer .07 .20
137 Steve Avery .02 .10
138 Bill Haselman .02 .10
139 Tripp Cromer .02 .10
140 Frank Viola .07 .20
141 Rene Gonzales .02 .10
142 Curt Schilling .07 .20
143 Tim Wallach .02 .10
144 Bobby Munoz .02 .10
145 Brady Anderson .07 .20
146 Rod Beck .02 .10
147 Mike LaValliere .02 .10
148 Greg Hibbard .02 .10
149 Kenny Lofton .07 .20
150 Dwight Gooden .07 .20
151 Greg Gagne .02 .10
152 Ray McDavid .02 .10
153 Chris Donnels .02 .10
154 Dan Wilson .02 .10
155 Todd Stottlemyre .02 .10
156 David McCarty .02 .10
157 Paul Wagner .02 .10
158 Orlando Miller 1.25 3.00
Brandon Wilson
Derek Jeter
Mike Neal
159 Mike Fetters .02 .10
160 Scott Lydy .02 .10
161 Darrell Whitmore .02 .10
162 Bob MacDonald .02 .10
163 Vinny Castilla .07 .20
164 Denis Boucher .02 .10
165 Ivan Rodriguez .10 .30
166 Ron Gant .07 .20
167 Tim Davis .02 .10
168 Steve Dixon .02 .10
169 Scott Fletcher .02 .10
170 Terry Mulholland .02 .10
171 Greg Myers .02 .10
172 Brett Butler .07 .20
173 Bob Wickman .02 .10
174 Dave Martinez .02 .10
175 Fernando Valenzuela .07 .20
176 Craig Grebeck .02 .10
177 Shawn Boskie .02 .10
178 Albie Lopez .02 .10
179 Butch Huskey .02 .10
180 George Brett .50 1.25
181 Juan Guzman .02 .10
182 Eric Anthony .02 .10
183 Rob Dibble .07 .20
184 Craig Shipley .02 .10
185 Kevin Tapani .02 .10
186 Marcus Moore .02 .10
187 Graeme Lloyd .02 .10
188 Mike Bordick .02 .10
189 Chris Hammond .02 .10
190 Cecil Fielder .07 .20
191 Curt Leskanic .02 .10
192 Lou Frazier .02 .10
193 Steve Dreyer RC .02 .10
194 Javier Lopez .07 .20
195 Edgar Martinez .10 .30
196 Allen Watson .02 .10
197 John Flaherty .02 .10
198 Kurt Stillwell .02 .10
199 Danny Jackson .02 .10
200 Cal Ripken .60 1.50
201 Mike Bell FDP RC .02 .10
202 Alan Benes FDP RC .08 .25
203 Matt Farner FDP RC .02 .10
204 Jeff Granger .02 .10
205 B.Kieschnick FDP RC .02 .10
206 Jeremy Lee FDP RC .02 .10
207 C.Peterson FDP RC .02 .10
208 Alan Rice FDP RC .02 .10
209 Billy Wagner FDP RC .60 1.50
210 Kelly Wunsch FDP RC .08 .25
211 Tom Candiotti .02 .10
212 Domingo Jean .02 .10
213 John Burkett .02 .10
214 George Bell .02 .10
215 Dan Plesac .02 .10
216 Manny Ramirez .20 .50
217 Mike Maddux .02 .10
218 Kevin McReynolds .02 .10
219 Pat Borders .02 .10
220 Doug Drabek .02 .10
221 Larry Luebbers RC .02 .10
222 Trevor Hoffman .10 .30
223 Pat Meares .02 .10
224 Danny Miceli .02 .10
225 Greg Vaughn .02 .10
226 Scott Hemond .02 .10
227 Pat Rapp .02 .10
228 Kirk Gibson .07 .20
229 Lance Painter .02 .10
230 Larry Walker .07 .20
231 Benji Gil .02 .10
232 Mark Wohlers .02 .10
233 Rich Amaral .02 .10
234 Eric Pappas .02 .10
235 Scott Cooper .02 .10
236 Mike Butcher .02 .10
237 Curtis Pride RC .20 .50
Shawn Green
Mark Sweeney RC
Eddie Davis RC
238 Kim Batiste .02 .10
239 Paul Assenmacher .02 .10
240 Will Clark .10 .30
241 Jose Offerman .02 .10
242 Todd Frohwirth .02 .10

243 Tim Raines .07 .20
244 Rick Wilkins .02 .10
245 Bret Saberhagen .07 .20
246 Thomas Howard .02 .10
247 Stan Belinda .02 .10
248 Rickey Henderson .20 .50
249 Brian Williams .02 .10
250 Barry Larkin .10 .30
251 Jose Valentin .02 .10
252 Lenny Webster .02 .10
253 Blas Minor .02 .10
254 Tim Teufel .02 .10
255 Bobby Witt .02 .10
256 Walt Weiss .02 .10
257 Chad Kreuter .02 .10
258 Roberto Mejia .02 .10
259 Cliff Floyd .07 .20
260 Julio Franco .07 .20
261 Rafael Belliard .02 .10
262 Marc Newfield .02 .10
263 Gerald Perry .02 .10
264 Ken Ryan .02 .10
265 Chili Davis .07 .20
266 Dave West .02 .10
267 Royce Clayton .02 .10
268 Pedro Martinez .20 .50
269 Mark Hutton .02 .10
270 Frank Thomas .20 .50
271 Brad Pennington .02 .10
272 Mike Harkey .02 .10
273 Sandy Alomar Jr. .02 .10
274 Dave Gallagher .02 .10
275 Wally Joyner .07 .20
276 Ricky Trlicek .02 .10
277 Al Osuna .02 .10
278 Pokey Reese .02 .10
279 Kevin Higgins .02 .10
280 Rick Aguilera .02 .10
281 Orlando Merced .02 .10
282 Mike Mohler .02 .10
283 John Jaha .02 .10
284 Robb Nen .07 .20
285 Travis Fryman .07 .20
286 Mark Thompson .02 .10
287 Mike Lansing .02 .10
288 Craig Lefferts .02 .10
289 Damon Berryhill .02 .10
290 Randy Johnson .20 .50
291 Jeff Reed .02 .10
292 Danny Darwin .02 .10
293 J.T. Snow .07 .20
294 Tyler Green .02 .10
295 Chris Hoiles .02 .10
296 Roger McDowell .02 .10
297 Spike Owen .02 .10
298 Salomon Torres .02 .10
299 Wilson Alvarez .02 .10
300 Ryne Sandberg .30 .75
301 Derek Lilliquist .02 .10
302 Howard Johnson .02 .10
303 Greg Cadaret .02 .10
304 Pat Hentgen .02 .10
305 Craig Biggio .10 .30
306 Scott Service .02 .10
307 Melvin Nieves .02 .10
308 Mike Trombley .02 .10
309 Carlos Garcia .02 .10
310 Robin Yount UER .30 .75
(listed with 111 triples in
1988; should be 11)
311 Marcos Armas .02 .10
312 Rich Rodriguez .02 .10
313 Justin Thompson .02 .10
314 Danny Sheaffer .02 .10
315 Ken Hill .02 .10
316 Chad Ogea .02 .10
Duff Brumley
Terrell Wade RC
Chris Michalak
317 Cris Carpenter .02 .10
318 Jeff Blauser .02 .10
319 Ted Power .02 .10
320 Ozzie Smith .30 .75
321 John Dopson .02 .10
322 Chris Turner .02 .10
323 Pete Incaviglia .02 .10
324 Alan Mills .02 .10
325 Jody Reed .02 .10
326 Rich Monteleone .02 .10
327 Mark Carreon .02 .10
328 Donn Pall .02 .10
329 Matt Walbeck .02 .10
330 Charles Nagy .02 .10
331 Jeff McKnight .02 .10
332 Jose Lind .02 .10
333 Mike Timlin .02 .10
334 Doug Jones .02 .10
335 Kevin Mitchell .02 .10
336 Luis Lopez .02 .10
337 Shane Mack .02 .10
338 Randy Tomlin .02 .10
339 Matt Mieske .02 .10
340 Mark McGwire .50 1.25
341 Nigel Wilson .02 .10
342 Danny Gladden .02 .10
343 Mo Sanford .02 .10
344 Sean Berry .02 .10
345 Kevin Brown .07 .20
346 Greg Olson .02 .10
347 Dave Magadan .02 .10
348 Rene Arocha .02 .10
349 Carlos Quintana .02 .10
350 Jim Abbott .10 .30
351 Gary DiSarcina .02 .10
352 Ben Rivera .02 .10
353 Carlos Hernandez .02 .10
354 Darren Lewis .02 .10
355 Harold Reynolds .07 .20
356 Scott Ruffcorn .02 .10
357 Mark Gubicza .02 .10
358 Paul Sorrento .02 .10
359 Anthony Young .02 .10
360 Mark Grace .10 .30
361 Rob Butler .02 .10
362 Kevin Bass .02 .10
363 Eric Helfand .02 .10
364 Derek Bell .02 .10
365 Scott Erickson .02 .10
366 Al Martin .02 .10
367 Ricky Bones .02 .10
368 Jeff Branson .02 .10
369 Luis Ortiz .20 .50
David Bell RC
Jason Giambi
George Arias
370 Benito Santiago .07 .20
(See also 379)
371 John Doherty .02 .10
372 Joe Girardi .02 .10
373 Tim Scott .02 .10
374 Marvin Freeman .02 .10
375 Deion Sanders .10 .30
376 Roger Salkeld .02 .10
377 Bernard Gilkey .02 .10
378 Tony Fossas .02 .10
379 Mark McLemore UER .02 .10
(Card number is 370)
380 Darren Daulton .07 .20
381 Chuck Finley .07 .20
382 Mitch Webster .02 .10
383 Gerald Williams .02 .10
384 Frank Thomas AS .10 .30
Fred McGriff AS
385 Roberto Alomar AS .07 .20
Robby Thompson AS
386 Wade Boggs AS .07 .20
Matt Williams AS
387 Cal Ripken AS .20 .50
Jeff Blauser AS
388 Ken Griffey Jr. AS .20 .50
Len Dykstra AS
389 Juan Gonzalez AS .07 .20
David Justice AS
390 George Belle AS .30 .75
Barry Bonds AS
391 Mike Stanley AS .20 .50
Mike Piazza AS
392 Jack McDowell AS .10 .30
Greg Maddux AS
393 Jimmy Key AS .07 .20
Tom Glavine AS
394 Jeff Montgomery AS .02 .10
Randy Myers AS
395 Checklist 1-198 .02 .10
396 Checklist 199-396 .02 .10
397 Tim Salmon .10 .30
398 Todd Benzinger .02 .10
399 Frank Castillo .02 .10
400 Ken Griffey Jr. .30 .75
401 John Kruk .07 .20
402 Dave Telgheder .02 .10
403 Gary Gaetti .07 .20
404 Jim Edmonds .20 .50
405 Don Slaught .02 .10
406 Jose Oquendo .02 .10
407 Bruce Ruffin .02 .10
408 Phil Clark .02 .10
409 Joe Klink .02 .10
410 Lou Whitaker .07 .20
411 Kevin Seitzer .02 .10
412 Darrin Fletcher .02 .10
413 Kenny Rogers .07 .20
414 Bill Pecota .02 .10
415 Dave Fleming .02 .10
416 Luis Alicea .02 .10
417 Paul Quantrill .02 .10
418 Damion Easley .02 .10
419 Wes Chamberlain .02 .10
420 Harold Baines .07 .20
421 Scott Radinsky .02 .10
422 Rey Sanchez .02 .10
423 Junior Ortiz .02 .10
424 Jeff Kent .10 .30
425 Brian McRae .02 .10
426 Ed Sprague .02 .10
427 Tom Edens .02 .10
428 Willie Greene .02 .10
429 Bryan Hickerson .02 .10
430 Dave Winfield .07 .20
431 Pedro Astacio .02 .10
432 Mike Gallego .02 .10
433 Dave Burba .02 .10
434 Bob Walk .02 .10
435 Darryl Hamilton .02 .10
436 Vince Horsman .02 .10
437 Bob Natal .02 .10
438 Mike Henneman .02 .10
439 Willie Blair .02 .10
440 Dennis Martinez .07 .20
441 Dan Peltier .02 .10
442 Tony Tarasco .02 .10
443 John Cummings .02 .10
444 Geronimo Pena .02 .10
445 Aaron Sele .02 .10
446 Stan Javier .02 .10
447 Mike Williams .02 .10
448 Greg Pirkl .02 .10
Roberto Petagine
D.J.Boston
Shawn Wooten RC
449 Jim Poole .02 .10
450 Carlos Baerga .02 .10
451 Bob Scanlan .02 .10
452 Lance Johnson .02 .10
453 Eric Hillman .02 .10
454 Keith Miller .02 .10
455 Dave Stewart .07 .20
456 Pete Harnisch .02 .10
457 Roberto Kelly .02 .10
458 Tim Worrell .02 .10
459 Pedro Munoz .02 .10
460 Orel Hershiser .07 .20
461 Randy Velarde .02 .10
462 Trevor Wilson .02 .10
463 Jerry Goff .02 .10
464 Bill Wegman .02 .10
465 Dennis Eckersley .07 .20
466 Jeff Conine .07 .20
467 Joe Boever .02 .10
468 Dante Bichette .07 .20
469 Jeff Shaw .02 .10
470 Rafael Palmeiro .10 .30
471 Phil Leftwich RC .02 .10
472 Jay Buhner .07 .20
473 Bob Tewksbury .02 .10
474 Tim Naehring .02 .10
475 Tom Glavine .10 .30
476 Dave Hollins .02 .10
477 Arthur Rhodes .02 .10
478 Joey Cora .02 .10
479 Mike Morgan .02 .10
480 Albert Belle .07 .20
481 John Franco .07 .20
482 Hipolito Pichardo .02 .10
483 Duane Ward .02 .10
484 Luis Gonzalez .07 .20
485 Joe Oliver .02 .10
486 Wally Whitehurst .02 .10
487 Mike Benjamin .02 .10
488 Eric Davis .07 .20
489 Scott Kamieniecki .02 .10
490 Kent Hrbek .07 .20
491 John Hope RC .02 .10
492 Jesse Orosco .02 .10
493 Troy Neel .02 .10
494 Ryan Bowen .02 .10
495 Mickey Tettleton .02 .10
496 Chris Jones .02 .10
497 John Wetteland .07 .20
498 David Hulse .02 .10
499 Greg Maddux .30 .75
500 Bo Jackson .20 .50
501 Donovan Osborne .02 .10
502 Mike Greenwell .02 .10
503 Steve Frey .02 .10
504 Jim Eisenreich .02 .10
505 Robby Thompson .02 .10
506 Leo Gomez .02 .10
507 Dave Staton .02 .10
508 Wayne Kirby .02 .10
509 Tim Bogar .02 .10
510 David Cone .07 .20
511 Devon White .07 .20
512 Xavier Hernandez .02 .10
513 Tim Costo .02 .10
514 Gene Harris .02 .10
515 Jack McDowell .02 .10
516 Kevin Gross .02 .10
517 Scott Leius .02 .10
518 Lloyd McClendon .02 .10
519 Alex Diaz RC .02 .10
520 Wade Boggs .10 .30
521 Bob Welch .02 .10
522 Henry Cotto .02 .10
523 Mike Moore .02 .10
524 Tim Laker .02 .10
525 Andres Galarraga .07 .20
526 Jamie Moyer .07 .20
527 Norberto Martin .02 .10
Ruben Santana
Jason Hardtke
Chris Sexton RC
528 Sid Bream .02 .10
529 Erik Hanson .02 .10
530 Ray Lankford .07 .20
531 Rob Deer .02 .10
532 Rod Correia .02 .10
533 Roger Mason .02 .10
534 Mike Devereaux .02 .10
535 Jeff Montgomery .02 .10
536 Dwight Smith .02 .10
537 Jeremy Hernandez .02 .10
538 Ellis Burks .07 .20
539 Bobby Jones .02 .10
540 Paul Molitor .07 .20
541 Jeff Juden .02 .10
542 Chris Sabo .02 .10
543 Larry Casian .02 .10
544 Jeff Gardner .02 .10
545 Ramon Martinez .02 .10
546 Paul O'Neill .10 .30
547 Steve Hosey .02 .10
548 Dave Nilsson .02 .10
549 Ron Darling .02 .10
550 Matt Williams .07 .20
551 Jack Armstrong .02 .10
552 Bill Krueger .02 .10
553 Freddie Benavides .02 .10
554 Jeff Fassero .02 .10
555 Chuck Knoblauch .07 .20
556 Guillermo Velasquez .02 .10
557 Joel Johnston .02 .10
558 Tom Lampkin .02 .10
559 Todd Van Poppel .02 .10
560 Gary Sheffield .07 .20
561 Skeeter Barnes .02 .10
562 Darren Holmes .02 .10
563 John Vander Wal .02 .10
564 Mike Ignasiak .02 .10
565 Fred McGriff .10 .30
566 Luis Polonia .02 .10
567 Mike Perez .02 .10
568 John Valentin .02 .10
569 Mike Felder .02 .10
570 Tommy Greene .02 .10
571 David Segui .02 .10
572 Roberto Hernandez .02 .10
573 Steve Wilson .02 .10
574 Willie McGee .07 .20
575 Randy Myers .02 .10
576 Darrin Jackson .02 .10
577 Eric Plunk .02 .10
578 Mike Macfarlane .02 .10
579 Doug Brocail .02 .10
580 Steve Finley .07 .20
581 John Roper .02 .10
582 Danny Cox .02 .10
583 Chip Hale .02 .10
584 Scott Bullett .02 .10
585 Kevin Reimer .02 .10
586 Brent Gates .02 .10
587 Matt Turner .02 .10
588 Rich Rowland .02 .10
589 Kent Bottenfield .02 .10
590 Marquis Grissom .07 .20
591 Doug Strange .02 .10
592 Jay Howell .02 .10
593 Omar Vizquel .10 .30
594 Rheal Cormier .02 .10
595 Andre Dawson .07 .20
596 Hilly Hathaway .02 .10
597 Todd Pratt .02 .10
598 Mike Mussina .10 .30
599 Alex Fernandez .02 .10
600 Don Mattingly .50 1.25
601 Frank Thomas MOG .10 .30
602 Ryne Sandberg MOG .20 .50
603 Wade Boggs MOG .07 .20
604 Cal Ripken MOG .30 .75
605 Barry Bonds MOG .30 .75
606 Ken Griffey Jr. MOG .20 .50
607 Kirby Puckett MOG .10 .30
608 Darren Daulton MOG .02 .10
609 Paul Molitor MOG .02 .10
610 Terry Steinbach .02 .10
611 Todd Worrell .02 .10
612 Jim Thome .10 .30
613 Chuck McElroy .02 .10
614 John Habyan .02 .10
615 Sid Fernandez .02 .10
616 Eddie Zambrano .02 .10
Glenn Murray
Chad Mottola
Jermaine Allensworth RC
617 Steve Bedrosian .02 .10
618 Rob Ducey .02 .10
619 Tom Browning .02 .10
620 Tony Gwynn .25 .60
621 Carl Willis .02 .10
622 Kevin Young .02 .10
623 Rafael Novoa .02 .10
624 Jerry Browne .02 .10
625 Charlie Hough .07 .20
626 Chris Gomez .02 .10
627 Steve Reed .02 .10
628 Kirk Rueter .02 .10
629 Matt Whiteside .02 .10
630 David Justice .07 .20
631 Brad Holman .02 .10
632 Brian Jordan .07 .20
633 Scott Bankhead .02 .10
634 Torey Lovullo .02 .10
635 Len Dykstra .07 .20
636 Ben McDonald .02 .10
637 Steve Howe .02 .10
638 Jose Vizcaino .02 .10
639 Bill Swift .02 .10
640 Darryl Strawberry .07 .20
641 Steve Farr .02 .10
642 Tom Kramer .02 .10
643 Joe Orsulak .02 .10
644 Tom Henke .02 .10
645 Joe Carter .07 .20
646 Ken Caminiti .07 .20
647 Reggie Sanders .07 .20
648 Andy Ashby .02 .10
649 Derek Parks .02 .10
650 Andy Van Slyke .10 .30
651 Juan Bell .02 .10
652 Roger Smithberg .02 .10
653 Chuck Carr .02 .10
654 Bill Gullickson .02 .10
655 Charlie Hayes .02 .10
656 Chris Nabholz .02 .10
657 Karl Rhodes .02 .10
658 Pete Smith .02 .10
659 Bret Boone .07 .20
660 Gregg Jefferies .02 .10
661 Bob Zupcic .02 .10
662 Steve Sax .02 .10
663 Mariano Duncan .02 .10
664 Jeff Tackett .02 .10
665 Mark Langston .02 .10
666 Steve Buechele .02 .10
667 Candy Maldonado .02 .10
668 Woody Williams .07 .20
669 Tim Wakefield .10 .30
670 Danny Tartabull .02 .10
671 Charlie O'Brien .02 .10
672 Felix Jose .02 .10
673 Bobby Ayala .02 .10
674 Scott Servais .02 .10
675 Roberto Alomar .10 .30
676 Pedro A.Martinez RC .02 .10
677 Eddie Guardado .07 .20
678 Mark Lewis .02 .10
679 Jaime Navarro .02 .10
680 Ruben Sierrra .07 .20
681 Rick Renteria .02 .10
682 Storm Davis .02 .10
683 Cory Snyder .02 .10
684 Ron Karkovice .02 .10
685 Juan Gonzalez .07 .20
686 Chris Howard .10 .30
Carlos Delgado
Jason Kendall
Paul Bako
687 John Smoltz .10 .30
688 Brian Dorsett .02 .10
689 Omar Olivares .02 .10
690 Mo Vaughn .07 .20
691 Joe Grahe .02 .10
692 Mickey Morandini .02 .10
693 Tino Martinez .10 .30
694 Brian Barnes .02 .10
695 Mike Stanley .02 .10
696 Mark Clark .02 .10
697 Dave Hansen .02 .10
698 Willie Wilson .02 .10
699 Pete Schourek .02 .10
700 Barry Bonds .60 1.50
701 Kevin Appier .07 .20
702 Tony Fernandez .02 .10
703 Darryl Kile .07 .20
704 Archi Cianfrocco .02 .10
705 Jose Rijo .02 .10
706 Brian Harper .02 .10
707 Zane Smith .02 .10
708 Dave Henderson .02 .10
709 Angel Miranda UER .02 .10
(no Topps logo on back)
710 Orestes Destrade .02 .10
711 Greg Gohr .02 .10
712 Eric Young .02 .10
713 Todd Williams .02 .10
Ron Watson
Kirk Bullinger
Mike Welch
714 Tim Spehr .02 .10
715 Hank Aaron 715 HR .20 .50
716 Nate Minchey .02 .10
717 Mike Blowers .02 .10
718 Kent Mercker .02 .10
719 Tom Pagnozzi .02 .10
720 Roger Clemens .40 1.00
721 Eduardo Perez .02 .10
722 Milt Thompson .02 .10
723 Gregg Olson .02 .10
724 Kirk McCaskill .02 .10
725 Sammy Sosa .20 .50
726 Alvaro Espinoza .02 .10
727 Henry Rodriguez .02 .10
728 Jim Leyritz .02 .10
729 Steve Scarsone .02 .10
730 Bobby Bonilla .07 .20
731 Chris Gwynn .02 .10
732 Al Leiter .07 .20
733 Bip Roberts .02 .10
734 Mark Portugal .02 .10
735 Terry Pendleton .07 .20
736 Dave Valle .02 .10
737 Paul Kilgus .02 .10
738 Greg A. Harris .02 .10
739 Jon Ratliff DP RC .02 .10
740 Kirk Presley DP RC .02 .10
741 Josue Estrada DP RC .02 .10
742 Wayne Gomes DP RC .02 .10
743 Pat Watkins DP RC .02 .10
744 Jamey Wright DP RC .08 .25
745 Jay Powell DP RC .02 .10
746 Ryan McGuire DP RC .02 .10
747 Marc Barcelo DP RC .02 .10
748 Sloan Smith DP RC .02 .10
749 John Wasdin DP RC .02 .10
750 Marc Vlades DP .02 .10
751 Dan Ehler DP RC .02 .10
752 Andre King DP RC .02 .10
753 Greg Keagle DP RC .02 .10
754 Jason Myers DP RC .02 .10
755 Dax Winslett DP RC .02 .10
756 Casey Whitten DP RC .02 .10
757 Tony Fuduric DP RC .02 .10
758 Greg Norton DP RC .08 .25
759 Jeff D'Amico DP RC .02 .10
760 Ryan Hancock DP RC .02 .10
761 David Cooper DP RC .02 .10
762 Kevin Orie DP RC .02 .10
763 John O'Donoghue .02 .10
Mike Oquist
764 Cory Bailey RC .02 .10
Scott Hatteberg
765 Mark Holzemer .02 .10
Paul Swingle RC
766 James Baldwin .02 .10
Rod Bolton
767 Jerry Di Poto .08 .25
Julian Tavarez RC
768 Danny Bautista .02 .10
Sean Bergman
769 Bob Hamelin .02 .10
Joe Vitiello
770 Mark Kiefer .02 .10
Troy O'Leary
771 Denny Hocking .02 .10
Oscar Munoz RC
772 Russ Davis .02 .10
Brien Taylor
773 Kyle Abbott .08 .25
Miguel Jimenez
774 Kevin King .02 .10
Eric Plantenberg RC
775 Jon Shave .02 .10
Desi Wilson
776 Domingo Cedeno .02 .10
Paul Spoljaric
777 Chipper Jones .20 .50
Ryan Klesko
778 Steve Trachsel .02 .10
Turk Wendell
779 Johnny Ruffin .02 .10
Jerry Spradlin RC
780 Jason Bates .02 .10
John Burke
781 Carl Everett .07 .20
Dave Weathers
782 Gary Mota .02 .10
James Mouton
783 Raul Mondesi .07 .20
Ben Van Ryn
784 Gabe White .07 .20
Rondell White
785 Brook Fordyce .07 .20
Bill Pulsipher
786 Kevin Foster RC .02 .10
Gene Schall
787 Rich Aude RC .02 .10
Midre Cummings
788 Brian Barber .02 .10
Rich Batchelor
789 Brian Johnson RC .02 .10
Scott Sanders
790 Ricky Faneyte .02 .10
J.R. Phillips
791 Checklist 3 .02 .10
792 Checklist 4 .02 .10

1994 Topps Gold

The 1994 Topps Gold set is parallel to the basic issue. They were inserted one per wax or mini pack, two per mini jumbo, three per rack pack, four per jumbo, five per jumbo rack and ten per factory set. The only difference between the Gold issue and the basic cards is gold foil on the player's name and the Topps logo. As in previous Gold Sets, player cards (cards 395-96 and 791-92) replace the Checklist cards.

*STARS: 1.5X TO 4X BASIC CARDS
*ROOKIES: 1.25X TO 3X BASIC CARDS
395 Bill Brennan .15 .40
396 Jeff Bronkey .15 .40
791 Mike Cook .15 .40
792 Dan Pasqua .15 .40

1994 Topps Spanish

Issued in complete factory set form only, these 792 standard-size cards parallel the regular Topps issue. These cards have the same front photos but are billingual. The factory set also contains the Topps Spanish Legends 10-card set. That set which is entitled "Topps Legends" features retired Latin players.

*STARS: 3X to 6X BASIC CARDS
L1 Felipe Alou .30 .75
L2 Ruben Amaro .08 .25
L3 Luis Aparicio .40 1.00
L4 Rod Carew .40 1.00
L5 Chico Carrasquel .20 .50
L6 Orlando Cepeda .40 1.00
L7 Juan Marichal .40 1.00
L8 Minnie Minoso .30 .75
L9 Cookie Rojas .08 .25
L10 Luis Tiant .20 .50

1994 Topps Black Gold

Randomly inserted one in every 72 packs, this 44-card standard-size set was issued in two series of 22. Cards were also issued three per 1994 Topps factory set. Collectors had a chance, through redemption cards to receive all or part of the set. There are seven Winner redemption cards for a total 51 cards associated with this set. The set is considered complete with the 44 player cards. Card fronts feature color player action photos. The player's name at bottom and the team name at top are screened in gold foil. The backs contain a player photo and statistical rankings. The winner cards were redeemable until January 31, 1995

COMPLETE SET (44) 10.00 25.00
COMPLETE SERIES 1 (22) 6.00 15.00
COMPLETE SERIES 2 (22) 4.00 10.00
THREE PER FACTORY SET
1 Roberto Alomar .25 .60
2 Carlos Baerga .07 .20
3 Albert Belle .15 .40
4 Joe Carter .15 .40
5 Cecil Fielder .15 .40
6 Travis Fryman .15 .40
7 Juan Gonzalez .15 .40
8 Ken Griffey Jr. .60 1.50
9 Chris Hoiles .07 .20
10 Randy Johnson .40 1.00
11 Kenny Lofton .15 .40
12 Jack McDowell .07 .20
13 Paul Molitor .15 .40
14 Jeff Montgomery .07 .20
15 John Olerud .15 .40
16 Rafael Palmeiro .25 .60
17 Kirby Puckett .40 1.00
18 Cal Ripken 1.25 3.00
19 Tim Salmon .25 .60
20 Mike Stanley .07 .20
21 Frank Thomas .40 1.00
22 Robin Ventura .15 .40
23 Jeff Bagwell .25 .60
24 Jay Bell .15 .40
25 Craig Biggio .25 .60
26 Jeff Blauser .07 .20
27 Barry Bonds 1.25 3.00
28 Darren Daulton .15 .40
29 Len Dykstra .15 .40
30 Andres Galarraga .15 .40
31 Ron Gant .15 .40
32 Tom Glavine .25 .60
33 Mark Grace .25 .60
34 Marquis Grissom .15 .40
35 Gregg Jefferies .07 .20
36 David Justice .15 .40
37 John Kruk .15 .40
38 Greg Maddux .60 1.50
39 Fred McGriff .25 .60
40 Randy Myers .07 .20
41 Mike Piazza .75 2.00
42 Sammy Sosa .40 1.00
43 Robby Thompson .07 .20
44 Matt Williams .15 .40
A Winner A 1-11 .07 .20
B Winner B 12-22 .07 .20
C Winner C 23-33 .07 .20
D Winner D 34-44 .07 .20
AB Winner AB 1-22 .07 .20
CD Winner CD 23-44 .07 .20
ABCD Winner ABCD 1-44 .07 .20

1994 Topps Traded

This set consists of 132 standard-size cards featuring traded players in their new uniforms, rookies and draft choices. Factory sets consisted of 140 cards including a set of eight Topps Finest cards. Card fronts feature a player photo with the player's name, team and position at the bottom. The horizontal backs have a player photo to the left with complete career statisics and highlights. Rookie Cards include Rusty Greer, Ben Grieve, Paul Konerko Terrence Long and Chan Ho Park.

COMP.FACT.SET (140) 20.00 40.00
1T Paul Wilson .02 .10
2T Bill Taylor RC .40 1.00
3T Dan Wilson .02 .10
4T Mark Smith .02 .10
5T Toby Borland RC .08 .25
6T Dave Clark .02 .10
7T Dennis Martinez .07 .20
8T Dave Gallagher .02 .10
9T Josias Manzanillo .02 .10
10T Brian Anderson RC .40 1.00
11T Damon Berryhill .02 .10
12T Alex Cole .02 .10
13T Jacob Shumate RC .08 .25
14T Oddibe McDowell .02 .10
15T Willie Banks .02 .10
16T Jerry Browne .02 .10
17T Donnie Elliott .02 .10
18T Ellis Burks .07 .20
19T Chuck McElroy .02 .10
20T Luis Polonia .02 .10
21T Brian Harper .02 .10
22T Mark Portugal .02 .10
23T Dave Henderson .02 .10
24T Mark Acre RC .08 .25
25T Julio Franco .07 .20
26T Darren Hall RC .08 .25
27T Eric Anthony .02 .10
28T Sid Fernandez .02 .10
29T Rusty Greer RC .60 1.50
30T Riccardo Ingram RC .08 .25
31T Gabe White .02 .10
32T Tim Belcher .02 .10
33T Terrence Long RC .40 1.00
34T Mark Dalesandro RC .08 .25
35T Mike Kelly .02 .10
36T Jack Morris .07 .20
37T Jeff Brantley .02 .10
38T Larry Barnes RC .08 .25
39T Brian R. Hunter .02 .10
40T Otis Nixon .02 .10
41T Bret Wagner .02 .10
42T Pedro Martinez TR .20 .50
Delino Deshields
43T Heathcliff Slocumb .02 .10
44T Ben Grieve RC .40 1.00
45T John Hudek RC .08 .25
46T Shawon Dunston .02 .10
47T Greg Colbrunn .02 .10
48T Joey Hamilton .02 .10
49T Marvin Freeman .02 .10
50T Terry Mulholland .02 .10
51T Keith Mitchell .02 .10
52T Dwight Smith .02 .10
53T Shawn Boskie .02 .10
54T Kevin Witt RC .40 1.00
55T Ron Gant .07 .20
56T Trenidad Hubbard RC 4.00 10.00
Jason Schmidt RC

Card	Low	High
Larry Sutton		
Stephen Larkin RC		
57T Jody Reed	.02	.10
58T Rick Helling	.02	.10
59T John Powell	.02	.10
60T Eddie Murray	.20	.50
61T Joe Hall RC	.08	.25
62T Jorge Fabregas	.02	.10
63T Mike Mordecai RC	.08	.25
64T Ed Vosberg	.02	.10
65T Rickey Henderson	.20	.50
66T Tim Grieve RC	.08	.25
67T Jon Lieber	.07	.20
68T Chris Howard	.02	.10
69T Matt Walbeck	.02	.10
70T Chan Ho Park RC	.60	1.50
71T Bryan Eversgerd RC	.08	.25
72T John Dettmer	.02	.10
73T Erik Hanson	.02	.10
74T Mike Thurman RC	.08	.25
75T Bobby Ayala	.02	.10
76T Rafael Palmeiro	.10	.30
77T Bret Boone	.07	.20
78T Paul Shuey	.02	.10
79T Kevin Foster RC	.08	.25
80T Dave Magadan	.02	.10
81T Bip Roberts	.02	.10
82T Howard Johnson	.02	.10
83T Xavier Hernandez	.02	.10
84T Ross Powell RC	.08	.25
85T Doug Million RC	.08	.25
86T Geronimo Berroa	.02	.10
87T Mark Farris RC	.08	.25
88T Butch Henry	.02	.10
89T Junior Felix	.02	.10
90T Bo Jackson	.20	.50
91T Hector Carrasco	.02	.10
92T Charlie O'Brien	.02	.10
93T Omar Vizquel	.10	.30
94T David Segui	.02	.10
95T Dustin Hermanson	.02	.10
96T Gar Finnvold RC	.08	.25
97T Dave Stevens	.02	.10
98T Corey Pointer RC	.08	.25
99T Felix Fermin	.02	.10
100T Lee Smith	.07	.20
101T Reid Ryan RC	.40	1.00
102T Bobby Munoz	.02	.10
103T Deion Sanders TR	.10	.30
Roberto Kelly		
104T Turner Ward	.02	.10
105T W.VanLandingham RC	.08	.25
106T Vince Coleman	.02	.10
107T Stan Javier	.02	.10
108T Darrin Jackson	.02	.10
109T C.J. Nitkowski RC	.08	.25
110T Anthony Young	.02	.10
111T Kurt Miller	.02	.10
112T Paul Konerko RC	6.00	15.00
113T Walt Weiss	.02	.10
114T Daryl Boston	.02	.10
115T Will Clark	.10	.30
116T Matt Smith RC	.08	.25
117T Mark Leiter	.02	.10
118T Gregg Olson	.02	.10
119T Tony Pena	.02	.10
120T Jose Vizcaino	.02	.10
121T Rick White RC	.08	.25
122T Rich Rowland	.02	.10
123T Jeff Reboulet	.02	.10
124T Greg Hibbard	.02	.10
125T Chris Sabo	.02	.10
126T Doug Jones	.02	.10
127T Tony Fernandez	.02	.10
128T Carlos Reyes RC	.08	.25
129T Kevin L.Brown RC	.40	1.00
130T Ryne Sandberg Farewell	.50	1.25
131T Ryne Sandberg Farewell	.50	1.25
132T Checklist 1-132	.02	.10

1994 Topps Traded Finest Inserts

Each Topps Traded factory set contained a complete eight card set of Finest Inserts. These cards are numbered separately and designed differently from the base cards. Each Finest Insert features a action shot of a player set against purple chrome background. The set highlights the top performers midway through the 1994 season, detailing their performances through July. The cards are numbered on back "X of 8".

Card	Low	High
COMPLETE SET (8)	2.00	5.00
1 Greg Maddux	.30	.75
2 Mike Piazza	.40	1.00
3 Matt Williams	.07	.20
4 Raul Mondesi	.07	.20
5 Ken Griffey Jr.	.30	.75
6 Kenny Lofton	.07	.20
7 Frank Thomas	.20	.50
8 Manny Ramirez	.20	.50

1995 Topps

These 660 standard-size cards feature color action player photos with white borders on the fronts. This set was released in two series. The first series contained 396 cards while the second series had 264 cards. Cards were distributed in 11-card packs (SRP $1.29), jumbo packs and factory sets. One "Own The Game" instant winner card has been inserted in every 120 packs. Rookie cards in this set include Rey Ordonez. Due to the 1994 baseball strike, it was publicly announced that production for this set was the lowest print run since 1966.

Card	Low	High
COMPLETE SET (660)	50.00	80.00
COMP.HOBBY SET (677)	50.00	100.00
COMP.RETAIL SET (677)	50.00	100.00
COMP.SERIES 1 (396)	25.00	40.00
COMP.SERIES 2 (264)	25.00	40.00
1 Frank Thomas	.30	.75
2 Mickey Morandini	.05	.15
3 Babe Ruth 100th B-Day	.75	2.00
4 Scott Cooper	.05	.15
5 David Cone	.10	.30
6 Jacob Shumate	.05	.15
7 Trevor Hoffman	.10	.30
8 Shane Mack	.05	.15
9 Delino DeShields	.05	.15
10 Matt Williams	.10	.30
11 Sammy Sosa	.30	.75
12 Gary DiSarcina	.05	.15
13 Kenny Rogers	.10	.30
14 Jose Vizcaino	.05	.15
15 Lou Whitaker	.10	.30
16 Ron Darling	.05	.15
17 Dave Nilsson	.05	.15
18 Chris Hammond	.05	.15
19 Sid Bream	.05	.15
20 Denny Martinez	.10	.30
21 Orlando Merced	.05	.15
22 John Wetteland	.10	.30
23 Mike Devereaux	.05	.15
24 Rene Arocha	.05	.15
25 Jay Buhner	.10	.30
26 Darren Holmes	.05	.15
27 Hal Morris	.05	.15
28 Brian Buchanan RC	.05	.15
29 Keith Miller	.05	.15
30 Paul Molitor	.10	.30
31 Dave West	.05	.15
32 Tony Tarasco	.05	.15
33 Scott Sanders	.05	.15
34 Eddie Zambrano	.05	.15
35 Ricky Bones	.05	.15
36 John Valentin	.05	.15
37 Kevin Tapani	.05	.15
38 Tim Wallach	.05	.15
39 Darren Lewis	.05	.15
40 Travis Fryman	.10	.30
41 Mark Leiter	.05	.15
42 Jose Bautista	.05	.15
43 Pete Smith	.05	.15
44 Bret Barberie	.05	.15
45 Dennis Eckersley	.10	.30
46 Ken Hill	.05	.15
47 Chad Ogea	.05	.15
48 Pete Harnisch	.05	.15
49 James Baldwin	.05	.15
50 Mike Mussina	.20	.50
51 Al Martin	.05	.15
52 Mark Thompson	.05	.15
53 Matt Smith	.05	.15
54 Joey Hamilton	.05	.15
55 Edgar Martinez	.20	.50
56 John Smiley	.05	.15
57 Rey Sanchez	.05	.15
58 Mike Timlin	.05	.15
59 Ricky Bottalico	.05	.15
60 Jim Abbott	.20	.50
61 Mike Kelly	.05	.15
62 Brian Jordan	.10	.30
63 Ken Ryan	.05	.15
64 Matt Mieske	.05	.15
65 Rick Aguilera	.05	.15
66 Ismael Valdes	.05	.15
67 Royce Clayton	.05	.15
68 Junior Felix	.05	.15
69 Harold Reynolds	.10	.30
70 Juan Gonzalez	.10	.30
71 Kelly Stinnett	.05	.15
72 Carlos Reyes	.05	.15
73 Dave Weathers	.05	.15
74 Mel Rojas	.05	.15
75 Doug Drabek	.05	.15
76 Charles Nagy	.05	.15
77 Tim Raines	.10	.30
78 Midre Cummings	.05	.15
79 Gene Schall	.05	.15
Scott Talanoa		
Harold Williams		
Ray Brown RC		
80 Rafael Palmeiro	.20	.50
81 Charlie Hayes	.05	.15
82 Ray Lankford	.10	.30
83 Tim Davis	.05	.15
84 C.J. Nitkowski	.05	.15
85 Andy Ashby	.05	.15
86 Gerald Williams	.05	.15
87 Terry Shumpert	.05	.15
88 Heathcliff Slocumb	.05	.15
89 Domingo Cedeno	.05	.15
90 Mark Grace	.20	.50
91 Brad Woodall RC	.05	.15
92 Gar Finnvold	.05	.15
93 Jaime Navarro	.05	.15
94 Carlos Hernandez	.05	.15
95 Mark Langston	.05	.15
96 Chuck Carr	.05	.15
97 Mike Gardiner	.05	.15
98 Dave McCarty	.05	.15
99 Cris Carpenter	.05	.15
100 Barry Bonds	.75	2.00
101 David Segui	.05	.15
102 Scott Brosius	.10	.30
103 Mariano Duncan	.05	.15
104 Kenny Lofton	.10	.30
105 Ken Caminiti	.10	.30
106 Darrin Jackson	.05	.15
107 Jim Poole	.05	.15
108 Wil Cordero	.05	.15
109 Danny Miceli	.05	.15
110 Walt Weiss	.05	.15
111 Tom Pagnozzi	.05	.15
112 Terrence Long	.05	.15
113 Bret Boone	.10	.30
114 Daryl Boston	.05	.15
115 Wally Joyner	.10	.30
116 Rob Butler	.05	.15
117 Rafael Belliard	.05	.15
118 Luis Lopez	.05	.15
119 Tony Fossas	.05	.15
120 Len Dykstra	.10	.30
121 Mike Morgan	.05	.15
122 Denny Hocking	.05	.15
123 Kevin Gross	.05	.15
124 Todd Benzinger	.05	.15
125 John Doherty	.05	.15
126 Eduardo Perez	.05	.15
127 Dan Smith	.05	.15
128 Joe Orsulak	.05	.15
129 Brent Gates	.05	.15
130 Jeff Conine	.10	.30
131 Doug Henry	.05	.15
132 Paul Sorrento	.05	.15
133 Mike Hampton	.10	.30
134 Tim Spehr	.05	.15
135 Julio Franco	.10	.30
136 Mike Dyer	.05	.15
137 Chris Sabo	.05	.15
138 Rheal Cormier	.05	.15
139 Paul Konerko	.40	1.00
140 Dante Bichette	.10	.30
141 Chuck McElroy	.05	.15
142 Mike Stanley	.05	.15
143 Bob Hamelin	.05	.15
144 Tommy Greene	.05	.15
145 John Smoltz	.20	.50
146 Ed Sprague	.05	.15
147 Ray McDavid	.05	.15
148 Otis Nixon	.05	.15
149 Turk Wendell	.05	.15
150 Chris James	.05	.15
151 Derek Parks	.05	.15
152 Jose Offerman	.05	.15
153 Tony Clark	.05	.15
154 Chad Curtis	.05	.15
155 Mark Portugal	.05	.15
156 Bill Pulsipher	.05	.15
157 Troy Neel	.05	.15
158 Dave Winfield	.10	.30
159 Bill Wegman	.05	.15
160 Benito Santiago	.10	.30
161 Jose Mesa	.05	.15
162 Luis Gonzalez	.10	.30
163 Alex Fernandez	.05	.15
164 Freddie Benavides	.05	.15
165 Ben McDonald	.05	.15
166 Blas Minor	.05	.15
167 Bret Wagner	.05	.15
168 Mac Suzuki	.05	.15
169 Roberto Mejia	.05	.15
170 Wade Boggs	.20	.50
171 Pokey Reese	.05	.15
172 Hipolito Pichardo	.05	.15
173 Kim Batiste	.05	.15
174 Darren Hall	.05	.15
175 Tom Glavine	.20	.50
176 Phil Plantier	.05	.15
177 Chris Howard	.05	.15
178 Karl Rhodes	.05	.15
179 LaTroy Hawkins	.05	.15
180 Raul Mondesi	.10	.30
181 Jeff Reed	.05	.15
182 Milt Cuyler	.05	.15
183 Jim Edmonds	.20	.50
184 Hector Fajardo	.05	.15
185 Jeff Kent	.10	.30
186 Wilson Alvarez	.05	.15
187 Geronimo Berroa	.05	.15
188 Billy Spiers	.05	.15
189 Derek Lilliquist	.05	.15
190 Craig Biggio	.20	.50
191 Roberto Hernandez	.05	.15
192 Bob Natal	.05	.15
193 Bobby Ayala	.05	.15
194 Travis Miller RC	.05	.15
195 Bob Tewksbury	.05	.15
196 Rondell White	.10	.30
197 Steve Cooke	.05	.15
198 Jeff Branson	.05	.15
199 Derek Jeter	.75	2.00
200 Tim Salmon	.20	.50
201 Steve Frey	.05	.15
202 Kent Mercker	.05	.15
203 Randy Johnson	.30	.75
204 Todd Worrell	.05	.15
205 Mo Vaughn	.10	.30
206 Howard Johnson	.05	.15
207 John Wasdin	.05	.15
208 Eddie Williams	.05	.15
209 Tim Belcher	.05	.15
210 Jeff Montgomery	.05	.15
211 Kirt Manwaring	.05	.15
212 Ben Grieve	.05	.15
213 Pat Hentgen	.05	.15
214 Shawon Dunston	.05	.15
215 Mike Greenwell	.05	.15
216 Alex Diaz	.05	.15
217 Pat Mahomes	.05	.15
218 Dave Hansen	.05	.15
219 Kevin Rogers	.05	.15
220 Cecil Fielder	.10	.30
221 Andrew Lorraine	.05	.15
222 Jack Armstrong	.05	.15
223 Todd Hundley	.05	.15
224 Mark Acre	.05	.15
225 Darrell Whitmore	.05	.15
226 Randy Milligan	.05	.15
227 Wayne Kirby	.05	.15
228 Darryl Kile	.10	.30
229 Bob Zupcic	.05	.15
230 Jay Bell	.10	.30
231 Dustin Hermanson	.05	.15
232 Harold Baines	.10	.30
233 Alan Benes	.05	.15
234 Felix Fermin	.05	.15
235 Ellis Burks	.10	.30
236 Jeff Brantley	.05	.15
237 Brian Hunter	.05	.15
Jose Malave		
Karim Garcia RC		
Shane Pullen		
238 Matt Nokes	.05	.15
239 Ben Rivera	.05	.15
240 Joe Carter	.10	.30
241 Jeff Granger	.05	.15
242 Terry Pendleton	.10	.30
243 Melvin Nieves	.05	.15
244 Frankie Rodriguez	.05	.15
245 Darryl Hamilton	.05	.15
246 Brooks Kieschnick	.05	.15
247 Todd Hollandsworth	.05	.15
248 Joe Rosselli	.05	.15
249 Bill Gullickson	.05	.15
250 Chuck Knoblauch	.10	.30
251 Kurt Miller	.05	.15
252 Bobby Jones	.05	.15
253 Lance Blankenship	.05	.15
254 Matt Whiteside	.05	.15
255 Darrin Fletcher	.05	.15
256 Eric Plunk	.05	.15
257 Shane Reynolds	.05	.15
258 Norberto Martin	.05	.15
259 Mike Thurman	.05	.15
260 Andy Van Slyke	.20	.50
261 Dwight Smith	.05	.15
262 Allen Watson	.05	.15
263 Dan Wilson	.05	.15
264 Brent Mayne	.05	.15
265 Bip Roberts	.05	.15
266 Sterling Hitchcock	.05	.15
267 Alex Gonzalez	.05	.15
268 Greg Harris	.05	.15
269 Ricky Jordan	.05	.15
270 Johnny Ruffin	.05	.15
271 Mike Stanton	.05	.15
272 Rich Rowland	.05	.15
273 Steve Trachsel	.05	.15
274 Pedro Munoz	.05	.15
275 Ramon Martinez	.06	.15
276 Dave Henderson	.05	.15
277 Chris Gomez	.05	.15
278 Joe Grahe	.05	.15
279 Rusty Greer	.10	.30
280 John Franco	.10	.30
281 Mike Bordick	.05	.15
282 Jeff D'Amico	.05	.15
283 Dave Magadan	.05	.15
284 Tony Pena	.05	.15
285 Greg Swindell	.05	.15
286 Doug Million	.05	.15
287 Gabe White	.05	.15
288 Trey Beamon	.05	.15
289 Arthur Rhodes	.05	.15
290 Juan Guzman	.05	.15
291 Jose Oquendo	.05	.15
292 Willie Blair	.05	.15
293 Eddie Taubensee	.05	.15
294 Steve Howe	.05	.15
295 Greg Maddux	.50	1.25
296 Mike Macfarlane	.05	.15
297 Curt Schilling	.10	.30
298 Phil Clark	.05	.15
299 Woody Williams	.05	.15
300 Jose Canseco	.20	.50
301 Aaron Sele	.05	.15
302 Carl Willis	.05	.15
303 Steve Buechele	.05	.15
304 Dave Burba	.05	.15
305 Orel Hershiser	.10	.30
306 Damion Easley	.05	.15
307 Mike Henneman	.05	.15
308 Josias Manzanillo	.05	.15
309 Kevin Seitzer	.05	.15
310 Ruben Sierra	.10	.30
311 Bryan Harvey	.05	.15
312 Jim Thome	.20	.50
313 Ramon Castro RC	.15	.40
314 Lance Johnson	.05	.15
315 Marquis Grissom	.10	.30
316 Terrell Wade	.05	.15
Juan Acevedo		
Matt Arrandale		
Eddie Priest RC		
317 Paul Wagner	.05	.15
318 Jamie Moyer	.10	.30
319 Todd Zeile	.05	.15
320 Chris Bosio	.05	.15
321 Steve Reed	.05	.15
322 Erik Hanson	.05	.15
323 Luis Polonia	.05	.15
324 Ryan Klesko	.10	.30
325 Kevin Appier	.10	.30
326 Jim Eisenreich	.05	.15
327 Randy Knorr	.05	.15
328 Craig Shipley	.05	.15
329 Tim Naehring	.05	.15
330 Randy Myers	.05	.15
331 Alex Cole	.05	.15
332 Jim Gott	.05	.15
333 Mike Jackson	.05	.15
334 John Flaherty	.05	.15
335 Chili Davis	.10	.30
336 Benji Gil	.05	.15
337 Jason Jacome	.05	.15
338 Stan Javier	.05	.15
339 Mike Fetters	.05	.15
340 Rich Renteria	.05	.15
341 Kevin Witt	.05	.15
342 Scott Servais	.05	.15
343 Craig Grebeck	.05	.15
344 Kirk Rueter	.05	.15
345 Don Slaught	.05	.15
346 Armando Benitez	.05	.15
347 Ozzie Smith	.50	1.25
348 Mike Blowers	.05	.15
349 Armando Reynoso	.05	.15
350 Barry Larkin	.20	.50
351 Mike Williams	.05	.15
352 Scott Kamieniecki	.05	.15
353 Gary Gaetti	.10	.30
354 Todd Stottlemyre	.05	.15
355 Fred McGriff	.20	.50
356 Tim Mauser	.05	.15
357 Chris Gwynn	.05	.15
358 Frank Castillo	.05	.15
359 Jeff Reboulet	.05	.15
360 Roger Clemens	.60	1.50
361 Mark Carreon	.05	.15
362 Chad Kreuter	.05	.15
363 Mark Farris	.05	.15
364 Bob Welch	.05	.15
365 Dean Palmer	.10	.30
366 Jeromy Burnitz	.10	.30
367 B.J. Surhoff	.10	.30
368 Mike Butcher	.05	.15
369 Brad Clontz	.05	.15
Steve Phoenix		
Scott Gentile		
Bucky Buckles RC		
370 Eddie Murray	.30	.75
371 Orlando Miller	.05	.15
372 Ron Karkovice	.05	.15
373 Richie Lewis	.05	.15
374 Lenny Webster	.05	.15
375 Jeff Tackett	.05	.15
376 Tom Urbani	.05	.15
377 Tino Martinez	.20	.50
378 Mark Dewey	.05	.15
379 Charles O'Brien	.05	.15
380 Terry Mulholland	.05	.15
381 Thomas Howard	.05	.15
382 Chris Haney	.05	.15
383 Billy Hatcher	.05	.15
384 Jeff Bagwell AS	.20	.50
Frank Thomas AS		
385 Bret Boone AS	.10	.30
Carlos Baerga AS		
386 Matt Williams AS	.10	.30
Wade Boggs AS		
387 Wil Cordero AS	.30	.75
Cal Ripken AS		
388 Barry Bonds AS	.40	1.00
Ken Griffey AS		
389 Tony Gwynn AS	.10	.30
Albert Belle AS		
390 Dante Bichette AS	.20	.50
Kirby Puckett AS		
391 Mike Piazza AS	.30	.75
Mike Stanley AS		
392 Greg Maddux AS	.30	.75
David Cone AS		
393 Danny Jackson AS	.05	.15
Jimmy Key AS		
394 John Franco AS	.05	.15
Lee Smith AS		
395 Checklist 1-198	.05	.15
396 Checklist 199-396	.05	.15
397 Ken Griffey Jr.	.50	1.25
398 Rick Heiserman RC	.05	.15
399 Don Mattingly	.75	2.00
400 Henry Rodriguez	.05	.15
401 Lenny Harris	.05	.15
402 Ryan Thompson	.05	.15
403 Darren Oliver	.05	.15
404 Omar Vizquel	.20	.50
405 Jeff Bagwell	.20	.50
406 Doug Webb RC	.05	.15
407 Todd Van Poppel	.05	.15
408 Leo Gomez	.05	.15
409 Mark Whiten	.05	.15
410 Pedro A.Martinez	.05	.15
411 Reggie Sanders	.10	.30
412 Kevin Foster	.05	.15
413 Danny Tartabull	.05	.15
414 Jeff Blauser	.05	.15
415 Mike Magnante	.05	.15
416 Tom Candiotti	.05	.15
417 Rod Beck	.05	.15
418 Jody Reed	.05	.15
419 Vince Coleman	.05	.15
420 Danny Jackson	.05	.15
421 Ryan Nye RC	.05	.15
422 Larry Walker	.10	.30
423 Russ Johnson DP	.05	.15
424 Pat Borders	.05	.15
425 Lee Smith	.10	.30
426 Paul O'Neill	.20	.50
427 Devon White	.10	.30
428 Jim Bullinger	.05	.15
429 Greg Hansell	.05	.15
Brian Sackinsky		
Carey Paige		
Rob Welch RC		
430 Steve Avery	.05	.15
431 Tony Gwynn	.40	1.00
432 Pat Meares	.05	.15
433 Bill Swift	.05	.15
434 David Wells	.10	.30
435 John Briscoe	.05	.15
436 Roger Pavlik	.05	.15
437 Jayson Peterson RC	.05	.15
438 Roberto Alomar	.20	.50
439 Billy Brewer	.05	.15
440 Gary Sheffield	.10	.30
441 Lou Frazier	.05	.15
442 Terry Steinbach	.05	.15
443 Jay Payton RC	.30	.75
444 Jason Bere	.05	.15
445 Denny Neagle	.10	.30
446 Andres Galarraga	.10	.30
447 Hector Carrasco	.05	.15
448 Bill Risley	.05	.15
449 Andy Benes	.05	.15
450 Jim Leyritz	.05	.15
451 Jose Oliva	.05	.15
452 Greg Vaughn	.05	.15
453 Rich Monteleone	.05	.15
454 Tony Eusebio	.05	.15
455 Chuck Finley	.10	.30
456 Kevin Brown	.10	.30
457 Joe Boever	.05	.15
458 Bobby Munoz	.05	.15
459 Bret Saberhagen	.10	.30
460 Kurt Abbott	.05	.15
461 Bobby Witt	.05	.15
462 Cliff Floyd	.10	.30
463 Mark Clark	.05	.15
464 Andujar Cedeno	.05	.15
465 Marvin Freeman	.05	.15
466 Mike Piazza	.50	1.25
467 Willie Greene	.05	.15
468 Pat Kelly	.05	.15
469 Carlos Delgado	.10	.30
470 Willie Banks	.05	.15
471 Matt Walbeck	.05	.15
472 Mark McGwire	.75	2.00
473 M.Christensen RC	.05	.15
474 Alan Trammell	.10	.30
475 Tom Gordon	.05	.15
476 Greg Colbrunn	.05	.15
477 Darren Daulton	.10	.30
478 Albie Lopez	.05	.15
479 Robin Ventura	.10	.30
480 Eddie Perez RC	.15	.40
Jason Kendall		
Einar Diaz		
Bret Hemphill		
481 Bryan Eversgerd	.05	.15
482 Dave Fleming	.05	.15
483 Scott Livingstone	.05	.15
484 Pete Schourek	.05	.15
485 Bernie Williams	.20	.50
486 Mark Lemke	.05	.15
487 Eric Karros	.10	.30
488 Scott Ruffcorn	.05	.15
489 Billy Ashley	.05	.15
490 Rico Brogna	.05	.15
491 John Burkett	.05	.15
492 Cade Gaspar RC	.05	.15
493 Jorge Fabregas	.05	.15
494 Greg Gagne	.05	.15
495 Doug Jones	.05	.15
496 Troy O'Leary	.05	.15
497 Pat Rapp	.05	.15
498 Butch Henry	.05	.15
499 John Olerud	.10	.30
500 John Hudek	.05	.15
501 Jeff King	.05	.15
502 Bobby Bonilla	.10	.30
503 Albert Belle	.10	.30
504 Rick Wilkins	.05	.15
505 John Jaha	.05	.15
506 Nigel Wilson	.05	.15
507 Sid Fernandez	.05	.15
508 Deion Sanders	.20	.50
509 Gil Heredia	.05	.15
510 Scott Elarton RC	.15	.40
511 Melido Perez	.05	.15
512 Greg McMichael	.05	.15
513 Rusty Meacham	.05	.15
514 Shawn Green	.10	.30
515 Carlos Garcia	.05	.15
516 Dave Stevens	.05	.15
517 Eric Young	.05	.15
518 Omar Daal	.05	.15
519 Kirk Gibson	.10	.30
520 Spike Owen	.05	.15
521 Jacob Cruz RC	.10	.30
522 Sandy Alomar Jr.	.05	.15
523 Steve Bedrosian	.05	.15
524 Ricky Gutierrez	.05	.15
525 Dave Veres	.05	.15
526 Gregg Jefferies	.05	.15
527 Jose Valentin	.05	.15
528 Robb Nen	.10	.30
529 Jose Rijo	.05	.15
530 Sean Berry	.05	.15
531 Mike Gallego	.05	.15
532 Roberto Kelly	.05	.15
533 Kevin Stocker	.05	.15
534 Kirby Puckett	.30	.75
535 Chipper Jones	.30	.75
536 Russ Davis	.05	.15
537 Jon Lieber	.05	.15
538 Trey Moore RC	.05	.15
539 Joe Girardi	.05	.15
540 Quilvio Veras	.05	.15
Arquimedez Pozo		
Miguel Cairo RC		
Jason Camilli		
541 Tony Phillips	.05	.15
542 Brian Anderson	.05	.15
543 Ivan Rodriguez	.20	.50
544 Jeff Cirillo	.05	.15
545 Joey Cora	.05	.15
546 Chris Hoiles	.05	.15
547 Bernard Gilkey	.05	.15
548 Mike Lansing	.05	.15
549 Jimmy Key	.10	.30
550 Mark Wohlers	.05	.15
551 Chris Clemons RC	.05	.15
552 Vinny Castilla	.10	.30
553 Mark Guthrie	.05	.15
554 Mike Lieberthal	.10	.30
555 Tommy Davis RC	.05	.15
556 Robby Thompson	.05	.15
557 Danny Bautista	.05	.15
558 Will Clark	.20	.50
559 Rickey Henderson	.30	.75
560 Todd Jones	.05	.15
561 Jack McDowell	.05	.15
562 Carlos Rodriguez	.05	.15
563 Mark Eichhorn	.05	.15
564 Jeff Nelson	.05	.15
565 Eric Anthony	.05	.15
566 Randy Velarde	.05	.15
567 Javier Lopez	.10	.30
568 Kevin Mitchell	.05	.15
569 Steve Karsay	.05	.15
570 Brian Meadows RC	.05	.15
571 Rey Ordonez RC	.30	.75
Mike Metcalfe		
Kevin Orie		
Ray Holbert		
572 John Kruk	.10	.30
573 Scott Leius	.05	.15
574 John Patterson	.05	.15
575 Kevin Brown	.10	.30
576 Mike Moore	.05	.15
577 Manny Ramirez	.20	.50
578 Jose Lind	.05	.15
579 Derrick May	.05	.15
580 Cal Eldred	.05	.15
581 David Bell	.30	.75
Joel Chelmis		
Lino Diaz		
Aaron Boone RC		
582 J.T. Snow	.10	.30
583 Luis Sojo	.05	.15
584 Moises Alou	.10	.30
585 Dave Clark	.05	.15
586 Dave Hollins	.05	.15
587 Nomar Garciaparra	.75	2.00
588 Cal Ripken	1.00	2.50
589 Pedro Astacio	.05	.15
590 J.R. Phillips	.05	.15
591 Jeff Frye	.05	.15
592 Bo Jackson	.30	.75
593 Steve Ontiveros	.05	.15
594 David Nied	.05	.15
595 Brad Ausmus	.10	.30
596 Carlos Baerga	.05	.15
597 James Mouton	.05	.15
598 Ozzie Guillen	.10	.30
599 Ozzie Timmons	.30	.75
Curtis Goodwin		
Johnny Damon		
Jeff Abbott RC		
600 Yorkis Perez	.05	.15
601 Rich Rodriguez	.05	.15
602 Mark McLemore	.05	.15
603 Jeff Fassero	.05	.15
604 John Roper	.05	.15
605 Mark Johnson RC	.15	.40
606 Wes Chamberlain	.05	.15
607 Felix Jose	.05	.15
608 Tony Longmire	.05	.15
609 Duane Ward	.05	.15
610 Brett Butler	.10	.30
611 W.VanLandingham	.05	.15
612 Mickey Tettleton	.05	.15
613 Brady Anderson	.10	.30
614 Reggie Jefferson	.05	.15
615 Mike Kingery	.05	.15
616 Derek Bell	.05	.15
617 Scott Erickson	.05	.15
618 Bob Wickman	.05	.15
619 Phil Leftwich	.05	.15
620 David Justice	.10	.30
621 Paul Wilson	.05	.15
622 Pedro Martinez	.20	.50
623 Terry Mathews	.05	.15
624 Brian McRae	.05	.15
625 Bruce Ruffin	.05	.15
626 Steve Finley	.10	.30
627 Ron Gant	.10	.30
628 Rafael Bournigal	.05	.15
629 Darryl Strawberry	.10	.30
630 Luis Alicea	.05	.15
631 Mark Smith	.05	.15
Scott Klingenbeck		
632 Cory Bailey	.05	.15
Scott Hatteberg		
633 Todd Greene	.10	.30
Troy Percival		
634 Rod Bolton	.05	.15
Olmedo Saenz		
635 Steve Kline	.05	.15
Herb Perry		
636 Sean Bergman	.05	.15
Shannon Penn		
637 Joe Randa	.10	.30
Joe Vitiello		
638 Jose Mercedes	.05	.15
Duane Singleton		
639 Marc Barcelo	.05	.15
Marty Cordova		
640 Andy Pettitte	.10	.30
Ruben Rivera		
641 Willie Adams	.05	.15
Scott Spiezio		
642 Eddy Diaz RC	.05	.15
Desi Relaford		
643 Terrell Lowery	.05	.15

Jon Shave
644 Angel Martinez .05 .15
Paul Spoljaric
645 Tony Graffanino .05 .15
Damon Hollins
646 Darron Cox .05 .15
Doug Glanville
647 Tim Belk .05 .15
Pat Watkins
648 Rod Pedraza .05 .15
Phil Schneider
649 Vic Darensbourg .05 .15
Marc Valdes
650 Rick Huisman .05 .15
Roberto Petagine
651 Roger Cedeno .05 .15
Ron Coomer RC
652 Shane Andrews .15 .40
Carlos Perez RC
653 Jason Isringhausen .10 .30
Chris Roberts
654 Wayne Gomes .05 .15
Kevin Jordan
655 Esteban Loaiza .05 .15
Steve Pegues
656 Terry Bradshaw .05 .15
John Frascatore
657 Andres Berumen .05 .15
Bryce Florie
658 Dan Carlson .05 .15
Keith Williams
659 Checklist .05 .15
660 Checklist .05 .15

1995 Topps Cyberstats

The 396-card Cyberstats insert set was issued one per pack and three per jumbo pack. Each 1995 Topps series had 198 Cyberstat cards. The idea was to present prorated statistics for the 1994 strike shortened season. The photos on front are the same as the basic issue. The difference is that the photo is given a glossy or metallic finish. The backs contain yearly and career statistics, including the prorated 1994 numbers.

COMPLETE SET (396) 25.00 60.00
COMP.SERIES 1 (198) 10.00 25.00
COMP.SERIES 2 (198) 15.00 40.00
*STARS: 1X TO 2.5X BASIC CARDS

1995 Topps Cyber Season in Review

This seven-card set was distributed exclusively in 1995 Topps hobby factory sets. It continues the Cyberstats insert theme used in the regular issue product, which presented "what if" statistics to fill in the strike-shortened 1994 season. The Season in Review cards commemorate projected accomplishments including Barry Bonds' 61 home runs and Kenny Lofton's World Series MVP.

COMPLETE SET (7) 4.00 10.00
1 Barry Bonds 1.50 4.00
2 Jose Canseco .75 2.00
3 Juan Gonzalez .60 1.50
4 Fred McGriff .40 1.00
5 Carlos Baerga .20 .50
6 Ryan Klesko .40 1.00
7 Kenny Lofton .30 .75

1995 Topps Finest Inserts

This 15-card standard-size set was inserted one every 36 Topps series two packs. This set featured the top 15 players in total bases from the 1994 season. The fronts feature a player photo, with his team identification and name on the bottom of the card. The horizontal backs feature another player photo along with a breakdown of how many of each type of hit each player got on the way to their season total. The set is sequenced in order of how they finished in the majors for the 1994 season.

COMPLETE SET (15) 25.00 60.00
SER.2 ODDS 1:36 HOB/RET, 1:20 JUM
1 Jeff Bagwell 1.25 3.00
2 Albert Belle .75 2.00
3 Ken Griffey Jr. 3.00 8.00
4 Frank Thomas 2.00 5.00
5 Matt Williams .75 2.00
6 Dante Bichette .75 2.00
7 Barry Bonds 5.00 12.00
8 Moises Alou .75 2.00
9 Andres Galarraga .75 2.00
10 Kenny Lofton .75 2.00
11 Rafael Palmeiro 1.25 3.00
12 Tony Gwynn 2.50 6.00
13 Kirby Puckett 2.00 5.00
14 Jose Canseco 1.25 3.00
15 Jeff Conine .75 2.00

1995 Topps League Leaders

Randomly inserted in jumbo packs at a rate of one in three and retail packs at a rate of one in six, this 50-card standard-size set showcases those that were among league leaders in various categories. Card fronts feature a player photo with a black background. The player's name appears in gold foil at the bottom and the category with which he led the league or was among the leaders is in yellow letters up the right side. The backs contain various graphs and where the player placed among the leaders.

COMPLETE SET (50) 20.00 50.00
COMPLETE SERIES 1 (25) 8.00 20.00
COMPLETE SERIES 2 (25) 12.50 30.00
STATED ODDS 1:6 RETAIL, 1:3 JUMBO
LL1 Albert Belle .25 .60
LL2 Kevin Mitchell .10 .30
LL3 Wade Boggs .40 1.00
LL4 Tony Gwynn .75 2.00
LL5 Moises Alou .25 .60
LL6 Andres Galarraga .25 .60
LL7 Matt Williams .25 .60
LL8 Barry Bonds 1.50 4.00
LL9 Frank Thomas .60 1.50
LL10 Jose Canseco .40 1.00
LL11 Jeff Bagwell .40 1.00
LL12 Kirby Puckett .60 1.50
LL13 Julio Franco .25 .60
LL14 Albert Belle .25 .60
LL15 Fred McGriff .40 1.00
LL16 Kenny Lofton .25 .60
LL17 Otis Nixon .10 .30
LL18 Brady Anderson .25 .60
LL19 Deion Sanders .40 1.00
LL20 Chuck Carr .10 .30
LL21 Pat Hentgen .10 .30
LL22 Andy Benes .10 .30
LL23 Roger Clemens 1.25 3.00
LL24 Greg Maddux 1.00 2.50
LL25 Pedro Martinez .10 .30
LL26 Paul O'Neill .40 1.00
LL27 Jeff Bagwell .40 1.00
LL28 Frank Thomas .60 1.50
LL29 Hal Morris .10 .30
LL30 Kenny Lofton .25 .60
LL31 Ken Griffey Jr. 1.00 2.50
LL32 Jeff Bagwell .40 1.00
LL33 Albert Belle .25 .60
LL34 Fred McGriff .40 1.00
LL35 Cecil Fielder .25 .60
LL36 Matt Williams .25 .60
LL37 Joe Carter .25 .60
LL38 Dante Bichette .25 .60
LL39 Frank Thomas .60 1.50
LL40 Mike Piazza 1.00 2.50
LL41 Craig Biggio .40 1.00
LL42 Vince Coleman .10 .30
LL43 Marquis Grissom .25 .60
LL44 Chuck Knoblauch .25 .60
LL45 Darren Lewis .10 .30
LL46 Randy Johnson .60 1.50
LL47 Jose Rijo .10 .30
LL48 Chuck Finley .25 .60
LL49 Bret Saberhagen .25 .60
LL50 Kevin Appier .25 .60

1995 Topps Opening Day

This 10-card standard-size set was inserted into all retail factory sets. The borderless fronts feature the player's photo set against a prismatic star background and the player's name on the bottom. In the lower right, the player's opening day highlight is mentioned and there is an "Opening Day" verbiage and logo in the upper right. The horizontal back has a player photo, description of the player's opening day as well as a line score for the player.

COMPLETE SET (10) 10.00 25.00
1 Kevin Appier .20 .50
2 Dante Bichette .40 1.00
3 Ken Griffey Jr. 6.00 15.00
4 Todd Hundley .40 1.00
5 John Jaha .20 .50
6 Fred McGriff .60 1.50
7 Raul Mondesi .40 1.00
8 Manny Ramirez 2.50 6.00
9 Danny Tartabull .20 .50
10 Devon White .40 1.00

1995 Topps Traded

This set contains 165 standard-size cards and was sold in 11-card packs for $1.29. The set features rookies, draft picks and players who had been traded. The fronts contain a photo with a white border. The backs have a player picture in a scoreboard and his statistics and information. Subsets featured are: At the Break (1T-10T) and All-Stars (156T-164T). Rookie Cards in this set include Michael Barrett, Carlos Beltran, Ben Davis, Hideo Nomo and Richie Sexson.

COMPLETE SET (165) 15.00 40.00
1T Frank Thomas ATB .25 .60
2T Ken Griffey Jr. ATB .40 1.00
3T Barry Bonds ATB .50 1.25
4T Albert Belle ATB .15 .40
5T Cal Ripken ATB .60 1.50
6T Mike Piazza ATB .40 1.00
7T Tony Gwynn ATB .25 .60
8T Jeff Bagwell ATB .15 .40
9T Mo Vaughn ATB .07 .20
10T Matt Williams ATB .07 .20
11T Ray Durham .15 .40
12T Juan LeBron RC 2.50 6.00
Card pictures Carlos Beltran
13T Shawn Green .15 .40
14T Kevin Gross .07 .20
15T Jon Nunnally .07 .20
16T Brian Maxcy RC .08 .25
17T Mark Kiefer .07 .20
18T Carlos Beltran UER RC 5.00 12.00
Card pictures Juan LeBron
19T Mike Mimbs RC .08 .25
20T Larry Walker .15 .40
21T Chad Curtis .07 .20
22T Jeff Barry .07 .20
23T Joe Oliver .07 .20
24T Tomas Perez RC .08 .25
25T Michael Barrett RC .40 1.00
26T Brian McRae .07 .20
27T Derek Bell .07 .20
28T Ray Durham .15 .40
29T Todd Williams .07 .20
30T Ryan Jaroncyk RC .08 .25
31T Todd Steverson .07 .20
32T Mike Devereaux .07 .20
33T Rheal Cormier .07 .20
34T Benny Santiago .15 .40
35T Bobby Higginson RC .40 1.00
36T Jack McDowell .07 .20
37T Mike MacFarlane .07 .20
38T Tony McKnight RC .08 .25
39T Brian Hunter .07 .20
40T Hideo Nomo RC 1.50 4.00
41T Brett Butler .15 .40
42T Donovan Osborne .07 .20
43T Scott Karl .07 .20
44T Tony Phillips .07 .20
45T Marty Cordova .07 .20
46T Dave Mlicki .07 .20
47T Bronson Arroyo RC 2.50 6.00
48T John Burkett .07 .20
49T J.D. Smart RC .08 .25
50T Mickey Tettleton .07 .20
51T Todd Stottlemyre .07 .20
52T Mike Perez .07 .20
53T Terry Mulholland .07 .20
54T Edgardo Alfonzo .07 .20
55T Zane Smith .07 .20
56T Jacob Brumfield .07 .20
57T Andujar Cedeno .07 .20
58T Jose Parra .07 .20
59T Manny Alexander .07 .20
60T Tony Tarasco .07 .20
61T Orel Hershiser .15 .40
62T Tim Scott .07 .20
63T Felix Rodriguez RC .08 .25
64T Ken Hill .07 .20
65T Marquis Grissom .15 .40
66T Lee Smith .15 .40
67T Jason Bates .07 .20
68T Felipe Lira .07 .20
69T Alex Hernandez RC .08 .25
70T Tony Fernandez .07 .20
71T Scott Radinsky .07 .20
72T Jose Canseco .25 .60
73T Mark Grudzielanek RC .40 1.00
74T Ben Davis RC .08 .25
75T Jim Abbott .25 .60
76T Roger Bailey .07 .20
77T Gregg Jefferies .07 .20
78T Erik Hanson .07 .20
79T Brad Radke RC .40 1.00
80T Jaime Navarro .07 .20
81T John Wetteland .15 .40
82T Chad Fonville RC .08 .25
83T John Mabry .07 .20
84T Glenallen Hill .07 .20
85T Ken Caminiti .15 .40
86T Tom Goodwin .07 .20
87T Darren Bragg .07 .20
88T Pat Ahearne .08 .25
Gary Rath
Larry Wimberly
Robbie Bell RC
89T Jeff Russell .07 .20
90T Dave Gallagher .07 .20
91T Steve Finley .15 .40
92T Vaughn Eshelman .07 .20
93T Kevin Jarvis .07 .20
94T Mark Gubicza .07 .20
95T Tim Wakefield .15 .40
96T Bob Tewksbury .07 .20
97T Sid Roberson RC .08 .25
98T Tom Henke .07 .20
99T Michael Tucker .07 .20
100T Jason Bates .07 .20
101T Otis Nixon .07 .20
102T Mark Whiten .07 .20
103T Dilson Torres RC .08 .25
104T Melvin Bunch RC .08 .25
105T Terry Pendleton .15 .40
106T Corey Jenkins RC .08 .25
107T Glenn Dishman RC .08 .25
Rob Grable
108T Reggie Taylor RC .08 .25
109T Curtis Goodwin .07 .20
110T David Cone .15 .40
111T Antonio Osuna .07 .20
112T Paul Shuey .07 .20
113T Doug Jones .07 .20
114T Mark McLemore .07 .20
115T Kevin Ritz .07 .20
116T John Kruk .15 .40
117T Trevor Wilson .07 .20
118T Jerald Clark .07 .20
119T Julian Tavarez .07 .20
120T Tim Pugh .07 .20
121T Todd Zeile .07 .20
122T Mark Sweeney UER 1.50 4.00
George Arias
Richie Sexson RC
Brian Schneider
123T Bobby Witt .07 .20
124T Hideo Nomo .60 1.50
125T Joey Cora .07 .20
126T Jim Scharrer RC .08 .25
127T Paul Quantrill .07 .20
128T Chipper Jones ROY .25 .60
129T Kenny James RC .08 .25
130T Lyle Mouton 1.25 3.00
Mariano Rivera
131T Tyler Green .07 .20
132T Brad Clontz .07 .20
133T Jon Nunnally .07 .20
134T Dave Magadan .07 .20
135T Al Leiter .15 .40
136T Bret Barberie .07 .20
137T Bill Swift .07 .20
138T Scott Cooper .07 .20
139T Roberto Kelly .07 .20
140T Charlie Hayes .07 .20
141T Pete Harnisch .07 .20
142T Rich Amaral .07 .20
143T Rudy Seanez .07 .20
144T Pat Listach .07 .20
145T Quilvio Veras .07 .20
146T Jose Olmeda RC .08 .25
147T Roberto Petagine .07 .20
148T Kevin Brown .15 .40
149T Phil Plantier .07 .20
150T Carlos Perez .15 .40
151T Pat Borders .07 .20
152T Tyler Green .07 .20
153T Stan Belinda .07 .20
154T Dave Stewart .15 .40
155T Andre Dawson .15 .40
156T Frank Thomas AS .25 .60
Fred McGriff UER
(McGriff's team shown as Blue Jays)
157T Carlos Baerga AS .15 .40
Craig Biggio
158T Wade Boggs AS .15 .40
Matt Williams
159T Cal Ripken AS .40 1.00
Ozzie Smith
160T Ken Griffey Jr. AS .40 1.00
Tony Gwynn
161T Albert Belle AS .50 1.25
Barry Bonds
162T Kirby Puckett .25 .60
Len Dykstra
163T Ivan Rodriguez AS .40 1.00
Mike Piazza
164T Randy Johnson AS .60 1.50
Hideo Nomo
165T Checklist .07 .20

1995 Topps Traded Proofs

Little is known about these cards, the one sample we have has a photo of Shawn Green used on his 1995 Topps Traded card but the back is the one used in the regular 1995 Topps set. There may be more cards so all additional information is appreciated.

NNO Shawn Green 4.00 10.00

1995 Topps Traded Power Boosters

This 10-card standard-size set was inserted in packs at a rate of one in 36. The set is comprised of parallel cards for the first 10 cards of the regular Topps Traded set which was the "At the Break" subset. The cards are done on extra-thick stock. The fronts have an action photo on a "Power Boosted" background, which is similar to diffraction technology, with the words "at the break" on the left side. The backs have a head shot and player information including his mid-season statistics for 1995 and previous years.

COMPLETE SET (10) 30.00 80.00
STATED ODDS 1:36
1 Frank Thomas 4.00 10.00
2 Ken Griffey Jr. 6.00 15.00
3 Barry Bonds 8.00 20.00
4 Albert Belle 2.50 6.00
5 Cal Ripken 10.00 25.00
6 Mike Piazza 6.00 15.00
7 Tony Gwynn 4.00 10.00
8 Jeff Bagwell 2.50 6.00
9 Mo Vaughn 1.25 3.00
10 Matt Williams 1.25 3.00

1996 Topps

This set consists of 440 standard-size cards. These cards were issued in 12-card foil packs with a suggested retail price of $1.29. The fronts feature full-color photos surrounded by a white background. Information on the backs includes a player photo, season and career stats and text. First series subsets include Star Power (1-6, 8-12), Draft Picks (13-26), AAA Stars (101-104), and Future Stars (210-219). A special Mickey Mantle card was issued as card number 7 (his uniform number) and became the last card to be issued as card number 7 in the Topps brand set. Rookie Cards in this set include Sean Casey, Geoff Jenkins and Daryle Ward.

COMPLETE SET (440) 15.00 40.00
COMP.HOBBY SET (449) 15.00 40.00
COMP.CEREAL SET (444) 25.00 50.00
COMP.SERIES 1 (220) 8.00 20.00
COMP.SERIES 2 (220) 8.00 20.00
COMMON CARD (1-440) .07 .20
COMMON RC .08 .25
1 Tony Gwynn STP .10 .30
2 Mike Piazza STP .20 .50
3 Greg Maddux STP .20 .50
4 Jeff Bagwell STP .07 .20
5 Larry Walker STP .07 .20
6 Barry Larkin STP .07 .20
7 Mickey Mantle 1.50 4.00
8 Tom Glavine STP UER .07 .20
Won 21 games in June 95
9 Craig Biggio STP .07 .20
10 Barry Bonds STP .30 .75
11 H.Slocumb STP .07 .20
12 Matt Williams STP .07 .20
13 Todd Helton .40 1.00
14 Mark Redman .08 .25
15 Michael Barrett .08 .25
16 Ben Davis .08 .25
17 Juan LeBron .08 .25
18 Tony McKnight .08 .25
19 Ryan Jaroncyk .08 .25
20 Corey Jenkins .08 .25
21 Jim Scharrer .08 .25
22 Mark Bellhorn RC .40 1.00
23 Jarrod Washburn RC .30 .75
24 Geoff Jenkins RC .30 .75
25 Sean Casey RC 1.50 4.00
26 Brett Tomko RC .15 .40
27 Tony Fernandez .07 .20
28 Rich Becker .07 .20
29 Andujar Cedeno .07 .20
30 Paul Molitor .07 .20
31 Brent Gates .07 .20
32 Glenallen Hill .07 .20
33 Mike Macfarlane .07 .20
34 Manny Alexander .07 .20
35 Todd Zeile .07 .20
36 Joe Girardi .07 .20
37 Tony Tarasco .07 .20
38 Tim Belcher .07 .20
39 Tom Goodwin .07 .20
40 Orel Hershiser .07 .20
41 Tripp Cromer .07 .20
42 Sean Bergman .07 .20
43 Troy Percival .07 .20
44 Kevin Stocker .07 .20
45 Albert Belle .07 .20
46 Tony Eusebio .07 .20
47 Sid Roberson .07 .20
48 Todd Hollandsworth .07 .20
49 Mark Wohlers .07 .20
50 Kirby Puckett .20 .50
51 Darren Holmes .07 .20
52 Ron Karkovice .07 .20
53 Al Martin .07 .20
54 Pat Rapp .07 .20
55 Mark Grace .10 .30
56 Greg Gagne .07 .20
57 Stan Javier .07 .20
58 Scott Sanders .07 .20
59 J.T. Snow .07 .20
60 David Justice .07 .20
61 Royce Clayton .07 .20
62 Kevin Foster .07 .20
63 Tim Naehring .07 .20
64 Orlando Miller .07 .20
65 Mike Mussina .10 .30
66 Jim Eisenreich .07 .20
67 Felix Fermin .07 .20
68 Bernie Williams .10 .30
69 Robb Nen .07 .20
70 Ron Gant .07 .20
71 Felipe Lira .07 .20
72 Jacob Brumfield .07 .20
73 John Mabry .07 .20
74 Mark Carreon .07 .20
75 Carlos Baerga .07 .20
76 Jim Dougherty .07 .20
77 Ryan Thompson .07 .20
78 Scott Leius .07 .20
79 Roger Pavlik .07 .20
80 Gary Sheffield .07 .20
81 Julian Tavarez .07 .20
82 Andy Ashby .07 .20
83 Mark Lemke .07 .20
84 Omar Vizquel .10 .30
85 Darren Daulton .07 .20
86 Mike Lansing .07 .20
87 Rusty Greer .07 .20
88 Dave Stevens .07 .20
89 Jose Offerman .07 .20
90 Tom Henke .07 .20
91 Troy O'Leary .07 .20
92 Michael Tucker .07 .20
93 Marvin Freeman .07 .20
94 Alex Diaz .07 .20
95 John Wetteland .07 .20
96 Cal Ripken 2131 .75 2.00
97 Mike Mimbs .07 .20
98 Bobby Higginson .07 .20
99 Edgardo Alfonzo .07 .20
100 Frank Thomas .20 .50
101 Steve Gibralter .20 .50
Bob Abreu
102 Brian Givens .08 .25
T.J. Mathews
103 Chris Pritchett .08 .25
Trenidad Hubbard
104 Eric Owens .08 .25
Butch Huskey
105 Doug Drabek .07 .20
106 Tomas Perez .07 .20
107 Mark Leiter .07 .20
108 Joe Oliver .07 .20
109 Tony Castillo .07 .20
110 Checklist (1-110) .07 .20
111 Kevin Seitzer .07 .20
112 Pete Schourek .07 .20
113 Sean Berry .07 .20
114 Todd Stottlemyre .07 .20
115 Joe Carter .07 .20
116 Jeff King .07 .20
117 Dan Wilson .07 .20
118 Kurt Abbott .07 .20
119 Lyle Mouton .07 .20
120 Jose Rijo .07 .20
121 Curtis Goodwin .07 .20
122 Jose Valentin .07 .20
123 Ellis Burks .07 .20
124 David Cone .07 .20
125 Eddie Murray .20 .50
126 Brian Jordan .07 .20
127 Darrin Fletcher .07 .20
128 Curt Schilling .07 .20
129 Ozzie Guillen .07 .20
130 Kenny Rogers .07 .20
131 Tom Pagnozzi .07 .20
132 Garret Anderson .07 .20
133 Bobby Jones .07 .20
134 Chris Gomez .07 .20
135 Mike Stanley .07 .20
136 Hideo Nomo .20 .50
137 Jon Nunnally .07 .20
138 Tim Wakefield .07 .20
139 Steve Finley .07 .20
140 Ivan Rodriguez .10 .30
141 Quilvio Veras .07 .20
142 Mike Fetters .07 .20
143 Mike Greenwell .07 .20
144 Bill Pulsipher .07 .20
145 Mark McGwire .50 1.25
146 Frank Castillo .07 .20
147 Greg Vaughn .07 .20
148 Pat Hentgen .07 .20
149 Walt Weiss .07 .20
150 Randy Johnson .20 .50
151 David Segui .07 .20
152 Benji Gil .07 .20
153 Tom Candiotti .07 .20
154 Geronimo Berroa .07 .20
155 John Franco .07 .20
156 Jay Bell .07 .20
157 Mark Gubicza .07 .20
158 Hal Morris .07 .20
159 Wilson Alvarez .07 .20
160 Derek Bell .07 .20
161 Ricky Bottalico .07 .20
162 Bret Boone .07 .20
163 Brad Radke .07 .20
164 John Valentin .07 .20
165 Steve Avery .07 .20
166 Mark McLemore .07 .20
167 Danny Jackson .07 .20
168 Tino Martinez .10 .30
169 Shane Reynolds .07 .20
170 Terry Pendleton .07 .20
171 Jim Edmonds .07 .20
172 Esteban Loaiza .07 .20
173 Ray Durham .07 .20
174 Carlos Perez .07 .20
175 Raul Mondesi .07 .20
176 Steve Ontiveros .07 .20
177 Chipper Jones .20 .50
178 Otis Nixon .07 .20
179 John Burkett .07 .20
180 Gregg Jefferies .07 .20
181 Denny Martinez .07 .20
182 Ken Caminiti .07 .20
183 Doug Jones .07 .20
184 Brian McRae .07 .20
185 Don Mattingly .50 1.25
186 Mel Rojas .07 .20
187 Marty Cordova .07 .20
188 Vinny Castilla .07 .20
189 John Smoltz .10 .30
190 Travis Fryman .07 .20
191 Chris Hoiles .07 .20
192 Chuck Finley .07 .20
193 Ryan Klesko .07 .20
194 Alex Fernandez .07 .20
195 Dante Bichette .07 .20
196 Eric Karros .07 .20
197 Roger Clemens .40 1.00
198 Randy Myers .07 .20
199 Tony Phillips .07 .20
200 Cal Ripken .60 1.50
201 Rod Beck .07 .20
202 Chad Curtis .07 .20
203 Jack McDowell .07 .20
204 Gary Gaetti .07 .20
205 Ken Griffey Jr. .30 .75
206 Ramon Martinez .07 .20
207 Jeff Kent .07 .20
208 Brad Ausmus .07 .20
209 Devon White .07 .20
210 Jason Giambi .07 .20
211 Nomar Garciaparra .30 .75
212 Billy Wagner .07 .20
213 Todd Greene .07 .20
214 Paul Wilson .07 .20
215 Johnny Damon .10 .30
216 Alan Benes .07 .20
217 Karim Garcia .07 .20
218 Dustin Hermanson .07 .20
219 Derek Jeter .50 1.25
220 Checklist (111-220) .07 .20
221 Kirby Puckett STP .10 .30
222 Cal Ripken STP .30 .75
223 Albert Belle STP .07 .20
224 Randy Johnson STP .10 .30
225 Wade Boggs STP .07 .20
226 Carlos Baerga STP .07 .20
227 Ivan Rodriguez STP .07 .20
228 Mike Mussina STP .07 .20
229 Frank Thomas STP .10 .30
230 Ken Griffey Jr. STP .20 .50
231 Jose Mesa STP .07 .20
232 Matt Morris RC .60 1.50
233 Craig Wilson RC .30 .75
234 Alvie Shepherd .08 .25
235 Randy Winn RC .30 .75
236 David Yocum RC .08 .25
237 Jason Brester RC .08 .25
238 Shane Monahan RC .08 .25
239 Brian McNichol RC .08 .25
240 Reggie Taylor .08 .25
241 Garrett Long .08 .25
242 Jonathan Johnson .08 .25
243 Jeff Liefer RC .08 .25
244 Brian Powell .08 .25
245 Brian Buchanan RC .08 .25
246 Mike Piazza .30 .75
247 Edgar Martinez .10 .30
248 Chuck Knoblauch .07 .20
249 Andres Galarraga .07 .20
250 Tony Gwynn .25 .60
251 Lee Smith .07 .20
252 Sammy Sosa .20 .50
253 Jim Thome .10 .30
254 Frank Rodriguez .07 .20
255 Charlie Hayes .07 .20
256 Bernard Gilkey .07 .20
257 John Smiley .07 .20
258 Brady Anderson .07 .20
259 Rico Brogna .07 .20
260 Kirt Manwaring .07 .20
261 Len Dykstra .07 .20
262 Tom Glavine .10 .30
263 Vince Coleman .07 .20
264 John Olerud .07 .20
265 Orlando Merced .07 .20
266 Kent Mercker .07 .20
267 Terry Steinbach .07 .20
268 Brian L. Hunter .07 .20
269 Jeff Fassero .07 .20
270 Jay Buhner .07 .20
271 Jeff Brantley .07 .20
272 Tim Raines .07 .20
273 Jimmy Key .07 .20
274 Mo Vaughn .07 .20
275 Andre Dawson .07 .20
276 Jose Mesa .07 .20
277 Brett Butler .07 .20
278 Luis Gonzalez .07 .20
279 Steve Sparks .07 .20
280 Chili Davis .07 .20
281 Carl Everett .07 .20
282 Jeff Cirillo .07 .20
283 Thomas Howard .07 .20
284 Paul O'Neill .10 .30
285 Pat Meares .07 .20
286 Mickey Tettleton .07 .20
287 Rey Sanchez .07 .20
288 Bip Roberts .07 .20
289 Roberto Alomar .10 .30
290 Ruben Sierra .07 .20
291 John Flaherty .07 .20
292 Bret Saberhagen .07 .20
293 Barry Larkin .10 .30
294 Sandy Alomar Jr. .07 .20
295 Ed Sprague .07 .20
296 Gary DiSarcina .07 .20
297 Marquis Grissom .07 .20
298 John Frascatore .07 .20
299 Will Clark .10 .30
300 Barry Bonds .60 1.50
301 Ozzie Smith UER .30 .75
Padres is listed as Padre
302 Dave Nilsson .07 .20
303 Pedro Martinez .10 .30
304 Joey Cora .07 .20
305 Rick Aguilera .07 .20
306 Craig Biggio .10 .30
307 Jose Vizcaino .07 .20
308 Jeff Montgomery .07 .20
309 Moises Alou .07 .20
310 Robin Ventura .07 .20
311 David Wells .07 .20
312 Delino DeShields .07 .20
313 Trevor Hoffman .07 .20
314 Andy Benes .07 .20
315 Deion Sanders .10 .30
316 Jim Bullinger .07 .20
317 John Jaha .07 .20
318 Greg Maddux .30 .75
319 Tim Salmon .10 .30
320 Ben McDonald .07 .20
321 Sandy Martinez .07 .20
322 Dan Miceli .07 .20
323 Wade Boggs .10 .30
324 Ismael Valdes .07 .20
325 Juan Gonzalez .07 .20
326 Charles Nagy .07 .20
327 Ray Lankford .07 .20
328 Mark Portugal .07 .20
329 Bobby Bonilla .07 .20
330 Reggie Sanders .07 .20
331 Jamie Brewington RC .08 .25
332 Aaron Sele .07 .20

333 Pete Harnisch .07 .20
334 Cliff Floyd .07 .20
335 Cal Eldred .07 .20
336 Jason Bates .07 .20
337 Tony Clark .07 .20
338 Jose Herrera .07 .20
339 Alex Ochoa .07 .20
340 Mark Loretta .07 .20
341 Donne Wall .07 .20
342 Jason Kendall .07 .20
343 Shannon Stewart .07 .20
344 Brooks Kieschnick .07 .20
345 Chris Snopek .07 .20
346 Ruben Rivera .07 .20
347 Jeff Suppan .07 .20
348 Phil Nevin .07 .20
349 John Wasdin .07 .20
350 Jay Payton .07 .20
351 Tim Crabtree .07 .20
352 Rick Krivda .07 .20
353 Bob Wolcott .07 .20
354 Jimmy Haynes .07 .20
355 Herb Perry .07 .20
356 Ryne Sandberg .30 .75
357 Harold Baines .07 .20
358 Chad Ogea .07 .20
359 Lee Tinsley .07 .20
360 Matt Williams .07 .20
361 Randy Velarde .07 .20
362 Jose Canseco .10 .30
363 Larry Walker .07 .20
364 Kevin Appier .07 .20
365 Darryl Hamilton .07 .20
366 Jose Lima .07 .20
367 Javy Lopez .07 .20
368 Dennis Eckersley .07 .20
369 Jason Isringhausen .07 .20
370 Mickey Morandini .07 .20
371 Scott Cooper .07 .20
372 Jim Abbott .10 .30
373 Paul Sorrento .07 .20
374 Chris Hammond .07 .20
375 Lance Johnson .07 .20
376 Kevin Brown .07 .20
377 Luis Alicea .07 .20
378 Andy Pettitte .10 .30
379 Dean Palmer .07 .20
380 Jeff Bagwell .10 .30
381 Jaime Navarro .07 .20
382 Rondell White .07 .20
383 Erik Hanson .07 .20
384 Pedro Munoz .07 .20
385 Heathcliff Slocumb .07 .20
386 Wally Joyner .07 .20
387 Bob Tewksbury .07 .20
388 David Bell .07 .20
389 Fred McGriff .10 .30
390 Mike Henneman .07 .20
391 Robby Thompson .07 .20
392 Norm Charlton .07 .20
393 Cecil Fielder .07 .20
394 Benito Santiago .07 .20
395 Rafael Palmeiro .10 .30
396 Ricky Bones .07 .20
397 Rickey Henderson .20 .50
398 C.J. Nitkowski .07 .20
399 Shawon Dunston .07 .20
400 Manny Ramirez .10 .30
401 Bill Swift .07 .20
402 Chad Fonville .07 .20
403 Joey Hamilton .07 .20
404 Alex Gonzalez .07 .20
405 Roberto Hernandez .07 .20
406 Jeff Blauser .07 .20
407 LaTroy Hawkins .07 .20
408 Greg Colbrunn .07 .20
409 Todd Hundley .07 .20
410 Glenn Dishman .07 .20
411 Joe Vitiello .07 .20
412 Todd Worrell .07 .20
413 Wil Cordero .07 .20
414 Ken Hill .07 .20
415 Carlos Garcia .07 .20
416 Bryan Rekar .07 .20
417 Shawn Green .07 .20
418 Tyler Green .07 .20
419 Mike Blowers .07 .20
420 Kenny Lofton .07 .20
421 Denny Neagle .07 .20
422 Jeff Conine .07 .20
423 Mark Langston .07 .20
424 Steve Cox .30 .75
Jesse Ibarra
Derrek Lee
Ron Wright RC
425 Jim Bonnici .40 1.00
Billy Owens
Richie Sexson
Daryle Ward RC
426 Kevin Jordan .08 .25
Bobby Morris
Desi Relaford
Adam Riggs RC
427 Tim Harkrider .08 .25
Rey Ordonez
Neifi Perez
Enrique Wilson
428 Bartolo Colon .20 .50
Doug Million
Rafael Orellano
Ray Ricken
429 Jeff D'Amico .08 .25
Marty Janzen RC
Gary Rath
Clint Sodowsky
430 Matt Drews .08 .25
Rich Hunter RC
Matt Ruebel
Bret Wagner
431 Jaime Bluma .08 .25
David Coggin
Steve Montgomery
Brandon Reed RC
432 Mike Figga .60 1.50
Raul Ibanez
Paul Konerko
Julio Mosquera
433 Brian Barber .07 .20
Marc Kroon
Marc Valdes
Don Wengert
434 George Arias .20 .50
Chris Haas RC
Scott Rolen
Scott Spiezio
435 Brian Banks 1.00 2.50
Vladimir Guerrero
Andruw Jones
Billy McMillon
436 Roger Cedeno .15 .40
Derrick Gibson
Ben Grieve
Shane Spencer RC
437 Anton French .08 .25
Demond Smith
DaRond Stovall RC
Keith Williams
438 Michael Coleman RC .08 .25
Jacob Cruz
Richard Hidalgo
Charles Peterson
439 Trey Beamon .07 .20
Yamil Benitez
Jermaine Dye
Angel Echevarria
440 Checklist .07 .20
F7 M.Mantle Last Day 2.00 5.00
NNO Mickey Mantle TRIB 1.25 3.00
Promotes the Mantle Foundation
Black and White Photo

1996 Topps Classic Confrontations

These cards were inserted at a rate of one in every five-card Series one retail pack sold at Walmart. The first ten cards showcase hitters, while the last five cards feature pitchers. Inside white borders, the fronts show player cutouts on a brownish rock background featuring a shadow image of the player. The player's name is gold foil stamped across the bottom. The horizontal backs of the hitters' cards are aqua and present headshots and statistics. The backs of the pitchers cards are purple and present the same information.

COMPLETE SET (15) 2.50 6.00
CC1 Ken Griffey Jr. .25 .60
CC2 Cal Ripken .50 1.25
CC3 Edgar Martinez .08 .25
CC4 Kirby Puckett .15 .40
CC5 Frank Thomas .15 .40
CC6 Barry Bonds .50 1.25
CC7 Reggie Sanders .05 .15
CC8 Andres Galarraga .05 .15
CC9 Tony Gwynn .20 .50
CC10 Mike Piazza .25 .60
CC11 Randy Johnson .15 .40
CC12 Mike Mussina .08 .25
CC13 Roger Clemens .30 .75
CC14 Tom Glavine .08 .25
CC15 Greg Maddux .25 .60

1996 Topps Mantle

Randomly inserted in Series one packs at a rate of one in nine hobby packs, one in six retail packs and one in two jumbo packs; these cards are reprints of the original Mickey Mantle cards issued from 1951 through 1969. The fronts look the same except for a commemorative stamp, while the backs clearly state that they are "Mickey Mantle Commemorative" cards and have a 1996 copyright date. These cards honor Yankee great Mickey Mantle, who passed away in August 1995 after a gallant battle against cancer. Based on evidence from an uncut sheet auctioned off at the 1996 Kit Young Hawaii Trade Show, some collectors/dealers believe that cards 15 through 19 were slightly shorter printed in relation to the other 14 cards.

COMPLETE SET (19) 60.00 120.00
COMMON MANTLE (3-14) 3.00 8.00
COM.MANTLE SP (15-19) 4.00 10.00
SER.1 ODDS 1:9 HOB, 1:6 RET, 1:2 JUM
FOUR PER CEREAL FACT.SET
CARDS 15-19 SHORTPRINTED BY 20%
FINEST SER.2 ODDS 1:18 RET, 1:12 ANCO
REF.SER.2 ODDS 1:96 HOB, 1:144 RET
RDMP.SER.2 ODDS 1:72 ANCO, 1:108 RET
1 Mickey Mantle 10.00 25.00
1951 Bowman
2 Mickey Mantle 10.00 25.00
1952 Topps

1996 Topps Mantle Finest

Randomly inserted in Series two packs at a rate of one in 18 and one in 12 ANCO, this 19-card set is a reprint of the regular insert set using Finest technology. Each card front is covered with the exclusive Topps Finest Protector to guarantee its brilliant uncirculated condition.

COMPLETE SET (19) 60.00 120.00
COMMON MANTLE (1-14) 3.00 8.00
COM.MANTLE SP (15-19) 4.00 10.00
SER.2 STATED ODDS 1:18 RET, 1:12 ANCO
1 Mickey Mantle 6.00 15.00
1951 Bowman
2 Mickey Mantle 6.00 15.00
1952 Topps
3 Mickey Mantle 3.00 8.00
1953 Topps

1996 Topps Masters of the Game

Cards from this 20-card standard-size set were randomly inserted into first-series hobby packs at a rate of one in 18. In addition, every factory set contained two Masters of the Game cards. The cards are numbered with a "MG" prefix in the lower left corner.

COMPLETE SET (20) 12.50 30.00
SER.1 STATED ODDS 1:18 HOBBY
TWO PER HOBBY FACTORY SET
1 Dennis Eckersley .40 1.00
2 Denny Martinez .40 1.00
3 Eddie Murray 1.00 2.50
4 Paul Molitor .40 1.00
5 Ozzie Smith 1.50 4.00
6 Rickey Henderson 1.00 2.50
7 Tim Raines .40 1.00
8 Lee Smith .40 1.00
9 Cal Ripken 3.00 8.00
10 Chili Davis .40 1.00
11 Wade Boggs .60 1.50
12 Tony Gwynn 1.25 3.00
13 Don Mattingly 2.50 6.00
14 Bret Saberhagen .40 1.00
15 Kirby Puckett 1.00 2.50
16 Joe Carter .40 1.00
17 Roger Clemens 2.00 5.00
18 Barry Bonds 3.00 8.00
19 Greg Maddux 1.50 4.00
20 Frank Thomas 1.00 2.50

1996 Topps Mystery Finest

Randomly inserted in first-series packs at a rate of one in 36 hobby and retail packs and one in eight jumbo packs, this 26-card standard-size set features a bit of a mystery. The fronts have opaque coating that must be removed before the player can be identified. After the opaque coating is removed, the fronts feature a player photo surrounded by silver borders. The backs feature a choice of players along with a corresponding mystery finest trivia fact. Some of these cards were also issued with refractor fronts.

COMPLETE SET (26) 50.00 120.00
SER.1 STATED ODDS 1:36 HOB/RET, 1:8 JUM
*REF: 1.25X TO 3X BASIC MYSTERY FINEST
REF.SER.1 ODDS 1:216 HOB/RET, 1:36 JUM
M1 Hideo Nomo 2.00 5.00
M2 Greg Maddux 3.00 8.00
M3 Randy Johnson 2.00 5.00
M4 Chipper Jones 2.00 5.00
M5 Marty Cordova .75 2.00
M6 Garret Anderson .75 2.00
M7 Cal Ripken 6.00 15.00
M8 Kirby Puckett 2.00 5.00
M9 Tony Gwynn 2.50 6.00
M10 Manny Ramirez 1.25 3.00
M11 Jim Edmonds .75 2.00
M12 Mike Piazza 3.00 8.00
M13 Barry Bonds 6.00 15.00
M14 Raul Mondesi .75 2.00
M15 Sammy Sosa 2.00 5.00
M16 Ken Griffey Jr. 3.00 8.00
M17 Albert Belle .75 2.00
M18 Dante Bichette .75 2.00
M19 Mo Vaughn .75 2.00
M20 Jeff Bagwell 1.25 3.00
M21 Frank Thomas 2.00 5.00
M22 Hideo Nomo 2.00 5.00
M23 Cal Ripken 6.00 15.00
M24 Mike Piazza 3.00 8.00
M25 Ken Griffey Jr. 3.00 8.00
M26 Frank Thomas 2.00 5.00

1996 Topps Power Boosters

Randomly inserted into packs, these cards are a metallic version of 25 of the first 26 cards from the basic Topps set. Card numbers 1-6 and 8-12 were issued at a rate of one every 36 first series retail packs, while numbers 13-26 were issued in hobby packs at a rate of one in 36. Inserted in place of two basic cards, they are printed on 28 point stock and the fronts have prismatic foil printing. Card number 7, which is Mickey Mantle in the regular set, was not issued in a Power Booster form. A first year card of Sean Casey highlights this set.

COMPLETE SET (25) 75.00 150.00
COMP. STAR POWER SET (11) 25.00 50.00
COMMON (1-6/8-12) .75 2.00
STR.PWR.SER.1 ODDS 1:36 RETAIL
COMP. DRAFT PICKS SET (14) 1.25 3.00
COMMON (12-26) .75 2.00
DP SER.1 STATED ODDS 1:36 HOBBY
1 Tony Gwynn 2.50 6.00
2 Mike Piazza 3.00 8.00
3 Greg Maddux 3.00 8.00
4 Jeff Bagwell 1.25 3.00
5 Larry Walker .75 2.00
6 Barry Larkin 1.25 3.00
8 Tom Glavine 1.25 3.00
9 Craig Biggio 1.25 3.00
10 Barry Bonds 6.00 15.00
11 Heathcliff Slocumb .75 2.00
12 Matt Williams .75 2.00
13 Todd Helton 3.00 8.00
14 Mark Redman .75 2.00
15 Michael Barrett .75 2.00
16 Ben Davis .75 2.00
17 Juan LeBron .75 2.00
18 Tony McKnight .75 2.00
19 Ryan Jaroncyk .75 2.00
20 Corey Jenkins .75 2.00
21 Jim Scharrer .75 2.00
22 Mark Bellhorn 4.00 10.00
23 Jarrod Washburn 3.00 8.00
24 Geoff Jenkins 3.00 8.00
25 Sean Casey 6.00 15.00
26 Brett Tomko 2.00 5.00

1996 Topps Profiles

Randomly inserted into Series one and two packs at a rate of one in 12 hobby and retail packs, one in six jumbo packs and one in eight ANCO packs;, this 20-card standard-size set features 10 players from each league. One card from the first series and two from the second series were also included in all Topps factory sets. Topps spokesmen Kirby Puckett (AL) and Tony Gwynn (NL) give opinions on players within their league. The fronts feature a player photo set against a silver-foil background. The player's name is on the bottom. A photo of either Gwynn or Puckett as well as the words "Profiles by ..." is on the right. The backs feature a player photo, some career data as well as Gwynn's or Puckett's opinion about the featured player. The cards are numbered with either an "AL or NL" prefix on the back depending on the player's league. The cards are sequenced in alphabetical order within league.

COMPLETE SET (40) 15.00 40.00
COMPLETE SERIES 1 (20) 12.50 30.00
COMPLETE SERIES 2 (20) 4.00 10.00
STAT.ODDS 1:12 HOB/RET, 1:6 JUM, 1:8 ANCO
1 SER.1 AND 2 SER.2 PER HOB.FACT.SET
AL1 Roberto Alomar .30 .75
AL2 Carlos Baerga .20 .50
AL3 Albert Belle .20 .50
AL4 Cecil Fielder .20 .50
AL5 Ken Griffey Jr. .75 2.00
AL6 Randy Johnson .50 1.25
AL7 Paul O'Neill .30 .75
AL8 Cal Ripken 1.50 4.00
AL9 Frank Thomas .50 1.25
AL10 Mo Vaughn .20 .50
AL11 Jay Buhner .20 .50
AL12 Marty Cordova .20 .50
AL13 Jim Edmonds .20 .50
AL14 Juan Gonzalez .20 .50
AL15 Kenny Lofton .20 .50
AL16 Edgar Martinez .30 .75
AL17 Don Mattingly 1.25 3.00
AL18 Mark McGwire 1.25 3.00
AL19 Rafael Palmeiro .30 .75
AL20 Tim Salmon .30 .75
NL1 Jeff Bagwell .30 .75
NL2 Derek Bell .20 .50
NL3 Barry Bonds 1.50 4.00
NL4 Greg Maddux .75 2.00
NL5 Fred McGriff .30 .75
NL6 Raul Mondesi .20 .50
NL7 Mike Piazza .75 2.00
NL8 Reggie Sanders .20 .50
NL9 Sammy Sosa .50 1.25
NL10 Larry Walker .20 .50
NL11 Dante Bichette .20 .50
NL12 Andres Galarraga .20 .50
NL13 Ron Gant .20 .50
NL14 Tom Glavine .30 .75
NL15 Chipper Jones .50 1.25
NL16 David Justice .20 .50
NL17 Barry Larkin .30 .75
NL18 Hideo Nomo .50 1.25
NL19 Gary Sheffield .20 .50
NL20 Matt Williams .20 .50

1996 Topps Road Warriors

This 20-card set was inserted only into Series two WalMart packs at a rate of one per pack and featured leading hitters of the majors. The set is sequenced in alphabetical order.

COMPLETE SET (20) 5.00 12.00
RW1 Derek Bell .15 .40
RW2 Albert Belle .15 .40
RW3 Craig Biggio .25 .60
RW4 Barry Bonds 1.25 3.00
RW5 Jay Buhner .15 .40
RW6 Jim Edmonds .15 .40
RW7 Gary Gaetti .15 .40
RW8 Ron Gant .15 .40
RW9 Edgar Martinez .25 .60
RW10 Tino Martinez .25 .60
RW11 Mark McGwire 1.00 2.50
RW12 Mike Piazza .60 1.50
RW13 Manny Ramirez .25 .60
RW14 Tim Salmon .25 .60
RW15 Reggie Sanders .15 .40
RW16 Frank Thomas .40 1.00
RW17 John Valentin .15 .40
RW18 Mo Vaughn .15 .40
RW19 Robin Ventura .15 .40
RW20 Matt Williams .15 .40

1996 Topps Wrecking Crew

Randomly inserted in Series two hobby packs at a rate of one in 18, this 15-card set honors some of the hottest home run producers in the League. One card from this set was also inserted into Topps Hobby Factory sets. The cards feature color action player photos with foil stamping.

COMPLETE SET (15) 25.00 60.00
SER.2 STATED ODDS 1:18 HOBBY
ONE PER HOBBY FACTORY SET
WC1 Jeff Bagwell 1.25 3.00
WC2 Albert Belle .75 2.00
WC3 Barry Bonds 6.00 15.00
WC4 Jose Canseco 1.25 3.00
WC5 Joe Carter .75 2.00
WC6 Cecil Fielder .75 2.00
WC7 Ron Gant .75 2.00
WC8 Juan Gonzalez .75 2.00
WC9 Ken Griffey Jr 3.00 8.00
WC10 Fred McGriff 1.25 3.00
WC11 Mark McGwire 5.00 12.00
WC12 Mike Piazza 3.00 8.00
WC13 Frank Thomas 2.00 5.00
WC14 Mo Vaughn .75 2.00

1997 Topps

This 495-card set was primarily distributed in first and second series 11-card packs with a suggested retail price of $1.29. In addition, eight-card retail packs, 40-card jumbo packs and 504-card factory sets (containing the complete 495-card set plus a random selection of eight insert cards and one hermetically sealed Willie Mays or Mickey Mantle Reprint insert) were made available. The card fronts feature a color action player photo with a gloss coating and a spot matte finish on the outside border with gold foil stamping. The backs carry another player photo, player information and statistics. The set includes the following subsets: Season Highlights (100-104, 462-466), Prospects (200-207, 487-494), the first ever expansion team cards of the Arizona Diamondbacks (249-251,468-469 and the Tampa Bay Devil Rays (252-253, 470-472) and Draft Picks (269-274, 477-483). Card 42 is a special Jackie Robinson tribute card commemorating the 50th anniversary of his contribution to baseball history and numbered for his Dodgers uniform number. Card number 7 does not exist because it was retired in honor of Mickey Mantle. Card number 84 does not exist because Mike Fetters' card was incorrectly numbered 61. Card number 277 does not exist because Chipper Jones' card was incorrectly numbered 276. Rookie Cards include Kris Benson and Eric Chavez. The Derek Jeter autograph card found at the end of our checklist was seeded one every 576 second series packs.

COMPLETE SET (495) 40.00 80.00
COMP.SERIES 1 (275) 20.00 40.00
COMP.SERIES 2 (220) 20.00 40.00
1 Barry Bonds .60 1.50
2 Tom Pagnozzi .07 .20
3 Terrell Wade .07 .20
4 Jose Valentin .07 .20
5 Mark Clark .07 .20
6 Brady Anderson .07 .20
8 Wade Boggs .10 .30
9 Scott Stahoviak .07 .20
10 Andres Galarraga .07 .20
11 Steve Avery .07 .20
12 Rusty Greer .07 .20
13 Derek Jeter .50 1.25
14 Ricky Bottalico .07 .20
15 Andy Ashby .07 .20
16 Paul Shuey .07 .20
17 F.P. Santangelo .07 .20
18 Royce Clayton .07 .20
19 Mike Mohler .07 .20
20 Mike Piazza .30 .75
21 Jaime Navarro .07 .20
22 Billy Wagner .07 .20
23 Mike Timlin .07 .20
24 Garret Anderson .07 .20
25 Ben McDonald .07 .20
26 Mel Rojas .07 .20
27 John Burkett .07 .20
28 Jeff King .07 .20
29 Reggie Jefferson .07 .20
30 Kevin Appier .07 .20
31 Felipe Lira .07 .20
32 Kevin Tapani .07 .20
33 Mark Portugal .07 .20
34 Carlos Garcia .07 .20
35 Joey Cora .07 .20
36 David Segui .07 .20
37 Mark Grace .10 .30
38 Erik Hanson .07 .20
39 Jeff D'Amico .07 .20
40 Jay Buhner .07 .20
41 B.J. Surhoff .07 .20
42 Jackie Robinson TRIB .20 .50
43 Roger Pavlik .07 .20
44 Hal Morris .07 .20
45 Mariano Duncan .07 .20
46 Harold Baines .07 .20
47 Jorge Fabregas .07 .20
48 Jose Herrera .07 .20
49 Jeff Cirillo .07 .20
50 Tom Glavine .10 .30
51 Pedro Astacio .07 .20
52 Mark Gardner .07 .20
53 Arthur Rhodes .07 .20
54 Troy O'Leary .07 .20
55 Bip Roberts .07 .20
56 Mike Lieberthal .07 .20
57 Shane Andrews .07 .20
58 Scott Karl .07 .20
59 Gary DiSarcina .07 .20
60 Andy Pettitte .10 .30
61 Kevin Elster .07 .20
61B Mike Fetters UER .07 .20
Card was intended as number 84
62 Mark McGwire .50 1.25
63 Dan Wilson .07 .20
64 Mickey Morandini .07 .20
65 Chuck Knoblauch .07 .20
66 Tim Wakefield .07 .20
67 Raul Mondesi .07 .20
68 Todd Jones .07 .20
69 Albert Belle .07 .20
70 Trevor Hoffman .07 .20
71 Eric Young .07 .20
72 Robert Perez .07 .20
73 Butch Huskey .07 .20
74 Brian McRae .07 .20
75 Jim Edmonds .07 .20
76 Mike Henneman .07 .20
77 Frank Rodriguez .07 .20
78 Danny Tartabull .07 .20
79 Robb Nen .07 .20
80 Reggie Sanders .07 .20
81 Ron Karkovice .07 .20
82 Benito Santiago .07 .20
83 Mike Lansing .07 .20
85 Craig Biggio .10 .30
86 Mike Bordick .07 .20
87 Ray Lankford .07 .20
88 Charles Nagy .07 .20
89 Paul Wilson .07 .20
90 John Wetteland .07 .20
91 Tom Candiotti .07 .20
92 Carlos Delgado .07 .20
93 Derek Bell .07 .20
94 Mark Lemke .07 .20
95 Edgar Martinez .10 .30
96 Rickey Henderson .20 .50
97 Greg Myers .07 .20
98 Jim Leyritz .07 .20
99 Mark Johnson .07 .20
100 Dwight Gooden HL .07 .20
101 Al Leiter HL .07 .20
102 John Mabry HL .07 .20
103 Alex Ochoa HL .07 .20
104 Mike Piazza HL .20 .50
105 Jim Thome .10 .30
106 Ricky Otero .07 .20
107 Jamey Wright .07 .20
108 Frank Thomas .20 .50
109 Jody Reed .07 .20
110 Orel Hershiser .07 .20
111 Terry Steinbach .07 .20
112 Mark Loretta .07 .20
113 Turk Wendell .07 .20
114 Marvin Benard .07 .20
115 Kevin Brown .07 .20
116 Robert Person .07 .20
117 Joey Hamilton .07 .20
118 Francisco Cordova .07 .20
119 John Smiley .07 .20
120 Travis Fryman .07 .20
121 Jimmy Key .07 .20
122 Tom Goodwin .07 .20
123 Mike Greenwell .07 .20
124 Juan Gonzalez .07 .20
125 Pete Harnisch .07 .20
126 Roger Cedeno .07 .20
127 Ron Gant .07 .20
128 Mark Langston .07 .20
129 Tim Crabtree .07 .20
130 Greg Maddux .30 .75
131 W.VanLandingham .07 .20
132 Wally Joyner .07 .20
133 Randy Myers .07 .20
134 John Valentin .07 .20
135 Bret Boone .07 .20
136 Bruce Ruffin .07 .20
137 Chris Snopek .07 .20
138 Paul Molitor .07 .20
139 Mark McLemore .07 .20
140 Rafael Palmeiro .10 .30
141 Herb Perry .07 .20
142 Luis Gonzalez .07 .20
143 Doug Drabek .07 .20
144 Ken Ryan .07 .20
145 Todd Hundley .07 .20
146 Ellis Burks .07 .20
147 Ozzie Guillen .07 .20
148 Rich Becker .07 .20
149 Sterling Hitchcock .07 .20
150 Bernie Williams .10 .30
151 Mike Stanley .07 .20
152 Roberto Alomar .10 .30
153 Jose Mesa .07 .20
154 Steve Trachsel .07 .20
155 Alex Gonzalez .07 .20
156 Troy Percival .07 .20
157 John Smoltz .10 .30
158 Pedro Martinez .10 .30
159 Jeff Conine .07 .20
160 Bernard Gilkey .07 .20
161 Jim Eisenreich .07 .20
162 Mickey Tettleton .07 .20
163 Justin Thompson .07 .20
164 Jose Offerman .07 .20
165 Tony Phillips .07 .20
166 Ismael Valdes .07 .20
167 Ryne Sandberg UER .30 .75
Card has him with 252 homers in 1996
168 Matt Mieske .07 .20
169 Geronimo Berroa .07 .20
170 Otis Nixon .07 .20
171 John Mabry .07 .20
172 Shawon Dunston .07 .20
173 Omar Vizquel .10 .30
174 Chris Hoiles .07 .20
175 Dwight Gooden .07 .20
176 Wilson Alvarez .07 .20
177 Todd Hollandsworth .07 .20
178 Roger Salkeld .07 .20
179 Rey Sanchez .07 .20
180 Rey Ordonez .07 .20
181 Denny Martinez .07 .20
182 Ramon Martinez .07 .20
183 Dave Wilson .07 .20
184 Marquis Grissom .07 .20
185 Randy Velarde .07 .20
186 Ron Coomer .07 .20
187 Tino Martinez .10 .30
188 Jeff Brantley .07 .20
189 Steve Finley .07 .20
190 Andy Benes .07 .20
191 Terry Adams .07 .20
192 Mike Blowers .07 .20
193 Russ Davis .07 .20
194 Darryl Hamilton .07 .20
195 Jason Kendall .07 .20
196 Johnny Damon .10 .30
197 Dave Martinez .07 .20
198 Mike Macfarlane .07 .20
199 Norm Charlton .07 .20
200 Doug Million RC .08 .25
Damian Moss
Bobby Rodgers
201 Geoff Jenkins .07 .20
Raul Ibanez
Mike Cameron
202 Sean Casey .10 .30
Jim Bonnici
Dmitri Young
203 Jed Hansen .07 .20
Homer Bush
Felipe Crespo
204 Kevin Orie .07 .20
Gabe Alvarez
Aaron Boone
205 Ben Davis .07 .20
Kevin Brown
Bobby Estalella
206 Billy McMillon RC .15 .40
Bubba Trammell
Dante Powell
207 Jarrod Washburn .07 .20
Marc Wilkins RC
Glendon Rusch
208 Brian Hunter .07 .20
209 Jason Giambi .07 .20
210 Henry Rodriguez .07 .20
211 Edgar Renteria .07 .20
212 Edgardo Alfonzo .07 .20
213 Fernando Vina .07 .20
214 Shawn Green .07 .20
215 Ray Durham .07 .20
216 Joe Randa .07 .20

217 Armando Reynoso .07 .20
218 Eric Davis .07 .20
219 Bob Tewksbury .07 .20
220 Jacob Cruz .07 .20
221 Glenallen Hill .07 .20
222 Gary Gaetti .07 .20
223 Donne Wall .07 .20
224 Brad Clontz .07 .20
225 Marty Janzen .07 .20
226 Todd Worrell .07 .20
227 John Franco .07 .20
228 David Wells .07 .20
229 Gregg Jefferies .07 .20
230 Tim Naehring .07 .20
231 Thomas Howard .07 .20
232 Roberto Hernandez .07 .20
233 Kevin Ritz .07 .20
234 Julian Tavarez .07 .20
235 Ken Hill .07 .20
236 Greg Gagne .07 .20
237 Bobby Chouinard .07 .20
238 Joe Carter .07 .20
239 Jermaine Dye .07 .20
240 Antonio Osuna .07 .20
241 Julio Franco .07 .20
242 Mike Grace .07 .20
243 Aaron Sele .07 .20
244 David Justice .07 .20
245 Sandy Alomar Jr. .07 .20
246 Jose Canseco .10 .30
247 Paul O'Neill .10 .30
248 Sean Berry .07 .20
249 Nick Bierbrodt .08 .25
Kevin Sweeney RC
250 Larry Rodriguez RC .08 .25
Vladimir Nunez RC
251 Ron Hartman .08 .25
David Hayman RC
252 Alex Sanchez .15 .40
Matthew Quatraro RC
253 Ronni Seberino RC .08 .25
Pablo Ortega RC
254 Rex Hudler .07 .20
255 Orlando Miller .07 .20
256 Mariano Rivera .20 .50
257 Brad Radke .07 .20
258 Bobby Higginson .07 .20
259 Jay Bell .07 .20
260 Mark Grudzielanek .07 .20
261 Lance Johnson .07 .20
262 Ken Caminiti .07 .20
263 J.T. Snow .07 .20
264 Gary Sheffield .07 .20
265 Darrin Fletcher .07 .20
266 Eric Owens .07 .20
267 Luis Castillo .07 .20
268 Scott Rolen .10 .30
269 Todd Noel .08 .25
John Oliver RC
270 Robert Stratton RC .15 .40
Corey Lee RC
271 Gil Meche RC .40 1.00
Matt Halloran RC
272 Eric Milton RC .15 .40
Dee Brown RC
273 Josh Garrett .15 .40
Chris Reitsma RC
274 A.J.Zapp RC .30 .75
Jason Marquis
275 Checklist .07 .20
276 Checklist .07 .20
277 Chipper Jones UER .20 .50
incorrectly numbered 276
278 Orlando Merced .07 .20
279 Ariel Prieto .07 .20
280 Al Leiter .07 .20
281 Pat Meares .07 .20
282 Darryl Strawberry .07 .20
283 Jamie Moyer .07 .20
284 Scott Servais .07 .20
285 Delino DeShields .07 .20
286 Danny Graves .07 .20
287 Gerald Williams .07 .20
288 Todd Greene .07 .20
289 Rico Brogna .07 .20
290 Derrick Gibson .07 .20
291 Joe Girardi .07 .20
292 Darren Lewis .07 .20
293 Nomar Garciaparra .30 .75
294 Greg Colbrunn .07 .20
295 Jeff Bagwell .10 .30
296 Brent Gates .07 .20
297 Jose Vizcaino .07 .20
298 Alex Ochoa .07 .20
299 Sid Fernandez .07 .20
300 Ken Griffey Jr. .30 .75
301 Chris Gomez .07 .20
302 Wendell Magee .07 .20
303 Darren Oliver .07 .20
304 Mel Nieves .07 .20
305 Sammy Sosa .20 .50
306 George Arias .07 .20
307 Jack McDowell .07 .20
308 Stan Javier .07 .20
309 Kimera Bartee .07 .20
310 James Baldwin .07 .20
311 Rocky Coppinger .07 .20
312 Keith Lockhart .07 .20
313 C.J. Nitkowski .07 .20
314 Allen Watson .07 .20
315 Darryl Kile .07 .20
316 Amaury Telemaco .07 .20
317 Jason Isringhausen .07 .20
318 Manny Ramirez .10 .30
319 Terry Pendleton .07 .20
320 Tim Salmon .10 .30
321 Eric Karros .07 .20
322 Mark Whiten .07 .20
323 Rick Krivda .07 .20
324 Brett Butler .07 .20
325 Randy Johnson .20 .50
326 Eddie Taubensee .07 .20
327 Mark Leiter .07 .20
328 Kevin Gross .07 .20
329 Ernie Young .07 .20
330 Pat Hentgen .07 .20
331 Rondell White .07 .20
332 Bobby Witt .07 .20
333 Eddie Murray .20 .50
334 Tim Raines .07 .20
335 Jeff Fassero .07 .20
336 Chuck Finley .07 .20
337 Willie Adams .07 .20
338 Chan Ho Park .07 .20
339 Jay Powell .07 .20
340 Ivan Rodriguez .10 .30
341 Jermaine Allensworth .07 .20
342 Jay Payton .07 .20
343 T.J. Mathews .07 .20
344 Tony Batista .07 .20
345 Ed Sprague .07 .20
346 Jeff Kent .07 .20
347 Scott Erickson .07 .20
348 Jeff Suppan .07 .20
349 Pete Schourek .07 .20
350 Kenny Lofton .07 .20
351 Alan Benes .07 .20
352 Fred McGriff .10 .30
353 Charlie O'Brien .07 .20
354 Darren Bragg .07 .20
355 Alex Fernandez .07 .20
356 Al Martin .07 .20
357 Bob Wells .07 .20
358 Chad Mottola .07 .20
359 Devon White .07 .20
360 David Cone .07 .20
361 Bobby Jones .07 .20
362 Scott Sanders .07 .20
363 Karim Garcia .07 .20
364 Kirt Manwaring .07 .20
365 Chili Davis .07 .20
366 Mike Hampton .07 .20
367 Chad Ogea .07 .20
368 Curt Schilling .07 .20
369 Phil Nevin .07 .20
370 Roger Clemens .40 1.00
371 Willie Greene .07 .20
372 Kenny Rogers .07 .20
373 Jose Rijo .07 .20
374 Bobby Bonilla .07 .20
375 Mike Mussina .10 .30
376 Curtis Pride .07 .20
377 Todd Walker .07 .20
378 Jason Bere .07 .20
379 Heathcliff Slocumb .07 .20
380 Dante Bichette .07 .20
381 Carlos Baerga .07 .20
382 Livan Hernandez .07 .20
383 Jason Schmidt .07 .20
384 Kevin Stocker .07 .20
385 Matt Williams .07 .20
386 Bartolo Colon .07 .20
387 Will Clark .10 .30
388 Dennis Eckersley .07 .20
389 Brooks Kieschnick .07 .20
390 Ryan Klesko .07 .20
391 Mark Carreon .07 .20
392 Tim Worrell .07 .20
393 Dean Palmer .07 .20
394 Wil Cordero .07 .20
395 Javy Lopez .07 .20
396 Rich Aurilia .07 .20
397 Greg Vaughn .07 .20
398 Vinny Castilla .07 .20
399 Jeff Montgomery .07 .20
400 Cal Ripken .60 1.50
401 Walt Weiss .07 .20
402 Brad Ausmus .07 .20
403 Ruben Rivera .07 .20
404 Mark Wohlers .07 .20
405 Rick Aguilera .07 .20
406 Tony Clark .07 .20
407 Lyle Mouton .07 .20
408 Bill Pulsipher .07 .20
409 Jose Rosado .07 .20
410 Tony Gwynn .25 .60
411 Cecil Fielder .07 .20
412 John Flaherty .07 .20
413 Lenny Dykstra .07 .20
414 Ugueth Urbina .07 .20
415 Brian Jordan .07 .20
416 Bob Abreu .10 .30
417 Craig Paquette .07 .20
418 Sandy Martinez .07 .20
419 Jeff Blauser .07 .20
420 Barry Larkin .10 .30
421 Kevin Seitzer .07 .20
422 Tim Belcher .07 .20
423 Paul Sorrento .07 .20
424 Cal Eldred .07 .20
425 Robin Ventura .07 .20
426 John Olerud .07 .20
427 Bob Wolcott .07 .20
428 Matt Lawton .07 .20
429 Rod Beck .07 .20
430 Shane Reynolds .07 .20
431 Mike James .07 .20
432 Steve Wojciechowski .07 .20
433 Vladimir Guerrero .20 .50
434 Dustin Hermanson .07 .20
435 Marty Cordova .07 .20
436 Marc Newfield .07 .20
437 Todd Stottlemyre .07 .20
438 Jeffrey Hammonds .07 .20
439 Dave Stevens .07 .20
440 Hideo Nomo .20 .50
441 Mark Thompson .07 .20
442 Mark Lewis .07 .20
443 Quinton McCracken .07 .20
444 Cliff Floyd .07 .20
445 Denny Neagle .07 .20
446 John Jaha .07 .20
447 Mike Sweeney .07 .20
448 John Wasdin .07 .20
449 Chad Curtis .07 .20
450 Mo Vaughn .07 .20
451 Donovan Osborne .07 .20
452 Ruben Sierra .07 .20
453 Michael Tucker .07 .20
454 Kurt Abbott .07 .20
455 Andruw Jones UER .10 .30
Birthdate is incorrectly listed as 1-22-67, should be 1-22-77
456 Shannon Stewart .07 .20
457 Scott Brosius .07 .20
458 Juan Guzman .07 .20
459 Ron Villone .07 .20
460 Moises Alou .07 .20
461 Larry Walker .07 .20
462 Eddie Murray SH .10 .30
463 Paul Molitor SH .07 .20
464 Hideo Nomo SH .07 .20
465 Barry Bonds SH .30 .75
466 Todd Hundley SH .07 .20
467 Rheal Cormier .07 .20
468 Jason Conti RC .08 .25
Jhensy Sandoval
469 Rod Barajas .60 1.50
Jackie Rexrode RC
470 Cedric Bowers RC .08 .25
Jared Sandberg RC
471 Chei Gunner RC .08 .25
Paul Wilder
472 Mike Decelle .08 .25
Marcus McCain RC
473 Todd Zeile .07 .20
474 Neifi Perez .07 .20
475 Jeromy Burnitz .07 .20
476 Trey Beamon .07 .20
477 Braden Looper RC .30 .75
John Patterson
478 Danny Peoples .20 .50
Jake Westbrook RC
479 Eric Chavez .75 2.00
Adam Eaton RC
480 Joe Lawrence RC .08 .25
Pete Tucci
481 Kris Benson .20 .50
Billy Koch RC
482 John Nicholson .08 .25
Andy Prater RC
483 Mark Johnson RC .30 .75
Mark Kotsay
484 Armando Benitez .07 .20
485 Mike Matheny .07 .20
486 Jeff Reed .07 .20
487 Mark Bellhorn .07 .20
Russ Johnson
Enrique Wilson
488 Ben Grieve .07 .20
Richard Hidalgo
Scott Morgan RC
489 Paul Konerko .10 .30
Derrek Lee UER
spelled Derek on back
Ron Wright
490 Wes Helms RC .50 1.25
Bill Mueller
Brad Seitzer
491 Jeff Abbott .07 .20
Shane Monahan
Edgard Velazquez
492 Jimmy Anderson RC .08 .25
Ron Blazier
Gerald Witasick
493 Darin Blood .07 .20
Heath Murray
Carl Pavano
494 Nelson Figueroa RC .08 .25
Mark Redman
Mike Villano
495 Checklist .07 .20
496 Checklist .07 .20
NNO Derek Jeter AU 100.00 175.00

1997 Topps All-Stars

Randomly inserted in Series one hobby and retail packs at a rate of one in 18 and one in every six jumbo packs, this 22-card set printed on rainbow foilboard features the top 11 players from each league and from each position as voted by the Topps Sports Department. The fronts carry a photo of a "first team" all-star player while the backs carry a different photo of that player alongside the "second team" and "third team" selections. Only the "first team" players are checklisted listed below.

COMPLETE SET (22) 10.00 25.00
SER.1 STATED ODDS 1:18 HOB/RET, 1:6 JUM
AS1 Ivan Rodriguez .40 1.00
AS2 Todd Hundley .25 .60
AS3 Frank Thomas .60 1.50
AS4 Andres Galarraga .25 .60
AS5 Chuck Knoblauch .25 .60
AS6 Eric Young .25 .60
AS7 Jim Thome .40 1.00
AS8 Chipper Jones .60 1.50
AS9 Cal Ripken 2.00 5.00
AS10 Barry Larkin .40 1.00
AS11 Albert Belle .25 .60
AS12 Barry Bonds 2.00 5.00
AS13 Ken Griffey Jr. 1.00 2.50
AS14 Ellis Burks .25 .60
AS15 Juan Gonzalez .25 .60
AS16 Gary Sheffield .25 .60
AS17 Andy Pettitte .40 1.00
AS18 Tom Glavine .40 1.00
AS19 Pat Hentgen .25 .60
AS20 John Smoltz .40 1.00
AS21 Roberto Hernandez .25 .60
AS22 Mark Wohlers .25 .60

1997 Topps Awesome Impact

Randomly inserted in second series 11-card retail packs at a rate of 1:18, cards from this 20-card set feature a selection of top young stars and prospects. Each card front features a color player action shot cut out against a silver prismatic background.

COMPLETE SET (20) 40.00 100.00
SER.2 STATED ODDS 1:18 RETAIL
AI1 Jaime Bluma 1.25 3.00
AI2 Tony Clark 1.25 3.00
AI3 Jermaine Dye 1.25 3.00
AI4 Nomar Garciaparra 5.00 12.00
AI5 Vladimir Guerrero 3.00 8.00
AI6 Todd Hollandsworth 1.25 3.00
AI7 Derek Jeter 8.00 20.00
AI8 Andruw Jones 2.00 5.00
AI9 Chipper Jones 3.00 8.00
AI10 Jason Kendall 1.25 3.00
AI11 Brooks Kieschnick 1.25 3.00
AI12 Alex Ochoa 1.25 3.00
AI13 Rey Ordonez 1.25 3.00
AI14 Neifi Perez 1.25 3.00
AI15 Edgar Renteria 1.25 3.00
AI16 Mariano Rivera 3.00 8.00
AI17 Ruben Rivera 1.25 3.00
AI18 Scott Rolen 2.00 5.00
AI19 Billy Wagner 1.25 3.00
AI20 Todd Walker 1.25 3.00

1997 Topps Hobby Masters

Randomly inserted in first and second series hobby packs at a rate of one in 36, cards from this 10-card set honor twenty players picked by hobby dealers from across the country as their all-time favorites. Cards 1-10 were issued in first series packs and 11-20 in second series packs. Printed on 28-point diffraction foilboard, one card replaces two regular cards when inserted in packs. The fronts feature borderless color player photos on a background of the player's profile. The backs carry player information.

COMPLETE SET (20) 30.00 80.00
COMPLETE SERIES 1 (10) 15.00 40.00
COMPLETE SERIES 2 (10) 15.00 40.00
STATED ODDS 1:36 HOBBY
HM1 Ken Griffey Jr. 2.50 6.00
HM2 Cal Ripken 5.00 12.00
HM3 Greg Maddux 2.50 6.00
HM4 Albert Belle .60 1.50
HM5 Tony Gwynn 2.00 5.00
HM6 Jeff Bagwell 1.00 2.50
HM7 Randy Johnson 1.50 4.00
HM8 Raul Mondesi .60 1.50
HM9 Juan Gonzalez .60 1.50
HM10 Kenny Lofton .60 1.50
HM11 Frank Thomas 1.50 4.00
HM12 Mike Piazza 2.50 6.00
HM13 Chipper Jones 1.50 4.00
HM14 Brady Anderson .60 1.50
HM15 Ken Caminiti .60 1.50
HM16 Barry Bonds 5.00 12.00
HM17 Mo Vaughn .60 1.50
HM18 Derek Jeter 4.00 10.00
HM19 Sammy Sosa 1.50 4.00
HM20 Andres Galarraga .60 1.50

1997 Topps Inter-League Finest

Randomly inserted in Series one hobby and retail packs at a rate of one in 36 and jumbo packs at a rate of one in 10; this 14-card set features top individual match-ups from inter-league rivalries. One player from each major league team is represented on each side of this double-sided set with a color photo and is covered with the patented Finest clear protector.

COMPLETE SET (14) 25.00 60.00
SER.1 ODDS 1:36 HOB/RET,1:10 JUM
*REF.: 1X TO 2.5X BASIC INTER-LG
REF.SER.1 ODDS 1:216 HOB/RET, 1:56 JUM
ILM1 Mark McGwire 4.00 10.00
Barry Bonds
ILM2 Tim Salmon 2.50 6.00
Mike Piazza
ILM3 Ken Griffey Jr. 2.50 6.00
Dante Bichette
ILM4 Juan Gonzalez 2.00 5.00
Tony Gwynn
ILM5 Frank Thomas 1.50 4.00
Sammy Sosa
ILM6 Albert Belle .60 1.50
Barry Larkin
ILM7 Johnny Damon .60 1.50
Brian Jordan
ILM8 Paul Molitor .60 1.50
Jeff King
ILM9 John Jaha 1.00 2.50
Jeff Bagwell
ILM10 Bernie Williams 1.00 2.50
Todd Hundley
ILM11 Joe Carter .60 1.50
Henry Rodriguez
ILM12 Cal Ripken 5.00 12.00
Gregg Jefferies
ILM13 Mo Vaughn 1.50 4.00
Chipper Jones
ILM14 Travis Fryman .60 1.50
Gary Sheffield

1997 Topps Mantle

Randomly inserted at the rate of one in 12 Series one hobby/retail packs and one every three jumbo packs, this 16-card set features authentic reprints of Topps Mickey Mantle cards that were not reprinted last year. Each card is stamped with the commemorative gold foil logo.

COMPLETE SET (16) 50.00 100.00
COMMON (21-36) 3.00 8.00
SER.1 ODDS 1:12 HOB/RET,1:3 JUM
COMMON FINEST (21-36) 3.00 8.00
FINEST SER.2 1:24 HOB/RET, 1:6 JUM
COMMON REF. (21-36) 12.50 30.00
REF.SER.2 1:216 HOB/RET,1:60 JUM

1997 Topps Mays

Randomly inserted at the rate of one in eight first series hobby/retail packs and one every two jumbo packs; cards from this 27-card set feature reprints of both the Topps and Bowman vintage Mays cards . Each card front is highlighted by a special commemorative gold foil stamp. Randomly inserted in first series hobby packs only (at the rate of one in 2,400) are personally signed cards. A special 4 1/4" by 5 3/4" jumbo reprint of the 1952 Topps Willie Mays card was made available exclusively in special series one Wal-Mart boxes. Each box (shaped much like a cereal box) contained ten eight-card retail packs and the aforementioned jumbo card and retailed for $10.

COMPLETE SET (27) 50.00 100.00
COMMON MAYS (3-27) 1.50 4.00
SER.1 ODDS 1:8 HOB/RET, 1:2 JUM
COMMON FINEST (1-27) 1.50 4.00
*51-'52 FINEST: .4X TO 1X BASIC MAYS REPRINTS
FINEST SER.2 1:20 HOB/RET,1:4 JUM
COMMON REF. (1-27) 4.00 10.00
*51-'52 REF: 1X TO 2.5X BASIC MAYS REPRINTS
REF.SER.2 1:180 HOB/RET,1:48 JUM
1 Willie Mays 3.00 8.00
1951 Bowman
2 Willie Mays 2.50 6.00
1952 Topps
J261 W.Mays 1952 Jumbo 3.00 8.00

1997 Topps Mays Autographs

Acording to Topps, Mays signed about 65 each of the following cards: 51B, 52T, 53T, 55B, 55T, 57T, 58T, 60T, 60T AS, 61T, 61T AS, 63T, 64T, 65T, 66T, 69T, 70T, 72T, 73T. The cards all have a "Certified Topps Autograph" stamp on them.

COMMON CARD (1953-1958) 100.00 200.00
COMMON CARD (1960-1973) 60.00 120.00
SER.1 ODDS 1:2400 H/R, 1:625 JUM
1 Willie Mays 100.00 200.00
1951 Bowman
2 Willie Mays 100.00 200.00
1952 Topps

1997 Topps Season's Best

This 25-card set was randomly inserted into Topps Series two packs at a rate of one every six hobby/retail packs and one per jumbo pack; this set features five top players from each of the following five statistical categories: Leading Looters (top base stealers), Bleacher Reachers (top home run hitters), Hill Toppers (most wins), Number Crunchers (most RBI's), Kings of Swings (top slugging percentages). The fronts display color player photos printed on prismatic illusion foilboard. The backs carry another player photo and statistics.

COMPLETE SET (25) 10.00 25.00
SER.2 STATED ODDS 1:6 HOB/RET, 1:1 JUM
SB1 Tony Gwynn 1.00 2.50
SB2 Frank Thomas .75 2.00
SB3 Ellis Burks .30 .75
SB4 Paul Molitor .30 .75
SB5 Chuck Knoblauch .30 .75
SB6 Mark McGwire 2.00 5.00
SB7 Brady Anderson .30 .75
SB8 Ken Griffey Jr. 1.25 3.00
SB9 Albert Belle .30 .75
SB10 Andres Galarraga .30 .75
SB11 Andres Galarraga .30 .75
SB12 Albert Belle .30 .75
SB13 Juan Gonzalez .30 .75
SB14 Mo Vaughn .30 .75
SB15 Rafael Palmeiro .50 1.25
SB16 John Smoltz .50 1.25
SB17 Andy Pettitte .50 1.25
SB18 Pat Hentgen .30 .75
SB19 Mike Mussina .50 1.25
SB20 Andy Benes .30 .75
SB21 Kenny Lofton .30 .75
SB22 Tom Goodwin .30 .75
SB23 Otis Nixon .30 .75
SB24 Eric Young .30 .75
SB25 Lance Johnson .30 .75

1997 Topps Sweet Strokes

This 15-card retail only set was randomly inserted in series one retail packs at a rate of one in 12. Printed on Rainbow foilboard, the set features color photos of some of Baseball's top hitters.

COMPLETE SET (15) 15.00 40.00
SER.1 STATED ODDS 1:12 RETAIL
SS1 Roberto Alomar .60 1.50
SS2 Jeff Bagwell .60 1.50
SS3 Albert Belle .40 1.00
SS4 Barry Bonds 3.00 8.00
SS5 Mark Grace .60 1.50
SS6 Ken Griffey Jr. 1.50 4.00
SS7 Tony Gwynn 1.25 3.00
SS8 Chipper Jones 1.00 2.50
SS9 Edgar Martinez .60 1.50
SS10 Mark McGwire 2.50 6.00
SS11 Rafael Palmeiro .60 1.50
SS12 Mike Piazza 1.50 4.00
SS13 Gary Sheffield .40 1.00
SS14 Frank Thomas 1.00 2.50
SS15 Mo Vaughn .40 1.00

1997 Topps Team Timber

Randomly inserted into all second series hobby/retail packs at a rate of 1:36 and second series Hobby Collector (jumbo) packs at a rate of 1:8, cards from this 16-card set highlight a selection of baseball's top sluggers. Each card features a simulated wood-grain stock, but the fronts are UV-coated, making the cards bow noticeably.

COMPLETE SET (16) 15.00 40.00
SER.2 STATED ODDS 1:36 HOB/RET, 1:8 JUM
TT1 Ken Griffey Jr. 1.50 4.00
TT2 Ken Caminiti .40 1.00
TT3 Bernie Williams .60 1.50
TT4 Jeff Bagwell .60 1.50
TT5 Frank Thomas 1.00 2.50
TT6 Andres Galarraga .40 1.00
TT7 Barry Bonds 3.00 8.00
TT8 Rafael Palmeiro .60 1.50
TT9 Brady Anderson .40 1.00
TT10 Juan Gonzalez .40 1.00
TT11 Mo Vaughn .40 1.00
TT12 Mark McGwire 2.50 6.00
TT13 Gary Sheffield .40 1.00
TT14 Albert Belle .40 1.00
TT15 Chipper Jones 1.00 2.50
TT16 Mike Piazza 1.50 4.00

1998 Topps

This 503-card set was distributed in two separate series: 282 cards in first series and 221 cards in second series. 11-card packs carried a suggested retail price of $1.29. Cards were also distributed in Home Team Advantage jumbo packs and hobby, retail and Christmas factory sets. Card fronts feature color action player photos printed on 16 pt. stock with player information and career statistics on the back. Card number 7 was permanently retired in 1996 to honor Mickey Mantle. Series one contains the following subsets: Draft Picks (245-249), Prospects (250-259), Season Highlights (265-269), Interleague (270-274) Checklists (275-276) and World Series (277-283). Series two contains Season Highlights (474-478), Interleague (479-483), Prospects (484-495/498-501) and Checklists (502-503). Rookie Cards of note include Ryan Anderson, Michael Cuddyer, Jack Cust and Troy Glaus. This set also features Topps long-awaited first regular-issue Alex Rodriguez card (504). The superstar shortstop was left out of all Topps sets for the first four years of his career due to a problem between Topps and Rodriguez's agent Scott Boras. Finally, as part of an agreement with the Baseball Hall of Fame, Topps produced commemorative admission tickets featuring Roberto Clemente memorabilia from the Hall in the form of a Topps card. These were the standard admission tickets for the shrine, and were also included one per case in 1998 Topps series two baseball.

COMPLETE SET (503) 40.00 80.00
COMP.HOBBY SET (511) 60.00 120.00
COMP.RETAIL SET (511) 60.00 120.00
COMP.SERIES 1 (282) 20.00 40.00
COMP.SERIES 2 (221) 20.00 40.00
1 Tony Gwynn .25 .60
2 Larry Walker .07 .20
3 Billy Wagner .07 .20
4 Denny Neagle .07 .20
5 Vladimir Guerrero .20 .50
6 Kevin Brown .10 .30
8 Mariano Rivera .20 .50
9 Tony Clark .07 .20
10 Deion Sanders .10 .30
11 Francisco Cordova .07 .20
12 Matt Williams .07 .20
13 Carlos Baerga .07 .20
14 Mo Vaughn .07 .20
15 Bobby Witt .07 .20
16 Matt Stairs .07 .20
17 Chan Ho Park .07 .20
18 Mike Bordick .07 .20
19 Michael Tucker .07 .20
20 Frank Thomas .20 .50
21 Roberto Clemente .40 1.00
22 Dmitri Young .07 .20
23 Steve Trachsel .07 .20
24 Jeff Kent .07 .20
25 Scott Rolen .10 .30
26 John Thomson .07 .20
27 Joe Vitiello .07 .20
28 Eddie Guardado .07 .20
29 Charlie Hayes .07 .20
30 Juan Gonzalez .07 .20
31 Garret Anderson .07 .20
32 John Jaha .07 .20
33 Omar Vizquel .10 .30
34 Brian Hunter .07 .20
35 Jeff Bagwell .10 .30
36 Mark Lemke .07 .20
37 Doug Glanville .07 .20
38 Dan Wilson .07 .20
39 Steve Cooke .07 .20
40 Chili Davis .07 .20
41 Mike Cameron .07 .20
42 F.P. Santangelo .07 .20
43 Brad Ausmus .07 .20
44 Gary DiSarcina .07 .20
45 Pat Hentgen .07 .20
46 Wilton Guerrero .07 .20
47 Devon White .07 .20
48 Danny Patterson .07 .20
49 Pat Meares .07 .20
50 Rafael Palmeiro .10 .30
51 Mark Gardner .07 .20
52 Jeff Blauser .07 .20
53 Dave Hollins .07 .20
54 Carlos Garcia .07 .20
55 Ben McDonald .07 .20
56 John Mabry .07 .20
57 Trevor Hoffman .07 .20
58 Tony Fernandez .07 .20
59 Rich Loiselle .07 .20
60 Mark Leiter .07 .20
61 Pat Kelly .07 .20
62 John Flaherty .07 .20
63 Roger Bailey .07 .20
64 Tom Gordon .07 .20
65 Ryan Klesko .07 .20
66 Darryl Hamilton .07 .20
67 Jim Eisenreich .07 .20
68 Butch Huskey .07 .20
69 Mark Grudzielanek .07 .20
70 Marquis Grissom .07 .20
71 Mark McLemore .07 .20
72 Gary Gaetti .07 .20
73 Greg Gagne .07 .20
74 Lyle Mouton .07 .20
75 Jim Edmonds .07 .20
76 Shawn Green .07 .20
77 Greg Vaughn .07 .20
78 Terry Adams .07 .20
79 Kevin Polcovich .07 .20
80 Troy O'Leary .07 .20
81 Jeff Shaw .07 .20
82 Rich Becker .07 .20
83 David Wells .07 .20
84 Steve Karsay .07 .20
85 Charles Nagy .07 .20
86 B.J. Surhoff .07 .20
87 Jamey Wright .07 .20
88 James Baldwin .07 .20
89 Edgardo Alfonzo .07 .20
90 Jay Buhner .07 .20
91 Brady Anderson .07 .20
92 Scott Servais .07 .20
93 Edgar Renteria .07 .20
94 Mike Lieberthal .07 .20
95 Rick Aguilera .07 .20
96 Walt Weiss .07 .20
97 Deivi Cruz .07 .20

98 Kurt Abbott	.07	.20
99 Henry Rodriguez	.07	.20
100 Mike Piazza	.30	.75
101 Bill Taylor	.07	.20
102 Todd Zeile	.07	.20
103 Rey Ordonez	.07	.20
104 Willie Greene	.07	.20
105 Tony Womack	.07	.20
106 Mike Sweeney	.07	.20
107 Jeffrey Hammonds	.07	.20
108 Kevin Orie	.07	.20
109 Alex Gonzalez	.07	.20
110 Jose Canseco	.10	.30
111 Paul Sorrento	.07	.20
112 Joey Hamilton	.07	.20
113 Brad Radke	.07	.20
114 Steve Avery	.07	.20
115 Esteban Loaiza	.07	.20
116 Stan Javier	.07	.20
117 Chris Gomez	.07	.20
118 Royce Clayton	.07	.20
119 Orlando Merced	.07	.20
120 Kevin Appier	.07	.20
121 Mel Nieves	.07	.20
122 Joe Girardi	.07	.20
123 Rico Brogna	.07	.20
124 Kent Mercker	.07	.20
125 Manny Ramirez	.10	.30
126 Jeromy Burnitz	.07	.20
127 Kevin Foster	.07	.20
128 Matt Morris	.07	.20
129 Jason Dickson	.07	.20
130 Tom Glavine	.10	.30
131 Wally Joyner	.07	.20
132 Rick Reed	.07	.20
133 Todd Jones	.07	.20
134 Dave Martinez	.07	.20
135 Sandy Alomar Jr.	.07	.20
136 Mike Lansing	.07	.20
137 Sean Berry	.07	.20
138 Doug Jones	.07	.20
139 Todd Stottlemyre	.07	.20
140 Jay Bell	.07	.20
141 Jaime Navarro	.07	.20
142 Chris Hoiles	.07	.20
143 Joey Cora	.07	.20
144 Scott Spiezio	.07	.20
145 Joe Carter	.07	.20
146 Jose Guillen	.07	.20
147 Damion Easley	.07	.20
148 Lee Stevens	.07	.20
149 Alex Fernandez	.07	.20
150 Randy Johnson	.20	.50
151 J.T. Snow	.07	.20
152 Chuck Finley	.07	.20
153 Bernard Gilkey	.07	.20
154 David Segui	.07	.20
155 Dante Bichette	.07	.20
156 Kevin Stocker	.07	.20
157 Carl Everett	.07	.20
158 Jose Valentin	.07	.20
159 Pokey Reese	.07	.20
160 Derek Jeter	.50	1.25
161 Roger Pavlik	.07	.20
162 Mark Wohlers	.07	.20
163 Ricky Bottalico	.07	.20
164 Ozzie Guillen	.07	.20
165 Mike Mussina	.10	.30
166 Gary Sheffield	.07	.20
167 Hideo Nomo	.20	.50
168 Mark Grace	.10	.30
169 Aaron Sele	.07	.20
170 Darryl Kile	.07	.20
171 Shawn Estes	.07	.20
172 Vinny Castilla	.07	.20
173 Ron Coomer	.07	.20
174 Jose Rosado	.07	.20
175 Kenny Lofton	.07	.20
176 Jason Giambi	.07	.20
177 Hal Morris	.07	.20
178 Darren Bragg	.07	.20
179 Orel Hershiser	.07	.20
180 Ray Lankford	.07	.20
181 Hideki Irabu	.07	.20
182 Kevin Young	.07	.20
183 Javy Lopez	.07	.20
184 Jeff Montgomery	.07	.20
185 Mike Holtz	.07	.20
186 George Williams	.07	.20
187 Cal Eldred	.07	.20
188 Tom Candiotti	.07	.20
189 Glenallen Hill	.07	.20
190 Brian Giles	.07	.20
191 Dave Mlicki	.07	.20
192 Garrett Stephenson	.07	.20
193 Jeff Frye	.07	.20
194 Joe Oliver	.07	.20
195 Bob Hamelin	.07	.20
196 Luis Sojo	.07	.20
197 LaTroy Hawkins	.07	.20
198 Kevin Elster	.07	.20
199 Jeff Reed	.07	.20
200 Dennis Eckersley	.07	.20
201 Bill Mueller	.07	.20
202 Russ Davis	.07	.20
203 Armando Benitez	.07	.20
204 Quilvio Veras	.07	.20
205 Tim Naehring	.07	.20
206 Quinton McCracken	.07	.20
207 Raul Casanova	.07	.20
208 Matt Lawton	.07	.20
209 Luis Alicea	.07	.20
210 Luis Gonzalez	.07	.20
211 Allen Watson	.07	.20
212 Gerald Williams	.07	.20
213 David Bell	.07	.20
214 Todd Hollandsworth	.07	.20
215 Wade Boggs	.10	.30
216 Jose Mesa	.07	.20
217 Jamie Moyer	.07	.20
218 Darren Daulton	.07	.20
219 Mickey Morandini	.07	.20
220 Rusty Greer	.07	.20
221 Jim Bullinger	.07	.20
222 Jose Offerman	.07	.20
223 Matt Karchner	.07	.20
224 Woody Williams	.07	.20
225 Mark Loretta	.07	.20
226 Mike Hampton	.07	.20
227 Willie Adams	.07	.20
228 Scott Hatteberg	.07	.20
229 Rich Amaral	.07	.20
230 Terry Steinbach	.07	.20
231 Glendon Rusch	.07	.20
232 Bret Boone	.07	.20
233 Robert Person	.07	.20
234 Jose Hernandez	.07	.20
235 Doug Drabek	.07	.20
236 Jason McDonald	.07	.20
237 Chris Widger	.07	.20
238 Tom Martin	.07	.20
239 Dave Burba	.07	.20
240 Pete Rose Jr.	.07	.20
241 Bobby Ayala	.07	.20
242 Tim Wakefield	.07	.20
243 Dennis Springer	.07	.20
244 Tim Belcher	.07	.20
245 Jon Garland	.10	.30
Geoff Goetz		
246 Glenn Davis	.10	.30
Lance Berkman		
247 Vernon Wells	.10	.30
Aaron Akin		
248 Adam Kennedy	.07	.20
Jason Romano		
249 Jason Dellaero	.07	.20
Troy Cameron		
250 Alex Sanchez	.07	.20
Jared Sandberg		
251 Pablo Ortega	.07	.20
James Manias		
252 Jason Conti RC	.07	.20
Mike Stoner		
253 John Patterson	.07	.20
Larry Rodriguez		
254 Adrian Beltre	.10	.30
Ryan Minor RC		
Aaron Boone		
255 Ben Grieve	.07	.20
Brian Buchanan		
Dermal Brown		
256 Kerry Wood	.10	.30
Carl Pavano		
Gil Meche		
257 David Ortiz	1.00	2.50
Daryle Ward		
Richie Sexson		
258 Randy Winn	.07	.20
Juan Encarnacion		
Andrew Vessel		
259 Kris Benson	.07	.20
Travis Smith		
Courtney Duncan RC		
260 Chad Hermansen	.07	.20
Brent Butler		
Warren Morris RC		
261 Ben Davis	.07	.20
Eli Marrero		
Ramon Hernandez		
262 Eric Chavez	.10	.30
Russell Branyan		
Russ Johnson		
263 Todd Dunwoody RC	.07	.20
John Barnes		
Ryan Jackson		
264 Matt Clement	.60	1.50
Roy Halladay		
Brian Fuentes RC		
265 Randy Johnson SH	.10	.30
266 Kevin Brown SH	.07	.20
267 Ricardo Rincon SH	.07	.20
Francisco Cordova		
268 N.Garciaparra SH	.20	.50
269 Tino Martinez SH	.07	.20
270 Chuck Knoblauch IL	.07	.20
271 Pedro Martinez IL	.10	.30
272 Denny Neagle IL	.07	.20
273 Juan Gonzalez IL	.07	.20
274 Andres Galarraga IL	.07	.20
275 Checklist	.07	.20
276 Checklist	.07	.20
277 Moises Alou WS	.07	.20
278 Sandy Alomar Jr. WS	.07	.20
279 Gary Sheffield WS	.07	.20
280 Matt Williams WS	.07	.20
281 Livan Hernandez WS	.07	.20
282 Chad Ogea WS	.07	.20
283 Marlins Champs	.07	.20
284 Tino Martinez	.10	.30
285 Roberto Alomar	.10	.30
286 Jeff King	.07	.20
287 Brian Jordan	.07	.20
288 Darin Erstad	.07	.20
289 Ken Caminiti	.07	.20
290 Jim Thome	.10	.30
291 Paul Molitor	.07	.20
292 Ivan Rodriguez	.10	.30
293 Bernie Williams	.10	.30
294 Todd Hundley	.07	.20
295 Andres Galarraga	.07	.20
296 Greg Maddux	.30	.75
297 Edgar Martinez	.07	.20
298 Ron Gant	.07	.20
299 Derek Bell	.07	.20
300 Roger Clemens	.40	1.00
301 Rondell White	.07	.20
302 Barry Larkin	.10	.30
303 Robin Ventura	.07	.20
304 Jason Kendall	.07	.20
305 Chipper Jones	.20	.50
306 John Franco	.07	.20
307 Sammy Sosa	.20	.50
308 Troy Percival	.07	.20
309 Chuck Knoblauch	.07	.20
310 Ellis Burks	.07	.20
311 Al Martin	.07	.20
312 Tim Salmon	.10	.30
313 Moises Alou	.07	.20
314 Lance Johnson	.07	.20
315 Justin Thompson	.07	.20
316 Will Clark	.10	.30
317 Barry Bonds	.60	1.50
318 Craig Biggio	.10	.30
319 John Smoltz	.10	.30
320 Cal Ripken	.60	1.50
321 Ken Griffey Jr.	.30	.75
322 Paul O'Neill	.10	.30
323 Todd Helton	.10	.30
324 John Olerud	.07	.20
325 Mark McGwire	.50	1.25
326 Jose Cruz Jr.	.07	.20
327 Jeff Cirillo	.07	.20
328 Dean Palmer	.07	.20
329 John Wetteland	.07	.20
330 Steve Finley	.07	.20
331 Albert Belle	.07	.20
332 Curt Schilling	.07	.20
333 Raul Mondesi	.07	.20
334 Andruw Jones	.10	.30
335 Nomar Garciaparra	.30	.75
336 David Justice	.07	.20
337 Andy Pettitte	.10	.30
338 Pedro Martinez	.10	.30
339 Travis Miller	.07	.20
340 Chris Stynes	.07	.20
341 Gregg Jefferies	.07	.20
342 Jeff Fassero	.07	.20
343 Craig Counsell	.07	.20
344 Wilson Alvarez	.07	.20
345 Bip Roberts	.07	.20
346 Kelvim Escobar	.07	.20
347 Mark Bellhorn	.07	.20
348 Cory Lidle RC	.60	1.50
349 Fred McGriff	.10	.30
350 Chuck Carr	.07	.20
351 Bob Abreu	.07	.20
352 Juan Guzman	.07	.20
353 Fernando Vina	.07	.20
354 Andy Benes	.07	.20
355 Dave Nilsson	.07	.20
356 Bobby Bonilla	.07	.20
357 Ismael Valdes	.07	.20
358 Carlos Perez	.07	.20
359 Kirk Rueter	.07	.20
360 Bartolo Colon	.07	.20
361 Mel Rojas	.07	.20
362 Johnny Damon	.10	.30
363 Geronimo Berroa	.07	.20
364 Reggie Sanders	.07	.20
365 Jermaine Allensworth	.07	.20
366 Orlando Cabrera	.07	.20
367 Jorge Fabregas	.07	.20
368 Scott Stahoviak	.07	.20
369 Ken Cloude	.07	.20
370 Donovan Osborne	.07	.20
371 Roger Cedeno	.07	.20
372 Neifi Perez	.07	.20
373 Chris Holt	.07	.20
374 Cecil Fielder	.07	.20
375 Marty Cordova	.07	.20
376 Tom Goodwin	.07	.20
377 Jeff Suppan	.07	.20
378 Jeff Brantley	.07	.20
379 Mark Langston	.07	.20
380 Shane Reynolds	.07	.20
381 Mike Fetters	.07	.20
382 Todd Greene	.07	.20
383 Ray Durham	.07	.20
384 Carlos Delgado	.07	.20
385 Jeff D'Amico	.07	.20
386 Brian McRae	.07	.20
387 Alan Benes	.07	.20
388 Heathcliff Slocumb	.07	.20
389 Eric Young	.07	.20
390 Travis Fryman	.07	.20
391 David Cone	.07	.20
392 Otis Nixon	.07	.20
393 Jeremi Gonzalez	.07	.20
394 Jeff Juden	.07	.20
395 Jose Vizcaino	.07	.20
396 Ugueth Urbina	.07	.20
397 Ramon Martinez	.07	.20
398 Robb Nen	.07	.20
399 Harold Baines	.07	.20
400 Delino DeShields	.07	.20
401 John Burkett	.07	.20
402 Sterling Hitchcock	.07	.20
403 Mark Clark	.07	.20
404 Terrell Wade	.07	.20
405 Scott Brosius	.07	.20
406 Chad Curtis	.07	.20
407 Brian Johnson	.07	.20
408 Roberto Kelly	.07	.20
409 Dave Dellucci RC	.15	.40
410 Michael Tucker	.07	.20
411 Mark Kotsay	.07	.20
412 Mark Lewis	.07	.20
413 Ryan McGuire	.07	.20
414 Shawon Dunston	.07	.20
415 Brad Rigby	.07	.20
416 Scott Erickson	.07	.20
417 Bobby Jones	.07	.20
418 Darren Oliver	.07	.20
419 John Smiley	.07	.20
420 T.J. Mathews	.07	.20
421 Dustin Hermanson	.07	.20
422 Mike Timlin	.07	.20
423 Willie Blair	.07	.20
424 Manny Alexander	.07	.20
425 Bob Tewksbury	.07	.20
426 Pete Schourek	.07	.20
427 Reggie Jefferson	.07	.20
428 Ed Sprague	.07	.20
429 Jeff Conine	.07	.20
430 Roberto Hernandez	.07	.20
431 Tom Pagnozzi	.07	.20
432 Jaret Wright	.07	.20
433 Livan Hernandez	.07	.20
434 Andy Ashby	.07	.20
435 Todd Dunn	.07	.20
436 Bobby Higginson	.07	.20
437 Rod Beck	.07	.20
438 Jim Leyritz	.07	.20
439 Matt Williams	.07	.20
440 Brett Tomko	.07	.20
441 Joe Randa	.07	.20
442 Chris Carpenter	.07	.20
443 Dennis Reyes	.07	.20
444 Al Leiter	.07	.20
445 Jason Schmidt	.07	.20
446 Ken Hill	.07	.20
447 Shannon Stewart	.07	.20
448 Enrique Wilson	.07	.20
449 Fernando Tatis	.07	.20
450 Jimmy Key	.07	.20
451 Darrin Fletcher	.07	.20
452 John Valentin	.07	.20
453 Kevin Tapani	.07	.20
454 Eric Karros	.07	.20
455 Jay Bell	.07	.20
456 Walt Weiss	.07	.20
457 Devon White	.07	.20
458 Carl Pavano	.07	.20
459 Mike Lansing	.07	.20
460 John Flaherty	.07	.20
461 Richard Hidalgo	.07	.20
462 Quinton McCracken	.07	.20
463 Karim Garcia	.07	.20
464 Miguel Cairo	.07	.20
465 Edwin Diaz	.07	.20
466 Bobby Smith	.07	.20
467 Yamil Benitez	.07	.20
468 Rich Butler	.07	.20
469 Ben Ford RC	.07	.20
470 Bubba Trammell	.07	.20
471 Brent Brede	.07	.20
472 Brooks Kieschnick	.07	.20
473 Carlos Castillo	.07	.20
474 Brad Radke SH	.07	.20
475 Roger Clemens SH	.20	.50
476 Curt Schilling SH	.07	.20
477 John Olerud SH	.07	.20
478 Mark McGwire SH	.25	.60
479 Mike Piazza	.20	.50
Ken Griffey Jr. IL		
480 Jeff Bagwell	.10	.30
Frank Thomas IL		
481 Chipper Jones	.10	.30
Nomar Garciaparra IL		
482 Larry Walker	.07	.20
Juan Gonzalez IL		
483 Gary Sheffield	.07	.20
Tino Martinez IL		
484 Derrick Gibson	.07	.20
Michael Coleman		
Norm Hutchins		
485 Braden Looper	.07	.20
Cliff Politte		
Brian Rose		
486 Eric Milton	.07	.20
Jason Marquis		
Corey Lee		
487 A.J.Hinch	.10	.30
Mark Osborne		
Robert Fick RC		
488 Aramis Ramirez	.10	.30
Alex Gonzalez		
Sean Casey		
489 Donnie Bridges	.07	.20
Tim Drew RC		
490 Ntema Ndungidi RC	.07	.20
Darnell McDonald		
491 Ryan Anderson RC	.07	.20
Mark Mangum		
492 J.J.Davis	.50	1.25
Troy Glaus RC		
493 Jayson Werth RC	.07	.20
Dan Reichert		
494 John Curtice RC	.30	.75
Michael Cuddyer RC		
495 Jack Cust RC	.20	.50
Jason Standridge		
496 Brian Anderson	.07	.20
497 Tony Saunders	.07	.20
498 Vladimir Nunez	.07	.20
Jhensy Sandoval		
499 Brad Penny	.10	.30
Nick Bierbrodt		
500 Dustin Carr	.07	.20
Luis Cruz RC		
501 Cedric Bowers	.07	.20
Marcus McCain		
502 Checklist	.07	.20
503 Checklist	.07	.20
504 Alex Rodriguez	.75	2.00

1998 Topps Minted in Cooperstown

Randomly inserted in first and second series packs at the rate of one in eight, this 503 card set is a parallel version of the base set. The set is distinguished by the special "Minted in Cooperstown" logo stamped on each card. Similar to the regular set, card number 7 does not exist.

*STARS: 5X TO 12X BASIC CARDS
*ROOKIES: 6X TO 15X BASIC CARDS
STATED ODDS: 1:8

1998 Topps Inaugural Devil Rays

This 503 card set was issued by Topps only in factory set form. Just as for the teams which began play in 1993, special sets with a Devil Rays logo was issued. The sets were sold only through retail outlets. These sets apparently did not sell well enough at the stadium and were later closed out to one of the home shopping networks. The logo is in gold foil and is in the middle of the card.

COMP.FACT.SET (503)	60.00	120.00

*STARS: 1.5X TO 4X BASIC CARDS
*ROOKIES: 2.5X TO 6X BASIC CARDS

1998 Topps Inaugural Diamondbacks

Similar to the Devil Rays set, Topps issued a factory set with the Diamond Backs logo to honor the first season the Arizona Diamondbacks played. The sets were issued in factory form and were only available through the Diamondback retail outlet.

COMP.FACT.SET (503)	60.00	120.00

*STARS: 1.5X TO 4X BASIC CARDS
*ROOKIES: 2.5X TO 6X BASIC CARDS

1998 Topps Baby Boomers

Randomly inserted in retail packs only at the rate of one in 36, this 15-card set features color photos of young players who have already made their mark in the game dispite less than three years in the majors.

COMPLETE SET (15)	20.00	50.00
SER.1 STATED ODDS 1:36 RETAIL		
BB1 Derek Jeter	5.00	12.00
BB2 Scott Rolen	1.25	3.00
BB3 Nomar Garciaparra	3.00	8.00
BB4 Jose Cruz Jr.	.75	2.00
BB5 Darin Erstad	.75	2.00
BB6 Todd Helton	1.25	3.00
BB7 Tony Clark	.75	2.00
BB8 Jose Guillen	.75	2.00
BB9 Andruw Jones	1.25	3.00
BB10 Vladimir Guerrero	2.00	5.00
BB11 Mark Kotsay	.75	2.00
BB12 Todd Greene	.75	2.00
BB13 Andy Pettitte	1.25	3.00
BB14 Justin Thompson	.75	2.00
BB15 Alan Benes	.75	2.00

1998 Topps Clemente

Randomly inserted in first and second series packs at the rate of one in 18, cards from this 19-card set honor the memory of Roberto Clemente on the 25th anniversary of his untimely death with conventional reprints of his Topps cards. All odd numbered cards were seeded in first series packs. All even numbered cards were seeded in second series packs.

COMPLETE SET (19)	60.00	120.00
COMPLETE SERIES 1 (10)	30.00	60.00
COMPLETE SERIES 2 (9)	30.00	60.00
COMMON CARD (2-19)	3.00	8.00
STATED ODDS 1:18		
1 Roberto Clemente 1955	6.00	15.00

1998 Topps Clemente Memorabilia Madness

As a major promotion for 1998 Topps series one, Topps created 46 different Roberto Clemente exchange cards for a total of 854 prizes. All 46 prizes (including the quantity available of each prize) is detailed explicitly in the listings below. The quantity is noted immediately after the prize. All 854 exchange cards looked identical to each other on front and almost identical to each other on back. Card fronts feature a blue, purple and white dot matrix head shot of Clemente surrounded by burgundy borders. Card backs featured extensive guidelines and rules for the exchange program. The only difference for each card were the few sentences on back detailing which specific prize each of the 46 different cards could be exchanged for. Lucky collectors that got their hands on these scarce exchange cards had until August 31st, 1998 to redeem their prizes. Odds for pulling one of these cards was approximately 1:3,708 hobby packs and approximately 1:1,020 hobby collector packs. Prices for almost all of these exchange cards have been excluded due to scarcity and lack of market information.

COMMON CARD (1-46)	100.00	200.00
SER.1 ODDS 1:3708 HOBBY, 1:1020 HTA		
SER.1 WILD CARD ODDS 1:72		
NNO Wild Card	.40	1.00

1998 Topps Clemente Sealed

Each 1998 Topps hobby factory set contained one of 19 different hermetically sealed Roberto Clemente reprint cards. The actual cards are identical to standard Clemente reprints available in 1998 Topps packs. The difference in these special cards is the clear plastic seal entirely encasing the card. Each seal is stamped with a gold foil logo on the card back stating "Factory Topps Seal 1998".

*SEALED: .4X TO 1X BASIC CLEMENTE

1998 Topps Clemente Tins

This four-tin set features reproductions of four different Roberto Clemente Topps cards printed on commemorative tins with a suggested retail price of $4.99. The tops of the tins feature color reprints of the card fronts with the backs carrying reproductions of the card backs. The cards highlighted are from the years 1955, 1956, 1965, and 1971. Inside each of these tins is a hermetically-sealed commemorative reprint of one of Clemente's 19 original Topps baseball cards dating from 1955 through 1973.

COMMON TIN (1-4)	2.00	5.00

1998 Topps Clemente Tribute

Randomly inserted in packs at the rate of one in 12, this five-card set honors the memory of Roberto Clemente on the 25th anniversary of his untimely death and features color photos printed on mirror foilboard on newly designed cards.

COMPLETE SET (5)	3.00	8.00
COMMON (RC1-RC5)	.75	2.00
SER.1 STATED ODDS 1:12		

1998 Topps Clout Nine

Randomly inserted in Topps Series two packs at the rate of one in 72, this nine-card set features color photos of the top players statiscally at each of the nine playing positions.

COMPLETE SET (9)	15.00	40.00
SER.2 STATED ODDS 1:72		
C1 Edgar Martinez	1.50	4.00
C2 Mike Piazza	4.00	10.00
C3 Frank Thomas	2.50	6.00
C4 Craig Biggio	1.50	4.00
C5 Vinny Castilla	1.00	2.50
C6 Jeff Blauser	1.00	2.50
C7 Barry Bonds	8.00	20.00
C8 Ken Griffey Jr.	4.00	10.00
C9 Larry Walker	1.00	2.50

1998 Topps Etch-A-Sketch

Randomly inserted in Topps Series one packs at the rate of one in 36, this nine-card set features drawings by artist George Vlosich III of some of baseball's hottest superstars using an Etch A Sketch as a canvas.

COMPLETE SET (9)	12.50	30.00
SER.1 STATED ODDS 1:36		
ES1 Albert Belle	.50	1.25
ES2 Barry Bonds	4.00	10.00
ES3 Ken Griffey Jr.	2.00	5.00
ES4 Greg Maddux	2.00	5.00
ES5 Hideo Nomo	1.25	3.00
ES6 Mike Piazza	2.00	5.00
ES7 Cal Ripken	4.00	10.00
ES8 Frank Thomas	1.25	3.00
ES9 Mo Vaughn	.50	1.25

1998 Topps Flashback

Randomly inserted in Topps Series one packs at the rate of one in 72, these two-sided cards of top players feature photographs of how they looked "then" as rookies on one side and how they look "now" as stars on the other.

COMPLETE SET (10)	30.00	80.00
SER.1 STATED ODDS 1:72		
FB1 Barry Bonds	10.00	25.00
FB2 Ken Griffey Jr.	5.00	12.00
FB3 Paul Molitor	1.25	3.00
FB4 Randy Johnson	3.00	8.00
FB5 Cal Ripken	10.00	25.00
FB6 Tony Gwynn	4.00	10.00
FB7 Kenny Lofton	1.25	3.00
FB8 Gary Sheffield	1.25	3.00
FB9 Deion Sanders	2.00	5.00
FB10 Brady Anderson	1.25	3.00

1998 Topps Focal Points

Randomly inserted in Topps Series two hobby packs only at the rate of one in 36, this 15-card set features color photos of current superstars with a special focus on the skills that have put them at the top.

COMPLETE SET (15)	30.00	80.00
SER.2 STATED ODDS 1:36 HOBBY		
FP1 Juan Gonzalez	.75	2.00
FP2 Nomar Garciaparra	3.00	8.00
FP3 Jose Cruz Jr.	.75	2.00
FP4 Cal Ripken	6.00	15.00
FP5 Ken Griffey Jr.	3.00	8.00
FP6 Ivan Rodriguez	1.25	3.00
FP7 Larry Walker	.75	2.00
FP8 Barry Bonds	6.00	15.00
FP9 Roger Clemens	4.00	10.00
FP10 Frank Thomas	2.00	5.00
FP11 Chuck Knoblauch	.75	2.00
FP12 Mike Piazza	3.00	8.00
FP13 Greg Maddux	3.00	8.00
FP14 Vladimir Guerrero	2.00	5.00
FP15 Andruw Jones	1.25	3.00

1998 Topps HallBound

Randomly inserted in Topps Series one hobby packs only at the rate of one in 36, this 15-card set features color photos of top stars who are bound for the Hall of Fame printed on foil mirrorboard cards.

COMPLETE SET (15)	30.00	80.00
SER.1 STATED ODDS 1:36 HOBBY		
HB1 Paul Molitor	.75	2.00
HB2 Tony Gwynn	2.50	6.00
HB3 Wade Boggs	1.25	3.00
HB4 Roger Clemens	4.00	10.00
HB5 Dennis Eckersley	.75	2.00
HB6 Cal Ripken	6.00	15.00
HB7 Greg Maddux	3.00	8.00
HB8 Rickey Henderson	1.25	3.00
HB9 Ken Griffey Jr.	3.00	8.00
HB10 Frank Thomas	2.00	5.00
HB11 Mark McGwire	5.00	12.00
HB12 Barry Bonds	6.00	15.00
HB13 Mike Piazza	3.00	8.00
HB14 Juan Gonzalez	.75	2.00
HB15 Randy Johnson	2.00	5.00

1998 Topps Milestones

Randomly inserted in Topps Series two retail packs only at the rate of one in 36, this ten-card set features color photos of players with the ability to set new records in the sport.

COMPLETE SET (10) 20.00 50.00
SER.2 STATED ODDS 1:36 RETAIL
MS1 Barry Bonds 5.00 12.00
MS2 Roger Clemens 3.00 8.00
MS3 Dennis Eckersley .60 1.50
MS4 Juan Gonzalez .60 1.50
MS5 Ken Griffey Jr. 2.50 6.00
MS6 Tony Gwynn 2.00 5.00
MS7 Greg Maddux 2.50 6.00
MS8 Mark McGwire 4.00 10.00
MS9 Cal Ripken 5.00 12.00
MS10 Frank Thomas 1.50 4.00

1998 Topps Mystery Finest

Randomly inserted in first series packs at the rate of one in 36, this 20-card set features color action player photos which showcase five of the 1997 season's most intriguing inter-league matchups.

COMPLETE SET (20) 30.00 80.00
SER.1 STATED ODDS 1:36
*REFRACTOR: 1X TO 2.5X BASIC MYS.FIN.
REFRACTOR SER.1 STATED ODDS: 1:144
ILM1 Chipper Jones 2.00 5.00
ILM2 Cal Ripken 6.00 15.00
ILM3 Greg Maddux 3.00 8.00
ILM4 Rafael Palmeiro 1.25 3.00
ILM5 Todd Hundley .75 2.00
ILM6 Derek Jeter 5.00 12.00
ILM7 John Olerud .75 2.00
ILM8 Tino Martinez 1.25 3.00
ILM9 Larry Walker .75 2.00
ILM10 Ken Griffey Jr. 3.00 8.00
ILM11 Andres Galarraga .75 2.00
ILM12 Randy Johnson 2.00 5.00
ILM13 Mike Piazza 3.00 8.00
ILM14 Jim Edmonds .75 2.00
ILM15 Eric Karros .75 2.00
ILM16 Tim Salmon 1.25 3.00
ILM17 Sammy Sosa 2.00 5.00
ILM18 Frank Thomas 2.00 5.00
ILM19 Mark Grace 1.25 3.00
ILM20 Albert Belle .75 2.00

1998 Topps Mystery Finest Bordered

Randomly inserted in Topps Series two packs at the rate of one in 36, this 20-card set features bordered color player photos of current hot players.

COMPLETE SET (20) 40.00 100.00
SER.2 STATED ODDS 1:36
*BORDERED REF: .75X TO 2X BORDERED
BORDERED REF.SER.2 ODDS 1:108
*BORDERLESS: .6X TO 1.5X BORDERED
BORDERLESS SER.2 ODDS 1:72
*BORDERLESS REF: 1.25X TO 3X BORDERED
BORDERLESS REF.SER.2 ODDS 1:288
M1 Nomar Garciaparra 3.00 8.00
M2 Chipper Jones 2.00 5.00
M3 Scott Rolen 1.25 3.00
M4 Albert Belle .75 2.00
M5 Mo Vaughn .75 2.00
M6 Jose Cruz Jr. .75 2.00
M7 Mark McGwire 5.00 12.00
M8 Derek Jeter 5.00 12.00
M9 Tony Gwynn 2.50 6.00
M10 Frank Thomas 2.00 5.00
M11 Tino Martinez 1.25 3.00
M12 Greg Maddux 3.00 8.00
M13 Juan Gonzalez .75 2.00
M14 Larry Walker .75 2.00
M15 Mike Piazza 3.00 8.00
M16 Cal Ripken 6.00 15.00
M17 Jeff Bagwell 1.25 3.00
M18 Andruw Jones 1.25 3.00
M19 Barry Bonds 6.00 15.00
M20 Ken Griffey Jr. 3.00 8.00

1998 Topps Rookie Class

Randomly inserted in Topps Series two packs at the rate of one in 12, this 10-card set features color photos of top young stars with less than one year's playing time in the Majors. The backs carry player information.

COMPLETE SET (10) 2.50 6.00
SER.2 STATED ODDS 1:12
R1 Travis Lee .30 .75
R2 Richard Hidalgo .30 .75
R3 Todd Helton .50 1.25
R4 Paul Konerko .30 .75
R5 Mark Kotsay .30 .75
R6 Derrek Lee .30 .75
R7 Eli Marrero .30 .75
R8 Fernando Tatis .30 .75
R9 Juan Encarnacion .30 .75
R10 Ben Grieve .30 .75

1999 Topps

The 1999 Topps set consisted of 462 standard-size cards. Each 11 card pack carried a suggested retail price of $1.29 per pack. Cards were also distributed in 40-card Home Team advantage jumbo packs, hobby, retail and Christmas factory sets. The Mark McGwire number 220 card was issued in 70 different varieties to honor his record setting season. The Sammy Sosa number 461 card was issued in 66 different varieties to honor his 1998 season. Basic sets are considered complete with any one of the 70 McGwire and 66 Sosa variations. A.J. Burnett, Pat Burrell, and Alex Escobar are the most notable Rookie Cards in the set. Card number 7 was not issued as Topps continues to honor the memory of Mickey Mantle. The Christmas factory set contains one Nolan Ryan finest reprint card as an added bonus, while the hobby and retail factory sets just contained the regular sets in a factory box.

COMPLETE SET (462) 30.00 80.00
COMP.HOBBY SET (462) 40.00 80.00
COMP.X-MAS SET (463) 40.00 80.00
COMP. SERIES 1 (241) 15.00 40.00
COMP. SERIES 2 (221) 15.00 40.00
COMP.MAC HR SET (70) 250.00 500.00
COMP.SOSA HR SET (66) 100.00 250.00
1 Roger Clemens .40 1.00
2 Andres Galarraga .07 .20
3 Scott Brosius .07 .20
4 John Flaherty .07 .20
5 Jim Leyritz .07 .20
6 Ray Durham .07 .20
8 Jose Vizcaino .07 .20
9 Will Clark .10 .30
10 David Wells .07 .20
11 Jose Guillen .07 .20
12 Scott Hatteberg .07 .20
13 Edgardo Alfonzo .07 .20
14 Mike Bordick .07 .20
15 Manny Ramirez .10 .30
16 Greg Maddux .30 .75
17 David Segui .07 .20
18 Darryl Strawberry .07 .20
19 Brad Radke .07 .20
20 Kerry Wood .07 .20
21 Matt Anderson .07 .20
22 Derrek Lee .10 .30
23 Mickey Morandini .07 .20
24 Paul Konerko .07 .20
25 Travis Lee .07 .20
26 Ken Hill .07 .20
27 Kenny Rogers .07 .20
28 Paul Sorrento .07 .20
29 Quilvio Veras .07 .20
30 Todd Walker .07 .20
31 Ryan Jackson .07 .20
32 John Olerud .07 .20
33 Doug Glanville .07 .20
34 Nolan Ryan .75 2.00
35 Ray Lankford .07 .20
36 Mark Loretta .07 .20
37 Jason Dickson .07 .20
38 Sean Bergman .07 .20
39 Quinton McCracken .07 .20
40 Bartolo Colon .07 .20
41 Brady Anderson .07 .20
42 Chris Stynes .07 .20
43 Jorge Posada .10 .30
44 Justin Thompson .07 .20
45 Johnny Damon .10 .30
46 Armando Benitez .07 .20
47 Brant Brown .07 .20
48 Charlie Hayes .07 .20
49 Darren Dreifort .07 .20
50 Juan Gonzalez .07 .20
51 Chuck Knoblauch .07 .20
52 Todd Helton .10 .30
53 Rick Reed .07 .20
54 Chris Gomez .07 .20
55 Gary Sheffield .07 .20
56 Rod Beck .07 .20
57 Rey Sanchez .07 .20
58 Garret Anderson .07 .20
59 Jimmy Haynes .07 .20
60 Steve Woodard .07 .20
61 Rondell White .07 .20
62 Vladimir Guerrero .20 .50
63 Eric Karros .07 .20
64 Russ Davis .07 .20
65 Mo Vaughn .07 .20
66 Sammy Sosa .20 .50
67 Troy Percival .07 .20
68 Kenny Lofton .07 .20
69 Bill Taylor .07 .20
70 Mark McGwire .50 1.25
71 Roger Cedeno .07 .20
72 Javy Lopez .07 .20
73 Damion Easley .07 .20
74 Andy Pettitte .10 .30
75 Tony Gwynn .25 .60
76 Ricardo Rincon .07 .20
77 F.P. Santangelo .07 .20
78 Jay Bell .07 .20
79 Scott Servais .07 .20
80 Jose Canseco .10 .30
81 Roberto Hernandez .07 .20
82 Todd Dunwoody .07 .20
83 John Wetteland .07 .20
84 Mike Caruso .07 .20
85 Derek Jeter .50 1.25
86 Aaron Sele .07 .20
87 Jose Lima .07 .20
88 Ryan Christenson .07 .20
89 Jeff Cirillo .07 .20
90 Jose Hernandez .07 .20
91 Mark Kotsay .07 .20
92 Darren Bragg .07 .20
93 Albert Belle .07 .20
94 Matt Lawton .07 .20
95 Pedro Martinez .10 .30
96 Greg Vaughn .07 .20
97 Neifi Perez .07 .20
98 Gerald Williams .07 .20
99 Derek Bell .07 .20
100 Ken Griffey Jr. .30 .75
101 David Cone .07 .20
102 Brian Johnson .07 .20
103 Dean Palmer .07 .20
104 Javier Valentin .07 .20
105 Trevor Hoffman .07 .20
106 Butch Huskey .07 .20
107 Dave Martinez .07 .20
108 Billy Wagner .07 .20
109 Shawn Green .07 .20
110 Ben Grieve .07 .20
111 Tom Goodwin .07 .20
112 Jaret Wright .07 .20
113 Aramis Ramirez .07 .20
114 Dmitri Young .07 .20
115 Hideki Irabu .07 .20
116 Roberto Kelly .07 .20
117 Jeff Fassero .07 .20
118 Mark Clark UER .07 .20
1997 and Career Victory totals are wrong
119 Jason McDonald .07 .20
120 Matt Williams .07 .20
121 Dave Burba .07 .20
122 Bret Saberhagen .07 .20
123 Deivi Cruz .07 .20
124 Chad Curtis .07 .20
125 Scott Rolen .10 .30
126 Lee Stevens .07 .20
127 J.T. Snow .07 .20
128 Rusty Greer .07 .20
129 Brian Meadows .07 .20
130 Jim Edmonds .07 .20
131 Ron Gant .07 .20
132 A.J. Hinch UER .07 .20
Photo is a reverse negative
133 Shannon Stewart .07 .20
134 Brad Fullmer .07 .20
135 Cal Eldred .07 .20
136 Matt Walbeck .07 .20
137 Carl Everett .07 .20
138 Walt Weiss .07 .20
139 Fred McGriff .10 .30
140 Darin Erstad .07 .20
141 Dave Nilsson .07 .20
142 Eric Young .07 .20
143 Dan Wilson .07 .20
144 Jeff Reed .07 .20
145 Brett Tomko .07 .20
146 Terry Steinbach .07 .20
147 Seth Greisinger .07 .20
148 Pat Meares .07 .20
149 Livan Hernandez .07 .20
150 Jeff Bagwell .10 .30
151 Bob Wickman .07 .20
152 Omar Vizquel .10 .30
153 Eric Davis .07 .20
154 Larry Sutton .07 .20
155 Magglio Ordonez .07 .20
156 Eric Milton .07 .20
157 Darren Lewis .07 .20
158 Rick Aguilera .07 .20
159 Mike Lieberthal .07 .20
160 Robb Nen .07 .20
161 Brian Giles .07 .20
162 Jeff Brantley .07 .20
163 Gary DiSarcina .07 .20
164 John Valentin .07 .20
165 David Dellucci .07 .20
166 Chan Ho Park .07 .20
167 Masato Yoshii .07 .20
168 Jason Schmidt .07 .20
169 LaTroy Hawkins .07 .20
170 Bret Boone .07 .20
171 Jerry DiPoto .07 .20
172 Mariano Rivera .20 .50
173 Mike Cameron .07 .20
174 Scott Erickson .07 .20
175 Charles Johnson .07 .20
176 Bobby Jones .07 .20
177 Francisco Cordova .07 .20
178 Todd Jones .07 .20
179 Jeff Montgomery .07 .20
180 Mike Mussina .10 .30
181 Bob Abreu .07 .20
182 Ismael Valdes .07 .20
183 Andy Fox .07 .20
184 Woody Williams .07 .20
185 Denny Neagle .07 .20
186 Jose Valentin .07 .20
187 Darrin Fletcher .07 .20
188 Gabe Alvarez .07 .20
189 Eddie Taubensee .07 .20
190 Edgar Martinez .10 .30
191 Jason Kendall .07 .20
192 Darryl Kile .07 .20
193 Jeff King .07 .20
194 Rey Ordonez .07 .20
195 Andruw Jones .10 .30
196 Tony Fernandez .07 .20
197 Jamey Wright .07 .20
198 B.J. Surhoff .07 .20
199 Vinny Castilla .07 .20
200 David Wells HL .07 .20
201 Mark McGwire HL .25 .60
202 Sammy Sosa HL .10 .30
203 Roger Clemens HL .20 .50
204 Kerry Wood HL .07 .20
205 Lance Berkman .15 .40
Mike Frank
Gabe Kapler
206 Alex Escobar RC .15 .40
Ricky Ledee
Mike Stoner
207 Peter Bergeron RC .08 .25
Jeremy Giambi
George Lombard
208 Michael Barrett .08 .25
Ben Davis
Robert Fick
209 Pat Cline .08 .25
Ramon Hernandez
Jayson Werth
210 Bruce Chen .08 .25
Chris Enochs
Ryan Anderson
211 Mike Lincoln .08 .25
Octavio Dotel
Brad Penny
212 Chuck Abbott RC .08 .25
Brent Butler
Danny Klassen
213 Chris C.Jones .08 .25
Jeff Urban RC
214 Arturo McDowell RC .08 .25
Tony Torcato
215 Josh McKinley RC .08 .25
Jason Tyner
216 Matt Burch .08 .25
Seth Etherton RC
UER back Etherton
217 Mamon Tucker RC .08 .25
Rick Elder
218 J.M.Gold .08 .25
Ryan Mills RC
219 Adam Brown .08 .25
Choo Freeman RC
220A Mark McGwire HR 1 15.00 40.00
220B Mark McGwire HR 2 6.00 15.00
220C Mark McGwire HR 3 6.00 15.00
220D Mark McGwire HR 4 6.00 15.00
220E Mark McGwire HR 5 6.00 15.00
220F Mark McGwire HR 6 6.00 15.00
220G Mark McGwire HR 7 6.00 15.00
220H Mark McGwire HR 8 6.00 15.00
220I Mark McGwire HR 9 6.00 15.00
220J M.McGwire HR 10 6.00 15.00
220K M.McGwire HR 11 6.00 15.00
220L M.McGwire HR 12 6.00 15.00
220M M.McGwire HR 13 6.00 15.00
220N M.McGwire HR 14 6.00 15.00
220O M.McGwire HR 15 6.00 15.00
220P M.McGwire HR 16 6.00 15.00
220Q M.McGwire HR 17 6.00 15.00
220R M.McGwire HR 18 6.00 15.00
220S M.McGwire HR 19 6.00 15.00
220T M.McGwire HR 20 6.00 15.00
220U M.McGwire HR 21 6.00 15.00
220V M.McGwire HR 22 6.00 15.00
220W M.McGwire HR 23 6.00 15.00
220X M.McGwire HR 24 6.00 15.00
220Y M.McGwire HR 25 6.00 15.00
220Z M.McGwire HR 26 6.00 15.00
220AA M.McGwire HR 27 6.00 15.00
220AB M.McGwire HR 28 6.00 15.00
220AC M.McGwire HR 29 6.00 15.00
220AD M.McGwire HR 30 6.00 15.00
220AE M.McGwire HR 31 6.00 15.00
220AF M.McGwire HR 32 6.00 15.00
220AG M.McGwire HR 33 6.00 15.00
220AH M.McGwire HR 34 6.00 15.00
220AI M.McGwire HR 35 6.00 15.00
220AJ M.McGwire HR 36 6.00 15.00
220AK M.McGwire HR 37 6.00 15.00
220AL M.McGwire HR 38 6.00 15.00
220AM M.McGwire HR 39 6.00 15.00
220AN M.McGwire HR 40 6.00 15.00
220AO M.McGwire HR 41 6.00 15.00
220AP M.McGwire HR 42 6.00 15.00
220AQ M.McGwire HR 43 6.00 15.00
220AR M.McGwire HR 44 6.00 15.00
220AS M.McGwire HR 45 6.00 15.00
220AT M.McGwire HR 46 6.00 15.00
220AU M.McGwire HR 47 6.00 15.00
220AV M.McGwire HR 48 6.00 15.00
220AW M.McGwire HR 49 6.00 15.00
220AX M.McGwire HR 50 6.00 15.00
220AY M.McGwire HR 51 6.00 15.00
220AZ M.McGwire HR 52 6.00 15.00
220BB M.McGwire HR 53 6.00 15.00
220CC M.McGwire HR 54 6.00 15.00
220DD M.McGwire HR 55 6.00 15.00
220EE M.McGwire HR 56 6.00 15.00
220FF M.McGwire HR 57 6.00 15.00
220GG M.McGwire HR 58 6.00 15.00
220HH M.McGwire HR 59 6.00 15.00
220II M.McGwire HR 60 6.00 15.00
220JJ M.McGwire HR 61 12.50 30.00
220KK M.McGwire HR 62 15.00 40.00
220LL M.McGwire HR 63 6.00 15.00
220MM M.McGwire HR 64 6.00 15.00
220NN M.McGwire HR 65 6.00 15.00
220OO M.McGwire HR 66 6.00 15.00
220PP M.McGwire HR 67 6.00 15.00
220QQ M.McGwire HR 68 6.00 15.00
220RR M.McGwire HR 69 6.00 15.00
220SS M.McGwire HR 70 50.00 100.00
221 Larry Walker LL .07 .20
222 Bernie Williams LL .07 .20
223 Mark McGwire LL .25 .60
224 Ken Griffey Jr. LL .20 .50
225 Sammy Sosa LL .10 .30
226 Juan Gonzalez LL .07 .20
227 Dante Bichette LL .07 .20
228 Alex Rodriguez LL .20 .50
229 Sammy Sosa LL .10 .30
230 Derek Jeter LL .25 .60
231 Greg Maddux LL .20 .50
232 Roger Clemens LL .20 .50
233 Ricky Ledee WS .07 .20
234 Chuck Knoblauch WS .07 .20
235 Bernie Williams WS .07 .20
236 Tino Martinez WS .07 .20
237 Orl. Hernandez WS .07 .20
238 Scott Brosius WS .07 .20
239 Andy Pettitte WS .07 .20
240 Mariano Rivera WS .10 .30
241 Checklist 1 .07 .20
242 Checklist 2 .07 .20
243 Tom Glavine .10 .30
244 Andy Benes .07 .20
245 Sandy Alomar Jr. .07 .20
246 Wilton Guerrero .07 .20
247 Alex Gonzalez .07 .20
248 Roberto Alomar .10 .30
249 Ruben Rivera .07 .20
250 Eric Chavez .07 .20
251 Ellis Burks .07 .20
252 Richie Sexson .07 .20
253 Steve Finley .07 .20
254 Dwight Gooden .07 .20
255 Dustin Hermanson .07 .20
256 Kirk Rueter .07 .20
257 Steve Trachsel .07 .20
258 Gregg Jefferies .07 .20
259 Matt Stairs .07 .20
260 Shane Reynolds .07 .20
261 Gregg Olson .07 .20
262 Kevin Tapani .07 .20
263 Matt Morris .07 .20
264 Carl Pavano .07 .20
265 Nomar Garciaparra .30 .75
266 Kevin Young .07 .20
267 Rick Helling .07 .20
268 Matt Franco .07 .20
269 Brian McRae .07 .20
270 Cal Ripken .60 1.50
271 Jeff Abbott .07 .20
272 Tony Batista .07 .20
273 Bill Simas .07 .20
274 Brian Hunter .07 .20
275 John Franco .07 .20
276 Devon White .07 .20
277 Rickey Henderson .20 .50
278 Chuck Finley .07 .20
279 Mike Blowers .07 .20
280 Mark Grace .10 .30
281 Randy Winn .07 .20
282 Bobby Bonilla .07 .20
283 David Justice .07 .20
284 Shane Monahan .07 .20
285 Kevin Brown .10 .30
286 Todd Zeile .07 .20
287 Al Martin .07 .20
288 Troy O'Leary .07 .20
289 Darryl Hamilton .07 .20
290 Tino Martinez .10 .30
291 David Ortiz .20 .50
292 Tony Clark .07 .20
293 Ryan Minor .07 .20
294 Mark Leiter .07 .20
295 Wally Joyner .07 .20
296 Cliff Floyd .07 .20
297 Shawn Estes .07 .20
298 Pat Hentgen .07 .20
299 Scott Elarton .07 .20
300 Alex Rodriguez .30 .75
301 Ozzie Guillen .07 .20
302 Hideo Nomo .20 .50
303 Ryan McGuire .07 .20
304 Brad Ausmus .07 .20
305 Alex Gonzalez .07 .20
306 Brian Jordan .07 .20
307 John Jaha .07 .20
308 Mark Grudzielanek .07 .20
309 Juan Guzman .07 .20
310 Tony Womack .07 .20
311 Dennis Reyes .07 .20
312 Marty Cordova .07 .20
313 Ramiro Mendoza .07 .20
314 Robin Ventura .07 .20
315 Rafael Palmeiro .10 .30
316 Ramon Martinez .07 .20
317 Pedro Astacio .07 .20
318 Dave Hollins .07 .20
319 Tom Candiotti .07 .20
320 Al Leiter .07 .20
321 Rico Brogna .07 .20
322 Reggie Jefferson .07 .20
323 Bernard Gilkey .07 .20
324 Jason Giambi .07 .20
325 Craig Biggio .10 .30
326 Troy Glaus .10 .30
327 Delino DeShields .07 .20
328 Fernando Vina .07 .20
329 John Smoltz .10 .30
330 Jeff Kent .07 .20
331 Roy Halladay .20 .50
332 Andy Ashby .07 .20
333 Tim Wakefield .07 .20
334 Roger Clemens .40 1.00
335 Bernie Williams .10 .30
336 Desi Relaford .07 .20
337 John Burkett .07 .20
338 Mike Hampton .07 .20
339 Royce Clayton .07 .20
340 Mike Piazza .30 .75
341 Jeremi Gonzalez .07 .20
342 Mike Lansing .07 .20
343 Jamie Moyer .07 .20
344 Ron Coomer .07 .20
345 Barry Larkin .10 .30
346 Fernando Tatis .07 .20
347 Chili Davis .07 .20
348 Bobby Higginson .07 .20
349 Hal Morris .07 .20
350 Larry Walker .07 .20
351 Carlos Guillen .07 .20
352 Miguel Tejada .07 .20
353 Travis Fryman .07 .20
354 Jarrod Washburn .07 .20
355 Chipper Jones .20 .50
356 Todd Stottlemyre .07 .20
357 Henry Rodriguez .07 .20
358 Eli Marrero .07 .20
359 Alan Benes .07 .20
360 Tim Salmon .10 .30
361 Luis Gonzalez .07 .20
362 Scott Spiezio .07 .20
363 Chris Carpenter .07 .20
364 Bobby Howry .07 .20
365 Raul Mondesi .07 .20
366 Ugueth Urbina .07 .20
367 Tom Evans .07 .20
368 Kerry Ligtenberg RC .08 .25
369 Adrian Beltre .07 .20
370 Ryan Klesko .07 .20
371 Wilson Alvarez .07 .20
372 John Thomson .07 .20
373 Tony Saunders .07 .20
374 Dave Mlicki .07 .20
375 Ken Caminiti .07 .20
376 Jay Buhner .07 .20
377 Bill Mueller .07 .20
378 Jeff Blauser .07 .20
379 Edgar Renteria .07 .20
380 Jim Thome .10 .30
381 Joey Hamilton .07 .20
382 Calvin Pickering .07 .20
383 Marquis Grissom .07 .20
384 Omar Daal .07 .20
385 Curt Schilling .07 .20
386 Jose Cruz Jr. .07 .20
387 Chris Widger .07 .20
388 Pete Harnisch .07 .20
389 Charles Nagy .07 .20
390 Tom Gordon .07 .20
391 Bobby Smith .07 .20
392 Derrick Gibson .07 .20
393 Jeff Conine .07 .20
394 Carlos Perez .07 .20
395 Barry Bonds .60 1.50
396 Mark McLemore .07 .20
397 Juan Encarnacion .07 .20
398 Wade Boggs .10 .30
399 Ivan Rodriguez .10 .30
400 Moises Alou .07 .20
401 Jeromy Burnitz .07 .20
402 Sean Casey .07 .20
403 Jose Offerman .07 .20
404 Joe Fontenot .07 .20
405 Kevin Millwood .07 .20
406 Lance Johnson .07 .20
407 Richard Hidalgo .07 .20
408 Mike Jackson .07 .20
409 Brian Anderson .07 .20
410 Jeff Shaw .07 .20
411 Preston Wilson .07 .20
412 Todd Hundley .07 .20
413 Jim Parque .07 .20
414 Justin Baughman .07 .20
415 Dante Bichette .07 .20
416 Paul O'Neill .10 .30
417 Miguel Cairo .07 .20
418 Randy Johnson .20 .50
419 Jesus Sanchez .07 .20
420 Carlos Delgado .07 .20
421 Ricky Ledee .07 .20
422 Orlando Hernandez .07 .20
423 Frank Thomas .20 .50
424 Pokey Reese .07 .20
425 Carlos Lee .15 .40
Mike Lowell
Kit Pellow RC
426 Michael Cuddyer .08 .25
Mark DeRosa
Jerry Hairston Jr.
427 Marlon Anderson .15 .40
Ron Belliard
Orlando Cabrera
428 Micah Bowie .08 .25
Phil Norton RC
Randy Wolf
429 Jack Cressend RC .15 .40
Jason Rakers
John Rocker
430 Ruben Mateo .08 .25
Scott Morgan
Mike Zywica RC
431 Jason LaRue .08 .25
Matt LeCroy
Mitch Meluskey
432 Gabe Kapler .15 .40
Armando Rios
Fernando Seguignol
433 Adam Kennedy .08 .25
Mickey Lopez RC
Jackie Rexrode
434 Jose Fernandez RC .08 .25
Jeff Liefer
Chris Truby
435 Corey Koskie .20 .50
Doug Mientkiewicz RC
Damon Minor
436 Roosevelt Brown RC .08 .25
Dernell Stenson
Vernon Wells
437 A.J. Burnett RC .30 .75
Billy Koch
John Nicholson
438 Matt Belisle .08 .25
Matt Roney RC
439 Austin Kearns .60 1.50
Chris George RC
440 Nate Bump RC .08 .25
Nate Cornejo
441 Brad Lidge .60 1.50
Mike Nannini RC
442 Matt Holliday 1.50 4.00
Jeff Winchester RC
443 Adam Everett .20 .50
Chip Ambres RC
444 Pat Burrell .60 1.50
Eric Valent RC
445 Roger Clemens SK .20 .50
446 Kerry Wood SK .07 .20
447 Curt Schilling SK .07 .20
448 Randy Johnson SK .10 .30
449 Pedro Martinez SK .10 .30
450 Jeff Bagwell AT .20 .50
Andres Galarraga
Mark McGwire
451 John Olerud AT .07 .20
Jim Thome
Tino Martinez
452 Alex Rodriguez AT .25 .60
Nomar Garciaparra
Derek Jeter
453 Vinny Castilla AT .10 .30
Chipper Jones
Scott Rolen
454 Sammy Sosa AT .20 .50
Ken Griffey Jr.
Juan Gonzalez
455 Barry Bonds AT .30 .75
Manny Ramirez
Larry Walker
456 Frank Thomas AT .20 .50
Tim Salmon
David Justice
457 Travis Lee AT .07 .20
Todd Helton
Ben Grieve
458 Vladimir Guerrero AT .07 .20
Greg Vaughn
Bernie Williams
459 Mike Piazza AT .20 .50
Ivan Rodriguez
Jason Kendall
460 Roger Clemens AT .20 .50
Kerry Wood
Greg Maddux
461A Sammy Sosa HR 1 6.00 15.00
461B Sammy Sosa HR 2 2.50 6.00
461C Sammy Sosa HR 3 2.50 6.00
461D Sammy Sosa HR 4 2.50 6.00
461E Sammy Sosa HR 5 2.50 6.00
461F Sammy Sosa HR 6 2.50 6.00
461G Sammy Sosa HR 7 2.50 6.00
461H Sammy Sosa HR 8 2.50 6.00
461I Sammy Sosa HR 9 2.50 6.00
461J Sammy Sosa HR 10 2.50 6.00
461K Sammy Sosa HR 11 2.50 6.00
461L Sammy Sosa HR 12 2.50 6.00
461M Sammy Sosa HR 13 2.50 6.00
461N Sammy Sosa HR 14 2.50 6.00
461O Sammy Sosa HR 15 2.50 6.00
461P Sammy Sosa HR 16 2.50 6.00
461Q Sammy Sosa HR 17 2.50 6.00
461R Sammy Sosa HR 18 2.50 6.00
461S Sammy Sosa HR 19 2.50 6.00
461T Sammy Sosa HR 20 2.50 6.00
461U Sammy Sosa HR 21 2.50 6.00
461V Sammy Sosa HR 22 2.50 6.00
461W Sammy Sosa HR 23 2.50 6.00
461X Sammy Sosa HR 24 2.50 6.00
461Y Sammy Sosa HR 25 2.50 6.00
461Z Sammy Sosa HR 26 2.50 6.00
461AA S.Sosa HR 27 2.50 6.00
461AB S.Sosa HR 28 2.50 6.00
461AC S.Sosa HR 29 2.50 6.00
461AD S.Sosa HR 30 2.50 6.00
461AE S.Sosa HR 31 2.50 6.00
461AF S.Sosa HR 32 2.50 6.00
461AG S.Sosa HR 33 2.50 6.00
461AH S.Sosa HR 34 2.50 6.00
461AI S.Sosa HR 35 2.50 6.00
461AJ S.Sosa HR 36 2.50 6.00
461AK S.Sosa HR 37 2.50 6.00
461AL S.Sosa HR 38 2.50 6.00
461AM S.Sosa HR 39 2.50 6.00
461AN S.Sosa HR 40 2.50 6.00
461AO S.Sosa HR 41 2.50 6.00

Card	Low	High
461AP S.Sosa HR 42	2.50	6.00
461AR S.Sosa HR 43	2.50	6.00
461AS S.Sosa HR 44	2.50	6.00
461AT S.Sosa HR 45	2.50	6.00
461AU S.Sosa HR 46	2.50	6.00
461AV S.Sosa HR 47	2.50	6.00
461AW S.Sosa HR 48	2.50	6.00
461AX S.Sosa HR 49	2.50	6.00
461AY S.Sosa HR 50	2.50	6.00
461AZ S.Sosa HR 51	2.50	6.00
461BB S.Sosa HR 52	2.50	6.00
461CC S.Sosa HR 53	2.50	6.00
461DD S.Sosa HR 54	2.50	6.00
461EE S.Sosa HR 55	2.50	6.00
461FF S.Sosa HR 56	2.50	6.00
461GG S.Sosa HR 57	2.50	6.00
461HH S.Sosa HR 58	2.50	6.00
461II S.Sosa HR 59	2.50	6.00
461JJ S.Sosa HR 60	2.50	6.00
461KK S.Sosa HR 61	6.00	15.00
461LL S.Sosa HR 62	8.00	20.00
461MM S.Sosa HR 63	3.00	8.00
461NN S.Sosa HR 64	3.00	8.00
461OO S.Sosa HR 65	3.00	8.00
461PP S.Sosa HR 66	10.00	25.00
462 Checklist	.07	.20
463 Checklist	.07	.20

1999 Topps MVP Promotion

This is a partial parallel to the regular Topps set. Draft pick and Prospect cards were not included in series one but were included in series two. The front of the card features the same photo as the basic issue card but is adorned with a bold gold foil MVP Promotion logo. The back features contest guidelines for the Topps MVP Promotion. If the featured player was awarded player of the week status (as determined by Topps) his card was then redeemable at season's end for a special set of all the weekly winners. Only 100 of each MVP Promotion card was produced. Stated odds were as follows: series 1 hobby packs 1:515, series 1 Home Team Advantage packs 1:142 and series 2 hobby packs 1:504, Series 2 Home Team Advantage 1:139 and series 2 retail 1:504. The exchange deadline to redeem winning cards was December 31st, 1999. Winning prize cards were mailed out between February 15th, 2000 and April 30th, 2000. The winning cards were the following numbers (which correspond to the regular Topps set): 35, 52. 70, 96, 101, 125, 127, 139, 159, 198, 248, 265, 290, 292, 300, 315, 340, 346, 350, 352, 355, 360, 365, 416, and 418. Since Topps destroyed these Winner exchange cards once they received them, they're in noticeably shorter supply than other cards from this set. Despite this fact, no noticeable premiums in secondary trading levels have been detected for these cards.

*STARS: 20X TO 50X BASIC CARDS
*ROOKIES: 8X TO 20X BASIC CARDS
SER.1 ODDS 1:515 HOB, 1:142 HTA
SER.2 ODDS 1:504 HOB, 1:139 HTA, 1:504 RET

Card	Low	High
35 Ray Lankford W	4.00	10.00
52 Todd Helton W	6.00	15.00
70 Mark McGwire W	25.00	60.00
96 Greg Vaughn W	4.00	10.00
101 David Cone W	4.00	10.00
125 Scott Rolen W	6.00	15.00
127 J.T. Snow W	4.00	10.00
139 Fred McGriff W	6.00	15.00
159 Mike Lieberthal W	4.00	10.00
198 B.J. Surhoff W	4.00	10.00
248 Roberto Alomar W	6.00	15.00
265 Nomar Garciaparra W	15.00	40.00
290 Tino Martinez W	6.00	15.00
292 Tony Clark W	4.00	10.00
300 Alex Rodriguez W	15.00	40.00
315 Rafael Palmeiro W	6.00	15.00
340 Mike Piazza W	15.00	40.00
346 Fernando Tatis W	4.00	10.00
350 Larry Walker W	4.00	10.00
352 Miguel Tejada W	4.00	10.00
355 Chipper Jones W	10.00	25.00
360 Tim Salmon W	6.00	15.00
365 Raul Mondesi W	4.00	10.00
416 Paul O'Neill W	6.00	15.00
418 Randy Johnson W	10.00	25.00

1999 Topps MVP Promotion Exchange

This 25-card set was available only to those lucky collectors who obtained one of the twenty-five winning player cards from the 1999 Topps MVP Promotion parallel set. Each week, throughout the 1999 season, Topps named a new Player of the Week, and that player's Topps MVP Promotion parallel card was made redeemable for this 25-card set. The deadline to exchange the winning cards was December 31st, 1999. The exchange cards shipped out in mid-February, 2000.

Card	Low	High
COMP.FACT.SET (25)	20.00	50.00
MVP1 Raul Mondesi	.60	1.50
MVP2 Tim Salmon	1.00	2.50
MVP3 Fernando Tatis	.60	1.50
MVP4 Larry Walker	.60	1.50
MVP5 Fred McGriff	1.00	2.50
MVP6 Nomar Garciaparra	2.50	6.00
MVP7 Rafael Palmeiro	1.00	2.50
MVP8 Randy Johnson	1.50	4.00
MVP9 Mike Lieberthal	.60	1.50
MVP10 B.J. Surhoff	.60	1.50
MVP11 Todd Helton	1.00	2.50
MVP12 Tino Martinez	1.00	2.50
MVP13 Scott Rolen	1.00	2.50
MVP14 Mike Piazza	2.50	6.00
MVP15 David Cone	.60	1.50
MVP16 Tony Clark	.60	1.50
MVP17 Roberto Alomar	1.00	2.50
MVP18 Miguel Tejada	.60	1.50
MVP19 Alex Rodriguez	2.50	6.00
MVP20 J.T. Snow	.60	1.50
MVP21 Ray Lankford	.60	1.50
MVP22 Greg Vaughn	.60	1.50
MVP23 Paul O'Neill	1.00	2.50
MVP24 Chipper Jones	1.50	4.00
MVP25 Mark McGwire	4.00	10.00

1999 Topps Oversize

Inserted one per Home Team Advantage and one per Hobby box, these cards feature sixteen of the leading players in an oversize version. The photos are the same as the regular Topps cards. We have numbered the cards with A and B prefixes to denote series one versus series two distribution, although Topps decided to number each series 1 through 8.

Card	Low	High
COMPLETE SERIES 1 (8)	6.00	15.00
COMPLETE SERIES 2 (8)	6.00	15.00

1999 Topps All-Matrix

This 30-card insert set consists of three thematic subsets (Club 40 are numbers 1-13, '99 Rookie Rush are number's 14-23 and Club K are numbers 24-30). All 30-cards feature silver foil dot-matrix technology. Cards were seeded exclusively into series 2 packs as follows: 1:18 hobby, 1:18 retail and 1:5 Home Team Advantage.

COMPLETE SET (30) 40.00 80.00
SER.2 ODDS 1:18 HOB/RET, 1:5 HTA

Card	Low	High
AM1 Mark McGwire	4.00	10.00
AM2 Sammy Sosa	1.50	4.00
AM3 Ken Griffey Jr.	2.50	6.00
AM4 Greg Vaughn	.60	1.50
AM5 Albert Belle	.60	1.50
AM6 Vinny Castilla	.60	1.50
AM7 Jose Canseco	1.00	2.50
AM8 Juan Gonzalez	.60	1.50
AM9 Manny Ramirez	1.00	2.50
AM10 Andres Galarraga	.60	1.50
AM11 Rafael Palmeiro	1.00	2.50
AM12 Alex Rodriguez	2.50	6.00
AM13 Mo Vaughn	.60	1.50
AM14 Eric Chavez	.60	1.50
AM15 Gabe Kapler	1.25	3.00
AM16 Calvin Pickering	.60	1.50
AM17 Ruben Mateo	.75	2.00
AM18 Roy Halladay	1.50	4.00
AM19 Jeremy Giambi	.60	1.50
AM20 Alex Gonzalez	.60	1.50
AM21 Ron Belliard	1.25	3.00
AM22 Marlon Anderson	1.25	3.00
AM23 Carlos Lee	1.25	3.00
AM24 Kerry Wood	.60	1.50
AM25 Roger Clemens	3.00	8.00
AM26 Curt Schilling	.60	1.50
AM27 Kevin Brown	1.00	2.50
AM28 Randy Johnson	1.50	4.00
AM29 Pedro Martinez	1.00	2.50
AM30 Orlando Hernandez	.60	1.50

1999 Topps All-Topps Mystery Finest

Randomly inserted in Topps Series two packs at the the rate of one in 36, this 33-card set features 11 three-player positional parallels of the All-Topps subset printed using Finest technology. All three players are printed on the back, but the collector has to peel off the opaque protector to reveal who is on the front.

COMPLETE SET (33) 125.00 250.00
SER.2 ODDS 1:36 HOB/RET, 1:8 HTA
*REFRACTORS: 1X TO 2.5X BASIC ATMF
SER.2 REF.ODDS 1:144 HOB/RET, 1:32 HTA

Card	Low	High
M1 Jeff Bagwell	2.00	5.00
M2 Andres Galarraga	1.25	3.00
M3 Mark McGwire	8.00	20.00
M4 John Olerud	1.25	3.00
M5 Jim Thome	2.00	5.00
M6 Tino Martinez	2.00	5.00
M7 Alex Rodriguez	5.00	12.00
M8 Nomar Garciaparra	5.00	12.00
M9 Derek Jeter	8.00	20.00
M10 Vinny Castilla	1.25	3.00
M11 Chipper Jones	3.00	8.00
M12 Scott Rolen	2.00	5.00
M13 Sammy Sosa	3.00	8.00
M14 Ken Griffey Jr.	5.00	12.00
M15 Juan Gonzalez	1.25	3.00
M16 Barry Bonds	10.00	25.00
M17 Manny Ramirez	2.00	5.00
M18 Larry Walker	1.25	3.00
M19 Frank Thomas	3.00	8.00
M20 Tim Salmon	2.00	5.00
M21 Dave Justice	1.25	3.00
M22 Travis Lee	1.25	3.00
M23 Todd Helton	2.00	5.00
M24 Ben Grieve	1.25	3.00
M25 Vladimir Guerrero	3.00	8.00
M26 Greg Vaughn	1.25	3.00
M27 Bernie Williams	2.00	5.00
M28 Mike Piazza	5.00	12.00
M29 Ivan Rodriguez	2.00	5.00
M30 Jason Kendall	1.25	3.00
M31 Roger Clemens	6.00	15.00
M32 Kerry Wood	1.25	3.00
M33 Greg Maddux	5.00	12.00

1999 Topps Autographs

Inserted one in every 532 first series hobby packs, one in every 146 first series Home Team Advantage packs,d one in every 501 second series hobby packs and one in every 138 second series Home Team Advantage packs, these cards feature an assortment of young and old players affixing their signature to these cards. Cards A1-A8 were distributed exclusively in first series packs and cards A9-A16 were distributed exclusively in second series packs. The fronts feature a player photo with the authentic autograph on the bottom.

SER.1 ODDS 1:532 HOB, 1:146 HTA
SER.2 ODDS 1:501 HOB, 1:138 HTA

Card	Low	High
A1 Roger Clemens	30.00	60.00
A2 Chipper Jones	20.00	50.00
A3 Scott Rolen	10.00	25.00
A4 Alex Rodriguez	50.00	100.00
A5 Andres Galarraga	6.00	15.00
A6 Rondell White	6.00	15.00
A7 Ben Grieve	4.00	10.00
A8 Troy Glaus	10.00	25.00
A9 Moises Alou	6.00	15.00
A10 Barry Bonds	40.00	80.00
A11 Vladimir Guerrero	12.50	30.00
A12 Andruw Jones	6.00	15.00
A13 Darin Erstad	6.00	15.00
A14 Shawn Green	6.00	15.00
A15 Eric Chavez	4.00	10.00
A16 Pat Burrell	10.00	25.00

1999 Topps Hall of Fame Collection

This 10 card set features Hall of Famers with photos of the plaques and a silhoutted photo. These cards were inserted one every 12 hobby packs and one every three HTA packs.

COMPLETE SET (10) 10.00 20.00
SER.1 ODDS 1:12 HOB/RET, 1:3 HTA

Card	Low	High
HOF1 Mike Schmidt	1.50	4.00
HOF2 Brooks Robinson	.75	2.00
HOF3 Stan Musial	1.25	3.00
HOF4 Willie McCovey	.75	2.00
HOF5 Eddie Mathews	.75	2.00
HOF6 Reggie Jackson	.75	2.00
HOF7 Ernie Banks	.75	2.00
HOF8 Whitey Ford	.75	2.00
HOF9 Bob Feller	.75	2.00
HOF10 Yogi Berra	.75	2.00

1999 Topps Lords of the Diamond

This die-cut insert set was inserted one every 18 hobby packs and one every five HTA packs. The words "Lords of the Diamond" are printed on the top while the players name is at the bottom. The middle of the card has the players photo.

COMPLETE SET (15) 25.00 50.00
SER.1 ODDS 1:18 HOB/RET, 1:5 HTA

Card	Low	High
LD1 Ken Griffey Jr.	1.50	4.00
LD2 Chipper Jones	1.00	2.50
LD3 Sammy Sosa	1.00	2.50
LD4 Frank Thomas	1.00	2.50
LD5 Mark McGwire	2.50	6.00
LD6 Jeff Bagwell	.60	1.50
LD7 Alex Rodriguez	1.50	4.00
LD8 Juan Gonzalez	.40	1.00
LD9 Barry Bonds	3.00	8.00
LD10 Nomar Garciaparra	1.50	4.00
LD11 Darin Erstad	.40	1.00
LD12 Tony Gwynn	1.25	3.00
LD13 Andres Galarraga	.40	1.00
LD14 Mike Piazza	1.50	4.00
LD15 Greg Maddux	1.50	4.00

1999 Topps New Breed

Fifteen of the young stars of the game are featured in this insert set. The cards were seeded into the 99 Topps packs at a rate of one every 18 hobby packs and one every five HTA packs.

COMPLETE SET (15) 12.50 25.00
SER.1 ODDS 1:18 HOB/RET, 1:5 HTA

Card	Low	High
NB1 Darin Erstad	.30	.75
NB2 Brad Fullmer	.30	.75
NB3 Kerry Wood	.30	.75
NB4 Nomar Garciaparra	1.25	3.00
NB5 Travis Lee	.30	.75
NB6 Scott Rolen	.50	1.25
NB7 Todd Helton	.50	1.25
NB8 Vladimir Guerrero	.75	2.00
NB9 Derek Jeter	2.00	5.00
NB10 Alex Rodriguez	1.25	3.00
NB11 Ben Grieve	.30	.75
NB12 Andruw Jones	.50	1.25
NB13 Paul Konerko	.30	.75
NB14 Aramis Ramirez	.30	.75
NB15 Adrian Beltre	.30	.75

1999 Topps Picture Perfect

This 10 card insert set was inserted one every eight hobby packs and one every two HTA packs. These cards all contain a minor, very difficult to determine mistake and part of the charm is to figure out what the error is in the card.

COMPLETE SET (10) 7.50 15.00
SER.1 ODDS 1:8 HOB/RET, 1:2 HTA

Card	Low	High
P1 Ken Griffey Jr.	.60	1.50
P2 Kerry Wood	.15	.40
P3 Pedro Martinez	.25	.60
P4 Mark McGwire	1.00	2.50
P5 Greg Maddux	.60	1.50
P6 Sammy Sosa	.40	1.00
P7 Greg Vaughn	.15	.40
P8 Juan Gonzalez	.15	.40
P9 Jeff Bagwell	.25	.60
P10 Derek Jeter	1.00	2.50

1999 Topps Power Brokers

This 20 card set features leading baseball players. They were inserted at a seeded rate of one every 36 hobby/retail packs and one every eight HTA packs.

COMPLETE SET (20) 60.00 120.00
SER.1 ODDS 1:36 HOB/RET, 1:8 HTA
*REFRACTORS: 1X TO 2.5X BASIC BROKERS
SER.1 REF.ODDS 1:144 HOB/RET, 1:32 HTA

Card	Low	High
PB1 Mark McGwire	5.00	12.00
PB2 Andres Galarraga	.75	2.00
PB3 Ken Griffey Jr.	3.00	8.00
PB4 Sammy Sosa	2.00	5.00
PB5 Juan Gonzalez	.75	2.00
PB6 Alex Rodriguez	3.00	8.00
PB7 Frank Thomas	2.00	5.00
PB8 Jeff Bagwell	1.25	3.00
PB9 Vinny Castilla	.75	2.00
PB10 Mike Piazza	3.00	8.00
PB11 Greg Vaughn	.75	2.00
PB12 Barry Bonds	6.00	15.00
PB13 Mo Vaughn	.75	2.00
PB14 Jim Thome	1.25	3.00
PB15 Larry Walker	.75	2.00
PB16 Chipper Jones	2.00	5.00
PB17 Nomar Garciaparra	3.00	8.00
PB18 Manny Ramirez	1.25	3.00
PB19 Roger Clemens	4.00	10.00
PB20 Kerry Wood	.75	2.00

1999 Topps Record Numbers

Randomly inserted in Series two hobby and retail packs at the rate of one in eight and HTA packs at a rate of one in two, this 10-card set features action color photos of record-setting players with silver foil highlights.

COMPLETE SET (10) 7.50 15.00
SER.2 ODDS 1:8 HOB/RET, 1:2 HTA

Card	Low	High
RN1 Mark McGwire	1.00	2.50
RN2 Mike Piazza	.60	1.50
RN3 Curt Schilling	.15	.40
RN4 Ken Griffey Jr.	.60	1.50
RN5 Sammy Sosa	.40	1.00
RN6 Nomar Garciaparra	.60	1.50
RN7 Kerry Wood	.15	.40
RN8 Roger Clemens	.75	2.00
RN9 Cal Ripken	1.25	3.00
RN10 Mark McGwire	1.00	2.50

1999 Topps Record Numbers Gold

Randomly seeded in series two packs, these scarce gold-foiled cards parallel the more common "silver-foiled" Record Numbers inserts. The print run for each card was based upon the statistic specified on the card. Erroneous stated odds for these Gold cards were unfortunately printed on all series two wrappers. According to sources at Topps the correct pack odds are as follows: RN1 1:151,320 hob, 1:38,016 HTA, 1:138,567 ret, RN2 1:28,317 hob, 1:7,797 HTA, 1:28,340 ret, RN3 1:32,134 hob, 1:8,848 HTA, 1:32,160 ret, RN4 1:29,288 hob, 1:8,064 HTA, 1:29,312 ret, RN5 1:907,920 hob, 1:133,056 HTA, 1:1,524,420 ret, RN6 1:605,280 hob, 1:88,704 HTA, 1:1,016,280 ret, RN7 1:907,920 hob, 1:133,056 HTA, 1:1,524,420 ret, RN8 1:907,920 hob, 1:133,056 HTA, 1:1,524,420 ret, RN9 1:3891 hob, 1:1069 HTA, 1:3888 ret, RN10 1:63,312 hob, 1:17,741 HTA, 1:63,510 ret. No pricing is available for cards with print runs of 30 or less.

Card	Low	High
RN1 Mark McGwire/70	50.00	100.00
RN2 Mike Piazza/362	6.00	15.00
RN3 Curt Schilling/319	3.00	8.00
RN4 Ken Griffey Jr./350	8.00	20.00
RN5 Sammy Sosa/20		
RN6 N.Garciaparra/30		
RN7 Kerry Wood/20		
RN8 Roger Clemens/20		
RN9 Cal Ripken/2632	6.00	15.00
RN10 Mark McGwire/162	15.00	40.00

1999 Topps Ryan

These cards reflect the Nolan Ryan Reprints of earlier Topps cards featuring the pitcher known for "Texas Heat". These cards are replicas of Ryan's cards and have a commemorative sticker placed on them as well. The cards were seeded one every 18 hobby/retail packs and one every five HTA packs. Odd-numbered cards (i.e. 1, 3, 5 etc.) were distributed in first series packs and even numbered cards were distributed in second series packs.

Card	Low	High
COMPLETE SET (27)	30.00	80.00
COMPLETE SERIES 1 (14)	15.00	40.00
COMPLETE SERIES 2 (13)	15.00	40.00
COMMON CARD (1-27)	2.00	5.00

STATED ODDS 1:18 HOB/RET, 1:5 HTA
1 Nolan Ryan 1968 UER 4.00 10.00
All the Ryan Rookie parallels in this set have the word sensational misspelled

1999 Topps Ryan Autographs

Nolan Ryan signed a selection of all 27 cards for this reprint set. The autographed cards were issued one every 4,250 series one hobby packs, one in every 5,007 series two hobby packs and one every 1,176 series one HTA packs.

Card	Low	High
COMMON CARD (1-13)	125.00	200.00
COMMON CARD (14-27)	100.00	200.00

SER.1 ODDS 1:4260 HOB, 1:1172 HTA
SER.2 ODDS 1:5007 HOB
1 Nolan Ryan 1968 300.00 500.00

1999 Topps Traded

This set contains 121 cards and was distributed as factory boxed sets only. The fronts feature color action player photo. The backs carry player information. Rookie Cards include Sean Burroughs, Josh Hamilton, Corey Patterson and Alfonso Soriano.

Card	Low	High
COMP.FACT.SET (122)	20.00	50.00
COMPLETE SET (121)	12.50	30.00
T1 Seth Etherton	.07	.20
T2 Mark Harriger RC	.08	.25
T3 Matt Wise RC	.08	.25
T4 Carlos E. Hernandez RC	.15	.40
T5 Julio Lugo RC	.30	.75
T6 Mike Nannini	.07	.20
T7 Justin Bowles RC	.08	.25
T8 Mark Mulder RC	.60	1.50
T9 Roberto Vaz RC	.08	.25
T10 Felipe Lopez RC	.60	1.50
T11 Matt Belisle	.20	.50
T12 Micah Bowie	.07	.20
T13 Ruben Quevedo RC	.08	.25
T14 Jose Garcia RC	.08	.25
T15 David Kelton RC	.08	.25
T16 Phil Norton	.07	.20
T17 Corey Patterson RC	.40	1.00
T18 Ron Walker RC	.08	.25
T19 Paul Hoover RC	.08	.25
T20 Ryan Rupe RC	.08	.25
T21 J.D. Closser RC	.15	.40
T22 Rob Ryan RC	.08	.25
T23 Steve Colyer RC	.08	.25
T24 Bubba Crosby RC	.25	.60
T25 Luke Prokopec RC	.08	.25
T26 Matt Blank RC	.08	.25
T27 Josh McKinley	.07	.20
T28 Nate Bump	.07	.20
T29 G.Chiaramonte RC	.08	.25
T30 Arturo McDowell	.07	.20
T31 Tony Torcato	.07	.20
T32 Dave Roberts RC	.25	.60
T33 C.C. Sabathia RC	3.00	8.00
T34 Sean Spencer RC	.08	.25
T35 Chip Ambres	.07	.20
T36 A.J. Burnett	.40	1.00
T37 Mo Bruce RC	.08	.25
T38 Jason Tyner	.07	.20
T39 Mamon Tucker	.07	.20
T40 Sean Burroughs RC	.25	.60
T41 Kevin Eberwein RC	.08	.25
T42 Junior Herndon RC	.08	.25
T43 Bryan Wolff RC	.08	.25
T44 Pat Burrell	.50	1.25
T45 Eric Valent	.07	.20
T46 Carlos Pena RC	.20	.50
T47 Mike Zywica	.07	.20
T48 Adam Everett	.10	.30
T49 Juan Pena RC	.15	.40
T50 Adam Dunn RC	1.50	4.00
T51 Austin Kearns	.50	1.25
T52 Jacobo Sequea RC	.08	.25
T53 Choo Freeman	.07	.20
T54 Jeff Winchester	.07	.20
T55 Matt Burch	.07	.20
T56 Chris George	.07	.20
T57 Scott Mullen RC	.08	.25
T58 Kit Pellow	.07	.20
T59 Mark Quinn RC	.08	.25
T60 Nate Cornejo	.08	.25
T61 Ryan Mills	.07	.20
T62 Kevin Beirne RC	.08	.25
T63 Kip Wells RC	.15	.40
T64 Juan Rivera RC	.40	1.00
T65 Alfonso Soriano RC	2.00	5.00
T66 Josh Hamilton RC	3.00	8.00
T67 Josh Girdley RC	.08	.25
T68 Kyle Snyder RC	.08	.25
T69 Mike Paradis RC	.08	.25
T70 Jason Jennings RC	.25	.60
T71 David Walling RC	.08	.25
T72 Omar Ortiz RC	.08	.25
T73 Jay Gehrke RC	.15	.40
T74 Casey Burns RC	.15	.40
T75 Carl Crawford RC	1.50	4.00
T76 Reggie Sanders	.07	.20
T77 Will Clark	.10	.30
T78 David Wells	.07	.20
T79 Paul Konerko	.07	.20
T80 Armando Benitez	.07	.20
T81 Brant Brown	.07	.20
T82 Mo Vaughn	.07	.20
T83 Jose Canseco	.10	.30
T84 Albert Belle	.07	.20
T85 Dean Palmer	.07	.20
T86 Greg Vaughn	.07	.20
T87 Mark Clark	.07	.20
T88 Pat Meares	.07	.20
T89 Eric Davis	.07	.20
T90 Brian Giles	.07	.20
T91 Jeff Brantley	.07	.20
T92 Bret Boone	.07	.20
T93 Ron Gant	.07	.20
T94 Mike Cameron	.07	.20
T95 Charles Johnson	.07	.20
T96 Denny Neagle	.07	.20
T97 Brian Hunter	.07	.20
T98 Jose Hernandez	.07	.20
T99 Rick Aguilera	.07	.20
T100 Tony Batista	.07	.20
T101 Roger Cedeno	.07	.20
T102 C.Gubanich RC	.08	.25
T103 Tim Belcher	.07	.20
T104 Bruce Aven	.07	.20
T105 Brian Daubach RC	.15	.40
T106 Ed Sprague	.07	.20
T107 Michael Tucker	.07	.20
T108 Homer Bush	.07	.20
T109 Armando Reynoso	.07	.20
T110 Brook Fordyce	.07	.20
T111 Matt Mantei	.07	.20
T112 Dave Mlicki	.07	.20
T113 Kenny Rogers	.07	.20
T114 Livan Hernandez	.07	.20
T115 Butch Huskey	.07	.20
T116 David Segui	.07	.20
T117 Darryl Hamilton	.07	.20
T118 Terry Mulholland	.07	.20
T119 Randy Velarde	.07	.20
T120 Bill Taylor	.07	.20
T121 Kevin Appier	.07	.20

1999 Topps Traded Autographs

Inserted one per factory box set, this 75-card set features autographed parallel version of the first 75 cards of the basic 1999 Topps Traded set. The card fronts have a light faded image on the base to accentuate the signature.

Card	Low	High
COMPLETE SET (75)	400.00	800.00
T1 Seth Etherton	2.00	5.00
T2 Mark Harriger	3.00	8.00
T3 Matt Wise	3.00	8.00
T4 Carlos E. Hernandez	3.00	8.00
T5 Julio Lugo	3.00	8.00
T6 Mike Nannini	2.00	5.00
T7 Justin Bowles	3.00	8.00
T8 Mark Mulder	6.00	15.00
T9 Roberto Vaz	2.00	5.00
T10 Felipe Lopez	3.00	8.00
T11 Matt Belisle	2.00	5.00
T12 Micah Bowie	2.00	5.00
T13 Ruben Quevedo	2.00	5.00
T14 Jose Garcia	3.00	8.00
T15 David Kelton	2.00	5.00
T16 Phil Norton	3.00	8.00
T17 Corey Patterson	6.00	15.00
T18 Ron Walker	2.00	5.00
T19 Paul Hoover	3.00	8.00
T20 Ryan Rupe	2.00	5.00
T21 J.D. Closser	3.00	8.00
T22 Rob Ryan	2.00	5.00
T23 Steve Colyer	2.00	5.00
T24 Bubba Crosby	3.00	8.00
T25 Luke Prokopec	2.00	5.00
T26 Matt Blank	3.00	8.00
T27 Josh McKinley	2.00	5.00
T28 Nate Bump	3.00	8.00
T29 G.Chiaramonte	2.00	5.00
T30 Arturo McDowell	2.00	5.00
T31 Tony Torcato	2.00	5.00
T32 Dave Roberts	6.00	15.00
T33 C.C. Sabathia	75.00	150.00
T34 Sean Spencer	2.00	5.00
T35 Chip Ambres	2.00	5.00
T36 A.J. Burnett	6.00	15.00
T37 Mo Bruce	2.00	5.00
T38 Jason Tyner	2.00	5.00
T39 Mamon Tucker	2.00	5.00
T40 Sean Burroughs	6.00	15.00
T41 Kevin Eberwein	2.00	5.00
T42 Junior Herndon	2.00	5.00
T43 Bryan Wolff	3.00	8.00

Card	Low	High
T44 Pat Burrell	8.00	20.00
T45 Eric Valent	3.00	8.00
T46 Carlos Pena	6.00	15.00
T47 Mike Zywica	3.00	8.00
T48 Adam Everett	6.00	15.00
T49 Juan Pena	3.00	8.00
T50 Adam Dunn	40.00	80.00
T51 Austin Kearns	12.50	30.00
T52 Jacobo Sequea	2.00	5.00
T53 Choo Freeman	3.00	8.00
T54 Jeff Winchester	2.00	5.00
T55 Matt Burch	3.00	8.00
T56 Chris George	2.00	5.00
T57 Scott Mullen	2.00	5.00
T58 Kit Pellow	2.00	5.00
T59 Mark Quinn	2.00	5.00
T60 Nate Cornejo	2.00	5.00
T61 Ryan Mills	2.00	5.00
T62 Kevin Beirne	3.00	8.00
T63 Kip Wells	3.00	8.00
T64 Juan Rivera	3.00	8.00
T65 Alfonso Soriano	30.00	60.00
T66 Josh Hamilton	100.00	200.00
T67 Josh Girdley	2.00	5.00
T68 Kyle Snyder	2.00	5.00
T69 Mike Paradis	2.00	5.00
T70 Jason Jennings	8.00	20.00
T71 David Walling	2.00	5.00
T72 Omar Ortiz	3.00	8.00
T73 Jay Gehrke	3.00	8.00
T74 Casey Burns	3.00	8.00
T75 Carl Crawford	30.00	60.00

2000 Topps

This 478 card set was issued in two separate series. The first series (containing cards 1-239) was released in December, 1999. The second series (containing cards 240-479) was released in April, 2000. The cards were issued in various formats including an eleven card hobby or retail pack with an SRP of $1.29 and a 40 card HomeTeam Advantage jumbo pack. Cards 1-200 and 240-440 are individual player cards with subsets as follows: Prospects (201-208/441-448), Draft Picks (209-220/449-455), Season Highlights (217-221/456-460), Post Season Highlights (222-228), 20th Century's Best (229-235/468-474), Magic Moments (236-240/475-479) and League Leaders (461-467). After the success Topps had with the multiple versions of Mark McGwire 220 and Sammy Sosa 461 in 1999, they made five versions each of the Magic Moments cards this year. Each Magic Moment variation featured different gold foil text on front commemorating a specific achievement in the featured player's career. Please note, that basic hand-collected sets are considered complete with the inclusion of any one of each of these Magic Moment cards. A reprint of the 1985 Mark McGwire Rookie Card was inserted one every 36 hobby and retail first series packs and one every eight HTA first series packs. Card number 7 was not issued as Topps continues to honor the memory of Mickey Mantle who wore that number during his career. Players with notable Rookie Cards in this set include Ben Sheets and Barry Zito.

Card	Low	High
COMPLETE SET (478)	20.00	50.00
COMP.HOBBY SET (478)	30.00	60.00
COMP. SERIES 1 (239)	10.00	25.00
COMP. SERIES 2 (240)	10.00	25.00
MCGWIRE MM SET (5)	5.00	12.00
AARON MM SET (5)	4.00	10.00
RIPKEN MM SET (5)	6.00	15.00
BOGGS MM SET (5)	1.25	3.00
GWYNN MM SET (5)	2.50	6.00
GRIFFEY MM SET (5)	3.00	8.00
BONDS MM SET (5)	5.00	12.00
SOSA MM SET (5)	3.00	8.00
JETER MM SET (5)	5.00	12.00
A.ROD MM SET (5)	3.00	8.00
1 Mark McGwire	.50	1.25
2 Tony Gwynn	.25	.60
3 Wade Boggs	.10	.30
4 Cal Ripken	.60	1.50
5 Matt Williams	.07	.20
6 Jay Buhner	.07	.20
8 Jeff Conine	.07	.20
9 Todd Greene	.07	.20
10 Mike Lieberthal	.07	.20
11 Steve Avery	.07	.20
12 Bret Saberhagen	.07	.20
13 Magglio Ordonez	.07	.20
14 Brad Radke	.07	.20
15 Derek Jeter	.50	1.25
16 Javy Lopez	.07	.20
17 Russ Davis	.07	.20
18 Armando Benitez	.07	.20
19 B.J. Surhoff	.07	.20
20 Darryl Kile	.07	.20
21 Mark Lewis	.07	.20
22 Mike Williams	.07	.20
23 Mark McLemore	.07	.20
24 Sterling Hitchcock	.07	.20
25 Darin Erstad	.07	.20
26 Ricky Gutierrez	.07	.20
27 John Jaha	.07	.20
28 Homer Bush	.07	.20
29 Darrin Fletcher	.07	.20
30 Mark Grace	.10	.30
31 Fred McGriff	.10	.30
32 Omar Daal	.07	.20
33 Eric Karros	.07	.20
34 Orlando Cabrera	.07	.20
35 J.T. Snow	.07	.20
36 Luis Castillo	.07	.20
37 Rey Ordonez	.07	.20
38 Bob Abreu	.07	.20
39 Warren Morris	.07	.20
40 Juan Gonzalez	.07	.20
41 Mike Lansing	.07	.20
42 Chili Davis	.07	.20
43 Dean Palmer	.07	.20
44 Hank Aaron	.30	.75
45 Jeff Bagwell	.10	.30
46 Jose Valentin	.07	.20
47 Shannon Stewart	.07	.20
48 Kent Bottenfield	.07	.20
49 Jeff Shaw	.07	.20
50 Sammy Sosa	.20	.50
51 Randy Johnson	.20	.50
52 Benny Agbayani	.07	.20
53 Dante Bichette	.07	.20
54 Pete Harnisch	.07	.20
55 Frank Thomas	.20	.50
56 Jorge Posada	.10	.30
57 Todd Walker	.07	.20
58 Juan Encarnacion	.07	.20
59 Mike Sweeney	.07	.20
60 Pedro Martinez	.10	.30
61 Lee Stevens	.07	.20
62 Brian Giles	.07	.20
63 Chad Ogea	.07	.20
64 Ivan Rodriguez	.10	.30
65 Roger Cedeno	.07	.20
66 David Justice	.07	.20
67 Steve Trachsel	.07	.20
68 Eli Marrero	.07	.20
69 Dave Nilsson	.07	.20
70 Ken Caminiti	.07	.20
71 Tim Raines	.07	.20
72 Brian Jordan	.07	.20
73 Jeff Blauser	.07	.20
74 Bernard Gilkey	.07	.20
75 John Flaherty	.07	.20
76 Brent Mayne	.07	.20
77 Jose Vidro	.07	.20
78 David Bell	.07	.20
79 Bruce Aven	.07	.20
80 John Olerud	.07	.20
81 Pokey Reese	.07	.20
82 Woody Williams	.07	.20
83 Ed Sprague	.07	.20
84 Joe Girardi	.07	.20
85 Barry Larkin	.10	.30
86 Mike Caruso	.07	.20
87 Bobby Higginson	.07	.20
88 Roberto Kelly	.07	.20
89 Edgar Martinez	.10	.30
90 Mark Kotsay	.07	.20
91 Paul Sorrento	.07	.20
92 Eric Young	.07	.20
93 Carlos Delgado	.07	.20
94 Troy Glaus	.07	.20
95 Ben Grieve	.07	.20
96 Jose Lima	.07	.20
97 Garret Anderson	.07	.20
98 Luis Gonzalez	.07	.20
99 Carl Pavano	.07	.20
100 Alex Rodriguez	.30	.75
101 Preston Wilson	.07	.20
102 Ron Gant	.07	.20
103 Brady Anderson	.07	.20
104 Rickey Henderson	.20	.50
105 Gary Sheffield	.07	.20
106 Mickey Morandini	.07	.20
107 Jim Edmonds	.07	.20
108 Kris Benson	.07	.20
109 Adrian Beltre	.07	.20
110 Alex Fernandez	.07	.20
111 Dan Wilson	.07	.20
112 Mark Clark	.07	.20
113 Greg Vaughn	.07	.20
114 Neifi Perez	.07	.20
115 Paul O'Neill	.10	.30
116 Jermaine Dye	.07	.20
117 Todd Jones	.07	.20
118 Terry Steinbach	.07	.20
119 Greg Norton	.07	.20
120 Curt Schilling	.07	.20
121 Todd Zeile	.07	.20
122 Edgardo Alfonzo	.07	.20
123 Ryan McGuire	.07	.20
124 Rich Aurilia	.07	.20
125 John Smoltz	.10	.30
126 Bob Wickman	.07	.20
127 Richard Hidalgo	.07	.20
128 Chuck Finley	.07	.20
129 Billy Wagner	.07	.20
130 Todd Hundley	.07	.20
131 Dwight Gooden	.07	.20
132 Russ Ortiz	.07	.20
133 Mike Lowell	.07	.20
134 Reggie Sanders	.07	.20
135 John Valentin	.07	.20
136 Brad Ausmus	.07	.20
137 Chad Kreuter	.07	.20
138 David Cone	.07	.20
139 Brook Fordyce	.07	.20
140 Roberto Alomar	.10	.30
141 Charles Nagy	.07	.20
142 Brian Hunter	.07	.20
143 Mike Mussina	.10	.30
144 Robin Ventura	.10	.30
145 Kevin Brown	.10	.30
146 Pat Hentgen	.07	.20
147 Ryan Klesko	.07	.20
148 Derek Bell	.07	.20
149 Andy Sheets	.07	.20
150 Larry Walker	.07	.20
151 Scott Williamson	.07	.20
152 Jose Offerman	.07	.20
153 Doug Mientkiewicz	.07	.20
154 John Snyder RC	.15	.40
155 Sandy Alomar Jr.	.07	.20
156 Joe Nathan	.07	.20
157 Lance Johnson	.07	.20
158 Odalis Perez	.07	.20
159 Hideo Nomo	.20	.50
160 Steve Finley	.07	.20
161 Dave Martinez	.07	.20
162 Matt Walbeck	.07	.20
163 Bill Spiers	.07	.20
164 Fernando Tatis	.07	.20
165 Kenny Lofton	.07	.20
166 Paul Byrd	.07	.20
167 Aaron Sele	.07	.20
168 Eddie Taubensee	.07	.20
169 Reggie Jefferson	.07	.20
170 Roger Clemens	.40	1.00
171 Francisco Cordova	.07	.20
172 Mike Bordick	.07	.20
173 Wally Joyner	.07	.20
174 Marvin Benard	.07	.20
175 Jason Kendall	.07	.20
176 Mike Stanley	.07	.20
177 Chad Allen	.07	.20
178 Carlos Beltran	.07	.20
179 Deivi Cruz	.07	.20
180 Chipper Jones	.20	.50
181 Vladimir Guerrero	.20	.50
182 Dave Burba	.07	.20
183 Tom Goodwin	.07	.20
184 Brian Daubach	.07	.20
185 Jay Bell	.07	.20
186 Roy Halladay	.07	.20
187 Miguel Tejada	.07	.20
188 Armando Rios	.07	.20
189 Fernando Vina	.07	.20
190 Eric Davis	.07	.20
191 Henry Rodriguez	.07	.20
192 Joe McEwing	.07	.20
193 Jeff Kent	.07	.20
194 Mike Jackson	.07	.20
195 Mike Morgan	.07	.20
196 Jeff Montgomery	.07	.20
197 Jeff Zimmerman	.07	.20
198 Tony Fernandez	.07	.20
199 Jason Giambi	.07	.20
200 Jose Canseco	.10	.30
201 Alex Gonzalez	.07	.20
202 Jack Cust / Mike Colangelo / Dee Brown	.15	.40
203 Felipe Lopez / Alfonso Soriano / Pablo Ozuna	.20	.50
204 Erubiel Durazo / Pat Burrell / Nick Johnson	.15	.40
205 John Sneed RC / Kip Wells / Matt Blank	.15	.40
206 Josh Kalinowski / Michael Tejera / Chris Mears RC	.15	.40
207 Roosevelt Brown / Corey Patterson / Lance Berkman	.15	.40
208 Kit Pellow / Kevin Barker / Russ Branyan	.15	.40
209 B.J. Garbe / Larry Bigbie RC	.20	.50
210 Eric Munson / Bobby Bradley RC	.15	.40
211 Josh Girdley / Kyle Snyder	.15	.40
212 Chance Caple RC / Jason Jennings	.15	.40
213 Ryan Christianson / Brett Myers RC	.40	1.00
214 Jason Stumm / Rob Purvis RC	.15	.40
215 David Walling / Mike Paradis	.15	.40
216 Omar Ortiz / Jay Gehrke	.15	.40
217 David Cone HL	.07	.20
218 Jose Jimenez HL	.07	.20
219 Chris Singleton HL	.07	.20
220 Fernando Tatis HL	.07	.20
221 Todd Helton HL	.07	.20
222 Kevin Millwood DIV	.07	.20
223 Todd Pratt DIV	.07	.20
224 Orl.Hernandez DIV	.07	.20
225 Pedro Martinez DIV	.10	.30
226 Tom Glavine LCS	.07	.20
227 Bernie Williams LCS	.07	.20
228 Mariano Rivera WS	.10	.30
229 Tony Gwynn 20CB	.25	.60
230 Wade Boggs 20CB	.10	.30
231 Lance Johnson CB	.07	.20
232 Mark McGwire 20CB	.50	1.25
233 R.Henderson 20CB	.20	.50
234 R.Henderson 20CB	.20	.50
235 Roger Clemens 20CB	.40	1.00
236A M.McGwire MM 1st HR	.75	2.00
236B M.McGwire MM 1987 ROY	.75	2.00
236C M.McGwire MM 62nd HR	.75	2.00
236D M.McGwire MM 70th HR	.75	2.00
236E M.McGwire MM 500th HR	.75	2.00
237A H.Aaron MM 1st Career HR	.75	2.00
237B H.Aaron MM 1957 MVP	.75	2.00
237C H.Aaron MM 3000th Hit	.75	2.00
237D H.Aaron MM 715th HR	.75	2.00
237E H.Aaron MM 755th HR	.75	2.00
238A C.Ripken MM 1982 ROY	1.50	4.00
238B C.Ripken MM 1991 MVP	1.50	4.00
238C C.Ripken MM 2131 Game	1.50	4.00
238D C.Ripken MM Streak Ends	1.50	4.00
238E C.Ripken MM 400th HR	1.50	4.00
239A W.Boggs MM 1983 Batting	.30	.75
239B W.Boggs MM 1988 Batting	.30	.75
239C W.Boggs MM 2000th Hit	.30	.75
239D W.Boggs MM 1996 Champs	.30	.75
239E W.Boggs MM 3000th Hit	.30	.75
240A T.Gwynn MM 1984 Batting	.60	1.50
240B T.Gwynn MM 1984 NLCS	.60	1.50
240C T.Gwynn MM 1995 Batting	.60	1.50
240D T.Gwynn MM 1998 NLCS	.60	1.50
240E T.Gwynn MM 3000th Hit	.60	1.50
241 Tom Glavine	.10	.30
242 David Wells	.07	.20
243 Kevin Appier	.07	.20
244 Troy Percival	.07	.20
245 Ray Lankford	.07	.20
246 Marquis Grissom	.07	.20
247 Randy Winn	.07	.20
248 Miguel Batista	.07	.20
249 Darren Dreifort	.07	.20
250 Barry Bonds	.60	1.50
251 Harold Baines	.07	.20
252 Cliff Floyd	.07	.20
253 Freddy Garcia	.07	.20
254 Kenny Rogers	.07	.20
255 Ben Davis	.07	.20
256 Charles Johnson	.07	.20
257 Bubba Trammell	.07	.20
258 Desi Relaford	.07	.20
259 Al Martin	.07	.20
260 Andy Pettitte	.10	.30
261 Carlos Lee	.07	.20
262 Matt Lawton	.07	.20
263 Andy Fox	.07	.20
264 Chan Ho Park	.07	.20
265 Billy Koch	.07	.20
266 Dave Roberts	.07	.20
267 Carl Everett	.07	.20
268 Orel Hershiser	.07	.20
269 Trot Nixon	.07	.20
270 Rusty Greer	.07	.20
271 Will Clark	.10	.30
272 Quilvio Veras	.07	.20
273 Rico Brogna	.07	.20
274 Devon White	.07	.20
275 Tim Hudson	.07	.20
276 Mike Hampton	.07	.20
277 Miguel Cairo	.07	.20
278 Darren Oliver	.07	.20
279 Jeff Cirillo	.07	.20
280 Al Leiter	.07	.20
281 Shane Andrews	.07	.20
282 Carlos Febles	.07	.20
283 Pedro Astacio	.07	.20
284 Juan Guzman	.07	.20
285 Orlando Hernandez	.07	.20
286 Paul Konerko	.07	.20
287 Tony Clark	.07	.20
288 Aaron Boone	.07	.20
289 Ismael Valdes	.07	.20
290 Moises Alou	.07	.20
291 Kevin Tapani	.07	.20
292 John Franco	.07	.20
293 Todd Zeile	.07	.20
294 Jason Schmidt	.07	.20
295 Johnny Damon	.10	.30
296 Scott Brosius	.07	.20
297 Travis Fryman	.07	.20
298 Jose Vizcaino	.07	.20
299 Eric Chavez	.07	.20
300 Mike Piazza	.30	.75
301 Matt Clement	.07	.20
302 Cristian Guzman	.07	.20
303 C.J. Nitkowski	.07	.20
304 Michael Tucker	.07	.20
305 Brett Tomko	.07	.20
306 Mike Lansing	.07	.20
307 Eric Owens	.07	.20
308 Livan Hernandez	.07	.20
309 Rondell White	.07	.20
310 Todd Stottlemyre	.07	.20
311 Chris Carpenter	.07	.20
312 Ken Hill	.07	.20
313 Mark Loretta	.07	.20
314 John Rocker	.07	.20
315 Richie Sexson	.07	.20
316 Ruben Mateo	.07	.20
317 Joe Randa	.07	.20
318 Mike Sirotka	.07	.20
319 Jose Rosado	.07	.20
320 Matt Mantei	.07	.20
321 Kevin Millwood	.07	.20
322 Gary Disarcina	.07	.20
323 Dustin Hermanson	.07	.20
324 Mike Stanton	.07	.20
325 Kirk Rueter	.07	.20
326 Damian Miller RC	.15	.40
327 Doug Glanville	.07	.20
328 Scott Rolen	.10	.30
329 Ray Durham	.07	.20
330 Butch Huskey	.07	.20
331 Mariano Rivera	.20	.50
332 Darren Lewis	.07	.20
333 Mike Timlin	.07	.20
334 Mark Grudzielanek	.07	.20
335 Mike Cameron	.07	.20
336 Kelvim Escobar	.07	.20
337 Bret Boone	.07	.20
338 Mo Vaughn	.07	.20
339 Craig Biggio	.10	.30
340 Michael Barrett	.07	.20
341 Marlon Anderson	.07	.20
342 Bobby Jones	.07	.20
343 John Halama	.07	.20
344 Todd Ritchie	.07	.20
345 Chuck Knoblauch	.07	.20
346 Rick Reed	.07	.20
347 Kelly Stinnett	.07	.20
348 Tim Salmon	.10	.30
349 A.J. Hinch	.07	.20
350 Jose Cruz Jr.	.07	.20
351 Roberto Hernandez	.07	.20
352 Edgar Renteria	.07	.20
353 Jose Hernandez	.07	.20
354 Brad Fullmer	.07	.20
355 Trevor Hoffman	.07	.20
356 Troy O'Leary	.07	.20
357 Justin Thompson	.07	.20
358 Kevin Young	.07	.20
359 Hideki Irabu	.07	.20
360 Jim Thome	.10	.30
361 Steve Karsay	.07	.20
362 Octavio Dotel	.07	.20
363 Omar Vizquel	.10	.30
364 Raul Mondesi	.07	.20
365 Shane Reynolds	.07	.20
366 Bartolo Colon	.07	.20
367 Chris Widger	.07	.20
368 Gabe Kapler	.07	.20
369 Bill Simas	.07	.20
370 Tino Martinez	.10	.30
371 John Thomson	.07	.20
372 Delino Deshields	.07	.20
373 Carlos Perez	.07	.20
374 Eddie Perez	.07	.20
375 Jeromy Burnitz	.07	.20
376 Jimmy Haynes	.07	.20
377 Travis Lee	.07	.20
378 Darryl Hamilton	.07	.20
379 Jamie Moyer	.07	.20
380 Alex Gonzalez	.07	.20
381 John Wetteland	.07	.20
382 Vinny Castilla	.07	.20
383 Jeff Suppan	.07	.20
384 Jim Leyritz	.07	.20
385 Robb Nen	.07	.20
386 Wilson Alvarez	.07	.20
387 Andres Galarraga	.07	.20
388 Mike Remlinger	.07	.20
389 Geoff Jenkins	.07	.20
390 Matt Stairs	.07	.20
391 Bill Mueller	.07	.20
392 Mike Lowell	.07	.20
393 Andy Ashby	.07	.20
394 Ruben Rivera	.07	.20
395 Todd Helton	.10	.30
396 Bernie Williams	.10	.30
397 Royce Clayton	.07	.20
398 Manny Ramirez	.10	.30
399 Kerry Wood	.07	.20
400 Ken Griffey Jr.	.30	.75
401 Enrique Wilson	.07	.20
402 Joey Hamilton	.07	.20
403 Shawn Estes	.07	.20
404 Ugueth Urbina	.07	.20
405 Albert Belle	.07	.20
406 Rick Helling	.07	.20
407 Steve Parris	.07	.20
408 Eric Milton	.07	.20
409 Dave Mlicki	.07	.20
410 Shawn Green	.07	.20
411 Jaret Wright	.07	.20
412 Tony Womack	.07	.20
413 Vernon Wells	.07	.20
414 Ron Belliard	.07	.20
415 Ellis Burks	.07	.20
416 Scott Erickson	.07	.20
417 Rafael Palmeiro	.10	.30
418 Damion Easley	.07	.20
419 Jamey Wright	.07	.20
420 Corey Koskie	.07	.20
421 Bobby Howry	.07	.20
422 Ricky Ledee	.07	.20
423 Dmitri Young	.07	.20
424 Sidney Ponson	.07	.20
425 Greg Maddux	.30	.75
426 Jose Guillen	.07	.20
427 Jon Lieber	.07	.20
428 Andy Benes	.07	.20
429 Randy Velarde	.07	.20
430 Sean Casey	.07	.20
431 Torii Hunter	.07	.20
432 Ryan Rupe	.07	.20
433 David Segui	.07	.20
434 Todd Pratt	.07	.20
435 Nomar Garciaparra	.30	.75
436 Denny Neagle	.07	.20
437 Ron Coomer	.07	.20
438 Chris Singleton	.07	.20
439 Tony Batista	.07	.20
440 Andruw Jones	.10	.30
441 Aubrey Huff / Sean Burroughs / Adam Piatt	.07	.20
442 Rafael Furcal / Travis Dawkins / Jason Dellaero	.15	.40
443 Mike Lamb RC / Joe Crede / Wilton Veras	.40	1.00
444 Julio Zuleta RC / Jorge Toca / Dernell Stenson	.15	.40
445 Garry Maddox Jr. RC / Gary Matthews Jr. / Tim Raines Jr.	.15	.40
446 Mark Mulder / C.C. Sabathia / Matt Riley	.15	.40
447 Scott Downs RC / Chris George / Matt Belisle	.15	.40
448 Doug Mirabelli / Ben Petrick / Jayson Werth	.15	.40
449 Josh Hamilton / Corey Myers RC	.20	.50
450 Ben Christensen RC / Richard Stahl RC	.15	.40
451 Ben Sheets RC / Barry Zito	1.00	2.50
452 Kurt Ainsworth / Ty Howington RC	.15	.40
453 Vince Faison RC / Rick Asadoorian	.15	.40
454 Keith Reed RC / Jeff Heaverlo	.15	.40
455 Mike MacDougal / Brad Baker RC	.15	.40
456 Mark McGwire SH	.25	.60
457 Cal Ripken SH	.30	.75
458 Wade Boggs SH	.07	.20
459 Tony Gwynn SH	.10	.30
460 Jesse Orosco SH	.07	.20
461 Larry Walker / Nomar Garciaparra LL	.10	.30
462 Ken Griffey Jr. / Mark McGwire LL	.20	.50
463 Manny Ramirez / Mark McGwire LL	.20	.50
464 Pedro Martinez / Randy Johnson LL	.10	.30
465 Pedro Martinez / Randy Johnson LL	.10	.30
466 Derek Jeter / Luis Gonzalez LL	.20	.50
467 Larry Walker / Manny Ramirez LL	.10	.30
468 Tony Gwynn 20CB	.25	.60
469 Mark McGwire 20CB	.50	1.25
470 Frank Thomas 20CB	.10	.30
471 Harold Baines 20CB	.07	.20
472 Roger Clemens 20CB	.40	1.00
473 John Franco 20CB	.07	.20
474 John Franco 20CB	.07	.20
475A K.Griffey Jr. MM 350th HR	.75	2.00
475B K.Griffey Jr. MM 1997 MVP	.75	2.00
475C K.Griffey Jr. MM HR Dad	.75	2.00
475D K.Griffey Jr. MM 1992 AS MVP	.75	2.00
475E K.Griffey Jr. MM 50 HR 1997	.75	2.00
476A B.Bonds MM 400HR/400SB	1.25	3.00
476B B.Bonds MM 40HR/40SB	1.25	3.00
476C B.Bonds MM 1993 MVP	1.25	3.00
476D B.Bonds MM 1990 MVP	1.25	3.00
476E B.Bonds MM 1992 MVP	1.25	3.00
477A S.Sosa MM 20 HR June	.75	2.00
477B S.Sosa MM 66 HR 1998	.75	2.00
477C S.Sosa MM 60 HR 1999	.75	2.00
477D S.Sosa MM 1998 MVP	.75	2.00
477E S.Sosa MM HR's 61/62	.75	2.00
478A D.Jeter MM 1996 ROY	1.25	3.00
478B D.Jeter MM Wins 1999 WS	1.25	3.00
478C D.Jeter MM Wins 1998 WS	1.25	3.00
478D D.Jeter MM Wins 1996 WS	1.25	3.00
478E D.Jeter MM 17 GM Hit Streak	1.25	3.00
479A A.Rodriguez MM 40HR/40SB	.75	2.00
479B A.Rodriguez MM 100th HR	.75	2.00
479C A.Rodriguez MM 1996 POY	.75	2.00
479D A.Rodriguez MM Wins 1 Million	.75	2.00
479E A.Rodriguez MM 1996 Batting Leader	.75	2.00
NNO M. McGwire 85 Reprint	2.00	5.00

2000 Topps 20th Century Best Sequential

Inserted into first series hobby packs at an overall rate of one in 869 and one in 239 HTA packs, and into series two hobby packs at one in 362 and one in 100 HTA packs, these cards parallel the Century's Best subset within the base 2000 Topps set (cards 229-235/468-474). These insert cards, unlike the regular cards, feature "CB" prefixed numbering on back and have dramatic sparkling foil-coated fronts. Each card is sequentially numbered to the featured players highlighted career statistic.

Card	Low	High
CB1 T.Gwynn AVG/339	15.00	40.00
CB2 W.Boggs 2B/578	8.00	20.00
CB3 L.Johnson 3B/117	10.00	25.00
CB4 M.McGwire HR/522	20.00	50.00
CB5 Rickey Henderson SB/1334	6.00	15.00
CB6 Rickey Henderson RUN/2103	6.00	15.00
CB7 R.Clemens WIN/247	30.00	60.00
CB8 Tony Gwynn HIT/3067	6.00	15.00
CB9 Mark McGwire SLG/587	20.00	50.00
CB10 Frank Thomas OBP/440	12.50	30.00
CB11 Harold Baines RBI/1583	3.00	8.00
CB12 Roger Clemens K's/3316	10.00	25.00
CB13 John Franco ERA/264	5.00	12.00
CB14 John Franco SV/416	5.00	12.00

2000 Topps Home Team Advantage

These cards were distributed exclusively in a 479-card factory set. Each set contained the 478-card base issue 2000 Topps set plus one Hank Aaron Chrome Reprint card. All of the base cards within Home Team Advantage factory sets were stamped with a special "HTA" gold foil logo on the card front. Oddly, cards 222-228 (Divisional Playoffs), 229-235 (20th Century's Best), 461-467 (League Leaders) and 468-474 (20th Century Best) did NOT feature the gold-foil HTA tag. Thus, those cards are identical to basic issue Topps cards and are not included within our checklist for this set (though they are included within the complete factory set).

Card	Low	High
COMP.FACT.SET (479)	40.00	80.00

*HTA: .75X TO 2X BASIC CARDS

2000 Topps MVP Promotion

Inserted one in every 510 first series hobby and retail packs and one in every 140 first series HTA packs, this set is an almost complete parallel of the regular Topps set. The cards in the first series parallel cards number 1 through 201 and second series parallels cards 241-440. Card numbers 7 and 44 were never produced for this set. Each MVP Promotion parallel card has a prominent gold foil MVP logo on the front and contest rules and guidelines on back. Only 100 of each of these cards were printed and a new winner was announced each week throughout the 2000 season as Topps selected their top player of the week. Winning cards could be redeemed for a complete set of exchange cards featuring every weekly winning player. Winning cards were verified through either calling 1-888-Go-Topps or checking on the Topps web site prior to the deadline. The exchange deadline for these cards was December 31st, 2000. The winning cards were the following numbers (in correspondence with the basic issue 2000 Topps card): 13, 15, 45, 50, 53, 55, 60, 72, 87, 90, 93, 107, 109, 116, 148, 165, 180, 199, 250, 271, 350, 395, 398, 403 and 427. Since Topps destroyed these Winner exchange cards once they received them, they're in noticeably shorter supply than other cards from this set. Despite this fact, no noticeable premiums in secondary trading levels have been detected for these cards.

*STARS: 30X TO 60X BASIC CARDS

Card	Low	High
13 Magglio Ordonez W	6.00	12.00
15 Derek Jeter W	40.00	80.00
45 Jeff Bagwell W	10.00	20.00
50 Sammy Sosa W	15.00	30.00
53 Dante Bichette W	6.00	12.00
55 Frank Thomas W	15.00	30.00
60 Pedro Martinez W	10.00	20.00
72 Brian Jordan W	6.00	12.00
87 Bobby Higginson W	6.00	12.00
90 Mark Kotsay W	6.00	12.00
93 Carlos Delgado W	6.00	12.00
107 Jim Edmonds W	6.00	12.00
109 Adrian Beltre W	6.00	12.00
116 Jermaine Dye W	6.00	12.00
148 Derek Bell W	6.00	12.00
165 Kenny Lofton W	6.00	12.00
180 Chipper Jones W	15.00	30.00
199 Jason Giambi W	6.00	12.00
250 Barry Bonds W	50.00	100.00
271 Will Clark W	10.00	20.00
350 Jose Cruz Jr. W	6.00	12.00
395 Todd Helton W	10.00	20.00
398 Manny Ramirez W	10.00	20.00
403 Shawn Estes W	6.00	12.00
427 Jon Lieber W	6.00	12.00

2000 Topps MVP Promotion Exchange

This 25-card set was available only to those lucky collectors who obtained one of the twenty-five winning player cards from the 2000 Topps MVP Promotion parallel set. Each week, throughout the 2000 season, Topps named a new Player of the Week, and that player's Topps MVP Promotion parallel card was made redeemable for this 25-card set. The deadline to exchange the winning cards was 12/31/00.

COMPLETE SET (25)	20.00	50.00
MVP1 Pedro Martinez	1.00	2.50
MVP2 Jim Edmonds	.60	1.50
MVP3 Derek Bell	.60	1.50
MVP4 Jermaine Dye	.60	1.50
MVP5 Jose Cruz Jr.	.60	1.50
MVP6 Todd Helton	1.00	2.50
MVP7 Brian Jordan	.60	1.50
MVP8 Shawn Estes	.60	1.50
MVP9 Dante Bichette	.60	1.50
MVP10 Carlos Delgado	.60	1.50
MVP11 Bobby Higginson	.60	1.50
MVP12 Mark Kotsay	.60	1.50
MVP13 Magglio Ordonez	.60	1.50
MVP14 Jon Lieber	.60	1.50
MVP15 Frank Thomas	1.50	4.00
MVP16 Manny Ramirez	1.00	2.50
MVP17 Sammy Sosa	1.50	4.00
MVP18 Will Clark	1.00	2.50
MVP19 Jeff Bagwell	1.00	2.50
MVP20 Derek Jeter	4.00	10.00
MVP21 Adrian Beltre	.60	1.50
MVP22 Kenny Lofton	.60	1.50
MVP23 Barry Bonds	4.00	10.00
MVP24 Jason Giambi	.60	1.50
MVP25 Chipper Jones	1.50	4.00

2000 Topps Oversize

Each 2000 Topps hobby and Home Team Advantage box has one of these cards as a chiptopper. A chiptopper is a card that lies on top of the packs within the sealed box. These cards are exact parallels of their corresponding base issue card except, of course, for their larger size (3" by 5") and 1-8 numbering on back. Please note, for checklisting purposes, we've added "A" and "B" prefixes to each card number to signify which cards were seeded in first versus second series packs.

COMPLETE SERIES 1 (8)	8.00	20.00
COMPLETE SERIES 2 (8)	6.00	15.00
A1 Mark McGwire	1.25	3.00
A2 Hank Aaron	.75	2.00
A3 Derek Jeter	1.25	3.00
A4 Sammy Sosa	.50	1.25
A5 Alex Rodriguez	.75	2.00
A6 Chipper Jones	.50	1.25
A7 Cal Ripken	1.50	4.00
A8 Pedro Martinez	.30	.75
B1 Barry Bonds	1.50	4.00
B2 Orlando Hernandez	.20	.50
B3 Mike Piazza	.75	2.00
B4 Manny Ramirez	.30	.75
B5 Ken Griffey Jr.	.75	2.00
B6 Rafael Palmeiro	.30	.75
B7 Greg Maddux	.75	2.00
B8 Nomar Garciaparra	.75	2.00

2000 Topps 21st Century

Inserted one every 18 first series hobby and retail packs and one every five first series HTA packs, these 10 cards feature players who are among those expected to be among the best players in the first part of the 21st century.

COMPLETE SET (10)	4.00	10.00
C1 Ben Grieve	.15	.40
C2 Alex Gonzalez	.15	.40
C3 Derek Jeter	1.00	2.50
C4 Sean Casey	.15	.40
C5 Nomar Garciaparra	.60	1.50
C6 Alex Rodriguez	.60	1.50
C7 Scott Rolen	.25	.60
C8 Andruw Jones	.25	.60
C9 Vladimir Guerrero	.40	1.00
C10 Todd Helton	.25	.60

2000 Topps Aaron

For their year 2000 product, Topps chose to reprint cards of All-Time Home Run King, Hank Aaron. The cards were inserted one every 18 hobby and retail pack and one every five HTA packs in both first and second series. The even year cards were released in the first series and the odd year cards were issued in the second series. Each card can be easily detected from the original cards issued from the 1950-70s by the large gold foil logo on front and the glossy card stock.

COMPLETE SET (23)	50.00	100.00
COMMON CARD (1-23)	2.00	5.00
1 Hank Aaron 1954	4.00	10.00

2000 Topps Aaron Autographs

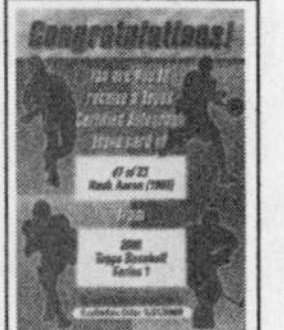

Due to the fact that Topps could not obtain actual signed Hank Aaron cards prior to pack out for first series in December, 2000 - Topps inserted into first series packs at a rate of one in 4361 hobby and retail and 1 in 1199 first series HTA packs exchange cards of which were redeemable (prior to the May 31st, 2000 deadline) for a signed Hank Aaron Reprint card. The 12 exchange cards distributed in series one were redeemable exclusively for specific even year Reprint cards. The 11 odd year Autographs were obtained by Topps well in time for the second series release in April, 2000 and thus those actual autographed cards were seeded directly into the series two packs.

COMMON CARD (2-23)	200.00	400.00
1 Hank Aaron 1954	300.00	500.00

2000 Topps Aaron Chrome

Issued one every 72 Hobby or Retail packs and one every 16 HTA packs for both first and second series, these cards parallel the Aaron reprint set. They are issued using the Chrome treatment Topps uses on many of their products. In this set, the odd year cards were issued in the first series and the even year cards in the second series.

COMPLETE SET (23)	80.00	200.00
COMMON CARD (1-23)	4.00	10.00
*CHROME REF: 1X TO 2.5X CHROME		
CH.REF.ODDS 1:288 HOB/RET, 1:76 HTA		
1 Hank Aaron 1954	6.00	15.00

2000 Topps All-Star Rookie Team

Randomly inserted into packs at one in 36 HOB/RET packs and one in eight HTA packs, this 10-card insert set features players that had break-through seasons their first year. Card backs carry a "RT" prefix.

COMPLETE SET (10)	10.00	25.00
RT1 Mark McGwire	2.00	5.00
RT2 Chuck Knoblauch	.30	.75
RT3 Chipper Jones	.75	2.00
RT4 Cal Ripken	2.50	6.00
RT5 Manny Ramirez	.50	1.25
RT6 Jose Canseco	.50	1.25
RT7 Ken Griffey Jr.	1.25	3.00
RT8 Mike Piazza	1.25	3.00
RT9 Dwight Gooden	.30	.75
RT10 Billy Wagner UER	.30	.75
Les Cain's name is spelled Less		

2000 Topps All-Topps

Inserted one every 12 first series hobby and retail packs and one every three first series HTA packs, this set features 10 star National Leaguers, 10 star American Leaguers, and a comparision to Hall of Famers at their respective position. Each card is printed on silver foil-board with selective metalization. The National League players were issued in series one, while the American League players were issued in series two.

COMPLETE SET (20)	10.00	20.00
COMPLETE N.L.(10)	4.00	10.00
COMPLETE A.L. (10)	4.00	10.00
AT1 Greg Maddux	.60	1.50
AT2 Mike Piazza	.60	1.50
AT3 Mark McGwire	1.00	2.50
AT4 Craig Biggio	.25	.60
AT5 Chipper Jones	.40	1.00
AT6 Barry Larkin	.25	.60
AT7 Barry Bonds	1.25	3.00
AT8 Andruw Jones	.25	.60
AT9 Sammy Sosa	.40	1.00
AT10 Larry Walker	.15	.40
AT11 Pedro Martinez	.25	.60
AT12 Ivan Rodriguez	.25	.60
AT13 Rafael Palmeiro	.25	.60
AT14 Roberto Alomar	.25	.60
AT15 Cal Ripken	1.25	3.00
AT16 Derek Jeter	1.00	2.50
AT17 Albert Belle	.15	.40
AT18 Ken Griffey Jr.	.60	1.50
AT19 Manny Ramirez	.25	.60
AT20 Jose Canseco	.25	.60

2000 Topps Autographs

Inserted at various level of difficulty, these players signed autographs for the 2000 Topps product. Group A players were inserted one every 7589 first series hobby and retail packs and one every 2087 first series HTA packs. Group A players were issued at a rate of one in every 5840 second series hobby and retail packs, and one every 1607 HTA packs. Group B players were inserted one every 4553 first series hobby and retail packs and one every 1252 first series HTA packs. Group B players were inserted at a rate of one every 2337 second series hobby and retail packs, and one every 643 HTA packs. Group C players were inserted one every 1518 first series hobby and retail packs and one every 417 first series HTA packs. Group C players were inserted one every 1169 second series hobby and retail packs, and one in every 321 HTA packs. Group D players were inserted one every 911 first series hobby and retails packs and one every 250 first series HTA packs. Group D players were inserted one in every 701 second series hobby and retail packs, and one in every 193 HTA packs. Group E autographs were issued one every 1138 first series hobby and retail packs and one every 313 first series HTA packs. Group E players were inserted one in every 1754 second series hobby and retail packs, and one in every 482 HTA packs. Originally intended to be a straight numerical run of TA1-TA15 for series one, cards TA 4 (Sean Casey) and TA 15 (Carlos Beltran) were dropped and replaced with TA 20 (Vladimir Guerrero) and TA 27 (Mike Sweeney).

TA1 Alex Rodriguez A	50.00	100.00
TA2 Tony Gwynn A	30.00	60.00
TA3 Vinny Castilla B	10.00	25.00
TA4 Sean Casey B	10.00	25.00
TA5 Shawn Green C	15.00	40.00
TA6 Rey Ordonez C	6.00	15.00
TA7 Matt Lawton C	6.00	15.00
TA8 Tony Womack C	6.00	15.00
TA9 Gabe Kapler D	10.00	25.00
TA10 Pat Burrell D	10.00	25.00
TA11 Preston Wilson D	10.00	25.00
TA12 Troy Glaus D	15.00	40.00
TA13 Carlos Beltran D	6.00	15.00
TA14 Josh Girdley E	6.00	15.00
TA15 B.J. Garbe E	6.00	15.00
TA16 Derek Jeter A	75.00	150.00
TA17 Cal Ripken A	100.00	200.00
TA18 Ivan Rodriguez B	20.00	50.00
TA19 Rafael Palmeiro B	30.00	60.00
TA20 Vladimir Guerrero B	20.00	50.00
TA21 Raul Mondesi C	10.00	25.00
TA22 Scott Rolen C	15.00	40.00
TA23 Billy Wagner C	15.00	40.00
TA24 Fernando Tatis C	6.00	15.00
TA25 Ruben Mateo D	6.00	15.00
TA26 Carlos Febles D	6.00	15.00
TA27 Mike Sweeney D	10.00	25.00
TA28 Alex Gonzalez D	6.00	15.00
TA29 Miguel Tejada D	15.00	40.00
TA30 Josh Hamilton E	30.00	60.00

2000 Topps Combos

Randomly inserted into packs at one in 18 hobby and retail packs, and one in every five HTA packs, this 10-card insert set showcases player groupings unified by a common theme, such as Home Run Kings, and features artist renderings of each player reminiscent of Topps' classic 1959 set. Card backs carry a "TC" prefix.

COMPLETE SET (10)	12.50	25.00
TC1 Roberto Alomar Manny Ramirez Kenny Lofton Jim Thome	.60	1.50
TC2 Tom Glavine Greg Maddux John Smoltz	1.25	3.00
TC3 Derek Jeter Bernie Williams Tino Martinez	1.50	4.00
TC4 Ivan Rodriguez Mike Piazza	1.00	2.50
TC5 Nomar Garciaparra Alex Rodriguez Derek Jeter	1.00	2.50
TC6 Sammy Sosa Mark McGwire	.60	1.50
TC7 Pedro Martinez Randy Johnson	.60	1.50
TC8 Barry Bonds Ken Griffey Jr.	1.50	4.00
TC9 Chipper Jones Ivan Rodriguez	.60	1.50
TC10 Cal Ripken Tony Gwynn Wade Boggs	.60	1.50

2000 Topps Hands of Gold

Inserted on every 18 first series hobby and retail packs and one every five first series HTA packs, this seven card set features players who have won at least five Gold Gloves. Each card is foil-stamped, die-cut and specially embossed.

COMPLETE SET (7)	3.00	8.00
HG1 Barry Bonds	1.25	3.00
HG2 Ivan Rodriguez	.25	.60
HG3 Ken Griffey Jr.	.60	1.50
HG4 Roberto Alomar	.25	.60
HG5 Tony Gwynn	.50	1.25
HG6 Omar Vizquel	.25	.60
HG7 Greg Maddux	.60	1.50

2000 Topps Own the Game

Randomly inserted into series two hobby and retail packs at a rate one in every 12, and one in every three series two HTA packs, this 30-card insert set features the top statistical leaders in major league baseball. Card backs carry an "OTG" prefix.

COMPLETE SET (30)	20.00	50.00
OTG1 Derek Jeter	2.00	5.00
OTG2 B.J. Surhoff	.30	.75
OTG3 Luis Gonzalez	.30	.75
OTG4 Manny Ramirez	.50	1.25
OTG5 Rafael Palmeiro	.50	1.25
OTG6 Mark McGwire	2.00	5.00
OTG7 Mark McGwire	2.00	5.00
OTG8 Sammy Sosa	.75	2.00
OTG9 Ken Griffey Jr.	1.25	3.00
OTG10 Larry Walker	.30	.75
OTG11 Nomar Garciaparra	1.25	3.00
OTG12 Derek Jeter	2.00	5.00
OTG13 Larry Walker	.30	.75
OTG14 Mark McGwire	2.00	5.00
OTG15 Manny Ramirez	.50	1.25
OTG16 Pedro Martinez	.50	1.25
OTG17 Randy Johnson	.75	2.00
OTG18 Kevin Millwood	.30	.75
OTG19 Randy Johnson	.75	2.00
OTG20 Pedro Martinez	.50	1.25
OTG21 Kevin Brown	.50	1.25
OTG22 Chipper Jones	.75	2.00
OTG23 Ivan Rodriguez	.50	1.25
OTG24 Mariano Rivera	.75	2.00
OTG25 Scott Williamson	.30	.75
OTG26 Carlos Beltran	.30	.75
OTG27 Randy Johnson	.75	2.00
OTG28 Pedro Martinez	.50	1.25
OTG29 Sammy Sosa	.75	2.00
OTG30 Manny Ramirez	.50	1.25

2000 Topps Perennial All-Stars

This set is inserted into first series hobby and retail packs at a rate of one in 18 and first series HTA packs at a rate of one every five packs. These 10 cards feature players who consistently achieve All-Star recognition.

COMPLETE SET (10)	8.00	20.00
PA1 Ken Griffey Jr.	.60	1.50
PA2 Derek Jeter	1.00	2.50
PA3 Sammy Sosa	.40	1.00
PA4 Cal Ripken	1.25	3.00
PA5 Mike Piazza	.60	1.50
PA6 Nomar Garciaparra	.60	1.50
PA7 Jeff Bagwell	.25	.60
PA8 Barry Bonds	1.25	3.00
PA9 Alex Rodriguez	.60	1.50
PA10 Mark McGwire	1.00	2.50

2000 Topps Power Players

Inserted into hobby and retail first series packs at a rate of one in eight and first series HTA packs at a rate one every other pack, this set features 20 of the best sluggers in baseball.

COMPLETE SET (20)	10.00	25.00
P1 Juan Gonzalez	.15	.40
P2 Ken Griffey Jr.	.60	1.50
P3 Mark McGwire	1.00	2.50
P4 Nomar Garciaparra	.60	1.50
P5 Barry Bonds	1.25	3.00
P6 Mo Vaughn	.15	.40
P7 Larry Walker	.15	.40
P8 Alex Rodriguez	.60	1.50
P9 Jose Canseco	.25	.60
P10 Jeff Bagwell	.25	.60
P11 Manny Ramirez	.25	.60
P12 Albert Belle	.15	.40
P13 Frank Thomas	.40	1.00
P14 Mike Piazza	.60	1.50
P15 Chipper Jones	.40	1.00
P16 Sammy Sosa	.40	1.00
P17 Vladimir Guerrero	.40	1.00
P18 Scott Rolen	.25	.60
P19 Raul Mondesi	.15	.40
P20 Derek Jeter	1.00	2.50

2000 Topps Stadium Autograph Relics

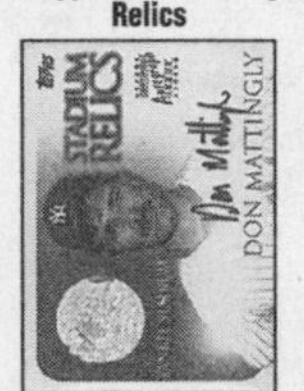

Exclusively inserted into first series HTA jumbo packs at a rate of one in 165 first series packs, and one in every 135 second series HTA packs, these cards feature a piece of a major league stadium (mostly infield bases) as well as as a photo and an autograph of the featured superstar who played there. Among the venerable ballparks included in this set are Wrigley Field, Fenway Park and Yankee Stadium.

SR1 Don Mattingly	75.00	150.00
SR2 Carl Yastrzemski	60.00	120.00
SR3 Ernie Banks	50.00	100.00
SR4 Johnny Bench	50.00	100.00
SR5 Willie Mays	125.00	250.00
SR6 Mike Schmidt	60.00	120.00
SR7 Lou Brock	40.00	80.00
SR8 Al Kaline	50.00	100.00
SR9 Paul Molitor	20.00	50.00
SR10 Eddie Mathews	60.00	120.00

2000 Topps Limited

These parallel cards were issued exclusively in factory set form (an attractive black box with a glossy teal overlay) and offered collectors the chance to get an upgraded premium version of the basic 2000 Topps. Each factory set contained a total of 619 cards including the complete 478 card basic Topps set plus the following insert sets: 21st Century Topps, Aaron Reprints, All-Star Rookie Team, All-Topps, Combos, Hands of Gold, Own the Game, Perennial All-Stars, Power Players and the Mark McGwire 1985 Reprint. Collectors received only one of five different variations of the Magic Moments subset cards (236-240/475-479) per factory set. Each card has thick gloss and features a "Limited Edition" gold foil stamp on front. Stated print run was originally 6000 serial numbered sets but actual production turned out to be 4,000 sets (with only 800 copies of each of the Magic Moments variation subset cards). Each factory box is serial numbered x/4000 but the individual cards are not numbered in any way. The sets were distributed in late September, 2000.

COMP.FACT.SET (619)	60.00	150.00
COMPLETE SET (478)	50.00	100.00
*STARS: 1.5X TO 4X BASIC CARDS		
*ROOKIES: 1.5X TO 4X BASIC CARDS		
*MAGIC MOMENTS: .75X TO 2X BASIC MM		

2000 Topps Limited 21st Century

These inserts were seeded at one complete set per sealed Topps Limited factory set. This is a complete parallel of the 21st Century insert that is found in 2000 Topps, and can be easily distinguished by the thicker card stock, glossy finish, and the words "Limited Edition" stamped in gold lettering on each card. Please note that only 4000 sets were produced.

COMPLETE SET (10)	10.00	25.00
*LIMITED: 1X TO 2.5X TOPPS 21ST CENT.		

2000 Topps Limited Aaron

These inserts were seeded at one complete set per sealed Topps Limited factory set. This is a complete parallel of the Aaron insert that is found in 2000 Topps, and can be easily distinguished by the thicker card stock, glossy finish, and the words "Limited Edition" stamped in gold lettering on each card. Please note that only 4000 sets were produced.

COMPLETE SET (23)	50.00	100.00
*LIMITED: .3X TO .8X TOPPS AARON		
1 Hank Aaron 1954	4.00	10.00

2000 Topps Limited All-Star Rookie Team

These inserts were seeded at one complete set per sealed Topps Limited factory set. This is a complete parallel of the All-Star Rookie Team insert that is found in 2000 Topps, and can be easily distinguished by the thicker card stock, glossy finish, and the words "Limited Edition" stamped in gold lettering on each card. Please note that only 4000 sets were produced.

COMPLETE SET (10)	12.50	30.00
*LIMITED: .5X TO 1.2X TOPPS AS ROOK.		

2000 Topps Limited All-Topps

These inserts were seeded at one complete set per sealed Topps Limited factory set. This is a complete parallel of the All-Topps insert that is found in 2000 Topps, and can be easily distinguished by the thicker card stock, glossy finish, and the words "Limited Edition" stamped in gold lettering on each card. Please note that only 4000 sets were produced.

COMPLETE SET (20)	15.00	40.00
*LIMITED: 1X TO 2.5X TOPPS ALL-TOPPS		

2000 Topps Limited Combos

These inserts were seeded at one complete set per sealed Topps Limited factory set. This is a complete parallel of the Combos insert that is found in 2000 Topps, and can be easily distinguished by the thicker card stock, glossy finish, and the words "Limited Edition" stamped in gold lettering on each card. Please note that only 4000 sets were produced.

COMPLETE SET (10)	20.00	50.00
*LIMITED: .75X TO 2X TOPPS COMBOS		

2000 Topps Limited Hands of Gold

These inserts were seeded at one complete set per sealed Topps Limited factory set. This is a complete parallel of the Hands of Gold insert that is found in 2000 Topps, and can be easily distinguished by the thicker card stock, glossy finish, and the words "Limited Edition" stamped in gold lettering on each card. Please note that only 4000 sets were produced.

COMPLETE SET (7)	6.00	15.00
*LIMITED: 1X TO 2.5X TOPPS HANDS		

2000 Topps Limited Own the Game

These inserts were seeded at one complete set per sealed Topps Limited factory set. This is a complete parallel of the Own the Game insert that is found in 2000 Topps, and can be easily distinguished by the thicker card stock, glossy finish, and the words "Limited Edition" stamped in gold lettering on each card. Please note that only 4000 sets were produced.

COMPLETE SET (30)	25.00	60.00
*LIMITED: .5X TO 1.2X TOPPS OTG		

2000 Topps Limited Perennial All-Stars

These inserts were seeded at one complete set per sealed Topps Limited factory set. This is a complete parallel of the Perennial All-Stars insert that is found in 2000 Topps, and can be easily distinguished by the thicker card stock, glossy finish, and the words "Limited Edition" stamped in gold lettering on each card. Please note that only 4000 sets were produced.

COMPLETE SET (10)	15.00	40.00
*LIMITED: 1X TO 2.5X TOPPS PER.AS		

2000 Topps Limited Power Players

These inserts were seeded at one complete set per sealed Topps Limited factory set. This is a complete parallel of the Power Players insert that is found in 2000 Topps, and can be easily distinguished by the thicker card stock, glossy finish, and the words "Limited Edition" stamped in gold lettering on each card. Please note that only 4000 sets were produced.

COMPLETE SET (20)	20.00	50.00
*LIMITED: 1X TO 2.5X TOPPS POWER		

2000 Topps Traded

The 2000 Topps Traded sets were released in October, 2000 and featured a 135-card base set, and one additional autograph card. The set carried a suggested retail price of $29.99. Please note that each card in the base set carried a "T" prefix before the card number. Topps announced that due to the unavailability of certain players previously scheduled to sign autographs, Topps will include a small quantity of autographed cards from the 2000 Topps Baseball Rookies/Traded set into its 2000 Bowman Baseball Draft Picks and Prospects set. Notable Rookie Cards include Cristian Guerrero and J.R. House.

COMP.FACT.SET (136)	25.00	40.00
COMPLETE SET (135)	15.00	30.00
FACT.SET PRICE IS FOR SEALED SETS		
T1 Mike MacDougal	.10	.30
T2 Andy Tracy RC	.10	.30
T3 Brandon Phillips RC	.40	1.00
T4 Brandon Inge RC	.75	2.00
T5 Robbie Morrison RC	.10	.30
T6 Josh Pressley RC	.10	.30
T7 Todd Moser RC	.10	.30
T8 Rob Purvis	.10	.30
T9 Chance Caple	.07	.20
T10 Ben Sheets	.40	1.00
T11 Russ Jacobson RC	.10	.30
T12 Brian Cole RC	.10	.30
T13 Brad Baker	.07	.20
T14 Alex Cintron RC	.10	.30
T15 Lyle Overbay RC	.30	.75
T16 Mike Edwards RC	.10	.30
T17 Sean McGowan RC	.10	.30
T18 Jose Molina	.07	.20
T19 Marcos Castillo RC	.10	.30
T20 Josue Espada RC	.10	.30
T21 Alex Gordon RC	.10	.30
T22 Rob Pugmire RC	.10	.30
T23 Jason Stumm	.07	.20
T24 Ty Howington	.07	.20
T25 Brett Myers	.25	.60
T26 Maicer Izturis RC	.10	.30
T27 John McDonald	.07	.20
T28 W.Rodriguez RC	.10	.30
T29 Carlos Zambrano RC	2.00	5.00
T30 Alejandro Diaz RC	.10	.30
T31 Geraldo Guzman RC	.10	.30
T32 J.R. House RC	.10	.30
T33 Elvin Nina RC	.10	.30
T34 Juan Pierre RC	.25	.60
T35 Ben Johnson RC	.50	1.25
T36 Jeff Bailey RC	.10	.30
T37 Miguel Olivo RC	.20	.50
T38 F.Rodriguez RC	.75	2.00
T39 Tony Pena Jr. RC	.10	.30
T40 Miguel Cabrera RC	8.00	20.00
T41 Asdrubal Oropeza RC	.10	.30
T42 Junior Zamora RC	.10	.30
T43 Jovanny Cedeno RC	.10	.30
T44 John Sneed	.10	.30
T45 Josh Kalinowski	.10	.30
T46 Mike Young RC	2.00	5.00
T47 Rico Washington RC	.10	.30
T48 Chad Durbin RC	.10	.30
T49 Junior Brignac RC	.10	.30
T50 Carlos Hernandez RC	.10	.30
T51 Cesar Izturis RC	.20	.50
T52 Oscar Salazar RC	.10	.30
T53 Pat Strange RC	.10	.30
T54 Rick Asadoorian	.10	.30
T55 Keith Reed	.07	.20
T56 Leo Estrella RC	.10	.30
T57 Wascar Serrano RC	.10	.30
T58 Richard Gomez RC	.10	.30
T59 Ramon Santiago RC	.10	.30
T60 Jovanny Sosa RC	.10	.30
T61 Aaron Rowand RC	.50	1.25
T62 Junior Guerrero RC	.10	.30
T63 Luis Terrero RC	.10	.30
T64 Brian Sanches RC	.10	.30
T65 Scott Sobkowiak RC	.10	.30
T66 Gary Majewski RC	.10	.30
T67 Barry Zito	.50	1.25
T68 Ryan Christianson	.07	.20
T69 Cristian Guerrero RC	.10	.30
T70 T.De La Rosa RC	.10	.30
T71 Andrew Beinbrink RC	.10	.30
T72 Ryan Knox RC	.10	.30
T73 Alex Graman RC	.10	.30
T74 Juan Guzman RC	.10	.30
T75 Ruben Salazar RC	.10	.30
T76 Luis Matos RC	.10	.30
T77 Tony Mota RC	.10	.30
T78 Doug Davis	.10	.30
T79 Ben Christensen	.07	.20
T80 Mike Lamb	.20	.50
T81 Adrian Gonzalez RC	3.00	8.00
T82 Mike Stodolka RC	.10	.30
T83 Adam Johnson RC	.10	.30
T84 Matt Wheatland RC	.10	.30
T85 Corey Smith RC	.10	.30
T86 Rocco Baldelli RC	.50	1.25
T87 Keith Bucktrot RC	.10	.30
T88 Adam Wainwright RC	.75	2.00
T89 Scott Thorman RC	.30	.75
T90 Tripper Johnson RC	.10	.30
T91 Jim Edmonds Cards	.10	.30
T92 Masato Yoshii	.07	.20
T93 Adam Kennedy	.07	.20
T94 Darryl Kile	.10	.30
T95 Mark McLemore	.07	.20
T96 Ricky Gutierrez	.07	.20
T97 Juan Gonzalez	.10	.30
T98 Melvin Mora	.10	.30
T99 Dante Bichette	.10	.30
T100 Lee Stevens	.07	.20
T101 Roger Cedeno	.07	.20
T102 John Olerud	.10	.30
T103 Eric Young	.07	.20
T104 Mickey Morandini	.07	.20
T105 Travis Lee	.07	.20
T106 Greg Vaughn	.07	.20
T107 Todd Zeile	.10	.30
T108 Chuck Finley	.10	.30
T109 Ismael Valdes	.07	.20
T110 Reggie Sanders	.10	.30
T111 Pat Hentgen	.07	.20
T112 Ryan Klesko	.10	.30
T113 Derek Bell	.07	.20
T114 Hideo Nomo	.30	.75
T115 Aaron Sele	.07	.20
T116 Fernando Vina	.07	.20
T117 Wally Joyner	.10	.30
T118 Brian Hunter	.07	.20
T119 Joe Girardi	.07	.20
T120 Omar Daal	.07	.20
T121 Brook Fordyce	.07	.20
T122 Jose Valentin	.07	.20
T123 Curt Schilling	.10	.30
T124 B.J. Surhoff	.10	.30
T125 Henry Rodriguez	.07	.20
T126 Mike Bordick	.07	.20
T127 David Justice	.10	.30
T128 Charles Johnson	.10	.30
T129 Will Clark	.20	.50
T130 Dwight Gooden	.10	.30
T131 David Segui	.07	.20
T132 Denny Neagle	.10	.30
T133 Jose Canseco	.20	.50
T134 Bruce Chen	.07	.20
T135 Jason Bere	.07	.20

2000 Topps Traded Autographs

Randomly inserted into 2000 Topps Traded sets at a rate of one per sealed factory set, this 80-card set features autographed cards of some of the Major League's most talented prospects. Card backs carry a "TTA" prefix.

TTA1 Mike MacDougal	3.00	8.00
TTA2 Andy Tracy	2.00	5.00
TTA3 Brandon Phillips	20.00	50.00
TTA4 Brandon Inge	12.50	30.00
TTA5 Robbie Morrison	2.00	5.00
TTA6 Josh Pressley	2.00	5.00
TTA7 Todd Moser	2.00	5.00
TTA8 Rob Purvis	3.00	8.00
TTA9 Chance Caple	2.00	5.00
TTA10 Ben Sheets	15.00	40.00
TTA11 Russ Jacobson	2.00	5.00
TTA12 Brian Cole	2.00	5.00
TTA13 Brad Baker	2.00	5.00
TTA14 Alex Cintron	3.00	8.00
TTA15 Lyle Overbay	10.00	25.00
TTA16 Mike Edwards	2.00	5.00
TTA17 Sean McGowan	2.00	5.00
TTA18 Jose Molina	2.00	5.00
TTA19 Marcos Castillo	2.00	5.00
TTA20 Josue Espada	2.00	5.00
TTA21 Alex Gordon	2.00	5.00
TTA22 Rob Pugmire	2.00	5.00
TTA23 Jason Stumm	2.00	5.00
TTA24 Ty Howington	2.00	5.00
TTA25 Brett Myers	10.00	25.00
TTA26 Maicer Izturis	3.00	8.00
TTA27 John McDonald	2.00	5.00
TTA28 Wilfredo Rodriguez	2.00	5.00
TTA29 Carlos Zambrano	30.00	60.00
TTA30 Alejandro Diaz	2.00	5.00
TTA31 Geraldo Guzman	2.00	5.00
TTA32 J.R. House	2.00	5.00
TTA33 Elvin Nina	2.00	5.00
TTA34 Juan Pierre	8.00	20.00
TTA35 Ben Johnson	10.00	25.00
TTA36 Jeff Bailey	2.00	5.00
TTA37 Miguel Olivo	5.00	12.00
TTA38 F.Rodriguez	10.00	25.00
TTA39 Tony Pena Jr.	2.00	5.00
TTA40 Miguel Cabrera	300.00	550.00
TTA41 Asdrubal Oropeza	2.00	5.00
TTA42 Junior Zamora	2.00	5.00
TTA43 Jovanny Cedeno	2.00	5.00
TTA44 John Sneed	2.00	5.00
TTA45 Josh Kalinowski	3.00	8.00
TTA46 Mike Young	75.00	150.00
TTA47 Rico Washington	2.00	5.00
TTA48 Chad Durbin	2.00	5.00
TTA49 Junior Brignac	2.00	5.00
TTA50 Carlos Hernandez	3.00	8.00
TTA51 Cesar Izturis	6.00	15.00
TTA52 Oscar Salazar	2.00	5.00
TTA53 Pat Strange	2.00	5.00
TTA54 Rick Asadoorian	3.00	8.00
TTA55 Keith Reed	2.00	5.00
TTA56 Leo Estrella	2.00	5.00
TTA57 Wascar Serrano	2.00	5.00
TTA58 Richard Gomez	2.00	5.00
TTA59 Ramon Santiago	6.00	15.00
TTA60 Jovanny Sosa	2.00	5.00
TTA61 Aaron Rowand	8.00	20.00
TTA62 Junior Guerrero	2.00	5.00
TTA63 Luis Terrero	3.00	8.00
TTA64 Brian Sanches	2.00	5.00
TTA65 Scott Sobkowiak	2.00	5.00
TTA66 Gary Majewski	3.00	8.00
TTA67 Barry Zito	12.50	30.00
TTA68 Ryan Christianson	2.00	5.00
TTA69 Cristian Guerrero	2.00	5.00
TTA70 Tomas De La Rosa	2.00	5.00
TTA71 Andrew Beinbrink	3.00	8.00
TTA72 Ryan Knox	2.00	5.00

TTA73 Alex Graman 2.00 5.00
TTA74 Juan Guzman 2.00 5.00
TTA75 Ruben Salazar 2.00 5.00
TTA76 Luis Matos 2.00 5.00
TTA77 Tony Mota 2.00 5.00
TTA78 Doug Davis 6.00 15.00
TTA79 Ben Christensen 2.00 5.00
TTA80 Mike Lamb 6.00 15.00

2001 Topps

The 2001 Topps set featured 790 cards and was issued over two series. The set looks to bring back some of the heritage that Topps established in the past by bringing back Manager cards, dual-player prospect cards, and the 2000 season highlight cards. Notable Rookie Cards include Hee Seop Choi. Please note that some cards have been discovered with nothing printed on front but blank white except for the players name and 50th Topps anniversary logo printed in Gold. Factory sets include five special cards inserted specifically in those sets. Card number 7 was not issued as Topps continued to honor the memory of Mickey Mantle.

COMPLETE SET (790) 40.00 80.00
COMP.FACT.BLUE SET (795) 60.00 120.00
COMP.SERIES 1 (405) 20.00 40.00
COMP. SERIES 2 (385) 20.00 40.00
COMMON (1-6/8-791) .07 .20
COMMON (352-376/727-751) .08 .25
1 Cal Ripken .60 1.50
2 Chipper Jones .20 .50
3 Roger Cedeno .07 .20
4 Garret Anderson .07 .20
5 Robin Ventura .07 .20
6 Daryle Ward .07 .20
8 Craig Paquette .07 .20
9 Phil Nevin .07 .20
10 Jermaine Dye .07 .20
11 Chris Singleton .07 .20
12 Mike Stanton .07 .20
13 Brian Hunter .07 .20
14 Mike Redmond .07 .20
15 Jim Thome .10 .30
16 Brian Jordan .07 .20
17 Joe Girardi .07 .20
18 Steve Woodard .07 .20
19 Dustin Hermanson .07 .20
20 Shawn Green .07 .20
21 Todd Stottlemyre .07 .20
22 Dan Wilson .07 .20
23 Todd Pratt .07 .20
24 Derek Lowe .07 .20
25 Juan Gonzalez .07 .20
26 Clay Bellinger .07 .20
27 Jeff Fassero .07 .20
28 Pat Meares .07 .20
29 Eddie Taubensee .07 .20
30 Paul O'Neill .10 .30
31 Jeffrey Hammonds .07 .20
32 Pokey Reese .07 .20
33 Mike Mussina .10 .30
34 Rico Brogna .07 .20
35 Jay Buhner .07 .20
36 Steve Cox .07 .20
37 Quilvio Veras .07 .20
38 Marquis Grissom .07 .20
39 Shigetoshi Hasegawa .07 .20
40 Shane Reynolds .07 .20
41 Adam Piatt .07 .20
42 Luis Polonia .07 .20
43 Brook Fordyce .07 .20
44 Preston Wilson .07 .20
45 Ellis Burks .07 .20
46 Armando Rios .07 .20
47 Chuck Finley .07 .20
48 Dan Plesac .07 .20
49 Shannon Stewart .07 .20
50 Mark McGwire .50 1.25
51 Mark Loretta .07 .20
52 Gerald Williams .07 .20
53 Eric Young .07 .20
54 Peter Bergeron .07 .20
55 Dave Hansen .07 .20
56 Arthur Rhodes .07 .20
57 Bobby Jones .07 .20
58 Matt Clement .07 .20
59 Mike Benjamin .07 .20
60 Pedro Martinez .10 .30
61 Jose Canseco .10 .30
62 Matt Anderson .07 .20
63 Torii Hunter .07 .20
64 Carlos Lee UER .07 .20
1999 Charlotte Games Played are wrong
65 David Cone .07 .20
66 Rey Sanchez .07 .20
67 Eric Chavez .07 .20
68 Rick Helling .07 .20
69 Manny Alexander .07 .20
70 John Franco .07 .20
71 Mike Bordick .07 .20
72 Andres Galarraga .07 .20
73 Jose Cruz Jr. .07 .20
74 Mike Matheny .07 .20
75 Randy Johnson .20 .50
76 Richie Sexson .07 .20
77 Vladimir Nunez .07 .20
78 Harold Baines .07 .20
79 Aaron Boone .07 .20
80 Darin Erstad .07 .20
81 Alex Gonzalez .07 .20
82 Gil Heredia .07 .20
83 Shane Andrews .07 .20
84 Todd Hundley .07 .20
85 Bill Mueller .07 .20
86 Mark McLemore .07 .20
87 Scott Spiezio .07 .20
88 Kevin McGlinchy .07 .20
89 Bubba Trammell .07 .20
90 Manny Ramirez .10 .30
91 Mike Lamb .07 .20
92 Scott Karl .07 .20
93 Brian Buchanan .07 .20
94 Chris Turner .07 .20
95 Mike Sweeney .07 .20
96 John Wetteland .07 .20
97 Rob Bell .07 .20
98 Pat Rapp .07 .20
99 John Burkett .07 .20
100 Derek Jeter .50 1.25
101 J.D. Drew .07 .20
102 Jose Offerman .07 .20
103 Rick Reed .07 .20
104 Will Clark .10 .30
105 Rickey Henderson .20 .50
106 Dave Berg .07 .20
107 Kirk Rueter .07 .20
108 Lee Stevens .07 .20
109 Jay Bell .07 .20
110 Fred McGriff .10 .30
111 Julio Zuleta .07 .20
112 Brian Anderson .07 .20
113 Orlando Cabrera .07 .20
114 Alex Fernandez .07 .20
115 Derek Bell .07 .20
116 Eric Owens .07 .20
117 Brian Bohanon .07 .20
118 Dennys Reyes .07 .20
119 Mike Stanley .07 .20
120 Jorge Posada .10 .30
121 Rich Becker .07 .20
122 Paul Konerko .07 .20
123 Mike Remlinger .07 .20
124 Travis Lee .07 .20
125 Ken Caminiti .07 .20
126 Kevin Barker .07 .20
127 Paul Quantrill .07 .20
128 Ozzie Guillen .07 .20
129 Kevin Tapani .07 .20
130 Mark Johnson .07 .20
131 Randy Wolf .07 .20
132 Michael Tucker .07 .20
133 Darren Lewis .07 .20
134 Joe Randa .07 .20
135 Jeff Cirillo .07 .20
136 David Ortiz .20 .50
137 Herb Perry .07 .20
138 Jeff Nelson .07 .20
139 Chris Stynes .07 .20
140 Johnny Damon .10 .30
141 Jeff Reboulet .07 .20
142 Jason Schmidt .07 .20
143 Charles Johnson .07 .20
144 Pat Burrell .07 .20
145 Gary Sheffield .07 .20
146 Tom Glavine .10 .30
147 Jason Isringhausen .07 .20
148 Chris Carpenter .07 .20
149 Jeff Suppan .07 .20
150 Ivan Rodriguez .10 .30
151 Luis Sojo .07 .20
152 Ron Villone .07 .20
153 Mike Sirotka .07 .20
154 Chuck Knoblauch .07 .20
155 Jason Kendall .07 .20
156 Dennis Cook .07 .20
157 Bobby Estalella .07 .20
158 Jose Guillen .07 .20
159 Thomas Howard .07 .20
160 Carlos Delgado .07 .20
161 Benji Gil .07 .20
162 Tim Bogar .07 .20
163 Kevin Elster .07 .20
164 Einar Diaz .07 .20
165 Andy Benes .07 .20
166 Adrian Beltre .07 .20
167 David Bell .07 .20
168 Turk Wendell .07 .20
169 Pete Harnisch .07 .20
170 Roger Clemens .40 1.00
171 Scott Williamson .07 .20
172 Kevin Jordan .07 .20
173 Brad Penny .07 .20
174 John Flaherty .07 .20
175 Troy Glaus .07 .20
176 Kevin Appier .07 .20
177 Walt Weiss .07 .20
178 Tyler Houston .07 .20
179 Michael Barrett .07 .20
180 Mike Hampton .07 .20
181 Francisco Cordova .07 .20
182 Mike Jackson .07 .20
183 David Segui .07 .20
184 Carlos Febles .07 .20
185 Roy Halladay .07 .20
186 Seth Etherton .07 .20
187 Charlie Hayes .07 .20
188 Fernando Tatis .07 .20
189 Steve Trachsel .07 .20
190 Livan Hernandez .07 .20
191 Joe Oliver .07 .20
192 Stan Javier .07 .20
193 B.J. Surhoff .07 .20
194 Rob Ducey .07 .20
195 Barry Larkin .10 .30
196 Danny Patterson .07 .20
197 Bobby Howry .07 .20
198 Dmitri Young .07 .20
199 Brian Hunter .07 .20
200 Alex Rodriguez .30 .75
201 Hideo Nomo .20 .50
202 Luis Alicea .07 .20
203 Warren Morris .07 .20
204 Antonio Alfonseca .07 .20
205 Edgardo Alfonzo .07 .20
206 Mark Grudzielanek .07 .20
207 Fernando Vina .07 .20
208 Willie Greene .07 .20
209 Homer Bush .07 .20
210 Jason Giambi .07 .20
211 Mike Morgan .07 .20
212 Steve Karsay .07 .20
213 Matt Lawton .07 .20
214 Wendell Magee Jr. .07 .20
215 Rusty Greer .07 .20
216 Keith Lockhart .07 .20
217 Billy Koch .07 .20
218 Todd Hollandsworth .07 .20
219 Raul Ibanez .07 .20
220 Tony Gwynn .25 .60
221 Carl Everett .07 .20
222 Hector Carrasco .07 .20
223 Jose Valentin .07 .20
224 Deivi Cruz .07 .20
225 Bret Boone .07 .20
226 Kurt Abbott .07 .20
227 Melvin Mora .07 .20
228 Danny Graves .07 .20
229 Jose Jimenez .07 .20
230 James Baldwin .07 .20
231 C.J. Nitkowski .07 .20
232 Jeff Zimmerman .07 .20
233 Mike Lowell .07 .20
234 Hideki Irabu .07 .20
235 Greg Vaughn .07 .20
236 Omar Daal .07 .20
237 Darren Dreifort .07 .20
238 Gil Meche .07 .20
239 Damian Jackson .07 .20
240 Frank Thomas .20 .50
241 Travis Miller .07 .20
242 Jeff Frye .07 .20
243 Dave Magadan .07 .20
244 Luis Castillo .07 .20
245 Bartolo Colon .07 .20
246 Steve Kline .07 .20
247 Shawon Dunston .07 .20
248 Rick Aguilera .07 .20
249 Omar Olivares .07 .20
250 Craig Biggio .10 .30
251 Scott Schoeneweis .07 .20
252 Dave Veres .07 .20
253 Ramon Martinez .07 .20
254 Jose Vidro .07 .20
255 Todd Helton .10 .30
256 Greg Norton .07 .20
257 Jacque Jones .07 .20
258 Jason Grimsley .07 .20
259 Dan Reichert .07 .20
260 Robb Nen .07 .20
261 Mark Clark .07 .20
262 Scott Hatteberg .07 .20
263 Doug Brocail .07 .20
264 Mark Johnson .07 .20
265 Eric Davis .07 .20
266 Terry Shumpert .07 .20
267 Kevin Millar .07 .20
268 Ismael Valdes .07 .20
269 Richard Hidalgo .07 .20
270 Randy Velarde .07 .20
271 Bengie Molina .07 .20
272 Tony Womack .07 .20
273 Enrique Wilson .07 .20
274 Jeff Brantley .07 .20
275 Rick Ankiel .07 .20
276 Terry Mulholland .07 .20
277 Ron Belliard .07 .20
278 Terrence Long .07 .20
279 Alberto Castillo .07 .20
280 Royce Clayton .07 .20
281 Joe McEwing .07 .20
282 Jason McDonald .07 .20
283 Ricky Bottalico .07 .20
284 Keith Foulke .07 .20
285 Brad Radke .07 .20
286 Gabe Kapler .07 .20
287 Pedro Astacio .07 .20
288 Armando Reynoso .07 .20
289 Darryl Kile .07 .20
290 Reggie Sanders .07 .20
291 Esteban Yan .07 .20
292 Joe Nathan .07 .20
293 Jay Payton .07 .20
294 Francisco Cordero .07 .20
295 Gregg Jefferies .07 .20
296 LaTroy Hawkins .07 .20
297 Jeff Tam RC .15 .40
298 Jacob Cruz .07 .20
299 Chris Holt .07 .20
300 Vladimir Guerrero .20 .50
301 Marvin Benard .07 .20
302 Alex Ramirez .07 .20
303 Mike Williams .07 .20
304 Sean Bergman .07 .20
305 Juan Encarnacion .07 .20
306 Russ Davis .07 .20
307 Hanley Frias .07 .20
308 Ramon Hernandez .07 .20
309 Matt Walbeck .07 .20
310 Bill Spiers .07 .20
311 Bob Wickman .07 .20
312 Sandy Alomar Jr. .07 .20
313 Eddie Guardado .07 .20
314 Shane Halter .07 .20
315 Geoff Jenkins .07 .20
316 Brian Meadows .07 .20
317 Damian Miller .07 .20
318 Darrin Fletcher .07 .20
319 Rafael Furcal .07 .20
320 Mark Grace .10 .30
321 Mark Mulder .07 .20
322 Joe Torre MG .10 .30
323 Bobby Cox MG .07 .20
324 Mike Scioscia MG .07 .20
325 Mike Hargrove MG .07 .20
326 Jimy Williams MG .07 .20
327 Jerry Manuel MG .07 .20
328 Buck Showalter MG .07 .20
329 Charlie Manuel MG .07 .20
330 Don Baylor MG .07 .20
331 Phil Garner MG .07 .20
332 Jack McKeon MG .07 .20
333 Tony Muser MG .07 .20
334 Buddy Bell MG .07 .20
335 Tom Kelly MG .07 .20
336 John Boles MG .07 .20
337 Art Howe MG .07 .20
338 Larry Dierker MG .07 .20
339 Lou Piniella MG .07 .20
340 Davey Johnson MG .07 .20
341 Larry Rothschild MG .07 .20
342 Davey Lopes MG .07 .20
343 Johnny Oates MG .07 .20
344 Felipe Alou MG .07 .20
345 Jim Fregosi MG .07 .20
346 Bobby Valentine MG .07 .20
347 Terry Francona MG .07 .20
348 Gene Lamont MG .07 .20
349 Tony LaRussa MG .07 .20
350 Bruce Bochy MG .07 .20
351 Dusty Baker MG .07 .20
352 Adrian Gonzalez .60 1.50
Adam Johnson
353 Matt Wheatland .08 .25
Bryan Digby
354 Tripper Johnson .08 .25
Scott Thorman
355 Phil Dumatrait .20 .50
Adam Wainwright
356 Scott Heard .08 .25
David Parrish RC
357 Rocco Baldelli .15 .40
Mark Folsom RC
358 Dominic Rich RC .08 .25
Aaron Herr
359 Mike Stodolka .08 .25
Sean Burnett
360 Derek Thompson .08 .25
Corey Smith
361 Danny Borrell RC .08 .25
Jason Bourgeois RC
362 Chin-Feng Chen .20 .50
Corey Patterson
Josh Hamilton
363 Ryan Anderson .20 .50
Barry Zito
C.C. Sabathia
364 Scott Sobkowiak .20 .50
David Walling
Ben Sheets
365 Ty Howington .08 .25
Josh Kalinowski
Josh Girdley
366 Hee Seop Choi RC .20 .50
Aaron McNeal
Jason Hart
367 Bobby Bradley .15 .40
Kurt Ainsworth
Chin-Hui Tsao
368 Mike Glendenning .08 .25
Kenny Kelly
Juan Silvestre
369 J.R. House .08 .25
Ramon Castro
Ben Davis
370 Chance Caple .15 .40
Rafael Soriano RC
Pasqual Coco
371 Travis Hafner RC 1.50 4.00
Eric Munson
Bucky Jacobsen
372 Jason Conti .08 .25
Chris Wakeland
Brian Cole
373 Scott Seabol .30 .75
Aubrey Huff
Joe Crede
374 Adam Everett .08 .25
Jose Ortiz
Keith Ginter
375 Carlos Hernandez .08 .25
Geraldo Guzman
Adam Eaton
376 Bobby Kielty .15 .40
Milton Bradley
Juan Rivera
377 Mark McGwire GM .25 .60
378 Don Larsen GM .07 .20
379 Bobby Thomson GM .07 .20
380 Bill Mazeroski GM .07 .20
381 Reggie Jackson GM .10 .30
382 Kirk Gibson GM .07 .20
383 Roger Maris GM .10 .30
384 Cal Ripken GM .30 .75
385 Hank Aaron GM .20 .50
386 Joe Carter GM .07 .20
387 Cal Ripken SH .60 1.50
388 Randy Johnson SH .10 .30
389 Ken Griffey Jr. SH .30 .75
390 Troy Glaus SH .07 .20
391 Kazuhiro Sasaki SH .07 .20
392 Sammy Sosa LL .10 .30
Troy Glaus
393 Todd Helton LL .07 .20
Edgar Martinez
394 Todd Helton LL .20 .50
Nomar Garciaparra
395 Barry Bonds LL .30 .75
Jason Giambi
396 Todd Helton LL .07 .20
Manny Ramirez
397 Todd Helton LL .07 .20
Darin Erstad
398 Kevin Brown LL .10 .30
Pedro Martinez
399 Randy Johnson LL .10 .30
Pedro Martinez
400 Will Clark HL .10 .30
401 New York Mets HL .20 .50
402 New York Yankees HL .30 .75
403 Seattle Mariners HL .07 .20
404 Mike Hampton HL .07 .20
405 New York Yankees HL .40 1.00
406 N.Y. Yankees Champs .75 2.00
407 Jeff Bagwell .10 .30
408 Brant Brown .07 .20
409 Brad Fullmer .07 .20
410 Dean Palmer .07 .20
411 Greg Zaun .07 .20
412 Jose Vizcaino .07 .20
413 Jeff Abbott .07 .20
414 Travis Fryman .07 .20
415 Mike Cameron .07 .20
416 Matt Mantei .07 .20
417 Alan Benes .07 .20
418 Mickey Morandini .07 .20
419 Troy Percival .07 .20
420 Eddie Perez .07 .20
421 Vernon Wells .07 .20
422 Ricky Gutierrez .07 .20
423 Carlos Hernandez .07 .20
424 Chan Ho Park .07 .20
425 Armando Benitez .07 .20
426 Sidney Ponson .07 .20
427 Adrian Brown .07 .20
428 Ruben Mateo .07 .20
429 Alex Ochoa .07 .20
430 Jose Rosado .07 .20
431 Masato Yoshii .07 .20
432 Corey Koskie .07 .20
433 Andy Pettitte .10 .30
434 Brian Daubach .07 .20
435 Sterling Hitchcock .07 .20
436 Timo Perez .07 .20
437 Shawn Estes .07 .20
438 Tony Armas Jr. .07 .20
439 Danny Bautista .07 .20
440 Randy Winn .07 .20
441 Wilson Alvarez .07 .20
442 Rondell White .07 .20
443 Jeromy Burnitz .07 .20
444 Kelvim Escobar .07 .20
445 Paul Bako .07 .20
446 Javier Vazquez .07 .20
447 Eric Gagne .07 .20
448 Kenny Lofton .07 .20
449 Mark Kotsay .07 .20
450 Jamie Moyer .07 .20
451 Delino DeShields .07 .20
452 Rey Ordonez .07 .20
453 Russ Ortiz .07 .20
454 Dave Burba .07 .20
455 Eric Karros .07 .20
456 Felix Martinez .07 .20
457 Tony Batista .07 .20
458 Bobby Higginson .07 .20
459 Jeff D'Amico .07 .20
460 Shane Spencer .07 .20
461 Brent Mayne .07 .20
462 Glendon Rusch .07 .20
463 Chris Gomez .07 .20
464 Jeff Shaw .07 .20
465 Damon Buford .07 .20
466 Mike DiFelice .07 .20
467 Jimmy Haynes .07 .20
468 Billy Wagner .07 .20
469 A.J. Hinch .07 .20
470 Gary DiSarcina .07 .20
471 Tom Lampkin .07 .20
472 Adam Eaton .07 .20
473 Brian Giles .07 .20
474 John Thomson .07 .20
475 Cal Eldred .07 .20
476 Ramiro Mendoza .07 .20
477 Scott Sullivan .07 .20
478 Scott Rolen .10 .30
479 Todd Ritchie .07 .20
480 Pablo Ozuna .07 .20
481 Carl Pavano .07 .20
482 Matt Morris .07 .20
483 Matt Stairs .07 .20
484 Tim Belcher .07 .20
485 Lance Berkman .07 .20
486 Brian Meadows .07 .20
487 Bob Abreu .07 .20
488 John VanderWal .07 .20
489 Donnie Sadler .07 .20
490 Damion Easley .07 .20
491 David Justice .07 .20
492 Ray Durham .07 .20
493 Todd Zeile .07 .20
494 Desi Relaford .07 .20
495 Cliff Floyd .07 .20
496 Scott Downs .07 .20
497 Barry Bonds .50 1.25
498 Jeff D'Amico .07 .20
499 Octavio Dotel .07 .20
500 Kent Mercker .07 .20
501 Craig Grebeck .07 .20
502 Roberto Hernandez .07 .20
503 Matt Williams .07 .20
504 Bruce Aven .07 .20
505 Brett Tomko .07 .20
506 Kris Benson .07 .20
507 Neifi Perez .07 .20
508 Alfonso Soriano .10 .30
509 Keith Osik .07 .20
510 Matt Franco .07 .20
511 Steve Finley .07 .20
512 Olmedo Saenz .07 .20
513 Esteban Loaiza .07 .20
514 Adam Kennedy .07 .20
515 Scott Elarton .07 .20
516 Moises Alou .07 .20
517 Bryan Rekar .07 .20
518 Darryl Hamilton .07 .20
519 Osvaldo Fernandez .07 .20
520 Kip Wells .07 .20
521 Bernie Williams .10 .30
522 Mike Darr .07 .20
523 Marlon Anderson .07 .20
524 Derrek Lee .10 .30
525 Ugueth Urbina .07 .20
526 Vinny Castilla .07 .20
527 David Wells .07 .20
528 Jason Marquis .07 .20
529 Orlando Palmeiro .07 .20
530 Carlos Perez .07 .20
531 J.T. Snow .07 .20
532 Al Leiter .07 .20
533 Jimmy Anderson .07 .20
534 Brett Laxton .07 .20
535 Butch Huskey .07 .20
536 Orlando Hernandez .07 .20
537 Magglio Ordonez .07 .20
538 Willie Blair .07 .20
539 Kevin Sefcik .07 .20
540 Chad Curtis .07 .20
541 John Halama .07 .20
542 Andy Fox .07 .20
543 Juan Guzman .07 .20
544 Frank Menechino RC .07 .20
545 Raul Mondesi .07 .20
546 Tim Salmon .10 .30
547 Ryan Rupe .07 .20
548 Jeff Reed .07 .20
549 Mike Mordecai .07 .20
550 Jeff Kent .07 .20
551 Wiki Gonzalez .07 .20
552 Kenny Rogers .07 .20
553 Kevin Young .07 .20
554 Brian Johnson .07 .20
555 Tom Goodwin .07 .20
556 Tony Clark UER .07 .20
0 games, 208 At-Bats
557 Mac Suzuki .07 .20
558 Brian Moehler .07 .20
559 Jim Parque .07 .20
560 Mariano Rivera .20 .50
561 Trot Nixon .07 .20
562 Mike Mussina .10 .30
563 Nelson Figueroa .07 .20
564 Alex Gonzalez .07 .20
565 Benny Agbayani .07 .20
566 Ed Sprague .07 .20
567 Scott Erickson .07 .20
568 Abraham Nunez .07 .20
569 Jerry DiPoto .07 .20
570 Sean Casey .07 .20
571 Wilton Veras .07 .20
572 Joe Mays .07 .20
573 Bill Simas .07 .20
574 Doug Glanville .07 .20
575 Scott Sauerbeck .07 .20
576 Ben Davis .07 .20
577 Jesus Sanchez .07 .20
578 Ricardo Rincon .07 .20
579 John Olerud .07 .20
580 Curt Schilling .07 .20
581 Alex Cora .07 .20
582 Pat Hentgen .07 .20
583 Javy Lopez .07 .20
584 Ben Grieve .07 .20
585 Frank Castillo .07 .20
586 Kevin Stocker .07 .20
587 Mark Sweeney .07 .20
588 Ray Lankford .07 .20
589 Turner Ward .07 .20
590 Felipe Crespo .07 .20
591 Omar Vizquel .10 .30
592 Mike Lieberthal .07 .20
593 Ken Griffey Jr. .30 .75
594 Troy O'Leary .07 .20
595 Dave Mlicki .07 .20
596 Manny Ramirez Sox .10 .30
597 Mike Lansing .07 .20
598 Rich Aurilia .07 .20
599 Russell Branyan .07 .20
600 Russ Johnson .07 .20
601 Greg Colbrunn .07 .20
602 Andruw Jones .10 .30
603 Henry Blanco .07 .20
604 Jarrod Washburn .07 .20
605 Tony Eusebio .07 .20
606 Aaron Sele .07 .20
607 Charles Nagy .07 .20
608 Ryan Klesko .07 .20
609 Dante Bichette .07 .20
610 Bill Haselman .07 .20
611 Jerry Spradlin .07 .20
612 A. Rodriguez Rangers .30 .75
613 Jose Silva .07 .20
614 Darren Oliver .07 .20
615 Pat Mahomes .07 .20
616 Roberto Alomar .10 .30
617 Edgar Renteria .07 .20
618 Jon Lieber .07 .20
619 John Rocker .07 .20
620 Miguel Tejada .07 .20
621 Mo Vaughn .07 .20
622 Jose Lima .07 .20
623 Kerry Wood .07 .20
624 Mike Timlin .07 .20
625 Wil Cordero .07 .20
626 Albert Belle .07 .20
627 Bobby Jones .07 .20
628 Doug Mirabelli .07 .20
629 Jason Tyner .07 .20
630 Andy Ashby .07 .20
631 Jose Hernandez .07 .20
632 Devon White .07 .20
633 Ruben Rivera .07 .20
634 Steve Parris .07 .20
635 David McCarty .07 .20
636 Jose Canseco .10 .30
637 Todd Walker .07 .20
638 Stan Spencer .07 .20
639 Wayne Gomes .07 .20
640 Freddy Garcia .07 .20
641 Jeremy Giambi .07 .20
642 Luis Lopez .07 .20
643 John Smoltz .10 .30
644 Kelly Stinnett .07 .20
645 Kevin Brown .07 .20
646 Wilton Guerrero .07 .20
647 Al Martin .07 .20
648 Woody Williams .07 .20
649 Brian Rose .07 .20
650 Rafael Palmeiro .10 .30
651 Pete Schourek .07 .20
652 Kevin Jarvis .07 .20
653 Mark Redman .07 .20
654 Ricky Ledee .07 .20
655 Larry Walker .07 .20
656 Paul Byrd .07 .20
657 Jason Bere .07 .20
658 Rick White .07 .20
659 Calvin Murray .07 .20
660 Greg Maddux .30 .75
661 Ron Gant .07 .20
662 Eli Marrero .07 .20
663 Graeme Lloyd .07 .20
664 Trevor Hoffman .07 .20
665 Nomar Garciaparra .30 .75
666 Glenallen Hill .07 .20
667 Matt LeCroy .07 .20
668 Justin Thompson .07 .20
669 Brady Anderson .07 .20
670 Miguel Batista .07 .20
671 Erubiel Durazo .07 .20
672 Kevin Millwood .07 .20
673 Mitch Meluskey .07 .20
674 Luis Gonzalez .07 .20
675 Edgar Martinez .10 .30
676 Robert Person .07 .20
677 Benito Santiago .07 .20
678 Todd Jones .07 .20
679 Tino Martinez .10 .30
680 Carlos Beltran .07 .20
681 Gabe White .07 .20
682 Bret Saberhagen .07 .20
683 Jeff Conine .07 .20
684 Jaret Wright .07 .20
685 Bernard Gilkey .07 .20
686 Garrett Stephenson .07 .20
687 Jamey Wright .07 .20
688 Sammy Sosa .20 .50
689 John Jaha .07 .20
690 Ramon Martinez .07 .20
691 Robert Fick .07 .20
692 Eric Milton .07 .20
693 Denny Neagle .07 .20
694 Ron Coomer .07 .20
695 John Valentin .07 .20
696 Placido Polanco .07 .20
697 Tim Hudson .07 .20
698 Marty Cordova .07 .20
699 Chad Kreuter .07 .20
700 Frank Catalanotto .07 .20
701 Tim Wakefield .07 .20
702 Jim Edmonds .07 .20
703 Michael Tucker .07 .20
704 Cristian Guzman .07 .20
705 Joey Hamilton .07 .20
706 Mike Piazza .30 .75
707 Dave Martinez .07 .20
708 Mike Hampton .07 .20
709 Bobby Bonilla .07 .20
710 Juan Pierre .07 .20
711 John Parrish .07 .20
712 Kory DeHaan .07 .20
713 Brian Tollberg .07 .20
714 Chris Truby .07 .20
715 Emil Brown .07 .20
716 Ryan Dempster .07 .20
717 Rich Garces .07 .20
718 Mike Myers .07 .20
719 Luis Ordaz .07 .20
720 Kazuhiro Sasaki .07 .20
721 Mark Quinn .07 .20
722 Ramon Ortiz .07 .20
723 Kerry Ligtenberg .07 .20
724 Rolando Arrojo .07 .20
725 Tsuyoshi Shinjo RC .20 .50
726 Ichiro Suzuki RC 5.00 12.00
727 Roy Oswalt .30 .75
Pat Strange
Jon Rauch
728 Phil Wilson RC 1.40 4.00
Jake Peavy RC
Darwin Cubillan RC UER
Sic, Peavey
729 Steve Smyth RC .08 .25
Mike Bynum
Nathan Haynes
730 Michael Cuddyer .08 .25
Joe Lawrence
Choo Freeman
731 Carlos Pena .08 .25
Larry Barnes
DeWayne Wise
732 Travis Dawkins .08 .25
Erick Almonte
Felipe Lopez
733 Alex Escobar .08 .25
Eric Valent
Brad Wilkerson
734 Toby Hall .08 .25

Rod Barajas		
Jeff Goldbach		
735 Jason Romano	.15	.40
Marcus Giles		
Pablo Ozuna		
736 Dee Brown	.08	.25
Jack Cust		
Vernon Wells		
737 David Espinosa	.08	.25
Luis Montanez RC		
738 Anthony Pluta RC	.08	.25
Justin Wayne RC		
739 Josh Axelson RC	.08	.25
Carmen Cali RC		
740 Shaun Boyd RC	.08	.25
Chris Morris RC		
741 Tommy Arko RC	.08	.25
Dan Moylan RC		
742 Luis Cotto RC	.08	.25
Luis Escobar		
743 Brandon Mims RC	.08	.25
Blake Williams RC		
744 Chris Russ RC	.08	.25
Bryan Edwards		
745 Joe Torres	.08	.25
Ben Diggins		
746 Hugh Quattlebaum RC	1.25	3.00
Edwin Encarnacion RC		
747 Brian Bass RC	.08	.25
Odannis Ayala RC		
748 Jason Kaanoi	.08	.25
Michael Matthews RC UER		
name misspelled Mathews		
749 Stuart McFarland RC	.08	.25
Adam Sterrett RC		
750 David Krynzel	.60	1.50
Grady Sizemore		
751 Keith Bucktrot	.08	.25
Dane Sardinha		
752 Anaheim Angels TC	.07	.20
753 Ariz. Diamondbacks TC	.07	.20
754 Atlanta Braves TC	.07	.20
755 Baltimore Orioles TC	.07	.20
756 Boston Red Sox TC	.07	.20
757 Chicago Cubs TC	.07	.20
758 Chicago White Sox TC	.07	.20
759 Cincinnati Reds TC	.07	.20
760 Cleveland Indians TC	.07	.20
761 Colorado Rockies TC	.07	.20
762 Detroit Tigers TC	.07	.20
763 Florida Marlins TC	.07	.20
764 Houston Astros TC	.07	.20
765 K.C. Royals TC	.07	.20
766 L.A. Dodgers TC	.07	.20
767 Milw. Brewers TC	.07	.20
768 Minnesota Twins TC	.07	.20
769 Montreal Expos TC	.07	.20
770 New York Mets TC	.07	.20
771 New York Yankees TC	.40	1.00
772 Oakland Athletics TC	.07	.20
773 Phil. Phillies TC	.07	.20
774 Pittsburgh Pirates TC	.07	.20
775 San Diego Padres TC	.07	.20
776 San Francisco Giants TC	.07	.20
777 Seattle Mariners TC	.07	.20
778 St. Louis Cardinals TC	.07	.20
779 T.B. Devil Rays TC	.07	.20
780 Texas Rangers TC	.07	.20
781 Toronto Blue Jays TC	.07	.20
782 Bucky Dent GM	.07	.20
783 Jackie Robinson GM	.20	.50
784 Roberto Clemente GM	.25	.60
785 Nolan Ryan GM	.30	.75
786 Kerry Wood GM	.07	.20
787 Rickey Henderson GM	.07	.20
788 Lou Brock GM	.10	.30
789 David Wells GM	.07	.20
790 Andruw Jones GM	.07	.20
791 Carlton Fisk GM	.07	.20
TK Bo Jackson	60.00	120.00
Deion Sanders Bat		
NNO Bobby Thomson	30.00	60.00
Ralph Branca		
1991 Bowman Autograph		

2001 Topps Employee

Topps created as a special bonus for their employees, a "parallel" factory set of the 2001 Topps set with a special employee logo embossed on the card. It is believed approximately 150 of these cards were produced.

*STARS: 6X TO 15X BASIC CARDS
CARD NO.7 DOES NOT EXIST

726 Ichiro Suzuki	60.00	150.00

2001 Topps Gold

Randomly inserted into first series packs at a rate of 1:17 Hobby/Retail and 1:4 HTA and second series packs at a rate of 1:14 Hobby/Retail and 1:3 HTA, this 790-card set is a complete parallel of the 2001 Topps base set. These cards were produced with a special gold-foil border on front and were individually serial numbered to 2001 on back. Please note that card number 7 does not exist.

*STARS: 10X TO 25X BASIC CARDS
*PROSPECTS 352-376/725/751: 4X TO 10X
*ROOKIES 352-376/725-751: 4X TO 10X

2001 Topps Home Team Advantage

This factory-sealed 790-card set was issued exclusively to Topps network of Home Team Advantage baseball card shops. The sets were packaged in attractive gold foil boxes and each card features a distinctive "HTA" foil stamp on front.

COMP.HTA.GOLD SET (790)	60.00	120.00

*HTA: .75X TO 2X BASIC CARDS

2001 Topps Limited

These attractive cards parallel the basic 2001 Topps set. The product was distributed exclusively in factory set format. Each set contained the 790-card basic set plus five Topps Archives Reserve Future Rookie Reprints chrome inserts wrapped together in a plastic cello pack. The sets were distributed through hobby dealers in attractive wood boxes and carried a suggested retail price of $173. Each Topps Limited card was printed on 20 pt. stock paper featuring glossy fronts and backs and a "Limited Edition" gold foil logo on front. Though the cards lack individual serial-numbering, Topps announced production at 3,805 sets. Each set states that total on the bottom of the wooden box.

COMP.FACT.SET (790)	60.00	150.00

*STARS: 1.5X TO 4X BASIC CARDS
*ROOKIES: 1.5X TO 4X BASIC CARDS

2001 Topps A Look Ahead

Randomly inserted into packs at 1:25 Hobby/Retail and 1:5 HTA, this 10-card insert takes a look a players that are on their way to Cooperstown. Card backs carry a "LA" prefix.

COMPLETE SET (10)	12.50	30.00
LA1 Vladimir Guerrero	1.00	2.50
LA2 Derek Jeter	2.50	6.00
LA3 Todd Helton	.60	1.50
LA4 Alex Rodriguez	1.50	4.00
LA5 Ken Griffey Jr.	1.50	4.00
LA6 Nomar Garciaparra	1.50	4.00
LA7 Chipper Jones	1.00	2.50
LA8 Ivan Rodriguez	.60	1.50
LA9 Pedro Martinez	.60	1.50
LA10 Rick Ankiel	.40	1.00

2001 Topps A Tradition Continues

Randomly inserted into packs at 1:17 Hobby/Retail and 1:5 HTA, this 30-card insert features players that look to carry the tradition of Major League Baseball well into the 21st century. Card backs carry a "TRC" prefix.

COMPLETE SET (30)	50.00	100.00
TRC1 Chipper Jones	1.25	3.00
TRC2 Cal Ripken	4.00	10.00
TRC3 Mike Piazza	2.00	5.00
TRC4 Ken Griffey Jr.	2.00	5.00
TRC5 Randy Johnson	1.25	3.00
TRC6 Derek Jeter	3.00	8.00
TRC7 Scott Rolen	.75	2.00
TRC8 Nomar Garciaparra	2.00	5.00
TRC9 Roberto Alomar	.75	2.00
TRC10 Greg Maddux	2.00	5.00
TRC11 Ivan Rodriguez	.75	2.00
TRC12 Jeff Bagwell	.75	2.00
TRC13 Alex Rodriguez	2.00	5.00
TRC14 Pedro Martinez	.75	2.00
TRC15 Sammy Sosa	1.25	3.00
TRC16 Jim Edmonds	.50	1.25
TRC17 Mo Vaughn	.50	1.25
TRC18 Barry Bonds	3.00	8.00
TRC19 Larry Walker	.50	1.25
TRC20 Mark McGwire	3.00	8.00
TRC21 Vladimir Guerrero	1.25	3.00
TRC22 Andruw Jones	.75	2.00
TRC23 Todd Helton	.75	2.00
TRC24 Kevin Brown	.50	1.25
TRC25 Tony Gwynn	1.50	4.00
TRC26 Manny Ramirez	.75	2.00
TRC27 Roger Clemens	2.50	6.00
TRC28 Frank Thomas	1.25	3.00
TRC29 Shawn Green	.50	1.25
TRC30 Jim Thome	.75	2.00

2001 Topps Base Hit Autograph Relics

Inserted in series two packs at a rate of one in 1,1462 hobby or retail packs and one in 325 HTA packs, these 28 cards features managers along with a game-used base piece and an autograph.

BH1 Mike Scioscia	40.00	80.00
BH2 Larry Dierker	20.00	50.00
BH3 Art Howe	40.00	80.00
BH4 Jim Fregosi	20.00	50.00
BH5 Bobby Cox	50.00	100.00
BH6 Davey Lopes	20.00	50.00
BH7 Tony LaRussa	40.00	80.00
BH8 Don Baylor	40.00	80.00
BH9 Larry Rothschild	20.00	50.00
BH10 Buck Showalter	20.00	50.00
BH11 Davey Johnson	20.00	50.00
BH12 Felipe Alou	40.00	80.00
BH13 Charlie Manuel	30.00	60.00
BH14 Lou Piniella	40.00	80.00
BH15 John Boles	20.00	50.00
BH16 Bobby Valentine	40.00	80.00
BH17 Mike Hargrove	40.00	80.00
BH18 Bruce Bochy	20.00	50.00
BH19 Terry Francona	100.00	200.00
BH20 Gene Lamont	20.00	50.00
BH21 Johnny Oates	50.00	100.00
BH22 Jimy Williams	20.00	50.00
BH23 Jack McKeon	40.00	80.00
BH24 Buddy Bell	40.00	80.00
BH25 Tony Muser	20.00	50.00
BH26 Phil Garner	40.00	80.00
BH27 Tom Kelly	20.00	50.00
BH28 Jerry Manuel	20.00	50.00

2001 Topps Before There Was Topps

Issued in series two packs at a rate of one in 25 hobby/retail packs and one in five HTA packs; these 10 cards feature superstars who concluded their career before Topps started their dominance of the card market.

COMPLETE SET (10)	15.00	40.00
BT1 Lou Gehrig	2.50	6.00
BT2 Babe Ruth	4.00	10.00
BT3 Cy Young	1.25	3.00
BT4 Walter Johnson	1.25	3.00
BT5 Ty Cobb	2.00	5.00
BT6 Rogers Hornsby	1.25	3.00
BT7 Honus Wagner	1.25	3.00
BT8 Christy Mathewson	1.25	3.00
BT9 Grover Alexander	1.25	3.00
BT10 Joe DiMaggio	2.50	6.00

2001 Topps Combos

Randomly inserted into packs at a rate of 1:12 Hobby/Retail and 1:4 HTA, this 20-card insert set pairs up players that have put up similar statistics throughout their carrers. Card backs carry a "TC" prefix. Instead of having photographs, these cards feature drawings of the featured players.

COMPLETE SET (20)	25.00	60.00
COMPLETE SERIES 1 (10)	12.50	30.00
COMPLETE SERIES 2 (10)	12.50	30.00
TC1 Derek Jeter	2.00	5.00
Yogi Berra		
Whitey Ford		
Don Mattingly		
Reggie Jackson		
TC2 Chipper Jones	.60	1.50
Mike Schmidt		
TC3 Brooks Robinson	1.50	4.00
Cal Ripken		
TC4 Bob Gibson	.60	1.50
Pedro Martinez		
TC5 Ivan Rodriguez	.60	1.50
Johnny Bench		
TC6 Ernie Banks	1.00	2.50
Alex Rodriguez		
TC7 Joe Morgan	.60	1.50
Ken Griffey Jr.		
Barry Larkin		
Johnny Bench		
TC8 Vladmir Guerrero	.60	1.50
Roberto Clemente		
TC9 Ken Griffey Jr.	.75	2.00
Hank Aaron		
TC10 Casey Stengel MG	.60	1.50
Joe Torre MG		
TC11 Kevin Brown	1.25	3.00
Sandy Koufax		
Don Drysdale UER		
Card states the Dodgers swept the 1965 World Series		
They won the Series in 7 games		
TC12 Mark McGwire	1.50	4.00
Sammy Sosa		
Roger Maris		
Babe Ruth		
TC13 Ted Williams	1.25	3.00
Carl Yastrzemski		
Nomar Garciaparra		
TC14 Greg Maddux	1.00	2.50
Roger Clemens		
Cy Young		
TC15 Tony Gwynn	1.25	3.00
Ted Williams		
TC16 Cal Ripken	2.00	5.00
Lou Gehrig		
TC17 Sandy Koufax	2.00	5.00
Randy Johnson		
Warren Spahn		
Steve Carlton		
TC18 Mike Piazza	.75	2.00
Josh Gibson		
TC19 Barry Bonds	1.50	4.00
Willie Mays		
TC20 Jackie Robinson	.60	1.50
Larry Doby		

2001 Topps Golden Anniversary

Randomly inserted into packs at 1:10 Hobby/Retail and 1:1 HTA, this 50-card insert celibrates Topp's 50th Anniversary by taking a look at some of the all-time greats. Card backs carry a "GA" prefix.

COMPLETE SET (50)	40.00	80.00
GA1 Hank Aaron	2.00	5.00
GA2 Ernie Banks	1.00	2.50
GA3 Mike Schmidt	2.00	5.00
GA4 Willie Mays	2.00	5.00
GA5 Johnny Bench	1.00	2.50
GA6 Tom Seaver	.60	1.50
GA7 Frank Robinson	.60	1.50
GA8 Sandy Koufax	3.00	8.00
GA9 Bob Gibson	.60	1.50
GA10 Ted Williams	2.00	5.00
GA11 Cal Ripken	3.00	8.00
GA12 Tony Gwynn	1.25	3.00
GA13 Mark McGwire	2.50	6.00
GA14 Ken Griffey Jr.	1.50	4.00
GA15 Greg Maddux	1.50	4.00
GA16 Roger Clemens	2.00	5.00
GA17 Barry Bonds	2.50	6.00
GA18 Rickey Henderson	1.00	2.50
GA19 Mike Piazza	1.50	4.00
GA20 Jose Canseco	.60	1.50
GA21 Derek Jeter	2.50	6.00
GA22 N.Garciaparra UER	1.50	4.00
Card has incorrect bat and throw information		
Garciaparra bats and throws righthanded		
GA23 Alex Rodriguez	1.50	4.00
GA24 Sammy Sosa	1.00	2.50
GA25 Ivan Rodriguez	.60	1.50
GA26 Vladimir Guerrero	1.00	2.50
GA27 Chipper Jones	1.00	2.50
GA28 Jeff Bagwell	.60	1.50
GA29 Pedro Martinez	.60	1.50
GA30 Randy Johnson	1.00	2.50
GA31 Pat Burrell	.40	1.00
GA32 Josh Hamilton	.75	2.00
GA33 Ryan Anderson	.40	1.00
GA34 Corey Patterson	.40	1.00
GA35 Eric Munson	.40	1.00
GA36 Sean Burroughs	.40	1.00
GA37 C.C. Sabathia	.40	1.00
GA38 Chin-Feng Chen	.40	1.00
GA39 Barry Zito	.60	1.50
GA40 Adrian Gonzalez	2.50	6.00
GA41 Mark McGwire	2.50	6.00
GA42 Nomar Garciaparra	1.50	4.00
GA43 Todd Helton	.60	1.50
GA44 Matt Williams	.40	1.00
GA45 Troy Glaus	.40	1.00
GA46 Geoff Jenkins	.40	1.00
GA47 Frank Thomas	1.00	2.50
GA48 Mo Vaughn	.40	1.00
GA49 Barry Larkin	.60	1.50
GA50 J.D. Drew	.40	1.00

2001 Topps Golden Anniversary Autographs

Randomly inserted into packs, this 98-card insert features authentic autographs of both modern day and former greats. Card backs carry a "GAA" prefix followed by the players initials. Please note that the Andy Pafko, Lou Brock, Rafael Furcal and Todd Zeile cards all packed out in series one packs as exchange cards with a redemption deadline of November 30th, 2001. In addition, Carlos Silva, Eddy Furniss, Phil Merrell and Carlos Silva packed out as exchange cards in series two packs with a redemption deadline of April 30th, 2003.

SER.1 GROUP A 1:22866 H/R, 1:5056 HTA
SER.2 GROUP A ODDS 1: 10,583 H/R, 1:2,355 HTA
SER.1 GROUP B 1:3054 H/R, 1:678 HTA
SER.2 GROUP B ODDS 1:11,781 H/R, 1:2,612 HTA
SER.1 GROUP C 1:1431 H/R, 1:318 HTA
SER.2 GROUP C 1:4236 H/R, 1:942 HTA
SER.1 GROUP D ODDS 1:18339 H/R, 1:4095 HTA
SER.2 GROUP D 1:981 H/R, 1:218 HTA
SER.1 GROUP E ODDS 1:13737 H/R, 1:3,056 HTA
SER.2 GROUP E 1:14157 H/R, 1:3139 HTA
SER.1 GROUP F 1:11015 H/R, 1:2438 HTA
SER.2 GROUP F 1:3532 H/R, 1:785 HTA
SER.1 GROUP G 1:625 H/R, 1:139 HTA
SER.2 GROUP G 1:3532 H/R, 1:785 HTA
SER.2 GROUP H 1:2,037 H/R, 1:452 HTA
SER.2 GROUP I 1:481 H/R, 1:107 HTA

GAAAG A.Gonzalez G	30.00	60.00
GAAAH Aaron Herr I2	8.00	20.00
GAAAJ A. Johnson G1-I2	4.00	10.00
GAAAO Augie Ojeda B2	50.00	100.00
GAAAP Andy Pafko C1	10.00	25.00
GAABB Barry Bonds B2	150.00	250.00
GAABE Brian Esposito I2	4.00	10.00
GAABG Bob Gibson C2	12.50	30.00
GAABK Bobby Kielty I2	4.00	10.00
GAABO Ben Oglivie D2	8.00	20.00
GAABR B.Robinson B	20.00	50.00
GAABT Brian Tollberg I2	4.00	10.00
GAACC Chris Clapinski I2	4.00	10.00
GAACD Chad Durbin I2	4.00	10.00
GAACE Carl Erskine D2	6.00	15.00
GAACJ Chipper Jones B1	60.00	120.00
GAACL Colby Lewis I2	12.50	30.00
GAACR Chris Richard I2	4.00	10.00
GAACS Carlos Silva I2	4.00	10.00
GAACY C. Yastrzemski C2	60.00	120.00
GAADA Dick Allen C1	12.50	30.00
GAADA Denny Abreu I2	4.00	10.00
GAADG Dick Groat D2	10.00	25.00
GAADT D. Thompson I2	4.00	10.00
GAAEB Ernie Banks B1	50.00	100.00
GAAEB Eric Byrnes I2	10.00	25.00
GAAEF Eddy Furniss I2	4.00	10.00
GAAEM Eric Munson G2	4.00	10.00
GAAER E. Ramirez I2	4.00	10.00
GAAGB George Bell D2	15.00	40.00
GAAGG G. Guzman I2	4.00	10.00
GAAGM G. Matthews Jr. D2	8.00	20.00
GAAGS G. Sizemore I2	40.00	80.00
GAAGT G.Templeton C	6.00	15.00
GAAHA Hank Aaron B1	250.00	350.00
GAAJB Johnny Bench C2	40.00	80.00
GAAJC Jorge Cantu I2	6.00	15.00
GAAJL John Lackey I2	10.00	25.00
GAAJM J. Marquis G1	6.00	15.00
GAAJR Joe Rudi C1	6.00	15.00
GAAJR Juan Rincon I2	12.50	30.00
GAAJS Juan Salas I2	4.00	10.00
GAAJV Jose Vidro F1	4.00	10.00
GAAJW Justin Wayne H2	4.00	10.00
GAAKG Kevin Gregg B2	8.00	20.00
GAAKH Ken Holtzman D2	4.00	10.00
GAAKT Kent Tekulve D2	4.00	10.00
GAALB Lou Brock B1	30.00	60.00
GAALM L. Montanez H2	10.00	25.00
GAALR Luis Rivas I2	4.00	10.00
GAAMB M. Bradley G2	6.00	15.00
GAAMC Mike Cuellar C1	6.00	15.00
GAAMG M. Glendenning I2	4.00	10.00
GAAML Matt Lawton F2	4.00	10.00
GAAML Mike Lamb G1	4.00	10.00
GAAMM Mike Mussina		
GAAMO M.Ordonez B	8.00	20.00
GAAMS Mike Schmidt B1	60.00	120.00
GAAMS Mike Sweeney F2	6.00	15.00
GAAMS Mike Stodolka I2	4.00	10.00
GAAMW M.Wheatland G	4.00	10.00
GAAMW M. Wenner I2	4.00	10.00
GAANG Nick Green I2	4.00	10.00
GAANJ Neil Jenkins I2	4.00	10.00
GAANR Nolan Ryan A2	175.00	350.00
GAAPB Pat Burrell G1	6.00	15.00
GAAPM Phil Merrell I2	4.00	10.00
GAARA Rick Ankiel D1	10.00	25.00
GAARB R. Baldelli G1-I2	10.00	25.00
GAARC Rod Carew B1	30.00	60.00
GAARF Rafael Furcal G1	6.00	15.00
GAARJ R. Jackson A2	125.00	200.00
GAARS Ron Swoboda C1	10.00	25.00
GAASH Scott Heard G1	4.00	10.00
GAASK Sandy Koufax A1	800.00	950.00
GAASM Stan Musial A2	175.00	300.00
GAASR Scott Rolen F2	10.00	25.00
GAAST Scott Thorman I2	4.00	10.00
GAATA Tony Alvarez I2	4.00	10.00
GAATH Todd Helton B2	40.00	80.00
GAATJ T. Johnson I2	4.00	10.00
GAATS Tom Seaver A2	100.00	175.00
GAAVL Vernon Law C1	10.00	25.00
GAAWD Willie Davis D2	15.00	40.00
GAAWF Whitey Ford C2	40.00	80.00
GAAWH W.Hernandez C	20.00	50.00
GAAWM Willie Mays A1	350.00	450.00
GAAWW Wilbur Wood D2	6.00	15.00
GAAYB Yogi Berra B1	40.00	80.00
GAAYH Yamid Haad I2	4.00	10.00
GAAYT Y. Torrealba I2	15.00	40.00
GAACCS Corey Smith I2	4.00	10.00
GAAGHB George Brett A2	175.00	300.00
GAAJDD J.D. Drew E2	10.00	25.00
GAAMAB Mike Bynum I2	4.00	10.00
GAAMFL M. Lockwood I2	4.00	10.00
GAAMJS M. Stodolka G1	4.00	10.00
GAAMJW M. Wheatland I2	6.00	15.00
GAATDLR T. De la Rosa I2	4.00	10.00

2001 Topps Hit Parade Bat Relics

Issued in retail packs at odds of one in 2,607 these six cards feature players who have achieved major career milestones along with a piece of memorabilia.

HP1 Reggie Jackson	40.00	80.00
HP2 Dave Winfield	40.00	80.00
HP3 Eddie Murray	40.00	80.00
HP4 Rickey Henderson	40.00	80.00
HP5 Robin Yount	40.00	80.00
HP6 Carl Yastrzemski	50.00	100.00

2001 Topps King of Kings Relics

Randomly inserted into packs at 1:2056 Hobby/Retail and 1:457 HTA, this four-card insert features game-used memorabilia from Nolan Ryan, Rickey Henderson, and Hank Aaron. Please note that a special fourth card containing game-used memorabila of all three were inserted into HTA packs at 1:8903. Card backs carry a "KKG" prefix.

KKR1 Hank Aaron	40.00	80.00
KKR2 Nolan Ryan	40.00	80.00
KKR3 Rickey Henderson	15.00	40.00
KKR4 Mark McGwire B	30.00	60.00
KKR5 Bob Gibson A	15.00	40.00
KKR6 Nolan Ryan B	40.00	80.00
KKGE Hank Aaron	175.00	300.00
Nolan Ryan		
Rickey Henderson		
KKLE2 Mark Mcgwire	300.00	500.00
Bob Gibson		
Nolan Ryan		

2001 Topps Noteworthy

Inserted in hobby/retail packs at a rate of one in eight and HTA packs at a rate of one per pack; this 50-card set feature a mix of active and retired players who achieved significant feats during their career.

COMPLETE SET (50)	40.00	80.00
TN1 Mark McGwire	1.50	4.00
TN2 Derek Jeter	1.50	4.00
TN3 Sammy Sosa	.60	1.50
TN4 Todd Helton	.40	1.00
TN5 Alex Rodriguez	1.00	2.50
TN6 Chipper Jones	.60	1.50
TN7 Barry Bonds	1.50	4.00
TN8 Ken Griffey Jr.	1.00	2.50
TN9 Nomar Garciaparra	1.00	2.50
TN10 Frank Thomas	.60	1.50
TN11 Randy Johnson	.60	1.50
TN12 Cal Ripken	2.00	5.00
TN13 Mike Piazza	1.00	2.50
TN14 Ivan Rodriguez	.40	1.00
TN15 Jeff Bagwell	.40	1.00
TN16 Vladimir Guerrero	.60	1.50
TN17 Greg Maddux	1.00	2.50
TN18 Tony Gwynn	.75	2.00
TN19 Larry Walker	.40	1.00
TN20 Juan Gonzalez	.40	1.00
TN21 Scott Rolen	.40	1.00
TN22 Jason Giambi	.40	1.00
TN23 Jeff Kent	.40	1.00
TN24 Pat Burrell	.40	1.00
TN25 Pedro Martinez	.40	1.00
TN26 Willie Mays	1.50	4.00
TN27 Whitey Ford	.40	1.00
TN28 Jackie Robinson	.60	1.50
TN29 Ted Williams UER	1.50	4.00
Card has wrong year for his last at-bat		
TN30 Babe Ruth	3.00	8.00
TN31 Warren Spahn	.40	1.00
TN32 Nolan Ryan	2.50	6.00
TN33 Yogi Berra	.60	1.50
TN34 Mike Schmidt	1.50	4.00
TN35 Steve Carlton	.40	1.00
TN36 Brooks Robinson	.40	1.00
TN37 Bob Gibson	.40	1.00
TN38 Reggie Jackson	.40	1.00
TN39 Johnny Bench	.60	1.50
TN40 Ernie Banks	.60	1.50
TN41 Eddie Mathews	.60	1.50
TN42 Don Mattingly	1.50	4.00
TN43 Duke Snider	.40	1.00
TN44 Hank Aaron	1.50	4.00
TN45 Roberto Clemente	2.00	5.00
TN46 Harmon Killebrew	.60	1.50
TN47 Frank Robinson	.40	1.00
TN48 Stan Musial	1.25	3.00
TN49 Lou Brock	.40	1.00
TN50 Joe Morgan	.40	1.00

2001 Topps Originals Relics

Randomly inserted into packs at different rates depening which series these cards were inserted in, this ten-card insert set features game-used jersey cards of players like Roberto Clemente and Carl Yastrzemski. Please note that the Willie Mays card is actually a game-used jacket.

SER.1 STATED ODDS 1:1172 H/R, 1:260 HTA
SER.2 STATED ODDS 1:1023 H/R, 1:227 HTA

1 Roberto Clemente 55	50.00	100.00
2 Carl Yastrzemski 60	15.00	40.00
3 Mike Schmidt 73	15.00	40.00
4 Wade Boggs 83	10.00	25.00
5 Chipper Jones 91	10.00	25.00
6 Willie Mays 52	20.00	50.00
7 Lou Brock 62	10.00	25.00
8 Dave Parker 74	6.00	15.00
9 Barry Bonds 86	20.00	50.00
10 Alex Rodriguez 98	10.00	25.00

2001 Topps Team Topps Legends Autographs

These signed cards were inserted into various 2001-2003 Topps products. As these cards were inserted into different products and some were exchange cards. Most players in this set were featured on reprinted versions of their classic Topps "rookie" and "final" cards. The checklist was originally comprised of cards TT1-TT50 (with each player having an R and F suffix (i.e. Willie Mays is featured on TT1F with his 1973 card and TT1R with his 1952 card). In late 2002 and throughout 2003, additional players were added to the set with checklist numbering outside of the TT1-TT50 schematic. The numbering for these late additions was based on player's initials (i.e. Lou Brock's card is TT-LB) and only reprints of their rookie-year cards were produced.

BOW.BEST GROUP A ODDS 1:404
BOW.BEST GROUP B ODDS 1:87
BOW.HERITAGE GROUP 1 ODDS 1:1570
BOW.HERITAGE GROUP 2 ODDS 1:1556
BOW.HERITAGE GROUP 3 ODDS 1:1937
BOW.HERITAGE GROUP 4 ODDS 1:1453
BOW.HERITAGE GROUP 5 ODDS 1:1899
TOPPS TRD.GROUP A ODDS 1:1567
TOPPS TRD.GROUP B ODDS 1:1881
TOPPS TRD.GROUP C ODDS 1:626
TOPPS TRD.GROUP D ODDS 1:TBD
TOPPS AMER.PIE EXCH.DEADLINE 11/01/03
TOPPS GALLERY EXCH.DEADLINE 06/30/03
02 TOPPS EXCH.DEADLINE 12/01/03

TT1F Willie Mays 73	100.00	200.00
T'02-TA'02/A		
TT1R Willie Mays 52	125.00	200.00
AP		
TT2F Hank Aaron 76		
TT3F Stan Musial 63		
TT3R Stan Musial 58 AS	50.00	100.00
TT6F Whitey Ford 67	20.00	50.00
TT/A-T10'02		
TT6R Whitey Ford 53	30.00	60.00
T'02/F-TA'02/B		
TT7R Nolan Ryan 68	125.00	200.00
T206'02/A-TA'02/A		
TT8F Carl Yastrzemski 83	20.00	50.00
TT8R Carl Yastrzemski 60	50.00	100.00
AP-T'02/A-TA'02/B-T10'02		
TT9R Brooks Robinson 57	30.00	60.00
TT10F Frank Robinson 75	10.00	25.00
BH5-TH'02/2		
TT10R Frank Robinson 57	20.00	50.00
GL-T'02/A-TA'02/B		
TT11R Tom Seaver 67	30.00	60.00
TA'02/A		
TT11F Tom Seaver 87		
TT12R Duke Snider 52	40.00	80.00
TT13F Warren Spahn 65	15.00	40.00
BH1-TT-T'02/B-TA'02/B		
TT13R Warren Spahn 52	30.00	60.00
AP-BB/A-TT/C		
TT14F Johnny Bench 83	30.00	60.00
TT14R Johnny Bench 68	60.00	120.00
AP		
TT15R Reggie Jackson 69	75.00	150.00
AP-TA'02/A		
TT16R Al Kaline 54	30.00	60.00
TT17F Willie McCovey 80		
TT18F Bob Gibson 75	15.00	40.00
AP'02		
TT18R Bob Gibson 59	20.00	50.00
AP-BB/A-T'02/A		
TT19R Mike Schmidt 73	60.00	120.00
TT20F Harmon Killebrew 75		
TT20R Harmon Killebrew 55	50.00	100.00
TT21R Bob Feller 52 BH2	10.00	25.00
TT23F Gil McDougald 60	6.00	15.00
GL-TA'02/B		
TT23R Gil McDougald 52	10.00	25.00
BB/B		
TT24F Jimmy Piersall 67		
TT24R Jimmy Piersall 56		
TT25F Luis Tiant 83	6.00	15.00
GL EXCH		
TT25R Luis Tiant 65	6.00	15.00
AP-BB/B-'02 TA/B		
TT26F Minnie Minoso 64		
TT27F Andy Pafko 59	6.00	15.00
GL		
TT27R Andy Pafko 52	10.00	25.00
BB/B-BH/3-GL		
TT28F Herb Score 62	6.00	15.00
BB/B-GL-TT/B		
TT28R Herb Score 56	6.00	15.00
BB/B-TA'02/B		
TT29F Bill Skowron 67	6.00	15.00
TT29R Bill Skowron 54	6.00	15.00
AP-BB/A-T206'02/C		
TT30F Maury Wills 72		
TT31F Clete Boyer 71	6.00	15.00
TA'02/B		
TT31R Clete Boyer 57	6.00	15.00
AP-BB/B		
TT32F Hank Bauer 61		
TT33F Vida Blue 87	6.00	15.00
T'02/C/TR		
TT33R Vida Blue 70	6.00	15.00

AP-T206'02/B-TH'02/4
TT34R Don Larsen 56 10.00 25.00
TT35F Joe Pepitone 73 6.00 15.00
TT/A
TT35R Joe Pepitone 62 10.00 25.00
AP
TT36F Enos Slaughter 59 10.00 25.00
BH4-TT/A
TT36R Enos Slaughter 52 15.00 40.00
TAR'02
TT37F Tug McGraw 65 10.00 25.00
BB/B
TT37R Tug McGraw 65 15.00 40.00
AP-BB/B-TT/B
TT38R Fergie Jenkins 66 6.00 15.00
TT40R Gaylord Perry 62 10.00 25.00
TT43F Bobby Thomson 60 6.00 15.00
TT-TH'02/3
TT43R Bobby Thomson 52 6.00 15.00
AP-TT/D-T'02/B-T10'02
TT46F Robin Roberts 66 T'02/E 12.50 30.00
TT46R Robin Roberts 52 20.00 50.00
TT47F Frank Howard 73 6.00 15.00
TT/A-TH'02/1
TT47R Frank Howard 60 6.00 15.00
AP-T'02/D-TA'02/B
TT48F Bobby Richardson 66 6.00 15.00
TT/A-T'02/B-T10'02
TT48R Bobby Richardson 57 10.00 25.00
AP-BB/B
TT49R Tony Kubek 57 50.00 100.00
AP-TA/B
TT50F Mickey Lolich 80 6.00 15.00
TT/A
TT50R Mickey Lolich 64 6.00 15.00
AP-T'02/C-TA'02/B-TH'02/1
TT51RF Ralph Branca 52 12.50 30.00
TT/D-T'02/E
TTGC Gary Carter 75 10.00 25.00
TTGG Goose Gossage 73 10.00 25.00
TAR'02
TTGN Craig Nettles 69 10.00 25.00
02 'TAR
TTJB Jim Bunning 65 10.00 25.00
TTJM Joe Morgan 65 15.00 40.00
TTJP Jim Palmer 66 15.00 40.00
TAR '02
TTJS Johnny Sain 52 10.00 25.00
TTLA Luis Aparicio 56 10.00 25.00
TTLB Lou Brock 62 30.00 60.00
TTPB Paul Blair 65 4.00 10.00
TTRY Robin Yount 75 40.00 80.00
TTVL Vern Law 52 6.00 15.00

2001 Topps Through the Years Reprints

Randomly inserted into packs at 1:8 Hobby/Retail and 1:1 HTA, this 50-card set takes a look at some of the best players to every make it onto a Topps trading card.

COMPLETE SET (50) 60.00 120.00
1 Yogi Berra '57 1.25 3.00
2 Roy Campanella '56 1.25 3.00
3 Willie Mays '53 2.00 5.00
4 Andy Pafko '52 1.25 3.00
5 Jackie Robinson '52 1.25 3.00
6 Stan Musial '59 1.50 4.00
7 Duke Snider '56 1.25 3.00
8 Warren Spahn '56 1.25 3.00
9 Ted Williams '54 UER 3.00 8.00
Williams is spelled William
Also wrong birthdate
10 Eddie Mathews '55 1.25 3.00
11 Willie McCovey '60 1.25 3.00
12 Frank Robinson '69 1.25 3.00
13 Ernie Banks '66 1.25 3.00
14 Hank Aaron '65 2.00 5.00
15 Sandy Koufax '61 2.50 6.00
16 Bob Gibson '68 1.25 3.00
17 Harmon Killebrew '67 1.25 3.00
18 Whitey Ford '64 1.25 3.00
19 Roberto Clemente '63 3.00 8.00
20 Juan Marichal '62 1.25 3.00
21 Johnny Bench '70 1.25 3.00
22 Willie Stargell '73 1.25 3.00
23 Joe Morgan '74 1.25 3.00
24 Carl Yastrzemski '71 1.50 4.00
25 Reggie Jackson '76 1.25 3.00
26 Tom Seaver '78 1.25 3.00
27 Steve Carlton '77 1.25 3.00
28 Jim Palmer '79 1.25 3.00
29 Rod Carew '72 1.25 3.00
30 George Brett '75 3.00 8.00
31 Roger Clemens '85 2.50 6.00
32 Don Mattingly '84 3.00 8.00
33 Ryne Sandberg '89 2.00 5.00
34 Mike Schmidt '81 2.00 5.00
35 Cal Ripken '82 4.00 10.00
36 Tony Gwynn '83 1.50 4.00
37 Ozzie Smith '87 2.00 5.00
38 Wade Boggs '88 1.25 3.00
39 Nolan Ryan '80 2.50 6.00
40 Robin Yount '86 1.25 3.00
41 Mark McGwire '99 2.50 6.00
42 Ken Griffey Jr. '92 1.50 4.00
43 Sammy Sosa '90 1.25 3.00
44 Alex Rodriguez '98 1.50 4.00
45 Barry Bonds '94 2.50 6.00
46 Mike Piazza '95 1.50 4.00
47 Chipper Jones '91 1.25 3.00
48 Greg Maddux '96 1.50 4.00
49 Nomar Garciaparra '97 1.50 4.00
50 Derek Jeter '93 3.00 8.00

2001 Topps What Could Have Been

Inserted at a rate of one in 25 hobby/retail packs or one in five HTA packs, these 10 cards feature stars of the Negro leagues who never got to play in the majors while they were at their peak.

COMPLETE SET (10) 10.00 25.00
WCB1 Josh Gibson 2.00 5.00
WCB2 Satchel Paige 1.25 3.00
WCB3 Buck Leonard .75 2.00
WCB4 James Bell 1.25 3.00
WCB5 Rube Foster 1.25 3.00
WCB6 Martin DiHigo .75 2.00
WCB7 William Johnson .75 2.00
WCB8 Mule Suttles .75 2.00
WCB9 Ray Dandridge .75 2.00
WCB10 John Lloyd .75 2.00

2001 Topps Traded

The 2001 Topps Traded product was released in October 2001, and features a 265-card base set. The 2001 Topps Traded and the 2001 Topps Chrome Traded were combined and sold together. Each pack contained eight 2001 Topps Traded and two 2001 Topps Chrome Traded cards for a total of ten cards in each pack. The 265-card set is broken down as follows: 99 cards highlighting player deals made during the 2000 off-season and 2001 season; 60 future stars who have never appeared alone on a Topps card; 55 rookies who make their premiere on a Topps card; six managers (T145-T150) who've either switched teams or were newly hired for the 2001 season and 45 traded reprints (T100 through T144) of rookie cards featured in past Topps Traded sets. The packs carried a 3.00 per pack SRP and came 24 packs to a box.

COMPLETE SET (265) 100.00 175.00
COMMON (T1-T99/T145-T265) .15 .40
COMMON (100-144) .40 1.00
T1 Sandy Alomar Jr. .15 .40
T2 Kevin Appier .20 .50
T3 Brad Ausmus .20 .50
T4 Derek Bell .15 .40
T5 Bret Boone .20 .50
T6 Rico Brogna .15 .40
T7 Ellis Burks .20 .50
T8 Ken Caminiti .20 .50
T9 Roger Cedeno .15 .40
T10 Royce Clayton .15 .40
T11 Enrique Wilson .15 .40
T12 Rheal Cormier .15 .40
T13 Eric Davis .20 .50
T14 Shawon Dunston .15 .40
T15 Andres Galarraga .20 .50
T16 Tom Gordon .15 .40
T17 Mark Grace .30 .75
T18 Jeffrey Hammonds .15 .40
T19 Dustin Hermanson .15 .40
T20 Quinton McCracken .15 .40
T21 Todd Hundley .15 .40
T22 Charles Johnson .20 .50
T23 Marquis Grissom .20 .50
T24 Jose Mesa .15 .40
T25 Brian Boehringer .15 .40
T26 John Rocker .20 .50
T27 Jeff Frye .15 .40
T28 Reggie Sanders .20 .50
T29 David Segui .15 .40
T30 Mike Sirotka .15 .40
T31 Fernando Tatis .15 .40
T32 Steve Trachsel .15 .40
T33 Ismael Valdes .15 .40
T34 Randy Velarde .15 .40
T35 Ryan Kohlmeier .15 .40
T36 Mike Bordick .20 .50
T37 Kent Bottenfield .15 .40
T38 Pat Rapp .15 .40
T39 Jeff Nelson .15 .40
T40 Ricky Bottalico .15 .40
T41 Luke Prokopec .15 .40
T42 Hideo Nomo .50 1.25
T43 Bill Mueller .20 .50
T44 Roberto Kelly .15 .40
T45 Chris Holt .15 .40
T46 Mike Jackson .15 .40
T47 Devon White .20 .50
T48 Gerald Williams .15 .40
T49 Eddie Taubensee .15 .40
T50 Brian Hunter UER .15 .40
Brian R Hunter pictured
Brian L Hunter stats
T51 Nelson Cruz .15 .40
T52 Jeff Fassero .15 .40
T53 Bubba Trammell .15 .40
T54 Bo Porter .15 .40
T55 Greg Norton .15 .40
T56 Benito Santiago .20 .50
T57 Ruben Rivera .15 .40
T58 Dee Brown .15 .40
T59 Jose Canseco UER .30 .75
2000 strikeout totals are wrong
T60 Chris Michalak .15 .40
T61 Tim Worrell .15 .40
T62 Matt Clement .20 .50
T63 Bill Pulsipher .15 .40
T64 Troy Brohawn RC .15 .40
T65 Mark Kotsay .20 .50
T66 Jimmy Rollins .20 .50
T67 Shea Hillenbrand .20 .50
T68 Ted Lilly .15 .40
T69 Jermaine Dye .20 .50
T70 Jerry Hairston Jr. .15 .40
T71 John Mabry .15 .40
T72 Kurt Abbott .15 .40
T73 Eric Owens .15 .40
T74 Jeff Brantley .15 .40
T75 Roy Oswalt .50 1.25
T76 Doug Mientkiewicz .20 .50
T77 Rickey Henderson .50 1.25
T78 Jason Grimsley .15 .40
T79 Christian Parker RC .15 .40
T80 Donne Wall .15 .40
T81 Alex Arias .15 .40
T82 Willis Roberts .15 .40
T83 Ryan Minor .15 .40
T84 Jason LaRue .15 .40
T85 Ruben Sierra .20 .50
T86 Johnny Damon .30 .75
T87 Juan Gonzalez .20 .50
T88 C.C. Sabathia .20 .50
T89 Tony Batista .15 .40
T90 Jay Witasick .15 .40
T91 Brent Abernathy .15 .40
T92 Paul LoDuca .20 .50
T93 Wes Helms .15 .40
T94 Mark Wohlers .15 .40
T95 Rob Bell .15 .40
T96 Tim Redding .15 .40
T97 Bud Smith RC .15 .40
T98 Adam Dunn .30 .75
T99 Ichiro Suzuki 8.00 20.00
Albert Pujols ROY
T100 Carlton Fisk 81 .50 1.25
T101 Tim Raines 81 .40 1.00
T102 Juan Marichal 74 .40 1.00
T103 Dave Winfield 81 .40 1.00
T104 Reggie Jackson 82 .50 1.25
T105 Cal Ripken 82 2.50 6.00
T106 Ozzie Smith 82 1.25 3.00
T107 Tom Seaver 83 .50 1.25
T108 Lou Piniella 74 .40 1.00
T109 Dwight Gooden 84 .40 1.00
T110 Bret Saberhagen 84 .40 1.00
T111 Gary Carter 85 .40 1.00
T112 Jack Clark 85 .40 1.00
T113 R. Henderson 85 .75 2.00
T114 Barry Bonds 86 2.00 5.00
T115 Bobby Bonilla 86 .40 1.00
T116 Jose Canseco 86 .50 1.25
T117 Will Clark 86 .50 1.25
T118 Andres Galarraga 86 .40 1.00
T119 Bo Jackson 86 .75 2.00
T120 Wally Joyner 86 .40 1.00
T121 Ellis Burks 87 .40 1.00
T122 David Cone 87 .40 1.00
T123 Greg Maddux 87 1.25 3.00
T124 Willie Randolph 76 .40 1.00
T125 Dennis Eckersley 87 .40 1.00
T126 Matt Williams 87 .40 1.00
T127 Joe Morgan 81 .40 1.00
T128 Fred McGriff 87 .50 1.25
T129 Roberto Alomar 88 .50 1.25
T130 Lee Smith 88 .40 1.00
T131 David Wells 88 .40 1.00
T132 Ken Griffey Jr. 89 1.25 3.00
T133 Deion Sanders 89 .50 1.25
T134 Nolan Ryan 89 1.50 4.00
T135 David Justice 90 .40 1.00
T136 Joe Carter 91 .40 1.00
T137 Jack Morris 92 .40 1.00
T138 Mike Piazza 93 1.25 3.00
T139 Barry Bonds 93 2.00 5.00
T140 Terrence Long 94 .40 1.00
T141 Ben Grieve 94 .40 1.00
T142 Richie Sexson 95 .40 1.00
George Arias
Mark Sweeney
Brian Schneider
T143 Sean Burroughs 99 .40 1.00
T144 Alfonso Soriano 99 .50 1.25
T145 Bob Boone MG .20 .50
T146 Larry Bowa MG .20 .50
T147 Bob Brenly MG .15 .40
T148 Buck Martinez MG .15 .40
T149 L. McClendon MG .15 .40
T150 Jim Tracy MG .15 .40
T151 Jared Abruzzo RC .15 .40
T152 Kurt Ainsworth .15 .40
T153 Willie Bloomquist .20 .50
T154 Ben Broussard .15 .40
T155 Bobby Bradley .15 .40
T156 Mike Bynum .15 .40
T157 A.J. Hinch .15 .40
T158 Ryan Christianson .15 .40
T159 Carlos Silva .15 .40
T160 Joe Crede .50 1.25
T161 Jack Cust .15 .40
T162 Ben Diggins .15 .40
T163 Phil Dumatrait .15 .40
T164 Alex Escobar .15 .40
T165 Miguel Olivo .15 .40
T166 Chris George .15 .40
T167 Marcus Giles .20 .50
T168 Keith Ginter .15 .40
T169 Josh Girdley .15 .40
T170 Tony Alvarez .15 .40
T171 Scott Seabol .15 .40
T172 Josh Hamilton .30 .75
T173 Jason Hart .15 .40
T174 Israel Alcantara .15 .40
T175 Jake Peavy .75 2.00
T176 Stubby Clapp RC .15 .40
T177 D'Angelo Jimenez .15 .40
T178 Nick Johnson .20 .50
T179 Ben Johnson .20 .50
T180 Larry Bigbie .15 .40
T181 Allen Levrault .15 .40
T182 Felipe Lopez .20 .50
T183 Sean Burnett .15 .40
T184 Nick Neugebauer .15 .40
T185 Austin Kearns .20 .50
T186 Corey Patterson .15 .40
T187 Carlos Pena .15 .40
T188 R. Rodriguez RC .15 .40
T189 Juan Rivera .15 .40
T190 Grant Roberts .15 .40
T191 Adam Pettyjohn RC .15 .40
T192 Jared Sandberg .15 .40
T193 Xavier Nady .15 .40
T194 Dane Sardinha .15 .40
T195 Shawn Sonnier .15 .40
T196 Rafael Soriano .15 .40
T197 Brian Specht RC .15 .40
T198 Aaron Myette .15 .40
T199 Juan Uribe RC .20 .50
T200 Jayson Werth .15 .40
T201 Brad Wilkerson .15 .40
T202 Horacio Estrada .15 .40
T203 Joel Pineiro .20 .50
T204 Matt LeCroy .15 .40
T205 Michael Coleman .15 .40
T206 Ben Sheets .30 .75
T207 Eric Byrnes .15 .40
T208 Sean Burroughs .15 .40
T209 Ken Harvey .15 .40
T210 Travis Hafner 1.50 4.00
T211 Erick Almonte .15 .40
T212 Jason Belcher RC .15 .40
T213 Wilson Betemit RC .60 1.50
T214 Hank Blalock RC 1.00 2.50
T215 Danny Borrell .15 .40
T216 John Buck RC .20 .50
T217 Freddie Bynum RC .15 .40
T218 Noel Devarez RC .15 .40
T219 Juan Diaz RC .15 .40
T220 Felix Diaz RC .15 .40
T221 Josh Fogg RC .15 .40
T222 Matt Ford RC .15 .40
T223 Scott Heard .15 .40
T224 Ben Hendrickson RC .15 .40
T225 Cody Ross RC .60 1.50
T226 A. Hernandez RC .15 .40
T227 Alfredo Amezaga RC .15 .40
T228 Bob Keppel RC .15 .40
T229 Ryan Madson RC .30 .75
T230 Octavio Martinez RC .15 .40
T231 Hee Seop Choi .20 .50
T232 Thomas Mitchell .15 .40
T233 Luis Montanez .15 .40
T234 Andy Morales RC .15 .40
T235 Justin Morneau RC 3.00 8.00
T236 Toe Nash RC .15 .40
T237 V. Pascucci RC .15 .40
T238 Roy Smith RC .15 .40
T239 Antonio Perez RC .20 .50
T240 Chad Petty RC .15 .40
T241 Steve Smyth .15 .40
T242 Jose Reyes RC 3.00 8.00
T243 Eric Reynolds RC .15 .40
T244 Dominic Rich .15 .40
T245 J. Richardson RC .15 .40
T246 Ed Rogers RC .15 .40
T247 Albert Pujols RC 30.00 60.00
T248 Esix Snead RC .15 .40
T249 Luis Torres RC .15 .40
T250 Matt White RC .15 .40
T251 Blake Williams .15 .40
T252 Chris Russ .15 .40
T253 Joe Kennedy RC .20 .50
T254 Jeff Randazzo RC .15 .40
T255 Beau Hale RC .15 .40
T256 Brad Hennessey RC .50 1.25
T257 Jake Gautreau RC .15 .40
T258 Jeff Mathis RC .20 .50
T259 Aaron Heilman RC .20 .50
T260 B. Sardinha RC .15 .40
T261 Irvin Guzman RC 1.50 4.00
T262 Gabe Gross RC .20 .50
T263 J.D. Martin RC .15 .40
T264 Chris Smith RC .15 .40
T265 Kenny Baugh RC .15 .40

2001 Topps Traded Gold

This set is a parallel to the 2001 Topps Traded set. Inserted into the 2001 Topps Traded at a rate of one in three, these cards are serial numbered to 2001 have have a gold foil border.

*STARS: 4X TO 10X BASIC CARDS
*REPRINTS: 1.5X TO 4X BASIC
*ROOKIES: 1X TO 2.5X BASIC

2001 Topps Traded Autographs

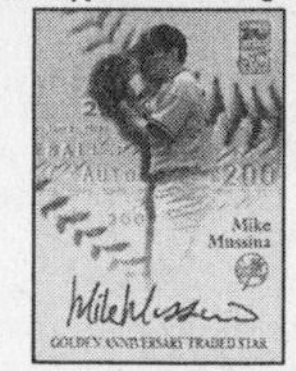

Inserted at a rate of one in 626, these cards share the same design as the 2001 Topps Golden Anniversary Autographs. The only difference is the front bottom of the card reads "Golden Anniversary Traded Star". The cards carry a 'TTA' prefix.

TTAJD Johnny Damon 15.00 40.00
TTAMM Mike Mussina 12.50 30.00

2001 Topps Traded Dual Jersey Relics

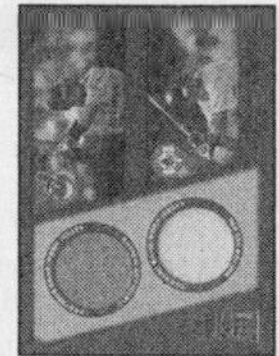

Inserted at a rate of one in 376, these cards highlight a player who has switched teams and feature a swatch of game-used jersey from both his former and current teams. The cards carry a 'TRR' prefix. Ben Grieve packed out as an exchange card.

TTRBG Ben Grieve 6.00 15.00
TTRDH D. Hermanson 6.00 15.00
TTRFT Fernando Tatis 6.00 15.00
TTRMR Manny Ramirez Sox 8.00 20.00

2001 Topps Traded Farewell Dual Bat Relic

Inserted at a rate of one in 4693, this card features bat pieces from both Cal Ripken and Tony Gwynn and is a farewell tribute to both players. The card carries a 'FR' prefix.

FRRG Cal Ripken 60.00 120.00
Tony Gwynn

2001 Topps Traded Hall of Fame Bat Relic

Inserted at a rate of one in 2796, this card features bat pieces from both Kirby Puckett and Dave Winfield and commemorates their entrance in Cooperstown. The card carries a 'HFR' prefix.

HFRPW Kirby Puckett 20.00 50.00
Dave Winfield

2001 Topps Traded Relics

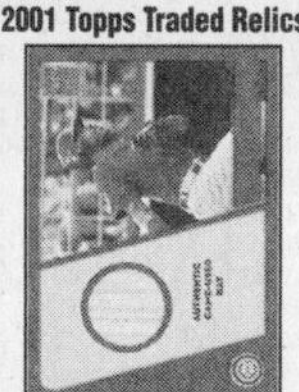

Inserted at a rate of one in 29, this 33-card set features game used bats or jersey swatches for players who have switched teams this season. All jersey swatches represent each player's new team. The cards carry a 'TTR' prefix. An exchange card for a Matt Stairs Jersey card was packed out.

AG A. Galarraga Bat 4.00 10.00
BB1 Bobby Bonilla Bat 4.00 10.00
BB2 Bret Boone Jsy 4.00 10.00
BM Bill Mueller Jsy 6.00 15.00
CJ C. Johnson Jsy 4.00 10.00
DB Derek Bell Bat 4.00 10.00
DN Denny Neagle Jsy 4.00 10.00
DW David Wells Jsy 4.00 10.00
ED Eric Davis Bat 4.00 10.00
EW E. Wilson Bat 4.00 10.00
FM Fred McGriff Bat 6.00 15.00
GW G. Williams Bat 4.00 10.00
HR Hideo Nomo Jsy 20.00 50.00
JC Jose Canseco Bat 6.00 15.00
JD J. Dye Bat SP 4.00 10.00
JD1 J. Damon Bat 6.00 15.00
JD2 Johnny Damon Jsy 6.00 15.00
JG Juan Gonzalez Bat 4.00 10.00
JH J. Hammonds Jsy 4.00 10.00
KC Ken Caminiti Bat 4.00 10.00
KS K. Stinnett Bat SP 4.00 10.00
MG1 Mark Grace Bat 6.00 15.00
MG2 M. Grissom Bat 4.00 10.00
MH M. Hampton Jsy 4.00 10.00
MS M. Stairs Jsy EXCH 4.00 10.00
NP Neifi Perez Bat 4.00 10.00
RB Rico Brogna Jsy 4.00 10.00
RG Ron Gant Bat 4.00 10.00
ROC R. Cedeno Jsy 4.00 10.00
RS Ruben Sierra Bat 4.00 10.00
RSC R. Clayton Bat 4.00 10.00
SA S. Alomar Jr. Bat 4.00 10.00
TH Todd Hundley Jsy 4.00 10.00
TR Tim Raines Jsy 4.00 10.00

2001 Topps Traded Rookie Relics

Inserted at a rate of one in 91, this 18-card set features bat pieces or jersey swatches for rookies. The cards carry a 'TRR' prefix. An exchange card for the Ed Rogers Bat card was seeded into packs.

TRRAB Angel Berroa Jsy 4.00 10.00
TRRAP A. Pujols Bat SP 100.00 175.00
TRRBO Bill Ortega Jsy 3.00 8.00
TRRER E.Rogers Bat SP EXCH 4.00 10.00
TRRHC H. Cota Jsy 3.00 8.00
TRRJL Jason Lane Jsy 3.00 8.00
TRRJS Jae Seo Jsy 3.00 8.00
TRRJS Jamal Strong Jsy 3.00 8.00
TRRJV Jose Valverde Jsy 3.00 8.00
TRRJY Jason Young Jsy 3.00 8.00
TRRNC Nate Cornejo Jsy 3.00 8.00
TRRNN N. Neugebauer Jsy 3.00 8.00
TRRPF P. Feliz Jsy SP 3.00 8.00
TRRRS Richard Stahl Jsy 3.00 8.00
TRRSB S. Burroughs Jsy 3.00 8.00
TRRTS T. Shinjo Bat SP 4.00 10.00
TRRWB W. Betemit Bat 4.00 10.00
TRRWR Wilkin Ruan Jsy 3.00 8.00

2001 Topps Traded Who Would Have Thought

Inserted at a rate of one in eight, this 20-card set portrays players who fans thought would never be traded. The cards carry a 'WWHT' prefix.

COMPLETE SET (20) 15.00 40.00
WWHT1 Nolan Ryan 2.50 6.00
WWHT2 Ozzie Smith 1.50 4.00
WWHT3 Tom Seaver .60 1.50
WWHT4 Steve Carlton .60 1.50
WWHT5 Reggie Jackson .60 1.50
WWHT6 Frank Robinson .60 1.50
WWHT7 Keith Hernandez .60 1.50
WWHT8 Andre Dawson .60 1.50
WWHT9 Lou Brock .60 1.50
WWHT10 D. Eckersley .60 1.50
WWHT11 Dave Winfield .60 1.50
WWHT12 Rod Carew .60 1.50
WWHT13 Willie Randolph .60 1.50
WWHT14 Dwight Gooden .60 1.50
WWHT15 Carlton Fisk .60 1.50
WWHT16 Dale Murphy .60 1.50
WWHT17 Paul Molitor .60 1.50
WWHT18 Gary Carter .60 1.50
WWHT19 Wade Boggs .60 1.50
WWHT20 Willie Mays 2.00 5.00

2002 Topps

The complete set of 2002 Topps consists of 718 cards issued in two separate series. The first series of 364 cards was distributed in November, 2001 and the second series of 354 cards followed up in April, 2002. Please note, the first series is numbered 1-365, but card number seven does not exist (the number was "retired" in 1996 by Topps to honor Mickey Mantle). Similar to the 1999 McGwire and Sosa home run cards, Barry Bonds is featured on card number 365 with 73 different versions to commemorate each of the homers he smashed during the 2001 season. The first series set is considered complete with any "one" of these variations. The cards were issued either in 10 card hobby/retail packs with an SRP of $1.29 or 37 card HTA packs with an SRP of $5 per pack. The hobby packs were issued 36 to a box and 12 boxes to a case. The HTA packs were issued 12 to a box and eight to a case. Cards numbered 277-305 feature managers; cards numbered 307-325/671-690 feature leading prospects; cards numbered 326-331/691-695 feature 2001 draft picks; cards numbered 332-336 feature leading highlights of the 2001 season; cards numbered 337-348 feature league leaders; cards numbered 349-356 feature the eight teams which made the playoffs; cards numbered 357-364 feature major league baseball's stirring tribute to the events of September 11, 2001; cards 641-670 feature Team Cards; 696-713 are Gold Glove subsets, 714-715 are Cy Young subsets, 716-717 are MVP subsets and 718-719 are Rookie of the Year subsets. Notable Rookie Cards include Joe Mauer and Kazuhisa Ishii. Also, Topps repurchased more than 21,000 actual vintage Topps cards and randomly seeded them into packs as follows - Ser.1 Home Team Advantage 1:169, ser.1 retail 1:tbd, ser.2 hobby 1:431, ser.2 Home Team Advantage 1:113 and ser.2 retail 1:331. Brown-boxed hobby factory sets were issued in May, 2002 containing the full 718-card basic set and five Topps Archives Reprints inserts. Green-boxed retail factory sets were issued in late August, 2002 containing the full 718-card basic set and cards 1-5 of a 10-card Draft Picks set. There has been a recently discovered variation of card 160 in which there is a correct back picture for Albert Pujols (#160). While Topps has confirmed this variation, it is unknown what percent of the print run has the correct back photo.

COMPLETE SET (718) 30.00 80.00
COMP.FACT.BROWN SET (723) 40.00 80.00
COMP.FACT.GREEN SET (723) 40.00 80.00
COMP. SERIES 1 (365) 15.00 40.00
COMPLETE SERIES 2 (354) 15.00 40.00
COMMON CARD (1-6/8-719) .07 .20
COMMON (307-331) .20 .50
COMMON CARD (332-364) .20 .50
1 Pedro Martinez .10 .30
2 Mike Stanton .07 .20
3 Brad Penny .07 .20
4 Mike Matheny .07 .20
5 Johnny Damon .10 .30
6 Bret Boone .07 .20
8 Chris Truby .07 .20
9 B.J. Surhoff .07 .20
10 Mike Hampton .07 .20
11 Juan Pierre .07 .20
12 Mark Buehrle .07 .20
13 Bob Abreu .07 .20
14 David Cone .07 .20
15 Aaron Sele UER .07 .20
Card lists him as being born in New Mexico
He was born in Minnesota
16 Fernando Tatis .07 .20
17 Bobby Jones .07 .20
18 Rick Helling .07 .20
19 Dmitri Young .07 .20
20 Mike Mussina UER .10 .30
Career win total is wrong
21 Mike Sweeney .07 .20
22 Cristian Guzman .07 .20
23 Ryan Kohlmeier .07 .20
24 Adam Kennedy .07 .20
25 Larry Walker .07 .20
26 Eric Davis UER .07 .20
2000 Stolen Base totals are wrong
27 Jason Tyner .07 .20
28 Eric Young .07 .20
29 Jason Marquis .07 .20
30 Luis Gonzalez .07 .20
31 Kevin Tapani .07 .20
32 Orlando Cabrera .07 .20
33 Marty Cordova UER .07 .20
Career homer total, 1003
34 Brad Ausmus .07 .20
35 Livan Hernandez .07 .20
36 Alex Gonzalez .07 .20
37 Edgar Renteria .07 .20
38 Bengie Molina .07 .20
39 Frank Menechino .07 .20
40 Rafael Palmeiro .10 .30
41 Brad Fullmer .07 .20
42 Julio Zuleta .07 .20
43 Darren Dreifort .07 .20
44 Trot Nixon .07 .20
45 Trevor Hoffman .07 .20
46 Vladimir Nunez .07 .20
47 Mark Kotsay .07 .20
48 Kenny Rogers .07 .20
49 Ben Petrick .07 .20
50 Jeff Bagwell .10 .30
51 Juan Encarnacion .07 .20
52 Ramiro Mendoza .07 .20
53 Brian Meadows .07 .20
54 Chad Curtis .07 .20
55 Aramis Ramirez .07 .20
56 Mark McLemore .07 .20
57 Dante Bichette .07 .20
58 Scott Schoeneweis .07 .20
59 Jose Cruz Jr. .07 .20
60 Roger Clemens .40 1.00
61 Jose Guillen .07 .20
62 Darren Oliver .07 .20
63 Chris Reitsma .07 .20
64 Jeff Abbott .07 .20
65 Robin Ventura .07 .20
66 Denny Neagle .07 .20
67 Al Martin .07 .20
68 Benito Santiago .07 .20
69 Roy Oswalt .07 .20
70 Juan Gonzalez .07 .20
71 Garret Anderson .07 .20
72 Bobby Bonilla .07 .20
73 Danny Bautista .07 .20
74 J.T. Snow .07 .20
75 Derek Jeter .50 1.25
76 John Olerud .07 .20
77 Kevin Appier .07 .20
78 Phil Nevin .07 .20
79 Sean Casey .07 .20
80 Troy Glaus .07 .20
81 Joe Randa .07 .20

82 Jose Valentin .07 .20
83 Ricky Bottalico .07 .20
84 Todd Zeile .07 .20
85 Barry Larkin .10 .30
86 Bob Wickman .07 .20
87 Jeff Shaw .07 .20
88 Greg Vaughn .07 .20
89 Fernando Vina .07 .20
90 Mark Mulder .07 .20
91 Paul Bako .07 .20
92 Aaron Boone .07 .20
93 Esteban Loaiza .07 .20
94 Richie Sexson .07 .20
95 Alfonso Soriano .07 .20
96 Tony Womack .07 .20
97 Paul Shuey .07 .20
98 Melvin Mora .07 .20
99 Tony Gwynn .25 .60
100 Vladimir Guerrero .20 .50
101 Keith Osik .07 .20
102 Bud Smith .07 .20
103 Scott Williamson .07 .20
104 Daryle Ward .07 .20
105 Doug Mientkiewicz .07 .20
106 Stan Javier .07 .20
107 Russ Ortiz .07 .20
108 Wade Miller .07 .20
109 Luke Prokopec .07 .20
110 Andruw Jones UER .10 .30
Career SB total, 1442
111 Ron Coomer .07 .20
112 Dan Wilson UER .07 .20
Career SB total, 1245
113 Luis Castillo .07 .20
114 Derek Bell .07 .20
115 Gary Sheffield .07 .20
116 Ruben Rivera .07 .20
117 Paul O'Neill .10 .30
118 Craig Paquette .07 .20
119 Kelvin Escobar .07 .20
120 Brad Radke .07 .20
121 Jorge Fabregas .07 .20
122 Randy Winn .07 .20
123 Tom Goodwin .07 .20
124 Jaret Wright .07 .20
125 Manny Ramirez .10 .30
126 Al Leiter .07 .20
127 Ben Davis .07 .20
128 Frank Catalanotto .07 .20
129 Jose Cabrera .07 .20
130 Magglio Ordonez .07 .20
131 Jose Macias .07 .20
132 Ted Lilly .07 .20
133 Chris Holt .07 .20
134 Eric Milton .07 .20
135 Shannon Stewart .07 .20
136 Omar Olivares .07 .20
137 David Segui .07 .20
138 Jeff Nelson .07 .20
139 Matt Williams .07 .20
140 Ellis Burks .07 .20
141 Jason Bere .07 .20
142 Jimmy Haynes .07 .20
143 Ramon Hernandez .07 .20
144 Craig Counsell UER .07 .20
Card pictures Greg Colbrunn
Some vital stats are wrong as well
145 John Smoltz .10 .30
146 Homer Bush .07 .20
147 Quilvio Veras .07 .20
148 Esteban Yan .07 .20
149 Ramon Ortiz .07 .20
150 Carlos Delgado .07 .20
151 Lee Stevens .07 .20
152 Wil Cordero .07 .20
153 Mike Bordick .07 .20
154 John Flaherty .07 .20
155 Omar Daal .07 .20
156 Todd Ritchie .07 .20
157 Carl Everett .07 .20
158 Scott Sullivan .07 .20
159 Deivi Cruz .07 .20
160 Albert Pujols UER .40 1.00
Placido Polanco pictured on back
160A Albert Pujols COR
Pujols correctly pictured on back
161 Royce Clayton .07 .20
162 Jeff Suppan .07 .20
163 C.C. Sabathia .07 .20
164 Jimmy Rollins .07 .20
165 Rickey Henderson .20 .50
166 Rey Ordonez .07 .20
167 Shawn Estes .07 .20
168 Reggie Sanders .07 .20
169 Jon Lieber .07 .20
170 Armando Benitez .07 .20
171 Mike Remlinger .07 .20
172 Billy Wagner .07 .20
173 Troy Percival .07 .20
174 Devon White .07 .20
175 Ivan Rodriguez .10 .30
176 Dustin Hermanson .07 .20
177 Brian Anderson .07 .20
178 Graeme Lloyd .07 .20
179 Russel Branyan .07 .20
180 Bobby Higginson .07 .20
181 Alex Gonzalez .07 .20
182 John Franco .07 .20
183 Sidney Ponson .07 .20
184 Jose Mesa .07 .20
185 Todd Hollandsworth .07 .20
186 Kevin Young .07 .20
187 Tim Wakefield .07 .20
188 Craig Biggio .10 .30
189 Jason Isringhausen .07 .20
190 Mark Quinn .07 .20
191 Glendon Rusch .07 .20
192 Damian Miller .07 .20
193 Sandy Alomar Jr. .07 .20
194 Scott Brosius .07 .20
195 Dave Martinez .07 .20
196 Danny Graves .07 .20
197 Shea Hillenbrand .07 .20
198 Jimmy Anderson .07 .20
199 Travis Lee .07 .20
200 Randy Johnson .20 .50
201 Carlos Beltran .07 .20
202 Jerry Hairston .07 .20
203 Jesus Sanchez .07 .20
204 Eddie Taubensee .07 .20
205 David Wells .07 .20
206 Russ Davis .07 .20
207 Michael Barrett .07 .20
208 Marquis Grissom .07 .20
209 Byung-Hyun Kim .07 .20
210 Hideo Nomo .20 .50
211 Ryan Rupe .07 .20
212 Ricky Gutierrez .07 .20
213 Darryl Kile .07 .20
214 Rico Brogna .07 .20
215 Terrence Long .07 .20
216 Mike Jackson .07 .20
217 Jamey Wright .07 .20
218 Adrian Beltre .07 .20
219 Benny Agbayani .07 .20
220 Chuck Knoblauch .07 .20
221 Randy Wolf .07 .20
222 Andy Ashby .07 .20
223 Corey Koskie .07 .20
224 Roger Cedeno .07 .20
225 Ichiro Suzuki .40 1.00
226 Keith Foulke .07 .20
227 Ryan Minor .07 .20
228 Shawon Dunston .07 .20
229 Alex Cora .07 .20
230 Jeromy Burnitz .07 .20
231 Mark Grace .10 .30
232 Aubrey Huff .07 .20
233 Jeffrey Hammonds .07 .20
234 Olmedo Saenz .07 .20
235 Brian Jordan .07 .20
236 Jeremy Giambi .07 .20
237 Joe Girardi .07 .20
238 Eric Gagne .07 .20
239 Masato Yoshii .07 .20
240 Greg Maddux .30 .75
241 Bryan Rekar .07 .20
242 Ray Durham .07 .20
243 Torii Hunter .07 .20
244 Derrek Lee .10 .30
245 Jim Edmonds .07 .20
246 Einar Diaz .07 .20
247 Brian Bohanon .07 .20
248 Ron Belliard .07 .20
249 Mike Lowell .07 .20
250 Sammy Sosa .20 .50
251 Richard Hidalgo .07 .20
252 Bartolo Colon .07 .20
253 Jorge Posada .10 .30
254 LaTroy Hawkins .07 .20
255 Paul LoDuca .07 .20
256 Carlos Febles .07 .20
257 Nelson Cruz .07 .20
258 Edgardo Alfonzo .07 .20
259 Joey Hamilton .07 .20
260 Cliff Floyd .07 .20
261 Wes Helms .07 .20
262 Jay Bell .07 .20
263 Mike Cameron .07 .20
264 Paul Konerko .07 .20
265 Jeff Kent .07 .20
266 Robert Fick .07 .20
267 Allen Levrault .07 .20
268 Placido Polanco .07 .20
269 Marlon Anderson .07 .20
270 Mariano Rivera .20 .50
271 Chan Ho Park .07 .20
272 Jose Vizcaino .07 .20
273 Jeff D'Amico .07 .20
274 Mark Gardner .07 .20
275 Travis Fryman .07 .20
276 Darren Lewis .07 .20
277 Bruce Bochy MG .07 .20
278 Jerry Manuel MG .07 .20
279 Bob Brenly MG .07 .20
280 Don Baylor MG .07 .20
281 Davey Lopes MG .07 .20
282 Jerry Narron MG .07 .20
283 Tony Muser MG .07 .20
284 Hal McRae MG .07 .20
285 Bobby Cox MG .07 .20
286 Larry Dierker MG .07 .20
287 Phil Garner MG .07 .20
288 Joe Kerrigan MG .07 .20
289 Bobby Valentine MG .07 .20
290 Dusty Baker MG .07 .20
291 Lloyd McClendon MG .07 .20
292 Mike Scioscia MG .07 .20
293 Buck Martinez MG .07 .20
294 Larry Bowa MG .07 .20
295 Tony LaRussa MG .07 .20
296 Jeff Torborg MG .07 .20
297 Tom Kelly MG .07 .20
298 Mike Hargrove MG .07 .20
299 Art Howe MG .07 .20
300 Lou Piniella MG .07 .20
301 Charlie Manuel MG .07 .20
302 Buddy Bell MG .07 .20
303 Tony Perez MG .07 .20
304 Bob Boone MG .07 .20
305 Joe Torre MG .10 .30
306 Jim Tracy MG .07 .20
307 Jason Lane PROS .20 .50
308 Chris George PROS .20 .50
309 Hank Blalock PROS UER .40 1.00
Bio has him throwing lefty
310 Joe Borchard PROS .20 .50
311 Marlon Byrd PROS .20 .50
312 R. Cabrera PROS RC .20 .50
313 F. Sanchez PROS RC .75 2.00
314 S. Wiggins PROS RC .20 .50
315 J. Maule PROS RC .20 .50
316 D. Cesar PROS RC .20 .50
317 Boof Bonser PROS .20 .50
318 J. Tolentino PROS RC .20 .50
319 Earl Snyder PROS RC .20 .50
320 T. Wade PROS RC .20 .50
321 N. Calzado PROS RC .20 .50
322 Eric Glaser PROS RC .20 .50
323 C. Kuzmic PROS RC .20 .50
324 Nic Jackson PROS RC .20 .50
325 Mike Rivera PROS .20 .50
326 Jason Bay PROS RC 1.50 4.00
327 Chris Smith DP .20 .50
328 Jake Gautreau DP .20 .50
329 Gabe Gross DP .20 .50
330 Kenny Baugh DP .20 .50
331 J.D. Martin DP .20 .50
332 Barry Bonds HL .50 1.25
500th Homer
333 Rickey Henderson HL .20 .50
Sets record for career walks
334 Bud Smith HL .20 .50
335 R. Henderson HL 3000 .20 .50
336 Barry Bonds HL .50 1.25
73 homers in a season
337 Ichiro Suzuki .20 .50
Jason Giambi
Roberto Alomar LL
338 Alex Rodriguez .20 .50
Ichiro Suzuki
Bret Boone LL
339 Alex Rodriguez .20 .50
Jim Thome
Rafael Palmeiro LL
340 Bret Boone .20 .50
Juan Gonzalez
Alex Rodriguez LL
341 Freddy Garcia .20 .50
Mike Mussina
Joe Mays LL
342 Hideo Nomo .20 .50
Mike Mussina
Roger Clemens LL
343 Larry Walker .20 .50
Todd Helton
Moises Alou
Lance Berkman LL
344 Sammy Sosa .30 .75
Todd Helton
Barry Bonds LL
345 Barry Bonds .30 .75
Sammy Sosa
Luis Gonzalez LL
346 Sammy Sosa .20 .50
Todd Helton
Luis Gonzalez LL
347 Randy Johnson .20 .50
Curt Schilling
John Burkett LL
348 Randy Johnson .20 .50
Curt Schilling
Chan Ho Park LL
349 Seattle Mariners PB .20 .50
350 Oakland Athletics PB .20 .50
351 New York Yankees PB .20 .50
352 Cleveland Indians PB .20 .50
353 Ariz. Diamondbacks PB .20 .50
354 Atlanta Braves PB .20 .50
355 St. Louis Cardinals PB .20 .50
356 Houston Astros PB .20 .50
357 Ariz.Diamondbacks .20 .50
Colorado Rockies UWS
358 Mike Piazza UWS .20 .50
359 Braves-Phillies UWS .20 .50
360 Curt Schilling UWS .20 .50
361 Roger Clemens .20 .50
Lee Mazzilli UWS
362 Sammy Sosa UWS .10 .30
363 Tom Lampkin .20 .50
Ichiro Suzuki
Bret Boone UWS
364 Barry Bonds .30 .75
Jeff Bagwell UWS
365 Barry Bonds HR 1 6.00 15.00
365 Barry Bonds HR 2 4.00 10.00
365 Barry Bonds HR 3 4.00 10.00
365 Barry Bonds HR 4 4.00 10.00
365 Barry Bonds HR 5 4.00 10.00
365 Barry Bonds HR 6 4.00 10.00
365 Barry Bonds HR 7 4.00 10.00
365 Barry Bonds HR 8 4.00 10.00
365 Barry Bonds HR 9 4.00 10.00
365 Barry Bonds HR 10 4.00 10.00
365 Barry Bonds HR 11 4.00 10.00
365 Barry Bonds HR 12 4.00 10.00
365 Barry Bonds HR 13 4.00 10.00
365 Barry Bonds HR 14 4.00 10.00
365 Barry Bonds HR 15 4.00 10.00
365 Barry Bonds HR 16 4.00 10.00
365 Barry Bonds HR 17 4.00 10.00
365 Barry Bonds HR 18 4.00 10.00
365 Barry Bonds HR 19 4.00 10.00
365 Barry Bonds HR 20 4.00 10.00
365 Barry Bonds HR 21 4.00 10.00
365 Barry Bonds HR 22 4.00 10.00
365 Barry Bonds HR 23 4.00 10.00
365 Barry Bonds HR 24 4.00 10.00
365 Barry Bonds HR 25 4.00 10.00
365 Barry Bonds HR 26 4.00 10.00
365 Barry Bonds HR 27 4.00 10.00
365 Barry Bonds HR 28 4.00 10.00
365 Barry Bonds HR 29 4.00 10.00
365 Barry Bonds HR 30 4.00 10.00
365 Barry Bonds HR 31 4.00 10.00
365 Barry Bonds HR 32 UER 4.00 10.00
No pitcher is listed on this card
365 Barry Bonds HR 33 4.00 10.00
365 Barry Bonds HR 34 4.00 10.00
365 Barry Bonds HR 35 4.00 10.00
365 Barry Bonds HR 36 4.00 10.00
365 Barry Bonds HR 37 4.00 10.00
365 Barry Bonds HR 38 4.00 10.00
365 Barry Bonds HR 39 4.00 10.00
365 Barry Bonds HR 40 4.00 10.00
365 Barry Bonds HR 41 4.00 10.00
365 Barry Bonds HR 42 4.00 10.00
365 Barry Bonds HR 43 4.00 10.00
365 Barry Bonds HR 44 4.00 10.00
365 Barry Bonds HR 45 4.00 10.00
365 Barry Bonds HR 46 4.00 10.00
365 Barry Bonds HR 47 4.00 10.00
365 Barry Bonds HR 48 4.00 10.00
365 Barry Bonds HR 49 4.00 10.00
365 Barry Bonds HR 50 4.00 10.00
365 Barry Bonds HR 51 4.00 10.00
365 Barry Bonds HR 52 4.00 10.00
365 Barry Bonds HR 53 4.00 10.00
365 Barry Bonds HR 54 4.00 10.00
365 Barry Bonds HR 55 4.00 10.00
365 Barry Bonds HR 56 4.00 10.00
365 Barry Bonds HR 57 4.00 10.00
365 Barry Bonds HR 58 4.00 10.00
365 Barry Bonds HR 59 4.00 10.00
365 Barry Bonds HR 60 4.00 10.00
365 Barry Bonds HR 61 6.00 15.00
365 Barry Bonds HR 62 4.00 10.00
365 Barry Bonds HR 63 4.00 10.00
365 Barry Bonds HR 64 4.00 10.00
365 Barry Bonds HR 65 4.00 10.00
365 Barry Bonds HR 66 4.00 10.00
365 Barry Bonds HR 67 4.00 10.00
365 Barry Bonds HR 68 4.00 10.00
365 Barry Bonds HR 69 4.00 10.00
365 Barry Bonds HR 70 6.00 15.00
365 Barry Bonds HR 71 4.00 10.00
365 Barry Bonds HR 72 4.00 10.00
365 Barry Bonds HR 73 20.00 50.00
366 Pat Meares .07 .20
367 Mike Lieberthal .07 .20
368 Larry Bigbie .07 .20
369 Ron Gant .07 .20
370 Moises Alou .07 .20
371 Chad Kreuter .07 .20
372 Willis Roberts .07 .20
373 Toby Hall .07 .20
374 Miguel Batista .07 .20
375 John Burkett .07 .20
376 Cory Lidle .07 .20
377 Nick Neugebauer .07 .20
378 Jay Payton .07 .20
379 Steve Karsay .07 .20
380 Eric Chavez .07 .20
381 Kelly Stinnett .07 .20
382 Jarrod Washburn .07 .20
383 Rick White .07 .20
384 Jeff Conine .07 .20
385 Fred McGriff .10 .30
386 Marvin Benard .07 .20
387 Joe Crede .07 .20
388 Dennis Cook .07 .20
389 Rick Reed .07 .20
390 Tom Glavine .10 .30
391 Rondell White .07 .20
392 Matt Morris .07 .20
393 Pat Rapp .07 .20
394 Robert Person .07 .20
395 Omar Vizquel .10 .30
396 Jeff Cirillo .07 .20
397 Dave Mlicki .07 .20
398 Jose Ortiz .07 .20
399 Ryan Dempster .07 .20
400 Curt Schilling .07 .20
401 Peter Bergeron .07 .20
402 Kyle Lohse .07 .20
403 Craig Wilson UER .07 .20
Homer totals are wrong
404 David Justice .07 .20
405 Darin Erstad .07 .20
406 Jose Mercedes .07 .20
407 Carl Pavano .07 .20
408 Albie Lopez .07 .20
409 Alex Ochoa .07 .20
410 Chipper Jones .20 .50
411 Tyler Houston .07 .20
412 Dean Palmer .07 .20
413 Damian Jackson .07 .20
414 Josh Towers .07 .20
415 Rafael Furcal .07 .20
416 Mike Morgan .07 .20
417 Herb Perry .07 .20
418 Mike Sirotka .07 .20
419 Mark Wohlers .07 .20
420 Nomar Garciaparra .30 .75
421 Felipe Lopez .07 .20
422 Joe McEwing .07 .20
423 Jacque Jones .07 .20
424 Julio Franco .07 .20
425 Frank Thomas .20 .50
426 So Taguchi RC .30 .75
427 Kazuhisa Ishii RC .20 .50
428 D'Angelo Jimenez .07 .20
429 Chris Stynes .07 .20
430 Kerry Wood .07 .20
431 Chris Singleton .07 .20
432 Erubiel Durazo .07 .20
433 Matt Lawton .07 .20
434 Bill Mueller .07 .20
435 Jose Canseco .10 .30
436 Ben Grieve .07 .20
437 Terry Mulholland .07 .20
438 David Bell .07 .20
439 A.J. Pierzynski .07 .20
440 Adam Dunn .07 .20
441 Jon Garland .07 .20
442 Jeff Fassero .07 .20
443 Julio Lugo .07 .20
444 Carlos Guillen .07 .20
445 Orlando Hernandez .07 .20
446 Mark Loretta UER .07 .20
Photo is Curtis Leskanic
447 Scott Spiezio .07 .20
448 Kevin Millwood .07 .20
449 Jamie Moyer .07 .20
450 Todd Helton .10 .30
451 Todd Walker .07 .20
452 Jose Lima .07 .20
453 Brook Fordyce .07 .20
454 Aaron Rowand .07 .20
455 Barry Zito .07 .20
456 Eric Owens .07 .20
457 Charles Nagy .07 .20
458 Raul Ibanez .07 .20
459 Joe Mays .07 .20
460 Jim Thome .10 .30
461 Adam Eaton .07 .20
462 Felix Martinez .07 .20
463 Vernon Wells .07 .20
464 Dennis Sadler .07 .20
465 Tony Clark .07 .20
466 Jose Hernandez .07 .20
467 Ramon Martinez .07 .20
468 Rusty Greer .07 .20
469 Rod Barajas .07 .20
470 Lance Berkman .07 .20
471 Brady Anderson .07 .20
472 Pedro Astacio .07 .20
473 Shane Halter .07 .20
474 Bret Prinz .07 .20
475 Edgar Martinez .10 .30
476 Steve Trachsel .07 .20
477 Gary Matthews Jr. .07 .20
478 Ismael Valdes .07 .20
479 Juan Uribe .07 .20
480 Shawn Green .07 .20
481 Kirk Rueter .07 .20
482 Damion Easley .07 .20
483 Chris Carpenter .07 .20
484 Kris Benson .07 .20
485 Antonio Alfonseca .07 .20
486 Kyle Farnsworth .07 .20
487 Brandon Lyon .07 .20
488 Hideki Irabu .07 .20
489 David Ortiz .20 .50
490 Mike Piazza .30 .75
491 Derek Lowe .07 .20
492 Chris Gomez .07 .20
493 Mark Johnson .07 .20
494 John Rocker .07 .20
495 Eric Karros .07 .20
496 Bill Haselman .07 .20
497 Dave Veres .07 .20
498 Pete Harnisch .07 .20
499 Tomokazu Ohka .07 .20
500 Barry Bonds .50 1.25
501 David Dellucci .07 .20
502 Wendell Magee .07 .20
503 Tom Gordon .07 .20
504 Javier Vazquez .07 .20
505 Ben Sheets .07 .20
506 Wilton Guerrero .07 .20
507 John Halama .07 .20
508 Mark Redman .07 .20
509 Jack Wilson .07 .20
510 Bernie Williams .10 .30
511 Miguel Cairo .07 .20
512 Denny Hocking .07 .20
513 Tony Batista .07 .20
514 Mark Grudzielanek .07 .20
515 Jose Vidro .07 .20
516 Sterling Hitchcock .07 .20
517 Billy Koch .07 .20
518 Matt Clement .07 .20
519 Bruce Chen .07 .20
520 Roberto Alomar .10 .30
521 Orlando Palmeiro .07 .20
522 Steve Finley .07 .20
523 Danny Patterson .07 .20
524 Terry Adams .07 .20
525 Tino Martinez .10 .30
526 Tony Armas Jr. .07 .20
527 Geoff Jenkins .07 .20
528 Kerry Robinson .07 .20
529 Corey Patterson .07 .20
530 Brian Giles .07 .20
531 Jose Jimenez .07 .20
532 Joe Kennedy .07 .20
533 Armando Rios .07 .20
534 Osvaldo Fernandez .07 .20
535 Ruben Sierra .07 .20
536 Octavio Dotel .07 .20
537 Luis Sojo .07 .20
538 Brent Butler .07 .20
539 Pablo Ozuna UER .07 .20
Games played for Portland is wrong for 2002
540 Freddy Garcia .07 .20
541 Chad Durbin .07 .20
542 Orlando Merced .07 .20
543 Michael Tucker .07 .20
544 Roberto Hernandez .07 .20
545 Pat Burrell .07 .20
546 A.J. Burnett .07 .20
547 Bubba Trammell .07 .20
548 Scott Elarton .07 .20
549 Mike Darr .07 .20
550 Ken Griffey Jr. .30 .75
551 Ugueth Urbina .07 .20
552 Todd Jones .07 .20
553 Delino Deshields .07 .20
554 Adam Piatt .07 .20
555 Jason Kendall .07 .20
556 Hector Ortiz .07 .20
557 Turk Wendell .07 .20
558 Rob Bell .07 .20
559 Sun Woo Kim .07 .20
560 Raul Mondesi .07 .20
561 Brent Abernathy .07 .20
562 Seth Etherton .07 .20
563 Shawn Wooten .07 .20
564 Jay Buhner .07 .20
565 Andres Galarraga .07 .20
566 Shane Reynolds .07 .20
567 Rod Beck .07 .20
568 Dee Brown .07 .20
569 Pedro Feliz .07 .20
570 Ryan Klesko .07 .20
571 John Vander Wal UER .07 .20
Home Run Total in 1999 was 64
572 Nick Bierbrodt .07 .20
573 Joe Nathan .07 .20
574 James Baldwin .07 .20
575 J.D. Drew .07 .20
576 Greg Colbrunn .07 .20
577 Doug Glanville .07 .20
578 Brandon Duckworth .07 .20
579 Shawn Chacon .07 .20
580 Rich Aurilia .07 .20
581 Chuck Finley .07 .20
582 Abraham Nunez .07 .20
583 Kenny Lofton .07 .20
584 Brian Daubach .07 .20
585 Miguel Tejada .07 .20
586 Nate Cornejo .07 .20
587 Kazuhiro Sasaki .07 .20
588 Chris Richard .07 .20
589 Armando Reynoso .07 .20
590 Tim Hudson .07 .20
591 Neifi Perez .07 .20
592 Steve Cox .07 .20
593 Henry Blanco .07 .20
594 Ricky Ledee .07 .20
595 Tim Salmon .10 .30
596 Luis Rivas .07 .20
597 Jeff Zimmerman .07 .20
598 Matt Stairs .07 .20
599 Preston Wilson .07 .20
600 Mark McGwire .50 1.25
601 Timo Perez UER .07 .20
Biographical Information is that of Aaron Rowand's
602 Matt Anderson .07 .20
603 Todd Hundley .07 .20
604 Rick Ankiel .07 .20
605 Tsuyoshi Shinjo .07 .20
606 Woody Williams .07 .20
607 Jason LaRue .07 .20
608 Carlos Lee .07 .20
609 Russ Johnson .07 .20
610 Scott Rolen .10 .30
611 Brent Mayne .07 .20
612 Darrin Fletcher .07 .20
613 Ray Lankford .07 .20
614 Troy O'Leary .07 .20
615 Javier Lopez .07 .20
616 Randy Velarde .07 .20
617 Vinny Castilla .07 .20
618 Milton Bradley .07 .20
619 Ruben Mateo .07 .20
620 Jason Giambi Yankees .07 .20
621 Andy Benes .07 .20
622 Joe Mauer RC 4.00 10.00
623 Andy Pettitte .10 .30
624 Jose Offerman .07 .20
625 Mo Vaughn .07 .20
626 Steve Sparks .07 .20
627 Mike Matthews .07 .20
628 Robb Nen .07 .20
629 Kip Wells .07 .20
630 Kevin Brown .07 .20
631 Arthur Rhodes .07 .20
632 Gabe Kapler .07 .20
633 Jermaine Dye .07 .20
634 Josh Beckett .07 .20
635 Pokey Reese .07 .20
636 Benji Gil .07 .20
637 Marcus Giles .07 .20
638 Julian Tavarez .07 .20
639 Jason Schmidt .07 .20
640 Alex Rodriguez .30 .75
641 Anaheim Angels TC .07 .20
642 Arizona Diamondbacks TC .10 .30
643 Atlanta Braves TC .07 .20
644 Baltimore Orioles TC .07 .20
645 Boston Red Sox TC .07 .20
646 Chicago Cubs TC .07 .20
647 Chicago White Sox TC .07 .20
648 Cincinnati Reds TC .07 .20
649 Cleveland Indians TC .07 .20
650 Colorado Rockies TC .07 .20
651 Detroit Tigers TC .07 .20
652 Florida Marlins TC .07 .20
653 Houston Astros TC .07 .20
654 Kansas City Royals TC .07 .20
655 Los Angeles Dodgers TC .07 .20
656 Milwaukee Brewers TC .07 .20
657 Minnesota Twins TC .07 .20
658 Montreal Expos TC .07 .20
659 New York Mets TC .07 .20
660 New York Yankees TC .20 .50
661 Oakland Athletics TC .07 .20
662 Philadelphia Phillies TC .07 .20
663 Pittsburgh Pirates TC .07 .20
664 San Diego Padres TC .07 .20
665 San Francisco Giants TC .07 .20
666 Seattle Mariners TC .10 .30
667 St. Louis Cardinals TC .07 .20
668 T.B. Devil Rays TC .07 .20
669 Texas Rangers TC .07 .20
670 Toronto Blue Jays TC .07 .20
671 Juan Cruz PROS .20 .50
672 Kevin Cash PROS RC .20 .50
673 Jimmy Gobble PROS RC .20 .50
674 Mike Hill PROS RC .20 .50
675 T.Buchholz PROS RC .20 .50
676 Bill Hall PROS .20 .50
677 B.Roneberg PROS RC .20 .50
678 R.Huffman PROS RC .20 .50
679 Chris Tritle PROS RC .20 .50
680 Nate Espy PROS RC .20 .50
681 Nick Alvarez PROS RC .20 .50
682 Jason Botts PROS RC .20 .50
683 Ryan Gripp PROS RC .20 .50
684 Dan Phillips PROS RC .20 .50
685 Pablo Arias PROS RC .20 .50
686 J.Rodriguez PROS RC .20 .50
687 Rich Harden PROS RC 1.25 3.00
688 Neal Frendling PROS RC .20 .50
689 Rich Thompson PROS RC .20 .50
690 G.Montalbano PROS RC .20 .50
691 Len Dinardo DP RC .20 .50
692 Ryan Raburn DP RC .20 .50
693 Josh Barfield DP RC 1.00 2.50
694 David Bacani DP RC .20 .50
695 Dan Johnson DP RC .40 1.00
696 Mike Mussina GG .07 .20
697 Ivan Rodriguez GG .10 .30
698 Doug Mientkiewicz GG .07 .20
699 Roberto Alomar GG .07 .20
700 Eric Chavez GG .07 .20
701 Omar Vizquel GG .07 .20
702 Mike Cameron GG .07 .20
703 Torii Hunter GG .07 .20
704 Ichiro Suzuki GG .20 .50
705 Greg Maddux GG .20 .50
706 Brad Ausmus GG .07 .20
707 Todd Helton GG .07 .20
708 Fernando Vina GG .07 .20
709 Scott Rolen GG .07 .20
710 Orlando Cabrera GG .07 .20
711 Andruw Jones GG .07 .20
712 Jim Edmonds GG .07 .20
713 Larry Walker GG .07 .20
714 Roger Clemens CY .20 .50
715 Randy Johnson CY .10 .30
716 Ichiro Suzuki MVP .20 .50
717 Barry Bonds MVP .30 .75
718 Ichiro Suzuki ROY .20 .50
719 Albert Pujols ROY .20 .50

2002 Topps Gold

Inserted one per 19 first series hobby packs, one per 15 first series retail packs, one per 5 first series HTA packs, one per 12 second series hobby packs, one per 9 second series retail packs and one per three second series HTA packs, this set parallels cards 1-330 and 366-695 of the 2002 Topps set. Each card features bold, gold-foil borders on front and 2002 serial-numbered sets were produced.

*GOLD 1-306/366-670: 8X TO 20X BASIC
*GOLD 307-330/671-695: 1.5X TO 4X BASIC
*GOLD 426-427: 1.5X TO 4X BASIC
622 Joe Mauer 10.00 25.00

2002 Topps Home Team Advantage

This is a parallel to the Topps set. Each of these cards, which were available only in the blue factory sets have the words "Home Team Advantage" stamped on them in gold foil except for cards #332-364 - those are identical to the base issue cards thus are not part of this checklist.

COMP.FACT.SET (718) 40.00 80.00
*HTA: .75X TO 2X BASIC
*BONDS HR 70: .2X TO .5X BASIC HR 70

2002 Topps Limited

This 790 card factory set was issued in October, 2002. It had a SRP of $150 and parallels the regular Topps set except for the reprinting of all 73 Barry Bonds 365 cards. These cards can be differentiated from the regular cards by their "glossy" finish on the front. Though the cards are not serial-numbered, Topps announced that 1,950 sets were issued.

COMP.FACT.SET (790) 60.00 150.00
*LTD STARS: 1.5X TO 4X BASIC CARDS
*307-331/426-427/622/671-695: 1.5X TO 4X
*BONDS HR: .2X TO .5X BASIC BONDS HR
622 Joe Mauer 30.00 60.00

2002 Topps 1952 Reprints

Inserted at a rate of one in 25 hobby, one in five HTA packs and one in 16 retail packs, these nineteen reprint cards feature players who participated in the 1952 World Series which was won by the New York Yankees.

COMPLETE SET (19) 20.00 50.00
COMPLETE SERIES 1 (9) 10.00 25.00
COMPLETE SERIES 2 (10) 10.00 25.00
52R1 Roy Campanella 2.00 5.00
52R2 Duke Snider 1.50 4.00
52R3 Carl Erskine 1.50 4.00
52R4 Andy Pafko 1.50 4.00
52R5 Johnny Mize 1.50 4.00
52R6 Billy Martin 1.50 4.00
52R7 Phil Rizzuto 2.00 5.00
52R8 Gil McDougald 1.50 4.00
52R9 Allie Reynolds 1.50 4.00
52R10 Jackie Robinson 2.00 5.00
52R11 Preacher Roe 1.50 4.00
52R12 Gil Hodges 2.00 5.00
52R13 Billy Cox 1.50 4.00
52R14 Yogi Berra 2.00 5.00
52R15 Gene Woodling 1.50 4.00
52R16 Johnny Sain 1.50 4.00
52R17 Ralph Houk 1.50 4.00
52R18 Joe Collins 1.50 4.00
52R19 Hank Bauer 1.50 4.00

2002 Topps 1952 Reprints Autographs

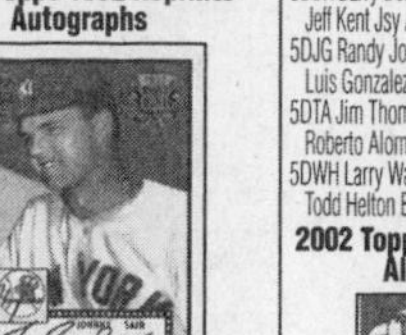

Inserted in series one packs at a rate of one in 10,268 hobby packs, one in 2826 HTA packs and one in 8,005 retail packs and series two packs at a rate of 1:7524 hobby, one in 1985 HTA packs and one in 5839 retail packs these eleven cards feature signed copies of the 1952 reprints. Phil Rizzuto did not return his cards in time for inclusion in this product and those cards could be redeemed until December 1st, 2003. Due to scarcity, no pricing is provided for these cards. These cards were released in different series and we have notated that information next to the player's name in our checklist.

APA Andy Pafko S1 75.00 150.00
CEA Carl Erskine S1 50.00 100.00
DSA Duke Snider S1 75.00 150.00
GMA Gil McDougald S1 30.00 60.00
HBA Hank Bauer S2
JBA Joe Black S1 50.00 100.00
JSA Johnny Sain S2
PRA Preacher Roe S2
PRA Phil Rizzuto S1 75.00 150.00
RHA Ralph Houk S2
YBA Yogi Berra S2

2002 Topps 1952 World Series Highlights

Inserted in first and second series packs at a rate of one in 25 hobby, one in five HTA and one in 16 retail packs, these eleven cards feature highlights of the 1952 World Series. Next to the card, we have notated whether they were released in the first or second series.

COMPLETE SET (7) 4.00 10.00
COMPLETE SERIES 1 (3) 1.50 4.00
COMPLETE SERIES 2 (4) 2.50 6.00
52WS1 Dodgers Line Up 1 .75 2.00
52WS2 Billy Martin's Homer 2 .75 2.00
52WS3 Dodgers Celebrate 1 .75 2.00
52WS4 Yanks Slip Dodgers 2 .75 2.00
52WS5 Carl Erskine 1 .75 2.00
52WS6 Casey Stengel MG .75 2.00
Allie Reynolds 2
52WS7 Allie Reynolds .75 2.00
Relieves Ed Lopat 2

2002 Topps 5-Card Stud Aces Relics

Inserted into second series packs at a rate of one in 1180 hobby, one in 293 HTA and one in 966 retail, these five cards feature some of the best pitchers in baseball along with a game jersey swatch "relic".

5AGM Greg Maddux Jsy 30.00 60.00
5AMH Mike Hampton Jsy 10.00 25.00
5AMM Mark Mulder Jsy 10.00 25.00
5APM Pedro Martinez Jsy 15.00 40.00
5ARJ Randy Johnson Jsy 15.00 40.00

2002 Topps 5-Card Stud Deuces are Wild Relics

Inserted into second series packs at an overall rate of one in 1962 hobby, one in 487 HTA and one in 1609 retail, these five cards feature memorabilia game bat and game jersey relics from two of the stars from the same team. These cards were issued in different odds depending on which series they were from and we have notated which group next to the card in the checklist.

SER.2 A ODDS 1:3078 H, 1:796 HTA, 1:2422 R
SER.2 B ODDS 1:5410 H, 1:1254 HTA, 1:4827 R
5DBG Bret Boone Jsy 15.00 40.00
Freddy Garcia Jsy A
5DBK Barry Bonds Jsy 40.00 80.00
Jeff Kent Jsy A
5DJG Randy Johnson Jsy 30.00 60.00
Luis Gonzalez Bat B
5DTA Jim Thome Jsy 30.00 60.00
Roberto Alomar Bat B
5DWH Larry Walker Bat 30.00 60.00
Todd Helton Bat B

2002 Topps 5-Card Stud Jack of All Trades Relics

Inserted into second series packs at an overall rate of one in 1350 Hobby packs, one in 333 HTA packs and one on 1119 retail packs, these five cards feature some of the best five-tool players in the field along with a game-used memorabilia relic from their career. These cards were issued at different odds depending on the player and we have notated that information in our checklist.

5JAJ Andruw Jones A 15.00 40.00
5JBB Barry Bonds Uni A 30.00 60.00
5JBW Bernie Williams Uni A 15.00 40.00
5JIR Ivan Rodriguez A 15.00 40.00
5JRO Roberto Alomar B 30.00 60.00

2002 Topps 5-Card Stud Kings of the Clubhouse Relics

Inserted into packs at an overall rate of one in 1449 hobby packs, one in 334 HTA packs and one in 1119 retail packs, these five cards feature some of the most effective and highly driven clubhouse leaders along with a game-used memorabilia relic from their career. Depending on the player, these cards were issued in two groups and we have notated that information in our checklist.

SER.2 A ODDS 1:1570 H, 1:358 HTA, 1:1211 R
SER.2B ODDS 1:18883 H,1:4943 HTA,1:14736 R
5KEM Edgar Martinez Jsy A 15.00 40.00
5KPO Paul O'Neill B 30.00 60.00
5KRJ Randy Johnson Jsy A 15.00 40.00
5KTG Tom Glavine Uni A 15.00 40.00
5KTH Todd Helton A 15.00 40.00

2002 Topps 5-Card Stud Three of a Kind Relics

Inserted into packs at an overall rate of one in 2039 Hobby packs, one in 524 HTA packs and one in retail 1609 packs, these five cards feature memorabilia relics from three stars from the same team. Depending on the card, these cards were issued as part of two groups, and we have notated that information next to the card in our checklist

SER.2 A ODDS 1:3078 H, 1:796 HTA, 1:2422 R
SER.2 B ODDS 1:6043 H, 1:1532 HTA, 1:4827 R
5TBDB A.J. Burnett Uni 30.00 60.00
Ryan Dempster Uni
Josh Beckett Uni A
5TFBJ Rafael Furcal 30.00 60.00
Wilson Betemit
Andruw Jones B
5TLOC Carlos Lee 30.00 60.00
Magglio Ordonez
Jose Canseco B
5TPSW Jorge Posada 30.00 60.00
Alfonso Soriano
Bernie Williams B
5TSPA Tsuyoshi Shinjo Uni 30.00 60.00
Mike Piazza Uni
Edgardo Alfonzo Uni A

2002 Topps All-World Team

Inserted into second series packs at a rate of one in 12 packs and one in 4 HTA packs, these 25 cards feature an international mix of upper-echelon stars. These cards are extremely thick as well.

COMPLETE SET (25) 30.00 60.00
AW1 Ichiro Suzuki 1.50 4.00
AW2 Barry Bonds 2.00 5.00
AW3 Pedro Martinez .60 1.50
AW4 Juan Gonzalez .60 1.50
AW5 Larry Walker .60 1.50
AW6 Sammy Sosa .75 2.00
AW7 Mariano Rivera .75 2.00
AW8 Vladimir Guerrero .75 2.00
AW9 Alex Rodriguez 1.25 3.00
AW10 Albert Pujols 1.50 4.00
AW11 Luis Gonzalez .60 1.50
AW12 Ken Griffey Jr. 1.25 3.00
AW13 Kazuhiro Sasaki .60 1.50
AW14 Bob Abreu .60 1.50
AW15 Todd Helton .60 1.50
AW16 Nomar Garciaparra 1.25 3.00
AW17 Miguel Tejada .60 1.50
AW18 Roger Clemens 1.50 4.00
AW19 Mike Piazza 1.25 3.00
AW20 Carlos Delgado .60 1.50
AW21 Derek Jeter 2.00 5.00
AW22 Hideo Nomo .75 2.00
AW23 Randy Johnson .75 2.00
AW24 Ivan Rodriguez .60 1.50
AW25 Chan Ho Park .60 1.50

2002 Topps Autographs

Inserted at varying odds, these 40 cards feature authentic autographs. Alex Rodriguez, Barry Bonds and Xavier Nady did not return their cards in time for series one packout, thus exchange cards were seeded into packs. Those cards could be redeemed until December 1st, 2003. First series cards have a numerical card number on back (i.e. TA-1) and series two cards have card numbering based on player's initials (i.e. TA-AB).

SER.1 A 1:15,402 H, 1:4256 HTA, 1:12,008 R
SER.2 A 1:10,071 H, 1:2404, 1:7702 R
SER.1 B 1:49,599 H, 1:12,312 HTA, 1:46,944 R
SER.2 B 1:1867 H, 1:487 HTA, 1:1449 R
SER.1 C 1:4104 H, 1:1130 HTA, 1:3238 R
SER.2 C 1:10,071 H, 1:2646 HTA, 1:7702 R
SER.1 D 1:9853 H, 1:2714 HTA, 1:7284 R
SER.2 D 1:1885 H, 1:496 HTA, 1:1449 R
SER.1 E 1:4104 H, 1:1130 HTA, 1:3238 R
SER.2 E 1:5023 H, 1:1323 HTA, 1:3851 R
SER.2 F 1:985 H, 1:271 HTA, 1:776 R
SER.2 F 1:940 H, 1:247 HTA, 1:725 R
SER.2 G 1:3017 H, 1:794 HTA, 1:2327 R
NO A1 PRICING DUE TO SCARCITY
TA1 Carlos Delgado B1 15.00 40.00
TA2 Ivan Rodriguez A1
TA3 Miguel Tejada C1 12.50 30.00
TA4 Geoff Jenkins E1 6.00 15.00
TA5 Johnny Damon A1
TA6 Tim Hudson C1 15.00 40.00
TA7 Terrence Long E1 4.00 10.00
TA8 Gabe Kapler C1 10.00 25.00
TA9 Magglio Ordonez C1 10.00 25.00
TA10 Barry Bonds A1
TA11 Pat Burrell C1 10.00 25.00
TA12 Mike Mussina A1
TA13 Eric Valent F1 4.00 10.00
TA14 Xavier Nady F1 4.00 10.00
TA15 Cristian Guerrero F1 4.00 10.00
TA16 Ben Sheets F1 10.00 25.00
TA17 Corey Patterson C1 6.00 15.00
TA18 Carlos Pena F1 4.00 10.00
TA19 Alex Rodriguez 60.00 120.00
D1/A2 EXCH
TAAB Adrian Beltre B2 12.50 30.00
TAAE Alex Escobar F2 4.00 10.00
TABG Brian Giles B2 12.50 30.00
TABW Brad Wilkerson G2 4.00 10.00
TABGR Ben Grieve B2 8.00 20.00
TACF Cliff Floyd C2 10.00 25.00
TACG Cristian Guzman B2 8.00 20.00
TADJ Jermaine Dye D2 10.00 25.00
TAJH Josh Hamilton E2 12.50 30.00
TAJO Jose Ortiz D2 6.00 15.00
TAJR Jimmy Rollins D2 20.00 50.00
TAJW Justin Wayne D2 6.00 15.00
TAKG Keith Ginter F2 4.00 10.00
TAMS Mike Sweeney B2 12.50 30.00
TANJ Nick Johnson F2 6.00 15.00
TARF Rafael Furcal B2 12.50 30.00
TARK Ryan Klesko B2 12.50 30.00
TARO Roy Oswalt F2 6.00 15.00
TARP Rafael Palmeiro A2 40.00 80.00
TARS Richie Sexson B2 12.50 30.00
TATG Troy Glaus A2 20.00 50.00

2002 Topps Coaches Collection Relics

Inserted at overall odds of one in 236 retail packs, these 26 cards feature memorabilia from either a coach or a manager currently involved in major league baseball. The Billy Williams jersey card was not available when these cards were packed and that card could be redeemed until April 30th, 2004.

SER.2 BAT ODDS 1:404 RETAIL
SER.2 UNIFORM ODDS 1:565 RETAIL
OVERALL SER.2 ODDS 1:236 RETAIL
CCAH Art Howe Bat 10.00 25.00
CCAT Alan Trammell Bat 15.00 40.00
CCBB Bruce Bochy Bat 10.00 25.00
CCBM Buck Martinez Bat 10.00 25.00
CCBV Bobby Valentine Bat 15.00 40.00
CCBW Billy Williams Jsy 15.00 40.00
CCBBE Buddy Bell Bat 15.00 40.00
CCBBR Bob Brenly Bat 15.00 40.00
CCDB Dusty Baker Bat 15.00 40.00
CCDL Davey Lopes Bat 15.00 40.00
CCDBA Don Baylor Bat 15.00 40.00
CCEH Elrod Hendricks Bat 10.00 25.00
CCEM Eddie Murray Bat 30.00 60.00
CCFW Frank White Bat 15.00 40.00
CCHM Hal McRae Jsy 4.00 10.00
CCJT Joe Torre Jsy 6.00 15.00
CCKG Ken Griffey Sr. Jsy 4.00 10.00
CCLB Larry Bowa Bat 15.00 40.00
CCLP Lance Parrish Bat 15.00 40.00
CCMH Mike Hargrove Bat 15.00 40.00
CCMS Mike Scioscia Bat 15.00 40.00
CCMW Mookie Wilson Bat 15.00 40.00
CCPG Phil Garner Bat 15.00 40.00
CCPM Paul Molitor Bat 15.00 40.00
CCTP Tony Perez Jsy 4.00 10.00
CCWR Willie Randolph Bat 15.00 40.00

2002 Topps Draft Picks

This 10-card set was distributed in two separate cello-wrapped five-card packets. Cards 1-5 were distributed in late August, 2002 as a bonus in green-boxed 2002 Topps retail factory sets. Cards 6-10 were distributed in November, 2002 within 2002 Topps Holiday factory sets. The cards are designed in the same manner as the Draft Picks and Prospects subsets from the basic 2002 Topps set and feature a selection of players chosen in the 2002 MLB Draft.

COMPLETE SET (10) 15.00 40.00
COMP.SERIES 1 SET (5) 6.00 15.00
COMP.SERIES 2 SET (5) 10.00 25.00
1 Scott Moore 2.00 5.00
2 Val Majewski 1.50 4.00
3 Brian Slocum 1.50 4.00
4 Chris Gruler 1.50 4.00
5 Mark Schramek 1.50 4.00
6 Joe Saunders 3.00 8.00
7 Jeff Francis 3.00 8.00
8 Royce Ring 1.50 4.00
9 Greg Miller 1.50 4.00
10 Brandon Weeden 1.50 4.00

2002 Topps East Meets West

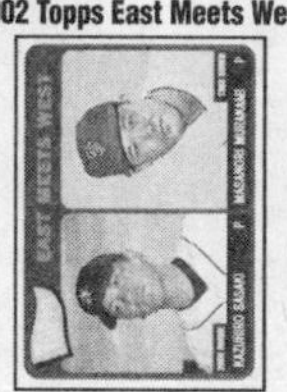

Issued at a rate of one in 24, these eight cards feature Masanori Murakami along with eight other Japanese players who have also played in the major leagues.

COMPLETE SET (8) 6.00 15.00
EWHI Hideki Irabu .75 2.00
Masanori Murakami
EWHN Hideo Nomo .75 2.00
Masanori Murakami
EWKS Kazuhiro Sasaki .75 2.00
Masanori Murakami
EWMS Mac Suzuki .75 2.00
Masanori Murakami
EWMY Masato Yoshii .75 2.00
Masanori Murakami
EWSH S. Hasagawa .75 2.00
Masanori Murakami
EWTO Tomo Ohka .75 2.00
Masanori Murakami
EWTS Tsuyoshi Shinjo .75 2.00
Masanori Murakami

2002 Topps East Meets West Relics

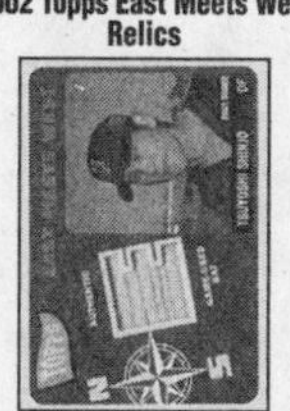

Inserted in packs at different odds depending on whether it is a bat or jersey card, these three cards feature game-used relics from Japanese born players.

SR1 BAT 1:12296 H,1:3380 HTA,1:9606 R
SER.1 JSY 1:3419 H, 1:939 HTA, 1:2685 R
EWRHN Hideo Nomo Jsy 20.00 50.00
EWRKS K. Sasaki Jsy 10.00 25.00
EWRTS T. Shinjo Bat 10.00 25.00

2002 Topps Ebbets Field Seat Relics

Inserted at a rate of one in 9,116 hobby packs, one in 2516 HTA packs and one in 7,222 retail packs, these nine cards feature not only the player but a slice of a seat used at Brooklyn's Ebbetts Field.

EFRAP Andy Pafko 75.00 150.00
EFRBC Billy Cox 200.00 300.00
EFRCF Carl Furillo 75.00 150.00

EFRDS Duke Snider 150.00 250.00
EFRGH Gil Hodges 150.00 250.00
EFRJB Joe Black 75.00 150.00
EFRJR Jackie Robinson 200.00 300.00
EFRRC Roy Campanella 200.00 300.00
EFRPWR Pee Wee Reese 200.00 300.00

2002 Topps Ebbets Field/Yankee Stadium Seat Dual Relics

Featuring a slice of a seat from both Ebbetts Field and from Yankee Stadium, these cards feature a selection of leading players from the 1952 World Series paired up with actual pieces of stadium seats taken from the historic Ebbets Field and Yankee Stadium ballparks. The Snider/Berra card was inserted at a rate of one in 86,070 series one hobby packs and the Rizzuto/Pafko card was inserted ata rate of one in 59,511 series two hobby packs. Only 52 copies of each card were produced. Both cards were intended to be hand-numbered (i.e. 1/52, 2/52 etc.) but due to production errors only the Snider/Berra card packed out as such.

RP Phil Rizzuto
Andy Pafko
SB Duke Snider
Yogi Berra

2002 Topps Ebbets Field/Yankee Stadium Seat Dual Relics Autographs

Inserted into first series packs at stated odds of one in 15,670 HTA packs and second series packs at a rate of one in 11,908 HTA packs, these cards feature a stadium seat along with an autograph of both featured players on these cards. Each card was issued to 25 serial numbered sets and due to market scarcity, no pricing is provided. The Rizzuto/Pafko card from series two was seeded into packs as an exchange card with a deadline of April 30th, 2004.

RP Phil Rizzuto
Andy Pafko 2
SB Duke Snider
Yogi Berra 1

2002 Topps Hall of Fame Vintage BuyBacks AutoProofs

In one of the most ambitious efforts put forth by a manufacturer in hobby history, Topps went into the secondary market and bought more than 3,500 vintage Topps cards (including an amazing selection from the 1950's and 1960's) featuring almost two dozen Hall of Famers (including stars such as Nolan Ryan, Yogi Berra and Carl Yastrzemski) for this far-reaching AutoProofs promotion. In most cases, 100 count lots of each vintage card were used (a staggering figure considering the scarcity of many of the 1950's and 1960's cards) with a few of the more common cards from the early 1980's tallying 200 or 300 count lots. After repurchase, each card was signed by the featured athlete, serial-numbered to a specific amount (exact print runs provided in our checklist) and affixed with a Topps hologram of authenticity on back. The cards were distributed across many 2002 Topps products - starting off with 2002 Topps series one baseball in November, 2001. Odds for finding these cards in packs is as follows: series 1 - 1:2341 hobby and 1:1841 retail; series 2 - 1:2341 hobby, 1:1841 retail.

OC2 Orl Cepeda 82 KM/200 10.00 25.00
SC7 S.Carlton 84 LL V/100 10.00 25.00
SC8 Steve Carlton 85/200 10.00 25.00
BR17 B.Robinson 82 KM/200 15.00 40.00
EW10 Earl Weaver 87/100 10.00 25.00
FJ33 F.Jenkins 84/100 10.00 25.00
GP26 G.Perry 82/100 10.00 25.00
GP29 G.Perry 83/100 10.00 25.00
GP30 G.Perry 83 SV/200 10.00 25.00
RF15 R.Fingers 81/300 10.00 25.00
RF16 R.Fingers 81 LL/100 10.00 25.00
RF18 R.Fingers 82/100 10.00 25.00
RF19 Rollie Fingers 82 IA/200 10.00 25.00
RF21 Rollie Fingers 82 KM/300 10.00 25.00
RF22 Rollie Fingers 83/200 10.00 25.00
RF24 Rollie Fingers 84/200 10.00 25.00
RF27 R.Fingers 85/300 10.00 25.00
RF28 Rollie Fingers 86/100 10.00 25.00
SC10 Steve Carlton 87/200 10.00 25.00

2002 Topps Hobby Masters

Inserted at a rate of one in 25 hobby and one in 16 retail packs, these 20 cards feature some of the leading players in the game.

COMPLETE SET (20) 30.00 80.00
HM1 Mark McGwire 3.00 8.00
HM2 Derek Jeter 3.00 8.00
HM3 Chipper Jones 1.25 3.00
HM4 Roger Clemens 2.50 6.00
HM5 Vladimir Guerrero 1.25 3.00
HM6 Ichiro Suzuki 2.50 6.00
HM7 Todd Helton 1.25 3.00
HM8 Alex Rodriguez 2.00 5.00
HM9 Albert Pujols 2.50 6.00
HM10 Sammy Sosa 1.25 3.00
HM11 Ken Griffey Jr. 2.00 5.00
HM12 Randy Johnson 1.25 3.00
HM13 Nomar Garciaparra 2.00 5.00
HM14 Ivan Rodriguez 1.25 3.00
HM15 Manny Ramirez 1.25 3.00
HM16 Barry Bonds 3.00 8.00
HM17 Mike Piazza 2.00 5.00
HM18 Pedro Martinez 1.25 3.00
HM19 Jeff Bagwell 1.25 3.00
HM20 Luis Gonzalez 1.25 3.00

2002 Topps Like Father Like Son Relics

These combination memorabilia cards feature famous baseball families with two generations of fathers and sons. The card designs are each based upon the original Topps design of the father's rookie card season (aka The Boone Family card features a 1973 Topps style to honor the year Bob Boone had his Rookie Card issued). The cards were seeded exclusively into retail packs at a rate of 1:1304.

SER.1 GROUP A ODDS 1:6259 RETAIL
SER.1 GROUP B ODDS 1:6259 RETAIL
SER.1 GROUP C ODDS 1:2235 RETAIL
FSAL Sandy Alomar Sr. Bat 40.00 80.00
Sandy Alomar Jr. Bat
Roberto Alomar Bat
FSBE Yogi Berra Jsy 40.00 80.00
Dale Berra Jsy
FSBON Bobby Bonds Uni 40.00 80.00
Barry Bonds Uni
FSBOO Bob Boone Jsy 40.00 80.00
Aaron Boone Jsy
Bret Boone Bat
FSCR Jose Cruz Sr. 40.00 80.00
Jose Cruz Jr.

2002 Topps Own the Game

Issued at a rate of one in 12 hobby packs and one in eight retail packs, these 30 cards feature players who are among the league leaders for their position.

COMPLETE SET (30) 15.00 40.00
OG1 Moises Alou .40 1.00
OG2 Roberto Alomar .60 1.50
OG3 Luis Gonzalez .40 1.00
OG4 Bret Boone .40 1.00
OG5 Barry Bonds 2.50 6.00
OG6 Jim Thome .60 1.50
OG7 Jimmy Rollins .40 1.00
OG8 Cristian Guzman .40 1.00
OG9 Lance Berkman .40 1.00
OG10 Mike Sweeney .40 1.00
OG11 Rich Aurilia .40 1.00
OG12 Ichiro Suzuki 2.00 5.00
OG13 Luis Gonzalez .40 1.00
OG14 Ichiro Suzuki 2.00 5.00
OG15 Jimmy Rollins .40 1.00
OG16 Roger Cedeno .40 1.00
OG17 Barry Bonds 2.50 6.00
OG18 Jim Thome .60 1.50
OG19 Curt Schilling .40 1.00
OG20 Roger Clemens 2.00 5.00
OG21 Curt Schilling .40 1.00
OG22 Brad Radke .40 1.00
OG23 Greg Maddux 1.50 4.00
OG24 Mark Mulder .40 1.00
OG25 Jeff Shaw .40 1.00
OG26 Mariano Rivera 1.00 2.50
OG27 Randy Johnson 1.00 2.50
OG28 Pedro Martinez .60 1.50
OG29 John Burkett .40 1.00
OG30 Tim Hudson .40 1.00

2002 Topps Prime Cuts Autograph Relics

Inserted into first series packs at a rate of one in 88,678 hobby and one in 24,624 HTA and second series packs at one in 8927 hobby and one in 2360 HTA packs, these eight cards feature both a memorabilia relic from the player's career as well as their autograph. Cards from series one were issued to a stated print run of 60 serial numbered sets while cards from series two were issued to a stated print run of 50 serial numbered sets. We have notated next to the players name which series the card was issued in.

NO PRICING DUE TO SCARCITY
PCAAE Alex Escobar S2
PCABB Barry Bonds S1
PCAJH Josh Hamilton S2
PCANJ Nick Johnson S2
PCATH Toby Hall S2
PCAWB Wilson Betemit S2
PCAXN Xavier Nady S2
PCACPE Carlos Pena S2

2002 Topps Prime Cuts Barrel Relics

Inserted in second series packs at a rate of one in 7824 hobby packs and one in 2063 HTA packs, these eight cards feature a piece from the selected player bat barrel. These cards were issued to a stated print run of 50 serial numbered sets.

NO PRICING DUE TO SCARCITY
PCAAD Adam Dunn
PCAAG Alexis Gomez
PCAAR Aaron Rowand
PCACP Corey Patterson
PCAJC Joe Crede
PCAMG Marcus Giles
PCARS Ruben Salazar
PCASB Sean Burroughs

2002 Topps Prime Cuts Pine Tar Relics

Inserted in packs at stated odds of one in 4,420 hobby packs and one in 1214 HTA packs for first series packs and one in 1043 hobby and one in 275 HTA packs for second series packs, these 20 cards feature pieces from the pine tar section of the player's bat. We have notated which series the player was issued in next to his name in our checklist. These cards have a stated print run of 200 serial numbered sets.

PCPAD Adam Dunn 2 20.00 50.00
PCPAE Alex Escobar 2 20.00 50.00
PCPAG Alexis Gomez 2 20.00 50.00
PCPAP Albert Pujols 1 40.00 80.00
PCPAR Aaron Rowand 2 20.00 50.00
PCPBB Barry Bonds 1 40.00 80.00
PCPCP Corey Patterson 2 20.00 50.00
PCPJC Joe Crede 2 20.00 50.00
PCPJH Josh Hamilton 2 50.00 100.00
PCPLG Luis Gonzalez 1 20.00 50.00
PCPMG Marcus Giles 2 20.00 50.00
PCPNJ Nick Johnson 2 20.00 50.00
PCPRS Ruben Salazar 2 20.00 50.00
PCPSB Sean Burroughs 2 20.00 50.00
PCPTG Tony Gwynn 1 30.00 60.00
PCPTH Todd Helton 1 20.00 50.00
PCPTH Toby Hall 2 20.00 50.00
PCPWB Wilson Betemit 2 20.00 50.00
PCPXN Xavier Nady 2 20.00 50.00
PCPCPE Carlos Pena 2 20.00 50.00

2002 Topps Prime Cuts Trademark Relics

Issued in first series packs at a rate of one in 8,868 hobby and one in 2428 HTA packs and second series packs at a rate of one in 2087 hobby and one in 549 HTA packs, these cards feature a slice of bat taken from the trademark section of a game used bat. Only 100 serial numbered copies of each card were produced. First and second series distribution information is detailed after the player's name in our set checklist.

PCTAD Adam Dunn 2 30.00 60.00
PCTAE Alex Escobar 2 30.00 60.00
PCTAG Alexis Gomez 2 30.00 60.00
PCTAP Albert Pujols 1 60.00 120.00
PCTAR Aaron Rowand 2 30.00 60.00
PCTBB Barry Bonds 1 60.00 120.00
PCTCP Corey Patterson 2 30.00 60.00
PCTJC Joe Crede 2 30.00 60.00
PCTJH Josh Hamilton 2 60.00 120.00
PCTLG Luis Gonzalez 1 30.00 60.00
PCTMG Marcus Giles 2 30.00 60.00
PCTNJ Nick Johnson 2 30.00 60.00
PCTRS Ruben Salazar 2 30.00 60.00

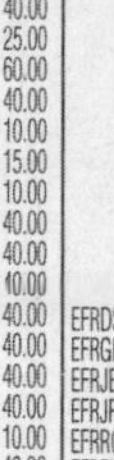

PCTSB Sean Burroughs 2 30.00 60.00
PCTTG Tony Gwynn 1 50.00 100.00
PCTTH Todd Helton 1 40.00 80.00
PCTTH Toby Hall 2 30.00 60.00
PCTWB Wilson Betemit 2 30.00 60.00
PCTXN Xavier Nady 2 30.00 60.00
PCTCPE Carlos Pena 2 30.00 60.00

2002 Topps Ring Masters

Issued at a rate of one in 25 hobby packs and one in 16 retail packs, these 10 cards feature players who have earned World Series rings in their career.

COMPLETE SET (10) 10.00 25.00
RM1 Derek Jeter 2.00 5.00
RM2 Mark McGwire 2.00 5.00
RM3 Mariano Rivera .75 2.00
RM4 Gary Sheffield .60 1.50
RM5 Al Leiter .60 1.50
RM6 Chipper Jones .75 2.00
RM7 Roger Clemens 1.50 4.00
RM8 Greg Maddux 1.25 3.00
RM9 Roberto Alomar .60 1.50
RM10 Paul O'Neill .60 1.50

2002 Topps Summer School Battery Mates Relics

Issued at a rate of one in 4,4401 hobby packs and one in 3,477 retail packs, these two cards feature a pitcher and catcher from the same team.

BMLP Al Leiter 15.00 40.00
Mike Piazza
BMML Greg Maddux 15.00 40.00
Javy Lopez

2002 Topps Summer School Heart of the Order Relics

Issued at an overall rate of one in 4,247 hobby packs and one in 3,325 retail packs, these four cards feature relics from three key players from a team's lineup.

SER.1 A 1:8,220 H, 1:2253 HTA, 1:6452 R
SER.1 B 1:8,778 H, 1:2411 HTA, 1:6862 R
HTOARB Bob Abreu 40.00 80.00
Scott Rolen
Pat Burrell A
HTOKBA Jeff Kent 50.00 100.00
Barry Bonds
Rich Aurilia A
HTOOWM Paul O'Neill 40.00 80.00
Bernie Williams
Tino Martinez A
HTOTGA Jim Thome 40.00 80.00
Juan Gonzalez
Roberto Alomar B

2002 Topps Summer School Hit and Run Relics

Issued at an overall rate of one in 4,241 hobby packs and one in 3,325 HTA packs, these three cards feature relics from some of the leading young stars in baseball.

SER.1 A 1:24591 H, 1:6760 HTA, 1:19649 R
SER.1 B 1:12296 H, 1:3380 HTA, 1:9606 R
SER.1 C 1:8788 H, 1:2411 HTA, 1:6862 R
HRRDE Darin Erstad Bat B 6.00 15.00
{UER Name spelled Darrin on front
HRRJD J.Damon Bat A 10.00 25.00
HRRRF R.Furcal Jsy C 6.00 15.00

2002 Topps Summer School Turn Two Relics

Issued at a rate of one in 4,401 hobby packs and one in 3,477 retail packs, these two cards feature relics from two of the best double play combination in baseball's history.

TTRTW Alan Trammell 20.00 50.00
Lou Whitaker
TTRVA Omar Vizquel 20.00 50.00
Roberto Alomar

2002 Topps Summer School Two Bagger Relics

Issued at an overall rate of one in 3,733 hobby packs and one in 2,941 retail packs, these three cards feature game-used relics from leading hitters in the game.

SER.1 A 1:4401 H, 1:1210 HTA, 1:3477 R
SER.1 B 1:24591 H,1:6760 HTA,1:19649 R
2BSR Scott Rolen Jsy A 10.00 25.00
2BTG Tony Gwynn Bat B 15.00 40.00
2BTH Todd Helton Jsy A 10.00 25.00

2002 Topps Yankee Stadium Seat Relics

Inserted into second series packs at a stated rate of one in 579 Hobby, one in 1472 HTA and one in 4313 Retail, these nine cards feature retired Yankee greats along with a piece of a seat used in the originaly Yankee Stadium.

YSRAR Allie Reynolds 60.00 150.00
YSRBM Billy Martin 150.00 250.00
YSRGM Gil McDougald 60.00 150.00
YSRGW Gene Woodling 60.00 150.00
YSRHB Hank Bauer 100.00 200.00
YSRJC Joe Collins 60.00 150.00
YSRJM Johnny Mize 30.00 60.00
YSRPR Phil Rizzuto 150.00 250.00
YSRYB Yogi Berra 150.00 250.00

2002 Topps Traded

This 275 card set was released in October, 2002. These cards were issued in 10 card hobby packs which were issued 24 packs to a box and 12 boxes to a case with an SRP of $3 per pack. In addition, this product was also issued in 35 count HTA packs. Cards numbered 1 to 100 were issued one per pack. Cards from previous traded sets were repurchased by Topps and were issued at a stated rate of one in 24 Hobby and Retail Packs and one in 10 HTA packs. However, there is no way of being able to identify that these cards are anything but original cards as no marking or stamping is on these cards.

COMPLETE SET (275) 100.00 200.00
COMMON CARD (T1-T110) .75 2.00
COMMON CARD (T111-T275) .15 .40
T1 Jeff Weaver .75 2.00
T2 Jay Powell .75 2.00
T3 Alex Gonzalez .75 2.00
T4 Jason Isringhausen .75 2.00
T5 Tyler Houston .75 2.00
T6 Ben Broussard .75 2.00
T7 Chuck Knoblauch .75 2.00
T8 Brian L. Hunter .75 2.00
T9 Dustan Mohr .75 2.00
T10 Eric Hinske .75 2.00
T11 Roger Cedeno .75 2.00
T12 Eddie Perez .75 2.00
T13 Jeromy Burnitz .75 2.00
T14 Bartolo Colon .75 2.00
T15 Rick Helling .75 2.00
T16 Dan Plesac .75 2.00
T17 Scott Strickland .75 2.00
T18 Antonio Alfonseca .75 2.00
T19 Ricky Gutierrez .75 2.00
T20 John Valentin .75 2.00
T21 Raul Mondesi .75 2.00
T22 Ben Davis .75 2.00
T23 Nelson Figueroa .75 2.00
T24 Earl Snyder .75 2.00
T25 Robin Ventura .75 2.00
T26 Jimmy Haynes .75 2.00
T27 Kenny Kelly .75 2.00
T28 Morgan Ensberg .40 1.00
T29 Reggie Sanders .75 2.00
T30 Shigetoshi Hasegawa .75 2.00
T31 Mike Timlin .75 2.00
T32 Russell Branyan .75 2.00
T33 Alan Embree .75 2.00
T34 D'Angelo Jimenez .75 2.00
T35 Kent Mercker .75 2.00
T36 Jesse Orosco .75 2.00
T37 Gregg Zaun .75 2.00
T38 Reggie Taylor .75 2.00
T39 Andres Galarraga .75 2.00
T40 Chris Truby .75 2.00
T41 Bruce Chen .75 2.00
T42 Darren Lewis .75 2.00
T43 Ryan Kohlmeier .75 2.00
T44 John McDonald .75 2.00
T45 Omar Daal .75 2.00
T46 Matt Clement .75 2.00
T47 Glendon Rusch .75 2.00
T48 Chan Ho Park .75 2.00
T49 Benny Agbayani .75 2.00
T50 Juan Gonzalez .75 2.00
T51 Carlos Baerga .75 2.00
T52 Tim Raines .75 2.00
T53 Kevin Appier .75 2.00
T54 Marty Cordova .75 2.00
T55 Jeff D'Amico .75 2.00
T56 Dmitri Young .75 2.00
T57 Roosevelt Brown .75 2.00
T58 Dustin Hermanson .75 2.00
T59 Jose Rijo .75 2.00
T60 Todd Ritchie .75 2.00
T61 Lee Stevens .75 2.00
T62 Placido Polanco .75 2.00
T63 Eric Young .75 2.00
T64 Chuck Finley .75 2.00
T65 Dicky Gonzalez .75 2.00
T66 Jose Macias .75 2.00
T67 Gabe Kapler .75 2.00
T68 Sandy Alomar Jr. .75 2.00
T69 Henry Blanco .75 2.00
T70 Julian Tavarez .75 2.00
T71 Paul Bako .75 2.00
T72 Scott Rolen 1.25 3.00
T73 Brian Jordan .75 2.00
T74 Rickey Henderson 1.50 4.00
T75 Kevin Mench .75 2.00
T76 Hideo Nomo 1.50 4.00
T77 Jeremy Giambi .75 2.00
T78 Brad Fullmer .75 2.00
T79 Carl Everett .75 2.00
T80 David Wells .75 2.00
T81 Aaron Sele .75 2.00
T82 Todd Hollandsworth .75 2.00
T83 Vicente Padilla .75 2.00
T84 Kenny Lofton .75 2.00
T85 Corky Miller .75 2.00
T86 Josh Fogg .75 2.00
T87 Cliff Floyd .75 2.00
T88 Craig Paquette .75 2.00
T89 Jay Payton .75 2.00
T90 Carlos Pena .75 2.00
T91 Juan Encarnacion .75 2.00
T92 Rey Sanchez .75 2.00
T93 Ryan Dempster .75 2.00
T94 Mario Encarnacion .75 2.00
T95 Jorge Julio .75 2.00
T96 John Mabry .75 2.00
T97 Todd Zeile .75 2.00
T98 Johnny Damon Sox 1.25 3.00
T99 Deivi Cruz .75 2.00
T100 Gary Sheffield .75 2.00
T101 Ted Lilly .75 2.00
T102 Todd Van Poppel .75 2.00
T103 Shawn Estes .75 2.00
T104 Cesar Izturis .75 2.00
T105 Ron Coomer .75 2.00
T106 Grady Little MG RC .75 2.00
T107 Jimy Williams MG .75 2.00
T108 Tony Pena MG .75 2.00
T109 Frank Robinson MG 1.25 3.00
T110 Ron Gardenhire MG .75 2.00
T111 Dennis Tankersley .15 .40
T112 Alejandro Cadena RC .15 .40
T113 Justin Reid RC .15 .40
T114 Nate Field RC .15 .40
T115 Rene Reyes RC .15 .40
T116 Nelson Castro RC .15 .40
T117 Miguel Olivo .15 .40
T118 David Espinosa .15 .40
T119 Chris Bootcheck RC .15 .40
T120 Rob Henkel RC .15 .40
T121 Steve Bechler RC .15 .40
T122 Mark Outlaw RC .15 .40
T123 Henry Pichardo RC .15 .40
T124 Michael Floyd RC .15 .40
T125 Richard Lane RC .15 .40
T126 Pete Zamora RC .15 .40
T127 Javier Colina .15 .40
T128 Greg Sain RC .15 .40
T129 Ronnie Merrill .15 .40
T130 Gavin Floyd RC .40 1.00
T131 Josh Bonifay RC .15 .40
T132 Tommy Marx RC .15 .40
T133 Gary Cates Jr. RC .15 .40
T134 Neal Cotts RC .40 1.00
T135 Angel Berroa .15 .40
T136 Elio Serrano RC .15 .40
T137 J.J. Putz RC .20 .50
T138 Ruben Gotay RC .20 .50
T139 Eddie Rogers .15 .40
T140 Wily Mo Pena .15 .40
T141 Tyler Yates RC .15 .40
T142 Colin Young RC .15 .40
T143 Chance Caple .15 .40
T144 Ben Howard RC .15 .40
T145 Ryan Bukvich RC .15 .40
T146 Cliff Bartosh RC .15 .40
T147 Brandon Claussen .15 .40
T148 Cristian Guerrero .15 .40
T149 Derrick Lewis .15 .40
T150 Eric Miller RC .15 .40
T151 Justin Huber RC .30 .75
T152 Adrian Gonzalez .15 .40
T153 Brian West RC .15 .40
T154 Chris Baker RC .15 .40
T155 Drew Henson .15 .40
T156 Scott Hairston RC .20 .50
T157 Jason Simontacchi RC .15 .40
T158 Jason Arnold RC .15 .40
T159 Brandon Phillips .15 .40
T160 Adam Roller RC .15 .40
T161 Scotty Layfield RC .15 .40
T162 Freddie Money RC .15 .40
T163 Noochie Varner RC .15 .40
T164 Terrance Hill RC .15 .40
T165 Jeremy Hill RC .15 .40
T166 Carlos Cabrera RC .15 .40
T167 Jose Morban RC .15 .40
T168 Kevin Frederick RC .15 .40
T169 Mark Teixeira .60 1.50
T170 Brian Rogers .15 .40
T171 Anastacio Martinez RC .15 .40
T172 Bobby Jenks RC .60 1.50
T173 David Gil RC .15 .40
T174 Andres Torres .15 .40
T175 James Barrett RC .15 .40
T176 Jimmy Journell .15 .40
T177 Brett Kay RC .15 .40
T178 Jason Young RC .15 .40
T179 Mark Hamilton RC .15 .40
T180 Jose Bautista RC 3.00 8.00
T181 Blake McGinley RC .15 .40
T182 Ryan Mottl RC .15 .40
T183 Jeff Austin RC .15 .40
T184 Xavier Nady .15 .40
T185 Kyle Kane RC .15 .40
T186 Travis Foley RC .15 .40
T187 Nathan Kaup RC .15 .40
T188 Eric Cyr .15 .40
T189 Josh Cisneros RC .15 .40
T190 Brad Nelson RC .15 .40
T191 Clint Weibl RC .15 .40
T192 Ron Calloway RC .15 .40
T193 Jung Bong .15 .40
T194 Rolando Viera RC .15 .40
T195 Jason Bulger RC .15 .40
T196 Chone Figgins RC .60 1.50
T197 Jimmy Alvarez RC .15 .40
T198 Joel Crump RC .15 .40
T199 Ryan Doumit RC .25 .60
T200 Demetrius Heath RC .15 .40
T201 John Ennis RC .15 .40
T202 Doug Sessions RC .15 .40
T203 Clinton Hosford RC .15 .40
T204 Chris Narveson RC .15 .40
T205 Ross Peeples RC .15 .40
T206 Alex Requena RC .15 .40
T207 Matt Erickson RC .15 .40
T208 Brian Forystek RC .15 .40
T209 Dewon Brazelton .15 .40
T210 Nathan Haynes .15 .40
T211 Jack Cust .15 .40
T212 Jesse Foppert RC .20 .50
T213 Jesus Cota RC .15 .40
T214 Juan M. Gonzalez RC .15 .40
T215 Tim Kalita RC .15 .40
T216 Manny Delcarmen RC .20 .50
T217 Jim Kavourias RC .15 .40
T218 C.J. Wilson RC .50 1.25
T219 Edwin Yan RC .15 .40
T220 Andy Van Hekken .15 .40
T221 Michael Cuddyer .15 .40
T222 Jeff Verplancke RC .15 .40
T223 Mike Wilson RC .15 .40
T224 Corwin Malone RC .15 .40
T225 Chris Snelling RC .25 .60
T226 Joe Rogers RC .15 .40
T227 Jason Bay 1.50 4.00
T228 Ezequiel Astacio RC .15 .40
T229 Joey Hammond RC .15 .40
T230 Chris Duffy RC .20 .50
T231 Mark Prior .60 1.50
T232 Hansel Izquierdo RC .15 .40
T233 Franklyn German RC .15 .40
T234 Alexis Gomez .15 .40
T235 Jorge Padilla RC .15 .40
T236 Ryan Snare RC .15 .40
T237 Deivis Santos .15 .40
T238 Taggert Bozied RC .20 .50
T239 Mike Peeples RC .15 .40
T240 Ronald Acuna RC .15 .40
T241 Koyie Hill .15 .40
T242 Garrett Guzman RC .15 .40
T243 Ryan Church RC .40 1.00
T244 Tony Fontana RC .15 .40
T245 Keto Anderson RC .15 .40
T246 Brad Bouras RC .15 .40
T247 Jason Dubois RC .20 .50
T248 Angel Guzman RC .30 .75
T249 Joel Hanrahan RC .15 .40
T250 Joe Jiannetti RC .15 .40
T251 Sean Pierce RC .15 .40
T252 Jake Mauer RC .15 .40
T253 Marshall McDougall RC .15 .40
T254 Edwin Almonte RC .15 .40
T255 Shawn Riggans RC .15 .40
T256 Steven Shell RC .15 .40
T257 Kevin Hooper RC .15 .40
T258 Michael Frick RC .15 .40
T259 Travis Chapman RC .15 .40
T260 Tim Hummel RC .15 .40
T261 Adam Morrissey RC .15 .40
T262 Dontrelle Willis RC 1.25 3.00
T263 Justin Sherrod RC .15 .40
T264 Gerald Smiley RC .15 .40
T265 Tony Miller RC .15 .40
T266 Nolan Ryan WW 1.00 2.50
T267 Reggie Jackson WW .25 .60
T268 Steve Garvey WW .15 .40
T269 Wade Boggs WW .25 .60
T270 Sammy Sosa WW .40 1.00
T271 Curt Schilling WW .15 .40
T272 Mark Grace WW .25 .60
T273 Jason Giambi WW .15 .40
T274 Ken Griffey Jr. WW .60 1.50
T275 Roberto Alomar WW .25 .60

2002 Topps Traded Gold

Inserted at a stated rate of one in three hobby and retail and one per HTA pack, this is a paralle of the 2002 Topps Traded set. Each card has "gold" borders and were issued to a stated print run of 2002 serial numbered sets.

*GOLD 1-110: .6X TO 1.5X BASIC
*GOLD 111-275: 2.5X TO 6X BASIC
*GOLD RC'S 111-275: 1.5X TO 4X BASIC RC'S
T262 Dontrelle Willis 3.00 8.00

2002 Topps Traded Farewell Relic

Inserted at a stated rate of one in 590 Hobby, one in 169 HTA and in 595 Retail packs, this one card set features one-time MVP Jose Canseco along with a game-used bat piece from his career. Canseco had announced his retirement during the 2002 season in an failed attempt to return to the majors.

FWJC Jose Canseco Bat 6.00 15.00

2002 Topps Traded Hall of Fame Relic

Inserted at a stated rate of one in 1533 Hobby Packs, one in 439 HTA packs and one in 1574 Retail packs, this one card set features Ozzie Smith along with a game-used bat piece from his career. Ozzie Smith was inducted into the HOF in 2002.

HOFOS Ozzie Smith Bat 12.50 30.00

2002 Topps Traded Signature Moves

Inserted at overall odds of one in 91 Hobby or Retail packs and one in 26 HTA packs, these 26 cards feature a mix of basically prospects along with a couple of stars who moved to new teams for 2002 and signed these cards for inclusion in the Topps Traded set. Since there were nine different insertion odds for these cards we have notated both the insertion odds for each group along with which group the player belong to.

A ODDS 1:15,292 H, 1:4288 HTA, 1:22,032 R
B ODDS 1:3846 H, 1:1105 HTA, 1:3840 R
C ODDS 1:6147 H, 1:1778 HTA, 1:6418 R
D ODDS 1:1917 H, 1:548 HTA, 1:1953 R
E ODDS 1:341 H, 1:97 HTA, 1:342 R
F ODDS 1:2247 H, 1:645 HTA, 1:2261 R
G ODDS 1:568 H, 1:162 HTA, 1:571 R
GROUP H ODDS 1:256 H/R, 1:73 HTA
I ODDS 1:1023 H, 1:293 HTA, 1:1025 R
OVERALL ODDS 1:91 HOB/RET, 1:26 HTA
AC Antoine Cameron D 4.00 10.00
AM Andy Morales H 3.00 8.00
BB Boof Bonser E 4.00 10.00
BC Brandon Claussen E 4.00 10.00
CS Chris Smith G 3.00 8.00
CU Chase Utley E 75.00 150.00
CW Corwin Malone H 3.00 8.00
DT Dennis Tankersley F 4.00 10.00
FJ Forrest Johnson E 4.00 10.00
JD Johnny Damon Sox B 15.00 40.00
JD Jeff DaVanon I 3.00 8.00
JM Jake Mauer G 4.00 10.00
JM Justin Morneau H 10.00 25.00
JP Juan Pena E 4.00 10.00
JS Juan Silvestre D 4.00 10.00
JW Justin Wayne E 4.00 10.00
KI Kazuhisa Ishii A 15.00 40.00
MC Matt Cooper E 4.00 10.00
MO Moises Alou B 6.00 15.00
MT Marcus Thames G 5.00 12.00
RA Roberto Alomar C 30.00 60.00
RH Ryan Hannaman E 4.00 10.00
RM Ramon Moreta H 4.00 10.00
TB Tony Blanco E 4.00 10.00
TL Todd Linden H 4.00 10.00
VD Victor Diaz H 4.00 10.00

2002 Topps Traded Tools of the Trade Dual Relics

Inserted at overall odds of one in 539 Hobby, one in 155 HTA and one in 542 Retail packs, these three cards feature two game-used relics from the featured players. As these cards were issued in different insertion ratios, we have notated that information as to the player's specific group next to their name in our checklist.

A ODDS 1:3407 H, 1:972 HTA, 1:3672 R
B ODDS 1:639 H, 1:183 HTA, 1:642 R
DTRRCP Chan Ho Park Jsy-Jsy B 6.00 15.00
DTRRHN Hideo Nomo Jsy-Jsy A 15.00 40.00
DTRRMO Moises Alou Jsy-Jsy B 6.00 15.00

2002 Topps Traded Tools of the Trade Relics

Inserted at overall odds for bats of one in 34 Hobby and Retail and one in 10 HTA and for jerseys at one in 426 Hobby, one in 122 HTA and one in 427 retail, these 35 cards feature players who switched teams for the 2002 season along with a game-used memorabilia piece. We have notated in our checklist what type of memorabilia piece on each player's card. In addition, since the bat cards were inserted at three different odds, we have notated that information as to the card's group next to their name in our checklist.

BAT A 1:1203 H, 1:344 HTA, 1:1224 R
BAT B 1:1807 H, 1:517 HTA, 1:1836 R
BAT C 1:35 H/R, 1:10 HTA
AB Roberto Alomar Bat C 4.00 10.00
AG Andres Galarraga Bat C 3.00 8.00
BF Brad Fullmer Bat C 3.00 8.00
BJ Brian Jordan Bat C 3.00 8.00
CE Carl Everett Bat C 3.00 8.00
CK Chuck Knoblauch Bat C 3.00 8.00
CP Carlos Pena Bat A 4.00 10.00
DB David Bell Bat C 3.00 8.00
DJ Dave Justice Bat C 3.00 8.00
EY Eric Young Bat C 3.00 8.00
GS Gary Sheffield Bat C 3.00 8.00
HB Rickey Henderson Bat C 4.00 10.00
JBU Jeromy Burnitz Bat C 3.00 8.00
JCI Jeff Cirillo Bat B 3.00 8.00
JDB Johnny Damon Sox Bat C 4.00 10.00
JG Juan Gonzalez Jsy 3.00 8.00
JP Josh Phelps Jsy 3.00 8.00
JV John Vander Wal Bat C 3.00 8.00
KL Kenny Lofton Bat C 3.00 8.00
MA Moises Alou Bat C 3.00 8.00
MLB Matt Lawton Bat C 3.00 8.00
MT Michael Tucker Bat C 3.00 8.00
MVB Mo Vaughn Bat C 3.00 8.00
MVJ Mo Vaughn Jsy 3.00 8.00
PP Placido Polanco Bat A 4.00 10.00
RS Reggie Sanders Bat C 3.00 8.00
RV Robin Ventura Bat C 3.00 8.00
RW Rondell White Bat C 3.00 8.00
SI Ruben Sierra Bat C 3.00 8.00
SR Scott Rolen Bat A 10.00 25.00
TC Tony Clark Bat C 3.00 8.00
TM Tino Martinez Bat C 4.00 10.00
TR Tim Raines Bat C 3.00 8.00
TS Tsuyoshi Shinjo Bat C 3.00 8.00
VC Vinny Castilla Bat C 3.00 8.00

2003 Topps

The first series of 366 cards was released in November, 2002. The second series of 354 cards were released in April, 2003. The set was issued either in 10 card hobby packs or 36 card HTA packs. The regular packs were issued 36 packs to a box and 12 boxes to a case with an SRP of $1.59. The HTA packs were issued 12 packs to a box and eight boxes to a case with an SRP of $5 per pack. The following subsets were issued in the first series: 262 through 291 basically featured current managers, cards numbered 292 through 321 featured players in their first year on a Topps card, cards numbered 322 through 331 featured two players who were expected to be major rookies during the 2003 season, cards numbered 332 through 336 honored players who achieved major feats during 2002, cards numbered 337 through 352 featured league leaders, cards 354 and 355 had post season highlights and cards 356 through 367 honored the best players in the American League. Second series subsets included Team Checklists (630-659); Draft Picks (660-674); Prospects (675-684); Award Winners (685-708) All-Stars (709-719) and World Series (720-721). As has been Topps tradition since 1997, there was no card number 7 issued in honor of the memory of Mickey Mantle.

COMPLETE SET (720) 40.00 80.00
COMPLETE SERIES 1 (366) 20.00 40.00
COMPLETE SERIES 2 (354) 20.00 40.00
COMMON CARD (1-6/8-721) .07 .20
COMMON (292-331/660-684) .20 .50
1 Alex Rodriguez .30 .75
2 Dan Wilson .07 .20
3 Jimmy Rollins .07 .20
4 Jermaine Dye .07 .20
5 Steve Karsay .07 .20
6 Timo Perez .07 .20
8 Jose Vidro .07 .20
9 Eddie Guardado .07 .20
10 Mark Prior .10 .30
11 Curt Schilling .07 .20
12 Dennis Cook .07 .20
13 Andruw Jones .10 .30
14 David Segui .07 .20
15 Trot Nixon .07 .20
16 Kerry Wood .07 .20
17 Magglio Ordonez .07 .20
18 Jason LaRue .07 .20
19 Danys Baez .07 .20
20 Todd Helton .10 .30
21 Denny Neagle .07 .20
22 Dave Mlicki .07 .20
23 Roberto Hernandez .07 .20
24 Odalis Perez .07 .20
25 Nick Neugebauer .07 .20
26 David Ortiz .20 .50
27 Andres Galarraga .07 .20
28 Edgardo Alfonzo .07 .20
29 Chad Bradford .07 .20
30 Jason Giambi .07 .20
31 Brian Giles .07 .20
32 Deivi Cruz .07 .20
33 Robb Nen .07 .20
34 Jeff Nelson .07 .20
35 Edgar Renteria .07 .20
36 Aubrey Huff .07 .20
37 Brandon Duckworth .07 .20
38 Juan Gonzalez .07 .20
39 Sidney Ponson .07 .20
40 Eric Hinske .07 .20
41 Kevin Appier .07 .20
42 Danny Bautista .07 .20
43 Javier Lopez .07 .20
44 Jeff Conine .07 .20
45 Carlos Baerga .07 .20
46 Ugueth Urbina .07 .20
47 Mark Buehrle .07 .20
48 Aaron Boone .07 .20
49 Jason Simontacchi .07 .20
50 Sammy Sosa .20 .50
51 Jose Jimenez .07 .20
52 Bobby Higginson .07 .20
53 Luis Castillo .07 .20
54 Orlando Merced .07 .20
55 Brian Jordan .07 .20
56 Eric Young .07 .20
57 Bobby Kielty .07 .20
58 Luis Rivas .07 .20
59 Brad Wilkerson .07 .20
60 Roberto Alomar .10 .30
61 Roger Clemens .40 1.00
62 Scott Hatteberg .07 .20
63 Andy Ashby .07 .20
64 Mike Williams .07 .20
65 Ron Gant .07 .20
66 Benito Santiago .07 .20
67 Bret Boone .07 .20
68 Matt Morris .07 .20
69 Troy Glaus .07 .20
70 Austin Kearns .07 .20
71 Jim Thome .10 .30
72 Rickey Henderson .20 .50
73 Luis Gonzalez .07 .20
74 Brad Fullmer .07 .20
75 Herbert Perry .07 .20
76 Randy Wolf .07 .20
77 Miguel Tejada .07 .20
78 Jimmy Anderson .07 .20
79 Ramon Martinez .07 .20
80 Ivan Rodriguez .10 .30
81 John Flaherty .07 .20
82 Shannon Stewart .07 .20
83 Orlando Palmeiro .07 .20
84 Rafael Furcal .07 .20
85 Kenny Rogers .07 .20
86 Terry Adams .07 .20
87 Mo Vaughn .07 .20
88 Jose Cruz Jr. .07 .20
89 Mike Matheny .07 .20
90 Alfonso Soriano .07 .20
91 Orlando Cabrera .07 .20
92 Jeffrey Hammonds .07 .20
93 Hideo Nomo .20 .50
94 Carlos Febles .07 .20
95 Billy Wagner .07 .20
96 Alex Gonzalez .07 .20
97 Todd Zeile .07 .20
98 Omar Vizquel .10 .30
99 Jose Rijo .07 .20
100 Ichiro Suzuki .40 1.00
101 Steve Cox .07 .20
102 Hideki Irabu .07 .20
103 Roy Halladay .07 .20
104 David Eckstein .07 .20
105 Greg Maddux .30 .75
106 Jay Gibbons .07 .20
107 Travis Driskill .07 .20
108 Fred McGriff .10 .30
109 Frank Thomas .20 .50
110 Shawn Green .07 .20
111 Ruben Quevedo .07 .20
112 Jacque Jones .07 .20
113 Tomo Ohka .07 .20
114 Joe McEwing .07 .20
115 Ramiro Mendoza .07 .20
116 Mark Mulder .07 .20
117 Mike Lieberthal .07 .20
118 Jack Wilson .07 .20
119 Randall Simon .07 .20
120 Bernie Williams .10 .30
121 Marvin Benard .07 .20
122 Jamie Moyer .07 .20
123 Andy Benes .07 .20
124 Tino Martinez .10 .30
125 Esteban Yan .07 .20
126 Juan Uribe .07 .20
127 Jason Isringhausen .07 .20
128 Chris Carpenter .07 .20
129 Mike Cameron .07 .20
130 Gary Sheffield .07 .20
131 Geronimo Gil .07 .20

132 Brian Daubach .07 .20
133 Corey Patterson .07 .20
134 Aaron Rowand .07 .20
135 Chris Reitsma .07 .20
136 Bob Wickman .07 .20
137 Cesar Izturis .07 .20
138 Jason Jennings .07 .20
139 Brandon Inge .07 .20
140 Larry Walker .07 .20
141 Ramon Santiago .07 .20
142 Vladimir Nunez .07 .20
143 Jose Vizcaino .07 .20
144 Mark Quinn .07 .20
145 Michael Tucker .07 .20
146 Darren Dreifort .07 .20
147 Ben Sheets .07 .20
148 Corey Koskie .07 .20
149 Tony Armas Jr. .07 .20
150 Kazuhisa Ishii .07 .20
151 Al Leiter .07 .20
152 Steve Trachsel .07 .20
153 Mike Stanton .07 .20
154 David Justice .07 .20
155 Marlon Anderson .07 .20
156 Jason Kendall .07 .20
157 Brian Lawrence .07 .20
158 J.T. Snow .07 .20
159 Edgar Martinez .10 .30
160 Pat Burrell .07 .20
161 Kerry Robinson .07 .20
162 Greg Vaughn .07 .20
163 Carl Everett .07 .20
164 Vernon Wells .07 .20
165 Jose Mesa .07 .20
166 Troy Percival .07 .20
167 Erubiel Durazo .07 .20
168 Jason Marquis .07 .20
169 Jerry Hairston Jr. .07 .20
170 Vladimir Guerrero .20 .50
171 Byung-Hyun Kim .07 .20
172 Marcus Giles .07 .20
173 Johnny Damon .10 .30
174 Jon Lieber .07 .20
175 Terrence Long .07 .20
176 Sean Casey .07 .20
177 Adam Dunn .07 .20
178 Juan Pierre .07 .20
179 Wendell Magee .07 .20
180 Barry Zito .07 .20
181 Aramis Ramirez .07 .20
182 Pokey Reese .07 .20
183 Jeff Kent .07 .20
184 Russ Ortiz .07 .20
185 Ruben Sierra .07 .20
186 Brent Abernathy .07 .20
187 Ismael Valdes UER .07 .20
Card does not include 2002 Rangers stats
188 Tom Wilson .07 .20
189 Craig Counsell .07 .20
190 Mike Mussina .10 .30
191 Ramon Hernandez .07 .20
192 Adam Kennedy .07 .20
193 Tony Womack .07 .20
194 Wes Helms .07 .20
195 Tony Batista .07 .20
196 Rolando Arrojo .07 .20
197 Kyle Farnsworth .07 .20
198 Gary Bennett .07 .20
199 Scott Sullivan .07 .20
200 Albert Pujols .40 1.00
201 Kirk Rueter .07 .20
202 Phil Nevin .07 .20
203 Kip Wells .07 .20
204 Ron Coomer .07 .20
205 Jeromy Burnitz .07 .20
206 Kyle Lohse .07 .20
207 Mike DeJean .07 .20
208 Paul Lo Duca .07 .20
209 Carlos Beltran .07 .20
210 Roy Oswalt .07 .20
211 Mike Lowell .07 .20
212 Robert Fick .07 .20
213 Todd Jones .07 .20
214 C.C. Sabathia .07 .20
215 Danny Graves .07 .20
216 Todd Hundley .07 .20
217 Tim Wakefield .07 .20
218 Derek Lowe .07 .20
219 Kevin Millwood .07 .20
220 Jorge Posada .10 .30
221 Bobby J. Jones .07 .20
222 Carlos Guillen .07 .20
223 Fernando Vina .07 .20
224 Ryan Rupe .07 .20
225 Kelvim Escobar .07 .20
226 Ramon Ortiz .07 .20
227 Junior Spivey .07 .20
228 Juan Cruz .07 .20
229 Melvin Mora .07 .20
230 Lance Berkman .07 .20
231 Brent Butler .07 .20
232 Shane Halter .07 .20
233 Derrek Lee .10 .30
234 Matt Lawton .07 .20
235 Chuck Knoblauch .07 .20
236 Eric Gagne .07 .20
237 Alex Sanchez .07 .20
238 Denny Hocking .07 .20
239 Eric Milton .07 .20
240 Rey Ordonez .07 .20
241 Orlando Hernandez .07 .20
242 Robert Person .07 .20
243 Sean Burroughs .07 .20
244 Jeff Cirillo .07 .20
245 Mike Lamb .07 .20
246 Jose Valentin .07 .20
247 Ellis Burks .07 .20
248 Shawn Chacon .07 .20
249 Josh Beckett .07 .20
250 Nomar Garciaparra .30 .75
251 Craig Biggio .10 .30
252 Joe Randa .07 .20
253 Mark Grudzielanek .07 .20
254 Glendon Rusch .07 .20
255 Michael Barrett .07 .20
256 Omar Daal .07 .20
257 Elmer Dessens .07 .20
258 Wade Miller .07 .20
259 Adrian Beltre .07 .20
260 Vicente Padilla .07 .20
261 Kazuhiro Sasaki .07 .20
262 Mike Scioscia MG .07 .20
263 Bobby Cox MG .07 .20
264 Mike Hargrove MG .07 .20
265 Grady Little MG RC .07 .20
266 Alex Gonzalez UER .07 .20
2002 stats are listed as all zero's
267 Jerry Manuel MG .07 .20
268 Bob Boone MG .07 .20
269 Joel Skinner MG .07 .20
270 Clint Hurdle MG .07 .20
271 Miguel Batista UER .07 .20
All 2002 Stats are 0's
272 Bob Brenly MG .07 .20
273 Jeff Torborg MG .07 .20
274 Jimy Williams MG UER .07 .20
Career managerial record is wrong
275 Tony Pena MG .07 .20
276 Jim Tracy MG .07 .20
277 Jerry Royster MG .07 .20
278 Ron Gardenhire MG .07 .20
279 Frank Robinson MG .10 .30
280 John Halama .07 .20
281 Joe Torre MG .10 .30
282 Art Howe MG .07 .20
283 Larry Bowa MG .07 .20
284 Lloyd McClendon MG .07 .20
285 Bruce Bochy MG .07 .20
286 Dusty Baker MG .07 .20
287 Lou Piniella MG .07 .20
288 Tony LaRussa MG .07 .20
289 Todd Walker .07 .20
290 Jerry Narron MG .07 .20
291 Carlos Tosca MG .07 .20
292 Chris Duncan FY RC 1.25 3.00
293 Franklin Gutierrez FY RC .40 1.00
294 Adam LaRoche FY .20 .50
295 Manuel Ramirez FY RC .20 .50
296 Il Kim FY RC .20 .50
297 Wayne Lydon FY RC .20 .50
298 Daryl Clark FY RC .20 .50
299 Sean Pierce FY .20 .50
300 Andy Marte FY RC 1.25 3.00
301 Matthew Peterson FY RC .20 .50
302 Gonzalo Lopez FY RC .20 .50
303 Bernie Castro FY RC .20 .50
304 Cliff Lee FY 1.25 3.00
305 Jason Perry FY RC .20 .50
306 Jaime Bubela FY RC .20 .50
307 Alexis Rios FY .40 1.00
308 Brendan Harris FY RC .20 .50
309 R.Nivar-Martinez FY RC .20 .50
310 Terry Tiffee FY RC .20 .50
311 Kevin Youkilis FY RC .75 2.00
312 Ruddy Lugo FY RC .20 .50
313 C.J. Wilson FY 1.00 2.50
314 Mike McNutt FY RC .20 .50
315 Jeff Clark FY RC .20 .50
316 Mark Malaska FY RC .20 .50
317 Doug Waechter FY RC .20 .50
318 Derell McCall FY RC .20 .50
319 Scott Tyler FY RC .20 .50
320 Craig Brazell FY RC .20 .50
321 Walter Young FY .20 .50
322 Marlon Byrd .20 .50
Jorge Padilla FS
323 Chris Snelling .20 .50
Shin-Soo Choo FS
324 Hank Blalock .20 .50
Mark Teixeira FS
325 Josh Hamilton .40 1.00
Carl Crawford FS
326 Orlando Hudson .20 .50
Josh Phelps FS
327 Jack Cust .20 .50
Rene Reyes FS
328 Angel Berroa .20 .50
Alexis Gomez FS
329 Michael Cuddyer .20 .50
Michael Restovich FS
330 Juan Rivera .20 .50
Marcus Thames FS
331 Brandon Puffer .20 .50
Jung Bong FS
332 Mike Cameron SH .07 .20
333 Shawn Green SH .07 .20
334 Oakland A's SH .07 .20
335 Jason Giambi SH .07 .20
336 Derek Lowe SH .07 .20
337 Manny Ramirez .10 .30
Mike Sweeney
Bernie Williams LL
338 Alfonso Soriano .07 .20
Alex Rodriguez
Derek Jeter LL
339 Alex Rodriguez .10 .30
Jim Thome
Rafael Palmeiro LL
340 Alex Rodriguez .20 .50
Magglio Ordonez
Miguel Tejada LL
341 Pedro Martinez .07 .20
Derek Lowe
Barry Zito LL
342 Pedro Martinez .10 .30
Roger Clemens
Mike Mussina LL
343 Larry Walker .20 .50
Vladimir Guerrero
Todd Helton LL
344 Sammy Sosa .20 .50
Albert Pujols
Shawn Green LL
345 Sammy Sosa .20 .50
Lance Berkman
Shawn Green LL
346 Lance Berkman .07 .20
Albert Pujols
Pat Burrell LL
347 Randy Johnson .10 .30
Greg Maddux
Tom Glavine LL
348 Randy Johnson .10 .30
Curt Schilling
Kerry Wood LL
349 Francisco Rodriguez .07 .20
Darin Erstad
Tim Salmon
AL Division Series
350 Minnesota Twins .10 .30
St Louis Cardinals
AL and NL Division Series
351 Anaheim Angels .10 .30
San Francisco Giants
AL and NL Division Series
352 Jim Edmonds .10 .30
Scott Rolen
NL Division Series
353 Adam Kennedy ALCS .07 .20
354 J.T. Snow WS .10 .30
355 David Bell NLCS .10 .30
356 Jason Giambi AS .07 .20
357 Alfonso Soriano AS .07 .20
358 Alex Rodriguez AS .20 .50
359 Eric Chavez AS .07 .20
360 Torii Hunter AS .07 .20
361 Bernie Williams AS .07 .20
362 Garret Anderson AS .07 .20
363 Jorge Posada AS .07 .20
364 Derek Lowe AS .07 .20
365 Barry Zito AS .07 .20
366 Manny Ramirez AS .10 .30
367 Mike Scioscia AS .07 .20
368 Francisco Rodriguez .07 .20
369 Chris Hammond .07 .20
370 Chipper Jones .20 .50
371 Chris Singleton .07 .20
372 Cliff Floyd .07 .20
373 Bobby Hill .07 .20
374 Antonio Osuna .07 .20
375 Barry Larkin .10 .30
376 Charles Nagy .07 .20
377 Denny Stark .07 .20
378 Dean Palmer .07 .20
379 Eric Owens .07 .20
380 Randy Johnson .20 .50
381 Jeff Suppan .07 .20
382 Eric Karros .07 .20
383 Luis Vizcaino .07 .20
384 Johan Santana .30 .75
385 Javier Vazquez .07 .20
386 John Thomson .07 .20
387 Nick Johnson .07 .20
388 Mark Ellis .07 .20
389 Doug Glanville .07 .20
390 Ken Griffey Jr. .30 .75
391 Bubba Trammell .07 .20
392 Livan Hernandez .07 .20
393 Desi Relaford .07 .20
394 Eli Marrero .07 .20
395 Jared Sandberg .07 .20
396 Barry Bonds .50 1.25
397 Esteban Loaiza .07 .20
398 Aaron Sele .07 .20
399 Geoff Blum .07 .20
400 Derek Jeter .50 1.25
401 Eric Byrnes .07 .20
402 Mike Timlin .07 .20
403 Mark Kotsay .07 .20
404 Rich Aurilia .07 .20
405 Joel Pineiro .07 .20
406 Chuck Finley .07 .20
407 Bengie Molina .07 .20
408 Steve Finley .07 .20
409 Julio Franco .07 .20
410 Marty Cordova .07 .20
411 Shea Hillenbrand .07 .20
412 Mark Bellhorn .07 .20
413 Jon Garland .07 .20
414 Reggie Taylor .07 .20
415 Milton Bradley .07 .20
416 Carlos Pena .07 .20
417 Andy Fox .07 .20
418 Brad Ausmus .07 .20
419 Brent Mayne .07 .20
420 Paul Quantrill .07 .20
421 Carlos Delgado .07 .20
422 Kevin Mench .07 .20
423 Joe Kennedy .07 .20
424 Mike Crudale .07 .20
425 Mark McLemore .07 .20
426 Bill Mueller .07 .20
427 Rob Mackowiak .07 .20
428 Ricky Ledee .07 .20
429 Ted Lilly .07 .20
430 Sterling Hitchcock .07 .20
431 Scott Strickland .07 .20
432 Damion Easley .07 .20
433 Torii Hunter .07 .20
434 Brad Radke .07 .20
435 Geoff Jenkins .07 .20
436 Paul Byrd .07 .20
437 Morgan Ensberg .07 .20
438 Mike Maroth .07 .20
439 Mike Hampton .07 .20
440 Adam Hyzdu .07 .20
441 Vance Wilson .07 .20
442 Todd Ritchie .07 .20
443 Tom Gordon .07 .20
444 John Burkett .07 .20
445 Rodrigo Lopez .07 .20
446 Tim Spooneybarger .07 .20
447 Quinton Mccracken .07 .20
448 Tim Salmon .10 .30
449 Jarrod Washburn .07 .20
450 Pedro Martinez .10 .30
451 Dustan Mohr .07 .20
452 Julio Lugo .07 .20
453 Scott Stewart .07 .20
454 Armando Benitez .07 .20
455 Raul Mondesi .07 .20
456 Robin Ventura .07 .20
457 Bobby Abreu .07 .20
458 Josh Fogg .07 .20
459 Ryan Klesko .07 .20
460 Tsuyoshi Shinjo .07 .20
461 Jim Edmonds .07 .20
462 Cliff Politte .07 .20
463 Chan Ho Park .07 .20
464 John Mabry .07 .20
465 Woody Williams .07 .20
466 Jason Michaels .07 .20
467 Scott Schoeneweis .07 .20
468 Brian Anderson .07 .20
469 Brett Tomko .07 .20
470 Scott Erickson .07 .20
471 Kevin Millar Sox .07 .20
472 Danny Wright .07 .20
473 Jason Schmidt .07 .20
474 Scott Williamson .07 .20
475 Einar Diaz .07 .20
476 Jay Payton .07 .20
477 Juan Acevedo .07 .20
478 Ben Grieve .07 .20
479 Raul Ibanez .07 .20
480 Richie Sexson .07 .20
481 Rick Reed .07 .20
482 Pedro Astacio .07 .20
483 Adam Piatt .07 .20
484 Bud Smith .07 .20
485 Tomas Perez .07 .20
486 Adam Eaton .07 .20
487 Rafael Palmeiro .10 .30
488 Jason Tyner .07 .20
489 Scott Rolen .10 .30
490 Randy Winn .07 .20
491 Ryan Jensen .07 .20
492 Trevor Hoffman .07 .20
493 Craig Wilson .07 .20
494 Jeremy Giambi .07 .20
495 Daryle Ward .07 .20
496 Shane Spencer .07 .20
497 Andy Pettitte .10 .30
498 John Franco .07 .20
499 Felipe Lopez .07 .20
500 Mike Piazza .30 .75
501 Cristian Guzman .07 .20
502 Jose Hernandez .07 .20
503 Octavio Dotel .07 .20
504 Brad Penny .07 .20
505 Dave Veres .07 .20
506 Ryan Dempster .07 .20
507 Joe Crede .07 .20
508 Chad Hermansen .07 .20
509 Gary Matthews Jr. .07 .20
510 Matt Franco .07 .20
511 Ben Weber .07 .20
512 Dave Berg .07 .20
513 Michael Young .10 .30
514 Frank Catalanotto .07 .20
515 Darin Erstad .07 .20
516 Matt Williams .07 .20
517 B.J. Surhoff .07 .20
518 Kerry Ligtenberg .07 .20
519 Mike Bordick .07 .20
520 Arthur Rhodes .07 .20
521 Joe Girardi .07 .20
522 D'Angelo Jimenez .07 .20
523 Paul Konerko .07 .20
524 Jose Macias .07 .20
525 Joe Mays .07 .20
526 Marquis Grissom .07 .20
527 Neifi Perez .07 .20
528 Preston Wilson .07 .20
529 Jeff Weaver .07 .20
530 Eric Chavez .07 .20
531 Placido Polanco .07 .20
532 Matt Mantei .07 .20
533 James Baldwin .07 .20
534 Toby Hall .07 .20
535 Brendan Donnelly .07 .20
536 Benji Gil .07 .20
537 Damian Moss .07 .20
538 Jorge Julio .07 .20
539 Matt Clement .07 .20
540 Brian Moehler .07 .20
541 Lee Stevens .07 .20
542 Jimmy Haynes .07 .20
543 Terry Mulholland .07 .20
544 Dave Roberts .07 .20
545 J.C. Romero .07 .20
546 Bartolo Colon .07 .20
547 Roger Cedeno .07 .20
548 Mariano Rivera .20 .50
549 Billy Koch .07 .20
550 Manny Ramirez .10 .30
551 Travis Lee .07 .20
552 Oliver Perez .07 .20
553 Tim Worrell .07 .20
554 Rafael Soriano .07 .20
555 Damian Miller .07 .20
556 John Smoltz .10 .30
557 Willis Roberts .07 .20
558 Tim Hudson .07 .20
559 Moises Alou .07 .20
560 Gary Glover .07 .20
561 Corky Miller .07 .20
562 Ben Broussard .07 .20
563 Gabe Kapler .07 .20
564 Chris Woodward .07 .20
565 Paul Wilson .07 .20
566 Todd Hollandsworth .07 .20
567 So Taguchi .07 .20
568 John Olerud .07 .20
569 Reggie Sanders .07 .20
570 Jake Peavy .07 .20
571 Kris Benson .07 .20
572 Todd Pratt .07 .20
573 Ray Durham .07 .20
574 Boomer Wells .07 .20
575 Chris Widger .07 .20
576 Shawn Wooten .07 .20
577 Tom Glavine .10 .30
578 Antonio Alfonseca .07 .20
579 Keith Foulke .07 .20
580 Shawn Estes .07 .20
581 Mark Grace .10 .30
582 Dmitri Young .07 .20
583 A.J. Burnett .07 .20
584 Richard Hidalgo .07 .20
585 Mike Sweeney .07 .20
586 Alex Cora .07 .20
587 Matt Stairs .07 .20
588 Doug Mientkiewicz .07 .20
589 Fernando Tatis .07 .20
590 David Weathers .07 .20
591 Cory Lidle .07 .20
592 Dan Plesac .07 .20
593 Jeff Bagwell .10 .30
594 Steve Sparks .07 .20
595 Sandy Alomar Jr. .07 .20
596 John Lackey .07 .20
597 Rick Helling .07 .20
598 Mark DeRosa .07 .20
599 Carlos Lee .07 .20
600 Garret Anderson .07 .20
601 Vinny Castilla .07 .20
602 Ryan Drese .07 .20
603 LaTroy Hawkins .07 .20
604 David Bell .07 .20
605 Freddy Garcia .07 .20
606 Miguel Cairo .07 .20
607 Scott Spiezio .07 .20
608 Mike Remlinger .07 .20
609 Tony Graffanino .07 .20
610 Russell Branyan .07 .20
611 Chris Magruder .07 .20
612 Jose Contreras RC .40 1.00
613 Carl Pavano .07 .20
614 Kevin Brown .07 .20
615 Tyler Houston .07 .20
616 A.J. Pierzynski .07 .20
617 Tony Fiore .07 .20
618 Peter Bergeron .07 .20
619 Rondell White .07 .20
620 Brett Myers .07 .20
621 Kevin Young .07 .20
622 Kenny Lofton .07 .20
623 Ben Davis .07 .20
624 J.D. Drew .07 .20
625 Chris Gomez .07 .20
626 Karim Garcia .07 .20
627 Ricky Gutierrez .07 .20
628 Mark Redman .07 .20
629 Juan Encarnacion .07 .20
630 Anaheim Angels TC .10 .30
631 Ariz.Diamondbacks TC .07 .20
632 Atlanta Braves TC .07 .20
633 Baltimore Orioles TC .07 .20
634 Boston Red Sox TC .07 .20
635 Chicago Cubs TC .07 .20
636 Chicago White Sox TC .07 .20
637 Cincinnati Reds TC .07 .20
638 Cleveland Indians TC .07 .20
639 Colorado Rockies TC .07 .20
640 Detroit Tigers TC .07 .20
641 Florida Marlins TC .07 .20
642 Houston Astros TC .07 .20
643 Kansas City Royals TC .07 .20
644 Los Angeles Dodgers TC .07 .20
645 Milwaukee Brewers TC .07 .20
646 Minnesota Twins TC .07 .20
647 Montreal Expos TC .07 .20
648 New York Mets TC .07 .20
649 New York Yankees TC .10 .30
650 Oakland Athletics TC .07 .20
651 Philadelphia Phillies TC .07 .20
652 Pittsburgh Pirates TC .07 .20
653 San Diego Padres TC .07 .20
654 San Francisco Giants TC .07 .20
655 Seattle Mariners TC .07 .20
656 St. Louis Cardinals TC .07 .20
657 T.B. Devil Rays TC .07 .20
658 Texas Rangers TC .07 .20
659 Toronto Blue Jays TC .07 .20
660 Bryan Bullington DP RC .20 .50
661 Jeremy Guthrie DP .20 .50
662 Joey Gomes DP RC .20 .50
663 E.Bastida-Martinez DP RC .20 .50
664 Brian Wright DP RC .20 .50
665 B.J. Upton DP .30 .75
666 Jeff Francis DP .20 .50
667 Drew Meyer DP .20 .50
668 Jeremy Hermida DP .30 .75
669 Khalil Greene DP .30 .75
670 Darrell Rasner DP RC .20 .50
671 Cole Hamels DP .75 2.00
672 James Loney DP .25 .60
673 Sergio Santos DP .20 .50
674 Jason Pridie DP .20 .50
675 Brandon Phillips .20 .50
Victor Martinez
676 Hee Seop Choi .20 .50
Nic Jackson
677 Dontrelle Willis .30 .75
Jason Stokes
678 Chad Tracy .20 .50
Lyle Overbay
679 Joe Borchard .20 .50
Corwin Malone
680 Joe Mauer 1.25 3.00
Justin Morneau
681 Drew Henson .20 .50
Brandon Claussen
682 Chase Utley .30 .75
Gavin Floyd
683 Taggert Bozied .20 .50
Xavier Nady
684 Aaron Heilman .20 .50
Jose Reyes
685 Kenny Rogers AW .07 .20
686 Bengie Molina AW .07 .20
687 John Olerud AW .07 .20
688 Bret Boone AW .07 .20
689 Eric Chavez AW .07 .20
690 Alex Rodriguez AW .20 .50
691 Darin Erstad AW .07 .20
692 Ichiro Suzuki AW .20 .50
693 Torii Hunter AW .07 .20
694 Greg Maddux AW .20 .50
695 Brad Ausmus AW .07 .20
696 Todd Helton AW .07 .20
697 Fernando Vina AW .07 .20
698 Scott Rolen AW .07 .20
699 Edgar Renteria AW .07 .20
700 Andruw Jones AW .07 .20
701 Larry Walker AW .07 .20
702 Jim Edmonds AW .07 .20
703 Barry Zito AW .07 .20
704 Randy Johnson AW .10 .30
705 Miguel Tejada AW .07 .20
706 Barry Bonds AW .30 .75
707 Eric Hinske AW .07 .20
708 Jason Jennings AW .07 .20
709 Todd Helton AS .07 .20
710 Jeff Kent AS .07 .20
711 Edgar Renteria AS .07 .20
712 Scott Rolen AS .07 .20
713 Barry Bonds AS .30 .75
714 Sammy Sosa AS .10 .30
715 Vladimir Guerrero AS .10 .30
716 Mike Piazza AS .20 .50
717 Curt Schilling AS .07 .20
718 Randy Johnson AS .10 .30
719 Bobby Cox AS .07 .20
720 Anaheim Angels WS .10 .30
721 Anaheim Angels WS .20 .50

2003 Topps Black

Inserted at a stated rate of one in 16 HTA series one packs and one in 10 HTA series 2 packs, this is a partial parallel to the Topps set. Only cards numbered from 1 through 331 were printed (though card number 7 does not exist, thus 330 cards comprise the series one set). However, the second series was issued in complete parallel form. These cards were issued to a stated print run of 52 serial numbered sets.

COM 1-291/368-659/685-721 10.00 25.00
SEMIS 1-291/368-659/685-721 15.00 30.00
UNL 1-291/368-659/685-721 20.00 40.00
COM. 292-331/660-684 10.00 25.00
UNL 292-331/660-684 15.00 30.00
COM. 292-331/612/660-684 10.00 25.00
SEMIS 292-331/612/660-684 15.00 30.00
UNL 92-331/612/660-684 20.00 40.00
292 Chris Duncan FY 30.00 60.00
300 Andy Marte FY 20.00 50.00

2003 Topps Box Bottoms

These cards were issued as a four-card sheet on the bottom of first and second series Home Team Advantage boxes. The sheets were not perforated, but did include dotted lines between each card indicating where the cards should be cut if they were to be separated. The cards are identical parallels to the basic issue 2003 Topps cards (including the same checklist numbers on the card backs). The key difference is the readily noticeable plain cardboard stock used for these Box Bottom parallels as averse to the high gloss card stock used for the basic issue cards.

*BOX BOTTOM CARDS: 1X TO 2.5X BASIC
1 Alex Rodriguez 1 .75 2.00
10 Mark Prior 4 .30 .75
11 Curt Schilling 1 .20 .50
20 Todd Helton 1 .30 .75
50 Sammy Sosa 2 .50 1.25
73 Luis Gonzalez 1 .20 .50
77 Miguel Tejada 4 .20 .50
80 Ivan Rodriguez 4 .30 .75
90 Alfonso Soriano 2 .20 .50
150 Kazuhisa Ishii 2 .20 .50
160 Pat Burrell 4 .20 .50
177 Adam Dunn 3 .20 .50
180 Barry Zito 3 .20 .50
200 Albert Pujols 2 1.00 2.50
230 Lance Berkman 3 .20 .50
250 Nomar Garciaparra 3 .75 2.00
368 Francisco Rodriguez 5 .20 .50
370 Chipper Jones 8 .50 1.25
380 Randy Johnson 8 .50 1.25
387 Nick Johnson 7 .20 .50
390 Ken Griffey Jr. 6 .75 2.00
396 Barry Bonds 5 1.25 3.00
433 Torii Hunter 5 .20 .50
450 Pedro Martinez 6 .30 .75
489 Scott Rolen 8 .30 .75
500 Mike Piazza 6 .75 2.00
530 Eric Chavez 6 .20 .50
550 Manny Ramirez 7 .30 .75
558 Tim Hudson 7 .20 .50
585 Mike Sweeney 8 .20 .50
593 Jeff Bagwell 5 .30 .75
600 Garret Anderson 7 .20 .50

2003 Topps Gold

Inserted at a stated rate of one in 16 first series hobby packs and one in five first series HTA packs, this is a partial parallel to the first series set. For the first series, nly cards numbered from 1 through 331 were printed. The second series was issued in its totality for this parallel. The second series cards were also issued at a stated rate of one in seven hobby packs, one in two HTA packs and one in five retail packs. All gold cards were issued to a stated print run of 2003 serial numbered sets.

*GOLD 1-291/368-659/685-721: 6X TO 15X
*GOLD: 292-331/660-684: 3X TO 8X
*GOLD RC's: 292-331/612/660-684: 3X TO 8X

2003 Topps Home Team Advantage

This is a parallel to the Topps set. Each of these cards, which were available only in the blue factory sets have the words "Home Team Advantage" stamped on them in gold foil.

COMP.FACT.SET (720) 40.00 80.00
*HTA: .75X TO 2X BASIC
DISTRIBUTED IN FACTORY SET FORM
CARD 7 DOES NOT EXIST

2003 Topps All-Stars

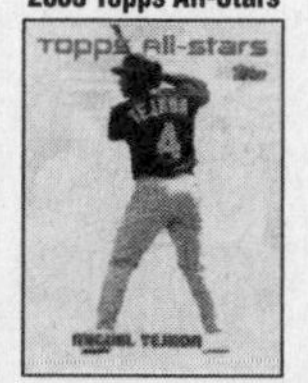

Issued at a stated rate of one in 15 second series hobby packs and one in five second series HTA packs, this 20 card set features most of the leading players in baseball.

COMPLETE SET (20) 20.00 50.00
1 Alfonso Soriano .75 2.00
2 Barry Bonds 2.50 6.00
3 Ichiro Suzuki 2.00 5.00
4 Alex Rodriguez 1.50 4.00
5 Miguel Tejada .75 2.00
6 Nomar Garciaparra 1.50 4.00
7 Jason Giambi .75 2.00
8 Manny Ramirez .75 2.00
9 Derek Jeter 2.50 6.00
10 Garret Anderson .75 2.00
11 Barry Zito .75 2.00
12 Sammy Sosa 1.00 2.50
13 Adam Dunn .75 2.00
14 Vladimir Guerrero 1.00 2.50
15 Mike Piazza 1.50 4.00
16 Shawn Green .75 2.00
17 Luis Gonzalez .75 2.00
18 Todd Helton .75 2.00
19 Torii Hunter .75 2.00
20 Curt Schilling .75 2.00

2003 Topps Autographs

Issued at varying stated odds, these 38 cards feature a mix of prospect and starts who signed cards for inclusion in the 2003 Topps product. The following players did not return their cards in time for inclusion in series 1 packs and these cards could be redeemed until November 30, 2004: Darin Erstad and Scott Rolen.

GROUP A1 SER.1 1:8910 H, 1: 2533 HTA
GROUP B1 SER.1 1:24,710 H, 1:7037 HTA
GROUP C1 SER.1 1:11,097 H, 1:3167 HTA
GROUP D1 SER.1 1:20,144 H, 1:5758 HTA
GROUP E1 SER.1 1:11,730 H, 1:3333 HTA
GROUP F1 SER.1 1:2209 H, 1:395 HTA
GROUP G1 SER.1 1:3471 H, 1:460 HTA
GROUP A2 1:31,408 H, 1:8808 HTA, 1:26,208 R
GROUP B2 1:5188 H, 1:1460 HTA, 1:4368 R
GROUP C2 1:864 H, 1:232 HTA, 1:708 R
GROUP D2 1:790 H, 1:214 HTA, 1:647 R
AJ Andruw Jones A1 40.00 80.00
AK1 Austin Kearns F1 4.00 10.00
AK2 Austin Kearns C2 4.00 10.00
AP Albert Pujols B2 150.00 300.00
AS Alfonso Soriano A1 30.00 60.00
BH Brad Hawpe D2 8.00 20.00
BS Ben Sheets E1 6.00 15.00
BU B.J. Upton D2 15.00 40.00
BZ Barry Zito C2 6.00 15.00
CE Clint Everts D2 4.00 10.00
CF Cliff Floyd C2 10.00 25.00
DE Darin Erstad B1 10.00 25.00
DW Dontrelle Willis D2 5.00 12.00
EC Eric Chavez A1 15.00 40.00
EH Eric Hinske C2 6.00 15.00

EM Eric Milton C1	6.00	15.00
HB Hank Blalock F1	10.00	25.00
JB Josh Beckett C2	20.00	50.00
JDM J.D. Martin G1	4.00	10.00
JL Jason Lane G1	6.00	15.00
JM Joe Mauer F1	30.00	60.00
JPH Josh Phelps C2	6.00	15.00
JV Jose Vidro C2	6.00	15.00
LB Lance Berkman A2	6.00	15.00
MB Mark Buehrle C1	10.00	25.00
MO Magglio Ordonez B2	4.00	10.00
MP Mark Prior F1	10.00	25.00
MTE Mark Teixeira F1	15.00	40.00
MTH Marcus Thames G1	4.00	10.00
MT1 Miguel Tejada A1	30.00	60.00
MT2 Miguel Tejada C2	15.00	40.00
NN Nick Neugebauer D1	6.00	15.00
OH Orlando Hudson G1	4.00	10.00
PK Paul Konerko C2	15.00	40.00
PL1 Paul Lo Duca F1	6.00	15.00
PL2 Paul Lo Duca C2	10.00	25.00
SR Scott Rolen A1	30.00	60.00
TH Torii Hunter C2	10.00	25.00

2003 Topps Blue Backs

Issued in the style of the 1951 Topps Blue Back set, these 40 cards were inserted into first series packs at a stated rate of one in 12 hobby packs and one in four HTA packs.

COMPLETE SET (40)	40.00	80.00
BB1 Albert Pujols	1.50	4.00
BB2 Ichiro Suzuki	1.50	4.00
BB3 Sammy Sosa	.75	2.00
BB4 Kazuhisa Ishii	.75	2.00
BB5 Alex Rodriguez	1.25	3.00
BB6 Derek Jeter	2.00	5.00
BB7 Vladimir Guerrero	.75	2.00
BB8 Ken Griffey Jr.	1.25	3.00
BB9 Jason Giambi	.75	2.00
BB10 Todd Helton	.75	2.00
BB11 Mike Piazza	1.25	3.00
BB12 Nomar Garciaparra	1.25	3.00
BB13 Chipper Jones	.75	2.00
BB14 Ivan Rodriguez	.75	2.00
BB15 Luis Gonzalez	.75	2.00
BB16 Pat Burrell	.75	2.00
BB17 Mark Prior	.75	2.00
BB18 Adam Dunn	.75	2.00
BB19 Jeff Bagwell	.75	2.00
BB20 Austin Kearns	.75	2.00
BB21 Alfonso Soriano	.75	2.00
BB22 Jim Thome	.75	2.00
BB23 Bernie Williams	.75	2.00
BB24 Pedro Martinez	.75	2.00
BB25 Lance Berkman	.75	2.00
BB26 Randy Johnson	.75	2.00
BB27 Rafael Palmeiro	.75	2.00
BB28 Richie Sexson	.75	2.00
BB29 Troy Glaus	.75	2.00
BB30 Shawn Green	.75	2.00
BB31 Larry Walker	.75	2.00
BB32 Eric Hinske	.75	2.00
BB33 Andruw Jones	.75	2.00
BB34 Barry Bonds	2.00	5.00
BB35 Curt Schilling	.75	2.00
BB36 Greg Maddux	1.25	3.00
BB37 Jimmy Rollins	.75	2.00
BB38 Eric Chavez	.75	2.00
BB39 Scott Rolen	.75	2.00
BB40 Mike Sweeney	.75	2.00

2003 Topps Blue Chips Autographs

SEEDED IN VARIOUS 03-06 TOPPS BRANDS		
AH Aubrey Huff	6.00	15.00
BC Bobby Crosby	6.00	15.00
BEP Brandon Phillips	8.00	20.00
BF Ben Fritz	4.00	10.00
BS Brian Slocum	4.00	10.00
CCE Clint Everts	4.00	10.00
CH Cole Hamels	40.00	80.00
CN Clint Nageotte	4.00	10.00
CT Chad Tracy	4.00	10.00
JG Jay Gibbons	4.00	10.00
JHA J.J. Hardy	8.00	20.00
JHU Justin Huber	4.00	10.00
JR Jeremy Reed	4.00	10.00
JRB Jason Bay	6.00	15.00
KH Kris Honel	4.00	10.00
MB Milton Bradley	4.00	10.00
OH Orlando Hudson	4.00	10.00
RN Ramon Nivar	4.00	10.00
VM Val Majewski	4.00	10.00
ZG Zack Greinke	10.00	25.00

2003 Topps Draft Picks

COMPLETE SET (10)	50.00	100.00
COMPLETE SERIES 1 (5)	30.00	60.00
COMPLETE SERIES 2 (5)	20.00	40.00
1-5 ISSUED IN RETAIL SETS		
6-10 DISTRIBUTED IN HOLIDAY SETS		
1 Brandon Wood	6.00	15.00
2 Ryan Wagner	1.25	3.00
3 Sean Rodriguez	3.00	8.00
4 Chris Lubanski	3.00	8.00
5 Chad Billingsley	6.00	15.00
6 Javi Herrera	1.50	4.00
7 Brian McFall	1.25	3.00
8 Nick Markakis	6.00	15.00
9 Adam Miller	5.00	12.00
10 Daric Barton	5.00	12.00

2003 Topps Farewell to Riverfront Stadium Relics

Issued at a stated rate of one in 37 second series HTA packs, this 10 card set featured leading current and retired Cincinnati Reds players since 1970 as well as a piece of Riverfront Stadium.

AD Adam Dunn	10.00	25.00
AK Austin Kearns	10.00	25.00
BL Barry Larkin	10.00	25.00
DC Dave Concepcion	10.00	25.00
JB Johnny Bench	15.00	40.00
JM Joe Morgan	10.00	25.00
KG Ken Griffey Jr.	10.00	25.00
PO Paul O'Neill	10.00	25.00
TP Tony Perez	10.00	25.00
TS Tom Seaver	10.00	25.00

2003 Topps First Year Player Bonus

Issued as five card bonus "packs" these 10 cards featured players in their first year on a Topps card. Cards number 1 through 5 were issued in a sealed clear cello pack within the "red" hobby factory sets while cards number 6-10 were issued in the "blue" Sears/JC Penney factory sets.

1 Ismael Castro		
2 Branden Florence		
3 Michael Garciaparra	2.00	5.00
4 Pete LaForest	2.00	5.00
5 Hanley Ramirez	6.00	15.00
6 Rajai Davis		
7 Gary Schneidmiller		
8 Corey Shafer		
9 Thomari Story-Harden		
10 Bryan Grace		

2003 Topps Flashback

This set, featuring basically retired players, was inserted at a stated rate of one in 12 HTA first series packs. Only Mike Piazza and Randy Johnson were active at the time this set was issued.

AR Al Rosen	2.00	5.00
BM Bill Madlock	2.00	5.00
CY Carl Yastrzemski	5.00	12.00
DM Dale Murphy	2.00	5.00
EM Eddie Mathews	2.50	6.00
GB George Brett	5.00	12.00
HK Harmon Killebrew	2.50	6.00
JP Jim Palmer	2.00	5.00
LD Lenny Dykstra	2.00	5.00
MP Mike Piazza	4.00	10.00
NR Nolan Ryan	6.00	15.00
RJ Randy Johnson	2.50	6.00
RR Robin Roberts	2.00	5.00
TS Tom Seaver	2.00	5.00
WS Warren Spahn	2.00	5.00

2003 Topps Hit Parade

Issued at a stated rate of one in 15 hobby packs, one in 5 HTA packs and one in 10 retail packs, this 30 card set feature active players in the top 10 of home runs, runs batted in or hits.

COMPLETE SET (30)	30.00	60.00
1 Barry Bonds	2.00	5.00
2 Sammy Sosa	.75	2.00
3 Rafael Palmeiro	.75	2.00
4 Fred McGriff	.75	2.00
5 Ken Griffey Jr.	1.25	3.00
6 Juan Gonzalez	.75	2.00
7 Andres Galarraga	.75	2.00
8 Jeff Bagwell	.75	2.00
9 Frank Thomas	.75	2.00
10 Matt Williams	.75	2.00
11 Barry Bonds	2.00	5.00
12 Rafael Palmeiro	.75	2.00
13 Fred McGriff	.75	2.00
14 Andres Galarraga	.75	2.00
15 Ken Griffey Jr.	1.25	3.00
16 Sammy Sosa	.75	2.00
17 Jeff Bagwell	.75	2.00
18 Juan Gonzalez	.75	2.00
19 Frank Thomas	.75	2.00
20 Matt Williams	.75	2.00
21 Rickey Henderson	.75	2.00
22 Rafael Palmeiro	.75	2.00
23 Roberto Alomar	.75	2.00
24 Barry Bonds	2.00	5.00
25 Mark Grace	.75	2.00
26 Fred McGriff	.75	2.00
27 Julio Franco	.75	2.00
28 Craig Biggio	.75	2.00
29 Andres Galarraga	.75	2.00
30 Barry Larkin	.75	2.00

2003 Topps Hobby Masters

Inserted into first series packs at stated odds of one in 18 Hobby packs and one in six HTA packs, these 20 cards feature some of the most popular players in the hobby.

COMPLETE SET (20)	15.00	40.00
HM1 Ichiro Suzuki	1.50	4.00
HM2 Kazuhisa Ishii	.75	2.00
HM3 Derek Jeter	2.00	5.00
HM4 Sammy Sosa	.75	2.00
HM5 Alex Rodriguez	1.25	3.00
HM6 Mike Piazza	1.25	3.00
HM7 Chipper Jones	.75	2.00
HM8 Vladimir Guerrero	.75	2.00
HM9 Nomar Garciaparra	1.25	3.00
HM10 Todd Helton	.75	2.00
HM11 Jason Giambi	.75	2.00
HM12 Ken Griffey Jr.	1.25	3.00
HM13 Albert Pujols	1.50	4.00
HM14 Ivan Rodriguez	.75	2.00
HM15 Mark Prior	.75	2.00
HM16 Adam Dunn	.75	2.00
HM17 Randy Johnson	.75	2.00
HM18 Barry Bonds	2.00	5.00
HM19 Alfonso Soriano	.75	2.00
HM20 Pat Burrell	.75	2.00

2003 Topps Own the Game

Inserted into first series packs at stated odds of one in 12 hobby and one in four HTA, these 30 cards feature players who put up big numbers during the 2002 season.

COMPLETE SET (30)	20.00	50.00
OG1 Ichiro Suzuki	1.50	4.00
OG2 Todd Helton	.75	2.00
OG3 Larry Walker	.75	2.00
OG4 Mike Sweeney	.75	2.00
OG5 Sammy Sosa	.75	2.00
OG6 Lance Berkman	.75	2.00
OG7 Alex Rodriguez	1.25	3.00
OG8 Jim Thome	.75	2.00
OG9 Shawn Green	.75	2.00
OG10 Nomar Garciaparra	1.25	3.00
OG11 Miguel Tejada	.75	2.00
OG12 Jason Giambi	.75	2.00
OG13 Magglio Ordonez	.75	2.00
OG14 Manny Ramirez	.75	2.00
OG15 Alfonso Soriano	.75	2.00
OG16 Johnny Damon	.75	2.00
OG17 Derek Jeter	2.00	5.00
OG18 Albert Pujols	1.50	4.00
OG19 Luis Castillo	.75	2.00
OG20 Barry Bonds	2.00	5.00
OG21 Garret Anderson	.75	2.00
OG22 Jimmy Rollins	.75	2.00
OG23 Curt Schilling	.75	2.00
OG24 Barry Zito	.75	2.00
OG25 Randy Johnson	.75	2.00
OG26 Tom Glavine	.75	2.00
OG27 Roger Clemens	1.50	4.00
OG28 Pedro Martinez	.75	2.00
OG29 Derek Lowe	.75	2.00
OG30 John Smoltz	.75	2.00

2003 Topps Prime Cuts Relics

Inserted into first series packs at a stated rate of one in 37,066 hobby packs and one in 5067 HTA packs and second series packs at a rate of one in 116,208 hobby, one in 1480 HTA and one in 4368 retail packs, these 31 cards featured game-used bat pieces taken from the barrel of the bat. Each of these cards were issued to a stated print run of 50 serial numbered sets.

AD1 Adam Dunn 1	50.00	100.00
AD2 Adam Dunn 2	50.00	100.00
AP Albert Pujols 1	125.00	200.00
AR1 Alex Rodriguez 1	75.00	150.00
AR2 Alex Rodriguez 2	75.00	150.00
AS Alfonso Soriano 2	50.00	100.00
BBO Barry Bonds 2	125.00	200.00
BW Bernie Williams 1	60.00	120.00
CD Carlos Delgado 2	50.00	100.00
EC Eric Chavez 2	50.00	100.00
EM Edgar Martinez 2	60.00	120.00
FT Frank Thomas 1	60.00	120.00
HB Hank Blalock 2	60.00	120.00
IR Ivan Rodriguez 1	60.00	120.00
JG Juan Gonzalez 1	50.00	100.00
JP Jorge Posada 2	60.00	120.00
LB Lance Berkman 1	40.00	80.00
LG Luis Gonzalez 2	50.00	100.00
MP Mark Prior 2	60.00	120.00
MP Mike Piazza 1	60.00	120.00
MV Mo Vaughn 1	50.00	100.00
NG1 Nomar Garciaparra 1	60.00	120.00
NG2 Nomar Garciaparra 2	60.00	120.00
RA1 Roberto Alomar 1	60.00	120.00
RA2 Roberto Alomar 2	60.00	120.00
RH Rickey Henderson 2	60.00	120.00
RJ Randy Johnson 2	60.00	120.00
RP Rafael Palmeiro 2	60.00	120.00
TG Tony Gwynn 2	60.00	120.00
TH Todd Helton 1	60.00	120.00
TM Tino Martinez 2	60.00	120.00

2003 Topps Prime Cuts Autograph Relics

Inserted into first series packs at stated odds of one in 27,661 hobby and one in 7,917 HTA packs or second series packs at stated odds of one in 232,416 hobb packs, one in 8808 HTA packs or one in 28,598 retail packs, these ten cards feature players who signed the relics cut from the barrel of the bat they used in a game. These cards were issued to a stated print run of 50 serial numbered sets.

AJ Andruw Jones 1	125.00	200.00
AP Albert Pujols 2		
CJ Chipper Jones 1	125.00	200.00
DE Darin Erstad 1		
EC Eric Chavez 1	90.00	150.00
LB Lance Berkman 2	125.00	200.00
MO Magglio Ordonez 2	100.00	175.00
MT Miguel Tejada 1	125.00	200.00
RP Rafael Palmeiro 1		
SR Scott Rolen 1		

2003 Topps Prime Cuts Pine Tar Relics

Inserted into first series packs at a stated rate of one in 9266 hobby packs and one in 1267 HTA packs and second series packs at a rate of one in 4288 hobby, one in 587 HTA and one in 928 retail, these 42 cards featured game-used bat pieces taken from the handle of the bat. Each of these cards were issued to a stated print run of 200 serial numbered sets.

AD1 Adam Dunn 1	30.00	60.00
AD2 Adam Dunn 2	30.00	60.00
AJ Andruw Jones 1	40.00	80.00
AP1 Albert Pujols 1	60.00	120.00
AP2 Albert Pujols 2	60.00	120.00
AR1 Alex Rodriguez 1	50.00	100.00
AR2 Alex Rodriguez 2	50.00	100.00
AS1 Alfonso Soriano 1	30.00	60.00
AS2 Alfonso Soriano 2	30.00	60.00
BBO Barry Bonds 2	60.00	120.00
BW Bernie Williams 1	40.00	80.00
CD Carlos Delgado 2	30.00	60.00
CJ Chipper Jones 1	40.00	80.00
DE Darin Erstad 1	30.00	60.00
EC1 Eric Chavez 1	30.00	60.00
EC2 Eric Chavez 2	30.00	60.00
EM Edgar Martinez 2	40.00	80.00
FT Frank Thomas 1	40.00	80.00
HB Hank Blalock 2	30.00	60.00
IR Ivan Rodriguez 1	40.00	80.00
JG Juan Gonzalez 1	30.00	60.00
JP Jorge Posada 2	40.00	80.00
LB1 Lance Berkman 1	30.00	60.00
LB2 Lance Berkman 2	30.00	60.00
LG Luis Gonzalez 2	30.00	60.00
MO Magglio Ordonez 2	30.00	60.00
MP Mark Prior 2	40.00	80.00
MP Mike Piazza 1	40.00	80.00
MT Miguel Tejada 1	30.00	60.00
MV Mo Vaughn 1	30.00	60.00
NG1 Nomar Garciaparra 1	40.00	80.00
NG2 Nomar Garciaparra 2	40.00	80.00
RA1 Roberto Alomar 1	40.00	80.00
RA2 Roberto Alomar 2	40.00	80.00
RH Rickey Henderson 2	40.00	80.00
RJ Randy Johnson 2	40.00	80.00
RP1 Rafael Palmeiro 1	40.00	80.00
RP2 Rafael Palmeiro 2	40.00	80.00
SR Scott Rolen 1	40.00	80.00
TG Tony Gwynn 2	40.00	80.00
TH Todd Helton 1	40.00	80.00
TM Tino Martinez 2	40.00	80.00

2003 Topps Prime Cuts Trademark Relics

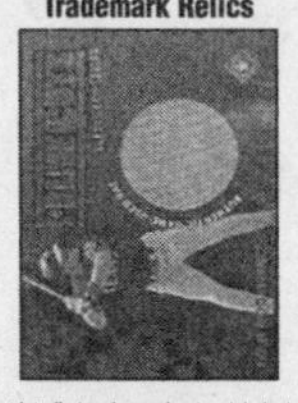

Inserted into first series packs at a stated rate of one in 18,533 hobby packs and one in 2533 HTA packs or second series packs at a rate of one in 12,912 hobby, one in 881 HTA or one in 1857 retail; these 42 cards featured game-used bat pieces taken from the middle of the bat. Each of these cards were issued to a stated print run of 100 serial numbered sets.

AD1 Adam Dunn 1	40.00	80.00
AD2 Adam Dunn 2	40.00	80.00
AJ Andruw Jones 1	50.00	100.00
AP1 Albert Pujols 1	75.00	150.00
AP2 Albert Pujols 2	75.00	150.00
AR1 Alex Rodriguez 1	60.00	120.00
AR2 Alex Rodriguez 2	60.00	120.00
AS1 Alfonso Soriano 1	50.00	100.00
AS2 Alfonso Soriano 2	50.00	100.00
BBO Barry Bonds 2	75.00	150.00
BW Bernie Williams 1	50.00	100.00
CD Carlos Delgado 2	40.00	80.00
CJ Chipper Jones 1	50.00	100.00
DE Darin Erstad 1	40.00	80.00
EC1 Eric Chavez 1	40.00	80.00
EC2 Eric Chavez 2	40.00	80.00
EM Edgar Martinez 2	50.00	100.00
FT Frank Thomas 1	50.00	100.00
HB Hank Blalock 2	40.00	80.00
IR Ivan Rodriguez 1	50.00	100.00
JG Juan Gonzalez 1	40.00	80.00
JP Jorge Posada 2	50.00	100.00
LB1 Lance Berkman 1	40.00	80.00
LB2 Lance Berkman 2	40.00	80.00
LG Luis Gonzalez 2	40.00	80.00
MO Magglio Ordonez 2	40.00	80.00
MP Mark Prior 2	50.00	100.00
MP Mike Piazza 1	50.00	100.00
MT Miguel Tejada 1	40.00	80.00
MV Mo Vaughn 1	40.00	80.00
NG1 Nomar Garciaparra 1	50.00	100.00
NG2 Nomar Garciaparra 2	50.00	100.00
RA1 Roberto Alomar 1	50.00	100.00
RA2 Roberto Alomar 2	50.00	100.00
RH Rickey Henderson 2	50.00	100.00
RJ Randy Johnson 2	50.00	100.00
RP1 Rafael Palmeiro 1	50.00	100.00
RP2 Rafael Palmeiro 2	50.00	100.00
SR Scott Rolen 1	50.00	100.00
TG Tony Gwynn 2	50.00	100.00
TH Todd Helton 1	50.00	100.00
TM Tino Martinez 2	50.00	100.00

2003 Topps Record Breakers

Inserted into packs at a stated rate of one in six hobby, one in two HTA and one in four retail, these 101 cards feature a mix of active and retired players who hold some sort of season, team, league or major league record.

COMPLETE SET (100)	60.00	120.00
COMPLETE SERIES 1 (50)	30.00	60.00
COMPLETE SERIES 2 (50)	30.00	60.00
AG Andres Galarraga 1	.60	1.50
AR1 Alex Rodriguez 1	1.00	2.50
AR2 Alex Rodriguez 2	1.00	2.50
BB1 Barry Bonds 1	1.50	4.00
BB2 Barry Bonds 2	1.50	4.00
BF Bob Feller 2	.60	1.50
BG Bob Gibson 1	.60	1.50
CB Craig Biggio 2	.60	1.50
CD1 Carlos Delgado 1	.60	1.50
CD2 Carlos Delgado 2	.60	1.50
CF Cliff Floyd 1	.60	1.50
CJ Chipper Jones 1	.60	1.50
CK Chuck Klein 1	.60	1.50
CS Curt Schilling 1	.60	1.50
DE Darin Erstad 2	.60	1.50
DG Dwight Gooden 2	.60	1.50
DM Don Mattingly 1	1.50	4.00
EM Edgar Martinez 2	.60	1.50
EM Eddie Mathews 1	.60	1.50
FJ Fergie Jenkins 1	.60	1.50
FM Fred McGriff 1	.60	1.50
FR1 Frank Robinson 1	.75	2.00
FR2 Frank Robinson 2	.75	2.00
FT Frank Thomas 2	.60	1.50
GA Garret Anderson 2	.60	1.50
GB1 George Brett 1	1.50	4.00
GB2 George Brett 2	1.50	4.00
GF1 George Foster 1	.60	1.50
GF2 George Foster 2	.60	1.50
GM Greg Maddux 2	1.00	2.50
GS Gary Sheffield 1	.60	1.50
HG Hank Greenberg 1	.75	2.00
HK Harmon Killebrew 1	.75	2.00
HW Hack Wilson 1	.75	2.00
IS Ichiro Suzuki 2	1.25	3.00
JB1 Jeff Bagwell 1	.60	1.50
JB2 Jeff Bagwell 2	.60	1.50
JD Johnny Damon 2	.60	1.50
JG Jason Giambi 1	.60	1.50
JK Jeff Kent 2	.60	1.50
JME Jose Mesa 2	.60	1.50
JM1 Juan Marichal 1	.60	1.50
JM2 Juan Marichal 2	.60	1.50
JO John Olerud 1	.60	1.50
JP Jim Palmer 2	.60	1.50
JR Jim Rice 2	.60	1.50
JS John Smoltz 2	.60	1.50
JT Jim Thome 2	.60	1.50
KG1 Ken Griffey Jr. 1	1.00	2.50
KG2 Ken Griffey Jr. 2	1.00	2.50
LA Luis Aparicio 2	.60	1.50
LBR1 Lou Brock 1	.75	2.00
LBR2 Lou Brock 2	.75	2.00
LB1 Lance Berkman 1	.60	1.50
LB2 Lance Berkman 2	.60	1.50
LC Luis Castillo 1	.60	1.50
LD Lenny Dykstra 2	.60	1.50
LG1 Luis Gonzalez 1	.60	1.50
LG2 Luis Gonzalez 2	.60	1.50
LW Larry Walker 2	.60	1.50
MP Mike Piazza 1	1.00	2.50
MR Manny Ramirez 2	.60	1.50
MS Mike Sweeney 1	.60	1.50
MSC Mike Schmidt 1	1.50	4.00
NG Nomar Garciaparra 2	1.00	2.50
NR Nolan Ryan 1	2.00	5.00
PM Pedro Martinez 1	.60	1.50
PM Paul Molitor 2	.60	1.50
PW Preston Wilson 1	.60	1.50
RA Roberto Alomar 2	.60	1.50
RC Roger Clemens 1	1.25	3.00
RCA Rod Carew 1	.75	2.00
RG Ron Guidry 1	.60	1.50
RH1 Rickey Henderson 1	.60	1.50
RH2 Rickey Henderson 2	.60	1.50
RJ1 Randy Johnson 1	.60	1.50
RJ2 Randy Johnson 2	.60	1.50
RP Rafael Palmeiro 1	.60	1.50
RS1 Richie Sexson 1	.60	1.50
RS2 Richie Sexson 2	.60	1.50
RY1 Robin Yount 1	.75	2.00
RY2 Robin Yount 2	.75	2.00
SG1 Shawn Green 1	.60	1.50
SG2 Shawn Green 2	.60	1.50
SS1 Sammy Sosa 1	.60	1.50
SS2 Sammy Sosa 2	.60	1.50
TG Troy Glaus 1	.60	1.50
TG1 Tony Gwynn 1	1.00	2.50
TG2 Tony Gwynn 2	1.00	2.50
TH1 Todd Helton 1	.60	1.50
TH2 Todd Helton 2	.60	1.50
TK Ted Kluszewski 2	.75	2.00
TR Tim Raines 2	.60	1.50
TS1 Tom Seaver 1	.75	2.00
TS2 Tom Seaver 2	.75	2.00
VG1 Vladimir Guerrero 1	.60	1.50
VG2 Vladimir Guerrero 2	.60	1.50
WB Wade Boggs 2	.75	2.00
WM Willie Mays 2	2.00	5.00
WS Willie Stargell 2	.75	2.00

2003 Topps Record Breakers Autographs

This 19 card set partially parallels the Record Breaker insert set. Most of the cards, except for Luis Gonzalez, were inserted into first series packs at a stated rate of one in 6941 hobby packs and one in 1178 HTA packs. The second series cards were issued at a stated rate of one in 2218 hobby, one in 634 HTA and one in 1850 retail packs.

GROUP A1 SER.1 1:6941 H, 1:1178 HTA		
GROUP B1 SER.1 1:34,320 H, 1:9744 HTA		
GRP 2 SER.2 1:2218 H, 1:634 HTA, 1:1850 R		
CF Cliff Floyd A1	8.00	20.00
CJ Chipper Jones A1	50.00	100.00
DM Don Mattingly 2	60.00	120.00
FJ Fergie Jenkins A1	8.00	20.00
GF George Foster 2	8.00	20.00
HK Harmon Killebrew A1	50.00	100.00
JM Juan Marichal 2	30.00	60.00
LA Luis Aparicio 2	8.00	20.00
LB Lance Berkman 2	20.00	50.00
LBR Lou Brock 2	30.00	60.00
LG Luis Gonzalez B1	8.00	20.00
MS Mike Schmidt A1	60.00	120.00
RP Rafael Palmeiro A1	40.00	80.00
RS Richie Sexson A1	8.00	20.00
RY Robin Yount A1	40.00	80.00
SG Shawn Green A1	30.00	60.00
SW Mike Sweeney A1	8.00	20.00
TG Troy Glaus A1		
WM Willie Mays 2	100.00	175.00

2003 Topps Record Breakers Relics

This 40 card set partially parallels the Record Breaker insert set. These cards, depending on the group they belonged to, were inserted into first and second series packs at different rates and we have noted all that information in our headers.

BAT A1 SER.1 ODDS 1:13,528 H, 1:4872 HTA		
BAT B1 SER.1 ODDS 1:9058 H, 1:1689 HTA		
BAT C1 SER.1 ODDS 1:743 H, 1:90 HTA		
UNI A1 SER.1 ODDS 1:6178 H, 1:700 HTA		
UNI B1 SER.1 ODDS 1:355 H, 1:51 HTA		
BAT 2 SER.2 ODDS 1:191 H, 1:59 HTA		
UNI A2 SER.2 ODDS 1:5235, 1:400 HTA		
UNI B2 SER.2 ODDS 1:418, 1:176 HTA		
UNI C2 SER.2 ODDS 1:1151, 1:87 HTA		
AR1 Alex Rodriguez Uni B1	6.00	15.00
AR2 Alex Rodriguez Uni B2	6.00	15.00
CD1 Carlos Delgado Uni B1	4.00	10.00
CD2 Carlos Delgado Uni B2	4.00	10.00
CJ Chipper Jones Uni B1	6.00	15.00
DE Darin Erstad Uni A2	4.00	10.00
DG Dwight Gooden Uni B2	4.00	10.00
DM Don Mattingly Bat C1	10.00	25.00
EM Edgar Martinez Bat 2	6.00	15.00
FR1 Frank Robinson Bat C1	6.00	15.00
FR2 Frank Robinson Bat 2	6.00	15.00
FT Frank Thomas Bat 2	6.00	15.00
GB1 George Brett Bat C1	10.00	25.00
GB2 George Brett Bat 2	10.00	25.00
HG Hank Greenberg Bat B1	15.00	40.00
HW Hack Wilson Bat A1	30.00	60.00
JB Jeff Bagwell Uni B1	6.00	15.00
JR Jim Rice Uni B2	4.00	10.00
LBE Lance Berkman Bat C1	4.00	10.00
LC Luis Castillo Bat C1	4.00	10.00
LG Luis Gonzalez Bat 2	4.00	10.00
LGO Luis Gonzalez Uni B1	4.00	10.00
MP Mike Piazza Bat C1	10.00	25.00
MS Mike Sweeney Bat C1	4.00	10.00
NR Nolan Ryan Uni A1	20.00	50.00
NRA Nolan Ryan Uni C2	15.00	40.00
PM Pedro Martinez Uni B1	6.00	15.00
RH Rickey Henderson Bat C1	6.00	15.00
RHO Rogers Hornsby Bat 2	15.00	40.00
RS Richie Sexson Uni C2	4.00	10.00
RY1 Robin Yount Uni B1	6.00	15.00
RY2 Robin Yount Bat 2	6.00	15.00
SG Shawn Green Uni B1	4.00	10.00
TG Tony Gwynn 2B Bat 2	6.00	15.00
TG2 Tony Gwynn Avg Bat 2	6.00	15.00
TH1 Todd Helton Uni B1	6.00	15.00
TH2 Todd Helton Uni B2	6.00	15.00
TK Ted Kluszewski Bat 2	6.00	15.00
TR Tim Raines Bat 2	4.00	10.00
WB Wade Boggs Bat 2	6.00	15.00

2003 Topps Record Breakers Nolan Ryan

Inserted at a stated rate of one in two HTA packs, this seven card set features all-time strikeout king Nolan Ryan. Each of these cards commemorate one of his record setting seven no-hitters.

COMPLETE SET (7)	30.00	60.00
COMMON CARD (NR1-NR7)	4.00	10.00

2003 Topps Record Breakers Nolan Ryan Autographs

Inserted at a stated rate of one in 1894 HTA packs, this three card set honors Nolan Ryan and the teams he tossed no-hitters for.

COMMON CARD	125.00	200.00

2003 Topps Red Backs

Inserted in second series packs at a stated rate of one in 12 hobby and one in eight retail; this 40-card set features leading players in the style of the 1951 Topps Red Back set.

COMPLETE SET (40)	50.00	100.00
1 Nomar Garciaparra	1.50	4.00
2 Ichiro Suzuki	2.00	5.00
3 Alex Rodriguez	1.50	4.00
4 Sammy Sosa	1.00	2.50

5 Barry Bonds 2.50 6.00
6 Vladimir Guerrero 1.00 2.50
7 Derek Jeter 2.50 6.00
8 Miguel Tejada .75 2.00
9 Alfonso Soriano .75 2.00
10 Manny Ramirez .75 2.00
11 Adam Dunn .75 2.00
12 Jason Giambi .75 2.00
13 Mike Piazza 1.50 4.00
14 Scott Rolen .75 2.00
15 Shawn Green .75 2.00
16 Randy Johnson 1.00 2.50
17 Todd Helton .75 2.00
18 Garret Anderson .75 2.00
19 Curt Schilling .75 2.00
20 Albert Pujols 2.00 5.00
21 Chipper Jones 1.00 2.50
22 Luis Gonzalez .75 2.00
23 Mark Prior .75 2.00
24 Jim Thome .75 2.00
25 Ivan Rodriguez .75 2.00
26 Torii Hunter .75 2.00
27 Lance Berkman .75 2.00
28 Troy Glaus .75 2.00
29 Andruw Jones .75 2.00
30 Barry Zito .75 2.00
31 Jeff Bagwell .75 2.00
32 Magglio Ordonez .75 2.00
33 Pat Burrell .75 2.00
34 Mike Sweeney .75 2.00
35 Rafael Palmeiro .75 2.00
36 Larry Walker .75 2.00
37 Carlos Delgado .75 2.00
38 Brian Giles .75 2.00
39 Pedro Martinez .75 2.00
40 Greg Maddux 1.50 4.00

2003 Topps Turn Back the Clock Autographs

This five card set was inserted at a stated rate of one in 134 HTA packs except for Bill Madlock who signed fewer cards and his card was inserted at a stated rate of one in 268 HTA packs.

GROUP A SER.1 ODDS 1:134 HTA
GROUP B SER.1 ODDS 1:268 HTA
BM Bill Madlock B 6.00 15.00
DM Dale Murphy A 10.00 25.00
HK Harmon Killebrew A
JP Jim Palmer A 8.00 20.00
LD Lenny Dykstra A 8.00 20.00

2003 Topps Traded

This 275 card-set was released in October, 2003. The set was issued in 10 card packs with an $3 SRP which came 24 packs to a box and 12 boxes to a case. Cards numbered 1 through 115 feature veterans who were traded while cards 116 through 120 feature managers. Cards numbered 121 through 165 featured prospects and cards 166 through 275 feature Rookie Cards. All of these cards were issued with a "T" prefix.

COMPLETE SET (275) 20.00 50.00
COMMON CARD (T1-T120) .07 .20
COMMON CARD (121-165) .15 .40
T1 Juan Pierre .07 .20
T2 Mark Grudzielanek .07 .20
T3 Tanyon Sturtze .07 .20
T4 Greg Vaughn .07 .20
T5 Greg Myers .07 .20
T6 Randall Simon .07 .20
T7 Todd Hundley .07 .20
T8 Marlon Anderson .07 .20
T9 Jeff Reboulet .07 .20
T10 Alex Sanchez .07 .20
T11 Mike Rivera .07 .20
T12 Todd Walker .07 .20
T13 Ray King .07 .20
T14 Shawn Estes .07 .20
T15 Gary Matthews Jr. .07 .20
T16 Jaret Wright .07 .20
T17 Edgardo Alfonzo .07 .20
T18 Omar Daal .07 .20
T19 Ryan Rupe .07 .20
T20 Tony Clark .07 .20
T21 Jeff Suppan .07 .20
T22 Mike Stanton .07 .20
T23 Ramon Martinez .07 .20
T24 Armando Rios .07 .20
T25 Johnny Estrada .07 .20
T26 Joe Girardi .07 .20
T27 Ivan Rodriguez .10 .30
T28 Robert Fick .07 .20
T29 Rick White .07 .20
T30 Robert Person .07 .20
T31 Alan Benes .07 .20
T32 Chris Carpenter .07 .20
T33 Chris Widger .07 .20
T34 Travis Hafner .07 .20
T35 Mike Venafro .07 .20
T36 Jon Lieber .07 .20
T37 Orlando Hernandez .07 .20
T38 Aaron Myette .07 .20
T39 Paul Bako .07 .20
T40 Erubiel Durazo .07 .20
T41 Mark Guthrie .07 .20
T42 Steve Avery .07 .20
T43 Damian Jackson .07 .20
T44 Rey Ordonez .07 .20
T45 John Flaherty .07 .20
T46 Byung-Hyun Kim .07 .20
T47 Tom Goodwin .07 .20
T48 Elmer Dessens .07 .20
T49 Al Martin .07 .20
T50 Gene Kingsale .07 .20
T51 Lenny Harris .07 .20
T52 David Ortiz Sox .20 .50
T53 Jose Lima .07 .20
T54 Mike Difelice .07 .20
T55 Jose Hernandez .07 .20
T56 Todd Zeile .07 .20
T57 Roberto Hernandez .07 .20
T58 Albie Lopez .07 .20
T59 Roberto Alomar .10 .30
T60 Russ Ortiz .07 .20
T61 Brian Daubach .07 .20
T62 Carl Everett .07 .20
T63 Jeromy Burnitz .07 .20
T64 Mark Bellhorn .07 .20
T65 Ruben Sierra .07 .20
T66 Mike Fetters .07 .20
T67 Armando Benitez .07 .20
T68 Deivi Cruz .07 .20
T69 Jose Cruz Jr. .07 .20
T70 Jeremy Fikac .07 .20
T71 Jeff Kent .07 .20
T72 Andres Galarraga .07 .20
T73 Rickey Henderson .20 .50
T74 Royce Clayton .07 .20
T75 Troy O'Leary .07 .20
T76 Ron Coomer .07 .20
T77 Greg Colbrunn .07 .20
T78 Wes Helms .07 .20
T79 Kevin Millwood .07 .20
T80 Damion Easley .07 .20
T81 Bobby Kielty .07 .20
T82 Keith Osik .07 .20
T83 Ramiro Mendoza .07 .20
T84 Shea Hillenbrand .07 .20
T85 Shannon Stewart .07 .20
T86 Eddie Perez .07 .20
T87 Ugueth Urbina .07 .20
T88 Orlando Palmeiro .07 .20
T89 Graeme Lloyd .07 .20
T90 John Vander Wal .07 .20
T91 Gary Bennett .07 .20
T92 Shane Reynolds .07 .20
T93 Steve Parris .07 .20
T94 Julio Lugo .07 .20
T95 John Halama .07 .20
T96 Carlos Baerga .07 .20
T97 Jim Parque .07 .20
T98 Mike Williams .07 .20
T99 Fred McGriff .10 .30
T100 Kenny Rogers .07 .20
T101 Matt Herges .07 .20
T102 Jay Bell .07 .20
T103 Esteban Yan .07 .20
T104 Eric Owens .07 .20
T105 Aaron Fultz .07 .20
T106 Rey Sanchez .07 .20
T107 Jim Thome .10 .30
T108 Aaron Boone .07 .20
T109 Raul Mondesi .07 .20
T110 Kenny Lofton .07 .20
T111 Jose Guillen .07 .20
T112 Aramis Ramirez .07 .20
T113 Sidney Ponson .07 .20
T114 Scott Williamson .07 .20
T115 Robin Ventura .07 .20
T116 Dusty Baker MG .07 .20
T117 Felipe Alou MG .07 .20
T118 Buck Showalter MG .07 .20
T119 Jack McKeon MG .07 .20
T120 Art Howe MG .07 .20
T121 Bobby Crosby PROS .15 .40
T122 Adrian Gonzalez PROS .15 .40
T123 Kevin Cash PROS .15 .40
T124 Shin-Soo Choo PROS .15 .40
T125 Chin-Feng Chen PROS .40 1.00
T126 Miguel Cabrera PROS .40 1.00
T127 Jason Young PROS .15 .40
T128 Alex Herrera PROS .15 .40
T129 Jason Dubois PROS .15 .40
T130 Jeff Mathis PROS .15 .40
T131 Casey Kotchman PROS .15 .40
T132 Ed Rogers PROS .15 .40
T133 Wilson Betemit PROS .15 .40
T134 Jim Kavourias PROS .15 .40
T135 Taylor Buchholz PROS .15 .40
T136 Adam LaRoche PROS .15 .40
T137 D.McPherson PROS .15 .40
T138 Jesus Cota PROS .15 .40
T139 Clint Nageotte PROS .15 .40
T140 Boof Bonser PROS .15 .40
T141 Walter Young PROS .15 .40
T142 Joe Crede PROS .15 .40
T143 Denny Bautista PROS .15 .40
T144 Victor Diaz PROS .15 .40
T145 Chris Narveson PROS .15 .40
T146 Gabe Gross PROS .15 .40
T147 Jimmy Journell PROS .15 .40
T148 Rafael Soriano PROS .15 .40
T149 Jerome Williams PROS .15 .40
T150 Aaron Cook PROS .15 .40
T151 An. Martinez PROS .15 .40
T152 Scott Hairston PROS .15 .40
T153 John Buck PROS .15 .40
T154 Ryan Ludwick PROS .15 .40
T155 Chris Bootcheck PROS .15 .40
T156 John Rheinecker PROS .15 .40
T157 Jason Lane PROS .15 .40
T158 Shelley Duncan PROS .75 2.00
T159 Adam Wainwright PROS .15 .40
T160 Jason Arnold PROS .15 .40
T161 Jonny Gomes PROS .25 .60
T162 James Loney PROS .20 .50
T163 Mike Fontenot PROS .15 .40
T164 Khalil Greene PROS .40 1.00
T165 Sean Burnett PROS .15 .40
T166 David Martinez FY RC .15 .40
T167 Felix Pie FY RC 1.50 4.00
T168 Joe Valentine FY RC .15 .40
T169 Brandon Webb FY RC 1.25 3.00
T170 Matt Diaz FY RC .30 .75
T171 Lew Ford FY RC .20 .50
T172 Jeremy Griffiths FY RC .15 .40
T173 Matt Hensley FY RC .15 .40
T174 Charlie Manning FY RC .15 .40
T175 Elizardo Ramirez FY RC .20 .50
T176 Greg Aquino FY RC .15 .40
T177 Felix Sanchez FY RC .15 .40
T178 Kelly Shoppach FY RC .30 .75
T179 Bubba Nelson FY RC .20 .50
T180 Mike O'Keefe FY RC .15 .40
T181 Hanley Ramirez FY RC 2.00 5.00
T182 T.Wellemeyer FY RC .15 .40
T183 Dustin Moseley FY RC .15 .40
T184 Eric Crozier FY RC .20 .50
T185 Ryan Shealy FY RC 1.00 2.50
T186 Jer. Bonderman FY RC 1.25 3.00
T187 T.Story-Harden FY RC .15 .40
T188 Dusty Brown FY RC .15 .40
T189 Rob Hammock FY RC .15 .40
T190 Jorge Piedra FY RC .20 .50
T191 Chris De La Cruz FY RC .15 .40
T192 Eli Whiteside FY RC .15 .40
T193 Jason Kubel FY RC .40 1.00
T194 Jon Schuerholz FY RC .15 .40
T195 St. Randolph FY RC .15 .40
T196 Andy Sisco FY RC .15 .40
T197 Sean Smith FY RC .20 .50
T198 Jon-Mark Sprowl FY RC .15 .40
T199 Matt Kata FY RC .15 .40
T200 Robinson Cano FY RC 6.00 15.00
T201 Nook Logan FY RC .20 .50
T202 Ben Francisco FY RC .15 .40
T203 Arnie Munoz FY RC .15 .40
T204 Ozzie Chavez FY RC .15 .40
T205 Eric Riggs FY RC .20 .50
T206 Beau Kemp FY RC .15 .40
T207 Travis Wong FY RC .20 .50
T208 Dustin Yount FY RC .20 .50
T209 Brian McCann FY RC 2.50 6.00
T210 Wilton Reynolds FY RC .20 .50
T211 Matt Bruback FY RC .15 .40
T212 Andrew Brown FY RC .20 .50
T213 Edgar Gonzalez FY RC .15 .40
T214 Eider Torres FY RC .15 .40
T215 Aquilino Lopez FY RC .15 .40
T216 Bobby Basham FY RC .15 .40
T217 Tim Olson FY RC .15 .40
T218 Nathan Panther FY RC .15 .40
T219 Bryan Grace FY RC .15 .40
T220 Dusty Gomon FY RC .20 .50
T221 Wil Ledezma FY RC .15 .40
T222 Josh Willingham FY RC .40 1.00
T223 David Cash FY RC .15 .40
T224 Oscar Villarreal FY RC .15 .40
T225 Jeff Duncan FY RC .15 .40
T226 Kade Johnson FY RC .15 .40
T227 L.Steidlmayer FY RC .15 .40
T228 Brandon Watson FY RC .15 .40
T229 Jose Morales FY RC .15 .40
T230 Mike Gallo FY RC .15 .40
T231 Tyler Adamczyk FY RC .15 .40
T232 Adam Stern FY RC .15 .40
T233 Brennan King FY RC .15 .40
T234 Dan Haren FY RC .30 .75
T235 Mi. Hernandez FY RC .15 .40
T236 Ben Fritz FY RC .15 .40
T237 Clay Hensley FY RC .15 .40
T238 Tyler Johnson FY RC .15 .40
T239 Pete LaForest FY RC .15 .40
T240 Tyler Martin FY RC .15 .40
T241 J.D. Durbin FY RC .15 .40
T242 Shane Victorino FY RC .40 1.00
T243 Rajai Davis FY RC .15 .40
T244 Ismael Castro FY RC .15 .40
T245 C.Wang FY RC 1.25 3.00
T246 Travis Ishikawa FY RC .30 .75
T247 Corey Shafer FY RC .15 .40
T248 G.Schneidmiller FY RC .15 .40
T249 Dave Pember FY RC .15 .40
T250 Keith Stamler FY RC .15 .40
T251 Tyson Graham FY RC .15 .40
T252 Ryan Cameron FY RC .15 .40
T253 E.Eckenstahler FY .15 .40
T254 Ma. Peterson FY RC .15 .40
T255 D. McGowan FY RC .20 .50
T256 Pr. Redman FY RC .15 .40
T257 Haj Turay FY RC .15 .40
T258 Carlos Guzman FY RC .20 .50
T259 Matt DeMarco FY RC .15 .40
T260 Derek Michaelis FY RC .15 .40
T261 Brian Burgamy FY RC .15 .40
T262 Jay Sitzman FY RC .15 .40
T263 Chris Fallon FY RC .15 .40
T264 Mike Adams FY RC .15 .40
T265 Clint Barmes FY RC .40 1.00
T266 Eric Reed FY RC .15 .40
T267 Willie Eyre FY RC .15 .40
T268 Carlos Duran FY RC .15 .40
T269 Nick Trzesniak FY RC .15 .40
T270 Ferdin Tejeda FY RC .15 .40
T271 Mi. Garciaparra FY RC .15 .40
T272 Michael Hinckley FY RC .20 .50
T273 Br. Florence FY RC .15 .40
T274 Trent Oeltjen FY RC .20 .50
T275 Mike Neu FY RC .15 .40

2003 Topps Traded Gold

*GOLD 1-120: 5X TO 12X BASIC
*GOLD 121-165: 2.5X TO 6X BASIC
*GOLD 166-275: 1.5X TO 4X BASIC
STATED ODDS 1:2 HOB/RET, 1:1 HTA
STATED PRINT RUN 2003 SERIAL #'d SETS
T245 Chien-Ming Wang FY 6.00 15.00

2003 Topps Traded Future Phenoms Relics

GROUP A ODDS 1:2330 HOB/RET, 1:669 HTA
GROUP B ODDS 1:505 HOB/RET, 1:144 HTA
GROUP C ODDS 1:101 HOB/RET, 1:29 HTA
BP Brandon Phillips Bat B 3.00 8.00
CC Chin-Feng Chen Jsy C 10.00 25.00
CDC Carl Crawford Bat C 3.00 8.00
CS Chris Snelling Bat C 3.00 8.00
HB Hank Blalock Bat C 3.00 8.00
JM Justin Morneau Bat C 3.00 8.00
JT Joe Thurston Jsy C 3.00 8.00
MB Marlon Byrd Bat C 3.00 8.00
MR Michael Restovich Bat B 3.00 8.00
MT Mark Teixeira Bat B 4.00 10.00
RB Rocco Baldelli Bat B 3.00 8.00
TAH Trey Hodges Jsy C 3.00 8.00
TH Travis Hafner Bat C 3.00 8.00
WB Wilson Betemit Bat C 3.00 8.00
WPB Willie Bloomquist Bat A 6.00 15.00

2003 Topps Traded Hall of Fame Relics

STATED ODDS 1:1009 HOB/RET, 1:289 HTA
EM Eddie Murray Bat 10.00 25.00
GC Gary Carter Uni 6.00 15.00

2003 Topps Traded Hall of Fame Dual Relic

STATED ODDS 1:2015 HOB/RET, 1:578 HTA
CM Gary Carter Uni 12.50 30.00
Eddie Murray Bat

2003 Topps Traded Signature Moves Autographs

GROUP A ODDS 1:280 HOB/RET, 1:80 HTA
GROUP B ODDS 1:114 HOB/RET, 1:33 HTA
BC Bartolo Colon A 6.00 15.00
BU B.J. Upton B 10.00 25.00
CF Cliff Floyd A 6.00 15.00
DB David Bell A 6.00 15.00
EA Erick Almonte B 4.00 10.00
ER Elizardo Ramirez B 4.00 10.00
FP Felix Pie B 35.00 60.00
IR Robert Fick A 4.00 10.00
JB Joe Borchard B 4.00 10.00
JC Jose Cruz Jr. A 4.00 10.00
JF Jesse Foppert B 4.00 10.00
JG Joey Gomes B 4.00 10.00
JJC Jack Cust A 4.00 10.00
JL James Loney B 10.00 25.00
JR Jose Reyes B 12.50 30.00
JS Jason Stokes A 4.00 10.00
KG Khalil Greene A 10.00 25.00
MT Mark Teixeira A 10.00 25.00
VM Victor Martinez B 8.00 20.00
WY Walter Young B 4.00 10.00

2003 Topps Traded Transactions Bat Relics

GROUP A ODDS 1:168 HOB/RET, 1:48 HTA
GROUP B ODDS 1:78 HOB/RET, 1:22 HTA
AG Andres Galarraga A 3.00 8.00
CF Cliff Floyd B 3.00 8.00
DB David Bell B 3.00 8.00
EA Edgardo Alfonzo B 3.00 8.00
ED Erubiel Durazo B 3.00 8.00
EK Eric Karros B 3.00 8.00
FL Felipe Lopez A 3.00 8.00
FM Fred McGriff B 4.00 10.00
JC Jose Cruz Jr. B 3.00 8.00
JG Jeremy Giambi A 3.00 8.00
JK Jeff Kent B 3.00 8.00
JP Juan Pierre B 3.00 8.00
JT Jim Thome A 4.00 10.00
KL Kenny Lofton A 4.00 10.00
KM Kevin Millwood B 4.00 10.00
PW Preston Wilson A 3.00 8.00
RD Ray Durham A 3.00 8.00
RF Robert Fick A 3.00 8.00
RO Rey Ordonez B 3.00 8.00
RS Ruben Sierra A 3.00 8.00
RW Rondell White B 3.00 8.00
SH Tsuyoshi Shinjo B 3.00 8.00
SS Shane Spencer A 3.00 8.00
TG Tom Glavine A 4.00 10.00
TZ Todd Zeile A 3.00 8.00

2003 Topps Traded Transactions Dual Relics

STATED ODDS 1:421 HOB/RET, 1:120 HTA
IR Ivan Rodriguez Marlins-Rgr 8.00 20.00
JT Jim Thome Phils-Indians 8.00 20.00
KM Kevin Millwood Phils-Braves 6.00 15.00

2004 Topps

This 366-card standard-size first series was released in November, 2003. In addition, a 366-card second series was released in April, 2004. The cards were issued in 10-card hobby or retail packs with an $1.59 SRP which came 36 packs to a box and 12 boxes to a case. In addition, these cards were also issued in 35-card HTA packs with an $5 SRP which came 12 packs to a box and eight boxes to a case. Please note that insert cards were issued in different rates in retail packs as they were in hobby packs. In addition, to continuing honoring the memory of Mickey Mantle, there was no card number 7 issued in this set. Both cards numbered 267 and 274 are numbered as 267 and thus no card number 274 exists. Please note the following subsets were issued: Managers (268-296); First Year Cards (297-326); Future Stars (327-331); Highlights (332-336); League Leaders (337-348); Post-Season Play (349-355); American League All-Stars (356-367). The second series had the following subsets: Team Card (638-667), Draft Picks (668-687), Prospects (688-692), Combo Cards (693-695), Gold Gloves (696-713), Award Winners (714-718), National League All-Stars (719-729) and World Series Highlights (730-733).

COMP.HOBBY SET (737) 40.00 80.00
COMP.HOLIDAY SET (742) 40.00 80.00
COMP.RETAIL SET (737) 40.00 80.00
COMP.ASTROS SET (737) 40.00 80.00
COMP.CUBS SET (737) 40.00 80.00
COMP.RED SOX SET (737) 40.00 80.00
COMP.YANKEES SET (737) 40.00 80.00
COMPLETE SET (732) 30.00 80.00
COMPLETE SERIES 1 (366) 15.00 40.00
COMPLETE SERIES 2 (366) 15.00 40.00
COMMON CARD (1-6/8-732) .07 .20
COMMON (297-326/668-687) .20 .50
COMMON (327-331/688-692) .20 .50
CARDS 7 AND 274 DO NOT EXIST
SCIOSCIA AND J.CASTRO NUMBERED 267
1 Jim Thome .12 .30
2 Reggie Sanders .07 .20
3 Mark Kotsay .07 .20
4 Edgardo Alfonzo .07 .20
5 Ben Davis .07 .20
6 Mike Matheny .07 .20
8 Marlon Anderson .07 .20
9 Chan Ho Park .12 .30
10 Ichiro Suzuki .30 .75
11 Kevin Millwood .07 .20
12 Bengie Molina .07 .20
13 Tom Glavine .12 .30
14 Junior Spivey .07 .20
15 Marcus Giles .07 .20
16 David Segui .07 .20
17 Kevin Millar .07 .20
18 Corey Patterson .07 .20
19 Aaron Rowand .07 .20
20 Derek Jeter .50 1.25
21 Jason LaRue .07 .20
22 Chris Hammond .07 .20
23 Jay Payton .07 .20
24 Bobby Higginson .07 .20
25 Lance Berkman .12 .30
26 Juan Pierre .07 .20
27 Brent Mayne .07 .20
28 Fred McGriff .07 .20
29 Richie Sexson .07 .20
30 Tim Hudson .12 .30
31 Mike Piazza .20 .50
32 Brad Radke .07 .20
33 Jeff Weaver .07 .20
34 Ramon Hernandez .07 .20
35 David Bell .07 .20
36 Craig Wilson .07 .20
37 Jake Peavy .07 .20
38 Tim Worrell .07 .20
39 Gil Meche .07 .20
40 Albert Pujols .50 1.25
41 Michael Young .07 .20
42 Josh Phelps .07 .20
43 Brendan Donnelly .07 .20
44 Steve Finley .07 .20
45 John Smoltz .20 .50
46 Jay Gibbons .07 .20
47 Trot Nixon .07 .20
48 Carl Pavano .07 .20
49 Frank Thomas .20 .50
50 Mark Prior .12 .30
51 Danny Graves .07 .20
52 Milton Bradley UER .07 .20
53 Jose Jimenez .07 .20
54 Shane Halter .07 .20
55 Mike Lowell .07 .20
56 Geoff Blum .07 .20
57 Michael Tucker UER .07 .20
Dee Brown pictured
58 Paul Lo Duca .07 .20
59 Vicente Padilla .07 .20
60 Jacque Jones .07 .20
61 Fernando Tatis .07 .20
62 Ty Wigginton .07 .20
63 Pedro Astacio .07 .20
64 Andy Pettitte .12 .30
65 Terrence Long .07 .20
66 Cliff Floyd .07 .20
67 Mariano Rivera .20 .50
68 Carlos Silva .07 .20
69 Marlon Byrd .07 .20
70 Mark Mulder .07 .20
71 Kerry Ligtenberg .07 .20
72 Carlos Guillen .07 .20
73 Fernando Vina .07 .20
74 Lance Carter .07 .20
75 Hank Blalock .07 .20
76 Jimmy Rollins .12 .30
77 Francisco Rodriguez .12 .30
78 Javy Lopez .07 .20
79 Jerry Hairston Jr. .07 .20
80 Andruw Jones .07 .20
81 Rodrigo Lopez .07 .20
82 Johnny Damon .12 .30
83 Hee Seop Choi .07 .20
84 Miguel Olivo .07 .20
85 Jon Garland .07 .20
86 Matt Lawton .07 .20
87 Juan Uribe .07 .20
88 Steve Sparks .07 .20
89 Tim Spooneybarger .07 .20
90 Jose Vidro .07 .20
91 Luis Rivas .07 .20
92 Hideo Nomo .20 .50
93 Javier Vazquez .07 .20
94 Al Leiter .07 .20
95 Darren Dreifort .07 .20
96 Alex Cintron .07 .20
97 Zach Day .07 .20
98 Jorge Posada .12 .30
99 John Halama .07 .20
100 Alex Rodriguez .30 .75
101 Orlando Palmeiro .07 .20
102 Dave Berg .07 .20
103 Brad Fullmer .07 .20
104 Mike Hampton .07 .20
105 Willis Roberts .07 .20
106 Ramiro Mendoza .07 .20
107 Juan Cruz .07 .20
108 Esteban Loaiza .07 .20
109 Russell Branyan .07 .20
110 Todd Helton .12 .30
111 Braden Looper .07 .20
112 Octavio Dotel .07 .20
113 Mike MacDougal .07 .20
114 Cesar Izturis .07 .20
115 Johan Santana .20 .50
116 Jose Contreras .07 .20
117 Placido Polanco .07 .20
118 Jason Phillips .07 .20
119 Adam Eaton .07 .20
120 Vernon Wells .07 .20
121 Ben Grieve .07 .20
122 Randy Winn .07 .20
123 Ismael Valdes .07 .20
124 Eric Owens .07 .20
125 Curt Schilling .12 .30
126 Russ Ortiz .07 .20
127 Mark Buehrle .12 .30
128 Danys Baez .07 .20
129 Dmitri Young .07 .20
130 Kazuhisa Ishii .07 .20
131 A.J. Pierzynski .07 .20
132 Michael Barrett .07 .20
133 Joe McEwing .07 .20
134 Alex Cora .07 .20
135 Tom Wilson .07 .20
136 Carlos Zambrano .12 .30
137 Brett Tomko .07 .20
138 Shigetoshi Hasegawa .07 .20
139 Jarrod Washburn .07 .20
140 Greg Maddux .30 .75
141 Craig Counsell .07 .20
142 Reggie Taylor .07 .20
143 Omar Vizquel .12 .30
144 Alex Gonzalez .07 .20
145 Billy Wagner .07 .20
146 Brian Jordan .07 .20
147 Wes Helms .07 .20
148 Kyle Lohse .07 .20
149 Timo Perez .07 .20
150 Jason Giambi .07 .20
151 Erubiel Durazo .07 .20
152 Mike Lieberthal .07 .20
153 Jason Kendall .07 .20
154 Xavier Nady .07 .20
155 Kirk Rueter .07 .20
156 Mike Cameron .07 .20
157 Miguel Cairo .07 .20
158 Woody Williams .07 .20
159 Toby Hall .07 .20
160 Bernie Williams .12 .30
161 Darin Erstad .07 .20
162 Matt Mantei .07 .20
163 Geronimo Gil .07 .20
164 Bill Mueller .07 .20
165 Damian Miller .07 .20
166 Tony Graffanino .07 .20
167 Sean Casey .07 .20
168 Brandon Phillips .07 .20
169 Mike Remlinger .07 .20
170 Adam Dunn .12 .30
171 Carlos Lee .07 .20
172 Juan Encarnacion .07 .20
173 Angel Berroa .07 .20
174 Desi Relaford .07 .20
175 Paul Quantrill .07 .20
176 Ben Sheets .07 .20
177 Eddie Guardado .07 .20
178 Rocky Biddle .07 .20
179 Mike Stanton .07 .20
180 Eric Chavez .07 .20
181 Jason Michaels .07 .20
182 Terry Adams .07 .20
183 Kip Wells .07 .20
184 Brian Lawrence .07 .20
185 Bret Boone .07 .20
186 Tino Martinez .12 .30
187 Aubrey Huff .07 .20
188 Kevin Mench .07 .20
189 Tim Salmon .07 .20
190 Carlos Delgado .07 .20
191 John Lackey .07 .20
192 Oscar Villarreal .07 .20
193 Luis Matos .07 .20
194 Derek Lowe .07 .20
195 Mark Grudzielanek .07 .20
196 Tom Gordon .07 .20
197 Matt Clement .07 .20
198 Byung-Hyun Kim .07 .20
199 Brandon Inge .07 .20
200 Nomar Garciaparra .20 .50
201 Antonio Osuna .07 .20
202 Jose Mesa .07 .20
203 Bo Hart .07 .20
204 Jack Wilson .07 .20
205 Ray Durham .07 .20
206 Freddy Garcia .07 .20
207 J.D. Drew .07 .20
208 Einar Diaz .07 .20
209 Roy Halladay .20 .50
210 David Eckstein UER .07 .20
Adam Kennedy pictured
211 Jason Marquis .07 .20
212 Jorge Julio .07 .20
213 Tim Wakefield .07 .20
214 Moises Alou .07 .20
215 Bartolo Colon .07 .20
216 Jimmy Haynes .07 .20
217 Preston Wilson .07 .20
218 Luis Castillo .07 .20
219 Richard Hidalgo .07 .20
220 Manny Ramirez .20 .50
221 Mike Mussina .12 .30
222 Randy Wolf .07 .20
223 Kris Benson .07 .20
224 Ryan Klesko .07 .20
225 Rich Aurilia .07 .20
226 Kelvim Escobar .07 .20
227 Francisco Cordero .07 .20
228 Kazuhiro Sasaki .07 .20
229 Danny Bautista .07 .20
230 Rafael Furcal .07 .20
231 Travis Driskill .07 .20
232 Kyle Farnsworth .07 .20
233 Jose Valentin .07 .20
234 Felipe Lopez .07 .20
235 C.C. Sabathia .12 .30
236 Brad Penny .07 .20
237 Brad Ausmus .07 .20
238 Raul Ibanez .07 .20
239 Adrian Beltre .07 .20
240 Rocco Baldelli .07 .20
241 Orlando Hudson .07 .20
242 Dave Roberts .07 .20
243 Doug Mientkiewicz .07 .20
244 Brad Wilkerson .07 .20
245 Scott Strickland .07 .20
246 Ryan Franklin .07 .20
247 Chad Bradford .07 .20
248 Gary Bennett .07 .20
249 Jose Cruz Jr. .07 .20
250 Jeff Kent .07 .20
251 Josh Beckett .12 .30
252 Ramon Ortiz .07 .20
253 Miguel Batista .07 .20
254 Jung Bong .07 .20
255 Deivi Cruz .07 .20
256 Alex Gonzalez .07 .20
257 Shawn Chacon .07 .20
258 Runelvys Hernandez .07 .20
259 Joe Mays .07 .20
260 Eric Gagne .07 .20
261 Dustan Mohr UER .07 .20
1998 Kinston stats are wrong
262 Tomokazu Ohka .07 .20
263 Eric Byrnes .07 .20
264 Frank Catalanotto .07 .20
265 Cristian Guzman .07 .20
266 Orlando Cabrera .07 .20
267A Juan Castro .07 .20
267B M.Scioscia MG UER 274 .07 .20
268 Bob Brenly MG .07 .20
269 Bobby Cox MG .07 .20
270 Mike Hargrove MG .07 .20
271 Grady Little MG .07 .20
272 Dusty Baker MG .07 .20
273 Jerry Manuel MG .07 .20

275 Eric Wedge MG .07 .20
276 Clint Hurdle MG .07 .20
277 Alan Trammell MG .07 .20
278 Jack McKeon MG .07 .20
279 Jimy Williams MG .07 .20
280 Tony Pena MG .07 .20
281 Jim Tracy MG .07 .20
282 Ned Yost MG .07 .20
283 Ron Gardenhire MG .07 .20
284 Frank Robinson MG .07 .20
285 Art Howe MG .07 .20
286 Joe Torre MG .12 .30
287 Ken Macha MG .07 .20
288 Larry Bowa MG .07 .20
289 Lloyd McClendon MG .07 .20
290 Bruce Bochy MG .07 .20
291 Felipe Alou MG .07 .20
292 Bob Melvin MG .07 .20
293 Tony LaRussa MG .12 .30
294 Lou Piniella MG .07 .20
295 Buck Showalter MG .07 .20
296 Carlos Tosca MG .07 .20
297 Anthony Acevedo FY RC .20 .50
298 Anthony Lerew FY RC .20 .50
299 Blake Hawksworth FY RC .20 .50
300 Brayan Pena FY RC .20 .50
301 Casey Myers FY RC .20 .50
302 Craig Ansman FY RC .20 .50
303 David Murphy FY RC .50 1.25
304 Dave Crouthers FY RC .20 .50
305 Dioner Navarro FY RC .30 .75
306 Donald Levinski FY RC .20 .50
307 Jesse Roman FY RC .20 .50
308 Sung Jung FY RC .20 .50
309 Jon Knott FY RC .20 .50
310 Josh Labandeira FY RC .20 .50
311 Kenny Perez FY RC .20 .50
312 Khalid Ballouli FY RC .20 .50
313 Kyle Davies FY RC .20 .50
314 Marcus McBeth FY RC .20 .50
315 Matt Creighton FY RC .20 .50
316 Chris O'Riordan FY RC .20 .50
317 Mike Gosling FY RC .20 .50
318 Nic Ungs FY RC .20 .50
319 Omar Falcon FY RC .20 .50
320 Rodney Choy Foo FY RC .20 .50
321 Tim Frend FY RC .20 .50
322 Todd Self FY RC .20 .50
323 Tydus Meadows FY RC .20 .50
324 Yadier Molina FY RC 1.25 3.00
325 Zach Duke FY RC .30 .75
326 Zach Miner FY RC .30 .75
327 Bernie Castro .30 .75
Khalil Greene FS
328 Ryan Madson .20 .50
Elizardo Ramirez FS
329 Rich Harden .20 .50
Bobby Crosby FS
330 Zack Greinke .30 .75
Jimmy Gobble FS
331 Bobby Jenks .20 .50
Casey Kotchman FS
332 Sammy Sosa HL .20 .50
333 Kevin Millwood HL .07 .20
334 Rafael Palmeiro HL .12 .30
335 Roger Clemens HL .25 .60
336 Eric Gagne HL .07 .20
337 Bill Mueller .50 1.25
Manny Ramirez
Derek Jeter
AL Batting Avg LL
338 Vernon Wells .30 .75
Ichiro Suzuki
Michael Young
AL Hits LL
339 Alex Rodriguez .30 .75
Frank Thomas
Carlos Delgado
AL Home Runs LL
340 Carlos Delgado .30 .75
Alex Rodriguez
Bret Boone
AL RBI's LL
341 Pedro Martinez .12 .30
Tim Hudson
Esteban Loaiza
AL ERA LL
342 Esteban Loaiza .20 .50
Pedro Martinez
Roy Halladay
AL Strikeouts LL
343 Albert Pujols .50 1.25
Todd Helton
Edgar Renteria
NL Batting Avg LL
344 Albert Pujols .50 1.25
Todd Helton
Juan Pierre
NL Hits LL
345 Jim Thome .12 .30
Richie Sexson
Javy Lopez
NL Home Runs LL
346 Preston Wilson .12 .30
Gary Sheffield
Jim Thome
NL RBI's LL
347 Jason Schmidt .12 .30
Kevin Brown
Mark Prior
NL ERA LL
348 Kerry Wood .12 .30
Mark Prior
Javier Vazquez
NL Strikeouts LL
349 Roger Clemens .25 .60
David Wells ALDS
350 Kerry Wood .12 .30
Mark Prior NLDS
351 Josh Beckett .20 .50
Miguel Cabrera
Ivan Rodriguez NLCS
352 Jason Giambi .20 .50
Mariano Rivera
Aaron Boone ALCS
353 Derek Lowe .12 .30
Ivan Rodriguez AL/NLDS
354 Pedro Martinez .25 .60
Jorge Posada
Roger Clemens ALCS
355 Juan Pierre WS .07 .20
356 Carlos Delgado AS .07 .20
357 Bret Boone AS .07 .20
358 Alex Rodriguez AS .30 .75
359 Bill Mueller AS .07 .20
360 Vernon Wells AS .12 .30
361 Garret Anderson AS .07 .20
362 Magglio Ordonez AS .12 .30
363 Jorge Posada AS .12 .30
364 Roy Halladay AS .20 .50
365 Andy Pettitte AS .12 .30
366 Frank Thomas AS .20 .50
367 Jody Gerut AS .07 .20
368 Sammy Sosa .20 .50
369 Joe Crede .07 .20
370 Gary Sheffield .07 .20
371 Coco Crisp .07 .20
372 Torii Hunter .07 .20
373 Derrek Lee .07 .20
374 Adam Everett .07 .20
375 Miguel Tejada .12 .30
376 Jeremy Affeldt .07 .20
377 Robin Ventura .07 .20
378 Scott Podsednik .07 .20
379 Matthew LeCroy .07 .20
380 Vladimir Guerrero .20 .50
381 Tike Redman .07 .20
382 Jeff Nelson .07 .20
383 Cliff Lee .12 .30
384 Bobby Abreu .07 .20
385 Josh Fogg .07 .20
386 Trevor Hoffman .12 .30
387 Jesse Foppert .07 .20
388 Edgar Martinez .12 .30
389 Edgar Renteria .07 .20
390 Chipper Jones .20 .50
391 Eric Munson .07 .20
392 Dewon Brazelton .07 .20
393 John Thomson .07 .20
394 Chris Woodward .07 .20
395 Adam LaRoche .07 .20
396 Elmer Dessens .07 .20
397 Johnny Estrada .07 .20
398 Damian Moss .07 .20
399 Gabe Kapler .07 .20
400 Dontrelle Willis .07 .20
401 Troy Glaus .07 .20
402 Raul Mondesi .07 .20
403 Shane Reynolds .07 .20
404 Kurt Ainsworth .07 .20
405 Pedro Martinez .12 .30
406 Eric Karros .07 .20
407 Billy Koch .07 .20
408 Scott Schoeneweis .07 .20
409 Paul Wilson .07 .20
410 Mike Sweeney .07 .20
411 Jason Bay .12 .30
412 Mark Redman .07 .20
413 Jason Jennings .07 .20
414 Rondell White .07 .20
415 Todd Hundley .07 .20
416 Shannon Stewart .07 .20
417 Jae Weong Seo .07 .20
418 Livan Hernandez .07 .20
419 Mark Ellis .07 .20
420 Pat Burrell .07 .20
421 Mark Loretta .07 .20
422 Robb Nen .07 .20
423 Joel Pineiro .07 .20
424 Jason Simontacchi .07 .20
425 Sterling Hitchcock .07 .20
426 Rey Ordonez .07 .20
427 Greg Myers .07 .20
428 Shane Spencer .07 .20
429 Carlos Baerga .07 .20
430 Garret Anderson .07 .20
431 Horacio Ramirez .07 .20
432 Brian Roberts .07 .20
433 Damian Jackson .07 .20
434 Doug Glanville .07 .20
435 Brian Daubach .07 .20
436 Alex Escobar .07 .20
437 Alex Sanchez .07 .20
438 Jeff Bagwell .12 .30
439 Darrell May .07 .20
440 Shawn Green .07 .20
441 Geoff Jenkins .07 .20
442 Endy Chavez .07 .20
443 Nick Johnson .07 .20
444 Jose Guillen .07 .20
445 Tomas Perez .07 .20
446 Phil Nevin .07 .20
447 Jason Schmidt .07 .20
448 Julio Mateo .07 .20
449 So Taguchi .07 .20
450 Randy Johnson .20 .50
451 Paul Byrd .07 .20
452 Chone Figgins .07 .20
453 Larry Bigbie .07 .20
454 Scott Williamson .07 .20
455 Ramon Martinez .07 .20
456 Roberto Alomar .12 .30
457 Ryan Dempster .07 .20
458 Ryan Ludwick .07 .20
459 Ramon Santiago .07 .20
460 Jeff Conine .07 .20
461 Brad Lidge .07 .20
462 Ken Harvey .07 .20
463 Guillermo Mota .07 .20
464 Rick Reed .07 .20
465 Joey Eischen .07 .20
466 Wade Miller .07 .20
467 Steve Karsay .07 .20
468 Chase Utley .20 .50
469 Matt Stairs .07 .20
470 Yorvit Torrealba .07 .20
471 Joe Kennedy .07 .20
472 Reed Johnson .07 .20
473 Victor Zambrano .07 .20
474 Jeff Davanon .07 .20
475 Luis Gonzalez .07 .20
476 Eli Marrero .07 .20
477 Ray King .07 .20
478 Jack Cust .07 .20
479 Omar Daal .07 .20
480 Todd Walker .07 .20
481 Shawn Estes .07 .20
482 Chris Reitsma .07 .20
483 Jake Westbrook .07 .20
484 Jeremy Bonderman .07 .20
485 A.J. Burnett .12 .30
486 Roy Oswalt .12 .30
487 Kevin Brown .07 .20
488 Eric Milton .07 .20
489 Claudio Vargas .07 .20
490 Roger Cedeno .07 .20
491 David Wells .07 .20
492 Scott Hatteberg .07 .20
493 Ricky Ledee .07 .20
494 Eric Young .07 .20
495 Armando Benitez .07 .20
496 Dan Haren .07 .20
497 Carl Crawford .12 .30
498 Laynce Nix .07 .20
499 Eric Hinske .07 .20
500 Ivan Rodriguez .12 .30
501 Scot Shields .07 .20
502 Brandon Webb .07 .20
503 Mark DeRosa .07 .20
504 Jhonny Peralta .07 .20
505 Adam Kennedy .07 .20
506 Tony Batista .07 .20
507 Jeff Suppan .07 .20
508 Kenny Lofton .07 .20
509 Scott Sullivan .07 .20
510 Ken Griffey Jr. .30 .75
511 Billy Traber .07 .20
512 Larry Walker .12 .30
513 Mike Maroth .07 .20
514 Todd Hollandsworth .07 .20
515 Kirk Saarloos .07 .20
516 Carlos Beltran .07 .20
517 Juan Rivera .07 .20
518 Roger Clemens .25 .60
519 Karim Garcia .07 .20
520 Jose Reyes .12 .30
521 Brandon Duckworth .07 .20
522 Brian Giles .07 .20
523 J.T. Snow .07 .20
524 Jamie Moyer .07 .20
525 Jason Isringhausen .07 .20
526 Julio Lugo .07 .20
527 Mark Teixeira .20 .50
528 Cory Lidle .07 .20
529 Lyle Overbay .07 .20
530 Troy Percival .07 .20
531 Robby Hammock .07 .20
532 Robert Fick .07 .20
533 Jason Johnson .07 .20
534 Brandon Lyon .07 .20
535 Antonio Alfonseca .07 .20
536 Tom Goodwin .07 .20
537 Paul Konerko .12 .30
538 D'Angelo Jimenez .07 .20
539 Ben Broussard .07 .20
540 Magglio Ordonez .12 .30
541 Ellis Burks .07 .20
542 Carlos Pena .12 .30
543 Chad Fox .07 .20
544 Jerome Robertson .07 .20
545 Travis Hafner .07 .20
546 Joe Randa .07 .20
547 Wil Cordero .07 .20
548 Brady Clark .07 .20
549 Ruben Sierra .07 .20
550 Barry Zito .07 .20
551 Brett Myers .07 .20
552 Oliver Perez .07 .20
553 Trey Hodges .07 .20
554 Benito Santiago .07 .20
555 David Ross .07 .20
556 Ramon Vazquez .07 .20
557 Joe Nathan .07 .20
558 Dan Wilson .07 .20
559 Joe Mauer .20 .50
560 Jim Edmonds .12 .30
561 Shawn Wooten .07 .20
562 Matt Kata .07 .20
563 Vinny Castilla .07 .20
564 Marty Cordova .07 .20
565 Aramis Ramirez .07 .20
566 Carl Everett .07 .20
567 Ryan Freel .07 .20
568 Jason Davis .07 .20
569 Mark Bellhorn Sox .07 .20
570 Craig Monroe .07 .20
571 Roberto Hernandez .07 .20
572 Tim Redding .07 .20
573 Kevin Appier .07 .20
574 Jeromy Burnitz .07 .20
575 Miguel Cabrera .20 .50
576 Ramon Nivar .07 .20
577 Casey Blake .07 .20
578 Aaron Boone .07 .20
579 Jermaine Dye .07 .20
580 Jerome Williams .07 .20
581 John Olerud .07 .20
582 Scott Rolen .12 .30
583 Bobby Kielty .07 .20
584 Travis Lee .07 .20
585 Jeff Cirillo .07 .20
586 Scott Spiezio .07 .20
587 Stephen Randolph .07 .20
588 Melvin Mora .07 .20
589 Mike Timlin .07 .20
590 Kerry Wood .07 .20
591 Tony Womack .07 .20
592 Jody Gerut .07 .20
593 Franklyn German .07 .20
594 Morgan Ensberg .07 .20
595 Odalis Perez .07 .20
596 Michael Cuddyer .07 .20
597 Jon Lieber .07 .20
598 Mike Williams .07 .20
599 Jose Hernandez .07 .20
600 Alfonso Soriano .07 .20
601 Marquis Grissom .07 .20
602 Matt Morris .07 .20
603 Damian Rolls .07 .20
604 Juan Gonzalez .07 .20
605 Aquilino Lopez .07 .20
606 Jose Valverde .07 .20
607 Kenny Rogers .07 .20
608 Joe Borowski .07 .20
609 Josh Bard .07 .20
610 Austin Kearns .07 .20
611 Chin-Hui Tsao .07 .20
612 Wil Ledezma .07 .20
613 Aaron Guiel .07 .20
614 LaTroy Hawkins .07 .20
615 Tony Armas Jr. .07 .20
616 Steve Trachsel .07 .20
617 Ted Lilly .07 .20
618 Todd Pratt .07 .20
619 Sean Burroughs .07 .20
620 Rafael Palmeiro .12 .30
621 Jeremi Gonzalez .07 .20
622 Quinton McCracken .07 .20
623 David Ortiz .20 .50
624 Randall Simon .07 .20
625 Wily Mo Pena .07 .20
626 Nate Cornejo .07 .20
627 Brian Anderson .07 .20
628 Corey Koskie .07 .20
629 Keith Foulke Sox .07 .20
630 Rheal Cormier .07 .20
631 Sidney Ponson .07 .20
632 Gary Matthews Jr. .07 .20
633 Herbert Perry .07 .20
634 Shea Hillenbrand .07 .20
635 Craig Biggio .12 .30
636 Barry Larkin .12 .30
637 Arthur Rhodes .07 .20
638 Anaheim Angels TC .07 .20
639 Arizona Diamondbacks TC .07 .20
640 Atlanta Braves TC .07 .20
641 Baltimore Orioles TC .07 .20
642 Boston Red Sox TC .10 .30
643 Chicago Cubs TC .07 .20
644 Chicago White Sox TC .07 .20
645 Cincinnati Reds TC .07 .20
646 Cleveland Indians TC .07 .20
647 Colorado Rockies TC .07 .20
648 Detroit Tigers TC .07 .20
649 Florida Marlins TC .07 .20
650 Houston Astros TC .07 .20
651 Kansas City Royals TC .07 .20
652 Los Angeles Dodgers TC .07 .20
653 Milwaukee Brewers TC .07 .20
654 Minnesota Twins TC .07 .20
655 Montreal Expos TC .07 .20
656 New York Mets TC .07 .20
657 New York Yankees TC .20 .50
658 Oakland Athletics TC .07 .20
659 Philadelphia Phillies TC .07 .20
660 Pittsburgh Pirates TC .07 .20
661 San Diego Padres TC .07 .20
662 San Francisco Giants TC .07 .20
663 Seattle Mariners TC .07 .20
664 St. Louis Cardinals TC .07 .20
665 Tampa Bay Devil Rays TC .07 .20
666 Texas Rangers TC .07 .20
667 Toronto Blue Jays TC .07 .20
668 Kyle Sleeth DP RC .20 .50
669 Bradley Sullivan DP RC .20 .50
670 Carlos Quentin DP RC .75 2.00
671 Conor Jackson DP RC 1.25 3.00
672 Jeffrey Allison DP RC .20 .50
673 Matthew Moses DP RC .30 .75
674 Tim Stauffer DP RC .30 .75
675 Estee Harris DP RC .20 .50
676 David Aardsma DP RC .20 .50
677 Omar Quintanilla DP RC .20 .50
678 Aaron Hill DP .07 .20
679 Tony Richie DP RC .20 .50
680 Lastings Milledge DP RC 1.25 3.00
681 Brad Snyder DP RC .20 .50
682 Jason Hirsh DP RC .20 .50
683 Logan Kensing DP RC .20 .50
684 Chris Lubanski DP .20 .50
685 Ryan Harvey DP .20 .50
686 Ryan Wagner DP .20 .50
687 Rickie Weeks DP .20 .50
688 Grady Sizemore .30 .75
Jeremy Guthrie
689 Edwin Jackson .20 .50
Greg Miller
690 Jeremy Reed .20 .50
Neal Cotts
691 Adam Loewen .50 1.25
Nick Markakis
692 B.J. Upton .30 .75
Delmon Young
693 Kings of New York .50 1.25
Alex Rodriguez
Derek Jeter
694 Fan Favorites .50 1.25
Ichiro Suzuki
Albert Pujols
695 South Philly Sluggers .30 .75
Jim Thome
Mike Schmidt
696 Mike Mussina GG .12 .30
697 Bengie Molina GG .07 .20
698 John Olerud GG .07 .20
699 Bret Boone GG .07 .20
700 Eric Chavez GG .07 .20
701 Alex Rodriguez GG .30 .75
702 Mike Cameron GG UER .07 .20
Pictures Randy Winn
703 Ichiro Suzuki GG .30 .75
704 Torii Hunter GG .07 .20
705 Mike Hampton GG .07 .20
706 Mike Matheny GG .07 .20
707 Derrek Lee GG .07 .20
708 Luis Castillo GG .07 .20
709 Scott Rolen GG .12 .30
710 Edgar Renteria GG .07 .20
711 Andruw Jones GG .07 .20
712 Jose Cruz Jr. GG .07 .20
713 Jim Edmonds GG .12 .30
714 Roy Halladay CY .20 .50
715 Eric Gagne CY .07 .20
716 Alex Rodriguez MVP .30 .75
717 Angel Berroa ROY .07 .20
718 Dontrelle Willis ROY .07 .20
719 Todd Helton AS .12 .30
720 Marcus Giles AS .07 .20
721 Edgar Renteria AS .07 .20
722 Scott Rolen AS .12 .30
723 Albert Pujols AS .50 1.25
724 Gary Sheffield AS .07 .20
725 Javy Lopez AS .07 .20
726 Eric Gagne AS .07 .20
727 Randy Wolf AS .07 .20
728 Bobby Cox AS .07 .20
729 Scott Podsednik AS .07 .20
730 Alex Gonzalez WS .07 .20
731 Brad Penny WS .07 .20
732 Josh Beckett .12 .30
Ivan Rodriguez
Alex Gonzalez WS
733 Josh Beckett WS MVP .12 .30

2004 Topps Black

COM. (1-6/8-331/368-695) 6.00 15.00
SEMIS 1-296/368-667/693-695 10.00 25.00
UNL 1-296/368-667/693-695 20.00 40.00
COM. 297-326/668-687 6.00 15.00
SEMIS 297-326/668-687 10.00 25.00
UNL 297-326/668-687 15.00 40.00
COM. 327-331/688-692 6.00 15.00
SEMIS 327-331/688-692 10.00 25.00
UNL 327-331/688-692 20.00 40.00
SERIES 1 ODDS 1:13 HTA
SERIES 2 ODDS 1:12 HTA
STATED PRINT RUN 53 SERIAL #'d SETS
CARDS 7 AND 274 DO NOT EXIST
SCIOSCIA AND J.CASTRO NUMBERED 267
10 Ichiro Suzuki 25.00 60.00
20 Derek Jeter 40.00 100.00
40 Albert Pujols 40.00 100.00
100 Alex Rodriguez 25.00 60.00
140 Greg Maddux 25.00 60.00
324 Yadier Molina FY 40.00 100.00
510 Ken Griffey Jr. 25.00 60.00
518 Roger Clemens 20.00 50.00
670 Carlos Quentin DP 25.00 60.00
671 Conor Jackson DP 40.00 100.00
680 Lastings Milledge DP 40.00 100.00
693 Kings of New York 40.00 100.00
Alex Rodriguez
Derek Jeter
694 Fan Favorites 40.00 100.00
Ichiro Suzuki
Albert Pujols
695 South Philly Sluggers 25.00 60.00
Jim Thome
Mike Schmidt

2004 Topps Box Bottoms

The player list in our checklist has the player's name as well as what sheet his card is located on. Sheets 1-4 were issued on the bottom of first series HTA boxes and sheets 5-8 on second series.

*BOX BOTTOM CARDS: 1X TO 2.5X BASIC
ONE 4-CARD SHEET PER HTA BOX

2004 Topps Gold

*GOLD 1-296/368-667/693-695: 6X TO 15X
*GOLD 297-326/668-687: 1.25X TO 3X
*GOLD 327-331/688-692: 6X TO 15X
SERIES 1 ODDS 1:11 HOB, 1:3 HTA, 1:10 RET
SERIES 2 ODDS 1:8 HOB, 1:2 HTA, 1:8 RET
STATED PRINT RUN 2004 SERIAL #'d SETS
CARDS 7 AND 274 DO NOT EXIST
SCIOSCIA AND J.CASTRO NUMBERED 267

2004 Topps All-Star Patch Relics

SER.2 ODDS 1:7698 H, 1:2208 HTA, 1:7819 R
STATED PRINT RUN 15 SETS
CARDS ARE NOT SERIAL-NUMBERED
PRINT RUN INFO PROVIDED BY TOPPS
NO PRICING DUE TO SCARCITY

2004 Topps 1st Edition

*1ST ED 1-296: 1.25X TO 3X BASIC
*1ST ED 297-RC'S: X TO X BASIC
*1ST ED 327-331/688-: 1.25X TO 3X BASIC
DISTRIBUTED IN 1ST EDITION BOXES
CARDS 7 AND 274 DO NOT EXIST
SCIOSCIA AND J.CASTRO NUMBERED 267

2004 Topps All-Star Stitches Jersey Relics

SERIES 1 ODDS 1:137 HOB/RET, 1:39 HTA
AB Aaron Boone 4.00 10.00
AJ Andruw Jones 4.00 10.00
AR Alex Rodriguez 6.00 15.00
BD Brendan Donnelly 4.00 10.00
BW Billy Wagner 4.00 10.00
CE Carl Everett 4.00 10.00
EG Eddie Guardado 4.00 10.00
EGA Eric Gagne 4.00 10.00
EL Esteban Loaiza 4.00 10.00
EM Edgar Martinez 4.00 10.00
ER Edgar Renteria 4.00 10.00
HB Hank Blalock 4.00 10.00
JL Javy Lopez 4.00 10.00
JM Jamie Moyer 4.00 10.00
JP Jorge Posada 4.00 10.00
JS Jason Schmidt 4.00 10.00
JV Jose Vidro 4.00 10.00
KF Keith Foulke 4.00 10.00
KW Kerry Wood 4.00 10.00
ML Mike Lowell 4.00 10.00
MM Mark Mulder 4.00 10.00
MMO Melvin Mora 4.00 10.00
NG Nomar Garciaparra 6.00 15.00
PL Paul Lo Duca 4.00 10.00
PW Preston Wilson 4.00 10.00
RF Rafael Furcal 4.00 10.00
RH Ramon Hernandez 4.00 10.00
RO Russ Ortiz 4.00 10.00
RW Randy Wolf 4.00 10.00
RWH Rondell White 4.00 10.00
SH Shigetoshi Hasegawa 4.00 10.00
SR Scott Rolen 4.00 10.00
TG Troy Glaus 4.00 10.00
TH Todd Helton 4.00 10.00
VW Vernon Wells 4.00 10.00
WW Woody Williams 4.00 10.00

2004 Topps All-Stars

COMPLETE SET (20) 8.00 20.00
SERIES 2 ODDS 1:16 H, 1:4 HTA
TAS1 Jason Giambi .40 1.00
TAS2 Ichiro Suzuki 1.50 4.00
TAS3 Alex Rodriguez 1.50 4.00
TAS4 Albert Pujols 2.50 6.00
TAS5 Alfonso Soriano .40 1.00
TAS6 Nomar Garciaparra 1.00 2.50
TAS7 Andruw Jones .40 1.00
TAS8 Carlos Delgado .40 1.00
TAS9 Gary Sheffield .40 1.00
TAS10 Jorge Posada .60 1.50
TAS11 Magglio Ordonez .60 1.50
TAS12 Kerry Wood .40 1.00
TAS13 Garret Anderson .40 1.00
TAS14 Bret Boone .40 1.00
TAS15 Hank Blalock .40 1.00
TAS16 Mike Lowell .40 1.00
TAS17 Todd Helton .60 1.50
TAS18 Vernon Wells .40 1.00
TAS19 Roger Clemens 1.25 3.00
TAS20 Scott Rolen .60 1.50

2004 Topps American Treasures Presidential Signatures

Randomly inserted into packs, this set features a "cut" signature from each of the United State Presidents. Each of these cards feature the cut signature against a United States flag background while the back features an informational blurb about that president.

SER.1 ODDS 1:175,770 HOBBY, 1:52,080 HTA
SER.1 ODDS 1:138,240 RETAIL
STATED PRINT RUN 1 SERIAL #'d SET
NO PRICING DUE TO SCARCITY

2004 Topps American Treasures Presidential Signatures Dual

This card is similar to the basic American Treasures Presidential Cut Signatures but feature two signatures from George H. Bush and his son George W. Bush. Only one copy of this card was produced and it was seeded exclusively into first series Home Team Advantage packs.

SERIES 1 ODDS 1:208,320 HTA
STATED PRINT RUN 1 SERIAL #'d CARD
NO PRICING DUE TO SCARCITY
GB2 George H.W. Bush
George W. Bush

2004 Topps American Treasures Signatures

Building on the popularity and interest the first series Presidential Autographs gave this product, Topps issed 17 signed cards of famed Americans past and present as very tough inserts (one in 658,152 hobby, one in 98,256 HTA and one in 1,156,384 retail packs). Each of these cards were issued to a stated print run of one serial numbered set.

SER.2 ODDS 1:658,152 HOBBY, 1:98,256 HTA
SER.2 ODDS 1:156,384 RETAIL
STATED PRINT RUN 1 SERIAL #'d SET
NO PRICING DUE TO SCARCITY

2004 Topps American Treasures Signatures Dual

This card which was issued at a stated rate of one in 1,196,512 HTA packs feature signatures of Mark Twain/Samuel Clemens. Samuel Clemens, who wrote under the pseudonym of Mark Twain, signed items both ways during his lifetime and Topps found one type of each signature to put on this card. This card was issued to a stated print run of one serial numbered set.

SERIES 2 STATED ODDS 1:196,512 HTA
STATED PRINT RUN 1 SERIAL #'d CARD
NO PRICING DUE TO SCARCITY
MT Mark Twain
Samuel Clemens

2004 Topps Autographs

Please note Josh Beckett, Mike Lowell, Mark Prior, Ivan Rodriguez and Scott Rolen did not return their cards in time for inclusion into packs and the exchange date for these cards were November 30th, 2005 for Series one exchange cards and April 30th, 2006 for Series two exchange cards. Cards issued in first series packs carry a "1" and cards from series 2 carry a "2" after their group seeding notes within our checklist.

SER.1 B 1:7362 H, 1:1911 HTA, 1:7472 R
SER.1 C 1:10,900 H, 1:2741 HTA, 1:11,059 R
SER.1 D 1:1053 H, 1:273 HTA, 1:1055 R
SER.1 E 1:5278 H, 1:1640 HTA, 1:6284 R
SER.1 F 1:1229 H, 1:318 HTA, 1:1229 R
SER.1 G 1:2340 H, 1:668 HTA, 1:1881 R
SER.1 H 1:1167 H, 1:351 HTA, 1:1229 R
SER.2 A 1:10,530 H, 1:2848 HTA, 1:9774 R
SER.2 B 1:1504 H, 1:391 HTA, 1:1422 R
SER.2 C 1:1319 H, 1:333 HTA, 1:1303 R
AB Aaron Boone B2 15.00 40.00
AH Aubrey Huff B2 6.00 15.00
AK Austin Kearns B1 6.00 15.00
BB Bobby Brownlie C2 10.00 25.00
BS Benito Santiago D1 10.00 25.00
BU B.J. Upton F1 10.00 25.00
CF Cliff Floyd D1 6.00 15.00

DM Dustin McGowan C2	4.00	10.00
DW Dontrelle Willis B2	10.00	25.00
EH Eric Hinske H1	4.00	10.00
ER Elizardo Ramirez H1	4.00	10.00
GA Garret Anderson B2	10.00	25.00
HB Hank Blalock D1	6.00	15.00
IR Ivan Rodriguez B2	10.00	25.00
JB Josh Beckett B1	8.00	20.00
JG Jay Gibbons A1	6.00	15.00
JP1 Josh Phelps G1	4.00	10.00
JP2 Jorge Posada B2	10.00	25.00
JV Jose Vidro F1	4.00	10.00
KG Khalil Greene H1	10.00	25.00
LB Lance Berkman A2	20.00	50.00
MC Miguel Cabrera C2	10.00	25.00
ML Mike Lowell F1	6.00	15.00
MO Magglio Ordonez F1	6.00	15.00
MP Mark Prior D1	10.00	25.00
MS Mike Sweeney D1	6.00	15.00
MT Mark Teixeira D1	15.00	40.00
PK Paul Konerko G1	5.00	12.00
PL Paul Lo Duca E1	6.00	15.00
SP Scott Podsednik B2	10.00	25.00
TH Torii Hunter C1	6.00	15.00
VM Victor Martinez D1	6.00	15.00
ZG Zack Greinke C2	8.00	20.00

2004 Topps Derby Digs Jersey Relics

SERIES 1 ODDS 1:585 H, 1:167 HTA, 1:586 R

AP Albert Pujols	10.00	25.00
BB Bret Boone	4.00	10.00
CD Carlos Delgado	4.00	10.00
GA Garret Anderson	4.00	10.00
JE Jim Edmonds	4.00	10.00
JG Jason Giambi	4.00	10.00
RS Richie Sexson	4.00	10.00

2004 Topps Draft Pick Bonus

COMPLETE SET (10)	10.00	25.00
COMP.RETAIL SET (5)	6.00	15.00
COMP.HOLIDAY SET (10)	4.00	10.00

1-5 ISSUED IN BLUE RETAIL FACT.SET
6-15 ISSUED IN GREEN HOLIDAY FACT.SET

1 Josh Johnson	.50	1.25
2 Donny Lucy	.50	1.25
3 Greg Golson	.50	1.25
4 K.C. Herren	.50	1.25
5 Jeff Marquez	.50	1.25
6 Mark Rogers	.75	2.00
7 Eric Hurley	.50	1.25
8 Gio Gonzalez	1.25	3.00
9 Thomas Diamond	.50	1.25
10 Matt Bush	.75	2.00
11 Kyle Waldrop	.50	1.25
12 Neil Walker	2.50	6.00
13 Mike Ferris	.50	1.25
14 Ray Liotta	.50	1.25
15 Philip Hughes	4.00	10.00

2004 Topps Fall Classic Covers

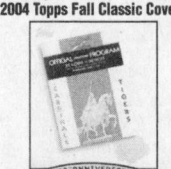

COMPLETE SET (99)	120.00	240.00
COMPLETE SERIES 1 (48)	60.00	120.00
COMPLETE SERIES 2 (51)	60.00	120.00
COMMON CARD	1.50	4.00

SERIES 1 ODDS 1:12 HOB/RET, 1:4 HTA
SERIES 2 ODDS 1:12 HOB/RET, 1:5 HTA
EVEN YEARS DISTRIBUTED IN SERIES 1
ODD YEARS DISTRIBUTED IN SERIES 2

2004 Topps First Year Player Bonus

COMPLETE SET (10)	8.00	20.00
COMPLETE SERIES 1 (5)	4.00	10.00
COMPLETE SERIES 2 (5)	4.00	10.00

1-5 ISSUED IN BROWN HOBBY FACT.SETS
6-10 ISSUED IN JC PENNEY FACT.SETS

1 Travis Blackley	.50	1.25
2 Rudy Guillen	.50	1.25
3 Ervin Santana	1.25	3.00
4 Wanell Severino	.50	1.25
5 Kevin Kouzmanoff	3.00	8.00
6 Alberto Callaspo	1.25	3.00
7 Bobby Brownlie	.50	1.25
8 Travis Hanson	.50	1.25
9 Joaquin Arias	1.25	3.00
10 Merkin Valdez	.50	1.25

2004 Topps Hit Parade

COMPLETE SET (30)	12.50	30.00

SERIES 2 ODDS 1:7 HOB, 1:2 HTA, 1:9 RET

HP1 Sammy Sosa HR	1.00	2.50
HP2 Rafael Palmeiro HR	.60	1.50
HP3 Fred McGriff HR	.40	1.00
HP4 Ken Griffey Jr. HR	1.50	4.00
HP5 Juan Gonzalez HR	.40	1.00
HP6 Frank Thomas HR	1.00	2.50
HP7 Andres Galarraga HR	.40	1.00
HP8 Jim Thome HR	.60	1.50
HP9 Jeff Bagwell HR	.60	1.50
HP10 Gary Sheffield HR	.40	1.00
HP11 Rafael Palmeiro RBI	.60	1.50
HP12 Sammy Sosa RBI	1.00	2.50
HP13 Fred McGriff RBI	.40	1.00
HP14 Andres Galarraga RBI	.40	1.00
HP15 Juan Gonzalez RBI	.40	1.00
HP16 Frank Thomas RBI	1.00	2.50
HP17 Jeff Bagwell RBI	.60	1.50
HP18 Ken Griffey Jr. RBI	1.50	4.00
HP19 Ruben Sierra RBI	.40	1.00
HP20 Gary Sheffield RBI	.40	1.00
HP21 Rafael Palmeiro Hits	.60	1.50
HP22 Roberto Alomar Hits Card number in Blue	.60	1.50
HP22A Roberto Alomar Hits Card number in White	.60	1.50
HP23 Julio Franco Hits	.40	1.00
HP24 Andres Galarraga Hits	.40	1.00
HP25 Fred McGriff Hits	.40	1.00
HP26 Craig Biggio Hits	.60	1.50
HP27 Barry Larkin Hits	.60	1.50
HP28 Steve Finley Hits	.40	1.00
HP29 B.J. Surhoff Hits	.40	1.00
HP30 Jeff Bagwell Hits	.60	1.50

2004 Topps Hobby Masters

COMPLETE SET (20)	12.50	30.00

SERIES 1 ODDS 1:12 HOBBY, 1:4 HTA

1 Albert Pujols	2.50	6.00
2 Mark Prior	.60	1.50
3 Alex Rodriguez	1.50	4.00
4 Nomar Garciaparra	1.00	2.50
5 Barry Bonds	2.00	5.00
6 Sammy Sosa	1.00	2.50
7 Alfonso Soriano	.40	1.00
8 Ichiro Suzuki	1.50	4.00
9 Derek Jeter	2.50	6.00
10 Jim Thome	.60	1.50
11 Jason Giambi	.40	1.00
12 Mike Piazza	1.00	2.50
13 Barry Zito	.40	1.00
14 Randy Johnson	1.00	2.50
15 Adam Dunn	.60	1.50
16 Vladimir Guerrero	1.00	2.50
17 Gary Sheffield	.40	1.00
18 Carlos Delgado	.40	1.00
19 Chipper Jones	1.00	2.50
20 Dontrelle Willis	.40	1.00

2004 Topps Own the Game

COMPLETE SET (30)	12.50	30.00

SERIES 1 ODDS 1:18 HOB/RET, 1:6 HTA

1 Jim Thome	.60	1.50
2 Albert Pujols	2.50	6.00
3 Alex Rodriguez	1.50	4.00
4 Barry Bonds	2.00	5.00
5 Ichiro Suzuki	1.50	4.00
6 Derek Jeter	2.50	6.00
7 Nomar Garciaparra	1.00	2.50
8 Alfonso Soriano	.40	1.00
9 Gary Sheffield	.40	1.00
10 Jason Giambi	.40	1.00
11 Todd Helton	.60	1.50
12 Garret Anderson	.40	1.00
13 Carlos Delgado	.40	1.00
14 Manny Ramirez	1.00	2.50
15 Richie Sexson	.40	1.00
16 Vernon Wells	.40	1.00
17 Preston Wilson	.40	1.00
18 Frank Thomas	1.00	2.50
19 Shawn Green	.40	1.00
20 Rafael Furcal	.40	1.00
21 Juan Pierre	.40	1.00
22 Javy Lopez	.40	1.00
23 Edgar Renteria	.40	1.00
24 Mark Prior	.60	1.50
25 Pedro Martinez	.60	1.50
26 Kerry Wood	.40	1.00
27 Curt Schilling	.60	1.50
28 Roy Halladay	1.00	2.50
29 Eric Gagne	.40	1.00
30 Brandon Webb	.40	1.00

2004 Topps Presidential First Pitch Seat Relics

SERIES 2 ODDS 1:592 H, 1:169 HTA, 1:592 R

BC Bill Clinton	20.00	50.00
CC Calvin Coolidge	10.00	25.00
DE Dwight Eisenhower	10.00	25.00
FR Franklin D. Roosevelt	15.00	40.00
GB George W. Bush	20.00	50.00
GF Gerald Ford	15.00	40.00
HH Herbert Hoover	10.00	25.00
HT Harry Truman	10.00	25.00
JK John F. Kennedy	20.00	50.00
LJ Lyndon B. Johnson	10.00	25.00
RN Richard Nixon	20.00	50.00
RR Ronald Reagan	30.00	60.00
WH Warren Harding	10.00	25.00
WT William Taft	10.00	25.00
WW Woodrow Wilson	10.00	25.00
GHB George H.W. Bush	15.00	40.00

2004 Topps Presidential Pastime

COMPLETE SET (42)	50.00	100.00

SERIES 2 ODDS 1:6 HOB, 1:2 HTA, 1:6 RET

PP1 George Washington	2.00	5.00
PP2 John Adams	1.25	3.00
PP3 Thomas Jefferson	2.00	5.00
PP4 James Madison	1.25	3.00
PP5 James Monroe	1.25	3.00
PP6 John Quincy Adams	1.25	3.00
PP7 Andrew Jackson	1.25	3.00
PP8 Martin Van Buren	1.25	3.00
PP9 William Harrison	1.25	3.00
PP10 John Tyler	1.25	3.00
PP11 James Polk	1.25	3.00
PP12 Zachary Taylor	1.25	3.00
PP13 Millard Fillmore	1.25	3.00
PP14 Franklin Pierce	1.25	3.00
PP15 James Buchanan	1.25	3.00
PP16 Abraham Lincoln	2.00	5.00
PP17 Andrew Johnson	1.25	3.00
PP18 Ulysses S. Grant	1.50	4.00
PP19 Rutherford B. Hayes	1.25	3.00
PP20 James Garfield	1.25	3.00
PP21 Chester Arthur	1.25	3.00
PP22 Grover Cleveland	1.25	3.00
PP23 Benjamin Harrison	1.25	3.00
PP24 William McKinley	1.25	3.00
PP25 Theodore Roosevelt	1.50	4.00
PP26 William Taft	1.25	3.00
PP27 Woodrow Wilson	1.25	3.00
PP28 Warren Harding	1.25	3.00
PP29 Calvin Coolidge	1.25	3.00
PP30 Herbert Hoover	1.25	3.00
PP31 Franklin D. Roosevelt	1.50	4.00
PP32 Harry Truman	1.25	3.00
PP33 Dwight Eisenhower	1.25	3.00
PP34 John F. Kennedy	1.50	4.00
PP35 Lyndon B. Johnson	1.25	3.00
PP36 Richard Nixon	1.50	4.00
PP37 Gerald Ford	1.50	4.00
PP38 Jimmy Carter	1.25	3.00
PP39 Ronald Reagan	4.00	10.00
PP40 George H.W. Bush	1.50	4.00
PP41 Bill Clinton	2.00	5.00
PP42 George W. Bush	2.00	5.00

2004 Topps Team Set Prospect Bonus

COMP.ASTROS SET (5)	3.00	8.00
COMP.CUBS SET (5)	3.00	8.00
COMP.RED SOX SET (5)	3.00	8.00
COMP.YANKEES SET (5)	3.00	8.00

A1-A5 ISSUED IN ASTROS FACTORY SET
C1-C5 ISSUED IN CUBS FACTORY SET
R1-R5 ISSUED IN RED SOX FACTORY SET
Y1-Y5 ISSUED IN YANKEES FACTORY SET

A1 Brooks Conrad	.75	2.00
A2 Hector Gimenez	.75	2.00
A3 Kevin Davidson	.75	2.00
A4 Chris Burke	.75	2.00
A5 John Buck	.75	2.00
C1 Bobby Brownlie	.75	2.00
C2 Felix Pie	.75	2.00
C3 Jon Connolly	.75	2.00
C4 David Kelton	.75	2.00
C5 Ricky Nolasco	1.25	3.00
R1 David Murphy	2.00	5.00
R2 Kevin Youkilis	1.25	3.00
R3 Juan Cedeno	.75	2.00
R4 Matt Murton	.75	2.00
R5 Kenny Perez	.75	2.00
Y1 Rudy Guillen	.75	2.00
Y2 David Parrish	.75	2.00
Y3 Brad Halsey	.75	2.00
Y4 Hector Made	.75	2.00
Y5 Robinson Cano	2.00	5.00

2004 Topps Series Seats Relics

SERIES 2 ODDS 1:316 HOB/RET, 1:89 HTA

AK Al Kaline	10.00	25.00
BF Bob Feller	6.00	15.00
BM Bill Mazeroski	10.00	25.00
BP Boog Powell	6.00	15.00
BR Brooks Robinson	6.00	15.00
FR Frank Robinson	6.00	15.00
HK Harmon Killebrew	10.00	25.00
JP Jim Palmer	6.00	15.00
LA Luis Aparicio	6.00	15.00
LP Lou Piniella	6.00	15.00
PM Paul Molitor	6.00	15.00
RJ Reggie Jackson	6.00	15.00
RY Robin Yount	10.00	25.00
WM Willie Mays	15.00	40.00
WS Warren Spahn	10.00	25.00

2004 Topps Series Stitches Relics

SER.2 GROUP A 1:829 H, 1:236 HTA, 1:832 R
SER.2 GROUP B 1:980 H, 1:280 HTA, 1:984 R
SER.2 GROUP C 1:686 H, 1:196 HTA, 1:686 R

AS Alfonso Soriano Bat B	6.00	15.00
CJ Chipper Jones Jsy C	6.00	15.00
DG Dwight Gooden Jsy A	4.00	10.00
DJ David Justice Bat B	6.00	15.00
FR Frank Robinson Bat B	6.00	15.00
GB George Brett Bat A	15.00	40.00
GC Gary Carter Jkt C	4.00	10.00
HK Harmon Killebrew Bat A	15.00	40.00
JB Johnny Bench Bat A	10.00	25.00
JBE Josh Beckett Jsy C	4.00	10.00
JC Joe Carter Bat B	6.00	15.00
JCA Jose Canseco Bat C	10.00	25.00
KG Kirk Gibson Bat B	6.00	15.00
KP Kirby Puckett Bat B	10.00	25.00
LD Lenny Dykstra Bat A	6.00	15.00
MS Mike Schmidt Uni A	15.00	40.00
PO Paul O'Neill Bat A	10.00	25.00
RC Roger Clemens Uni C	8.00	20.00
RJ Randy Johnson Jsy A	6.00	15.00
RJA Reggie Jackson Bat B	10.00	25.00
RY Robin Yount Uni A	6.00	15.00
SG Steve Garvey Bat B	6.00	15.00
TS Tom Seaver Uni A	6.00	15.00
WM Willie Mays Bat A	20.00	50.00

2004 Topps Legends Autographs

ISSUED IN VARIOUS 03-05 TOPPS BRANDS
SER.1 ODDS 1:399 H, 1:421 HTA, 1:494 R
SER.2 ODDS 1:766 H, 1:216 HTA, 1:802 R

AD Andre Dawson	6.00	15.00
BC Bert Campaneris	6.00	15.00
BP Boog Powell	6.00	15.00
CE Carl Erskine	6.00	15.00
DE Dwight Evans	10.00	25.00
DJ Davey Johnson	4.00	10.00
JP Jim Piersall	6.00	15.00
JP Johnny Podres	10.00	25.00
JR Joe Rudi	6.00	15.00
LB Lou Brock		
LD Lenny Dykstra		
NR Nolan Ryan	125.00	200.00
SA Sparky Anderson	6.00	15.00
SG Steve Garvey	6.00	15.00
WM Willie Mays	125.00	200.00

2004 Topps World Series Highlights

COMPLETE SET (30)	15.00	40.00
COMPLETE SERIES 1 (15)	8.00	20.00
COMPLETE SERIES 2 (15)	8.00	20.00

SERIES 1 ODDS 1:18 HOB/RET, 1:6 HTA
SERIES 2 ODDS 1:18 HOB/RET, 1:7 HTA

AJ Andruw Jones 2	.40	1.00
AK Al Kaline 2	1.00	2.50
BM Bill Mazeroski 1	.60	1.50
BR Brooks Robinson 1	.60	1.50
BT Bobby Thomson 2	.60	1.50
CF Carlton Fisk 1	.60	1.50
CY Carl Yastrzemski 1	1.00	2.50
DB Dusty Baker 2	.40	1.00
DJ David Justice 2	.40	1.00
DL Don Larsen 1	.40	1.00
DS Duke Snider 2	.60	1.50
FR Frank Robinson 2	.60	1.50
JB Johnny Bench 2	1.00	2.50
JC Joe Carter 2	.40	1.00
JCA Jose Canseco 2	.60	1.50
JP1 Jim Palmer 1	.40	1.00
JP2 Johnny Podres 2	.40	1.00
KG Kirk Gibson 1	.40	1.00
KP Kirby Puckett 1	1.00	2.50
LB Lou Brock 1	.60	1.50
LG Luis Gonzalez 2	.40	1.00
MS Mike Schmidt 1	1.50	4.00
OS Ozzie Smith 2	1.50	4.00
RJ Reggie Jackson 1	.60	1.50
RY Robin Yount 1	1.00	2.50
SM Stan Musial 1	1.50	4.00
TS Tom Seaver 1	.60	1.50
WF Whitey Ford 2	.60	1.50
WM1 Willie Mays 1	2.00	5.00
WM2 Willie McCovey 2	.60	1.50

2004 Topps World Series Highlights Autographs

SERIES 1 ODDS 1:74 HTA
SERIES 2 ODDS 1:69 HTA

AK Al Kaline 2	15.00	40.00
BM Bill Mazeroski 1	15.00	40.00
BR Brooks Robinson 1	15.00	40.00
BT Bobby Thomson 2	10.00	25.00
CF Carlton Fisk 1	40.00	80.00
DB Dusty Baker 2	10.00	25.00
DJ David Justice 2	10.00	25.00
DL Don Larsen 1	10.00	25.00
DS Duke Snider 2	15.00	40.00
HK Harmon Killebrew 1	20.00	50.00
JB Johnny Bench 2	30.00	60.00
JP1 Jim Palmer 1	10.00	25.00
JP2 Johnny Podres 2	10.00	25.00
KG Kirk Gibson 1	10.00	25.00
LB Lou Brock 1	15.00	40.00
MS Mike Schmidt 1	30.00	60.00
RJ Reggie Jackson 2	30.00	60.00
RY Robin Yount 1	15.00	40.00
SM Stan Musial 2	40.00	80.00
WF Whitey Ford 2	15.00	40.00

2004 Topps Traded

This 220-card set was released in October, 2004. The set was issued in 11-card hobby and retail packs (including one puzzle piece) which had an $3 SRP and which came 24 packs to a box and 12 boxes to a case. Cards numbered 1-65 feature players who were traded, while cards numbered 66 through 70 feature managers who took over teams after the basic set was issued and cards 71 through 90 are high draft picks, cards numbered 91 through 110 are prospect cards and cards numbered 111-220 feature Rookie Cards. Please note, an additional card (#T221) featuring Barry Bonds was distributed by Topps directly to hobby shop accounts enrolled in the Home Team Advantage program in early January, 2005. Collectors could obtain the card by purchasing a pack of 2005 Topps series 1 baseball. The program was limited to one card per customer.

COMPLETE SET (220)	20.00	50.00
COMMON CARD (1-70)	.07	.20
COMMON CARD (71-90)	.20	.50
COMMON CARD (91-110)	.20	.50
COMMON CARD (111-220)	.20	.50

BONDS AVAIL VIA HTA SHOP EXCHANGE
PLATE ODDS 1:1151 H, 1:1173 R, 1:327 HTA
PLATE PRINT RUN 1 SET PER COLOR
BLACK-CYAN-MAGENTA-YELLOW ISSUED
NO PLATE PRICING DUE TO SCARCITY

T1 Pokey Reese	.07	.20
T2 Tony Womack	.07	.20
T3 Richard Hidalgo	.07	.20
T4 Juan Uribe	.07	.20
T5 J.D. Drew	.07	.20
T6 Alex Gonzalez	.07	.20
T7 Carlos Guillen	.07	.20
T8 Doug Mientkiewicz	.07	.20
T9 Fernando Vina	.07	.20
T10 Milton Bradley	.07	.20
T11 Kelvim Escobar	.07	.20
T12 Ben Grieve	.07	.20
T13 Brian Jordan	.07	.20
T14 A.J. Pierzynski	.07	.20
T15 Billy Wagner	.07	.20
T16 Terrence Long	.07	.20
T17 Carlos Beltran	.07	.20
T18 Carl Everett	.07	.20
T19 Reggie Sanders	.07	.20
T20 Javy Lopez	.07	.20
T21 Jay Payton	.07	.20
T22 Octavio Dotel	.07	.20
T23 Eddie Guardado	.07	.20
T24 Andy Pettitte	.12	.30
T25 Richie Sexson	.07	.20
T26 Ronnie Belliard	.07	.20
T27 Michael Tucker	.07	.20
T28 Brad Fullmer	.07	.20
T29 Freddy Garcia	.07	.20
T30 Bartolo Colon	.07	.20
T31 Larry Walker Cards	.12	.30
T32 Mark Kotsay	.07	.20
T33 Jason Marquis	.07	.20
T34 Dustan Mohr	.07	.20
T35 Javier Vazquez	.07	.20
T36 Nomar Garciaparra	.20	.50
T37 Tino Martinez	.12	.30
T38 Hee Seop Choi	.07	.20
T39 Damian Miller	.07	.20
T40 Jose Lima	.07	.20
T41 Ty Wigginton	.07	.20
T42 Raul Ibanez	.07	.20
T43 Danys Baez	.07	.20
T44 Tony Clark	.07	.20
T45 Greg Maddux	.30	.75
T46 Victor Zambrano	.07	.20
T47 Orlando Cabrera Sox	.07	.20
T48 Jose Cruz Jr.	.07	.20
T49 Kris Benson	.07	.20
T50 Alex Rodriguez	.30	.75
T51 Steve Finley	.07	.20
T52 Ramon Hernandez	.07	.20
T53 Esteban Loaiza	.07	.20
T54 Ugueth Urbina	.07	.20
T55 Jeff Weaver	.07	.20
T56 Flash Gordon	.07	.20
T57 Jose Contreras	.07	.20
T58 Paul Lo Duca	.07	.20
T59 Junior Spivey	.07	.20
T60 Curt Schilling	.12	.30
T61 Brad Penny	.07	.20
T62 Braden Looper	.07	.20
T63 Miguel Cairo	.07	.20
T64 Juan Encarnacion	.07	.20
T65 Miguel Batista	.07	.20
T66 Terry Francona MG	.07	.20
T67 Lee Mazzilli MG	.07	.20
T68 Al Pedrique MG	.07	.20
T69 Ozzie Guillen MG	.07	.20
T70 Phil Garner MG	.07	.20
T71 Matt Bush DP RC	.30	.75
T72 Homer Bailey DP RC	.30	.75
T73 Greg Golson DP RC	.20	.50
T74 Kyle Waldrop DP RC	.20	.50
T75 Richie Robnett DP RC	.20	.50
T76 Jay Rainville DP RC	.20	.50
T77 Bill Bray DP RC	.20	.50
T78 Philip Hughes DP RC	1.50	4.00
T79 Scott Elbert DP RC	.20	.50
T80 Josh Fields DP RC	.30	.75
T81 Justin Orenduff DP RC	.30	.75
T82 Dan Putnam DP RC	.20	.50
T83 Chris Nelson DP RC	.20	.50
T84 Blake DeWitt DP RC	.75	2.00
T85 J.P. Howell DP RC	.20	.50
T86 Huston Street DP RC	.50	1.25
T87 Kurt Suzuki DP RC	.60	1.50
T88 Erick San Pedro DP RC	.20	.50
T89 Matt Tuiasosopo DP RC	.50	1.25
T90 Matt Macri DP RC	.30	.75
T91 Chad Tracy PROS	.20	.50
T92 Scott Hairston PROS	.20	.50
T93 Jonny Gomes PROS	.20	.50
T94 Chin-Feng Chen PROS	.20	.50
T95 Chien-Ming Wang PROS	1.00	2.50
T96 Dustin McGowan PROS	.20	.50
T97 Chris Burke PROS	.20	.50
T98 Denny Bautista PROS	.20	.50
T99 Preston Larrison PROS	.20	.50
T100 Kevin Youkilis PROS	.30	.75
T101 John Maine PROS	.20	.50
T102 Guillermo Quiroz PROS	.20	.50
T103 Dave Krynzel PROS	.20	.50
T104 David Kelton PROS	.20	.50
T105 Edwin Encarnacion PROS	.30	.75
T106 Chad Gaudin PROS	.20	.50
T107 Sergio Mitre PROS	.20	.50
T108 Laynce Nix PROS	.20	.50
T109 David Parrish PROS	.20	.50
T110 Brandon Claussen PROS	.20	.50
T111 Frank Francisco FY RC	.20	.50
T112 Brian Dallimore FY RC	.20	.50
T113 Jim Crowell FY RC	.20	.50
T114 Andres Blanco FY RC	.20	.50
T115 Eduardo Villacis FY RC	.20	.50
T116 Kazuhito Tadano FY RC	.20	.50
T117 Aarom Baldiris FY RC	.20	.50
T118 Justin Germano FY RC	.20	.50
T119 Joey Gathright FY RC	.20	.50
T120 Franklyn Gracesqui FY RC	.20	.50
T121 Chin-Lung Hu FY RC	.20	.50
T122 Scott Olsen FY RC	.20	.50
T123 Tyler Davidson FY RC	.20	.50
T124 Fausto Carmona FY RC	.30	.75
T125 Tim Hutting FY RC	.20	.50
T126 Ryan Meaux FY RC	.20	.50
T127 Jon Connolly FY RC	.20	.50
T128 Hector Made FY RC	.20	.50
T129 Jamie Brown FY RC	.20	.50
T130 Paul McAnulty FY RC	.20	.50
T131 Chris Saenz FY RC	.20	.50
T132 Marland Williams FY RC	.20	.50
T133 Mike Huggins FY RC	.20	.50
T134 Jesse Crain FY RC	.20	.50
T135 Chad Bentz FY RC	.20	.50
T136 Kazuo Matsui FY RC	.30	.75
T137 Paul Maholm FY RC	.30	.75
T138 Brock Jacobsen FY RC	.20	.50
T139 Casey Daigle FY RC	.20	.50
T140 Nyjer Morgan FY RC	.20	.50
T141 Tom Mastny FY RC	.20	.50
T142 Kody Kirkland FY RC	.20	.50
T143 Jose Capellan FY RC	.20	.50
T144 Felix Hernandez FY RC	4.00	10.00
T145 Shawn Hill FY RC	.20	.50
T146 Danny Gonzalez FY RC	.20	.50
T147 Scott Dohmann FY RC	.20	.50
T148 Tommy Murphy FY RC	.20	.50
T149 Akinori Otsuka FY RC	.20	.50
T150 Miguel Perez FY RC	.20	.50
T151 Mike Rouse FY RC	.20	.50
T152 Ramon Ramirez FY RC	.20	.50
T153 Luke Hughes FY RC	.20	.50
T154 Howie Kendrick FY RC	3.00	8.00
T155 Ryan Budde FY RC	.20	.50
T156 Charlie Zink FY RC	.20	.50
T157 Warner Madrigal FY RC	.20	.50
T158 Jason Szuminski FY RC	.20	.50
T159 Chad Chop FY RC	.20	.50
T160 Shingo Takatsu FY RC	.20	.50
T161 Matt Lemanczyk FY RC	.20	.50
T162 Wardell Starling FY RC	.20	.50
T163 Nick Gorneault FY RC	.20	.50
T164 Scott Proctor FY RC	.20	.50
T165 Brooks Conrad FY RC	.20	.50
T166 Hector Gimenez FY RC	.20	.50
T167 Kevin Howard FY RC	.20	.50
T168 Vince Perkins FY RC	.20	.50
T169 Brock Peterson FY RC	.20	.50
T170 Chris Shelton FY RC	.20	.50
T171 Erick Aybar FY RC	.30	.75
T172 Paul Bacot FY RC	.20	.50
T173 Matt Capps FY RC	.20	.50
T174 Kory Casto FY RC	.20	.50
T175 Juan Cedeno FY RC	.20	.50
T176 Vito Chiaravalloti FY RC	.20	.50
T177 Alec Zumwalt FY RC	.20	.50
T178 J.J. Furmaniak FY RC	.20	.50
T179 Lee Gwaltney FY RC	.20	.50
T180 Donald Kelly FY RC	.30	.75
T181 Benji DeQuin FY RC	.20	.50
T182 Brant Colamarino FY RC	.20	.50
T183 Juan Gutierrez FY RC	.20	.50
T184 Carl Loadenthal FY RC	.20	.50
T185 Ricky Nolasco FY RC	.30	.75
T186 Jeff Salazar FY RC	.20	.50
T187 Rob Tejeda FY RC	.20	.50
T188 Alex Romero FY RC	.20	.50
T189 Yoann Torrealba FY RC	.20	.50
T190 Carlos Sosa FY RC	.20	.50
T191 Tim Bittner FY RC	.20	.50
T192 Chris Aguila FY RC	.20	.50
T193 Jason Frasor FY RC	.20	.50
T194 Reid Gorecki FY RC	.20	.50
T195 Dustin Nippert FY RC	.20	.50
T196 Javier Guzman FY RC	.20	.50
T197 Harvey Garcia FY RC	.20	.50
T198 Ivan Ochoa FY RC	.20	.50
T199 David Wallace FY RC	.20	.50
T200 Joel Zumaya FY RC	1.25	3.00
T201 Casey Kopitzke FY RC	.20	.50
T202 Lincoln Holdzkom FY RC	.20	.50
T203 Chad Santos FY RC	.20	.50
T204 Brian Pilkington FY RC	.20	.50
T205 Terry Jones FY RC	.20	.50
T206 Jerome Gamble FY RC	.20	.50
T207 Brad Eldred FY RC	.20	.50
T208 David Pauley FY RC	.30	.75
T209 Kevin Davidson FY RC	.20	.50
T210 Damaso Espino FY RC	.20	.50
T211 Tom Farmer FY RC	.20	.50
T212 Michael Mooney FY RC	.20	.50
T213 James Tomlin FY RC	.20	.50
T214 Greg Thissen FY RC	.20	.50
T215 Calvin Hayes FY RC	.20	.50
T216 Fernando Cortez FY RC	.20	.50
T217 Sergio Silva FY RC	.20	.50
T218 Jon de Vries FY RC	.20	.50
T219 Don Sutton FY RC	.20	.50
T220 Leo Nunez FY RC	.20	.50
T221 Barry Bonds HTA	2.00	5.00

2004 Topps Traded Blue

ODDS 1:4574 H, 1:4925 R, 1:1238 HTA
STATED PRINT RUN 1 SERIAL #'d SET
NO PRICING DUE TO SCARCITY

2004 Topps Traded Gold

*GOLD 1-70: 6X TO 15X BASIC
*GOLD 71-90: 1.2X TO 3X BASIC
*GOLD 91-110: 1.2X TO 3X BASIC
*GOLD 111-220: 1.2X TO 3X BASIC
STATED ODDS 1:2 HOB/RET, 1:1 HTA
STATED PRINT RUN 2004 SERIAL #'d SETS

2004 Topps Traded Future Phenoms Relics

GROUP A ODDS 1:184 H/R, 1:53 HTA
GROUP B ODDS 1:65 H/R, 1:27 HTA

AG Adrian Gonzalez Bat A	3.00	8.00
BC Bobby Crosby Bat A	4.00	10.00
BU B.J. Upton Bat A	6.00	15.00
DN Dioner Navarro Bat B	3.00	8.00
DY Delmon Young Bat A	6.00	15.00
ED Eric Duncan Bat B	2.00	5.00
EJ Edwin Jackson Jsy B	2.00	5.00
JH J.J. Hardy Bat B	6.00	15.00
JM Justin Morneau Bat A	4.00	10.00
JW Jayson Werth Bat A	6.00	15.00
KC Kevin Cash Bat B	2.00	5.00
KM Kazuo Matsui Bat A	4.00	10.00
LM Lastings Milledge Bat B	4.00	10.00
MM Mark Malaska Jsy A	3.00	8.00
NG Nick Green Bat A	3.00	8.00
RN Ramon Nivar Bat A	3.00	8.00
VM Victor Martinez Bat A	4.00	10.00

2004 Topps Traded Hall of Fame Relics

A ODDS 1:3388 H, 1:3518 R, 1:966 HTA
B ODDS 1:1011 H, 1:1026 R, 1:289 HTA

DE Dennis Eckersley Jsy B	6.00	15.00
PM Paul Molitor Bat A	6.00	15.00

2004 Topps Traded Hall of Fame Dual Relic

ODDS 1:3388 H, 1:3518 R, 1:966 HTA

ME Paul Molitor Bat	10.00	25.00
Dennis Eckersley Jsy		

2004 Topps Traded Puzzle

COMPLETE PUZZLE (110)	25.00	50.00
COMMON PIECE (1-110)	.20	.50
ONE PER PACK		
1 Puzzle Piece 1	.20	.50
2 Puzzle Piece 2	.20	.50
3 Puzzle Piece 3	.20	.50
4 Puzzle Piece 4	.20	.50
5 Puzzle Piece 5	.20	.50
6 Puzzle Piece 6	.20	.50
7 Puzzle Piece 7	.20	.50
8 Puzzle Piece 8	.20	.50
9 Puzzle Piece 9	.20	.50
10 Puzzle Piece 10	.20	.50
11 Puzzle Piece 11	.20	.50
12 Puzzle Piece 12	.20	.50
13 Puzzle Piece 13	.20	.50
14 Puzzle Piece 14	.20	.50
15 Puzzle Piece 15	.20	.50
16 Puzzle Piece 16	.20	.50
17 Puzzle Piece 17	.20	.50
18 Puzzle Piece 18	.20	.50
19 Puzzle Piece 19	.20	.50
20 Puzzle Piece 20	.20	.50
21 Puzzle Piece 21	.20	.50
22 Puzzle Piece 22	.20	.50
23 Puzzle Piece 23	.20	.50
24 Puzzle Piece 24	.20	.50
25 Puzzle Piece 25	.20	.50
26 Puzzle Piece 26	.20	.50
27 Puzzle Piece 27	.20	.50
28 Puzzle Piece 28	.20	.50
29 Puzzle Piece 29	.20	.50
30 Puzzle Piece 30	.20	.50
31 Puzzle Piece 31	.20	.50
32 Puzzle Piece 32	.20	.50
33 Puzzle Piece 33	.20	.50
34 Puzzle Piece 34	.20	.50
35 Puzzle Piece 35	.20	.50
36 Puzzle Piece 36	.20	.50
37 Puzzle Piece 37	.20	.50
38 Puzzle Piece 38	.20	.50
39 Puzzle Piece 39	.20	.50
40 Puzzle Piece 40	.20	.50
41 Puzzle Piece 41	.20	.50
42 Puzzle Piece 42	.20	.50
43 Puzzle Piece 43	.20	.50
44 Puzzle Piece 44	.20	.50
45 Puzzle Piece 45	.20	.50
46 Puzzle Piece 46	.20	.50
47 Puzzle Piece 47	.20	.50
48 Puzzle Piece 48	.20	.50
49 Puzzle Piece 49	.20	.50
50 Puzzle Piece 50	.20	.50
51 Puzzle Piece 51	.20	.50
52 Puzzle Piece 52	.20	.50
53 Puzzle Piece 53	.20	.50
54 Puzzle Piece 54	.20	.50
55 Puzzle Piece 55	.20	.50
56 Puzzle Piece 56	.20	.50
57 Puzzle Piece 57	.20	.50
58 Puzzle Piece 58	.20	.50
59 Puzzle Piece 59	.20	.50
60 Puzzle Piece 60	.20	.50
61 Puzzle Piece 61	.20	.50
62 Puzzle Piece 62	.20	.50
63 Puzzle Piece 63	.20	.50
64 Puzzle Piece 64	.20	.50
65 Puzzle Piece 65	.20	.50
66 Puzzle Piece 66	.20	.50
67 Puzzle Piece 67	.20	.50
68 Puzzle Piece 68	.20	.50
69 Puzzle Piece 69	.20	.50
70 Puzzle Piece 70	.20	.50
71 Puzzle Piece 71	.20	.50
72 Puzzle Piece 72	.20	.50
73 Puzzle Piece 73	.20	.50
74 Puzzle Piece 74	.20	.50
75 Puzzle Piece 75	.20	.50
76 Puzzle Piece 76	.20	.50
77 Puzzle Piece 77	.20	.50
78 Puzzle Piece 78	.20	.50
79 Puzzle Piece 79	.20	.50
80 Puzzle Piece 80	.20	.50
81 Puzzle Piece 81	.20	.50
82 Puzzle Piece 82	.20	.50
83 Puzzle Piece 83	.20	.50
84 Puzzle Piece 84	.20	.50
85 Puzzle Piece 85	.20	.50
86 Puzzle Piece 86	.20	.50
87 Puzzle Piece 87	.20	.50
88 Puzzle Piece 88	.20	.50
89 Puzzle Piece 89	.20	.50
90 Puzzle Piece 90	.20	.50
91 Puzzle Piece 91	.20	.50
92 Puzzle Piece 92	.20	.50
93 Puzzle Piece 93	.20	.50
94 Puzzle Piece 94	.20	.50
95 Puzzle Piece 95	.20	.50
96 Puzzle Piece 96	.20	.50
97 Puzzle Piece 97	.20	.50
98 Puzzle Piece 98	.20	.50
99 Puzzle Piece 99	.20	.50
100 Puzzle Piece 100	.20	.50
101 Puzzle Piece 101	.20	.50
102 Puzzle Piece 102	.20	.50
103 Puzzle Piece 103	.20	.50
104 Puzzle Piece 104	.20	.50
105 Puzzle Piece 105	.20	.50
106 Puzzle Piece 106	.20	.50
107 Puzzle Piece 107	.20	.50
108 Puzzle Piece 108	.20	.50
109 Puzzle Piece 109	.20	.50
110 Puzzle Piece 110	.20	.50

2004 Topps Traded Signature Cuts

STATED ODDS 1:91,472 HOB, 1:39,600 HTA
STATED PRINT RUN 1 SERIAL #'d SET
NO PRICING DUE TO SCARCITY
BR Babe Ruth
CH Catfish Hunter
JM Johnny Mize
RM Roger Maris
WS Warren Spahn

2004 Topps Traded Signature Moves

A ODDS 1:675 H, 1:684 R, 1:193 HTA
B ODDS 1:169 H/R, 1:48 HTA
EXCHANGE DEADLINE 12/31/06

AR Alex Rodriguez A	100.00	175.00
AW Adam Wainwright B	12.50	30.00
EM Eli Marrero B	4.00	10.00
FV Fernando Vina B	4.00	10.00
JV Javier Vazquez A	6.00	15.00
MB Milton Bradley B	6.00	15.00
MK Mark Kotsay B	6.00	15.00
MN Mike Neu B	4.00	10.00

2004 Topps Traded Transactions Relics

STATED ODDS 1:106 H, 1:107 R, 1:30 HTA

AP Andy Pettitte Bat	4.00	10.00
AR Alex Rodriguez Yanks Jsy	10.00	25.00
BJ Brian Jordan Bat	3.00	8.00
CE Carl Everett Bat	3.00	8.00
GS Gary Sheffield Bat	4.00	10.00
HC Hee Seop Choi Bat	3.00	8.00
IR Ivan Rodriguez Bat	4.00	10.00
JB Jeromy Burnitz Bat	3.00	8.00
JG Juan Gonzalez Bat	3.00	8.00
JL Javy Lopez Bat	3.00	8.00
KL Kenny Lofton Bat	3.00	8.00
KM Kazuo Matsui Bat	3.00	8.00
MT Miguel Tejada Bat	3.00	8.00
RA Roberto Alomar Bat	4.00	10.00
RC Roger Clemens Bat	6.00	15.00
RLS Richie Sexson Bat	3.00	8.00
RP Rafael Palmeiro Bat	4.00	10.00
RS Reggie Sanders Bat	3.00	8.00
RW Rondell White Bat	3.00	8.00
VG Vladimir Guerrero Bat	4.00	10.00

2004 Topps Traded Transactions Dual Relics

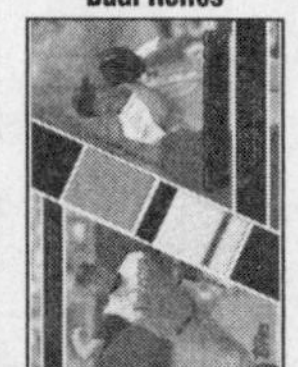

STATED ODDS 1:562 H, 1:563 R, 1:160 HTA

AR Alex Rodriguez Rgr-Yanks	10.00	25.00
CS Curt Schilling D'backs-Sox	6.00	15.00
RP Rafael Palmeiro O's-Rgr	6.00	15.00

2005 Topps

This 367-card first series was released in November, 2004 while the 366 card second series was issued in April. The set was issued in 10-card hobby/retail packs with a $2 SRP which came 36 packs to a box and 12 boxes to a case. These cards were also issued in 35-card HTA packs with a $5 SRP which came 20 packs to a box and two boxes to a case. Please note that card number 7 was not issued. In addition, the following subets were issued in the first series: Managers (267-296); First year cards (297-326); Prospects (327-331); Season Highlights (332-336); League Leaders (337-348); Post-Season (349-355); AL All-Stars (356-367). In addition, card number 368, which was not on the original checklist, honored the Boston Red Sox World Championship. Subsets in the second series included Team Cards (638-667); First Year players (668-687); Multi player prospect cards (688-694); Award Winners (695-718); NL All-Stars (719-730) and World Series Cards (731-734).

Card		
COMP.HOBBY SET (737)	40.00	80.00
COMP.HOLIDAY SET (742)	40.00	80.00
COMP.CUBS SET (737)	40.00	80.00
COMP.GIANTS SET (737)	40.00	80.00
COMP.NATIONALS SET (737)	40.00	80.00
COMP.RED SOX SET (737)	40.00	80.00
COMP.TIGERS SET (737)	40.00	80.00
COMP.YANKEES SET (737)	40.00	80.00
COMPLETE SET (732)	40.00	80.00
COMPLETE SERIES 1 (366)	20.00	40.00
COMPLETE SERIES 2 (366)	20.00	40.00
COMMON (1-6/8-296)	.07	.20
COMMON (297-326/668-687)	.20	.50
COMMON CARD 327-	.20	.50
COM (349-355/368/731-734)	.20	.50
CARD NUMBER 7 DOES NOT EXIST		
OVERALL PLATE SER.1 ODDS 1:154 HTA		
OVERALL PLATE SER.2 ODDS 1:112 HTA		
PLATE PRINT RUN 1 SET PER COLOR		
BLACK-CYAN-MAGENTA-YELLOW ISSUED		
NO PLATE PRICING DUE TO SCARCITY		
1 Alex Rodriguez	.30	.75
2 Placido Polanco	.07	.20
3 Torii Hunter	.07	.20
4 Lyle Overbay	.07	.20
5 Johnny Damon	.12	.30
6 Johnny Estrada	.07	.20
8 Francisco Rodriguez	.12	.30
9 Jason LaRue	.07	.20
10 Sammy Sosa	.20	.50
11 Randy Wolf	.07	.20
12 Jason Bay	.07	.20
13 Tom Glavine	.12	.30
14 Michael Tucker	.07	.20
15 Brian Giles	.07	.20
16 Dan Wilson	.07	.20
17 Jim Edmonds	.12	.30
18 Danys Baez	.07	.20
19 Roy Halladay	.20	.50
20 Hank Blalock	.07	.20
21 Darin Erstad	.07	.20
22 Robby Hammock	.07	.20
23 Mike Hampton	.07	.20
24 Mark Bellhorn	.07	.20
25 Jim Thome	.12	.30
26 Scott Schoeneweis	.07	.20
27 Jody Gerut	.07	.20
28 Vinny Castilla	.07	.20
29 Luis Castillo	.07	.20
30 Ivan Rodriguez	.12	.30
31 Craig Biggio	.12	.30
32 Joe Randa	.07	.20
33 Adrian Beltre	.07	.20
34 Scott Podsednik	.07	.20
35 Cliff Floyd	.07	.20
36 Livan Hernandez	.07	.20
37 Eric Byrnes	.07	.20
38 Gabe Kapler	.07	.20
39 Jack Wilson	.07	.20
40 Gary Sheffield	.07	.20
41 Chan Ho Park	.12	.30
42 Carl Crawford	.12	.30
43 Miguel Batista	.07	.20
44 David Bell	.07	.20
45 Jeff DaVanon	.07	.20
46 Brandon Webb	.12	.30
47 Bronson Arroyo	.07	.20
48 Melvin Mora	.07	.20
49 David Ortiz	.20	.50
50 Andruw Jones	.07	.20
51 Chone Figgins	.07	.20
52 Danny Graves	.07	.20
53 Preston Wilson	.07	.20
54 Jeremy Bonderman	.07	.20
55 Chad Fox	.07	.20
56 Dan Miceli	.07	.20
57 Jimmy Gobble	.07	.20
58 Darren Dreifort	.07	.20
59 Matt LeCroy	.07	.20
60 Jose Vidro	.07	.20
61 Al Leiter	.07	.20
62 Javier Vazquez	.07	.20
63 Erubiel Durazo	.07	.20
64 Doug Glanville	.07	.20
65 Scot Shields	.07	.20
66 Edgardo Alfonzo	.07	.20
67 Ryan Franklin	.07	.20
68 Francisco Cordero	.07	.20
69 Brett Myers	.07	.20
70 Curt Schilling	.12	.30
71 Matt Kata	.07	.20
72 Mark DeRosa	.07	.20
73 Rodrigo Lopez	.07	.20
74 Tim Wakefield	.07	.20
75 Frank Thomas	.20	.50
76 Jimmy Rollins	.12	.30
77 Barry Zito	.07	.20
78 Hideo Nomo	.20	.50
79 Brad Wilkerson	.07	.20
80 Adam Dunn	.12	.30
81 Billy Traber	.07	.20
82 Fernando Vina	.07	.20
83 Nate Robertson	.07	.20
84 Brad Ausmus	.07	.20
85 Mike Sweeney	.07	.20
86 Kip Wells	.07	.20
87 Chris Reitsma	.07	.20
88 Zach Day	.07	.20
89 Tony Clark	.07	.20
90 Bret Boone	.07	.20
91 Mark Loretta	.07	.20
92 Jerome Williams	.07	.20
93 Randy Winn	.07	.20
94 Marlon Anderson	.07	.20
95 Aubrey Huff	.07	.20
96 Kevin Mench	.07	.20
97 Frank Catalanotto	.07	.20
98 Flash Gordon	.07	.20
99 Scott Hatteberg	.07	.20
100 Albert Pujols	.50	1.25
101 Jose/Bengie Molina	.07	.20
102 Oscar Villarreal	.07	.20
103 Jay Gibbons	.07	.20
104 Byung-Hyun Kim	.07	.20
105 Joe Borowski	.07	.20
106 Mark Grudzielanek	.07	.20
107 Mark Buehrle	.12	.30
108 Paul Wilson	.07	.20
109 Ronnie Belliard	.07	.20
110 Reggie Sanders	.07	.20
111 Tim Redding	.07	.20
112 Brian Lawrence	.07	.20
113 Darrell May	.07	.20
114 Jose Hernandez	.07	.20
115 Ben Sheets	.07	.20
116 Johan Santana	.20	.50
117 Billy Wagner	.07	.20
118 Mariano Rivera	.20	.50
119 Steve Trachsel	.07	.20
120 Akinori Otsuka	.07	.20
121 Bobby Kielty	.07	.20
122 Orlando Hernandez	.07	.20
123 Raul Ibanez	.07	.20
124 Mike Matheny	.07	.20
125 Vernon Wells	.07	.20
126 Jason Isringhausen	.07	.20
127 Jose Guillen	.07	.20
128 Danny Bautista	.07	.20
129 Marcus Giles	.07	.20
130 Javy Lopez	.07	.20
131 Kevin Millar	.07	.20
132 Kyle Farnsworth	.07	.20
133 Carl Pavano	.07	.20
134 D'Angelo Jimenez	.07	.20
135 Casey Blake	.07	.20
136 Matt Holliday	.20	.50
137 Bobby Higginson	.07	.20
138 Nate Field	.07	.20
139 Alex Gonzalez	.07	.20
140 Jeff Kent	.07	.20
141 Aaron Guiel	.07	.20
142 Shawn Green	.07	.20
143 Bill Hall	.07	.20
144 Shannon Stewart	.07	.20
145 Juan Rivera	.07	.20
146 Coco Crisp	.07	.20
147 Mike Mussina	.12	.30
148 Eric Chavez	.07	.20
149 Jon Lieber	.07	.20
150 Vladimir Guerrero	.20	.50
151 Alex Cintron	.07	.20
152 Horacio Ramirez	.07	.20
153 Sidney Ponson	.07	.20
154 Trot Nixon	.07	.20
155 Greg Maddux	.30	.75
156 Edgar Renteria	.07	.20
157 Ryan Freel	.07	.20
158 Matt Lawton	.07	.20
159 Shawn Chacon	.07	.20
160 Josh Beckett	.12	.30
161 Ken Harvey	.07	.20
162 Juan Cruz	.07	.20
163 Juan Encarnacion	.07	.20
164 Wes Helms	.07	.20
165 Brad Radke	.07	.20
166 Claudio Vargas	.07	.20
167 Mike Cameron	.07	.20
168 Billy Koch	.07	.20
169 Bobby Crosby	.07	.20
170 Mike Lieberthal	.07	.20
171 Rob Mackowiak	.07	.20
172 Sean Burroughs	.07	.20
173 J.T. Snow Jr.	.07	.20
174 Paul Konerko	.12	.30
175 Luis Gonzalez	.07	.20
176 John Lackey	.07	.20
177 Antonio Alfonseca	.07	.20
178 Brian Roberts	.07	.20
179 Bill Mueller	.07	.20
180 Carlos Lee	.07	.20
181 Corey Patterson	.07	.20
182 Sean Casey	.07	.20
183 Cliff Lee	.12	.30
184 Jason Jennings	.07	.20
185 Dmitri Young	.07	.20
186 Juan Uribe	.07	.20
187 Andy Pettitte	.12	.30
188 Juan Gonzalez	.07	.20
189 Pokey Reese	.07	.20
190 Jason Phillips	.07	.20
191 Rocky Biddle	.07	.20
192 Lew Ford	.07	.20
193 Mark Mulder	.07	.20
194 Bobby Abreu	.07	.20
195 Jason Kendall	.07	.20
196 Terrence Long	.07	.20
197 A.J. Pierzynski	.07	.20
198 Eddie Guardado	.07	.20
199 So Taguchi	.07	.20
200 Jason Giambi	.07	.20
201 Tony Batista	.07	.20
202 Kyle Lohse	.07	.20
203 Trevor Hoffman	.12	.30
204 Tike Redman	.07	.20
205 Matt Herges	.07	.20
206 Gil Meche	.07	.20
207 Chris Carpenter	.20	.50
208 Ben Broussard	.07	.20
209 Eric Young	.07	.20
210 Doug Waechter	.07	.20
211 Jarrod Washburn	.07	.20
212 Chad Tracy	.07	.20
213 John Smoltz	.20	.50
214 Jorge Julio	.07	.20
215 Todd Walker	.07	.20
216 Shingo Takatsu	.07	.20
217 Jose Acevedo	.07	.20
218 David Riske	.07	.20
219 Shawn Estes	.07	.20
220 Lance Berkman	.12	.30
221 Carlos Guillen	.07	.20
222 Jeremy Affeldt	.07	.20
223 Cesar Izturis	.07	.20
224 Scott Sullivan	.07	.20
225 Kazuo Matsui	.07	.20
226 Josh Fogg	.07	.20
227 Jason Schmidt	.07	.20
228 Jason Marquis	.07	.20
229 Scott Spiezio	.07	.20
230 Miguel Tejada	.12	.30
231 Bartolo Colon	.07	.20
232 Jose Valverde	.07	.20
233 Derrek Lee	.07	.20
234 Scott Williamson	.07	.20
235 Joe Crede	.07	.20
236 John Thomson	.07	.20
237 Mike MacDougal	.07	.20
238 Eric Gagne	.07	.20
239 Alex Sanchez	.07	.20
240 Miguel Cabrera	.20	.50
241 Luis Rivas	.07	.20
242 Adam Everett	.07	.20
243 Jason Johnson	.07	.20
244 Travis Hafner	.07	.20
245 Jose Valentin	.07	.20
246 Stephen Randolph	.07	.20
247 Rafael Furcal	.07	.20
248 Adam Kennedy	.07	.20
249 Luis Matos	.07	.20
250 Mark Prior	.12	.30
251 Angel Berroa	.07	.20
252 Phil Nevin	.07	.20
253 Oliver Perez	.07	.20
254 Orlando Hudson	.07	.20
255 Braden Looper	.07	.20
256 Khalil Greene	.07	.20
257 Tim Worrell	.07	.20
258 Carlos Zambrano	.12	.30
259 Odalis Perez	.07	.20
260 Gerald Laird	.07	.20
261 Jose Cruz Jr.	.07	.20
262 Michael Barrett	.07	.20
263 Michael Young UER	.12	.30
Rod Barajas pictured sliding		
264 Toby Hall	.07	.20
265 Woody Williams	.07	.20
266 Rich Harden	.07	.20
267 Mike Scioscia MG	.07	.20
268 Al Pedrique MG	.07	.20
269 Bobby Cox MG	.07	.20
270 Lee Mazzilli MG	.07	.20
271 Terry Francona MG	.12	.30
272 Dusty Baker MG	.07	.20
273 Ozzie Guillen MG	.12	.30
274 Dave Miley MG	.07	.20
275 Eric Wedge MG	.07	.20
276 Clint Hurdle MG	.07	.20
277 Alan Trammell MG	.07	.20
278 Jack McKeon MG	.07	.20
279 Phil Garner MG	.07	.20
280 Tony Pena MG	.07	.20
281 Jim Tracy MG	.07	.20
282 Ned Yost MG	.07	.20
283 Ron Gardenhire MG	.07	.20
284 Frank Robinson MG	.12	.30
285 Art Howe MG	.07	.20
286 Joe Torre MG	.12	.30
287 Ken Macha MG	.07	.20
288 Larry Bowa MG	.07	.20
289 Lloyd McClendon MG	.07	.20
290 Bruce Bochy MG	.07	.20
291 Felipe Alou MG	.07	.20
292 Bob Melvin MG	.07	.20
293 Tony LaRussa MG	.12	.30
294 Lou Piniella MG	.07	.20
295 Buck Showalter MG	.07	.20
296 John Gibbons MG	.07	.20
297 Steve Doetsch FY RC	.20	.50
298 Melky Cabrera FY RC	.50	1.25
299 Luis Ramirez FY RC	.20	.50
300 Chris Seddon FY RC	.20	.50
301 Nate Schierholtz FY	.20	.50
302 Ian Kinsler FY RC	.60	1.50
303 Brandon Moss FY RC	.75	2.00
304 Chadd Blasko FY RC	.30	.75
305 Jeremy West FY RC	.20	.50
306 Sean Marshall FY RC	.50	1.25
307 Matt DeSalvo FY RC	.20	.50
308 Ryan Sweeney FY RC	.30	.75
309 Matthew Lindstrom FY RC	.20	.50
310 Ryan Goleski FY RC	.20	.50
311 Brett Harper FY RC	.20	.50
312 Chris Roberson FY RC	.20	.50
313 Andre Ethier FY RC	1.50	4.00
314 Chris Denorfia FY RC	.20	.50
315 Ian Bladergroen FY RC	.20	.50
316 Darren Fenster FY RC	.20	.50
317 Kevin West FY RC	.20	.50
318 Chaz Lytle FY RC	.30	.75
319 James Jurries FY RC	.20	.50
320 Matt Rogelstad FY RC	.20	.50
321 Wade Robinson FY RC	.20	.50
322 Jake Dittler FY	.20	.50
323 Brian Stavisky FY RC	.20	.50
324 Kole Strayhorn FY RC	.20	.50
325 Jose Vaquedano FY RC	.20	.50
326 Elvys Quezada FY RC	.20	.50
327 John Maine	.20	.50
Val Majewski FS		
328 Rickie Weeks	.30	.75
J.J. Hardy FS		
329 Gabe Gross	.20	.50
Guillermo Quiroz FS		
330 David Wright	.75	2.00
Craig Brazell FS		
331 Dallas McPherson	.30	.75
Jeff Mathis FS		
332 Randy Johnson SH	.20	.50
333 Randy Johnson SH	.20	.50
334 Ichiro Suzuki SH	.30	.75
335 Ken Griffey Jr. SH	.30	.75
336 Greg Maddux SH	.30	.75
337 Ichiro Suzuki	.30	.75
Melvin Mora		
Vladimir Guerrero LL		
338 Ichiro Suzuki	.12	.30
Michael Young		
Vladimir Guerrero LL		
339 Manny Ramirez	.12	.30
Paul Konerko		
David Ortiz LL		
340 Miguel Tejada	.12	.30
David Ortiz		
Manny Ramirez LL		
341 Johan Santana	.20	.50
Curt Schilling		
Jake Westbrook LL		
342 Johan Santana	.20	.50
Pedro Martinez		
Curt Schilling LL		
343 Todd Helton	.12	.30
Mark Loretta		
Adrian Beltre LL		
344 Juan Pierre	.07	.20
Mark Loretta		
Jack Wilson LL		
345 Adrian Beltre	.12	.30
Adam Dunn		
Albert Pujols LL		
346 Vinny Castilla	.50	1.25
Scott Rolen		
Albert Pujols LL		
347 Jake Peavy	.07	.20
Randy Johnson		
Ben Sheets LL		
348 Randy Johnson	.20	.50
Ben Sheets		
Jason Schmidt LL		
349 Alex Rodriguez	.75	2.00
Ruben Sierra ALDS		
350 Larry Walker	1.25	3.00
Albert Pujols NLDS		
351 Curt Schilling	.50	1.25
David Ortiz ALDS		
352 Curt Schilling WS2	.30	.75
353 Sox Celebration	.50	1.25
David Ortiz		
Curt Schilling ALCS		
354 Cards Celebration	1.25	3.00
Albert Pujols		
Jim Edmonds NLCS		
355 Mark Bellhorn WS1	.20	.50
356 Paul Konerko AS	.12	.30
357 Alfonso Soriano AS	.12	.30
358 Miguel Tejada AS	.12	.30
359 Melvin Mora AS	.07	.20
360 Vladimir Guerrero AS	.20	.50
361 Ichiro Suzuki AS	.30	.75
362 Manny Ramirez AS	.20	.50
363 Ivan Rodriguez AS	.12	.30
364 Johan Santana AS	.20	.50
365 Paul Konerko AS	.12	.30
366 David Ortiz AS	.20	.50
367 Bobby Crosby AS	.07	.20
368 Sox Celebration	.50	1.25
Manny Ramirez		
Derek Lowe WS4		
369 Garret Anderson	.07	.20
370 Randy Johnson	.20	.50
371 Charles Thomas	.07	.20
372 Rafael Palmeiro	.12	.30
373 Kevin Youkilis	.07	.20
374 Freddy Garcia	.07	.20
375 Magglio Ordonez	.12	.30
376 Aaron Harang	.07	.20
377 Grady Sizemore	.12	.30
378 Chin-Hui Tsao	.07	.20
379 Eric Munson	.07	.20
380 Juan Pierre	.07	.20
381 Brad Lidge	.07	.20
382 Brian Anderson	.07	.20
383 Alex Cora	.07	.20
384 Brady Clark	.07	.20
385 Todd Helton	.12	.30
386 Chad Cordero	.07	.20
387 Kris Benson	.07	.20
388 Brad Halsey	.07	.20
389 Jermaine Dye	.07	.20
390 Manny Ramirez	.20	.50
391 Daryle Ward	.07	.20
392 Adam Eaton	.07	.20
393 Brett Tomko	.07	.20
394 Bucky Jacobsen	.07	.20
395 Dontrelle Willis	.07	.20
396 B.J. Upton	.12	.30
397 Rocco Baldelli	.07	.20
398 Ted Lilly	.07	.20
399 Ryan Drese	.07	.20
400 Ichiro Suzuki	.30	.75
401 Brendan Donnelly	.07	.20
402 Brandon Lyon	.07	.20
403 Nick Green	.07	.20
404 Jerry Hairston Jr.	.07	.20
405 Mike Lowell	.07	.20
406 Kerry Wood	.07	.20
407 Carl Everett	.07	.20
408 Hideki Matsui	.30	.75
409 Omar Vizquel	.12	.30
410 Joe Kennedy	.07	.20
411 Carlos Pena	.12	.30
412 Armando Benitez	.07	.20
413 Carlos Beltran	.07	.20
414 Kevin Appier	.07	.20
415 Jeff Weaver	.07	.20
416 Chad Moeller	.07	.20
417 Joe Mays	.07	.20
418 Termel Sledge	.07	.20
419 Richard Hidalgo	.07	.20
420 Kenny Lofton	.07	.20
421 Justin Duchscherer	.07	.20
422 Eric Milton	.07	.20
423 Jose Mesa	.07	.20
424 Ramon Hernandez	.07	.20
425 Jose Reyes	.12	.30
426 Joel Pineiro	.07	.20
427 Matt Morris	.07	.20
428 John Halama	.07	.20
429 Gary Matthews Jr.	.07	.20
430 Ryan Madson	.07	.20
431 Mark Kotsay	.07	.20
432 Carlos Delgado	.07	.20
433 Casey Kotchman	.07	.20
434 Greg Aquino	.07	.20
435 Eli Marrero	.07	.20
436 David Newhan	.07	.20
437 Mike Timlin	.07	.20
438 LaTroy Hawkins	.07	.20
439 Jose Contreras	.07	.20
440 Ken Griffey Jr.	.30	.75
441 C.C. Sabathia	.12	.30
442 Brandon Inge	.07	.20
443 Pete Munro	.07	.20
444 John Buck	.07	.20
445 Hee Seop Choi	.07	.20
446 Chris Capuano	.07	.20
447 Jesse Crain	.07	.20
448 Geoff Jenkins	.07	.20
449 Brian Schneider	.07	.20
450 Mike Piazza	.20	.50
451 Jorge Posada	.12	.30
452 Nick Swisher	.20	.50
453 Kevin Millwood	.07	.20
454 Mike Gonzalez	.07	.20
455 Jake Peavy	.07	.20
456 Dustin Hermanson	.07	.20
457 Jeremy Reed	.07	.20
458 Julian Tavarez	.07	.20
459 Geoff Blum	.07	.20
460 Alfonso Soriano	.12	.30
461 Alexis Rios	.12	.30
462 David Eckstein	.07	.20
463 Shea Hillenbrand	.07	.20
464 Russ Ortiz	.07	.20
465 Kurt Ainsworth	.07	.20
466 Orlando Cabrera	.07	.20
467 Carlos Silva	.07	.20
468 Ross Gload	.07	.20

469 Josh Phelps .07 .20
470 Marquis Grissom .07 .20
471 Mike Maroth .07 .20
472 Guillermo Mota .07 .20
473 Chris Burke .07 .20
474 David DeJesus .07 .20
475 Jose Lima .07 .20
476 Cristian Guzman .07 .20
477 Nick Johnson .07 .20
478 Victor Zambrano .07 .20
479 Rod Barajas .07 .20
480 Damian Miller .07 .20
481 Chase Utley .12 .30
482 Todd Pratt .07 .20
483 Sean Burnett .07 .20
484 Boomer Wells .07 .20
485 Dustan Mohr .07 .20
486 Bobby Madritsch .07 .20
487 Ray King .07 .20
488 Reed Johnson .07 .20
489 R.A. Dickey .07 .20
490 Scott Kazmir .20 .50
491 Tony Womack .07 .20
492 Tomas Perez .07 .20
493 Esteban Loaiza .07 .20
494 Tomo Ohka .07 .20
495 Mike Lamb .07 .20
496 Ramon Ortiz .07 .20
497 Richie Sexson .07 .20
498 J.D. Drew .07 .20
499 David Segui .07 .20
500 Barry Bonds .40 1.00
501 Aramis Ramirez .07 .20
502 Wily Mo Pena .07 .20
503 Jeromy Burnitz .07 .20
504 Craig Monroe .07 .20
505 Nomar Garciaparra .20 .50
506 Brandon Backe .07 .20
507 Marcus Thames .07 .20
508 Derek Lowe .07 .20
509 Doug Davis .07 .20
510 Joe Mauer .20 .50
511 Endy Chavez .07 .20
512 Bernie Williams .12 .30
513 Mark Redman .07 .20
514 Jason Michaels .07 .20
515 Craig Wilson .07 .20
516 Ryan Klesko .07 .20
517 Ray Durham .07 .20
518 Jose Lopez .07 .20
519 Jeff Suppan .07 .20
520 Julio Lugo .07 .20
521 Mike Wood .07 .20
522 David Bush .07 .20
523 Juan Rincon .07 .20
524 Paul Quantrill .07 .20
525 Marlon Byrd .07 .20
526 Roy Oswalt .12 .30
527 Rondell White .07 .20
528 Troy Glaus .07 .20
529 Scott Hairston .07 .20
530 Chipper Jones .20 .50
531 Daniel Cabrera .07 .20
532 Doug Mientkiewicz .07 .20
533 Glendon Rusch .07 .20
534 Jon Garland .07 .20
535 Austin Kearns .07 .20
536 Jake Westbrook .07 .20
537 Aaron Miles .07 .20
538 Omar Infante .07 .20
539 Paul Lo Duca .07 .20
540 Morgan Ensberg .07 .20
541 Tony Graffanino .07 .20
542 Milton Bradley .07 .20
543 Keith Ginter .07 .20
544 Justin Morneau .20 .50
545 Tony Armas Jr. .07 .20
546 Mike Stanton .07 .20
547 Kevin Brown .07 .20
548 Marco Scutaro .07 .20
549 Tim Hudson .12 .30
550 Pat Burrell .07 .20
551 Ty Wigginton .07 .20
552 Jeff Cirillo .07 .20
553 Jim Brower .07 .20
554 Jamie Moyer .07 .20
555 Larry Walker .12 .30
556 Dewon Brazelton .07 .20
557 Brian Jordan .07 .20
558 Josh Towers .07 .20
559 Shigetoshi Hasegawa .07 .20
560 Octavio Dotel .07 .20
561 Travis Lee .07 .20
562 Michael Cuddyer .07 .20
563 Junior Spivey .07 .20
564 Zack Greinke .12 .30
565 Roger Clemens .25 .60
566 Chris Shelton .07 .20
567 Ugueth Urbina .07 .20
568 Rafael Betancourt .07 .20
569 Willie Harris .07 .20
570 Todd Hollandsworth .07 .20
571 Keith Foulke .07 .20
572 Larry Bigbie .07 .20
573 Paul Byrd .07 .20
574 Troy Percival .07 .20
575 Pedro Martinez .12 .30
576 Matt Clement .07 .20
577 Ryan Wagner .07 .20
578 Jeff Francis .07 .20
579 Jeff Conine .07 .20
580 Wade Miller .07 .20
581 Matt Stairs .07 .20
582 Gavin Floyd .07 .20
583 Kazuhisa Ishii .07 .20
584 Victor Santos .07 .20
585 Jacque Jones .07 .20
586 Sunny Kim .07 .20
587 Dan Kolb .07 .20
588 Cory Lidle .07 .20
589 Jose Castillo .07 .20
590 Alex Gonzalez .07 .20
591 Kirk Rueter .07 .20
592 Joibert Cabrera .07 .20
593 Erik Bedard .07 .20
594 Ben Grieve .07 .20
595 Ricky Ledee .07 .20
596 Mark Hendrickson .07 .20
597 Laynce Nix .07 .20
598 Jason Frasor .07 .20
599 Kevin Gregg .07 .20
600 Derek Jeter .50 1.25
601 Luis Terrero .07 .20
602 Jaret Wright .07 .20
603 Edwin Jackson .07 .20
604 Dave Roberts .07 .20
605 Moises Alou .07 .20
606 Aaron Rowand .07 .20
607 Kazuhito Tadano .07 .20
608 Luis A. Gonzalez .07 .20
609 A.J. Burnett .12 .30
610 Jeff Bagwell .12 .30
611 Brad Penny .07 .20
612 Craig Counsell .07 .20
613 Corey Koskie .07 .20
614 Mark Ellis .07 .20
615 Felix Rodriguez .07 .20
616 Jay Payton .07 .20
617 Hector Luna .07 .20
618 Miguel Olivo .07 .20
619 Rob Bell .07 .20
620 Scott Rolen .12 .30
621 Ricardo Rodriguez .07 .20
622 Eric Hinske .07 .20
623 Tim Salmon .07 .20
624 Adam LaRoche .07 .20
625 B.J. Ryan .07 .20
626 Roberto Alomar .12 .30
627 Steve Finley .07 .20
628 Joe Nathan .07 .20
629 Scott Linebrink .07 .20
630 Vicente Padilla .07 .20
631 Raul Mondesi .07 .20
632 Yadier Molina .12 .30
633 Tino Martinez .12 .30
634 Mark Teixeira .20 .50
635 Kelvim Escobar .07 .20
636 Pedro Feliz .07 .20
637 Rich Aurilia .07 .20
638 Los Angeles Angels TC .07 .20
639 Arizona Diamondbacks TC .07 .20
640 Atlanta Braves TC .12 .30
641 Baltimore Orioles TC .07 .20
642 Boston Red Sox TC .20 .50
643 Chicago Cubs TC .12 .30
644 Chicago White Sox TC .07 .20
645 Cincinnati Reds TC .07 .20
646 Cleveland Indians TC .07 .20
647 Colorado Rockies TC .07 .20
648 Detroit Tigers TC .07 .20
649 Florida Marlins TC .07 .20
650 Houston Astros TC .07 .20
651 Kansas City Royals TC .07 .20
652 Los Angeles Dodgers TC .07 .20
653 Milwaukee Brewers TC .07 .20
654 Minnesota Twins TC .07 .20
655 Montreal Expos TC .07 .20
656 New York Mets TC .07 .20
657 New York Yankees TC .20 .50
658 Oakland Athletics TC .07 .20
659 Philadelphia Phillies TC .07 .20
660 Pittsburgh Pirates TC .07 .20
661 San Diego Padres TC .07 .20
662 San Francisco Giants TC .07 .20
663 Seattle Mariners TC .07 .20
664 St. Louis Cardinals TC .12 .30
665 Tampa Bay Devil Rays TC .07 .20
666 Texas Rangers TC .07 .20
667 Toronto Blue Jays TC .07 .20
668 Billy Butler FY RC 1.00 2.50
669 Wes Swackhamer FY RC .20 .50
670 Matt Campbell FY RC .20 .50
671 Ryan Webb FY .20 .50
672 Glen Perkins FY RC .20 .50
673 Michael Rogers FY RC .20 .50
674 Kevin Melillo FY RC .20 .50
675 Erik Cordier FY RC .20 .50
676 Landon Powell FY RC .20 .50
677 Justin Verlander FY RC 4.00 10.00
678 Eric Nielsen FY RC .20 .50
679 Alexander Smit FY RC .20 .50
680 Ryan Garko FY RC .20 .50
681 Bobby Livingston FY RC .20 .50
682 Jeff Niemann FY RC .50 1.25
683 Wladimir Balentien FY RC .30 .75
684 Chip Cannon FY RC .20 .50
685 Yorman Bazardo FY RC .20 .50
686 Mike Bourn FY RC .50 1.25
687 Andy LaRoche FY RC 1.00 2.50
688 Felix Hernandez .75 2.00
Justin Leone
689 Ryan Howard 1.00 2.50
Cole Hamels
690 Matt Cain .20 .50
Merkin Valdez
691 Andy Marte .50 1.25
Jeff Francoeur UER
Francoeur's stat line says pitching instead of hitting
692 Chad Billingsley .20 .50
Joel Guzman
693 Jerry Hairston Jr. .07 .20
Scott Hairston
694 Miguel Tejada .12 .30
Lance Berkman
695 Kenny Rogers GG .07 .20
696 Ivan Rodriguez GG .12 .30
697 Darin Erstad GG .07 .20
698 Bret Boone GG .07 .20
699 Eric Chavez GG .07 .20
700 Derek Jeter GG .50 1.25
701 Vernon Wells GG .07 .20
702 Ichiro Suzuki GG .30 .75
703 Torii Hunter GG .07 .20
704 Greg Maddux GG .30 .75
705 Mike Matheny GG .07 .20
706 Todd Helton GG .12 .30
707 Luis Castillo GG .07 .20
708 Scott Rolen GG .12 .30
709 Cesar Izturis GG .07 .20
710 Jim Edmonds GG .12 .30
711 Andruw Jones GG .07 .20
712 Steve Finley GG .07 .20
713 Johan Santana CY .20 .50
714 Roger Clemens CY .25 .60
715 Vladimir Guerrero MVP .20 .50
716 Barry Bonds MVP .40 1.00
717 Bobby Crosby ROY .07 .20
718 Jason Bay ROY .07 .20
719 Albert Pujols AS .50 1.25
720 Mark Loretta AS .07 .20
721 Edgar Renteria AS .07 .20
722 Scott Rolen AS .12 .30
723 J.D. Drew AS .07 .20
724 Jim Edmonds AS .12 .30
725 Johnny Estrada AS .07 .20
726 Jason Schmidt AS .07 .20
727 Chris Carpenter AS .20 .50
728 Eric Gagne AS .07 .20
729 Jason Bay AS .07 .20
730 Bobby Cox MG AS .07 .20
731 David Ortiz .50 1.25
Mark Bellhorn WS1
732 Curt Schilling WS2 .30 .75
733 Manny Ramirez .50 1.25
Pedro Martinez WS3
734 Red Sox Win .30 .75
Johnny Damon
Derek Lowe WS4

2005 Topps 1st Edition

*1st ED 1-296/332-348/356-367: 1.25X TO 3X
*1st ED 369-667/693-69: 1.25X TO 3X
*1st ED 297-326/668-687: .6X TO 1.5X
*1st ED 327-331/688-692: .6X TO 1.5X
*1st ED 349-355/368/731-734: 1.25X TO 3X
ISSUED IN SER.1 & 2 1ST EDITION BOXES
CARD NUMBER 7 DOES NOT EXIST

2005 Topps Black

COMMON (1-6/8-331/369-734) 8.00 20.00
COMMON 297-326/668-687 8.00 20.00
COMMON 327-331/688-692 8.00 20.00
COMMON 731-734 8.00 20.00
SERIES 1 ODDS 1:13 HTA
SERIES 2 ODDS 1:9 HTA
STATED PRINT RUN 54 SERIAL #'d SETS
CARD NUMBER 7 DOES NOT EXIST
1 Alex Rodriguez 30.00 80.00
2 Placido Polanco 8.00 20.00
3 Torii Hunter 8.00 20.00
4 Lyle Overbay 8.00 20.00
5 Johnny Damon 12.00 30.00
6 Johnny Estrada 8.00 20.00
8 Francisco Rodriguez 12.00 30.00
9 Jason LaRue 8.00 20.00
10 Sammy Sosa 20.00 50.00
11 Randy Wolf 8.00 20.00
12 Jason Bay 8.00 20.00
13 Tom Glavine 12.00 30.00
14 Michael Tucker 8.00 20.00
15 Brian Giles 8.00 20.00
16 Dan Wilson 8.00 20.00
17 Jim Edmonds 12.00 30.00
18 Danys Baez 8.00 20.00
19 Roy Halladay 20.00 50.00
20 Hank Blalock 8.00 20.00
21 Darin Erstad 8.00 20.00
22 Robby Hammock 8.00 20.00
23 Mike Hampton 8.00 20.00
24 Mark Bellhorn 8.00 20.00
25 Jim Thome 12.00 30.00
26 Scott Schoeneweis 8.00 20.00
27 Jody Gerut 8.00 20.00
28 Vinny Castilla 8.00 20.00
29 Luis Castillo 8.00 20.00
30 Ivan Rodriguez 12.00 30.00
31 Craig Biggio 12.00 30.00
32 Joe Randa 8.00 20.00
33 Adrian Beltre 8.00 20.00
34 Scott Podsednik 8.00 20.00
35 Cliff Floyd 8.00 20.00
36 Livan Hernandez 8.00 20.00
37 Eric Byrnes 8.00 20.00
38 Gabe Kapler 8.00 20.00
39 Jack Wilson 8.00 20.00
40 Gary Sheffield 8.00 20.00
41 Chan Ho Park 12.00 30.00
42 Carl Crawford 12.00 30.00
43 Miguel Batista 8.00 20.00
44 David Bell 8.00 20.00
45 Jeff DaVanon 8.00 20.00
46 Brandon Webb 12.00 30.00
47 Bronson Arroyo 8.00 20.00
48 Melvin Mora 8.00 20.00
49 David Ortiz 20.00 50.00
50 Andruw Jones 8.00 20.00
51 Chone Figgins 8.00 20.00
52 Danny Graves 8.00 20.00
53 Preston Wilson 8.00 20.00
54 Jeremy Bonderman 8.00 20.00
55 Chad Fox 8.00 20.00
56 Dan Miceli 8.00 20.00
57 Jimmy Gobble 8.00 20.00
58 Darren Dreifort 8.00 20.00
59 Matt LeCroy 8.00 20.00
60 Jose Vidro 8.00 20.00
61 Al Leiter 8.00 20.00
62 Javier Vazquez 8.00 20.00
63 Erubiel Durazo 8.00 20.00
64 Doug Glanville 8.00 20.00
65 Scot Shields 8.00 20.00
66 Edgardo Alfonzo 8.00 20.00
67 Ryan Franklin 8.00 20.00
68 Francisco Cordero 8.00 20.00
69 Brett Myers 8.00 20.00
70 Curt Schilling 12.00 30.00
71 Matt Kata 8.00 20.00
72 Mark DeRosa 8.00 20.00
73 Rodrigo Lopez 8.00 20.00
74 Tim Wakefield 8.00 20.00
75 Frank Thomas 20.00 50.00
76 Jimmy Rollins 12.00 30.00
77 Barry Zito 8.00 20.00
78 Hideo Nomo 20.00 50.00
79 Brad Wilkerson 8.00 20.00
80 Adam Dunn 12.00 30.00
81 Billy Traber 8.00 20.00
82 Fernando Vina 8.00 20.00
83 Nate Robertson 8.00 20.00
84 Brad Ausmus 8.00 20.00
85 Mike Sweeney 8.00 20.00
86 Kip Wells 8.00 20.00
87 Chris Reitsma 8.00 20.00
88 Zach Day 8.00 20.00
89 Tony Clark 8.00 20.00
90 Bret Boone 8.00 20.00
91 Mark Loretta 8.00 20.00
92 Jerome Williams 8.00 20.00
93 Randy Winn 8.00 20.00
94 Marlon Anderson 8.00 20.00
95 Aubrey Huff 8.00 20.00
96 Kevin Mench 8.00 20.00
97 Frank Catalanotto 8.00 20.00
98 Flash Gordon 8.00 20.00
99 Scott Hatteberg 8.00 20.00
100 Albert Pujols 50.00 120.00
101 Jose/Bengie Molina 8.00 20.00
102 Oscar Villarreal 8.00 20.00
103 Jay Gibbons 8.00 20.00
104 Byung-Hyun Kim 8.00 20.00
105 Joe Borowski 8.00 20.00
106 Mark Grudzielanek 8.00 20.00
107 Mark Buehrle 12.00 30.00
108 Paul Wilson 8.00 20.00
109 Ronnie Belliard 8.00 20.00
110 Reggie Sanders 8.00 20.00
111 Tim Redding 8.00 20.00
112 Brian Lawrence 8.00 20.00
113 Darrell May 8.00 20.00
114 Jose Hernandez 8.00 20.00
115 Ben Sheets 8.00 20.00
116 Johan Santana 20.00 50.00
117 Billy Wagner 8.00 20.00
118 Mariano Rivera 20.00 50.00
119 Steve Trachsel 8.00 20.00
120 Akinori Otsuka 8.00 20.00
121 Bobby Kielty 8.00 20.00
122 Orlando Hernandez 8.00 20.00
123 Raul Ibanez 8.00 20.00
124 Mike Matheny 8.00 20.00
125 Vernon Wells 8.00 20.00
126 Jason Isringhausen 8.00 20.00
127 Jose Guillen 8.00 20.00
128 Danny Bautista 8.00 20.00
129 Marcus Giles 8.00 20.00
130 Javy Lopez 8.00 20.00
131 Kevin Millar 8.00 20.00
132 Kyle Farnsworth 8.00 20.00
133 Carl Pavano 8.00 20.00
134 D'Angelo Jimenez 8.00 20.00
135 Casey Blake 8.00 20.00
136 Matt Holliday 20.00 50.00
137 Bobby Higginson 8.00 20.00
138 Nate Field 8.00 20.00
139 Alex Gonzalez 8.00 20.00
140 Jeff Kent 8.00 20.00
141 Aaron Guiel 8.00 20.00
142 Shawn Green 8.00 20.00
143 Bill Hall 8.00 20.00
144 Shannon Stewart 8.00 20.00
145 Juan Rivera 8.00 20.00
146 Coco Crisp 8.00 20.00
147 Mike Mussina 12.00 30.00
148 Eric Chavez 8.00 20.00
149 Jon Lieber 8.00 20.00
150 Vladimir Guerrero 20.00 50.00
151 Alex Cintron 8.00 20.00
152 Horacio Ramirez 8.00 20.00
153 Sidney Ponson 8.00 20.00
154 Trot Nixon 8.00 20.00
155 Greg Maddux 30.00 80.00
156 Edgar Renteria 8.00 20.00
157 Ryan Freel 8.00 20.00
158 Matt Lawton 8.00 20.00
159 Shawn Chacon 8.00 20.00
160 Josh Beckett 12.00 30.00
161 Ken Harvey 8.00 20.00
162 Juan Cruz 8.00 20.00
163 Juan Encarnacion 8.00 20.00
164 Wes Helms 8.00 20.00
165 Brad Radke 8.00 20.00
166 Claudio Vargas 8.00 20.00
167 Mike Cameron 8.00 20.00
168 Billy Koch 8.00 20.00
169 Bobby Crosby 8.00 20.00
170 Mike Lieberthal 8.00 20.00
171 Rob Mackowiak 8.00 20.00
172 Sean Burroughs 8.00 20.00
173 J.T. Snow Jr. 8.00 20.00
174 Paul Konerko 12.00 30.00
175 Luis Gonzalez 8.00 20.00
176 John Lackey 8.00 20.00
177 Antonio Alfonseca 8.00 20.00
178 Brian Roberts 8.00 20.00
179 Bill Mueller 8.00 20.00
180 Carlos Lee 8.00 20.00
181 Corey Patterson 8.00 20.00
182 Sean Casey 8.00 20.00
183 Cliff Lee 12.00 30.00
184 Jason Jennings 8.00 20.00
185 Dmitri Young 8.00 20.00
186 Juan Uribe 8.00 20.00
187 Andy Pettitte 12.00 30.00
188 Juan Gonzalez 8.00 20.00
189 Pokey Reese 8.00 20.00
190 Jason Phillips 8.00 20.00
191 Rocky Biddle 8.00 20.00
192 Lew Ford 8.00 20.00
193 Mark Mulder 8.00 20.00
194 Bobby Abreu 8.00 20.00
195 Jason Kendall 8.00 20.00
196 Terrence Long 8.00 20.00
197 A.J. Pierzynski 8.00 20.00
198 Eddie Guardado 8.00 20.00
199 So Taguchi 8.00 20.00
200 Jason Giambi 8.00 20.00
201 Tony Batista 8.00 20.00
202 Kyle Lohse 8.00 20.00
203 Trevor Hoffman 12.00 30.00
204 Tike Redman 8.00 20.00
205 Matt Herges 8.00 20.00
206 Gil Meche 8.00 20.00
207 Chris Carpenter 20.00 50.00
208 Ben Broussard 8.00 20.00
209 Eric Young 8.00 20.00
210 Doug Waechter 8.00 20.00
211 Jarrod Washburn 8.00 20.00
212 Chad Tracy 8.00 20.00
213 John Smoltz 20.00 50.00
214 Jorge Julio 8.00 20.00
215 Todd Walker 8.00 20.00
216 Shingo Takatsu 8.00 20.00
217 Jose Acevedo 8.00 20.00
218 David Riske 8.00 20.00
219 Shawn Estes 8.00 20.00
220 Lance Berkman 12.00 30.00
221 Carlos Guillen 8.00 20.00
222 Jeremy Affeldt 8.00 20.00
223 Cesar Izturis 8.00 20.00
224 Scott Sullivan 8.00 20.00
225 Kazuo Matsui 8.00 20.00
226 Josh Fogg 8.00 20.00
227 Jason Schmidt 8.00 20.00
228 Jason Marquis 8.00 20.00
229 Scott Spiezio 8.00 20.00
230 Miguel Tejada 12.00 30.00
231 Bartolo Colon 8.00 20.00
232 Jose Valverde 8.00 20.00
233 Derrek Lee 8.00 20.00
234 Scott Williamson 8.00 20.00
235 Joe Crede 8.00 20.00
236 John Thomson 8.00 20.00
237 Mike MacDougal 8.00 20.00
238 Eric Gagne 8.00 20.00
239 Alex Sanchez 8.00 20.00
240 Miguel Cabrera 20.00 50.00
241 Luis Rivas 8.00 20.00
242 Adam Everett 8.00 20.00
243 Jason Johnson 8.00 20.00
244 Travis Hafner 8.00 20.00
245 Jose Valentin 8.00 20.00
246 Stephen Randolph 8.00 20.00
247 Rafael Furcal 8.00 20.00
248 Adam Kennedy 8.00 20.00
249 Luis Matos 8.00 20.00
250 Mark Prior 12.00 30.00
251 Angel Berroa 8.00 20.00
252 Phil Nevin 8.00 20.00
253 Oliver Perez 8.00 20.00
254 Orlando Hudson 8.00 20.00
255 Braden Looper 8.00 20.00
256 Khalil Greene 8.00 20.00
257 Tim Worrell 8.00 20.00
258 Carlos Zambrano 12.00 30.00
259 Odalis Perez 8.00 20.00
260 Gerald Laird 8.00 20.00
261 Jose Cruz Jr. 8.00 20.00
262 Michael Barrett 8.00 20.00
263 Michael Young UER 12.00 30.00
264 Toby Hall 8.00 20.00
265 Woody Williams 8.00 20.00
266 Rich Harden 8.00 20.00
267 Mike Scioscia MG 8.00 20.00
268 Al Pedrique MG 8.00 20.00
269 Bobby Cox MG 8.00 20.00
270 Lee Mazzilli MG 8.00 20.00
271 Terry Francona MG 12.00 30.00
272 Dusty Baker MG 8.00 20.00
273 Ozzie Guillen MG 12.00 30.00
274 Dave Miley MG 8.00 20.00
275 Eric Wedge MG 8.00 20.00
276 Clint Hurdle MG 8.00 20.00
277 Alan Trammell MG 8.00 20.00
278 Jack McKeon MG 8.00 20.00
279 Phil Garner MG 8.00 20.00
280 Tony Pena MG 8.00 20.00
281 Jim Tracy MG 8.00 20.00
282 Ned Yost MG 8.00 20.00
283 Ron Gardenhire MG 8.00 20.00
284 Frank Robinson MG 12.00 30.00
285 Art Howe MG 8.00 20.00
286 Joe Torre MG 12.00 30.00
287 Ken Macha MG 8.00 20.00
288 Larry Bowa MG 8.00 20.00
289 Lloyd McClendon MG 8.00 20.00
290 Bruce Bochy MG 8.00 20.00
291 Felipe Alou MG 8.00 20.00
292 Bob Melvin MG 8.00 20.00
293 Tony LaRussa MG 12.00 30.00
294 Lou Piniella MG 8.00 20.00
295 Buck Showalter MG 8.00 20.00
296 John Gibbons MG 8.00 20.00
297 Steve Doetsch FY 8.00 20.00
298 Melky Cabrera FY 20.00 50.00
299 Luis Ramirez FY 8.00 20.00
300 Chris Seddon FY 8.00 20.00
301 Nate Schierholtz FY 8.00 20.00
302 Ian Kinsler FY 60.00 150.00
303 Brandon Moss FY 30.00 80.00
304 Chadd Blasko FY 12.00 30.00
305 Jeremy West FY 8.00 20.00
306 Sean Marshall FY 20.00 50.00
307 Matt DeSalvo FY 8.00 20.00
308 Ryan Sweeney FY 12.00 30.00
309 Matthew Lindstrom FY 8.00 20.00
310 Ryan Goleski FY 8.00 20.00
311 Brett Harper FY 8.00 20.00
312 Chris Roberson FY 8.00 20.00
313 Andre Ethier FY 60.00 150.00
314 Chris Denorfia FY 8.00 20.00
315 Ian Bladergroen FY 8.00 20.00
316 Darren Fenster FY 8.00 20.00
317 Kevin West FY 8.00 20.00
318 Chaz Lytle FY 12.00 30.00
319 James Jurries FY 8.00 20.00
320 Matt Rogelstad FY 8.00 20.00
321 Wade Robinson FY 8.00 20.00
322 Jake Dittler FY 8.00 20.00
323 Brian Stavisky FY 8.00 20.00
324 Kole Strayhorn FY 8.00 20.00
325 Jose Vaquedano FY 8.00 20.00
326 Elvys Quezada FY 8.00 20.00
327 John Maine 8.00 20.00
Val Majewski FS
328 Rickie Weeks 12.00 30.00
J.J. Hardy FS
329 Gabe Gross 8.00 20.00
Guillermo Quiroz FS
330 David Wright 30.00 80.00
Craig Brazell FS
331 Dallas McPherson 12.00 30.00
Jeff Mathis FS
369 Garret Anderson 8.00 20.00
370 Randy Johnson 20.00 50.00
371 Charles Thomas 8.00 20.00
372 Rafael Palmeiro 12.00 30.00
373 Kevin Youkilis 8.00 20.00
374 Freddy Garcia 8.00 20.00
375 Magglio Ordonez 12.00 30.00
376 Aaron Harang 8.00 20.00
377 Grady Sizemore 12.00 30.00
378 Chin-Hui Tsao 8.00 20.00
379 Eric Munson 8.00 20.00
380 Juan Pierre 8.00 20.00
381 Brad Lidge 8.00 20.00
382 Brian Anderson 8.00 20.00
383 Alex Cora 8.00 20.00
384 Brady Clark 8.00 20.00
385 Todd Helton 12.00 30.00
386 Chad Cordero 8.00 20.00
387 Kris Benson 8.00 20.00
388 Brad Halsey 8.00 20.00
389 Jermaine Dye 8.00 20.00
390 Manny Ramirez 20.00 50.00
391 Daryle Ward 8.00 20.00
392 Adam Eaton 8.00 20.00
393 Brett Tomko 8.00 20.00
394 Bucky Jacobsen 8.00 20.00
395 Dontrelle Willis 8.00 20.00
396 B.J. Upton 12.00 30.00
397 Rocco Baldelli 8.00 20.00
398 Ted Lilly 8.00 20.00
399 Ryan Drese 8.00 20.00
400 Ichiro Suzuki 30.00 80.00
401 Brendan Donnelly 8.00 20.00
402 Brandon Lyon 8.00 20.00
403 Nick Green 8.00 20.00
404 Jerry Hairston Jr. 8.00 20.00
405 Mike Lowell 8.00 20.00
406 Kerry Wood 8.00 20.00
407 Carl Everett 8.00 20.00
408 Hideki Matsui 30.00 80.00
409 Omar Vizquel 12.00 30.00
410 Joe Kennedy 8.00 20.00
411 Carlos Pena 12.00 30.00
412 Armando Benitez 8.00 20.00
413 Carlos Beltran 8.00 20.00
414 Kevin Appier 8.00 20.00
415 Jeff Weaver 8.00 20.00
416 Chad Moeller 8.00 20.00
417 Joe Mays 8.00 20.00
418 Termel Sledge 8.00 20.00
419 Richard Hidalgo 8.00 20.00
420 Kenny Lofton 8.00 20.00
421 Justin Duchscherer 8.00 20.00
422 Eric Milton 8.00 20.00
423 Jose Mesa 8.00 20.00
424 Ramon Hernandez 8.00 20.00
425 Jose Reyes 12.00 30.00
426 Joel Pineiro 8.00 20.00
427 Matt Morris 8.00 20.00
428 John Halama 8.00 20.00
429 Gary Matthews Jr. 8.00 20.00
430 Ryan Madson 8.00 20.00
431 Mark Kotsay 8.00 20.00
432 Carlos Delgado 8.00 20.00
433 Casey Kotchman 8.00 20.00
434 Greg Aquino 8.00 20.00
435 Eli Marrero 8.00 20.00
436 David Newhan 8.00 20.00
437 Mike Timlin 8.00 20.00
438 LaTroy Hawkins 8.00 20.00
439 Jose Contreras 8.00 20.00
440 Ken Griffey Jr. 30.00 80.00
441 C.C. Sabathia 12.00 30.00
442 Brandon Inge 8.00 20.00
443 Pete Munro 8.00 20.00
444 John Buck 8.00 20.00
445 Hee Seop Choi 8.00 20.00
446 Chris Capuano 8.00 20.00
447 Jesse Crain 8.00 20.00
448 Geoff Jenkins 8.00 20.00
449 Brian Schneider 8.00 20.00
450 Mike Piazza 20.00 50.00
451 Jorge Posada 12.00 30.00
452 Nick Swisher 20.00 50.00
453 Kevin Millwood 8.00 20.00
454 Mike Gonzalez 8.00 20.00
455 Jake Peavy 8.00 20.00
456 Dustin Hermanson 8.00 20.00
457 Jeremy Reed 8.00 20.00
458 Julian Tavarez 8.00 20.00
459 Geoff Blum 8.00 20.00
460 Alfonso Soriano 12.00 30.00
461 Alexis Rios 12.00 30.00
462 David Eckstein 8.00 20.00
463 Shea Hillenbrand 8.00 20.00
464 Russ Ortiz 8.00 20.00
465 Kurt Ainsworth 8.00 20.00
466 Orlando Cabrera 8.00 20.00
467 Carlos Silva 8.00 20.00
468 Ross Gload 8.00 20.00
469 Josh Phelps 8.00 20.00
470 Marquis Grissom 8.00 20.00
471 Mike Maroth 8.00 20.00
472 Guillermo Mota 8.00 20.00
473 Chris Burke 8.00 20.00
474 David DeJesus 8.00 20.00
475 Jose Lima 8.00 20.00
476 Cristian Guzman 8.00 20.00
477 Nick Johnson 8.00 20.00
478 Victor Zambrano 8.00 20.00
479 Rod Barajas 8.00 20.00
480 Damian Miller 8.00 20.00
481 Chase Utley 12.00 30.00
482 Todd Pratt 8.00 20.00
483 Sean Burnett 8.00 20.00
484 Boomer Wells 8.00 20.00
485 Dustan Mohr 8.00 20.00
486 Bobby Madritsch 8.00 20.00
487 Ray King 8.00 20.00
488 Reed Johnson 8.00 20.00
489 R.A. Dickey 8.00 20.00
490 Scott Kazmir 20.00 50.00
491 Tony Womack 8.00 20.00
492 Tomas Perez 8.00 20.00
493 Esteban Loaiza 8.00 20.00
494 Tomo Ohka 8.00 20.00
495 Mike Lamb 8.00 20.00
496 Ramon Ortiz 8.00 20.00
497 Richie Sexson 8.00 20.00
498 J.D. Drew 8.00 20.00
499 David Segui 8.00 20.00
500 Barry Bonds 40.00 100.00
501 Aramis Ramirez 8.00 20.00
502 Wily Mo Pena 8.00 20.00
503 Jeromy Burnitz 8.00 20.00
504 Craig Monroe 8.00 20.00
505 Nomar Garciaparra 20.00 50.00
506 Brandon Backe 8.00 20.00
507 Marcus Thames 8.00 20.00
508 Derek Lowe 8.00 20.00
509 Doug Davis 8.00 20.00
510 Joe Mauer 20.00 50.00
511 Endy Chavez 8.00 20.00
512 Bernie Williams 12.00 30.00
513 Mark Redman 8.00 20.00
514 Jason Michaels 8.00 20.00
515 Craig Wilson 8.00 20.00
516 Ryan Klesko 8.00 20.00
517 Ray Durham 8.00 20.00
518 Jose Lopez 8.00 20.00
519 Jeff Suppan 8.00 20.00
520 Julio Lugo 8.00 20.00
521 Mike Wood 8.00 20.00
522 David Bush 8.00 20.00
523 Juan Rincon 8.00 20.00
524 Paul Quantrill 8.00 20.00
525 Marlon Byrd 8.00 20.00
526 Roy Oswalt 12.00 30.00
527 Rondell White 8.00 20.00
528 Troy Glaus 8.00 20.00
529 Scott Hairston 8.00 20.00
530 Chipper Jones 20.00 50.00
531 Daniel Cabrera 8.00 20.00
532 Doug Mientkiewicz 8.00 20.00
533 Glendon Rusch 8.00 20.00
534 Jon Garland 8.00 20.00
535 Austin Kearns 8.00 20.00
536 Jake Westbrook 8.00 20.00
537 Aaron Miles 8.00 20.00
538 Omar Infante 8.00 20.00
539 Paul Lo Duca 8.00 20.00
540 Morgan Ensberg 8.00 20.00
541 Tony Graffanino 8.00 20.00
542 Milton Bradley 8.00 20.00
543 Keith Ginter 8.00 20.00
544 Justin Morneau 20.00 50.00
545 Tony Armas Jr. 8.00 20.00
546 Mike Stanton 8.00 20.00
547 Kevin Brown 8.00 20.00
548 Marco Scutaro 8.00 20.00
549 Tim Hudson 12.00 30.00
550 Pat Burrell 8.00 20.00
551 Ty Wigginton 8.00 20.00
552 Jeff Cirillo 8.00 20.00
553 Jim Brower 8.00 20.00
554 Jamie Moyer 8.00 20.00
555 Larry Walker 12.00 30.00
556 Dewon Brazelton 8.00 20.00
557 Brian Jordan 8.00 20.00
558 Josh Towers 8.00 20.00
559 Shigetoshi Hasegawa 8.00 20.00
560 Octavio Dotel 8.00 20.00
561 Travis Lee 8.00 20.00
562 Michael Cuddyer 8.00 20.00
563 Junior Spivey 8.00 20.00
564 Zack Greinke 12.00 30.00
565 Roger Clemens 25.00 60.00
566 Chris Shelton 8.00 20.00
567 Ugueth Urbina 8.00 20.00
568 Rafael Betancourt 8.00 20.00
569 Willie Harris 8.00 20.00
570 Todd Hollandsworth 8.00 20.00
571 Keith Foulke 8.00 20.00
572 Larry Bigbie 8.00 20.00
573 Paul Byrd 8.00 20.00
574 Troy Percival 8.00 20.00
575 Pedro Martinez 12.00 30.00
576 Matt Clement 8.00 20.00
577 Ryan Wagner 8.00 20.00
578 Jeff Francis 8.00 20.00
579 Jeff Conine 8.00 20.00
580 Wade Miller 8.00 20.00

581 Matt Stairs 8.00 20.00
582 Gavin Floyd 8.00 20.00
583 Kazuhisa Ishii 8.00 20.00
584 Victor Santos 8.00 20.00
585 Jacque Jones 8.00 20.00
586 Sunny Kim 8.00 20.00
587 Dan Kolb 8.00 20.00
588 Cory Lidle 8.00 20.00
589 Jose Castillo 8.00 20.00
590 Alex Gonzalez 8.00 20.00
591 Kirk Rueter 8.00 20.00
592 Jolbert Cabrera 8.00 20.00
593 Erik Bedard 8.00 20.00
594 Ben Grieve 8.00 20.00
595 Ricky Ledee 8.00 20.00
596 Mark Hendrickson 8.00 20.00
597 Laynce Nix 8.00 20.00
598 Jason Frasor 8.00 20.00
599 Kevin Gregg 8.00 20.00
600 Derek Jeter 50.00 125.00
601 Luis Terrero 8.00 20.00
602 Jaret Wright 8.00 20.00
603 Edwin Jackson 8.00 20.00
604 Dave Roberts 8.00 20.00
605 Moises Alou 8.00 20.00
606 Aaron Rowand 8.00 20.00
607 Kazuhito Tadano 8.00 20.00
608 Luis A. Gonzalez 8.00 20.00
609 A.J. Burnett 12.00 30.00
610 Jeff Bagwell 12.00 30.00
611 Brad Penny 8.00 20.00
612 Craig Counsell 8.00 20.00
613 Corey Koskie 8.00 20.00
614 Mark Ellis 8.00 20.00
615 Felix Rodriguez 8.00 20.00
616 Jay Payton 8.00 20.00
617 Hector Luna 8.00 20.00
618 Miguel Olivo 8.00 20.00
619 Rob Bell 8.00 20.00
620 Scott Rolen 12.00 30.00
621 Ricardo Rodriguez 8.00 20.00
622 Eric Hinske 8.00 20.00
623 Tim Salmon 8.00 20.00
624 Adam LaRoche 8.00 20.00
625 B.J. Ryan 8.00 20.00
626 Roberto Alomar 12.00 30.00
627 Steve Finley 8.00 20.00
628 Joe Nathan 8.00 20.00
629 Scott Linebrink 8.00 20.00
630 Vicente Padilla 8.00 20.00
631 Raul Mondesi 8.00 20.00
632 Yadier Molina 12.00 30.00
633 Tino Martinez 12.00 30.00
634 Mark Teixeira 20.00 50.00
635 Kelvim Escobar 8.00 20.00
636 Pedro Feliz 8.00 20.00
637 Rich Aurilia 8.00 20.00
638 Los Angeles Angels TC 8.00 20.00
639 Arizona Diamondbacks TC 8.00 20.00
640 Atlanta Braves TC 12.00 30.00
641 Baltimore Orioles TC 8.00 20.00
642 Boston Red Sox TC 20.00 50.00
643 Chicago Cubs TC 12.00 30.00
644 Chicago White Sox TC 8.00 20.00
645 Cincinnati Reds TC 8.00 20.00
646 Cleveland Indians TC 8.00 20.00
647 Colorado Rockies TC 8.00 20.00
648 Detroit Tigers TC 8.00 20.00
649 Florida Marlins TC 8.00 20.00
650 Houston Astros TC 8.00 20.00
651 Kansas City Royals TC 8.00 20.00
652 Los Angeles Dodgers TC 8.00 20.00
653 Milwaukee Brewers TC 8.00 20.00
654 Minnesota Twins TC 8.00 20.00
655 Montreal Expos TC 8.00 20.00
656 New York Mets TC 8.00 20.00
657 New York Yankees TC 20.00 50.00
658 Oakland Athletics TC 8.00 20.00
659 Philadelphia Phillies TC 8.00 20.00
660 Pittsburgh Pirates TC 8.00 20.00
661 San Diego Padres TC 8.00 20.00
662 San Francisco Giants TC 8.00 20.00
663 Seattle Mariners TC 8.00 20.00
664 St. Louis Cardinals TC 12.00 30.00
665 Tampa Bay Devil Rays TC 8.00 20.00
666 Texas Rangers TC 8.00 20.00
667 Toronto Blue Jays TC 8.00 20.00
668 Billy Butler FY 40.00 100.00
669 Wes Swackhamer FY 8.00 20.00
670 Matt Campbell FY 8.00 20.00
671 Ryan Webb FY 8.00 20.00
672 Glen Perkins FY 8.00 20.00
673 Michael Rogers FY 8.00 20.00
674 Kevin Melillo FY 8.00 20.00
675 Erik Cordier FY 8.00 20.00
676 Landon Powell FY 8.00 20.00
677 Justin Verlander FY 150.00 400.00
678 Eric Nielsen FY 8.00 20.00
679 Alexander Smit FY 8.00 20.00
680 Ryan Garko FY 8.00 20.00
681 Bobby Livingston FY 8.00 20.00
682 Jeff Niemann FY 20.00 50.00
683 Wladimir Balentien FY 12.00 30.00
684 Chip Cannon FY 8.00 20.00
685 Yorman Bazardo FY 8.00 20.00
686 Mike Bourn FY 20.00 50.00
687 Andy LaRoche FY 40.00 100.00
688 Felix Hernandez 30.00 80.00
Justin Leone
689 Ryan Howard 40.00 100.00
Cole Hamels
690 Matt Cain 8.00 20.00
Merkin Valdez
691 Andy Marte 20.00 50.00
Jeff Francoeur
692 Chad Billingsley 8.00 20.00
Joel Guzman
693 Jerry Hairston Jr. 8.00 20.00
Scott Hairston
694 Miguel Tejada 12.00 30.00
Lance Berkman
695 Kenny Rogers GG 8.00 20.00
696 Ivan Rodriguez GG 12.00 30.00
697 Darin Erstad GG 8.00 20.00
698 Bret Boone GG 8.00 20.00
699 Eric Chavez GG 8.00 20.00
700 Derek Jeter GG 50.00 125.00
701 Vernon Wells GG 8.00 20.00
702 Ichiro Suzuki GG 30.00 80.00
703 Torii Hunter GG 8.00 20.00
704 Greg Maddux GG 30.00 80.00
705 Mike Matheny GG 8.00 20.00
706 Todd Helton GG 12.00 30.00
707 Luis Castillo GG 8.00 20.00
708 Scott Rolen GG 12.00 30.00
709 Cesar Izturis GG 8.00 20.00
710 Jim Edmonds GG 12.00 30.00
711 Andruw Jones GG 8.00 20.00
712 Steve Finley GG 8.00 20.00
713 Johan Santana CY 20.00 50.00
714 Roger Clemens CY 25.00 60.00
715 Vladimir Guerrero MVP 20.00 50.00
716 Barry Bonds MVP 40.00 100.00
717 Bobby Crosby ROY 8.00 20.00
718 Jason Bay ROY 8.00 20.00
719 Albert Pujols AS 50.00 120.00
720 Mark Loretta AS 8.00 20.00
721 Edgar Renteria AS 8.00 20.00
722 Scott Rolen AS 12.00 30.00
723 J.D. Drew AS 8.00 20.00
724 Jim Edmonds AS 12.00 30.00
725 Johnny Estrada AS 8.00 20.00
726 Jason Schmidt AS 8.00 20.00
727 Chris Carpenter AS 20.00 50.00
728 Eric Gagne AS 8.00 20.00
729 Jason Bay AS 8.00 20.00
730 Bobby Cox MG AS 8.00 20.00
731 David Ortiz 20.00 50.00
Mark Bellhorn WS1
732 Curt Schilling WS2 12.00 30.00
733 Manny Ramirez 20.00 50.00
Pedro Martinez WS3
734 Red Sox Win 12.00 30.00
Johnny Damon
Derek Lowe WS4

2005 Topps Box Bottoms

ONE 4-CARD SHEET PER HTA BOX
1 Alex Rodriguez 1 .75 2.00
10 Sammy Sosa 1 .50 1.25
20 Hank Blalock 2 .20 .50
25 Jim Thome 2 .30 .75
30 Ivan Rodriguez 3 .30 .75
40 Gary Sheffield 1 .20 .50
47 Hideo Nomo 4 .50 1.25
80 Adam Dunn 2 .30 .75
100 Albert Pujols 3 1.25 3.00
120 Akinori Otsuka 4 .20 .50
150 Vladimir Guerrero 1 .50 1.25
200 Jason Giambi 2 .20 .50
216 Shingo Takatsu 4 .20 .50
225 Kazuo Matsui 4 .20 .50
230 Miguel Tejada 3 .30 .75
240 Miguel Cabrera 3 .50 1.25
369 Garret Anderson 8 .20 .50
385 Todd Helton 6 .30 .75
390 Manny Ramirez 7 .50 1.25
395 Dontrelle Willis 7 .20 .50
406 Kerry Wood 5 .20 .50
431 Mark Kotsay 6 .20 .50
450 Mike Piazza 5 .50 1.25
455 Jake Peavy 8 .20 .50
460 Alfonso Soriano 6 .30 .75
500 Barry Bonds 5 1.00 2.50
505 Nomar Garciaparra 7 .50 1.25
510 Joe Mauer 7 .50 1.25
526 Roy Oswalt 6 .30 .75
530 Chipper Jones 5 .50 1.25
550 Pat Burrell 8 .20 .50
620 Scott Rolen 8 .30 .75

2005 Topps Gold

*1st ED 1-296/332-348
*GOLD 297-326/668-687: 2X TO 5X
*GOLD 327-331/688-692: 2X TO 5X
*GOLD 731-734: 3X TO 8X
SERIES 1 ODDS 1:8 HOB, 1:3 HTA, 1:10 RET
SERIES 2 ODDS 1:5 HOB, 1:2 HTA, 1:6 RET
STATED PRINT RUN 2005 SERIAL #'d SETS
CARD NUMBER 7 DOES NOT EXIST

2005 Topps 1955 World Series Cut Signature

SER.2 ODDS 1:297,056 H, 1:77,616 HTA
SER.2 ODDS 1:171,072 R
STATED PRINT RUN 1 SERIAL #'d SET
NO PRICING DUE TO SCARCITY

2005 Topps 1955 World Series Dual Cut Signatures

SER.2 ODDS 1:51,744 HTA
STATED PRINT RUN 1 SERIAL #'d SET
NO PRICING DUE TO SCARCITY

2005 Topps 1955 World Series Dual Match-Ups Autographs

SER.2 ODDS 1:9002 H, 1:2587 HTA, 1:9004 R
STATED PRINT RUN 50 SERIAL #'d SETS
SER.2 EXCH.DEADLINE 04/30/07
NO PRICING DUE TO SCARCITY

2005 Topps A-Rod Spokesman

COMPLETE SET (4) 4.00 10.00
SER.2 ODDS 1:24 HOB, 1:8 HTA, 1:24 RET
1 Alex Rodriguez 1994 1.25 3.00
2 Alex Rodriguez 1995 1.25 3.00
3 Alex Rodriguez 1996 1.25 3.00
4 Alex Rodriguez 1997 1.25 3.00

2005 Topps A-Rod Spokesman Autographed Jersey Relics

SER.2 ODDS 1:89,117 H, 1:22,176 HTA
SER.2 ODDS 1:85,536 R
STATED PRINT RUN 13 SERIAL #'d SETS
NO PRICING DUE TO SCARCITY
EXCHANGE DEADLINE 04/30/07

2005 Topps A-Rod Spokesman Autographs

SER.2 ODDS 1:22,279 H, 1:6749 HTA
SER.2 ODDS 1:24,439 R
PRINT RUNS B/WN 1-200 COPIES PER
NO PRICING ON QTY OF 25 OR LESS
1 Alex Rodriguez 1994/1
2 Alex Rodriguez 1995/25
3 Alex Rodriguez 1996/100 100.00 200.00
4 Alex Rodriguez 1997/200 100.00 175.00

2005 Topps A-Rod Spokesman Jersey Relics

SER.2 ODDS 1:3550 H, 1:1015 HTA, 1:3564 R
PRINT RUNS B/WN 1-800 COPIES PER
NO PRICING ON QTY OF 1
1 Alex Rodriguez 1994/1
2 Alex Rodriguez 1995/50 30.00 60.00
3 Alex Rodriguez 1996/300 8.00 20.00
4 Alex Rodriguez 1997/800 6.00 15.00

2005 Topps All-Star Patches Relics

SER.2 ODDS 1:3495 H, 1:1001 HTA, 1:3491 R
STATED PRINT RUN 25 SERIAL #'d SETS
NO PRICING DUE TO SCARCITY

2005 Topps All-Star Stitches Relics

SERIES 1 ODDS 1:96 H, 1:27 HTA, 1:60 R
AP Albert Pujols 8.00 20.00
AS Alfonso Soriano 4.00 10.00
BA Bobby Abreu 4.00 10.00
BL Barry Larkin 4.00 10.00
BS Ben Sheets 4.00 10.00
CB Carlos Beltran 4.00 10.00
CC Carl Crawford 4.00 10.00
CP Carl Pavano 4.00 10.00
CS C.C. Sabathia 4.00 10.00
CZ Carlos Zambrano 4.00 10.00
DK Danny Kolb 4.00 10.00
DO David Ortiz 4.00 10.00
EL Esteban Loaiza 4.00 10.00
ER Edgar Renteria 4.00 10.00
FG Tom Gordon 4.00 10.00
FR Francisco Rodriguez 4.00 10.00
GS Gary Sheffield 4.00 10.00
HB Hank Blalock 4.00 10.00
IR Ivan Rodriguez 4.00 10.00
JE Johnny Estrada 4.00 10.00
JG Jason Giambi 4.00 10.00
JK Jeff Kent 4.00 10.00
JN Joe Nathan 4.00 10.00
JT Jim Thome 4.00 10.00
JW Jack Wilson 4.00 10.00
KH Ken Harvey 4.00 10.00
LB Lance Berkman 4.00 10.00
MA Moises Alou 4.00 10.00
MC Miguel Cabrera 4.00 10.00
ML Mike Lowell 4.00 10.00
MLA Matt Lawton 4.00 10.00
MLO Mark Loretta 4.00 10.00
MM Mark Mulder 4.00 10.00
MP Mike Piazza 4.00 10.00
MR Manny Ramirez 4.00 10.00
MRI Mariano Rivera 4.00 10.00
MT Miguel Tejada 4.00 10.00
MY Michael Young 4.00 10.00
PL Paul Lo Duca 4.00 10.00
RB Ronnie Belliard 4.00 10.00
SR Scott Rolen 4.00 10.00
SS Sammy Sosa 4.00 10.00
TG Tom Glavine 4.00 10.00
TH Todd Helton 4.00 10.00
TL Ted Lilly 4.00 10.00
VG Vladimir Guerrero 4.00 10.00
VM Victor Martinez 4.00 10.00

2005 Topps All-Stars

COMPLETE SET (15) 10.00 25.00
SER.2 ODDS 1:9 HOBBY, 1:3 HTA
1 Todd Helton .60 1.50
2 Albert Pujols 2.50 6.00
3 Vladimir Guerrero 1.00 2.50
4 Ichiro Suzuki 1.50 4.00
5 Randy Johnson 1.00 2.50
6 Manny Ramirez 1.00 2.50
7 Sammy Sosa 1.00 2.50
8 Alfonso Soriano .60 1.50
9 Jim Thome .60 1.50
10 Barry Bonds 2.00 5.00
11 Roger Clemens 1.25 3.00
12 Mike Piazza 1.00 2.50
13 Derek Jeter 2.50 6.00
14 Alex Rodriguez 1.50 4.00
15 Carlos Beltran .40 1.00

2005 Topps Autographs

Carlos Beltran and Zack Greinke did not return their cards in time to be included within first series packs, thus exchange cards with a deadline redemption date of November 30th, 2006 were placed into packs in their place.

SER.1 A 1:2683 H, 1:767 HTA, 1:2238 R
SER.1 B 1:3950 H, 1:1129 HTA, 1:3300 R
SER.1 C 1:305 H, 1:87 HTA, 1:254 R
SER.1 D 1:2913 H, 1:833 HTA, 1:2432 R
SER.2 A 1:178,234H, 1:51,744HTA,1:171,072R
SER.2 B 1:89,117 H, 1:22,176 HTA, 1:85,536 R
SER.2 C 1:2751 H, 1:780 HTA, 1:2715 R
SER.2 D 1:1367 H, 1:390 HTA, 1:1369 R
SER.2 E 1:2039 H, 1:586 HTA, 1:2061 R
SER.2 F 1:285 H, 1:129 HTA, 1:301 R
SER.2 GROUP A PRINT RUN 25 COPIES
SER.2 GROUP B PRINT RUN 50 COPIES
SER.2 GROUP A-B ARE NOT SERIAL #'d
PRINT RUN INFO PROVIDED BY TOPPS
SER.1 EXCH.DEADLINE 11/30/06
SER.2 EXCH.DEADLINE 04/30/07
NO GROUP A2 PRICING DUE TO SCARCITY
AR Alex Rodriguez A1 100.00 175.00
AR2 Alex Rodriguez B2/50 * 100.00 200.00
ARI Alexis Rios C1 4.00 10.00
BB Billy Butler E2 20.00 50.00
BBO Barry Bonds A2/25 *
CC Carl Crawford D2 10.00 25.00
CK Casey Kotchman C1 4.00 10.00
CT Chad Tracy C1 4.00 10.00
CW Craig Wilson D2 6.00 15.00
DD David DeJesus C1 4.00 10.00
DM Dallas McPherson D1 4.00 10.00
DW David Wright C1 10.00 25.00
EC Eric Chavez A1 10.00 25.00
EC2 Eric Chavez C2 10.00 25.00
ECO Erik Cordier F2 4.00 10.00
EG Eric Gagne C2 15.00 40.00
FH Felix Hernandez D2 20.00 40.00
GP Glen Perkins F2 6.00 15.00
IR Ivan Rodriguez C2 30.00 60.00
JB Jason Bay D2 10.00 25.00
JC Jose Capellan B1 4.00 10.00
JM Justin Morneau C1 12.50 30.00
JMA John Maine C1 15.00 40.00
JS Johan Santana C2 15.00 40.00
JSM Jeff Mathis C1 4.00 10.00
LP Landon Powell F2 6.00 15.00
MB Milton Bradley D2 10.00 25.00
MC Miguel Cabrera C1 10.00 25.00
MCA Matt Campbell F2 4.00 10.00
MH Matt Holliday C1 6.00 15.00
ML Mark Loretta D2 6.00 15.00
MR Michael Rogers F2 4.00 10.00
SK Scott Kazmir C2 10.00 25.00
TH Torii Hunter A1 10.00 25.00
TS Termel Sledge E2 4.00 10.00
VW Vernon Wells A1 10.00 25.00
ZG Zack Greinke C1 10.00 25.00

2005 Topps Barry Bonds Chase to 715

COMMON CARD 15.00 40.00
SER.2 ODDS 1:2539 H, 1:722 HTA, 1:2516 R
STATED PRINT RUN 1 SERIAL #'d SET

2005 Topps Barry Bonds Home Run History

COMP.SERIES 3 (48) 20.00 50.00
COMP.06 UPDATE (26) 10.00 25.00
COMP.07 UPDATE (22) 20.00 50.00
COMMON CARD (1-754) 1.25 3.00
COMMON HR 1 15.00 40.00
COMMON HR 100/200/300/400 6.00 15.00
COMMON HR 500/600 6.00 15.00
COMMON HR 661/700 3.00 8.00
COMMON HR 755-762 2.00 5.00
05 SER.2 ODDS 1:4 H, 1:1 HTA, 1:4 R
05 UPDATE ODDS 1:4 H, 1:1 HTA, 1:4 R
06 SER.1 ODDS 1:4 HOB, 1:4 MINI, 1:4 RET
06 SER.1 ODDS 1:2 RACK
06 UPDATE ODDS 1:6 HOB,1:6 RET
07 UPDATE ODDS 1:12 HOBBY
05 SER.2 EXCH ODDS 1:178,234 HOB
05 SER.2 EXCH ODDS 1:51,744 HTA
05 SER.2 EXCH ODDS 1:171,072 RET
07 UPDATE ODDS 1:12 H,1:3 HTA,1:12 R
EXCH CARD PRINT RUN 25 COPIES
EXCH.CARD PRINT RUN INFO FROM TOPPS
NO EXCH CARD PRICING DUE TO SCARCITY
1-330 ISSUED IN 05 SERIES 2 PACKS
331-660 ISSUED IN 05 UPDATE PACKS
661-708 ISSUED IN 06 SERIES 1 PACKS
709-734 ISSUED IN 06 UPDATE PACKS
735-575 ISSUED IN 07 UPDATE PACKS
1/100/200/300/400/500/600 ARE GOLD FOIL
661/700/755/766 ARE SILVER FOIL

2005 Topps Barry Bonds MVP

SER.2 ODDS 1:2613 H, 1:743 HTA, 1:2592 R
PRINT RUNS B/WN 25-500 COPIES PER
NO PRICING ON QTY OF 25
1 Barry Bonds 1990/25
2 Barry Bonds 1992/50
3 Barry Bonds 1993/100 12.00 30.00
4 Barry Bonds 2001/200 10.00 25.00
5 Barry Bonds 2002/300 10.00 25.00
6 Barry Bonds 2003/400 8.00 20.00
7 Barry Bonds 2004/500 8.00 20.00

2005 Topps Barry Bonds MVP Autographed Jersey Relics

SER.2 ODDS 1:22,176 HTA
STATED PRINT RUN 1 SERIAL #'d SET
NO PRICING DUE TO SCARCITY
EXCHANGE DEADLINE 04/30/07

2005 Topps Barry Bonds MVP Autographs

SER.2 ODDS 1:222,792 H, 1:51,744 HTA
SER.2 ODDS 1:171,072 R
PRINT RUNS B/WN 1-7 COPIES PER
NO PRICING DUE TO SCARCITY

2005 Topps Barry Bonds MVP Jersey Relics

SER.2 ODDS 1:2613 H, 1:743 HTA, 1:2592 R
PRINT RUNS B/WN 25-500 COPIES PER
NO PRICING ON QTY OF 25
1 Barry Bonds 1990/25
2 Barry Bonds 1992/50
3 Barry Bonds 1993/100 50.00 100.00
4 Barry Bonds 2001/200 30.00 60.00
5 Barry Bonds 2002/300 20.00 50.00
6 Barry Bonds 2003/400 15.00 40.00
7 Barry Bonds 2004/500 12.50 30.00

2005 Topps Celebrity Threads Jersey Relics

SERIES 1 ODDS 1:562 H, 1:161 HTA, 1:468 R
RELICS ARE FROM CELEBRITY AS EVENT
CC Cesar Cedeno 4.00 10.00
CF Cecil Fielder 6.00 15.00
DW Dave Winfield 4.00 10.00
GG Goose Gossage 4.00 10.00
HR Harold Reynolds 4.00 10.00
MS Mike Scott 4.00 10.00
OS Ozzie Smith 8.00 20.00
RF Rollie Fingers 4.00 10.00

2005 Topps Dem Bums

COMPLETE SET (21) 20.00 50.00
SERIES 1 ODDS 1:12 H, 1:4 HTA, 1:12 R
BB Bob Borkowski 1.25 3.00
CE Carl Erskine 1.25 3.00
CF Carl Furillo 1.25 3.00
CL Clem Labine 1.25 3.00
DH Don Hoak 1.25 3.00
DN Don Newcombe 1.25 3.00
DS Duke Snider 2.00 5.00
DZ Don Zimmer 1.25 3.00
ER Ed Roebuck 1.25 3.00
GS George Shuba 1.25 3.00
JB Joe Black 1.25 3.00
JG Jim Gilliam 1.25 3.00
JH Jim Hughes 1.25 3.00
JP Johnny Podres 1.25 3.00
JR Jackie Robinson 2.00 5.00
KS Karl Spooner 1.25 3.00
RC Roy Campanella 2.00 5.00
RCR Roger Craig 1.25 3.00
RM Russ Meyer 1.25 3.00
RW Rube Walker 1.25 3.00
WA Walter Alston 1.25 3.00

2005 Topps Dem Bums Autographs

SERIES 1 ODDS 1:150 HTA
SERIES 2 ODDS 1:182 HTA
SER.2 EXCH.DEADLINE 04/30/07
CE Carl Erskine 15.00 40.00
CL Clem Labine 15.00 40.00
DN Don Newcombe 20.00 50.00
DS Duke Snider 20.00 50.00
DZ Don Zimmer 20.00 50.00
ER Ed Roebuck 20.00 50.00
JP Johnny Podres 15.00 40.00
RC Roger Craig 15.00 40.00

2005 Topps Dem Bums Cut Signatures

SER.1 ODDS 1:347,438 H, 1:71,104 HTA
SER.1 ODDS 1:436,320 R
STATED PRINT RUN 1 SERIAL #'d SET
NO PRICING DUE TO SCARCITY

2005 Topps Derby Digs Ball Relics

SER.2 ODDS 1:63,655 H, 1:17,248 HTA
SER.2 ODDS 1:57,024 R
STATED PRINT RUN 10 SERIAL #'d SETS
NO PRICING DUE TO SCARCITY

2005 Topps Derby Digs Jersey Relics

SER.1 ODDS 1:11,208 HOBBY, 1:3232 HTA
SER.1 ODDS 1:9630 RETAIL
STATED PRINT RUN 100 SERIAL #'d SETS
DO David Ortiz 15.00 40.00
HB Hank Blalock 10.00 25.00
JT Jim Thome 15.00 40.00
LB Lance Berkman 10.00 25.00
MT Miguel Tejada 10.00 25.00
SS Sammy Sosa 15.00 40.00

2005 Topps Factory Set Draft Picks Bonus

COMPLETE SET (5) 10.00 20.00
ONE SET PER FACTORY SET
1 Beau Jones 2.00 5.00
2 Cliff Pennington .75 2.00
3 Chris Volstad 2.00 5.00
4 Ricky Romero 1.25 3.00
5 Jay Bruce 6.00 15.00

2005 Topps Factory Set First Year Draft Bonus

COMPLETE SET (10) 15.00 30.00
ONE SET PER GREEN HOLIDAY FACT.SET
1 Nick Webber .75 2.00
2 Aaron Thompson 1.25 3.00
3 Matt Garza 1.25 3.00
4 Tyler Greene .75 2.00
5 Ryan Braun 8.00 20.00
6 C.J. Henry 1.25 3.00
7 Ryan Zimmerman 6.00 15.00
8 John Mayberry Jr. 2.00 5.00
9 Cesar Carrillo 1.25 3.00
10 Mark McCormick .75 2.00

2005 Topps Factory Set First Year Player Bonus

COMPLETE SERIES 1 (5)	6.00	15.00
1-5 ISSUED IN RED HOBBY SETS		
1 Bill McCarthy	.75	2.00
2 John Hudgins	.75	2.00
3 Kyle Nichols	.75	2.00
4 Thomas Pauly	.75	2.00
5 Philip Humber	2.00	5.00

2005 Topps Factory Set Team Bonus

Issued five per selected Topps factory sets, these cards feature leading prospects from seven-different organizations.

COMP.CUBS SET (5)	6.00	15.00
COMP.GIANTS SET (5)	6.00	15.00
COMP.NATIONALS SET (5)	6.00	15.00
COMP.RED SOX SET (5)	6.00	15.00
COMP.TIGERS SET (5)	6.00	15.00
COMP.YANKEES SET (5)	6.00	15.00
C1-C5 ISSUED IN CUBS FACTORY SET		
G1-G5 ISSUED IN GIANTS FACTORY SET		
N1-N5 ISSUED IN NATIONALS FACTORY SET		
R1-R5 ISSUED IN RED SOX FACTORY SET		
T1-T5 ISSUED IN TIGERS FACTORY SET		
Y1-Y5 ISSUED IN YANKEES FACTORY SET		
C1 Casey McGehee	2.50	6.00
C2 Andy Santana	.75	2.00
C3 Buck Coats	.75	2.00
C4 Kevin Collins	.75	2.00
C5 Brandon Sing	.75	2.00
G1 Pat Misch	.75	2.00
G2 J.B. Thurmond	.75	2.00
G3 Billy Sadler	.75	2.00
G4 Jonathan Sanchez	3.00	8.00
G5 Fred Lewis	1.25	3.00
N1 Daryl Thompson	.75	2.00
N2 Ender Chavez	.75	2.00
N3 Ryan Church	.75	2.00
N4 Brendan Harris	.75	2.00
N5 Darrell Rasner	.75	2.00
R1 Stefan Bailie	.75	2.00
R2 Willy Mota	.75	2.00
R3 Matt Van Der Bosch	.75	2.00
R4 Mike Garber	.75	2.00
R5 Dustin Pedroia	2.50	6.00
T1 Eulogio de la Cruz	.75	2.00
T2 Humberto Sanchez	1.25	3.00
T3 Danny Zell	.75	2.00
T4 Kyle Sleeth	.75	2.00
T5 Curtis Granderson	1.25	3.00
Y1 T.J. Beam	.75	2.00
Y2 Ben Jones	.75	2.00
Y3 Robinson Cano	2.00	5.00
Y4 Steven White	.75	2.00
Y5 Philip Hughes	1.25	3.00

2005 Topps Grudge Match

COMPLETE SET (10)	5.00	12.00
SERIES 1 ODDS 1:24 H, 1:8 HTA, 1:18 R		
1 Jorge Posada	.60	1.50
Pedro Martinez		
2 Mike Piazza	1.25	3.00
Roger Clemens		
3 Mariano Rivera	1.00	2.50
Luis Gonzalez		
4 Jim Edmonds	.60	1.50
Carlos Zambrano		
5 Aaron Boone	.40	1.00
Tim Wakefield		
6 Manny Ramirez	1.00	2.50
Roger Clemens		
7 Michael Tucker	.40	1.00
Eric Gagne		
8 Ivan Rodriguez	.60	1.50
J.T. Snow		
9 Alex Rodriguez	1.50	4.00
Bronson Arroyo		
10 Corky Miller	1.00	2.50
Sammy Sosa		

2005 Topps Hit Parade

COMPLETE SET (30)	30.00	60.00
SER.2 ODDS 1:12 H, 1:4 HTA, 1:12 R		
HR1 Barry Bonds HR	2.00	5.00

HR2 Sammy Sosa HR	1.00	2.50
HR3 Rafael Palmeiro HR	.60	1.50
HR4 Ken Griffey Jr. HR	1.50	4.00
HR5 Jeff Bagwell HR	.60	1.50
HR6 Frank Thomas HR	1.00	2.50
HR7 Juan Gonzalez HR	.40	1.00
HR8 Jim Thome HR	.60	1.50
HR9 Gary Sheffield HR	.40	1.00
HR10 Manny Ramirez HR	1.00	2.50
HIT1 Rafael Palmeiro HIT	.60	1.50
HIT2 Barry Bonds HIT	2.00	5.00
HIT3 Roberto Alomar HIT	.60	1.50
HIT4 Craig Biggio HIT	.60	1.50
HIT5 Julio Franco HIT	.40	1.00
HIT6 Steve Finley HIT	.40	1.00
HIT7 Jeff Bagwell HIT	.60	1.50
HIT8 B.J. Surhoff HIT	.40	1.00
HIT9 Marquis Grissom HIT	.40	1.00
HIT10 Sammy Sosa HIT	1.00	2.50
RBI1 Barry Bonds RBI	2.00	5.00
RBI2 Rafael Palmeiro RBI	.60	1.50
RBI3 Sammy Sosa RBI	1.00	2.50
RBI4 Jeff Bagwell RBI	.60	1.50
RBI5 Ken Griffey Jr. RBI	1.50	4.00
RBI6 Frank Thomas RBI	1.00	2.50
RBI7 Juan Gonzalez RBI	.40	1.00
RBI8 Gary Sheffield RBI	.40	1.00
RBI9 Ruben Sierra RBI	.40	1.00
RBI10 Manny Ramirez RBI	1.00	2.50

2005 Topps Hobby Masters

COMPLETE SET (20)	12.50	30.00
SERIES 1 ODDS 1:18 HOBBY, 1:6 HTA		
1 Alex Rodriguez	1.50	4.00
2 Sammy Sosa	1.00	2.50
3 Ichiro Suzuki	1.50	4.00
4 Albert Pujols	2.50	6.00
5 Derek Jeter	2.50	6.00
6 Jim Thome	.60	1.50
7 Vladimir Guerrero	1.00	2.50
8 Nomar Garciaparra	1.00	2.50
9 Mike Piazza	1.00	2.50
10 Jason Giambi	.40	1.00
11 Ivan Rodriguez	.60	1.50
12 Alfonso Soriano	.60	1.50
13 Dontrelle Willis	.40	1.00
14 Chipper Jones	1.00	2.50
15 Mark Prior	.60	1.50
16 Todd Helton	.60	1.50
17 Randy Johnson	1.00	2.50
18 Hank Blalock	.40	1.00
19 Ken Griffey Jr.	1.50	4.00
20 Roger Clemens	1.25	3.00

2005 Topps Midsummer Covers Ball Relics

SER.1 ODDS 1:46,325 H, 1:3333 HTA
SER.2 ODDS 1:17,474 H, 1:3610 HTA
STATED PRINT RUN 10 SERIAL #'d SETS
NO PRICING DUE TO SCARCITY

2005 Topps On Deck Circle Relics

SER.2 ODDS 1:1493 H, 1:425 HTA, 1:1488 R		
STATED PRINT RUN 275 SETS		
CARDS ARE NOT SERIAL-NUMBERED		
PRINT RUN INFO PROVIDED BY TOPPS		
AP Albert Pujols	15.00	40.00
AR Alex Rodriguez	15.00	40.00
AS Alfonso Soriano	4.00	10.00
CB Carlos Beltran	4.00	10.00
HB Hank Blalock	4.00	10.00
IR Ivan Rodriguez	6.00	15.00
JT Jim Thome	6.00	15.00
SR Scott Rolen	6.00	15.00
SS Sammy Sosa	6.00	15.00
TH Todd Helton	6.00	15.00

2005 Topps Own the Game

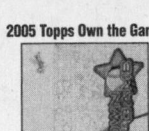

COMPLETE SET (30)	12.50	30.00
SERIES 1 ODDS 1:12 H, 1:4 HTA, 1:12 R		
1 Ichiro Suzuki	1.50	4.00
2 Todd Helton	.60	1.50
3 Adrian Beltre	.40	1.00
4 Albert Pujols	2.50	6.00
5 Adam Dunn	.60	1.50
6 Jim Thome	.60	1.50
7 Miguel Tejada	.60	1.50
8 David Ortiz	1.00	2.50
9 Manny Ramirez	1.00	2.50
10 Scott Rolen	.60	1.50
11 Gary Sheffield	.40	1.00
12 Vladimir Guerrero	1.00	2.50
13 Jim Edmonds	.60	1.50
14 Ivan Rodriguez	.60	1.50
15 Lance Berkman	.60	1.50
16 Michael Young	.60	1.50
17 Juan Pierre	.40	1.00
18 Craig Biggio	.60	1.50
19 Johnny Damon	.60	1.50
20 Jimmy Rollins	.60	1.50
21 Scott Podsednik	.40	1.00
22 Bobby Abreu	.40	1.00
23 Lyle Overbay	.40	1.00
24 Carl Crawford	.60	1.50
25 Mark Loretta	.40	1.00
26 Vinny Castilla	.40	1.00
27 Curt Schilling	.60	1.50
28 Johan Santana	1.00	2.50
29 Randy Johnson	1.00	2.50
30 Pedro Martinez	.60	1.50

2005 Topps Power Brokers Cut Signatures

SER.2 ODDS 1:99,019H,1:22,176R,1:85,536R
STATED PRINT RUN 1 SERIAL #'d SET
NO PRICING DUE TO SCARCITY

2005 Topps Spokesman Jersey Relic

SER.1 ODDS 1:5627 H, 1:1604 HTA, 1:4692 R		
RELIC IS EVENT WORN		
AR Alex Rodriguez	20.00	50.00

2005 Topps Team Topps Autographs

These cards were issued in some late season 2005 Topps products.

BOWMAN DRAFT ODDS 1:697 H		
TOP.UP.ODDS 1:5374H,1:1537 HTA,1:5347R		
BH Ben Hendrickson BD	4.00	10.00
JK Josh Kroeger BD	4.00	10.00
KS Kurt Suzuki TU	4.00	10.00

2005 Topps Touch Em All Base Relics

SER.1 ODDS 1:13,493 H, 1:3878 HTA
SER.1 ODDS 1:11,440 R
SER.2 ODDS 1:8329 H, 1:2352 HTA
SER.2 ODDS 1:8146 R
STATED PRINT RUN 50 SERIAL #'d SETS
NO PRICING DUE TO SCARCITY

2005 Topps World Champions Red Sox Relics

SER.2 A ODDS 1:649 H, 1:185 HTA, 1:648 R		
SER.2 B ODDS 1:311 H, 1:89 HTA, 1:310 R		
BM Bill Mueller Bat A	6.00	15.00
BM2 Bill Mueller Jsy B	6.00	15.00
CS Curt Schilling Jsy B	6.00	15.00
DL Derek Lowe Jsy B	6.00	15.00
DMI Doug Mientkiewicz Bat B	6.00	15.00
DO David Ortiz Bat B	6.00	15.00
DO2 David Ortiz Jsy B	6.00	15.00
DR Dave Roberts Bat A	6.00	15.00
JD Johnny Damon Bat A	6.00	15.00
JD2 Johnny Damon Jsy B	6.00	15.00
KM Kevin Millar Bat B	6.00	15.00
KY Kevin Youkilis Bat A	4.00	10.00
MR Manny Ramirez Bat A	6.00	15.00
MR2 Manny Ramirez Home Jsy B	6.00	15.00
MR3 Manny Ramirez Road Jsy B	6.00	15.00
OC Orlando Cabrera Bat A	6.00	15.00
OC2 Orlando Cabrera Jsy B	6.00	15.00
PM Pedro Martinez Uni A	6.00	15.00
PR Pokey Reese Bat B	4.00	10.00
TN Trot Nixon Bat A	6.00	15.00

2005 Topps World Treasures Cut Signatures

SER.1 ODDS 1:135,475 HOB, 1:42,662 HTA
SER.1 ODDS 1:109,080 RETAIL
STATED PRINT RUN 1 SERIAL #'d SET
NO PRICING DUE TO SCARCITY

2005 Topps World Treasures Dual Signatures

SERIES 1 ODDS 1:213,312 HTA
STATED PRINT RUN 1 SERIAL #'d SET
NO PRICING DUE TO SCARCITY

2005 Topps Update

This 330-card set was released in November, 2005. The set was issued in 10-card packs with a $1.50 SRP which came 36 packs to a box and eight boxes to a case. It is also important to note that a factory set consisting of just the base set (no inserts) was also included in the sealed hobby cases. The basic set consists of cards 1-84 featuring either players who were traded/signed as free agents after the original 2005 Topps set was released. Cards numbered 85-89 feature managers with new teams. Cards numbered 90-110 feature prospects, who previously had cards, who made an impact in baseball in 2005. Cards numbered 111 through 115 feature players who set records in 2005. Cards numbered 116 through 134 feature post-season highlights. Cards numbered 135 through 146 feature 2005 league leaders. Cards numbered 147 through 194 feature a mix of award winners and 2005 All-Stars. Cards numbered 195 through 202 feature players who were in the 2005 All-Star Home Run Derby. Cards numbered 203 through 220 feature players with tremendous futures. Cards numbered 221 through 310 feature Rookie Cards of players who had not been on Topps cards previously. Cards 311 through 330 feature some of the leading players selected in the 2005 amateur draft.

COMPLETE SET (330)	15.00	40.00
COMP.FACT.SET (330)	25.00	40.00
COMMON CARD (1-330)	.07	.20
COM (90-110/203-220)	.20	.50
COMMON (116-134)	.20	.50
COM (14/66/221-310)	.12	.30
COMMON (311-330)	.30	.75
PLATE ODDS 1:2009 H, 1:582 HTA, 1:2009 R		
PLATE PRINT RUN 1 SET PER COLOR		
BLACK-CYAN-MAGENTA-YELLOW ISSUED		
NO PLATE PRICING DUE TO SCARCITY		
1 Sammy Sosa	.20	.50
2 Jeff Francoeur	.20	.50
3 Tony Clark	.07	.20
4 Michael Tucker	.07	.20
5 Mike Matheny	.07	.20
6 Eric Young	.07	.20
7 Jose Valentin	.07	.20
8 Matt Lawton	.07	.20
9 Juan Rivera	.07	.20
10 Shawn Green	.07	.20
11 Aaron Boone	.07	.20
12 Woody Williams	.07	.20
13 Brad Wilkerson	.07	.20
14 Anthony Reyes RC	.20	.50
15 Russ Adams	.07	.20
16 Gustavo Chacin	.07	.20
17 Michael Restovich	.07	.20
18 Humberto Quintero	.07	.20
19 Matt Ginter	.07	.20
20 Scott Podsednik	.07	.20
21 Byung-Hyun Kim	.07	.20
22 Orlando Hernandez	.07	.20
23 Mark Grudzielanek	.07	.20
24 Jody Gerut	.07	.20
25 Adrian Beltre	.07	.20
26 Scott Schoeneweis	.07	.20
27 Marlon Anderson	.07	.20
28 Jason Vargas	.07	.20
29 Claudio Vargas	.07	.20
30 Jason Kendall	.07	.20
31 Aaron Small	.07	.20
32 Juan Cruz	.07	.20
33 Placido Polanco	.07	.20
34 Jorge Sosa	.07	.20
35 John Olerud	.07	.20
36 Ryan Langerhans	.07	.20
37 Randy Winn	.07	.20
38 Zach Duke	.07	.20
39 Garrett Atkins	.07	.20
40 Al Leiter	.07	.20
41 Shawn Chacon	.07	.20
42 Mark DeRosa	.07	.20
43 Miguel Ojeda	.07	.20
44 A.J. Pierzynski	.07	.20
45 Carlos Lee	.07	.20
46 LaTroy Hawkins	.07	.20
47 Nick Green	.07	.20
48 Shawn Estes	.07	.20
49 Eli Marrero	.07	.20
50 Jeff Kent	.07	.20
51 Joe Randa	.07	.20
52 Jose Hernandez	.07	.20
53 Joe Blanton	.07	.20
54 Huston Street	.07	.20
55 Marlon Byrd	.07	.20
56 Alex Sanchez	.07	.20
57 Livan Hernandez	.07	.20
58 Chris Young	.12	.30
59 Brad Eldred	.07	.20
60 Terrence Long	.07	.20
61 Phil Nevin	.07	.20
62 Kyle Farnsworth	.07	.20
63 Jon Lieber	.07	.20
64 Antonio Alfonseca	.07	.20
65 Tony Graffanino	.07	.20
66 Tadahito Iguchi RC	.20	.50
67 Brad Thompson	.07	.20
68 Jose Vidro	.07	.20
69 Jason Phillips	.07	.20
70 Carl Pavano	.07	.20
71 Pokey Reese	.07	.20
72 Jerome Williams	.07	.20
73 Kazuhisa Ishii	.07	.20
74 Zach Day	.07	.20
75 Edgar Renteria	.07	.20
76 Mike Myers	.07	.20
77 Jeff Cirillo	.07	.20
78 Endy Chavez	.07	.20
79 Jose Guillen	.07	.20
80 Ugueth Urbina	.07	.20
81 Vinny Castilla	.07	.20
82 Javier Vazquez	.07	.20
83 Willy Taveras	.07	.20
84 Mark Mulder	.07	.20
85 Mike Hargrove MG	.07	.20
86 Buddy Bell MG	.07	.20
87 Charlie Manuel MG	.07	.20
88 Willie Randolph MG	.07	.20
89 Bob Melvin MG	.07	.20
90 Chris Lambert PROS	.12	.30
91 Homer Bailey PROS	.12	.30
92 Ervin Santana PROS	.12	.30
93 Bill Bray PROS	.12	.30
94 Thomas Diamond PROS	.12	.30
95 Trevor Plouffe PROS	.12	.30
96 James Houser PROS	.12	.30
97 Jake Stevens PROS	.12	.30
98 Anthony Whittington PROS	.12	.30
99 Philip Hughes PROS	.20	.50
100 Greg Golson PROS	.12	.30
101 Paul Maholm PROS	.12	.30
102 Carlos Quentin PROS	.20	.50
103 Dan Johnson PROS	.12	.30
104 Mark Rogers PROS	.12	.30
105 Neil Walker PROS	.12	.30
106 Omar Quintanilla PROS	.12	.30
107 Blake DeWitt PROS	.20	.50
108 Taylor Tankersley PROS	.12	.30
109 David Murphy PROS	.20	.50
110 Felix Hernandez PROS	.50	1.25
111 Craig Biggio HL	.12	.30
112 Greg Maddux HL	.30	.75
113 Bobby Abreu HL	.07	.20
114 Alex Rodriguez HL	.30	.75
115 Trevor Hoffman HL	.12	.30
116 A.J. Pierzynski	.20	.50
Tadahito Iguchi ALDS		
117 Reggie Sanders NLDS	.12	.30
118 Bengie Molina	.12	.30
Ervin Santana ALDS		
119 Chris Burke	.20	.50
Lance Berkman		
Adam LaRoche NLDS		
120 Garret Anderson ALCS	.12	.30
121 A.J. Pierzynski ALCS	.12	.30
122 Paul Konerko ALCS	.20	.50
123 Joe Crede ALCS	.12	.30
124 Mark Buehrle	.20	.50
Jon Garland ALCS		
125 Freddy Garcia	.12	.30
Jose Contreras ALCS		
126 Reggie Sanders NLCS	.12	.30
127 Roy Oswalt NLCS	.20	.50
128 Roger Clemens NLCS	.40	1.00
129 Albert Pujols NLCS	.75	2.00
130 Roy Oswalt NLCS	.20	.50
131 Joe Crede	.12	.30
Bobby Jenks WS		
132 Paul Konerko	.20	.50
Scott Podsednik WS		
133 Geoff Blum WS	.12	.30
134 White Sox Sweep WS	.12	.30
135 Alex Rodriguez	.20	.50
David Ortiz		
Manny Ramirez AL HR		
136 Michael Young	.12	.30
Alex Rodriguez		
Vladimir Guerrero AL BA		
137 David Ortiz	.20	.50
Mark Teixeira		
Manny Ramirez AL RBI		
138 Bartolo Colon	.12	.30
Jon Garland		
Cliff Lee AL Wins		
139 Kevin Millwood	.12	.30
Johan Santana		
Mark Buehrle AL ERA		
140 Johan Santana	.20	.50
Randy Johnson		
John Lackey AL K's		
141 Andruw Jones	.07	.20
Derrek Lee		
Albert Pujols NL HR		
142 Derrek Lee	.07	.20
Albert Pujols		
Miguel Cabrera NL BA		
143 Andruw Jones	.07	.20
Albert Pujols		
Pat Burrell NL RBI		
144 Dontrelle Willis	.20	.50
Chris Carpenter		
Roy Oswalt NL Wins		
145 Roger Clemens	.25	.60
Andy Pettitte		
Dontrelle Willis NL ERA		
146 Jake Peavy	.20	.50
Chris Carpenter		
Pedro Martinez NL K's		
147 Mark Teixeira AS	.20	.50
148 Brian Roberts AS	.07	.20
149 Michael Young AS	.12	.30
150 Alex Rodriguez AS	.30	.75
151 Johnny Damon AS	.12	.30
152 Vladimir Guerrero AS	.20	.50
153 Manny Ramirez AS	.20	.50
154 David Ortiz AS	.20	.50
155 Mariano Rivera AS	.20	.50
156 Joe Nathan AS	.07	.20
157 Albert Pujols AS	.50	1.25
158 Jeff Kent AS	.07	.20
159 Felipe Lopez AS	.07	.20
160 Morgan Ensberg AS	.07	.20
161 Miguel Cabrera AS	.20	.50
162 Ken Griffey Jr. AS	.30	.75
163 Andruw Jones AS	.07	.20
164 Paul Lo Duca AS	.07	.20
165 Chad Cordero AS	.07	.20
166 Ken Griffey Jr. Comeback	.30	.75
167 Jason Giambi Comeback	.07	.20
168 Willy Taveras ROY	.07	.20
169 Huston Street ROY	.07	.20
170 Chris Carpenter AS	.20	.50
171 Bartolo Colon AS	.07	.20
172 Bobby Cox AS MG	.07	.20
173 Ozzie Guillen AS MG	.12	.30
174 Andruw Jones POY	.07	.20
175 Johnny Damon AS	.12	.30
176 Alex Rodriguez AS	.30	.75
177 David Ortiz AS	.20	.50
178 Manny Ramirez AS	.20	.50
179 Miguel Tejada AS	.12	.30
180 Vladimir Guerrero AS	.20	.50
181 Mark Teixeira AS	.20	.50
182 Ivan Rodriguez AS	.12	.30
183 Brian Roberts AS	.07	.20
184 Mark Buehrle AS	.12	.30
185 Bobby Abreu AS	.07	.20
186 Carlos Beltran AS	.07	.20
187 Albert Pujols AS	.50	1.25
188 Derrek Lee AS	.07	.20
189 Jim Edmonds AS	.12	.30
190 Aramis Ramirez AS	.07	.20
191 Mike Piazza AS	.20	.50
192 Jeff Kent AS	.07	.20
193 David Eckstein AS	.07	.20
194 Chris Carpenter AS	.20	.50
195 Bobby Abreu HR	.07	.20
196 Ivan Rodriguez HR	.12	.30
197 Carlos Lee HR	.07	.20
198 David Ortiz HR	.20	.50
199 Hee-Seop Choi HR	.07	.20
200 Andruw Jones HR	.07	.20
201 Mark Teixeira HR	.20	.50
202 Jason Bay HR	.07	.20
203 Hanley Ramirez FUT	.20	.50
204 Shin-Soo Choo FUT	.20	.50
205 Justin Huber FUT	.12	.30
206 Nelson Cruz FUT RC	.50	1.25
207 Edwin Encarnacion FUT	.20	.50
208 Miguel Montero FUT RC	.75	2.00
209 William Bergolla FUT	.12	.30
210 Luis Montanez FUT	.12	.30
211 Francisco Liriano FUT	.20	.50
212 Kevin Thompson FUT	.12	.30
213 B.J. Upton FUT	.20	.50
214 Conor Jackson FUT	.20	.50
215 Delmon Young FUT	.30	.75
216 Andy LaRoche FUT	.60	1.50
217 Ryan Garko FUT	.12	.30
218 Josh Barfield FUT	.20	.50
219 Chris B.Young FUT	.50	1.25
220 Justin Verlander FUT	2.50	6.00
221 Drew Anderson FY RC	.12	.30
222 Luis Hernandez FY RC	.12	.30
223 Jim Burt FY RC	.12	.30
224 Mike Morse FY RC	.30	.75
225 Elliot Johnson FY RC	.12	.30
226 C.J. Smith FY RC	.12	.30
227 Casey McGehee FY RC	.40	1.00
228 Brian Miller FY RC	.12	.30
229 Chris Vines FY RC	.12	.30
230 D.J. Houlton FY RC	.12	.30
231 Chuck Tiffany FY RC	.30	.75
232 Humberto Sanchez FY RC	.20	.50
233 Baltazar Lopez FY RC	.12	.30
234 Russ Martin FY RC	.50	1.25
235 Dana Eveland FY RC	.12	.30
236 Johan Silva FY RC	.12	.30
237 Adam Harben FY RC	.12	.30
238 Brian Bannister FY RC	.20	.50
239 Adam Boeve FY RC	.12	.30
240 Thomas Oldham FY RC	.12	.30
241 Cody Haerther FY RC	.12	.30
242 Dan Santin FY RC	.12	.30
243 Daniel Haigwood FY RC	.12	.30
244 Craig Tatum FY RC	.12	.30
245 Martin Prado FY RC	.75	2.00
246 Errol Simonitsch FY RC	.12	.30
247 Lorenzo Scott FY RC	.12	.30
248 Hayden Penn FY RC	.12	.30
249 Heath Totten FY RC	.12	.30
250 Nick Masset FY RC	.12	.30
251 Pedro Lopez FY RC	.12	.30
252 Ben Harrison FY	.12	.30
253 Mike Spidale FY RC	.12	.30
254 Jeremy Harts FY RC	.12	.30
255 Danny Zell FY RC	.12	.30
256 Kevin Collins FY RC	.12	.30
257 Tony Arnerich FY RC	.12	.30
258 Matt Albers FY RC	.12	.30
259 Ricky Barrett FY RC	.12	.30
260 Hernan Iribarren FY RC	.12	.30
261 Sean Tracey FY RC	.12	.30
262 Jerry Owens FY RC	.12	.30
263 Steve Nelson FY RC	.12	.30
264 Brandon McCarthy FY RC	.20	.50
265 David Shepard FY RC	.12	.30
266 Steven Bondurant FY RC	.12	.30
267 Billy Sadler FY RC	.12	.30
268 Ryan Feierabend FY RC	.12	.30
269 Stuart Pomeranz FY RC	.12	.30
270 Shaun Marcum FY	.30	.75
271 Erik Schindewolf FY RC	.12	.30
272 Stefan Bailie FY RC	.12	.30
273 Mike Esposito FY RC UER	.12	.30
Photo is Darwinson Salazar		
274 Buck Coats FY RC	.12	.30
275 Andy Sides FY RC	.12	.30
276 Micah Schnurstein FY RC	.12	.30
277 Jesse Gutierrez FY RC	.12	.30
278 Jake Postlewait FY RC	.12	.30
279 Willy Mota FY RC	.12	.30
280 Ryan Speier FY RC	.12	.30
281 Frank Mata FY RC	.12	.30
282 Jair Jurrjens FY RC	.60	1.50
283 Nick Touchstone FY RC	.12	.30
284 Matthew Kemp FY RC	1.50	4.00
285 Vinny Rottino FY RC	.12	.30
286 J.B. Thurmond FY RC	.12	.30
287 Kelvin Pichardo FY RC	.12	.30
288 Scott Mitchinson FY RC	.12	.30
289 Darwinson Salazar FY RC	.12	.30
290 George Kottaras FY RC	.20	.50
291 Kenny Durost FY RC	.12	.30
292 Jonathan Sanchez FY RC	.50	1.25
293 Brandon Moorhead FY RC	.12	.30
294 Kennard Bibbs FY RC	.12	.30
295 David Gassner FY RC	.12	.30
296 Micah Furtado FY RC	.12	.30
297 Ismael Ramirez FY RC	.12	.30
298 Carlos Gonzalez FY RC	1.25	3.00
299 Brandon Sing FY RC	.12	.30
300 Jason Motte FY RC	.20	.50
301 Chuck James FY RC	.30	.75
302 Andy Santana FY RC	.12	.30
303 Manny Parra FY RC	.30	.75
304 Chris B.Young FY RC	.50	1.25
305 Juan Senreiso FY RC	.12	.30
306 Franklin Morales FY RC	.20	.50
307 Jared Gothreaux FY RC	.12	.30
308 Jayce Tingler FY RC	.12	.30
309 Matt Brown FY RC	.12	.30
310 Frank Diaz FY RC	.12	.30
311 Stephen Drew DP RC	1.50	4.00
312 Jered Weaver DP RC	1.25	3.00
313 Ryan Braun DP RC	3.00	8.00
314 John Mayberry Jr. DP RC	.75	2.00
315 Aaron Thompson DP RC	.50	1.25
316 Cesar Carrillo DP RC	.50	1.25
317 Jacoby Ellsbury DP RC	2.00	5.00
318 Matt Garza DP RC	.50	1.25
319 Cliff Pennington DP RC	.30	.75
320 Colby Rasmus DP RC	1.50	4.00
321 Chris Volstad DP RC	.75	2.00
322 Ricky Romero DP RC	.50	1.25
323 Ryan Zimmerman DP RC	2.50	6.00
324 C.J. Henry DP RC	.50	1.25
325 Jay Bruce DP RC	2.50	6.00
326 Beau Jones DP RC	.75	2.00
327 Mark McCormick DP RC	.30	.75
328 Eli Iorg DP RC	.30	.75
329 Andrew McCutchen DP RC	2.50	6.00
330 Mike Costanzo DP RC	.30	.75

2005 Topps Update Blue

ODDS 1:8035 H, 1:2341 HTA, 1:8035 R
STATED PRINT RUN 1 SERIAL #'d SET
NO PRICING DUE TO SCARCITY

2005 Topps Update Box Bottoms

*BOX BOTTOM: 1X TO 2.5X BASIC
*BOX BOTTOM: .6X TO 1.5X BASIC RC
ONE FOUR-CARD SHEET PER HTA BOX
CL: 1/10/20/22/25/45/50/57/70/84/110
CL: 224/264/311-313

2005 Topps Update Gold

*GOLD 1-89: 6X TO 15X BASIC
*GOLD 90-110: 2X TO 5X BASIC
*GOLD 111-115/135-202: 6X TO 15X BASIC
*GOLD: 116-134: 3X TO 8X BASIC
*GOLD: 203-220: 2X TO 5X BASIC
*GOLD 14/66/221-310: 2X TO 5X BASIC
*GOLD 311-330: 2X TO 5X BASIC
STATED ODDS 1:4 H, 1:1 HTA, 1:4 R
STATED PRINT RUN 2005 SERIAL #'d SETS
220 Justin Verlander FUT 10.00 25.00

2005 Topps Update All-Star Patches

STATED ODDS 1:910 H, 1:268 HTA, 1:910 R
PRINT RUNS B/WN 20-70 COPIES PER
NO PRICING ON QTY OF 25 OR LESS
AJ Andruw Jones/70 12.50 30.00
AP Albert Pujols/35 30.00 60.00
AR Alex Rodriguez/50 15.00 40.00
ARA Aramis Ramirez/60 10.00 25.00
BA Bobby Abreu/65 10.00 25.00
BC Bartolo Colon/60 10.00 25.00
BL Brad Lidge/65 10.00 25.00
BR Brian Roberts/25
BW Billy Wagner/50 10.00 25.00
CB Carlos Beltran/60 10.00 25.00
CC Chris Carpenter/70 10.00 25.00
CCO Chad Cordero/65 6.00 15.00
CL Carlos Lee/65 10.00 25.00
DE David Eckstein/65 12.50 30.00
DL Derrek Lee/65 12.50 30.00
DO David Ortiz/70 12.50 30.00
DW Dontrelle Willis/60 10.00 25.00
FL Felipe Lopez/35 8.00 20.00
GS Gary Sheffield/50 10.00 25.00
IR Ivan Rodriguez/25
IS Ichiro Suzuki/50 20.00 50.00
JB Jason Bay/50 10.00 25.00
JD Johnny Damon/60 12.50 30.00
JE Jim Edmonds/50 10.00 25.00
JG Jon Garland/70 12.50 30.00
JI Jason Isringhausen/65 10.00 25.00
JK Jeff Kent/65 10.00 25.00
JN Joe Nathan/65 6.00 15.00
JP Jake Peavy/60 10.00 25.00
JS Johan Santana/60 12.50 30.00
JSM John Smoltz/65 12.50 30.00
KR Kenny Rogers/50 6.00 15.00
LC Luis Castillo/20
LG Luis Gonzalez/70 10.00 25.00
LH Livan Hernandez/50 10.00 25.00
MA Moises Alou/65 6.00 15.00
MB Mark Buehrle/60 10.00 25.00
MC Miguel Cabrera/70 12.50 30.00
MCL Matt Clement/70 10.00 25.00
ME Morgan Ensberg/60 10.00 25.00
MM Melvin Mora/30 12.50 30.00
MP Mike Piazza/50 15.00 40.00
MR Manny Ramirez/65 12.50 30.00
MRI Mariano Rivera/65 15.00 40.00
MT Miguel Tejada/60 10.00 25.00
MTE Mark Teixeira/60 12.50 30.00
MY Michael Young/50 10.00 25.00
PK Paul Konerko/60 10.00 25.00
RO Roy Oswalt/60 10.00 25.00
SP Scott Podsednik/65 10.00 25.00

2005 Topps Update All-Star Stitches

GROUP A ODDS 1:131 H, 1:81 HTA, 1:127 R
GROUP B ODDS 1:91 H, 1:45 HTA, 1:91 R
GROUP C ODDS 1:100 H, 1:41 HTA, 1:100 R
GROUP D ODDS 1:109 H, 1:34 HTA, 1:109 R
GROUP E ODDS 1:98 H, 1:29 HTA, 1:98 R
GROUP F ODDS 1:272 H, 1:89 HTA, 1:272 R
AJ Andruw Jones C 4.00 10.00
AP Albert Pujols E 8.00 20.00
AR Alex Rodriguez D 6.00 15.00
ARA Aramis Ramirez E 3.00 8.00
BA Bobby Abreu B 3.00 8.00
BC Bartolo Colon D 3.00 8.00
BL Brad Lidge D 3.00 8.00
BR Brian Roberts C 3.00 8.00
BW Billy Wagner C 3.00 8.00
CB Carlos Beltran D 3.00 8.00
CC Chris Carpenter E 4.00 10.00
CCO Chad Cordero D 3.00 8.00
CL Carlos Lee E 3.00 8.00
DE David Eckstein B 6.00 15.00
DL Derrek Lee F 4.00 10.00
DO David Ortiz E 4.00 10.00
DW Dontrelle Willis F 3.00 8.00
FL Felipe Lopez B 3.00 8.00
GS Gary Sheffield D 3.00 8.00
IR Ivan Rodriguez A 4.00 10.00
IS Ichiro Suzuki A 8.00 20.00
JB Jason Bay C 3.00 8.00
JD Johnny Damon B 4.00 10.00
JE Jim Edmonds A 3.00 8.00
JG Jon Garland E 4.00 10.00
JI Jason Isringhausen E 3.00 8.00
JK Jeff Kent C 3.00 8.00
JN Joe Nathan D 3.00 8.00
JP Jake Peavy D 3.00 8.00
JS Johan Santana C 4.00 10.00
JSM John Smoltz D 4.00 10.00
KR Kenny Rogers A 3.00 8.00
LC Luis Castillo B 3.00 8.00
LG Luis Gonzalez C 3.00 8.00
LH Livan Hernandez F 3.00 8.00
MA Moises Alou C 3.00 8.00
MB Mark Buehrle B 3.00 8.00
MC Miguel Cabrera E 4.00 10.00
MCL Matt Clement B 3.00 8.00
ME Morgan Ensberg B 3.00 8.00
MM Melvin Mora B 3.00 8.00
MP Mike Piazza E 4.00 10.00
MR Manny Ramirez E 4.00 10.00
MRI Mariano Rivera B 4.00 10.00
MT Miguel Tejada B 3.00 8.00
MTE Mark Teixeira C 4.00 10.00
MY Michael Young A 3.00 8.00
PK Paul Konerko B 3.00 8.00
RO Roy Oswalt A 3.00 8.00
SP Scott Podsednik A 6.00 15.00

2005 Topps Update Barry Bonds Home Run History

SEE 05 TOPPS BONDS HRH FOR PRICING

2005 Topps Update Derby Digs Jersey Relics

STATED ODDS 1:3320 H,1:637 HTA,1:3320 R
STATED PRINT RUN 100 SERIAL #'d SETS
AJ Andruw Jones 10.00 25.00
BA Bobby Abreu 10.00 25.00
CL Carlos Lee 6.00 15.00
DO David Ortiz 10.00 25.00
IR Ivan Rodriguez 10.00 25.00
JB Jason Bay 6.00 15.00
MT Mark Teixeira 10.00 25.00

2005 Topps Update Hall of Fame Bat Relics

A ODDS 1:6406 H, 1:2012 HTA, 1:6406 R
B ODDS 1:1860 H, 1:548 HTA, 1:1860 R
RS Ryne Sandberg B 8.00 20.00
WB Wade Boggs A 6.00 15.00

2005 Topps Update Hall of Fame Dual Bat Relic

ODDS 1:13,392 H, 1:3815 HTA, 1:13,392 R
STATED PRINT RUN 200 SERIAL #'d CARDS
BS Wade Boggs 12.50 30.00
Ryne Sandberg

2005 Topps Update Legendary Sacks Relics

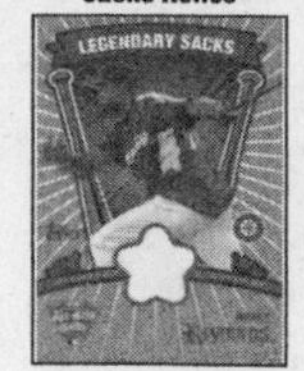

Please note that while the cards say "Game-Used Jersey" the material embedded in the cards look to be game-used base material.

STATED ODDS 1:965 H, 1:281 HTA, 1:965 R
STATED PRINT RUN 300 SERIAL #'d SETS
CARDS FEATURE CELEBRITY JSY SWATCH
AD Andre Dawson 6.00 15.00
BJ Bo Jackson 10.00 25.00
DW Dave Winfield 6.00 15.00
HR Harold Reynolds 6.00 15.00
JA Jim Abbott 6.00 15.00
LW Lou Whitaker 6.00 15.00
MF Mark Fidrych 10.00 25.00
OS Ozzie Smith 10.00 25.00
RF Rollie Fingers 6.00 15.00

2005 Topps Update Midsummer Covers Ball Relics

STATED ODDS 1:524 H, 1:512 HTA
STATED PRINT RUN 150 SERIAL #'d SETS
AP Albert Pujols 20.00 50.00
AR Alex Rodriguez 15.00 40.00
BR Brian Roberts 10.00 25.00
CB Carlos Beltran 10.00 25.00
DL Derrek Lee 15.00 40.00
DW Dontrelle Willis 10.00 25.00
IS Ichiro Suzuki 30.00 60.00
MT Miguel Tejada 10.00 25.00
RC Roger Clemens 15.00 40.00
VG Vladimir Guerrero 15.00 40.00

2005 Topps Update Signature Moves

A ODDS 1:317,088H,1:103,008HTA,1:40,176R
B ODDS 1:126,836 H,1:51,504 HTA,1:40,176 R
C ODDS 1:1220 H, 1:339 HTA, 1:1220 R
D ODDS 1:1128 H, 1:323 HTA, 1:1128 R
E ODDS 1:916 H, 1:262 HTA, 1:916 R
GROUP A PRINT RUN 15 #'d CARDS
GROUP B PRINT RUN 25 #'d CARDS
GROUP C PRINT RUN 275 #'d CARDS
GROUP D PRINT RUN 475 #'d SETS
NO GROUP A-B PRICING DUE TO SCARCITY
RED ODDS 1:6676 H, 1:1908 HTA, 1:6676 R
RED FOIL PRINT RUN 25 SERIAL #'d SETS
NO RED FOIL PRICING DUE TO SCARCITY
BB Barry Bonds A/15
BL Bobby Livingston D/475 6.00 15.00
BS Benito Santiago E 8.00 20.00
CJS C.J. Smith D/475 6.00 15.00
GK George Kottaras D/475 8.00 20.00
GP Glen Perkins C/275 8.00 20.00
HS Humberto Sanchez E 10.00 25.00
JP Jake Postlewait C/275 6.00 15.00
JV Justin Verlander C/275 50.00 100.00
KI Kazuhisa Ishii C/275 10.00 25.00
MA Matt Albers D/475 6.00 15.00
MM Mark Mulder C/275 10.00 25.00
PM Pedro Martinez B/25
RS Richie Sexson C/275 10.00 25.00
TC Travis Chick D/475 6.00 15.00
TG Troy Glaus C/275 10.00 25.00
TH Tim Hudson C/275 10.00 25.00
TW Tony Womack E 8.00 20.00

2005 Topps Update Touch Em All Base Relics

STATED ODDS 1:238 H, 1:77 HTA, 1:238 R
STATED PRINT RUN 1000 SERIAL #'d SETS
AP Albert Pujols 10.00 25.00
AR Alex Rodriguez 8.00 20.00
DL Derrek Lee 6.00 15.00
DO David Ortiz 6.00 15.00
GS Gary Sheffield 4.00 10.00
IR Ivan Rodriguez 6.00 15.00
IS Ichiro Suzuki 10.00 25.00
MR Manny Ramirez 6.00 15.00
MT Miguel Tejada 4.00 10.00
VG Vladimir Guerrero 6.00 15.00

2005 Topps Update Washington Nationals Inaugural Lineup

COMPLETE SET (10) 2.50 6.00
STATED ODDS 1:10 H, 1:4 HTA, 1:10 R
BS Brian Schneider .40 1.00
BW Brad Wilkerson .40 1.00
CG Cristian Guzman .40 1.00
JG Jose Guillen .40 1.00
JV Jose Vidro .40 1.00
LH Livan Hernandez .40 1.00
NJ Nick Johnson .40 1.00
TS Termel Sledge .40 1.00
VC Vinny Castilla .40 1.00
TEAM Team Photo .40 1.00

2005 Topps Update Washington Nationals Inaugural Lineup Ball Relics

These exceedingly scarce cards (only five serial #'d sets issued) each feature a swatch of leather material derived from a ball actually used at the first home game played for the 2005 season of the Washington Nationals. The checklist features the eight position players in the starting lineup in addition to Opening Day starting pitcher Livan Hernandez. Finally, a tenth card featuring a photo of the entire starting lineup standing on the base line as they're being introduced rounds out the 10-card set.

ODDS 1:49,104 H, 1:14,715 HTA, 1:40,176 R
STATED PRINT RUN 5 SERIAL #'d SETS
NO PRICING DUE TO SCARCITY

2005 Topps 1955 National

Each collector who purchased a VIP ticket for the 2005 Sports Collectors National Convention in Chicago received this four-card set of 1955 stars who were not issued in the original set. The card numbers assigned matched those numbers not used in the original 1955 Topps set and the card size matches the original 1955 measurements.

COMPLETE SET (4) 8.00 20.00
175 Stan Musial 6.00 15.00
186 Whitey Ford 2.50 6.00
203 Bob Feller 1.50 4.00
209 Herb Score 1.50 4.00

2005 Topps XXL Cubs

COMPLETE SET (4) 2.00 5.00
ONE 4-CARD SET PER PACK
1 Derrek Lee .40 1.00
2 Mark Prior .60 1.50
3 Nomar Garciaparra 1.00 2.50
4 Greg Maddux 1.50 4.00

2005 Topps XXL Red Sox

COMPLETE SET (4) 2.00 5.00
ONE 4-CARD SET PER PACK
1 David Ortiz 1.00 2.50
2 Manny Ramirez 1.00 2.50
3 Johnny Damon .60 1.50
4 Curt Schilling .60 1.50

2005 Topps XXL Yankees

COMPLETE SET (4) 4.00 10.00
ONE 4-CARD SET PER PACK
1 Alex Rodriguez 1.50 4.00
2 Derek Jeter 2.50 6.00
3 Hideki Matsui 1.50 4.00
4 Randy Johnson 1.00 2.50

2006 Topps Pre-Production

This three-card set was released to hobby dealers and media in January, 2006 to preview the upcoming 2006 Topps Series I product.

COMPLETE SET (3) .75 2.00
3-CARD SETS MAILED TO HOBBY DEALERS
PP1 Ichiro Suzuki .75 2.00
PP2 Alex Rodriguez .75 2.00
PP3 Albert Pujols 1.25 3.00

2006 Topps

This 659-card set was issued over two series. The first series was released in February, 2006 and the second series was released in June, 2006. The cards were issued in a myriad of forms including 10-card hobby packs with an $1.59 SRP which came 36 packs to a box and 10 boxes to a case. Retail packs consisted of 12-card packs with an $1.99 SRP and those cards came 24 packs to a box and 20 boxes to a case. There were also rack packs which had 18 cards and a $2.99 SRP and those packs came 24 packs to a box and three boxes to a case. There were also special packs issued for Target and Walmart. Card number 297, Alex Gordon, was pulled from circulation almost immediately, although a few copies in various forms of production were located in packs. In addition, Pete Mackanin and John Koronka cards were changed for the factory sets. This product has many sub sets including Award Winners (243-265); Managers/Team Cards (266-295, 586-615); Rookies (296-330), 616-645), Team Stars (326-330). Assorted Multi-Player Cards (646-660). A few Alay Soler cards were inserted into series two packs unannounced and those cards are very scarce.

COMP.HOBBY SET (664) 50.00 80.00
COMP.HOLIDAY SET (659) 50.00 80.00
COMP.CARDINALS SET (664) 50.00 80.00
COMP.CUBS SET (664) 50.00 80.00
COMP.PIRATES SET (664) 50.00 80.00
COMP.RED SOX SET (664) 50.00 80.00
COMP.YANKEES SET (664) 50.00 80.00
COMPLETE SET (659) 30.00 80.00
COMPLETE SERIES 1 (329) 15.00 40.00
COMPLETE SERIES 2 (330) 15.00 40.00
COMMON CARD (1-660) .07 .20
COMP.SER.1 SET EXCLUDES CARD 297
CARD 297 NOT INTENDED FOR RELEASE
CARDS 287b AND 312b ISSUED IN FACT.SET
2 TICKETS EXCH.CARD RANDOM IN PACKS
OVERALL PLATE SER.1 ODDS 1:246 HTA
OVERALL PLATE SER.2 ODDS 1:193 HTA
PLATE PRINT RUN 1 SET PER COLOR
BLACK-CYAN-MAGENTA-YELLOW ISSUED
NO PLATE PRICING DUE TO SCARCITY
1 Alex Rodriguez .30 .75
2 Jose Valentin .07 .20
3 Garrett Atkins .07 .20
4 Scott Hatteberg .07 .20
5 Carl Crawford .12 .30
6 Armando Benitez .07 .20
7 Mickey Mantle UER .60 1.50
High single home run season credited to wrong year
Length of longest homer in cartoon is also wrong
8 Mike Morse .07 .20
9 Damian Miller .07 .20
10 Clint Barmes .07 .20
11 Michael Barrett .07 .20
12 Coco Crisp .07 .20
13 Tadahito Iguchi .07 .20
14 Chris Snyder .07 .20
15 Brian Roberts .07 .20
16 David Wright .30 .75
17 Victor Santos .07 .20
18 Trevor Hoffman .12 .30
19 Jeremy Reed .07 .20
20 Bobby Abreu .07 .20
21 Lance Berkman .12 .30
22 Zach Day .07 .20
23 Jonny Gomes .07 .20
24 Jason Marquis .07 .20
25 Chipper Jones .20 .50
26 Scott Hairston .07 .20
27 Ryan Dempster .07 .20
28 Brandon Inge .07 .20
29 Aaron Harang .07 .20
30 Jon Garland .07 .20
31 Pokey Reese .07 .20
32 Mike MacDougal .07 .20
33 Mike Lieberthal .07 .20
34 Cesar Izturis .07 .20
35 Brad Wilkerson .07 .20
36 Jeff Suppan .07 .20
37 Adam Everett .07 .20
38 Bengie Molina .07 .20
39 Rickie Weeks .12 .30
40 Jorge Posada .12 .30
41 Rheal Cormier .07 .20
42 Reed Johnson .07 .20
43 Laynce Nix .07 .20
44 Carl Everett .07 .20
45 Greg Maddux .30 .75
46 Jeff Francis .07 .20
47 Felipe Lopez .07 .20
48 Dan Johnson .07 .20
49 Humberto Cota .07 .20
50 Manny Ramirez .20 .50
51 Juan Uribe .07 .20
52 Jaret Wright .07 .20
53 Tomo Ohka .07 .20
54 Mike Matheny .07 .20
55 Joe Mauer .20 .50
56 Jarrod Washburn .07 .20
57 Randy Winn .07 .20
58 Pedro Feliz .07 .20
59 Kenny Rogers .07 .20
60 Rocco Baldelli .07 .20
61 Eric Hinske .07 .20
62 Damaso Marte .07 .20
Front lists him as a Pirate, back says White Sox
63 Desi Relaford .07 .20
64 Juan Encarnacion .07 .20
65 Nomar Garciaparra .20 .50
66 Shawn Estes .07 .20
67 Brian Jordan .07 .20
68 Steve Kline .07 .20
69 Braden Looper .07 .20
70 Carlos Lee .07 .20
71 Tom Glavine .12 .30
72 Craig Biggio .12 .30
73 Steve Finley .07 .20
74 David Newhan .07 .20
75 Eric Gagne .07 .20
76 Tony Graffanino .07 .20
77 Dallas McPherson .07 .20
78 Nick Punto .07 .20
79 Mark Kotsay .07 .20
80 Kerry Wood .07 .20
81 Kyle Farnsworth .07 .20
82 Huston Street .07 .20
83 Endy Chavez .07 .20
84 So Taguchi .07 .20
85 Hank Blalock .07 .20
86 Brad Radke .07 .20
87 Chien-Ming Wang .12 .30
88 B.J. Surhoff .07 .20
89 Glendon Rusch .07 .20
90 Mark Buehrle .12 .30
91 Rafael Betancourt .07 .20
92 Lance Cormier .07 .20
93 Alex Gonzalez .07 .20
94 Matt Stairs .07 .20
95 Andy Pettitte .12 .30
96 Jesse Crain .07 .20
97 Kenny Lofton .07 .20
98 Geoff Blum .07 .20
99 Mark Redman .07 .20
100 Barry Bonds .40 1.00
101 Chad Orvella .07 .20
102 Xavier Nady .07 .20
103 Junior Spivey UER .07 .20
Card forgets to credit the 2nd Washington Senators term from 1961-71
104 Bernie Williams .12 .30
105 Victor Martinez .12 .30
106 Nook Logan .07 .20
107 Mark Teahen .07 .20
108 Mike Lamb .07 .20
109 Jayson Werth .12 .30
110 Mariano Rivera .20 .50
111 Erubiel Durazo .07 .20
112 Ryan Vogelsong .07 .20
113 Bobby Madritsch .07 .20
114 Travis Lee .07 .20
115 Adam Dunn .12 .30
116 David Riske .07 .20
117 Troy Percival .07 .20
118 Chad Tracy .07 .20
119 Andy Marte .07 .20
120 Edgar Renteria .07 .20
121 Jason Giambi .07 .20
122 Justin Morneau .20 .50
123 J.T. Snow .07 .20
124 Danys Baez .07 .20
125 Carlos Delgado .07 .20
126 John Buck .07 .20
127 Shannon Stewart .07 .20
128 Mike Cameron .07 .20
129 Joe McEwing .07 .20
130 Richie Sexson .07 .20
131 Rod Barajas .07 .20
132 Russ Adams .07 .20
133 J.D. Closser .07 .20
134 Ramon Ortiz .07 .20
135 Josh Beckett .12 .30
136 Ryan Freel .07 .20
137 Victor Zambrano .07 .20
138 Ronnie Belliard .07 .20
139 Jason Michaels .07 .20
140 Brian Giles .07 .20
141 Randy Wolf .07 .20
142 Robinson Cano .20 .50
143 Joe Blanton .07 .20
144 Esteban Loaiza .07 .20
145 Troy Glaus .07 .20
146 Matt Clement .07 .20
147 Geoff Jenkins .07 .20
148 John Thomson .07 .20
149 A.J. Pierzynski .07 .20
150 Pedro Martinez .12 .30
151 Roger Clemens .25 .60
152 Jack Wilson .07 .20
153 Ray King .07 .20
154 Ryan Church .07 .20
155 Paul Lo Duca .07 .20
156 Dan Wheeler .07 .20
157 Carlos Zambrano .12 .30
158 Mike Timlin .07 .20
159 Brandon Claussen UER .07 .20
Cincinnati is misspelled in cartoon
160 Travis Hafner .07 .20
161 Chris Shelton .07 .20
162 Rafael Furcal .07 .20
163 Tom Gordon .07 .20
Listed as a Yankee but in a Phillies uniform
164 Noah Lowry .07 .20
165 Larry Walker .12 .30
166 Dave Roberts .07 .20
167 Scott Schoeneweis .07 .20
168 Julian Tavarez .07 .20
169 Jhonny Peralta .07 .20
170 Vernon Wells .07 .20
171 Jorge Cantu .07 .20
172 Todd Greene .07 .20
173 Willy Taveras .07 .20
174 Corey Patterson .07 .20
175 Ivan Rodriguez .12 .30
176 Bobby Kielty .07 .20
177 Jose Reyes .12 .30
178 Barry Zito .07 .20
179 Deivi Cruz .07 .20
180 Mark Teixeira .20 .50
181 Chone Figgins .07 .20
182 Aaron Rowand .07 .20
183 Tim Wakefield .07 .20
184 Mike Maroth .07 .20
185 Johnny Damon .12 .30
186 Vicente Padilla .07 .20
187 Ryan Klesko .07 .20
188 Gary Matthews .07 .20
189 Jose Mesa .07 .20
190 Nick Johnson .07 .20
191 Freddy Garcia .07 .20
192 Larry Bigbie UER .07 .20
Photo is Brian Roberts
193 Chris Ray .07 .20
194 Torii Hunter .07 .20
195 Mike Sweeney .07 .20
196 Brad Penny .07 .20
197 Jason Frasor .07 .20
198 Kevin Mench .07 .20
199 Adam Kennedy .07 .20
200 Albert Pujols .50 1.25
201 Jody Gerut .07 .20
202 Luis Gonzalez UER .07 .20
The wrong Luis Gonzalez's career stats are posted
203 Zack Greinke .12 .30
204 Miguel Cairo .07 .20
205 Jimmy Rollins .12 .30
206 Edgardo Alfonzo .07 .20
207 Billy Wagner .07 .20
208 B.J. Ryan .07 .20
209 Orlando Hudson .07 .20
210 Preston Wilson .07 .20
211 Melvin Mora .07 .20
212 Bill Mueller .07 .20
213 Javy Lopez .07 .20
214 Wilson Betemit .07 .20
215 Garret Anderson .07 .20
216 Russell Branyan .07 .20
217 Jeff Weaver .07 .20
218 Doug Mientkiewicz UER .07 .20
Final out of 2004 WS incorrectly described
219 Mark Ellis .07 .20
220 Jason Bay .07 .20
221 Adam LaRoche .07 .20
222 C.C. Sabathia .12 .30
223 Humberto Quintero .07 .20
224 Bartolo Colon .07 .20
225 Ichiro Suzuki UER .30 .75
Career Stats are all incorrect
226 Brett Tomko .07 .20
227 Corey Koskie .07 .20
228 David Eckstein .07 .20
229 Cristian Guzman .07 .20
230 Jeff Kent UER .07 .20
Credited with 1312 RBI's in 2005
231 Chris Capuano .07 .20
232 Rodrigo Lopez .07 .20
233 Jason Phillips .07 .20
234 Luis Rivas .07 .20
235 Cliff Floyd .07 .20
236 Gil Meche .07 .20
237 Adam Eaton .07 .20
238 Matt Morris .07 .20
239 Kyle Davies .07 .20
240 David Wells .07 .20
241 John Smoltz .20 .50
242 Felix Hernandez .20 .50
243 Kenny Rogers GG .07 .20
244 Mark Teixeira GG .20 .50
245 Orlando Hudson GG .07 .20
246 Derek Jeter GG .50 1.25
247 Eric Chavez GG .07 .20
248 Torii Hunter GG .07 .20
249 Vernon Wells GG .07 .20
250 Ichiro Suzuki GG .30 .75
251 Greg Maddux GG .30 .75
252 Mike Matheny GG .07 .20
253 Derrek Lee GG .07 .20
254 Luis Castillo GG .07 .20
255 Omar Vizquel GG .12 .30
256 Mike Lowell GG .07 .20
257 Andruw Jones GG .07 .20
258 Jim Edmonds GG .12 .30
259 Bobby Abreu GG .07 .20
260 Bartolo Colon CY UER .07 .20
2005 record does not match between the front and the back
261 Chris Carpenter CY .20 .50
262 Alex Rodriguez MVP .30 .75
263 Albert Pujols MVP .50 1.25
264 Huston Street ROY .07 .20
265 Ryan Howard ROY .30 .75
266 Bob Melvin MG .07 .20
267 Bobby Cox MG .07 .20
268 Baltimore Orioles TC .07 .20
269 Boston Red Sox TC .12 .30
270 Chicago White Sox TC .07 .20
271 Dusty Baker MG .07 .20
272 Jerry Narron MG .07 .20
273 Cleveland Indians TC .07 .20
274 Clint Hurdle MG .07 .20

275 Detroit Tigers TC .07 .20
276 Jack McKeon MG .07 .20
277 Phil Garner MG .07 .20
278 Kansas City Royals TC UER .07 .20
The stadium is pictured but not the team
279 Jim Tracy MG .07 .20
280 Los Angeles Angels TC .07 .20
281 Milwaukee Brewers TC .07 .20
282 Minnesota Twins TC .07 .20
283 Willie Randolph MG .07 .20
284 New York Yankees TC .12 .30
285 Oakland Athletics TC .07 .20
286 Charlie Manuel MG .07 .20
287a Pete Mackanin MG ERR .07 .20
Lloyd McClendon is pictured
287b Pete Mackanin MG COR .07 .20
288 Bruce Bochy MG .07 .20
289 Felipe Alou MG .07 .20
290 Seattle Mariners TC .07 .20
291 Tony LaRussa MG .12 .30
292 Tampa Bay Devil Rays TC .07 .20
293 Texas Rangers TC .07 .20
294 Toronto Blue Jays TC .07 .20
295 Frank Robinson MG .07 .20
296 Anderson Hernandez (RC) .20 .50
297A Alex Gordon (RC) Full 100.00 200.00
297B Alex Gordon Cut Out 30.00 60.00
297C Alex Gordon Blank Gold 12.50 30.00
297D Alex Gordon Blank Silver
298 Jason Botts (RC) .20 .50
299 Jeff Mathis (RC) .20 .50
300 Ryan Garko (RC) .20 .50
301 Charlton Jimerson (RC) .20 .50
302 Chris Denorfia (RC) .20 .50
303 Anthony Reyes (RC) .20 .50
304 Bryan Bullington (RC) .20 .50
305 Chuck James (RC) .20 .50
306 Danny Sandoval RC .20 .50
307 Walter Young (RC) .20 .50
308 Fausto Carmona (RC) .20 .50
309 Francisco Liriano (RC) .50 1.25
310 Hong-Chih Kuo (RC) .50 1.25
311 Joe Saunders (RC) .20 .50
312a John Koronka (RC) .20 .50
Pictured in Cubs uniform
312b John Koronka (RC) .20 .50
Pictured in Rangers uniform
313 Robert Andino RC .20 .50
314 Shaun Marcum (RC) .20 .50
315 Tom Gorzelanny (RC) .20 .50
316 Craig Breslow RC .20 .50
317 Chris DeMaria RC .20 .50
Front lists him as a Brewer, Back has him as a Royal
318 Brayan Pena (RC) .20 .50
319 Rich Hill (RC) .20 .50
320 Rick Short (RC) .20 .50
321 C.J. Wilson (RC) .30 .75
322 Marshall McDougall (RC) .20 .50
323 Darrell Rasner (RC) .20 .50
324 Brandon Watson (RC) .20 .50
325 Paul McAnulty (RC) .20 .50
326 Derek Jeter .50 1.25
Alex Rodriguez TS
327 Miguel Tejada .12 .30
Melvin Mora TS
328 Marcus Giles .20 .50
Chipper Jones TS
329 Manny Ramirez .20 .50
David Ortiz TS
330 Michael Barrett .30 .75
Greg Maddux TS
331 Matt Holliday .20 .50
332 Orlando Cabrera .07 .20
333 Ryan Langerhans .07 .20
334 Lew Ford .07 .20
335 Mark Prior .12 .30
336 Ted Lilly .07 .20
337 Michael Young .12 .30
338 Livan Hernandez .07 .20
339 Yadier Molina .12 .30
340 Eric Chavez .07 .20
341 Miguel Batista .07 .20
342 Bruce Chen .07 .20
343 Sean Casey .07 .20
344 Doug Davis .07 .20
345 Andruw Jones .07 .20
346 Hideki Matsui .20 .50
347 Joe Randa .07 .20
348 Reggie Sanders .07 .20
349 Jason Jennings .07 .20
350 Joe Nathan .07 .20
351 Jose Lopez .07 .20
352 John Lackey .07 .20
353 Claudio Vargas .07 .20
354 Grady Sizemore .12 .30
355 Jon Papelbon (RC) 1.00 2.50
356 Luis Matos .07 .20
357 Orlando Hernandez .07 .20
358 Jamie Moyer .07 .20
359 Chase Utley .20 .50
360 Moises Alou .07 .20
361 Chad Cordero .07 .20
362 Brian McCann .07 .20
363 Jermaine Dye .07 .20
364 Ryan Madson .07 .20
365 Aramis Ramirez .07 .20
366 Matt Treanor .07 .20
367 Ray Durham .07 .20
368 Khalil Greene .07 .20
369 Mike Hampton .07 .20
370 Mike Mussina .12 .30
371 Brad Hawpe .07 .20
372 Marlon Byrd .07 .20
373 Woody Williams .07 .20
374 Victor Diaz .07 .20
375 Brady Clark .07 .20
376 Luis Gonzalez .07 .20
377 Raul Ibanez .12 .30
378 Tony Clark .07 .20
379 Shawn Chacon .07 .20
380 Marcus Giles .07 .20
381 Odalis Perez .07 .20
382 Steve Trachsel .07 .20
383 Russ Ortiz .07 .20
384 Toby Hall .07 .20
385 Bill Hall .07 .20
386 Luke Hudson .07 .20
387 Ken Griffey Jr. .30 .75
388 Tim Hudson .12 .30
389 Brian Moehler .07 .20
390 Jake Peavy .07 .20
391 Casey Blake .07 .20
392 Sidney Ponson .07 .20
393 Brian Schneider .07 .20
394 J.J. Hardy .07 .20
395 Austin Kearns .07 .20
396 Pat Burrell .07 .20
397 Jason Vargas .07 .20
398 Ryan Howard .30 .75
399 Joe Crede .07 .20
400 Vladimir Guerrero .20 .50
401 Roy Halladay .20 .50
402 David Dellucci .07 .20
403 Brandon Webb .12 .30
404 Marlon Anderson .07 .20
405 Miguel Tejada .12 .30
406 Ryan Doumit .07 .20
407 Kevin Youkilis .07 .20
408 Jon Lieber .07 .20
409 Edwin Encarnacion .07 .20
410 Miguel Cabrera .20 .50
411 A.J. Burnett .12 .30
412 David Bell .07 .20
413 Gregg Zaun .07 .20
414 Lance Niekro .07 .20
415 Shawn Green .07 .20
416 Roberto Hernandez .07 .20
417 Jay Gibbons .07 .20
418 Johnny Estrada .07 .20
419 Omar Vizquel .12 .30
420 Gary Sheffield .07 .20
421 Brad Halsey .07 .20
422 Aaron Cook .07 .20
423 David Ortiz .12 .30
424 Tony Womack .07 .20
425 Joe Kennedy .07 .20
426 Dustin McGowan .07 .20
427 Carl Pavano .07 .20
428 Nick Green .07 .20
429 Francisco Cordero .07 .20
430 Octavio Dotel .07 .20
431 Julio Franco .07 .20
432 Brett Myers .07 .20
433 Casey Kotchman .07 .20
434 Frank Catalanotto .07 .20
435 Paul Konerko .12 .30
436 Keith Foulke .07 .20
437 Juan Rivera .07 .20
438 Todd Pratt .07 .20
439 Ben Broussard .07 .20
440 Scott Kazmir .12 .30
441 Rich Aurilia .07 .20
442 Craig Monroe .07 .20
443 Danny Kolb .07 .20
444 Curtis Granderson .12 .30
445 Jeff Francoeur .20 .50
446 Dustin Hermanson .07 .20
447 Jacque Jones .07 .20
448 Bobby Crosby .07 .20
449 Jason LaRue .07 .20
450 Derrek Lee .07 .20
451 Curt Schilling .12 .30
452 Jake Westbrook .07 .20
453 Daniel Cabrera .07 .20
454 Bobby Jenks .07 .20
455 Dontrelle Willis .07 .20
456 Brad Lidge .07 .20
457 Shea Hillenbrand .07 .20
458 Luis Castillo .07 .20
459 Mark Hendrickson .07 .20
460 Randy Johnson .20 .50
461 Placido Polanco .07 .20
462 Aaron Boone .07 .20
463 Todd Walker .07 .20
464 Nick Swisher .20 .50
465 Joel Pineiro .07 .20
466 Jay Payton .07 .20
467 Cliff Lee .12 .30
468 Johan Santana .20 .50
469 Josh Willingham .07 .20
470 Jeremy Bonderman .07 .20
471 Runelvys Hernandez .07 .20
472 Duaner Sanchez .07 .20
473 Jason Lane .07 .20
474 Trot Nixon .07 .20
475 Ramon Hernandez .07 .20
476 Mike Lowell .07 .20
477 Chan Ho Park .12 .30
478 Doug Waechter .07 .20
479 Carlos Silva .07 .20
480 Jose Contreras .07 .20
481 Vinny Castilla .07 .20
482 Chris Reitsma .07 .20
483 Jose Guillen .07 .20
484 Aaron Hill .07 .20
485 Kevin Millwood .07 .20
486 Wily Mo Pena .07 .20
487 Rich Harden .07 .20
488 Chris Carpenter .20 .50
489 Jason Bartlett .07 .20
490 Magglio Ordonez .12 .30
491 John Rodriguez .07 .20
492 Bob Wickman .07 .20
493 Eddie Guardado .07 .20
494 Kip Wells .07 .20
495 Adrian Beltre .07 .20
496 Jose Capellan (RC) .20 .50
497 Scott Podsednik .07 .20
498 Brad Thompson .07 .20
499 Aaron Heilman .07 .20
500 Derek Jeter .50 1.25
501 Emil Brown .07 .20
502 Morgan Ensberg .07 .20
503 Nate Bump .07 .20
504 Phil Nevin .07 .20
505 Jason Schmidt .07 .20
506 Michael Cuddyer .07 .20
507 John Patterson .07 .20
508 Danny Haren .07 .20
509 Freddy Sanchez .07 .20
510 J.D. Drew .07 .20
511 Dmitri Young .07 .20
512 Eric Milton .07 .20
513 Ervin Santana .07 .20
514 Mark Loretta .07 .20
515 Mark Grudzielanek .07 .20
516 Derrick Turnbow .07 .20
517 Denny Bautista .07 .20
518 Lyle Overbay .07 .20
519 Julio Lugo .07 .20
520 Carlos Beltran .07 .20
521 Jose Cruz Jr. .07 .20
522 Jason Isringhausen .07 .20
523 Bronson Arroyo .07 .20
524 Ben Sheets .07 .20
525 Zach Duke .07 .20
526 Ryan Wagner .07 .20
527 Jose Vidro .07 .20
528 Doug Mirabelli .07 .20
529 Kris Benson .07 .20
530 Carlos Guillen .07 .20
531 Juan Pierre .07 .20
532 Scot Shields .07 .20
533 Scott Hatteberg .07 .20
534 Tim Stauffer .07 .20
535 Jim Edmonds .12 .30
536 Scot Eyre .07 .20
537 Ben Johnson .07 .20
538 Mark Mulder .07 .20
539 Juan Rincon .07 .20
540 Gustavo Chacin .07 .20
541 Oliver Perez .07 .20
542 Chris Young .07 .20
543 Edinson Volquez .07 .20
544 Mark Bellhorn .07 .20
545 Kelvim Escobar .07 .20
546 Andy Sisco .07 .20
547 Derek Lowe .07 .20
548 Sean Burroughs .07 .20
549 Erik Bedard .07 .20
550 Alfonso Soriano .12 .30
551 Matt Murton .07 .20
552 Eric Byrnes .07 .20
553 Chris Duffy .07 .20
554 Kazuo Matsui .07 .20
555 Scott Rolen .12 .30
556 Rob Mackowiak .07 .20
557 Chris Burke .07 .20
558 Jeromy Burnitz .07 .20
559 Jerry Hairston Jr. .07 .20
560 Jim Thome .12 .30
561 Miguel Olivo .07 .20
562 Jose Castillo .07 .20
563 Brad Ausmus .07 .20
564 Yorvit Torrealba .07 .20
565 David DeJesus .07 .20
566 Paul Byrd .07 .20
567 Brandon Backe .07 .20
568 Aubrey Huff .07 .20
569 Mike Jacobs .07 .20
570 Todd Helton .12 .30
571 Angel Berroa .07 .20
572 Todd Jones .07 .20
573 Jeff Bagwell .12 .30
574 Darin Erstad .07 .20
575 Roy Oswalt .12 .30
576 Rondell White .07 .20
577 Alex Rios .12 .30
578 Wes Helms .07 .20
579 Javier Vazquez .07 .20
580 Frank Thomas .20 .50
581 Brian Fuentes .07 .20
582 Francisco Rodriguez .12 .30
583 Craig Counsell .07 .20
584 Jorge Sosa .07 .20
585 Mike Piazza .20 .50
586 Mike Scioscia MG .07 .20
587 Joe Torre MG .12 .30
588 Ken Macha MG .07 .20
589 John Gibbons MG .07 .20
590 Joe Maddon MG .07 .20
591 Eric Wedge MG .07 .20
592 Mike Hargrove MG .07 .20
593 Sam Perlozzo MG .07 .20
594 Buck Showalter MG .07 .20
595 Terry Francona MG .07 .20
596 Buddy Bell MG .07 .20
597 Jim Leyland MG .07 .20
598 Ron Gardenhire MG .07 .20
599 Ozzie Guillen MG .07 .20
600 Ned Yost MG .07 .20
601 Atlanta Braves TC .07 .20
602 Philadelphia Phillies TC .07 .20
603 New York Mets TC .12 .30
604 Washington Nationals TC .07 .20
605 Florida Marlins TC .07 .20
606 Houston Astros TC .07 .20
607 Chicago Cubs TC .07 .20
608 St. Louis Cardinals TC .12 .30
609 Pittsburgh Pirates TC .07 .20
610 Cincinnati Reds TC .07 .20
611 Colorado Rockies TC .07 .20
612 Los Angeles Dodgers TC .12 .30
613 San Francisco Giants TC .07 .20
614 San Diego Padres TC .07 .20
615 Arizona Diamondbacks TC .07 .20
616 Kenji Johjima RC .50 1.25
617 Ryan Zimmerman (RC) 1.00 2.50
618 Craig Hansen RC .50 1.25
619 Joey Devine RC .20 .50
620 Hanley Ramirez (RC) .50 1.25
621 Scott Olsen (RC) .20 .50
622 Jason Bergmann RC .20 .50
623 Geovany Soto (RC) .50 1.25
624 J.J. Furmaniak (RC) .20 .50
625 Jeremy Accardo RC .20 .50
626 Mark Woodyard (RC) .20 .50
627 Matt Capps (RC) .20 .50
628 Tim Corcoran RC .20 .50
629 Ryan Jorgensen RC .20 .50
630 Ronny Paulino (RC) .20 .50
631 Dan Uggla (RC) .50 1.25
632 Ian Kinsler (RC) .60 1.50
633 Josh Barfield (RC) .20 .50
634 Reggie Abercrombie (RC) .20 .50
635 Joel Zumaya (RC) .50 1.25
636 Matt Cain (RC) .50 1.25
637 Conor Jackson (RC) .30 .75
638 Brian Anderson (RC) .20 .50
639 Prince Fielder (RC) .75 2.00
640 Jeremy Hermida (RC) .20 .50
641 Justin Verlander (RC) 1.50 4.00
642 Brian Bannister (RC) .20 .50
643 Willie Eyre (RC) .20 .50
644 Ricky Nolasco (RC) .20 .50
645 Paul Maholm (RC) .20 .50
646 Johnny Damon .12 .30
Jason Giambi
647 Rondell White .07 .20
Lew Ford UER
Michael Cuddyer is pictured
648 Orlando Hernandez .07 .20
Orlando Hudson
649 Adam Dunn .30 .75
Ken Griffey Jr.
650 Pat Burrell .07 .20
Mike Lieberthal
651 Jose Reyes .12 .30
Kaz Matsui
652 Hank Blalock .12 .30
Michael Young
653 Prince Fielder .30 .75
Rickie Weeks
654 Travis Lee .07 .20
Rocco Baldelli
655 Derrek Lee .07 .20
Aramis Ramirez
656 Grady Sizemore .12 .30
Aaron Boone
657 Luis Gonzalez .07 .20
Shawn Green
Koyie Hill
658 Ivan Rodriguez .12 .30
Carlos Guillen
659 Alex Rodriguez .30 .75
Gary Sheffield
660 Ervin Santana .12 .30
Francisco Rodriguez
RC1 Alay Soler 15.00 40.00

2006 Topps Black

COMMON CARD (1-660) 6.00 15.00
SEMISTARS 10.00 25.00
UNLISTED STARS 50.00 40.00
SERIES 1 ODDS 1:18 HTA
SERIES 2 ODDS 1:14 HTA
STATED PRINT RUN 55 SERIAL #'d SETS
CARD 297 DOES NOT EXIST

2006 Topps Box Bottoms

ONE 4-CARD SHEET PER HTA BOX
1 Alex Rodriguez .75 2.00
16 David Wright .75 2.00
20 Bobby Abreu .20 .50
25 Chipper Jones .50 1.25
50 Manny Ramirez .50 1.25
70 Carlos Lee .20 .50
90 Mark Buehrle .30 .75
100 Barry Bonds 1.00 2.50
115 Adam Dunn .30 .75
125 Carlos Delgado .20 .50
150 Pedro Martinez .30 .75
151 Roger Clemens .60 1.50
180 Mark Teixeira .50 1.25
194 Torii Hunter .20 .50
200 Albert Pujols 1.25 3.00
225 Ichiro Suzuki .75 2.00
337 Michael Young .30 .75
345 Andruw Jones .20 .50
357 Orlando Hernandez .20 .50
390 Jake Peavy .20 .50
405 Miguel Tejada .30 .75
423 David Ortiz .30 .75
450 Derrek Lee .20 .50
468 Johan Santana .50 1.25
550 Alfonso Soriano .30 .75
560 Jim Thome .30 .75
570 Todd Helton .30 .75
599 Ozzie Guillen MG .20 .50
616 Kenji Johjima .50 1.25
637 Conor Jackson .30 .75
639 Prince Fielder .75 2.00
659 Alex Rodriguez .75 2.00
Gary Sheffield

2006 Topps Gold

*GOLD 1-295/326-615/646-660: 6X TO 15X
*GOLD 296-325/616-645: 2.5X TO 6X
SER.1 ODDS 1:15 HOB, 1:4 HTA, 1:26 MINI
SER.1 ODDS 1:8 RACK, 1:14 RET
SER.2 ODDS 1:11 HOB, 1:4 HTA, 1:21 MINI
SER.2 ODDS 1:6 RACK, 1:11 RET
STATED PRINT RUN 2006 SERIAL #'d SETS
CARD 297 DOES NOT EXIST

2006 Topps Platinum

SER.1 ODDS 1:29,000 HOBBY, 1:9,930 HTA
SER.1 ODDS 1:52,000 MINI, 1:15,000 RACK
SER.1 ODDS 1:27,000 RETAIL
SER.2 ODDS 1:23,500 HOBBY, 1:14,000 HTA
SER.2 ODDS 1:35,000 MINI, 1:12,000 RACK
SER.2 ODDS 1:26,000 RETAIL
STATED PRINT RUN 1 SERIAL #'d SET
NO PRICING DUE TO SCARCITY
CARD 297 DOES NOT EXIST

2006 Topps 2K All-Stars

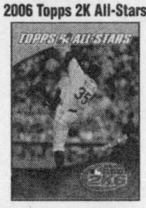

SER.1 ODDS 1:18 H, 1:18 HTA, 1:18 MINI
SER.1 ODDS 1:6 RACK, 1:18 RETAIL
1-6 ISSUED IN 2K ALL-STAR GAMES
7-11 ISSUED IN SER.1 TOPPS PACKS
1 Derek Jeter 4.00 10.00
2 Andruw Jones .60 1.50
3 Miguel Cabrera 1.50 4.00
4 Derrek Lee .60 1.50
5 Mariano Rivera 1.50 4.00
6 Ivan Rodriguez 1.00 2.50
7 Vladimir Guerrero 1.50 4.00
8 Albert Pujols 4.00 10.00
9 Alex Rodriguez 2.50 6.00
10 Alfonso Soriano 1.00 2.50
11 Dontrelle Willis .60 1.50

2006 Topps 2K All-Stars Autograph

RANDOM INSERT IN 06 2K ALL-STAR GAME
STATED PRINT RUN 100 COPIES
AJ Andruw Jones

2006 Topps Autographs

SER.1 A 1:681,120 HOBBY, 1:152,750 HTA
SER.1 A 1:220,032 RACK
SER.1 B 1:14500 H,1:2932 HTA,1:26,900 MINI
SER.1 B 1:7124 RACK, 1:11,500 RETAIL
SER.1 C 1:17400 H,1:4966 HTA, 1:28,622 MINI
SER.1 C 1:8400 RACK, 1:14,000 RET
SER.1 D 1:42,570 H, 1:11,841 HTA
SER.1 D 1:70,000 MINI, 1:20,000 RACK
SER.1 D 1:33,000 RETAIL
SER.1 E 1:3451 H, 1:980 HTA, 1:5800 MINI
SER.1 E 1:1650 RACK, 1:2900 RET
SER.1 F 1:2090 H, 1:560 HTA, 1:3480 MINI
SER.1 F 1:995 RACK, 1:1750 RETAIL
SER.1 G 1:3481 H, 1:944 HTA, 1:5800 MINI
SER.1 G 1:1660 RACK, 1:2900 RETAIL
SER.1 H 1:430 H, 1:121 HTA, 1:725 MINI
SER.1 H 1:207 RACK, 1:363 RETAIL
OVERALL SER.1 AU-GU ODDS 1:137 H/R
OVERALL SER.1 AU-GU ODDS 1:47 HTA
GROUP A PRINT RUN 10 #'d CARDS
GROUP B PRINT RUN 100 #'d SETS
GROUP C PRINT RUN 200 #'d SETS
GROUP D PRINT RUN 250 #'d CARDS
NO GROUP A PRICING DUE TO SCARCITY
B.LIVINGSTON ISSUED IN SER.2 PACKS
EXCHANGE DEADLINE 02/28/08
AG Alex Gordon H 10.00 25.00
AL Anthony Lerew H 4.00 10.00
AR Alex Rodriguez B/100 250.00 500.00
ARE Anthony Reyes H 10.00 25.00
BB Barry Bonds A/10
BC Brian Cashman B/100 125.00 200.00
BL Bobby Livingston F2 4.00 10.00
BW Brad Wilkerson E 6.00 15.00
CB Craig Breslow H 4.00 10.00
CG Carlos Guillen E 6.00 15.00
CJ Chuck James G 15.00 40.00
DD Doug DeVore H 4.00 10.00
DO David Ortiz B/100 90.00 150.00
DR Darrell Rasner H 4.00 10.00
DW Dave Winfield B/100 90.00 150.00
EC Eric Chavez C/200 40.00 80.00
FC Fausto Carmona H 4.00 10.00
FL Francisco Liriano H 6.00 15.00
GN Graig Nettles E 10.00 25.00
GS Gary Sheffield C/200 20.00 50.00
HR Horacio Ramirez F 4.00 10.00
JB Jason Botts H 4.00 10.00
JJ Josh Johnson H 10.00 25.00
JM Jeff Mathis F 4.00 10.00
LC Lance Cormier E 6.00 15.00
LH Livan Hernandez F 6.00 15.00
MB Milton Bradley C/200 15.00 40.00
MY Michael Young E 10.00 25.00
NC Nelson Cruz G 8.00 20.00
RG Ryan Garko F 6.00 15.00
RH Rich Hill H 12.50 30.00
RO Roy Oswalt F 10.00 25.00
RS Ryne Sandberg B/100 90.00 150.00
SO Scott Olsen H 4.00 10.00
TS Termel Sledge E 6.00 15.00
WB Wade Boggs D/250 40.00 80.00

2006 Topps Autographs Green

SER.2 A 1:160,000 HOBBY, 1:48,000 HTA
SER.2 A 1:350,000 MINI, 1:90,000 RACK
SER.2 A 1:150,000 RETAIL
SER.2 B 1:70,000 HOBBY, 1:12,000 HTA
SER.2 B 1:125,000 MINI, 1:33,000 RACK
SER.2 B 1:80,000 RETAIL
SER.2 C 1:4060 H, 1:1150 HTA, 1:6800 MINI
SER.2 C 1:1400 R, 1:1940 RACK
SER.2 D 1:4750 H, 1:1000 HTA, 1:6500 MINI
SER.2 D 1:4750 R, 1:2000 RACK
SER.2 E 1:2030 H, 1:575 HTA, 1:3390 MINI
SER.2 E 1:2025 R, 1:966 RACK
SER.2 F 1:510 H, 1:190 HTA, 1:1125 MINI
SER.2 F 1:506 R, 1:325 RACK
GROUP A PRINT RUN 50 CARDS
GROUP B PRINT RUN 120 CARDS
GROUP C PRINT RUN 250 SETS
A-C ARE NOT SERIAL-NUMBERED
A-C PRINT RUNS PROVIDED BY TOPPS
NO GROUP A PRICING DUE TO SCARCITY
EXCHANGE DEADLINE 06/30/08
AJ Andruw Jones C/250 * 30.00 60.00
AR Alex Rodriguez A/50 *
BB Barry Bonds B/120 * 350.00 500.00
BC Brandon Claussen F 4.00 10.00
BM Brandon McCarthy E 6.00 15.00
BR Brian Roberts C/250 * 30.00 60.00
CB Clint Barmes E 6.00 15.00
CO Chad Orvella F 4.00 10.00
CV Claudio Vargas F 4.00 10.00
DD Doug Drabek C/250 * 10.00 25.00
DJ Dan Johnson D 6.00 15.00
DS Darryl Strawberry C/250 * 20.00 50.00
DSN Duke Snider C/250 * 40.00 80.00
GA Garrett Atkins D 6.00 15.00
GC Gary Carter C/250 * 15.00 40.00
JB Jose Bautista F 20.00 50.00
JF Jeff Francis D 6.00 15.00
JP Jonathan Papelbon F 15.00 40.00
RC Robinson Cano E 8.00 20.00
RZ Ryan Zimmerman E 20.00 50.00
SK Scott Kazmir D 10.00 25.00
WP Wily Mo Pena C/250 * 15.00 40.00

2006 Topps Barry Bonds Chase to 715

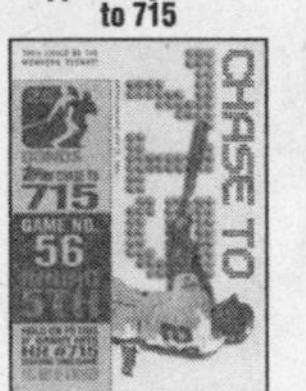

COMMON CARD 20.00 50.00
SER.1 ODDS 1:4800 HOBBY, 1:5400 HTA
SER.1 ODDS 1:10,900 MINI, 1:3076 RACK
SER.1 ODDS 1:5,300 RETAIL
STATED PRINT RUN 1 SERIAL #'d SET

2006 Topps Barry Bonds Home Run History

SEE 05 TOPPS BONDS HRH FOR PRICING

2006 Topps United States Constitution

COMPLETE SET (42) 30.00 60.00
SER.2 ODDS 1:8 HOBBY, 1:2 HTA, 1:16 MINI
SER.2 ODDS 1:8 RETAIL, 1:4 RACK
AB Abraham Baldwin .75 2.00
AH Alexander Hamilton .75 2.00
BF Benjamin Franklin 1.25 3.00
CP Charles Pinckney .75 2.00
DB David Brearly .75 2.00
DC Daniel Carroll .75 2.00
DJ Daniel of St. Thomas Jenifer .75 2.00
GB Gunning Bedford Jr. .75 2.00
GC George Clymer .75 2.00
GM Gouverneur Morris .75 2.00
GR George Read .75 2.00
GW George Washington 1.25 3.00
HW Hugh Williamson .75 2.00
JB John Blair .75 2.00
JD Jonathan Dayton .75 2.00
JI Jared Ingersoll .75 2.00
JL John Langdon .75 2.00
JM James Madison .75 2.00
JR John Rutledge .75 2.00
JW James Wilson .75 2.00
NG Nicholas Gilman .75 2.00
PB Pierce Butler .75 2.00
RB Richard Bassett .75 2.00
RK Rufus King .75 2.00
RM Robert Morris .75 2.00
RS Roger Sherman .75 2.00
TF Thomas Fitzsimons .75 2.00
TM Thomas Mifflin .75 2.00
WB William Blount .75 2.00
WF William Few .75 2.00
WJ William Samuel Johnson .75 2.00
WL William Livingston .75 2.00
WP William Paterson .75 2.00
CCP Charles Cotesworth Pinckney .75 2.00
JBR Jacob Broom .75 2.00
JDI John Dickinson .75 2.00
JMC James McHenry .75 2.00
NGO Nathaniel Gorham .75 2.00
RDS Richard Dobbs Spaight .75 2.00
HDR1 Header Card 1 .75 2.00
HDR2 Header Card 2 .75 2.00
HDR3 Header Card 3 .75 2.00

2006 Topps United States Constitution Cut Signatures

SER.2 ODDS 1:300,000 HOBBY
SER.2 ODDS 1:80,000 HTA
SER.2 ODDS 1:450,000 MINI
SER.2 ODDS 1:150,000 RETAIL
STATED PRINT RUN 1 SET
NO PRICING DUE TO SCARCITY

2006 Topps Declaration of Independence

COMPLETE SET (56) 70.00 120.00
SER.1 ODDS 1:8 HOBBY, 1:4 HTA, 1:12 MINI
SER.1 ODDS 1:4 RACK, 1:6 RETAIL
AC Abraham Clark 1.25 3.00
AM Arthur Middleton 1.25 3.00
BF Benjamin Franklin 2.00 5.00
BG Button Gwinnett 1.25 3.00
BH Benjamin Harrison 1.25 3.00
BR Benjamin Rush 1.25 3.00
CB Carter Braxton 1.25 3.00
CC Charles Carroll 1.25 3.00
CR Caesar Rodney 1.25 3.00
EG Elbridge Gerry 1.25 3.00
ER Edward Rutledge 1.25 3.00
FH Francis Hopkinson 1.25 3.00
FL Francis Lewis 1.25 3.00
FLL Francis Lightfoot Lee 1.25 3.00
GC George Clymer 1.25 3.00
GR George Ross 1.25 3.00
GRE George Read 1.25 3.00
GT George Taylor 1.25 3.00
GW George Walton 1.25 3.00
GWY George Wythe 1.25 3.00
JA John Adams 1.25 3.00
JB Josiah Bartlett 1.25 3.00
JH John Hancock 2.00 5.00
JHA John Hart 1.25 3.00
JHE Joseph Hewes 1.25 3.00
JM John Morton 1.25 3.00
JP John Penn 1.25 3.00
JS James Smith 1.25 3.00
JW James Wilson 1.25 3.00
JWI John Witherspoon 1.25 3.00
LH Lyman Hall 1.25 3.00
LM Lewis Morris 1.25 3.00
MT Matthew Thornton 1.25 3.00
OW Oliver Wolcott 1.25 3.00
PL Philip Livingston 1.25 3.00
RHL Richard Henry Lee 1.25 3.00
RM Robert Morris 1.25 3.00
RS Roger Sherman 1.25 3.00
RST Richard Stockton 1.25 3.00
RTP Robert Treat Paine 1.25 3.00
SA Samuel Adams 2.00 5.00
SC Samuel Chase 1.25 3.00
SH Stephen Hopkins 1.25 3.00
SHU Samuel Huntington 1.25 3.00
TH Thomas Heyward Jr. 1.25 3.00
TJ Thomas Jefferson 2.00 5.00
TL Thomas Lynch Jr. 1.25 3.00
TM Thomas McKean 1.25 3.00
TN Thomas Nelson Jr. 1.25 3.00
TS Thomas Stone 1.25 3.00
WE William Ellery 1.25 3.00
WF William Floyd 1.25 3.00
WH William Hooper 1.25 3.00
WP William Paca 1.25 3.00
WW William Whipple 1.25 3.00
WWI William Williams 1.25 3.00

2006 Topps Declaration of Independence Cut Signatures

SER.1 ODDS 1:255,375 HOBBY
SER.1 ODDS 1:102,624 HTA

SER.1 ODDS 1:320,576 MINI
SER.1 ODDS 1:145,104 RETAIL
STATED PRINT RUN 1 SERIAL #'d SET
NO PRICING DUE TO SCARCITY

2006 Topps Factory Set Rookie Bonus

COMP.RETAIL SET (5) 6.00 15.00
COMP.HOBBY SET (5) 6.00 15.00
COMP.HOLIDAY SET (10) 10.00 25.00
1-5 ISSUED IN RETAIL FACTORY SETS
6-10 ISSUED IN HOBBY FACTORY SETS
11-20 ISSUED IN HOLIDAY FACTORY SETS
1 Nick Markakis 1.00 2.50
2 Kelly Shoppach .40 1.00
3 Jordan Tata .40 1.00
4 Ruddy Lugo .40 1.00
5 Josh Wilson .40 1.00
6 Fernando Nieve .40 1.00
7 Sendy Rleal .40 1.00
8 Jason Kubel .40 1.00
9 James Loney .60 1.50
10 Fabio Castro .40 1.00
11 Jonathan Broxton .40 1.00
12 Eliezer Alfonzo .40 1.00
13 Jason Hirsh .40 1.00
14 Rajai Davis .40 1.00
15 Henry Owens .40 1.00
16 Kevin Frandsen .40 1.00
17 Matt Garza .40 1.00
18 Chris Duncan .60 1.50
19 Chris Coste 1.00 2.50
20 Jeff Karstens .40 1.00

2006 Topps Factory Set Team Bonus

COMP.CARDINALS SET (5) 6.00 15.00
COMP.CUBS SET (5) 6.00 15.00
COMP.PIRATES SET (5) 6.00 15.00
COMP.RED SOX SET (5) 10.00 25.00
COMP.YANKEES SET (5) 8.00 20.00
BRS1-5 ISSUED IN RED SOX FACTORY SET
CC1-5 ISSUED IN CUBS FACTORY SET
NYY1-5 ISSUED IN YANKEES FACTORY SET
PP1-5 ISSUED IN PIRATES FACTORY SET
SLC1-5 ISSUED IN CARDINALS FACTORY SET
BRS1 Jonathan Papelbon 2.00 5.00
BRS2 Manny Ramirez 1.00 2.50
BRS3 David Ortiz .60 1.50
BRS4 Josh Beckett .60 1.50
BRS5 Curt Schilling .60 1.50
CC1 Sean Marshall .60 1.50
CC2 Freddie Bynum .40 1.00
CC3 Derrek Lee .40 1.00
CC4 Juan Pierre .40 1.00
CC5 Carlos Zambrano .60 1.50
NYY1 Wil Nieves .40 1.00
NYY2 Alex Rodriguez 1.50 4.00
NYY3 Derek Jeter 2.50 6.00
NYY4 Mariano Rivera 1.00 2.50
NYY5 Randy Johnson 1.00 2.50
PP1 Matt Capps .40 1.00
PP2 Paul Maholm .40 1.00
PP3 Nate McLouth .40 1.00
PP4 John Van Benschoten .40 1.00
PP5 Jason Bay .40 1.00
SLC1 Adam Wainwright 1.00 2.50
SLC2 Skip Schumaker .40 1.00
SLC3 Albert Pujols 2.50 6.00
SLC4 Jim Edmonds .60 1.50
SLC5 Scott Rolen .60 1.50

2006 Topps Hit Parade

COMPLETE SET (30) 35.00 60.00
SER.2 ODDS 1:18 H, 1:6 HTA, 1:27 MINI
SER.2 ODDS 1:18 R, 1:9 RACK
HR1 Barry Bonds HR 3.00 8.00
HR2 Ken Griffey Jr HR 2.50 6.00
HR3 Jeff Bagwell HR 1.00 2.50
HR4 Gary Sheffield HR .60 1.50
HR5 Frank Thomas HR 1.50 4.00
HR6 Manny Ramirez HR 1.50 4.00
HR7 Jim Thome HR 1.00 2.50
HR8 Alex Rodriguez HR 2.50 6.00
HR9 Mike Piazza HR 1.50 4.00
HIT1 Craig Biggio HIT 1.00 2.50
HIT2 Barry Bonds HIT 3.00 8.00
HIT3 Julio Franco HIT .60 1.50
HIT4 Steve Finley HIT .60 1.50
HIT5 Gary Sheffield HIT .60 1.50
HIT6 Jeff Bagwell HIT 1.00 2.50
HIT7 Ken Griffey Jr HIT 2.50 6.00
HIT8 Omar Vizquel HIT 1.00 2.50
HIT9 Marquis Grissom HIT .60 1.50
HR10 Carlos Delgado HR .60 1.50
RBI1 Barry Bonds RBI 3.00 8.00
RBI2 Ken Griffey Jr RBI 2.50 6.00
RBI3 Jeff Bagwell RBI 1.00 2.50
RBI4 Gary Sheffield RBI .60 1.50
RBI5 Frank Thomas RBI 1.50 4.00
RBI6 Manny Ramirez RBI 1.50 4.00
RBI7 Ruben Sierra RBI .60 1.50
RBI8 Jeff Kent RBI .60 1.50
RBI9 Luis Gonzalez RBI .60 1.50
HIT10 Bernie Williams HIT 1.00 2.50
RBI10 Alex Rodriguez RBI 2.50 6.00

2006 Topps Hobby Masters

COMPLETE SET (20) 8.00 20.00
SER.1 ODDS 1:18 HOBBY, 1:6 HTA
HM1 Derrek Lee .40 1.00
HM2 Albert Pujols 2.50 6.00
HM3 Nomar Garciaparra 1.00 2.50
HM4 Alfonso Soriano .60 1.50
HM5 Derek Jeter 2.50 6.00
HM6 Miguel Tejada .60 1.50
HM7 Alex Rodriguez 1.50 4.00
HM8 Jim Edmonds UER .40 1.00
Back Photo is Andruw Jones
HM9 Mark Prior .60 1.50
HM10 Roger Clemens 1.25 3.00
HM11 Randy Johnson 1.00 2.50
HM12 Manny Ramirez 1.00 2.50
HM13 Curt Schilling .60 1.50
HM14 Vladimir Guerrero 1.00 2.50
HM15 Barry Bonds 2.00 5.00
HM16 Ichiro Suzuki 1.50 4.00
HM17 Pedro Martinez .60 1.50
HM18 Carlos Beltran .40 1.00
HM19 David Ortiz .60 1.50
HM20 Andruw Jones .40 1.00

2006 Topps Home Run Derby Contest

SER.2 ODDS 1:48,000 H, 1:14,000 HTA
SER.2 ODDS 1:23,500 MINI, 1:12,000 R
SER.2 ODDS 1:7,000 RACK
STATED PRINT RUN 10 SERIAL #'d SETS
NO PRICING DUE TO SCARCITY

2006 Topps Mantle Collection

COMPLETE SET (10) 60.00 120.00
SER.1 ODDS 1:36 HOB, 1:36 HTA, 1:36 MINI
SER.1 ODDS 1:12 RACK, 1:36 RETAIL
BLACK SER.1 ODDS 1:4,665 HTA
BLACK PRINT RUN 7 SERIAL #'d SETS
NO BLACK PRICING DUE TO SCARCITY
*GOLD p/r 477-977: 1.25X TO 3X BASIC
*GOLD p/r 277-377: 1.5X TO 4X BASIC
*GOLD p/r 177: 2X TO 5X BASIC
*GOLD p/r 77: 4X TO 10X BASIC
GOLD SER.1 ODDS 1:1500 HOB, 1:2332 HTA
GOLD SER.1 ODDS 1:3376 MINI, 1:970 RACK
GOLD SER.1 ODDS 1:1500 RETAIL
GOLD PRINT RUNS B/WN 77-977 PER
1996 Mickey Mantle 96 6.00 15.00
1997 Mickey Mantle 97 6.00 15.00
1998 Mickey Mantle 98 6.00 15.00
1999 Mickey Mantle 99 6.00 15.00
2000 Mickey Mantle 00 6.00 15.00
2001 Mickey Mantle 01 6.00 15.00
2002 Mickey Mantle 02 6.00 15.00
2003 Mickey Mantle 03 6.00 15.00
2004 Mickey Mantle 04 6.00 15.00
2005 Mickey Mantle 05 6.00 15.00

2006 Topps Mantle Collection Bat Relics

SER.1 ODDS 1:4540 HOBBY, 1:8552 HTA
SER.1 ODDS 1:14,000 MINI, 1:6500 RETAIL
PRINT RUNS B/WN 77-167 COPIES PER
BLACK SER.1 ODDS 1:4,665 HTA
BLACK PRINT RUN 7 SERIAL #'d SETS
NO BLACK PRICING DUE TO SCARCITY
1996 Mickey Mantle 96/77 40.00 80.00
1997 Mickey Mantle 97/87 40.00 80.00
1998 Mickey Mantle 98/97 40.00 80.00
1999 Mickey Mantle 99/107 40.00 80.00
2000 Mickey Mantle 00/117 40.00 80.00
2001 Mickey Mantle 01/127 40.00 80.00
2002 Mickey Mantle 02/137 40.00 80.00
2003 Mickey Mantle 03/147 40.00 80.00
2004 Mickey Mantle 04/157 40.00 80.00
2005 Mickey Mantle 05/167 40.00 80.00

2006 Topps Mantle Home Run History

COMPLETE SET (501) 500.00 900.00
COMP.06 SERIES 1-2 SET (1-101) 60.00 120.00
COMP.06 UPDATE (102-201) 60.00 120.00
COMP.07 SERIES 1 SET (202-301) 75.00 150.00
COMP.07 SERIES 2 SET (302-401) 125.00 250.00
COMP.07 UPDATE (402-501) 125.00 250.00
COMP.08 TOPPS (502-536) 20.00 50.00
COMMON CARD (1-201) .40 1.00
COMMON CARD (202-301) 1.00 2.50
COMMON CARD (302-536) .75 2.00
SER.1 ODDS 1:4 HOBBY, 1:1 HTA, 1:4 MINI
SER.1 ODDS 1:2 RACK, 1:4 RETAIL
SER.2 ODDS 1:4 HOBBY, 1:1 HTA, 1:8 MINI
SER.2 ODDS 1:2 RACK, 1:4 RETAIL
UPDATE ODDS 1:4 HOB,1:4 RET
07 SER.1 ODDS 1:9 H, 1:2 HTA, 1:9 K-MART
07 SER.1 ODDS 1:9 RACK, 1:9 TARGET
07 SER.1 ODDS 1:9 WAL-MART
07 SER.2 ODDS 1:9 HOBBY
07 UPDATE ODDS 1:9 HOB, 1:9 RET
08 SER.1 ODDS 1:9 HOB, 1:9 RET
CARD 1 ISSUED IN SERIES 1 PACKS
CARDS 2-101 ISSUED IN SERIES 2 PACKS
CARDS 102-201 ISSUED IN UPDATE PACKS
CARDS 202-301 ISSUED IN 07 SERIES 1
CARDS 302-401 ISSUED IN 07 SERIES 2
CARDS 402-501 ISSUED IN 07 UPDATE
CARDS 502-537 ISSUED IN 08 SERIES 1

2006 Topps Mantle Home Run History Bat Relics

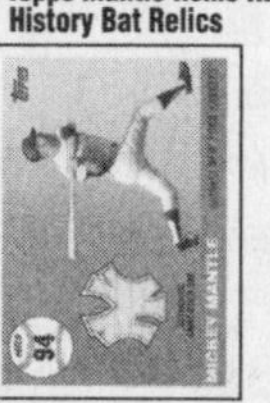

COMMON CARD (R1-R536) 50.00 100.00
SER.1 ODDS 1:681,120 H, 1:102,624 HTA
SER.2 ODDS 1:6250 H, 1:16,000 HTA
SER.2 ODDS 1:21,000 MINI, 1:1575 R
UPD ODDS 1:5100 H,1:1859 HTA,1:5800 R
07 SER.1 ODDS 1:14,618 H, 1:494 HTA
07 SER.1 ODDS 1:32,000 K-MART
07 SER.1 ODDS 1:16,225 RACK
07 SER.1 ODDS 1:32,00 WAL-MART
07 SER.2 ODDS 1:12,106 HOBBY, 1:693 HTA
07 UPD. ODDS 1:5,550 HOBBY
07 UPD. ODDS 1:1,475 HTA
07 UPD. ODDS 1:5,550 RETAIL
08 SER.1 ODDS 1:29,331 H,1:1492 HTA
08 SER.1 ODDS 1:207,000 RETAIL
1 ISSUED IN SERIES 1 PACKS
2-101 ISSUED IN SERIES 2 PACKS
102-201 ISSUED IN UPDATE PACKS
202-301 ISSUED IN 07 SERIES 1 PACKS
302-401 ISSUED IN 07 SERIES 2 PACKS
402-501 ISSUED IN 07 UPDATE
502-536 ISSUED IN 08 SERIES 1
STATED PRINT RUN 7 SERIAL #'d SETS

2006 Topps Mantle Home Run History Cut Signature

SER.1 ODDS 1:308,872 HTA
STATED PRINT RUN 1 SERIAL #'d CARD
NO PRICING DUE TO SCARCITY
CS1 Mickey Mantle

2006 Topps Opening Day Team vs. Team

COMPLETE SET (15) 6.00 15.00
SER.2 ODDS 1:6 HOBBY, 1:3 HTA, 1:24 MINI
SER.2 ODDS 1:6 RACK, 1:12 RETAIL
AM Houston Astros vs. Marlins .60 1.50
AY Oakland Athletics vs. Yankees .60 1.50
BP Milwaukee Brewers vs. Pirates .60 1.50
DB Los Angeles Dodgers vs. Braves .60 1.50
JT Toronto Blue Jays vs. Twins .60 1.50
MA Seattle Mariners vs. Angels .60 1.50
MN New York Mets vs. Nationals .60 1.50
OD Baltimore Orioles vs. Devil Rays .60 1.50
PC Philadelphia Phillies vs. Cardinals .60 1.50
PG San Diego Padres vs. Giants .60 1.50
RC Cincinnati Reds vs. Cubs .60 1.50
RD Colorado Rockies vs. Diamondbacks .60 1.50
RR Texas Rangers vs. Red Sox .60 1.50
RT Kansas City Royals vs. Tigers .60 1.50
WI Chicago White Sox vs. Indians .60 1.50

2006 Topps Opening Day Team vs. Team Relics

SER.2 A ODDS 1:8800 H, 1:22,000 HTA
SER.2 A ODDS 1:25,000 MINI, 1:2100 R
SER.2 B ODDS 1:610 H, 1:2850 HTA
SER.2 B ODDS 1:3075 MINI, 1:1200 R
GROUP A PRINT RUN 50 SERIAL #'d SETS
NO GROUP A PRICING DUE TO SCARCITY
EXCHANGE DEADLINE 06/30/08
AY Oakland Athletics Base B 6.00 15.00
BP Milwaukee Brewers Ball A
DB Los Angeles Dodgers Ball A
OD Baltimore Orioles Base B 6.00 15.00
PG San Diego Padres Ball A
RD Colorado Rockies Base B 6.00 15.00
RT Kansas City Royals Base B 10.00 25.00
WI Chicago White Sox Ball A

2006 Topps Own the Game

COMPLETE SET (30) 20.00 50.00
SER.1 ODDS 1:12 HOB, 1:4 HTA, 1:12 MINI
SER.1 ODDS 1:6 RACK, 1:8 RETAIL
OG1 Derrek Lee .40 1.00
OG2 Michael Young .60 1.50
OG3 Albert Pujols 2.50 6.00
OG4 Roger Clemens 1.25 3.00
OG5 Andy Pettitte .60 1.50
OG6 Dontrelle Willis .40 1.00
OG7 Michael Young .60 1.50
OG8 Ichiro Suzuki 1.50 4.00
OG9 Derek Jeter 2.50 6.00
OG10 Andruw Jones .40 1.00
OG11 Alex Rodriguez 1.50 4.00
OG12 David Ortiz .60 1.50
OG13 David Ortiz .60 1.50
OG14 Manny Ramirez 1.00 2.50
OG15 Mark Teixeira UER 1.00 2.50
Name is spelled Teixiera
OG16 Albert Pujols 2.50 6.00
OG17 Alex Rodriguez 1.50 4.00
OG18 Derek Jeter 2.50 6.00
OG19 Chad Cordero .40 1.00
OG20 Francisco Rodriguez .60 1.50
OG21 Mariano Rivera 1.00 2.50
OG22 Chone Figgins .40 1.00
OG23 Jose Reyes .60 1.50
OG24 Scott Podsednik .40 1.00
OG25 Jake Peavy .40 1.00
OG26 Johan Santana 1.00 2.50
OG27 Pedro Martinez .60 1.50
OG28 Dontrelle Willis .40 1.00
OG29 Chris Carpenter 1.00 2.50
OG30 Bartolo Colon .40 1.00

2006 Topps Rookie of the Week

COMPLETE SET (25) 15.00 40.00
COMMON CARD (1-13) .50 1.25
ISSUED ONE PER WEEK VIA HTA SHOPS
1 Mickey Mantle 52 4.00 10.00
2 Barry Bonds 87 2.50 6.00
3 Roger Clemens 85 1.50 4.00
4 Ernie Banks 54 1.25 3.00
5 Nolan Ryan 68 3.00 8.00
The spelling mistake on the word sensational was finally corrected
6 Albert Pujols 01 3.00 8.00
7 Roberto Clemente 55 4.00 10.00
8 Frank Robinson 57 .50 1.25
9 Brooks Robinson 57 .75 2.00
10 Harmon Killebrew 55 1.25 3.00
11 Reggie Jackson 69 .75 2.00
12 George Brett 75 2.50 6.00
13 Ichiro Suzuki 01 2.00 5.00
14 Cal Ripken 82 5.00 12.00
15 Tom Seaver 68 .75 2.00
16 Johnny Bench 68 1.25 3.00
17 Mike Schmidt 73 2.00 5.00
18 Derek Jeter 93 3.00 8.00
19 Bob Gibson 59 .75 2.00
20 Ozzie Smith 79 2.00 5.00
21 Rickey Henderson 80 1.25 3.00
22 Tony Gwynn 83 1.25 3.00
23 Wade Boggs 83 .75 2.00
24 Ryne Sandberg 83 2.50 6.00
25 Mickey Mantle TBD 4.00 10.00

2006 Topps Stars

COMPLETE SET (15) 6.00 15.00
SER.2 ODDS 1:12 HOBBY, 1:4 HTA
AP Albert Pujols 2.00 5.00
AR Alex Rodriguez 1.25 3.00
AS Alfonso Soriano .50 1.25
BB Barry Bonds 1.50 4.00
DJ Derek Jeter 2.00 5.00
DO David Ortiz .50 1.25
HM Hideki Matsui .75 2.00
IS Ichiro Suzuki 1.25 3.00
MC Miguel Cabrera .75 2.00
MR Manny Ramirez .75 2.00
MT Miguel Tejada .50 1.25
PM Pedro Martinez .50 1.25
RC Roger Clemens 1.00 2.50
TH Todd Helton .50 1.25
VG Vladimir Guerrero .75 2.00

2006 Topps Target Factory Set Mantle Memorabilia

The card was packaged exclusively with 2006 Topps Factory sets sold in Target stores. Each factory set contained the complete Series 1 and Series 2 sets as well as the Mantle 1952 Topps reprint relic card. The original set SRP was $59.99.

MMR52 Mickey Mantle 52T 20.00 50.00

2006 Topps Team Topps Autographs

ISSUED IN VARIOUS 06 TOPPS PRODUCTS
SEE '03 TOPPS BLUE CHIPS FOR ADD'L INFO
BF Bob Feller 10.00 25.00
CS Chris Snyder 4.00 10.00
DD Doug Drabek 6.00 15.00
DS Duke Snider 15.00 40.00
DZ Don Zimmer 6.00 15.00
ED Eric Davis 6.00 15.00
JF Josh Fields 6.00 15.00
JL Jim Leyritz 4.00 10.00
JP Johnny Podres 6.00 15.00
JP1 Jimmy Piersall 6.00 15.00
MC Mike Cuellar 6.00 15.00
MP Manny Parra 10.00 25.00
MR Mickey Rivers 6.00 15.00
RS Ryan Sweeney 4.00 10.00
SE Scott Elbert 4.00 10.00
TJ Tommy John 6.00 15.00

2006 Topps Trading Places

COMPLETE SET (20) 10.00 25.00
SER.2 ODDS 1:18 H, 1:4 HTA, 1:32 MINI
SER.2 ODDS 1:18 R, 1:8 RACK
AS Alfonso Soriano 1.00 2.50
BM Bill Mueller .60 1.50
BW Brad Wilkerson .60 1.50
CC Coco Crisp .60 1.50
CD Carlos Delgado .60 1.50
CP Corey Patterson .60 1.50
ER Edgar Renteria .60 1.50
FT Frank Thomas 1.50 4.00
JD Johnny Damon 1.00 2.50
JP Juan Pierre .60 1.50
JT Jim Thome 1.00 2.50
KL Kenny Lofton .60 1.50
MB Milton Bradley .60 1.50
NG Nomar Garciaparra 1.50 4.00
PW Preston Wilson .60 1.50
RF Rafael Furcal .60 1.50
RH Ramon Hernandez .60 1.50
TG Troy Glaus .60 1.50
JDN Juan Encarnacion .60 1.50
MJP Mike Piazza 1.50 4.00

2006 Topps Wal-Mart

These cards were issued in three-card cello packs within sealed series one Wal-Mart Bonus Boxes. Each Bonus Box carried a $9.97 suggested retail price and contained ten mini packs of series one cards plus the aforementioned three-card cello pack. The mini packs each contained six cards, thus each sealed Bonus Box contained 63 cards in all.

COMPLETE SERIES 1 (18) 12.50 30.00
COMPLETE SERIES 2 (18) 12.50 30.00
THREE PER WAL-MART BLASTER BOX
S1 CARDS ISSUED IN SERIES 1 PACKS
S2 CARDS ISSUED IN SERIES 2 PACKS
WM1 Stan Musial 52 S1 2.00 5.00
WM2 Ted Williams 87 S1 3.00 8.00
WM3 Yogi Berra 54 S2 1.25 3.00
WM4 Joe Mauer 96 UPD 1.00 2.50
WM5 Mickey Mantle 02 S1 4.00 10.00
WM6 Mickey Mantle 57 S2 4.00 10.00
WM7 Alex Rodriguez 58 S2 2.00 5.00
WM8 Carlos Zambrano 92 UPD 1.00 2.50
WM9 Gary Carter 60 S2 .50 1.25
WM10 Roy Oswalt 61 S2 .75 2.00
WM11 Mickey Mantle 70 UPD 6.00 15.00
WM12 Randy Johnson 62 UPD 1.50 4.00
WM13 Carlos Lee 64 S1 .50 1.25
WM14 Johan Santana 65 S2 1.25 3.00
WM15 Roberto Clemente 66 S2 4.00 10.00
WM16 Carl Yastrzemski 67 S2 2.00 5.00
WM17 Chase Utley 63 UPD 1.50 4.00
WM18 Pedro Martinez 68 UPD 1.00 2.50
WM19 Jason Bay 69 UPD 1.00 2.50
WM20 Alex Rodriguez 59 UPD 2.50 6.00
WM21 Chipper Jones 72 S2 1.25 3.00
WM22 Ichiro Suzuki 01 S1 2.00 5.00
WM23 Bobby Abreu 94 S1 .50 1.25
WM24 Tom Seaver 95 S1 .75 2.00
WM25 Alfonso Soriano 76 S2 .75 2.00
WM26 Andruw Jones 92 S1 .50 1.25
WM27 Hanley Ramirez 71 UPD 1.50 4.00
WM28 Adam Dunn 91 S1 .75 2.00
WM29 Carl Crawford 00 UPD 1.00 2.50
WM30 Mark Teixeira 81 S1 1.25 3.00
WM31 Albert Pujols 82 S2 3.00 8.00
WM32 Cal Ripken 83 S2 5.00 12.00
WM33 Ryne Sandberg 84 S1 2.50 6.00
WM34 Don Mattingly 85 S1 2.50 6.00
WM35 Roger Clemens 86 S1 1.50 4.00
WM36 Jose Reyes 53 S2 .75 2.00
WM37 Curt Schilling 80 UPD 1.00 2.50
WM38 Derrek Lee 56 S2 .50 1.25
WM39 Miguel Cabrera 73 S2 1.25 3.00
WM40 Manny Ramirez 88 UPD 1.00 2.50
WM41 Barry Bonds 89 S1 2.50 6.00
WM42 Barry Bonds 74 S2 2.50 6.00
WM43 Jeff Francoeur 98 UPD 1.50 4.00
WM44 Livan Hernandez 75 S2 .50 1.25
WM45 Derek Jeter 77 S2 3.00 8.00
WM46 David Ortiz 97 S1 .75 2.00
WM47 Carlos Delgado 78 UPD 1.00 2.50
WM48 Ivan Rodriguez 99 S1 .75 2.00
WM49 Todd Helton 05 UPD 1.00 2.50
WM50 Barry Bonds 79 UPD 2.50 6.00
WM51 Miguel Tejada 55 UPD 1.00 2.50
WM52 Alex Rodriguez 03 S1 2.00 5.00
WM53 Vladimir Guerrero 04 S1 1.25 3.00
WM54 Paul Konerko 90 UPD 1.00 2.50

2006 Topps Trading Places Autographs

SER.2 A ODDS 1:110,000 HOBBY
SER.2 A ODDS 1:28,000 HTA
SER.2 A ODDS 1:250,000 MINI
SER.2 A ODDS 1:160,000 RACK
SER.2 A ODDS 1:150,000 RETAIL
SER.2 B ODDS 1:18,000 H, 1:5100 HTA
SER.2 B ODDS 1:30,000 MINI, 1:17,000 R
SER.2 B ODDS 1:8700 RACK
SER.2 C ODDS 1:4280 H, 1:1175 HTA
SER.2 C ODDS 1:7200 MINI, 1:4200 R
SER.2 C ODDS 1:2040 RACK
GROUP A PRINT RUN 75 CARDS
GROUP B PRINT RUN 225 SETS
A-B ARE NOT SERIAL-NUMBERED
A-B PRINT RUNS PROVIDED BY TOPPS
BR B.J. Ryan B 15.00 40.00
BW Billy Wagner C 12.50 30.00
JE Johnny Estrada C 4.00 10.00
KJ Kenji Johjima A 90.00 150.00
ML Mike Lowell C 10.00 25.00
PL Paul LoDuca B 15.00 40.00
TS Termel Sledge C 4.00 10.00

2006 Topps Trading Places Autographed Relics

SER.2 ODDS 1:31,500 HOBBY, 1:8000 HTA
SER.2 ODDS 78,000 MINI, 1:52,000 RETAIL
STATED PRINT RUN 25 SERIAL #'d SETS
NO PRICING DUE TO SCARCITY

2006 Topps Trading Places Relics

SER.2 A ODDS 1:645 HOBBY 1:115 HTA
SER.2 A ODDS 1:1355 MINI, 1:810 RETAIL
SER.2 B ODDS 1:410 HOBBY 1:120 HTA
SER.2 B ODDS 1:903 MINI, 1:500 RETAIL
AS Alfonso Soriano Bat A 3.00 8.00
BM Bill Mueller Bat A 3.00 8.00
BR B.J. Ryan Jsy B 3.00 8.00
CP Corey Patterson Bat A 3.00 8.00
ER Edgar Renteria Bat A 3.00 8.00
JD Johnny Damon Jsy B 6.00 15.00
JE Johnny Estrada Bat B 3.00 8.00
JP Juan Pierre Bat A 3.00 8.00
JT Jim Thome Bat A 6.00 15.00
KJ Kenji Johjima Bat B 6.00 15.00
KL Kenny Lofton Bat B 3.00 8.00
MB Milton Bradley Bat B 3.00 8.00
ML Mike Lowell Bat A 3.00 8.00
NG Nomar Garciaparra Bat A 4.00 10.00
PL Paul Lo Duca Bat A 3.00 8.00
PW Preston Wilson Bat A 3.00 8.00
RH Ramon Hernandez Bat B 3.00 8.00
TS Terrmel Sledge Bat B 3.00 8.00
BW1 Billy Wagner Jsy B 3.00 8.00
BW2 Brad Wilkerson Bat B 3.00 8.00

2006 Topps World Series Champion Relics

SER.1 A ODDS 1:23,755 H, 1:9329 HTA
SER.1 A ODDS 1:55,000 MINI, 1:27,000 R
SER.1 B ODDS 1:11,289 H, 1:2544 HTA
SER.1 B ODDS 1:24,000 MINI, 1:11,500 R
SER.1 C ODDS 1:1941 H, 1:880 HTA
SER.1 C ODDS 1:5100 MINI, 1:2500 R
SER.1 D ODDS 1:3144 H, 1:2168 HTA
SER.1 D ODDS 1:9200 MINI, 1:4700 R
SER.1 E ODDS 1:4984 H, 1:3346 HTA
SER.1 E ODDS 1:14,500 MINI, 1:7200 R
SER.1 F ODDS 1:1006 H, 1:617 HTA
SER.1 F ODDS 1:2800 MINI, 1:1430 R
SER.1 G ODDS 1:1396 H, 1:465 HTA
SER.1 G ODDS 1:3500 MINI, 1:1750 R
OVERALL SER.1 AU-GU ODDS 1:137 H/R
OVERALL SER.1 AU-GU ODDS 1:47 HTA
GROUP A PRINT RUN 100 SETS
GROUP A ARE NOT SERIAL-NUMBERED
GROUP A PRINT RUN PROVIDED BY TOPPS
AP A.J. Pierzynski Bat E 10.00 25.00
AR Aaron Rowand Bat D 10.00 25.00
BJ Bobby Jenks Glv A/100 * 250.00 350.00
CEB Carl Everett Bat F 6.00 15.00
CEU Carl Everett Uni A/100 * 60.00 120.00
FT Frank Thomas Uni F 10.00 25.00
JC Joe Crede Bat D 15.00 40.00
JD Jermaine Dye Bat C 10.00 25.00
JG Jon Garland Uni F 6.00 15.00
JU Juan Uribe Bat B 10.00 25.00
MB Mark Buehrle Glv A/100 * 150.00 250.00
PKB Paul Konerko Bat G 8.00 20.00
PKU Paul Konerko Uni G 8.00 20.00
SP Scott Podsednik Bat C 10.00 25.00
TI Tadahito Iguchi Bat C 8.00 20.00
TP Timo Perez Bat C 6.00 15.00
WH Willie Harris Bat F 4.00 10.00

2006 Topps Update

This 330-card set was released in November, 2006. This set was issued in 12-card packs with an $2 SRP and those packs came 36 to a box and 12 boxes to a case. The first 132 cards in this set feature players who were either new to their team in 2006 or made an unexpected impact and were not in the first two Topps series. Cards numbered 133-170 feature 2006 Rookies while cards numbered 171-181 are Season Highlights. Cards number 182-201 are a Postseason Highlight subset, cards 202-217 are an League Leader subset while cards 218-282 form an All-Star subset. Cards numbered 283-290 celebrate players who participated in the Home Run Derby, cards 291-320 were Team Leader cards and the set concluded with Classic Duos (321-330). Cory Lidle, who perished in a plane crash while this set was in production, was issued as an "in memoriam" card.

COMPLETE SET (330) 20.00 50.00
COMMON CARD (1-132) .07 .20

COMMON ROOKIE (133-170) .20 .50
COMMON CARD (171-330) .12 .30
UNLISTED STARS 171-330 .30 .75
1-330 PLATE ODDS 1:85 HTA
PLATE PRINT RUN 1 SET PER COLOR
BLACK-CYAN-MAGENTA-YELLOW ISSUED
NO PLATE PRICING DUE TO SCARCITY
1 Austin Kearns .07 .20
2 Adam Eaton .07 .20
3 Juan Encarnacion .07 .20
4 Jarrod Washburn .07 .20
5 Alex Gonzalez .07 .20
6 Toby Hall .07 .20
7 Preston Wilson .07 .20
8 Ramon Ortiz .07 .20
9 Jason Michaels .07 .20
10 Jeff Weaver .07 .20
11 Russell Branyan .07 .20
12 Brett Tomko .07 .20
13 Doug Mientkiewicz .07 .20
14 David Wells .07 .20
15 Corey Koskie .07 .20
16 Russ Ortiz .07 .20
17 Carlos Pena .12 .30
18 Mark Hendrickson .07 .20
19 Julian Tavarez .07 .20
20 Jeff Conine .07 .20
21 Dioner Navarro .07 .20
22 Bob Wickman .07 .20
23 Felipe Lopez .07 .20
24 Eddie Guardado .07 .20
25 David Dellucci .07 .20
26 Ryan Wagner .07 .20
27 Nick Green .07 .20
28 Gary Majewski .07 .20
29 Shea Hillenbrand .07 .20
30 Jae Seo .07 .20
31 Royce Clayton .07 .20
32 Dave Riske .07 .20
33 Joey Gathright .07 .20
34 Robinson Tejada .07 .20
35 Edwin Jackson .07 .20
36 Aubrey Huff .07 .20
37 Akinori Otsuka .07 .20
38 Juan Castro UER .07 .20
Key Stat does not match actual stat
39 Zach Day .07 .20
40 Jeremy Accardo .07 .20
41 Shawn Green .07 .20
42 Kazuo Matsui .07 .20
43 J.J. Putz .07 .20
44 David Ross .07 .20
45 Scott Williamson .07 .20
46 Joe Borchard .07 .20
47 Elmer Dessens .07 .20
48 Odalis Perez .07 .20
49 Kelly Shoppach .07 .20
50 Brandon Phillips .07 .20
51 Guillermo Mota .07 .20
52 Alex Cintron .07 .20
53 Denny Bautista .07 .20
54 Josh Bard .07 .20
55 Julio Lugo .07 .20
56 Doug Mirabelli .07 .20
57 Kip Wells .07 .20
58 Adrian Gonzalez .12 .30
59 Shawn Chacon .07 .20
60 Marcus Thames .07 .20
61 Craig Wilson .07 .20
62 Cory Sullivan .07 .20
63 Ben Broussard .07 .20
64 Todd Walker .07 .20
65 Greg Maddux .30 .75
66 Xavier Nady .07 .20
67 Oliver Perez .07 .20
68 Sean Casey .07 .20
69 Kyle Lohse .07 .20
70 Carlos Lee .07 .20
71 Rheal Cormier .07 .20
72 Ronnie Belliard .07 .20
73 Cory Lidle .07 .20
74 David Bell .07 .20
75 Wilson Betemit .07 .20
76 Danys Baez .07 .20
77 Mike Stanton .07 .20
78 Kevin Mench .07 .20
79 Sandy Alomar Jr. .07 .20
80 Cesar Izturis .07 .20
81 Jeremy Affeldt .07 .20
82 Matt Stairs .07 .20
83 Hector Luna .07 .20
84 Tony Graffanino .07 .20
85 J.P Howell .07 .20
86 Bengie Molina .07 .20
87 Maicer Izturis .07 .20
88 Marco Scutaro .07 .20
89 Daryle Ward .07 .20
90 Sal Fasano .07 .20
91 Oscar Villarreal .07 .20
92 Gabe Gross .07 .20
93 Phil Nevin .07 .20
94 Damon Hollins .07 .20
95 Juan Cruz .07 .20
96 Marlon Anderson .07 .20
97 Jason Davis .07 .20
98 Ryan Shealy .07 .20
99 Francisco Cordero .07 .20
100 Bobby Abreu .07 .20
101 Roberto Hernandez .07 .20
102 Gary Bennett .07 .20
103 Aaron Sele .07 .20
104 Nook Logan .07 .20
105 Alfredo Amezaga .07 .20
106 Chris Woodward .07 .20
107 Kevin Jarvis .07 .20
108 B.J. Upton .07 .20
109 Alan Embree .07 .20
110 Milton Bradley .07 .20
111 Pete Orr .07 .20
112 Jeff Cirillo .07 .20
113 Corey Patterson .07 .20
114 Josh Paul .07 .20
115 Fernando Rodney .07 .20
116 Jerry Hairston Jr. .07 .20
117 Scott Proctor .07 .20
118 Ambiorix Burgos .07 .20
119 Jose Bautista .20 .50
120 Livan Hernandez .07 .20
121 John McDonald .07 .20
122 Ronny Cedeno .07 .20
123 Nate Robertson .07 .20
124 Jamey Carroll .07 .20
125 Alex Escobar .07 .20
126 Endy Chavez .07 .20
127 Jorge Julio .07 .20
128 Kenny Lofton .07 .20
129 Matt Diaz .07 .20
130 Dave Bush .07 .20
131 Jose Molina .07 .20
132 Mike MacDougal .07 .20
133 Ben Zobrist (RC) .50 1.25
134 Shane Komine RC .30 .75
135 Casey Janssen RC .20 .50
136 Kevin Frandsen (RC) .20 .50
137 John Rheinecker (RC) .20 .50
138 Matt Kemp (RC) 1.00 2.50
139 Scott Mathieson (RC) .20 .50
140 Jered Weaver (RC) .50 1.25
141 Joel Guzman (RC) .20 .50
142 Anibal Sanchez (RC) .20 .50
143 Melky Cabrera (RC) .30 .75
144 Howie Kendrick (RC) .50 1.25
145 Cole Hamels (RC) .75 2.00
146 Willy Aybar (RC) .20 .50
147 Jamie Shields RC .60 1.50
148 Kevin Thompson (RC) .20 .50
149 Jon Lester RC .75 2.00
150 Stephen Drew (RC) .50 1.25
151 Andre Ethier (RC) .75 2.00
152 Jordan Tata RC .20 .50
153 Mike Napoli RC .60 1.50
154 Kason Gabbard (RC) .20 .50
155 Lastings Milledge (RC) .20 .50
156 Erick Aybar (RC) .20 .50
157 Fausto Carmona (RC) .20 .50
158 Russ Martin (RC) .30 .75
159 David Pauley (RC) .20 .50
160 Andy Marte (RC) .20 .50
161 Carlos Quentin (RC) .30 .75
162 Franklin Gutierrez (RC) .20 .50
163 Taylor Buchholz (RC) .20 .50
164 Josh Johnson (RC) .50 1.25
165 Chad Billingsley (RC) .30 .75
166 Kendry Morales (RC) .50 1.25
167 Adam Loewen (RC) .20 .50
168 Yusmeiro Petit (RC) .20 .50
169 Matt Albers (RC) .20 .50
170 John Maine (RC) .30 .75
171 Alex Rodriguez SH .50 1.25
172 Mike Piazza SH .30 .75
173 Cory Sullivan SH .12 .30
174 Anibal Sanchez SH .12 .30
175 Trevor Hoffman SH .20 .50
176 Barry Bonds SH .60 1.50
177 Derek Jeter SH .75 2.00
178 Jose Reyes SH .20 .50
179 Manny Ramirez SH .30 .75
180 Vladimir Guerrero SH .30 .75
181 Mariano Rivera SH .30 .75
182 Mark Kotsay PH .12 .30
183 Derek Jeter PH .75 2.00
184 Carlos Delgado PH .12 .30
185 Frank Thomas PH .30 .75
186 Albert Pujols PH .75 2.00
187 Magglio Ordonez PH .20 .50
188 Carlos Delgado PH .12 .30
189 Kenny Rogers PH .12 .30
190 Tom Glavine PH .20 .50
191 Placido Polanco .12 .30
Jeff Suppan PH
192 Jose Reyes PH .20 .50
193 Endy Chavez .20 .50
Yadier Molina PH
194 Craig Monroe PH .12 .30
195 Justin Verlander 1.00 2.50
Joel Zumaya PH
196 Paul LoDuca .12 .30
Carlos Beltran PH
197 Albert Pujols .75 2.00
Jim Edmonds
Scott Rolen PH
198 Anthony Reyes PH .12 .30
199 Chris Carpenter PH .30 .75
200 David Eckstein PH .12 .30
201 Jered Weaver PH .30 .75
202 David Ortiz .20 .50
Jermaine Dye
Travis Hafner LL
203 Joe Mauer .75 2.00
Derek Jeter
Robinson Cano LL
204 David Ortiz .30 .75
Justin Morneau
Raul Ibanez LL
205 Carl Crawford .20 .50
Chone Figgins
Ichiro Suzuki LL
206 Johan Santana .30 .75
Chien-Ming Wang
Jon Garland LL
207 Johan Santana .30 .75
Roy Halladay
C.C. Sabathia LL UER
The heading on the back for ERA was mistakenly labeled for Wins
208 Johan Santana .30 .75
Jeremy Bonderman
John Lackey LL
209 Francisco Rodriguez .20 .50
Bobby Jenks
B.J. Ryan LL
210 Ryan Howard .75 2.00
Albert Pujols
Alfonso Soriano LL
211 Freddy Sanchez .75 2.00
Miguel Cabrera
Albert Pujols LL
212 Ryan Howard .75 2.00
Albert Pujols
Lance Berkman LL
213 Jose Reyes .30 .75
Juan Pierre
Hanley Ramirez LL
214 Derek Lowe .20 .50
Brandon Webb
Carlos Zambrano LL
215 Roy Oswalt .30 .75
Chris Carpenter
Brandon Webb LL
216 Aaron Harang .30 .75
Jake Peavy
John Smoltz LL
217 Trevor Hoffman .20 .50
Billy Wagner
Joe Borowski LL
218 Ichiro Suzuki AS .50 1.25
219 Derek Jeter AS .75 2.00
220 Alex Rodriguez AS .50 1.25
221 David Ortiz AS .20 .50
222 Vladimir Guerrero AS .30 .75
223 Ivan Rodriguez AS .20 .50
224 Vernon Wells AS .12 .30
225 Mark Loretta AS .12 .30
226 Kenny Rogers AS .12 .30
227 Alfonso Soriano AS .20 .50
228 Carlos Beltran AS .12 .30
229 Albert Pujols AS .75 2.00
230 Jason Bay AS .12 .30
231 Edgar Renteria AS .12 .30
232 David Wright AS .50 1.25
233 Chase Utley AS .30 .75
234 Paul LoDuca AS .12 .30
235 Brad Penny AS .12 .30
236 Derrick Turnbow AS .12 .30
237 Mark Redman AS .12 .30
238 Francisco Liriano AS .30 .75
239 A.J. Pierzynski AS .12 .30
240 Grady Sizemore AS .20 .50
241 Jose Contreras AS .12 .30
242 Jermaine Dye AS .12 .30
243 Jason Schmidt AS .12 .30
244 Nomar Garciaparra AS .30 .75
245 Scott Kazmir AS .20 .50
246 Johan Santana AS .30 .75
247 Chris Capuano AS .12 .30
248 Magglio Ordonez AS .20 .50
249 Gary Matthews Jr. AS .12 .30
250 Carlos Lee AS .12 .30
251 David Eckstein AS .12 .30
252 Michael Young AS .20 .50
253 Matt Holliday AS .30 .75
254 Lance Berkman AS .20 .50
255 Scott Rolen AS .20 .50
256 Bronson Arroyo AS .12 .30
257 Barry Zito AS .12 .30
258 Brian McCann AS .12 .30
259 Jose Lopez AS .12 .30
260 Chris Carpenter AS .30 .75
261 Roy Halladay AS .30 .75
262 Jim Thome AS .20 .50
263 Dan Uggla AS .30 .75
264 Mariano Rivera AS .30 .75
265 Roy Oswalt AS .20 .50
266 Tom Gordon AS .12 .30
267 Troy Glaus AS .12 .30
268 Bobby Jenks AS .12 .30
269 Freddy Sanchez AS .12 .30
270 Paul Konerko AS .20 .50
271 Joe Mauer AS .30 .75
272 B.J. Ryan AS .12 .30
273 Ryan Howard AS .50 1.25
274 Brian Fuentes AS .12 .30
275 Miguel Cabrera AS .30 .75
276 Brandon Webb AS .20 .50
277 Mark Buehrle AS .20 .50
278 Trevor Hoffman AS .20 .50
279 Jonathan Papelbon AS .60 1.50
280 Andruw Jones AS .12 .30
281 Miguel Tejada AS .20 .50
282 Carlos Zambrano AS .20 .50
283 Ryan Howard HRD .50 1.25
284 David Wright HRD .50 1.25
285 Miguel Cabrera HRD .30 .75
286 David Ortiz HRD .20 .50
287 Jermaine Dye HRD .12 .30
288 Miguel Tejada HRD .20 .50
289 Lance Berkman HRD .20 .50
290 Troy Glaus HRD .12 .30
291 David Wright .50 1.25
Tom Glavine TL
292 Ryan Howard .50 1.25
Tom Gordon TL
293 Miguel Cabrera .30 .75
Dontrelle Willis TL
294 Andruw Jones .30 .75
John Smoltz TL
295 Alfonso Soriano .20 .50
Alfonso Soriano TL
296 Albert Pujols .75 2.00
Chris Carpenter TL
297 Adam Dunn .20 .50
Bronson Arroyo TL
298 Lance Berkman .20 .50
Roy Oswalt TL
299 Chris Capuano .50 1.25
Prince Fielder TL
300 Freddy Sanchez .12 .30
Jason Bay TL
301 Carlos Zambrano .20 .50
Juan Pierre TL
302 Adrian Gonzalez .20 .50
Trevor Hoffman TL
303 Derek Lowe .12 .30
Rafael Furcal TL
304 Omar Vizquel .20 .50
Jason Schmidt TL
305 Brandon Webb .20 .50
Chad Tracy TL
306 Matt Holliday .30 .75
Garrett Atkins TL
307 Alex Rodriguez .20 .50
Chien-Ming Wang TL
308 Curt Schilling .20 .50
David Ortiz TL
309 Roy Halladay .30 .75
Vernon Wells TL
310 Miguel Tejada .20 .50
Erik Bedard TL
311 Carl Crawford .20 .50
Scott Kazmir TL
312 Jeremy Bonderman .20 .50
Magglio Ordonez TL
313 Justin Morneau .30 .75
Johan Santana TL
314 Jon Garland .12 .30
Jermaine Dye TL
315 Travis Hafner .20 .50
C.C. Sabathia TL
316 Emil Brown .12 .30
Mark Grudzielanek TL UER
Grudzielanek's name spelled incorrectly
317 Frank Thomas .30 .75
Barry Zito TL
318 Jered Weaver .30 .75
Vladimir Guerrero TL UER
Ervin Santana was actual team leader in Wins
319 Michael Young .20 .50
Gary Matthews TL
320 Ichiro Suzuki .50 1.25
J.J. Putz TL
321 Derek Jeter .75 2.00
Robinson Cano CD
322 Chris Carpenter .30 .75
Mark Mulder CD
323 Jason Schmidt .20 .50
Trevor Hoffman CD
324 David Wright .50 1.25
Paul Lo Duca CD
325 Lance Berkman .20 .50
Roy Oswalt CD
326 Derek Jeter .75 2.00
Jose Reyes CD
327 Cliff Floyd .50 1.25
David Wright CD
328 Francisco Liriano .30 .75
Johan Santana CD
329 J.D. Drew .30 .75
Stephen Drew CD
330 Jeff Weaver .30 .75
Jered Weaver CD

2006 Topps Update 1st Edition

*1ST ED 1-132: 3X TO 8X BASIC
*1ST ED 133-170: 1.2X TO 3X BASIC RC
*1ST ED 171-330: 2X TO 5X BASIC
STATED ODDS 1:36 HOB, 1:12 HTA

2006 Topps Update Black

COMMON CARD (1-132) 4.00 10.00
COMMON ROOKIE (133-170) 4.00 10.00
COMMON CARD (171-330) 4.00 10.00
STATED ODDS 1:7 HTA
STATED PRINT RUN 55 SER.#'d SETS
1 Austin Kearns 4.00 10.00
2 Adam Eaton 4.00 10.00
3 Juan Encarnacion 4.00 10.00
4 Jarrod Washburn 4.00 10.00
5 Alex Gonzalez 4.00 10.00
6 Toby Hall 4.00 10.00
7 Preston Wilson 4.00 10.00
8 Ramon Ortiz 4.00 10.00
9 Jason Michaels 4.00 10.00
10 Jeff Weaver 4.00 10.00
11 Russell Branyan 4.00 10.00
12 Brett Tomko 4.00 10.00
13 Doug Mientkiewicz 4.00 10.00
14 David Wells 4.00 10.00
15 Corey Koskie 4.00 10.00
16 Russ Ortiz 4.00 10.00
17 Carlos Pena 6.00 15.00
18 Mark Hendrickson 4.00 10.00
19 Julian Tavarez 4.00 10.00
20 Jeff Conine 4.00 10.00
21 Dioner Navarro 4.00 10.00
22 Bob Wickman 4.00 10.00
23 Felipe Lopez 4.00 10.00
24 Eddie Guardado 4.00 10.00
25 David Dellucci 4.00 10.00
26 Ryan Wagner 4.00 10.00
27 Nick Green 4.00 10.00
28 Gary Majewski 4.00 10.00
29 Shea Hillenbrand 4.00 10.00
30 Jae Seo 4.00 10.00
31 Royce Clayton 4.00 10.00
32 Dave Riske 4.00 10.00
33 Joey Gathright 4.00 10.00
34 Robinson Tejada 4.00 10.00
35 Edwin Jackson 4.00 10.00
36 Aubrey Huff 4.00 10.00
37 Akinori Otsuka 4.00 10.00
38 Juan Castro 4.00 10.00
39 Zach Day 4.00 10.00
40 Jeremy Accardo 4.00 10.00
41 Shawn Green 4.00 10.00
42 Kazuo Matsui 4.00 10.00
43 J.J. Putz 4.00 10.00
44 David Ross 4.00 10.00
45 Scott Williamson 4.00 10.00
46 Joe Borchard 4.00 10.00
47 Elmer Dessens 4.00 10.00
48 Odalis Perez 4.00 10.00
49 Kelly Shoppach 4.00 10.00
50 Brandon Phillips 4.00 10.00
51 Guillermo Mota 4.00 10.00
52 Alex Cintron 4.00 10.00
53 Denny Bautista 4.00 10.00
54 Josh Bard 4.00 10.00
55 Julio Lugo 4.00 10.00
56 Doug Mirabelli 4.00 10.00
57 Kip Wells 4.00 10.00
58 Adrian Gonzalez 6.00 15.00
59 Shawn Chacon 4.00 10.00
60 Marcus Thames 4.00 10.00
61 Craig Wilson 4.00 10.00
62 Cory Sullivan 4.00 10.00
63 Ben Broussard 4.00 10.00
64 Todd Walker 4.00 10.00
65 Greg Maddux 15.00 40.00
66 Xavier Nady 4.00 10.00
67 Oliver Perez 4.00 10.00
68 Sean Casey 4.00 10.00
69 Kyle Lohse 4.00 10.00
70 Carlos Lee 4.00 10.00
71 Rheal Cormier 4.00 10.00
72 Ronnie Belliard 4.00 10.00
73 Cory Lidle 4.00 10.00
74 David Bell 4.00 10.00
75 Wilson Betemit 4.00 10.00
76 Danys Baez 4.00 10.00
77 Mike Stanton 4.00 10.00
78 Kevin Mench 4.00 10.00
79 Sandy Alomar Jr. 4.00 10.00
80 Cesar Izturis 4.00 10.00
81 Jeremy Affeldt 4.00 10.00
82 Matt Stairs 4.00 10.00
83 Hector Luna 4.00 10.00
84 Tony Graffanino 4.00 10.00
85 J.P Howell 4.00 10.00
86 Bengie Molina 4.00 10.00
87 Maicer Izturis 4.00 10.00
88 Marco Scutaro 4.00 10.00
89 Daryle Ward 4.00 10.00
90 Sal Fasano 4.00 10.00
91 Oscar Villarreal 4.00 10.00
92 Gabe Gross 4.00 10.00
93 Phil Nevin 4.00 10.00
94 Damon Hollins 4.00 10.00
95 Juan Cruz 4.00 10.00
96 Marlon Anderson 4.00 10.00
97 Jason Davis 4.00 10.00
98 Ryan Shealy 4.00 10.00
99 Francisco Cordero 4.00 10.00
100 Bobby Abreu 4.00 10.00
101 Roberto Hernandez 4.00 10.00
102 Gary Bennett 4.00 10.00
103 Aaron Sele 4.00 10.00
104 Nook Logan 4.00 10.00
105 Alfredo Amezaga 4.00 10.00
106 Chris Woodward 4.00 10.00
107 Kevin Jarvis 4.00 10.00
108 B.J. Upton 4.00 10.00
109 Alan Embree 4.00 10.00
110 Milton Bradley 4.00 10.00
111 Pete Orr 4.00 10.00
112 Jeff Cirillo 4.00 10.00
113 Corey Patterson 4.00 10.00
114 Josh Paul 4.00 10.00
115 Fernando Rodney 4.00 10.00
116 Jerry Hairston Jr. 4.00 10.00
117 Scott Proctor 4.00 10.00
118 Ambiorix Burgos 4.00 10.00
119 Jose Bautista 10.00 25.00
120 Livan Hernandez 4.00 10.00
121 John Mcdonald 4.00 10.00
122 Ronny Cedeno 4.00 10.00
123 Nate Robertson 4.00 10.00
124 Jamey Carroll 4.00 10.00
125 Alex Escobar 4.00 10.00
126 Endy Chavez 4.00 10.00
127 Jorge Julio 4.00 10.00
128 Kenny Lofton 4.00 10.00
129 Matt Diaz 4.00 10.00
130 Dave Bush 4.00 10.00
131 Jose Molina 4.00 10.00
132 Mike MacDougal 4.00 10.00
133 Ben Zobrist 10.00 25.00
134 Shane Komine 6.00 15.00
135 Casey Janssen 4.00 10.00
136 Kevin Frandsen 4.00 10.00
137 John Rheinecker 4.00 10.00
138 Matt Kemp 20.00 50.00
139 Scott Mathieson 4.00 10.00
140 Jered Weaver 10.00 25.00
141 Joel Guzman 4.00 10.00
142 Anibal Sanchez 4.00 10.00
143 Melky Cabrera 6.00 15.00
144 Howie Kendrick 10.00 25.00
145 Cole Hamels 15.00 40.00
146 Willy Aybar 4.00 10.00
147 James Shields 12.00 30.00
148 Kevin Thompson 4.00 10.00
149 Jon Lester 15.00 40.00
150 Stephen Drew 10.00 25.00
151 Andre Ethier 15.00 40.00
152 Jordan Tata 4.00 10.00
153 Mike Napoli 12.00 30.00
154 Kason Gabbard 4.00 10.00
155 Lastings Milledge 4.00 10.00
156 Erick Aybar 4.00 10.00
157 Fausto Carmona 4.00 10.00
158 Russ Martin 6.00 15.00
159 David Pauley 4.00 10.00
160 Andy Marte 4.00 10.00
161 Carlos Quentin 6.00 15.00
162 Franklin Gutierrez 4.00 10.00
163 Taylor Buchholz 4.00 10.00
164 Josh Johnson 10.00 25.00
165 Chad Billingsley 6.00 15.00
166 Kendry Morales 10.00 25.00
167 Adam Loewen 4.00 10.00
168 Yusmeiro Petit 4.00 10.00
169 Matt Albers 4.00 10.00
170 John Maine 6.00 15.00
171 Alex Rodriguez SH 15.00 40.00
172 Mike Piazza SH 10.00 25.00
173 Cory Sullivan SH 4.00 10.00
174 Anibal Sanchez SH 4.00 10.00
175 Trevor Hoffman SH 6.00 15.00
176 Barry Bonds SH 20.00 50.00
177 Derek Jeter SH 25.00 60.00
178 Jose Reyes SH 6.00 15.00
179 Manny Ramirez SH 10.00 25.00
180 Vladimir Guerrero SH 10.00 25.00
181 Mariano Rivera SH 10.00 25.00
182 Mark Kotsay PH 4.00 10.00
183 Derek Jeter PH 25.00 60.00
184 Carlos Delgado PH 4.00 10.00
185 Frank Thomas PH 10.00 25.00
186 Albert Pujols PH 25.00 60.00
187 Magglio Ordonez PH 6.00 15.00
188 Carlos Delgado PH 4.00 10.00
189 Kenny Rogers PH 4.00 10.00
190 Tom Glavine PH 6.00 15.00
191 Placido Polanco 4.00 10.00
Jeff Suppan PH
192 Jose Reyes PH 6.00 15.00
193 Endy Chavez 6.00 15.00
Yadier Molina PH
194 Craig Monroe PH 4.00 10.00
195 Justin Verlander 30.00 80.00
Joel Zumaya PH
196 Paul LoDuca 4.00 10.00
Carlos Beltran PH
197 Albert Pujols 25.00 60.00
Jim Edmonds
Scott Rolen PH
198 Anthony Reyes PH 4.00 10.00
199 Chris Carpenter PH 10.00 25.00
200 David Eckstein PH 4.00 10.00
201 Jered Weaver PH 10.00 25.00
202 David Ortiz 6.00 15.00
Jermaine Dye
Travis Hafner LL
203 Joe Mauer 25.00 60.00
Derek Jeter
Robinson Cano LL
204 David Ortiz 10.00 25.00
Justin Morneau
Raul Ibanez LL
205 Carl Crawford 6.00 15.00
Chone Figgins
Ichiro Suzuki LL
206 Johan Santana 10.00 25.00
Chien-Ming Wang
Jon Garland LL
207 Johan Santana 10.00 25.00
Roy Halladay
C.C. Sabathia LL
208 Johan Santana 10.00 25.00
Jeremy Bonderman
John Lackey LL
209 Francisco Rodriguez 6.00 15.00
Bobby Jenks
B.J. Ryan LL
210 Ryan Howard 25.00 60.00
Albert Pujols
Alfonso Soriano LL
211 Freddy Sanchez 25.00 60.00
Miguel Cabrera
Albert Pujols LL
212 Ryan Howard 25.00 60.00
Albert Pujols
Lance Berkman LL
213 Jose Reyes 6.00 15.00
Juan Pierre
Hanley Ramirez LL
214 Derek Lowe 6.00 15.00
Brandon Webb
Carlos Zambrano LL
215 Roy Oswalt 10.00 25.00
Chris Carpenter
Brandon Webb LL
216 Aaron Harang 10.00 25.00
Jake Peavy
John Smoltz LL
217 Trevor Hoffman 6.00 15.00
Billy Wagner
Joe Borowski LL
218 Ichrio Suzuki AS 15.00 40.00
219 Derek Jeter AS 25.00 60.00
220 Alex Rodriguez AS 15.00 40.00
221 David Ortiz AS 6.00 15.00
222 Vladimir Guererro AS 10.00 25.00
223 Ivan Rodriguez AS 6.00 15.00
224 Vernon Wells AS 4.00 10.00
225 Mark Loretta AS 4.00 10.00
226 Kenny Rogers AS 4.00 10.00
227 Alfonso Soriano AS 6.00 15.00
228 Carlos Beltran AS 4.00 10.00
229 Albert Pujols AS 25.00 60.00
230 Jason Bay AS 4.00 10.00
231 Edgar Renteria AS 4.00 10.00
232 David Wright AS 15.00 40.00
233 Chase Utley AS 10.00 25.00
234 Paul LoDuca AS 4.00 10.00
235 Brad Penny AS 4.00 10.00
236 Derrick Turnbow AS 4.00 10.00
237 Mark Redman AS 4.00 10.00
238 Francisco Liriano AS 10.00 25.00
239 A.J. Pierzynski AS 4.00 10.00
240 Grady Sizemore AS 6.00 15.00
241 Jose Contreras AS 4.00 10.00
242 Jermaine Dye AS 4.00 10.00
243 Jason Schmidt AS 4.00 10.00
244 Nomar Garciaparra AS 10.00 25.00
245 Scott Kazmir AS 6.00 15.00
246 Johan Santana AS 10.00 25.00
247 Chris Capuano AS 4.00 10.00
248 Maggio Ordonez AS 6.00 15.00
249 Gary Matthews Jr. AS 4.00 10.00
250 Carlos Lee AS 4.00 10.00
251 David Eckstein AS 4.00 10.00
252 Michael Young AS 6.00 15.00
253 Matt Holliday AS 10.00 25.00
254 Lance Berkman AS 6.00 15.00
255 Scott Rolen AS 6.00 15.00
256 Bronson Arroyo AS 4.00 10.00
257 Barry Zito AS 4.00 10.00
258 Brian McCann AS 4.00 10.00
259 Jose Lopez AS 4.00 10.00
260 Chris Carpenter AS 10.00 25.00
261 Roy Halladay AS 10.00 25.00
262 Jim Thome AS 6.00 15.00
263 Dan Uggla AS 10.00 25.00
264 Mariano Rivera AS 10.00 25.00
265 Roy Oswalt AS 6.00 15.00
266 Tom Gordon AS 4.00 10.00
267 Troy Glaus AS 4.00 10.00
268 Bobby Jenks AS 4.00 10.00
269 Freddy Sanchez AS 4.00 10.00
270 Paul Konerko AS 6.00 15.00
271 Joe Mauer AS 10.00 25.00
272 B.J. Ryan AS 4.00 10.00
273 Ryan Howard AS 15.00 40.00
274 Brian Fuentes AS 4.00 10.00
275 Miguel Cabrera AS 10.00 25.00
276 Brandon Webb AS 6.00 15.00
277 Mark Buerhle AS 6.00 15.00
278 Trevor Hoffman AS 6.00 15.00
279 Jonathan Papelbon AS 20.00 50.00
280 Andruw Jones AS 4.00 10.00
281 Miguel Tejada AS 6.00 15.00
282 Carlos Zambrano AS 6.00 15.00
283 Ryan Howard HRD 15.00 40.00
284 David Wright HRD 15.00 40.00
285 Miguel Cabrera HRD 10.00 25.00
286 David Ortiz HRD 6.00 15.00
287 Jermaine Dye HRD 4.00 10.00
288 Miguel Tejada HRD 6.00 15.00
289 Lance Berkman HRD 6.00 15.00
290 Troy Glaus HRD 4.00 10.00
291 David Wright 15.00 40.00
Tom Glavine TL
292 Ryan Howard 15.00 40.00
Tom Gordon TL
293 Miguel Cabrera 10.00 25.00
Dontrelle Willis TL
294 Andruw Jones 10.00 25.00
John Smoltz TL
295 Alfonso Soriano 6.00 15.00
Alfonso Soriano TL
296 Albert Pujols 25.00 60.00
Chris Carpenter TL
297 Adam Dunn 6.00 15.00
Bronson Arroyo TL
298 Lance Berkman 6.00 15.00
Roy Oswalt TL
299 Chris Capuano 15.00 40.00
Prince Fielder TL
300 Freddy Sanchez 4.00 10.00
Jason Bay TL
301 Carlos Zambrano 6.00 15.00
Juan Pierre TL
302 Adrian Gonzalez 6.00 15.00
Trevor Hoffman TL
303 Derek Lowe 4.00 10.00
Rafael Furcal TL
304 Omar Vizquel 6.00 15.00
Jason Schmidt TL
305 Brandon Webb 6.00 15.00
Chad Tracy TL
306 Matt Holliday 10.00 25.00
Garrett Atkins TL
307 Alex Rodriguez 6.00 15.00
Chien-Ming Wang TL
308 Curt Schilling 6.00 15.00
David Ortiz TL
309 Roy Halladay 10.00 25.00
Vernon Wells TL
310 Miguel Tejada 6.00 15.00
Erik Bedard TL
311 Carl Crawford 6.00 15.00
Scott Kazmir TL
312 Jeremy Bonderman 6.00 15.00
Magglio Ordonez TL
313 Justin Morneau 10.00 25.00
Johan Santana TL
314 Jon Garland 4.00 10.00
Jermaine Dye TL
315 Travis Hafner 6.00 15.00
C.C. Sabathia TL
316 Emil Brown 4.00 10.00
Mark Grundzielanek TL
317 Frank Thomas 10.00 25.00
Barry Zito TL
318 Jered Weaver 10.00 25.00
Vladimir Guerrero TL
319 Michael Young 6.00 15.00
Gary Mathews TL
320 Ichiro Suzuki 15.00 40.00
J.J. Putz TL
321 Derek Jeter 25.00 60.00
Robinson Cano CD
322 Chris Carpenter 10.00 25.00
Mark Mulder CD
323 Jason Schmidt 6.00 15.00
Trevor Hoffman CD
324 David Wright 15.00 40.00
Paul Lo Duca CD
325 Lance Berkman 6.00 15.00
Roy Oswalt CD
326 Derek Jeter 25.00 60.00
Jose Reyes CD
327 Cliff Floyd 15.00 40.00
David Wright CD
328 Francisco Liriano 10.00 25.00
Johan Santana CD
329 J.D. Drew 10.00 25.00
Stephen Drew CD
330 Jeff Weaver 10.00 25.00
Jered Weaver CD

2006 Topps Update Gold

*GOLD 1-132: 2X TO 5X BASIC
*GOLD 133-170: .75X TO 2X BASIC RC
*GOLD 171-330: 1.2X TO 3X BASIC
STATED ODDS 1:4 HOB, 1:2 HTA, 1:6 RET
STATED PRINT RUN 2006 SER.#'d SETS

2006 Topps Update Platinum

ODDS 1:12,000 H,1:8800 HTA,1:12,000 R
STATED PRINT RUN 1 SERIAL #'d SET
NO PRICING DUE TO SCARCITY

2006 Topps Update All Star Autographs

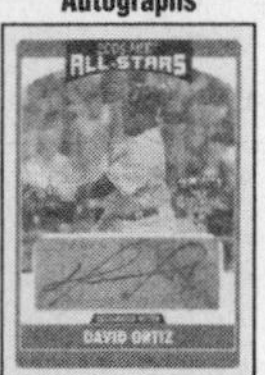

ODDS 1:48,000 H,1:16,000 HTA,1:57,000 R
STATED PRINT RUN 25 SER.#'d SETS
NO PRICING DUE TO SCARCITY
AR Alex Rodriguez
DO David Ortiz
DW David Wright

2006 Topps Update All Star Stitches

STATED ODDS 1:43 H,1:15 HTA,1:53 R
PATCH ODDS 1:2300 HOBBY,1:377 HTA
PATCH PRINT RUN 10 SER. #'d SETS
NO PATCH PRICING DUE TO SCARCITY
AJ Andruw Jones Jsy 5.00 12.00
AJP A.J. Pierzynski Jsy 4.00 10.00
AP Albert Pujols Jsy 12.50 30.00
AR Alex Rodriguez Jsy 6.00 15.00
AS Alfonso Soriano Jsy 5.00 12.00
BA Bronson Arroyo Jsy 5.00 12.00
BF Brian Fuentes Jsy 3.00 8.00
BJ Bobby Jenks Jsy 4.00 10.00
BM Brian McCann Jsy 6.00 15.00
BP Brad Penny Jsy 4.00 10.00
BR B.J. Ryan Jsy 4.00 10.00
BW Brandon Webb Jsy 5.00 12.00
CB Carlos Beltran Jsy 4.00 10.00
CC Chris Carpenter Jsy 5.00 12.00
CFC Chris Capuano Jsy 3.00 8.00
CL Carlos Lee Jsy 4.00 10.00
CU Chase Utley Jsy 5.00 12.00
CZ Carlos Zambrano Jsy 4.00 10.00
DE David Eckstein Jsy 6.00 15.00
DO David Ortiz Jsy 5.00 12.00
DT Derrick Turnbow Jsy 3.00 8.00
DU Dan Uggla Jsy 4.00 10.00
DW David Wright Jsy 8.00 20.00
ER Edgar Renteria Jsy 4.00 10.00
FS Freddy Sanchez Jsy 5.00 12.00
GM Gary Matthews Jr. Jsy 3.00 8.00
GS Grady Sizemore Jsy 5.00 12.00
IR Ivan Rodriguez Jsy 5.00 12.00
JB Jason Bay Jsy 6.00 15.00
JC Jose Contreras Jsy 4.00 10.00
JD Jermaine Dye Jsy 4.00 10.00
JDS Jason Schmidt Jsy 4.00 10.00
JL Jose Lopez Jsy 3.00 8.00
JM Joe Mauer Jsy 5.00 12.00
JP Jonathan Papelbon Jsy 8.00 20.00
JR Jose Reyes Jsy 3.00 8.00
JS Johan Santana Jsy 4.00 10.00
JT Jim Thome Jsy 5.00 12.00
KR Kenny Rogers Jsy 4.00 10.00
LB Lance Berkman Jsy 4.00 10.00
MAR Mark Redman Jsy 4.00 10.00
MB Mark Buehrle Jsy 4.00 10.00
MC Miguel Cabrera Jsy 5.00 12.00
MH Matt Holliday Jsy 5.00 12.00
ML Mark Loretta Jsy 4.00 10.00
MO Magglio Ordonez Jsy 4.00 10.00
MR Mariano Rivera Jsy 5.00 12.00
MT Miguel Tejada Jsy 3.00 8.00
MY Michael Young Jsy 3.00 8.00
PK Paul Konerko Jsy 4.00 10.00
PL Paul LoDuca Jsy 3.00 8.00
RC Robinson Cano Jsy 6.00 15.00
RH Roy Halladay Jsy 4.00 10.00
RJH Ryan Howard Jsy 12.50 30.00
RO Roy Oswalt Jsy 3.00 8.00
SK Scott Kazmir Jsy 4.00 10.00
SR Scott Rolen Jsy 5.00 12.00
TEG Troy Glaus Jsy 3.00 8.00
TG Tom Gordon Jsy 4.00 10.00
TH Trevor Hoffman Jsy 3.00 8.00
TMG Tom Glavine Jsy 5.00 12.00
VG Vladimir Guerrero Jsy 4.00 10.00
VW Vernon Wells Jsy 4.00 10.00

2006 Topps Update All Star Stitches Dual

STATED ODDS 1:2550 HOBBY,1:752 HTA
STATED PRINT RUN 50 SER.#'d SETS
CJ Andruw Jones 10.00 25.00
Miguel Cabrera
HS Johan Santana 10.00 25.00
Roy Halladay
HT Jim Thome Jsy 20.00 50.00
Ryan Howard Jsy
MM Joe Mauer 10.00 25.00
Brian McCann
PW David Wright 30.00 60.00
Albert Pujols
RH Mariano Rivera Jsy 30.00 60.00
Trevor Hoffman Jsy
RO David Ortiz 20.00 50.00
Alex Rodriguez
SS Ichiro Suzuki 20.00 50.00
Alfonso Soriano
TG Miguel Tejada 10.00 25.00
Vladimir Guerrero
WS Grady Sizemore Jsy 12.50 30.00
Vernon Wells Jsy

2006 Topps Update Barry Bonds 715

STATED ODDS 1:36 H,1:36 HTA,1:36 R
BB Barry Bonds 2.00 5.00

2006 Topps Update Barry Bonds Home Run History Autographs

ODDS 1:42,400 H,1:15,141 HTA,1:50,000 R
STATED PRINT RUN 5 SER.#'d SETS
NO PRICING DUE TO SCARCITY

2006 Topps Update Barry Bonds 715 Relics

ODDS 1:5000 H,1:1827 HTA,1:5950 R
STATED PRINT RUN 715 SER.#'d SETS
BB Barry Bonds Jsy 20.00 50.00

2006 Topps Update Box Bottoms

HTA1 Shawn Green .20 .50
HTA2 Austin Kearns .20 .50
HTA3 Brandon Phillips .20 .50
HTA4 Jered Weaver .50 1.25
HTA5 Carlos Lee .20 .50
HTA6 Bobby Abreu .20 .50
HTA7 Shea Hillenbrand .20 .50
HTA8 Cole Hamels .75 2.00
HTA9 Greg Maddux .75 2.00
HTA10 B.J. Upton .20 .50
HTA11 Aubrey Huff .20 .50
HTA12 Stephen Drew .50 1.25
HTA13 Sean Casey .20 .50
HTA14 Jeff Conine .20 .50
HTA15 Johan Santana .50 1.25
Francisco Liriano
HTA16 Melky Cabrera .30 .75

2006 Topps Update Derby Digs Jerseys

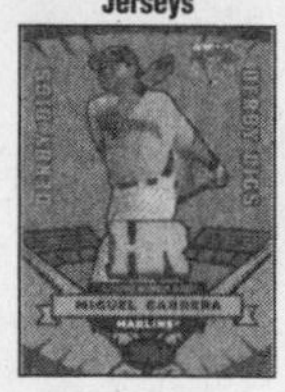

ODDS 1:4200 H,1:1631 HTA, 1:5700 R
NO PRICING DUE TO SCARCITY

2006 Topps Update Midsummer Covers Baseball Relics

STATED ODDS 1:7750 HOBBY
STATED PRINT RUN 10 SERIAL #'d SETS
NO PRICING DUE TO SCARCITY

2006 Topps Update Rookie Debut

COMPLETE SET (45) 15.00 40.00
STATED ODDS 1:4 HOB, 1:4 RET
RD1 Joel Zumaya 1.00 2.50
RD2 Ian Kinsler 1.25 3.00
RD3 Kenji Johjima 1.00 2.50
RD4 Josh Barfield .40 1.00
RD5 Nick Markakis 1.00 2.50
RD6 Dan Uggla 1.00 2.50
RD7 Eric Reed .40 1.00
RD8 Carlos Martinez .40 1.00
RD9 Angel Pagan .40 1.00
RD10 Jason Childers .40 1.00
RD11 Ruddy Lugo .40 1.00
RD12 James Loney .60 1.50
RD13 Fernando Nieve .40 1.00
RD14 Reggie Abercrombie .40 1.00
RD15 Boone Logan .40 1.00
RD16 Brian Bannister .40 1.00
RD17 Ricky Nolasco .40 1.00
RD18 Willie Eyre .40 1.00
RD19 Fabio Castro .40 1.00
RD20 Jordan Tata .40 1.00
RD21 Taylor Buchholz .40 1.00
RD22 Sean Marshall .60 1.50
RD23 John Rheinecker .40 1.00
RD24 Casey Janssen .40 1.00
RD25 Russ Martin .60 1.50
RD26 Yusmeiro Petit .40 1.00
RD27 Kendry Morales 1.00 2.50
RD28 Alay Soler .40 1.00
RD29 Jered Weaver 1.00 2.50
RD30 Matt Kemp 2.00 5.00
RD31 Enrique Gonzalez .40 1.00
RD32 Lastings Milledge .40 1.00
RD33 Jamie Shields 1.25 3.00
RD34 David Pauley .40 1.00
RD35 Zach Jackson .40 1.00
RD36 Zach Minor .40 1.00
RD37 Jon Lester 1.50 4.00
RD38 Chad Billingsley .60 1.50
RD39 Scott Thorman .40 1.00
RD40 Anibal Sanchez .40 1.00
RD41 Mike Thompson .40 1.00
RD42 T.J. Beam .40 1.00
RD43 Stephen Drew 1.00 2.50
RD44 Joe Saunders .40 1.00
RD45 Carlos Quentin .60 1.50

2006 Topps Update Rookie Debut Autographs

A ODDS 1:10,600 H,1:4416 HTA,1:15,500 R
B ODDS 1:5600 H, 1:2163 HTA,1:7500 R
C ODDS 1:2200 H, 1:815 HTA,1:2650 R
D ODDS 1:1180 H, 1:415 HTA,1:1500 R
NO GROUP A PRICING DUE TO SCARCITY
AL Adam Loewen B 20.00 50.00
BL Bobby Livingston C 6.00 15.00
EF Emiliano Fruto C 6.00 15.00
FC Fausto Carmona C 6.00 15.00
IK Ian Kinsler A
JL Jon Lester D 15.00 40.00
JS Jeremy Sowers B 6.00 15.00
MA Matt Albers A
MN Mike Napoli D 15.00 40.00
MP Martin Prado D 10.00 25.00
RA Reggie Abercrombie A
RN Ricky Nolasco D 6.00 15.00
ST Scott Thorman C 6.00 15.00
YP Yusmeiro Petit D 6.00 15.00

2006 Topps Update Signature Moves

A ODDS 1:300,000 H,1:53,000 HTA,1:57,000 R
B ODDS 1:100,000 H,1:30,000 HTA,1:57,000 R
C-D ODDS 1:17,500 H,1:6624 HTA,1:22,000 R
E ODDS 1:9800 H,1:2600 HTA,1:10,500 R
NO PRICING DUE TO SCARCITY

2006 Topps Update Touch 'Em All Base Relics

STATED ODDS 1:610 HOBBY,1:90 HTA
AP Albert Pujols 12.50 30.00
AR Alex Rodriguez 10.00 25.00
CB Carlos Beltran 5.00 12.00
DO David Ortiz 8.00 20.00
DW David Wright 10.00 25.00
IS Ichiro Suzuki 10.00 25.00
JM Joe Mauer 6.00 15.00
MT Miguel Tejada 5.00 12.00
MY Michael Young 5.00 12.00
RH Ryan Howard 10.00 25.00

2006 Topps All-Star FanFest

1 Ichiro Suzuki 1.50 4.00
2 Roberto Clemente 3.00 8.00
3 Albert Pujols 2.50 6.00
4 Mickey Mantle 3.00 8.00
5 Alex Rodriguez 1.50 4.00

2007 Topps Pre-Production

This three-card set was released to hobby dealers and media in January, 2007 to preview the upcoming 2007 Topps Series I product.

COMPLETE SET (3) 4.00 10.00
1 David Ortiz .75 2.00
2 David Wright 2.00 5.00
3 Ryan Howard 2.00 5.00

2007 Topps

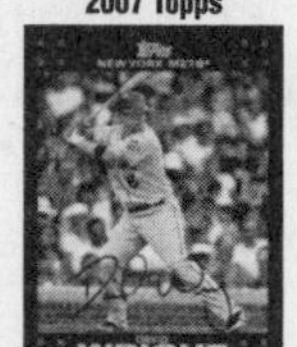

This 661-card set was released over two series. The first series was issued in February, 2007 while the second series

COMP.HOBBY SET (661) 40.00 80.00
COMP.HOLIDAY SET (661) 40.00 80.00
COMP.CARDINALS SET (661) 40.00 80.00
COMP.CUBS SET (661) 40.00 80.00
COMP.DODGERS SET (661) 40.00 80.00
COMP.RED SOX SET (661) 40.00 80.00
COMP.YANKEES SET (661) 40.00 80.00
COMP.SET w/o VAR. (661) 40.00 80.00
COMPLETE SERIES 1 (330) 15.00 40.00
COMP.SERIES 1 w/o #40 (329) 10.00 25.00
COMPLETE SERIES 2 (331) 25.00 50.00
COMMON CARD (1-330) .07 .20
COMMON RC .20 .50
SER.1 VAR. ODDS 1:3700 WAL-MART
SER.2 VAR.ODDS 1:30 HOBBY
NO SER.1 VAR.PRICING DUE TO SCARTIY
OVERALL PLATE SER.1 ODDS 1:98 HTA
OVERALL PLATE SER.2 ODDS 1:139 HTA
PLATE PRINT RUN 1 SET PER COLOR
BLACK-CYAN-MAGENTA-YELLOW ISSUED
NO PLATE PRICING DUE TO SCARCITY
1 John Lackey .07 .20
2 Nick Swisher .20 .50
3 Brad Lidge .07 .20
4 Bengie Molina .07 .20
5 Bobby Abreu .07 .20
6 Edgar Renteria .07 .20
7 Mickey Mantle .60 1.50
8 Preston Wilson .07 .20
9 Ryan Dempster .07 .20
10 C.C. Sabathia .12 .30
11 Julio Lugo .07 .20
12 J.D. Drew .07 .20
13 Miguel Batista .07 .20
14 Eliezer Alfonzo .07 .20
15a Andrew Miller RC .50 1.25
15b Andrew Miller RC .50 1.25
Posed
16 Jason Varitek .20 .50
17 Saul Rivera .07 .20
18 Orlando Hernandez .07 .20
19 Alfredo Amezaga .07 .20
20a Delmon Young (RC) .30 .75
Face Right
20b Delmon Young (RC) .30 .75
Face Left
21 Chris Britton .07 .20
22 Corey Patterson .07 .20
23 Josh Bard .07 .20
24 Tom Gordon .07 .20
25 Gary Matthews .07 .20
26 Jason Jennings .07 .20
27 Joey Gathright .07 .20
28 Brandon Inge .07 .20
29 Pat Neshek .30 .75
30 Bronson Arroyo .07 .20
31 Jay Payton .07 .20
32 Andy Pettitte .12 .30
33 Ervin Santana .07 .20
Fascimile signature is Johan Santana
34 Paul Konerko .12 .30
35 Joel Zumaya .12 .30
36 Gregg Zaun .07 .20
37 Tony Gwynn Jr. .07 .20
38 Adam LaRoche .07 .20
39 Jim Edmonds .12 .30
40a Derek Jeter 5.00 12.00
Mickey Mantle and George W.Bush in background
40b Derek Jeter .50 1.25
41 Rich Hill .07 .20
42 Livan Hernandez .07 .20
43 Aubrey Huff .07 .20
44 Todd Greene .07 .20
45 Andre Ethier .12 .30
46 Jeremy Sowers .07 .20
47 Ben Broussard .07 .20
48 Darren Oliver .07 .20
49 Nook Logan .07 .20
50 Miguel Cabrera .20 .50
51 Carlos Lee .07 .20
52 Jose Castillo .07 .20
53 Mike Piazza .20 .50
54 Daniel Cabrera .07 .20
55 Cole Hamels .20 .50
56 Mark Loretta .07 .20
57 Brian Fuentes .07 .20
58 Todd Coffey .07 .20
59 Brent Clevlen .07 .20
60 John Smoltz .20 .50
61 Jason Grilli .07 .20
62 Dan Wheeler .07 .20
63 Scott Proctor .07 .20
64 Bobby Kielty .07 .20
65 Dan Uggla .12 .30
66 Lyle Overbay .07 .20
67 Geoff Jenkins .07 .20
68 Michael Barrett .07 .20
69 Casey Fossum .07 .20
70 Ivan Rodriguez .12 .30
71 Jose Lopez .07 .20
72 Jake Westbrook .07 .20
73 Moises Alou .07 .20
74 Jose Valverde .07 .20
75 Jered Weaver .12 .30
76 Lastings Milledge .12 .30
77 Austin Kearns .07 .20
78 Adam Loewen .07 .20
79 Josh Barfield .07 .20
80 Johan Santana .20 .50
81 Ian Kinsler .12 .30
82 Ian Snell .07 .20
83 Mike Lowell .07 .20
84 Elizardo Ramirez .07 .20
85 Scott Rolen .12 .30
86 Shannon Stewart .07 .20
87 Alexis Gomez .07 .20
88 Jimmy Gobble .07 .20
89 Jamey Carroll .07 .20
90 Chipper Jones .20 .50
91 Carlos Silva .07 .20
92 Joe Crede .07 .20
93 Mike Napoli .12 .30
94 Willy Taveras .07 .20
95 Rafael Furcal .07 .20
96 Phil Nevin .07 .20
97 Dave Bush .07 .20
98 Marcus Giles .07 .20
99 Joe Blanton .07 .20
100 Dontrelle Willis .07 .20
101 Scott Kazmir .12 .30
102 Jeff Kent .07 .20
103 Pedro Feliz .07 .20
104 Johnny Estrada .07 .20
105 Travis Hafner .07 .20
106 Ryan Garko .07 .20
107 Rafael Soriano .07 .20
108 Wes Helms .07 .20
109 Billy Wagner .07 .20
110 Aaron Rowand .07 .20
111 Felipe Lopez .07 .20
112 Jeff Conine .07 .20
113 Nick Markakis .20 .50
114 John Koronka .07 .20
115 B.J. Ryan .07 .20
116 Tim Wakefield .07 .20
117 David Ross .07 .20
118 Emil Brown .07 .20
119 Michael Cuddyer .07 .20
120 Jason Giambi .07 .20
121 Alex Cintron .07 .20
122 Luke Scott .07 .20
123 Chone Figgins .07 .20
124 Huston Street .07 .20
125 Carlos Delgado .07 .20
126 Daryle Ward .07 .20
127 Chris Duncan .07 .20
128 Damian Miller .07 .20
129 Aramis Ramirez .07 .20
130 Albert Pujols .50 1.25
131 Chris Snyder .07 .20
132 Ray Durham .07 .20
133 Gary Sheffield .07 .20
134 Mike Jacobs .07 .20
135a Troy Tulowitzki (RC) 1.25 3.00
135b Troy Tulowitzki (RC) 1.25 3.00
Throw
136 Jon Rauch .07 .20
137 Jay Gibbons .07 .20
138 Adrian Gonzalez .12 .30
139 Prince Fielder .12 .30
140 Freddy Sanchez .07 .20
141 Rich Aurilia .07 .20
142 Trot Nixon .07 .20
143 Vicente Padilla .07 .20
144 Jack Wilson .07 .20
145 Jake Peavy .07 .20
146 Luke Hudson .07 .20
147 Javier Vazquez .07 .20
148 Scott Podsednik .07 .20
149 Magglio Ordonez .12 .30
Ivan Rodriguez CC
150 Todd Helton .12 .30
151 Kendry Morales .12 .30
152 Adam Everett .07 .20
153 Bob Wickman .07 .20
154 Bill Hall .07 .20
155 Jeremy Bonderman .07 .20
156 Ryan Theriot .07 .20
157 Rocco Baldelli .07 .20
158 Noah Lowry .07 .20
159 Jason Michaels .07 .20
160 Justin Verlander .25 .60
161 Eduardo Perez .07 .20
162 Chris Ray .07 .20
163 Dave Roberts .07 .20
164 Zach Duke .07 .20
165 Mark Buehrle .12 .30
166 Hank Blalock .07 .20
167 Royce Clayton .07 .20
168 Mark Teahen .07 .20
169 Todd Jones .07 .20
170 Chien-Ming Wang .12 .30
171 Nick Punto .07 .20
172 Morgan Ensberg .07 .20
173 Rob Mackowiak .07 .20
174 Frank Catalanotto .07 .20
175 Matt Murton .07 .20
176 Alfonso Soriano .12 .30
Carlos Beltran CC
177 Francisco Cordero .07 .20
178 Jason Marquis .07 .20
179 Joe Nathan .07 .20
180 Roy Halladay UER .20 .50
Bio is Joe Nathan's
181 Melvin Mora .07 .20
182 Ramon Ortiz .07 .20
183 Jose Valentin .07 .20
184 Gil Meche .07 .20
185 B.J. Upton .07 .20
186 Grady Sizemore .12 .30
187 Matt Cain .12 .30
188 Eric Byrnes .07 .20
189 Carl Crawford .12 .30
190 J.J. Putz .07 .20
191 Cla Meredith .07 .20
192 Matt Capps .07 .20
193 Rod Barajas .07 .20
194 Edwin Encarnacion .07 .20
195 James Loney .12 .30
196 Johnny Damon .12 .30
197 Freddy Garcia .07 .20
198 Mike Redmond .07 .20
199 Ryan Shealy .07 .20
200 Carlos Beltran .07 .20
201 Chuck James .07 .20
202 Mark Ellis .07 .20
203 Brad Ausmus .07 .20
204 Juan Rivera .07 .20
205 Cory Sullivan .07 .20
206 Ben Sheets .07 .20
207 Mark Mulder .07 .20
208 Carlos Quentin .07 .20
209 Jonathan Broxton .07 .20
210 Kazuo Matsui .07 .20
211 Armando Benitez .07 .20
212 Richie Sexson .07 .20
213 Josh Johnson .20 .50
214 Brian Schneider .07 .20
215 Craig Monroe .07 .20
216 Chris Duffy .07 .20
217 Chris Coste .07 .20
218 Clay Hensley .07 .20
219 Chris Gomez .07 .20
220 Hideki Matsui .20 .50
221 Robinson Tejada UER .07 .20
Tejeda is misspelled on front
222 Scott Hatteberg .07 .20
223 Jeff Francis .07 .20
224 Matt Thornton .07 .20
225 Robinson Cano .20 .50
226 Chicago White Sox .07 .20
227 Oakland Athletics .07 .20
228 St. Louis Cardinals .07 .20
229 New York Mets .07 .20
230 Barry Zito .07 .20
231 Baltimore Orioles .07 .20
232 Seattle Mariners .07 .20
233 Houston Astros .07 .20
234 Pittsburgh Pirates .07 .20
235 Reed Johnson .07 .20
236 Boston Red Sox .20 .50
237 Cincinnati Reds .07 .20
238 Philadelphia Phillies .07 .20
239 New York Yankees .20 .50
240 Chris Carpenter .07 .20
241 Atlanta Braves .07 .20
242 San Francisco Giants .07 .20
243 Joe Torre MG .12 .30
244 Tampa Bay Devil Rays .07 .20
245 Chad Tracy .07 .20
246 Clint Hurdle MG .07 .20
247 Mike Scioscia MG UER .07 .20
Incorrect Career Stats
248 Ron Gardenhire MG UER .07 .20
Incorrect Career Stats
249 Tony LaRussa MG UER .12 .30
Stats in header and in text do not agree
250 Anibal Sanchez .07 .20
251 Charlie Manuel MG .07 .20
252 John Gibbons MG .07 .20
253 Jim Tracy MG .07 .20
254 Jerry Narron MG .07 .20
255 Brad Penny .07 .20
256 Bobby Cox MG .07 .20
257 Bob Melvin MG .07 .20
258 Mike Hargrove MG UER .07 .20
Stats are those of Tony LaRussa
259 Phil Garner MG UER .07 .20
Stats are those of Tony LaRussa
260 David Wright .30 .75
261 Vinny Rottino (RC) .20 .50
262 Ryan Braun RC .20 .50
263 Kevin Kouzmanoff (RC) .20 .50
264 David Murphy (RC) .20 .50
265 Jimmy Rollins .12 .30
266 Joe Maddon MG .12 .30
267 Grady Little MG .07 .20
268 Ryan Sweeney (RC) .20 .50
269 Fred Lewis (RC) .30 .75
270 Alfonso Soriano .12 .30
271a Delwyn Young (RC) .20 .50
271b Delwyn Young (RC) .20 .50
Swing
272 Jeff Salazar (RC) .20 .50
273 Miguel Montero (RC) .20 .50
274 Shawn Riggans (RC) .20 .50
275 Greg Maddux .30 .75
276 Brian Stokes (RC) .20 .50
277 Philip Humber (RC) .20 .50
278 Scott Moore (RC) .20 .50
279 Adam Lind (RC) .20 .50
280 Curt Schilling .12 .30
281 Chris Narveson (RC) .20 .50
282 Oswaldo Navarro RC .20 .50
283 Drew Anderson RC .20 .50
284 Jerry Owens (RC) .20 .50
285 Stephen Drew .07 .20
286 Joaquin Arias (RC) .20 .50
287 Jose Garcia RC .20 .50
288 Shane Youman RC .20 .50
289 Brian Burres (RC) UER .20 .50
Height and Weight amounts are incorrect
290 Matt Holliday .20 .50
291 Ryan Feierabend (RC) .20 .50
292a Josh Fields (RC) .20 .50
292b Josh Fields (RC) .20 .50
Running
293 Glen Perkins (RC) .20 .50
294 Mike Rabelo RC .20 .50
295 Jorge Posada .12 .30
296 Ubaldo Jimenez (RC) 1.25 3.00
297 Brad Ausmus GG .07 .20
298 Eric Chavez GG .07 .20
299 Orlando Hudson GG .07 .20
300 Vladimir Guerrero .20 .50
301 Derek Jeter GG .50 1.25
302 Scott Rolen GG .12 .30
303 Mark Grudzielanek GG .07 .20
304 Kenny Rogers GG .07 .20
305 Frank Thomas .20 .50
306 Mike Cameron GG .07 .20
307 Torii Hunter GG .07 .20
308 Albert Pujols GG .50 1.25
309 Mark Teixeira GG .20 .50
310 Jonathan Papelbon .20 .50
311 Greg Maddux GG .30 .75
312 Carlos Beltran GG .07 .20
313 Ichiro Suzuki GG .30 .75
314 Andruw Jones GG .07 .20
315 Manny Ramirez .20 .50
316 Vernon Wells GG .07 .20
317 Omar Vizquel GG .12 .30
318 Ivan Rodriguez GG .12 .30
319 Brandon Webb CY .12 .30
320 Magglio Ordonez .12 .30
321 Johan Santana CY .20 .50
322 Ryan Howard MVP .30 .75
323 Justin Morneau MVP .20 .50
324 Hanley Ramirez ROY .20 .50
325 Joe Mauer .20 .50
326 Justin Verlander ROY .25 .60
327 Bobby Abreu .50 1.25
Derek Jeter CC UER
Abreu's career homer total is incorrect
328 Carlos Delgado .30 .75
David Wright CC
329 Yadier Molina .12 .30
Albert Pujols CC
330 Ryan Howard .30 .75
331 Kelly Johnson .07 .20
332 Chris Young .07 .20
333 Mark Kotsay .07 .20
334 A.J. Burnett .12 .30
335 Brian McCann .07 .20
336 Woody Williams .07 .20
337 Jason Isringhausen .07 .20
338 Juan Pierre .07 .20
339 Jonny Gomes .07 .20
340 Roger Clemens .25 .60
341 Akinori Iwamura RC .50 1.25
342 Bengie Molina .07 .20
343 Shin-Soo Choo .12 .30
344 Kenji Johjima .07 .20
345 Joe Borowski .07 .20
346 Shawn Green .07 .20
347 Chicago Cubs .07 .20
348 Rodrigo Lopez .07 .20
349 Brian Giles .07 .20
350 Chase Utley .20 .50
351 Mark DeRosa .07 .20
352 Carl Pavano .07 .20
353 Kyle Lohse .07 .20
354 Chris Iannetta .07 .20
355 Oliver Perez .07 .20
356 Curtis Granderson .12 .30
357 Sean Casey .07 .20
358 Jason Tyner .07 .20
359 Jon Garland .07 .20
360 David Ortiz .12 .30
361 Adam Kennedy .07 .20
362 Chris Burke .07 .20
363 Bobby Crosby .07 .20
364 Conor Jackson .07 .20
365 Tim Hudson .12 .30
366 Rickie Weeks .12 .30
367 Cristian Guzman .07 .20
368 Mark Prior .12 .30
369 Ben Zobrist .07 .20
370 Troy Glaus .07 .20
371 Kenny Lofton .07 .20
372 Shane Victorino .07 .20
373 Cliff Lee .12 .30
374 Adrian Beltre .07 .20
375 Miguel Olivo .07 .20
376 Endy Chavez .07 .20

377 Zack Segovia (RC) .20 .50
378 Ramon Hernandez .07 .20
379 Chris Young .07 .20
380 Jason Schmidt .07 .20
381 Ronny Paulino .07 .20
382 Kevin Millwood .07 .20
383 Jon Lester .20 .50
384 Alex Gonzalez .07 .20
385 Brad Hawpe .07 .20
386 Placido Polanco .07 .20
387 Nate Robertson .07 .20
388 Torii Hunter .07 .20
389 Gavin Floyd .07 .20
390 Roy Oswalt .12 .30
391 Kelvim Escobar .07 .20
392 Craig Wilson .07 .20
393 Milton Bradley .07 .20
394 Aaron Hill .07 .20
395 Matt Diaz .07 .20
396 Chris Capuano .07 .20
397 Juan Encarnacion .07 .20
398 Jacque Jones .07 .20
399 James Shields .07 .20
400 Ichiro Suzuki .30 .75
401 Matt Kemp .12 .30
402 Matt Morris .07 .20
403 Casey Blake .07 .20
404 Corey Hart .07 .20
405 Josh Willingham .07 .20
406 Ryan Madson .07 .20
407 Nick Johnson .07 .20
408 Kevin Millar .07 .20
409 Khalil Greene .07 .20
410 Tom Glavine .12 .30
411a Jason Bay .12 .30
411b Jason Bay No Sig 2.00 5.00
412 Gerald Laird .07 .20
413 Coco Crisp .07 .20
414 Brandon Phillips .07 .20
415 Aaron Cook .07 .20
416 Mark Redman .07 .20
417 Mike Maroth .07 .20
418 Boof Bonser .07 .20
419 Jorge Cantu .07 .20
420 Jeff Weaver .07 .20
421 Melky Cabrera .07 .20
422 Francisco Rodriguez .12 .30
423 Mike Lamb .07 .20
424 Dan Haren .07 .20
425 Tomo Ohka .07 .20
426 Jeff Francoeur .20 .50
427 Randy Wolf .07 .20
428 So Taguchi .07 .20
429 Carlos Zambrano .12 .30
430 Justin Morneau .20 .50
431 Luis Gonzalez .07 .20
432 Takashi Saito .07 .20
433 Brandon Morrow RC 1.00 2.50
434 Victor Martinez .12 .30
435 Felix Hernandez .20 .50
436 Ricky Nolasco .07 .20
437 Paul LoDuca .07 .20
437b Paul LoDuca No Sig 2.00 5.00
438 Chad Cordero .07 .20
439 Miguel Tejada .12 .30
440 Mark Teixeira .20 .50
441 Pat Burrell .07 .20
442 Paul Maholm .07 .20
443 Mike Cameron .07 .20
444 Josh Beckett .12 .30
445 Pablo Ozuna .07 .20
446 Jaret Wright .07 .20
447 Angel Berroa .07 .20
448 Fernando Rodney .07 .20
449 Francisco Liriano .20 .50
450 Ken Griffey Jr. .30 .75
451 Bobby Jenks .07 .20
452 Mike Mussina .12 .30
453 Howie Kendrick .07 .20
454 Milwaukee Brewers .07 .20
455 Dan Johnson .07 .20
456 Ted Lilly .07 .20
457 Mike Hampton .07 .20
458 J.J. Hardy .07 .20
459 Jeff Suppan .07 .20
460 Jose Reyes .12 .30
461 Jae Seo .07 .20
462 Edgar Gonzalez .07 .20
463 Russell Martin .07 .20
464 Omar Vizquel .12 .30
465 Jhonny Peralta .07 .20
466 Raul Ibanez .12 .30
467 Hanley Ramirez .20 .50
468 Kerry Wood .07 .20
469 Ryan Church .07 .20
470 Gary Sheffield .07 .20
471 David Wells .07 .20
472 David Dellucci .07 .20
473 Xavier Nady .07 .20
474 Michael Young .12 .30
475 Kevin Youkilis .07 .20
476 Aaron Harang .07 .20
477 Brian Lawrence .07 .20
478 Octavio Dotel .07 .20
479 Chris Shelton .07 .20
480 Matt Garza .07 .20
481a Jim Thome .12 .30
481b Jim Thome No Sig 2.00 5.00
482 Jose Contreras .07 .20
483 Kris Benson .07 .20
484 John Maine .07 .20
485 Tadahito Iguchi .07 .20
486 Wandy Rodriguez .07 .20
487 Eric Chavez .07 .20
488 Vernon Wells .07 .20
489 Doug Davis .07 .20
490 Andruw Jones .07 .20
491 David Eckstein .07 .20
492 Michael Barrett .07 .20
493 Greg Norton .07 .20
494 Orlando Hudson .07 .20
495 Wilson Betemit .07 .20
496 Ryan Klesko .07 .20
497 Fausto Carmona .07 .20
498 Jarrod Washburn .07 .20
499 Aaron Boone .07 .20
500 Pedro Martinez .12 .30
501 Mike O'Connor .07 .20
502 Brian Roberts .07 .20
503 Jeff Cirillo .07 .20
504 Brett Myers .07 .20
505 Jose Bautista .12 .30
506 Akinori Otsuka .07 .20
507 Shea Hillenbrand .07 .20
508 Ryan Langerhans .07 .20
509 Josh Fogg .07 .20
510 Alex Rodriguez .30 .75
511 Kenny Rogers .07 .20
512 Jason Kubel .07 .20
513 Jermaine Dye .07 .20
514 Mark Grudzielanek .07 .20
515 Josh Phelps .07 .20
516 Bartolo Colon .07 .20
517 Craig Biggio .12 .30
518 Esteban Loaiza .07 .20
519 Alex Rios .12 .30
520 Adam Dunn .12 .30
521 Derrick Turnbow .07 .20
522 Anthony Reyes .07 .20
523 Derrek Lee .07 .20
524 Ty Wigginton .07 .20
525 Jeremy Hermida .07 .20
526 Derek Lowe .07 .20
527 Randy Winn .07 .20
528 Paul Byrd .07 .20
529 Chris Snelling .07 .20
530 Brandon Webb .12 .30
531 Julio Franco .07 .20
532 Jose Vidro .07 .20
533 Erik Bedard .07 .20
534 Terrmel Sledge .07 .20
535 Jon Lieber .07 .20
536 Tom Gorzelanny .07 .20
537 Kip Wells .07 .20
538 Wily Mo Pena .07 .20
539 Eric Milton .07 .20
540 Chad Billingsley .07 .20
541 David DeJesus .07 .20
542 Omar Infante .07 .20
543 Rondell White .07 .20
544 Juan Uribe .07 .20
545 Miguel Cairo .07 .20
546 Orlando Cabrera .07 .20
547 Byung-Hyun Kim .07 .20
548 Jason Kendall .07 .20
549 Horacio Ramirez .07 .20
550 Trevor Hoffman .12 .30
551 Ronnie Belliard .07 .20
552 Chris Woodward .07 .20
553 Ramon Martinez .07 .20
554 Elizardo Ramirez .07 .20
555 Andy Marte .07 .20
556 John Patterson .07 .20
557 Scott Olsen .07 .20
558 Steve Trachsel .07 .20
559 Doug Mientkiewicz .07 .20
560 Randy Johnson .20 .50
561 Chan Ho Park .12 .30
562 Jamie Moyer .07 .20
563 Mike Gonzalez .07 .20
564 Nelson Cruz .12 .30
565 Alex Cora .07 .20
566 Ryan Freel .07 .20
567 Chris Stewart RC .20 .50
568 Carlos Guillen .07 .20
569 Jason Bartlett .07 .20
570 Mariano Rivera .20 .50
571 Norris Hopper .07 .20
572 Alex Escobar .07 .20
573 Gustavo Chacin .07 .20
574 Brandon McCarthy .07 .20
575 Seth McClung .07 .20
576 Yuniesky Betancourt .07 .20
577 Jason LaRue .07 .20
578 Dustin Pedroia .25 .60
579 Taylor Tankersley .07 .20
580 Garret Anderson .07 .20
581 Mike Sweeney .07 .20
582 Scott Thorman .07 .20
583 Joe Inglett .07 .20
584 Clint Barmes .07 .20
585 Willie Bloomquist .07 .20
586 Willy Aybar .07 .20
587 Brian Bannister .07 .20
588 Jose Guillen .07 .20
UER Y.Betancourt Pictured
589 Brad Wilkerson .07 .20
590 Lance Berkman .12 .30
591 Toronto Blue Jays .07 .20
592 Florida Marlins .07 .20
593 Washington Nationals .07 .20
594 Los Angeles Angels .07 .20
595 Cleveland Indians .07 .20
596 Texas Rangers .07 .20
597 Detroit Tigers .07 .20
598 Arizona Diamondbacks .07 .20
599 Kansas City Royals .07 .20
600 Ryan Zimmerman .12 .30
601 Colorado Rockies .07 .20
602 Minnesota Twins .07 .20
603 Los Angeles Dodgers .07 .20
604 San Diego Padres .07 .20
605 Bruce Bochy MG .07 .20
606 Ron Washington MG .07 .20
607 Manny Acta MG .07 .20
608 Sam Perlozzo MG .07 .20
609 Terry Francona MG .12 .30
610 Jim Leyland MG .07 .20
611 Eric Wedge MG .07 .20
612 Ozzie Guillen MG .07 .20
613 Buddy Bell MG .07 .20
614 Bob Geren MG .07 .20
615 Lou Piniella MG .07 .20
616 Fredi Gonzalez MG .07 .20
617 Ned Yost MG .07 .20
618 Willie Randolph MG .07 .20
619 Bud Black MG .07 .20
620 Garrett Atkins .07 .20
621 Alexi Casilla RC .30 .75
622 Matt Chico (RC) .20 .50
623 Alejandro De Aza RC .30 .75
624 Jeremy Brown .07 .20
625 Josh Hamilton (RC) .75 2.00
626 Doug Slaten RC .20 .50
627 Andy Cannizaro RC .20 .50
628 Juan Salas (RC) .20 .50
629 Levale Speigner RC .20 .50
630a Daisuke Matsuzaka English RC .75 2.00
630b Daisuke Matsuzaka Japanese 1.50 4.00
630c Daisuke Matsuzaka No Sig 1.50 4.00
631 Elijah Dukes RC .30 .75
632 Kevin Cameron RC .20 .50
633 Juan Perez RC .20 .50
634a Alex Gordon RC .60 1.50
634b Alex Gordon No Sig 2.00 5.00
635 Juan Lara RC .20 .50
636 Mike Rabelo .20 .50
637 Justin Hampson (RC) .20 .50
638 Cesar Jimenez RC .20 .50
639 Joe Smith RC .20 .50
640 Kei Igawa RC .50 1.25
641 Hideki Okajima RC 1.00 2.50
642 Sean Henn (RC) .20 .50
643 Jay Marshall RC .20 .50
644 Jared Burton RC .20 .50
645 Angel Sanchez RC .20 .50
646 Devern Hansack RC .20 .50
647 Juan Morillo (RC) .20 .50
648 Hector Gimenez (RC) .20 .50
649 Brian Barden RC .20 .50
650 Alex Rodriguez .30 .75
Jason Giambi CC
651 Jason Michaels .07 .20
Travis Hafner CC
652 Josh Johnson .20 .50
Miguel Olivo CC
653 Sean Casey .07 .20
Placido Polanco CC
654 Ivan Rodriguez .12 .30
Fernando Rodney CC
655 Dan Uggla .20 .50
Hanley Ramirez CC
656 Carlos Beltran .12 .30
Jose Reyes CC
657 Alex Rodriguez .50 1.25
Derek Jeter CC
658 Aaron Rowand .12 .30
Jimmy Rollins CC
659 Angel Berroa .07 .20
Andres Blanco CC
660a Yadier Molina .12 .30
660b Yadier Molina No Sig 2.00 5.00
661 Barry Bonds 4.00 10.00

2007 Topps 1st Edition

*1st ED: 3X TO 8X BASIC
*1st ED RC: 1.25X TO 3X BASIC
SER.1 ODDS 1:36 HOBBY, 1:5 HTA
SER.2 ODDS 1:36 HOBBY, 1:5 HTA

2007 Topps Copper

COMMON CARD (1-660) 6.00 15.00
UNLISTED STARS 10.00 25.00
SER.1 ODDS 1:7 HTA
SER.2 ODDS 1:10 HTA
STATED PRINT RUN 56 SERIAL #'d SETS
7 Mickey Mantle 75.00 150.00
15 Andrew Miller 100.00 150.00
29 Pat Neshek 30.00 60.00
40 Derek Jeter 400.00 800.00
53 Mike Piazza 15.00 40.00
58 Todd Coffey 10.00 25.00
130 Albert Pujols 30.00 60.00
170 Chien-Ming Wang 30.00 60.00
236 Boston Red Sox CL 6.00 15.00
239 New York Yankees CL 10.00 25.00
260 David Wright 15.00 40.00
275 Greg Maddux 15.00 40.00
301 Derek Jeter GG 40.00 80.00
305 Frank Thomas 15.00 40.00
308 Albert Pujols GG 30.00 60.00
311 Greg Maddux GG 15.00 40.00
313 Ichiro Suzuki GG 15.00 40.00
322 Ryan Howard MVP 15.00 40.00
327 Bobby Abreu 20.00 50.00
Derek Jeter CC
328 Carlos Delgado 15.00 40.00
David Wright CC
329 Yadier Molina 10.00 25.00
Albert Pujols CC
330 Ryan Howard 15.00 40.00
340 Roger Clemens 20.00 50.00
341 Akinori Iwamura 15.00 40.00
360 David Ortiz 20.00 50.00
362 Chris Burke 10.00 25.00
400 Ichiro Suzuki 30.00 60.00
403 Casey Blake 15.00 40.00
413 Coco Crisp 10.00 25.00
444 Josh Beckett 10.00 25.00
450 Ken Griffey Jr. 30.00 60.00
460 Jose Reyes 10.00 25.00
475 Kevin Youkilis 10.00 25.00
510 Alex Rodriguez 20.00 50.00
625 Josh Hamilton 30.00 60.00
630 Daisuke Matsuzaka 100.00 150.00
634 Alex Gordon 15.00 40.00
641 Hideki Okajima 20.00 50.00
650 Alex Rodriguez 15.00 40.00
Jason Giambi CC
657 Alex Rodriguez 20.00 50.00
Derek Jeter CC

2007 Topps Gold

*GOLD: 6X TO 15X BASIC
*GOLD RC: 2.5X TO 6X BASIC RC
SER.1 ODDS 1:11 H, 1:3 HTA, 1:24 K-MART
SER.1 ODDS 1:6 RACK, 1:11 TARGET
SER.1 ODDS 1:24 WAL-MART
SER.2 ODDS 1:11 HOBBY, 1:2 HTA
STATED PRINT RUN 2007 SER.#'d SETS
40 Derek Jeter 125.00 250.00

2007 Topps Platinum

SER.1 ODDS 1:26,000 H, 1:3200 HTA
SER.1 ODDS 1:45000 K-MART,1:8500 RACK
SER.1 ODDS 1:26000 TAR,1:45000 WAL-MART
SER.2 ODDS 1:24,000 HOBBY , 1:2900 HTA
STATED PRINT RUN 1 SERIAL #'d SET
NO PRICING DUE TO SCARCITY

2007 Topps Red Back

COMP.SERIES 1 (330) 40.00 80.00
COMP.SERIES 2 (330) 40.00 80.00
*RED: 1X TO 2.5X BASIC
*RED RC: .5X TO 1.2X BASIC RC
SER.1 ODDS 2:1 H, 10:1 HTA, 3:1 RACK
40 Derek Jeter 15.00 40.00

2007 Topps 1952 Mantle Reprint Relic

SER.1 ODDS 1:158,700 H, 1:8721 HTA
SER.1 ODDS 1:602,600 K-MART
SER.1 ODDS 1:127,100 TARGET
SER 1 ODDS 1:602,600 WAL-MART
STATED PRINT RUN 52 SERIAL #'d SETS
NO PRICING DUE TO SCARCITY
52MM Mickey Mantle Bat 125.00 250.00

2007 Topps 1953 Mantle Reprint Relic

SER.2 ODDS 1:199,750 HOBBY, 1:10,500 HTA
STATED PRINT RUN 53 SER.#'d SETS
NO PRICING DUE TO SCARCITY
53MM Mickey Mantle

2007 Topps Alex Rodriguez Road to 500

COMPLETE SET (126-175)
COMMON CARD (1-75/101-425) 1.25 3.00
COMMON CARD (76-100) 15.00 40.00
COMMON CARD (401-425) 6.00 15.00
COMMON CARD (451-475) 4.00 10.00
COMMON CARD (476-499) 4.00 10.00
SER.1 ODDS 1:36 H, 1:5 HTA, 1:36 K-MART
SER.1 ODDS 1:36 RACK, 1:36 TARGET
SER.1 ODDS 1:36 WAL-MART
FINEST ODDS TWO PER AROD BOX TOPPER
HERITAGE ODDS 1:24 HOBBY/RETAIL
OPENING DAY ODDS 1:36 H, 1:36 R
MOMENTS ODDS TWO PER BOX TOPPER
CO-SIG ODDS TWO PER AROD BOX TOPPER
BOWMAN ODDS 1:6 HOBBY, 1:2 HTA
SER.2 ODDS 1:36 HOBBY, 1:5 HTA
T.CHROME ODDS TWO PER BOX TOPPER
ALLEN AND GINTER ODDS 1:24 H, 1:24 R
BOW.CHR. ODDS 1:9 HOBBY
TURKEY RED ODDS 1:24 HOBBY/RETAIL
BOW.HER ODDS TWO PER BOX TOPPER
UPDATE ODDS 1:36 H, 1:5 HTA, 1:36 R
TOPPS 52 ODDS 1:20 H, 1:20 R
CARDS 1-25 ISSUED IN SERIES 1
CARDS 26-50 ISSUED IN FINEST
CARDS 51-75 ISSUED IN HERITAGE
CARDS 76-100 ISSUED IN OPENING DAY
CARDS 101-125 ISSUED IN MOMENTS
CARDS 126-175 ISSUED IN BOWMAN
CARDS 176-200 ISSUED IN CO-SIGNERS
CARDS 201-225 ISSUED IN SERIES 2
CARDS 226-250 ISSUED IN TOP.CHROME
CARDS 251-275 ISSUED IN ALLEN GINTER
CARDS 276-300 ISSUED IN BOW.CHR.
CARDS 301-325 ISSUSED IN TUR.RED
CARDS 326-350 ISSUED IN 08 FINEST
CARDS 351-375 ISSUED IN BOW.HER.
CARDS 376-400 ISSUED IN UPDATE
CARDS 401-425 ISSUED IN BOW.BEST
CARDS 426-450 ISSUED IN BOW.DRAFT
CARDS 451-475 ISSUED IN BOW.STERL.
CARDS 476-500 ISSUED IN TOPPS 52
ARHR500 Alex Rodriguez 500HR 10.00 25.00

2007 Topps Alex Rodriguez Road to 500 Autographs

SER.1 ODDS 1:1,111,000 H, 1:122,100 HTA
SER.1 ODDS 1:1,000,000 K-MART
SER.1 ODDS 1:127,100 TARGET
SER.1 ODDS 1,000,000 WAL-MART
FINEST ODDS 1:788 BOXES
HERITAGE ODDS 1:100,500 HOBBY/RETAIL
OPEN.DAY ODDS 1:171,146 H, 1:256,960 R
MOMENTS ODDS 1:803 BOX TOPPERS
BOWMAN ODDS 34,931 H, 1:11,000 HTA
CO-SIG ODDS 1:1687 BOX TOPPERS
SER.2 ODDS 1:750,000 HOBBY
SER.2 ODDS 1:173,160 HTA
ALLEN GINTER ODDS 1:64,496 HOBBY
CHROME ODDS 1:1866 BOX TOPPERS
ALLEN GINTER ODDS 1:122,200 RETAIL
BOW.CHR. ODDS 1:57,500 HOBBY
TURKEY RED ODDS 1:50,000 HOBBY
TURKEY RED ODDS 1:50,000 RETAIL
BOW.HER ODDS 1:773 HOBBY BOXES
UPD.ODDS 1:500,000 H, 1:33,500 HTA
UPD.ODDS 1:11,000 RETAIL
TOPPS 52 ODDS 1:16,000 H, 1:77,000 R
CARDS 1-25 ISSUED IN SERIES 1
CARDS 26-50 ISSUED IN FINEST
CARDS 51-75 ISSUED IN HERITAGE
CARDS 76-100 ISSUED IN OPENING DAY
CARDS 101-125 ISSUED IN MOMENTS
CARDS 126-175 ISSUED IN BOWMAN
CARDS 176-200 ISSUED IN CO-SIGNERS
CARDS 201-225 ISSUED IN SER.2
CARDS 226-250 ISSUED IN TOPPS CHROME
CARDS 251-275 ISSUED IN ALLEN GINTER
CARDS 276-300 ISSUED IN BOWMAN CHROME
CARDS 301-325 ISSUED IN TURKEY RED
CARDS 326-250 ISSUED IN 08 FINEST
CARDS 351-375 ISSUED IN BOW.HERITAGE
CARDS 376-400 ISSUED IN UPDATE
CARDS 401-425 ISSUED IN BOW.BEST
CARDS 426-450 ISSUED IN BOW.DRAFT
CARDS 451-475 ISSUED IN BOW.STERL.
CARDS 476-500 ISSUED IN TOPPS 52
STATED PRINT RUN 1 SER.#'d SET
NO PRICING DUE TO SCARCITY

2007 Topps All Stars

COMPLETE SET (12) 6.00 15.00
SER.1 ODDS ONE PER RACK PACK
AS1 Alfonso Soriano .60 1.50
AS2 Paul Konerko .60 1.50
AS3 Carlos Beltran .40 1.00
AS4 Troy Glaus .40 1.00
AS5 Jason Bay .60 1.50
AS6 Vladimir Guerrero 1.00 2.50
AS7 Chase Utley 1.00 2.50
AS8 Michael Young .60 1.50
AS9 David Wright 1.50 4.00
AS10 Gary Matthews .40 1.00
AS11 Brad Penny .40 1.00
AS12 Roy Halladay UER 1.00 2.50
Header line for stats is in incorrect order

2007 Topps All Star Rookies

COMPLETE SET (10) 6.00 15.00
SER.1 ODDS ONE PER RACK PACK
ASR1 Prince Fielder .60 1.50
ASR2 Dan Uggla .60 1.50
ASR3 Ryan Zimmerman .60 1.50
ASR4 Hanley Ramirez 1.00 2.50
ASR5 Melky Cabrera .40 1.00
ASR6 Andre Ethier .60 1.50
ASR7 Nick Markakis 1.00 2.50
ASR8 Justin Verlander 1.25 3.00
ASR9 Francisco Liriano 1.00 2.50
ASR10 Russell Martin .40 1.00

2007 Topps DiMaggio Streak

COMPLETE SET (56) 20.00 50.00
COMMON CARD .60 1.50
SER.2 ODDS 1:9 HOBBY

2007 Topps DiMaggio Streak Before the Streak

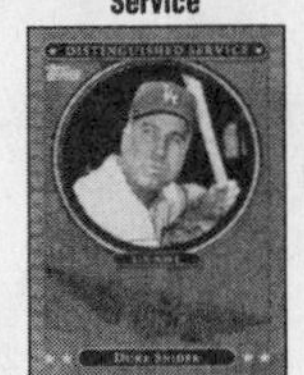

COMPLETE SET (61) 20.00 50.00
COMMON CARD .60 1.50
SER.2 ODDS 1:9 HOBBY

2007 Topps Distinguished Service

COMPLETE SET (30) 10.00 25.00
COMP.SERIES 1 (1-20) 6.00 15.00
COMP.SERIES 2 (21-30) 5.00 12.00
SER.1 ODDS 1:12 H, 1:12 HTA, 1:12 K-MART
SER.1 ODDS 1:12 RACK, 1:12 WAL-MART
SER.2 ODDS 1:12 HOBBY, 1:2 HTA
DS1 Duke Snider .60 1.50
DS2 Yogi Berra 1.00 2.50
DS3 Bob Feller .40 1.00
DS4 Bobby Doerr .40 1.00
DS5 Monte Irvin .40 1.00
DS6 Dwight D. Eisenhower .40 1.00
DS7 George Marshall .40 1.00
DS8 Franklin D. Roosevelt .40 1.00
DS9 Harry Truman .40 1.00
DS10 Douglas Macarthur .40 1.00
DS11 Ralph Kiner .60 1.50
DS12 Hank Sauer .40 1.00
DS13 Elmer Valo .40 1.00
DS14 Sibby Sisti .40 1.00
DS15 Hoyt Wilhelm .40 1.00
DS16 James Doolittle .40 1.00
DS17 Curtis Lemay .40 1.00
DS18 Omar Bradley .40 1.00
DS19 Chester Nimitz .40 1.00
DS20 Mark Clark .40 1.00
DS21 Joe DiMaggio 2.50 6.00
DS22 Warren Spahn .60 1.50
DS23 Stan Musial 1.50 4.00
DS24 Red Schoendienst .40 1.00
DS25 Ted Williams 2.50 6.00
DS26 Winston Churchill .40 1.00
DS27 Charles de Gaulle .40 1.00
DS28 George Bush .40 1.00
DS29 John F. Kennedy 1.00 2.50
DS30 Richard Bong .40 1.00

2007 Topps Distinguished Service Autographs

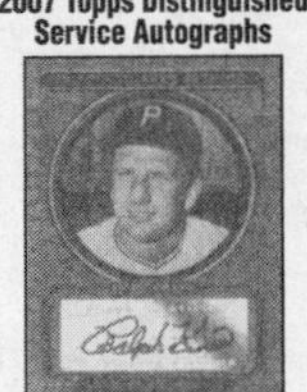

SER.1 ODDS 1:20,000 H, 1:830 HTA
SER.1 ODDS 1:41,225 K-MART,1:9200 RACK
SER.1 ODDS 1:20,000 TARGET
SER.1 ODDS 1:41,225 WAL-MART
BD Bobby Doerr 20.00 50.00
BF Bob Feller 30.00 60.00
DS Duke Snider 40.00 80.00
MI Monte Irvin 30.00 60.00
RK Ralph Kiner 40.00 80.00

2007 Topps Distinguished Service Cuts

SER.1 ODDS 1:505,600 H, 1:61,000 HTA
SER.1 ODDS 1:1,000,000 K-MART
SER.1 ODDS 1:138,000 TARGET
SER.1 ODDS 1:1,000,000 WAL-MART
SER.2 ODDS 1:165,000 HOBBY
SER.2 ODDS 1:57,720 HTA
STATED PRINT RUN 1 SER.#'d SET
NO PRICING DUE TO SCARCITY

2007 Topps Factory Set All Star Bonus

1 Alex Rodriguez 1.50 4.00
2 David Wright 1.50 4.00
3 David Ortiz .60 1.50
4 Ichiro Suzuki 1.50 4.00
5 Ryan Howard 1.50 4.00

2007 Topps Factory Set Cardinals Team Bonus

1 Skip Schumaker .40 1.00
2 Josh Hancock .40 1.00
3 Tyler Johnson .40 1.00
4 Randy Keisler .40 1.00
5 Randy Flores .40 1.00

2007 Topps Factory Set Cubs Team Bonus

1 Ronny Cedeno .40 1.00
2 Cesar Izturis .40 1.00
3 Neal Cotts .40 1.00
4 Wade Miller .40 1.00
5 Michael Wuertz .40 1.00

2007 Topps Factory Set Dodgers Team Bonus

1 Chin-Hui Tsao .60 1.50
2 Olmedo Saenz .40 1.00
3 Brett Tomko .40 1.00
4 Marlon Anderson .40 1.00
5 Brady Clark .40 1.00

2007 Topps Factory Set Red Sox Team Bonus

1 Daisuke Matsuzaka 1.50 4.00
2 Eric Hinske .40 1.00
3 Brendan Donnelly .40 1.00
4 Hideki Okajima 2.00 5.00
5 J.C. Romero .40 1.00

2007 Topps Factory Set Rookie Bonus

COMPLETE SET (20) 12.50 30.00
1 Felix Pie .40 1.00
2 Rick Vanden Hurk .40 1.00
3 Jeff Baker .40 1.00
4 Don Kelly .40 1.00
5 Matt Lindstrom .40 1.00
6 Chase Wright 1.00 2.50
7 Jon Coutlangus .40 1.00
8 Lee Gardner .40 1.00
9 Gustavo Molina .40 1.00
10 Kory Casto .40 1.00
11 Daisuke Matsuzaka 1.50 4.00
12 Tim Lincecum 6.00 15.00
13 Phil Hughes 2.00 5.00
14 Ryan Braun 2.00 5.00
15 Billy Butler .60 1.50
16 Jarrod Saltalamacchia .60 1.50
17 Hideki Okajima 2.00 5.00
18 Akinori Iwamura 1.00 2.50
19a Joba Chamberlain 2.00 5.00
19b Joba Chamberlain Houston Astros UER 2.00
5.00
20 Hunter Pence 2.00 5.00

2007 Topps Factory Set Yankees Team Bonus

1 Darrell Rasner .40 1.00
2 Phil Hughes 2.00 5.00
3 Wil Nieves .40 1.00
4 Kei Igawa 1.00 2.50
5 Kevin Thompson .40 1.00

2007 Topps Flashback Fridays

COMPLETE SET (25) 6.00 15.00
ISSUED VIA HTA SHOPS
FF1 Ryan Howard .75 2.00
FF2 Derek Jeter 1.25 3.00
FF3 Ken Griffey Jr .75 2.00
FF4 Miguel Tejada .30 .75
FF5 David Wright .75 2.00
FF6 Alfonso Soriano .30 .75
FF7 Matt Holliday .50 1.25
FF8 Jason Bay .30 .75
FF9 Ryan Zimmerman .30 .75
FF10 Alex Rodriguez .75 2.00
FF11 Jermaine Dye .20 .50
FF12 Miguel Cabrera .50 1.25
FF13 Johan Santana .50 1.25
FF14 Brandon Webb .30 .75
FF15 Ivan Rodriguez .30 .75
FF16 Ichiro Suzuki .75 2.00
FF17 Michael Young .30 .75
FF18 David Ortiz .30 .75
FF19 Roger Clemens .60 1.50
FF20 Frank Thomas .50 1.25
FF21 Trevor Hoffman .30 .75
FF22 Gary Matthews .20 .50
FF23 Rafael Furcal .20 .50
FF24 Chipper Jones .50 1.25
FF25 Albert Pujols 1.25 3.00

2007 Topps Generation Now

SER.1 ODDS 1:4 H, 1:4 K-MART, 1:4 RACK
SER.1 ODDS 1:4 TARGET, 1:4 WAL-MART
SER.2 ODDS 1:4 HOBBY
UPDATE ODDS 1:4 HOB, 1:4 RET
CARDS OF SAME PLAYER EQUALLY PRICED
GN1 Ryan Howard 1.25 3.00
GN51 Chase Utley .75 2.00
GN85 Chien-Ming Wang .50 1.25
GN103 Mike Napoli .50 1.25

GN117 Justin Morneau .75 2.00
GN147 David Wright 1.25 3.00
GN187 Jered Weaver .50 1.25
GN195 Andre Ethier .50 1.25
GN219 Ryan Zimmerman .50 1.25
GN279 Russell Martin .30 .75
GN283 Justin Verlander 1.00 2.50
GN299 Hanley Ramirez .75 2.00
GN350 Nick Markakis .75 2.00
GN360 Nick Swisher .75 2.00
GN397 Prince Fielder .50 1.25
GN425 Ian Kinsler .50 1.25
GN452 Kenji Johjima .75 2.00
GN481 Jonathan Papelbon .75 2.00
GN516 Jose Reyes .50 1.25
GN520 Curtis Granderson .50 1.25
GN551 Josh Barfield .30 .75

2007 Topps Generation Now Autographs

SER.1 ODDS 1:50,850 H, 1:2070 HTA
SER.1 ODDS 1:101,000 K-MART,1:18,396 RACK
SER.1 ODDS 1:50,850 TARGET
SER.1 ODDS 1:101,000 WAL-MART
SER.2 ODDS 1:94,000 HOBBY
SER.2 ODDS 1:1370 HTA
UPDATE ODDS 1:11,000 H, 1:5500 HTA
UPDATE ODDS 1:10,800 RETAIL
STATED PRINT RUN 1 SERIAL #'d SET
NO PRICING DUE TO SCARCITY

2007 Topps Generation Now Vintage

RANDOM INSERTS IN K-MART PACKS
1-18 ISSUED IN SER.1 PACKS
19-36 ISSUED IN SER.2 PACKS
37-54 ISSUED IN 07 UPDATE PACKS
GNV1 Ryan Howard .75 2.00
GNV2 Jeff Francoeur .50 1.25
GNV3 Nick Swisher .50 1.25
GNV4 Joey Gathright .20 .50
GNV5 Jhonny Peralta .20 .50
GNV6 Willy Taveras .20 .50
GNV7 Cory Sullivan .20 .50
GNV8 Chris Young .20 .50
GNV9 Jered Weaver .30 .75
GNV10 Jonathan Papelbon .50 1.25
GNV11 Russell Martin .20 .50
GNV12 Hanley Ramirez .50 1.25
GNV13 Justin Verlander .60 1.50
GNV14 Matt Cain .30 .75
GNV15 Kenji Johjima .50 1.25
GNV16 Angel Pagan .20 .50
GNV17 Brandon Phillips .20 .50
GNV18 Mark Teahen .20 .50
GNV19 Stephen Drew .20 .50
GNV20 Nick Markakis .50 1.25
GNV21 Anibal Sanchez .20 .50
GNV22 Jeremy Hermida .20 .50
GNV23 James Loney .30 .75
GNV24 Prince Fielder .30 .75
GNV25 Josh Barfield .20 .50
GNV26 Ian Kinsler .30 .75
GNV27 Ryan Zimmerman .30 .75
GNV28 David Wright .75 2.00
GNV29 Jose Reyes .30 .75
GNV30 Delmon Young .30 .75
GNV31 Zach Duke .20 .50
GNV32 Brian McCann .20 .50
GNV33 Bobby Jenks .20 .50
GNV34 Robinson Cano .50 1.25
GNV35 Jose Lopez .20 .50
GNV36 Daisuke Matsuzaka .75 2.00
GNV37 Alex Rios .30 .75
GNV38 Cole Hamels .50 1.25
GNV39 Matt Kemp .30 .75
GNV40 Dan Uggla .30 .75
GNV41 Scott Kazmir .30 .75
GNV42 J.J. Hardy .20 .50
GNV43 Hunter Pence 1.00 2.50
GNV44 Jason Bay .30 .75
GNV45 James Shields .20 .50
GNV46 Chase Utley .50 1.25
GNV47 Justin Morneau .50 1.25
GNV48 Chien-Ming Wang .30 .75
GNV49 Troy Tulowitzki 1.25 3.00
GNV50 Joe Mauer .50 1.25
GNV51 Brandon Webb .30 .75
GNV52 Matt Holliday .50 1.25
GNV53 Grady Sizemore .30 .75
GNV54 Homer Bailey .30 .75

2007 Topps Gibson Home Run History

COMPLETE SET (110) 60.00 120.00
COMMON GIBSON .60 1.50
SER.1 ODDS 1:9 H, 1:2 HTA, 1:9 K-MART
SER.1 ODDS 1:9 RACK, 1:9 TARGET
SER.1 ODDS 1:9 WAL-MART
CARDS 1-110 ISSUED IN SERIES 1 PACKS

2007 Topps Highlights Autographs

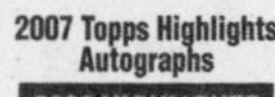

SER.1 A 1:50,842 H, 1:2105 HTA
SER.1 A 1:101,000 K-MART,1:18,396 RACK
SER.1 A 1:50,842 TARGET
SER.1 A 1:101,000 WAL-MART
SER.2 A 1:37,162 HOBBY, 1:523 HTA
SER.1 B 1:24,150 H, 1:1034 HTA
SER.1 B 1:51,800 K-MART, 1:12,264 RACK
SER.1 B 1:25,420 TARGET
SER.1 B 1:51,800 WAL-MART
SER.2 B 1:7330 HOBBY, 1:105 HTA
SER.1 C 1:13,000 H, 1:555 HTA
SER.1 C 1:27,300 K-MART, 1:7350 RACK
SER.1 C 1:13,600 TARGET
SER.1 C 1:27,300 WAL-MART
SER.2 C 1:7330 HOBBY, 1:105 HTA
SER.1 D 1:4916 H, 1:208 HTA
SER.1 D 1:10,250 K-MART, 1:2628 RACK
SER.1 D 1:5100 TARGET, 1:10,250 WAL-MART
SER.2 D 1:12,198 HOBBY, 1:174 HTA
SER.1 E 1:2460 H, 1:52 HTA, 1:5125 K-MART
SER.1 E 1:1314 RACK, 1:2550 TARGET
SER.1 E 1:5125 WAL-MART
SER.2 E 1:1410 HOBBY, 1:20 HTA
SER.1 F 1:1256 H, 1:52 HTA, 1:2564 K-MART
SER.1 F 1:657 RACK, 1:1277 TARGET
SER.1 F 1:2564 WAL-MART
SER.1 G 1:376 H, 1:16 HTA, 1:789 K-MART
SER.1 G 1:203 RACK,1:393 TARGET
SER.1 G 1:789 WAL-MART
GROUP A1 PRINT RUN B/WN 25-50 PER
GROUP B1 PRINT RUN 100 SETS
GROUP C1 PRINT RUN 250 SETS
A1-C1 ARE NOT SERIAL-NUMBERED
A1-C1 PRINT RUNS PROVIDED BY TOPPS
NO GROUP A1 PRICING DUE TO SCARCITY
EXCH * = PARTIAL EXCHANGE
EXCHANGE DEADLINE 02/28/09
AB Aaron Boone E2 4.00 10.00
AJ Andruw Jones B2 12.50 30.00
AM Andrew Miller G 12.50 30.00
AP Albert Pujols A2 150.00 200.00
AP Albert Pujols A/25 *
APA Angel Pagan G 4.00 10.00
AR Alex Rodriguez A/25 *
AR Anthony Reyes E2 6.00 15.00
AS Anibal Sanchez G 4.00 10.00
CG Curtis Granderson B2 15.00 40.00
CMS Curt Schilling A/25 *
CQ Carlos Quentin F 6.00 15.00
CW Chien-Ming Wang B/100 * 100.00 200.00
CW Craig Wilson E2 6.00 15.00
DO David Ortiz B/100 * 60.00 120.00
DO David Ortiz B2 12.50 30.00
DT Derrick Turnbow D2 6.00 15.00
DU Dan Uggla E2 8.00 20.00
DW David Wright D 30.00 60.00
DW David Wright C2 30.00 60.00
DWW Dontrelle Willis E 10.00 25.00
DWW Dontrelle Willis C2 6.00 15.00
DY Delmon Young E 10.00 25.00
EC Endy Chavez B2 10.00 25.00
EF Emiliano Fruto G 4.00 10.00
ES Ervin Santana E2 4.00 10.00
GS Gary Sheffield A/25 *
HR Hanley Ramirez G 8.00 20.00
JAS John Smoltz C/250 * 20.00 50.00
JD Johnny Damon A/25 *
JD Johnny Damon B2 30.00 60.00
JEM Justin Morneau E 10.00 25.00
JF Josh Fields F 6.00 15.00
JG Jon Garland E2 4.00 10.00
JH John Hattig G 4.00 10.00
JL James Loney G 6.00 15.00
JM John Maine F 10.00 25.00
JS Johan Santana C/250 * 40.00 80.00
JT Jim Thome A2 20.00 50.00
JV Justin Verlander B2 8.00 20.00
JZ Joel Zumaya E2 8.00 20.00
KE Kelvim Escobar C2 6.00 15.00
KM Kevin Mench D 4.00 10.00
KM Kendry Morales B2 4.00 10.00
LM Lastings Milledge E2 4.00 10.00
MC Miguel Cabrera C/250 * 12.50 30.00
MC Melky Cabrera E2 8.00 20.00
MH Matt Holliday G 6.00 15.00
MN Mike Napoli G 10.00 25.00
MP Mike Piazza A/50 * 90.00 150.00
MTC Matt Cain D2 6.00 15.00
PL Paul LoDuca B2 12.50 30.00
RC Robinson Cano E2 15.00 40.00
RH Ryan Howard B/100 * 75.00 150.00
RH Ryan Howard A2 40.00 80.00
RM Russell Martin C2 10.00 25.00
RZ Ryan Zimmerman E 15.00 40.00
RZ Ryan Zimmerman C2 12.50 30.00
SC Shawn Chacon E2 4.00 10.00
SP Scott Podsednik E2 4.00 10.00
SR Shawn Riggans E2 4.00 10.00
SSC Shin-Soo Choo B2 12.50 30.00
ST Steve Trachsel A2 10.00 25.00
TG Tom Glavine B2 30.00 60.00
TH Travis Hafner D 10.00 25.00
TT Troy Tulowitzki G 6.00 15.00
VG Vladimir Guerrero A/25 *
VG Vladimir Guerrero A2 40.00 80.00

2007 Topps Highlights Relics

SER.1 A 1:933 H, 1:33 HTA, 1:2160 K-MART
SER.1 A 1:1070 TARGET, 1:2160 WAL-MART
SER.2 A 1:2435 HOBBY, 1:138 HTA
SER.1 B 1:726 H, 1:19 HTA, 1:1270 K-MART
SER.1 B 1:631 TARGET, 1:1270 WAL-MART
SER.2 B 1:609 HOBBY, 1:35 HTA
SER.1 C 1:2468 H, 1:87 HTA, 1:5675 K-MART
SER.1 C 1:2825 TARGET, 1:5675 WAL-MART
SER.2 C 1:1420 HOBBY, 1:80 HTA
SER.2 D 1:533 HOBBY, 1:30 HTA
SER.2 E 1:1705 HOBBY, 1:96 HTA
AB Adrian Beltre B2 3.00 8.00
AER Alex Rodriguez C2 8.00 20.00
AJ Andruw Jones E2 3.00 8.00
ALR Anthony Reyes B2 4.00 10.00
AP Albert Pujols Pants B 8.00 20.00
AP Albert Pujols B2 8.00 20.00
AP2 Albert Pujols Jsy B 8.00 20.00
AR Alex Rodriguez Jsy B 8.00 20.00
AR Aramis Ramirez D2 3.00 8.00
AR2 Alex Rodriguez Bat A 8.00 20.00
AS Alfonso Soriano Bat A 4.00 10.00
AS Alfonso Soriano A2 4.00 10.00
BB Barry Bonds B2
BM Brian McCann Bat A 3.00 8.00
CB Craig Biggio Pants A 4.00 10.00
CD Carlos Delgado Bat B 3.00 8.00
CIB Carlos Beltran Jsy B 3.00 8.00
CJ Chipper Jones B2 3.00 8.00
CQ Carlos Quentin Bat A 3.00 8.00
CS Curt Schilling Jsy A 3.00 8.00
DE David Eckstein A2 5.00 12.00
DO David Ortiz Bat B 4.00 10.00
DO David Ortiz D2 4.00 10.00
DW Dontrelle Willis Jsy B 4.00 10.00
DW David Wright D2 5.00 12.00
DW2 Dontrelle Willis Pants B 4.00 10.00
DWW Dontrelle Willis E2 4.00 10.00
ER Edgar Renteria Bat B 3.00 8.00
FT Frank Thomas Bat B 4.00 10.00
GA Garrett Atkins A2 3.00 8.00
GS Gary Sheffield Bat B 3.00 8.00
GS Grady Sizemore A2 5.00 12.00
IR Ivan Rodriguez Bat C 3.00 8.00
IS Ichiro Suzuki Bat A 8.00 20.00
JAS John Smoltz Pants A 4.00 10.00
JB Jason Bay Jsy A 3.00 8.00
JB2 Jason Bay Bat A 3.00 8.00
JD Jermaine Dye C2 3.00 8.00
JDD Johnny Damon A2 4.00 10.00
JM Justin Morneau Bat B 3.00 8.00
JPM Joe Mauer Bat A 4.00 10.00
JR Jose Reyes Jsy A 3.00 8.00
JS Johan Santana Jsy A 4.00 10.00
JT Jim Thome B2 5.00 12.00
JV Justin Verlander A2 5.00 12.00
LB Lance Berkman C2 3.00 8.00
MAR Manny Ramirez Jsy B 3.00 8.00
MAR2 Manny Ramirez Bat C 3.00 8.00
MC Matt Cain B2 3.00 8.00
MCT Mark Teixeira B2 3.00 8.00
MEC Melky Cabrera B2 4.00 10.00
MO Magglio Ordonez Bat B 4.00 10.00
MR Mariano Rivera Jsy A 4.00 10.00
MR Manny Ramirez D2 3.00 8.00
MT Miguel Tejada Bat A 3.00 8.00
MT Miguel Tejada B2 3.00 8.00
NS Nick Swisher D2 4.00 10.00
PK Paul Konerko Bat A 3.00 8.00
PK Paul Konerko B2 3.00 8.00
PM Pedro Martinez D2 3.00 8.00
RC Robinson Cano Pants A 4.00 10.00
RC Robinson Cano B2 4.00 10.00
RH Ryan Howard Bat B 6.00 15.00
RH Roy Halladay B2 3.00 8.00
RJH Ryan Howard B2 6.00 15.00
RO Roy Oswalt Jsy A 3.00 8.00
SK Scott Kazmir Jsy B 3.00 8.00
SK Scott Kazmir C2 3.00 8.00
SR Scott Rolen Jsy A 4.00 10.00
TG Tom Glavine A2 4.00 10.00
TG1 Tom Glavine Jsy A 4.00 10.00
TG2 Troy Glaus Bat B 3.00 8.00
VG Vladimir Guerrero D2 4.00 10.00
VW Vernon Wells Bat A 3.00 8.00
VW Vernon Wells D2 3.00 8.00

2007 Topps Hit Parade

SER.2 ODDS 1:9 HOBBY, 1:2 HTA
HP1 Barry Bonds 2.00 5.00
HP2 Ken Griffey Jr. 1.50 4.00
HP3 Frank Thomas 1.00 2.50
HP4 Jim Thome .60 1.50
HP5 Manny Ramirez 1.00 2.50
HP6 Alex Rodriguez 1.50 4.00
HP7 Gary Sheffield .40 1.00
HP8 Mike Piazza 1.00 2.50
HP9 Carlos Delgado .40 1.00
HP10 Chipper Jones 1.00 2.50
HP11 Barry Bonds 2.00 5.00
HP12 Ken Griffey Jr. 1.50 4.00
HP13 Frank Thomas 1.00 2.50
HP14 Manny Ramirez 1.00 2.50
HP15 Gary Sheffield .40 1.00
HP16 Jeff Kent .40 1.00
HP17 Alex Rodriguez 1.50 4.00
HP18 Luis Gonzalez .40 1.00
HP19 Jim Thome .60 1.50
HP20 Mike Piazza 1.00 2.50
HP21 Craig Biggio .60 1.50
HP22 Barry Bonds 2.00 5.00
HP23 Julio Franco .40 1.00
HP24 Steve Finley .40 1.00
HP25 Omar Vizquel .60 1.50
HP26 Ken Griffey Jr. 1.50 4.00
HP27 Gary Sheffield .40 1.00
HP28 Luis Gonzalez .40 1.00
HP29 Ivan Rodriguez .60 1.50
HP30 Bernie Williams .60 1.50

2007 Topps Hobby Masters

COMPLETE SET (20) 10.00 25.00
SER.1 ODDS 1:6 H, 1:4 HTA
HM1 David Wright 1.50 4.00
HM2 Albert Pujols 2.50 6.00
HM3 David Ortiz .60 1.50
HM4 Ryan Howard 1.50 4.00
HM5 Alfonso Soriano .60 1.50
HM6 Delmon Young .60 1.50
HM7 Jered Weaver .60 1.50
HM8 Derek Jeter 2.50 6.00
HM9 Freddy Sanchez .40 1.00
HM10 Alex Rodriguez 1.50 4.00
HM11 Johan Santana 1.00 2.50
HM12 Ichiro Suzuki 1.50 4.00
HM13 Andruw Jones .40 1.00
HM14 Vladimir Guerrero 1.00 2.50
HM15 Miguel Cabrera 1.00 2.50
HM16 Todd Helton .60 1.50
HM17 Manny Ramirez 1.00 2.50
HM18 Carlos Beltran .40 1.00
HM19 Justin Morneau 1.00 2.50
HM20 Francisco Liriano 1.00 2.50

2007 Topps Homerun Derby Contest

RANDOM INSERTS IN SER.2 PACKS
STATED ODDS 999 SER.#'d SETS
AB Adrian Beltre .60 1.50
AD Adam Dunn 1.00 2.50
AER Alex Rodriguez 2.50 6.00
AJ Andruw Jones .60 1.50
AL Adam LaRoche .60 1.50
AP Albert Pujols 4.00 10.00
AR Aramis Ramirez .60 1.50
AS Alfonso Soriano 1.00 2.50
BH Bill Hall .60 1.50
CB Carlos Beltran .60 1.50
CD Carlos Delgado .60 1.50
CL Carlos Lee .60 1.50
CM Craig Monroe .60 1.50
CU Chase Utley 1.50 4.00
DO David Ortiz 1.00 2.50
DU Dan Uggla 1.00 2.50
DW David Wright 2.50 6.00
DY Delmon Young 1.00 2.50
FT Frank Thomas 1.50 4.00
GA Garrett Atkins .60 1.50
GS Grady Sizemore 1.00 2.50
JB Jason Bay 1.00 2.50
JC Joe Crede .60 1.50
JD Jermaine Dye .60 1.50
JDD Johnny Damon 1.00 2.50
JF Jeff Francoeur 1.50 4.00
JG Jason Giambi .60 1.50
JM Justin Morneau 1.50 4.00
JT Jim Thome 1.00 2.50
KG Ken Griffey Jr 2.50 6.00
LB Lance Berkman 1.00 2.50
MC Miguel Cabrera 1.50 4.00
MH Matt Holliday 1.50 4.00
MMT Marcus Thames .60 1.50
MOT Miguel Tejada 1.00 2.50
MP Mike Piazza 1.50 4.00
MR Manny Ramirez 1.50 4.00
MT Mark Teixeira 1.50 4.00
NS Nick Swisher 1.50 4.00
PB Pat Burrell .60 1.50
PF Prince Fielder 1.00 2.50
PK Paul Konerko 1.00 2.50
RH Ryan Howard 2.50 6.00
RI Raul Ibanez 1.00 2.50
RS Richie Sexson .60 1.50
TG Troy Glaus .60 1.50
TH Travis Hafner .60 1.50
TKH Torii Hunter .60 1.50
VG Vladimir Guerrero 1.50 4.00
VW Vernon Wells .60 1.50

2007 Topps In the Name Letter Relics

SER.1 ODDS 1:8292 H, 1:488 HTA
STATED PRINT RUN 1 SERIAL #'d SET
NO PRICING DUE TO SCARCITY

2007 Topps Mickey Mantle Story

COMPLETE SET (57) 50.00 100.00
COMP.SERIES 1 (1-15) 8.00 20.00
COMP.SERIES 2 (16-30) 8.00 20.00
COMP.UPD.SET (31-45) 12.50 30.00
COMP.08 SER.1 SET (46-57) 6.00 15.00
COMP.08 SER.2 SET (58-67) 6.00 15.00
COMP.08 UPD SET (68-77) 6.00 15.00
COMMON MANTLE (1-77) .75 2.00
SER.1 ODDS 1:18 H, 1:18 HTA, 1:18 K-MART
SER.1 ODDS 1:18 RACK, 1:18 TARGET
SER.1 ODDS 1:18 WAL-MART
SER.2 ODDS 1:18 H,1:3 HTA,1:18 R
UPDATE ODDS 1:18 H, 1:3 HTA, 1:18 R
08 SER.1 ODDS 1:18 H, 1:3 HTA
08 SER.2 ODDS 1:18 H,1:3 HTA, 1:18 R
08 UPD.ODDS 1:18 HOBBY
1-15 ISSUED IN SERIES 1
16-30 ISSUED IN SERIES 2
31-45 ISSUED IN UPDATE
46-57 ISSSUED IN 08 SERIES 1
58-65 ISSUED IN 08 SERIES 2
66-77 ISSUED IN 08 UPDATE

2007 Topps Opening Day Team vs. Team

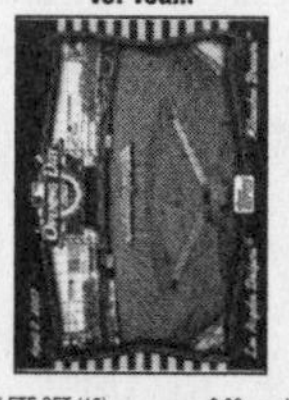

COMPLETE SET (15) 6.00 15.00
SER.2 ODDS 1:12 HOBBY, 1:3 HTA
OD1 New York Mets / St. Louis Cardinals .40 1.00
OD2 Atlanta Braves / Philadelphia Phillies .40 1.00
OD3 Florida Marlins / Washington Nationals .40 1.00
OD4 Tampa Bay Devil Rays / New York Yankees 1.00 2.50
OD5 Toronto Blue Jays / Detroit Tigers .40 1.00
OD6 Cleveland Indians / Chicago White Sox .40 1.00
OD7 Los Angeles Dodgers / Milwaukee Brewers .40 1.00
OD8 Chicago Cubs / Cincinnati Reds .40 1.00
OD9 Arizona Diamondbacks / Colorado Rockies .40 1.00
OD10 Boston Red Sox / Kansas City Royals 1.00 2.50
OD11 Oakland Athletics / Seattle Mariners .40 1.00
OD12 Baltimore Orioles / Minnesota Twins .40 1.00
OD13 Pittsburgh Pirates / Houston Astros .40 1.00
OD14 Texas Rangers / Los Angeles Angels .40 1.00
OD15 San Diego Padres / San Francisco Giants .40 1.00

2007 Topps Own the Game

COMPLETE SET (25) 10.00 25.00
SER.1 ODDS 1:6 H, 1:2 HTA, 1:6 K-MART
SER.1 ODDS 1:6 RACK, 1:6 TARGET
SER.1 ODDS 1:6 WAL-MART
OTG1 Ryan Howard 1.50 4.00
OTG2 David Ortiz .60 1.50
OTG3 Alfonso Soriano .60 1.50
OTG4 Albert Pujols 2.50 6.00
OTG5 Lance Berkman .60 1.50
OTG6 Jermaine Dye .40 1.00
OTG7 Travis Hafner .40 1.00
OTG8 Jim Thome .60 1.50
OTG9 Carlos Beltran .40 1.00
OTG10 Adam Dunn .60 1.50
OTG11 Ryan Howard 1.50 4.00
OTG12 David Ortiz .60 1.50
OTG13 Albert Pujols 2.50 6.00
OTG14 Lance Berkman .60 1.50
OTG15 Justin Morneau 1.00 2.50
OTG16 Andruw Jones .40 1.00
OTG17 Jermaine Dye .40 1.00
OTG18 Travis Hafner .40 1.00
OTG19 Alex Rodriguez 1.50 4.00
OTG20 David Wright 1.50 4.00
OTG21 Johan Santana 1.00 2.50
OTG22 Chris Carpenter 1.00 2.50
OTG23 Brandon Webb .60 1.50
OTG24 Roy Oswalt .60 1.50
OTG25 Roy Halladay 1.00 2.50

2007 Topps Rookie Stars

COMPLETE SET (10) 6.00 15.00
SER.2 ODDS 1:9 HOBBY
RS1 Daisuke Matsuzaka 1.25 3.00
RS2 Kevin Kouzmanoff .30 .75
RS3 Elijah Dukes .50 1.25
RS4 Andrew Miller .75 2.00
RS5 Kei Igawa .75 2.00
RS6 Troy Tulowitzki 2.00 5.00
RS7 Ubaldo Jimenez 2.00 5.00
RS8 Alex Gordon 1.00 2.50
RS9 Josh Hamilton 1.25 3.00
RS10 Delmon Young .50 1.25

2007 Topps Stars

COMPLETE SET (15) 6.00 15.00
SER.2 ODDS 1:9 HOBBY
TS1 Ryan Howard 1.25 3.00
TS2 Alfonso Soriano .50 1.25
TS3 Todd Helton .50 1.25
TS4 Johan Santana .75 2.00
TS5 David Wright 1.25 3.00
TS6 Albert Pujols 2.00 5.00
TS7 Daisuke Matsuzaka 1.25 3.00
TS8 Miguel Cabrera .75 2.00
TS9 David Ortiz .50 1.25
TS10 Alex Rodriguez 1.25 3.00
TS11 Vladimir Guerrero .75 2.00
TS12 Ichiro Suzuki 1.25 3.00
TS13 Derek Jeter 2.00 5.00
TS14 Lance Berkman .50 1.25
TS15 Ryan Zimmerman .50 1.25

2007 Topps Target Factory Set Mantle Memorabilia

COMMON MANTLE MEMORABILIA 15.00 40.00
DISTRIBUTED WITH TOPPS TARGET FACT.SETS
MMR53 Mickey Mantle 53T 15.00 40.00
MMR56 Mickey Mantle 56T 15.00 40.00
MMR57 Mickey Mantle 57T 15.00 40.00

2007 Topps Target Factory Set Red Backs

1 Mickey Mantle 3.00 8.00
2 Ted Williams 2.50 6.00

2007 Topps Trading Places

COMPLETE SET (25) 6.00 15.00
SER.2 ODDS 1:9 HOBBY
TP1 Jeff Weaver .40 1.00
TP2 Frank Thomas 1.00 2.50
TP3 Mike Piazza 1.00 2.50
TP4 Alfonso Soriano .60 1.50
TP5 Freddy Garcia .40 1.00
TP6 Jason Marquis .40 1.00
TP7 Ted Lilly .40 1.00
TP8 Mark Loretta .40 1.00
TP9 Marcus Giles .40 1.00
TP10 Barry Zito .40 1.00
TP11 Andy Pettitte .60 1.50
TP12 J.D. Drew .40 1.00
TP13 Gary Matthews .40 1.00
TP14 Jay Payton .40 1.00
TP15 Aubrey Huff .40 1.00
TP16 Brian Bannister .40 1.00
TP17 Jeff Conine .40 1.00
TP18 Gary Sheffield .40 1.00
TP19 Shea Hillenbrand .40 1.00
TP20 Wes Helms .40 1.00
TP21 Frank Catalanotto .40 1.00
TP22 Adam LaRoche .40 1.00
TP23 Mike Gonzalez .40 1.00
TP24 Greg Maddux 1.50 4.00
TP25 Jason Schmidt .40 1.00

2007 Topps Trading Places Autographs

SER.2 ODDS 1:3,055 HOBBY, 1:44 HTA
AH Aubrey Huff 6.00 15.00
AL Adam LaRoche 4.00 10.00
BB Brian Bannister 5.00 12.00
FC Frank Catalanotto 4.00 10.00
FG Freddy Garcia 6.00 15.00
GS Gary Sheffield 15.00 40.00
JS Jason Schmidt 6.00 15.00
MG Mike Gonzalez 4.00 10.00
SH Shea Hillenbrand 4.00 10.00
WH Wes Helms 4.00 10.00

2007 Topps Trading Places Relics

SER.2 ODDS 1:2,435 HOBBY, 1:137 HTA
AP Andy Pettitte 5.00 12.00
AS Alfonso Soriano 5.00 12.00
BZ Barry Zito 4.00 10.00
FT Frank Thomas 5.00 12.00
GM Greg Maddux 5.00 12.00
GS Gary Sheffield 5.00 12.00
JW Jeff Weaver 4.00 10.00
MG Marcus Giles 4.00 10.00
ML Mark Loretta 4.00 10.00
MP Mike Piazza 6.00 15.00

2007 Topps Unlock the Mick

COMPLETE SET (5) 3.00 8.00
COMMON MANTLE 1.00 2.50
SER.1 ODDS 1:18 H, 1:18 HTA, 1:18 K-MART
SER.1 ODDS 1:18 RACK, 1:18 TARGET
SER.1 ODDS 1:18 WAL-MART

2007 Topps Wal-Mart

COMP.SERIES 1 (18) 15.00 40.00
STATED ODDS 1:4 WAL-MART
SER.1 ODDS 3 PER $9.99 WAL-MART BOX
SER.1 ODDS 6 PER $19.99 WAL-MART BOX
1-18 ISSUED IN SERIES 1
19-36 ISSUED IN SERIES 2
37-54 ISSUED IN UPDATE
WM1 Frank Thomas 41 PB 1.00 2.50
WM2 Mike Piazza 34 DS 1.00 2.50
WM3 Ivan Rodriguez 22 Caramel .60 1.50
WM4 David Ortiz T207 .60 1.50
WM5 David Wright 1887 AG 1.50 4.00
WM6 Greg Maddux 52T 1.50 4.00
WM7 Mickey Mantle 51T 3.00 8.00
WM8 Jose Reyes 65T .60 1.50
WM9 John Smoltz T205 1.00 2.50
WM10 Jim Edmonds 56T .60 1.50
WM11 Ryan Howard 58T 1.50 4.00
WM12 Miguel Cabrera T206 1.00 2.50
WM13 Carlos Delgado 10 Turkey .40 1.00
WM14 Miguel Tejada 55B .60 1.50
WM15 Ichiro Suzuki 33 DeLong 1.50 4.00
WM16 Albert Pujols 49B 2.50 6.00
WM17 Derek Jeter 91 SC 2.50 6.00
WM18 Vladimir Guerrero 61 Baz 1.00 2.50
WM19 Lance Berkman .60 1.50
WM20 Chase Utley 1.00 2.50
WM21 Gary Matthews .40 1.00
WM22 Johan Santana 1.00 2.50
WM23 Todd Helton .60 1.50
WM24 Carlos Beltran .40 1.00
WM25 Alex Rodriguez 1.50 4.00
WM26 Cole Hamels 1.00 2.50
WM27 Daisuke Matsuzaka 1.50 4.00
WM28 Kei Igawa 1.00 2.50
WM29 Hanley Ramirez 1.00 2.50
WM30 Joe Mauer 1.00 2.50
WM31 Brandon Webb .60 1.50
WM32 Michael Young .60 1.50
WM33 Nick Swisher 1.00 2.50
WM34 Jason Bay .60 1.50
WM35 Manny Ramirez 1.00 2.50
WM36 Ryan Zimmerman .60 1.50
WM37 Grady Sizemore .60 1.50
WM38 Matt Holliday 1.00 2.50
WM39 Jimmy Rollins .60 1.50
WM40 Magglio Ordonez .60 1.50
WM41 Prince Fielder .60 1.50
WM42 Jorge Posada .60 1.50
WM43 Hideki Okajima 2.00 5.00
WM44 Dan Uggla .60 1.50
WM45 Jake Peavy .40 1.00
WM46 Carlos Lee .40 1.00
WM47 C.C. Sabathia .60 1.50
WM48 Gary Sheffield .40 1.00
WM49 Tim Lincecum 6.00 15.00
WM50 J.J. Putz .40 1.00
WM51 Justin Verlander 1.25 3.00
WM52 Akinori Iwamura 1.00 2.50
WM53 Adam LaRoche .40 1.00
WM54 Alfonso Soriano .60 1.50

2007 Topps Williams 406

COMPLETE SET (36) 12.50 30.00
COMP.SERIES 1 (18) 6.00 15.00
COMP.SERIES 2 (18) 6.00 15.00

377 Zack Segovia (RC) .20 .50
378 Ramon Hernandez .07 .20
379 Chris Young .07 .20
380 Jason Schmidt .07 .20
381 Ronny Paulino .07 .20
382 Kevin Millwood .07 .20
383 Jon Lester .20 .50
384 Alex Gonzalez .07 .20
385 Brad Hawpe .07 .20
386 Placido Polanco .07 .20
387 Nate Robertson .07 .20
388 Torii Hunter .07 .20
389 Gavin Floyd .07 .20
390 Roy Oswalt .12 .30
391 Kelvim Escobar .07 .20
392 Craig Wilson .07 .20
393 Milton Bradley .07 .20
394 Aaron Hill .07 .20
395 Matt Diaz .07 .20
396 Chris Capuano .07 .20
397 Juan Encarnacion .07 .20
398 Jacque Jones .07 .20
399 James Shields .07 .20
400 Ichiro Suzuki .30 .75
401 Matt Kemp .12 .30
402 Matt Morris .07 .20
403 Casey Blake .07 .20
404 Corey Hart .07 .20
405 Josh Willingham .07 .20
406 Ryan Madson .07 .20
407 Nick Johnson .07 .20
408 Kevin Millar .07 .20
409 Khalil Greene .07 .20
410 Tom Glavine .12 .30
411a Jason Bay .12 .30
411b Jason Bay No Sig 2.00 5.00
412 Gerald Laird .07 .20
413 Coco Crisp .07 .20
414 Brandon Phillips .07 .20
415 Aaron Cook .07 .20
416 Mark Redman .07 .20
417 Mike Maroth .07 .20
418 Boof Bonser .07 .20
419 Jorge Cantu .07 .20
420 Jeff Weaver .07 .20
421 Melky Cabrera .07 .20
422 Francisco Rodriguez .12 .30
423 Mike Lamb .07 .20
424 Dan Haren .07 .20
425 Tomo Ohka .07 .20
426 Jeff Francoeur .20 .50
427 Randy Wolf .07 .20
428 So Taguchi .07 .20
429 Carlos Zambrano .12 .30
430 Justin Morneau .20 .50
431 Luis Gonzalez .07 .20
432 Takashi Saito .07 .20
433 Brandon Morrow RC 1.00 2.50
434 Victor Martinez .12 .30
435 Felix Hernandez .20 .50
436 Ricky Nolasco .07 .20
437 Paul LoDuca .07 .20
437b Paul LoDuca No Sig 2.00 5.00
438 Chad Cordero .07 .20
439 Miguel Tejada .12 .30
440 Mark Teixeira .20 .50
441 Pat Burrell .07 .20
442 Paul Maholm .07 .20
443 Mike Cameron .07 .20
444 Josh Beckett .12 .30
445 Pablo Ozuna .07 .20
446 Jaret Wright .07 .20
447 Angel Berroa .07 .20
448 Fernando Rodney .07 .20
449 Francisco Liriano .20 .50
450 Ken Griffey Jr. .30 .75
451 Bobby Jenks .07 .20
452 Mike Mussina .12 .30
453 Howie Kendrick .07 .20
454 Milwaukee Brewers .07 .20
455 Dan Johnson .07 .20
456 Ted Lilly .07 .20
457 Mike Hampton .07 .20
458 J.J. Hardy .07 .20
459 Jeff Suppan .07 .20
460 Jose Reyes .12 .30
461 Jae Seo .07 .20
462 Edgar Gonzalez .07 .20
463 Russell Martin .07 .20
464 Omar Vizquel .12 .30
465 Jhonny Peralta .07 .20
466 Raul Ibanez .12 .30
467 Hanley Ramirez .20 .50
468 Kerry Wood .07 .20
469 Ryan Church .07 .20
470 Gary Sheffield .07 .20
471 David Wells .07 .20
472 David Dellucci .07 .20
473 Xavier Nady .07 .20
474 Michael Young .12 .30
475 Kevin Youkilis .07 .20
476 Aaron Harang .07 .20
477 Brian Lawrence .07 .20
478 Octavio Dotel .07 .20
479 Chris Shelton .07 .20
480 Matt Garza .07 .20
481a Jim Thome .12 .30
481b Jim Thome No Sig 2.00 5.00
482 Jose Contreras .07 .20
483 Kris Benson .07 .20
484 John Maine .07 .20
485 Tadahito Iguchi .07 .20
486 Wandy Rodriguez .07 .20
487 Eric Chavez .07 .20
488 Vernon Wells .07 .20
489 Doug Davis .07 .20
490 Andruw Jones .07 .20
491 David Eckstein .07 .20
492 Michael Barrett .07 .20
493 Greg Norton .07 .20
494 Orlando Hudson .07 .20
495 Wilson Betemit .07 .20
496 Ryan Klesko .07 .20
497 Fausto Carmona .07 .20
498 Jarrod Washburn .07 .20
499 Aaron Boone .07 .20
500 Pedro Martinez .12 .30
501 Mike O'Connor .07 .20
502 Brian Roberts .07 .20
503 Jeff Cirillo .07 .20
504 Brett Myers .07 .20
505 Jose Bautista .12 .30
506 Akinori Otsuka .07 .20
507 Shea Hillenbrand .07 .20
508 Ryan Langerhans .07 .20
509 Josh Fogg .07 .20
510 Alex Rodriguez .30 .75
511 Kenny Rogers .07 .20
512 Jason Kubel .07 .20
513 Jermaine Dye .07 .20
514 Mark Grudzielanek .07 .20
515 Josh Phelps .07 .20
516 Bartolo Colon .07 .20
517 Craig Biggio .12 .30
518 Esteban Loaiza .07 .20
519 Alex Rios .12 .30
520 Adam Dunn .12 .30
521 Derrick Turnbow .07 .20
522 Anthony Reyes .07 .20
523 Derrek Lee .07 .20
524 Ty Wigginton .07 .20
525 Jeremy Hermida .07 .20
526 Derek Lowe .07 .20
527 Randy Winn .07 .20
528 Paul Byrd .07 .20
529 Chris Snelling .07 .20
530 Brandon Webb .12 .30
531 Julio Franco .07 .20
532 Jose Vidro .07 .20
533 Erik Bedard .07 .20
534 Termel Sledge .07 .20
535 Jon Lieber .07 .20
536 Tom Gorzelanny .07 .20
537 Kip Wells .07 .20
538 Wily Mo Pena .07 .20
539 Eric Milton .07 .20
540 Chad Billingsley .07 .20
541 David DeJesus .07 .20
542 Omar Infante .07 .20
543 Rondell White .07 .20
544 Juan Uribe .07 .20
545 Miguel Cairo .07 .20
546 Orlando Cabrera .07 .20
547 Byung-Hyun Kim .07 .20
548 Jason Kendall .07 .20
549 Horacio Ramirez .07 .20
550 Trevor Hoffman .12 .30
551 Ronnie Belliard .07 .20
552 Chris Woodward .07 .20
553 Ramon Martinez .07 .20
554 Elizardo Ramirez .07 .20
555 Andy Marte .07 .20
556 John Patterson .07 .20
557 Scott Olsen .07 .20
558 Steve Trachsel .07 .20
559 Doug Mientkiewicz .07 .20
560 Randy Johnson .20 .50
561 Chan Ho Park .12 .30
562 Jamie Moyer .07 .20
563 Mike Gonzalez .07 .20
564 Nelson Cruz .12 .30
565 Alex Cora .07 .20
566 Ryan Freel .07 .20
567 Chris Stewart RC .20 .50
568 Carlos Guillen .07 .20
569 Jason Bartlett .07 .20
570 Mariano Rivera .20 .50
571 Norris Hopper .07 .20
572 Alex Escobar .07 .20
573 Gustavo Chacin .07 .20
574 Brandon McCarthy .07 .20
575 Seth McClung .07 .20
576 Yuniesky Betancourt .07 .20
577 Jason LaRue .07 .20
578 Dustin Pedroia .25 .60
579 Taylor Tankersley .07 .20
580 Garrett Anderson .07 .20
581 Mike Sweeney .07 .20
582 Scott Thorman .07 .20
583 Joe Inglett .07 .20
584 Clint Barmes .07 .20
585 Willie Bloomquist .07 .20
586 Willy Aybar .07 .20
587 Brian Bannister .07 .20
588 Jose Guillen .07 .20
UER Y.Betancourt Pictured
589 Brad Wilkerson .07 .20
590 Lance Berkman .12 .30
591 Toronto Blue Jays .07 .20
592 Florida Marlins .07 .20
593 Washington Nationals .07 .20
594 Los Angeles Angels .07 .20
595 Cleveland Indians .07 .20
596 Texas Rangers .07 .20
597 Detroit Tigers .07 .20
598 Arizona Diamondbacks .07 .20
599 Kansas City Royals .07 .20
600 Ryan Zimmerman .12 .30
601 Colorado Rockies .07 .20
602 Minnesota Twins .07 .20
603 Los Angeles Dodgers .07 .20
604 San Diego Padres .07 .20
605 Bruce Bochy MG .07 .20
606 Ron Washington MG .07 .20
607 Manny Acta MG .07 .20
608 Sam Perlozzo MG .07 .20
609 Terry Francona MG .12 .30
610 Jim Leyland MG .07 .20
611 Eric Wedge MG .07 .20
612 Ozzie Guillen MG .07 .20
613 Buddy Bell MG .07 .20
614 Bob Geren MG .07 .20
615 Lou Piniella MG .07 .20
616 Fredi Gonzalez MG .07 .20
617 Ned Yost MG .07 .20
618 Willie Randolph MG .07 .20
619 Bud Black MG .07 .20
620 Garrett Atkins .07 .20
621 Alexi Casilla RC .30 .75
622 Matt Chico (RC) .20 .50
623 Alejandro De Aza RC .30 .75
624 Jeremy Brown .07 .20
625 Josh Hamilton (RC) .75 2.00
626 Doug Slaten RC .20 .50
627 Andy Cannizaro RC .20 .50
628 Juan Salas (RC) .20 .50
629 Levale Speigner RC .20 .50
630a Daisuke Matsuzaka English RC .75 2.00
630b Daisuke Matsuzaka Japanese 1.50 4.00
630c Daisuke Matsuzaka No Cig 1.50 4.00
631 Elijah Dukes RC .30 .75
632 Kevin Cameron RC .20 .50
633 Juan Perez RC .20 .50
634a Alex Gordon RC .60 1.50
634b Alex Gordon No Sig 2.00 5.00
635 Juan Lara RC .20 .50
636 Mike Rabelo .20 .50
637 Justin Hampson (RC) .20 .50
638 Cesar Jimenez RC .20 .50
639 Joe Smith RC .20 .50
640 Kei Igawa RC .50 1.25
641 Hideki Okajima RC 1.00 2.50
642 Sean Henn (RC) .20 .50
643 Jay Marshall RC .20 .50
644 Jared Burton RC .20 .50
645 Angel Sanchez RC .20 .50
646 Devern Hansack RC .20 .50
647 Juan Morillo (RC) .20 .50
648 Hector Gimenez (RC) .20 .50
649 Brian Barden RC .20 .50
650 Alex Rodriguez .30 .75
Jason Giambi CC
651 Jason Michaels .07 .20
Travis Hafner CC
652 Josh Johnson .20 .50
Miguel Olivo CC
653 Sean Casey .07 .20
Placido Polanco CC
654 Ivan Rodriguez .12 .30
Fernando Rodney CC
655 Dan Uggla .20 .50
Hanley Ramirez CC
656 Carlos Beltran .12 .30
Jose Reyes CC
657 Alex Rodriguez .50 1.25
Derek Jeter CC
658 Aaron Rowand .12 .30
Jimmy Rollins CC
659 Angel Berroa .07 .20
Andres Blanco CC
660a Yadier Molina .12 .30
660b Yadier Molina No Sig 2.00 5.00
661 Barry Bonds 4.00 10.00

2007 Topps 1st Edition

*1st ED: 3X TO 8X BASIC
*1st ED RC: 1.25X TO 3X BASIC
SER.1 ODDS 1:36 HOBBY, 1:5 HTA
SER.2 ODDS 1:36 HOBBY, 1:5 HTA

2007 Topps Copper

COMMON CARD (1-660) 6.00 15.00
UNLISTED STARS 10.00 25.00
SER.1 ODDS 1:7 HTA
SER.2 ODDS 1:7 HTA
STATED PRINT RUN 56 SERIAL #'d SETS
7 Mickey Mantle 75.00 150.00
15 Andrew Miller 100.00 150.00
29 Pat Neshek 30.00 60.00
40 Derek Jeter 400.00 800.00
53 Mike Piazza 15.00 40.00
58 Todd Coffey 10.00 25.00
130 Albert Pujols 30.00 60.00
170 Chien-Ming Wang 30.00 60.00
236 Boston Red Sox CL 6.00 15.00
239 New York Yankees CL 10.00 25.00
260 David Wright 15.00 40.00
275 Greg Maddux 15.00 40.00
301 Derek Jeter GG 40.00 80.00
305 Frank Thomas 15.00 40.00
308 Albert Pujols GG 30.00 60.00
311 Greg Maddux GG 15.00 40.00
313 Ichiro Suzuki GG 15.00 40.00
322 Ryan Howard MVP 15.00 40.00
327 Bobby Abreu 20.00 50.00
Derek Jeter CC
328 Carlos Delgado 15.00 40.00
David Wright CC
329 Yadier Molina 10.00 25.00
Albert Pujols CC
330 Ryan Howard 15.00 40.00
340 Roger Clemens 20.00 50.00
341 Akinori Iwamura 15.00 40.00
360 David Ortiz 20.00 50.00
362 Chris Burke 10.00 25.00
400 Ichiro Suzuki 30.00 60.00
403 Casey Blake 15.00 40.00
413 Coco Crisp 10.00 25.00
444 Josh Beckett 10.00 25.00
450 Ken Griffey Jr. 30.00 60.00
460 Jose Reyes 10.00 25.00
475 Kevin Youkilis 10.00 25.00
510 Alex Rodriguez 20.00 50.00
625 Josh Hamilton 30.00 60.00
630 Daisuke Matsuzaka 100.00 150.00
634 Alex Gordon 15.00 40.00
641 Hideki Okajima 20.00 50.00
650 Alex Rodriguez 15.00 40.00
Jason Giambi CC
657 Alex Rodriguez 20.00 50.00
Derek Jeter CC

2007 Topps Gold

*GOLD: 6X TO 15X BASIC
*GOLD RC: 2.5X TO 6X BASIC RC
SER.1 ODDS 1:11 H, 1:3 HTA, 1:24 K-MART
SER.1 ODDS 1:6 RACK, 1:11 TARGET
SER.1 ODDS 1:24 WAL-MART
SER.2 ODDS 1:11 HOBBY, 1:2 HTA
STATED PRINT RUN 2007 SER.#'d SETS
40 Derek Jeter 125.00 250.00

2007 Topps Platinum

SER.1 ODDS 1:26,000 H, 1:3200 HTA
SER.1 ODDS 1:45000 K-MART,1:8500 RACK
SER.1 ODDS 1:26000 TAR,1:45000 WAL-MART
SER.2 ODDS 1:24,000 HOBBY , 1:2900 HTA
STATED PRINT RUN 1 SERIAL #'d SET
NO PRICING DUE TO SCARCITY

2007 Topps Red Back

COMP.SERIES 1 (330) 40.00 80.00
COMP.SERIES 2 (330) 40.00 80.00
*RED: 1X TO 2.5X BASIC
*RED RC: .5X TO 1.2X BASIC RC
SER.1 ODDS 2:1 H, 10:1 HTA, 3:1 RACK
40 Derek Jeter 15.00 40.00

2007 Topps 1952 Mantle Reprint Relic

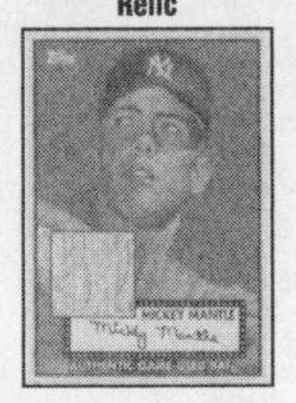

SER.1 ODDS 1:158,700 H, 1:8721 HTA
SER.1 ODDS 1:602,600 K-MART
SER.1 ODDS 1:127,100 TARGET
SER.1 ODDS 1:602,600 WAL-MART
STATED PRINT RUN 52 SERIAL #'d SETS
NO PRICING DUE TO SCARCITY
52MM Mickey Mantle Bat 125.00 250.00

2007 Topps 1953 Mantle Reprint Relic

SER.2 ODDS 1:199,750 HOBBY, 1:10,500 HTA
STATED PRINT RUN 53 SER.#'d SETS
NO PRICING DUE TO SCARCITY
53MM Mickey Mantle

2007 Topps Alex Rodriguez Road to 500

COMPLETE SET (126-175)
COMMON CARD (1-75/101-425) 1.25 3.00
COMMON CARD (76-100) 15.00 40.00
COMMON CARD (401-425) 6.00 15.00
COMMON CARD (451-475) 4.00 10.00
COMMON CARD (476-499) 4.00 10.00
SER.1 ODDS 1:36 H, 1:5 HTA, 1:36 K-MART
SER.1 ODDS 1:36 RACK, 1:36 TARGET
SER.1 ODDS 1:36 WAL-MART
FINEST ODDS TWO PER AROD BOX TOPPER
HERITAGE ODDS 1:24 HOBBY/RETAIL
OPENING DAY ODDS 1:36 H, 1:36 R
MOMENTS ODDS TWO PER BOX TOPPER
CO-SIG ODDS TWO PER AROD BOX TOPPER
BOWMAN ODDS 1:6 HOBBY, 1:2 HTA
SER.2 ODDS 1:36 HOBBY, 1:5 HTA
T.CHROME ODDS TWO PER BOX TOPPER
ALLEN AND GINTER ODDS 1:24 H, 1:24 R
BOW.CHR. ODDS 1:9 HOBBY
TURKEY RED ODDS 1:24 HOBBY/RETAIL
BOWHER ODDS TWO PER BOX TOPPER
UPDATE ODDS 1:36 H, 1:5 HTA, 1:36 R
TOPPS 52 ODDS 1:20 H, 1:20 R
CARDS 1-25 ISSUED IN SERIES 1
CARDS 26-50 ISSUED IN FINEST
CARDS 51-75 ISSUED IN HERITAGE
CARDS 76-100 ISSUED IN OPENING DAY
CARDS 101-125 ISSUED IN MOMENTS
CARDS 126-175 ISSUED IN BOWMAN
CARDS 176-200 ISSUED IN CO-SIGNERS
CARDS 201-225 ISSUED IN SERIES 2
CARDS 226-250 ISSUED IN TOP.CHROME
CARDS 251-275 ISSUED IN ALLEN GINTER
CARDS 276-300 ISSUED IN BOW.CHR.
CARDS 301-325 ISSUED IN TUR.RED
CARDS 326-350 ISSUED IN 08 FINEST
CARDS 351-375 ISSUED IN BOW.HER.
CARDS 376-400 ISSUED IN UPDATE
CARDS 401-425 ISSUED IN BOW.BEST
CARDS 426-450 ISSUED IN BOW.DRAFT
CARDS 451-475 ISSUED IN BOW.STERL.
CARDS 476-500 ISSUED IN TOPPS 52
ARHR500 Alex Rodriguez 500HR 10.00 25.00

2007 Topps Alex Rodriguez Road to 500 Autographs

SER.1 ODDS 1:1,111,000 H, 1:122,100 HTA
SER.1 ODDS 1:1,000,000 K-MART
SER.1 ODDS 1:127,100 TARGET
SER.1 ODDS 1,000,000 WAL-MART
FINEST ODDS 1:788 BOXES
HERITAGE ODDS 1:100,500 HOBBY/RETAIL
OPEN.DAY ODDS 1:171,146 H, 1:256,960 R
MOMENTS ODDS 1:603 BOX TOPPERS
BOWMAN ODDS 34,931 H, 1:11,000 HTA
CO-SIG ODDS 1:1687 BOX TOPPERS
SER.2 ODDS 1:750,000 HOBBY
SER.2 ODDS 1:173,160 HTA
ALLEN GINTER ODDS 1:64,496 HOBBY
CHROME ODDS 1:1866 BOX TOPPERS
ALLEN GINTER ODDS 1:122,200 RETAIL
BOW.CHR. ODDS 1:57,500 HOBBY
TURKEY RED ODDS 1:50,000 HOBBY
TURKEY RED ODDS 1:50,000 RETAIL
BOW.HER ODDS 1:773 HOBBY BOXES
UPD.ODDS 1:500,000 H, 1:33,500 HTA
UPD.ODDS 1:11,000 RETAIL
TOPPS 52 ODDS 1:16,000 H, 1:77,000 R
CARDS 1-25 ISSUED IN SERIES 1
CARDS 26-50 ISSUED IN FINEST
CARDS 51-75 ISSUED IN HERITAGE
CARDS 76-100 ISSUED IN OPENING DAY
CARDS 101-125 ISSUED IN MOMENTS
CARDS 126-175 ISSUED IN BOWMAN
CARDS 176-200 ISSUED IN CO-SIGNERS
CARDS 201-225 ISSUED IN SER.2
CARDS 226-250 ISSUED IN TOPPS CHROME
CARDS 251-275 ISSUED IN ALLEN GINTER
CARDS 276-300 ISSUED IN BOWMAN CHROME
CARDS 301-325 ISSUED IN TURKEY RED
CARDS 326-250 ISSUED IN 08 FINEST
CARDS 351-375 ISSUED IN BOW.HERITAGE
CARDS 376-400 ISSUED IN UPDATE
CARDS 401-425 ISSUED IN BOW.BEST
CARDS 426-450 ISSUED IN BOW.DRAFT
CARDS 451-475 ISSUED IN BOW.STERL.
CARDS 476-500 ISSUED IN TOPPS 52
STATED PRINT RUN 1 SER.#'d SET
NO PRICING DUE TO SCARCITY

2007 Topps All Stars

COMPLETE SET (12) 6.00 15.00
SER.1 ODDS ONE PER RACK PACK
AS1 Alfonso Soriano .60 1.50
AS2 Paul Konerko .60 1.50
AS3 Carlos Beltran .40 1.00
AS4 Troy Glaus .40 1.00
AS5 Jason Bay .60 1.50
AS6 Vladimir Guerrero 1.00 2.50
AS7 Chase Utley 1.00 2.50
AS8 Michael Young .60 1.50
AS9 David Wright 1.50 4.00
AS10 Gary Matthews .40 1.00
AS11 Brad Penny .40 1.00
AS12 Roy Halladay UER 1.00 2.50
Header line for stats is in incorrect order

2007 Topps All Star Rookies

COMPLETE SET (10) 6.00 15.00
SER.1 ODDS ONE PER RACK PACK
ASR1 Prince Fielder .60 1.50
ASR2 Dan Uggla .60 1.50
ASR3 Ryan Zimmerman .60 1.50
ASR4 Hanley Ramirez 1.00 2.50
ASR5 Melky Cabrera .40 1.00
ASR6 Andre Ethier .60 1.50
ASR7 Nick Markakis 1.00 2.50
ASR8 Justin Verlander 1.25 3.00
ASR9 Francisco Liriano 1.00 2.50
ASR10 Russell Martin .40 1.00

2007 Topps DiMaggio Streak

COMPLETE SET (56) 20.00 50.00
COMMON CARD .60 1.50
SER.2 ODDS 1:9 HOBBY

2007 Topps DiMaggio Streak Before the Streak

COMPLETE SET (61) 20.00 50.00
COMMON CARD .60 1.50
SER.2 ODDS 1:9 HOBBY

2007 Topps Distinguished Service

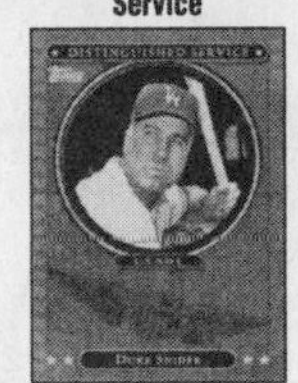

COMPLETE SET (30) 10.00 25.00
COMP.SERIES 1 (1-20) 6.00 15.00
COMP.SERIES 2 (21-30) 5.00 12.00
SER.1 ODDS 1:12 H, 1:12 HTA, 1:12 K-MART
SER.1 ODDS 1:12 RACK, 1:12 WAL-MART
SER.2 ODDS 1:12 HOBBY, 1:2 HTA
DS1 Duke Snider .60 1.50
DS2 Yogi Berra 1.00 2.50
DS3 Bob Feller .40 1.00
DS4 Bobby Doerr .40 1.00
DS5 Monte Irvin .40 1.00
DS6 Dwight D. Eisenhower .40 1.00
DS7 George Marshall .40 1.00
DS8 Franklin D. Roosevelt .40 1.00
DS9 Harry Truman .40 1.00
DS10 Douglas Macarthur .40 1.00
DS11 Ralph Kiner .60 1.50
DS12 Hank Sauer .40 1.00
DS13 Elmer Valo .40 1.00
DS14 Sibby Sisti .40 1.00
DS15 Hoyt Wilhelm .40 1.00
DS16 James Doolittle .40 1.00
DS17 Curtis Lemay .40 1.00
DS18 Omar Bradley .40 1.00
DS19 Chester Nimitz .40 1.00
DS20 Mark Clark .40 1.00
DS21 Joe DiMaggio 2.50 6.00
DS22 Warren Spahn .60 1.50
DS23 Stan Musial 1.50 4.00
DS24 Red Schoendienst .40 1.00
DS25 Ted Williams 2.50 6.00
DS26 Winston Churchill .40 1.00
DS27 Charles de Gaulle .40 1.00
DS28 George Bush .40 1.00
DS29 John F. Kennedy 1.00 2.50
DS30 Richard Bong .40 1.00

2007 Topps Distinguished Service Autographs

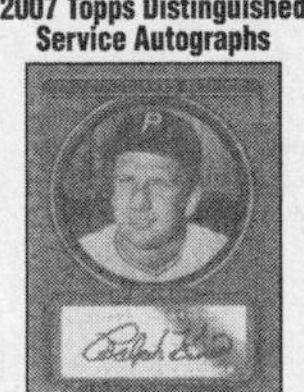

SER.1 ODDS 1:20,000 H, 1:830 HTA
SER.1 ODDS 1:41,225 K-MART,1:9200 RACK
SER.1 ODDS 1:20,000 TARGET
SER.1 ODDS 1:41,225 WAL-MART
BD Bobby Doerr 20.00 50.00
BF Bob Feller 30.00 60.00
DS Duke Snider 40.00 80.00
MI Monte Irvin 30.00 60.00
RK Ralph Kiner 40.00 80.00

2007 Topps Distinguished Service Cuts

SER.1 ODDS 1:505,600 H, 1:61,000 HTA
SER.1 ODDS 1:1,000,000 K-MART
SER.1 ODDS 1:138,000 TARGET
SER.1 ODDS 1:1,000,000 WAL-MART
SER.2 ODDS 1:165,000 HOBBY
SER.2 ODDS 1:57,720 HTA
STATED PRINT RUN 1 SER.#'d SET
NO PRICING DUE TO SCARCITY

2007 Topps Factory Set All Star Bonus

1 Alex Rodriguez 1.50 4.00
2 David Wright 1.50 4.00
3 David Ortiz .60 1.50
4 Ichiro Suzuki 1.50 4.00
5 Ryan Howard 1.50 4.00

2007 Topps Factory Set Cardinals Team Bonus

1 Skip Schumaker .40 1.00
2 Josh Hancock .40 1.00
3 Tyler Johnson .40 1.00
4 Randy Keisler .40 1.00
5 Randy Flores .40 1.00

2007 Topps Factory Set Cubs Team Bonus

1 Ronny Cedeno .40 1.00
2 Cesar Izturis .40 1.00
3 Neal Cotts .40 1.00
4 Wade Miller .40 1.00
5 Michael Wuertz .40 1.00

2007 Topps Factory Set Dodgers Team Bonus

1 Chin-Hui Tsao .60 1.50
2 Olmedo Saenz .40 1.00
3 Brett Tomko .40 1.00
4 Marlon Anderson .40 1.00
5 Brady Clark .40 1.00

2007 Topps Factory Set Red Sox Team Bonus

1 Daisuke Matsuzaka 1.50 4.00
2 Eric Hinske .40 1.00
3 Brendan Donnelly .40 1.00
4 Hideki Okajima 2.00 5.00
5 J.C. Romero .40 1.00

2007 Topps Factory Set Rookie Bonus

COMPLETE SET (20) 12.50 30.00
1 Felix Pie .40 1.00
2 Rick Vanden Hurk .40 1.00
3 Jeff Baker .40 1.00
4 Don Kelly .40 1.00
5 Matt Lindstrom .40 1.00
6 Chase Wright 1.00 2.50
7 Jon Coutlangus .40 1.00
8 Lee Gardner .40 1.00
9 Gustavo Molina .40 1.00
10 Kory Casto .40 1.00
11 Daisuke Matsuzaka 1.50 4.00
12 Tim Lincecum 6.00 15.00
13 Phil Hughes 2.00 5.00
14 Ryan Braun 2.00 5.00
15 Billy Butler .60 1.50
16 Jarrod Saltalamacchia .60 1.50
17 Hideki Okajima 2.00 5.00
18 Akinori Iwamura 1.00 2.50
19a Joba Chamberlain 2.00 5.00
19b Joba Chamberlain Houston Astros UER 2.00 5.00
20 Hunter Pence 2.00 5.00

2007 Topps Factory Set Yankees Team Bonus

1 Darrell Rasner .40 1.00
2 Phil Hughes 2.00 5.00
3 Wil Nieves .40 1.00
4 Kei Igawa 1.00 2.50
5 Kevin Thompson .40 1.00

2007 Topps Flashback Fridays

COMPLETE SET (25) 6.00 15.00
ISSUED VIA HTA SHOPS
FF1 Ryan Howard .75 2.00
FF2 Derek Jeter 1.25 3.00
FF3 Ken Griffey Jr .75 2.00
FF4 Miguel Tejada .30 .75
FF5 David Wright .75 2.00
FF6 Alfonso Soriano .30 .75
FF7 Matt Holliday .50 1.25
FF8 Jason Bay .30 .75
FF9 Ryan Zimmerman .30 .75
FF10 Alex Rodriguez .75 2.00
FF11 Jermaine Dye .20 .50
FF12 Miguel Cabrera .50 1.25
FF13 Johan Santana .50 1.25
FF14 Brandon Webb .30 .75
FF15 Ivan Rodriguez .30 .75
FF16 Ichiro Suzuki .75 2.00
FF17 Michael Young .30 .75
FF18 David Ortiz .30 .75
FF19 Roger Clemens .60 1.50
FF20 Frank Thomas .50 1.25
FF21 Trevor Hoffman .30 .75
FF22 Gary Matthews .20 .50
FF23 Rafael Furcal .20 .50
FF24 Chipper Jones .50 1.25
FF25 Albert Pujols 1.25 3.00

2007 Topps Generation Now

SER.1 ODDS 1:4 H, 1:4 K-MART, 1:4 RACK
SER.1 ODDS 1:4 TARGET, 1:4 WAL-MART
SER.2 ODDS 1:4 HOBBY
UPDATE ODDS 1:4 HOB, 1:4 RET
CARDS OF SAME PLAYER EQUALLY PRICED
GN1 Ryan Howard 1.25 3.00
GN51 Chase Utley .75 2.00
GN85 Chien-Ming Wang .50 1.25
GN103 Mike Napoli .50 1.25

GN117 Justin Morneau .75 2.00
GN147 David Wright 1.25 3.00
GN187 Jered Weaver .50 1.25
GN195 Andre Ethier .50 1.25
GN219 Ryan Zimmerman .50 1.25
GN279 Russell Martin .30 .75
GN283 Justin Verlander 1.00 2.50
GN299 Hanley Ramirez .75 2.00
GN350 Nick Markakis .75 2.00
GN360 Nick Swisher .75 2.00
GN397 Prince Fielder .50 1.25
GN425 Ian Kinsler .50 1.25
GN452 Kenji Johjima .75 2.00
GN481 Jonathan Papelbon .75 2.00
GN516 Jose Reyes .50 1.25
GN520 Curtis Granderson .50 1.25
GN551 Josh Barfield .30 .75

2007 Topps Generation Now Autographs

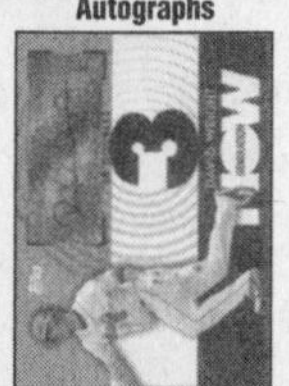

SER.1 ODDS 1:50,850 H, 1:2070 HTA
SER.1 ODDS 1:101,000 K-MART,1:18,396 RACK
SER.1 ODDS 1:50,850 TARGET
SER.1 ODDS 1:101,000 WAL-MART
SER.2 ODDS 1:94,000 HOBBY
SER.2 ODDS 1:1370 HTA
UPDATE ODDS 1:11,000 H, 1:5500 HTA
UPDATE ODDS 1:10,800 RETAIL
STATED PRINT RUN 1 SERIAL #'d SET
NO PRICING DUE TO SCARCITY

2007 Topps Generation Now Vintage

RANDOM INSERTS IN K-MART PACKS
1-18 ISSUED IN SER.1 PACKS
19-36 ISSUED IN SER.2 PACKS
37-54 ISSUED IN 07 UPDATE PACKS
GNV1 Ryan Howard .75 2.00
GNV2 Jeff Francoeur .50 1.25
GNV3 Nick Swisher .50 1.25
GNV4 Joey Gathright .20 .50
GNV5 Jhonny Peralta .20 .50
GNV6 Willy Taveras .20 .50
GNV7 Cory Sullivan .20 .50
GNV8 Chris Young .20 .50
GNV9 Jered Weaver .30 .75
GNV10 Jonathan Papelbon .50 1.25
GNV11 Russell Martin .20 .50
GNV12 Hanley Ramirez .50 1.25
GNV13 Justin Verlander .60 1.50
GNV14 Matt Cain .30 .75
GNV15 Kenji Johjima .50 1.25
GNV16 Angel Pagan .20 .50
GNV17 Brandon Phillips .20 .50
GNV18 Mark Teahen .20 .50
GNV19 Stephen Drew .20 .50
GNV20 Nick Markakis .50 1.25
GNV21 Anibal Sanchez .20 .50
GNV22 Jeremy Hermida .20 .50
GNV23 James Loney .30 .75
GNV24 Prince Fielder .30 .75
GNV25 Josh Barfield .20 .50
GNV26 Ian Kinsler .30 .75
GNV27 Ryan Zimmerman .30 .75
GNV28 David Wright .75 2.00
GNV29 Jose Reyes .30 .75
GNV30 Delmon Young .30 .75
GNV31 Zach Duke .20 .50
GNV32 Brian McCann .20 .50
GNV33 Bobby Jenks .20 .50
GNV34 Robinson Cano .50 1.25
GNV35 Jose Lopez .20 .50
GNV36 Daisuke Matsuzaka .75 2.00
GNV37 Alex Rios .30 .75
GNV38 Cole Hamels .50 1.25
GNV39 Matt Kemp .30 .75
GNV40 Dan Uggla .30 .75
GNV41 Scott Kazmir .30 .75
GNV42 J.J. Hardy .20 .50
GNV43 Hunter Pence 1.00 2.50
GNV44 Jason Bay .30 .75
GNV45 James Shields .20 .50
GNV46 Chase Utley .50 1.25
GNV47 Justin Morneau .50 1.25
GNV48 Chien-Ming Wang .30 .75
GNV49 Troy Tulowitzki 1.25 3.00
GNV50 Joe Mauer .50 1.25
GNV51 Brandon Webb .30 .75
GNV52 Matt Holliday .50 1.25
GNV53 Grady Sizemore .30 .75
GNV54 Homer Bailey .30 .75

2007 Topps Gibson Home Run History

COMPLETE SET (110) 60.00 120.00
COMMON GIBSON .60 1.50
SER.1 ODDS 1:9 H, 1:2 HTA, 1:9 K-MART
SER.1 ODDS 1:9 RACK, 1:9 TARGET
SER.1 ODDS 1:9 WAL-MART
CARDS 1-110 ISSUED IN SERIES 1 PACKS

2007 Topps Highlights Autographs

SER.1 A 1:50,842 H, 1:2105 HTA
SER.1 A 1:101,000 K-MART,1:18,396 RACK
SER.1 A 1:50,842 TARGET
SER.1 A 1:101,000 WAL-MART
SER.2 A 1:37,162 HOBBY, 1:523 HTA
SER.1 B 1:24,150 H, 1:1034 HTA
SER.1 B 1:51,800 K-MART, 1:12,264 RACK
SER.1 B 1:25,420 TARGET
SER.1 B 1:51,800 WAL-MART
SER.2 B 1:7330 HOBBY, 1:105 HTA
SER.1 C 1:13,000 H, 1:555 HTA
SER.1 C 1:27,300 K-MART, 1:7350 RACK
SER.1 C 1:13,600 TARGET
SER.1 C 1:27,300 WAL-MART
SER.2 C 1:7330 HOBBY, 1:105 HTA
SER.1 D 1:4916 H, 1:208 HTA
SER.1 D 1:10,250 K-MART, 1:2628 RACK
SER.1 D 1:5100 TARGET, 1:10,250 WAL-MART
SER.2 D 1:12,198 HOBBY, 1:174 HTA
SER.1 E 1:2460 H, 1:52 HTA, 1:5125 K-MART
SER.1 E 1:1314 RACK, 1:2550 TARGET
SER.1 E 1:5125 WAL-MART
SER.2 E 1:1410 HOBBY, 1:20 HTA
SER.1 F 1:1256 H, 1:52 HTA, 1:2564 K-MART
SER.1 F 1:657 RACK, 1:1277 TARGET
SER.1 F 1:2564 WAL-MART
SER.1 G 1:376 H, 1:16 HTA, 1:789 K-MART
SER.1 G 1:203 RACK,1:393 TARGET
SER.1 G 1:789 WAL-MART
GROUP A1 PRINT RUN B/WN 25-50 PER
GROUP B1 PRINT RUN 100 SETS
GROUP C1 PRINT RUN 250 SETS
A1-C1 ARE NOT SERIAL-NUMBERED
A1-C1 PRINT RUNS PROVIDED BY TOPPS
NO GROUP A1 PRICING DUE TO SCARCITY
EXCH * = PARTIAL EXCHANGE
EXCHANGE DEADLINE 02/28/09
AB Aaron Boone E2 4.00 10.00
AJ Andruw Jones B2 12.50 30.00
AM Andrew Miller G 12.50 30.00
AP Albert Pujols A2 150.00 200.00
AP Albert Pujols A/25 *
APA Angel Pagan G 4.00 10.00
AR Alex Rodriguez A/25 *
AR Anthony Reyes E2 6.00 15.00
AS Anibal Sanchez G 4.00 10.00
CG Curtis Granderson B2 15.00 40.00
CMS Curt Schilling A/25 *
CQ Carlos Quentin F 6.00 15.00
CW Chien-Ming Wang B/100 * 100.00 200.00
CW Craig Wilson E2 6.00 15.00
DO David Ortiz B/100 * 60.00 120.00
DO David Ortiz B2 12.50 30.00
DT Derrick Turnbow D2 6.00 15.00
DU Dan Uggla E2 8.00 20.00
DW David Wright D 30.00 60.00
DW David Wright C2 30.00 60.00
DWW Dontrelle Willis E 10.00 25.00
DWW Dontrelle Willis C2 6.00 15.00
DY Delmon Young E 10.00 25.00
EC Endy Chavez B2 10.00 25.00
EF Emiliano Fruto G 4.00 10.00
ES Ervin Santana E2 4.00 10.00
GS Gary Sheffield A/25 *
HR Hanley Ramirez G 8.00 20.00
JAS John Smoltz C/250 * 20.00 50.00
JD Johnny Damon A/25 *
JD Johnny Damon B2 30.00 60.00
JEM Justin Morneau E 10.00 25.00
JF Josh Fields F 6.00 15.00
JG Jon Garland E2 4.00 10.00
JH John Hattig G 4.00 10.00
JL James Loney G 6.00 15.00
JM John Maine F 10.00 25.00
JS Johan Santana C/250 * 40.00 80.00
JT Jim Thome A2 20.00 50.00
JV Justin Verlander B2 8.00 20.00
JZ Joel Zumaya E2 8.00 20.00
KE Kelvim Escobar C2 6.00 15.00
KM Kevin Mench D 4.00 10.00
KM Kendry Morales B2 4.00 10.00
LM Lastings Milledge E2 4.00 10.00
MC Miguel Cabrera C/250 * 12.50 30.00
MC Melky Cabrera E2 8.00 20.00
MH Matt Holliday G 6.00 15.00
MN Mike Napoli G 10.00 25.00
MP Mike Piazza A/50 * 90.00 150.00
MTC Matt Cain D2 6.00 15.00
PL Paul LoDuca B2 12.50 30.00
RC Robinson Cano E2 15.00 40.00
RH Ryan Howard B/100 * 75.00 150.00
RH Ryan Howard A2 40.00 80.00
RM Russell Martin C2 10.00 25.00
RZ Ryan Zimmerman E 15.00 40.00
RZ Ryan Zimmerman C2 12.50 30.00
SC Shawn Chacon E2 4.00 10.00
SP Scott Podsednik E2 4.00 10.00
SR Shawn Riggans E2 4.00 10.00
SSC Shin-Soo Choo B2 12.50 30.00
ST Steve Trachsel A2 10.00 25.00
TG Tom Glavine B2 30.00 60.00
TH Travis Hafner D 10.00 25.00
TT Troy Tulowitzki G 6.00 15.00
VG Vladimir Guerrero A/25 *
VG Vladimir Guerrero A2 40.00 80.00

2007 Topps Highlights Relics

SER.1 A 1:933 H, 1:33 HTA, 1:2160 K-MART
SER.1 A 1:1070 TARGET, 1:2160 WAL-MART
SER.2 A 1:2435 HOBBY, 1:138 HTA
SER.1 B 1:726 H, 1:19 HTA, 1:1270 K-MART
SER.1 B 1:631 TARGET, 1:1270 WAL-MART
SER.2 B 1:609 HOBBY, 1:35 HTA
SER.1 C 1:2468 H, 1:87 HTA, 1:5675 K-MART
SER.1 C 1:2825 TARGET, 1:5675 WAL-MART
SER.2 C 1:1420 HOBBY, 1:80 HTA
SER.2 D 1:533 HOBBY, 1:30 HTA
SER.2 E 1:1705 HOBBY, 1:96 HTA
AB Adrian Beltre B2 3.00 8.00
AER Alex Rodriguez C2 8.00 20.00
AJ Andruw Jones E2 3.00 8.00
ALR Anthony Reyes B2 4.00 10.00
AP Albert Pujols Pants B 8.00 20.00
AP Albert Pujols B2 8.00 20.00
AP2 Albert Pujols Jsy B 8.00 20.00
AR Alex Rodriguez Jsy B 8.00 20.00
AR Aramis Ramirez D2 3.00 8.00
AR2 Alex Rodriguez Bat A 8.00 20.00
AS Alfonso Soriano Bat A 4.00 10.00
AS Alfonso Soriano A2 4.00 10.00
BB Barry Bonds B2
BM Brian McCann Bat A 3.00 8.00
CB Craig Biggio Pants A 4.00 10.00
CD Carlos Delgado Bat B 3.00 8.00
CIB Carlos Beltran Jsy B 3.00 8.00
CJ Chipper Jones B2 3.00 8.00
CQ Carlos Quentin Bat A 3.00 8.00
CS Curt Schilling Jsy A 3.00 8.00
DE David Eckstein A2 5.00 12.00
DO David Ortiz Bat B 4.00 10.00
DO David Ortiz D2 4.00 10.00
DW Dontrelle Willis Jsy B 4.00 10.00
DW David Wright D2 5.00 12.00
DW2 Dontrelle Willis Pants B 4.00 10.00
DWW Dontrelle Willis E2 4.00 10.00
ER Edgar Renteria Bat B 3.00 8.00
FT Frank Thomas Bat B 4.00 10.00
GA Garrett Atkins A2 3.00 8.00
GS Gary Sheffield Bat B 3.00 8.00
GS Grady Sizemore A2 5.00 12.00
IR Ivan Rodriguez Bat C 3.00 8.00
IS Ichiro Suzuki Bat A 8.00 20.00
JAS John Smoltz Pants A 4.00 10.00
JB Jason Bay Jsy A 3.00 8.00
JB2 Jason Bay Bat A 3.00 8.00
JD Jermaine Dye C2 3.00 8.00
JDD Johnny Damon A2 4.00 10.00
JM Justin Morneau Bat B 3.00 8.00
JPM Joe Mauer Bat A 4.00 10.00
JR Jose Reyes Jsy A 3.00 8.00
JS Johan Santana Jsy A 4.00 10.00
JT Jim Thome B2 5.00 12.00
JV Justin Verlander A2 5.00 12.00
LB Lance Berkman C2 3.00 8.00
MAR Manny Ramirez Jsy B 3.00 8.00
MAR2 Manny Ramirez Bat C 3.00 8.00
MC Matt Cain B2 3.00 8.00
MCT Mark Teixeira B2 3.00 8.00
MEC Melky Cabrera B2 4.00 10.00
MO Magglio Ordonez Bat B 4.00 10.00
MR Mariano Rivera Jsy A 4.00 10.00
MR Manny Ramirez D2 3.00 8.00
MT Miguel Tejada Bat A 3.00 8.00
MT Miguel Tejada B2 3.00 8.00
NS Nick Swisher D2 4.00 10.00
PK Paul Konerko Bat A 3.00 8.00
PK Paul Konerko B2 3.00 8.00
PM Pedro Martinez D2 3.00 8.00
RC Robinson Cano Pants A 4.00 10.00
RC Robinson Cano B2 4.00 10.00
RH Ryan Howard Bat B 6.00 15.00
RH Roy Halladay B2 3.00 8.00
RJH Ryan Howard B2 6.00 15.00
RO Roy Oswalt Jsy A 3.00 8.00
SK Scott Kazmir Jsy B 3.00 8.00
SK Scott Kazmir C2 3.00 8.00
SR Scott Rolen Jsy A 4.00 10.00
TG Tom Glavine A2 4.00 10.00
TG1 Tom Glavine Jsy A 4.00 10.00
TG2 Troy Glaus Bat B 3.00 8.00
VG Vladimir Guerrero D2 4.00 10.00
VW Vernon Wells Bat A 3.00 8.00
VW Vernon Wells D2 3.00 8.00

2007 Topps Hit Parade

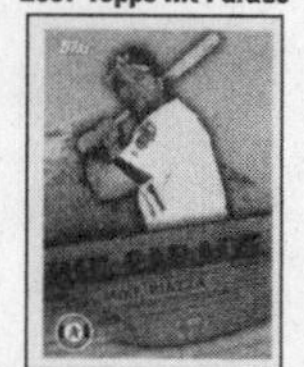

SER.2 ODDS 1:9 HOBBY, 1:2 HTA
HP1 Barry Bonds 2.00 5.00
HP2 Ken Griffey Jr. 1.50 4.00
HP3 Frank Thomas 1.00 2.50
HP4 Jim Thome .60 1.50
HP5 Manny Ramirez 1.00 2.50
HP6 Alex Rodriguez 1.50 4.00
HP7 Gary Sheffield .40 1.00
HP8 Mike Piazza 1.00 2.50
HP9 Carlos Delgado .40 1.00
HP10 Chipper Jones 1.00 2.50
HP11 Barry Bonds 2.00 5.00
HP12 Ken Griffey Jr. 1.50 4.00
HP13 Frank Thomas 1.00 2.50
HP14 Manny Ramirez 1.00 2.50
HP15 Gary Sheffield .40 1.00
HP16 Jeff Kent .40 1.00
HP17 Alex Rodriguez 1.50 4.00
HP18 Luis Gonzalez .40 1.00
HP19 Jim Thome .60 1.50
HP20 Mike Piazza 1.00 2.50
HP21 Craig Biggio .60 1.50
HP22 Barry Bonds 2.00 5.00
HP23 Julio Franco .40 1.00
HP24 Steve Finley .40 1.00
HP25 Omar Vizquel .60 1.50
HP26 Ken Griffey Jr. 1.50 4.00
HP27 Gary Sheffield .40 1.00
HP28 Luis Gonzalez .40 1.00
HP29 Ivan Rodriguez .60 1.50
HP30 Bernie Williams .60 1.50

2007 Topps Hobby Masters

COMPLETE SET (20) 10.00 25.00
SER.1 ODDS 1:6 H, 1:4 HTA
HM1 David Wright 1.50 4.00
HM2 Albert Pujols 2.50 6.00
HM3 David Ortiz .60 1.50
HM4 Ryan Howard 1.50 4.00
HM5 Alfonso Soriano .60 1.50
HM6 Delmon Young .60 1.50
HM7 Jered Weaver .60 1.50
HM8 Derek Jeter 2.50 6.00
HM9 Freddy Sanchez .40 1.00
HM10 Alex Rodriguez 1.50 4.00
HM11 Johan Santana 1.00 2.50
HM12 Ichiro Suzuki 1.50 4.00
HM13 Andruw Jones .40 1.00
HM14 Vladimir Guerrero 1.00 2.50
HM15 Miguel Cabrera 1.00 2.50
HM16 Todd Helton .60 1.50
HM17 Manny Ramirez 1.00 2.50
HM18 Carlos Beltran .40 1.00
HM19 Justin Morneau 1.00 2.50
HM20 Francisco Liriano 1.00 2.50

2007 Topps Homerun Derby Contest

RANDOM INSERTS IN SER.2 PACKS
STATED ODDS 999 SER.#'d SETS
AB Adrian Beltre .60 1.50
AD Adam Dunn 1.00 2.50
AER Alex Rodriguez 2.50 6.00
AJ Andruw Jones .60 1.50
AL Adam LaRoche .60 1.50
AP Albert Pujols 4.00 10.00
AR Aramis Ramirez .60 1.50
AS Alfonso Soriano 1.00 2.50
BH Bill Hall .60 1.50
CB Carlos Beltran .60 1.50
CD Carlos Delgado .60 1.50
CL Carlos Lee .60 1.50
CM Craig Monroe .60 1.50
CU Chase Utley 1.50 4.00
DO David Ortiz 1.00 2.50
DU Dan Uggla 1.00 2.50
DW David Wright 2.50 6.00
DY Delmon Young 1.00 2.50
FT Frank Thomas 1.50 4.00
GA Garrett Atkins .60 1.50
GS Grady Sizemore 1.00 2.50
JB Jason Bay 1.00 2.50
JC Joe Crede .60 1.50
JD Jermaine Dye .60 1.50
JDD Johnny Damon 1.00 2.50
JF Jeff Francoeur 1.50 4.00
JG Jason Giambi .60 1.50
JM Justin Morneau 1.50 4.00
JT Jim Thome 1.00 2.50
KG Ken Griffey Jr 2.50 6.00
LB Lance Berkman 1.00 2.50
MC Miguel Cabrera 1.50 4.00
MH Matt Holliday 1.50 4.00
MMT Marcus Thames .60 1.50
MOT Miguel Tejada 1.00 2.50
MP Mike Piazza 1.50 4.00
MR Manny Ramirez 1.50 4.00
MT Mark Teixeira 1.50 4.00
NS Nick Swisher 1.50 4.00
PB Pat Burrell .60 1.50
PF Prince Fielder 1.00 2.50
PK Paul Konerko 1.00 2.50
RH Ryan Howard 2.50 6.00
RI Raul Ibanez 1.00 2.50
RS Richie Sexson .60 1.50
TG Troy Glaus .60 1.50
TH Travis Hafner .60 1.50
TKH Torii Hunter .60 1.50
VG Vladimir Guerrero 1.50 4.00
VW Vernon Wells .60 1.50

2007 Topps In the Name Letter Relics

SER.1 ODDS 1:8292 H, 1:488 HTA
STATED PRINT RUN 1 SERIAL #'d SET
NO PRICING DUE TO SCARCITY

2007 Topps Mickey Mantle Story

COMPLETE SET (57) 50.00 100.00
COMP.SERIES 1 (1-15) 8.00 20.00
COMP.SERIES 2 (16-30) 8.00 20.00
COMP.UPD.SET (31-45) 12.50 30.00
COMP.08 SER.1 SET (46-57) 6.00 15.00
COMP.08 SER.2 SET (58-67) 6.00 15.00
COMP.08 UPD SET (68-77) 6.00 15.00
COMMON MANTLE (1-77) .75 2.00
SER.1 ODDS 1:18 H, 1:18 HTA, 1:18 K-MART
SER.1 ODDS 1:18 RACK, 1:18 TARGET
SER.1 ODDS 1:18 WAL-MART
SER.2 ODDS 1:18 H,1:3 HTA,1:18 R
UPDATE ODDS 1:18 H, 1:3 HTA, 1:18 R
08 SER.1 ODDS 1:18 H, 1:3 HTA
08 SER.2 ODDS 1:18 H,1:3 HTA, 1:18 R
08 UPD.ODDS 1:18 HOBBY
1-15 ISSUED IN SERIES 1
16-30 ISSUED IN SERIES 2
31-45 ISSUED IN UPDATE
46-57 ISSSUED IN 08 SERIES 1
58-65 ISSUED IN 08 SERIES 2
66-77 ISSUED IN 08 UPDATE

2007 Topps Opening Day Team vs. Team

COMPLETE SET (15) 6.00 15.00
SER.2 ODDS 1:12 HOBBY, 1:3 HTA
OD1 New York Mets / St. Louis Cardinals .40 1.00
OD2 Atlanta Braves / Philadelphia Phillies .40 1.00
OD3 Florida Marlins / Washington Nationals .40 1.00
OD4 Tampa Bay Devil Rays / New York Yankees 1.00 2.50
OD5 Toronto Blue Jays / Detroit Tigers .40 1.00
OD6 Cleveland Indians / Chicago White Sox .40 1.00
OD7 Los Angeles Dodgers / Milwaukee Brewers .40 1.00
OD8 Chicago Cubs / Cincinnati Reds .40 1.00
OD9 Arizona Diamondbacks / Colorado Rockies .40 1.00
OD10 Boston Red Sox / Kansas City Royals 1.00 2.50
OD11 Oakland Athletics / Seattle Mariners .40 1.00
OD12 Baltimore Orioles / Minnesota Twins .40 1.00
OD13 Pittsburgh Pirates / Houston Astros .40 1.00
OD14 Texas Rangers / Los Angeles Angels .40 1.00
OD15 San Diego Padres / San Francisco Giants .40 1.00

2007 Topps Own the Game

COMPLETE SET (25) 10.00 25.00
SER.1 ODDS 1:6 H, 1:2 HTA, 1:6 K-MART
SER.1 ODDS 1:6 RACK, 1:6 TARGET
SER.1 ODDS 1:6 WAL-MART
OTG1 Ryan Howard 1.50 4.00
OTG2 David Ortiz .60 1.50
OTG3 Alfonso Soriano .60 1.50
OTG4 Albert Pujols 2.50 6.00
OTG5 Lance Berkman .60 1.50
OTG6 Jermaine Dye .40 1.00
OTG7 Travis Hafner .40 1.00
OTG8 Jim Thome .60 1.50
OTG9 Carlos Beltran .40 1.00
OTG10 Adam Dunn .60 1.50
OTG11 Ryan Howard 1.50 4.00
OTG12 David Ortiz .60 1.50
OTG13 Albert Pujols 2.50 6.00
OTG14 Lance Berkman .60 1.50
OTG15 Justin Morneau 1.00 2.50
OTG16 Andruw Jones .40 1.00
OTG17 Jermaine Dye .40 1.00
OTG18 Travis Hafner .40 1.00
OTG19 Alex Rodriguez 1.50 4.00
OTG20 David Wright 1.50 4.00
OTG21 Johan Santana 1.00 2.50
OTG22 Chris Carpenter 1.00 2.50
OTG23 Brandon Webb .60 1.50
OTG24 Roy Oswalt .60 1.50
OTG25 Roy Halladay 1.00 2.50

2007 Topps Rookie Stars

COMPLETE SET (10) 6.00 15.00
SER.2 ODDS 1:9 HOBBY
RS1 Daisuke Matsuzaka 1.25 3.00
RS2 Kevin Kouzmanoff .30 .75
RS3 Elijah Dukes .50 1.25
RS4 Andrew Miller .75 2.00
RS5 Kei Igawa .75 2.00
RS6 Troy Tulowitzki 2.00 5.00
RS7 Ubaldo Jimenez 2.00 5.00
RS8 Alex Gordon 1.00 2.50
RS9 Josh Hamilton 1.25 3.00
RS10 Delmon Young .50 1.25

2007 Topps Stars

COMPLETE SET (15) 6.00 15.00
SER.2 ODDS 1:9 HOBBY
TS1 Ryan Howard 1.25 3.00
TS2 Alfonso Soriano .50 1.25
TS3 Todd Helton .50 1.25
TS4 Johan Santana .75 2.00
TS5 David Wright 1.25 3.00
TS6 Albert Pujols 2.00 5.00
TS7 Daisuke Matsuzaka 1.25 3.00
TS8 Miguel Cabrera .75 2.00
TS9 David Ortiz .50 1.25
TS10 Alex Rodriguez 1.25 3.00
TS11 Vladimir Guerrero .75 2.00
TS12 Ichiro Suzuki 1.25 3.00
TS13 Derek Jeter 2.00 5.00
TS14 Lance Berkman .50 1.25
TS15 Ryan Zimmerman .50 1.25

2007 Topps Target Factory Set Mantle Memorabilia

COMMON MANTLE MEMORABILIA 15.00 40.00
DISTRIBUTED WITH TOPPS TARGET FACT.SETS
MMR53 Mickey Mantle 53T 15.00 40.00
MMR56 Mickey Mantle 56T 15.00 40.00
MMR57 Mickey Mantle 57T 15.00 40.00

2007 Topps Target Factory Set Red Backs

1 Mickey Mantle 3.00 8.00
2 Ted Williams 2.50 6.00

2007 Topps Trading Places

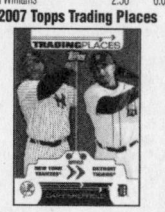

COMPLETE SET (25) 6.00 15.00
SER.2 ODDS 1:9 HOBBY
TP1 Jeff Weaver .40 1.00
TP2 Frank Thomas 1.00 2.50
TP3 Mike Piazza 1.00 2.50
TP4 Alfonso Soriano .60 1.50
TP5 Freddy Garcia .40 1.00
TP6 Jason Marquis .40 1.00
TP7 Ted Lilly .40 1.00
TP8 Mark Loretta .40 1.00
TP9 Marcus Giles .40 1.00
TP10 Barry Zito .40 1.00
TP11 Andy Pettitte .60 1.50
TP12 J.D. Drew .40 1.00
TP13 Gary Matthews .40 1.00
TP14 Jay Payton .40 1.00
TP15 Aubrey Huff .40 1.00
TP16 Brian Bannister .40 1.00
TP17 Jeff Conine .40 1.00
TP18 Gary Sheffield .40 1.00
TP19 Shea Hillenbrand .40 1.00
TP20 Wes Helms .40 1.00
TP21 Frank Catalanotto .40 1.00
TP22 Adam LaRoche .40 1.00
TP23 Mike Gonzalez .40 1.00
TP24 Greg Maddux 1.50 4.00
TP25 Jason Schmidt .40 1.00

2007 Topps Trading Places Autographs

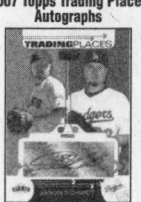

SER.2 ODDS 1:3,055 HOBBY, 1:44 HTA
AH Aubrey Huff 6.00 15.00
AL Adam LaRoche 4.00 10.00
BB Brian Bannister 5.00 12.00
FC Frank Catalanotto 4.00 10.00
FG Freddy Garcia 6.00 15.00
GS Gary Sheffield 15.00 40.00
JS Jason Schmidt 6.00 15.00
MG Mike Gonzalez 4.00 10.00
SH Shea Hillenbrand 4.00 10.00
WH Wes Helms 4.00 10.00

2007 Topps Trading Places Relics

SER.2 ODDS 1:2,435 HOBBY, 1:137 HTA
AP Andy Pettitte 5.00 12.00
AS Alfonso Soriano 5.00 12.00
BZ Barry Zito 4.00 10.00
FT Frank Thomas 5.00 12.00
GM Greg Maddux 5.00 12.00
GS Gary Sheffield 5.00 12.00
JW Jeff Weaver 4.00 10.00
MG Marcus Giles 4.00 10.00
ML Mark Loretta 4.00 10.00
MP Mike Piazza 6.00 15.00

2007 Topps Unlock the Mick

COMPLETE SET (5) 3.00 8.00
COMMON MANTLE 1.00 2.50
SER.1 ODDS 1:18 H, 1:18 HTA, 1:18 K-MART
SER.1 ODDS 1:18 RACK, 1:18 TARGET
SER.1 ODDS 1:18 WAL-MART

2007 Topps Wal-Mart

COMP.SERIES 1 (18) 15.00 40.00
STATED ODDS 1:4 WAL-MART
SER.1 ODDS 3 PER $9.99 WAL-MART BOX
SER.1 ODDS 6 PER $19.99 WAL-MART BOX
1-18 ISSUED IN SERIES 1
19-36 ISSUED IN SERIES 2
37-54 ISSUED IN UPDATE
WM1 Frank Thomas 41 PB 1.00 2.50
WM2 Mike Piazza 34 DS 1.00 2.50
WM3 Ivan Rodriguez 22 Caramel .60 1.50
WM4 David Ortiz T207 .60 1.50
WM5 David Wright 1887 AG 1.50 4.00
WM6 Greg Maddux 52T 1.50 4.00
WM7 Mickey Mantle 51T 3.00 8.00
WM8 Jose Reyes 65T .60 1.50
WM9 John Smoltz T205 1.00 2.50
WM10 Jim Edmonds 56T .60 1.50
WM11 Ryan Howard 58T 1.50 4.00
WM12 Miguel Cabrera T206 1.00 2.50
WM13 Carlos Delgado 10 Turkey .40 1.00
WM14 Miguel Tejada 55B .60 1.50
WM15 Ichiro Suzuki 33 DeLong 1.50 4.00
WM16 Albert Pujols 49B 2.50 6.00
WM17 Derek Jeter 91 SC 2.50 6.00
WM18 Vladimir Guerrero 61 Baz 1.00 2.50
WM19 Lance Berkman .60 1.50
WM20 Chase Utley 1.00 2.50
WM21 Gary Matthews .40 1.00
WM22 Johan Santana 1.00 2.50
WM23 Todd Helton .60 1.50
WM24 Carlos Beltran .40 1.00
WM25 Alex Rodriguez 1.50 4.00
WM26 Cole Hamels 1.00 2.50
WM27 Daisuke Matsuzaka 1.50 4.00
WM28 Kei Igawa 1.00 2.50
WM29 Hanley Ramirez 1.00 2.50
WM30 Joe Mauer 1.00 2.50
WM31 Brandon Webb .60 1.50
WM32 Michael Young .60 1.50
WM33 Nick Swisher 1.00 2.50
WM34 Jason Bay .60 1.50
WM35 Manny Ramirez 1.00 2.50
WM36 Ryan Zimmerman .60 1.50
WM37 Grady Sizemore .60 1.50
WM38 Matt Holliday 1.00 2.50
WM39 Jimmy Rollins .60 1.50
WM40 Magglio Ordonez .60 1.50
WM41 Prince Fielder .60 1.50
WM42 Jorge Posada .60 1.50
WM43 Hideki Okajima 2.00 5.00
WM44 Dan Uggla .60 1.50
WM45 Jake Peavy .40 1.00
WM46 Carlos Lee .40 1.00
WM47 C.C. Sabathia .60 1.50
WM48 Gary Sheffield .40 1.00
WM49 Tim Lincecum 6.00 15.00
WM50 J.J. Putz .40 1.00
WM51 Justin Verlander 1.25 3.00
WM52 Akinori Iwamura 1.00 2.50
WM53 Adam LaRoche .40 1.00
WM54 Alfonso Soriano .60 1.50

2007 Topps Williams 406

COMPLETE SET (36) 12.50 30.00
COMP.SERIES 1 (18) 6.00 15.00
COMP.SERIES 2 (18) 6.00 15.00

COMMON WILLIAMS .60 1.50
SER.1 ODDS 1:4 TARGET

2007 Topps World Champion Relics

SER.1 ODDS 1:7550 H, 1:226 HTA
SER.1 ODDS 1:14,750 K-MART
SER.1 ODDS 1:7550 TARGET
SER.1 ODDS 1:14,750 WAL-MART
STATED PRINT RUN 100 SETS
CARDS ARE NOT SERIAL NUMBERED
PRINT RUNS PROVIDED BY TOPPS
WCR1 Jeff Weaver Jsy/100 * 20.00 50.00
WCR2 Chris Duncan Jsy/100 * 40.00 80.00
WCR3 Chris Carpenter Jsy/100 * 60.00 120.00
WCR4 Yadier Molina Jsy/100 * 60.00 120.00
WCR5 Albert Pujols Bat/100 * 75.00 150.00
WCR6 Jim Edmonds Jsy/100 * 40.00 80.00
WCR7 Ronnie Belliard Bat/100 * 40.00 80.00
WCR8 So Taguchi Bat/100 * 60.00 120.00
WCR9 Juan Encarnacion Bat/100 * 20.00 50.00
WCR10 Scott Rolen Jsy/100 * 40.00 80.00
WCR11 Anthony Reyes Jsy/100 * 40.00 80.00
WCR12 Preston Wilson Bat/100 * 30.00 60.00
WCR13 Jeff Suppan Jsy/100 * 30.00 60.00
WCR14 Adam Wainwright Jsy/100 * 40.00 80.00
WCR15 David Eckstein Bat/100 * 20.00 50.00

2007 Topps World Domination

WD1 Ryan Howard 1.50 4.00
WD2 Justin Morneau 1.00 2.50
WD3 Ivan Rodriguez .60 1.50
WD4 Albert Pujols 2.50 6.00
WD5 Jorge Cantu .40 1.00
WD6 Johan Santana 1.00 2.50
WD7 Ichiro Suzuki 1.50 4.00
WD8 Chien-Ming Wang .60 1.50
WD9 Mariano Rivera 1.00 2.50
WD10 Andruw Jones .40 1.00

2007 Topps Update

This 334-card set was released in October, 2007. The set was issued through both hobby and retail channels. The hobby packs were created in two forms: 10-card wax packs with an $1.59 SRP which came 36 packs to a box and 12 boxes per case. The other form were the 50-card HTA pack with an $10 SRP which came 10 packs per box and six boxes per case. While a few rookies were interspersed throughout the set, most of the 2007 rookies were issued betwwen cards 147-202. The other subset is a Classic Combos grouping (275-284).

COMP.SET w/o SPs (330) 20.00 50.00
COMMON CARD (1-330) .12 .30
COMMON ROOKIE (1-330) .20 .50
1-330 PLATE ODDS 1:54 HTA
PLATE PRINT RUN 1 SET PER COLOR
BLACK-CYAN-MAGENTA-YELLOW ISSUED
NO PLATE PRICING DUE TO SCARCITY
1 Tony Armas Jr. .12 .30
2 Shannon Stewart .12 .30
3 Jason Marquis .12 .30
4 Josh Wilson .12 .30
5 Steve Trachsel .12 .30
6 J.D. Drew .12 .30
7 Ronnie Belliard .12 .30
8 Trot Nixon .12 .30
9 Adam LaRoche .12 .30
10 Mark Loretta .12 .30
11 Matt Morris .12 .30
12 Marlon Anderson .12 .30
13 Jorge Julio .12 .30
14 Brady Clark .12 .30
15 David Wells .12 .30
16 Francisco Rosario .12 .30
17 Jason Ellison .12 .30
18 Adam Jones .20 .50
19 Russell Branyan .12 .30
20 Rob Bowen .12 .30
21 J.D. Durbin .12 .30
22 Jeff Salazar .12 .30
23 Tadahito Iguchi .12 .30
24 Brad Hennessey .12 .30
25 Mark Hendrickson .12 .30
26 Kameron Loe .12 .30
27 Yusmeiro Petit .12 .30
28 Olmedo Saenz .12 .30
29 Carlos Silva .12 .30
30 Kevin Frandsen .12 .30
31 Tony Pena .12 .30
32 Russ Ortiz .12 .30
33 Hong-Chih Kuo .12 .30
34 Paul McAnulty .12 .30
35 Hiram Bocachica .12 .30
36 Justin Germano .12 .30
37 Jason Simontacchi .12 .30
38 Jose Cruz .12 .30
39 Wilfredo Ledezma .12 .30
40 Chris Denorfia UER .12 .30
(wrong name on front; Carlos Carrasco)
41 Ryan Langerhans .12 .30
42 Chris Snelling .12 .30
43 Ubaldo Jimenez .75 2.00
44 Scott Spiezio .12 .30
45 Byung-Hyun Kim .12 .30
46 Brandon Lyon .12 .30
47 Scott Hairston .12 .30
48 Chad Durbin .12 .30
49 Sammy Sosa .30 .75
50 Jason Smith .12 .30
51 Zach Greinke .20 .50
52 Armando Benitez .12 .30
53 Randy Messenger .12 .30
54 Mark Teixeira .30 .75
55 Mike Maroth .12 .30
56 Jamie Burke .12 .30
57 Carlos Marmol .20 .50
58 David Weathers .12 .30
59 Ryan Doumit .12 .30
60 Michael Barrett .12 .30
61 Shawn Chacon .12 .30
62 Mike Fontenot .12 .30
63 Cesar Izturis .12 .30
64 Cliff Floyd .12 .30
65 Angel Pagan .12 .30
66 Aaron Miles .12 .30
67 Tony Graffanino .12 .30
68 Kevin Mench .12 .30
69 Claudio Vargas .12 .30
70 Jose Capellan .12 .30
71 A.J. Pierzynski .12 .30
72 Darin Erstad .12 .30
73 Boone Logan .12 .30
74 Luis Castillo .12 .30
75 Marcus Thames .12 .30
76 Neifi Perez .12 .30
77 Esteban German .12 .30
78 Tony Pena .12 .30
79 Adam Wainwright .20 .50
80 Reggie Sanders .12 .30
81 Kelly Shoppach .12 .30
82 Rafael Betancourt .12 .30
83 Tom Mastny .12 .30
84 Kyle Farnsworth .12 .30
85 Rick Ankiel .12 .30
86 Kevin Thompson .12 .30
87 Jeff Karstens .12 .30
88 Eric Hinske .12 .30
89 Doug Mirabelli .12 .30
90 Julian Tavarez .12 .30
91 Carlos Pena .20 .50
92 Brendan Harris .12 .30
93 Chris Sampson .12 .30
94 Al Reyes .12 .30
95 Dmitri Young .12 .30
96 Jason Bergmann .12 .30
97 Shawn Hill .12 .30
98 Greg Dobbs .12 .30
99 Carlos Ruiz .12 .30
100a Abraham Nunez .12 .30
100b Jacoby Ellsbury (RC) 30.00 60.00
101 Jayson Werth .20 .50
102 Adam Eaton .12 .30
103 Antonio Alfonseca .12 .30
104 Jorge Sosa .12 .30
105 Ramon Castro .12 .30
106 Ruben Gotay .12 .30
107 Damion Easley .12 .30
108 David Newhan .12 .30
109 Jason Wood .12 .30
110 Reggie Abercrombie .12 .30
111 Kevin Gregg .12 .30
112 Henry Owens .12 .30
113 Willie Harris .12 .30
114 Pete Orr .12 .30
115 Casey Janssen .12 .30
116 Jason Frasor .12 .30
117 Jeremy Accardo .12 .30
118 John McDonald .12 .30
119 Matt Stairs .12 .30
120 Jason Phillips .12 .30
121 Justin Duchscherer .12 .30
122 Rich Harden .12 .30
123 Jack Cust .12 .30
124 Lenny DiNardo .12 .30
125 Joe Kennedy .12 .30
126 Chad Gaudin .12 .30
127 Marco Scutaro .12 .30
128 Brad Thompson .12 .30
129 Dustin Moseley .12 .30
130 Eric Gagne .12 .30
131 Marlon Byrd .12 .30
132 Scot Shields .12 .30
133 Victor Diaz .12 .30
134 Reggie Willits .12 .30
135 Jose Molina .12 .30
136 Ramon Vazquez .12 .30
137 Erick Aybar .12 .30
138 Sean Marshall .12 .30
139 Casey Kotchman .12 .30
140 Ryan Spilborghs .12 .30
141 Cameron Maybin RC .30 .75
142 Jeremy Guthrie .12 .30
143 Jeff Baker .12 .30
144 Edwin Jackson .12 .30
145 Macay McBride .12 .30
146 Freddie Bynum .12 .30
147 Eric Patterson .12 .30
148 Dustin McGowan .12 .30
149 Homer Bailey (RC) .30 .75
150 Ryan Braun (RC) 1.00 2.50
151 Tony Abreu RC .50 1.25
152 Tyler Clippard (RC) .30 .75
153 Mark Reynolds RC 1.50 4.00
154 Jesse Litsch RC .30 .75
155 Carlos Gomez RC .30 .75
156 Matt DeSalvo (RC) .20 .50
157 Andy LaRoche (RC) .20 .50
158 Tim Lincecum RC 3.00 8.00
159 Jarrod Saltalamacchia (RC) .30 .75
160 Hunter Pence (RC) 1.00 2.50
161 Brandon Wood (RC) .20 .50
162 Phil Hughes (RC) 1.00 2.50
163 Rocky Cherry RC .50 1.25
164 Chase Wright RC .50 1.25
165 Dallas Braden RC 1.25 3.00
166 Felix Pie (RC) .20 .50
167 Zach McClellan RC .20 .50
168 Rick Vanden Hurk RC .20 .50
169 Micah Owings (RC) .20 .50
170 Jon Coutlangus (RC) .20 .50
171 Andy Sonnanstine RC .20 .50
172 Yunel Escobar (RC) .20 .50
173 Kevin Slowey (RC) .50 1.25
174 Curtis Thigpen (RC) .20 .50
175 Masumi Kuwata RC .20 .50
176 Kurt Suzuki (RC) .20 .50
177 Travis Buck (RC) .20 .50
178 Matt Lindstrom (RC) .20 .50
179 Jesus Flores RC .20 .50
180 Joakim Soria RC .20 .50
181 Nathan Haynes (RC) .20 .50
182 Matthew Brown RC .20 .50
183 Travis Metcalf RC .30 .75
184 Yovani Gallardo (RC) .50 1.25
185 Nate Schierholtz (RC) .20 .50
186 Kyle Kendrick RC .50 1.25
187 Kevin Melillo (RC) .20 .50
188 Ryan Rowland-Smith .12 .30
189 Lee Gronkiewicz RC .20 .50
190 Eulogio De La Cruz (RC) .30 .75
191 Brett Carroll RC .20 .50
192 Terry Evans RC .20 .50
193 Chase Headley (RC) .20 .50
194 Guillermo Rodriguez RC .20 .50
195 Marcus McBeth (RC) .20 .50
196 Brian Wolfe (RC) .20 .50
197 Troy Cate RC .20 .50
198 Mike Zagurski RC .20 .50
199 Yoel Hernandez RC .12 .30
200 Brad Salmon RC .20 .50
201 Alberto Arias RC .20 .50
202 Danny Putnam (RC) .20 .50
203 Jamie Vermilyea RC .20 .50
204 Kyle Lohse .12 .30
205 Sammy Sosa .30 .75
206 Tom Glavine .20 .50
207 Prince Fielder .20 .50
208 Mark Buehrle .20 .50
209 Troy Tulowitzki .75 2.00
210 Daisuke Matsuzaka RC .75 2.00
211 Randy Johnson .30 .75
212 Justin Verlander .40 1.00
213 Trevor Hoffman .20 .50
214 Alex Rodriguez .50 1.25
215 Ivan Rodriguez .20 .50
216 David Ortiz .20 .50
217 Placido Polanco .12 .30
218 Derek Jeter .75 2.00
219 Alex Rodriguez .50 1.25
220 Vladimir Guerrero .30 .75
221 Magglio Ordonez .20 .50
222 Ichiro Suzuki .50 1.25
223 Russell Martin .12 .30
224 Prince Fielder .20 .50
225 Chase Utley .30 .75
226 Jose Reyes .20 .50
227 David Wright .50 1.25
228 Carlos Beltran .12 .30
229 Barry Bonds .60 1.50
230 Ken Griffey Jr. .50 1.25
231 Torii Hunter .12 .30
232 Jonathan Papelbon .30 .75
233 J.J. Putz .12 .30
234 Francisco Rodriguez .20 .50
235 C.C. Sabathia .20 .50
236 Johan Santana .30 .75
237 Justin Verlander .40 1.00
238 Francisco Cordero .12 .30
239 Mike Lowell .12 .30
240 Cole Hamels .30 .75
241 Trevor Hoffman .20 .50
242 Manny Ramirez .30 .75
243 Jake Peavy .12 .30
244 Brad Penny .12 .30
245 Takashi Saito .12 .30
246 Ben Sheets .12 .30
247 Hideki Okajima .60 1.50
248 Roy Oswalt .20 .50
249 Billy Wagner .12 .30
250 Carl Crawford .20 .50
251 Chris Young .12 .30
252 Brian McCann .12 .30
253 Derrek Lee .12 .30
254 Albert Pujols .75 2.00
255 Dmitri Young .12 .30
256 Orlando Hudson .12 .30
257 J.J. Hardy .12 .30
258 Miguel Cabrera .30 .75
259 Freddy Sanchez .12 .30
260 Matt Holliday .30 .75
261 Carlos Lee .12 .30
262 Aaron Rowand .12 .30
263 Alfonso Soriano .20 .50
264 Victor Martinez .20 .50
265 Jorge Posada .20 .50
266 Justin Morneau .30 .75
267 Brian Roberts .12 .30
268 Carlos Guillen .12 .30
269 Grady Sizemore .20 .50
270 Josh Beckett .20 .50
271 Dan Haren .12 .30
272 Bobby Jenks .12 .30
273 John Lackey .12 .30
274 Gil Meche .12 .30
275 Mike Fontenot .12 .30
Khalil Greene
276 Alex Rodriguez .50 1.25
Russell Martin
277 Troy Tulowitzki .75 2.00
Jose Reyes
278 Jorge Posada .75 2.00
Derek Jeter
Alex Rodriguez
279 Chase Utley .50 1.25
Ichiro Suzuki
280 Carl Crawford .20 .50
Carlos Guillen
281 Cole Hamels .30 .75
Russell Martin
282 Jonathan Papelbon .30 .75
Jorge Posada
283 Carl Crawford .20 .50
Victor Martinez
284 Alfonso Soriano .20 .50
J.J. Hardy
285 Justin Morneau .30 .75
286 Prince Fielder .20 .50
287 Alex Rios .20 .50
288 Vladimir Guerrero .30 .75
289 Albert Pujols .75 2.00
290 Ryan Howard .50 1.25
291 Magglio Ordonez .20 .50
292 Matt Holliday .30 .75
293 Wilson Betemit .12 .30
294 Todd Wellemeyer .12 .30
295 Scott Baker .12 .30
296 Edgar Gonzalez .12 .30
297 J.P. Howell .12 .30
298 Shaun Marcum .12 .30
299 Edinson Volquez .12 .30
300 Kason Gabbard .12 .30
301 Bob Howry .12 .30
302 J.A. Happ .75 2.00
303 Scott Feldman .20 .50
304 D'Angelo Jimenez .12 .30
305 Orlando Palmeiro .12 .30
306 Paul Bako .12 .30
307 Kyle Davies .12 .30
308 Gabe Gross .12 .30
309 John Wasdin .12 .30
310 Jon Knott .12 .30
311 Josh Phelps .12 .30
312a Joba Chamberlain RC 1.00 2.50
312b Joba Chamberlain 90.00 150.00
Reverse Negative
312c Joba Chamberlain UER
Houston Astros
313 Octavio Dotel .12 .30
314 Craig Monroe .12 .30
315 Edward Mujica .12 .30
316 Brandon Watson .12 .30
317 Chris Schroder .12 .30
318 Scott Proctor .12 .30
319 Ty Wigginton .12 .30
320 Troy Percival .12 .30
321 Scott Linebrink .12 .30
322 David Murphy .12 .30
323 Jorge Cantu .12 .30
324 Dan Wheeler .12 .30
325 Jason Kendall .12 .30
326 Milton Bradley .12 .30
327 Justin Upton RC 1.50 4.00
328 Kenny Lofton .12 .30
329 Roger Clemens .40 1.00
330 Brian Burres .12 .30
SO1 Poley Walnuts 12.50 30.00

2007 Topps Update 1st Edition

*1ST ED VET: 2X TO 5X BASIC
*1ST ED RC: 1.2X TO 3X BASIC RC
STATED ODDS 1:36 HOB, 1:5 HTA

2007 Topps Update Copper

COMMON CARD 2.50 6.00
STATED ODDS 1:4 HTA
STATED PRINT RUN 56 SER.#'d SETS

2007 Topps Update Gold

*GOLD VET: 2.5X TO 6X BASIC
*GOLD RC: 1.5X TO 4X BASIC RC
STATED ODDS 1:4 HOB, 1:4 RET
STATED PRINT RUN 2007 SER.#'d SETS

2007 Topps Update Platinum

STATED ODDS 1:9700 H, 1:1085 HTA
STATED ODDS 1:9700 RETAIL
STATED PRINT RUN 1 SER.#'d SET
NO PRICING DUE TO SCARCITY

2007 Topps Update Red Back

COMPLETE SET (330) 30.00 60.00
*RED VET: .5X TO 1.2X BASIC
*RED RC: .5X TO 1.2X BASIC RC
STATED ODDS XXX

2007 Topps Update 1954 Mantle Reprint Relic

STATED ODDS 1:73,000 HOBBY
STATED ODDS 1:67,200 HTA
STATED ODDS 1:10,800 RETAIL
STATED PRINT RUN 54 SER.#'d SETS
NO PRICING DUE TO SCARCITY

2007 Topps Update 2007 Highlights Autographs

GROUP A ODDS 1:14,900 H, 1:252 HTA
GROUP A ODDS 1:14,900 RETAIL
GROUP B ODDS 1:925 H, 19 HTA
GROUP B ODDS 1:1,165 RETAIL
GROUP C ODDS 1:10,100 H, 1:165 HTA
GROUP C ODDS 1:9,700 RETAIL
GROUP D ODDS 1:22,000 H,1:88 HTA
GROUP D ODDS 1:18,400 RETAIL
GROUP E ODDS 1:7,200 H, 1:125 HTA
GROUP E ODDS 1:7,605 RETAIL
GROUP F ODDS 1:7,000 H, 1:123 HTA
GROUP F ODDS 1:7,352 RETAIL
GROUP G ODDS 1:5,025 H, 1:105 HTA
GROUP G ODDS 1:6,563 RETAIL
AC Asdrubal Cabrera G 8.00 20.00
AE Andre Ethier B 6.00 15.00
AG Alex Gordon B 10.00 25.00
AH Aaron Heilman B 4.00 10.00
AJ Andruw Jones A 10.00 25.00
AL Anthony Lerew B 4.00 10.00
AP Albert Pujols A 150.00 200.00
AR Alex Rodriguez A 100.00 175.00
AS Alfonso Soriano A
BB Brian Bruney B 4.00 10.00
CJ Conor Jackson B 4.00 10.00
CS C.C. Sabathia B 8.00 20.00
DE Damion Easley F 4.00 10.00
DW David Wright A 40.00 80.00
FC Francisco Cordero B 4.00 10.00
GS Gary Sheffield B 10.00 25.00
JR Jimmy Rollins B 12.50 30.00
JS Jarrod Saltalamacchia B 4.00 10.00
JT Jim Thome A 30.00 60.00
MC Miguel Cairo E 4.00 10.00
PF Prince Fielder B 10.00 25.00
RB Rod Barajas C 4.00 10.00
RC Robinson Cano B 15.00 40.00
RH Ryan Howard A 40.00 80.00
RW Ron Washington D 10.00 25.00
TT Troy Tulowitzki B 10.00 25.00

2007 Topps Update All-Star Patches

STATED ODDS 1:2,500 H,1:249 HTA
STATED PRINT RUN 10 SER.#'d SETS
NO PRICING DUE TO SCARCITY

2007 Topps Update All-Star Stitches

STATED ODDS 1:45 H,1:10 HTA,1:55 R
AIR Alex Rios 3.00 8.00
AP Albert Pujols 8.00 20.00
AR Alex Rodriguez 6.00 15.00
ARR Aaron Rowand 3.00 8.00
BF Brian Fuentes 3.00 8.00
BJ Bobby Jenks 3.00 8.00
BM Brian McCann 5.00 12.00
BR Brian Roberts 3.00 8.00
BS Ben Sheets 3.00 8.00
BW Brandon Webb 3.00 8.00
CB Carlos Beltran 3.00 8.00
CC Carl Crawford 3.00 8.00
CH Cole Hamels 4.00 10.00
CL Carlos Lee 3.00 8.00
CS C.C. Sabathia 5.00 12.00
CU Chase Utley 5.00 12.00
CY Chris Young 3.00 8.00
DO David Ortiz 6.00 15.00
DW David Wright 6.00 15.00
DY Dmitri Young 3.00 8.00
FC Francisco Cordero 3.00 8.00
FR Francisco Rodriguez 3.00 8.00
FS Freddy Sanchez 3.00 8.00
GM Gil Meche 3.00 8.00
GS Grady Sizemore 5.00 12.00
HO Hideki Okajima 5.00 12.00
IR Ivan Rodriguez 5.00 12.00
IS Ichiro Suzuki 10.00 25.00
JB Josh Beckett 5.00 12.00
JEP Jake Peavy 3.00 8.00
JH J.J. Hardy 3.00 8.00
JL John Lackey 3.00 8.00
JM Justin Morneau 3.00 8.00
JP J.J. Putz 3.00 8.00
JR Jose Reyes 5.00 12.00
JRP Jorge Posada 5.00 12.00
JRV Jose Valverde 3.00 8.00
JS Johan Santana 5.00 12.00
JV Justin Verlander 5.00 12.00
MH Matt Holliday 5.00 12.00
ML Mike Lowell 5.00 12.00
MR Manny Ramirez 5.00 12.00
MY Michael Young
OH Orlando Hudson 3.00 8.00
PF Prince Fielder 5.00 12.00
RH Ryan Howard 6.00 15.00
RM Russell Martin 5.00 12.00
RO Roy Oswalt 3.00 8.00
TH Torii Hunter 3.00 8.00
TS Takashi Saito 5.00 12.00
TWH Trevor Hoffman 3.00 8.00
VM Victor Martinez 3.00 8.00

2007 Topps Update All-Star Stitches Dual

STATED ODDS 1:5600 H, 1:490 HTA
STATED PRINT RUN 25 SER.#'d SETS
NO PRICING DUE TO SCARCITY

2007 Topps Update All-Star Stitches Triple

STATED ODDS 1:5600 H, 1:490 HTA
STATED PRINT RUN 25 SER.#'d SETS
NO PRICING DUE TO SCARCITY

2007 Topps Update Barry Bonds 756

STATED ODDS 1:36 H, 1:5 HTA, 1:36 R
HRK Barry Bonds 1.25 3.00

2007 Topps Update Barry Bonds 756 Relic

STATED ODDS 1:5,145 H,1:1,400 HTA
STATED ODDS 1:5,145 RETAIL
STATED PRINT RUN 756 SER.#'d SETS
HRKR Barry Bonds 20.00 50.00

2007 Topps Update Barry Bonds 756 Relic Autographs

STATED ODDS 1:278,000 HOBBY
STATED ODDS 1:67,200 HTA
STATED PRINT RUN 20 SER.#'d SETS
NO PRICING DUE TO SCARCITY

2007 Topps Update Chrome

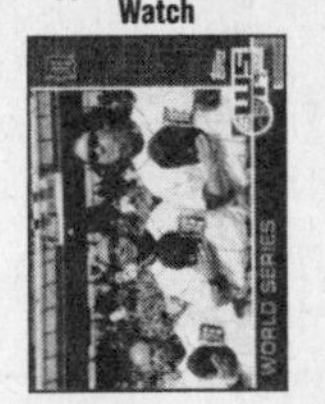

STATED PRINT RUN 415 SER.#'d SETS
TRC1 Homer Bailey 2.50 6.00
TRC2 Ryan Braun 8.00 20.00
TRC3 Tony Abreu 4.00 10.00
TRC4 Tyler Clippard 2.50 6.00
TRC5 Mark Reynolds 12.00 30.00
TRC6 Jesse Litsch 2.50 6.00
TRC7 Carlos Gomez 2.50 6.00
TRC8 Matt DeSalvo 1.50 4.00
TRC9 Andy LaRoche 1.50 4.00
TRC10 Tim Lincecum [illegible] [illegible]
TRC11 Jarrod Saltalamacchia 2.50 6.00
TRC12 Hunter Pence 8.00 20.00
TRC13 Brandon Wood 1.50 4.00
TRC14 Phil Hughes 8.00 20.00
TRC15 Rocky Cherry 4.00 10.00
TRC16 Chase Wright 4.00 10.00
TRC17 Dallas Braden 10.00 25.00
TRC18 Felix Pie 1.50 4.00
TRC19 Zach McClellan 1.50 4.00
TRC20 Rick Vanden Hurk 1.50 4.00
TRC21 Micah Owings 1.50 4.00
TRC22 Jon Coutlangus 1.50 4.00
TRC23 Andy Sonnanstine 1.50 4.00
TRC24 Yunel Escobar 1.50 4.00
TRC25 Kevin Slowey 4.00 10.00
TRC26 Curtis Thigpen 1.50 4.00
TRC27 Masumi Kuwata 1.50 4.00
TRC28 Kurt Suzuki 1.50 4.00
TRC29 Travis Buck 1.50 4.00
TRC30 Matt Lindstrom 1.50 4.00
TRC31 Jesus Flores 1.50 4.00
TRC32 Joakim Soria 1.50 4.00
TRC33 Nathan Haynes 1.50 4.00
TRC34 Matthew Brown 1.50 4.00
TRC35 Travis Metcalf 2.50 6.00
TRC36 Yovani Gallardo 4.00 10.00
TRC37 Nate Schierholtz 1.50 4.00
TRC38 Kyle Kendrick 4.00 10.00
TRC39 Kevin Melillo 1.50 4.00
TRC40 Cameron Maybin 2.50 6.00
TRC41 Lee Gronkiewicz 1.50 4.00
TRC42 Eulogio De La Cruz 2.50 6.00
TRC43 Brett Carroll 1.50 4.00
TRC44 Terry Evans 1.50 4.00
TRC45 Chase Headley 1.50 4.00
TRC46 Guillermo Rodriguez 1.50 4.00
TRC47 Marcus McBeth 1.50 4.00
TRC48 Brian Wolfe 1.50 4.00
TRC49 Troy Cate 1.50 4.00
TRC50 Justin Upton 12.00 30.00
TRC52 Brad Salmon 1.50 4.00
TRC53 Alberto Arias 1.50 4.00
TRC54 Danny Putnam 1.50 4.00
TRC55 Jamie Vermilyea 1.50 4.00

2007 Topps Update Target

COMMON CARD .75 2.00

2007 Topps Update World Series Watch

COMPLETE SET (15) 8.00 20.00
STATED ODDS 1:36 H, 1:5 HTA, 1:36 R
WSW1 New York Mets .75 2.00
WSW2 Detroit Tigers .75 2.00
WSW3 Boston Red Sox 2.00 5.00
WSW4 Milwaukee Brewers .75 2.00
WSW5 Cleveland Indians .75 2.00
WSW6 Los Angeles Angels .75 2.00
WSW7 San Diego Padres .75 2.00
WSW8 Los Angeles Dodgers .75 2.00
WSW9 Philadelphia Phillies .75 2.00
WSW10 Chicago Cubs .75 2.00
WSW11 St. Louis Cardinals .75 2.00
WSW12 Arizona Diamondbacks .75 2.00
WSW13 New York Yankees 2.00 5.00
WSW14 Seattle Mariners .75 2.00
WSW15 Atlanta Braves .75 2.00

2008 Topps

This 330-card first series was released in February, 2008. The set was issued in myriad forms both in and outside the hobby. The packs were issued into the hobby in 10-card packs, with an $1.59 SRP, which came 36 packs to a box and 12 boxes to a case. The HTA packs had 46-cards (44 cards if a relic card was inserted), with an $10 SRP, which came 10 packs to a box and six boxes to a case. Card number 234, which featured the Boston Red Sox celebrating their 2007 World Series victory was issued in a regular version and in a photoshopped version in which Presidential Candidate (and noted Yankee fan) Rudy Giuliani was placed into the celebration. The Guiliani card was issued at an officially announced stated rate of one in two of the earliest boxes.

COMP.HOBBY SET (660) 40.00 80.00
COMP.CUBS SET (660) 40.00 80.00
COMP.DODGERS SET (660) 40.00 80.00
COMP.METS SET (660) 40.00 80.00
COMP.RED SOX SET (660) 40.00 80.00

COMP.TIGERS SET (660) 40.00 80.00
COMP.YANKEES SET (660) 40.00 80.00
COMP.SET w/o VAR (660) 40.00 80.00
COMP.SERIES 1 (331) 15.00 40.00
COMP.SERIES 2 (330) 15.00 40.00
COMMON CARD (1-660) .12 .30
COMMON RC (1-660) .25 .60
SERIES 1 SET DOES NOT INCLUDE FS1
SERIES 1 SET DOES NOT INCLUDE #234C
SER.2 SET DOES NOT INCLUDE #661
SER.2 SET DOES NOT INCLUDE NNO CARDS
SER.1 PLATE ODDS 1:1348 HOBBY
SER.2 PLATE ODDS 1:900 HOBBY
PLATE PRINT RUN 1 SET PER COLOR
BLACK-CYAN-MAGENTA-YELLOW ISSUED
NO PLATE PRICING DUE TO SCARCITY
1 Alex Rodriguez .50 1.25
2 Barry Zito .12 .30
3 Jeff Suppan .12 .30
4 Rick Ankiel .12 .30
5 Scott Kazmir .20 .50
6 Felix Pie .12 .30
7 Mickey Mantle 1.00 2.50
8 Stephen Drew .12 .30
9 Randy Wolf .12 .30
10 Miguel Cabrera .30 .75
11 Yorvit Torrealba .12 .30
12 Jason Bartlett .12 .30
13 Kendry Morales .12 .30
14 Lenny DiNardo .12 .30
15 Magglio Ordonez .50 1.25
Ichiro Suzuki
Placido Polanco
16 Kevin Gregg .12 .30
17 Cristian Guzman .12 .30
18 J.D. Durbin .12 .30
19 Robinson Tejeda .12 .30
20 Daisuke Matsuzaka .30 .75
21 Edwin Encarnacion .12 .30
22 Ron Washington MG .12 .30
23 Chin-Lung Hu (RC) .40 1.00
24 Alex Rodriguez .50 1.25
Magglio Ordonez
Vladimir Guerrero
25 Kaz Matsui .12 .30
26 Manny Ramirez .30 .75
27 Bob Melvin MG .12 .30
28 Kyle Kendrick .12 .30
29 Anibal Sanchez .12 .30
30 Jimmy Rollins .20 .50
31 Ronny Paulino .12 .30
32 Howie Kendrick .12 .30
33 Joe Mauer .30 .75
34 Aaron Cook .12 .30
35 Cole Hamels .30 .75
36 Brendan Harris .12 .30
37 Jason Marquis .12 .30
38 Preston Wilson .12 .30
39 Yovanni Gallardo .12 .30
40 Miguel Tejada .20 .50
41 Rich Aurilia .12 .30
42 Corey Hart .12 .30
43 Ryan Dempster .12 .30
44 Jonathan Broxton .12 .30
45 Dontrelle Willis .12 .30
46 Zack Greinke .20 .50
47 Orlando Cabrera .12 .30
48 Zach Duke .12 .30
49 Orlando Hernandez .12 .30
50 Jake Peavy .12 .30
51 Erik Bedard .12 .30
52 Trevor Hoffman .20 .50
53 Hank Blalock .12 .30
54 Victor Martinez .20 .50
55 Chris Young .12 .30
56 Seth Smith (RC) .25 .60
57 Wladimir Balentien (RC) .25 .60
58 Matt Holliday .30 .75
Ryan Howard
Miguel Cabrera
59 Grady Sizemore .20 .50
60 Jose Reyes .20 .50
61 Alex Rodriguez .20 .50
Carlos Pena
David Ortiz
62 Rich Thompson RC .40 1.00
63 Jason Michaels .12 .30
64 Mike Lowell .12 .30
65 Billy Wagner .12 .30
66 Brad Wilkerson .12 .30
67 Wes Helms .12 .30
68 Kevin Millar .12 .30
69 Bobby Cox MG .12 .30
70 Dan Uggla .20 .50
71 Jarrod Washburn .12 .30
72 Mike Piazza .30 .75
73 Mike Napoli .20 .50
74 Garrett Atkins .12 .30
75 Felix Hernandez .30 .75
76 Ivan Rodriguez .20 .50
77 Angel Guzman .12 .30
78 Radhames Liz RC .40 1.00
79 Omar Vizquel .20 .50
80 Alex Rios .20 .50
81 Ray Durham .12 .30
82 So Taguchi .12 .30
83 Mark Reynolds .12 .30
84 Brian Fuentes .12 .30
85 Jason Bay .20 .50
86 Scott Podsednik .12 .30
87 Maicer Izturis .12 .30
88 Jack Cust .12 .30
89 Josh Willingham .12 .30
90 Vladimir Guerrero .30 .75
91 Marcus Giles .12 .30
92 Ross Detwiler RC .60 1.50
93 Kenny Lofton .12 .30
94 Bud Black MG .12 .30
95 John Lackey .12 .30
96 Sam Fuld RC .75 2.00
97 Clint Sammons (RC) .25 .60
98 Ryan Howard .40 1.00
Chase Utley
99 David Ortiz .20 .50
Manny Ramirez
100 Ryan Howard .40 1.00
101 Ryan Braun ROY .40 1.00
102 Ross Ohlendorf RC .40 1.00
103 Jonathan Albaladejo RC .40 1.00
104 Kevin Youkilis .20 .50
105 Roger Clemens .40 1.00
106 Josh Bard .12 .30
107 Shawn Green .12 .30
108 B.J. Ryan .12 .30
109 Joe Nathan .12 .30
110 Justin Morneau .30 .75
111 Ubaldo Jimenez .20 .50
112 Jacque Jones .12 .30
113 Kevin Frandsen .12 .30
114 Mike Fontenot .12 .30
115 Johan Santana .30 .75
116 Chuck James .12 .30
117 Boof Bonser .12 .30
118 Marco Scutaro .12 .30
119 Jeremy Hermida .12 .30
120 Andruw Jones .12 .30
121 Mike Cameron .12 .30
122 Jason Varitek .30 .75
123 Terry Francona MG .20 .50
124 Bob Geren MG .12 .30
125 Tim Hudson .20 .50
126 Brandon Jones RC .60 1.50
127 Steve Pearce RC .40 1.00
128 Kenny Lofton .12 .30
129 Kevin Hart (RC) .25 .60
130 Justin Upton .20 .50
131 Norris Hopper .12 .30
132 Ramon Vazquez .12 .30
133 Mike Bacsik .12 .30
134 Matt Stairs .12 .30
135 Brad Penny .12 .30
136 Robinson Cano .30 .75
137 Jamey Carroll .12 .30
138 Dan Wheeler .12 .30
139 Johnny Estrada .12 .30
140 Brandon Webb .20 .50
141 Ryan Klesko .12 .30
142 Chris Duncan .12 .30
143 Willie Harris .12 .30
144 Jerry Owens .12 .30
145 Magglio Ordonez .20 .50
146 Aaron Hill .12 .30
147 Marlon Anderson .12 .30
148 Gerald Laird .12 .30
149 Luke Hochevar RC .40 1.00
150 Alfonso Soriano .20 .50
151 Adam Loewen .12 .30
152 Bronson Arroyo .12 .30
153 Luis Mendoza (RC) .25 .60
154 David Ross .12 .30
155 Carlos Zambrano .20 .50
156 Brandon McCarthy .12 .30
157 Tim Redding .12 .30
158 Jose Bautista UER .20 .50
Wrong photo
159 Luke Scott .12 .30
160 Ben Sheets .12 .30
161 Matt Garza .12 .30
162 Andy Laroche .12 .30
163 Doug Davis .12 .30
164 Nate Schierholtz .12 .30
165 Tim Lincecum .50 1.25
166 Andy Sonnanstine .12 .30
167 Jason Hirsh .12 .30
168 Phil Hughes .30 .75
169 Adam Lind .12 .30
170 Scott Rolen .20 .50
171 John Maine .12 .30
172 Chris Ray .12 .30
173 Jamie Moyer .12 .30
174 Julian Tavarez .12 .30
175 Delmon Young .20 .50
176 Troy Patton (RC) .25 .60
177 Josh Anderson (RC) .25 .60
178 Dustin Pedroia ROY .40 1.00
179 Chris B. Young .12 .30
180 Jose Valverde .12 .30
181 Joe Borowski .12 .30
Bobby Jenks
J.J. Putz
182 Billy Buckner (RC) .25 .60
183 Paul Byrd .12 .30
184 Tadahito Iguchi .12 .30
185 Yunel Escobar .12 .30
186 Lastings Milledge .12 .30
187 Dustin McGowan .12 .30
188 Kei Igawa .12 .30
189 Esteban German .12 .30
190 Russell Martin .12 .30
191 Orlando Hudson .12 .30
192 Jim Edmonds .20 .50
193 J.J. Hardy .12 .30
194 Chad Billingsley .12 .30
195 Todd Helton .20 .50
196 Ross Gload .12 .30
197 Melky Cabrera .12 .30
198 Shannon Stewart .12 .30
199 Adrian Beltre .12 .30
200 Manny Ramirez .30 .75
201 Matt Capps .12 .30
202 Mike Lamb .12 .30
203 Jason Tyner .12 .30
204 Rafael Furcal .12 .30
205 Gil Meche .12 .30
206 Geoff Jenkins .12 .30
207 Jeff Kent .12 .30
208 David DeJesus .12 .30
209 Andy Phillips .12 .30
210 Mark Teahen .12 .30
211 Lyle Overbay .12 .30
212 Moises Alou .12 .30
213 Michael Barrett .12 .30
214 C.J. Wilson .12 .30
215 Bobby Jenks .12 .30
216 Ryan Garko .12 .30
217 Josh Beckett .20 .50
218 Clint Hurdle MG .12 .30
219 Kevin Kouzmanoff .12 .30
220 Roy Oswalt .20 .50
221 Ian Snell .12 .30
222 Mark Grudzielanek .12 .30
223 Odalis Perez .12 .30
224 Mark Buehrle .20 .50
225 Hunter Pence .30 .75
226 Kurt Suzuki .12 .30
227 Alfredo Amezaga .12 .30
228 Geoff Blum .12 .30
229 Dustin Pedroia .40 1.00
230 Roy Halladay .30 .75
231 Casey Blake .12 .30
232 Clay Buchholz (RC) .60 1.50
233 Jimmy Rollins MVP .20 .50
234a Boston Red Sox .50 1.25
234b Boston Red Sox 3.00 8.00
Rudy Giuliani celebrating with team
234c Boston Red Sox 30.00 60.00
Rudy Giuliani celebrating with team Red
235 Rich Harden .12 .30
236 Joe Koshansky (RC) .25 .60
237 Eric Wedge MG .12 .30
238 Shane Victorino .12 .30
239 Richie Sexson .12 .30
240 Jim Thome .20 .50
241 Ervin Santana .12 .30
242 Manny Acta .12 .30
243 Akinori Iwamura .12 .30
244 Adam Wainwright .20 .50
245 Dan Haren .12 .30
246 Jason Isringhausen .12 .30
247 Edgar Gonzalez .12 .30
248 Jose Contreras .12 .30
249 Chris Sampson .12 .30
250 Jonathan Papelbon .20 .50
251 Dan Johnson .12 .30
252 Dmitri Young .12 .30
253 Bronson Sardinha (RC) .25 .60
254 David Murphy .12 .30
255 Brandon Phillips .12 .30
256 Alex Rodriguez MVP .50 1.25
257 Austin Kearns .12 .30
Dimitri Young
258 Manny Ramirez .30 .75
Kevin Youkilis
259 Emilio Bonifacio RC .60 1.50
260 Chad Cordero .12 .30
261 Josh Barfield .12 .30
262 Brett Myers .12 .30
263 Nook Logan .12 .30
264 Byung-Hyun Kim .12 .30
265 Fredi Gonzalez .12 .30
266 Ryan Doumit .12 .30
267 Chris Burke .12 .30
268 Daric Barton (RC) .25 .60
269 James Loney .20 .50
270 C.C. Sabathia .20 .50
271 Chad Tracy .12 .30
272 Anthony Reyes .12 .30
273 Rafael Soriano .12 .30
274 Jermaine Dye .12 .30
275 C.C. Sabathia .20 .50
276 Brad Ausmus .12 .30
277 Aubrey Huff .12 .30
278 Xavier Nady .12 .30
279 Damion Easley .12 .30
280 Willie Randolph MG .12 .30
281 Carlos Ruiz .12 .30
282 Jon Lester .30 .75
283 Jorge Sosa .12 .30
284 Lance Broadway (RC) .25 .60
285 Tony LaRussa MG .20 .50
286 Jeff Clement (RC) .40 1.00
287 Justin Morneau .30 .75
Johan Santana
Joe Mauer
288 Ivan Rodriguez .40 1.00
Justin Verlander
289 Justin Ruggiano RC .40 1.00
290 Edgar Renteria .12 .30
291 Eugenio Velez RC .25 .60
292 Mark Loretta .12 .30
293 Gavin Floyd .12 .30
294 Brian McCann .20 .50
295 Tim Wakefield .12 .30
296 Paul Konerko .20 .50
297 Jorge Posada .20 .50
298 Prince Fielder .20 .50
Ryan Howard
Adam Dunn
299 Cesar Izturis .12 .30
300 Chien-Ming Wang .20 .50
301 Chris Duffy .12 .30
302 Horacio Ramirez .12 .30
303 Jose Lopez .12 .30
304 Jose Vidro .12 .30
305 Carlos Delgado .20 .50
306 Scott Olsen .12 .30
307 Shawn Hill .12 .30
308 Felipe Lopez .12 .30
309 Ryan Church .12 .30
310 Kelvim Escobar .12 .30
311 Jeremy Guthrie .12 .30
312 Ramon Hernandez .12 .30
313 Kameron Loe .12 .30
314 Ian Kinsler .20 .50
315 David Weathers .12 .30
316 Scott Hatteberg .12 .30
317 Cliff Lee .20 .50
318 Ned Yost MG .12 .30
319 Joey Votto (RC) 1.00 2.50
320 Ichiro Suzuki .50 1.25
321 J.R. Towles RC .40 1.00
322 Scott Kazmir .30 .75
Johan Santana
Erik Bedard
323 Jose Valverde .20 .50
Francisco Cordero
Trevor Hoffman
324 Jake Peavy .12 .30
325 Jim Leyland MG .12 .30
326 Matt Holliday .30 .75
Chipper Jones
Hanley Ramirez
327 Jake Peavy .12 .30
Aaron Harang
John Smoltz
328 Nyjer Morgan (RC) .25 .60
329 Lou Piniella MG .12 .30
330 Curtis Granderson .20 .50
331 Dave Roberts .12 .30
332 Grady Sizemore .20 .50
Jhonny Peralta
333 Jayson Nix (RC) .25 .60
334 Oliver Perez .12 .30
335 Eric Byrnes .12 .30
336 Jhonny Peralta .12 .30
337 Livan Hernandez .12 .30
338 Matt Diaz .12 .30
339 Troy Percival .12 .30
340 David Wright .40 1.00
341 Daniel Cabrera .12 .30
342 Matt Belisle .12 .30
343 Kason Gabbard .12 .30
344 Mike Rabelo .12 .30
345 Carl Crawford .20 .50
346 Adam Everett .12 .30
347 Chris Capuano .12 .30
348 Craig Monroe .12 .30
349 Mike Mussina .20 .50
350 Mark Teixeira .30 .75
351 Bobby Crosby .12 .30
352 Miguel Batista .12 .30
353 Brendan Ryan .12 .30
354 Edwin Jackson .12 .30
355 Brian Roberts .12 .30
356 Manny Corpas .12 .30
357 Jeremy Accardo .12 .30
358 John Patterson .12 .30
359 Evan Meek RC .25 .60
360 David Ortiz .20 .50
361 Wesley Wright RC .25 .60
362 Fernando Hernandez RC .25 .60
363 Brian Barton RC .40 1.00
364 Al Reyes .12 .30
365 Derrek Lee .12 .30
366 Jeff Weaver .12 .30
367 Khalil Greene .12 .30
368 Michael Bourn .12 .30
369 Luis Castillo .12 .30
370 Adam Dunn .20 .50
371 Rickie Weeks .20 .50
372 Matt Kemp .20 .50
373 Casey Kotchman .12 .30
374 Jason Jennings .12 .30
375 Fausto Carmona .12 .30
376 Willy Taveras .12 .30
377 Jake Westbrook .12 .30
378 Ozzie Guillen .12 .30
379 Hideki Okajima .12 .30
380 Grady Sizemore .20 .50
381 Jeff Francoeur .20 .50
382 Micah Owings .12 .30
383 Jered Weaver .12 .30
384 Carlos Quentin .20 .50
385 Troy Tulowitzki .30 .75
386 Julio Lugo .12 .30
387 Sean Marshall .12 .30
388 Jorge Cantu .12 .30
389 Callix Crabbe (RC) .25 .60
390 Troy Glaus .12 .30
391 Nick Markakis .30 .75
392 Joey Gathright .12 .30
393 Michael Cuddyer .12 .30
394 Mark Ellis .12 .30
395 Lance Berkman .20 .50
396 Randy Johnson .30 .75
397 Brian Wilson .30 .75
398 Kenji Johjima .12 .30
399 Jarrod Saltalamacchia .12 .30
400 Matt Holliday .30 .75
401 Scott Hairston .12 .30
402 Taylor Buchholz .12 .30
403 Nate Robertson .12 .30
404 Cecil Cooper .12 .30
405 Travis Hafner .12 .30
406 Takashi Saito .12 .30
407 Johnny Damon .20 .50
408 Edinson Volquez .12 .30
409 Jason Giambi .12 .30
410 Alex Gordon .20 .50
411 Jason Kubel .12 .30
412 Joel Zumaya .12 .30
413 Wandy Rodriguez .12 .30
414 Andrew Miller .12 .30
415 Derek Lowe .12 .30
416 Elijah Dukes .12 .30
417 Brian Bass (RC) .25 .60
418 Dioner Navarro .12 .30
419 Bengie Molina .12 .30
420 Nick Swisher .30 .75
421 Brandon Backe .12 .30
422 Erick Aybar .12 .30
423 Mike Scioscia MG .12 .30
424 Aaron Harang .12 .30
425 Hanley Ramirez .30 .75
426 Franklin Gutierrez .12 .30
427 Carlos Guillen .12 .30
428 Jair Jurrjens .12 .30
429 Billy Butler .12 .30
430 Ryan Braun .40 1.00
431 Delwyn Young .12 .30
432 Jason Kendall .12 .30
433 Carlos Silva .12 .30
434 Ron Gardenhire MG .12 .30
435 Torii Hunter .12 .30
436 Joe Blanton .12 .30
437 Brandon Wood .12 .30
438 Jay Payton .12 .30
439 Josh Hamilton .30 .75
440 Pedro Martinez .20 .50
441 Miguel Olivo .12 .30
442 Luis Gonzalez .12 .30
443 Greg Dobbs .12 .30
444 Jack Wilson .12 .30
445 Hideki Matsui .30 .75
446 Randor Bierd RC .25 .60
447 Chipper Jones .30 .75
Mark Teixeira
448 Cameron Maybin .12 .30
449 Braden Looper .12 .30
450 Prince Fielder .20 .50
451 Brian Giles .12 .30
452 Kevin Slowey .12 .30
453 Josh Fogg .12 .30
454 Mike Hampton .12 .30
455 Derek Jeter .75 2.00
456 Chone Figgins .12 .30
457 Josh Fields .12 .30
458 Brad Hawpe .12 .30
459 Mike Sweeney .12 .30
460 Chase Utley .30 .75
461 Jacoby Ellsbury .50 1.25
462 Freddy Sanchez .12 .30
463 John McLaren .12 .30
464 Rocco Baldelli .12 .30
465 Huston Street .12 .30
466 Miguel Cabrera .30 .75
Ivan Rodriguez
467 Nick Blackburn RC .40 1.00
468 Gregor Blanco (RC) .25 .60
469 Brian Bocock RC .25 .60
470 Tom Gorzelanny .12 .30
471 Brian Schneider .12 .30
472 Shaun Marcum .12 .30
473 Joe Maddon .12 .30
474 Yuniesky Betancourt .12 .30
475 Adrian Gonzalez .20 .50
476 Johnny Cueto RC .40 1.00
477 Ben Broussard .12 .30
478 Geovany Soto .30 .75
479 Bobby Abreu .12 .30
480 Matt Cain .12 .30
481 Manny Parra .25 .60
482 Kazuo Fukumori RC .40 1.00
483 Mike Jacobs .12 .30
484 Todd Jones .12 .30
485 J.J. Putz .12 .30
486 Javier Vazquez .12 .30
487 Corey Patterson .12 .30
488 Mike Gonzalez .12 .30
489 Joakim Soria .12 .30
490 Albert Pujols .75 2.00
491 Cliff Floyd .12 .30
492 Harvey Garcia (RC) .25 .60
493 Steve Holm RC .25 .60
494 Paul Maholm .12 .30
495 James Shields .12 .30
496 Brad Lidge .12 .30
497 Cla Meredith .12 .30
498 Matt Chico .12 .30
499 Milton Bradley .12 .30
500 Chipper Jones .30 .75
501 Elliot Johnson (RC) .25 .60
502 Alex Cora .12 .30
503 Jeremy Bonderman .12 .30
504 Conor Jackson .12 .30
505 B.J. Upton .20 .50
506 Jay Gibbons .12 .30
507 Mark DeRosa .12 .30
508 John Danks .12 .30
509 Alex Gonzalez .12 .30
510 Justin Verlander .40 1.00
511 Jeff Francis .12 .30
512 Placido Polanco .12 .30
513 Rick Vanden Hurk .12 .30
514 Tony Pena .12 .30
515 A.J. Burnett .20 .50
516 Jason Schmidt .12 .30
517 Bill Hall .12 .30
518 Ian Stewart .12 .30
519 Travis Buck .12 .30
520 Vernon Wells .12 .30
521 Jayson Werth .20 .50
522 Nate McLouth .12 .30
523 Noah Lowry .12 .30
524 Rajai Davis .20 .50
525 Gary Matthews .12 .30
526 Juan Encarnacion .12 .30
527 Marlon Byrd .12 .30
528 Paul Lo Duca .12 .30
529 Masahide Kobayashi RC .40 1.00
530 Ryan Zimmerman .20 .50
531 Hiroki Kuroda RC .40 1.00
532 Tim Lahey RC .25 .60
533 Kyle McClellan RC .25 .60
534 Matt Tupman RC .25 .60
535 Francisco Rodriguez .20 .50
536 Albert Pujols .20 .50
Prince Fielder
537 Scott Moore .12 .30
538 Alex Romero (RC) .40 1.00
539 Clete Thomas RC .40 1.00
540 John Smoltz .30 .75
541 Adam Jones .20 .50
542 Adam Kennedy .12 .30
543 Carlos Lee .12 .30
544 Chad Gaudin .12 .30
545 Chris Young .12 .30
546 Francisco Liriano .20 .50
547 Fred Lewis .12 .30
548 Garrett Olson .12 .30
549 Gregg Zaun .12 .30
550 Curt Schilling .20 .50
551 Erick Threets (RC) .25 .60
552 J.D. Drew .12 .30
553 Jo-Jo Reyes .12 .30
554 Joe Borowski .12 .30
555 Josh Beckett .20 .50
556 John Gibbons .12 .30
557 John McDonald .12 .30
558 John Russell .12 .30
559 Jonny Gomes .12 .30
560 Aramis Ramirez .12 .30
561 Matt Tolbert RC .40 1.00
562 Ronnie Belliard .12 .30
563 Ramon Troncoso RC .25 .60
564 Frank Catalanotto .12 .30
565 A.J. Pierzynski .12 .30
566 Kevin Millwood .12 .30
567 David Eckstein .12 .30
568 Jose Guillen .12 .30
569 Brad Hennessey .12 .30
570 Homer Bailey .20 .50
571 Eric Gagne .12 .30
572 Adam Eaton .12 .30
573 Tom Gordon .12 .30
574 Scott Baker .12 .30
575 Ty Wigginton .12 .30
576 Dave Bush .12 .30
577 John Buck .12 .30
578 Ricky Nolasco .12 .30
579 Jesse Litsch .12 .30
580 Ken Griffey Jr. .50 1.25
581 Kazuo Matsui .12 .30
582 Dusty Baker .12 .30
583 Nick Punto .12 .30
584 Ryan Theriot .12 .30
585 Brian Bannister .12 .30
586 Coco Crisp .12 .30
587 Chris Snyder .12 .30
588 Tony Gwynn .12 .30
589 Dave Trembley .12 .30
590 Mariano Rivera .30 .75
591 Rico Washington (RC) .25 .60
592 Matt Morris .12 .30
593 Randy Wells RC .40 1.00
594 Mike Morse .12 .30
595 Francisco Cordero .12 .30
596 Joba Chamberlain .20 .50
597 Kyle Davies .12 .30
598 Bruce Bochy .12 .30
599 Austin Kearns .12 .30
600 Tom Glavine .20 .50
601 Felipe Paulino RC .40 1.00
602 Lyle Overbay .12 .30
Vernon Wells
603 Blake DeWitt (RC) .60 1.50
604 Wily Mo Pena .12 .30
605 Andre Ethier .20 .50
606 Jason Bergmann .12 .30
607 Ryan Spilborghs .12 .30
608 Brian Burres .12 .30
609 Ted Lilly .12 .30
610 Carlos Beltran .12 .30
611 Garret Anderson .12 .30
612 Kelly Johnson .12 .30
613 Melvin Mora .12 .30
614 Rich Hill .12 .30
615 Pat Burrell .12 .30
616 Jon Garland .12 .30
617 Asdrubal Cabrera .20 .50
618 Pat Neshek .12 .30
619 Sergio Mitre .12 .30
620 Gary Sheffield .12 .30
621 Denard Span .20 .50
622 Jorge De La Rosa .12 .30
623 Trey Hillman MG .12 .30
624 Joe Torre MG .20 .50
625 Greg Maddux .40 1.00
626 Mike Redmond .12 .30
627 Mike Pelfrey .12 .30
628 Andy Pettitte .20 .50
629 Eric Chavez .12 .30
630 Chris Carpenter .30 .75
631 Joe Girardi MG .20 .50
632 Charlie Manuel MG .12 .30
633 Adam LaRoche .12 .30
634 Kenny Rogers .12 .30
635 Michael Young .20 .50
636 Rafael Betancourt .12 .30
637 Jose Castillo .12 .30
638 Juan Pierre .12 .30
639 Juan Uribe .12 .30
640 Carlos Pena .20 .50
641 Marcus Thames .12 .30
642 Mark Kotsay .12 .30
643 Matt Murton .12 .30
644 Reggie Willits .12 .30
645 Andy Marte .12 .30
646 Rajai Davis .12 .30
647 Randy Winn .12 .30
648 Ryan Freel .12 .30
649 Joe Crede .12 .30
650 Frank Thomas .30 .75
651 Martin Prado .12 .30
652 Rod Barajas .12 .30
653 Endy Chavez .12 .30
654 Willy Aybar .12 .30
655 Aaron Rowand .12 .30
656 Darin Erstad .12 .30
657 Jeff Keppinger .12 .30
658 Kerry Wood .12 .30
659 Vicente Padilla .12 .30
660 Yadier Molina .20 .50
661 Johan Santana 150.00 250.00
Front of card reads Santana Tosses 1st No-No
FS1 Kazuo Uzuki .75 2.00
NNO Alexei Ramirez 50.00 100.00
NNO Kosuke Fukudome 10.00 25.00
NNO Yasuhiko Yabuta 40.00 80.00

2008 Topps Black

SER.1 ODDS 1:95 HOBBY
SER.2 ODDS 1:63 HOBBY
STATED PRINT RUN 57 SER.#'d SETS
1 Alex Rodriguez 15.00 40.00
2 Barry Zito 6.00 15.00
3 Jeff Suppan 6.00 15.00
4 Rick Ankiel 6.00 15.00
5 Scott Kazmir 6.00 15.00
6 Felix Pie 6.00 15.00
7 Mickey Mantle 60.00 120.00
8 Stephen Drew 6.00 15.00
9 Randy Wolf 6.00 15.00
10 Miguel Cabrera 10.00 25.00
11 Yorvit Torrealba 6.00 15.00
12 Jason Bartlett 6.00 15.00
13 Kendry Morales 6.00 15.00
14 Lenny DiNardo 6.00 15.00
15 Magglio Ordonez 15.00 40.00
Ichiro Suzuki
Placido Polanco
16 Kevin Gregg 6.00 15.00
17 Cristian Guzman 6.00 15.00
18 J.D. Durbin 6.00 15.00
19 Robinson Tejeda 6.00 15.00
20 Daisuke Matsuzaka 10.00 25.00
21 Edwin Encarnacion 6.00 15.00
22 Ron Washington MG 6.00 15.00
23 Chin-Lung Hu 30.00 60.00
24 Alex Rodriguez 10.00 25.00
Magglio Ordonez
Vladimir Guerrero
25 Kaz Matsui 6.00 15.00
26 Manny Ramirez 10.00 25.00
27 Bob Melvin MG 6.00 15.00
28 Kyle Kendrick 6.00 15.00
29 Anibal Sanchez 6.00 15.00
30 Jimmy Rollins 10.00 25.00
31 Ronny Paulino 6.00 15.00
32 Howie Kendrick 6.00 15.00
33 Joe Mauer 10.00 25.00
34 Aaron Cook 6.00 15.00
35 Cole Hamels 10.00 25.00
36 Brendan Harris 6.00 15.00
37 Jason Marquis 6.00 15.00
38 Preston Wilson 6.00 15.00
39 Yovanni Gallardo 6.00 15.00
40 Miguel Tejada 6.00 15.00
41 Rich Aurilia 6.00 15.00
42 Corey Hart 6.00 15.00
43 Ryan Dempster 6.00 15.00
44 Jonathan Broxton 6.00 15.00
45 Dontrelle Willis 6.00 15.00
46 Zack Greinke 6.00 15.00
47 Orlando Cabrera 6.00 15.00
48 Zach Duke 6.00 15.00
49 Orlando Hernandez 6.00 15.00
50 Jake Peavy 10.00 25.00
51 Erik Bedard 6.00 15.00
52 Trevor Hoffman 6.00 15.00
53 Hank Blalock 6.00 15.00
54 Victor Martinez 6.00 15.00
55 Chris Young 6.00 15.00
56 Seth Smith 6.00 15.00
57 Wladimir Balentien 6.00 15.00
58 Matt Holliday 10.00 25.00
Ryan Howard
Miguel Cabrera
59 Grady Sizemore 10.00 25.00
60 Jose Reyes 10.00 25.00
61 Alex Rodriguez 6.00 15.00
Carlos Pena
David Ortiz
62 Rich Thompson 6.00 15.00
63 Jason Michaels 6.00 15.00
64 Mike Lowell 10.00 25.00
65 Billy Wagner 6.00 15.00
66 Brad Wilkerson 6.00 15.00
67 Wes Helms 6.00 15.00
68 Kevin Millar 6.00 15.00
69 Bobby Cox MG 6.00 15.00
70 Dan Uggla 6.00 15.00
71 Jarrod Washburn 6.00 15.00
72 Mike Piazza 20.00 50.00
73 Mike Napoli 6.00 15.00
74 Garrett Atkins 6.00 15.00
75 Felix Hernandez 10.00 25.00
76 Ivan Rodriguez 10.00 25.00
77 Angel Guzman 6.00 15.00
78 Radhames Liz 10.00 25.00
79 Omar Vizquel 6.00 15.00
80 Alex Rios 6.00 15.00
81 Ray Durham 6.00 15.00
82 So Taguchi 6.00 15.00
83 Mark Reynolds 6.00 15.00
84 Brian Fuentes 6.00 15.00
85 Jason Bay 10.00 25.00
86 Scott Podsednik 6.00 15.00
87 Maicer Izturis 6.00 15.00
88 Jack Cust 6.00 15.00
89 Josh Willingham 6.00 15.00
90 Vladimir Guerrero 10.00 25.00
91 Marcus Giles 6.00 15.00
92 Ross Detwiler 10.00 25.00
93 Kenny Lofton 6.00 15.00
94 Bud Black MG 6.00 15.00
95 John Lackey 6.00 15.00
96 Sam Fuld 6.00 15.00
97 Clint Sammons 6.00 15.00
98 Ryan Howard 12.50 30.00
Chase Utley
99 David Ortiz 12.50 30.00
Manny Ramirez
100 Ryan Howard 12.50 30.00
101 Ryan Braun ROY 12.50 30.00
102 Ross Ohlendorf 10.00 25.00
103 Jonathan Albaladejo 6.00 15.00
104 Kevin Youkilis 10.00 25.00
105 Roger Clemens 12.00 30.00
106 Josh Bard 6.00 15.00
107 Shawn Green 6.00 15.00
108 B.J. Ryan 6.00 15.00
109 Joe Nathan 6.00 15.00
110 Justin Morneau 6.00 15.00
111 Ubaldo Jimenez 6.00 15.00
112 Jacque Jones 6.00 15.00
113 Kevin Frandsen 6.00 15.00
114 Mike Fontenot 6.00 15.00
115 Johan Santana 12.50 30.00
116 Chuck James 6.00 15.00
117 Boof Bonser 6.00 15.00
118 Marco Scutaro 6.00 15.00
119 Jeremy Hermida 6.00 15.00
120 Andruw Jones 6.00 15.00
121 Mike Cameron 6.00 15.00
122 Jason Varitek 10.00 25.00
123 Terry Francona MG 6.00 15.00
124 Bob Geren MG 6.00 15.00
125 Tim Hudson 6.00 15.00
126 Brandon Jones 6.00 15.00
127 Steve Pearce 10.00 25.00
128 Kenny Lofton 6.00 15.00
129 Kevin Hart 6.00 15.00
130 Justin Upton 10.00 25.00
131 Norris Hopper 6.00 15.00
132 Ramon Vazquez 6.00 15.00
133 Mike Bacsik 6.00 15.00
134 Matt Stairs 6.00 15.00
135 Brad Penny 6.00 15.00

136 Robinson Cano 10.00 25.00
137 Jamey Carroll 6.00 15.00
138 Dan Wheeler 6.00 15.00
139 Johnny Estrada 6.00 15.00
140 Brandon Webb 6.00 15.00
141 Ryan Klesko 6.00 15.00
142 Chris Duncan 6.00 15.00
143 Willie Harris 6.00 15.00
144 Jerry Owens 6.00 15.00
145 Magglio Ordonez 10.00 25.00
146 Aaron Hill 6.00 15.00
147 Marlon Anderson 6.00 15.00
148 Gerald Laird 6.00 15.00
149 Luke Hochevar 10.00 25.00
150 Alfonso Soriano 10.00 25.00
151 Adam Loewen 6.00 15.00
152 Bronson Arroyo 6.00 15.00
153 Luis Mendoza 6.00 15.00
154 David Ross 6.00 15.00
155 Carlos Zambrano 6.00 15.00
156 Brandon McCarthy 6.00 15.00
157 Tim Redding 6.00 15.00
158 Jose Bautista UER 6.00 15.00
Wrong photo
159 Luke Scott 6.00 15.00
160 Ben Sheets 6.00 15.00
161 Matt Garza 6.00 15.00
162 Andy Laroche 6.00 15.00
163 Doug Davis 6.00 15.00
164 Nate Schierholtz 6.00 15.00
165 Tim Lincecum 10.00 25.00
166 Andy Sonnanstine 6.00 15.00
167 Jason Hirsh 6.00 15.00
168 Phil Hughes 12.50 30.00
169 Adam Lind 6.00 15.00
170 Scott Rolen 10.00 25.00
171 John Maine 6.00 15.00
172 Chris Ray 6.00 15.00
173 Jamie Moyer 6.00 15.00
174 Julian Tavarez 6.00 15.00
175 Delmon Young 10.00 25.00
176 Troy Patton 6.00 15.00
177 Josh Anderson 6.00 15.00
178 Dustin Pedroia ROY 10.00 25.00
179 Chris Young 6.00 15.00
180 Jose Valverde 6.00 15.00
181 Joe Borowski 6.00 15.00
Bobby Jenks
J.J. Putz
182 Billy Buckner 6.00 15.00
183 Paul Byrd 6.00 15.00
184 Tadahito Iguchi 6.00 15.00
185 Yunel Escobar 6.00 15.00
186 Lastings Milledge 6.00 15.00
187 Dustin McGowan 6.00 15.00
188 Kei Igawa 6.00 15.00
189 Esteban German 6.00 15.00
190 Russell Martin 6.00 15.00
191 Orlando Hudson 6.00 15.00
192 Jim Edmonds 6.00 15.00
193 J.J. Hardy 6.00 15.00
194 Chad Billingsley 6.00 15.00
195 Todd Helton 10.00 25.00
196 Ross Gload 6.00 15.00
197 Melky Cabrera 6.00 15.00
198 Shannon Stewart 6.00 15.00
199 Adrian Beltre 6.00 15.00
200 Manny Ramirez 10.00 25.00
201 Matt Capps 6.00 15.00
202 Mike Lamb 6.00 15.00
203 Jason Tyner 6.00 15.00
204 Rafael Furcal 6.00 15.00
205 Gil Meche 6.00 15.00
206 Geoff Jenkins 6.00 15.00
207 Jeff Kent 6.00 15.00
208 David DeJesus 6.00 15.00
209 Andy Phillips 6.00 15.00
210 Mark Teahen 6.00 15.00
211 Lyle Overbay 6.00 15.00
212 Moises Alou 6.00 15.00
213 Michael Barrett 6.00 15.00
214 C.J. Wilson 6.00 15.00
215 Bobby Jenks 6.00 15.00
216 Ryan Garko 6.00 15.00
217 Josh Beckett 15.00 40.00
218 Clint Hurdle MG 6.00 15.00
219 Kevin Kouzmanoff 6.00 15.00
220 Roy Oswalt 6.00 15.00
221 Ian Snell 6.00 15.00
222 Mark Grudzielanek 6.00 15.00
223 Odalis Perez 6.00 15.00
224 Mark Buehrle 6.00 15.00
225 Hunter Pence 12.50 30.00
226 Kurt Suzuki 6.00 15.00
227 Alfredo Amezaga 6.00 15.00
228 Geoff Blum 6.00 15.00
229 Dustin Pedroia 12.50 30.00
230 Roy Halladay 6.00 15.00
231 Casey Blake 6.00 15.00
232 Clay Buchholz 30.00 60.00
233 Jimmy Rollins MVP 10.00 25.00
234 Boston Red Sox 30.00 60.00
235 Rich Harden 6.00 15.00
236 Joe Koshansky 6.00 15.00
237 Eric Wedge MG 6.00 15.00
238 Shane Victorino 6.00 15.00
239 Richie Sexson 6.00 15.00
240 Jim Thome 10.00 25.00
241 Ervin Santana 6.00 15.00
242 Manny Acta 6.00 15.00
243 Akinori Iwamura 6.00 15.00
244 Adam Wainwright 6.00 15.00
245 Dan Haren 6.00 15.00
246 Jason Isringhausen 6.00 15.00
247 Edgar Gonzalez 6.00 15.00
248 Jose Contreras 6.00 15.00
249 Chris Sampson 6.00 15.00
250 Jonathan Papelbon 12.50 30.00
251 Dan Johnson 6.00 15.00
252 Dmitri Young 6.00 15.00
253 Bronson Sardinha 6.00 15.00
254 David Murphy 6.00 15.00
255 Brandon Phillips 6.00 15.00
256 Alex Rodriguez MVP 15.00 40.00
257 Austin Kearns 6.00 15.00
Dmitri Young
258 Manny Ramirez 10.00 25.00
Kevin Youkilis
259 Emilio Bonifacio 6.00 15.00
260 Chad Cordero 6.00 15.00
261 Josh Barfield 6.00 15.00
262 Brett Myers 6.00 15.00
263 Nook Logan 6.00 15.00
264 Byung-Hyun Kim 6.00 15.00
265 Fredi Gonzalez 6.00 15.00
266 Ryan Doumit 6.00 15.00
267 Chris Burke 6.00 15.00
268 Daric Barton 6.00 15.00
269 James Loney 12.50 30.00
270 C.C. Sabathia 6.00 15.00
271 Chad Tracy 6.00 15.00
272 Anthony Reyes 6.00 15.00
273 Rafael Soriano 6.00 15.00
274 Jermaine Dye 6.00 15.00
275 C.C. Sabathia 6.00 15.00
276 Brad Ausmus 6.00 15.00
277 Aubrey Huff 6.00 15.00
278 Xavier Nady 6.00 15.00
279 Damion Easley 6.00 15.00
280 Willie Randolph MG 6.00 15.00
281 Carlos Ruiz 6.00 15.00
282 Jon Lester 10.00 25.00
283 Jorge Sosa 6.00 15.00
284 Lance Broadway 6.00 15.00
285 Tony LaRussa MG 6.00 15.00
286 Jeff Clement 6.00 15.00
287 Justin Morneau 12.50 30.00
Johan Santana
Joe Mauer
288 Ivan Rodriguez 10.00 25.00
Justin Verlander
289 Justin Ruggiano 6.00 15.00
290 Edgar Renteria 6.00 15.00
291 Eugenio Velez 6.00 15.00
292 Mark Loretta 6.00 15.00
293 Gavin Floyd 6.00 15.00
294 Brian McCann 6.00 15.00
295 Tim Wakefield 6.00 15.00
296 Paul Konerko 6.00 15.00
297 Jorge Posada 10.00 25.00
298 Prince Fielder 10.00 25.00
Ryan Howard
Adam Dunn
299 Cesar Izturis 6.00 15.00
300 Chien-Ming Wang 12.50 30.00
301 Chris Duffy 6.00 15.00
302 Horacio Ramirez 6.00 15.00
303 Jose Lopez 6.00 15.00
304 Jose Vidro 6.00 15.00
305 Carlos Delgado 6.00 15.00
306 Scott Olsen 6.00 15.00
307 Shawn Hill 6.00 15.00
308 Felipe Lopez 6.00 15.00
309 Ryan Church 6.00 15.00
310 Kelvim Escobar 6.00 15.00
311 Jeremy Guthrie 6.00 15.00
312 Ramon Hernandez 6.00 15.00
313 Kameron Loe 6.00 15.00
314 Ian Kinsler 6.00 15.00
315 David Weathers 6.00 15.00
316 Scott Hatteberg 6.00 15.00
317 Cliff Lee 6.00 15.00
318 Ned Yost MG 6.00 15.00
319 Joey Votto 10.00 25.00
320 Ichiro Suzuki 20.00 50.00
321 J.R. Towles 10.00 25.00
322 Scott Kazmir 10.00 25.00
Johan Santana
Erik Bedard
323 Jose Valverde 6.00 15.00
Francisco Cordero
Trevor Hoffman
324 Jake Peavy 10.00 25.00
325 Jim Leyland MG 6.00 15.00
326 Matt Holliday 10.00 25.00
Chipper Jones
Hanley Ramirez
327 Jake Peavy 10.00 25.00
Aaron Harang
John Smoltz
328 Nyjer Morgan 6.00 15.00
329 Lou Piniella 6.00 15.00
330 Curtis Granderson 10.00 25.00
331 Dave Roberts 6.00 15.00
332 Grady Sizemore 10.00 25.00
Jhonny Peralta
333 Jayson Nix 6.00 15.00
334 Oliver Perez 6.00 15.00
335 Eric Byrnes 6.00 15.00
336 Jhonny Peralta 6.00 15.00
337 Livan Hernandez 6.00 15.00
338 Matt Diaz 6.00 15.00
339 Troy Percival 6.00 15.00
340 David Wright 12.50 30.00
341 Daniel Cabrera 6.00 15.00
342 Matt Belisle 6.00 15.00
343 Kason Gabbard 6.00 15.00
344 Mike Rabelo 6.00 15.00
345 Carl Crawford 6.00 15.00
346 Adam Everett 6.00 15.00
347 Chris Capuano 6.00 15.00
348 Craig Monroe 6.00 15.00
349 Mike Mussina 6.00 15.00
350 Mark Teixeira 10.00 25.00
351 Bobby Crosby 6.00 15.00
352 Miguel Batista 6.00 15.00
353 Brendan Ryan 15.00 40.00
354 Edwin Jackson 6.00 15.00
355 Brian Roberts 6.00 15.00
356 Manny Corpas 6.00 15.00
357 Jeremy Accardo 6.00 15.00
358 John Patterson 6.00 15.00
359 Evan Meek 6.00 15.00
360 David Ortiz 12.50 30.00
361 Wesley Wright 10.00 25.00
362 Fernando Hernandez 6.00 15.00
363 Brian Barton 12.50 30.00
364 Al Reyes 6.00 15.00
365 Derrek Lee 6.00 15.00
366 Jeff Weaver 6.00 15.00
367 Khalil Greene 6.00 15.00
368 Michael Bourn 6.00 15.00
369 Luis Castillo 6.00 15.00
370 Adam Dunn 6.00 15.00
371 Rickie Weeks 6.00 15.00
372 Matt Kemp 6.00 15.00
373 Casey Kotchman 6.00 15.00
374 Jason Jennings 6.00 15.00
375 Fausto Carmona 6.00 15.00
376 Willy Taveras 6.00 15.00
377 Jake Westbrook 6.00 15.00
378 Ozzie Guillen 6.00 15.00
379 Hideki Okajima 10.00 25.00
380 Grady Sizemore 10.00 25.00
381 Jeff Francoeur 10.00 25.00
382 Micah Owings 10.00 25.00
383 Jered Weaver 6.00 15.00
384 Carlos Quentin 6.00 15.00
385 Troy Tulowitzki 10.00 25.00
386 Julio Lugo 6.00 15.00
387 Sean Marshall 6.00 15.00
388 Jorge Cantu 6.00 15.00
389 Callix Crabbe 6.00 15.00
390 Troy Glaus 6.00 15.00
391 Nick Markakis 10.00 25.00
392 Joey Gathright 6.00 15.00
393 Michael Cuddyer 6.00 15.00
394 Mark Ellis 6.00 15.00
395 Lance Berkman 6.00 15.00
396 Randy Johnson 10.00 25.00
397 Brian Wilson 6.00 15.00
398 Kenji Johjima 6.00 15.00
399 Jarrod Saltalamacchia 6.00 15.00
400 Matt Holliday 6.00 15.00
401 Scott Hairston 6.00 15.00
402 Taylor Buchholz 6.00 15.00
403 Nate Robertson 6.00 15.00
404 Cecil Cooper 6.00 15.00
405 Travis Hafner 6.00 15.00
406 Takashi Saito 10.00 25.00
407 Johnny Damon 6.00 15.00
408 Edinson Volquez 10.00 25.00
409 Jason Giambi 10.00 25.00
410 Ryan Howard 10.00 25.00
411 Jason Kubel 6.00 15.00
412 Joel Zumaya 6.00 15.00
413 Wandy Rodriguez 6.00 15.00
414 Andrew Miller 6.00 15.00
415 Derek Lowe 10.00 25.00
416 Elijah Dukes 6.00 15.00
417 Brian Bass 10.00 25.00
418 Dioner Navarro 6.00 15.00
419 Bengie Molina 6.00 15.00
420 Nick Swisher 6.00 15.00
421 Brandon Backe 6.00 15.00
422 Erick Aybar 6.00 15.00
423 Mike Scioscia 6.00 15.00
424 Aaron Harang 6.00 15.00
425 Hanley Ramirez 10.00 25.00
426 Franklin Gutierrez 6.00 15.00
427 Carlos Guillen 6.00 15.00
428 Jair Jurrjens 6.00 15.00
429 Billy Butler 6.00 15.00
430 Ryan Braun 15.00 40.00
431 Delwyn Young 6.00 15.00
432 Jason Kendall 6.00 15.00
433 Carlos Silva 6.00 15.00
434 Ron Gardenhire MG 6.00 15.00
435 Torii Hunter 6.00 15.00
436 Joe Blanton 6.00 15.00
437 Brandon Wood 6.00 15.00
438 Jay Payton 6.00 15.00
439 Josh Hamilton 30.00 60.00
440 Pedro Martinez 10.00 25.00
441 Miguel Olivo 6.00 15.00
442 Luis Gonzalez 6.00 15.00
443 Greg Dobbs 6.00 15.00
444 Jack Wilson 6.00 15.00
445 Hideki Matsui 12.50 30.00
446 Randor Bierd 6.00 15.00
447 Chipper Jones 10.00 25.00
Mark Teixeira
448 Cameron Maybin 12.50 30.00
449 Braden Looper 6.00 15.00
450 Prince Fielder 12.50 30.00
451 Brian Giles 6.00 15.00
452 Kevin Slowey 10.00 25.00
453 Josh Fogg 6.00 15.00
454 Mike Hampton 6.00 15.00
455 Derek Jeter 40.00 80.00
456 Chone Figgins 6.00 15.00
457 Josh Fields 6.00 15.00
458 Brad Hawpe 6.00 15.00
459 Mike Sweeney 6.00 15.00
460 Chase Utley 12.50 30.00
461 Jacoby Ellsbury 20.00 50.00
462 Freddy Sanchez 6.00 15.00
463 John McLaren 6.00 15.00
464 Rocco Baldelli 6.00 15.00
465 Huston Street 6.00 15.00
466 Miguel Cabrera 10.00 25.00
Ivan Rodriguez
467 Nick Blackburn 15.00 40.00
468 Gregor Blanco 6.00 15.00
469 Brian Bocock 10.00 25.00
470 Tom Gorzelanny 6.00 15.00
471 Brian Schneider 6.00 15.00
472 Shaun Marcum 6.00 15.00
473 Joe Maddon 6.00 15.00
474 Yuniesky Betancourt 6.00 15.00
475 Adrian Gonzalez 6.00 15.00
476 Johnny Cueto 12.50 30.00
477 Ben Broussard 6.00 15.00
478 Geovany Soto 15.00 40.00
479 Bobby Abreu 6.00 15.00
480 Matt Cain 6.00 15.00
481 Manny Parra 6.00 15.00
482 Kazuo Fukumori 10.00 25.00
483 Mike Jacobs 6.00 15.00
484 Todd Jones 6.00 15.00
485 J.J. Putz 6.00 15.00
486 Javier Vazquez 6.00 15.00
487 Corey Patterson 6.00 15.00
488 Mike Gonzalez 6.00 15.00
489 Joakim Soria 6.00 15.00
490 Albert Pujols 20.00 50.00
491 Cliff Floyd 6.00 15.00
492 Harvey Garcia 6.00 15.00
493 Steve Holm 6.00 15.00
494 Paul Maholm 6.00 15.00
495 James Shields 6.00 15.00
496 Brad Lidge 6.00 15.00
497 Cla Meredith 6.00 15.00
498 Matt Chico 6.00 15.00
499 Milton Bradley 6.00 15.00
500 Chipper Jones 12.50 30.00
501 Elliot Johnson 6.00 15.00
502 Alex Cora 6.00 15.00
503 Jeremy Bonderman 10.00 25.00
504 Conor Jackson 6.00 15.00
505 B.J. Upton 6.00 15.00
506 Jay Gibbons 6.00 15.00
507 Mark DeRosa 6.00 15.00
508 John Danks 6.00 15.00
509 Alex Gonzalez 6.00 15.00
510 Justin Verlander 10.00 25.00
511 Jeff Francis 6.00 15.00
512 Placido Polanco 6.00 15.00
513 Rick Vanden Hurk 6.00 15.00
514 Tony Pena 6.00 15.00
515 A.J. Burnett 6.00 15.00
516 Jason Schmidt 6.00 15.00
517 Bill Hall 6.00 15.00
518 Ian Stewart 6.00 15.00
519 Travis Buck 6.00 15.00
520 Vernon Wells 6.00 15.00
521 Jayson Werth 6.00 15.00
522 Nate McLouth 15.00 40.00
523 Noah Lowry 6.00 15.00
524 Raul Ibanez 6.00 15.00
525 Gary Matthews 6.00 15.00
526 Juan Encarnacion 6.00 15.00
527 Marlon Byrd 6.00 15.00
528 Paul Lo Duca 6.00 15.00
529 Masahide Kobayashi 10.00 25.00
530 Ryan Zimmerman 10.00 25.00
531 Hiroki Kuroda 12.50 30.00
532 Tim Lahey 6.00 15.00
533 Kyle McClellan 6.00 15.00
534 Matt Tupman 6.00 15.00
535 Francisco Rodriguez 6.00 15.00
536 Albert Pujols 12.50 30.00
Prince Fielder
537 Scott Moore 6.00 15.00
538 Alex Romero 6.00 15.00
539 Clete Thomas 6.00 15.00
540 John Smoltz 10.00 25.00
541 Adam Jones 6.00 15.00
542 Adam Kennedy 6.00 15.00
543 Carlos Lee 6.00 15.00
544 Chad Gaudin 6.00 15.00
545 Chris Young 6.00 15.00
546 Francisco Liriano 6.00 15.00
547 Fred Lewis 6.00 15.00
548 Garrett Olson 6.00 15.00
549 Gregg Zaun 6.00 15.00
550 Curt Schilling 10.00 25.00
551 Erick Threets 6.00 15.00
552 J.D. Drew 6.00 15.00
553 Jo-Jo Reyes 6.00 15.00
554 Joe Borowski 6.00 15.00
555 Josh Beckett 10.00 25.00
556 John Gibbons 6.00 15.00
557 John McDonald 6.00 15.00
558 John Russell 6.00 15.00
559 Jonny Gomes 6.00 15.00
560 Aramis Ramirez 6.00 15.00
561 Matt Tolbert 10.00 25.00
562 Ronnie Belliard 6.00 15.00
563 Ramon Troncoso 6.00 15.00
564 Frank Catalanotto 6.00 15.00
565 A.J. Pierzynski 6.00 15.00
566 Kevin Millwood 6.00 15.00
567 David Eckstein 6.00 15.00
568 Jose Guillen 6.00 15.00
569 Brad Hennessey 6.00 15.00
570 Homer Bailey 6.00 15.00
571 Eric Gagne 6.00 15.00
572 Adam Eaton 6.00 15.00
573 Tom Gordon 6.00 15.00
574 Scott Baker 6.00 15.00
575 Ty Wigginton 6.00 15.00
576 Dave Bush 6.00 15.00
577 John Buck 6.00 15.00
578 Ricky Nolasco 6.00 15.00
579 Jesse Litsch 6.00 15.00
580 Ken Griffey Jr. 20.00 50.00
581 Kazuo Matsui 6.00 15.00
582 Dusty Baker 6.00 15.00
583 Nick Punto 6.00 15.00
584 Ryan Theriot 6.00 15.00
585 Brian Bannister 10.00 25.00
586 Coco Crisp 10.00 25.00
587 Chris Snyder 6.00 15.00
588 Tony Gwynn 10.00 25.00
589 Dave Trembley 6.00 15.00
590 Mariano Rivera 12.50 30.00
591 Rico Washington 6.00 15.00
592 Matt Morris 6.00 15.00
593 Randy Wells 6.00 15.00
594 Mike Morse 6.00 15.00
595 Francisco Cordero 6.00 15.00
596 Joba Chamberlain 20.00 50.00
597 Kyle Davies 6.00 15.00
598 Bruce Bochy 6.00 15.00
599 Austin Kearns 6.00 15.00
600 Tom Glavine 10.00 25.00
601 Felipe Paulino 6.00 15.00
602 Lyle Overbay 6.00 15.00
Vernon Wells
603 Blake DeWitt 15.00 40.00
604 Wily Mo Pena 6.00 15.00
605 Andre Ethier 10.00 25.00
606 Jason Bergmann 6.00 15.00
607 Ryan Spilborghs 6.00 15.00
608 Brian Burres 6.00 15.00
609 Ted Lilly 6.00 15.00
610 Carlos Beltran 6.00 15.00
611 Garret Anderson 6.00 15.00
612 Kelly Johnson 6.00 15.00
613 Melvin Mora 6.00 15.00
614 Rich Hill 6.00 15.00
615 Pat Burrell 6.00 15.00
616 Jon Garland 6.00 15.00
617 Asdrubal Cabrera 6.00 15.00
618 Pat Neshek 6.00 15.00
619 Sergio Mitre 6.00 15.00
620 Gary Sheffield 6.00 15.00
621 Denard Span 6.00 15.00
622 Jorge De La Rosa 6.00 15.00
623 Trey Hillman MG 6.00 15.00
624 Joe Torre MG 12.50 30.00
625 Greg Maddux 15.00 40.00
626 Mike Redmond 6.00 15.00
627 Mike Pelfrey 6.00 15.00
628 Andy Pettitte 10.00 25.00
629 Eric Chavez 6.00 15.00
630 Chris Carpenter 6.00 15.00
631 Joe Girardi MG 6.00 15.00
632 Charlie Manuel MG 6.00 15.00
633 Adam LaRoche 6.00 15.00
634 Kenny Rogers 6.00 15.00
635 Michael Young 6.00 15.00
636 Rafael Betancourt 6.00 15.00
637 Jose Castillo 6.00 15.00
638 Juan Pierre 6.00 15.00
639 Juan Uribe 6.00 15.00
640 Carlos Pena 6.00 15.00
641 Marcus Thames 6.00 15.00
642 Mark Kotsay 6.00 15.00
643 Matt Murton 6.00 15.00
644 Reggie Willits 6.00 15.00
645 Andy Marte 6.00 15.00
646 Rajai Davis 6.00 15.00
647 Randy Winn 6.00 15.00
648 Ryan Freel 6.00 15.00
649 Joe Crede 6.00 15.00
650 Frank Thomas 12.50 30.00
651 Martin Prado 6.00 15.00
652 Rod Barajas 6.00 15.00
653 Endy Chavez 6.00 15.00
654 Willy Aybar 6.00 15.00
655 Aaron Rowand 6.00 15.00
656 Darin Erstad 6.00 15.00
657 Jeff Keppinger 6.00 15.00
658 Kerry Wood 6.00 15.00
659 Vicente Padilla 6.00 15.00
660 Yadier Molina 6.00 15.00

2008 Topps Gold Border

*GOLD: 3X TO 8X BASIC
*GOLD RC: 2X TO 5X BASIC RC
SER.1 ODDS 1:9 H,1:3 HTA,1:11 R
SER.2 ODDS 1:5 H,1:2 HTA,1:12 R
STATED PRINT RUN 2008 SER.#'d SETS
234b Boston Red Sox
Rudy Giuliani celebrating with team

2008 Topps Gold Foil

*GOLD FOIL: 1X TO 2.5X BASIC
*GOLD FOIL RC: .6X TO 1.5X BASIC RC
RANDOM INSERTS IN PACKS
234b Boston Red Sox 4.00 10.00
Rudy Giuliani celebrating with team

2008 Topps Platinum

SER.1 ODDS 1:16,500 H,1:10,000 HTA
SER.1 ODDS 1:25,000 RETAIL
SER.2 ODDS 1:12,500 H,1:2950 HTA
SER.2 ODDS 1:21,000 RETAIL
STATED PRINT RUN 1 SER.#'d SET
NO PRICING DUE TO SCARCITY

2008 Topps 1955 Reprint Relic

STATED ODDS 1:400,000 H,1:11,000 HTA
STATED ODDS 1:176,000 RETAIL
STATED PRINT RUN 55 SER.#'d SETS
NO PRICING DUE TO SCARCITY
MM55 Mickey Mantle Bat

2008 Topps 1956 Reprint Relic

SER.2 ODDS 1:43,030 HOBBY
SER.2 ODDS 1:5249 HTA
STATED PRINT RUN 56 SER.#'d SETS
56MM Mickey Mantle 90.00 150.00

2008 Topps 50th Anniversary All Rookie Team

COMPLETE SET (110) 50.00 100.00
COMP.SER.1 SET (55) 20.00 50.00
COMP.SER.2 SET (55) 20.00 50.00
SER.1 ODDS 1:5 HOB, 1:5 RET
SER.2 ODDS 1:5 HOB,1:5 HTA,1:5 RET
AR1 Darryl Strawberry .40 1.00
AR2 Gary Sheffield .40 1.00
AR3 Dwight Gooden .40 1.00
AR4 Melky Cabrera .40 1.00
AR5 Gary Carter .40 1.00
AR6 Lou Piniella .40 1.00
AR7 Dave Justice .40 1.00
AR8 Andre Dawson .60 1.50
AR9 Mark Ellis .40 1.00
AR10 Dave Johnson .40 1.00
AR11 Jermaine Dye .40 1.00
AR12 Dan Johnson .40 1.00
AR13 Alfonso Soriano .60 1.50
AR14 Prince Fielder .60 1.50
AR15 Hanley Ramirez 1.00 2.50
AR16 Matt Holliday 1.00 2.50
AR17 Justin Verlander 1.25 3.00
AR18 Mark Teixeira 1.00 2.50
AR19 Julio Franco .40 1.00
AR20 Ivan Rodriguez .60 1.50
AR21 Jason Bay .60 1.50
AR22 Brandon Webb .60 1.50
AR23 Dontrelle Willis .40 1.00
AR24 Brad Wilkerson .40 1.00
AR25 Dan Uggla .60 1.50
AR26 Ozzie Smith 1.50 4.00
AR27 Andruw Jones .40 1.00
AR28 Garret Anderson .40 1.00
AR29 Jimmy Rollins .60 1.50
AR30 Brian McCann .60 1.50
AR31 Scott Podsednik .40 1.00
AR32 Garrett Atkins .40 1.00
AR33 Billy Wagner .40 1.00
AR34 Chipper Jones 1.00 2.50
AR35 Roger McDowell .40 1.00
AR36 Austin Kearns .40 1.00
AR37 Boog Powell .40 1.00
AR38 Ron Swoboda .40 1.00
AR39 Roy Oswalt .60 1.50
AR40 Mike Piazza 1.00 2.50
AR41 Albert Pujols 2.50 6.00
AR42 Ichiro Suzuki 1.50 4.00
AR43 C.C. Sabathia .60 1.50
AR44 Todd Helton .60 1.50
AR45 Scott Rolen .60 1.50
AR46 Derek Jeter 2.50 6.00
AR47 Shawn Green .40 1.00
AR48 Manny Ramirez 1.00 2.50
AR49 Tom Seaver UER .60 1.50
Position listed as shortstop
AR50 Kenny Lofton .40 1.00
AR51 Francisco Liriano .60 1.50
AR52 Ryan Zimmerman .60 1.50
AR53 Jeff Francoeur .60 1.50
AR54 Joe Mauer 1.00 2.50
AR55 Magglio Ordonez .60 1.50
AR56 Carlos Beltran .40 1.00
AR57 Andre Ethier .60 1.50
AR58 Brian Bannister .40 1.00
AR59 Chris Young .40 1.00
AR60 Troy Tulowitzki 1.00 2.50
AR61 Hideki Okajima .40 1.00
AR62 Delmon Young .60 1.50
AR63 Craig Wilson .40 1.00
AR64 Hunter Pence 1.00 2.50
AR65 Tadahito Iguchi .40 1.00
AR66 Mark Kotsay .40 1.00
AR67 Nick Markakis 1.00 2.50
AR68 Russ Adams .40 1.00
AR69 Russ Martin .60 1.50
AR70 James Loney .60 1.50
AR71 Ryan Braun 1.25 3.00
AR72 Jonny Gomes .40 1.00
AR73 Carlos Ruiz .40 1.00
AR74 Willy Taveras .40 1.00
AR75 Joe Torre .60 1.50
AR76 Jeff Kent .40 1.00
AR77 Huston Street .40 1.00
AR78 Dustin Pedroia 1.25 3.00
AR79 Gustavo Chacin .40 1.00
AR80 Adam Dunn .60 1.50
AR81 Pat Burrell .40 1.00
AR82 Rocco Baldelli .40 1.00
AR83 Chad Tracy .40 1.00
AR84 Adam LaRoche .40 1.00
AR85 Aaron Miles .40 1.00
AR86 Khalil Greene .40 1.00
AR87 Daniel Cabrera .40 1.00
AR88 Mike Gonzalez .40 1.00
AR89 Ty Wigginton .40 1.00
AR90 Angel Berroa .40 1.00
AR91 Moises Alou .40 1.00
AR92 Miguel Olivo .40 1.00
AR93 Nick Johnson .40 1.00
AR94 Eric Hinske .40 1.00
AR95 Ramon Santiago .40 1.00
AR96 Jason Jennings .40 1.00
AR97 Adam Kennedy .40 1.00
AR98 Mike Lamb .40 1.00
AR99 Rafael Furcal .40 1.00
AR100 Jay Payton .40 1.00
AR101 Bengie Molina .40 1.00
AR102 Mark Redman .40 1.00
AR103 Alex Gonzalez .40 1.00
AR104 Ray Durham .40 1.00
AR105 Miguel Cairo .40 1.00
AR106 Kerry Wood .40 1.00
AR107 Dmitri Young .40 1.00
AR108 Jose Cruz .40 1.00
AR109 Jose Guillen .40 1.00
AR110 Scott Hatteberg .40 1.00

2008 Topps 50th Anniversary All Rookie Team Gold

COMMON CARD 5.00 12.00
SEMISTARS 8.00 20.00
UNLISTED STARS 12.50 30.00
SER.1 ODDS 1:1290 H,1:1100 HTA
SER.1 ODDS 1:1290 RETAIL
SER.2 ODDS 1:740 HOB,1:505 HTA
SER.2 ODDS 1:1100 RETAIL
STATED PRINT RUN 99 SER.#'d SETS
AR1 Darryl Strawberry 5.00 12.00
AR2 Gary Sheffield 5.00 12.00
AR3 Dwight Gooden 5.00 12.00
AR4 Melky Cabrera 5.00 12.00
AR5 Gary Carter 5.00 12.00
AR6 Lou Piniella 5.00 12.00
AR7 Dave Justice 5.00 12.00
AR8 Andre Dawson 8.00 20.00
AR9 Mark Ellis 5.00 12.00
AR10 Dave Johnson 5.00 12.00
AR11 Jermaine Dye 5.00 12.00
AR12 Dan Johnson 5.00 12.00
AR13 Alfonso Soriano 8.00 20.00
AR14 Prince Fielder 8.00 20.00
AR15 Hanley Ramirez 12.00 30.00
AR16 Matt Holliday 12.00 30.00
AR17 Justin Verlander 15.00 40.00
AR18 Mark Teixeira 12.00 30.00
AR19 Julio Franco 5.00 12.00
AR20 Ivan Rodriguez 8.00 20.00
AR21 Jason Bay 8.00 20.00
AR22 Brandon Webb 8.00 20.00
AR23 Dontrelle Willis 5.00 12.00
AR24 Brad Wilkerson 5.00 12.00
AR25 Dan Uggla 8.00 20.00
AR26 Ozzie Smith 15.00 40.00
AR27 Andruw Jones 5.00 12.00
AR28 Garret Anderson 5.00 12.00
AR29 Jimmy Rollins 8.00 20.00
AR30 Brian McCann 8.00 20.00
AR31 Scott Podsednik 5.00 12.00
AR32 Garrett Atkins 5.00 12.00
AR33 Billy Wagner 5.00 12.00
AR34 Chipper Jones 12.00 30.00
AR35 Roger McDowell 5.00 12.00
AR36 Austin Kearns 5.00 12.00
AR37 Boog Powell 5.00 12.00
AR38 Ron Swoboda 5.00 12.00
AR39 Roy Oswalt 8.00 20.00
AR40 Mike Piazza 12.00 30.00
AR41 Albert Pujols 20.00 50.00
AR42 Ichiro Suzuki 15.00 40.00
AR43 C.C. Sabathia 8.00 20.00
AR44 Todd Helton 8.00 20.00
AR45 Scott Rolen 8.00 20.00
AR46 Derek Jeter 20.00 50.00
AR47 Shawn Green 5.00 12.00
AR48 Manny Ramirez 12.00 30.00
AR49 Tom Seaver 8.00 20.00
AR50 Kenny Lofton 5.00 12.00
AR51 Francisco Liriano 8.00 20.00
AR52 Ryan Zimmerman 8.00 20.00
AR53 Jeff Francoeur 8.00 20.00
AR54 Joe Mauer 12.00 30.00
AR55 Magglio Ordonez 8.00 20.00
AR56 Carlos Beltran 5.00 12.00
AR57 Andre Ethier 8.00 20.00
AR58 Brian Bannister 5.00 12.00
AR59 Chris Young 5.00 12.00
AR60 Troy Tulowitzki 12.00 30.00
AR61 Hideki Okajima 5.00 12.00
AR62 Delmon Young 8.00 20.00
AR63 Craig Wilson 15.00 40.00
AR64 Hunter Pence 12.00 30.00
AR65 Tadahito Iguchi 5.00 12.00
AR66 Mark Kotsay 5.00 12.00
AR67 Nick Markakis 12.00 30.00
AR68 Russ Adams 5.00 12.00
AR69 Russ Martin 10.00 25.00
AR70 James Loney 8.00 20.00
AR71 Ryan Braun 12.50 30.00
AR72 Jonny Gomes 5.00 12.00
AR73 Carlos Ruiz 5.00 12.00
AR74 Willy Taveras 5.00 12.00
AR75 Joe Torre 8.00 20.00
AR76 Jeff Kent 5.00 12.00
AR77 Huston Street 5.00 12.00
AR78 Dustin Pedroia 15.00 40.00
AR79 Gustavo Chacin 5.00 12.00
AR80 Adam Dunn 8.00 20.00
AR81 Pat Burrell 5.00 12.00
AR82 Rocco Baldelli 5.00 12.00
AR83 Chad Tracy 5.00 12.00
AR84 Adam LaRoche 5.00 12.00
AR85 Aaron Miles 5.00 12.00
AR86 Khalil Greene 5.00 12.00
AR87 Daniel Cabrera 5.00 12.00
AR88 Mike Gonzalez 5.00 12.00
AR89 Ty Wigginton 5.00 12.00
AR90 Angel Berroa 5.00 12.00
AR91 Moises Alou 5.00 12.00
AR92 Miguel Olivo 5.00 12.00
AR93 Nick Johnson 5.00 12.00
AR94 Eric Hinske 5.00 12.00
AR95 Ramon Santiago 5.00 12.00
AR96 Jason Jennings 5.00 12.00
AR97 Adam Kennedy 8.00 20.00
AR98 Mike Lamb 5.00 12.00
AR99 Rafael Furcal 5.00 12.00
AR100 Jay Payton 5.00 12.00
AR101 Bengie Molina 5.00 12.00
AR102 Mark Redman 5.00 12.00
AR103 Alex Gonzalez 5.00 12.00
AR104 Ray Durham 5.00 12.00
AR105 Miguel Cairo 5.00 12.00
AR106 Kerry Wood 5.00 12.00
AR107 Dmitri Young 10.00 25.00
AR108 Jose Cruz 5.00 12.00
AR109 Jose Guillen 5.00 12.00
AR110 Scott Hatteberg 5.00 12.00

2008 Topps 50th Anniversary All Rookie Team Autographs

SER.1 ODDS 1:7194 H, 1:365 HTA
SER.1 ODDS 1:50,000 RETAIL
SER.2 ODDS 1:13,017 HOB,1:432 HTA
SER.2 ODDS 1:34,310 RETAIL
STATED PRINT RUN 25 SER.#'d SETS
NO PRICING DUE TO SCARCITY

2008 Topps 50th Anniversary All Rookie Team Relics

SER.1 ODDS 1:7178 H, 1:366 HTA
SER.1 ODDS 1:50,700 RETAIL

SER.2 ODDS 1:2378 H,1:290 HTA
STATED PRINT RUN 50 SER.#'d SETS
AD Andre Dawson 30.00 60.00
AD Adam Dunn 12.50 30.00
AE Andre Ethier 20.00 50.00
AJ Andruw Jones 12.50 30.00
AP Albert Pujols
AS Alfonso Soriano 12.50 30.00
BM Brian McCann 10.00 25.00
BW Brandon Webb 15.00 40.00
CJ Chipper Jones 15.00 40.00
CS C.C. Sabathia 12.50 30.00
DG Dwight Gooden 10.00 25.00
DJ Dave Justice 12.50 30.00
DS Darryl Strawberry 20.00 50.00
DU Dan Uggla 12.50 30.00
DW Dontrelle Willis 12.50 30.00
FL Francisco Liriano 15.00 40.00
GA Garret Anderson 10.00 25.00
GC Gary Carter 20.00 50.00
GS Gary Sheffield 30.00 60.00
HR Hanley Ramirez 10.00 25.00
IR Ivan Rodriguez 12.50 30.00
IS Ichiro Suzuki 30.00 60.00
JB Jason Bay 30.00 60.00
JM Joe Mauer 8.00 20.00
JR Jimmy Rollins 15.00 40.00
JV Justin Verlander 15.00 40.00
MH Matt Holliday 20.00 50.00
MO Magglio Ordonez 20.00 50.00
MP Mike Piazza 20.00 50.00
MT Mark Teixeira 15.00 40.00
NJ Nick Johnson 30.00 60.00
NM Nick Markakis 40.00 80.00
OS Ozzie Smith 15.00 40.00
PB Pat Burrell 12.50 30.00
PF Prince Fielder 15.00 40.00
RB Rocco Baldelli 12.50 30.00
RO Roy Oswalt 10.00 25.00
SP Scott Podsednik
TH Todd Helton 10.00 25.00
TS Tom Seaver 12.50 30.00

2008 Topps Barry Bonds Home Run Triple Relic

RANDOM INSERTS IN PACKS
NO PRICING DUE TO SCARCITY
BB Barry Bonds

2008 Topps Campaign 2008

COMPLETE SET (12) 12.50 30.00
STATED ODDS 1:9 H,1:2 HTA,1:9 R
AG Al Gore
AS Arnold Schwarzenegger
BO Barack Obama 8.00 20.00
BR Bill Richardson .60 1.50
DK Dennis Kucinich .60 1.50
FT Fred Thompson .60 1.50
HC Hillary Clinton 2.00 5.00
JB Joseph Biden 2.00 5.00
JE John Edwards 1.00 2.50
JM John McCain 2.00 5.00
MH Mike Huckabee 1.00 2.50
MR Mitt Romney 1.00 2.50
RG Rudy Giuliani 1.00 2.50
RP Ron Paul .60 1.50
SP Sarah Palin 12.50 30.00
SP Sarah Palin Pageant 30.00 60.00

2008 Topps Campaign 2008 Gold

COMPLETE SET 50.00 100.00
*GOLD: .75X TO 2X BASIC
STATED ODDS 1:5 HTA
BO Barack Obama 20.00 50.00
JB Joseph Biden 5.00 12.00

2008 Topps Campaign 2008 Cut Signatures

STATED ODDS 1:125,000 H,1:7500 HTA
STATED ODDS 1:170,000 RETAIL
PRINT RUNS b/wn 15-18 COPIES PER
NO PRICING DUE TO SCARCITY
BO Barack Obama/15
FT Fred Thompson/15
HC Hillary Clinton/18
JE John Edwards/15
JM John McCain/13

2008 Topps Campaign 2008 Letter Patches

SER.2 ODDS 1:2642 H,1:322 HTA
STATED PRINT RUN 50 SER.#'d SETS
BO Barack Obama O 60.00 120.00
BO Barack Obama B 60.00 120.00
BO Barack Obama A 60.00 120.00
BO Barack Obama M 60.00 120.00
BO Barack Obama A 60.00 120.00
HC Hillary Clinton C 30.00 60.00
HC Hillary Clinton L 30.00 60.00
HC Hillary Clinton I 30.00 60.00
HC Hillary Clinton N 30.00 60.00
HC Hillary Clinton T 30.00 60.00
HC Hillary Clinton O 30.00 60.00
HC Hillary Clinton N 30.00 60.00
JM John McCain M 30.00 60.00
JM John McCain c 30.00 60.00
JM John McCain C 30.00 60.00
JM John McCain A 30.00 60.00
JM John McCain I 30.00 60.00
JM John McCain N 30.00 60.00

2008 Topps Commemorative Patch Relics

SER.2 ODDS 1:792 HOB,1:97 HTA
STATED PRINT RUN 100 SER.#'d SETS
AP Andy Pettitte 30.00 60.00
AR Alex Rodriguez 50.00 100.00
BA Bobby Abreu 20.00 50.00
BS Brian Schneider 10.00 25.00
BW Billy Wagner 10.00 25.00
CB Carlos Beltran 10.00 25.00
CD Carlos Delgado 10.00 25.00
CMW Chien-Ming Wang 50.00 100.00
DJ Derek Jeter 60.00 120.00
DW David Wright 20.00 50.00
EC Endy Chavez 8.00 20.00
HM Hideki Matsui 50.00 100.00
JC Joba Chamberlain 50.00 100.00
JD Johnny Damon 30.00 60.00
JG Jason Giambi 40.00 80.00
JM John Maine 10.00 25.00
JP Jorge Posada 20.00 50.00
JR Jose Reyes 12.50 30.00
LC Luis Castillo 8.00 20.00
MA Moises Alou 8.00 20.00
MC Melky Cabrera 20.00 50.00
MM Mike Mussina 40.00 80.00
MP Mike Pelfrey 12.50 30.00
MR Mariano Rivera 20.00 50.00
OH Orlando Hernandez 8.00 20.00
OP Oliver Perez 8.00 20.00
PH Phil Hughes 20.00 50.00
PM Pedro Martinez 10.00 25.00
RC Robinson Cano 30.00 60.00
RMC Ryan Church 10.00 25.00

2008 Topps Dick Perez

WMDP1 Manny Ramirez .60 1.50
WMDP2 Cameron Maybin .25 .60
WMDP3 Ryan Howard .75 2.00
WMDP4 David Ortiz .40 1.00
WMDP5 Tim Lincecum 1.00 2.50
WMDP6 David Wright .75 2.00
WMDP7 Mickey Mantle 2.00 5.00
WMDP8 Joba Chamberlain .40 1.00
WMDP9 Ichiro Suzuki 1.00 2.50
WMDP10 Prince Fielder .40 1.00
WMDP11 Jacoby Ellsbury 1.00 2.50
WMDP12 Jake Peavy .25 .60
WMDP13 Miguel Cabrera .60 1.50
WMDP14 Josh Beckett .40 1.00
WMDP15 Jimmy Rollins .40 1.00
WMDP16 Torii Hunter .25 .60
WMDP17 Alfonso Soriano .40 1.00
WMDP18 Jose Reyes .40 1.00
WMDP19 C.C. Sabathia .40 1.00
WMDP20 Alex Rodriguez 1.00 2.50
WMDP21 Ryan Braun .75 2.00
WMDP22 Johan Santana .60 1.50
WMDP23 Matt Holliday .60 1.50
WMDP24 Ervin Santana .25 .60
WMDP25 Daisuke Matsuzaka .60 1.50
WMDP26 Josh Hamilton .60 1.50
WMDP27 Chipper Jones .60 1.50
WMDP28 Lance Berkman .40 1.00
WMDP29 Hanley Ramirez .60 1.50
WMDP30 Mariano Rivera .60 1.50

2008 Topps Highlights Autographs

SER.1 A ODDS 1:32,000 H,1:1463 HTA
SER.1 A ODDS 1:159,000 RETAIL
SER.2 A ODDS 1:28,927 H,1:965 HTA
SER.2 A ODDS 1:76,245 RETAIL
UPD.A ODDS 1:38,362 HOBBY
SER.1 B ODDS 1:4792 H,1:244 HTA
SER.1 B ODDS 1:33,333 RETAIL
SER.2 B ODDS 1:923 H,1:31 HTA
SER.2 B ODDS 1:2451 RETAIL
UPD.B ODDS 1:11,066 HOBBY
SER.1 C ODDS 1:958 H,1:49 HTA
SER.1 C ODDS 1:6470 RETAIL
SER.2 C ODDS 1:651 H,1:87 HTA
SER.2 C ODDS 1:6862 RETAIL
UPD.C ODDS 1:4082 HOBBY
SER.1 D ODDS 1:1425 H,1:70 HTA
SER.1 D ODDS 1:14,250 RETAIL
SER.2 D ODDS 1:15,370 H,1:181 HTA
SER.2 D ODDS 1:14,296 RETAIL
UPD.D ODDS 1:5587 HOBBY
SER.1 E ODDS 1:1075 H,1:117 HTA
SER.1 E ODDS 1:880 RETAIL
SER.2 E ODDS 1:814 H,1:27 HTA
SER.2 E ODDS 1:2144 RETAIL
UPD.E ODDS 1:6851 HOBBY
SER.1 F ODDS 1:895 H,1:23 HTA
SER.1 F ODDS 1:1370 RETAIL
SER.2 F ODDS 1:3254 H,1:108 HTA
SER.2 F ODDS 1:8578 RETAIL
UPD.F ODDS 1:1116 HOBBY
SER.1 G ODDS 1:3070 H,1:224 HTA
SER.1 G ODDS 1:4055 RETAIL
UPD.G ODDS 1:1109 HOBBY
UPD.H ODDS 1:1985 HOBBY
NO GROUP A PRICING AVAILABLE
NO GROUP A2 PRICING AVAILABLE
AC Asdrubal Cabrera C UPD 6.00 15.00
AG Armando Galarraga D UPD 6.00 15.00
AH Aaron Heilman B2 6.00 15.00
AK Austin Kearns F2 4.00 10.00
AL Adam Lind C 4.00 10.00
AP Albert Pujols A
AS Alfonso Soriano A
BB Billy Butler C UPD 10.00 25.00
BC Bobby Crosby B2 6.00 15.00
BD Blake DeWitt C UPD 12.50 30.00
BDB Brian Barton F UPD 4.00 10.00
BP Brandon Phillips B UPD 4.00 10.00
BP Brad Penny B 10.00 25.00
BR B.J. Ryan D UPD 4.00 10.00
CB Clay Buchholz C 10.00 25.00
CC Carl Crawford B2 8.00 20.00
CD Carlos Delgado A2
CF Chone Figgins B2 6.00 15.00
CG Carlos Gomez C UPD 4.00 10.00
CJ Chipper Jones A UPD
CK Clayton Kershaw B UPD 40.00 80.00
CM Craig Monroe B2 6.00 15.00
CMW Chien-Ming Wang B 100.00 150.00
CMW Chien-Ming Wang A2
CP Carlos Pena C 8.00 20.00
CR Carlos Ruiz F UPD 4.00 10.00
CV Carlos Villanueva F 4.00 10.00
CV Claudio Vargas C2 4.00 10.00
CW Chase Wright E2 4.00 10,00
DB Daric Barton G 4.00 10.00
DB Dallas Braden C2 12.50 30.00
DE Darin Erstad B2 4.00 10.00
DH Dan Haren B 4.00 10.00
DM Dustin McGowan C UPD 6.00 15.00
DM Dustin Moseley F 4.00 10.00
DO David Ortiz A2
DW David Wright A UPD
DW David Wright B 30.00 60.00
DW David Wright A2
DY Delwyn Young E2 4.00 10.00
EC Eric Chavez B2 4.00 10.00
ED Eulogio De La Cruz C 4.00 10.00
EL Evan Longoria A UPD
ES Ervin Santana C 4.00 10.00
ES Ervin Santana E2 4.00 10.00
EV Edinson Volquez D UPD 8.00 20.00
FC Fausto Carmona C 6.00 15.00
FC Fausto Carmona E2 4.00 10.00
FL Francisco Liriano B2 6.00 15.00
FS Freddy Sanchez C 6.00 15.00
GS Greg Smith UPD
GS Gary Sheffield B 10.00 25.00
HCK Hong-Chih Kuo C2 6.00 15.00
HK Howie Kendrick D 4.00 10.00
HR Hanley Ramirez B 15.00 40.00
JA Josh Anderson E 4.00 10.00
JAB Jason Bartlett D2 4.00 10.00
JAR Jo-Jo Reyes C2 4.00 10.00
JB Jay Bruce B UPD
JB Jeremy Bonderman B2 6.00 15.00
JBR John Buck D 4.00 10.00
JBR Jose Reyes B 30.00 60.00
JC Joba Chamberlain B2 12.50 30.00
JD Johnny Damon A
JD Johnny Damon A2
JEM Justin Morneau B 10.00 25.00
JF Josh Fields C 4.00 10.00
JH Josh Hamilton B UPD 20.00 50.00
JKM John Maine B2 6.00 15.00
JL John Lackey C 5.00 12.00
JLC Jorge Cantu C2 4.00 10.00
JM Jose Molina D 4.00 10.00
JM Justin Morneau A2
JP Jake Peavy B 15.00 40.00
JR Jo-Jo Reyes E UPD 4.00 10.00
JR Jimmy Rollins B 40.00 80.00
JR Jimmy Rollins A2
JS Jeff Salazar G UPD 4.00 10.00
JTD Jermaine Dye B2 4.00 10.00
JTD Jermaine Dye B 4.00 10.00
JV Joey Votto C UPD 20.00 50.00
JV Jason Varitek B 40.00 80.00
JW Josh Willingham B2 6.00 15.00
JZ Joel Zumaya B2 6.00 15.00
KM Kendry Morales B2 4.00 10.00
LB Lance Broadway E 4.00 10.00
LC Luis Castillo C 4.00 10.00
MB Mike Bacsik F 4.00 10.00
MC Melky Cabrera B2 10.00 25.00
ME Mark Ellis F 4.00 10.00
MG Matt Garza C 4.00 10.00
MG Matt Garza B2 4.00 10.00
MK Masa Kobayashi C UPD 6.00 15.00
MMT Marcus Thames B2 4.00 10.00
MR Manny Ramirez A
MS Max Scherzer B UPD 10.00 25.00
MT Mark Teixeira A2
MW Mark Worrell H UPD 4.00 10.00
MY Michael Young B 6.00 15.00
NJM Nyjer Morgan E 4.00 10.00
NM Nick Markakis B UPD 10.00 25.00
NM Nick Markakis C 10.00 25.00
NM Nick Markakis B2 6.00 15.00
NR Nate Robertson B2 4.00 10.00
PF Prince Fielder B2 15.00 40.00
PF Prince Fielder B 30.00 60.00
PH Philip Humber D2 4.00 10.00
PJF Pedro Feliciano B2 6.00 15.00
RB Ryan Braun A UPD 60.00 120.00
RB Ryan Braun B2 20.00 50.00
RC Robinson Cano B2 12.50 30.00
RC Ramon Castro D 4.00 10.00
RH Rich Hill D 6.00 15.00
RJC Robinson Cano B 30.00 60.00
RJM Randy Messenger F 4.00 10.00
RM Russell Martin C 6.00 15.00
RM Russ Martin B2 6.00 15.00
RN Ricky Nolasco B2 4.00 10.00
RP Ronny Paulino E2 4.00 10.00
RR Ryan Roberts E2 4.00 10.00
SF Sam Fuld E 10.00 25.00
SH Steve Holm F UPD 4.00 10.00
SM Scott Moore F 4.00 10.00
SS Seth Smith G UPD 4.00 10.00
SS Seth Smith E 4.00 10.00
SV Shane Victorino B2 12.50 30.00
TG Tom Gorzelanny E2 4.00 10.00
TG Tom Gorzelanny F 4.00 10.00
TT Taylor Tankersley B2 4.00 10.00
UJ Ubaldo Jimenez F 6.00 15.00
VG Vladimir Guerrero A
VG Vladimir Guerrero A2
WN Wil Nieves C 4.00 10.00
YG Yovani Gallardo C 8.00 20.00
YP Yusmeiro Petit UPD
ZG Zack Greinke C UPD 12.50 30.00
ZG Zack Greinke E2 12.50 30.00

2008 Topps Highlights Relics

SER.1 A ODDS 1:3597 H,1:183 HTA
SER.1 A ODDS 1:25,000 RETAIL
SER.2 A ODDS 1:85 H, 1:11 HTA
SER.1 B ODDS 1:21,250 H,1:958 HTA
SER.1 B ODDS 1:7500 RETAIL
SER.2 B ODDS 1:108 H, 1:14 HTA
SER.1 C ODDS 1:1725 H,1:705 HTA
SER.1 C ODDS 1:3050 RETAIL
SER.2 C ODDS 1:651 H, 1:80 HTA
SER.1 D ODDS 1:244 RETAIL
SER.1 D ODDS 1:1965 H,1:33 HTA
AG Alex Gordon B2 5.00 12.00
AP Albert Pujols B2 6.00 15.00
AP Albert Pujols D 6.00 15.00
AR Aramis Ramirez B2 3.00 8.00
BP Brandon Phillips B2 3.00 8.00
BU B.J. Upton C2 3.00 8.00
BW Brandon Webb C2 3.00 8.00
CB Carlos Beltran Bat C 3.00 8.00
CC Carl Crawford D 3.00 8.00
CC Carl Crawford Pants B2 3.00 8.00
CM Cameron Maybin Bat C2 3.00 8.00
CM Cameron Maybin D 3.00 8.00
CMW Chien-Ming Wang Jsy B2 8.00 20.00
CS Curt Schilling Jsy D 4.00 10.00
CU Chase Utley Jsy B2 5.00 12.00
DL Derrek Lee B2 3.00 8.00
DO David Ortiz D 4.00 10.00
DO1 David Ortiz B2 4.00 10.00
DO2 David Ortiz B2 4.00 10.00
DU Dan Uggla Jsy B2 3.00 8.00
DW David Wright Jsy C2 5.00 12.00
DW David Wright D 5.00 12.00
DWW Dontrelle Willis D 3.00 8.00
DY Delmon Young Jsy B2 3.00 8.00
EC Eric Chavez D 3.00 8.00
HR Hanley Ramirez B2 3.00 8.00
IR Ivan Rodriguez D 5.00 12.00
IS Ichiro Suzuki D 6.00 15.00
IS Ichiro Suzuki C2 6.00 15.00
JB Jeremy Bonderman B2 3.00 8.00
JL James Loney B2 3.00 8.00
JP Jake Peavy B2 3.00 8.00
JR Jose Reyes A2 5.00 12.00
JR Jose Reyes A 5.00 12.00
JT Jim Thome C2 3.00 8.00
JV Justin Verlander D 5.00 12.00
LB Lance Berkman C 3.00 8.00
MH Matt Holliday B 3.00 8.00
MR Manny Ramirez D 4.00 10.00
MT Miguel Tejada D 3.00 8.00
PF Prince Fielder A 4.00 10.00
PF Prince Fielder B2 4.00 10.00
RB Ryan Braun B2 6.00 15.00
RF Rafael Furcal C2 3.00 8.00
RH Ryan Howard B2 5.00 12.00
RO Roy Oswalt A2 3.00 8.00
RZ Ryan Zimmerman B2 3.00 8.00
ST Scott Thorman B2 3.00 8.00
TH Todd Helton D 3.00 8.00
VG Vladimir Guerrero A 4.00 10.00
VG Vladimir Guerrero B2 4.00 10.00

2008 Topps Highlights Relics Autographs

SER.2 ODDS 1:17,356 H,1:577 HTA
SER.2 ODDS 1:45,747 RETAIL
STATED PRINT RUN 25 SER.#'d SETS
NO PRICING DUE TO SCARCITY

2008 Topps Highlights Relics Dual

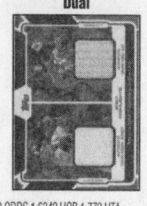

SER.2 ODDS 1:6342 HOB,1:773 HTA
STATED PRINT RUN 25 SER.#'d SETS
NO PRICING DUE TO SCARCITY

2008 Topps Historical Campaign Match-Ups

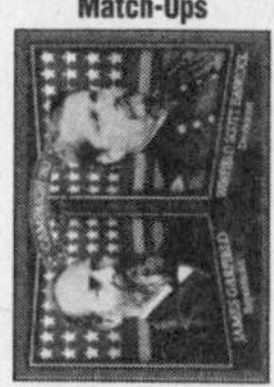

COMPLETE SET (55) 30.00 60.00
SER.2 ODDS 1:6 HOB,1:6 HTA,1:6 RET
1792 George Washington / John Adams 1.00 2.50
1796 John Adams / Thomas Jefferson 1.00 2.50
1800 Thomas Jefferson / Aaron Burr .75 2.00
1804 Thomas Jefferson / Charles Pinckney .75 2.00
1808 James Madison / Charles Pinckney .60 1.50
1812 James Madison / DeWitt Clinton .60 1.50
1816 James Monroe / Rufus King .60 1.50
1820 James Monroe / John Quincy Adams .60 1.50
1824 John Quincy Adams / Andrew Jackson .60 1.50
1828 Andrew Jackson / John Quincy Adams .60 1.50
1832 Andrew Jackson / Henry Clay .40 1.00
1836 Martin Van Buren / William Henry Harrison .40 1.00
1840 William Henry Harrison / Martin Van Buren .50 1.25
1844 James K. Polk / Henry Clay .40 1.00
1848 Zachary Taylor / Lewis Cass .40 1.00
1852 Franklin Pierce / Winfield Scott .40 1.00
1856 James Buchanan / John C. Fremont .50 1.25
1860 Abraham Lincoln / John C. Breckinridge .75 2.00
1864 Abraham Lincoln / George B. McClellan .75 2.00
1868 Ulysses S. Grant / Horatio Seymour .50 1.25
1872 Ulysses S. Grant / Horace Greeley .50 1.25
1876 Rutherford B. Hayes / Samuel J. Tilden .40 1.00
1880 James Garfield / Winfield Scott Hancock .40 1.00
1884 Grover Cleveland / James G. Blaine .40 1.00
1888 Benjamin Harrison / Grover Cleveland .40 1.00
1892 Grover Cleveland / Benjamin Harrison .40 1.00
1896 William McKinley / William Jennings Bryan .50 1.25
1900 William McKinley / William Jennings Bryan .40 1.00
1904 Theodore Roosevelt / Alton B. Parker .60 1.50
1908 William H. Taft / William Jennings Bryan .50 1.25
1912 Woodrow Wilson / Theodore Roosevelt .60 1.50
1916 Woodrow Wilson / Charles Evans Hughes .40 1.00
1920 Warren G. Harding / James M. Cox .40 1.00
1924 Calvin Coolidge / John W. Davis .40 1.00
1928 Herbert Hoover / Al Smith .40 1.00
1932 Franklin D. Roosevelt / Herbert Hoover .60 1.50
1936 Franklin D. Roosevelt / Alf Landon .50 1.25
1940 Franklin D. Roosevelt / Wendell Willkie .60 1.50
1944 Franklin D. Roosevelt / Thomas E. Dewey .50 1.25
1948 Harry S Truman / Thomas E. Dewey .50 1.25
1952 Dwight D. Eisenhower / Adlai Stevenson .60 1.50
1956 Dwight D. Eisenhower / Adlai Stevenson .60 1.50
1960 John F. Kennedy / Richard Nixon 1.25 3.00
1964 Lyndon B. Johnson / Barry Goldwater .60 1.50
1968 Richard Nixon / Hubert H. Humphrey .40 1.00
1972 Richard Nixon / George McGovern .60 1.50
1976 Jimmy Carter / Gerald Ford .75 2.00
1980 Ronald Reagan / Jimmy Carter 1.25 3.00
1984 Ronald Reagan / Walter Mondale .75 2.00
1988 George Bush / Michael Dukakis .60 1.50
1992 Bill Clinton / George Bush .75 2.00
1996 Bill Clinton / Bob Dole .75 2.00
2000 George W. Bush / Al Gore .75 2.00
2004 George W. Bush / John Kerry .75 2.00
2008D Hillary Clinton / Barack Obama 1.50 4.00

2008 Topps Historical Campaign Match-Ups Cut Signatures

SER.2 ODDS 1:80,000 HOBBY
SER.2 ODDS 1:14,000 HTA
SER.2 ODDS 1:96,000 RETAIL
STATED PRINT RUN 1 SER.#'d SETS
NO PRICING DUE TO SCARCITY

2008 Topps In the Name Relics

STATED ODDS 1:17,908 HOBBY
STATED ODDS 1:1046 HTA
EACH CARD IS #'d ONE-OF-ONE
TOTAL PRINT RUNS LISTED BELOW
PRINT RUNS PROVIDED BY TOPPS
NO PRICING DUE TO SCARCITY

2008 Topps K-Mart

COMPLETE SET (30) 15.00 40.00
RANDOM INSERTS IN KMART PACKS
RV1 Chin Lung Hu 1.25 3.00
RV2 Steve Pearce 1.25 3.00
RV3 Luke Hochevar 1.25 3.00
RV4 Joey Votto 3.00 8.00
RV5 Clay Buchholz 2.00 5.00
RV6 Emilio Bonifacio 2.00 5.00
RV7 Daric Barton .75 2.00
RV8 Eugenio Velez .75 2.00
RV9 J.R. Towles 1.25 3.00
RV10 Wladimir Balentien .75 2.00
RV11 Ross Detwiler 2.00 5.00
RV12 Troy Patton .75 2.00
RV13 Brandon Jones 2.00 5.00
RV14 Billy Buckner .75 2.00
RV15 Ross Ohlendorf 1.25 3.00
RV16 Nick Blackburn 1.25 3.00
RV17 Masahide Kobayashi 1.25 3.00
RV18 Jayson Nix .75 2.00
RV19 Blake DeWitt 2.00 5.00
RV20 Hiroki Kuroda 1.25 3.00
RV21 Matt Tolbert 1.25 3.00
RV22 Brian Bass .75 2.00
RV23 Fernando Hernandez .75 2.00
RV24 Kazuo Fukumori 1.25 3.00
RV25 Brian Barton 1.25 3.00
RV26 Clete Thomas 1.25 3.00
RV27 Rico Washington .75 2.00
RV28 Erick Threets .75 2.00
RV29 Callix Crabbe .75 2.00
RV30 Johnny Cueto 1.25 3.00

2008 Topps of the Class

RANDOM INSERTS IN PACKS
NNO David Wright .60 1.50

2008 Topps Own the Game

COMPLETE SET (25) 6.00 15.00
STATED ODDS 1:6 HOB, 1:6 RET
OTG1 Alex Rodriguez 1.25 3.00
OTG2 Prince Fielder .50 1.25
OTG3 Ryan Howard 1.00 2.50
OTG4 Carlos Pena .50 1.25
OTG5 Adam Dunn .50 1.25
OTG6 Matt Holliday .75 2.00
OTG7 David Ortiz .50 1.25
OTG8 Jim Thome .50 1.25
OTG9 Lance Berkman .50 1.25
OTG10 Miguel Cabrera .75 2.00
OTG11 Alex Rodriguez 1.25 3.00
OTG12 Magglio Ordonez .50 1.25
OTG13 Matt Holliday .75 2.00
OTG14 Ryan Howard 1.00 2.50
OTG15 Vladimir Guererro .75 2.00
OTG16 Carlos Pena .50 1.25
OTG17 Mike Lowell .30 .75
OTG18 Miguel Cabrera .75 2.00
OTG19 Prince Fielder .50 1.25
OTG20 Carlos Lee .30 .75
OTG21 Jake Peavy .30 .75
OTG22 John Lackey .30 .75
OTG23 Brandon Webb .50 1.25
OTG24 Brad Penny .30 .75
OTG25 Fausto Carmona .30 .75

2008 Topps Presidential Stamp Collection

SER.1 ODDS 1:1950 H, 1:1240 HTA
SER.1 ODDS 1:3300 RETAIL
SER.2 ODDS 1:1600 H,1:700 HTA
SER.2 ODDS 1:2000 RETAIL
STATED PRINT RUN 90 SER.#'d SETS
ALL VERSIONS PRICED EQUALLY
AJ1 Andrew Jackson 40.00 80.00
AJO1 Andrew Johnson 20.00 50.00
AL1 Abraham Lincoln 60.00 120.00
AL2 Abraham Lincoln 60.00 120.00
AL3 Abraham Lincoln 60.00 120.00
AL4 Abraham Lincoln 60.00 120.00
AL6 Abraham Lincoln 60.00 120.00
BH1 Benjamin Harrison 30.00 60.00
CAA1 Chester A. Arthur 50.00 100.00
DDE1 Dwight D. Eisenhower 40.00 80.00
FDR1 Franklin Delano Roosevelt 40.00 80.00
FP1 Franklin Pierce 30.00 60.00
GC1 Grover Cleveland 40.00 80.00
GW1 George Washington 30.00 60.00
GW2 George Washington 30.00 60.00
GW3 George Washington 30.00 60.00
GW4 George Washington 30.00 60.00
GW5 George Washington 30.00 60.00
GW6 George Washington 30.00 60.00
GW7 George Washington 30.00 60.00
GW8 George Washington 30.00 60.00
GW9 George Washington 30.00 60.00
GW10 George Washington 30.00 60.00
GW11 George Washington 30.00 60.00
GW12 George Washington 30.00 60.00
GW13 George Washington 30.00 60.00
HH1 Herbert Hoover 20.00 50.00
HST1 Harry S. Truman 30.00 60.00
JB1 James Buchanan 50.00 100.00
JFK1 John F. Kennedy 50.00 100.00
JFK2 John F. Kennedy 50.00 100.00
JG1 James Garfield 30.00 60.00
JG2 James Garfield 30.00 60.00
JKP1 James K. Polk 30.00 60.00
JM1 James Monroe 30.00 60.00
JM2 James Monroe 30.00 60.00
JMA1 James Madison 50.00 100.00
JQA1 John Quincy Adams 20.00 50.00
JT1 John Tyler 20.00 50.00
LBJ1 Lyndon B. Johnson 30.00 60.00
MF1 Millard Fillmore 30.00 60.00
MVB1 Martin Van Buren 30.00 60.00
RBH1 Rutherford B. Hayes 50.00 100.00
RBH2 Rutherford B. Hayes 50.00 100.00
RN1 Richard Nixon 30.00 60.00
RR1 Ronald Reagan 30.00 60.00
TJ1 Thomas Jefferson 50.00 100.00
TJ2 Thomas Jefferson 50.00 100.00
TJ3 Thomas Jefferson 50.00 100.00
TJ4 Thomas Jefferson 50.00 100.00
TR1 Teddy Roosevelt 30.00 60.00
TR2 Theodore Roosevelt 30.00 60.00
TR3 Theodore Roosevelt 30.00 60.00
USG1 Ulysses S. Grant 30.00 60.00
USG2 Ulysses S. Grant 30.00 60.00
WGH1 Warren G. Harding 30.00 60.00
WGH2 Warren G. Harding 30.00 60.00
WHH1 William Henry Harrison 30.00 60.00
WHT1 William Howard Taft 30.00 60.00
WM1 William McKinley 20.00 50.00
WW1 Woodrow Wilson 30.00 60.00
WW2 Woodrow Wilson 20.00 50.00
ZT1 Zachary Taylor 20.00 50.00

2008 Topps Red Hot Rookie Redemption

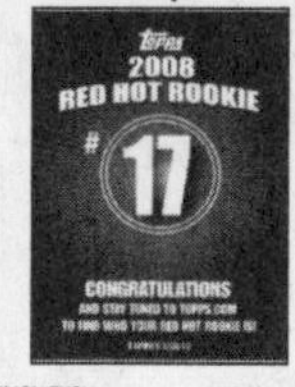

COMMON EXCH 6.00 15.00
RANDOM INSERTS IN SER.2 PACKS
EXCHANGE DEADLINE 5/30/2010
1 Jay Bruce AU 15.00 40.00
2 Justin Masterson 3.00 8.00
3 John Bowker 1.25 3.00
4 Kosuke Fukudome 4.00 10.00
5 Mike Aviles 2.00 5.00
6 Chris Davis 3.00 8.00
7 Chris Volstad 1.25 3.00
8 Jeff Samardzija 4.00 10.00
9 Brad Ziegler 6.00 15.00
10 Gio Gonzalez 2.00 5.00
11 Clayton Kershaw 6.00 15.00
12 Daniel Murphy 6.00 15.00
13 Chris Dickerson 2.00 5.00
14 Pablo Sandoval 8.00 20.00
15 Nick Evans 1.25 3.00
16 Clayton Richard 1.25 3.00
17 Evan Longoria AU 50.00 100.00
18 Taylor Teagarden 2.00 5.00
19 Collin Balester 1.25 3.00
20 Lou Montanez 1.25 3.00

2008 Topps Replica Mini Jerseys

STATED ODDS 1:412 H,1:19 HTA
STATED ODDS 1:8300 RETAIL
PRINT RUNS B/WN 379-539 COPIES PER
AIR Alex Rios/539 5.00 12.00
AP Albert Pujols 10.00 25.00
AR Alex Rodriguez/539 10.00 25.00

BW Brandon Webb 5.00 12.00
CC Carl Crawford/539 5.00 12.00
CH Cole Hamels 6.00 15.00
CMS Curt Schilling 6.00 15.00
CS C.C. Sabathia/539 5.00 12.00
CU Chase Utley 6.00 15.00
DAO David Ortiz 8.00 20.00
DO David Ortiz 8.00 20.00
DP Dustin Pedroia 10.00 25.00
DW David Wright 8.00 20.00
GS Grady Sizemore/539 6.00 15.00
HO Hideki Okajima 8.00 20.00
IS Ichiro Suzuki 10.00 25.00
JAV Jason Varitek 6.00 15.00
JB Josh Beckett 10.00 25.00
JCL Julio Lugo 6.00 15.00
JDD J.D. Drew 6.00 15.00
JE Jacoby Ellsbury 15.00 40.00
JL Jon Lester 8.00 20.00
JM Justin Morneau/539 5.00 12.00
JP Jake Peavy 6.00 15.00
JR Jose Reyes 6.00 15.00
JRP Jonathan Papelbon 8.00 20.00
JV Justin Verlander/539 6.00 15.00
KY Kevin Youkilis 6.00 15.00
MH Matt Holliday 6.00 15.00
ML Mike Lowell 10.00 25.00
MR Manny Ramirez 10.00 25.00
MT Mike Timlin 6.00 15.00
PF Prince Fielder 8.00 20.00
RH Ryan Howard/379 8.00 20.00
RM Russell Martin 5.00 12.00

2008 Topps Retail Relics

ONE PER RETAIL BLASTER BOX
NO PRICING ON SOME DUE TO SCARCITY
AB Angel Berroa UPD 3.00 8.00
AC Asdrubal Cabrera UPD 3.00 8.00
AD Adam Dunn 3.00 8.00
AER Alex Rodriguez UPD
AH Aaron Harang 3.00 8.00
AL Adam LaRoche 3.00 8.00
AR Aramis Ramirez UPD 3.00 8.00
AR Aaron Rowand 3.00 8.00
BA Bronson Arroyo 3.00 8.00
BC Bobby Crosby 3.00 8.00
BG Brian Giles 3.00 8.00
BH Brad Hawpe 3.00 8.00
BJ Bobby Jenks 3.00 8.00
BKA Bobby Abreu 3.00 8.00
BP Brad Penny 3.00 8.00
BS Ben Sheets 3.00 8.00
BW Brandon Webb 3.00 8.00
CB Carlos Beltran 3.00 8.00
CC Chris Capuano 3.00 8.00
CC Coco Crisp UPD
CD Carlos Delgado 3.00 8.00
CDC Carl Crawford 3.00 8.00
CG Curtis Granderson UPD 3.00 8.00
CJC Chris Carpenter 3.00 8.00
CK Casey Kotchman 3.00 8.00
DE Darin Erstad 3.00 8.00
DN Dioner Navarro UPD 3.00 8.00
DP Dustin Pedroia UPD 5.00 12.00
DW David Wright UPD 5.00 12.00
EB Erik Bedard UPD 3.00 8.00
EC Eric Chavez UPD 3.00 8.00
EC Eric Chavez 3.00 8.00
EE Edwin Encarnacion 3.00 8.00
FL Fred Lewis
FR Francisco Rodriguez 3.00 8.00
GA Garrett Atkins 3.00 8.00
HB Hank Blalock 3.00 8.00
HK Hong-Chih Kuo UPD 4.00 10.00
IK Ian Kinsler UPD 3.00 8.00
IR Ivan Rodriguez 3.00 8.00
IS Ian Snell 3.00 8.00
JB Jason Bay 4.00 10.00
JD Jermaine Dye 3.00 8.00
JE Johnny Estrada UPD 3.00 8.00
JE Jim Edmonds 3.00 8.00
JF Jeff Francis UPD 3.00 8.00
JL Jon Lester UPD 4.00 10.00
JL Jon Lester 4.00 10.00
JM John Maine UPD 3.00 8.00
JP Jake Peavy 3.00 8.00
JR Justin Ruggiano UPD 3.00 8.00
JR Jimmy Rollins 3.00 8.00
JRH Rich Harden 3.00 8.00
KG Khalil Greene 3.00 8.00
KH Kevin Hart UPD 3.00 8.00
KM Kendry Morales 3.00 8.00
KW Kerry Wood UPD 3.00 8.00
KW Kerry Wood 3.00 8.00
LB Lance Berkman 3.00 8.00
LH Livan Hernandez 3.00 8.00
LM Lastings Milledge UPD 3.00 8.00
MB Mark Buehrle 3.00 8.00
MH Mike Hampton 3.00 8.00
MK Matt Kemp UPD 3.00 8.00
MM Mark Mulder UPD 3.00 8.00
MM Melvin Mora 3.00 8.00
MMM Mike Mussina 3.00 8.00
MS Mike Sweeney 3.00 8.00
MT Mark Teahen 3.00 8.00
MY Michael Young 3.00 8.00
OG Ozzie Guillen 3.00 8.00
OG Ozzie Guillen UPD 3.00 8.00
PB Pat Burrell 3.00 8.00
PM Pedro Martinez 3.00 8.00
RB Rocco Baldelli UPD 3.00 8.00
RF Rafael Furcal 3.00 8.00
RF Rafael Furcal UPD 3.00 8.00
RH Roy Halladay 3.00 8.00
RW Rickie Weeks 3.00 8.00
SC Sean Casey UPD 3.00 8.00
SK Scott Kazmir 3.00 8.00
TG Troy Glaus 3.00 8.00
TH Todd Helton 3.00 8.00
TH Todd Helton UPD 3.00 8.00
TP Tony Pena 3.00 8.00
VW Vernon Wells 3.00 8.00
ZG Zack Greinke 3.00 8.00
LB1 Lance Broadway

2008 Topps Silk Collection

SER.2 ODDS 1:300 HOB, 1:139 RET
STATED PRINT RUN 100 SER.#'d SETS
1-100 FOUND IN SERIES 2
UPD ODDS 1:246 HOBBY
STATED PRINT RUN 100 SER.#'d SETS
101-200 FOUND IN UPDATE
SC1 Alex Rodriguez 30.00 60.00
SC2 Scott Kazmir 8.00 20.00
SC3 Ivan Rodriguez 8.00 20.00
SC4 Joe Mauer 15.00 40.00
SC5 Ken Griffey Jr. 20.00 50.00
SC6 Nick Markakis 6.00 15.00
SC7 Mickey Mantle 50.00 100.00
SC8 Erik Bedard 6.00 15.00
SC9 Derrek Lee 15.00 40.00
SC10 Miguel Cabrera 8.00 20.00
SC11 Yovani Gallardo 6.00 15.00
SC12 Victor Martinez 6.00 15.00
SC13 Curtis Granderson 10.00 25.00
SC14 Chris Young 6.00 15.00
SC15 Jimmy Rollins 15.00 40.00
SC16 Dan Uggla 6.00 15.00
SC17 Felix Hernandez 6.00 15.00
SC18 Alex Rios 15.00 40.00
SC19 Jason Bay 40.00 80.00
SC20 Jose Reyes 10.00 25.00
SC21 Mike Lowell 10.00 25.00
SC22 Carl Crawford 6.00 15.00
SC23 Chipper Jones 20.00 50.00
SC24 Troy Glaus 10.00 25.00
SC25 Cole Hamels 20.00 50.00
SC26 Chris Young 8.00 20.00
SC27 Torii Hunter 8.00 20.00
SC28 Hideki Matsui 10.00 25.00
SC29 Freddy Sanchez 6.00 15.00
SC30 Josh Beckett 10.00 25.00
SC31 Mark Buehrle 6.00 15.00
SC32 Brian Bannister 15.00 40.00
SC33 Carlos Beltran 8.00 20.00
SC34 Dontrelle Willis 6.00 15.00
SC35 Vladimir Guerrero 15.00 40.00
SC36 Matt Holliday 8.00 20.00
SC37 Adam Dunn 6.00 15.00
SC38 Gary Matthews 6.00 15.00
SC39 Travis Hafner 15.00 40.00
SC40 Chase Utley 20.00 50.00
SC41 Vernon Wells 8.00 20.00
SC42 Lance Berkman 10.00 25.00
SC43 Jeff Francis 6.00 15.00
SC44 Curt Schilling 10.00 25.00
SC45 Alfonso Soriano 15.00 40.00
SC46 Jarrod Saltalamacchia 6.00 15.00
SC47 Hideki Okajima 10.00 25.00
SC48 Pedro Martinez 20.00 50.00
SC49 Jorge Posada 15.00 40.00
SC50 Justin Upton 15.00 40.00
SC51 Tom Gorzelanny 10.00 25.00
SC52 Carlos Delgado 6.00 15.00
SC53 Edgar Renteria 6.00 15.00
SC54 Chien-Ming Wang 30.00 60.00
SC55 C.C. Sabathia 6.00 15.00
SC56 B.J. Upton 6.00 15.00
SC57 Delmon Young 8.00 20.00
SC58 Tim Lincecum 20.00 50.00
SC59 Carlos Zambrano 6.00 15.00
SC60 Magglio Ordonez 6.00 15.00
SC61 Brandon Webb 20.00 50.00
SC62 Ben Sheets 8.00 20.00
SC63 Brad Penny 20.00 50.00
SC64 John Lackey 6.00 15.00
SC65 Hanley Ramirez 8.00 20.00
SC66 Gary Sheffield 20.00 50.00
SC67 Ubaldo Jimenez 6.00 15.00
SC68 Barry Zito 6.00 15.00
SC69 Daisuke Matsuzaka 20.00 50.00
SC70 Justin Morneau 10.00 25.00
SC71 Jacoby Ellsbury 60.00 120.00
SC72 John Smoltz 20.00 50.00
SC73 Chris Carpenter 10.00 25.00
SC74 Ryan Braun 20.00 50.00
SC75 Prince Fielder 10.00 25.00
SC76 Carlos Lee 6.00 15.00
SC77 Ryan Zimmerman 15.00 40.00
SC78 Troy Tulowitzki 6.00 15.00
SC79 Michael Young 6.00 15.00
SC80 Johan Santana 15.00 40.00
SC81 Hunter Pence 6.00 15.00
SC82 Adrian Gonzalez 6.00 15.00
SC83 Jake Peavy 6.00 15.00
SC84 Derek Jeter 60.00 120.00
SC85 Ichiro Suzuki 20.00 50.00
SC86 Miguel Tejada 6.00 15.00
SC87 Trevor Hoffman 6.00 15.00
SC88 Kevin Youkilis 20.00 50.00
SC89 David Wright 20.00 50.00
SC90 Albert Pujols 60.00 120.00
SC91 Todd Helton 10.00 25.00
SC92 Rich Harden 6.00 15.00
SC93 Fausto Carmona 6.00 15.00
SC94 Mark Teixeira 6.00 15.00
SC95 Justin Verlander 10.00 25.00
SC96 Tim Hudson 6.00 15.00
SC97 Jeff Francoeur 15.00 40.00
SC98 Manny Ramirez 15.00 40.00
SC99 David Ortiz 15.00 40.00
SC100 Ryan Howard 15.00 40.00
SC101 Johan Santana 6.00 15.00
SC102 Cristian Guzman 4.00 10.00
SC103 Brendan Harris 4.00 10.00
SC104 Randy Wolf 4.00 10.00
SC105 Cliff Lee 6.00 15.00
SC106 Roy Halladay 6.00 15.00
SC107 Dustin Pedroia 10.00 25.00
SC108 Chris Iannetta 4.00 10.00
SC109 Kerry Wood 6.00 15.00
SC110 Jim Edmonds 6.00 15.00
SC111 Jon Rauch 4.00 10.00
SC112 Ryan Sweeney 4.00 10.00
SC113 Ryan Ludwick 6.00 15.00
SC114 George Sherrill 5.00 12.00
SC115 Matt Garza 5.00 12.00
SC116 Nate McLouth 30.00 60.00
SC117 Eric Hinske 6.00 15.00
SC118 Adrian Gonzalez 4.00 10.00
SC119 Carlos Marmol 5.00 12.00
SC120 Jose Valverde 4.00 10.00
SC121 Shane Victorino 10.00 25.00
SC122 Brad Wilkerson 5.00 12.00
SC123 Dana Eveland 6.00 15.00
SC124 Luke Scott 5.00 12.00
SC125 Mike Cameron 5.00 12.00
SC126 Ervin Santana 10.00 25.00
SC127 Ryan Dempster 5.00 12.00
SC128 Geoff Jenkins 4.00 10.00
SC129 Billy Wagner 6.00 15.00
SC130 Pedro Feliz 4.00 10.00
SC131 Stephen Drew 4.00 10.00
SC132 Mark Hendrickson 4.00 10.00
SC133 Orlando Hudson 4.00 10.00
SC134 Pat Burrell 6.00 15.00
SC135 Russ Martin 12.50 30.00
SC136 James Loney 5.00 12.00
SC137 Justin Masterson 20.00 50.00
SC138 Matt Kemp 6.00 15.00
SC139 Hiroki Kuroda 6.00 15.00
SC140 Joe Crede 4.00 10.00
SC141 Joakim Soria 4.00 10.00
SC142 Armando Galarraga 6.00 15.00
SC143 Jason Varitek 6.00 15.00
SC144 Aaron Cook 5.00 12.00
SC145 Orlando Cabrera 4.00 10.00
SC146 Ian Kinsler 6.00 15.00
SC147 Carlos Gomez 6.00 15.00
SC148 Mike Aviles 10.00 25.00
SC149 Carlos Guillen 5.00 12.00
SC150 Erik Bedard 4.00 10.00
SC151 J.D. Drew 5.00 12.00
SC152 Marco Scutaro 4.00 10.00
SC153 James Shields 6.00 15.00
SC154 Cesar Izturis 4.00 10.00
SC155 Akinori Iwamura 8.00 20.00
SC156 Aramis Ramirez 5.00 12.00
SC157 Joe Mauer 6.00 15.00
SC158 Brad Lidge 8.00 20.00
SC159 Milton Bradley 4.00 10.00
SC160 Jay Bruce 12.50 30.00
SC161 Andrew Miller 5.00 12.00
SC162 Mark Reynolds 4.00 10.00
SC163 Johnny Damon 8.00 20.00
SC164 Michael Bourn 6.00 15.00
SC165 Andre Ethier 10.00 25.00
SC166 Carlos Pena 6.00 15.00
SC167 Joe Nathan 6.00 15.00
SC168 Cody Ross 4.00 10.00
SC169 Joba Chamberlain 10.00 25.00
SC170 Clayton Kershaw 8.00 20.00
SC171 Francisco Rodriguez 6.00 15.00
SC172 Mark DeRosa 5.00 12.00
SC173 Ben Sheets 4.00 10.00
SC174 Brian Wilson 4.00 10.00
SC175 Emil Brown 4.00 10.00
SC176 Geovany Soto 8.00 20.00
SC177 Jason Giambi 6.00 15.00
SC178 Shaun Marcum 5.00 12.00
SC179 Edinson Volquez 5.00 12.00
SC180 Max Scherzer 8.00 20.00
SC181 Kelly Johnson 5.00 12.00
SC182 Mariano Rivera 10.00 25.00
SC183 Chris Perez 8.00 20.00
SC184 Jose Guillen 4.00 10.00
SC185 Kyle Lohse 10.00 25.00
SC186 Kosuke Fukudome 12.50 30.00
SC187 Takashi Saito 12.50 30.00
SC188 Mike Mussina 12.50 30.00
SC189 J.J. Putz 4.00 10.00
SC190 Evan Longoria 20.00 50.00
SC191 Jered Weaver 5.00 12.00
SC192 Grady Sizemore 12.50 30.00
SC193 Carlos Gonzalez 6.00 15.00
SC194 Brian McCann 5.00 12.00
SC195 Jonathan Papelbon 5.00 12.00
SC196 Dioner Navarro 5.00 12.00
SC197 Bobby Abreu 5.00 12.00
SC198 Carlos Quentin 5.00 12.00
SC199 Josh Hamilton 20.00 50.00
SC200 Dan Haren 4.00 10.00

2008 Topps Stars

COMPLETE SET (25) 8.00 20.00
SER.2 ODDS 1:6 HOB, 1:6 RET
TS1 Alex Rodriguez 1.25 3.00
TS2 Magglio Ordonez .50 1.25
TS3 Justin Morneau .75 2.00
TS4 Josh Beckett .50 1.25
TS5 David Wright 1.00 2.50
TS6 Jimmy Rollins .50 1.25
TS7 Ichiro Suzuki 1.25 3.00
TS8 Chipper Jones .75 2.00
TS9 Brandon Webb .50 1.25
TS10 Ryan Howard 1.00 2.50
TS11 Derek Jeter 2.00 5.00
TS12 Vladimir Guerrero .75 2.00
TS13 Manny Ramirez .75 2.00
TS14 Jake Peavy .30 .75
TS15 David Ortiz .50 1.25
TS16 Jose Reyes .50 1.25
TS17 Miguel Cabrera .75 2.00
TS18 Victor Martinez .50 1.25
TS19 C.C. Sabathia .50 1.25
TS20 Prince Fielder .50 1.25
TS21 Alfonso Soriano .50 1.25
TS22 Grady Sizemore .50 1.25
TS23 Albert Pujols 2.00 5.00
TS24 Pedro Martinez .50 1.25
TS25 Matt Holliday .75 2.00

2008 Topps Trading Card History

COMPLETE SET (75) 20.00 50.00
SER.1 ODDS 1:12 HOBBY
SER.2 ODDS 1:6 HOBBY
TCH1 Jacoby Ellsbury 1.50 4.00
TCH2 Joba Chamberlain .60 1.50
TCH3 Daisuke Matsuzaka 1.00 2.50
TCH4 Price Fielder .60 1.50
TCH5 Clay Buchholz 1.00 2.50
TCH6 Alex Rodriguez 1.50 4.00
TCH7 Mickey Mantle 2.50 6.00
TCH8 Ryan Braun 1.25 3.00
TCH9 Albert Pujols 2.50 6.00
TCH10 Joe Mauer 1.00 2.50
TCH11 Jose Reyes .60 1.50
TCH12 Joey Votto 1.50 4.00
TCH13 Johan Santana 1.00 2.50
TCH14 Hunter Pence 1.00 2.50
TCH15 Hideki Okajima .40 1.00
TCH16 Cameron Maybin .40 1.00
TCH17 Roger Clemens 1.25 3.00
TCH18 Tim Lincecum 1.50 4.00
TCH19 Mark Teixeira 1.00 2.50
Jeff Francoeur
TCH20 Justin Upton .60 1.50
TCH21 Alfonso Soriano .60 1.50
TCH22 Pedro Martinez .60 1.50
TCH23 Chien-Ming Wang .60 1.50
TCH24 Ichiro Suzuki 1.50 4.00
TCH25 Grady Sizemore .60 1.50
TCH26 Ryan Howard 1.25 3.00
TCH27 David Wright 1.25 3.00
TCH28 Chin-Lung Hu .60 1.50
TCH29 Jimmy Rollins .60 1.50
TCH30 Ken Griffey Jr 1.50 4.00
TCH31 Chipper Jones 1.00 2.50
TCH32 Justin Verlander 1.25 3.00
TCH33 Manny Ramirez 1.00 2.50
TCH34 Chase Utley 1.00 2.50
TCH35 Ivan Rodriguez .60 1.50
TCH36 Josh Beckett .60 1.50
TCH37 Tom Glavine .60 1.50
TCH38 Vladimir Guerrero 1.00 2.50
TCH39 Lance Berkman .60 1.50
TCH40 Gary Sheffield .40 1.00
TCH41 Luke Hochevar .60 1.50
TCH42 David Ortiz .60 1.50
TCH43 Miguel Cabrera 1.00 2.50
TCH44 Andruw Jones .40 1.00
TCH45 Hideki Matsui 1.00 2.50
TCH46 C.C. Sabathia .60 1.50
TCH47 Magglio Ordonez .60 1.50
TCH48 Pedro Martinez .60 1.50
TCH49 Curtis Granderson .60 1.50
TCH50 Derek Jeter 2.50 6.00
TCH51 Victor Martinez .60 1.50
TCH52 Hanley Ramirez 1.00 2.50
TCH53 Jake Peavy .40 1.00
TCH54 Brandon Webb .60 1.50
TCH55 Matt Holliday 1.00 2.50
TCH56 Hiroki Kuroda .60 1.50
TCH57 Mike Lowell .40 1.00
TCH58 Carlos Lee .40 1.00
TCH59 Nick Markakis 1.00 2.50
TCH60 Carlos Beltran .40 1.00
TCH61 Francisco Rodriguez .60 1.50
TCH62 Troy Tulowitzki 1.00 2.50
TCH63 Russ Martin .60 1.50
TCH64 Justin Morneau 1.00 2.50
TCH65 Phil Hughes 1.00 2.50
TCH66 Torii Hunter .40 1.00
TCH67 Adam Dunn .60 1.50
TCH68 Raul Ibanez .60 1.50
TCH69 Robinson Cano 1.00 2.50
TCH70 Brad Hawpe .40 1.00
TCH71 Michael Young .60 1.50
TCH72 Jim Thome .60 1.50
TCH73 Chris Young .40 1.00
TCH74 Carlos Zambrano .60 1.50
TCH75 Felix Hernandez 1.00 2.50

2008 Topps World Champion Relics

STATED ODDS 1:4792 H, 1:244 HTA
STATED ODDS 1:33,333 RETAIL
STATE PRINT RUN 100 SER.#'d SETS
WCR1 Josh Beckett 50.00 100.00
WCR2 Hideki Okajima 30.00 60.00
WCR3 Curt Schilling 40.00 80.00
WCR4 Jason Varitek 40.00 80.00
WCR5 Mike Lowell 30.00 60.00
WCR6 Jacoby Ellsbury 60.00 120.00
WCR7 Dustin Pedroia 30.00 60.00
WCR8 Jonathan Papelbon 30.00 60.00
WCR9 Julio Lugo 20.00 50.00
WCR10 Manny Ramirez 30.00 60.00
WCR11 David Ortiz 30.00 60.00
WCR12 Eric Gagne 30.00 60.00
WCR13 Jon Lester 30.00 60.00
WCR14 J.D. Drew 30.00 60.00
WCR15 Kevin Youkilis 40.00 80.00

2008 Topps World Champion Relics Autographs

STATED ODDS 1:14,417 H, 1:732 HTA
STATED ODDS 1:99,000 RETAIL
PRINT RUNS B/WN 25-50 COPIES PER
NO PRICING ON MOST DUE TO SCARCITY
WCAR1 Josh Beckett/50
WCAR2 Hideki Okajima/50
WCAR3 Curt Schilling/50
WCAR4 Jason Varitek/50
WCAR5 Mike Lowell/50
WCAR6 Jacoby Ellsbury/25
WCAR7 Dustin Pedroia/25
WCAR8 Jonathan Papelbon/50
WCAR9 Julio Lugo/50
WCAR10 Manny Ramirez/50 100.00 200.00

2008 Topps Year in Review

COMPLETE SET (178) 50.00 100.00
COMP.SER.1.SET (60) 12.50 30.00
COMP.SER.2.SET (60) 12.50 30.00
COMP.UPD SET (58) 12.50 30.00
SER.1 ODDS 1:6 HOB, 1:6 RET
SER.2 ODDS 1:6 HOB, 1:6 RET
UPD ODDS 1:6 HOBBY
YR1 Paul Lo Duca .30 .75
YR2 Felix Hernandez .75 2.00
YR3 Ian Snell .30 .75
YR4 Carlos Beltran .30 .75
YR5 Daisuke Matsuzaka .75 2.00
YR6 Jose Reyes .50 1.25
YR7 Alex Rodriguez 1.25 3.00
YR8 Scott Kazmir .50 1.25
YR9 Adam Everett .30 .75
YR10 Josh Beckett .75 2.00
Josh Hamilton
YR11 Craig Monroe .30 .75
YR12 Justin Morneau .75 2.00
YR13 Roy Halladay .75 2.00
YR14 Jeff Suppan .30 .75
YR15 Marco Scutaro .30 .75
YR16 Ivan Rodriguez .50 1.25
YR17 Dimtri Young .30 .75
YR18 Mark Buehrle .50 1.25
YR19 Alex Rodriguez 1.25 3.00
YR20 Joe Saunders .30 .75
YR21 Russell Martin .30 .75
YR22 Manny Ramirez .75 2.00
YR23 Chase Utley .75 2.00
YR24 Travis Hafner .30 .75
YR25 Jake Peavy .30 .75
YR26 Shawn Hill .30 .75
YR27 Daisuke Matsuzaka .75 2.00
YR28 Matt Belisle .30 .75
YR29 Troy Tulowitzki .75 2.00
YR30 Andruw Jones .30 .75
YR31 Phil Hughes .75 2.00
YR32 Derrek Lee .30 .75
YR33 Ichiro Suzuki 1.25 3.00
YR34 Julio Franco .30 .75
YR35 Chien-Ming Wang .50 1.25
YR36 Hideki Matsui .75 2.00
YR37 Brad Penny .30 .75
YR38 Jack Wilson .30 .75
YR39 Francisco Cordero .30 .75
YR40 Omar Vizquel .50 1.25
YR41 Tim Lincecum 1.25 3.00
YR42 Bartolo Colon .30 .75
YR43 Fred Lewis .30 .75
YR44 Jeff Kent .30 .75
YR45 Randy Johnson .75 2.00
YR46 Rafael Furcal .30 .75
YR47 Delmon Young .50 1.25
YR48 Andrew Miller .30 .75
YR49 David Ortiz .50 1.25
Mike Lowell
YR50 Justin Verlander 1.00 2.50
YR51 C.C. Sabathia .50 1.25
YR52 Felipe Lopez .30 .75
YR53 Oliver Perez .30 .75
YR54 John Smoltz .75 2.00
YR55 Mark Reynolds .30 .75
YR56 Jeremy Accardo .30 .75
YR57 Todd Helton .50 1.25
YR58 Adrian Beltre .30 .75
YR59 Carlos Delgado .30 .75
YR60 Chris Young .30 .75
YR61 Roy Halladay .75 2.00
YR62 Kevin Youkilis .50 1.25
YR63 Joe Blanton .30 .75
YR64 Chad Gaudin .30 .75
YR65 Derek Lowe .30 .75
YR66 C.C. Sabathia .50 1.25
YR67 Luis Castillo .30 .75
YR68 Curt Schilling .50 1.25
YR69 Pedro Feliz .30 .75
YR70 James Shields .30 .75
YR71 Masumi Kuwata .30 .75
YR72 Raul Ibanez .50 1.25
YR73 Justin Verlander 1.00 2.50
YR74 Tim Lincecum 1.25 3.00
YR75 Hideki Matsui .75 2.00
YR76 Julio Franco .30 .75
YR77 Russell Branyan .30 .75
YR78 Chipper Jones .75 2.00
YR79 Chone Figgins .30 .75
YR80 Chris Young .30 .75
YR81 Sammy Sosa .75 2.00
YR82 Miguel Tejada .50 1.25
YR83 Wil Ledezma .30 .75
YR84 Victor Martinez .50 1.25
YR85 Dustin McGowan .30 .75
YR86 Mike Fontenot .30 .75
YR87 Mark Ellis .30 .75
YR88 Ryan Howard 1.00 2.50
YR89 Frank Thomas .75 2.00
YR90 Aubrey Huff .30 .75
YR91 Jake Peavy .30 .75
YR92 Dan Haren .30 .75
YR93 Damian Miller .30 .75
YR94 Billy Butler .30 .75
YR95 Dmitri Young .30 .75
YR96 Chipper Jones .75 2.00
YR97 Justin Morneau .75 2.00
YR98 Erik Bedard .30 .75
YR99 Scott Hatteberg .30 .75
YR100 Vladimir Guerrero .75 2.00
YR101 Ichiro Suzuki 1.25 3.00
YR102 Jose Reyes .50 1.25
YR103 Ryan Garko .30 .75
YR104 Jeff Francoeur .50 1.25
YR105 Joe Mauer .75 2.00
YR106 Manny Ramirez .75 2.00
YR107 Chase Utley .75 2.00
YR108 Magglio Ordonez .50 1.25
YR109 Chris Young .30 .75
YR110 B.J. Upton .50 1.25
YR111 Willie Harris .30 .75
YR112 Shelley Duncan .30 .75
YR113 Jon Lester .75 2.00
YR114 Travis Buck .30 .75
YR115 Ryan Raburn .30 .75
YR116 Eric Byrnes .30 .75
YR117 Kenny Lofton .30 .75
YR118 Jason Isringhausen .30 .75
YR119 Todd Helton .50 1.25
YR120 Carl Crawford .50 1.25
YR121 Mark Teixeira .75 2.00
YR122 Alex Gordon .50 1.25
YR123 Jermaine Dye .30 .75
YR124 Vladimir Guerrero .75 2.00
YR125 Alex Rodriguez 1.25 3.00
YR126 Tom Glavine .50 1.25
YR127 Scott Rolen .50 1.25
YR128 Billy Wagner .30 .75
YR129 Rick Ankiel .30 .75
YR130 Jack Cust .30 .75
YR131 Mike Mussina .50 1.25
YR132 Maggio Ordonez .50 1.25
YR133 Placido Polanco .30 .75
YR134 Russell Branyan .30 .75
YR135 David Price .75 2.00
YR136 Mike Cameron .30 .75
YR137 Brandon Webb .50 1.25
YR138 Cameron Maybin .30 .75
YR139 Johan Santana .75 2.00
YR140 Bobby Jenks .30 .75
YR141 Garret Anderson .30 .75
YR142 Jarrod Saltalamacchia .30 .75
YR143 Adrian Gonzalez .50 1.25
YR144 Carlos Guillen .30 .75
YR145 Tom Shearn .30 .75
YR146 John Lackey .30 .75
YR147 Jayson Werth .50 1.25
YR148 Aaron Harang .30 .75
YR149 Chien-Ming Wang .50 1.25
YR150 Scott Baker .30 .75
YR151 Clay Buchholz .75 2.00
YR152 Tom Glavine .50 1.25
YR153 Pedro Martinez .50 1.25
YR154 Doug Davis .30 .75
YR155 Brandon Phillips .30 .75
YR156 Jason Varitek .75 2.00
YR157 Jim Thome .50 1.25
YR158 Alex Rodriguez 1.25 3.00
YR159 Curtis Granderson .50 1.25
YR160 Scott Kazmir .50 1.25
YR161 Marlon Byrd .30 .75
YR162 David Ortiz .50 1.25
YR163 Greg Maddux 1.00 2.50
YR164 Johnny Damon .50 1.25
YR165 Carlos Lee .30 .75
YR166 Jim Thome .50 1.25
YR167 Frank Thomas .75 2.00
YR168 Greg Maddux 1.00 2.50
YR169 Matt Holliday .75 2.00
YR170 J.R. Towles .50 1.25
YR171 Lance Berkman .50 1.25
YR172 Melky Cabrera .30 .75
YR173 Vladimir Guerrero .75 2.00
YR174 Nick Markakis .75 2.00
YR175 Prince Fielder .50 1.25
YR176 Moises Alou .30 .75
YR177 Micah Owings .30 .75
YR178 Carlos Zambrano .50 1.25

2008 Topps Update

This set was released on October 22, 2008. The base set consists of 330 cards.

COMP.SET w/o VAR (330) 20.00 50.00
COMMON CARD (1-330) .12 .30
COMMON ROOKIE (1-330) .20 .50
1-330 PLATE ODDS 1:457 HOBBY
PLATE PRINT RUN 1 SET PER COLOR
BLACK-CYAN-MAGENTA-YELLOW ISSUED
NO PLATE PRICING DUE TO SCARCITY
UH1A Kosuke Fukudome RC .60 1.50
UH1B Kosuke Fukudome VAR 15.00 40.00
Upside-down photo
UH2 Sean Casey .12 .30
UH3 Freddie Bynum .12 .30
UH4 Brent Lillibridge (RC) .20 .50
UH5 Chipper Jones AS .30 .75
UH6 Yamid Haad .12 .30
UH7 Josh Anderson .12 .30
UH8 Jeff Mathis .12 .30
UH9 Shawn Riggans .12 .30
UH10A Evan Longoria RC 1.00 2.50
UH10B Evan Longoria VAR 40.00 80.00
(Upside-down photo
UH11 Matt Holliday AS .30 .75
UH12 Trot Nixon .12 .30
UH13 Geoff Blum .12 .30
UH14 Bartolo Colon .12 .30
UH15 Kevin Cash .12 .30
UH16 Paul Janish (RC) .20 .50
UH17 Russell Martin AS .12 .30
UH18 Andy Phillips .12 .30
UH19 Johnny Estrada .12 .30
UH20 Justin Masterson RC .50 1.25
UH21 Darrell Rasner .12 .30
UH22 Brian Moehler .12 .30
UH23 Cristian Guzman AS .12 .30
UH24 Tony Armas Jr. .12 .30
UH25 Lance Berkman AS .20 .50
UH26 Chris Iannetta .12 .30
UH27 Reid Brignac .20 .50
UH28 Miguel Tejada AS .20 .50
UH29 Ryan Ludwick AS .12 .30
UH30 Brendan Harris .12 .30
UH31 Marco Scutaro .12 .30
UH32 Cody Ross .12 .30
UH33 Carlos Marmol .20 .50
UH34 Nate McLouth AS .12 .30
UH35 Hanley Ramirez AS .30 .75
UH36 Xavier Nady .12 .30
UH37 Connor Robertson .12 .30
UH38 Carlos Villanueva .12 .30
UH39 Jose Molina .12 .30
UH40 Jon Rauch .12 .30
UH41 Joe Mauer AS .30 .75
UH42 Chip Ambres .12 .30
UH43 Jason Bartlett .12 .30
UH44 Ryan Sweeney .12 .30
UH45 Eric Hurley (RC) .20 .50
UH46 Kevin Youkilis AS .20 .50
UH47 Dustin Pedroia AS .40 1.00
UH48 Grant Balfour .12 .30
UH49 Ryan Ludwick .12 .30
UH50 Matt Garza .12 .30
UH51 Fernando Tatis .12 .30
UH52 Derek Jeter AS .75 2.00
UH53 Justin Duchscherer AS .12 .30
UH54 Matt Ginter .12 .30
UH55 Cesar Izturis .12 .30
UH56 Roy Halladay AS .30 .75
UH57 Ramon Castro .12 .30
UH58 Scott Kazmir AS .20 .50
UH59 Cliff Lee AS .20 .50
UH60 Jim Edmonds .20 .50
UH61 Randy Wolf .12 .30
UH62 Matt Albers .12 .30
UH63 Eric Bruntlett .12 .30
UH64 Joe Nathan AS .12 .30
UH65 Alex Rodriguez AS .50 1.25
UH66 Robinson Cancel .12 .30
UH67 Jamey Carroll .12 .30
UH68 Jonathan Papelbon AS .20 .50
UH69 Chad Moeller .12 .30
UH70 George Sherrill .12 .30
UH71 Mariano Rivera AS .30 .75
UH72 Pete Orr .12 .30
UH73 Jonathan Albaladejo RC .30 .75
UH74 Corey Patterson .12 .30
UH75 Matt Treanor .12 .30
UH76 Francisco Rodriguez AS .20 .50
UH77 Ervin Santana AS .12 .30
UH78 Dallas Braden .20 .50
UH79 Willie Harris .12 .30
UH80 Erik Bedard .12 .30
UH81 J.C. Romero .12 .30
UH82 Joe Saunders AS .12 .30
UH83 George Sherrill AS .12 .30
UH84 Julian Tavarez .12 .30
UH85 Chad Gaudin .12 .30
UH86 David Aardsma .12 .30
UH87 Ryan Langerhans .12 .30
UH88 Dan Haren .12 .30
Russell Martin
UH89 Joakim Soria AS .12 .30
UH90 Dan Haren .12 .30
UH91 Billy Buckner .12 .30
UH92 Eric Hinske .12 .30
UH93 Chris Coste .12 .30
UH94 Edinson Volquez .12 .30
Russell Martin
UH95 Ichiro Suzuki AS .50 1.25
UH96 Vladimir Nunez .12 .30
UH97 Sean Gallagher .12 .30
UH98 Denny Bautista .12 .30
UH99 Hanley Ramirez .20 .50
David Ortiz
UH100 Jay Bruce (RC) .75 2.00

UH100B Jay Bruce VAR 20.00 50.00
Upside-down photo
UH101 Dioner Navarro AS .12 .30
UH102 Matt Murton .12 .30
UH103 Chris Burke .12 .30
UH104 Omar Infante .12 .30
UH105 Dan Giese (RC) .20 .50
UH106 Carlos Guillen .30 .75
Josh Hamilton
UH107 Jason Varitek AS .30 .75
UH108 Shin- Soo Choo .20 .50
UH109 Alberto Callaspo .12 .30
UH110 Jose Valverde .12 .30
UH111 Brandon Boggs (RC) .30 .75
UH112 Josh Hamilton .30 .75
J.D. Drew
UH113 Justin Morneau AS .30 .75
UH114 Billy Traber .12 .30
UH115 Mike Lamb .12 .30
UH116 Odalis Perez .12 .30
UH117 Jed Lowrie (RC) .50 1.25
UH118 Justin Morneau .30 .75
David Ortiz
UH119 Ken Griffey Jr. HL .50 1.25
UH120 Angel Berroa .12 .30
UH121 Jacque Jones .12 .30
UH122 DeWayne Wise .12 .30
UH123 Matt Joyce RC .50 1.25
UH124 Alex Rodriguez .60 1.50
Evan Longoria
UH125 John Smoltz HL .30 .75
UH126 Morgan Ensberg .12 .30
UH127 Michael Young .20 .50
Derek Jeter
UH128 LaTroy Hawkins .12 .30
UH129 Nick Adenhart (RC) .20 .50
UH130 Mike Cameron .12 .30
UH131 Manny Ramirez HL .30 .75
UH132 Jorge De La Rosa .12 .30
UH133 Tadahito Iguchi .12 .30
UH134 Joey Devine .12 .30
UH135 Jose Arredondo RC .30 .75
UH136 Hanley Ramirez .75 2.00
Albert Pujols
UH137 Evan Longoria HL .60 1.50
UH138 T.J. Beam .12 .30
UH139 Jon Lieber .12 .30
UH140 Dana Eveland .12 .30
UH141 Michael Aubrey RC .30 .75
UH142 Adrian Gonzalez .30 .75
Matt Holliday
UH143 Chipper Jones HL .30 .75
UH144 Robinson Tejeda .12 .30
UH145 Kip Wells .12 .30
UH146 Carlos Gonzalez (RC) .50 1.25
UH147 Josh Banks (RC) .20 .50
UH148 David Wright AS .40 1.00
UH149 Paul Hoover .12 .30
UH150 Jon Lester HL .30 .75
UH151 Darin Erstad .12 .30
UH152 Steve Trachsel .12 .30
UH153 Armando Galarraga RC .30 .75
UH154 Grady Sizemore HRD .20 .50
UH155 Jay Bruce HL .50 1.25
UH156 Juan Rincon .12 .30
UH157 Mark Hendrickson .12 .30
UH158 Chad Durbin .12 .30
UH159 Mike Aviles RC .30 .75
UH160 Orlando Cabrera .12 .30
UH161 Asdrubal Cabrera HL .20 .50
UH162 Eric Stults .12 .30
UH163 Miguel Cairo .12 .30
UH164 Jason LaRue .12 .30
UH165 Burke Badenhop RC .30 .75
UH166 Ryan Braun HRD .40 1.00
UH167 Justin Morneau HRD .30 .75
UH168 Ben Zobrist .12 .30
UH169 Eulogio De La Cruz .12 .30
UH170 Greg Smith (RC) .20 .50
UH171 Brian Bixler (RC) .20 .50
UH172 Evan Longoria HRD .60 1.50
UH173 Randy Johnson HL .30 .75
UH174 D.J. Carrasco .12 .30
UH175 Luis Vizcaino .12 .30
UH176 Brad Wilkerson UER .12 .30
Shown batting righty; Wilkerson is a left
UH177 Emmanuel Burriss RC .30 .75
UH178 Lance Berkman HRD .20 .50
UH179 Johnny Damon HL .20 .50
UH180 Scott Rolen .20 .50
UH181 Runelvys Hernandez .12 .30
UH182 Sidney Ponson .12 .30
UH183 Greg Reynolds RC .30 .75
UH184 Chase Utley HRD .30 .75
UH185 Joey Votto HL .50 1.25
UH186 Wes Littleton .12 .30
UH187 Rod Barajas .12 .30
UH188 Ray Durham .12 .30
UH189 Micah Hoffpauir RC .60 1.50
UH190 Manny Ramirez AS .30 .75
UH191 Ian Kinsler AS .20 .50
UH192 Craig Hansen .12 .30
UH193 Jeremy Affeldt .12 .30
UH194 Gary Bennett .12 .30
UH195 Chris Carter (RC) .30 .75
UH196 Dan Uggla HRD .20 .50
UH197 Michael Young AS .20 .50
UH198 Andy LaRoche .12 .30
UH199 Lance Cormier .12 .30
UH200 Luke Scott .12 .30
UH201 Travis Denker RC .30 .75
UH202 Josh Hamilton .30 .75
UH203 Joe Crede AS .12 .30
UH204 Franquelis Osoria .12 .30
UH205 Octavio Dotel .12 .30
UH206 Russell Branyan .12 .30
UH207 Alberto Gonzalez RC .30 .75
UH208 Kerry Wood AS .12 .30
UH209 Carlos Guillen AS .12 .30
UH210 Joe Saunders .12 .30
UH211 Brett Tomko .12 .30
UH212 Guillermo Mota .12 .30
UH213 German Duran RC .30 .75
UH214 Carlos Zambrano AS .20 .50
UH215 Josh Hamilton AS .30 .75
UH216 Jason Bay .20 .50
UH217 Willy Aybar .12 .30
UH218 Salomon Torres .12 .30
UH219 Damaso Marte .12 .30
UH220 Geoff Jenkins .12 .30
UH221 J.D. Drew AS .12 .30
UH222 Dave Borkowski .12 .30
UH223 Jeff Ridgway RC .30 .75
UH224 Angel Pagan .12 .30
UH225 Ryan Tucker (RC) .20 .50
UH226 Brian McCann AS .20 .50
UH227 Carlos Quentin AS .12 .30
UH228 Joe Blanton .12 .30
UH229 Adrian Gonzalez AS .20 .50
UH230 Jason Jennings .12 .30
UH231 Chris Davis RC .50 1.25
UH232 Geovany Soto AS .30 .75
UH233 Grady Sizemore AS .20 .50
UH234 Carl Pavano .12 .30
UH235 Eddie Guardado .12 .30
UH236 Chris Snelling .12 .30
UH237 Manny Ramirez .30 .75
UH238 Dan Uggla AS .20 .50
UH239 Milton Bradley AS .12 .30
UH240 Clayton Kershaw RC 1.00 2.50
UH241 Chase Utley AS .30 .75
UH242 Raul Chavez .12 .30
UH243 Joe Mather RC .30 .75
UH244 Brandon Webb AS .20 .50
UH245 Ryan Braun .40 1.00
UH246 Kelvin Jimenez .12 .30
UH247 Scott Podsednik .12 .30
UH248 Doug Mientkiewicz .12 .30
UH249 Chris Volstad (RC) .20 .50
UH250 Pedro Feliz .12 .30
UH251 Mark Redman .12 .30
UH252 Tony Clark .12 .30
UH253 Josh Johnson .20 .50
UH254 Jose Castillo .12 .30
UH255 Brian Horwitz RC .20 .50
UH256 Aramis Ramirez AS .12 .30
UH257 Casey Blake .12 .30
UH258 Arthur Rhodes .12 .30
UH259 Aaron Boone .12 .30
UH260 Emil Brown .12 .30
UH261 Matt Macri (RC) .20 .50
UH262 Brian Wilson AS .30 .75
UH263 Eric Patterson .12 .30
UH264 David Ortiz .20 .50
UH265 Tony Abreu .12 .30
UH266 Rob Mackowiak .12 .30
UH267 Gregorio Petit RC .30 .75
UH268 Alfonso Soriano AS .20 .50
UH269 Robert Andino .12 .30
UH270 Justin Duchscherer .12 .30
UH271 Brad Thompson .12 .30
UH272 Guillermo Quiroz .12 .30
UH273 Chris Perez RC .30 .75
UH274 Albert Pujols AS .75 2.00
UH275 Rich Harden .12 .30
UH276 Corey Hart AS .12 .30
UH277 John Rheinecker .12 .30
UH278 So Taguchi .12 .30
UH279 Alex Hinshaw RC .30 .75
UH280 Max Scherzer RC .60 1.50
UH281 Chris Aguila .12 .30
UH282 Carlos Marmol AS .20 .50
UH283 Alex Cintron .12 .30
UH284 Curtis Thigpen .12 .30
UH285 Kosuke Fukudome AS .40 1.00
UH286 Aaron Cook AS .12 .30
UH287 Chase Headley .12 .30
UH288 Evan Longoria AS .60 1.50
UH289 Chris Gomez .12 .30
UH290 Carlos Gomez .12 .30
UH291 Jonathan Herrera RC .30 .75
UH292 Ryan Dempster AS .12 .30
UH293 Adam Dunn .20 .50
UH294 Mark Teixeira .30 .75
UH295 Aaron Miles .12 .30
UH296 Gabe Gross .12 .30
UH297 Cory Wade (RC) .20 .50
UH298 Dan Haren AS .12 .30
UH299 Jolbert Cabrera .12 .30
UH300 C.C. Sabathia .20 .50
UH301 Tony Pena .12 .30
UH302 Brandon Moss .12 .30
UH303 Taylor Teagarden RC .30 .75
UH304 Brad Lidge AS .12 .30
UH305 Ben Francisco .12 .30
UH306 Casey Kotchman .12 .30
UH307 Greg Norton .12 .30
UH308 Shelley Duncan .12 .30
UH309 John Bowker (RC) .20 .50
UH310 Kyle Lohse .12 .30
UH311 Oscar Salazar .12 .30
UH312 Ivan Rodriguez .20 .50
UH313 Tim Lincecum AS .50 1.25
UH314 Wilson Betemit .12 .30
UH315 Sean Rodriguez (RC) .20 .50
UH316 Ben Sheets AS .12 .30
UH317 Brian Buscher .12 .30
UH318 Kyle Farnsworth .12 .30
UH319 Ruben Gotay .12 .30
UH320 Heath Bell .20 .50
UH321 Jeff Niemann (RC) .20 .50
UH322 Edinson Volquez AS .12 .30
UH323 Jorge Velandia .12 .30
UH324 Ken Griffey Jr. .50 1.25
UH325 Clay Hensley .12 .30
UH326 Kevin Mench .12 .30
UH327 Hernan Iribarren (RC) .30 .75
UH328 Billy Wagner AS .12 .30
UH329 Jeremy Sowers .12 .30
UH330 Johan Santana .30 .75

2008 Topps Update Black

COMMON CARD (1-330) 4.00 10.00
STATED ODDS 1:59 HOBBY
STATED PRINT RUN 57 SER.#'d SETS
UH1 Kosuke Fukudome 12.00 30.00
UH2 Sean Casey 10.00 25.00
UH3 Freddie Bynum 4.00 10.00
UH4 Brent Lillibridge 4.00 10.00
UH5 Chipper Jones AS 6.00 15.00
UH6 Yamid Haad 4.00 10.00
UH7 Josh Anderson 4.00 10.00
UH8 Jeff Mathis 4.00 10.00
UH9 Shawn Riggans 4.00 10.00
UH10 Evan Longoria 20.00 50.00
UH11 Matt Holliday AS 10.00 25.00
UH12 Trot Nixon 4.00 10.00
UH13 Geoff Blum 4.00 10.00
UH14 Bartolo Colon 4.00 10.00
UH15 Kevin Cash 4.00 10.00
UH16 Paul Janish 4.00 10.00
UH17 Russ Martin AS 15.00 40.00
UH18 Andy Phillips 4.00 10.00
UH19 Johnny Estrada 4.00 10.00
UH20 Justin Masterson 30.00 60.00
UH21 Darrell Rasner 4.00 10.00
UH22 Brian Moehler 4.00 10.00
UH23 Cristian Guzman AS 4.00 10.00
UH24 Tony Armas Jr. 4.00 10.00
UH25 Lance Berkman AS 6.00 15.00
UH26 Chris Iannetta 4.00 10.00
UH27 Reid Brignac 6.00 15.00
UH28 Miguel Tejada AS 6.00 15.00
UH29 Ryan Ludwick AS 4.00 10.00
UH30 Brendan Harris 4.00 10.00
UH31 Marco Scutaro 4.00 10.00
UH32 Cody Ross 4.00 10.00
UH33 Carlos Marmol 6.00 15.00
UH34 Nate McLouth AS 12.50 30.00
UH35 Hanley Ramirez AS 10.00 25.00
UH36 Xavier Nady 4.00 10.00
UH37 Connor Robertson 4.00 10.00
UH38 Carlos Villanueva 4.00 10.00
UH39 Jose Molina 4.00 10.00
UH40 Jon Rauch 4.00 10.00
UH41 Joe Mauer AS 10.00 25.00
UH42 Chip Ambres 4.00 10.00
UH43 Jason Bartlett 4.00 10.00
UH44 Ryan Sweeney 4.00 10.00
UH45 Eric Hurley 4.00 10.00
UH46 Kevin Youkilis AS 10.00 25.00
UH47 Dustin Pedroia AS 10.00 25.00
UH48 Grant Balfour 4.00 10.00
UH49 Ryan Ludwick 6.00 15.00
UH50 Matt Garza 4.00 10.00
UH51 Fernando Tatis 4.00 10.00
UH52 Derek Jeter AS 25.00 60.00
UH53 Justin Duchscherer AS 4.00 10.00
UH54 Matt Ginter 4.00 10.00
UH55 Cesar Izturis 4.00 10.00
UH56 Roy Halladay AS 10.00 25.00
UH57 Ramon Castro 4.00 10.00
UH58 Scott Kazmir AS 6.00 15.00
UH59 Cliff Lee AS 6.00 15.00
UH60 Jim Edmonds 6.00 15.00
UH61 Randy Wolf 4.00 10.00
UH62 Matt Albers 4.00 10.00
UH63 Eric Bruntlett 4.00 10.00
UH64 Joe Nathan AS 4.00 10.00
UH65 Alex Rodriguez AS 10.00 25.00
UH66 Robinson Cancel 4.00 10.00
UH67 Jamey Carroll 4.00 10.00
UH68 Jonathan Papelbon AS 6.00 15.00
UH69 Chad Moeller 4.00 10.00
UH70 George Sherrill 4.00 10.00
UH71 Mariano Rivera AS 10.00 25.00
UH72 Pete Orr 4.00 10.00
UH73 Jonathan Albaladejo 6.00 15.00
UH74 Corey Patterson 4.00 10.00
UH75 Matt Treanor 4.00 10.00
UH76 Francisco Rodriguez AS 6.00 15.00
UH77 Ervin Santana AS 4.00 10.00
UH78 Dallas Braden 6.00 15.00
UH79 Willie Harris 4.00 10.00
UH80 Erik Bedard 4.00 10.00
UH81 J.C. Romero 4.00 10.00
UH82 Joe Saunders AS 4.00 10.00
UH83 George Sherrill AS 4.00 10.00
UH84 Julian Tavarez 4.00 10.00
UH85 Chad Gaudin 4.00 10.00
UH86 David Aardsma 4.00 10.00
UH87 Ryan Langerhans 4.00 10.00
UH88 Dan Haren 4.00 10.00
Russ Martin
UH89 Joakim Soria AS 4.00 10.00
UH90 Dan Haren 4.00 10.00
UH91 Billy Buckner 4.00 10.00
UH92 Eric Hinske 4.00 10.00
UH93 Chris Coste 4.00 10.00
UH94 Edinson Volquez 4.00 10.00
Russ Martin
UH95 Ichiro Suzuki AS 20.00 50.00
UH96 Vladimir Nunez 4.00 10.00
UH97 Sean Gallagher 4.00 10.00
UH98 Denny Bautista 4.00 10.00
UH99 Hanley Ramirez 6.00 15.00
David Ortiz
UH100 Jay Bruce 10.00 25.00
UH101 Dioner Navarro AS 4.00 10.00
UH102 Matt Murton 4.00 10.00
UH103 Chris Burke 4.00 10.00
UH104 Omar Infante 4.00 10.00
UH105 Dan Giese 4.00 10.00
UH106 Carlos Guillen 12.50 30.00
Josh Hamilton
UH107 Jason Varitek AS 10.00 25.00
UH108 Shin- Soo Choo 6.00 15.00
UH109 Alberto Callaspo 4.00 10.00
UH110 Jose Valverde 4.00 10.00
UH111 Brandon Boggs 6.00 15.00
UH112 Josh Hamilton 12.50 30.00
J.D. Drew
UH113 Justin Morneau AS 10.00 25.00
UH114 Billy Traber 4.00 10.00
UH115 Mike Lamb 4.00 10.00
UH116 Odalis Perez 4.00 10.00
UH117 Jed Lowrie 12.50 30.00
UH118 Justin Morneau 10.00 25.00
David Ortiz
UH119 Ken Griffey Jr. HL 15.00 40.00
UH120 Angel Berroa 4.00 10.00
UH121 Jacque Jones 4.00 10.00
UH122 DeWayne Wise 4.00 10.00
UH123 Matt Joyce 10.00 25.00
UH124 Alex Rodriguez 20.00 50.00
Evan Longoria
UH125 John Smoltz HL 10.00 25.00
UH126 Morgan Ensberg 4.00 10.00
UH127 Michael Young 6.00 15.00
Derek Jeter
UH128 LaTroy Hawkins 4.00 10.00
UH129 Nick Adenhart 10.00 25.00
UH130 Mike Cameron 4.00 10.00
UH131 Manny Ramirez HL 12.50 30.00
UH132 Jorge De La Rosa 4.00 10.00
UH133 Tadahito Iguchi 4.00 10.00
UH134 Joey Devine 4.00 10.00
UH135 Jose Arredondo 6.00 15.00
UH136 Hanley Ramirez 25.00 60.00
Albert Pujols
UH137 Evan Longoria HL 15.00 40.00
UH138 T.J. Beam 4.00 10.00
UH139 Jon Lieber 4.00 10.00
UH140 Dana Eveland 4.00 10.00
UH141 Michael Aubrey 6.00 15.00
UH142 Adrian Gonzalez 10.00 25.00
Matt Holliday
UH143 Chipper Jones HL 6.00 15.00
UH144 Robinson Tejeda 4.00 10.00
UH145 Kip Wells 4.00 10.00
UH146 Carlos Gonzalez 10.00 25.00
UH147 Josh Banks 4.00 10.00
UH148 David Wright AS 12.50 30.00
UH149 Paul Hoover 4.00 10.00
UH150 Jon Lester HL 12.50 30.00
UH151 Darin Erstad 4.00 10.00
UH152 Steve Trachsel 4.00 10.00
UH153 Armando Galarraga 6.00 15.00
UH154 Grady Sizemore HRD 6.00 15.00
UH155 Jay Bruce HL 10.00 25.00
UH156 Juan Rincon 4.00 10.00
UH157 Mark Hendrickson 4.00 10.00
UH158 Chad Durbin 4.00 10.00
UH159 Mike Aviles 6.00 15.00
UH160 Orlando Cabrera 4.00 10.00
UH161 Asdrubal Cabrera HL 6.00 15.00
UH162 Eric Stults 4.00 10.00
UH163 Miguel Cairo 4.00 10.00
UH164 Jason LaRue 4.00 10.00
UH165 Burke Badenhop 6.00 15.00
UH166 Ryan Braun HRD 12.50 30.00
UH167 Justin Morneau HRD 10.00 25.00
UH168 Ben Zobrist 4.00 10.00
UH169 Eulogio De La Cruz 4.00 10.00
UH170 Greg Smith 4.00 10.00
UH171 Brian Bixler 4.00 10.00
UH172 Evan Longoria HRD 15.00 40.00
UH173 Randy Johnson HL 10.00 25.00
UH174 D.J. Carrasco 4.00 10.00
UH175 Luis Vizcaino 4.00 10.00
UH176 Brad Wilkerson 4.00 10.00
UH177 Emmanuel Burriss 6.00 15.00
UH178 Lance Berkman HRD 6.00 15.00
UH179 Johnny Damon HL 6.00 15.00
UH180 Scott Rolen 6.00 15.00
UH181 Runelvys Hernandez 4.00 10.00
UH182 Sidney Ponson 4.00 10.00
UH183 Greg Reynolds 6.00 15.00
UH184 Chase Utley HRD 10.00 25.00
UH185 Joey Votto HL 15.00 40.00
UH186 Wes Littleton 4.00 10.00
UH187 Rod Barajas 4.00 10.00
UH188 Ray Durham 4.00 10.00
UH189 Micah Hoffpauir 12.00 30.00
UH190 Manny Ramirez AS 10.00 25.00
UH191 Ian Kinsler AS 6.00 15.00
UH192 Craig Hansen 4.00 10.00
UH193 Jeremy Affeldt 4.00 10.00
UH194 Gary Bennett 4.00 10.00
UH195 Chris Carter 6.00 15.00
UH196 Dan Uggla HRD 6.00 15.00
UH197 Michael Young AS 6.00 15.00
UH198 Andy LaRoche 4.00 10.00
UH199 Lance Cormier 4.00 10.00
UH200 Luke Scott 4.00 10.00
UH201 Travis Denker 6.00 15.00
UH202 Josh Hamilton 12.50 30.00
UH203 Joe Crede AS 4.00 10.00
UH204 Franquelis Osoria 4.00 10.00
UH205 Octavio Dotel 4.00 10.00
UH206 Russell Branyan 4.00 10.00
UH207 Alberto Gonzalez 6.00 15.00
UH208 Kerry Wood AS 4.00 10.00
UH209 Carlos Guillen AS 4.00 10.00
UH210 Joe Saunders 4.00 10.00
UH211 Brett Tomko 4.00 10.00
UH212 Guillermo Mota 4.00 10.00
UH213 German Duran 6.00 15.00
UH214 Carlos Zambrano AS 6.00 15.00
UH215 Josh Hamilton AS 12.50 30.00
UH216 Jason Bay 12.50 30.00
UH217 Willy Aybar 4.00 10.00
UH218 Salomon Torres 4.00 10.00
UH219 Damaso Marte 4.00 10.00
UH220 Geoff Jenkins 4.00 10.00
UH221 J.D. Drew AS 4.00 10.00
UH222 Dave Borkowski 4.00 10.00
UH223 Jeff Ridgway 6.00 15.00
UH224 Angel Pagan 4.00 10.00
UH225 Ryan Tucker 4.00 10.00
UH226 Brian McCann AS 6.00 15.00
UH227 Carlos Quentin AS 4.00 10.00
UH228 Joe Blanton 4.00 10.00
UH229 Adrian Gonzalez AS 6.00 15.00
UH230 Jason Jennings 4.00 10.00
UH231 Chris Davis 10.00 25.00
UH232 Geovany Soto AS 10.00 25.00
UH233 Grady Sizemore AS 6.00 15.00
UH234 Carl Pavano 4.00 10.00
UH235 Eddie Guardado 4.00 10.00
UH236 Chris Snelling 4.00 10.00
UH237 Manny Ramirez 20.00 50.00
UH238 Dan Uggla AS 6.00 15.00
UH239 Milton Bradley AS 4.00 10.00
UH240 Clayton Kershaw 20.00 50.00
UH241 Chase Utley AS 10.00 25.00
UH242 Raul Chavez 4.00 10.00
UH243 Joe Mather 6.00 15.00
UH244 Brandon Webb AS 6.00 15.00
UH245 Ryan Braun 12.50 30.00
UH246 Kelvin Jimenez 4.00 10.00
UH247 Scott Podsednik 4.00 10.00
UH248 Doug Mientkiewicz 4.00 10.00
UH249 Chris Volstad 4.00 10.00
UH250 Pedro Feliz 4.00 10.00
UH251 Mark Redman 4.00 10.00
UH252 Tony Clark 4.00 10.00
UH253 Josh Johnson 6.00 15.00
UH254 Jose Castillo 4.00 10.00
UH255 Brian Horwitz 4.00 10.00
UH256 Aramis Ramirez AS 4.00 10.00
UH257 Casey Blake 10.00 25.00
UH258 Arthur Rhodes 4.00 10.00
UH259 Aaron Boone 4.00 10.00
UH260 Emil Brown 4.00 10.00
UH261 Matt Macri 4.00 10.00
UH262 Brian Wilson AS 10.00 25.00
UH263 Eric Patterson 4.00 10.00
UH264 David Ortiz 6.00 15.00
UH265 Tony Abreu 4.00 10.00
UH266 Rob Mackowiak 4.00 10.00
UH267 Gregorio Petit 6.00 15.00
UH268 Alfonso Soriano AS 6.00 15.00
UH269 Robert Andino 4.00 10.00
UH270 Justin Duchscherer 4.00 10.00
UH271 Brad Thompson 4.00 10.00
UH272 Guillermo Quiroz 4.00 10.00
UH273 Chris Perez 6.00 15.00
UH274 Albert Pujols AS 12.50 30.00
UH275 Rich Harden 4.00 10.00
UH276 Corey Hart AS 4.00 10.00
UH277 John Rheinecker 4.00 10.00
UH278 So Taguchi 4.00 10.00
UH279 Alex Hinshaw 6.00 15.00
UH280 Max Scherzer 12.00 30.00
UH281 Chris Aguila 4.00 10.00
UH282 Carlos Marmol AS 6.00 15.00
UH283 Alex Cintron 4.00 10.00
UH284 Curtis Thigpen 4.00 10.00
UH285 Kosuke Fukudome AS 10.00 25.00
UH286 Aaron Cook AS 4.00 10.00
UH287 Chase Headley 4.00 10.00
UH288 Evan Longoria AS 15.00 40.00
UH289 Chris Gomez 4.00 10.00
UH290 Carlos Gomez 6.00 15.00
UH291 Jonathan Herrera 6.00 15.00
UH292 Ryan Dempster AS 4.00 10.00
UH293 Adam Dunn 6.00 15.00
UH294 Mark Teixeira 10.00 25.00
UH295 Aaron Miles 4.00 10.00
UH296 Gabe Gross 4.00 10.00
UH297 Cory Wade 4.00 10.00
UH298 Dan Haren AS 4.00 10.00
UH299 Jolbert Cabrera 4.00 10.00
UH300 C.C. Sabathia 6.00 15.00
UH301 Tony Pena 4.00 10.00
UH302 Brandon Moss 4.00 10.00
UH303 Taylor Teagarden 6.00 15.00
UH304 Brad Lidge AS 4.00 10.00
UH305 Ben Francisco 4.00 10.00
UH306 Casey Kotchman 4.00 10.00
UH307 Greg Norton 4.00 10.00
UH308 Shelley Duncan 4.00 10.00
UH309 John Bowker 4.00 10.00
UH310 Kyle Lohse 4.00 10.00
UH311 Oscar Salazar 4.00 10.00
UH312 Ivan Rodriguez 6.00 15.00
UH313 Tim Lincecum AS 15.00 40.00
UH314 Wilson Betemit 4.00 10.00
UH315 Sean Rodriguez 4.00 10.00
UH316 Ben Sheets AS 4.00 10.00
UH317 Brian Buscher 4.00 10.00
UH318 Kyle Farnsworth 4.00 10.00
UH319 Ruben Gotay 4.00 10.00
UH320 Heath Bell 6.00 15.00
UH321 Jeff Niemann 4.00 10.00
UH322 Edinson Volquez AS 4.00 10.00
UH323 Jorge Velandia 4.00 10.00
UH324 Ken Griffey Jr. 15.00 40.00
UH325 Clay Hensley 4.00 10.00
UH326 Kevin Mench 4.00 10.00
UH327 Hernan Iribarren 6.00 15.00
UH328 Billy Wagner AS 4.00 10.00
UH329 Jeremy Sowers 4.00 10.00
UH330 Johan Santana 10.00 25.00

2008 Topps Update Gold Border

*GLD BDR VET: 2X TO 5X BASIC
*GLD BDR RC: 1.2X TO 3X BASIC RC
STATED ODDS 1:5 HOBBY
STATED PRINT RUN 2008 SER.#'d SETS

2008 Topps Update Gold Foil

*GLD FOIL VET: 1X TO 2.5X BASIC
*GLD FOIL RC: .6X TO 1.5X BASIC RC
STATED ODDS 1:2 HOBBY

2008 Topps Update Platinum

STATED ODDS 1:9434 HOBBY
STATED PRINT RUN 1 SER.#'d SET
NO PRICING DUE TO SCARCITY

2008 Topps Update 1957 Mickey Mantle Reprint Relic

STATED ODDS 17,982 HOBBY
STATED PRINT RUN 57 SER.#'d SETS
MMR57 Mickey Mantle Bat/57 60.00 120.00

2008 Topps Update 2008 Presidential Picks

STATED ODDS 1:15,984 HOBBY
STATED PRINT RUN 100 SER.#'d SETS
BO Barack Obama 150.00 250.00
JM John McCain 40.00 80.00

2008 Topps Update All-Star Jumbo Patches

STATED ODDS 1:4496 HOBBY
STATED PRINT RUN 6 SER.#'d SETS
NO PRICING DUE TO SCARCITY

2008 Topps Update All-Star Jumbo Patches Autographs

STATED ODDS 1:23,017 HOBBY
STATED PRINT RUN 6 SER.#'d SETS
NO PRICING DUE TO SCARCITY

2008 Topps Update All-Star Stitches

STATED ODDS 1:44 HOBBY
AC Aaron Cook 3.00 8.00
AER Alex Rodriguez 6.00 15.00
AG Adrian Gonzalez 3.00 8.00
AP Albert Pujols 6.00 15.00
AR Aramis Ramirez 3.00 8.00
AS Alfonso Soriano 3.00 8.00
BL Brad Lidge 5.00 12.00
BM Brian McCann 4.00 10.00
BS Ben Sheets 3.00 8.00
BTW Brandon Webb 3.00 8.00
BW Brian Wilson
CAG Carlos Guillen 3.00 8.00
CG Cristian Guzman 3.00 8.00
CH Corey Hart 3.00 8.00
CJ Chipper Jones 4.00 10.00
CL Cliff Lee 4.00 10.00
CM Carlos Marmol 3.00 8.00
CQ Carlos Quentin 3.00 8.00
CU Chase Utley 4.00 10.00
CZ Carlos Zambrano 4.00 10.00
DH Dan Haren 3.00 8.00
DN Dioner Navarro 4.00 10.00
DO David Ortiz 4.00 10.00
DP Dustin Pedroia 5.00 12.00
DU Dan Uggla 3.00 8.00
DW David Wright 5.00 12.00
EL Evan Longoria 12.50 30.00
ES Ervin Santana 3.00 8.00
EV Edinson Volquez 3.00 8.00
FR Francisco Rodriguez 4.00 10.00
GFS George Sherrill 3.00 8.00
GPS Geovany Soto 5.00 12.00
GS Grady Sizemore 4.00 10.00
HR Hanley Ramirez 3.00 8.00
IK Ian Kinsler 3.00 8.00
IS Ichiro Suzuki 8.00 20.00
JC Joe Crede 3.00 8.00
JCD Justin Duchscherer 4.00 10.00
JD J.D. Drew 4.00 10.00
JEM Justin Morneau 4.00 10.00
JES Joe Saunders
JH Josh Hamilton 8.00 20.00
JM Joe Mauer 4.00 10.00
JN Joe Nathan 3.00 8.00
JP Jonathan Papelbon 4.00 10.00
JS Joakim Soria 3.00 8.00
JV Jason Varitek 4.00 10.00
KF Kosuke Fukudome 10.00 25.00
KW Kerry Wood 3.00 8.00
KY Kevin Youkilis 3.00 8.00
LB Lance Berkman 4.00 10.00
MB Milton Bradley 3.00 8.00
MH Matt Holliday 3.00 8.00
MR Manny Ramirez 4.00 10.00
MSR Mariano Rivera 4.00 10.00
MT Miguel Tejada 3.00 8.00
MY Michael Young 3.00 8.00
NM Nate McLouth 5.00 12.00
RB Ryan Braun 4.00 10.00
RD Ryan Dempster 3.00 8.00
RH Roy Halladay 3.00 8.00
RL Ryan Ludwick 5.00 12.00
RM Russ Martin 3.00 8.00
SK Scott Kazmir 3.00 8.00
TL Tim Lincecum 12.50 30.00
WW Billy Wagner 3.00 8.00

2008 Topps Update All-Star Stitches Gold

*GOLD: .75X TO 2X BASIC
STATED ODDS 1:373 HOBBY
STATED PRINT RUN 50 SER.#'d SETS
AER Alex Rodriguez 30.00 60.00
EL Evan Longoria 20.00 50.00
IS Ichiro Suzuki 20.00 50.00
KY Kevin Youkilis 30.00 60.00

2008 Topps Update All-Star Stitches Platinum

STATED ODDS 1:23,017 HOBBY
STATED PRINT RUN 1 SER.#'d SET
NO PRICING DUE TO SCARCITY

2008 Topps Update All-Star Stitches Autographs

STATED ODDS 1:6394 HOBBY
STATED PRINT RUN 25 SER.#'d SETS
CJ Chipper Jones 100.00 200.00
DP Dustin Pedroia 75.00 150.00
DU Dan Uggla 10.00 25.00
EV Edinson Volquez 30.00 60.00
HR Hanley Ramirez 30.00 60.00
JH Josh Hamilton 50.00 100.00
JV Jason Varitek 50.00 100.00
RB Ryan Braun 40.00 80.00
RM Russ Martin 100.00 175.00
TL Tim Lincecum 100.00 200.00

2008 Topps Update All-Star Stitches Dual

STATED ODDS 1:5994
STATED PRINT RUN 25 SER.#'d SETS
NO PRICING ON FEW DUE TO SCARCITY
BP Lance Berkman
Albert Pujols
FL Kosuke Fukudome 40.00 80.00
Ichiro Suzuki
HB Josh Hamilton 12.50 30.00
Ryan Braun
HW Dan Haren
Brandon Webb
LS Cliff Lee 10.00 25.00
Ben Sheets
IV Tim Lincecum 12.50 30.00
Edinson Volquez
RR Alex Rodriguez
Manny Ramirez
RR Mariano Rivera 30.00 60.00
Francisco Rodriguez
RT Hanley Ramirez 8.00 20.00
Miguel Tejada
UU Chase Utley 20.00 50.00
Dan Uggla

2008 Topps Update All-Star Stitches Triple

STATED ODDS 1:5994 HOBBY
STATED PRINT RUN 25 SER.#'d SETS
NO PRICING ON FEW DUE TO SCARCITY
HFB M. Holliday/K. Fukudome/R. Braun 20.00 50.00
HRS J. Hamilton/M. Ramirez/I. Suzuki 30.00 60.00
KHY I. Kinsler/M. Bradley/M. Young 8.00 20.00
MMN Joe Mauer/Justin Morneau/Joe Nathan
MNM R. Martin/D. Navarro/B. McCann 40.00 80.00
PDY D. Pedroia/J.D. Drew/D. Ortiz 20.00 50.00
PGB A. Pujols/A. Gonzalez/L. Berkman 30.00 60.00

RSS F. Rodriguez/E. Santana/J. Saunders 30.00 60.00
RWJ A. Rodriguez/D. Wright/C. Jones 40.00 80.00
WLW K. Wood/B. Lidge/B. Wagner 20.00 50.00
ZSD C. Zambrano/A. Ramirez/R. Dempster 50.00 100.00

2008 Topps Update Chrome

ONE PER BOX TOPPER
CHR1 Jay Bruce 5.00 12.00
CHR2 Dan Giese 2.00 5.00
CHR3 Brandon Boggs 3.00 8.00
CHR4 Jed Lowrie 5.00 12.00
CHR5 Matt Joyce 5.00 12.00
CHR6 Nick Adenhart 2.00 5.00
CHR7 Jose Arredondo 3.00 8.00
CHR8 Michael Aubrey 3.00 8.00
CHR9 Josh Banks 2.00 5.00
CHR10 Armando Galarraga 3.00 8.00
CHR11 Mike Aviles 3.00 8.00
CHR12 Burke Badenhop 3.00 8.00
CHR13 Reid Brignac 3.00 8.00
CHR14 Emmanuel Burriss 3.00 8.00
CHR15 Greg Reynolds 3.00 8.00
CHR16 Chris Volstad 2.00 5.00
CHR17 Brian Bixler 2.00 5.00
CHR18 Chris Carter 3.00 8.00
CHR19 Travis Denker 3.00 8.00
CHR20 Alberto Gonzalez 3.00 8.00
CHR21 Robinzon Diaz 2.00 5.00
CHR22 Brett Gardner 5.00 12.00
CHR23 Micah Hoffpauir 6.00 15.00
CHR24 Hernan Iribarren 3.00 8.00
CHR25 Greg Smith 2.00 5.00
CHR26 German Duran 3.00 8.00
CHR27 Kosuke Fukudome 6.00 15.00
CHR28 Ryan Tucker 2.00 5.00
CHR29 Paul Janish 2.00 5.00
CHR30 Clayton Kershaw 5.00 12.00
CHR31 Chris Davis 5.00 12.00
CHR32 Joe Mather 3.00 8.00
CHR33 Nick Hundley 2.00 5.00
CHR34 Brian Horwitz 2.00 5.00
CHR35 Carlos Gonzalez 5.00 12.00
CHR36 Matt Macri 2.00 5.00
CHR37 Gregorio Petit 3.00 8.00
CHR38 Chris Perez 3.00 8.00
CHR39 Alex Hinshaw 3.00 8.00
CHR40 Max Scherzer 6.00 15.00
CHR41 Jonathan Van Every 2.00 5.00
CHR42 Jonathan Herrera 3.00 8.00
CHR43 Cory Wade 2.00 5.00
CHR44 Max Ramirez 2.00 5.00
CHR45 John Bowker 2.00 5.00
CHR46 Sean Rodriguez 2.00 5.00
CHR47 Jeff Niemann 2.00 5.00
CHR48 Taylor Teagarden 3.00 8.00
CHR49 Mark Worrell 2.00 5.00
CHR50 Evan Longoria 10.00 25.00
CHR51 Chris Smith 2.00 5.00
CHR52 Brent Lillibridge 2.00 5.00
CHR53 Colt Morton 3.00 8.00
CHR54 Eric Hurley 2.00 5.00
CHR55 Justin Masterson 5.00 12.00

2008 Topps Update First Couples

COMPLETE SET (41) 15.00 40.00
STATED ODDS 1:6 HOBBY
FC1 George Washington .75 2.00
Martha Washington
FC2 John Adams .60 1.50
Abagail Adams
FC3 Thomas Jefferson .60 1.50
Martha Jefferson
FC4 James Madison .40 1.00
Dolley Madison
FC5 James Monroe .40 1.00
Elizabeth Kortright Monroe
FC6 John Quincy Adams .40 1.00
Louisa Catherine Adams
FC7 Andrew Jackson .40 1.00
Rachel Jackson
FC8 Martin Van Buren .40 1.00
Hannah Van Buren
FC9 William Henry Harrison .40 1.00
Anna Harrison
FC10 John Tyler .40 1.00
Julia Tyler
FC11 James K. Polk .40 1.00
(Sarah Polk
FC12 Zachary Taylor .40 1.00
Margaret Taylor
FC13 Millard Fillmore .40 1.00
Abigail Fillmore
FC14 Franklin Pierce .40 1.00
Jane M. Pierce
FC15 Abraham Lincoln .75 2.00
Mary Lincoln
FC16 Andrew Johnson .40 1.00
Eliza Johnson
FC17 Ulysses S. Grant .40 1.00
Julia Grant
FC18 Rutherford B. Hayes .40 1.00
Lucy Hayes
FC19 James A. Garfield .40 1.00
Lucretia Garfield
FC20 Chester A. Arthur .40 1.00
Ellen Arthur
FC21 Grover Cleveland .40 1.00
Frances Cleveland
FC22 Benjamin Harrison .40 1.00
Caroline Harrison
FC23 William McKinley .40 1.00
Ida McKinley
FC24 Theodore Roosevelt .60 1.50
Edith Roosevelt
FC25 William H. Taft .40 1.00
Helen Taft
FC26 Woodrow Wilson .40 1.00
Edith Wilson
FC27 Warren G. Harding .40 1.00
(Florence Harding
FC28 Calvin Coolidge .40 1.00
Grace Coolidge
FC29 Herbert Hoover .40 1.00
Lou Hoover
FC30 Franklin D. Roosevelt .60 1.50
(Eleanor Roosevelt
FC31 Harry S. Truman .40 1.00
(Bess Truman
FC32 Dwight D. Eisenhower .60 1.50
Mamie Eisenhower
FC33 John F. Kennedy 1.00 2.50
Jacqueline Kennedy Onassis
FC34 Lyndon B. Johnson .60 1.50
(Lady Bird Johnson
FC35 Richard M. Nixon .60 1.50
(Pat Nixon
FC36 Gerald R. Ford .60 1.50
(Betty Ford
FC37 Jimmy Carter .60 1.50
(Rosalynn Carter
FC38 Ronald Reagan 1.00 2.50
(Nancy Reagan
FC39 George Bush .60 1.50
(Barbara Bush
FC40 Bill Clinton .75 2.00
(Hillary Rodham Clinton
FC41 George W. Bush .75 2.00
(Laura Bush

2008 Topps Update First Lady Cut Signatures

STATED ODDS 1:47,952 HOBBY
STATED PRINT RUN 1 SER.#'d SETS
NO PRICING DUE TO SCARCITY

2008 Topps Update Ring of Honor 1986 New York Mets

COMPLETE SET (10) 5.00 12.00
STATED ODDS 1:18 HOBBY
GOLD ODDS 1:11,743 HOBBY
GOLD PRINT RUN 25 SER.#'d SETS
NO GOLD PRICING AVAILABLE
DG Dwight Gooden .60 1.50
DJ Davey Johnson .60 1.50
DS Darryl Strawberry .60 1.50
GC Gary Carter .60 1.50
HJ Howard Johnson .60 1.50
JO Jesse Orosco .60 1.50
KH Keith Hernandez .60 1.50
KM Kevin Mitchell .60 1.50
RD Ron Darling .60 1.50
RK Ray Knight .60 1.50

2008 Topps Update Ring of Honor 1986 New York Mets Autographs

STATED ODDS 1:2849 HOBBY
DG Dwight Gooden 12.50 30.00
DJ Davey Johnson 10.00 25.00
DS Darryl Strawberry 15.00 40.00
GC Gary Carter 15.00 40.00
HJ Howard Johnson 12.50 30.00
JO Jesse Orosco 15.00 40.00
KH Keith Hernandez 15.00 40.00
KM Kevin Mitchell 12.50 30.00
RD Ron Darling 10.00 25.00
RK Ray Knight 12.50 30.00

2008 Topps Update Ring of Honor World Series Champions

COMPLETE SET (10) 5.00 12.00
STATED ODDS 1:16 HOBBY
GOLD ODDS 1:11,743 HOBBY
GOLD PRINT RUN 25 SER.#'d SETS
NO GOLD PRICING AVAILABLE
BS Bruce Sutter .60 1.50
DC David Cone COR .60 1.50
DC1 David Cone UER .60 1.50
Last name misspelled
DJ David Justice .60 1.50
DS Duke Snider 1.00 2.50
JP Johnny Podres .60 1.50
LA Luis Aparicio .60 1.50
MI Monte Irvin .60 1.50
ML Mike Lowell .60 1.50
OC Orlando Cepeda .60 1.50
RK Ray Knight .60 1.50
WF Whitey Ford 1.00 2.50

2008 Topps Update Ring of Honor World Series Champions Autographs

STATED ODDS 1:2569 HOBBY
BS Bruce Sutter 30.00 60.00
DC David Cone 30.00 60.00
DJ David Justice 30.00 60.00
DS Duke Snider 30.00 60.00
JP Johnny Podres 15.00 40.00
LA Luis Aparicio 15.00 40.00
MI Monte Irvin 15.00 40.00
ML Mike Lowell 20.00 50.00
OC Orlando Cepeda 30.00 60.00
WF Whitey Ford 30.00 60.00

2008 Topps Update Sketches

STATED ODDS 1:214 HOBBY
ANNCD PRINT RUN 1 COPY PER
MULTIPLE VERSIONS OF EACH
NO PRICING DUE TO SCARCITY

2008 Topps Update Take Me Out To The Ballgame

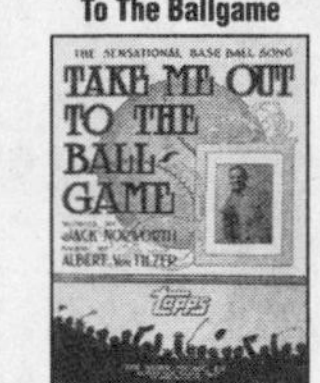

STATED ODDS 1:72 HOBBY
BG 100th Anniversary .75 2.00

2008 Topps Update World Baseball Classic Preview

COMPLETE SET (25) 8.00 20.00
STATED ODDS 1:9 HOBBY
WBC1 Daisuke Matsuzaka .60 1.50
WBC2 Alexei Ramirez 1.00 2.50
WBC3 Derrek Lee .25 .60
WBC4 Akinori Iwamura .25 .60
WBC5 Chase Utley .60 1.50
WBC6 Jose Reyes .40 1.00
WBC7 Jake Peavy .25 .60
WBC8 Justin Huber .25 .60
WBC9 Justin Morneau .60 1.50
WBC10 Ichiro Suzuki 1.00 2.50
WBC11 Adrian Gonzalez .40 1.00
WBC12 Carlos Zambrano .40 1.00
WBC13 Miguel Cabrera .60 1.50
WBC14 Carlos Beltran .25 .60
WBC15 Albert Pujols 1.50 4.00
WBC16 Paul Bell .25 .60
WBC17 Frank Catalanotto .25 .60
WBC18 Jason Varitek .60 1.50
WBC19 Andruw Jones .25 .60
WBC20 Johan Santana .60 1.50
WBC21 Carlos Lee .25 .60
WBC22 David Ortiz .40 1.00
WBC23 Francisco Rodriguez .40 1.00
WBC24 Chin-Lung Hu .40 1.00
WBC25 Kosuke Fukudome .75 2.00

2009 Topps

This set was released on February 4, 2009. The base set consists of 349 cards.

COMP.HOBBY SET (660) 40.00 80.00
COMP.HOLIDAY SET (660) 40.00 80.00
COMP.ALLSTAR SET (660) 40.00 80.00
COMP.CUBS SET (660) 40.00 80.00
COMP.METS SET (660) 40.00 80.00
COMP.RED SOX SET (660) 40.00 80.00
COMP.YANKEES SET (660) 40.00 80.00
COMP.SET w/o SP's (660) 40.00 80.00
COMP.SER.1 SET w/o SP's (330) 15.00 40.00
COMP.SER.2 SET w/o SP's (330) 15.00 40.00
COMMON CARD (1-696) .15 .40
SER.1 SP VAR ODDS 1:95 HOBBY
SER.2 SP VAR ODDS 1:82 HOBBY
COMMON RC (1-696) .30 .75
SER.1 PLATE ODDS 1:925 HOBBY
SER.2 PLATE ODDS 1:1056 HOBBY
PLATE PRINT RUN 1 SET PER COLOR
BLACK-CYAN-MAGENTA-YELLOW ISSUED
NO PLATE PRICING DUE TO SCARCITY
1a Alex Rodriguez .60 1.50
1b Babe Ruth SP 20.00 50.00
2a Omar Vizquel .25 .60
2b Pee Wee Reese SP 6.00 15.00
3 Andy Marte .15 .40
4 Chipper Jones 1.00 2.50
Albert Pujols
Matt Holliday LL
5 John Lackey .15 .40
6 Raul Ibanez .25 .60
7 Mickey Mantle 1.25 3.00
8 Terry Francona MG .25 .60
9 Dallas McPherson .15 .40
10a Dan Uggla .25 .60
10b Rogers Hornsby SP 6.00 15.00
11 Fernando Tatis .15 .40
12 Andrew Carpenter RC .50 1.25
13 Ryan Langerhans .15 .40
14 Jon Rauch .15 .40
15 Nate McLouth .15 .40
16 Evan Longoria HL .50 1.25
17 Bobby Cox MG .15 .40
18 George Sherrill .15 .40
19 Edgar Gonzalez .15 .40
20 Brad Lidge .15 .40
21 Jack Wilson .15 .40
22 Evan Longoria .50 1.25
David Price CC
23 Gerald Laird .15 .40
24 Frank Thomas .40 1.00
25 Jon Lester .40 1.00
26 Jason Giambi .15 .40
27 Jonathon Niese RC .50 1.25
28 Mike Lowell .15 .40
29 Jerry Hairston .15 .40
30a Ken Griffey Jr. .60 1.50
30b Jackie Robinson SP 8.00 20.00
31 Ian Stewart .15 .40
32 Daric Barton .15 .40
33 Jose Guillen .15 .40
34 Brandon Inge .15 .40
35 David Price RC .75 2.00
36 Kevin Slowey .25 .60
37 Erick Aybar .15 .40
38 Eric Wedge MG .15 .40
39 Stephen Drew .15 .40
40 Carl Crawford .25 .60
41 Mike Mussina .25 .60
42 Jeff Francoeur .25 .60
43 Joe Mauer .50 1.25
Dustin Pedroia
Milton Bradley LL
44a Geoff Jenkins .15 .40
44b Barack Obama SP 12.50 30.00
45 Aubrey Huff .15 .40
46 Brad Ziegler .15 .40
47 Jose Valverde .15 .40
48 Mike Napoli .25 .60
49 Kazuo Matsui .15 .40
50 David Ortiz .25 .60
51 Will Venable RC .30 .75
52 Marco Scutaro .15 .40
53 Jonathan Sanchez .15 .40
54 Dusty Baker MG .15 .40
55 J.J. Hardy .15 .40
56 Edwin Encarnacion .15 .40
57 Jo-Jo Reyes .15 .40
58 Travis Snider RC .50 1.25
59 Eric Gagne .15 .40
60a Mariano Rivera .40 1.00
60b Cy Young SP 5.00 12.00
61 Lance Berkman .25 .60
Carlos Lee CC
62 Brian Barton .15 .40
63 Josh Outman RC .50 1.25
64 Miguel Montero .15 .40
65 Mike Pelfrey .15 .40
66a Dustin Pedroia .40 1.00
66b Ty Cobb SP 12.50 30.00
67 Andruw Jones .15 .40
68 Kyle Lohse .15 .40
69 Rich Aurilia .15 .40
70 Jermaine Dye .15 .40
71 Mat Gamel RC .75 2.00
72 David Dellucci .15 .40
73 Shane Victorino .15 .40
74 Trey Hillman MG .15 .40
75 Rich Harden .15 .40
76 Marcus Thames .15 .40
77 Jed Lowrie .25 .60
78 Tim Lincecum .60 1.50
79 David Eckstein .15 .40
80 Brian McCann .25 .60
81 Ryan Howard .25 .60
Adam Dunn
Carlos Delgado LL
82 Miguel Cairo .15 .40
83 Ryan Garko .15 .40
84 Rod Barajas .15 .40
85 Justin Verlander .50 1.25
86 Kila Kaaihue (RC) .50 1.25
87 Brad Hawpe .15 .40
88 Fredi Gonzalez MG .15 .40
89 Jon Lester/Jason Bay HL .40 1.00
90 Justin Morneau .40 1.00
91 Cody Ross .15 .40
92 Luis Castillo .15 .40
93 James Parr (RC) .30 .75
94 Adam Lind .15 .40
95 Andrew Miller .15 .40
96 Dexter Fowler (RC) .50 1.25
97 Willie Harris .15 .40
98 Akinori Iwamura .15 .40
99 Juan Castro .15 .40
100 David Wright .50 1.25
101 Nick Hundley .15 .40
102 Garrett Atkins .15 .40
103 Kyle Kendrick .15 .40
104 Brandon Moss .15 .40
105 Francisco Liriano .15 .40
106 Marlon Byrd .15 .40
107 Pedro Feliz .15 .40
108 Alcides Escobar RC .75 2.00
109 Tom Gorzelanny .15 .40
110 Hideki Matsui .40 1.00
111 Troy Percival .15 .40
112 Hideki Okajima .15 .40
113 Chris Young .15 .40
114 Chris Dickerson .15 .40
115a Kevin Youkilis .25 .60
115b George Sisler SP 8.00 20.00
116 Omar Infante .15 .40
117 Ron Gardenhire MG .15 .40
118 Josh Johnson .25 .60
119 Craig Counsell .15 .40
120 Mark Teixeira .40 1.00
121 Greg Golson (RC) .30 .75
122 Joe Mather .15 .40
123 Casey Blake .15 .40
124 Reed Johnson .15 .40
125 Roy Oswalt .25 .60
126 Orlando Hudson .15 .40
127 Miguel Cabrera .40 1.00
Carlos Quentin
Alex Rodriguez LL
128 Johnny Cueto .15 .40
129 Angel Berroa .15 .40
130 Vladimir Guerrero .40 1.00
131 Joe Torre MG .25 .60
132 Juan Pierre .15 .40
133 Brandon Jones .15 .40
134 Evan Longoria .50 1.25
135 Carlos Delgado .15 .40
136 Tim Hudson .25 .60
137 Angel Salome (RC) .30 .75
138 Ubaldo Jimenez .25 .60
139 Matt Stairs HL .15 .40
140 Brandon Webb .25 .60
141 Mark Teahen .15 .40
142 Brad Penny .15 .40
143 Matt Joyce .15 .40
144 Matt Tuiasosopo (RC) .30 .75
145 Alex Gordon .25 .60
146 Glen Perkins .15 .40
147 Ryan Howard .50 1.25
David Wright
Adrian Gonzalez LL
148 Ty Wigginton .25 .60
149 Juan Uribe .15 .40
150 Kosuke Fukudome .40 1.00
151 Carl Pavano .15 .40
152 Cody Ransom .15 .40
153 Lastings Milledge .15 .40
154 A.J. Pierzynski .15 .40
155 Roy Halladay .40 1.00
156 Carlos Pena .25 .60
157 Brandon Webb .25 .60
Dan Haren CC
158 Ray Durham .15 .40
159 Matt Antonelli RC .50 1.25
160 Evan Longoria .50 1.25
161 Brendan Harris .15 .40
162 Mike Cameron .15 .40
163 Ross Gload .15 .40
164 Bob Geren MG .15 .40
165 Matt Kemp .25 .60
166 Jeff Baker .15 .40
167 Aaron Harang .15 .40
168 Mark DeRosa .25 .60
169 Juan Miranda RC .50 1.25
170a CC Sabathia .25 .60
170b CC Sabathia 5.00 12.00
Yankees SP
171 Jeff Bailey .15 .40
172 Yadier Molina .25 .60
173 Manny Delcarmen .15 .40
174 James Shields .15 .40
175 Jeff Samardzija .25 .60
176 Josh Hamilton .40 1.00
Justin Morneau
Miguel Cabrera LL
177 Eric Hinske .15 .40
178 Frank Catalanotto .15 .40
179 Rafael Furcal .15 .40
180 Cliff Lee .25 .60
181 Jerry Manuel MG .15 .40
182 Daniel Murphy RC .75 2.00
183 Jason Michaels .15 .40
184 Bobby Parnell RC .50 1.25
185 Randy Johnson .25 .60
186 Ryan Madson .15 .40
187 Jon Garland .15 .40
188 Josh Bard .15 .40
189 Jay Payton .15 .40
190 Chien-Ming Wang .25 .60
191 Shane Victorino HL .15 .40
192 Collin Balester .15 .40
193 Zack Greinke .25 .60
194 Jeremy Guthrie .15 .40
195a Tim Lincecum .60 1.50
195b Christy Mathewson SP 8.00 20.00
196 Jason Motte (RC) .50 1.25
197 Ronnie Belliard .15 .40
198 Conor Jackson .15 .40
199 Ramon Castro .15 .40
200a Chase Utley .40 1.00
200b Jimmie Foxx SP 6.00 15.00
201 Jarrod Saltalamacchia .40 1.00
Josh Hamilton CC
202 Gaby Sanchez RC .50 1.25
203 Jair Jurrjens .15 .40
204 Andy Sonnanstine .15 .40
205a Miguel Tejada .25 .60
205b Honus Wagner SP 8.00 20.00
206 Johan Santana .60 1.50
Tim Lincecum
Jake Peavy LL
207 Joe Blanton .15 .40
208 James McDonald RC .75 2.00
209 Alfredo Amezaga .15 .40
210a Geovany Soto .25 .60
210b Roy Campanella SP 10.00 25.00
211 Ryan Rowland-Smith .15 .40
212 Denard Span .15 .40
213 Jeremy Sowers .15 .40
214 Scott Elbert (RC) .30 .75
215 Ian Kinsler .25 .60
216 Joe Maddon MG .15 .40
217 Albert Pujols 1.00 2.50
218 Emmanuel Burriss .15 .40
219 Shin-Soo Choo .25 .60
220 Jay Bruce .25 .60
221 Cliff Lee .40 1.00
Roy Halladay
Daisuke Matsuzaka LL
222 Mark Sweeney .15 .40
223 Dave Roberts .15 .40
224 Max Scherzer .25 .60
225 Aaron Cook .15 .40
226 Neal Cotts .15 .40
227 Freddy Sandoval (RC) .30 .75
228 Scott Rolen .25 .60
229 Cesar Izturis .15 .40
230 Justin Upton .25 .60
231 Xavier Nady .15 .40
232 Gabe Kapler .15 .40
233 Erik Bedard .15 .40
234 John Russell MG .15 .40
235 Chad Billingsley .15 .40
236 Kelly Johnson .15 .40
237 Aaron Cunningham RC .30 .75
238 Jorge Cantu .15 .40
239 Brandon League .15 .40
240a Ryan Braun .50 1.25
240b Mel Ott SP 8.00 20.00
241 David Newhan .15 .40
242 Ricky Nolasco .15 .40
243 Chase Headley .15 .40
244 Sean Rodriguez .15 .40
245 Pat Burrell .15 .40
246 B.J. Upton .50 1.25
Carl Crawford
Evan Longoria HL
247 Yuniesky Betancourt .15 .40
248 Scott Lewis (RC) .30 .75
249 Jack Hannahan .15 .40
250 Josh Hamilton .40 1.00
251 Greg Smith .15 .40
252 Brandon Wood .15 .40
253 Edgar Renteria .15 .40
254 Cito Gaston MG .15 .40
255 Joe Crede .25 .60
256 Reggie Abercrombie .15 .40
257 George Kottaras (RC) .30 .75
258 Casey Kotchman .15 .40
259 Tim Lincecum .60 1.50
Dan Haren
Johan Santana LL
260 Manny Ramirez .40 1.00
261 Jose Bautista .25 .60
262 Mike Gonzalez .15 .40
263 Elijah Dukes .15 .40
264 Dave Bush .15 .40
265 Carlos Zambrano .25 .60
266 Todd Wellemeyer .15 .40
267 Michael Bowden (RC) .30 .75
268 Chris Burke .15 .40
269 Hunter Pence .25 .60
270a Grady Sizemore .25 .60
270b Tris Speaker SP 8.00 20.00
271 Cliff Lee .25 .60
272 Chan Ho Park .25 .60
273 Brian Roberts .15 .40
274 Alex Hinshaw .15 .40
275 Alex Rios .25 .60
276 Geovany Soto .25 .60
277 Asdrubal Cabrera .25 .60
278 Philadelphia Phillies HL .15 .40
279 Ryan Church .15 .40
280 Joe Saunders .15 .40
281 Tug Hulett .15 .40
282 Chris Lambert (RC) .30 .75
283 John Baker .15 .40
284 Luis Ayala .15 .40
285 Justin Duchscherer .15 .40
286 Odalis Perez .15 .40
287a Greg Maddux .50 1.25
287b Walter Johnson SP 6.00 15.00
288 Guillermo Quiroz .15 .40
289 Josh Banks .15 .40
290a Albert Pujols 1.00 2.50
290b Lou Gehrig SP 12.50 30.00
291 Chris Coste .15 .40
292 Francisco Cervelli RC .75 2.00
293 Brian Bixler .15 .40
294 Brandon Boggs .15 .40
295 Derrek Lee .15 .40
296 Reid Brignac .15 .40
297 Bud Black MG .15 .40
298 Jonathan Van Every .15 .40
299 Cole Hamels HL .40 1.00
300 Ichiro Suzuki .60 1.50
301 Clint Barmes .15 .40
302 Brian Giles .15 .40
303 Zach Duke .15 .40
304 Jason Kubel .15 .40
305a Ivan Rodriguez .25 .60
305b Thurman Munson SP 15.00 40.00
306 Javier Vazquez .15 .40
307 A.J. Burnett .40 1.00
Ervin Santana
Roy Halladay LL
308 Chris Duncan .15 .40
309 Humberto Sanchez (RC) .30 .75
310 Johan Santana .40 1.00
311 Kelly Shoppach .15 .40
312 Ryan Sweeney .15 .40
313 Jamey Carroll .15 .40
314 Matt Treanor .15 .40
315 Hiroki Kuroda .15 .40
316 Brian Stokes .15 .40
317 Jarrod Saltalamacchia .15 .40
318 Manny Acta MG .15 .40
319 Brian Fuentes .15 .40
320a Miguel Cabrera .40 1.00
320b Johnny Mize SP 8.00 20.00
321 Scott Kazmir .40 1.00
David Price CC
322 John Buck .15 .40
323 Vicente Padilla .15 .40
324 Mark Reynolds .15 .40
325 Dustin McGowan .15 .40
326 Manny Ramirez HL .40 1.00
327 Phil Coke RC .50 1.25
328 Doug Mientkiewicz .15 .40
329 Gil Meche .15 .40
330 Daisuke Matsuzaka .40 1.00
331 Luke Scott .15 .40
332 Chone Figgins .15 .40
333 Jeremy Sowers .15 .40
Aaron Laffey
334 Blake DeWitt .15 .40
335 Chris Young .15 .40
336 Jordan Schafer (RC) .50 1.25
337 Bobby Jenks .15 .40
338 Daniel Cabrera .15 .40
339 Jim Leyland MG .15 .40
340a Joe Mauer .40 1.00
340b Wade Boggs SP 6.00 15.00
341 Willy Taveras .15 .40
342 Gerald Laird .15 .40
343 Ian Snell .15 .40
344 J.R. Towles .15 .40
345 Stephen Drew .15 .40
346 Mike Cameron .15 .40
347 Jason Bartlett .15 .40
348 Tony Pena .15 .40
349 Justin Masterson .15 .40
350a Dustin Pedroia .50 1.25
350b Ryne Sandberg SP 8.00 20.00
351 Chris Snyder .15 .40
352 Gregor Blanco .15 .40
353a Derek Jeter 1.00 2.50
353b Cal Ripken Jr. SP 8.00 20.00
354 Mike Aviles .15 .40
355a John Smoltz .40 1.00
355b Jim Palmer SP 5.00 12.00
356 Ervin Santana .15 .40
357 Huston Street .15 .40
358 Chad Tracy .15 .40
359 Jason Varitek .40 1.00
360 Jorge Posada .25 .60
361 Alex Rios .25 .60
Vernon Wells
362 Luke Montz RC .30 .75
363 Jhonny Peralta .15 .40
364 Kevin Millwood .15 .40
365 Mark Buehrle .25 .60
366 Alexi Casilla .15 .40
367 Bobby Abreu .15 .40
368 Trevor Hoffman .25 .60
369 Matt Harrison .15 .40
370 Victor Martinez .25 .60
371 Jeff Francis .15 .40
372 Rickie Weeks .25 .60
373 Joe Martinez RC .50 1.25
374 Kevin Kouzmanoff .15 .40
375 Carlos Quentin .25 .60
376 Rajai Davis .15 .40
377 Trevor Crowe RC .30 .75
378 Mark Hendrickson .15 .40
379 Howie Kendrick .15 .40
380 Aramis Ramirez .15 .40
381 Sharon Martis RC .50 1.25
382 Wily Mo Pena .15 .40
383 Everth Cabrera RC .50 1.25
384 Bob Melvin MG .15 .40
385 Mike Jacobs .15 .40
386 Jonathan Papelbon .25 .60
387 Adam Everett .15 .40
388 Humberto Quintero .15 .40
389 Garrett Olson .15 .40
390 Joey Votto .40 1.00
391 Dan Haren .15 .40
392 Brandon Phillips .15 .40
393 Alex Cintron .15 .40
394 Barry Zito .15 .40
395 Magglio Ordonez .25 .60
396 Alex Cora .15 .40
397 Carlos Ruiz .15 .40
398 Cameron Maybin .15 .40
399 Wandy Rodriguez .15 .40
400a Alfonso Soriano .25 .60
400b Frank Robinson SP 6.00 15.00
401 Tony La Russa MG .25 .60
402 Nick Blackburn .15 .40
403 Trevor Cahill RC .75 2.00
404 Matt Capps .15 .40
405 Todd Helton .25 .60
406 Mark Ellis .15 .40
407 Dave Trembley MG .15 .40

408 Ronny Paulino .15 .40
409 Jesse Chavez RC .30 .75
410 Lou Piniella MG .15 .40
411 Troy Tulowitzki .40 1.00
412 Taylor Teagarden .25 .60
413 Ruben Gotay .15 .40
414 Cha Seung Baek .15 .40
415a Josh Beckett .25 .60
415b Bob Gibson SP 10.00 25.00
416 Josh Whitesell RC .50 1.25
417 Jason Marquis .15 .40
418 Andy Pettitte .25 .60
419 Braden Looper .15 .40
420 Scott Baker .15 .40
421 B.J. Ryan .15 .40
422 Hank Blalock .15 .40
423 Melvin Mora .15 .40
424 Jorge Campillo .15 .40
425 Curtis Granderson .25 .60
426 Pablo Sandoval .50 1.25
427 Brian Duensing RC .50 1.25
428 Jamie Moyer .15 .40
429 Mike Hampton .15 .40
430 Francisco Rodriguez .25 .60
431 Ramon Hernandez .15 .40
432 Wladimir Balentien .15 .40
433 Coco Crisp .15 .40
434 Carlos Guillen .40 1.00
Miguel Cabrera
435 Carlos Lee .15 .40
436 Ryan Theriot .15 .40
437 Austin Kearns .15 .40
438 Mark Loretta .15 .40
439 Ryan Spilborghs .15 .40
440 Fausto Carmona .15 .40
441 Andrew Bailey RC .75 2.00
442 Cliff Pennington .15 .40
443 Gavin Floyd .15 .40
444 Jody Gerut .15 .40
445 Joe Nathan .15 .40
446 Matt Holliday .40 1.00
447 Freddy Sanchez .15 .40
448 Jeff Clement .15 .40
449 Mike Fontenot .15 .40
450 Hanley Ramirez .40 1.00
451 Ryan Perry RC .75 2.00
452 Orlando Cabrera .15 .40
453 Javier Valentin .15 .40
454 Carlos Silva .15 .40
455 Adam Jones .25 .60
456 Jason Kendall .15 .40
457 John Maine .15 .40
458 Jeremy Bonderman .15 .40
459 Brian Bannister .15 .40
460 Nick Markakis .40 1.00
461 Mike Scioscia MG .15 .40
462 James Loney .25 .60
463 Brian Wilson .40 1.00
464 Bobby Crosby .15 .40
465 Troy Glaus .15 .40
466 Wilson Betemit .15 .40
467 Chris Volstad .15 .40
468 Derek Lowe .15 .40
469 Michael Cuddyer .15 .40
470 Lance Berkman .25 .60
471 Kerry Wood .15 .40
472 Bill Hall .15 .40
473 Jered Weaver .15 .40
474 Franklin Gutierrez .15 .40
475a Chipper Jones .40 1.00
475b Mike Schmidt SP 8.00 20.00
476a Edinson Volquez .15 .40
476b Juan Marichal SP 5.00 12.00
477 Josh Willingham .15 .40
478 Jose Molina .15 .40
479 Brad Nelson (RC) .30 .75
480 Prince Fielder .25 .60
481 Nyjer Morgan .15 .40
482 Jason Jaramillo (RC) .30 .75
483 John Lannan .15 .40
484 Chris Carpenter .40 1.00
485 Aaron Rowand .15 .40
486 J.J. Putz .15 .40
487 Travis Hafner .15 .40
488 Ozzie Guillen MG .15 .40
489 Matt Guerrier .15 .40
490a Joba Chamberlain .25 .60
490b Nolan Ryan SP 8.00 20.00
491 Paul Bako .15 .40
492 Andre Ethier .25 .60
493 Ramiro Pena RC .50 1.25
494 Gary Matthews .15 .40
495a Eric Chavez .15 .40
495b Brooks Robinson SP 8.00 20.00
496 Charlie Manuel MG .15 .40
497 Clint Hurdle MG .15 .40
498 Kyle Davies .15 .40
499 Edwin Moreno (RC) .30 .75
500 Ryan Howard .50 1.25
501 Jeff Suppan .15 .40
502 Yovani Gallardo .15 .40
503 Carlos Gonzalez .25 .60
504 Felix Pie .15 .40
505 Scott Olsen .15 .40
506 Paul Konerko .25 .60
507 Melky Cabrera .15 .40
508 Kenji Johjima .25 .60
509 Lou Montanez .15 .40
510 Ryan Ludwick .25 .60
511 Chad Qualls .15 .40
512 Steve Pearce .15 .40
513 Bronson Arroyo .15 .40
514 Nick Hundley .15 .40
515a Gary Sheffield .15 .40
515b Reggie Jackson SP 10.00 25.00
516 Brian Anderson .15 .40
517 Kevin Frandsen .15 .40
518 Chris Perez .15 .40
519 Dioner Navarro .15 .40
520a Adrian Gonzalez .25 .60
520b Tony Gwynn SP 6.00 15.00
521 Dana Eveland .15 .40
522 Gio Gonzalez .15 .40
523 Brandon Morrow .15 .40
524 Andy LaRoche .15 .40
525 Jimmy Rollins .25 .60
526 Bruce Bochy MG .15 .40
527 Jason Isringhausen .15 .40
528 Nick Swisher .40 1.00
529 Fernando Rodney .15 .40
530 Felix Hernandez .40 1.00
531 Frank Francisco .15 .40
532 Garret Anderson .15 .40
533 Darin Erstad .15 .40
534 Skip Schumaker .15 .40
535 Ryan Doumit .15 .40
536 Khalil Greene .15 .40
537 Anthony Reyes .15 .40
538 Carlos Guillen .15 .40
539 Miguel Olivo .15 .40
540 Russell Martin .15 .40
541 Jason Bay .25 .60
542 Chris Ray .15 .40
543 Travis Ishikawa .15 .40
544 Pat Neshek .25 .60
545 Matt Garza .15 .40
546 Matt Cain .15 .40
547 Jack Cust .15 .40
548 John Danks .15 .40
549 Randy Winn .15 .40
550 Carlos Beltran .15 .40
551 Tim Redding .15 .40
552 Eric Byrnes .15 .40
553 Jeff Karstens .15 .40
554 Adam LaRoche .15 .40
555 Joe Girardi MG .25 .60
556 Brendan Ryan .15 .40
557 Jayson Werth .25 .60
558 Edgar Renteria .15 .40
559 Esteban German .15 .40
560 Adrian Beltre .15 .40
561 Ryan Freel .15 .40
562 Cecil Cooper MG .15 .40
563 Francisco Cordero .15 .40
564 Jesus Flores .15 .40
565 Jose Lopez .15 .40
566 Dontrelle Willis .15 .40
567 Willy Aybar .15 .40
568 Greg Reynolds .15 .40
569 Ted Lilly .15 .40
570 David DeJesus .15 .40
571 Noah Lowry .15 .40
572 Michael Bourn .15 .40
573 Adam Wainwright .25 .60
574 Nate Schierholtz .15 .40
575 Clayton Kershaw .40 1.00
576 Don Wakamatsu MG .15 .40
577 Jose Contreras .15 .40
578 Adam Kennedy .15 .40
579 Rocco Baldelli .15 .40
580 Scott Kazmir .15 .40
581 David Purcey .15 .40
582 Yunel Escobar .15 .40
583 Brett Anderson RC .50 1.25
584 Ron Washington MG .15 .40
585 Alexei Ramirez .25 .60
586 Nelson Cruz .25 .60
587 Adam Dunn .25 .60
588 Jorge De La Rosa .15 .40
589 Rickey Romero (RC) .75 2.00
590 Johnny Damon .25 .60
591 Elvis Andrus RC .50 1.25
592 Fred Lewis .15 .40
593 Kenshin Kawakami RC .50 1.25
594 Milton Bradley .15 .40
595a Vernon Wells .15 .40
595b Robin Yount SP 6.00 15.00
596 Radhames Liz .15 .40
597 Randy Wolf .15 .40
598 Micah Owings .15 .40
599 Placido Polanco .15 .40
600a Jake Peavy .15 .40
600b Greg Maddux SP 10.00 25.00
601 Ryan Howard .50 1.25
Jimmy Rollins
602 Carlos Gomez .15 .40
603 Jose Reyes .25 .60
604 Gregg Zaun .15 .40
605 Rick Ankiel .15 .40
606 Nick Johnson .15 .40
607 Jarrod Washburn .15 .40
608 Cristian Guzman .15 .40
609 Juan Rivera .15 .40
610a Michael Young .25 .60
610b Paul Molitor SP 10.00 25.00
611 Jeremy Hermida .15 .40
612 Joel Pineiro .15 .40
613 Kendry Morales .15 .40
614 David Murphy .15 .40
615 Robinson Cano .40 1.00
616 Koji Uehara RC .50 1.25
617 Shaun Marcum .15 .40
618 Brandon Backe .15 .40
619 Chris Carter .15 .40
620 Ryan Zimmerman .25 .60
621 Oliver Perez .15 .40
622 Kurt Suzuki .15 .40
623 Aaron Hill .15 .40
624 Ben Francisco .15 .40
625 Jim Thome .25 .60
626 Scott Hairston .15 .40
627 Billy Butler .15 .40
628 Justin Upton .25 .60
Chris Young
629 Lyle Overbay .15 .40
630 A.J. Burnett .25 .60
631 Colby Rasmus (RC) .75 2.00
632 Brett Myers .15 .40
633 David Patton RC .50 1.25
634 Chris Davis .15 .40
635 Joakim Soria .15 .40
636 Armando Galarraga .15 .40
637 Donald Veal RC .50 1.25
638 Eugenio Velez .15 .40
639 Corey Hart .15 .40
640 B.J. Upton .25 .60
641 Jesse Litsch .15 .40
642 Ken Macha MG .15 .40
643 David Freese RC 2.50 6.00
644 Alfredo Aceves RC .50 1.25
645 Paul Maholm .15 .40
646 Chris Iannetta .15 .40
647 Manny Parra .15 .40
648 J.D. Drew .15 .40
649 Luke Hochevar .15 .40
650a Cole Hamels .40 1.00
650b Steve Carlton SP 10.00 25.00
651 Jake Westbrook .15 .40
652 Doug Davis .15 .40
653 Nick Evans .15 .40
654 Brian Schneider .15 .40
655 Bengie Molina .15 .40
656 Delmon Young .25 .60
657 Aaron Heilman .15 .40
658 Rick Porcello RC 1.00 2.50
659 Torii Hunter .15 .40
660a Jacoby Ellsbury .40 1.00
660b Carl Yastrzemski SP 8.00 20.00

2009 Topps Gold Border

*GOLD VET: 2X TO 5X BASIC
*GOLD RC: 1X TO 2.5X BASIC RC
SER.1 ODDS 1:7 HOBBY
SER.2 ODDS 1:5 HOBBY
STATED PRINT RUN 2009 SER.#'d SETS
7 Mickey Mantle 8.00 20.00
658 Rick Porcello 5.00 12.00

2009 Topps Platinum

SER.1 ODDS 1:13,500 HOBBY
SER.2 ODDS 1:13,500 HOBBY
STATED PRINT RUN 1 SER.#'d SET
NO PRICING DUE TO SCARCITY

2009 Topps Target

*VETS: .5X TO 1.2X BASIC TOPPS CARDS
*RC: .5X TO 1.2X BASIC TOPPS RC CARDS

2009 Topps Target Legends Gold

*GOLD: .6X TO 1.5X BASIC
RANDOM INSERTS IN TARGET PACKS

2009 Topps Wal Mart Black Border

*VETS: .5X TO 1.2X BASIC TOPPS CARDS
*RC: .5X TO 1.2X BASIC TOPPS RC CARDS

2009 Topps 1952 Autographs

STATED ODDS 1:60,000 HOBBY
NNO Billy Crystal 100.00 175.00

2009 Topps 1958 Reprint Relic

STATED ODDS 1:50,000 HOBBY
STATED PRINT RUN 58 SER.#'d SETS
NO PRICING DUE TO SCARCITY
MMR58 Mickey Mantle Jsy/58

2009 Topps 1959 Reprint Relic

STATED ODDS 1:60,000 HOBBY
STATED PRINT RUN 59 SER.#'d SETS
NO PRICING DUE TO SCARCITY
MMR59 Mickey Mantle Jsy

2009 Topps 1960 Reprint Relic

STATED ODDS 1:34,000 UPD HOB.PACK
STATED PRINT RUN 60 SER.#'d SETS
NO PRICING DUE TO SCARCITY
MMR60 Mickey Mantle

2009 Topps American Legends Cut Signature

STATED ODDS 1:142:200 HOBBY
UPDATE ODDS 1:150,000 HOBBY
STATED PRINT RUN 1 SER.#'d SET
NO PRICING DUE TO SCARCITY

2009 Topps Career Best Autographs

GROUP A1 ODDS 1:6708 HOBBY
GROUP A2 ODDS 1:3140 HOBBY
GROUP B1 ODDS 1:416 HOBBY
GROUP B2 ODDS 1:613 HOBBY
UPDATE ODDS 1:352 HOBBY
MOST GROUP A PRICING NOT AVAILABLE
AE Andre Ethier UPD 6.00 15.00
AG Armando Galarraga B1 3.00 8.00
AI Akinori Iwamura B1 5.00 12.00
AI Akinori Iwamura B2 5.00 12.00
AJ Andruw Jones UPD 5.00 12.00
AK Austin Kearns B2 3.00 8.00
AP Albert Pujols A1
AR Aramis Ramirez A1 10.00 25.00
AR Alex Rodriguez A2 75.00 150.00
BD Blake DeWitt B2 6.00 15.00
BM Brandon Moss A2 3.00 8.00
BR Brian Roberts A1
BZ Ben Zobrist UPD 6.00 15.00
CB Chad Billingsley A1
CC Carl Crawford A1
CD Carlos Delgado A1
CD Chris Dickerson B2 3.00 8.00
CF Chone Figgins A2 5.00 12.00
CG Curtis Granderson B1 10.00 25.00
CG Carlos Gomez B2 6.00 15.00
CJ Conor Jackson A1
CK Clayton Kershaw A1
CK Clayton Kershaw B2 8.00 20.00
CV Chris Volstad B2 3.00 8.00
CW C.J. Wilson B1 3.00 8.00
CWJ Chipper Jones A1
DM Dallas McPherson B1 3.00 8.00
DMM Dustin McGowan B1 3.00 8.00
DO David Ortiz A1 20.00 50.00
DP Dustin Pedroia A1
DP David Price A2 20.00 50.00
DU Dan Uggla A1
DW David Wright A1
DW David Wright A2
EK Eddie Kunz B1 3.00 8.00
EL Evan Longoria A1
EL Evan Longoria A2 30.00 60.00
FC Fausto Carmona B2 3.00 8.00
FH Felix Hernandez A1
FH Felix Hernandez A2 12.50 30.00
FL Fred Lewis B2 3.00 8.00
GA Garrett Atkins B1 3.00 8.00
GS Gary Sheffield UPD 10.00 25.00
GS Greg Smith B1 3.00 8.00
GS Gary Sheffield A2
HB Heath Bell UPD 3.00 8.00
HR Hanley Ramirez A1 12.50 30.00
IR Ivan Rodriguez UPD 20.00 50.00
JB Jay Bruce A1
JB Jeff Baker B2 3.00 8.00
JD Johnny Damon A2 30.00 60.00
JG Jason Giambi UPD 15.00 40.00
JH Josh Hamilton A1
JH Josh Hamilton A2 20.00 50.00
JL Jon Lester A1
JL Jon Lester A2 10.00 25.00
JN Jayson Nix UPD 3.00 8.00
JN Jeff Niemann A2 3.00 8.00
JR Jose Reyes A1
JS Jeff Samardzija A2 8.00 20.00
KG Kevin Gregg UPD 3.00 8.00
KK Kevin Kouzmanoff A2 6.00 15.00
LB Lance Berkman A2 10.00 25.00
LH Luke Hochevar B1 4.00 10.00
MA Mike Aviles A2
MB Milton Bradley UPD 4.00 10.00
MC Matt Cain UPD
MG Mat Gamel B1 6.00 15.00
MH Matt Holliday UPD 20.00 50.00
MJ Matt Joyce UPD
MS Max Scherzer A1
NM Nate McLouth UPD 12.50 30.00
NM Nick Markakis A1 20.00 50.00
OH Orlando Hudson UPD 5.00 12.00
PF Prince Fielder A1
PF Prince Fielder B2 10.00 25.00
PM Peter Moylan UPD 3.00 8.00
PN Pat Neshek B1 5.00 12.00
RB Ryan Braun A1
RC Ryan Church UPD
RC Robinson Cano B2 15.00 40.00
RG Ryan Garko A1
RH Rich Hill UPD 3.00 8.00
RH Ryan Howard A1
RH Ryan Howard A2 75.00 150.00
RI Raul Ibanez UPD 15.00 40.00
RM Russ Martin A1
RO Roy Oswalt UPD 6.00 15.00
RO Roy Oswalt A2 10.00 25.00
RP Ronny Paulino B1 3.00 8.00
SK Scott Kazmir A1
SP Steve Pearce B1 3.00 8.00
SR Sean Rodriguez B1 12.50 30.00
SV Shane Victorino B1 15.00 40.00
TS Travis Snider B1 6.00 15.00
VG Vladimir Guerrero UPD 15.00 40.00
YG Yovani Gallardo B1 6.00 15.00
YG Yovani Gallardo A2 6.00 15.00
ZG Zack Greinke B1 6.00 15.00
AMS Andy Sonnanstine A2 3.00 8.00
ASO Alfonso Soriano A2 30.00 60.00
GTS Greg Smith B2 3.00 8.00
JCH Joba Chamberlain A2 15.00 40.00

2009 Topps Career Best Relics

GROUP A1 ODDS 1:70 HOBBY
GROUP A2 ODDS 1:344 HOBBY
GROUP B1 ODDS 1:146 HOBBY
GROUP B2 ODDS 1:92 HOBBY
AB Angel Berroa Bat B2 2.50 6.00
AE Andre Ethier Jsy B2 2.50 6.00
AER Alex Rodriguez Bat A1 6.00 15.00
AG Alex Gordon Jsy A1 4.00 10.00
AG Alex Gordon Jsy B2 2.50 6.00
AP Albert Pujols Jsy A1 6.00 15.00
AR Aramis Ramirez Jsy B1 2.50 6.00
AR Alex Rodriguez Jsy A2 6.00 15.00
BM Brian McCann Bat A1 2.50 6.00
CB Carlos Beltran Pants B2 2.50 6.00
CG Curtis Granderson Jsy A1 3.00 8.00
CG Curtis Granderson Jsy B2 3.00 8.00
CGG Cristian Guzman Bat A1 2.50 6.00
CH Cole Hamels Jsy B2 4.00 10.00
CJ Conor Jackson Bat A1 2.50 6.00
CJ Conor Jackson Jsy B2 2.50 6.00
CM Cameron Maybin Bat B1 2.50 6.00
DM Daisuke Matsuzaka Jsy A1 4.00 10.00
DO David Ortiz Bat A1 4.00 10.00
DW David Wright Bat A1 5.00 12.00
DW David Wright Jsy B1 5.00 12.00
EC Eric Chavez Bat B2 2.50 6.00
FS Freddy Sanchez Jsy A1 2.50 6.00
GA Garret Anderson Jsy A2 4.00 10.00
HO Hideki Okajima Jsy B1 3.00 8.00
IK Ian Kinsler Jsy B2 2.50 6.00
IS Ichiro Suzuki Jsy A1 10.00 25.00
JA Josh Anderson Jsy A1 3.00 8.00
JB Jeremy Bonderman Jsy A1 2.50 6.00
JB Jay Bruce Bat A2 4.00 10.00
JC Johnny Cueto Jsy A1 2.50 6.00
JC Jorge Cantu Bat A2 2.50 6.00
JD Jermaine Dye Jsy A1 2.50 6.00
JD J.D. Drew Bat A2 3.00 8.00
JE Jacoby Ellsbury Jsy A1 8.00 20.00
JH Jeremy Hermida Jsy A1 2.50 6.00
JM Justin Morneau Bat A1 2.50 6.00
JP Jonathan Papelbon Jsy B1 2.50 6.00
JP Jose Reyes Jsy A1 3.00 8.00
LG Luis Gonzalez Bat A2 2.50 6.00
MA Mike Aviles Jsy B2 2.50 6.00
MC Miguel Cabrera Bat A2 4.00 10.00
MK Matt Kemp Jsy B2 3.00 8.00
MO Magglio Ordonez Bat A2 4.00 10.00
OD Octavio Dotel Jsy B2 2.50 6.00
PF Prince Fielder Jsy A1 3.00 8.00
PF Prince Fielder Jsy A2 3.00 8.00
RB Ryan Braun Jsy B1 4.00 10.00
RC Robinson Cano Bat B2 3.00 8.00
RD Ray Durham Bat A2 2.50 6.00
RF Rafael Furcal Bat A2 3.00 8.00
RG Ryan Garko Jsy A1 2.50 6.00
RH Ryan Howard Jsy A1 5.00 12.00
RH Ryan Howard Bat B2 5.00 12.00
SK Scott Kazmir Jsy A1 2.50 6.00
VM Victor Martinez Bat A1 2.50 6.00
VM Victor Martinez Jsy B2 2.50 6.00
ARA Aramis Ramirez Jsy B2 2.50 6.00
JBE Josh Beckett Jsy B2 3.00 8.00
JCU Johnny Cueto Jsy A2 2.50 6.00
RBA Rocco Baldelli Bat B2 2.50 6.00
RBR Ryan Braun Jsy A2 4.00 10.00

2009 Topps Career Best Relics Silver

*SILVER 99: .6X TO 1.5X BASIC
STATED ODDS 1:1033 HOBBY
STATED PRINT RUN 99 SER.#'d SETS

2009 Topps Career Best Relic Autographs

SER.1 ODDS 1:2210 HOBBY
SER.2 ODDS 1:2845 HOBBY
STATED PRINT RUN 50 SER.#'d SETS
AER Alex Rodriguez Bat 100.00 200.00
AI Akinori Iwamura 8.00 20.00
AK Austin Kearns 12.50 30.00
AR Aramis Ramirez Jsy 8.00 20.00
BD Blake DeWitt 10.00 25.00
CC Carl Crawford Jsy 8.00 20.00
DP Dustin Pedroia Jsy 50.00 100.00
DW David Wright Bat 20.00 50.00
EL Evan Longoria 50.00 100.00
FC Fausto Carmona 10.00 25.00
FH Felix Hernandez 20.00 50.00
FL Fred Lewis 8.00 20.00
HR Hanley Ramirez Jsy 20.00 50.00
JC Joba Chamberlain 20.00 50.00
JH Josh Hamilton Jsy 10.00 25.00
JH Josh Hamilton 10.00 25.00
JL Jon Lester 20.00 50.00
JR Jose Reyes Jsy 30.00 60.00
NM Nick Markakis Jsy 20.00 50.00
PF Prince Fielder Jsy 12.50 30.00
RB Ryan Braun Jsy 20.00 50.00

2009 Topps Career Best Relics Dual

STATED ODDS 1:472 HOBBY
STATED PRINT RUN 99 SER.#'d SETS
BL Ryan Braun Jsy/Evan Longoria Jsy 12.50 30.00
CP Miguel Cabrera Bat/Albert Pujols Jsy 12.50 30.00
EP Jacoby Ellsbury Jsy/Dustin Pedroia Jsy 15.00 40.00
FH Prince Fielder Bat/Ryan Howard Jsy 6.00 15.00
GJ Tom Glavine Jsy/Randy Johnson Jsy 6.00 15.00
GO Vladimir Guerrero Jsy/David Ortiz Jsy 20.00 50.00
HB Josh Hamilton Jsy/Ryan Braun Jsy 12.50 30.00
HC Ryan Howard Jsy/Miguel Cabrera Bat 6.00 15.00
HR Ryan Howard Jsy/Alex Rodriguez Bat 15.00 40.00
HU Ryan Howard Jsy/Chase Utley Jsy 10.00 25.00
LC Tim Lincecum Jsy/Matt Cain Jsy 10.00 25.00
LS Evan Longoria Jsy/Geovany Soto Jsy 8.00 20.00
MM Joe Mauer Jsy/Brian McCann Jsy 8.00 20.00
OL Magglio Ordonez Bat/Carlos Lee Bat 6.00 15.00
OP Roy Oswalt Jsy/Jake Peavy Jsy 6.00 15.00
OR David Ortiz Bat/Alex Rodriguez Bat 12.50 30.00
PB Hunter Pence Bat/Ryan Braun Jsy 12.50 30.00
PK Dustin Pedroia Jsy/Ian Kinsler Jsy 8.00 20.00
RB Alex Rios Jsy/Carlos Beltran Pants 10.00 25.00
RR Jimmy Rollins Jsy/Jose Reyes Jsy 6.00 15.00
RU Hanley Ramirez Jsy/Dan Uggla Jsy 6.00 15.00
SM Ichiro Jsy/Daisuke Matsuzaka Jsy 30.00 60.00
TS Jim Thome Jsy/Gary Sheffield Bat 6.00 15.00
UU Justin Upton Bat/B.J. Upton Bat 6.00 15.00
VP Jason Varitek Bat/Jorge Posada Uni 6.00 15.00
WJ David Wright Pants/Chipper Jones Jsy 10.00 25.00
WL David Wright Jsy/Evan Longoria Jsy 12.50 30.00
ZL Ryan Zimmerman Jsy/Evan Longoria Jsy 8.00 20.00
OPU David Ortiz Bat/Albert Pujols Jsy 8.00 20.00
RRA Jimmy Rollins Jsy/Hanley Ramirez Jsy 6.00 15.00

2009 Topps Career Best Jumbo Jerseys

SER.1 ODDS 1:1800 HOBBY
SER.2 ODDS 1:7122 HOBBY
SER.1 PRINT RUN 20 SER.#'d SETS
SER.2 PRINT RUN 10 SER.#'d SETS
NO PRICING DUE TO SCARCITY

2009 Topps Career Best Relics Quad

STATED ODDS 1:2854 HOBBY
STATED PRINT RUN 20 SER.#'d SETS
NO PRICING DUE TO SCARCITY

2009 Topps Factory Set JCPenney Bonus

COMPLETE SET (5) 3.00 8.00
JCP1 Rick Porcello 1.25 3.00
JCP2 David Price 1.00 2.50
JCP3 Koji Uehara .60 1.50
JCP4 Colby Rasmus 1.00 2.50
JCP5 Jordan Schafer .60 1.50

2009 Topps Factory Set Rookie Bonus

COMPLETE SET (20) 8.00 20.00
1 David Price 1.00 2.50
2 Rick Porcello 1.25 3.00
3 Ryan Perry 1.00 2.50
4 Brett Anderson .60 1.50
5 David Freese 3.00 8.00
6 Koji Uehara .60 1.50
7 Elvis Andrus .60 1.50
8 Trevor Cahill 1.00 2.50
9 Andrew Bailey 1.00 2.50
10 Jordan Schafer .60 1.50
11 Colby Rasmus 1.00 2.50
12 Kenshin Kawakami .60 1.50
13 Michael Bowden .40 1.00
14 Edwin Moreno .40 1.00
15 Ricky Romero 1.00 2.50
16 Tommy Hanson 1.25 3.00
17 Ramiro Pena .60 1.50
18 Freddy Sandoval .40 1.00
19 Andrew McCutchen 1.50 4.00
20 George Kottaras .40 1.00

2009 Topps Factory Set Target Ruth Chrome Gold Refractors

COMPLETE SET (3) 15.00 40.00
1 Babe Ruth 8.00 20.00
2 Babe Ruth 8.00 20.00
3 Babe Ruth 8.00 20.00

2009 Topps In the Name Letter Relics

STATED ODDS 1:2975 HOBBY
STATED PRINT RUN 1 SER.#'d SET
NO PRICING DUE TO SCARCITY

2009 Topps Legendary Letters Commemorative Patch

STATED ODDS 1:630 HOBBY
EACH LETTER SER.#'d TO 50
COMBINED PRINT RUNS LISTED BELOW
BG Bob Gibson/300 * 10.00 25.00
Letters spellGIBSON (each letter serial #'d/50)
BR Babe Ruth/200 * 12.50 30.00
Letters spellRUTH (each letter serial #'d/50)
CM Christy Mathewson/450 * 6.00 15.00
Letters spellMATHEWSON (each letter serial #'d/50)
CR Cal Ripken Jr./300 * 30.00 60.00
Letters spellRIPKEN (each letter serial #'d/50)
CY Cy Young/250 * 12.50 30.00
Letters spellYOUNG (each letter serial #'d/50)
GS George Sisler/300 * 4.00 10.00
Letters spellSISLER (each letter serial #'d/50)
HW Honus Wagner/300 * 10.00 25.00
Letters spellWAGNER (each letter serial #'d/50)
JF Jimmie Foxx/200 * 4.00 10.00
Letters spellFOXX (each letter serial #'d/50)
JM Johnny Mize/200 * 6.00 15.00
Letters spellMIZE (each letter serial #'d/50)
JR Jackie Robinson/400 * 8.00 20.00
Letters spellROBINSON (each letter serial #'d/50)
LG Lou Gehrig/300 * 12.50 30.00
Letters spellGEHRIG (each letter serial #'d/50)
MM Mickey Mantle/300 * 15.00 40.00
Letters spellMANTLE (each letter serial #'d/50)
MO Mel Ott/150 * 4.00 10.00
Letters spellOTT (each letter serial #'d/50)
NR Nolan Ryan/200 * 12.50 30.00
Letters spellRYAN (each letter serial #'d/50)
RC Roy Campanella/500 * 8.00 20.00
Letters spellCAMPANELLA (each letter serial #'d/50)
RH Rogers Hornsby/350 * 4.00 10.00
Letters spellHORNSBY (each letter serial #'d/50)
TC Ty Cobb/200 * 12.50 30.00
Letters spellCOBB (each letter serial #'d/50)
TM Thurman Munson/300 * 10.00 25.00
Letters spellMUNSON (each letter serial #'d/50)
TS Tris Speaker/350 * 5.00 12.00
Letters spellSPEAKER (each letter serial #'d/50)
WJ Walter Johnson/350 * 5.00 12.00
Letters spellJOHNSON (each letter serial #'d/50)
CMY Carl Yastrzemski/550 * 12.50 30.00
Letters spellYASTRZEMSKI (each letter serial #'d/50)
PWR Pee Wee Reese/250 * 8.00 20.00
Letters spellREESE (each letter serial #'d/50)

2009 Topps Legends Chrome Target Cereal

COMPLETE SET (30) 30.00 60.00
RANDOM INSERTS IN TARGET CEREAL PACKS
GR1 Ted Williams 4.00 10.00
GR2 Bob Gibson 1.00 2.50
GR3 Babe Ruth 4.00 10.00
GR4 Roy Campanella 1.50 4.00
GR5 Ty Cobb 2.50 6.00
GR6 Cy Young 1.50 4.00
GR7 Mickey Mantle 5.00 12.00
GR8 Walter Johnson 1.50 4.00
GR9 Roberto Clemente 4.00 10.00
GR10 Jimmie Foxx 1.50 4.00
GR11 Christy Mathewson 1.50 4.00
GR12 Jackie Robinson 1.50 4.00
GR13 Ty Cobb 2.50 6.00
GR14 Honus Wagner 1.50 4.00
GR15 Lou Gehrig 3.00 8.00
GR16 Nolan Ryan 5.00 12.00
GR17 Cal Ripken Jr 6.00 15.00
GR18 Thurman Munson 1.50 4.00
GR19 Rogers Hornsby 1.00 2.50
GR20 George Sisler 1.00 2.50
LLG21 Rickey Henderson 1.50 4.00
LLG22 Ozzie Smith 2.50 6.00
LLG23 Babe Ruth 4.00 10.00
LLG24 Roger Maris 2.50 6.00
LLG25 Nolan Ryan 5.00 12.00
LLG26 Reggie Jackson 1.00 2.50
LLG27 Frank Robinson 1.00 2.50
LLG28 Ryne Sandberg 3.00 8.00
LLG29 Steve Carlton .60 1.50
LLG30 Johnny Bench 1.50 4.00

2009 Topps Legends Chrome Target Cereal Refractors

*REF: .5X TO 1.2X BASIC
RANDOM INSERTS IN TARGET PACKS

2009 Topps Legends Chrome Target Cereal Gold Refractors

*GOLD REF: .75X TO 2X BASIC
RANDOM INSERTS IN TARGET PACKS

2009 Topps Legends Chrome Wal Mart Cereal

RANDOM INSERTS IN WALMART CEREAL PACKS
PR1 Ted Williams 4.00 10.00
PR2 Jackie Robinson 1.50 4.00
PR3 Babe Ruth 4.00 10.00
PR4 Honus Wagner 1.50 4.00
PR5 Lou Gehrig 3.00 8.00
PR6 Nolan Ryan 5.00 12.00
PR7 Mickey Mantle 5.00 12.00
PR8 Thurman Munson 1.50 4.00
PR9 Cal Ripken Jr. 6.00 15.00
PR10 George Sisler 1.00 2.50
PR11 Mel Ott 1.50 4.00
PR12 Bob Gibson 1.00 2.50
PR13 Jackie Robinson 1.50 4.00
PR14 Roy Campanella 1.50 4.00
PR15 Ty Cobb 2.50 6.00
PR16 Cy Young 1.50 4.00
PR17 Cal Ripken Jr 6.00 15.00
PR18 Walter Johnson 1.50 4.00
PR19 Lou Gehrig 3.00 8.00
PR20 Jimmie Foxx 1.50 4.00
PR21 Babe Ruth 4.00 10.00
PR22 Rogers Hornsby 1.00 2.50
PR23 Johnny Mize 1.00 2.50
PR24 Ty Cobb 2.50 6.00
PR25 Tris Speaker 1.00 2.50
PR26 Rickey Henderson 1.50 4.00
PR27 Ozzie Smith 2.50 6.00
PR28 Nolan Ryan 5.00 12.00
PR29 Reggie Jackson 1.00 2.50
PR30 Frank Robinson 1.00 2.50

2009 Topps Legends Chrome Wal Mart Cereal Refractors

*REF: .5X TO 1.2X BASIC
RANDOM INSERTS IN TARGET PACKS

2009 Topps Legends Chrome Wal Mart Cereal Gold Refractors

*GOLD REF: .75X TO 2X BASIC
RANDOM INSERTS IN TARGET PACKS

2009 Topps Legends Commemorative Patch

SERIES 1 ODDS 1:343 HOBBY
UPDATE RANDOMLY INSERTED
1-100 ISSUED IN SERIES 1
101-150 ISSUED IN UPDATE
LPR1 Babe Ruth 15.00 40.00
1921 World Series
LPR2 Babe Ruth 15.00 40.00
1927 World Series
LPR3 Lou Gehrig 12.50 30.00
1928 World Series
LPR4 Lou Gehrig 12.50 30.00
1933 All-Star Game
LPR5 Jimmie Foxx 8.00 20.00
1934 All-Star Game
LPR6 Mel Ott 4.00 10.00
1934 All-Star Game
LPR7 Ted Williams 6.00 15.00
1946 All-Star Game
LPR8 Ted Williams 6.00 15.00
1949 All-Star Game
LPR9 Jackie Robinson 8.00 20.00
1949 All-Star Game
LPR10 Roy Campanella 12.50 30.00
1949 All-Star Game
LPR11 Mickey Mantle 12.50 30.00
(1951 World Series
LPR12 Mickey Mantle 12.50 30.00
(1952 World Series
LPR13 Ted Williams 6.00 15.00
1953 All-Star Game
LPR14 Roy Campanella 12.50 30.00
1953 All-Star Game
LPR15 Ted Williams 6.00 15.00
1954 All-Star Game
LPR16 Mickey Mantle 12.50 30.00
(1954 All-Star Game
LPR17 Duke Snider 10.00 25.00
1954 All-Star Game
LPR18 Whitey Ford 8.00 20.00
1954 All-Star Game
LPR19 Jackie Robinson 8.00 20.00
1955 World Series
LPR20 Mickey Mantle 12.50 30.00
(1956 World Series
LPR21 Don Larsen 4.00 10.00
1956 World Series
LPR22 Ted Williams 6.00 15.00
1960 All-Star Game, Yankee Stadium
LPR23 Ernie Banks 8.00 20.00
1960 All-Star Game, Yankee Stadium
LPR24 Roberto Clemente 8.00 20.00
(1961 All-Star Game, Candlestick Park
LPR25 Roberto Clemente 8.00 20.00
(1962 All-Star Game, RFK Stadium
LPR26 Roberto Clemente 8.00 20.00
(1962 All-Star Game, Wrigley Field
LPR27 Ernie Banks 8.00 20.00
1962 All-Star Game, Wrigley Field
LPR28 Mickey Mantle 12.50 30.00
(1962 World Series
LPR29 Roberto Clemente 8.00 20.00
(1963 All-Star Game
LPR30 Nolan Ryan 10.00 25.00
1969 World Series
LPR31 Tom Seaver 10.00 25.00
1969 World Series
LPR32 Roberto Clemente 8.00 20.00
(1971 All-Star Game
LPR33 Thurman Munson 8.00 20.00
1971 All-Star Game
LPR34 Carl Yastrzemski 10.00 25.00
1971 All-Star Game
LPR35 Nolan Ryan 10.00 25.00
1972 All-Star Game
LPR36 Bob Gibson 8.00 20.00
1972 All-Star Game
LPR37 Carl Yastrzemski 10.00 25.00
1972 All-Star Game
LPR38 Nolan Ryan 10.00 25.00
1973 All-Star Game
LPR39 Tom Seaver 10.00 25.00
1973 All-Star Game
LPR40 Reggie Jackson 10.00 25.00
1973 World Series
LPR41 Reggie Jackson 10.00 25.00
1977 World Series
LPR42 Thurman Munson 8.00 20.00
1978 World Series
LPR43 Cal Ripken 12.50 30.00
1983 All-Star Game
LPR44 Mike Schmidt 10.00 25.00
1983 All-Star Game
LPR45 Cal Ripken 12.50 30.00
1983 World Series
LPR46 Nolan Ryan 10.00 25.00

1985 All-Star Game
LPR47 Cal Ripken 12.50 30.00
1985 All-Star Game
LPR48 Nolan Ryan 10.00 25.00
1989 All-Star Game
LPR49 Cal Ripken 12.50 30.00
1989 All-Star Game
LPR50 Cal Ripken 12.50 30.00
2001 All-Star Game
LPR51 Cy Young 10.00 25.00
1903 World Series
LPR52 Christy Mathewson 10.00 25.00
1905 World Series
LPR53 Honus Wagner 10.00 25.00
1909 World Series
LPR54 Walter Johnson 10.00 25.00
1924 World Series
LPR55 Rogers Hornsby 10.00 25.00
1926 World Series
LPR56 Lou Gehrig 12.50 30.00
1927 World Series
LPR57 Babe Ruth 15.00 40.00
1928 World Series
LPR58 Jimmie Foxx 8.00 20.00
1929 World Series
LPR59 Jimmie Foxx 8.00 20.00
1930 World Series
LPR60 Babe Ruth 15.00 40.00
1933 MLB All-Star Game
LPR61 Lou Gehrig 12.50 30.00
1934 MLB All-Star Game
LPR62 Johnny Mize 10.00 25.00
1946 MLB All-Star Game
LPR63 Pee Wee Reese 6.00 15.00
1949 MLB All-Star Game
LPR64 Jackie Robinson 8.00 20.00
1951 MLB All-Star Game
LPR65 Johnny Mize 10.00 25.00
1951 World Series
LPR66 Mickey Mantle 12.50 30.00
1953 MLB All-Star Game
LPR67 Jackie Robinson 8.00 20.00
1954 MLB All-Star Game
LPR68 Roy Campanella 12.50 30.00
1955 World Series
LPR69 Mickey Mantle 12.50 30.00
1960 MLB All-Star Game (Yankee Stadium)
LPR70 Brooks Robinson 10.00 25.00
1961 MLB All-Star Game (Candlestick Park)
LPR71 Bill Mazeroski 10.00 25.00
1962 MLB All-Star Game (RFK Stadium)
LPR72 Frank Robinson 10.00 25.00
1962 MLB All-Star Game (Wrigley Field)
LPR73 Carl Yastrzemski 10.00 25.00
1963 MLB All-Star Game
LPR74 Juan Marichal 10.00 25.00
1965 MLB All-Star Game
LPR75 Brooks Robinson 10.00 25.00
1966 MLB All-Star Game
LPR76 Frank Robinson 10.00 25.00
1966 World Series
LPR77 Steve Carlton 8.00 20.00
1969 MLB All-Star Game
LPR78 Jim Palmer 8.00 20.00
1970 World Series
LPR79 Frank Robinson 10.00 25.00
1971 MLB All-Star Game
LPR80 Jim Palmer 8.00 20.00
1972 MLB All-Star Game
LPR81 Reggie Jackson 10.00 25.00
1973 MLB All-Star Game
LPR82 Thurman Munson 8.00 20.00
1977 World Series
LPR83 Mike Schmidt 10.00 25.00
1980 World Series
LPR84 Robin Yount 10.00 25.00
1982 MLB All-Star Game
LPR85 Robin Yount 10.00 25.00
1983 MLB All-Star Game
LPR86 Ryne Sandberg 12.50 30.00
1984 MLB All-Star Game
LPR87 Tony Gwynn 8.00 20.00
1985 MLB All-Star Game
LPR88 Mike Schmidt 10.00 25.00
1989 MLB All-Star Game
LPR89 Paul Molitor 10.00 25.00
1993 World Series
LPR90 Frank Thomas 12.50 30.00
1994 MLB All-Star Game
LPR91 Chipper Jones 10.00 25.00
1995 World Series
LPR92 John Smoltz 10.00 25.00
1996 MLB-Star Game
LPR93 Wade Boggs 10.00 25.00
1996 World Series
LPR94 Greg Maddux 12.50 30.00
1997 MLB All-Star Game
LPR95 Tony Gwynn 8.00 20.00
1998 MLB All-Star Game
LPR96 Mariano Rivera 10.00 25.00
1999 World Series
LPR97 Manny Ramirez 10.00 25.00
2004 World Series
LPR98 Albert Pujols 15.00 40.00
2006 World Series
LPR99 Ichiro Suzuki 12.50 30.00
2007 MLB All-Star Game
LPR100 Alex Rodriguez 10.00 25.00
2008 MLB All-Star Game
LPR101 Babe Ruth 15.00 40.00
LPR102 Babe Ruth 15.00 40.00
LPR103 Lou Gehrig 12.50 30.00
LPR104 Hank Greenberg 10.00 25.00
LPR105 Jimmie Foxx 8.00 20.00
LPR106 Lou Gehrig 12.50 30.00
LPR107 Stan Musial 8.00 20.00
LPR108 Hank Greenberg 10.00 25.00
LPR109 Pee Wee Reese 6.00 15.00
LPR110 Johnny Mize 10.00 25.00
LPR111 Jackie Robinson 8.00 20.00
LPR112 Roy Campanella 12.50 30.00
LPR113 Whitey Ford 8.00 20.00
LPR114 Robin Roberts 4.00 10.00
LPR115 Roy Campanella 12.50 30.00
LPR116 Johnny Mize 10.00 25.00
LPR117 Jackie Robinson 8.00 20.00
LPR118 Mickey Mantle 12.50 30.00
LPR119 Ernie Banks 8.00 20.00
LPR120 Duke Snider 10.00 25.00
LPR121 Mickey Mantle 12.50 30.00
LPR122 Brooks Robinson 10.00 25.00
LPR123 Mickey Mantle 12.50 30.00
LPR124 Whitey Ford 8.00 20.00
LPR125 Duke Snider 10.00 25.00
LPR126 Bob Gibson 8.00 20.00
LPR127 Ernie Banks 8.00 20.00
LPR128 Frank Robinson 10.00 25.00
LPR129 Jim Palmer 8.00 20.00
LPR130 Bob Gibson 8.00 20.00
LPR131 Steve Carlton 8.00 20.00
LPR132 Reggie Jackson 10.00 25.00
LPR133 Willie McCovey 10.00 25.00
LPR134 Carl Yastrzemski 10.00 25.00
LPR135 Tom Seaver 10.00 25.00
LPR136 Brooks Robinson 10.00 25.00
LPR137 Frank Robinson 10.00 25.00
LPR138 Thurman Munson 8.00 20.00
LPR139 Thurman Munson 8.00 20.00
LPR140 Carl Yastrzemski 10.00 25.00
LPR141 Nolan Ryan 10.00 25.00
LPR142 Robin Yount 10.00 25.00
LPR143 Reggie Jackson 10.00 25.00
LPR144 Cal Ripken 12.50 30.00
LPR145 Wade Boggs 10.00 25.00
LPR146 Mike Schmidt 10.00 25.00
LPR147 Ryne Sandberg 12.50 30.00
LPR148 Paul Molitor 10.00 25.00
LPR149 Cal Ripken 12.50 30.00
LPR150 Tony Gwynn 8.00 20.00

2009 Topps Legends of the Game

COMPLETE SET (75) 40.00 80.00
COMP.UPD.SET (25) 8.00 20.00
STATED ODDS 1:6 HOBBY
1-25 ISSUED IN TOPPS 1
26-50 ISSUED IN TOPPS 2
51-75 ISSUED IN UPDATE
*GOLD: 1.5X TO 4X BASIC
GOLD SER.1 ODDS 1:1975 HOBBY
GOLD SER.2 ODDS 1:1725 HOBBY
GOLD UPD.ODDS 1:950 HOBBY
GOLD PRINT RUN 99 SER.#'d SETS
*PLATINUM: 4X TO 10X BASIC
PLAT.SER.1 ODDS 1:8200 HOBBY
PLAT.SER.2 ODDS 1:6900 HOBBY
PLAT.UPD.ODDS 1:3800 HOBBY
PLATINUM PRINT RUN 25 SER.#'d SETS
LG1 Cy Young .75 2.00
LG2 Honus Wagner .75 2.00
LG3 Christy Mathewson .75 2.00
LG4 Ty Cobb 1.25 3.00
LG5 Walter Johnson .75 2.00
LG6 Tris Speaker .50 1.25
LG7 Babe Ruth 2.00 5.00
LG8 George Sisler .50 1.25
LG9 Rogers Hornsby .50 1.25
LG10 Jimmie Foxx .75 2.00
LG11 Lou Gehrig 1.50 4.00
LG12 Mel Ott .75 2.00
LG13 Jackie Robinson .75 2.00
LG14 Johnny Mize .50 1.25
LG15 Pee Wee Reese .50 1.25
LG16 Roy Campanella .75 2.00
LG17 Ted Williams 2.00 5.00
LG18 Roger Maris .75 2.00
LG19 Bob Gibson .50 1.25
LG20 Mickey Mantle 2.50 6.00
LG21 Roberto Clemente 2.00 5.00
LG22 Thurman Munson .75 2.00
LG23 Carl Yastrzemski 1.25 3.00
LG24 Nolan Ryan 2.50 6.00
LG25 Cal Ripken Jr. 3.00 8.00
LGAP Albert Pujols 2.00 5.00
LGAR Alex Rodriguez 1.25 3.00
LGBR Brooks Robinson .50 1.25
LGCJ Chipper Jones .75 2.00
LGFR Frank Robinson .50 1.25
LGFT Frank Thomas .75 2.00
LGGM Greg Maddux 1.00 2.50
LGIS Ichiro Suzuki 1.25 3.00
LGJM Juan Marichal .30 .75
LGJP Jim Palmer .30 .75
LGJS John Smoltz .75 2.00
LGMR Mariano Rivera .75 2.00
LGMS Mike Schmidt 1.25 3.00
LGPM Paul Molitor .75 2.00
LGRJ Reggie Jackson .50 1.25
LGRS Ryne Sandberg 1.50 4.00
LGRY Robin Yount .75 2.00
LGSC Steve Carlton .30 .75
LGTG Tony Gwynn .75 2.00
LGTH Trevor Hoffman .50 1.25
LGVG Vladimir Guerrero .75 2.00
LGWB Wade Boggs .50 1.25
LGMRA Manny Ramirez .75 2.00
LGRJO Randy Johnson .50 1.25
LGTGL Tom Glavine .50 1.25
LGU01 Cy Young .75 2.00
LGU02 Honus Wagner .75 2.00
LGU03 Christy Mathewson .75 2.00
LGU04 Ty Cobb 1.25 3.00
LGU05 Tris Speaker .50 1.25
LGU06 Babe Ruth 2.00 5.00
LGU07 George Sisler .50 1.25
LGU08 Rogers Hornsby .50 1.25
LGU09 Jimmie Foxx .75 2.00
LGU10 Johnny Mize .50 1.25
LGU11 Nolan Ryan 2.50 6.00
LGU12 Juan Marichal .30 .75
LGU13 Steve Carlton .30 .75
LGU14 Reggie Jackson .50 1.25
LGU15 Frank Robinson .50 1.25
LGU16 Wade Boggs .50 1.25
LGU17 Paul Molitor .75 2.00
LGU18 Babe Ruth 2.00 5.00
LGU19 Nolan Ryan 2.50 6.00
LGU20 Frank Robinson .50 1.25
LGU21 Reggie Jackson .50 1.25
LGU22 Wade Boggs .50 1.25
LGU23 Rogers Hornsby .50 1.25
LGU24 Paul Molitor .75 2.00
LGU25 Johnny Mize .50 1.25

2009 Topps Legends of the Game Autographs

STATED ODDS 1:110,000 HOBBY
UPDATE CARDS RANDOM INSERTS
STATED PRINT RUN 1 SER.#'d SET
NO PRICING DUE TO SCARCITY

2009 Topps Legends of the Game Career Best

RANDOM INSERTS IN PACKS
BR Babe Ruth 2.50 6.00
CY Cy Young 1.00 2.50
GS George Sisler .60 1.50
HW Honus Wagner 1.00 2.50
JF Jimmie Foxx 1.00 2.50
JR Jackie Robinson 1.00 2.50
LG Lou Gehrig 2.00 5.00
MM Mickey Mantle 3.00 8.00
MO Mel Ott 1.00 2.50
RC Roy Campanella 1.00 2.50
RH Rogers Hornsby .60 1.50
TC Ty Cobb 1.50 4.00
TS Tris Speaker .60 1.50
WJ Walter Johnson 1.00 2.50
CZM Christy Mathewson 1.00 2.50

2009 Topps Legends of the Game Career Best Cut Signatures

STATED ODDS 1:780,000 HOBBY
STATED PRINT RUN 1 SER.#'d SET
NO PRICING DUE TO SCARCITY

2009 Topps Legends of the Game Career Best Relics

STATED ODDS 1:15,500 HOBBY
NO PRICING DUE TO SCARCITY

2009 Topps Legends of the Game Nickname Letter Patch

RANDOM INSERTS IN PACKS
EACH LETTER SER.#'d TO 50
COMBINED PRINT RUNS LISTED BELOW
BG Bob Gibson/250 * 10.00 25.00
Letters spell GIBBY (each letter serial #'d/50)
BO Barack Obama/800 * 20.00 50.00
Letters spell COMMANDER IN CHIEF (each letter serial #'d/50)
BR Babe Ruth/350 * 15.00 40.00
Letters spell BAMBINO (each letter serial #'d/50)
BR Brooks Robinson/650 * 6.00 15.00
Letters spell VACUUM CLEANER (each letter #'d/50)
CM Christy Mathewson/300 * 4.00 10.00
Letters spell BIG SIX (each letter serial #'d/50)
CMY Carl Yastrzemski/150 * 10.00 25.00
Letters spell YAZ (each letter serial #'d/50)
CR Cal Ripken Jr./350 * 30.00 60.00
Letters spell IRON MAN (each letter serial #'d/50)
CY Cy Young/350 * 4.00 10.00
Letters spell CYCLONE (each letter serial #'d/50)
FR Frank Robinson/400 * 6.00 15.00
Letters spell THE JUDGE (each letter #'d/50)
GM Greg Maddux/300 * 10.00 25.00
Letters spell MAD DOG (each letter #'d/50)
GS George Sisler/400 * 4.00 10.00
Letters spell GORGEOUS (each letter serial #'d/50)
HW Honus Wagner/400 * 5.00 12.00
Letters spell DUTCHMAN (each letter serial #'d/50)
JB Joe Biden/650 * 4.00 10.00
Letters spell VICE PRESIDENT (each letter serial #'d/50)
JF Jimmie Foxx/400 * 4.00 10.00
Letters spell THE BEAST (each letter serial #'d/50)
JM Johnny Mize/450 * 4.00 10.00
Letters spell THE BIG CAT (each letter serial #'d/50)
JM Juan Marichal/700 * 4.00 10.00
Letters spell DOMINICAN DANDY (each letter #'d/50)
JR Jackie Robinson/300 * 12.50 30.00
Letters spell JACKIE (each letter serial #'d/50)
LG Lou Gehrig/450 * 12.50 30.00
Letters spell IRON HORSE (each letter serial #'d/50)
MIO Michelle Obama/450 * 12.50 30.00
Letters spell FIRST LADY (each letter serial #'d/50)
MM Mickey Mantle/350 * 15.00 40.00
Letters spell THE MICK (each letter serial #'d/50)
MM2 Mickey Mantle/650 * 15.00 40.00
Letters spell COMMERCE COMET (each letter serial #'d/50)
MO Mel Ott/300 * 4.00 10.00
Letters spell MASTER (each letter serial #'d/50)
NR Nolan Ryan/700 * 12.50 30.00
Letters spell THE RYAN EXPRESS (each letter serial #'d/50)
PM Paul Molitor/350 * 6.00 15.00
Letters spell IGNITOR (each letter #'d/50)
PWR Pee Wee Reese/300 * 6.00 15.00
Letters spell PEE WEE (each letter serial #'d/50)
RC Roy Campanella/250 * 10.00 25.00
Letters spell CAMPY (each letter serial #'d/50)
RCW Roberto Clemente/300 * 20.00 50.00
Letters spell ARRIBA (each letter serial #'d/50)
RH Rogers Hornsby/250 * 4.00 10.00
Letters spell RAJAH (each letter serial #'d/50)
RJ Reggie Jackson/500 * 6.00 15.00
Letters spell MR. OCTOBER (each letter #'d/50)
RM Roger Maris/700 * 10.00 25.00
Letters spell AGAINST ALL ODDS (each letter serial #'d/50)
TC Ty Cobb/350 * 12.50 30.00
Letters spell GA PEACH (each letter serial #'d/50)
TM Thurman Munson/330 * 15.00 40.00
Letters spell THE WALL (each letter serial #'d/50)
TS Tris Speaker/450 * 4.00 10.00
Letters spell GREY EAGLE (each letter serial #'d/50)
TW Ted Williams/650 * 12.50 30.00
Letters spell TEDDY BALLGAME (each letter serial #'d/50)
WB Wade Boggs/500 * 5.00 12.00
Letters spell CHICKEN MAN (each letter #'d/50)
WJ Walter Johnson/400 * 8.00 20.00
Letters spell BIG TRAIN (each letter serial #'d/50)

2009 Topps Legends of the Game Cut Signatures

STATED ODDS 1:142,200 HOBBY
UPDATE ODDS 1:90,000 HOBBY
STATED PRINT RUN 1 SER.#'d SET
NO PRICING DUE TO SCARCITY

2009 Topps Legends of the Game Framed Stamps

SERIES 1 ODDS 1:1555 HOBBY
SERIES 2 ODDS 1:9400 HOBBY
SERIES 1 PRINT RUN 95 SER.#'d SETS
SERIES 2 PRINT RUN 90 SER.#'d SETS
BR1 Babe Ruth 20.00 50.00
BR2 Babe Ruth 20.00 50.00
BR3 Babe Ruth 20.00 50.00
BR4 Babe Ruth 20.00 50.00
BR5 Babe Ruth 20.00 50.00
BR6 Babe Ruth 20.00 50.00
BR7 Babe Ruth 20.00 50.00
BR8 Babe Ruth 20.00 50.00
BR9 Babe Ruth 20.00 50.00
CM1 Christy Mathewson 12.50 30.00
CY1 Cy Young 8.00 20.00
GS1 George Sisler 4.00 10.00
HW1 Honus Wagner 20.00 50.00
JF1 Jimmie Foxx 12.50 30.00
JR1 Jackie Robinson 10.00 25.00
JR2 Jackie Robinson 10.00 25.00
JR3 Jackie Robinson 10.00 25.00
JR4 Jackie Robinson 10.00 25.00
JR5 Jackie Robinson 10.00 25.00
JR6 Jackie Robinson 10.00 25.00
JR7 Jackie Robinson 10.00 25.00
LG1 Lou Gehrig 30.00 60.00
LG2 Lou Gehrig 30.00 60.00
LG3 Lou Gehrig 30.00 60.00
MM1 Mickey Mantle 30.00 60.00
MM2 Mickey Mantle 30.00 60.00
RC1 Roberto Clemente 30.00 60.00
RH1 Rogers Hornsby 12.50 30.00
TC1 Ty Cobb 15.00 40.00
TS1 Tris Speaker 10.00 25.00
WJ1 Walter Johnson 15.00 40.00

2009 Topps Legends of the Game Relics

SERIES 1 ODDS 1:6750 HOBBY
SERIES 2 ODDS 1:6300 HOBBY
UPDATE ODDS 1:4075 HOBBY
STATED PRINT RUN 20 SER.#'d SETS
NO PRICING DUE TO SCARCITY

2009 Topps Red Hot Rookie Redemption

In mid-June 2009, it was announced that 10 percent of the Gordon Beckham redemptions (#RHR2) would feature a certified autograph.

COMPLETE SET (10) 15.00 40.00
COMMON EXCHANGE 6.00 15.00
STATED ODDS 1:36 HOBBY
1:10 G.BECKHAM CARDS ARE SIGNED
EXCHANGE DEADLINE 6/30/2010
RHR1 Fernando Martinez 3.00 8.00
RHR2A Gordon Beckham 4.00 10.00
RHR2B Gordon Beckham AU
RHR3 Andrew McCutchen 5.00 12.00
RHR4 Tommy Hanson 4.00 10.00
RHR5 Nolan Reimold 1.25 3.00
RHR6 Neftali Feliz 4.00 10.00
RHR7 Mat Latos 4.00 10.00
RHR8 Julio Borbon 2.00 5.00
RHR9 Jhoulys Chacin 2.00 5.00
RHR10 Chris Coghlan 3.00 8.00

2009 Topps Ring Of Honor

COMPLETE SET (100) 30.00 60.00
COMP.UPD SET (25) 6.00 15.00
STATED ODDS 1:6 HOBBY
101-125 ISSUED IN UPDATE
RH1 David Justice .40 1.00
RH2 Whitey Ford .60 1.50
RH3 Orlando Cepeda .40 1.00
RH4 Cole Hamels 1.00 2.50
RH5 Darryl Strawberry .40 1.00
RH6 Johnny Bench 1.00 2.50
RH7 David Ortiz .60 1.50
RH8 Derek Jeter 2.50 6.00
RH9 Dwight Gooden .40 1.00
RH10 Brooks Robinson .60 1.50
RH11 Ivan Rodriguez .60 1.50
RH12 David Eckstein .40 1.00
RH13 Derek Jeter 2.50 6.00
RH14 Paul Molitor 1.00 2.50
RH15 Don Zimmer .40 1.00
RH16 Jermaine Dye .40 1.00
RH17 Gary Sheffield .40 1.00
RH18 Bob Gibson .60 1.50
RH19 Pedro Martinez .60 1.50
RH20 Manny Ramirez 1.00 2.50
RH21 Johnny Podres .40 1.00
RH22 Johnny Podres .40 1.00
RH23 Mariano Rivera 1.00 2.50
RH24 Curt Schilling .60 1.50
RH25 Lou Piniella .40 1.00
RH26 Roberto Clemente 2.50 6.00
RH27 Kevin Mitchell .40 1.00
RH28 Frank Robinson .60 1.50
RH29 Francisco Rodriguez .60 1.50
RH30 Troy Glaus .40 1.00
RH31 Tony LaRussa .60 1.50
RH32 Mike Schmidt 1.50 4.00
RH33 Brad Lidge .40 1.00
RH34 Randy Johnson .60 1.50
RH35 Duke Snider .60 1.50
RH36 Rollie Fingers .40 1.00
RH37 Luis Gonzalez .40 1.00
RH38 Josh Beckett .60 1.50
RH39 Gary Carter .40 1.00
RH40 Bob Gibson .60 1.50
RH41 Andy Pettitte .60 1.50
RH42 Reggie Jackson .60 1.50
RH43 Jim Leyland .40 1.00
RH44 Mariano Rivera 1.00 2.50
RH45 Albert Pujols 2.50 6.00
RH46 Don Larsen .40 1.00
RH47 Roger Clemens 1.25 3.00
RH48 Tom Glavine .60 1.50
RH49 Ryan Howard 1.25 3.00
RH50 Reggie Jackson .60 1.50
RH51 Carlos Ruiz .40 1.00
RH52 Tyler Johnson .40 1.00
RH53 Jason Varitek 1.00 2.50
RH54 Darryl Strawberry .40 1.00
RH55 Dusty Baker .40 1.00
RH56 Dustin Pedroia 1.25 3.00
RH57 Jayson Werth .60 1.50
RH58 Garret Anderson .40 1.00
RH59 Dontrelle Willis .40 1.00
RH60 David Justice .40 1.00
RH61 Luis Aparicio .40 1.00
RH62 John Smoltz 1.00 2.50
RH63 Miguel Cabrera 1.00 2.50
RH64 Yadier Molina .60 1.50
RH65 Jacoby Ellsbury 1.00 2.50
RH66 Mark Buehrle .60 1.50
RH67 Johnny Damon .60 1.50
RH68 Brad Penny .40 1.00
RH69 Joe Torre .60 1.50
RH70 Chris Carpenter 1.00 2.50
RH71 Bobby Cox .40 1.00
RH72 Jonathan Papelbon .60 1.50
RH73 Joe Girardi .60 1.50
RH74 Aaron Rowand .40 1.00
RH75 Daisuke Matzusaka 1.00 2.50
RH76 Babe Ruth 2.50 6.00
RH77 Jackie Robinson 1.00 2.50
RH78 Chris Duncan .40 1.00
RH79 Christy Mathewson 1.00 2.50
RH80 Cy Young 1.00 2.50
RH81 Jermaine Dye .40 1.00
RH82 Honus Wagner 1.00 2.50
RH83 Chone Figgins .40 1.00
RH84 Walter Johnson 1.00 2.50
RH85 Jon Garland .40 1.00
RH86 Mel Ott 1.00 2.50
RH87 Jimmie Foxx 1.00 2.50
RH88 Hideki Okajima .40 1.00
RH89 Johnny Mize .60 1.50
RH90 Rogers Hornsby .60 1.50
RH91 Miguel Cabrera 1.00 2.50
RH92 Pee Wee Reese .60 1.50
RH93 Darin Erstad .40 1.00
RH94 Tris Speaker .60 1.50
RH95 Steve Garvey .40 1.00
RH96 Lou Gehrig 2.00 5.00
RH97 Babe Ruth 2.50 6.00
RH98 David Ortiz .60 1.50
RH99 Thurman Munson 1.00 2.50
RH100 Roy Campanella 1.00 2.50

2009 Topps Ring Of Honor Autographs

SERIES 1 ODDS 1:4000 HOBBY
SERIES 2 ODDS 1:4350 HOBBY
UPDATE ODDS 1:3900 HOBBY
NO PRICING DUE TO SCARCITY

2009 Topps Silk Collection

SER.1 ODDS 1:241 HOBBY
SER.2 ODDS 1:280 HOBBY
UPDATE ODDS 1:163 HOBBY
STATED PRINT RUN 50 SER.#'d SETS
1-100 ISSUED IN SERIES 1
101-200 ISSUED IN SERIES 2
201-300 ISSUED IN UPDATE
S1 David Wright 12.00 30.00
S2 Nate McLouth 4.00 10.00
S3 Brandon Jones 4.00 10.00
S4 Mike Mussina 6.00 15.00
S5 Kevin Youkilis 6.00 15.00
S6 Kyle Lohse 4.00 10.00
S7 Rich Aurilia 4.00 10.00
S8 Rich Harden 4.00 10.00
S9 Chase Headley 4.00 10.00
S10 Vladimir Guerrero 10.00 25.00
S11 Denard Span 4.00 10.00
S12 Andrew Miller 4.00 10.00
S13 Justin Upton 6.00 15.00
S14 Aaron Cook 4.00 10.00
S15 Travis Snider 6.00 15.00
S16 Scott Rolen 6.00 15.00
S17 Chad Billingsley 4.00 10.00
S18 Brandon Wood 4.00 10.00
S19 Brad Lidge 4.00 10.00
S20 Dexter Fowler 6.00 15.00
S21 Ian Kinsler 6.00 15.00
S22 Joe Crede 6.00 15.00
S23 Jay Bruce 6.00 15.00
S24 Frank Thomas 10.00 25.00
S25 Roy Halladay 10.00 25.00
S26 Justin Duchscherer 4.00 10.00
S27 Carl Crawford 6.00 15.00
S28 Jeff Francoeur 6.00 15.00
S29 Mike Napoli 6.00 15.00
S30 Ryan Braun 12.00 30.00
S31 Yuniesky Betancourt 4.00 10.00
S32 James Shields 4.00 10.00
S33 Hunter Pence 6.00 15.00
S34 Ian Stewart 4.00 10.00
S35 David Price 10.00 25.00
S36 Hideki Okajima 4.00 10.00
S37 Brad Penny 4.00 10.00
S38 Ivan Rodriguez 6.00 15.00
S39 Chris Duncan 4.00 10.00
S40 Johan Santana 10.00 25.00
S41 Joe Saunders 4.00 10.00
S42 Jose Valverde 4.00 10.00
S43 Tim Lincecum 15.00 40.00
S44 Miguel Tejada 6.00 15.00
S45 Geovany Soto 6.00 15.00
S46 Mark DeRosa 6.00 15.00
S47 Yadier Molina 6.00 15.00
S48 Collin Balester 4.00 10.00
S49 Zack Greinke 6.00 15.00
S50 Manny Ramirez 10.00 25.00
S51 Brian Giles 4.00 10.00
S52 J.J. Hardy 4.00 10.00
S53 Jarrod Saltalamacchia 4.00 10.00
S54 Aubrey Huff 4.00 10.00
S55 Carlos Zambrano 6.00 15.00
S56 Ken Griffey Jr. 15.00 40.00
S57 Daric Barton 4.00 10.00
S58 Randy Johnson 6.00 15.00
S59 Jon Garland 4.00 10.00
S60 Daisuke Matsuzaka 10.00 25.00
S61 Miguel Cabrera 10.00 25.00
S62 Orlando Hudson 4.00 10.00
S63 Johnny Cueto 4.00 10.00
S64 Omar Vizquel 6.00 15.00
S65 Derrek Lee 4.00 10.00
S66 Brad Ziegler 4.00 10.00
S67 Shane Victorino 4.00 10.00
S68 Roy Oswalt 6.00 15.00
S69 Cliff Lee 6.00 15.00
S70 Ichiro Suzuki 15.00 40.00
S71 Casey Blake 4.00 10.00
S72 Kelly Shoppach 4.00 10.00
S73 Ryan Sweeney 4.00 10.00
S74 Carlos Pena 6.00 15.00
S75 Carlos Delgado 4.00 10.00
S76 Tim Hudson 6.00 15.00
S77 Brandon Webb 6.00 15.00
S78 Adam Lind 4.00 10.00
S79 Akinori Iwamura 4.00 10.00
S80 Mariano Rivera 10.00 25.00
S81 Pat Burrell 4.00 10.00
S82 Mark Teixeira 10.00 25.00
S83 Matt Kemp 6.00 15.00
S84 Jeff Samardzija 6.00 15.00
S85 Kosuke Fukudome 10.00 25.00
S86 Aaron Harang 4.00 10.00
S87 Conor Jackson 4.00 10.00
S88 Andy Sonnanstine 4.00 10.00
S89 Joe Blanton 4.00 10.00
S90 CC Sabathia 6.00 15.00
S91 Greg Maddux 12.00 30.00
S92 Gabe Kapler 4.00 10.00
S93 Garrett Atkins 4.00 10.00
S94 Hideki Matsui 10.00 25.00
S95 Chien-Ming Wang 6.00 15.00
S96 Josh Johnson 6.00 15.00
S97 Dustin McGowan 4.00 10.00
S98 Gil Meche 4.00 10.00
S99 Justin Morneau 10.00 25.00
S100 Evan Longoria 12.00 30.00
S101 Joe Mauer 10.00 25.00
S102 Derek Jeter 25.00 60.00
S103 Jorge Posada 6.00 15.00
S104 Victor Martinez 6.00 15.00
S105 Carlos Quentin 6.00 15.00
S106 Jonathan Papelbon 6.00 15.00
S107 Brandon Phillips 4.00 10.00
S108 Alfonso Soriano 6.00 15.00
S109 Carlos Lee 4.00 10.00
S110 Joe Nathan 4.00 10.00
S111 Jeremy Bonderman 4.00 10.00
S112 Nick Markakis 10.00 25.00
S113 Troy Glaus 4.00 10.00
S114 Travis Hafner 4.00 10.00
S115 Joba Chamberlain 6.00 15.00
S116 Melky Cabrera 4.00 10.00
S117 Kenji Johjima 6.00 15.00
S118 Carlos Guillen 4.00 10.00
S119 Matt Cain 4.00 10.00
S120 Clayton Kershaw 10.00 25.00
S121 Yunel Escobar 4.00 10.00
S122 Michael Young 6.00 15.00
S123 Stephen Drew 4.00 10.00
S124 Justin Masterson 4.00 10.00
S125 Mike Aviles 4.00 10.00
S126 Josh Beckett 6.00 15.00
S127 Fausto Carmona 4.00 10.00
S128 Gavin Floyd 4.00 10.00
S129 Hanley Ramirez 10.00 25.00
S130 Adam Jones 6.00 15.00
S131 Jered Weaver 4.00 10.00
S132 Edinson Volquez 4.00 10.00
S133 Prince Fielder 6.00 15.00
S134 Adrian Gonzalez 6.00 15.00
S135 Jimmy Rollins 6.00 15.00
S136 Felix Hernandez 10.00 25.00
S137 Ryan Doumit 4.00 10.00
S138 Russell Martin 4.00 10.00
S139 Carlos Beltran 4.00 10.00
S140 Nelson Cruz 6.00 15.00
S141 Jeremy Hermida 4.00 10.00
S142 Robinson Cano 10.00 25.00
S143 Armando Galarraga 4.00 10.00
S144 Luke Hochevar 4.00 10.00
S145 Delmon Young 6.00 15.00
S146 Chris Young 4.00 10.00
S147 Dustin Pedroia 12.00 30.00
S148 Ervin Santana 4.00 10.00
S149 Jhonny Peralta 4.00 10.00
S150 Alexi Casilla 4.00 10.00
S151 Kevin Kouzmanoff 4.00 10.00
S152 Aramis Ramirez 4.00 10.00
S153 Joey Votto 10.00 25.00
S154 Barry Zito 4.00 10.00
S155 Cameron Maybin 4.00 10.00
S156 Todd Helton 6.00 15.00
S157 Curtis Granderson 6.00 15.00
S158 Jamie Moyer 4.00 10.00
S159 Wladimir Balentien 4.00 10.00
S160 John Maine 4.00 10.00
S161 Chris Carpenter 10.00 25.00
S162 Andre Ethier 6.00 15.00
S163 Yovani Gallardo 4.00 10.00
S164 Nick Hundley 4.00 10.00
S165 Brandon Morrow 4.00 10.00
S166 Jason Bay 6.00 15.00
S167 Randy Winn 4.00 10.00
S168 Willy Aybar 4.00 10.00
S169 David DeJesus 4.00 10.00
S170 Scott Kazmir 4.00 10.00
S171 Johnny Damon 6.00 15.00
S172 Carlos Gomez 4.00 10.00
S173 Jose Reyes 6.00 15.00
S174 Rick Ankiel 4.00 10.00
S175 Ryan Zimmerman 6.00 15.00
S176 Jim Thome 6.00 15.00
S177 Chris Davis 4.00 10.00
S178 Paul Maholm 4.00 10.00
S179 Manny Parra 4.00 10.00
S180 Rickie Weeks 6.00 15.00
S181 Dan Haren 4.00 10.00
S182 Magglio Ordonez 6.00 15.00
S183 Troy Tulowitzki 10.00 25.00
S184 Freddy Sanchez 4.00 10.00
S185 James Loney 6.00 15.00
S186 Michael Cuddyer 4.00 10.00
S187 Lance Berkman 6.00 15.00
S188 Chipper Jones 10.00 25.00
S189 Eric Chavez 4.00 10.00
S190 Ryan Howard 12.00 30.00
S191 Gary Sheffield 4.00 10.00
S192 Eric Byrnes 4.00 10.00
S193 Jayson Werth 6.00 15.00
S194 Adrian Beltre 4.00 10.00
S195 Fred Lewis 4.00 10.00
S196 Vernon Wells 4.00 10.00
S197 Jake Peavy 4.00 10.00
S198 Joakim Soria 4.00 10.00
S199 B.J. Upton 6.00 15.00
S200 J.D. Drew 4.00 10.00
S201 Ivan Rodriguez 6.00 15.00
S202 Felipe Lopez 4.00 10.00
S203 David Hernandez 4.00 10.00
S204 Brian Fuentes 4.00 10.00
S205 Jonathan Broxton 4.00 10.00
S206 Tommy Hanson 12.00 30.00
S207 Daniel Schlereth 4.00 10.00
S208 Gordon Beckham 25.00 60.00
S209 Sean O'Sullivan 4.00 10.00
S210 Gabe Gross 4.00 10.00
S211 Orlando Hudson 4.00 10.00
S212 Matt Murton 4.00 10.00
S213 Rich Hill 4.00 10.00
S214 J.A. Happ 6.00 15.00
S215 Kris Medlen 6.00 15.00
S216 Daniel Bard 4.00 10.00
S217 Laynce Nix 4.00 10.00
S218 Jake Fox 6.00 15.00
S219 Carl Pavano 4.00 10.00
S220 Clayton Richard 4.00 10.00
S221 Edwin Jackson 4.00 10.00
S222 Gary Sheffield 4.00 10.00
S223 Kyle Blanks 6.00 15.00
S224 Vin Mazzaro 4.00 10.00
S225 Juan Uribe 4.00 10.00
S226 David Ross 4.00 10.00
S227 Russell Branyan 4.00 10.00
S228 David Eckstein 4.00 10.00
S229 Wilkin Ramirez 4.00 10.00
S230 John Mayberry Jr. 4.00 10.00
S231 Sean West 6.00 15.00
S232 Matt Lindstrom 4.00 10.00
S233 Jermey Reed 4.00 10.00
S234 Emilio Bonifacio 4.00 10.00
S235 Gerardo Parra 6.00 15.00
S236 Joe Crede 6.00 15.00
S237 Tony Gwynn 4.00 10.00
S238 Kevin Gregg 4.00 10.00
S239 CC Sabathia 6.00 15.00
S240 Nick Green 4.00 10.00
S241 Anthony Swarzak 4.00 10.00
S242 Livan Hernandez 4.00 10.00
S243 Chris Coghlan 10.00 25.00
S244 Jeff Weaver 4.00 10.00
S245 Alfredo Figaro 4.00 10.00
S246 Aaron Poreda 4.00 10.00
S247 Delwyn Young 6.00 15.00
S248 Fernando Martinez 10.00 25.00
S249 Gaby Sanchez 6.00 15.00
S250 Derek Holland 6.00 15.00
S251 Jayson Nix 4.00 10.00
S252 Raul Ibanez 6.00 15.00
S253 Andrew McCutchen 15.00 40.00
S254 Edgar Renteria 4.00 10.00
S255 Chris Perez 4.00 10.00
S256 Maicer Izturis 4.00 10.00
S257 Mark Kotsay 4.00 10.00
S258 Jason Giambi 4.00 10.00
S259 Tyler Greene 4.00 10.00
S260 Omar Vizquel 6.00 15.00
S261 Diory Hernandez 4.00 10.00
S262 Ben Zobrist 4.00 10.00
S263 Landon Powell 4.00 10.00
S264 Ty Wigginton 6.00 15.00
S265 Randy Johnson 6.00 15.00
S266 Jordan Zimmermann 4.00 10.00

S267 Victor Martinez 6.00 15.00
S268 Andruw Jones 4.00 10.00
S269 Jason Vargas 4.00 10.00
S270 Brad Bergensen 4.00 10.00
S271 Craig Stammen 4.00 10.00
S272 Matt LaPorta 10.00 25.00
S273 Takashi Saito 4.00 10.00
S274 Kevin Millar 4.00 10.00
S275 Randy Wells 4.00 10.00
S276 Javier Vazquez 4.00 10.00
S277 Mark Teixeira 10.00 25.00
S278 Cesar Izturis 4.00 10.00
S279 Omir Santos 4.00 10.00
S280 Jeff Niemann 4.00 10.00
S281 Chris Getz 4.00 10.00
S282 Brad Penny 4.00 10.00
S283 Mark DeRosa 6.00 15.00
S284 Jon Garland 4.00 10.00
S285 Matt Holliday 10.00 25.00
S286 Casey McGehee 4.00 10.00
S287 Brett Cecil 4.00 10.00
S288 Ryan Langerhans 4.00 10.00
S289 Endy Chavez 4.00 10.00
S290 Heath Bell 6.00 15.00
S291 Scott Podsednik 4.00 10.00
S292 Scott Richmond 4.00 10.00
S293 David Huff 4.00 10.00
S294 Ramon Castro 4.00 10.00
S295 Sean Marshall 6.00 15.00
S296 Ramon Ramirez 4.00 10.00
S297 Nolan Reimold 4.00 10.00
S298 Nate McLouth 4.00 10.00
S299 Matt Palmer 4.00 10.00
S300 Ken Griffey Jr. 15.00 40.00

2009 Topps Target Legends

RANDOM INSERTS IN TARGET PACKS
LLG1 Ted Williams 2.50 6.00
LLG2 Jackie Robinson 1.00 2.50
LLG3 Babe Ruth 2.50 6.00
LLG4 Honus Wagner 1.00 2.50
LLG5 Lou Gehrig 2.00 5.00
LLG6 Nolan Ryan 3.00 8.00
LLG7 Mickey Mantle 3.00 8.00
LLG8 Thurman Munson 1.00 2.50
LLG9 Cal Ripken Jr. 4.00 10.00
LLG10 George Sisler .60 1.50
LLG11 Mel Ott 1.00 2.50
LLG11 Mel Ott 1.00 2.50
LLG12 Bob Gibson .60 1.50
LLG12 Bob Gibson .60 1.50
LLG13 Babe Ruth 2.50 6.00
LLG13 Babe Ruth 2.50 6.00
LLG14 Roy Campanella 1.00 2.50
LLG14 Roy Campanella 1.00 2.50
LLG15 Ty Cobb 1.50 4.00
LLG15 Ty Cobb 1.50 4.00
LLG16 Cy Young 1.00 2.50
LLG16 Cy Young 1.00 2.50
LLG17 Mickey Mantle 3.00 8.00
LLG17 Mickey Mantle 3.00 8.00
LLG18 Walter Johnson 1.00 2.50
LLG18 Walter Johnson 1.00 2.50
LLG19 Pee Wee Reese .60 1.50
LLG19 Pee Wee Reese .60 1.50
LLG20 Jimmie Foxx 1.00 2.50
LLG20 Jimmie Foxx 1.00 2.50
LLG21 Rickey Henderson 1.00 2.50
LLG22 Ozzie Smith 1.50 4.00
LLG23 Babe Ruth 2.50 6.00
LLG24 Roger Maris 1.00 2.50
LLG25 Nolan Ryan 3.00 8.00
LLG26 Reggie Jackson .60 1.50
LLG27 Frank Robinson .60 1.50
LLG28 Ryne Sandberg 2.00 5.00
LLG29 Steve Carlton .40 1.00
LLG30 Johnny Bench 1.00 2.50

2009 Topps Topps Town

COMPLETE SET (75) 15.00 40.00
COMP.UPD.SET (25) 5.00 12.00
RANDOM INSERTS IN PACKS
UPDATE ODDS 1:9 HOBBY
1-50 ISSUED IN TOPPS
51-75 ISSUED IN UPDATE
COMP.GOLD SET (50) 40.00 80.00
COMP.UPD.GLD.SET (25) 8.00 20.00
*GOLD: 1X TO 2.5X BASIC
GOLD RANDOMLY INSERTED
TTT1 Alex Rodriguez .75 2.00
TTT2 Roy Halladay .50 1.25
TTT3 Grady Sizemore .30 .75
TTT4 Brandon Webb .30 .75
TTT5 Evan Longoria .60 1.50
TTT6 Johan Santana .50 1.25
TTT7 Hanley Ramirez .50 1.25
TTT8 Alex Gordon .30 .75
TTT9 Ryan Howard .60 1.50
TTT10 Jake Peavy .20 .50
TTT11 Nick Markakis .50 1.25
TTT12 Justin Morneau .50 1.25
TTT13 Albert Pujols 1.25 3.00
TTT14 CC Sabathia .30 .75
TTT15 Alfonso Soriano .30 .75
TTT16 Ichiro Suzuki .75 2.00
TTT17 Francisco Rodriguez .30 .75
TTT18 Miguel Cabrera .50 1.25
TTT19 Carlos Quentin .30 .75
TTT20 Lance Berkman .30 .75
TTT21 Chipper Jones .50 1.25
TTT22 Tim Lincecum .75 2.00
TTT23 Josh Hamilton .50 1.25
TTT24 Jay Bruce .30 .75
TTT25 Daisuke Matsuzaka .50 1.25
TTT26 Joe Mauer .50 1.25
TTT27 David Ortiz .30 .75
TTT28 Jimmy Rollins .30 .75
TTT29 Derek Jeter 1.25 3.00
TTT30 Ryan Braun .60 1.50
TTT31 Vladimir Guerrero .50 1.25
TTT32 David Wright .60 1.50
TTT33 Carlos Lee .20 .50
TTT34 Dustin Pedroia .60 1.50
TTT35 Prince Fielder .30 .75
TTT36 Ian Kinsler .30 .75
TTT37 Justin Upton .30 .75
TTT38 Kosuke Fukudome .50 1.25
TTT39 Carlos Zambrano .30 .75
TTT40 Nate McLouth .20 .50
TTT41 Manny Ramirez .50 1.25
TTT42 Kevin Youkilis .30 .75
TTT43 Curtis Granderson .30 .75
TTT44 Todd Helton .30 .75
TTT45 Alex Rios .30 .75
TTT46 Roy Oswalt .30 .75
TTT47 Carlos Beltran .20 .50
TTT48 Mark Teixeira .50 1.25
TTT49 Daisuke Matsuzaka .50 1.25
TTT50 Chase Utley .50 1.25
TTT51 Mariano Rivera .50 1.25
TTT52 Torii Hunter .20 .50
TTT53 Felix Hernandez .50 1.25
TTT54 Adam Jones .30 .75
TTT55 Vernon Wells .20 .50
TTT56 Josh Beckett .30 .75
TTT57 Joey Votto .50 1.25
TTT58 Adrian Gonzalez .30 .75
TTT59 Justin Verlander .60 1.50
TTT60 Dan Uggla .30 .75
TTT61 Zack Greinke .30 .75
TTT62 Russell Martin .20 .50
TTT63 Jose Reyes .30 .75
TTT64 Jorge Posada .30 .75
TTT65 Raul Ibanez .30 .75
TTT66 Chris Carpenter .50 1.25
TTT67 Carl Crawford .30 .75
TTT68 Michael Young .30 .75
TTT69 Victor Martinez .30 .75
TTT70 Hunter Pence .30 .75
TTT71 Troy Tulowitzki .50 1.25
TTT72 Jacoby Ellsbury .50 1.25
TTT73 Matt Cain .20 .50
TTT74 Brian McCann .30 .75
TTT75 Alexei Ramirez .30 .75

2009 Topps Turkey Red

COMPLETE SET (150) 75.00 150.00
COMP.UPD.SET (50) 20.00 50.00
STATED ODDS 1:4 HOBBY
UPDATE ODDS 1:4 HOBBY
1-100 ISSUED IN TOPPS
101-150 ISSUED IN UPDATE
TR1 Babe Ruth 2.50 6.00
TR2 Evan Longoria 1.25 3.00
TR3 Jimmie Foxx 1.00 2.50
TR4 Alex Rios .60 1.50
TR5 Nick Markakis 1.00 2.50
TR6 Ian Kinsler .60 1.50
TR7 Andre Ethier .60 1.50
TR8 Ryan Ludwick .60 1.50
TR9 Tim Lincecum 1.50 4.00
TR10 Jackie Robinson 1.00 2.50
TR11 Bengie Molina .40 1.00
TR12 Jermaine Dye .40 1.00
TR13 Brian Giles .40 1.00
TR14 Chase Utley 1.00 2.50
TR15 David Ortiz .60 1.50
TR16 Joe Mauer 1.00 2.50
TR17 Conor Jackson .40 1.00
TR18 Jose Lopez .40 1.00
TR19 Brian McCann .60 1.50
TR20 George Sisler .60 1.50
TR21 Garret Anderson .40 1.00
TR22 Cliff Lee .60 1.50
TR23 Garrett Atkins .40 1.00
TR24 Curtis Granderson .60 1.50
TR25 Alex Rodriguez 1.50 4.00
TR26 Cristian Guzman .40 1.00
TR27 Aubrey Huff .40 1.00
TR28 Delmon Young .60 1.50
TR29 Carlos Quentin .60 1.50
TR30 Christy Mathewson 1.00 2.50
TR31 Justin Upton .60 1.50
TR32 Shane Victorino .40 1.00
TR33 Joey Votto 1.00 2.50
TR34 Kelly Johnson .40 1.00
TR35 David Wright 1.25 3.00
TR36 Jacoby Ellsbury 1.00 2.50
TR37 Kevin Kouzmanoff .40 1.00
TR38 Hunter Pence .60 1.50
TR39 Corey Hart .40 1.00
TR40 Kosuke Fukudome 1.00 2.50
TR41 Cole Hamels 1.00 2.50
TR42 Geovany Soto .60 1.50
TR43 Torii Hunter .40 1.00
TR44 Ervin Santana .40 1.00
TR45 Miguel Cabrera 1.00 2.50
TR46 Josh Johnson .60 1.50
TR47 Carlos Gomez .40 1.00
TR48 Nate McLouth .40 1.00
TR49 Ben Sheets .40 1.00
TR50 Tris Speaker .60 1.50
TR51 Josh Hamilton 1.00 2.50
TR52 Rich Harden .40 1.00
TR53 Francisco Rodriguez .60 1.50
TR54 Alex Gordon .60 1.50
TR55 Manny Ramirez 1.00 2.50
TR56 Carlos Zambrano .60 1.50
TR57 Brandon Webb .60 1.50
TR58 Alfonso Soriano .60 1.50
TR59 Mel Ott 1.00 2.50
TR60 Carlos Lee .40 1.00
TR61 Lou Gehrig 2.00 5.00
TR62 Adam Jones .60 1.50
TR63 Josh Beckett .60 1.50
TR64 Prince Fielder .60 1.50
TR65 Jimmy Rollins .60 1.50
TR66 Justin Morneau 1.00 2.50
TR67 Dan Uggla .60 1.50
TR68 Lance Berkman .60 1.50
TR69 Chipper Jones 1.00 2.50
TR70 Jon Lester 1.00 2.50
TR71 Albert Pujols 2.50 6.00
TR72 Ryan Braun 1.25 3.00
TR73 Grady Sizemore .60 1.50
TR74 Carlos Beltran .40 1.00
TR75 Hanley Ramirez 1.00 2.50
TR76 Jay Bruce .60 1.50
TR77 Derek Jeter 2.50 6.00
TR78 Matt Cain .40 1.00
TR79 Roy Campanella 1.00 2.50
TR80 Rogers Hornsby .60 1.50
TR81 Ryan Zimmerman .60 1.50
TR82 Dustin Pedroia 1.25 3.00
TR83 B.J. Upton .60 1.50
TR84 Jose Reyes .60 1.50
TR85 Johnny Mize .60 1.50
TR86 Magglio Ordonez .60 1.50
TR87 Ty Cobb 1.50 4.00
TR88 Michael Young .60 1.50
TR89 Todd Helton .60 1.50
TR90 Walter Johnson 1.00 2.50
TR91 Matt Kemp .60 1.50
TR92 Adrian Gonzalez .60 1.50
TR93 Pee Wee Reese .60 1.50
TR94 Ryan Doumit .40 1.00
TR95 Ryan Howard 1.25 3.00
TR96 Ichiro Suzuki 1.50 4.00
TR97 Cy Young 1.00 2.50
TR98 Mark Teixeira 1.00 2.50
TR99 Vladimir Guerrero 1.00 2.50
TR100 Honus Wagner 1.00 2.50
TR101 Ty Cobb 1.50 4.00
TR102 David Price 1.00 2.50
TR103 Jorge Posada .60 1.50
TR104 Brian Roberts .40 1.00
TR105 Tris Speaker .60 1.50
TR106 John Lackey .40 1.00
TR107 Miguel Tejada .60 1.50
TR108 Dan Haren .40 1.00
TR109 Troy Tulowitzki 1.00 2.50
TR110 Yunel Escobar .40 1.00
TR111 Koji Uehara .60 1.50
TR112 Vernon Wells .40 1.00
TR113 Jimmie Foxx 1.00 2.50
TR114 CC Sabathia .60 1.50
TR115 Alexei Ramirez .60 1.50
TR116 Rick Porcello 1.25 3.00
TR117 Gary Sheffield .40 1.00
TR118 Ryan Dempster .40 1.00
TR119 Shin-Soo Choo .60 1.50
TR120 Adam Dunn .60 1.50
TR121 Edinson Volquez .40 1.00
TR122 Kevin Youkilis .60 1.50
TR123 Roy Halladay 1.00 2.50
TR124 Justin Verlander 1.25 3.00
TR125 Max Scherzer .60 1.50
TR126 Jorge Cantu .40 1.00
TR127 Roy Oswalt .60 1.50
TR128 Tommy Hanson 1.25 3.00
TR129 Raul Ibanez .60 1.50
TR130 Johan Santana 1.00 2.50
TR131 Jermaine Dye .40 1.00
TR132 Mariano Rivera 1.00 2.50
TR133 Rogers Hornsby .60 1.50
TR134 Daisuke Matsuzaka 1.00 2.50
TR135 Andrew McCutchen 1.50 4.00
TR136 Jake Peavy .40 1.00
TR137 Jason Bay .60 1.50
TR138 Ken Griffey 1.50 4.00
TR139 Chris Carpenter 1.00 2.50
TR140 Carl Crawford .60 1.50
TR141 Victor Martinez .60 1.50
TR142 Brad Hawpe .40 1.00
TR143 Aaron Hill .40 1.00
TR144 Randy Johnson .60 1.50
TR145 Gordon Beckham 1.25 3.00
TR146 Jordan Zimmermann .40 1.00
TR147 Freddy Sanchez .40 1.00
TR148 Carlos Pena .60 1.50
TR149 Johnny Cueto .40 1.00
TR150 Babe Ruth 2.50 6.00

2009 Topps Wal Mart Legends

RANDOM INSERTS IN WALMART PACKS
LLP1 Ted Williams 2.50 6.00
LLP2 Bob Gibson .60 1.50
LLP3 Babe Ruth 2.50 6.00
LLP4 Roy Campanella 1.00 2.50
LLP5 Ty Cobb 1.50 4.00
LLP6 Cy Young 1.00 2.50
LLP7 Mickey Mantle 3.00 8.00
LLP8 Walter Johnson 1.00 2.50
LLP9 Roberto Clemente 2.50 6.00
LLP10 Jimmie Foxx 1.00 2.50
LLP11 Johnny Mize .60 1.50
LLP11 Johnny Mize .60 1.50
LLP12 Jackie Robinson 1.00 2.50
LLP12 Jackie Robinson 1.00 2.50
LLP13 Babe Ruth 2.50 6.00
LLP13 Babe Ruth 2.50 6.00
LLP14 Honus Wagner 1.00 2.50
LLP14 Honus Wagner 1.00 2.50
LLP15 Lou Gehrig 2.00 5.00
LLP15 Lou Gehrig 2.00 5.00
LLP16 Nolan Ryan 3.00 8.00
LLP16 Nolan Ryan 3.00 8.00
LLP17 Mickey Mantle 3.00 8.00
LLP17 Mickey Mantle 3.00 8.00
LLP18 Thurman Munson 1.00 2.50
LLP18 Thurman Munson 1.00 2.50
LLP19 Christy Mathewson 1.00 2.50
LLP19 Christy Mathewson 1.00 2.50
LLP20 George Sisler .60 1.50
LLP20 George Sisler .60 1.50
LLP21 Babe Ruth 2.50 6.00
LLP22 Rickey Henderson 1.00 2.50
LLP23 Roger Maris 1.00 2.50
LLP24 Nolan Ryan 3.00 8.00
LLP25 Reggie Jackson .60 1.50
LLP26 Steve Carlton .40 1.00
LLP27 Tony Gwynn 1.00 2.50
LLP28 Paul Molitor 1.00 2.50
LLP29 Brooks Robinson .60 1.50
LLP30 Wade Boggs .60 1.50

2009 Topps Wal Mart Legends Gold

*GOLD: .6X TO 1.5X BASIC
RANDOM INSERTS IN WAL MART PACKS

2009 Topps WBC Autographs

COMMON CARD 10.00 25.00
STATED ODDS 1:1418 HOBBY
STATED PRINT RUN 100 SER.#'d SETS
BM Brian McCann 15.00 40.00
CD Carlos Delgado 12.50 30.00
CG Curtis Granderson 15.00 40.00
CR Carlos Ruiz 10.00 25.00
DO David Ortiz 20.00 50.00
DP Dustin Pedroia 50.00 100.00
DW David Wright 75.00 150.00
JR Jose Reyes 20.00 50.00
RB Ryan Braun 20.00 50.00
AIR Alex Rios 10.00 25.00

2009 Topps WBC Autograph Relics

STATED ODDS 1:14,200 HOBBY
STATED PRINT RUN 50 SER.#'d SETS
CR Carlos Ruiz 15.00 40.00
JR Jose Reyes 20.00 50.00

2009 Topps WBC Stars

COMPLETE SET (25) 12.50 30.00
STATED ODDS 1:12 HOBBY
BCS1 David Wright 1.25 3.00
BCS2 Jin Young Kee .60 1.50
BCS3 Yulieski Gourriel .40 1.00
BCS4 Hiroyuki Nakajima .60 1.50
BCS5 Ichiro Suzuki 1.50 4.00
BCS6 Jose Reyes .60 1.50
BCS7 Yu Darvish 4.00 10.00
BCS8 Carlos Lee .40 1.00
BCS9 Fu-Te Ni .60 1.50
BCS10 Derek Jeter 2.50 6.00
BCS11 Adrian Gonzalez .60 1.50
BCS12 Dylan Lindsay .60 1.50
BCS13 Greg Halman .60 1.50
BCS14 Miguel Cabrera 1.00 2.50
BCS15 Chris Denorfia .40 1.00
BCS16 Aroldis Chapman 1.50 4.00
BCS17 Alex Rios .60 1.50
BCS18 Luke Hughes .40 1.00
BCS19 Gregor Blanco .40 1.00
BCS20 Bernie Williams .60 1.50
BCS21 Phillippe Aumont 1.00 2.50
BCS22 Shuichi Murata .60 1.50
BCS23 Frederich Cepeda .60 1.50
BCS24 Dustin Pedroia 1.25 3.00
BCS25 David Ortiz .60 1.50

2009 Topps WBC Stars Relics

STATED ODDS 1:219 HOBBY
AC Aroldis Chapman 12.50 30.00
BW Bernie Williams 4.00 10.00
DL Dylan Lindsay 3.00 8.00
FC Frederich Cepeda 3.00 8.00
GH Greg Halman 3.00 8.00
HR Hanley Ramirez 4.00 10.00
MO Magglio Ordonez 3.00 8.00
PA Phillippe Aumont 4.00 10.00
RM Russell Martin 4.00 10.00
FTN Fu-Te Ni 4.00 10.00
JRO Jimmy Rollins 5.00 12.00
LJY Jin Young Lee 3.00 8.00

2009 Topps WBC Stamp Collection

STATED ODDS 1:9400 HOBBY
STATED PRINT RUN 90 SER.#'d SETS
WBC1 Professional Baseball 10.00 25.00
WBC2 Centennial of Baseball 15.00 40.00
WBC3 Take Me Out to the Ball Game 10.00 25.00
WBC4 USA 12.50 30.00

2009 Topps World Baseball Classic Rising Star Redemption

COMPLETE SET (10) 8.00 20.00
1 Lee Jin Young .60 1.50
2 Derek Jeter 4.00 10.00
3 Gift Ngoepe .60 1.50
4 Ubaldo Jimenez 1.00 2.50
5 Sidney De Jong .60 1.50
6 Yoennis Cespedes 5.00 12.00
7 Yu Darvish 6.00 15.00
8 Dae Ho Lee .60 1.50
9 Jung Keun Bong .60 1.50
10 Daisuke Matsuzaka 1.50 4.00
NNO Exchange Card

2009 Topps World Champion Autographs

STATED ODDS 1:20,000 HOBBY
CR Carlos Ruiz 60.00 120.00
JW Jayson Werth 60.00 120.00
SV Shane Victorino 100.00 200.00

2009 Topps World Champion Relics

STATED ODDS 1:5600 HOBBY
STATED PRINT RUN 100 SER.#'d SETS
CH Cole Hamels Jsy 30.00 60.00
CU Chase Utley Jsy 40.00 80.00
JR Jimmy Rollins Jsy 40.00 80.00
PB Pat Burrell Bat 20.00 50.00
RH Ryan Howard Jsy 50.00 100.00

2009 Topps World Champion Relics Autographs

STATED ODDS 1:11,400 HOBBY
PRINT RUNS B/WN 8-50 COPIES PER
NO HAMELS PRICING AVAILABLE
CH Cole Hamels Jsy
JR Jimmy Rollins Jsy 75.00 150.00
RH Ryan Howard Jsy 200.00 400.00

2009 Topps Update

COMP.SET w/o VAR (330) 20.00 50.00
COMMON CARD (1-330) .12 .30
COMMON SP VAR (1-330) 5.00 12.00
SP VAR ODDS 1:32 HOBBY
COMMON RC (1-330) .30 .75
PRINTING PLATE ODDS 1:615 HOBBY
PLATE PRINT RUN 1 SET PER COLOR
BLACK-CYAN-MAGENTA-YELLOW ISSUED
NO PLATE PRICING DUE TO SCARCITY
UH1 Ivan Rodriguez .20 .50
UH2 Felipe Lopez .12 .30
UH3 Michael Saunders RC .50 1.25
UH4 David Hernandez RC .30 .75
UH5 Brian Fuentes .12 .30
UH6 Josh Barfield .12 .30
UH7 Brayan Pena .12 .30
UH8 Lance Broadway .12 .30
UH9 Jonathan Broxton .12 .30
UH10 Tommy Hanson RC 1.00 2.50
UH11 Daniel Schlereth RC .30 .75
UH12 Edwin Maysonet .12 .30
UH13 Scott Hairston .12 .30
UH14 Yadier Molina .20 .50
UH15 Jacoby Ellsbury .30 .75
UH16 Brian Buscher .12 .30
UH17 Derek Jeter .75 2.00
David Wright
UH18 John Grabow .12 .30
UH19 Nelson Cruz .20 .50
UH20 Gordon Beckham RC 1.00 2.50
UH21 Matt Diaz .12 .30
UH22 Brett Gardner .12 .30
UH23 Sean O'Sullivan RC .30 .75
UH24 Gabe Gross .12 .30
UH25 Orlando Hudson .12 .30
UH26 Ryan Howard .40 1.00
UH27 Josh Reddick RC .50 1.25
UH28 Matt Murton .12 .30
UH29 Rich Hill .12 .30
UH30 J.A. Happ .20 .50
UH31 Adam Jones .20 .50
UH32 Kris Medlen RC .50 1.25
UH33 Daniel Bard RC .30 .75
UH34 Laynce Nix .12 .30
UH35 Tom Gorzelanny .12 .30
UH36 Paul Konerko .20 .50
Jermaine Dye
UH37 Adam Kennedy .12 .30
UH38 Justin Upton .20 .50
UH39 Jake Fox .20 .50
UH40 Carl Pavano .12 .30
UH41 Xavier Paul (RC) .30 .75
UH42 Eric Hinske .12 .30
UH43 Koyie Hill .12 .30
UH44 Seth Smith .12 .30
UH45 Brad Ausmus .12 .30
UH46 Clayton Richard .12 .30
UH47a Carlos Beltran .12 .30
UH47b Duke Snider SP 6.00 15.00
UH48a Albert Pujols .75 2.00
UH48b Roger Maris SP 6.00 15.00
UH49 Edwin Jackson .12 .30
UH50 Gary Sheffield .12 .30
UH51 Jesus Guzman RC .30 .75
UH52a Kyle Blanks RC .50 1.25
UH52b Bo Jackson SP 5.00 12.00
UH53 Clete Thomas .12 .30
UH54 Vin Mazzaro RC .30 .75
UH55 Ben Zobrist .12 .30
UH56 Wes Helms .12 .30
UH57 Juan Uribe .12 .30
UH58 Omar Quintanilla .12 .30
UH59 David Ross .12 .30
UH60 Brandon Inge .12 .30
UH61 Jamie Hoffmann RC .30 .75
UH62 Russell Branyan .12 .30
UH63 Mark Rzepczynski RC .50 1.25
UH64 Alex Gonzalez .12 .30
UH65a Joe Mauer .30 .75
UH65b Paul Molitor SP 5.00 12.00
UH66 Jhoulys Chacin RC .50 1.25
UH67 Brandon McCarthy .12 .30
UH68 David Eckstein .12 .30
UH69 Joe Girardi .75 2.00
Derek Jeter
UH70 Wilkin Ramirez RC .30 .75
UH71a Chase Utley .30 .75
UH71b Rogers Hornsby SP 5.00 12.00
UH71c Ryne Sandberg SP 6.00 15.00
UH72 John Mayberry Jr. (RC) .30 .75
UH73 Sean West (RC) .50 1.25
UH74 Mitch Maier .12 .30
UH75 Matt Lindstrom .12 .30
UH76 Scott Rolen .20 .50
UH77 Jeremy Reed .12 .30
UH78 LaTroy Hawkins .12 .30
UH79 Robert Andino .12 .30
UH80 Matt Stairs .12 .30
UH81 Mark Teixeira .30 .75
UH82 David Wright .40 1.00
UH83 Emilio Bonifacio .12 .30
UH84 Gerardo Parra RC .50 1.25
UH85 Joe Crede .20 .50
UH86 Carlos Pena .20 .50
UH87 Jake Peavy .12 .30
UH88 Jim Leyland .12 .30
Tony La Russa
UH89 Phil Hughes .20 .50
UH90 Orlando Cabrera .12 .30
UH91 Anderson Hernandez .12 .30
UH92 Edwin Encarnacion .12 .30
UH93 Pedro Martinez .20 .50
UH94 Jarrod Washburn .12 .30
UH95 Ryan Freel .12 .30
UH96 Tony Gwynn .12 .30
UH97 Juan Castro .12 .30
UH98a Hanley Ramirez .30 .75
UH98b Honus Wagner SP 5.00 12.00
UH99 Kevin Gregg .12 .30
UH100 CC Sabathia .20 .50
UH101 Nick Green .12 .30
UH102 Brett Hayes (RC) .30 .75
UH103a Evan Longoria .40 1.00
UH103b Wade Boggs SP 5.00 12.00
UH104 Geoff Blum .12 .30
UH105 Luis Valbuena .20 .50
UH106 Jonny Gomes .12 .30
UH107 Anthony Swarzak (RC) .30 .75
UH108 Chris Tillman RC .50 1.25
UH109 Orlando Hudson .12 .30
UH110 Justin Masterson .12 .30
UH111 Livan Hernandez .12 .30
UH112 Kyle Farnsworth .12 .30
UH113 Francisco Rodriguez .20 .50
UH114 Chris Coghlan RC .75 2.00
UH115 Jeff Weaver .12 .30
UH116 Alfredo Figaro RC .30 .75
UH117 Alex Rios .20 .50
UH118 Blake Hawksworth (RC) .30 .75
UH119 Bud Norris RC .30 .75
UH120 Aaron Poreda RC .30 .75
UH121 Brandon Inge .12 .30
UH122 Kevin Youkilis .75 2.00
David Wright
Derek Jeter
Shane Victorino
UH123 Ryan Braun .40 1.00
UH124 Delwyn Young .20 .50
UH125 Fernando Martinez RC .75 2.00
UH126 Matt Tolbert .12 .30
UH127 Shane Robinson RC .30 .75
UH128 Chone Figgins .12 .30
UH129 Shane Victorino .12 .30
UH130 Randy Johnson .20 .50
UH131 Derek Jeter .75 2.00
UH132 Joe Thurston .12 .30
UH133 Graham Taylor RC .50 1.25
UH134 Derek Holland RC .50 1.25
UH135 Ryan Perry .40 1.00
Rick Porcello
UH136 Raul Ibanez .20 .50
UH137 Ross Ohlendorf .12 .30
UH138 Ryan Church .12 .30
UH139 Brian Moehler .12 .30
UH140 Jack Wilson .12 .30
UH141 Jason Hammel .12 .30
UH142 Jorge Posada .20 .50
UH143 Matt Maloney (RC) .30 .75
UH144 Ronny Cedeno .12 .30
UH145 Micah Hoffpauir .12 .30
UH146 Juan Cruz .12 .30
UH147 Jayson Nix .12 .30
UH148a Jason Bay .20 .50
UH148b Tris Speaker SP 5.00 12.00
UH149 Joel Hanrahan .20 .50
UH150a Raul Ibanez .20 .50
UH150b Ty Cobb SP 5.00 12.00
UH151 Jayson Werth .20 .50
UH152 Barbaro Canizares RC .30 .75
UH153a Ichiro Suzuki .50 1.25
UH153b George Sisler SP 5.00 12.00
UH154 Gerardo Parra .20 .50
UH155 Andrew McCutchen (RC) 1.25 3.00
UH156 Heath Bell .20 .50
UH157 Josh Hamilton .30 .75
UH158 Wilson Valdez .12 .30
UH159 Chad Billingsley .12 .30
UH160 Edgar Renteria .12 .30
UH161 Andrew Bailey .30 .75
UH162 Chris Perez .12 .30
UH163 Alejandro De Aza .12 .30
UH164 Brett Tomko .12 .30
UH165 Maicer Izturis .12 .30
UH166 Mike Redmond .12 .30
UH167 Julio Borbon RC .50 1.25
UH168 Paul Phillips .12 .30
UH169 Mark Kotsay .12 .30
UH170 Jason Giambi .12 .30
UH171 Trevor Hoffman .20 .50
UH172 Tyler Greene (RC) .30 .75
UH173 David Robertson .12 .30
UH174 Omar Vizquel .20 .50
UH175 Jody Gerut .12 .30
UH176 Diory Hernandez RC .30 .75
UH177 Neftali Feliz RC 1.00 2.50
UH178 Josh Beckett .20 .50
UH179 Carl Crawford .20 .50
UH180 Mariano Rivera .30 .75
UH181 Zach Duke .12 .30
UH182 Mark Buehrle .20 .50
UH183 Guillermo Quiroz .12 .30
UH184 Francisco Cordero .12 .30
UH185 Kevin Correia .12 .30
UH186a Zack Greinke .20 .50
UH186b Christy Mathewson SP 5.00 12.00
UH187 Ryan Franklin .20 .50
UH188 Jeff Francouer .20 .50
UH189 Michael Young .20 .50
Josh Hamilton
Ian Kinsler
UH190 Ken Griffey Jr. .50 1.25
UH191 Ben Zobrist .12 .30
UH192 Prince Fielder .20 .50
UH193 Landon Powell (RC) .30 .75
UH194 Ty Wigginton .20 .50
UH195 P.J. Walters RC .30 .75
UH196 Brian Fuentes .12 .30
UH197 Dan Haren .12 .30
UH198a Roy Halladay .30 .75
UH198b Cy Young SP 5.00 12.00
UH199 Mike Rivera .12 .30
UH200 Randy Johnson .20 .50
UH201 Jordan Zimmermann RC .30 .75
UH202 Angel Berroa .12 .30
UH203 Ben Francisco .12 .30
UH204 Brian Barden .12 .30
UH205 Dallas Braden .20 .50
UH206 Chris Burke .12 .30
UH207 Garrett Jones .20 .50
UH208 Chad Gaudin .12 .30
UH209 Andruw Jones .12 .30
UH210 Jason Vargas .12 .30
UH211 Brad Bergesen (RC) .30 .75
UH212 Ian Kinsler .20 .50
UH213 Josh Johnson .20 .50
UH214 Jason Grilli .12 .30
UH215 Felix Hernandez .30 .75
UH216 Mat Latos RC 1.00 2.50
UH217 Craig Stammen RC .30 .75
UH218 Cliff Lee .20 .50
UH219 Ken Takahashi RC .50 1.25
UH220 Matt LaPorta RC .75 2.00
UH221 Adrian Gonzalez .20 .50
UH222 Ted Lilly .12 .30
UH223 Jack Hannahan .12 .30
UH224 Takashi Saito .12 .30
UH225 Gregorio Petit .12 .30
UH226 Kevin Hart .12 .30
UH227 Edwin Jackson .12 .30
UH228 Jason LaRue .12 .30
UH229 Kevin Millar .12 .30
UH230 Freddy Sanchez .12 .30
UH231 Josh Bard .12 .30
UH232a Tim Lincecum .50 1.25
UH232b Nolan Ryan CAL SP 6.00 15.00
UH232c Nolan Ryan NYM SP 6.00 15.00
UH233 Ramon Santiago .12 .30
UH234 Mike Sweeney .12 .30
UH235 Joe Nathan .12 .30
UH236 Kris Benson .12 .30
UH237 Dustin Pedroia .40 1.00
UH238 Kevin Cash .12 .30
UH239 George Sherrill .12 .30
UH240 Jason Marquis .12 .30
UH241 Dewayne Wise .12 .30
UH242 Randy Wells .12 .30
UH243 Jonathan Papelbon .20 .50
UH244 Johan Santana .30 .75
UH245 Mariano Rivera .30 .75
UH246 Javier Vazquez .12 .30
UH247 Lastings Milledge .12 .30
UH248 Chan Ho Park .20 .50
UH249 Brian McCann .20 .50
UH250a Mark Teixeira .30 .75
UH250c Johnny Mize NYG SP 5.00 12.00
UH250b Johnny Mize NYY SP 5.00 12.00
UH251 Ian Snell .12 .30
UH252 Justin Verlander .40 1.00
UH253a Prince Fielder .20 .50
UH253b Reggie Jackson CAL SP 5.00 12.00
UH253c Reggie Jackson OAK SP 5.00 12.00
UH254 Cesar Izturis .12 .30
UH255 Omir Santos RC .30 .75
UH256 Tim Wakefield .12 .30
UH257 Adrian Gonzalez .20 .50
UH258 Nyjer Morgan .12 .30
UH259 Victor Martinez .20 .50
UH260a Ryan Howard .40 1.00
UH260b Willie McCovey SP 5.00 12.00
UH261 Aaron Bates RC .30 .75
UH262 Jeff Niemann .12 .30
UH263 Matt Holliday .30 .75
UH264 Adam LaRoche .12 .30
UH265 Justin Morneau .30 .75
UH266 Jonathan Broxton .12 .30
UH267 Miguel Cairo .12 .30
UH268 Chris Getz .12 .30
UH269 Cliff Floyd .12 .30
UH270 David Ortiz .50 1.25
Alex Rodriguez
UH271 Frank Catalanotto .12 .30
UH272 Carlos Pena .20 .50
UH273 Mark Lowe .12 .30
UH274 Joe Mauer .30 .75
UH275 Ryan Garko .12 .30
UH276 Brad Penny .12 .30
UH277 Orlando Hudson .12 .30
UH278 Gaby Sanchez RC .50 1.25
UH279 Ross Detwiler .12 .30
UH280 Mark DeRosa .20 .50
UH281a Kevin Youkilis .20 .50
UH281b Jimmie Foxx SP 5.00 12.00
UH282 Victor Martinez .20 .50
UH283 Freddy Sanchez .12 .30
UH284 Mark Melancon RC .30 .75
UH285 Ryan Franklin .20 .50
UH286 Sidney Ponson .12 .30
UH287 Matt Joyce .12 .30
UH288 Jon Garland .12 .30
UH289 Nick Johnson .12 .30
UH290 Jason Michaels .12 .30
UH291 Ross Gload .12 .30
UH292 Yuniesky Betancourt .12 .30
UH293 Aaron Hill .12 .30
UH294 Josh Anderson .12 .30
UH295 Miguel Tejada .20 .50
UH296 Casey McGehee .12 .30
UH297 Brett Cecil RC .30 .75
UH298 Jason Bartlett .12 .30
UH299 Ryan Langerhans .12 .30
UH300 Albert Pujols .75 2.00
UH301 Ryan Zimmerman .20 .50
UH302 Casey Kotchman .12 .30
UH303 Luke French (RC) .30 .75
UH304 Nick Swisher .30 .75
Johnny Damon
UH305 Michael Young .20 .50
UH306 Endy Chavez .12 .30
UH307 Heath Bell .20 .50
UH308 Matt Cain .12 .30
UH309 Scott Podsednik .12 .30
UH310 Scott Richmond .12 .30
UH311 David Huff RC .30 .75
UH312 Ryan Hanigan .12 .30
UH313 Jeff Baker .12 .30
UH314 Brad Hawpe .12 .30
UH315 Jerry Hairston Jr. .12 .30
UH316 Hunter Pence .40 1.00
Ryan Braun
UH317 Nelson Cruz .20 .50
UH318a Carl Crawford .20 .50
UH318b Rickey Henderson SP 5.00 12.00
UH319 Ramon Castro .12 .30
UH320 Mark Schlereth .12 .30
Daniel Schlereth
UH321 Hunter Pence .20 .50
UH322 Sean Marshall .20 .50

UH323 Ramon Ramirez .12 .30
UH324 Nolan Reimold (RC) .30 .75
UH325a Torii Hunter .12 .30
UH325b Frank Robinson SP 5.00 12.00
UH326 Nate McLouth .12 .30
UH327 Julio Lugo .12 .30
UH328 Matt Palmer .12 .30
UH329 Curtis Granderson .20 .50
UH330a Ken Griffey Jr. .50 1.25
UH330b Babe Ruth Braves SP 8.00 20.00
UH330c Babe Ruth Sox SP 8.00 20.00

2009 Topps Update Black

STATED ODDS 1:44 HOBBY
STATED PRINT RUN 58 SER.#'d SETS
UH1 Ivan Rodriguez 8.00 20.00
UH2 Felipe Lopez 5.00 12.00
UH3 Michael Saunders 8.00 20.00
UH4 David Hernandez 5.00 12.00
UH5 Brian Fuentes 5.00 12.00
UH6 Josh Barfield 5.00 12.00
UH7 Brayan Pena 5.00 12.00
UH8 Lance Broadway 5.00 12.00
UH9 Jonathan Broxton 5.00 12.00
UH10 Tommy Hanson 12.00 30.00
UH11 Daniel Schlereth 5.00 12.00
UH12 Edwin Maysonet 5.00 12.00
UH13 Scott Hairston 5.00 12.00
UH14 Yadier Molina 8.00 20.00
UH15 Jacoby Ellsbury 10.00 25.00
UH16 Brian Buscher 5.00 12.00
UH17 Derek Jeter 20.00 50.00
David Wright
UH18 John Grabow 5.00 12.00
UH19 Nelson Cruz 8.00 20.00
UH20 Gordon Beckham 12.00 30.00
UH21 Matt Diaz 5.00 12.00
UH22 Brett Gardner 5.00 12.00
UH23 Sean O'Sullivan 5.00 12.00
UH24 Gabe Gross 5.00 12.00
UH25 Orlando Hudson 5.00 12.00
UH26 Ryan Howard 12.00 30.00
UH27 Josh Reddick 8.00 20.00
UH28 Matt Murton 5.00 12.00
UH29 Rich Hill 5.00 12.00
UH30 J.A. Happ 8.00 20.00
UH31 Adam Jones 8.00 20.00
UH32 Kris Medlen 8.00 20.00
UH33 Daniel Bard 5.00 12.00
UH34 Laynce Nix 5.00 12.00
UH35 Tom Gorzelanny 5.00 12.00
UH36 Paul Konerko 8.00 20.00
Jermaine Dye
UH37 Adam Kennedy 5.00 12.00
UH38 Justin Upton 8.00 20.00
UH39 Jake Fox 8.00 20.00
UH40 Carl Pavano 5.00 12.00
UH41 Xavier Paul 5.00 12.00
UH42 Eric Hinske 5.00 12.00
UH43 Koyie Hill 5.00 12.00
UH44 Seth Smith 5.00 12.00
UH45 Brad Ausmus 5.00 12.00
UH46 Clayton Richard 5.00 12.00
UH47 Carlos Beltran 5.00 12.00
UH48 Albert Pujols 20.00 50.00
UH49 Edwin Jackson 5.00 12.00
UH50 Gary Sheffield 5.00 12.00
UH51 Jesus Guzman 5.00 12.00
UH52 Kyle Blanks 8.00 20.00
UH53 Clete Thomas 5.00 12.00
UH54 Vin Mazzaro 5.00 12.00
UH55 Ben Zobrist 5.00 12.00
UH56 Wes Helms 5.00 12.00
UH57 Juan Uribe 5.00 12.00
UH58 Omar Quintanilla 5.00 12.00
UH59 David Ross 5.00 12.00
UH60 Brandon Inge 5.00 12.00
UH61 Jamie Hoffmann 5.00 12.00
UH62 Russell Branyan 5.00 12.00
UH63 Mark Rzepczynski 8.00 20.00
UH64 Alex Gonzalez 5.00 12.00
UH65 Joe Mauer 10.00 25.00
UH66 Jhoulys Chacin 8.00 20.00
UH67 Brandon McCarthy 5.00 12.00
UH68 David Eckstein 5.00 12.00
UH69 Joe Girardi 20.00 50.00
Derek Jeter
UH70 Wilkin Ramirez 5.00 12.00
UH71 Chase Utley 10.00 25.00
UH72 John Mayberry Jr. 5.00 12.00
UH73 Sean West 8.00 20.00
UH74 Mitch Maier 5.00 12.00
UH75 Matt Lindstrom 5.00 12.00
UH76 Scott Rolen 8.00 20.00
UH77 Jeremy Reed 5.00 12.00
UH78 LaTroy Hawkins 5.00 12.00
UH79 Robert Andino 5.00 12.00
UH80 Matt Stairs 5.00 12.00
UH81 Mark Teixeira 10.00 25.00
UH82 David Wright 12.00 30.00
UH83 Emilio Bonifacio 5.00 12.00
UH84 Gerardo Parra 8.00 20.00
UH85 Joe Crede 8.00 20.00
UH86 Carlos Pena 8.00 20.00
UH87 Jake Peavy 5.00 12.00
UH88 Jim Leyland 5.00 12.00
Tony La Russa
UH89 Phil Hughes 8.00 20.00
UH90 Orlando Cabrera 5.00 12.00
UH91 Anderson Hernandez 5.00 12.00
UH92 Edwin Encarnacion 5.00 12.00
UH93 Pedro Martinez 8.00 20.00
UH94 Jarrod Washburn 5.00 12.00
UH95 Ryan Freel 5.00 12.00
UH96 Tony Gwynn 5.00 12.00
UH97 Juan Castro 5.00 12.00
UH98 Hanley Ramirez 10.00 25.00
UH99 Kevin Gregg 5.00 12.00
UH100 CC Sabathia 8.00 20.00
UH101 Nick Green 5.00 12.00
UH102 Brett Hayes 5.00 12.00
UH103 Evan Longoria 12.00 30.00
UH104 Geoff Blum 5.00 12.00
UH105 Luis Valbuena 8.00 20.00
UH106 Jonny Gomes 5.00 12.00
UH107 Anthony Swarzak 5.00 12.00
UH108 Chris Tillman 8.00 20.00
UH109 Orlando Hudson 5.00 12.00
UH110 Justin Masterson 5.00 12.00
UH111 Livan Hernandez 5.00 12.00
UH112 Kyle Farnsworth 5.00 12.00
UH113 Francisco Rodriguez 8.00 20.00
UH114 Chris Coghlan 10.00 25.00
UH115 Jeff Weaver 5.00 12.00
UH116 Alfredo Figaro 5.00 12.00
UH117 Alex Rios 8.00 20.00
UH118 Blake Hawksworth 5.00 12.00
UH119 Bud Norris 5.00 12.00
UH120 Aaron Poreda 5.00 12.00
UH121 Brandon Inge 5.00 12.00
UH122 Kevin Youkilis 20.00 50.00
David Wright
Derek Jeter
Shane Victorino
UH123 Ryan Braun 12.00 30.00
UH124 Delwyn Young 8.00 20.00
UH125 Fernando Martinez 10.00 25.00
UH126 Matt Tolbert 5.00 12.00
UH127 Shane Robinson 5.00 12.00
UH128 Chone Figgins 5.00 12.00
UH129 Shane Victorino 5.00 12.00
UH130 Randy Johnson 8.00 20.00
UH131 Derek Jeter 20.00 50.00
UH132 Joe Thurston 5.00 12.00
UH133 Graham Taylor 8.00 20.00
UH134 Derek Holland 8.00 20.00
UH135 Ryan Perry 12.00 30.00
Rick Porcello
UH136 Raul Ibanez 8.00 20.00
UH137 Ross Ohlendorf 5.00 12.00
UH138 Ryan Church 5.00 12.00
UH139 Brian Moehler 5.00 12.00
UH140 Jack Wilson 5.00 12.00
UH141 Jason Hammel 5.00 12.00
UH142 Jorge Posada 8.00 20.00
UH143 Matt Maloney 5.00 12.00
UH144 Ronny Cedeno 5.00 12.00
UH145 Micah Hoffpauir 5.00 12.00
UH146 Juan Cruz 5.00 12.00
UH147 Jayson Nix 5.00 12.00
UH148 Jason Bay 8.00 20.00
UH149 Joel Hanrahan 5.00 12.00
UH150 Raul Ibanez 8.00 20.00
UH151 Jayson Werth 8.00 20.00
UH152 Barbaro Canizares 5.00 12.00
UH153 Ichiro Suzuki 15.00 40.00
UH154 Gerardo Parra 8.00 20.00
UH155 Andrew McCutchen 15.00 40.00
UH156 Heath Bell 8.00 20.00
UH157 Josh Hamilton 10.00 25.00
UH158 Wilson Valdez 5.00 12.00
UH159 Chad Billingsley 5.00 12.00
UH160 Edgar Renteria 5.00 12.00
UH161 Andrew Bailey 10.00 25.00
UH162 Chris Perez 5.00 12.00
UH163 Alejandro De Aza 5.00 12.00
UH164 Brett Tomko 5.00 12.00
UH165 Maicer Izturis 5.00 12.00
UH166 Mike Redmond 5.00 12.00
UH167 Julio Borbon 8.00 20.00
UH168 Paul Phillips 5.00 12.00
UH169 Mark Kotsay 5.00 12.00
UH170 Jason Giambi 5.00 12.00
UH171 Trevor Hoffman 8.00 20.00
UH172 Tyler Greene 5.00 12.00
UH173 David Robertson 5.00 12.00
UH174 Omar Vizquel 8.00 20.00
UH175 Jody Gerut 5.00 12.00
UH176 Diory Hernandez 5.00 12.00
UH177 Neftali Feliz 12.00 30.00
UH178 Josh Beckett 8.00 20.00
UH179 Carl Crawford 8.00 20.00
UH180 Mariano Rivera 10.00 25.00
UH181 Zach Duke 5.00 12.00
UH182 Mark Buehrle 8.00 20.00
UH183 Guillermo Quiroz 5.00 12.00
UH184 Francisco Cordero 5.00 12.00
UH185 Kevin Correia 5.00 12.00
UH186 Zack Greinke 6.00 15.00
UH187 Ryan Franklin 8.00 20.00
UH188 Jeff Francoeur 8.00 20.00
UH189 Michael Young 6.00 15.00
Josh Hamilton
Ian Kinsler
UH190 Ken Griffey Jr. 15.00 40.00
UH191 Ben Zobrist 5.00 12.00
UH192 Prince Fielder 6.00 15.00
UH193 Landon Powell 5.00 12.00
UH194 Ty Wigginton 8.00 20.00
UH195 P.J. Walters 5.00 12.00
UH196 Brian Fuentes 5.00 12.00
UH197 Dan Haren 5.00 12.00
UH198 Roy Halladay 10.00 25.00
UH199 Mike Rivera 5.00 12.00
UH200 Randy Johnson 8.00 20.00
UH201 Jordan Zimmermann 5.00 12.00
UH202 Angel Berroa 5.00 12.00
UH203 Ben Francisco 5.00 12.00
UH204 Brian Barden 5.00 12.00
UH205 Dallas Braden 8.00 20.00
UH206 Chris Burke 5.00 12.00
UH207 Garrett Jones 8.00 20.00
UH208 Chad Gaudin 5.00 12.00
UH209 Andruw Jones 5.00 12.00
UH210 Jason Vargas 5.00 12.00
UH211 Brad Bergesen 5.00 12.00
UH212 Ian Kinsler 8.00 20.00
UH213 Josh Johnson 8.00 20.00
UH214 Jason Grilli 5.00 12.00
UH215 Felix Hernandez 12.00 30.00
UH216 Mat Latos 12.00 30.00
UH217 Craig Stammen 5.00 12.00
UH218 Cliff Lee 8.00 20.00
UH219 Ken Takahashi 5.00 12.00
UH220 Matt LaPorta 10.00 25.00
UH221 Adrian Gonzalez 8.00 20.00
UH222 Ted Lilly 5.00 12.00
UH223 Jack Hannahan 5.00 12.00
UH224 Takashi Saito 5.00 12.00
UH225 Gregorio Petit 5.00 12.00
UH226 Kevin Hart 5.00 12.00
UH227 Edwin Jackson 5.00 12.00
UH228 Jason LaRue 5.00 12.00
UH229 Kevin Millar 5.00 12.00
UH230 Freddy Sanchez 5.00 12.00
UH231 Josh Bard 5.00 12.00
UH232 Tim Lincecum 15.00 40.00
UH233 Ramon Santiago 5.00 12.00
UH234 Mike Sweeney 5.00 12.00
UH235 Joe Nathan 5.00 12.00
UH236 Kris Benson 5.00 12.00
UH237 Dustin Pedroia 12.00 30.00
UH238 Kevin Cash 5.00 12.00
UH239 George Sherrill 5.00 12.00
UH240 Jason Marquis 5.00 12.00
UH241 Dewayne Wise 5.00 12.00
UH242 Randy Wells 5.00 12.00
UH243 Jonathan Papelbon 8.00 20.00
UH244 Johan Santana 10.00 25.00
UH245 Mariano Rivera 10.00 25.00
UH246 Javier Vazquez 5.00 12.00
UH247 Lastings Milledge 5.00 12.00
UH248 Chan Ho Park 8.00 20.00
UH249 Brian McCann 8.00 20.00
UH250 Mark Teixeira 10.00 25.00
UH251 Ian Snell 5.00 12.00
UH252 Justin Verlander 15.00 40.00
UH253 Prince Fielder 6.00 15.00
UH254 Cesar Izturis 5.00 12.00
UH255 Omir Santos 5.00 12.00
UH256 Tim Wakefield 5.00 12.00
UH257 Adrian Gonzalez 8.00 20.00
UH258 Nyjer Morgan 5.00 12.00
UH259 Victor Martinez 8.00 20.00
UH260 Ryan Howard 12.00 30.00
UH261 Aaron Bates 5.00 12.00
UH262 Jeff Niemann 5.00 12.00
UH263 Matt Holliday 10.00 25.00
UH264 Adam LaRoche 5.00 12.00
UH265 Justin Morneau 10.00 25.00
UH266 Jonathan Broxton 5.00 12.00
UH267 Miguel Cairo 5.00 12.00
UH268 Chris Getz 5.00 12.00
UH269 Cliff Floyd 5.00 12.00
UH270 David Ortiz 15.00 40.00
Alex Rodriguez
UH271 Frank Catalanotto 5.00 12.00
UH272 Carlos Pena 8.00 20.00
UH273 Mark Lowe 5.00 12.00
UH274 Joe Mauer 10.00 25.00
UH275 Ryan Garko 5.00 12.00
UH276 Brad Penny 5.00 12.00
UH277 Orlando Hudson 5.00 12.00
UH278 Gaby Sanchez 6.00 15.00
UH279 Ross Detwiler 5.00 12.00
UH280 Mark DeRosa 8.00 20.00
UH281 Kevin Youkilis 8.00 20.00
UH282 Victor Martinez 8.00 20.00
UH283 Freddy Sanchez 5.00 12.00
UH284 Mark Melancon 5.00 12.00
UH285 Ryan Franklin 8.00 20.00
UH286 Sidney Ponson 5.00 12.00
UH287 Matt Joyce 5.00 12.00
UH288 Jon Garland 5.00 12.00
UH289 Nick Johnson 5.00 12.00
UH290 Jason Michaels 5.00 12.00
UH291 Ross Gload 5.00 12.00
UH292 Yuniesky Betancourt 5.00 12.00
UH293 Aaron Hill 5.00 12.00
UH294 Josh Anderson 5.00 12.00
UH295 Miguel Tejada 8.00 20.00
UH296 Casey McGehee 5.00 12.00
UH297 Brett Cecil 5.00 12.00
UH298 Jason Bartlett 5.00 12.00
UH299 Ryan Langerhans 5.00 12.00
UH300 Albert Pujols 20.00 50.00
UH301 Ryan Zimmerman 8.00 20.00
UH302 Casey Kotchman 5.00 12.00
UH303 Luke French 5.00 12.00
UH304 Nick Swisher 12.00 30.00
Johnny Damon
UH305 Michael Young 8.00 20.00
UH306 Endy Chavez 5.00 12.00
UH307 Heath Bell 8.00 20.00
UH308 Matt Cain 8.00 20.00
UH309 Scott Podsednik 5.00 12.00
UH310 Scott Richmond 5.00 12.00
UH311 David Huff 5.00 12.00
UH312 Ryan Hanigan 5.00 12.00
UH313 Jeff Baker 5.00 12.00
UH314 Brad Hawpe 5.00 12.00
UH315 Jerry Hairston Jr. 5.00 12.00
UH316 Hunter Pence 12.00 30.00
Ryan Braun
UH317 Nelson Cruz 8.00 20.00
UH318 Carl Crawford 8.00 20.00
UH319 Ramon Castro 5.00 12.00
UH320 Mark Schlereth 5.00 12.00
Daniel Schlereth
UH321 Hunter Pence 8.00 20.00
UH322 Sean Marshall 8.00 20.00
UH323 Ramon Ramirez 5.00 12.00
UH324 Nolan Reimold 5.00 12.00
UH325 Torii Hunter 5.00 12.00
UH326 Nate McLouth 5.00 12.00
UH327 Julio Lugo 5.00 12.00
UH328 Matt Palmer 5.00 12.00
UH329 Curtis Granderson 8.00 20.00
UH330 Ken Griffey Jr. 15.00 40.00

2009 Topps Update Gold Border

*GOLD VET: 2.5X TO 6X BASIC
*GOLD RC: 1X TO 2.5X BASIC RC
STATED ODDS 1:3 HOBBY
STATED PRINT RUN 2009 SER.#'d SETS

2009 Topps Update Platinum

STATED ODDS 1:6250 HOBBY
STATED PRINT RUN 1 SER.#'d SET
NO PRICING DUE TO SCARCITY

2009 Topps Update Target

*VETS: .5X TO 1.2X BASIC TOPPS CARDS
*RC: .5X TO 1.2X BASIC TOPSP RC CARDS

2009 Topps Update All-Star Jumbo Patches

STATED ODDS 1:2040 HOBBY
STATED PRINT RUN 6 SER.#'d SETS
NO PRICING DUE TO SCARCITY

2009 Topps Update All-Star Jumbo Patches Autographs

RANDOM INSERTS IN PACKS
STATED PRINT RUN 6 SER.#'d SETS
NO PRICING DUE TO SCARCITY

2009 Topps Update All-Star Stitches

STATED ODDS 1:58 HOBBY
AST1 Chase Utley 5.00 12.00
AST2 Nelson Cruz 3.00 8.00
AST3 Adam Jones 4.00 10.00
AST4 Justin Upton 3.00 8.00
AST5 Albert Pujols 15.00 40.00
AST6 Ben Zobrist 4.00 10.00
AST7 Joe Mauer 5.00 12.00
AST8 Yadier Molina 10.00 25.00
AST9 Mark Teixeira 5.00 12.00
AST10 David Wright 5.00 12.00
AST11 Carlos Pena 3.00 8.00
AST12 Hanley Ramirez 4.00 10.00
AST13 Adrian Gonzalez 4.00 10.00
AST14 Francisco Rodriguez 4.00 10.00
AST15 Evan Longoria 6.00 15.00
AST16 Brandon Inge 5.00 12.00
AST17 Shane Victorino 5.00 12.00
AST18 Raul Ibanez 5.00 12.00
AST19 Jason Bay 4.00 10.00
AST20 Jayson Werth 6.00 15.00
AST21 Ichiro Suzuki 10.00 25.00
AST22 Heath Bell 3.00 8.00
AST23 Andrew Bailey 3.00 8.00
AST24 Chad Billingsley 3.00 8.00
AST25 Josh Hamilton 4.00 10.00
AST26 Trevor Hoffman 3.00 8.00
AST27 Josh Beckett 4.00 10.00
AST28 Zach Duke 4.00 10.00
AST29 Mark Buehrle 5.00 12.00
AST30 Zack Greinke 5.00 12.00
AST31 Francisco Cordero 3.00 8.00
AST32 Ryan Franklin 12.50 30.00
AST33 Brian Fuentes 3.00 8.00
AST34 Dan Haren 3.00 8.00
AST35 Roy Halladay 4.00 10.00
AST36 Josh Johnson 3.00 8.00
AST37 Felix Hernandez 4.00 10.00
AST38 Ted Lilly 3.00 8.00
AST39 Edwin Jackson 4.00 10.00
AST40 Tim Lincecum 6.00 15.00
AST41 Joe Nathan 4.00 10.00
AST42 Jason Marquis 3.00 8.00
AST43 Jonathan Papelbon 3.00 8.00
AST44 Johan Santana 4.00 10.00
AST45 Mariano Rivera 4.00 10.00
AST46 Brian McCann 4.00 10.00
AST47 Justin Verlander 5.00 12.00
AST48 Prince Fielder 4.00 10.00
AST49 Tim Wakefield 4.00 10.00
AST50 Ryan Braun 4.00 10.00
AST51 Victor Martinez 3.00 8.00
AST52 Ryan Zimmerman 4.00 10.00
AST53 Orlando Hudson 3.00 8.00
AST54 Kevin Youkilis 3.00 8.00
AST55 Freddy Sanchez 3.00 8.00
AST56 Aaron Hill 4.00 10.00
AST57 Miguel Tejada 3.00 8.00
AST58 Jason Bartlett 3.00 8.00
AST59 Ryan Howard 8.00 20.00
AST60 Michael Young 3.00 8.00
AST61 Brad Hawpe 3.00 8.00
AST62 Carl Crawford 3.00 8.00
AST63 Hunter Pence 3.00 8.00
AST64 Curtis Granderson 4.00 10.00
AST65 Jonathan Broxton 3.00 8.00
AST66 Matt Cain 3.00 8.00

2009 Topps Update All-Star Stitches Gold

*GOLD: .75X TO 2X BASIC
STATED ODDS 1:616 HOBBY
STATED PRINT RUN 50 SER.#'d SETS

2009 Topps Update All-Star Stitches Platinum

STATED ODDS 1:30,442 HOBBY
STATED PRINT RUN 1 SER.#'d SET
NO PRICING DUE TO SCARCITY

2009 Topps Update All-Star Stitches Autographs

STATED ODDS 1:5500 HOBBY
STATED PRINT RUN 25 SER.#'d SETS
NO PRICING DUE TO SCARCITY

2009 Topps Update All-Star Stitches Dual

STATED ODDS 1:8154 HOBBY
STATED PRINT RUN 25 SER.#'d SETS
NO PRICING DUE TO SCARCITY

2009 Topps Update All-Star Stitches Triple

STATED ODDS 1:3238 HOBBY
STATED PRINT RUN 25 SER.#'d SETS
NO PRICING DUE TO SCARCITY

2009 Topps Update Career Quest Autographs

STATED ODDS 1:546 HOBBY
AM Andrew McCutchen 10.00 25.00
DH David Hernandez 3.00 8.00
DS Daniel Schlereth 3.00 8.00
GB Gordon Beckham 10.00 25.00
JZ Jordan Zimmermann 4.00 10.00
KU Koji Uehara 20.00 50.00
MG Mat Gamel 4.00 10.00
RB Reid Brignac 4.00 10.00
RP Ryan Perry 4.00 10.00
TH Tommy Hanson 10.00 25.00
VM Vin Mazzaro 4.00 10.00
RPO Rick Porcello 12.50 30.00

2009 Topps Update Chrome Rookie Refractors

ONE PER BOX TOPPER
CHR1 Michael Saunders 3.00 8.00
CHR2 David Hernandez 2.00 5.00
CHR3 Tommy Hanson 6.00 15.00
CHR4 Daniel Schlereth 2.00 5.00
CHR5 Gordon Beckham 8.00 20.00
CHR6 Sean O'Sullivan 2.00 5.00
CHR7 Josh Reddick 3.00 8.00
CHR8 Kris Medlen 3.00 8.00
CHR9 Daniel Bard 2.00 5.00
CHR10 Xavier Paul 2.00 5.00
CHR11 Jesus Guzman 2.00 5.00
CHR12 Kyle Blanks 3.00 8.00
CHR13 Vin Mazzaro 2.00 5.00
CHR14 Jamie Hoffmann 2.00 5.00
CHR15 Mark Rzepczynski 3.00 8.00
CHR16 Jhoulys Chacin 3.00 8.00
CHR17 Wilkin Ramirez 2.00 5.00
CHR18 John Mayberry Jr. 2.00 5.00
CHR19 Sean West 3.00 8.00
CHR20 Gerardo Parra 3.00 8.00
CHR21 Brett Hayes 2.00 5.00
CHR22 Anthony Swarzak 2.00 5.00
CHR23 Chris Tillman 3.00 8.00
CHR24 Chris Coghlan 5.00 12.00
CHR25 Alfredo Figaro 2.00 5.00
CHR26 Blake Hawksworth 2.00 5.00
CHR27 Bud Norris 2.00 5.00
CHR28 Aaron Poreda 2.00 5.00
CHR29 Fernando Martinez 5.00 12.00
CHR30 Shane Robinson 2.00 5.00
CHR31 Graham Taylor 3.00 8.00
CHR32 Derek Holland 3.00 8.00
CHR33 Matt Maloney 2.00 5.00
CHR34 Barbaro Canizares 2.00 5.00
CHR35 Andrew McCutchen 8.00 20.00
CHR36 Julio Borbon 3.00 8.00
CHR37 Tyler Greene 2.00 5.00
CHR38 Diory Hernandez 2.00 5.00
CHR39 Neftali Feliz 6.00 15.00
CHR40 Landon Powell 2.00 5.00
CHR41 P.J. Walters 2.00 5.00
CHR42 Jordan Zimmermann 2.00 5.00
CHR43 Brad Bergesen 2.00 5.00
CHR44 Mat Latos 6.00 15.00
CHR45 Craig Stammen 2.00 5.00
CHR46 Ken Takahashi 3.00 8.00
CHR47 Matt LaPorta 5.00 12.00
CHR48 Omir Santos 2.00 5.00
CHR49 Aaron Bates 2.00 5.00
CHR50 Gaby Sanchez 3.00 8.00
CHR51 Mark Melancon 2.00 5.00
CHR52 Brett Cecil 2.00 5.00
CHR53 Luke French 2.00 5.00
CHR54 David Huff 2.00 5.00
CHR55 Nolan Reimold 2.00 5.00

2009 Topps Update Legends of the Game Team Name Letter Patch

STATED ODDS 1:408 HOBBY
STATED PRINT RUN 50 SER.#'d SETS
BR Babe Ruth/50 * 8.00 20.00
Letters spell Red Sox (each letter serial #'d/50)
CM Christy Mathewson/50 * 4.00 10.00
Letters spell New York (each letter serial #'d/50)
CY Cy Young/50 * 4.00 10.00
Letters spell Boston (each letter serial #'d/50)
GS George Sisler/50 * 4.00 10.00
Letters spell St. Louis (each letter serial #'d/50)
HW Honus Wagner/50 * 6.00 15.00
Letters spell Pirates (each letter serial #'d/50)
JF Jimmie Foxx/50 * 8.00 20.00
Letters spell Red Sox (each letter serial #'d/50)
JM Johnny Mize/50 * 4.00 10.00
Letters spell Cardinals (each letter serial #'d/50)
JR Jackie Robinson/50 * 6.00 15.00
Letters spell Dodgers (each letter serial #'d/50)
LG Lou Gehrig/50 * 12.50 30.00
Letters spell New York (each letter serial #'d/50)
MM Mickey Mantle/50 * 12.50 30.00
Letters spell New York (each letter serial #'d/50)
PR Pee Wee Reese/50 * 6.00 15.00
Letters spell Dodgers (each letter serial #'d/50)
RC Roy Campanella/50 * 10.00 25.00
Letters spell Dodgers (each letter serial #'d/50)
RH Rogers Hornsby/50 * 12.50 30.00
Letters spell Cardinals (each letter serial #'d/50)
TC Ty Cobb/50 * 10.00 25.00
Letters spell Detroit (each letter serial #'d/50)
TM Thurman Munson/50 * 10.00 25.00
Letters spell New York (each letter serial #'d/50)
TS Tris Speaker/50 * 4.00 10.00
Letters spell Boston (each letter serial #'d/50)
WJ Walter Johnson/50 * 8.00 20.00
Letters spell Washington (each letter serial #'d/50)
BR2 Babe Ruth/50 * 8.00 20.00
Letters spell New York (each letter serial #'d/50)

2009 Topps Update Propaganda

COMPLETE SET (30) 8.00 20.00
STATED ODDS 1:6 HOBBY
PP01 Adam Dunn .50 1.25
PP02 Adrian Gonzalez .50 1.25
PP03 Albert Pujols 2.00 5.00
PP04 Andrew McCutchen 1.25 3.00
PP05 Alfonso Soriano .50 1.25
PP06 Carlos Quentin .50 1.25
PP07 Chipper Jones .75 2.00
PP08 David Wright 1.00 2.50
PP09 Dustin Pedroia 1.00 2.50
PP10 Evan Longoria 1.00 2.50
PP11 Grady Sizemore .50 1.25
PP12 Hanley Ramirez .75 2.00
PP13 Hunter Pence .50 1.25
PP14 Ichiro Suzuki 1.25 3.00
PP15 Andrew Bailey .75 2.00
PP16 Jay Bruce .50 1.25
PP17 Joe Mauer .75 2.00
PP18 Josh Hamilton .75 2.00
PP19 Justin Upton .50 1.25
PP20 Manny Ramirez .75 2.00
PP21 Mark Teixeira .75 2.00
PP22 Miguel Cabrera .75 2.00
PP23 Nick Markakis .75 2.00
PP24 Roy Halladay .75 2.00
PP25 Ryan Braun 1.00 2.50
PP26 Ryan Howard 1.00 2.50
PP27 Tim Lincecum 1.25 3.00
PP28 Todd Helton .50 1.25
PP29 Vladimir Guerrero .75 2.00
PP30 Zack Greinke .50 1.25

2009 Topps Update Stadium Stamp Collection

STATED ODDS 1:2280 HOBBY
STATED PRINT RUN 90 SER.#'d SETS
SSC1 Polo Grounds 12.50 30.00
SSC2 Forbes Field 10.00 25.00
SSC3 Wrigley Field 12.50 30.00
SSC4 Yankee Stadium 15.00 40.00
SSC5 Tiger Stadium 12.50 30.00
SSC6 Shibe Park 10.00 25.00
SSC7 Crosley Field 10.00 25.00
SSC8 Comiskey Park 10.00 25.00
SSC9 Fenway Park 12.50 30.00
SSC10 Ebbets Field 10.00 25.00

2009 Topps Update WBC Stitches Dual

STATED ODDS 1:3285 HOBBY
STATED PRINT RUN 25 SER.#'d SETS
NO PRICING DUE TO SCARCITY

2009 Topps Update WBC Stitches Triple

STATED ODDS 1:1294 HOBBY
STATED PRINT RUN 25 SER.#'d SETS
NO PRICING DUE TO SCARCITY

2010 Topps

COMP.HOBBY.SET (661) 40.00 80.00
COMP.ALLSTAR.SET (661) 40.00 80.00
COMP.PHILLIES SET (661) 40.00 80.00
COMP.RED SOX SET (661) 40.00 80.00
COMP.YANKEES SET (661) 40.00 80.00
COMP.SET w/o SPs (660) 30.00 60.00
COMP.SER. 1 SET w/o SPs (330) 12.50 30.00
COMP.SER. 2 SET w/o SPs (330) 12.50 30.00
COMMON CARD (1-660) .15 .40
COMMON RC (1-660) .25 .60
COMMON SP VAR (1-660) 6.00 15.00
COMMON PIE SP (1-660) 15.00 40.00
SER. 1 PRINTING PLATE ODDS 1:1417 HOBBY
SER. 2 PRINTING PLATE ODDS 1:1642 HOBBY
PLATE PRINT RUN 1 SET PER COLOR
BLACK-CYAN-MAGENTA-YELLOW ISSUED
NO PLATE PRICING DUE TO SCARCITY
661B ISSUED IN FACTORY SETS
1A Prince Fielder .25 .60
1B Hank Greenberg SP 8.00 20.00
2 Buster Posey RC 5.00 12.00
3 Derrek Lee .15 .40
4 Hanley Ramirez 1.00 2.50
Pablo Sandoval
Albert Pujols
5 Texas Rangers .15 .40
6 Chicago White Sox .15 .40
7 Mickey Mantle 1.25 3.00
8 Joe Mauer 1.00 2.50
Ichiro Suzuki
Derek Jeter
9 Tim Lincecum NL CY .60 1.50
10 Clayton Kershaw .40 1.00
11 Orlando Cabrera .15 .40
12 Doug Davis .15 .40
13 Melvin Mora .15 .40
14 Ted Lilly .15 .40
15 Bobby Abreu .15 .40
16 Johnny Cueto .15 .40
17 Dexter Fowler .15 .40
18 Tim Stauffer .15 .40
19 Felipe Lopez .15 .40
20A Tommy Hanson .25 .60
20B Warren Spahn SP 6.00 15.00
21 Cristian Guzman .15 .40
22 Anthony Swarzak .15 .40
23 Shane Victorino .25 .60
24 John Maine .15 .40
25 Adam Jones .25 .60
26 Zach Duke .15 .40
27 Lance Berkman .25 .60
Mike Hampton
28 Jonathan Sanchez .15 .40
29 Aubrey Huff .15 .40
30 Victor Martinez .25 .60
31 Jason Grilli .15 .40
32 Cincinnati Reds .15 .40
33 Adam Moore RC .25 .60
34 Michael Dunn RC .25 .60
35 Rick Porcello .25 .60
36 Tobi Stoner RC .40 1.00
37 Garret Anderson .15 .40
38 Houston Astros .15 .40
39 Jeff Baker .15 .40
40 Josh Johnson .25 .60
41 Los Angeles Dodgers .25 .60
42 Prince Fielder .25 .60
Ryan Howard
Albert Pujols
43 Marco Scutaro .15 .40
44 Howie Kendrick .15 .40
45 David Hernandez .15 .40
46 Chad Tracy .15 .40
47 Brad Penny .15 .40
48 Joey Votto .40 1.00
49 Jorge De La Rosa .15 .40
50A Zack Greinke .25 .60
50B Cy Young SP 6.00 15.00
51 Eric Young Jr .15 .40
52 Billy Butler .15 .40
53 Craig Counsell .15 .40
54 John Lackey .15 .40
55 Manny Ramirez .40 1.00
56A Andy Pettitte .25 .60
56B Whitey Ford SP 8.00 20.00
57 CC Sabathia .25 .60
58 Kyle Blanks .15 .40
59 Kevin Gregg .15 .40
60 David Wright .50 1.25
61 Skip Schumaker .15 .40
62 Kevin Millwood .15 .40
63 Josh Bard .15 .40
64 Drew Stubbs RC .60 1.50
65A Nick Swisher .40 1.00
65B Nick Swisher 30.00 60.00
Pie in the face
66 Kyle Phillips RC .25 .60
67 Matt LaPorta .40 1.00
68 Brandon Inge .25 .60
69 Kansas City Royals .15 .40
70 Cole Hamels .40 1.00
71 Mike Hampton .15 .40
72 Milwaukee Brewers .15 .40
73 Adam Wainwright .40 1.00
Chris Carpenter
Jorge De La Rosa
74 Casey Blake .15 .40
75 Adrian Gonzalez .25 .60
76 Joe Saunders .15 .40
77 Kenshin Kawakami .25 .60
78 Cesar Izturis .15 .40
79 Francisco Cordero .15 .40
80A Tim Lincecum .60 1.50
80B Christy Mathewson SP 8.00 20.00
81 Ryan Theriot .15 .40
82 Jason Marquis .15 .40
83 Mark Teahen .15 .40
84 Nate Robertson .15 .40
85A Ken Griffey Jr. .60 1.50
85B Jackie Robinson SP 8.00 20.00
86 Gil Meche .15 .40
87 Darin Erstad .15 .40
88A Jerry Hairston Jr. .15 .40
88B Jerry Hairston Jr. 15.00 40.00
Pie in the face
89 J.A. Happ .25 .60
90A Ian Kinsler .25 .60
90B Rogers Hornsby SP 8.00 20.00
91 Erik Bedard .15 .40
92 David Eckstein .15 .40
93 Joe Nathan .15 .40
94A Ivan Rodriguez .25 .60
94B Carlton Fisk SP 8.00 20.00
95A Carl Crawford .25 .60
95B Rickey Henderson SP 8.00 20.00
96 Jon Garland .15 .40
97 Luis Durango RC .25 .60
98 Cesar Ramos (RC) .25 .60
99 Garrett Jones .25 .60
100A Albert Pujols 1.00 2.50
100B Stan Musial SP 8.00 20.00
101 Scott Baker .15 .40
102 Minnesota Twins .15 .40
103 Daniel Murphy .15 .40
104 New York Mets .25 .60
105 Madison Bumgarner RC .60 1.50
106 Chris Carpenter .40 1.00
Tim Lincecum
Jair Jurrjens
107 Scott Hairston .15 .40
108 Erick Aybar .15 .40
109 Justin Masterson .15 .40
110A Andrew McCutchen .40 1.00
110B Willie Stargell SP 8.00 20.00
111 Ty Wigginton .15 .40
112 Kevin Correia .15 .40
113 Willy Taveras .15 .40
114 Chris Iannetta .15 .40
115 Gordon Beckham .25 .60
116A Carlos Gomez .15 .40
116B Robin Yount SP 8.00 20.00
117 David DeJesus .15 .40
118 Brandon Morrow .15 .40
119 Wilkin Ramirez .15 .40
120A Jorge Posada .25 .60
120B Jorge Posada 30.00 60.00
Pie in the face
121 Brett Anderson .25 .60
122 Carlos Ruiz .15 .40
123A Jeff Samardzija .15 .40
123B Jeff Samardzija 75.00 150.00
Abe Lincoln Variation SP
124 Rickie Weeks .25 .60
125A Ichiro Suzuki .60 1.50
125B George Sisler SP 6.00 15.00
126 John Smoltz .40 1.00
127 Hank Blalock .15 .40
128 Garrett Mock .15 .40
129 Reid Gorecki (RC) .40 1.00
130A Vladimir Guerrero .40 1.00
130B Reggie Jackson SP 6.00 15.00
131 Dustin Richardson RC .25 .60
132 Cliff Lee .25 .60
133 Freddy Sanchez .15 .40
134 Philadelphia Phillies .15 .40
135A Ryan Dempster .15 .40
135B Ryan Dempster 75.00 150.00
Abe Lincoln Variation SP
136 Adam Wainwright .25 .60
137 Oakland Athletics .15 .40
138 Carlos Pena .40 1.00
Mark Teixeira
Jason Bay
139 Frank Francisco .15 .40
140 Matt Holliday .40 1.00
141 Chone Figgins .15 .40
142 Tim Hudson .25 .60
143 Omar Vizquel .25 .60
144 Rich Harden .15 .40
145 Justin Upton .25 .60
146 Yunel Escobar .15 .40
147 Huston Street .15 .40
148 Cody Ross .15 .40
149 Jose Guillen .15 .40

150 Joe Mauer .40 1.00
151 Mat Gamel .15 .40
152 Nyjer Morgan .15 .40
153 Justin Duchscherer .15 .40
154 Pedro Feliz .15 .40
155 Zack Greinke AL CY .25 .60
156 Tony Gwynn Jr. .15 .40
157 Mike Sweeney .15 .40
158 Jeff Niemann .15 .40
159 Vernon Wells .15 .40
160 Miguel Tejada .25 .60
161 Denard Span .15 .40
162 Wade Davis (RC) .25 .60
163 Josh Butler RC .25 .60
164 Carlos Carrasco (RC) .60 1.50
165A Brandon Phillips .15 .40
165B Joe Morgan SP 6.00 15.00
166 Eric Byrnes .15 .40
167 San Diego Padres .15 .40
168 Brad Kilby RC .25 .60
169 Pittsburgh Pirates .15 .40
170 Jason Bay .25 .60
171 Felix Hernandez .50 1.25
CC Sabathia
Justin Verlander
172 Joe Mauer AL MVP .40 1.00
173 Kendry Morales .15 .40
174 Mike Gonzalez .15 .40
175A Josh Hamilton .40 1.00
175B Roger Maris SP 8.00 20.00
176 Yovani Gallardo .15 .40
177 Adam Lind .25 .60
178 Kerry Wood .15 .40
179 Ryan Spilborghs .15 .40
180 Jayson Nix .15 .40
181 Nick Johnson .15 .40
182 Coco Crisp .15 .40
183 Jonathan Papelbon .25 .60
184 Jeff Francoeur .25 .60
185A Hideki Matsui .40 1.00
185B Hideki Matsui 40.00 80.00
Pie in the face
186 Andrew Bailey .15 .40
187 Will Venable .15 .40
188 Joe Blanton .15 .40
189 Adrian Beltre .15 .40
190 Pablo Sandoval .25 .60
191 Mat Latos .15 .40
192 Andruw Jones .15 .40
193 Shairon Martis .15 .40
194 Neill Walker (RC) .40 1.00
195 James Shields .15 .40
196 Ian Desmond (RC) .40 1.00
197 Cleveland Indians .15 .40
198 Florida Marlins .15 .40
199 Seattle Mariners .15 .40
200A Roy Halladay .40 1.00
200B Walter Johnson SP 8.00 20.00
201 Detroit Tigers .15 .40
202 San Francisco Giants .15 .40
203 Zack Greinke .25 .60
Felix Hernandez
Roy Halladay
204 Elvis Andrus .25 .60
Ian Kinsler
205 Chris Coghlan .15 .40
206 Albert Pujols .25 .60
Prince Fielder
Ryan Howard
207 Colby Rasmus .40 1.00
208 Tim Wakefield .15 .40
209 Alexei Ramirez .15 .40
210 Josh Beckett .25 .60
211 Kelly Shoppach .15 .40
212 Magglio Ordonez .25 .60
213 Ricky Nolasco .15 .40
214 Matt Kemp .25 .60
215 Max Scherzer .15 .40
216 Mike Cameron .15 .40
217 Gio Gonzalez .15 .40
218 Fernando Martinez .15 .40
219 Kevin Hart .15 .40
220 Randy Johnson .25 .60
221 Russell Branyan .15 .40
222A Curtis Granderson .25 .60
222B Curtis Granderson SP 12.50 30.00
223 Ryan Church .15 .40
224 Rod Barajas .15 .40
225A David Price .40 1.00
225B David Price 40.00 80.00
Pie in the face
226 Juan Rivera .15 .40
227 Josh Thole RC .40 1.00
228 Chris Pettit RC .25 .60
229 Daniel McCutchen RC .40 1.00
230 Jonathan Broxton .15 .40
231 Luke Scott .15 .40
232 St. Louis Cardinals .25 .60
233 Mark Teixeira .40 1.00
Jason Bay
Adam Lind
234 Tampa Bay Rays .15 .40
235 Neftali Feliz .15 .40
236 Andrew Bailey AL ROY .15 .40
237 Ryan Braun .25 .60
Prince Fielder
238 Ian Stewart .15 .40
239 Juan Uribe .15 .40
240 Ricky Romero .15 .40
241 Rocco Baldelli .15 .40
242 Bobby Jenks .15 .40
243 Asdrubal Cabrera .25 .60
244 Barry Zito .15 .40
245 Lance Berkman .25 .60
246 Leo Nunez .15 .40
247 Andre Ethier .25 .60
248 Jason Kendall .15 .40
249 Jon Niese .15 .40
250A Mark Teixeira .40 1.00
250B Mark Teixeira 40.00 80.00
Pie in the face
250C Lou Gehrig SP 10.00 25.00
251 John Lannan .15 .40
252 Ronny Cedeno .15 .40
253 Bengie Molina .15 .40
254 Edwin Jackson .15 .40
255 Chris Davis .15 .40
256 Akinori Iwamura .15 .40
257 Bobby Crosby .15 .40
258 Edwin Encarnacion .15 .40
259 Daniel Hudson RC .40 1.00
260 New York Yankees .40 1.00
261 Matt Carson (RC) .25 .60
262 Homer Bailey .15 .40
263 Placido Polanco .15 .40
264 Arizona Diamondbacks .15 .40
265 Los Angeles Angels .15 .40
266 Humberto Quintero .15 .40
267 Toronto Blue Jays .15 .40
268 Juan Pierre .15 .40
269 Alex Rodriguez .40 1.00
Derek Jeter
Robinson Cano
270 Michael Brantley RC .25 .60
271 Jermaine Dye .15 .40
272 Jair Jurrjens .15 .40
273 Pat Neshek .15 .40
274 Stephen Drew .15 .40
275 Chris Coghlan NL ROY .15 .40
276 Matt Lindstrom .15 .40
277 Jarrod Washburn .15 .40
278 Carlos Delgado .15 .40
279 Randy Wolf .15 .40
280 Mark DeRosa .15 .40
281 Braden Looper .15 .40
282 Washington Nationals .15 .40
283 Adam Kennedy .15 .40
284 Ross Ohlendorf .15 .40
285 Kurt Suzuki .15 .40
286 Javier Vazquez .15 .40
287 Jhonny Peralta .15 .40
288 Boston Red Sox .25 .60
289 Lyle Overbay .15 .40
290 Orlando Hudson .15 .40
291 Austin Kearns .15 .40
292 Tommy Manzella (RC) .25 .60
293 Brent Dlugach (RC) .25 .60
294A Adam Dunn .25 .60
294B Babe Ruth SP 12.50 30.00
295 Kevin Youkilis .25 .60
296 Atlanta Braves .15 .40
297 Ben Zobrist .15 .40
298 Baltimore Orioles .15 .40
299 Gary Sheffield .15 .40
300A Chase Utley .40 1.00
300B Ryne Sandberg SP 8.00 20.00
301 Jack Cust .15 .40
302 Kevin Youkilis .25 .60
David Ortiz
303 Chris Snyder .15 .40
304 Adam LaRoche .15 .40
305 Juan Francisco RC .40 1.00
306A Milton Bradley .25 .60
306B Milton Bradley 60.00 120.00
Abe Lincoln Variation SP
Lincoln pictured on the scoreboard
307 Henry Rodriguez RC .25 .60
308 Robinzon Diaz .15 .40
309 Gerald Laird .15 .40
310 Elvis Andrus .25 .60
311 Jose Valverde .15 .40
312 Tyler Flowers RC .40 1.00
313 Jason Kubel .15 .40
314 Angel Pagan .15 .40
315 Scott Kazmir .15 .40
316 Chris Young .15 .40
317 Ryan Doumit .15 .40
318 Nate Schierholtz .15 .40
319 Ryan Franklin .15 .40
320 Brian McCann .25 .60
321 Pat Burrell .15 .40
322 Travis Buck .15 .40
323 Jim Thome .25 .60
324 Alex Rios .25 .60
325 Julio Lugo .15 .40
326A Tyler Colvin RC .40 1.00
326B Tyler Colvin 50.00 100.00
Abe Lincoln Variation SP
327 Albert Pujols NL MVP 1.00 2.50
328 Chicago Cubs .25 .60
329 Colorado Rockies .15 .40
330 Brandon Allen (RC) .25 .60
331A Ryan Braun .50 1.25
331B Eddie Mathews SP 8.00 20.00
332 Brad Hawpe .15 .40
333 Ryan Ludwick .15 .40
334 Jayson Werth .25 .60
335 Jordan Norberto RC .25 .60
336 C.J. Wilson .15 .40
337 Carlos Zambrano .25 .60
338 Brett Cecil .15 .40
339 Jose Reyes .25 .60
340 John Buck .15 .40
341 Texas Rangers .15 .40
342 Melky Cabrera .15 .40
343 Brian Bruney .15 .40
344 Brett Myers .15 .40
345 Chris Volstad .15 .40
346 Taylor Teagarden .15 .40
347 Aaron Harang .15 .40
348 Jordan Zimmermann .15 .40
349 Felix Pie .15 .40
350 Prince Fielder .25 .60
Ryan Braun
351 Koji Uehara .25 .60
352 Cameron Maybin .15 .40
353A Jason Heyward RC 1.50 4.00
353B Jason Heyward 50.00 100.00
Pie in the face
354A Evan Longoria .50 1.25
354B Johnny Mize SP 6.00 15.00
355 James Russell RC .60 1.50
356 Los Angeles Angels .15 .40
357 Scott Downs .15 .40
358 Mark Buehrle .25 .60
359 Aramis Ramirez .15 .40
360 Justin Morneau .40 1.00
361 Washington Nationals .15 .40
362 Travis Snider .15 .40
363 Joba Chamberlain .25 .60
364 Trevor Hoffman .25 .60
365 Logan Ondrusek RC .25 .60
366 Hiroki Kuroda .15 .40
367 Wandy Rodriguez .15 .40
368 Wade LeBlanc .15 .40
369a David Ortiz .25 .60
369b Jimmie Foxx 6.00 15.00
370A Robinson Cano .40 1.00
370B Robinson Cano 30.00 60.00
Pie in the face 8/12/09
370C Robinson Cano 30.00 60.00
Pie in the face 8/28/09
370D Mel Ott SP 6.00 15.00
371 Nick Hundley .15 .40
372 Philadelphia Phillies .15 .40
373 Clint Barmes .15 .40
374 Scott Feldman .15 .40
375 Mike Leake RC .75 2.00
376 Esmil Rogers RC .25 .60
377A Felix Hernandez .40 1.00
377B Tom Seaver SP 8.00 20.00
378 George Sherrill .15 .40
379 Phil Hughes .15 .40
380 J.D. Drew .15 .40
381 Miguel Montero .15 .40
382 Kyle Davies .15 .40
383 Derek Lowe .15 .40
384 Chris Johnson RC .60 1.50
385 Torii Hunter .15 .40
386 Dan Haren .15 .40
387 Josh Fields .15 .40
388 Joel Pineiro .15 .40
389 Troy Tulowitzki .40 1.00
390 Ervin Santana .15 .40
391 Manny Parra .15 .40
392 Carlos Monasterios RC .40 1.00
393 Jason Frasor .15 .40
394 Luis Castillo .15 .40
395 Jenry Mejia RC .40 1.00
396 Jake Westbrook .15 .40
397 Colorado Rockies .15 .40
398 Carlos Gonzalez .25 .60
399A Matt Garza .15 .40
399B Matt Garza 12.50 30.00
UPD Pie in the face
400A Alex Rodriguez .60 1.50
400B Alex Rodriguez 50.00 100.00
Pie in the face 5/16/09
400C Alex Rodriguez 50.00 100.00
Pie in the face 8/7/09
400D Frank Robinson SP 8.00 20.00
401 Chad Billingsley .15 .40
402 J.P. Howell .15 .40
403A Jimmy Rollins .25 .60
403B Ozzie Smith SP 8.00 20.00
404 Mariano Rivera .40 1.00
405 Dustin McGowan .15 .40
406 Jeff Francis .15 .40
407 Nick Punto .15 .40
408 Detroit Tigers .15 .40
409A Kosuke Fukudome .40 1.00
409B Richie Ashburn SP 10.00 25.00
410 Oakland Athletics .15 .40
411 Jack Wilson .15 .40
412 San Francisco Giants .15 .40
413 J.J. Hardy .15 .40
414 Sean West .15 .40
415 Cincinnati Reds .15 .40
416 Ruben Tejada RC .40 1.00
417 Dallas Braden .25 .60
418 Aaron Laffey .15 .40
419 David Aardsma .15 .40
420 Shin-Soo Choo .25 .60
421 Doug Fister .15 .40
422A Vin Mazzaro .15 .40
422B Francisco Cervelli 30.00 60.00
Pie in the face
423 Brad Bergesen .15 .40
424 David Herndon RC .25 .60
425 Dontrelle Willis .15 .40
426 Mark Reynolds .15 .40
427 Brandon Webb .25 .60
428 Baltimore Orioles .15 .40
429 Seth Smith .15 .40
430 Kazuo Matsui .15 .40
431 John Raynor RC .25 .60
432 A.J. Burnett .25 .60
433 Julio Borbon .15 .40
434 Kevin Slowey .15 .40
435A Nelson Cruz .25 .60
435B Nelson Cruz 15.00 30.00
Pie in the face
436 New York Mets .25 .60
437 Luke Hochevar .15 .40
438 Jason Bartlett .15 .40
439 Emilio Bonifacio .15 .40
440 Willie Harris .15 .40
441 Clete Thomas .15 .40
442 Dan Runzler RC .40 1.00
443 Jason Hammel .15 .40
444 Yuniesky Betancourt .15 .40
445 Miguel Olivo .15 .40
446 Gavin Floyd .15 .40
447 Jeremy Guthrie .15 .40
448 Joakim Soria .15 .40
449 Ryan Sweeney .15 .40
450A Omir Santos .15 .40
450B Omir Santos UPD Cup SP 12.50 30.00
451 Michael Saunders .15 .40
452 Allen Craig RC .60 1.50
453 Jesse English (RC) .25 .60
454 James Loney .15 .40
455 St. Louis Cardinals .25 .60
456 Clayton Richard .15 .40
457 Kanekoa Texeira RC .25 .60
458 Todd Wellemeyer .15 .40
459 Joel Zumaya .15 .40
460 Aaron Cunningham .15 .40
461 Tyson Ross RC .25 .60
462 Alcides Escobar .25 .60
463 Carlos Marmol .25 .60
464 Francisco Liriano .15 .40
465 Chien-Ming Wang .25 .60
466 Jered Weaver .15 .40
467A Fausto Carmona .15 .40
467B Mitch Talbot 15.00 30.00
Pie in the face
468 Delmon Young .25 .60
469 Alex Burnett RC .25 .60
470 New York Yankees .40 1.00
471 Drew Butera (RC) .25 .60
472 Toronto Blue Jays .15 .40
473 Jason Varitek .40 1.00
474 Kyle Kendrick .15 .40
475A Johnny Damon .25 .60
475B Johnny Damon 50.00 100.00
Pie in the face
476A Yadier Molina .25 .60
476B Thurman Munson SP 8.00 20.00
477 Nate McLouth .15 .40
478 Conor Jackson .15 .40
479A Chris Carpenter .40 1.00
479B Dizzy Dean SP 8.00 20.00
480 Boston Red Sox .25 .60
481 Scott Rolen .25 .60
482 Mike McCoy RC .25 .60
483 Daisuke Matsuzaka .40 1.00
484 Mike Fontenot .15 .40
485 Jesus Flores .15 .40
486 Raul Ibanez .25 .60
487 Dan Uggla .25 .60
488 Delwyn Young .15 .40
489A Russell Martin .15 .40
489B Roy Campanella SP 8.00 20.00
490 Michael Bourn .15 .40
491 Rafael Furcal .15 .40
492 Brian Wilson .40 1.00
493A Travis Ishikawa .15 .40
493B Travis Ishikawa UPD Cup SP 15.00 40.00
494 Andrew Miller .15 .40
495 Carlos Pena .25 .60
496 Rajai Davis .15 .40
497 Edgar Renteria .15 .40
498 Sergio Santos (RC) .25 .60
499 Michael Bowden .15 .40
500 Brad Lidge .15 .40
501 Jake Peavy .15 .40
502 Jhoulys Chacin .15 .40
503 Austin Jackson RC .40 1.00
504 Jeff Mathis .15 .40
505 Andy Marte .15 .40
506 Jose Lopez .15 .40
507 Francisco Rodriguez .25 .60
508A Chris Getz .15 .40
508B Chris Getz UPD Cup SP 12.50 30.00
509A Todd Helton .25 .60
509B Ike Davis 20.00 50.00
Pie in the face
510 Justin Upton .25 .60
Mark Reynolds
511 Chicago Cubs .25 .60
512 Scot Shields .15 .40
513 Scott Sizemore RC .40 1.00
514 Rafael Soriano .15 .40
515 Seattle Mariners .15 .40
516 Marlon Byrd .15 .40
517 Cliff Pennington .15 .40
518 Corey Hart .15 .40
519 Alexi Casilla .15 .40
520 Randy Wells .15 .40
521 Jeremy Bonderman .15 .40
522 Jordan Schafer .15 .40
523 Phil Coke .15 .40
524 Dusty Hughes RC .25 .60
525 David Huff .15 .40
526 Carlos Guillen .15 .40
527 Brandon Wood .15 .40
528 Brian Bannister .15 .40
529 Carlos Lee .15 .40
530 Steve Pearce .15 .40
531 Matt Cain .25 .60
532A Hunter Pence .25 .60
532B Dale Murphy SP 8.00 20.00
533 Gary Matthews Jr. .15 .40
534 Hideki Okajima .15 .40
535 Andy Sonnanstine .15 .40
536 Matt Palmer .15 .40
537 Michael Cuddyer .15 .40
538 Travis Hafner .15 .40
539 Arizona Diamondbacks .15 .40
540 Sean Rodriguez .15 .40
541 Jason Motte .15 .40
542 Heath Bell .15 .40
543 Adam Jones .40 1.00
Nick Markakis
544 Kevin Kouzmanoff .15 .40
545 Fred Lewis .15 .40
546 Bud Norris .15 .40
547 Brett Gardner .15 .40
548 Minnesota Twins .15 .40
549A Derek Jeter 1.00 2.50
549B Pee Wee Reese SP 8.00 20.00
550 Freddy Garcia .15 .40
551 Everth Cabrera .15 .40
552 Chris Tillman .15 .40
553 Florida Marlins .15 .40
554 Ramon Hernandez .15 .40
555 B.J. Upton .25 .60
556 Chicago White Sox .15 .40
557 Aaron Hill .15 .40
558 Ronny Paulino .15 .40
559A Nick Markakis .40 1.00
559B Eddie Murray SP 8.00 20.00
560 Ryan Rowland-Smith .15 .40
561 Ryan Zimmerman .25 .60
562 Carlos Quentin .25 .60
563 Bronson Arroyo .15 .40
564 Houston Astros .15 .40
565 Franklin Morales .15 .40
566 Maicer Izturis .15 .40
567 Mike Pelfrey .15 .40
568 Jarrod Saltalamacchia .15 .40
569A Jacoby Ellsbury .40 1.00
569B Tris Speaker SP 8.00 20.00
570 Josh Willingham .15 .40
571 Brandon Lyon .15 .40
572 Clay Buchholz .25 .60
573 Johan Santana .40 1.00
574 Milwaukee Brewers .15 .40
575 Ryan Perry .15 .40
576 Paul Maholm .15 .40
577 Jason Jaramillo .15 .40
578 Aaron Rowand .15 .40
579A Trevor Cahill .15 .40
579B Juan Miranda 15.00 40.00
Pie in the face
580 Ian Snell .15 .40
581 Chris Dickerson .15 .40
582 Martin Prado .15 .40
583 Anibal Sanchez .15 .40
584 Matt Capps .15 .40
585 Dioner Navarro .15 .40
586 Roy Oswalt .25 .60
587 David Murphy .15 .40
588 Landon Powell .15 .40
589 Edinson Volquez .15 .40
590A Ryan Howard .50 1.25
590B Ernie Banks SP 8.00 20.00
591 Fernando Rodney .15 .40
592 Brian Roberts .15 .40
593 Derek Holland .15 .40
594 Andy LaRoche .15 .40
595 Mike Lowell .15 .40
596 Brendan Ryan .15 .40
597 J.R. Towles .15 .40
598 Alberto Callaspo .15 .40
599 Jay Bruce .25 .60
600A Hanley Ramirez .40 1.00
600B Honus Wagner SP 8.00 20.00
601 Blake DeWitt .15 .40
602 Kansas City Royals .15 .40
603 Gerardo Parra .15 .40
604 Atlanta Braves .15 .40
605 A.J. Pierzynski .15 .40
606 Chad Qualls .15 .40
607 Ubaldo Jimenez .25 .60
608 Pittsburgh Pirates .15 .40
609 Jeff Suppan .15 .40
610 Alex Gordon .25 .60
611 Josh Outman .15 .40
612 Lastings Milledge .15 .40
613 Eric Chavez .15 .40
614 Kelly Johnson .15 .40
615A Justin Verlander .50 1.25
615B Nolan Ryan SP 10.00 25.00
616 Franklin Gutierrez .15 .40
617 Luis Valbuena .15 .40
618 Jorge Cantu .15 .40
619 Mike Napoli .25 .60
620 Geovany Soto .25 .60
621 Aaron Cook .15 .40
622 Cleveland Indians .15 .40
623 Miguel Cabrera .40 1.00
624 Carlos Beltran .15 .40
625 Grady Sizemore .25 .60
626 Glen Perkins .15 .40
627 Jeremy Hermida .15 .40
628 Ross Detwiler .15 .40
629 Oliver Perez .15 .40
630 Ben Francisco .15 .40
631 Marc Rzepczynski .15 .40
632 Daric Barton .15 .40
633 Daniel Bard .15 .40
634 Casey Kotchman .15 .40
635 Carl Pavano .15 .40
636 Evan Longoria .50 1.25
B.J. Upton
637 Babe Ruth 1.00 2.50
Lou Gehrig
638 Paul Konerko .25 .60
639 Los Angeles Dodgers .25 .60
640 Matt Diaz .15 .40
641 Chase Headley .15 .40
642 San Diego Padres .15 .40
643 Michael Young .25 .60
644 David Purcey .15 .40
645 Texas Rangers .15 .40
646 Trevor Crowe .15 .40
647 Alfonso Soriano .25 .60
648 Brian Fuentes .15 .40
649 Casey McGehee .15 .40
650A Dustin Pedroia .50 1.25
650B Ty Cobb SP 8.00 20.00
651 Mike Aviles .15 .40
652A Chipper Jones .40 1.00
652B Mickey Mantle SP 10.00 25.00
653A Nolan Reimold .25 .60
653B Nolan Reimold UPD Cup SP 12.50 30.00
654 Collin Balester .15 .40
655 Ryan Madson .15 .40
656 Jon Lester .40 1.00
657 Chris Young .15 .40
658 Tommy Hunter .15 .40
659 Nick Blackburn .15 .40
660 Brandon McCarthy .15 .40
661A Stephen Strasburg 20.00 50.00
Million Card Giveaway
661B Stephen Strasburg FS 5.00 12.00
Issue in Factory Sets
661C Stephen Strasburg 250.00 500.00
Million Card Giveaway AU/299
661D Stephen Strasburg UPD 4.00 10.00
Wearing White Jersey Arm Back
661E Stephen Strasburg UPD SP VAR 75.00 150.00
Wearing Grey Jersey
661F Stephen Strasburg UPD 40.00 80.00
Pie in the Face
661G Bob Gibson UPD SP VAR 8.00 20.00

2010 Topps Black

SER.1 ODDS 1:96 HOBBY
SER.2 ODDS 1:112 HOBBY
STATED PRINT RUN 59 SER.#'d SETS
1 Prince Fielder 5.00 12.00
2 Buster Posey 30.00 80.00
3 Derrek Lee 4.00 10.00
4 Hanley Ramirez 20.00 50.00
Pablo Sandoval
Albert Pujols
5 Texas Rangers 5.00 12.00
6 Chicago White Sox 5.00 12.00
7 Mickey Mantle 25.00 60.00
8 Joe Mauer 20.00 50.00
Ichiro Suzuki
Derek Jeter
9 Tim Lincecum NL CY 12.00 30.00
10 Clayton Kershaw 8.00 20.00
11 Orlando Cabrera 5.00 12.00
12 Doug Davis 5.00 12.00
13 Melvin Mora 5.00 12.00
14 Ted Lilly 5.00 12.00
15 Bobby Abreu 5.00 12.00
16 Johnny Cueto 5.00 12.00
17 Dexter Fowler 5.00 12.00
18 Tim Stauffer 5.00 12.00
19 Felipe Lopez 5.00 12.00
20 Tommy Hanson 6.00 15.00
21 Cristian Guzman 5.00 12.00
22 Anthony Swarzak 5.00 12.00
23 Shane Victorino 6.00 15.00
24 John Maine 5.00 12.00
25 Adam Jones 6.00 15.00
26 Zach Duke 5.00 12.00
27 Lance Berkman 6.00 15.00
Mike Hampton
28 Jonathan Sanchez 5.00 12.00
29 Aubrey Huff 5.00 12.00
30 Victor Martinez 6.00 15.00
31 Jason Grilli 5.00 12.00
32 Cincinnati Reds 5.00 12.00
33 Adam Moore 5.00 12.00
34 Michael Dunn 5.00 12.00
35 Rick Porcello 3.00 8.00
36 Tobi Stoner 5.00 12.00
37 Garrett Anderson 5.00 12.00
38 Houston Astros 5.00 12.00
39 Jeff Baker 5.00 12.00
40 Josh Johnson 6.00 15.00
41 Los Angeles Dodgers 5.00 12.00
42 Prince Fielder 5.00 12.00
Ryan Howard
Albert Pujols
43 Marco Scutaro 5.00 12.00
44 Howie Kendrick 5.00 12.00
45 David Hernandez 5.00 12.00
46 Chad Tracy 5.00 12.00
47 Brad Penny 5.00 12.00
48 Joey Votto 8.00 20.00
49 Jorge De La Rosa 5.00 12.00
50 Zack Greinke 5.00 12.00
51 Eric Young Jr 5.00 12.00
52 Billy Butler 5.00 12.00
53 Craig Counsell 5.00 12.00
54 John Lackey 5.00 12.00
55 Manny Ramirez 8.00 20.00
56 Andy Pettitte 6.00 15.00
57 CC Sabathia 6.00 15.00
58 Kyle Blanks 5.00 12.00
59 Kevin Gregg 5.00 12.00
60 David Wright 10.00 25.00
61 Skip Schumaker 5.00 12.00
62 Kevin Millwood 5.00 12.00
63 Josh Beckett 5.00 12.00
64 Drew Stubbs 8.00 20.00
65 Nick Swisher 10.00 25.00
66 Kyle Phillips 5.00 12.00
67 Matt LaPorta 8.00 20.00
68 Brandon Inge 6.00 15.00
69 Kansas City Royals 5.00 12.00
70 Cole Hamels 8.00 20.00
71 Mike Hampton 5.00 12.00
72 Milwaukee Brewers 5.00 12.00
73 Adam Wainwright 10.00 25.00
Chris Carpenter
Jorge De La Rosa
74 Casey Blake 5.00 12.00
75 Adrian Gonzalez 6.00 15.00
76 Joe Saunders 5.00 12.00
77 Kenshin Kawakami 6.00 15.00
78 Cesar Izturis 5.00 12.00
79 Francisco Cordero 5.00 12.00
80 Tim Lincecum 12.00 30.00
81 Ryan Theriot 5.00 12.00
82 Jason Marquis 5.00 12.00
83 Mark Teahen 5.00 12.00
84 Nate Robertson 5.00 12.00
85 Ken Griffey Jr. 12.00 30.00
86 Gil Meche 5.00 12.00
87 Darin Erstad 5.00 12.00
88 Jerry Hairston Jr. 5.00 12.00
89 J.A. Happ 6.00 15.00
90 Ian Kinsler 6.00 15.00
91 Erik Bedard 5.00 12.00
92 David Eckstein 5.00 12.00
93 Joe Nathan 5.00 12.00
94 Ivan Rodriguez 6.00 15.00
95 Carl Crawford 6.00 15.00
96 Jon Garland 5.00 12.00
97 Luis Durango 5.00 12.00
98 Cesar Ramos 5.00 12.00
99 Garrett Jones 6.00 15.00
100 Albert Pujols 20.00 50.00
101 Scott Baker 5.00 12.00
102 Minnesota Twins 5.00 12.00
103 Daniel Murphy 5.00 12.00
104 New York Mets 6.00 15.00
105 Madison Bumgarner 8.00 20.00
106 Chris Carpenter 12.00 30.00
Tim Lincecum
Jair Jurrjens
107 Scott Hairston 5.00 12.00
108 Erick Aybar 5.00 12.00
109 Justin Masterson 5.00 12.00
110 Andrew McCutchen 8.00 20.00
111 Ty Wigginton 5.00 12.00
112 Kevin Correia 5.00 12.00
113 Willy Taveras 5.00 12.00
114 Chris Iannetta 5.00 12.00
115 Gordon Beckham 6.00 15.00
116 Carlos Gomez 5.00 12.00
117 David DeJesus 5.00 12.00
118 Brandon Morrow 5.00 12.00
119 Wilkin Ramirez 5.00 12.00
120 Jorge Posada 6.00 15.00
121 Brett Anderson 8.00 20.00
122 Carlos Ruiz 5.00 12.00
123 Jeff Samardzija 5.00 12.00
124 Rickie Weeks 8.00 20.00
125 Ichiro Suzuki 12.00 30.00
126 John Smoltz 8.00 20.00
127 Hank Blalock 5.00 12.00
128 Garrett Mock 5.00 12.00
129 Reid Gorecki 6.00 15.00
130 Vladimir Guerrero 8.00 20.00
131 Dustin Richardson 5.00 12.00
132 Cliff Lee 6.00 15.00
133 Freddy Sanchez 5.00 12.00
134 Philadelphia Phillies 5.00 12.00
135 Ryan Dempster 5.00 12.00
136 Adam Wainwright 6.00 15.00
137 Oakland Athletics 5.00 12.00
138 Carlos Pena 8.00 20.00
Mark Teixeira
Jason Bay
139 Frank Francisco 5.00 12.00
140 Matt Holliday 8.00 20.00
141 Chone Figgins 5.00 12.00
142 Tim Hudson 8.00 20.00
143 Omar Vizquel 6.00 15.00
144 Rich Harden 5.00 12.00
145 Justin Upton 6.00 15.00
146 Yunel Escobar 5.00 12.00
147 Huston Street 5.00 12.00
148 Cody Ross 5.00 12.00
149 Jose Guillen 5.00 12.00
150 Joe Mauer 8.00 20.00
151 Mat Gamel 5.00 12.00
152 Nyjer Morgan 5.00 12.00
153 Justin Duchscherer 5.00 12.00
154 Pedro Feliz 5.00 12.00
155 Zack Greinke AL CY 5.00 12.00
156 Tony Gwynn Jr. 5.00 12.00
157 Mike Sweeney 5.00 12.00
158 Jeff Niemann 5.00 12.00
159 Vernon Wells 5.00 12.00
160 Miguel Tejada 6.00 15.00
161 Denard Span 5.00 12.00
162 Wade Davis 5.00 12.00
163 Josh Butler 5.00 12.00
164 Carlos Carrasco 8.00 20.00
165 Brandon Phillips 5.00 12.00
166 Eric Byrnes 5.00 12.00
167 San Diego Padres 5.00 12.00
168 Brad Kilby 5.00 12.00
169 Pittsburgh Pirates 5.00 12.00
170 Jason Bay 6.00 15.00
171 Felix Hernandez 12.00 30.00
CC Sabathia
Justin Verlander
172 Joe Mauer AL MVP 8.00 20.00
173 Kendry Morales 5.00 12.00
174 Mike Gonzalez 5.00 12.00
175 Josh Hamilton 8.00 20.00
176 Yovani Gallardo 5.00 12.00
177 Adam Lind 6.00 15.00
178 Kerry Wood 5.00 12.00
179 Ryan Spilborghs 5.00 12.00
180 Jayson Nix 5.00 12.00
181 Nick Johnson 5.00 12.00
182 Coco Crisp 5.00 12.00
183 Jonathan Papelbon 6.00 15.00
184 Jeff Francoeur 5.00 12.00
185 Hideki Matsui 8.00 20.00
186 Andrew Bailey 5.00 12.00
187 Will Venable 5.00 12.00
188 Joe Blanton 5.00 12.00
189 Adrian Beltre 5.00 12.00
190 Pablo Sandoval 6.00 15.00
191 Mat Latos 5.00 12.00
192 Andruw Jones 5.00 12.00
193 Shairon Martis 5.00 12.00
194 Neil Walker 8.00 20.00
195 James Shields 5.00 12.00
196 Ian Desmond 8.00 20.00
197 Cleveland Indians 5.00 12.00
198 Florida Marlins 5.00 12.00
199 Seattle Mariners 5.00 12.00
200 Roy Halladay 8.00 20.00
201 Detroit Tigers 5.00 12.00
202 San Francisco Giants 5.00 12.00
203 Zack Greinke 8.00 20.00
Felix Hernandez
Roy Halladay
204 Elvis Andrus 6.00 15.00
Ian Kinsler
205 Chris Coghlan 4.00 10.00
206 Albert Pujols 5.00 12.00
Prince Fielder
Ryan Howard
207 Colby Rasmus 8.00 20.00
208 Tim Wakefield 5.00 12.00
209 Alexei Ramirez 5.00 12.00
210 Josh Beckett 6.00 15.00
211 Kelly Shoppach 5.00 12.00
212 Magglio Ordonez 6.00 15.00
213 Ricky Nolasco 5.00 12.00
214 Matt Kemp 6.00 15.00
215 Max Scherzer 5.00 12.00
216 Mike Cameron 5.00 12.00
217 Gio Gonzalez 6.00 15.00
218 Fernando Martinez 5.00 12.00
219 Kevin Hart 5.00 12.00
220 Randy Johnson 6.00 15.00
221 Russell Branyan 5.00 12.00
222 Curtis Granderson 6.00 15.00
223 Ryan Church 5.00 12.00
224 Rod Barajas 5.00 12.00
225 David Price 8.00 20.00
226 Juan Rivera 5.00 12.00
227 Josh Thole 6.00 15.00
228 Chris Pettit 5.00 12.00
229 Daniel McCutchen 6.00 15.00
230 Jonathan Broxton 5.00 12.00
231 Luke Scott 5.00 12.00
232 St. Louis Cardinals 6.00 15.00
233 Mark Teixeira 8.00 20.00
Jason Bay
Adam Lind
234 Tampa Bay Rays 5.00 12.00

235 Neftali Feliz 4.00 10.00
236 Andrew Bailey AL ROY 5.00 12.00
237 Ryan Braun 5.00 12.00
Prince Fielder
238 Ian Stewart 5.00 12.00
239 Juan Uribe 5.00 12.00
240 Ricky Romero 5.00 12.00
241 Rocco Baldelli 5.00 12.00
242 Bobby Jenks 5.00 12.00
243 Asdrubal Cabrera 8.00 20.00
244 Barry Zito 5.00 12.00
245 Lance Berkman 6.00 15.00
246 Leo Nunez 5.00 12.00
247 Andre Ethier 5.00 12.00
248 Jason Kendall 5.00 12.00
249 Jon Niese 5.00 12.00
250 Mark Teixeira 8.00 20.00
251 John Lannan 5.00 12.00
252 Ronny Cedeno 5.00 12.00
253 Bengie Molina 5.00 12.00
254 Edwin Jackson 5.00 12.00
255 Chris Davis 5.00 12.00
256 Akinori Iwamura 5.00 12.00
257 Bobby Crosby 5.00 12.00
258 Edwin Encarnacion 5.00 12.00
259 Daniel Hudson 6.00 15.00
260 New York Yankees 8.00 20.00
261 Matt Carson 5.00 12.00
262 Homer Bailey 5.00 12.00
263 Placido Polanco 5.00 12.00
264 Arizona Diamondbacks 5.00 12.00
265 Los Angeles Angels 5.00 12.00
266 Humberto Quintero 5.00 12.00
267 Toronto Blue Jays 5.00 12.00
268 Juan Pierre 5.00 12.00
269 Alex Rodriguez 20.00 50.00
Derek Jeter
Robinson Cano
270 Michael Brantley 5.00 12.00
271 Jermaine Dye 5.00 12.00
272 Jair Jurrjens 5.00 12.00
273 Pat Neshek 5.00 12.00
274 Stephen Drew 4.00 10.00
275 Chris Coghlan NL ROY 4.00 10.00
276 Matt Lindstrom 5.00 12.00
277 Jarrod Washburn 5.00 12.00
278 Carlos Delgado 5.00 12.00
279 Randy Wolf 5.00 12.00
280 Mark DeRosa 5.00 12.00
281 Braden Looper 5.00 12.00
282 Washington Nationals 5.00 12.00
283 Adam Kennedy 5.00 12.00
284 Ross Ohlendorf 5.00 12.00
285 Kurt Suzuki 5.00 12.00
286 Javier Vazquez 5.00 12.00
287 Jhonny Peralta 5.00 12.00
288 Boston Red Sox 6.00 15.00
289 Lyle Overbay 5.00 12.00
290 Orlando Hudson 5.00 12.00
291 Austin Kearns 5.00 12.00
292 Tommy Manzella 5.00 12.00
293 Brent Dlugach 5.00 12.00
294 Adam Dunn 8.00 20.00
295 Kevin Youkilis 6.00 15.00
296 Atlanta Braves 5.00 12.00
297 Ben Zobrist 5.00 12.00
298 Baltimore Orioles 5.00 12.00
299 Gary Sheffield 5.00 12.00
300 Chase Utley 8.00 20.00
301 Jack Cust 5.00 12.00
302 Kevin Youkilis 6.00 15.00
David Ortiz
303 Chris Snyder 5.00 12.00
304 Adam LaRoche 5.00 12.00
305 Juan Francisco 6.00 15.00
306 Milton Bradley 5.00 12.00
307 Henry Rodriguez 5.00 12.00
308 Robinzon Diaz 5.00 12.00
309 Gerald Laird 5.00 12.00
310 Elvis Andrus 6.00 15.00
311 Jose Valverde 5.00 12.00
312 Tyler Flowers 6.00 15.00
313 Jason Kubel 5.00 12.00
314 Angel Pagan 5.00 12.00
315 Scott Kazmir 5.00 12.00
316 Chris Young 5.00 12.00
317 Ryan Doumit 5.00 12.00
318 Nate Schierholtz 5.00 12.00
319 Ryan Franklin 5.00 12.00
320 Brian McCann 6.00 15.00
321 Pat Burrell 5.00 12.00
322 Travis Buck 5.00 12.00
323 Jim Thome 6.00 15.00
324 Alex Rios 6.00 15.00
325 Julio Lugo 5.00 12.00
326 Tyler Colvin 6.00 15.00
327 Albert Pujols NL MVP 20.00 50.00
328 Chicago Cubs 6.00 15.00
329 Colorado Rockies 5.00 12.00
330 Brandon Allen 5.00 12.00
331 Ryan Braun 10.00 25.00
332 Brad Hawpe 5.00 12.00
333 Ryan Ludwick 5.00 12.00
334 Jayson Werth 8.00 20.00
335 Jordan Norberto 5.00 12.00
336 C.J. Wilson 5.00 12.00
337 Carlos Zambrano 6.00 15.00
338 Brett Cecil 5.00 12.00
339 Jose Reyes 6.00 15.00
340 John Buck 5.00 12.00
341 Texas Rangers 5.00 12.00
342 Melky Cabrera 5.00 12.00
343 Brian Bruney 5.00 12.00
344 Brett Myers 5.00 12.00
345 Chris Volstad 5.00 12.00
346 Taylor Teagarden 5.00 12.00
347 Aaron Harang 5.00 12.00
348 Jordan Zimmermann 5.00 12.00
349 Felix Pie 5.00 12.00
350 Prince Fielder 5.00 12.00
Ryan Braun
351 Koji Uehara 6.00 15.00
352 Cameron Maybin 4.00 10.00
353 Jason Heyward 100.00 175.00
354 Evan Longoria 10.00 25.00
355 James Russell 8.00 20.00
356 Los Angeles Angels 5.00 12.00
357 Scott Downs 5.00 12.00
358 Mark Buehrle 8.00 20.00
359 Aramis Ramirez 5.00 12.00
360 Justin Morneau 10.00 25.00
361 Washington Nationals 5.00 12.00
362 Travis Snider 5.00 12.00
363 Joba Chamberlain 6.00 15.00
364 Trevor Hoffman 8.00 20.00
365 Logan Ondrusek 5.00 12.00
366 Hiroki Kuroda 5.00 12.00
367 Wandy Rodriguez 5.00 12.00
368 Wade LeBlanc 5.00 12.00
369 David Ortiz 6.00 15.00
370 Robinson Cano 10.00 25.00
371 Nick Hundley 5.00 12.00
372 Philadelphia Phillies 5.00 12.00
373 Clint Barmes 5.00 12.00
374 Scott Feldman 5.00 12.00
375 Mike Leake 10.00 25.00
376 Esmil Rogers 5.00 12.00
377 Felix Hernandez 10.00 25.00
378 George Sherrill 5.00 12.00
379 Phil Hughes 5.00 12.00
380 J.D. Drew 5.00 12.00
381 Miguel Montero 5.00 12.00
382 Kyle Davies 5.00 12.00
383 Derek Lowe 5.00 12.00
384 Chris Johnson 12.00 30.00
385 Torii Hunter 5.00 12.00
386 Dan Haren 5.00 12.00
387 Josh Fields 5.00 12.00
388 Joel Pineiro 5.00 12.00
389 Troy Tulowitzki 10.00 25.00
390 Ervin Santana 5.00 12.00
391 Manny Parra 5.00 12.00
392 Carlos Monasterios 6.00 15.00
393 Jason Frasor 5.00 12.00
394 Luis Castillo 5.00 12.00
395 Henry Mejia 8.00 20.00
396 Jake Westbrook 5.00 12.00
397 Colorado Rockies 5.00 12.00
398 Carlos Gonzalez 8.00 20.00
399 Matt Garza 5.00 12.00
400 Alex Rodriguez 12.00 30.00
401 Chad Billingsley 5.00 12.00
402 J.P. Howell 5.00 12.00
403 Jimmy Rollins 6.00 15.00
404 Mariano Rivera 8.00 20.00
405 Dustin McGowan 5.00 12.00
406 Jeff Francis 5.00 12.00
407 Nick Punto 5.00 12.00
408 Detroit Tigers 5.00 12.00
409 Kosuke Fukudome 8.00 20.00
410 Oakland Athletics 5.00 12.00
411 Jack Wilson 5.00 12.00
412 San Francisco Giants 5.00 12.00
413 J.J. Hardy 5.00 12.00
414 Sean West 5.00 12.00
415 Cincinnati Reds 5.00 12.00
416 Ruben Tejada 6.00 15.00
417 Dallas Braden 6.00 15.00
418 Aaron Laffey 5.00 12.00
419 David Aardsma 5.00 12.00
420 Shin-Soo Choo 8.00 20.00
421 Doug Fister 5.00 12.00
422 Vin Mazzaro 5.00 12.00
423 Brad Bergesen 5.00 12.00
424 David Herndon 5.00 12.00
425 Dontrelle Willis 5.00 12.00
426 Mark Reynolds 5.00 12.00
427 Brandon Webb 6.00 15.00
428 Baltimore Orioles 5.00 12.00
429 Seth Smith 5.00 12.00
430 Kazuo Matsui 5.00 12.00
431 John Raynor 5.00 12.00
432 A.J. Burnett 6.00 15.00
433 Julio Borbon 5.00 12.00
434 Kevin Slowey 5.00 12.00
435 Nelson Cruz 8.00 20.00
436 New York Mets 6.00 15.00
437 Luke Hochevar 5.00 12.00
438 Jason Bartlett 5.00 12.00
439 Emilio Bonifacio 5.00 12.00
440 Willie Harris 5.00 12.00
441 Clete Thomas 5.00 12.00
442 Dan Runzler 6.00 15.00
443 Jason Hammel 5.00 12.00
444 Yuniesky Betancourt 5.00 12.00
445 Miguel Olivo 5.00 12.00
446 Gavin Floyd 5.00 12.00
447 Jeremy Guthrie 5.00 12.00
448 Joakim Soria 5.00 12.00
449 Ryan Sweeney 5.00 12.00
450 Omir Santos 5.00 12.00
451 Michael Saunders 5.00 12.00
452 Allen Craig 12.00 30.00
453 Jesse English 5.00 12.00
454 James Loney 6.00 15.00
455 St. Louis Cardinals 6.00 15.00
456 Clayton Richard 5.00 12.00
457 Kanekoa Texeira 5.00 12.00
458 Todd Wellemeyer 5.00 12.00
459 Joel Zumaya 5.00 12.00
460 Aaron Cunningham 5.00 12.00
461 Tyson Ross 5.00 12.00
462 Alcides Escobar 6.00 15.00
463 Carlos Marmol 8.00 20.00
464 Francisco Liriano 5.00 12.00
465 Chien-Ming Wang 5.00 12.00
466 Jered Weaver 5.00 12.00
467 Fausto Carmona 5.00 12.00
468 Delmon Young 6.00 15.00
469 Alex Burnett 5.00 12.00
470 New York Yankees 8.00 20.00
471 Drew Butera 5.00 12.00
472 Toronto Blue Jays 5.00 12.00
473 Jason Vantek 8.00 20.00
474 Kyle Kendrick 5.00 12.00
475 Johnny Damon 6.00 15.00
476 Yadier Molina 6.00 15.00
477 Nate McLouth 5.00 12.00
478 Conor Jackson 5.00 12.00
479 Chris Carpenter 10.00 25.00
480 Boston Red Sox 6.00 15.00
481 Scott Rolen 6.00 15.00
482 Mike McCoy 5.00 12.00
483 Daisuke Matsuzaka 8.00 20.00
484 Mike Fontenot 5.00 12.00
485 Jesus Flores 5.00 12.00
486 Raul Ibanez 6.00 15.00
487 Dan Uggla 6.00 15.00
488 Delwyn Young 8.00 20.00
489 Russell Martin 4.00 10.00
490 Michael Bourn 5.00 12.00
491 Rafael Furcal 5.00 12.00
492 Brian Wilson 12.00 30.00
493 Travis Ishikawa 6.00 15.00
494 Andrew Miller 5.00 12.00
495 Carlos Pena 6.00 15.00
496 Rajai Davis 5.00 12.00
497 Edgar Renteria 5.00 12.00
498 Sergio Santos 5.00 12.00
499 Michael Bowden 5.00 12.00
500 Brad Lidge 5.00 12.00
501 Jake Peavy 4.00 10.00
502 Jhoulys Chacin 5.00 12.00
503 Austin Jackson 5.00 12.00
504 Jeff Mathis 5.00 12.00
505 Andy Marte 5.00 12.00
506 Jose Lopez 5.00 12.00
507 Francisco Rodriguez 6.00 15.00
508 Chris Getz 5.00 12.00
509 Todd Helton 6.00 15.00
510 Justin Upton 6.00 15.00
Mark Reynolds
511 Chicago Cubs 6.00 15.00
512 Scot Shields 5.00 12.00
513 Scott Sizemore 6.00 15.00
514 Rafael Soriano 5.00 12.00
515 Seattle Mariners 5.00 12.00
516 Marlon Byrd 5.00 12.00
517 Cliff Pennington 5.00 12.00
518 Corey Hart 5.00 12.00
519 Alexi Casilla 5.00 12.00
520 Randy Wells 5.00 12.00
521 Jeremy Bonderman 5.00 12.00
522 Jordan Schafer 5.00 12.00
523 Phil Coke 5.00 12.00
524 Dusty Hughes 5.00 12.00
525 David Huff 5.00 12.00
526 Carlos Guillen 5.00 12.00
527 Brandon Wood 5.00 12.00
528 Brian Bannister 5.00 12.00
529 Carlos Lee 5.00 12.00
530 Steve Pearce 5.00 12.00
531 Matt Cain 6.00 15.00
532 Hunter Pence 5.00 12.00
533 Gary Matthews Jr. 5.00 12.00
534 Hideki Okajima 5.00 12.00
535 Andy Sonnanstine 5.00 12.00
536 Matt Palmer 5.00 12.00
537 Michael Cuddyer 5.00 12.00
538 Travis Hafner 5.00 12.00
539 Arizona Diamondbacks 5.00 12.00
540 Sean Rodriguez 5.00 12.00
541 Jason Motte 5.00 12.00
542 Heath Bell 8.00 20.00
543 Adam Jones 10.00 25.00
Nick Markakis
544 Kevin Kouzmanoff 5.00 12.00
545 Fred Lewis 5.00 12.00
546 Bud Norris 5.00 12.00
547 Brett Gardner 5.00 12.00
548 Minnesota Twins 5.00 12.00
549 Derek Jeter 20.00 50.00
550 Freddy Garcia 5.00 12.00
551 Everth Cabrera 5.00 12.00
552 Chris Tillman 5.00 12.00
553 Florida Marlins 5.00 12.00
554 Ramon Hernandez 5.00 12.00
555 B.J. Upton 6.00 15.00
556 Chicago White Sox 5.00 12.00
557 Aaron Hill 5.00 12.00
558 Ronny Paulino 5.00 12.00
559 Nick Markakis 10.00 25.00
560 Ryan Rowland-Smith 5.00 12.00
561 Ryan Zimmerman 6.00 15.00
562 Carlos Quentin 6.00 15.00
563 Bronson Arroyo 5.00 12.00
564 Houston Astros 5.00 12.00
565 Franklin Morales 5.00 12.00
566 Maicer Izturis 5.00 12.00
567 Mike Pelfrey 5.00 12.00
568 Jarrod Saltalamacchia 5.00 12.00
569 Jacoby Ellsbury 8.00 20.00
570 Josh Willingham 5.00 12.00
571 Brandon Lyon 5.00 12.00
572 Clay Buchholz 6.00 15.00
573 Johan Santana 8.00 20.00
574 Milwaukee Brewers 5.00 12.00
575 Ryan Perry 5.00 12.00
576 Paul Maholm 5.00 12.00
577 Jason Jaramillo 5.00 12.00
578 Aaron Rowand 5.00 12.00
579 Trevor Cahill 5.00 12.00
580 Ian Snell 5.00 12.00
581 Chris Dickerson 5.00 12.00
582 Martin Prado 5.00 12.00
583 Anibal Sanchez 5.00 12.00
584 Matt Capps 5.00 12.00
585 Dioner Navarro 5.00 12.00
586 Roy Oswalt 6.00 15.00
587 David Murphy 5.00 12.00
588 Landon Powell 5.00 12.00
589 Edinson Volquez 5.00 12.00
590 Ryan Howard 10.00 25.00
591 Fernando Rodney 5.00 12.00
592 Brian Roberts 5.00 12.00
593 Derek Holland 5.00 12.00
594 Andy LaRoche 5.00 12.00
595 Mike Lowell 5.00 12.00
596 Brendan Ryan 5.00 12.00
597 J.R. Towles 5.00 12.00
598 Alberto Callaspo 5.00 12.00
599 Jay Bruce 6.00 15.00
600 Hanley Ramirez 8.00 20.00
601 Blake DeWitt 5.00 12.00
602 Kansas City Royals 5.00 12.00
603 Gerardo Parra 5.00 12.00
604 Atlanta Braves 5.00 12.00
605 A.J. Pierzynski 5.00 12.00
606 Chad Qualls 5.00 12.00
607 Ubaldo Jimenez 6.00 15.00
608 Pittsburgh Pirates 5.00 12.00
609 Jeff Suppan 5.00 12.00
610 Alex Gordon 6.00 15.00
611 Josh Outman 5.00 12.00
612 Lastings Milledge 5.00 12.00
613 Eric Chavez 5.00 12.00
614 Kelly Johnson 5.00 12.00
615 Justin Verlander 12.00 30.00
616 Franklin Gutierrez 5.00 12.00
617 Luis Valbuena 5.00 12.00
618 Jorge Cantu 5.00 12.00
619 Mike Napoli 8.00 20.00
620 Geovany Soto 6.00 15.00
621 Aaron Cook 5.00 12.00
622 Cleveland Indians 5.00 12.00
623 Miguel Cabrera 10.00 25.00
624 Carlos Beltran 5.00 12.00
625 Grady Sizemore 6.00 15.00
626 Glen Perkins 5.00 12.00
627 Jeremy Hermida 5.00 12.00
628 Ross Detwiler 5.00 12.00
629 Oliver Perez 5.00 12.00
630 Ben Francisco 5.00 12.00
631 Marc Rzepczynski 5.00 12.00
632 Daric Barton 5.00 12.00
633 Daniel Bard 5.00 12.00
634 Casey Kotchman 5.00 12.00
635 Carl Pavano 5.00 12.00
636 Evan Longoria 10.00 25.00
B.J. Upton
637 Babe Ruth 20.00 50.00
Lou Gehrig
638 Paul Konerko 8.00 20.00
639 Los Angeles Dodgers 6.00 15.00
640 Matt Diaz 5.00 12.00
641 Chase Headley 5.00 12.00
642 San Diego Padres 5.00 12.00
643 Michael Young 6.00 15.00
644 David Purcey 5.00 12.00
645 Texas Rangers 5.00 12.00
646 Trevor Crowe 5.00 12.00
647 Alfonso Soriano 6.00 15.00
648 Brian Fuentes 5.00 12.00
649 Casey McGehee 5.00 12.00
650 Dustin Pedroia 10.00 25.00
651 Mike Aviles 5.00 12.00
652 Chipper Jones 8.00 20.00
653 Nolan Reimold 6.00 15.00
654 Collin Balester 5.00 12.00
655 Ryan Madson 5.00 12.00
656 Jon Lester 10.00 25.00
657 Chris Young 5.00 12.00
658 Tommy Hunter 5.00 12.00
659 Nick Blackburn 5.00 12.00
660 Brandon McCarthy 5.00 12.00
661 Stephen Strasburg UPD

2010 Topps Copper

*COPPER VET: 4X TO 10X BASIC
*COPPER RC: 2.5X TO 6X BASIC RC
STATED ODDS 1:11 WM RETAIL
STATED PRINT RUN 399 SER.#'d SETS

2010 Topps Gold Border

*GOLD VET: 2X TO 5X BASIC
*GOLD RC: 1.2X TO 3X BASIC RC
STATED ODDS 1:6 HOBBY
STATED PRINT RUN 2010 SER.#'d SETS
1-330 ISSUED IN SERIES 1
331-660 ISSUE IN SERIES 2

2010 Topps Platinum

SER.1 ODDS 1:12,900 HOBBY
SER.2 ODDS 1:16,000 HOBBY
STATED PRINT RUN 1 SER.#'d SET
1-330 ISSUED IN SERIES 1
331-660 ISSUE IN SERIES 2
NO PRICING DUE TO SCARCITY

2010 Topps Target

*VETS: .5X TO 1.2X BASIC TOPPS CARDS
*RC: .5X TO 1.2X BASIC TOPPS RC CARDS

2010 Topps Wal Mart Black Border

*VETS: .5X TO 1.2X BASIC TOPPS CARDS
*RC: .5X TO 1.2X BASIC TOPPS RC CARDS

2010 Topps 2020

COMPLETE SET (20) 6.00 15.00
STATED ODDS 1:6 HOBBY
T1 Ryan Braun 1.00 2.50
T2 Gordon Beckham .50 1.25
T3 Andre Ethier .50 1.25
T4 David Price .75 2.00
T5 Justin Upton .50 1.25
T6 Hunter Pence .50 1.25
T7 Ryan Howard 1.00 2.50
T8 Buster Posey 3.00 8.00
T9 Madison Bumgarner .75 2.00
T10 Evan Longoria 1.00 2.50
T11 Joe Mauer .75 2.00
T12 Chris Coghlan .30 .75
T13 Andrew McCutchen .75 2.00
T14 Ubaldo Jimenez .50 1.25
T15 Pablo Sandoval .50 1.25
T16 David Wright 1.00 2.50
T17 Tommy Hanson .50 1.25
T18 Clayton Kershaw .75 2.00
T19 Zack Greinke .50 1.25
T20 Matt Kemp .50 1.25

2010 Topps Baseball Legends Cut Sigs

STATED ODDS 1:289,000 HOBBY
NO PRICING DUE TO SCARCITY

2010 Topps Blue Back

INSERTED IN WAL MART PACKS
31-45 ISSUED IN UPD WM PACKS
1 Babe Ruth 2.50 6.00
2 Stan Musial 1.50 4.00
3 George Sisler 1.00 2.50
4 Tim Lincecum 1.50 4.00
5 Ichiro Suzuki 1.50 4.00
6 Roy Halladay 1.00 2.50
7 Walter Johnson 1.00 2.50
8 Nolan Ryan 3.00 8.00
9 Hanley Ramirez 1.00 2.50
10 Derek Jeter 2.50 6.00
11 Tom Seaver .60 1.50
12 Roger Maris 1.00 2.50
13 Honus Wagner 1.00 2.50
14 Vladimir Guerrero 1.00 2.50
15 Mel Ott 1.00 2.50
16 Mickey Mantle 3.00 8.00
17 Cal Ripken Jr. 4.00 10.00
18 Cy Young 1.00 2.50
19 Jackie Robinson 1.00 2.50
20 Jimmie Foxx 1.00 2.50
21 Lou Gehrig 2.00 5.00
22 Rogers Hornsby .60 1.50
23 Ty Cobb 1.50 4.00
24 Dizzy Dean .40 1.00
25 Reggie Jackson .60 1.50
26 Warren Spahn .60 1.50
27 Albert Pujols 2.50 6.00
28 Chipper Jones 1.00 2.50
29 Mariano Rivera 1.00 2.50
30 David Wright 1.25 3.00
31 Babe Ruth 2.50 6.00
32 Jimmie Foxx 1.00 2.50
33 Rogers Hornsby .60 1.50
34 Ty Cobb 1.50 4.00
35 Dizzy Dean .40 1.00
36 Reggie Jackson .60 1.50
37 Nolan Ryan 3.00 8.00
38 Tom Seaver .60 1.50
39 Roger Maris 1.00 2.50
40 Vladimir Guerrero 1.00 2.50
41 Roy Campanella 1.00 2.50
42 Johnny Mize .60 1.50
43 Christy Mathewson 1.00 2.50
44 Carl Yastrzemski 1.00 2.50
45 Joe Mauer 1.00 2.50

2010 Topps Cards Your Mom Threw Out

COMPLETE SET (174) 40.00 100.00
SER.1 ODDS 1:3 HOBBY
SER.2 ODDS 1:3 HOBBY
UPD ODDS 1:3 HOBBY
CMT1 Mickey Mantle 3.00 8.00
CMT2 Jackie Robinson 1.00 2.50
CMT3 Ernie Banks 1.00 2.50
CMT4 Duke Snider .60 1.50
CMT5 Luis Aparicio .40 1.00
CMT6 Frank Robinson .60 1.50
CMT7 Orlando Cepeda .40 1.00
CMT8 Bob Gibson .60 1.50
CMT9 Carl Yastrzemski 1.00 2.50
CMT10 Roger Maris 1.00 2.50
CMT11 Mickey Mantle 3.00 8.00
CMT12 Stan Musial 1.50 4.00
CMT13 Brooks Robinson .60 1.50
CMT14 Juan Marichal .40 1.00
CMT15 Jim Palmer .40 1.00
CMT16 Willie McCovey .60 1.50
CMT17 Mickey Mantle 3.00 8.00
CMT18 Reggie Jackson .60 1.50
CMT19 Steve Carlton .40 1.00
CMT20 Thurman Munson 1.00 2.50
CMT21 Tom Seaver .60 1.50
CMT22 Johnny Bench 1.00 2.50
CMT23 Dave Winfield .40 1.00
CMT24 Robin Yount 1.00 2.50
CMT25 Mike Schmidt 1.50 4.00
CMT26 Reggie Jackson .60 1.50
CMT27 Nolan Ryan 3.00 8.00
CMT28 Ozzie Smith 1.50 4.00
CMT29 Rickey Henderson 1.00 2.50
CMT30 Eddie Murray 1.00 2.50
CMT31 Paul Molitor 1.00 2.50
CMT32 Ryne Sandberg 2.00 5.00
CMT33 Don Mattingly 2.00 5.00
CMT34 Dwight Gooden .40 1.00
CMT35 Tony Gwynn 1.00 2.50
CMT36 Bo Jackson 1.00 2.50
CMT37 Nolan Ryan 3.00 8.00
CMT38 Gary Sheffield .40 1.00
CMT39 Frank Thomas 1.00 2.50
CMT40 Chipper Jones 1.00 2.50
CMT41 Manny Ramirez 1.00 2.50
CMT42 Derek Jeter 2.50 6.00
CMT43 Tony Gwynn 1.00 2.50
CMT44 Mike Piazza 1.00 2.50
CMT45 Cal Ripken 4.00 10.00
CMT46 Pedro Martinez .60 1.50
CMT47 Alex Rodriguez 1.50 4.00
CMT48 Ivan Rodriguez .60 1.50
CMT49 Randy Johnson .60 1.50
CMT50 Ichiro Suzuki 1.50 4.00
CMT51 Albert Pujols 2.50 6.00
CMT52 Kevin Youkilis .60 1.50
CMT53 Alfonso Soriano .60 1.50
CMT54 Ryan Howard 1.25 3.00
Cole Hamels
CMT55 Alex Gordon .60 1.50
CMT56 Dustin Pedroia 1.25 3.00
CMT57 Tim Lincecum 1.50 4.00
CMT58 Evan Longoria 1.25 3.00
CMT59 Phil Rizzuto .60 1.50
CMT60 Mickey Mantle 3.00 8.00
CMT61 Al Kaline 1.00 2.50
CMT62 Yogi Berra 1.00 2.50
CMT63 Ernie Banks 1.00 2.50
CMT64 Whitey Ford .60 1.50
CMT65 Duke Snider .60 1.50
CMT66 Warren Spahn .60 1.50
CMT67 Willie McCovey .60 1.50
CMT68 Brooks Robinson .60 1.50
CMT69 Roger Maris 1.00 2.50
CMT70 Harmon Killebrew 1.00 2.50
CMT71 Eddie Mathews 1.00 2.50
CMT72 Carl Yastrzemski 1.00 2.50
CMT73 Gaylord Perry .40 1.00
CMT74 Jim Bunning .40 1.00
CMT75 Rod Carew .60 1.50
CMT76 Nolan Ryan 3.00 8.00
CMT77 Johnny Bench 1.00 2.50
CMT78 Frank Robinson .60 1.50
CMT79 Juan Marichal .40 1.00
CMT80 Reggie Jackson .60 1.50
CMT81 Willie McCovey .60 1.50
CMT82 George Brett 2.00 5.00
CMT83 Dennis Eckersley .40 1.00
CMT84 Tom Seaver .60 1.50
CMT85 Eddie Murray 1.00 2.50
CMT86 Paul Molitor 1.00 2.50
CMT87 Joe Morgan .40 1.00
CMT88 Rickey Henderson 1.00 2.50
CMT89 Steve Carlton .40 1.00
CMT90 Tony Gwynn 1.00 2.50
CMT91 Ryne Sandberg 2.00 5.00
CMT92 Robin Yount 1.00 2.50
CMT93 Mike Schmidt 1.50 4.00
CMT94 Don Mattingly 2.00 5.00
CMT95 Darryl Strawberry .40 1.00
CMT96 Randy Johnson .60 1.50
CMT97 Frank Thomas 1.00 2.50
CMT98 Ken Griffey Jr. 1.50 4.00
CMT99 Cal Ripken 4.00 10.00
CMT100 Ozzie Smith 1.50 4.00
CMT101 Bo Jackson 1.00 2.50
CMT102 Babe Ruth 2.50 6.00
CMT103 Manny Ramirez 1.00 2.50
CMT104 John Smoltz 1.00 2.50
CMT105 Derek Jeter 2.50 6.00
CMT106 Alex Rodriguez 1.50 4.00
CMT107 Chipper Jones 1.00 2.50
CMT108 Mariano Rivera 1.00 2.50
CMT109 Joe Mauer 1.00 2.50
CMT110 Cole Hamels 1.00 2.50
CMT111 Ichiro Suzuki 2.50 6.00
Albert Pujols
CMT112 Andre Ethier .60 1.50
CMT113 Justin Verlander 1.25 3.00
CMT114 Derek Jeter 2.50 6.00
CMT115 Ryan Zimmerman .60 1.50
CMT116 Rick Porcello .40 1.00
CMT117 Eddie Mathews 1.00 2.50
CMT118 John Podres .40 1.00
CMT119 Tom Lasorda .40 1.00
CMT120 Harmon Killebrew 1.00 2.50
CMT121 Jackie Robinson 1.00 2.50
CMT122 Yogi Berra/Mickey Mantle 3.00 8.00
CMT123 Roger Maris 1.00 2.50
CMT124 Lew Burdette .40 1.00
CMT125 Roger Maris 1.00 2.50
CMT126 Carl Yastrzemski 1.00 2.50
CMT127 Lou Brock .60 1.50
CMT128 Willie McCovey .60 1.50
CMT129 Willie Stargell .60 1.50
CMT130 Ernie Banks 1.00 2.50
CMT131 Robin Roberts .40 1.00
CMT132 Brooks Robinson .60 1.50
CMT133 Tom Seaver .60 1.50
CMT134 Mickey Mantle 3.00 8.00
CMT135 Nolan Ryan 3.00 8.00
CMT136 Steve Garvey .40 1.00
CMT137 Frank Robinson .60 1.50
CMT138 Luis Aparicio .40 1.00
CMT139 Nolan Ryan 3.00 8.00
CMT140 Yogi Berra/Roy Campanella 1.00 2.50
CMT141 Reggie Jackson .60 1.50
CMT142 Mark Fidrych .40 1.00
CMT143 Andre Dawson .60 1.50
CMT144 Dale Murphy 1.00 2.50
CMT145 Lou Brock/Carl Yastrzemski 1.00 2.50
CMT146 Ozzie Smith 1.50 4.00
CMT147 Rickey Henderson 1.00 2.50
CMT148 Wade Boggs .60 1.50
CMT149 Darryl Strawberry .40 1.00
CMT150 Dave Winfield .40 1.00
CMT151 Paul Molitor 1.00 2.50
CMT152 Barry Larkin .60 1.50
CMT153 Eddie Murray 1.00 2.50
CMT154 Craig Biggio .60 1.50
CMT155 Larry Walker .60 1.50
CMT156 Nolan Ryan 3.00 8.00
CMT157 Don Mattingly 2.00 5.00
CMT158 Frank Thomas 1.00 2.50
CMT159 Billy Wagner .40 1.00
CMT160 Derek Jeter 2.50 6.00
CMT161 Chipper Jones 1.00 2.50
CMT162 Derek Jeter 2.50 6.00
CMT163 Mike Piazza/Ken Griffey Jr. 1.50 4.00
CMT164 Alex Rodriguez/Nomar
Garciaparra/Derek Jeter 2.50 6.00
CMT165 Barry Zito/Ben Sheets .40 1.00
CMT166 Vladimir Guerrero 1.00 2.50
CMT167 Jason Bay .60 1.50
CMT168 Josh Hamilton/Carl Crawford 1.00 2.50
CMT169 Jim Thome/Mike Schmidt 1.50 4.00
CMT170 Ian Kinsler .60 1.50
CMT171 Ryan Zimmerman .60 1.50
CMT172 Ubaldo Jimenez .60 1.50
CMT173 Joey Votto 1.00 2.50
CMT174 David Price 1.00 2.50

2010 Topps Cards Your Mom Threw Out Original Back

*ORIG: .6X TO 1.5X BASIC
STATED ODDS 1:36 HOBBY

2010 Topps Commemorative Patch

1-50 ISSUED IN SERIES 1
51-100 ISSUED IN SERIES 2
101-150 ISSUED IN UPDATE
MCP1 Tris Speaker 5.00 12.00
MCP2 Babe Ruth 8.00 20.00
MCP3 Babe Ruth 8.00 20.00
MCP4 Mel Ott 4.00 10.00
MCP5 Dizzy Dean 6.00 15.00
MCP6 Jimmie Foxx 4.00 10.00
MCP7 Hank Greenberg 4.00 10.00
MCP8 Lou Gehrig 5.00 12.00
MCP9 Lou Gehrig 5.00 12.00
MCP10 Ralph Kiner 4.00 10.00
MCP11 Johnny Mize 4.00 10.00
MCP12 Robin Roberts 4.00 10.00
MCP13 Monte Irvin 4.00 10.00
MCP14 Duke Snider 5.00 12.00
MCP15 Eddie Mathews 5.00 12.00
MCP16 Mickey Mantle 8.00 20.00
MCP17 Roger Maris 6.00 15.00
MCP18 Johnny Podres 4.00 10.00
MCP19 Bob Gibson 4.00 10.00
MCP20 Juan Marichal 4.00 10.00
MCP21 Orlando Cepeda 4.00 10.00
MCP22 Al Kaline 4.00 10.00
MCP23 Frank Robinson 4.00 10.00
MCP24 Bobby Murcer 4.00 10.00
MCP25 Willie Stargell 4.00 10.00
MCP26 Johnny Bench 5.00 12.00
MCP27 Ozzie Smith 5.00 12.00
MCP28 Eddie Murray 4.00 10.00
MCP29 Gary Carter 4.00 10.00
MCP30 Dennis Eckersley 4.00 10.00
MCP31 Ryne Sandberg 4.00 10.00
MCP32 Gary Sheffield 4.00 10.00
MCP33 Frank Thomas 5.00 12.00
MCP34 Vladimir Guerrero 4.00 10.00
MCP35 Ichiro Suzuki 4.00 10.00
MCP36 Curt Schilling 4.00 10.00
MCP37 Chipper Jones 4.00 10.00
MCP38 Ryan Zimmerman 4.00 10.00
MCP39 Roy Halladay 5.00 12.00
MCP40 Grady Sizemore 4.00 10.00
MCP41 Manny Ramirez 4.00 10.00
MCP42 Tim Lincecum 5.00 12.00
MCP43 Evan Longoria 8.00 20.00
MCP44 David Wright 5.00 12.00
MCP45 Chase Utley 5.00 12.00
MCP46 Mariano Rivera 5.00 12.00
MCP47 Joe Mauer 8.00 20.00
MCP48 Albert Pujols 6.00 15.00
MCP49 Ichiro Suzuki 5.00 12.00
MCP50 Mark Teixeira 5.00 12.00
MCP51 Richie Ashburn 5.00 12.00
MCP52 Johnny Bench 5.00 12.00
MCP53 Yogi Berra 4.00 10.00
MCP54 Rod Carew 8.00 20.00
MCP55 Orlando Cepeda 4.00 10.00
MCP56 Rickey Henderson 4.00 10.00
MCP57 Bob Feller 4.00 10.00
MCP58 Rollie Fingers 5.00 12.00
MCP59 Carlton Fisk
MCP60 Catfish Hunter 5.00 12.00
MCP61 Monte Irvin 4.00 10.00
MCP62 Reggie Jackson 4.00 10.00
MCP63 Fergie Jenkins 4.00 10.00
MCP64 Al Kaline 5.00 12.00
MCP65 George Kell 4.00 10.00
MCP66 Harmon Killebrew 8.00 20.00
MCP67 Ralph Kiner 4.00 10.00
MCP68 Juan Marichal 5.00 12.00
MCP69 Eddie Mathews 5.00 12.00
MCP70 Bill Mazeroski 5.00 12.00
MCP71 Willie McCovey 4.00 10.00
MCP72 Joe Morgan 4.00 10.00
MCP73 Eddie Murray 4.00 10.00
MCP74 Ryne Sandberg 4.00 10.00
MCP75 Tom Seaver 5.00 12.00
MCP76 Hal Newhouser 5.00 12.00
MCP77 Phil Niekro
MCP78 Jim Palmer
MCP79 Tony Perez 5.00 12.00
MCP80 Phil Rizzuto 5.00 12.00
MCP81 Robin Roberts 4.00 10.00
MCP82 Brooks Robinson 4.00 10.00
MCP83 Mike Schmidt 5.00 12.00
MCP84 Red Schoendienst 5.00 12.00
MCP85 Ozzie Smith 5.00 12.00
MCP86 Warren Spahn
MCP87 Willie Stargell 4.00 10.00
MCP88 Hoyt Wilhelm 4.00 10.00
MCP89 Jimmie Foxx 4.00 10.00
MCP90 Mickey Mantle 8.00 20.00
MCP91 Jackie Robinson 4.00 10.00
MCP92 Lou Gehrig 4.00 10.00
MCP93 Babe Ruth 8.00 20.00
MCP94 Albert Pujols 6.00 15.00
MCP95 David Wright 5.00 12.00
MCP96 Mariano Rivera 5.00 12.00
MCP97 Ryan Howard 6.00 15.00
MCP98 Ryan Braun 5.00 12.00
MCP99 Joe Mauer 8.00 20.00
MCP100 CC Sabathia 5.00 12.00
MCP101 Tris Speaker 5.00 12.00
MCP102 Dizzy Dean 6.00 15.00
MCP103 Lou Gehrig 5.00 12.00
MCP104 Jimmie Foxx 4.00 10.00
MCP105 Hank Greenberg 4.00 10.00
MCP106 Bob Feller 5.00 12.00
MCP107 Mel Ott 4.00 10.00
MCP108 Johnny Mize 4.00 10.00
MCP109 Phil Rizzuto 5.00 12.00
MCP110 Enos Slaughter 5.00 12.00
MCP111 Pee Wee Reese 5.00 12.00
MCP112 Stan Musial 10.00 25.00
MCP113 Hal Newhouser 5.00 12.00
MCP114 Red Schoendienst 5.00 12.00
MCP115 Yogi Berra 4.00 10.00
MCP116 Larry Doby 6.00 15.00
MCP117 Richie Ashburn 5.00 12.00
MCP118 Whitey Ford
MCP119 Johnny Podres 4.00 10.00
MCP120 Duke Snider 5.00 12.00
MCP121 Roger Maris 8.00 20.00
MCP122 Lou Brock 6.00 15.00
MCP123 Luis Aparicio 5.00 12.00

MCP124 Eddie Mathews 5.00 12.00
MCP125 Rollie Fingers 5.00 12.00
MCP126 Reggie Jackson 4.00 10.00
MCP127 Joe Morgan 5.00 12.00
MCP128 Johnny Bench 5.00 12.00
MCP129 Steve Carlton 4.00 10.00
MCP130 Barry Larkin 4.00 10.00
MCP131 Roberto Alomar 5.00 12.00
MCP132 Greg Maddux 4.00 10.00
MCP133 Derek Jeter 10.00 25.00
MCP134 Mike Piazza
MCP135 Derek Jeter 10.00 25.00
MCP136 Chipper Jones 4.00 10.00
MCP137 Alex Rodriguez 5.00 12.00
MCP138 Roy Halladay 5.00 12.00
MCP139 Josh Beckett 5.00 12.00
MCP140 Hideki Matsui 12.50 30.00
MCP141 Lance Berkman
MCP142 Ryan Braun 5.00 12.00
MCP143 Andre Ethier 4.00 10.00
MCP144 Justin Morneau 5.00 12.00
MCP145 Joe Mauer 8.00 20.00
MCP146 Chase Utley 5.00 12.00
MCP147 Vladimir Guerrero 4.00 10.00
MCP148 Evan Longoria 8.00 20.00
MCP149 Derek Jeter 10.00 25.00
MCP150 Albert Pujols 6.00 15.00

2010 Topps Factory Set All Star Bonus

COMPLETE SET (5) 1.25 3.00
AS1 Hideki Matsui 1.00 2.50
AS2 Kendry Morales .40 1.00
AS3 Torii Hunter .40 1.00
AS4 Scott Kazmir .40 1.00
AS5 Bobby Abreu .40 1.00

2010 Topps Factory Set Phillies Team Bonus

COMPLETE SET (5) 2.50 6.00
PHI1 Roy Halladay 1.00 2.50
PHI2 Ryan Howard 1.25 3.00
PHI3 Chase Utley 1.00 2.50
PHI4 Jimmy Rollins .60 1.50
PHI5 Jayson Werth .60 1.50

2010 Topps Factory Set Red Sox Team Bonus

COMPLETE SET (5) 3.00 8.00
BOS1 Dustin Pedroia 1.25 3.00
BOS2 Jacoby Ellsbury 1.00 2.50
BOS3 Victor Martinez .60 1.50
BOS4 John Lackey .40 1.00
BOS5 Daisuke Matsuzaka 1.00 2.50

2010 Topps Factory Set Retail Bonus

COMPLETE SET (5) 6.00 15.00
RS1 Ryan Howard 1.25 3.00
RS2 Ichiro Suzuki 1.50 4.00
RS3 Hanley Ramirez 1.00 2.50
RS4 Derek Jeter 2.50 6.00
RS5 Albert Pujols 2.50 6.00

2010 Topps Factory Set Target Ruth Chrome Gold Refractors

COMPLETE SET (3) 15.00 40.00
COMMON RUTH 8.00 20.00
1 Babe Ruth 8.00 20.00
2 Babe Ruth 8.00 20.00
3 Babe Ruth 8.00 20.00

2010 Topps Factory Set Wal Mart Mantle Chrome Gold Refractors

COMPLETE SET (3) 20.00 50.00
COMMON MANTLE 10.00 25.00
1 Mickey Mantle 10.00 25.00
2 Mickey Mantle 10.00 25.00
3 Mickey Mantle 10.00 25.00

2010 Topps Factory Set Yankees Team Bonus

COMPLETE SET (5) 4.00 10.00
NYY1 Derek Jeter 2.50 6.00
NYY2 Alex Rodriguez 1.50 4.00
NYY3 Mariano Rivera 1.00 2.50
NYY4 Mark Teixeira 1.00 2.50
NYY5 Curtis Granderson .60 1.50

2010 Topps History of the Game

STATED ODDS 1:6 HOBBY
HOG1 Baseball Invented .40 1.00
HOG2 First Game Played .40 1.00
HOG3 National League Created .40 1.00
HOG4 AL Elevated to Major League .40 1.00
HOG5 First World Series Game Played .40 1.00
HOG6 Taft Attends Opening Day .40 1.00
HOG7 Ruth Sold to the Yankees 1.25 3.00
HOG8 Baseball hits the Airwaves .40 1.00
HOG9 Gehrig Replaces Wally Pipp 1.00 2.50
HOG10 Ruth Sets Season HR Mark 1.25 3.00
HOG11 First MLB AS Game Played .40 1.00
HOG12 First Night Game Played .40 1.00
HOG13 Ruth Retires with 715 HR 1.25 3.00
HOG14 First Hall of Fame Class .40 1.00
HOG15 Robinson Plays in first game 1.00 2.50
HOG16 First Televised Baseball Game .40 1.00
HOG17 Dodgers & Giants move to CA .40 1.00
HOG18 Maris Breaks Ruth HR Record .75 2.00
HOG19 First MLB Draft .40 1.00
HOG20 Frank Robinson MVP .40 1.00
HOG21 DH rule created .40 1.00
HOG22 Ryan Throws 7th No-Hitter 1.50 4.00
HOG23 Ripken Breaks Gehrig Streak 2.00 5.00
HOG24 Interleague Play Introduced .40 1.00
HOG25 1st MLB game played in Japan .40 1.00

2010 Topps History of the World Series

COMPLETE SET (25) 8.00 20.00
STATED ODDS 1:6 HOBBY
HWS1 Christy Mathewson .75 2.00
HWS2 Walter Johnson .75 2.00
HWS3 Babe Ruth 2.00 5.00
HWS4 Rogers Hornsby .50 1.25
HWS5 Babe Ruth 2.00 5.00
HWS6 Mickey Mantle 2.50 6.00
HWS7 Mel Ott .75 2.00
HWS8 Enos Slaughter .30 .75
HWS9 Bob Feller .30 .75
HWS10 Whitey Ford .50 1.25
HWS11 Johnny Podres .30 .75
HWS12 Yogi Berra .75 2.00
HWS13 Yogi Berra .75 2.00
HWS14 Jim Palmer .30 .75
HWS15 Bob Gibson .50 1.25
HWS16 Brooks Robinson .50 1.25
HWS17 Dennis Eckersley .30 .75
HWS18 Paul Molitor .75 2.00
HWS19 Jason Varitek .75 2.00
HWS20 Edgar Renteria .30 .75
HWS21 Derek Jeter 2.00 5.00
HWS22 Alex Gonzalez .30 .75
HWS23 Cole Hamels .75 2.00
HWS24 Chase Utley .75 2.00
HWS25 New York Yankees .75 2.00

2010 Topps In The Name Letter Relics

STATED ODDS 1:4300 HOBBY
STATED PRINT RUN 1 SER.#'d SET
NO PRICING DUE TO SCARCITY

2010 Topps Legendary Lineage

STATED ODDS 1:4 HOBBY
UPDATE ODDS 1:8 HOBBY
1-30 ISSUED IN SERIES 1
31-60 ISSUED IN SERIES 2
61-75 ISSUED IN UPDATE
LL1 Willie McCovey 1.00 2.50
Ryan Howard
LL2 Mickey Mantle 2.50 6.00
Chipper Jones
LL3 Babe Ruth 2.00 5.00
Alex Rodriguez
LL4 Lou Gehrig 1.50 4.00
Mark Teixeira
LL5 Ty Cobb 1.25 3.00
Curtis Granderson
LL6 Jimmie Foxx .75 2.00
Manny Ramirez
LL7 George Sisler 1.25 3.00
Ichiro Suzuki
LL8 Tris Speaker .50 1.25
Grady Sizemore
LL9 Honus Wagner .75 2.00
Hanley Ramirez
LL10 Johnny Bench .75 2.00
Ivan Rodriguez
LL11 Mike Schmidt 1.00 2.50
Evan Longoria
LL12 Ozzie Smith 1.25 3.00
Jose Reyes
LL13 Reggie Jackson .50 1.25
Adam Dunn
LL14 Warren Spahn .50 1.25
Tommy Hanson
LL15 Duke Snider .50 1.25
Andre Ethier
LL16 Stan Musial 2.00 5.00
Albert Pujols
LL17 Cal Ripken 3.00 8.00
Derek Jeter
LL18 Gary Carter .30 .75
David Wright
LL19 Whitey Ford .50 1.25
CC Sabathia
LL20 Frank Thomas .50 1.25
Prince Fielder
LL21 Hank Greenberg 1.00 2.50
Ryan Braun
LL22 Frank Robinson .75 2.00
Vladimir Guerrero
LL23 Jackie Robinson .75 2.00
Matt Kemp
LL24 Bob Gibson 1.25 3.00
Tim Lincecum
LL25 Tom Seaver .75 2.00
Roy Halladay
LL26 Dennis Eckersley .75 2.00
Mariano Rivera
LL27 Tony Gwynn .75 2.00
Joe Mauer
LL28 Nolan Ryan .50 1.25
Zack Greinke
LL29 Carl Yastrzemski .75 2.00
Kevin Youkilis
LL30 Rickey Henderson .50 1.25
Carl Crawford
LL31 Joe Mauer .75 2.00
Johnny Bench
LL32 Orlando Cepeda .50 1.25
Pablo Sandoval
LL33 Carlton Fisk .50 1.25
Victor Martinez
LL34 Eddie Mathews .75 2.00
Chipper Jones
LL35 Al Kaline .75 2.00
Miguel Cabrera
LL36 Andre Dawson .50 1.25
Alfonso Soriano
LL37 Jackie Robinson 1.25 3.00
Ichiro Suzuki
LL38 Cal Ripken Jr. 3.00 8.00
Hanley Ramirez
LL39 Phil Rizzuto 2.00 5.00
Derek Jeter
LL40 Harmon Killebrew .75 2.00
Justin Morneau
LL41 Jimmie Foxx .50 1.25
Prince Fielder
LL42 Lou Gehrig 2.00 5.00
Albert Pujols
LL43 Mike Schmidt 1.25 3.00
Alex Rodriguez
LL44 Bo Jackson .50 1.25
Justin Upton
LL45 Babe Ruth 1.00 2.50
Ryan Howard
LL46 Luis Aparicio .30 .75
Alexei Ramirez
LL47 Frank Robinson 1.00 2.50
Ryan Braun
LL48 Stan Musial 1.25 3.00
Matt Holliday
LL49 Lou Brock .50 1.25
Carl Crawford
LL50 Tris Speaker .75 2.00
Jacoby Ellsbury
LL51 Juan Marichal 1.25 3.00
Tim Lincecum
LL52 Dale Murphy .75 2.00
Matt Kemp
LL53 Nolan Ryan 1.00 2.50
Justin Verlander
LL54 Ozzie Smith 1.25 3.00
Elvis Andrus
LL55 Rickey Henderson .75 2.00
B.J. Upton
LL56 Brooks Robinson .50 1.25
Ryan Zimmerman
LL57 Yogi Berra .75 2.00
Jorge Posada
LL58 Honus Wagner .75 2.00
Andrew McCutchen
LL59 Mickey Mantle 2.50 6.00
Mark Teixeira
LL60 Ryne Sandberg 1.50 4.00
Chase Utley
LL61 Dave Winfield 2.00 5.00
Jason Heyward
LL62 Walter Johnson 2.00 5.00
Stephen Strasburg
LL63 Victor Martinez 1.00 2.50
Carlos Santana
LL64 Rod Carew .75 2.00
Robinson Cano
LL65 Bob Gibson .50 1.25
Ubaldo Jimenez
LL66 Miguel Cabrera 1.25 3.00
Mike Stanton
LL67 Hank Greenberg .75 2.00
Ike Davis
LL68 Mark Teixeira .75 2.00
Logan Morrison
LL69 Tom Seaver 1.00 2.50
Mike Leake
LL70 Ernie Banks 1.25 3.00
Starlin Castro
LL71 Jim Palmer .75 2.00
Brian Matusz
LL72 Larry Walker .50 1.25
Justin Morneau
LL73 Steve Carlton .75 2.00
Jon Lester
LL74 Johnny Bench 3.00 8.00
Buster Posey
LL75 Joe Nathan .50 1.25
Drew Storen

2010 Topps Legendary Lineage Relics

SER.1 ODDS 1:7540 HOBBY
SER.2 ODDS 1:6075 HOBBY
STATED PRINT RUN 50 SER.#'d SETS
BC Lou Brock 10.00 25.00
Carl Crawford
BM Yogi Berra 60.00 120.00
Jorge Posada
CR Johnny Bench 12.50 30.00
Ivan Rodriguez
CS Orlando Cepeda 15.00 40.00
Pablo Sandoval
CW Gary Carter 15.00 40.00
David Wright
ER Dennis Eckersley 40.00 80.00
Mariano Rivera
FR Jimmie Foxx 30.00 60.00
Manny Ramirez
GB Hank Greenberg 30.00 60.00
Ryan Braun
HU Rickey Henderson 30.00 60.00
B.J. Upton
KC Al Kaline 30.00 60.00
Miguel Cabrera
KM Harmon Killebrew 10.00 25.00
Justin Morneau
MH Willie McCovey 12.50 30.00
Ryan Howard
MJ Eddie Mathews 60.00 120.00
Chipper Jones
MJ Mickey Mantle 60.00 120.00
Chipper Jones
MK Dale Murphy 20.00 50.00
Matt Kemp
MP Stan Musial 75.00 150.00
Albert Pujols
MT Mickey Mantle 75.00 150.00
Mark Teixeira
RB Frank Robinson 10.00 25.00
Ryan Braun
RH Babe Ruth 60.00 120.00
Ryan Howard
RJ Cal Ripken
Derek Jeter
RR Cal Ripken Jr 20.00 50.00
Hanley Ramirez
SE Duke Snider 50.00 100.00
Andre Ethier
SH Warren Spahn 60.00 120.00
Tommy Hanson
SL Mike Schmidt 20.00 50.00
Evan Longoria
SR Mike Schmidt 40.00 80.00
Alex Rodriguez
SS George Sisler 60.00 120.00
Ichiro Suzuki
SU Ryne Sandberg 12.50 30.00
Chase Utley
TF Frank Thomas 60.00 120.00
Prince Fielder
WR Honus Wagner 50.00 100.00
Hanley Ramirez
BMA Johnny Bench 40.00 80.00
Joe Mauer
SSI Tris Speaker 20.00 50.00
Grady Sizemore

2010 Topps Legends Gold Chrome Target Cereal

INSERTED IN TARGET PACKS
GC1 Babe Ruth 6.00 15.00
GC2 Honus Wagner 2.50 6.00
GC3 Ichiro Suzuki 4.00 10.00
GC4 Nolan Ryan 8.00 20.00
GC5 Jackie Robinson 2.50 6.00
GC6 Tom Seaver 1.50 4.00
GC7 Derek Jeter 6.00 15.00
GC8 George Sisler 2.50 6.00
GC9 Roger Maris 2.50 6.00
GC10 Lou Gehrig 5.00 12.00
GC11 Mickey Mantle 8.00 20.00
GC12 Willie McCovey 1.50 4.00
GC13 Ty Cobb 4.00 10.00
GC14 Warren Spahn 1.50 4.00
GC15 Albert Pujols 6.00 15.00
GC16 Lou Gehrig 5.00 12.00
GC17 Mariano Rivera 2.50 6.00
GC18 Jimmie Foxx 2.50 6.00
GC19 Babe Ruth 6.00 15.00
GC20 Honus Wagner 2.50 6.00

2010 Topps Legends Platinum Chrome Wal Mart Cereal

INSERTED IN WAL MART PACKS
PC1 Mickey Mantle 8.00 20.00
PC2 Jackie Robinson 2.50 6.00
PC3 Ty Cobb 4.00 10.00
PC4 Warren Spahn 1.50 4.00
PC5 Albert Pujols 6.00 15.00
PC6 Lou Gehrig 5.00 12.00
PC7 Mariano Rivera 2.50 6.00
PC8 Jimmie Foxx 2.50 6.00
PC9 Cy Young 2.50 6.00
PC10 Honus Wagner 2.50 6.00
PC11 Babe Ruth 6.00 15.00
PC12 Mickey Mantle 8.00 20.00
PC13 Ichiro Suzuki 4.00 10.00
PC14 Nolan Ryan 8.00 20.00
PC15 Jackie Robinson 2.50 6.00
PC16 Tom Seaver 1.50 4.00
PC17 Derek Jeter 6.00 15.00
PC18 Ty Cobb 4.00 10.00
PC19 Roger Maris 2.50 6.00
PC20 Lou Gehrig 5.00 12.00

2010 Topps Logoman HTA

DISTRIBUTED IN HTA STORES
1 Albert Pujols 1.50 4.00
2 Hanley Ramirez .60 1.50
3 Mike Schmidt 1.00 2.50
4 CC Sabathia .40 1.00
5 Babe Ruth 1.50 4.00
6 George Sisler .60 1.50
7 Gordon Beckham .40 1.00
8 Tris Speaker .40 1.00
9 Ryan Braun .75 2.00
10 Jackie Robinson .60 1.50
11 Stan Musial 1.00 2.50
12 Ichiro Suzuki 1.00 2.50
13 Manny Ramirez .60 1.50
14 Ty Cobb 1.00 2.50
15 Tommy Hanson .40 1.00
16 Joe Mauer .60 1.50
17 David Ortiz .40 1.00
18 Tim Lincecum 1.00 2.50
19 Andrew McCutchen .60 1.50
20 Reggie Jackson .40 1.00
21 Nolan Ryan 2.00 5.00
22 Evan Longoria .75 2.00
23 Johan Santana .60 1.50
24 Mark Teixeira .60 1.50
25 Pablo Sandoval .40 1.00
26 Jimmie Foxx .60 1.50
27 Roy Halladay .60 1.50
28 Lou Gehrig 1.25 3.00
29 Alex Rodriguez 1.00 2.50
30 Thurman Munson .60 1.50
31 Mel Ott .60 1.50
32 Mickey Mantle 2.00 5.00
33 Johnny Mize .40 1.00
34 Rogers Hornsby .40 1.00
35 Chase Utley .60 1.50
36 Walter Johnson .60 1.50
37 Zack Greinke .40 1.00
38 Honus Wagner .60 1.50
39 Roy Campanella .60 1.50
40 Prince Fielder .40 1.00
41 Cal Ripken Jr. 2.50 6.00
42 Carl Yastrzemski .60 1.50
43 David Wright .75 2.00
44 Tom Seaver .40 1.00
45 Cy Young .60 1.50
46 Christy Mathewson .60 1.50
47 Justin Morneau .60 1.50
48 Ryan Howard .75 2.00
49 Rick Porcello .25 .60
50 Nolan Reimold .40 1.00

2010 Topps Manufactured Hat Logo Patch

SER.1 ODDS 1:432 HOBBY
SER.2 ODDS 1:420 HOBBY
STATED PRINT RUN 99 SER.#'d SETS
1-186 ISSUED IN SERIES 1
187-416 ISSUED IN SERIES 2
VAR.OF SAME PLAYER EQUALLY PRICED
MHR1 Babe Ruth 20.00 50.00
MHR2 Babe Ruth 20.00 50.00
MHR3 George Sisler 8.00 20.00
MHR4 George Sisler 8.00 20.00
MHR5 Honus Wagner 5.00 12.00
MHR6 Jackie Robinson 40.00 80.00
MHR7 Jimmie Foxx 8.00 20.00
MHR8 Jimmie Foxx 8.00 20.00
MHR9 Johnny Mize 5.00 12.00
MHR10 Johnny Mize 5.00 12.00
MHR11 Johnny Mize 5.00 12.00
MHR12 Lou Gehrig 8.00 20.00
MHR13 Mel Ott 10.00 25.00
MHR14 Rogers Hornsby 4.00 10.00
MHR15 Rogers Hornsby 4.00 10.00
MHR16 Roy Campanella 10.00 25.00
MHR17 Thurman Munson 10.00 25.00
MHR18 Tris Speaker 10.00 25.00
MHR19 Ty Cobb 10.00 25.00
MHR20 Ty Cobb 10.00 25.00
MHR21 Mickey Mantle 12.50 30.00
MHR22 Richie Ashburn 10.00 25.00
MHR23 Bo Jackson 8.00 20.00
MHR24 Bo Jackson 8.00 20.00
MHR25 Paul Molitor 10.00 25.00
MHR26 Paul Molitor 10.00 25.00
MHR27 Paul Molitor 10.00 25.00
MHR28 Tony Gwynn 6.00 15.00
MHR29 Tony Gwynn 6.00 15.00
MHR30 Tony Gwynn 6.00 15.00
MHR31 Al Kaline 8.00 20.00
MHR32 Andre Dawson 6.00 15.00
MHR33 Andre Dawson 6.00 15.00
MHR34 Bob Feller 6.00 15.00
MHR35 Bob Gibson 15.00 40.00
MHR36 Bobby Murcer 6.00 15.00
MHR37 Carl Erskine 10.00 25.00
MHR38 Carl Erskine 10.00 25.00
MHR39 Curt Schilling 6.00 15.00
MHR40 Curt Schilling 6.00 15.00
MHR41 Curt Schilling 6.00 15.00
MHR42 Dale Murphy 10.00 25.00
MHR43 Dale Murphy 10.00 25.00
MHR44 Dizzy Dean 6.00 15.00
MHR45 Dizzy Dean 6.00 15.00
MHR46 Duke Snider 8.00 20.00
MHR47 Duke Snider 8.00 20.00
MHR48 Duke Snider 8.00 20.00
MHR49 Dwight Gooden 6.00 15.00
MHR50 Dwight Gooden 6.00 15.00
MHR51 Eddie Mathews 10.00 25.00
MHR52 Eddie Mathews 10.00 25.00
MHR53 Eddie Murray 10.00 25.00
MHR54 Eddie Murray 10.00 25.00
MHR55 Eddie Murray 10.00 25.00
MHR56 Eddie Murray 10.00 25.00
MHR57 Fergie Jenkins 8.00 20.00
MHR58 Fergie Jenkins 8.00 20.00
MHR59 Frank Robinson 8.00 20.00
MHR60 Frank Robinson 8.00 20.00
MHR61 Frank Thomas 10.00 25.00
MHR62 Frank Thomas 10.00 25.00
MHR63 Frank Thomas 10.00 25.00
MHR64 Gary Carter 10.00 25.00
MHR65 Gary Carter 10.00 25.00
MHR66 George Kell 8.00 20.00
MHR67 Hank Greenberg 5.00 12.00
MHR68 Jim Palmer 6.00 15.00
MHR69 Jim Palmer 6.00 15.00
MHR70 Jim Palmer 6.00 15.00
MHR71 Jimmy Piersall 12.50 30.00
MHR72 Johnny Bench 10.00 25.00
MHR73 Johnny Bench 10.00 25.00
MHR74 Johnny Podres 12.50 30.00
MHR75 Johnny Podres 12.50 30.00
MHR76 Juan Marichal 8.00 20.00
MHR77 Juan Marichal 8.00 20.00
MHR78 Monte Irvin 6.00 15.00
MHR79 Nolan Ryan 20.00 50.00
MHR80 Nolan Ryan 20.00 50.00
MHR81 Nolan Ryan 20.00 50.00
MHR82 Nolan Ryan 20.00 50.00
MHR83 Orlando Cepeda 4.00 10.00
MHR84 Orlando Cepeda 4.00 10.00
MHR85 Ozzie Smith 15.00 40.00
MHR86 Ozzie Smith 15.00 40.00
MHR87 Ralph Kiner 6.00 15.00
MHR88 Reggie Jackson 15.00 40.00
MHR89 Reggie Jackson 15.00 40.00
MHR90 Reggie Jackson 15.00 40.00
MHR91 Reggie Jackson 15.00 40.00
MHR92 Reggie Jackson 15.00 40.00
MHR93 Robin Roberts 12.50 30.00
MHR94 Robin Yount 12.50 30.00
MHR95 Robin Yount 12.50 30.00
MHR96 Roger Maris 12.50 30.00
MHR97 Roger Maris 12.50 30.00
MHR98 Roger Maris 12.50 30.00
MHR99 Stan Musial 12.50 30.00
MHR100 Steve Carlton 8.00 20.00
MHR101 Steve Carlton 8.00 20.00
MHR102 Tom Seaver 12.50 30.00
MHR103 Tom Seaver 12.50 30.00
MHR104 Tony Perez 6.00 15.00
MHR105 Warren Spahn 10.00 25.00
MHR106 Warren Spahn 10.00 25.00
MHR107 Willie McCovey 6.00 15.00
MHR108 Willie McCovey 6.00 15.00
MHR109 Willie Stargell 12.50 30.00
MHR110 Rickey Henderson 20.00 50.00
MHR111 Rickey Henderson 20.00 50.00
MHR112 Rickey Henderson 20.00 50.00
MHR113 Rickey Henderson 20.00 50.00
MHR114 Carlton Fisk 8.00 20.00
MHR115 Carlton Fisk 8.00 20.00
MHR116 Dennis Eckersley 8.00 20.00
MHR117 Dennis Eckersley 8.00 20.00
MHR118 Ryne Sandberg 15.00 40.00
MHR119 Ryne Sandberg 15.00 40.00
MHR120 Lou Brock 8.00 20.00
MHR121 Carl Yastrzemski 10.00 25.00
MHR122 Ernie Banks 10.00 25.00
MHR123 Mike Schmidt 12.50 30.00
MHR124 Alex Rodriguez 12.50 30.00
MHR125 Alex Rodriguez 12.50 30.00
MHR126 Alex Rodriguez 12.50 30.00
MHR127 Kevin Youkilis 10.00 25.00
MHR128 Vladimir Guerrero 10.00 25.00
MHR129 Vladimir Guerrero 10.00 25.00
MHR130 Chipper Jones 8.00 20.00
MHR131 Dustin Pedroia 12.50 30.00
MHR132 Ian Kinsler 4.00 10.00
MHR133 Dustin Pedroia 12.50 30.00
MHR134 Ryan Howard 12.50 30.00
MHR135 Prince Fielder 8.00 20.00
MHR136 David Wright 10.00 25.00
MHR137 Carl Crawford 6.00 15.00
MHR138 Justin Upton 10.00 25.00
MHR139 Dan Haren 4.00 10.00
MHR140 Randy Johnson 10.00 25.00
MHR141 Randy Johnson 10.00 25.00
MHR142 Randy Johnson 10.00 25.00
MHR143 Randy Johnson 10.00 25.00
MHR144 Randy Johnson 10.00 25.00
MHR145 Randy Johnson 10.00 25.00
MHR146 David Ortiz 10.00 25.00
MHR147 Roy Halladay 10.00 25.00
MHR148 Tim Lincecum 20.00 50.00
MHR149 Pablo Sandoval 10.00 25.00
MHR150 Albert Pujols 30.00 60.00
MHR151 Hanley Ramirez 6.00 15.00
MHR152 Nick Markakis 8.00 20.00
MHR153 Ichiro Suzuki 20.00 50.00
MHR154 Adam Jones 4.00 10.00
MHR155 Evan Longoria 10.00 25.00
MHR156 Joe Mauer 12.50 30.00
MHR157 Matt Kemp 8.00 20.00
MHR158 Justin Verlander 8.00 20.00
MHR159 Zack Greinke 8.00 20.00
MHR160 Miguel Cabrera 8.00 20.00
MHR161 Chase Utley 12.50 30.00
MHR162 Adam Dunn 6.00 15.00
MHR163 Manny Ramirez 6.00 15.00
MHR164 Manny Ramirez 6.00 15.00
MHR165 Grady Sizemore 12.50 30.00
MHR166 Felix Hernandez 12.50 30.00
MHR167 Mark Teixeira 10.00 25.00
MHR168 Joey Votto 15.00 40.00
MHR169 Ryan Braun 12.50 30.00
MHR170 Mariano Rivera 12.50 30.00
MHR171 Tommy Hanson 6.00 15.00
MHR172 Matt Cain 6.00 15.00
MHR173 Josh Johnson 10.00 25.00
MHR174 Clayton Kershaw 4.00 10.00
MHR175 Jon Lester 10.00 25.00
MHR176 Elvis Andrus 5.00 12.00
MHR177 Dexter Fowler 5.00 12.00
MHR178 Rick Porcello 6.00 15.00
MHR179 Andrew McCutchen 8.00 20.00
MHR180 Colby Rasmus 10.00 25.00
MHR181 Chris Coghlan 4.00 10.00
MHR182 Nolan Reimold 5.00 12.00
MHR183 Buster Posey 30.00 60.00
MHR184 Koji Uehara 5.00 12.00
MHR185 Madison Bumgarner 12.50 30.00
MHR186 Neftali Feliz 6.00 15.00
MHR187 Mark Teixeira 10.00 25.00
MHR188 Vladimir Guerrero 10.00 25.00
MHR189 Joe Mauer 12.50 30.00
MHR190 Max Scherzer 4.00 10.00
MHR191 Adrian Gonzalez 4.00 10.00
MHR192 Josh Beckett 10.00 25.00
MHR193 Jose Reyes 10.00 25.00
MHR194 Ryan Braun 12.50 30.00
MHR195 Cliff Lee 4.00 10.00
MHR196 Kendry Morales 5.00 12.00
MHR197 Tim Lincecum 20.00 50.00
MHR198 Prince Fielder 8.00 20.00
MHR199 Ichiro Suzuki 20.00 50.00
MHR200 Chipper Jones 8.00 20.00
MHR201 Chase Utley 12.50 30.00
MHR202 Felix Hernandez 12.50 30.00
MHR203 Nolan Reimold 5.00 12.00
MHR204 Albert Pujols 30.00 60.00
MHR205 Torii Hunter 6.00 15.00
MHR206 Evan Longoria 10.00 25.00
MHR207 CC Sabathia 8.00 20.00
MHR208 Mariano Rivera 12.50 30.00
MHR209 B.J. Upton 6.00 15.00
MHR210 Justin Upton 10.00 25.00
MHR211 Ivan Rodriguez 6.00 15.00
MHR212 Curtis Granderson 5.00 12.00
MHR213 Josh Hamilton 8.00 20.00
MHR214 Tim Hudson 8.00 20.00
MHR215 Neftali Feliz 6.00 15.00
MHR216 Babe Ruth 20.00 50.00
MHR217 Adam Lind 4.00 10.00
MHR218 David Price 8.00 20.00
MHR219 Tommy Hanson 6.00 15.00
MHR220 Andrew McCutchen 8.00 20.00
MHR221 Adam Dunn 6.00 15.00
MHR222 Victor Martinez 5.00 12.00
MHR223 Pablo Sandoval 10.00 25.00
MHR224 Ricky Romero 5.00 12.00
MHR225 Brian McCann 4.00 10.00
MHR226 Jered Weaver 5.00 12.00
MHR227 Andrew Bailey 4.00 10.00
MHR228 Joe Saunders 4.00 10.00
MHR229 Colby Rasmus 10.00 25.00
MHR230 Nick Markakis 8.00 20.00
MHR231 Mark Reynolds 5.00 12.00
MHR232 Ryan Howard 12.50 30.00
MHR233 Stephen Drew 4.00 10.00
MHR234 David Ortiz 10.00 25.00
MHR235 Kenshin Kawakami 6.00 15.00
MHR236 Michael Young 4.00 10.00
MHR237 Jayson Werth 8.00 20.00
MHR238 John Lackey 4.00 10.00
MHR239 Dustin Pedroia 12.50 30.00
MHR240 Travis Snider 6.00 15.00
MHR241 Rajai Davis 8.00 20.00
MHR242 Edgar Renteria 4.00 10.00
MHR243 Justin Morneau 10.00 25.00
MHR244 Jimmy Rollins 8.00 20.00
MHR245 Elvis Andrus 5.00 12.00
MHR246 David Wright 10.00 25.00
MHR247 Javier Vazquez 6.00 15.00
MHR248 Jorge Posada 6.00 15.00
MHR249 Carlos Beltran 8.00 20.00
MHR250 Jonathan Broxton 4.00 10.00
MHR251 Adam Jones 4.00 10.00
MHR252 Alex Rodriguez 12.50 30.00
MHR253 Koji Uehara 5.00 12.00
MHR254 Brandon Webb 6.00 15.00
MHR255 Kevin Kouzmanoff 8.00 20.00
MHR256 Ryan Zimmerman 12.50 30.00
MHR257 Brian Roberts 5.00 12.00
MHR258 Alfonso Soriano 4.00 10.00
MHR259 Jason Varitek 8.00 20.00
MHR260 Aramis Ramirez 4.00 10.00
MHR261 Jeremy Guthrie 6.00 15.00
MHR262 Johnny Cueto 5.00 12.00
MHR263 Jacoby Ellsbury 10.00 25.00
MHR264 Carlos Quentin 4.00 10.00
MHR265 Kosuke Fukudome 6.00 15.00
MHR266 Grady Sizemore 12.50 30.00
MHR267 Troy Tulowitzki 8.00 20.00
MHR268 Alexei Ramirez 4.00 10.00
MHR269 Jeff Francis 4.00 10.00
MHR270 Jay Bruce 4.00 10.00
MHR271 Rick Porcello 6.00 15.00
MHR272 Gordon Beckham 6.00 15.00
MHR273 Justin Verlander 8.00 20.00
MHR274 Magglio Ordonez 8.00 20.00
MHR275 Miguel Cabrera 8.00 20.00
MHR276 Jake Peavy 4.00 10.00
MHR277 Ryan Ludwick 4.00 10.00
MHR278 Todd Helton 6.00 15.00
MHR279 Carlos Lee 4.00 10.00
MHR280 Mark Buehrle 6.00 15.00
MHR281 Billy Butler 6.00 15.00
MHR282 Chris Coghlan 4.00 10.00
MHR283 Brett Anderson 4.00 10.00
MHR284 Lance Berkman 4.00 10.00
MHR285 Chone Figgins 4.00 10.00
MHR286 Ubaldo Jimenez 5.00 12.00
MHR287 Jason Kubel 6.00 15.00
MHR288 Manny Ramirez 6.00 15.00
MHR289 Joe Nathan 5.00 12.00
MHR290 Jimmie Foxx 8.00 20.00
MHR291 J.J. Hardy 8.00 20.00
MHR292 Mike Cameron 4.00 10.00
MHR293 Roy Oswalt 4.00 10.00
MHR294 Carlos Delgado 5.00 12.00
MHR295 Rogers Hornsby 4.00 10.00
MHR296 Hunter Pence 4.00 10.00
MHR297 Scott Kazmir 8.00 20.00
MHR298 Tris Speaker 10.00 25.00
MHR299 Jhoulys Chacin 4.00 10.00
MHR300 Michael Cuddyer 8.00 20.00
MHR301 Zack Greinke 8.00 20.00
MHR302 Jeff Francoeur 4.00 10.00
MHR303 Matt Kemp 8.00 20.00
MHR304 Dan Haren 4.00 10.00
MHR305 Andy Pettitte 4.00 10.00
MHR306 David DeJesus 4.00 10.00
MHR307 A.J. Burnett 5.00 12.00
MHR308 Ty Cobb 10.00 25.00
MHR309 Johnny Mize 5.00 12.00
MHR310 Joakim Soria 6.00 15.00
MHR311 Chris Carpenter 6.00 15.00
MHR312 Asdrubal Cabrera 10.00 25.00
MHR313 Shane Victorino 12.50 30.00
MHR314 Andre Ethier 6.00 15.00
MHR315 Kurt Suzuki 6.00 15.00
MHR316 Honus Wagner 5.00 12.00
MHR317 Clayton Kershaw 4.00 10.00
MHR318 Zach Duke 4.00 10.00
MHR319 Shin-Soo Choo 10.00 25.00
MHR320 Matt Cain 6.00 15.00
MHR321 Russell Martin 5.00 12.00
MHR322 Joba Chamberlain 4.00 10.00
MHR323 Jason Bay 5.00 12.00
MHR324 Delmon Young 6.00 15.00
MHR325 Matt Holliday 6.00 15.00
MHR326 Scott Rolen 8.00 20.00
MHR327 Adam Wainwright 5.00 12.00
MHR328 Hanley Ramirez 6.00 15.00
MHR329 Cal Ripken Jr. 30.00 60.00
MHR330 Mickey Mantle 12.50 30.00
MHR331 Chase Headley 4.00 10.00
MHR332 Rich Harden 4.00 10.00
MHR333 Garrett Jones 5.00 12.00
MHR334 Dexter Fowler 5.00 12.00
MHR335 Ian Kinsler 4.00 10.00
MHR336 Raul Ibanez 6.00 15.00
MHR337 Roy Halladay 10.00 25.00
MHR338 Ryan Spilborghs 6.00 15.00
MHR339 Cole Hamels 10.00 25.00
MHR340 Thurman Munson 10.00 25.00
MHR341 Robinson Cano 6.00 15.00
MHR342 Matt LaPorta 5.00 12.00
MHR343 Travis Hafner 5.00 12.00
MHR344 Lou Gehrig 8.00 20.00
MHR345 Nelson Cruz 6.00 15.00
MHR346 Derrek Lee 6.00 15.00
MHR347 Juan Marichal 8.00 20.00
MHR348 Rollie Fingers 5.00 12.00
MHR349 Carl Yastrzemski 10.00 25.00
MHR350 Frank Robinson 8.00 20.00
MHR351 Joe Morgan 6.00 15.00
MHR352 Steve Carlton 8.00 20.00
MHR353 Catfish Hunter 10.00 25.00
MHR354 Willie Stargell 12.50 30.00
MHR355 Early Wynn 5.00 12.00
MHR356 Larry Doby 5.00 12.00
MHR357 Bill Mazeroski 6.00 15.00
MHR358 Carlton Fisk 8.00 20.00
MHR359 Dave Winfield 5.00 12.00
MHR360 Enos Slaughter 10.00 25.00
MHR361 Ernie Banks 10.00 25.00
MHR362 Joe Morgan 6.00 15.00
MHR363 Rollie Fingers 5.00 12.00
MHR364 Phil Rizzuto 8.00 20.00
MHR365 Bo Jackson 8.00 20.00
MHR366 Dave Winfield 5.00 12.00
MHR367 Babe Ruth 20.00 50.00
MHR368 Luis Aparicio 5.00 12.00
MHR369 Duke Snider 8.00 20.00
MHR370 Richie Ashburn 10.00 25.00
MHR371 Early Wynn 5.00 12.00
MHR372 Yogi Berra 10.00 25.00
MHR373 Lou Brock 8.00 20.00
MHR374 Roger Maris 12.50 30.00
MHR375 Orlando Cepeda 4.00 10.00
MHR376 Catfish Hunter 10.00 25.00
MHR377 Ralph Kiner 6.00 15.00
MHR378 Bob Gibson 15.00 40.00
MHR379 Robin Yount 12.50 30.00

MHR380 Harmon Killebrew 10.00 25.00
MHR381 Orlando Cepeda 4.00 10.00
MHR382 Steve Carlton 8.00 20.00
MHR383 Bob Feller 6.00 15.00
MHR384 Dennis Eckersley 8.00 20.00
MHR385 Robin Roberts 12.50 30.00
MHR386 Willie McCovey 6.00 15.00
MHR387 Hank Greenberg 5.00 12.00
MHR388 Johnny Bench 10.00 25.00
MHR389 Eddie Murray 10.00 25.00
MHR390 Red Schoendienst 5.00 12.00
MHR391 Roger Maris 12.50 30.00
MHR392 Tris Speaker 10.00 25.00
MHR393 Dale Murphy 10.00 25.00
MHR394 Fergie Jenkins 8.00 20.00
MHR395 Frank Robinson 8.00 20.00
MHR396 Willie McCovey 6.00 15.00
MHR397 George Kell 8.00 20.00
MHR398 Dave Winfield 5.00 12.00
MHR399 Ozzie Smith 15.00 40.00
MHR400 Rogers Hornsby 4.00 10.00
MHR401 Jim Palmer 6.00 15.00
MHR402 Carlton Fisk 8.00 20.00
MHR403 Duke Snider 8.00 20.00
MHR404 Gary Carter 10.00 25.00
MHR405 Luis Aparicio 5.00 12.00
MHR406 Andre Dawson 6.00 15.00
MHR407 Hal Newhouser 8.00 20.00
MHR408 Al Kaline 8.00 20.00
MHR409 Bo Jackson 8.00 20.00
MHR410 Johnny Mize 5.00 12.00
MHR411 Mike Schmidt 12.50 30.00
MHR412 Jim Bunning 6.00 15.00
MHR413 Tony Perez 6.00 15.00
MHR414 Dizzy Dean 6.00 15.00
MHR415 Frank Thomas 10.00 25.00
MHR416 Stan Musial 12.50 30.00

2010 Topps Manufactured MLB Logoman Patch

RANDOM INSERTS IN VARIOUS 2010 PRODUCTS
STATED PRINT RUN 50 SER.#'d SETS
LM1 Albert Pujols 60.00 120.00
LM2 Hanley Ramirez 12.50 30.00
LM3 Mike Schmidt 40.00 80.00
LM4 Nick Markakis 30.00 60.00
LM5 CC Sabathia
LM6 Babe Ruth 40.00 80.00
LM7 George Sisler
LM8 Gordon Beckham 30.00 60.00
LM9 Adrian Gonzalez 20.00 50.00
LM10 Ozzie Smith 40.00 80.00
LM11 Yogi Berra
LM12 Tris Speaker 15.00 40.00
LM13 Ryan Braun 15.00 40.00
LM14 Juan Marichal 15.00 40.00
LM21 Joe Mauer 20.00 50.00
LM22 David Ortiz 15.00 40.00
LM23 Tim Lincecum
LM25 Miguel Cabrera 15.00 40.00
LM27 Lou Gehrig 40.00 80.00
LM28 Stan Musial 20.00 50.00
LM29 Whitey Ford 20.00 50.00
LM30 Ty Cobb
LM31 Dustin Pedroia 20.00 50.00
LM32 Evan Longoria 20.00 50.00
LM33 Clayton Kershaw 15.00 40.00
LM36 Frank Robinson 20.00 50.00
LM37 Johnny Bench 20.00 50.00
LM38 Ryne Sandberg 30.00 60.00
LM39 Reggie Jackson 20.00 50.00
LM40 Nolan Ryan 30.00 60.00
LM41 Steve Carlton
LM42 Johnny Podres
LM43 Jim Palmer
LM44 Jimmie Foxx 15.00 40.00
LM45 Robin Yount
LM46 Justin Upton 12.50 30.00
LM47 Alfonso Soriano 12.50 30.00
LM48 Grady Sizemore 15.00 40.00
LM49 Matt Kemp 12.50 30.00
LM50 B.J. Upton 12.50 30.00
LM52 Roy Halladay 40.00 80.00
LM54 Chipper Jones 40.00 80.00
LM55 Alex Rodriguez 40.00 80.00
LM56 Andre Dawson 15.00 40.00
LM57 Tony Gwynn 30.00 60.00
LM58 Mickey Mantle 50.00 100.00
LM59 Johnny Mize 15.00 40.00
LM61 Walter Johnson
LM62 Honus Wagner
LM63 Bob Gibson 15.00 40.00
LM64 Warren Spahn
LM65 Dizzy Dean
LM66 Roy Campanella 15.00 40.00
LM67 Cal Ripken Jr. 40.00 80.00
LM68 Carl Yastrzemski
LM69 Mel Ott
LM70 Roger Maris
LM72 Justin Verlander
LM73 Aaron Hill 12.50 30.00
LM74 Josh Beckett 12.50 30.00
LM75 Adam Wainwright 15.00 40.00
LM77 Derrek Lee 30.00 60.00
LM78 Chase Utley 30.00 60.00
LM79 Zack Greinke 50.00 100.00
LM81 Tom Seaver 20.00 50.00
LM82 Cy Young 20.00 50.00
LM83 Christy Mathewson 15.00 40.00
LM84 Thurman Munson 15.00 40.00
LM85 Eddie Mathews 60.00 120.00
LM88 Willie Stargell 12.50 30.00
LM90 Ernie Banks 30.00 60.00
LM91 Felix Hernandez 15.00 40.00
LM92 Prince Fielder 15.00 40.00
LM93 David Wright 40.00 80.00
LM94 Kevin Youkilis 15.00 40.00
LM95 Justin Morneau 15.00 40.00
LM96 Ryan Howard 20.00 50.00
LM97 Todd Helton 30.00 60.00
LM98 Rick Porcello 12.50 30.00
LM99 Nolan Reimold 12.50 30.00
LM100 Dan Haren 12.50 30.00

2010 Topps Mickey Mantle Reprint Relics

SERIES 1 ODDS 1:88,000
UPDATE ODDS 1:60,000 HOBBY
SER.1 PRINT RUN 61 SER.#'d SETS
SER.2 PRINT RUN 62 SER.#'d SETS
UPD PRINT RUN 63 SER.#'d SETS
MMR61 Mickey Mantle Bat/61 150.00 400.00
MMR66 Mickey Mantle Bat/63 90.00 150.00
MMR62 Mickey Mantle Bat/62

2010 Topps Mickey Mouse All-Stars

COMPLETE SET (10) 20.00 50.00
COMP.FANFEST SET (5) 10.00 25.00
COMP.UPDATE SET (5) 10.00 25.00
MM1 All Star Game 2.50 6.00
MM2 American League 2.50 6.00
MM3 National League 2.50 6.00
MM4 Los Angeles Angels 2.50 6.00
MM5 Los Angeles Dodgers 2.50 6.00
MM6 Atlanta Braves 2.50 6.00
MM7 Chicago Cubs 2.50 6.00
MM8 New York Mets 2.50 6.00
MM9 New York Yankees 4.00 10.00
MM10 San Francisco Giants 2.50 6.00

2010 Topps Million Card Giveaway

COMMON CARD 1.50 4.00
RANDOM INSERTS IN VAR.TOPPS PRODUCTS
TMC1 Roy Campanella 1.50 4.00
TMC2 Gary Carter 1.50 4.00
TMC3 Bob Gibson 1.50 4.00
TMC4 Ichiro Suzuki 1.50 4.00
TMC5 Mickey Mantle 1.50 4.00
TMC6 Mickey Mantle 1.50 4.00
TMC7 Roger Maris 1.50 4.00
TMC8 Thurman Munson 1.50 4.00
TMC9 Mike Schmidt 1.50 4.00
TMC10 Carl Yastrzemski 1.50 4.00
TMC11 Roy Campanella 1.50 4.00
TMC12 Gary Carter 1.50 4.00
TMC13 Bob Gibson 1.50 4.00
TMC14 Ichiro Suzuki 1.50 4.00
TMC15 Mickey Mantle 1.50 4.00
TMC16 Mickey Mantle 1.50 4.00
TMC17 Roger Maris 1.50 4.00
TMC18 Thurman Munson 1.50 4.00
TMC19 Mike Schmidt 1.50 4.00
TMC20 Carl Yastrzemski 1.50 4.00
TMC21 Roy Campanella 1.50 4.00
TMC22 Gary Carter 1.50 4.00
TMC23 Bob Gibson 1.50 4.00
TMC24 Ichiro Suzuki 1.50 4.00
TMC25 Mickey Mantle 1.50 4.00
TMC26 Roger Maris 1.50 4.00
TMC27 Thurman Munson 1.50 4.00
TMC28 Mike Schmidt 1.50 4.00
TMC29 Carl Yastrzemski 1.50 4.00
TMC30 Mickey Mantle 1.50 4.00

2010 Topps Peak Performance

STATED ODDS 1:4 HOBBY
UPDATE ODDS 1:8 HOBBY
1-50 ISSUED IN SERIES 1
51-100 ISSUED IN SERIES 2
101-125 ISSUED IN UPDATE
1 Albert Pujols 2.00 5.00
2 Tim Lincecum 1.25 3.00
3 Honus Wagner .75 2.00
4 Walter Johnson .75 2.00
5 Babe Ruth 2.00 5.00
6 Steve Carlton .30 .75
7 Grady Sizemore .50 1.25
8 Justin Morneau .75 2.00
9 Bob Gibson .50 1.25
10 Christy Mathewson .75 2.00
11 Mel Ott .75 2.00
12 Lou Gehrig 1.50 4.00
13 Mariano Rivera .75 2.00
14 Raul Ibanez .50 1.25
15 Alex Rodriguez 1.25 3.00
16 Vladimir Guerrero .75 2.00
17 Reggie Jackson .50 1.25
18 Mickey Mantle 2.50 6.00
19 Tris Speaker .50 1.25
20 Mark Teixeira .75 2.00
21 Jimmie Foxx .75 2.00
22 George Sisler .75 2.00
23 Stan Musial 1.25 3.00
24 Willie Stargell .50 1.25
25 Chase Utley .75 2.00
26 Joe Mauer .75 2.00
27 Tom Seaver .50 1.25
28 Johnny Mize .50 1.25
29 Roy Campanella .75 2.00
30 Prince Fielder .50 1.25
31 Manny Ramirez .75 2.00
32 Ryan Howard 1.00 2.50
33 Cy Young .75 2.00
34 Ichiro Suzuki 1.25 3.00
35 Miguel Cabrera .75 2.00
36 Dizzy Dean .30 .75
37 Hanley Ramirez .75 2.00
38 David Ortiz .50 1.25
39 Chipper Jones .75 2.00
40 Alfonso Soriano .50 1.25
41 David Wright 1.00 2.50
42 Ryan Braun 1.00 2.50
43 Dustin Pedroia 1.00 2.50
44 Roy Halladay .50 1.25
45 Jackie Robinson .50 1.25
46 Rogers Hornsby .50 1.25
47 Roger Maris .75 2.00
48 Curt Schilling .50 1.25
49 Evan Longoria 1.00 2.50
50 Ty Cobb 1.25 3.00
51 Luis Aparicio .30 .75
52 Lance Berkman .50 1.25
53 Ubaldo Jimenez .50 1.25
54 Ian Kinsler .50 1.25
55 George Kell .30 .75
56 Felix Hernandez .75 2.00
57 Max Scherzer .30 .75
58 Magglio Ordonez .50 1.25
59 Derek Jeter 2.00 5.00
60 Mike Schmidt 1.25 3.00
61 Hunter Pence .50 1.25
62 Jason Bay .50 1.25
63 Clay Buchholz .50 1.25
64 Josh Hamilton .75 2.00
65 Willie McCovey .50 1.25
66 Aaron Hill .30 .75
67 Derrek Lee .30 .75
68 Andre Ethier .50 1.25
69 Ryan Zimmerman .50 1.25
70 Joe Morgan .30 .75
71 Carlos Lee .30 .75
72 Chad Billingsley .30 .75
73 Adam Dunn .50 1.25
74 Dan Uggla .50 1.25
75 Jermaine Dye .30 .75
76 Monte Irvin .30 .75
77 Curtis Granderson .50 1.25
78 Mark Reynolds .30 .75
79 Matt Kemp .50 1.25
80 Ozzie Smith 1.25 3.00
81 Brandon Phillips .30 .75
82 Yogi Berra .75 2.00
83 Bobby Abreu .30 .75
84 Catfish Hunter .30 .75
85 Justin Upton .50 1.25
86 Justin Verlander 1.00 2.50
87 Troy Tulowitzki .75 2.00
88 Phil Rizzuto .75 2.00
89 B.J. Upton .50 1.25
90 Richie Ashburn .50 1.25
91 Matt Cain .50 1.25
92 Joey Votto .75 2.00
93 Robin Roberts .30 .75
94 Nick Markakis .75 2.00
95 Al Kaline .75 2.00
96 Dan Haren .30 .75
97 Thurman Munson .75 2.00
98 Victor Martinez .50 1.25
99 Brian McCann .50 1.25
100 Zack Greinke .50 1.25
101 Stephen Strasburg 2.00 5.00
102 Vladimir Guerrero .75 2.00
103 Hideki Matsui .75 2.00
104 Chone Figgins .30 .75
105 John Lackey .30 .75
106 Max Scherzer .30 .75
107 Carlos Pena .50 1.25
108 Ubaldo Jimenez .50 1.25
109 Colby Rasmus .75 2.00
110 Jered Weaver .30 .75
111 Ryan Zimmerman .50 1.25
112 Jason Heyward 2.00 5.00
113 Carlos Santana 1.00 2.50
114 Mike Leake 1.00 2.50
115 Ike Davis .75 2.00
116 Starlin Castro 1.25 3.00
117 Mike Stanton 1.25 3.00
118 Austin Jackson .50 1.25
119 Dustin Pedroia 1.00 2.50
120 Tyler Colvin .50 1.25
121 Brennan Boesch .75 2.00
122 Dallas Braden .50 1.25
123 Edwin Jackson .30 .75
124 Daniel Nava .50 1.25
125 Roy Halladay .75 2.00

2010 Topps Peak Performance Autographs

SER.1 A ODDS 1:19,950 HOBBY
SER.2 A ODDS 1:6800 HOBBY
UPD A ODDS 1:9310 HOBBY
SER.1 B ODDS 1:1125 HOBBY
SER.2 B ODDS 1:826 HOBBY
UPD B ODDS 1:914 HOBBY
SER.1 C ODDS 1:600 HOBBY
SER.2 C ODDS 1:526 HOBBY
UPD C ODDS 1:1775 HOBBY
SER.1 D ODDS 1:1850 HOBBY
AB Andrew Bailey B2 4.00 10.00
AC Andrew Carpenter 3.00 8.00
AD Jason Donald UPD 3.00 8.00
AE Andre Ethier B2 12.50 30.00
AE Andre Ethier UPD B 10.00 25.00
AG Adrian Gonzalez UPD A 10.00 25.00
AH Aaron Hill B2 4.00 10.00
AL Adam Lind UPD B 4.00 10.00
AM Andrew McCutchen UPD B 6.00 15.00
AP Albert Pujols A1
AR Alex Rodriguez A1
AS Alfonso Soriano UPD A
AS Alfonso Soriano A1
BA Brett Anderson C2
BM Brian McCann A2
BM Peter Moylan 6.00 15.00
BP Buster Posey B1 40.00 80.00
CB Clay Buchholz B2 6.00 15.00
CB Collin Balester C1 3.00 8.00
CC Chris Coghlan UPD B 4.00 10.00
CF Chone Figgins B1
CF Chone Figgins UPD B 4.00 10.00
CG Curtis Granderson B1
CJ Chipper Jones A1
CK Clayton Kershaw C1 10.00 25.00
CM Cameron Maybin C1
CM Cameron Maybin C2 3.00 8.00
CP Carlos Pena UPD B 4.00 10.00
CR Cal Ripken Jr A2
CR Carlos Ruiz C2 5.00 12.00
CR Colby Rasmus UPD B 5.00 12.00
CV Chris Volstad C2 3.00 8.00
CY Chris Young C1 3.00 8.00
DB Dallas Braden C2 5.00 12.00
DB Daniel Bard B1 8.00 20.00
DG Dwight Gooden A1
DM Daniel Murphy B2 4.00 10.00
DO David Ortiz A1
DP Dustin Pedroia B2 10.00 25.00
DP Dustin Pedroia B1 12.50 30.00
DS Denard Span B2 4.00 10.00
DS Drew Stubbs UPD B 6.00 15.00
DS Daniel Stange 3.00 8.00
DS Daniel Schlereth C1 3.00 8.00
DW David Wright A2
DW David Wright UPD A 15.00 40.00
DW David Wright A1
EC Everth Cabrera C2 3.00 8.00
ES Ervin Santana UPD B 4.00 10.00
EV Edinson Volquez B2 3.00 8.00
FC Fausto Carmona B2 4.00 10.00
FC Fausto Carmona UPD B 4.00 10.00
FJ Fergie Jenkins A1
FM Franklin Morales D1 3.00 8.00
FP Felipe Paulino 6.00 15.00
FR Frank Robinson A1
GB Gordon Beckham B1 12.50 30.00
GC Gary Carter B1 10.00 25.00
GG Gio Gonzalez C2 3.00 8.00
GK George Kell B2 12.50 30.00
GP Glen Perkins 3.00 8.00
HB Heath Bell UPD C 4.00 10.00
HK Howie Kendrick B2 4.00 10.00
HP Hunter Pence A2
HR Hanley Ramirez A2
HR Hanley Ramirez B1 8.00 20.00
JB Jason Bartlett B2 4.00 10.00
JB Jose Bautista UPD C 12.50 30.00
JB Jay Bruce C1 8.00 20.00
JC Johnny Cueto UPD B 4.00 10.00
JC Johnny Cueto C1 4.00 10.00
JD Jermaine Dye B2 4.00 10.00
JF Jeff Francoeur A2
JJ Josh Johnson 6.00 15.00
JL Jon Lester B2 8.00 20.00
JL John Lackey UPD A 6.00 15.00
JM Joe Morgan A2
JM Justin Masterson UPD B 4.00 10.00
JM Juan Marichal A1
JO Josh Outman B2 3.00 8.00
JP Jhonny Peralta B2 5.00 12.00
JR Juan Rivera B2 4.00 10.00
JS Joe Saunders B2 5.00 12.00
JU Justin Upton A2
JU Justin Upton UPD A 8.00 20.00
KG Kevin Gregg UPD B 4.00 10.00
KK Kevin Kouzmanoff UPD B 4.00 10.00
KS Kurt Suzuki 3.00 8.00
KU Koji Uehara A2
LA Luis Aparicio A2
LM Lou Marson C2 3.00 8.00
LS Lee Smith A1
MB Milton Bradley B1 4.00 10.00
MC Matt Capps UPD B 4.00 10.00
MG Mat Gamel C1 4.00 10.00
MN Mike Napoli B2 10.00 25.00
MR Manny Ramirez A2
MR Manny Ramirez A1
MS Mike Schmidt A2
MS Max Scherzer UPD B 4.00 10.00
MS Max Scherzer B1 4.00 10.00
MT Matt Tolbert B2
MT Matt Tolbert 3.00 8.00
MY Michael Young A2
NE Nick Evans C2 3.00 8.00
NF Neftali Feliz UPD B 6.00 15.00
NM Nyjer Morgan UPD B 3.00 8.00
NS Nick Swisher B2 20.00 50.00
OS Ozzie Smith A2
PF Prince Fielder A2
PF Prince Fielder UPD A 12.50 30.00
PF Prince Fielder A1
PH Phil Hughes B2 10.00 25.00
PH Phil Hughes B1 8.00 20.00
PP Placido Polanco UPD B 5.00 12.00
PS Pablo Sandoval UPD B 5.00 12.00
RB Ryan Braun UPD A 20.00 50.00
RB Ryan Braun B1 20.00 50.00
RC Robinson Cano A2
RC Robinson Cano UPD A 20.00 50.00
RC Robinson Cano B1 12.50 30.00
RH Ryan Howard A2
RH Ryan Howard UPD A 30.00 60.00
RH Ryan Howard A1
RI Raul Ibanez A2
RN Ricky Nolasco UPD B 3.00 8.00
RP Ryan Perry C2 3.00 8.00
RP Ryan Perry C1 4.00 10.00
RR Ricky Romero UPD C 3.00 8.00
RR Randy Ruiz B1 6.00 15.00
RW Randy Wells A2
RW Randy Wells UPD C 3.00 8.00
SR Sean Rodriguez UPD B 3.00 8.00
SV Shane Victorino C1 10.00 25.00
TC Trevor Cahill B2 4.00 10.00
TC Trevor Cahill UPD B 5.00 12.00
TH Torii Hunter A2
TH Tommy Hanson UPD B 8.00 20.00
TH Tommy Hanson B1 10.00 25.00
TS Travis Snider B2 5.00 12.00
TT Troy Tulowitzki B1 6.00 15.00
TW Tim Wood UPD C 3.00 8.00
UJ Ubaldo Jimenez C1
UJ Ubaldo Jimenez B2 12.50 30.00
UJ Ubaldo Jimenez UPD B 6.00 15.00
VG Vladimir Guerrero UPD A
VG Vladimir Guerrero A1
VW Vernon Wells UPD A 10.00 25.00
WD Wade Davis B2 5.00 12.00
WD Wade Davis B1 10.00 25.00
WM Willie McCovey A2
AES Alcides Escobar UPD B 3.00 8.00
BPA Bobby Parnell C1 3.00 8.00
CBI Chad Billingsley C2 5.00 12.00
CCR Carl Crawford UPD A 8.00 20.00
CGE Chris Getz C2 3.00 8.00
CGO Carlos Gomez B2 3.00 8.00
DMC Dustin McGowan B2 3.00 8.00
JDE Joey Devine C2 4.00 10.00
JFR Jeff Francis B2 4.00 10.00
JLM Jason Motte C2 5.00 12.00
JMI Jose Mijares D1 3.00 8.00
JMO Justin Morneau A2
JRE Josh Reddick C2 4.00 10.00
JSO Joakim Soria B2 4.00 10.00
MCA Matt Cain UPD B 8.00 20.00
MSC Max Scherzer B2 4.00 10.00

2010 Topps Peak Performance Autograph Relics

SERIES 1 ODDS 1:3740 HOBBY
SERIES 2ODDS 1:4350 HOBBY
STATED PRINT RUN 50 SER.#'d SETS
CB Chad Billingsley S2
CG Curtis Granderson 15.00 40.00
DO David Ortiz 30.00 60.00
DW David Wright S2
DW David Wright 30.00 60.00
FH Felix Hernandez S2
GB Gordon Beckham 75.00 150.00
HP Hunter Pence S2 12.50 30.00
HR Hanley Ramirez S2 15.00 40.00
JJ Josh Johnson 12.50 30.00
JM Justin Morneau S2 20.00 50.00
JU Justin Upton S2 15.00 40.00
KM Kendry Morales
MK Matt Kemp S2 20.00 50.00
PF Prince Fielder S2
PF Prince Fielder 20.00 50.00
RB Ryan Braun 20.00 50.00
RH Ryan Howard S2 50.00 100.00
RH Ryan Howard 40.00 80.00
RI Raul Ibanez
TT Troy Tulowitzki S2 15.00 40.00

2010 Topps Peak Performance Dual Relics

STATED ODDS 1:6315 HOBBY
STATED PRINT RUN 50 SER.#'d SETS
BF Ryan Braun
Prince Fielder
BR Gordon Beckham 30.00 60.00
Alexei Ramirez
GY Adrian Gonzalez
Kevin Youkilis
HJ Felix Hernandez 50.00 100.00
Ubaldo Jimenez
HP Ryan Howard
Albert Pujols
IF Ichiro Suzuki 30.00 60.00
Kosuke Fukudome
KE Matt Kemp 20.00 50.00
Andre Ethier
LB Carlos Lee 8.00 20.00
Lance Berkman
LS Tim Lincecum 40.00 80.00
Pablo Sandoval
RT Alex Rodriguez
Mark Teixeira
SR CC Sabathia
Mariano Rivera
SU Ryne Sandberg 20.00 50.00
Chase Utley
UU B.J. Upton 20.00 50.00
Justin Upton
WL David Wright 20.00 50.00
Evan Longoria
RTU Hanley Ramirez 30.00 60.00
Troy Tulowitzki

2010 Topps Peak Performance Jumbo Relics

STATED ODDS 1:5425 HOBBY
STATED PRINT RUN 20 SER.#'d SETS
NO PRICING DUE TO SCARCITY

2010 Topps Peak Performance Relics

SER.1 A ODDS 1:1555 HOBBY
SER.1 B ODDS 1:71 HOBBY
SER.1 C ODDS 1:153 HOBBY
SER.2 ODDS 1:49 HOBBY
AC Asdrubal Cabrera B 4.00 10.00
AE Alcides Escobar C 3.00 8.00
AG Adrian Gonzalez S2 3.00 8.00
AH Aaron Hill S2 3.00 8.00
AJ Adam Jones S2 3.00 8.00
AJ Adam Jones B 3.00 8.00
AK Al Kaline S2 8.00 20.00
AL Adam LaRoche A 3.00 8.00
AM Andrew McCutchen S2 3.00 8.00
AP Andy Pettitte S2 3.00 8.00
AP Albert Pujols B 8.00 20.00
AR Alexei Ramirez B 3.00 8.00
AR Aramis Ramirez C 3.00 8.00
AS Alfonso Soriano S2 5.00 12.00
BG Bob Gibson A 10.00 25.00
BM Brian McCann C 3.00 8.00
BP Buster Posey S2 12.50 30.00
BR Brad Lidge B 3.00 8.00
CC Chris Coghlan S2 3.00 8.00
CF Carlton Fisk A 8.00 20.00
CH Catfish Hunter S2
CH Cole Hamels B 3.00 8.00
CJ Chipper Jones S2 4.00 10.00
CJ Chipper Jones B 6.00 15.00
CL Cliff Lee B 4.00 10.00
CR Colby Rasmus S2 4.00 10.00
CR Cal Ripken Jr. B 8.00 20.00
CS CC Sabathia S2 3.00 8.00
CU Chase Utley B 4.00 10.00
CZ Carlos Zambrano S2 3.00 8.00
DE Dennis Eckersley B 3.00 8.00
DG Dwight Gooden B 3.00 8.00
DH Dan Haren S2 3.00 8.00
DL Derrek Lee S2 4.00 10.00
DL Derrek Lee B 3.00 8.00
DM Daniel Murphy A 3.00 8.00
DO David Ortiz S2 3.00 8.00
DO David Ortiz B 3.00 8.00
DP David Price S2 4.00 10.00
DP Dustin Pedroia B 4.00 10.00
DU Dan Uggla S2 3.00 8.00
DU Dan Uggla B 4.00 10.00
DW Dave Winfield C 4.00 10.00
DW David Wright C 4.00 10.00
DY Delmon Young B 3.00 8.00
EL Evan Longoria B 4.00 10.00
FC Fausto Carmona B 3.00 8.00
FH Felix Hernandez S2 3.00 8.00
FH Felix Hernandez B 3.00 8.00
GB Gordon Beckham S2 3.00 8.00
GK George Kell S2 8.00 20.00
GS Grady Sizemore S2 3.00 8.00
GS Gary Sheffield A 4.00 10.00
HG Hank Greenberg B 12.50 30.00
HM Hideki Matsui B 8.00 20.00
HR Hanley Ramirez S2 3.00 8.00
HW Honus Wagner S2 40.00 80.00
HW Honus Wagner A 60.00 120.00
IK Ian Kinsler S2 3.00 8.00
IS Ichiro Suzuki S2 8.00 20.00
IS Ichiro Suzuki B 8.00 20.00
JB Jason Bulger B 3.00 8.00
JC Johnny Cueto S2 EXCH 4.00 10.00
JD J.D. Drew B 3.00 8.00
JE Jacoby Ellsbury B 4.00 10.00
JG Jody Gerut B 3.00 8.00
JH Josh Hamilton S2 4.00 10.00
JH Jeremy Hermida B 3.00 8.00
JM Justin Morneau S2 4.00 10.00
JM Johnny Mize A 15.00 40.00
JP Willie Stargell S2 10.00 25.00
JP Jonathan Papelbon B 3.00 8.00
JR Jose Reyes B 3.00 8.00
JS Joakim Soria B 3.00 8.00
JV Joey Votto S2 3.00 8.00
JW Jayson Werth A 5.00 12.00
JZ Jordan Zimmermann B 4.00 10.00
KF Kosuke Fukudome S2 3.00 8.00
KF Kosuke Fukudome B 3.00 8.00
KJ Kenji Johjima B 3.00 8.00
KK Kenshin Kawakami S2 3.00 8.00
LB Lance Berkman S2 5.00 12.00
MC Matt Cain S2 4.00 10.00
MC Matt Cain B 3.00 8.00
MF Mike Fontenot S2 3.00 8.00
MG Mat Gamel C 3.00 8.00
MI Monte Irvin S2
MK Matt Kemp C 3.00 8.00
MM Melvin Mora B 4.00 10.00
MO Mel Ott S2 6.00 15.00
MO Mel Ott A 6.00 15.00
MP Manny Parra C 3.00 8.00
MS Mike Schmidt A 15.00 40.00
MT Mark Teixeira S2 3.00 8.00
MY Michael Young B 3.00 8.00
NF Neftali Feliz S2 3.00 8.00
NM Nick Markakis S2 3.00 8.00
NS Nick Swisher S2 4.00 10.00
NS Nick Swisher C 4.00 10.00
OS Ozzie Smith S2 5.00 12.00
PF Prince Fielder S2 3.00 8.00
PF Prince Fielder B 3.00 8.00
PH Phil Hughes S2 3.00 8.00
PM Paul Molitor B 4.00 10.00
PS Pablo Sandoval S2 EXCH 4.00 10.00
RA Richie Ashburn S2 10.00 25.00
RA Rick Ankiel B 4.00 10.00
RB Ryan Braun B 3.00 8.00
RC Roy Campanella S2 8.00 20.00
RD Ryan Dempster S2 3.00 8.00
RH Ryan Howard S2 3.00 8.00
RH Rich Harden B 3.00 8.00
RP Rick Porcello S2 3.00 8.00
RR Robin Roberts S2 15.00 40.00
RT Ryan Theriot S2 3.00 8.00
RW Rickie Weeks C 3.00 8.00
SC Shin-Soo Choo B 4.00 10.00
TG Tony Gwynn B 3.00 8.00
TH Tim Hudson B 3.00 8.00
TL Ted Lilly S2 3.00 8.00
TM Thurman Munson S2 12.50 30.00
TM Thurman Munson A 15.00 40.00
TS Tris Speaker S2 12.50 30.00
TS Tris Speaker A 12.50 30.00
TT Troy Tulowitzki S2 3.00 8.00
TT Troy Tulowitzki B 4.00 10.00
UJ Ubaldo Jimenez S2 4.00 10.00
YB Yogi Berra S2 12.50 30.00
YG Yovani Gallardo S2 3.00 8.00
YG Yovani Gallardo B 3.00 8.00
ZG Zack Greinke S2 4.00 10.00
AH1 Aaron Hill Bat B 4.00 10.00
AH2 Aaron Hill Jsy B 4.00 10.00
ARA Aramis Ramirez S2 4.00 10.00
BRU Babe Ruth A 150.00 250.00
GSI George Sisler S2 10.00 25.00
GSI George Sisler A 15.00 40.00
GSO Geovany Soto S2 4.00 10.00
GSO Geovany Soto C 4.00 10.00
JBO Jeremy Bonderman B 3.00 8.00
JMI Johnny Mize S2 8.00 20.00
JPO Jorge Posada B 5.00 12.00
JV1 Joey Votto Bat B 4.00 10.00
JV2 Joey Votto Jsy B 4.00 10.00
JWI Josh Willingham B 3.00 8.00
KY1 Kevin Youkilis Bat B 3.00 8.00
KY2 Kevin Youkilis Jsy C 3.00 8.00
MCA Melky Cabrera B 4.00 10.00
MMA Mickey Mantle A 50.00 100.00
PWR Pee Wee Reese S2 12.50 30.00
PWR Pee Wee Reese A 30.00 60.00
RCA Robinson Cano S2 4.00 10.00
RHE Rickey Henderson B 6.00 15.00
RHO Rogers Hornsby S2 15.00 40.00
RHO Ryan Howard B 5.00 12.00
SK1 Scott Kazmir Rays Jsy B 3.00 8.00
SK2 Scott Kazmir LAA Jsy C 3.00 8.00
THA Tommy Hanson B 4.00 10.00

2010 Topps Peak Performance Relics Blue

*BLUE: 1X TO 2.5X BASIC
RANDOM INSERTS IN SER.2 PACKS
STATED PRINT RUN 99 SER.#'d SETS

2010 Topps Red Back

INSERTED IN TARGET PACKS
31-45 ISSUED IN UPD TARGET PACKS
1 Mickey Mantle 3.00 8.00
2 Rogers Hornsby .60 1.50
3 Warren Spahn .60 1.50
4 Jackie Robinson 1.00 2.50
5 Ty Cobb 1.50 4.00
6 Cy Young 1.00 2.50
7 Albert Pujols 2.50 6.00
8 Mariano Rivera 1.00 2.50
9 Jimmie Foxx 1.00 2.50
10 Reggie Jackson .60 1.50
11 Lou Gehrig 2.00 5.00
12 Dizzy Dean .40 1.00
13 Chipper Jones 1.00 2.50
14 Cal Ripken Jr. 4.00 10.00
15 David Wright 1.25 3.00
16 Babe Ruth 2.50 6.00
17 Honus Wagner 1.00 2.50
18 Ichiro Suzuki 1.50 4.00
19 Nolan Ryan 3.00 8.00
20 Stan Musial 1.50 4.00
21 Tom Seaver .60 1.50
22 Derek Jeter 2.50 6.00
23 Roy Halladay 1.00 2.50
24 Mel Ott 1.00 2.50
25 George Sisler 1.00 2.50
26 Roger Maris 1.00 2.50
27 Walter Johnson 1.00 2.50
28 Vladimir Guerrero 1.00 2.50
29 Tim Lincecum 1.50 4.00
30 Hanley Ramirez 1.00 2.50
31 Babe Ruth 2.50 6.00
32 Jimmie Foxx 1.00 2.50
33 Rogers Hornsby .60 1.50
34 Warren Spahn .60 1.50
35 Reggie Jackson .60 1.50
36 Nolan Ryan 3.00 8.00
37 Tom Seaver .60 1.50
38 George Sisler 1.00 2.50
39 Roger Maris 1.00 2.50
40 Vladimir Guerrero 1.00 2.50
41 Thurman Munson 1.00 2.50
42 Johnny Mize .60 1.50
43 Pee Wee Reese .60 1.50
44 Hank Greenberg 1.00 2.50
45 Ryan Braun 1.25 3.00

2010 Topps Red Hot Rookie Redemption

COMPLETE SET (10) 20.00 50.00
STATED ODDS 1:36 HOBBY
RHR1 Carlos Santana 2.50 6.00
RHR2 Jose Tabata 2.00 5.00
RHR3 Brennan Boesch 2.00 5.00
RHR4 Mike Stanton 3.00 8.00
RHR5 Starlin Castro 3.00 8.00
RHR6 Logan Morrison 1.25 3.00
RHR7 Dominic Brown 3.00 8.00
RHR8 Stephen Strasburg 10.00 25.00
RHR9 Mike Minor 1.25 3.00
RHR10A Brett Wallace 2.00 5.00
RHR10B Brett Wallace AU

2010 Topps Series 2 Attax Code Cards

COMPLETE SET (27) 5.00 12.00
1 Jason Bay .50 1.25
2 Lance Berkman .50 1.25
3 Billy Butler .30 .75
4 Stephen Drew .30 .75
5 Yunel Escobar .30 .75
6 Yovani Gallardo .30 .75
7 Zack Greinke .50 1.25
8 Felix Hernandez .75 2.00
9 Matt Holliday .75 2.00
10 Torii Hunter .30 .75
11 Josh Johnson .50 1.25
12 Matt Kemp .50 1.25
13 Ian Kinsler .50 1.25
14 Derrek Lee .30 .75
15 Jon Lester .75 2.00
16 Tim Lincecum 1.25 3.00
17 Justin Morneau .75 2.00
18 Alexei Ramirez .30 .75
19 Alex Rodriguez 1.25 3.00
20 Pablo Sandoval .50 1.25
21 Max Scherzer .30 .75
22 Grady Sizemore .50 1.25
23 B.J. Upton .50 1.25
24 Chase Utley .75 2.00
25 Justin Verlander 1.00 2.50
26 Joey Votto .75 2.00
27 Ryan Zimmerman .50 1.25

2010 Topps Silk Collection

SER.1 ODDS 1:373 HOBBY
SER.2 ODDS 1:431 HOBBY
UPDATE ODDS 1:412 HOBBY
STATED PRINT RUN 50 SER.#'d SETS
1-50 ISSUED IN SERIES 1
51-100 ISSUED IN SERIES 2
101-200 ISSUED IN UPDATE
S1 Prince Fielder 6.00 15.00
S2 Buster Posey
S3 Derrek Lee 4.00 10.00
S4 Mickey Mantle 25.00 60.00
S5 Clayton Kershaw 10.00 25.00
S6 Bobby Abreu 4.00 10.00
S7 Johnny Cueto 4.00 10.00
S8 Dexter Fowler 4.00 10.00
S9 Felipe Lopez 4.00 10.00
S10 Tommy Hanson 6.00 15.00
S11 Shane Victorino 6.00 15.00
S12 Adam Jones 6.00 15.00
S13 Victor Martinez 6.00 15.00

S14 Rick Porcello 4.00 10.00
S15 Garret Anderson 4.00 10.00
S16 Josh Johnson 6.00 15.00
S17 Marco Scutaro 4.00 10.00
S18 Howie Kendrick 4.00 10.00
S19 Joey Votto 10.00 25.00
S20 Jorge De La Rosa 4.00 10.00
S21 Zack Greinke 6.00 15.00
S22 Eric Young Jr
S23 Billy Butler 4.00 10.00
S24 John Lackey 4.00 10.00
S25 Manny Ramirez 10.00 25.00
S26 CC Sabathia 6.00 15.00
S27 David Wright 12.00 30.00
S28 Nick Swisher 10.00 25.00
S29 Matt LaPorta 10.00 25.00
S30 Brandon Inge 6.00 15.00
S31 Cole Hamels 10.00 25.00
S32 Adrian Gonzalez 6.00 15.00
S33 Joe Saunders 4.00 10.00
S34 Tim Lincecum 15.00 40.00
S35 Ken Griffey Jr. 15.00 40.00
S36 J.A. Happ 6.00 15.00
S37 Ian Kinsler 6.00 15.00
S38 Ivan Rodriguez 6.00 15.00
S39 Carl Crawford 6.00 15.00
S40 Jon Garland 4.00 10.00
S41 Albert Pujols 25.00 60.00
S42 Madison Bumgarner
S43 Andrew McCutchen 10.00 25.00
S44 Gordon Beckham 6.00 15.00
S45 Jorge Posada 6.00 15.00
S46 Ichiro Suzuki 15.00 40.00
S47 Vladimir Guerrero 10.00 25.00
S48 Cliff Lee 6.00 15.00
S49 Freddy Sanchez 4.00 10.00
S50 Ryan Dempster 4.00 10.00
S51 Adam Wainwright 6.00 15.00
S52 Matt Holliday 10.00 25.00
S53 Chone Figgins 4.00 10.00
S54 Tim Hudson 6.00 15.00
S55 Rich Harden 4.00 10.00
S56 Justin Upton 6.00 15.00
S57 Joe Mauer 10.00 25.00
S58 Vernon Wells 4.00 10.00
S59 Miguel Tejada 6.00 15.00
S60 Denard Span 4.00 10.00
S61 Brandon Phillips 4.00 10.00
S62 Jason Bay 6.00 15.00
S63 Kendry Morales 4.00 10.00
S64 Josh Hamilton 10.00 25.00
S65 Yovani Gallardo 4.00 10.00
S66 Adam Lind 6.00 15.00
S67 Hideki Matsui 10.00 25.00
S68 Will Venable 4.00 10.00
S69 Joe Blanton 4.00 10.00
S70 Adrian Beltre 4.00 10.00
S71 Pablo Sandoval 6.00 15.00
S72 Roy Halladay 10.00 25.00
S73 Chris Coghlan 4.00 10.00
S74 Colby Rasmus 10.00 25.00
S75 Alexei Ramirez 4.00 10.00
S76 Josh Beckett 6.00 15.00
S77 Matt Kemp 6.00 15.00
S78 Max Scherzer 4.00 10.00
S79 Randy Johnson 6.00 15.00
S80 Curtis Granderson 6.00 15.00
S81 David Price 10.00 25.00
S82 Neftali Feliz 4.00 10.00
S83 Ricky Romero 4.00 10.00
S84 Lance Berkman 6.00 15.00
S85 Andre Ethier 6.00 15.00
S86 Mark Teixeira 10.00 25.00
S87 Edwin Jackson 4.00 10.00
S88 Akinori Iwamura 4.00 10.00
S89 Michael Brantley
S90 Jair Jurrjens 4.00 10.00
S91 Stephen Drew 4.00 10.00
S92 Javier Vazquez 4.00 10.00
S93 Orlando Hudson 4.00 10.00
S94 Adam Dunn 6.00 15.00
S95 Kevin Youkilis 6.00 15.00
S96 Chase Utley 10.00 25.00
S97 Tyler Flowers
S98 Brian McCann 6.00 15.00
S99 Jim Thome 6.00 15.00
S100 Alex Rios 6.00 15.00
S101 Geovany Soto 6.00 15.00
S102 Joakim Soria 4.00 10.00
S103 Chad Billingsley 4.00 10.00
S104 Jacoby Ellsbury 10.00 25.00
S105 Justin Morneau 10.00 25.00
S106 Jeff Francis 4.00 10.00
S107 Francisco Rodriguez 6.00 15.00
S108 Torii Hunter 4.00 10.00
S109 A.J Burnett 6.00 15.00
S110 Chris Young 6.00 15.00
S111 Bud Norris 4.00 10.00
S112 Todd Helton 6.00 15.00
S113 Shin-Soo Choo 6.00 15.00
S114 Matt Cain 6.00 15.00
S115 Jered Weaver 4.00 10.00
S116 Jason Bartlett 4.00 10.00
S117 Chris Carpenter 10.00 25.00
S118 Kosuke Fukudome 10.00 25.00
S119 Roy Oswalt 6.00 15.00
S120 Alex Rodriguez 15.00 40.00
S121 Dan Haren 4.00 10.00
S122 Hiroki Kuroda 4.00 10.00
S123 Hunter Pence 6.00 15.00
S124 Jeremy Guthrie 4.00 10.00
S125 Grady Sizemore 6.00 15.00
S126 Mark Reynolds 4.00 10.00
S127 Johnny Damon 6.00 15.00
S128 Aaron Rowand 4.00 10.00
S129 Carlos Beltran 4.00 10.00
S130 Alfonso Soriano 6.00 15.00
S131 Nelson Cruz 6.00 15.00
S132 Edinson Volquez 4.00 10.00
S133 Jayson Werth 6.00 15.00
S134 Mariano Rivera 10.00 25.00
S135 Brandon Webb 6.00 15.00
S136 Jordan Zimmermann 4.00 10.00
S137 Michael Young 6.00 15.00
S138 Daisuke Matsuzaka 10.00 25.00
S139 Ubaldo Jimenez 6.00 15.00
S140 Evan Longoria 12.00 30.00
S141 Brad Lidge 4.00 10.00
S142 Carlos Zambrano 6.00 15.00
S143 Heath Bell 6.00 15.00
S144 Trevor Cahill 4.00 10.00
S145 Carlos Gonzalez 6.00 15.00
S146 Jose Reyes 6.00 15.00
S147 Ian Snell 4.00 10.00
S148 Manny Parra 4.00 10.00
S149 Michael Cuddyer 4.00 10.00
S150 Melky Cabrera 4.00 10.00
S151 Justin Verlander 12.00 30.00
S152 Delmon Young 6.00 15.00
S153 Kelly Johnson 4.00 10.00
S154 Derek Lowe 4.00 10.00
S155 Derek Jeter 25.00 60.00
S156 Paul Maholm 4.00 10.00
S157 Mike Napoli 6.00 15.00
S158 Aramis Ramirez 4.00 10.00
S159 Alex Gordon 6.00 15.00
S160 Jorge Cantu 4.00 10.00
S161 Brad Hawpe 4.00 10.00
S162 Troy Tulowitzki 10.00 25.00
S163 Casey Kotchman 4.00 10.00
S164 Carlos Guillen 4.00 10.00
S165 J.D. Drew 4.00 10.00
S166 Dustin Pedroia 12.00 30.00
S167 Francisco Liriano 4.00 10.00
S168 Jimmy Rollins 6.00 15.00
S169 Wade LeBlanc 4.00 10.00
S170 Miguel Cabrera 10.00 25.00
S171 Jeremy Hermida 4.00 10.00
S172 Koji Uehara 6.00 15.00
S173 Tommy Hunter 4.00 10.00
S174 Dustin McGowan 4.00 10.00
S175 Corey Hart 4.00 10.00
S176 Jake Peavy 4.00 10.00
S177 Jason Varitek 10.00 25.00
S178 Chris Dickerson 4.00 10.00
S179 Robinson Cano 10.00 25.00
S180 Michael Bourn 4.00 10.00
S181 Chris Volstad 4.00 10.00
S182 Mark Buehrle 6.00 15.00
S183 Jarrod Saltalamacchia 4.00 10.00
S184 Aaron Hill 4.00 10.00
S185 Carlos Pena 6.00 15.00
S186 Luke Hochevar 4.00 10.00
S187 Derek Holland 4.00 10.00
S188 Carlos Quentin 6.00 15.00
S189 J.J. Hardy 4.00 10.00
S190 Ryan Zimmerman 6.00 15.00
S191 Travis Snider 4.00 10.00
S192 Russell Martin 4.00 10.00
S193 Brian Roberts 4.00 10.00
S194 Ryan Ludwick 4.00 10.00
S195 Aaron Cook 4.00 10.00
S196 Jay Bruce 6.00 15.00
S197 Kevin Slowey 4.00 10.00
S198 Johan Santana 10.00 25.00
S199 Carlos Lee 4.00 10.00
S200 David Ortiz 6.00 15.00
S201 Doug Davis 4.00 10.00
S202 Coco Crisp 4.00 10.00
S203 Jason Kendall 4.00 10.00
S204 Jason Bay 6.00 15.00
S205 Jim Thome 6.00 15.00
S206 Omar Vizquel 6.00 15.00
S207 Jose Valverde 6.00 15.00
S208 Adam Kennedy 4.00 10.00
S209 Kelly Shoppach 4.00 10.00
S210 Akinori Iwamura 4.00 10.00
S211 Brad Penny 4.00 10.00
S212 Kevin Millwood 6.00 15.00
S213 Cliff Lee 6.00 15.00
S214 Andruw Jones 4.00 10.00
S215 Rod Barajas 4.00 10.00
S216 Pedro Feliz 4.00 10.00
S217 Mike Gonzalez
S218 Placido Polanco 4.00 10.00
S219 Jhan Marinez 4.00 10.00
S220 Bobby Wilson 4.00 10.00
S221 Kris Medlen 4.00 10.00
S222 Aaron Heilman 4.00 10.00
S223 Shaun Marcum 4.00 10.00
S224 Alfredo Simon 4.00 10.00
S225 Matt Thornton 4.00 10.00
S226 Billy Wagner 4.00 10.00
S227 Troy Glaus 4.00 10.00
S228 Jesus Feliciano 4.00 10.00
S229 Dana Eveland 4.00 10.00
S230 Scott Olsen 4.00 10.00
S231 Corey Patterson 4.00 10.00
S232 Livan Hernandez 4.00 10.00
S233 Bill Hall 4.00 10.00
S234 Josh Reddick 4.00 10.00
S235 Xavier Nady 4.00 10.00
S236 Koyie Hill 4.00 10.00
S237 Tom Gorzelanny 4.00 10.00
S238 Kevin Frandsen 4.00 10.00
S239 Mark Kotsay 4.00 10.00
S240 Arthur Rhodes 4.00 10.00
S241 Micah Owings 4.00 10.00
S242 Shelley Duncan 4.00 10.00
S243 Mike Redmond 4.00 10.00
S244 Chris Perez 4.00 10.00
S245 Don Kelly 4.00 10.00
S246 Alex Avila 4.00 10.00
S247 Geoff Blum 4.00 10.00
S248 Mitch Maier 4.00 10.00
S249 Roy Halladay 10.00 25.00
S250 Matt Daley 4.00 10.00
S251 Vicente Padilla 4.00 10.00
S252 Kila Ka'aihue 6.00 15.00
S253 Dave Bush 4.00 10.00
S254 Jody Gerut 4.00 10.00
S255 George Kottaras 4.00 10.00
S256 LaTroy Hawkins 4.00 10.00
S257 Brendan Harris 4.00 10.00
S258 Alex Cora 4.00 10.00
S259 Randy Winn 4.00 10.00
S260 Matt Harrison 4.00 10.00
S261 Pat Burrell 4.00 10.00
S262 Mark Ellis 4.00 10.00
S263 Conor Jackson 4.00 10.00
S264 Matt Downs 4.00 10.00
S265 Jeff Clement 4.00 10.00
S266 Joel Hanrahan 6.00 15.00
S267 John Jaso 4.00 10.00
S268 John Danks 4.00 10.00
S269 Eugenio Velez 4.00 10.00
S270 Jason Vargas 4.00 10.00
S271 Rob Johnson 4.00 10.00
S272 Gabe Gross 4.00 10.00
S273 David Freese 8.00 20.00
S274 Jamie Garcia 6.00 15.00
S275 Gabe Kapler 4.00 10.00
S276 Colby Lewis 4.00 10.00
S277 Carlos Santana 12.00 30.00
S278 Cole Gillespie 4.00 10.00
S279 Jonny Venters 4.00 10.00
S280 Jeff Suppan 4.00 10.00
S281 Lance Zawadzki 4.00 10.00
S282 Mike Leake 12.00 30.00
S283 John Ely 4.00 10.00
S284 Mike Stanton 15.00 40.00
S285 Rhyne Hughes 4.00 10.00
S286 Jeanmar Gomez 6.00 15.00
S287 Brennan Boesch 10.00 25.00
S288 Austin Jackson 6.00 15.00
S289 Alex Sanabia 4.00 10.00
S290 Jason Donald 4.00 10.00
S291 Andrew Cashner 4.00 10.00
S292 Josh Bell 4.00 10.00
S293 Travis Wood 6.00 15.00
S294 Mike Stanton 15.00 40.00
S295 Jose Tabata 10.00 25.00
S296 Jake Arrieta 6.00 15.00
S297 Carlos Santana 12.00 30.00
S298 Sam Demel 4.00 10.00
S299 Felix Doubront 4.00 10.00
S300 Stephen Strasburg 40.00 80.00

2010 Topps Tales of the Game

STATED ODDS 1:6 HOBBY
TOG1 Spikes Up .75 2.00
TOG2 The Curse of the Bambino 1.25 3.00
TOG3 Ruth Calls His Shot 1.25 3.00
TOG4 Topps Dumps 1952 .40 1.00
TOG5 Robinson Steals Home .75 2.00
TOG6 Let's Play Two .75 2.00
TOG7 Maz Hits Series Walk-Off .60 1.50
TOG8 Maris Chases #61 .75 2.00
TOG9 Mantle HR Facade 1.50 4.00
TOG10 Piersall Runs Backwards .40 1.00
TOG11 1969 Amazin' Mets .60 1.50
TOG12 Reggie has Tower Power .60 1.50
TOG13 Carlton Fisk: The Wave .60 1.50
TOG14 Reggie's WS HR Hat Trick .60 1.50
TOG15 Ozzie Smith Flips Out .75 2.00
TOG16 Bo Knows Wall Climbing .75 2.00
TOG17 Boggs: Chicken? .60 1.50
TOG18 Prince: BP HR at Age 12 .50 1.25
TOG19 Old Cal Clutch 2.00 5.00
TOG20 Jeter: The Flip 1.25 3.00
TOG21 Schilling's Bloody Sock .60 1.50
TOG22 Pesky's Pole .40 1.00
TOG23 Manny Being Manny .75 2.00
TOG24 The Great Ham-Bino .75 2.00
TOG25 Yanks Dig Up Ortiz' Jersey .60 1.50

2010 Topps Topps Town

RANDOM INSERTS IN PACKS
TTT1 Joe Mauer .50 1.25
TTT2 David Wright .60 1.50
TTT3 Hanley Ramirez .50 1.25
TTT4 Adrian Gonzalez .30 .75
TTT5 Evan Longoria .60 1.50
TTT6 Ichiro Suzuki .75 2.00
TTT7 Josh Hamilton .50 1.25
TTT8 Zack Greinke .30 .75
TTT9 Roy Halladay .50 1.25
TTT10 Tim Lincecum .75 2.00
TTT11 Brian McCann .30 .75
TTT12 Miguel Tejada .30 .75
TTT13 Ryan Howard .60 1.50
TTT14 Albert Pujols 1.25 3.00
TTT15 Miguel Cabrera .50 1.25
TTT16 Kevin Youkilis .30 .75
TTT17 Todd Helton .30 .75
TTT18 Vladimir Guerrero .50 1.25
TTT19 Justin Upton .30 .75
TTT20 Adam Jones .30 .75
TTT21 Adam Dunn .30 .75
TTT22 Andrew McCutchen .50 1.25
TTT23 CC Sabathia .30 .75
TTT24 Ryan Braun .60 1.50
TTT25 Manny Ramirez .50 1.25

2010 Topps Topps Town Gold

*GOLD: .75X TO 2X BASIC
RANDOM INSERTS IN PACKS

2010 Topps Turkey Red

STATED ODDS 1:4 HOBBY
1-50 ISSUED IN SERIES 1
51-100 ISSUED IN SERIES 2
101-150 ISSUED IN UPDATE
TR1 Ryan Howard 1.00 2.50
TR2 Miguel Tejada .50 1.25
TR3 Nolan Ryan 2.50 6.00
TR4 Albert Pujols 2.00 5.00
TR5 Josh Beckett .50 1.25
TR6 Justin Upton .50 1.25
TR7 Andre Ethier .50 1.25
TR8 Tommy Hanson .50 1.25
TR9 Josh Johnson .50 1.25
TR10 Jonathan Papelbon .50 1.25
TR11 Cole Hamels .75 2.00
TR12 Manny Ramirez .75 2.00
TR13 Yovani Gallardo .30 .75
TR14 Kevin Youkilis .50 1.25
TR15 Hank Greenberg .75 2.00
TR16 Ozzie Smith 1.25 3.00
TR17 Derrek Lee .30 .75
TR18 Ryan Braun 1.00 2.50
TR19 Cal Ripken Jr. 3.00 8.00
TR20 CC Sabathia .50 1.25
TR21 Johnny Bench .75 2.00
TR22 Tim Lincecum 1.25 3.00
TR23 Mike Schmidt 1.25 3.00
TR24 Clayton Kershaw .75 2.00
TR25 Ernie Banks .75 2.00
TR26 Dexter Fowler .30 .75
TR27 Edwin Jackson .30 .75
TR28 Mickey Mantle 2.50 6.00
TR29 Gordon Beckham .50 1.25
TR30 Victor Martinez .50 1.25
TR31 Mel Ott .75 2.00
TR32 Zack Greinke .50 1.25
TR33 Roy Halladay .75 2.00
TR34 David Wright 1.00 2.50
TR35 Stephen Drew .30 .75
TR36 Matt Holliday .75 2.00
TR37 Chase Utley .75 2.00
TR38 Rick Porcello .30 .75
TR39 Vladimir Guerrero .75 2.00
TR40 Mark Teixeira .75 2.00
TR41 Evan Longoria 1.00 2.50
TR42 Ian Kinsler .50 1.25
TR43 Adrian Gonzalez .50 1.25
TR44 Matt Kemp .50 1.25
TR45 Ryne Sandberg 1.50 4.00
TR46 Babe Ruth 2.00 5.00
TR47 Curtis Granderson .50 1.25
TR48 Willie McCovey .50 1.25
TR49 Josh Hamilton .75 2.00
TR50 Pablo Sandoval .50 1.25
TR51 Torii Hunter .30 .75
TR52 Adam Dunn .50 1.25
TR53 Alexei Ramirez .30 .75
TR54 Andrew McCutchen .75 2.00
TR55 Aaron Hill .30 .75
TR56 Alcides Escobar .50 1.25
TR57 Jimmie Foxx .75 2.00
TR58 Joey Votto .75 2.00
TR59 Jose Reyes .50 1.25
TR60 Al Kaline .75 2.00
TR61 Felix Hernandez .75 2.00
TR62 Troy Tulowitzki .75 2.00
TR63 Nate McLouth .30 .75
TR64 Justin Morneau .75 2.00
TR65 Prince Fielder .50 1.25
TR66 Nelson Cruz .50 1.25
TR67 Grady Sizemore .50 1.25
TR68 Hanley Ramirez .75 2.00
TR69 Brooks Robinson .50 1.25
TR70 Jackie Robinson .75 2.00
TR71 Nick Markakis .75 2.00
TR72 Roy Oswalt .50 1.25
TR73 Chad Billingsley .30 .75
TR74 Tom Seaver .50 1.25
TR75 B.J. Upton .50 1.25
TR76 Chris Coghlan .30 .75
TR77 Luis Aparicio .30 .75
TR78 Dan Haren .30 .75
TR79 Raul Ibanez .50 1.25
TR80 Kosuke Fukudome .75 2.00
TR81 Denard Span .30 .75
TR82 Joe Morgan .30 .75
TR83 Yogi Berra .75 2.00
TR84 Dustin Pedroia 1.00 2.50
TR85 Lou Gehrig 1.50 4.00
TR86 Billy Butler .30 .75
TR87 Jake Peavy .30 .75
TR88 Eddie Mathews .75 2.00
TR89 Ubaldo Jimenez .50 1.25
TR90 Johan Santana .75 2.00
TR91 Buster Posey 3.00 8.00
TR92 George Sisler .75 2.00
TR93 Ian Desmond .50 1.25
TR94 Kurt Suzuki .30 .75
TR95 Ty Cobb 1.25 3.00
TR96 Magglio Ordonez .50 1.25
TR97 Chase Headley .30 .75
TR98 Hunter Pence .50 1.25
TR99 Ryan Ludwick .30 .75
TR100 Derek Jeter 2.00 5.00
TR101 Hideki Matsui .75 2.00
TR102 Kelly Johnson .30 .75
TR103 Jason Heyward 2.00 5.00
TR104 Adam Jones .50 1.25
TR105 John Lackey .30 .75
TR106 Roy Campanella .75 2.00
TR107 Aramis Ramirez .30 .75
TR108 Carlos Quentin .50 1.25
TR109 Brandon Phillips .30 .75
TR110 Shin-Soo Choo .50 1.25
TR111 Ian Stewart .30 .75
TR112 Miguel Cabrera .75 2.00
TR113 Josh Johnson .50 1.25
TR114 Carlos Lee .30 .75
TR115 Joakim Soria .30 .75
TR116 Jonathan Broxton .30 .75
TR117 Carlos Gomez .30 .75
TR118 Joe Mauer .75 2.00
TR119 Jason Bay .50 1.25
TR120 Curtis Granderson .50 1.25
TR121 A.J. Burnett .50 1.25
TR122 Ben Sheets .30 .75
TR123 Roy Halladay .75 2.00
TR124 Ryan Doumit .30 .75
TR125 Kyle Blanks .30 .75
TR126 Matt Cain .50 1.25
TR127 Ichiro Suzuki 1.25 3.00
TR128 Chris Carpenter .75 2.00
TR129 Matt Garza .30 .75
TR130 Vladimir Guerrero .75 2.00
TR131 Vernon Wells .30 .75
TR132 Ryan Zimmerman .50 1.25
TR133 Lou Brock .50 1.25
TR134 Rod Carew .50 1.25
TR135 Orlando Cepeda .30 .75
TR136 Rogers Hornsby .50 1.25
TR137 Walter Johnson .75 2.00
TR138 Christy Mathewson .75 2.00
TR139 Johnny Mize .50 1.25
TR140 Thurman Munson .75 2.00
TR141 Pee Wee Reese .50 1.25
TR142 Tris Speaker .50 1.25
TR143 Honus Wagner .75 2.00
TR144 Cy Young .75 2.00
TR145 Robin Yount .75 2.00
TR146 Duke Snider .50 1.25
TR147 Frank Robinson .50 1.25
TR148 Stephen Strasburg 2.00 5.00
TR149 Mike Stanton 1.25 3.00
TR150 Starlin Castro 1.25 3.00

2010 Topps Vintage Legends Collection

COMPLETE SET (60) 15.00 40.00
COM.UPDATE SET (25) 5.00 12.00
STATED ODDS 1:4 HOBBY
26-50 ISSUED IN UPDATE
VLC1 Lou Gehrig 1.50 4.00
VLC2 Johnny Mize .50 1.25
VLC3 Reggie Jackson .50 1.25
VLC4 Tris Speaker .50 1.25
VLC5 George Sisler .75 2.00
VLC6 Willie McCovey .50 1.25
VLC7 Tom Seaver .50 1.25
VLC8 Walter Johnson .75 2.00
VLC9 Ozzie Smith 1.25 3.00
VLC10 Babe Ruth 2.00 5.00
VLC11 Christy Mathewson .75 2.00
VLC12 Jackie Robinson .75 2.00
VLC13 Eddie Murray .75 2.00
VLC14 Mel Ott .75 2.00
VLC15 Jimmie Foxx .75 2.00
VLC16 Thurman Munson .75 2.00
VLC17 Mike Schmidt 1.25 3.00
VLC18 Johnny Bench .75 2.00
VLC19 Rogers Hornsby .50 1.25
VLC20 Ty Cobb 1.25 3.00
VLC21 Nolan Ryan 2.50 6.00
VLC22 Roy Campanella .75 2.00
VLC23 Cy Young .75 2.00
VLC24 Pee Wee Reese .50 1.25
VLC25 Honus Wagner .75 2.00
VLC26 Johnny Mize .50 1.25
VLC27 Cy Young .75 2.00
VLC28 Ozzie Smith 1.25 3.00
VLC29 Nolan Ryan 2.50 6.00
VLC30 George Sisler .75 2.00
VLC31 Babe Ruth 2.00 5.00
VLC32 Reggie Jackson .50 1.25
VLC33 Christy Mathewson .75 2.00
VLC34 Mike Schmidt 1.25 3.00
VLC35 Mel Ott .75 2.00
VLC36 Ty Cobb 1.25 3.00
VLC37 Eddie Murray .75 2.00
VLC38 Lou Gehrig 1.50 4.00
VLC39 Roy Campanella .75 2.00
VLC40 Tom Seaver .50 1.25
VLC41 Honus Wagner .75 2.00
VLC42 Jackie Robinson .75 2.00
VLC43 Johnny Bench .75 2.00
VLC44 Pee Wee Reese .50 1.25
VLC45 Thurman Munson .75 2.00
VLC46 Rogers Hornsby .50 1.25
VLC47 Jimmie Foxx .75 2.00
VLC48 Willie McCovey .50 1.25
VLC49 Tris Speaker .50 1.25
VLC50 Walter Johnson .75 2.00

2010 Topps When They Were Young

STATED ODDS 1:6 HOBBY
AP Aaron Poreda .40 1.00
AR Alex Rodriguez 1.50 4.00
BR Brian Roberts .40 1.00
CM Charlie Morton .40 1.00
CR Cody Ross .40 1.00
CS Clint Sammons .40 1.00
DM Daniel McCutchen .60 1.50
DO David Ortiz .60 1.50
DW David Wright 1.25 3.00
GB Gordon Beckham .60 1.50
JB Jason Berken .40 1.00
JD Johnny Damon .60 1.50
JV Justin Verlander 1.25 3.00
RD Ryan Doumit .40 1.00
RM Russell Martin .40 1.00
RN Ricky Nolasco .40 1.00
SO Scott Olsen .40 1.00
YM Yadier Molina .60 1.50

2010 Topps World Champion Autograph Relics

STATED ODDS 1:7,500 HOBBY
STATED PRINT RUN 50 SER.#'d SETS
AR Alex Rodriguez 150.00 300.00
CS CC Sabathia 150.00 300.00
MC Melky Cabrera 30.00 60.00
MR Mariano Rivera 125.00 250.00
RC Robinson Cano 60.00 120.00

2010 Topps World Champion Autographs

STATED ODDS 1:22,600 HOBBY
STATED PRINT RUN 50 SER.#'d SETS
AR Alex Rodriguez 125.00 250.00
CS CC Sabathia 125.00 250.00
MC Melky Cabrera 20.00 50.00
MR Mariano Rivera 100.00 200.00
RC Robinson Cano 50.00 100.00

2010 Topps World Champion Relics

STATED ODDS 1:3750 HOBBY
STATED PRINT RUN 100 SER.#'d SETS
AP Andy Pettitte 20.00 50.00
AR Alex Rodriguez 30.00 60.00
BG Brett Gardner 15.00 40.00
CS CC Sabathia 20.00 50.00
EH Eric Hinske 15.00 40.00
HM Hideki Matsui 40.00 80.00
JD Johnny Damon 20.00 50.00
JG Joe Girardi 15.00 40.00
JH Jerry Hairston Jr. 15.00 40.00
JP Jorge Posada 20.00 50.00
MC Melky Cabrera 15.00 40.00
MR Mariano Rivera 15.00 40.00
MT Mark Teixeira 30.00 60.00
NS Nick Swisher 15.00 40.00
RC Robinson Cano 20.00 50.00

2010 Topps Update

COMP.SET w/o SPs (330) 20.00 50.00
COMMON CARD (1-330) .12 .30
COMMON SP VAR (1-330) 6.00 15.00
COMMON RC (1-330) .30 .75
PRINTING PLATE ODDS 1:1550 HOBBY
PLATE PRINT RUN 1 SET PER COLOR
BLACK-CYAN-MAGENTA-YELLOW ISSUED
NO PLATE PRICING DUE TO SCARCITY
US1 Vladimir Guerrero .30 .75
US2 Dayan Viciedo RC .50 1.25
US3 Sam Demel RC .30 .75
US4 Alex Cora .12 .30
US5 Troy Glaus .12 .30
US6 Adam Ottavino RC .30 .75
US7 Ryan LeCure (RC) .30 .75
US8 Fred Lewis .12 .30
US9 Danny Worth RC .30 .75
US10 Hideki Matsui .30 .75
US11 Vernon Wells .12 .30
US12 Jason Michaels .12 .30
US13 Max Scherzer .30 .75
US14 Ike Davis .30 .75
US15A Ike Davis RC .75 2.00
US15B Willie McCovey VAR SP 6.00 15.00
US16 Felipe Paulino .12 .30
US17 Marlon Byrd .12 .30
US18 Omar Beltre (RC) .30 .75
US19 Russell Branyan .12 .30
US20 Jason Bay .20 .50
US21 Roy Oswalt .20 .50
US22 Ty Wigginton .12 .30
US23 Andy Pettitte .20 .50
US24 Vladimir Guerrero .30 .75
Miguel Cabrera
US25A Andrew Bailey .12 .30
US25B Philadelphia Athletics VAR SP 6.00 15.00
US26 Jesus Feliciano RC .30 .75
US27 Koyie Hill .12 .30
US28 Bill Hall .12 .30
US29 Livan Hernandez .12 .30
US30 Roy Halladay .30 .75
US31 Corey Patterson .12 .30
US32 Doug Davis .12 .30
US33 Matt Capps .12 .30
US34 Shaun Marcum .12 .30
US35 Ryan Braun .40 1.00
US36 Omar Vizquel .20 .50
US37 Alex Avila .12 .30
US38 Chris Young .12 .30
US39 Kila Ka'aihue .20 .50
US40 Evan Longoria .40 1.00
US41 Anthony Slama RC .30 .75
US42 Conor Jackson .12 .30
US43 Brennan Boesch .30 .75
US44 Scott Rolen .20 .50
US45A David Price .30 .75
US45B Steve Carlton VAR SP 6.00 15.00
US46 Colby Lewis .12 .30
US47 Jody Gerut .12 .30
US48 Geoff Blum .12 .30
US49 Bobby Wilson .12 .30
US50A Mike Stanton RC 1.25 3.00
US50B Reggie Jackson VAR SP 6.00 15.00
US51 Tom Gorzelanny .12 .30
US52 Andy Oliver RC .30 .75
US53 Gordon Smith RC .30 .75
US54 Akinori Iwamura .12 .30
US55 Stephen Strasburg .75 2.00
US56 Matt Holliday .30 .75
US57 Derek Jeter .75 2.00
Elvis Andrus
US58A Brian Wilson .30 .75
US58B New York Giants VAR SP 6.00 15.00
US59A Jeanmar Gomez RC .50 1.25
US59B Jeanmar Gomez 10.00 25.00
Pie in the face SP
US60 Miguel Tejada .20 .50
US61 Alfredo Simon .12 .30
US62 Chris Narveson .12 .30
US63 David Ortiz .20 .50
US64 Jose Valverde .12 .30
US65 Victor Martinez .30 .75
Robinson Cano
US66 Ronnie Belliard .12 .30
US67 Kyle Farnsworth .12 .30
US68 John Danks .12 .30
US69 Lance Cormier .12 .30
US70 Jonathan Broxton .12 .30
US71 Jason Giambi .12 .30
US72 Milton Bradley .12 .30
US73 Torii Hunter .12 .30
US74 Ryan Church .12 .30
US75 Jason Heyward .75 2.00
US76 Jose Tabata .30 .75
US77 John Axford RC .30 .75
US78 Jon Link RC .30 .75
US79 Jonny Gomes .12 .30
US80 David Ortiz .20 .50
US81 Rich Harden .12 .30
US82 Emmanuel Burriss .12 .30
US83 Jeff Suppan .12 .30
US84 Melvin Mora .12 .30
US85A Starlin Castro RC 1.25 3.00
US85B Andre Dawson VAR SP 6.00 15.00
US86 Matt Guerrier .12 .30
US87 Trevor Plouffe (RC) .30 .75
US88 Lance Berkman .20 .50
US89 Frank Herrmann RC .30 .75
US90 Rafael Furcal .12 .30
US91 Nick Johnson .12 .30
US92 Pedro Feliciano .12 .30
US93 Jon Rauch .12 .30
US94 Reid Brignac .12 .30
US95 Jamie Moyer .12 .30
US96 John Bowker .12 .30
US97 Troy Tulowitzki .30 .75
Matt Holliday
US98 Yunel Escobar .12 .30
US99 Jose Bautista .20 .50
US100A Roy Halladay .30 .75
US100B Robin Roberts VAR SP 6.00 15.00
US101 Jake Westbrook .12 .30
US102 Chris Carter RC .50 1.25
US103 Matt Tuiasosopo .12 .30
US104 Paul Konerko .20 .50
US105 Chone Figgins .12 .30
US106 Orlando Cabrera .12 .30
US107 Matt Capps .12 .30
US108 John Buck .12 .30
US109 Luke Hughes (RC) .30 .75
US110 Curtis Granderson .20 .50
US111 Willie Bloomquist .12 .30
US112 Chad Qualls .12 .30
US113 Brad Ziegler .12 .30
US114 Kenley Jansen RC 1.25 3.00
US115 Brad Lincoln RC .50 1.25
US116 Brandon Morrow .12 .30
US117 Martin Prado .12 .30
US118 Jose Bautista .20 .50
US119 Adam LaRoche .12 .30
US120 Brennan Boesch RC .75 2.00
US121 J.A. Happ .20 .50
US122 Darnell McDonald .12 .30
US123 Alberto Callaspo .12 .30
US124 Chris Young .12 .30
US125 Adam Wainwright .20 .50
US126 Elvis Andrus .20 .50
US127 Nick Swisher .30 .75
US128 Reed Johnson .12 .30
US129 Gregor Blanco .12 .30
US130 Ichiro Suzuki .50 1.25
US131 Takashi Saito .12 .30
US132 Corey Hart .12 .30
US133 Javier Vazquez .12 .30
US134 Rick Ankiel .12 .30
US135 Starlin Castro .50 1.25
US136 Jarrod Saltalamacchia .12 .30
US137 Austin Kearns .12 .30
US138 Brandon League .12 .30
US139 Jorge Cantu .12 .30
US140 Josh Hamilton .30 .75
US141 Phil Hughes .12 .30
US142 Mike Cameron .12 .30
US143 Jonathan Lucroy RC .30 .75
US144 Eric Patterson .12 .30
US145 Adrian Beltre .12 .30
US146 Peter Bourjos RC .50 1.25
US147 Argenis Diaz RC .50 1.25
US148 J.J. Putz .12 .30
US149A Kevin Russo RC .30 .75
US149B Babe Ruth VAR SP 10.00 25.00
US150 Hanley Ramirez .30 .75
US151 Kerry Wood .12 .30
US152 Ian Kennedy .20 .50
US153 Brian McCann .20 .50
US154 Jose Guillen .12 .30
US155 Ivan Rodriguez .20 .50
US156 Matt Thornton .12 .30
US157 Jason Marquis .12 .30
US158 CC Sabathia .20 .50
Carl Crawford
US159 Octavio Dotel .12 .30
US160 Josh Johnson .20 .50
US161 Matt Holliday .30 .75
US162 Hong-Chih Kuo .12 .30
US163 Marco Scutaro .12 .30
US164 Gaby Sanchez .12 .30
US165 Omar Infante .12 .30
US166 Jon Garland .12 .30
US167 Ramon Santiago .12 .30
US168 Wilson Ramos RC .75 2.00
US169 Ryan Ludwick .12 .30
US170 Carl Crawford .20 .50
US171 Cristian Guzman .12 .30
US172 Josh Donaldson RC .50 1.25
US173 Lorenzo Cain RC .50 1.25
US174 Matt Lindstrom .12 .30
US175A Drew Storen RC .50 1.25
US175B Bruce Sutter VAR SP 6.00 15.00
US176 Felipe Lopez .12 .30
US177 Chris Heisey RC .50 1.25
US178 Jim Edmonds .20 .50
US179 Juan Pierre .12 .30
US180 David Wright .40 1.00
US181 J.P. Arencibia RC .50 1.25
US182 Randy Wolf .12 .30
US183 Luis Atilano RC .30 .75
US184 Blake DeWitt .12 .30
US185A Brian Matusz RC .75 2.00
US185B Jim Palmer VAR SP 6.00 15.00
US186 Scott Hairston .12 .30
US187 Phil Hughes .30 .75
David Price
US188 Orlando Hudson .12 .30
US189 Derek Lee .12 .30
US190 John Lackey .12 .30
US191 Danny Valencia RC 2.00 5.00
US192 Daniel Nava RC .50 1.25
US193 Ryan Theriot .12 .30

US194 Vernon Wells .12 .30
US195 Mark DeRosa .12 .30
US196 Aubrey Huff .12 .30
US197 Sean Marshall .12 .30
US198 Francisco Cervelli .12 .30
US199 Jhonny Peralta .12 .30
US200A Albert Pujols .75 2.00
US200B St. Louis Browns VAR SP 6.00 15.00
US201 Jeffrey Marquez RC .50 1.25
US202 Mitch Moreland RC .50 1.25
US203A Jon Jay RC .50 1.25
US203B Tony Gwynn VAR SP 6.00 15.00
US204 Carlos Silva .12 .30
US205 Ben Sheets .12 .30
US206 Garret Anderson .12 .30
US207 Jerry Hairston Jr. .12 .30
US208 Jeff Keppinger .12 .30
US209 Bengie Molina .12 .30
US210 Ubaldo Jimenez .20 .50
US211 Daniel Hudson .20 .50
US212 Mitch Talbot .12 .30
US213 Alex Gonzalez .12 .30
US214A Jason Heyward .75 2.00
US214B Dave Winfield VAR SP 6.00 15.00
US215 Albert Pujols .75 2.00
Ryan Braun
US216 John Baker .12 .30
US217 Yorvit Torrealba .12 .30
US218 Kevin Gregg .12 .30
US219 Bobby Crosby .12 .30
US220A Jon Lester .30 .75
US220B Boston Americans VAR SP 6.00 15.00
US221 Heath Bell .20 .50
US222 Ted Lilly .12 .30
US223 Henry Blanco .12 .30
US224 Scott Olsen .12 .30
US225A Josh Bell (RC) .30 .75
US225B Brooks Robinson VAR SP 6.00 15.00
US226 Scott Podsednik .12 .30
US227 Mark Kotsay .12 .30
US228 Brandon Phillips .12 .30
Martin Prado
US229 Joe Saunders .12 .30
US230 Robinson Cano .30 .75
US231 Gabe Kapler .12 .30
US232 Jason Kendall .12 .30
US233 Brendan Harris .12 .30
US234 Matt Downs RC .30 .75
US235 Jose Tabata RC .75 2.00
US236 Matt Daley .12 .30
US237 Jhan Marinez RC .30 .75
US238 Mark Ellis .12 .30
US239 Gabe Gross .12 .30
US240 Adrian Gonzalez .20 .50
US241 Joey Votto .30 .75
US242 Shelley Duncan .12 .30
US243 Michael Bourn .12 .30
US244 Mike Redmond .12 .30
US245 Placido Polanco .12 .30
US246 LaTroy Hawkins .12 .30
US247 Nick Swisher .30 .75
US248 Matt Harrison .12 .30
US249 Rafael Soriano .12 .30
US250 Miguel Cabrera .30 .75
US251A Jake Arrieta RC .50 1.25
US251B Jake Arrieta 12.50 30.00
Pie in the face SP
US252 Jim Thome .20 .50
US253 Mike Minor RC .50 1.25
US254 Chris Perez .12 .30
US255 Kevin Millwood .12 .30
US256 Mike Gonzalez .12 .30
US257 Joel Hanrahan .20 .50
US258 Dana Eveland .12 .30
US259 Yadier Molina .20 .50
US260A Andre Ethier .20 .50
US260B Brooklyn Dodgers VAR SP 6.00 15.00
US261 Jason Vargas .12 .30
US262 Rob Johnson .12 .30
US263 Randy Winn .12 .30
US264 Vicente Padilla .12 .30
US265 Ryan Howard .40 1.00
US266 Billy Wagner .12 .30
US267 Eugenio Velez .12 .30
US268 Logan Morrison RC .50 1.25
US269 Dave Bush .12 .30
US270 Vladimir Guerrero .30 .75
US271 Travis Wood (RC) .50 1.25
US272 Brian Stokes .12 .30
US273 John Jaso .12 .30
US274 Stephen Strasburg .75 2.00
Ivan Rodriguez
US275 Hong-Chih Kuo .12 .30
US276A Austin Jackson .20 .50
US276B Rickey Henderson VAR SP 6.00 15.00
US277 Micah Owings .12 .30
US278 Brad Penny .12 .30
US279 Hanley Ramirez .30 .75
US280 Alex Rodriguez .50 1.25
US281 Jose Valverde .12 .30
US282 Rhyne Hughes RC .30 .75
US283 Kevin Frandsen .12 .30
US284 Josh Reddick .12 .30
US285 Jaime Garcia .20 .50
US286 Arthur Rhodes .12 .30
US287 Alex Sanabia RC .30 .75
US288 Jonny Venters RC .30 .75
US289 Adam Kennedy .12 .30
US290 Justin Verlander .40 1.00
US291 Corey Hart .12 .30
US292 Kelly Shoppach .12 .30
US293 Pat Burrell .12 .30
US294 Aaron Heilman .12 .30
US295 Andrew Cashner RC .30 .75
US296 Lance Zawadzki RC .30 .75
US297 Don Kelly (RC) .30 .75
US298 David Freese .20 .50
US299 Xavier Nady .12 .30
US300 Cliff Lee .20 .50
US301 Jeff Clement .12 .30
US302 Pedro Feliz .12 .30
US303 Brandon Phillips .12 .30
US304 Kris Medlen .12 .30
US305 Cliff Lee .20 .50
US306 Dan Haren .12 .30
US307 Carlos Santana .40 1.00
US308 Matt Thornton .12 .30
US309 Andruw Jones .12 .30
US310 Derek Jeter .75 2.00
US311 Felix Doubront RC .30 .75
US312 Coco Crisp .12 .30
US313 Mitch Maier .12 .30
US314 Cole Gillespie RC .30 .75
US315A Edwin Jackson .12 .30
US315B Edwin Jackson 10.00 25.00
Pie in the face SP
US316 Rod Barajas .12 .30
US317A Mike Leake .40 1.00
US317B Babe Ruth VAR SP 8.00 20.00
US318A Domonic Brown RC 1.25 3.00
US318B Bo Jackson VAR SP 6.00 15.00
US319 Josh Tomlin RC .75 2.00
US320A Joe Mauer .30 .75
US320B Washington Senators VAR SP 6.0015.00
US321 Jason Donald RC .30 .75
US322 John Ely RC .30 .75
US323 Ryan Kalish RC .50 1.25
US324 George Kottaras .12 .30
US325 Ian Kinsler .20 .50
US326 Miguel Cabrera .30 .75
US327 Mike Stanton .50 1.25
US328 Adrian Beltre .12 .30
US329 Jose Reyes .30 .75
Hanley Ramirez
US330A Carlos Santana RC 1.00 2.50
US330B Cleveland Naps VAR SP 6.00 15.00
US330C Johnny Bench VAR SP 6.00 15.00

2010 Topps Update Black

STATED ODDS 1:105 HOBBY
STATED PRINT RUN 59 SER.#'d SETS
US1 Vladimir Guerrero 10.00 25.00
US2 Dayan Viciedo 8.00 20.00
US3 Sam Demel 5.00 12.00
US4 Alex Cora 5.00 12.00
US5 Troy Glaus 5.00 12.00
US6 Adam Ottavino 5.00 12.00
US7 Sam LeCure 5.00 12.00
US8 Fred Lewis 5.00 12.00
US9 Danny Worth 5.00 12.00
US10 Hideki Matsui 10.00 25.00
US11 Vernon Wells 5.00 12.00
US12 Jason Michaels 5.00 12.00
US13 Max Scherzer 5.00 12.00
US14 Ike Davis 10.00 25.00
US15 Ike Davis 10.00 25.00
US16 Felipe Paulino 5.00 12.00
US17 Marlon Byrd 5.00 12.00
US18 Omar Beltre 5.00 12.00
US19 Russell Branyan 5.00 12.00
US20 Jason Bay 8.00 20.00
US21 Roy Oswalt 8.00 20.00
US22 Ty Wigginton 5.00 12.00
US23 Andy Pettitte 8.00 20.00
US24 Vladimir Guerrero 10.00 25.00
Miguel Cabrera
US25 Andrew Bailey 5.00 12.00
US26 Jesus Feliciano 5.00 12.00
US27 Koyie Hill 5.00 12.00
US28 Bill Hall 5.00 12.00
US29 Livan Hernandez 5.00 12.00
US30 Roy Halladay 10.00 25.00
US31 Corey Patterson 5.00 12.00
US32 Doug Davis 5.00 12.00
US33 Matt Capps 5.00 12.00
US34 Shaun Marcum 5.00 12.00
US35 Ryan Braun 12.00 30.00
US36 Omar Vizquel 8.00 20.00
US37 Alex Avila 5.00 12.00
US38 Chris Young 5.00 12.00
US39 Kila Ka'aihue 8.00 20.00
US40 Evan Longoria 12.00 30.00
US41 Anthony Slama 5.00 12.00
US42 Conor Jackson 5.00 12.00
US43 Brennan Boesch 10.00 25.00
US44 Scott Rolen 8.00 20.00
US45 David Price 10.00 25.00
US46 Colby Lewis 5.00 12.00
US47 Jody Gerut 5.00 12.00
US48 Geoff Blum 5.00 12.00
US49 Bobby Wilson 5.00 12.00
US50 Mike Stanton 15.00 40.00
US51 Tom Gorzelanny 5.00 12.00
US52 Andy Oliver 5.00 12.00
US53 Jordan Smith 5.00 12.00
US54 Akinori Iwamura 5.00 12.00
US55 Stephen Strasburg 12.00 30.00
US56 Matt Holliday 10.00 25.00
US57 Derek Jeter 25.00 60.00
Elvis Andrus
US58 Brian Wilson 12.00 30.00
US59 Jeanmar Gomez 6.00 15.00
US60 Miguel Tejada 8.00 20.00
US61 Alfredo Simon 5.00 12.00
US62 Chris Narveson 5.00 12.00
US63 David Ortiz 8.00 20.00
US64 Jose Valverde 5.00 12.00
US65 Victor Martinez 10.00 25.00
Robinson Cano
US66 Ronnie Belliard 5.00 12.00
US67 Kyle Farnsworth 5.00 12.00
US68 John Danks 5.00 12.00
US69 Lance Cormier 5.00 12.00
US70 Jonathan Broxton 5.00 12.00
US71 Jason Giambi 5.00 12.00
US72 Milton Bradley 5.00 12.00
US73 Torii Hunter 5.00 12.00
US74 Ryan Church 5.00 12.00
US75 Jason Heyward 25.00 60.00
US76 Jose Tabata 10.00 25.00
US77 John Axford 5.00 12.00
US78 Jon Link 5.00 12.00
US79 Jonny Gomes 5.00 12.00
US80 David Ortiz 8.00 20.00
US81 Rich Harden 5.00 12.00
US82 Emmanuel Burriss 5.00 12.00
US83 Jeff Suppan 5.00 12.00
US84 Melvin Mora 5.00 12.00
US85 Starlin Castro 15.00 40.00
US86 Matt Guerrier 5.00 12.00
US87 Trevor Plouffe 5.00 12.00
US88 Lance Berkman 8.00 20.00
US89 Frank Herrmann 5.00 12.00
US90 Rafael Furcal 5.00 12.00
US91 Nick Johnson 5.00 12.00
US92 Pedro Feliciano 5.00 12.00
US93 Jon Rauch 5.00 12.00
US94 Reid Brignac 5.00 12.00
US95 Jamie Moyer 5.00 12.00
US96 John Bowker 5.00 12.00
US97 Troy Tulowitzki 10.00 25.00
Matt Holliday
US98 Yunel Escobar 5.00 12.00
US99 Jose Bautista 8.00 20.00
US100 Roy Halladay 10.00 25.00
US101 Jake Westbrook 5.00 12.00
US102 Chris Carter 8.00 20.00
US103 Matt Tuiasosopo 5.00 12.00
US104 Paul Konerko 8.00 20.00
US105 Chone Figgins 5.00 12.00
US106 Orlando Cabrera 5.00 12.00
US107 Matt Capps 5.00 12.00
US108 John Buck 5.00 12.00
US109 Luke Hughes 5.00 12.00
US110 Curtis Granderson 8.00 20.00
US111 Willie Bloomquist 5.00 12.00
US112 Chad Qualls 5.00 12.00
US113 Brad Ziegler 5.00 12.00
US114 Kenley Jansen 20.00 50.00
US115 Brad Lincoln 8.00 20.00
US116 Brandon Morrow 5.00 12.00
US117 Martin Prado 5.00 12.00
US118 Jose Bautista 8.00 20.00
US119 Adam LaRoche 5.00 12.00
US120 Brennan Boesch 10.00 25.00
US121 J.A. Happ 8.00 20.00
US122 Darnell McDonald 5.00 12.00
US123 Alberto Callaspo 5.00 12.00
US124 Chris Young 5.00 12.00
US125 Adam Wainwright 8.00 20.00
US126 Elvis Andrus 8.00 20.00
US127 Nick Swisher 12.00 30.00
US128 Reed Johnson 5.00 12.00
US129 Gregor Blanco 5.00 12.00
US130 Ichiro Suzuki 15.00 40.00
US131 Takashi Saito 5.00 12.00
US132 Corey Hart 5.00 12.00
US133 Javier Vazquez 5.00 12.00
US134 Rick Ankiel 5.00 12.00
US135 Starlin Castro 15.00 40.00
US136 Jarrod Saltalamacchia 5.00 12.00
US137 Austin Kearns 5.00 12.00
US138 Brandon League 5.00 12.00
US139 Jorge Cantu 5.00 12.00
US140 Josh Hamilton 10.00 25.00
US141 Phil Hughes 5.00 12.00
US142 Mike Cameron 5.00 12.00
US143 Jonathan Lucroy 5.00 12.00
US144 Eric Patterson 5.00 12.00
US145 Adrian Beltre 5.00 12.00
US146 Peter Bourjos 8.00 20.00
US147 Argenis Diaz 8.00 20.00
US148 J.J. Putz 5.00 12.00
US149 Kevin Russo 5.00 12.00
US150 Hanley Ramirez 10.00 25.00
US151 Kerry Wood 5.00 12.00
US152 Ian Kennedy 8.00 20.00
US153 Brian McCann 8.00 20.00
US154 Jose Guillen 5.00 12.00
US155 Ivan Rodriguez 8.00 20.00
US156 Matt Thornton 5.00 12.00
US157 Jason Marquis 5.00 12.00
US158 CC Sabathia 8.00 20.00
Carl Crawford
US159 Octavio Dotel 5.00 12.00
US160 Josh Johnson 6.00 15.00
US161 Matt Holliday 10.00 25.00
US162 Hong-Chih Kuo 5.00 12.00
US163 Marco Scutaro 5.00 12.00
US164 Gaby Sanchez 5.00 12.00
US165 Omar Infante 5.00 12.00
US166 Jon Garland 5.00 12.00
US167 Ramon Santiago 5.00 12.00
US168 Wilson Ramos 12.00 30.00
US169 Ryan Ludwick 5.00 12.00
US170 Carl Crawford 8.00 20.00
US171 Cristian Guzman 5.00 12.00
US172 Josh Donaldson 5.00 12.00
US173 Lorenzo Cain 8.00 20.00
US174 Matt Lindstrom 5.00 12.00
US175 Drew Storen 8.00 20.00
US176 Felipe Lopez 5.00 12.00
US177 Chris Heisey 6.00 15.00
US178 Jim Edmonds 8.00 20.00
US179 Juan Pierre 5.00 12.00
US180 David Wright 12.00 30.00
US181 J.P. Arencibia 8.00 20.00
US182 Randy Wolf 5.00 12.00
US183 Luis Atilano 5.00 12.00
US184 Blake DeWitt 5.00 12.00
US185 Brian Matusz 10.00 25.00
US186 Scott Hairston 5.00 12.00
US187 Phil Hughes 10.00 25.00
David Price
US188 Orlando Hudson 5.00 12.00
US189 Derrek Lee 5.00 12.00
US190 John Lackey 5.00 12.00
US191 Danny Valencia 25.00 60.00
US192 Daniel Nava 6.00 15.00
US193 Ryan Theriot 5.00 12.00
US194 Vernon Wells 5.00 12.00
US195 Mark DeRosa 5.00 12.00
US196 Aubrey Huff 5.00 12.00
US197 Sean Marshall 5.00 12.00
US198 Francisco Cervelli 5.00 12.00
US199 Jhonny Peralta 5.00 12.00
US200 Albert Pujols 25.00 60.00
US201 Jeffrey Marquez 8.00 20.00
US202 Mitch Moreland 6.00 15.00
US203 Jon Jay 6.00 15.00
US204 Carlos Silva 5.00 12.00
US205 Ben Sheets 5.00 12.00
US206 Garret Anderson 5.00 12.00
US207 Jerry Hairston Jr. 5.00 12.00
US208 Jeff Keppinger 5.00 12.00
US209 Bengie Molina 5.00 12.00
US210 Ubaldo Jimenez 6.00 15.00
US211 Daniel Hudson 6.00 15.00
US212 Mitch Talbot 5.00 12.00
US213 Alex Gonzalez 5.00 12.00
US214 Jason Heyward 25.00 60.00
US215 Albert Pujols 25.00 60.00
Ryan Braun
US216 John Baker 5.00 12.00
US217 Yorvit Torrealba 5.00 12.00
US218 Kevin Gregg 5.00 12.00
US219 Bobby Crosby 5.00 12.00
US220 Jon Lester 12.00 30.00
US221 Heath Bell 8.00 20.00
US222 Ted Lilly 5.00 12.00
US223 Henry Blanco 5.00 12.00
US224 Scott Olsen 5.00 12.00
US225 Josh Bell 5.00 12.00
US226 Scott Podsednik 5.00 12.00
US227 Mark Kotsay 5.00 12.00
US228 Brandon Phillips 5.00 12.00
Martin Prado
US229 Joe Saunders 5.00 12.00
US230 Robinson Cano 10.00 25.00
US231 Gabe Kapler 5.00 12.00
US232 Jason Kendall 5.00 12.00
US233 Brendan Harris 5.00 12.00
US234 Matt Downs 5.00 12.00
US235 Jose Tabata 10.00 25.00
US236 Matt Daley 5.00 12.00
US237 Jhan Marinez 5.00 12.00
US238 Mark Ellis 5.00 12.00
US239 Gabe Gross 5.00 12.00
US240 Adrian Gonzalez 8.00 20.00
US241 Joey Votto 10.00 25.00
US242 Shelley Duncan 5.00 12.00
US243 Michael Bourn 5.00 12.00
US244 Mike Redmond 5.00 12.00
US245 Placido Polanco 5.00 12.00
US246 LaTroy Hawkins 5.00 12.00
US247 Nick Swisher 12.00 30.00
US248 Matt Harrison 5.00 12.00
US249 Rafael Soriano 5.00 12.00
US250 Miguel Cabrera 12.00 30.00
US251 Jake Arrieta 8.00 20.00
US252 Jim Thome 8.00 20.00
US253 Mike Minor 6.00 15.00
US254 Chris Perez 5.00 12.00
US255 Kevin Millwood 5.00 12.00
US256 Mike Gonzalez 5.00 12.00
US257 Joel Hanrahan 8.00 20.00
US258 Dana Eveland 5.00 12.00
US259 Yadier Molina 8.00 20.00
US260 Andre Ethier 6.00 15.00
US261 Jason Vargas 5.00 12.00
US262 Rob Johnson 5.00 12.00
US263 Randy Winn 5.00 12.00
US264 Vicente Padilla 5.00 12.00
US265 Ryan Howard 12.00 30.00
US266 Billy Wagner 5.00 12.00
US267 Eugenio Velez 5.00 12.00
US268 Logan Morrison 8.00 20.00
US269 Dave Bush 5.00 12.00
US270 Vladimir Guerrero 10.00 25.00
US271 Travis Wood 6.00 15.00
US272 Brian Stokes 5.00 12.00
US273 John Jaso 5.00 12.00
US274 Stephen Strasburg 12.00 30.00
Ivan Rodriguez
US275 Hong-Chih Kuo 5.00 12.00
US276 Austin Jackson 6.00 15.00
US277 Micah Owings 5.00 12.00
US278 Brad Penny 5.00 12.00
US279 Hanley Ramirez 10.00 25.00
US280 Alex Rodriguez 15.00 40.00
US281 Jose Valverde 5.00 12.00
US282 Rhyne Hughes 5.00 12.00
US283 Kevin Frandsen 5.00 12.00
US284 Josh Reddick 5.00 12.00
US285 Jaime Garcia 8.00 20.00
US286 Arthur Rhodes 5.00 12.00
US287 Alex Sanabia 5.00 12.00
US288 Jonny Venters 5.00 12.00
US289 Adam Kennedy 5.00 12.00
US290 Justin Verlander 15.00 40.00
US291 Corey Hart 5.00 12.00
US292 Kelly Shoppach 5.00 12.00
US293 Pat Burrell 5.00 12.00
US294 Aaron Heilman 5.00 12.00
US295 Andrew Cashner 5.00 12.00
US296 Lance Zawadzki 5.00 12.00
US297 Don Kelly 5.00 12.00
US298 David Freese 8.00 20.00
US299 Xavier Nady 5.00 12.00
US300 Cliff Lee 8.00 20.00
US301 Jeff Clement 5.00 12.00
US302 Pedro Feliz 5.00 12.00
US303 Brandon Phillips 5.00 12.00
US304 Kris Medlen 5.00 12.00
US305 Cliff Lee 8.00 20.00
US306 Dan Haren 5.00 12.00
US307 Carlos Santana 12.00 30.00
US308 Matt Thornton 5.00 12.00
US309 Andruw Jones 5.00 12.00
US310 Derek Jeter 25.00 60.00
US311 Felix Doubront 5.00 12.00
US312 Coco Crisp 5.00 12.00
US313 Mitch Maier 5.00 12.00
US314 Cole Gillespie 5.00 12.00
US315 Edwin Jackson 5.00 12.00
US316 Rod Barajas 5.00 12.00
US317 Mike Leake 12.00 30.00
US318 Domonic Brown 15.00 40.00
US319 Josh Tomlin 12.00 30.00
US320 Joe Mauer 10.00 25.00
US321 Jason Donald 5.00 12.00
US322 John Ely 6.00 15.00
US323 Ryan Kalish 6.00 15.00
US324 George Kottaras 5.00 12.00
US325 Ian Kinsler 8.00 20.00
US326 Miguel Cabrera 12.00 30.00
US327 Mike Stanton 15.00 40.00
US328 Adrian Beltre 5.00 12.00
US329 Jose Reyes 10.00 25.00
Hanley Ramirez
US330 Carlos Santana 12.00 30.00

2010 Topps Update Gold

*GOLD VET: 2X TO 5X BASIC
*GOLD RC: .75X TO 2X BASIC RC
STATED ODDS 1:6 HOBBY
STATED PRINT RUN 2010 SER.#'d SETS
US55 Stephen Strasburg 3.00 8.00
US274 Stephen Strasburg 3.00 8.00
Ivan Rodriguez

2010 Topps Update Target

*VETS: .5X TO 1.2X BASIC TOPPS UPD CARDS
*RC: .5X TO 1.2X BASIC TOPPS UPD RC CARDS

2010 Topps Update Wal Mart Black Border

*VETS: .5X TO 1.2X BASIC TOPPS UPD CARDS
*RC: .5X TO 1.2X BASIC TOPPS UPD RC CARDS

2010 Topps Update All-Star Jumbo Patches

STATED ODDS 1:5207 HOBBY
STATED PRINT RUN 6 SER.#'d SETS
NO PRICING DUE TO SCARCITY

2010 Topps Update All-Star Jumbo Patches Autographs

STATED ODDS 1:34,500 HOBBY
STATED PRINT RUN 6 SER.#'d SETS
NO PRICING DUE TO SCARCITY

2010 Topps Update All-Star Stitches

STATED ODDS 1:53 HOBBY
AB Andrew Bailey 3.00 8.00
AE Andre Ethier 3.00 8.00
AG Adrian Gonzalez 3.00 8.00
AP Andy Pettitte 5.00 12.00
AR Alex Rodriguez 5.00 12.00
AW Adam Wainwright 4.00 10.00
BM Brian McCann 4.00 10.00
BP Brandon Phillips 3.00 8.00
BW Brian Wilson 5.00 12.00
CB Clay Buchholz 3.00 8.00
CC Carl Crawford 3.00 8.00
CH Corey Hart 3.00 8.00
CL Cliff Lee 4.00 10.00
CY Chris Young 3.00 8.00
DJ Derek Jeter 10.00 25.00
DO David Ortiz 3.00 8.00
DP David Price 4.00 10.00
DW David Wright 3.00 8.00
EA Elvis Andrus 4.00 10.00
EL Evan Longoria 5.00 12.00
EM Evan Meek 3.00 8.00
FC Fausto Carmona 3.00 8.00
HB Heath Bell 4.00 10.00
HR Hanley Ramirez 3.00 8.00
IK Ian Kinsler 3.00 8.00
IS Ichiro Suzuki 10.00 25.00
JB Jose Bautista 4.00 10.00
JH Josh Hamilton 4.00 10.00
JJ Josh Johnson 3.00 8.00
JL Jon Lester 3.00 8.00
JM Joe Mauer 5.00 12.00
JR Jose Reyes 4.00 10.00
JS Joakim Soria 3.00 8.00
JV Justin Verlander 3.00 8.00
JW Jered Weaver 3.00 8.00
MB Marlon Byrd 4.00 10.00
MC Miguel Cabrera 4.00 10.00
MH Matt Holliday 4.00 10.00
MP Martin Prado 3.00 8.00
MT Matt Thornton 3.00 8.00
NF Neftali Feliz 4.00 10.00
OI Omar Infante 3.00 8.00
PH Phil Hughes 4.00 10.00
PK Paul Konerko 3.00 8.00
RB Ryan Braun 3.00 8.00
RC Robinson Cano 5.00 12.00
RF Rafael Furcal 3.00 8.00
RH Roy Halladay 5.00 12.00
RS Rafael Soriano 3.00 8.00
SR Scott Rolen 4.00 10.00
TC Trevor Cahill 3.00 8.00
TH Torii Hunter 3.00 8.00
TL Tim Lincecum 8.00 20.00
TT Troy Tulowitzki 4.00 10.00
TW Ty Wigginton 4.00 10.00
UJ Ubaldo Jimenez 3.00 8.00
VG Vladimir Guerrero 3.00 8.00
VM Victor Martinez 3.00 8.00
VW Vernon Wells 3.00 8.00
YG Yovani Gallardo 3.00 8.00
YM Yadier Molina 4.00 10.00
ABE Adrian Beltre 4.00 10.00
APU Albert Pujols 8.00 20.00
ARH Arthur Rhodes 3.00 8.00
CCA Chris Carpenter 4.00 10.00
CCS CC Sabathia 4.00 10.00
DPE Dustin Pedroia 4.00 10.00
HCK Hong-Chih Kuo 4.00 10.00
JBR Jonathan Broxton 3.00 8.00
JBU John Buck 3.00 8.00
JHE Jason Heyward 6.00 15.00
JVO Joey Votto 5.00 12.00
MBO Michael Bourn 3.00 8.00
MCA Matt Capps 3.00 8.00
RHO Ryan Howard 4.00 10.00
THU Tim Hudson 3.00 8.00

2010 Topps Update All-Star Stitches Gold

*GOLD: .6X TO 1.5X BASIC
STATED ODDS 1:1047 HOBBY
STATED PRINT RUN 50 SER.#'d SETS

2010 Topps Update All-Star Stitches Platinum

STATED ODDS 1:52,300 HOBBY
STATED PRINT RUN 1 SER.#'d SET
NO PRICING DUE TO SCARCITY

2010 Topps Update All-Star Stitches Autographs

STATED ODDS 1:10,666 HOBBY
STATED PRINT RUN 25 SER.#'d SETS
NO PRICING DUE TO SCARCITY

2010 Topps Update All-Star Stitches Dual

STATED ODDS 1:15,900 HOBBY
STATED PRINT RUN 25 SER.#'d SETS
NO PRICING DUE TO SCARCITY

2010 Topps Update All-Star Stitches Triple

STATED ODDS 1:7,700 HOBBY
STATED PRINT RUN 25 SER.#'d SETS
NO PRICING DUE TO SCARCITY

2010 Topps Update Attax Code Cards

28 Jered Weaver .30 .75
29 Hideki Matsui .75 2.00
30 Mark Reynolds .30 .75
31 Justin Upton .50 1.25
32 Jason Heyward 2.00 5.00
33 Brian McCann .50 1.25
34 Adam Jones .50 1.25
35 Nick Markakis .75 2.00
36 Kevin Youkilis .50 1.25
37 Victor Martinez .50 1.25
38 John Lackey .30 .75
39 Starlin Castro 1.25 3.00
40 Alfonso Soriano .50 1.25
41 Jake Peavy .30 .75
42 Paul Konerko .50 1.25
43 Carlos Santana 1.00 2.50
44 Shin-Soo Choo .50 1.25
45 Mike Leake 1.00 2.50
46 Ubaldo Jimenez .50 1.25
47 Miguel Cabrera .75 2.00
48 Austin Jackson .75 2.00
49 Hanley Ramirez .75 2.00
50 Mike Stanton 1.25 3.00
51 Hunter Pence .50 1.25
52 Joakim Soria .30 .75
53 Andre Ethier .50 1.25
54 Clayton Kershaw .75 2.00
55 Ryan Braun 1.00 2.50
56 Joe Mauer .75 2.00
57 Francisco Liriano .30 .75
58 Ike Davis .75 2.00
59 David Wright 1.00 2.50
60 Robinson Cano .75 2.00
61 Derek Jeter 2.00 5.00
62 Kurt Suzuki .30 .75
63 Roy Halladay .75 2.00
64 Ryan Howard 1.00 2.50
65 Andrew McCutchen .75 2.00
66 Albert Pujols 2.00 5.00
67 Adam Wainwright .50 1.25
68 Adrian Gonzalez .50 1.25
69 Buster Posey 3.00 8.00
70 Matt Cain .50 1.25
71 Ichiro Suzuki 1.25 3.00
72 Evan Longoria 1.00 2.50
73 David Price .75 2.00
74 Josh Hamilton .75 2.00
75 Vernon Wells .30 .75
76 Stephen Strasburg 2.00 5.00
77 Adam Dunn .50 1.25

2010 Topps Update Baseball Legends Cut Signatures

STATED ODDS 1:310,000 HOBBY
STATED PRINT RUN 1 SER.#'d SET
NO PRICING DUE TO SCARCITY

2010 Topps Update Chrome Rookie Refractors

ONE PER BOX TOPPER
CHR01 Stephen Strasburg 10.00 25.00
CHR02 Wilson Ramos 4.00 10.00
CHR03 Lance Zawadzki 1.50 4.00
CHR04 Jesus Feliciano 1.50 4.00
CHR05 Logan Morrison 2.50 6.00
CHR06 Josh Donaldson 1.50 4.00
CHR07 Travis Wood 2.50 6.00
CHR08 Cole Gillespie 1.50 4.00
CHR09 Ryan Kalish 2.50 6.00
CHR10 Domonic Brown 6.00 15.00
CHR11 Jason Donald 1.50 4.00
CHR12 Jeffrey Marquez 2.50 6.00
CHR13 Adam Ottavino 1.50 4.00
CHR14 Luke Hughes 1.50 4.00
CHR15 Jose Tabata 4.00 10.00
CHR16 Josh Bell 1.50 4.00
CHR17 Jon Link 1.50 4.00
CHR18 John Ely 1.50 4.00
CHR19 Jeanmar Gomez 2.50 6.00
CHR20 Mike Stanton 6.00 15.00
CHR21 Luis Atilano 1.50 4.00
CHR22 Chris Heisey 2.50 6.00
CHR23 Jake Arrieta 2.50 6.00
CHR24 Jonathan Lucroy 1.50 4.00
CHR25 Andrew Cashner 1.50 4.00
CHR26 Sam LeCure 1.50 4.00
CHR27 Danny Valencia 10.00 25.00
CHR28 Rhyne Hughes 1.50 4.00
CHR29 Kenley Jansen 6.00 15.00
CHR30 Ike Davis 4.00 10.00
CHR31 Lorenzo Cain 2.50 6.00
CHR32 Jonny Venters 1.50 4.00
CHR33 Andy Oliver 1.50 4.00
CHR34 Jon Jay 2.50 6.00
CHR35 Drew Storen 2.50 6.00
CHR36 Omar Beltre 1.50 4.00
CHR37 Alex Sanabia 1.50 4.00
CHR38 Jordan Smith 1.50 4.00
CHR39 Trevor Plouffe 1.50 4.00
CHR40 Starlin Castro 6.00 15.00
CHR41 Jhan Marinez 1.50 4.00
CHR42 Brad Lincoln 2.50 6.00
CHR43 Kevin Russo 1.50 4.00
CHR44 Frank Herrmann 1.50 4.00
CHR45 Brennan Boesch 4.00 10.00
CHR46 Daniel Nava 2.50 6.00
CHR47 Sam Demel 1.50 4.00
CHR48 Dayan Viciedo 2.50 6.00
CHR49 Felix Doubront 1.50 4.00
CHR50 Carlos Santana 5.00 12.00
CHR51 Josh Tomlin 4.00 10.00
CHR52 Anthony Slama 1.50 4.00
CHR53 Chris Carter 2.50 6.00
CHR54 J.P. Arencibia 2.50 6.00
CHR55 Mitch Moreland 2.50 6.00
CHR56 Peter Bourjos 2.50 6.00
CHR57 Argenis Diaz 2.50 6.00
CHR58 Mike Minor 2.50 6.00
CHR59 Brian Matusz 4.00 10.00
CHR60 Jason Heyward 10.00 25.00
CHR61 Mike Stanton 6.00 15.00
CHR62 Ike Davis 4.00 10.00
CHR63 Carlos Santana 5.00 12.00
CHR64 Austin Jackson 2.50 6.00
CHR65 Mike Leake 5.00 12.00
CHR66 Brennan Boesch 5.00 12.00
CHR67 Stephen Strasburg 10.00 25.00
CHR68 Jose Tabata 4.00 10.00
CHR69 Starlin Castro 6.00 15.00
CHR70 Danny Worth 1.50 4.00

2010 Topps Update Manufactured Bat Barrel

STATED ODDS 1:380 HOBBY
STATED PRINT RUN 99 SER.#'d SETS
BLACK ODDS 1:1960 HOBBY
BLACK PRINT RUN 25 SER.#'d SETS
NO BLACK PRICING DUE TO SCARCITY
PINK ODDS 1:44,000 HOBBY
PINK PRINT RUN 1 SER.#'d SET
NO PINK PRICING DUE TO SCARCITY
MB1 Ryan Braun 6.00 15.00
MB2 Derek Jeter 30.00 60.00
MB3 Torii Hunter 8.00 20.00
MB4 Chase Utley 10.00 25.00
MB5 Justin Upton 6.00 15.00
MB6 David Wright 10.00 25.00
MB7 Troy Tulowitzki 8.00 20.00
MB8 Kevin Youkilis 8.00 20.00
MB9 Jose Reyes 8.00 20.00
MB10 Albert Pujols 20.00 50.00
MB11 Jimmy Rollins 8.00 20.00
MB12 Victor Martinez 8.00 20.00
MB13 Shane Victorino 8.00 20.00
MB14 Matt Holliday 10.00 25.00
MB15 Prince Fielder 6.00 15.00
MB16 Hideki Matsui 30.00 60.00
MB17 Nick Markakis 10.00 25.00
MB18 Alfonso Soriano 5.00 12.00
MB19 Shin-Soo Choo 10.00 25.00
MB20 Evan Longoria 12.50 30.00
MB21 Joey Votto 15.00 40.00
MB22 Andrew McCutchen 10.00 25.00
MB23 Mark Reynolds 4.00 10.00
MB24 Andre Ethier 6.00 15.00
MB25 Robinson Cano 10.00 25.00
MB26 Casey McGehee 5.00 12.00
MB27 Paul Konerko 5.00 12.00
MB28 Adam Lind 6.00 15.00
MB29 Dustin Pedroia 8.00 20.00
MB30 Jason Heyward 20.00 50.00
MB31 Billy Butler 6.00 15.00
MB32 Justin Morneau 8.00 20.00
MB33 Aaron Hill 6.00 15.00
MB34 Pablo Sandoval 8.00 20.00
MB35 Miguel Cabrera 10.00 25.00
MB36 Ryan Zimmerman 8.00 20.00
MB37 Hunter Pence 6.00 15.00
MB38 Adrian Gonzalez 5.00 12.00
MB39 Adam Dunn 6.00 15.00
MB40 Vladimir Guerrero 6.00 15.00
MB41 Jason Bay 8.00 20.00
MB42 Matt Kemp 4.00 10.00
MB43 Dan Uggla 5.00 12.00
MB44 Brandon Phillips 5.00 12.00
MB45 Alex Rodriguez 15.00 40.00
MB46 Manny Ramirez 8.00 20.00
MB47 Nick Swisher 8.00 20.00
MB48 Vernon Wells 8.00 20.00
MB49 Corey Hart 5.00 12.00
MB50 Joe Mauer 12.50 30.00
MB51 David Ortiz 6.00 15.00
MB52 Josh Hamilton 12.50 30.00
MB53 Kendry Morales 8.00 20.00
MB54 Colby Rasmus 12.50 30.00
MB55 Chipper Jones 15.00 40.00
MB56 Lance Berkman 4.00 10.00
MB57 James Loney 5.00 12.00
MB58 Ian Kinsler 6.00 15.00
MB59 Carl Crawford 5.00 12.00
MB60 Hanley Ramirez 6.00 15.00
MB61 Buster Posey 30.00 60.00
MB62 Ike Davis 10.00 25.00
MB63 Adam Jones 6.00 15.00
MB64 Brian McCann 6.00 15.00
MB65 Mark Teixeira 12.50 30.00
MB66 Kurt Suzuki 5.00 12.00
MB67 Mike Stanton 12.50 30.00
MB68 Jayson Werth 10.00 25.00
MB69 Nelson Cruz 6.00 15.00
MB70 Ryan Howard 12.50 30.00
MB71 Martin Prado 6.00 15.00
MB72 Michael Young 5.00 15.00
MB73 Ben Zobrist 8.00 20.00
MB74 Carlos Lee 6.00 15.00
MB75 Ichiro Suzuki 30.00 60.00
MB76 Carlos Quentin 4.00 10.00
MB77 B.J. Upton 6.00 15.00
MB78 Alex Rios 5.00 12.00
MB79 Magglio Ordonez 8.00 20.00
MB80 Jose Bautista 8.00 20.00
MB81 Garrett Jones 5.00 12.00
MB82 Carlos Pena 8.00 20.00
MB83 Jay Bruce 8.00 20.00
MB84 Austin Jackson 8.00 20.00

MB85 Chris Young 4.00 10.00
MB86 Alexei Ramirez 6.00 15.00
MB87 Carlos Gonzalez 8.00 20.00
MB88 Howie Kendrick 5.00 12.00
MB89 Ryan Ludwick 6.00 15.00
MB90 Miguel Tejada 6.00 15.00
MB91 Derrek Lee 5.00 12.00
MB92 Adrian Beltre 5.00 12.00
MB93 Gordon Beckham 8.00 20.00
MB94 Yadier Molina 8.00 20.00
MB95 Starlin Castro 12.50 30.00
MB96 Stephen Drew 4.00 10.00
MB97 Carlos Santana 10.00 25.00
MB98 Bobby Abreu 8.00 20.00
MB99 Ty Wigginton 6.00 15.00
MB100 Scott Rolen 8.00 20.00
MB101 Grady Sizemore 6.00 15.00
MB102 Miguel Montero 5.00 12.00
MB103 Todd Helton 6.00 15.00
MB104 Chris Coghlan 5.00 12.00
MB105 Curtis Granderson 5.00 12.00
MB106 Troy Glaus 5.00 12.00
MB107 Placido Polanco 6.00 15.00
MB108 Elvis Andrus 6.00 15.00
MB109 Aramis Ramirez 6.00 15.00
MB110 Jose Tabata 6.00 15.00
MB111 Ian Desmond 5.00 12.00
MB112 Craig Biggio 10.00 25.00
MB113 Bernie Williams 8.00 20.00
MB114 Frank Robinson 8.00 20.00
MB115 Babe Ruth 40.00 80.00
MB116 Jimmie Foxx 8.00 20.00
MB117 Yogi Berra 10.00 25.00
MB118 Lou Gehrig 20.00 50.00
MB119 Tris Speaker 8.00 20.00
MB120 Roy Campanella 10.00 25.00
MB121 Bobby Murcer 12.50 30.00
MB122 Jimmy Piersall 6.00 15.00
MB123 Bo Jackson 12.50 30.00
MB124 Frank Thomas 10.00 25.00
MB125 Rogers Hornsby 10.00 25.00
MB126 Lou Brock 8.00 20.00
MB127 Richie Ashburn 12.50 30.00
MB128 Steve Garvey 8.00 20.00
MB129 Larry Doby 8.00 20.00
MB130 Jackie Robinson 12.50 30.00
MB131 Andre Dawson 8.00 20.00
MB132 Tony Gwynn 10.00 25.00
MB133 Don Mattingly 12.50 30.00
MB134 Carl Yastrzemski 10.00 25.00
MB135 Hank Greenberg 10.00 25.00
MB136 Dale Murphy 12.50 30.00
MB137 Paul Molitor 8.00 20.00
MB138 Eddie Murray 10.00 25.00
MB139 Mike Piazza 8.00 20.00
MB140 Ty Cobb 15.00 40.00
MB141 Al Kaline 12.50 30.00
MB142 Joe Morgan 8.00 20.00
MB143 Willie McCovey 8.00 20.00
MB144 Bill Mazeroski 8.00 20.00
MB145 George Sisler 6.00 15.00
MB146 Carlton Fisk 8.00 20.00
MB147 Sal Bando 4.00 10.00
MB148 Rod Carew 8.00 20.00
MB149 Orlando Cepeda 8.00 20.00
MB150 Mickey Mantle 40.00 80.00
MB151 Mike Schmidt 15.00 40.00
MB152 Rickey Henderson 20.00 50.00
MB153 Monte Irvin 5.00 12.00
MB154 George Kell 8.00 20.00
MB155 Pee Wee Reese 8.00 20.00
MB156 Robin Yount 12.50 30.00
MB157 Tony Perez 6.00 15.00
MB158 Ryne Sandberg 12.50 30.00
MB159 Luis Aparicio 10.00 25.00
MB160 Honus Wagner 12.50 30.00
MB161 Roger Maris 15.00 40.00
MB162 Duke Snider 8.00 20.00
MB163 Willie Stargell 10.00 25.00
MB164 Dave Winfield 6.00 15.00
MB165 Johnny Mize 6.00 15.00
MB166 Phil Rizzuto 8.00 20.00
MB167 Johnny Bench 10.00 25.00
MB168 Ozzie Smith 12.50 30.00
MB169 Reggie Jackson 10.00 25.00
MB170 Thurman Munson 12.50 30.00
MB171 Harmon Killebrew 12.50 30.00
MB172 Eddie Mathews 8.00 20.00
MB173 Ralph Kiner 8.00 20.00
MB174 Brooks Robinson 10.00 25.00
MB175 Mel Ott 8.00 20.00

2010 Topps Update Manufactured Rookie Logo Patch

STATED ODDS 1:1125 HOBBY
STATED PRINT RUN 500 SER.#'d SETS
AJ Austin Jackson 5.00 12.00
JH Jason Heyward 8.00 20.00
SS Stephen Strasburg 20.00 50.00

2010 Topps Update More Tales of the Game

COMPLETE SET
STATED ODDS 1:6 HOBBY
1 Joel Youngblood .40 1.00
2 Triple Billing .40 1.00
3 Seven Touchdowns .40 1.00
4 Eddie Mathews .75 2.00
5 Babe Ruth 1.25 3.00
6 Intracity Sweep .40 1.00
7 Mike Schmidt .75 2:00
8 Mile-High Humidor .40 1.00
9 Andre Dawson .75 2.00
Alex Rodriguez
10 Walter Johnson .75 2.00
11 Warren Spahn .60 1.50
12 There's No Tying in Baseball .40 1.00
13 Harry Truman .40 1.00
14 Stephen Strasburg 1.25 3.00
15 Roy Halladay .75 2.00

2010 Topps Update Peek Performance Autographs

GROUP A ODDS 1:2450 HOBBY
GROUP B ODDS 1:834 HOBBY
AC Andrew Cashner B 3.00 8.00
AJ Austin Jackson A 8.00 20.00
AO Adam Ottavino B 4.00 10.00
BB Brennan Boesch B 4.00 10.00
BL Brad Lincoln A 4.00 10.00
BP Buster Posey A 50.00 100.00
CH Chris Heisey B
CS Carlos Santana A 8.00 20.00
ID Ike Davis A 10.00 25.00
JD Jason Donald B 3.00 8.00
JE John Ely B 3.00 8.00
JH Jason Heyward A 50.00 100.00
JT Jose Tabata A 8.00 20.00
JV Jonny Venters B 4.00 10.00
LA Luis Atilano B 3.00 8.00
ML Mike Leake A 8.00 20.00
SC Starlin Castro A 10.00 25.00
SS Stephen Strasburg A 100.00 175.00
AOL Andy Oliver B 5.00 12.00
DST Drew Storen A 4.00 10.00
JCA Jason Castro B 4.00 10.00
MST Mike Stanton A 15.00 40.00
TCO Tyler Colvin A 5.00 12.00

2010 Topps Update Platinum

UNPRICED 1/1 ODDS 1:17,500 HOBBY

2011 Topps

COMP.HOBBY.SET (660) 30.00 60.00
COMP.ALLSTAR.SET (660) 30.00 60.00
COMP.SET w/o SP's (660) 30.00 60.00
COMP.SER.1 w/o SP's (330) 12.50 30.00
COMP.SER.2 w/o SP's (330) 12.50 30.00
COMMON CARD (1-660) .15 .40
COMMON RC (1-660) .25 .60
COMMON SP VAR (1-660) 6.00 15.00
SER.1 PLATE ODDS 1:1500 HOBBY
PLATE PRINT RUN 1 SET PER COLOR
BLACK-CYAN-MAGENTA-YELLOW ISSUED
NO PLATE PRICING DUE TO SCARCITY
1 Ryan Braun .50 1.25
2 Jake Westbrook .15 .40
3 Jon Lester .40 1.00
4 Jason Kubel .15 .40
5A Joey Votto .40 1.00
5B Lou Gehrig SP 10.00 25.00
6 Neftali Feliz .15 .40
7 Mickey Mantle 1.25 3.00
8 Julio Borbon .15 .40
9 Gil Meche .15 .40
10 Stephen Strasburg .75 2.00
11 Roy Halladay .40 1.00
Adam Wainwright
Ubaldo Jimenez LL
12 Carlos Marmol .25 .60
13 Billy Wagner .15 .40
14 Randy Wolf .15 .40
15 David Wright .50 1.25
16 Aramis Ramirez .15 .40
17 Mark Ellis .15 .40
18 Kevin Millwood .15 .40
19 Derek Lowe .15 .40
20 Hanley Ramirez .40 1.00
21 Michael Cuddyer .15 .40
22 Barry Zito .15 .40
23 Jaime Garcia .25 .60
24 Neil Walker .15 .40
25A Carl Crawford .25 .60
25B Carl Crawford Red Sox SP 20.00 50.00
25C Carl Yastrzemski SP 6.00 15.00
26 Neftali Feliz .15 .40
27 Ben Zobrist .15 .40
28 Carlos Carrasco .15 .40
29 Josh Hamilton .40 1.00
30 Gio Gonzalez .15 .40
31 Erick Aybar .15 .40
32 Chris Johnson .15 .40
33 Max Scherzer .15 .40
34 Rick Ankiel .15 .40
35 Shin-Soo Choo .25 .60
36 Ted Lilly .15 .40
37 Vicente Padilla .15 .40
38 Ryan Dempster .15 .40
39 Ian Kennedy .25 .60
40 Justin Upton .25 .60
41 Freddy Garcia .15 .40
42 Mariano Rivera .40 1.00
43 Brendan Ryan .15 .40
44A Martin Prado .15 .40
44B Rogers Hornsby SP 6.00 15.00
45 Hunter Pence .25 .60
46 Hong-Chih Kuo .15 .40
47 Kevin Correia .15 .40
48 Andrew Cashner .15 .40
49 Los Angeles Angels TC .15 .40
50A Alex Rodriguez .60 1.50
50B Mike Schmidt SP 8.00 20.00
51 David Eckstein .15 .40
52 Tampa Bay Rays TC .15 .40
53 Arizona Diamondbacks TC .15 .40
54 Brian Fuentes .15 .40
55 Matt Joyce .15 .40
56 Johan Santana .40 1.00
57 Mark Trumbo (RC) .40 1.00
58 Edgar Renteria .15 .40
59 Gaby Sanchez .15 .40
60 Andrew McCutchen .40 1.00
61 David Price .40 1.00
62 Jonathan Papelbon .25 .60
63 Edinson Volquez .15 .40
64 Yorvit Torrealba .15 .40
65 Chris Sale RC .40 1.00
66 R.A. Dickey .15 .40
67 Vladimir Guerrero .40 1.00
68 Cleveland Indians TC .15 .40
69 Brett Gardner .15 .40
70 Kyle Drabek RC .40 1.00
71 Trevor Hoffman .25 .60
72 Jair Jurrjens .15 .40
73 James McDonald .15 .40
74 Tyler Clippard .15 .40
75 Jered Weaver .15 .40
76 Tom Gorzelanny .15 .40
77 Tim Hudson .25 .60
78 Mike Stanton .25 .60
79 Kurt Suzuki .15 .40
80A Desmond Jennings RC .60 1.50
80B Jackie Robinson SP 8.00 20.00
81 Omar Infante .15 .40
82 Josh Johnson .40 1.00
Adam Wainwright
Roy Halladay LL
83 Greg Halman RC .40 1.00
84 Roger Bernadina .15 .40
85 Jack Wilson .15 .40
86 Carlos Silva .15 .40
87 Daniel Descalso RC .25 .60
88 Brian Bogusevic (RC) .25 .60
89 Placido Polanco .15 .40
90A Yadier Molina .25 .60
90B Yogi Berra SP 8.00 20.00
91 Lucas May RC .25 .60
92 Chris Narveson .15 .40
93A Paul Konerko .25 .60
93B Frank Thomas SP 6.00 15.00
94 Ryan Raburn .15 .40
95 Pedro Alvarez RC .40 1.00
96 Zach Duke .15 .40
97 Carlos Gomez .15 .40
98 Bronson Arroyo .15 .40
99 Ben Revere RC .40 1.00
100A Albert Pujols 1.00 2.50
100B Stan Musial SP 6.00 15.00
101 Gregor Blanco .15 .40
102A CC Sabathia .25 .60
102B Christy Mathewson SP 6.00 15.00
103 Cliff Lee .40 1.00
104 Ian Stewart .15 .40
105 Jonathan Lucroy .15 .40
106 Felix Pie .15 .40
107 Aubrey Huff .15 .40
108 Zack Greinke .25 .60
109 Josh Hamilton .40 1.00
Miguel Cabrera
Joe Mauer LL
110 Aroldis Chapman RC .75 2.00
111 Kevin Gregg .15 .40
112 Jorge Cantu .15 .40
113 Arthur Rhodes .15 .40
114 Russell Martin .15 .40
115 Jason Varitek .40 1.00
116 Russell Branyan .15 .40
117 Brett Sinkbeil RC .25 .60
118 Howie Kendrick .15 .40
119 Jason Bay .25 .60
120 Mat Latos .15 .40
121 Brandon Inge .15 .40
122 Bobby Jenks .15 .40
123 Mike Lowell .15 .40
124 CC Sabathia .40 1.00
Jon Lester
David Price LL
125 Evan Meek .15 .40
126 San Diego Padres TC .15 .40
127 Chris Volstad .15 .40
128 Manny Ramirez .40 1.00
129 Lucas Duda RC .40 1.00
130 Robinson Cano .40 1.00
131 Kevin Kouzmanoff .15 .40
132 Brian Duensing .15 .40
133 Miguel Tejada .25 .60
134 Carlos Gonzalez .40 1.00
Joey Votto
Omar Infante LL
135A Mike Stanton .25 .60
135B Dale Murphy SP 6.00 15.00
136 Jason Marquis .15 .40
137 Xavier Nady .15 .40
138 Albert Pujols 1.00 2.50
Carlos Gonzalez
Joey Votto LL
139 Eric Young Jr. .15 .40
140 Brett Anderson .25 .60
141 Ubaldo Jimenez .25 .60
142 Johnny Cueto .15 .40
143 Jeremy Jeffress RC .25 .60
144 Lance Berkman .25 .60
145 Freddie Freeman RC 1.00 2.50
146 Roy Halladay .40 1.00
147 Jon Niese .15 .40
148 Ricky Romero .15 .40
149 David Aardsma .15 .40
150A Miguel Cabrera .40 1.00
150B Hank Greenberg SP 6.00 15.00
151 Fausto Carmona .15 .40
152 Baltimore Orioles TC .15 .40
153 A.J. Pierzynski .15 .40
154 Marlon Byrd .15 .40
155 Alex Rodriguez .60 1.50
156 Josh Thole .15 .40
157 New York Mets TC .25 .60
158 Casey Blake .15 .40
159 Chris Perez .15 .40
160 Josh Tomlin .15 .40
161 Chicago White Sox TC .15 .40
162 Ronny Cedeno .15 .40
163 Carlos Pena .25 .60
164 Koji Uehara .15 .40
165 Jeremy Hellickson RC .75 2.00
166 Josh Johnson .25 .60
167 Clay Hensley .15 .40
168 Felix Hernandez .40 1.00
169 Chipper Jones .40 1.00
170 David DeJesus .15 .40
171 Garrett Jones .15 .40
172 Lyle Overbay .15 .40
173 Jose Lopez .15 .40
174 Roy Oswalt .25 .60
175 Brennan Boesch .25 .60
176 Daniel Hudson .15 .40
177 Brian Matusz .40 1.00
178 Heath Bell .25 .60
179 Armando Galarraga .15 .40
180 Paul Maholm .15 .40
181 Magglio Ordonez .25 .60
182 Jeremy Bonderman .15 .40
183 Stephen Strasburg .75 2.00
184 Brandon Morrow .15 .40
185 Peter Bourjos .25 .60
186 Carl Pavano .15 .40
187 Milwaukee Brewers TC .15 .40
188 Pablo Sandoval .25 .60
189 Kerry Wood .15 .40
190 Coco Crisp .15 .40
191 Jay Bruce .25 .60
192 Cincinnati Reds TC .15 .40
193 Cory Luebke RC .25 .60
194 Andres Torres .15 .40
195 Nick Markakis .40 1.00
196 Jose Ceda RC .25 .60
197 Aaron Hill .15 .40
198A Buster Posey .50 1.25
198B Johnny Bench SP 8.00 20.00
199A Jimmy Rollins .25 .60
199B Ozzie Smith SP 6.00 15.00
200A Ichiro Suzuki .60 1.50
200B Ty Cobb SP 8.00 20.00
201 Mike Napoli .25 .60
202 Jose Bautista .40 1.00
Paul Konerko
Miguel Cabrera LL
203 Dillon Gee RC .40 1.00
204 Oakland Athletics TC .15 .40
205 Ty Wigginton .15 .40
206 Chase Headley .15 .40
207 Angel Pagan .15 .40
208 Clay Buchholz .25 .60
209A Carlos Santana .40 1.00
209B Roy Campanella SP 6.00 15.00
20B Honus Wagner SP 6.00 15.00
210 Brian Wilson .40 1.00
211 Joey Votto .40 1.00
212 Pedro Feliz .15 .40
213 Brandon Snyder (RC) .25 .60
214 Chase Utley .40 1.00
215 Edwin Encarnacion .15 .40
216 Jose Bautista .25 .60
217 Yunel Escobar .15 .40
218 Victor Martinez .25 .60
219A Carlos Ruiz .15 .40
219B Thurman Munson SP 6.00 15.00
220 Todd Helton .25 .60
221 Scott Hairston .15 .40
222 Matt Lindstrom .15 .40
223 Gregory Infante RC .25 .60
224 Milton Bradley .15 .40
225 Josh Willingham .15 .40
226 Jose Guillen .15 .40
227 Nate McLouth .15 .40
228 Scott Rolen .25 .60
229 Jonathan Sanchez .15 .40
230 Aaron Cook .15 .40
231 Mark Buehrle .25 .60
232 Jamie Moyer .15 .40
233 Ramon Hernandez .15 .40
234 Miguel Montero .15 .40
235 Felix Hernandez .40 1.00
Clay Buchholz
David Price LL
236 Nelson Cruz .25 .60
237 Jason Vargas .15 .40
238 Pedro Ciriaco RC .25 .60
239 Jhoulys Chacin .15 .40
240 Andre Ethier .25 .60
241 Wandy Rodriguez .15 .40
242 Brad Lidge .15 .40
243 Omar Vizquel .25 .60
244 Mike Aviles .15 .40
245 Neil Walker .15 .40
246 John Lannan .15 .40
247A Starlin Castro .40 1.00
247B Ernie Banks SP 6.00 15.00
248 Wade LeBlanc .15 .40
249 Aaron Harang .15 .40
250A Carlos Gonzalez .25 .60
250B Mel Ott SP 6.00 15.00
251 Alcides Escobar .15 .40
252 Michael Saunders .15 .40
253 Jim Thome .25 .60
254 Lars Anderson RC .40 1.00
255 Torii Hunter .15 .40
256 Tyler Colvin .25 .60
257 Travis Hafner .15 .40
258 Rafael Soriano .15 .40
259 Kyle Davies .15 .40
260 Freddy Sanchez .15 .40
261 Alexei Ramirez .15 .40
262 Alex Gordon .25 .60
263 Joel Pineiro .15 .40
264 Ryan Perry .15 .40
265 John Danks .15 .40
266 Rickie Weeks .25 .60
267 Jose Contreras .15 .40
268 Jake McGee (RC) .25 .60
269 Stephen Drew .15 .40
270 Ubaldo Jimenez .25 .60
271A Adam Dunn .25 .60
271B Babe Ruth SP 10.00 25.00
272 J.J. Hardy .15 .40
273 Derrek Lee .15 .40
274 Michael Brantley .15 .40
275 Clayton Kershaw .40 1.00
276 Miguel Olivo .15 .40
277 Trevor Hoffman .25 .60
278 Marco Scutaro .15 .40
279 Nick Swisher .40 1.00
280 Andrew Bailey .15 .40
281 Kevin Slowey .15 .40
282 Buster Posey .50 1.25
283 Colorado Rockies TC .15 .40
284 Reid Brignac .15 .40
285 Hank Conger RC .40 1.00
286 Melvin Mora .15 .40
287 Scott Cousins RC .25 .60
288 Matt Capps .15 .40
289 Yuniesky Betancourt .15 .40
290 Ike Davis .25 .60
291 Juan Gutierrez .15 .40
292 Darren Ford RC .25 .60
293A Justin Morneau .40 1.00
293B Harmon Killebrew SP 6.00 15.00
294 Luke Scott .15 .40
295 Jon Jay .15 .40
296 John Buck .15 .40
297 Jason Jaramillo .15 .40
298 Jeff Keppinger .15 .40
299 Chris Carpenter .40 1.00
300A Roy Halladay .40 1.00
300B Walter Johnson SP 6.00 15.00
301 Seth Smith .15 .40
302 Adrian Beltre .15 .40
303 Emilio Bonifacio .15 .40
304 Jim Thome .25 .60
305 James Loney .25 .60
306 Miguel Cabrera .60 1.50
Alex Rodriguez
Jose Bautista LL
307 Alex Rios .25 .60
308 Ian Desmond .25 .60
309 Chicago Cubs TC .25 .60
310 Alex Gonzalez .15 .40
311 James Shields .15 .40
312 Gaby Sanchez .15 .40
313 Chris Coghlan .15 .40
314 Ryan Kalish .25 .60
315A David Ortiz .25 .60
315B Jimmie Foxx SP 6.00 15.00
316 Chris Young .15 .40
317 Yonder Alonso RC .40 1.00
318 Albert Pujols 1.00 2.50
Adam Dunn
Joey Votto LL
319 Atlanta Braves TC .15 .40
320 Michael Young .25 .60
321 Jeremy Guthrie .15 .40
322 Brent Morel RC .25 .60
323 C.J. Wilson .15 .40
324 Boston Red Sox TC .25 .60
325 Jayson Werth .25 .60
326 Ozzie Martinez RC .25 .60
327 Christian Guzman .15 .40
328 David Price .40 1.00
329 Brett Wallace .15 .40
330A Derek Jeter 1.00 2.50
330B Phil Rizzuto SP 6.00 15.00
331 Carlos Guillen .15 .40
332 Melky Cabrera .15 .40
333 Tom Wilhelmsen RC .25 .60
334 St. Louis Cardinals TC .25 .60
335 Buster Posey .50 1.25
336 Chris Heisey .15 .40
337 Jordan Walden .15 .40
338 Jason Hammel .15 .40
339 Alexi Casilla .15 .40
340 Evan Longoria .50 1.25
341 Kyle Kendrick .15 .40
342 Jorge De La Rosa .15 .40
343 Mason Tobin RC .25 .60
344 Michael Kohn RC .25 .60
345 Austin Jackson .15 .40
346 Jose Bautista .25 .60
347 Darwin Barney RC .75 2.00
348 Landon Powell .15 .40
349 Drew Stubbs .25 .60
350A Francisco Liriano .15 .40
350B Adrian Gonzalez Red Sox SP 10.00 25.00
351 Jacoby Ellsbury .40 1.00
352 Colby Lewis .15 .40
353 Cliff Pennington .15 .40
354 Scott Baker .15 .40
355A Justin Verlander .50 1.25
355B Bob Feller SP 6.00 15.00
356 Alfonso Soriano .25 .60
357 Mike Cameron .15 .40
358 Paul Janish .15 .40
359 Roy Halladay .40 1.00
360 Ivan Rodriguez .25 .60
361 Florida Marlins TC .15 .40
362 Doug Fister .15 .40
363 Aaron Rowand .15 .40
364 Tim Wakefield .15 .40
365 Adam Lind .25 .60
366 Joe Nathan .15 .40
367 Hiroki Kuroda .15 .40
368 Brian Broderick RC .25 .60
369 Wilson Betemit .15 .40
370 Matt Garza .15 .40
371 Taylor Teagarden .15 .40
372 Jarrod Saltalamacchia .15 .40
373 Trever Miller .15 .40
374 Washington Nationals TC .15 .40
375A Matt Kemp .25 .60
375B Andre Dawson SP 6.00 15.00
376 Clayton Richard .15 .40
377 Esmil Rogers .15 .40
378 Mark Reynolds .15 .40
379 Ben Francisco .15 .40
380 Jose Reyes .25 .60
381 Michael Gonzalez .15 .40
382 Travis Snider .15 .40
383 Ryan Ludwick .15 .40
384 Nick Hundley .15 .40
385 Ichiro Suzuki .60 1.50
386 Barry Enright .15 .40
387 Danny Valencia .25 .60
388 Kenley Jansen .25 .60
389 Carlos Quentin .15 .40
390 Danny Valencia .25 .60
391 Phil Coke .15 .40
392 Kris Medlen .15 .40
393A Jake Arrieta .15 .40
393B Jim Palmer SP 6.00 15.00
394 Austin Jackson .15 .40
395 Tyler Flowers .15 .40
396 Adam Jones .25 .60
397 Sean Rodriguez .15 .40
398 Pittsburgh Pirates TC .15 .40
399 Adam Moore .15 .40
400 Troy Tulowitzki .40 1.00
401 Michael Crotta RC .25 .60
402 Jack Cust .15 .40
403 Felix Hernandez .40 1.00
404 Chris Capuano .15 .40
405A Ian Kinsler .25 .60
405B Ryne Sandberg SP 6.00 15.00
406 John Lackey .15 .40
407 Jonathan Broxton .15 .40
408 Denard Span .15 .40
409 Vin Mazzaro .15 .40
410A Prince Fielder .25 .60
410B Reggie Jackson SP 6.00 15.00
411 Josh Bell .15 .40
412 Samuel Deduno RC .25 .60
413 Derek Holland .15 .40
414 Jose Molina .15 .40
415 Brian McCann .25 .60
416 Everth Cabrera .15 .40
417 Miguel Cairo .15 .40
418 Zach Britton RC .60 1.50
419 Kelly Johnson .15 .40
420 Ryan Howard .50 1.25
421 Domonic Brown .40 1.00
422 Juan Pierre .15 .40
423 Hideki Okajima .15 .40
424 New York Yankees TC .25 .60
425A Adrian Gonzalez .25 .60
425B Johnny Mize SP 6.00 15.00
426 Travis Buck .15 .40
427 Brad Emaus RC .25 .60
428 Brett Myers .15 .40
429 Skip Schumaker .15 .40
430 Trevor Crowe .15 .40
431 Marcos Mateo RC .25 .60
432 Matt Harrison .15 .40
433 Curtis Granderson .25 .60
434 Mark DeRosa .15 .40
435A Elvis Andrus .25 .60
435B Pee Wee Reese SP 6.00 15.00
436 Trevor Cahill .15 .40
437 Jordan Schafer .15 .40
438 Ryan Theriot .15 .40
439 Ervin Santana .15 .40
440 Grady Sizemore .25 .60
441 Rafael Furcal .15 .40
442 Brad Bergesen .15 .40
443 Brian Roberts .15 .40
444 Brett Cecil .15 .40
445 Mitch Talbot .15 .40
446 Brandon Beachy RC .60 1.50
447 Toronto Blue Jays TC .15 .40
448 Colby Rasmus .40 1.00
449 Austin Kearns .15 .40
450A Mark Teixeira .40 1.00
450B Mickey Mantle SP 10.00 25.00
451 Livan Hernandez .15 .40
452 David Freese .25 .60
453 Joe Saunders .15 .40
454 Alberto Callaspo .15 .40
455 Logan Morrison .15 .40
456 Ryan Doumit .15 .40
457 Brandon Allen .15 .40
458 Javier Vazquez .15 .40
459 Frank Francisco .15 .40
460A Cole Hamels .40 1.00
460B Robin Roberts SP 6.00 15.00
461 Eric Sogard RC .25 .60
462 Daric Barton .15 .40
463 Will Venable .15 .40
464 Daniel Bard .15 .40
465 Yovani Gallardo .15 .40
466 Johnny Damon .25 .60
467 Wade Davis .15 .40
468 Chone Figgins .15 .40
469 Joe Blanton .15 .40
470 Billy Butler .15 .40
471 Tim Collins RC .25 .60
472 Jason Kendall .15 .40
473 Chad Billingsley .15 .40
474 Jeff Mathis .15 .40
475 Phil Hughes .15 .40
476 Matt LaPorta .15 .40
477 Franklin Gutierrez .15 .40
478 Mike Minor .15 .40
479 Justin Duchscherer .15 .40
480A Dustin Pedroia .50 1.25
480B Roberto Alomar SP 6.00 15.00
481 Randy Wells .15 .40
482 Eric Hinske .15 .40
483 Justin Smoak RC .25 .60
484 Gerardo Parra .15 .40
485 Delmon Young .25 .60
486 Francisco Rodriguez .25 .60
487 Chris Snyder .15 .40
488 Brayan Villarreal RC .25 .60
489 Marc Rzepczynski .15 .40
490A Matt Holliday .40 1.00
490B Duke Snider SP 6.00 15.00
491 Fernando Abad RC .25 .60
492 A.J. Burnett .25 .60
493 Ryan Sweeney .15 .40
494 Drew Storen .15 .40
495 Shane Victorino .25 .60
496 Gavin Floyd .15 .40
497 Alex Avila .15 .40
498 Scott Feldman .15 .40
499 J.A. Happ .25 .60
500 Kevin Youkilis .25 .60
501 Tsuyoshi Nishioka RC .75 2.00
502 Jeff Baker .15 .40
503 Nathan Adcock RC .25 .60
504 Jhonny Peralta .15 .40
505A Tommy Hanson .25 .60
505B Greg Maddux SP 6.00 15.00
506 Aneury Rodriguez RC .25 .60
507 Huston Street .15 .40
508 Homer Bailey .15 .40
509 Michael Bourn .15 .40
510A Jason Heyward .50 1.25
510B Hank Aaron SP 8.00 20.00
511 Philadelphia Phillies TC .15 .40
512 Octavio Dotel .15 .40
513 Adam LaRoche .15 .40
514 Kelly Shoppach .15 .40
515 Carlos Beltran .15 .40
516A Mike Leake .25 .60
516B Tom Seaver SP 6.00 15.00
517 Fred Lewis .15 .40
518 Michael Morse .15 .40
519 Corey Hart .15 .40
520 Jorge Posada .25 .60
521 Joaquin Benoit .15 .40
522 Asdrubal Cabrera .25 .60
523 Mike Nickeas (RC) .25 .60
524 Michael Martinez RC .40 1.00
525 Vernon Wells .15 .40
526 Jason Donald .15 .40
527 Kila Ka'aihue .15 .40
528 Bobby Abreu .15 .40
529 Maicer Izturis .15 .40
530A Felix Hernandez .40 1.00
530B Sandy Koufax SP 12.50 30.00
531 Juan Rivera .15 .40
532 Erik Bedard .15 .40
533 Lorenzo Cain .15 .40
534 Bud Norris .15 .40
535 Rich Harden .15 .40
536 Tony Sipp .15 .40
537 Jake Peavy .15 .40
538 Jason Motte .15 .40
539 Brandon Lyon .15 .40
540 Joakim Soria .15 .40
541 John Jaso .15 .40
542 Mike Pelfrey .15 .40
543 Texas Rangers TC .15 .40
544 Justin Masterson .15 .40
545 Jose Tabata .25 .60
546 Pat Burrell .15 .40
547 Albert Pujols 1.00 2.50
548 Ryan Franklin .15 .40
549 Jayson Nix .15 .40
550 Joe Mauer .40 1.00
551 Marcus Thames .15 .40
552 San Francisco Giants TC .15 .40
553 Kyle Lohse .15 .40
554 Cedric Hunter RC .25 .60
555 Madison Bumgarner .15 .40
556 B.J. Upton .25 .60
557 Wes Helms .15 .40
558 Carlos Zambrano .25 .60
559 Reggie Willits .15 .40
560 Chris Iannetta .15 .40
561 Luke Gregerson .15 .40
562 Gordon Beckham .25 .60
563 Josh Rodriguez RC .25 .60
564 Jeff Samardzija .15 .40
565 Mark Teahen .15 .40
566 Jordan Zimmermann .15 .40
567 Dallas Braden .15 .40
568 Kansas City Royals TC .15 .40
569 Cameron Maybin .15 .40
570A Matt Cain .25 .60
570B Bert Blyleven SP 6.00 15.00
571 Jeremy Affeldt .15 .40
572 Brad Hawpe .15 .40
573 Nyjer Morgan .15 .40
574 Brandon Kintzler RC .25 .60
575 Rod Barajas .15 .40
576 Jed Lowrie .25 .60
577 Mike Fontenot .15 .40
578 Willy Aybar .15 .40
579 Jeff Niemann .15 .40
580 Chris Young .15 .40
581 Fernando Rodney .15 .40
582 Kosuke Fukudome .40 1.00
583 Ryan Spilborghs .15 .40
584 Jason Bartlett .15 .40
585 Dan Johnson .15 .40
586 Carlos Lee .15 .40
587 J.P. Arencibia .25 .60
588 Rajai Davis .15 .40
589 Seattle Mariners TC .15 .40
590A Tim Lincecum .40 1.00
590B Juan Marichal SP 6.00 15.00
591 John Axford .15 .40
592 Dayan Viciedo .15 .40
593 Francisco Cordero .15 .40
594 Jose Valverde .15 .40
595 Michael Pineda RC .75 2.00
596 Anibal Sanchez .15 .40
597 Rick Porcello .15 .40
598 Jonny Gomes .15 .40
599 Travis Ishikawa .15 .40
600A Neftali Feliz .15 .40
600B John Smoltz SP 6.00 15.00
601 J.J. Putz .15 .40
602 Ivan DeJesus RC .25 .60
603 David Murphy .15 .40
604 Joe Paterson RC .40 1.00
605 Brandon Belt RC 1.00 2.50
606 Juan Miranda .15 .40
607 Daniel Murphy .15 .40
608 Casey McGehee .15 .40
609 Juan Francisco .15 .40
610 Josh Beckett .25 .60
611 Geovany Soto .25 .60
612 Detroit Tigers TC .15 .40
613 Dexter Fowler .15 .40
614 Minnesota Twins TC .15 .40
615 Shaun Marcum .15 .40
616 Ross Ohlendorf .15 .40
617 Joel Zumaya .15 .40
618 Josh Lueke RC .25 .60
619 Jonny Venters .15 .40
620 Luke Hochevar .15 .40
621 Omar Beltre .15 .40
622 Matt Thornton .15 .40
623 Leo Nunez .15 .40
624 Luke French .15 .40
625 Ruben Tejada .15 .40
626A Dan Haren .15 .40
626B Nolan Ryan SP 10.00 25.00
627 Kyle Blanks .15 .40
628 Blake DeWitt .15 .40

629 Ivan Nova .25 .60
630A Brandon Phillips .15 .40
630B Joe Morgan SP 6.00 15.00
631 Houston Astros TC .15 .40
632 Scott Kazmir .15 .40
633 Aaron Crow RC .40 1.00
634 Mitch Moreland .15 .40
635 Jason Heyward .50 1.25
636 Chris Tillman .15 .40
637 Ricky Nolasco .15 .40
638 Ryan Madson .15 .40
639 Pedro Beato RC .25 .60
640A Dan Uggla .25 .60
640B Eddie Mathews SP 6.00 15.00
641 Travis Wood .15 .40
642 Jason Hammel .15 .40
643 Jaime Garcia .25 .60
644 Joel Hanrahan .25 .60
645A Adam Wainwright .25 .60
645B Bob Gibson SP 6.00 15.00
646 Los Angeles Dodgers TC .25 .60
647 Jeanmar Gomez .15 .40
648 Cody Ross .15 .40
649 Joba Chamberlain .25 .60
650A Josh Hamilton .40 1.00
650B Frank Robinson SP 6.00 15.00
651A Kendrys Morales .15 .40
651B Eddie Murray SP 6.00 15.00
652 Edwin Jackson .15 .40
653 J.D. Drew .15 .40
654 Chris Getz .15 .40
655 Starlin Castro .40 1.00
656 Raul Ibanez .25 .60
657 Nick Blackburn .15 .40
658 Mitch Maier .15 .40
659 Clint Barmes .15 .40
660A Ryan Zimmerman .25 .60
660B Brooks Robinson SP 6.00 15.00

2011 Topps Black

SER.1 ODDS 1:100 HOBBY
STATED PRINT RUN 60 SER.#'d SETS
1 Ryan Braun 12.00 30.00
2 Jake Westbrook 6.00 15.00
3 Jon Lester 10.00 25.00
4 Jason Kubel 6.00 15.00
5 Joey Votto 10.00 25.00
6 Neftali Feliz 6.00 15.00
7 Mickey Mantle 50.00 120.00
8 Julio Borbon 6.00 15.00
9 Gil Meche 6.00 15.00
10 Stephen Strasburg 20.00 50.00
11 Roy Halladay 10.00 25.00
Adam Wainwright
Ubaldo Jimenez LL
12 Carlos Marmol 8.00 20.00
13 Billy Wagner 6.00 15.00
14 Randy Wolf 6.00 15.00
15 David Wright 12.00 30.00
16 Aramis Ramirez 6.00 15.00
17 Mark Ellis 6.00 15.00
18 Kevin Millwood 6.00 15.00
19 Derek Lowe 6.00 15.00
20 Hanley Ramirez 10.00 25.00
21 Michael Cuddyer 6.00 15.00
22 Barry Zito 6.00 15.00
23 Jaime Garcia 8.00 20.00
24 Neil Walker 6.00 15.00
25 Carl Crawford 8.00 20.00
26 Neftali Feliz 6.00 15.00
27 Ben Zobrist 6.00 15.00
28 Carlos Carrasco 6.00 15.00
29 Josh Hamilton 10.00 25.00
30 Gio Gonzalez 6.00 15.00
31 Erick Aybar 6.00 15.00
32 Chris Johnson 6.00 15.00
33 Max Scherzer 6.00 15.00
34 Rick Ankiel 6.00 15.00
35 Shin-Soo Choo 6.00 15.00
36 Ted Lilly 6.00 15.00
37 Vicente Padilla 6.00 15.00
38 Ryan Dempster 6.00 15.00
39 Ian Kennedy 10.00 25.00
40 Justin Upton 10.00 25.00
41 Freddy Garcia 6.00 15.00
42 Mariano Rivera 10.00 25.00
43 Brendan Ryan 6.00 15.00
44 Martin Prado 6.00 15.00
45 Hunter Pence 8.00 20.00
46 Hong-Chih Kuo 6.00 15.00
47 Kevin Correia 6.00 15.00
48 Andrew Cashner 6.00 15.00
49 Los Angeles Angels TC 6.00 15.00
50 Alex Rodriguez 15.00 40.00
51 David Eckstein 6.00 15.00
52 Tampa Bay Rays TC 6.00 15.00
53 Arizona Diamondbacks TC 6.00 15.00
54 Brian Fuentes 6.00 15.00
55 Matt Joyce 6.00 15.00
56 Johan Santana 10.00 25.00
57 Mark Trumbo 8.00 20.00
58 Edgar Renteria 6.00 15.00
59 Gaby Sanchez 6.00 15.00
60 Andrew McCutchen 12.00 30.00
61 David Price 10.00 25.00
62 Jonathan Papelbon 8.00 20.00
63 Edinson Volquez 6.00 15.00
64 Yorvit Torrealba 6.00 15.00
65 Chris Sale 6.00 15.00
66 R.A. Dickey 6.00 15.00
67 Vladimir Guerrero 10.00 25.00
68 Cleveland Indians TC 6.00 15.00
69 Brett Gardner 6.00 15.00
70 Kyle Drabek 6.00 15.00
71 Trevor Hoffman 8.00 20.00
72 Jair Jurrjens 6.00 15.00
73 James McDonald 6.00 15.00
74 Tyler Clippard 6.00 15.00
75 Jered Weaver 6.00 15.00
76 Tom Gorzelanny 6.00 15.00
77 Tim Hudson 8.00 20.00
78 Mike Stanton 8.00 20.00
79 Kurt Suzuki 6.00 15.00
80 Desmond Jennings 10.00 25.00
81 Omar Infante 6.00 15.00
82 Josh Johnson 10.00 25.00
Adam Wainwright
Roy Halladay LL
83 Greg Halman 6.00 15.00
84 Roger Bernadina 6.00 15.00
85 Jack Wilson 6.00 15.00
86 Carlos Silva 6.00 15.00
87 Daniel Descalso 6.00 15.00
88 Brian Bogusevic 6.00 15.00
89 Placido Polanco 6.00 15.00
90 Yadier Molina 8.00 20.00
91 Lucas May 6.00 15.00
92 Chris Narveson 6.00 15.00
93 Paul Konerko 10.00 25.00
94 Ryan Raburn 6.00 15.00
95 Pedro Alvarez 8.00 20.00
96 Zach Duke 6.00 15.00
97 Carlos Gomez 6.00 15.00
98 Bronson Arroyo 6.00 15.00
99 Ben Revere 8.00 20.00
100 Albert Pujols 25.00 60.00
101 Gregor Blanco 6.00 15.00
102 CC Sabathia 8.00 20.00
103 Cliff Lee 10.00 25.00
104 Ian Stewart 6.00 15.00
105 Jonathan Lucroy 6.00 15.00
106 Felix Pie 6.00 15.00
107 Aubrey Huff 6.00 15.00
108 Zack Greinke 8.00 20.00
109 Josh Hamilton 10.00 25.00
Miguel Cabrera
Joe Mauer LL
110 Aroldis Chapman 12.00 30.00
111 Kevin Gregg 6.00 15.00
112 Jorge Cantu 6.00 15.00
113 Arthur Rhodes 6.00 15.00
114 Russell Martin 6.00 15.00
115 Jason Varitek 10.00 25.00
116 Russell Branyan 6.00 15.00
117 Brett Sinkbeil 6.00 15.00
118 Howie Kendrick 6.00 15.00
119 Jason Bay 8.00 20.00
120 Mat Latos 6.00 15.00
121 Brandon Inge 6.00 15.00
122 Bobby Jenks 6.00 15.00
123 Mike Lowell 6.00 15.00
124 CC Sabathia 10.00 25.00
Jon Lester
David Price LL
125 Evan Meek 6.00 15.00
126 San Diego Padres TC 6.00 15.00
127 Chris Volstad 6.00 15.00
128 Manny Ramirez 10.00 25.00
129 Lucas Duda 10.00 25.00
130 Robinson Cano 10.00 25.00
131 Kevin Kouzmanoff 6.00 15.00
132 Brian Duensing 6.00 15.00
133 Miguel Tejada 8.00 20.00
134 Carlos Gonzalez 10.00 25.00
Joey Votto
Omar Infante LL
135 Mike Stanton 8.00 20.00
136 Jason Marquis 6.00 15.00
137 Xavier Nady 6.00 15.00
138 Albert Pujols 25.00 60.00
Carlos Gonzalez
Joey Votto LL
139 Eric Young Jr. 6.00 15.00
140 Brett Anderson 8.00 20.00
141 Ubaldo Jimenez 8.00 20.00
142 Johnny Cueto 6.00 15.00
143 Jeremy Jeffress 6.00 15.00
144 Lance Berkman 8.00 20.00
145 Freddie Freeman 15.00 40.00
146 Roy Halladay 10.00 25.00
147 Jon Niese 6.00 15.00
148 Ricky Romero 6.00 15.00
149 David Aardsma 6.00 15.00
150 Miguel Cabrera 10.00 25.00
151 Fausto Carmona 6.00 15.00
152 Baltimore Orioles TC 6.00 15.00
153 A.J. Pierzynski 6.00 15.00
154 Marlon Byrd 6.00 15.00
155 Alex Rodriguez 15.00 40.00
156 Josh Thole 6.00 15.00
157 New York Mets TC 8.00 20.00
158 Casey Blake 6.00 15.00
159 Chris Perez 6.00 15.00
160 Josh Tomlin 6.00 15.00
161 Chicago White Sox TC 6.00 15.00
162 Ronny Cedeno 6.00 15.00
163 Carlos Pena 8.00 20.00
164 Koji Uehara 6.00 15.00
165 Jeremy Hellickson 12.00 30.00
166 Josh Johnson 8.00 20.00
167 Clay Hensley 6.00 15.00
168 Felix Hernandez 10.00 25.00
169 Chipper Jones 10.00 25.00
170 David DeJesus 6.00 15.00
171 Garrett Jones 6.00 15.00
172 Lyle Overbay 6.00 15.00
173 Jose Lopez 6.00 15.00
174 Roy Oswalt 8.00 20.00
175 Brennan Boesch 8.00 20.00
176 Daniel Hudson 6.00 15.00
177 Brian Matusz 10.00 25.00
178 Heath Bell 10.00 25.00
179 Armando Galarraga 6.00 15.00
180 Paul Maholm 6.00 15.00
181 Magglio Ordonez 8.00 20.00
182 Jeremy Bonderman 6.00 15.00
183 Stephen Strasburg 20.00 50.00
184 Brandon Morrow 6.00 15.00
185 Peter Bourjos 8.00 20.00
186 Carl Pavano 6.00 15.00
187 Milwaukee Brewers TC 6.00 15.00
188 Pablo Sandoval 8.00 20.00
189 Kerry Wood 6.00 15.00
190 Coco Crisp 6.00 15.00
191 Jay Bruce 8.00 20.00
192 Cincinnati Reds TC 6.00 15.00
193 Cory Luebke 6.00 15.00
194 Andres Torres 6.00 15.00
195 Nick Markakis 10.00 25.00
196 Jose Ceda 5.00 12.00
197 Aaron Hill 6.00 15.00
198 Buster Posey 12.00 30.00
199 Jimmy Rollins 8.00 20.00
200 Ichiro Suzuki 15.00 40.00
201 Mike Napoli 10.00 25.00
202 Jose Bautista 6.00 15.00
Paul Konerko
Miguel Cabrera LL
203 Dillon Gee 10.00 25.00
204 Oakland Athletics TC 6.00 15.00
205 Ty Wigginton 6.00 15.00
206 Chase Headley 6.00 15.00
207 Angel Pagan 6.00 15.00
208 Clay Buchholz 8.00 20.00
209 Carlos Santana 10.00 25.00
210 Brian Wilson 10.00 25.00
211 Joey Votto 10.00 25.00
212 Pedro Feliz 6.00 15.00
213 Brandon Snyder 6.00 15.00
214 Chase Utley 10.00 25.00
215 Edwin Encarnacion 6.00 15.00
216 Jose Bautista 8.00 20.00
217 Yunel Escobar 6.00 15.00
218 Victor Martinez 8.00 20.00
219 Carlos Ruiz 6.00 15.00
220 Todd Helton 8.00 20.00
221 Scott Hairston 6.00 15.00
222 Matt Lindstrom 6.00 15.00
223 Gregory Infante 6.00 15.00
224 Milton Bradley 6.00 15.00
225 Josh Willingham 6.00 15.00
226 Jose Guillen 6.00 15.00
227 Nate McLouth 6.00 15.00
228 Scott Rolen 8.00 20.00
229 Jonathan Sanchez 6.00 15.00
230 Aaron Cook 6.00 15.00
231 Mark Buehrle 8.00 20.00
232 Jamie Moyer 6.00 15.00
233 Ramon Hernandez 6.00 15.00
234 Miguel Montero 6.00 15.00
235 Felix Hernandez 10.00 25.00
Clay Buchholz
David Price LL
236 Nelson Cruz 8.00 20.00
237 Jason Vargas 6.00 15.00
238 Pedro Ciriaco 6.00 15.00
239 Jhoulys Chacin 6.00 15.00
240 Andre Ethier 8.00 20.00
241 Wandy Rodriguez 6.00 15.00
242 Brad Lidge 6.00 15.00
243 Omar Vizquel 8.00 20.00
244 Mike Aviles 6.00 15.00
245 Neil Walker 6.00 15.00
246 John Lannan 6.00 15.00
247 Starlin Castro 10.00 25.00
248 Wade LeBlanc 6.00 15.00
249 Aaron Harang 6.00 15.00
250 Carlos Gonzalez 8.00 20.00
251 Alcides Escobar 6.00 15.00
252 Michael Saunders 6.00 15.00
253 Jim Thome 8.00 20.00
254 Lars Anderson 8.00 20.00
255 Torii Hunter 6.00 15.00
256 Tyler Colvin 8.00 20.00
257 Travis Hafner 6.00 15.00
258 Rafael Soriano 6.00 15.00
259 Kyle Davies 6.00 15.00
260 Freddy Sanchez 6.00 15.00
261 Alexei Ramirez 6.00 15.00
262 Alex Gordon 8.00 20.00
263 Joel Pineiro 6.00 15.00
264 Ryan Perry 6.00 15.00
265 John Danks 6.00 15.00
266 Rickie Weeks 8.00 20.00
267 Jose Contreras 6.00 15.00
268 Jake McGee 6.00 15.00
269 Stephen Drew 6.00 15.00
270 Ubaldo Jimenez 8.00 20.00
271 Adam Dunn 8.00 20.00
272 J.J. Hardy 6.00 15.00
273 Derrek Lee 6.00 15.00
274 Michael Brantley 6.00 15.00
275 Clayton Kershaw 10.00 25.00
276 Miguel Olivo 6.00 15.00
277 Trevor Hoffman 8.00 20.00
278 Marco Scutaro 6.00 15.00
279 Nick Swisher 10.00 25.00
280 Andrew Bailey 6.00 15.00
281 Kevin Slowey 6.00 15.00
282 Buster Posey 12.00 30.00
283 Colorado Rockies TC 6.00 15.00
284 Reid Brignac 6.00 15.00
285 Hank Conger 8.00 20.00
286 Melvin Mora 6.00 15.00
287 Scott Cousins 6.00 15.00
288 Matt Capps 6.00 15.00
289 Yuniesky Betancourt 6.00 15.00
290 Ike Davis 8.00 20.00
291 Juan Gutierrez 6.00 15.00
292 Darren Ford 6.00 15.00
293 Justin Morneau 10.00 25.00
294 Luke Scott 6.00 15.00
295 Jon Jay 6.00 15.00
296 John Buck 6.00 15.00
297 Jason Jaramillo 6.00 15.00
298 Jeff Keppinger 6.00 15.00
299 Chris Carpenter 10.00 25.00
300 Roy Halladay 10.00 25.00
301 Seth Smith 6.00 15.00
302 Adrian Beltre 6.00 15.00
303 Emilio Bonifacio 6.00 15.00
304 Jim Thome 8.00 20.00
305 James Loney 8.00 20.00
306 Miguel Cabrera 6.00 15.00
Alex Rodriguez
Jose Bautista LL
307 Alex Rios 8.00 20.00
308 Ian Desmond 8.00 20.00
309 Chicago Cubs TC 8.00 20.00
310 Alex Gonzalez 6.00 15.00
311 James Shields 6.00 15.00
312 Gaby Sanchez 6.00 15.00
313 Chris Coghlan 6.00 15.00
314 Ryan Kalish 8.00 20.00
315 David Ortiz 8.00 20.00
316 Chris Young 6.00 15.00
317 Yonder Alonso 6.00 15.00
318 Albert Pujols 25.00 60.00
Adam Dunn
Joey Votto LL
319 Atlanta Braves TC 6.00 15.00
320 Michael Young 10.00 25.00
321 Jeremy Guthrie 6.00 15.00
322 Brent Morel 6.00 15.00
323 C.J. Wilson 6.00 15.00
324 Boston Red Sox TC 8.00 20.00
325 Jayson Werth 8.00 20.00
326 Ozzie Martinez 6.00 15.00
327 Christian Guzman 6.00 15.00
328 David Price 10.00 25.00
329 Brett Wallace 6.00 15.00
330 Derek Jeter 25.00 60.00
331 Carlos Guillen 6.00 15.00
332 Melky Cabrera 6.00 15.00
333 Tom Wilhelmsen 20.00 50.00
334 St. Louis Cardinals 15.00 40.00
335 Buster Posey 12.00 30.00
336 Chris Heisey 6.00 15.00
337 Jordan Walden 15.00 40.00
338 Jason Hammel 6.00 15.00
339 Alexi Casilla 6.00 15.00
340 Evan Longoria 12.00 30.00
341 Kyle Kendrick 6.00 15.00
342 Jorge De La Rosa 6.00 15.00
343 Mason Tobin 6.00 15.00
344 Michael Kohn 6.00 15.00
345 Austin Jackson 6.00 15.00
346 Jose Bautista 8.00 20.00
347 Darwin Barney 12.00 30.00
348 Landon Powell 6.00 15.00
349 Drew Stubbs 10.00 25.00
350 Francisco Liriano 6.00 15.00
351 Jacoby Ellsbury 15.00 40.00
352 Colby Lewis 6.00 15.00
353 Cliff Pennington 6.00 15.00
354 Scott Baker 6.00 15.00
355 Justin Verlander 15.00 40.00
356 Alfonso Soriano 8.00 20.00
357 Mike Cameron 6.00 15.00
358 Paul Janish 6.00 15.00
359 Roy Halladay 10.00 25.00
360 Ivan Rodriguez 8.00 20.00
361 Florida Marlins 6.00 15.00
362 Doug Fister 6.00 15.00
363 Aaron Rowand 6.00 15.00
364 Tim Wakefield 6.00 15.00
365 Adam Lind 8.00 20.00
366 Joe Nathan 12.00 30.00
367 Hiroki Kuroda 15.00 40.00
368 Brian Broderick 6.00 15.00
369 Wilson Betemit 6.00 15.00
370 Matt Garza 6.00 15.00
371 Taylor Teagarden 6.00 15.00
372 Jarrod Saltalamacchia 6.00 15.00
373 Trever Miller 6.00 15.00
374 Washington Nationals 6.00 15.00
375 Matt Kemp 8.00 20.00
376 Clayton Richard 6.00 15.00
377 Esmil Rogers 6.00 15.00
378 Mark Reynolds 6.00 15.00
379 Ben Francisco 6.00 15.00
380 Jose Reyes 8.00 20.00
381 Michael Gonzalez 6.00 15.00
382 Travis Snider 6.00 15.00
383 Ryan Ludwick 6.00 15.00
384 Nick Hundley 6.00 15.00
385 Ichiro Suzuki 15.00 40.00
386 Barry Enright 6.00 15.00
387 Danny Valencia 8.00 20.00
388 Kenley Jansen 10.00 25.00
389 Carlos Quentin 5.00 12.00
390 Danny Valencia 12.00 30.00
391 Phil Coke 6.00 15.00
392 Kris Medlen 6.00 15.00
393 Jake Arrieta 12.00 30.00
394 Austin Jackson 6.00 15.00
395 Tyler Flowers 6.00 15.00
396 Adam Jones 8.00 20.00
397 Sean Rodriguez 6.00 15.00
398 Pittsburgh Pirates 30.00 80.00
399 Adam Moore 6.00 15.00
400 Troy Tulowitzki 20.00 50.00
401 Michael Crotta 6.00 15.00
402 Jack Cust 6.00 15.00
403 Felix Hernandez 10.00 25.00
404 Chris Capuano 6.00 15.00
405 Ian Kinsler 8.00 20.00
406 John Lackey 6.00 15.00
407 Jonathan Broxton 6.00 15.00
408 Denard Span 6.00 15.00
409 Vin Mazzaro 6.00 15.00
410 Prince Fielder 6.00 15.00
411 Josh Bell 6.00 15.00
412 Samuel Deduno 6.00 15.00
413 Derek Holland 6.00 15.00
414 Jose Molina 6.00 15.00
415 Brian McCann 8.00 20.00
416 Everth Cabrera 6.00 15.00
417 Miguel Cairo 6.00 15.00
418 Zach Britton 10.00 25.00
419 Kelly Johnson 6.00 15.00
420 Ryan Howard 12.00 30.00
421 Domonic Brown 10.00 25.00
422 Juan Pierre 6.00 15.00
423 Hideki Okajima 12.00 30.00
424 New York Yankees 12.00 30.00
425 Adrian Gonzalez 8.00 20.00
426 Travis Buck 6.00 15.00
427 Brad Emaus 6.00 15.00
428 Brett Myers 6.00 15.00
429 Skip Schumaker 6.00 15.00
430 Trevor Crowe 6.00 15.00
431 Marcos Mateo 12.00 30.00
432 Matt Harrison 6.00 15.00
433 Curtis Granderson 8.00 20.00
434 Mark DeRosa 6.00 15.00
435 Elvis Andrus 8.00 20.00
436 Trevor Cahill 6.00 15.00
437 Jordan Schafer 6.00 15.00
438 Ryan Theriot 6.00 15.00
439 Ervin Santana 6.00 15.00
440 Grady Sizemore 8.00 20.00
441 Rafael Furcal 6.00 15.00
442 Brad Bergesen 6.00 15.00
443 Brian Roberts 6.00 15.00
444 Brett Cecil 6.00 15.00
445 Mitch Talbot 6.00 15.00
446 Brandon Beachy 10.00 25.00
447 Toronto Blue Jays 6.00 15.00
448 Colby Rasmus 10.00 25.00
449 Austin Kearns 6.00 15.00
450 Mark Teixeira 10.00 25.00
451 Livan Hernandez 6.00 15.00
452 David Freese 10.00 25.00
453 Joe Saunders 12.00 30.00
454 Alberto Callaspo 6.00 15.00
455 Logan Morrison 6.00 15.00
456 Ryan Doumit 6.00 15.00
457 Brandon Allen 6.00 15.00
458 Javier Vazquez 6.00 15.00
459 Frank Francisco 6.00 15.00
460 Cole Hamels 10.00 25.00
461 Eric Sogard 6.00 15.00
462 Daric Barton 6.00 15.00
463 Will Venable 6.00 15.00
464 Daniel Bard 6.00 15.00
465 Yovani Gallardo 6.00 15.00
466 Johnny Damon 8.00 20.00
467 Wade Davis 6.00 15.00
468 Chone Figgins 6.00 15.00
469 Joe Blanton 6.00 15.00
470 Billy Butler 6.00 15.00
471 Tim Collins 5.00 12.00
472 Jason Kendall 6.00 15.00
473 Chad Billingsley 6.00 15.00
474 Jeff Mathis 6.00 15.00
475 Phil Hughes 6.00 15.00
476 Matt LaPorta 6.00 15.00
477 Franklin Gutierrez 6.00 15.00
478 Mike Minor 6.00 15.00
479 Justin Duchscherer 6.00 15.00
480 Dustin Pedroia 12.00 30.00
481 Randy Wells 6.00 15.00
482 Eric Hinske 6.00 15.00
483 Justin Smoak 25.00 60.00
484 Gerardo Parra 6.00 15.00
485 Delmon Young 8.00 20.00
486 Francisco Rodriguez 8.00 20.00
487 Chris Snyder 12.00 30.00
488 Brayan Villarreal 6.00 15.00
489 Marc Rzepczynski 6.00 15.00
490 Matt Holliday 10.00 25.00
491 Fernando Abad 5.00 12.00
492 A.J. Burnett 8.00 20.00
493 Ryan Sweeney 6.00 15.00
494 Drew Storen 6.00 15.00
495 Shane Victorino 8.00 20.00
496 Gavin Floyd 6.00 15.00
497 Alex Avila 12.00 30.00
498 Scott Feldman 6.00 15.00
499 J.A. Happ 8.00 20.00
500 Kevin Youkilis 8.00 20.00
501 Tsuyoshi Nishioka 12.00 30.00
502 Jeff Baker 6.00 15.00
503 Nathan Adcock 6.00 15.00
504 Jhonny Peralta 6.00 15.00
505 Tommy Hanson 8.00 20.00
506 Aneury Rodriguez 5.00 12.00
507 Huston Street 6.00 15.00
508 Homer Bailey 6.00 15.00
509 Michael Bourn 6.00 15.00
510 Jason Heyward 12.00 30.00
511 Philadelphia Phillies 12.00 30.00
512 Octavio Dotel 6.00 15.00
513 Adam LaRoche 6.00 15.00
514 Kelly Shoppach 6.00 15.00
515 Carlos Beltran 6.00 15.00
516 Mike Leake 8.00 20.00
517 Fred Lewis 6.00 15.00
518 Michael Morse 6.00 15.00
519 Corey Hart 6.00 15.00
520 Jorge Posada 15.00 40.00
521 Joaquin Benoit 6.00 15.00
522 Asdrubal Cabrera 10.00 25.00
523 Mike Nickeas 6.00 15.00
524 Michael Martinez 20.00 50.00
525 Vernon Wells 6.00 15.00
526 Jason Donald 6.00 15.00
527 Kila Ka'aihue 6.00 15.00
528 Bobby Abreu 6.00 15.00
529 Maicer Izturis 6.00 15.00
530 Felix Hernandez 10.00 25.00
531 Juan Rivera 6.00 15.00
532 Erik Bedard 6.00 15.00
533 Lorenzo Cain 6.00 15.00
534 Bud Norris 6.00 15.00
535 Rich Harden 6.00 15.00
536 Tony Sipp 15.00 40.00
537 Jake Peavy 6.00 15.00
538 Jason Motte 6.00 15.00
539 Brandon Lyon 6.00 15.00
540 Joakim Soria 6.00 15.00
541 John Jaso 6.00 15.00
542 Mike Pelfrey 6.00 15.00
543 Texas Rangers 6.00 15.00
544 Justin Masterson 6.00 15.00
545 Jose Tabata 8.00 20.00
546 Pat Burrell 6.00 15.00
547 Albert Pujols 30.00 80.00
548 Ryan Franklin 6.00 15.00
549 Jayson Nix 6.00 15.00
550 Joe Mauer 10.00 25.00
551 Marcus Thames 6.00 15.00
552 San Francisco Giants 6.00 15.00
553 Kyle Lohse 6.00 15.00
554 Cedric Hunter 6.00 15.00
555 Madison Bumgarner 6.00 15.00
556 B.J. Upton 8.00 20.00
557 Wes Helms 6.00 15.00
558 Carlos Zambrano 8.00 20.00
559 Reggie Willits 6.00 15.00
560 Chris Iannetta 6.00 15.00
561 Luke Gregerson 6.00 15.00
562 Gordon Beckham 8.00 20.00
563 Josh Rodriguez 6.00 15.00
564 Jeff Samardzija 12.00 30.00
565 Mark Teahen 6.00 15.00
566 Jordan Zimmermann 6.00 15.00
567 Dallas Braden 6.00 15.00
568 Kansas City Royals 6.00 15.00
569 Cameron Maybin 5.00 12.00
570 Matt Cain 8.00 20.00
571 Jeremy Affeldt 6.00 15.00
572 Brad Hawpe 6.00 15.00
573 Nyjer Morgan 6.00 15.00
574 Brandon Kintzler 6.00 15.00
575 Rod Barajas 6.00 15.00
576 Jed Lowrie 8.00 20.00
577 Mike Fontenot 6.00 15.00
578 Willy Aybar 6.00 15.00
579 Jeff Niemann 6.00 15.00
580 Chris Young 6.00 15.00
581 Fernando Rodney 6.00 15.00
582 Kosuke Fukudome 10.00 25.00
583 Ryan Spilborghs 6.00 15.00
584 Jason Bartlett 6.00 15.00
585 Dan Johnson 6.00 15.00
586 Carlos Lee 6.00 15.00
587 J.P. Arencibia 15.00 40.00
588 Rajai Davis 6.00 15.00
589 Seattle Mariners 25.00 60.00
590 Tim Lincecum 10.00 25.00
591 John Axford 6.00 15.00
592 Dayan Viciedo 6.00 15.00
593 Francisco Cordero 6.00 15.00
594 Jose Valverde 6.00 15.00
595 Michael Pineda 12.00 30.00
596 Anibal Sanchez 6.00 15.00
597 Rick Porcello 6.00 15.00
598 Jonny Gomes 6.00 15.00
599 Travis Ishikawa 6.00 15.00
600 Neftali Feliz 6.00 15.00
601 J.J. Putz 6.00 15.00
602 Ivan DeJesus 6.00 15.00
603 David Murphy 6.00 15.00
604 Joe Paterson 10.00 25.00
605 Brandon Belt 15.00 40.00
606 Juan Miranda 6.00 15.00
607 Daniel Murphy 6.00 15.00
608 Casey McGehee 6.00 15.00
609 Juan Francisco 6.00 15.00
610 Josh Beckett 8.00 20.00
611 Geovany Soto 8.00 20.00
612 Detroit Tigers 6.00 15.00
613 Dexter Fowler 6.00 15.00
614 Minnesota Twins 6.00 15.00
615 Shaun Marcum 6.00 15.00
616 Ross Ohlendorf 6.00 15.00
617 Joel Zumaya 6.00 15.00
618 Josh Lueke 6.00 15.00
619 Jonny Venters 6.00 15.00
620 Luke Hochevar 6.00 15.00
621 Omar Beltre 6.00 15.00
622 Matt Thornton 6.00 15.00
623 Leo Nunez 6.00 15.00
624 Luke French 6.00 15.00
625 Ruben Tejada 6.00 15.00
626 Dan Haren 6.00 15.00
627 Kyle Blanks 6.00 15.00
628 Blake DeWitt 6.00 15.00
629 Ivan Nova 10.00 25.00
630 Brandon Phillips 6.00 15.00
631 Houston Astros 6.00 15.00
632 Scott Kazmir 6.00 15.00
633 Aaron Crow 8.00 20.00
634 Mitch Moreland 6.00 15.00
635 Jason Heyward 25.00 60.00
636 Chris Tillman 6.00 15.00
637 Ricky Nolasco 6.00 15.00
638 Ryan Madson 6.00 15.00
639 Pedro Beato 4.00 10.00
640 Dan Uggla 8.00 20.00
641 Travis Wood 6.00 15.00
642 Jason Hammel 6.00 15.00
643 Jaime Garcia 30.00 80.00
644 Joel Hanrahan 10.00 25.00
645 Adam Wainwright 8.00 20.00
646 Los Angeles Dodgers 8.00 20.00
647 Jeanmar Gomez 6.00 15.00
648 Cody Ross 6.00 15.00
649 Joba Chamberlain 8.00 20.00
650 Josh Hamilton 10.00 25.00
651 Kendrys Morales 6.00 15.00
652 Edwin Jackson 6.00 15.00
653 J.D. Drew 6.00 15.00
654 Chris Getz 6.00 15.00
655 Starlin Castro 15.00 40.00
656 Raul Ibanez 8.00 20.00
657 Nick Blackburn 6.00 15.00
658 Mitch Maier 6.00 15.00
659 Clint Barmes 6.00 15.00
660 Ryan Zimmerman 8.00 20.00

2011 Topps Cognac Diamond Anniversary

*COGNAC VET: 1.5X TO 4X BASIC
*COGNAC RC: 1X TO 2.5X BASIC RC
*COGNAC SP: .2X TO .5X BASIC SP
STATED ODDS 1:2 UPDATE HOBBY
STATED SP ODDS 1:41 UPDATE HOBBY

2011 Topps Diamond Anniversary

*DIAMOND VET: 2X TO 5X BASIC
*DIAMOND RC: 1.2X TO 3X BASIC RC
*DIAMOND SP: .3X TO .8X BASIC SP
SER.1 STATED ODDS 1:4 HOBBY

2011 Topps Diamond Anniversary Authentic Diamonds

ISSUED VIA ONLINE REDEMPTION
STATED PRINT RUN 1 SER.#'d SET
NO PRICING DUE TO SCARCITY

2011 Topps Diamond Anniversary Factory Set Limited Edition

COMPLETE SET (660) 30.00 80.00
*FACT.SET LTD: .5X TO 1.2X BASIC

2011 Topps Factory Set Red Border

*RED VET: 4X TO 10X BASIC
*RED RC: 2.5X TO 6X BASIC RC
ONE PACK OF FIVE RED PER FACT.SET
STATED PRINT RUN 245 SER.#'d SETS

2011 Topps Gold

*GOLD VET: 2X TO 5X BASIC
*GOLD RC: 1.2X TO 3X BASIC RC
SER.1 ODDS 1:8 HOBBY
STATED PRINT RUN 2011 SER.#'d SETS

2011 Topps Gold Canary Diamond

STATED PRINT RUN 1 SER.#'d SET
NO PRICING DUE TO SCARCITY

2011 Topps Hope Diamond Anniversary

*HOPE VET: 8X TO 20X BASIC
*HOPE RC: 5X TO 12X BASIC RC
*HOPE SP: X TO X BASIC SP
STATED ODDS 1:35 UPDATE HOBBY
STATED SP ODDS 1:1340 UPDATE HOBBY
STATED PRINT RUN 60 SER.#'d SETS

2011 Topps Platinum

SER.1 ODDS 1:33,000 HOBBY
STATED PRINT RUN 1 SER.#'d SET
NO PRICING DUE TO SCARCITY

2011 Topps Sparkle

APPX.ODDDS ONE PER HOBBY CASE
1 Ryan Braun 12.50 30.00
3 Jon Lester 15.00 40.00
5 Joey Votto 12.50 30.00
15 David Wright 20.00 50.00
20 Hanley Ramirez 8.00 20.00
23 Jaime Garcia 12.50 30.00
25 Carl Crawford 20.00 50.00
35 Shin-Soo Choo 20.00 50.00
40 Justin Upton 10.00 25.00
42 Mariano Rivera 15.00 40.00
44 Martin Prado 10.00 25.00
50 Alex Rodriguez 20.00 50.00
60 Andrew McCutchen 12.50 30.00
61 David Price 8.00 20.00
67 Vladimir Guerrero 15.00 40.00
70 Kyle Drabek 12.50 30.00
75 Jered Weaver 10.00 25.00
78 Mike Stanton 12.50 30.00
80 Desmond Jennings 10.00 25.00
100 Albert Pujols 30.00 60.00
102 CC Sabathia 15.00 40.00
108 Zack Greinke 10.00 25.00
110 Aroldis Chapman 15.00 40.00
120 Mat Latos 10.00 25.00
128 Manny Ramirez 12.50 30.00
140 Brett Anderson 10.00 25.00
150 Miguel Cabrera 10.00 25.00
165 Jeremy Hellickson 10.00 25.00
166 Josh Johnson 10.00 25.00
169 Chipper Jones 12.50 30.00
174 Roy Oswalt 12.50 30.00
177 Brian Matusz 10.00 25.00
195 Nick Markakis 20.00 50.00
200 Ichiro Suzuki 12.50 30.00
208 Clay Buchholz 10.00 25.00
209 Carlos Santana 12.50 30.00
210 Brian Wilson 12.50 30.00
214 Chase Utley 12.50 30.00
216 Jose Bautista 12.50 30.00
218 Victor Martinez 10.00 25.00
236 Nelson Cruz 8.00 20.00
240 Andre Ethier 10.00 25.00
241 Wandy Rodriguez 12.50 30.00
247 Starlin Castro 20.00 50.00
250 Carlos Gonzalez 8.00 20.00
255 Torii Hunter 10.00 25.00
269 Stephen Drew 10.00 25.00
270 Ubaldo Jimenez 12.50 30.00
271 Adam Dunn 10.00 25.00
275 Clayton Kershaw 8.00 20.00
290 Ike Davis 12.50 30.00
293 Justin Morneau 12.50 30.00
294 Luke Scott 12.50 30.00
299 Chris Carpenter 8.00 20.00
300 Roy Halladay 20.00 50.00
307 Alex Rios 10.00 25.00
315 David Ortiz 10.00 25.00
320 Michael Young 12.50 30.00
322 Brent Morel 8.00 20.00
330 Derek Jeter 40.00 80.00
335 Buster Posey 12.50 30.00
340 Evan Longoria 10.00 25.00
345 Austin Jackson 12.50 30.00
350 Francisco Liriano 8.00 20.00
351 Jacoby Ellsbury 12.50 30.00
355 Justin Verlander 12.50 30.00
356 Alfonso Soriano 8.00 20.00
375 Matt Kemp 10.00 25.00
378 Mark Reynolds 10.00 25.00
380 Jose Reyes 10.00 25.00
389 Carlos Quentin 8.00 20.00
396 Adam Jones 15.00 40.00
400 Troy Tulowitzki 10.00 25.00
405 Ian Kinsler 10.00 25.00
407 Jonathan Broxton 8.00 20.00
410 Prince Fielder 15.00 40.00
415 Brian McCann 10.00 25.00

419 Kelly Johnson 8.00 20.00
420 Ryan Howard 10.00 25.00
425 Adrian Gonzalez 10.00 25.00
435 Elvis Andrus 8.00 20.00
436 Trevor Cahill 12.50 30.00
441 Rafael Furcal 10.00 25.00
450 Mark Teixeira 12.50 30.00
455 Logan Morrison 8.00 20.00
460 Cole Hamels 10.00 25.00
465 Yovani Gallardo 8.00 20.00
470 Billy Butler 8.00 20.00
473 Chad Billingsley 12.50 30.00
478 Mike Minor 8.00 20.00
480 Dustin Pedroia 10.00 25.00
485 Delmon Young 10.00 25.00
490 Matt Holliday 8.00 20.00
500 Kevin Youkilis 8.00 20.00
505 Tommy Hanson 10.00 25.00
510 Jason Heyward 10.00 25.00
519 Corey Hart 12.50 30.00
520 Jorge Posada 10.00 25.00
525 Vernon Wells 10.00 25.00
530 Felix Hernandez 10.00 25.00
545 Jose Tabata 12.50 30.00
550 Joe Mauer 12.50 30.00
555 Madison Bumgarner 12.50 30.00
560 Chris Iannetta 12.50 30.00
562 Gordon Beckham 12.50 30.00
567 Dallas Braden 10.00 25.00
570 Matt Cain 12.50 30.00
586 Carlos Lee 15.00 40.00
590 Tim Lincecum 20.00 50.00
610 Josh Beckett 10.00 25.00
613 Dexter Fowler 12.50 30.00
626 Dan Haren 10.00 25.00
627 Kyle Blanks 8.00 20.00
630 Brandon Phillips 10.00 25.00
640 Dan Uggla 8.00 20.00
645 Adam Wainwright 10.00 25.00
650 Josh Hamilton 12.50 30.00
651 Kendrys Morales 8.00 20.00
652 Edwin Jackson 8.00 20.00
660 Ryan Zimmerman 10.00 25.00

2011 Topps Sparkle Double

NO PRICING DUE TO SCARCITY
340 Evan Longoria
510 Jason Heyward
590 Tim Lincecum

2011 Topps Target

*VETS: .5X TO 1.2X BASIC TOPPS CARDS
*RC: .5X TO 1.2X BASIC TOPPS RC CARDS

2011 Topps Wal Mart Black Border

*VETS: .5X TO 1.2X BASIC TOPPS CARDS
*RC: .5X TO 1.2X BASIC TOPPS RC CARDS

2011 Topps 60

COMPLETE SET (150) 30.00 80.00
COMP.SER.1 SET (50) 10.00 25.00
COMP.SER.2 SET (50) 10.00 25.00
COMP.UPD.SET (50) 10.00 25.00
SER.1 ODDS 1:4 HOBBY
UPD.ODDS 1:4 HOBBY
1-50 ISSUED IN SERIES 1
51-100 ISSUED IN SERIES 2
101-150 ISSUED IN UPDATE
1 Ryan Howard 1.00 2.50
2 Andre Dawson .50 1.25
3 Babe Ruth 2.00 5.00
4 Gary Carter .30 .75
5 Lou Gehrig 1.50 4.00
6 Robinson Cano .75 2.00
7 Mickey Mantle 2.50 6.00
8 Felix Hernandez .75 2.00
9 Ian Kinsler .50 1.25
10 Alex Rodriguez 1.25 3.00
11 Troy Tulowitzki .75 2.00
12 Prince Fielder .50 1.25
13 Jonathan Papelbon .50 1.25
14 Barry Larkin .50 1.25
15 Jason Heyward 1.00 2.50
16 Carl Crawford .50 1.25
17 Dale Murphy .75 2.00
18 Keith Hernandez .30 .75
19 Andre Ethier .50 1.25
20 Manny Ramirez .75 2.00
21 Tommy Hanson .50 1.25
22 Clay Buchholz .50 1.25
23 Neftali Feliz .30 .75
24 Josh Johnson .50 1.25
25 Orlando Cepeda .30 .75
26 Derek Jeter 2.00 5.00
27 David Wright 1.00 2.50
28 Billy Butler .30 .75
29 Ryan Zimmerman .50 1.25
30 Nick Markakis .75 2.00
31 Justin Upton .50 1.25
32 Adam Dunn .50 1.25
33 Johan Santana .75 2.00
34 Mark Reynolds .30 .75
35 Frank Thomas .75 2.00
36 Adam Jones .50 1.25
37 Stephen Strasburg 1.50 4.00
38 Ryan Braun 1.00 2.50
39 Adam Wainwright .50 1.25
40 Michael Young .50 1.25
41 Shin-Soo Choo .50 1.25
42 Mat Latos .30 .75
43 Chipper Jones .75 2.00
44 Duke Snider .50 1.25
45 Hanley Ramirez .75 2.00
46 Ike Davis .50 1.25
47 Nolan Ryan 2.50 6.00
48 Buster Posey 1.00 2.50
49 Josh Hamilton .75 2.00
50 Miguel Cabrera .75 2.00
51 Walter Johnson .75 2.00
52 Felix Hernandez .75 2.00
53 Jose Bautista .50 1.25
54 Ryan Zimmerman .50 1.25
55 Mariano Rivera .75 2.00
56 Roberto Alomar .50 1.25
57 Sandy Koufax 2.50 6.00
58 Hank Aaron 1.50 4.00
59 Roy Campanella .75 2.00
60 Mel Ott .75 2.00
61 Tom Seaver .50 1.25
62 Mike Stanton .50 1.25
63 Evan Longoria 1.00 2.50
64 Jorge Posada .50 1.25
65 Don Mattingly 1.50 4.00
66 Paul Molitor .75 2.00
67 Andrew McCutchen .75 2.00
68 Joey Votto .75 2.00
69 David Price .75 2.00
70 Chris Carpenter .75 2.00
71 Willie Stargell .50 1.25
72 Eddie Mathews .50 1.25
73 Nelson Cruz .50 1.25
74 Chase Utley .75 2.00
75 CC Sabathia .50 1.25
76 Joe Mauer .75 2.00
77 Dave Winfield .30 .75
78 Francisco Liriano .30 .75
79 Rickey Henderson .75 2.00
80 Thurman Munson .75 2.00
81 Brian McCann .50 1.25
82 Shane Victorino .50 1.25
83 Hunter Pence .50 1.25
84 Starlin Castro .75 2.00
85 Johnny Bench .75 2.00
86 Dustin Pedroia 1.00 2.50
87 Clayton Kershaw .75 2.00
88 Mark Teixeira .75 2.00
89 Jered Weaver .30 .75
90 Greg Maddux 1.00 2.50
91 David Ortiz .50 1.25
92 Alfonso Soriano .50 1.25
93 Carlos Gonzalez .50 1.25
94 Torii Hunter .30 .75
95 Jon Lester .75 2.00
96 Tim Lincecum .75 2.00
97 Jackie Robinson .75 2.00
98 Marlon Byrd .30 .75
99 Jacoby Ellsbury .75 2.00
100 Albert Pujols 2.00 5.00
101 Joe DiMaggio 2.00 5.00
102 Hank Aaron 1.50 4.00
103 Alex Rodriguez 1.25 3.00
104 Alex Rodriguez 1.25 3.00
105 Rogers Hornsby .50 1.25
106 Jimmie Foxx .75 2.00
107 Johnny Mize .50 1.25
108 Babe Ruth 2.00 5.00
109 Luis Aparicio .30 .75
110 Carlton Fisk .50 1.25
111 Reggie Jackson .50 1.25
112 Reggie Jackson .50 1.25
113 Willie McCovey .50 1.25
114 Nolan Ryan 2.50 6.00
115 Nolan Ryan 2.50 6.00
116 Nolan Ryan 2.50 6.00
117 Fergie Jenkins .30 .75
118 Joe Morgan .30 .75
119 Tom Seaver .50 1.25
120 Ozzie Smith 1.25 3.00
121 Pee Wee Reese .50 1.25
122 Roberto Alomar .50 1.25
123 Andre Dawson .50 1.25
124 Rickey Henderson .75 2.00
125 Paul Molitor .75 2.00
126 Frank Robinson .50 1.25
127 Duke Snider .50 1.25
128 Frank Thomas .75 2.00
129 Ty Cobb 1.25 3.00
130 Lou Gehrig 1.50 4.00
131 Christy Mathewson .75 2.00
132 George Sisler .75 2.00
133 Tris Speaker .50 1.25
134 Honus Wagner .75 2.00
135 Cy Young .75 2.00
136 Bert Blyleven .30 .75
137 Steve Garvey .30 .75
138 Roger Maris .75 2.00
139 Dan Uggla .50 1.25
140 Eric Hosmer 2.50 6.00
141 Danny Duffy .50 1.25
142 Tyler Chatwood .30 .75
143 Lance Berkman .50 1.25
144 Zach Britton .75 2.00
145 Michael Pineda 1.00 2.50
146 Freddie Freeman 1.25 3.00
147 Kyle Drabek .50 1.25
148 Craig Kimbrel .75 2.00
149 Drew Storen .30 .75
150 Sandy Koufax 2.50 6.00

2011 Topps 60 Autograph Relics

COMMON CARD 20.00 50.00
SER.1 ODDS 1:3970 HOBBY
STATED PRINT RUN 50 SER.#'d SETS
AC Aroldis Chapman S2 30.00 60.00
AD Andre Dawson 50.00 100.00
AG Adrian Gonzalez S2 50.00 100.00
AK Al Kaline 60.00 120.00
BM Brian Matusz 75.00 150.00
BW Bernie Williams S2 50.00 100.00
CF Carlton Fisk S2 50.00 100.00
DP David Price S2 30.00 60.00
DS Duke Snider 50.00 100.00
FH Felix Hernandez 40.00 80.00
GC Gary Carter 20.00 50.00
HR Hanley Ramirez 30.00 60.00
IK Ian Kinsler 20.00 50.00
JH Jason Heyward S2 50.00 100.00
JV Joey Votto S2 40.00 80.00
RC Robinson Cano 50.00 100.00
RH Ryan Howard 60.00 120.00
RO Roy Oswalt S2 40.00 80.00
RS Ryne Sandberg S2 30.00 60.00
TS Tom Seaver S2 60.00 120.00

2011 Topps 60 Autographs

SER.1 ODDS 1:342 HOBBY
UPD.ODDS 1:620 HOBBY
EXCHANGE DEADLINE 1/31/2014
EXCH * IS PARTIAL EXCHANGE
AC Andrew Cashner S2 6.00 15.00
AC Andrew Cashner UPD 3.00 8.00
AD Andre Dawson 20.00 50.00
AE Andre Ethier 8.00 20.00
AG Alex Gordon 5.00 12.00
AG Adrian Gonzalez UPD 20.00 50.00
AJ Adam Jones 8.00 20.00
AK Al Kaline EXCH * 20.00 50.00
AM Andrew McCutchen 10.00 25.00
AP Albert Pujols 150.00 300.00
AP Albert Pujols UPD EXCH 150.00 300.00
AR Alex Rodriguez
AT Andres Torres S2 5.00 12.00
BA Brett Anderson UPD 4.00 10.00
BC Brett Cecil UPD 3.00 8.00
BD Blake DeWitt 8.00 20.00
BL Barry Larkin 30.00 60.00
BL Brandon League UPD 3.00 8.00
BM Brian McCann 10.00 25.00
BP Buster Posey S2 15.00 40.00
CB Clay Buchholz 4.00 10.00
CB Clay Buchholz UPD 6.00 15.00
CC Carl Crawford 6.00 15.00
CD Chris Dickerson 8.00 20.00
CF Chone Figgins 4.00 10.00
CG Chris Getz 3.00 8.00
CG Gio Gonzalez S2 5.00 12.00
CH Chris Heisey UPD 5.00 12.00
CL Cliff Lee 30.00 60.00
CL Cliff Lee S2 30.00 60.00
CP Carlos Pena S2 5.00 12.00
CR Colby Rasmus UPD 10.00 25.00
CT Chris Tillman 10.00 25.00
CU Chase Utley S2 20.00 50.00
CV Chris Volstad EXCH * 3.00 8.00
CY Chris B. Young UPD 4.00 10.00
DB Domonic Brown 12.50 30.00
DB Daniel Bard UPD 4.00 10.00
DG Dwight Gooden S2 8.00 20.00
DM Daniel McCutchen UPD 3.00 8.00
DS Duke Snider 12.50 30.00
DS Darryl Strawberry S2 8.00 20.00
DS Drew Stubbs UPD 5.00 12.00
DW David Wright S2 20.00 50.00
DW David Wright UPD 15.00 40.00
FD Felix Doubront 6.00 15.00
FF Freddie Freeman S2 15.00 40.00
FH Felix Hernandez S2 12.50 30.00
FH Felix Hernandez UPD 12.50 30.00
FR Fernando Rodney UPD 3.00 8.00
GB Gordon Beckham 5.00 12.00
GC Gary Carter 10.00 25.00
GC Gary Carter UPD 10.00 25.00
GP Glen Perkins 4.00 10.00
GS Gaby Sanchez S2 5.00 12.00
GS Gaby Sanchez UPD 3.00 8.00
HA Hank Aaron UPD 125.00 250.00
HP Hunter Pence 10.00 25.00
HR Hanley Ramirez 8.00 20.00
IK Ian Kinsler 8.00 20.00
IK Ian Kennedy S2 8.00 20.00
JB Jose Bautista S2 12.50 30.00
JB Jose Bautista UPD 10.00 25.00
JC Joba Chamberlain 8.00 20.00
JF Jeff Francis 3.00 8.00
JH Jason Heyward 20.00 50.00
JH Josh Hamilton UPD 15.00 40.00
JJ Josh Johnson 5.00 12.00
JJ Josh Johnson UPD 4.00 10.00
JN Jon Niese UPD 4.00 10.00
JP Jonathan Papelbon 8.00 20.00
JP Jhonny Peralta S2 5.00 12.00
JT Josh Tomlin 5.00 12.00
JT Josh Tomlin S2 5.00 12.00
JT Josh Thole UPD EXCH 4.00 10.00
JZ Jordan Zimmermann UPD EXCH 4.00 10.00
KD Kyle Drabek S2 5.00 12.00
KH Keith Hernandez 8.00 20.00
KJ Kevin Jepsen 3.00 8.00
KU Koji Uehara 8.00 20.00
LC Lorenzo Cain S2 5.00 12.00
LM Logan Morrison S2 6.00 15.00
MB Marlon Byrd 5.00 12.00
MB Madison Bumgarner S2 10.00 25.00
MC Miguel Cabrera S2 50.00 100.00
MF Mark Fidrych 10.00 25.00
MH Matt Harrison 3.00 8.00
ML Mike Leake S2 5.00 12.00
MN Mike Napoli 10.00 25.00
MR Manny Ramirez 20.00 50.00
MR Mark Reynolds S2 6.00 15.00
NW Neil Walker 8.00 20.00
OC Orlando Cepeda 20.00 50.00
PB Peter Bourjos EXCH 15.00 40.00
PF Prince Fielder 12.50 30.00
PS Pablo Sandoval UPD 5.00 12.00
RC Robinson Cano 20.00 50.00
RC Robinson Cano S2 20.00 50.00
RH Ryan Howard
RK Ryan Kalish 12.50 30.00
RK Ralph Kiner S2 15.00 40.00
RP Rick Porcello S2 5.00 12.00
RW Randy Wells 4.00 10.00
RZ Ryan Zimmerman S2 8.00 20.00
SC Starlin Castro S2 12.50 30.00
SK Sandy Koufax UPD 200.00 400.00
SV Shane Victorino S2 8.00 20.00
TB Taylor Buchholz S2 5.00 12.00
TC Tyler Colvin 8.00 20.00
TC Trevor Cahill S2 5.00 12.00
TH Tommy Hanson 8.00 20.00
TH Tim Hudson UPD 10.00 25.00
TT Troy Tulowitzki 12.50 30.00
TW Travis Wood 5.00 12.00
TW Travis Wood S2
TW Travis Wood UPD 3.00 8.00
VM Vin Mazzaro 3.00 8.00
WD Wade Davis 4.00 10.00
WL Wade LeBlanc S2
WV Will Venable 6.00 15.00
ACA Asdrubal Cabrera S2 8.00 20.00
APA Angel Pagan S2 5.00 12.00
APA Angel Pagan UPD 3.00 8.00
BDU Brian Duensing 4.00 10.00
BJU B.J. Upton 5.00 12.00
BMA Brian Matusz 8.00 20.00
CCO Chris Coghlan 3.00 8.00
DBA Daric Barton 3.00 8.00
DSN Drew Storen EXCH 5.00 12.00
DST Drew Stubbs 6.00 15.00
FCA Fausto Carmona EXCH 5.00 12.00
JBR Jay Bruce UPD 10.00 25.00
JJA Jon Jay UPD 8.00 20.00
JNI Jeff Niemann UPD 3.00 8.00
LMA Lou Marson 4.00 10.00
MSC Max Scherzer 5.00 12.00
SSC Shin-Soo Choo S2 8.00 20.00

2011 Topps 60 Autographs Diamond Anniversary

STATED PRINT RUN 10 SER.#'d SETS
NO PRICING DUE TO SCARCITY

2011 Topps 60 Dual Relics

STATED PRINT RUN 50 SER.#'d SETS
1 Josh Hamilton 12.50 30.00
Carlos Gonzalez
2 Joey Votto 15.00 40.00
Miguel Cabrera
3 Robinson Cano 20.00 50.00
Dustin Pedroia
4 Jon Lester 15.00 40.00
Clayton Kershaw
5 Buster Posey 30.00 60.00
Jason Heyward
6 Roberto Alomar 15.00 40.00
Bert Blyleven
7 Hank Aaron 30.00 60.00
Chipper Jones
8 Lou Gehrig 100.00 175.00
Cal Ripken Jr.
9 Bob Gibson 20.00 50.00
Adam Wainwright
10 Joe Morgan 20.00 50.00
Chase Utley
11 Ichiro Suzuki 12.50 30.00
Torii Hunter
12 Mark Teixeira 50.00 100.00
Jorge Posada
13 Mariano Rivera 12.50 30.00
Carlos Marmol
14 Josh Beckett 6.00 15.00
John Lackey
15 Josh Johnson 10.00 25.00
Clay Buchholz

2011 Topps 60 Jumbo Relics

SER.1 ODDS 1:4953 HOBBY
STATED PRINT RUN 20 SER.#'d SETS
NO PRICING DUE TO SCARCITY

2011 Topps 60 Relics

SER.1 ODDS 1:47 HOBBY
AD Andre Dawson 5.00 12.00
AG Adrian Gonzalez 3.00 8.00
AJ Adam Jones S2 5.00 12.00
AR Aramis Ramirez 3.00 8.00
AR Aramis Ramirez S2 3.00 8.00
AS Alfonso Soriano S2 3.00 8.00
BL Barry Larkin 4.00 10.00
BR Babe Ruth 250.00 400.00
CB Carlos Beltran 3.00 8.00
CK Clayton Kershaw S2 4.00 10.00
CM Carlos Marmol 3.00 8.00
CM Carlos Marmol S2 3.00 8.00
CS Curt Schilling 4.00 10.00
CU Chase Utley S2 5.00 12.00
CZ Carlos Zambrano 3.00 8.00
DB Daniel Bard S2 3.00 8.00
DJ Derek Jeter 8.00 25.00
DJ Derek Jeter S2 10.00 25.00
DM Don Mattingly 6.00 15.00
DO David Ortiz S2 5.00 12.00
DP Dustin Pedroia 5.00 12.00
DW Dave Winfield 4.00 10.00
EL Evan Longoria 8.00 20.00
FC Fausto Carmona 3.00 8.00
FH Felix Hernandez 3.00 8.00
GC Gary Carter 4.00 10.00
GG Goose Gossage 4.00 10.00
GS Geovany Soto 3.00 8.00
GS Geovany Soto S2 3.00 8.00
HA Hank Aaron S2 15.00 40.00
HJ Howard Johnson 4.00 10.00
IK Ian Kinsler S2 3.00 8.00
IS Ichiro Suzuki 8.00 20.00
JA Jonathan Albaladejo 3.00 8.00
JB Josh Beckett S2 3.00 8.00
JC Joba Chamberlain 3.00 8.00
JE Jacoby Ellsbury 4.00 10.00
JH Josh Hamilton 6.00 15.00
JH Jason Heyward S2 5.00 12.00
JL Jon Lester S2 4.00 10.00
JM Joe Morgan 5.00 12.00
JR Jimmy Rollins 4.00 10.00
JR Jackie Robinson S2 40.00 80.00
JU Justin Upton 3.00 8.00
JW Jered Weaver 3.00 8.00
KF Kosuke Fukudome 3.00 8.00
LB Lew Burdette 4.00 10.00
MB Marlon Byrd S2 3.00 8.00
MG Matt Garza 3.00 8.00
MH Matt Holliday 5.00 12.00
MK Matt Kemp 3.00 8.00
ML Mat Latos S2 3.00 8.00
MP Mike Piazza 4.00 10.00
MR Manny Ramirez 3.00 8.00
MR Mark Reynolds S2 3.00 8.00
MS Marco Scutaro S2 3.00 8.00
MT Mark Teixeira 4.00 10.00
MT Mark Teixeira S2 4.00 10.00
MY Michael Young S2 4.00 10.00
NR Nolan Ryan 10.00 25.00
NS Nick Swisher S2 4.00 10.00
OS Ozzie Smith 10.00 25.00
PF Prince Fielder 3.00 8.00
PF Prince Fielder S2 4.00 10.00
PH Phil Hughes S2 3.00 8.00
PS Pablo Sandoval S2 4.00 10.00
RA Roberto Alomar 5.00 12.00
RC Roy Campanella S2 10.00 25.00
RD Ryan Dempster S2 3.00 8.00
RH Ryan Howard 5.00 12.00
RH Rickey Henderson S2 5.00 12.00
RI Raul Ibanez 4.00 10.00
RR Robin Roberts 10.00 25.00
RZ Ryan Zimmerman S2 3.00 8.00
SB Sal Bando 5.00 12.00
SC Starlin Castro S2 4.00 10.00
SG Steve Garvey 4.00 10.00
SV Shane Victorino S2 4.00 10.00
TC Tyler Colvin 4.00 10.00
TC Tyler Colvin S2 3.00 8.00
TG Tony Gwynn 4.00 10.00
TH Torii Hunter 3.00 8.00
TT Troy Tulowitzki 5.00 12.00
VG Vladimir Guerrero S2 3.00 8.00
VM Victor Martinez 3.00 8.00
WB Wade Boggs 4.00 10.00
YB Yogi Berra 8.00 20.00
ABE Adrian Beltre 3.00 8.00
AGO Alex Gordon 4.00 10.00
AJB A.J. Burnett 4.00 10.00
APE Andy Pettitte 4.00 10.00
ARO Alex Rodriguez 6.00 15.00
BGA Brett Gardner 6.00 15.00
BGA Brett Gardner S2 4.00 10.00
CCS CC Sabathia 4.00 10.00
DLE Derrek Lee 3.00 8.00
DMC Daniel McCutchen 3.00 8.00
DWR David Wright 4.00 10.00
JCH Joba Chamberlain S2 3.00 8.00
JDA Johnny Damon 4.00 10.00
JDD J.D. Drew 3.00 8.00
JDD J.D. Drew S2 3.00 8.00
JLA John Lackey S2 3.00 8.00
JLO Jed Lowrie S2 3.00 8.00
JPA Jonathan Papelbon 3.00 8.00
JPO Jorge Posada 4.00 10.00
MBY Marlon Byrd 3.00 8.00
MRI Mariano Rivera 5.00 12.00
PHU Phil Hughes 3.00 8.00
PWR Pee Wee Reese 8.00 20.00
RCA Robinson Cano 5.00 12.00
RCA Robinson Cano S2 5.00 12.00
RHE Rickey Henderson 5.00 12.00
RWE Randy Wells S2 3.00 8.00
SCA Starlin Castro 4.00 10.00
SSC Shin-Soo Choo 3.00 8.00

2011 Topps 60 Relics Diamond Anniversary

*DA: .75X TO 2X BASIC
STATED PRINT RUN 99 SER.#'d SETS
DJ Derek Jeter S2 20.00 50.00
HA Hank Aaron S2 20.00 50.00
RH Rickey Henderson S2 15.00 40.00

2011 Topps 60 Years of Topps

COMPLETE SET (118) 30.00 60.00
COMP.SER.1 SET (59) 12.50 30.00
COMP.SER.2 SET (59) 12.50 30.00
SER.1 ODDS 1:3 HOBBY
1-59 ISSUED IN SER.1
59-118 ISSUED IN SER.2
*ORIGINAL BACK: .6X TO 1.5X BASIC
ORIGINAL ODDS 1:36 HOBBY
1 Jackie Robinson .75 2.00
2 Roy Campanella .75 2.00
3 Monte Irvin .30 .75
4 Ernie Banks .75 2.00
5 Phil Rizzuto .50 1.25
6 Mickey Mantle 2.50 6.00
7 Pee Wee Reese .50 1.25
8 Roger Maris .75 2.00
9 Stan Musial 1.25 3.00
10 Juan Marichal .30 .75
11 Gaylord Perry .30 .75
12 Frank Robinson .50 1.25
13 Bob Gibson .50 1.25
14 Lou Brock .50 1.25
15 Al Kaline .75 2.00
16 Tony Perez .30 .75
17 Frank Robinson .50 1.25
Brooks Robinson
18 Tom Seaver .50 1.25
19 Reggie Jackson .50 1.25
20 Nolan Ryan 2.50 6.00
21 Rod Carew .50 1.25
22 Carlton Fisk .50 1.25
23 Mike Schmidt 1.25 3.00
24 Carl Yastrzemski .75 2.00
25 Robin Yount .75 2.00
26 Bruce Sutter .30 .75
27 Phil Niekro 2.50 6.00
Nolan Ryan
28 Eddie Murray .75 2.00
29 Paul Molitor .75 2.00
30 Andre Dawson .50 1.25
31 Jim Palmer .30 .75
32 Ozzie Smith 1.25 3.00
33 Tony Gwynn .75 2.00
34 Steve Garvey .30 .75
35 Dave Winfield .30 .75
36 Dennis Eckersley .30 .75
37 Greg Maddux 1.00 2.50
38 Bo Jackson .75 2.00
39 Bernie Williams .50 1.25
40 Roberto Alomar .50 1.25
41 Frank Thomas .75 2.00
42 Jim Edmonds .50 1.25
43 Mike Piazza .75 2.00
44 Barry Larkin .50 1.25
45 Mickey Mantle 2.50 6.00
46 Mariano Rivera .75 2.00
47 Bob Abreu .30 .75
48 Mike Piazza .75 2.00
Ivan Rodriguez
Jason Kendall
49 Alex Rodriguez 1.25 3.00
50 Manny Ramirez .75 2.00
51 Vladimir Guerrero .75 2.00
52 Cliff Lee .75 2.00
53 Mark Teixeira .75 2.00
54 Justin Verlander 1.00 2.50
55 Ryan Howard 1.00 2.50
56 Troy Tulowitzki .75 2.00
57 Johnny Cueto .30 .75
58 Joe Mauer .75 2.00
59 Albert Pujols 2.00 5.00
60 Yogi Berra .75 2.00
61 Warren Spahn .50 1.25
62 Jackie Robinson .75 2.00
63 Ed Mathews .50 1.25
64 Mickey Mantle 2.50 6.00
65 Brooks Robinson .50 1.25
66 Luis Aparicio .30 .75
67 Richie Ashburn .50 1.25
68 Harmon Killebrew .75 2.00
69 Stan Musial 1.25 3.00
70 Orlando Cepeda .30 .75
71 Duke Snider .50 1.25
72 Carl Yastrzemski .75 2.00
73 Frank Robinson .50 1.25
74 Roger Maris .75 2.00
75 Steve Carlton .30 .75
76 Ernie Banks .75 2.00
77 Johnny Bench .75 2.00
78 Tom Seaver .50 1.25
79 Gaylord Perry .30 .75
80 Nolan Ryan 2.50 6.00
81 Rich Gossage .30 .75
82 Dave Parker .30 .75
83 Reggie Jackson .50 1.25
84 Dave Winfield .30 .75
85 Don Sutton .30 .75
86 Gary Carter .30 .75
87 Eddie Murray .75 2.00
88 Ron Guidry .30 .75
89 Jim Palmer .30 .75
90 Steve Garvey .30 .75
91 Cal Ripken Jr. 3.00 8.00
92 Rickey Henderson .75 2.00
93 Andre Dawson .50 1.25
94 Don Mattingly 1.50 4.00
95 Ozzie Smith 1.25 3.00
96 Dale Murphy .75 2.00
97 Paul Molitor .75 2.00
98 Curt Schilling .50 1.25
99 Larry Walker .50 1.25
100 Wade Boggs .50 1.25
101 Craig Biggio .50 1.25
102 Manny Ramirez .75 2.00
103 Frank Thomas .75 2.00
104 Derek Jeter 2.00 5.00
105 Tony Gwynn .75 2.00
106 Mariano Rivera .75 2.00
107 Roy Halladay .75 2.00
108 Chris Carpenter .75 2.00
109 David Ortiz .50 1.25
110 Josh Beckett .50 1.25
111 Albert Pujols 2.00 5.00
112 Alex Rodriguez/Derek Jeter 2.00 5.00
113 Billy Butler .30 .75
114 Hanley Ramirez .75 2.00
115 Josh Hamilton .75 2.00
116 Ryan Braun 1.00 2.50
117 Evan Longoria/David Price 1.00 2.50
118 Buster Posey 1.00 2.50

2011 Topps 60 Years of Topps Original Back

*ORIGINAL BACK: .6X TO 1.5X BASIC
SER.1 ODDS 1:36 HOBBY
1-59 ISSUED IN SER.1
60-118 ISSUED IN SER.2

2011 Topps 60th Anniversary Reprint Autographs

SER.1 ODDS 1:14,750 HOBBY
EXCHANGE DEADLINE 1/31/2014
AK Al Kaline S2 60.00 120.00
BG Bob Gibson EXCH 40.00 80.00
BR Brooks Robinson 40.00 80.00
DM Don Mattingly
EB Ernie Banks EXCH 40.00 80.00
EM Eddie Murray S2 60.00 120.00
FR Frank Robinson EXCH 40.00 80.00
HA Henry Aaron S2 250.00 350.00
JB Johnny Bench EXCH
MS Mike Schmidt S2 60.00 120.00
NR Nolan Ryan S2
PM Paul Molitor S2 50.00 100.00
RJ Reggie Jackson 100.00 200.00
RS Ryne Sandberg 75.00 150.00
SK Sandy Koufax S2 300.00 600.00
SM Stan Musial S2 250.00 350.00
TG Tony Gwynn S2 50.00 100.00
TS Tom Seaver EXCH 60.00 120.00
WB Wade Boggs S2 50.00 100.00
YB Yogi Berra EXCH

2011 Topps 60th Anniversary Reprint Relic Autographs

SER.1 ODDS 1:33,350 HOBBY
NO PRICING DUE TO SCARCITY
EXCHANGE DEADLINE 1/31/2014

2011 Topps 60th Anniversary Reprint Relics

SER.1 ODDS 1:7817 HOBBY
STATED PRINT RUN 60 SER.#'d SETS
AD Andre Dawson S2 60.00 120.00
AK Al Kaline S2 20.00 50.00
AR Alex Rodriguez 30.00 60.00
BB Bert Blyleven S2 20.00 50.00
BG Bob Gibson 50.00 100.00
BR Brooks Robinson 40.00 80.00
CF Carlton Fisk S2 20.00 50.00
CY Carl Yastrzemski 30.00 60.00
DJ Derek Jeter 125.00 250.00
DM Don Mattingly
DM Dale Murphy S2 20.00 50.00
DW Dave Winfield S2 30.00 60.00
EB Ernie Banks 50.00 100.00
EM Eddie Murray S2 20.00 50.00
FR Frank Robinson 20.00 50.00
FT Frank Thomas S2 30.00 60.00
HA Henry Aaron S2 20.00 50.00
HK Harmon Killebrew S2 20.00 50.00
JB Johnny Bench 30.00 60.00
JM Joe Mauer 30.00 60.00
JM Joe Morgan S2 50.00 100.00
JR Jackie Robinson 20.00 50.00
LB Lou Brock S2 20.00 50.00
MS Mike Schmidt S2 40.00 80.00
NR Nolan Ryan 50.00 100.00
NR Nolan Ryan S2 50.00 100.00
PM Paul Molitor S2 30.00 60.00
RA Roberto Alomar S2 30.00 60.00
RC Roy Campanella 30.00 60.00
RH Rickey Henderson 30.00 60.00
RJ Reggie Jackson 20.00 50.00
RS Ryne Sandberg 30.00 60.00
SK Sandy Koufax S2 50.00 100.00
SM Stan Musial S2 30.00 60.00
TG Tony Gwynn S2 40.00 80.00
TM Thurman Munson 30.00 60.00
TS Tom Seaver 40.00 80.00
WB Wade Boggs S2 20.00 50.00
WM Willie McCovey 30.00 60.00
YB Yogi Berra 20.00 50.00

2011 Topps Before There Was Topps

COMPLETE SET (7) 4.00 10.00
COMMON CARD .75 2.00
BTT1 American Tobacco 1909 T206 .75 2.00
BTT2 American Tobacco 1911 T205 .75 2.00
BTT3 American Tobacco 1911 T201 .75 2.00
BTT4 Exhibit Supply Company 1921 .75 2.00
BTT5 Goudey 1933 .75 2.00
BTT6 Gum Inc 1939 Play Ball .75 2.00
BTT7 Bowman 1948-1955 .75 2.00

2011 Topps Black Diamond Wrapper Redemption

COMPLETE SET (60) 60.00 120.00
1 Cliff Lee 2.00 5.00
2 Roy Halladay 2.00 5.00
3 Zack Greinke 1.25 3.00
4 David Wright 2.50 6.00
5 Justin Upton 1.25 3.00
6 Joey Votto 2.00 5.00
7 CC Sabathia 1.25 3.00
8 Ichiro Suzuki 3.00 8.00
9 Jered Weaver .75 2.00
10 Adrian Gonzalez 1.25 3.00
11 Albert Pujols 5.00 12.00
12 Joe Mauer 2.00 5.00
13 Adam Dunn 1.25 3.00
14 Ryan Zimmerman 1.25 3.00
15 Adam Jones 1.25 3.00
16 Tim Lincecum 2.00 5.00
17 Carlos Gonzalez 1.25 3.00
18 Mark Teixeira 2.00 5.00
19 Mat Latos 1.25 3.00
20 Ubaldo Jimenez 1.25 3.00
21 Prince Fielder 1.25 3.00
22 Victor Martinez 1.25 3.00
23 Ian Kinsler 1.25 3.00
24 Dan Uggla 1.25 3.00
25 Justin Morneau 2.00 5.00
26 Brian McCann 1.25 3.00
27 Josh Johnson 1.25 3.00
28 Roy Oswalt 1.25 3.00
29 Chase Utley 2.00 5.00
30 Jose Reyes 1.25 3.00
31 Felix Hernandez 2.00 5.00
32 Alex Rodriguez 3.00 8.00
33 Troy Tulowitzki 2.00 5.00
34 Dustin Pedroia 2.50 6.00
35 Adam Wainwright 1.25 3.00

36 David Price 2.00 5.00
37 Jon Lester 2.00 5.00
38 Josh Hamilton 2.00 5.00
39 Aroldis Chapman 2.50 6.00
40 Jason Heyward 2.50 6.00
41 Ryan Braun 2.50 6.00
42 Matt Holliday 2.00 5.00
43 Buster Posey 2.50 6.00
44 Nick Markakis 2.00 5.00
45 Kevin Youkilis 1.25 3.00
46 Clayton Kershaw 2.00 5.00
47 Evan Longoria 2.50 6.00
48 Andre Ethier 1.25 3.00
49 Hanley Ramirez 2.00 5.00
50 Robinson Cano 2.00 5.00
51 Andrew McCutchen 2.00 5.00
52 Martin Prado .75 2.00
53 Carl Crawford 1.25 3.00
54 Derek Jeter 5.00 12.00
55 Torii Hunter .75 2.00
56 Mark Reynolds .75 2.00
57 Miguel Cabrera 2.00 5.00
58 Mike Stanton 1.25 3.00
59 Starlin Castro 2.00 5.00
60 Ryan Howard 2.50 6.00

2011 Topps Black Diamond Wrapper Redemption Autographs

STATED PRINT RUN 60 SER.#'d SETS
RA1 Monte Irvin 50.00 100.00
RA2 Irv Noren 12.50 30.00
RA3 Roy Sievers 30.00 60.00
RA4 Vernon Law 100.00 175.00
RA5 Bill Pierce 75.00 150.00
RA6 Eddie Yost 20.00 50.00
RA7 John Antonelli 30.00 60.00
RA8 Charlie Silvera 50.00 100.00
RA9 Roy Smalley 50.00 100.00
RA10 Curt Simmons 125.00 250.00
RA11 Ned Garver 40.00 80.00
RA12 Bobby Shantz 60.00 120.00
RA13 Joe Presko 75.00 150.00
RA14 Bob Friend 20.00 50.00
RA15 Jerry Coleman 100.00 200.00
RA16 Virgil Trucks 75.00 150.00
RA17 Chuck Diering 20.00 50.00
RA18 Lou Brissie 40.00 80.00
RA19 Joe DeMaestri 40.00 80.00
RA20 Randy Jackson 30.00 60.00
RA21 Ivan Delock 30.00 60.00
RA22 Bob DelGreco 75.00 150.00
RA23 Dick Groat 30.00 60.00
RA24 Johnny Groth 20.00 50.00
RA25 Eddie Robinson 30.00 60.00
RA26 Cloyd Boyer 60.00 120.00
RA27 Harry Perkowski
RA28 Al Dark
RA29 Joe Astroth 75.00 150.00
RA30 Del Crandall 20.00 50.00
RA31 Ralph Branca 40.00 80.00
RA32 Red Schoendienst 75.00 150.00
RA33 Yogi Berra
RA34 Joe Garagiola 60.00 120.00

2011 Topps CMG Reprints

COMPLETE SET (30) 12.50 30.00
STATED ODDS 1:8 HOBBY
CMGR1 Babe Ruth 2.00 5.00
CMGR2 Babe Ruth 2.00 5.00
CMGR3 Hank Greenberg .75 2.00
CMGR4 Babe Ruth 2.00 5.00
CMGR5 Babe Ruth 2.00 5.00
CMGR6 Christy Mathewson .75 2.00
CMGR7 Jackie Robinson .75 2.00
CMGR8 Cy Young .75 2.00
CMGR9 George Sisler .75 2.00
CMGR10 Honus Wagner .75 2.00
CMGR11 Honus Wagner .75 2.00
CMGR12 Honus Wagner .75 2.00
CMGR13 Honus Wagner .75 2.00
CMGR14 Jackie Robinson .75 2.00
CMGR15 Jimmie Foxx .75 2.00
CMGR16 Jimmie Foxx .75 2.00
CMGR17 Jimmie Foxx .75 2.00
CMGR18 Johnny Mize/Enos Slaughter .50 1.25
CMGR19 Walter Johnson .75 2.00
CMGR20 Lou Gehrig 1.50 4.00
CMGR21 Lou Gehrig 1.50 4.00
CMGR22 Mel Ott .75 2.00
CMGR23 Rogers Hornsby .50 1.25
CMGR24 Lou Gehrig 1.50 4.00
CMGR25 Ty Cobb 1.25 3.00
CMGR26 Ty Cobb 1.25 3.00
CMGR27 Ty Cobb 1.25 3.00
CMGR28 Ty Cobb 1.25 3.00
CMGR29 Ty Cobb 1.25 3.00
CMGR30 Walter Johnson .75 2.00

2011 Topps Commemorative Patch

RANDOM INSERTS IN PACKS
AC Aroldis Chapman S2 5.00 12.00
AE Andre Ethier 4.00 10.00
AG Adrian Gonzalez 6.00 15.00
AG Adrian Gonzalez S2 6.00 15.00
AJ Adam Jones 5.00 12.00
AK Al Kaline UPD 10.00 25.00
AM Andrew McCutchen 5.00 12.00
AM Andrew McCutchen S2 5.00 12.00
AP Albert Pujols 8.00 20.00
AP Albert Pujols S2 8.00 20.00
AW Adam Wainwright 5.00 12.00
BA Brett Anderson S2 4.00 10.00
BB Brandon Belt UPD 8.00 20.00
BF Bob Feller S2 5.00 12.00
BG Bob Gibson UPD 8.00 20.00
BL Barry Larkin UPD 8.00 20.00
BM Brandon Morrow 4.00 10.00
BM Brian McCann S2 6.00 15.00
BM Bill Mazeroski UPD 8.00 20.00
BP Buster Posey 6.00 15.00
BP Buster Posey S2 6.00 15.00
BR Brian Roberts S2 5.00 12.00
BR Babe Ruth UPD 12.50 30.00
BW Brian Wilson S2 5.00 12.00
CB Chad Billingsley S2 5.00 12.00
CF Carlton Fisk UPD 6.00 15.00
CH Cole Hamels 5.00 12.00
CK Clayton Kershaw 5.00 12.00
CL Cliff Lee S2 6.00 15.00
CR Cal Ripken Jr. S2 12.50 30.00
CS Carlos Santana 5.00 12.00
CU Chase Utley 8.00 20.00
DG Dee Gordon UPD 5.00 12.00
DJ Derek Jeter 12.50 30.00
DL Derrek Lee S2 5.00 12.00
DO David Ortiz 6.00 15.00
DP David Price UPD 5.00 12.00
DW David Wright 5.00 12.00
DW David Wright S2 5.00 12.00
EH Eric Hosmer UPD 10.00 25.00
EL Evan Longoria 6.00 15.00
EM Eddie Murray UPD 12.50 30.00
FF Freddie Freeman UPD 8.00 20.00
FH Felix Hernandez 5.00 12.00
FH Felix Hernandez S2 5.00 12.00
FJ Fergie Jenkins UPD 5.00 12.00
FR Frank Robinson UPD 5.00 12.00
FT Frank Thomas UPD 8.00 20.00
GG Gio Gonzalez 4.00 10.00
GP Gaylord Perry UPD 5.00 12.00
GS Grady Sizemore S2 5.00 12.00
HA Hank Aaron S2 12.50 30.00
HA Hank Aaron UPD 8.00 20.00
HP Hunter Pence 5.00 12.00
ID Ian Desmond 4.00 10.00
IK Ian Kinsler S2 4.00 10.00
IS Ichiro Suzuki 8.00 20.00
IS Ichiro Suzuki S2 8.00 20.00
JB Josh Bell 4.00 10.00
JB Jose Bautista S2 6.00 15.00
JB Johnny Bench UPD 10.00 25.00
JF Jimmie Foxx UPD 6.00 15.00
JH Jason Heyward 6.00 15.00
JM Joe Mauer 6.00 15.00
JM Juan Marichal UPD 5.00 12.00
JP Jim Palmer S2 6.00 15.00
JR Jose Reyes 6.00 15.00
JR Jose Reyes S2 6.00 15.00
JS John Smoltz UPD 5.00 12.00
JU Justin Upton 4.00 10.00
JV Joey Votto 8.00 20.00
JW Jered Weaver S2 5.00 12.00
KS Kurt Suzuki 4.00 10.00
KU Koji Uehara 4.00 10.00
LA Luis Aparicio UPD 10.00 25.00
MB Madison Bumgarner S2 5.00 12.00
MC Miguel Cabrera 5.00 12.00
MG Matt Garza S2 5.00 12.00
MH Matt Holliday 4.00 10.00
MI Monte Irvin UPD 6.00 15.00
MK Matt Kemp S2 6.00 15.00
ML Mat Latos 4.00 10.00
ML Mat Latos S2 4.00 10.00
MP Martin Prado S2 5.00 12.00
MP Michael Pineda UPD 5.00 12.00
MR Manny Ramirez 4.00 10.00
MR Mark Reynolds S2 4.00 10.00
MS Mike Schmidt S2 8.00 20.00
MS Mike Schmidt UPD 8.00 20.00
NM Nick Markakis 5.00 12.00
NR Nolan Ryan S2 10.00 25.00
NR Nolan Ryan UPD 12.50 30.00
OS Ozzie Smith UPD 10.00 25.00
PA Pedro Alvarez S2 5.00 12.00
PF Prince Fielder S2 5.00 12.00
PM Paul Molitor UPD 6.00 15.00
PO Paul O'Neill UPD 12.50 30.00
PS Pablo Sandoval 5.00 12.00
RA Roberto Alomar S2 6.00 15.00
RA Roberto Alomar UPD 6.00 15.00
RB Ryan Braun S2 6.00 15.00
RB Ryan Braun UPD 5.00 12.00
RC Robinson Cano S2 6.00 15.00
RF Rollie Fingers UPD 6.00 15.00
RH Roy Halladay 6.00 15.00
RH Rickey Henderson S2 6.00 15.00
RH Rickey Henderson UPD 6.00 15.00
RJ Reggie Jackson S2 6.00 15.00
RJ Reggie Jackson UPD 10.00 25.00
RM Roger Maris UPD 8.00 20.00
RS Ryne Sandberg UPD 12.50 30.00
RZ Ryan Zimmerman 5.00 12.00
RZ Ryan Zimmerman S2 5.00 12.00
SC Starlin Castro 5.00 12.00
SD Stephen Drew S2 4.00 10.00
SG Steve Garvey UPD 12.50 30.00
SS Stephen Strasburg 6.00 15.00
TC Trevor Cahill 4.00 10.00
TG Tony Gwynn S2 6.00 15.00
TH Torii Hunter 4.00 10.00
TL Tim Lincecum 6.00 15.00
TS Tom Seaver S2 6.00 15.00
TS Tom Seaver UPD 6.00 15.00
VW Vernon Wells 4.00 10.00
WM Willie McCovey UPD 6.00 15.00
ZB Zach Britton UPD 5.00 12.00
BMA Brian Matusz 4.00 10.00
CFI Carlton Fisk UPD 6.00 15.00
CLE Carlos Lee S2 4.00 10.00
FJE Fergie Jenkins UPD 5.00 12.00
IDA Ike Davis 4.00 10.00
ISU Ichiro Suzuki 8.00 20.00
ISU Ichiro Suzuki S2 8.00 20.00
JBA Jose Bautista UPD 4.00 10.00
JHA Josh Hamilton 6.00 15.00
JMI Johnny Mize UPD 8.00 20.00
JMO Joe Morgan UPD 5.00 12.00
JWE Jayson Werth S2 5.00 12.00
JWR Jayson Werth UPD 5.00 12.00
NRY Nolan Ryan S2 10.00 25.00
NRY Nolan Ryan UPD 12.50 30.00
PMO Paul Molitor UPD 6.00 15.00
RAL Roberto Alomar S2 6.00 15.00
RAL Roberto Alomar UPD 6.00 15.00
RED Red Schoendienst UPD 8.00 20.00
RHO Ryan Howard 6.00 15.00
RJA Reggie Jackson UPD 10.00 25.00
RZI Ryan Zimmerman S2 5.00 12.00
SSC Shin-Soo Choo 6.00 15.00
THA Tommy Hanson 4.00 10.00

2011 Topps Cut Signatures

SER.1 ODDS 1:500,000 HOBBY
STATED PRINT RUN 1 SER.#'d SET
NO PRICING DUE TO SCARCITY

2011 Topps Diamond Anniversary Autographs

SER.1 ODDS 1:14,750 HOBBY
HERITAGE ODDS 1:7500 HOBBY
SOME HARPER ISSUED IN 2010 BOW.STER.
STATED PRINT RUN 60 SER.#'d SETS
60AAK Al Kaline 40.00 80.00
60ANR Nolan Ryan 50.00 100.00
60AAC Andrew Cashner 40.00 80.00
60AAE Andre Ethier 40.00 80.00
60ABG Bob Gibson 60.00 120.00
60ABH Bryce Harper 300.00 500.00
60ABM Brian McCann 30.00 60.00
60ABR Brooks Robinson 75.00 150.00
60ACB Clay Buchholz 20.00 50.00
60ACG Carlos Gonzalez 50.00 100.00
60ADM Don Mattingly 150.00 250.00
60ADO David Ortiz 30.00 60.00
60AEB Ernie Banks 75.00 150.00
60AEL Evan Longoria 100.00 175.00
60AEM Eddie Murray 60.00 120.00
60AFJ Fergie Jenkins 30.00 60.00
60AFR Frank Robinson 60.00 120.00
60AGC Gary Carter 20.00 50.00
60AHR Hanley Ramirez 40.00 80.00
60AIK Ian Kinsler 30.00 60.00
60AJB Johnny Bench 40.00 80.00
60AJH Jason Heyward 60.00 120.00
60AJJ Josh Johnson 30.00 60.00
60AKO Keith Olbermann 40.00 80.00
60AMK Matt Kemp 40.00 80.00
60AMR Mariano Rivera 100.00 200.00
60AMS Mike Schmidt 75.00 150.00
60ANC Nelson Cruz 30.00 60.00
60APS Pablo Sandoval 40.00 80.00
60ASB Sy Berger 30.00 60.00
60ASM Stan Musial 200.00 350.00
60ATG Tony Gwynn 75.00 150.00
60ATP Tony Perez 20.00 50.00

2011 Topps Diamond Die Cut

DDC1 Ryan Braun 8.00 20.00
DDC2 Mickey Mantle 20.00 50.00
DDC3 Aaron Hill 2.50 6.00
DDC4 Tim Hudson 4.00 10.00
DDC5 CC Sabathia 4.00 10.00
DDC6 Shin-Soo Choo 4.00 10.00
DDC7 Andrew McCutchen 6.00 15.00
DDC8 Hank Aaron 12.00 30.00
DDC9 Max Scherzer 2.50 6.00
DDC10 Miguel Cabrera 6.00 15.00
DDC11 Brian Matusz 6.00 15.00
DDC12 Jackie Robinson 6.00 15.00
DDC13 Chipper Jones 6.00 15.00
DDC14 Johan Santana 6.00 15.00
DDC15 Andre Ethier 4.00 10.00
DDC16 Justin Upton 4.00 10.00
DDC17 Johnny Cueto 2.50 6.00
DDC18 Gordon Beckham 4.00 10.00
DDC19 Alex Rios 4.00 10.00
DDC20 Nolan Ryan 20.00 50.00
DDC21 Rickey Henderson 6.00 15.00
DDC22 Carlos Marmol 4.00 10.00
DDC23 Matt Cain 4.00 10.00
DDC24 Adam Wainwright 4.00 10.00
DDC25 Vladimir Guerrero 6.00 15.00
DDC26 Mike Minor 2.50 6.00
DDC27 Ricky Romero 2.50 6.00
DDC28 Delmon Young 4.00 10.00
DDC29 Brett Anderson 4.00 10.00
DDC30 Evan Longoria 8.00 20.00
DDC31 Brett Wallace 2.50 6.00
DDC32 Cal Ripken Jr. 25.00 60.00
DDC33 Tommy Hanson 4.00 10.00
DDC34 Mark Buehrle 4.00 10.00
DDC35 Mariano Rivera 6.00 15.00
DDC36 Stephen Drew 2.50 6.00
DDC37 Ubaldo Jimenez 4.00 10.00
DDC38 Alexei Ramirez 2.50 6.00
DDC39 Thurman Munson 6.00 15.00
DDC40 Felix Hernandez 6.00 15.00
DDC41 Adrian Beltre 2.50 6.00
DDC42 Ian Kinsler 2.50 6.00
DDC43 Billy Butler 2.50 6.00
DDC44 Carlos Ruiz 2.50 6.00
DDC45 Stephen Strasburg 12.00 30.00
DDC46 Vernon Wells 2.50 6.00
DDC47 Ian Desmond 4.00 10.00
DDC48 Matt Holliday 6.00 15.00
DDC49 Ike Davis 4.00 10.00
DDC50 Ryan Howard 8.00 20.00
DDC51 Andrew Bailey 2.50 6.00
DDC52 David Ortiz 4.00 10.00
DDC53 Jimmy Rollins 4.00 10.00
DDC54 Ernie Banks 4.00 10.00
DDC55 Ryan Zimmerman 4.00 10.00
DDC56 Alex Rodriguez 10.00 25.00
DDC57 Brian McCann 4.00 10.00
DDC58 Tim Lincecum 6.00 15.00
DDC59 Freddie Freeman 10.00 25.00
DDC60 David Wright 8.00 20.00
DDC61 Carlos Quentin 2.50 6.00
DDC62 Adam Jones 4.00 10.00
DDC63 Brandon Morrow 2.50 6.00
DDC64 Chris Sale 4.00 10.00
DDC65 Reggie Jackson 4.00 10.00
DDC66 Carl Yastrzemski 6.00 15.00
DDC67 Sandy Koufax 20.00 50.00
DDC68 Nick Markakis 6.00 15.00
DDC69 Jair Jurrjens 2.50 6.00
DDC70 Josh Hamilton 6.00 15.00
DDC71 Prince Fielder 4.00 10.00
DDC72 Cole Hamels 6.00 15.00
DDC73 Kelly Johnson 2.50 6.00
DDC74 Colby Rasmus 6.00 15.00
DDC75 Tony Gwynn 6.00 15.00
DDC76 Hank Greenberg 6.00 15.00
DDC77 Tom Seaver 4.00 10.00
DDC78 Bob Gibson 4.00 10.00
DDC79 Fausto Carmona 2.50 6.00
DDC80 Joe Mauer 6.00 15.00
DDC81 Jose Bautista 4.00 10.00
DDC82 Yunel Escobar 2.50 6.00
DDC83 Jeremy Hellickson 8.00 20.00
DDC84 Josh Beckett 4.00 10.00
DDC85 Hanley Ramirez 6.00 15.00
DDC86 Yadier Molina 4.00 10.00
DDC87 Corey Hart 2.50 6.00
DDC88 Hunter Pence 4.00 10.00
DDC89 Roger Maris 6.00 15.00
DDC90 Ichiro Suzuki 10.00 25.00
DDC91 Martin Prado 2.50 6.00
DDC92 Starlin Castro 6.00 15.00
DDC93 Kendry Morales 2.50 6.00
DDC94 Marlon Byrd 2.50 6.00
DDC95 Domonic Brown 6.00 15.00
DDC96 Dave Winfield 2.50 6.00
DDC97 Wade Boggs 4.00 10.00
DDC98 Heath Bell 4.00 10.00
DDC99 Dan Haren 2.50 6.00
DDC100 Albert Pujols 15.00 40.00
DDC101 Nelson Cruz 4.00 10.00
DDC102 Yovani Gallardo 2.50 6.00
DDC103 Howie Kendrick 2.50 6.00
DDC104 Desmond Jennings 6.00 15.00
DDC105 Troy Tulowitzki 6.00 15.00
DDC106 Gaby Sanchez 2.50 6.00
DDC107 Joakim Soria 2.50 6.00
DDC108 Clayton Kershaw 6.00 15.00
DDC109 Mike Schmidt 10.00 25.00
DDC110 Roy Halladay 6.00 15.00
DDC111 Jered Weaver 2.50 6.00
DDC112 Babe Ruth 15.00 40.00
DDC113 Wandy Rodriguez 2.50 6.00
DDC114 Torii Hunter 2.50 6.00
DDC115 Josh Johnson 4.00 10.00
DDC116 Justin Verlander 8.00 20.00
DDC117 Clay Buchholz 4.00 10.00
DDC118 Danny Valencia 4.00 10.00
DDC119 Kurt Suzuki 2.50 6.00
DDC120 David Price 6.00 15.00
DDC121 Daniel Hudson 2.50 6.00
DDC122 Neftali Feliz 2.50 6.00
DDC123 Michael Young 4.00 10.00
DDC124 Jose Reyes 4.00 10.00
DDC125 Robinson Cano 6.00 15.00
DDC126 Billy Wagner 2.50 6.00
DDC127 Miguel Montero 2.50 6.00
DDC128 Kevin Youkilis 4.00 10.00
DDC129 Austin Jackson 2.50 6.00
DDC130 Chase Utley 6.00 15.00
DDC131 Rickie Weeks 4.00 10.00
DDC132 Manny Ramirez 6.00 15.00
DDC133 Carlos Santana 6.00 15.00
DDC134 Aramis Ramirez 2.50 6.00
DDC135 Jason Heyward 8.00 20.00
DDC136 Chris Young 2.50 6.00
DDC137 Tyler Colvin 4.00 10.00
DDC138 Jon Jay 2.50 6.00
DDC139 Nick Swisher 6.00 15.00
DDC140 Mark Teixeira 6.00 15.00
DDC141 Jose Tabata 4.00 10.00
DDC142 Francisco Liriano 2.50 6.00
DDC143 Mike Stanton 4.00 10.00
DDC144 Grady Sizemore 4.00 10.00
DDC145 Justin Morneau 6.00 15.00
DDC146 Jon Lester 6.00 15.00
DDC147 Chris Carpenter 6.00 15.00
DDC148 Mark Reynolds 2.50 6.00
DDC149 Scott Rolen 4.00 10.00
DDC150 Carlos Gonzalez 4.00 10.00
DDC151 Derek Jeter 15.00 40.00
DDC152 Lou Gehrig 12.00 30.00
DDC153 Ryne Sandberg 12.00 30.00
DDC154 Jay Bruce 4.00 10.00
DDC155 Eric Hosmer 20.00 50.00

2011 Topps Diamond Die Cut Black

*BLACK: 1.2X TO 3X BASIC
ISSUED VIA ONLINE REDEMPTION
STATED PRINT RUN 60 SER.#'D SETS

2011 Topps Diamond Duos

COMPLETE SET (30) 6.00 15.00
STATED ODDS 1:4 HOBBY
BD Ryan Braun .75 2.00
Ike Davis
BW Lance Berkman .40 1.00
Brett Wallace
BY Wade Boggs .40 1.00
Kevin Youkilis
CC Ty Cobb 1.00 2.50
Miguel Cabrera
CS Steve Carlton .25 .60
CC Sabathia
GT Carlos Gonzalez .60 1.50
Troy Tulowitzki
HF Jason Heyward 1.00 2.50
Freddie Freeman
HG Josh Hamilton .60 1.50
Vladimir Guerrero
HH Ryan Howard .75 2.00
Jason Heyward
HJ Rickey Henderson .60 1.50
Desmond Jennings
HM Tommy Hanson .40 1.00
Mike Minor
JC Derek Jeter 1.50 4.00
Robinson Cano
JJ Reggie Jackson .40 1.00
Adam Jones
KA Ian Kinsler .40 1.00
Elvis Andrus
KL Clayton Kershaw .60 1.50
Mat Latos
KT Harmon Killebrew .60 1.50
Jim Thome
LJ Barry Larkin 1.50 4.00
Derek Jeter
LZ Evan Longoria .75 2.00
Ryan Zimmerman
MH Greg Maddux .75 2.00
Jeremy Hellickson
MP Joe Mauer .75 2.00
Buster Posey
PC Albert Pujols 1.50 4.00
Miguel Cabrera
PG David Price .60 1.50
Matt Garza
RS Hanley Ramirez .60 1.50
Mike Stanton
SC Tom Seaver .75 2.00
Aroldis Chapman
TR Frank Thomas .60 1.50
Manny Ramirez
TU Hisanori Takahashi .25 .60
Koji Uehara
UR Chase Utley .60 1.50
Jimmy Rollins
US Justin Upton .40 1.00
Mike Stanton
VG Joey Votto .60 1.50
Adrian Gonzalez
HHO Rogers Hornsby .60 1.50
Matt Holliday

2011 Topps Diamond Duos Series 2

COMPLETE SET (30) 6.00 15.00
DD1 Roy Halladay .60 1.50
Roy Oswalt
DD2 Chase Utley .60 1.50
Robinson Cano
DD3 Cliff Lee .60 1.50
Zack Greinke
DD4 Adrian Gonzalez .40 1.00
Carl Crawford
DD5 Dan Uggla .75 2.00
Jason Heyward
DD6 Ryan Braun .75 2.00
Carlos Gonzalez
DD7 Frank Thomas .60 1.50
Adam Dunn
DD8 Zack Greinke .40 1.00
Yovani Gallardo
DD9 Adrian Beltre .40 1.00
Elvis Andrus
DD10 Adrian Gonzalez .40 1.00
Kevin Youkilis
DD11 Carl Crawford .60 1.50
Jacoby Ellsbury
DD12 Troy Tulowitzki .60 1.50
Hanley Ramirez
DD13 Aroldis Chapman .40 1.00
Chris Sale
DD14 Ryan Zimmerman .40 1.00
Jayson Werth
DD15 Tim Lincecum .60 1.50
Brian Wilson
DD16 Josh Hamilton .60 1.50
Joey Votto
DD17 Buster Posey .75 2.00
Neftali Feliz
DD18 Roy Halladay .60 1.50
Felix Hernandez
DD19 Miguel Cabrera .60 1.50
Victor Martinez
DD20 Clayton Kershaw .60 1.50
Madison Bumgarner
DD21 David Price .60 1.50
Jon Lester
DD22 Troy Tulowitzki .60 1.50
Ubaldo Jimenez
DD23 Cliff Lee .60 1.50
CC Sabathia
DD24 Andrew McCutchen .60 1.50
Pedro Alvarez
DD25 Mark Teixeira .60 1.50
Adrian Gonzalez
DD26 Alex Rodriguez .75 2.00
Evan Longoria
DD27 Josh Johnson .75 2.00
Justin Verlander
DD28 Albert Pujols 1.50 4.00
Matt Holliday
DD29 Hank Aaron 1.25 3.00
Jason Heyward
DD30 Sandy Koufax 2.00 5.00
Clayton Kershaw

2011 Topps Diamond Duos Relics

STATED ODDS 1:12,500 HOBBY
STATED PRINT RUN 50 SER.#'d SETS
DDR1 Derek Jeter 50.00 100.00
Robinson Cano
DDR2 Joe Mauer 50.00 100.00
Buster Posey
DDR3 Albert Pujols 30.00 60.00
Miguel Cabrera
DDR4 Ryan Howard 40.00 80.00
Jason Heyward
DDR5 Josh Hamilton 20.00 50.00
Vladimir Guerrero
DDR6 Evan Longoria 40.00 80.00
Ryan Zimmerman
DDR7 Chase Utley 30.00 60.00
Jimmy Rollins
DDR8 Joey Votto 10.00 25.00
Adrian Gonzalez
DDR9 Hanley Ramirez 30.00 60.00
Mike Stanton
DDR10 Barry Larkin 50.00 100.00
Derek Jeter
DDR11 Reggie Jackson 30.00 60.00
Adam Jones
DDR12 Ty Cobb 50.00 100.00
Miguel Cabrera
DDR13 Wade Boggs 30.00 60.00
Kevin Youkilis
DDR14 Clayton Kershaw 30.00 60.00
Mat Latos
DDR15 Justin Upton 10.00 25.00
Mike Stanton

2011 Topps Diamond Duos Relics Series 2

STATED PRINT RUN 50 SER.#'d SETS
DDR1 Chase Utley 20.00 50.00
Robinson Cano
DDR2 Hank Aaron 40.00 80.00
Jason Heyward
DDR3 Miguel Cabrera 12.50 30.00
Victor Martinez
DDR4 Roy Campanella
Buster Posey
DDR5 Ryan Braun 12.50 30.00
Carlos Gonzalez
DDR6 Jon Lester 20.00 50.00
Kevin Youkilis
DDR7 Roberto Alomar 30.00 60.00
Robinson Cano
DDR8 Ian Kinsler 15.00 40.00
Nelson Cruz
DDR9 Tim Lincecum 50.00 100.00
Buster Posey
DDR10 Josh Hamilton 20.00 50.00
Joey Votto
DDR11 Buster Posey 20.00 50.00
Neftali Feliz
DDR12 Roy Halladay 12.50 30.00
Felix Hernandez
DDR13 Alex Rodriguez 40.00 80.00
Evan Longoria
DDR14 Josh Johnson 20.00 50.00
Justin Verlander
DDR15 Albert Pujols 50.00 100.00
Matt Holliday

2011 Topps Diamond Giveaway

COMPLETE SET (30) 40.00 100.00
COMP.SER.1 SET (10) 12.50 30.00
COMP.SER.2 SET (10) 12.50 30.00
COMP.UPD.SET (10) 12.50 30.00
APPX.SER.1 ODDS 1:9 HOBBY
TDG1 Mickey Mantle 2.00 5.00
TDG2 Jackie Robinson 2.00 5.00
TDG3 Reggie Jackson 2.00 5.00
TDG4 Albert Pujols 2.00 5.00
TDG5 Derek Jeter 2.00 5.00
TDG6 Roy Halladay 2.00 5.00
TDG7 Derek Jeter 2.00 5.00
TDG8 Albert Pujols 2.00 5.00
TDG9 Ryan Howard 2.00 5.00
TDG10 Tim Lincecum 2.00 5.00
TDG11 Tony Gwynn 2.00 5.00
TDG12 Mike Schmidt 2.00 5.00
TDG13 Nolan Ryan 2.00 5.00
TDG14 Jason Heyward 2.00 5.00
TDG15 Troy Tulowitzki 2.00 5.00
TDG16 Buster Posey 2.00 5.00
TDG17 Ryan Braun 2.00 5.00
TDG18 Evan Longoria 2.00 5.00
TDG19 Joe Mauer 2.00 5.00
TDG20 Kevin Youkilis 2.00 5.00
TDG21 Mickey Mantle 2.00 5.00
TDG22 Sandy Koufax 2.00 5.00
TDG23 Cal Ripken Jr. 2.00 5.00
TDG24 Adrian Gonzalez 2.00 5.00
TDG25 Adrian Beltre 2.00 5.00
TDG26 Carl Crawford 2.00 5.00
TDG27 Victor Martinez 2.00 5.00
TDG28 Cliff Lee 2.00 5.00
TDG29 Jose Bautista 2.00 5.00
TDG30 Prince Fielder 2.00 5.00

2011 Topps Diamond Stars

COMPLETE SET (25) 10.00 25.00
DS1 Evan Longoria .75 2.00
DS2 Troy Tulowitzki .60 1.50
DS3 Joe Mauer .60 1.50
DS4 Adrian Gonzalez .40 1.00
DS5 Joey Votto .60 1.50
DS6 Buster Posey .75 2.00
DS7 Chase Utley .60 1.50
DS8 David Wright .75 2.00
DS9 Hanley Ramirez .60 1.50
DS10 Albert Pujols 1.50 4.00
DS11 Roy Halladay .60 1.50
DS12 Alex Rodriguez 1.00 2.50
DS13 Jason Heyward .75 2.00
DS14 Miguel Cabrera .60 1.50
DS15 Cliff Lee .60 1.50
DS16 Felix Hernandez .60 1.50
DS17 Matt Holliday .60 1.50
DS18 Robinson Cano .60 1.50
DS19 Josh Hamilton .60 1.50
DS20 Ichiro Suzuki 1.00 2.50
DS21 Carl Crawford .40 1.00
DS22 Ryan Howard .75 2.00
DS23 Josh Johnson .40 1.00
DS24 Ryan Braun .75 2.00
DS25 Carlos Gonzalez .40 1.00

2011 Topps Glove Manufactured Leather Nameplates

SER.1 ODDS 1:461 HOBBY
BLACK: .5X TO 1.2X BASIC
SER.1 BLACK ODDS 1:1815 HOBBY
UPD.BLACK ODDS 1:935 HOBBY
BLACK PRINT RUN 99 SER.#'d SETS
SER.1 NICKNAME ODDS 1:200,000 HOBBY
UPD.NICKNAME ODDS 1:87,500 HOBBY
NICKNAME PRINT RUN 1 SER.#'d SET
NO NICKNAME PRICING AVAILABLE
AD Andre Dawson S2 4.00 10.00
AD Andre Dawson UPD 4.00 10.00
AE Andre Ethier 4.00 10.00
AG Adrian Gonzalez 4.00 10.00
AM Andrew McCutchen 4.00 10.00
AP Albert Pujols 8.00 20.00
AR Alex Rodriguez 5.00 12.00
AR Alex Rodriguez UPD 5.00 12.00
AW Adam Wainwright 6.00 15.00
BB Billy Butler 4.00 10.00
BB Brandon Belt UPD 4.00 10.00
BF Bob Feller S2 6.00 15.00
BG Bob Gibson S2 8.00 20.00
BM Bill Mazeroski S2 5.00 12.00
BP Buster Posey 10.00 25.00
BR Babe Ruth S2 10.00 25.00
BR Babe Ruth UPD 10.00 25.00
BW Brian Wilson UPD 4.00 10.00
BZ Ben Zobrist UPD 4.00 10.00
CC Carl Crawford 4.00 10.00
CF Carlton Fisk S2 4.00 10.00
CF Carlton Fisk UPD 4.00 10.00
CG Carlos Gonzalez 5.00 12.00
CH Cole Hamels UPD 4.00 10.00
CK Clayton Kershaw 4.00 10.00
CR Cal Ripken Jr. S2 10.00 25.00
CU Chase Utley 6.00 15.00
CY Carl Yastrzemski S2 6.00 15.00
DD Danny Duffy UPD 4.00 10.00
DJ Derek Jeter 10.00 25.00
DM Don Mattingly S2 6.00 15.00
DP David Price 4.00 10.00
DS Duke Snider UPD 4.00 10.00
DW David Wright 8.00 20.00
EH Eric Hosmer UPD 6.00 15.00
EL Evan Longoria 6.00 15.00
EM Eddie Murray S2 8.00 20.00
FH Felix Hernandez 4.00 10.00
FJ Fergie Jenkins S2 4.00 10.00
FJ Fergie Jenkins UPD 4.00 10.00
FR Frank Robinson S2 4.00 10.00
FR Frank Robinson UPD 4.00 10.00
FT Frank Thomas S2 4.00 10.00
FT Frank Thomas UPD 4.00 10.00
GM Greg Maddux S2 6.00 15.00
HA Hank Aaron S2 4.00 10.00
HA Hank Aaron UPD 4.00 10.00
HG Hank Greenberg S2 5.00 12.00
HK Harmon Killebrew S2 8.00 20.00
HP Hunter Pence 4.00 10.00
HR Hanley Ramirez 4.00 10.00
IS Ichiro Suzuki 8.00 20.00
JB Johnny Bench S2 8.00 20.00
JB Jose Bautista UPD 5.00 12.00
JD Joe DiMaggio UPD 6.00 15.00
JF Jimmie Foxx S2 4.00 10.00
JF Jimmie Foxx UPD 4.00 10.00
JH Josh Hamilton 6.00 15.00
JH Jim Hunter S2 4.00 10.00
JJ Josh Johnson 4.00 10.00
JL Jon Lester 5.00 12.00
JM Joe Mauer 8.00 20.00
JM Johnny Mize S2 4.00 10.00
JM Johnny Mize UPD 4.00 10.00
JP Jim Palmer S2 6.00 15.00
JS James Shields UPD 4.00 10.00
JT Julio Teheran UPD 4.00 10.00
JU Justin Upton 4.00 10.00
JV Joey Votto 8.00 20.00
JW Jayson Werth UPD 4.00 10.00
KY Kevin Youkilis UPD 4.00 10.00
LA Luis Aparicio S2 4.00 10.00
LA Luis Aparicio UPD 4.00 10.00
LB Lance Berkman UPD 4.00 10.00
LG Lou Gehrig S2 8.00 20.00
MC Miguel Cabrera 4.00 10.00
MC Miguel Cabrera UPD 4.00 10.00
MH Matt Holliday 6.00 15.00
MI Monte Irvin S2 5.00 12.00
MK Matt Kemp UPD 4.00 10.00
ML Mat Latos 4.00 10.00
MM Mickey Mantle S2 12.50 30.00
MO Mel Ott S2 5.00 12.00
MP Martin Prado 4.00 10.00
MP Michael Pineda UPD 5.00 12.00
MS Mike Stanton 5.00 12.00
MS Mike Schmidt S2 8.00 20.00
MS Max Scherzer UPD 4.00 10.00
MT Mark Teixeira 5.00 12.00
NC Nelson Cruz 6.00 15.00
NM Nick Markakis 6.00 15.00
NR Nolan Ryan S2 8.00 20.00
NR Nolan Ryan UPD 8.00 20.00
OC Orlando Cepeda S2 4.00 10.00
OS Ozzie Smith S2 4.00 10.00

OS Ozzie Smith UPD 4.00 10.00
PM Paul Molitor UPD 4.00 10.00
PN Phil Niekro S2 6.00 15.00
PR Phil Rizzuto S2 6.00 15.00
RA Richie Ashburn S2 5.00 12.00
RA Roberto Alomar UPD 4.00 10.00
RB Ryan Braun 5.00 12.00
RC Robinson Cano 6.00 15.00
RC Roy Campanella S2 5.00 12.00
RH Ryan Howard 8.00 20.00
RH Rogers Hornsby S2 4.00 10.00
RH Rogers Hornsby UPD 4.00 10.00
RJ Reggie Jackson S2 4.00 10.00
RJ Reggie Jackson UPD 4.00 10.00
RS Ryne Sandberg S2 6.00 15.00
RZ Ryan Zimmerman 4.00 10.00
SC Starlin Castro 6.00 15.00
SK Sandy Koufax S2 10.00 25.00
SM Stan Musial S2 10.00 25.00
SS Stephen Strasburg 8.00 20.00
TC Trevor Cahill 4.00 10.00
TG Tony Gwynn S2 5.00 12.00
TH Torii Hunter 4.00 10.00
TH Travis Hafner UPD 4.00 10.00
TL Tim Lincecum 8.00 20.00
TM Thurman Munson S2 6.00 15.00
TN Tsuyoshi Nishioka UPD 5.00 12.00
TS Tom Seaver S2 5.00 12.00
TS Tom Seaver UPD 5.00 12.00
UJ Ubaldo Jimenez 4.00 10.00
VM Victor Martinez 4.00 10.00
WF Whitey Ford S2 5.00 12.00
WM Willie McCovey S2 4.00 10.00
WM Willie McCovey UPD 4.00 10.00
WS Willie Stargell S2 5.00 12.00
ZB Zach Britton UPD 4.00 10.00
ADU Adam Dunn UPD 4.00 10.00
ARO Alex Rodriguez UPD 5.00 12.00
BRO Brooks Robinson S2 8.00 20.00
CCS CC Sabathia 5.00 12.00
DMU Dale Murphy S2 6.00 15.00
JAS Jerry Sands UPD 4.00 10.00
JHE Jason Heyward 10.00 25.00
JMA Juan Marichal S2 6.00 15.00
JMO Joe Morgan UPD 4.00 10.00
JVE Justin Verlander 5.00 12.00
JWE Jered Weaver UPD 4.00 10.00
NOR Nolan Ryan UPD 8.00 20.00
NRY Nolan Ryan UPD 8.00 20.00
PWR Pee Wee Reese UPD 4.00 10.00
RHA Roy Halladay 6.00 15.00
RHE Rickey Henderson S2 4.00 10.00
RHE Rickey Henderson UPD 4.00 10.00
RJA Reggie Jackson S2 4.00 10.00
SSC Shin-Soo Choo 6.00 15.00

2011 Topps Glove Manufactured Leather Nameplates Nickname

SER1 ODDS 1:200,000 HOBBY
UPD.ODDS 1:87,500 HOBBY
STATED PRINT RUN 1 SER.#'d SET
NO PRICING DUE TO SCARCITY

2011 Topps History of Topps

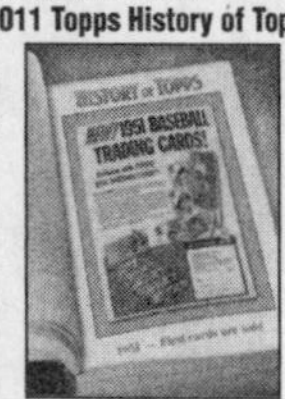

COMPLETE SET (10) 3.00 8.00
STATED ODDS 1:18 HOBBY
HOT1 Topps Is Founded .40 1.00
HOT2 1951- First Cards Are Sold .40 1.00
HOT3 1952- Berger Creates First Set .40 1.00
HOT4 1957- Topps Sets Card Size .40 1.00
HOT5 1972- Topps Goes Public .40 1.00
HOT6 1974- First Topps Traded Set .40 1.00
HOT7 1989- Reintroduces of Bowman .40 1.00
HOT8 1994- Topps Moves To NYC .40 1.00
HOT9 2007- Eisner Buy Topps .40 1.00
HOT10 2009- Gets MLB Exclusive .40 1.00

2011 Topps In The Name Letter Relics

STATED ODDS 1:4067 HOBBY
STATED PRINT RUN 1 SER.#'d SET
NO PRICING DUE TO SCARCITY

2011 Topps Kimball Champions

COMPLETE SET (150) 40.00 100.00
COMP.SER.1 SET (50) 12.50 30.00
COMP.SER.2 SET (50) 12.50 30.00
COMP.UPD SET (50) 12.50 30.00
SER.1 ODDS 1:4 HOBBY
UPD.ODDS 1:4 HOBBY
KC1 Ubaldo Jimenez .40 1.00
KC2 Derek Jeter 1.50 4.00
KC3 Carlos Santana .60 1.50
KC4 Johan Santana .60 1.50
KC5 Carlos Gonzalez .40 1.00
KC6 Clay Buchholz .40 1.00
KC7 Mickey Mantle 2.00 5.00
KC8 Ryan Braun .75 2.00
KC9 Chase Utley .60 1.50
KC10 Ichiro Suzuki 1.00 2.50
KC11 Starlin Castro .60 1.50
KC12 Torii Hunter .25 .60
KC13 Ty Cobb 1.00 2.50
KC14 Clayton Kershaw .60 1.50
KC15 David Price .60 1.50
KC16 Aroldis Chapman .75 2.00
KC17 Chris Carpenter .60 1.50
KC18 Andrew McCutchen .60 1.50
KC19 Brandon Morrow .25 .60
KC20 Roy Halladay .60 1.50
KC21 Shin-Soo Choo .40 1.00
KC22 Victor Martinez .40 1.00
KC23 Mat Latos .25 .60
KC24 Josh Johnson .40 1.00
KC25 Vladimir Guerrero .60 1.50
KC26 Justin Morneau .60 1.50
KC27 Nick Markakis .60 1.50
KC28 Mike Stanton .40 1.00
KC29 Jered Weaver .25 .60
KC30 David Wright .75 2.00
KC31 Nelson Cruz .40 1.00
KC32 Alex Rios .40 1.00
KC33 Martin Prado .25 .60
KC34 Joey Votto .60 1.50
KC35 Jon Lester .60 1.50
KC36 Hanley Ramirez .60 1.50
KC37 Stephen Strasburg 1.25 3.00
KC38 Roy Oswalt .40 1.00
KC39 CC Sabathia .40 1.00
KC40 Albert Pujols 1.50 4.00
KC41 Pablo Sandoval .40 1.00
KC42 Mariano Rivera .60 1.50
KC43 Pee Wee Reese .40 1.00
KC44 Hunter Pence .40 1.00
KC45 David Ortiz .40 1.00
KC46 Mel Ott .60 1.50
KC47 Brett Anderson .40 1.00
KC48 Justin Upton .40 1.00
KC49 Jose Bautista .40 1.00
KC50 Miguel Cabrera .60 1.50
KC51 Hank Aaron 1.25 3.00
KC52 Sandy Koufax 2.00 5.00
KC53 Carlton Fisk .40 1.00
KC54 Nolan Ryan 2.00 5.00
KC55 Stan Musial 1.00 2.50
KC56 Steve Carlton .25 .60
KC57 Tom Seaver .40 1.00
KC58 Mel Ott .60 1.50
KC59 Tony Gwynn .60 1.50
KC60 Johnny Bench .60 1.50
KC61 Greg Maddux .75 2.00
KC62 Luis Aparicio .25 .60
KC63 Juan Marichal .25 .60
KC64 Jackie Robinson .60 1.50
KC65 Bob Gibson .40 1.00
KC66 Yogi Berra .60 1.50
KC67 Pee Wee Reese .40 1.00
KC68 Reggie Jackson .40 1.00
KC69 Robin Roberts .25 .60
KC70 Roy Campanella .60 1.50
KC71 Brooks Robinson .40 1.00
KC72 Ernie Banks .60 1.50
KC73 Phil Rizzuto .60 1.50
KC74 Eddie Murray .60 1.50
KC75 Bob Feller .25 .60
KC76 Lou Brock .40 1.00
KC77 Frank Robinson .40 1.00
KC78 Eddie Mathews .40 1.00
KC79 Barry Larkin .40 1.00
KC80 Roger Maris .60 1.50
KC81 Craig Biggio .40 1.00
KC82 Mike Schmidt 1.00 2.50
KC83 Don Mattingly 1.25 3.00
KC84 Ryne Sandberg 1.25 3.00
KC85 Willie McCovey .40 1.00
KC86 Whitey Ford .60 1.50
KC87 Andre Dawson .40 1.00
KC88 Jim Palmer .25 .60
KC89 Duke Snider .40 1.00
KC90 Hank Greenberg .60 1.50
KC91 Dale Murphy .60 1.50
KC92 Frank Thomas .60 1.50
KC93 Wade Boggs .40 1.00
KC94 Carl Yastrzemski .60 1.50
KC95 Lou Gehrig 1.25 3.00
KC96 Cal Ripken Jr. 2.50 6.00
KC97 Paul Molitor .60 1.50
KC98 Gary Carter .40 1.00
KC99 Ty Cobb 1.00 2.50
KC100 Babe Ruth 1.50 4.00
KC101 Babe Ruth 1.50 4.00
KC102 Willie McCovey .40 1.00
KC103 Zach Britton .60 1.50
KC104 Jimmie Foxx .60 1.50
KC105 Honus Wagner .60 1.50
KC106 Gary Carter .25 .60
KC107 Dan Uggla .40 1.00
KC108 Lance Berkman .40 1.00
KC109 Trevor Cahill .25 .60
KC110 Hank Aaron 1.25 3.00
KC111 Tris Speaker .40 1.00
KC112 Cole Hamels .60 1.50
KC113 Alex Rodriguez 1.00 2.50
KC114 Felix Hernandez .60 1.50
KC115 Ty Cobb 1.00 2.50
KC116 Johnny Mize .40 1.00
KC117 Curtis Granderson .40 1.00
KC118 Cliff Lee .60 1.50
KC119 Matt Holliday .60 1.50
KC120 Frank Robinson .40 1.00
KC121 Luis Aparicio .25 .60
KC122 Christy Mathewson .60 1.50
KC123 Bert Blyleven .25 .60
KC124 Frank Thomas .60 1.50
KC125 Nolan Ryan 2.00 5.00
KC126 Danny Duffy .40 1.00
KC127 Justin Verlander .75 2.00
KC128 Carlton Fisk .40 1.00
KC129 George Sisler .60 1.50
KC130 Adrian Gonzalez .40 1.00
KC131 Adam Dunn .40 1.00
KC132 Tom Seaver .40 1.00
KC133 Ozzie Smith 1.00 2.50
KC134 Miguel Cabrera .60 1.50
KC135 Carl Crawford .40 1.00
KC136 Paul Molitor .60 1.50
KC137 Joe Morgan .25 .60
KC138 Rogers Hornsby .40 1.00
KC139 James Shields .25 .60
KC140 Michael Pineda .75 2.00
KC141 Andre Dawson .40 1.00
KC142 Ryan Howard .75 2.00
KC143 Kyle Drabek .40 1.00
KC144 Reggie Jackson .40 1.00
KC145 Eric Hosmer 2.00 5.00
KC146 Vladimir Guerrero .60 1.50
KC147 Mark Teixeira .60 1.50
KC148 Jose Reyes .40 1.00
KC149 Cy Young .60 1.50
KC150 Joe DiMaggio 1.50 4.00

2011 Topps Lost Cards

COMPLETE SET (10) 6.00 15.00
STATED ODDS 1:12 HOBBY
*ORIGINAL BACK: .6X TO 1.5X BASIC
ORIGINAL ODDS 1:108 HOBBY
LC1 Stan Musial 1.25 3.00
LC2 Duke Snider .50 1.25
LC3 Mickey Mantle 2.50 6.00
LC4 Roy Campanella .75 2.00
LC5 Stan Musial 1.25 3.00
LC6 Whitey Ford .50 1.25
LC7 Bob Feller .30 .75
LC8 Mickey Mantle 2.50 6.00
LC9 Stan Musial 1.25 3.00
LC10 Stan Musial 1.25 3.00

2011 Topps Mickey Mantle Reprint Relics

SER.1 ODDS 1:115,000 HOBBY
UPD.ODDS 1:52,500 HOBBY
PRINT RUNS B/WN 64-66 COPIES PER
MMRR1 Mickey Mantle Jsy/64 125.00 250.00
MMRR2 Mickey Mantle Bat/65 125.00 250.00
MMRR3 Mickey Mantle Jsy/66 125.00 250.00

2011 Topps Prime 9 Player of the Week Refractors

COMPLETE SET (9) 10.00 25.00
PNR1 Johnny Bench 1.00 2.50
PNR2 Albert Pujols 2.50 6.00
PNR3 Jackie Robinson 1.00 2.50
PNR4 Derek Jeter 2.50 6.00
PNR5 Mike Schmidt 1.50 4.00
PNR6 Hank Aaron 2.00 5.00
PNR7 Mickey Mantle 3.00 8.00
PNR8 Ichiro Suzuki 1.50 4.00
PNR9 Sandy Koufax 3.00 8.00

2011 Topps Silk Collection

SER.1 ODDS 1:396 HOBBY
UPD.ODDS 1:221 HOBBY
STATED PRINT RUN 50 SER.#'d SETS
1 Ryan Kalish 6.00 15.00
2 Jose Bautista 6.00 15.00
3 Carlos Gonzalez 6.00 15.00
4 Justin Upton 6.00 15.00
5 Chipper Jones 10.00 25.00
6 Ubaldo Jimenez 6.00 15.00
7 Brett Wallace 4.00 10.00
8 Roy Oswalt 6.00 15.00
9 Brennan Boesch 6.00 15.00
10 Albert Pujols 25.00 60.00
11 Jaime Garcia 6.00 15.00
12 Kevin Kouzmanoff 4.00 10.00
13 Brett Anderson 6.00 15.00
14 Ian Desmond 6.00 15.00
15 Adam Dunn 6.00 15.00
16 David Wright 12.00 30.00
17 Andrew Bailey 4.00 10.00
18 Torii Hunter 4.00 10.00
19 Max Scherzer 4.00 10.00
20 Carl Crawford 6.00 15.00
21 Michael Young 6.00 15.00
22 Chris Carpenter 10.00 25.00
23 Chase Utley 10.00 25.00
24 Clay Buchholz 6.00 15.00
25 Stephen Drew 4.00 10.00
26 Alex Gordon 6.00 15.00
27 Shin-Soo Choo 6.00 15.00
28 Miguel Cabrera 10.00 25.00
29 Andrew McCutchen 10.00 25.00
30 Victor Martinez 6.00 15.00
31 Jered Weaver 5.00 12.00
32 Clayton Kershaw 10.00 25.00
33 Ichiro Suzuki 15.00 40.00
34 Mike Stanton 6.00 15.00
35 Vladimir Guerrero 10.00 25.00
36 Cliff Lee 10.00 25.00
37 Miguel Montero 4.00 10.00
38 Howie Kendrick 4.00 10.00
39 Jon Lester 10.00 25.00
40 Nick Swisher 10.00 25.00
41 Magglio Ordonez 6.00 15.00
42 Carlos Santana 10.00 25.00
43 Ryan Braun 12.00 30.00
44 Carlos Pena 6.00 15.00
45 Tim Hudson 6.00 15.00
46 Alex Rodriguez 15.00 40.00
47 Aaron Hill 4.00 10.00
48 Chris Young 4.00 10.00
49 Johan Santana 10.00 25.00
50 James Shields 4.00 10.00
51 C.J. Wilson 4.00 10.00
52 Mariano Rivera 10.00 25.00
53 Marlon Byrd 4.00 10.00
54 Martin Prado 4.00 10.00
55 Joey Votto 10.00 25.00
56 Paul Konerko 6.00 15.00
57 Mark Buehrle 6.00 15.00
58 Fausto Carmona 4.00 10.00
59 Nelson Cruz 6.00 15.00
60 Wandy Rodriguez 4.00 10.00
61 Derek Lee 4.00 10.00
62 Ricky Romero 4.00 10.00
63 Carlos Marmol 6.00 15.00
64 Johnny Cueto 4.00 10.00
65 Starlin Castro 10.00 25.00
66 Zack Greinke 6.00 15.00
67 Scott Rolen 6.00 15.00
68 Nick Markakis 10.00 25.00
69 Jimmy Rollins 6.00 15.00
70 John Danks 4.00 10.00
71 Ike Davis 6.00 15.00
72 Brandon Morrow 4.00 10.00
73 Derek Jeter 25.00 60.00
74 Peter Bourjos 6.00 15.00
75 Roy Halladay 10.00 25.00
76 Alex Rios 6.00 15.00
77 Hanley Ramirez 10.00 25.00
78 Jon Jay 4.00 10.00
79 Justin Morneau 10.00 25.00
80 Aramis Ramirez 4.00 10.00
81 Todd Helton 6.00 15.00
82 Andre Ethier 6.00 15.00
83 Stephen Strasburg 20.00 50.00
84 Adrian Beltre 4.00 10.00
85 Brian Wilson 10.00 25.00
86 Kurt Suzuki 4.00 10.00
87 David Price 10.00 25.00
88 Jason Kubel 4.00 10.00
89 Hunter Pence 6.00 15.00
90 Alexei Ramirez 4.00 10.00
91 Billy Wagner 6.00 15.00
92 Michael Cuddyer 4.00 10.00
93 Jeremy Hellickson 12.00 30.00
94 CC Sabathia 6.00 15.00
95 Josh Johnson 6.00 15.00
96 Brian Matusz 10.00 25.00
97 Mat Latos 6.00 15.00
98 Rickie Weeks 6.00 15.00
99 Heath Bell 6.00 15.00
100 David Ortiz 6.00 15.00
101 Trevor Cahill 4.00 10.00
102 Felix Hernandez 10.00 25.00
103 Shane Victorino 6.00 15.00
104 Michael Bourn 4.00 10.00
105 Josh Hamilton 10.00 25.00
106 Corey Hart 4.00 10.00
107 John Lackey 4.00 10.00
108 Kevin Youkilis 6.00 15.00
109 Daric Barton 4.00 10.00
110 Danny Valencia 6.00 15.00
111 Edwin Jackson 4.00 10.00
112 Jason Bartlett 4.00 10.00
113 Matt Cain 6.00 15.00
114 Rick Porcello 4.00 10.00
115 Huston Street 4.00 10.00
116 Dan Uggla 6.00 15.00
117 Ryan Ludwick 4.00 10.00
118 Elvis Andrus 6.00 15.00
119 Ivan Rodriguez 6.00 15.00
120 Casey McGehee 4.00 10.00
121 Adam Wainwright 6.00 15.00
122 Dustin Pedroia 12.00 30.00
123 Travis Snider 4.00 10.00
124 Jason Heyward 12.00 30.00
125 Phil Hughes 4.00 10.00
126 Dan Haren 4.00 10.00
127 J.P. Arencibia 6.00 15.00
128 Matt Kemp 6.00 15.00
129 Denard Span 4.00 10.00
130 Drew Storen 4.00 10.00
131 Jonathan Broxton 4.00 10.00
132 Adrian Gonzalez 6.00 15.00
133 Adam Jones 6.00 15.00
134 Joba Chamberlain 6.00 15.00
135 Carlos Beltran 4.00 10.00
136 Evan Longoria 12.00 30.00
137 Adam Lind 6.00 15.00
138 Joe Mauer 10.00 25.00
139 Brian McCann 6.00 15.00
140 Francisco Liriano 4.00 10.00
141 Chris Tillman 4.00 10.00
142 Troy Tulowitzki 10.00 25.00
143 Grady Sizemore 6.00 15.00
144 Jose Tabata 6.00 15.00
145 Drew Stubbs 6.00 15.00
146 Austin Jackson 4.00 10.00
147 Franklin Gutierrez 4.00 10.00
148 Kendrys Morales 4.00 10.00
149 Carlos Quentin 4.00 10.00
150 Wade Davis 4.00 10.00
151 Jose Valverde 4.00 10.00
152 Logan Morrison 4.00 10.00
153 Delmon Young 6.00 15.00
154 Alfonso Soriano 6.00 15.00
155 Colby Rasmus 10.00 25.00
156 Mike Minor 4.00 10.00
157 Yovani Gallardo 4.00 10.00
158 Chris Iannetta 4.00 10.00
159 Cody Ross 4.00 10.00
160 Jorge Posada 6.00 15.00
161 Dallas Braden 4.00 10.00
162 Dexter Fowler 4.00 10.00
163 Shaun Marcum 4.00 10.00
164 Kyle Blanks 4.00 10.00
165 B.J. Upton 6.00 15.00
166 Matt Holliday 10.00 25.00
167 Joakim Soria 4.00 10.00
168 Jake Arrieta 4.00 10.00
169 Ryan Doumit 4.00 10.00
170 Curtis Granderson 6.00 15.00
171 Madison Bumgarner 4.00 10.00
172 Buster Posey 12.00 30.00
173 Kelly Johnson 4.00 10.00
174 Chad Billingsley 4.00 10.00
175 Cole Hamels 10.00 25.00
176 Justin Verlander 12.00 30.00
177 Domonic Brown 10.00 25.00
178 Billy Butler 4.00 10.00
179 Jacoby Ellsbury 10.00 25.00
180 Will Venable 4.00 10.00
181 Ian Kinsler 6.00 15.00
182 Tommy Hanson 6.00 15.00
183 Kosuke Fukudome 10.00 25.00
184 Ryan Zimmerman 6.00 15.00
185 Geovany Soto 6.00 15.00
186 Matt Garza 4.00 10.00
187 Prince Fielder 6.00 15.00
188 Mark Reynolds 4.00 10.00
189 Mark Teixeira 10.00 25.00
190 Carlos Lee 4.00 10.00
191 Brian Roberts 4.00 10.00
192 Kila Ka'aihue 4.00 10.00
193 Brett Myers 4.00 10.00
194 Vernon Wells 4.00 10.00
195 Jose Reyes 6.00 15.00
196 Brandon Phillips 4.00 10.00
197 Josh Beckett 6.00 15.00
198 Gordon Beckham 6.00 15.00
199 Tim Lincecum 10.00 25.00
200 Jeff Niemann 4.00 10.00
201 Adrian Gonzalez 6.00 15.00
202 Josh Willingham 4.00 10.00
203 Jose Iglesias 6.00 15.00
204 Mike Napoli 6.00 15.00
205 Conor Jackson 4.00 10.00
206 Tim Stauffer 4.00 10.00
207 Carlos Pena 6.00 15.00
208 Rick Ankiel 4.00 10.00
209 Russell Martin 4.00 10.00
210 Zach Britton 10.00 25.00
211 Brian Fuentes 4.00 10.00
212 Angel Sanchez 4.00 10.00
213 Andruw Jones 4.00 10.00
214 Jerry Sands 15.00 40.00
215 Brandon Belt 8.00 20.00
216 Jonathan Herrera 4.00 10.00
217 Yuniesky Betancourt 4.00 10.00
218 Mitchell Boggs 4.00 10.00
219 Andy Dirks 4.00 10.00
220 Zack Greinke 6.00 15.00
221 Jeff Francis 4.00 10.00
222 Nolan Reimold 4.00 10.00
223 Freddy Garcia 4.00 10.00
224 Aaron Harang 4.00 10.00
225 Kerry Wood 4.00 10.00
226 Orlando Cabrera 4.00 10.00
227 Lyle Overbay 4.00 10.00
228 Scott Downs 4.00 10.00
229 Sean Burnett 4.00 10.00
230 Victor Martinez 6.00 15.00
231 Logan Forsythe 4.00 10.00
232 Brandon McCarthy 4.00 10.00
233 Joe Mather 4.00 10.00
234 Edgar Renteria 4.00 10.00
235 Scott Sizemore 4.00 10.00
236 Jeff Francoeur 6.00 15.00
237 Kyle Farnsworth 4.00 10.00
238 Jon Rauch 4.00 10.00
239 Brad Penny 4.00 10.00
240 Fernando Salas 6.00 15.00
241 Doug Davis 4.00 10.00
242 Pete Kozma 10.00 25.00
243 Alfredo Amezaga 4.00 10.00
244 Mark Melancon 4.00 10.00
245 Rafael Soriano 4.00 10.00
246 Alex White 4.00 10.00
247 Bartolo Colon 4.00 10.00
248 Trystan Magnuson 4.00 10.00
249 Omar Infante 4.00 10.00
250 Carl Crawford 6.00 15.00
251 Matt Guerrier 4.00 10.00
252 Alexi Amarista 4.00 10.00
253 Humberto Quintero 4.00 10.00
254 Reed Johnson 4.00 10.00
255 Darren Oliver 4.00 10.00
256 Alex Cobb 4.00 10.00
257 Josh Collmenter 4.00 10.00
258 Michael Pineda 12.00 30.00
259 Jon Garland 4.00 10.00
260 Lance Berkman 6.00 15.00
261 Eduardo Sanchez 6.00 15.00
262 John Mayberry 4.00 10.00
263 Brendan Ryan 4.00 10.00
264 Bruce Chen 4.00 10.00
265 Alexi Ogando 10.00 25.00
266 Brad Ziegler 4.00 10.00
267 Jason Giambi 4.00 10.00
268 Charlie Furbush 4.00 10.00
269 Julio Teheran 12.00 30.00
270 Vladimir Guerrero 10.00 25.00
271 Xavier Nady 4.00 10.00
272 Kevin Gregg 4.00 10.00
273 Jason Bourgeois 4.00 10.00
274 Derrek Lee 4.00 10.00
275 Adrian Beltre 4.00 10.00
276 Daniel Moskos 4.00 10.00
277 Carlos Peguero 6.00 15.00
278 Tyler Chatwood 4.00 10.00
279 Orlando Hudson 4.00 10.00
280 Jayson Werth 6.00 15.00
281 Philip Humber 4.00 10.00
282 Brandon League 4.00 10.00
283 J.P. Howell 4.00 10.00
284 Michael Dunn 4.00 10.00
285 Miguel Tejada 6.00 15.00
286 Jamey Carroll 4.00 10.00
287 Arthur Rhodes 4.00 10.00
288 Bill Hall 4.00 10.00
289 David DeJesus 4.00 10.00
290 Adam Dunn 6.00 15.00
291 Charlie Morton 4.00 10.00
292 J.J. Hardy 4.00 10.00
293 Kevin Correia 4.00 10.00
294 Alcides Escobar 4.00 10.00
295 Danny Duffy 6.00 15.00
296 Justin Turner 4.00 10.00
297 John Buck 4.00 10.00
298 Sergio Santos 4.00 10.00
299 Todd Frazier 6.00 15.00
300 Cliff Lee 10.00 25.00

2011 Topps Target Hanger Pack Exclusives

ONE PER TARGET HANGER PACK
THP1 Albert Pujols 3.00 8.00
THP2 Derek Jeter 3.00 8.00
THP3 Mat Latos .50 1.25
THP4 Hanley Ramirez 1.25 3.00
THP5 Miguel Cabrera 1.25 3.00
THP6 Aroldis Chapman 1.50 4.00
THP7 Chase Utley 1.25 3.00
THP8 Ryan Braun 1.50 4.00
THP9 David Price 1.25 3.00
THP10 Joey Votto 1.25 3.00
THP11 David Wright 1.50 4.00
THP12 Carlos Gonzalez .75 2.00
THP13 David Ortiz .75 2.00
THP14 Andre Ethier .75 2.00
THP15 Roy Halladay 1.25 3.00
THP16 Cliff Lee 1.25 3.00
THP17 Dan Uggla .75 2.00
THP18 Mark Teixeira 1.25 3.00
THP19 Felix Hernandez 1.25 3.00
THP20 Buster Posey 1.50 4.00
THP21 Ryan Zimmerman .75 2.00
THP22 Ian Kinsler .75 2.00
THP23 Mike Stanton .75 2.00
THP24 Troy Tulowitzki 1.25 3.00
THP25 Zack Greinke .75 2.00
THP26 Pedro Alvarez .75 2.00
THP27 Jon Lester 1.25 3.00
THP28 Justin Upton .75 2.00
THP29 Clayton Kershaw 1.25 3.00
THP30 Carl Crawford .75 2.00

2011 Topps Target Red Diamond

COMPLETE SET (30) 40.00 80.00
RANDOM INSERTS IN TARGET PACKS
RDT1 Babe Ruth 3.00 8.00
RDT2 Derek Jeter 3.00 8.00
RDT3 Ty Cobb 2.00 5.00
RDT4 Josh Hamilton 1.25 3.00
RDT5 Albert Pujols 3.00 8.00
RDT6 Jason Heyward 1.50 4.00
RDT7 Mickey Mantle 4.00 10.00
RDT8 Ryan Braun 1.50 4.00
RDT9 Honus Wagner 1.25 3.00
RDT10 Jackie Robinson 1.25 3.00
RDT11 Roy Halladay 1.25 3.00
RDT12 Carlos Gonzalez .75 2.00
RDT13 Ichiro Suzuki 2.00 5.00
RDT14 Roy Campanella 1.25 3.00
RDT15 Miguel Cabrera 1.25 3.00
RDT16 Adrian Gonzalez .75 2.00
RDT17 CC Sabathia .75 2.00
RDT18 Ryan Howard 1.50 4.00
RDT19 Adrian Beltre .50 1.25
RDT20 Sandy Koufax 4.00 10.00
RDT21 Evan Longoria 1.50 4.00
RDT22 Robinson Cano 1.25 3.00
RDT23 Adam Dunn .75 2.00
RDT24 Joe Mauer 1.25 3.00
RDT25 Tim Lincecum 1.25 3.00
RDT26 Victor Martinez .75 2.00
RDT27 Ubaldo Jimenez .75 2.00
RDT28 Matt Holliday 1.25 3.00
RDT29 Josh Johnson .75 2.00
RDT30 Hank Aaron 2.50 6.00

2011 Topps Topps Town

COMPLETE SET (50) 6.00 15.00
STATED ODDS 1:1 HOBBY
TT1 Miguel Cabrera .50 1.25
TT2 Dan Haren .20 .50
TT3 Brett Wallace .20 .50
TT4 Brett Anderson .30 .75
TT5 Roy Halladay .50 1.25
TT6 Vernon Wells .20 .50
TT7 Joe Mauer .50 1.25
TT8 Jose Reyes .30 .75
TT9 Adam Jones .30 .75
TT10 Josh Hamilton .50 1.25
TT11 Chris Young .20 .50
TT12 Mat Latos .20 .50
TT13 Chase Utley .50 1.25
TT14 Shin-Soo Choo .30 .75
TT15 David Wright .60 1.50
TT16 Nick Markakis .50 1.25
TT17 Aroldis Chapman .75 2.00
TT18 Ryan Zimmerman .30 .75
TT19 Andrew McCutchen .50 1.25
TT20 Ichiro Suzuki .75 2.00
TT21 Starlin Castro .50 1.25
TT22 Jason Heyward .60 1.50
TT23 Evan Longoria .60 1.50
TT24 Josh Johnson .30 .75
TT25 Ryan Howard .60 1.50
TT26 Matt Garza .20 .50
TT27 Andre Ethier .30 .75
TT28 David Ortiz .30 .75
TT29 Carlos Gonzalez .30 .75
TT30 Ryan Braun .60 1.50
TT31 Manny Ramirez .50 1.25
TT32 Mike Stanton .30 .75
TT33 Victor Martinez .30 .75
TT34 Felix Hernandez .50 1.25
TT35 David Price .50 1.25
TT36 Robinson Cano .50 1.25
TT37 Billy Butler .20 .50
TT38 Justin Verlander .60 1.50
TT39 Adrian Gonzalez .30 .75
TT40 Buster Posey .60 1.50
TT41 Carlos Santana .50 1.25
TT42 Kevin Youkilis .30 .75
TT43 Vladimir Guerrero .50 1.25
TT44 Ubaldo Jimenez .30 .75
TT45 Hanley Ramirez .50 1.25
TT46 Joey Votto .50 1.25
TT47 Dustin Pedroia .60 1.50
TT48 Troy Tulowitzki .50 1.25
TT49 CC Sabathia .30 .75
TT50 Albert Pujols 1.25 3.00

2011 Topps Topps Town Series 2

COMPLETE SET (50) 6.00 15.00
TT1 Tim Lincecum .50 1.25
TT2 Mark Reynolds .20 .50
TT3 Cliff Lee .50 1.25
TT4 Logan Morrison .20 .50
TT5 Grady Sizemore .30 .75
TT6 Todd Helton .30 .75
TT7 Adrian Gonzalez .30 .75
TT8 Ryan Ludwick .20 .50
TT9 Dan Uggla .30 .75
TT10 Justin Upton .30 .75
TT11 Kendrys Morales .20 .50
TT12 Justin Morneau .50 1.25
TT13 Zack Greinke .30 .75
TT14 Derek Jeter 1.25 3.00
TT15 Jose Bautista .30 .75
TT16 Adam Wainwright .30 .75
TT17 Nelson Cruz .30 .75
TT18 Brandon Phillips .20 .50
TT19 Victor Martinez .30 .75
TT20 Clayton Kershaw .50 1.25
TT21 Adam Dunn .30 .75
TT22 Chone Figgins .20 .50
TT23 Matt Holliday .50 1.25
TT24 Neftali Feliz .20 .50
TT25 Pedro Alvarez .30 .75
TT26 Trevor Cahill .20 .50
TT27 Mark Teixeira .50 1.25
TT28 Aramis Ramirez .20 .50
TT29 Chris Coghlan .20 .50
TT30 Carl Crawford .30 .75
TT31 Jon Lester .50 1.25
TT32 Cole Hamels .50 1.25
TT33 Austin Jackson .20 .50
TT34 Ike Davis .30 .75
TT35 Ian Kinsler .30 .75
TT36 Hunter Pence .30 .75
TT37 Jeremy Hellickson .60 1.50
TT38 Brian Matusz .50 1.25
TT39 Clay Buchholz .30 .75
TT40 Lance Berkman .30 .75
TT41 Angel Pagan .20 .50
TT42 Torii Hunter .20 .50
TT43 Chris Carpenter .50 1.25
TT44 B.J. Upton .30 .75
TT45 Martin Prado .20 .50
TT46 Roy Oswalt .30 .75
TT47 Jay Bruce .30 .75
TT48 Joakim Soria .20 .50
TT49 Jayson Werth .30 .75
TT50 Phil Hughes .20 .50

2011 Topps Toys R Us Purple Diamond

COMPLETE SET (10) 12.50 30.00
RANDOM INSERTS IN TRU PACKS
PDC1 Buster Posey 6.00 15.00
PDC2 Troy Tulowitzki 1.25 3.00
PDC3 Evan Longoria 1.50 4.00
PDC4 Tim Lincecum 1.25 3.00
PDC5 Alex Rodriguez 2.00 5.00
PDC6 CC Sabathia .75 2.00
PDC7 Joe Mauer 1.25 3.00
PDC8 Robinson Cano 1.25 3.00
PDC9 Starlin Castro 1.25 3.00
PDC10 Ryan Howard 1.50 4.00

2011 Topps Value Box Chrome Refractors

COMPLETE SET (3) 4.00 10.00
ONE PER $14.99 RETAIL VALUE BOX
MBC1 Mickey Mantle 2.50 6.00
MBC2 Jackie Robinson .75 2.00
MBC3 Babe Ruth 2.00 5.00

2011 Topps Wal Mart Blue Diamond

COMPLETE SET (30) 30.00 60.00
RANDOM INSERTS IN WAL MART PACKS
BDW1 Albert Pujols 3.00 8.00
BDW2 Derek Jeter 3.00 8.00
BDW3 Mat Latos .50 1.25
BDW4 Hanley Ramirez 1.25 3.00
BDW5 Miguel Cabrera 1.25 3.00
BDW6 Aroldis Chapman 1.50 4.00
BDW7 Chase Utley 1.25 3.00
BDW8 Ryan Braun 1.50 4.00
BDW9 David Price 1.25 3.00
BDW10 Joey Votto 1.25 3.00
BDW11 David Wright 1.50 4.00
BDW12 Carlos Gonzalez .75 2.00
BDW13 David Ortiz .75 2.00
BDW14 Andre Ethier .75 2.00
BDW15 Roy Halladay 1.25 3.00
BDW16 Cliff Lee 1.25 3.00
BDW17 Dan Uggla .75 2.00
BDW18 Mark Teixeira 1.25 3.00

BDW19 Felix Hernandez 1.25 3.00
BDW20 Buster Posey 1.50 4.00
BDW21 Ryan Zimmerman .75 2.00
BDW22 Ian Kinsler .75 2.00
BDW23 Mike Stanton .75 2.00
BDW24 Troy Tulowitzki 1.25 3.00
BDW25 Zack Greinke .75 2.00
BDW26 Pedro Alvarez .75 2.00
BDW27 Jon Lester 1.25 3.00
BDW28 Justin Upton .75 2.00
BDW29 Clayton Kershaw 1.25 3.00
BDW30 Carl Crawford .75 2.00

2011 Topps Wal Mart Hanger Pack Exlcusives

ONE PER WAL MART HANGER PACK
WHP1 Babe Ruth 6.00 15.00
WHP2 Derek Jeter 6.00 15.00
WHP3 Ty Cobb 4.00 10.00
WHP4 Josh Hamilton 2.50 6.00
WHP5 Albert Pujols 6.00 15.00
WHP6 Jason Heyward 3.00 8.00
WHP7 Mickey Mantle 8.00 20.00
WHP8 Ryan Braun 3.00 8.00
WHP9 Honus Wagner 2.50 6.00
WHP10 Jackie Robinson 2.50 6.00
WHP11 Roy Halladay 2.50 6.00
WHP12 Carlos Gonzalez 1.50 4.00
WHP13 Ichiro Suzuki 4.00 10.00
WHP14 Roy Campanella 2.50 6.00
WHP15 Miguel Cabrera 2.50 6.00
WHP16 Adrian Gonzalez 1.50 4.00
WHP17 CC Sabathia 1.50 4.00
WHP18 Ryan Howard 3.00 8.00
WHP19 Adrian Beltre 1.00 2.50
WHP20 Sandy Koufax 8.00 20.00
WHP21 Evan Longoria 3.00 8.00
WHP22 Robinson Cano 2.50 6.00
WHP23 Adam Dunn 1.50 4.00
WHP24 Joe Mauer 2.50 6.00
WHP25 Tim Lincecum 2.50 6.00
WHP26 Victor Martinez 1.50 4.00
WHP27 Ubaldo Jimenez 1.50 4.00
WHP28 Matt Holliday 2.50 6.00
WHP29 Josh Johnson 1.50 4.00
WHP30 Hank Aaron 5.00 12.00

2011 Topps World Champion Autograph Relics

STATED ODDS 1:7941 HOBBY
STATED PRINT RUN 50 SER.#'d SETS
EXCHANGE DEADLINE 1/31/2014
BP Buster Posey 300.00 600.00
CR Cody Ross EXCH 150.00 250.00
FS Freddy Sanchez EXCH 125.00 250.00
MB Madison Bumgarner 100.00 200.00
PS Pablo Sandoval 150.00 250.00

2011 Topps World Champion Autographs

STATED ODDS 1:33,000 HOBBY
STATED PRINT RUN 50 SER.#'d SETS
EXCHANGE DEADLINE 1/31/2014
WCA1 Buster Posey 175.00 350.00
WCA2 Madison Bumgarner 100.00 200.00
WCA3 Pablo Sandoval 100.00 200.00
WCA4 Cody Ross 100.00 200.00
WCA5 Freddy Sanchez 100.00 200.00

2011 Topps World Champion Relics

STATED ODDS 1:6250 HOBBY
STATED PRINT RUN 100 SER.#'d SETS
EXCHANGE DEADLINE 1/31/2014
WCR1 Buster Posey 100.00 200.00
WCR2 Madison Bumgarner 60.00 120.00
WCR3 Pablo Sandoval 50.00 100.00
WCR4 Cody Ross EXCH 75.00 150.00
WCR5 Freddy Sanchez 40.00 80.00
WCR6 Tim Lincecum 100.00 200.00
WCR7 Matt Cain 40.00 80.00
WCR8 Jonathan Sanchez EXCH 75.00 150.00
WCR9 Brian Wilson 75.00 150.00
WCR10 Juan Uribe EXCH 40.00 80.00
WCR11 Aubrey Huff EXCH 60.00 120.00
WCR12 Edgar Renteria 50.00 100.00
WCR13 Andres Torres EXCH 40.00 80.00
WCR14 Pat Burrell 40.00 80.00
WCR15 Mike Fontenot 40.00 80.00

2011 Topps Update

COMP.SET w/o SP's (330) 20.00 50.00
COMMON CARD (1-330) .12 .30
COMMON SP VAR (1-330) 5.00 12.00
COMMON RC (1-330) .25 .60
PRINTING PLATE ODDS 1:846 HOBBY
PLATE PRINT RUN 1 SET PER COLOR
BLACK-CYAN-MAGENTA-YELLOW ISSUED
NO PLATE PRICING DUE TO SCARCITY
US1 Adrian Gonzalez .20 .50
US2 Ty Wigginton .12 .30
US3 Blake Beavan .20 .50
US4A Brian McCann .20 .50
US4B Carlton Fisk SP 5.00 12.00
US5 Josh Willingham .12 .30
US6 Prince Fielder .20 .50
US7 Nate Schierholtz .12 .30
US8 David Robertson .12 .30
US9 Jose Iglesias RC .40 1.00
US10A Jose Bautista .20 .50
US10B Hank Aaron SP 6.00 15.00
US11 Jason Pridie .12 .30
US12 Greg Dobbs .12 .30
US13 Koyie Hill .12 .30
US14 Alex Avila .12 .30
US15 Aaron Heilman .12 .30
US16 Wellington Castillo .12 .30
US17 Craig Gentry .12 .30
US18A Robinson Cano .30 .75
US18B Joe DiMaggio SP 8.00 20.00
US19 Mike Napoli .20 .50
US20 Adrian Gonzalez .20 .50
US21A Prince Fielder .20 .50
US21B Willie McCovey SP 5.00 12.00
US22 Randall Delgado RC .40 1.00
US23 Chance Ruffin RC .25 .60
US24 Rex Brothers RC .25 .60
US25 Tim Stauffer .12 .30
US26 Jered Weaver .12 .30
US27 Joey Devine .12 .30
US28 Adam Kennedy .12 .30
US29 Mike MacDougal .12 .30
US30 Dustin Ackley RC 1.00 2.50
US31A Curtis Granderson .20 .50
US31B Paul O'Neill SP 5.00 12.00
US32 Matt Stairs .12 .30
US33 Jayson Nix .12 .30
US34 David Ross .12 .30
US35 Eduardo Nunez RC .25 .60
US36 Josh Judy RC .25 .60
US37 Rick Ankiel .12 .30
US38A Josh Hamilton .30 .75
US38B Roger Maris SP 5.00 12.00
US39 Eduardo Sanchez RC .40 1.00
US40 Brian Fuentes .12 .30
US41 Lou Marson .12 .30
US42A David Ortiz .20 .50
US42B Frank Thomas SP 5.00 12.00
US43 Carlos Quentin .12 .30
US44 Matt Treanor .12 .30
US45 Peter Moylan .12 .30
US46 Angel Sanchez .12 .30
US47 Paul Goldschmidt RC 1.25 3.00
US48 Scott Hairston .12 .30
US49 Rickie Weeks .20 .50
US50A Jered Weaver .12 .30
US50B Nolan Ryan SP 8.00 20.00
US51 Andruw Jones .12 .30
US52 Lance Berkman .20 .50
US53 Koji Uehara .12 .30
US54 Jerry Sands RC 1.00 2.50
US55 Anthony Rizzo RC .40 1.00
US56 Ryan Adams RC .25 .60
US57 Tony Campana RC .60 1.50
US58A Tim Lincecum .30 .75
US58B Bert Blyleven SP 5.00 12.00
US59A Matt Kemp .20 .50
US59B Rickey Henderson SP 5.00 12.00
US60 Heath Bell .20 .50
US61 Nick Masset .12 .30
US62 Jason Marquis .12 .30
US63 Doug Fister .12 .30
US64 J.C. Romero .12 .30
US65 Mitchell Boggs .12 .30
US66 Andy Dirks RC .25 .60
US67 Miguel Olivo .12 .30
US68 Tyler Clippard .12 .30
US69 Gerald Laird .12 .30
US70 Michael Wuertz .12 .30
US71 Jeff Francis .12 .30
US72 Colby Rasmus .30 .75
US73 Juan Nicasio .12 .30
US74 Henry Blanco .12 .30
US75 Gio Gonzalez .12 .30
US76 Nolan Reimold .12 .30
US77 Freddy Garcia .12 .30
US78 David Ortiz .20 .50
US79 Chris Dickerson .12 .30
US80 Jose Bautista .20 .50
US81 Aaron Harang .12 .30
US82 Mark Ellis .12 .30
US83 Brandon Belt .50 1.25
US84 Pablo Sandoval .20 .50
US85A Roy Halladay .30 .75
US85B Tom Seaver SP 5.00 12.00
US86 Rafael Furcal .12 .30
US87 Clayton Mortensen .12 .30
US88 Orlando Cabrera .12 .30
US89 Sean O'Sullivan .12 .30
US90 James Russell .12 .30
US91 Brandon League .12 .30
US92 Hunter Pence .20 .50
US93 Matt Downs .12 .30
US94 Ryan Vogelsong .12 .30
US95 Lyle Overbay .12 .30
US96 Ryan Hanigan .12 .30
US97 Cody Eppley RC .25 .60
US98 Alexi Ogando .30 .75
US99 Carlos Villanueva .12 .30
US100 Cliff Lee .30 .75
US101 Scott Downs .12 .30
US102 Sean Burnett .12 .30
US103 Josh Collmenter RC .25 .60
US104 Logan Forsythe RC .25 .60
US105 Joel Hanrahan .20 .50
US106 Ryan Ludwick .12 .30
US107 Brandon McCarthy .12 .30
US108 Ubaldo Jimenez .12 .30
US109 Jair Jurrjens .12 .30
US110 Edgar Renteria .12 .30
US111 Scott Sizemore .12 .30
US112 Lonnie Chisenhall RC .40 1.00
US113 Chris Perez .12 .30
US114 Lance Lynn RC .25 .60
US115 Kerry Wood .12 .30
US116 Shawn Camp .12 .30
US117 Michael Stutes RC .40 1.00
US118 Michael Pineda .40 1.00
US119 Jeff Francoeur .20 .50
US120 Bobby Parnell .12 .30
US121 Jon Rauch .12 .30
US122 Alfredo Aceves .12 .30
US123 Brad Penny .12 .30
US124 Xavier Paul .12 .30
US125 Joel Peralta .12 .30
US126 Adrian Gonzalez .20 .50
US127 Rickie Weeks .20 .50
US128 Mariano Rivera .30 .75
US129 Brooks Conrad .12 .30
US130 David Robertson .12 .30
US131 Jeff Keppinger .12 .30
US132 Jose Altuve RC .40 1.00
US133 Fernando Salas .20 .50
US134 Michael Bourn .12 .30
US135 Grant Balfour .12 .30
US136 Brandon Crawford .12 .30
US137 Willie Bloomquist .12 .30
US138A Michael Young .12 .30
US138B Paul Molitor SP 5.00 12.00
US139 Rafael Soriano .12 .30
US140A Clayton Kershaw .30 .75
US140B Sandy Koufax SP 6.00 15.00
US141 Mike Cameron .12 .30
US142 Alex White RC .25 .60
US143 Craig Kimbrel .30 .75
US144 Kevin Youkilis .20 .50
US145 Bartolo Colon .12 .30
US146 Jordan Walden .12 .30
US147 C.J. Wilson .12 .30
US148 Alex Presley RC .60 1.50
US149 Omar Infante .12 .30
US150 Adrian Beltre .12 .30
US151 Cory Gearrin RC .25 .60
US152 Julio Teheran RC .75 2.00
US153 Matt Guerrier .12 .30
US154A Cliff Lee .30 .75
US154B Babe Ruth SP 6.00 15.00
US155 Eric Hosmer RC 2.00 5.00
US156 Humberto Quintero .12 .30
US157 Reed Johnson .12 .30
US158 Darren Oliver .12 .30
US159 Alex Cobb RC .25 .60
US160 Victor Martinez .20 .50
US161 Conor Jackson .12 .30
US162 Troy Tulowitzki .30 .75
US163 Adrian Beltre .12 .30
US164 Hector Noesi .40 1.00
US165 Al Albuquerque RC .25 .60
US166 David Ortiz .20 .50
US167 Brandan Ryan .12 .30
US168 Bruce Chen .12 .30
US169 Ezequiel Carrera RC .25 .60
US170 Brad Ziegler .12 .30
US171 Matt Lindstrom .12 .30
US172 Jonny Venters .12 .30
US173 Charlie Furbush RC .25 .60
US174 Jacob Turner RC 1.00 2.50
US175 Mike Trout RC 1.50 4.00
US176 Xavier Nady .12 .30
US177 Rene Tosoni RC .25 .60
US178 Jason Bourgeois .12 .30
US179 Michael Pineda .40 1.00
US180 Daniel Moskos RC .25 .60
US181 Jo Jo Reyes .12 .30
US182 Ronny Paulino .12 .30
US183 Carlos Peguero RC .40 1.00
US184 Tyler Chatwood RC .25 .60
US185 Orlando Hudson .12 .30
US186 J.D. Martinez RC .40 1.00
US187 Bobby Wilson .12 .30
US188 Eric Hosmer 1.00 2.50
US189 Wilson Valdez .12 .30
US190 Alexi Ogando .30 .75
US191 Andy Sonnanstine .12 .30
US192 Mike Moustakas RC .60 1.50
US193 Lonnie Chisenhall .20 .50
US194 Jason Kipnis RC .75 2.00
US195A Joey Votto .30 .75
US195B Larry Walker SP 5.00 12.00
US196 Philip Humber .12 .30
US197 Brandon League .12 .30
US198 Kevin Jepsen .12 .30
US199 Micah Owings .12 .30
US200 Vladimir Guerrero .30 .75
US201 Hisanori Takahashi .12 .30
US202 Derrek Lee .12 .30
US203 Juan Nicasio RC .25 .60
US204 Brian Wilson .30 .75
US205 D.J. LeMahieu RC .25 .60
US206 J.P. Howell .12 .30
US207A Jay Bruce .20 .50
US207B Frank Robinson SP 5.00 12.00
US208 Javier Lopez .12 .30
US209 Rubby De La Rosa RC .60 1.50
US210 Jayson Werth .20 .50
US211 Dustin Moseley .12 .30
US212 Pat Neshek .12 .30
US213 Louis Coleman RC .25 .60
US214 Matt Daley .12 .30
US215 Michael Dunn .12 .30
US216 Takashi Saito .12 .30
US217 Elliot Johnson .12 .30
US218 Matt Kemp .20 .50
US219 George Sherrill .12 .30
US220 Adam Dunn .20 .50
US221 Jamey Carroll .12 .30
US222 Chris Gimenez .12 .30
US223 Arthur Rhodes .12 .30
US224 Bill Hall .12 .30
US225 David DeJesus .12 .30
US226 Steve Pearce .12 .30
US227 Kosuke Fukudome .30 .75
US228 Zach Britton .30 .75
US229A Asdrubal Cabrera .20 .50
US229B Roberto Alomar SP 8.00 20.00
US230A Miguel Cabrera .30 .75
US230B Al Kaline SP 5.00 12.00
US231 Charlie Blackmon RC .25 .60
US232 Miguel Tejada .20 .50
US233 John McDonald .12 .30
US234 Brandon Crawford RC .25 .60
US235 Charlie Morton .12 .30
US236 Jose Morales .12 .30
US237 Ryan Roberts .12 .30
US238A Carlos Beltran .20 .50
US238B Darryl Strawberry SP 5.00 12.00
US239 J.J. Hardy .12 .30
US240 Blake Tekotte RC .25 .60
US241 Brandon Wood .12 .30
US242 Matt Holliday .30 .75
US243 Chris Denorfia .12 .30
US244 Francisco Rodriguez .20 .50
US245 Kevin Correia .12 .30
US246 Alcides Escobar .12 .30
US247 Zack Cozart RC .60 1.50
US248 Octavio Dotel .12 .30
US249A Starlin Castro .20 .50
US249B Ozzie Smith SP 5.00 12.00
US250 Zack Greinke .20 .50
US251 Justin Turner .12 .30
US252 Derek Jeter .75 2.00
US253 Scott Linebrink .12 .30
US254 Dustin Ackley .50 1.25
US255 Allen Craig .12 .30
US256 Mark Kotsay .12 .30
US257 Erik Bedard .12 .30
US258A Andre Ethier .20 .50
US258B Monte Irvin SP 5.00 12.00
US259 Andre Ethier .20 .50
US260A Matt Holliday .30 .75
US260B Ty Cobb SP 5.00 12.00
US261 John Buck .12 .30
US262 Javy Guerra (RC) .40 1.00
US263 Chad Qualls .12 .30
US264 Alex White .12 .30
US265 Willie Harris .12 .30
US266 Jason Isringhausen .12 .30
US267 Sam Fuld .12 .30
US268 Yadier Molina .20 .50
US269 Sergio Santos .12 .30
US270 Todd Frazier RC .40 1.00
US271 Eric O'Flaherty .12 .30
US272 Jorge Cantu .12 .30
US273 Miguel Montero .12 .30
US274 Jeff Karstens .12 .30
US275 Michael Cuddyer .12 .30
US276 Yuniesky Betancourt .12 .30
US277 Sam LeCure .12 .30
US278A Jacoby Ellsbury .30 .75
US278B Tris Speaker SP 5.00 12.00
US279 Trevor Plouffe .12 .30
US280 Kyle Farnsworth .12 .30
US281 Mark Melancon .12 .30
US282 Brad Hand RC .25 .60
US283 Latroy Hawkins .12 .30
US284 Laynce Nix .12 .30
US285 David Purcey .12 .30
US286 Rich Thompson .12 .30
US287 Matt Joyce .12 .30
US288 Eric Thames RC .25 .60
US289 Eric Chavez .12 .30
US290 Sean Burroughs .12 .30
US291A Andrew McCutchen .30 .75
US291B Andre Dawson SP 5.00 12.00
US292 Mike Adams .12 .30
US293 Howie Kendrick .12 .30
US294 Edwin Jackson .12 .30
US295 Wilson Ramos .12 .30
US296 Bobby Jenks .12 .30
US297 Chase D'Arnaud RC .40 1.00
US298 Yorvit Torrealba .12 .30
US299 Robinson Cano .30 .75
US300 Carl Crawford .20 .50
US301 Tom Gorzelanny .12 .30
US302 Alex Torres RC .25 .60
US303 Juan Uribe .12 .30
US304 Hunter Pence .20 .50
US305 Carlos Beltran .20 .50
US306 Brandon Phillips .12 .30
US307 Casey Coleman .12 .30
US308 Kyle Seager RC .40 1.00
US309A Paul Konerko .20 .50
US309B Jimmie Foxx SP 5.00 12.00
US310 Scott Rolen .20 .50
US311 Drew Butera .12 .30
US312 Danny Duffy RC .40 1.00
US313 Tyson Ross .12 .30
US314 Armando Galarraga .12 .30
US315 Carlos Pena .20 .50
US316 Justin Upton .20 .50
US317 Craig Counsell .12 .30
US318 Brayan Pena .12 .30
US319 Corey Patterson .12 .30
US320 Russell Martin .12 .30
US321 Gaby Sanchez .12 .30
US322 Fernando Martinez .12 .30
US323 Jhonny Peralta .12 .30
US324 Melvin Mora .12 .30
US325 Jason Giambi .12 .30
US326 Trevor Bell .12 .30
US327 Blake Beavan RC .40 1.00
US328 Kevin Gregg .12 .30
US329 Dee Gordon RC .60 1.50
US330 Lance Berkman .20 .50

2011 Topps Update Cognac Diamond Anniversary

*COGNAC VET: 2X TO 5X BASIC
*COGNAC RC: 1X TO 2.5X BASIC RC
*COGNAC SP: .25X TO .6X BASIC SP
STATED ODDS 1:3 HOBBY
STATED SP ODDS 1:81 HOBBY

2011 Topps Update Black

*BLACK: 12X TO 30X BASIC
*BLACK RC: 6X TP 15X BASIC
STATED ODDS 1:58 HOBBY
STATED PRINT RUN 60 SER.#'d SETS

2011 Topps Update Diamond Anniversary

*DIAMOND VET: 2X TO 5X BASIC
*DIAMOND RC: 1X TO 2.5X BASIC RC
*DIAMOND SP: .25X TO .6X BASIC SP
STATED ODDS 1:4 HOBBY
STATED SP ODDS 1:79 HOBBY

2011 Topps Update Gold

*GOLD VET: 2X TO 5X BASIC
*GOLD RC: 1X TO 2.5X BASIC RC
STATED ODDS 1:3 HOBBY
STATED PRINT RUN 2011 SER.#'d SETS

2011 Topps Update Gold Canary Diamond

STATED ODDS 1:4100 HOBBY
STATED PRINT RUN 1 SER.#'D SET
NO PRICING DUE TO SCARCITY

2011 Topps Update Hope Diamond Anniversary

*HOPE VET: 12X TO 30X BASIC
*HOPE RC: 6X TO 15X BASIC RC
*HOPE SP: .75X TO 2X BASIC SP
STATED ODDS 1:68 HOBBY
STATED SP ODDS 1:2627 HOBBY
STATED PRINT RUN 60 SER.#'d SETS

2011 Topps Update Platinum

STATED ODDS 1:4100 HOBBY
STATED PRINT RUN 1 SER.#'D SET
NO PRICING DUE TO SCARCITY

2011 Topps Update Target Red Border

*TARGET: 2X TO 5X BASIC
*TARGET RC: 1X TO 2.5X BASIC RC
FOUND IN TARGET RETAIL PACKS

2011 Topps Update Wal Mart Blue Border

*WM: 2X TO 5X BASIC
*WM RC: 1X TO 2.5X BASIC RC
FOUND IN WAL MART RETAIL PACKS

2011 Topps Update All-Star Stitches

STATED ODDS 1:51 HOBBY
AS1 Jose Bautista 4.00 10.00
AS2 Alex Avila 4.00 10.00
AS3 Robinson Cano 5.00 12.00
AS4 Adrian Gonzalez 4.00 10.00
AS5 Curtis Granderson 4.00 10.00
AS6 Josh Hamilton 5.00 12.00
AS7 David Ortiz 4.00 10.00
AS8 Carlos Quentin 3.00 8.00
AS9 Jered Weaver 3.00 8.00
AS10 Tim Lincecum 5.00 12.00
AS11 Gio Gonzalez 3.00 8.00
AS12 Brandon League 3.00 8.00
AS13 Alexi Ogando 3.00 8.00
AS14 Chris Perez 4.00 10.00
AS15 Justin Verlander 5.00 12.00
AS16 David Robertson 4.00 10.00
AS17 Michael Young 3.00 8.00
AS18 Kevin Youkilis 3.00 8.00
AS19 Josh Beckett 4.00 10.00
AS20 C.J. Wilson 3.00 8.00
AS21 Adrian Beltre 3.00 8.00
AS22 Asdrubal Cabrera 4.00 10.00
AS23 Miguel Cabrera 5.00 12.00
AS24 Michael Cuddyer 4.00 10.00
AS25 Jacoby Ellsbury 4.00 10.00
AS26 Matt Joyce 4.00 10.00
AS27 Howie Kendrick 3.00 8.00
AS28 Paul Konerko 3.00 8.00
AS29 Justin Upton 4.00 10.00
AS30 Jhonny Peralta 4.00 10.00
AS31 Brian McCann 3.00 8.00
AS32 Prince Fielder 4.00 10.00
AS33 Rickie Weeks 3.00 8.00
AS34 Lance Berkman 4.00 10.00
AS35 Matt Kemp 4.00 10.00
AS36 Heath Bell 3.00 8.00
AS37 Tyler Clippard 3.00 8.00
AS38 Pablo Sandoval 4.00 10.00
AS39 Roy Halladay 5.00 12.00
AS40 Joel Hanrahan 4.00 10.00
AS41 Jair Jurrjens 4.00 10.00
AS42 Clayton Kershaw 5.00 12.00
AS43 Craig Kimbrel 5.00 12.00
AS44 Cliff Lee 5.00 12.00
AS45 Troy Tulowitzki 3.00 8.00
AS46 Jonny Venters 4.00 10.00
AS47 Joey Votto 5.00 12.00
AS48 Brian Wilson 5.00 12.00
AS49 Jay Bruce 4.00 10.00
AS50 Carlos Beltran 3.00 8.00
AS51 Starlin Castro 5.00 12.00
AS52 Andre Ethier 3.00 8.00
AS53 Matt Holliday 4.00 10.00
AS54 Yadier Molina 4.00 10.00
AS55 Miguel Montero 4.00 10.00
AS56 Andrew McCutchen 4.00 10.00
AS57 Hunter Pence 4.00 10.00
AS58 Brandon Phillips 4.00 10.00
AS59 Scott Rolen 4.00 10.00
AS60 Gaby Sanchez 3.00 8.00
AS61 Kevin Correia 3.00 8.00
AS62 Russell Martin 4.00 10.00
AS63 Jose Valverde 4.00 10.00
AS64 Jose Reyes 5.00 12.00
AS65 Ryan Braun 4.00 10.00
AS66 Felix Hernandez 3.00 8.00
AS67 Jon Lester 4.00 10.00
AS68 David Price 4.00 10.00
AS69 James Shields 3.00 8.00
AS70 Matt Cain 4.00 10.00
AS71 Cole Hamels 4.00 10.00
AS72 Ryan Vogelsong 4.00 10.00
AS73 Placido Polanco 4.00 10.00
AS74 Shane Victorino 4.00 10.00
AS75 Ricky Romero 3.00 8.00

2011 Topps Update All-Star Stitches Diamond Anniversary

*DIAMOND: .75X TO 2X BASIC
STATED ODDS 1:759 HOBBY
STATED PRINT RUN 60 SER.#'d SETS

2011 Topps Update All-Star Stitches Gold Canary Diamond

STATED ODDS 1:45,000 HOBBY
STATED PRINT RUN 1 SER.#'d SET
NO PRICING DUE TO SCARCITY

2011 Topps Update All-Star Stitches Autographs

STATED ODDS 1:11,675 HOBBY
STATED PRINT RUN 25 SER.#'d SETS
NO PRICING DUE TO SCARCITY

2011 Topps Update All-Star Stitches Dual

STATED ODDS 1:13,825 HOBBY
STATED PRINT RUN 25 SER.#'d SETS
NO PRICING DUE TO SCARCITY

2011 Topps Update All-Star Stitches Jumbo Patches

STATED ODDS 1:2,500 HOBBY
STATED PRINT RUN 6 SER.#'d SETS
NO PRICING DUE TO SCARCITY

2011 Topps Update All-Star Stitches Jumbo Patches Autographs

STATED ODDS 1:18,725 HOBBY
STATED PRINT RUN 6 SER.#'d SETS
NO PRICING DUE TO SCARCITY

2011 Topps Update All-Star Stitches Triple

STATED ODDS 1:4450 HOBBY
STATED PRINT RUN 25 SER.#'d SETS
NO PRICING DUE TO SCARCITY

2011 Topps Update Diamond Duos

COMPLETE SET (30) 6.00 15.00
STATED ODDS 1:8 HOBBY
DD1 Felix Hernandez .75 2.00
Michael Pineda
DD2 Andre Ethier .40 1.00
Matt Kemp
DD3 Jered Weaver .25 .60
Dan Haren
DD4 Albert Pujols 1.50 4.00
Lance Berkman
DD5 Eric Hosmer 2.00 5.00
Brandon Belt
DD6 Brett Anderson .40 1.00
Trevor Cahill
DD7 Starlin Castro .75 2.00
Darwin Barney
DD8 Joey Votto .60 1.50
Jay Bruce
DD9 Zack Greinke .40 1.00
Shaun Marcum
DD10 Michael Pineda .60 1.50
Zach Britton
DD11 Adam Dunn .40 1.00
Paul Konerko
DD12 Matt Holliday .60 1.50
Colby Rasmus
DD13 Mike Stanton .40 1.00
Logan Morrison
DD14 Jose Bautista .40 1.00
Adam Lind
DD15 Joe DiMaggio 1.50 4.00
Derek Jeter
DD16 Eric Hosmer 2.00 5.00
Danny Duffy
DD17 Craig Kimbrel .60 1.50
Julio Teheran
DD18 Adrian Gonzalez .40 1.00
Jose Bautista
DD19 Justin Verlander .75 2.00
Max Scherzer
DD20 Hank Aaron 1.25 3.00
jose Bautista
DD21 David Price .60 1.50
James Shields
DD22 Ricky Romero .40 1.00
Kyle Drabek
DD23 David Ortiz .60 1.50
Vladimir Guerrero
DD24 Evan Longoria .75 2.00
Ben Zobrist
DD25 Eric Hosmer 2.00 5.00
Freddie Freeman
DD26 Buster Posey .75 2.00
Brian McCann
DD27 Grady Sizemore .40 1.00
Shin-Soo Choo
DD28 Brandon Phillips .25 .60
Howie Kendrick
DD29 Matt Kemp 1.00 2.50
Jerry Sands
DD30 Sandy Koufax 2.00 5.00
Ryan Braun

2011 Topps Update Diamond Duos Dual Relics

STATED ODDS 1:4650 HOBBY
STATED PRINT RUN 50 SER.#'d SETS
DD1 Felix Hernandez 15.00 40.00
Michael Pineda
DD2 Andre Ethier 20.00 50.00
Matt Kemp
DD3 Jered Weaver 20.00 50.00
Dan Haren
DD4 Albert Pujols 40.00 80.00
Lance Berkman
DD5 Eric Hosmer 50.00 100.00
Brandon Belt
DD6 Brett Anderson 6.00 15.00
Trevor Cahill
DD7 Starlin Castro 30.00 60.00
Darwin Barney
DD8 Joey Votto 15.00 40.00
Jay Bruce
DD9 Zack Greinke 15.00 40.00
Shaun Marcum
DD10 Michael Pineda 15.00 40.00
Zach Britton
DD11 Adam Dunn 20.00 50.00
Paul Konerko
DD12 Matt Holliday 10.00 25.00
Colby Rasmus
DD13 Mike Stanton 12.50 30.00
Logan Morrison
DD14 Jose Bautista 15.00 40.00
Adam Lind
DD15 Joe DiMaggio 100.00 175.00
Derek Jeter

2011 Topps Update Next 60 Autographs

STATED ODDS 1:566 HOBBY
EXCHANGE DEADLINE 9/30/2014
AC Aroldis Chapman 10.00 25.00
AJ Austin Jackson 6.00 15.00
AO Alexi Ogando 4.00 10.00
BB Brandon Belt 10.00 25.00
BW Brett Wallace 4.00 10.00
CK Craig Kimbrel 10.00 25.00
CS Chris Sale 4.00 10.00
DA Dustin Ackley 12.50 30.00
DD Danny Duffy 4.00 10.00
DH Daniel Hudson 3.00 8.00
EH Eric Hosmer EXCH 50.00 100.00
FF Freddie Freeman 10.00 25.00
JH Jeremy Hellickson 12.50 30.00
JJ Jeremy Jeffress 3.00 8.00
JS Jerry Sands 4.00 10.00
JW Jordan Walden 4.00 10.00
KD Kyle Drabek 3.00 8.00
MM Mike Moustakas 12.50 30.00
MP Michael Pineda 10.00 25.00
MS Mike Stanton 12.50 30.00
MT Mark Trumbo 8.00 20.00
NF Neftali Feliz 4.00 10.00
SC Starlin Castro 12.50 30.00
JT1 Jose Tabata 5.00 12.00
JT2 Julio Teheran 6.00 15.00

2011 Topps Update Topps Town

COMPLETE SET (50) 10.00
STATED ODDS 1:8 HOBBY
TTU1 Eric Hosmer 1.50 4.00
TTU2 Francisco Liriano .20 .50
TTU3 Prince Fielder .30 .75
TTU4 Carlos Beltran .20 .50
TTU5 Ricky Romero .20 .50
TTU6 Vernon Wells .20 .50
TTU7 Rickie Weeks .30 .75
TTU8 Brian Wilson .50 1.25
TTU9 Colby Rasmus .50 1.25
TTU10 Zach Britton .50 1.25
TTU11 Wandy Rodriguez .20 .50
TTU12 Gaby Sanchez .20 .50
TTU13 Shane Victorino .30 .75
TTU14 Matt Garza .20 .50
TTU15 Francisco Rodriguez .30 .75
TTU16 Drew Stubbs .30 .75
TTU17 James Shields .20 .50
TTU18 Heath Bell .20 .50
TTU19 Fausto Carmona .20 .50
TTU20 Freddie Freeman .75 2.00
TTU21 Chad Billingsley .20 .50
TTU22 Stephen Drew .20 .50
TTU23 Jimmy Rollins .30 .75
TTU24 Vladimir Guerrero .50 1.25
TTU25 Gio Gonzalez .20 .50
TTU26 Curtis Granderson .30 .75
TTU27 Neil Walker .20 .50
TTU28 Alfonso Soriano .30 .75
TTU29 Michael Young .30 .75
TTU30 Paul Konerko .30 .75
TTU31 Adam Lind .30 .75
TTU32 Ben Zobrist .20 .50
TTU33 Travis Hafner .20 .50
TTU34 Jhoulys Chacin .20 .50
TTU35 Jaime Garcia .30 .75
TTU36 Jered Weaver .20 .50
TTU37 Max Scherzer .20 .50
TTU38 Alex Rodriguez .75 2.00
TTU39 Jacoby Ellsbury .50 1.25
TTU40 Matt Kemp .30 .75
TTU41 Michael Bourn .20 .50
TTU42 Kurt Suzuki .20 .50
TTU43 Brian McCann .30 .75
TTU44 CC Sabathia .30 .75
TTU45 Josh Beckett .30 .75
TTU46 Adrian Beltre .20 .50
TTU47 Drew Storen .20 .50
TTU48 Ian Desmond .30 .75
TTU49 Matt Cain .30 .75
TTU50 Michael Pineda .60 1.50

1952 Topps Advertising Panels

These three card strips feature a regular 1952 Topps card and ad information on the back. These cards are not numbered in the traditional sense. Any additions to this list or any Advertising Panel list will be appreciated

COMPLETE SET 100.00 200.00
1 Bob Mahoney 75.00 150.00
Robin Roberts
Sid Hudson
2 Bob Wellman 50.00 100.00
Lou Kretlow
Ray Scarborough
3 Wally Westlake 50.00 100.00
Dizzy Trout
Irv Noren
4 Eddie Joost 50.00 100.00
Willie Jones
Gordon Goldsberry

1953 Topps Advertising Panels

These three card strips feature a regular 53 Topps card on the front and advertising information on the back.

COMPLETE SET 300.00 600.00
1 Johnny Mize 60.00 120.00
Clem Koshorek
Toby Atwell
2 Jim Hearn 50.00 100.00
Johnny Groth
Sherm Lollar
3 Mickey Mantle 250.00 500.00
Johnny Wyrostek
Sal Yvars

1954 Topps Advertising Panels

1 Granny Hamner 50.00 100.00
Richie Ashburn
Johnny Schmitz

1955 Topps Advertising Panels

These panels feature regular 1955 Topps cards on the front and advertising information on the back. These items have been seen with advertising for the 1955 Topps Double Header set affixed as well.

COMPLETE SET 150.00 300.00
1 Dave Jolly 25.00 50.00
Jim Pendleton
Karl Spooner
2 Danny Schell 25.00 50.00
Jake Thies
Howie Pollet
3 Jackie Robinson 125.00 250.00
Bill Taylor
Curt Roberts

1956 Topps Advertising Panels

These panels feature regular 1956 Topps cards on the front and advertising information on the back.

COMPLETE SET	25.00	50.00
1 Bob Grim	25.00	50.00
Dusty Rhodes		
Each Card is printed twice		
2 Johnny O'Brien	25.00	50.00
Harvey Haddix		
Frank House		

1957 Topps Advertising Panels

Issued in three card strips to promote the upcoming 1957 Topps set, these three card panels are somewhat different in that the backs of these cards were composites of other cards as well as an advertisment for Topps/Bazooka bubble gum.

COMPLETE SET	200.00	400.00
1 Dick Williams	30.00	60.00
Brooks Lawrence		
Lou Skizas		
2 Jim Piersall	75.00	150.00
Pee Wee Reese		
Harvey Kuenn		
3 Hector Lopez	40.00	80.00
Johnny Logan		
Billy Martin		
4 Tom Sturdivant	50.00	100.00
Elston Howard		
Clem Labine		
5 Brooks Lawrence	30.00	60.00
Lou Skizas		
Bob Boyd		

1959 Topps Advertising Panels

The fronts of these cards feature standard 1959 Topps cards while the backs feature cards of either Nellie Fox or Ted Kluszewski.

COMPLETE SET	400.00	800.00
1 Don McMahon	25.00	50.00
Red Wilson		
Bob Boyd		
2 Joe Pignatano	25.00	50.00
Sam Jones		
Jack Urban		
3 Billy Hunter	25.00	50.00
Chuck Stobbs		
Carl Sawatski		
4 Vito Valentinelli	25.00	50.00
Ken Lehman		
Ed Bouchee		
5 Mel Roach	50.00	100.00
Brooks Lawrence		
Warren Spahn		
6 Harvey Kuenn	25.00	50.00
Alex Grammas		
Bob Cerv		
7 Bob Cerv	250.00	500.00
Jim Bolger		
Mickey Mantle		

1960 Topps Advertising Panels

These panels were issued to promote the upcoming Topps set. The fronts feature standard 1960 Topps cards while the backs feature advertising information.

COMPLETE SET	200.00	400.00
1 Wayne Terwilliger	20.00	50.00
Kent Hadley		
Faye Throneberry		
2 Hank Foiles	20.00	50.00
Hobie Landrith		
Hal Smith		
3 Cal McLish	150.00	300.00
Hal Smith		
Ernie Banks		
Jim Grant		
Al Kaline		
Jerry Casale		
Milt Pappas		
Wally Moon		

1961 Topps Advertising Panels

Used to promote the upcoming Topps sets; these fronts show standard 1961 Topps cards on the front with advertising information on the back.

COMPLETE SET	100.00	200.00
1 Dan Dobbek	20.00	50.00
Russ Nixon		
1960 NL Pitching Leaders		
2 Jack Kralick	20.00	50.00
Dick Stigman		
Joe Christopher		
3 Ed Roebuck	20.00	50.00
Bob Schmidt		
Zoilo Versalles		
4 Lindy Shows Larry	20.00	50.00
Johnny Blanchard		
Johnny Kucks		

1962 Topps Advertising Panels

These panels feature standard 1962 Topps cards on the front as well as a Roger Maris card back.

COMPLETE SET	75.00	150.00
1 AL Home Run Leaders	50.00	100.00
Barney Schultz		
Carl Sawatski		
2 NL Strikeout Leaders	50.00	100.00
Carroll Hardy		
Carl Sawatski		
3 Darrell Johnson	50.00	100.00
AL Strikeout Leaders		
Jim Kaat		
4 Norm Larker	50.00	100.00
Al Schroll		
Jim King		

1963 Topps Advertising Panels

These Panels features regular 1963 Topps cards on the front and a Stan Musial ad/endorsement on the back.

COMPLETE SET	75.00	150.00
1 Elston Howard	40.00	80.00
Bob Veale		
Cal Koonce		
2 Hoyt Wilhelm	50.00	100.00
Don Lock		
Bob Duliba		

1964 Topps Advertising Panels

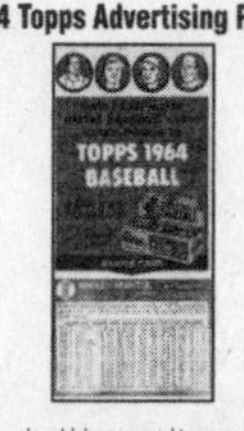

These panels, which were used to promote the 1964 Topps set; feature standard 1964 Topps cards on the front and a Mickey Mantle card back.

COMPLETE SET	150.00	300.00
1 Walt Alston	40.00	80.00
Bill Henry		
Vada Pinson		
2 Jimmie Hall	20.00	50.00
Ernie Broglio		
A.L. ERA Leaders		
3 Mickey Mantle	250.00	500.00
Jim Davenport		
Boog Powell		
4 Denis Menke	20.00	50.00
Dean Chance		
Tim Harkness		
5 Hoyt Wilhelm	40.00	80.00
Curt Flood		
Bill Bruton		
6 Carl Willey	20.00	50.00
White Sox Rookies		
Bob Friend		

1965 Topps Advertising Panels

This panel features three players on the front and an advertising for the upcoming Topps Embossed insert set.

1 Ron Herbel	20.00	50.00
Joe Gibbon		
Ed Charles		

1966 Topps Advertising Panels

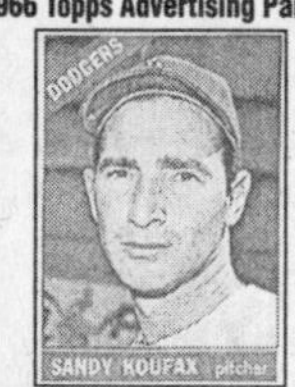

This panel was issued to preview the 1966 Topps baseball set. As is traditional for these panels, they were issued in three card strips. The back of these inserts features information on the upcoming "rub-off" insert set

1 Sandy Koufax	125.00	250.00
Jim Fregosi		
Don Mossi		
2 Jim Lonborg	50.00	100.00
Howie Koplitz		
Luis Aparicio		

1967 Topps Advertising Panels

Described as a salesman's sample; the front of this panel features standard 1967 Topps cards on the front and advertising information on the back

COMPLETE SET	50.00	100.00
1 Earl Battey	20.00	50.00
Manny Mota		
Gene Brabender		
2 Ron Fairly	30.00	60.00
Bobby Murcer		
Stan Bahnsen		
Curt Simmons		

2003 Topps 205

This 165 card series one set was released in July, 2003. The 175 card series two set was released several months later in February, 204. These cards were issued in eight-card packs which came 20 packs to a box and 10 boxes to a case. Cards number 1 through 120 feature veterans. Please note that 15 of these cards were issued with variations and we have notated the differences in these cards in our checklist. Cards number 121 through 130 feature propsects who were about ready to jump into the majors. Cards numbered 131 through 144 feature some players in their first year of cards. Card number number 145 features Louis Sockalexis who was supposedly the player the Cleveland Indians named their team in honor of. (This supposition has been buttressed by recently redisovered newspaper clippings from 1897). Cards numbered 146 to 150 feature various "reprints" of some of the tougher T-205 cards. Also randomly inserted in packs were cards featuring "repurchased" tobacco cards. Those cards were inserted at a stated rate of one in 336 for 1st series cards and one in 295 for second series cards. The second series featured the following subsets: T205 Reprints from cards 151 through 154, retired players from card 155 through 160; prospects from cards 161 through 169. First year players from cards 170 through 192. In addition, 10 players had 2 variations in the second series and we have notated this information along with some players who were issued in shorter quantity we have put an SP next to that player's name.

COMPLETE SERIES 1 (165)	15.00	40.00
COMPLETE SERIES 2 (175)	75.00	125.00
COMP.SERIES 2 w/o SP's (155)	15.00	40.00
COM (1-130/161-169/193-315)	.20	.50
COMMON (131-145/170-192)	.20	.50
COMMON (146-150)	.40	1.00
COMMON SP	1.00	2.50
SERIES 2 SP STATED ODDS 1:5		
1A Barry Bonds w/Cap	1.25	3.00
1B Barry Bonds w/Helmet	1.25	3.00
2 Bret Boone	.20	.50
3A Albert Pujols Clear Logo	1.00	2.50
3B Albert Pujols White Logo	1.00	2.50
4 Carl Crawford	.20	.50
5 Bartolo Colon	.20	.50
6 Cliff Floyd	.20	.50
7 John Olerud	.20	.50
8A Jason Giambi Full Jkt	.20	.50
8B Jason Giambi Partial Jkt	.20	.50
9 Edgardo Alfonzo	.20	.50
10 Ivan Rodriguez	.30	.75
11 Jim Edmonds	.20	.50
12A Mike Piazza Orange	.75	2.00
12B Mike Piazza Yellow	.75	2.00
13 Greg Maddux	.75	2.00
14 Jose Vidro	.20	.50
15A Vlad Guerrero Clear Logo	.50	1.25
15B V.Guerrero White Logo	.50	1.25
16 Bernie Williams	.30	.75
17 Roger Clemens	1.00	2.50
18A Miguel Tejada Blue	.20	.50
18B Miguel Tejada Green	.20	.50
19 Carlos Delgado	.20	.50
20A Alfonso Soriano w/Bat	.20	.50
20B Alf. Soriano Sunglasses	.20	.50
21 Bobby Cox MG	.20	.50
22 Mike Scioscia	.20	.50
23 John Smoltz	.30	.75
24 Luis Gonzalez	.20	.50
25 Shawn Green	.20	.50
26 Raul Ibanez	.20	.50
27 Andruw Jones	.30	.75
28 Josh Beckett	.20	.50
29 Derek Lowe	.20	.50
30 Todd Helton	.30	.75
31 Barry Larkin	.30	.75
32 Jason Jennings	.20	.50
33 Darin Erstad	.20	.50
34 Magglio Ordonez	.20	.50
35 Mike Sweeney	.20	.50
36 Kazuhisa Ishii	.20	.50
37 Ron Gardenhire MG	.20	.50
38 Tim Hudson	.20	.50
39 Tim Salmon	.30	.75
40A Pat Burrell Black Bat	.20	.50
40B Pat Burrell Brown Bat	.20	.50
41 Manny Ramirez	.30	.75
42 Nick Johnson	.20	.50
43 Tom Glavine	.30	.75
44 Mark Mulder	.20	.50
45 Brian Jordan	.20	.50
46 Rafael Palmeiro	.30	.75
47 Vernon Wells	.20	.50
48 Bob Brenly MG	.20	.50
49 C.C. Sabathia	.20	.50
50A A.Rodriguez Look Ahead	.75	2.00
50B A.Rodriguez Look Away	.75	2.00
51A Sammy Sosa Head Duck	.50	1.25
51B Sammy Sosa Head Left	.50	1.25
52 Paul Konerko	.20	.50
53 Craig Biggio	.30	.75
54 Moises Alou	.20	.50
55 Johnny Damon	.30	.75
56 Torii Hunter	.20	.50
57 Omar Vizquel	.30	.75
58 Orlando Hernandez	.20	.50
59 Barry Zito	.20	.50
60 Lance Berkman	.20	.50
61 Carlos Beltran	.20	.50
62 Edgar Renteria	.20	.50
63 Ben Sheets	.20	.50
64 Doug Mientkiewicz	.20	.50
65 Troy Glaus	.20	.50
66 Preston Wilson	.20	.50
67 Kerry Wood	.20	.50
68 Frank Thomas	.50	1.25
69 Jimmy Rollins	.20	.50
70 Brian Giles	.20	.50
71 Bobby Higginson	.20	.50
72 Larry Walker	.20	.50
73 Randy Johnson	.50	1.25
74 Tony LaRussa MG	.20	.50
75A Derek Jeter w/Gold Trim	1.25	3.00
75B D.Jeter w/o Gold Trim	1.25	3.00
76 Bobby Abreu	.20	.50
77A A.Dunn Closed Mouth	.20	.50
77B Adam Dunn Open Mouth	.20	.50
78 Ryan Klesko	.20	.50
79 Francisco Rodriguez	.20	.50
80 Scott Rolen	.30	.75
81 Roberto Alomar	.30	.75
82 Joe Torre MG	.30	.75
83 Jim Thome	.30	.75
84 Kevin Millwood	.20	.50
85 J.T. Snow	.20	.50
86 Trevor Hoffman	.20	.50
87 Jay Gibbons	.20	.50
88A Mark Prior New Logo	.30	.75
88B Mark Prior Old Logo	.30	.75
89 Rich Aurilia	.20	.50
90 Chipper Jones	.50	1.25
91 Richie Sexson	.20	.50
92 Gary Sheffield	.20	.50
93 Pedro Martinez	.30	.75
94 Rodrigo Lopez	.20	.50
95 Al Leiter	.20	.50
96 Jorge Posada	.30	.75
97 Luis Castillo	.20	.50
98 Aubrey Huff	.20	.50
99 A.J. Pierzynski	.20	.50
100A I.Suzuki Look Ahead	1.00	2.50
100B Ichiro Suzuki Look Right	1.00	2.50
101 Eric Chavez	.20	.50
102 Brett Myers	.20	.50
103 Jason Kendall	.20	.50
104 Jeff Kent	.20	.50
105 Eric Hinske	.20	.50
106 Jacque Jones	.20	.50
107 Phil Nevin	.20	.50
108 Roy Oswalt	.20	.50
109 Curt Schilling	.20	.50
110A N.Garciaparra w/Gold Trim	.75	2.00
110B N.Garciaparra w/o Gold Trim	.75	2.00
111 Garret Anderson	.20	.50
112 Eric Gagne	.20	.50
113 Javier Vazquez	.20	.50
114 Jeff Bagwell	.30	.75
115 Mike Lowell	.20	.50
116 Carlos Pena	.20	.50
117 Ken Griffey Jr.	.75	2.00
118 Tony Batista	.20	.50
119 Edgar Martinez	.30	.75
120 Austin Kearns	.20	.50
121 Jason Stokes PROS	.20	.50
122 Jose Reyes PROS	.20	.50
123 Rocco Baldelli PROS	.20	.50
124 Joe Borchard PROS	.20	.50
125 Joe Mauer PROS	.50	1.25
126 Gavin Floyd PROS	.20	.50
127 Mark Teixeira PROS	.30	.75
128 Jeremy Guthrie PROS	.20	.50
129 B.J. Upton PROS	.50	1.25
130 Khalil Greene PROS	.50	1.25
131 Hanley Ramirez FY RC	2.00	5.00
132 Andy Marte FY RC	1.50	4.00
133 J.D. Durbin FY RC	.20	.50
134 Jason Kubel FY RC	.50	1.25
135 Craig Brazell FY RC	.20	.50
136 Bryan Bullington FY RC	.20	.50
137 Jose Contreras FY RC	.40	1.00
138 Brian Burgamy FY RC	.20	.50
139 E.Bastida-Martinez FY RC	.20	.50
140 Joey Gomes FY RC	.20	.50
141 Ismael Castro FY RC	.25	.60
142 Travis Wong FY RC	.25	.60
143 Mi.Garciaparra FY RC	.20	.50
144 Arnaldo Munoz FY RC	.20	.50
145 Louis Sockalexis FY XRC	.20	.50
146 Richard Hoblitzell REP	.40	1.00
147 George Graham REP	.40	1.00
148 Hal Chase REP	.40	1.00
149 John McGraw REP	.60	1.50
150 Bobby Wallace REP	.40	1.00
151 David Shean REP	.40	1.00
152 Richard Hoblitzell REP SP	1.00	2.50
153 Hal Chase REP	.40	1.00
154 Hooks Wiltse REP	.40	1.00
155 George Brett RET	1.25	3.00
156 Willie Mays RET	1.25	3.00
157 Honus Wagner RET SP	4.00	10.00
158 Nolan Ryan RET	1.50	4.00
159 Reggie Jackson RET	.60	1.50
160 Mike Schmidt RET	1.25	3.00
161 Josh Barfield PROS	.20	.50
162 Grady Sizemore PROS	.50	1.25
163 Justin Morneau PROS	.20	.50
164 Laynce Nix PROS	.20	.50
165 Zack Greinke PROS	.20	.50
166 Victor Martinez PROS	.30	.75
167 Jeff Mathis PROS	.20	.50
168 Casey Kotchman PROS	.20	.50
169 Gabe Gross PROS	.20	.50
170 Edwin Jackson FY RC	.25	.60
171 Delmon Young FY SP RC	4.00	10.00
172 Eric Duncan FY SP RC	2.50	6.00
173 Brian Snyder FY SP RC	2.00	5.00
174 Chris Lubanski FY SP RC	2.00	5.00
175 Ryan Harvey FY SP RC	2.50	6.00
176 Nick Markakis FY SP RC	3.00	8.00
177 Chad Billingsley FY SP RC	3.00	8.00
178 Elizardo Ramirez FY RC	.25	.60
179 Ben Francisco FY RC	.20	.50
180 Franklin Gutierrez FY SP RC	2.00	5.00
181 Aaron Hill FY SP RC	2.00	5.00
182 Kevin Correia FY RC	.20	.50
183 Kelly Shoppach FY RC	.40	1.00
184 Felix Pie FY SP RC	3.00	8.00
185 Adam Loewen FY SP RC	2.00	5.00
186 Danny Garcia FY RC	.20	.50
187 Rickie Weeks FY SP RC	3.00	8.00
188 Robby Hammock FY SP RC	1.50	4.00
189 Ryan Wagner FY SP RC	1.50	4.00
190 Matt Kata FY SP RC	1.50	4.00
191 Bo Hart FY SP RC	1.50	4.00
192 Brandon Webb FY SP RC	2.50	6.00
193 Bengie Molina	.20	.50
194 Junior Spivey	.20	.50
195 Gary Sheffield	.20	.50
196 Jason Johnson	.20	.50
197 David Ortiz	.50	1.25
198 Roberto Alomar	.30	.75
199 Wily Mo Pena	.20	.50
200 Sammy Sosa	.50	1.25
201 Jay Payton	.20	.50
202 Dmitri Young	.20	.50
203 Derrek Lee	.30	.75
204A Jeff Bagwell w/Hat	.30	.75
204B Jeff Bagwell w/o Hat	.30	.75
205 Runelvys Hernandez	.20	.50
206 Kevin Brown	.20	.50
207 Wes Helms	.20	.50
208 Eddie Guardado	.20	.50
209 Orlando Cabrera	.20	.50
210 Alfonso Soriano	.20	.50
211 Ty Wigginton	.20	.50
212A Rich Harden Look Left	.30	.75
212B Rich Harden Look Right	.30	.75
213 Mike Lieberthal	.20	.50
214 Brian Giles	.20	.50
215 Jason Schmidt	.20	.50
216 Jamie Moyer	.20	.50
217 Matt Morris	.20	.50
218 Victor Zambrano	.20	.50
219 Roy Halladay	.20	.50
220 Mike Hampton	.20	.50
221 Kevin Millar Sox	.20	.50
222 Hideo Nomo	.50	1.25
223 Milton Bradley	.20	.50
224 Jose Guillen	.20	.50
225 Derek Jeter	1.25	3.00
226 Rondell White	.20	.50
227A Hank Blalock Blue Jsy	.20	.50
227B Hank Blalock White Jsy	.20	.50
228 Shigetoshi Hasegawa	.20	.50
229 Mike Mussina	.30	.75
230 Cristian Guzman	.20	.50
231A Todd Helton Blue	.30	.75
231B Todd Helton Green	.30	.75
232 Kenny Lofton	.20	.50
233 Carl Everett	.20	.50
234 Shea Hillenbrand	.20	.50
235 Brad Fullmer	.20	.50
236 Bernie Williams	.30	.75
237 Vicente Padilla	.20	.50
238 Tim Worrell	.20	.50
239 Juan Gonzalez	.20	.50
240 Ichiro Suzuki	1.00	2.50
241 Aaron Boone	.20	.50
242 Shannon Stewart	.20	.50
243A Barry Zito Blue	.20	.50
243B Barry Zito Green	.20	.50
244 Reggie Sanders	.20	.50
245 Scott Podsednik	.20	.50
246 Miguel Cabrera	.50	1.25
247 Angel Berroa	.20	.50
248 Carlos Zambrano	.20	.50
249 Marlon Byrd	.20	.50
250 Mark Prior	.30	.75
251 Esteban Loaiza	.20	.50
252 David Eckstein	.20	.50
253 Alex Cintron	.20	.50
254 Melvin Mora	.20	.50
255 Russ Ortiz	.20	.50
256 Carlos Lee	.20	.50
257 Tino Martinez	.30	.75
258 Randy Wolf	.20	.50
259 Jason Phillips	.20	.50
260 Vladimir Guerrero	.50	1.25
261 Brad Wilkerson	.20	.50
262 Ivan Rodriguez	.30	.75
263 Matt Lawton	.20	.50
264 Adam Dunn	.20	.50
265 Joe Borowski	.20	.50
266 Jody Gerut	.20	.50
267 Alex Rodriguez	.75	2.00
268 Brendan Donnelly	.20	.50
269A Randy Johnson Grey	.50	1.25
269B Randy Johnson Pink	.50	1.25
270 Nomar Garciaparra	.75	2.00
271 Javy Lopez	.20	.50
272 Travis Hafner	.20	.50
273 Juan Pierre	.20	.50
274 Morgan Ensberg	.20	.50
275 Albert Pujols	1.00	2.50
276 Jason LaRue	.20	.50
277 Paul Lo Duca	.20	.50
278 Andy Pettitte	.30	.75
279 Mike Piazza	.75	2.00
280A Jim Thome Blue	.30	.75
280B Jim Thome Green	.30	.75
281 Marquis Grissom	.20	.50
282 Woody Williams	.20	.50
283A Curt Schilling Look Ahead	.20	.50
283B Curt Schilling Look Right	.20	.50
284A Chipper Jones Blue	.50	1.25
284B Chipper Jones Yellow	.50	1.25
285 Deivi Cruz	.20	.50
286 Johnny Damon	.30	.75
287 Chin-Hui Tsao	.20	.50
288 Alex Gonzalez	.20	.50
289 Billy Wagner	.20	.50
290 Jason Giambi	.20	.50
291 Keith Foulke	.20	.50
292 Jerome Williams	.20	.50
293 Livan Hernandez	.20	.50
294 Aaron Guiel	.20	.50
295 Randall Simon	.20	.50
296 Byung-Hyun Kim	.20	.50
297 Jorge Julio	.20	.50
298 Miguel Batista	.20	.50
299 Rafael Furcal	.20	.50
300A Dontrelle Willis No Smile	.50	1.25
300B Dontrelle Willis Smile SP	1.50	4.00
301 Alex Sanchez	.20	.50
302 Shawn Chacon	.20	.50
303 Matt Clement	.20	.50
304 Luis Matos	.20	.50
305 Steve Finley	.20	.50
306 Marcus Giles	.20	.50
307 Boomer Wells	.20	.50
308 Jeromy Burnitz	.20	.50
309 Mike MacDougal	.20	.50
310 Mariano Rivera	.50	1.25
311 Adrian Beltre	.20	.50
312 Mark Loretta	.20	.50
313 Ugueth Urbina	.20	.50
314 Bill Mueller	.20	.50
315 Johan Santana	.30	.75
NNO Vintage Buyback		

2003 Topps 205 American Beauty

*AMER.BTY: 1.25X TO 3X BASIC
*AMER.BTY PURPLE: 4X TO 10X BASIC
PURPLE CARDS ARE 10% OF PRINT RUN
CL: 1/20/50/51/100/146-150

2003 Topps 205 Bazooka Blue

SERIES 2 STATED ODDS 1:2744 PACKS
SERIES 2 STATED ODDS 1:208 MINI BOXES
STATED PRINT RUN 1 SET
NO PRICING DUE TO SCARCITY

2003 Topps 205 Bazooka Red

SERIES 1 STATED ODDS 1:1573 PACKS
SERIES 2 STATED ODDS 1:691 PACKS
SERIES 2 STATED ODDS 1:52 MINI BOXES
SERIES 1 STATED PRINT RUN 5 SETS
SERIES 2 STATED PRINT RUN 4 SETS
NO PRICING DUE TO SCARCITY

2003 Topps 205 Brooklyn

*BROOKLYN C 1-130: .75X TO 2X BASIC
*BROOKLYN U 1-130: 1.25X TO 3X BASIC
*BROOKLYN U 131-144: 1.25X TO 3X BASIC
*BROOKLYN R 1-130: 2X TO 5X BASIC
*BROOKLYN R 131-144: 2X TO 5X BASIC
BROOKLYN 5 PRINT RUN 5 SETS
NO BROOKLYN 5 PRICING DUE TO SCARCITY
SEE BECKETT.COM FOR C/U/R/5 SCHEMATIC
SCHEMATIC IS IN OPG SUBSCRIPTION AREA
*BRKLYN 151-315: 2X TO 5X BASIC
*BRKLYN 151-315: .6X TO 1.5X BASIC SP
151-315 SERIES 2 STATED ODDS 1:12
151-315 STATED PRINT RUN 205 SETS
151-315 ARE NOT SERIAL-NUMBERED
151-315 PRINT RUN PROVIDED BY TOPPS

2003 Topps 205 Brooklyn Exclusive Pose

*BROOKLYN EP: 1X TO 2.5X POLAR EP
OVERALL BROOKLYN SERIES 2 ODDS 1:12
STATED PRINT RUN 205 SETS
CARDS ARE NOT SERIAL-NUMBERED
PRINT RUN PROVIDED BY TOPPS

2003 Topps 205 Cycle

*CYCLE 121-145: 1.25X TO 3X BASIC
*CYCLE PURPLE 121-130: 4X TO 10X BASIC
*CYCLE PURPLE 131-145: 3X TO 8X BASIC
PURPLE CARDS ARE 10% OF PRINT RUN

2003 Topps 205 Drum

*DRUM: 2X TO 5X BASIC
*DRUM: .6X TO 1.5X BASIC SP

2003 Topps 205 Drum Exclusive Pose

*DRUM EP: 1X TO 2.5X POLAR EP

2003 Topps 205 Honest

*HONEST: 1.25X TO 3X BASIC
*HONEST PURPLE: 4X TO 10X BASIC
PURPLE CARDS ARE 10% OF PRINT RUN
CL: 1/3/8/12/15/18/20/40/50/51/75/77/88
CL: 100/110

2003 Topps 205 Piedmont

*PIEDMONT: 1.25X TO 3X BASIC
*PIEDMONT PURPLE: 4X TO 10X BASIC
PURPLE CARDS ARE 10% OF PRINT RUN
CL: 2-19/21-49/

2003 Topps 205 Polar Bear

*POLAR BEAR: .75X TO 2X BASIC
*POLAR BEAR: .25X TO .6X BASIC SP

2003 Topps 205 Polar Bear Exclusive Pose

316 Willie Mays EP	2.50	6.00
317 Delmon Young EP	3.00	8.00
318 Rickie Weeks EP	2.50	6.00
319 Ryan Wagner EP	.75	2.00

320 Brandon Webb EP 1.00 2.50
321 Chris Lubanski EP 1.00 2.50
322 Ryan Harvey EP 2.00 5.00
323 Nick Markakis EP 2.50 6.00
324 Chad Billingsley EP 2.50 6.00
325 Aaron Hill EP .75 2.00
326 Brian Snyder EP .75 2.00
327 Eric Duncan EP 2.50 6.00
328 Sammy Sosa EP 1.00 2.50
329 Alfonso Soriano EP .75 2.00
330 Ichiro Suzuki EP 2.00 5.00
331 Alex Rodriguez EP 1.50 4.00
332 Nomar Garciaparra EP 1.50 4.00
333 Albert Pujols EP 2.00 5.00
334 Jim Thome EP .75 2.00
335 Dontrelle Willis EP 1.00 2.50

2003 Topps 205 Sovereign

*SOVEREIGN: 1.25X TO 3X BASIC
*SOVEREIGN: .4X TO 1X BASIC SP
*SOV.GREEN: 2.5X TO 6X BASIC
*SOV.GREEN: 1.25X TO 3X BASIC SP
SOV.GREEN CARDS ARE 25% OF PRINT RUN

2003 Topps 205 Sovereign Exclusive Pose

*SOVEREIGN EP: .6X TO 1.5X POLAR EP
*SOV.GREEN EP: 1.25X TO 3X POLAR EP
SOV.GREEN CARDS ARE 25% OF PRINT RUN

2003 Topps 205 Sweet Caporal

*SWEET CAP: 1.25X TO 3X BASIC
*SWEET CAP PURPLE: 4X TO 10X BASIC
PURPLE CARDS ARE 10% OF PRINT RUN
CL: 70-99/101-120

2003 Topps 205 Autographs

These cards feature autographs of leading players. These cards were inserted at varying odds and we have noted what group the player belongs to in our checklist. Though lacking serial numbering, representatives at Topps publicly announced only 50 copies of Hank Aaron's card were produced - making it, by far, the scarcest card in this set.

SER.1 GROUP A1 ODDS 1:2434
SER.1 GROUP B1 ODDS 1:608
SER.1 GROUP C1 ODDS 1:1460
SER.1 GROUP D1 ODDS 1:122
SER.2 GROUP A2 ODDS 1:5816
SER.2 GROUP B2 ODDS 1:646
SER.2 GROUP C2 ODDS 1:49
A2 STATED PRINT RUN 50 CARDS
A2 IS NOT SERIAL-NUMBERED
A2 PRINT RUN PROVIDED BY TOPPS
CF Cliff Floyd B1 8.00 20.00
DW Dontrelle Willis C2 5.00 12.00
ED Eric Duncan C2 8.00 20.00
FP Felix Pie C2 15.00 40.00
HA Hank Aaron A2 SP/50 150.00 250.00
JR Jose Reyes D1 10.00 25.00
JW Jerome Williams B2 6.00 15.00
LB Lance Berkman B1 12.50 30.00
LC Luis Castillo C2 4.00 10.00
MB Marlon Byrd D1 4.00 10.00
MO Magglio Ordonez C1 8.00 20.00
MS Mike Sweeney B1 8.00 20.00
PL Paul Lo Duca D1 6.00 15.00
RH Rich Harden C2 12.50 30.00
RWA Ryan Wagner C2 6.00 15.00
SR Scott Rolen A1 15.00 40.00
TH Torii Hunter D1 6.00 15.00

2003 Topps 205 Relics

Randomly inserted into packs, these 43 cards feature game-used memorabilia pieces of the featured players. Please note that many of these cards were inserted in different rates and we have noted both the insert ratio as well as the group the player belongs to in our checklisting information.

COM.UNI A1/RELIC A2 6.00 15.00
COM.BAT B-D1/UNI E1/RELIC B2 4.00 10.00
COMMON BAT E-H1/UNI F-M1 3.00 8.00
SER.1 BAT GROUP A1 ODDS 1:1216
SER.1 BAT GROUP B1 ODDS 1:972
SER.1 BAT GROUP C1 ODDS 1:270
SER.1 BAT GROUP D1 ODDS 1:365
SER.1 BAT GROUP E1 ODDS 1:561
SER.1 BAT GROUP F1 ODDS 1:486
SER.1 BAT GROUP G1 ODDS 1:91
SER.1 BAT GROUP H1 ODDS 1:203
SER.1 UNI GROUP A1 ODDS 1:4884
SER.1 UNI GROUP B1 ODDS 1:456
SER.1 UNI GROUP C1 ODDS 1:1460
SER.1 UNI GROUP D1 ODDS 1:1216
SER.1 UNI GROUP E1 ODDS 1:973
SER.1 UNI GROUP F1 ODDS 1:608
SER.1 UNI GROUP G1 ODDS 1:61
SER.1 UNI GROUP H1 ODDS 1:183
SER.1 UNI GROUP I1 ODDS 1:83
SER.1 UNI GROUP J1 ODDS 1:324
SER.1 UNI GROUP K1 ODDS 1:317
SER.1 UNI GROUP L1 ODDS 1:243
SER.1 UNI GROUP M1 ODDS 1:221
SER.2 RELIC GROUP A ODDS 1:79
SER.2 RELIC GROUP B ODDS 1:16
AB A.J. Burnett Jsy G1 3.00 8.00
AD Adam Dunn Bat G1 3.00 8.00
AJ Andruw Jones Jsy B2 UER 6.00 15.00
Chipper Jones is pictured
AL Al Leiter Jsy I1 3.00 8.00
APB Albert Pujols Bat A2 10.00 25.00
AP1 Albert Pujols Uni E1 8.00 20.00
AP2 Albert Pujols Hat A2 10.00 25.00
ARA Aramis Ramirez Bat B2 4.00 10.00
AR1 Alex Rodriguez Jsy H1 6.00 15.00
AR2 Alex Rodriguez Bat B2 6.00 15.00
AS1 Alfonso Soriano Uni G1 3.00 8.00
AS2 Alfonso Soriano Bat A2 6.00 15.00
BB1 Barry Bonds Uni B1 10.00 25.00
BB2 Bret Boone Bat A2 6.00 15.00
BD Brandon Duckworth Jsy B2 4.00 10.00
BG1 Brian Giles Bat G1 3.00 8.00
BG2 Brian Giles Bat A2 6.00 15.00
BP Brad Penny Jsy B2 4.00 10.00
BW1 Bernie Williams Bat D1 6.00 15.00
BW2 Bernie Williams Jsy A2 8.00 20.00
BZ Barry Zito Jsy K1 3.00 8.00
CB Craig Biggio Uni B2 6.00 15.00
CD Carlos Delgado Jsy B2 4.00 10.00
CG Cristian Guzman Jsy B2 4.00 10.00
CJB Chipper Jones Bat A2 8.00 20.00
CP Corey Patterson Bat A2 6.00 15.00
CS1 Curt Schilling Jsy B1 4.00 10.00
CS2 Curt Schilling Bat B2 4.00 10.00
DE Darin Erstad Uni A2 6.00 15.00
DL Derek Lowe Hat A1 6.00 15.00
DW Dontrelle Willis Uni B2 6.00 15.00
EC Eric Chavez Bat G1 3.00 8.00
EG Eric Gagne Jsy G1 3.00 8.00
EMA Edgar Martinez Jsy B2 6.00 15.00
EMU Eddie Murray Bat A2 10.00 25.00
FM Fred McGriff Bat B2 6.00 15.00
FR Frank Robinson Bat A2 8.00 20.00
FT Frank Thomas Jsy B2 6.00 15.00
GA Garret Anderson Uni L1 3.00 8.00
GB George Brett Jsy A2 12.50 30.00
GC Gary Carter Bat A2 6.00 15.00
GM1 Greg Maddux Jsy B1 6.00 15.00
GM2 Greg Maddux Bat A2 8.00 20.00
GS Gary Sheffield Bat B2 4.00 10.00
HB Hank Blalock Bat B2 4.00 10.00
IR Ivan Rodriguez Bat A2 8.00 20.00
JB1 Jeff Bagwell Uni G1 4.00 10.00
JB2 Jeff Bagwell Bat A2 8.00 20.00
JC Jose Canseco Bat B2 6.00 15.00
JD Johnny Damon Bat B1 6.00 15.00
JE Jim Edmonds Jsy A2 6.00 15.00
JG Jason Giambi Bat A2 6.00 15.00
JGI Jeremy Giambi Jsy B2 4.00 10.00
JGO Juan Gonzalez Bat B2 4.00 10.00
JJ Jason Jennings Jsy G1 3.00 8.00
JK Jeff Kent Bat C1 4.00 10.00
JO John Olerud Jsy B2 4.00 10.00
JP Jorge Posada Bat A2 8.00 20.00
JS John Smoltz Jsy B1 6.00 15.00
JT Jim Thome Bat F1 4.00 10.00
KB Kevin Brown Jsy B2 4.00 10.00
KI Kazuhisa Ishii Jsy I1 3.00 8.00
KL1 Kenny Lofton Bat G1 3.00 8.00
KL2 Kenny Lofton Uni B2 4.00 10.00
LB Lance Berkman Bat C1 4.00 10.00
LC Luis Castillo Jsy G1 3.00 8.00
LG1 Luis Gonzalez Jsy J1 3.00 8.00
LG2 Luis Gonzalez Bat A2 6.00 15.00
LW Larry Walker Jsy B2 4.00 10.00
MC Mike Cameron Jsy B2 4.00 10.00
MG Mark Grace Bat A2 8.00 20.00
MGR Marquis Grissom Bat B2 4.00 10.00
MM Mark Mulder Uni A2 6.00 15.00
MO Magglio Ordonez Jsy M1 3.00 8.00
MP1 Mike Piazza Bat C1 6.00 15.00
MP2 Mike Piazza Bat A2 8.00 20.00
MR Manny Ramirez Bat H1 4.00 10.00
MSC Mike Schmidt Bat A2 12.50 30.00
MSW Mike Sweeney Bat H1 3.00 8.00
MTE Miguel Tejada Bat B2 4.00 10.00
MTI Mark Teixeira Bat B2 6.00 15.00
MV Mo Vaughn Jsy I1 3.00 8.00
NG1 Nomar Garciaparra Jsy G1 6.00 15.00
NG2 Nomar Garciaparra Bat A2 8.00 20.00
NJ Nick Johnson Bat D1 4.00 10.00
NR Nolan Ryan Uni A2 30.00 60.00
PM1 Pedro Martinez Jsy F1 4.00 10.00
PM2 Pedro Martinez Jsy A2 8.00 20.00
PO Paul O'Neill Uni B2 6.00 15.00
RA1 Roberto Alomar Bat G1 4.00 10.00
RA2 Roberto Alomar Uni B2 6.00 15.00
RBB Rocco Baldelli Bat B2 4.00 10.00
RBJ Rocco Baldelli Jsy B2 4.00 10.00
RC Roger Clemens Uni A2 8.00 20.00
RF1 Rafael Furcal Bat E1 3.00 8.00
RF2 Rafael Furcal Bat A2 6.00 15.00
RH Rickey Henderson Bat B2 6.00 15.00
RJ1 Randy Johnson Jsy C1 6.00 15.00
RJ2 Randy Johnson Jsy A2 8.00 20.00
RO Roy Oswalt Jsy I1 3.00 8.00
RP1 Rafael Palmeiro Jsy H1 4.00 10.00
RP2 Rafael Palmeiro Bat A2 8.00 20.00
RV Robin Ventura Bat B2 4.00 10.00
SB Sean Burroughs Bat B2 4.00 10.00
SR1 Scott Rolen Bat A1 6.00 15.00
SR2 Scott Rolen Uni A2 8.00 20.00
SS Sammy Sosa Jsy A2 8.00 20.00
SST Shannon Stewart Bat B2 4.00 10.00
TG Troy Glaus Uni A2 6.00 15.00
TH Todd Helton Jsy D1 6.00 15.00
TM Tino Martinez Bat B2 6.00 15.00
TP Troy Percival Uni G1 3.00 8.00
TS Tsuyoshi Shinjo Bat B2 4.00 10.00
VG Vladimir Guerrero Bat A2 8.00 20.00
VW Vernon Wells Jsy A2 6.00 15.00
WB Wade Boggs Bat A2 8.00 20.00

2003 Topps 205 Triple Folder Polar Bear

COMPLETE SET (100) 20.00 50.00
COMPLETE SERIES 1 (50) 10.00 25.00
COMPLETE SERIES 2 (50) 10.00 25.00
ONE PER PACK
*BROOKLYN: 3X TO 8X BASIC
SERIES 1 BROOKLYN ODDS 1:72
SERIES 2 BROOKLYN ODDS 1:29
TF1 Barry Bonds 1.00 2.50
Jason LaRue
TF2 Alfonso Soriano 1.00 2.50
Derek Jeter
TF3 Alex Rodriguez .60 1.50
Miguel Tejada
TF4 Nomar Garciaparra 1.00 2.50
Derek Jeter
TF5 Omar Vizquel .60 1.50
Alex Rodriguez
TF6 Paul Konerko .40 1.00
Omar Vizquel
TF7 Paul Konerko .40 1.00
Magglio Ordonez
TF8 Doug Mientkiewicz .40 1.00
Darin Erstad
TF9 Jason Kendall .40 1.00
Jimmy Rollins
TF10 Shawn Green .40 1.00
Roberto Alomar
TF11 Derek Jeter 1.00 2.50
Roberto Alomar
TF12 Bobby Abreu .40 1.00
Luis Castillo
TF13 Randy Johnson .40 1.00
Curt Schilling
TF14 Mike Piazza .60 1.50
Kerry Wood
TF15 Roger Clemens .75 2.00
Jorge Posada
TF16 Ichiro Suzuki .75 2.00
Ryan Klesko
TF17 Alfonso Soriano .40 1.00
Chipper Jones
TF18 Barry Bonds 1.00 2.50
Nick Johnson
TF19 Chipper Jones .40 1.00
Andruw Jones
TF20 Bobby Abreu .40 1.00
Paul Konerko
TF21 Rafael Palmeiro .60 1.50
Alex Rodriguez
TF22 Eric Hinske .40 1.00
Carlos Delgado
TF23 Nomar Garciaparra .40 1.00
Jay Gibbons
TF24 Mike Piazza .60 1.50
Luis Gonzalez
TF25 J.T. Snow .40 1.00
Vladimir Guerrero
TF26 Jason Giambi .40 1.00
Bernie Williams
TF27 Miguel Tejada .40 1.00
Richie Sexson
TF28 Doug Mientkiewicz .40 1.00
Jimmy Rollins
TF29 Eric Chavez 1.00 2.50
Derek Jeter
TF30 Alfonso Soriano .40 1.00
Bret Boone
TF31 Chipper Jones .60 1.50
Mike Piazza
TF32 Ichiro Suzuki .75 2.00
Bret Boone
TF33 Bobby Abreu .60 1.50
Mike Piazza
TF34 Jimmy Rollins .40 1.00
Pat Burell
TF35 Ichiro Suzuki .75 2.00
Miguel Tejada
TF36 Jason LaRue 1.00 2.50
Barry Bonds
TF37 Derek Jeter 1.00 2.50
Alfonso Soriano
TF38 Miguel Tejada .60 1.50
Alex Rodriguez
TF39 Derek Jeter 1.00 2.50
Nomar Garciaparra
TF40 Alex Rodriguez .60 1.50
Omar Vizquel
TF41 Curt Schilling .40 1.00
Randy Johnson
TF42 Jorge Posada .75 2.00
Roger Clemens
TF43 Ryan Klesko .75 2.00
Ichiro Suzuki
TF44 Nick Johnson 1.00 2.50
Barry Bonds
TF45 Alex Rodriguez .60 1.50
Rafael Palmeiro
TF46 Vladimir Guerrero .40 1.00
J.T. Snow
TF47 Derek Jeter 1.00 2.50
Eric Chavez
TF48 Bret Boone .75 2.00
Ichiro Suzuki
TF49 Mike Piazza .60 1.50
Bobby Abreu
TF50 Miguel Tejada .75 2.00
Ichiro Suzuki
TF51 Juan Pierre .40 1.00
Jim Thome
TF52 Kevin Millwood .40 1.00
Jim Thome
TF53 Hank Blalock .40 1.00
Jorge Posada
TF54 Deivi Cruz .40 1.00
Hank Blalock
TF55 Rafael Furcal .40 1.00
Ty Wigginton
TF56 Jim Thome .40 1.00
Nomar Garciaparra
TF57 Craig Biggio .40 1.00
Jason Giambi
TF58 Aaron Boone .40 1.00
Jason Giambi
TF59 Jason Giambi .40 1.00
Bernie Williams
TF60 Cristian Guzman .40 1.00
Jody Gerut
TF61 Todd Helton .40 1.00
Jose Reyes
TF62 Derek Jeter 1.00 2.50
Hank Blalock
TF63 Mike Piazza .40 1.00
Jimmy Rollins
TF64 Bernie Williams 1.00 2.50
Derek Jeter
TF65 Andruw Jones .40 1.00
Rafael Furcal
TF66 Mike Piazza .60 1.50
Andruw Jones
TF67 Mike Piazza .60 1.50
Cliff Floyd
TF68 Jason Kendall .75 2.00
Albert Pujols
TF69 Nomar Garciaparra .60 1.50
Manny Ramirez
TF70 Jorge Posada .60 1.50
Alex Rodriguez
TF71 Derek Jeter 1.00 2.50
Alex Rodriguez
TF72 Mike Sweeney .60 1.50
Alex Rodriguez
TF73 Marquis Grissom .40 1.00
Ivan Rodriguez
TF74 Jason Phillips .40 1.00
Gary Sheffield
TF75 Chipper Jones .40 1.00
Gary Sheffield
TF76 Junior Spivey .40 1.00
Gary Sheffield
TF77 Al Leiter .75 2.00
Ichiro Suzuki
TF78 Jose Vidro .40 1.00
Jim Thome
TF79 Jimmy Rollins .40 1.00
Paul Lo Duca
TF80 Alex Rodriguez .60 1.50
Rafael Palmeiro
TF81 Albert Pujols .75 2.00
Jim Edmonds
TF82 Eric Chavez .40 1.00
Mike Sweeney
TF83 Cristian Guzman .40 1.00
Jimmy Rollins
TF84 Alfonso Soriano .40 1.00
Bernie Williams
TF85 Ichiro Suzuki .75 2.00
Derek Jeter
TF86 Jimmy Rollins .40 1.00
Derrek Lee
TF87 Shawn Green .40 1.00
Paul Lo Duca
TF88 Carlos Delgado .40 1.00
Jorge Posada
TF89 Dmitri Young .40 1.00
C.C. Sabathia
TF90 Dontrelle Willis .40 1.00
Shawn Chacon
TF91 Edgar Martinez .60 1.50
Alex Rodriguez
TF92 Edgar Martinez .40 1.00
Carlos Delgado
TF93 Edgar Martinez .40 1.00
Esteban Loaiza
TF94 Roy Halladay .40 1.00
C.C. Sabathia
TF95 Ichiro Suzuki .75 2.00
Albert Pujols
TF96 Ichiro Suzuki .75 2.00
Shigetoshi Hasegawa
TF97 Geoff Jenkins .40 1.00
Aaron Boone
TF98 Nomar Garciaparra .60 1.50
Alfonso Soriano
TF99 Jorge Posada .40 1.00
Alfonso Soriano
TF100 Vernon Wells .40 1.00
Garret Anderson

2003 Topps 205 Triple Folder Autographs

SERIES 2 STATED ODDS 1:355 HOBBY
STATED PRINT RUN 205 SETS
CARDS ARE NOT SERIAL-NUMBERED
PRINT RUN PROVIDED BY TOPPS
DW Dontrelle Willis 10.00 25.00
JW Jerome Williams 15.00 40.00
RH Rich Harden 30.00 60.00
RW Ryan Wagner 15.00 40.00

2003 Topps 205 World Series Line-Ups

SERIES 2 ODDS 1:27,440 PACKS
SERIES 2 ODDS 1:1960 MINI BOXES
STATED PRINT RUN 1 SET
NO PRICING DUE TO SCARCITY

2002 Topps 206 Olbermann Promos

This five card set, issued exclusively through Beckett Sports Collectibles Vintage magazine, featured famed television sports announcer and noted card collector Keith Olbermann. These five cards feature Olbermann in a variety of poses similar to poses of the old tobacco cards.

COMPLETE SET 2.00 5.00
COMMON CARD .40 1.00

2002 Topps 206

Issued in three separate series this 526-card set featured a mix of veterans, rookies and retired greats in the general style of the classic T-206 set issued more than 90 years prior. Series one consists of cards 1-180 and went live in February, 2002, series two consists of cards 181-307 - including 96 variations - and went live in early August, 2002 and series three consists of cards 308-456 - including 15 variations and a total of 55 short prints seeded at a rate of one per pack - and went live in January, 2003. Each pack contained eight cards with an SRP of $4. Packs were issued 20 per box and each case had 10 boxes. The following subsets were issued as part of the set: Prospects (131-140/261-270/399-418); First Year Players (141-155/271-285/419-432), Retired Stars (156-170/286-298/433-448) and Reprints (171-180/299-307/449-456). The First Year Player subset cards 141-155 and 277-285 were inserted at stated odds of one in two packs making them short-prints in comparison to other cards in the set. According to press release notes, Topps purchased more than 4,000 original Tobacco cards and also randomly inserted those in packs. They created a "holder" for these smaller cards inside the standard-size cards of the Topps 206 set. Stated pack odds for these "repurchased" Tobacco cards was 1:110 for series one, 1:179 for series two and 1:101 for series three.

COMPLETE SET (525) 110.00 220.00
COMPLETE SERIES 1 (180) 25.00 60.00
COMPLETE SERIES 2 (180) 25.00 60.00
COMPLETE SERIES 3 (165) 50.00 100.00
COM(1-140/181-270/308-418) .20 .50
COMMON (141-155/271-285) .20 .50
COMMON RC (308-418) .20 .50
COMMON SP (308-398) .75 2.00
COMMON FYP SP (.40 1.00
COMMON RET SP (433-447) .75 2.00
1 Vladimir Guerrero .50 1.25
2 Sammy Sosa .50 1.25
3 Garret Anderson .20 .50
4 Rafael Palmeiro .30 .75
5 Juan Gonzalez .20 .50
6 John Smoltz .30 .75
7 Mark Mulder .20 .50
8 Jon Lieber .20 .50
9 Greg Maddux .75 2.00
10 Moises Alou .20 .50
11 Joe Randa .20 .50
12 Bobby Abreu .20 .50
13 Juan Pierre .20 .50
14 Kerry Wood .20 .50
15 Craig Biggio .30 .75
16 Curt Schilling .20 .50
17 Brian Jordan .20 .50
18 Edgardo Alfonzo .20 .50
19 Darren Dreifort .20 .50
20 Todd Helton .30 .75
21 Ramon Ortiz .20 .50
22 Ichiro Suzuki 1.00 2.50
23 Jimmy Rollins .20 .50
24 Darin Erstad .20 .50
25 Shawn Green .20 .50
26 Tino Martinez .30 .75
27 Bret Boone .20 .50
28 Alfonso Soriano .20 .50
29 Chan Ho Park .20 .50
30 Roger Clemens 1.00 2.50
31 Cliff Floyd .20 .50
32 Johnny Damon .30 .75
33 Frank Thomas .50 1.25
34 Barry Bonds 1.25 3.00
35 Luis Gonzalez .20 .50
36 Carlos Lee .20 .50
37 Roberto Alomar .30 .75
38 Carlos Delgado .20 .50
39 Nomar Garciaparra .75 2.00
40 Jason Kendall .20 .50
41 Scott Rolen .30 .75
42 Tom Glavine .30 .75
43 Ryan Klesko .20 .50
44 Brian Giles .20 .50
45 Bud Smith .20 .50
46 Charles Nagy .20 .50
47 Tony Gwynn .60 1.50
48 C.C. Sabathia UER .20 .50
Credited with incorrect victory total in 2001
49 Frank Catalanotto .20 .50
50 Jerry Hairston .20 .50
51 Jeromy Burnitz .20 .50
52 David Justice .20 .50
53 Bartolo Colon .20 .50
54 Andres Galarraga .20 .50
55 Jeff Weaver .20 .50
56 Terrence Long .20 .50
57 Tsuyoshi Shinjo .20 .50
58 Barry Zito .20 .50
59 Mariano Rivera .50 1.25
60 John Olerud .20 .50
61 Randy Johnson .50 1.25
62 Kenny Lofton .20 .50
63 Jermaine Dye .20 .50
64 Troy Glaus .20 .50
65 Larry Walker .20 .50
66 Hideo Nomo .50 1.25
67 Mike Mussina .30 .75
68 Paul LoDuca .20 .50
69 Magglio Ordonez .20 .50
70 Paul O'Neill .30 .75
71 Sean Casey .20 .50
72 Lance Berkman .20 .50
73 Adam Dunn .20 .50
74 Aramis Ramirez .20 .50
75 Rafael Furcal .20 .50
76 Gary Sheffield .20 .50
77 Todd Hollandsworth .20 .50
78 Chipper Jones .50 1.25
79 Bernie Williams .30 .75
80 Richard Hidalgo .20 .50
81 Eric Chavez .20 .50
82 Mike Piazza .75 2.00
83 J.D. Drew .20 .50
84 Ken Griffey Jr. .75 2.00
85 Joe Kennedy .20 .50
86 Joel Pineiro .20 .50
87 Josh Towers .20 .50
88 Andruw Jones .30 .75
89 Carlos Beltran .20 .50
90 Mike Cameron .20 .50
91 Albert Pujols 1.00 2.50
92 Alex Rodriguez .75 2.00
93 Omar Vizquel .30 .75
94 Juan Encarnacion .20 .50
95 Jeff Bagwell .30 .75
96 Jose Canseco .30 .75
97 Ben Sheets .20 .50
98 Mark Grace .30 .75
99 Mike Sweeney .20 .50
100 Mark McGwire 1.25 3.00
101 Ivan Rodriguez .30 .75
102 Rich Aurilia .20 .50
103 Cristian Guzman .20 .50
104 Roy Oswalt .20 .50
105 Tim Hudson .20 .50
106 Brent Abernathy .20 .50
107 Mike Hampton .20 .50
108 Miguel Tejada .20 .50
109 Bobby Higginson .20 .50
110 Edgar Martinez .30 .75
111 Jorge Posada .30 .75
112 Jason Giambi Yankees .20 .50
113 Pedro Astacio .20 .50
114 Kazuhiro Sasaki .20 .50
115 Preston Wilson .20 .50
116 Jason Bere .20 .50
117 Mark Quinn .20 .50
118 Pokey Reese .20 .50
119 Derek Jeter 1.25 3.00
120 Shannon Stewart .20 .50
121 Jeff Kent .20 .50
122 Jeremy Giambi .20 .50
123 Pat Burrell .20 .50
124 Jim Edmonds .20 .50
125 Mark Buehrle .20 .50
126 Kevin Brown .20 .50
127 Raul Mondesi .20 .50
128 Pedro Martinez .30 .75
129 Jim Thome .30 .75
130 Russ Ortiz .20 .50
131 Br.Duckworth PROS .20 .50
132 Ryan Jamison PROS .20 .50
133 Brandon Inge PROS .20 .50
134 Felipe Lopez PROS .20 .50
135 Jason Lane PROS .20 .50
136 F.Johnson PROS RC .20 .50
137 Greg Nash PROS .20 .50
138 Covelli Crisp PROS .75 2.00
139 Nick Neugebauer PROS .20 .50
140 Dustan Mohr PROS .20 .50
141 Freddy Sanchez FYP RC .75 2.00
142 Justin Backsmeyer FYP RC .20 .50
143 Jorge Julio FYP .20 .50
144 Ryan Mottl FYP RC .20 .50
145 Chris Tritle FYP RC .20 .50
146 Noochie Varner FYP RC .20 .50
147 Brian Rogers FYP .20 .50
148 Michael Hill FYP RC .20 .50
149 Luis Pineda FYP .20 .50
150 Rich Thompson FYP RC .20 .50
151 Bill Hall FYP .20 .50
152 Juan Dominguez FYP RC .20 .50
153 Justin Woodrow FYP .20 .50
154 Nic Jackson FYP RC .20 .50
155 Laynce Nix FYP RC .60 1.50
156 Hank Aaron RET 2.00 5.00
157 Ernie Banks RET 1.00 2.50
158 Johnny Bench RET 1.00 2.50
159 George Brett RET 2.00 5.00
160 Carlton Fisk RET .60 1.50
161 Bob Gibson RET .60 1.50
162 Reggie Jackson RET .60 1.50
163 Don Mattingly RET 2.00 5.00
164 Kirby Puckett RET 1.00 2.50
165 Frank Robinson RET .60 1.50
166 Nolan Ryan RET 2.50 6.00
167 Tom Seaver RET .60 1.50
168 Mike Schmidt RET 2.00 5.00
169 Dave Winfield RET .40 1.00
170 Carl Yastrzemski RET 1.25 3.00
171 Frank Chance REP .40 1.00
172 Ty Cobb REP 2.00 5.00
173 Sam Crawford REP .40 1.00
174 Johnny Evers REP .40 1.00
175 John McGraw REP .60 1.50
176 Eddie Plank REP 1.00 2.50
177 Tris Speaker REP 1.00 2.50
178 Joe Tinker REP .40 1.00
179 H.Wagner Orange REP 3.00 8.00
180 Cy Young REP 1.00 2.50
181 Javier Vazquez .20 .50
182A Mark Mulder Green Jsy .20 .50
182B Mark Mulder White Jsy .20 .50
183A R.Clemens Blue Jsy 1.00 2.50
183B R.Clemens Pinstripes 1.00 2.50
184 Kazuhisa Ishii RC .30 .75
185 Roberto Alomar .30 .75
186 Lance Berkman .20 .50
187A A.Dunn Arms Folded .20 .50
187B Adam Dunn w/Bat .20 .50
188A Aramis Ramirez w/Bat .20 .50
188B Aramis Ramirez w/o Bat .20 .50
189 Chuck Knoblauch .20 .50
190 Nomar Garciaparra .75 2.00
191 Brad Penny .20 .50
192A Gary Sheffield w/Bat .20 .50
192B Gary Sheffield w/o Bat .20 .50
193 Alfonso Soriano .20 .50
194 Andruw Jones .30 .75
195A R.Johnson Black Jsy .50 1.25
195B R.Johnson Purple Jsy .50 1.25
196A C.Patterson Blue Jsy .20 .50
196B C.Patterson Pinstripes .20 .50
197 Milton Bradley .20 .50
198A J.Damon Blue Jsy/Cap .30 .75
198B J.Damon Blue Jsy/Hlmt .30 .75
198C J.Damon White Jsy .30 .75
199A Paul Lo Duca Blue Jsy .20 .50
199B Paul Lo Duca White Jsy .20 .50
200A Albert Pujols Red Jsy 1.00 2.50
200B Albert Pujols Running 1.00 2.50
200C Albert Pujols w/Bat 1.00 2.50
201 Scott Rolen .30 .75
202A J.D. Drew Running .20 .50
202B J.D. Drew w/Bat .20 .50
202C J.D. Drew White Jsy .20 .50
203 Vladimir Guerrero .50 1.25
204A Jason Giambi Blue Jsy .20 .50
204B Jason Giambi Grey Jsy .20 .50
204C Jason Giambi Pinstripes .20 .50
205A Moises Alou Grey Jsy .20 .50
205B Moises Alou Pinstripes .20 .50
206A Mag. Ordonez Signing .20 .50
206B Magglio Ordonez w/Bat .20 .50
207 Carlos Febles .20 .50
208 So Taguchi RC .30 .75
209A Raf. Palmeiro One Hand .30 .75
209B Raf. Palmeiro Two Hands .30 .75
210 David Wells .20 .50
211 Orlando Cabrera .20 .50
212 Sammy Sosa .50 1.25
213 Armando Benitez .20 .50
214 Wes Helms .20 .50
215A Mar. Rivera Arms Folded .50 1.25
215B Mar. Rivera Holding Ball .50 1.25
216 Jimmy Rollins .20 .50
217 Matt Lawton .20 .50
218A Shawn Green w/Bat .20 .50
218B Shawn Green w/o Bat .20 .50
219A Bernie Williams w/Bat .30 .75
219B Bernie Williams w/o Bat .30 .75
220A Bret Boone Blue Jsy .20 .50
220B Bret Boone White Jsy .20 .50
221A Alex Rodriguez Blue Jsy .75 2.00
221B Alex Rodriguez One Hand .75 2.00
221C Alex Rodriguez Two Hands .75 2.00
222 Roger Cedeno .20 .50
223 Marty Cordova .20 .50
224 Fred McGriff .30 .75
225A Chipper Jones Batting .50 1.25
225B Chipper Jones Running .50 1.25
226 Kerry Wood .20 .50
227A Larry Walker Grey Jsy .20 .50

Card	Low	High
227B Larry Walker Purple Jsy	.20	.50
228 Robin Ventura	.20	.50
229 Robert Fick	.20	.50
230A Tino Martinez Black Glove	.30	.75
230B Tino Martinez Throwing	.30	.75
230C Tino Martinez w/Bat	.30	.75
231 Ben Petrick	.20	.50
232 Neifi Perez	.20	.50
233 Pedro Martinez	.30	.75
234A Brian Jordan Grey Jsy	.20	.50
234B Brian Jordan White Jsy	.20	.50
235 Freddy Garcia	.20	.50
236A Derek Jeter Batting	1.25	3.00
236B Derek Jeter Blue Jsy	1.25	3.00
236C Derek Jeter Kneeling	1.25	3.00
237 Ben Grieve	.20	.50
238A Barry Bonds Black Jsy	1.25	3.00
238B B.Bonds w/Wrist Band	1.25	3.00
238C B.Bonds w/o Wrist Band	1.25	3.00
239 Luis Gonzalez	.20	.50
240 Shane Halter	.20	.50
241A Brian Giles Black Jsy	.20	.50
241B Brian Giles Grey Jsy	.20	.50
242 Bud Smith	.20	.50
243 Richie Sexson	.20	.50
244A Barry Zito Green Jsy	.20	.50
244B Barry Zito White Jsy	.20	.50
245 Eric Milton	.20	.50
246A Ivan Rodriguez Blue Jsy	.30	.75
246B I.Rodriguez Grey Jsy	.30	.75
246C I.Rodriguez White Jsy	.30	.75
247 Toby Hall	.20	.50
248A Mike Piazza Black Jsy	.75	2.00
248B Mike Piazza Grey Jsy	.75	2.00
249 Ruben Sierra	.20	.50
250A Tsuyoshi Shinjo Cap	.20	.50
250B Tsuyoshi Shinjo Helmet	.20	.50
251A Jer. Dye Green Jsy	.20	.50
251B Jermaine Dye White Jsy	.20	.50
252 Roy Oswalt	.20	.50
253 Todd Helton	.30	.75
254 Adrian Beltre	.20	.50
255 Doug Mientkiewicz	.20	.50
256A Ichiro Suzuki Blue Jsy	1.00	2.50
256B Ichiro Suzuki w/Bat	1.00	2.50
256C Ichiro Suzuki White Jsy	1.00	2.50
257A C.C. Sabathia Blue Jsy	.20	.50
257B C.C. Sabathia White Jsy	.20	.50
258 Paul Konerko	.20	.50
259 Ken Griffey Jr.	.75	2.00
260A Jeromy Burnitz w/Bat	.20	.50
260B Jeromy Burnitz w/o Bat	.20	.50
261 Hank Blalock PROS	.30	.75
262 Mark Prior PROS	.30	.75
263 Josh Beckett PROS	.20	.50
264 Carlos Pena PROS	.20	.50
265 Sean Burroughs PROS	.20	.50
266 Austin Kearns PROS	.20	.50
267 Chin-Hui Tsao PROS	.20	.50
268 Dewon Brazelton PROS	.20	.50
269 J.D. Martin PROS	.20	.50
270 Marlon Byrd PROS	.20	.50
271 Joe Mauer FYP RC	4.00	10.00
272 Jason Botts FYP RC	.20	.50
273 Mauricio Lara FYP RC	.20	.50
274 Jonny Gomes FYP RC	1.00	2.50
275 Gavin Floyd FYP RC	.40	1.00
276 Alex Requena FYP RC	.20	.50
277 Jimmy Gobble FYP RC	.20	.50
278 Chris Duffy FYP RC	.20	.50
279 Colt Griffin FYP RC	.20	.50
280 Ryan Church FYP RC	.40	1.00
281 Beltran Perez FYP RC	.20	.50
282 Clint Nageotte FYP RC	.30	.75
283 Justin Schuda FYP RC	.20	.50
284 Scott Hairston FYP RC	.30	.75
285 Mario Ramos FYP RC	.20	.50
286A Tom Seaver White Sox RET	.60	1.50
286B Tom Seaver Mets RET	.60	1.50
287A H.Aaron White Jsy RET	2.00	5.00
287B H.Aaron Blue Jsy RET	2.00	5.00
288 Mike Schmidt RET	2.00	5.00
289A R.Yount Blue Jsy RET	1.00	2.50
289B R.Yount P'stripes RET	1.00	2.50
290 Joe Morgan RET	.40	1.00
291 Frank Robinson RET	.60	1.50
292A Reggie Jackson A's RET	.60	1.50
292B Reggie Jackson Yanks RET	.60	1.50
293A Nolan Ryan Astros RET	2.50	6.00
293B N.Ryan Rangers RET	2.50	6.00
294 Dave Winfield RET	.40	1.00
295 Willie Mays RET	2.00	5.00
296 Brooks Robinson RET	.60	1.50
297A Mark McGwire A's RET	2.50	6.00
297B M.McGwire Cards RET	2.50	6.00
298 Honus Wagner RET	1.00	2.50
299A Sherry Magee REP	.40	1.00
299B Sherry Magie UER REP	.40	1.00
300 Frank Chance REP	.40	1.00
301A Joe Doyle NY REP	.40	1.00
301B Joe Doyle NY Nat'l REP	.40	1.00
302 John McGraw REP	.60	1.50
303 Jimmy Collins REP	.40	1.00
304 Buck Herzog REP	.40	1.00
305 Sam Crawford REP	.40	1.00
306 Cy Young REP	1.00	2.50
307 Honus Wagner Blue REP	3.00	8.00
308A A.Rodriguez Blue Jsy SP	1.50	4.00
308B A.Rodriguez White Jsy	.75	2.00
309 Vernon Wells	.20	.50
310A B.Bonds w/Elbow Pad	1.25	3.00
310B B.Bonds w/o Elbow Pad SP	2.50	6.00
311 Vicente Padilla	.20	.50
312A A.Soriano w/Wristband	.20	.50
312B A.Soriano w/o Wristband SP	.75	2.00
313 Mike Piazza	.75	2.00
314 Jacque Jones	.20	.50
315 Shawn Green SP	.75	2.00
316 Paul Byrd	.20	.50
317 Lance Berkman	.20	.50
318 Larry Walker	.20	.50
319 Ken Griffey Jr. SP	1.50	4.00
320 Shea Hillenbrand	.20	.50
321 Jay Gibbons	.20	.50
322 Andruw Jones	.30	.75
323 Luis Gonzalez SP	.75	2.00
324 Garret Anderson	.20	.50
325 Roy Halladay	.20	.50
326 Randy Winn	.20	.50
327 Matt Morris	.20	.50
328 Robb Nen	.20	.50
329 Trevor Hoffman	.20	.50
330 Kip Wells	.20	.50
331 Orlando Hernandez	.20	.50
332 Rey Ordonez	.20	.50
333 Torii Hunter	.20	.50
334 Geoff Jenkins	.20	.50
335 Eric Karros	.20	.50
336 Mike Lowell	.20	.50
337 Nick Johnson	.20	.50
338 Randall Simon	.20	.50
339 Ellis Burks	.20	.50
340A S.Sosa Blue Jsy SP	1.00	2.50
340B Sammy Sosa White Jsy	.50	1.25
341 Pedro Martinez	.30	.75
342 Junior Spivey	.20	.50
343 Vinny Castilla	.20	.50
344 Randy Johnson SP	1.00	2.50
345 Chipper Jones SP	1.00	2.50
346 Orlando Hudson	.20	.50
347 Albert Pujols SP	2.00	5.00
348 Rondell White	.20	.50
349 Vladimir Guerrero	.50	1.25
350A Mark Prior Red SP	.60	1.50
350B Mark Prior Yellow	.30	.75
351 Eric Gagne	.20	.50
352 Todd Zeile	.20	.50
353 Manny Ramirez SP	.75	2.00
354 Kevin Millwood	.20	.50
355 Troy Percival	.20	.50
356A Jason Giambi Batting SP	.75	2.00
356B Jason Giambi Throwing	.20	.50
357 Bartolo Colon	.20	.50
358 Jeremy Giambi	.20	.50
359 Jose Cruz Jr.	.20	.50
360A I.Suzuki Blue Jsy SP	2.00	5.00
360B I.Suzuki White Jsy	1.00	2.50
361 Eddie Guardado	.20	.50
362 Ivan Rodriguez	.30	.75
363 Carl Crawford	.20	.50
364 Jason Simontacchi RC	.20	.50
365 Kenny Lofton	.20	.50
366 Raul Mondesi	.20	.50
367 A.J. Pierzynski	.20	.50
368 Ugueth Urbina	.20	.50
369 Rodrigo Lopez	.20	.50
370A N.Garciaparra One Bat SP	1.50	4.00
370B N.Garciaparra Two Bats	.75	2.00
371 Craig Counsell	.20	.50
372 Barry Larkin	.30	.75
373 Carlos Pena	.20	.50
374 Luis Castillo	.20	.50
375 Raul Ibanez	.20	.50
376 Kazuhisa Ishii SP	.75	2.00
377 Derek Lowe	.20	.50
378 Curt Schilling	.20	.50
379 Jim Thome Phillies	.30	.75
380A Derek Jeter Blue SP	2.50	6.00
380B Derek Jeter Seats	1.25	3.00
381 Pat Burrell	.20	.50
382 Jamie Moyer	.20	.50
383 Eric Hinske	.20	.50
384 Scott Rolen	.30	.75
385 Miguel Tejada SP	.75	2.00
386 Andy Pettitte	.30	.75
387 Mike Lieberthal	.20	.50
388 Al Leiter	.20	.50
389 Todd Helton SP	.75	2.00
390A Adam Dunn Bat SP	.75	2.00
390B Adam Dunn Glove	.20	.50
391 Cliff Floyd	.20	.50
392 Tim Salmon	.30	.75
393 Joe Torre MG	.30	.75
394 Bobby Cox MG	.20	.50
395 Tony LaRussa MG	.20	.50
396 Art Howe MG	.20	.50
397 Bob Brenly MG	.20	.50
398 Ron Gardenhire MG	.20	.50
399 Mike Cuddyer PROS	.20	.50
400 Joe Mauer PROS	4.00	10.00
401 Mark Teixeira PROS	.50	1.25
402 Hee Seop Choi PROS	.20	.50
403 Angel Berroa PROS	.20	.50
404 Jesse Foppert PROS RC	.30	.75
405 Bobby Crosby PROS	.50	1.25
406 Jose Reyes PROS	.30	.75
407 C.Kotchman PROS RC	.40	1.00
408 Aaron Heilman PROS	.20	.50
409 Adrian Gonzalez PROS	.20	.50
410 Delwyn Young PROS RC	.40	1.00
411 Brett Myers PROS	.20	.50
412 Justin Huber PROS RC	.30	.75
413 Drew Henson PROS	.20	.50
414 T.Bozied PROS RC	.30	.75
415 Dontrelle Willis PROS RC	1.25	3.00
416 Rocco Baldelli PROS	.20	.50
417 Jason Stokes PROS RC	.20	.50
418 Brandon Phillips PROS	.20	.50
419 Jake Blalock FYP RC	.20	.50
420 Micah Schilling FYP RC	.40	1.00
421 Denard Span FYP RC	.40	1.00
422A J.Loney Red FYP RC	1.50	4.00
422B J.Loney w/Sky FYP RC	1.50	4.00
423A W.Bankston Blue FYP RC	.75	2.00
423B W.Bankston w/Sky FYP RC	.75	2.00
424 Jeremy Hermida FYP RC	2.00	5.00
425 C.Granderson FYP RC	2.00	5.00
426A J.Pridie Red FYP RC	.40	1.00
426B J.Pridie w/Sky FYP RC	.40	1.00
427 Larry Broadway FYP RC	.20	.50
428A K.Greene Green FYP RC	3.00	8.00
428B K.Greene Red FYP RC	3.00	8.00
429 Joey Votto FYP RC	6.00	15.00
430A B.Upton Grey FYP RC	2.00	5.00
430B B.Upton w/People FYP RC	2.00	5.00
431A S.Santos Gold FYP RC	.40	1.00
431B S.Santos Grey FYP RC	.40	1.00
432 Brian Dopirak FYP RC	.40	1.00
433 Ozzie Smith RET SP	1.50	4.00
434 Wade Boggs RET SP	1.00	2.50
435 Yogi Berra RET SP	1.50	4.00
436 Al Kaline RET SP	1.50	4.00
437 Robin Roberts RET SP	.75	2.00
438 Rob. Clemente RET SP	3.00	8.00
439 Gary Carter RET SP	.75	2.00
440 Fergie Jenkins RET SP	.75	2.00
441 Orlando Cepeda RET SP	.75	2.00
442 Rod Carew RET SP	1.00	2.50
443 Ha. Killebrew RET SP	1.50	4.00
444 Duke Snider RET SP	1.00	2.50
445 Stan Musial RET SP	2.50	6.00
446 Hank Greenberg RET SP	1.50	4.00
447 Lou Brock RET SP	1.00	2.50
448 Jim Palmer RET	.40	1.00
449 John McGraw REP	.60	1.50
450 Mordecai Brown REP	.40	1.00
451 Christy Mathewson REP	.60	1.50
452 Sam Crawford REP	.40	1.00
453 Bill O'Hara REP	.40	1.00
454 Joe Tinker REP	.40	1.00
455 Nap Lajoie REP	.60	1.50
456 Honus Wagner Red REP	3.00	8.00
NNO Repurchased Tobacco Card		

2002 Topps 206 American Beauty

Inserted into third series packs as a stated rate of one in 15,316 these five cards were issued with the very scarce American Beauty back. These cards were issued to a stated print run of five sets so no pricing is provided due to scarcity.

308 A.Rodriguez White Jsy
310 B.Bonds w/Elbow Pad
312 A.Soriano w/Wristband
370 N.Garciaparra Two Bats
456 Honus Wagner Red REP

2002 Topps 206 Carolina Brights

Randomly inserted in second series packs and using the "Carolina Brights" backs, these cards parallel the Topps 206 second series cards.

*CAROLINA 181-270: 3X TO 8X BASIC
*CAROLINA RC's 181-270: 1X TO 2.5X
*CAROLINA 271-285: 1.25X TO 3X BASIC
*CAROLINA 286-307: 2X TO 5X BASIC

2002 Topps 206 Cycle

Randomly inserted in first series packs and using the "Cycle" backs, this is a complete parallel of the Topps 206 first series.

*CYCLE 1-140: 5X TO 12X BASIC CARDS
*CYCLE 141-155: 1.25X TO 3X BASIC
*CYCLE 156-180: 3X TO 8X BASIC

2002 Topps 206 Drum

Issued at a stated rate of one in 3711 third series packs, these five cards feature "Drum" backs. These cards have a stated print run of 20 sets and no pricing is provided due to market scarcity.

324 Garret Anderson
356 Jason Giambi Batting
360 I.Suzuki White Jsy
390 Adam Dunn Glove
400 Joe Mauer PROS

2002 Topps 206 Lenox

Issued at a stated rate of one in 7422 third series packs, these five cards feature "Lenox" backs. These cards have a stated print run of 10 sets and no pricing is provided due to market scarcity.

308 A.Rodriguez Blue Jsy
340 Sammy Sosa White Jsy
349 Vladimir Guerrero
353 Manny Ramirez
416 Rocco Baldelli PROS

2002 Topps 206 Piedmont Black

Randomly inserted in second series packs and using the "Piedmont" backs, these cards parallel the Topps 206 second series cards. The words on the back are in black ink and thus these cards are called Piedmont Black

*P'MONT.BLACK 181-270: 1.5X TO 4X BASIC
*P'MONT.BLACK RC's 181-270: .5X TO 1.2X
*P'MONT.BLACK 271-285: .6X TO 1.5X
*P'MONT.BLACK 286-307: 1X TO 2.5X

2002 Topps 206 Piedmont Red

Randomly inserted in second series packs and using the "Piedmont" backs, these cards parallel the Topps 206 second series cards. The words on the back are in black ink and thus these cards are called Piedmont Red.

*P'MONT.RED 181-270: 3X TO 8X BASIC
*P'MONT.RED RC's 181-270: 1X TO 2.5X
*P'MONT.RED 271-285: 1.25X TO 3X
*P'MONT.RED 286-307: 2X TO 5X BASIC

2002 Topps 206 Polar Bear

Randomly inserted into approximately two out of every three packs and using the "Polar Bear" backs, this is a complete parallel of the Topps 206 set. Cards 1-180 were distributed in first series packs, 181-307 in second series packs and 308-456 in third series packs. The set is actually complete at 525 cards, but the checklist runs from 1-307 with 96 variations intermingled within.

*POLAR 1-140/181-270/308-418: 1.25X TO 3X
*RC 1-140/181-270/308-418: .5X TO 1.2X
*FYP 141-155/271-285: .5X TO 1.2X
*SP 308-418: .6X TO 1.5X SP
*FYP 419-432: .5X TO 1.2X
*RT/RP 156-180/286-307/448-456: .75X TO 2X
*RET 443-447: .75X TO 2X

2002 Topps 206 Sweet Caporal Black

Randomly inserted into packs, this is a parallel to the T206 third series. These cards have the words "Sweet Caporal" in black on the back.

*BLACK 308-418: 2.5X TO 6X BASIC
*BLACK SP 308-418: 1.25X TO 3X BASIC
*BLACK RC 308-418: 1X TO 2.5X BASIC
*BLACK 419-432: 1.25X TO 3X BASIC
*BLACK 433-447: .75X TO 2X BASIC
*BLACK 448-456: 1.5X TO 4X BASIC

2002 Topps 206 Sweet Caporal Blue

Randomly inserted into packs, this is a parallel to the T206 third series. These cards have the words "Sweet Caporal" in blue on the back.

*BLUE 308-418: 2X TO 5X BASIC
*BLUE SP 308-418: 1X TO 2.5X BASIC
*BLUE RC 308-418: .75X TO 2X BASIC
*BLUE 419-432: 1X TO 2.5X BASIC
*BLUE 433-447: .6X TO 1.5X BASIC
*BLUE 448-456: 1.25X TO 3X BASIC

2002 Topps 206 Sweet Caporal Red

Randomly inserted into packs, this is a parallel to the T206 third series. These cards have the words "Sweet Caporal" in blue on the back.

*RED 308-418: 1.5X TO 4X BASIC
*RED SP 308-418: .75X TO 2X BASIC
*RED RC 308-418: .6X TO 1.5X BASIC
*RED 419-432: .75X TO 2X BASIC
*RED 433-447: .5X TO 1.2X BASIC
*RED 448-456: 1X TO 2.5X BASIC

2002 Topps 206 Tolstoi

Randomly inserted in first series packs and using the "Tolstoi" backs, this is a complete parallel of the Topps 206 first series.

*TOLSTOI 1-140: 1.5X TO 4X BASIC
*TOLSTOI 141-155: .4X TO 1X BASIC
*TOLSTOI 156-180: 1X TO 2.5X BASIC

2002 Topps 206 Tolstoi Red

Randomly inserted in packs and using the "Tolstoi" backs, this is a complete parallel of the Topps 206 first series. These cards are differentiated from the more common Tolstoi backs as the color on the back is red. These cards were printed at a stated rate of 25 percent of the total Tolstoi run.

*TOLSTOI RED 1-140: 3X TO 8X BASIC
*TOLSTOI RED 141-155: .6X TO 1.5X BASIC
*TOLSTOI RED 156-180: 2X TO 5X BASIC

2002 Topps 206 Uzit

Randomly inserted into packs, this is a parallel to the T206 third series. These cards have "Uzit" on the back.

*UZIT 308-418: 3X TO 8X BASIC
*UZIT SP 308-418: 1.5X TO 4X BASIC
*UZIT RC 308-418: 1.5X TO 4X BASIC
*UZIT 419-432: 1.5X TO 4X BASIC
*UZIT 433-447: 1X TO 2.5X BASIC
*UZIT 448-456: 2X TO 5X BASIC

2002 Topps 206 Autographs

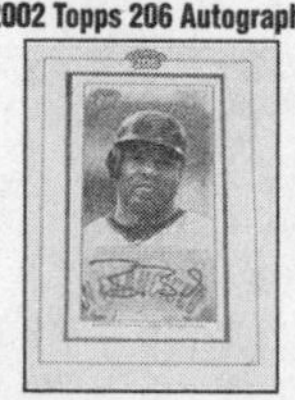

Inserted at an overall stated rate of one in 41 series one packs, one in 55 series two packs and varying group specific odds in series three packs (see details below), these cards feature a mix of young players and veteran stars who autographed cards for the T206 product.

SER.1 GROUP A1 ODDS 1:1067
SER.1 GROUP B1 ODDS 1:1122
SER.1 GROUP C1 ODDS 1:532
SER.1 GROUP D1 ODDS 1:444
SER.1 GROUP E1 ODDS 1:532
SER.1 GROUP F1 ODDS 1:121
SER.1 GROUP G1 ODDS 1:118
SER.2 GROUP A2 ODDS 1:511
SER.2 GROUP B2 ODDS 1:893
SER.2 GROUP C2 ODDS 1:1557
SER.2 GROUP D2 ODDS 1:106
SER.2 GROUP E2 ODDS 1:638
SER.2 GROUP F2 ODDS 1:596
SER.2 GROUP G2 ODDS 1:526
SER.3 GROUP A3 ODDS 1:810
SER.3 GROUP B3 ODDS 1:442
SER.3 GROUP C3 ODDS 1:411
SER.3 GROUP D3 ODDS 1:393
SER.3 GROUP E3 ODDS 1:393
SER.3 GROUP F3 ODDS 1:384
SER.3 GROUP G3 ODDS 1:383

Card	Low	High
AP Albert Pujols A2	200.00	400.00
AR Alex Rodriguez A1	60.00	120.00
BB Barry Bonds A1	150.00	250.00
BG Brian Giles G1	6.00	15.00
BI Brandon Inge D1	6.00	15.00
BS Ben Sheets E2	6.00	15.00
BSM Bud Smith B2	6.00	15.00
BZ Barry Zito D1	12.50	30.00
CG Cristian Guzman G1	4.00	10.00
CT Chris Tritle G2	4.00	10.00
DB Dewon Brazelton D2	4.00	10.00
DE David Eckstein G3	12.50	30.00
DH Drew Henson D3	4.00	10.00
EC Eric Chavez A2	10.00	25.00
FJ Forrest Johnson F1	4.00	10.00
FL Felipe Lopez C1	6.00	15.00
GF Gavin Floyd D2	6.00	15.00
GN Greg Nash F1	4.00	10.00
HB Hank Blalock D2	6.00	15.00
JC Jose Cruz Jr. A3	6.00	15.00
JD Johnny Damon Sox B2	15.00	40.00
JDM J.D. Martin D2	4.00	10.00
JE Jim Edmonds C1	15.00	40.00
JJ Jorge Julio F1	4.00	10.00
JM Joe Mauer D2	60.00	120.00
JR Jimmy Rollins G1	12.50	30.00
JV Jose Vidro B3	6.00	15.00
KI Kazuhisa Ishii A2	15.00	40.00
LB Lance Berkman A2	20.00	50.00
LG Luis Gonzalez C2	6.00	15.00
MA Moises Alou A2	10.00	25.00
MB Milton Bradley C3	6.00	15.00
MB Marlon Byrd D2	4.00	10.00
ML Mike Lamb F3	4.00	10.00
MO Magglio Ordonez E1	6.00	15.00
MP Mark Prior D2	6.00	15.00
MT Marcus Thames E3	4.00	10.00
RC Roger Clemens B1	75.00	150.00
RJ Ryan Jamison F1	4.00	10.00
RS Richie Sexson F2	6.00	15.00
SR Scott Rolen A2	15.00	40.00
ST So Taguchi A2	15.00	40.00

2002 Topps 206 Relics

Issued in first series packs at overall stated odds of one in 11 and second series packs at overall stated odds of one in 12 and third series packs at various odds, these 109 cards feature either a bat sliver or a jersey/uniform swatch. Representatives at Topps announced that only 25 copies of the Honus Wagner blue Bat and Honus Wagner Red Bat and 100 copies of the Ty Cobb Bat card (both seeded into second series packs) were produced. In addition, in early 2005, the Beckett staff managed to confirm with Topps that 300 copies of Wagner's Orange background card were also produced. Please note, all first series Relics feature light yellow frames (surrounding the mini-sized card), all second series Relics feature light blue frames and third series Relics feature light pink frames.

SER.1 BAT GROUP A1 ODDS 1:166
SER.1 BAT GROUP B1 ODDS 1:1780
SER.2 BAT GROUP A2 ODDS 1:35,217
SER.2 BAT GROUP B2 ODDS 1:8991
SER.2 BAT GROUP C2 ODDS 1:2097
SER.2 BAT GROUP D2 ODDS 1:75
SER.2 BAT GROUP E2 ODDS 1:1377
SER.2 BAT GROUP F2 ODDS 1:893
SER.2 BAT GROUP G2 ODDS 1:248
SER.2 BAT GROUP H2 ODDS 1:319
SER.2 BAT GROUP I2 ODDS 1:447
SER.2 BAT OVERALL ODDS 1:40
SER.3 BAT GROUP A3 ODDS 1:15,316
SER.3 BAT GROUP B3 ODDS 1:390
SER.3 BAT GROUP C3 ODDS 1:370
SER.3 BAT GROUP D3 ODDS 1:34
SER.3 BAT GROUP E3 ODDS 1:187
SER.3 BAT GROUP F3 ODDS 1:185
SER.1 UNI GROUP A1 ODDS 1:14
SER.1 UNI GROUP B1 ODDS 1:74
SER.2 UNI GROUP A2 ODDS 1:372
SER.2 UNI GROUP B2 ODDS 1:27
SER.2 UNI GROUP C2 ODDS 1:62
SER.2 UNI GROUP D2 ODDS 1:447
SER.2 UNI OVERALL ODDS 1:18
SER.3 UNI GROUP A3 ODDS 1:247
SER.3 UNI GROUP B3 ODDS 1:185
SER.3 UNI GROUP C3 ODDS 1:62
SER.3 UNI GROUP D3 ODDS 1:187
SER.3 UNI GROUP E3 ODDS 1:27
SER.3 UNI GROUP F3 ODDS 1:176

Card	Low	High
AB A.J. Burnett Jsy B2	3.00	8.00
AD2 Adam Dunn Bat D2	6.00	15.00
AD3 Adam Dunn Bat C3	6.00	15.00
AJ1 Andruw Jones Jsy A1	4.00	10.00
AJ2 Andruw Jones Jsy C2	4.00	10.00
AJ3 Andruw Jones Uni E3	4.00	10.00
AP1 Albert Pujols Bat A1	8.00	20.00
AP2 Albert Pujols Jsy B2	8.00	20.00
AP3 Albert Pujols Bat D3	8.00	20.00
ARA Aramis Ramirez Bat D2	6.00	15.00
AR2 Alex Rodriguez Bat D2	8.00	20.00
AR3 Alex Rodriguez Bat D3	6.00	15.00
AS1 Alfonso Soriano Bat A1	6.00	15.00
AS2 Alfonso Soriano Bat I2	3.00	8.00
AS3 Alfonso Soriano Bat D3	3.00	8.00
BB1 Barry Bonds Jsy A1	10.00	25.00
BB2 Barry Bonds Uni C2	10.00	25.00
BD Brandon Duckworth Jsy B2	3.00	8.00
BH Buck Herzog Bat G2	20.00	50.00
BL Barry Larkin Jsy B2	4.00	10.00
BP Brad Penny Jsy B2	3.00	8.00
BW1 Bernie Williams Jsy A1	4.00	10.00
BW2 Bernie Williams Jsy B2	4.00	10.00
BW3 Bernie Williams Uni A3	6.00	15.00
BZ1 Barry Zito Jsy A1	3.00	8.00
BZ3 Barry Zito Uni C3	3.00	8.00
CB Craig Biggio Jsy B1	4.00	10.00
CD Carlos Delgado Jsy A1	3.00	8.00
CF1 Cliff Floyd Jsy A1	3.00	8.00
CF2 Cliff Floyd Jsy B2	3.00	8.00
CG Cristian Guzman Jsy B2	3.00	8.00
CJ1 Chipper Jones Jsy A1	6.00	15.00
CJ2 Chipper Jones Jsy B2	6.00	15.00
CJ3 Chipper Jones Uni B3	6.00	15.00
CL Carlos Lee Jsy A1	3.00	8.00
CP Corey Patterson Bat F3	3.00	8.00
CS2 Curt Schilling Bat D2	6.00	15.00
CS3 Curt Schilling Bat D3	3.00	8.00
DE Darin Erstad Jsy B2	3.00	8.00
DM Doug Mientkiewicz Uni D3	3.00	8.00
EC2 Eric Chavez Bat H2	3.00	8.00
EC3 Eric Chavez Uni E3	3.00	8.00
EM1 Edgar Martinez Jsy A1	4.00	10.00
EM2 Edgar Martinez Jsy B2	4.00	10.00
FM Fred McGriff Bat D2	6.00	15.00
FT1 Frank Thomas Jsy A1	6.00	15.00
FT2 Frank Thomas Jsy B2	6.00	15.00
FT3 Frank Thomas Uni C3	6.00	15.00
GM1 Greg Maddux Jsy A1	6.00	15.00
GM2 Greg Maddux Jsy C2	6.00	15.00
GS2 Gary Sheffield Bat D2	6.00	15.00
GS3 Gary Sheffield Bat B3	6.00	15.00
HW1 H.Wag Oran Bat B1/300 *	250.00	400.00
HW2 H.Wagner Blue Bat A2/25 *		
HW3 H.Wagner Red Bat A3/25 *		
IR1 Ivan Rodriguez Jsy A1	4.00	10.00
IR2 Ivan Rodriguez Uni A2	4.00	10.00
IR3 Ivan Rodriguez Bat D3	4.00	10.00
JB1 Jeff Bagwell Jsy A1	4.00	10.00
JB2 Jeff Bagwell Uni C2	4.00	10.00
JB3 Jeff Bagwell Bat D3	4.00	10.00
JD J.Damon Sox Bat D2	4.00	10.00
JE1 Jim Edmonds Jsy A1	3.00	8.00
JE3 Jim Edmonds Uni F3	3.00	8.00
JG Juan Gonzalez Bat D2	6.00	15.00
JH Josh Hamilton Bat D2	8.00	20.00
JJ Jason Jennings Jsy B2	3.00	8.00
JK Jeff Kent Uni B2	3.00	8.00
JO1 John Olerud Jsy A1	3.00	8.00
JO2 John Olerud Jsy B2	3.00	8.00
JT Joe Tinker Bat G2	30.00	60.00
JW Jeff Weaver Jsy A1	3.00	8.00
KB Kevin Brown Jsy B2	3.00	8.00
KL Kenny Lofton Jsy B1	3.00	8.00
LG Luis Gonzalez Uni E3	3.00	8.00
LW1 Larry Walker Jsy A1	3.00	8.00
LW2 Larry Walker Jsy B2	3.00	8.00
MC Mike Cameron Jsy A1	3.00	8.00
MG Mark Grace Bat D2	6.00	15.00
MO Maglio Ordonez Jsy A1	3.00	8.00
MP1 Mike Piazza Jsy A1	6.00	15.00
MP2 Mike Piazza Uni C2	6.00	15.00
MP3 Mike Piazza Uni C3	6.00	15.00
MT2 Miguel Tejada Bat H2	3.00	8.00
MT3 Miguel Tejada Uni E3	3.00	8.00
MV2 Mo Vaughn Bat D2	6.00	15.00
MV3 Mo Vaughn Uni E3	3.00	8.00
MW Matt Williams Jsy B2	3.00	8.00
NG Nomar Garciaparra Bat C3	8.00	20.00
NJ Nick Johnson Bat E3	3.00	8.00
PB Pat Burrell Bat B3	6.00	15.00
PM Pedro Martinez Uni A3	6.00	15.00
PO Paul O'Neill Jsy A1	4.00	10.00
PW Preston Wilson Jsy B2	3.00	8.00
RA1 Roberto Alomar Jsy A1	4.00	10.00
RA2 Roberto Alomar Bat D2	6.00	15.00
RA3 Roberto Alomar Bat D3	4.00	10.00
RD Ryan Dempster Jsy B2	3.00	8.00
RH2 Rickey Henderson Bat D2	8.00	20.00
RH3 Rickey Henderson Bat D3	6.00	15.00
RJ1 Randy Johnson Jsy A1	6.00	15.00
RJ2 Randy Johnson Jsy C2	6.00	15.00
RJ3 Randy Johnson Uni A3	8.00	20.00
RP2 Rafael Palmeiro Jsy B2	4.00	10.00
RP3 Rafael Palmeiro Uni B3	4.00	10.00
RV Robin Ventura Bat D2	6.00	15.00
SB Sean Burroughs Bat D2	4.00	10.00
SC Sam Crawford Bat A1	30.00	60.00
SCR Sam Crawford Bat C2	30.00	60.00
SG1 Shawn Green Jsy A1	3.00	8.00
SG2 Shawn Green Jsy C2	3.00	8.00
SR Scott Rolen Bat D3	4.00	10.00
SS Shannon Stewart Bat A1	6.00	15.00
TC Ty Cobb Bat B2/100 *	550.00	700.00
TL Travis Lee Bat D2	4.00	10.00
TM1 Tino Martinez Jsy A1	4.00	10.00
TM2 Tino Martinez Bat D2	6.00	15.00
WB Wilson Betemit Bat D3	3.00	8.00
BBO1 Bret Boone Jsy B1	3.00	8.00
BBO2 Bret Boone Jsy D2	3.00	8.00
CHP Chan Ho Park Bat A1	6.00	15.00
JCA Jose Canseco Bat A1	6.00	15.00
JCO Jimmy Collins Bat F2 UER Eddie Collins pictured	40.00	80.00
JEV1 Johnny Evers Jsy A1	30.00	60.00
JEV2 Johnny Evers Bat G2	30.00	60.00
JMA Joe Mays Jsy B2	3.00	8.00
JMC1 John McGraw Bat A1	50.00	100.00
JMC2 John McGraw Bat E2	50.00	100.00
JTH1 Jim Thome Jsy A1	4.00	10.00
JTH2 Jim Thome Bat D2	6.00	15.00
JTH3 Jim Thome Uni C3	4.00	10.00
TGL1 Tom Glavine Jsy A1	4.00	10.00
TGL2 Tom Glavine Jsy A2	4.00	10.00
TGW1 Tony Gwynn Jsy A1	6.00	15.00
TGW2 Tony Gwynn Jsy B2	6.00	15.00

TGW3 Tony Gwynn Uni E3 6.00 15.00
THA Toby Hall Jsy B2 3.00 8.00
THE1 Todd Helton Jsy A1 4.00 10.00
THE2 Todd Helton Jsy C2 4.00 10.00
THE3 Todd Helton Uni E3 4.00 10.00
TSH2 Tsuyoshi Shinjo Bat D2 6.00 15.00
TSH3 Tsuyoshi Shinjo Bat D3 3.00 8.00
TSP Tris Speaker Bat A1 40.00 80.00
JAGI Jason Giambi Jsy A1 3.00 8.00
JEGI Jeremy Giambi Jsy A1 3.00 8.00

2002 Topps 206 Team 206 Series 1

Inserted at an approximate rate of one per pack (only not in a pack when an autograph or relic card was inserted), these 20 cards feature the leading players from the 206 first series in a more modern design.

COMPLETE SET (20) 6.00 15.00
T2061 Barry Bonds 1.00 2.50
T2062 Ivan Rodriguez .25 .60
T2063 Luis Gonzalez .20 .50
T2064 Jason Giambi Yankees .20 .50
T2065 Pedro Martinez .25 .60
T2066 Larry Walker .20 .50
T2067 Bob Abreu .20 .50
T2068 Derek Jeter 1.00 2.50
T2069 Bret Boone .20 .50
T20610 Mike Piazza .60 1.50
T20611 Alex Rodriguez .60 1.50
T20612 Roger Clemens .75 2.00
T20613 Albert Pujols .75 2.00
T20614 Randy Johnson .40 1.00
T20615 Sammy Sosa .40 1.00
T20616 Cristian Guzman .20 .50
T20617 Shawn Green .20 .50
T20618 Curt Schilling .20 .50
T20619 Ichiro Suzuki .75 2.00
T20620 Chipper Jones .40 1.00

2002 Topps 206 Team 206 Series 2

Inserted at an approximate rate of one per pack (only not in a pack when an autograph or relic card was inserted), these 20 cards feature the leading players from the 206 second series in a more modern design.

COMPLETE SET (25) 6.00 15.00
T2061 Alex Rodriguez .60 1.50
T2062 Sammy Sosa .40 1.00
T2063 Jason Giambi .20 .50
T2064 Nomar Garciaparra .60 1.50
T2065 Ichiro Suzuki .75 2.00
T2066 Chipper Jones .40 1.00
T2067 Derek Jeter 1.00 2.50
T2068 Barry Bonds 1.00 2.50
T2069 Mike Piazza .60 1.50
T20610 Randy Johnson .40 1.00
T20611 Shawn Green .20 .50
T20612 Todd Helton .25 .60
T20613 Luis Gonzalez .20 .50
T20614 Albert Pujols .75 2.00
T20615 Curt Schilling .20 .50
T20616 Scott Rolen .25 .60
T20617 Ivan Rodriguez .25 .60
T20618 Roberto Alomar .25 .60
T20619 Cristian Guzman .20 .50
T20620 Bret Boone .20 .50
T20621 Barry Zito .20 .50
T20622 Larry Walker .20 .50
T20623 Eric Chavez .20 .50
T20624 Roger Clemens .75 2.00
T20625 Pedro Martinez .25 .60

2002 Topps 206 Team 206 Series 3

Inserted at an approximate rate of one per pack (only not in a pack when an autograph or relic card was inserted), these 30 cards feature the leading players from the 206 third series in a more modern design.

COMPLETE SET (30) 6.00 15.00
1 Ichiro Suzuki .75 2.00
2 Kazuhisa Ishii .25 .60
3 Alex Rodriguez .60 1.50
4 Mark Prior .25 .60
5 Derek Jeter 1.00 2.50
6 Sammy Sosa .40 1.00
7 Nomar Garciaparra .60 1.50
8 Mike Piazza .60 1.50
9 Jason Giambi .20 .50
10 Vladimir Guerrero .40 1.00
11 Curt Schilling .20 .50
12 Jim Thome Phillies .25 .60
13 Adam Dunn .20 .50
14 Albert Pujols .75 2.00
15 Pat Burrell .20 .50
16 Chipper Jones .40 1.00
17 Randy Johnson .40 1.00
18 Todd Helton .25 .60
19 Luis Gonzalez .20 .50
20 Alfonso Soriano .20 .50
21 Shawn Green .20 .50
22 Pedro Martinez .25 .60
23 Lance Berkman .20 .50
24 Ivan Rodriguez .25 .60
25 Larry Walker .20 .50
26 Andruw Jones .25 .60
27 Ken Griffey Jr. .60 1.50
28 Manny Ramirez .25 .60
29 Barry Bonds 1.00 2.50
30 Miguel Tejada .20 .50

2009 Topps 206 Hawaii Trade Conference

1 Honus Wagner
2 Lou Gehrig
3 Babe Ruth
4 Rogers Hornsby
5 Jackie Robinson
6 Ty Cobb

2009 Topps 206

COMPLETE SET (350) 100.00 200.00
COMP.SET w/o SP's (300) 20.00 50.00
COMMON CARD (1-300) .15 .40
COMMON ROOKIE (1-300) .30 .75
COMMON SP VAR (1-300) .75 2.00
SP VAR ODDS 1:4 HOBBY
SP VAR HAVE NO CARD NUMBERS
OVERALL PLATE ODDS 1:285 HOBBY
PLATE PRINT RUN 1 SET PER COLOR
BLACK-CYAN-MAGENTA-YELLOW ISSUED
NO PLATE PRICING DUE TO SCARCITY
1a Ryan Howard .50 1.25
1b Ryan Howard VAR SP 2.50 6.00
2 Erick Aybar .15 .40
3 Carlos Quentin .25 .60
4 Juan Pierre .15 .40
5 Chris Young .15 .40
6 John Mayberry (RC) .30 .75
7 Rocco Baldelli .15 .40
8 Dan Uggla .25 .60
9 Matt Holliday .40 1.00
10a Andrew McCutchen (RC) 1.25 3.00
10b Andrew McCutchen VAR SP 3.00 8.00
11 Adam Jones .25 .60
12 Ian Stewart .15 .40
13 Bobby Parnell RC .50 1.25
14 Scott Rolen .25 .60
15 Max Scherzer .25 .60
16 Jonny Gomes .15 .40
17 Jonathan Broxton .15 .40
18 Kenji Johjima .25 .60
19a Mel Ott .40 1.00
19b Mel Ott VAR SP 2.00 5.00
20 Geovany Soto .25 .60
21 Ivan Rodriguez .25 .60
22 Josh Reddick RC .50 1.25
23a Koji Uehara RC .50 1.25
23b Koji Uehara VAR SP 1.25 3.00
24 David Ortiz .25 .60
25 Magglio Ordonez .25 .60
26 Chien-Ming Wang .25 .60
27 Andrew Carpenter RC .50 1.25
28a Kenshin Kawakami RC .50 1.25
28b Kenshin Kawakami VAR SP 1.25 3.00
29 Kerry Wood .15 .40
30 Justin Morneau .40 1.00
31 Andy Sonnanstine .15 .40
32 Stephen Drew .15 .40
33 Jay Bruce .25 .60
34 Andre Ethier .25 .60
35 Erik Bedard .15 .40
36a Jimmie Foxx .40 1.00
36b Jimmie Foxx VAR SP 2.00 5.00
37 Rich Harden .15 .40
38 Hunter Pence .25 .60
39 Jayson Werth .25 .60
40 Daniel Schlereth RC .30 .75
41a David Hernandez RC .30 .75
41b David Hernandez VAR SP .75 2.00
42 Jason Marquis .15 .40
43 Hideki Matsui .40 1.00
44a Michael Bowden (RC) .30 .75
44b Michael Bowden VAR SP .75 2.00
45 Derek Lowe .15 .40
46 Cliff Lee .25 .60
47 Rickie Weeks .25 .60
48 Carlos Pena .25 .60
49a Walter Johnson .40 1.00
49b Walter Johnson VAR SP 2.00 5.00
50 Joe Crede .25 .60
51 Zack Greinke .25 .60
52 Kevin Kouzmanoff .15 .40
53 Wilkin Ramirez RC .30 .75
54 Jonathan Papelbon .25 .60
55 Chris Volstad .15 .40
56 Robinson Cano .40 1.00
57a Matt LaPorta RC .75 2.00
57b Matt LaPorta VAR SP 2.00 5.00
58 Brian Roberts .15 .40
59 David Huff RC .30 .75
60 Daniel Murphy RC .75 2.00
61a Derek Holland RC .50 1.25
61b Derek Holland VAR SP 1.25 3.00
62 Dan Haren .15 .40
63 Bronson Arroyo .15 .40
64 Corey Hart .15 .40
65 Troy Glaus .15 .40
66a Ty Cobb .60 1.50
66b Ty Cobb VAR SP 3.00 8.00
67 Alfonso Soriano .25 .60
68 Luke Hochevar .15 .40
69 Jimmy Rollins .25 .60
70 Matt Tuiasosopo (RC) .30 .75
71a Dustin Pedroia .50 1.25
71b Dustin Pedroia VAR SP 2.50 6.00
72a Rick Porcello RC 1.00 2.50
72b Rick Porcello VAR SP 2.50 6.00
73 Joba Chamberlain .25 .60
74 Greg Golson (RC) .30 .75
75 Jair Jurrjens .15 .40
76 Trevor Crowe RC .30 .75
77 Joe Nathan .15 .40
78 Hank Blalock .15 .40
79 Bobby Abreu .15 .40
80 Jim Thome .25 .60
81 Orlando Hudson .15 .40
82 Randy Johnson .25 .60
83a Rogers Hornsby .25 .60
83b Rogers Hornsby VAR SP 1.25 3.00
84 Mike Fontenot .15 .40
85 Kazuo Matsui .15 .40
86 Kurt Suzuki .15 .40
87a Ryan Perry RC .75 2.00
87b Ryan Perry VAR SP 2.00 5.00
88 Melvin Mora .15 .40
89 Ubaldo Jimenez .25 .60
90a Alex Rodriguez .60 1.50
90b Alex Rodriguez VAR SP 3.00 8.00
91 John Lannan .15 .40
92 Javier Vazquez .15 .40
93 Victor Martinez .25 .60
94 Francisco Liriano .15 .40
95 Matt Garza .15 .40
96 Vladimir Guerrero .40 1.00
97 Gavin Floyd .15 .40
98 Matt Kemp .25 .60
99 Adrian Gonzalez .25 .60
100 Ramiro Pena RC .50 1.25
101 J.D. Drew .15 .40
102a Hanley Ramirez .40 1.00
102b Hanley Ramirez VAR SP 2.00 5.00
103a Andrew Bailey RC .75 2.00
103b Andrew Bailey VAR SP 2.00 5.00
104 Mark Melancon RC .30 .75
105 Lou Montanez .15 .40
106 Jeff Francis .15 .40
107a Fernando Martinez RC .75 2.00
107b Fernando Martinez VAR SP 2.00 5.00
108 Alex Rios .25 .60
109 Justin Upton .25 .60
110 Chris Dickerson .15 .40
111 Mike Cameron .15 .40
112 Felix Hernandez .40 1.00
113a Tris Speaker .25 .60
113b Tris Speaker VAR SP 1.25 3.00
114 Carlos Zambrano .25 .60
115 Michael Bourn .15 .40
116a Chase Utley .40 1.00
116b Chase Utley VAR SP 2.00 5.00
117 Jordan Schafer (RC) .50 1.25
118 Kevin Youkilis .25 .60
119 Curtis Granderson .25 .60
120a Derek Jeter 1.00 2.50
120b Derek Jeter VAR SP 5.00 12.00
121 Francisco Cervelli RC .75 2.00
122 Nick Markakis .40 1.00
123 Brad Hawpe .15 .40
124 Johan Santana .40 1.00
125 Adam Lind .15 .40
126 Brandon Webb .25 .60
127 Javier Valentin .15 .40
128 James Loney .25 .60
129a Ichiro Suzuki .60 1.50
129b Ichiro Suzuki VAR SP 3.00 8.00
130a Honus Wagner .40 1.00
130b Honus Wagner VAR SP 2.00 5.00
131 Kosuke Fukudome .40 1.00
132 Carlos Lee .15 .40
133 Shane Victorino .15 .40
134 Travis Snider RC .50 1.25
135 Jon Lester .40 1.00
136 Edgar Renteria .15 .40
137a Mark Teixeira .40 1.00
137b Mark Teixeira VAR SP 2.00 5.00
138a Elvis Andrus RC .50 1.25
138b Elvis Andrus VAR SP 1.25 3.00
139 Chipper Jones .40 1.00
140 Jeremy Sowers .15 .40
141 Prince Fielder .25 .60
142a Evan Longoria .50 1.25
142b Evan Longoria VAR SP 2.50 6.00
143a Cy Young .40 1.00
143b Cy Young VAR SP 2.00 5.00
144 Neftali Feliz RC 1.00 2.50
145 David DeJesus .15 .40
146 Tony Gwynn Jr. .15 .40
147 Fernando Perez (RC) .30 .75
148 Josh Beckett .25 .60
149 Josh Johnson .25 .60
150 A.J. Burnett .25 .60
151 Wade LeBlanc RC .50 1.25
152 Luke Scott .15 .40
153 Dexter Fowler (RC) .50 1.25
154a Mickey Mantle 1.25 3.00
154b Mickey Mantle VAR SP 6.00 15.00
155 Adam Dunn .25 .60
156 Brian McCann .25 .60
157 Brandon Phillips .15 .40
158 Mat Gamel RC .75 2.00
159 Rick Ankiel .15 .40
160a Thurman Munson .40 1.00
160b Thurman Munson VAR SP 2.00 5.00
161 Jermaine Dye .15 .40
162 Billy Butler .15 .40
163 Cole Hamels .40 1.00
164 Luis Valbuena RC .50 1.25
165 John Smoltz .40 1.00
166 Joel Zumaya .15 .40
167 Nick Swisher .40 1.00
168 Aaron Cunningham RC .30 .75
169 Carlos Beltran .15 .40
170 Jhonny Peralta .15 .40
171a David Wright .50 1.25
171b David Wright VAR SP 2.50 6.00
172 Michael Young .25 .60
173 Howie Kendrick .15 .40
174a Gordon Beckham RC 1.00 2.50
174b Gordon Beckham VAR SP 2.50 6.00
175a Manny Ramirez .40 1.00
175b Manny Ramirez VAR SP 2.00 5.00
176 Barry Zito .15 .40
177a Pee Wee Reese .25 .60
177b Pee Wee Reese VAR SP 1.25 3.00
178 Bobby Scales RC .50 1.25
179 Roy Oswalt .25 .60
180 Jack Cust .15 .40
181a David Price RC .75 2.00
181b David Price VAR SP 2.00 5.00
182 Daisuke Matsuzaka .40 1.00
183 Jeremy Bonderman .15 .40
184 Jorge Posada .25 .60
185 Brian Duensing RC .50 1.25
186 Yunel Escobar .15 .40
187 Travis Hafner .15 .40
188 Glen Perkins .15 .40
189 Scott Kazmir .15 .40
190 Jon Garland .15 .40
191 Paul Konerko .25 .60
192 Rafael Furcal .15 .40
193 Jake Peavy .15 .40
194 George Kottaras (RC) .30 .75
195 Jacoby Ellsbury .40 1.00
196 Jeremy Hermida .15 .40
197 Brett Anderson RC .50 1.25
198 Brad Nelson (RC) .30 .75
199 Nolan Reimold (RC) .30 .75
200 Todd Helton .25 .60
201 John Maine .15 .40
202 Vernon Wells .15 .40
203 Chris Young .15 .40
204 Johnny Cueto .15 .40
205 J.J. Hardy .15 .40
206 Yadier Molina .25 .60
207a Jackie Robinson .40 1.00
207b Jackie Robinson VAR SP 2.00 5.00
208 Derrek Lee .15 .40
209 Gil Meche .15 .40
210 Pat Burrell .15 .40
211 Jordan Zimmermann RC .30 .75
212 Jason Bay .25 .60
213 Chris Coghlan RC .75 2.00
214 Jason Giambi .15 .40
215 Vin Mazzaro RC .30 .75
216 Ryan Freel .15 .40
217 Garrett Atkins .15 .40
218 Francisco Rodriguez .25 .60
219 Roy Halladay .40 1.00
220 Conor Jackson .15 .40
221 Joey Votto .40 1.00
222 Clayton Kershaw .40 1.00
223 Ken Griffey Jr. .60 1.50
224a Roy Campanella .40 1.00
224b Roy Campanella VAR SP 2.00 5.00
225 Jeff Samardzija .25 .60
226 Lance Berkman .25 .60
227 Brad Lidge .15 .40
228 Will Venable RC .30 .75
229 Mike Lowell .15 .40
230 Miguel Cabrera .40 1.00
231a CC Sabathia .25 .60
231b CC Sabathia VAR SP 1.25 3.00
232 Daniel Bard RC .30 .75
233 Garret Anderson .15 .40
234a Grady Sizemore .25 .60
234b Grady Sizemore VAR SP 1.25 3.00
235 Yovani Gallardo .15 .40
236 James Shields .15 .40
237a Christy Mathewson .40 1.00
237b Christy Mathewson VAR SP 2.00 5.00
238 Mark Buehrle .25 .60
239 Joakim Soria .15 .40
240 Kyle Blanks RC .50 1.25
241 Kris Medlen RC .50 1.25
242 Milton Bradley .15 .40
243 Miguel Tejada .25 .60
244 Daric Barton .15 .40
245 Ricky Romero (RC) .75 2.00
246 Felix Pie .15 .40
247 Huston Street .15 .40
248 Mariano Rivera .40 1.00
249 Ryan Zimmerman .25 .60
250 Tim Hudson .25 .60
251 Francisco Cordero .15 .40
252 Ryan Braun .50 1.25
253 Akinori Iwamura .15 .40
254a Johnny Mize .25 .60
254b Johnny Mize VAR SP 1.25 3.00
255 A.J. Pierzynski .15 .40
256 Alex Gordon .25 .60
257 Nate McLouth .15 .40
258 Aaron Bates RC .30 .75
259 Jason Varitek 2.00 5.00
260 Andrew Miller .15 .40
261 Johnny Damon .25 .60
262a Tommy Hanson RC 1.00 2.50
262b Tommy Hanson VAR SP 2.50 6.00
263 Aubrey Huff .15 .40
264 Ryan Garko .15 .40
265 Carlos Delgado .15 .40
266 Josh Hamilton .40 1.00
267 Jered Weaver .15 .40
268a Aaron Poreda RC .30 .75
268b Aaron Poreda VAR SP .75 2.00
269 Russell Martin .15 .40
270 Matt Cain .15 .40
271a Lou Gehrig .75 2.00
271b Lou Gehrig VAR SP 4.00 10.00
272 Aramis Ramirez .15 .40
273 Brian Bannister .15 .40
274a Colby Rasmus (RC) .75 2.00
274b Colby Rasmus VAR SP 2.00 5.00
275 Justin Masterson .15 .40
276 Justin Verlander .50 1.25
277 Andy Pettitte .25 .60
278 David Freese RC 2.50 6.00
279 Casey Kotchman .15 .40
280 Fausto Carmona .15 .40
281 Joe Mauer .40 1.00
282 Ian Kinsler .25 .60
283 Joe Saunders .15 .40
284 Alexei Ramirez .25 .60
285 Chad Billingsley .15 .40
286a Tim Lincecum .60 1.50
286b Tim Lincecum VAR SP 3.00 8.00
287a Babe Ruth 1.00 2.50
287b Babe Ruth VAR SP 5.00 12.00
288 Ryan Theriot .15 .40
289 Josh Whitesell RC .50 1.25
290 Trevor Cahill RC .40 1.00
291 Jonathan Niese RC .50 1.25
292 Jeremy Guthrie .15 .40
293 Troy Tulowitzki .40 1.00
294 Jose Reyes .25 .60
295 Cristian Guzman .15 .40
296 Mat Latos RC 1.00 2.50
297 Micah Owings .15 .40
298 Trevor Hoffman .25 .60
299a Albert Pujols 1.00 2.50
299b Albert Pujols VAR SP 5.00 12.00
300a George Sisler .25 .60
300b George Sisler VAR SP 1.25 3.00

2009 Topps 206 Bronze

*BRONZE VET: .6X TO 1.5X BASIC
*BRONZE RC: .5X TO 1.2X BASIC RC
APPX.ODDS 1 PER HOBBY PACK

2009 Topps 206 Mini Piedmont

*PIEDMONT VET: .75X TO 2X BASIC
*PIEDMONT RC: .6X TO 1.5X BASIC RC
*PIEDMONT VAR: .5X TO 1.2X BASIC VAR
OVERALL ONE MINI PER PACK
VARIATION ODDS 1:20 HOBBY
OVERALL PLATE ODDS 1:332 HOBBY
PLATE PRINT RUN 1 SET PER COLOR
BLACK-CYAN-MAGENTA-YELLOW ISSUED
NO PLATE PRICING DUE TO SCARCITY

2009 Topps 206 Mini Carolina Brights

STATED ODDS 1:1331 HOBBY
STATED PRINT RUN 1 SER.#'d SETS
NO PRICING DUE TO SCARCITY

2009 Topps 206 Mini Cycle

*CYCLE VET: 6X TO 15X BASIC VET
*CYCLE RC: 3X TO 8X BASIC RC
STATED ODDS 1:22 HOBBY
STATED PRINT RUN 99 SER.#'d SETS

2009 Topps 206 Mini Framed Cloth

STATED ODDS 1:160 HOBBY
STATED PRINT RUN 50 SER.#'d SETS
1 Ryan Howard 15.00 40.00
10 Andrew McCutchen 20.00 50.00
19 Mel Ott 10.00 25.00
23 Koji Uehara 6.00 15.00
28 Kenshin Kawakami 6.00 15.00
36 Jimmie Foxx 10.00 25.00
41 David Hernandez 4.00 10.00
44 Michael Bowden 5.00 12.00
49 Walter Johnson 10.00 25.00
57 Matt LaPorta 10.00 25.00
61 Derrek Holland 8.00 20.00
66 Ty Cobb 20.00 50.00
71 Dustin Pedroia 15.00 40.00
72 Rick Porcello 15.00 40.00
83 Rogers Hornsby 8.00 20.00
87 Ryan Perry 10.00 25.00
90 Alex Rodriguez 20.00 50.00
102 Hanley Ramirez 10.00 25.00
103 Andrew Bailey 10.00 25.00
107 Fernando Martinez 10.00 25.00
113 Tris Speaker 6.00 15.00
116 Chase Utley 10.00 25.00
120 Derek Jeter 30.00 80.00
129 Ichiro Suzuki 20.00 50.00
130 Honus Wagner 10.00 25.00
137 Mark Teixeira 10.00 25.00
138 Elvis Andrus 6.00 15.00
142 Evan Longoria 15.00 40.00
143 Cy Young 10.00 25.00
154 Mickey Mantle 40.00 100.00
160 Thurman Munson 10.00 25.00
171 David Wright 15.00 40.00
174 Gordon Beckham 15.00 40.00
175 Manny Ramirez 10.00 25.00
177 Pee Wee Reese 6.00 15.00
181 David Price 12.00 30.00
207 Jackie Robinson 10.00 25.00
224 Roy Campanella 10.00 25.00
231 CC Sabathia 6.00 15.00
234 Grady Sizemore 6.00 15.00
237 Christy Mathewson 10.00 25.00
254 Johnny Mize 6.00 15.00
262 Tommy Hanson 15.00 40.00
268 Aaron Poreda 4.00 10.00
271 Lou Gehrig 25.00 60.00
274 Colby Rasmus 10.00 25.00
286 Tim Lincecum 20.00 50.00
287 Babe Ruth 30.00 80.00
299 Albert Pujols 30.00 80.00
300 George Sisler 6.00 15.00

2009 Topps 206 Mini Old Mill

*OLD MILL: 3X TO 8X BASIC VET
*OLD MILL RC: 1.5X TO 4X BASIC RC
STATED ODDS 1:20 HOBBY
120 Derek Jeter 8.00 20.00

2009 Topps 206 Mini Piedmont Gold

*GOLD VET: 8X TO 20X BASIC VET
*GOLD RC: 4X TO 10X BASIC RC
STATED ODDS 1:159 HOBBY
STATED PRINT RUN 50 SER.#'d SETS

2009 Topps 206 Mini Polar Bear

*POLAR VET: 2X TO 5X BASIC VET
*POLAR RC: 1X TO 2.5X BASIC RC
STATED ODDS 1:10 HOBBY
120 Derek Jeter 6.00 15.00

2009 Topps 206 Autographs

STATED ODDS 1:66 HOBBY
EXCHANGE DEADLINE 11/30/2012
NFA1 David Wright 10.00 25.00
NFA2 Johnny Cueto 4.00 10.00
NFA3 Evan Longoria 12.50 30.00
NFA4 Gio Gonzalez 3.00 8.00
NFA5 Juan Rivera 3.00 8.00
NFA6 Ryan Braun 15.00 40.00
NFA7 Joba Chamberlain 10.00 25.00
NFA8 Dustin Pedroia 12.50 30.00
NFA9 Jay Bruce 8.00 20.00
NFA10 Jordan Zimmermannn 4.00 10.00
NFA11 Ryan Howard 30.00 60.00
NFA12 Max Scherzer 3.00 8.00
NFA13 Heath Bell 3.00 8.00
NFA14 Jonathan Papelbon 8.00 20.00
NFA15 Jhonny Peralta 3.00 8.00
NFA16 Milton Bradley 3.00 8.00

2009 Topps 206 Checklists

COMPLETE SET (7) 5.00 12.00
APPX.ODDS 1:3 HOBBY
1 Mickey Mantle 1.00 2.50
2 Mickey Mantle 1.00 2.50
3 Mickey Mantle 1.00 2.50
4 Mickey Mantle 1.00 2.50
5 Mickey Mantle 1.00 2.50
6 Mickey Mantle 1.00 2.50
7 Mickey Mantle 1.00 2.50

2009 Topps 206 Mini Framed Autograph

STATED ODDS 1:18 HOBBY
EXCHANGE DEADLINE 11/30/2012
FMA1 Gordon Beckham 10.00 25.00
FMA2 Koji Uehara 15.00 40.00
FMA3 Ryan Perry 8.00 20.00
FMA4 Elvis Andrus 6.00 15.00
FMA5 Jonathan Van Every 3.00 8.00
FMA6 Glen Perkins 3.00 8.00
FMA7 Jordan Zimmermann 4.00 10.00
FMA8 Daniel Schlereth 3.00 8.00
FMA9 Chris Volstad 3.00 8.00
FMA10 Ryan Braun 12.50 30.00
FMA11 Nick Evans 4.00 10.00
FMA12 Fernando Martinez 5.00 12.00
FMA13 Shairon Martis 3.00 8.00
FMA14 James Parr 3.00 8.00
FMA15 Mat Gamel 4.00 10.00
FMA16 Michael Bowden 5.00 12.00
FMA17 David Hernandez 4.00 10.00
FMA18 Chris Young 4.00 10.00
FMA19 Denard Span 5.00 12.00
FMA20 Phil Hughes 8.00 20.00
FMA21 Jason Motte 8.00 20.00
FMA22 Clayton Kershaw 8.00 20.00
FMA23 Justin Masterson 8.00 20.00
FMA24 Vinny Mazzaro 3.00 8.00
FMA25 Scott Elbert 4.00 10.00
FMA26 Rich Hill 3.00 8.00
FMA27 Luke Montz 3.00 8.00
FMA28 Curtis Granderson 12.50 30.00
FMA29 Kila Ka'aihue 3.00 8.00
FMA30 Josh Outman 3.00 8.00

2009 Topps 206 Mini Framed Relics Piedmont

STATED ODDS 1:71 HOBBY
FR1 Alex Rodriguez Bat 8.00 20.00
FR2 Ryan Howard 6.00 15.00
FR3 David Wright 5.00 12.00
FR4 Albert Pujols 10.00 25.00
FR5 Evan Longoria 6.00 15.00
FR6 Chipper Jones 6.00 15.00
FR7 Carlos Beltran 3.00 8.00
FR8 Ichiro Suzuki 6.00 15.00
FR9 Hanley Ramirez 3.00 8.00
FR10 Carl Crawford 3.00 8.00
FR11 David Ortiz Jsy 3.00 8.00
FR12 Nick Markakis 4.00 10.00
FR13 Michael Young 3.00 8.00
FR14 Hideki Matsui 6.00 15.00
FR15 Ryan Braun 4.00 10.00
FR16 Robinson Cano 5.00 12.00
FR17 Miguel Tejada 3.00 8.00
FR18 Phil Hughes 3.00 8.00
FR19 Cole Hamels 4.00 10.00
FR20 James Loney 3.00 8.00
FR21 Brian McCann 4.00 10.00
FR22 Ty Cobb Bat 50.00 100.00
FR23 Jimmie Foxx Bat 20.00 50.00
FR24 Jackie Robinson Bat 20.00 50.00
FR25 Babe Ruth 100.00 175.00

2009 Topps 206 Mini Framed Relics Old Mill

*OLD MILL: .4X TO 1X PIEDMONT
STATED ODDS 1:105 HOBBY

2009 Topps 206 Mini Framed Relics Polar Bear

*POLAR: .6X TO 1.5X PIEDMONT
RANDOM INSERTS IN PACKS

2010 Topps 206

COMPLETE SET (350) 100.00 200.00
COMP.SET w/o SP's (300) 20.00 50.00
COMMON CARD (1-300) .15 .40
COMMON ROOKIE (1-300) .30 .75
COMMON SP VAR (301-350) .60 1.50
SP VAR HAVE NO CARD NUMBERS
PLATE PRINT RUN 1 SET PER COLOR
BLACK-CYAN-MAGENTA-YELLOW ISSUED
NO PLATE PRICING DUE TO SCARCITY
1 Matt Holliday .40 1.00
2 Willie Stargell .25 .60
3 Nate McLouth .15 .40
4 David Ortiz .25 .60
5 Will Venable .15 .40
6 Denard Span .15 .40
7 Ted Lilly .15 .40
8 Shane Victorino .25 .60
9 Zack Greinke .25 .60
10 Conor Jackson .15 .40
11 Brandon Inge .25 .60
12 Chris Iannetta .15 .40
13 Tim Hudson .25 .60
14 Rafael Furcal .15 .40
15 Mordecai Brown .15 .40
16 Johan Santana .40 1.00
17 Mike Leake RC 1.00 2.50
18 Travis Snider .15 .40
19 Carlos Ruiz .15 .40
20 Mark DeRosa .15 .40
21 Jason Kubel .15 .40
22 Kevin Kouzmanoff .15 .40
23 Matt Cain .25 .60
24 Starlin Castro RC 1.25 3.00
25 Jackie Robinson .40 1.00
26 Stan Musial .60 1.50
27 Derek Holland .15 .40
28 Chris Young .15 .40
29 John Lackey .15 .40
30 Yunel Escobar .15 .40
31 Colby Rasmus .40 1.00
32 Brad Hawpe .15 .40
33 Justin Upton .25 .60
34 Zach Duke .15 .40
35 Ryan Dempster .15 .40
36 Mark Reynolds .15 .40
37 Gordon Beckham .25 .60
38 Derrek Lee .15 .40
39 Yovani Gallardo .15 .40
40 Hiroki Kuroda .15 .40
41 Brian McCann .25 .60
42 A.J. Burnett .25 .60
43 Martin Prado .15 .40
44 Bryan Anderson (RC) .30 .75
45 Adrian Gonzalez .25 .60
46 Carlos Quentin .25 .60
47 Rickie Weeks .25 .60
48 David Price .40 1.00
49 Vernon Wells .15 .40
50 Ricky Nolasco .15 .40
51 Asdrubal Cabrera .25 .60
52 Ichiro Suzuki .60 1.50
53 Felix Hernandez .40 1.00
54 Kevin Slowey .15 .40
55 Stephen Strasburg RC 2.00 5.00
56 Nick Markakis .40 1.00
57 Aaron Harang .15 .40
58 Justin Verlander .50 1.25
59 Thurman Munson .40 1.00
60 Jason Heyward RC 2.00 5.00
61 Carlos Zambrano .25 .60
62 Geovany Soto .25 .60
63 Fausto Carmona .15 .40
64 Bobby Abreu .15 .40
65 Aaron Hill .15 .40
66 Marco Scutaro .15 .40
67 Cristian Guzman .15 .40
68 Garrett Atkins .15 .40
69 Honus Wagner .40 1.00
70 Luke Hochevar .15 .40
71 Paul Maholm .15 .40
72 Pablo Sandoval .25 .60
73 Dustin Pedroia .50 1.25
74 Carlos Gomez .15 .40
75 Jeff Francis .15 .40
76 Clay Buchholz .25 .60
77 Scott Sizemore RC .50 1.25
78 Placido Polanco .15 .40
79 Shin-Soo Choo .25 .60
80 Akinori Iwamura .15 .40
81 Adam Lind .25 .60
82 Nick Swisher .40 1.00
83 Carlos Lee .15 .40
84 Cal Ripken Jr. 1.50 4.00
85 Josh Beckett .25 .60
86 Chris Carpenter .40 1.00
87 Cole Hamels .40 1.00
88 Jeremy Bonderman .15 .40
89 Matt Kemp .25 .60
90 Jon Lester .40 1.00
91 Mickey Mantle 1.25 3.00
92 Andre Ethier .25 .60
93 Cody Ross .15 .40

94 Jorge Posada .25 .60
95 Grady Sizemore .25 .60
96 Evan Longoria .50 1.25
97 Javier Vazquez .15 .40
98 Nolan Ryan 1.25 3.00
99 Christy Mathewson .40 1.00
100 Howie Kendrick .15 .40
101 Andy Pettitte .25 .60
102 Kevin Millwood .15 .40
103 James Shields .15 .40
104 Joey Votto .40 1.00
105 Brian Roberts .15 .40
106 Kazuo Matsui .15 .40
107 Derek Lowe .15 .40
108 Alexei Ramirez .15 .40
109 Carlos Beltran .15 .40
110 Mike Napoli .25 .60
111 Mark Teixeira .40 1.00
112 Ryan Zimmerman .25 .60
113 Chase Utley .40 1.00
114 Alex Rodriguez .60 1.50
115 Yadier Molina .25 .60
116 B.J. Upton .25 .60
117 Freddy Sanchez .15 .40
118 Roy Oswalt .25 .60
119 Matt Garza .15 .40
120 Ken Griffey Jr. .60 1.50
121 Orlando Cabrera .15 .40
122 Cy Young .40 1.00
123 Kurt Suzuki .15 .40
124 Josh Hamilton .40 1.00
125 Prince Fielder .25 .60
126 Jason Marquis .15 .40
127 Nick Blackburn .15 .40
128 Mat Latos .15 .40
129 John Maine .15 .40
130 Nelson Cruz .25 .60
131 Troy Tulowitzki .40 1.00
132 Mike Cameron .15 .40
133 Edwin Jackson .15 .40
134 Todd Helton .25 .60
135 Delmon Young .25 .60
136 Chris Volstad .15 .40
137 Troy Glaus .15 .40
138 J.A. Happ .25 .60
139 Barry Zito .15 .40
140 Ian Kinsler .25 .60
141 Ivan Rodriguez .25 .60
142 Bengie Molina .15 .40
143 Michael Cuddyer .15 .40
144 Curtis Granderson .25 .60
145 Jay Bruce .25 .60
146 Brett Anderson .25 .60
147 Roy Halladay .40 1.00
148 Andre Dawson .25 .60
149 Scott Kazmir .15 .40
150 Ryan Ludwick .15 .40
151 Chris Getz .15 .40
152 Cliff Lee .25 .60
153 Ryan Braun .50 1.25
154 Orlando Hudson .15 .40
155 Jake Peavy .15 .40
156 Chris Tillman .15 .40
157 Edinson Volquez .15 .40
158 Jenrry Mejia RC .50 1.25
159 Frank Robinson .25 .60
160 Erick Aybar .15 .40
161 Neftali Feliz .15 .40
162 Derek Jeter 1.00 2.50
163 Max Scherzer .15 .40
164 Joba Chamberlain .25 .60
165 Ty Cobb .60 1.50
166 Austin Jackson RC .50 1.25
167 Mike Pelfrey .15 .40
168 Nolan Reimold .25 .60
169 Michael Bourn .15 .40
170 Ian Stewart .15 .40
171 Ian Desmond (RC) .50 1.25
172 Kid Elberfeld .15 .40
173 Aramis Ramirez .15 .40
174 Clayton Kershaw .40 1.00
175 Dan Haren .15 .40
176 Hanley Ramirez .40 1.00
177 Gavin Floyd .15 .40
178 Jimmy Rollins .25 .60
179 Drew Stubbs RC .75 2.00
180 Gil Meche .15 .40
181 Wade Davis (RC) .30 .75
182 Lou Gehrig .75 2.00
183 Carlos Pena .25 .60
184 Chipper Jones .40 1.00
185 Babe Ruth 1.00 2.50
186 Mark Buehrle .25 .60
187 Chris Coghlan .15 .40
188 Rich Harden .15 .40
189 Nick Johnson .15 .40
190 Kenshin Kawakami .25 .60
191 Victor Martinez .25 .60
192 Johnny Cueto .15 .40
193 Buster Posey RC 3.00 8.00
194 Brett Myers .15 .40
195 Stephen Drew .15 .40
196 Adam Jones .25 .60
197 Travis Hafner .15 .40
198 David DeJesus .15 .40
199 Vladimir Guerrero .40 1.00
200 Corey Hart .15 .40
201 Franklin Gutierrez .15 .40
202 Alex Gordon .25 .60
203 Allen Craig RC .75 2.00
204 Justin Morneau .40 1.00
205 Koji Uehara .25 .60
206 Jacoby Ellsbury .40 1.00
207 Carlos Guillen .15 .40
208 Chone Figgins .15 .40
209 Torii Hunter .15 .40
210 Hunter Pence .25 .60
211 Jered Weaver .25 .60
212 Pedro Feliz .15 .40
213 Joel Pineiro .15 .40
214 John Danks .15 .40
215 Jason Bay .25 .60
216 Wandy Rodriguez .15 .40
217 Alex Rios .25 .60
218 Joe Mauer .40 1.00
219 Edgar Renteria .15 .40
220 Rick Porcello .15 .40
221 Albert Pujols 1.00 2.50
222 Tom Seaver .25 .60
223 Kyle Blanks .15 .40
224 Tommy Hanson .15 .40
225 Adam Wainwright .25 .60
226 Jonathan Sanchez .15 .40
227 Chad Billingsley .15 .40
228 Francisco Liriano .15 .40
229 Jose Lopez .15 .40
230 Jair Jurrjens .15 .40
231 Justin Masterson .15 .40
232 Joe Saunders .15 .40
233 Frank Chance .15 .40
234 Dan Uggla .25 .60
235 Jeff Francoeur .25 .60
236 Johnny Bench .40 1.00
237 Carl Pavano .15 .40
238 Ubaldo Jimenez .25 .60
239 Lance Berkman .25 .60
240 Casey McGehee .15 .40
241 Manny Ramirez .40 1.00
242 Julio Borbon .15 .40
243 Alcides Escobar .25 .60
244 Russell Martin .15 .40
245 Chien-Ming Wang .25 .60
246 Raul Ibanez .25 .60
247 Jhoulys Chacin .15 .40
248 Yogi Berra .40 1.00
249 Rick Ankiel .15 .40
250 Ryan Doumit .15 .40
251 Hideki Matsui .40 1.00
252 Michael Young .25 .60
253 Elvis Andrus .25 .60
254 Reggie Jackson .25 .60
255 Tim Lincecum .60 1.50
256 Brandon Webb .25 .60
257 Ryan Howard .50 1.25
258 Scott Rolen .25 .60
259 Carlos Gonzalez .25 .60
260 Billy Butler .15 .40
261 Daniel McCutchen RC .50 1.25
262 Melvin Mora .15 .40
263 CC Sabathia .25 .60
264 Al Kaline .40 1.00
265 James Loney .25 .60
266 Rajai Davis .15 .40
267 Manny Parra .15 .40
268 Kosuke Fukudome .40 1.00
269 Miguel Cabrera .40 1.00
270 Ricky Romero .15 .40
271 Chris Davis .15 .40
272 Carl Crawford .25 .60
273 Robinson Cano .40 1.00
274 Adrian Beltre .15 .40
275 Andrew McCutchen .40 1.00
276 Jason Bartlett .15 .40
277 Johnny Evers .15 .40
278 Adam Dunn .25 .60
279 Glen Perkins .15 .40
280 Ben Zobrist .15 .40
281 Melky Cabrera .15 .40
282 Jose Reyes .25 .60
283 Ervin Santana .15 .40
284 Alfonso Soriano .25 .60
285 Jayson Werth .25 .60
286 Kevin Youkilis .25 .60
287 Daisuke Matsuzaka .40 1.00
288 Scott Baker .15 .40
289 David Wright .50 1.25
290 Magglio Ordonez .25 .60
291 Daniel Murphy .25 .60
292 Josh Johnson .25 .60
293 Jeff Niemann .15 .40
294 Willie Keeler .15 .40
295 Tommy Manzella (RC) .30 .75
296 Brandon Phillips .15 .40
297 Miguel Montero .15 .40
298 Kendry Morales .15 .40
299 Dexter Fowler .15 .40
300 Trevor Cahill .15 .40
301 Kendry Morales SP .60 1.50
302 Alex Rodriguez SP 2.50 6.00
303 Brian McCann SP 1.00 2.50
304 Roy Halladay SP 1.50 4.00
305 Jacoby Ellsbury SP 1.50 4.00
306 Adrian Gonzalez SP 1.00 2.50
307 Gordon Beckham SP 1.00 2.50
308 Cliff Lee SP 1.00 2.50
309 Shin-Soo Choo SP 1.00 2.50
310 Evan Longoria SP 2.00 5.00
311 Rick Porcello SP .60 1.50
312 Ian Kinsler SP 1.00 2.50
313 Zack Greinke SP 1.00 2.50
314 Hunter Pence SP 1.00 2.50
315 Ryan Braun SP 2.00 5.00
316 Joe Mauer SP 1.50 4.00
317 Ryan Zimmerman SP 1.00 2.50
318 Matt Kemp SP 1.00 2.50
319 Aaron Hill SP .60 1.50
320 Chris Coghlan SP .60 1.50
321 Albert Pujols SP 4.00 10.00
322 Ubaldo Jimenez SP 1.00 2.50
323 Pablo Sandoval SP 1.00 2.50
324 Joey Votto SP 1.50 4.00
325 Andrew McCutchen SP 1.50 4.00
326 Carlos Zambrano SP 1.00 2.50
327 Rajai Davis SP .60 1.50
328 Adam Jones SP 1.00 2.50
329 Jason Bay SP 1.00 2.50
330 Justin Upton SP 1.00 2.50
331 Stephen Strasburg SP 4.00 10.00
332 Babe Ruth SP 4.00 10.00
333 Tim Lincecum SP 2.50 6.00
334 Tom Seaver SP 1.00 2.50
335 Wade Davis SP .60 1.50
336 Ryan Howard SP 2.00 5.00
337 Ian Desmond SP 1.00 2.50
338 Austin Jackson SP 1.00 2.50
339 Neftali Feliz SP .60 1.50
340 Mickey Mantle SP 5.00 12.00
341 Jason Heyward SP 4.00 10.00
342 Stephen Drew SP .60 1.50
343 Stan Musial SP 2.50 6.00
344 Tim Lincecum SP 2.50 6.00
345 Mickey Mantle SP 5.00 12.00
346 Justin Upton SP 1.00 2.50
347 Albert Pujols SP 4.00 10.00
348 Ryan Braun SP 2.00 5.00
349 Joe Mauer SP 1.50 4.00
350 Roy Halladay SP 1.50 4.00

2010 Topps 206 Bronze

COMPLETE SET (300) 50.00 100.00
*BRONZE VET: .6X TO 1.5X BASIC
*BRONZE RC: .5X TO 1.2X BASIC RC

2010 Topps 206 Mini Piedmont

*PIEDMONT VET: 1X TO 2.5X BASIC
*PIEDMONT RC: .6X TO 1.5X BASIC RC
PLATE PRINT RUN 1 SET PER COLOR
BLACK-CYAN-MAGENTA-YELLOW ISSUED
NO PLATE PRICING DUE TO SCARCITY
84 Cal Ripken Jr. 5.00 12.00

2010 Topps 206 Mini American Caramel

*AC VET: 1.5X TO 4X BASIC VET
*AC RC: .75X TO 2X BASIC RC

2010 Topps 206 Mini Carolina Brights

STATED PRINT RUN 1 SER.#'d SET
NO PRICING DUE TO SCARCITY

2010 Topps 206 Mini Cycle

*CYCLE VET: 6X TO 15X BASIC VET
*CYCLE RC: 3X TO 8X BASIC RC
STATED PRINT RUN 99 SER.#'d SETS
84 Cal Ripken Jr. 50.00 100.00

2010 Topps 206 Mini Old Mill

*OLD MILL: 2.5X TO 6X BASIC VET
*OLD MILL RC: 1.2X TO 3X BASIC RC
84 Cal Ripken Jr. 20.00 50.00

2010 Topps 206 Mini Polar Bear

*POLAR VET: 2X TO 5X BASIC VET
*POLAR RC: 1X TO 2.5X BASIC RC
84 Cal Ripken Jr. 15.00 40.00

2010 Topps 206 Cut Signatures

STATED PRINT RUN 1 SER.#'d SET
NO PRICING DUE TO SCARCITY

2010 Topps 206 Dual Relics

STATED PRINT RUN 99 SER.#'d SETS
AD Adam Dunn 8.00 20.00
AP Albert Pujols 30.00 60.00
AR Alex Rodriguez 20.00 50.00
BM Brian McCann 5.00 12.00
CC Carl Crawford 5.00 12.00
DW David Wright 5.00 12.00
GS Grady Sizemore 5.00 12.00
JB Johnny Bench 10.00 25.00
JH Josh Hamilton 8.00 20.00
MM Mickey Mantle 75.00 150.00
MR Manny Ramirez 5.00 12.00
NM Nick Markakis 12.50 30.00
NR Nolan Ryan 20.00 50.00
PF Prince Fielder 5.00 12.00
RH Ryan Howard 12.50 30.00
RS Ryne Sandberg 10.00 25.00
SV Shane Victorino 8.00 20.00
WS Willie Stargell 8.00 20.00
APE Andy Pettitte 6.00 15.00
JRO Jimmy Rollins 8.00 20.00

2010 Topps 206 Mini Framed American Caramel Autographs

EXCH DEADLINE 8/31/2013
AC Asdrubal Cabrera 10.00 25.00
AH Aaron Hill
AP Albert Pujols
AR Alex Rios 12.50 30.00
BU B.J. Upton 5.00 12.00
CB Chad Billingsley 6.00 15.00
CG Chris Getz 4.00 10.00
CS CC Sabathia 50.00 100.00
CT Chris Tillman 4.00 10.00
DB Dallas Braden 4.00 10.00
DO David Ortiz
DS Duke Snider 10.00 25.00
DW David Wright
EC Eric Chavez 3.00 8.00
FM Franklin Morales 3.00 8.00
FP Felipe Paulino 3.00 8.00
HR Hanley Ramirez 10.00 25.00
JD Joey Devine 3.00 8.00
JH Joel Hanrahan 3.00 8.00
JL Jed Lowrie 4.00 10.00
JP Johnny Podres 6.00 15.00
JU Justin Upton 8.00 20.00
KS Kurt Suzuki 3.00 8.00
MB Milton Bradley 3.00 8.00
MC Melky Cabrera 4.00 10.00
MH Matt Holliday
MM Miguel Montero 3.00 8.00
MR Manny Ramirez
MY Michael Young 6.00 15.00
NM Nick Markakis 6.00 15.00
OC Orlando Cabrera 4.00 10.00
PF Prince Fielder 12.50 30.00
PP Placido Polanco 6.00 15.00
RC Robinson Cano 50.00 100.00
RG Ryan Garko 3.00 8.00
RI Raul Ibanez 6.00 15.00
SP Steve Pearce 3.00 8.00
SR Sean Rodriguez 3.00 8.00
SS Stephen Strasburg 100.00 175.00
TC Tyler Colvin 8.00 20.00
TH Torii Hunter 10.00 25.00
VM Vin Mazzaro 3.00 8.00
ARO Alex Rodriguez 100.00 175.00
MBU Madison Bumgarner
MCA Matt Cain 15.00 40.00

2010 Topps 206 Mini Carolina Brights Red Chrome

STATED PRINT RUN 1 SER.#'d SET
NO PRICING DUE TO SCARCITY

2010 Topps 206 Mini Dual Relics Booklet

STATED PRINT RUN 99 SER.#'d SETS
MBR1 Albert Pujols 40.00 80.00
Ryan Howard
MBR2 Prince Fielder 10.00 25.00
Ryan Braun
MBR3 Evan Longoria 15.00 40.00
David Wright
MBR4 Ichiro Suzuki 60.00 120.00
Albert Pujols
MBR5 Joe Mauer 12.50 30.00
Johnny Bench
MBR6 Hanley Ramirez 10.00 25.00
Jimmy Rollins
MBR7 Adam Jones 15.00 40.00
Nick Markakis
MBR8 Tim Lincecum 10.00 25.00
Zack Greinke
MBR9 Grady Sizemore 20.00 50.00
Ichiro Suzuki
MBR10 Tim Lincecum 40.00 80.00
Roy Halladay
MBR11 Ian Kinsler 12.50 30.00
Gordon Beckham
MBR12 Chase Utley 40.00 80.00
Ryan Howard
MBR13 Shin-Soo Choo 20.00 50.00
Grady Sizemore
MBR14 Miguel Cabrera 10.00 25.00
Prince Fielder
MBR15 Justin Upton 10.00 25.00
Matt Kemp
MBR16 Carlton Fisk 10.00 25.00
Ivan Rodriguez
MBR17 David Wright 15.00 40.00
Jose Reyes
MBR18 Matt Kemp 20.00 50.00
Andre Ethier
MBR19 CC Sabathia 15.00 40.00
Andy Pettitte
MBR20 Hanley Ramirez 10.00 25.00
Dan Uggla
MBR21 Dustin Pedroia 12.50 30.00
Kevin Youkilis
MBR22 Hunter Pence 10.00 25.00
Josh Hamilton
MBR23 Prince Fielder 10.00 25.00
Pablo Sandoval
MBR24 Joe Mauer 15.00 40.00
Brian McCann
MBR25 Mickey Mantle 125.00 250.00
Babe Ruth

2010 Topps 206 Mini Framed Relics Piedmont

AG Alex Gordon 3.00 8.00
AJ Adam Jones 3.00 8.00
AP Albert Pujols 10.00 25.00
BM Bobby Murcer 6.00 15.00
BP Brandon Phillips 3.00 8.00
CB Clint Barmes 3.00 8.00
CC Carl Crawford 3.00 8.00
CG Curtis Granderson 4.00 10.00
CJ Conor Jackson 3.00 8.00
CM Carlos Marmol 3.00 8.00
CR Cal Ripken Jr. 12.50 30.00
CS Curt Schilling 3.00 8.00
CU Chase Utley 5.00 12.00
CZ Carlos Zambrano 3.00 8.00
DO David Ortiz 3.00 8.00
DU Dan Uggla 3.00 8.00
EJ Edwin Jackson 3.00 8.00
EV Edinson Volquez 3.00 8.00
FT Frank Thomas 4.00 10.00
GS Geovany Soto 3.00 8.00
IK Ian Kinsler 3.00 8.00
JD Johnny Damon 3.00 8.00
JE Johnny Evers 20.00 50.00
JR Jimmy Rollins 3.00 8.00
JV Jason Varitek 3.00 8.00
JW Josh Willingham 3.00 8.00
KJ Kelly Johnson 3.00 8.00
KM Kevin Millwood 3.00 8.00
KS Kevin Slowey 3.00 8.00
KW Kerry Wood 3.00 8.00
LC Luis Castillo 3.00 8.00
LH Livan Hernandez 3.00 8.00
MC Miguel Cabrera 4.00 10.00
MM Mickey Mantle 30.00 60.00
MR Mariano Rivera 4.00 10.00
MT Miguel Tejada 3.00 8.00
NS Nate Schierholtz 3.00 8.00
PK Paul Konerko 3.00 8.00
RH Rickey Henderson 8.00 20.00
SC Shin-Soo Choo 3.00 8.00
TG Tony Gwynn Jr. 3.00 8.00
YB Yogi Berra 8.00 20.00
YE Yunel Escobar 3.00 8.00
YG Yovani Gallardo 3.00 8.00
ZG Zack Greinke 3.00 8.00
BMC Brian McCann 3.00 8.00
GSI Grady Sizemore 3.00 8.00
JVO Joey Votto 6.00 15.00
RHO Ryan Howard 6.00 15.00
TGL Troy Glaus 3.00 8.00

2010 Topps 206 Mini Framed Relics Old Mill

*OLD MILL: .75X TO 2X PIEDMONT
CR Cal Ripken Jr. 50.00 100.00

2010 Topps 206 Mini Framed Relics Polar Bear

*POLAR BEAR: .6X TO 1.5X PIEDMONT
RH Rickey Henderson 50.00 100.00

2010 Topps 206 Mini Framed Autographs Piedmont

EXCH DEADLINE 8/31/2013
AJ Adam Jones 4.00 10.00
AL Adam Lind 3.00 8.00
BM Bengie Molina 6.00 15.00
BS Brian Schneider 5.00 12.00
CC Chris Coghlan 3.00 8.00
CF Chone Figgins 5.00 12.00
CP Cliff Pennington 3.00 8.00
CR Colby Rasmus 6.00 15.00
CT Clete Thomas 3.00 8.00
CY Chris Young 3.00 8.00
DB Daric Barton 3.00 8.00
DM Daniel Murphy 3.00 8.00
DP Dustin Pedroia EXCH 20.00 50.00
EC Everth Cabrera 3.00 8.00
EV Eugenio Velez 3.00 8.00
FC Francisco Cervelli 6.00 15.00
FM Fernando Martinez 3.00 8.00
GB Gordon Beckham 10.00 25.00
HB Heath Bell 4.00 10.00
JB Gregor Blanco 3.00 8.00
JC Jeff Clement 3.00 8.00
JF Jeff Francis 3.00 8.00
JK Jason Kubel 3.00 8.00
JL John Lannan 3.00 8.00
JP Jhonny Peralta 3.00 8.00
JT J.R. Towles 3.00 8.00
JW Josh Willingham 3.00 8.00
JZ Jordan Zimmermann 4.00 10.00
MB Mitch Boggs 3.00 8.00
MS Max Scherzer 5.00 12.00
MT Matt Tolbert 3.00 8.00
NC Nelson Cruz 5.00 12.00
NF Neftali Feliz 5.00 12.00
NM Nyjer Morgan 4.00 10.00
PP Placido Polanco 5.00 12.00
PS Pablo Sandoval 6.00 15.00
RB Ryan Braun EXCH 15.00 40.00
RH Ryan Howard 20.00 50.00
RP Ryan Perry 3.00 8.00
RZ Ryan Zimmerman 12.50 30.00
SC Shin-Soo Choo 8.00 20.00
SG Sammy Gervacio 3.00 8.00
SS Scott Sizemore 3.00 8.00
SS Stephen Strasburg
TC Trevor Crowe 3.00 8.00
TG Tom Gorzelanny 4.00 10.00
TH Tommy Hanson 5.00 12.00
TT Troy Tulowitzki EXCH 10.00 25.00
WV Will Venable 3.00 8.00
CRI Cal Ripken Jr. EXCH 150.00 250.00
RPO Rick Porcello EXCH 8.00 20.00

2010 Topps 206 Mini Framed Autographs Old Mill

EXCH DEADLINE 8/31/2013
NO PRICING DUE TO SCARCITY

2010 Topps 206 Mini Framed Autographs Polar Bear

*POLAR BEAR: .5X TO 1.2X PIEDMONT
EXCH DEADLINE 8/31/2013

2010 Topps 206 Mini Framed Silk

STATED PRINT RUN 50 SER.#'d SETS
S1 Jackie Robinson 10.00 25.00
S2 Will Venable 4.00 10.00
S3 Cy Young 10.00 25.00
S4 Lou Gehrig 20.00 50.00
S5 Johan Santana 10.00 25.00
S6 Matt Cain 6.00 15.00
S7 John Lackey 4.00 10.00
S8 Honus Wagner 10.00 25.00
S9 David Price 10.00 25.00
S10 Ichiro Suzuki 15.00 40.00
S11 Felix Hernandez 10.00 25.00
S12 Nick Markakis 10.00 25.00
S13 Jason Heyward 25.00 60.00
S14 Shin-Soo Choo 6.00 15.00
S15 Christy Mathewson 10.00 25.00
S16 Adam Lind 6.00 15.00
S17 Chris Carpenter 10.00 25.00
S18 Andre Ethier 6.00 15.00
S19 Grady Sizemore 6.00 15.00
S20 Nolan Ryan 30.00 80.00
S21 Ty Cobb 15.00 40.00
S22 Chase Utley 10.00 25.00
S23 Thurman Munson 10.00 25.00
S24 Babe Ruth 25.00 60.00
S25 Mordecai Brown 4.00 10.00
S26 Josh Hamilton 10.00 25.00
S27 Prince Fielder 6.00 15.00
S28 Mat Latos 4.00 10.00
S29 Nelson Cruz 6.00 15.00
S30 Kid Elberfeld 4.00 10.00
S31 Curtis Granderson 6.00 15.00
S32 Frank Chance 4.00 10.00
S33 Johnny Evers 4.00 10.00
S34 Chipper Jones 10.00 25.00
S35 Buster Posey 40.00 100.00
S36 Justin Morneau 10.00 25.00
S37 Torii Hunter 4.00 10.00
S38 Jason Bay 6.00 15.00
S39 Tommy Hanson 6.00 15.00
S40 Adam Wainwright 6.00 15.00
S41 Ubaldo Jimenez 6.00 15.00
S42 Manny Ramirez 10.00 25.00
S43 Willie Keeler 4.00 10.00
S44 CC Sabathia 6.00 15.00
S45 Miguel Cabrera 10.00 25.00
S46 Adam Dunn 6.00 15.00
S47 Daisuke Matsuzaka 10.00 25.00
S48 David Wright 12.00 30.00
S49 Josh Johnson 6.00 15.00
S50 Kendry Morales 4.00 10.00

2010 Topps 206 Mini Historical Events

COMPLETE SET (20) 5.00 12.00
HE1 Jan 5th 1909 .60 1.50
Colombia recognizes Panama's independence
HE2 Feb 16th 1909 .60 1.50
1st subway car with side doors goes into service (NYC)
HE3 Mar 4th 1909 .60 1.50
President Taft inaugurated at 27th U.S. President during 10" snowstorm
HE4 Mar 30th 1909 .60 1.50
Queensboro Bridge opens, linking Manhattan & Queens
HE5 Apr 18th 1909 .60 1.50
Joan of Arc beatified
HE6 Jul 8th 1909 .60 1.50
1st pro baseball game (Minor League) played under lights
HE7 Jul 25th 1909 .60 1.50
France's Louis Bleriot, makes 1st airplane flight across English Channel
HE8 Jul 30th 1909 .60 1.50
Wright Brothers deliver 1st military plane to the army
HE9 Aug 7th 1909 .60 1.50
U.S. re-issues 1st Lincoln penny
HE10 Sept 2nd 1909 .60 1.50
1st junior high school in U.S. opens (Columbus, OH)
HE11 Jan 3rd 1910 .60 1.50
British miners strike for 8-hour working day
HE12 Feb 8th 1910 .60 1.50
The Boy Scouts of America is incorporated by William D. Boyce
HE13 Feb 23rd 1910 .60 1.50
1st radio contest held (Philadelphia)
HE14 Apr 14th 1910 .60 1.50
President Taft begins tradition of throwing out first pitch on Opening Day
HE15 May 18th 1910 .60 1.50
Earth Passes through tail of Comet Halley
HE16 Jul 1st 1910 .60 1.50
Chicago's Comiskey Park opens, St Louis Browns beat White Sox 2-0
HE17 Sep 12th 1910 .60 1.50
World's 1st female cop, Alice Stebbins Wells, appointed (LAPD)
HE18 Nov 12th 1910 .60 1.50
1st Movie stunt: man jumps into Hudson River from a burning balloon
HE19 Nov 27th 1910 .60 1.50
NY's Penn Station opens as world's largest railway terminal
HE20 Dec 16th 1910 .60 1.50
First short flight in a plane with a Jet Engine

2010 Topps 206 Mini Piedmont Gold Chrome

STATED PRINT RUN 50 SER.#'d SETS
C1 Jackie Robinson 8.00 20.00
C2 Will Venable 3.00 8.00
C3 Cy Young 8.00 20.00
C4 Lou Gehrig 15.00 40.00
C5 Johan Santana 8.00 20.00
C6 Matt Cain 5.00 12.00
C7 John Lackey 3.00 8.00
C8 Honus Wagner 8.00 20.00
C9 David Price 8.00 20.00
C10 Ichiro Suzuki 12.00 30.00
C11 Felix Hernandez 8.00 20.00
C12 Nick Markakis 8.00 20.00
C13 Jason Heyward 20.00 50.00
C14 Shin-Soo Choo 5.00 12.00
C15 Christy Mathewson 8.00 20.00
C16 Adam Lind 5.00 12.00
C17 Chris Carpenter 8.00 20.00
C18 Andre Ethier 5.00 12.00
C19 Grady Sizemore 5.00 12.00
C20 Nolan Ryan 25.00 60.00
C21 Ty Cobb 12.00 30.00
C22 Chase Utley 8.00 20.00
C23 Thurman Munson 8.00 20.00
C24 Babe Ruth 20.00 50.00
C25 Mordecai Brown 3.00 8.00
C26 Josh Hamilton 8.00 20.00
C27 Prince Fielder 5.00 12.00
C28 Mat Latos 3.00 8.00
C29 Nelson Cruz 5.00 12.00
C30 Kid Elberfeld 3.00 8.00
C31 Curtis Granderson 5.00 12.00
C32 Frank Chance 3.00 8.00
C33 Johnny Evers 3.00 8.00
C34 Chipper Jones 8.00 20.00
C35 Buster Posey 30.00 80.00
C36 Justin Morneau 8.00 20.00
C37 Torii Hunter 3.00 8.00
C38 Jason Bay 5.00 12.00
C39 Tommy Hanson 5.00 12.00
C40 Adam Wainwright 5.00 12.00
C41 Ubaldo Jimenez 5.00 12.00
C42 Manny Ramirez 8.00 20.00
C43 Willie Keeler 3.00 8.00
C44 CC Sabathia 5.00 12.00
C45 Miguel Cabrera 8.00 20.00
C46 Adam Dunn 5.00 12.00
C47 Daisuke Matsuzaka 8.00 20.00
C48 David Wright 10.00 25.00
C49 Josh Johnson 5.00 12.00
C50 Kendry Morales 3.00 8.00

2010 Topps 206 Mini Personalities

COMPLETE SET (10) 40.00 80.00
STATED PRINT RUN 206 SER.#'d SETS
TP1 Chris Holmes 4.00 10.00
TP2 Jim McKenna 4.00 10.00
TP3 Loretta Micali 4.00 10.00
TP4 Clay Luraschi 4.00 10.00
TP5 Joe Del Toro 4.00 10.00
TP6 Tom Mozeleski 4.00 10.00
TP7 Ed Yablonski 4.00 10.00
TP8 Olga M. Vega 4.00 10.00
TP9 Adam Gandolfo 4.00 10.00
TP10 Kathy Szulewski 4.00 10.00

2010 Topps 206 Original-Cut Signature Booklet

STATED PRINT RUN 1 SER.#'d SET
NO PRICING DUE TO SCARCITY

2010 Topps 206 Stamps

SR1 Honus Wagner 20.00 50.00
SR2 Cy Young
SR3 Babe Ruth 50.00 100.00
SR4 Babe Ruth 50.00 100.00
SR5 Babe Ruth 50.00 100.00
SR6 Babe Ruth 50.00 100.00
SR7 Babe Ruth 50.00 100.00
SR8 Babe Ruth 50.00 100.00
SR9 Ty Cobb 15.00 40.00
SR10 Ty Cobb 15.00 40.00
SR11 Johnny Mize 15.00 40.00
SR12 Johnny Mize 15.00 40.00
SR13 Johnny Mize 15.00 40.00
SR14 Johnny Mize 15.00 40.00
SR15 Mel Ott
SR16 Mel Ott
SR17 Mel Ott
SR18 Jimmie Foxx 15.00 40.00
SR19 Jimmie Foxx 15.00 40.00
SR20 Jimmie Foxx 15.00 40.00
SR21 Lou Gehrig 20.00 50.00
SR22 Lou Gehrig 20.00 50.00
SR23 Lou Gehrig 20.00 50.00
SR24 Lou Gehrig 20.00 50.00
SR25 Lou Gehrig 20.00 50.00
SR26 Lou Gehrig 20.00 50.00
SR27 Lou Gehrig 20.00 50.00
SR28 Lou Gehrig 20.00 50.00
SR29 Lou Gehrig 20.00 50.00
SR30 Lou Gehrig 20.00 50.00
SR31 Lou Gehrig 20.00 50.00
SR32 Jackie Robinson 15.00 40.00
SR33 Jackie Robinson 15.00 40.00
SR34 Jackie Robinson 15.00 40.00
SR35 Jackie Robinson 15.00 40.00
SR36 Jackie Robinson 15.00 40.00
SR37 Jackie Robinson 15.00 40.00
SR38 Mickey Mantle 60.00 120.00
SR39 Mickey Mantle 60.00 120.00
SR40 Mickey Mantle 60.00 120.00
SR41 Mickey Mantle 60.00 120.00
SR42 Mickey Mantle 60.00 120.00
SR43 Mickey Mantle 60.00 120.00
SR44 Mickey Mantle 60.00 120.00
SR45 Mickey Mantle 60.00 120.00
SR46 Stan Musial 15.00 40.00
SR47 Thurman Munson 15.00 40.00
SR48 Thurman Munson 15.00 40.00
SR49 Nolan Ryan 40.00 80.00
SR50 Nolan Ryan 40.00 80.00
SR51 Cal Ripken Jr. 50.00 100.00
SR52 Cal Ripken Jr. 50.00 100.00
SR53 Albert Pujols

2006 Topps 52

This 327-card set was released in January, 2007. This product was issued in eight-card packs with an $5 SRP which came 20 packs per box and eight boxes for a case. With the exception of Mickey Mantle (card #311), every player in the set was qualified to be a Topps Rookie Card in 2006. A few players were issued with either their team's current logo or the logo that team used in 1952 and Mantle was issued in six different colors. In addition, a few cards were short printed and those cards were inserted into packs at a stated rate of one in five.

COMP.SET w/o SPs (275) 40.00 80.00
COMMON CARD (1-275) .20 .50
COMMON LOGO VAR. 1.25 3.00
LOGO VAR.STATED ODDS 1:5 H,1:5 R
COMMON SP 1.00 2.50
SP STATED ODDS 1:5 H, 1:5 R
1 Howie Kendrick (RC) .50 1.25
2 Enrique Gonzalez (RC) .20 .50
3 Chuck James (RC) .20 .50
4 Chris Britton RC .20 .50
5 David Pauley (RC) .20 .50
6 Angel Pagan (RC) .20 .50
7 Pat Neshek RC 2.00 5.00
8 Walter Young (RC) .20 .50
9 Chris Denorfia (RC) .20 .50
10 Rafael Perez RC .20 .50
11 Ryan Spilborghs (RC) .20 .50
12 Jon Huber RC .20 .50
13 Jordan Tata RC .20 .50
14 Eric Reed (RC) .20 .50
15 Norris Hopper RC .20 .50
16 Scott Olsen (RC) .20 .50
17 Fernando Nieve (RC) .20 .50
18 Chris Booker (RC) .20 .50
19 Chad Billingsley (RC) .30 .75
20 Carlos Villanueva RC .20 .50
21 Craig Hansen RC .50 1.25
22 Dave Gassner (RC) .20 .50
23 Mike Pelfrey RC .50 1.25
24 Matt Smith RC .30 .75
25 Chris Roberson (RC) .20 .50
26 John Van Benschoten (RC) .20 .50
27 Kevin Frandsen (RC) .20 .50
28 Les Walrond (RC) .20 .50
29 James Shields RC .60 1.50
30 Russell Martin (RC) .30 .75
31 Ben Zobrist (RC) .50 1.25
32 John Rheinecker (RC) .20 .50
33 Francisco Rosario (RC) .20 .50
34 Santiago Ramirez (RC) .20 .50
35 Mike Napoli RC .60 1.50
36 Tony Pena Jr. (RC) .20 .50
37A Jeff Karstens RC .20 .50
37B Jeff Karstens 52 Logo 1.25 3.00
38 Phil Stockman (RC) .20 .50
39 Kurt Birkins RC .20 .50
40 Dustin Pedroia (RC) 4.00 10.00
41 Buck Coats (RC) .20 .50
42 Jim Johnson RC .20 .50
43 Angel Guzman (RC) .20 .50
44 Kelly Shoppach (RC) .20 .50
45 Josh Wilson (RC) .20 .50
46 Jack Hannahan RC .20 .50
47 Ricky Nolasco (RC) .20 .50
48 T.J. Bohn (RC) .20 .50
49 Joel Zumaya (RC) .50 1.25
50 Phil Barzilla RC .20 .50
51 Justin Huber (RC) .20 .50
52A Willy Aybar (RC) .20 .50
52B Willy Aybar 52 Logo 1.25 3.00
53 Tony Gwynn Jr. (RC) .20 .50
54 Chris Barnwell RC .20 .50

55 Henry Owens RC .20 .50
56 Jeff Bajenaru (RC) .20 .50
57 Jonah Bayliss RC .20 .50
58 Josh Sharpless RC .20 .50
59 Eliezer Alfonzo RC .20 .50
60 Bobby Livingston (RC) .20 .50
61 John Gall (RC) .20 .50
62 Ruddy Lugo (RC) .20 .50
63 Fabio Castro RC .20 .50
64 Casey Janssen RC .20 .50
65 Mike O'Connor RC .20 .50
66 Kendry Morales (RC) .50 1.25
67 James Hoey RC .20 .50
68 Dustin Moseley (RC) .20 .50
69 Peter Moylan RC .20 .50
70 Manny Delcarmen (RC) .20 .50
71 Rich Hill (RC) .20 .50
72 Boone Logan RC .20 .50
73 Cody Ross (RC) .50 1.25
74 Fausto Carmona (RC) .20 .50
75 Ramon Ramirez (RC) .20 .50
76 Zach Miner (RC) .20 .50
77 Hanley Ramirez UER (RC) .50 1.25
Carlos M. Martinez pictured
78 Josh Johnson (RC) .50 1.25
79 Taylor Buchholz (RC) .20 .50
80 Joe Nelson (RC) .20 .50
81 Hong-Chih Kuo (RC) .50 1.25
82 Chris Mabeus (RC) .20 .50
83 Willie Eyre (RC) .20 .50
84 John Maine (RC) .30 .75
85 Yurendell DeCaster (RC) .20 .50
86 Mike Thompson RC .20 .50
87 Brian Wilson RC 3.00 8.00
88A Matt Cain (RC) .50 1.25
88B Matt Cain 52 Logo 3.00 8.00
89 Sean Green RC .20 .50
90 Tyler Johnson (RC) .20 .50
91 Jason Childers RC .20 .50
92 Wes Littleton (RC) .20 .50
93 Ty Taubenheim RC .30 .75
94 Saul Rivera (RC) .20 .50
95 Reggie Willits RC .50 1.25
96 Carlos Quentin (RC) .30 .75
97 Macay McBride (RC) .20 .50
98 Brandon Fahey RC .20 .50
99 Sean Marshall (RC) .30 .75
100 Sean Tracey (RC) .20 .50
101 Brian Slocum (RC) .20 .50
102 Choo Freeman (RC) .20 .50
103 Brent Clevlen (RC) .30 .75
104 Josh Willingham (RC) .30 .75
105 Chris Resop (RC) .20 .50
106 Chris Sampson RC .20 .50
107A James Loney (RC) .30 .75
107B James Loney 52 Logo 2.00 5.00
108 Matt Kemp (RC) 1.00 2.50
109 Jason Kubel (RC) .20 .50
110 Brian Bannister (RC) .20 .50
111 Kevin Thompson (RC) .20 .50
112 Jeremy Brown (RC) .20 .50
113 Brian Sanches (RC) .20 .50
114 Nate McLouth (RC) .20 .50
115 Ben Johnson (RC) .20 .50
116 Jonathan Sanchez (RC) .50 1.25
117 Mark Lowe (RC) .20 .50
118 Skip Schumaker (RC) .20 .50
119 Jason Hammel (RC) .20 .50
120 Drew Meyer (RC) .20 .50
121 Melvin Dorta RC .20 .50
122 Jeff Mathis (RC) .20 .50
123 Davis Romero (RC) .20 .50
124 Joey Devine RC .20 .50
125 Sendy Rleal RC .20 .50
126 Freddie Bynum (RC) .20 .50
127 Brian Anderson (RC) .20 .50
128 Jeremy Sowers (RC) .20 .50
129 Ryan Shealy (RC) .20 .50
130 Reggie Abercrombie (RC) .20 .50
131 Matt Albers (RC) .20 .50
132 Lastings Milledge (RC) .20 .50
133 Robert Andino RC .20 .50
134 Chris Demaria RC .20 .50
135 Boof Bonser (RC) .30 .75
136 Alay Soler RC .20 .50
137 Wil Nieves (RC) .20 .50
138 Mike Rouse (RC) .20 .50
139 Carlos Ruiz (RC) .20 .50
140 Matt Capps (RC) .20 .50
141 Travis Ishikawa (RC) .20 .50
142 Josh Kinney RC .20 .50
143 Josh Rupe (RC) .20 .50
144 Shaun Marcum (RC) .20 .50
145 Jason Bergmann RC .20 .50
146 Tommy Murphy (RC) .20 .50
147 Martin Prado (RC) .30 .75
148 Val Majewski (RC) .20 .50
149 Ian Kinsler (RC) .60 1.50
150 Joe Winkelsas (RC) .20 .50
151 Agustin Montero (RC) .20 .50
152 Joe Inglett RC .20 .50
153 Manuel Corpas RC .20 .50
154 Yusmeiro Petit (RC) .20 .50
155 Mark Woodyard (RC) .20 .50
156 Jeff Fulchino RC .20 .50
157 Stephen Andrade (RC) .20 .50
158 Tim Hamulack (RC) .20 .50
159 Colter Bean (RC) .20 .50
160 Anderson Hernandez (RC) .20 .50
161 Kevin Reese (RC) .20 .50
162 Jason Windsor (RC) .20 .50
163A Paul Maholm (RC) .20 .50
163B Paul Maholm 52 Logo 1.25 3.00
164 Jeremy Accardo RC .20 .50
165 Joel Guzman (RC) .20 .50
166 Erick Aybar (RC) .20 .50
167 Scott Thorman (RC) .20 .50
168 Adam Loewen (RC) .20 .50
169 Carlos Marmol RC .60 1.50
170 Bill Bray (RC) .20 .50
171 Edward Mujica RC .20 .50
172 Jeremy Hermida (RC) .20 .50
173 Taylor Tankersley (RC) .20 .50
174 Bobby Keppel (RC) .20 .50
175 Chris B. Young (RC) .20 .50
176 Josh Rabe RC .20 .50
177 T.J. Beam (RC) .20 .50
178A Shane Komine RC .30 .75
178B Shane Komine 52 Logo 2.00 5.00
179 Scott Mathieson (RC) .20 .50
180 Josh Barfield (RC) .20 .50
181 Justin Knoedler (RC) .20 .50
182 Emiliano Fruto RC .20 .50
183 Adam Wainwright (RC) .50 1.25
184 Nick Masset (RC) .20 .50
185 Ryan Roberts RC .20 .50
186 Brandon Watson (RC) .20 .50
187 Chris Bootcheck (RC) .20 .50
188 Dan Ortmeier (RC) .20 .50
189 Kevin Barry (RC) .20 .50
190 Cory Morris RC .20 .50
191 Kason Gabbard (RC) .20 .50
192 Tom Mastny (RC) .20 .50
193 David Aardsma (RC) .20 .50
194 Anthony Reyes (RC) .20 .50
195 Mike Jacobs (RC) .20 .50
196 Conor Jackson (RC) .30 .75
197 Kenji Johjima RC .50 1.25
198 Jack Taschner (RC) .20 .50
199 Renyel Pinto (RC) .20 .50
200 Chad Santos (RC) .20 .50
201 Aaron Rakers (RC) .20 .50
202 Franklin Gutierrez (RC) .20 .50
203 Chris Coste RC .50 1.25
204 Chris Iannetta RC .20 .50
205 Mike Vento (RC) .20 .50
206 Ryan O'Malley RC .20 .50
207 Jason Botts (RC) .20 .50
208 John Hattig (RC) .20 .50
209 Brandon Harper RC .20 .50
210 Ryan Theriot RC .60 1.50
211 Travis Hughes (RC) .20 .50
212 Paul Hoover (RC) .20 .50
213 Brayan Pena (RC) .20 .50
214 Craig Breslow RC .20 .50
215 Eude Brito (RC) .20 .50
216A Melky Cabrera (RC) .30 .75
216B Melky Cabrera 52 Logo 2.00 5.00
217A Jonathan Broxton (RC) .20 .50
217B Jonathan Broxton 52 Logo 1.25 3.00
218 Bryan Corey (RC) .20 .50
219 Ron Flores RC .20 .50
220 Andrew Brown (RC) .20 .50
221 Jaime Bubela (RC) .20 .50
222 Jason Bulger (RC) .20 .50
223 Alberto Callaspo (RC) .20 .50
224 Jose Capellan (RC) .20 .50
225A Cole Hamels (RC) .75 2.00
225B Cole Hamels 52 Logo 5.00 12.00
226 Bernie Castro (RC) .20 .50
227 Shin-Soo Choo (RC) .30 .75
228 Doug Clark (RC) .20 .50
229 Roy Corcoran RC .20 .50
230 Tim Corcoran RC .20 .50
231 Nelson Cruz (RC) .30 .75
232 Rajai Davis (RC) .30 .75
233A Chris Duncan (RC) .30 .75
233B Chris Duncan 52 Logo 2.00 5.00
234 Scott Dunn (RC) .20 .50
235 Mike Esposito (RC) .20 .50
236 Scott Feldman RC .20 .50
237 Luis Figueroa RC .20 .50
238 Bartolome Fortunato (RC) .20 .50
239 Alejandro Freire RC .20 .50
240 J.J. Furmaniak (RC) .20 .50
241 Nick Markakis (RC) .50 1.25
242 Matt Garza (RC) .20 .50
243 Justin Germano (RC) .20 .50
244 Alexis Gomez (RC) .20 .50
245 Tom Gorzelanny (RC) .20 .50
246 Dan Uggla (RC) .50 1.25
247 Jeremy Guthrie (RC) .20 .50
248 Stephen Drew (RC) .50 1.25
249 Brendan Harris (RC) .20 .50
250 Jeff Harris RC .20 .50
251 Corey Hart (RC) .20 .50
252 Chris Heintz RC .20 .50
253 Prince Fielder (RC) .75 2.00
254 Francisco Liriano (RC) .50 1.25
255 Jason Hirsh (RC) .20 .50
256 J.R. House (RC) .20 .50
257 Zach Jackson (RC) .20 .50
258 Charlton Jimerson (RC) .20 .50
259 Greg Jones (RC) .20 .50
260 Mitch Jones (RC) .20 .50
261 Ryan Jorgensen RC .20 .50
262 Logan Kensing (RC) .20 .50
263 John Koronka (RC) .20 .50
264 Anthony Lerew (RC) .20 .50
265 Anibal Sanchez (RC) .20 .50
266 Juan Mateo RC .20 .50
267 Paul McAnulty (RC) .20 .50
268 Dustin McGowan (RC) .20 .50
269 Marty McLeary (RC) .20 .50
270 Ryan Zimmerman (RC) 1.00 2.50
271 Dustin Nippert (RC) .20 .50
272 Eric O'Flaherty RC .20 .50
273 Ronny Paulino (RC) .20 .50
274 Tony Pena (RC) .20 .50
275 Hayden Penn (RC) .20 .50
276 Miguel Perez SP (RC) 1.00 2.50
277 Paul Phillips SP (RC) 1.00 2.50
278 Omar Quintanilla SP (RC) 1.00 2.50
279 Guillermo Quiroz SP (RC) 1.00 2.50
280 Darrell Rasner SP (RC) 1.00 2.50
281 Kenny Ray SP (RC) 1.00 2.50
282 Royce Ring SP (RC) 1.00 2.50
283 Brian Rogers SP RC 1.00 2.50
284 Ed Rogers SP (RC) 1.00 2.50
285 Danny Sandoval SP RC 1.00 2.50
286 Joe Saunders SP (RC) 1.00 2.50
287 Chris Schroder SP RC 1.00 2.50
288 Mike Smith SP (RC) 1.00 2.50
289 Travis Smith SP (RC) 1.00 2.50
290 Geovany Soto SP (RC) 2.50 6.00
291 Brian Sweeney SP (RC) 1.00 2.50
292 Jon Switzer SP (RC) 1.00 2.50
293 Joe Thurston SP (RC) 1.00 2.50
294 Jermaine Van Buren SP (RC) 1.00 2.50
295 Ryan Garko SP (RC) 1.00 2.50
296 Cla Meredith SP (RC) 1.00 2.50
297 Luke Scott SP (RC) 1.00 2.50
298 Andy Marte SP (RC) 1.00 2.50
299 Jered Weaver SP (RC) 2.50 6.00
300 Freddy Guzman SP (RC) 1.00 2.50
301 Jonathan Papelbon SP (RC) 5.00 12.00
302 John-Ford Griffin SP (RC) UER 1.00 2.50
Photo is Anthony Lerew
303 Jon Lester SP RC 4.00 10.00
304 Shawn Hill SP (RC) 1.00 2.50
305 Brian Myrow SP RC 1.00 2.50
306 Anderson Garcia SP RC 1.00 2.50
307 Andre Ethier SP (RC) 4.00 10.00
308 Ben Hendrickson SP (RC) 1.00 2.50
309 Alejandro Machado SP (RC) 1.00 2.50
310 Justin Verlander SP (RC) 8.00 20.00
311A Mickey Mantle SP Blue 12.00 30.00
311B Mickey Mantle Black 2.50 6.00
311C Mickey Mantle Green 2.50 6.00
311D Mickey Mantle Orange 2.50 6.00
311E Mickey Mantle Red 2.50 6.00
311F Mickey Mantle Yellow 2.50 6.00
312 Steve Stemle SP RC 1.00 2.50

2006 Topps 52 Chrome

COMMON CARD .75 2.00
SEMISTARS 1.25 3.00
UNLISTED STARS 2.00 5.00
STATED ODDS 1:5 H, 1:7 R
STATED PRINT RUN 1952 SER.#'d SETS
1 Howie Kendrick 2.00 5.00
2 David Pauley .75 2.00
3 Chris Denorfia .75 2.00
4 Jordan Tata .75 2.00
5 Fernando Nieve .75 2.00
6 Craig Hansen 2.00 5.00
7 Mickey Mantle 6.00 15.00
8 James Shields 2.50 6.00
9 Francisco Rosario .75 2.00
10 Jeff Karstens .75 2.00
11 Buck Coats .75 2.00
12 Josh Wilson .75 2.00
13 Joel Zumaya 2.00 5.00
14 Tony Gwynn Jr. .75 2.00
15 Jonah Bayliss .75 2.00
16 John Gall .75 2.00
17 Mike O'Connor .75 2.00
18 Peter Moylan .75 2.00
19 Cody Ross 2.00 5.00
20 Hanley Ramirez UER 2.00 5.00
Carlos M. Martinez pictured
21 Hong-Chih Kuo 2.00 5.00
22 Yurendell DeCaster .75 2.00
23 Sean Green .75 2.00
24 Ty Taubenheim 1.25 3.00
25 Macay McBride .75 2.00
26 Brian Slocum .75 2.00
27 Chris Resop .75 2.00
28 Jason Kubel .75 2.00
29 Brian Sanches .75 2.00
30 Mark Lowe .75 2.00
31 Melvin Dorta .75 2.00
32 Sendy Rleal .75 2.00
33 Ryan Shealy .75 2.00
34 Robert Andino .75 2.00
35 Wil Nieves .75 2.00
36 Travis Ishikawa .75 2.00
37 Jason Bergmann .75 2.00
38 Ian Kinsler 2.50 6.00
39 Manuel Corpas .75 2.00
40 Stephen Andrade .75 2.00
41 Kevin Reese .75 2.00
42 Joel Guzman .75 2.00
43 Carlos Marmol 2.50 6.00
44 Taylor Tankersley .75 2.00
45 T.J. Beam .75 2.00
46 Justin Knoedler .75 2.00
47 Ryan Roberts .75 2.00
48 Kevin Barry .75 2.00
49 David Aardsma .75 2.00
50 Kenji Johjima 2.00 5.00
51 Aaron Rakers .75 2.00
52 Mike Vento .75 2.00
53 Brandon Harper .75 2.00
54 Brayan Pena .75 2.00
55 Jonathan Broxton .75 2.00
56 Jaime Bubela .75 2.00
57 Cole Hamels 3.00 8.00
58 Roy Corcoran .75 2.00
59 Chris Duncan 1.25 3.00
60 Luis Figueroa .75 2.00
61 Kendry Morales 2.00 5.00
62 Tom Gorzelanny .75 2.00
63 Brendan Harris .75 2.00
64 Anibal Sanchez .75 2.00
65 Zach Jackson .75 2.00
66 Ryan Jorgensen .75 2.00
67 Josh Johnson 2.00 5.00
68 Marty McLeary .75 2.00
69 Ronny Paulino .75 2.00
70 Tyler Johnson .75 2.00
71 Reggie Abercrombie .75 2.00
72 Nick Markakis 2.00 5.00
73 J.J. Furmaniak .75 2.00
74 Prince Fielder 3.00 8.00
75 Enrique Gonzalez .75 2.00
76 Angel Pagan .75 2.00
77 Rafael Perez .75 2.00
78 Eric Reed .75 2.00
79 Chris Booker .75 2.00
80 Dave Gassner .75 2.00
81 John Van Benschoten .75 2.00
82 Russell Martin 1.25 3.00
83 Santiago Ramirez .75 2.00
84 Phil Stockman .75 2.00
85 Jim Johnson .75 2.00
86 Jack Hannahan .75 2.00
87 Phil Barzilla .75 2.00
88 Chris Barnwell .75 2.00
89 Josh Sharpless .75 2.00
90 Chris Roberson .75 2.00

2006 Topps 52 Chrome Refractors

*CHROME REF: .6X TO 1.5X CHROME
STATED ODDS 1:19 H, 1:20 R
STATED PRINT RUN 552 SER.#'d SETS

2006 Topps 52 Chrome Gold Refractors

COMMON CARD 5.00 12.00
SEMISTARS 8.00 20.00
UNLISTED STARS 12.50 30.00
STATED ODDS 1:207 H, 1:207 R
STATED PRINT RUN 52 SER.#'d SETS
7 Mickey Mantle 200.00 300.00

2006 Topps 52 Debut Flashbacks

COMPLETE SET (20) 15.00 40.00
STATED ODDS 1:6 H, 1:6 R
*CHROME: .75X TO 2X BASIC
CHROME ODDS 1:25 H, 1:25 R
CHR.PRINT RUN 1952 SER.#'d SETS
DF1 Dontrelle Willis .50 1.25
DF2 Carlos Beltran .50 1.25
DF3 Albert Pujols 3.00 8.00
DF4 Ichiro Suzuki 2.00 5.00
DF5 Mike Piazza 1.25 3.00
DF6 Nomar Garciaparra 1.25 3.00
DF7 Scott Rolen .75 2.00
DF8 Mariano Rivera 1.25 3.00
DF9 David Ortiz .75 2.00
DF10 Johnny Damon .75 2.00
DF11 Tom Glavine .75 2.00
DF12 David Wright 2.00 5.00
DF13 Greg Maddux 2.00 5.00
DF14 Manny Ramirez 1.25 3.00
DF15 Alex Rodriguez 2.00 5.00
DF16 Roger Clemens 1.50 4.00
DF17 Alfonso Soriano .75 2.00
DF18 Frank Thomas 1.25 3.00
DF19 Chipper Jones 1.25 3.00
DF20 Ivan Rodriguez .75 2.00

2006 Topps 52 Debut Flashbacks Chrome Refractors

*CHROME REF: 1.25X TO 3X BASIC
STATED ODDS 1:87 H, 1:88 R
STATED PRINT RUN 552 SER.#'d SETS

2006 Topps 52 Debut Flashbacks Chrome Gold Refractors

GOLD REF: 4X TO 10X BASIC
STATED ODDS 1:931 H, 1:931 R
STATED PRINT RUN 52 SER.#'d SETS

2006 Topps 52 Dynamic Duos

COMPLETE SET (15) 8.00 20.00
STATED ODDS 1:4 H, 1:4 R
DD1 Stephen Drew 1.25 3.00
Carlos Quentin
DD2 Jonathan Papelbon 2.50 6.00
Jon Lester
DD3 Joel Zumaya 4.00 10.00
Justin Verlander
DD4 Dan Uggla 1.25 3.00
Hanley Ramirez
DD5 Jonathan Broxton .75 2.00
Chad Billingsley
DD6 Francisco Liriano 1.25 3.00
Matt Garza
DD7 Lastings Milledge .75 2.00
John Maine
DD8 Chris Coste 2.00 5.00
Cole Hamels
DD9 Mike Napoli 1.50 4.00
Howie Kendrick
DD10 Joe Inglett .50 1.25
Andy Marte
DD11 Jeremy Hermida .50 1.25
Josh Willingham
DD12 Matt Kemp 2.50 6.00
James Loney
DD13 Andre Ethier 2.00 5.00
Russell Martin
DD14 Melky Cabrera .75 2.00
Jeff Karstens
DD15 Ricky Nolasco 1.25 3.00
Scott Olsen
Josh Johnson
Anibal Sanchez

2006 Topps 52 Ticket to Stardom

STATED ODDS 1:6068 H, 1:6068 R
STATED PRINT RUN 10 SER.#'d SETS
NO PRICING DUE TO SCARCITY

2006 Topps 52 Signatures

GROUP A ODDS 1:11,000 H, 1:52,000 R
GROUP B ODDS 1:2580 H, 1:9500 R
GROUP C ODDS 1:130 H, 1:410 R
GROUP D ODDS 1:912 H, 1:3000 R
GROUP E ODDS 1:111 H, 1:372 R
GROUP F ODDS 1:104 H, 1:358 R
GROUP G ODDS 1:32 H, 1:115 R
GROUP H ODDS 1:85 H, 1:300 R
GROUP I ODDS 1:30 H, 1:111 R
GROUP J ODDS 1:20 H, 1:76 R
NO A-B PRICING DUE TO SCARCITY
EXCH DEADLINE 12/31/08
ASTERISK = PARTIAL EXCHANGE
AG Angel Guzman E 3.00 8.00
AL Anthony Lerew H 3.00 8.00
AP Angel Pagan F 6.00 15.00
AR Alex Rodriguez A
AS Anibal Sanchez H 6.00 15.00
BA Brian Anderson D 5.00 12.00
BB Boof Bonser C 8.00 20.00
BC Buck Coats G 3.00 8.00
BPB Brian Bannister E 10.00 25.00
BS Brian Slocum I 3.00 8.00
BZ Ben Zobrist F 5.00 12.00
CHJ Chuck James F 6.00 15.00
CI Chris Iannetta E 5.00 12.00
CM Chris Mabeus I 3.00 8.00
DU Dan Uggla E 8.00 20.00
DW David Wright B
EA Erick Aybar J 3.00 8.00
EG Enrique Gonzalez J 3.00 8.00
EM Edward Mujica J 3.00 8.00
FC Fabio Castro G 3.00 8.00
FG Franklin Gutierrez H 6.00 15.00
HK Howie Kendrick C 12.50 30.00
JAP Albert Pujols A
JD Johnny Damon A
JFS Joe Saunders C 8.00 20.00
JG Joel Guzman F 3.00 8.00
JK Josh Kinney J 5.00 12.00
JP Jonathan Papelbon G 8.00 20.00
JS Josh Sharpless I 3.00 8.00
JV Justin Verlander C 50.00 100.00
JVB John Van Benschoten I 3.00 8.00
JWK Jeff Karstens G 8.00 20.00
JZ Joel Zumaya C 20.00 50.00
KM Kendry Morales G 10.00 25.00
MA Matt Albers I 3.00 8.00
MG Matt Garza C 10.00 25.00
MK Matt Kemp G 15.00 40.00
MN Mike Napoli G 12.50 30.00
MTC Matt Cain C 12.50 30.00
RA Reggie Abercrombie G 3.00 8.00
RO Ryan O'Malley G 3.00 8.00
SD Stephen Drew C 20.00 50.00
SM Scott Mathieson I 3.00 8.00
TJB T.J. Bohn I 3.00 8.00
TM Tom Mastny J 3.00 8.00
WB Bill Bray E 3.00 8.00
YD Yurendell DeCaster J 3.00 8.00
YP Yusmeiro Petit E 3.00 8.00

2006 Topps 52 Signatures Red Ink

STATED ODDS 1:235 H, 1:840 R
STATED PRINT RUN 52 SER.#'d SETS
EXCH DEADLINE 12/31/08
AG Angel Guzman 12.50 30.00
AL Anthony Lerew 20.00 50.00
AP Angel Pagan 30.00 60.00
AR Alex Rodriguez
AS Anibal Sanchez 20.00 50.00
BA Brian Anderson 12.50 30.00
BB Boof Bonser 20.00 50.00
BC Buck Coats 12.50 30.00
BPB Brian Bannister 50.00 100.00
BS Brian Slocum 20.00 50.00
BZ Ben Zobrist 20.00 50.00
CHJ Chuck James 20.00 50.00
CI Chris Iannetta 30.00 60.00
CM Chris Mabeus 12.50 30.00
DU Dan Uggla 20.00 50.00
DW David Wright
EA Erick Aybar 12.50 30.00
EF Emiliano Fruto 12.50 30.00
EG Enrique Gonzalez 12.50 30.00
EM Edward Mujica 12.50 30.00
FC Fabio Castro 30.00 60.00
FG Franklin Gutierrez 12.50 30.00
HK Howie Kendrick 30.00 60.00
JAP Albert Pujols
JD Johnny Damon
JFS Joe Saunders 12.50 30.00
JG Joel Guzman 12.50 30.00
JK Josh Kinney 20.00 50.00
JP Jonathan Papelbon 30.00 60.00
JS Josh Sharpless 12.50 30.00
JV Justin Verlander 75.00 150.00
JVB John Van Benschoten 12.50 30.00
JWK Jeff Karstens 20.00 50.00
JZ Joel Zumaya 50.00 100.00
KM Kendry Morales 40.00 80.00
MA Matt Albers 12.50 30.00
MG Matt Garza 20.00 50.00
MK Matt Kemp 50.00 100.00
MN Mike Napoli 50.00 100.00
MTC Matt Cain 75.00 150.00
RA Reggie Abercrombie 12.50 30.00
RO Ryan O'Malley 20.00 50.00
SD Stephen Drew 50.00 100.00
SM Scott Mathieson 20.00 50.00
TJB T.J. Bohn 12.50 30.00
TM Tom Mastny 20.00 50.00
WB Bill Bray 12.50 30.00
YD Yurendell DeCaster 12.50 30.00
YP Yusmeiro Petit 20.00 50.00

2007 Topps 52

This 227-card set was released in December, 2007. The set was issued in both hobby and retail channels. The hobby packs consisted of eight cards with an $3 SRP which came 20 packs to a box and eight boxes to a case. Some of the more popular 2007 rookies were also created in shorter printed action variations and the final fourteen cards in the set were also short-printed. These shorter printed cards were inserted into packs at a stated rate of one in six for either hobby or retail. No cards numbered 198-200 were printed in this set.

COMP.SET w/o SPs (202) 20.00 50.00
COMMON CARD (1-227) .25 .60
COMMON ACTION VARIATION 2.00 5.00
ACT.VAR.STATED ODDS 1:6 H, 1:6 R
COMMON SP 2.00 5.00
SP STATED ODDS 1:6 H, 1:6 R
1 Akinori Iwamura RC .60 1.50
2 Angel Sanchez RC .25 .60
3 Luis Hernandez (RC) .25 .60
4 Joaquin Arias (RC) .25 .60
5a Troy Tulowitzki (RC) 1.50 4.00
5b Troy Tulowitzki 2.50 6.00
Action SP
6 Jesus Flores RC .25 .60
7 Mickey Mantle 2.00 5.00
8 Kory Casto (RC) .25 .60
9 Tony Abreu RC .60 1.50
10 Kevin Kouzmanoff (RC) .25 .60
11 Travis Buck (RC) .25 .60
12 Kurt Suzuki (RC) .25 .60
13 Matt DeSalvo (RC) .25 .60
14 Jerry Owens (RC) .25 .60
15 Alex Gordon RC .75 2.00
16 Jeff Baker (RC) .25 .60
17 Ben Francisco (RC) .25 .60
18 Nate Schierholtz (RC) .25 .60
19 Nathan Haynes (RC) .25 .60
20a Ryan Braun (RC) 1.25 3.00
20b Ryan Braun 3.00 8.00
Action SP
21 Brian Barden RC .25 .60
22 Sean Barker RC .25 .60
23 Alejandro De Aza RC .40 1.00
24 Jamie Burke (RC) .25 .60
25 Michael Bourn (RC) .25 .60
26 Jeff Salazar (RC) .25 .60
27 Chase Headley (RC) .25 .60
28 Chris Basak RC .25 .60
29 Mike Fontenot (RC) .25 .60
30a Hunter Pence (RC) 1.25 3.00
30b Hunter Pence 3.00 8.00
Action SP
31 Masumi Kuwata RC .25 .60
32 Ryan Rowland-Smith RC .25 .60
33 Tyler Clippard (RC) .40 1.00
34 Matt Lindstrom (RC) .25 .60
35 Fred Lewis (RC) .40 1.00
36 Brett Carroll RC .25 .60
37 Alexi Casilla RC .40 1.00
38 Nick Gorneault (RC) .25 .60
39 Dennis Sarfate (RC) .25 .60
40 Felix Pie (RC) .25 .60
41 Miguel Montero (RC) .25 .60
42 Danny Putnam (RC) .25 .60
43 Shane Youman RC .25 .60
44 Andy LaRoche (RC) .25 .60
45 Jarrod Saltalamacchia (RC) .40 1.00
46 Kei Igawa RC .60 1.50
47 Don Kelly (RC) .25 .60
48 Fernando Cortez (RC) .25 .60
49 Travis Metcalf RC .40 1.00
50a Daisuke Matsuzaka RC 1.00 2.50
50b Daisuke Matsuzaka 3.00 8.00
Action SP
51 Edwar Ramirez RC .60 1.50
52 Ryan Sweeney (RC) .25 .60
53 Shawn Riggans (RC) .25 .60
54 Billy Sadler (RC) .25 .60
55 Billy Butler (RC) .40 1.00
56 Andy Cavazos RC .25 .60
57 Sean Henn (RC) .25 .60
58 Brian Esposito (RC) .25 .60
59 Brandon Morrow RC 1.25 3.00
60 Adam Lind (RC) .25 .60
61 Joe Smith RC .25 .60
62 Chris Stewart RC .25 .60
63 Eulogio De La Cruz (RC) .40 1.00
64 Sean Gallagher (RC) .25 .60
65 Carlos Gomez RC .40 1.00
66 Jailen Peguero RC .25 .60
67 Juan Perez RC .25 .60
68 Levale Speigner RC .25 .60
69 Jamie Vermilyea RC .25 .60
70a Delmon Young (RC) .40 1.00
70b Delmon Young 2.00 5.00
Action SP
71 Jo-Jo Reyes (RC) .25 .60
72 Zack Segovia (RC) .25 .60
73 Andy Sonnanstine RC .25 .60
74 Chase Wright RC .60 1.50
75 Josh Fields (RC) .25 .60
76 Jon Knott (RC) .25 .60
77 Guillermo Rodriguez RC .25 .60
78 Jon Coutlangus (RC) .25 .60
79 Kevin Cameron RC .25 .60
80 Mark Reynolds RC 2.00 5.00
81 Brian Stokes (RC) .25 .60
82 Alberto Arias RC .25 .60
83 Yoel Hernandez RC .25 .60
84 David Murphy (RC) .25 .60
85 Josh Hamilton (RC) 1.00 2.50
86 Justin Hampson (RC) .25 .60
87 Doug Slaten RC .25 .60
88 Joseph Bisenius RC .25 .60
89 Troy Cate RC .25 .60
90 Homer Bailey (RC) .40 1.00
91 Jacoby Ellsbury (RC) 2.00 5.00
92 Devern Hansack RC .25 .60
93 Zach McClellan RC .25 .60
94 Vinny Rottino (RC) .25 .60
95 Elijah Dukes RC .40 1.00
96 Ryan Z. Braun UER RC .25 .60
Facsimile auto of Ryan J. Braun
97 Lee Gardner (RC) .25 .60
98 Joakim Soria RC .25 .60
99 Jason Miller (RC) .25 .60
100a Hideki Okajima RC 1.25 3.00
100b Hideki Okajima 3.00 8.00
Action SP
101 John Danks RC .40 1.00
102 Garrett Jones (RC) .60 1.50
103 Jensen Lewis RC .25 .60
104 Clay Rapada RC .25 .60
105 Kyle Kendrick RC .60 1.50
106 Eric Stults RC .25 .60
107 Jared Burton RC .25 .60
108 Julio DePaula RC .40 1.00
109 Jesse Litsch RC .40 1.00
110 Micah Owings (RC) .25 .60
111 Cory Doyne (RC) .25 .60
112 Jay Marshall RC .25 .60
113 Mike Schultz RC .25 .60
114 Juan Salas (RC) .25 .60
115 Matt Chico (RC) .25 .60
116 Brad Salmon RC .25 .60
117 Jeff Bailey (RC) .25 .60
118 Gustavo Molina RC .25 .60
119 Brian Burres (RC) .25 .60
120 Yovani Gallardo (RC) .60 1.50

121 Hector Gimenez (RC) .25 .60
122 Kelvin Jimenez RC .25 .60
123 Rick Vanden Hurk RC .25 .60
124 Billy Petrick (RC) .25 .60
125 Andrew Miller RC .60 1.50
126 Rocky Cherry RC .60 1.50
127 Jordan De Jong RC .25 .60
128 Eric Hull RC .25 .60
129 Kevin Mahar RC .25 .60
130a Tim Lincecum RC 4.00 10.00
130b Tim Lincecum 3.00 8.00
Action SP
131 Garrett Olson (RC) .25 .60
132 Neal Musser RC .25 .60
133 Mike Rabelo RC .25 .60
134 Dennis Dove (RC) .25 .60
135 J.D. Durbin (RC) .25 .60
136 Jose Garcia RC .25 .60
137 Marcus McBeth (RC) .25 .60
138 Curtis Thigpen (RC) .25 .60
139 Mike Zagurski RC .25 .60
140 Kevin Slowey (RC) .60 1.50
141 Dewon Day RC .25 .60
142 Glen Perkins (RC) .25 .60
143 Brian Wolfe (RC) .25 .60
144 Dallas Braden RC 1.50 4.00
145 J.A. Happ (RC) 1.50 4.00
146 Lee Gronkiewicz RC .25 .60
147 Cesar Jimenez RC .25 .60
148 Mark McLemore (RC) .25 .60
149 Connor Robertson RC .25 .60
150a Phil Hughes (RC) 1.25 3.00
150b Phil Hughes 3.00 8.00
Action SP
151 Matthew Brown RC .25 .60
152 Ryan Feierabend (RC) .25 .60
153 Brendan Ryan (RC) .25 .60
154 Terry Evans RC .25 .60
155 Eric Patterson (RC) .25 .60
156 Patrick Misch (RC) .25 .60
157 Darren Clarke RC .25 .60
158 Kevin Melillo (RC) .25 .60
159 Edwin Bellorin RC .25 .60
160 Ubaldo Jimenez (RC) 1.50 4.00
161 Ryan Budde (RC) .25 .60
162 Brian Buscher RC .40 1.00
163 Juan Gutierrez RC .25 .60
164 Franklin Morales (RC) .40 1.00
165 Carmen Pignatiello (RC) .25 .60
166 Jair Jurrjens (RC) .40 1.00
167 Manny Acosta (RC) .25 .60
168 Ian Stewart RC .25 .60
169 Daniel Barone (RC) .25 .60
170a Justin Upton RC 2.00 5.00
170b Justin Upton 3.00 8.00
Action SP
171 Tommy Watkins RC .40 1.00
172 Ross Wolf RC .25 .60
173 Jack Cassel RC .25 .60
174 Asdrubal Cabrera RC 1.25 3.00
175 Mauro Zarate RC .25 .60
176 Aaron Laffey RC .60 1.50
177 Marcus Gwyn RC .25 .60
178 Danny Richar RC .25 .60
179 Joel Hanrahan (RC) .40 1.00
180 Cameron Maybin RC .40 1.00
181 John Lannan RC .25 .60
182 Shelley Duncan (RC) .60 1.50
183 Brandon Wood (RC) .25 .60
184 Delwyn Young (RC) .25 .60
185 Manny Parra (RC) .25 .60
186 Ehren Wassermann RC .25 .60
187 Jose A. Reyes RC .25 .60
188 Jose Ascanio RC .25 .60
190a Alvin Colina RC .60 1.50
190b Joba Chamberlain 5.00 12.00
Action SP
191 Yunel Escobar (RC) .25 .60
192 Carlos Maldonado (RC) .25 .60
193 Dan Meyer (RC) .25 .60
194 Scott Moore (RC) .25 .60
195 Romulo Sanchez RC .25 .60
196 Tom Shearn (RC) .25 .60
197 Craig Stansberry (RC) .25 .60
201 Joba Chamberlain RC 1.25 3.00
202 John Nelson SP (RC) 2.00 5.00
203 Phil Dumatrait (RC) .25 .60
204 Brandon Moss (RC) .25 .60
205 Beltran Perez (RC) .25 .60
206 Drew Anderson RC .25 .60
207 Brett Campbell RC .25 .60
208 Andy Cannizaro SP RC 2.00 5.00
209 Travis Chick SP (RC) 2.00 5.00
210 Francisco Cruceta SP (RC) 2.00 5.00
211 Jose Diaz SP (RC) 2.00 5.00
212 Jeff Fiorentino SP (RC) 2.00 5.00
213 Tim Gradoville SP RC 2.00 5.00
214 Kevin Hooper SP (RC) 2.00 5.00
215 Philip Humber SP (RC) 2.00 5.00
216 Juan Lara SP RC 2.00 5.00
217 Mitch Maier SP RC 2.00 5.00
218 Juan Morillo SP (RC) 2.00 5.00
219 A.J. Murray SP RC 2.00 5.00
220 Chris Narveson SP (RC) 2.00 5.00
221 Oswaldo Navarro SP RC 2.00 5.00

2007 Topps 52 Black Back

STATED ODDS 1:6 HOBBY
1 Akinori Iwamura 2.50 6.00
2 Angel Sanchez 1.00 2.50
3 Luis Hernandez 1.00 2.50
4 Joaquin Arias 1.00 2.50
5 Troy Tulowitzki 6.00 15.00
6 Jesus Flores 1.00 2.50
7 Mickey Mantle 8.00 20.00
8 Kory Casto 1.00 2.50
9 Tony Abreu 2.50 6.00
10 Kevin Kouzmanoff 1.00 2.50
11 Travis Buck 1.00 2.50
12 Kurt Suzuki 1.00 2.50
13 Matt DeSalvo 1.00 2.50
14 Jerry Owens 1.00 2.50
15 Alex Gordon 3.00 8.00
16 Jeff Baker 1.00 2.50
17 Ben Francisco 1.00 2.50
18 Nate Schierholtz 1.00 2.50
19 Nathan Haynes 1.00 2.50
20 Ryan Braun 5.00 12.00
21 Brian Barden 1.00 2.50
22 Sean Barker 1.00 2.50
23 Alejandro De Aza 1.50 4.00
24 Jamie Burke 1.00 2.50
25 Michael Bourn 1.00 2.50
26 Jeff Salazar 1.00 2.50
27 Chase Headley 1.00 2.50
28 Chris Basak 1.00 2.50
29 Mike Fontenot 1.00 2.50
30 Hunter Pence 5.00 12.00
31 Masumi Kuwata 1.00 2.50
32 Ryan Rowland-Smith 1.00 2.50
33 Tyler Clippard 1.50 4.00
34 Matt Lindstrom 1.00 2.50
35 Fred Lewis 1.50 4.00
36 Brett Carroll 1.00 2.50
37 Alexi Casilla 1.50 4.00
38 Nick Gorneault 1.00 2.50
39 Dennis Sarfate 1.00 2.50
40 Felix Pie 1.00 2.50
41 Miguel Montero 1.00 2.50
42 Danny Putnam 1.00 2.50
43 Shane Youman 1.00 2.50
44 Andy LaRoche 1.00 2.50
45 Jarrod Saltalamacchia 1.50 4.00
46 Kei Igawa 2.50 6.00
47 Don Kelly 1.00 2.50
48 Fernando Cortez 1.00 2.50
49 Travis Metcalf 1.50 4.00
50 Daisuke Matsuzaka 4.00 10.00
51 Edward Ramirez 2.50 6.00
52 Ryan Sweeney 1.00 2.50
53 Shawn Riggans 1.00 2.50
54 Billy Sadler 1.00 2.50
55 Billy Butler 1.50 4.00
56 Andy Cavazos 1.00 2.50
57 Sean Henn 1.00 2.50
58 Brian Esposito 1.00 2.50
59 Brandon Morrow 5.00 12.00
60 Adam Lind 1.00 2.50
61 Joe Smith 1.00 2.50
62 Chris Stewart 1.00 2.50
63 Eulogio De La Cruz 1.50 4.00
64 Sean Gallagher 1.00 2.50
65 Carlos Gomez 1.50 4.00
66 Jailen Peguero 1.00 2.50
67 Juan Perez 1.00 2.50
68 Levale Speigner 1.00 2.50
69 Jamie Vermilyea 1.00 2.50
70 Delmon Young 1.50 4.00
71 Jo-Jo Reyes 1.00 2.50
72 Zack Segovia 1.00 2.50
73 Andy Sonnanstine 1.00 2.50
74 Chase Wright 2.50 6.00
75 Josh Fields 1.00 2.50
76 Jon Knott 1.00 2.50
77 Guillermo Rodriguez 1.00 2.50
78 Jon Coutlangus 1.00 2.50
79 Kevin Cameron 1.00 2.50
80 Mark Reynolds 8.00 20.00
81 Brian Stokes 1.00 2.50
82 Alberto Arias 1.00 2.50
83 Yoel Hernandez 1.00 2.50
84 David Murphy 1.00 2.50
85 Josh Hamilton 4.00 10.00
86 Justin Hampson 1.00 2.50
87 Doug Slaten 1.00 2.50
88 Joseph Bisenius 1.00 2.50
89 Troy Cate 1.00 2.50
90 Homer Bailey 1.50 4.00
91 Jacoby Ellsbury 8.00 20.00
92 Devern Hansack 1.00 2.50
93 Zach McClellan 1.00 2.50
94 Vinny Rottino 1.00 2.50
95 Elijah Dukes 1.50 4.00
96 Ryan Z. Braun UER 1.00 2.50
Facsimile auto of Ryan J.Braun
97 Lee Gardner 1.00 2.50
98 Joakim Soria 1.00 2.50
99 Jason Miller 1.00 2.50
100 Hideki Okajima 5.00 12.00
101 John Danks 1.50 4.00
102 Garrett Jones 2.50 6.00
103 Jensen Lewis 1.00 2.50
104 Clay Rapada 1.00 2.50
105 Kyle Kendrick 2.50 6.00
106 Eric Stults 1.00 2.50
110 Micah Owings 1.00 2.50
113 Mike Schultz 1.00 2.50
115 Matt Chico 1.00 2.50
120 Yovani Gallardo 2.50 6.00
125 Andrew Miller 2.50 6.00

2007 Topps 52 Chrome

STATED ODDS 1:3 H, 1:6 R
STATED PRINT RUN 1952 SER.#'d SETS
1 Akinori Iwamura 1.50 4.00
2 Angel Sanchez .60 1.50
3 Luis Hernandez .60 1.50
4 Troy Tulowitzki 4.00 10.00
5 Joaquin Arias .60 1.50
6 Jesus Flores .60 1.50
7 Brandon Wood .60 1.50
8 Kory Casto .60 1.50
9 Kevin Kouzmanoff .60 1.50
10 Tony Abreu 1.50 4.00
11 Travis Buck .60 1.50
12 Kurt Suzuki .60 1.50
13 Alejandro De Aza .60 1.50
14 Alex Gordon 2.00 5.00
15 Jerry Owens .60 1.50
16 Ryan J. Braun 3.00 8.00
17 Michael Bourn .60 1.50
18 Hunter Pence 3.00 8.00
19 Jeff Baker .60 1.50
20 Ben Francisco .60 1.50
21 Nate Schierholtz .60 1.50
22 Nathan Haynes .60 1.50
23 Andrew Miller 1.50 4.00
24 Sean Barker .60 1.50
25 Matt DeSalvo .60 1.50
26 Fred Lewis 1.00 2.50
27 Jamie Burke .60 1.50
28 Jeff Salazar .60 1.50
29 Chase Headley .60 1.50
30 Chris Basak .60 1.50
31 Mike Fontenot .60 1.50
32 Felix Pie .60 1.50
33 Masumi Kuwata .60 1.50
34 Daisuke Matsuzaka 2.50 6.00
35 Tim Lincecum 10.00 25.00
36 Jarrod Saltalamacchia 1.00 2.50
37 Tyler Clippard 1.00 2.50
38 Billy Butler 1.00 2.50
39 Matt Lindstrom .60 1.50
40 Brett Carroll .60 1.50
41 Alexi Casilla 1.00 2.50
42 Nick Gorneault .60 1.50
43 Matt Chico .60 1.50
44 Adam Lind .60 1.50
45 Miguel Montero .60 1.50
46 Danny Putnam .60 1.50
47 Delmon Young 1.00 2.50
48 Josh Fields .60 1.50
49 Carlos Gomez 1.00 2.50
50 Mark Reynolds 5.00 12.00
51 Shane Youman .60 1.50
52 Andy LaRoche .60 1.50
53 Kei Igawa 1.50 4.00
54 Don Kelly .60 1.50
55 Cameron Maybin 1.00 2.50
56 Travis Metcalf 1.00 2.50
57 Ubaldo Jimenez 4.00 10.00
58 Ryan Sweeney .60 1.50
59 Shawn Riggans .60 1.50
60 Jacoby Ellsbury 5.00 12.00
61 Andy Cavazos .60 1.50
62 Josh Hamilton 2.50 6.00
63 Homer Bailey 1.00 2.50
64 Sean Henn .60 1.50
65 Elijah Dukes 1.00 2.50
66 Brian Esposito .60 1.50
67 Brandon Morrow 3.00 8.00
68 Joe Smith .60 1.50
69 Chris Stewart .60 1.50
70 Eulogio De La Cruz 1.00 2.50
71 Sean Gallagher .60 1.50
72 Jailen Peguero .60 1.50
73 Juan Perez .60 1.50
74 Levale Speigner .60 1.50
75 Jamie Vermilyea .60 1.50
76 Hideki Okajima 3.00 8.00
77 Eric Patterson .60 1.50
78 Zack Segovia .60 1.50
79 Kyle Kendrick 1.50 4.00
80 Andy Sonnanstine .60 1.50
81 Chase Wright 1.50 4.00
82 Jon Knott .60 1.50
83 Guillermo Rodriguez .60 1.50
84 Jon Coutlangus .60 1.50
85 Kevin Cameron .60 1.50
86 Brian Stokes .60 1.50
87 Alberto Arias .60 1.50
88 Delwyn Young .60 1.50
89 David Murphy .60 1.50
90 Micah Owings .60 1.50
91 Yovani Gallardo 1.50 4.00
92 Justin Hampson .60 1.50
93 Doug Slaten .60 1.50
94 Justin Upton 5.00 12.00
95 Joba Chamberlain 3.00 8.00

2007 Topps 52 Chrome Refractors

*CHR.REF: .75X TO 2X BASIC CHROME
STATED ODDS 1:9 H, 1:25 R
STATED PRINT RUN 552 SER.#'d SETS

2007 Topps 52 Chrome Gold Refractors

STATED ODDS 1:89 H, 1:300 R
STATED PRINT RUN 52 SER.#'d SETS
1 Akinori Iwamura 10.00 25.00
2 Angel Sanchez 4.00 10.00
3 Luis Hernandez 4.00 10.00
4 Troy Tulowitzki 25.00 60.00
5 Joaquin Arias 4.00 10.00
6 Jesus Flores 4.00 10.00
7 Brandon Wood 4.00 10.00

8 Kory Casto 4.00 10.00
9 Kevin Kouzmanoff 4.00 10.00
10 Tony Abreu 10.00 25.00
11 Travis Buck 4.00 10.00
12 Kurt Suzuki 4.00 10.00
13 Alejandro De Aza 6.00 15.00
14 Alex Gordon 12.00 30.00
15 Jerry Owens 4.00 10.00
16 Ryan J. Braun 20.00 50.00
17 Michael Bourn 4.00 10.00
18 Hunter Pence 20.00 50.00
19 Jeff Baker 4.00 10.00
20 Ben Francisco 4.00 10.00
21 Nate Schierholtz 4.00 10.00
22 Nathan Haynes 4.00 10.00
23 Andrew Miller 10.00 25.00
24 Sean Barker 4.00 10.00
25 Matt DeSalvo 4.00 10.00
26 Fred Lewis 6.00 15.00
27 Jamie Burke 4.00 10.00
28 Jeff Salazar 4.00 10.00
29 Chase Headley 4.00 10.00
30 Chris Basak 4.00 10.00
31 Mike Fontenot 4.00 10.00
32 Felix Pie 4.00 10.00
33 Masumi Kuwata 4.00 10.00
34 Daisuke Matsuzaka 15.00 40.00
35 Tim Lincecum 60.00 150.00
36 Jarrod Saltalamacchia 6.00 15.00
37 Tyler Clippard 6.00 15.00
38 Billy Butler 6.00 15.00
39 Matt Lindstrom 4.00 10.00
40 Brett Carroll 4.00 10.00
41 Alexi Casilla 6.00 15.00
42 Nick Gorneault 4.00 10.00
43 Matt Chico 4.00 10.00
44 Adam Lind 4.00 10.00
45 Miguel Montero 4.00 10.00
46 Danny Putnam 4.00 10.00
47 Delmon Young 6.00 15.00
48 Josh Fields 4.00 10.00
49 Carlos Gomez 6.00 15.00
50 Mark Reynolds 30.00 80.00
51 Shane Youman 4.00 10.00
52 Andy LaRoche 4.00 10.00
53 Kei Igawa 10.00 25.00
54 Don Kelly 4.00 10.00
55 Cameron Maybin 6.00 15.00
56 Travis Metcalf 6.00 15.00
57 Ubaldo Jimenez 25.00 60.00
58 Ryan Sweeney 4.00 10.00
59 Shawn Riggans 4.00 10.00
60 Jacoby Ellsbury 30.00 80.00
61 Andy Cavazos 4.00 10.00
62 Josh Hamilton 15.00 40.00
63 Homer Bailey 6.00 15.00
64 Sean Henn 4.00 10.00
65 Elijah Dukes 6.00 15.00
66 Brian Esposito 4.00 10.00
67 Brandon Morrow 20.00 50.00
68 Joe Smith 4.00 10.00
69 Chris Stewart 4.00 10.00
70 Eulogio De La Cruz 6.00 15.00
71 Sean Gallagher 4.00 10.00
72 Jailen Peguero 4.00 10.00
73 Juan Perez 4.00 10.00
74 Levale Speigner 4.00 10.00
75 Jamie Vermilyea 4.00 10.00
76 Hideki Okajima 20.00 50.00
77 Eric Patterson 4.00 10.00
78 Zack Segovia 4.00 10.00
79 Kyle Kendrick 10.00 25.00
80 Andy Sonnanstine 4.00 10.00
81 Chase Wright 10.00 25.00
82 Jon Knott 4.00 10.00
83 Guillermo Rodriguez 4.00 10.00
84 Jon Coutlangus 4.00 10.00
85 Kevin Cameron 4.00 10.00
86 Brian Stokes 4.00 10.00
87 Alberto Arias 4.00 10.00
88 Delwyn Young 4.00 10.00
89 David Murphy 4.00 10.00
90 Micah Owings 4.00 10.00
91 Yovani Gallardo 10.00 25.00
92 Justin Hampson 4.00 10.00
93 Doug Slaten 4.00 10.00
94 Justin Upton 30.00 80.00
95 Joba Chamberlain 20.00 50.00

2007 Topps 52 Debut Flashbacks

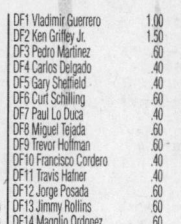

COMPLETE SET (15) 6.00 15.00
STATED ODDS 1:6 H, 1:6 R
COMPLETE CHR.SET (15) 10.00 25.00
*CHROME: .6X TO 1.5X BASIC
CHROME ODDS 1:16 H, 1:46 R
CHR.PRINT RUN 1952 SER.#'d SETS
CHR.REF: 1X TO 2.5X BASIC
CHR.REF ODDS 1:55 H, 1:170 R
CHR.REF PRINT RUN 552 SER.#'d SETS
DF1 Vladimir Guerrero 1.00 2.50
DF2 Ken Griffey Jr. 1.50 4.00
DF3 Pedro Martinez .60 1.50
DF4 Carlos Delgado .40 1.00
DF5 Gary Sheffield .40 1.00
DF6 Curt Schilling .60 1.50
DF7 Paul Lo Duca .40 1.00
DF8 Miguel Tejada .60 1.50
DF9 Trevor Hoffman .60 1.50
DF10 Francisco Cordero .40 1.00
DF11 Travis Hafner .40 1.00
DF12 Jorge Posada .60 1.50
DF13 Jimmy Rollins .60 1.50
DF14 Magglio Ordonez .60 1.50
DF15 Jim Edmonds .60 1.50

2007 Topps 52 Debut Flashbacks Chrome Gold Refractors

*GOLD REF: 3X TO 8X BASIC
STATED ODDS 1:609 H, 1:1700 R
STATED PRINT RUN 52 SER.#'d SETS

2007 Topps 52 Diamond Debut Tix

STATED ODDS 1:649 HOBBY
STATED PRINT RUN 20 SER.#'d SETS
NO PRICING DUE TO SCARCITY

2007 Topps 52 Dynamic Duos

COMPLETE SET (15) 6.00 15.00
STATED ODDS 1:4 H, 1:4 R
DD1 Tim Lincecum 6.00 15.00
Nate Schierholtz
DD2 Joba Chamberlain 2.00 5.00
Phil Hughes
DD3 Ryan Braun 2.00 5.00
Yovani Gallardo
DD4 Kyle Kendrick 1.00 2.50
Michael Bourn
DD5 Delmon Young .60 1.50
Elijah Dukes
DD6 Hideki Okajima 1.50 4.00
Daisuke Matsuzaka
DD7 Justin Upton 3.00 8.00
Mark Reynolds
DD8 Eric Patterson .40 1.00
Felix Pie
DD9 Josh Hamilton 1.50 4.00
Homer Bailey
DD10 Ubaldo Jimenez 2.50 6.00
Troy Tulowitzki
DD11 Alex Gordon 1.25 3.00
Billy Butler
DD12 Delwyn Young .40 1.00
Andy LaRoche
DD13 Andrew Miller .60 1.50
Cameron Maybin
DD14 Joe Smith .60 1.50
Carlos Gomez
DD15 David Murphy .60 1.50
Jarrod Saltalamacchia

2007 Topps 52 Signatures

GROUP A ODDS 1:4750 H, 1:13,401 R
GROUP B ODDS 1:150 H, 1:429 R
GROUP C ODDS 1:3149 H, 1:19,065 R
GROUP D ODDS 1:1049 H, 1:3000 R
GROUP E ODDS 1:54 H, 1:162 R
GROUP F ODDS 1:9 H, 1:29 R
EXCHANGE DEADLINE 11/30/09
AA Alberto Arias F 3.00 8.00
AC Alexi Casilla F 3.00 8.00
AG Alex Gordon B 30.00 60.00
AL Andy LaRoche B 10.00 25.00
AS Angel Sanchez E 3.00 8.00
ASL Aaron Laffey F 6.00 15.00
BB Brian Barden F 3.00 8.00
BC Brett Carroll F 3.00 8.00
BE Brian Esposito F 3.00 8.00
BF Ben Francisco F 3.00 8.00
BP Billy Petrick E 3.00 8.00
BPB Brian Buscher E 3.00 8.00
BW Brian Wolfe E 3.00 8.00
CD Cory Doyne F 3.00 8.00
CH Chase Headley E 5.00 12.00
CM Cameron Maybin B 20.00 50.00
CS Chris Stewart B 3.00 8.00
CW Chase Wright B 8.00 20.00
DC Darren Clarke F 3.00 8.00
ER Edwar Ramirez F 5.00 12.00
FC Francisco Cordero A 50.00 100.00
FL Fred Lewis B 5.00 12.00
FP Felix Pie B 10.00 25.00
GS Gary Sheffield A 20.00 50.00
HO Hideki Okajima B 30.00 60.00
HP Hunter Pence B 20.00 50.00
JA Joaquin Arias B 3.00 8.00
JB Jared Burton B 8.00 20.00
JC Jon Coutlangus B 3.00 8.00
JCH Joba Chamberlain B 150.00 250.00
JH Joel Hanrahan D 10.00 25.00
JJR Jo-Jo Reyes B 3.00 8.00
JL Jensen Lewis F 3.00 8.00
JM Jason Miller D 5.00 12.00
JP Jorge Posada A 60.00 120.00
JR Jimmy Rollins A
JRB Joseph Bisenius F 3.00 8.00
JSS Jarrod Saltalamacchia B 10.00 25.00
JU Justin Upton B 40.00 80.00
KS Kurt Suzuki B 3.00 8.00
LS Levale Speigner F 3.00 8.00
MB Michael Bourn B 10.00 25.00
MBB Matthew Brown F 3.00 8.00
MJZ Mike Zagurski E 3.00 8.00
ML Matt Lindstrom B 6.00 15.00
MM Mark McLemore E 3.00 8.00
NG Nick Gorneault B 6.00 15.00
NH Nathan Haynes F 3.00 8.00
PD Phil Dumatrait E 3.00 8.00
RB Ryan Braun B 50.00 100.00
RC Rocky Cherry C 5.00 12.00
RDB Ryan Budde E 3.00 8.00
RZB Ryan Z. Braun B 3.00 8.00
TB Travis Buck B 5.00 12.00
TL Tim Lincecum B 75.00 150.00
TM Travis Metcalf B 10.00 25.00
TPC Troy Cate F 3.00 8.00
YG Yovani Gallardo B 10.00 25.00
ZS Zack Segovia E 3.00 8.00

2007 Topps 52 Signatures Red Ink

STATED ODDS 1:88 HOBBY
STATED PRINT RUN 52 SER.#'d SETS
EXCH DEADLINE 12/31/08
AA Alberto Arias 10.00 25.00
AC Alexi Casilla 10.00 25.00
AG Alex Gordon 60.00 120.00
AI Akinori Iwamura 30.00 60.00
AL Andy LaRoche 30.00 60.00
AM Andrew Miller 30.00 60.00
AS Angel Sanchez 10.00 25.00
ASL Aaron Laffey 20.00 50.00
BB Brian Barden 10.00 25.00
BC Brett Carroll 10.00 25.00
BE Brian Esposito 10.00 25.00
BF Ben Francisco 10.00 25.00
BP Billy Petrick 10.00 25.00
BPB Brian Buscher 10.00 25.00
BS Brian Stokes 10.00 25.00
BW Brian Wolfe 10.00 25.00
CD Cory Doyne 10.00 25.00
CH Chase Headley 20.00 50.00
CM Cameron Maybin 40.00 80.00
CS Chris Stewart 10.00 25.00
CW Chase Wright 30.00 60.00
DC Darren Clarke 10.00 25.00
ER Edwar Ramirez 15.00 40.00
FC Francisco Cordero 100.00 200.00
FL Fred Lewis 10.00 25.00
FP Felix Pie 20.00 50.00
GS Gary Sheffield 40.00 80.00
HO Hideki Okajima 50.00 100.00
HP Hunter Pence 75.00 150.00
JA Joaquin Arias 10.00 25.00
JB Jared Burton 15.00 40.00
JC Jon Coutlangus 10.00 25.00
JCH Joba Chamberlain 200.00 300.00
JH Joel Hanrahan 20.00 50.00
JJR Jo-Jo Reyes 10.00 25.00
JL Jensen Lewis 10.00 25.00
JM Jason Miller 10.00 25.00
JP Jorge Posada 100.00 200.00
JR Jimmy Rollins
JRB Joseph Bisenius 10.00 25.00
JSS Jarrod Saltalamacchia 20.00 50.00
JU Justin Upton 75.00 150.00
KK Kevin Kouzmanoff 10.00 25.00
KS Kurt Suzuki 20.00 50.00
LS Levale Speigner 10.00 25.00
MB Michael Bourn 30.00 60.00
MBB Matthew Brown 10.00 25.00
MJZ Mike Zagurski 20.00 50.00
ML Matt Lindstrom 15.00 40.00
MM Mark McLemore 10.00 25.00
NG Nick Gorneault 15.00 40.00
NH Nathan Haynes 10.00 25.00
PD Phil Dumatrait 10.00 25.00
PH Phil Hughes 60.00 120.00
PL Paul Lo Duca 20.00 50.00
RB Ryan Braun 100.00 175.00
RC Rocky Cherry 20.00 50.00
RDB Ryan Budde 20.00 50.00
RZB Ryan Braun 15.00 40.00
TB Travis Buck 15.00 40.00
TC Tyler Clippard 30.00 60.00
TL Tim Lincecum 150.00 300.00
TM Travis Metcalf 20.00 50.00
TPC Troy Cate 10.00 25.00
YG Yovani Gallardo 40.00 80.00
ZS Zack Segovia 20.00 50.00

2007 Topps 52 Signatures Combos

STATED ODDS 1:1094 HOBBY
STATED PRINT RUN 25 SER.#'d SETS
NO PRICING DUE TO SCARCITY
EXCHANGE DEADLINE 11/30/09

2006 Topps AFLAC

COMMON CARD 5.00 12.00
EACH PLAYER ISSUED 100 OF OWN CARD
APPX.250 SETS DIST.AT 06 AFLAC GAME
BB Blake Beavan 12.50 30.00
BK Brett Krill 6.00 15.00
CC Christian Colon 5.00 12.00
CR Cameron Rupp 6.00 15.00
DB Drake Britton 5.00 12.00
DD Derek Dietrich 10.00 25.00
DM D.J. LeMahieu 5.00 12.00
DR Danny Rams 5.00 12.00
ED Evan Danieli 6.00 15.00
EG Erik Goeddel 6.00 15.00
FF Freddie Freeman 40.00 80.00
GP Greg Peavey 8.00 20.00
HM Hunter Morris 10.00 25.00
JG Jon Gilmore 8.00 20.00
JH Jason Heyward 90.00 150.00
JL Joe Leftridge 5.00 12.00
JS Josh Smoker 12.50 30.00
JT John Tolisano 8.00 20.00
JV Josh Vitters 12.50 30.00
KB Kyle Blair 5.00 12.00
KK Kevin Keyes 5.00 12.00
MB Madison Bumgarner 30.00 60.00
MH Matt Harvey 8.00 20.00
MM Michael Main 12.50 30.00
NN Nick Noonan 8.00 20.00
NR Neil Ramirez 10.00 25.00
PD Paul Demny 5.00 12.00
RP Rick Porcello 30.00 60.00
RS Robert Stock 12.50 30.00
SB Steven Brooks 6.00 15.00
SS Sequoyah Stonecipher 12.50 30.00
TA Tim Alderson 5.00 12.00
YG Yasmani Grandal 6.00 15.00

2006 Topps AFLAC Promo

BB Blake Beavan 5.00 12.00
BK Brett Krill 3.00 8.00
CC Christian Colon 2.50 6.00
CR Cameron Rupp 3.00 8.00
DB Drake Britton 3.00 8.00
DD Derek Dietrich 5.00 12.00
DM D.J. LeMahieu 2.50 6.00
DR Danny Rams 4.00 10.00
ED Evan Danieli 2.50 6.00
EG Erik Goeddel 3.00 8.00
FF Freddie Freeman 30.00 60.00
GP Greg Peavey 4.00 10.00
HM Hunter Morris 4.00 10.00
JG Jon Gilmore 5.00 12.00
JH Jason Heyward 60.00 120.00
JJ Justin Jackson 5.00 12.00
JL Joe Leftridge 3.00 8.00
JS Josh Smoker 10.00 25.00
JT John Tolisano 4.00 10.00
JV Josh Vitters 20.00 50.00
KB Kyle Blair 2.50 6.00
KD Kentrail Davis 4.00 10.00
KK Kevin Keyes 2.50 6.00
MB Madison Bumgarner 10.00 25.00
MB2 Michael Burgess 10.00 25.00
MH Matt Harvey 6.00 15.00
MM Michael Main 4.00 10.00
NN Nick Noonan 5.00 12.00
NR Neil Ramirez 3.00 8.00
PD Paul Demny 5.00 12.00
RP Rick Porcello 20.00 50.00
RS Robert Stock 6.00 15.00
SB Steven Brooks 2.50 6.00
SR Sam Runion 4.00 10.00
SS Sequoyah Stonecipher 3.00 8.00
TA Tim Alderson 6.00 15.00
TR Tanner Robles 2.50 6.00
YG Yasmani Grandal 8.00 20.00

2007 Topps AFLAC

AB Andy Burns 4.00 10.00
AF Anthony Ferrara 10.00 25.00
AH Aaron Hicks 12.50 30.00
AM Alex Meyer 6.00 15.00
AN Adrian Nieto 6.00 15.00
AW Austin Wright 6.00 15.00
BD Brett DeVall 6.00 15.00
BH B.J. Hermsen 4.00 10.00
BN Billy Nicholson CO 4.00 10.00
BW Brett Warren 6.00 15.00
CA Chris Amezquita 4.00 10.00
CE Cecil Espy CO 4.00 10.00
CM Clark Murphy 4.00 10.00
DH Destin Hood 6.00 15.00
DM Daniel Marrs 4.00 10.00
EM Ethan Martin 10.00 25.00
GC Gerrit Cole 15.00 40.00
GL Garrison Lassiter 4.00 10.00
HM Harold Martinez 6.00 15.00
IG Isaac Galloway 4.00 10.00
JA Jack Armstrong 4.00 10.00
JC Jarred Cosart 12.50 30.00
JS Jordan Swagerty 4.00 10.00
KM Kevin Maris CO 4.00 10.00
KS Kyle Skipworth 15.00 40.00
MH Manny Hermosillo CO 4.00 10.00
MP Michael Palazzone 4.00 10.00
MS Mike Sheppard Jr. CO 6.00 15.00
OM Quinton Miller 10.00 25.00
RO Ricky Oropesa 4.00 10.00
ROS Ryan O'Sullivan 4.00 10.00
SG Sonny Gray 4.00 10.00
SS Scott Silverstein 6.00 15.00
TB Tim Beckham 40.00 80.00
TH Taylor Hightower 4.00 10.00
TM Tim Melville 6.00 15.00
WF Wesley Freeman 4.00 10.00
WK Walker Kelly 10.00 25.00
XA Xavier Avery 6.00 15.00

2003 Topps All-Time Fan Favorites

This 150-card set was released in May, 2003. This set was issued in six card packs with an $3 SRP which came 24 packs to a box and eight boxes to a case. These cards were issued in different styles with photos purporting to be from that era in which the faux card was issued. While most of the photos are close to the era they are supposed to be from, some photos such as the 64 Brooks Robinson design and the 54 Tom Lasorda are obviously not from the correct time period. The Monte Irvin card was issued in equal quantities with or without the facsmile autograph. A set is considered complete with only one of the Irvin cards. A notable card in this set is the first mainstream card of legendary broadcaster Ernie Harwell who was the Tigers announcers for more than 40 years.

COMPLETE SET (150) 20.00 50.00
1 Willie Mays 1.25 3.00
2 Whitey Ford .40 1.00
3 Stan Musial 1.00 2.50
4 Paul Blair .15 .40
5 Harold Reynolds .25 .60
6 Bob Friend .25 .60
7 Rod Carew .40 1.00
8 Kirk Gibson .25 .60
9 Graig Nettles .25 .60
10 Ozzie Smith 1.00 2.50
11 Tony Perez .25 .60
12 Tim Wallach .15 .40
13 Bert Campaneris .25 .60
14 Cory Snyder .15 .40
15 Dave Parker .25 .60
16 Darrell Evans .25 .60
17 Joe Pepitone .25 .60
18 Don Sutton .25 .60
19 Dale Murphy .40 1.00
20 George Brett 1.25 3.00
21 Carlton Fisk .40 1.00
22 Bob Watson .15 .40
23 Wally Joyner .25 .60
24 Paul Molitor .25 .60
25 Keith Hernandez .25 .60
26 Jerry Koosman .25 .60
27 George Bell .25 .60
28 Boog Powell .40 1.00
29 Bruce Sutter .25 .60
30 Ernie Banks .60 1.50
31 Steve Lyons .15 .40
32 Earl Weaver .25 .60
33 Dave Stieb .25 .60
34 Alan Trammell .25 .60
35 Bret Saberhagen .25 .60
36 J.R. Richard .25 .60
37 Mickey Rivers .15 .40
38 Juan Marichal .25 .60
39 Gaylord Perry .25 .60
40 Don Mattingly 1.25 3.00
41 Bob Grich .25 .60
42 Steve Sax .25 .60
43 Sparky Anderson .25 .60
44 Luis Aparicio .25 .60
45 Fergie Jenkins .25 .60
46 Jim Palmer .25 .60
47 Howard Johnson .25 .60
48 Dwight Evans .40 1.00
49 Bill Buckner .25 .60
50 Cal Ripken 2.00 5.00
51 Jose Cruz .25 .60
52 Tony Oliva .25 .60
53 Bobby Richardson .25 .60
54 Luis Tiant .25 .60
55 Warren Spahn .40 1.00
56 Phil Rizzuto .40 1.00
57 Eric Davis .25 .60
58 Vida Blue .25 .60
59 Steve Balboni .15 .40
60 Mike Schmidt 1.25 3.00
61 Ken Griffey Sr. .25 .60
62 Jim Abbott .40 1.00
63 Whitey Herzog .25 .60
64 Rich Gossage .25 .60
65 Tony Armas .25 .60
66 Bill Skowron .40 1.00
67 Don Newcombe .25 .60
68 Bill Madlock .25 .60
69 Lance Parrish .25 .60
70 Reggie Jackson .40 1.00
71 Willie Wilson .25 .60
72 Terry Pendleton .25 .60
73 Jim Piersall .25 .60
74 George Foster .25 .60
75 Bob Horner .25 .60
76 Chris Sabo .25 .60
77 Fred Lynn .25 .60
78 Jim Rice .25 .60
79 Maury Wills .25 .60
80 Yogi Berra .60 1.50
81 Johnny Sain .40 1.00
82 Tom Lasorda .25 .60
83 Bill Mazeroski .40 1.00
84 John Kruk .25 .60
85 Bob Feller .25 .60
86 Frank Robinson .40 1.00
87 Red Schoendienst .25 .60
88 Gary Carter .25 .60
89 Andre Dawson .25 .60
90 Tim McCarver .25 .60
91 Robin Yount .60 1.50
92 Phil Niekro .25 .60
93 Joe Morgan .25 .60
94 Darren Daulton .25 .60
95 Bobby Thomson .25 .60
96 Alvin Davis .15 .40
97 Robin Roberts .40 1.00
98 Kirby Puckett .60 1.50
99 Jack Clark .25 .60
100 Hank Aaron 1.25 3.00
101 Orlando Cepeda .25 .60
102 Vern Law .25 .60
103 Cecil Cooper .25 .60
104 Don Larsen .25 .60
105 Mario Mendoza .15 .40
106 Tony Gwynn .75 2.00
107 Ernie Harwell .25 .60
108A Monte Irvin .25 .60
108B Monte Irvin NO AU ERR .25 .60
109 Tommy John .25 .60
110 Rollie Fingers .25 .60
111 Johnny Podres .25 .60
112 Jeff Reardon .25 .60
113 Buddy Bell .25 .60
114 Dwight Gooden .25 .60
115 Garry Templeton .25 .60
116 Johnny Bench .60 1.50
117 Joe Rudi .25 .60
118 Ron Guidry .25 .60
119 Vince Coleman .25 .60
120 Al Kaline .60 1.50
121 Carl Yastrzemski 1.00 2.50
122 Hank Bauer .25 .60
123 Mark Fidrych .25 .60
124 Paul O'Neill .40 1.00
125 Ron Cey .25 .60
126 Willie McGee .25 .60
127 Harmon Killebrew .60 1.50
128 Dave Concepcion .25 .60
129 Harold Baines .25 .60
130 Lou Brock .40 1.00
131 Lee Smith .25 .60
132 Willie McCovey .25 .60
133 Steve Garvey .25 .60
134 Kent Tekulve .25 .60
135 Tom Seaver .40 1.00
136 Bo Jackson .60 1.50
137 Walt Weiss .15 .40
138 Brook Jacoby .15 .40
139 Dennis Eckersley .25 .60
140 Duke Snider .40 1.00
141 Lenny Dykstra .25 .60
142 Greg Luzinski .25 .60
143 Jim Bunning .25 .60
144 Jose Canseco .40 1.00
145 Ron Santo .40 1.00
146 Bert Blyleven .25 .60
147 Wade Boggs .40 1.00
148 Brooks Robinson .40 1.00
149 Ray Knight .25 .60
150 Nolan Ryan 1.50 4.00

2003 Topps All-Time Fan Favorites Chrome Refractors

Inserted at a stated rate of one in 18, this is a parallel to the basic set. These cards were produced using the Topps Chrome technology and were issued to a stated print run of 299 serial numbered sets.

*CHROME REF: 3X TO 8X BASIC

2003 Topps All-Time Fan Favorites Archives Autographs

This 165-card set was issued at different odds depending on what group the player belonged to. Please note that exchange cards with a redemption deadline of April 30th, 2005, were seeded into packs for the following players: Dave Concepcion, Bob Feller, Tug McGraw, Paul O'Neill and Kirby Puckett. In addition, exchange cards were produced for a small percentage of Eric Davis cards (though the bulk of his real autographs did make pack out).

GROUP A STATED ODDS 1:218
GROUP B STATED ODDS 1:759
GROUP C STATED ODDS 1:116
GROUP D STATED ODDS 1:45
GROUP E STATED ODDS 1:87
GROUP F STATED ODDS 1:1028
GROUP G STATED ODDS 1:838
GROUP H STATED ODDS 1:818
GROUP I STATED ODDS 1:796
GROUP J STATED ODDS 1:111
GROUP K STATED ODDS 1:759
GROUP L STATED ODDS 1:744
AD Alvin Davis D 4.00 10.00
ADA Andre Dawson A 40.00 80.00
AK Al Kaline A 75.00 150.00
AO Al Oliver D 6.00 15.00
AT Alan Trammell C 15.00 40.00
BB Bert Blyleven D 12.50 30.00
BBE Buddy Bell C 6.00 15.00
BBI Buddy Biancalana D 4.00 10.00
BBU Bill Buckner C 6.00 15.00
BC Bert Campaneris E 4.00 10.00
BF Bob Feller C 12.50 30.00
BFR Bob Friend D 12.50 30.00
BGR Bob Grich D 4.00 10.00
BH Bob Horner J 6.00 15.00
BJ Bo Jackson A 40.00 80.00
BJA Brook Jacoby E 4.00 10.00
BL Bill Lee D 4.00 10.00
BMA Bill Madlock D 4.00 10.00
BMZ Bill Mazeroski A 50.00 100.00
BP Boog Powell D 6.00 15.00
BRO Brooks Robinson A 50.00 100.00
BS Bill Skowron D 6.00 15.00
BSA Bret Saberhagen A 20.00 50.00
BSU Bruce Sutter C 10.00 25.00
BT Bobby Thomson A 40.00 80.00
BW Bob Watson C 6.00 15.00
CC Cecil Cooper E 4.00 10.00
CF Carlton Fisk A 50.00 100.00
CL Carney Lansford C 6.00 15.00
CLE Chet Lemon D 4.00 10.00
CN Cory Snyder C 6.00 15.00
CR Cal Ripken A 175.00 300.00
CS Chris Sabo H 12.50 30.00
CSP Chris Speier C 10.00 25.00
CY Carl Yastrzemski A 100.00 200.00
DC Dave Concepcion A 40.00 80.00
DD Darren Daulton C 6.00 15.00
DDE Doug DeCinces C 6.00 15.00
DE Darrell Evans D 4.00 10.00
DEC Dennis Eckersley A 40.00 80.00
DEV Dwight Evans A 50.00 100.00
DG Dwight Gooden A 40.00 80.00
DL Don Larsen D 6.00 15.00
DM Dale Murphy A 50.00 100.00
DN Don Newcombe A 40.00 80.00
DON Don Mattingly A 75.00 150.00
DP Dave Parker A 40.00 80.00
DS Dave Stieb C 10.00 25.00
DSN Duke Snider A 50.00 100.00
DSU Don Sutton A 40.00 80.00
EB Ernie Banks A 75.00 150.00
ED Eric Davis I 6.00 15.00
EH Ernie Harwell C 50.00 100.00
EW Earl Weaver D 10.00 25.00
FJ Fergie Jenkins C 6.00 15.00
FL Fred Lynn A 30.00 60.00
FR Frank Robinson A 50.00 100.00
GB George Bell D 4.00 10.00
GBR George Brett A 175.00 300.00
GC Gary Carter A 60.00 120.00
GF George Foster D 6.00 15.00
GL Greg Luzinski C 6.00 15.00
GN Graig Nettles D 6.00 15.00
GP Gaylord Perry B 10.00 25.00
GT Garry Templeton C 6.00 15.00
HA Hank Aaron A 175.00 300.00
HB Hank Bauer A 40.00 80.00
HBA Harold Baines C 6.00 15.00
HJ Howard Johnson K 4.00 10.00
HK Harmon Killebrew A 100.00 200.00
HR Harold Reynolds A 40.00 80.00
JA Jim Abbott D 6.00 15.00
JB Jim Bunning A 75.00 150.00
JBE Johnny Bench A 75.00 150.00
JC Jack Clark B 10.00 25.00
JCA Joe Carter A 40.00 80.00
JCR Jose Cruz D 4.00 10.00
JK Jerry Koosman F 10.00 25.00
JKR John Kruk A 50.00 100.00
JM Joe Morgan A 40.00 80.00
JMA Juan Marichal A 50.00 100.00
JMO John Montefusco D 4.00 10.00
JOS Jose Canseco A 50.00 100.00
JP Jim Palmer A 50.00 100.00
JPE Joe Pepitone E 4.00 10.00
JR J.R. Richard E 4.00 10.00
JRE Jeff Reardon D 4.00 10.00
JRI Jim Rice A 40.00 80.00
JRU Joe Rudi E 4.00 10.00
KG Ken Griffey Sr. A 40.00 80.00
KGI Kirk Gibson A 40.00 80.00
KH Keith Hernandez A 40.00 80.00
KM Kevin Mitchell L 4.00 10.00
KP Kirby Puckett A 60.00 120.00
KS Kevin Seitzer D 4.00 10.00
KT Kent Tekulve C 10.00 25.00
LA Luis Aparicio D 10.00 25.00
LB Lou Brock A 50.00 100.00
LD Lenny Dykstra G 6.00 15.00
LDU Leon Durham D 4.00 10.00
LP Lance Parrish D 6.00 15.00
LS Lee Smith J 6.00 15.00
LT Luis Tiant A 40.00 80.00
MCG Willie McGee A 50.00 100.00
MF Mark Fidrych J 10.00 25.00
MI Monte Irvin A 40.00 80.00
MM Mario Mendoza E 4.00 10.00
MP Mike Pagliarulo E 4.00 10.00
MR Mickey Rivers E 4.00 10.00
MS Mike Schmidt A 150.00 250.00
MW Maury Wills E 6.00 15.00
NR Nolan Ryan A 175.00 300.00
OC Orlando Cepeda A 50.00 100.00
OS Ozzie Smith A 75.00 150.00
PB Paul Blair J 6.00 15.00
PM Paul Molitor A 40.00 80.00
PN Phil Niekro A 40.00 80.00
PO Paul O'Neill A 50.00 100.00
PR Phil Rizzuto A 50.00 100.00
RCA Rod Carew A 50.00 100.00
RCE Ron Cey D 4.00 10.00
RD Rob Dibble C 6.00 15.00
RDA Ron Darling C 6.00 15.00
RF Rollie Fingers A 40.00 80.00
RG Rich Gossage A 40.00 80.00
RGU Ron Guidry C 6.00 15.00
RJ Reggie Jackson A 75.00 150.00
RK Ralph Kiner A 50.00 100.00
RKI Ron Kittle D 4.00 10.00
RR Robin Roberts B 10.00 25.00
RS Red Schoendienst C 6.00 15.00
RSA Ron Santo D 12.50 30.00
RY Ray Knight J 4.00 10.00
RYO Robin Yount A 75.00 150.00
SA Sparky Anderson A 40.00 80.00
SB Steve Balboni E 4.00 10.00
SG Steve Garvey B 10.00 25.00
SL Steve Lyons C 6.00 15.00
SM Stan Musial A 100.00 200.00
SS Steve Sax D 4.00 10.00
SY Steve Yeager E 4.00 10.00
TA Tony Armas D 4.00 10.00
TG Tony Gwynn A 75.00 150.00
TH Tom Herr D 4.00 10.00
TJ Tommy John B 6.00 15.00
TL Tom Lasorda A 40.00 80.00
TM Tim McCarver A 40.00 80.00
TMC Tug McGraw D 10.00 25.00
TP Terry Pendleton B 6.00 15.00
TPE Tony Perez A 50.00 100.00
TSE Tom Seaver A 75.00 150.00
TW Tim Wallach E 4.00 10.00
VB Vida Blue C 6.00 15.00
VC Vince Coleman J 4.00 10.00
WB Wade Boggs A 50.00 100.00
WF Whitey Ford A 75.00 150.00
WH Whitey Herzog C 10.00 25.00
WHE Willie Hernandez D 4.00 10.00
WJ Wally Joyner J 4.00 10.00
WM Willie Mays A 175.00 300.00
WMC Willie McCovey A 50.00 100.00
WS Warren Spahn D 15.00 40.00
WW Walt Weiss D 4.00 10.00
WWI Willie Wilson A 40.00 80.00
YB Yogi Berra A 75.00 150.00

2003 Topps All-Time Fan Favorites Best Seat in the House Relics

Inserted at a stated rate of one in 13 special relic packs, these five cards feature a group of stars from a team along with a piece of a set from a now retired ballpark.

BS1 Brooks Robinson 10.00 25.00
Frank Robinson
Jim Palmer
BS2 Bob Grich 10.00 25.00
Rod Carew
Wally Joyner
BS3 Dave Parker 10.00 25.00
Kent Tekulve
Willie Stargell
Phil Garner
BS4 Paul Molitor 10.00 25.00
Robin Yount
Rollie Fingers
BS5 Bob Horner 10.00 25.00
Dale Murphy
Phil Niekro

2003 Topps All-Time Fan Favorites Relics

Issued one per special "relic" box-topper pack, these 43 cards feature players from the basic set along with a game-used memorabilia piece.

ADA Andre Dawson Bat 4.00 10.00
AT Alan Trammell Bat 4.00 10.00
BFR Bob Friend Jsy 4.00 10.00
BH Bob Horner Bat 4.00 10.00
BJ Bo Jackson Bat 10.00 25.00
BR Bobby Richardson Bat 6.00 15.00
CF Curt Flood Bat 4.00 10.00
CS Chris Sabo Bat 4.00 10.00
DEC Dennis Eckersley Uni 4.00 10.00
DM Dale Murphy Bat 6.00 15.00
DON Don Mattingly Bat 12.50 30.00
DP Dave Parker Bat 4.00 10.00
FL Fred Lynn Bat 4.00 10.00
GBR George Brett Uni 12.50 30.00
GC Gary Carter Bat 4.00 10.00
GF George Foster Bat 4.00 10.00
GL Greg Luzinski Bat 4.00 10.00
HBA Harold Baines Bat 6.00 15.00
HR Harold Reynolds Bat 4.00 10.00
JCR Jose Cruz Bat 4.00 10.00
JM Joe Morgan Bat 4.00 10.00
JOS Jose Canseco Bat 6.00 15.00
JRI Jim Rice Bat 4.00 10.00
JRU Joe Rudi Bat 4.00 10.00
KGI Kirk Gibson Bat 4.00 10.00
KH Keith Hernandez Bat 4.00 10.00
KM Kevin Mitchell Bat 4.00 10.00
KP Kirby Puckett Bat 10.00 25.00
LD Lenny Dykstra Bat 4.00 10.00
LP Lance Parrish Bat 6.00 15.00
MCG Willie McGee Bat 6.00 15.00
MS Mike Schmidt Bat 12.50 30.00
MW Maury Wills Bat 4.00 10.00
NC Norm Cash Jsy 20.00 50.00
PO Paul O'Neill Bat 6.00 15.00
RCA Rod Carew Bat 6.00 15.00
RDA Ron Darling Jsy 4.00 10.00
SG Steve Garvey Bat 4.00 10.00
TMC Tug McGraw Jsy 4.00 10.00
VC Vince Coleman Bat 4.00 10.00
WHE Willie Hernandez Jsy 4.00 10.00
WJ Wally Joyner Bat 4.00 10.00
WS Willie Stargell Bat 6.00 15.00

2004 Topps All-Time Fan Favorites

This 150-card set was released in June, 2004. This set was issued in six card packs with an $5 SRP which came 24 packs to a box and 10 boxes to a case. This set has several noticable 1st cards including former commissioners Peter Ueberroth and Fay Vincent, long-time umpire Eric Gregg and long time Yankee Stadium public address announcer legend Bob Shepard.

COMPLETE SET (150) 20.00 50.00
1 Willie Mays 1.50 4.00
2 Bob Gibson .50 1.25
3 Dave Stieb .30 .75
4 Tim McCarver .30 .75
5 Reggie Jackson .50 1.25
6 John Candelaria .30 .75
7 Lenny Dykstra .30 .75
8 Tony Oliva .30 .75
9 Frank Viola .30 .75
10 Don Mattingly 1.50 4.00
11 Garry Maddox .30 .75
12 Randy Jones .30 .75
13 Joe Carter .30 .75
14 Orlando Cepeda .30 .75
15 Bob Sheppard ANC .50 1.25
16 Bobby Grich .30 .75
17 George Scott .30 .75
18 Mickey Rivers .30 .75
19 Ron Santo .50 1.25
20 Mike Schmidt 1.25 3.00
21 Luis Aparicio .30 .75
22 Cesar Geronimo .30 .75
23 Jack Morris .30 .75
24 Jeffrey Loria OWNER .30 .75
25 George Brett 1.50 4.00
26 Paul O'Neill .50 1.25
27 Reggie Smith .30 .75
28 Robin Yount .75 2.00
29 Andre Dawson .50 1.25
30 Whitey Ford .50 1.25
31 Ralph Kiner .50 1.25
32 Will Clark .50 1.25
33 Keith Hernandez .30 .75
34 Tony Fernandez .30 .75
35 Willie McGee .30 .75
36 Harmon Killebrew .75 2.00
37 Dave Kingman .30 .75
38 Kirk Gibson .30 .75
39 Terry Steinbach .30 .75
40 Frank Robinson .50 1.25
41 Chet Lemon .30 .75
42 Mike Cuellar .30 .75
43 Darrell Evans .30 .75
44 Don Kessinger .30 .75
45 Dave Concepcion .30 .75
46 Sparky Anderson .30 .75
47 Bret Saberhagen .30 .75
48 Brett Butler .30 .75
49 Kent Hrbek .30 .75
50 Hank Aaron 1.50 4.00
51 Rudolph Giuliani .75 2.00
52 Clete Boyer .30 .75
53 Mookie Wilson .30 .75
54 Dave Stewart .30 .75
55 Gary Matthews Sr. .30 .75
56 Roy Face .30 .75
57 Vida Blue .30 .75
58 Jimmy Key .30 .75
59 Al Hrabosky .30 .75
60 Al Kaline .75 2.00
61 Mike Scott .30 .75
62 Jack McDowell .30 .75
63 Reggie Jackson .50 1.25
64 Earl Weaver .30 .75
65 Ernie Harwell ANC .50 1.25
66 David Justice .30 .75
67 Wilbur Wood .30 .75
68 Mike Boddicker .30 .75
69 Don Zimmer .30 .75
70 Jim Palmer .30 .75
71 Doug DeCinces .30 .75
72 Ryne Sandberg 1.50 4.00
73 Don Newcombe .30 .75
74 Denny Martinez .30 .75
75 Carl Yastrzemski .75 2.00
76 Bake McBride .30 .75
77 Andy Van Slyke .30 .75
78 Bruce Sutter .30 .75
79 Bobby Valentine .30 .75
80 Johnny Bench .75 2.00
81 Orel Hershiser .30 .75
82 Cecil Fielder .30 .75
83 Lou Whitaker .30 .75
84 Alan Trammell .30 .75
85 Sam McDowell .30 .75
86 Ray Knight .30 .75
87 Gregg Jefferies .30 .75
88 Ben Oglivie .30 .75
89 Billy Beane .30 .75
90 Yogi Berra .75 2.00
91 Jose Canseco .50 1.25
92 Bobby Bonilla .30 .75
93 Darren Daulton .30 .75
94 Harold Reynolds .30 .75
95 Lou Brock .50 1.25
96 Pete Incaviglia .30 .75
97 Eric Gregg UMP .30 .75
98 Devon White .30 .75
99 Kelly Gruber .30 .75
100 Nolan Ryan 2.50 6.00
101 Carlton Fisk .50 1.25
102 George Foster .30 .75
103 Dennis Eckersley .30 .75
104 Rick Sutcliffe .30 .75
105 Cal Ripken 3.00 8.00
106 Norm Cash .30 .75
107 Charlie Hough .30 .75
108 Paul Molitor .75 2.00
109 Maury Wills .30 .75
110 Tom Seaver .50 1.25
111 Brooks Robinson .50 1.25
112 Jim Rice .50 1.25
113 Dwight Gooden .30 .75
114 Harold Baines .30 .75
115 Tim Raines .30 .75
116 Roy Smalley .30 .75
117 Richie Allen .30 .75
118 Ron Swoboda .30 .75
119 Ron Guidry .30 .75
120 Duke Snider .50 1.25
121 Ferguson Jenkins .30 .75
122 Mark Fidrych UER .30 .75
Posing as a lefty
123 Buddy Bell .30 .75
124 Bo Jackson .75 2.00
125 Stan Musial 1.25 3.00
126 Jesse Barfield .30 .75
127 Tony Gwynn .75 2.00
128 Phil Garner .30 .75
129 Dale Murphy .50 1.25
130 Wade Boggs .50 1.25
131 Sid Fernandez .30 .75
132 Monte Irvin .30 .75
133 Peter Ueberroth COM .30 .75
134 Gary Gaetti .30 .75
135 Gorman Thomas .30 .75
136 Dave Lopes .30 .75
137 Sy Berger .30 .75
138 Buck O'Neil UER .30 .75
Wrong birth year on back
139 Herb Score .30 .75
140 Rod Carew .50 1.25
141 Joe Buck ANC .50 1.25
142 Willie Horton .30 .75
143 Hal McRae .30 .75
144 Rollie Fingers .30 .75
145 Tom Brunansky .30 .75
146 Fay Vincent COM .30 .75
147 Gary Carter .30 .75
148 Bobby Richardson .30 .75
149 Steve Garvey .30 .75
150 Don Larsen .30 .75

2004 Topps All-Time Fan Favorites Refractors

*REFRACTORS: 3X TO 8X BASIC
STATED ODDS 1:19
STATED PRINT RUN 299 SERIAL #'d SETS

2004 Topps All-Time Fan Favorites Autographs

A few players did not return their autograph in time for inclusion in packs and those autographs could be redeemed until May 31, 2006. Please note, Topps was unable to fulfill the Richie Allen exchange card with the promised player and sent out a selection of 2004 Topps World Series Heroes Autographs including Whitey Ford and Duke Snider in their place.

GROUP A ODDS 1:69,360
GROUP B ODDS 1:648
GROUP C ODDS 1:102
GROUP D ODDS 1:5662
GROUP E ODDS 1:181
GROUP F ODDS 1:208
GROUP G ODDS 1:509
GROUP H ODDS 1:356
GROUP I ODDS 1:58
GROUP J ODDS 1:148
GROUP K ODDS 1:128
GROUP L ODDS 1:135
GROUP M ODDS 1:104
GROUP N ODDS 1:228
OVERALL AUTO ODDS 1:12
GROUP A PRINT RUN 10 CARDS
GROUP B PRINT RUN 50 SETS
GROUP C PRINT RUN 100 SETS
GROUP D PRINT RUN 150 CARDS
CARDS ARE NOT SERIAL-NUMBERED
PRINT RUNS PROVIDED BY TOPPS
NO GROUP A PRICING DUE TO SCARCITY
R.ALLEN EXCH UNABLE TO BE FULFILLED
04 WS HL AU'S REPLACE ALLEN EXCH
AD Andre Dawson C 15.00 40.00
AH Al Hrabosky L 4.00 10.00
AK Al Kaline B 60.00 120.00
AT Alan Trammell C 15.00 40.00
AV Andy Van Slyke C 30.00 60.00
BB Billy Beane C 40.00 80.00
BBE Buddy Bell N 4.00 10.00
BG Bob Gibson C 30.00 60.00
BGR Bobby Grich I 4.00 10.00
BJ Bo Jackson B 60.00 120.00
BO Ben Oglivie I 4.00 10.00
BON Buck O'Neil K 50.00 100.00
BR Bobby Richardson F 10.00 25.00
BRO Brooks Robinson B 30.00 60.00
BSA Bret Saberhagen C 15.00 40.00
BSU Bruce Sutter F 12.50 30.00
BV Bobby Valentine C 15.00 40.00
CF Carlton Fisk B 40.00 80.00
CG Cesar Geronimo C 15.00 40.00
CH Charlie Hough G 6.00 15.00
CL Chet Lemon M 4.00 10.00
CR Cal Ripken B 175.00 300.00
CY Carl Yastrzemski B 75.00 150.00
DC Dave Concepcion C 15.00 40.00
DD Darren Daulton L 4.00 10.00
DDE Doug DeCinces E 6.00 15.00
DE Darrell Evans I 4.00 10.00
DEC Dennis Eckersley C 20.00 50.00
DG Dwight Gooden B 20.00 50.00
DJ David Justice E 10.00 25.00
DK Dave Kingman E 15.00 40.00
DKE Don Kessinger M 6.00 15.00
DL Dave Lopes M 4.00 10.00
DLA Don Larsen C 10.00 25.00
DM Dale Murphy B 40.00 80.00
DON Don Mattingly B 75.00 150.00
DS Dave Stewart H 4.00 10.00
DSN Duke Snider C 30.00 60.00
DST Dave Stieb J 4.00 10.00
DZ Don Zimmer I 10.00 25.00
EG Eric Gregg I 6.00 15.00
EH Ernie Harwell E 20.00 50.00
EW Earl Weaver M 6.00 15.00
FJ Ferguson Jenkins F 10.00 25.00
FR Frank Robinson C 30.00 60.00
FVI Fay Vincent C 30.00 60.00
FVI1 Frank Viola I 6.00 15.00
GB George Brett B 125.00 200.00
GC Gary Carter B 20.00 50.00
GF George Foster I 8.00 20.00
GMA Gary Matthews Sr. J 4.00 10.00
GS George Scott K 8.00 20.00
HA Hank Aaron B 175.00 300.00
HB Harold Baines C 15.00 40.00
HK Harmon Killebrew C 60.00 120.00
HR Harold Reynolds C 10.00 25.00
JB Jesse Barfield J 4.00 10.00
JB1 Joe Buck C 15.00 40.00
JBE Johnny Bench C 60.00 120.00
JC Joe Carter C 15.00 40.00
JCA Jose Canseco C 30.00 60.00
JKE Jimmy Key C 10.00 25.00
JM Jack McDowell K 4.00 10.00
JMO Jack Morris K 4.00 10.00
JP Jim Palmer B 40.00 80.00
JR Jim Rice C 15.00 40.00
KG Kirk Gibson B 20.00 50.00
KH Keith Hernandez B 20.00 50.00
LA Luis Aparicio C 15.00 40.00
LB Lou Brock C 30.00 60.00
LD Lenny Dykstra C 10.00 25.00
MB Mike Boddicker J 4.00 10.00
MF Mark Fidrych C 30.00 60.00
MI Monte Irvin C 12.50 30.00
MR Mickey Rivers M 4.00 10.00
MS Mike Schmidt B
MSC Mike Scott M 4.00 10.00
MW Maury Wills I 4.00 10.00
MWI Mookie Wilson L 4.00 10.00
NR Nolan Ryan D 90.00 150.00
OC Orlando Cepeda C 30.00 60.00
OH Orel Hershiser E 15.00 40.00
PI Pete Incaviglia E 6.00 15.00
PM Paul Molitor B 20.00 50.00
PO Paul O'Neill B 40.00 80.00
PU Peter Ueberroth C 60.00 120.00
RC Rod Carew C 30.00 60.00
RF Rollie Fingers C 15.00 40.00
RG Ron Guidry C 15.00 40.00
RJO Randy Jones L 4.00 10.00
RJ2 Reggie Jackson C 50.00 100.00
RK Ralph Kiner G 15.00 40.00
RKN Ray Knight C 10.00 25.00
RS Ron Santo I 20.00 50.00
RSU Rick Sutcliffe C 30.00 60.00
RSW Ron Swoboda N 6.00 15.00
RY Robin Yount B 75.00 150.00
RYN Ryne Sandberg C 75.00 150.00
SA Sparky Anderson C 15.00 40.00
SB Sy Berger H 15.00 40.00
SF Sid Fernandez C 10.00 25.00
SG Steve Garvey C 15.00 40.00
SM Stan Musial C 75.00 150.00
SM1 Sam McDowell C 15.00 40.00
TB Tom Brunansky F 10.00 25.00
TF Tony Fernandez F 4.00 10.00
TG Tony Gwynn B 75.00 150.00
TM Tim McCarver E 10.00 25.00
TO Tony Oliva E 15.00 40.00
TR Tim Raines E 4.00 10.00
TSE Tom Seaver B 60.00 120.00
VB Vida Blue F 6.00 15.00
WB Wade Boggs B 40.00 80.00
WF Whitey Ford C 40.00 80.00
WH Willie Horton K 6.00 15.00
WM Willie Mays B
WMC Willie McGee C 15.00 40.00
WW Wilbur Wood I 6.00 15.00
YB Yogi Berra C 50.00 100.00

2004 Topps All-Time Fan Favorites Best Seat in the House Relics

STATED ODDS 1:10 RELIC PACKS
BS1 Tom Seaver 10.00 25.00
George Foster
Johnny Bench
BS2 Frank Robinson 6.00 15.00
Jim Palmer
Brooks Robinson
BS3 Dave Parker 6.00 15.00
Bill Madlock
Bill Mazeroski
BS4 Kent Hrbek 10.00 25.00
Rod Carew
Harmon Killebrew

2004 Topps All-Time Fan Favorites Relics

ONE PER RELIC PACK
BR Brooks Robinson Bat 4.00 10.00
BS Bret Saberhagen Jsy 3.00 8.00
CF Carlton Fisk Bat 4.00 10.00
CY Carl Yastrzemski Bat 10.00 25.00
DE Dennis Eckersley Uni 4.00 10.00
DJ David Justice Bat 3.00 8.00
DP Dave Parker Uni 3.00 8.00
DS Darryl Strawberry Bat 3.00 8.00
EW Earl Weaver Jsy 3.00 8.00
FR Frank Robinson Jsy 3.00 8.00
FRB Frank Robinson Bat 3.00 8.00
GB George Brett Uni 8.00 20.00
GC Gary Carter Jsy 3.00 8.00
GF George Foster Bat 3.00 8.00
GN Graig Nettles Bat 3.00 8.00
HK Harmon Killebrew Jsy 10.00 25.00
HR Harold Reynolds Bat 3.00 8.00
JC Jose Canseco Jsy 4.00 10.00
JCB Jose Canseco Bat 4.00 10.00
JM Joe Morgan Bat 3.00 8.00
JP Jim Palmer Uni 3.00 8.00
JR Jim Rice Jsy 3.00 8.00
KG Kirk Gibson Bat 3.00 8.00
KH Keith Hernandez Bat 3.00 8.00
KP Kirby Puckett Jsy 6.00 15.00
LB Lou Brock Jsy 4.00 10.00
MS Mike Schmidt Bat 8.00 20.00
MW Maury Wills Jsy 3.00 8.00
NR Nolan Ryan Jsy 15.00 40.00
RC Rod Carew Bat 4.00 10.00
RJ Reggie Jackson Bat 4.00 10.00
TP Tony Perez Bat 3.00 8.00
WB Wade Boggs Uni 4.00 10.00
WM Willie Mays Uni 20.00 50.00

2005 Topps All-Time Fan Favorites

This 142-card set was released in June, 2005. The set was issued in six-card hobby and retail packs. The hobby packs had an $5 SRP and came 24 packs to a box and eight boxes to a case. The retail packs had an $3 SRP and also came 24 packs to a box and eight boxes to a case. Please note that the retail boxes had no "memorabilia" cards in them. Sid Bream used three different Bible verses during the course of signing his cards.

COMPLETE SET (142) 20.00 50.00
COMMON CARD (1-142) .25 .60
OVERALL PLATE ODDS 1:1414 HOB/RET
PLATE PRINT RUN 1 SET PER COLOR
BLACK-CYAN-MAGENTA-YELLOW ISSUED
NO PLATE PRICING DUE TO SCARCITY
1 Andy Van Slyke .25 .60
2 Bill Freehan .25 .60
3 Bo Jackson .60 1.50
4 Mark Grace .40 1.00
5 Chuck Knoblauch .25 .60
6 Candy Maldonado .25 .60
7 David Cone .25 .60
8 Don Mattingly 1.25 3.00
9 Darryl Strawberry .25 .60
10 Dick Williams .25 .60
11 Frank Robinson .40 1.00
12 Glenn Hubbard .25 .60
13 Jim Abbott .25 .60
14 Jeff Brantley
15 John Elway UER 1.50 4.00
Back has him drafted by wrong Football team
16 Jim Leyland .25 .60
17 Jesse Orosco .25 .60
18 Joe Pepitone .25 .60
19 J.R. Richard .25 .60
20 Jerome Walton .25 .60
21 Kevin Maas .25 .60
22 Lou Brock .40 1.00
23 Lou Whitaker .25 .60
24 Carl Erskine .25 .60
25 John Candelaria .25 .60
26 Mike Norris .25 .60
27 Nolan Ryan 1.50 4.00
28 Pedro Guerrero .25 .60
29 Roger Craig .25 .60
30 Ron Gant .25 .60
31 Sid Bream .25 .60
32 Sid Fernandez .25 .60
33 Tony LaRussa .40 1.00
34 Tom Seaver .40 1.00
35 Yogi Berra .60 1.50
36 Andre Dawson .40 1.00
37 Al Kaline .60 1.50
38 Brett Butler .25 .60
39 Bob Gibson .40 1.00
40 Bill Mazeroski .40 1.00
41 Matty Alou .25 .60
42 Chet Lemon .25 .60
43 Cal Ripken 2.50 6.00
44 Dusty Baker .25 .60
45 Dwight Gooden .25 .60
46 Dave Winfield .25 .60
47 Ernie Banks .60 1.50
48 Gary Carter .25 .60
49 Howard Johnson .25 .60
50 Mike Schmidt 1.25 3.00
51 Matt Williams .25 .60
52 Ozzie Smith 1.00 2.50
53 Atlee Hammaker .25 .60
54 Cleon Jones .25 .60
55 Dave Johnson .25 .60
56 Denny McLain .25 .60
57 Don Zimmer .25 .60
58 Gregg Jefferies .25 .60
59 Jay Buhner .25 .60
60 Johnny Bench .60 1.50
61 George Brett 1.25 3.00
62 Dale Murphy .25 .60
63 Bob Welch .25 .60
64 Paul O'Neill .40 1.00
65 Mark Lemke .25 .60
66 Kevin McReynolds .25 .60
67 Jesus Alou .25 .60
68 Joe Pignatano .25 .60
69 Jim Lonborg .25 .60
70 Jerry Grote .25 .60
71 Joaquin Andujar .25 .60
72 Gary Gaetti .25 .60
73 Edgar Martinez .40 1.00
74 Ron Darling .25 .60
75 Duke Snider .40 1.00
76 Dave Magadan .25 .60
77 Doug Drabek .25 .60
78 Carl Yastrzemski .75 2.00
79 Mitch Williams .25 .60
80 Marvin Miller PA .25 .60
81 Michael Kay ANC .25 .60
82 Lonnie Smith .25 .60
83 John Wetteland .25 .60
84 Johnny Podres .25 .60
85 Joe Morgan .25 .60
86 Juan Marichal .25 .60
87 Jeffrey Leonard .25 .60
88 Bob Feller .25 .60
89 Brooks Robinson .40 1.00
90 Clem Labine .25 .60
91 Barry Lyons .25 .60
92 Harmon Killebrew .60 1.50
93 Jim Frey .25 .60
94 John Kruk .25 .60
95 Ed Kranepool .25 .60
96 Jose Oquendo .25 .60
97 Johnny Pesky .25 .60
98 John Tudor .25 .60
99 Keith Hernandez .25 .60
100 Monte Irvin .25 .60
101 Marty Barrett .25 .60
102 Oscar Gamble .25 .60
103 Hank Bauer .25 .60
104 Ron Blomberg .25 .60
105 Rod Carew .40 1.00
106 Rick Dempsey .25 .60
107 Walt Jockety GM .25 .60
108 Tom Kelly .25 .60
109 Steve Carlton .25 .60
110 Rick Monday .25 .60
111 Rob Dibble .25 .60
112 Shawon Dunston .25 .60
113 Tony Gwynn .75 2.00
114 Tom Niedenfuer .25 .60
115 Bob Dernier .25 .60
116 Anthony Young .25 .60
117 Reggie Jackson .60 1.50
118 Steve Garvey .25 .60
119 Tim Raines .25 .60
120 Whitey Ford .40 1.00
121 Rafael Santana .25 .60
122 Scott Brosius .25 .60
123 Stan Musial 1.00 2.50
124 Ron Santo .40 1.00
125 Wade Boggs .40 1.00
126 Jose Canseco .40 1.00
127 Brady Anderson .25 .60
128 Vida Blue .25 .60
129 Charlie Hough .25 .60
130 Jim Kaat .25 .60
131 Zane Smith .25 .60
132 Bob Boone .25 .60
133 Travis Fryman .25 .60
134 Harold Baines .25 .60
135 Orlando Cepeda .25 .60
136 Mike Cuellar .25 .60
137 Tito Fuentes .25 .60
138 Daryl Boston .25 .60
139 Jim Leyritz .25 .60
140 Moose Skowron .25 .60
141 Theo Epstein GM .25 .60
142 Barry Bonds 1.25 3.00

2005 Topps All-Time Fan Favorites Refractors

*REF: 2.5X TO 6X BASIC
STATED ODDS 1:19 H, 1:19 R
STATED PRINT RUN 299 SERIAL #'d SETS

2005 Topps All-Time Fan Favorites Refractors Gold

STATED ODDS 1:225 H, 1:225 R
STATED PRINT RUN 25 SERIAL #'d SETS
NO PRICING DUE TO SCARCITY

2005 Topps All-Time Fan Favorites Autographs

Among players and other personages signing their first major manufacturer autographs for this product included Dr. Jim Beckett, John Elway (first as a baseball player); Marvin Miller and Walt Jockety. Unfortunately, Red Sox GM Theo Epstien di not honor his commitment to sign cards for this set. An exchange card for Epstein was originally placed into packs and Topps sent a variety of different signed cards to collectors that sent in their Epstein exchange as a replacement.

GROUP A ODDS 1:34,438 H, 1:93,312 R
GROUP B ODDS 1:1456 H, 1:1421 R
GROUP C ODDS 1:397 H, 1:462 R
GROUP D ODDS 1:1467 H, 1:1414 R
GROUP E ODDS 1:43 H, 1:233 R
GROUP F ODDS 1:37 H, 1:122 R
GROUP G ODDS 1:1165 H, 1079 R
GROUP H ODDS 1:57 H, 1:97 R
GROUP I ODDS 1:108 H, 1:153 R
OVERALL AUTO ODDS 1:12
GROUP A PRINT RUN 15 CARDS
GROUP B PRINT RUN 40 SETS
GROUP C PRINT RUN 90 SETS
CARDS ARE NOT SERIAL-NUMBERED
PRINT RUNS PROVIDED BY TOPPS
NO GROUP A PRICING DUE TO SCARCITY
EXCHANGE DEADLINE 05/31/07
AD Andre Dawson B/40 *
AH Atlee Hammaker H 4.00 10.00
AK Al Kaline E 20.00 50.00
AY Anthony Young F 4.00 10.00
BB Brett Butler F 4.00 10.00
BF Bill Freehan H 12.50 30.00
BFE Bob Feller E 30.00 60.00
BG Bob Gibson C/90 * 50.00 100.00
BJ Bo Jackson E 30.00 60.00
BL Barry Lyons G 4.00 10.00
BLB Barry Bonds A/15 *
BM Bill Mazeroski E 30.00 60.00
BR Brooks Robinson C/90 * 75.00 150.00
BW Bob Welch F 4.00 10.00
CH Charlie Hayes F 4.00 10.00
CJ Cleon Jones H 10.00 25.00
CK Chuck Knoblauch E 12.50 30.00
CL Clem Labine E 10.00 25.00
CLE Chet Lemon H 10.00 25.00
CM Candy Maldonado H 4.00 10.00
CR Cal Ripken C/90 * 125.00 250.00
CY Carl Yastrzemski C/90 * 75.00 150.00
DC David Cone E 6.00 15.00
DD Doug Drabek E 6.00 15.00
DG Dwight Gooden D 10.00 25.00
DJ Dave Johnson E 6.00 15.00
DM Don Mattingly D 50.00 100.00
DMA Dave Magadan F 4.00 10.00
DMC Denny McLain F 10.00 25.00
DMU Dale Murphy F 10.00 25.00
DS Darryl Strawberry E 12.50 30.00
DSN Duke Snider B/40 *
DW Dave Winfield C/90 * 50.00 100.00
DWI Dick Williams C/90 * 15.00 40.00
DZ Don Zimmer B/40 *
EB Ernie Banks B/40 *
EM Edgar Martinez E 10.00 25.00
FR Frank Robinson D 30.00 60.00
GC Gary Carter E 10.00 25.00
GG Gary Gaetti H 4.00 10.00
GH Glenn Hubbard F 4.00 10.00
GJ Gregg Jefferies E 6.00 15.00
HJ Howard Johnson F 4.00 10.00
HK Harmon Killebrew E 40.00 80.00
JA Jim Abbott E 10.00 25.00
JAN Joaquin Andujar H 4.00 10.00
JBE Dr. Jim Beckett C/90 * 50.00 100.00
JBR Jeff Brantley E 10.00 25.00
JBU Jay Buhner E 10.00 25.00
JE John Elway B/40 *
JG Jerry Grote F 10.00 25.00
JK John Kruk F 4.00 10.00
JLE Jim Leyland F 15.00 40.00
JLO Jim Lonborg F 6.00 15.00
JMA Juan Marichal C/90 * 20.00 50.00
JO Jesse Orosco E 10.00 25.00
JOQ Jose Oquendo I 4.00 10.00
JP Joe Pignatano F 10.00 25.00
JPE Joe Pepitone F 10.00 25.00
JPO Johnny Podres B/40 *
JPY Johnny Pesky F 15.00 40.00
JR J.R. Richard E 10.00 25.00
JT John Tudor F 15.00 40.00
JW Jerome Walton F 4.00 10.00
JWE John Wetteland E 10.00 25.00
KM Kevin Maas E 6.00 15.00
KMC Kevin McReynolds F 4.00 10.00
LS Lonnie Smith I 4.00 10.00
LW Lou Whitaker C/90 * 10.00 25.00
MB Marty Barrett H 4.00 10.00
MI Monte Irvin E 10.00 25.00
MK Michael Kay ANC C/90 * 12.50 30.00
MLE Mark Lemke H 6.00 15.00
MNO Mike Norris I 4.00 10.00
MS Mike Schmidt B/40 *
MW Matt Williams F 10.00 25.00
MWI Mitch Williams E 6.00 15.00
NR Nolan Ryan B/40 *
OG Oscar Gamble H 6.00 15.00
OS Ozzie Smith E 30.00 60.00
PO Paul O'Neill E 15.00 40.00
RB Ron Blomberg F 4.00 10.00
RCR Roger Craig E 10.00 25.00
RD Rick Dempsey I 4.00 10.00
RG Ron Gant C/90 * 20.00 50.00
RJ Reggie Jackson B/40 *
RM Rick Monday E 10.00 25.00
RS Rafael Santana F 4.00 10.00
RSA Ron Santo C/90 * 20.00 50.00
SB Sid Bream F 6.00 15.00
SBR Scott Brosius C/90 * 20.00 50.00
SC Steve Carlton C/90 * 30.00 60.00
SD Shawon Dunston E 10.00 25.00
SF Sid Fernandez E 6.00 15.00
SG Steve Garvey E 15.00 40.00
SM Stan Musial B/40 *
TG Tony Gwynn C/90 * 50.00 100.00
TK Tom Kelly F 6.00 15.00
TL Tony LaRussa E 15.00 40.00
TN Tom Niedenfuer H 4.00 10.00
TR Tim Raines E 10.00 25.00
TS Tom Seaver B/40 *
WB Wade Boggs B/40 *
WF Whitey Ford C/90 * 75.00 150.00
YB Yogi Berra C/90 * 40.00 80.00

2005 Topps All-Time Fan Favorites Autographs Rainbow

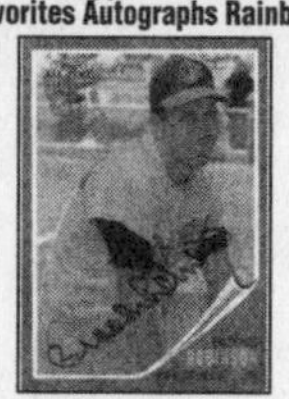

STATED ODDS 1:543 H, 1:933 R
STATED PRINT RUN 10 SERIAL #'d SETS
NO PRICING DUE TO SCARCITY
EXCHANGE DEADLINE 05/31/07

2005 Topps All-Time Fan Favorites Best Seat in the House Relics

GROUP A ODDS 1:170 BOX LOADER
GROUP B ODDS 1:14 BOX LOADER
GROUP A PRINT RUN 50 CARDS
GROUP B PRINT RUN 125 SETS
RAINBOW ODDS 1:56 BOX LOADER
RAINBOW PRINT RUN 25 SERIAL #'d SETS
NO RAINBOW PRICING DUE TO SCARCITY
CR Cal Ripken 10.00 25.00
Frank Robinson B/125
JD Dave Johnson 6.00 15.00
Rick Dempsey B/125
KMLW Al Kaline 10.00 25.00
Lou Whitaker
Chet Lemon
Denny McLain B/125
MFBJ Don Mattingly 15.00 40.00
Whitey Ford
Yogi Berra
Reggie Jackson A/50
RR Brooks Robinson 10.00 25.00
Cal Ripken B/125
RRRD Brooks Robinson 10.00 25.00
Rick Dempsey
Frank Robinson
Cal Ripken B/125

2005 Topps All-Time Fan Favorites Jim Beckett Promo

PROMO ISSUED IN BECKETT BASEBALL
JB Dr. Jim Beckett 2.00 5.00

2005 Topps All-Time Fan Favorites League Leaders Tri-Signers

STATED ODDS 1:5194 H, 1:5632 R
STATED PRINT RUN 50 SERIAL #'d SETS
EXCHANGE DEADLINE 05/31/07
JSB Reggie Jackson 300.00 500.00
Mike Schmidt
George Brett EXCH
MBG Don Mattingly 150.00 250.00
Wade Boggs
Dwight Gooden
RSM Frank Robinson
Duke Snider
Stan Musial

2005 Topps All-Time Fan Favorites Originals Relics

STATED ODDS 1:17 BOX-LOADER
STATED PRINT RUN 50 SERIAL #'d SETS
PRINT RUNS INTERMINGLE DIFT.CARDS
ACTUAL VINTAGE CARDS USED
AD Andre Dawson Bat 10.00 25.00
BJ Bo Jackson Jsy 20.00 50.00
DM Dale Murphy Bat 15.00 40.00
GC Gary Carter Bat 10.00 25.00

JR Jim Rice Bat 10.00 25.00
NR Nolan Ryan Jsy 30.00 60.00
RC Rod Carew Bat 15.00 40.00
RJ Reggie Jackson Bat 15.00 40.00
TG Tony Gwynn Jsy 20.00 50.00
WB Wade Boggs Bat 15.00 40.00

2005 Topps All-Time Fan Favorites Relics

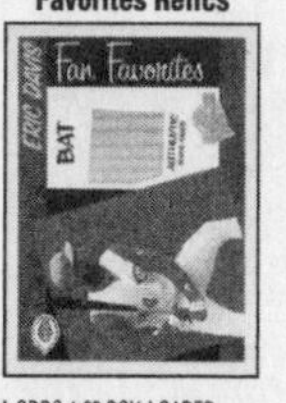

GROUP A ODDS 1:83 BOX-LOADER
GROUP B ODDS 1:31 BOX-LOADER
GROUP C ODDS 1:3 BOX-LOADER
GROUP D ODDS 1:3 BOX-LOADER
GROUP A PRINT RUN 50 SERIAL #'d SETS
GROUP B PRINT RUN 135 SERIAL #'d SETS
GROUP C PRINT RUN 200 SERIAL #'d SETS
GROUP D PRINT RUN 350 SERIAL #'d SETS
RAINBOW ODDS 1:13 BOX-LOADER
RAINBOW PRINT RUN 25 SERIAL #'d SETS
NO RAINBOW PRICING DUE TO SCARCITY
AD Andre Dawson Bat D/350 4.00 10.00
BD Bucky Dent Bat C/200 4.00 10.00
BJ Bo Jackson Bat C/200 6.00 15.00
BR Brooks Robinson Bat D/350 6.00 15.00
BS Bruce Sutter Jsy D/350 4.00 10.00
CF Cecil Fielder Bat C/200 6.00 15.00
CY Carl Yastrzemski Bat A/50
DM Dale Murphy Bat C/200 6.00 15.00
DS Darryl Strawberry Bat D/350 4.00 10.00
ED Eric Davis Bat C/200 4.00 10.00
GC Gary Carter Bat D/350 4.00 10.00
JC Joe Carter Bat D/350 4.00 10.00
JCC Jose Canseco Bat D/350 5.00 15.00
JR Jim Rice Bat C/200 4.00 10.00
KH Keith Hernandez Bat C/200 4.00 10.00
LD Lenny Dykstra Bat C/200 4.00 10.00
MW Mookie Wilson Bat B/135 4.00 10.00
NR Nolan Ryan Jsy B/135 15.00 40.00
PO Paul O'Neill Bat C/200 6.00 15.00
RC Rod Carew Bat C/200 6.00 15.00
RJ Reggie Jackson Bat D/350 6.00 15.00
SM Stan Musial Bat A/50
TG Tony Gwynn Jsy C/200 6.00 15.00
VC Vince Coleman Bat C/200 4.00 10.00
WB Wade Boggs Bat C/200 6.00 15.00
WJ Wally Joyner Bat C/200 4.00 10.00
WM Willie McGee Bat D/350 6.00 15.00

2005 Topps All-Time Fan Favorites Rookie Dual Autographs

STATED ODDS 1:8356 H, 1:8448 R
STATED PRINT RUN 50 SERIAL #'d SETS
EXCHANGE DEADLINE 05/31/07
RB Nolan Ryan
Johnny Bench

2007 Topps All-Star FanFest

This seven card set was given to attendees of the 2007 MLB All-Star FanFest in San Francisco.

COMPLETE SET (7) 3.00 8.00
1 Tim Lincecum 1.25 3.00
2 Barry Bonds .40 1.00
3 Alex Rodriguez .30 .75
4 David Wright .30 .75
5 Ryan Howard .30 .75
6 Daisuke Matsuzaka .30 .75
7 Mickey Mantle .60 1.50

2008 Topps All-Star FanFest

COMPLETE SET (8) 20.00 50.00
1 Babe Ruth 5.00 12.00
2 Jackie Robinson 2.00 5.00
3 Alex Rodriguez 3.00 8.00
4 David Wright 2.50 6.00
5 Lou Gehrig 4.00 10.00
6 Joba Chamberlain 1.25 3.00
7 Mickey Mantle 6.00 15.00
8 Johan Santana 2.00 5.00

2008 Topps All-Star FanFest Patch

STATED PRINT RUN 375 SER.#'d SETS
NO CARD NUMBERS
CARDS LISTED ALPHABETICALLY
1 Lou Gehrig 20.00 50.00
2 Mickey Mantle 30.00 60.00
3 Thurman Munson 15.00 40.00
4 Jose Reyes 12.50 30.00
5 Babe Ruth 30.00 60.00
6 Johan Santana 12.50 30.00
7 Tom Seaver 12.50 30.00
8 David Wright 12.50 30.00

2009 Topps All-Star FanFest

1 Albert Pujols
2 Ryan Ludwick
3 Rick Ankiel
4 Yadier Molina
5 Khalil Greene

2009 Topps All-Star FanFest Patch

1 Albert Pujols
2 Ryan Howard
3 Ichiro Suzuki

2010 Topps All-Star FanFest

COMPLETE SET (6) 15.00 40.00
WR1 Torii Hunter 1.25 3.00
WR2 Hideki Matsui 3.00 8.00
WR3 Kendry Morales 1.25 3.00
WR4 Nolan Ryan 10.00 25.00
WR5 Rod Carew 2.00 5.00
WR6 Stephen Strasburg 8.00 20.00

2006 Topps Allen and Ginter National Promos

COMPLETE SET (8) 15.00 30.00
*MINIS: .6X TO 1.5X BASE CARDS
NCC2 Kirk Gibson 1.25 3.00
NCC4 Vladimir Guerrero 1.00 2.50
NCC6 Nolan Ryan 4.00 10.00
NCC7 Jered Weaver .75 2.00
NCC8 Matt Kemp .75 2.00

2006 Topps Allen and Ginter

This 350-card set was release in August, 2006. The set was issued in seven-card hobby packs with an $4 SRP. Those packs came 24 to a box and there were 12 boxes in a case. In addition, there were also six-card retail packs issued and those packs came 24 packs to a box and 20 boxes to a case. There were some subsets included in this set including Rookies (251-265); Retired Greats (266-290); Managers (291-300); Modern Personalities (301-314); Reprinted Allen and Ginters (316-319); Famous People of the Past (326-349).

COMPLETE SET (350) 60.00 120.00
COMP.SET w/o SP's (300) 15.00 40.00
SP STATED ODDS 1:2 HOBBY, 1:2 RETAIL
SP CL: 5/15/25/35/45/50-59/65/85/105/115
SP CL: 125/135/145/150-159/165/175/185
SP CL: 205/215/235/245/251/255-256/265
SP CL: 285/295/305/315/325/335/345
FRAMED ORIGINALS ODDS 1:3227 H, 1:3227 R
1 Albert Pujols 1.00 2.50
2 Aubrey Huff .15 .40
3 Mark Teixeira .40 1.00
4 Vernon Wells .15 .40
5 Ken Griffey Jr. SP 2.00 5.00
6 Nick Swisher .40 1.00
7 Jose Reyes .25 .60
8 David Wright .60 1.50
9 Vladimir Guerrero .40 1.00
10 Andruw Jones .15 .40
11 Ramon Hernandez .15 .40
12 Miguel Tejada .25 .60
13 Juan Pierre .15 .40
14 Jim Thome .25 .60
15 Austin Kearns SP 1.25 3.00
16 Jhonny Peralta .15 .40
17 Clint Barmes .15 .40
18 Angel Berroa .15 .40
19 Nomar Garciaparra .40 1.00
20 Joe Nathan .15 .40
21 Brandon Webb .25 .60
22 Chad Tracy .15 .40
23 Derek Jeter 1.00 2.50
24 Conor Jackson (RC) .25 .60
25 Jason Giambi SP 1.25 3.00
26 Johnny Estrada .15 .40
27 Luis Gonzalez .15 .40
28 Javier Vazquez .15 .40
29 Orlando Hudson .15 .40
30 Shawn Green .15 .40
31 Mark Buehrle .25 .60
32 Wily Mo Pena .15 .40
33 C.C. Sabathia .25 .60
34 Ronnie Belliard .15 .40
35 Travis Hafner SP 1.25 3.00
36 Mike Jacobs (RC) .15 .40
37 Roy Oswalt .25 .60
38 Zack Greinke .25 .60
39 J.D. Drew .15 .40
40 Jeff Kent .15 .40
41 Ben Sheets .15 .40
42 Luis Castillo .15 .40
43 Carlos Delgado .15 .40
44 Cliff Floyd .15 .40
45 Danny Haren SP 1.25 3.00
46 Bobby Abreu .15 .40
47 Jeromy Burnitz .15 .40
48 Khalil Greene .15 .40
49 Moises Alou .15 .40
50 Alex Rodriguez SP 2.00 5.00
51 Ervin Santana SP 1.25 3.00
52 Bartolo Colon SP 1.25 3.00
53 John Smoltz SP 1.25 3.00
54 David Ortiz SP 1.25 3.00
55 Hideki Matsui SP 1.25 3.00
56 Jermaine Dye SP 1.25 3.00
57 Victor Martinez SP 1.25 3.00
58 Willy Taveras SP 1.25 3.00
59 Brady Clark SP 1.25 3.00
60 Justin Morneau .40 1.00
61 Xavier Nady .15 .40
62 Rich Harden .15 .40
63 Jack Wilson .15 .40
64 Brian Giles .15 .40
65 Jon Lieber SP 1.25 3.00
66 Dan Johnson .15 .40
67 Billy Wagner .15 .40
68 Rickie Weeks .25 .60
69 Chris Ray (RC) .15 .40
70 Chris Shelton .15 .40
71 Dmitri Young .15 .40
72 Ivan Rodriguez .25 .60
73 Jeremy Bonderman .15 .40
74 Justin Verlander (RC) 1.25 3.00
75 Randy Johnson .40 1.00
76 Magglio Ordonez .25 .60
77 Brandon Inge .15 .40
78 Placido Polanco .15 .40
79 Ryan Howard .60 1.50
80 Jason Bay .15 .40
81 Sean Casey .15 .40
82 Jeremy Hermida (RC) .15 .40
83 Mike Cameron .15 .40
84 Trevor Hoffman .25 .60
85 Mike Matheny SP 1.25 3.00
86 Steve Finley .15 .40
87 Adam Everett .15 .40
88 Jason Isringhausen .15 .40
89 Jonny Gomes .15 .40
90 Barry Zito .15 .40
91 Bobby Crosby .15 .40
92 Eric Chavez .15 .40
93 Frank Thomas .40 1.00
94 Huston Street .15 .40
95 Jorge Posada .25 .60
96 Casey Kotchman UER .15 .40
Birthdate is incorrect
97 Darin Erstad .15 .40
98 Chipper Jones .40 1.00
99 Jeff Francoeur .40 1.00
100 Barry Bonds .75 2.00
101 Alfonso Soriano .25 .60
102 Brandon Claussen .15 .40
103 Aaron Boone .15 .40
104 Roger Clemens .50 1.25
105 Andy Pettitte SP 1.25 3.00
106 Nick Johnson .15 .40
107 Tom Gordon .15 .40
108 Orlando Hernandez .15 .40
109 Francisco Rodriguez .25 .60
110 Orlando Cabrera .15 .40
111 Edgar Renteria .15 .40
112 Tim Hudson .25 .60
113 Coco Crisp .15 .40
114 Matt Clement .15 .40
115 Greg Maddux SP 2.00 5.00
116 Paul Konerko .25 .60
117 Felipe Lopez .15 .40
118 Garrett Atkins .15 .40
119 Akinori Otsuka .15 .40
120 Craig Biggio .25 .60
121 Danys Baez .15 .40
122 Brad Penny .15 .40
123 Eric Gagne .15 .40
124 Lew Ford .15 .40
125 Mariano Rivera SP 1.25 3.00
126 Carlos Beltran .15 .40
127 Pedro Martinez .25 .60
128 Todd Helton .25 .60
129 Aaron Rowand .15 .40
130 Mike Lieberthal .15 .40
131 Oliver Perez .15 .40
132 Ryan Klesko .15 .40
133 Randy Winn .15 .40
134 Yuniesky Betancourt .15 .40
135 David Eckstein SP 1.25 3.00
136 Chad Orvella .15 .40
137 Toby Hall .15 .40
138 Hank Blalock .15 .40
139 B.J. Ryan .15 .40
140 Roy Halladay .40 1.00
141 Livan Hernandez .15 .40
142 John Patterson .15 .40
143 Bengie Molina .15 .40
144 Brad Wilkerson .15 .40
145 Jorge Cantu SP 1.25 3.00
146 Mark Mulder .15 .40
147 Felix Hernandez .40 1.00
148 Paul Lo Duca .15 .40
149 Prince Fielder (RC) .60 1.50
150 Johnny Damon SP 1.25 3.00
151 Ryan Langerhans SP 1.25 3.00
152 Kris Benson SP 1.25 3.00
153 Curt Schilling SP 1.25 3.00
154 Manny Ramirez SP 1.25 3.00
155 Robinson Cano SP 1.25 3.00
156 Derrek Lee SP 1.25 3.00
157 A.J. Pierzynski SP 1.25 3.00
158 Adam Dunn SP 1.25 3.00
159 Cliff Lee SP 1.25 3.00
160 Grady Sizemore .25 .60
161 Jeff Francis .15 .40
162 Dontrelle Willis .15 .40
163 Brad Ausmus .15 .40
164 Preston Wilson .15 .40
165 Derek Lowe SP 1.25 3.00
166 Chris Capuano .15 .40
167 Joe Mauer .40 1.00
168 Torii Hunter .15 .40
169 Chase Utley .40 1.00
170 Zach Duke .15 .40
171 Jason Schmidt .15 .40
172 Adrian Beltre .15 .40
173 Eddie Guardado .15 .40
174 Richie Sexson .15 .40
175 Miguel Cabrera SP 1.25 3.00
176 Julio Lugo .15 .40
177 Francisco Cordero .15 .40
178 Kevin Millwood .15 .40
179 A.J. Burnett .25 .60
180 Jose Guillen .15 .40
181 Larry Bigbie .15 .40
182 Raul Ibanez .25 .60

Card	Low	High
183 Jake Peavy	.15	.40
184 Pat Burrell	.15	.40
185 Tom Glavine SP	1.25	3.00
186 J.J. Hardy	.15	.40
187 Emil Brown	.15	.40
188 Lance Berkman	.25	.60
189 Marcus Giles	.15	.40
190 Scott Podsednik	.15	.40
191 Chone Figgins	.15	.40
192 Melvin Mora	.15	.40
193 Mark Loretta	.15	.40
194 Carlos Zambrano	.25	.60
195 Chien-Ming Wang	.25	.60
196 Mark Prior	.25	.60
197 Bobby Jenks	.15	.40
198 Brian Fuentes	.15	.40
199 Garret Anderson	.15	.40
200 Ichiro Suzuki	.60	1.50
201 Brian Roberts	.15	.40
202 Jason Kendall	.15	.40
203 Milton Bradley	.15	.40
204 Jimmy Rollins	.25	.60
205 Brett Myers SP	1.25	3.00
206 Joe Randa	.15	.40
207 Mike Piazza	.40	1.00
208 Matt Morris	.15	.40
209 Omar Vizquel	.25	.60
210 Jeremy Reed	.15	.40
211 Chris Carpenter	.40	1.00
212 Jim Edmonds	.25	.60
213 Scott Kazmir	.25	.60
214 Travis Lee	.15	.40
215 Michael Young SP	1.25	3.00
216 Rod Barajas	.15	.40
217 Gustavo Chacin	.15	.40
218 Lyle Overbay	.15	.40
219 Troy Glaus	.15	.40
220 Chad Cordero	.15	.40
221 Jose Vidro	.15	.40
222 Scott Rolen	.25	.60
223 Carl Crawford	.25	.60
224 Rocco Baldelli	.15	.40
225 Mike Mussina	.25	.60
226 Kelvim Escobar	.15	.40
227 Corey Patterson	.15	.40
228 Javy Lopez	.15	.40
229 Jonathan Papelbon (RC)	.75	2.00
230 Aramis Ramirez	.15	.40
231 Tadahito Iguchi	.15	.40
232 Morgan Ensberg	.15	.40
233 Mark Grudzielanek	.15	.40
234 Mike Sweeney	.15	.40
235 Shawn Chacon SP	1.25	3.00
236 Nick Punto	.15	.40
237 Geoff Jenkins	.15	.40
238 Carlos Lee	.15	.40
239 David DeJesus	.15	.40
240 Brad Lidge	.15	.40
241 Bob Wickman	.15	.40
242 Jon Garland	.15	.40
243 Kerry Wood	.15	.40
244 Bronson Arroyo	.15	.40
245 Matt Holliday SP	1.50	4.00
246 Josh Beckett	.25	.60
247 Johan Santana	.40	1.00
248 Rafael Furcal	.15	.40
249 Shannon Stewart	.15	.40
250 Gary Sheffield	.15	.40
251 Josh Barfield SP (RC)	1.25	3.00
252 Kenji Johjima RC	.40	1.00
253 Ian Kinsler (RC)	.50	1.25
254 Brian Anderson (RC)	.15	.40
255 Matt Cain SP (RC)	1.25	3.00
256 Josh Willingham SP (RC)	1.25	3.00
257 John Koronka (RC)	.15	.40
258 Chris Duffy (RC)	.15	.40
259 Brian McCann (RC)	.16	.40
260 Hanley Ramirez (RC)	.40	1.00
261 Hong-Chih Kuo (RC)	.40	1.00
262 Francisco Liriano (RC)	.40	1.00
263 Anderson Hernandez (RC)	.15	.40
264 Ryan Zimmerman (RC)	.75	2.00
265 Brian Bannister SP (RC)	1.25	3.00
266 Nolan Ryan	1.00	2.50
267 Frank Robinson	.15	.40
268 Roberto Clemente	1.25	3.00
269 Hank Greenberg	.40	1.00
270 Napolean Lajoie	.25	.60
271 Lloyd Waner	.25	.60
272 Paul Waner	.25	.60
273 Frankie Frisch	.25	.60
274 Moose Skowron	.15	.40
275 Mickey Mantle	1.25	3.00
276 Brooks Robinson	.25	.60
277 Carl Yastrzemski	.60	1.50
278 Johnny Pesky	.15	.40
279 Stan Musial	.60	1.50
280 Bill Mazeroski	.25	.60
281 Harmon Killebrew	.40	1.00
282 Monte Irvin	.15	.40
283 Bob Gibson	.25	.60
284 Ted Williams	1.00	2.50
285 Yogi Berra SP	1.25	3.00
286 Ernie Banks	.40	1.00
287 Bobby Doerr	.15	.40
288 Josh Gibson	.40	1.00
289 Bob Feller	.15	.40
290 Cal Ripken	1.50	4.00
291 Bobby Cox MG	.15	.40
292 Terry Francona MG	.15	.40
293 Dusty Baker MG	.15	.40
294 Ozzie Guillen MG	.15	.40
295 Jim Leyland MG SP	1.25	3.00
296 Willie Randolph MG	.15	.40
297 Joe Torre MG	.25	.60
298 Felipe Alou MG	.15	.40
299 Tony La Russa MG	.25	.60
300 Frank Robinson MG	.15	.40
301 Mike Tyson	.60	1.50
302 Duke Paoa Kahanamoku	.15	.40
303 Jennie Finch	1.00	2.50
304 Brandi Chastain	.15	.40
305 Danica Patrick SP	3.00	8.00
306 Wendy Guey	.15	.40
307 Hulk Hogan	.50	1.25
308 Carl Lewis	.15	.40
309 John Wooden	.25	.60
310 Randy Couture	.75	2.00
311 Andy Irons	.15	.40
312 Takeru Kobayashi	.50	1.25
313 Leon Spinks	.15	.40
314 Jim Thorpe	.25	.60
315 Jerry Bailey SP	1.25	3.00
316 Adrian C. Anson REP	.25	.60
317 John M. Ward REP	.15	.40
318 Mike Kelly REP	.15	.40
319 Capt. Jack Glasscock REP	.15	.40
320 Aaron Hill	.15	.40
321 Derrick Turnbow	.15	.40
322 Nick Markakis (RC)	.40	1.00
323 Brad Hawpe	.15	.40
324 Kevin Mench	.15	.40
325 John Lackey SP	1.25	3.00
326 Chester A. Arthur	.15	.40
327 Ulysses S. Grant	.15	.40
328 Abraham Lincoln	.15	.40
329 Grover Cleveland	.15	.40
330 Benjamin Harrison	.15	.40
331 Theodore Roosevelt	.15	.40
332 Rutherford B. Hayes	.15	.40
333 Chancellor Otto Von Bismarck	.15	.40
334 Kaiser Wilhelm II	.15	.40
335 Queen Victoria SP	1.25	3.00
336 Pope Leo XIII	.15	.40
337 Thomas Edison	.15	.40
338 Orville Wright	.15	.40
339 Wilbur Wright	.15	.40
340 Nathaniel Hawthorne	.15	.40
341 Herman Melville	.15	.40
342 Stonewall Jackson	.15	.40
343 Robert E. Lee	.15	.40
344 Andrew Carnegie	.15	.40
345 John Rockefeller SP	1.25	3.00
346 Bob Fitzsimmons	.15	.40
347 Billy The Kid	.15	.40
348 Buffalo Bill	.15	.40
349 Jesse James	.15	.40
350 Statue Of Liberty	.15	.40
NNO Framed Originals	60.00	120.00

2006 Topps Allen and Ginter Mini

*MINI 1-350: 1X TO 2.5X BASIC
*MINI 1-350: 1X TO 2.5X BASIC RC's
APPX.15 MINIS PER 24-CT SEALED BOX
*MINI SP 1-350: .6X TO 1.5X BASIC SP
*MINI SP 1-350: .6X TO 1.5X BASIC SP RC's
MINI SP ODDS 1:13 H, 1:13 R

Card	Low	High
COMMON CARD (351-375)	20.00	50.00
SEMISTARS 351-375	30.00	60.00
UNLISTED STARS 351-375	30.00	60.00

351-375 RANDOM WITHIN RIP CARDS
OVERALL PLATE ODDS 1:865 H, 1:865 R
PLATE PRINT RUN 1 SET PER COLOR
BLACK-CYAN-MAGENTA-YELLOW ISSUED
NO PLATE PRICING DUE TO SCARCITY

Card	Low	High
351 Albert Pujols EXT	75.00	150.00
352 Alex Rodriguez EXT	50.00	100.00
353 Andruw Jones EXT	20.00	50.00
354 Barry Bonds EXT	40.00	80.00
355 Cal Ripken EXT	75.00	150.00
356 David Ortiz EXT	40.00	80.00
357 David Wright EXT	50.00	100.00
358 Derek Jeter EXT	75.00	150.00
359 Derrek Lee EXT	20.00	50.00
360 Hideki Matsui EXT	30.00	60.00
361 Ichiro Suzuki EXT	40.00	80.00
362 Johan Santana EXT	30.00	60.00
363 Josh Gibson EXT	20.00	50.00
364 Ken Griffey Jr. EXT	60.00	120.00
365 Manny Ramirez EXT	30.00	60.00
366 Mickey Mantle EXT	75.00	150.00
367 Miguel Cabrera EXT	20.00	50.00
368 Miguel Tejada EXT	20.00	50.00
369 Mike Piazza EXT	30.00	60.00
370 Nolan Ryan EXT	60.00	120.00
371 Roberto Clemente EXT	125.00	200.00
372 Roger Clemens EXT	40.00	80.00
373 Scott Rolen EXT	30.00	60.00
374 Ted Williams EXT	50.00	100.00
375 Vladimir Guerrero EXT	30.00	60.00

2006 Topps Allen and Ginter Mini A and G Back

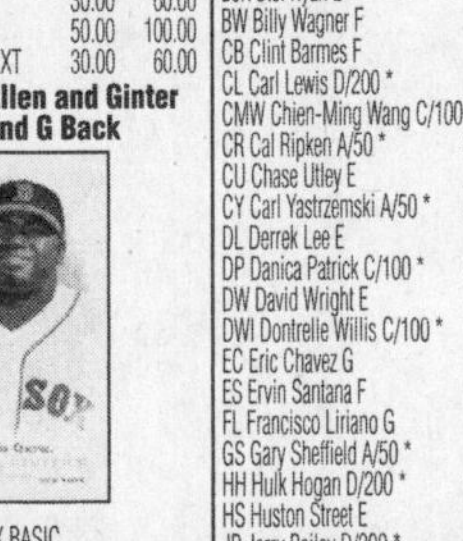

*A & G BACK: 2X TO 5X BASIC
*A & G BACK: 1.5X TO 4X BASIC RC's
STATED ODDS 1:5 H, 1:5 R
*A & G BACK SP: 1X TO 2.5X BASIC SP
*A & G BACK SP: 1X TO 2.5X BASIC SP RC's
SP STATED ODDS 1:65 H, 1:65 R

2006 Topps Allen and Ginter Mini Bazooka

STATED ODDS 1:125 H, 1:266 R
STATED PRINT RUN 25 SERIAL #'d SETS
NO PRICING DUE TO SCARCITY

2006 Topps Allen and Ginter Mini Black

*BLACK: 4X TO 10X BASIC
*BLACK: 2.5X TO 6X BASIC RC's
STATED ODDS 1:10 H, 1:10 R
*BLACK SP: 1.5X TO 4X BASIC SP
*BLACK SP: 1.5X TO 4X BASIC SP RC's
SP STATED ODDS 1:130 H, 1:130 R

2006 Topps Allen and Ginter Mini No Card Number

*NO NBR: 6X TO 15X BASIC
*NO NBR: 4X TO 10X BASIC RC's
*NO NBR: 2X TO 5X BASIC SP
*NO NBR: 2X TO 5X BASIC SP RC's
STATED ODDS 1:60 H, 1:168 R
STATED PRINT RUN 50 SETS
CARDS ARE NOT SERIAL-NUMBERED
PRINT RUN INFO PROVIDED BY TOPPS

2006 Topps Allen and Ginter Mini Wood

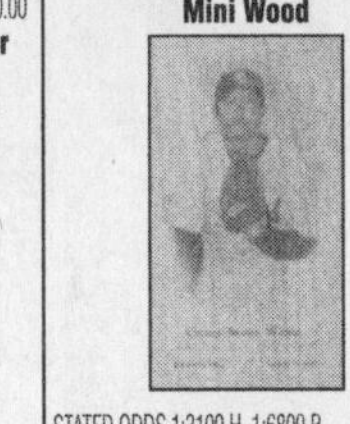

STATED ODDS 1:3100 H, 1:6800 R
STATED PRINT RUN 1 SERIAL #'d SET
NO PRICING DUE TO SCARCITY

2006 Topps Allen and Ginter Autographs

GROUP A ODDS 1:2467 H, 1:3850 R
GROUP B ODDS 1:14,500 H, 1:32,000 R
GROUP C ODDS 1:2200 H, 1:4300 R
GROUP D ODDS 1:548 H, 1:1090 R
GROUP E ODDS 1:473 H, 1:1000 R
GROUP F ODDS 1:250 H, 1:520 R
GROUP G ODDS 1:158 H, 1:299 R
GROUP A PRINT RUN 50 CARDS PER
GROUP A BONDS PRINT RUN 25 CARDS
GROUP B PRINT RUN 75 CARDS PER
GROUP C PRINT RUN 100 CARDS PER
GROUP D PRINT RUN 200 CARDS PER
GROUP A-D ARE NOT SERIAL-NUMBERED
A-D PRINT RUNS PROVIDED BY TOPPS
NO BONDS PRICING DUE TO SCARCITY

Card	Low	High
AI Andy Irons D/200 *	100.00	175.00
AR Alex Rodriguez A/50 *	400.00	500.00
BB Barry Bonds A/25 *		
BC Brandi Chastain D/200 *	30.00	60.00
BF Bob Feller E	20.00	50.00
BJR B.J. Ryan E	8.00	20.00
BW Billy Wagner F	10.00	25.00
CB Clint Barmes F	8.00	20.00
CL Carl Lewis D/200 *	60.00	120.00
CMW Chien-Ming Wang C/100 *	500.00	600.00
CR Cal Ripken A/50 *	350.00	400.00
CU Chase Utley E	40.00	80.00
CY Carl Yastrzemski A/50 *	250.00	400.00
DL Derrek Lee E	15.00	40.00
DP Danica Patrick C/100 *	400.00	600.00
DW David Wright E	40.00	80.00
DWI Dontrelle Willis C/100 *	15.00	40.00
EC Eric Chavez G	6.00	15.00
ES Ervin Santana F	6.00	15.00
FL Francisco Liriano G	12.50	30.00
GS Gary Sheffield A/50 *	60.00	120.00
HH Hulk Hogan D/200 *	125.00	250.00
HS Huston Street E	10.00	25.00
JB Jerry Bailey D/200 *	50.00	100.00
JB1 Josh Barfield G	6.00	15.00
JF Jennie Finch D/200 *	90.00	150.00
JG Jonny Gomes G	6.00	15.00
JS Johan Santana C/100 *	75.00	150.00
JW John Wooden D/200 *	125.00	250.00
KJ Kenji Johjima A/50 *	50.00	100.00
LF Lew Ford G	5.00	12.00
LS Leon Spinks D/200 *	40.00	80.00
MC Miguel Cabrera C/100 *	75.00	150.00
MT Mike Tyson D/200 *	250.00	350.00
MY Michael Young E	10.00	25.00
NR Nolan Ryan A/50 *	350.00	450.00
OS Ozzie Smith B/75 *	100.00	200.00
PF Prince Fielder F	20.00	50.00
RA Randy Couture E	125.00	225.00
RC Robinson Cano G	30.00	60.00
RH Ryan Howard F	50.00	100.00
RZ Ryan Zimmerman F	30.00	60.00
SK Scott Kazmir F	10.00	25.00
SM Stan Musial A/50 *	300.00	400.00
TG Tony Gwynn A/50 *	200.00	300.00
TH Travis Hafner F	8.00	20.00
TK Takeru Kobayashi D/200 *	60.00	120.00
VG Vladimir Guerrero A/50 *	200.00	300.00
VM Victor Martinez E	15.00	40.00
WG Wendy Guey F	8.00	20.00
WMP Wily Mo Pena G	8.00	20.00

2006 Topps Allen and Ginter Autographs Red Ink

RANDOM INSERTS WITHIN RIP CARDS
STATED PRINT RUN 10 SETS
CARDS ARE NOT SERIAL-NUMBERED
PRINT RUN IFNO PROVIDED BY TOPPS
NO PRICING DUE TO SCARCITY
AR Alex Rodriguez
DW David Wright

2006 Topps Allen and Ginter N43

Card	Low	High
COMPLETE SET (15)	50.00	100.00

STATED ODDS 1:2 SEALED HOBBY BOXES

Card	Low	High
1 Alex Rodriguez	3.00	8.00
2 Barry Bonds	4.00	10.00
3 Albert Pujols	5.00	12.00
4 Josh Gibson	2.00	5.00
5 Nolan Ryan	5.00	12.00
6 Ichiro Suzuki	3.00	8.00
7 Mickey Mantle	6.00	15.00
8 Ted Williams	5.00	12.00
9 David Wright	3.00	8.00
10 Ken Griffey Jr.	3.00	8.00
11 Mark Teixeira	2.00	5.00
12 Adrian C. Anson	1.25	3.00
13 Mike Tyson	3.00	8.00
14 Kenji Johjima	2.00	5.00
15 Ryan Zimmerman	4.00	10.00

2006 Topps Allen and Ginter N43 Autographs

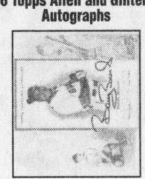

STATED ODDS 1:1970 HOBBY BOXES
STATED PRINT RUN 10 SERIAL #'d SETS
NO PRICING DUE TO SCARCITY
AR Alex Rodriguez
BB Barry Bonds

2006 Topps Allen and Ginter N43 Relics

STATED ODDS 1:379 HOBBY BOXES
STATED PRINT RUN 50 SERIAL #'d SETS

Card	Low	High
AP Albert Pujols Uni	40.00	80.00
JG Josh Gibson Model Bat	200.00	300.00

2006 Topps Allen and Ginter Dick Perez

Card	Low	High
COMPLETE SET (30)	10.00	25.00

ONE PEREZ OR DECOY PER PACK
ORIGINALS RANDOM WITHIN RIP CARDS
ORIGINALS PRINT RUN 1 SERIAL #'d SET
NO ORIG. PRICING DUE TO SCARCITY

Card	Low	High
1 Shawn Green	.25	.60
2 Andruw Jones	.25	.60
3 Miguel Tejada	.40	1.00
4 David Ortiz	.40	1.00
5 Derrek Lee	.25	.60
6 Paul Konerko	.40	1.00
7 Ken Griffey Jr.	1.00	2.50
8 Travis Hafner	.25	.60
9 Todd Helton	.40	1.00
10 Ivan Rodriguez	.40	1.00
11 Miguel Cabrera	.60	1.50
12 Lance Berkman	.40	1.00
13 Mike Sweeney	.25	.60
14 Vladimir Guerrero	.60	1.50
15 Rafael Furcal	.25	.60
16 Carlos Lee	.25	.60
17 Johan Santana	.60	1.50
18 David Wright	1.00	2.50
19 Alex Rodriguez	1.00	2.50
20 Huston Street	.25	.60
21 Bobby Abreu	.25	.60
22 Jason Bay	.25	.60
23 Jake Peavy	.25	.60
24 Ichiro Suzuki	1.00	2.50
25 Barry Bonds	1.25	3.00
26 Albert Pujols	1.50	4.00
27 Aubrey Huff	.25	.60
28 Mark Teixeira	.60	1.50
29 Vernon Wells	.25	.60
30 Alfonso Soriano	.40	1.00

2006 Topps Allen and Ginter Postcards

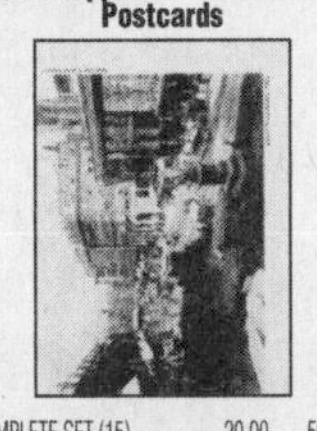

Card	Low	High
COMPLETE SET (15)	20.00	50.00

STATED ODDS 1:2 HOBBY BOXES
PERSONALIZED ODDS 1:3000 HOB.BOXES
PERSONALIZED PRINT RUN 1 #'d SET
NO PERSONALIZED PRICING AVAILABLE

Card	Low	High
AP Albert Pujols	4.00	10.00
AR Alex Rodriguez	2.50	6.00
BB Barry Bonds	3.00	8.00
CR Cal Ripken	6.00	15.00
DJ Derek Jeter	4.00	10.00
DO David Ortiz	1.00	2.50
DW David Wright	2.50	6.00
IS Ichiro Suzuki	2.50	6.00
JG Josh Gibson	1.50	4.00
KG Ken Griffey Jr.	2.50	6.00
MM Mickey Mantle	5.00	12.00
MR Manny Ramirez	1.50	4.00
MT Miguel Tejada	1.00	2.50
TW Ted Williams	4.00	10.00
VG Vladimir Guerrero	1.50	4.00

2006 Topps Allen and Ginter Relics

GROUP A ODDS 1:2800 H, 1:4950 R
GROUP B ODDS 1:2000 H, 1:3900 R
GROUP C ODDS 1:140 H, 1:248 R
GROUP D ODDS 1:178 H, 1:413 R
GROUP E ODDS 1:128 H, 1:275 R
GROUP F ODDS 1:60 H, 1:118 R
GROUP G ODDS 1:66 H, 1:152 R
GROUP H ODDS 1:111 H, 1:174 R
GROUP I ODDS 1:178 H, 1:413 R
GROUP A ARE NOT SERIAL-NUMBERED
GROUP A QTY PROVIDED BY TOPPS

Card	Low	High
AP Albert Pujols Uni F	8.00	20.00
APE Andy Pettitte Jsy F	4.00	10.00
AR Alex Rodriguez Jsy C	8.00	20.00
BB Barry Bonds Uni G	10.00	25.00
BC Bobby Crosby Uni E	3.00	8.00
BM Brandon McCarthy Jsy E	3.00	8.00
CB Carlos Beltran Jsy H	3.00	8.00
CBA Clint Barmes Jsy G	3.00	8.00
CD Carlos Delgado Jsy F	3.00	8.00
CMW Chien-Ming Wang Jsy F	20.00	50.00
CS Curt Schilling Jsy F	4.00	10.00
CU Chase Utley Jsy G	6.00	15.00
DO David Ortiz Jsy G	4.00	10.00
DW David Wright Jsy H	6.00	15.00
DWI Dontrelle Willis Jsy I	3.00	8.00
EC Eric Chavez Uni E	3.00	8.00
FH Felix Hernandez Jsy C	4.00	10.00
FT Frank Thomas Bat F	6.00	15.00
GB George W. Bush Tie A/150 *	200.00	300.00
GS Gary Sheffield Bat E	3.00	8.00
HCK Hong-Chih Kuo Jsy D	8.00	20.00
HM Hideki Matsui Uni G	6.00	15.00
HS Huston Street Jsy D	3.00	8.00
JC Jorge Cantu Jsy E	3.00	8.00
JD Johnny Damon Jsy C	4.00	10.00
JDY Jermaine Dye Uni G	3.00	8.00
JF Jeff Francoeur Bat C	6.00	15.00
JG Jonny Gomes Jsy F	3.00	8.00
JK John F. Kennedy Sweater A/250 *	200.00	300.00
JP Jake Peavy Jsy C	3.00	8.00
JS Johan Santana Jsy G	4.00	10.00
JT Jim Thome Uni C	4.00	10.00
MB Mark Buehrle Uni F	3.00	8.00
MC Miguel Cabrera Uni B	6.00	15.00
MH Matt Holliday Jsy F	4.00	10.00
MM Mickey Mantle Uni D	75.00	150.00
MP Mark Prior Jsy G	3.00	8.00
MPZ Mike Piazza Bat C	4.00	10.00
MR Manny Ramirez Jsy H	4.00	10.00
MT Miguel Tejada Uni E	3.00	8.00
NS Nick Swisher Jsy E	3.00	8.00
PK Paul Konerko Uni D	3.00	8.00
PM Pedro Martinez Jsy I	4.00	10.00
RC Robinson Cano Uni F	8.00	20.00
RH Ryan Howard Bat C	12.50	30.00
RL Ryan Langerhans Bat C	3.00	8.00
RO Roy Oswalt Jsy G	3.00	8.00
TH Travis Hafner Jsy D	3.00	8.00
VG Vladimir Guerrero Bat F	4.00	10.00
VM Victor Martinez Jsy D	3.00	8.00
WT Willy Taveras Jsy H	3.00	8.00
ZD Zach Duke Jsy C	3.00	8.00

2006 Topps Allen and Ginter Rip Cards

1-50 STATED ODDS 1:265 HOBBY
1-4 PRINT RUN 10 SERIAL #'d SETS
5-9 PRINT RUN 15 SERIAL #'d SETS
10-19 PRINT RUN 25 SERIAL #'d SETS
20-50 PRINT RUN 99 SERIAL #'d SETS
1-19 NO PRICING DUE TO SCARCITY
ALL LISTED PRICES ARE FOR RIPPED
UNRIPPED HAVE ADD'L CARDS WITHIN

Card	Low	High
COMMON UNRIPPED (20-50)	75.00	150.00
UNRIPPED (30/35/43)	100.00	200.00
UNRIPPED (45/47/49)	100.00	200.00
RIP20 Kenji Johjima/99	15.00	40.00
RIP21 Cap Anson/99	15.00	40.00
RIP22 Ryan Zimmerman/99	20.00	50.00
RIP23 Andruw Jones/99	10.00	25.00
RIP24 Barry Bonds at Wall/99	15.00	40.00
RIP25 Cal Ripken/99	30.00	60.00
RIP26 David Ortiz/99	10.00	25.00
RIP27 Hideki Matsui/99	10.00	25.00
RIP28 Ken Griffey Jr./99	15.00	40.00
RIP29 Manny Ramirez/99	10.00	25.00
RIP30 Mickey Mantle w/Bat/99	50.00	100.00
RIP31 Alex Rodriguez Bat Out/99	15.00	40.00
RIP32 Miguel Cabrera/99	6.00	15.00
RIP33 Miguel Tejada/99	6.00	15.00
RIP34 Pedro Martinez/99	10.00	25.00
RIP35 Albert Pujols w/Bat/99	30.00	60.00
RIP36 Alex Rodriguez Hands Out/99	15.00	40.00
RIP37 Alex Rodriguez Derek Jeter	15.00	40.00
RIP38 Barry Bonds 700/99	15.00	40.00
RIP39 Derek Jeter/99	20.00	50.00
RIP40 Ichiro Suzuki/99	15.00	40.00
RIP41 Ichiro Suzuki Hideki Matsui	15.00	40.00
RIP42 Josh Gibson/99	15.00	40.00
RIP43 Mickey Mantle Swing/99	50.00	100.00
RIP44 Jonathan Papelbon/99	20.00	50.00
RIP45 Mickey Mantle Ted Williams	50.00	100.00
RIP46 Albert Pujols Back/99	30.00	60.00
RIP47 Roberto Clemente/99	30.00	60.00
RIP48 Roger Clemens/99	15.00	40.00
RIP49 Ted Williams/99	30.00	60.00
RIP50 Vladimir Guerrero/99	10.00	25.00

2007 Topps Allen and Ginter

This 350-card set was released in August, 2007. The set was issued in both hobby and retail versions. The hobby packs, which had an $4 SRP, consisted of eight-cards which came 24 packs to a box and 12 boxes to a case. Similar to the 2006 set, many non-baseball players were interspersed throughout this set. There were also a group of short-printed cards, which were inserted at a stated rate of one in two hobby or retail packs. In addition, some original 19th century Allen and Ginter cards were repurchased for this product and those original cards (featuring both sports and non-sport subjects) were inserted at a stated rate of one in 17, 072 hobby and one in 34, 654 retail packs.

Card	Low	High
COMPLETE SET (350)	60.00	120.00
COMP.SET w/o SP's (300)	20.00	50.00
COMMON CARD	.12	.30
COMMON RC	.20	.50
COMMON SP	1.25	3.00

SP STATED ODDS 1:2 HOBBY, 1:2 RETAIL
SP CL: 5/43/48/58/63/107/110/119/130/137
SP CL: 152/159/178/193/194/203/219/222
SP CL: 224/243/263/301/302/303/306/307
SP CL: 308/309/310/316/317/318/319/320
SP CL: 321/322/325/326/327/330/331/334
SP CL: 335/336/339/340/345/348/349/350
FRAMED ORIGINALS ODDS 1:17,072 HOBBY
FRAMED ORIGINALS ODDS 1:34,654 RETAIL

Card	Low	High
1 Ryan Howard	.50	1.25
2 Mike Gonzalez	.12	.30
3 Austin Kearns	.12	.30
4 Josh Hamilton (RC)	.75	2.00
5 Stephen Drew SP	1.25	3.00
6 Matt Murton	.12	.30
7 Mickey Mantle	1.00	2.50
8 Howie Kendrick	.12	.30
9 Alexander Graham Bell	.12	.30
10 Jason Bay	.20	.50
11 Hank Blalock	.12	.30
12 Johan Santana	.30	.75
13 Eleanor Roosevelt	.12	.30
14 Kei Igawa RC	.50	1.25
15 Jeff Francoeur	.30	.75
16 Carl Crawford	.20	.50
17 Jhonny Peralta	.12	.30
18 Mariano Rivera	.30	.75
19 Mario Andretti	.30	.75
20 Vladimir Guerrero	.30	.75
21 Adam Wainwright	.20	.50
22 Huston Street	.12	.30
23 Cael Sanderson	.12	.30
24 Susan B. Anthony	.12	.30
25 Jay Payton	.12	.30
26 P.T. Barnum	.12	.30
27 Scott Podsednik	.12	.30
28 Willie Randolph	.12	.30
29 Sean Casey	.12	.30
30 Eiffel Tower	.12	.30
31 Kenji Johjima	.30	.75
32 Felix Hernandez	.30	.75
33 Elijah Dukes RC	.30	.75
34 Mark Grudzielanek	.12	.30
35 J.D. Drew	.12	.30
36 Kevin Kouzmanoff	.12	.30
37 Jonathan Papelbon	.30	.75
38 Bobby Crosby	.12	.30
39 Brooklyn Bridge	.12	.30
40 Adam Dunn	.20	.50
41 Lyle Overbay	.12	.30
42 Brian Fuentes	.12	.30
43 Scott Rolen SP	1.25	3.00
44 Matt Lindstrom (RC)	.20	.50
45 Carlos Zambrano	.20	.50
46 Cole Hamels	.30	.75
47 Matt Kemp	.20	.50
48 Gary Matthews SP	1.25	3.00
49 J.J. Putz	.12	.30
50 Albert Pujols	.75	2.00
51 Dan Haren	.12	.30
52 Aaron Harang	.12	.30
53 Ferris Wheel	.12	.30
54 Juan Rivera	.12	.30
55 Ken Griffey Jr.	.50	1.25
56 Chien-Ming Wang	.20	.50
57 Sean Henn (RC)	.20	.50
58 Mike Mussina SP	1.25	3.00
59 Ian Snell	.12	.30
60 Josh Barfield	.12	.30
61 Justin Morneau	.30	.75
62 Dwight D. Eisenhower	.12	.30
63 Bengie Molina SP	1.25	3.00
64 Brett Myers	.12	.30
65 Andy Marte	.12	.30
66 Bill Hall	.12	.30
67 Ryan Shealy	.12	.30
68 Joe B. Scott	.12	.30
69 Mike Rabelo RC	.20	.50
70 Jermaine Dye	.12	.30
71 Andre Ethier	.20	.50
72 Bruce Lee	.12	.30
73 Nick Punto	.12	.30
74 Ervin Santana	.12	.30
75 Troy Tulowitzki (RC)	1.25	3.00
76 Garret Anderson	.12	.30
77 Ryan Freel	.12	.30
78 Carlos Guillen	.12	.30
79 John Smoltz	.30	.75
80 Chase Utley	.30	.75
81 Mike Sweeney	.12	.30
82 Joe Frazier	.30	.75
83 Brad Lidge	.12	.30
84 Casey Blake	.12	.30
85 Ivan Rodriguez	.20	.50
86 Roy Oswalt	.20	.50
87 Akinori Iwamura RC	.50	1.25
88 Francisco Rodriguez	.20	.50
89 John Lackey	.20	.50
90 Miguel Cabrera	.30	.75
91 Kevin Mench	.12	.30
92 Victor Martinez	.20	.50
93 Chad Tracy	.12	.30
94 Charlie Manuel	.12	.30
95 Hanley Ramirez	.30	.75
96 Dontrelle Willis	.12	.30
97 Doug Slaten RC	.20	.50
98 Noah Lowry	.12	.30
99 Shawn Green	.12	.30
100 David Ortiz	.20	.50
101 Mark Reynolds RC	1.50	4.00
102 Preston Wilson	.12	.30
103 Mohandas Gandhi	.12	.30
104 Jeff Kent	.12	.30
105 Lance Berkman	.20	.50
106 C.C. Sabathia	.20	.50
107 Jason Varitek SP	1.25	3.00
108 Mark Twain	.12	.30
109 Melvin Mora	.12	.30
110 Michael Young SP	1.25	3.00
111 Scott Hatteberg	.12	.30
112 Erik Bedard	.12	.30
113 Sitting Bull	.12	.30
114 Homer Bailey (RC)	.30	.75
115 Mark Teahen	.12	.30
116 Ryan Braun (RC)	1.00	2.50
117 John Miles	.12	.30
118 Coco Crisp	.12	.30
119 Hunter Pence SP (RC)	2.00	5.00
120 Delmon Young (RC)	.30	.75
121 Aramis Ramirez	.12	.30
122 Magglio Ordonez	.20	.50
123 Tadahito Iguchi	.12	.30
124 Mark Selby	.12	.30
125 Gil Meche	.12	.30
126 Curt Schilling	.20	.50
127 Brandon Phillips	.12	.30
128 Milton Bradley	.12	.30
129 Craig Monroe	.12	.30
130 Jason Schmidt SP	1.25	3.00

2007 Topps Allen and Ginter

131 Nick Markakis .30 .75
132 Paul Konerko .20 .50
133 Carlos Gomez RC .30 .75
134 Garrett Atkins .12 .30
135 Jered Weaver .20 .50
136 Edgar Renteria .12 .30
137 Jason Isringhausen SP 1.25 3.00
138 Ray Durham .12 .30
139 Bob Baffert .12 .30
140 Nick Swisher .30 .75
141 Brian McCann .12 .30
142 Orlando Hudson .12 .30
143 Brian Bannister .12 .30
144 Manny Acta .12 .30
145 Jose Vidro .12 .30
146 Carlos Quentin .12 .30
147 Billy Butler (RC) .30 .75
148 Kenny Rogers .12 .30
149 Tom Gordon .12 .30
150 Derek Jeter .75 2.00
151 Bob Wickman .12 .30
152 Carlos Lee SP 1.25 3.00
153 Willy Taveras .12 .30
154 Paul LoDuca .12 .30
155 Ben Sheets .12 .30
156 Brian Roberts .12 .30
157 Freddy Adu .12 .30
158 Jason Kendall .12 .30
159 Michael Barrett SP 1.25 3.00
160 Frank Thomas .30 .75
161 Manny Ramirez .30 .75
162 Stanley Glenn .12 .30
163 Robinson Cano .30 .75
164 Phil Hughes (RC) 1.00 2.50
165 Joe Mauer .30 .75
166 Derrek Lee .12 .30
167 Jeff Weaver .12 .30
168 Joe Smith RC .12 .30
169 Louis Pasteur .12 .30
170 Gary Sheffield .12 .30
171 Luis Castillo .12 .30
172 Joe Torre .20 .50
173 Andy LaRoche (RC) .20 .50
174 Jamie Fischer .12 .30
175 Carlos Beltran .12 .30
176 Bronson Arroyo .12 .30
177 Rafael Furcal .12 .30
178 Juan Pierre SP 1.25 3.00
179 Matt Cain .20 .50
180 Alfonso Soriano .20 .50
181 Joe Borowski .12 .30
182 Conor Jackson .12 .30
183 Groundhog Day .12 .30
184 Pat Burrell .12 .30
185 Troy Glaus .12 .30
186 Joel Zumaya .20 .50
187 Russell Martin .12 .30
188 Josh Willingham .12 .30
189 Jarrod Saltalamacchia (RC) .30 .75
190 Scott Kazmir .20 .50
191 Jeremy Hermida .12 .30
192 Tower Bridge .12 .30
193 Rich Hill SP 1.25 3.00
194 Francisco Cordero SP 1.25 3.00
195 Mike Piazza .30 .75
196 Brad Ausmus .12 .30
197 Greg Louganis .12 .30
198 Frank Catalanotto .12 .30
199 Alejandro De Aza RC .30 .75
200 David Wright .50 1.25
201 Freddy Sanchez .12 .30
202 Shea Hillenbrand .12 .30
203 Justin Verlander SP 1.25 3.00
204 Alex Gordon RC .60 1.50
205 Jimmy Rollins .20 .50
206 Mike Napoli .20 .50
207 Chris Burke .12 .30
208 Chipper Jones .30 .75
209 Randy Johnson .30 .75
210 Daisuke Matsuzaka RC .75 2.00
211 Orlando Cabrera .12 .30
212 B.J. Upton .12 .30
213 Lou Piniella MG .12 .30
214 Mike Cameron .12 .30
215 Luis Gonzalez .12 .30
216 Rickie Weeks .20 .50
217 Hideki Okajima RC 1.00 2.50
218 Johnny Estrada .12 .30
219 Dan Uggla SP 1.25 3.00
220 Ryan Zimmerman .20 .50
221 Tony Gwynn Jr. .12 .30
222 Rocco Baldelli SP 1.25 3.00
223 Xavier Nady .12 .30
224 Josh Bard SP 1.25 3.00
225 Raul Ibanez .20 .50
226 Chris Carpenter .30 .75
227 Matt DeSalvo (RC) .20 .50
228 Jack the Ripper .12 .30
229 Eric Chavez .12 .30
230 Jose Reyes .20 .50
231 Glen Perkins (RC) .20 .50
232 Gregg Zaun .12 .30
233 Jim Thome .20 .50
234 Joe Crede .12 .30
235 Barry Zito .20 .50
236 Yoel Hernandez RC .20 .50
237 Kelly Johnson .12 .30
238 Chris Young .12 .30
239 Fyodor Dostoevsky .12 .30
240 Miguel Tejada .20 .50
241 Doug Mientkiewicz .12 .30
242 Bobby Jenks .12 .30
243 Brad Hawpe SP 1.25 3.00
244 Jay Marshall RC .20 .50
245 Brad Penny .12 .30
246 Johnny Damon .20 .50
247 Dave Roberts .12 .30
248 Ron Washington .12 .30
249 Mike Aponte .12 .30
250 Brandon Webb .20 .50
251 Andy Pettitte .20 .50
252 Bud Black .12 .30
253 Michael Cuddyer .12 .30
254 Chris Stewart RC .20 .50
255 Mark Teixeira .30 .75
256 Hideki Matsui .30 .75
257 Curtis Granderson .20 .50
258 A.J. Pierzynski .12 .30
259 Tony La Russa .20 .50
260 Andruw Jones .12 .30
261 Torii Hunter .12 .30
262 Mark Loretta .12 .30
263 Jim Edmonds SP 1.25 3.00
264 Aaron Rowand .12 .30
265 Roy Halladay .30 .75
266 Freddy Garcia .12 .30
267 Reggie Sanders .12 .30
268 Washington Monument .12 .30
269 Franklin D. Roosevelt .12 .30
270 Alex Rodriguez .50 1.25
271 Wes Helms .12 .30
272 Mia Hamm .12 .30
273 Jorge Posada .20 .50
274 Tim Lincecum RC 3.00 8.00
275 Bobby Abreu .12 .30
276 Zach Duke .12 .30
277 Carlos Delgado .12 .30
278 Julio Juarez .12 .30
279 Brandon Inge .12 .30
280 Todd Helton .20 .50
281 Marcus Giles .12 .30
282 Josh Johnson .30 .75
283 Chris Capuano .12 .30
284 B.J. Ryan .12 .30
285 Nick Johnson .12 .30
286 Khalil Greene .12 .30
287 Travis Hafner .12 .30
288 Ted Lilly .12 .30
289 Jim Leyland .12 .30
290 Prince Fielder .20 .50
291 Trevor Hoffman .20 .50
292 Brian Giles .12 .30
293 Omar Vizquel .20 .50
294 Julio Lugo .12 .30
295 Jake Peavy .12 .30
296 Adrian Beltre .12 .30
297 Josh Beckett .20 .50
298 Harry S. Truman .12 .30
299 Mark Buehrle .20 .50
300 Ichiro Suzuki .50 1.25
301 Chris Duncan SP 1.25 3.00
302 Augie Garrido SP CO 1.25 3.00
303 Tyler Clippard SP (RC) 1.25 3.00
304 Ramon Hernandez .12 .30
305 Jeremy Bonderman .12 .30
306 Morgan Ensberg SP 1.25 3.00
307 J.J. Hardy SP 1.25 3.00
308 Mark Zupan SP 1.25 3.00
309 Laila Ali SP 1.25 3.00
310 Greg Maddux SP 1.50 4.00
311 David Ross .12 .30
312 Chris Duffy .12 .30
313 Moises Alou .12 .30
314 Yadier Molina .20 .50
315 Corey Patterson .12 .30
316 Dan O'Brien SP 1.25 3.00
317 Michael Bourn SP (RC) 1.25 3.00
318 Jonny Gomes SP 1.25 3.00
319 Ken Jennings SP 1.25 3.00
320 Barry Bonds SP 1.50 4.00
321 Gary Hall Jr. SP 1.25 3.00
322 Kerri Walsh SP 1.25 3.00
323 Craig Biggio .20 .50
324 Ian Kinsler .20 .50
325 Grady Sizemore SP 1.25 3.00
326 Alex Rios SP 1.25 3.00
327 Ted Toles SP 1.25 3.00
328 Jason Jennings .12 .30
329 Vernon Wells .12 .30
330 Bob Geren SP MG 1.25 3.00
331 Dennis Rodman SP 1.25 3.00
332 Tom Glavine .20 .50
333 Pedro Martinez .20 .50
334 Gustavo Molina SP RC 1.25 3.00
335 Bartolo Colon SP 1.25 3.00
336 Misty May-Treanor SP 1.25 3.00
337 Randy Winn .12 .30
338 Eric Byrnes .12 .30
339 Jason McElwain SP 1.25 3.00
340 Placido Polanco SP 1.25 3.00
341 Adrian Gonzalez .20 .50
342 Chad Cordero .12 .30
343 Jeff Francis .12 .30
344 Lastings Milledge .20 .50
345 Sammy Sosa SP 1.25 3.00
346 Jacque Jones .12 .30
347 Anibal Sanchez .12 .30
348 Roger Clemens SP 1.50 4.00
349 Jesse Litsch SP RC 1.25 3.00
350 Adam LaRoche SP 1.25 3.00
NNO Framed Originals 50.00 100.00

2007 Topps Allen and Ginter Mini

*MINI 1-350: 1X TO 2.5X BASIC
*MINI 1-350: .6X TO 1.5X BASIC RC's
APPX. ONE MINI PER PACK
*MINI SP 1-350: .6X TO 1.5X BASIC SP
*MINI SP 1-350: .6X TO 1.5X BASIC SP RC's
MINI SP ODDS 1:13 H, 1:13 R
COMMON CARD (351-390) 15.00 40.00
351-390 RANDOM WITHIN RIP CARDS
OVERALL PLATE ODDS 1:788 HOBBY
PLATE PRINT RUN 1 SET PER COLOR
BLACK-CYAN-MAGENTA-YELLOW ISSUED
NO PLATE PRICING DUE TO SCARCITY
351 Alex Rodriguez EXT 40.00 80.00
352 Ryan Zimmerman EXT 20.00 50.00
353 Prince Fielder EXT 40.00 80.00
354 Gary Sheffield EXT 15.00 40.00
355 Jermaine Dye EXT 15.00 40.00
356 Hanley Ramirez EXT 15.00 40.00
357 Jose Reyes EXT 30.00 60.00
358 Miguel Tejada EXT 20.00 50.00
359 Elijah Dukes EXT 15.00 40.00
360 Ryan Howard EXT 30.00 60.00
361 Vladimir Guerrero EXT 15.00 40.00
362 Ichiro Suzuki EXT 40.00 80.00
363 Jason Bay EXT 15.00 40.00
364 Justin Morneau EXT 15.00 40.00
365 Michael Young EXT 15.00 40.00
366 Adam Dunn EXT 15.00 40.00
367 Alfonso Soriano EXT 20.00 50.00
368 Jake Peavy EXT 20.00 50.00
369 Nick Swisher EXT 20.00 50.00
370 David Wright EXT 30.00 60.00
371 Brandon Webb EXT 20.00 50.00
372 Brian McCann EXT 20.00 50.00
373 Frank Thomas EXT 20.00 50.00
374 Albert Pujols EXT 30.00 60.00
375 Russell Martin EXT 20.00 50.00
376 Felix Hernandez EXT 15.00 40.00
377 Barry Bonds EXT 40.00 80.00
378 Lance Berkman EXT 15.00 40.00
379 Joe Mauer EXT 30.00 60.00
380 B.J. Upton EXT 15.00 40.00
381 Todd Helton EXT 15.00 40.00
382 Paul Konerko EXT 20.00 50.00
383 Grady Sizemore EXT 20.00 50.00
384 Magglio Ordonez EXT 15.00 40.00
385 Dan Uggla EXT 20.00 50.00
386 J.D. Drew EXT 15.00 40.00
387 Adam LaRoche EXT 15.00 40.00
388 Carlos Beltran EXT 15.00 40.00
389 Derek Jeter EXT 40.00 80.00
390 Daisuke Matsuzaka EXT 75.00 200.00

2007 Topps Allen and Ginter Mini A and G Back

*A & G BACK: 1.25X TO 3X BASIC
*A & G BACK: .75X TO 2X BASIC RC's
STATED ODDS 1:5 H, 1:5 R
*A & G BACK SP: .75X TO 2X BASIC SP
*A & G BACK SP: .75X TO 2X BASIC SP RC's
SP STATED ODDS 1:65 H, 1:65 R

2007 Topps Allen and Ginter Mini Bazooka

STATED ODDS 1:213 H, 1:214 R
STATED PRINT RUN 25 SERIAL #'d SETS
NO PRICING DUE TO SCARCITY

2007 Topps Allen and Ginter Mini Black

*BLACK: 2X TO 5X BASIC
*BLACK: 1.5X TO 4X BASIC RC's
STATED ODDS 1:10 H, 1:10 R
*BLACK SP: 1.5X TO 4X BASIC SP
*BLACK SP: 1.5X TO 4X BASIC SP RC's
SP STATED ODDS 1:130 H, 1:130 R

2007 Topps Allen and Ginter Mini Black No Number

*BLK NO NBR: 2.5X TO 6X BASIC
*BLK NO NBR: 2X TO 5X BASIC RC's
*BLK NO NBR: 1.5X TO 4X BASIC SP
*BLK NO NBR: 1.5X TO 4X BASIC SP RC's
RANDOM INSERTS IN PACKS
210 Daisuke Matsuzaka 6.00 15.00

2007 Topps Allen and Ginter Mini No Card Number

*NO NBR: 10X TO 25X BASIC
*NO NBR: 6X TO 15X BASIC RC's
*NO NBR: 2.5X TO 6X BASIC SP
*NO NBR: 2.5X TO 6X BASIC SP RC's
STATED ODDS 1:106 H, 1:108 R
STATED PRINT RUN 50 SETS
CARDS ARE NOT SERIAL-NUMBERED
PRINT RUN INFO PROVIDED BY TOPPS
7 Mickey Mantle 40.00 80.00
50 Albert Pujols 30.00 60.00
55 Ken Griffey Jr. 40.00 80.00
56 Chien-Ming Wang 30.00 60.00
150 Derek Jeter 40.00 80.00
270 Alex Rodriguez 30.00 60.00
300 Ichiro Suzuki 40.00 80.00
320 Barry Bonds SP 40.00 80.00

2007 Topps Allen and Ginter Mini Wood

STATED ODDS 1:3507 HOBBY
STATED PRINT RUN 1 SERIAL #'d SET
NO PRICING DUE TO SCARCITY

2007 Topps Allen and Ginter Autographs

GROUP A ODDS 1:64,496 H, 1:122200 R
GROUP B ODDS 1:3261 H, 1:6522 R
GROUP C ODDS 1:13,987 H, 1:27,642 R
GROUP D ODDS 1:288 H, 1:578 R
GROUP E ODDS 1:6789 H, 1:13,578 R
GROUP F ODDS 1:162 H, 1:324 R
GROUP G ODDS 1:680 H, 1:1362 R
GROUP A PRINT RUN 25 CARDS PER
GROUP B PRINT RUN 100 CARDS PER
GROUP C PRINT RUN 120 CARDS PER
GROUP D PRINT RUN 200 CARDS PER
GROUP A-D ARE NOT SERIAL-NUMBERED
A-D PRINT RUNS PROVIDED BY TOPPS
NO PUJOLS PRICING DUE TO SCARCITY
EXCH DEADLINE 7/31/2009
AE Andre Ethier F 10.00 25.00
AG Augie Garrido D/200 * 30.00 60.00
AG2 Adrian Gonzalez F 12.50 30.00
AI Akinori Iwamura F 10.00 25.00
AP Albert Pujols A/25 *
AR Alex Rodriguez E/225 * 125.00 250.00
BB Bob Baffert D/200 * 30.00 60.00
BC Brian Cashman B/100 * 40.00 80.00
BH Bill Hall G 6.00 15.00
BPB Brian Bannister F 10.00 25.00
CG Curtis Granderson F 10.00 25.00
CH Cole Hamels F 10.00 25.00
CMW Chien-Ming Wang D/200 * 150.00 250.00
CS Cael Sanderson D/200 * 30.00 60.00
DO Dan O'Brien D/200 * 12.50 30.00
DR Dennis Rodman D/200 * 30.00 60.00
DW David Wright D/200 * 60.00 120.00
ES Ervin Santana F 6.00 15.00
FA Freddy Adu D/200 * 15.00 40.00
GH Gary Hall Jr. D/200 * 20.00 50.00
HK Howie Kendrick F 6.00 15.00
HR Hanley Ramirez F 15.00 40.00
JBS Joe B. Scott D/200 * 40.00 80.00
JF Jamie Fischer D/200 * 20.00 50.00
JH Jeremy Hermida G 5.00 12.00
JM Justin Morneau F 12.50 30.00
JMC Jason McElwain D/200 * 20.00 50.00
JMM John Miles D/200 * 12.50 30.00
JP Jonathan Papelbon F 15.00 40.00
JS Johan Santana B/100 * 60.00 120.00
JT Jim Thome B/100 * 100.00 200.00
KJ Ken Jennings D/200 * 30.00 60.00
KW Kerri Walsh D/200 * 40.00 80.00
LA Laila Ali D/200 * 60.00 120.00
MA Mike Aponte D/200 * 15.00 40.00
MEI Maicer Izturis F 6.00 15.00
MGA Mario Andretti D/200 * 40.00 80.00
MMT Misty May-Treanor D/200 * 50.00 100.00
MN Mike Napoli F 10.00 25.00
MS Mark Selby D/200 * 12.50 30.00
MZ Mark Zupan D/200 * 10.00 25.00
NL Nook Logan G 5.00 12.00
NM Nick Markakis F 10.00 25.00
RH Ryan Howard B/100 * 50.00 100.00
RM Russell Martin F 10.00 25.00
RZ Ryan Zimmerman F 12.50 30.00
SG Stanley Glenn D/200 * 40.00 80.00
SJF Joe Frazier C/120 * 150.00 250.00
TH Torii Hunter F 8.00 20.00
TS Tommie Smith D/200 * 40.00 80.00
TT Ted Toles D/200 * 15.00 40.00
TTT Troy Tulowitzki F 40.00 80.00

2007 Topps Allen and Ginter Autographs Red Ink

UNFRAMED RANDOM INSERTS IN RIP CARDS
FRAMED RANDOM INSERTS IN PACKS
STATED PRINT RUN 10 SETS
NO PRICING DUE TO SCARCITY
UNF EQUALS UNFRAMED

2007 Topps Allen and Ginter Cut Signatures

STATED ODDS 1:145,116 HOBBY
STATED ODDS 1:290,232 RETAIL
STATED PRINT RUN 1 SER.#'d SET
NO PRICING DUE TO SCARCITY
1 Franklin D. Roosevelt
2 Jack Dempsey
3 Orville Wright
4 General James Doolittle
5 Admiral Richard E. Byrd
6 Mother Teresa
7 Fidel Castro
8 Charles Lindbergh
9 Roy Rogers
10 William Randolph Hearst

2007 Topps Allen and Ginter Dick Perez

COMPLETE SET (30) 6.00 15.00
APPX.ONE PEREZ PER PACK
ORIGINALS RANDOM WITHIN RIP CARDS
ORIGINALS PRINT RUN 1 SERIAL #'d SET
NO ORIG. PRICING DUE TO SCARCITY
1 Brandon Webb .30 .75
2 Chipper Jones .50 1.25
3 Nick Markakis .50 1.25
4 Daisuke Matsuzaka .75 2.00
5 Alfonso Soriano .30 .75
6 Jermaine Dye .20 .50
7 Adam Dunn .30 .75
8 Grady Sizemore .30 .75
9 Troy Tulowitzki 1.25 3.00
10 Gary Sheffield .20 .50
11 Hanley Ramirez .50 1.25
12 Carlos Lee .20 .50
13 Mark Teahen .20 .50
14 Gary Matthews .20 .50
15 Andre Ethier .30 .75
16 Prince Fielder .30 .75
17 Joe Mauer .50 1.25
18 Jose Reyes .30 .75
19 Derek Jeter 1.25 3.00
20 Nick Swisher .50 1.25
21 Ryan Howard .75 2.00
22 Freddy Sanchez .20 .50
23 Greg Maddux .75 2.00
24 Raul Ibanez .30 .75
25 Barry Zito .20 .50
26 Jim Edmonds .30 .75
27 Delmon Young .30 .75
28 Michael Young .20 .50
29 Roy Halladay .50 1.25
30 Ryan Zimmerman .30 .75

2007 Topps Allen and Ginter Mini Emperors

STATED ODDS 1:72 H, 1:72 R
1 Julius Caesar 2.00 5.00
2 Caesar Augustus 2.00 5.00
3 Tiberius 2.00 5.00
4 Caligula 2.00 5.00
5 Claudius 2.00 5.00
6 Nero 2.00 5.00
7 Titus 2.00 5.00
8 Hadrian 2.00 5.00
9 Marcus Aurelius 2.00 5.00
10 Septimus Severus 2.00 5.00

2007 Topps Allen and Ginter Mini Flags

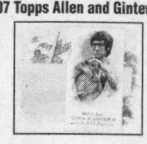

COMPLETE SET (50) 100.00 175.00
STATED ODDS 1:12 H, 1:12 R
1 Algeria 1.50 4.00
2 Argentina 1.50 4.00
3 Australia 1.50 4.00
4 Austria 1.50 4.00
5 Belgium 1.50 4.00
6 Brazil 1.50 4.00
7 Bulgaria 1.50 4.00
8 Canada 1.50 4.00
9 Chile 1.50 4.00
10 China 1.50 4.00
11 Colombia 1.50 4.00
12 Costa Rica 1.50 4.00
13 Denmark 1.50 4.00
14 Dominican Republic 1.50 4.00
15 Ecuador 1.50 4.00
16 Egypt 1.50 4.00
17 France 1.50 4.00
18 Germany 1.50 4.00
19 Greece 1.50 4.00
20 Greenland 1.50 4.00
21 Honduras 1.50 4.00
22 Iceland 1.50 4.00
23 India 1.50 4.00
24 Indonesia 1.50 4.00
25 Ireland 1.50 4.00
26 Israel 1.50 4.00
27 Italy 1.50 4.00
28 Ivory Coast 1.50 4.00
29 Jamaica 1.50 4.00
30 Japan 1.50 4.00
31 Kenya 1.50 4.00
32 Mexico 1.50 4.00
33 Morocco 1.50 4.00
34 Netherlands 1.50 4.00
35 Nigeria 1.50 4.00
36 Norway 1.50 4.00
37 Panama 1.50 4.00
38 Peru 1.50 4.00
39 Philippines 1.50 4.00
40 Portugal 1.50 4.00
41 Puerto Rico 1.50 4.00
42 Russian Federation 1.50 4.00
43 Spain 1.50 4.00
44 Switzerland 1.50 4.00
45 Taiwan 1.50 4.00
46 Thailand 1.50 4.00
47 Turkey 1.50 4.00
48 United Arab Emirates 1.50 4.00
49 United Kingdom 1.50 4.00
50 United States of America 1.50 4.00

2007 Topps Allen and Ginter Mini Snakes

STATED ODDS 1:144 H, 1:144 R
1 Arizona Coral Snake 8.00 20.00
2 Copperhead 8.00 20.00
3 Black Mamba 8.00 20.00
4 King Cobra 8.00 20.00
5 Cottonmouth 8.00 20.00

2007 Topps Allen and Ginter N43

STATED ODDS 1:3 HOBBY BOX LOADER
AP Albert Pujols 2.50 6.00
AR Alex Rodriguez 1.50 4.00
BB Barry Bonds 2.00 5.00
BL Bruce Lee .40 1.00
DJ Ch Felicity's Diamond Jim 4.00 10.00
DM Daisuke Matsuzaka 1.50 4.00
DW David Wright 1.50 4.00
GL Greg Louganis .40 1.00
IS Ichiro Suzuki 1.50 4.00
JF Joe Frazier 1.00 2.50
MA Mario Andretti 1.00 2.50
PF Prince Fielder .60 1.50
RH Ryan Howard 1.50 4.00
RZ Ryan Zimmerman .60 1.50
VG Vladimir Guerrero 1.00 2.50

2007 Topps Allen and Ginter N43 Autographs

GROUP A ODDS 1:1747 HOBBY BOX LOADER
GROUP B ODDS 1:1034 HOBBY BOX LOADER
GROUP A PRINT RUN 10 SER.#'d SETS
GROUP B PRINT RUN 50 SER.#'d SETS
NO GROUP A PRICING AVAILABLE
AR Alex Rodriguez A/10
DJ Ch Felicity's Diamond Jim B/50 300.00450.00
DW David Wright A/10
RH Ryan Howard A/10

2007 Topps Allen and Ginter N43 Relics

STATED ODDS 1:205 HOBBY BOX LOADER
STATED PRINT RUN 25 SER.#'d SETS
NO PRICING DUE TO SCARCITY

2007 Topps Allen and Ginter National Pride

STATED ODDS 1:2 HOBBY BOX LOADER
1 Kei Igawa 2.00 5.00
Daisuke Matsuzaka
Hideki Matsui
Ichiro Suzuki
2 Hideki Okajima 2.50 6.00
Akinori Iwamura
Kenji Johjima
Tadahito Iguchi
3 Bobby Abreu 1.25 3.00
Miguel Cabrera
Felix Hernandez
Johan Santana
4 Shin-Soo Choo .75 2.00
Chan Ho Park
Byung-Hyun Kim
Jae Kuk Ryu
5 Jason Bay 1.25 3.00
Russell Martin
Justin Morneau
Rich Harden
6 Hanley Ramirez 1.25 3.00
Manny Ramirez
Aramis Ramirez
Vladimir Guerrero
7 Jose Reyes 3.00 8.00
Pedro Martinez
David Ortiz
Albert Pujols
8 Carlos Beltran .75 2.00
Carlos Delgado
Ivan Rodriguez
Jorge Posada
9 Prince Fielder .75 2.00
Alex Rodriguez
Ryan Howard
David Wright
10 Brandon Webb 1.50 4.00
Justin Verlander
Greg Maddux
John Smoltz

2007 Topps Allen and Ginter Relics

GROUP A ODDS 1:1,160,000 H
GROUP A ODDS 1:243,648 R
GROUP B ODDS 1:31,376 H, 1:62,750 R
GROUP C ODDS 1:15,275 H, 1:30,550 R
GROUP D ODDS 1:383 H, 1:766 R
GROUP E ODDS 1:1530 H, 1:3068 R
GROUP F ODDS 1:510 H, 1:1022 R
GROUP G ODDS 1:109 H, 1:218 R
GROUP H ODDS 1:69 H, 1:140 R
GROUP I ODDS 1:340 H, 1:680 R
GROUP J ODDS 1:25 H, 1:48 R
GROUP B PRINT RUN 50 COPIES PER
GROUP C PRINT RUN 100 COPIES PER
GROUP D PRINT RUN 250 COPIES PER
GROUP B-D ARE NOT SERIAL-NUMBERED
GROUP B-D QTY PROVIDED BY TOPPS
NO WASHINGTON PRICING AVAILABLE
AER Alex Rodriguez Bat D/250 * 15.00 40.00
AL Adam LaRoche J 3.00 8.00
AP Albert Pujols Bat E 8.00 20.00
AR Aramis Ramirez J 3.00 8.00
AS Arthur Shorin B/50 * 150.00 300.00
BB Barry Bonds Pants D/250 * 20.00 50.00
BC Brian Cashman D/250 * 15.00 40.00
BL Bruce Lee D/250 * 225.00 325.00
BR Brian Roberts J 3.00 8.00
BZ Barry Zito Pants J 3.00 8.00
CB Carlos Beltran Bat I 3.00 8.00
CC Carl Crawford Bat H 3.00 8.00
CK Casey Kotchman J 3.00 8.00
CLC Coco Crisp Bat D 3.00 8.00
CMS Curt Schilling J 4.00 10.00
CP Corey Patterson Bat F 3.00 8.00
CT Chad Tracy Bat G 3.00 8.00
DAO David Ortiz Bat D/250 * 6.00 15.00
DL Derrek Lee Bat H 3.00 8.00
DO Dan O'Brien D/250 * 10.00 25.00
DW Dontrelle Willis J 3.00 8.00
EC Eric Chavez Pants J 3.00 8.00
EG Eric Gagne J 3.00 8.00
GH Gary Hall Jr. D/250 * 10.00 25.00
GW1 George Washington Hair A/1 *
GW2 George Washington Hair A/1 *
GW3 George Washington Hair A/1 *
HB Hank Blalock J 3.00 8.00
HR Hanley Ramirez Bat G 4.00 10.00
IR Ivan Rodriguez J 4.00 10.00
JB Jason Bay Bat H 3.00 8.00
JF Jamie Fischer D/250 * 10.00 25.00
JG Jason Giambi Bat H 3.00 8.00
JJ Julio Juarez D/250 * 8.00 20.00
KJ Ken Jennings D/250 * 10.00 25.00
KO Keith Olbermann C/100 * 75.00 200.00
KW Kerri Walsh D/250 * 10.00 25.00
LA Laila Ali D/250 * 20.00 50.00
MC1 Miguel Cabrera G 4.00 10.00
MC2 Miguel Cabrera Bat G 4.00 10.00
MCM Mike Mussina Pants J 4.00 10.00
MG Marcus Giles J 3.00 8.00
MH Mia Hamm D/250 * 15.00 40.00
MM Mickey Mantle Bat D/250 * 60.00 120.00
MMU Mark Mulder Pants J 3.00 8.00
MP Mike Piazza Bat H 4.00 10.00
MR Manny Ramirez Bat H 4.00 10.00
MT Miguel Tejada J 3.00 8.00
NS Nick Swisher Bat H 3.00 8.00
PF Prince Fielder Bat G 6.00 15.00
PK Paul Konerko Bat H 3.00 8.00
PL Paul LoDuca J 3.00 8.00
RA Rich Aurilia Bat G 3.00 8.00
RC Robinson Cano Bat F 4.00 10.00
RH Rich Harden Pants J 3.00 8.00
RW Randy Winn J 3.00 8.00
SD Stephen Drew J 3.00 8.00
SJF Joe Frazier D/250 * 20.00 50.00
SP Scott Podsednik Bat G 3.00 8.00
SR1 Scott Rolen G 4.00 10.00
SR2 Scott Rolen Bat G 4.00 10.00
SS Sammy Sosa Bat I 4.00 10.00
TG Troy Glaus Bat H 3.00 8.00
TN Trot Nixon Bat G 3.00 8.00
TS Tommie Smith D/250 * 12.50 30.00
VG Vladimir Guerrero Bat H 4.00 10.00

2007 Topps Allen and Ginter Rip Card

STATED ODDS 1:285 HOBBY
PRINT RUNS B/WN 10-99 COPIES PER
NO PRICING ON QTY 10 OR LESS
ALL LISTED PRICED ARE FOR RIPPED
UNRIPPED HAVE ADD'L CARDS WITHIN
1 Grady Sizemore/90 10.00 25.00
2 Miguel Cabrera/75 10.00 25.00
3 Adam Dunn/95 6.00 15.00
4 Jose Reyes/99 10.00 25.00
5 Alfonso Soriano/90 6.00 15.00
6 Chase Utley/99 10.00 25.00
7 Frank Thomas/95 10.00 25.00
8 Andruw Jones/95 10.00 25.00
9 Nick Markakis/75 10.00 25.00
10 Felix Hernandez/99 10.00 25.00
11 Jered Weaver/99 10.00 25.00
12 Ivan Rodriguez/99 10.00 25.00
13 Joe Mauer/99 10.00 25.00
14 Derek Jeter/99 20.00 50.00
15 Delmon Young/
16 Brandon Webb/10
17 Miguel Tejada/75 6.00 15.00
18 Vladimir Guerrero/75 10.00 25.00
19 Greg Maddux/99 15.00 40.00
20 Michael Young/99 6.00 15.00
21 Barry Zito/99 6.00 15.00

22 Russell Martin/95 6.00 15.00
23 Daisuke Matsuzaka/99 90.00 150.00
24 Stephen Drew/95 10.00 25.00
25 Alex Rodriguez/99 15.00 40.00
26 J.D. Drew/99 6.00 15.00
27 Paul Konerko/99 6.00 15.00
28 Josh Hamilton /90 20.00 50.00
29 Mike Piazza /99 10.00 25.00
30 Ryan Howard/10
31 Carl Crawford/99 6.00 15.00
32 Adam LaRoche/90 6.00 15.00
33 Bill Hall/95 6.00 15.00
34 Scott Kazmir/95 10.00 25.00
35 Gary Matthews/99 6.00 15.00
36 Gary Sheffield/99 6.00 15.00
37 Francisco Rodriguez/95 6.00 15.00
38 Todd Helton/99 10.00 25.00
39 Dontrelle Willis/10
40 David Wright/99 15.00 40.00
41 David Ortiz/10
42 Barry Bonds/99 20.00 50.00
43 Johan Santana/75 10.00 25.00
44 Albert Pujols/90 20.00 50.00
45 Carlos Lee/99 6.00 15.00
46 Cole Hamels/95 10.00 25.00
47 Prince Fielder/99 10.00 25.00
48 Hanley Ramirez/99 10.00 25.00
49 Ryan Zimmerman/90 10.00 25.00
50 Kei Igawa/75 10.00 25.00

2007 Topps Allen and Ginter National Mini Promos

NCC4 Grady Sizemore .75 2.00
NCC5 C.C. Sabathia .60 1.50
NCC6 Victor Martinez .60 1.50

2007 Topps Allen and Ginter National Promos

NCC4 Grady Sizemore .75 2.00
NCC5 C.C. Sabathia .60 1.50
NCC6 Victor Martinez .60 1.50

2008 Topps Allen and Ginter

COMP.SET w/o FUKU.(350) 50.00 100.00
COMP.SET w/o SPs (300) 15.00 40.00
COMMON CARD (1-300) .15 .40
COMMON RC (1-300) .40 1.00
COMMON SP (301-350) 1.25 3.00
SP STATED ODDS 1:2 HOBBY
FRAMED ORIG.ODDS 1:26,500 HOBBY
1 Alex Rodriguez .60 1.50
2 Juan Pierre .15 .40
3 Benjamin Franklin .25 .60
4 Roy Halladay .40 1.00
5 C.C. Sabathia .25 .60
6 Brian Barton RC .60 1.50
7 Mickey Mantle 1.25 3.00
8 Brian Bass (RC) .40 1.00
9 Ian Kinsler .25 .60
10 Manny Ramirez .40 1.00
11 Michael Cuddyer .15 .40
12 Ian Snell .15 .40
13 Mike Lowell .15 .40
14 Adrian Gonzalez .25 .60
15 B.J. Upton .25 .60
16 Hiroki Kuroda RC .60 1.50
17 Kenji Johjima .15 .40
18 James Loney .25 .60
19 Albert Einstein .25 .60
20 Vladimir Guerrero .40 1.00
21 Miguel Tejada .25 .60
22 Chin-Lung Hu (RC) .60 1.50
23 A.J. Burnett .25 .60
24 Bobby Jenks .15 .40
25 Aramis Ramirez .15 .40
26 Corey Hart .15 .40
27 Brad Hawpe .15 .40
28 Adam LaRoche .15 .40
29 Empire State Building .25 .60
30 Miguel Cabrera .40 1.00
31 Ryan Zimmerman .25 .60
32 Mark Ellis .15 .40
33 Nick Swisher .40 1.00
34 Bill Hall .15 .40
35 Eric Byrnes .15 .40
36 Michael Young .25 .60
37 Pedro Martinez .25 .60
38 Andruw Jones .15 .40
39 J.R. Towles RC .60 1.50
40 Justin Upton .25 .60
41 Paul Konerko .25 .60
42 Luke Scott .15 .40
43 Rickie Weeks .15 .40
44 Adam Wainwright .25 .60
45 Justin Morneau .40 1.00
46 Chris Young .15 .40
47 Chad Billingsley .15 .40
48 Kazuo Matsui .15 .40
49 Shane Victorino .15 .40
50 Albert Pujols 1.00 2.50
51 Brian McCann .25 .60
52 Carlos Delgado .15 .40
53 Chien-Ming Wang .25 .60
54 Takashi Saito .15 .40
55 Josh Beckett .25 .60
56 Nick Johnson .15 .40
57 Ben Sheets .15 .40
58 Johnny Damon .25 .60
59 Nicky Hayden .25 .60
60 Prince Fielder .25 .60
61 Adam Dunn .25 .60
62 Dustin Pedroia .50 1.25
63 Jacoby Ellsbury .60 1.50
64 Brad Penny .15 .40
65 Victor Martinez .25 .60
66 Joe Mauer .40 1.00
67 Kevin Kouzmanoff .15 .40
68 Frank Thomas .40 1.00
69 Stevie Williams .25 .60
70 Matt Holliday .40 1.00
71 Fausto Carmona .15 .40
72 Clayton Kershaw RC 2.00 5.00
73 Tadahito Iguchi .15 .40
74 Khalil Greene .15 .40
75 Travis Hafner .15 .40
76 Jim Thome .25 .60
77 Joba Chamberlain .25 .60
78 Ivan Rodriguez .25 .60
79 Jose Guillen .15 .40
80 Hanley Ramirez .40 1.00
81 Vernon Wells .15 .40
82 Jayson Nix (RC) .40 1.00
83 Masahide Kobayashi RC .60 1.50
84 Bonnie Blair .25 .60
85 Curtis Granderson .25 .60
86 Kelvim Escobar .15 .40
87 Aaron Rowand .15 .40
88 Troy Glaus .25 .60
89 Billy Wagner .15 .40
90 Jose Reyes .25 .60
91 Scott Rolen .25 .60
92 Dan Jansen .25 .60
93 David Eckstein .15 .40
94 Tom Gorzelanny .15 .40
95 Garrett Atkins .15 .40
96 Carlos Zambrano .25 .60
97 Jeff Francis .15 .40
98 Kazuo Fukumori RC .60 1.50
99 John Bowker (RC) .40 1.00
100 David Wright .50 1.25
101 Adrian Beltre .15 .40
102 Ray Durham .15 .40
103 Kerri Strug .25 .60
104 Orlando Hudson .15 .40
105 Jonathan Papelbon .25 .60
106 Brian Schneider .15 .40
107 Matt Biondi .25 .60
108 Alex Romero (RC) .60 1.50
109 Joey Chestnut .25 .60
110 Chase Utley .40 1.00
111 Dan Uggla .25 .60
112 Akinori Iwamura .15 .40
113 Curt Schilling .25 .60
114 Trevor Hoffman .25 .60
115 Alex Rios .15 .40
116 Mariano Rivera .40 1.00
117 Jeff Niemann (RC) .40 1.00
118 Geovany Soto .40 1.00
119 Billy Mitchell .25 .60
120 Derek Jeter 1.00 2.50
121 Yovani Gallardo .15 .40
122 The Gateway Arch .25 .60
123 Josh Willingham .15 .40
124 Greg Maddux .50 1.25
125 John Lackey .15 .40
126 Chris Young .15 .40
127 Billy Butler .15 .40
128 Golden Gate Bridge .25 .60
129 Joey Votto (RC) 1.50 4.00
130 Tim Wakefield .15 .40
131 Todd Helton .25 .60
132 Gary Matthews .15 .40
133 Wild Bill Hickok .25 .60
134 Jason Varitek .40 1.00
135 Robinson Cano .40 1.00
136 Javier Vazquez .15 .40
137 Annie Oakley .25 .60
138 Andy Pettitte .25 .60
139 Greg Reynolds RC .60 1.50
140 Jimmy Rollins .25 .60
141 Jermaine Dye .15 .40
142 Eugenio Velez RC .40 1.00
143 J.J. Hardy .15 .40
144 Grand Canyon .25 .60
145 Bobby Abreu .15 .40
146 Scott Kazmir .25 .60
147 James Fenimore Cooper .25 .60
148 Mark Buehrle .25 .60
149 Freddy Sanchez .15 .40
150 Johan Santana .40 1.00
151 Orlando Cabrera .15 .40
152 Lyle Overbay .15 .40
153 Clay Buchholz (RC) 1.00 2.50
154 Jesse Carlson RC .60 1.50
155 Troy Tulowitzki .40 1.00
156 Delmon Young .25 .60
157 Ross Ohlendorf RC .60 1.50
158 Mary Shelley .25 .60
159 James Shields .15 .40
160 Alfonso Soriano .25 .60
161 Randy Winn .15 .40
162 Austin Kearns .15 .40
163 Jeremy Hermida .15 .40
164 Jorge Posada .25 .60
165 Justin Verlander .50 1.25
166 Bram Stoker .25 .60
167 Marie Curie .25 .60
168 Melky Cabrera .15 .40
169 Howie Kendrick .15 .40
170 Jake Peavy .15 .40
171 J.D. Drew .15 .40
172 Pablo Picasso .25 .60
173 Rick Ankiel .15 .40
174 Jose Valverde .15 .40
175 Chipper Jones .40 1.00
176 Claude Monet .25 .60
177 Evan Longoria RC 2.00 5.00
178 Jose Vidro .15 .40
179 Hideki Matsui .40 1.00
180 Ryan Braun .50 1.25
181 Moises Alou .15 .40
182 Nate McLouth .15 .40
183 Harriet Tubman .25 .60
184 Felix Hernandez .40 1.00
185 Carlos Pena .25 .60
186 Jarrod Saltalamacchia .15 .40
187 Les Miles .25 .60
188 Kelly Johnson .15 .40
189 Rampage Jackson .40 1.00
190 Grady Sizemore .25 .60
191 Francisco Cordero .15 .40
192 Yunel Escobar .15 .40
193 Edwin Encarnacion .15 .40
194 Melvin Mora .15 .40
195 Russ Martin .15 .40
196 Edgar Renteria .15 .40
197 Bigfoot .40 1.00
198 Steve Holm RC .40 1.00
199 Daric Barton (RC) .40 1.00
200 David Ortiz .25 .60
201 Tim Lincecum .60 1.50
202 Jeff King .25 .60
203 Jhonny Peralta .15 .40
204 Julio Lugo .15 .40
205 J.J. Putz .15 .40
206 Jeff Francoeur .25 .60
207 Yuniesky Betancourt .15 .40
208 Bruce Jenner .25 .60
209 Clete Thomas RC .60 1.50
210 Carlos Lee .15 .40
211 Josh Hamilton .40 1.00
212 Pyotr Ilyich Tchaikovsky .25 .60
213 Brendan Harris .15 .40
214 Dustin McGowan .15 .40
215 Aaron Harang .15 .40
216 Brett Myers .15 .40
217 Frederich Nietzsche .25 .60
218 John Maine .15 .40
219 Charles Dickens .25 .60
220 Erik Bedard .15 .40
221 Tim Hudson .25 .60
222 Jeremy Bonderman .15 .40
223 Nyjer Morgan (RC) .40 1.00
224 Johnny Cueto RC .60 1.50
225 Roy Oswalt .25 .60
226 Rich Hill .15 .40
227 Frederick Douglass .25 .60
228 Derek Lowe .15 .40
229 Joe Blanton .15 .40
230 Carlos Beltran .15 .40
231 Huston Street .15 .40
232 Davy Crockett .25 .60
233 Pluto .25 .60
234 Jered Weaver .15 .40
235 Dan Haren .15 .40
236 Alex Gordon .25 .60
237 Zack Greinke .25 .60
238 Todd Clever .25 .60
239 Brian Bannister .15 .40
240 Magglio Ordonez .25 .60
241 Ryan Garko .15 .40
242 Takudzwa Ngwenya .25 .60
243 Gil Meche .15 .40
244 Mark Teahen .15 .40
245 Carlos Guillen .15 .40
246 Jeff Kent .15 .40
247 Lisa Leslie .40 1.00
248 Lastings Milledge .15 .40
249 Serena Williams .50 1.25
250 Ichiro Suzuki .60 1.50
251 Matt Cain .15 .40
252 Callix Crabbe (RC) .40 1.00
253 Nick Blackburn RC .60 1.50
254 Hunter Pence .40 1.00
255 Cole Hamels .40 1.00
256 Garret Anderson .15 .40
257 Luis Gonzalez .15 .40
258 Eric Chavez .15 .40
259 Francisco Rodriguez .25 .60
260 Mark Teixeira .40 1.00
261 Bob Motley .25 .60
262 Mark Spitz .25 .60
263 Yadier Molina .25 .60
264 Adam Jones .25 .60
265 Brian Roberts .25 .60
266 Matt Kemp .25 .60
267 Andrew Miller .15 .40
268 Dean Karnazes .25 .60
269 Gary Sheffield .15 .40
270 Lance Berkman .25 .60
271 Paul Lo Duca .15 .40
272 Matt Tolbert RC .60 1.50
273 Jay Bruce (RC) 1.50 4.00
274 John Smoltz .40 1.00
275 Nick Markakis .40 1.00
276 Oscar Wilde .25 .60
277 Dontrelle Willis .15 .40
278 Kevin Van Dam .25 .60
279 Jim Edmonds .25 .60
280 Brandon Webb .25 .60
281 Joe Nathan .15 .40
282 Jeanette Lee .25 .60
283 Andrew Litz .25 .60
284 Daisuke Matsuzaka .40 1.00
285 Brandon Phillips .15 .40
286 Pat Burrell .15 .40
287 Chris Carpenter .40 1.00
288 Pete Weber .25 .60
289 Derrek Lee .15 .40
290 Ken Griffey Jr. .60 1.50
291 Rich Thompson RC .60 1.50
292 Elijah Dukes .15 .40
293 Pedro Feliz .15 .40
294 Torii Hunter .15 .40
295 Chone Figgins .15 .40
296 Hideki Okajima .15 .40
297 Max Scherzer RC 1.25 3.00
298 Greg Smith RC .40 1.00
299 Rafael Furcal .15 .40
300 Ryan Howard .50 1.25
301 Felix Pie SP 1.25 3.00
302 Brad Lidge SP 1.25 3.00
303 Jason Bay SP 1.25 3.00
304 Victor Hugo SP 1.25 3.00
305 Randy Johnson SP 1.25 3.00
306 Carlos Gomez SP 1.25 3.00
307 Pat Neshek SP 1.25 3.00
308 Jed Lowrie SP (RC) 1.25 3.00
309 Ryan Church SP 1.25 3.00
310 Michael Bourn SP 1.25 3.00
311 B.J. Ryan SP 1.25 3.00
312 Brandon Wood SP 1.25 3.00
313 Harriet Beecher Stowe SP 1.25 3.00
314 Mike Cameron SP 1.25 3.00
315 Tom Glavine SP 1.25 3.00
316 Ervin Santana SP 1.25 3.00
317 Geoff Jenkins SP 1.25 3.00
318 Andre Ethier SP 1.25 3.00
319 Jason Giambi SP 1.25 3.00
320 Dmitri Young SP 1.25 3.00
321 Wily Mo Pena SP 1.25 3.00
322 Hank Blalock SP 1.25 3.00
323 James Bowie SP 1.25 3.00
324 Casey Kotchman SP 1.25 3.00
325 Stephen Drew SP 1.25 3.00
326 Adam Kennedy SP 1.25 3.00
327 A.J. Pierzynski SP 1.25 3.00
328 Richie Sexson SP 1.25 3.00
329 Jeff Clement SP (RC) 1.25 3.00
330 Luke Hochevar SP RC 1.25 3.00
331 Luis Castillo SP 1.25 3.00
332 Dave Roberts SP 1.25 3.00
333 Coco Crisp SP 1.25 3.00
334 Jo-Jo Reyes SP 1.25 3.00
335 Phil Hughes SP 1.25 3.00
336 Allen Fisher SP 1.25 3.00
337 Jason Schmidt SP 1.25 3.00
338 Placido Polanco SP 1.25 3.00
339 Jack Cust SP 1.25 3.00
340 Carl Crawford SP 1.25 3.00
341 Ty Wigginton SP 1.25 3.00
342 Aubrey Huff SP 1.25 3.00
343 Bengie Molina SP 1.25 3.00
344 Matt Diaz SP 1.25 3.00
345 Francisco Liriano SP 1.25 3.00
346 Brandon Boggs SP (RC) 1.25 3.00
347 David DeJesus SP 1.25 3.00
348 Justin Masterson SP RC 1.50 4.00
349 Frank Morris SP 1.25 3.00
350 Kevin Youkilis SP 1.25 3.00
NNO Kosuke Fukudome SP 10.00 25.00
NNO Framed Original 50.00 100.00

2008 Topps Allen and Ginter Mini

*MINI 1-300: .75X TO 2X BASIC
*MINI 1-300 RC: .5X TO 1.2X BASIC RC's
APPX. ONE MINI PER PACK
*MINI SP 300-350: .75X TO 2X BASIC SP
MINI SP ODDS 1:13 HOBBY
351-390 RANDOM WITHIN RIP CARDS
OVERALL PLATE ODDS 1:961 HOBBY
PLATE PRINT RUN 1 SET PER COLOR
BLACK-CYAN-MAGENTA-YELLOW ISSUED
NO PLATE PRICING DUE TO SCARCITY
351 Prince Fielder EXT 20.00 50.00
352 Justin Upton EXT 20.00 50.00
353 Russell Martin EXT 30.00 60.00
354 Cy Young EXT 20.00 50.00
355 Hanley Ramirez EXT 20.00 50.00
356 Grady Sizemore EXT 20.00 50.00
357 David Ortiz EXT 40.00 80.00
358 Dan Haren EXT 15.00 40.00
359 Honus Wagner EXT 30.00 60.00
360 Albert Pujols EXT 30.00 60.00
361 Hiroki Kuroda EXT 15.00 40.00
362 Evan Longoria EXT 30.00 60.00
363 Tris Speaker EXT 20.00 50.00
364 Josh Hamilton EXT 30.00 60.00
365 Johan Santana EXT 20.00 50.00
366 Derek Jeter EXT 40.00 80.00
367 Jake Peavy EXT 30.00 60.00
368 Troy Glaus EXT 15.00 40.00
369 Nick Swisher EXT 20.00 50.00
370 George Sisler EXT 20.00 50.00
371 Ichiro Suzuki EXT 40.00 80.00
372 Mark Teixeira EXT 20.00 50.00
373 Justin Verlander EXT 15.00 40.00
374 Jackie Robinson EXT 30.00 60.00
375 Vladimir Guerrero EXT 30.00 60.00
376 Delmon Young EXT 20.00 50.00
377 Lou Gehrig EXT 30.00 60.00
378 Tim Lincecum EXT 30.00 60.00
379 Ryan Zimmerman EXT 15.00 40.00
380 David Wright EXT 40.00 80.00
381 Matt Holliday EXT 20.00 50.00
382 Jose Reyes EXT 30.00 60.00
383 Christy Mathewson EXT 30.00 60.00
384 Hunter Pence EXT 20.00 50.00
385 Chase Utley EXT 20.00 50.00
386 Daisuke Matsuzaka EXT 20.00 50.00
387 Miguel Cabrera EXT 15.00 40.00
388 Torii Hunter EXT 15.00 40.00
389 Carlos Zambrano EXT 20.00 50.00
390 Alex Rodriguez EXT 30.00 60.00
391 Victor Martinez EXT 15.00 40.00
392 Justin Morneau EXT 15.00 40.00
393 Carlos Beltran EXT 15.00 40.00
394 Ryan Braun EXT 20.00 50.00
395 Alfonso Soriano EXT 20.00 50.00
396 Joba Chamberlain EXT 30.00 60.00
397 Nick Markakis EXT 20.00 50.00
398 Ty Cobb EXT 40.00 80.00
399 B.J. Upton EXT 15.00 40.00
400 Ryan Howard EXT 20.00 50.00

2008 Topps Allen and Ginter Mini A and G Back

*A & G BACK: 1X TO 2.5X BASIC
*A & G BACK RCs: .6X TO 1.5X BASIC RCs
STATED ODDS 1:5 HOBBY
*A & G BACK SP: 1X TO 2.5X BASIC SP
SP STATED ODDS 1:65 HOBBY

2008 Topps Allen and Ginter Mini Bazooka

STATED ODDS 1:301 HOBBY
STATED PRINT RUN 25 SER.#'d SETS
NO PRICING DUE TO SCARCITY

2008 Topps Allen and Ginter Mini Black

*BLACK: 1.5X TO 4X BASIC
*BLACK RCs: .75X TO 2X BASIC RCs
STATED ODDS 1:10 HOBBY
*BLACK SP: 1.2X TO 3X BASIC SP
SP STATED ODDS 1:130 HOBBY

2008 Topps Allen and Ginter Mini Framed Cloth

STATED ODDS 1:439 HOBBY
STATED PRINT RUN 10 SER.#'d SETS
NO PRICING DUE TO SCARCITY

2008 Topps Allen and Ginter Mini No Card Number

*NO NBR: 10X TO 25X BASIC
*NO NBR RCs: 4X TO 10X BASIC RCs
*NO NBR: 1.5X TO 4X BASIC SP
STATED ODDS 1:151 HOBBY
STATED PRINT RUN 50 SETS
CARDS ARE NOT SERIAL-NUMBERED
PRINT RUN INFO PROVIDED BY TOPPS
7 Mickey Mantle 30.00 60.00
16 Hiroki Kuroda 6.00 15.00
22 Chin-Lung Hu 6.00 15.00
39 J.R. Towles 6.00 15.00
72 Clayton Kershaw 6.00 15.00
153 Clay Buchholz 10.00 25.00
177 Evan Longoria 15.00 40.00
224 Johnny Cueto 10.00 25.00
253 Nick Blackburn 6.00 15.00
273 Jay Bruce 10.00 25.00
297 Max Scherzer 6.00 15.00

2008 Topps Allen and Ginter Mini Wood

STATED ODDS 1:4395 HOBBY
SOME CARDS FOUND IN RIP PACKS
STATED PRINT RUN 1 SER.#'d SETS
NO PRICING DUE TO SCARCITY

2008 Topps Allen and Ginter Autographs

GROUP A ODDS 1:277 HOBBY
GROUP B ODDS 1:256 HOBBY
GROUP C ODDS 1:135 HOBBY
GRP A PRINT RUNS B/W 90-240 COPIES PER
CARDS ARE NOT SERIAL-NUMBERED
PRINT RUNS PROVIDED BY TOPPS
EXCHANGE DEADLINE 7/31/2010
AE Andre Ethier C 10.00 25.00
AF Andrea Farina A/190 * 15.00 40.00
AFI Allen Fisher A/190 * 12.50 30.00
AIR Alex Rios B 6.00 15.00
AL Andrew Litz A/190 * 15.00 40.00
AM Adriano Moraes A/190 * EXCH 15.00 40.00
BB Bonnie Blair A/190 * 20.00 50.00
BJ Bruce Jenner A/190 * 30.00 60.00
BM Bob Motley A/190 * 30.00 60.00
BP Brad Penny A/240 * 10.00 25.00
BPB Brian Bannister C 5.00 12.00
BPM Billy Mitchell A/190 * 30.00 60.00
CB Clay Buchholz B 10.00 25.00
CC Carl Crawford A/240 * 10.00 25.00
CG Curtis Granderson B 10.00 25.00
DB Murray Campbell A/190 * 20.00 50.00
DJ Dan Jansen A/190 * 20.00 50.00
DK Dean Karnazes A/190 * 20.00 50.00
DO David Ortiz A/90 * 60.00 120.00
DW David Wright A/240 * 40.00 80.00
ES Ervin Santana C 4.00 10.00
FC Francisco Cordero C EXCH 5.00 12.00
FCC Fausto Carmona C 5.00 12.00
FM Frank Morris A/190 * 15.00 40.00
GJ Geoff Jenkins B 5.00 12.00
HP Hunter Pence A/90 * 30.00 60.00
HR Hanley Ramirez A/240 * 12.50 30.00
IK Ian Kinsler C 8.00 20.00
JBF Jeff Francoeur C 6.00 15.00
JC Joba Chamberlain B 10.00 25.00
JF Jeff Francis B 5.00 12.00
JJC Joey Chestnut A/190 * 20.00 50.00
JK Jeff King A/190 * EXCH 12.50 30.00
JL Jeanette Lee A/190 * 75.00 150.00
JR Jose Reyes A/90 * 60.00 120.00
JS Jarrod Saltalamacchia C 5.00 12.00
KS Kerri Strug A/190 * 30.00 60.00
KVD Kevin Van Dam A/190 * 20.00 50.00
LL Lisa Leslie A/190 * 20.00 50.00
LM Les Miles A/190 * EXCH 30.00 60.00
MB Matt Biondi A/190 * 20.00 50.00
MK Matt Kemp B 10.00 25.00
MR Manny Ramirez A/90 * 90.00 150.00
MS Mark Spitz A/190 * 30.00 60.00
MTH Matt Holliday A/90 * 100.00 150.00
NH Nicky Hayden A/240 * 20.00 50.00
NM Nick Markakis B 10.00 25.00
OH Orlando Hudson B 5.00 12.00
PF Prince Fielder A/90 * 20.00 50.00
PW Pete Weber A/190 * 15.00 40.00
RH Ryan Howard A/90 * 75.00 150.00
RJ Rampage Jackson A/190 * 60.00 120.00
SJW Serena Williams A/190 * 50.00 100.00
SW Stevie Williams A/240 * 15.00 40.00
TC Todd Clever A/190 * 20.00 50.00
TH Torii Hunter A/240 * 12.50 30.00
TLH Travis Hafner A/240 * 10.00 25.00
TN Takudzwa Ngwenya A/190 * 12.50 30.00

2008 Topps Allen and Ginter Autographs Red Ink

RANDOM INSERTS IN PACKS
SOME FOUND ONLY IN RIP PACKS
STATED PRINT RUN 10 SER.#'d SETS
NO PRICING DUE TO SCARCITY
EXCHANGE DEADLINE 7/31/2010

2008 Topps Allen and Ginter Cabinet Boxloader

STATED ODDS 1:3 HOBBY BOXES
BH1 Matt Holliday 3.00 8.00
Jamey Carroll
Michael Barrett
Brian Giles
BH2 Mike Lowell 4.00 10.00
Manny Ramirez
Jonathan Papelbon
Josh Beckett
BH3 Ryan Howard 4.00 10.00
Jimmy Rollins
Chase Utley
Cole Hamels
BH4 Alex Rodriguez 5.00 12.00
Frank Thomas
Jim Thome
BH5 Justin Verlander 4.00 10.00
Mark Buehrle
Clay Buchholz
HB1 General George Washington 3.00 8.00
General Nathanael Greene
HB2 General Horatio Gates 3.00 8.00
General John Burgoyne
HB3 General George Meade 3.00 8.00
General Robert E. Lee
HB4 Lt. Col. William B. Travis 3.00 8.00
Colonel James Bowie
Colonel Davy Crockett
General Antonio Lopez de Santa Anna
HB5 General Dwight Eisenhower 3.00 8.00
Field Marshal Bernard Montgomery

2008 Topps Allen and Ginter Cabinet Boxloader Autograph

STATED ODDS 1:322 HOBBY BOXES
STATED PRINT RUN 200 SER.#'d SETS
BF Bigfoot 30.00 60.00

2008 Topps Allen and Ginter Cut Signatures

STATED ODDS 1:138,500 HOBBY
STATED PRINT RUN 1 SER.#'d SET
NO PRICING DUE TO SCARCITY

2008 Topps Allen and Ginter Dick Perez Original Sketches

RANDOM INSERTS IN PACKS
STATED PRINT RUN 1 SER.#'d SET
NO PRICING DUE TO SCARCITY

2008 Topps Allen and Ginter DNA Relics

GROUP A ODDS 1:203,317 HOBBY
GROUP B ODDS 1:264,312 HOBBY
GROUP A PRINT RUN ONE SET
GROUP B PRINT RUN TEN SETS
CARDS ARE NOT SERIAL NUMBERED
PRINT RUN INFO PROVIDED BY TOPPS
NO PRICING DUE TO SCARCITY

2008 Topps Allen and Ginter Mini Ancient Icons

COMPLETE SET (20) 60.00 120.00
STATED ODDS 1:48 HOBBY
A1 Gilgamesh 3.00 8.00
A2 Marduk 3.00 8.00
A3 Beowulf 3.00 8.00
A4 Poseidon 3.00 8.00
A5 The Sphinx 3.00 8.00
A6 Tutankhamen 3.00 8.00
A7 Alexander the Great 3.00 8.00
A8 Cleopatra 3.00 8.00
A9 Sun Tzu 3.00 8.00
A10 Quetzalcoatl 3.00 8.00
A11 Isis 3.00 8.00
A12 Hercules 3.00 8.00
A13 King Arthur 3.00 8.00
A14 Miyamoto Musashi 3.00 8.00
A15 Genghis Khan 3.00 8.00
A16 Zeus 3.00 8.00
A17 Achilles 3.00 8.00
A18 Confucius 3.00 8.00
A19 Attila the Hun 3.00 8.00
A20 Romulus and Remus 3.00 8.00

2008 Topps Allen and Ginter Mini Baseball Icons

COMPLETE SET (17) 50.00 100.00
STATED ODDS 1:48 HOBBY
BI1 Cy Young 4.00 10.00
BI2 Walter Johnson 4.00 10.00
BI3 Jackie Robinson 5.00 12.00
BI4 Thurman Munson 4.00 10.00
BI5 Mel Ott 3.00 8.00
BI6 Honus Wagner 4.00 10.00
BI7 Pee Wee Reese 3.00 8.00
BI8 Tris Speaker 3.00 8.00
BI9 Christy Mathewson 4.00 10.00
BI10 Ty Cobb 4.00 10.00
BI11 Johnny Mize 3.00 8.00
BI12 Jimmie Foxx 4.00 10.00
BI13 Lou Gehrig 5.00 12.00
BI14 Roy Campanella 3.00 8.00
BI15 George Sisler 3.00 8.00
BI16 Rogers Hornsby 3.00 8.00
BI17 Babe Ruth 8.00 20.00

2008 Topps Allen and Ginter Mini Pioneers of Aviation

COMPLETE SET (5) 15.00 40.00
STATED ODDS 1:XX
PA1 Ornithopter 4.00 10.00
PA2 Linen Balloon 4.00 10.00
PA3 Piloted Glider 4.00 10.00
PA4 Aerial Steam Carriage 4.00 10.00
PA5 Aerodrome 4.00 10.00

2008 Topps Allen and Ginter Mini Team Orange

COMPLETE SET (10) 50.00 100.00
STATED ODDS 1:144 HOBBY
TO1 Cornelius Franks 4.00 10.00
TO2 Mittens McCluskey 4.00 10.00
TO3 Capt. W.P. Mantooth 4.00 10.00
TO4 Wheelbarrow Walker 4.00 10.00
TO5 Archibald Clinker 4.00 10.00
TO6 Minty Beans 4.00 10.00
TO7 Francisco Fiasco 4.00 10.00
TO8 Thurgood Cartwright IV 4.00 10.00
TO9 Enzo DiStubbs 4.00 10.00
TO10 Sir Wagonwheel Stevens 4.00 10.00

2008 Topps Allen and Ginter Mini World's Deadliest Sharks

COMPLETE SET (5) 20.00 50.00
STATED ODDS 1:XX
WDS1 Great White Shark 5.00 12.00
WDS2 Tiger Shark 5.00 12.00
WDS3 Bull Shark 5.00 12.00
WDS4 Oceanic Whitetip Shark 5.00 12.00
WDS5 Mako Shark 5.00 12.00

2008 Topps Allen and Ginter Mini World Leaders

COMPLETE SET (50) 30.00 60.00
STATED ODDS 1:12 HOBBY
WL1 Cristina Fernandez de Kirchner 1.50 4.00
WL2 Kevin Rudd 1.50 4.00
WL3 Guy Verhofstadt 1.50 4.00
WL4 Luiz Inacio Lula da Silva 1.50 4.00
WL5 Stephen Harper 1.50 4.00
WL6 Michelle Bachelet Jeria 1.50 4.00
WL7 Oscar Arias Sanchez 1.50 4.00
WL8 Mirek Topolanek 1.50 4.00
WL9 Anders Fogh Rasmussen 1.50 4.00
WL10 Leonel Fernandez Reyna 1.50 4.00
WL11 Mohamed Hosni Mubarak 1.50 4.00
WL12 Tarja Halonen 1.50 4.00
WL13 Nicolas Sarkozy 1.50 4.00
WL14 Yahya A.J.J. Jammeh 1.50 4.00
WL15 Angela Merkel 1.50 4.00
WL16 Konstandinos Karamanlis 1.50 4.00
WL17 Benedict XVI 2.00 5.00
WL18 Geir H. Haarde 1.50 4.00
WL19 Manmohan Singh 1.50 4.00
WL20 Susilo Bambang Yudhoyono 1.50 4.00
WL21 Bertie Ahern 1.50 4.00
WL22 Ehud Olmert 1.50 4.00
WL23 Bruce Golding 1.50 4.00
WL24 Yasuo Fukuda 1.50 4.00
WL25 Mwai Kibaki 1.50 4.00
WL26 Felipe de Jesus Calderon Hinojosa 1.50 4.00
WL27 Sanjaa Bayar 1.50 4.00
WL28 Armando Guebuza 1.50 4.00
WL29 Girija Prasad Koirala 1.50 4.00
WL30 Jan Peter Balkenende 1.50 4.00
WL31 Helen Clark 1.50 4.00
WL32 Jens Stoltenberg 1.50 4.00
WL33 Qaboos bin Said al-Said 1.50 4.00
WL34 Alan Garcia Perez 1.50 4.00
WL35 Gloria Macapagal-Arroyo 1.50 4.00
WL36 Donald Tusk 1.50 4.00
WL37 Vladimir Vladimirovich Putin 2.50 6.00
WL38 Robert Fico 1.50 4.00
WL39 Thabo Mbeki 1.50 4.00
WL40 Lee Myung-bak 1.50 4.00
WL41 Jose Luis Rodriguez Zapatero 1.50 4.00
WL42 Fredrik Reinfeldt 1.50 4.00
WL43 Pascal Couchepin 1.50 4.00
WL44 Jakaya Kikwete 1.50 4.00
WL45 Samak Sundaravej 1.50 4.00
WL46 Tenzin Gyatso 1.50 4.00
WL47 Patrick Manning 1.50 4.00
WL48 Gordon Brown 2.50 6.00
WL49 George W. Bush 3.00 8.00
WL50 Nguyen Tan Dung 1.50 4.00

2008 Topps Allen and Ginter N43

STATED ODDS 1:3 HOBBY BOXES
CG Curtis Granderson 2.00 5.00
CU Chase Utley 3.00 8.00
DO David Ortiz 2.00 5.00
DW David Wright 4.00 10.00
HR Hanley Ramirez 3.00 8.00
IS Ichiro Suzuki 5.00 12.00
JC Joba Chamberlain 2.00 5.00
JR Jose Reyes 3.00 8.00
MH Matt Holliday 3.00 8.00
MR Manny Ramirez 3.00 8.00
PF Prince Fielder 2.00 5.00
RB Ryan Braun 4.00 10.00
RH Ryan Howard 4.00 10.00
RZ Ryan Zimmerman 2.00 5.00
VG Vladimir Guerrero 3.00 8.00

2008 Topps Allen and Ginter N43 Autographs

STATED PRINT RUN 15 SER.#'d SETS
STATED ODDS 1:428 HOBBY BOXES
NO PRICING DUE TO SCARCITY
EXCHANGE DEADLINE 7/31/2010
CG Curtis Granderson
DO David Ortiz
DW David Wright
HR Hanley Ramirez
JC Joba Chamberlain EXCH
JR Jose Reyes
MH Matt Holliday
MR Manny Ramirez
PF Prince Fielder
RH Ryan Howard

2008 Topps Allen and Ginter N43 Relics

STATED PRINT RUN 25 SER.#'d SETS
STATED ODDS 1:256 HOBBY BOXES
NO PRICING DUE TO SCARCITY

2008 Topps Allen and Ginter N43 Relics Autographs

STATED PRINT RUN 5 SER.#'d SETS
STATED ODDS 1:2565 HOBBY BOXES
NO PRICING DUE TO SCARCITY
EXCHANGE DEADLINE 7/31/2010

2008 Topps Allen and Ginter National Convention

COMPLETE SET (7) 8.00 20.00
1 Babe Ruth 3.00 8.00
2 Lou Gerhig 2.50 6.00
3 Jackie Robinson 1.25 3.00
4 Don Larsen .50 1.25
5 Johnny Unitas 2.50 6.00
6 Roger Maris 1.25 3.00
7 Mickey Mantle 4.00 10.00

2008 Topps Allen and Ginter Relics

GROUP A ODDS 1:280 HOBBY
GROUP B ODDS 1:71 HOBBY
GROUP C ODDS 1:20 HOBBY
RELIC AU ODDS 1:26,431 HOBBY
GROUP A B/W 100-250 COPIES PER
CARDS ARE NOT SERIAL NUMBERED
PRINT RUN INFO PROVIDED BY TOPPS
AD1 Adam Dunn Jsy 3.00 8.00
AD2 Adam Dunn Bat 3.00 8.00
AER Alex Rodriguez Bat A 10.00 25.00
AF Andrea Farina A/250 * 5.00 12.00
AFI Allen Fisher A/250 * 8.00 20.00
AIR Alex Rios Bat B 3.00 8.00
AJP A.J. Pierzynski Jsy C 3.00 8.00
AK Austin Kearns Bat B 3.00 8.00
AL Andrew Litz A/250 * 8.00 20.00
AM Archie Moore A/100 * 15.00 40.00
AP1 Albert Pujols Jsy 6.00 15.00
AP2 Albert Pujols Bat 10.00 25.00
APB Aaron Pryor A/100 * 40.00 80.00
AR Aramis Ramirez Jsy B 3.00 8.00
ASM Adriano Moraes A/250 * 12.50 30.00
ATK Adam Kennedy Jsy C 3.00 8.00
AW Andre Ward A/100 * 15.00 40.00
BA Bobby Abreu Bat B 3.00 8.00
BB Bonnie Blair A/250 * 10.00 25.00
BC Bobby Crosby Jsy C 3.00 8.00
BF Bigfoot A/250 * 30.00 60.00
BH Brad Hawpe Jsy C 3.00 8.00
BJ Bruce Jenner A/250 * 6.00 15.00
BM Billy Mitchell A/250 * 20.00 50.00
BMM Brian McCann Jsy C 3.00 8.00
BR1 Brian Roberts Jsy 3.00 8.00
BR2 Brian Roberts Bat 3.00 8.00
CAM Carlos Marmol Jsy C 3.00 8.00
CC1 Carl Crawford Jsy 3.00 8.00
CC2 Carl Crawford Bat 3.00 8.00
CG Curtis Granderson Jsy C 3.00 8.00
CJ Chipper Jones Jsy C 4.00 10.00
CK Casey Kotchman Jsy B 3.00 8.00
CS Curt Schilling Jsy B 3.00 8.00
CU Chase Utley Jsy C 4.00 10.00
CZ Carlos Zambrano Jsy C 3.00 8.00
DG Danny Green A/100 * 30.00 60.00
DJ Dan Jansen A/250 * 8.00 20.00
DK Dean Karnazes A/250 * 10.00 25.00
DM Daisuke Matsuzaka Jsy A 6.00 15.00
DO1 David Ortiz Jsy 4.00 10.00
DO2 David Ortiz Bat 4.00 10.00
DRY Delwyn Young Jsy C 3.00 8.00
DW David Wright Jsy C 6.00 15.00
DY Dmitri Young Bat B 3.00 8.00
EC Eric Chavez Jsy A 3.00 8.00
EM Edison Miranda A/100 * 15.00 40.00
ER Edgar Renteria Bat B 3.00 8.00
FM Frank Morris A/250 * 6.00 15.00
GA Garret Anderson Jsy C 3.00 8.00
HB Hank Blalock Jsy B 3.00 8.00
IR1 Ivan Rodriguez Jsy B 3.00 8.00
IR2 Ivan Rodriguez Bat B 3.00 8.00
IS Ichiro Suzuki Jsy C 6.00 15.00
JB Jason Bay Jsy C 4.00 10.00
JC Joey Chestnut A/250 * 10.00 25.00
JCJ Joel Casamayor A/100 * 12.50 30.00
JD J.D. Drew Bat B 3.00 8.00
JDD Johnny Damon Bat C 3.00 8.00
JF Jeff Francoeur Jsy C 3.00 8.00
JFB Jeff Fenech A/100 * 15.00 40.00
JG Jay Gibbons Bat B 3.00 8.00
JJH J.J. Hardy Jsy C 3.00 8.00
JK Jeff Kent Bat B 3.00 8.00
JKI Jeff King A/250 * 10.00 25.00
JL Jeanette Lee A/250 * 30.00 60.00
JM Joe Mauer Jsy C 4.00 10.00
JS John Smoltz Jsy C 3.00 8.00
JT Jim Thome Jsy C 4.00 10.00
JTD Jermaine Dye Jsy C 3.00 8.00
JV1 Jason Varitek Bat 4.00 10.00
JV2 Jason Varitek Jsy 4.00 10.00
KP Kelly Pavlik A/100 * 40.00 80.00
KS Kerri Strug A/250 * 15.00 40.00
KVD Kevin Van Dam A/250 * 10.00 25.00
LB Lance Berkman Jsy C 3.00 8.00
LL Lisa Leslie A/250 * 12.50 30.00
LM Les Miles A/250 * 10.00 25.00
MB Matt Biondi A/250 * 8.00 20.00
MC Melky Cabrera Jsy C 3.00 8.00
MDC Matt Capps Jsy C 3.00 8.00
MH Mike Hampton Jsy C 3.00 8.00
MH Marcus Henderson AU/100 * 150.00 250.00
MK Matt Kemp Jsy C 3.00 8.00
MR Manny Ramirez Jsy C 4.00 10.00
MS Mark Spitz A/250 * 12.50 30.00
MT Mark Teixeira Jsy C 3.00 8.00
MY Michael Young Jsy C 3.00 8.00
NH Nicky Hayden A/250 * 10.00 25.00
PF Prince Fielder Bat B 3.00 8.00
PK Paul Konerko Jsy C 3.00 8.00
PL Paul Lo Duca Bat B 3.00 8.00
PW Pete Weber A/250 * 15.00 40.00
RF Rafael Furcal Bat B 3.00 8.00
RH Ryan Howard Jsy C 5.00 12.00
RJ Rampage Jackson A/250 * 15.00 40.00
RM Ray Mancini A/100 * 40.00 80.00
RO Roy Oswalt Jsy C 3.00 8.00
RS Richie Sexson Jsy C 3.00 8.00
SD Stephen Drew Jsy B 3.00 8.00
SJW Serena Williams A/250 * 12.50 30.00
SP Samuel Peter A/100 * 10.00 25.00
SW Stevie Williams A/250 * 8.00 20.00
TC Todd Clever A/250 * 10.00 25.00
TG Tom Glavine Jsy C 3.00 8.00
TH Tim Hudson Jsy C 3.00 8.00
TLH Todd Helton Jsy C 3.00 8.00
TN Takudzwa Ngwenya A/250 * 8.00 20.00
TPH Travis Hafner Jsy C 3.00 8.00
TSG Tom Gorzelanny Jsy C 3.00 8.00
TT Troy Tulowitzki Jsy C 3.00 8.00
VG Vladimir Guerrero Bat B 3.00 8.00
VM Victor Martinez Jsy C 3.00 8.00
WMP Wily Mo Pena Bat B 3.00 8.00

2008 Topps Allen and Ginter Rip Cards

STATED ODDS 1:189 HOBBY
PRINT RUNS B/WN 10-99 COPIES PER
NO PRICING ON QTY 10 OR LESS
ALL LISTED PRICED ARE FOR RIPPED
UNRIPPED HAVE ADD'L CARDS WITHIN
COMMON UNRIPPED p/r 99 50.00 120.00
COMMON UNRIPPED p/r 75 60.00 150.00
COMMON UNRIPPED p/r 50 75.00 200.00
COMMON UNRIPPED p/r 28 100.00 250.00
RC1 Erik Bedard/99 6.00 15.00
RC2 Jacoby Ellsbury/75 10.00 25.00
RC3 Chris Carpenter/99 6.00 15.00
RC4 Brandon Phillips/99 6.00 15.00
RC5 David Wright/99 10.00 25.00
RC6 Brian McCann/99 6.00 15.00
RC7 Mickey Mantle/10
RC8 Dan Uggla/75 6.00 15.00
RC9 James Loney/99 10.00 25.00
RC10 James Shields/99 6.00 15.00
RC11 Curtis Granderson/75 10.00 25.00
RC12 Jason Bay/99 6.00 15.00
RC13 Alex Gordon/75 10.00 25.00
RC14 Travis Hafner/99 6.00 15.00
RC15 Derek Jeter/28
RC16 Pedro Feliz/99 6.00 15.00
RC17 Thurman Munson/50 10.00 25.00
RC18 Grady Sizemore/75 10.00 25.00
RC19 Alex Rios/99 6.00 15.00
RC20 David Ortiz/50 10.00 25.00
RC21 Walter Johnson/28
RC22 Scott Rolen/99 10.00 25.00
RC23 John Smoltz/99 10.00 25.00
RC24 Mel Ott/28
RC25 Ryan Howard/50 10.00 25.00
RC26 Hiroki Kuroda/99 10.00 25.00
RC27 Johnny Damon/99 6.00 15.00
RC28 Jose Reyes/75 10.00 25.00
RC29 Felix Hernandez/99 10.00 25.00
RC30 John Lackey/99 6.00 15.00
RC31 Albert Pujols/10
RC32 Mark Teixeira/99 10.00 25.00
RC33 Jim Edmonds/99 6.00 15.00
RC34 Prince Fielder/50 10.00 25.00
RC35 Brian Bannister/99 6.00 15.00
RC36 Chipper Jones/50 10.00 25.00
RC37 Edgar Renteria/99 6.00 15.00
RC38 Roy Campanella/50 10.00 25.00
RC39 Troy Tulowitzki/99 10.00 25.00
RC40 Adam LaRoche/99 6.00 15.00
RC41 Phil Hughes/99 10.00 25.00
RC42 Pee Wee Reese/50 10.00 25.00
RC43 Adam Jones/99 6.00 15.00
RC44 Huston Street/99 6.00 15.00
RC45 Cliff Lee/99 6.00 15.00
RC46 Delmon Young/99 10.00 25.00
RC47 Joe Mauer/99 10.00 25.00
RC48 Johan Santana/28
RC49 Dmitri Young/99 6.00 15.00
RC50 Todd Helton/99 10.00 25.00
RC51 Carlos Beltran/75 10.00 25.00
RC52 J.J. Putz/99 6.00 15.00
RC53 Carlos Lee/99 6.00 15.00
RC54 Billy Butler/99 6.00 15.00
RC55 Miguel Cabrera/99 10.00 25.00
RC56 Derrek Lee/99 6.00 15.00
RC57 Alfonso Soriano/75 10.00 25.00
RC58 Cole Hamels/99 10.00 25.00
RC59 Hanley Ramirez/75 10.00 25.00
RC60 Adrian Gonzalez/99 6.00 15.00
RC61 B.J. Upton/99 6.00 15.00
RC62 Tim Lincecum/75 10.00 25.00
RC63 Gary Matthews/99 6.00 15.00
RC64 Justin Upton/75 10.00 25.00
RC65 Zack Greinke/99 6.00 15.00
RC66 Roy Oswalt/75 6.00 15.00
RC67 Jimmy Rollins/28
RC68 Miguel Tejada/99 6.00 15.00
RC69 Clay Buchholz/99 10.00 25.00
RC70 Andruw Jones/99 6.00 15.00
RC71 Chase Utley/75 10.00 25.00
RC72 Aaron Rowand/99 6.00 15.00
RC73 Johnny Mize/50 10.00 25.00
RC74 Jonathan Papelbon/75 10.00 25.00
RC75 Jarrod Saltalamacchia/99 6.00 15.00
RC76 Lance Berkman/50 6.00 15.00
RC77 Vernon Wells/99 6.00 15.00
RC78 Dontrelle Willis/99 6.00 15.00
RC79 Jim Thome/99 10.00 25.00
RC80 Torii Hunter/99 6.00 15.00
RC81 Russ Martin/75 6.00 15.00
RC82 Jake Peavy/99 10.00 25.00
RC83 Carlos Zambrano/99 6.00 15.00
RC84 Troy Glaus/99 6.00 15.00
RC85 Ryan Zimmerman/75 10.00 25.00
RC86 Evan Longoria/75 10.00 25.00
RC87 Yovani Gallardo/99 6.00 15.00
RC88 Jimmie Foxx/10
RC89 Josh Hamilton/75 10.00 25.00
RC90 Matt Holliday/50 10.00 25.00
RC91 Matt Cain/99 6.00 15.00
RC92 Francisco Cordero/99 6.00 15.00
RC93 Derek Lowe/99 6.00 15.00
RC94 Brandon Webb/75 6.00 15.00
RC95 Carlos Pena/99 6.00 15.00
RC96 Ichiro Suzuki/10
RC97 Khalil Greene/99 10.00 25.00
RC98 Rogers Hornsby/10
RC99 C.C. Sabathia/75 6.00 15.00
RC100 Victor Martinez/99 6.00 15.00

2008 Topps Allen and Ginter United States

COMPLETE SET (50) 10.00 25.00
STATED ODDS 1:XX
US1 Alex Rios .40 1.00
US2 Curt Schilling .40 1.00
US3 Brian Bannister .25 .60
US4 Torii Hunter .25 .60
US5 Chase Utley .60 1.50
US6 Roy Halladay .60 1.50
US7 Brad Ausmus .25 .60
US8 Ian Snell .25 .60
US9 Lastings Milledge .25 .60
US10 Nick Markakis .60 1.50
US11 Shane Victorino .25 .60
US12 Jason Schmidt .25 .60
US13 Curtis Granderson .40 1.00
US14 Scott Rolen .40 1.00
US15 Casey Blake .25 .60
US16 Nate Robertson .25 .60
US17 Brandon Webb .40 1.00
US18 Jonathan Papelbon .40 1.00
US19 Tim Stauffer .25 .60
US20 Mark Teixeira .60 1.50
US21 Chris Capuano .25 .60
US22 Jason Varitek .60 1.50
US23 Joe Mauer .60 1.50
US24 Dmitri Young .25 .60
US25 Ryan Howard .75 2.00
US26 Taylor Tankersley .25 .60
US27 Alex Gordon .40 1.00
US28 Barry Zito .40 1.00
US29 Chris Carpenter .60 1.50
US30 Derek Jeter 1.50 4.00
US31 Cody Ross .25 .60
US32 Alex Rodriguez 1.00 2.50
US33 Ryan Zimmerman .25 .60
US34 Travis Hafner .25 .60
US35 Nick Swisher .60 1.50
US36 Matt Holliday .60 1.50
US37 Jacoby Ellsbury 1.00 2.50
US38 Ken Griffey Jr. 1.00 2.50
US39 Paul Konerko .40 1.00
US40 Orlando Hudson .25 .60
US41 Mark Ellis .25 .60
US42 Todd Helton .40 1.00
US43 Adam Dunn .40 1.00
US44 Brandon Lyon .25 .60
US45 Daric Barton .25 .60
US46 David Wright .75 2.00
US47 Grady Sizemore .40 1.00
US48 Seth McClung .25 .60
US49 Pat Neshek .25 .60
US50 John Buck .25 .60

2008 Topps Allen and Ginter World's Greatest Victories

COMPLETE SET (20) 30.00 60.00
STATED ODDS 1:24 HOBBY
WGV1 Kerri Strug 2.50 6.00
WGV2 Mark Spitz 2.50 6.00
WGV3 Jonas Salk 2.00 5.00
WGV4 Man Walks on the Moon 2.00 5.00
WGV5 Jon Lester 3.00 8.00
WGV6 The Fall of the Berlin Wall 2.00 5.00
WGV7 David and Goliath 2.00 5.00
WGV8 Gary Carter and the '86 Mets 2.50 6.00
WGV9 The Battle of Gettysburg 2.00 5.00
WGV10 Deep Blue 2.00 5.00
WGV11 The Allied Forces 2.00 5.00
WGV12 Don Larsen 2.50 6.00
WGV13 Truman Defeats Dewey 2.00 5.00
WGV14 The American Revolution 2.00 5.00
WGV15 2004 ALCS 3.00 8.00
WGV16 The Battle of Thermopylae 2.00 5.00
WGV17 Brown v. Board of Education 2.00 5.00
WGV18 Team Orange 2.50 6.00
WGV19 Bill Mazeroski 2.50 6.00
WGV20 Cinderella 2.00 5.00

2009 Topps Allen and Ginter

COMPLETE SET (350) 30.00 60.00
COMP.SET w/o SP's (300) 12.50 30.00
COMMON CARD (1-300) .15 .40
COMMON RC (1-300) .40 1.00
COMMON SP (301-350) 1.25 3.00
SP STATED ODDS 1:2 HOBBY
1 Jay Bruce .25 .60
2 Zack Greinke .25 .60
3 Manny Parra .15 .40
4 Jorge Posada .25 .60
5 Luke Hochevar .15 .40
6 Adam Eaton .15 .40
7 John Smoltz .40 1.00
8 Matt Cain .15 .40
9 Ryan Theriot .15 .40
10 Chone Figgins .15 .40
11 Jacoby Ellsbury .40 1.00
12 Jermaine Dye .15 .40
13 Travis Hafner .15 .40
14 Troy Tulowitzki .40 1.00
15 Alfred Nobel .15 .40
16 Josh Johnson .25 .60
17 Manny Ramirez .40 1.00
18 Clyde Parris .40 1.00
19 Mike Pelfrey .15 .40
20 Adam Jones .25 .60
21 Robinson Cano .40 1.00
22 Mariano Rivera .40 1.00
23 Kristin Armstrong .15 .40
24 Steve Wiebe .15 .40
25 Evan Longoria .50 1.25
26 Charles Goodyear .15 .40
27 Chien-Ming Wang .25 .60
28 Ervin Santana .15 .40
29 Jonathan Papelbon .25 .60
30 Ryan Howard .50 1.25
31 Nick Markakis .30 .75
32 Jeremy Bonderman .15 .40
33 Florence Nightingale .15 .40
34 Ryan Dempster .15 .40
35 Geovany Soto .25 .60
36 Joba Chamberlain .25 .60
37 Andre Ethier .25 .60
38 Troy Glaus .15 .40
39 Hanley Ramirez .40 1.00
40 Jeremy Hermida .15 .40
41 Victor Martinez .25 .60
42 Mark Buehrle .25 .60
43 Koji Uehara RC .60 1.50
44 Freddy Sanchez .15 .40
45 Derrek Lee .15 .40
46 Brian Roberts .15 .40
47 J.J. Hardy .15 .40
48 Brigham Young .15 .40
49 Ubaldo Jimenez .25 .60
50 Pat Neshek .25 .60
51 Ryan Perry RC 1.00 2.50
52 Aaron Hill .15 .40
53 Clayton Kershaw .40 1.00
54 Carlos Guillen .15 .40
55 Alex Rios .25 .60
56 Daniel Murphy RC 1.00 2.50
57 Frank Evans .25 .60
58 Brad Hawpe .15 .40
59 Mark Reynolds .15 .40
60 Matt Holliday .40 1.00
61 Burke Kenny .15 .40
62 Dan Uggla .25 .60
63 Andrew Miller .15 .40
64 Jordan Zimmermann RC .40 1.00
65 Dexter Fowler (RC) .60 1.50
66 Alex Rodriguez .60 1.50
67 Ian Kinsler .25 .60
68 Jamie Moyer .15 .40
69 James Loney .25 .60
70 Rick Ankiel .15 .40
71 Albert Pujols 1.00 2.50
72 Carlos Lee .15 .40
73 Vernon Wells .15 .40
74 Matt Tuiasosopo (RC) .40 1.00
75 David Wright .50 1.25
76 Brandon Phillips .15 .40
77 Francisco Liriano .15 .40
78 Eric Byrnes .15 .40
79 Electron .15 .40
80 Joe Martinez RC .60 1.50
81 Willie Williams .40 1.00
82 Justin Verlander .50 1.25
83 Ludwig van Beethoven .15 .40
84 Justin Upton .25 .60
85 Jason Jaramillo (RC) .40 1.00
86 Michael Cuddyer .15 .40
87 Aaron Cook .15 .40
88 Brad Penny .15 .40
89 Elvis Andrus RC .60 1.50
90 Bobby Crosby .15 .40
91 Alex Gordon .25 .60
92 Joe Mauer .40 1.00
93 David DeJesus .15 .40
94 Paul Maholm .15 .40
95 David Patton RC .60 1.50
96 Geronimo .15 .40
97 Art Pennington .40 1.00
98 Josh Whitesell RC .60 1.50
99 Chris Duncan .15 .40
100 Ichiro Suzuki .60 1.50
101 Andrew Bailey RC 1.00 2.50
102 Edinson Volquez .15 .40
103 Aaron Harang .15 .40
104 Jeff Francoeur .25 .60
105 Kurt Suzuki .15 .40
106 Mike Jacobs .15 .40
107 Bryan Berg .15 .40
108 Alamo .15 .40
109 Samuel Morse .15 .40
110 Kevin Youkilis .25 .60
111 Jason Giambi .25 .60
112 Millito Navarro .40 1.00
113 Rafael Furcal .15 .40
114 Hideki Matsui .40 1.00
115 Ryan Doumit .15 .40
116 Charles Darwin .15 .40
117 Blake DeWitt .15 .40
118 Scott Olsen .15 .40
119 Scott Lewis (RC) .40 1.00
120 Edwin Moreno (RC) .40 1.00
121 Ryan Church .15 .40
122 Dontrelle Willis .15 .40
123 Barry Zito .15 .40
124 Donald Veal RC .60 1.50
125 Randy Johnson .25 .60
126 Trevor Crowe RC .40 1.00
127 J.D. Drew .15 .40
128 Red Moore .40 1.00
129 Brian Giles .15 .40
130 Johnny Damon .25 .60
131 Rickie Weeks .25 .60
132 Anna Tunnicliffe .15 .40
133 Roy Halladay .40 1.00
134 Jered Weaver .15 .40
135 Jeff Suppan .15 .40
136 Mickey Mantle 1.25 3.00
137 Mark Teixeira .40 1.00
138 Garrett Atkins .15 .40
139 Daisuke Matsuzaka .40 1.00
140 Loren Opstedahl .40 1.00
141 Carlos Zambrano .25 .60
142 LaShawn Merritt .15 .40
143 Robbie Maddison .15 .40
144 Joakim Soria .15 .40
145 Todd Wellemeyer .15 .40
146 Rich Harden .15 .40
147 Coco Crisp .15 .40
148 Brad Lidge .15 .40
149 Chipper Jones .40 1.00
150 Prince Fielder .25 .60
151 Cole Hamels .40 1.00
152 Phil Coke RC .60 1.50
153 CC Sabathia .25 .60
154 Corey Hart .15 .40
155 Yadier Molina .25 .60
156 Jayson Werth .25 .60
157 Jason Motte (RC) .60 1.50
158 Sigmund Freud .15 .40
159 Denard Span .25 .60
160 Max Scherzer .25 .60
161 Justin Morneau .40 1.00
162 Shane Victorino .25 .60
163 Matt Garza .15 .40
164 Erik Bedard .15 .40
165 Chase Utley .40 1.00
166 Gil Meche .15 .40
167 Jim Thome .25 .60
168 Adrian Gonzalez .25 .60
169 Kazuo Matsui .15 .40
170 Lance Berkman .25 .60
171 Brett Anderson RC .60 1.50
172 Jarrod Saltalamacchia .15 .40
173 Francisco Rodriguez .25 .60
174 John Lannan .15 .40
175 Alfonso Soriano .25 .60
176 Ramiro Pena RC .60 1.50
177 David Freese RC 3.00 8.00
178 Adam LaRoche .15 .40
179 Trevor Hoffman .25 .60
180 Russell Martin .15 .40
181 Aaron Rowand .15 .40
182 Jose Reyes .25 .60
183 Pedro Feliz .15 .40
184 Chris Young .15 .40
185 Dustin Pedroia .50 1.25
186 Adrian Beltre .15 .40
187 Brett Myers .15 .40
188 Chris Davis .15 .40
189 Casey Kotchman .15 .40
190 B.J. Upton .25 .60
191 Hiroki Kuroda .15 .40
192 Ryan Zimmerman .25 .60
193 Khalil Greene .15 .40
194 Brandon Morrow .15 .40
195 Kevin Kouzmanoff .15 .40
196 Joey Votto .40 1.00
197 Jhonny Peralta .15 .40
198 Raul Ibanez .25 .60
199 James McDonald RC .60 1.50
200 Carlos Quentin .25 .60
201 Travis Snider RC .60 1.50
202 Conor Jackson .15 .40
203 Scott Kazmir .15 .40
204 Casey Blake .15 .40
205 Ryan Braun .50 1.25
206 Miguel Tejada .25 .60
207 Jack Cust .15 .40
208 Michael Young .15 .40
209 St. Patrick's Cathedral .15 .40
210 Johan Santana .40 1.00
211 Kevin Millwood .15 .40
212 Mariel Zagunis .15 .40
213 Stephanie Brown Trafton .15 .40
214 Adam Dunn .25 .60
215 Jed Lowrie .25 .60
216 Derek Lowe .15 .40
217 Jorge Cantu .15 .40
218 Bobby Parnell RC .60 1.50
219 Nate McLouth .15 .40
220 Suez Canal .15 .40
221 Brandon Webb .25 .60
222 Akinori Iwamura .15 .40
223 Scott Rolen .25 .60
224 Tim Lincecum .60 1.50
225 David Price RC 1.00 2.50
226 Ricky Romero (RC) 1.00 2.50
227 Nelson Cruz .25 .60
228 Will Simpson/Archie Bunker .15 .40
229 Mark Ellis .15 .40
230 Torii Hunter .15 .40
231 David Murphy .15 .40
232 Everth Cabrera RC .60 1.50
233 John Lackey .15 .40
234 Wyatt Earp .15 .40
235 Roy Oswalt .25 .60
236 Edgar Renteria .15 .40
237 Walton Glenn Eller .15 .40
238 Vincent Van Gogh .15 .40
239 Chris Carpenter .40 1.00
240 Hank Blalock .15 .40
241 Trevor Cahill RC 1.00 2.50
242 Mark Teahen .15 .40
243 Alexander Cartwright .15 .40
244 Carlos Beltran .15 .40
245 Todd Helton .25 .60
246 General Custer .15 .40
247 Jeff Clement .15 .40
248 Colby Rasmus (RC) 1.00 2.50
249 John Higby .15 .40
250 Grady Sizemore .25 .60
251 Carl Crawford .25 .60
252 Lastings Milledge .15 .40
253 Miguel Cabrera .40 1.00
254 John Maine .15 .40
255 Aramis Ramirez .15 .40
256 Jose Lopez .15 .40
257 Heinrich Hertz .15 .40
258 Felix Hernandez .40 1.00
259 Napoleon Bonaparte .15 .40
260 Louis Braille .15 .40
261 John Danks .15 .40
262 Magglio Ordonez .25 .60
263 Brian Duensing RC .60 1.50
264 Carlos Pena .25 .60
265 Paul Konerko .25 .60
266 Johnny Cueto .15 .40
267 Melvin Mora .15 .40
268 Andy Pettitte .25 .60
269 Brian McCann .25 .60
270 Josh Outman RC .60 1.50
271 Jair Jurrjens .15 .40
272 Brad Nelson (RC) .40 1.00
273 Jason Bay .25 .60
274 Josh Hamilton .40 1.00
275 Vladimir Guerrero .40 1.00
276 Michael Phelps .75 2.00
277 Kerry Wood .15 .40
278 Herb Simpson .40 1.00
279 Jon Lester .25 .60
280 Shin-Soo Choo .25 .60
281 Jake Peavy .15 .40
282 Eric Chavez .15 .40
283 Mike Aviles .15 .40
284 Kenshin Kawakami RC .60 1.50
285 George Kottaras (RC) .40 1.00
286 Matt Kemp .25 .60
287 James Shields .15 .40
288 Joe Saunders .15 .40
289 Milky Way .15 .40
290 Cat Osterman .50 1.25
291 Josh Beckett .25 .60
292 Oliver Perez .15 .40
293 Ian Snell .15 .40
294 Tim Hudson .25 .60
295 Brett Gardner .15 .40
296 Bobby Abreu .15 .40
297 Kolan McConiughey .15 .40
298 Dan Haren .15 .40
299 Shairon Martis RC .60 1.50
300 David Ortiz .25 .60
301 Jonathan Sanchez SP 1.25 3.00
302 Stephen Drew SP 1.25 3.00
303 Rocco Baldelli SP 1.25 3.00
304 Yunel Escobar SP 1.25 3.00
305 Javier Vazquez SP 1.25 3.00
306 Cliff Lee SP 1.25 3.00
307 Hunter Pence SP 1.25 3.00
308 Fausto Carmona SP 1.25 3.00
309 Kosuke Fukudome SP 1.25 3.00
310 Old Faithful SP 1.25 3.00
311 Gavin Floyd SP 1.25 3.00
312 A.J. Burnett SP 1.25 3.00
313 Jeff Francis SP 1.25 3.00
314 Chad Billingsley SP 1.25 3.00
315 Andy LaRoche SP 1.25 3.00
316 Rick Porcello SP 2.50 6.00
317 John Baker SP 1.25 3.00
318 Delmon Young SP 1.25 3.00
319 Gary Sheffield SP 1.25 3.00
320 B.J. Ryan SP 1.25 3.00
321 Kelly Shoppach SP 1.25 3.00
322 Chris Volstad SP 1.25 3.00
323 Derek Jeter SP 3.00 8.00
324 Wladimir Balentien SP 1.25 3.00
325 Dioner Navarro SP 1.25 3.00
326 Cameron Maybin SP 1.25 3.00
327 Kenji Johjima SP 1.25 3.00
328 Matt LaPorta SP RC 2.00 5.00

329 Carlos Gomez SP 1.25 3.00
330 Cristian Guzman SP 1.25 3.00
331 Jeff Samardzija SP 1.25 3.00
332 Curtis Granderson SP 1.25 3.00
333 Nick Swisher SP 1.25 3.00
334 Pat Burrell SP 1.25 3.00
335 Justin Duchscherer SP 1.25 3.00
336 Ryan Ludwick SP 1.25 3.00
337 Billy Butler SP 1.25 3.00
338 Jason Wong SP 1.25 3.00
339 Jordan Schafer SP (RC) 1.25 3.00
340 Richard Galling SP 1.25 3.00
341 Edgar Gonzalez SP 1.25 3.00
342 Sitting Bull SP 1.25 3.00
343 Doc Holliday SP 1.25 3.00
344 Chris Young SP 1.25 3.00
345 Carlos Delgado SP 1.25 3.00
346 Dominique Wilkins SP 1.25 3.00
347 Yovani Gallardo SP 1.25 3.00
348 Justin Masterson SP 1.25 3.00
349 Aubrey Huff SP 1.25 3.00
350 Jimmy Rollins SP 1.25 3.00

2009 Topps Allen and Ginter Code

*CODE: 2X TO 5X BASIC
STATED ODDS 1:12 HOBBY

2009 Topps Allen and Ginter Mini

COMP.SET w/o EXT (350) 125.00 250.00
*MINI 1-300: .75X TO 2X BASIC
*MINI 1-300 RC: .5X TO 1.2X BASIC RC's
APPX. ONE MINI PER PACK
*MINI SP 301-350: .5X TO 1.2X BASIC SP
MINI SP ODDS 1:13 HOBBY
351-390 RANDOM WITHIN RIP CARDS
OVERALL PLATE ODDS 1:608 HOBBY
PLATE PRINT RUN 1 SET PER COLOR
BLACK-CYAN-MAGENTA-YELLOW ISSUED
NO PLATE PRICING DUE TO SCARCITY
351 Manny Ramirez EXT 40.00 80.00
352 Travis Snider EXT 30.00 60.00
353 CC Sabathia EXT 15.00 40.00
354 Nick Markakis EXT 20.00 50.00
355 Jon Lester EXT 15.00 40.00
356 Cole Hamels EXT 20.00 50.00
357 Edinson Volquez EXT 20.00 50.00
358 Hanley Ramirez EXT 20.00 50.00
359 Alex Rodriguez EXT 50.00 100.00
360 Francisco Rodriguez EXT 20.00 50.00
361 Albert Pujols EXT 60.00 120.00
362 Matt Holliday EXT 20.00 50.00
363 Max Scherzer EXT 15.00 40.00
364 Adam Dunn EXT 20.00 50.00
365 Randy Johnson EXT 20.00 50.00
366 Roy Halladay EXT 15.00 40.00
367 Joe Mauer EXT 30.00 60.00
368 Roy Oswalt EXT 15.00 40.00
369 Grady Sizemore EXT 20.00 50.00
370 Jacoby Ellsbury EXT 20.00 50.00
371 Nate McLouth EXT 15.00 40.00
372 Josh Johnson EXT 15.00 40.00
373 Geovany Soto EXT 20.00 50.00
374 Josh Beckett EXT 20.00 50.00
375 Brian McCann EXT 20.00 50.00
376 David Wright EXT 30.00 60.00
377 Adrian Gonzalez EXT 20.00 50.00
378 Tim Lincecum EXT 20.00 50.00
379 Dan Haren EXT 15.00 40.00
380 Alex Rios EXT 15.00 40.00
381 Rich Harden EXT 30.00 60.00
382 Victor Martinez EXT 20.00 50.00
383 Carlos Lee EXT 20.00 50.00
384 Chipper Jones EXT 30.00 60.00
385 Clayton Kershaw EXT 30.00 60.00
386 Daisuke Matsuzaka EXT 30.00 60.00
387 Carlos Beltran EXT 20.00 50.00
388 Scott Kazmir EXT 15.00 40.00
389 Mark Teixeira EXT 40.00 80.00
390 Justin Upton EXT 20.00 50.00
391 David Price EXT 40.00 80.00
392 Felix Hernandez EXT 20.00 50.00
393 Mariano Rivera EXT 40.00 80.00
394 Joba Chamberlain EXT 30.00 60.00
395 Justin Morneau EXT 20.00 50.00
396 Ryan Howard EXT 40.00 80.00
397 Evan Longoria EXT 40.00 80.00
398 Ryan Zimmerman EXT 15.00 40.00
399 Jason Bay EXT 30.00 60.00
400 Miguel Cabrera EXT 15.00 40.00

2009 Topps Allen and Ginter Mini A and G Back

*A & G BACK: 1X TO 2.5X BASIC
*A & G BACK RCs: .6X TO 1.5X BASIC RCs
STATED ODDS 1:5 HOBBY
*A & G BACK SP: .6X TO 1.5X BASIC SP
SP STATED ODDS 1:65 HOBBY

2009 Topps Allen and Ginter Mini Bazooka

STATED ODDS 1:191 HOBBY
STATED PRINT RUN 25 SER.#'d SETS
NO PRICING DUE TO SCARCITY

2009 Topps Allen and Ginter Mini Black

*BLACK: 2X TO 5X BASIC
*BLACK RCs: .75X TO 2X BASIC RCs
STATED ODDS 1:10 HOBBY
*BLACK SP: .75X TO 2X BASIC SP
SP STATED ODDS 1:130 HOBBY

2009 Topps Allen and Ginter Mini Framed Cloth

STATE ODDS 1:278 HOBBY
STATED PRINT RUN 10 SER.#'d SETS
NO PRICING DUE TO SCARCITY

2009 Topps Allen and Ginter Mini No Card Number

*NO NBR: 8X TO 20X BASIC
*NO NBR RCs: 3X TO 8X BASIC RCs
*NO NBR SP: 1.2X TO 3X BASIC SP
STATED ODDS 1:95 HOBBY
STATED PRINT RUN 50 SETS
11 Jacoby Ellsbury 20.00 50.00
22 Mariano Rivera 12.50 30.00
66 Alex Rodriguez 20.00 50.00
136 Mickey Mantle 40.00 80.00
149 Chipper Jones 20.00 50.00
246 General Custer 12.50 30.00
316 Rick Porcello 10.00 25.00
323 Derek Jeter 30.00 60.00
328 Matt LaPorta 6.00 15.00
332 Curtis Granderson 10.00 25.00
338 Jason Wong 10.00 25.00
348 Justin Masterson 10.00 25.00

2009 Topps Allen and Ginter Mini Wood

STATED ODDS 1:2780 HOBBY
STATED PRINT RUN 1 SER.#'d SET
NO PRICING DUE TO SCARCITY

2009 Topps Allen and Ginter Autographs

GROUP A ODDS 1:2730 HOBBY
GROUP B ODDS 1:51 HOBBY
CARDS ARE NOT SERIAL-NUMBERED
PRINT RUNS PROVIDED BY TOPPS
NO PHELPS PRICING DUE TO SCARCITY
EXCHANGE DEADLINE 6/30/2012
AC Alexi Casilla B 4.00 10.00
AP Art Pennington/239 * B 20.00 50.00
AR Alex Rios B 6.00 15.00
AT Anna Tunnicliffe/239 * B 8.00 20.00
BC Bob Crowley/239 * B 10.00 25.00
BK Burke Kenny/239 * B 10.00 25.00
BM Billy The Marlin/239 * B 10.00 25.00
BW Blake DeWitt B 4.00 10.00
BY Brock Yates/239 * B 10.00 25.00
CG Carlos Gomez B 5.00 12.00
CJ Conor Jackson B 4.00 10.00
CK Clayton Kershaw B 10.00 25.00
CM Cameron Maybin B 5.00 12.00
CO Cat Osterman/239 * B 30.00 60.00
CP Clyde Parris/239 * B 15.00 40.00
DO David Ortiz/49 * A 100.00 200.00
DS Denard Span B 6.00 15.00
DW David Wright/49 * A 100.00 200.00
EL Evan Longoria B 30.00 60.00
ES Ervin Santana B 4.00 10.00
FE Frank Evans/239 * B 15.00 40.00
HR Hanley Ramirez B 10.00 25.00
HS Herb Simpson/239 * B 15.00 40.00
HT Hannah Teter/239 * B 10.00 25.00
IK Iris Kyle SP/239 * B 10.00 25.00
JB Jay Bruce B 10.00 25.00
JC Joba Chamberlain/49 * A 75.00 150.00
JF Jeff Francoeur B 10.00 25.00
JH John Higby/239 * B 10.00 25.00
JJ Josh Johnson B 8.00 20.00
JM Justin Masterson B 6.00 15.00
JP Jonathan Papelbon B 10.00 25.00
JR Jose Reyes/49 * A 100.00 200.00
JW Jayson Werth/49 * A 90.00 150.00
KA Kristin Armstrong/239 * B 10.00 25.00
KM Kolan McConiughey/239 * B 8.00 20.00
LC Lynne Cox/239 * B 12.50 30.00
LM LaShawn Merritt/239 * B 8.00 20.00
LO Loren Opstedahl/239 * B 10.00 25.00
MC Miguel Cabrera/49 * A EXCH 75.00 150.00
MH Matt Holliday/49 * A 60.00 120.00
MK Matt Kemp B 10.00 25.00
MM Mike Metzger/239 * B 12.50 30.00
MN Millito Navarro/239 * B 20.00 50.00
MS Max Scherzer B 6.00 15.00
MZ Mariel Zagunis/239 * B 10.00 25.00
PH Phil Hughes B 10.00 25.00
RB Ryan Braun B 15.00 40.00
RC Ryan Church B 4.00 10.00
RF Richard Fosbury/239 * B 12.50 30.00
RH Ryan Howard/49 * A 100.00 175.00
RM Red Moore/239 * B 12.50 30.00
SB Stephanie Brown Trafton/239 * B 12.50 30.00
SD Shani Davis/239 * B 10.00 25.00
SO Scott Olsen B 4.00 10.00
SW Steve Wiebe/239 * B 12.50 30.00
TT Troy Tulowitzki B 10.00 25.00
WE Walton Glenn Eller/239 * B 10.00 25.00
WS Will Simpson 12.50 30.00
Archie Bunker/239 * B
WW Willie Williams/239 * B 15.00 40.00
YM Yuto Miyazawa/239 * B 20.00 50.00
BBE Bryan Berg/239 * B 12.50 30.00
BCA Brian Cappelletto/239 * B 8.00 20.00
DOW Dominique Wilkins/239 * B 15.00 40.00
JCU Jack Cust B 4.00 10.00
JOC Johnny Cueto B 4.00 10.00
JRI Juan Rivera B 4.00 10.00
MLO Mike Lowell B 8.00 20.00
MP1 Michael Phelps/8 * A EXCH
MP2 Michael Phelps/8 * A EXCH
MP3 Michael Phelps/8 * A EXCH
MP4 Michael Phelps/8 * A EXCH
MP5 Michael Phelps/8 * A EXCH
MP6 Michael Phelps/8 * A EXCH
MP7 Michael Phelps/8 * A EXCH
MP8 Michael Phelps/8 * A EXCH
RJH Rich Hill B 4.00 10.00
RMA Robbie Maddison/239 * B 10.00 25.00

2009 Topps Allen and Ginter Autographs Gold

RANDOM INSERTS IN PACKS
STATED PRINT RUN OF 1
CARDS ARE NOT SERIAL-NUMBERED
PRINT RUNS PROVIDED BY TOPPS
EXCHANGE DEADLINE 6/30/2012
MP1 Michael Phelps
MP2 Michael Phelps
MP3 Michael Phelps
MP4 Michael Phelps
MP5 Michael Phelps
MP6 Michael Phelps
MP7 Michael Phelps
MP8 Michael Phelps

2009 Topps Allen and Ginter Autographs Red Ink

STATED ODDS 1:1801 HOBBY
STATED PRINT RUN 10 SER.#'d SETS
NO PRICING DUE TO SCARCITY
EXCHANGE DEADLINE 6/30/2012

2009 Topps Allen and Ginter Cabinet Boxloaders

COMPLETE SET (10) 20.00 50.00
ONE CABINET/N43 PER HOBBY BOX
CB1 Yurendell de Caster 2.50 6.00
Gene Kingsale
CB2 Frederich Cepeda 3.00 8.00
Yulieski Gourriel
CB3 David Wright 4.00 10.00
Brian Roberts
CB4 Norichika Aoki 4.00 10.00
Daisuke Matsuzaka
CB5 Hisashi Iwakuma 4.00 10.00
Ichiro Suzuki
CB6 Thomas Jefferson 2.50 6.00
John Hancock
CB7 George Washington 3.00 8.00
Alexander Hamilton
CB8 Harry S Truman 3.00 8.00
Lester B. Pearson
CB9 Abraham Lincoln 3.00 8.00
Ulysses S. Grant
CB10 John F. Kennedy 3.00 8.00
Nikita Khrushchev

2009 Topps Allen and Ginter Cut Signatures

STATED ODDS 1:186,000 HOBBY
STATED PRINT RUN 1 SER.#'d SET
NO PRICING DUE TO SCARCITY

2009 Topps Allen and Ginter Dick Perez Original Sketches

RANDOM INSERTS IN PACKS
STATED PRINT RUN 1 SER.#'d SET
NO PRICING DUE TO SCARCITY

2009 Topps Allen and Ginter DNA Relics

STATED ODDS 1:186,000 HOBBY
STATED PRINT RUN 1 SER.#'d SET
NO PRICING DUE TO SCARCITY

2009 Topps Allen and Ginter Baseball Highlights

COMPLETE SET (25) 10.00 25.00
STATED ODDS 1:6 HOBBY
AGHS1 Aaron Boone .40 1.00
AGHS2 Ken Griffey Jr. 1.50 4.00
AGHS3 Randy Johnson .60 1.50
AGHS4 Carlos Zambrano .60 1.50
AGHS5 Josh Hamilton 1.00 2.50
AGHS6 Josh Beckett .60 1.50
AGHS7 Manny Ramirez 1.00 2.50
AGHS8 Derek Jeter 2.50 6.00
AGHS9 Frank Thomas 1.00 2.50
AGHS10 Jim Thome .60 1.50
AGHS11 Francisco Rodriguez .60 1.50
AGHS12 New York Yankees 1.00 2.50
AGHS13 David Wright 1.25 3.00
AGHS14 Ichiro Suzuki 1.50 4.00
AGHS15 Jon Lester 1.00 2.50
AGHS16 Alex Rodriguez 1.50 4.00
AGHS17 Chipper Jones 1.00 2.50
AGHS18 Derek Jeter 2.50 6.00
AGHS19 Albert Pujols 2.50 6.00
AGHS20 CC Sabathia .60 1.50
AGHS21 David Price 1.00 2.50
AGHS22 Ken Griffey Jr. 1.50 4.00
AGHS23 Brad Lidge .40 1.00
AGHS24 Mariano Rivera 1.00 2.50
AGHS25 Evan Longoria 1.25 3.00

2009 Topps Allen and Ginter Mini Creatures

COMPLETE SET (20) 75.00 150.00
STATED ODDS 1:48 HOBBY
LMT1 Bigfoot 3.00 8.00
LMT2 The Loch Ness Monster 3.00 8.00
LMT3 Grendel 3.00 8.00
LMT4 Unicorn 3.00 8.00
LMT5 The Invisible Man 3.00 8.00
LMT6 Kraken 3.00 8.00
LMT7 Medusa 3.00 8.00
LMT8 Sphinx 3.00 8.00
LMT9 Minotaur 3.00 8.00
LMT10 Dragon 3.00 8.00
LMT11 Leviathan 3.00 8.00
LMT12 Cyclops 3.00 8.00
LMT13 Vampire 3.00 8.00
LMT14 Griffin 3.00 8.00
LMT15 Chupacabra 3.00 8.00
LMT16 Cerberus 3.00 8.00
LMT17 Hydra 3.00 8.00
LMT18 Werewolf 3.00 8.00
LMT19 Fairy 3.00 8.00
LMT20 Yeti 3.00 8.00

2009 Topps Allen and Ginter Mini Creatures Autographs

RANDOM INSERTS IN PACKS
STATED PRINT RUN 10 SER.#'d SETS
NO PRICING DUE TO SCARCITY
CAI The Invisible Man

2009 Topps Allen and Ginter Mini Creatures Relics

RANDOM INSERTS IN PACKS
STATED PRINT RUN 10 SER.#'d SETS
NO PRICING DUE TO SCARCITY
CRB Bigfoot
CRL The Loch Ness Monster
CRU Unicorn
CRI The Invisible Man
RCY Yeti

2009 Topps Allen and Ginter Mini Extinct Creatures

RANDOM INSERTS IN PACKS
EA1 Velociraptor 12.50 30.00
EA2 Dodo 12.50 30.00
EA3 Xerces Blue 12.50 30.00
EA4 Labrador Duck 12.50 30.00
EA5 Eastern Elk 12.50 30.00

2009 Topps Allen and Ginter Mini Inventions of the Future

RANDOM INSERTS IN PACKS
FI1 Aeromobile 10.00 25.00
FI2 Clock Defier 10.00 25.00
FI3 Protecto-Bubble 10.00 25.00
FI4 Here-To-There-O-Matic 10.00 25.00
FI5 Mental Movies 10.00 25.00

2009 Topps Allen and Ginter Mini National Heroes

COMPLETE SET (40) 30.00 60.00
STATED ODDS 1:12 HOBBY
NH1 George Washington 2.00 5.00
NH2 Haile Selassie I 1.25 3.00
NH3 Toussaint L'Ouverture 1.25 3.00
NH4 Rigas Feraios 1.25 3.00
NH5 Yi Sun-sin 1.25 3.00
NH6 Giuseppe Garibaldi 1.25 3.00
NH7 Juan Santamaria 1.25 3.00
NH8 Tecun Uman 1.25 3.00
NH9 Jon Sigurosson 1.25 3.00
NH10 Mohandas Gandhi 2.00 5.00
NH11 Simon Bolivar 1.25 3.00
NH12 Alexander Nevsky 1.25 3.00
NH13 Lim Bo Seng 1.25 3.00
NH14 Sun Yat-sen 1.25 3.00
NH15 Tiradentes 1.25 3.00
NH16 Chiang Kai-Shek 1.25 3.00
NH17 William I 1.25 3.00
NH18 Severyn Nalyvaiko 1.25 3.00
NH19 Vasil Levski 1.25 3.00
NH20 Tadeusz Kosciuszko 1.25 3.00
NH21 Andranik Toros Ozanian 1.25 3.00
NH22 William Wallace 1.25 3.00
NH23 Oda Nobunaga 1.25 3.00
NH24 Milos Obilic 1.25 3.00
NH25 Niels Ebbeson 1.25 3.00
NH26 Jose Rizal 1.25 3.00
NH27 Alfonso Ugarte 1.25 3.00
NH28 Mustafa Ataturk 1.25 3.00
NH29 Nelson Mandela 1.25 3.00
NH30 El Cid 1.25 3.00
NH31 William Tell 1.25 3.00
NH32 Winston Churchill 1.25 3.00
NH33 Skanderbeg 1.25 3.00
NH34 General Jose de San Martin 1.25 3.00
NH35 Janos Damjanich 1.25 3.00
NH36 Joan of Arc 1.25 3.00
NH37 Abd al-Qadir 1.25 3.00
NH38 David Ben-Gurion 1.25 3.00
NH39 Benito Juarez 1.25 3.00
NH40 Marcus Garvey 1.25 3.00

2009 Topps Allen and Ginter Mini World's Biggest Hoaxes

COMPLETE SET (20) 12.50 30.00
STATED ODDS 1:12 HOBBY
HHB1 Charles Ponzi 1.25 3.00
HHB2 Alabama Changes Value of Pi 1.25 3.00
HHB3 The Runaway Bride 1.25 3.00
HHB4 Idaho 1.25 3.00
HHB5 The Turk 1.25 3.00
HHB6 Enron 1.25 3.00
HHB7 Anna Anderson 1.25 3.00
HHB8 Ferdinand Waldo Demara 1.25 3.00
HHB9 San Serriffe 1.25 3.00
HHB10 D.B. Cooper 1.25 3.00
HHB11 Wisconsin State Cap Collapses 1.25 3.00
HHB12 Victor Lustig 1.25 3.00
HHB13 The War of the Worlds 1.25 3.00
HHB14 George Parker 1.25 3.00
HHB15 The Bathtub Hoax 1.25 3.00
HHB16 The Cottingley Fairies 1.25 3.00
HHB17 James Reavis 1.25 3.00
HHB18 The Piltdown Man 1.25 3.00
HHB19 The Cardiff Giant 1.25 3.00
HHB20 Cold Fusion 1.25 3.00

2009 Topps Allen and Ginter N43

COMPLETE SET (15) 20.00 50.00
ONE CABINET/N43 PER HOBBY BOX
AP Albert Pujols 6.00 15.00
AR Alex Rodriguez 4.00 10.00
CJ Chipper Jones 2.50 6.00
DM Daisuke Matsuzaka 2.50 6.00
DW David Wright 3.00 8.00
EL Evan Longoria 3.00 8.00
GS Grady Sizemore 1.50 4.00
JB Jay Bruce 1.50 4.00
JH Josh Hamilton 2.50 6.00
JU Justin Upton 1.50 4.00
MC Miguel Cabrera 2.50 6.00
MR Manny Ramirez 2.50 6.00
RH Ryan Howard 3.00 8.00
TL Tim Lincecum 4.00 10.00
RHA Roy Halladay 2.50 6.00

2009 Topps Allen and Ginter N43 Autographs

STATED ODDS 1:270 HOBBY BOXES
STATED PRINT RUN 15 SER.#'d SETS
NO PRICING DUE TO SCARCITY
EXCHANGE DEADLINE 6/30/2012

2009 Topps Allen and Ginter N43 Relics

STATED ODDS 1:162 HOBBY BOXES
STATED PRINT RUN 25 SER.#'d SETS
NO PRICING DUE TO SCARCITY

2009 Topps Allen and Ginter N43 Relics Autographs

STATED ODDS 1:1621 HOBBY BOXES
STATED PRINT RUN 5 SER.#'d SETS
NO PRICING DUE TO SCARCITY
EXCHANGE DEADLINE 6/30/2012

2009 Topps Allen and Ginter National Pride

COMPLETE SET (75) 10.00 25.00
APPX.ODDS ONE PER HOBBY PACK
NP1 Ervin Santana .30 .75
NP2 Justin Upton .50 1.25
NP3 Jason Bay .50 1.25
NP4 Geovany Soto .50 1.25
NP5 Ryan Dempster .30 .75
NP6 Johnny Cueto .30 .75
NP7 Chipper Jones .75 2.00
NP8 Fausto Carmona .30 .75
NP9 Carlos Guillen .30 .75
NP10 Jose Reyes .50 1.25
NP11 Hiroki Kuroda .30 .75
NP12 Prince Fielder .50 1.25
NP13 Justin Morneau .75 2.00
NP14 Fransisco Rodriguez .50 1.25
NP15 Jorge Posada .50 1.25
NP16 Jake Peavy .30 .75
NP17 Felix Hernandez .75 2.00
NP18 Robinson Cano .75 2.00
NP19 Erik Bedard .30 .75
NP20 Akinori Iwamura .30 .75
NP21 Scott Hairston .30 .75
NP22 David Wright 1.00 2.50
NP23 Chien-Ming Wang .50 1.25
NP24 Chase Utley .75 2.00
NP25 Jonathan Sanchez .30 .75
NP26 Yunel Escobar .30 .75
NP27 John Lackey .30 .75
NP28 Melvin Mora .30 .75
NP29 Alfonso Soriano .50 1.25
NP30 Jose Contreras .30 .75
NP31 Grady Sizemore .50 1.25
NP32 Rich Harden .30 .75
NP33 Hanley Ramirez .75 2.00
NP34 Nick Markakis .75 2.00
NP35 Manny Ramirez .75 2.00
NP36 Yovani Gallardo .30 .75
NP37 Johan Santana .75 2.00
NP38 Mariano Rivera .75 2.00
NP39 Shin-Soo Choo .50 1.25
NP40 Hideki Matsui .75 2.00
NP41 Raul Ibanez .50 1.25
NP42 Edgar Renteria .30 .75
NP43 Jose Lopez .30 .75
NP44 Yuniesky Betancourt .30 .75
NP45 Evan Longoria 1.00 2.50
NP46 Carlos Ruiz .30 .75
NP47 Ryan Howard 1.00 2.50
NP48 Jorge Cantu .30 .75
NP49 Max Scherzer .50 1.25
NP50 Jair Jurrjens .30 .75
NP51 Albert Pujols 2.00 5.00
NP52 Daisuke Matsuzaka .75 2.00
NP53 Vladimir Guerrero .75 2.00
NP54 Carlos Zambrano .50 1.25
NP55 Kosuke Fukudome .75 2.00
NP56 Edinson Volquez .30 .75
NP57 Victor Martinez .50 1.25
NP58 Derek Jeter 2.00 5.00
NP59 Miguel Cabrera .75 2.00
NP60 Stephen Drew .30 .75
NP61 Mark Teahen .30 .75
NP62 Ryan Braun 1.00 2.50
NP63 Carlos Beltran .30 .75
NP64 Francisco Liriano .30 .75
NP65 Carlos Delgado .30 .75
NP66 Joba Chamberlain .50 1.25
NP67 Adrian Gonzalez .50 1.25
NP68 Ichiro Suzuki 1.25 3.00
NP69 Ryan Rowland-Smith .30 .75
NP70 Carlos Pena .50 1.25
NP71 Josh Hamilton .75 2.00
NP72 Edgar Gonzalez .30 .75
NP73 Carlos Lee .30 .75
NP74 Yadier Molina .50 1.25
NP75 Alex Rodriguez 1.25 3.00

2009 Topps Allen and Ginter Relics

GROUP A ODDS 1:100 HOBBY
GROUP B ODDS 1:215 HOBBY
GROUP D ODDS 1:17 HOBBY
GROUP C ODDS 1:39 HOBBY
CARDS ARE NOT SERIAL-NUMBERED
PRINT RUNS PROVIDED BY TOPPS
AL Adam LaRoche Jsy C 3.00 8.00
AP Albert Pujols Bat 15.00 40.00
AR Alex Rios Bat/90 * A 30.00 60.00
AS Alfonso Soriano Bat/191 * A 4.00 10.00
AT Anna Tunnicliffe Rashguard/250 * A 10.00
25.00
BC Bob Crowley A 10.00 25.00
BD Blake DeWitt Bat C 4.00 10.00
BK Burke Kenny Hair/250 * A 20.00 50.00
BU B.J. Upton Jsy D 3.00 8.00
BY Brock Yates/250 * A 8.00 20.00
BZ Barry Zito Pants A 3.00 8.00
CB Carlos Beltran Jsy C 3.00 8.00
CC Coco Crisp Bat A 5.00 12.00
CJ Chipper Jones Jsy C 4.00 10.00
CK Casey Kotchman Jsy A 3.00 8.00
CM Cameron Maybin Bat C 3.00 8.00
CO Cat Osterman/250 * A 15.00 40.00
CP Corey Patterson Bat C 3.00 8.00
CQ Carlos Quentin Jsy D 3.00 8.00
CS CC Sabathia Jsy 3.00 8.00
CU Chase Utley Jsy D 3.00 8.00
CW Chien-Ming Wang Jsy A 4.00 10.00
DM Daisuke Matsuzaka Jsy/110 * A 60.00 120.00
DO David Ortiz Jsy A 4.00 10.00
DW Dontrelle Willis Pants D 3.00 8.00
EC Eric Chavez Pants/210 * A 12.50 30.00
EG Eric Gagne Jsy B 3.00 8.00
EL Evan Longoria Jsy D 5.00 12.00
FL Fred Lewis Bat C 3.00 8.00
GS Gary Sheffield Bat A 3.00 8.00
HB Hank Blalock Bat A 3.00 8.00
HM Hideki Matsui Jsy B 10.00 25.00
HR Hanley Ramirez Bat/199 * A 12.50 30.00
HT Hannah Teter/250 * A 12.50 30.00
IK Iris Kyle Suit/250 * A 12.50 30.00
IS Ichiro Suzuki Jsy 6.00 15.00
JB Jay Bruce Jsy D 3.00 8.00
JD Jermaine Dye Bat C 3.00 8.00
JM Joe Mauer Jsy D 3.00 8.00
JR Jimmy Rollins Jsy D 3.00 8.00
JT Jim Thome Bat B 3.00 8.00
JU Justin Upton Jsy D 3.00 8.00
JW Jered Weaver Jsy D 3.00 8.00
KA Kristin Armstrong Jsy/250 * A 10.00 25.00
KF Kosuke Fukudome Jsy D 3.00 8.00
KM Kolan McConiughey/250 * A 8.00 20.00
LC Lynne Cox/250 * A 10.00 25.00
LM LaShawn Merritt/250 * A 8.00 20.00
LO Loren Opstedahl/250 * A 12.50 30.00
MC Mike Cameron Bat C 3.00 8.00
MH Matt Holliday Jsy D 3.00 8.00
MM Mickey Mantle Pants/250 * A 75.00 150.00
MO Magglio Ordonez Jsy D 3.00 8.00
MP Michael Phelps/250 * A 30.00 60.00
MR Manny Ramirez Jsy A 4.00 10.00
MT Mark Teixeira Jsy 4.00 10.00
MZ Mariel Zagunis Lame/250 * A 12.50 30.00
NM Nate McLouth Jsy D 3.00 8.00
NS Nick Swisher Bat/164 * A 15.00 40.00
PF Prince Fielder Bat C 3.00 8.00
RB Rocco Baldelli Bat 3.00 8.00
RC Robinson Cano Bat/195 * A 10.00 25.00
RD Ryan Doumit Jsy D 3.00 8.00
RF Richard Fosbury A 8.00 20.00
RH Ryan Howard Jsy 4.00 10.00
RL Ryan Ludwick Jsy D 3.00 8.00
RO Roy Oswalt Jsy A 8.00 20.00
RZ Ryan Zimmerman Bat C 3.00 8.00
SB Stephanie Brown Trafton/250 * A 8.00 20.00
SD Shani Davis/250 * A 8.00 20.00
SR Scott Rolen Jsy C 3.00 8.00
SW Steve Wiebe/250 * A 8.00 20.00
TH Travis Hafner Jsy C 3.00 8.00
TL Tim Lincecum Jsy D 8.00 20.00
VG Vladimir Guerrero Bat C 3.00 8.00
VW Vernon Wells Jsy A 3.00 8.00
WE Walton Glenn Eller/250 * A 12.50 30.00
WS Will Simpson/Archie Bunker/250 * A 10.00 25.00
YE Yunel Escobar Jsy D 3.00 8.00
YG Yovani Gallardo Jsy D 3.00 8.00
AER Alex Rodriguez Pants 12.50 30.00
AP2 Albert Pujols Hat/190 * 20.00 50.00
AP3 Albert Pujols Jsy/255 * 15.00 40.00
BBE Bryan Berg Card/250 * A 15.00 40.00
BCA Brian Cappelletto Shirt/250 * A 8.00 20.00
BTM Billy The Marlin Jsy/250 * A 10.00 25.00
DAW David Wright Btg Glv 12.50 30.00
DOW Dominique Wilkins/250 * A 10.00 25.00
GSI Grady Sizemore Jsy D 3.00 8.00
IS2 Ichiro Suzuki Bat 6.00 15.00
JHI John Higby/250 * A 10.00 25.00
JRH Rich Harden Pants A 3.00 8.00
MCA Miguel Cabrera Jsy C 3.00 8.00
MME Mike Metzger/250 * A 10.00 25.00
MMO Melvin Mora Bat C 3.00 8.00
MMU Mark Mulder Pants C 3.00 8.00
MR2 Manny Ramirez Bat/190 * C 8.00 20.00
MTE Miguel Tejada Jsy B 3.00 8.00
RB2 Rocco Baldelli Jsy 3.00 8.00
RH2 Ryan Howard Bat 5.00 12.00
RJB Ryan Braun Jsy D 4.00 10.00
RMA Robbie Maddison/250 * A 8.00 20.00
THU Tim Hudson Jsy A 3.00 8.00
TLH Todd Helton Jsy C 3.00 8.00
DAW2 David Wright Jsy 3.00 8.00

2009 Topps Allen and Ginter Rip Cards

STATED ODDS 1:257 HOBBY
PRINT RUNS B/WN 5-99 COPIES PER
NO PRICING ON QTY 25 OR LESS
ALL LISTED PRICED ARE FOR RIPPED
UNRIPPED HAVE ADD'L CARDS WITHIN
COMMON UNRIPPED p/r 99 40.00 80.00
COMMON UNRIPPED p/r 50 50.00 100.00
RC1 Stephen Drew/25
RC2 Carlos Zambrano/25
RC3 Carlos Quentin/25
RC4 Paul Konerko/99 6.00 15.00
RC5 Lance Berkman/10
RC6 Vladimir Guerrero
RC7 Bobby Abreu/25
RC8 Prince Fielder/10
RC9 Pat Neshek/99 6.00 15.00
RC10 Brian Giles/99 6.00 15.00
RC11 Jeff Francis/99 6.00 15.00
RC12 Jermaine Dye/50 6.00 15.00
RC13 Dan Uggla/50 6.00 15.00
RC14 Tim Hudson/50 6.00 15.00
RC15 Chris Young/50 6.00 15.00
RC16 Vernon Wells/10
RC17 Johnny Cueto/10
RC18 Brad Penny/25
RC19 John Lackey/99 6.00 15.00
RC20 Joey Votto/25
RC21 Todd Helton/25
RC22 Kevin Youkilis/5
RC23 Rafael Furcal/50 6.00 15.00
RC24 Dustin Pedroia/5
RC25 Alfonso Soriano/5
RC26 Derrek Lee/50 6.00 15.00
RC27 Cameron Maybin/99 6.00 15.00
RC28 Ryan Dempster/50 6.00 15.00
RC29 Jim Thome/25
RC30 Jonathan Papelbon/10
RC31 Yunel Escobar/99 6.00 15.00
RC32 Brian Roberts/25
RC33 John Smoltz/5
RC34 Joakim Soria/50 6.00 15.00
RC35 Cliff Lee/10
RC36 Delmon Young/25
RC37 Gary Sheffield/5
RC38 Miguel Tejada/50 6.00 15.00
RC39 Alex Gordon/25
RC40 Shane Victorino/99 6.00 15.00
RC41 Kerry Wood/25
RC42 Robinson Cano/10
RC43 Garrett Atkins/50 6.00 15.00
RC44 Fausto Carmona/99 6.00 15.00
RC45 Mike Jacobs/99 6.00 15.00
RC46 Kosuke Fukudome/25
RC47 Oliver Perez/99 6.00 15.00
RC48 Magglio Ordonez/10
RC49 James Loney/50 6.00 15.00
RC50 Ryan Braun/5
RC51 Jorge Posada/10
RC52 Rickie Weeks/99 6.00 15.00
RC53 Matt Kemp/10
RC54 Hunter Pence
RC55 Alex Rodriguez/5
RC56 Aubrey Huff/99 6.00 15.00
RC57 Chad Billingsley/50 6.00 15.00
RC58 Carlos Gomez/99 6.00 15.00
RC59 A.J. Burnett/10
RC60 Mike Aviles/99 6.00 15.00
RC61 Francisco Liriano/10
RC62 Joe Saunders/99 6.00 15.00
RC63 Derek Lowe/50 6.00 15.00
RC64 Travis Hafner/99 6.00 15.00
RC65 Michael Young
RC66 Andre Ethier/25
RC67 Carlos Delgado/10
RC68 Brad Lidge/25
RC69 Kevin Kouzmanoff/50 6.00 15.00
RC70 Jose Lopez/25
RC71 Ryan Ludwick/50 6.00 15.00
RC72 B.J. Upton/10
RC73 Zack Greinke/5
RC74 Melvin Mora/99 6.00 15.00
RC75 Derek Jeter
RC76 Yadier Molina/99 6.00 15.00
RC77 Carlos Pena/50 6.00 15.00
RC78 David Ortiz/10
RC79 Matt Cain/5
RC80 Aramis Ramirez/50 6.00 15.00
RC81 Rocco Baldelli/50 6.00 15.00
RC82 Carl Crawford/25
RC83 Jake Peavy/5
RC84 Jimmy Rollins/10
RC85 Brandon Phillips/50 6.00 15.00
RC86 Jose Reyes/5
RC87 Russell Martin/5
RC88 Victor Martinez/10
RC89 Chien-Ming Wang/5
RC90 Josh Hamilton/5
RC91 Jered Weaver/25
RC92 Ian Kinsler/5
RC93 Eric Chavez/99 6.00 15.00
RC94 Torii Hunter/25
RC95 Akinori Iwamura/25
RC96 Chase Utley/5
RC97 Johan Santana/5
RC98 Curtis Granderson/10
RC99 Mark Buehrle/50 6.00 15.00
RC100 Mickey Mantle/5

2010 Topps Allen and Ginter

COMPLETE SET (350) 60.00 120.00
COMP.SET w/o SPs (300) 15.00 40.00
COMMON CARD (1-300) .15 .40
COMMON RC (1-300) .40 1.00
COMMON SP (301-350) 1.25 3.00
SP STATED ODDS 1:2 HOBBY
1 Adam Lind .25 .60
2 Everth Cabrera .15 .40
3 Ryan Braun .50 1.25
4 Prince Fielder .25 .60
5 Edwin Jackson .15 .40
6 Madison Bumgarner RC 1.00 2.50
7 Ryan Howard .50 1.25
8 Miguel Tejada .25 .60
9 Kelly Kulick .15 .40
10 Gary Stewart .15 .40
11 Wade Davis (RC) .40 1.00
12 Jesus Flores .15 .40
13 B.J. Upton .25 .60
14 Shane Victorino .25 .60
15 Carlos Quentin .25 .60
16 Carl Pavano .15 .40
17 Johan Santana .40 1.00
18 Jose Lopez .15 .40
19 Tommy Hanson .25 .60
20 Sacagawea .15 .40
21 Ryan Kennelly .15 .40
22 Lucy .15 .40
23 Joe Mauer .40 1.00
24 Brandon Webb .25 .60
25 Max Scherzer .15 .40
26 Andy Pettitte .25 .60
27 Brad Hawpe .15 .40
28 Felipe Lopez .15 .40
29 Cole Hamels .40 1.00
30 Rafael Furcal .15 .40
31 Miguel Montero .15 .40
32 Joba Chamberlain .25 .60
33 Bengie Molina .15 .40
34 Delmon Young .25 .60
35 John Lackey .15 .40
36 Victor Martinez .25 .60
37 Daniel McCutchen RC .60 1.50
38 Tiago Della Vega .15 .40
39 Josh Johnson .25 .60
40 Carlos Beltran .15 .40
41 Daniel Hudson RC .60 1.50
42 Mark DeRosa .15 .40
43 Yovani Gallardo .15 .40
44 Chris Coghlan .15 .40
45 Justin Verlander .50 1.25
46 Chad Billingsley .15 .40
47 Drew Stubbs RC 1.00 2.50
48 Alan Francis .15 .40
49 Jenrry Mejia RC .60 1.50
50 Jason Bay .25 .60
51 Matt Holliday .40 1.00
52 Gavin Floyd .15 .40
53 Jason Heyward RC 2.50 6.00
54 Tony Hawk .40 1.00
55 Esmil Rogers RC .40 1.00
56 Shin-Soo Choo .25 .60
57 Jacoby Ellsbury .40 1.00
58 Colby Rasmus .40 1.00
59 Ivory Crockett .15 .40
60 Chris Davis .15 .40
61 Michael Cuddyer .15 .40
62 Matt Kemp .25 .60
63 Matt Carson (RC) .40 1.00
64 Josh Beckett .25 .60
65 Andre Ethier .25 .60
66 Orlando Hudson .15 .40

67 Carl Crawford .25 .60
68 Betelgeuse .15 .40
69 Clay Buchholz .25 .60
70 Joey Votto .40 1.00
71 Hunter Pence .25 .60
72 Erick Aybar .15 .40
73 Avery Jenkins .15 .40
74 Ryan Ludwick .15 .40
75 Jayson Werth .25 .60
76 Joakim Soria .15 .40
77 Ricky Romero .15 .40
78 Leonardo da Vinci .15 .40
79 James Loney .25 .60
80 Will Venable .15 .40
81 Cliff Lee .25 .60
82 Justin Upton .25 .60
83 David Wright .50 1.25
84 Elvis Andrus .25 .60
85 Yunel Escobar .15 .40
86 Andrew Bailey .15 .40
87 Alexei Ramirez .15 .40
88 Kosuke Fukudome .40 1.00
89 Joel Pineiro .15 .40
90 Kevin Kouzmanoff .15 .40
91 Carlos Zambrano .25 .60
92 Randy Oitker .15 .40
93 Brandon Inge .25 .60
94 Luke Hochevar .15 .40
95 Judson Laipply .15 .40
96 Roy Halladay .40 1.00
97 Zach Duke .15 .40
98 Johnny Cueto .15 .40
99 Anthony Gatto .15 .40
100 Matt LaPorta .40 1.00
101 Mark Buehrle .25 .60
102 Torii Hunter .15 .40
103 Niccolo Machiavelli .15 .40
104 Mahlon Duckett .15 .40
105 Nicolaus Copernicus .15 .40
106 Dustin Pedroia .50 1.25
107 Adam Dunn .25 .60
108 Paul Konerko .25 .60
109 Ian Kinsler .25 .60
110 Sherlock Holmes .15 .40
111 Josh Willingham .15 .40
112 Tyler Bradt .15 .40
113 Billy Butler .15 .40
114 Milton Bradley .15 .40
115 Trevor Hoffman .25 .60
116 Galileo Galilei .15 .40
117 Neil Walker (RC) .60 1.50
118 Eric Young Jr. (RC) .40 1.00
119 Dan Uggla .25 .60
120 Nick Swisher .40 1.00
121 Francisco Rodriguez .25 .60
122 Yadier Molina .25 .60
123 Mariano Rivera .40 1.00
124 Andrew McCutchen .40 1.00
125 Hideki Matsui .40 1.00
126 Chipper Jones .40 1.00
127 Albert Pujols 1.00 2.50
128 Hans Florine .15 .40
129 Johannes Gutenberg .15 .40
130 Area 51 .15 .40
131 Tyler Flowers RC .60 1.50
132 David Price .40 1.00
133 Nelson Cruz .25 .60
134 Vladimir Guerrero .40 1.00
135 Ken Blackburn .15 .40
136 Garrett Jones .15 .40
137 Ryan Zimmerman .25 .60
138 Javier Vazquez .15 .40
139 Miguel Cabrera .40 1.00
140 Brandon Allen (RC) .40 1.00
141 Matt Cain .25 .60
142 Ubaldo Jimenez .25 .60
143 Jorge Posada .25 .60
144 Stuart Scott .15 .40
145 Jim Thome .25 .60
146 Carlos Lee .15 .40
147 Cristian Guzman .15 .40
148 Anne Donovan .15 .40
149 Ichiro Suzuki .60 1.50
150 Grady Sizemore .25 .60
151 Kanekoa Texeira RC .40 1.00
152 The Parthenon .15 .40
153 Jay Bruce .25 .60
154 Juan Francisco RC .60 1.50
155 Carlos Carrasco (RC) 1.00 2.50
156 Cameron Maybin .15 .40
157 Kevin Youkilis .25 .60
158 Mark Teixeira .40 1.00
159 Denard Span .15 .40
160 Derrek Lee .15 .40
161 Luis Durango RC .40 1.00
162 Juan Pierre .15 .40
163 Raul Ibanez .25 .60
164 Kyle Blanks .15 .40
165 Nick Jacoby .15 .40
166 Chris Tillman .15 .40
167 Dan Haren .15 .40
168 Rickie Weeks .25 .60
169 Felix Hernandez .40 1.00
170 Adrian Gonzalez .25 .60
171 Michael Young .25 .60
172 Ian Desmond (RC) .60 1.50
173 Jimmy Rollins .25 .60
174 Eric Byrnes .15 .40
175 Tim Lincecum .60 1.50
176 Preston Pittman .15 .40
177 Pedro Feliz .15 .40
178 Josh Hamilton .40 1.00
179 Ben Zobrist .15 .40
180 Gordon Beckham .25 .60
181 Tyler Colvin RC .60 1.50
182 Chris Carpenter .40 1.00
183 Tommy Manzella (RC) .40 1.00
184 Jake Peavy .15 .40
185 X-Rays .15 .40
186 Jose Reyes .25 .60
187 Jair Jurrjens .15 .40
188 Jason Bartlett .15 .40
189 Howie Kendrick .15 .40
190 Randy Wolf .15 .40
191 Justin Morneau .40 1.00
192 Tom Knapp .15 .40
193 Tony Hoard .15 .40
Rory
194 Nyjer Morgan .15 .40
195 Sergio Santos (RC) .40 1.00
196 Scott Baker .15 .40
197 Johnny Damon .25 .60
198 A.J. Pierzynski .15 .40
199 Summer Sanders .15 .40
200 Lance Berkman .25 .60
201 Pablo Sandoval .25 .60
202 Aramis Ramirez .15 .40
203 Sig Hansen .15 .40
204 Russell Martin .15 .40
205 Meb Keflezighi .15 .40
206 J.D. Drew .15 .40
207 Wandy Rodriguez .15 .40
208 Evan Longoria .50 1.25
209 Alex Gordon .25 .60
210 Chris Johnson RC 1.00 2.50
211 Johnny Strange .15 .40
212 Ken Griffey Jr. .60 1.50
213 Mark Reynolds .15 .40
214 CC Sabathia .25 .60
215 Daniel Murphy .15 .40
216 Jordin Sparks .15 .40
217 James Shields .15 .40
218 Todd Helton .25 .60
219 Adam Wainwright .25 .60
220 Manny Ramirez .40 1.00
221 Mike Leake RC 1.25 3.00
222 Craig Gentry RC .40 1.00
223 Jason Kubel .15 .40
224 Ian Stewart .15 .40
225 Mark Teahen .15 .40
226 Brian McCann .25 .60
227 Henry Rodriguez RC .40 1.00
228 Chase Utley .40 1.00
229 Franklin Gutierrez .15 .40
230 Brian Roberts .15 .40
231 Travis Snider .15 .40
232 Hubertus Wawra .15 .40
233 Rick Ankiel .15 .40
234 Nick Johnson .15 .40
235 Carlos Guillen .15 .40
236 Shawn Johnson .40 1.00
237 Kevin Millwood .15 .40
238 Michael Brantley RC .40 1.00
239 Mike Cameron .15 .40
240 Aaron Hill .15 .40
241 Derek Lowe .15 .40
242 Jules Verne .15 .40
243 Jim Zapp .15 .40
244 Aaron Cook .15 .40
245 Michael Dunn RC .40 1.00
246 Geovany Soto .25 .60
247 Rajai Davis .15 .40
248 Jason Marquis .15 .40
249 Alfonso Soriano .25 .60
250 Magglio Ordonez .25 .60
251 Chase Headley .15 .40
252 Matt Garza .15 .40
253 Adam Moore RC .40 1.00
254 Rich Harden .15 .40
255 Robert Scott .15 .40
256 Rick Porcello .15 .40
257 Ervin Santana .15 .40
258 Ryan Dempster .15 .40
259 Scott Feldman .15 .40
260 Chris Young .15 .40
261 Adam Jones .25 .60
262 Zack Greinke .25 .60
263 Ruben Tejada RC .60 1.50
264 Captain Nemo .15 .40
265 Kendry Morales .15 .40
266 Adam LaRoche .15 .40
267 Martin Prado .15 .40
268 Brad Kilby RC .40 1.00
269 A.J. Burnett .25 .60
270 Max Poser .15 .40
271 King Tut .15 .40
272 David Blaine .15 .40
273 David DeJesus .15 .40
274 Nick Markakis .40 1.00
275 Clayton Kershaw .40 1.00
276 Daniel Runzler RC .60 1.50
277 Regis Philbin .15 .40
278 Jeff Francoeur .25 .60
279 Curtis Granderson .25 .60
280 Koji Uehara .25 .60
281 Kurt Suzuki .15 .40
282 Tyson Ross RC .40 1.00
283 Hank Presswood .15 .40
284 Dustin Richardson RC .40 1.00
285 Alex Rodriguez .60 1.50
286 Revolving Door .15 .40
287 Drew Brees .40 1.00
288 Bobby Jenks .15 .40
289 Hanley Ramirez .40 1.00
290 Jon Lester .40 1.00
291 Ron Teasley .15 .40
292 Chris Pettit RC .40 1.00
293 Troy Tulowitzki .40 1.00
294 Buster Posey RC 4.00 10.00
295 Josh Thole RC .60 1.50
296 Barry Zito .15 .40
297 Isaac Newton .15 .40
298 Jorge Cantu .15 .40
299 Robinson Cano .40 1.00
300 Nolan Reimold .25 .60
301 Gaby Sanchez SP 1.25 3.00
302 Daric Barton SP 1.25 3.00
303 Trevor Cahill SP 1.25 3.00
304 Carlos Pena SP 1.25 3.00
305 Kelly Johnson SP 1.25 3.00
306 Brandon Phillips SP 1.25 3.00
307 Akinori Iwamura SP 1.25 3.00
308 Adrian Beltre SP 1.25 3.00
309 Casey McGehee SP 1.25 3.00
310 Placido Polanco SP 1.25 3.00
311 Chone Figgins SP 1.25 3.00
312 Carlos Ruiz SP 1.25 3.00
313 Ryan Doumit SP 1.25 3.00
314 Ivan Rodriguez SP 1.25 3.00
315 Bobby Abreu SP 1.25 3.00
316 Nate McLouth SP 1.25 3.00
317 Alex Rios SP 1.25 3.00
318 Carlos Gonzalez SP 2.00 5.00
319 Austin Jackson SP RC 1.25 3.00
320 Scott Sizemore SP RC 1.25 3.00
321 Carlos Gomez SP 1.25 3.00
322 Gary Matthews SP 1.25 3.00
323 Angel Pagan SP 1.25 3.00
324 Randy Winn SP 1.25 3.00
325 Brett Gardner SP 1.25 3.00
326 Aaron Rowand SP 1.25 3.00
327 Vernon Wells SP 1.25 3.00
328 Jered Weaver SP 1.25 3.00
329 Troy Glaus SP 1.25 3.00
330 Jonathan Papelbon SP 1.25 3.00
331 Huston Street SP 1.25 3.00
332 Ricky Nolasco SP 1.25 3.00
333 Roy Oswalt SP 1.25 3.00
334 Brett Myers SP 1.25 3.00
335 Jonathan Broxton SP 1.25 3.00
336 Hiroki Kuroda SP 1.25 3.00
337 Joe Nathan SP 1.25 3.00
338 Francisco Liriano SP 1.25 3.00
339 Ben Sheets SP 1.25 3.00
340 Brad Lidge SP 1.25 3.00
341 Jon Garland SP 1.25 3.00
342 Erik Bedard SP 1.25 3.00
343 Brad Penny SP 1.25 3.00
344 Derek Holland SP 1.25 3.00
345 Stephen Drew SP 1.25 3.00
346 Ryan Theriot SP 1.25 3.00
347 Orlando Cabrera SP 1.25 3.00
348 Asdrubal Cabrera SP 2.00 5.00
349 Yuniesky Betancourt SP 1.25 3.00
350 Alcides Escobar SP 1.25 3.00

2010 Topps Allen and Ginter Mini

*MINI 1-300: .75X TO 2X BASIC
*MINI 1-300 RC: .5X TO 1.2X BASIC RC's
APPX. ONE MINI PER PACK
*MINI SP 301-350: .5X TO 1.2X BASIC SP
MINI SP ODDS 1:13 HOBBY
COMMON CARD (351-400) 20.00 50.00
351-400 RANDOM WITHIN RIP CARDS
STRASBURG 401 ISSUED IN PACKS
OVERALL PLATE ODDS 1:799 HOBBY
PLATE PRINT RUN 1 SET PER COLOR
BLACK-CYAN-MAGENTA-YELLOW ISSUED
NO PLATE PRICING DUE TO SCARCITY
351 Cole Hamels EXT 40.00 80.00
352 Billy Butler EXT 30.00 60.00
353 Daisuke Matsuzaka EXT 30.00 60.00
354 Stephen Drew EXT 30.00 60.00
355 Ryan Braun EXT 20.00 50.00
356 Mark Teixeira EXT 20.00 50.00
357 Chipper Jones EXT 40.00 80.00
358 Justin Morneau EXT 20.00 50.00
359 Adrian Gonzalez EXT 30.00 60.00
360 Dustin Pedroia EXT 30.00 60.00
361 Miguel Cabrera EXT 30.00 60.00
362 Carlos Beltran EXT 30.00 60.00
363 Lance Berkman EXT 30.00 60.00
364 Kevin Kouzmanoff EXT 30.00 60.00
365 A.J. Burnett EXT 20.00 50.00
366 Tim Lincecum EXT 20.00 50.00
367 Francisco Rodriguez EXT 20.00 50.00
368 Zack Greinke EXT 40.00 80.00
369 Andre Ethier EXT 20.00 50.00
370 Hideki Matsui EXT 30.00 60.00
371 Alexei Ramirez EXT 20.00 50.00
372 Grady Sizemore EXT 20.00 50.00
373 Joe Mauer EXT 30.00 60.00
374 Adam Lind EXT 30.00 60.00
375 Kurt Suzuki EXT 30.00 60.00
376 Rick Porcello EXT 30.00 60.00
377 Felix Hernandez EXT 30.00 60.00
378 Albert Pujols EXT 50.00 100.00
379 Adam Dunn EXT 30.00 60.00
380 Brandon Webb EXT 30.00 60.00
381 Pablo Sandoval EXT 40.00 80.00
382 Chris Young EXT 30.00 60.00
383 Tommy Hanson EXT 30.00 60.00
384 Adam Jones EXT 20.00 50.00
385 Joe Nathan EXT 20.00 50.00
386 Andy Pettitte EXT 30.00 60.00
387 Gordon Beckham EXT 40.00 80.00
388 Alfonso Soriano EXT 30.00 60.00
389 Hanley Ramirez EXT 30.00 60.00
390 Torii Hunter EXT 20.00 50.00
391 Matt Garza EXT 20.00 50.00
392 Johnny Cueto EXT 20.00 50.00
393 Prince Fielder EXT 30.00 60.00
394 Andrew McCutchen EXT 30.00 60.00
395 Ken Griffey Jr. EXT 50.00 100.00
396 Ryan Howard EXT 20.00 50.00
397 Todd Helton EXT 20.00 50.00
398 Kosuke Fukudome EXT 30.00 60.00
399 Roy Halladay EXT 20.00 50.00
400 Matt Kemp EXT 40.00 80.00
401 Stephen Strasburg 75.00 150.00

2010 Topps Allen and Ginter Mini A and G Back

*A & G BACK: 1X TO 2.5X BASIC
*A & G BACK RCs: .6X TO 1.5X BASIC RCs
STATED ODDS 1:5 HOBBY
*A & G BACK SP: .6X TO 1.5X BASIC SP
SP STATED ODDS 1:65 HOBBY

2010 Topps Allen and Ginter Mini Bazooka

STATED ODDS 1:280 HOBBY
STATED PRINT RUN 25 SER.#'D SETS
NO PRICING DUE TO SCARCITY

2010 Topps Allen and Ginter Mini Black

*BLACK: 2X TO 5X BASIC
*BLACK RCs: .75X TO 2X BASIC RCs
STATED ODDS 1:10 HOBBY
*BLACK SP: .75X TO 2X BASIC SP
SP STATED ODDS 1:130 HOBBY
294 Buster Posey 12.50 30.00

2010 Topps Allen and Ginter Mini No Card Number

*NO NBR: 8X TO 20X BASIC
*NO NBR RCs: 3X TO 8X BASIC RCs
*NO NBR SP: 1.2X TO 3X BASIC SP
STATED ODDS 1:140 HOBBY

2010 Topps Allen and Ginter Mini Silk

STATED ODDS 1:365 HOBBY
STATED PRINT RUN 10 SER.#'D SET
NO PRICING DUE TO SCARCITY

2010 Topps Allen and Ginter Mini Wood

STATED ODDS 1:3542 HOBBY
STATED PRINT RUN 1 SER.#'D SET
NO PRICING DUE TO SCARCITY

2010 Topps Allen and Ginter Autographs

ASTERISK EQUALS PARTIAL EXCHANGE
AD Anne Donovan 10.00 25.00
AE Alcides Escobar 6.00 15.00
AF Alan Francis 12.50 30.00
AG Alex Gordon 40.00 80.00
AJ Adam Jones 10.00 25.00
AL Adam Lind 5.00 12.00
AM Andrew McCutchen 12.50 30.00
AP Albert Pujols
AR Alexei Ramirez 8.00 20.00
BD Brian Duensing 5.00 12.00
CC Chris Coghlan 6.00 15.00
CK Clayton Kershaw 12.50 30.00
CM Cameron Maybin 4.00 10.00
CP Cliff Pennington 6.00 15.00
CR Colby Rasmus 12.50 30.00
CV Chris Volstad 4.00 10.00
CY Chris Young 4.00 10.00
DB David Blaine 50.00 100.00
DD Dale Davis 8.00 20.00
DM Daniel McCutchen 4.00 10.00
DP Dustin Pedroia 20.00 50.00
DS Drew Stubbs 8.00 20.00
DT Darren Taylor 10.00 25.00
EC Everth Cabrera 4.00 10.00
EL Evan Longoria
GS Gary Stewart 10.00 25.00
HF Hans Florine 12.50 30.00
HP Hank Presswood 20.00 50.00
HW Hubertus Wawra 12.50 30.00
IC Ivory Crockett 12.50 30.00
IK Ian Kinsler 8.00 20.00
JC Johnny Cueto 5.00 12.00
JF Jeff Francis 4.00 10.00
JH Jason Heyward 60.00 120.00
JK Jason Kubel 8.00 20.00
JL Judson Laipply 15.00 40.00
JM Jason Motte 5.00 12.00
JO Josh Outman 4.00 10.00
JP Jonathan Papelbon 30.00 60.00
JR Juan Rivera 5.00 12.00
JS Jordin Sparks 30.00 60.00
JU Justin Upton 15.00 40.00
JW Josh Willingham 5.00 12.00
JZ Jim Zapp 20.00 50.00
KB Ken Blackburn 10.00 25.00
KK Kelly Kulick 15.00 40.00
KU Koji Uehara 6.00 15.00
MB Michael Bourn 5.00 12.00
MC Miguel Cabrera 60.00 120.00
MD Mahlon Duckett 20.00 50.00
MH Matt Holliday 125.00 250.00
MK Matt Kemp 10.00 25.00
MM Marvin Miller 20.00 50.00
MP Mike Parsons 12.50 30.00
MS Max Scherzer 4.00 10.00
NF Neftali Feliz 6.00 15.00
PP Placido Polanco 10.00 25.00
PS Pablo Sandoval 12.50 30.00
RB Ryan Braun 75.00 150.00
RH Ryan Howard 100.00 175.00
RK Ryan Kennelly 10.00 25.00
RN Ricky Nolasco 4.00 10.00
RO Ross Ohlendorf 4.00 10.00
RP Rick Porcello 12.50 30.00
RS Robert Scott 20.00 50.00
RT Ron Teasley 20.00 50.00
RZ Ryan Zimmerman 12.50 30.00
SH Sig Hansen 30.00 60.00
SJ Shawn Johnson 60.00 120.00
SK Scott Kazmir
SS Stuart Scott 20.00 50.00
SS Stephen Strasburg 500.00 600.00
SV Shane Victorino 20.00 50.00
TB Tyler Bradt 12.50 30.00
TC Trevor Crowe 4.00 10.00
TH Tommy Hanson 12.50 30.00
TK Tom Knapp 12.50 30.00
TT Troy Tulowitzki 20.00 50.00
VW Vernon Wells 40.00 80.00
YE Yunel Escobar 5.00 12.00
YG Yovani Gallardo 8.00 20.00
ZS Zac Sunderland 10.00 25.00
AEI Andre Ethier EXCH * 12.50 30.00
AGA Anthony Gatto 12.50 30.00
AGO Adrian Gonzalez 20.00 50.00
AJE Avery Jenkins 50.00 100.00
BJU B.J. Upton 10.00 25.00
DBR Drew Brees 60.00 120.00
GSI Glenn Singleman 12.50 30.00
JCL Jeff Clement 5.00 12.00
JRT J.R. Towles 4.00 10.00
JST Johnny Strange 10.00 25.00
MKE Meb Keflezighi 15.00 40.00
MPO Max Poser 8.00 20.00
MTB Mitchell Boggs 5.00 12.00
PPI Preston Pittman 12.50 30.00
RHI Rich Hill 5.00 12.00
ROI Randy Oitker 12.50 30.00
RPE Ryan Perry 4.00 10.00
RPH Regis Philbin 20.00 50.00
RTH Tony Hoard 12.50 30.00
Rory
SSA Summer Sanders 30.00 60.00
TDV Tiago Della Vega 10.00 25.00
THA Tony Hawk 100.00 175.00

2010 Topps Allen and Ginter Autographs Red Ink

RANDOM INSERTS IN RIP CARDS
STATED PRINT RUN 10 SER.#'D SETS
NO PRICING DUE TO SCARCITY

2010 Topps Allen and Ginter Baseball Highlights

COMPLETE SET (15) 8.00 20.00
STATED ODDS 1:10 HOBBY
AGHS1 Chase Utley 1.00 2.50
AGHS2 Mark Buehrle .60 1.50
AGHS3 Derek Jeter 2.50 6.00
AGHS4 Mariano Rivera 1.00 2.50
AGHS5 Ichiro Suzuki 1.50 4.00
AGHS6 Johnny Damon .60 1.50
AGHS7 Carl Crawford .60 1.50
AGHS8 Dewayne Wise .40 1.00
AGHS9 Jimmy Rollins .60 1.50
AGHS10 Hideki Matsui 1.00 2.50
AGHS11 Andre Ethier .60 1.50
AGHS12 Troy Tulowitzki 1.00 2.50
AGHS13 Jonathan Sanchez .40 1.00
AGHS14 Mark Teixeira 1.00 2.50
AGHS15 Daniel Murphy .40 1.00

2010 Topps Allen and Ginter Book Cards

STATED ODDS 1:127,825 HOBBY
STATED PRINT RUN 1 SER.#'d SET
NO PRINCING DUE TO SCARCITY

2010 Topps Allen and Ginter Cabinets

ONE CABINET OR N43 PER BOX TOPPER
NCCB1 President Chester A. Arthur 2.00 5.00
Washington Roebling
John A. Roebling
Emily Roebling
NCCB2 Andrew McCutchen 2.50 6.00
NCCB3 President Herbert Hoover 2.00 5.00
Elwood Mead
NCCB4 Lance Berkman 2.00 5.00
Ivan Rodriguez
Carlos Lee
NCCB5 President Theodore Roosevelt 2.00 5.00
John Frank Stevens
George Washington Goethals
John Findlay Wallace
NCCB6 CC Sabathia 4.00 10.00
Mariano Rivera
Hideki Matsui
Derek Jeter
NCCB7 Joe Mauer 3.00 8.00
NCCB8 George Washington 2.00 5.00
Thomas Jefferson
Theodore Roosevelt
Abraham Lincoln
NCCB9 Jacoby Ellsbury 2.50 6.00
Andy Pettitte
Jorge Posada
NCCB10 Gerald R. Ford 2.00 5.00
Richard M. Nixon
Wally Hickel

2010 Topps Allen and Ginter Cabinet Relics

RANDOM BOX TOPPER INSERTS
STATED PRINT RUN 1 SER.#'d SET
NO PRINCING DUE TO SCARCITY

2010 Topps Allen and Ginter Cut Signatures

STATED ODDS 1:110,000 HOBBY
STATED PRINT RUN 1 SER.#'d SET
NO PRINCING DUE TO SCARCITY

2010 Topps Allen and Ginter DNA Relics

STATED ODDS 1:200,000 HOBBY
STATED PRINT RUN 1 SER.#'d SET
NO PRINCING DUE TO SCARCITY

2010 Topps Allen and Ginter Employee Autographs

RANDOM INSERTS IN PACKS
NO PRICING DUE TO SCARCITY

2010 Topps Allen and Ginter Mini Celestial Stars

RANDOM INSERTS IN PACKS
CS1 Mark Teixeira 6.00 15.00
CS2 Prince Fielder 4.00 10.00
CS3 Tim Lincecum 10.00 25.00
CS4 Derek Jeter 15.00 40.00
CS5 Dustin Pedroia 8.00 20.00
CS6 Cliff Lee 4.00 10.00
CS7 Evan Longoria 8.00 20.00
CS8 Ryan Howard 8.00 20.00
CS9 David Wright 8.00 20.00
CS10 Albert Pujols 15.00 40.00
CS11 Vladimir Guerrero 6.00 15.00
CS12 Johan Santana 6.00 15.00

2010 Topps Allen and Ginter Mini Creatures of Legend, Myth and Joy

STATED ODDS 1:288 HOBBY
CLMJ1 Santa Claus 10.00 25.00
CLMJ2 The Easter Bunny 10.00 25.00
CLMJ3 The Tooth Fairy 10.00 25.00
CLMJ4 Goldilocks 10.00 25.00
CLMJ5 Little Red Riding Hood 10.00 25.00
CLMJ6 Paul Bunyan 10.00 25.00
CLMJ7 Jack and the Beanstalk 10.00 25.00
CLMJ8 Peter Pan 10.00 25.00
CLMJ9 Three Little Pigs 10.00 25.00
CLMJ10 The Little Engine That Could 10.0025.00

2010 Topps Allen and Ginter Mini Lords of Olympus

COMPLETE SET (25) 20.00 50.00
STATED ODDS 1:12 HOBBY
LO1 Zeus 1.25 3.00
LO2 Poseidon 1.25 3.00
LO3 Hades 1.25 3.00
LO4 Hera 1.25 3.00
LO5 Athena 1.25 3.00
LO6 Apollo 1.25 3.00
LO7 Aphrodite 1.25 3.00
LO8 Hermes 1.25 3.00
LO9 Artemis 1.25 3.00
LO10 Gaea 1.25 3.00
LO11 Uranus 1.25 3.00
LO12 Cronos 1.25 3.00
LO13 Prometheus 1.25 3.00
LO14 Phoebe 1.25 3.00
LO15 Demeter 1.25 3.00
LO16 Persephone 1.25 3.00
LO17 Dionysus 1.25 3.00
LO18 Eros 1.25 3.00
LO19 Helios 1.25 3.00
LO20 Thanatos 1.25 3.00
LO21 Pan 1.25 3.00
LO22 Nemesis 1.25 3.00
LO23 The Fates 1.25 3.00
LO24 The Muses 1.25 3.00
LO25 Atlas 1.25 3.00

2010 Topps Allen and Ginter Mini Monsters of the Mesozoic

COMPLETE SET (25) 20.00 50.00
STATED ODDS 1:12 HOBBY
MM1 Tyrannosaurus Rex 1.25 3.00
MM2 Triceratops 1.25 3.00
MM3 Stegosaurus 1.25 3.00
MM4 Velociraptor 1.25 3.00
MM5 Allosaurus 1.25 3.00
MM6 Megalosaurus 1.25 3.00
MM7 Spinosaurus 1.25 3.00
MM8 Ankylosaurus 1.25 3.00
MM9 Apatosaurus 1.25 3.00
MM10 Brachiosaurus 1.25 3.00
MM11 Diplodocus 1.25 3.00
MM12 Iguanodon 1.25 3.00
MM13 Pachycephalosaurus 1.25 3.00
MM14 Pentaceratops 1.25 3.00
MM15 Protoceratops 1.25 3.00
MM16 Ultrasaurus 1.25 3.00
MM17 Dilophosaurus 1.25 3.00
MM18 Supersaurus 1.25 3.00
MM19 Nomingia 1.25 3.00
MM20 Oviraptor 1.25 3.00
MM21 Bambiraptor 1.25 3.00
MM22 Protarchaeopteryx 1.25 3.00
MM23 Carcharodontosaurus 1.25 3.00
MM24 Carnotaurus 1.25 3.00
MM25 Giganotosaurus 1.25 3.00

2010 Topps Allen and Ginter Mini Monsters of the Mesozoic Relics

STATED ODDS 1:174,000 HOBBY
STATED PRINT RUN 1 SER.#'d SET
NO PRICING DUE TO SCARCITY

2010 Topps Allen and Ginter Mini National Animals

COMPLETE SET (50) 30.00 60.00
STATED ODDS 1:8 HOBBY
NA1 Cougar 1.25 3.00
Argentina
NA2 Cuban Crocodile 1.25 3.00
Cuba
NA3 Falcon 1.25 3.00
Iceland
NA4 Cheetah 1.25 3.00
Kenya
NA5 Cow 1.25 3.00
Nepal
NA6 Kangaroo 1.25 3.00
Australia
NA7 Ostrich 1.25 3.00
Grenada
NA8 Chihuahua 1.25 3.00
Mexico
NA9 Jaguar 1.25 3.00
Brazil
NA10 Bull 1.25 3.00
Spain
NA11 Harpy Eagle 1.25 3.00
Panama
NA12 Markhor 1.25 3.00
Pakistan
NA13 African Elephant 1.25 3.00
South Africa
NA14 Barbary Macaque 1.25 3.00
Gibraltar
NA15 Giant Panda 1.25 3.00
People's Republic of China
NA16 Leopard 1.25 3.00
Somalia
NA17 Camel 1.25 3.00
Kuwait
NA18 Beaver 1.25 3.00
Canada
NA19 Alpaca 1.25 3.00
Peru
NA20 Lion 1.25 3.00
Belgium
NA21 Lynx 1.25 3.00
Romania
NA22 Stag 1.25 3.00
Ireland
NA23 Elk 1.25 3.00
Sweden
NA24 Condor 1.25 3.00
Colombia
NA25 Wisent 1.25 3.00
Poland
NA26 Gray Wolf 1.25 3.00
Turkey
NA27 Gallic Rooster 1.25 3.00
France
NA28 Sable Antelope 1.25 3.00
Zimbabwe
NA29 Flamingo 1.25 3.00
Bahamas
NA30 Koi 1.25 3.00
Japan
NA31 Ashy-faced Owl 1.25 3.00
Dominican Republic
NA32 Bulldog 1.25 3.00
United Kingdom
NA33 Brown Bear 1.25 3.00
Finland
NA34 White-tailed Deer 1.25 3.00
Honduras
NA35 Russian Bear 1.25 3.00
Russia
NA36 Dolphin 1.25 3.00
Greece
NA37 Komodo Dragon 1.25 3.00
Indonesia
NA38 Llama 1.25 3.00
Bolivia
NA39 Sheep 1.25 3.00
New Zealand
NA40 King Cobra 1.25 3.00
Republic of India
NA41 Green-and-black Streamertail 1.25 3.00
Jamaica
NA42 Carabao 1.25 3.00
Philippines
NA43 Water Buffalo 1.25 3.00
Vietnam
NA44 Israeli Gazelle 1.25 3.00
Israel
NA45 Italian Wolf 1.25 3.00
Italy
NA46 Ring Tailed Lemur 1.25 3.00
Madagascar
NA47 Tiger 1.25 3.00
South Korea
NA48 Dalmatian 1.25 3.00
Croatia
NA49 Zebra 1.25 3.00
Botswana
NA50 Bald Eagle 1.50 4.00
United States

2010 Topps Allen and Ginter Mini Saltiest Sailors

RANDOM INSERTS IN PACKS
WSS1 Blackbeard 40.00 80.00
WSS2 Ned Low 40.00 80.00
WSS3 Jack Rackham 40.00 80.00
WSS4 Stede Bonnet 40.00 80.00
WSS5 Black Bart 40.00 80.00
WSS6 Captain Kidd 40.00 80.00
WSS7 Henry Morgan 40.00 80.00
WSS8 Edward England 40.00 80.00
WSS9 Thomas Tew 40.00 80.00
WSS10 Charles Vane 40.00 80.00

2010 Topps Allen and Ginter Mini Sailors of the Seven Seas

COMPLETE SET (10) 10.00 25.00
STATED ODDS 1:24 HOBBY
SSS1 Christopher Columbus 1.50 4.00
SSS2 Sir Francis Drake 1.50 4.00
SSS3 Sir Walter Raleigh 1.50 4.00
SSS4 Vasco Nunez de Balboa 1.50 4.00
SSS5 Francisco Vasquez de Coronado 1.50 4.00
SSS6 Hernando de Cortes 1.50 4.00
SSS7 Hernando de Soto 1.50 4.00
SSS8 Henry Hudson 1.50 4.00
SSS9 Francisco Pizarro 1.50 4.00
SSS10 Juan Ponce de Leon 1.50 4.00

2010 Topps Allen and Ginter Mini World's Biggest

RANDOM INSERTS IN RETAIL PACKS
WB1 Blue Whale 2.00 5.00
WB2 Burj Khalifa 2.00 5.00
WB3 Prague Castle 2.00 5.00
WB4 General Sherman Sequoia 2.00 5.00
WB5 Mount Everest 2.00 5.00
WB6 Antarctica 6.00 15.00
WB7 Sahara 6.00 15.00
WB8 Angel Falls 6.00 15.00
WB9 The Amazon 6.00 15.00
WB10 Steamboat Geyser 6.00 15.00
WB11 Lake Pontchartrain Causeway 6.00 15.00
WB12 The Nile 6.00 15.00
WB13 Russia 6.00 15.00
WB14 Three Gorges Dam 6.00 15.00
WB15 Golden Jubilee 6.00 15.00
WB16 Polar Bear 6.00 15.00
WB17 African Elephant 6.00 15.00
WB18 Eastern Lowland Gorilla 6.00 15.00
WB19 Goliath Birdeater 6.00 15.00
WB20 World's Largest Collection of World's Smallest Versions of World's Largest 6.00 15.00
WB21 Large Hadron Collider 6.00 15.00
WB22 1966 Leonid Meteor Shower 6.00 15.00
WB23 Sedan Crater 6.00 15.00
WB24 Kuthodaw Pagoda 6.00 15.00
WB25 Spring Temple Buddha 6.00 15.00

2010 Topps Allen and Ginter Mini World's Greatest Word Smiths

COMPLETE SET (15) 12.50 30.00
STATED ODDS 1:24 HOBBY
WGWS1 Homer 1.50 4.00
WGWS2 William Shakespeare 1.50 4.00
WGWS3 Washington Irving 1.50 4.00
WGWS4 Miguel de Cervantes 1.50 4.00
WGWS5 Fyodor Dostoevsky 1.50 4.00
WGWS6 Victor Hugo 1.50 4.00
WGWS7 Shen Kuo 1.50 4.00
WGWS8 John Milton 1.50 4.00
WGWS9 Dante Alighieri 1.50 4.00
WGWS10 Edgar Allan Poe 1.50 4.00
WGWS11 Marcus Aurelius 1.50 4.00
WGWS12 Virgil 1.50 4.00
WGWS13 John Bunyan 1.50 4.00
WGWS14 Plato 1.50 4.00
WGWS15 Confucius 1.50 4.00

2010 Topps Allen and Ginter N43

AE Andre Ethier 1.25 3.00
AM Andrew McCutchen 2.00 5.00
AP Albert Pujols 5.00 12.00
AR Alex Rodriguez 3.00 8.00
BU B.J. Upton 1.25 3.00
EL Evan Longoria 2.50 6.00
HP Hunter Pence 1.25 3.00
HR Hanley Ramirez 2.00 5.00
JM Joe Mauer 2.00 5.00
JU Justin Upton 1.25 3.00
MT Mark Teixeira 2.00 5.00
NM Nick Markakis 2.00 5.00
PF Prince Fielder 1.25 3.00
RB Ryan Braun 2.50 6.00
RH Ryan Howard 2.50 6.00

2010 Topps Allen and Ginter Relics

STATED ODDS 1:11 HOBBY
AD Adam Dunn 3.00 8.00
AD Anne Donovan 5.00 12.00
AE Andre Ethier 3.00 8.00
AF Alan Francis 6.00 15.00
AG Adrian Gonzalez Bat 3.00 8.00
AH Aaron Hill 3.00 8.00
AJ Adam Jones 3.00 8.00
AJ Avery Jenkins 20.00 50.00
AL Adam Lind 3.00 8.00
AS Alfonso Soriano 3.00 8.00
BA Brett Anderson 3.00 8.00
BB Billy Butler 3.00 8.00
BM Brian McCann 3.00 8.00
BP Buster Posey 12.50 30.00
BR Brian Roberts 3.00 8.00
BU B.J. Upton 3.00 8.00
CC Chris Coghlan 3.00 8.00
CL Carlos Lee 3.00 8.00
CM Carlos Marmol 3.00 8.00
CQ Carlos Quentin 3.00 8.00
CR Colby Rasmus Bat 3.00 8.00
CV Chris Volstad
DB David Blaine 15.00 40.00
DD Dale Davis 4.00 10.00
DH Dan Haren 3.00 8.00
DT Darren Taylor 5.00 12.00
DU Dan Uggla 3.00 8.00
DW David Wright 5.00 12.00
EL Evan Longoria 3.00 8.00
GB Gordon Beckham 3.00 8.00
GS Grady Sizemore 3.00 8.00
GS Gary Stewart 5.00 12.00
HF Hans Florine 10.00 25.00
HR Hanley Ramirez 3.00 8.00
HW Hubertus Wawra 6.00 15.00
IC Ivory Crockett 5.00 12.00
IK Ian Kinsler 3.00 8.00
IR Ivan Rodriguez 3.00 8.00
IS Ichiro Suzuki 4.00 10.00
JB Jay Bruce 3.00 8.00
JD John Danks 3.00 8.00
JH Josh Hamilton 3.00 8.00
JJ Josh Johnson 3.00 8.00
JL Judson Laipply 5.00 12.00
JS Jordin Sparks 8.00 20.00
JS Johnny Strange 3.00 8.00
JV Joey Votto 3.00 8.00
KB Kyle Blanks 3.00 8.00
KB Ken Blackburn 4.00 10.00
KF Kosuke Fukudome 3.00 8.00
KK Kelly Kulick 8.00 20.00
KM Kendry Morales 3.00 8.00
LB Lance Berkman 6.00 15.00
MC Matt Cain 3.00 8.00
MK Matt Kemp 3.00 8.00
MK Meb Keflezighi 5.00 12.00
ML Mat Latos 3.00 8.00
MM Marvin Miller 5.00 12.00
MP Mike Parsons 4.00 10.00
MR Mark Reynolds 3.00 8.00
NC Nelson Cruz 3.00 8.00
NF Neftali Feliz 30.00 60.00
NM Nick Markakis 3.00 8.00
PF Prince Fielder 3.00 8.00
PP Preston Pittman 5.00 12.00
RB Ryan Braun 3.00 8.00
RC Robinson Cano 3.00 8.00
RH Ryan Howard 4.00 10.00
RK Ryan Kennelly 4.00 10.00
RN Ricky Nolasco 3.00 8.00
RO Randy Oitker 20.00 50.00
RP Regis Philbin 12.50 30.00
RZ Ryan Zimmerman 3.00 8.00
SD Stephen Drew 3.00 8.00
SH Sig Hansen 30.00 60.00
SJ Shawn Johnson 15.00 40.00
SS Stuart Scott 4.00 10.00
SV Shane Victorino 3.00 8.00
TB Tyler Bradt 6.00 15.00
TH Tony Hawk 20.00 50.00
TK Tom Knapp 12.50 30.00
TT Troy Tulowitzki 3.00 8.00
UJ Ubaldo Jimenez 3.00 8.00
YE Yunel Escobar 3.00 8.00
YG Yovani Gallardo 4.00 10.00
ZS Zac Sunderland 4.00 10.00
AGA Anthony Gatto 5.00 12.00
ARA Aramis Ramirez 3.00 8.00
DBR Drew Brees 10.00 25.00
DWR David Wright 3.00 8.00
GSI Glenn Singleman 4.00 10.00
JSA Jeff Samardzija 3.00 8.00
MCA Miguel Cabrera 3.00 8.00
MPO Max Poser 6.00 15.00
RTH Tony Hoard 12.50 30.00
Rory
SSA Summer Sanders 6.00 15.00
TDV Tiago Della Vega 5.00 12.00
THE Todd Helton 3.00 8.00
THU Torii Hunter 3.00 8.00
MCAB Melky Cabrera 3.00 8.00

2010 Topps Allen and Ginter Rip Cards

STATED ODDS 1:285 HOBBY
PRINT RUNS B/WN 5-99 COPIES PER
NO PRICING ON QTY 25 OR LESS
ALL LISTED PRICED ARE FOR RIPPED
UNRIPPED HAVE ADD'L CARDS WITHIN
COMMON UNRIPPED p/r 99 40.00 80.00
COMMON UNRIPPED p/r 50 50.00 100.00
RC1 Rick Ankiel/99 6.00 15.00
RC2 David Ortiz/25
RC3 Jayson Werth/25
RC4 Elijah Dukes/99 6.00 15.00
RC5 Carlos Gomez/99 6.00 15.00
RC6 Dan Uggla/25
RC7 Erik Bedard/50 6.00 15.00
RC8 Mariano Rivera/5
RC9 Derek Jeter/5
RC10 Raul Ibanez/25
RC11 Troy Glaus/50 6.00 15.00
RC12 Brian Roberts/25
RC13 Cliff Lee/25
RC14 Aramis Ramirez/50 6.00 15.00
RC15 Colby Rasmus/99 10.00 25.00
RC16 Ryan Zimmerman
RC17 CC Sabathia/5
RC18 Miguel Tejada/25
RC19 Mike Cameron/99 6.00 15.00
RC20 Corey Hart/99 6.00 15.00
RC21 Justin Upton/5
RC22 Brian McCann
RC23 Jon Lester
RC24 Yunel Escobar/99 6.00 15.00
RC25 Nick Swisher/50 15.00 40.00
RC26 B.J. Upton/25
RC27 Adam Wainwright/5
RC28 Nate McLouth/99 6.00 15.00
RC29 Ian Kinsler
RC30 Evan Longoria/5
RC31 Jay Bruce/50 10.00 25.00
RC32 Justin Verlander
RC33 Hunter Pence/50 10.00 25.00
RC34 Kendry Morales/50 6.00 15.00
RC35 James Loney/99 10.00 25.00
RC36 Brandon Phillips/50 6.00 15.00
RC37 Josh Beckett/5
RC38 Carlos Lee/50 6.00 15.00
RC39 Jimmy Rollins/5
RC40 Nick Markakis/25
RC41 Manny Ramirez/25
RC42 Chris Carpenter/5
RC43 Russ Martin/99 6.00 15.00
RC44 Derrek Lee/50 6.00 15.00
RC45 Orlando Hudson/99 6.00 15.00
RC46 Jason Bay/25
RC47 Johan Santana/5
RC48 Lastings Milledge/99 6.00 15.00
RC49 Aaron Hill/25
RC50 Denard Span/99 6.00 15.00
RC51 Jose Reyes/5
RC52 Tim Hudson/50 10.00 25.00
RC53 Joakim Soria/50 6.00 15.00
RC54 Chad Billingsley/99 6.00 15.00
RC55 Alex Rodriguez/5
RC56 Matt Holliday/5
RC57 Josh Johnson/25
RC58 Tyler Flowers/99 10.00 25.00
RC59 Bobby Abreu/25
RC60 Kyle Blanks/99 6.00 15.00
RC61 Jacoby Ellsbury/25
RC62 Carlos Pena/50 10.00 25.00
RC63 Magglio Ordonez/50 10.00 25.00
RC64 Elvis Andrus/99 10.00 25.00
RC65 Kevin Youkilis/5
RC66 Joey Votto/50 10.00 25.00
RC67 Yovani Gallardo/50 6.00 15.00
RC68 Clayton Kershaw/25
RC69 Delmon Young/99 10.00 25.00
RC70 Chase Utley/5
RC71 Scott Kazmir/99 6.00 15.00
RC72 Carl Crawford/5
RC73 Josh Hamilton
RC74 Tommy Manzella/99 6.00 15.00
RC75 Troy Tulowitzki/5
RC76 Jim Thome/50 10.00 25.00
RC77 Ichiro Suzuki/5
RC78 Dan Haren
RC79 Roy Oswalt/25
RC80 Michael Brantley/99 6.00 15.00
RC81 Franklin Gutierrez/50 6.00 15.00
RC82 Jered Weaver/50 6.00 15.00
RC83 Jake Peavy/25
RC84 Ubaldo Jimenez/25
RC85 Chris Coghlan/99 6.00 15.00
RC86 Nelson Cruz/50 10.00 25.00
RC87 Aaron Rowand/99 6.00 15.00
RC88 Ben Sheets/50 6.00 15.00
RC89 James Shields/50 6.00 15.00
RC90 Matt Cain/25
RC91 Travis Snider/99 6.00 15.00
RC92 Jonathan Broxton/50 6.00 15.00
RC93 Carlos Zambrano/99 10.00 25.00
RC94 Rich Harden/50 6.00 15.00
RC95 David Wright
RC96 Curtis Granderson/25
RC97 Victor Martinez/25
RC98 Vernon Wells/50 6.00 15.00
RC99 Shane Victorino/25
RC100 Vladimir Guerrero/25

2010 Topps Allen and Ginter This Day in History

COMPLETE SET (75) 10.00 25.00
TDH1 Chase Utley .60 1.50
TDH2 Stephen Drew .25 .60
TDH3 Aramis Ramirez .25 .60
TDH4 Lance Berkman .40 1.00
TDH5 Chipper Jones .60 1.50
TDH6 Brian Roberts .25 .60
TDH7 Jason Heyward 1.50 4.00
TDH8 Yunel Escobar .25 .60
TDH9 Pablo Sandoval .40 1.00
TDH10 David Ortiz .40 1.00
TDH11 Jason Bay .40 1.00
TDH12 Andre Ethier .40 1.00
TDH13 Adam Dunn .40 1.00
TDH14 Justin Verlander .75 2.00
TDH15 Manny Ramirez .60 1.50
TDH16 Carlos Gonzalez .40 1.00
TDH17 Joe Mauer .60 1.50
TDH18 Felix Hernandez .60 1.50
TDH19 Robinson Cano .60 1.50
TDH20 CC Sabathia .40 1.00
TDH21 Magglio Ordonez .40 1.00
TDH22 Grady Sizemore .40 1.00
TDH23 Dan Haren .25 .60
TDH24 Joey Votto .60 1.50
TDH25 Ryan Zimmerman .40 1.00
TDH26 Francisco Rodriguez .40 1.00
TDH27 Ken Griffey Jr. 1.00 2.50
TDH28 Jose Reyes .40 1.00
TDH29 Adam Jones .40 1.00
TDH30 Hideki Matsui .60 1.50
TDH31 Mark Teixeira .60 1.50
TDH32 Adrian Gonzalez .40 1.00
TDH33 Kosuke Fukudome .60 1.50
TDH34 Troy Tulowitzki .60 1.50
TDH35 Josh Johnson .40 1.00
TDH36 Hanley Ramirez .60 1.50
TDH37 Ichiro Suzuki 1.00 2.50
TDH38 Jim Thome .40 1.00
TDH39 Torii Hunter .25 .60
TDH40 Jake Peavy .25 .60
TDH41 Aaron Hill .25 .60
TDH42 Jorge Posada .40 1.00
TDH43 Jonathan Broxton .25 .60
TDH44 B.J. Upton .40 1.00
TDH45 Miguel Cabrera .60 1.50
TDH46 Yovani Gallardo .25 .60
TDH47 Brandon Phillips .25 .60
TDH48 Matt Holliday .60 1.50
TDH49 Justin Morneau .60 1.50
TDH50 Alex Rodriguez 1.00 2.50
TDH51 Gordon Beckham .40 1.00
TDH52 Justin Upton .40 1.00
TDH53 Nick Markakis .60 1.50
TDH54 Derrek Lee .25 .60
TDH55 Ryan Braun .75 2.00
TDH56 Jimmy Rollins .40 1.00
TDH57 Miguel Tejada .40 1.00
TDH58 Dan Uggla .40 1.00
TDH59 Hunter Pence .40 1.00
TDH60 Roy Halladay .60 1.50
TDH61 James Shields .25 .60
TDH62 Kevin Youkilis .40 1.00
TDH63 Alfonso Soriano .40 1.00
TDH64 Josh Hamilton .60 1.50
TDH65 Zack Greinke .40 1.00
TDH66 Curtis Granderson .40 1.00
TDH67 Josh Beckett .40 1.00
TDH68 Brian McCann .40 1.00
TDH69 Alexei Ramirez .25 .60
TDH70 Andrew McCutchen .60 1.50
TDH71 Billy Butler .25 .60
TDH72 Jay Bruce .40 1.00
TDH73 Ian Kinsler .40 1.00
TDH74 Carlos Lee .25 .60
TDH75 Mariano Rivera .60 1.50

2011 Topps Allen and Ginter

COMPLETE SET (350) 50.00 100.00
COMP.SET w/o SP's (300) 12.50 30.00
COMMON CARD (1-300) .15 .40
COMMON RC (1-300) .40 1.00
COMMON SP (301-350) 1.25 3.00
SP ODDS 1:2 HOBBY
1 Carlos Gonzalez .25 .60
2 Ty Wigginton .15 .40
3 Lou Holtz .15 .40
4 Jhoulys Chacin .15 .40
5 Aroldis Chapman RC 1.25 3.00
6 Micky Ward .15 .40
7 Mickey Mantle 1.25 3.00
8 Alexei Ramirez .15 .40
9 Joe Saunders .15 .40
10 Miguel Cabrera .40 1.00
11 Marc Forgione .15 .40
12 Hope Solo .60 1.50
13 Brett Anderson .25 .60
14 Adrian Beltre .15 .40
15 Diana Taurasi .15 .40
16 Gordon Beckham .25 .60
17 Jonathan Papelbon .25 .60
18 Daniel Hudson .15 .40
19 Daniel Bard .15 .40
20 Jeremy Hellickson RC 1.25 3.00
21 Logan Morrison .15 .40
22 Michael Bourn .15 .40
23 Aubrey Huff .15 .40
24 Kristi Yamaguchi .15 .40
25 Nelson Cruz .25 .60
26 Edwin Jackson .15 .40
27 Dillon Gee RC .60 1.50
28 John Lindsey RC .40 1.00
29 Johnny Cueto .15 .40
30 Hanley Ramirez .40 1.00
31 Jimmy Rollins .25 .60
32 Dirk Hayhurst .15 .40
33 Curtis Granderson .25 .60
34 Pedro Ciriaco RC .40 1.00
35 Adam Dunn .25 .60
36 Eric Sogard RC .40 1.00
37 Fausto Carmona .15 .40
38 Angel Pagan .15 .40
39 Stephen Drew .15 .40
40 John McEnroe .15 .40
41 Carlos Santana .40 1.00
42 Heath Bell .25 .60
43 Jake LaMotta .15 .40
44 Ozzie Martinez RC .40 1.00
45 Annika Sorenstam .15 .40
46 Edinson Volquez .15 .40
47 Phil Hughes .15 .40
48 Francisco Liriano .15 .40
49 Javier Vazquez .15 .40
50 Carl Crawford .25 .60
51 Tim Collins RC .40 1.00
52 Francisco Cordero .15 .40
53 Chipper Jones .40 1.00
54 Austin Jackson .15 .40
55 Dustin Pedroia .50 1.25
56 Scott Kazmir .15 .40
57 Derek Jeter 1.00 2.50
58 Alcides Escobar .15 .40
59 Jeremy Jeffress RC .40 1.00
60 Brandon Belt RC 1.50 4.00
61 Brian Roberts .15 .40
62 Alfonso Soriano .25 .60
63 Neil Walker .15 .40
64 Ricky Romero .15 .40
65 Ryan Howard .50 1.25
66 Starlin Castro .40 1.00
67 Delmon Young .25 .60
68 Max Scherzer .15 .40
69 Neftali Feliz .15 .40
70 Evan Longoria .50 1.25
71 Chris Perez .15 .40
72 Maxim Shmyrev .15 .40
73 Brandon Morrow .15 .40
74 Torii Hunter .15 .40
75 Jose Reyes .25 .60
76 Chase Headley .15 .40
77 Rafael Furcal .15 .40
78 Luke Scott .15 .40
79 Aimee Mullins .15 .40
80 Joey Votto .40 1.00
81 Yonder Alonso RC .60 1.50
82 Scott Rolen .25 .60
83 Mat Hoffman .15 .40
84 Gregory Infante RC .40 1.00
85 Chris Sale RC .60 1.50
86 Greg Halman RC .60 1.50
87 Colby Lewis .15 .40
88 David Ortiz .25 .60
89 John Axford .15 .40
90 Roy Halladay .40 1.00
91 Joel Pineiro .15 .40
92 Michael Pineda RC 1.25 3.00
93 Evan Lysacek .15 .40
94 Josh Rodriguez RC .40 1.00
95 Dan Uggla .25 .60
96 Daniel Boulud .15 .40
97 Zach Britton RC 1.00 2.50
98 Jason Bay .25 .60
99 Placido Polanco .15 .40
100 Albert Pujols 1.00 2.50
101 Peter Bourjos .25 .60
102 Wandy Rodriguez .15 .40
103 Andres Torres .15 .40
104 Huston Street .15 .40
105 Ubaldo Jimenez .25 .60
106 Jonathan Broxton .15 .40
107 L.L. Zamenhof .15 .40
108 Roy Oswalt .25 .60
109 Martin Prado .15 .40
110 Jake McGee (RC) .40 1.00
111 Pablo Sandoval .25 .60
112 Timothy Shieff .15 .40
113 Miguel Montero .15 .40
114 Brandon Phillips .15 .40
115 Shin-Soo Choo .25 .60
116 Josh Beckett .25 .60
117 Jonathan Sanchez .15 .40
118 Rafael Soriano .15 .40
119 Nancy Lopez .15 .40
120 Adrian Gonzalez .25 .60
121 J.D. Drew .15 .40
122 Ryan Dempster .15 .40
123 Rajai Davis .15 .40
124 Chad Billingsley .15 .40
125 Clayton Kershaw .40 1.00
126 Jair Jurrjens .15 .40
127 James Loney .25 .60
128 Michael Cuddyer .15 .40
129 Kelly Johnson .15 .40
130 Robinson Cano .40 1.00
131 Chris Iannetta .15 .40
132 Colby Rasmus .40 1.00
133 Geno Auriemma .25 .60
134 Matt Cain .25 .60
135 Kyle Petty .15 .40
136 Dick Vitale .15 .40
137 Carlos Beltran .15 .40
138 Matt Garza .15 .40
139 Tim Howard .15 .40
140 Felix Hernandez .40 1.00
141 Vernon Wells .15 .40
142 Michael Young .25 .60
143 Carlos Zambrano .25 .60
144 Jorge Posada .25 .60
145 Victor Martinez .25 .60
146 John Danks .15 .40
147 George Bush .25 .60
148 Sanya Richards .15 .40
149 Lars Anderson RC .60 1.50
150 Troy Tulowitzki .40 1.00
151 Brandon Beachy RC 1.00 2.50
152 Jordan Zimmermann .15 .40
153 Scott Cousins RC .40 1.00
154 Todd Helton .25 .60
155 Josh Johnson .25 .60
156 Marlon Byrd .15 .40
157 Corey Hart .15 .40
158 Billy Butler .15 .40
159 Shawn Michaels .15 .40
160 David Wright .50 1.25
161 Casey McGehee .15 .40
162 Mat Latos .15 .40
163 Ian Kennedy .25 .60
164 Heather Mitts .25 .60
165 Jo Frost .15 .40
166 Geovany Soto .25 .60
167 Adam LaRoche .15 .40
168 Carlos Marmol .25 .60
169 Dan Haren .15 .40
170 Tim Lincecum .40 1.00
171 John Lackey .15 .40
172 Yunesky Maya RC .40 1.00
173 Mariano Rivera .40 1.00
174 Joakim Soria .15 .40
175 Jose Bautista .25 .60
176 Brian Bogusevic (RC) .40 1.00
177 Aaron Crow RC .60 1.50
178 Ben Revere RC .60 1.50
179 Shane Victorino .25 .60
180 Kyle Drabek RC .60 1.50
181 Mark Buehrle .25 .60
182 Clay Buchholz .25 .60
183 Mike Napoli .25 .60
184 Pedro Alvarez RC .25 .60
185 Justin Upton .25 .60
186 Yunel Escobar .15 .40
187 Jim Nantz .15 .40
188 Daniel Descalso RC .40 1.00
189 Dexter Fowler .15 .40
190 Sue Bird .15 .40
191 Matt Guy .15 .40
192 Carl Pavano .15 .40
193 Jorge De La Rosa .15 .40
194 Rick Porcello .15 .40
195 Tommy Hanson .25 .60
196 Jered Weaver .15 .40
197 Jay Bruce .25 .60
198 Freddie Freeman RC 1.50 4.00
199 Jake Peavy .15 .40
200 Josh Hamilton .40 1.00
201 Andrew Romine RC .40 1.00
202 Nick Swisher .40 1.00
203 Aaron Hill .15 .40
204 Jim Thome .25 .60
205 Kendrys Morales .15 .40
206 Tsuyoshi Nishioka RC 1.25 3.00
207 Kosuke Fukudome .40 1.00
208 Marco Scutaro .15 .40
209 Guy Fieri .15 .40
210 Chase Utley .40 1.00
211 Francisco Rodriguez .25 .60
212 Aramis Ramirez .15 .40
213 Xavier Nady .15 .40
214 Elvis Andrus .25 .60
215 Andrew McCutchen .40 1.00
216 Jose Tabata .25 .60
217 Shaun Marcum .15 .40
218 Bobby Abreu .15 .40
219 Johan Santana .40 1.00
220 Prince Fielder .25 .60
221 Mark Rogers (RC) .40 1.00
222 James Shields .15 .40
223 Chuck Woolery .15 .40
224 Jason Kubel .15 .40
225 Jack LaLanne .15 .40
226 Andre Ethier .25 .60
227 Lucas Duda RC .60 1.50
228 Brandon Snyder (RC) .40 1.00
229 Juan Pierre .15 .40
230 Mark Teixeira .40 1.00
231 C.J. Wilson .15 .40
232 Picabo Street .15 .40
233 Ben Zobrist .15 .40
234 Chrissie Wellington .15 .40
235 Cole Hamels .40 1.00
236 B.J. Upton .25 .60
237 Carlos Quentin .15 .40
238 Rudy Ruettiger .15 .40
239 Brett Myers .15 .40
240 Matt Holliday .40 1.00
241 Ike Davis .25 .60
242 Cheryl Burke .15 .40
243 Mike Nickeas (RC) .40 1.00
244 Chone Figgins .15 .40
245 Brian McCann .25 .60
246 Ian Kinsler .25 .60
247 Yadier Molina .25 .60
248 Ervin Santana .15 .40
249 Carlos Ruiz .15 .40
250 Ichiro Suzuki .60 1.50
251 Ian Desmond .25 .60
252 Omar Infante .15 .40
253 Mike Minor .15 .40
254 Denard Span .15 .40
255 David Price .40 1.00
256 Hunter Pence .25 .60
257 Andrew Bailey .15 .40
258 Howie Kendrick .15 .40
259 Tim Hudson .25 .60
260 Alex Rodriguez .60 1.50
261 Carlos Pena .25 .60
262 Manny Pacquiao 2.50 6.00
263 Mark Trumbo (RC) .60 1.50
264 Adam Jones .25 .60
265 Buster Posey .50 1.25
266 Chris Coghlan .15 .40
267 Brett Sinkbeil RC .40 1.00
268 Dallas Braden .15 .40
269 Derrek Lee .15 .40
270 Kevin Youkilis .25 .60
271 Chris Young .15 .40
272 Wee Man .15 .40
273 Brent Morel RC .40 1.00
274 Stan Lee .15 .40
275 Justin Verlander .50 1.25
276 Desmond Jennings RC 1.00 2.50
277 Hank Conger RC .60 1.50
278 Travis Snider .15 .40
279 Brian Wilson .40 1.00
280 Adam Wainwright .25 .60
281 Adam Lind .25 .60
282 Reid Brignac .15 .40
283 Daric Barton .15 .40
284 Eric Jackson .15 .40
285 Alex Rios .25 .60
286 Cory Luebke RC .40 1.00
287 Yovani Gallardo .15 .40
288 Rickie Weeks .25 .60
289 Paul Konerko .25 .60
290 Cliff Lee .40 1.00
291 Grady Sizemore .25 .60
292 Wade Davis .15 .40
293 Prince William .40 1.00
Kate Middleton
294 Jacoby Ellsbury .40 1.00
295 Chris Carpenter .40 1.00
296 Derek Lowe .15 .40
297 Travis Hafner .15 .40
298 Peter Gammons .15 .40
299 Ana Julaton .15 .40
300 Ryan Braun .50 1.25
301 Gio Gonzalez SP 1.25 3.00
302 John Buck SP 1.25 3.00
303 Jaime Garcia SP 1.25 3.00
304 Madison Bumgarner SP 1.25 3.00
305 Justin Morneau SP 1.25 3.00
306 Josh Willingham SP 1.25 3.00
307 Ryan Ludwick SP 1.25 3.00
308 Jhonny Peralta SP 1.25 3.00
309 Kurt Suzuki SP 1.25 3.00
310 Matt Kemp SP 1.25 3.00
311 Ian Stewart SP 1.25 3.00
312 Cody Ross SP 1.25 3.00
313 Leo Nunez SP 1.25 3.00
314 Nick Markakis SP 1.25 3.00
315 Jayson Werth SP 1.25 3.00
316 Manny Ramirez SP 1.25 3.00
317 Brian Matusz SP 1.25 3.00
318 Brett Wallace SP 1.25 3.00
319 Jon Niese SP 1.25 3.00
320 Jon Lester SP 1.25 3.00
321 Mark Reynolds SP 1.25 3.00
322 Trevor Cahill SP 1.25 3.00
323 Orlando Hudson SP 1.25 3.00
324 Domonic Brown SP 1.25 3.00
325 Mike Stanton SP 1.25 3.00
326 Jason Castro SP 1.25 3.00
327 David DeJesus SP 1.25 3.00
328 Chris Johnson SP 1.25 3.00
329 Alex Gordon SP 1.25 3.00
330 CC Sabathia SP 1.25 3.00
331 Carlos Gomez SP 1.25 3.00
332 Luke Hochevar SP 1.25 3.00
333 Carlos Lee SP 1.25 3.00
334 Gaby Sanchez SP 1.25 3.00
335 Jason Heyward SP 1.50 4.00
336 Kevin Kouzmanoff SP 1.25 3.00
337 Drew Storen SP 1.25 3.00
338 Lance Berkman SP 1.25 3.00
339 Miguel Tejada SP 1.25 3.00
340 Ryan Zimmerman SP 1.25 3.00
341 Ricky Nolasco SP 1.25 3.00
342 Mike Pelfrey SP 1.25 3.00
343 Drew Stubbs SP 1.25 3.00
344 Danny Valencia SP 1.25 3.00
345 Zack Greinke SP 1.25 3.00
346 Brett Gardner SP 1.25 3.00
347 Josh Thole SP 1.25 3.00
348 Russell Martin SP 1.25 3.00
349 Yuniesky Betancourt SP 1.25 3.00
350 Joe Mauer SP 1.25 3.00

2011 Topps Allen and Ginter Code Cards

*MINI 1-300: 1.5X TO 4X BASIC
*MINI 1-300 RC: .75X TO 2X BASIC RC's
OVERALL CODE ODDS 1:8 HOBBY
301 Gio Gonzalez .75 2.00
302 John Buck .75 2.00
303 Jaime Garcia 1.25 3.00
304 Madison Bumgarner .75 2.00
305 Justin Morneau 2.00 5.00
306 Josh Willingham .75 2.00
307 Ryan Ludwick .75 2.00
308 Jhonny Peralta .75 2.00
309 Kurt Suzuki .75 2.00
310 Matt Kemp 1.25 3.00
311 Ian Stewart .75 2.00
312 Cody Ross .75 2.00
313 Leo Nunez .75 2.00
314 Nick Markakis 2.00 5.00
315 Jayson Werth 1.25 3.00
316 Manny Ramirez 2.00 5.00
317 Brian Matusz 2.00 5.00
318 Brett Wallace .75 2.00
319 Jon Niese .75 2.00
320 Jon Lester 2.00 5.00
321 Mark Reynolds .75 2.00
322 Trevor Cahill .75 2.00
323 Orlando Hudson .75 2.00
324 Domonic Brown 2.00 5.00
325 Mike Stanton 1.25 3.00
326 Jason Castro .75 2.00
327 David DeJesus .75 2.00
328 Chris Johnson .75 2.00
329 Alex Gordon 1.25 3.00
330 CC Sabathia 1.25 3.00
331 Carlos Gomez .75 2.00
332 Luke Hochevar .75 2.00
333 Carlos Lee .75 2.00
334 Gaby Sanchez .75 2.00
335 Jason Heyward 2.50 6.00
336 Kevin Kouzmanoff .75 2.00
337 Drew Storen .75 2.00
338 Lance Berkman 1.25 3.00
339 Miguel Tejada 1.25 3.00
340 Ryan Zimmerman 1.25 3.00
341 Ricky Nolasco .75 2.00
342 Mike Pelfrey .75 2.00
343 Drew Stubbs 1.25 3.00
344 Danny Valencia 1.25 3.00
345 Zack Greinke 1.25 3.00
346 Brett Gardner .75 2.00
347 Josh Thole .75 2.00
348 Russell Martin .75 2.00
349 Yuniesky Betancourt .75 2.00
350 Joe Mauer 2.00 5.00

2011 Topps Allen and Ginter Mini

*MINI 1-300: .75X TO 2X BASIC
*MINI 1-300 RC: .5X TO 1.2X BASIC RC's
*MINI SP 301-350: .5X TO 1.2X BASIC SP
MINI SP ODDS 1:13 HOBBY
COMMON CARD (351-400) 20.00 50.00
351-400 RANDOM WITHIN RIP CARDS
STATED PLATE ODDS 1:751 HOBBY
PLATE PRINT RUN 1 SET PER COLOR
BLACK-CYAN-MAGENTA-YELLOW ISSUED
NO PLATE PRICING DUE TO SCARCITY
351 Ryan Braun EXT
352 Jason Heyward EXT 20.00 50.00
353 Ichiro Suzuki EXCH 40.00 80.00
354 Kevin Youkilis EXT 30.00 60.00
355 Roy Halladay EXT 30.00 60.00
356 Starlin Castro EXT 20.00 50.00
357 Mickey Mantle EXT 60.00 120.00
358 Robinson Cano EXT 40.00 80.00
359 Dan Uggla EXT 20.00 50.00
360 Carl Crawford EXT 30.00 60.00

361 Hunter Pence EXT 30.00 60.00
362 Chase Utley EXT 40.00 80.00
363 Justin Upton EXT 20.00 50.00
364 Pedro Alvarez EXT 20.00 50.00
365 Dustin Pedroia EXT 20.00 50.00
366 Albert Pujols EXT 40.00 80.00
367 Mike Stanton EXT 30.00 60.00
368 Joe Mauer EXT 20.00 50.00
369 Evan Longoria EXT 20.00 50.00
370 Carlos Gonzalez EXT 20.00 50.00
371 Adam Dunn EXT 30.00 60.00
372 Derek Jeter EXT 100.00 175.00
373 Jose Bautista EXT 20.00 50.00
374 Ryan Zimmerman EXT 30.00 60.00
375 Troy Tulowitzki EXT 20.00 50.00
376 Mat Latos EXT 20.00 50.00
377 Clayton Kershaw EXT 20.00 50.00
378 Shin-Soo Choo EXT 20.00 50.00
379 Cliff Lee EXT 40.00 80.00
380 Adrian Gonzalez EXT 30.00 60.00
381 Tim Lincecum EXT 20.00 50.00
382 Zack Greinke EXT 20.00 50.00
383 Torii Hunter EXT 30.00 60.00
384 Felix Hernandez EXT 30.00 60.00
385 Aroldis Chapman EXT 20.00 50.00
386 Josh Hamilton EXT 30.00 60.00
387 Hanley Ramirez EXT 20.00 50.00
388 Jon Lester EXT 20.00 50.00
389 Billy Butler EXT 20.00 50.00
390 Miguel Cabrera EXT 20.00 50.00
391 Justin Morneau EXT 30.00 60.00
392 Ubaldo Jimenez EXT 20.00 50.00
393 Alex Rodriguez EXT 20.00 50.00
394 CC Sabathia EXT 30.00 60.00
395 Buster Posey EXT 20.00 50.00
396 Ryan Howard EXT 20.00 50.00
397 Mark Teixeira EXT 40.00 80.00
398 Brett Anderson EXT 20.00 50.00
399 David Wright EXT 30.00 60.00
400 Joey Votto EXT 20.00 50.00

2011 Topps Allen and Ginter Mini A and G Back

*A & G BACK: 1X TO 2.5X BASIC
*A & G BACK RCs: .6X TO 1.5X BASIC RCs
A & G BACK ODDS 1:5 HOBBY
*A & G BACK SP: .6X TO 1.5X BASIC SP
A & G BACK SP ODDS 1:65 HOBBY

2011 Topps Allen and Ginter Mini Bazooka

STATED ODDS 1:284 HOBBY
STATED PRINT RUN 25 SER.#'d SETS
NO PRICING DUE TO SCARCITY

2011 Topps Allen and Ginter Mini Black

*BLACK: 2X TO 5X BASIC
*BLACK RCs: .75X TO 2X BASIC RCs
BLACK ODDS 1:10 HOBBY
BLACK SP ODDS 1:130 HOBBY
*BLACK SP: .75X TO 2X BASIC SP

2011 Topps Allen and Ginter Mini No Card Number

*NO NBR: 8X TO 20X BASIC
*NO NBR RCs: 3X TO 8X BASIC RCs
*NO NBR SP: 1.2X TO 3X BASIC SP
STATED ODDS 1:142 HOBBY

2011 Topps Allen and Ginter Mini Silk

STATED ODDS 1:801 HOBBY
STATED PRINT RUN 10 SER.#'d SETS
NO PRICING DUE TO SCARCITY

2011 Topps Allen and Ginter Mini Wood

STATED ODDS 1:3436 HOBBY
STATED PRINT RUN 1 SER.#'d SET
NO PRICING DUE TO SCARCITY

2011 Topps Allen and Ginter Glossy Rookie Exclusive

STATED PRINT RUN 999 SER.#'d SETS
AGS1 Eric Hosmer 10.00 25.00
AGS2 Dustin Ackley 5.00 12.00
AGS3 Mike Moustakas 3.00 8.00
AGS4 Dee Gordon 3.00 8.00
AGS5 Anthony Rizzo 2.00 5.00
AGS6 Charlie Blackmon 1.25 3.00
AGS7 Brandon Crawford 1.25 3.00
AGS8 Juan Nicasio 1.25 3.00
AGS9 Prince William 5.00 12.00
Kate Middleton
AGS10 U.S. Navy SEALs 2.00 5.00

2011 Topps Allen and Ginter Ascent of Man

COMPLETE SET (26) 10.00 25.00
STATED ODDS 1:6 HOBBY
AOM1 Prokaryotes .60 1.50
AOM2 Eukaryotes .60 1.50
AOM3 Choanoflagellates .60 1.50
AOM4 Porifera .60 1.50
AOM5 Cnidarians .60 1.50
AOM6 Platyhelminthes .60 1.50
AOM7 Chordates .60 1.50
AOM8 Ostracoderms .60 1.50
AOM9 Placoderms .60 1.50
AOM10 Sarcopterygii .60 1.50
AOM11 Amphibians .60 1.50
AOM12 Reptiles .60 1.50
AOM13 Eutherians .60 1.50
AOM14 Haplorrhini .60 1.50
AOM15 Catarrhini .60 1.50
AOM16 Hominoidea .60 1.50
AOM17 Hominidae .60 1.50
AOM18 Homininae .60 1.50
AOM19 Hominini .60 1.50
AOM20 Hominina .60 1.50
AOM21 Australopithecus .60 1.50
AOM22 Homo habilis .60 1.50
AOM23 Homo erectus .60 1.50
AOM24 Homo sapiens .60 1.50
AOM25 Cro-Magnon Man .60 1.50
AOM26 Modern Man .60 1.50

2011 Topps Allen and Ginter Autographs

STATED ODDS 1:68 HOBBY
DUAL AUTO ODDS 1:56,000 HOBBY
EXCHANGE DEADLINE 6/30/2014
AC Aroldis Chapman 12.50 30.00
AG Adrian Gonzalez 60.00 120.00
AP Albert Pujols EXCH
AT Andres Torres 6.00 15.00
BW Brett Wallace 5.00 12.00
CF Chone Figgins 4.00 10.00
CS Chris Sale 6.00 15.00
CU Chase Utley 90.00 150.00
DD David DeJesus 4.00 10.00
DH Daniel Hudson 6.00 15.00
FS Freddy Sanchez 5.00 12.00
GG Gio Gonzalez 4.00 10.00
GO Al Gore 300.00 400.00
Keith Olbermann
JB Jose Bautista 12.50 30.00
JH Jason Heyward EXCH 50.00 100.00
JJ Josh Johnson 6.00 15.00
JM Joe Mauer EXCH 150.00 250.00
JT Jose Tabata 6.00 15.00
LH Lou Holtz 30.00 60.00
MC Miguel Cabrera EXCH 90.00 150.00
NC Nelson Cruz 10.00 25.00
RH Roy Halladay 200.00 350.00
RW Randy Wells 4.00 10.00
SC Starlin Castro 15.00 40.00
SM Sergio Mitre 6.00 15.00
UJ Ubaldo Jimenez 12.50 30.00
ADU Angelo Dundee 12.50 30.00
AJU Ana Julaton 40.00 80.00
AMU Aimee Mullins EXCH 10.00 25.00
APA Angel Pagan 4.00 10.00
ASO Annika Sorenstam EXCH 30.00 60.00
BMO Brent Morel 4.00 10.00
CBU Cheryl Burke EXCH 20.00 50.00
CCS CC Sabathia EXCH 75.00 150.00
CWE Chrissie Wellington 10.00 25.00
CWO Chuck Woolery 10.00 25.00
DBO Daniel Boulud 12.50 30.00
DHA Dirk Hayhurst 20.00 50.00
DTU Diana Taurasi 12.50 30.00
DVI Dick Vitale 20.00 50.00
EJA Eric Jackson 12.50 30.00
ELY Evan Lysacek 10.00 25.00
GAU Geno Auriemma EXCH 12.50 30.00
GFI Guy Fieri 20.00 50.00
GWB George W. Bush 400.00 700.00
HMI Heather Mitts 30.00 60.00
HSO Hope Solo EXCH 50.00 100.00
JHA Josh Hamilton 40.00 80.00
JLA Jake LaMotta EXCH 40.00 80.00
JMC John McEnroe EXCH 90.00 150.00
JNA Jim Nantz 10.00 25.00
JOF Jo Frost 15.00 40.00
KPE Kyle Petty 10.00 25.00
KYA Kristi Yamaguchi EXCH 50.00 100.00
LHO Larry Holmes EXCH 20.00 50.00
MFA Marc Forgione 8.00 20.00
MGU Matt Guy 10.00 25.00
MHO Mat Hoffman 12.50 30.00
MMO Mike Morse 5.00 12.00
MPA Manny Pacquiao 600.00 900.00
MSH Maxim Shmyrev EXCH 8.00 20.00
MWA Micky Ward 15.00 40.00
NJA Nick Jacoby EXCH 8.00 20.00
NLO Nancy Lopez 12.50 30.00
PGA Peter Gammons 20.00 50.00
PST Picabo Street 20.00 50.00
RJO Rafer Johnson EXCH 12.50 30.00
RRU Rudy Ruettiger 30.00 60.00
RTU Ron Turcotte EXCH 10.00 25.00
SBI Sue Bird 20.00 50.00
SLE Stan Lee 50.00 100.00
SMI Shawn Michaels EXCH 50.00 100.00
SRI Sanya Richards EXCH 10.00 25.00
THO Tim Howard 20.00 50.00
TSC Timothy Shieff 10.00 25.00
WEE Wee Man 20.00 50.00

2011 Topps Allen and Ginter Autographs Red Ink

STATED ODDS 1:1718 HOBBY
STATED PRINT RUN 10 SER.#'d SETS
NO PRICING DUE TO SCARITY
EXCHANGE DEADLINE 6/30/2014

2011 Topps Allen and Ginter Baseball Highlight Sketches

COMPLETE SET (25) 6.00 15.00
STATED ODDS 1:6 HOBBY
BHS1 Minnesota Twins .30 .75
BHS2 Jay Bruce .50 1.25
BHS3 Starlin Castro .75 2.00
BHS4 Roy Halladay .75 2.00
BHS5 Albert Pujols 2.00 5.00
BHS6 Jose Bautista .50 1.25
BHS7 CC Sabathia .50 1.25
BHS8 Cody Ross .30 .75
BHS9 Edwin Jackson .30 .75
BHS10 Ryan Howard 1.00 2.50
BHS11 Trevor Hoffman .50 1.25
BHS12 Armando Galarraga .30 .75
BHS13 San Francisco Giants .30 .75
BHS14 Mariano Rivera .75 2.00
BHS15 Aroldis Chapman 1.00 2.50
BHS16 Dallas Braden .30 .75
BHS17 Texas Rangers .30 .75
BHS18 Stephen Strasburg 1.50 4.00
BHS19 Matt Garza .30 .75
BHS20 Alex Rodriguez 1.25 3.00
BHS21 David Wright 1.00 2.50
BHS22 Ubaldo Jimenez .50 1.25
BHS23 Mark Teixeira .75 2.00
BHS24 Jason Heyward 1.00 2.50
BHS25 Ichiro Suzuki 1.25 3.00

2011 Topps Allen and Ginter Book Cards

STATED ODDS 1:48,000 HOBBY
STATED PRINT RUN 1 SER.#'d SET
NO PRICING DUE TO SCARCITY

2011 Topps Allen and Ginter Cabinet Baseball Highlights

STATED ODDS 1:2 HOBBY BOXES
CB1 Armando Galarraga 2.50 6.00
Miguel Cabrera
Jason Donald
CB2 Roy Halladay 2.50 6.00
Carlos Ruiz
Ryan Howard
CB3 Dallas Braden 2.00 5.00
Landon Powell
Daric Barton
CB4 Ichiro Suzuki 1.00 2.50
Jose Bautista
Felix Hernandez
CB5 Alex Rodriguez 4.00 10.00
Derek Jeter
Shaun Marcum
CB6 Albert Pujols 4.00 10.00
Tony La Russa
Ryan Dempster
CB7 Grand Canyon 2.00 5.00
Woodrow Wilson
Benjamin Harrison
Theodore Roosevelt
CB8 Yosemite National Park 2.00 5.00
Abraham Lincoln
John Conness
CB9 Yellowstone National Park 2.00 5.00
Ulysses S. Grant
Old Faithful
CB10 Redwood National Park 2.00 5.00
Lyndon B. Johnson
John E. Raker

2011 Topps Allen and Ginter Cabinet Baseball Highlights Relics

STATED ODDS 1:5010 HOBBY BOXES
STATED PRINT RUN 1 SER.#'d SET
NO PRICING DUE TO SCARCITY

2011 Topps Allen and Ginter Carnival Cuts Relics

STATED PRINT RUN 10 SER.#'d SETS
NO PRICING DUE TO SCARCITY

2011 Topps Allen and Ginter Cut Signatures

STATED ODDS 1:128,000 HOBBY.
STATED PRINT RUN 1 SER.#'d SET
NO PRICING DUE TO SCARCITY

2011 Topps Allen and Ginter DNA Relics

STATED ODDS 1:290,000 HOBBY
STATED PRINT RUN 1 SER.#'d SET
NO PRICING DUE TO SCARCITY

2011 Topps Allen and Ginter Employee Autographs

STATED PRINT RUN 10 SER.#'d SETS
NO PRICING DUE TO SCARCITY

2011 Topps Allen and Ginter Floating Fortresses

COMPLETE SET (20) 8.00 20.00
STATED ODDS 1:8 HOBBY
FF1 HMS Victory .60 1.50
FF2 Mary Rose .60 1.50
FF3 Henri Grace a Dieu .60 1.50
FF4 Michael .60 1.50
FF5 Sovereign of the Seas .60 1.50
FF6 HMS Indefatigable .60 1.50
FF7 Mahmudiye .60 1.50
FF8 Le Napoleon .60 1.50
FF9 USS Merrimack .60 1.50
FF10 USS Monitor .60 1.50
FF11 Lave .60 1.50
FF12 La Gloire .60 1.50
FF13 HMS Warrior .60 1.50
FF14 Solferino .60 1.50
FF15 USS Cairo .60 1.50
FF16 HMS Dreadnought .60 1.50
FF17 USS Texas .60 1.50
FF18 HMS Devastation .60 1.50
FF19 HMS Revenge .60 1.50
FF20 USS Pennsylvania .60 1.50

2011 Topps Allen and Ginter Hometown Heroes

COMPLETE SET (100) 10.00 25.00
HH1 Buster Posey .60 1.50
HH2 Colby Rasmus .50 1.25
HH3 Brian Wilson .50 1.25
HH4 Jason Kubel .20 .50
HH5 Chase Utley .50 1.25
HH6 Dan Haren .20 .50
HH7 CC Sabathia .30 .75
HH8 Stephen Drew .20 .50
HH9 Adam Wainwright .30 .75
HH10 Ryan Braun .60 1.50
HH11 Jason Heyward .60 1.50
HH12 Andrew McCutchen .50 1.25
HH13 Shane Victorino .30 .75
HH14 Carl Pavano .20 .50
HH15 Matt Holliday .50 1.25
HH16 Dan Uggla .30 .75
HH17 Scott Rolen .30 .75
HH18 Zack Greinke .30 .75
HH19 Nick Swisher .50 1.25
HH20 David Price .50 1.25
HH21 Jon Lester .50 1.25
HH22 John Danks .20 .50
HH23 Dustin Pedroia .60 1.50
HH24 Ryan Zimmerman .30 .75
HH25 Adam Dunn .30 .75
HH26 Torii Hunter .20 .50
HH27 Brandon Phillips .20 .50
HH28 Grady Sizemore .30 .75
HH29 Rick Porcello .20 .50
HH30 Dexter Fowler .20 .50
HH31 Jake Peavy .20 .50
HH32 Roy Halladay .50 1.25
HH33 Austin Jackson .20 .50
HH34 Chipper Jones .50 1.25
HH35 Alex Gordon .30 .75
HH36 Gordon Beckham .30 .75
HH37 Clayton Kershaw .50 1.25
HH38 Andre Ethier .30 .75
HH39 Tim Lincecum .50 1.25
HH40 Prince Fielder .30 .75
HH41 David DeJesus .20 .50
HH42 David Wright .60 1.50
HH43 Joba Chamberlain .30 .75
HH44 Delmon Young .30 .75
HH45 Ike Davis .30 .75
HH46 Jacoby Ellsbury .50 1.25
HH47 Phil Hughes .20 .50
HH48 Evan Longoria .60 1.50
HH49 Danny Valencia .30 .75
HH50 Josh Hamilton .50 1.25
HH51 Josh Beckett .30 .75
HH52 Ian Kinsler .30 .75
HH53 Justin Verlander .60 1.50
HH54 Joe Mauer .50 1.25
HH55 Justin Upton .30 .75
HH56 Brett Anderson .30 .75
HH57 Jordan Zimmermann .20 .50
HH58 Jimmy Rollins .30 .75
HH59 Brett Gardner .20 .50
HH60 Alex Rodriguez .75 2.00
HH61 Corey Hart .20 .50
HH62 Pedro Alvarez .30 .75
HH63 Cody Ross .20 .50
HH64 Matt Cain .30 .75
HH65 Adrian Gonzalez .30 .75
HH66 Derek Lowe .20 .50
HH67 Jon Jay .20 .50
HH68 Johnny Damon .30 .75
HH69 Yovani Gallardo .20 .50
HH70 Troy Tulowitzki .50 1.25
HH71 Chris Carpenter .50 1.25
HH72 Billy Butler .20 .50
HH73 Mark Teixeira .50 1.25
HH74 Jayson Werth .30 .75
HH75 Carl Crawford .30 .75
HH76 Adam Lind .30 .75
HH77 Mark Buehrle .30 .75
HH78 Manny Ramirez .50 1.25
HH79 Derek Jeter 1.25 3.00
HH80 Cliff Lee .50 1.25
HH81 Neil Walker .20 .50
HH82 Jim Thome .30 .75
HH83 Travis Hafner .20 .50
HH84 Matt Kemp .30 .75
HH85 Michael Young .30 .75
HH86 Kevin Youkilis .30 .75
HH87 Jeremy Hellickson .60 1.50
HH88 Roy Oswalt .30 .75
HH89 Todd Helton .30 .75
HH90 Ryan Howard .60 1.50
HH91 Madison Bumgarner .20 .50
HH92 Mike Napoli .30 .75
HH93 Lance Berkman .30 .75
HH94 C.J. Wilson .20 .50
HH95 Kyle Drabek .30 .75
HH96 Brian McCann .30 .75
HH97 Brandon Morrow .20 .50
HH98 Clay Buchholz .30 .75
HH99 Andrew Bailey .20 .50
HH100 Travis Snider .20 .50

2011 Topps Allen and Ginter Minds that Made the Future

COMPLETE SET (40) 20.00 50.00
STATED ODDS 1:8 HOBBY
MMF1 Leonardo da Vinci .60 1.50
MMF2 Alexander Graham Bell .60 1.50
MMF3 Eli Whitney .60 1.50
MMF4 Nicolaus Copernicus .60 1.50
MMF5 Johannes Gutenberg .60 1.50
MMF6 George Washington Carver .60 1.50
MMF7 Samuel Morse .60 1.50
MMF8 Granville Woods .60 1.50
MMF9 Elisha Otis .60 1.50
MMF10 Alessandro Volta .60 1.50
MMF11 Tycho Brahe .60 1.50
MMF12 Gregor Mendel .60 1.50
MMF13 Carl Linnaeus .60 1.50
MMF14 Johannes Kepler .60 1.50
MMF15 Isaac Newton .60 1.50
MMF16 Marie Curie .60 1.50
MMF17 Carl Friedrich Gauss .60 1.50
MMF18 Sigmund Freud .60 1.50
MMF19 Bernhard Riemann .60 1.50
MMF20 Leonhard Euler .60 1.50
MMF21 Robert Fulton .60 1.50
MMF22 Ada Lovelace .60 1.50
MMF23 Florence Nightingale .60 1.50
MMF24 Nikola Tesla .60 1.50
MMF25 Galileo Galilei .60 1.50
MMF26 Charles Darwin .60 1.50
MMF27 Louis Pasteur .60 1.50
MMF28 Guglielmo Marconi .60 1.50
MMF29 Antoine Lavoisier .60 1.50
MMF30 Michael Faraday .60 1.50
MMF31 Dmitri Mendeleev .60 1.50
MMF32 Robert Koch .60 1.50
MMF33 Euclid .60 1.50
MMF34 Archimedes .60 1.50
MMF35 Jagadish Chandra Bose .60 1.50
MMF36 Aristotle .60 1.50
MMF37 John Deere .60 1.50
MMF38 George Eastman .60 1.50
MMF39 Samuel Colt .60 1.50
MMF40 Benjamin Franklin .60 1.50

2011 Topps Allen and Ginter Mini Animals in Peril

COMPLETE SET (30) 20.00 50.00
STATED ODDS 1:12 HOBBY
AP1 Siberian Tiger .75 2.00
AP2 Mountain Gorilla .75 2.00
AP3 Arakan Forest Turtle .75 2.00
AP4 Darwin's Fox .75 2.00
AP5 Gharial .75 2.00
AP6 Vaquita .75 2.00
AP7 Dhole .75 2.00
AP8 Blue Whale .75 2.00
AP9 Bonobo .75 2.00
AP10 Ethiopian Wolf .75 2.00
AP11 Giant Panda .75 2.00
AP12 Snow Leopard .75 2.00
AP13 African Wild Dog .75 2.00
AP14 Indian Rhinoceros .75 2.00
AP15 Philippine Eagle .75 2.00
AP16 Markhor .75 2.00
AP17 Orangutan .75 2.00
AP18 Grevy's Zebra .75 2.00
AP19 Tasmanian Devil .75 2.00
AP20 Bengal Tiger .75 2.00
AP21 Whooping Crane .75 2.00
AP22 Sea Otter .75 2.00
AP23 Red Wolf .75 2.00
AP24 Key Deer .75 2.00
AP25 Black-Footed Ferret .75 2.00
AP26 Amur Leopard .75 2.00
AP27 Anderson's Salamander .75 2.00
AP28 Greater Bamboo Lemur .75 2.00
AP29 Hawaiian Monk Seal .75 2.00
AP30 Kakapo .75 2.00

2011 Topps Allen and Ginter Mini Fabulous Face Flocculence

FFF1 Abraham Lincoln 8.00 20.00
The Lincoln
FFF2 The Ironing Board 8.00 20.00
FFF3 The Conscientious Objector 8.00 20.00
FFF4 The Bib 8.00 20.00
FFF5 Charles Darwin 8.00 20.00
The Darwin
FFF6 The Neckbeard 8.00 20.00
FFF7 The Goat Patch 8.00 20.00
FFF8 Ambrose Burnside 8.00 20.00
Burnside's Sideburns
FFF9 Thunderchops 8.00 20.00
FFF10 Brian Wilson 15.00 40.00
The Closer

2011 Topps Allen and Ginter Mini Flora of the World

COMPLETE SET (5) 20.00 50.00
STATED ODDS 1:144 HOBBY
FOW1 Black-Eyed Susan 6.00 15.00
FOW2 Spurred Snapdragon 6.00 15.00
FOW3 Shirley Poppy 6.00 15.00
FOW4 Mexican Hat 6.00 15.00
FOW5 Sweet Alyssum 6.00 15.00

2011 Topps Allen and Ginter Mini Fortunes for the Taking

FFT1 The Oak Island Money Pit 10.00 25.00
FFT2 Captain Kidd's Treasure 10.00 25.00
FFT3 The Beale Ciphers 10.00 25.00
FFT4 The Amber Room 10.00 25.00
FFT5 The Devonshire Treasure of Cocos Island 10.00 25.00
FFT6 Blackbeard's Treasure 10.00 25.00
FFT7 The Treasure of Lima 10.00 25.00
FFT8 Montezuma's Treasure 10.00 25.00
FFT9 Butch Cassidy's Loot 10.00 25.00
FFT10 The Lost French Gold of Ohio 10.00 25.00

2011 Topps Allen and Ginter Mini Portraits of Penultimacy

COMPLETE SET (10) 5.00 12.00
STATED ODDS 1:12 HOBBY
PP1 Antonio Meucci .60 1.50
PP2 Mike Gellner .60 1.50
PP3 Dr. Watson .60 1.50
PP4 Igor .60 1.50
PP5 The Hare .60 1.50
PP6 Tonto .60 1.50
PP7 Antonio Salieri .60 1.50
PP8 Sancho Panza .60 1.50
PP9 Thomas E. Dewey .60 1.50
PP10 Toto .60 1.50

2011 Topps Allen and Ginter Mini Step Right Up

COMPLETE SET (10) 5.00 12.00
STATED ODDS 1:15 HOBBY
SRU1 The Bed of Nails .60 1.50
SRU2 Fire Breathing .60 1.50
SRU3 Fire Eating .60 1.50
SRU4 The Flea Circus .60 1.50
SRU5 The Human Cannonball .60 1.50
SRU6 The Human Blockhead .60 1.50
SRU7 Snake Charming .60 1.50
SRU8 The Strongman .60 1.50
SRU9 Knife Throwing .60 1.50
SRU10 Tightrope Walking .60 1.50

2011 Topps Allen and Ginter Mini Uninvited Guests

COMPLETE SET (10) 5.00 12.00
STATED ODDS 1:12 HOBBY
UG1 Bachelor's Grove Cemetery .60 1.50
UG2 The White House .60 1.50
UG3 Waverly Hills Sanatorium .60 1.50
UG4 The Villisca Axe Murder House .60 1.50
UG5 The Amityville Haunting .60 1.50
UG6 The Lemp Mansion .60 1.50
UG7 Alcatraz .60 1.50
UG8 The Winchester Mystery House .60 1.50
UG9 RMS Queen Mary .60 1.50
UG10 The Lizzie Borden House .60 1.50

2011 Topps Allen and Ginter Mini World's Most Mysterious Figures

COMPLETE SET (10) 5.00 12.00
STATED ODDS 1:15 HOBBY
WMF1 Rasputin .60 1.50
WMF2 The Poe Toaster .60 1.50
WMF3 Kasper Hauser .60 1.50
WMF4 Fulcanelli .60 1.50
WMF5 D.B. Cooper .60 1.50
WMF6 The Count of St. Germain .60 1.50
WMF7 The Man in the Iron Mask .60 1.50
WMF8 Nostradamus .60 1.50
WMF9 The Babushka Lady .60 1.50
WMF10 Captain Charles Johnson .60 1.50

2011 Topps Allen and Ginter N43

STATED ODDS 1:2 HOBBY BOXES
AC Aroldis Chapman 2.00 5.00
AP Albert Pujols 4.00 10.00
AW Adam Wainwright 1.25 3.00
CC Carl Crawford 1.25 3.00
CG Carlos Gonzalez 1.25 3.00
DP David Price 2.00 5.00
DW David Wright 2.50 6.00
HR Hanley Ramirez 2.00 5.00
JJ Josh Johnson 1.25 3.00
JV Joey Votto 2.00 5.00
MT Mark Teixeira 2.00 5.00
RC Robinson Cano 2.00 5.00
RH Roy Halladay 2.00 5.00
TL Tim Lincecum 2.00 5.00
UJ Ubaldo Jimenez 1.25 3.00

2011 Topps Allen and Ginter Relics

STATED ODDS 1:10 HOBBY
EXCHANGE DEADLINE 6/30/2014
AB1 Adrian Beltre Bat 10.00 25.00
AB2 Adrian Beltre Jsy 3.00 8.00
AD1 Adam Dunn Bat 3.00 8.00
AD2 Adam Dunn Jsy 3.00 8.00
AE Andre Ethier 3.00 8.00
AG Adrian Gonzalez 4.00 10.00
AH Aaron Hill 3.00 8.00
AJ Adam Jones 3.00 8.00
AL1 Adam Lind Bat 3.00 8.00
AL2 Adam Lind Jsy 3.00 8.00
AM1 Andrew McCutchen Bat 5.00 12.00
AM2 Andrew McCutchen Jsy 5.00 12.00
AP1 Albert Pujols Bat 10.00 25.00
AP2 Albert Pujols Jsy 30.00 60.00
AR Alex Rodriguez 5.00 12.00
AS Alfonso Soriano 4.00 10.00
BB Billy Butler 3.00 8.00
BD Blake DeWitt 3.00 8.00
BG Brett Gardner 3.00 8.00
BM Brian McCann 3.00 8.00
CB Carlos Beltran 5.00 12.00
CG Carlos Gomez 3.00 8.00
CJ Chipper Jones 5.00 12.00
CM Casey McGehee 3.00 8.00
CP Carlos Pena 3.00 8.00
CQ Carlos Quentin 3.00 8.00
CR Cody Ross 5.00 12.00
CU Chase Utley 4.00 10.00
DH Daniel Hudson 3.00 8.00
DJ Derek Jeter 10.00 25.00
DL Derrek Lee 3.00 8.00
DO David Ortiz 3.00 8.00
DP Dustin Pedroia 5.00 12.00
DS1 Drew Stubbs Bat 4.00 10.00
DS2 Drew Stubbs Jsy 3.00 8.00
DU1 Dan Uggla Bat 3.00 8.00
DU2 Dan Uggla Jsy 3.00 8.00
EA Elvis Andrus 3.00 8.00
EL1 Evan Longoria Bat 3.00 8.00
EL2 Evan Longoria Jsy 5.00 12.00
EV Edinson Volquez 3.00 8.00
FC Francisco Cervelli 3.00 8.00
FH Felix Hernandez 3.00 8.00
GB Gordon Beckham 3.00 8.00
GS Grady Sizemore 8.00 20.00
HK Howie Kendrick 3.00 8.00
HP Hunter Pence 3.00 8.00
HR1 Hanley Ramirez Bat 3.00 8.00
HR2 Hanley Ramirez Jsy 3.00 8.00
ID1 Ike Davis Bat 3.00 8.00
ID2 Ike Davis Jsy 3.00 8.00
IR Ivan Rodriguez 3.00 8.00
IS Ichiro Suzuki 6.00 15.00
JB Jason Bay 5.00 12.00
JC Joba Chamberlain 3.00 8.00
JD Johnny Damon 3.00 8.00
JE1 Jacoby Ellsbury Bat 5.00 12.00
JE2 Jacoby Ellsbury Jsy 3.00 8.00
JH Josh Hamilton 6.00 15.00
JJ Josh Johnson 3.00 8.00
JL James Loney 3.00 8.00
JM Joe Maddon 3.00 8.00
JP1 Jorge Posada Bat 4.00 10.00
JP2 Jorge Posada Jsy 4.00 10.00
JR Jimmy Rollins 5.00 12.00
JS Jarrod Saltalamacchia 3.00 8.00
JT Jose Tabata 4.00 10.00
JU Justin Upton 3.00 8.00
JV1 Joey Votto Bat 4.00 10.00
JV2 Joey Votto Jsy 8.00 20.00
JW Jayson Werth 3.00 8.00
KB Kyle Blanks 3.00 8.00
KF Kosuke Fukudome 4.00 10.00
KM Kendrys Morales 3.00 8.00
KS Kurt Suzuki 3.00 8.00
KY Kevin Youkilis 4.00 10.00
MB Mark Buehrle 3.00 8.00
MC Matt Cain 4.00 10.00
MR Mark Reynolds 3.00 8.00
MT Mark Teixeira 3.00 8.00
MY1 Michael Young Bat 3.00 8.00
MY2 Michael Young Jsy 3.00 8.00
NC Nelson Cruz 4.00 10.00
NF Neftali Feliz 3.00 8.00
NM Nick Markakis 5.00 12.00
NS Nick Swisher 3.00 8.00
PF Prince Fielder 3.00 8.00
PH Phil Hughes 3.00 8.00
PK Paul Konerko 6.00 15.00
PS1 Pablo Sandoval Bat 4.00 10.00
PS2 Pablo Sandoval Jsy 4.00 10.00
RB1 Ryan Braun Bat 4.00 10.00
RB2 Ryan Braun Jsy 4.00 10.00
RC Robinson Cano 3.00 8.00
RD Ryan Dempster 3.00 8.00
RH Ryan Howard 3.00 8.00
RM1 Russell Martin Bat 3.00 8.00
RM2 Russell Martin Jsy 3.00 8.00
RN Ricky Nolasco 3.00 8.00
RP Ryan Perry 3.00 8.00
RW1 Rickie Weeks Bat 3.00 8.00
RW2 Rickie Weeks Jsy 3.00 8.00
RZ Ryan Zimmerman 3.00 8.00
SC1 Starlin Castro Bat 5.00 12.00
SC2 Starlin Castro Jsy 5.00 12.00
SD Stephen Drew 5.00 12.00
SR Scott Rolen 5.00 12.00
SV1 Shane Victorino Bat 4.00 10.00
SV2 Shane Victorino Jsy 3.00 8.00
TC Tyler Colvin 3.00 8.00
TG Tony Gwynn Jr. 3.00 8.00
TH Tim Hudson 3.00 8.00
TT Troy Tulowitzki 3.00 8.00
TW Tim Wakefield 3.00 8.00
WV Will Venable 3.00 8.00
XN Xavier Nady 3.00 8.00
YE Yunel Escobar 4.00 10.00
ADU Angelo Dundee 4.00 10.00
AES Alcides Escobar 4.00 10.00
AJA1 Austin Jackson Bat 3.00 8.00
AJA2 Austin Jackson Jsy 3.00 8.00
AJB A.J. Burnett 3.00 8.00
AJP A.J. Pierzynski 6.00 15.00
AJU Ana Julaton 10.00 25.00
AMU Aimee Mullins 4.00 10.00
ARA1 Alexei Ramirez Bat 3.00 8.00
ARA2 Alexei Ramirez Jsy 3.00 8.00
ARM2 Aramis Ramirez Jsy 3.00 8.00
ARM1 Aramis Ramirez Bat 15.00 40.00
ASA Anibal Sanchez 3.00 8.00
ASO Annika Sorenstam 12.50 30.00
BBO Brennan Boesch 3.00 8.00
BJU B.J. Upton 3.00 8.00
CBU Cheryl Burke 10.00 25.00
CJO Chris Johnson 3.00 8.00
CRA Colby Rasmus 5.00 12.00
CWE Chrissie Wellington 6.00 15.00
CWO Chuck Woolery 5.00 12.00
DBO Daniel Boulud 6.00 15.00
DTU Diana Taurasi 6.00 15.00
DVA Dick Vitale 6.00 15.00
EJA Eric Jackson 5.00 12.00
ELY Evan Lysacek 5.00 12.00
GAU Geno Auriemma 6.00 15.00
GFI Guy Fieri 10.00 25.00
GSO Geovany Soto 3.00 8.00
HMI Heather Mitts 10.00 25.00
HSO Hope Solo 20.00 50.00
IDE Ian Desmond 3.00 8.00
JBA Jose Bautista 4.00 10.00
JBE Josh Beckett 3.00 8.00
JBR Jay Bruce 5.00 12.00
JDD J.D. Drew 3.00 8.00
JJA Jon Jay 3.00 8.00
JLA John Lackey 3.00 8.00
JLA Jake LaMotta 15.00 40.00
JLL Jack LaLanne 6.00 15.00
JLO Jed Lowrie 3.00 8.00
JMC John McEnroe 20.00 50.00
JMO Justin Morneau 3.00 8.00
JNA Jim Nantz 6.00 15.00
JOF Jo Frost 6.00 15.00
JPA Jonathan Papelbon 3.00 8.00
JRE Jose Reyes 6.00 15.00
JSA Jeff Samardzija 4.00 10.00
JVE Justin Verlander 4.00 10.00
KPE Kyle Petty 10.00 25.00
KYA Kristi Yamaguchi 10.00 25.00
LHO Lou Holtz 8.00 20.00
LHO Larry Holmes 10.00 25.00
MBY Marlon Byrd 3.00 8.00
MCA1 Melky Cabrera Bat 3.00 8.00
MCA2 Melky Cabrera Jsy 3.00 8.00
MCB Miguel Cabrera 4.00 10.00
MFA Marc Forgione 6.00 15.00
MGU Matt Guy 5.00 12.00
MHO Mat Hoffman 8.00 20.00
MPA Manny Pacquiao 75.00 150.00
MSH Maxim Shmyrev 8.00 20.00
MWA Micky Ward 5.00 12.00
NLO Nancy Lopez 12.50 30.00
PGA Peter Gammons 10.00 25.00
PST Picabo Street 10.00 25.00
RDO Ryan Doumit 3.00 8.00
RJO Rafer Johnson 6.00 15.00
RRU Rudy Ruettiger 10.00 25.00
RTU Ron Turcotte 8.00 20.00
SBI Sue Bird 6.00 15.00
SLE Stan Lee 20.00 50.00
SMI Shawn Michaels 12.50 30.00
SRI Sanya Richards 8.00 20.00
THA Tommy Hanson 3.00 8.00
THE Todd Helton 3.00 8.00
THO Tim Howard 8.00 20.00
TSC Timothy Shieff 6.00 15.00
WEE Wee Man 8.00 20.00

2011 Topps Allen and Ginter Rip Cards

OVERALL RIP ODDS 1:276 HOBBY
PRINT RUNS B/WN 10-99 COPIES PER
NO PRICING ON QTY 25 OR LESS
ALL LISTED PRICED ARE FOR RIPPED
UNRIPPED HAVE ADD'L CARDS WITHIN
COMMON UNRIPPED p/r 99 60.00 120.00
COMMON UNRIPPED p/r 75 60.00 120.00
COMMON UNRIPPED p/r 50 60.00 120.00
COMMON UNRIPPED p/r 25 100.00 250.00
COMMON UNRIPPED p/r 10 350.00 700.00
RC54 Jayson Werth/50 6.00 15.00
RC55 Jered Weaver/50 4.00 10.00

RC56 Francisco Liriano/50 4.00 10.00
RC57 Zack Greinke/50 6.00 15.00
RC58 Roy Oswalt/50 6.00 15.00
RC59 Hunter Pence/50 6.00 15.00
RC60 Adrian Beltre/50 4.00 10.00
RC61 Martin Prado/50 4.00 10.00
RC62 Jay Bruce/50 6.00 15.00
RC63 Jimmy Rollins/50 6.00 15.00
RC64 Paul Konerko/50 6.00 15.00
RC65 Brandon Phillips/50 4.00 10.00
RC66 Dan Haren/50 4.00 10.00
RC67 Andre Ethier/50 6.00 15.00
RC68 Matt Cain/50 6.00 15.00
RC69 Elvis Andrus/75 6.00 15.00
RC70 Jason Heyward/75 8.00 20.00
RC71 Ian Kinsler/75 6.00 15.00
RC72 Joakim Soria/75 4.00 10.00
RC73 Michael Young/75 6.00 15.00
RC74 Delmon Young/75 6.00 15.00
RC75 Mariano Rivera/75 8.00 20.00
RC76 Mat Latos/75 4.00 10.00
RC77 Colby Rasmus/75 8.00 20.00
RC78 Heath Bell/75 6.00 15.00
RC79 Shane Victorino/75 6.00 15.00
RC80 Derek Jeter/75 15.00 40.00
RC81 Billy Butler/75 4.00 10.00
RC82 Neftali Feliz/75 4.00 10.00
RC83 Carlos Santana/75 8.00 20.00
RC84 Gordon Beckham/99 6.00 15.00
RC85 Mike Stanton/99 6.00 15.00
RC86 Yovani Gallardo/99 4.00 10.00
RC87 Clay Buchholz/99 6.00 15.00
RC88 Pedro Alvarez/99 6.00 15.00
RC89 Matt Garza/99 4.00 10.00
RC90 Aroldis Chapman/99 8.00 20.00
RC91 David Ortiz/99 6.00 15.00
RC92 Jeremy Hellickson/99 8.00 20.00
RC93 Jacoby Ellsbury/99 8.00 20.00
RC94 Stephen Drew/99 4.00 10.00
RC95 Starlin Castro/99 8.00 20.00
RC96 Torii Hunter/99 4.00 10.00
RC97 Madison Bumgarner/99 4.00 10.00
RC99 Vernon Wells/99 4.00 10.00

2011 Topps Allen and Ginter State Map Relics

STATED PRINT RUN 50 SER.#'d SETS
1 New England 90.00 150.00
2 New York 90.00 150.00
3 Pennsylvania 60.00 120.00
New Jersey
4 Virginia 100.00 200.00
West Virginia
Maryland
Delaware
5 North Carolina 50.00 100.00
South Carolina
6 Kentucky 50.00 100.00
Tennessee
7 Michigan 50.00 100.00
8 Ohio 50.00 100.00
9 Indiana 60.00 120.00
10 Georgia 40.00 80.00
11 Florida 90.00 150.00
12 Alabama 50.00 100.00
13 Mississippi 50.00 100.00
14 Wisconsin 75.00 150.00
15 Illinois 50.00 100.00
16 Minnesota 60.00 120.00
17 Iowa 60.00 120.00
18 Arkansas 50.00 100.00
19 Missouri 50.00 100.00
20 Louisiana 50.00 100.00
21 North Dakota 40.00 80.00
22 South Dakota 50.00 100.00
23 Nebraska 60.00 120.00
24 Kansas 50.00 100.00
25 Oklahoma 50.00 100.00
26 Texas 90.00 150.00
27 Montana 40.00 80.00
28 Wyoming 30.00 60.00
29 Colorado 50.00 100.00
30 New Mexico 40.00 80.00
31 Idaho 50.00 100.00
32 Utah 60.00 120.00
33 Arizona 40.00 60.00
34 Washington 50.00 100.00
35 Oregon 50.00 100.00
36 Nevada 40.00 80.00
37 California 60.00 120.00
38 Alaska 50.00 100.00
39 Hawaii 75.00 150.00

2011 Topps Allen and Ginter Terrorabilia

STATED PRINT RUN 10 SER.#'d SETS
NO PRICING DUE TO SCARCITY

2009 Topps American Heritage American Icons

COMPLETE SET (10)
STATED ODDS 1:487 H, 1:655 R
PRINT RUN 99 SER.#'d SETS
AI1 Babe Ruth 25.00 60.00
AI2 Jackie Robinson 10.00 25.00
AI3 Lou Gehrig 20.00 50.00
AI4 Honus Wagner 10.00 25.00
AI5 Ty Cobb 15.00 40.00
AI6 Cy Young 10.00 25.00
AI7 Roy Campanella 10.00 25.00
AI8 Walter Johnson 10.00 25.00
AI9 Johnny Mize 6.00 15.00
AI10 Christy Mathewson 10.00 25.00

2009 Topps American Heritage American Legends

COMPLETE SET (18)
STATED ODDS 1:119 H, 1:200 R
PRINT RUN 199 SER.#'d SETS
AL1 Walter Johnson 6.00 15.00
AL2 George Sisler 4.00 10.00
AL3 Ty Cobb 10.00 25.00
AL4 Thurman Munson 6.00 15.00
AL5 Christy Mathewson 6.00 15.00
AL6 Johnny Mize 4.00 10.00
AL7 Mickey Mantle 15.00 40.00
AL8 Babe Ruth 15.00 40.00
AL9 Rogers Hornsby 4.00 10.00
AL10 Pee Wee Reese 4.00 10.00
AL11 Lou Gehrig 12.50 30.00
AL12 Cy Young 6.00 15.00
AL13 Jimmie Foxx 6.00 15.00
AL14 Honus Wagner 6.00 15.00
AL15 Roy Campanella 6.00 15.00
AL16 Jackie Robinson 6.00 15.00
AL17 Mel Ott 4.00 10.00
AL18 Tris Speaker 4.00 10.00

2009 Topps American Heritage American Legends Cut Signature

STATED ODDS 1:60,000 H, 1:47,500 R
PRINT RUN 1 SER.#'d SET
NOT PRICED DUE TO SCARCITY

2009 Topps American Heritage American Legends Cut Signature Dual

STATED ODDS 1:65,280 H
PRINT RUN 1 SER.#'d SET
NOT PRICED DUE TO SCARCITY

2009 Topps American Heritage American Legends Relics

STATED ODDS 1:1472 H, 1:1590 R
PRINT RUN 25 SER.#'d SETS
BR Babe Ruth Bat 100.00 200.00
GS George Sisler Bat
HW Honus Wagner Bat
JF Jimmie Foxx Bat 25.00 60.00
JM Johnny Mize Bat 15.00 40.00
JR Jackie Robinson Bat 15.00 40.00
LG Lou Gehrig Pants 75.00 150.00
MM Mickey Mantle Pants 50.00 100.00
MO Mel Ott Pants
PR Pee Wee Reese Bat 25.00 60.00
RC Roy Campanella Pants 15.00 40.00
RH Rogers Hornsby Bat 25.00 60.00
TC Ty Cobb Bat 50.00 100.00
TM Thurman Munson Jsy 25.00 60.00
TS Tris Speaker Bat 25.00 60.00

2009 Topps American Heritage American Legends Relics Dual

STATED ODDS 1:4950 H, 1:6500 R
PRINT RUN 20 SER.#'d SETS
NOT PRICED DUE TO SCARCITY

2009 Topps American Heritage American Legends Relics Eight

STATED ODDS 1:98,000 H
PRINT RUN 1 SER.#'d SET
NOT PRICED DUE TO SCARCITY

2009 Topps American Heritage Heroes

COMPLETE SET (150) 30.00 60.00
COMP.SET w/o SPs (125) 12.50 25.00
SP STATED ODDS 1:4
24 Frank Robinson .20 .50
26 Jackie Robinson .40 1.00
122 Jackie Robinson Breaks Color Barrier .40 1.00

2009 Topps American Heritage Heroes Chrome

COMPLETE SET (100)
*CHROME: .8X TO 2X BASIC CARDS
STATED PRINT RUN 1776 SER.#'d SETS
STATED ODDS 1:4

2009 Topps American Heritage Heroes Chrome Refractor

COMPLETE SET (100)
*REFRACTORS: 8X TO 20X BASIC CARDS
STATED ODDS 1:72
STATED PRINT RUN 76 SER.#'d SETS

2009 Topps American Heritage Heroes American Heroes Quad Cut Signatures

STATED PRINT RUN 1 SER. #'d SET
STATED ODDS 1:127,632
NOT PRICED DUE TO SCARCITY
LRKO Joe Louis
Jackie Robinson
Martin Luther King Jr.
Barack Obama

2009 Topps American Heritage Heroes Heroes of Sport

COMPLETE SET (25) 12.50 25.00
STATED ODDS 1:4
*GOLD/199: 3X TO 8X BASIC INSERTS
*PLATINUM/25: 5X TO 12X BASIC INSERTS
HS1 Jackie Robinson .60 1.50
HS2 Babe Ruth 1.50 4.00
HS4 Cy Young .60 1.50
HS6 Tris Speaker .40 1.00
HS7 Mickey Mantle 1.50 4.00
HS8 Thurman Munson .60 1.50
HS10 Frank Robinson .40 1.00
HS11 Christy Mathewson .60 1.50
HS12 Roy Campanella .60 1.50
HS14 Lou Gehrig 1.25 3.00
HS16 Rogers Hornsby .40 1.00
HS17 Stan Musial .60 1.50
HS18 Honus Wagner .60 1.50
HS19 Jimmie Foxx .60 1.50
HS20 Walter Johnson .60 1.50
HS22 Reggie Jackson .40 1.00
HS23 Ty Cobb 1.00 2.50
HS25 George Sisler .40 1.00

2009 Topps American Heritage Heroes Heroes of Sport 8-Piece Relics

UNPRICED PRINT RUN 1
STATED ODDS 1:191,448

2009 Topps American Heritage Heroes Heroes of Sport Autographs

STATED ODDS 1:6,000

2009 Topps American Heritage Heroes Heroes of Sport Cut Signatures

UNPRICED PRINT RUN 1
STATED ODDS 1:129,300

2009 Topps American Heritage Heroes Heroes of Sport Dual Relics

UNPRICED PRINT RUN 20
STATED ODDS 1:8,200

2009 Topps American Heritage Heroes Heroes of Sport Relics

STATED ODDS 1:234
HSR1 Jackie Robinson Bat 15.00 40.00
HSR2a Babe Ruth Bat 100.00 175.00
HSR2b Babe Ruth Jsy 125.00 200.00
HSR3 Mickey Mantle Pants 50.00 100.00
HSR4 Johnny Mize Bat 15.00 40.00
HSR7 Rogers Hornsby Bat 20.00 50.00
HSR9 Jimmie Foxx Bat 25.00 60.00
HSR10 Ty Cobb Bat 50.00 100.00
HSR11 Lou Gehrig Pants 75.00 150.00
HSR12 Frank Robinson Bat 10.00 25.00

2009 Topps American Heritage Heroes Presidential Medal of Freedom

COMPLETE SET (25) 8.00 20.00
STATED ODDS 1:4
MOF23 Frank Robinson .60 1.50

2001 Topps Archives

Issued in two series of 225 cards, this 450 card set features some of the first and last cards of retired superstars and other retired star players. The cards were issued in eight card packs with an SRP of $4. These packs were issued 20 packs to a box and eight boxes to a case. A very annoying feature of this set was the checklist numbers were so small that it was very difficult to tell what the number of the card was if a collector was trying to build a set.

COMPLETE SET (450) 80.00 160.00
COMP. SERIES 1 (225) 40.00 80.00
COMP. SERIES 2 (225) 40.00 80.00
1 Johnny Antonelli 52 .40 1.00
2 Yogi Berra 52 UER 1.00 2.50
Berra's first card was 51 Topps Red Back
3 Dom DiMaggio 52 UER .40 1.00
His first Topps card is 1951 Red Back
4 Carl Erskine 52 .40 1.00
5 Larry Doby 52 .40 1.00
6 Monte Irvin 52 .40 1.00
7 Vernon Law 52 .40 1.00
8 Eddie Mathews 52 1.00 2.50
9 Willie Mays 52 2.00 5.00
10 Gil McDougald 52 .40 1.00
11 Andy Pafko 52 .60 1.50
12 Phil Rizzuto 52 1.00 2.50
13 Preacher Roe 52 UER .40 1.00
His first Topps card is 51 Topps Red Back
14 Hank Sauer 52 UER .40 1.00
His first Topps card is 51 Topps Blue Back
15 Bobby Shantz 52 .40 1.00
16 Enos Slaughter 52 UER .40 1.00
His first Topps card is 51 Topps Blue Back
17 Warren Spahn 52 UER .60 1.50
His First Topps card was 1951 Topps Red Back
18 Mickey Vernon 52 UER .40 1.00
His First Topps Card was 1951 Topps Blue Back
19 Early Wynn 52 UER .40 1.00
His first Topps card is a 1951 Topps Red Back
20 Gaylord Perry 62 .40 1.00
21 Johnny Podres 53 .40 1.00
22 Ernie Banks 54 1.00 2.50
23 Moose Skowron 54 .40 1.00
24 Harmon Killebrew 55 1.00 2.50
25 Ted Williams 54 2.00 5.00
26 Jimmy Piersall 56 .40 1.00
27 Frank Thomas 56 .40 1.00
28 Bill Mazeroski 57 1.00 2.50
29 Bobby Richardson 57 .40 1.00
30 Frank Robinson 57 .60 1.50
31 Stan Musial 58 1.50 4.00
32 Johnny Callison 59 .40 1.00
33 Bob Gibson 59 .60 1.50
34 Frank Howard 60 .40 1.00
35 Willie McCovey 60 .40 1.00
36 Carl Yastrzemski 60 1.50 4.00
37 Jim Maloney 61 .40 1.00
38 Ron Santo 61 .60 1.50
39 Lou Brock 62 .60 1.50
40 Tim McCarver 62 .40 1.00
41 Joe Pepitone 62 .20 .50
42 Boog Powell 62 .60 1.50
43 Bill Freehan 63 .40 1.00
44 Dick Allen 64 .40 1.00
45 Willie Horton 64 .20 .50
46 Mickey Lolich 64 .40 1.00
47 Wilbur Wood 64 .20 .50
48 Bert Campaneris 65 .40 1.00
49 Rod Carew 67 .60 1.50
50 Luis Aparicio 56 .40 1.00
51 Joe Morgan 65 .40 1.00
52 Luis Tiant 65 .40 1.00
53 Bobby Murcer 66 .40 1.00
54 Don Sutton 66 .40 1.00
55 Ken Holtzman 67 .20 .50
56 Reggie Smith 67 .40 1.00
57 Hal McRae 68 .40 1.00
58 Roy White 68 UER .40 1.00
His Rookie Card is 66 Topps
59 Reggie Jackson 69 .60 1.50
60 Graig Nettles 69 .40 1.00
61 Joe Rudi 69 .40 1.00
62 Vida Blue 70 .40 1.00
63 Darrell Evans 70 .40 1.00
64 David Concepcion 71 .40 1.00
65 Bobby Grich 71 .40 1.00
66 Greg Luzinski 71 .40 1.00
67 Ron Cey 72 .40 1.00
68 George Hendrick 72 .20 .50
69 Dwight Evans 73 .60 1.50
70 Gary Matthews 73 .20 .50
71 Mike Schmidt 73 3.00 8.00
72 Jim Kaat 60 .40 1.00
73 Dave Winfield 74 .40 1.00
74 Gary Carter 75 .60 1.50
75 Dennis Eckersley 76 .40 1.00
76 Kent Tekulve 76 .40 1.00
77 Andre Dawson 77 .60 1.50
78 Denny Martinez 77 .40 1.00
79 Bruce Sutter 77 .40 1.00
80 Jack Morris 78 .40 1.00
81 Ozzie Smith 80 2.00 5.00
82 Lee Smith 80 .40 1.00
83 Don Mattingly 84 3.00 8.00
84 Joe Carter 85 .40 1.00
85 Kirby Puckett 85 1.00 2.50
86 Joe Adcock 52 .40 1.00
87 Gus Bell 52 UER .20 .50
His first Topps card is 1951 Topps Red Back
88 Roy Campanella 52 1.00 2.50
89 Jackie Jensen 52 .40 1.00
90 Johnny Mize 52 .60 1.50
91 Allie Reynolds 52 .40 1.00
92 Al Rosen 52 UER .40 1.00
His first Topps card is a 1951 Topps Red Back
93 Hal Newhouser 53 .40 1.00
94 Harvey Kuenn 54 .40 1.00
95 Nellie Fox 56 1.00 2.50
96 Elston Howard 56 .60 1.50
97 Sal Maglie 57 .40 1.00
98 Roger Maris 58 1.00 2.50
99 Norm Cash 60 UER .40 1.00
His Rookie Card was in 1959 Topps
100 Thurman Munson 70 1.00 2.50
101 Roy Campanella 57 UER 1.00 2.50
His first Topps card is in 1952
102 Larry Doby 59 .40 1.00
103 Dom Dimaggio 53 .40 1.00
104 Johnny Mize 53 .40 1.00
105 Allie Reynolds 53 .40 1.00
106 Preacher Roe 54 .40 1.00
107 Hal Newhouser 55 .20 .50
108 Monte Irvin 56 .40 1.00
109 Carl Erskine 59 .40 1.00
110 Enos Slaughter 59 .40 1.00
111 Gil McDougald 60 .40 1.00
112 Andy Pafko 59 .40 1.00
113 Sal Maglie 59 .20 .50
114 Johnny Antonelli 61 .20 .50
115 Phil Rizzuto 61 .60 1.50
116 Yogi Berra 62 1.00 2.50
117 Jim Wynn 77 .20 .50
118 Mickey Vernon 63 .20 .50
119 Gus Bell 64 .20 .50
120 Ted Williams 58 1.25 3.00
121 Frank Thomas 65 .20 .50
122 Bobby Richardson 66 .40 1.00
123 Gaylord Perry 83 .40 1.00
124 Vernon Law 67 .20 .50
125 Jimmy Piersall 67 .20 .50
126 Moose Skowron 67 .20 .50
127 Joe Adcock 63 .20 .50
128 Johnny Podres 69 .40 1.00
129 Ernie Banks 71 1.00 2.50
130 Jim Maloney 72 .20 .50
131 Johnny Callison 73 .20 .50
132 Eddie Mathews 68 .60 1.50
133 Joe Pepitone 73 .20 .50
134 Warren Spahn 65 .60 1.50
135 Bill Mazeroski 72 .60 1.50
136 Norm Cash 74 .40 1.00
137 Bob Gibson 75 .60 1.50
138 Harmon Killebrew 75 1.00 2.50
139 Frank Robinson 75 .60 1.50
140 Ron Santo 75 .60 1.50
141 Hank Sauer 59 .20 .50
142 Bobby Shantz 64 .20 .50
143 Nellie Fox 65 .60 1.50
144 Elston Howard 68 .60 1.50
145 Jackie Jensen 61 .40 1.00
146 Al Rosen 56 .40 1.00
147 Dick Allen 76 .20 .50
148 Bill Freehan 77 .40 1.00
149 Boog Powell 77 .40 1.00
150 Lou Brock 79 UER .60 1.50
Header for stats on back is for a pitcher
Brock was an outfielder
151 Rod Carew 86 .60 1.50
152 Wilbur Wood 79 .20 .50
153 Thurman Munson 79 1.00 2.50
154 Ken Holtzman 80 .20 .50
155 Willie Horton 80 .20 .50
156 Mickey Lolich 80 .20 .50
157 Tim McCarver 80 .20 .50
158 Willie McCovey 80 .40 1.00
159 Roy White 80 .20 .50
160 Bobby Murcer 83 .40 1.00
161 Joe Rudi 83 .20 .50
162 Reggie Smith 83 .20 .50
163 Luis Tiant 83 .20 .50
164 Bert Campaneris 84 .20 .50
165 Frank Howard 73 .20 .50
166 Harvey Kuenn 66 .20 .50
167 Greg Luzinski 85 .20 .50
168 Luis Aparicio 74 .40 1.00
169 Willie Mays 73 1.25 3.00
170 Roger Maris 68 1.00 2.50
171 Vida Blue 87 .20 .50
172 Bobby Grich 87 .20 .50
173 Reggie Jackson 87 .60 1.50
174 Hal McRae 87 .20 .50
175 Carl Yastrzemski 83 1.00 2.50
176 David Concepcion 88 .20 .50
177 Ron Cey 87 .20 .50
178 George Hendrick 88 .20 .50
179 Gary Matthews 88 .20 .50
180 Stan Musial 63 1.00 2.50
181 Graig Nettles 88 .20 .50
182 Don Sutton 88 .40 1.00
183 Kent Tekulve 86 .20 .50
184 Bruce Sutter 89 .40 1.00
185 Darrell Evans 90 .20 .50
186 Mike Schmidt 89 1.50 4.00
187 Jim Kaat 83 .20 .50
188 Dwight Evans 92 .60 1.50
189 Gary Carter 93 .40 1.00
190 Jack Morris 94 .20 .50
191 Joe Morgan 85 .40 1.00
192 Dave Winfield 95 .40 1.00
193 Andre Dawson 96 .40 1.00
194 Lee Smith 96 .20 .50
195 Ozzie Smith 96 1.50 4.00
196 Denny Martinez 97 .20 .50
197 Don Mattingly 96 1.50 4.00
198 Joe Carter 98 .40 1.00
199 Dennis Eckersley 98 .40 1.00
200 Kirby Puckett 96 1.00 2.50
201 Walter Alston MG 56 .40 1.00
202 Casey Stengel MG 60 .40 1.00
203 S. Anderson MG 71 .40 1.00
204 T. Lasorda MG 88 .40 1.00
205 Whitey Herzog MG 88 .20 .50
206 AL HR Leaders 70 .40 1.00
Harmon Killebrew
Frank Howard
Reggie Jackson
207 NL HR Leaders 68 .40 1.00
Hank Aaron
Jim Wynn
Ron Santo
Willie McCovey
208 AL HR Leaders 67 1.00 2.50
Brooks Robinson
Harmon Killebrew
Boog Powell
209 AL Batting Leaders 65 .40 1.00
Tony Oliva
Brooks Robinson
Elston Howard
210 NL HR Leaders 64 .40 1.00
Hank Aaron
Willie McCovey
Willie Mays
Orlando Cepeda
211 NL HR Leaders 63 .40 1.00
Hank Aaron
Frank Robinson
Willie Mays
Ernie Banks
Orlando Cepeda
212 AL HR Leaders 68 1.00 2.50
Carl Yastrzemski
Harmon Killebrew
Frank Howard
213 Ernie Banks 59 Thrill 1.00 2.50
214 Hank Aaron 59 Thrill 1.25 3.00
215 Willie Mays 59 Thrill 1.25 3.00
216 Al Kaline 59 Thrill 1.00 2.50
217 Stan Musial 59 Thrill 1.00 2.50
218 Duke Snider 59 Thrill .60 1.50
219 The Champs 67 .60 1.50
Frank Robinson
Hank Bauer MG
Brooks Robinson UER
All Cards have a 1965 Leaders Back
220 Pride of the NL 63 1.00 2.50
Willie Mays
Stan Musial
221 Whitey Ford WS 63 .60 1.50
222 Jerry Koosman WS 70 .20 .50
223 Bob Gibson WS 65 .60 1.50
224 Gil Hodges WS 60 .60 1.50
225 R. Jackson WS 78 .60 1.50
226 Hank Bauer 52 .40 1.00
227 Ralph Branca 52 .40 1.00
228 Joe Garagiola 52 .40 1.00
229 Bob Feller 52 .40 1.00
230 Dick Groat 52 .40 1.00
231 George Kell 52 .40 1.00
232 Bob Boone 73 .40 1.00
233 Minnie Minoso 52 .40 1.00
234 Billy Pierce 52 .40 1.00
235 Robin Roberts 52 .40 1.00
236 Johnny Sain 52 .40 1.00
237 Red Schoendienst 52 .40 1.00
238 Curt Simmons 52 .40 1.00
239 Duke Snider 52 .60 1.50
240 Bobby Thomson 52 .60 1.50
241 Hoyt Wilhelm 52 .60 1.50
242 Roy Face 53 .40 1.00
243 Ralph Kiner 53 .40 1.00
244 Hank Aaron 54 2.50 6.00
245 Al Kaline 54 1.00 2.50
246 Don Larsen 56 .40 1.00
247 Tug McGraw 65 .40 1.00
248 Don Newcombe 56 .60 1.50
249 Herb Score 56 .40 1.00
250 Clete Boyer 57 .40 1.00
251 Lindy McDaniel 57 .20 .50
252 Brooks Robinson 57 .60 1.50
253 Orlando Cepeda 58 .40 1.00
254 Larry Bowa 70 .40 1.00
255 Mike Cuellar 59 .40 1.00
256 Jim Perry 59 .40 1.00
257 Dave Parker 74 .40 1.00
258 Maury Wills 60 .40 1.00
259 Willie Davis 61 .20 .50
260 Juan Marichal 61 .40 1.00
261 Jim Bouton 62 .40 1.00
262 Dean Chance 62 .40 1.00
263 Sam McDowell 62 .40 1.00
264 Whitey Ford 53 .60 1.50
265 Bob Uecker 62 .60 1.50
266 Willie Stargell 63 .60 1.50
267 Rico Carty 64 .40 1.00
268 Tommy John 64 .40 1.00
269 Phil Niekro 64 .40 1.00
270 Paul Blair 65 .40 1.00
271 Steve Carlton 65 1.25 3.00
272 Jim Lonborg 65 .40 1.00
273 Tony Perez 65 .40 1.00
274 Ron Swoboda 65 .40 1.00
275 Fergie Jenkins 66 .40 1.00
276 Jim Palmer 66 .40 1.00
277 Sal Bando 67 .40 1.00
278 Tom Seaver 67 1.50 4.00
279 Johnny Bench 68 1.50 4.00
280 Nolan Ryan 68 UER 2.50 6.00
The word sensational is spelled incorrectly
281 Rollie Fingers 69 .40 1.00
282 Sparky Lyle 69 .40 1.00
283 Al Oliver 69 .40 1.00
284 Bob Watson 69 .40 1.00
285 Bill Buckner 70 .40 1.00
286 Bert Blyleven 71 .60 1.50
287 George Foster 71 .40 1.00
288 Al Hrabosky 71 .20 .50
289 Cecil Cooper 72 .40 1.00
290 Carlton Fisk 72 .60 1.50
291 Mickey Rivers 72 .40 1.00
292 Goose Gossage 73 .40 1.00
293 Rick Reuschel 73 .40 1.00
294 Bucky Dent 74 .40 1.00
295 Frank Tanana 74 .40 1.00
296 George Brett 75 3.00 8.00
297 Keith Hernandez 75 .40 1.00
298 Fred Lynn 75 .40 1.00
299 Robin Yount 75 1.00 2.50
300 Ron Guidry 76 .40 1.00
301 Jack Clark 77 .40 1.00
302 Mark Fidrych 77 .40 1.00
303 Dale Murphy 77 .60 1.50
304 Willie Hernandez 78 .20 .50
305 Lou Whitaker 78 .40 1.00
306 Kirk Gibson 81 .40 1.00
307 Wade Boggs 83 .60 1.50
308 Ryne Sandberg 83 2.50 6.00
309 Orel Hershiser 85 .40 1.00
310 Jimmy Key 85 .40 1.00
311 Richie Ashburn 52 .60 1.50
312 Smoky Burgess 52 .40 1.00
313 Gil Hodges 52 1.00 2.50
314 Ted Kluszewski 52 .60 1.50
315 Pee Wee Reese 52 1.00 2.50
316 Jackie Robinson 52 1.00 2.50
317 Jim Wynn 64 .20 .50
318 Satchel Paige 53 1.00 2.50
319 Roberto Clemente 55 2.50 6.00
320 Carl Furillo 56 .40 1.00
321 Don Drysdale 57 .60 1.50
322 Curt Flood 58 .40 1.00
323 Bob Allison 59 .40 1.00
324 Tony Conigliaro 64 .40 1.00
325 Dan Quisenberry 80 .40 1.00
326 Ralph Branca 52 .20 .50
327 Bob Feller 53 .20 .50
328 Satchel Paige 53 1.00 2.50
329 George Kell 58 .20 .50
330 Pee Wee Reese 58 .60 1.50
331 Bobby Thomson 60 .60 1.50
332 Carl Furillo 60 .20 .50
333 Hank Bauer 61 .20 .50
334 Herb Score 62 .40 1.00
335 Richie Ashburn 63 .60 1.50
336 Billy Pierce 64 .20 .50
337 Duke Snider 64 .60 1.50
338 Early Wynn 62 .20 .50
339 Robin Roberts 66 .40 1.00
340 Dick Groat 67 .20 .50
341 Curt Simmons 67 .20 .50
342 Bob Uecker 67 .60 1.50
343 Smoky Burgess 67 .20 .50
344 Jim Bouton 68 .20 .50
345 Roy Face 69 .20 .50
346 Don Drysdale 69 .60 1.50
347 Bob Allison 70 .20 .50
348 Clete Boyer 71 .20 .50
349 Dean Chance 71 .20 .50
350 Tony Conigliaro 71 .20 .50
351 Curt Flood 71 .20 .50
352 Hoyt Wilhelm 72 .20 .50
353 Ron Swoboda 73 .20 .50
354 Roberto Clemente 73 1.50 4.00
355 Tug McGraw 85 .20 .50
356 Orlando Cepeda 74 .20 .50
357 Joe Garagiola 52 .20 .50
358 Juan Marichal 74 .40 1.00
359 Sam McDowell 74 .20 .50
360 Johnny Sain 55 .20 .50
361 Ted Kluszewski 61 .40 1.00
362 Al Kaline 74 1.00 2.50
363 Lindy McDaniel 75 .20 .50
364 Don Newcombe 60 .40 1.00
365 Jim Perry 75 .20 .50
366 Hank Aaron 76 1.50 4.00
367 Don Larsen 65 .40 1.00
368 Mike Cuellar 77 .20 .50
369 Willie Davis 77 .20 .50
370 Ralph Kiner 53 .40 1.00
371 Minnie Minoso 64 .40 1.00
372 Larry Bowa 85 .20 .50
373 Brooks Robinson 77 .60 1.50
374 Bob Boone 90 .20 .50
375 Jim Lonborg 79 .20 .50
376 Paul Blair 80 .20 .50
377 Rico Carty 80 .20 .50
378 Sal Bando 81 .20 .50
379 Mark Fidrych 81 .20 .50
380 Al Hrabosky 82 .20 .50
381 Willie Stargell 82 .60 1.50
382 Johnny Bench 83 1.00 2.50
383 Dave Parker 91 .20 .50
384 Sparky Lyle 83 .20 .50
385 Fergie Jenkins 84 .40 1.00
386 Jim Palmer 84 .40 1.00
387 Whitey Ford 67 .60 1.50
388 Tony Perez 86 .40 1.00
389 Mickey Rivers 85 .20 .50
390 Bob Watson 85 .20 .50
391 Rollie Fingers 86 .40 1.00
392 George Foster 86 .20 .50
393 Al Oliver 86 .20 .50
394 Tom Seaver 87 .60 1.50
395 Maury Wills 72 .20 .50
396 Steve Carlton 87T .40 1.00
397 Cecil Cooper 88 .20 .50
398 Bill Buckner 88 .20 .50
399 Phil Niekro 87 .40 1.00
400 Red Schoendienst 62 .40 1.00
401 Ron Guidry 89 .20 .50
402 Willie Hernandez 89 .20 .50
403 Tommy John 89 .20 .50
404 Gil Hodges 63 1.00 2.50
405 Bucky Dent 84 .20 .50
406 Keith Hernandez 90 .20 .50
407 Dan Quisenberry 90 .20 .50
408 Fred Lynn 91 .20 .50
409 Rick Reuschel 91 .20 .50
410 Jackie Robinson 56 1.00 2.50
411 Goose Gossage 92 .20 .50
412 Bert Blyleven 93 .40 1.00
413 Jack Clark 93 .20 .50
414 Carlton Fisk 93 .60 1.50
415 Dale Murphy 93 .60 1.50
416 Frank Tanana 93 .20 .50
417 George Brett 94 1.50 4.00
418 Robin Yount 94 1.00 2.50
419 Kirk Gibson 95 .40 1.00
420 Lou Whitaker 95 .20 .50
421 R. Sandberg 97 UER 2.00 5.00
Card lists 1996 homers as 252
422 Jimmy Key 98 .20 .50
423 Nolan Ryan 94 1.50 4.00
424 Wade Boggs 00 .40 1.00
425 Orel Hershiser 00 .20 .50
426 Billy Martin MG 84 .60 1.50
427 Ralph Houk MG 62 .40 1.00
428 Chuck Tanner MG 72 .20 .50
429 Earl Weaver MG 71 .40 1.00
430 Leo Durocher MG 52 .40 1.00
431 AL HR Leaders 66 .40 1.00
Tony Conigliaro
Norm Cash
Willie Horton
432 NL HR Leaders 60 1.00 2.50
Ernie Banks
Hank Aaron
Eddie Mathews
Ken Boyer
433 AL Batting Leaders 62 .40 1.00
Norm Cash
Elston Howard
Al Kaline
Jimmy Piersall
434 Leading Firemen 79 .20 .50
Goose Gossage
Rollie Fingers
435 Strikeout Leaders 77 .60 1.50
Nolan Ryan
Tom Seaver
436 HR Leaders 74 .40 1.00
Reggie Jackson
Willie Stargell
437 RBI Leaders 73 .60 1.50
Johnny Bench
Dick Allen
438 Roger Maris 1.00 2.50
Blasts 61st 62
439 Carl Yastrzemski 1.00 2.50
World Series Game Two 68
440 Nolan Ryan RB 78 1.50 4.00
441 Baltimore Orioles 70 .40 1.00
442 Tony Perez RB 86 .20 .50
443 Steve Carlton RB 84 .20 .50
444 Wade Boggs RB 89 .40 1.00
445 Andre Dawson RB 89 .40 1.00
446 Whitey Ford RB 62 .60 1.50
447 Hank Aaron WS 59 1.50 4.00
448 Bob Gibson WS 69 .60 1.50
449 R.Clemente WS 72 1.50 4.00
450 Brooks Robinson .40 1.00
Orioles/WS 71

2001 Topps Archives Autographs

Inserted at overall odds of one in 20, these 159 cards feature the players signing their reprint cards. The set is checklisted TAA1-TAA170 but 11 cards do not exist as follows: 9, 15, 47, 72, 82, 84, 95, 105, 109, 159 and 161. The only first series exchange card was Keith Hernandez but unfortunately, Topps was unable to fulfill the card and sent collectors an array of other signed cards. The series two exchange card subjects were Juan Marichal, Jack Morris, Billy Pierce, Boog Powell, Ron Santo, Enos Slaughter, Ozzie Smith, Reggie Smith, Don Sutton, Bob Uecker, Jim Wynn and Robin Yount. Of these players, Juan Marichal, Ozzie Smith and Reggie Smith did not return any cards. The series one exchange date was April 30th, 2002 . The series two exchange deadline was exactly one year later - April 30th, 2003.

SER.1 GROUP A ODDS 1:3049
SER.2 GROUP A ODDS 1:2904
SER.1 GROUP B ODDS 1:872
SER.2 GROUP B ODDS 1:480
SER.1 GROUP C ODDS 1:697
SER.2 GROUP C ODDS 1:4782
SER.1 GROUP D ODDS 1:122
SER.2 GROUP D ODDS 1:662
SER.1 GROUP E ODDS 1:26
SER.2 GROUP E ODDS 1:209
SER.1 GROUP F ODDS 1:6097
SER.2 GROUP F ODDS 1:1455
SER.2 GROUP G ODDS 1:320
SER.2 GROUP H ODDS 1:412
SER.2 GROUP I ODDS 1:192
SER.2 GROUP J ODDS 1:38
SER.2 GROUP K ODDS 1:329
TAA1 Johnny Antonelli E1 6.00 15.00
TAA2 Hank Bauer E1 10.00 25.00
TAA3 Yogi Berra A2 SP/50 300.00 450.00
TAA4 Ralph Branca E1 10.00 25.00
TAA5 Dom DiMaggio E1 40.00 80.00
TAA6 Joe Garagiola E1 30.00 60.00
TAA7 Carl Erskine D1 15.00 40.00
TAA8 Bob Feller E1 15.00 40.00
TAA9 Does Not Exist
TAA10 Dick Groat D1 40.00 80.00
TAA11 Monte Irvin E1 15.00 40.00
TAA12 George Kell E1 15.00 40.00
TAA13 Vernon Law E1 10.00 25.00
TAA14 Bob Boone E1 10.00 25.00
TAA15 Does Not Exist
TAA16 W.Mays A2 SP/50 800.00 1200.00
TAA17 Gil McDougald E1 10.00 25.00
TAA18 Minnie Minoso E1 15.00 40.00
TAA19 Andy Pafko D2 15.00 40.00
TAA20 Billy Pierce E2 10.00 25.00
TAA21 P. Rizzuto B2 SP/200 75.00 150.00
TAA22 Robin Roberts C1 20.00 50.00
TAA23 Preacher Roe E1 10.00 25.00
TAA24 Johnny Sain E1 12.50 30.00
TAA25 Hank Sauer E1 20.00 50.00
TAA26 R. Schoendienst E1 15.00 40.00
TAA27 Bobby Shantz E1 6.00 15.00
TAA28 Curt Simmons E1 6.00 15.00
TAA29 Enos Slaughter E2 20.00 50.00
TAA30 Duke Snider B1 50.00 100.00
TAA31 Warren Spahn C2 75.00 150.00
TAA32 B.Thomson E1 10.00 25.00
TAA33 Mickey Vernon B2 6.00 15.00
TAA34 Hoyt Wilhelm D1 20.00 50.00
TAA35 Jim Wynn E2 6.00 15.00
TAA36 Roy Face E1 6.00 15.00
TAA37 Gaylord Perry C2 30.00 60.00
TAA38 Ralph Kiner B1 75.00 150.00
TAA39 Johnny Podres E2 15.00 40.00
TAA40 H.Aaron A2 SP/50 500.00 650.00
TAA41 E.Banks A2 SP/50 350.00 600.00
TAA42 Al Kaline B1 100.00 175.00
TAA43 Moose Skowron E1 10.00 25.00
TAA44 D.Larsen A1 SP/50 200.00 300.00
TAA45 H.Killebrew B1 150.00 250.00
TAA46 Tug McGraw E1 40.00 80.00
TAA47 Does Not Exist
TAA48 Don Newcombe E1 15.00 40.00
TAA49 Jim Piersall E2 10.00 25.00
TAA50 Herb Score E1 20.00 50.00
TAA51 Frank Thomas E1 6.00 15.00
TAA52 Clete Boyer D1 10.00 25.00
TAA53 Bill Mazeroski C2 50.00 100.00
TAA54 Lindy McDaniel E1 10.00 25.00
TAA55 B. Richardson E2 6.00 15.00
TAA56 B. Robinson A SP/50 175.00 300.00
TAA57 Frank Robinson B1 50.00 100.00
TAA58 Orlando Cepeda B1 60.00 120.00
TAA59 S. Musial A1 SP/50 275.00 400.00
TAA60 Larry Bowa D1 15.00 40.00
TAA61 Johnny Callison E2 10.00 25.00
TAA62 Mike Cuellar D1 20.00 50.00
TAA63 B. Gibson A1 SP/50 200.00 300.00
TAA64 Jim Perry E2 6.00 15.00
TAA65 Frank Howard E1 10.00 25.00
TAA66 Dave Parker E1 10.00 25.00
TAA67 Willie McCovey D2 75.00 150.00
TAA68 Maury Wills E1 6.00 15.00
TAA69 C. Yastrzemski F1 150.00 250.00
TAA70 Willie Davis E1 6.00 15.00
TAA71 Jim Maloney E2 10.00 25.00
TAA72 Does Not Exist
TAA73 Ron Santo E2 20.00 50.00
TAA74 Jim Bouton D1 15.00 40.00
TAA75 L. Brock A2 SP/50 175.00 300.00
TAA76 Dean Chance E1 6.00 15.00
TAA77 Tim McCarver B2 SP/200 40.00 80.00
TAA78 Sam McDowell D1 10.00 25.00
TAA79 Joe Pepitone E1 10.00 25.00
TAA80 Whitey Ford F1 100.00 200.00
TAA81 Boog Powell E2 10.00 25.00
TAA82 Does Not Exist
TAA83 Bill Freehan D2 6.00 15.00
TAA84 Does Not Exist
TAA85 Dick Allen B2 30.00 60.00
TAA86 Rico Carty E1 6.00 15.00
TAA87 Willie Horton E2 6.00 15.00
TAA88 Tommy John E1 6.00 15.00
TAA89 Mickey Lolich E2 6.00 15.00
TAA90 Phil Niekro D1 15.00 40.00
TAA91 Wilbur Wood E1 6.00 15.00
TAA92 Paul Blair E1 6.00 15.00
TAA93 B. Campaneris E2 10.00 25.00
TAA94 Steve Carlton D1 20.00 50.00
TAA95 Does Not Exist
TAA96 Jim Lonborg E1 6.00 15.00
TAA97 Luis Aparicio B1 30.00 60.00
TAA98 Tony Perez D1 20.00 50.00
TAA99 J. Morgan B2 SP/200 40.00 80.00
TAA100 Ron Swoboda D1 15.00 40.00
TAA101 Luis Tiant E2 6.00 15.00
TAA102 Fergie Jenkins D1 15.00 40.00
TAA103 Bobby Murcer D2 40.00 80.00
TAA104 Jim Palmer B1 50.00 100.00
TAA105 Does Not Exist
TAA106 Sal Bando E2 6.00 15.00
TAA107 Ken Holtzman B1 30.00 60.00
TAA108 T.Seaver A2 SP/50 175.00 300.00
TAA109 Does Not Exist
TAA110 J.Bench A1 SP/50 150.00 250.00
TAA111 Hal McRae E2 6.00 15.00
TAA112 Nolan Ryan A2 350.00 500.00
TAA113 Roy White D2 10.00 25.00
TAA114 Rollie Fingers C1 15.00 40.00
TAA115 R.Jackson A2 SP/50 175.00 300.00
TAA116 Sparky Lyle E1 10.00 25.00
TAA117 Graig Nettles D2 10.00 25.00
TAA118 Al Oliver E1 6.00 15.00
TAA119 Joe Rudi B2 10.00 25.00
TAA120 Bob Watson E1 6.00 15.00
TAA121 Vida Blue E2 6.00 15.00
TAA122 Bill Buckner E1 10.00 25.00
TAA123 Darrell Evans E1 6.00 15.00
TAA124 Bert Blyleven D1 20.00 50.00
TAA125 D.Concepcion D2 20.00 50.00
TAA126 George Foster E1 6.00 15.00
TAA127 Bobby Grich E1 6.00 15.00
TAA128 Al Hrabosky E1 10.00 25.00
TAA129 Greg Luzinski D1 10.00 25.00
TAA130 Cecil Cooper E1 6.00 15.00
TAA131 Ron Cey E2 6.00 15.00
TAA132 Carlton Fisk B1 60.00 120.00
TAA133 G.Hendrick E2 10.00 25.00
TAA134 Mickey Rivers E1 6.00 15.00
TAA135 Dwight Evans D2 15.00 40.00
TAA136 Rich Gossage E1 6.00 15.00
TAA137 G. Matthews B2 6.00 15.00
TAA138 Rick Reuschel E1 6.00 15.00
TAA139 Mike Schmidt A1 SP/50 275.00 400.00
TAA140 Bucky Dent D1 15.00 40.00
TAA141 Jim Kaat B2 15.00 40.00
TAA142 Frank Tanana E1 6.00 15.00
TAA143 Dave Winfield B2 SP/200 40.00 80.00
TAA144 G.Brett A1 SP/50 275.00 400.00
TAA145 G.Carter B2 SP/200 60.00 120.00
TAA146 Keith Hernandez D1
TAA147 Fred Lynn C1 20.00 50.00
TAA148 R.Yount B2 SP/200 100.00 175.00
TAA149 Dennis Eckersley B2 SP/200 40.00 80.00
TAA150 Ron Guidry E2 15.00 40.00
TAA151 Kent Tekulve D1 15.00 40.00
TAA152 Jack Clark E1 6.00 15.00
TAA153 A.Dawson B2 SP/200 40.00 80.00
TAA154 Mark Fidrych E1 30.00 60.00
TAA155 Dennis Martinez B2 SP/200 30.00 60.00
TAA156 Dale Murphy C1 20.00 50.00
TAA157 Bruce Sutter D2 30.00 60.00
TAA158 W.Hernandez D2 6.00 15.00
TAA159 Does Not Exist
TAA160 Lou Whitaker D2 15.00 40.00
TAA161 Does Not Exist
TAA162 Kirk Gibson E1 20.00 50.00
TAA163 Lee Smith D2 10.00 25.00
TAA164 Wade Boggs B1 60.00 120.00
TAA165 Ryne Sandberg B2 SP/200 125.00 200.00
TAA166 Don Mattingly D1 60.00 120.00
TAA167 J.Carter B2 SP/200 20.00 50.00
TAA168 Orel Hershiser D2 40.00 80.00
TAA169 Kirby Puckett A2 100.00 175.00
TAA170 Jimmy Key C1 20.00 50.00

2001 Topps Archives AutoProofs

Inserted at a rate of one in 2,444 in series one and one in 2,391 in series two these 10 cards feature players signing their actual cards. Each of these cards are serial numbered to 100. Willie McCovey and Willie Mays were both first series exchange cards with a redemption deadline of April 30th, 2002. Carlton Fisk, Robin Roberts and Hoyt Wilhelm were series two exchange cards with a redemption deadline of April 30th, 2003.

1 Wade Boggs 99 S1 40.00 80.00
2 Carlton Fisk 93 S2 50.00 100.00
3 Willie Mays 73 S1 100.00 200.00
4 Willie McCovey 80 S1 40.00 80.00
5 J.Palmer 82/84 EXCH S1 30.00 60.00
6 Robin Roberts 66 S2 40.00 80.00
7 Duke Snider 64 S2 40.00 80.00
8 Warren Spahn 65 S2 40.00 80.00
9 Hoyt Wilhelm 63 S2 40.00 80.00
10 Carl Yastrzemski 83 S1 75.00 150.00

2001 Topps Archives Bucks

Randomly inserted in packs, these three cards issued in the style of the old Baseball Bucks were good for money toward Topps 50th anniversary merchandise.

TB1 Willie Mays $1 4.00 10.00
TB2 Roberto Clemente $5 10.00 25.00
TB3 Jackie Robinson $10 10.00 25.00

2001 Topps Archives Future Rookie Reprints

Issued five per sealed Topps factory and HTA sets, these 20 cards feature Rookie Card reprints of today's leading players.

COMPLETE SET (20) 25.00 50.00
1 Barry Bonds 87 3.00 8.00
2 Chipper Jones 91 1.25 3.00
3 Cal Ripken 82 4.00 10.00
4 Shawn Green 92 .50 1.25
5 Frank Thomas 90 1.25 3.00
6 Derek Jeter 93 3.00 8.00
7 Geoff Jenkins 96 .50 1.25
8 Jim Edmonds 93 .50 1.25
9 Bernie Williams 90 .75 2.00
10 Sammy Sosa 90 1.25 3.00
11 Rickey Henderson 80 1.25 3.00
12 Calvin Reese 92 .50 1.25
13 Randy Johnson 89 1.25 3.00
14 Juan Gonzalez 90 .50 1.25
15 Gary Sheffield 89 .50 1.25
16 Manny Ramirez 92 .75 2.00
17 Pokey Reese 92 .50 1.25
18 Preston Wilson 93 .50 1.25
19 Jay Payton 95 .50 1.25
20 Rafael Palmeiro 87 .75 2.00

2001 Topps Archives Rookie Reprint Bat Relics

Inserted in series one packs at a rate of one in 1,356 and second series packs at a rate of one in 1,307 these six cards feature not only the rookie reprint but also a game used bat slice.

TARR1 Johnny Bench 10.00 25.00
TARR2 George Brett 20.00 50.00
TARR3 Fred Lynn 6.00 15.00
TARR4 Reggie Jackson 10.00 25.00
TARR5 Mike Schmidt 20.00 50.00
TARR6 Willie Stargell 10.00 25.00

2002 Topps Archives

This 200 card set was released in early April, 2002. These cards were issued in eight card packs which were issued in 20 pack boxes and were packed eight boxes to a case. The packs had an SRP of $4 per pack. This set was subtitled "Best Years" and it featured a reprint of the player's Topps card from their best year in the majors. Interestingly, Topps changed the backs of most of the cards to include the stats from that selected year. Also, in many of the cards, the text was changed to reflect the best year rather than using the original verbiage.

COMPLETE SET (200) 40.00 100.00
1 Willie Mays 62 2.00 5.00
2 Dale Murphy 83 .60 1.50
3 Dave Winfield 79 .40 1.00
4 Roger Maris 61 1.00 2.50
5 Ron Cey 77 .40 1.00
6 Lee Smith 91 .40 1.00
7 Len Dykstra 93 .40 1.00
8 Ray Fosse 70 .40 1.00
9 Warren Spahn 57 .60 1.50
10 Herb Score 56 .40 1.00
11 Jim Wynn 74 .40 1.00
12 Sam McDowell 70 .40 1.00
13 Fred Lynn 79 .40 1.00
14 Yogi Berra 54 1.00 2.50
15 Ron Santo 64 .60 1.50
16 Alvin Dark 53 .40 1.00
17 Bill Buckner 85 .40 1.00
18 Rollie Fingers 81 .40 1.00
19 Tony Gwynn 97 1.25 3.00
20 Red Schoendienst 53 .40 1.00
21 Gaylord Perry 72 .40 1.00
22 Jose Cruz 83 .40 1.00
23 Dennis Martinez 91 .40 1.00
24 Dave McNally 68 .40 1.00
25 Norm Cash 61 .40 1.00
26 Ted Kluszewski 54 UER .60 1.50
Card has Yogi Berra's stats on back
27 Rick Reuschel 77 .40 1.00
28 Bruce Sutter 77 .40 1.00
29 Don Larsen 56 .40 1.00
30 Claudell Washington 82 .40 1.00
31 Luis Aparicio 60 .40 1.00
32 Clete Boyer 62 .40 1.00
33 Goose Gossage 77 .40 1.00
34 Ray Knight 79 .40 1.00
35 Roy Campanella 53 1.00 2.50
36 Tug McGraw 71 .40 1.00
37 Bob Lemon 52 .40 1.00
38 Willie Stargell 71 .60 1.50
39 Roberto Clemente 66 2.00 5.00
40 Jim Fregosi 70 .40 1.00
41 Reggie Smith 77 .40 1.00
42 Dave Parker 78 .40 1.00
43 Darrell Evans 73 .40 1.00
44 Ryne Sandberg 90 1.50 4.00
45 Manny Mota 72 .40 1.00
46 Dennis Eckersley 92 .40 1.00
47 Nellie Fox 59 .60 1.50
48 Gil Hodges 54 1.00 2.50
49 Reggie Jackson 69 .60 1.50
50 Bobby Shantz 52 .40 1.00
51 Cecil Cooper 80 .40 1.00
52 Jim Kaat 66 .40 1.00
53 George Hendrick 80 .40 1.00
54 Johnny Podres 61 .40 1.00
55 Bob Gibson 68 .60 1.50
56 Vern Law 60 .40 1.00
57 Joe Adcock 56 .40 1.00
58 Jack Clark 87 .40 1.00
59 Bill Mazeroski 60 .60 1.50
60 Carl Yastrzemski 67 1.50 4.00
61 Bobby Murcer 71 .40 1.00
62 Davey Johnson 73 .40 1.00
63 Jim Palmer 75 .40 1.00
64 Roy Face 59 .40 1.00
65 Dean Chance 64 .40 1.00
66 Moose Skowron 60 .60 1.50
67 Dwight Evans 87 .60 1.50
68 Kirk Gibson 88 .40 1.00
69 Sal Bando 69 .40 1.00
70 Mike Schmidt 80 2.00 5.00
71 Bo Jackson 89 1.00 2.50
72 Chris Chambliss 76 .40 1.00
73 Fergie Jenkins 71 .40 1.00
74 Brooks Robinson 64 .60 1.50
75 Bobby Richardson 62 .40 1.00
76 Duke Snider 54 .60 1.50
77 Allie Reynolds 52 .60 1.50
78 Harmon Killebrew 66 1.00 2.50
79 Steve Carlton 72 .40 1.00
80 Bert Blyleven 73 .40 1.00
81 Phil Niekro 69 .40 1.00
82 Lew Burdette 56 .40 1.00
83 Hoyt Wilhelm 64 .40 1.00
84 Curt Flood 65 .40 1.00
85 Willie Hernandez 84 .40 1.00
86 Robin Yount 82 1.00 2.50
87 Robin Roberts 52 .40 1.00
88 Whitey Ford 61 .60 1.50
89 Tony Oliva 64 .60 1.50
90 Don Newcombe 56 .40 1.00
91 Al Oliver 82 .40 1.00
92 Mike Cuellar 69 .40 1.00
93 Mike Scott 86 .40 1.00
94 Dick Allen 66 .40 1.00
95 Jimmy Piersall 56 .40 1.00
96 Bill Freehan 68 .40 1.00
97 Willie Horton 65 .40 1.00
98 Bob Friend 60 .40 1.00
99 Ken Holtzman 73 .40 1.00
100 Rico Carty 70 .40 1.00
101 Gil McDougald 56 .40 1.00
102 Lee May 69 .40 1.00
103 Joe Pepitone 64 .40 1.00
104 Gene Tenace 75 .40 1.00
105 Gary Carter 85 .40 1.00
106 Tim McCarver 67 .40 1.00
107 Ernie Banks 58 1.00 2.50
108 George Foster 77 .40 1.00
109 Lou Brock 74 .60 1.50
110 Dick Groat 60 .40 1.00
111 Graig Nettles 77 .40 1.00
112 Boog Powell 69 .60 1.50
113 Joe Carter 86 .40 1.00
114 Juan Marichal 66 .40 1.00
115 Larry Doby 54 .40 1.00
116 Fernando Valenzuela 86 .40 1.00
117 Luis Tiant 68 .40 1.00
118 Early Wynn 59 .40 1.00
119 Bill Madlock 75 .40 1.00
120 Eddie Mathews 53 1.00 2.50
121 George Brett 80 2.00 5.00
122 Al Kaline 55 1.00 2.50
123 Frank Howard 69 .40 1.00
124 Mickey Lolich 71 .40 1.00
125 Kirby Puckett 88 1.00 2.50
126 Bob Cerv 58 .40 1.00
127 Will Clark 89 .60 1.50
128 Vida Blue 71 .40 1.00
129 Kevin Mitchell 89 .40 1.00
130 Bucky Dent 80 .40 1.00
131 Tom Seaver 69 .60 1.50
132 Jerry Koosman 76 .40 1.00
133 Orlando Cepeda 61 .40 1.00
134 Nolan Ryan 73 2.50 6.00
135 Tony Kubek 60 .60 1.50
136 Don Drysdale 62 .60 1.50
137 Paul Blair 69 .40 1.00
138 Elston Howard 63 .60 1.50
139 Joe Rudi 74 .40 1.00
140 Tommie Agee 70 .40 1.00
141 Richie Ashburn 58 .60 1.50
142 Jim Bunning 65 .60 1.50
143 Hank Sauer 52 .40 1.00
144 Greg Luzinski 77 .40 1.00
145 Ron Guidry 78 .40 1.00
146 Rod Carew 77 .60 1.50
147 Andre Dawson 87 .40 1.00
148 Keith Hernandez 79 .40 1.00
149 Carlton Fisk 77 .60 1.50
150 Cleon Jones 69 .40 1.00
151 Don Mattingly 85 2.00 5.00
152 Vada Pinson 63 .40 1.00
153 Ozzie Smith 87 1.50 4.00
154 Dave Concepcion 79 .40 1.00
155 Al Rosen 53 .40 1.00
156 Tommy John 68 .40 1.00
157 Bob Ojeda 86 .40 1.00
158 Frank Robinson 66 .60 1.50
159 Darryl Strawberry 87 .40 1.00
160 Bobby Bonds 73 .40 1.00
161 Bert Campaneris 70 .40 1.00
162 Catfish Hunter 74 .60 1.50
163 Bud Harrelson 70 .40 1.00
164 Dwight Gooden 85 .40 1.00
165 Wade Boggs 87 .60 1.50
166 Joe Morgan 76 .40 1.00
167 Ron Swoboda 67 .40 1.00
168 Hank Aaron 57 2.00 5.00
169 Steve Garvey 77 .40 1.00
170 Mickey Rivers 77 .40 1.00
171 Johnny Bench 70 1.00 2.50
172 Ralph Terry 62 .40 1.00
173 Billy Pierce 56 .40 1.00
174 Thurman Munson 76 1.00 2.50
175 Don Sutton 72 .40 1.00
176 Sparky Anderson 84 MG .40 1.00
177 Gil Hodges 69 MG 1.00 2.50
178 Davey Johnson 86 MG .40 1.00
179 Frank Robinson 89 MG .60 1.50
180 Red Schoendienst 67 MG .40 1.00
181 Roger Maris 61 AS 1.00 2.50
182 Willie Mays 62 AS 2.00 5.00
183 Luis Aparicio 60 AS .60 1.50
184 Nellie Fox 59 AS .60 1.50
185 Ernie Banks 58 AS 1.00 2.50
186 Orlando Cepeda 62 AS .40 1.00
187 Whitey Ford 61 AS .60 1.50
188 Bob Gibson 69 AS .60 1.50
189 Bill Mazeroski 59 AS .60 1.50
190 Hank Aaron 58 AS 2.00 5.00
191 1971 AL HR Leaders .40 1.00
Frank Howard
Harmon Killebrew
Carl Yastrzemski
192 1962 NL HR Leaders .60 1.50
Orlando Cepeda
Frank Robinson
Willie Mays
193 1967 NL RBI Leaders 1.00 2.50
Hank Aaron
Roberto Clemente
Dick Allen
194 1970 NL Win Leaders .40 1.00
Tom Seaver
Phil Niekro
Fergie Jenkins
Juan Marichal
195 1976 AL ERA Leaders .40 1.00
Jim Palmer
Catfish Hunter
Dennis Eckersley
196 Hank Aaron 76 HL 2.00 5.00
197 Brooks Robinson 78 HL .60 1.50
198 Tom Seaver 70 HL .60 1.50
199 Jim Palmer 71 HL .40 1.00
200 Lou Brock 75 HL .60 1.50

2002 Topps Archives Autographs

Issued at overall stated odds of one in 22 hobby packs and 1:22 retail packs, these 59 cards feature many of the players featured in the 2002 Topps Archives set. Since there were so many groups that the different players belong to 12 different groups. We have notated the group that these players belong to next to their name in our checklist.

GROUP A ODDS 1:19,803 HOB, 1:20,040 RET
GROUP B ODDS 1:12,872 HOB, 1:13,360 RET
GROUP C ODDS 1:11,193 HOB, 1:11,451 RET
GROUP D ODDS 1:8045 HOB, 1:8016 RET
GROUP E ODDS 1:753 HOB, 1:756 RET
GROUP F ODDS 1:3387 HOB, 1:3340 RET
GROUP G ODDS 1:1355 HOB, 1:1359 RET
GROUP H ODDS 1:1129 HOB, 1:1129 RET
GROUP I ODDS 1:847 HOB, 1:844 RET
GROUP J ODDS 1:59 HOB, 1:59 RET
GROUP K ODDS 1:748 HOB, 1:749 RET
GROUP L ODDS 1:45 HOB, 1:45 RET
TAAAD Alvin Dark 53 J 15.00 40.00
TAAAK Al Kaline 55 E 30.00 60.00
TAABB Bobby Bonds 73 J 20.00 50.00
TAABC Bert Campaneris 70 L 6.00 15.00
TAABD Bucky Dent 80 J 6.00 15.00
TAABH Bud Harrelson 70 L 10.00 25.00
TAABJ Bo Jackson 89 F
TAABP Billy Pierce 56 J 6.00 15.00
TAABS Bruce Sutter 77 J 15.00 40.00
TAACC Chris Chambliss 76 J 10.00 25.00
TAADA Dick Allen 66 J 15.00 40.00
TAADG Dwight Gooden 85 G
TAADM Dave McNally 68 L 20.00 50.00
TAADN Don Newcombe 56 I 10.00 25.00
TAADP Dave Parker 78 H 10.00 25.00
TAADS Duke Snider 54 E 60.00 120.00
TAADW Dave Winfield 79 D 40.00 80.00
TAAEB Ernie Banks 58 E 60.00 120.00
TAAFJ Fergie Jenkins 71 J 10.00 25.00
TAAFL Fred Lynn 79 J 6.00 15.00
TAAGB George Brett 80 E 150.00 250.00
TAAGC Gary Carter 85 E
TAAGF George Foster 77 L 6.00 15.00
TAAGH Willie Hernandez 84 L 6.00 15.00
TAAGL Greg Luzinski 77 J 6.00 15.00
TAAGP Gaylord Perry 72 J 10.00 25.00
TAAHA Hank Aaron 57 E 200.00 350.00
TAAHK Harmon Killebrew 69 E 40.00 80.00
TAAHW Hoyt Wilhelm 64 L 15.00 40.00
TAAJF Jim Fregosi 70 I 10.00 25.00
TAAJK Jim Kaat 66 J 10.00 25.00
TAAJP Jim Palmer 75 E 10.00 25.00
TAAJR Joe Rudi 74 J 6.00 15.00
TAAKH Keith Hernandez 79 J 10.00 25.00
TAAKM Kevin Mitchell 89 J 6.00 15.00
TAAKP Kirby Puckett 88 A 75.00 150.00
TAALB Lew Burdette 56 L 10.00 25.00
TAALD Len Dykstra 94 J 6.00 15.00
TAALS Lee Smith 91 H 6.00 15.00
TAAMR Mickey Rivers 77 L 6.00 15.00
TAAMS Mike Schmidt 80 B 60.00 120.00
TAARS Ron Santo 64 L 30.00 60.00
TAART Ralph Terry 62 J 10.00 25.00
TAARY Robin Yount 82 C 50.00 100.00
TAASB Sal Bando 69 L 6.00 15.00
TAASG Steve Garvey 77 J 10.00 25.00
TAATJ Tommy John 68 L 6.00 15.00
TAATO Tony Oliva 64 J 15.00 40.00
TAABPO Boog Powell 69 J 10.00 25.00
TAABRO B.Robinson 64 E 50.00 100.00
TAADEV Darrell Evans 73 J 6.00 15.00
TAADGR Dick Groat 60 L 10.00 25.00
TAAJBU Jim Bunning 65 L 15.00 40.00
TAAJCR Jose Cruz 83 K 6.00 15.00
TAAJKO Jerry Koosman 76 G
TAAJPI Jimmy Piersall 56 J 6.00 15.00
TAAJPO Johnny Podres 61 J 10.00 25.00
TAARCE Ron Cey 77 L 6.00 15.00
TAARSM Reggie Smith 77 L 10.00 15.00

2002 Topps Archives AutoProofs

Randomly inserted into 1:616 hobby packs and 1:617 retail packs, these 10 cards feature original Topps cards which were repurchased by Topps on the secondary market and then signed by the featured player. Since each player signed a different amount of cards, we have notated those stated print runs next to the players name in our checklist. Cards with a print run of 40 or fewer are not priced due to market scarcity.

GROUP A ODDS 1:128,720 H, 1:80,160 R
GROUP B ODDS 1:42,907 H, 1:40,080 R
GROUP C ODDS 1:17,163 H, 1:16,032 R
GROUP D ODDS 1:5254 H, 1:5344 R
GROUP E ODDS 1:8305 H, 1:8016 R
GROUP F ODDS 1:7151 H, 1:7287 R
GROUP G ODDS 1:6436 H, 1:6680 R
GROUP H ODDS 1:4597 H, 1:4453 R
GROUP I ODDS 1:3731 H, 1:3817 R
GROUP J ODDS 1:2258 H, 1:2290 R
NO PRICING ON QTY 16 OR LESS
1 Gary Carter 85 E/80 15.00 40.00
2 Jose Cruz 83 F/95 15.00 40.00
3 Steve Garvey 77 A/5
4 Bo Jackson 89 J/300 30.00 60.00
5 Kevin Mitchell 89 D/65 15.00 40.00
6 Kirby Puckett 88 D/65 60.00 120.00
7 Mike Schmidt 80 H/147 60.00 120.00
8 Ozzie Smith 87 G/105 50.00 100.00
9 Darryl Strawberry 87 I/181 15.00 40.00
10 Dave Winfield 79 B/16
11 Robin Yount 82 C/39 75.00 150.00

2002 Topps Archives Bat Relics

Randomly inserted into hobby and retail packs, these 19 cards feature players from the Archives set along with a game bat piece. Players in group A were inserted at stated odds of one in 106 while players in group B were inserted at stated odds of one in 282. We have notated what group each player is part of in our checklist.

GROUP A ODDS 1:106 HOB/RET
GROUP B ODDS 1:282 HOB/RET
TBRAD Andre Dawson 87 A 6.00 15.00
TBRBF Bill Freehan 68 A 6.00 15.00
TBRBR Brooks Robinson 64 A 8.00 20.00
TBRCY Carl Yastrzemski 67 B 15.00 40.00
TBRDE Dwight Evans 87 A 8.00 20.00
TBRDM Don Mattingly 85 A 15.00 40.00
TBRDP Dave Parker 78 A 6.00 15.00
TBRGB George Brett 80 A 15.00 40.00
TBRGC Gary Carter 85 A 6.00 15.00
TBRJB Johnny Bench 70 A 10.00 25.00
TBRJC Joe Carter 86 A 6.00 15.00
TBRJM Joe Morgan 76 B 6.00 15.00
TBRNC Norm Cash 61 A 6.00 15.00
TBRRJ Reggie Jackson 69 A 8.00 20.00
TBRRM Roger Maris 61 A 30.00 60.00
TBRRS Ron Santo 64 A 8.00 20.00
TBRRY Robin Yount 82 B 10.00 25.00
TBRWH Willie Horton 65 A 6.00 15.00
TBRWS Willie Stargell 71 A 8.00 20.00

2002 Topps Archives Reprints

Issued at a stated rate of five per sealed 2002 Topps Factory set, these 10 cards feature reprints of first Topps cards of some of the leading superstars in baseball.

COMPLETE SET (10) 10.00 25.00
1 Alex Rodriguez 98 1.25 3.00
2 Jason Giambi 94 .75 2.00
3 Pedro Martinez 93 .75 2.00
4 Ichiro Suzuki 01 1.50 4.00
5 Jeff Bagwell 91 .75 2.00
6 Ivan Rodriguez 91 .75 2.00
7 Mike Piazza 93 1.25 3.00
8 Nomar Garciaparra 95 1.25 3.00
9 Ken Griffey Jr. 89 1.25 3.00
10 Albert Pujols 01 1.50 4.00

2002 Topps Archives Seat Relics

Randomly inserted into hobby and retail packs, these 19 cards feature a player from the Archives set along with a piece of a seat from a ballpark they played in. There were three different groups of players and they were inserted at odds ranging from one in 80 packs to one in 1636 packs.

GROUP A ODDS 1:1629 HOB, 1:1636 RET
GROUP B ODDS 1:80 HOB, 1:80 RET
GROUP C ODDS 1:1160 HOB, 1:1162 RET
TSRBL Bob Lemon 52 B 6.00 15.00
TSRDP Dave Parker 78 B 6.00 15.00
TSRDS Duke Snider 54 B 8.00 20.00
TSREB Ernie Banks 58 B 10.00 25.00
TSREM Eddie Mathews 53 B 10.00 25.00
TSRHS Herb Score 56 B 6.00 15.00
TSRJB Jim Bunning 65 B 6.00 15.00
TSRJC Joe Carter 86 B 6.00 15.00
TSRJP Jim Palmer 75 B 6.00 15.00
TSRML Mickey Lolich 71 B 6.00 15.00
TSRNF Nellie Fox 59 B 8.00 20.00
TSRRA Richie Ashburn 58 B 8.00 20.00
TSRRC Rod Carew 77 B 8.00 20.00
TSRRG Ron Guidry 78 C 8.00 20.00
TSRSA Sparky Anderson 84 B 6.00 15.00
TSRSM Sam McDowell 70 B UER 6.00 15.00
Almost all of his major league seasons are listed as 1964
TSRTK Ted Kluszewski 54 B 8.00 20.00
TSRWS Warren Spahn 57 B 10.00 25.00
TSRYB Yogi Berra 54 B 15.00 40.00

2002 Topps Archives Uniform Relics

Inserted into hobby and retail packs at stated odds of one in 28, these 20 cards feature players from the Archives set along with a game-worn uniform swatch of that player.

TURBB Bobby Bonds 73 6.00 15.00
TURDC Dave Concepcion 79 6.00 15.00
TURDE Dennis Eckersley 92 6.00 15.00
TURDM Dale Murphy 83 8.00 20.00
TURDS Don Sutton 72 6.00 15.00
TURDW Dave Winfield 79 6.00 15.00
TURFL Fred Lynn 79 6.00 15.00
TURFR Frank Robinson 66 8.00 20.00
TURGB George Brett 80 15.00 40.00
TURGP Gaylord Perry 72 6.00 15.00
TURKP Kirby Puckett 88 10.00 25.00
TURNR Nolan Ryan 73 20.00 50.00
TUROC Orlando Cepeda 61 6.00 15.00
TUROS Ozzie Smith 87 10.00 25.00
TURPN Phil Niekro 69 6.00 15.00
TURRS Ryne Sandberg 90 15.00 40.00
TURSA Sparky Anderson 84 6.00 15.00
TURSG Steve Garvey 77 6.00 15.00
TURWB Wade Boggs 87 8.00 20.00
TURWC Will Clark 89 8.00 20.00

2001 Topps Archives Reserve

This 100 card set was issued in five card packs. These five card packs were issued in special display boxes which included one signed baseball per sealed box. These sealed boxes were issued six boxes to a case. The boxes (ball plus packs) had an SRP of $100 per box. All cards have a chrome-like finish to them.

COMPLETE SET (100) 50.00 100.00
1 Joe Adcock 52 .60 1.50
2 Brooks Robinson 57 1.00 2.50

3 Luis Aparicio 56 .60 1.50
4 Richie Ashburn 52 1.00 2.50
5 Hank Bauer 52 .60 1.50
6 Johnny Bench 68 2.50 6.00
7 Wade Boggs 83 1.00 2.50
8 Moose Skowron 54 .60 1.50
9 George Brett 75 4.00 10.00
10 Lou Brock 62 1.00 2.50
11 Roy Campanella 52 1.50 4.00
12 Willie Hernandez 78 .60 1.50
13 Steve Carlton 65 2.00 5.00
14 Gary Carter 75 1.00 2.50
15 Hoyt Wilhelm 52 1.00 2.50
16 Orlando Cepeda 58 .60 1.50
17 Roberto Clemente 55 4.00 8.00
18 Dale Murphy 77 1.00 2.50
19 Dave Concepcion 71 .60 1.50
20 Dom DiMaggio 52 .60 1.50
21 Larry Doby 52 .60 1.50
22 Don Drysdale 57 1.00 2.50
23 Dennis Eckersley 76 .60 1.50
24 Bob Feller 52 .60 1.50
25 Rollie Fingers 69 .60 1.50
26 Carlton Fisk 72 1.00 2.50
27 Nellie Fox 56 1.00 2.50
28 Mickey Rivers 72 .60 1.50
29 Tommy John 64 .60 1.50
30 Johnny Sain 52 .60 1.50
31 Keith Hernandez 75 .60 1.50
32 Gil Hodges 52 1.50 4.00
33 Elston Howard 56 1.00 2.50
34 Frank Howard 60 .60 1.50
35 Bob Gibson 59 1.00 2.50
36 Fergie Jenkins 66 .60 1.50
37 Jackie Jensen 52 .60 1.50
38 Al Kaline 54 1.50 4.00
39 Harmon Killebrew 55 1.50 4.00
40 Ralph Kiner 53 .60 1.50
41 Dick Groat 52 .60 1.50
42 Don Larsen 56 .60 1.50
43 Ralph Branca 52 .60 1.50
44 Mickey Lolich 64 .60 1.50
45 Juan Marichal 61 .60 1.50
46 Roger Maris 58 1.50 4.00
47 Bobby Thomson 52 1.00 2.50
48 Eddie Mathews 52 1.50 4.00
49 Don Mattingly 84 4.00 10.00
50 Willie McCovey 60 .60 1.50
51 Gil McDougald 52 .60 1.50
52 Tug McGraw 65 .60 1.50
53 Billy Pierce 52 .60 1.50
54 Minnie Minoso 52 .60 1.50
55 Johnny Mize 52 1.00 2.50
56 Roy Face 53 .60 1.50
57 Joe Morgan 65 .60 1.50
58 Thurman Munson 70 1.50 4.00
59 Stan Musial 58 2.00 5.00
60 Phil Niekro 64 .60 1.50
61 Paul Blair 65 .60 1.50
62 Andy Pafko 52 1.00 2.50
63 Satchel Paige 53 1.50 4.00
64 Tony Perez 65 .60 1.50
65 Sal Bando 67 .60 1.50
66 Jimmy Piersall 56 .60 1.50
67 Kirby Puckett 85 1.50 4.00
68 Phil Rizzuto 52 1.50 4.00
69 Robin Roberts 52 .60 1.50
70 Jackie Robinson 52 1.50 4.00
71 Ryne Sandberg 83 6.00 12.00
72 Mike Schmidt 73 4.00 10.00
73 Red Schoendienst 52 .60 1.50
74 Herb Score 56 .60 1.50
75 Enos Slaughter 52 .60 1.50
76 Ozzie Smith 80 3.00 8.00
77 Warren Spahn 52 1.00 2.50
78 Don Sutton 66 .60 1.50
79 Luis Tiant 65 .60 1.50
80 Ted Kluszewski 52 1.00 2.50
81 Whitey Ford 53 1.00 2.50
82 Maury Wills 60 .60 1.50
83 Dave Winfield 74 .60 1.50
84 Early Wynn 52 .60 1.50
85 Carl Yastrzemski 60 2.00 5.00
86 Robin Yount 75 1.50 4.00
87 Bob Allison 59 .60 1.50
88 Clete Boyer 57 .60 1.50
89 Reggie Jackson 69 1.00 2.50
90 Yogi Berra 52 1.50 4.00
91 Willie Mays 52 4.00 8.00
92 Jim Palmer 66 .60 1.50
93 Pee Wee Reese 52 1.50 4.00
94 Frank Robinson 57 1.00 2.50
95 Boog Powell 62 1.00 2.50
96 Willie Stargell 63 1.00 2.50
97 Nolan Ryan 68 UER 4.00 10.00
Sensational spelled incorrectly
98 Tom Seaver 67 2.50 6.00
99 Duke Snider 52 1.00 2.50
100 Bill Mazeroski 57 1.50 4.00

2001 Topps Archives Reserve Autographed Baseballs

Issued one per sealed box, these 30 players signed baseballs for inclusion in this product. Each player signed an amount of ball between 100 and 1000 and we have included that information next to the player's name.

1 Johnny Bench/100 50.00 100.00
2 Paul Blair/1000 10.00 25.00
3 Clete Boyer/1000 10.00 25.00
4 Ralph Branca/400 15.00 40.00
5 Roy Face/1000 15.00 40.00
6 Bob Feller/1000 15.00 40.00
7 Whitey Ford/100 40.00 80.00
8 Bob Gibson/1000 20.00 50.00
9 Dick Groat/1000 15.00 40.00
10 Frank Howard/1000 10.00 25.00
11 Reggie Jackson/100 50.00 100.00
12 Don Larsen/100 15.00 40.00
13 Mickey Lolich/500 10.00 25.00
14 Willie Mays/100 125.00 200.00
15 Gil McDougald/500 15.00 40.00
16 Tug McGraw/1000 20.00 50.00
17 Minnie Minoso/1000 15.00 40.00
18 Andy Pafko/500 15.00 40.00
19 Joe Pepitone/1000 10.00 25.00
20 Robin Roberts/1000 20.00 50.00
21 Frank Robinson/100 30.00 60.00
22 Nolan Ryan/100 75.00 150.00
23 Herb Score/500 10.00 25.00
24 Tom Seaver/100 50.00 100.00
25 Moose Skowron/1000 15.00 40.00
26 Warren Spahn/100 50.00 100.00
27 Bobby Thomson/400 15.00 40.00
28 Luis Tiant/500 10.00 25.00
29 Carl Yastrzemski/100 75.00 150.00
30 Maury Wills/1000 10.00 25.00

2001 Topps Archives Reserve Future Rookie Reprints

Issued five per Topps Limited factory set, these 20 cards are reprints of the featured players rookie card.

COMPLETE SET (20) 60.00 120.00
1 Barry Bonds 87 6.00 15.00
2 Chipper Jones 91 2.50 6.00
3 Cal Ripken 82 10.00 25.00
4 Shawn Green 92 1.00 2.50
5 Frank Thomas 90 2.50 6.00
6 Derek Jeter 93 8.00 20.00
7 Geoff Jenkins 96 1.00 2.50
8 Jim Edmonds 93 1.00 2.50
9 Bernie Williams 90 1.50 4.00
10 Sammy Sosa 90 2.50 6.00
11 Rickey Henderson 80 2.50 6.00
12 Tony Gwynn 83 3.00 8.00
13 Randy Johnson 89 2.50 6.00
14 Juan Gonzalez 90 1.00 2.50
15 Gary Sheffield 89 1.00 2.50
16 Manny Ramirez 92 1.50 4.00
17 Pokey Reese 92 1.00 2.50
18 Preston Wilson 93 1.00 2.50
19 Jay Payton 95 1.00 2.50
20 Rafael Palmeiro 87 1.50 4.00

2001 Topps Archives Reserve Rookie Reprint Autographs

Inserted one per 10 packs, these 27 cards feature autographs of the players rookie reprint card. Each player signed a different amount of cards and those are notated by groups A, B or C in our checklist. Cards 15, 20, 22, 24, 28, 30, 31, and 35 do not exist. Willie Mays did not return his cards in time for inclusion in the packout. Those cards could be redeemed until July 31, 2003.

ARA1 Willie Mays C 125.00 200.00
ARA2 Whitey Ford B 30.00 60.00
ARA3 Nolan Ryan A UER 125.00 200.00
The word sensational is incorrectly spelled
ARA4 Carl Yastrzemski B 50.00 100.00
ARA5 Frank Robinson B 20.00 50.00
ARA6 Tom Seaver A 30.00 60.00
ARA7 Warren Spahn A 50.00 100.00
ARA8 Johnny Bench A 60.00 120.00
ARA9 Reggie Jackson A 60.00 120.00
ARA10 Bob Gibson B 20.00 50.00
ARA11 Bob Feller D 8.00 20.00
ARA12 Gil McDougald A 10.00 25.00
ARA13 Luis Tiant A 8.00 20.00
ARA14 Minnie Minoso D 8.00 20.00
ARA16 Herb Score B 8.00 20.00
ARA17 Moose Skowron C 10.00 25.00
ARA18 Maury Wills D 8.00 20.00
ARA19 Clete Boyer A 8.00 20.00
ARA21 Don Larsen A 8.00 20.00
ARA23 Tug McGraw C 15.00 40.00
ARA25 Robin Roberts C 12.50 30.00
ARA26 Frank Howard A 8.00 20.00
ARA27 Mickey Lolich D 8.00 20.00
ARA29 Tommy John C 8.00 20.00
ARA32 Dick Groat D 10.00 25.00
ARA33 Roy Face D 8.00 20.00
ARA34 Paul Blair D 6.00 15.00

2001 Topps Archives Reserve Rookie Reprint Relics

Issued at a rate of one in 10 packs, these 51 cards feature not only a rookie reprint of the featured player but also a memorabilia piece relating to their career.

ARR1 B.Robinson Jsy 10.00 25.00
ARR2 Tony Conigliaro Jsy 15.00 40.00
ARR3 Frank Howard Jsy 6.00 15.00
ARR4 Don Sutton Jsy 6.00 15.00

ARR5 F.Jenkins Jsy 6.00 15.00
ARR6 Frank Robinson Jsy 10.00 25.00
ARR7 Don Mattingly Jsy 15.00 40.00
ARR8 Willie Stargell Jsy 10.00 25.00
ARR9 Moose Skowron Jsy 10.00 25.00
ARR10 Fred Lynn Jsy 6.00 15.00
ARR11 George Brett Jsy 15.00 40.00
ARR12 Nolan Ryan Jsy 20.00 50.00
ARR13 O.Cepeda Jsy 6.00 15.00
ARR14 R.Jackson Jsy 10.00 25.00
ARR15 Steve Carlton Jsy 10.00 25.00
ARR16 Tom Seaver Jsy 10.00 25.00
ARR17 T. Munson Jsy 15.00 40.00
ARR18 Yogi Berra Jsy 10.00 25.00
ARR19 W. McCovey Jsy 6.00 15.00
ARR20 Robin Yount Jsy 10.00 25.00
ARR21 Al Kaline Bat 10.00 25.00
ARR22 C. Yastrzemski Bat 15.00 40.00
ARR23 Carlton Fisk Bat 10.00 25.00
ARR24 Dale Murphy Bat 10.00 25.00
ARR25 Dave Winfield Bat 6.00 15.00
ARR26 Dick Groat Bat 6.00 15.00
ARR27 Dom DiMaggio Bat 10.00 25.00
ARR28 Don Mattingly Bat 15.00 40.00
ARR29 Gary Carter Bat 6.00 15.00
ARR30 George Kell Bat 10.00 25.00
ARR31 H. Killebrew Bat 10.00 25.00
ARR32 Jackie Jensen Bat 10.00 25.00
ARR33 J. Robinson Bat 40.00 80.00
ARR34 Jim Piersall Bat 6.00 15.00
ARR35 Joe Adcock Bat 6.00 15.00
ARR36 Joe Carter Bat 6.00 15.00
ARR37 Johnny Mize Bat 10.00 25.00
ARR38 Kirk Gibson Bat 6.00 15.00
ARR39 Mickey Vernon Bat 6.00 15.00
ARR40 Mike Schmidt Bat 15.00 40.00
ARR41 R. Sandberg Bat 15.00 40.00
ARR42 Ozzie Smith Bat 10.00 25.00
ARR43 T.Kluszewski Bat 10.00 25.00
ARR44 Wade Boggs Bat 10.00 25.00
ARR45 Willie Mays Bat 40.00 80.00
ARR46 Duke Snider Bat 10.00 25.00
ARR47 Harvey Kuenn Bat 6.00 15.00
ARR48 Robin Yount Bat 10.00 25.00
ARR49 R.Schoendienst Bat 6.00 15.00
ARR50 Elston Howard Bat 10.00 25.00
ARR51 Bob Allison Bat 6.00 15.00

2002 Topps Archives Reserve

This 100 card set was released in June, 2002. This 100 card set was issued in four card packs which came 10 packs to a box and four boxes to a case. Each box also contined an autographed baseball.

COMPLETE SET (100) 75.00 150.00
1 Lee Smith 91 .60 1.50
2 Gaylord Perry 72 .60 1.50
3 Al Oliver 82 .60 1.50
4 Goose Gossage 77 .60 1.50
5 Bill Madlock 75 .60 1.50
6 Rod Carew 77 1.00 2.50
7 Fred Lynn 79 .60 1.50
8 Frank Robinson 66 1.00 2.50
9 Al Kaline 55 1.50 4.00
10 Len Dykstra 93 .60 1.50
11 Carlton Fisk 77 1.00 2.50
12 Nellie Fox 59 1.00 2.50
13 Reggie Jackson 69 1.00 2.50
14 Bob Gibson 68 1.00 2.50
15 Bill Buckner 85 .60 1.50
16 Harmon Killebrew 69 1.50 4.00
17 Gary Carter 85 .60 1.50
18 Dave Winfield 79 .60 1.50
19 Ozzie Smith 87 2.50 6.00
20 Dwight Evans 87 1.00 2.50
21 Dave Concepcion 79 .60 1.50
22 Joe Morgan 76 .60 1.50
23 Clete Boyer 62 .60 1.50
24 Will Clark 89 1.00 2.50
25 Lee May 69 .60 1.50
26 Kevin Mitchell 89 .60 1.50
27 Roger Maris 61 1.50 4.00
28 Mickey Lolich 71 .60 1.50
29 Luis Aparicio 60 .60 1.50
30 George Foster 77 .60 1.50
31 Don Mattingly 85 3.00 8.00
32 Fernando Valenzuela 86 .60 1.50
33 Bobby Bonds 73 .60 1.50
34 Jim Palmer 75 .60 1.50
35 Dennis Eckersley 92 .60 1.50
36 Kirby Puckett 88 1.50 4.00
37 Jose Cruz 83 .60 1.50
38 Richie Ashburn 58 1.00 2.50
39 Whitey Ford 61 1.00 2.50
40 Robin Roberts 52 .60 1.50
41 Don Newcombe 56 .60 1.50
42 Roy Campanella 53 1.50 4.00
43 Dennis Martinez 91 .60 1.50
44 Larry Doby 54 .60 1.50
45 Steve Garvey 77 .60 1.50
46 Thurman Munson 76 1.50 4.00
47 Dale Murphy 83 1.00 2.50
48 Moose Skowron 60 1.00 2.50
49 Tom Seaver 69 1.00 2.50
50 Orlando Cepeda 61 .60 1.50
51 Graig Nettles 77 .60 1.50
52 Willie Stargell 71 1.00 2.50
53 Yogi Berra 54 1.50 4.00
54 Steve Carlton 72 .60 1.50
55 Don Sutton 72 .60 1.50
56 Brooks Robinson 64 1.00 2.50
57 Vida Blue 71 .60 1.50
58 Rollie Fingers 81 .60 1.50
59 Jim Bunning 65 .60 1.50
60 Nolan Ryan 73 4.00 10.00
61 Hank Aaron 57 3.00 8.00
62 Fergie Jenkins 71 .60 1.50
63 Andre Dawson 87 .60 1.50
64 Ernie Banks 58 1.50 4.00
65 Early Wynn 59 .60 1.50
66 Duke Snider 54 1.00 2.50
67 Red Schoendienst 53 .60 1.50
68 Don Drysdale 62 1.00 2.50
69 Catfish Hunter 74 1.00 2.50
70 George Brett 80 3.00 8.00
71 Elston Howard 63 1.00 2.50
72 Wade Boggs 87 1.00 2.50
73 Keith Hernandez 79 .60 1.50
74 Billy Pierce 56 .60 1.50
75 Ted Kluszewski 54 1.00 2.50
76 Carl Yastrzemski 67 2.50 6.00
77 Bert Blyleven 73 .60 1.50
78 Tony Oliva 64 .60 1.50
79 Joe Carter 86 .60 1.50
80 Johnny Bench 70 1.50 4.00
81 Tony Gwynn 97 2.00 5.00
82 Mike Schmidt 80 3.00 8.00
83 Phil Niekro 69 .60 1.50
84 Juan Marichal 66 .60 1.50
85 Eddie Mathews 53 1.50 4.00
86 Boog Powell 69 1.00 2.50
87 Dwight Gooden 85 .60 1.50
88 Darryl Strawberry 87 .60 1.50
89 Roberto Clemente 66 4.00 10.00
90 Ryne Sandberg 90 3.00 8.00
91 Jack Clark 87 .60 1.50
92 Willie Mays 62 3.00 8.00
93 Ron Guidry 78 .60 1.50
94 Kirk Gibson 88 .60 1.50
95 Lou Brock 74 1.00 2.50
96 Robin Yount 82 1.50 4.00
97 Bill Mazeroski 60 1.00 2.50
98 Dave Parker 78 .60 1.50
99 Hoyt Wilhelm 64 .60 1.50
100 Warren Spahn 57 1.00 2.50

2002 Topps Archives Reserve Autographed Baseballs

Inserted one per Archives Reserve box, these 21 autographed baseballs feature authentic signatures from some of baseball's best all-time players. Since the players signed a different amount of cards, we have notated that information next to their name in our checklist.

1 Luis Aparicio/1600 10.00 25.00
2 Ernie Banks/50
3 Yogi Berra/100 60.00 120.00
4 Lou Brock/400 20.00 50.00
5 Jim Bunning/500 30.00 60.00
6 Gary Carter/500 12.50 30.00
7 Goose Gossage/500 12.50 30.00
8 Fergie Jenkins/1000 10.00 25.00
9 Al Kaline/250 50.00 100.00
10 Harmon Killebrew/250 60.00 120.00
11 Willie Mays/50
12 Joe Morgan/250 20.00 50.00
13 Graig Nettles/1600 10.00 25.00
14 Jim Palmer/400 12.50 30.00
15 Gaylord Perry/500 12.50 30.00
16 Brooks Robinson/500 20.00 50.00
17 Mike Schmidt/250 60.00 120.00
18 Duke Snider/100 50.00 100.00
19 Dave Winfield/1650 15.00 40.00
20 Robin Yount/250 50.00 100.00

2002 Topps Archives Reserve Autographs

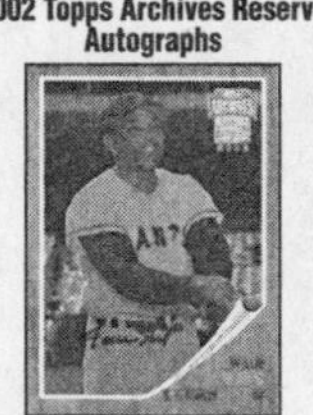

Inserted at overall stated odds of one in 15 hobby and one in 203 retail, these 17 cards feature the players signed the Archives reserve "reprint" of their key year card. Since the players all signed at a different rate based on their "group", we have listed their group affiliation next to their name in our checklist.

GROUP A ODDS 1:1077 RET
GROUP B ODDS 1:1421 RET
GROUP C ODDS 1:947 RET
GROUP D ODDS 1:1421 RET
GROUP E ODDS 1:718 RET
TRAAK Al Kaline 55 C 30.00 60.00
TRABR Brooks Robinson 64 B 12.50 30.00
TRADS Duke Snider 54 A 40.00 80.00
TRAEB Ernie Banks 58 A 50.00 100.00
TRAFJ Fergie Jenkins 71 E 6.00 15.00
TRAGC Gary Carter 85 B 12.50 30.00
TRAGN Graig Nettles 77 D 6.00 15.00
TRAGP Gaylord Perry 72 C 8.00 20.00
TRAHK H.Killebrew 69 C 40.00 80.00
TRAJM Joe Morgan 76 B 12.50 30.00
TRALA Luis Aparicio 60 D 8.00 20.00
TRALB Lou Brock 74 B 12.50 30.00
TRALS Lee Smith 91 E 6.00 15.00
TRAMS Mike Schmidt 80 A 60.00 120.00
TRARY Robin Yount 82 A 60.00 120.00
TRAWM Willie Mays 62 A 75.00 150.00
TRAYR Yogi Berra 54 A 60.00 120.00

2002 Topps Archives Reserve Bat Relics

Inserted at stated odds of one in 22 hobby packs, these 10 cards feature not only the player's "best card" but also a game-used bat piece from each player. The players belonged to different groups in terms of scarcity and we have put that information next to their name in our checklist.

TRRCF Carlton Fisk 77 B 6.00 15.00
TRRDW Dave Winfield 79 C 6.00 15.00
TRROC Orlando Cepeda 61 B 6.00 15.00
TRRRM Roger Maris 61 A 50.00 100.00
TRRTM Thurman Munson 76 B 15.00 40.00
TRRCY Carl Yastrzemski 67 B 15.00 40.00
TRRDM Don Mattingly 85 B 10.00 25.00
TRREM Eddie Mathews 53 B 8.00 20.00
TRRGB George Brett 80 B 10.00 25.00
TRRHA Hank Aaron 57 B 20.00 50.00

2002 Topps Archives Reserve Uniform Relics

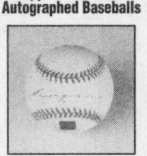

Inserted at stated odds of one in seven hobby packs, these 15 cards feature not only the player's "best card" but also a game-used bat piece from each player. The players belonged to different groups in terms of scarcity and we have put that information next to their name in our checklist.

BR Brooks Robinson 64 Uni D 6.00 15.00
EB Ernie Banks 58 Uni C 10.00 25.00
GC Gary Carter 85 Jsy C 8.00 20.00
JB Johnny Bench 70 Uni D 6.00 15.00
JM Juan Marichal 66 Jsy A 8.00 20.00
KP Kirby Puckett 88 Jsy D 6.00 15.00
NF Nellie Fox 59 Uni C 8.00 20.00
NR Nolan Ryan 73 Jsy D 15.00 40.00
RS Red Schoendienst 53 Jsy B 6.00 15.00
RY Robin Yount 82 Uni D 6.00 15.00
TG Tony Gwynn 97 Jsy D 6.00 15.00
WB Wade Boggs 87 Jsy D 6.00 15.00
WC Will Clark 89 Jsy C 8.00 20.00
WM Willie Mays 62 Uni C 20.00 50.00
WS Willie Stargell 71 Uni D 6.00 15.00

2009 Topps Attax

COMPLETE SET (220) 12.50 30.00
COMMON CARD .10 .25
1 Bobby Abreu .10 .25
2 Garret Anderson .10 .25
3 Rick Ankiel .10 .25
4 Mike Aviles .10 .25
5 Rocco Baldelli .10 .25
6 Jason Bay .15 .40
7 Josh Beckett .15 .40
8 Erik Bedard .10 .25
9 Ronnie Belliard .10 .25
10 Carlos Beltran .10 .25
11 Adrian Beltre .10 .25
12 Yuniesky Betancourt .10 .25
13 Chad Billingsley .10 .25
14 Casey Blake .10 .25
15 Hank Blalock .10 .25
16 Milton Bradley .10 .25
17 Ryan Braun .30 .75
18 Mark Buehrle .15 .40
19 A.J. Burnett .15 .40
20 Pat Burrell .10 .25
21 Billy Butler .10 .25
22 Eric Byrnes .10 .25
23 Orlando Cabrera .10 .25
24 Daniel Cabrera .10 .25
25 Mike Cameron .10 .25
26 Jorge Cantu .10 .25
27 Fausto Carmona .10 .25
28 Joba Chamberlain .15 .40
29 Eric Chavez .10 .25
30 Ryan Church .10 .25
31 Carl Crawford .15 .40
32 Joe Crede .15 .40
33 Bobby Crosby .10 .25
34 Johnny Cueto .10 .25
35 Johnny Damon .15 .40
36 Chris Davis .10 .25
37 David DeJesus .10 .25
38 Carlos Delgado .10 .25
39 Ryan Dempster .10 .25
40 Mark DeRosa .15 .40
41 Matt Diaz .10 .25
42 Ryan Doumit .10 .25
43 Stephen Drew .10 .25
44 J.D. Drew .10 .25
45 Adam Dunn .15 .40
46 Jermaine Dye .10 .25
47 Jim Edmonds .15 .40
48 Jacoby Ellsbury .25 .60
49 Edwin Encarnacion .10 .25
50 Yunel Escobar .10 .25
51 Andre Ethier .15 .40
52 Pedro Feliz .10 .25
53 Chone Figgins .10 .25
54 Jeff Francoeur .15 .40
55 Kosuke Fukudome .25 .60
56 Rafael Furcal .10 .25
57 Ryan Garko .10 .25
58 Jon Garland .10 .25
59 Matt Garza .10 .25
60 Jason Giambi .10 .25
61 Brian Giles .10 .25
62 Troy Glaus .10 .25
63 Carlos Gomez .10 .25
64 Adrian Gonzalez .15 .40
65 Curtis Granderson .15 .40
66 Ken Griffey Jr. .40 1.00
67 Vladimir Guerrero .25 .60
68 Carlos Guillen .10 .25
69 Jose Guillen .10 .25
70 Cristian Guzman .10 .25
71 Travis Hafner .10 .25
72 Bill Hall .10 .25
73 Cole Hamels .25 .60
74 Rich Harden .10 .25
75 J.J. Hardy .10 .25
76 Dan Haren .10 .25
77 Brendan Harris .10 .25
78 Corey Hart .10 .25
79 Brad Hawpe .10 .25
80 Todd Helton .15 .40
81 Jeremy Hermida .10 .25
82 Ramon Hernandez .10 .25
83 Felix Hernandez .25 .60
84 Trevor Hoffman .15 .40
85 Orlando Hudson .10 .25
86 Tim Hudson .15 .40
87 Aubrey Huff .10 .25
88 Torii Hunter .10 .25
89 Chris Iannetta .10 .25
90 Raul Ibanez .15 .40
91 Akinori Iwamura .10 .25
92 Conor Jackson .10 .25
93 Bobby Jenks .10 .25
94 Derek Jeter .60 1.50
95 Ubaldo Jimenez .15 .40
96 Kenji Johjima .15 .40
97 Kelly Johnson .10 .25
98 Randy Johnson .15 .40
99 Adam Jones .15 .40
100 Scott Kazmir .10 .25
101 Matt Kemp .15 .40
102 Howie Kendrick .10 .25
103 Jeff Kent .10 .25
104 Clayton Kershaw .25 .60
105 Ian Kinsler .15 .40
106 Paul Konerko .15 .40
107 Casey Kotchman .10 .25
108 Kevin Kouzmanoff .10 .25
109 Hiroki Kuroda .10 .25
110 Adam LaRoche .10 .25
111 Derrek Lee .10 .25
112 Carlos Lee .10 .25
113 Jon Lester .25 .60
114 Fred Lewis .10 .25
115 Brad Lidge .10 .25
116 Francisco Liriano .10 .25
117 James Loney .15 .40
118 Jose Lopez .10 .25
119 Derek Lowe .10 .25
120 Mike Lowell .10 .25
121 Jed Lowrie .15 .40
122 Ryan Ludwick .15 .40
123 John Maine .10 .25
124 Victor Martinez .15 .40
125 Pedro Martinez .15 .40
126 Justin Masterson .10 .25
127 Kaz Matsui .10 .25
128 Hideki Matsui .25 .60
129 Gary Matthews .10 .25
130 Joe Mauer .25 .60
131 Cameron Maybin .10 .25
132 Brian McCann .15 .40
133 Lastings Milledge .10 .25
134 Bengie Molina .10 .25
135 Yadier Molina .15 .40
136 Melvin Mora .10 .25
137 David Murphy .10 .25
138 Brett Myers .10 .25
139 Xavier Nady .10 .25
140 Joe Nathan .10 .25
141 Magglio Ordonez .15 .40
142 David Ortiz .15 .40
143 Roy Oswalt .15 .40
144 Lyle Overbay .10 .25
145 Jonathan Papelbon .15 .40
146 Dustin Pedroia .30 .75
147 Mike Pelfrey .10 .25
148 Carlos Pena .15 .40
149 Hunter Pence .15 .40
150 Jhonny Peralta .10 .25
151 Andy Pettitte .15 .40
152 Brandon Phillips .10 .25
153 Juan Pierre .10 .25
154 A.J. Pierzynski .10 .25
155 Placido Polanco .10 .25
156 Jorge Posada .15 .40
157 David Price .25 .60
158 J.J. Putz .10 .25
159 Aramis Ramirez .10 .25
160 Manny Ramirez .25 .60
161 Edgar Renteria .10 .25
162 Jose Reyes .15 .40
163 Mark Reynolds .10 .25
164 Alex Rios .15 .40
165 Mariano Rivera .25 .60
166 Brian Roberts .10 .25
167 Francisco Rodriguez .15 .40
168 Ivan Rodriguez .15 .40
169 Scott Rolen .15 .40
170 Jimmy Rollins .15 .40
171 Aaron Rowand .10 .25
172 CC Sabathia .15 .40
173 Jarrod Saltalamacchia .10 .25
174 Jeff Samardzija .15 .40
175 Freddy Sanchez .10 .25
176 Max Scherzer .15 .40
177 Brian Schneider .10 .25
178 Luke Scott .10 .25
179 Ben Sheets .10 .25
180 Gary Sheffield .10 .25
181 James Shields .10 .25
182 Grady Sizemore .15 .40
183 Travis Snider .15 .40
184 Chris Snyder .10 .25
185 Geovany Soto .15 .40
186 Denard Span .10 .25
187 Kurt Suzuki .10 .25
188 Mark Teahen .10 .25
189 Mark Teixeira .25 .60
190 Miguel Tejada .15 .40
191 Ryan Theriot .10 .25
192 Jim Thome .15 .40
193 Troy Tulowitzki .25 .60
194 Dan Uggla .15 .40
195 Justin Upton .15 .40
196 B.J. Upton .15 .40
197 Chase Utley .25 .60
198 Jose Valverde .10 .25
199 Jason Varitek .25 .60
200 Javier Vazquez .10 .25
201 Justin Verlander .30 .75
202 Shane Victorino .10 .25
203 Edinson Volquez .10 .25
204 Joey Votto .25 .60
205 Tim Wakefield .10 .25
206 Chien-Ming Wang .20 .50
207 Jered Weaver .10 .25
208 Rickie Weeks .15 .40
209 Vernon Wells .10 .25
210 Jayson Werth .15 .40
211 Ty Wigginton .15 .40
212 Josh Willingham .10 .25
213 Dontrelle Willis .10 .25
214 Randy Winn .10 .25
215 David Wright .30 .75
216 Kevin Youkilis .15 .40
217 Chris Young .10 .25
218 Delmon Young .15 .40
219 Michael Young .15 .40
220 Carlos Zambrano .15 .40

2009 Topps Attax Code Cards

1 Garrett Atkins .40 1.00
2 Lance Berkman .60 1.50
3 Jay Bruce .60 1.50
4 Miguel Cabrera 1.00 2.50
5 Prince Fielder .60 1.50
6 Alex Gordon .60 1.50
7 Roy Halladay 1.00 2.50
8 Josh Hamilton 1.00 2.50
9 Matt Holliday 1.00 2.50
10 Ryan Howard 1.25 3.00
11 Chipper Jones 1.00 2.50
12 John Lackey .40 1.00
13 Cliff Lee .60 1.50
14 Tim Lincecum 1.50 4.00
15 Evan Longoria 1.25 3.00
16 Nick Markakis 1.00 2.50
17 Russell Martin .40 1.00
18 Daisuke Matsuzaka 1.00 2.50
19 Nate McLouth .40 1.00
20 Justin Morneau 1.00 2.50
21 Jake Peavy .40 1.00
22 Albert Pujols 2.50 6.00
23 Carlos Quentin .60 1.50
24 Hanley Ramirez 1.00 2.50
25 Alex Rodriguez 1.50 4.00
26 Johan Santana 1.00 2.50
27 Alfonso Soriano .60 1.50
28 Ichiro Suzuki 1.50 4.00
29 Brandon Webb .60 1.50
30 Ryan Zimmerman .60 1.50

2009 Topps Attax Gold

1 Garrett Atkins .60 1.50
2 Lance Berkman 1.00 2.50
3 Jay Bruce 1.00 2.50
4 Miguel Cabrera 1.50 4.00
5 Prince Fielder 1.00 2.50
6 Alex Gordon 1.00 2.50
7 Roy Halladay 1.50 4.00
8 Josh Hamilton 1.50 4.00
9 Matt Holliday 1.50 4.00
10 Ryan Howard 2.00 5.00
11 Chipper Jones 1.50 4.00
12 John Lackey .60 1.50
13 Cliff Lee 1.00 2.50
14 Tim Lincecum 2.50 6.00
15 Evan Longoria 2.00 5.00
16 Nick Markakis 1.50 4.00
17 Russell Martin .60 1.50
18 Daisuke Matsuzaka 1.50 4.00
19 Nate McLouth .60 1.50
20 Justin Morneau 1.50 4.00
21 Barack Obama 2.00 5.00
22 Jake Peavy .60 1.50
23 Albert Pujols 4.00 10.00
24 Carlos Quentin 1.00 2.50
25 Hanley Ramirez 1.50 4.00
26 Alex Rodriguez 2.50 6.00
27 Johan Santana 1.50 4.00
28 Alfonso Soriano 1.00 2.50
29 Ichiro Suzuki 2.50 6.00
30 Brandon Webb 1.00 2.50
31 Ryan Zimmerman 1.00 2.50

2009 Topps Attax Gold Starter Pack Exclusives

1 Ty Cobb 10.00 25.00
2 Lou Gehrig 6.00 15.00
3 Greg Maddux 8.00 20.00
4 Mickey Mantle 8.00 20.00

5 Jackie Robinson 6.00 15.00
6 Babe Ruth 15.00 40.00
7 Nolan Ryan 8.00 20.00
8 Honus Wagner 4.00 10.00
9 Cy Young 6.00 15.00

2009 Topps Attax Silver Foil

1 Bobby Abreu .40 1.00
2 Rick Ankiel .40 1.00
3 Jason Bay .60 1.50
4 Josh Beckett .60 1.50
5 Carlos Beltran .40 1.00
6 Ryan Braun 1.25 3.00
7 Pat Burrell .40 1.00
8 Joba Chamberlain .60 1.50
9 Eric Chavez .40 1.00
10 Carlos Delgado .40 1.00
11 Adam Dunn .60 1.50
12 Adrian Gonzalez .60 1.50
13 Curtis Granderson .60 1.50
14 Vladimir Guerrero 1.00 2.50
15 Cole Hamels 1.00 2.50
16 Rich Harden .40 1.00
17 Dan Haren .40 1.00
18 Brad Hawpe .40 1.00
19 Felix Hernandez 1.00 2.50
20 Torii Hunter .40 1.00
21 Raul Ibanez .60 1.50
22 Derek Jeter 2.50 6.00
23 Scott Kazmir .40 1.00
24 Ian Kinsler .60 1.50
25 Carlos Lee .40 1.00
26 Jon Lester 1.00 2.50
27 Brad Lidge .40 1.00
28 Derek Lowe .40 1.00
29 Victor Martinez .60 1.50
30 Hideki Matsui 1.00 2.50
31 Joe Mauer 1.00 2.50
32 Brian McCann .60 1.50
33 Magglio Ordonez .60 1.50
34 David Ortiz .60 1.50
35 Roy Oswalt .60 1.50
36 Dustin Pedroia 1.25 3.00
37 Carlos Pena .60 1.50
38 Hunter Pence .60 1.50
39 Brandon Phillips .40 1.00
40 Aramis Ramirez .40 1.00
41 Manny Ramirez 1.00 2.50
42 Jose Reyes .60 1.50
43 Alex Rios .60 1.50
44 Francisco Rodriguez .60 1.50
45 Jimmy Rollins .60 1.50
46 Aaron Rowand .40 1.00
47 CC Sabathia .60 1.50
48 James Shields .40 1.00
49 Grady Sizemore .60 1.50
50 Geovany Soto .60 1.50
51 Mark Teixeira 1.00 2.50
52 Miguel Tejada .60 1.50
53 Jim Thome .60 1.50
54 Dan Uggla .60 1.50
55 B.J. Upton .60 1.50
56 Chase Utley 1.00 2.50
57 David Wright 1.25 3.00
58 Kevin Youkilis .60 1.50
59 Michael Young .60 1.50
60 Carlos Zambrano .60 1.50

2010 Topps Attax

COMPLETE SET (220) 12.50 30.00
COMMON CARD .10 .25
1 Bobby Abreu .10 .25
2 Brett Anderson .15 .40
3 Elvis Andrus .15 .40
4 Andrew Bailey .10 .25
5 Clint Barmes .10 .25
6 Jason Bartlett .10 .25
7 Jason Bay .15 .40
8 Josh Beckett .15 .40
9 Gordon Beckham .15 .40
10 Erik Bedard .10 .25
11 Heath Bell .15 .40
12 Carlos Beltran .10 .25
13 Adrian Beltre .10 .25
14 Lance Berkman .15 .40
15 Casey Blake .10 .25
16 Hank Blalock .10 .25
17 Ryan Braun .30 .75
18 Jonathan Broxton .10 .25
19 Jay Bruce .15 .40
20 Mark Buehrle .15 .40
21 A.J. Burnett .15 .40
22 Billy Butler .10 .25
23 Eric Byrnes .10 .25
24 Asdrubal Cabrera .15 .40
25 Everth Cabrera .10 .25
26 Miguel Cabrera .25 .60
27 Orlando Cabrera .10 .25
28 Matt Cain .15 .40
29 Alberto Callaspo .10 .25
30 Mike Cameron .10 .25
31 Robinson Cano .25 .60
32 Jorge Cantu .10 .25
33 Chris Carpenter .25 .60
34 Luis Castillo .10 .25
35 Joba Chamberlain .15 .40
36 Shin-Soo Choo .15 .40
37 Ryan Church .10 .25
38 Chris Coghlan .10 .25
39 Carl Crawford .15 .40
40 Joe Crede .10 .25
41 Nelson Cruz .15 .40
42 Mike Cuddyer .10 .25
43 Johnny Cueto .10 .25
44 Johnny Damon .15 .40
45 David DeJesus .10 .25
46 Ryan Dempster .10 .25
47 Mark DeRosa .10 .25
48 Matt Diaz .10 .25
49 J.D. Drew .10 .25
50 Stephen Drew .10 .25
51 Adam Dunn .15 .40
52 Jermaine Dye .10 .25
53 Jacoby Ellsbury .25 .60
54 Yunel Escobar .10 .25
55 Andre Ethier .15 .40
56 Scott Feldman .10 .25
57 Neftali Feliz .10 .25
58 Prince Fielder .15 .40
59 Chone Figgins .10 .25
60 Mike Fontenot .10 .25
61 Dexter Fowler .10 .25
62 Jeff Francoeur .15 .40
63 Kosuke Fukudome .25 .60
64 Rafael Furcal .10 .25
65 Yovani Gallardo .10 .25
66 Matt Garza .10 .25
67 Adrian Gonzalez .15 .40
68 Curtis Granderson .15 .40
69 Zack Greinke .15 .40
70 Ken Griffey Jr. .40 1.00
71 Vladimir Guerrero .25 .60
72 Cristian Guzman .10 .25
73 Travis Hafner .10 .25
74 Roy Halladay .25 .60
75 Cole Hamels .25 .60
76 Josh Hamilton .25 .60
77 Tommy Hanson .15 .40
78 J.A. Happ .15 .40
79 Dan Haren .10 .25
80 Corey Hart .10 .25
81 Brad Hawpe .10 .25
82 Todd Helton .15 .40
83 Felix Hernandez .25 .60
84 Ramon Hernandez .10 .25
85 Aaron Hill .10 .25
86 Matt Holliday .25 .60
87 Ryan Howard .30 .75
88 Orlando Hudson .10 .25
89 Torii Hunter .10 .25
90 Raul Ibanez .15 .40
91 Brandon Inge .15 .40
92 Bobby Jenks .10 .25
93 Derek Jeter .60 1.50
94 Ubaldo Jimenez .15 .40
95 Josh Johnson .15 .40
96 Kelly Johnson .10 .25
97 Adam Jones .15 .40
98 Chipper Jones .25 .60
99 Garrett Jones .10 .25
100 Scott Kazmir .10 .25
101 Matt Kemp .15 .40
102 Howie Kendrick .10 .25
103 Adam Kennedy .10 .25
104 Clayton Kershaw .25 .60
105 Ian Kinsler .15 .40
106 Paul Konerko .15 .40
107 Kevin Kouzmanoff .10 .25
108 Adam LaRoche .10 .25
109 Carlos Lee .10 .25
110 Cliff Lee .15 .40
111 Derrek Lee .10 .25
112 Jon Lester .25 .60
113 Brad Lidge .10 .25
114 Tim Lincecum .40 1.00
115 Adam Lind .15 .40
116 James Loney .15 .40
117 Evan Longoria .30 .75
118 Felipe Lopez .10 .25
119 Jose Lopez .10 .25
120 Mike Lowell .10 .25
121 Ryan Ludwick .10 .25
122 Nick Markakis .25 .60
123 Jason Marquis .10 .25
124 Victor Martinez .15 .40
125 Justin Masterson .10 .25
126 Joe Mauer .25 .60
127 Brian McCann .15 .40
128 Nate McLouth .10 .25
129 Andrew McCutchen .25 .60
130 Bengie Molina .10 .25
131 Yadier Molina .15 .40
132 Miguel Montero .10 .25
133 Melvin Mora .10 .25
134 Kendry Morales .10 .25
135 Justin Morneau .25 .60
136 Joe Nathan .10 .25
137 Dioner Navarro .10 .25
138 Magglio Ordonez .15 .40
139 David Ortiz .15 .40
140 Roy Oswalt .15 .40
141 Jonathan Papelbon .15 .40
142 Gerardo Parra .10 .25
143 Jake Peavy .10 .25
144 Dustin Pedroia .30 .75
145 Carlos Pena .15 .40
146 Hunter Pence .15 .40
147 Jhonny Peralta .10 .25
148 Andy Pettitte .15 .40
149 Brandon Phillips .10 .25
150 A.J. Pierzynski .10 .25
151 Placido Polanco .10 .25
152 Rick Porcello .10 .25
153 Jorge Posada .15 .40
154 David Price .25 .60
155 Albert Pujols .60 1.50
156 Carlos Quentin .15 .40
157 Alexei Ramirez .10 .25
158 Aramis Ramirez .10 .25
159 Hanley Ramirez .25 .60
160 Manny Ramirez .25 .60
161 Colby Rasmus .25 .60
162 Nolan Reimold .15 .40
163 Edgar Renteria .10 .25
164 Jose Reyes .15 .40
165 Mark Reynolds .10 .25
166 Alex Rios .15 .40
167 Mariano Rivera .25 .60
168 Brian Roberts .15 .40
169 Ryan Roberts .10 .25
170 Alex Rodriguez .40 1.00
171 Francisco Rodriguez .15 .40
172 Wandy Rodriguez .10 .25
173 Scott Rolen .15 .40
174 Jimmy Rollins .15 .40
175 Cody Ross .10 .25
176 Aaron Rowand .10 .25
177 CC Sabathia .15 .40
178 Freddy Sanchez .10 .25
179 Pablo Sandoval .15 .40
180 Johan Santana .25 .60
181 Skip Schumaker .10 .25
182 Luke Scott .10 .25
183 Grady Sizemore .15 .40
184 Travis Snider .10 .25
185 Alfonso Soriano .15 .40
186 Geovany Soto .15 .40
187 Denard Span .10 .25
188 Ian Stewart .10 .25
189 Huston Street .10 .25
190 Ichiro Suzuki .40 1.00
191 Kurt Suzuki .10 .25
192 Willy Taveras .10 .25
193 Mark Teahen .10 .25
194 Mark Teixeira .25 .60
195 Miguel Tejada .15 .40
196 Ryan Theriot .10 .25
197 Troy Tulowitzki .25 .60
198 Dan Uggla .15 .40
199 B.J. Upton .15 .40
200 Justin Upton .15 .40
201 Chase Utley .25 .60
202 Jose Valverde .10 .25
203 Javier Vazquez .10 .25
204 Justin Verlander .30 .75
205 Shane Victorino .15 .40
206 Joey Votto .25 .60
207 Adam Wainwright .15 .40
208 Jered Weaver .10 .25
209 Vernon Wells .10 .25
210 Jayson Werth .15 .40
211 Josh Willingham .10 .25
212 Randy Winn .10 .25
213 Kerry Wood .10 .25
214 David Wright .30 .75
215 Kevin Youkilis .15 .40
216 Chris Young .10 .25
217 Michael Young .15 .40
218 Carlos Zambrano .15 .40
219 Ryan Zimmerman .15 .40
220 Ben Zobrist .10 .25

2010 Topps Attax Code Cards

1 Lance Berkman .60 1.50
2 Ryan Braun 1.25 3.00
3 Chris Carpenter 1.00 2.50
4 Jacoby Ellsbury 1.00 2.50
5 Prince Fielder .60 1.50
6 Adrian Gonzalez .60 1.50
7 Curtis Granderson .60 1.50
8 Zack Greinke .60 1.50
9 Dan Haren .40 1.00
10 Felix Hernandez 1.00 2.50
11 Ryan Howard 1.25 3.00
12 Derek Jeter 2.50 6.00
13 Matt Kemp .60 1.50
14 Jon Lester 1.00 2.50
15 Tim Lincecum 1.50 4.00
16 Evan Longoria 1.25 3.00
17 Joe Mauer 1.00 2.50
18 Albert Pujols 2.50 6.00
19 Hanley Ramirez 1.00 2.50
20 Manny Ramirez 1.00 2.50
21 Alex Rodriguez 1.50 4.00
22 CC Sabathia .60 1.50
23 Pablo Sandoval .60 1.50
24 Grady Sizemore .60 1.50
25 Ichiro Suzuki 1.50 4.00
26 Mark Teixeira 1.00 2.50
27 Troy Tulowitzki 1.00 2.50
28 Justin Verlander 1.25 3.00
29 Joey Votto 1.00 2.50
30 David Wright 1.25 3.00

2010 Topps Attax Gold Foil

1 Lance Berkman 1.00 2.50
2 Ryan Braun 2.00 5.00
3 Chris Carpenter 1.50 4.00
4 Jacoby Ellsbury 1.50 4.00
5 Prince Fielder 1.00 2.50
6 Adrian Gonzalez 1.00 2.50
7 Curtis Granderson 1.00 2.50
8 Zack Greinke 1.00 2.50
9 Dan Haren .60 1.50
10 Felix Hernandez 1.50 4.00
11 Ryan Howard 2.00 5.00
12 Derek Jeter 4.00 10.00
13 Matt Kemp 1.00 2.50
14 Jon Lester 1.50 4.00
15 Tim Lincecum 2.50 6.00
16 Evan Longoria 2.00 5.00
17 Joe Mauer 1.50 4.00
18 Albert Pujols 4.00 10.00
19 Hanley Ramirez 1.50 4.00
20 Manny Ramirez 1.50 4.00
21 Alex Rodriguez 2.50 6.00
22 CC Sabathia 1.00 2.50
23 Pablo Sandoval 1.00 2.50
24 Grady Sizemore 1.00 2.50
25 Ichiro Suzuki 2.50 6.00
26 Mark Teixeira 1.50 4.00
27 Troy Tulowitzki 1.50 4.00
28 Justin Verlander 2.00 5.00
29 Joey Votto 1.50 4.00
30 David Wright 2.00 5.00

2010 Topps Attax Legends

1 Ty Cobb 4.00 10.00
2 Bob Gibson 1.50 4.00
3 Rickey Henderson 2.50 6.00
4 Reggie Jackson 1.25 3.00
5 Mickey Mantle 8.00 20.00
6 Jackie Robinson 2.50 6.00
7 Babe Ruth 6.00 15.00
8 Nolan Ryan 8.00 20.00
9 Mike Schmidt 4.00 10.00
10 Cy Young 2.50 6.00

2010 Topps Attax Silver Foil

1 Elvis Andrus .60 1.50
2 Jason Bay .60 1.50
3 Josh Beckett .60 1.50
4 Gordon Beckham .60 1.50
5 Carlos Beltran .40 1.00
6 Billy Butler .40 1.00
7 Miguel Cabrera 1.00 2.50
8 Matt Cain .60 1.50
9 Robinson Cano 1.00 2.50
10 Shin-Soo Choo .60 1.50
11 Chris Coghlan .40 1.00
12 Carl Crawford .60 1.50
13 Johnny Cueto .40 1.00
14 Johnny Damon .60 1.50
15 Adam Dunn .60 1.50
16 Yunel Escobar .40 1.00
17 Andre Ethier .60 1.50
18 Scott Feldman .40 1.00
19 Dexter Fowler .40 1.00
20 Yovani Gallardo .40 1.00
21 Roy Halladay 1.00 2.50
22 Cole Hamels 1.00 2.50
23 Josh Hamilton 1.00 2.50
24 Todd Helton .60 1.50
25 Aaron Hill .40 1.00
26 Matt Holliday 1.00 2.50
27 Torii Hunter .40 1.00
28 Ubaldo Jimenez .60 1.50
29 Josh Johnson .60 1.50
30 Howie Kendrick .40 1.00
31 Clayton Kershaw 1.00 2.50
32 Ian Kinsler .60 1.50
33 Carlos Lee .40 1.00
34 Derrek Lee .40 1.00
35 Adam Lind .60 1.50
36 Jose Lopez .40 1.00
37 Nick Markakis 1.00 2.50
38 Jason Marquis .40 1.00
39 Victor Martinez .60 1.50
40 Andrew McCutchen 1.00 2.50
41 Kendry Morales .40 1.00
42 Justin Morneau 1.00 2.50
43 David Ortiz .60 1.50
44 Dustin Pedroia 1.25 3.00
45 Carlos Pena .60 1.50
46 Hunter Pence .60 1.50
47 Aramis Ramirez .40 1.00
48 Nolan Reimold .60 1.50
49 Mark Reynolds .40 1.00
50 Mariano Rivera 1.00 2.50
51 Brian Roberts .60 1.50
52 Jimmy Rollins .60 1.50
53 Miguel Tejada .60 1.50
54 Dan Uggla .60 1.50
55 Chase Utley 1.00 2.50
56 Javier Vazquez .40 1.00
57 Adam Wainwright .60 1.50
58 Jered Weaver .40 1.00
59 Jayson Werth .60 1.50
60 Ryan Zimmerman .60 1.50

2010 Topps Attax Battle of the Ages

1 Ty Cobb .50 1.25
2 Prince Fielder .20 .50
3 Bob Gibson .20 .50
4 Zack Greinke .20 .50
5 Rickey Henderson .30 .75
6 Ryan Howard .40 1.00
7 Reggie Jackson .20 .50
8 Bo Jackson .30 .75
9 Derek Jeter .75 2.00
10 Jon Lester .30 .75
11 Tim Lincecum .50 1.25
12 Evan Longoria .40 1.00
13 Mickey Mantle 1.00 2.50
14 Joe Mauer .30 .75
15 Stan Musial .50 1.25
16 Jim Palmer .12 .30
17 Albert Pujols .75 2.00
18 Manny Ramirez .30 .75
19 Cal Ripken Jr. 1.25 3.00
20 Jackie Robinson .30 .75
21 Alex Rodriguez .50 1.25
22 Babe Ruth .75 2.00
23 Nolan Ryan 1.00 2.50
24 CC Sabathia .20 .50
25 Mike Schmidt .50 1.25
26 Tom Seaver .20 .50
27 Ichiro Suzuki .50 1.25
28 Justin Verlander .40 1.00
29 David Wright .40 1.00
30 Cy Young .30 .75

2010 Topps Attax Battle of the Ages Foil

*FOIL: 2X TO 5X BASIC
1 Ty Cobb 2.50 6.00
2 Prince Fielder 1.00 2.50
3 Bob Gibson 1.00 2.50
4 Zack Greinke 1.00 2.50
5 Rickey Henderson 1.50 4.00
6 Ryan Howard 2.00 5.00
7 Reggie Jackson 1.00 2.50
8 Bo Jackson 1.50 4.00
9 Derek Jeter 4.00 10.00
10 Jon Lester 1.50 4.00
11 Tim Lincecum 2.50 6.00
12 Evan Longoria 2.00 5.00
13 Mickey Mantle 5.00 12.00
14 Joe Mauer 1.50 4.00
15 Stan Musial 2.50 6.00
16 Jim Palmer .60 1.50
17 Albert Pujols 4.00 10.00
18 Manny Ramirez 1.50 4.00
19 Cal Ripken Jr. 6.00 15.00
20 Jackie Robinson 1.50 4.00
21 Alex Rodriguez 2.50 6.00
22 Babe Ruth 4.00 10.00
23 Nolan Ryan 5.00 12.00
24 CC Sabathia 1.00 2.50
25 Mike Schmidt 2.50 6.00
26 Tom Seaver 1.00 2.50
27 Ichiro Suzuki 2.50 6.00
28 Justin Verlander 2.00 5.00
29 David Wright 2.00 5.00
30 Cy Young 1.50 4.00

2011 Topps Attax

COMMON CARD (1-206) .10 .25
COMMON MASCOT (207-231) .60 1.50
COMMON STADIUM (232-260) .60 1.50
1 Adam Dunn .15 .40
2 Adam Jones .15 .40
3 Adam LaRoche .10 .25
4 Adam Lind .15 .40
5 Adam Wainwright .15 .40
6 Adrian Beltre .10 .25
7 Adrian Gonzalez .15 .40
8 Albert Pujols .60 1.50
9 Alex Rios .15 .40
10 Alex Rodriguez .40 1.00
11 Alexei Ramirez .10 .25
12 Alfonso Soriano .15 .40
13 Andre Ethier .15 .40
14 Andres Torres .10 .25
15 Andrew Bailey .10 .25
16 Andrew McCutchen .25 .60
17 Angel Pagan .10 .25
18 Aramis Ramirez .10 .25
19 Aroldis Chapman .30 .75
20 Aubrey Huff .10 .25
21 Austin Jackson .10 .25
22 B.J. Upton .15 .40
23 Ben Zobrist .10 .25
24 Billy Butler .10 .25
25 Bobby Abreu .10 .25
26 Brandon Morrow .10 .25
27 Brandon Phillips .10 .25
28 Brennan Boesch .15 .40
29 Brett Anderson .15 .40
30 Brett Gardner .10 .25
31 Brett Wallace .10 .25
32 Brian Matusz .25 .60
33A Brian McCann .15 .40
One Hand on Bat
33B Brian McCann
Two Hands on Bat
34 Brian Roberts .10 .25
35 Brian Wilson .25 .60
36 Buster Posey .30 .75
37 Carl Crawford .15 .40
38 Carlos Gonzalez .15 .40
39 Carlos Lee .10 .25
40 Carlos Marmol .15 .40
41 Carlos Pena .15 .40
42 Carlos Quentin .10 .25
43 Carlos Santana .25 .60
44 Carlos Zambrano .15 .40
45 Casey McGehee .10 .25
46 CC Sabathia .15 .40
47 Chase Headley .10 .25
48 Chase Utley .25 .60
49 Chipper Jones .25 .60
50 Chone Figgins .10 .25
51 Chris Carpenter .25 .60
52 Chris Coghlan .10 .25
53 Chris Johnson .10 .25
54 Chris Young .10 .25
55 Clay Buchholz .15 .40
56 Clayton Kershaw .25 .60
57 Cliff Lee .25 .60
58 Coco Crisp .10 .25
59 Colby Rasmus .25 .60
60 Cole Hamels .25 .60
61 Corey Hart .10 .25
62 Curtis Granderson .15 .40
63 Dan Haren .10 .25
64 Dan Uggla .15 .40
65 Danny Valencia .15 .40
66 David Ortiz .15 .40
67 David Price .25 .60
68 Bronson Arroyo .10 .25
69 David Wright .30 .75
70 Delmon Young .15 .40
71 Denard Span .10 .25
72 Derek Jeter .60 1.50
73 Derrek Lee .10 .25
74 Dexter Fowler .10 .25
75 Domonic Brown .25 .60
76 Drew Stubbs .15 .40
77 Dustin Pedroia .30 .75
78 Edinson Volquez .10 .25
79 Elvis Andrus .15 .40
80 Erick Aybar .10 .25
81 Evan Longoria .30 .75
82 Fausto Carmona .10 .25
83 Felix Hernandez .25 .60
84 Francisco Liriano .10 .25
85 Franklin Gutierrez .10 .25
86 Freddy Sanchez .10 .25
87 Gaby Sanchez .10 .25
88 Garrett Jones .10 .25
89 Geovany Soto .15 .40
90 Gordon Beckham .15 .40
91 Grady Sizemore .15 .40
92 Hanley Ramirez .25 .60
93 Heath Bell .15 .40
94 Hideki Matsui .25 .60
95 Howie Kendrick .10 .25
96 Hunter Pence .15 .40
97 Ian Desmond .15 .40
98 Ian Kinsler .15 .40
99 Ian Stewart .10 .25
100 Ichiro Suzuki .40 1.00
101 Ike Davis .15 .40
102 Jacoby Ellsbury .25 .60
103 James Loney .15 .40
104 Jason Bay .15 .40
105 Jason Heyward .30 .75
106 Jason Kubel .10 .25
107 Jay Bruce .15 .40
108 Jayson Werth .15 .40
109 Jered Weaver .10 .25
110 Jim Thome .15 .40
111 Joakim Soria .10 .25
112 Joe Mauer .25 .60
113 Joey Votto .25 .60
114 Johan Santana .25 .60
115 John Danks .10 .25
116 Jon Lester .25 .60
117 Jonathan Papelbon .15 .40
118 Jorge Posada .15 .40
119 Jose Bautista .15 .40
120 Jose Reyes .15 .40
121 Jose Tabata .15 .40
122 Jose Valverde .10 .25
123 Josh Beckett .15 .40
124 Josh Hamilton .25 .60
125 Josh Johnson .15 .40
126 Josh Willingham .10 .25
127 Juan Pierre .10 .25
128 Juan Uribe .10 .25
129 Justin Morneau .25 .60
130 Justin Upton .15 .40
131 Justin Verlander .30 .75
132 Kelly Johnson .10 .25
133 Kendry Morales .10 .25
134 Kevin Youkilis .15 .40
135 Koji Uehara .10 .25
136 Kosuke Fukudome .25 .60
137 Kurt Suzuki .10 .25
138 Lance Berkman .15 .40
139 Logan Morrison .10 .25
140 Luke Scott .10 .25
141 Magglio Ordonez .15 .40
142 Manny Ramirez .25 .60
143 Mariano Rivera .25 .60
144 Mark Reynolds .10 .25
145 Mark Teixeira .25 .60
146 Marlon Byrd .10 .25
147 Martin Prado .10 .25
148 Mat Latos .10 .25
149 Matt Cain .15 .40
150 Matt Garza .10 .25
151 Matt Holliday .25 .60
152 Matt Kemp .15 .40
153 Max Scherzer .10 .25
154A Michael Bourn .10 .25
Jersey #21
154B Michael Bourn
Jersey #42
155 Michael Cuddyer .10 .25
156 Michael Young .15 .40
157 Miguel Cabrera .25 .60
158 Miguel Montero .10 .25
159 Miguel Tejada .15 .40
160 Mike Napoli .15 .40
161 Mike Stanton .15 .40
162 Neftali Feliz .10 .25
163 Neil Walker .10 .25
164 Nelson Cruz .15 .40
165 Nick Markakis .25 .60
166 Nick Swisher .25 .60
167 Omar Infante .10 .25
168 Pablo Sandoval .15 .40
169 Paul Konerko .15 .40
170 Phil Hughes .10 .25
171 Placido Polanco .10 .25
172 Prince Fielder .15 .40
173 Rafael Furcal .10 .25
174 Raul Ibanez .15 .40
175 Rickie Weeks .15 .40
176 Ricky Nolasco .10 .25
177 Ricky Romero .10 .25
178 Robinson Cano .25 .60
179 Roy Halladay .25 .60
180 Roy Oswalt .15 .40
181 Ryan Braun .30 .75
182 Ryan Howard .30 .75
183 Ryan Zimmerman .15 .40
184 Scott Rolen .15 .40
185 Shane Victorino .15 .40
186 Shin-Soo Choo .15 .40
187 Starlin Castro .25 .60
188 Stephen Drew .10 .25
189 Stephen Strasburg .50 1.25
190 Tim Hudson .15 .40
191 Tim Lincecum .25 .60
192 Todd Helton .15 .40
193 Tommy Hanson .15 .40
194 Torii Hunter .10 .25
195 Travis Hafner .10 .25
196 Trevor Cahill .10 .25
197 Troy Tulowitzki .25 .60
198 Tyler Colvin .15 .40
199 Ubaldo Jimenez .15 .40
200 Vernon Wells .10 .25
201 Victor Martinez .15 .40
202 Vladimir Guerrero .25 .60
203 Wandy Rodriguez .10 .25
204 Yadier Molina .15 .40
205 Yovani Gallardo .10 .25
206 Zack Greinke .15 .40
207 A's Mascot .60 1.50
208 Bernie Brewer .60 1.50
209 Billy the Marlin .60 1.50
210 Blue Jays Mascot .60 1.50
211 Braves Mascot .60 1.50
212 Diamondbacks Mascot .60 1.50
213 Dinger .60 1.50
214 Fredbird .60 1.50
215 Gapper .60 1.50
216 Junction Jack .60 1.50
217 Mariner Moose .60 1.50
218 Mr. Met .75 2.00
219 Orioles Mascot .60 1.50
220 Paws .60 1.50
221 Phillie Phanatic .75 2.00
222 Pirate Parrot .60 1.50
223 Rangers Captain .60 1.50
224 Raymond .60 1.50
225 Royals Mascot .60 1.50
226 Screech .60 1.50
227 Slider .60 1.50
228 Swinging Friar .60 1.50
229 TC .60 1.50
230 Wally the Green Monster .75 2.00
231 White Sox Mascot .60 1.50
232 Angels Stadium of Anaheim .60 1.50
233 ATT Ballpark .60
234 Busch Stadium .60
235 Chase Field .60
236 Citi Field .60
237 Citizens Bank Park .60
238 Comerica Park .60
239 Dodger Stadium .60
240 Fenway Park .75 2.00
241 Great American Ball Park .60
242 Kauffman Stadium .60
243 Miller Park .60
244 Minute Maid Park .60
245 Nationals Park .60
246 Oriole Park at Camden Yards .60
247 Petco Park .60
248 PNC Park .60
249 Progressive Field .60
250 Rangers Ballpark in Arlington .60
251 Rogers Centre .60
252 Safeco Field .60
253 Target Field .60
254 Tropicana Field .60
255 Turner Field .60
256 U.S. Cellular Field .60
257 Wrigley Field .75 2.00
258 Yankee Stadium 1.25 3.00

2011 Topps Attax Foil

*1-206: 1X TO 2.5X BASIC
*207-258: .5X TO 1.2X BASIC

2011 Topps Attax Legends

A1 Mickey Mantle 8.00 20.00
A2 Babe Ruth 10.00 25.00

2005 Topps Barry Bonds Fan Giveaway

COMPLETE SET (1) 2.50 6.00
BB4 Barry Bonds 2.00 5.00

1996 Topps Chrome

The 1996 Topps Chrome set was issued in one series totalling 165 cards and features a selection of players from the 1996 Topps regular set. The four-card packs retailed for $3.00 each. Each chromium card is a replica of its regular version with the exception of the Topps Chrome logo replacing the traditional logo. Included in the set is a Mickey Mantle number 7 Commemorative card and a Cal Ripken Tribute card.

COMPLETE SET (165) 20.00 50.00
1 Tony Gwynn STP .50 1.25
2 Mike Piazza STP .75 2.00
3 Greg Maddux STP .75 2.00
4 Jeff Bagwell STP .30 .75
5 Larry Walker STP .30 .75
6 Barry Larkin STP .30 .75
7 Mickey Mantle COMM 4.00 10.00
8 Tom Glavine STP .30 .75
9 Craig Biggio STP .30 .75
10 Barry Bonds STP 1.00 2.50
11 H.Slocumb STP .30 .75
12 Matt Williams STP .30 .75
13 Todd Helton 1.50 4.00
14 Paul Molitor .30 .75
15 Glenallen Hill .30 .75
16 Troy Percival .30 .75
17 Albert Belle .30 .75
18 Mark Wohlers .30 .75
19 Kirby Puckett .75 2.00
20 Mark Grace .50 1.25
21 J.T. Snow .30 .75
22 David Justice .30 .75
23 Mike Mussina .50 1.25
24 Bernie Williams .50 1.25
25 Ron Gant .30 .75
26 Carlos Baerga .30 .75
27 Gary Sheffield .30 .75
28 Cal Ripken 2131 2.50 6.00
29 Frank Thomas .75 2.00
30 Kevin Seitzer .30 .75
31 Joe Carter .30 .75
32 Jeff King .30 .75
33 David Cone .30 .75
34 Eddie Murray .75 2.00
35 Brian Jordan .30 .75
36 Garret Anderson .30 .75
37 Hideo Nomo .75 2.00
38 Steve Finley .30 .75
39 Ivan Rodriguez .50 1.25
40 Quilvio Veras .30 .75
41 Mark McGwire 2.00 5.00
42 Greg Vaughn .30 .75
43 Randy Johnson .75 2.00
44 David Segui .30 .75
45 Derek Bell .30 .75
46 John Valentin .30 .75
47 Steve Avery .30 .75
48 Tino Martinez .50 1.25
49 Shane Reynolds .30 .75
50 Jim Edmonds .30 .75
51 Raul Mondesi .30 .75
52 Chipper Jones .75 2.00
53 Gregg Jefferies .30 .75
54 Ken Caminiti .30 .75
55 Brian McRae .30 .75
56 Don Mattingly 2.00 5.00
57 Marty Cordova .30 .75
58 Vinny Castilla .30 .75
59 John Smoltz .50 1.25
60 Travis Fryman .30 .75
61 Ryan Klesko .30 .75
62 Alex Fernandez .30 .75

63 Dante Bichette .30 .75
64 Eric Karros .30 .75
65 Roger Clemens 1.50 4.00
66 Randy Myers .30 .75
67 Cal Ripken 2.50 6.00
68 Rod Beck .30 .75
69 Jack McDowell .30 .75
70 Ken Griffey Jr. 1.25 3.00
71 Ramon Martinez .30 .75
72 Jason Giambi .30 .75
73 Nomar Garciaparra FS 1.25 3.00
74 Billy Wagner .30 .75
75 Todd Greene .30 .75
76 Paul Wilson .30 .75
77 Johnny Damon .50 1.25
78 Alan Benes .30 .75
79 Karim Garcia FS .30 .75
80 Derek Jeter FS 2.00 5.00
81 Kirby Puckett STP .50 1.25
82 Cal Ripken STP 1.25 3.00
83 Albert Belle STP .30 .75
84 Randy Johnson STP .50 1.25
85 Wade Boggs STP .30 .75
86 Carlos Baerga STP .30 .75
87 Ivan Rodriguez STP .30 .75
88 Mike Mussina STP .30 .75
89 Frank Thomas STP .50 1.25
90 Ken Griffey Jr. STP .75 2.00
91 Jose Mesa STP .30 .75
92 Matt Morris RC 2.00 5.00
93 Mike Piazza 1.25 3.00
94 Edgar Martinez .50 1.25
95 Chuck Knoblauch .30 .75
96 Andres Galarraga .30 .75
97 Tony Gwynn 1.00 2.50
98 Lee Smith .30 .75
99 Sammy Sosa .75 2.00
100 Jim Thome .50 1.25
101 Bernard Gilkey .30 .75
102 Brady Anderson .30 .75
103 Rico Brogna .30 .75
104 Len Dykstra .30 .75
105 Tom Glavine .50 1.25
106 John Olerud .30 .75
107 Terry Steinbach .30 .75
108 Brian Hunter .30 .75
109 Jay Buhner .30 .75
110 Mo Vaughn .30 .75
111 Jose Mesa .30 .75
112 Brett Butler .30 .75
113 Chili Davis .30 .75
114 Paul O'Neill .50 1.25
115 Roberto Alomar .50 1.25
116 Barry Larkin .50 1.25
117 Marquis Grissom .30 .75
118 Will Clark .50 1.25
119 Barry Bonds 2.00 5.00
120 Ozzie Smith 1.25 3.00
121 Pedro Martinez .50 1.25
122 Craig Biggio .50 1.25
123 Moises Alou .30 .75
124 Robin Ventura .30 .75
125 Greg Maddux 1.25 3.00
126 Tim Salmon .50 1.25
127 Wade Boggs .50 1.25
128 Ismael Valdes .30 .75
129 Juan Gonzalez .30 .75
130 Ray Lankford .30 .75
131 Bobby Bonilla .30 .75
132 Reggie Sanders .30 .75
133 Alex Ochoa .30 .75
134 Mark Loretta .30 .75
135 Jason Kendall .30 .75
136 Brooks Kieschnick .30 .75
137 Chris Snopek .30 .75
138 Ruben Rivera NOW .30 .75
139 Jeff Suppan .30 .75
140 John Wasdin .30 .75
141 Jay Payton .30 .75
142 Rick Krivda .30 .75
143 Jimmy Haynes .30 .75
144 Ryne Sandberg 1.25 3.00
145 Matt Williams .30 .75
146 Jose Canseco .50 1.25
147 Larry Walker .30 .75
148 Kevin Appier .30 .75
149 Javy Lopez .30 .75
150 Dennis Eckersley .30 .75
151 Jason Isringhausen .30 .75
152 Dean Palmer .30 .75
153 Jeff Bagwell .50 1.25
154 Rondell White .30 .75
155 Wally Joyner .30 .75
156 Fred McGriff .50 1.25
157 Cecil Fielder .30 .75
158 Rafael Palmeiro .50 1.25
159 Rickey Henderson .75 2.00
160 Shawon Dunston .30 .75
161 Manny Ramirez .50 1.25
162 Alex Gonzalez .30 .75
163 Shawn Green .30 .75
164 Kenny Lofton .30 .75
165 Jeff Conine .30 .75

1996 Topps Chrome Refractors

Randomly inserted at the rate of one in every 12 packs, this 165-card set is parallel to the regular Chrome set. The difference in design is the refractive quality of the cards.

*STARS: 2.5X TO 6X BASIC CARDS
*ROOKIES: 1.5X TO 4X BASIC CARDS
STATED ODDS 1:12 HOBBY

1996 Topps Chrome Masters of the Game

Randomly inserted in packs at a rate of one in 12, this 20-card set honors players who are masters of their playing positions. The fronts feature color action photography with brilliant color metallization.

COMPLETE SET (20) 25.00 60.00
STATED ODDS 1:12 HOBBY
*REF: 1X TO 2.5X BASIC CHR.MASTERS
REF.STATED ODDS 1:36 HOBBY
1 Dennis Eckersley .75 2.00
2 Denny Martinez .75 2.00
3 Eddie Murray 2.00 5.00
4 Paul Molitor .75 2.00
5 Ozzie Smith 3.00 8.00
6 Rickey Henderson 2.00 5.00
7 Tim Raines .75 2.00
8 Lee Smith .75 2.00
9 Cal Ripken 6.00 15.00
10 Chili Davis .75 2.00
11 Wade Boggs 1.25 3.00
12 Tony Gwynn 2.50 6.00
13 Don Mattingly 5.00 12.00
14 Bret Saberhagen .75 2.00
15 Kirby Puckett 2.00 5.00
16 Joe Carter .75 2.00
17 Roger Clemens 4.00 10.00
18 Barry Bonds 5.00 12.00
19 Greg Maddux 3.00 8.00
20 Frank Thomas 2.00 5.00

1996 Topps Chrome Wrecking Crew

Randomly inserted in packs at a rate of one in 24, this 15-card set features baseball's top hitters and is printed in color action photography with brilliant color metallization.

COMPLETE SET (15) 30.00 80.00
STATED ODDS 1:24 HOBBY
*REF: 1X TO 2.5X BASIC CHR.WRECKING
REF.STATED ODDS 1:72 HOBBY
WC1 Jeff Bagwell 1.50 4.00
WC2 Albert Belle 1.00 2.50
WC3 Barry Bonds 6.00 15.00
WC4 Jose Canseco 1.50 4.00
WC5 Joe Carter 1.00 2.50
WC6 Cecil Fielder 1.00 2.50
WC7 Ron Gant 1.00 2.50
WC8 Juan Gonzalez 1.00 2.50
WC9 Ken Griffey Jr. 4.00 10.00
WC10 Fred McGriff 1.50 4.00
WC11 Mark McGwire 6.00 15.00
WC12 Mike Piazza 4.00 10.00
WC13 Frank Thomas 2.50 6.00
WC14 Mo Vaughn 1.00 2.50
WC15 Matt Williams 1.00 2.50

1997 Topps Chrome

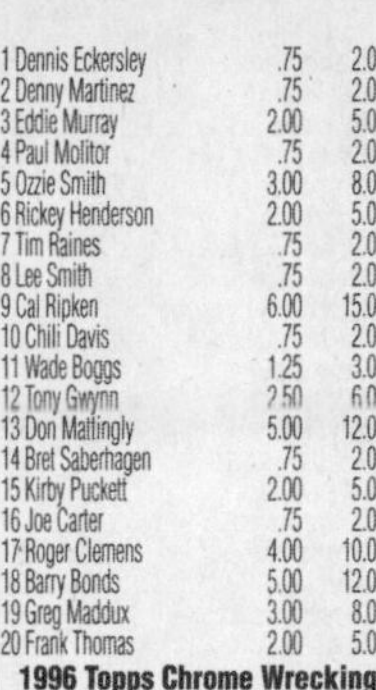

The 1997 Topps Chrome set was issued in one series totalling 165 cards and was distributed in four-card packs with a suggested retail price of $3.00. Using Chromium technology to highlight the cards, this set features a metalized version of the cards of some of the best players from the 1997 regular Topps Series one and two. An attractive 8 1/2" by 11" chrome promo sheet was sent to dealers advertising this set.

COMPLETE SET (165) 20.00 50.00
1 Barry Bonds 2.00 5.00
2 Jose Valentin .30 .75
3 Brady Anderson .30 .75
4 Wade Boggs .50 1.25
5 Andres Galarraga .30 .75
6 Rusty Greer .30 .75
7 Derek Jeter 2.00 5.00
8 Ricky Bottalico .30 .75
9 Mike Piazza 1.25 3.00
10 Garret Anderson .30 .75
11 Jeff King .30 .75
12 Kevin Appier .30 .75
13 Mark Grace .50 1.25
14 Jeff D'Amico .30 .75
15 Jay Buhner .30 .75
16 Hal Morris .30 .75
17 Harold Baines .30 .75
18 Jeff Cirillo .30 .75
19 Tom Glavine .50 1.25
20 Andy Pettitte .50 1.25
21 Mark McGwire 2.00 5.00
22 Chuck Knoblauch .30 .75
23 Raul Mondesi .30 .75
24 Albert Belle .30 .75
25 Trevor Hoffman .30 .75
26 Eric Young .30 .75
27 Brian McRae .30 .75
28 Jim Edmonds .30 .75
29 Robb Nen .30 .75
30 Reggie Sanders .30 .75
31 Mike Lansing .30 .75
32 Craig Biggio .50 1.25
33 Ray Lankford .30 .75
34 Charles Nagy .30 .75
35 Paul Wilson .30 .75
36 John Wetteland .30 .75
37 Derek Bell .30 .75
38 Edgar Martinez .50 1.25
39 Rickey Henderson .75 2.00
40 Jim Thome .50 1.25
41 Frank Thomas .75 2.00
42 Jackie Robinson .75 2.00
43 Terry Steinbach .30 .75
44 Kevin Brown .30 .75
45 Joey Hamilton .30 .75
46 Travis Fryman .30 .75
47 Juan Gonzalez .30 .75
48 Ron Gant .30 .75
49 Greg Maddux 1.25 3.00
50 Wally Joyner .30 .75
51 John Valentin .30 .75
52 Bret Boone .30 .75
53 Paul Molitor .30 .75
54 Rafael Palmeiro .50 1.25
55 Todd Hundley .30 .75
56 Ellis Burks .30 .75
57 Bernie Williams .50 1.25
58 Roberto Alomar .50 1.25
59 Jose Mesa .30 .75
60 Troy Percival .30 .75
61 John Smoltz .50 1.25
62 Jeff Conine .30 .75
63 Bernard Gilkey .30 .75
64 Mickey Tettleton .30 .75
65 Justin Thompson .30 .75
66 Tony Phillips .30 .75
67 Ryne Sandberg 1.25 3.00
68 Geronimo Berroa .30 .75
69 Todd Hollandsworth .30 .75
70 Rey Ordonez .30 .75
71 Marquis Grissom .30 .75
72 Tino Martinez .50 1.25
73 Steve Finley .30 .75
74 Andy Benes .30 .75
75 Jason Kendall .30 .75
76 Johnny Damon .50 1.25
77 Jason Giambi .30 .75
78 Henry Rodriguez .30 .75
79 Edgar Renteria .30 .75
80 Ray Durham .30 .75
81 Gregg Jefferies .30 .75
82 Roberto Hernandez .30 .75
83 Joe Carter .30 .75
84 Jermaine Dye .30 .75
85 Julio Franco .30 .75
86 David Justice .30 .75
87 Jose Canseco .50 1.25
88 Paul O'Neill .50 1.25
89 Mariano Rivera .75 2.00
90 Bobby Higginson .30 .75
91 Mark Grudzielanek .30 .75
92 Lance Johnson .30 .75
93 Ken Caminiti .30 .75
94 Gary Sheffield .30 .75
95 Luis Castillo .30 .75
96 Scott Rolen .50 1.25
97 Chipper Jones .75 2.00
98 Darryl Strawberry .30 .75
99 Nomar Garciaparra 1.25 3.00
100 Jeff Bagwell .50 1.25
101 Ken Griffey Jr. 1.25 3.00
102 Sammy Sosa .75 2.00
103 Jack McDowell .30 .75
104 James Baldwin .30 .75
105 Rocky Coppinger .30 .75
106 Manny Ramirez .50 1.25
107 Tim Salmon .50 1.25
108 Eric Karros .30 .75
109 Brett Butler .30 .75
110 Randy Johnson .75 2.00
111 Pat Hentgen .30 .75
112 Rondell White .30 .75
113 Eddie Murray .75 2.00
114 Ivan Rodriguez .50 1.25
115 Jermaine Allensworth .30 .75
116 Ed Sprague .30 .75
117 Kenny Lofton .30 .75
118 Alan Benes .30 .75
119 Fred McGriff .50 1.25
120 Alex Fernandez .30 .75
121 Al Martin .30 .75
122 Devon White .30 .75
123 David Cone .30 .75
124 Karim Garcia .30 .75
125 Chili Davis .30 .75
126 Roger Clemens 1.50 4.00
127 Bobby Bonilla .30 .75
128 Mike Mussina .50 1.25
129 Todd Walker .30 .75
130 Dante Bichette .30 .75
131 Carlos Baerga .30 .75
132 Matt Williams .30 .75
133 Will Clark .50 1.25
134 Dennis Eckersley .30 .75
135 Ryan Klesko .30 .75
136 Dean Palmer .30 .75
137 Javy Lopez .30 .75
138 Greg Vaughn .30 .75
139 Vinny Castilla .30 .75
140 Cal Ripken 2.50 6.00
141 Ruben Rivera .30 .75
142 Mark Wohlers .30 .75
143 Tony Clark .30 .75
144 Jose Rosado .30 .75
145 Tony Gwynn 1.00 2.50
146 Cecil Fielder .30 .75
147 Brian Jordan .30 .75
148 Bob Abreu .50 1.25
149 Barry Larkin .50 1.25
150 Robin Ventura .30 .75
151 John Olerud .30 .75
152 Rod Beck .30 .75
153 Vladimir Guerrero .75 2.00
154 Marty Cordova .30 .75
155 Todd Stottlemyre .30 .75
156 Hideo Nomo .75 2.00
157 Denny Neagle .30 .75
158 John Jaha .30 .75
159 Mo Vaughn .30 .75
160 Andruw Jones .50 1.25
161 Moises Alou .30 .75
162 Larry Walker .30 .75
163 Eddie Murray SH .50 1.25
164 Paul Molitor SH .30 .75
165 Checklist .30 .75

1997 Topps Chrome Refractors

Randomly inserted in packs at a rate of one in 12, this 165-card set is a parallel version of the regular Topps Chrome set and is similar in design. The difference is found in the refractive quality of the cards.

*STARS: 2.5X TO 6X BASE CARDS
STATED ODDS 1:12

1997 Topps Chrome All-Stars

Randomly inserted in packs at a rate of one in 24, this 22-card set features color player photos printed on rainbow foilboard. The set showcases the top three players from each position from both the American and National leagues as voted on by the Topps Sports Department.

COMPLETE SET (22) 40.00 100.00
STATED ODDS 1:24
*REF: 1X TO 2.5X BASIC CHROME AS
REFRACTOR STATED ODDS 1:72
AS1 Ivan Rodriguez 1.50 4.00
AS2 Todd Hundley 1.00 2.50
AS3 Frank Thomas 2.50 6.00
AS4 Andres Galarraga 1.00 2.50
AS5 Chuck Knoblauch 1.00 2.50
AS6 Eric Young 1.00 2.50
AS7 Jim Thome 1.50 4.00
AS8 Chipper Jones 2.50 6.00
AS9 Cal Ripken 8.00 20.00
AS10 Barry Larkin 1.50 4.00
AS11 Albert Belle 1.00 2.50
AS12 Barry Bonds 6.00 15.00
AS13 Ken Griffey Jr. 4.00 10.00
AS14 Ellis Burks 1.00 2.50
AS15 Juan Gonzalez 1.00 2.50
AS16 Gary Sheffield 1.00 2.50
AS17 Andy Pettitte 1.50 4.00
AS18 Tom Glavine 1.50 4.00
AS19 Pat Hentgen 1.00 2.50
AS20 John Smoltz 1.50 4.00
AS21 Roberto Hernandez 1.00 2.50
AS22 Mark Wohlers 1.00 2.50

1997 Topps Chrome Diamond Duos

Randomly inserted in packs at a rate of one in 36, this 10-card set features color player photos of two superstar teammates on double sided chromium cards.

COMPLETE SET (10) 20.00 50.00
STATED ODDS 1:36
*REF.: 1X TO 2.5X BASIC DIAM.DUOS
REFRACTOR STATED ODDS 1:108
DD1 Chipper Jones 2.00 5.00
Andruw Jones
DD2 Derek Jeter 5.00 12.00
Bernie Williams
DD3 Ken Griffey Jr. 3.00 8.00
Jay Buhner
DD4 Kenny Lofton 1.25 3.00
Manny Ramirez
DD5 Jeff Bagwell 1.25 3.00
Craig Biggio
DD6 Juan Gonzalez 1.25 3.00
Ivan Rodriguez
DD7 Cal Ripken 6.00 15.00
Brady Anderson
DD8 Mike Piazza 3.00 8.00
Hideo Nomo
DD9 Andres Galarraga .75 2.00
Dante Bichette
DD10 Frank Thomas 2.00 5.00
Albert Belle

1997 Topps Chrome Season's Best

Randomly inserted in packs at a rate of one in 18, this 25-card set features color player photos of the five top players from five statistical categories: most steals (Leading Looters), most home runs (Bleacher Reachers), most wins (Hill Toppers), most RBIs (Number Crunchers), and best slugging percentage (Kings of Swing).

COMPLETE SET (25) 25.00 60.00
STATED ODDS 1:18
*REF: 1X TO 2.5X BASIC SEAS.BEST
REFRACTOR STATED ODDS 1:54
1 Tony Gwynn 2.50 6.00
2 Frank Thomas 2.00 5.00
3 Ellis Burks .75 2.00
4 Paul Molitor .75 2.00
5 Chuck Knoblauch .75 2.00
6 Mark McGwire 5.00 12.00
7 Brady Anderson .75 2.00
8 Ken Griffey Jr. 3.00 8.00
9 Albert Belle .75 2.00
10 Andres Galarraga .75 2.00
11 Andres Galarraga .75 2.00
12 Albert Belle .75 2.00
13 Juan Gonzalez .75 2.00
14 Mo Vaughn .75 2.00
15 Rafael Palmeiro 1.25 3.00
16 John Smoltz 1.25 3.00
17 Andy Pettitte 1.25 3.00
18 Pat Hentgen .75 2.00
19 Mike Mussina 1.25 3.00
20 Andy Benes .75 2.00
21 Kenny Lofton .75 2.00
22 Tom Goodwin .75 2.00
23 Otis Nixon .75 2.00
24 Eric Young .75 2.00
25 Lance Johnson .75 2.00

1997 Topps Chrome Jumbos

This six-card set contains jumbo versions of the six featured players' regular Topps Chrome cards and measures approximately 3 3/4" by 5 1/4". One of these cards was found in a special box with five Topps Chrome packs issued through Wal-Mart. The cards are numbered according to their corresponding number in the regular set.

COMPLETE SET (6) 6.00 15.00
9 Mike Piazza 1.25 3.00
94 Gary Sheffield .50 1.25
97 Chipper Jones 1.00 2.50
101 Ken Griffey Jr. 1.00 2.50
102 Sammy Sosa .60 1.50
140 Cal Ripken Jr. 2.00 5.00

1998 Topps Chrome

The 1998 Topps Chrome set was issued in two separate series of 282 and 221 cards respectively with design and content paralleling the base 1998 Topps set. Four-card packs carried a suggested retail price of $3 each. Card fronts feature color action player photos printed with Chromium technology on metalized cards. The backs carry player information. As is tradition with Topps sets since 1996, card number seven was excluded from the set in honor of Mickey Mantle. Subsets are as follows: Prospects/Draft Picks (245-264/484-501), Season Highlights (265-269/474-478), Inter-League (270-274/479-483), Checklists (275-276/502-503) and World Series (277-283). After four years of being excluded from Topps products, superstar Alex Rodriguez finally made his Topps debut as card number 504. Notable Rookie Cards include Ryan Anderson, Michael Cuddyer, Jack Cust and Troy Glaus.

COMPLETE SET (503) 60.00 150.00
COMP. SERIES 1 (282) 30.00 80.00
COMP. SERIES 2 (221) 30.00 80.00
REF.STATED ODDS 1:12
1 Tony Gwynn 1.00 2.50
2 Larry Walker .30 .75
3 Billy Wagner .30 .75
4 Denny Neagle .30 .75
5 Vladimir Guerrero .75 2.00
6 Kevin Brown .50 1.25
8 Mariano Rivera .75 2.00
9 Tony Clark .30 .75
10 Deion Sanders .50 1.25
11 Francisco Cordova .30 .75
12 Matt Williams .30 .75
13 Carlos Baerga .30 .75
14 Mo Vaughn .30 .75
15 Bobby Witt .30 .75
16 Matt Stairs .30 .75
17 Chan Ho Park .30 .75
18 Mike Bordick .30 .75
19 Michael Tucker .30 .75
20 Frank Thomas .75 2.00
21 Roberto Clemente 2.00 5.00
22 Dmitri Young .30 .75
23 Steve Trachsel .30 .75
24 Jeff Kent .30 .75
25 Scott Rolen .50 1.25
26 John Thomson .30 .75
27 Joe Vitiello .30 .75
28 Eddie Guardado .30 .75
29 Charlie Hayes .30 .75
30 Juan Gonzalez .30 .75
31 Garret Anderson .30 .75
32 John Jaha .30 .75
33 Omar Vizquel .50 1.25
34 Brian Hunter .30 .75
35 Jeff Bagwell .50 1.25
36 Mark Lemke .30 .75
37 Doug Glanville .30 .75
38 Dan Wilson .30 .75
39 Steve Cooke .30 .75
40 Chili Davis .30 .75
41 Mike Cameron .30 .75
42 F.P. Santangelo .30 .75
43 Brad Ausmus .30 .75
44 Gary DiSarcina .30 .75
45 Pat Hentgen .30 .75
46 Wilton Guerrero .30 .75
47 Devon White .30 .75
48 Danny Patterson .30 .75
49 Pat Meares .30 .75
50 Rafael Palmeiro .50 1.25
51 Mark Gardner .30 .75
52 Jeff Blauser .30 .75
53 Dave Hollins .30 .75
54 Carlos Garcia .30 .75
55 Ben McDonald .30 .75
56 John Mabry .30 .75
57 Trevor Hoffman .30 .75
58 Tony Fernandez .30 .75
59 Rich Loiselle RC .30 .75
60 Mark Leiter .30 .75
61 Pat Kelly .30 .75
62 John Flaherty .30 .75
63 Roger Bailey .30 .75
64 Tom Gordon .30 .75
65 Ryan Klesko .30 .75
66 Darryl Hamilton .30 .75
67 Jim Eisenreich .30 .75
68 Butch Huskey .30 .75
69 Mark Grudzielanek .30 .75
70 Marquis Grissom .30 .75
71 Mark McLemore .30 .75
72 Gary Gaetti .30 .75
73 Greg Gagne .30 .75
74 Lyle Mouton .30 .75
75 Jim Edmonds .30 .75
76 Shawn Green .30 .75
77 Greg Vaughn .30 .75
78 Terry Adams .30 .75
79 Kevin Polcovich .30 .75
80 Troy O'Leary .30 .75
81 Jeff Shaw .30 .75
82 Rich Becker .30 .75
83 David Wells .30 .75
84 Steve Karsay .30 .75
85 Charles Nagy .30 .75
86 B.J. Surhoff .30 .75
87 Jamey Wright .30 .75
88 James Baldwin .30 .75
89 Edgardo Alfonzo .30 .75
90 Jay Buhner .30 .75
91 Brady Anderson .30 .75
92 Scott Servais .30 .75
93 Edgar Renteria .30 .75
94 Mike Lieberthal .30 .75
95 Rick Aguilera .30 .75
96 Walt Weiss .30 .75
97 Deivi Cruz .30 .75
98 Kurt Abbott .30 .75
99 Henry Rodriguez .30 .75
100 Mike Piazza 1.25 3.00
101 Billy Taylor .30 .75
102 Todd Zeile .30 .75
103 Rey Ordonez .30 .75
104 Willie Greene .30 .75
105 Tony Womack .30 .75
106 Mike Sweeney .30 .75
107 Jeffrey Hammonds .30 .75
108 Kevin Orie .30 .75
109 Alex Gonzalez .30 .75
110 Jose Canseco .50 1.25
111 Paul Sorrento .30 .75
112 Joey Hamilton .30 .75
113 Brad Radke .30 .75
114 Steve Avery .30 .75
115 Esteban Loaiza .30 .75
116 Stan Javier .30 .75
117 Chris Gomez .30 .75
118 Royce Clayton .30 .75
119 Orlando Merced .30 .75
120 Kevin Appier .30 .75
121 Mel Nieves .30 .75
122 Joe Girardi .30 .75
123 Rico Brogna .30 .75
124 Kent Mercker .30 .75
125 Manny Ramirez .50 1.25
126 Jeromy Burnitz .30 .75
127 Kevin Foster .30 .75
128 Matt Morris .30 .75
129 Jason Dickson .30 .75
130 Tom Glavine .50 1.25
131 Wally Joyner .30 .75
132 Rick Reed .30 .75
133 Todd Jones .30 .75
134 Dave Martinez .30 .75
135 Sandy Alomar Jr. .30 .75
136 Mike Lansing .30 .75
137 Sean Berry .30 .75
138 Doug Jones .30 .75
139 Todd Stottlemyre .30 .75
140 Jay Bell .30 .75
141 Jaime Navarro .30 .75
142 Chris Hoiles .30 .75
143 Joey Cora .30 .75
144 Scott Spiezio .30 .75
145 Joe Carter .30 .75
146 Jose Guillen .30 .75
147 Damion Easley .30 .75
148 Lee Stevens .30 .75
149 Alex Fernandez .30 .75
150 Randy Johnson .75 2.00
151 J.T. Snow .30 .75
152 Chuck Finley .30 .75
153 Bernard Gilkey .30 .75
154 David Segui .30 .75
155 Dante Bichette .30 .75
156 Kevin Stocker .30 .75
157 Carl Everett .30 .75
158 Jose Valentin .30 .75
159 Pokey Reese .30 .75
160 Derek Jeter 2.00 5.00
161 Roger Pavlik .30 .75
162 Mark Wohlers .30 .75
163 Ricky Bottalico .30 .75
164 Ozzie Guillen .30 .75
165 Mike Mussina .50 1.25
166 Gary Sheffield .30 .75
167 Hideo Nomo .75 2.00
168 Mark Grace .50 1.25
169 Aaron Sele .30 .75
170 Darryl Kile .30 .75
171 Shawn Estes .30 .75
172 Vinny Castilla .30 .75
173 Ron Coomer .30 .75
174 Jose Rosado .30 .75
175 Kenny Lofton .30 .75
176 Jason Giambi .30 .75
177 Hal Morris .30 .75
178 Darren Bragg .30 .75
179 Orel Hershiser .30 .75
180 Ray Lankford .30 .75
181 Hideki Irabu .30 .75
182 Kevin Young .30 .75
183 Javy Lopez .30 .75
184 Jeff Montgomery .30 .75
185 Mike Holtz .30 .75
186 George Williams .30 .75
187 Cal Eldred .30 .75
188 Tom Candiotti .30 .75
189 Glenallen Hill .30 .75
190 Brian Giles .30 .75
191 Dave Mlicki .30 .75
192 Garrett Stephenson .30 .75
193 Jeff Frye .30 .75
194 Joe Oliver .30 .75
195 Bob Hamelin .30 .75
196 Luis Sojo .30 .75
197 LaTroy Hawkins .30 .75
198 Kevin Elster .30 .75
199 Jeff Reed .30 .75
200 Dennis Eckersley .30 .75
201 Bill Mueller .30 .75
202 Russ Davis .30 .75
203 Armando Benitez .30 .75
204 Quilvio Veras .30 .75
205 Tim Naehring .30 .75
206 Quinton McCracken .30 .75
207 Raul Casanova .30 .75
208 Matt Lawton .30 .75
209 Luis Alicea .30 .75
210 Luis Gonzalez .30 .75
211 Allen Watson .30 .75
212 Gerald Williams .30 .75
213 David Bell .30 .75
214 Todd Hollandsworth .30 .75
215 Wade Boggs .50 1.25
216 Jose Mesa .30 .75
217 Jamie Moyer .30 .75
218 Darren Daulton .30 .75
219 Mickey Morandini .30 .75
220 Rusty Greer .30 .75
221 Jim Bullinger .30 .75
222 Jose Offerman .30 .75
223 Matt Karchner .30 .75
224 Woody Williams .30 .75
225 Mark Loretta .30 .75
226 Mike Hampton .30 .75
227 Willie Adams .30 .75
228 Scott Hatteberg .30 .75
229 Rich Amaral .30 .75
230 Terry Steinbach .30 .75
231 Glendon Rusch .30 .75
232 Bret Boone .30 .75
233 Robert Person .30 .75
234 Jose Hernandez .30 .75
235 Doug Drabek .30 .75
236 Jason McDonald .30 .75
237 Chris Widger .30 .75
238 Tom Martin .30 .75
239 Dave Burba .30 .75
240 Pete Rose Jr. RC .30 .75
241 Bobby Ayala .30 .75
242 Tim Wakefield .30 .75
243 Dennis Springer .30 .75
244 Tim Belcher .30 .75
245 Jon Garland .40 1.00
Geoff Goetz
246 Glenn Davis .40 1.00
Lance Berkman
247 Vernon Wells .40 1.00
Aaron Akin
248 Adam Kennedy .40 1.00
Jason Romano
249 Jason Dellaero .40 1.00
Troy Cameron
250 Alex Sanchez .40 1.00
Jared Sandberg
251 Pablo Ortega .40 1.00
James Manias
252 Jason Conti RC .40 1.00
Mike Stoner
253 John Patterson .40 1.00
Larry Rodriguez
254 Adrian Beltre .40 1.00
Ryan Minor RC
Aaron Boone
255 Ben Grieve .40 1.00
Brian Buchanan
Dermal Brown
256 Kerry Wood .40 1.00
Carl Pavano
Gil Meche
257 David Ortiz 2.00 5.00
Daryle Ward
Richie Sexson
258 Randy Winn .40 1.00
Juan Encarnacion
Andrew Vessel
259 Kris Benson .40 1.00
Travis Smith
Courtney Duncan RC
260 Chad Hermansen RC .40 1.00
Brent Butler
Warren Morris
261 Ben Davis .40 1.00

Eli Marrero
Ramon Hernandez
262 Eric Chavez .40 1.00
Russell Branyan
Russ Johnson
263 Todd Dunwoody RC .40 1.00
John Barnes
Ryan Jackson
264 Matt Clement 2.00 5.00
Roy Halladay
Brian Fuentes RC
265 Randy Johnson SH .50 1.25
266 Kevin Brown SH .30 .75
267 Ricardo Rincon SH .30 .75
268 N.Garciaparra SH .75 2.00
269 Tino Martinez SH .30 .75
270 Chuck Knoblauch IL .30 .75
271 Pedro Martinez IL .50 1.25
272 Denny Neagle IL .30 .75
273 Juan Gonzalez IL .30 .75
274 Andres Galarraga IL .30 .75
275 Checklist .30 .75
276 Checklist .30 .75
277 Moises Alou WS .30 .75
278 Sandy Alomar Jr. WS .30 .75
279 Gary Sheffield WS .30 .75
280 Matt Williams WS .30 .75
281 Livan Hernandez WS .30 .75
282 Chad Ogea WS .30 .75
283 Marlins Champs .30 .75
284 Tino Martinez .50 1.25
285 Roberto Alomar .50 1.25
286 Jeff King .30 .75
287 Brian Jordan .30 .75
288 Darin Erstad .30 .75
289 Ken Caminiti .30 .75
290 Jim Thome .50 1.25
291 Paul Molitor .30 .75
292 Ivan Rodriguez .50 1.25
293 Bernie Williams .50 1.25
294 Todd Hundley .30 .75
295 Andres Galarraga .30 .75
296 Greg Maddux 1.25 3.00
297 Edgar Martinez .50 1.25
298 Ron Gant .30 .75
299 Derek Bell .30 .75
300 Roger Clemens 1.50 4.00
301 Rondell White .30 .75
302 Barry Larkin .50 1.25
303 Robin Ventura .30 .75
304 Jason Kendall .30 .75
305 Chipper Jones .75 2.00
306 John Franco .30 .75
307 Sammy Sosa .75 2.00
308 Troy Percival .30 .75
309 Chuck Knoblauch .30 .75
310 Ellis Burks .30 .75
311 Al Martin .30 .75
312 Tim Salmon .50 1.25
313 Moises Alou .30 .75
314 Lance Johnson .30 .75
315 Justin Thompson .30 .75
316 Will Clark .50 1.25
317 Barry Bonds 2.00 5.00
318 Craig Biggio .50 1.25
319 John Smoltz .50 1.25
320 Cal Ripken 2.50 6.00
321 Ken Griffey Jr. 1.25 3.00
322 Paul O'Neill .50 1.25
323 Todd Helton .50 1.25
324 John Olerud .30 .75
325 Mark McGwire 2.00 5.00
326 Jose Cruz Jr. .30 .75
327 Jeff Cirillo .30 .75
328 Dean Palmer .30 .75
329 John Wetteland .30 .75
330 Steve Finley .30 .75
331 Albert Belle .30 .75
332 Curt Schilling .30 .75
333 Raul Mondesi .30 .75
334 Andruw Jones .50 1.25
335 Nomar Garciaparra 1.25 3.00
336 David Justice .30 .75
337 Andy Pettitte .50 1.25
338 Pedro Martinez .50 1.25
339 Travis Miller .30 .75
340 Chris Stynes .30 .75
341 Gregg Jefferies .30 .75
342 Jeff Fassero .30 .75
343 Craig Counsell .30 .75
344 Wilson Alvarez .30 .75
345 Bip Roberts .30 .75
346 Kelvim Escobar .30 .75
347 Mark Bellhorn .30 .75
348 Cory Lidle RC 3.00 8.00
349 Fred McGriff .50 1.25
350 Chuck Carr .30 .75
351 Bob Abreu .30 .75
352 Juan Guzman .30 .75
353 Fernando Vina .30 .75
354 Andy Benes .30 .75
355 Dave Nilsson .30 .75
356 Bobby Bonilla .30 .75
357 Ismael Valdes .30 .75
358 Carlos Perez .30 .75
359 Kirk Rueter .30 .75
360 Bartolo Colon .30 .75
361 Mel Rojas .30 .75
362 Johnny Damon .50 1.25
363 Geronimo Berroa .30 .75
364 Reggie Sanders .30 .75
365 Jermaine Allensworth .30 .75
366 Orlando Cabrera .30 .75
367 Jorge Fabregas .30 .75
368 Scott Stahoviak .30 .75
369 Ken Cloude .30 .75
370 Donovan Osborne .30 .75
371 Roger Cedeno .30 .75
372 Neifi Perez .30 .75
373 Chris Holt .30 .75
374 Cecil Fielder .30 .75
375 Marty Cordova .30 .75
376 Tom Goodwin .30 .75
377 Jeff Suppan .30 .75
378 Jeff Brantley .30 .75
379 Mark Langston .30 .75
380 Shane Reynolds .30 .75
381 Mike Fetters .30 .75
382 Todd Greene .30 .75
383 Ray Durham .30 .75
384 Carlos Delgado .30 .75
385 Jeff D'Amico .30 .75
386 Brian McRae .30 .75
387 Alan Benes .30 .75
388 Heathcliff Slocumb .30 .75
389 Eric Young .30 .75
390 Travis Fryman .30 .75
391 David Cone .30 .75
392 Otis Nixon .30 .75
393 Jeremi Gonzalez .30 .75
394 Jeff Juden .30 .75
395 Jose Vizcaino .30 .75
396 Ugueth Urbina .30 .75
397 Ramon Martinez .30 .75
398 Robb Nen .30 .75
399 Harold Baines .30 .75
400 Delino DeShields .30 .75
401 John Burkett .30 .75
402 Sterling Hitchcock .30 .75
403 Mark Clark .30 .75
404 Terrell Wade .30 .75
405 Scott Brosius .30 .75
406 Chad Curtis .30 .75
407 Brian Johnson .30 .75
408 Roberto Kelly .30 .75
409 Dave Dellucci RC .50 1.25
410 Michael Tucker .30 .75
411 Mark Kotsay .30 .75
412 Mark Lewis .30 .75
413 Ryan McGuire .30 .75
414 Shawon Dunston .30 .75
415 Brad Rigby .30 .75
416 Scott Erickson .30 .75
417 Bobby Jones .30 .75
418 Darren Oliver .30 .75
419 John Smiley .30 .75
420 T.J. Mathews .30 .75
421 Dustin Hermanson .30 .75
422 Mike Timlin .30 .75
423 Willie Blair .30 .75
424 Manny Alexander .30 .75
425 Bob Tewksbury .30 .75
426 Pete Schourek .30 .75
427 Reggie Jefferson .30 .75
428 Ed Sprague .30 .75
429 Jeff Conine .30 .75
430 Roberto Hernandez .30 .75
431 Tom Pagnozzi .30 .75
432 Jaret Wright .30 .75
433 Livan Hernandez .30 .75
434 Andy Ashby .30 .75
435 Todd Dunn .30 .75
436 Bobby Higginson .30 .75
437 Rod Beck .30 .75
438 Jim Leyritz .30 .75
439 Matt Williams .30 .75
440 Brett Tomko .30 .75
441 Joe Randa .30 .75
442 Chris Carpenter .30 .75
443 Dennis Reyes .30 .75
444 Al Leiter .30 .75
445 Jason Schmidt .30 .75
446 Ken Hill .30 .75
447 Shannon Stewart .30 .75
448 Enrique Wilson .30 .75
449 Fernando Tatis .30 .75
450 Jimmy Key .30 .75
451 Darrin Fletcher .30 .75
452 John Valentin .30 .75
453 Kevin Tapani .30 .75
454 Eric Karros .30 .75
455 Jay Bell .30 .75
456 Walt Weiss .30 .75
457 Devon White .30 .75
458 Carl Pavano .30 .75
459 Mike Lansing .30 .75
460 John Flaherty .30 .75
461 Richard Hidalgo .30 .75
462 Quinton McCracken .30 .75
463 Karim Garcia .30 .75
464 Miguel Cairo .30 .75
465 Edwin Diaz .30 .75
466 Bobby Smith .30 .75
467 Yamil Benitez .30 .75
468 Rich Butler RC .30 .75
469 Ben Ford RC .30 .75
470 Bubba Trammell .30 .75
471 Brent Brede .30 .75
472 Brooks Kieschnick .30 .75
473 Carlos Castillo .30 .75
474 Brad Radke SH .30 .75
475 Roger Clemens SH .75 2.00
476 Curt Schilling SH .30 .75
477 John Olerud SH .30 .75
478 Mark McGwire SH 1.00 2.50
479 Mike Piazza IL .75 2.00
Ken Griffey Jr.
480 Jeff Bagwell .50 1.25
Frank Thomas
481 Chipper Jones .50 1.25
Nomar Garciaparra IL
482 Larry Walker IL .30 .75
Juan Gonzalez IL
483 Gary Sheffield IL .30 .75
Tino Martinez IL
484 Derrick Gibson .40 1.00
Michael Coleman
Norm Hutchins
485 Braden Looper .40 1.00
Cliff Politte
Brian Rose
486 Eric Milton .40 1.00
Jason Marquis
Corey Lee
487 A.J.Hinch .40 1.00
Mark Osborne RC
Robert Fick
488 Aramis Ramirez .40 1.00
Alex Gonzalez
Sean Casey
489 Donnie Bridges .40 1.00
Tim Drew RC
490 Ntema Ndungidi RC .40 1.00
Darnell McDonald
491 Ryan Anderson RC .40 1.00
Mark Mangum
492 J.J.Davis 2.00 5.00
Troy Glaus RC
493 Jayson Werth RC .40 1.00
Dan Reichert
494 John Curtice RC 1.00 2.50
Michael Cuddyer RC
495 Jack Cust RC .75 2.00
Jason Standridge
496 Brian Anderson .40 1.00
497 Tony Saunders .40 1.00
498 Vladimir Nunez .40 1.00
Jhensy Sandoval
499 Brad Penny .40 1.00
Nick Bierbrodt
500 Dustin Carr .40 1.00
Luis Cruz RC
501 Cedric Bowers .40 1.00
Marcus McCain
502 Checklist .30 .75
503 Checklist .30 .75
504 Alex Rodriguez 1.50 4.00

1998 Topps Chrome Refractors

Randomly inserted in first and second series packs at the rate of one in 12, this set is parallel to the base set and is similar in design. The difference is found in the refractive quality of the cards.

*STARS: 2.5X TO 6X BASIC CARDS
*ROOKIES: 1.25X TO 3X BASIC
STATED ODDS 1:12

1998 Topps Chrome Baby Boomers

Randomly inserted in first series packs at the rate of one in 24, this 15 card set features color action photos printed on metalized cards with Chromium technology of young players who have already made their mark in the game with less than three years in the majors.

COMPLETE SET (15) 30.00 80.00
SER.1 STATED ODDS 1:24
*REF: .75X TO 2X BASIC CHR.BOOMERS
REFRACTOR SER.1 STATED ODDS 1:72
BB1 Derek Jeter 6.00 15.00
BB2 Scott Rolen 1.50 4.00
BB3 Nomar Garciaparra 4.00 10.00
BB4 Jose Cruz Jr. 1.00 2.50
BB5 Darin Erstad 1.00 2.50
BB6 Todd Helton 1.50 4.00
BB7 Tony Clark 1.00 2.50
BB8 Jose Guillen 1.00 2.50
BB9 Andruw Jones 1.50 4.00
BB10 Vladimir Guerrero 2.50 6.00
BB11 Mark Kotsay 1.00 2.50
BB12 Todd Greene 1.00 2.50
BB13 Andy Pettitte 1.50 4.00
BB14 Justin Thompson 1.00 2.50
BB15 Alan Benes 1.00 2.50

1998 Topps Chrome Clout Nine

Randomly seeded at a rate of one in 24 second series packs, cards from this nine-card set feature a selection of the league's top sluggers. The cards are a straight parallel of the previously released 1998 Topps Clout 9 set, except of course for the Chromium stock fronts.

COMPLETE SET (9) 25.00 60.00
SER.2 STATED ODDS 1:24
*REF: .75X TO 2X BASIC CHR.CLOUT
REFRACTOR SER.2 STATED ODDS 1:72
C1 Edgar Martinez 1.50 4.00
C2 Mike Piazza 4.00 10.00
C3 Frank Thomas 2.50 6.00
C4 Craig Biggio 1.50 4.00
C5 Vinny Castilla 1.00 2.50
C6 Jeff Blauser 1.00 2.50
C7 Barry Bonds 6.00 15.00
C8 Ken Griffey Jr. 4.00 10.00
C9 Larry Walker 1.00 2.50

1998 Topps Chrome Flashback

Randomly inserted in first series packs at the rate of one in 24, this 10-card set features two-sided cards with color action photos of top players printed on metalized cards with Chromium technology. One side displays how they looked "then" as rookies, while the other side shows how they look "now" as stars.

COMPLETE SET (10) 30.00 80.00
SER.1 STATED ODDS 1:24
*REF: .75X TO 2X BASIC CHR.FLASHBACK
REFRACTOR SER.1 STATED ODDS 1:72
FB1 Barry Bonds 6.00 15.00
FB2 Ken Griffey Jr. 4.00 10.00
FB3 Paul Molitor 1.00 2.50
FB4 Randy Johnson 2.50 6.00
FB5 Cal Ripken 8.00 20.00
FB6 Tony Gwynn 3.00 8.00
FB7 Kenny Lofton 1.00 2.50
FB8 Gary Sheffield 1.00 2.50
FB9 Deion Sanders 1.50 4.00
FB10 Brady Anderson 1.00 2.50

1998 Topps Chrome HallBound

Randomly inserted in first series packs at the rate of one in 24, this 15-card set features color photos printed on metalized cards with Chromium technology of top stars who are bound for the Hall of Fame in Cooperstown, New York.

COMPLETE SET (15) 60.00 150.00
SER.1 STATED ODDS 1:24
*REF: .75X TO 2X BASIC HALLBOUND
REFRACTOR SER.1 STATED ODDS 1:72
HB1 Paul Molitor 1.25 3.00
HB2 Tony Gwynn 4.00 10.00
HB3 Wade Boggs 2.00 5.00
HB4 Roger Clemens 6.00 15.00
HB5 Dennis Eckersley 1.25 3.00
HB6 Cal Ripken 10.00 25.00
HB7 Greg Maddux 5.00 12.00
HB8 Rickey Henderson 2.00 5.00
HB9 Ken Griffey Jr. 5.00 12.00
HB10 Frank Thomas 3.00 8.00
HB11 Mark McGwire 8.00 20.00
HB12 Barry Bonds 8.00 20.00
HB13 Mike Piazza 5.00 12.00
HB14 Juan Gonzalez 1.25 3.00
HB15 Randy Johnson 3.00 8.00

1998 Topps Chrome Milestones

Randomly seeded at a rate of one in every 24 second series packs, these 10 cards feature a selection of veteran stars that achieved specific career milestones in 1997. The cards are a straight parallel from the previously released 1998 Topps Milestones inserts except, of course, for the Chromium finish on the fronts.

COMPLETE SET (10) 50.00 120.00
SER.2 STATED ODDS 1:24
*REF: .75X TO 2X BASIC CHR.MILE
REFRACTOR SER.2 STATED ODDS 1:72
MS1 Barry Bonds 5.00 12.00
MS2 Roger Clemens 4.00 10.00
MS3 Dennis Eckersley .75 2.00
MS4 Juan Gonzalez .75 2.00
MS5 Ken Griffey Jr. 3.00 8.00
MS6 Tony Gwynn 2.50 6.00
MS7 Greg Maddux 3.00 8.00
MS8 Mark McGwire 5.00 12.00
MS9 Cal Ripken 6.00 15.00
MS10 Frank Thomas 2.00 5.00

1998 Topps Chrome Rookie Class

Randomly seeded at a rate of one in 12 second series packs, cards from this 10-card set feature a selection of the league's top rookies for 1998. The cards are a straight parallel of the previously released 1998 Topps Rookie Class set, except of course for the Chromium stock fronts.

COMPLETE SET (10) 8.00 20.00
SER.2 STATED ODDS 1:12
*REF: .75X TO 2X BASIC CHR.RK.CLASS
REFRACTOR SER.2 STATED ODDS 1:24
R1 Travis Lee .75 2.00
R2 Richard Hidalgo .75 2.00
R3 Todd Helton 1.25 3.00
R4 Paul Konerko .75 2.00
R5 Mark Kotsay .75 2.00
R6 Derrek Lee .75 2.00
R7 Eli Marrero .75 2.00
R8 Fernando Tatis .75 2.00
R9 Juan Encarnacion .75 2.00
R10 Ben Grieve .75 2.00

1999 Topps Chrome

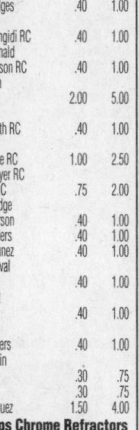

The 1999 Topps Chrome set totaled 462 cards (though is numbered 1-463 - card number 7 was never issued in honor of Mickey Mantle). The product was distributed in first and second series four-card packs each carrying a suggested retail price of $3. The first series cards were 1-6/8-242, second series cards 243-463. The card fronts feature action color player photos. The backs carry player information. The set contains the following subsets: Season Highlights (200-204), Prospects (205-212/425-437), Draft Picks (213-219/438-444), League Leaders (221-232), World Series (233-240), Strikeout Kings (445-449), All-Topps (450-460) and four Checklist Cards (241-242/462-463). The Mark McGwire Home Run Record Breaker card (220) was released in 70 different variations highlighting every home run that he hit in 1998. The Sammy Sosa Home Run Parade card (461) was issued in 66 different variations. A 462 card set of 1999 Topps Chrome is considered complete with any version of the McGwire 220 and Sosa 461. Rookie Cards of note include Pat Burrell and Alex Escobar

COMPLETE SET (462) 50.00 120.00
COMP. SERIES 1 (241) 25.00 60.00
COMP. SERIES 2 (221) 25.00 60.00
COMMON (1-6/8-463) .20 .50
COMMON (205-212/425-437) .40 1.00
1 Roger Clemens 1.50 4.00
2 Andres Galarraga .30 .75
3 Scott Brosius .30 .75
4 John Flaherty .20 .50
5 Jim Leyritz .20 .50
6 Ray Durham .30 .75
8 Jose Vizcaino .20 .50
9 Will Clark .50 1.25
10 David Wells .30 .75
11 Jose Guillen .30 .75
12 Scott Hatteberg .20 .50
13 Edgardo Alfonzo .20 .50
14 Mike Bordick .20 .50
15 Manny Ramirez .50 1.25
16 Greg Maddux 1.25 3.00
17 David Segui .20 .50
18 Darryl Strawberry .30 .75
19 Brad Radke .30 .75
20 Kerry Wood .30 .75
21 Matt Anderson .20 .50
22 Derrek Lee .50 1.25
23 Mickey Morandini .20 .50
24 Paul Konerko .30 .75
25 Travis Lee .20 .50
26 Ken Hill .20 .50
27 Kenny Rogers .30 .75
28 Paul Sorrento .20 .50
29 Quilvio Veras .20 .50
30 Todd Walker .20 .50
31 Ryan Jackson .20 .50
32 John Olerud .30 .75
33 Doug Glanville .20 .50
34 Nolan Ryan 2.50 6.00
35 Ray Lankford .30 .75
36 Mark Loretta .20 .50
37 Jason Dickson .20 .50
38 Sean Bergman .20 .50
39 Quinton McCracken .20 .50
40 Bartolo Colon .30 .75
41 Brady Anderson .30 .75
42 Chris Stynes .20 .50
43 Jorge Posada .50 1.25
44 Justin Thompson .20 .50
45 Johnny Damon .50 1.25
46 Armando Benitez .20 .50
47 Brant Brown .20 .50
48 Charlie Hayes .20 .50
49 Darren Dreifort .20 .50
50 Juan Gonzalez .30 .75
51 Chuck Knoblauch .30 .75
52 Todd Helton .50 1.25
53 Rick Reed .20 .50
54 Chris Gomez .20 .50
55 Gary Sheffield .30 .75
56 Rod Beck .20 .50
57 Rey Sanchez .20 .50
58 Garret Anderson .30 .75
59 Jimmy Haynes .20 .50
60 Steve Woodard .20 .50
61 Rondell White .30 .75
62 Vladimir Guerrero .75 2.00
63 Eric Karros .30 .75
64 Russ Davis .20 .50
65 Mo Vaughn .30 .75
66 Sammy Sosa .75 2.00
67 Troy Percival .30 .75
68 Kenny Lofton .30 .75
69 Bill Taylor .20 .50
70 Mark McGwire 2.00 5.00
71 Roger Cedeno .20 .50
72 Javy Lopez .30 .75
73 Damion Easley .20 .50
74 Andy Pettitte .50 1.25
75 Tony Gwynn 1.00 2.50
76 Ricardo Rincon .20 .50
77 F.P. Santangelo .20 .50
78 Jay Bell .30 .75
79 Scott Servais .20 .50
80 Jose Canseco .50 1.25
81 Roberto Hernandez .20 .50
82 Todd Dunwoody .20 .50
83 John Wetteland .30 .75
84 Mike Caruso .20 .50
85 Derek Jeter 2.00 5.00
86 Aaron Sele .20 .50
87 Jose Lima .20 .50
88 Ryan Christenson .20 .50
89 Jeff Cirillo .20 .50
90 Jose Hernandez .20 .50
91 Mark Kotsay .30 .75
92 Darren Bragg .20 .50
93 Albert Belle .30 .75
94 Matt Lawton .20 .50
95 Pedro Martinez .50 1.25
96 Greg Vaughn .20 .50
97 Neifi Perez .20 .50
98 Gerald Williams .20 .50
99 Derek Bell .20 .50
100 Ken Griffey Jr. 1.25 3.00
101 David Cone .30 .75
102 Brian Johnson .20 .50
103 Dean Palmer .30 .75
104 Javier Valentin .20 .50
105 Trevor Hoffman .30 .75
106 Butch Huskey .20 .50
107 Dave Martinez .20 .50
108 Billy Wagner .30 .75
109 Shawn Green .30 .75
110 Ben Grieve .20 .50
111 Tom Goodwin .20 .50
112 Jaret Wright .20 .50
113 Aramis Ramirez .30 .75
114 Dmitri Young .30 .75
115 Hideki Irabu .20 .50
116 Roberto Kelly .20 .50
117 Jeff Fassero .20 .50
118 Mark Clark .20 .50
119 Jason McDonald .20 .50
120 Matt Williams .30 .75
121 Dave Burba .20 .50
122 Bret Saberhagen .30 .75
123 Deivi Cruz .20 .50
124 Chad Curtis .20 .50
125 Scott Rolen .50 1.25
126 Lee Stevens .20 .50
127 J.T. Snow .30 .75
128 Rusty Greer .30 .75
129 Brian Meadows .20 .50
130 Jim Edmonds .30 .75
131 Ron Gant .30 .75
132 A.J. Hinch .20 .50
133 Shannon Stewart .30 .75
134 Brad Fullmer .20 .50
135 Cal Eldred .20 .50
136 Matt Walbeck .20 .50
137 Carl Everett .30 .75
138 Walt Weiss .20 .50
139 Fred McGriff .50 1.25
140 Darin Erstad .30 .75
141 Dave Nilsson .20 .50
142 Eric Young .20 .50
143 Dan Wilson .20 .50
144 Jeff Reed .20 .50
145 Brett Tomko .20 .50
146 Terry Steinbach .20 .50
147 Seth Greisinger .20 .50
148 Pat Meares .20 .50
149 Livan Hernandez .30 .75
150 Jeff Bagwell .50 1.25
151 Bob Wickman .20 .50
152 Omar Vizquel .50 1.25
153 Eric Davis .30 .75
154 Larry Sutton .20 .50
155 Magglio Ordonez .30 .75
156 Eric Milton .20 .50
157 Darren Lewis .20 .50
158 Rick Aguilera .20 .50
159 Mike Lieberthal .30 .75
160 Robb Nen .30 .75
161 Brian Giles .30 .75
162 Jeff Brantley .20 .50
163 Gary DiSarcina .20 .50
164 John Valentin .20 .50
165 Dave Dellucci .20 .50
166 Chan Ho Park .30 .75
167 Masato Yoshii .20 .50
168 Jason Schmidt .30 .75
169 LaTroy Hawkins .20 .50
170 Bret Boone .30 .75
171 Jerry DiPoto .20 .50
172 Mariano Rivera .75 2.00
173 Mike Cameron .20 .50
174 Scott Erickson .20 .50
175 Charles Johnson .30 .75
176 Bobby Jones .20 .50
177 Francisco Cordova .20 .50
178 Todd Jones .20 .50
179 Jeff Montgomery .20 .50
180 Mike Mussina .50 1.25
181 Bob Abreu .30 .75
182 Ismael Valdes .20 .50
183 Andy Fox .20 .50
184 Woody Williams .20 .50
185 Denny Neagle .20 .50
186 Jose Valentin .20 .50
187 Darrin Fletcher .20 .50
188 Gabe Alvarez .20 .50
189 Eddie Taubensee .20 .50
190 Edgar Martinez .50 1.25
191 Jason Kendall .30 .75
192 Darryl Kile .30 .75
193 Jeff King .20 .50
194 Rey Ordonez .20 .50
195 Andruw Jones .50 1.25
196 Tony Fernandez .20 .50
197 Jamey Wright .20 .50
198 B.J. Surhoff .30 .75
199 Vinny Castilla .30 .75
200 David Wells HL .20 .50
201 Mark McGwire HL 1.00 2.50
202 Sammy Sosa HL .50 1.25
203 Roger Clemens HL .75 2.00
204 Kerry Wood HL .20 .50
205 Gabe Kapler .40 1.00
Lance Berkman
Mike Frank
206 Alex Escobar RC .40 1.00
Ricky Ledee
Mike Stoner
207 Peter Bergeron RC .40 1.00
Jeremy Giambi
George Lombard
208 Michael Barrett .40 1.00
Ben Davis
Robert Fick
209 Jayson Werth .40 1.00
Ramon Hernandez
Pat Cline
210 Ryan Anderson .40 1.00
Bruce Chen
Chris Enochs
211 Brad Penny .40 1.00
Octavio Dotel
Mike Lincoln
212 Chuck Abbott RC .40 1.00
Brent Butler
Danny Klassen
213 Chris C.Jones .40 1.00
Jeff Urban RC
214 Arturo McDowell RC .40 1.00
Tony Torcato
215 Josh McKinley RC .40 1.00
Jason Tyner
216 Matt Burch .40 1.00
Seth Etheron RC
217 Mamon Tucker RC .40 1.00
Rick Elder
218 J.M.Gold .40 1.00
Ryan Mills RC
219 Andy Brown .40 1.00
Choo Freeman RC
220A Mark McGwire HR 1 20.00 50.00
220B Mark McGwire HR 2 12.50 30.00
220C Mark McGwire HR 3 12.50 30.00
220D Mark McGwire HR 4 12.50 30.00
220E Mark McGwire HR 5 12.50 30.00
220F Mark McGwire HR 6 12.50 30.00
220G Mark McGwire HR 7 12.50 30.00
220H Mark McGwire HR 8 12.50 30.00
220I Mark McGwire HR 9 12.50 30.00
220J M.McGwire HR 10 12.50 30.00
220K M.McGwire HR 11 12.50 30.00
220L M.McGwire HR 12 12.50 30.00
220M M.McGwire HR 13 12.50 30.00
220N M.McGwire HR 14 12.50 30.00
220O M.McGwire HR 15 12.50 30.00
220P M.McGwire HR 16 12.50 30.00
220Q M.McGwire HR 17 12.50 30.00
220R M.McGwire HR 18 12.50 30.00
220S M.McGwire HR 19 12.50 30.00
220T M.McGwire HR 20 12.50 30.00
220U M.McGwire HR 21 12.50 30.00
220V M.McGwire HR 22 12.50 30.00
220W M.McGwire HR 23 12.50 30.00
220X M.McGwire HR 24 12.50 30.00
220Y M.McGwire HR 25 12.50 30.00
220Z M.McGwire HR 26 12.50 30.00
220AA M.McGwire HR 27 12.50 30.00
220AB M.McGwire HR 28 12.50 30.00
220AC M.McGwire HR 29 12.50 30.00
220AD M.McGwire HR 30 12.50 30.00
220AE M.McGwire HR 31 12.50 30.00
220AF M.McGwire HR 32 12.50 30.00
220AG M.McGwire HR 33 12.50 30.00
220AH M.McGwire HR 34 12.50 30.00
220AI M.McGwire HR 35 12.50 30.00
220AJ M.McGwire HR 36 12.50 30.00
220AK M.McGwire HR 37 12.50 30.00
220AL M.McGwire HR 38 12.50 30.00
220AM M.McGwire HR 39 12.50 30.00
220AN M.McGwire HR 40 12.50 30.00
220AO M.McGwire HR 41 12.50 30.00
220AP M.McGwire HR 42 12.50 30.00
220AQ M.McGwire HR 43 12.50 30.00
220AR M.McGwire HR 44 12.50 30.00
220AS M.McGwire HR 45 12.50 30.00
220AT M.McGwire HR 46 12.50 30.00
220AU M.McGwire HR 47 12.50 30.00
220AV M.McGwire HR 48 12.50 30.00
220AW M.McGwire HR 49 12.50 30.00
220AX M.McGwire HR 50 12.50 30.00
220AY M.McGwire HR 51 12.50 30.00
220AZ M.McGwire HR 52 12.50 30.00
220BB M.McGwire HR 53 12.50 30.00
220CC M.McGwire HR 54 12.50 30.00
220DD M.McGwire HR 55 12.50 30.00
220EE M.McGwire HR 56 12.50 30.00
220FF M.McGwire HR 57 12.50 30.00
220GG M.McGwire HR 58 12.50 30.00
220HH M.McGwire HR 59 12.50 30.00
220II M.McGwire HR 60 12.50 30.00
220JJ M.McGwire HR 61 20.00 50.00
220KK M.McGwire HR 62 40.00 80.00
220LL M.McGwire HR 63 20.00 50.00
220MM M.McGwire HR 64 20.00 50.00
220NN M.McGwire HR 65 20.00 50.00
220OO M.McGwire HR 66 20.00 50.00
220PP M.McGwire HR 67 20.00 50.00
220QQ M.McGwire HR 68 20.00 50.00

220RR M.McGwire HR 69 20.00 50.00
220SS M.McGwire HR 70 60.00 120.00
221 Larry Walker LL .20 .50
222 Bernie Williams LL .30 .75
223 Mark McGwire LL 1.00 2.50
224 Ken Griffey Jr. LL .75 2.00
225 Sammy Sosa LL .50 1.25
226 Juan Gonzalez LL .20 .50
227 Dante Bichette LL .20 .50
228 Alex Rodriguez LL .75 2.00
229 Sammy Sosa LL .50 1.25
230 Derek Jeter LL 1.00 2.50
231 Greg Maddux LL .75 2.00
232 Roger Clemens LL .75 2.00
233 Ricky Ledee WS .20 .50
234 Chuck Knoblauch WS .20 .50
235 Bernie Williams WS .30 .75
236 Tino Martinez WS .30 .75
237 Orl. Hernandez WS .30 .75
238 Scott Brosius WS .20 .50
239 Andy Pettitte WS .30 .75
240 Mariano Rivera WS .50 1.25
241 Checklist .20 .50
242 Checklist .20 .50
243 Tom Glavine .50 1.25
244 Andy Benes .20 .50
245 Sandy Alomar Jr. .20 .50
246 Wilton Guerrero .20 .50
247 Alex Gonzalez .20 .50
248 Roberto Alomar .50 1.25
249 Ruben Rivera .20 .50
250 Eric Chavez .30 .75
251 Ellis Burks .30 .75
252 Richie Sexson .30 .75
253 Steve Finley .30 .75
254 Dwight Gooden .30 .75
255 Dustin Hermanson .20 .50
256 Kirk Rueter .20 .50
257 Steve Trachsel .20 .50
258 Gregg Jefferies .20 .50
259 Matt Stairs .20 .50
260 Shane Reynolds .20 .50
261 Gregg Olson .20 .50
262 Kevin Tapani .20 .50
263 Matt Morris .30 .75
264 Carl Pavano .30 .75
265 Nomar Garciaparra 1.25 3.00
266 Kevin Young .30 .75
267 Rick Helling .20 .50
268 Matt Franco .20 .50
269 Brian McRae .20 .50
270 Cal Ripken 2.50 6.00
271 Jeff Abbott .20 .50
272 Tony Batista .20 .50
273 Bill Simas .20 .50
274 Brian Hunter .20 .50
275 John Franco .30 .75
276 Devon White .30 .75
277 Rickey Henderson .75 2.00
278 Chuck Finley .30 .75
279 Mike Blowers .20 .50
280 Mark Grace .50 1.25
281 Randy Winn .20 .50
282 Bobby Bonilla .30 .75
283 David Justice .30 .75
284 Shane Monahan .20 .50
285 Kevin Brown .50 1.25
286 Todd Zeile .30 .75
287 Al Martin .20 .50
288 Troy O'Leary .20 .50
289 Darryl Hamilton .20 .50
290 Tino Martinez .50 1.25
291 David Ortiz .75 2.00
292 Tony Clark .20 .50
293 Ryan Minor .20 .50
294 Mark Leiter .20 .50
295 Wally Joyner .30 .75
296 Cliff Floyd .30 .75
297 Shawn Estes .20 .50
298 Pat Hentgen .20 .50
299 Scott Elarton .20 .50
300 Alex Rodriguez 1.25 3.00
301 Ozzie Guillen .30 .75
302 Hideo Nomo .75 2.00
303 Ryan McGuire .20 .50
304 Brad Ausmus .30 .75
305 Alex Gonzalez .20 .50
306 Brian Jordan .30 .75
307 John Jaha .20 .50
308 Mark Grudzielanek .20 .50
309 Juan Guzman .20 .50
310 Tony Womack .20 .50
311 Dennis Reyes .20 .50
312 Marty Cordova .20 .50
313 Ramiro Mendoza .20 .50
314 Robin Ventura .30 .75
315 Rafael Palmeiro .50 1.25
316 Ramon Martinez .20 .50
317 Pedro Astacio .20 .50
318 Dave Hollins .20 .50
319 Tom Candiotti .20 .50
320 Al Leiter .30 .75
321 Rico Brogna .20 .50
322 Reggie Jefferson .20 .50
323 Bernard Gilkey .20 .50
324 Jason Giambi .30 .75
325 Craig Biggio .50 1.25
326 Troy Glaus .50 1.25
327 Delino DeShields .20 .50
328 Fernando Vina .20 .50
329 John Smoltz .50 1.25
330 Jeff Kent .30 .75
331 Roy Halladay .75 2.00
332 Andy Ashby .20 .50
333 Tim Wakefield .30 .75
334 Roger Clemens 1.50 4.00
335 Bernie Williams .50 1.25
336 Desi Relaford .20 .50
337 John Burkett .20 .50
338 Mike Hampton .30 .75
339 Royce Clayton .20 .50
340 Mike Piazza 1.25 3.00
341 Jeremi Gonzalez .20 .50
342 Mike Lansing .20 .50
343 Jamie Moyer .30 .75
344 Ron Coomer .20 .50
345 Barry Larkin .50 1.25
346 Fernando Tatis .20 .50
347 Chili Davis .30 .75
348 Bobby Higginson .30 .75
349 Hal Morris .20 .50
350 Larry Walker .30 .75
351 Carlos Guillen .30 .75
352 Miguel Tejada .30 .75
353 Travis Fryman .30 .75
354 Jarrod Washburn .20 .50
355 Chipper Jones .75 2.00
356 Todd Stottlemyre .20 .50
357 Henry Rodriguez .20 .50
358 Eli Marrero .20 .50
359 Alan Benes .20 .50
360 Tim Salmon .50 1.25
361 Luis Gonzalez .30 .75
362 Scott Spiezio .20 .50
363 Chris Carpenter .30 .75
364 Bobby Howry .20 .50
365 Raul Mondesi .30 .75
366 Ugueth Urbina .20 .50
367 Tom Evans .20 .50
368 Kerry Ligtenberg RC .30 .75
369 Adrian Beltre .30 .75
370 Ryan Klesko .30 .75
371 Wilson Alvarez .20 .50
372 John Thomson .20 .50
373 Tony Saunders .20 .50
374 Dave Mlicki .30 .75
375 Ken Caminiti .30 .75
376 Jay Buhner .30 .75
377 Bill Mueller .30 .75
378 Jeff Blauser .20 .50
379 Edgar Renteria .30 .75
380 Jim Thome .50 1.25
381 Joey Hamilton .20 .50
382 Calvin Pickering .20 .50
383 Marquis Grissom .30 .75
384 Omar Daal .20 .50
385 Curt Schilling .30 .75
386 Jose Cruz Jr. .20 .50
387 Chris Widger .20 .50
388 Pete Harnisch .20 .50
389 Charles Nagy .20 .50
390 Tom Gordon .20 .50
391 Bobby Smith .20 .50
392 Derrick Gibson .20 .50
393 Jeff Conine .30 .75
394 Carlos Perez .20 .50
395 Barry Bonds 2.00 5.00
396 Mark McLemore .20 .50
397 Juan Encarnacion .20 .50
398 Wade Boggs .50 1.25
399 Ivan Rodriguez .50 1.25
400 Moises Alou .30 .75
401 Jeromy Burnitz .30 .75
402 Sean Casey .30 .75
403 Jose Offerman .20 .50
404 Joe Fontenot .20 .50
405 Kevin Millwood .30 .75
406 Lance Johnson .20 .50
407 Richard Hidalgo .20 .50
408 Mike Jackson .20 .50
409 Brian Anderson .20 .50
410 Jeff Shaw .20 .50
411 Preston Wilson .30 .75
412 Todd Hundley .20 .50
413 Jim Parque .20 .50
414 Justin Baughman .20 .50
415 Dante Bichette .30 .75
416 Paul O'Neill .50 1.25
417 Miguel Cairo .20 .50
418 Randy Johnson .75 2.00
419 Jesus Sanchez .20 .50
420 Carlos Delgado .30 .75
421 Ricky Ledee .20 .50
422 Orlando Hernandez .30 .75
423 Frank Thomas .75 2.00
424 Pokey Reese .20 .50
425 Carlos Lee .40 1.00
Mike Lowell
Kit Pellow RC
426 Michael Cuddyer .40 1.00
Mark DeRosa
Jerry Hairston Jr.
427 Marlon Anderson .40 1.00
Ron Belliard
Orlando Cabrera
428 Micah Bowie .40 1.00
Phil Norton RC
Randy Wolf
429 Jack Cressend RC .40 1.00
Jason Rakers
John Rocker
430 Ruben Mateo .40 1.00
Scott Morgan
Mike Zywica RC
431 Jason LaRue .40 1.00
Matt LeCroy
Mitch Meluskey
432 Gabe Kapler .40 1.00
Armando Rios
Fernando Seguignol
433 Adam Kennedy .40 1.00
Mickey Lopez RC
Jackie Rexrode
434 Jose Fernandez RC .40 1.00
Jeff Liefer
Chris Truby
435 Corey Koskie .60 1.50
Doug Mientkiewicz RC
Damon Minor
436 Roosevelt Brown RC .40 1.00
Dernell Stenson
Vernon Wells
437 A.J. Burnett RC .75 2.00
Billy Koch
John Nicholson
438 Matt Belisle .40 1.00
Matt Roney RC
439 Austin Kearns 1.50 4.00
Chris George RC
440 Nate Bump RC .40 1.00
Nate Cornejo
441 Brad Lidge 1.50 4.00
Mike Nannini RC
442 Matt Holliday 3.00 8.00
Jeff Winchester RC
443 Adam Everett .60 1.50
Chip Ambres RC
444 Pat Burrell 1.50 4.00
Eric Valent RC
445 Roger Clemens SK .75 2.00
446 Kerry Wood SK .20 .50
447 Curt Schilling SK .20 .50
448 Randy Johnson SK .50 1.25
449 Pedro Martinez SK .50 1.25
450 Jeff Bagwell AT .75 2.00
Andres Galarraga
Mark McGwire
451 John Olerud AT .30 .75
Jim Thome
Tino Martinez
452 Alex Rodriguez AT 1.00 2.50
Nomar Garciaparra
Derek Jeter
453 Vinny Castilla AT .50 1.25
Chipper Jones
Scott Rolen
454 Sammy Sosa AT .75 2.00
Ken Griffey Jr.
Juan Gonzalez
455 Barry Bonds AT 1.00 2.50
Manny Ramirez
Larry Walker
456 Frank Thomas AT .75 2.00
Tim Salmon
David Justice
457 Travis Lee AT .30 .75
Todd Helton
Ben Grieve
458 Vladimir Guerrero AT .30 .75
Greg Vaughn
Bernie Williams
459 Mike Piazza AT .75 2.00
Ivan Rodriguez
Jason Kendall
460 Roger Clemens AT .75 2.00
Kerry Wood
Greg Maddux
461A Sammy Sosa HR 1 8.00 20.00
461B Sammy Sosa HR 2 5.00 12.00
461C Sammy Sosa HR 3 5.00 12.00
461D Sammy Sosa HR 4 5.00 12.00
461E Sammy Sosa HR 5 5.00 12.00
461F Sammy Sosa HR 6 5.00 12.00
461G Sammy Sosa HR 7 5.00 12.00
461H Sammy Sosa HR 8 5.00 12.00
461I Sammy Sosa HR 9 5.00 12.00
461J Sammy Sosa HR 10 5.00 12.00
461K Sammy Sosa HR 11 5.00 12.00
461L Sammy Sosa HR 12 5.00 12.00
461M Sammy Sosa HR 13 5.00 12.00
461N Sammy Sosa HR 14 5.00 12.00
461O Sammy Sosa HR 15 5.00 12.00
461P Sammy Sosa HR 16 5.00 12.00
461Q Sammy Sosa HR 17 5.00 12.00
461R Sammy Sosa HR 18 5.00 12.00
461S Sammy Sosa HR 19 5.00 12.00
461T Sammy Sosa HR 20 5.00 12.00
461U Sammy Sosa HR 21 5.00 12.00
461V Sammy Sosa HR 22 5.00 12.00
461W Sammy Sosa HR 23 5.00 12.00
461X Sammy Sosa HR 24 5.00 12.00
461Y Sammy Sosa HR 25 5.00 12.00
461Z Sammy Sosa HR 26 5.00 12.00
461AA S.Sosa HR 27 5.00 12.00
461AB S.Sosa HR 28 5.00 12.00
461AC S.Sosa HR 29 5.00 12.00
461AD S.Sosa HR 30 5.00 12.00
461AE S.Sosa HR 31 5.00 12.00
461AF S.Sosa HR 32 5.00 12.00
461AG S.Sosa HR 33 5.00 12.00
461AH S.Sosa HR 34 5.00 12.00
461AI S.Sosa HR 35 5.00 12.00
461AJ S.Sosa HR 36 5.00 12.00
461AK S.Sosa HR 37 5.00 12.00
461AL S.Sosa HR 38 5.00 12.00
461AM S.Sosa HR 39 5.00 12.00
461AN S.Sosa HR 40 5.00 12.00
461AO S.Sosa HR 41 5.00 12.00
461AP S.Sosa HR 42 5.00 12.00
461AR S.Sosa HR 43 5.00 12.00
461AS S.Sosa HR 44 5.00 12.00
461AT S.Sosa HR 45 5.00 12.00
461AU S.Sosa HR 46 5.00 12.00
461AV S.Sosa HR 47 5.00 12.00
461AW S.Sosa HR 48 5.00 12.00
461AX S.Sosa HR 49 5.00 12.00
461AY S.Sosa HR 50 5.00 12.00
461AZ S.Sosa HR 51 5.00 12.00
461BB S.Sosa HR 52 5.00 12.00
461CC S.Sosa HR 53 5.00 12.00
461DD S.Sosa HR 54 5.00 12.00
461EE S.Sosa HR 55 5.00 12.00
461FF S.Sosa HR 56 5.00 12.00
461GG S.Sosa HR 57 5.00 12.00
461HH S.Sosa HR 58 5.00 12.00
461II S.Sosa HR 59 5.00 12.00
461JJ S.Sosa HR 60 5.00 12.00
461KK S.Sosa HR 61 8.00 20.00
461LL S.Sosa HR 62 12.50 30.00
461MM S.Sosa HR 63 8.00 20.00
461NN S.Sosa HR 64 8.00 20.00
461OO S.Sosa HR 65 8.00 20.00
461PP S.Sosa HR 66 30.00 60.00
462 Checklist .20 .50
463 Checklist .20 .50

1999 Topps Chrome Refractors

Randomly inserted in packs at the rate of one in 12, this 462-card set is parallel to the base set and is similar in design. The difference is found in the refractive quality of the card. It's estimated that only around 15 to 25 of each McGwire number 220 refractor was produced.

*STARS: 2.5X TO 6X BASIC CARDS
*ROOKIES: 1.25X TO 3X BASIC CARDS
MCGWIRE 220 HR 1 125.00 250.00
MCGWIRE 220 HR 2-60 60.00 120.00
MCGWIRE 220 HR 61 100.00 200.00
MCGWIRE 220 HR 62 150.00 300.00
MCGWIRE 220 HR 63-69 60.00 120.00
MCGWIRE 220 HR 70 200.00 400.00
SOSA 461 HR 1 30.00 60.00
SOSA 461 HR 2-60 10.00 25.00
SOSA 461 HR 61 20.00 50.00
SOSA 461 HR 62 40.00 80.00
SOSA 461 HR 63-65 10.00 25.00
SOSA 461 HR 66 60.00 120.00
REFRACTOR STATED ODDS 1:12
442 Matt Holliday 15.00 40.00
Jeff Winchester

1999 Topps Chrome All-Etch

Randomly inserted in Series two packs at the rate of one in six, this 30-card set features color player photos printed on All-Etch technology. A refractive parallel version of this set was also produced with an insertion rate of 1:24 packs.

COMPLETE SET (30) 40.00 100.00
SER.2 STATED ODDS 1:6
*REFRACTORS: .75X TO 2X BASIC ALL-ETCH
SER.2 REFRACTOR ODDS 1:24
AE1 Mark McGwire 5.00 12.00
AE2 Sammy Sosa 2.00 5.00
AE3 Ken Griffey Jr. 3.00 8.00
AE4 Greg Vaughn .50 1.25
AE5 Albert Belle .75 2.00
AE6 Vinny Castilla .75 2.00
AE7 Jose Canseco 1.25 3.00
AE8 Juan Gonzalez .75 2.00
AE9 Manny Ramirez 1.25 3.00
AE10 Andres Galarraga .75 2.00
AE11 Rafael Palmeiro 1.25 3.00
AE12 Alex Rodriguez 3.00 8.00
AE13 Mo Vaughn .75 2.00
AE14 Eric Chavez .75 2.00
AE15 Gabe Kapler 1.00 2.50
AE16 Calvin Pickering .50 1.25
AE17 Ruben Mateo 1.00 2.50
AE18 Roy Halladay 2.00 5.00
AE19 Jeremy Giambi .50 1.25
AE20 Alex Gonzalez .50 1.25
AE21 Ron Belliard 1.00 2.50
AE22 Marlon Anderson 1.00 2.50
AE23 Carlos Lee 1.00 2.50
AE24 Kerry Wood .75 2.00
AE25 Roger Clemens 4.00 10.00
AE26 Curt Schilling .75 2.00
AE27 Kevin Brown 1.25 3.00
AE28 Randy Johnson 2.00 5.00
AE29 Pedro Martinez 1.25 3.00
AE30 Orlando Hernandez .75 2.00

1999 Topps Chrome Early Road to the Hall

Randomly inserted in Series one packs at the rate of one in 12, this 10-card set features color photos of ten players with less than 10 years in the Majors but are already headed towards the Hall of Fame in Cooperstown, New York.

COMPLETE SET (10) 25.00 60.00
SER.1 STATED ODDS 1:12
*REFRACTORS: 3X TO 8X BASIC ROAD
SER.1 REFRACTOR ODDS 1:944 HOBBY
REF.PRINT RUN 100 SERIAL #'d SETS
ER1 Nomar Garciaparra 3.00 8.00
ER2 Derek Jeter 5.00 12.00
ER3 Alex Rodriguez 3.00 8.00
ER4 Juan Gonzalez .75 2.00
ER5 Ken Griffey Jr. 3.00 8.00
ER6 Chipper Jones 2.00 5.00
ER7 Vladimir Guerrero 2.00 5.00
ER8 Jeff Bagwell 1.25 3.00
ER9 Ivan Rodriguez 1.25 3.00
ER10 Frank Thomas 2.00 5.00

1999 Topps Chrome Fortune 15

Randomly inserted into Series two packs at the rate of one in 12, this 15-card set features color photos of the League's most elite veteran and rookie players. A refractor parallel version of this set was also produced with an insertion rate of 1:627 packs and sequentially numnbered to 100.

COMPLETE SET (15) 40.00 100.00
SER.2 STATED ODDS 1:12
*REFRACTORS: 4X TO 8X BASIC FORT.15
SER.2 REFRACTOR ODDS 1:627
REF.PRINT RUN 100 SERIAL #'d SETS
FF1 Alex Rodriguez 3.00 8.00
FF2 Nomar Garciaparra 3.00 8.00
FF3 Derek Jeter 5.00 12.00
FF4 Troy Glaus 1.25 3.00
FF5 Ken Griffey Jr. 3.00 8.00
FF6 Vladimir Guerrero 2.00 5.00
FF7 Kerry Wood .75 2.00
FF8 Eric Chavez .75 2.00
FF9 Greg Maddux 3.00 8.00
FF10 Mike Piazza 3.00 8.00
FF11 Sammy Sosa 2.00 5.00
FF12 Mark McGwire 5.00 12.00
FF13 Ben Grieve .50 1.25
FF14 Chipper Jones 2.00 5.00
FF15 Manny Ramirez 1.25 3.00

1999 Topps Chrome Lords of the Diamond

Randomly inserted in Series one packs at the rate of one in eight, this 15-card set features color photos of some of the true masters of the ballfield. A refractive parallel version of this set was also produced with an insertion rate of 1:24.

COMPLETE SET (15) 20.00 50.00
SER.1 STATED ODDS 1:8
*REFRACTORS: .6X TO 1.5X BASIC LORDS
SER.1 REFRACTOR ODDS 1:24
LD1 Ken Griffey Jr. 1.50 4.00
LD2 Chipper Jones 1.00 2.50
LD3 Sammy Sosa 1.00 2.50
LD4 Frank Thomas 1.00 2.50
LD5 Mark McGwire 2.50 6.00
LD6 Jeff Bagwell .60 1.50
LD7 Alex Rodriguez 1.50 4.00
LD8 Juan Gonzalez .40 1.00
LD9 Barry Bonds 2.50 6.00
LD10 Nomar Garciaparra 1.50 4.00
LD11 Darin Erstad .40 1.00
LD12 Tony Gwynn 1.25 3.00
LD13 Andres Galarraga .40 1.00
LD14 Mike Piazza 1.50 4.00
LD15 Greg Maddux 1.50 4.00

1999 Topps Chrome New Breed

Randomly inserted in Series one packs at the rate of one in 24, this 15-card set features color photos of some of today's young stars in Major League Baseball. A refractive parallel version of this set was also produced with an insertion rate of 1:72.

COMPLETE SET (15) 40.00 100.00
SER.1 STATED ODDS 1:24
*REFRACTORS: .6X TO 1.5X BASIC BREED
SER.1 REFRACTOR ODDS 1:72
NB1 Darin Erstad 1.25 3.00
NB2 Brad Fullmer .75 2.00
NB3 Kerry Wood 1.25 3.00
NB4 Nomar Garciaparra 5.00 12.00
NB5 Travis Lee .75 2.00
NB6 Scott Rolen 2.00 5.00
NB7 Todd Helton 2.00 5.00
NB8 Vladimir Guerrero 3.00 8.00
NB9 Derek Jeter 8.00 20.00
NB10 Alex Rodriguez 5.00 12.00
NB11 Ben Grieve .75 2.00
NB12 Andruw Jones 2.00 5.00
NB13 Paul Konerko 1.25 3.00
NB14 Aramis Ramirez 1.25 3.00
NB15 Adrian Beltre 1.25 3.00

1999 Topps Chrome Record Numbers

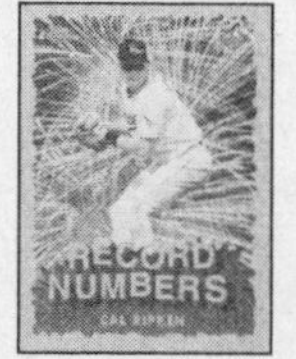

Randomly inserted in Series two packs at the rate of one in 36, this 10-card set features color photos of top Major League record-setters. A refractive parallel version of this set was also produced with an insertion rate of 1:144.

COMPLETE SET (10) 60.00 150.00
SER.2 STATED ODDS 1:36
*REFRACTORS: .75X TO 2X BASIC REC.NUM.
SER.2 REFRACTOR ODDS 1:144
RN1 Mark McGwire 8.00 20.00
RN2 Mike Piazza 5.00 12.00
RN3 Curt Schilling 1.25 3.00
RN4 Ken Griffey Jr. 5.00 12.00
RN5 Sammy Sosa 3.00 8.00
RN6 Nomar Garciaparra 5.00 12.00
RN7 Kerry Wood 1.25 3.00
RN8 Roger Clemens 6.00 15.00
RN9 Cal Ripken 10.00 25.00
RN10 Mark McGwire 8.00 20.00

1999 Topps Chrome Traded

This 121-card set features color photos on Chromium cards of 46 of the most notable transactions of the 1999 season and 75 newcomers accented with the Topps "Rookie Card" logo. The set was distributed only in factory boxes. Due to a very late ship date (January, 2000) this set caused some commotion in the hobby as to its status as a 1999 or 2000 product. Notable Rookie Cards include Carl Crawford, Adam Dunn, Josh Hamilton, Corey Patterson and Alfonso Soriano.

COMP.FACT SET (121) 50.00 100.00
T1 Seth Etherton .15 .40
T2 Mark Harriger RC .20 .50
T3 Matt Wise RC .20 .50
T4 Carlos E. Hernandez RC .30 .75
T5 Julio Lugo RC .50 1.25
T6 Mike Nannini .15 .40
T7 Justin Bowles RC .20 .50
T8 Mark Mulder RC 1.25 3.00
T9 Roberto Vaz RC .20 .50
T10 Felipe Lopez RC 1.25 3.00
T11 Matt Belisle .15 .40
T12 Micah Bowie .15 .40
T13 Ruben Quevedo RC .20 .50
T14 Jose Garcia RC .20 .50
T15 David Kelton RC .20 .50
T16 Phil Norton .15 .40
T17 Corey Patterson RC .75 2.00
T18 Ron Walker RC .20 .50
T19 Paul Hoover RC .20 .50
T20 Ryan Rupe RC .20 .50
T21 J.D. Closser RC .30 .75
T22 Rob Ryan RC .20 .50
T23 Steve Colyer RC .20 .50
T24 Bubba Crosby RC .50 1.25
T25 Luke Prokopec RC .20 .50
T26 Matt Blank RC .20 .50
T27 Josh McKinley .15 .40
T28 Nate Bump .20 .50
T29 G.Chiaramonte RC .20 .50
T30 Arturo McDowell .15 .40
T31 Tony Torcato .15 .40
T32 Dave Roberts RC .50 1.25
T33 C.C. Sabathia RC 4.00 10.00
T34 Sean Spencer RC .20 .50
T35 Chip Ambres .15 .40
T36 A.J. Burnett .75 2.00
T37 Mo Bruce RC .20 .50
T38 Jason Tyner .15 .40
T39 Mamon Tucker .15 .40
T40 Sean Burroughs RC .50 1.25
T41 Kevin Eberwein RC .20 .50
T42 Junior Herndon RC .20 .50
T43 Bryan Wolff RC .20 .50
T44 Pat Burrell 1.25 3.00
T45 Eric Valent .30 .75
T46 Carlos Pena RC .40 1.00
T47 Mike Zywica .15 .40
T48 Adam Everett .40 1.00
T49 Juan Pena RC .20 .50
T50 Adam Dunn RC 3.00 8.00
T51 Austin Kearns 1.25 3.00
T52 Jacobo Sequea RC .20 .50
T53 Choo Freeman .25 .60
T54 Jeff Winchester .15 .40
T55 Matt Burch .20 .50
T56 Chris George .15 .40
T57 Scott Mullen RC .20 .50
T58 Kit Pellow .20 .50
T59 Mark Quinn RC .20 .50
T60 Nate Cornejo .20 .50
T61 Ryan Mills .15 .40
T62 Kevin Beirne RC .20 .50
T63 Kip Wells RC .30 .75
T64 Juan Rivera RC .75 2.00
T65 Alfonso Soriano RC 4.00 10.00
T66 Josh Hamilton RC 5.00 12.00
T67 Josh Girdley RC .20 .50
T68 Kyle Snyder RC .20 .50
T69 Mike Paradis RC .20 .50
T70 Jason Jennings RC .50 1.25
T71 David Walling RC .20 .50
T72 Omar Ortiz RC .20 .50
T73 Jay Gehrke RC .20 .50
T74 Casey Burns RC .20 .50
T75 Carl Crawford RC 3.00 8.00
T76 Reggie Sanders .25 .60
T77 Will Clark .40 1.00
T78 David Wells .25 .60
T79 Paul Konerko .25 .60
T80 Armando Benitez .15 .40
T81 Brant Brown .15 .40
T82 Mo Vaughn .25 .60
T83 Jose Canseco .40 1.00
T84 Albert Belle .25 .60
T85 Dean Palmer .25 .60
T86 Greg Vaughn .15 .40
T87 Mark Clark .15 .40
T88 Pat Meares .15 .40
T89 Eric Davis .25 .60
T90 Brian Giles .25 .60
T91 Jeff Brantley .15 .40
T92 Bret Boone .25 .60
T93 Ron Gant .25 .60
T94 Mike Cameron .15 .40
T95 Charles Johnson .25 .60
T96 Denny Neagle .15 .40
T97 Brian Hunter .15 .40
T98 Jose Hernandez .15 .40
T99 Rick Aguilera .15 .40
T100 Tony Batista .15 .40
T101 Roger Cedeno .15 .40
T102 C.Gubanich RC .20 .50
T103 Tim Belcher .15 .40
T104 Bruce Aven .15 .40
T105 Brian Daubach RC .30 .75
T106 Ed Sprague .15 .40
T107 Michael Tucker .15 .40
T108 Homer Bush .15 .40
T109 Armando Reynoso .15 .40
T110 Brook Fordyce .15 .40
T111 Matt Mantei .15 .40
T112 Dave Mlicki .15 .40
T113 Kenny Rogers .25 .60
T114 Livan Hernandez .25 .60
T115 Butch Huskey .15 .40
T116 David Segui .15 .40
T117 Darryl Hamilton .15 .40
T118 Terry Mulholland .15 .40
T119 Randy Velarde .15 .40
T120 Bill Taylor .15 .40
T121 Kevin Appier .25 .60

2000 Topps Chrome

These cards parallel the regular Topps set and are issued using Topps' Chromium technology and color metallization. The first series product was released in February, 2000 and second series in May, 2000. Four card packs for each series carried an SRP of $3.00. Similar to the regular set, no card number 7 was issued and a Mark McGwire rookie reprint card was also inserted into packs. Also, like the base Topps set all of the Magic Moments subset cards (235-239 and 475-479) are available in five variations - each detailing a different highlight in the featured player's career. The base Chrome set is considered complete with any of the Magic Moments variations (for each player). Notable Rookie Cards include Rick Asadoorian, Ben Sheets and Barry Zito.

COMPLETE SET (478) 60.00 160.00
COMP. SERIES 1 (240) 30.00 80.00
COMP. SERIES 2 (240) 30.00 80.00
MCGWIRE MM SET (5) 20.00 50.00
AARON MM SET (5) 15.00 40.00
RIPKEN MM SET (5) 25.00 60.00
BOGGS MM SET (5) 5.00 12.00
GWYNN MM SET (5) 10.00 25.00
GRIFFEY MM SET (5) 12.50 30.00
BONDS MM SET (5) 20.00 50.00
SOSA MM SET (5) 12.50 30.00
JETER MM SET (5) 20.00 50.00
A.ROD MM SET (5) 15.00 40.00
1 Mark McGwire 2.00 5.00
2 Tony Gwynn 1.00 2.50
3 Wade Boggs .50 1.25
4 Cal Ripken 2.50 6.00
5 Matt Williams .30 .75
6 Jay Buhner .30 .75
7 Does Not Exist
8 Jeff Conine .30 .75
9 Todd Greene .30 .75
10 Mike Lieberthal .30 .75
11 Steve Avery .30 .75
12 Bret Saberhagen .30 .75
13 Magglio Ordonez .30 .75
14 Brad Radke .30 .75
15 Derek Jeter 2.00 5.00
16 Javy Lopez .30 .75
17 Russ Davis .30 .75
18 Armando Benitez .30 .75
19 B.J. Surhoff .30 .75
20 Darryl Kile .30 .75
21 Mark Lewis .30 .75
22 Mike Williams .30 .75
23 Mark McLemore .30 .75
24 Sterling Hitchcock .30 .75
25 Darin Erstad .30 .75
26 Ricky Gutierrez .30 .75
27 John Jaha .30 .75
28 Homer Bush .30 .75
29 Darrin Fletcher .30 .75
30 Mark Grace .50 1.25
31 Fred McGriff .50 1.25
32 Omar Daal .30 .75
33 Eric Karros .30 .75
34 Orlando Cabrera .30 .75
35 J.T. Snow .30 .75
36 Luis Castillo .30 .75
37 Rey Ordonez .30 .75
38 Bob Abreu .30 .75
39 Warren Morris .30 .75
40 Juan Gonzalez .30 .75
41 Mike Lansing .30 .75
42 Chili Davis .30 .75
43 Dean Palmer .30 .75
44 Hank Aaron 1.50 4.00
45 Jeff Bagwell .50 1.25
46 Jose Valentin .30 .75
47 Shannon Stewart .30 .75
48 Kent Bottenfield .30 .75
49 Jeff Shaw .30 .75
50 Sammy Sosa .75 2.00

51 Randy Johnson .75 2.00
52 Benny Agbayani .30 .75
53 Dante Bichette .30 .75
54 Pete Harnisch .30 .75
55 Frank Thomas .75 2.00
56 Jorge Posada .50 1.25
57 Todd Walker .30 .75
58 Juan Encarnacion .30 .75
59 Mike Sweeney .30 .75
60 Pedro Martinez .50 1.25
61 Lee Stevens .30 .75
62 Brian Giles .30 .75
63 Chad Ogea .30 .75
64 Ivan Rodriguez .50 1.25
65 Roger Cedeno .30 .75
66 David Justice .30 .75
67 Steve Trachsel .30 .75
68 Eli Marrero .30 .75
69 Dave Nilsson .30 .75
70 Ken Caminiti .30 .75
71 Tim Raines .30 .75
72 Brian Jordan .30 .75
73 Jeff Blauser .30 .75
74 Bernard Gilkey .30 .75
75 John Flaherty .30 .75
76 Brent Mayne .30 .75
77 Jose Vidro .30 .75
78 David Bell .30 .75
79 Bruce Aven .30 .75
80 John Olerud .30 .75
81 Pokey Reese .30 .75
82 Woody Williams .30 .75
83 Ed Sprague .30 .75
84 Joe Girardi .30 .75
85 Barry Larkin .50 1.25
86 Mike Caruso .30 .75
87 Bobby Higginson .30 .75
88 Roberto Kelly .30 .75
89 Edgar Martinez .50 1.25
90 Mark Kotsay .30 .75
91 Paul Sorrento .30 .75
92 Eric Young .30 .75
93 Carlos Delgado .30 .75
94 Troy Glaus .30 .75
95 Ben Grieve .30 .75
96 Jose Lima .30 .75
97 Garret Anderson .30 .75
98 Luis Gonzalez .30 .75
99 Carl Pavano .30 .75
100 Alex Rodriguez 1.25 3.00
101 Preston Wilson .30 .75
102 Ron Gant .30 .75
103 Brady Anderson .30 .75
104 Rickey Henderson .75 2.00
105 Gary Sheffield .30 .75
106 Mickey Morandini .30 .75
107 Jim Edmonds .30 .75
108 Kris Benson .30 .75
109 Adrian Beltre .30 .75
110 Alex Fernandez .30 .75
111 Dan Wilson .30 .75
112 Mark Clark .30 .75
113 Greg Vaughn .30 .75
114 Neifi Perez .30 .75
115 Paul O'Neill .50 1.25
116 Jermaine Dye .30 .75
117 Todd Jones .30 .75
118 Terry Steinbach .30 .75
119 Greg Norton .30 .75
120 Curt Schilling .30 .75
121 Todd Zeile .30 .75
122 Edgardo Alfonzo .30 .75
123 Ryan McGuire .30 .75
124 Rich Aurilia .30 .75
125 John Smoltz .50 1.25
126 Bob Wickman .30 .75
127 Richard Hidalgo .30 .75
128 Chuck Finley .30 .75
129 Billy Wagner .30 .75
130 Todd Hundley .30 .75
131 Dwight Gooden .30 .75
132 Russ Ortiz .30 .75
133 Mike Lowell .30 .75
134 Reggie Sanders .30 .75
135 John Valentin .30 .75
136 Brad Ausmus .30 .75
137 Chad Kreuter .30 .75
138 David Cone .30 .75
139 Brook Fordyce .30 .75
140 Roberto Alomar .50 1.25
141 Charles Nagy .30 .75
142 Brian Hunter .30 .75
143 Mike Mussina .50 1.25
144 Robin Ventura .50 1.25
145 Kevin Brown .50 1.25
146 Pat Hentgen .30 .75
147 Ryan Klesko .30 .75
148 Derek Bell .30 .75
149 Andy Sheets .30 .75
150 Larry Walker .30 .75
151 Scott Williamson .30 .75
152 Jose Offerman .30 .75
153 Doug Mientkiewicz .30 .75
154 John Snyder RC .40 1.00
155 Sandy Alomar Jr. .30 .75
156 Joe Nathan .30 .75
157 Lance Johnson .30 .75
158 Odalis Perez .30 .75
159 Hideo Nomo .75 2.00
160 Steve Finley .30 .75
161 Dave Martinez .30 .75
162 Matt Walbeck .30 .75
163 Bill Spiers .30 .75
164 Fernando Tatis .30 .75
165 Kenny Lofton .30 .75
166 Paul Byrd .30 .75
167 Aaron Sele .30 .75
168 Eddie Taubensee .30 .75
169 Reggie Jefferson .30 .75
170 Roger Clemens 1.50 4.00
171 Francisco Cordova .30 .75
172 Mike Bordick .30 .75
173 Wally Joyner .30 .75
174 Marvin Benard .30 .75
175 Jason Kendall .30 .75
176 Mike Stanley .30 .75
177 Chad Allen .30 .75
178 Carlos Beltran .30 .75
179 Deivi Cruz .30 .75
180 Chipper Jones .75 2.00
181 Vladimir Guerrero .75 2.00
182 Dave Burba .30 .75
183 Tom Goodwin .30 .75
184 Brian Daubach .30 .75
185 Jay Bell .30 .75
186 Roy Halladay .30 .75
187 Miguel Tejada .30 .75
188 Armando Rios .30 .75
189 Fernando Vina .30 .75
190 Eric Davis .30 .75
191 Henry Rodriguez .30 .75
192 Joe McEwing .30 .75
193 Jeff Kent .30 .75
194 Mike Jackson .30 .75
195 Mike Morgan .30 .75
196 Jeff Montgomery .30 .75
197 Jeff Zimmerman .30 .75
198 Tony Fernandez .30 .75
199 Jason Giambi .30 .75
200 Jose Canseco .50 1.25
201 Alex Gonzalez .30 .75
202 Jack Cust .40 1.00
Mike Colangelo
Dee Brown
203 Felipe Lopez .75 2.00
Alfonso Soriano
Pablo Ozuna
204 Erubiel Durazo .60 1.50
Pat Burrell
Nick Johnson
205 John Sneed RC .40 1.00
Kip Wells
Matt Blank
206 Josh Kalinowski .40 1.00
Michael Tejera
Chris Mears RC
207 Roosevelt Brown .60 1.50
Corey Patterson
Lance Berkman
208 Kit Pellow .40 1.00
Kevin Barker
Russ Branyan
209 B.J. Garbe 1.00 2.50
Larry Bigbie RC
210 Eric Munson .40 1.00
Bobby Bradley RC
211 Josh Girdley .40 1.00
Kyle Snyder
212 Chance Caple RC .40 1.00
Jason Jennings
213 Ryan Christianson 1.50 4.00
Brett Myers RC
214 Jason Stumm .40 1.00
Rob Purvis RC
215 David Walling .40 1.00
Mike Paradis
216 Omar Ortiz .40 1.00
Jay Gehrke
217 David Cone HL .30 .75
218 Jose Jimenez HL .30 .75
219 Chris Singleton HL .30 .75
220 Fernando Tatis HL .30 .75
221 Todd Helton HL .30 .75
222 Kevin Millwood DIV .30 .75
223 Todd Pratt DIV .30 .75
224 Orl. Hernandez DIV .30 .75
225 Pedro Martinez DIV .50 1.25
226 Tom Glavine LCS .30 .75
227 Bernie Williams LCS .30 .75
228 Mariano Rivera WS .50 1.25
229 Tony Gwynn 20CB 1.00 2.50
230 Wade Boggs 20CB .50 1.25
231 Lance Johnson CB .30 .75
232 Mark McGwire 20CB 2.00 5.00
233 R.Henderson 20CB .75 2.00
234 R.Henderson 20CB .75 2.00
235 Roger Clemens 20CB 1.50 4.00
236A Mark McGwire MM 5.00 12.00
1st HR
236B Mark McGwire MM 5.00 12.00
1987 ROY
236C Mark McGwire MM 5.00 12.00
62nd HR
236D Mark McGwire MM 5.00 12.00
70th HR
236E Mark McGwire MM 5.00 12.00
500th HR
237A Hank Aaron MM 4.00 10.00
1st Career HR
237B Hank Aaron MM 4.00 10.00
1957 MVP
237C Hank Aaron MM 4.00 10.00
3000th Hit
237D Hank Aaron MM 4.00 10.00
715th HR
237E Hank Aaron 4.00 10.00
MM 755th HR
238A Cal Ripken MM 6.00 15.00
1982 ROY
238B Cal Ripken MM 6.00 15.00
1991 MVP
238C Cal Ripken MM 6.00 15.00
2131 Game
238D Cal Ripken MM 6.00 15.00
Streak Ends
238E Cal Ripken MM 6.00 15.00
400th HR
239A Wade Boggs MM 1.25 3.00
1983 Batting
239B Wade Boggs MM 1.25 3.00
1988 Batting
239C Wade Boggs MM 1.25 3.00
2000th Hit
239D Wade Boggs MM 1.25 3.00
1996 Champs
239E Wade Boggs MM 1.25 3.00
3000th Hit
240A Tony Gwynn MM 2.50 6.00
1984 Batting
240B Tony Gwynn MM 2.50 6.00
1984 NLCS
240C Tony Gwynn MM 2.50 6.00
1995 Batting
240D Tony Gwynn MM 2.50 6.00
1998 NLCS
240E Tony Gwynn MM 2.50 6.00
3000th Hit
241 Tom Glavine .50 1.25
242 David Wells .30 .75
243 Kevin Appier .30 .75
244 Troy Percival .30 .75
245 Ray Lankford .30 .75
246 Marquis Grissom .30 .75
247 Randy Winn .30 .75
248 Miguel Batista .30 .75
249 Darren Dreifort .30 .75
250 Barry Bonds 1.50 4.00
251 Harold Baines .30 .75
252 Cliff Floyd .30 .75
253 Freddy Garcia .30 .75
254 Kenny Rogers .30 .75
255 Ben Davis .30 .75
256 Charles Johnson .30 .75
257 Bubba Trammell .30 .75
258 Desi Relaford .30 .75
259 Al Martin .30 .75
260 Andy Pettitte .50 1.25
261 Carlos Lee .30 .75
262 Matt Lawton .30 .75
263 Andy Fox .30 .75
264 Chan Ho Park .30 .75
265 Billy Koch .30 .75
266 Dave Roberts .30 .75
267 Carl Everett .30 .75
268 Orel Hershiser .30 .75
269 Trot Nixon .30 .75
270 Rusty Greer .30 .75
271 Will Clark .50 1.25
272 Quilvio Veras .30 .75
273 Rico Brogna .30 .75
274 Devon White .30 .75
275 Tim Hudson .30 .75
276 Mike Hampton .30 .75
277 Miguel Cairo .30 .75
278 Darren Oliver .30 .75
279 Jeff Cirillo .30 .75
280 Al Leiter .30 .75
281 Shane Andrews .30 .75
282 Carlos Febles .30 .75
283 Pedro Astacio .30 .75
284 Juan Guzman .30 .75
285 Orlando Hernandez .30 .75
286 Paul Konerko .30 .75
287 Tony Clark .30 .75
288 Aaron Boone .30 .75
289 Ismael Valdes .30 .75
290 Moises Alou .30 .75
291 Kevin Tapani .30 .75
292 John Franco .30 .75
293 Todd Zeile .30 .75
294 Jason Schmidt .30 .75
295 Johnny Damon .50 1.25
296 Scott Brosius .30 .75
297 Travis Fryman .30 .75
298 Jose Vizcaino .30 .75
299 Eric Chavez .30 .75
300 Mike Piazza 1.25 3.00
301 Matt Clement .30 .75
302 Cristian Guzman .30 .75
303 C.J. Nitkowski .30 .75
304 Michael Tucker .30 .75
305 Brett Tomko .30 .75
306 Mike Lansing .30 .75
307 Eric Owens .30 .75
308 Livan Hernandez .30 .75
309 Rondell White .30 .75
310 Todd Stottlemyre .30 .75
311 Chris Carpenter .30 .75
312 Ken Hill .30 .75
313 Mark Loretta .30 .75
314 John Rocker .30 .75
315 Richie Sexson .30 .75
316 Ruben Mateo .30 .75
317 Joe Randa .30 .75
318 Mike Sirotka .30 .75
319 Jose Rosado .30 .75
320 Matt Mantei .30 .75
321 Kevin Millwood .30 .75
322 Gary Disarcina .30 .75
323 Dustin Hermanson .30 .75
324 Mike Stanton .30 .75
325 Kirk Rueter .30 .75
326 Damian Miller RC .60 1.50
327 Doug Glanville .30 .75
328 Scott Rolen .50 1.25
329 Ray Durham .30 .75
330 Butch Huskey .30 .75
331 Mariano Rivera .75 2.00
332 Darren Lewis .30 .75
333 Mike Timlin .30 .75
334 Mark Grudzielanek .30 .75
335 Mike Cameron .30 .75
336 Kelvim Escobar .30 .75
337 Bret Boone .30 .75
338 Mo Vaughn .30 .75
339 Craig Biggio .50 1.25
340 Michael Barrett .30 .75
341 Marlon Anderson .30 .75
342 Bobby Jones .30 .75
343 John Halama .30 .75
344 Todd Ritchie .30 .75
345 Chuck Knoblauch .30 .75
346 Rick Reed .30 .75
347 Kelly Stinnett .30 .75
348 Tim Salmon .50 1.25
349 A.J. Hinch .30 .75
350 Jose Cruz Jr. .30 .75
351 Roberto Hernandez .30 .75
352 Edgar Renteria .30 .75
353 Jose Hernandez .30 .75
354 Brad Fullmer .30 .75
355 Trevor Hoffman .30 .75
356 Troy O'Leary .30 .75
357 Justin Thompson .30 .75
358 Kevin Young .30 .75
359 Hideki Irabu .30 .75
360 Jim Thome .50 1.25
361 Steve Karsay .30 .75
362 Octavio Dotel .30 .75
363 Omar Vizquel .50 1.25
364 Raul Mondesi .30 .75
365 Shane Reynolds .30 .75
366 Bartolo Colon .30 .75
367 Chris Widger .30 .75
368 Gabe Kapler .30 .75
369 Bill Simas .30 .75
370 Tino Martinez .50 1.25
371 John Thomson .30 .75
372 Delino Deshields .30 .75
373 Carlos Perez .30 .75
374 Eddie Perez .30 .75
375 Jeromy Burnitz .30 .75
376 Jimmy Haynes .30 .75
377 Travis Lee .30 .75
378 Darryl Hamilton .30 .75
379 Jamie Moyer .30 .75
380 Alex Gonzalez .30 .75
381 John Wetteland .30 .75
382 Vinny Castilla .30 .75
383 Jeff Suppan .30 .75
384 Jim Leyritz .30 .75
385 Robb Nen .30 .75
386 Wilson Alvarez .30 .75
387 Andres Galarraga .30 .75
388 Mike Remlinger .30 .75
389 Geoff Jenkins .30 .75
390 Matt Stairs .30 .75
391 Bill Mueller .30 .75
392 Mike Lowell .30 .75
393 Andy Ashby .30 .75
394 Ruben Rivera .30 .75
395 Todd Helton .50 1.25
396 Bernie Williams .50 1.25
397 Royce Clayton .30 .75
398 Manny Ramirez .50 1.25
399 Kerry Wood .30 .75
400 Ken Griffey Jr. 1.25 3.00
401 Enrique Wilson .30 .75
402 Joey Hamilton .30 .75
403 Shawn Estes .30 .75
404 Ugueth Urbina .30 .75
405 Albert Belle .30 .75
406 Rick Helling .30 .75
407 Steve Parris .30 .75
408 Eric Milton .30 .75
409 Dave Mlicki .30 .75
410 Shawn Green .30 .75
411 Jaret Wright .30 .75
412 Tony Womack .30 .75
413 Vernon Wells .30 .75
414 Ron Belliard .30 .75
415 Ellis Burks .30 .75
416 Scott Erickson .30 .75
417 Rafael Palmeiro .50 1.25
418 Damion Easley .30 .75
419 Jamey Wright .30 .75
420 Corey Koskie .30 .75
421 Bobby Howry .30 .75
422 Ricky Ledee .30 .75
423 Dmitri Young .30 .75
424 Sidney Ponson .30 .75
425 Greg Maddux 1.25 3.00
426 Jose Guillen .30 .75
427 Jon Lieber .30 .75
428 Andy Benes .30 .75
429 Randy Velarde .30 .75
430 Sean Casey .30 .75
431 Torii Hunter .30 .75
432 Ryan Rupe .30 .75
433 David Segui .30 .75
434 Todd Pratt .30 .75
435 Nomar Garciaparra 1.25 3.00
436 Denny Neagle .30 .75
437 Ron Coomer .30 .75
438 Chris Singleton .30 .75
439 Tony Batista .30 .75
440 Andruw Jones .50 1.25
441 Aubrey Huff .30 .75
Sean Burroughs
Adam Piatt
442 Rafael Furcal .60 1.50
Travis Dawkins
Jason Dellaero
443 Mike Lamb RC 1.50 4.00
Joe Crede
Wilton Veras
444 Julio Zuleta RC .40 1.00
Jorge Toca
Dernell Stenson
445 Garry Maddox Jr. RC .40 1.00
Gary Matthews Jr.
Tim Raines Jr.
446 Mark Mulder .60 1.50
C.C. Sabathia
Matt Riley
447 Scott Downs RC .40 1.00
Chris George
Matt Belisle
448 Doug Mirabelli .40 1.00
Ben Petrick
Jayson Werth
449 Josh Hamilton .60 1.50
Corey Myers RC
450 Ben Christensen RC .40 1.00
Richard Stahl
451 Ben Sheets RC 4.00 10.00
Barry Zito RC
452 Kurt Ainsworth .40 1.00
Ty Howington RC
453 Vince Faison RC .60 1.50
Rick Asadoorian
454 Keith Reed RC .40 1.00
Jeff Heaverlo
455 Mike MacDougal .40 1.00
Brad Baker RC
456 Mark McGwire SH 1.00 2.50
457 Cal Ripken SH 1.25 3.00
458 Wade Boggs SH .30 .75
459 Tony Gwynn SH .50 1.25
460 Jesse Orosco SH .30 .75
461 Larry Walker .50 1.25
Nomar Garciaparra LL
462 Ken Griffey Jr. .75 2.00
Mark McGwire LL
463 Manny Ramirez .75 2.00
Mark McGwire LL
464 Pedro Martinez .50 1.25
Randy Johnson LL
465 Pedro Martinez .50 1.25
Randy Johnson LL
466 Derek Jeter .75 2.00
Luis Gonzalez LL
467 Larry Walker .50 1.25
Manny Ramirez LL
468 Tony Gwynn 20CB 1.00 2.50
469 Mark McGwire 20CB 2.00 5.00
470 Frank Thomas 20CB .50 1.25
471 Harold Baines 20CB .30 .75
472 Roger Clemens 20CB 1.50 4.00
473 John Franco 20CB .30 .75
474 John Franco 20CB .30 .75
475A Ken Griffey Jr. MM 3.00 8.00
350th HR
475B Ken Griffey Jr. MM 3.00 8.00
1997 MVP
475C Ken Griffey Jr. MM 3.00 8.00
HR Dad
475D Ken Griffey Jr. MM 3.00 8.00
1992 AS MVP
475E Ken Griffey Jr. MM 3.00 8.00
50 HR 1997
476A Barry Bonds MM 5.00 12.00
400HR/400SB
476B Barry Bonds MM 5.00 12.00
40HR/40SB
476C Barry Bonds MM 5.00 12.00
1993 MVP
476D Barry Bonds MM 5.00 12.00
1990 MVP
476E Barry Bonds MM 5.00 12.00
1992 MVP
477A Sammy Sosa 3.00 8.00
MM 20 HR June
477B Sammy Sosa MM 3.00 8.00
66 HR 1998
477C Sammy Sosa MM 3.00 8.00
60 HR 1999
477D Sammy Sosa MM 3.00 8.00
1998 MVP
477E Sammy Sosa MM 3.00 8.00
HR's 61/62
478A Derek Jeter MM 5.00 12.00
1996 ROY
478B Derek Jeter MM 5.00 12.00
Wins 1999 WS
478C Derek Jeter MM 5.00 12.00
Wins 1998 WS
478D Derek Jeter MM 5.00 12.00
Wins 1996 WS
478E Derek Jeter MM 5.00 12.00
17 GM Hit Streak
479A Alex Rodriguez MM 4.00 10.00
40HR/40SB
479B Alex Rodriguez MM 4.00 10.00
100th HR
479C Alex Rodriguez 4.00 10.00
MM 1996 POY
479D Alex Rodriguez 4.00 10.00
MM Wins 1 Million
479E Alex Rodriguez MM 4.00 10.00
1996 Batting Leader
NNO M.McGwire 85 Reprint 3.00 8.00

2000 Topps Chrome Refractors

These cards which parallel the regular Topps Chrome set were issued at a rate of one in 12 packs. The Mark McGwire rookie reprint card was issued at a rate of one in 12,116 first series packs and are serial numbered to 70.

*STARS: 2.5X TO 6X BASIC CARDS
*PROSPECTS 202-216: 2.5X TO 6X BASIC
*ROOKIES 202-216: 2X TO 5X BASIC
*PROSPECTS 441-455: 2.5X TO 6X BASIC
*ROOKIES 441-455: 2X TO 5X BASIC
MCGWIRE MM SET (5) 75.00 150.00
MCGWIRE MM (236A-236E) 15.00 40.00
AARON MM SET (5) 60.00 120.00
AARON MM (237A-237E) 12.50 30.00
RIPKEN MM SET (5) 100.00 200.00
RIPKEN MM (238A-238E) 20.00 50.00
BOGGS MM SET (5) 15.00 40.00
BOGGS MM (239A-239E) 4.00 10.00
GWYNN MM SET (5) 40.00 80.00
GWYNN MM (240A-240E) 8.00 20.00
GRIFFEY MM SET (5) 50.00 100.00
GRIFFEY MM (475A-475E) 10.00 25.00
BONDS MM SET (5) 75.00 150.00
BONDS MM (476A-476E) 15.00 40.00
SOSA MM SET (5) 50.00 100.00
SOSA MM (477A-477E) 10.00 25.00
JETER MM SET (5) 75.00 150.00
JETER MM (478A-478E) 15.00 40.00
A.ROD MM SET (5) 60.00 120.00
A.ROD MM (479A-479E) 12.50 30.00

2000 Topps Chrome 21st Century

Inserted at a rate of one in 16, this 10 cards feature players who are expected to be the best in the first part of the 21st century. Card backs carry a "C" prefix.

COMPLETE SET (10) 15.00 40.00
*REF: 1X TO 2.5X BASIC 21ST CENT.
SER.1 REFRACTOR ODDS 1:80
C1 Ben Grieve .60 1.50
C2 Alex Gonzalez .60 1.50
C3 Derek Jeter 4.00 10.00
C4 Sean Casey .60 1.50
C5 Nomar Garciaparra 2.50 6.00
C6 Alex Rodriguez 2.50 6.00
C7 Scott Rolen 1.00 2.50
C8 Andruw Jones 1.00 2.50
C9 Vladimir Guerrero 1.50 4.00
C10 Todd Helton 1.00 2.50

2000 Topps Chrome All-Star Rookie Team

Randomly inserted into packs at one in 16, this 10-card insert set features players that made the All-Star game their rookie season. Card backs carry a "RT" prefix.

COMPLETE SET (10) 20.00 50.00
*REF: 1X TO 2.5X BASIC ASR TEAM
REFRACTOR STATED ODDS 1:80
RT1 Mark McGwire 4.00 10.00
RT2 Chuck Knoblauch .60 1.50
RT3 Chipper Jones 1.50 4.00
RT4 Cal Ripken 5.00 12.00
RT5 Manny Ramirez 1.00 2.50
RT6 Jose Canseco 1.00 2.50
RT7 Ken Griffey Jr. 2.50 6.00
RT8 Mike Piazza 2.50 6.00
RT9 Dwight Gooden .60 1.50
RT10 Billy Wagner .60 1.50

2000 Topps Chrome All-Topps

Inserted at a rate of one in 32 first and second series packs, these 10 cards feature the best players in the American and National Leagues. National League cards 91-10) were distributed in series one and American league (11-20) in series two. Card backs carry an "AT" prefix.

COMPLETE SET (20) 60.00 160.00
COMPLETE N.L. (10) 30.00 80.00
COMPLETE A.L.(10) 30.00 80.00
*REFRACTORS: 1X TO 2.5X BASIC ALL NL
REFRACTOR ODDS 1:160
AT1 Greg Maddux 4.00 10.00
AT2 Mike Piazza 4.00 10.00
AT3 Mark McGwire 6.00 15.00
AT4 Craig Biggio 1.50 4.00
AT5 Chipper Jones 2.50 6.00
AT6 Barry Larkin 1.50 4.00
AT7 Barry Bonds 5.00 12.00
AT8 Andruw Jones 1.50 4.00
AT9 Sammy Sosa 2.50 6.00
AT10 Larry Walker 1.00 2.50
AT11 Pedro Martinez 1.50 4.00
AT12 Ivan Rodriguez 1.50 4.00
AT13 Rafael Palmeiro 1.50 4.00
AT14 Roberto Alomar 1.50 4.00
AT15 Cal Ripken 8.00 20.00
AT16 Derek Jeter 6.00 15.00
AT17 Albert Belle 1.00 2.50
AT18 Ken Griffey Jr. 4.00 10.00
AT19 Manny Ramirez 1.50 4.00
AT20 Jose Canseco 1.50 4.00

2000 Topps Chrome Allegiance

This Topps Chrome exclusive set features 20 players who have spent their entire career with just one team. The Allegiance cards were issued at a rate of one in 16 and have a "TA" prefix.

COMPLETE SET (20) 50.00 120.00
*REF: 4X TO 10X BASIC ALLEGIANCE
SER.1 REFRACTOR ODDS 1:424 HOBBY
REFRACTOR PRINT RUN 100 SERIAL #'d SETS
TA1 Derek Jeter 6.00 15.00
TA2 Ivan Rodriguez 1.50 4.00
TA3 Alex Rodriguez 4.00 10.00
TA4 Cal Ripken 8.00 20.00
TA5 Mark Grace 1.50 4.00
TA6 Tony Gwynn 3.00 8.00
TA7 Tom Glavine 1.50 4.00
TA8 Frank Thomas 2.50 6.00
TA9 Manny Ramirez 1.50 4.00
TA10 Barry Larkin 1.50 4.00
TA11 Bernie Williams 1.50 4.00
TA12 Eric Karros 1.00 2.50
TA13 Vladimir Guerrero 2.50 6.00
TA14 Craig Biggio 1.50 4.00
TA15 Nomar Garciaparra 4.00 10.00
TA16 Andruw Jones 1.50 4.00
TA17 Jim Thome 1.50 4.00
TA18 Scott Rolen 1.50 4.00
TA19 Chipper Jones 2.50 6.00
TA20 Ken Griffey Jr. 4.00 10.00

2000 Topps Chrome Combos

Randomly inserted into series two packs at one in 16, this 10-card insert features a variety of player combinations, such as the 1999 MVP's. Card backs carry a "TC" prefix.

COMPLETE SET (10) 30.00 80.00
*REFRACTORS: 1X TO 2.5X BASIC COMBO
REFRACTOR ODDS 1:80
TC1 Roberto Alomar 1.00 2.50
Manny Ramirez
Kenny Lofton
Jim Thome
TC2 Tom Glavine 2.50 6.00
Greg Maddux
John Smoltz
TC3 Paul O'Neill 4.00 10.00
Derek Jeter
Bernie Williams
Tino Martinez
TC4 Ivan Rodriguez 2.50 6.00
Mike Piazza
TC5 Nomar Garciaparra 4.00 10.00
Alex Rodriguez
Derek Jeter
TC6 Sammy Sosa 4.00 10.00
Mark McGwire
TC7 Pedro Martinez 1.00 2.50
Randy Johnson
TC8 Barry Bonds 2.50 6.00
Ken Griffey Jr.
TC9 Chipper Jones 1.50 4.00
Ivan Rodriguez
TC10 Cal Ripken 5.00 12.00
Tony Gwynn
Wade Boggs

2000 Topps Chrome Kings

Randomly inserted into series two packs at one in 32, this 10-card insert features some of the greatest players in major league baseball. Card backs carry a "CK" prefix.

COMPLETE SET (10) 30.00 80.00
CK1 Mark McGwire 6.00 15.00
CK2 Sammy Sosa 2.50 6.00
CK3 Ken Griffey Jr. 4.00 10.00
CK4 Mike Piazza 4.00 10.00
CK5 Alex Rodriguez 4.00 10.00
CK6 Manny Ramirez 1.50 4.00
CK7 Barry Bonds 5.00 12.00
CK8 Nomar Garciaparra 4.00 10.00
CK9 Chipper Jones 2.50 6.00
CK10 Vladimir Guerrero 2.50 6.00

2000 Topps Chrome Kings Refractors

Randomly inserted into series two packs at one in 514, this 10-card insert is a complete parallel of the Chrome Kings insert. Each card was produced using Topps' "refractor" technology. Please note that each card was serial numbered to the amount of homeruns that the individual players had after the 1999 season. Production runs are listed below. Card backs carry a "CK" pefix.

COMPLETE SET (10) 125.00 300.00
CK1 Mark McGwire/522 12.50 30.00
CK2 Sammy Sosa/366 8.00 20.00
CK3 Ken Griffey Jr./398 10.00 25.00
CK4 Mike Piazza/240 10.00 25.00
CK5 Alex Rodriguez/148 20.00 50.00
CK6 Manny Ramirez/198 6.00 15.00
CK7 Barry Bonds/445 10.00 25.00
CK8 N.Garciaparra/96 20.00 50.00
CK9 Chipper Jones/153 8.00 20.00
CK10 V.Guerrero/92 15.00 40.00

2000 Topps Chrome New Millennium Stars

Randomly inserted into series two packs at one in 32, this 10-card insert features some of the major league's hottest young talent. Card backs carry a "NMS" prefix.

COMPLETE SET (10) 15.00 40.00
*REFRACTORS: 1X TO 2.5X BASIC MILL.
SER.2 REFRACTOR ODDS 1:160
NMS1 Nomar Garciaparra 4.00 10.00
NMS2 Vladimir Guerrero 2.50 6.00
NMS3 Sean Casey 1.00 2.50
NMS4 Richie Sexson 1.00 2.50
NMS5 Todd Helton 1.50 4.00
NMS6 Carlos Beltran 1.00 2.50
NMS7 Kevin Millwood 1.00 2.50
NMS8 Ruben Mateo 1.00 2.50
NMS9 Pat Burrell 2.00 5.00
NMS10 Alfonso Soriano 1.00 2.50

2000 Topps Chrome Own the Game

Randomly inserted into series two packs at one in 11, this 30-card insert features players that are amoung the major league's statistical leaders year after year. Card backs carry an "OTG" prefix.

COMPLETE SET (30) 80.00 200.00
*REFRACTORS: 1X TO 2.5X BASIC OWN
SER.2 REFRACTOR ODDS 1:55
OTG1 Derek Jeter 6.00 15.00
OTG2 B.J. Surhoff 1.00 2.50
OTG3 Luis Gonzalez 1.00 2.50
OTG4 Manny Ramirez 1.50 4.00
OTG5 Rafael Palmeiro 1.50 4.00
OTG6 Mark McGwire 6.00 15.00
OTG7 Mark McGwire 6.00 15.00
OTG8 Sammy Sosa 2.50 6.00
OTG9 Ken Griffey Jr. 4.00 10.00
OTG10 Larry Walker 1.00 2.50
OTG11 Nomar Garciaparra 4.00 10.00
OTG12 Derek Jeter 6.00 15.00
OTG13 Larry Walker 1.00 2.50
OTG14 Mark McGwire 6.00 15.00
OTG15 Manny Ramirez 1.50 4.00
OTG16 Pedro Martinez 1.50 4.00
OTG17 Randy Johnson 2.50 6.00
OTG18 Kevin Millwood 1.00 2.50
OTG19 Randy Johnson 2.50 6.00
OTG20 Pedro Martinez 1.50 4.00
OTG21 Kevin Brown 1.50 4.00
OTG22 Chipper Jones 2.50 6.00
OTG23 Ivan Rodriguez 1.50 4.00
OTG24 Mariano Rivera 2.50 6.00
OTG25 Scott Williamson 1.00 2.50
OTG26 Carlos Beltran 1.00 2.50
OTG27 Randy Johnson 2.50 6.00
OTG28 Pedro Martinez 1.50 4.00
OTG29 Sammy Sosa 2.50 6.00
OTG30 Manny Ramirez 1.50 4.00

2000 Topps Chrome Power Players

This 20 card set, issued at a rate of one in eight packs, features players who are the leading power hitters in the majors. Card backs carry a "P" prefix.

COMPLETE SET (20) 40.00 100.00
*REFRACTORS: 1X TO 2.5X BASIC POWER
SER.1 REFRACTOR ODDS 1:40
P1 Juan Gonzalez .60 1.50
P2 Ken Griffey Jr. 2.50 6.00
P3 Mark McGwire 4.00 10.00
P4 Nomar Garciaparra 2.50 6.00
P5 Barry Bonds 3.00 8.00
P6 Mo Vaughn .60 1.50
P7 Larry Walker .60 1.50

P8 Alex Rodriguez 2.50 6.00
P9 Jose Canseco 1.00 2.50
P10 Jeff Bagwell 1.00 2.50
P11 Manny Ramirez 1.00 2.50
P12 Albert Belle .60 1.50
P13 Frank Thomas 1.50 4.00
P14 Mike Piazza 2.50 6.00
P15 Chipper Jones 1.50 4.00
P16 Sammy Sosa 1.50 4.00
P17 Vladimir Guerrero 1.50 4.00
P18 Scott Rolen 1.00 2.50
P19 Raul Mondesi .60 1.50
P20 Derek Jeter 4.00 10.00

2000 Topps Chrome Traded

The 2000 Topps Chrome Traded set was released in late November, 2000 and features a 135-card base set. The set is an exact parallel of the Topps Traded set.This set was produced using Topps' chrome technology. Please note that card backs carry a "T" prefix. Each set came with 135 cards and carried a $99.99 suggested retail price. Notable Rookie Cards include Miguel Cabrera.

COMP.FACT.SET (135) 40.00 80.00
T1 Mike MacDougal .30 .75
T2 Andy Tracy RC .20 .50
T3 Brandon Phillips RC 1.00 2.50
T4 Brandon Inge RC 1.50 4.00
T5 Robbie Morrison RC .20 .50
T6 Josh Pressley RC .20 .50
T7 Todd Moser RC .20 .50
T8 Rob Purvis .25 .60
T9 Chance Caple .15 .40
T10 Ben Sheets 1.00 2.50
T11 Russ Jacobson RC .20 .50
T12 Brian Cole RC .20 .50
T13 Brad Baker .15 .40
T14 Alex Cintron RC .30 .75
T15 Lyle Overbay RC .75 2.00
T16 Mike Edwards RC .20 .50
T17 Sean McGowan RC .20 .50
T18 Jose Molina .15 .40
T19 Marcos Castillo RC .20 .50
T20 Josue Espada RC .20 .50
T21 Alex Gordon RC .20 .50
T22 Rob Pugmire RC .20 .50
T23 Jason Stumm .20 .50
T24 Ty Howington .15 .40
T25 Brett Myers .60 1.50
T26 Maicer Izturis RC .30 .75
T27 John McDonald .15 .40
T28 W.Rodriguez RC .20 .50
T29 Carlos Zambrano RC 4.00 10.00
T30 Alejandro Diaz RC .20 .50
T31 Geraldo Guzman RC .20 .50
T32 J.R. House RC .20 .50
T33 Elvin Nina RC .20 .50
T34 Juan Pierre RC .75 2.00
T35 Ben Johnson RC 1.25 3.00
T36 Jeff Bailey RC .20 .50
T37 Miguel Olivo RC .50 1.25
T38 F.Rodriguez RC 1.50 4.00
T39 Tony Pena Jr. RC .20 .50
T40 Miguel Cabrera RC 20.00 50.00
T41 Asdrubal Oropeza RC .20 .50
T42 Junior Zamora RC .30 .75
T43 Jovanny Cedeno RC .20 .50
T44 John Sneed .25 .60
T45 Josh Kalinowski .25 .60
T46 Mike Young RC 5.00 12.00
T47 Rico Washington RC .20 .50
T48 Chad Durbin RC .20 .50
T49 Junior Brignac RC .20 .50
T50 Carlos Hernandez RC .30 .75
T51 Cesar Izturis RC .50 1.25
T52 Oscar Salazar RC .20 .50
T53 Pat Strange RC .20 .50
T54 Rick Asadoorian .30 .75
T55 Keith Reed .15 .40
T56 Leo Estrella RC .20 .50
T57 Wascar Serrano RC .20 .50
T58 Richard Gomez RC .20 .50
T59 Ramon Santiago RC .20 .50
T60 Jovanny Sosa RC .20 .50
T61 Aaron Rowand RC 1.25 3.00
T62 Junior Guerrero RC .20 .50
T63 Luis Terrero RC .30 .75
T64 Brian Sanches RC .20 .50
T65 Scott Sobkowiak RC .20 .50
T66 Gary Majewski RC .30 .75
T67 Barry Zito 1.25 3.00
T68 Ryan Christianson .20 .50
T69 Cristian Guerrero RC .20 .50
T70 T.De La Rosa RC .20 .50
T71 Andrew Beinbrink RC .20 .50
T72 Ryan Knox RC .20 .50
T73 Alex Graman RC .20 .50
T74 Juan Guzman RC .20 .50
T75 Ruben Salazar RC .20 .50
T76 Luis Matos RC .30 .75
T77 Tony Mota RC .20 .50
T78 Doug Davis .25 .60
T79 Ben Christensen .15 .40
T80 Mike Lamb .50 1.25
T81 Adrian Gonzalez RC 5.00 12.00
T82 Mike Stodolka RC .20 .50
T83 Adam Johnson RC .20 .50
T84 Matt Wheatland RC .20 .50
T85 Corey Smith RC .20 .50
T86 Rocco Baldelli RC 1.50 4.00
T87 Keith Bucktrot RC .20 .50
T88 Adam Wainwright RC 2.00 5.00
T89 Scott Thorman RC .75 2.00
T90 Tripper Johnson RC .20 .50
T91 Jim Edmonds Cards .25 .60
T92 Masato Yoshii .15 .40
T93 Adam Kennedy .15 .40
T94 Darryl Kile .25 .60
T95 Mark McLemore .15 .40
T96 Ricky Gutierrez .15 .40
T97 Juan Gonzalez .25 .60
T98 Melvin Mora .25 .60
T99 Dante Bichette .25 .60
T100 Lee Stevens .15 .40
T101 Roger Cedeno .15 .40
T102 John Olerud .25 .60
T103 Eric Young .15 .40
T104 Mickey Morandini .15 .40
T105 Travis Lee .15 .40
T106 Greg Vaughn .15 .40
T107 Todd Zeile .25 .60
T108 Chuck Finley .25 .60
T109 Ismael Valdes .15 .40
T110 Reggie Sanders .25 .60
T111 Pat Hentgen .15 .40
T112 Ryan Klesko .25 .60
T113 Derek Bell .15 .40
T114 Hideo Nomo .60 1.50
T115 Aaron Sele .15 .40
T116 Fernando Vina .15 .40
T117 Wally Joyner .25 .60
T118 Brian Hunter .15 .40
T119 Joe Girardi .15 .40
T120 Omar Daal .15 .40
T121 Brook Fordyce .15 .40
T122 Jose Valentin .15 .40
T123 Curt Schilling .25 .60
T124 B.J. Surhoff .25 .60
T125 Henry Rodriguez .15 .40
T126 Mike Bordick .15 .40
T127 David Justice .25 .60
T128 Charles Johnson .25 .60
T129 Will Clark .40 1.00
T130 Dwight Gooden .25 .60
T131 David Segui .15 .40
T132 Denny Neagle .25 .60
T133 Jose Canseco .40 1.00
T134 Bruce Chen .15 .40
T135 Jason Bere .15 .40

2001 Topps Chrome

The 2001 Topps Chrome product was released in two separate series. The first series shipped in February 2001, and features a 331-card base set produced with Topps' special chrome technology. This set parallels the regular 2001 Topps base set in card design and photography but card numbering differs due to the fact that the manufacturer decided to select only the best 331 cards of the 405 card basic Topps set to be featured in this upgraded Chrome product. Each Topps Chrome pack contains four cards, and carried a suggested retail price of $2.99. Please note, card number 7 does not exist. The number was retired in Topps and Topps Chrome brands back in 1996 in honor of Yankees legend Mickey Mantle. Notable Rookie Cards include Jake Peavy and Albert Pujols.

COMPLETE SET (661) 150.00 300.00
COMP. SERIES 1 (331) 75.00 150.00
COMP. SERIES 2 (330) 75.00 150.00
1 Cal Ripken 2.50 6.00
2 Chipper Jones .75 2.00
3 Roger Cedeno .20 .50
4 Garret Anderson .30 .75
5 Robin Ventura .30 .75
6 Daryle Ward .20 .50
7 Does Not Exist
8 Phil Nevin .30 .75
9 Jermaine Dye .30 .75
10 Chris Singleton .20 .50
11 Mike Redmond .20 .50
12 Jim Thome .50 1.25
13 Brian Jordan .30 .75
14 Dustin Hermanson .20 .50
15 Shawn Green .30 .75
16 Todd Stottlemyre .20 .50
17 Dan Wilson .20 .50
18 Derek Lowe .30 .75
19 Juan Gonzalez .30 .75
20 Pat Meares .20 .50
21 Paul O'Neill .50 1.25
22 Jeffrey Hammonds .20 .50
23 Pokey Reese .20 .50
24 Mike Mussina .50 1.25
25 Rico Brogna .20 .50
26 Jay Buhner .30 .75
27 Steve Cox .20 .50
28 Quilvio Veras .20 .50
29 Marquis Grissom .30 .75
30 Shigetoshi Hasegawa .30 .75
31 Shane Reynolds .20 .50
32 Adam Piatt .20 .50
33 Preston Wilson .30 .75
34 Ellis Burks .30 .75
35 Armando Rios .20 .50
36 Chuck Finley .30 .75
37 Shannon Stewart .30 .75
38 Mark McGwire 2.00 5.00
39 Gerald Williams .20 .50
40 Eric Young .20 .50
41 Peter Bergeron .20 .50
42 Arthur Rhodes .20 .50
43 Bobby Jones .20 .50
44 Matt Clement .30 .75
45 Pedro Martinez .50 1.25
46 Jose Canseco .50 1.25
47 Matt Anderson .20 .50
48 Torii Hunter .30 .75
49 Carlos Lee .30 .75
50 Eric Chavez .30 .75
51 Rick Helling .20 .50
52 John Franco .30 .75
53 Mike Bordick .30 .75
54 Andres Galarraga .30 .75
55 Jose Cruz Jr. .20 .50
56 Mike Matheny .20 .50
57 Randy Johnson .75 2.00
58 Richie Sexson .30 .75
59 Vladimir Nunez .20 .50
60 Aaron Boone .30 .75
61 Darin Erstad .30 .75
62 Alex Gonzalez .20 .50
63 Gil Heredia .20 .50
64 Shane Andrews .20 .50
65 Todd Hundley .20 .50
66 Bill Mueller .30 .75
67 Mark McLemore .20 .50
68 Scott Spiezio .20 .50
69 Kevin McGlinchy .20 .50
70 Manny Ramirez .50 1.25
71 Mike Lamb .20 .50
72 Brian Buchanan .20 .50
73 Mike Sweeney .30 .75
74 John Wetteland .30 .75
75 Rob Bell .20 .50
76 John Burkett .20 .50
77 Derek Jeter 2.00 5.00
78 J.D. Drew .30 .75
79 Jose Offerman .20 .50
80 Rick Reed .20 .50
81 Will Clark .50 1.25
82 Rickey Henderson .75 2.00
83 Kirk Rueter .20 .50
84 Lee Stevens .20 .50
85 Jay Bell .30 .75
86 Fred McGriff .50 1.25
87 Julio Zuleta .20 .50
88 Brian Anderson .20 .50
89 Orlando Cabrera .30 .75
90 Alex Fernandez .20 .50
91 Derek Bell .20 .50
92 Eric Owens .20 .50
93 Dennys Reyes .20 .50
94 Mike Stanley .20 .50
95 Jorge Posada .50 1.25
96 Paul Konerko .30 .75
97 Mike Remlinger .20 .50
98 Travis Lee .20 .50
99 Ken Caminiti .30 .75
100 Kevin Barker .20 .50
101 Ozzie Guillen .30 .75
102 Randy Wolf .20 .50
103 Michael Tucker .20 .50
104 Darren Lewis .20 .50
105 Joe Randa .30 .75
106 Jeff Cirillo .20 .50
107 David Ortiz .75 2.00
108 Herb Perry .20 .50
109 Jeff Nelson .20 .50
110 Chris Stynes .20 .50
111 Johnny Damon .50 1.25
112 Jason Schmidt .30 .75
113 Charles Johnson .20 .50
114 Pat Burrell .30 .75
115 Gary Sheffield .30 .75
116 Tom Glavine .50 1.25
117 Jason Isringhausen .30 .75
118 Chris Carpenter .30 .75
119 Jeff Suppan .20 .50
120 Ivan Rodriguez .50 1.25
121 Luis Sojo .20 .50
122 Ron Villone .20 .50
123 Mike Sirotka .20 .50
124 Chuck Knoblauch .30 .75
125 Jason Kendall .30 .75
126 Bobby Estalella .20 .50
127 Jose Guillen .30 .75
128 Carlos Delgado .30 .75
129 Benji Gil .20 .50
130 Einar Diaz .20 .50
131 Andy Benes .20 .50
132 Adrian Beltre .30 .75
133 Roger Clemens 1.50 4.00
134 Scott Williamson .20 .50
135 Brad Penny .20 .50
136 Troy Glaus .30 .75
137 Kevin Appier .30 .75
138 Walt Weiss .20 .50
139 Michael Barrett .20 .50
140 Mike Hampton .30 .75
141 Francisco Cordova .20 .50
142 David Segui .20 .50
143 Carlos Febles .20 .50
144 Roy Halladay .30 .75
145 Seth Etherton .20 .50
146 Fernando Tatis .20 .50
147 Livan Hernandez .30 .75
148 B.J. Surhoff .30 .75
149 Barry Larkin .50 1.25
150 Bobby Howry .20 .50
151 Dmitri Young .30 .75
152 Brian Hunter .20 .50
153 Alex Rodriguez 1.25 3.00
154 Hideo Nomo .75 2.00
155 Warren Morris .20 .50
156 Antonio Alfonseca .20 .50
157 Edgardo Alfonzo .20 .50
158 Mark Grudzielanek .20 .50
159 Fernando Vina .20 .50
160 Homer Bush .20 .50
161 Jason Giambi .30 .75
162 Steve Karsay .20 .50
163 Matt Lawton .20 .50
164 Rusty Greer .30 .75
165 Billy Koch .20 .50
166 Todd Hollandsworth .20 .50
167 Raul Ibanez .20 .50
168 Tony Gwynn 1.00 2.50
169 Carl Everett .30 .75
170 Hector Carrasco .20 .50
171 Jose Valentin .20 .50
172 Deivi Cruz .20 .50
173 Bret Boone .30 .75
174 Melvin Mora .30 .75
175 Danny Graves .20 .50
176 Jose Jimenez .20 .50
177 James Baldwin .20 .50
178 C.J. Nitkowski .20 .50
179 Jeff Zimmerman .20 .50
180 Mike Lowell .30 .75
181 Hideki Irabu .20 .50
182 Greg Vaughn .20 .50
183 Omar Daal .20 .50
184 Darren Dreifort .20 .50
185 Gil Meche .20 .50
186 Damian Jackson .20 .50
187 Frank Thomas .75 2.00
188 Luis Castillo .20 .50
189 Bartolo Colon .30 .75
190 Craig Biggio .50 1.25
191 Scott Schoeneweis .20 .50
192 Dave Veres .20 .50
193 Ramon Martinez .20 .50
194 Jose Vidro .20 .50
195 Todd Helton .50 1.25
196 Greg Norton .20 .50
197 Jacque Jones .30 .75
198 Jason Grimsley .20 .50
199 Dan Reichert .20 .50
200 Robb Nen .30 .75
201 Scott Hatteberg .20 .50
202 Terry Shumpert .20 .50
203 Kevin Millar .30 .75
204 Ismael Valdes .20 .50
205 Richard Hidalgo .20 .50
206 Randy Velarde .20 .50
207 Bengie Molina .20 .50
208 Tony Womack .20 .50
209 Enrique Wilson .20 .50
210 Jeff Brantley .20 .50
211 Rick Ankiel .20 .50
212 Terry Mulholland .20 .50
213 Ron Belliard .20 .50
214 Terrence Long .20 .50
215 Alberto Castillo .20 .50
216 Royce Clayton .20 .50
217 Joe McEwing .20 .50
218 Jason McDonald .20 .50
219 Ricky Bottalico .20 .50
220 Keith Foulke .30 .75
221 Brad Radke .30 .75
222 Gabe Kapler .30 .75
223 Pedro Astacio .20 .50
224 Armando Reynoso .20 .50
225 Darryl Kile .30 .75
226 Reggie Sanders .30 .75
227 Esteban Yan .20 .50
228 Joe Nathan .30 .75
229 Jay Payton .20 .50
230 Francisco Cordero .20 .50
231 Gregg Jefferies .20 .50
232 LaTroy Hawkins .20 .50
233 Jacob Cruz .20 .50
234 Chris Holt .20 .50
235 Vladimir Guerrero .75 2.00
236 Marvin Benard .20 .50
237 Alex Ramirez .20 .50
238 Mike Williams .20 .50
239 Sean Bergman .20 .50
240 Juan Encarnacion .20 .50
241 Russ Davis .20 .50
242 Ramon Hernandez .20 .50
243 Sandy Alomar Jr. .20 .50
244 Eddie Guardado .20 .50
245 Shane Halter .20 .50
246 Geoff Jenkins .20 .50
247 Brian Meadows .20 .50
248 Damian Miller .20 .50
249 Darrin Fletcher .20 .50
250 Rafael Furcal .30 .75
251 Mark Grace .50 1.25
252 Mark Mulder .30 .75
253 Joe Torre MG .50 1.25
254 Bobby Cox MG .20 .50
255 Mike Scioscia MG .20 .50
256 Mike Hargrove MG .20 .50
257 Jimy Williams MG .20 .50
258 Jerry Manuel MG .20 .50
259 Charlie Manuel MG .20 .50
260 Don Baylor MG .30 .75
261 Phil Garner MG .30 .75
262 Tony Muser MG .20 .50
263 Buddy Bell MG .30 .75
264 Tom Kelly MG .20 .50
265 John Boles MG .20 .50
266 Art Howe MG .20 .50
267 Larry Dierker MG .20 .50
268 Lou Piniella MG .30 .75
269 Larry Rothschild MG .20 .50
270 Davey Lopes MG .30 .75
271 Johnny Oates MG .20 .50
272 Felipe Alou MG .20 .50
273 Bobby Valentine MG .20 .50
274 Tony LaRussa MG .20 .50
275 Bruce Bochy MG .20 .50
276 Dusty Baker MG .30 .75
277 Adrian Gonzalez 2.50 6.00
Adam Johnson
278 Matt Wheatland .40 1.00
Bryan Digby
279 Tripper Johnson .40 1.00
Scott Thorman
280 Phil Dumatrait .75 2.00
Adam Wainwright
281 Scott Heard .40 1.00
David Parrish RC
282 Rocco Baldelli .60 1.50
Mark Folsom
283 Dominic Rich RC .40 1.00
Aaron Herr
284 Mike Stodolka .40 1.00
Sean Burnett
285 Derek Thompson .40 1.00
Corey Smith
286 Danny Borrell .40 1.00
Jason Bourgeois RC
287 Chin-Feng Chen .75 2.00
Corey Patterson
Josh Hamilton
288 Ryan Anderson .75 2.00
Barry Zito
C.C. Sabathia
289 Scott Sobkowiak .75 2.00
David Walling
Ben Sheets
290 Ty Howington .40 1.00
Josh Kalinowski
Josh Girdley
291 Hee Seop Choi .75 2.00
Aaron McNeal
Jason Hart
292 Bobby Bradley .60 1.50
Kurt Ainsworth
Chin-Hui Tsao
293 Mike Glendenning .40 1.00
Kenny Kelly
Juan Silvestre
294 J.R. House .40 1.00
Ramon Castro
Ben Davis
295 Chance Caple .60 1.50
Rafael Soriano
Pasqual Coco
296 Travis Hafner RC 4.00 10.00
Eric Munson
Bucky Jacobsen
297 Jason Conti .40 1.00
Chris Wakeland
Brian Cole
298 Scott Seabol 1.00 2.50
Aubrey Huff
Joe Crede
299 Adam Everett .40 1.00
Jose Ortiz
Keith Ginter
300 Carlos Hernandez .40 1.00
Geraldo Guzman
Adam Eaton
301 Bobby Kielty .60 1.50
Milton Bradley
Juan Rivera
302 Mark McGwire GM 1.00 2.50
303 Don Larsen GM .30 .75
304 Bobby Thomson GM .30 .75
305 Bill Mazeroski GM .30 .75
306 Reggie Jackson GM .50 1.25
307 Kirk Gibson GM .30 .75
308 Roger Maris GM .50 1.25
309 Cal Ripken GM 1.25 3.00
310 Hank Aaron GM .75 2.00
311 Joe Carter GM .30 .75
312 Cal Ripken SH 1.25 3.00
313 Randy Johnson SH .50 1.25
314 Ken Griffey Jr. SH .75 2.00
315 Troy Glaus SH .30 .75
316 Kazuhiro Sasaki SH .30 .75
317 Sammy Sosa .50 1.25
Troy Glaus LL
318 Todd Helton .30 .75
Edgar Martinez LL
319 Todd Helton .75 2.00
Nomar Garicaparra LL
320 Barry Bonds .75 2.00
Jason Giambi LL
321 Todd Helton .30 .75
Manny Ramirez LL
322 Todd Helton .30 .75
Darin Erstad LL
323 Kevin Brown .50 1.25
Pedro Martinez LL
324 Randy Johnson .50 1.25
Pedro Martinez LL
325 Will Clark HL .50 1.25
326 New York Mets HL .75 2.00
327 New York Yankees HL 1.25 3.00
328 Seattle Mariners HL .30 .75
329 Mike Hampton HL .30 .75
330 New York Yankees HL 1.50 4.00
331 N.Y. Yankees Champs 3.00 8.00
332 Jeff Bagwell .50 1.25
333 Andy Pettitte .50 1.25
334 Tony Armas Jr. .20 .50
335 Jeromy Burnitz .30 .75
336 Javier Vazquez .30 .75
337 Eric Karros .30 .75
338 Brian Giles .30 .75
339 Scott Rolen .50 1.25
340 David Justice .30 .75
341 Ray Durham .30 .75
342 Todd Zeile .30 .75
343 Cliff Floyd .30 .75
344 Barry Bonds 2.00 5.00
345 Matt Williams .30 .75
346 Steve Finley .30 .75
347 Scott Elarton .20 .50
348 Bernie Williams .50 1.25
349 David Wells .30 .75
350 J.T. Snow .30 .75
351 Al Leiter .30 .75
352 Magglio Ordonez .30 .75
353 Raul Mondesi .30 .75
354 Tim Salmon .50 1.25
355 Jeff Kent .30 .75
356 Mariano Rivera .75 2.00
357 John Olerud .30 .75
358 Javy Lopez .30 .75
359 Ben Grieve .20 .50
360 Ray Lankford .30 .75
361 Ken Griffey Jr. 1.25 3.00
362 Rich Aurilia .20 .50
363 Andruw Jones .50 1.25
364 Ryan Klesko .30 .75
365 Roberto Alomar .50 1.25
366 Miguel Tejada .30 .75
367 Mo Vaughn .30 .75
368 Albert Belle .30 .75
369 Jose Canseco .50 1.25
370 Kevin Brown .30 .75
371 Rafael Palmeiro .50 1.25
372 Mark Redman .20 .50
373 Larry Walker .30 .75
374 Greg Maddux 1.25 3.00
375 Nomar Garciaparra 1.25 3.00
376 Kevin Millwood .30 .75
377 Edgar Martinez .50 1.25
378 Sammy Sosa .75 2.00
379 Tim Hudson .30 .75
380 Jim Edmonds .30 .75
381 Mike Piazza 1.25 3.00
382 Brant Brown .20 .50
383 Brad Fullmer .20 .50
384 Alan Benes .20 .50
385 Mickey Morandini .20 .50
386 Troy Percival .30 .75
387 Eddie Perez .20 .50
388 Vernon Wells .30 .75
389 Ricky Gutierrez .20 .50
390 Rondell White .30 .75
391 Kelvim Escobar .20 .50
392 Tony Batista .20 .50
393 Jimmy Haynes .20 .50
394 Billy Wagner .30 .75
395 A.J. Hinch .20 .50
396 Matt Morris .30 .75
397 Lance Berkman .30 .75
398 Jeff D'Amico .20 .50
399 Octavio Dotel .20 .50
400 Olmedo Saenz .20 .50
401 Esteban Loaiza .20 .50
402 Adam Kennedy .20 .50
403 Moises Alou .30 .75
404 Orlando Palmeiro .20 .50
405 Kevin Young .20 .50
406 Tom Goodwin .20 .50
407 Mac Suzuki .30 .75
408 Pat Hentgen .20 .50
409 Kevin Stocker .20 .50
410 Mark Sweeney .20 .50
411 Tony Eusebio .20 .50
412 Edgar Renteria .30 .75
413 John Rocker .30 .75
414 Jose Lima .20 .50
415 Kerry Wood .30 .75
416 Mike Timlin .20 .50
417 Jose Hernandez .20 .50
418 Jeremy Giambi .20 .50
419 Luis Lopez .20 .50
420 Mitch Meluskey .20 .50
421 Garrett Stephenson .20 .50
422 Jamey Wright .20 .50
423 John Jaha .20 .50
424 Placido Polanco .20 .50
425 Marty Cordova .20 .50
426 Joey Hamilton .20 .50
427 Travis Fryman .30 .75
428 Mike Cameron .20 .50
429 Matt Mantei .20 .50
430 Chan Ho Park .30 .75
431 Shawn Estes .20 .50
432 Danny Bautista .20 .50
433 Wilson Alvarez .20 .50
434 Kenny Lofton .30 .75
435 Russ Ortiz .20 .50
436 Dave Burba .20 .50
437 Felix Martinez .20 .50
438 Jeff Shaw .20 .50
439 Mike DiFelice .20 .50
440 Roberto Hernandez .20 .50
441 Bryan Rekar .20 .50
442 Ugueth Urbina .20 .50
443 Vinny Castilla .30 .75
444 Carlos Perez .20 .50
445 Juan Guzman .20 .50
446 Ryan Rupe .20 .50
447 Mike Mordecai .20 .50
448 Ricardo Rincon .20 .50
449 Curt Schilling .30 .75
450 Alex Cora .20 .50
451 Turner Ward .20 .50
452 Omar Vizquel .50 1.25
453 Russ Branyan .20 .50
454 Russ Johnson .20 .50
455 Greg Colbrunn .20 .50
456 Charles Nagy .20 .50
457 Wil Cordero .20 .50
458 Jason Tyner .20 .50
459 Devon White .30 .75
460 Kelly Stinnett .20 .50
461 Wilton Guerrero .20 .50
462 Jason Bere .20 .50
463 Calvin Murray .20 .50
464 Miguel Batista .20 .50
466 Luis Gonzalez .30 .75
467 Jaret Wright .20 .50
468 Chad Kreuter .20 .50
469 Armando Benitez .20 .50
470 Erubiel Durazo .20 .50
470 Sidney Ponson .20 .50
471 Adrian Brown .20 .50
472 Sterling Hitchcock .20 .50
473 Timo Perez .20 .50
474 Jamie Moyer .30 .75
475 Delino DeShields .20 .50
476 Glendon Rusch .20 .50
477 Chris Gomez .20 .50
478 Adam Eaton .20 .50
479 Pablo Ozuna .20 .50
480 Bob Abreu .30 .75
481 Kris Benson .20 .50
482 Keith Osik .20 .50
483 Darryl Hamilton .20 .50
484 Marlon Anderson .20 .50
485 Jimmy Anderson .20 .50
486 John Halama .20 .50
487 Nelson Figueroa .20 .50
488 Alex Gonzalez .20 .50
489 Benny Agbayani .20 .50
490 Ed Sprague .20 .50
491 Scott Erickson .20 .50
492 Doug Glanville .20 .50
493 Jesus Sanchez .20 .50
494 Mike Lieberthal .30 .75
495 Aaron Sele .20 .50
496 Pat Mahomes .20 .50
497 Ruben Rivera .20 .50
498 Wayne Gomes .20 .50
499 Freddy Garcia .30 .75
500 Al Martin .20 .50
501 Woody Williams .20 .50
502 Paul Byrd .20 .50
503 Rick White .20 .50
504 Trevor Hoffman .30 .75
505 Brady Anderson .30 .75
506 Robert Person .20 .50
507 Jeff Conine .30 .75
508 Chris Truby .20 .50
509 Emil Brown .20 .50
510 Ryan Dempster .20 .50
511 Ruben Mateo .20 .50
512 Alex Ochoa .20 .50
513 Jose Rosado .20 .50
514 Masato Yoshii .20 .50
515 Brian Daubach .20 .50
516 Jeff D'Amico .20 .50
517 Brent Mayne .20 .50
518 John Thomson .20 .50
519 Todd Ritchie .20 .50
520 John VanderWal .20 .50
521 Neifi Perez .20 .50
522 Chad Curtis .20 .50
523 Kenny Rogers .30 .75
524 Trot Nixon .30 .75
525 Sean Casey .30 .75
526 Wilton Veras .20 .50
527 Troy O'Leary .20 .50
528 Dante Bichette .30 .75
529 Jose Silva .20 .50
530 Darren Oliver .20 .50
531 Steve Parris .20 .50
532 David McCarty .20 .50
533 Todd Walker .20 .50
534 Brian Rose .20 .50
535 Pete Schourek .20 .50
536 Ricky Ledee .20 .50
537 Justin Thompson .20 .50
538 Benito Santiago .30 .75
539 Carlos Beltran .30 .75
540 Gabe White .20 .50
541 Bret Saberhagen .30 .75
542 Ramon Martinez .20 .50
543 John Valentin .20 .50
544 Frank Catalanotto .20 .50
545 Tim Wakefield .30 .75
546 Michael Tucker .20 .50
547 Juan Pierre .30 .75
548 Rich Garces .20 .50
549 Luis Ordaz .20 .50
550 Jerry Spradlin .20 .50
551 Corey Koskie .20 .50
552 Cal Eldred .20 .50
553 Alfonso Soriano .50 1.25
554 Kip Wells .20 .50
555 Orlando Hernandez .30 .75
556 Bill Simas .20 .50
557 Jim Parque .20 .50
558 Joe Mays .20 .50
559 Tim Belcher .20 .50
560 Shane Spencer .20 .50
561 Glenallen Hill .20 .50
562 Matt LeCroy .20 .50
563 Tino Martinez .50 1.25
564 Eric Milton .20 .50
565 Ron Coomer .20 .50
566 Cristian Guzman .20 .50
567 Kazuhiro Sasaki .30 .75
568 Mark Quinn .20 .50
569 Eric Gagne .30 .75
570 Kerry Ligtenberg .20 .50
571 Rolando Arrojo .20 .50
572 Jon Lieber .20 .50
573 Jose Vizcaino .20 .50
574 Jeff Abbott .20 .50
575 Carlos Hernandez .20 .50
576 Scott Sullivan .20 .50
577 Matt Stairs .20 .50
578 Tom Lampkin .20 .50
579 Donnie Sadler .20 .50
580 Desi Relaford .20 .50
581 Scott Downs .20 .50
582 Mike Mussina .50 1.25
583 Ramon Ortiz .20 .50
584 Mike Myers .20 .50
585 Frank Castillo .20 .50
586 Manny Ramirez Sox .50 1.25
587 Alex Rodriguez 1.25 3.00
588 Andy Ashby .20 .50
589 Felipe Crespo .20 .50
590 Bobby Bonilla .30 .75
591 Denny Neagle .20 .50
592 Dave Martinez .20 .50
593 Mike Hampton .30 .75
594 Gary DiSarcina .20 .50
595 Tsuyoshi Shinjo RC .75 2.00
596 Albert Pujols RC 30.00 60.00
597 Roy Oswalt 1.00 2.50
Pat Strange
Jon Rauch
598 Phil Wilson RC 4.00 10.00
Jake Peavy RC
Darwin Cubillan RC UER
Peavy is spelled incorrectly
599 Nathan Haynes .40 1.00
Steve Smyth RC
Mike Bynum
600 Joe Lawrence .40 1.00
Choo Freeman
Michael Cuddyer
601 Larry Barnes .40 1.00
DeWayne Wise
Carlos Pena
602 Feilpe Lopez .40 1.00
Gookie Dawkins
Eric Almonte RC

603 Brad Wilkerson .40 1.00
Alex Escobar
Eric Valent
604 Jeff Goldbach .40 1.00
Toby Hall
Rod Barajas
605 Marcus Giles .60 1.50
Pablo Ozuna
Jason Romano
606 Vernon Wells .40 1.00
Jack Cust
Dee Brown
607 Luis Montanez RC .40 1.00
David Espinosa
608 Anthony Pluta RC .40 1.00
Justin Wayne RC
609 Josh Axelson RC .40 1.00
Carmen Cali RC
610 Shaun Boyd RC .40 1.00
Chris Morris RC
611 Dan Moylan RC .40 1.00
Tommy Arko RC
612 Luis Cotto RC .40 1.00
Luis Escobar
613 Blake Williams RC .40 1.00
Brandon Mims RC
614 Chris Russ RC .40 1.00
Bryan Edwards
615 Joe Torres .40 1.00
Ben Diggins
616 Hugh Quattlebaum RC 4.00 10.00
Edwin Encarnacion RC
617 Brian Bass RC .40 1.00
Odannis Ayala RC
618 Jason Kaanoi .40 1.00
Michael Matthews RC UER
name misspelled Mathews
619 Stuart McFarland RC .40 1.00
Adam Sterrett RC
620 David Krynzel 2.00 5.00
Grady Sizemore
621 Keith Bucktrot .40 1.00
Dane Sardinha
622 Anaheim Angels TC .30 .75
623 Ariz. Diamondbacks TC .30 .75
624 Atlanta Braves TC .30 .75
625 Baltimore Orioles TC .30 .75
626 Boston Red Sox TC .30 .75
627 Chicago Cubs TC .30 .75
628 Chicago White Sox TC .30 .75
629 Cincinnati Reds TC .30 .75
630 Cleveland Indians TC .30 .75
631 Colorado Rockies TC .30 .75
632 Detroit Tigers TC .30 .75
633 Florida Marlins TC .30 .75
634 Houston Astros TC .30 .75
635 K.C. Royals TC .30 .75
636 L.A. Dodgers TC .30 .75
637 Milw. Brewers TC .30 .75
638 Minnesota Twins TC .30 .75
639 Montreal Expos TC .30 .75
640 New York Mets TC .30 .75
641 New York Yankees TC 1.50 4.00
642 Oakland Athletics TC .30 .75
643 Phil. Phillies TC .30 .75
644 Pittsburgh Pirates TC .30 .75
645 San Diego Padres TC .30 .75
646 S.F. Giants TC .30 .75
647 Seattle Mariners TC .30 .75
648 St. Louis Cardinals TC .30 .75
649 T. Bay Devil Rays TC .30 .75
650 Texas Rangers TC .30 .75
651 Toronto Blue Jays TC .30 .75
652 Bucky Dent GM .20 .50
653 Jackie Robinson GM .75 2.00
654 Roberto Clemente GM 1.00 2.50
655 Nolan Ryan GM 1.25 3.00
656 Kerry Wood GM .30 .75
657 Rickey Henderson GM .75 2.00
658 Lou Brock GM .50 1.25
659 David Wells GM .20 .50
660 Andruw Jones GM .30 .75
661 Carlton Fisk GM .30 .75

2001 Topps Chrome Retrofractors

Randomly inserted into packs at one in 12, this 661-card set is a complete parallel set of the 2001 Topps Chrome base set. Please note that these cards were produced with Topps Refractor technology.

*STARS: 2.5X TO 6X BASIC CARDS
*PROSPECTS 277-301/595-621: 2X TO 5X
*ROOKIES 277-301/595-621: 2X TO 5X
596 Albert Pujols 150.00 300.00
598 Phil Wilson 30.00 60.00
Jake Peavy
Darwin Cubillan
616 Hugh Quattlebaum 40.00 80.00
Edwin Encarnacion

2001 Topps Chrome Before There Was Topps

This set parallels the regular Before There Was Topps insert cards. These cards were inserted at a rate of one in 20 2001 Topps Chrome series two hobby/retail packs.

COMPLETE SET (10) 30.00 80.00
*REFRACTORS: 1.25X TO 3X BASIC BEFORE
SER.2 REFRACTOR ODDS 1:200 HOB/RET
BT1 Lou Gehrig 5.00 12.00
BT2 Babe Ruth 8.00 20.00
BT3 Cy Young 2.50 6.00
BT4 Walter Johnson 2.50 6.00
BT5 Ty Cobb 4.00 10.00
BT6 Rogers Hornsby 2.50 6.00
BT7 Honus Wagner 2.50 6.00
BT8 Christy Mathewson 2.50 6.00
BT9 Grover Alexander 2.50 6.00
BT10 Joe DiMaggio 5.00 12.00

2001 Topps Chrome Combos

Randomly insert into packs at 1:12 Hobby/Retail and 1:4 HTA, this 10-card insert pairs up players that have put up similar statistics throughout their careers. Card backs carry a "TC" prefix. Please note that these cards feature Topps' special chrome technology.

COMPLETE SET (20) 60.00 120.00
COMPLETE SERIES 1 (10) 30.00 60.00
COMPLETE SERIES 2 (10) 30.00 60.00
*REFRACTORS: 1.5X TO 4X BASIC COMBO
REFRACTOR ODDS 1:120 H/R
TC1 Derek Jeter 4.00 10.00
Yogi Berra
Whitey Ford
Don Mattingly
Reggie Jackson
TC2 Chipper Jones 1.25 3.00
Mike Schmidt
TC3 Brooks Robinson 3.00 8.00
Cal Ripken
TC4 Bob Gibson 1.25 3.00
Pedro Martinez
TC5 Ivan Rodriguez 1.25 3.00
Johnny Bench
TC6 Ernie Banks 2.00 5.00
Alex Rodriguez
TC7 Joe Morgan 1.25 3.00
Ken Griffey Jr.
Barry Larkin
Johnny Bench
TC8 Vladimir Guerrero 1.25 3.00
Roberto Clemente
TC9 Ken Griffey Jr. 2.00 5.00
Hank Aaron
TC10 Casey Stengel MG 1.25 3.00
Joe Torre
TC11 Kevin Brown 2.50 6.00
Sandy Koufax
Don Drysdale UER
Card states the Dodgers swept the 1965 World Series
They won the Series in 7 games
TC12 Mark McGwire 3.00 8.00
Sammy Sosa
Roger Maris
Babe Ruth
TC13 Ted Williams 2.00 5.00
Carl Yastrzemski
Nomar Garciaparra
TC14 Greg Maddux 2.00 5.00
Roger Clemens
Cy Young
TC15 Tony Gwynn 2.50 6.00
Ted Williams
TC16 Cal Ripken 4.00 10.00
Lou Gehrig
TC17 Sandy Koufax 4.00 10.00
Randy Johnson
Warren Spahn
Steve Carlton
TC18 Mike Piazza 1.50 4.00
Josh Gibson
TC19 Barry Bonds 3.00 8.00
Willie Mays
TC20 Jackie Robinson 1.25 3.00
Larry Doby

2001 Topps Chrome Golden Anniversary

Randomly inserted into packs at 1:10 Hobby/Retail, this 50-card insert celibrates Topp's 50th Anniversary by taking a look at some of the all-time greats. Card backs carry a "GA" prefix. Please note that these cards feature Topps' special chrome technology.

COMPLETE SET (50) 150.00 300.00
*REFRACTORS: 1.5X TO 4X BASIC ANNV.
SER.1 REFRACTOR ODDS 1:100
GA1 Hank Aaron 4.00 10.00
GA2 Ernie Banks 2.00 5.00
GA3 Mike Schmidt 4.00 10.00
GA4 Willie Mays 4.00 10.00
GA5 Johnny Bench 2.00 5.00
GA6 Tom Seaver 1.25 3.00
GA7 Frank Robinson 1.25 3.00
GA8 Sandy Koufax 6.00 15.00
GA9 Bob Gibson 1.25 3.00
GA10 Ted Williams 4.00 10.00
GA11 Cal Ripken 6.00 15.00
GA12 Tony Gwynn 2.50 6.00
GA13 Mark McGwire 5.00 12.00
GA14 Ken Griffey Jr. 3.00 8.00
GA15 Greg Maddux 3.00 8.00
GA16 Roger Clemens 4.00 10.00
GA17 Barry Bonds 5.00 12.00
GA18 Rickey Henderson 2.00 5.00
GA19 Mike Piazza 3.00 8.00
GA20 Jose Canseco 1.25 3.00
GA21 Derek Jeter 5.00 12.00
GA22 Nomar Garciaparra 3.00 8.00
GA23 Alex Rodriguez 3.00 8.00
GA24 Sammy Sosa 2.00 5.00
GA25 Ivan Rodriguez 1.25 3.00
GA26 Vladimir Guerrero 2.00 5.00
GA27 Chipper Jones 2.00 5.00
GA28 Jeff Bagwell 1.25 3.00
GA29 Pedro Martinez 1.25 3.00
GA30 Randy Johnson 2.00 5.00
GA31 Pat Burrell .75 2.00
GA32 Josh Hamilton 1.50 4.00
GA33 Ryan Anderson .75 2.00
GA34 Corey Patterson .75 2.00
GA35 Eric Munson .75 2.00
GA36 Sean Burroughs .75 2.00
GA37 C.C. Sabathia .75 2.00
GA38 Chin-Feng Chen .75 2.00
GA39 Barry Zito 1.25 3.00
GA40 Adrian Gonzalez 5.00 12.00
GA41 Mark McGwire 5.00 12.00
GA42 Nomar Garciaparra 3.00 8.00
GA43 Todd Helton 1.25 3.00
GA44 Matt Williams .75 2.00
GA45 Troy Glaus .75 2.00
GA46 Geoff Jenkins .75 2.00
GA47 Frank Thomas 2.00 5.00
GA48 Mo Vaughn .75 2.00
GA49 Barry Larkin 1.25 3.00
GA50 J.D. Drew .75 2.00

2001 Topps Chrome King Of Kings

Randomly inserted into packs at 1:5,157 series one hobby and 1:5,209 series one retail and 1:6383 series two hobby and 1:6,520 series two retail, this seven-card insert features game-used memorabilia from major superstars. Please note that a special fourth card containing game-used memorabila of all three were inserted into Hobby packs at 1:59,220. Card backs carry a "KKR" prefix.

SER.2 GROUP A ODDS 1:11,347 H, 1:11,520 R
SER.2 GROUP B ODDS 1:15,348 H, 1:15,648 R
KKR1 Hank Aaron 60.00 120.00
KKR2 Nolan Ryan Rangers 50.00 100.00
KKR3 Rickey Henderson 15.00 40.00
KKR5 Bob Gibson 10.00 25.00
KKR6 Nolan Ryan Angels 50.00 100.00
KKGE Hank Aaron
Nolan Ryan
Rickey Henderson

2001 Topps Chrome King Of Kings Refractors

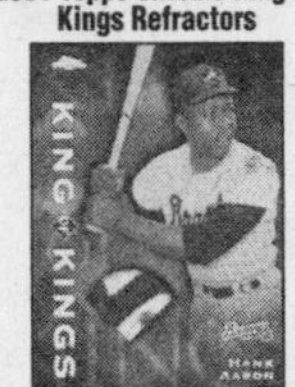

This insert is a complete parallel of the Chrome King of Kings insert set produced with Topps patented refractor technology. The first three cards were randomly inserted exclusively into first series hobby packs at 1:16,920. Cards 5 and 6 were randomly seeded exclusively into second series hobby packs at a rate of 1:23,022. Card number 4 in the set (intended to feature Mark McGwire) was never produced. Only ten of each card was printed and each is hand-numbered in thein blue pen on back. Please note that a special "Golden Edition" card containing game-used memorabilia of Aaron, Ryan and Henderson was inserted into first series hobby packs at a rate of 1:212,169. Only 5 copies of this card were produced. Card backs carry a "KKR" prefix. Due to scarcity, no pricing is provided.

KKR1 Hank Aaron/10
KKR2 Nolan Ryan Rangers/10
KKR3 Rickey Henderson/10
KKR5 Bob Gibson/10
KKR6 Nolan Ryan Angels/10
KKGE Hank Aaron
Nolan Ryan
Rickey Henderson/5

2001 Topps Chrome Originals

Randomly inserted into Hobby packs at 1:1783 and Retail packs at 1:1788, this ten-card insert features game-used jersey cards of players like Roberto Clemente and Carl Yastrzemski produced with Topps patented chrome technology.

SER.2 GROUP A ODDS 1:4863 H, 1:4943 R
SER.2 GROUP B ODDS 1:7855 H, 1:8229 R
SER.2 GROUP C ODDS 1:6588 H, 1:6803 R
SER.2 GROUP D ODDS 1:46,044 H, 1:57,600 R
SER.2 GROUP E ODDS 1:6588 H, 1:6797 R
REFRACT.1-5 SER.1 ODDS 1:9644 HOBBY
REFRACT.6-10 SER.2 ODDS 1:8372 HOBBY
REFRACTOR PRINT RUN 10 #'d SETS
NO REFRACTOR PRICE DUE TO SCARCITY
1 Roberto Clemente 175.00 300.00
2 Carl Yastrzemski 125.00 200.00
3 Mike Schmidt 75.00 150.00
4 Wade Boggs 30.00 60.00
5 Chipper Jones 40.00 80.00
6 Willie Mays 175.00 300.00
7 Lou Brock 30.00 60.00
8 Dave Parker 20.00 50.00
9 Barry Bonds 75.00 150.00
10 Alex Rodriguez 30.00 60.00

2001 Topps Chrome Past to Present

Randomly insert into packs at 1:18 Hobby/Retail, this 10-card insert pairs up players that have put up similar statistics throughout their careers. Card backs carry a "PTP" prefix. Please note that these cards feature Topps' special chrome technology.

COMPLETE SET (10) 30.00 60.00
*REFRACTORS: 1.5X TO 4X BASIC PAST
SER.1 REFRACTOR ODDS 1:180
PTP1 Phil Rizzuto 5.00 12.00
Derek Jeter
PTP2 Warren Spahn 3.00 8.00
Greg Maddux
PTP3 Yogi Berra 4.00 10.00
Jorge Posada
PTP4 Willie Mays 8.00 20.00
Barry Bonds
PTP5 Red Schoendienst 1.50 4.00
Fernando Vina
PTP6 Duke Snider 1.50 4.00
Shawn Green
PTP7 Bob Feller 1.50 4.00
Bartolo Colon
PTP8 Johnny Mize 1.50 4.00
Tino Martinez
PTP9 Larry Doby 1.50 4.00
Manny Ramirez
PTP10 Eddie Mathews 2.00 5.00
Chipper Jones

2001 Topps Chrome Through the Years Reprints

Randomly inserted into packs at 1:10 Hobby/Retail, this 50-card set takes a look at some of the best players to every make it onto a Topps trading card. Please note that these cards were produced with Topps chrome technology.

COMPLETE SET (50) 150.00 300.00
*REFRACTORS: 1.5X TO 4X BASIC THROUGH
SER.1 REFRACTOR ODDS 1:100
1 Yogi Berra 57 2.50 6.00
2 Roy Campanella 56 2.50 6.00
3 Willie Mays 53 4.00 10.00
4 Andy Pafko 52 2.50 6.00
5 Jackie Robinson 52 2.50 6.00
6 Stan Musial 59 3.00 8.00
7 Duke Snider 56 2.00 5.00
8 Warren Spahn 56 2.00 5.00
9 Ted Williams 54 6.00 15.00
10 Eddie Mathews 55 2.50 6.00
11 Willie McCovey 60 2.00 5.00
12 Frank Robinson 69 2.00 5.00
13 Ernie Banks 66 2.50 6.00
14 Hank Aaron 65 4.00 10.00
15 Sandy Koufax 61 5.00 12.00
16 Bob Gibson 68 2.00 5.00
17 Harmon Killebrew 67 2.50 6.00
18 Whitey Ford 64 2.00 5.00
19 Roberto Clemente 63 6.00 15.00
20 Juan Marichal 61 2.00 5.00
21 Johnny Bench 70 2.50 6.00
22 Willie Stargell 73 2.00 5.00
23 Joe Morgan 74 2.00 5.00
24 Carl Yastrzemski 71 3.00 8.00
25 Reggie Jackson 76 2.00 5.00
26 Tom Seaver 78 2.00 5.00
27 Steve Carlton 77 2.00 5.00
28 Jim Palmer 79 2.00 5.00
29 Rod Carew 72 2.00 5.00
30 George Brett 75 6.00 15.00
31 Roger Clemens 85 5.00 12.00
32 Don Mattingly 84 6.00 15.00
33 Ryne Sandberg 89 4.00 10.00
34 Mike Schmidt 81 4.00 10.00
35 Cal Ripken 82 8.00 20.00
36 Tony Gwynn 83 3.00 8.00
37 Ozzie Smith 87 4.00 10.00
38 Wade Boggs 88 2.00 5.00
39 Nolan Ryan 80 6.00 15.00
40 Robin Yount 86 2.50 6.00
41 Mark McGwire 99 5.00 12.00
42 Ken Griffey Jr. 92 3.00 8.00
43 Sammy Sosa 90 2.50 6.00
44 Alex Rodriguez 98 3.00 8.00
45 Barry Bonds 94 5.00 12.00
46 Mike Piazza 95 3.00 8.00
47 Chipper Jones 91 2.50 6.00
48 Greg Maddux 96 3.00 8.00
49 Nomar Garciaparra 97 3.00 8.00
50 Derek Jeter 93 6.00 15.00

2001 Topps Chrome What Could Have Been

Inserted a rate of one in 30 hobby/retail packs, these 10 cards parallel the regular What Could Have Been retail set.

COMPLETE SET (10) 15.00 40.00
*REFRACTORS: 1.5X TO 4X BASIC WHAT
SER.2 REFRACTOR ODDS 1:300 HOB/RET
WCB1 Josh Gibson 4.00 10.00
WCB2 Satchel Paige 1.50 4.00
WCB3 Buck Leonard 1.50 4.00
WCB4 James Bell 1.50 4.00
WCB5 Rube Foster 1.50 4.00
WCB6 Martin DiHigo 1.50 4.00
WCB7 William Johnson 1.50 4.00
WCB8 Mule Suttles 1.50 4.00
WCB9 Ray Dandridge 1.50 4.00
WCB10 John Lloyd 1.50 4.00

2001 Topps Chrome Traded

This set is a parallel to the 2001 Topps Traded set. Inserted into the 2001 Topps Traded at a rate of two per pack, these cards feature the patented "Chrome" technology which Topps uses.

COMPLETE SET (266) 75.00 150.00
COMMON (1-99/145-266) .30 .75
COMMON (100-144) .50 1.25
T1 Sandy Alomar Jr. .30 .75
T2 Kevin Appier .50 1.25
T3 Brad Ausmus .50 1.25
T4 Derek Bell .30 .75
T5 Bret Boone .50 1.25
T6 Rico Brogna .30 .75
T7 Ellis Burks .50 1.25
T8 Ken Caminiti .50 1.25
T9 Roger Cedeno .30 .75
T10 Royce Clayton .30 .75
T11 Enrique Wilson .30 .75
T12 Rheal Cormier .30 .75
T13 Eric Davis .50 1.25
T14 Shawon Dunston .30 .75
T15 Andres Galarraga .50 1.25
T16 Tom Gordon .30 .75
T17 Mark Grace .75 2.00
T18 Jeffrey Hammonds .30 .75
T19 Dustin Hermanson .30 .75
T20 Quinton McCracken .30 .75
T21 Todd Hundley .30 .75
T22 Charles Johnson .50 1.25
T23 Marquis Grissom .50 1.25
T24 Jose Mesa .30 .75
T25 Brian Boehringer .30 .75
T26 John Rocker .50 1.25
T27 Jeff Frye .30 .75
T28 Reggie Sanders .50 1.25
T29 David Segui .30 .75
T30 Mike Sirotka .30 .75
T31 Fernando Tatis .30 .75
T32 Steve Trachsel .30 .75
T33 Ismael Valdes .30 .75
T34 Randy Velarde .30 .75
T35 Ryan Kohlmeier .30 .75
T36 Mike Bordick .50 1.25
T37 Kent Bottenfield .30 .75
T38 Pat Rapp .30 .75
T39 Jeff Nelson .30 .75
T40 Ricky Bottalico .30 .75
T41 Luke Prokopec .30 .75
T42 Hideo Nomo 1.25 3.00
T43 Bill Mueller .50 1.25
T44 Roberto Kelly .30 .75
T45 Chris Holt .30 .75
T46 Mike Jackson .30 .75
T47 Devon White .50 1.25
T48 Gerald Williams .30 .75
T49 Eddie Taubensee .30 .75
T50 Brian Hunter UER .30 .75
Brian R Hunter pictured
Brian L Hunter stats
T51 Nelson Cruz .30 .75
T52 Jeff Fassero .30 .75
T53 Bubba Trammell .30 .75
T54 Bo Porter .30 .75
T55 Greg Norton .30 .75
T56 Benito Santiago .50 1.25
T57 Ruben Rivera .30 .75
T58 Dee Brown .30 .75
T59 Jose Canseco .75 2.00
T60 Chris Michalak .30 .75
T61 Tim Worrell .30 .75
T62 Matt Clement .50 1.25
T63 Bill Pulsipher .30 .75
T64 Troy Brohawn RC .40 1.00
T65 Mark Kotsay .50 1.25
T66 Jimmy Rollins .50 1.25
T67 Shea Hillenbrand .50 1.25
T68 Ted Lilly .30 .75
T69 Jermaine Dye .50 1.25
T70 Jerry Hairston Jr. .30 .75
T71 John Mabry .30 .75
T72 Kurt Abbott .30 .75
T73 Eric Owens .30 .75
T74 Jeff Brantley .30 .75
T75 Roy Oswalt 1.25 3.00
T76 Doug Mientkiewicz .50 1.25
T77 Rickey Henderson 1.25 3.00
T78 Jason Grimsley .30 .75
T79 Christian Parker RC .40 1.00
T80 Donne Wall .30 .75
T81 Alex Arias .30 .75
T82 Willis Roberts .30 .75
T83 Ryan Minor .30 .75
T84 Jason LaRue .30 .75
T85 Ruben Sierra .50 1.25
T86 Johnny Damon .75 2.00
T87 Juan Gonzalez .50 1.25
T88 C.C. Sabathia .50 1.25
T89 Tony Batista .30 .75
T90 Jay Witasick .30 .75
T91 Brent Abernathy .30 .75
T92 Paul LoDuca .50 1.25
T93 Wes Helms .30 .75
T94 Mark Wohlers .30 .75
T95 Rob Bell .30 .75
T96 Tim Redding .30 .75
T97 Bud Smith RC .40 1.00
T98 Adam Dunn .75 2.00
T99 Ichiro Suzuki 10.00 25.00
Albert Pujols ROY
T100 Carlton Fisk 81 .75 2.00
T101 Tim Raines 81 .50 1.25
T102 Juan Marichal 74 .50 1.25
T103 Dave Winfield 81 .50 1.25
T104 Reggie Jackson 82 .75 2.00
T105 Cal Ripken 82 4.00 10.00
T106 Ozzie Smith 82 2.00 5.00
T107 Tom Seaver 83 .75 2.00
T108 Lou Piniella 74 .50 1.25
T109 Dwight Gooden 84 .50 1.25
T110 Bret Saberhagen 84 .50 1.25
T111 Gary Carter 85 .50 1.25
T112 Jack Clark 85 .50 1.25
T113 Rickey Henderson 85 1.25 3.00
T114 Barry Bonds 86 3.00 8.00
T115 Bobby Bonilla 86 .50 1.25
T116 Jose Canseco 86 .75 2.00
T117 Will Clark 86 .75 2.00
T118 Andres Galarraga 86 .50 1.25
T119 Bo Jackson 86 1.25 3.00
T120 Wally Joyner 86 .50 1.25
T121 Ellis Burks 87 .50 1.25
T122 David Cone 87 .50 1.25
T123 Greg Maddux 87 2.00 5.00
T124 Willie Randolph 76 .50 1.25
T125 Dennis Eckersley 87 .50 1.25
T126 Matt Williams 87 .50 1.25
T127 Joe Morgan 81 .50 1.25
T128 Fred McGriff 87 .75 2.00
T129 Roberto Alomar 88 .75 2.00
T130 Lee Smith 88 .50 1.25
T131 David Wells 88 .50 1.25
T132 Ken Griffey Jr. 89 2.00 5.00
T133 Deion Sanders 89 .75 2.00
T134 Nolan Ryan 89 3.00 8.00
T135 David Justice 90 .50 1.25
T136 Joe Carter 91 .50 1.25
T137 Jack Morris 92 .50 1.25
T138 Mike Piazza 93 2.00 5.00
T139 Barry Bonds 93 3.00 8.00
T140 Terrence Long 94 .50 1.25
T141 Ben Grieve 94 .50 1.25
T142 Richie Sexson 95 .50 1.25
George Arias
Mark Sweeney
Brian Schneider
T143 Sean Burroughs 99 .50 1.25
T144 Alfonso Soriano 99 .75 2.00
T145 Bob Boone MG .50 1.25
T146 Larry Bowa MG .50 1.25
T147 Bob Brenly MG .30 .75
T148 Buck Martinez MG .30 .75
T149 L. McClendon MG .30 .75
T150 Jim Tracy MG .30 .75
T151 Jared Abruzzo RC .40 1.00
T152 Kurt Ainsworth .30 .75
T153 Willie Bloomquist .50 1.25
T154 Ben Broussard .30 .75
T155 Bobby Bradley .30 .75
T156 Mike Bynum .30 .75
T157 A.J. Hinch .30 .75
T158 Ryan Christianson .30 .75
T159 Carlos Silva .30 .75
T160 Joe Crede 1.25 3.00
T161 Jack Cust .30 .75
T162 Ben Diggins .30 .75
T163 Phil Dumatrait .30 .75
T164 Alex Escobar .30 .75
T165 Miguel Olivo .30 .75
T166 Chris George .30 .75
T167 Marcus Giles .50 1.25
T168 Keith Ginter .30 .75
T169 Josh Girdley .30 .75
T170 Tony Alvarez .30 .75
T171 Scott Seabol .30 .75
T172 Josh Hamilton .60 1.50
T173 Jason Hart .30 .75
T174 Israel Alcantara .30 .75
T175 Jake Peavy 3.00 8.00
T176 Stubby Clapp RC .40 1.00
T177 D'Angelo Jimenez .30 .75
T178 Nick Johnson .50 1.25
T179 Ben Johnson .50 1.25
T180 Larry Bigbie .30 .75
T181 Allen Levrault .30 .75
T182 Felipe Lopez .50 1.25
T183 Sean Burnett .30 .75
T184 Nick Neugebauer .30 .75
T185 Austin Kearns .50 1.25
T186 Corey Patterson .30 .75
T187 Carlos Pena .30 .75
T188 R. Rodriguez RC .40 1.00
T189 Juan Rivera .30 .75
T190 Grant Roberts .30 .75
T191 Adam Pettyjohn RC .40 1.00
T192 Jared Sandberg .30 .75
T193 Xavier Nady .30 .75
T194 Dane Sardinha .30 .75
T195 Shawn Sonnier .30 .75
T196 Rafael Soriano .40 1.00
T197 Brian Specht RC .40 1.00
T198 Aaron Myette .30 .75
T199 Juan Uribe RC .50 1.25
T200 Jayson Werth .30 .75
T201 Brad Wilkerson .30 .75
T202 Horacio Estrada .30 .75
T203 Joel Pineiro .50 1.25
T204 Matt LeCroy .30 .75
T205 Michael Coleman .30 .75
T206 Ben Sheets .75 2.00
T207 Eric Byrnes .30 .75
T208 Sean Burroughs .30 .75
T209 Ken Harvey .30 .75
T210 Travis Hafner 3.00 8.00
T211 Erick Almonte .40 1.00
T212 Jason Belcher RC .40 1.00
T213 Wilson Betemit RC 1.50 4.00
T214 Hank Blalock RC 2.50 6.00
T215 Danny Borrell .40 1.00
T216 John Buck RC .50 1.25
T217 Freddie Bynum RC .40 1.00
T218 Noel Devarez RC .40 1.00
T219 Juan Diaz RC .40 1.00
T220 Felix Diaz RC .40 1.00
T221 Josh Fogg RC .40 1.00
T222 Matt Ford RC .40 1.00
T223 Scott Heard .30 .75
T224 Ben Hendrickson RC .40 1.00
T225 Cody Ross RC 1.50 4.00
T226 A. Hernandez RC .40 1.00
T227 Alfredo Amezaga RC .40 1.00
T228 Bob Keppel RC .40 1.00
T229 Ryan Madson RC .75 2.00
T230 Octavio Martinez RC .40 1.00
T231 Hee Seop Choi .50 1.25
T232 Thomas Mitchell .30 .75
T233 Luis Montanez .40 1.00
T234 Andy Morales RC .40 1.00
T235 Justin Morneau RC 4.00 10.00
T236 Toe Nash RC .40 1.00
T237 V. Pascucci RC .40 1.00
T238 Roy Smith RC .40 1.00
T239 Antonio Perez RC .50 1.25
T240 Chad Petty RC .40 1.00
T241 Steve Smyth .40 1.00
T242 Jose Reyes RC 5.00 12.00
T243 Eric Reynolds RC .40 1.00
T244 Dominic Rich .40 1.00
T245 J. Richardson RC .40 1.00
T246 Ed Rogers RC .40 1.00
T247 Albert Pujols 40.00 80.00
T248 Esix Snead RC .40 1.00
T249 Luis Torres RC .40 1.00
T250 Matt White RC .40 1.00
T251 Blake Williams .40 1.00
T252 Chris Russ .40 1.00
T253 Joe Kennedy RC .50 1.25
T254 Jeff Randazzo RC .40 1.00
T255 Beau Hale RC .40 1.00
T256 Brad Hennessey RC .75 2.00
T257 Jake Gautreau RC .40 1.00
T258 Jeff Mathis RC .50 1.25
T259 Aaron Heilman RC .50 1.25
T260 B. Sardinha RC .40 1.00
T261 Irvin Guzman RC 3.00 8.00
T262 Gabe Gross RC .50 1.25
T263 J.D. Martin RC .40 1.00
T264 Chris Smith RC .40 1.00
T265 Kenny Baugh RC .40 1.00
T266 Ichiro Suzuki RC 10.00 25.00

2001 Topps Chrome Traded Retrofractors

This set is a parallel to the 2001 Topps Chrome Traded set. Inserted into the 2001 Topps Traded at a rate of one in 12, these cards feature grayback card stock with refractor technology on the front.

*STARS: 1.5X TO 4X BASIC CARDS
*REPRINTS: 1X TO 2.5X BASIC
*ROOKIES: 2.5X TO 6X BASIC
T99 Ichiro Suzuki 60.00 120.00
Albert Pujols ROY
T210 Travis Hafner 20.00 50.00
T235 Justin Morneau 15.00 40.00
T242 Jose Reyes 50.00 100.00
T247 Albert Pujols 150.00 300.00
T261 Irvin Guzman 50.00 100.00
T266 Ichiro Suzuki 50.00 100.00

2002 Topps Chrome

This product's first series, consisting of cards 1-6 and 8-331, was released in late January, 2002. The second series, consisting of cards 366-695, was released in early June, 2002. Both first and second series packs contained four cards and carried an SRP of $3. Sealed boxes contained 24 packs. The set parallels the 2002 Topps set except, of course, for the upgraded chrome card stock. Unlike the 1999 Topps Chrome product, featuring 70 variations of Mark McGwire's Home Run record card, the 2002 first series product did not include different variations of the Barry Bonds Home Run record cards. Please note, that just as in the basic 2002 Topps set there is no card number 7 as it is still retired in honor of Mickey Mantle. In addition, the foil-coated subset cards from the basic Topps set (cards 332-365 and 696-719) were NOT replicated for this Chrome set, thus it's considered complete at 660 cards. Notable Rookie Cards include Kazuhisa Ishii and Joe Mauer.

COMPLETE SET (660) 100.00 250.00
COMPLETE SERIES 1 (330) 50.00 125.00
COMPLETE SERIES 2 (330) 50.00 125.00
COMMON (1-331/366-695) .20 .50
COMMON (307-326/671-690) .60 1.50
COMMON (327-331/691-695) .60 1.50
1 Pedro Martinez .60 1.50
2 Mike Stanton .20 .50
3 Brad Penny .20 .50
4 Mike Matheny .20 .50
5 Johnny Damon .60 1.50
6 Bret Boone .40 1.00
7 Does Not Exist
8 Chris Truby .20 .50
9 B.J. Surhoff .40 1.00

10 Mike Hampton .40 1.00
11 Juan Pierre .40 1.00
12 Mark Buehrle .40 1.00
13 Bob Abreu .40 1.00
14 David Cone .40 1.00
15 Aaron Sele .20 .50
16 Fernando Tatis .20 .50
17 Bobby Jones .20 .50
18 Rick Helling .20 .50
19 Dmitri Young .40 1.00
20 Mike Mussina .60 1.50
21 Mike Sweeney .40 1.00
22 Cristian Guzman .20 .50
23 Ryan Kohlmeier .20 .50
24 Adam Kennedy .20 .50
25 Larry Walker .40 1.00
26 Eric Davis .40 1.00
27 Jason Tyner .20 .50
28 Eric Young .20 .50
29 Jason Marquis .20 .50
30 Luis Gonzalez .40 1.00
31 Kevin Tapani .20 .50
32 Orlando Cabrera .40 1.00
33 Marty Cordova .20 .50
34 Brad Ausmus .40 1.00
35 Livan Hernandez .40 1.00
36 Alex Gonzalez .20 .50
37 Edgar Renteria .40 1.00
38 Bengie Molina .20 .50
39 Frank Menechino .20 .50
40 Rafael Palmeiro .60 1.50
41 Brad Fullmer .20 .50
42 Julio Zuleta .20 .50
43 Darren Dreifort .20 .50
44 Trot Nixon .40 1.00
45 Trevor Hoffman .40 1.00
46 Vladimir Nunez .20 .50
47 Mark Kotsay .40 1.00
48 Kenny Rogers .40 1.00
49 Ben Petrick .20 .50
50 Jeff Bagwell .60 1.50
51 Juan Encarnacion .20 .50
52 Ramiro Mendoza .20 .50
53 Brian Meadows .20 .50
54 Chad Curtis .20 .50
55 Aramis Ramirez .40 1.00
56 Mark McLemore .20 .50
57 Dante Bichette .40 1.00
58 Scott Schoeneweis .20 .50
59 Jose Cruz Jr. .20 .50
60 Roger Clemens 2.00 5.00
61 Jose Guillen .40 1.00
62 Darren Oliver .20 .50
63 Chris Reitsma .20 .50
64 Jeff Abbott .20 .50
65 Robin Ventura .40 1.00
66 Denny Neagle .20 .50
67 Al Martin .20 .50
68 Benito Santiago .40 1.00
69 Roy Oswalt .40 1.00
70 Juan Gonzalez .40 1.00
71 Garret Anderson .40 1.00
72 Bobby Bonilla .40 1.00
73 Danny Bautista .20 .50
74 J.T. Snow .40 1.00
75 Derek Jeter 2.50 6.00
76 John Olerud .40 1.00
77 Kevin Appier .40 1.00
78 Phil Nevin .40 1.00
79 Sean Casey .40 1.00
80 Troy Glaus .40 1.00
81 Joe Randa .40 1.00
82 Jose Valentin .20 .50
83 Ricky Bottalico .20 .50
84 Todd Zeile .40 1.00
85 Barry Larkin .60 1.50
86 Bob Wickman .20 .50
87 Jeff Shaw .20 .50
88 Greg Vaughn .20 .50
89 Fernando Vina .20 .50
90 Mark Mulder .40 1.00
91 Paul Bako .20 .50
92 Aaron Boone .40 1.00
93 Esteban Loaiza .20 .50
94 Richie Sexson .40 1.00
95 Alfonso Soriano .40 1.00
96 Tony Womack .20 .50
97 Paul Shuey .20 .50
98 Melvin Mora .40 1.00
99 Tony Gwynn 1.25 3.00
100 Vladimir Guerrero 1.00 2.50
101 Keith Osik .20 .50
102 Bud Smith .20 .50
103 Scott Williamson .20 .50
104 Daryle Ward .20 .50
105 Doug Mientkiewicz .40 1.00
106 Stan Javier .20 .50
107 Russ Ortiz .20 .50
108 Wade Miller .20 .50
109 Luke Prokopec .20 .50
110 Andruw Jones .60 1.50
111 Ron Coomer .20 .50
112 Dan Wilson .20 .50
113 Luis Castillo .20 .50
114 Derek Bell .20 .50
115 Gary Sheffield .40 1.00
116 Ruben Rivera .20 .50
117 Paul O'Neill .60 1.50
118 Craig Paquette .20 .50
119 Kelvim Escobar .20 .50
120 Brad Radke .40 1.00
121 Jorge Fabregas .20 .50
122 Randy Winn .20 .50
123 Tom Goodwin .20 .50
124 Jaret Wright .20 .50
125 Barry Bonds HR 73 15.00 40.00
126 Al Leiter .20 .50
127 Ben Davis .20 .50
128 Frank Catalanotto .20 .50
129 Jose Cabrera .20 .50
130 Magglio Ordonez .40 1.00
131 Jose Macias .20 .50
132 Ted Lilly .20 .50
133 Chris Holt .20 .50
134 Eric Milton .20 .50
135 Shannon Stewart .20 .50
136 Omar Olivares .20 .50
137 David Segui .20 .50
138 Jeff Nelson .20 .50
139 Matt Williams .40 1.00
140 Ellis Burks .40 1.00
141 Jason Bere .20 .50
142 Jimmy Haynes .20 .50
143 Ramon Hernandez .20 .50
144 Craig Counsell .20 .50
145 John Smoltz .60 1.50
146 Homer Bush .20 .50
147 Quilvio Veras .20 .50
148 Esteban Yan .20 .50
149 Ramon Ortiz .20 .50
150 Carlos Delgado .40 1.00
151 Lee Stevens .20 .50
152 Wil Cordero .20 .50
153 Mike Bordick .40 1.00
154 John Flaherty .20 .50
155 Omar Daal .20 .50
156 Todd Ritchie .20 .50
157 Carl Everett .40 1.00
158 Scott Sullivan .20 .50
159 Deivi Cruz .20 .50
160 Albert Pujols 2.00 5.00
161 Royce Clayton .20 .50
162 Jeff Suppan .20 .50
163 C.C. Sabathia .40 1.00
164 Jimmy Rollins .40 1.00
165 Rickey Henderson 1.00 2.50
166 Rey Ordonez .20 .50
167 Shawn Estes .20 .50
168 Reggie Sanders .20 .50
169 Jon Lieber .20 .50
170 Armando Benitez .20 .50
171 Mike Remlinger .20 .50
172 Billy Wagner .40 1.00
173 Troy Percival .40 1.00
174 Devon White .40 1.00
175 Ivan Rodriguez .60 1.50
176 Dustin Hermanson .20 .50
177 Brian Anderson .20 .50
178 Graeme Lloyd .20 .50
179 Russell Branyan .20 .50
180 Bobby Higginson .40 1.00
181 Alex Gonzalez .20 .50
182 John Franco .40 1.00
183 Sidney Ponson .20 .50
184 Jose Mesa .20 .50
185 Todd Hollandsworth .20 .50
186 Kevin Young .20 .50
187 Tim Wakefield .40 1.00
188 Craig Biggio .60 1.50
189 Jason Isringhausen .40 1.00
190 Mark Quinn .20 .50
191 Glendon Rusch .20 .50
192 Damian Miller .20 .50
193 Sandy Alomar Jr. .20 .50
194 Scott Brosius .40 1.00
195 Dave Martinez .20 .50
196 Danny Graves .20 .50
197 Shea Hillenbrand .40 1.00
198 Jimmy Anderson .20 .50
199 Travis Lee .20 .50
200 Randy Johnson 1.00 2.50
201 Carlos Beltran .40 1.00
202 Jerry Hairston .20 .50
203 Jesus Sanchez .20 .50
204 Eddie Taubensee .20 .50
205 David Wells .40 1.00
206 Russ Davis .20 .50
207 Michael Barrett .20 .50
208 Marquis Grissom .40 1.00
209 Byung-Hyun Kim .40 1.00
210 Hideo Nomo 1.00 2.50
211 Ryan Rupe .20 .50
212 Ricky Gutierrez .20 .50
213 Darryl Kile .40 1.00
214 Rico Brogna .20 .50
215 Terrence Long .20 .50
216 Mike Jackson .20 .50
217 Jamey Wright .20 .50
218 Adrian Beltre .40 1.00
219 Benny Agbayani .20 .50
220 Chuck Knoblauch .40 1.00
221 Randy Wolf .20 .50
222 Andy Ashby .20 .50
223 Corey Koskie .20 .50
224 Roger Cedeno .20 .50
225 Ichiro Suzuki 2.00 5.00
226 Keith Foulke .40 1.00
227 Ryan Minor .20 .50
228 Shawon Dunston .20 .50
229 Alex Cora .20 .50
230 Jeromy Burnitz .40 1.00
231 Mark Grace .60 1.50
232 Aubrey Huff .40 1.00
233 Jeffrey Hammonds .20 .50
234 Olmedo Saenz .20 .50
235 Brian Jordan .40 1.00
236 Jeremy Giambi .20 .50
237 Joe Girardi .20 .50
238 Eric Gagne .40 1.00
239 Masato Yoshii .20 .50
240 Greg Maddux 1.50 4.00
241 Bryan Rekar .20 .50
242 Ray Durham .40 1.00
243 Torii Hunter .40 1.00
244 Derrek Lee .60 1.50
245 Jim Edmonds .40 1.00
246 Einar Diaz .20 .50
247 Brian Bohanon .20 .50
248 Ron Belliard .20 .50
249 Mike Lowell .40 1.00
250 Sammy Sosa 1.00 2.50
251 Richard Hidalgo .20 .50
252 Bartolo Colon .40 1.00
253 Jorge Posada .60 1.50
254 Latroy Hawkins .20 .50
255 Paul LoDuca .40 1.00
256 Carlos Febles .20 .50
257 Nelson Cruz .20 .50
258 Edgardo Alfonzo .20 .50
259 Joey Hamilton .20 .50
260 Cliff Floyd .40 1.00
261 Wes Helms .20 .50
262 Jay Bell .40 1.00
263 Mike Cameron .20 .50
264 Paul Konerko .40 1.00
265 Jeff Kent .40 1.00
266 Robert Fick .20 .50
267 Allen Levrault .20 .50
268 Placido Polanco .20 .50
269 Marlon Anderson .20 .50
270 Mariano Rivera 1.00 2.50
271 Chan Ho Park .40 1.00
272 Jose Vizcaino .20 .50
273 Jeff D'Amico .20 .50
274 Mark Gardner .20 .50
275 Travis Fryman .40 1.00
276 Darren Lewis .20 .50
277 Bruce Bochy MG .20 .50
278 Jerry Manuel MG .20 .50
279 Bob Brenly MG .20 .50
280 Don Baylor MG .40 1.00
281 Davey Lopes MG .20 .50
282 Jerry Narron MG .20 .50
283 Tony Muser MG .20 .50
284 Hal McRae MG .40 1.00
285 Bobby Cox MG .20 .50
286 Larry Dierker MG .20 .50
287 Phil Garner MG .40 1.00
288 Joe Kerrigan MG .20 .50
289 Bobby Valentine MG .40 1.00
290 Dusty Baker MG .40 1.00
291 Lloyd McClendon MG .20 .50
292 Mike Scioscia MG .20 .50
293 Buck Martinez MG .20 .50
294 Larry Bowa MG .40 1.00
295 Tony LaRussa MG .40 1.00
296 Jeff Torborg MG .20 .50
297 Tom Kelly MG .40 1.00
298 Mike Hargrove MG .20 .50
299 Art Howe MG .20 .50
300 Lou Piniella MG .40 1.00
301 Charlie Manuel MG .20 .50
302 Buddy Bell MG .40 1.00
303 Tony Perez MG .40 1.00
304 Bob Boone MG .40 1.00
305 Joe Torre MG .60 1.50
306 Jim Tracy MG .40 1.00
307 Jason Lane PROS .60 1.50
308 Chris George PROS .60 1.50
309 Hank Blalock PROS 1.00 2.50
310 Joe Borchard PROS .60 1.50
311 Marlon Byrd PROS .60 1.50
312 Ray. Cabrera PROS RC .60 1.50
313 Fr. Sanchez PROS RC 2.50 6.00
314 Scott Wiggins PROS RC .60 1.50
315 Jason Maule PROS RC .60 1.50
316 Dionys Cesar PROS RC .60 1.50
317 Boof Bonser PROS .60 1.50
318 Juan Tolentino PROS RC .60 1.50
319 Earl Snyder PROS RC .60 1.50
320 Travis Wade PROS RC .60 1.50
321 Nap. Calzado PROS RC .60 1.50
322 Eric Glaser PROS .60 1.50
323 Craig Kuzmic PROS RC .60 1.50
324 Nic Jackson PROS RC .60 1.50
325 Mike Rivera PROS .60 1.50
326 Jason Bay PROS RC 3.00 8.00
327 Chris Smith DP .60 1.50
328 Jake Gautreau DP .60 1.50
329 Gabe Gross DP .60 1.50
330 Kenny Baugh DP .60 1.50
331 J.D. Martin DP .60 1.50
366 Pat Meares .20 .50
367 Mike Lieberthal .40 1.00
368 Larry Bigbie .20 .50
369 Ron Gant .40 1.00
370 Moises Alou .40 1.00
371 Chad Kreuter .20 .50
372 Willis Roberts .20 .50
373 Toby Hall .20 .50
374 Miguel Batista .20 .50
375 John Burkett .20 .50
376 Cory Lidle .20 .50
377 Nick Neugebauer .20 .50
378 Jay Payton .20 .50
379 Steve Karsay .20 .50
380 Eric Chavez .40 1.00
381 Kelly Stinnett .20 .50
382 Jarrod Washburn .20 .50
383 Rick White .20 .50
384 Jeff Conine .40 1.00
385 Fred McGriff .60 1.50
386 Marvin Benard .20 .50
387 Joe Crede .40 1.00
388 Dennis Cook .20 .50
389 Rick Reed .20 .50
390 Tom Glavine .60 1.50
391 Rondell White .40 1.00
392 Matt Morris .40 1.00
393 Pat Rapp .20 .50
394 Robert Person .20 .50
395 Omar Vizquel .60 1.50
396 Jeff Cirillo .20 .50
397 Dave Mlicki .20 .50
398 Jose Ortiz .20 .50
399 Ryan Dempster .20 .50
400 Curt Schilling .40 1.00
401 Peter Bergeron .20 .50
402 Kyle Lohse .20 .50
403 Craig Wilson .20 .50
404 David Justice .40 1.00
405 Darin Erstad .40 1.00
406 Jose Mercedes .20 .50
407 Carl Pavano .40 1.00
408 Albie Lopez .20 .50
409 Alex Ochoa .20 .50
410 Chipper Jones 1.00 2.50
411 Tyler Houston .20 .50
412 Dean Palmer .40 1.00
413 Damian Jackson .20 .50
414 Josh Towers .20 .50
415 Rafael Furcal .40 1.00
416 Mike Morgan .20 .50
417 Herb Perry .20 .50
418 Mike Sirotka .20 .50
419 Mark Wohlers .20 .50
420 Nomar Garciaparra 1.50 4.00
421 Felipe Lopez .20 .50
422 Joe McEwing .20 .50
423 Jacque Jones .40 1.00
424 Julio Franco .40 1.00
425 Frank Thomas 1.00 2.50
426 So Taguchi RC 1.00 2.50
427 Kazuhisa Ishii RC 1.00 2.50
428 D'Angelo Jimenez .20 .50
429 Chris Stynes .20 .50
430 Kerry Wood .40 1.00
431 Chris Singleton .20 .50
432 Erubiel Durazo .20 .50
433 Matt Lawton .20 .50
434 Bill Mueller .40 1.00
435 Jose Canseco .60 1.50
436 Ben Grieve .20 .50
437 Terry Mulholland .20 .50
438 David Bell .20 .50
439 A.J. Pierzynski .40 1.00
440 Adam Dunn .40 1.00
441 Jon Garland .40 1.00
442 Jeff Fassero .20 .50
443 Julio Lugo .20 .50
444 Carlos Guillen .40 1.00
445 Orlando Hernandez .40 1.00
446 Mark Loretta .20 .50
447 Scott Spiezio .20 .50
448 Kevin Millwood .40 1.00
449 Jamie Moyer .40 1.00
450 Todd Helton .60 1.50
451 Todd Walker .20 .50
452 Jose Lima .20 .50
453 Brook Fordyce .20 .50
454 Aaron Rowand .40 1.00
455 Barry Zito .40 1.00
456 Eric Owens .20 .50
457 Charles Nagy .20 .50
458 Raul Ibanez .20 .50
459 Joe Mays .20 .50
460 Jim Thome .60 1.50
461 Adam Eaton .20 .50
462 Felix Martinez .20 .50
463 Vernon Wells .40 1.00
464 Donnie Sadler .20 .50
465 Tony Clark .20 .50
466 Jose Hernandez .20 .50
467 Ramon Martinez .20 .50
468 Rusty Greer .40 1.00
469 Rod Barajas .20 .50
470 Lance Berkman .40 1.00
471 Brady Anderson .40 1.00
472 Pedro Astacio .20 .50
473 Shane Halter .20 .50
474 Bret Prinz .20 .50
475 Edgar Martinez .60 1.50
476 Steve Trachsel .20 .50
477 Gary Matthews Jr. .20 .50
478 Ismael Valdes .20 .50
479 Juan Uribe .20 .50
480 Shawn Green .40 1.00
481 Kirk Rueter .20 .50
482 Damion Easley .20 .50
483 Chris Carpenter .40 1.00
484 Kris Benson .20 .50
485 Antonio Alfonseca .20 .50
486 Kyle Farnsworth .20 .50
487 Brandon Lyon .20 .50
488 Hideki Irabu .20 .50
489 David Ortiz 1.00 2.50
490 Mike Piazza 1.50 4.00
491 Derek Lowe .40 1.00
492 Chris Gomez .20 .50
493 Mark Johnson .20 .50
494 John Rocker .40 1.00
495 Eric Karros .40 1.00
496 Bill Haselman .20 .50
497 Dave Veres .20 .50
498 Pete Harnisch .20 .50
499 Tomokazu Ohka .20 .50
500 Barry Bonds 2.50 6.00
501 David Dellucci .20 .50
502 Wendell Magee .20 .50
503 Tom Gordon .20 .50
504 Javier Vazquez .40 1.00
505 Ben Sheets .40 1.00
506 Wilton Guerrero .20 .50
507 John Halama .20 .50
508 Mark Redman .20 .50
509 Jack Wilson .20 .50
510 Bernie Williams .60 1.50
511 Miguel Cairo .20 .50
512 Denny Hocking .20 .50
513 Tony Batista .20 .50
514 Mark Grudzielanek .20 .50
515 Jose Vidro .20 .50
516 Sterling Hitchcock .20 .50
517 Billy Koch .20 .50
518 Matt Clement .40 1.00
519 Bruce Chen .20 .50
520 Roberto Alomar .60 1.50
521 Orlando Palmeiro .20 .50
522 Steve Finley .40 1.00
523 Danny Patterson .20 .50
524 Terry Adams .20 .50
525 Tino Martinez .60 1.50
526 Tony Armas Jr. UER .20 .50
Career stats do not include pre-2001
527 Geoff Jenkins .20 .50
528 Kerry Robinson .20 .50
529 Corey Patterson .20 .50
530 Brian Giles .40 1.00
531 Jose Jimenez .20 .50
532 Joe Kennedy .20 .50
533 Armando Rios .20 .50
534 Osvaldo Fernandez .20 .50
535 Ruben Sierra .40 1.00
536 Octavio Dotel .20 .50
537 Luis Sojo .20 .50
538 Brent Butler .20 .50
539 Pablo Ozuna .20 .50
540 Freddy Garcia .40 1.00
541 Chad Durbin .20 .50
542 Orlando Merced .20 .50
543 Michael Tucker .20 .50
544 Roberto Hernandez .20 .50
545 Pat Burrell .40 1.00
546 A.J. Burnett .40 1.00
547 Bubba Trammell .20 .50
548 Scott Elarton .20 .50
549 Mike Darr .20 .50
550 Ken Griffey Jr. 1.50 4.00
551 Ugueth Urbina .20 .50
552 Todd Jones .20 .50
553 Delino Deshields .20 .50
554 Adam Piatt .20 .50
555 Jason Kendall .40 1.00
556 Hector Ortiz .20 .50
557 Turk Wendell .20 .50
558 Rob Bell .20 .50
559 Sun Woo Kim .20 .50
560 Raul Mondesi .40 1.00
561 Brent Abernathy .20 .50
562 Seth Etherton .20 .50
563 Shawn Wooten .20 .50
564 Jay Buhner .40 1.00
565 Andres Galarraga .40 1.00
566 Shane Reynolds .20 .50
567 Rod Beck .20 .50
568 Dee Brown .20 .50
569 Pedro Feliz .20 .50
570 Ryan Klesko .40 1.00
571 John Vander Wal .20 .50
572 Nick Bierbrodt .20 .50
573 Joe Nathan .40 1.00
574 James Baldwin .20 .50
575 J.D. Drew .40 1.00
576 Greg Colbrunn .20 .50
577 Doug Glanville .20 .50
578 Brandon Duckworth .20 .50
579 Shawn Chacon .20 .50
580 Rich Aurilia .20 .50
581 Chuck Finley .40 1.00
582 Abraham Nunez .20 .50
583 Kenny Lofton .40 1.00
584 Brian Daubach .20 .50
585 Miguel Tejada .40 1.00
586 Nate Cornejo .20 .50
587 Kazuhiro Sasaki .40 1.00
588 Chris Richard .20 .50
589 Armando Reynoso .20 .50
590 Tim Hudson .40 1.00
591 Neifi Perez .20 .50
592 Steve Cox .20 .50
593 Henry Blanco .20 .50
594 Ricky Ledee .20 .50
595 Tim Salmon .60 1.50
596 Luis Rivas .20 .50
597 Jeff Zimmerman .20 .50
598 Matt Stairs .20 .50
599 Preston Wilson .40 1.00
600 Mark McGwire 2.50 6.00
601 Timo Perez .20 .50
602 Matt Anderson .20 .50
603 Todd Hundley .20 .50
604 Rick Ankiel .20 .50
605 Tsuyoshi Shinjo .40 1.00
606 Woody Williams .20 .50
607 Jason LaRue .20 .50
608 Carlos Lee .40 1.00
609 Russ Johnson .20 .50
610 Scott Rolen .60 1.50
611 Brent Mayne .20 .50
612 Darrin Fletcher .20 .50
613 Ray Lankford .40 1.00
614 Troy O'Leary .20 .50
615 Javier Lopez .40 1.00
616 Randy Velarde .20 .50
617 Vinny Castilla .40 1.00
618 Milton Bradley .40 1.00
619 Ruben Mateo .20 .50
620 Jason Giambi Yankees .40 1.00
621 Andy Benes .20 .50
622 Joe Mauer RC 12.50 30.00
623 Andy Pettitte .60 1.50
624 Jose Offerman .20 .50
625 Mo Vaughn .40 1.00
626 Steve Sparks UER .20 .50
No 2001 Stats listed
627 Mike Matthews .20 .50
628 Robb Nen .40 1.00
629 Kip Wells .20 .50
630 Kevin Brown .40 1.00
631 Arthur Rhodes .20 .50
632 Gabe Kapler .40 1.00
633 Jermaine Dye .40 1.00
634 Josh Beckett .40 1.00
635 Pokey Reese .20 .50
636 Benji Gil .20 .50
637 Marcus Giles .40 1.00
638 Julian Tavarez .20 .50
639 Jason Schmidt .40 1.00
640 Alex Rodriguez 1.50 4.00
641 Anaheim Angels TC .40 1.00
642 Ariz. Diamondbacks TC .60 1.50
643 Atlanta Braves TC .40 1.00
644 Baltimore Orioles TC .40 1.00
645 Boston Red Sox TC .40 1.00
646 Chicago Cubs TC .40 1.00
647 Chicago White Sox TC .40 1.00
648 Cincinnati Reds TC .40 1.00
649 Cleveland Indians TC .40 1.00
650 Colorado Rockies TC .40 1.00
651 Detroit Tigers TC .40 1.00
652 Florida Marlins TC .40 1.00
653 Houston Astros TC .40 1.00
654 Kansas City Royals TC .40 1.00
655 Los Angeles Dodgers TC .40 1.00
656 Milwaukee Brewers TC .40 1.00
657 Minnesota Twins TC .40 1.00
658 Montreal Expos TC .40 1.00
659 New York Mets TC .40 1.00
660 New York Yankees TC 1.00 2.50
661 Oakland Athletics TC .40 1.00
662 Philadelphia Phillies TC .40 1.00
663 Pittsburgh Pirates TC .40 1.00
664 San Diego Padres TC .40 1.00
665 San Francisco Giants TC .40 1.00
666 Seattle Mariners TC .60 1.50
667 St. Louis Cardinals TC .40 1.00
668 T.B. Devil Rays TC .40 1.00
669 Texas Rangers TC .40 1.00
670 Toronto Blue Jays TC .40 1.00
671 Juan Cruz PROS .60 1.50
672 Kevin Cash PROS RC .60 1.50
673 Jimmy Gobble PROS RC .60 1.50
674 Mike Hill PROS RC .60 1.50
675 T.Buchholz PROS RC .60 1.50
676 Bill Hall PROS .60 1.50
677 B.Roneberg PROS RC .60 1.50
678 R.Huffman PROS RC .60 1.50
679 Chris Tritle PROS RC .60 1.50
680 Nate Espy PROS .60 1.50
681 Nick Alvarez PROS RC .60 1.50
682 Jason Botts PROS RC .60 1.50
683 Ryan Gripp PROS RC .60 1.50
684 Dan Phillips PROS RC .60 1.50
685 Pablo Arias PROS RC .60 1.50
686 J.Rodriguez PROS RC 1.00 2.50
687 Rich Harden PROS RC 3.00 8.00
688 Neal Frendling PROS RC .60 1.50
689 R.Thompson PROS RC .60 1.50
690 G.Montalbano PROS RC .60 1.50
691 Len Dinardo DP RC .60 1.50
692 Ryan Raburn DP RC .60 1.50
693 Josh Barfield DP RC 2.00 5.00
694 David Bacani DP RC .60 1.50
695 Dan Johnson DP RC 1.00 2.50

2002 Topps Chrome Black Refractors

Issued in second series hobby packs at a stated rate of one in 21, these cards parallel the 2002 Topps Chrome set. Black Refractors can be differentiated from the regular cards by their black borders. In addition, each card was serial-numbered to 50 in thin gold foil on the card back.

*BLACK: 6X TO 15X BASIC CARDS
*BLACK 307-331/671-695: 5X TO 12X BASIC
125 Barry Bonds HR 73 175.00 300.00
622 Joe Mauer 200.00 400.00

2002 Topps Chrome Gold Refractors

Inserted into first and second series packs at stated odds of one in four, these cards parallel the 2002 Topps Chrome set. The cards can be differentiated by their striking gold borders and refractive sheen on front.

*GOLD: 2X TO 5X BASIC
*GOLD 307-331/671-695: 1.25X TO 3X BASIC
622 Joe Mauer 40.00 80.00

2002 Topps Chrome 1952 Reprints

Issued in packs at stated odds of one in eight, these nineteen reprint cards feature players who participated in the 1952 World Series which was won by the New York Yankees.

COMPLETE SET (19) 20.00 50.00
COMPLETE SERIES 1 (9) 10.00 25.00
COMPLETE SERIES 2 (10) 10.00 25.00
*REF: .75X TO 2X BASIC 52 REPRINTS
52R1 Roy Campanella 2.00 5.00
52R2 Duke Snider 1.50 4.00
52R3 Carl Erskine 1.50 4.00
52R4 Andy Pafko 1.50 4.00
52R5 Johnny Mize 1.50 4.00
52R6 Billy Martin 1.50 4.00
52R7 Phil Rizzuto 2.00 5.00
52R8 Gil McDougald 1.50 4.00
52R9 Allie Reynolds 1.50 4.00
52R10 Jackie Robinson 2.00 5.00
52R11 Preacher Roe 1.50 4.00
52R12 Gil Hodges 2.00 5.00
52R13 Billy Cox 1.50 4.00
52R14 Yogi Berra 2.00 5.00
52R15 Gene Woodling 1.50 4.00
52R16 Johnny Sain 1.50 4.00
52R17 Ralph Houk 1.50 4.00
52R18 Joe Collins 1.50 4.00
52R19 Hank Bauer 1.50 4.00

2002 Topps Chrome 5-Card Stud Aces Relics

Inserted in second series packs at a stated rate of one in 140, these five cards feature leading pitchers along with a game-worn jersey swatch.

5AAL Al Leiter Jsy 6.00 15.00
5ABZ Barry Zito Jsy 6.00 15.00
5ACS Curt Schilling Jsy 6.00 15.00
5AKB Kevin Brown Jsy 6.00 15.00
5ATH Tim Hudson Jsy 6.00 15.00

2002 Topps Chrome 5-Card Stud Deuces are Wild Relics

Inserted in second series packs at an overall stated rate of one in 428, these three cards feature teammates as well as a piece of game-used memorabilia from each player.

SER.2 BAT ODDS 1:1098
SER.2 UNIFORM ODDS 1:704
5DBT Bernie Williams Bat 15.00 40.00
Tino Martinez Bat
5DCA Chipper Jones Bat 20.00 50.00
Andruw Jones Bat
5DRC Ryan Dempster Uni 6.00 15.00
Cliff Floyd Uni

2002 Topps Chrome 5-Card Stud Jack of all Trades Relics

Inserted in second series packs at a stated rate of one in 428, these three cards feature players who have all five tools along with a piece of game-used memorabilia of that player.

SER.2 BAT ODDS 1:1098
SER.2 JERSEY ODDS 1:704
5JAR Alex Rodriguez Bat
5JCJ Chipper Jones Jsy 10.00 25.00
5JMO Magglio Ordonez Bat 6.00 15.00

2002 Topps Chrome 5-Card Stud Kings of the Clubhouse Relics

Inserted in second series packs at a stated rate of one in 303, these three cards feature three of the best team leaders along with a piece of game-used memorabilia from the featured player.

SER.2 BAT ODDS 1:2204
SER.2 JERSEY ODDS 1:704
SER.2 UNIFORM ODDS 1:704
5KAR Alex Rodriguez Bat
5KJB Jeff Bagwell Uniform 8.00 20.00
5KTG Tony Gwynn Jsy 12.50 30.00

2002 Topps Chrome 5-Card Stud Three of a Kind Relics

Inserted into second series packs at a stated rate of one in 689, these three cards feature a group of three teammates along with a piece of game-used memorabilia from each player.

B='s Bat, J='s Jsy, U='s Uniform
5TAIR Alex Rodriguez Bat 40.00 80.00
Ivan Rodriguez Jsy
Rafael Palmeiro Uni
5TBEJ Bret Boone Bat 12.50 30.00
Edgar Martinez Bat

John Olerud Bat
5TJCL Jeff Bagwell Uni 40.00 80.00
Craig Biggio Bat
Lance Berkman Bat

2002 Topps Chrome Summer School Like Father Like Son Relics

Issued in packs at stated odds of one in 790, this card features memorabilia from Preston and Mookie Wilson.

FSCWI Preston Wilson Uni 6.00 15.00
Mookie Wilson Jsy

2002 Topps Chrome Summer School Battery Mates Relics

Inserted at overall odds of one in 349, these two cards feature memorabilia from a pitcher and catcher from the same team. The Hampton/Petrick card was seeded at a rate of 1:716 and the Glavine/Lopez at 1:681.

SER.1 GROUP A ODDS 1:716
SER.1 GROUP B ODDS 1:681
BMCGL Tom Glavine Jsy 10.00 25.00
Javier Lopez Jsy B
BMCHP Mike Hampton Jsy 6.00 15.00
Ben Petrick Jsy A UER
Card has two jersey swatches on it
but states jersey and bat

2002 Topps Chrome Summer School Top of the Order Relics

Inserted into packs at an overall rate of one in 106, these 12 cards featured players who lead off for their teams along with a memorabilia piece. Uniforms (a.k.a. pants), jerseys and bats were utilized for this set. Bat cards were seeded into five different groups at the following ratios: Group A 1:1383, Group B 1:1538, Group C 1:3170, Group D 1:2902, Group E 1:2544. Jersey cards were seeded into two groups as follows: Group A 1:790 and Group B 1:659. Uniform cards were seeded into three groups as follows: Group A 1:920, Group B 1:651 and Group C 1:614.

SER.1 BAT GROUP A ODDS 1:1383
SER.1 BAT GROUP B ODDS 1:1538
SER.1 BAT GROUP C ODDS 1:3170
SER.1 BAT GROUP D ODDS 1:2902
SER.1 BAT GROUP E ODDS 1:2544
SER.1 JSY GROUP A ODDS 1:790
SER.1 JSY GROUP B ODDS 1:659
SER.1 UNI GROUP A ODDS 1:920
SER.1 UNI GROUP B ODDS 1:651
SER.1 UNI GROUP C ODDS 1:614
TOCBA Benny Agbayani Uni C 6.00 15.00
TOCCB Craig Biggio Uni A 10.00 25.00
TOCCK Chuck Knoblauch Bat E 6.00 15.00
TOCJD Johnny Damon Bat B 10.00 25.00
TOCJK Jason Kendall Bat D 6.00 15.00
TOCJP Juan Pierre Bat A 6.00 15.00
TOCKL Kenny Lofton Uni B 6.00 15.00
TOCPB Peter Bergeron Jsy A 6.00 15.00
TOCPL Paul LoDuca Bat A 6.00 15.00
TOCRF Rafael Furcal Bat C 6.00 15.00
TOCRH R.Henderson Bat B 10.00 25.00
TOCSS Shannon Stewart Jsy B 6.00 15.00

2002 Topps Chrome Traded

Inserted at a stated rate of two per 2002 Topps Traded Hobby or Retail Pack and sever per 2002 Topps Traded HTA pack, this is a complete parallel of the 2002 Topps Traded set. Unlike the regular Topps Traded set, all cards are printed in equal quantities.

COMPLETE SET (275) 60.00 120.00
T1 Jeff Weaver .20 .50
T2 Jay Powell .20 .50
T3 Alex Gonzalez .20 .50
T4 Jason Isringhausen .30 .75
T5 Tyler Houston .20 .50
T6 Ben Broussard .20 .50
T7 Chuck Knoblauch .30 .75
T8 Brian L. Hunter .20 .50
T9 Dustan Mohr .20 .50
T10 Eric Hinske .20 .50
T11 Roger Cedeno .20 .50
T12 Eddie Perez .20 .50
T13 Jeromy Burnitz .30 .75
T14 Bartolo Colon .30 .75
T15 Rick Helling .20 .50
T16 Dan Plesac .20 .50
T17 Scott Strickland .20 .50
T18 Antonio Alfonseca .20 .50
T19 Ricky Gutierrez .20 .50
T20 John Valentin .20 .50
T21 Raul Mondesi .30 .75
T22 Ben Davis .20 .50
T23 Nelson Figueroa .20 .50
T24 Earl Snyder .20 .50
T25 Robin Ventura .30 .75
T26 Jimmy Haynes .20 .50
T27 Kenny Kelly .20 .50
T28 Morgan Ensberg .30 .75
T29 Reggie Sanders .30 .75
T30 Shigetoshi Hasegawa .30 .75
T31 Mike Timlin .20 .50
T32 Russell Branyan .20 .50
T33 Alan Embree .20 .50
T34 D'Angelo Jimenez .20 .50
T35 Kent Mercker .20 .50
T36 Jesse Orosco .20 .50
T37 Gregg Zaun .20 .50
T38 Reggie Taylor .20 .50
T39 Andres Galarraga .30 .75
T40 Chris Truby .20 .50
T41 Bruce Chen .20 .50
T42 Darren Lewis .20 .50
T43 Ryan Kohlmeier .20 .50
T44 John McDonald .20 .50
T45 Omar Daal .20 .50
T46 Matt Clement .30 .75
T47 Glendon Rusch .20 .50
T48 Chan Ho Park .30 .75
T49 Benny Agbayani .20 .50
T50 Juan Gonzalez .30 .75
T51 Carlos Baerga .20 .50
T52 Tim Raines .30 .75
T53 Kevin Appier .30 .75
T54 Marty Cordova .20 .50
T55 Jeff D'Amico .20 .50
T56 Dmitri Young .30 .75
T57 Roosevelt Brown .20 .50
T58 Dustin Hermanson .20 .50
T59 Jose Rijo .20 .50
T60 Todd Ritchie .20 .50
T61 Lee Stevens .20 .50
T62 Placido Polanco .20 .50
T63 Eric Young .20 .50
T64 Chuck Finley .30 .75
T65 Dicky Gonzalez .20 .50
T66 Jose Macias .20 .50
T67 Gabe Kapler .30 .75
T68 Sandy Alomar Jr. .20 .50
T69 Henry Blanco .20 .50
T70 Julian Tavarez .20 .50
T71 Paul Bako .20 .50
T72 Scott Rolen .50 1.25
T73 Brian Jordan .30 .75
T74 Rickey Henderson .75 2.00
T75 Kevin Mench .20 .50
T76 Hideo Nomo .75 2.00
T77 Jeremy Giambi .20 .50
T78 Brad Fullmer .20 .50
T79 Carl Everett .30 .75
T80 David Wells .30 .75
T81 Aaron Sele .20 .50
T82 Todd Hollandsworth .20 .50
T83 Vicente Padilla .20 .50
T84 Kenny Lofton .30 .75
T85 Corky Miller .20 .50
T86 Josh Fogg .20 .50
T87 Cliff Floyd .30 .75
T88 Craig Paquette .20 .50
T89 Jay Payton .20 .50
T90 Carlos Pena .20 .50
T91 Juan Encarnacion .20 .50
T92 Rey Sanchez .20 .50
T93 Ryan Dempster .20 .50
T94 Mario Encarnacion .20 .50
T95 Jorge Julio .20 .50
T96 John Mabry .20 .50
T97 Todd Zeile .30 .75
T98 Johnny Damon .50 1.25
T99 Deivi Cruz .20 .50
T100 Gary Sheffield .30 .75
T101 Ted Lilly .20 .50
T102 Todd Van Poppel .20 .50
T103 Shawn Estes .20 .50
T104 Cesar Izturis .20 .50
T105 Ron Coomer .20 .50
T106 Grady Little MG RC .20 .50
T107 Jimy Williams MGR .20 .50
T108 Tony Pena MGR .20 .50
T109 Frank Robinson MGR .50 1.25
T110 Ron Gardenhire MGR .20 .50
T111 Dennis Tankersley .20 .50
T112 Alejandro Cadena RC .40 1.00
T113 Justin Reid RC .40 1.00
T114 Nate Field RC .40 1.00
T115 Rene Reyes RC .40 1.00
T116 Nelson Castro RC .40 1.00
T117 Miguel Olivo .20 .50
T118 David Espinosa .20 .50
T119 Chris Bootcheck RC .40 1.00
T120 Rob Henkel RC .40 1.00
T121 Steve Bechler RC .40 1.00
T122 Mark Outlaw RC .40 1.00
T123 Henry Pichardo RC .40 1.00
T124 Michael Floyd RC .40 1.00
T125 Richard Lane RC .40 1.00
T126 Pete Zamora RC .40 1.00
T127 Javier Colina .20 .50
T128 Greg Sain RC .40 1.00
T129 Ronnie Merrill .20 .50
T130 Gavin Floyd RC 1.00 2.50
T131 Josh Bonifay RC .40 1.00
T132 Tommy Marx RC .40 1.00
T133 Gary Cates Jr. RC .40 1.00
T134 Neal Cotts RC 1.00 2.50
T135 Angel Berroa .20 .50
T136 Elio Serrano RC .40 1.00
T137 J.J. Putz RC .50 1.25
T138 Ruben Gotay RC .50 1.25
T139 Eddie Rogers .20 .50
T140 Wily Mo Pena .30 .75
T141 Tyler Yates RC .40 1.00
T142 Colin Young RC .30 .75
T143 Chance Caple .20 .50
T144 Ben Howard RC .40 1.00
T145 Ryan Bukvich RC .40 1.00
T146 Cliff Bartosh RC .40 1.00
T147 Brandon Claussen .20 .50
T148 Cristian Guerrero .20 .50
T149 Derrick Lewis .20 .50
T150 Eric Miller RC .40 1.00
T151 Justin Huber RC .75 2.00
T152 Adrian Gonzalez .20 .50
T153 Brian West RC .40 1.00
T154 Chris Baker RC .40 1.00
T155 Drew Henson .20 .50
T156 Scott Hairston RC .50 1.25
T157 Jason Simontacchi RC .40 1.00
T158 Jason Arnold RC .40 1.00
T159 Brandon Phillips .20 .50
T160 Adam Roller RC .40 1.00
T161 Scotty Layfield RC .40 1.00
T162 Freddie Money RC .40 1.00
T163 Noochie Varner RC .40 1.00
T164 Terrance Hill RC .40 1.00
T165 Jeremy Hill RC .40 1.00
T166 Carlos Cabrera RC .40 1.00
T167 Jose Morban RC .40 1.00
T168 Kevin Frederick RC .40 1.00
T169 Mark Teixeira 1.50 4.00
T170 Brian Rogers .20 .50
T171 Anastacio Martinez RC .40 1.00
T172 Bobby Jenks RC 1.50 4.00
T173 David Gil RC .40 1.00
T174 Andres Torres .20 .50
T175 James Barrett RC .40 1.00
T176 Jimmy Journell .20 .50
T177 Brett Kay RC .40 1.00
T178 Jason Young RC .40 1.00
T179 Mark Hamilton RC .40 1.00
T180 Jose Bautista RC 10.00 25.00
T181 Blake McGinley RC .40 1.00
T182 Ryan Mottl RC .40 1.00
T183 Jeff Austin RC .40 1.00
T184 Xavier Nady .20 .50
T185 Kyle Kane RC .40 1.00
T186 Travis Foley RC .40 1.00
T187 Nathan Kaup RC .40 1.00
T188 Eric Cyr .20 .50
T189 Josh Cisneros RC .40 1.00
T190 Brad Nelson RC .40 1.00
T191 Clint Weibl RC .40 1.00
T192 Ron Calloway RC .40 1.00
T193 Jung Bong .20 .50
T194 Rolando Viera RC .40 1.00
T195 Jason Bulger RC .40 1.00
T196 Chone Figgins RC 1.50 4.00
T197 Jimmy Alvarez RC .40 1.00
T198 Joel Crump RC .40 1.00
T199 Ryan Doumit RC .60 1.50
T200 Demetrius Heath RC .40 1.00
T201 John Ennis RC .40 1.00
T202 Doug Sessions RC .40 1.00
T203 Clinton Hosford RC .40 1.00
T204 Chris Narveson RC .40 1.00
T205 Ross Peeples RC .40 1.00
T206 Alex Requena RC .40 1.00
T207 Matt Erickson RC .40 1.00
T208 Brian Forystek RC .40 1.00
T209 Dewon Brazelton .20 .50
T210 Nathan Haynes .20 .50
T211 Jack Cust .20 .50
T212 Jesse Foppert RC .50 1.25
T213 Jesus Cota RC .40 1.00
T214 Juan M. Gonzalez RC .40 1.00
T215 Tim Kalita RC .40 1.00
T216 Manny Delcarmen RC .50 1.25
T217 Jim Kavourias RC .40 1.00
T218 C.J. Wilson RC 1.25 3.00
T219 Edwin Yan RC .40 1.00
T220 Andy Van Hekken .20 .50
T221 Michael Cuddyer .20 .50
T222 Jeff Verplancke RC .40 1.00
T223 Mike Wilson RC .40 1.00
T224 Corwin Malone RC .40 1.00
T225 Chris Snelling RC .60 1.50
T226 Joe Rogers RC .40 1.00
T227 Jason Bay 3.00 8.00
T228 Ezequiel Astacio RC .40 1.00
T229 Joey Hammond RC .40 1.00
T230 Chris Duffy RC .40 1.00
T231 Mark Prior .50 1.25
T232 Hansel Izquierdo RC .40 1.00
T233 Franklyn German RC .40 1.00
T234 Alexis Gomez .20 .50
T235 Jorge Padilla RC .40 1.00
T236 Ryan Snare RC .40 1.00
T237 Deivis Santos .20 .50
T238 Taggert Bozied RC .50 1.25
T239 Mike Peeples RC .40 1.00
T240 Ronald Acuna RC .40 1.00
T241 Koyie Hill .20 .50
T242 Garrett Guzman RC .40 1.00
T243 Ryan Church RC 1.00 2.50
T244 Tony Fontana RC .40 1.00
T245 Keto Anderson RC .40 1.00
T246 Brad Bouras RC .40 1.00
T247 Jason Dubois RC .50 1.25
T248 Angel Guzman RC .75 2.00
T249 Joel Hanrahan RC .40 1.00
T250 Joe Jiannetti RC .40 1.00
T251 Sean Pierce RC .40 1.00
T252 Jake Mauer RC .40 1.00
T253 Marshall McDougall RC .40 1.00
T254 Edwin Almonte RC .40 1.00
T255 Shawn Riggans RC .40 1.00
T256 Steven Shell RC .40 1.00
T257 Kevin Hooper RC .40 1.00
T258 Michael Frick RC .40 1.00
T259 Travis Chapman RC .40 1.00
T260 Tim Hummel RC .40 1.00
T261 Adam Morrissey RC .40 1.00
T262 Dontrelle Willis RC 2.50 6.00
T263 Justin Sherrod RC .40 1.00
T264 Gerald Smiley RC .40 1.00
T265 Tony Miller RC .40 1.00
T266 Nolan Ryan WW 2.00 5.00
T267 Reggie Jackson WW .50 1.25
T268 Steve Garvey WW .30 .75
T269 Wade Boggs WW .50 1.25
T270 Sammy Sosa WW .75 2.00
T271 Curt Schilling WW .30 .75
T272 Mark Grace WW .50 1.25
T273 Jason Giambi WW .20 .50
T274 Ken Griffey Jr. WW 1.25 3.00
T275 Roberto Alomar WW .50 1.25

2002 Topps Chrome Traded Black Refractors

Inserted at a stated rate of one in 56 Topps Traded hobby or retail packs and one in 16 HTA packs, this is a parallel of the Topps Chrome Traded set. These cards can be differentiated from the regular cards by their black borders and are printed to a stated print run of 100 serial numbered sets.

*BLACK REF: 4X TO 10X BASIC
*BLACK REF RC'S: 4X TO 10X BASIC RC'S
T262 Dontrelle Willis 50.00 100.00

2002 Topps Chrome Traded Refractors

nserted at a stated rate of one in 12 Topps Traded packs, this is a parallel of the Topps Chrome Traded set. These cards can be differentiated from the regular cards by their "refractive" sheen and are notated as refractors on the back of the card.

*REF: 2X TO 5X BASIC
*REF RC'S: 1.5X TO 4X BASIC RC'S
STATED ODDS 1:12 HOB/RET, 1:12 HTA
T262 Dontrelle Willis 10.00 25.00

2003 Topps Chrome

The first series of 2003 Topps Chrome was released in January, 2003. These cards were issued in four card packs which came 24 packs to a box and 10 boxes to a case with an SRP of $3 per pack. Cards numbered 201 through 220 feature players in their first year of Topps cards. The second series, which also consisted of 220 cards, was released in May, 2003. Cards number 421 through 430 were draft pick cards while cards 431 through 440 were two player prospect cards.

COMPLETE SET (440) 80.00 200.00
COMPLETE SERIES 1 (220) 40.00 100.00
COMPLETE SERIES 2 (220) 40.00 100.00
COMMON (1-200/221-420) .40 1.00
COMMON (201-220/421-440) .60 1.50
1 Alex Rodriguez 1.50 4.00
2 Eddie Guardado .40 1.00
3 Curt Schilling .60 1.50
4 Andruw Jones .60 1.50
5 Magglio Ordonez .60 1.50
6 Todd Helton .60 1.50
7 Odalis Perez .40 1.00
8 Edgardo Alfonzo .40 1.00
9 Eric Hinske .40 1.00
10 Danny Bautista .40 1.00
11 Sammy Sosa 1.00 2.50
12 Roberto Alomar .60 1.50
13 Roger Clemens 2.00 5.00
14 Austin Kearns .40 1.00
15 Luis Gonzalez .40 1.00
16 Mo Vaughn .40 1.00
17 Alfonso Soriano .40 1.00
18 Orlando Cabrera .40 1.00
19 Hideo Nomo 1.00 2.50
20 Omar Vizquel .60 1.50
21 Greg Maddux 1.50 4.00
22 Fred McGriff .60 1.50
23 Frank Thomas 1.00 2.50
24 Shawn Green .40 1.00
25 Jacque Jones .40 1.00
26 Bernie Williams .60 1.50
27 Corey Patterson .40 1.00
28 Cesar Izturis .40 1.00
29 Larry Walker .40 1.00
30 Darren Dreifort .40 1.00
31 Al Leiter .40 1.00
32 Jason Marquis .40 1.00
33 Sean Casey .40 1.00
34 Craig Counsell .40 1.00
35 Albert Pujols 2.00 5.00
36 Kyle Lohse .40 1.00
37 Paul Lo Duca .40 1.00
38 Roy Oswalt .40 1.00
39 Danny Graves .40 1.00
40 Kevin Millwood .40 1.00
41 Lance Berkman .40 1.00
42 Denny Hocking .40 1.00
43 Jose Valentin .40 1.00
44 Josh Beckett .40 1.00
45 Nomar Garciaparra 1.50 4.00
46 Craig Biggio .60 1.50
47 Omar Daal .40 1.00
48 Jimmy Rollins .40 1.00
49 Jermaine Dye .40 1.00
50 Edgar Renteria .40 1.00
51 Brandon Duckworth .40 1.00
52 Luis Castillo .40 1.00
53 Andy Ashby .40 1.00
54 Mike Williams .40 1.00
55 Benito Santiago .40 1.00
56 Bret Boone .40 1.00
57 Randy Wolf .40 1.00
58 Ivan Rodriguez .60 1.50
59 Shannon Stewart .40 1.00
60 Jose Cruz Jr. .40 1.00
61 Billy Wagner .40 1.00
62 Alex Gonzalez .40 1.00
63 Ichiro Suzuki 2.00 5.00
64 Joe McEwing .40 1.00
65 Mark Mulder .40 1.00
66 Mike Cameron .40 1.00
67 Corey Koskie .40 1.00
68 Marlon Anderson .40 1.00
69 Jason Kendall .40 1.00
70 J.T. Snow .40 1.00
71 Edgar Martinez .60 1.50
72 Vernon Wells .40 1.00
73 Vladimir Guerrero 1.00 2.50
74 Adam Dunn .40 1.00
75 Barry Zito .40 1.00
76 Jeff Kent .40 1.00
77 Russ Ortiz .40 1.00
78 Phil Nevin .40 1.00
79 Carlos Beltran .40 1.00
80 Mike Lowell .40 1.00
81 Bob Wickman .40 1.00
82 Junior Spivey .40 1.00
83 Melvin Mora .40 1.00
84 Derrek Lee .60 1.50
85 Chuck Knoblauch .40 1.00
86 Eric Gagne .40 1.00
87 Orlando Hernandez .40 1.00
88 Robert Person .40 1.00
89 Elmer Dessens .40 1.00
90 Wade Miller .40 1.00
91 Adrian Beltre .40 1.00
92 Kazuhiro Sasaki .40 1.00
93 Timo Perez .40 1.00
94 Jose Vidro .40 1.00
95 Geronimo Gil .40 1.00
96 Trot Nixon .40 1.00
97 Denny Neagle .40 1.00
98 Roberto Hernandez .40 1.00
99 David Ortiz 1.00 2.50
100 Robb Nen .40 1.00
101 Sidney Ponson .40 1.00
102 Kevin Appier .40 1.00
103 Javier Lopez .40 1.00
104 Jeff Conine .40 1.00
105 Mark Buehrle .40 1.00
106 Jason Simontacchi .40 1.00
107 Jose Jimenez .40 1.00
108 Brian Jordan .40 1.00
109 Brad Wilkerson .40 1.00
110 Scott Hatteberg .40 1.00
111 Matt Morris .40 1.00
112 Miguel Tejada .40 1.00
113 Rafael Furcal .40 1.00
114 Steve Cox .40 1.00
115 Roy Halladay .40 1.00
116 David Eckstein .40 1.00
117 Tomo Ohka .40 1.00
118 Jack Wilson .40 1.00
119 Randall Simon .40 1.00
120 Jamie Moyer .40 1.00
121 Andy Benes .40 1.00
122 Tino Martinez .60 1.50
123 Esteban Yan .40 1.00
124 Jason Isringhausen .40 1.00
125 Chris Carpenter .40 1.00
126 Aaron Rowand .40 1.00
127 Brandon Inge .40 1.00
128 Jose Vizcaino .40 1.00
129 Jose Mesa .40 1.00
130 Troy Percival .40 1.00
131 Jon Lieber .40 1.00
132 Brian Giles .40 1.00
133 Aaron Boone .40 1.00
134 Bobby Higginson .40 1.00
135 Luis Rivas .40 1.00
136 Troy Glaus .40 1.00
137 Jim Thome .60 1.50
138 Ramon Martinez .40 1.00
139 Jay Gibbons .40 1.00
140 Mike Lieberthal .40 1.00
141 Juan Uribe .40 1.00
142 Gary Sheffield .40 1.00
143 Ramon Santiago .40 1.00
144 Ben Sheets .40 1.00
145 Tony Armas Jr. .40 1.00
146 Kazuhisa Ishii .40 1.00
147 Erubiel Durazo .40 1.00
148 Jerry Hairston Jr. .40 1.00
149 Byung-Hyun Kim .40 1.00
150 Marcus Giles .40 1.00
151 Johnny Damon .60 1.50
152 Terrence Long .40 1.00
153 Juan Pierre .40 1.00
154 Aramis Ramirez .40 1.00
155 Brent Abernathy .40 1.00
156 Ismael Valdes .40 1.00
157 Mike Mussina .60 1.50
158 Ramon Hernandez .40 1.00
159 Adam Kennedy .40 1.00
160 Tony Womack .40 1.00
161 Tony Batista .40 1.00
162 Kip Wells .40 1.00
163 Jeromy Burnitz .40 1.00
164 Todd Hundley .40 1.00
165 Tim Wakefield .40 1.00
166 Derek Lowe .40 1.00
167 Jorge Posada .60 1.50
168 Ramon Ortiz .40 1.00
169 Brent Butler .40 1.00
170 Shane Halter .40 1.00
171 Matt Lawton .40 1.00
172 Alex Sanchez .40 1.00
173 Eric Milton .40 1.00
174 Vicente Padilla .40 1.00
175 Steve Karsay .40 1.00
176 Mark Prior .60 1.50
177 Kerry Wood .40 1.00
178 Jason LaRue .40 1.00
179 Danys Baez .40 1.00
180 Nick Neugebauer .40 1.00
181 Andres Galarraga .40 1.00
182 Jason Giambi .40 1.00
183 Aubrey Huff .40 1.00
184 Juan Gonzalez .40 1.00
185 Ugueth Urbina .40 1.00
186 Rickey Henderson 1.00 2.50
187 Brad Fullmer .40 1.00
188 Todd Zeile .40 1.00
189 Jason Jennings .40 1.00
190 Vladimir Nunez .40 1.00
191 David Justice .40 1.00
192 Brian Lawrence .40 1.00
193 Pat Burrell .40 1.00
194 Pokey Reese .40 1.00
195 Robert Fick .40 1.00
196 C.C. Sabathia .40 1.00
197 Fernando Vina .40 1.00
198 Sean Burroughs .40 1.00
199 Ellis Burks .40 1.00
200 Joe Randa .40 1.00
201 Chris Duncan FY RC 1.50 4.00
202 Franklin Gutierrez FY RC 1.25 3.00
203 Adam LaRoche FY .60 1.50
204 Manuel Ramirez FY RC 1.00 2.50
205 Il Kim FY RC .60 1.50
206 Daryl Clark FY RC .60 1.50
207 Sean Pierce FY .60 1.50
208 Andy Marte FY RC 3.00 8.00
209 Bernie Castro FY RC .60 1.50
210 Jason Perry FY RC 1.00 2.50
211 Jaime Bubela FY RC .60 1.50
212 Alexis Rios FY 1.00 2.50
213 Brendan Harris FY RC 1.00 2.50
214 R.Nivar-Martinez FY RC .60 1.50
215 Terry Tiffee FY RC .60 1.50
216 Kevin Youkilis FY RC 1.50 4.00
217 Derell McCall FY RC .60 1.50
218 Scott Tyler FY RC 1.00 2.50
219 Craig Brazell FY RC .60 1.50
220 Walter Young FY .60 1.50
221 Francisco Rodriguez .40 1.00
222 Chipper Jones 1.00 2.50
223 Chris Singleton .40 1.00
224 Cliff Floyd .40 1.00
225 Bobby Hill .40 1.00
226 Antonio Osuna .40 1.00
227 Barry Larkin .60 1.50
228 Dean Palmer .40 1.00
229 Eric Owens .40 1.00
230 Randy Johnson 1.00 2.50
231 Jeff Suppan .40 1.00
232 Eric Karros .40 1.00
233 Johan Santana .60 1.50
234 Javier Vazquez .40 1.00
235 John Thomson .40 1.00
236 Nick Johnson .40 1.00
237 Mark Ellis .40 1.00
238 Doug Glanville .40 1.00
239 Ken Griffey Jr. 1.50 4.00
240 Bubba Trammell .40 1.00
241 Livan Hernandez .40 1.00
242 Desi Relaford .40 1.00
243 Eli Marrero .40 1.00
244 Jared Sandberg .40 1.00
245 Barry Bonds 2.50 6.00
246 Aaron Sele .40 1.00
247 Derek Jeter 2.50 6.00
248 Eric Byrnes .40 1.00
249 Rich Aurilia .40 1.00
250 Joel Pineiro .40 1.00
251 Chuck Finley .40 1.00
252 Bengie Molina .40 1.00
253 Steve Finley .40 1.00
254 Marty Cordova .40 1.00
255 Shea Hillenbrand .40 1.00
256 Milton Bradley .40 1.00
257 Carlos Pena .40 1.00
258 Brad Ausmus .40 1.00
259 Carlos Delgado .40 1.00
260 Kevin Mench .40 1.00
261 Joe Kennedy .40 1.00
262 Mark McLemore .40 1.00
263 Bill Mueller .40 1.00
264 Ricky Ledee .40 1.00
265 Ted Lilly .40 1.00
266 Sterling Hitchcock .40 1.00
267 Scott Strickland .40 1.00
268 Damion Easley .40 1.00
269 Torii Hunter .40 1.00
270 Brad Radke .40 1.00
271 Geoff Jenkins .40 1.00
272 Paul Byrd .40 1.00
273 Morgan Ensberg .40 1.00
274 Mike Maroth .40 1.00
275 Mike Hampton .40 1.00
276 Flash Gordon .40 1.00
277 John Burkett .40 1.00
278 Rodrigo Lopez .40 1.00
279 Tim Spooneybarger .40 1.00
280 Quinton McCracken .40 1.00
281 Tim Salmon .60 1.50
282 Jarrod Washburn .40 1.00
283 Pedro Martinez .60 1.50
284 Julio Lugo .40 1.00
285 Armando Benitez .40 1.00
286 Raul Mondesi .40 1.00
287 Robin Ventura .40 1.00
288 Bobby Abreu .40 1.00
289 Josh Fogg .40 1.00
290 Ryan Klesko .40 1.00
291 Tsuyoshi Shinjo .40 1.00
292 Jim Edmonds .40 1.00
293 Chan Ho Park .40 1.00
294 John Mabry .40 1.00
295 Woody Williams .40 1.00
296 Scott Schoeneweis .40 1.00
297 Brian Anderson .40 1.00
298 Brett Tomko .40 1.00
299 Scott Erickson .40 1.00
300 Kevin Millar Sox .40 1.00
301 Danny Wright .40 1.00
302 Jason Schmidt .40 1.00
303 Scott Williamson .40 1.00
304 Einar Diaz .40 1.00
305 Jay Payton .40 1.00
306 Juan Acevedo .40 1.00
307 Ben Grieve .40 1.00
308 Raul Ibanez .40 1.00
309 Richie Sexson .40 1.00
310 Rick Reed .40 1.00
311 Pedro Astacio .40 1.00
312 Bud Smith .40 1.00
313 Tomas Perez .40 1.00
314 Rafael Palmeiro .60 1.50
315 Jason Tyner .40 1.00
316 Scott Rolen .60 1.50
317 Randy Winn .40 1.00
318 Ryan Jensen .40 1.00
319 Trevor Hoffman .40 1.00
320 Craig Wilson .40 1.00
321 Jeremy Giambi .40 1.00
322 Andy Pettitte .60 1.50
323 John Franco .40 1.00
324 Felipe Lopez .40 1.00
325 Mike Piazza 1.50 4.00
326 Cristian Guzman .40 1.00
327 Jose Hernandez .40 1.00
328 Octavio Dotel .40 1.00
329 Brad Penny .40 1.00
330 Dave Veres .40 1.00
331 Ryan Dempster .40 1.00
332 Joe Crede .40 1.00
333 Chad Hermansen .40 1.00
334 Gary Matthews Jr. .40 1.00
335 Frank Catalanotto .40 1.00
336 Darin Erstad .40 1.00
337 Matt Williams .40 1.00
338 B.J. Surhoff .40 1.00
339 Kerry Ligtenberg .40 1.00
340 Mike Bordick .40 1.00
341 Joe Girardi .40 1.00
342 D'Angelo Jimenez .40 1.00
343 Paul Konerko .40 1.00
344 Joe Mays .40 1.00
345 Marquis Grissom .40 1.00
346 Neifi Perez .40 1.00
347 Preston Wilson .40 1.00
348 Jeff Weaver .40 1.00
349 Eric Chavez .40 1.00
350 Placido Polanco .40 1.00
351 Matt Mantei .40 1.00
352 James Baldwin .40 1.00
353 Toby Hall .40 1.00
354 Benji Gil .40 1.00
355 Damian Moss .40 1.00
356 Jorge Julio .40 1.00
357 Matt Clement .40 1.00
358 Lee Stevens .40 1.00
359 Dave Roberts .40 1.00
360 J.C. Romero .40 1.00
361 Bartolo Colon .40 1.00
362 Roger Cedeno .40 1.00
363 Mariano Rivera 1.00 2.50
364 Billy Koch .40 1.00
365 Manny Ramirez .60 1.50
366 Travis Lee .40 1.00
367 Oliver Perez .40 1.00
368 Tim Worrell .40 1.00
369 Damian Miller .40 1.00
370 John Smoltz .60 1.50
371 Willis Roberts .40 1.00
372 Tim Hudson .40 1.00
373 Moises Alou .40 1.00
374 Corky Miller .40 1.00
375 Ben Broussard .40 1.00
376 Gabe Kapler .40 1.00
377 Chris Woodward .40 1.00
378 Todd Hollandsworth .40 1.00
379 So Taguchi .40 1.00
380 John Olerud .40 1.00
381 Reggie Sanders .40 1.00
382 Jake Peavy .40 1.00
383 Kris Benson .40 1.00
384 Ray Durham .40 1.00
385 Boomer Wells .40 1.00
386 Tom Glavine .60 1.50
387 Antonio Alfonseca .40 1.00
388 Keith Foulke .40 1.00
389 Shawn Estes .40 1.00
390 Mark Grace .60 1.50
391 Dmitri Young .40 1.00
392 A.J. Burnett .40 1.00
393 Richard Hidalgo .40 1.00

394 Mike Sweeney .40 1.00
395 Doug Mientkiewicz .40 1.00
396 Cory Lidle .40 1.00
397 Jeff Bagwell .60 1.50
398 Steve Sparks .40 1.00
399 Sandy Alomar Jr. .40 1.00
400 John Lackey .40 1.00
401 Rick Helling .40 1.00
402 Carlos Lee .40 1.00
403 Garret Anderson .40 1.00
404 Vinny Castilla .40 1.00
405 David Bell .40 1.00
406 Freddy Garcia .40 1.00
407 Scott Spiezio .40 1.00
408 Russell Branyan .40 1.00
409 Jose Contreras RC 1.25 3.00
410 Kevin Brown .40 1.00
411 Tyler Houston .40 1.00
412 A.J. Pierzynski .40 1.00
413 Peter Bergeron .40 1.00
414 Brett Myers .40 1.00
415 Kenny Lofton .40 1.00
416 Ben Davis .40 1.00
417 J.D. Drew .40 1.00
418 Ricky Gutierrez .40 1.00
419 Mark Redman .40 1.00
420 Juan Encarnacion .40 1.00
421 Bryan Bullington DP RC .60 1.50
422 Jeremy Guthrie DP .60 1.50
423 Joey Gomes DP RC .60 1.50
424 E.Bastida-Martinez DP RC .60 1.50
425 Brian Wright DP RC .60 1.50
426 B.J. Upton DP 1.00 2.50
427 Jeff Francis DP .60 1.50
428 Jeremy Hermida DP 1.00 2.50
429 Khalil Greene DP 1.00 2.50
430 Darrell Rasner DP RC .60 1.50
431 Brandon Phillips 1.00 2.50
Victor Martinez
432 Hee Seop Choi .60 1.50
Nic Jackson
433 Dontrelle Willis 1.00 2.50
Jason Stokes
434 Chad Tracy .60 1.50
Lyle Overbay
435 Joe Borchard .60 1.50
Corwin Malone
436 Joe Mauer 1.00 2.50
Justin Morneau
437 Drew Henson .60 1.50
Brandon Claussen
438 Chase Utley 1.00 2.50
Gavin Floyd
439 Taggert Bozied .60 1.50
Xavier Nady
440 Aaron Heilman .60 1.50
Jose Reyes

2003 Topps Chrome Black Refractors

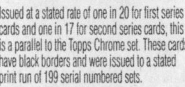

Issued at a stated rate of one in 20 for first series cards and one in 17 for second series cards, this is a parallel to the Topps Chrome set. These cards have black borders and were issued to a stated print run of 199 serial numbered sets.

*BLACK 1-200/221-420: 2X TO 5X
*BLACK 201-220/409/421-440: 2.5X TO 6X

2003 Topps Chrome Gold Refractors

Issued at a stated rate of one in eight for first series cards and two in eight for second series cards, this is a parallel to the Topps Chrome set. These cards have gold borders and were issued to a stated print run of 449 serial numbered sets.

*GOLD 1-200/221-420: 1.25X TO 3X
*GOLD 201-220/409/421-440: 1.5X TO 4X

2003 Topps Chrome Refractors

Issued at a stated rate of one in five, this is a parallel to the Topps Chrome set. These cards use the patented Topps Chrome technology and were issued to a stated print run of 699 serial numbered sets.

*REF 1-200/201-420: 1X TO 2.5X
*REF 201-220/409/421-440: 1.25X TO 3X

2003 Topps Chrome Silver Refractors

*SILVER REF 221-420: 1.25X TO 3X BASIC
*SILVER REF 421-440: 1.5X TO 4X BASIC
ONE PER SER.2 RETAIL EXCH.CARD
CARDS WERE ONLY PRODUCED FOR SER.2

2003 Topps Chrome Uncirculated X-Fractors

Issued at a box-topper, this is a parallel to the Topps Chrome set. Each of these cards were issued in a special case and each of these cards were issued to a stated print run of 50 serial numbered sets for first series cards and a stated print run of 57 serial numbered cards for second series cards.

*X-FRACT 1-200/221-420: 4X TO 10X
*X-FRACT 201-220/409/421-440: 5X TO 12X

2003 Topps Chrome Blue Backs Relics

Randomly inserted into packs, these 20 cards are authentic game-used memorabilia attached to a card which was in 1951 Blue Back design. These cards were issued in three different odds and we have notated those odds as well as what group the player belonged to in our checklist.

BAT ODDS 1:236 HOB/RET
UNI GROUP A ODDS 1:69 HOB/RET
UNI GROUP B ODDS 1:662 HOB/RET
AD Adam Dunn Uni B 6.00 15.00
AP Albert Pujols Uni A 10.00 25.00
AR Alex Rodriguez Bat 10.00 25.00
AS Alfonso Soriano Bat 6.00 15.00
BW Bernie Williams Bat 6.00 15.00
EC Eric Chavez Uni A 4.00 10.00
FT Frank Thomas Uni A 6.00 15.00
JB Josh Beckett Uni A 4.00 10.00
JBA Jeff Bagwell Uni A 4.00 10.00
JR Jimmy Rollins Uni A 4.00 10.00
KW Kerry Wood Uni A 4.00 10.00
LB Lance Berkman Bat 6.00 15.00
MO Magglio Ordonez Uni A 4.00 10.00
MP Mike Piazza Uni A 8.00 20.00
NG Nomar Garciaparra Bat 10.00 25.00
NJ Nick Johnson Bat 6.00 15.00
PK Paul Konerko Uni A 4.00 10.00
RA Roberto Alomar Bat 6.00 15.00
SG Shawn Green Uni A 4.00 10.00
TS Tsuyoshi Shinjo Bat 6.00 15.00

2003 Topps Chrome Record Breakers Relics

Randomly inserted into packs, these 40 cards feature a mix of active and retired players along with a game-used memorabilia piece. These cards were issued in a few different group and we have notated that information next to the player's name in our checklist.

BAT 1 ODDS 1:364 HOB/RET
BAT 2 ODDS 1:131 HOB/RET
UNI GROUP A1 ODDS 1:413 HOB/RET
UNI GROUP B1 ODDS 1:50 HOB/RET
UNI GROUP A2 ODDS 1:1707 HOB/RET
UNI GROUP B2 ODDS 1:127 HOB/RET
AR1 Alex Rodriguez Uni B1 6.00 15.00
AR2 Alex Rodriguez Bat 2 6.00 15.00
BB Barry Bonds Walks Uni B2 10.00 25.00
BB2 Barry Bonds Slg Uni B2 10.00 25.00
BB3 Barry Bonds Bat 2 10.00 25.00
CB Craig Biggio Uni B1 4.00 10.00
CD Carlos Delgado Uni B1 4.00 10.00
CF Cliff Floyd Bat 1 4.00 10.00
DE Darin Erstad Bat 2 4.00 10.00
DLE Dennis Eckersley Uni A2 6.00 15.00
DM Don Mattingly Bat 2 15.00 40.00
FT Frank Thomas Uni B1 6.00 15.00
HK Harmon Killebrew Uni B1 10.00 25.00
HR Harold Reynolds Bat 2 4.00 10.00
JB1 Jeff Bagwell Slg Uni B1 4.00 10.00
JB2 Jeff Bagwell RBI Uni B2 4.00 10.00
JC Jose Canseco Bat 2 6.00 15.00
JG Juan Gonzalez Uni B1 4.00 10.00
JM Joe Morgan Bat 1 4.00 10.00
JS John Smoltz Uni B2 4.00 10.00
KS Kazuhiro Sasaki Uni B1 4.00 10.00
LB Lou Brock Bat 1 8.00 20.00
LG1 Luis Gonzalez RBI Bat 1 4.00 10.00
LG2 Luis Gonzalez Avg Bat 2 4.00 10.00
LW Larry Walker Bat 1 4.00 10.00
MP Mike Piazza Uni B1 8.00 20.00
MR Manny Ramirez Bat 2 6.00 15.00
MS Mike Schmidt Uni A1 15.00 40.00
PM Paul Molitor Bat 2 4.00 10.00
RC Rod Carew Avg Bat 2 6.00 15.00
RC2 Rod Carew Hits Bat 2 6.00 15.00
RH1 R.Henderson A's Bat 1 6.00 15.00
RH2 R.Henderson Yanks Bat 2 6.00 15.00
RJ1 Randy Johnson ERA Uni B1 6.00 15.00
RJ2 Randy Johnson Wins Uni B2 6.00 15.00
RY Robin Yount Uni B1 10.00 25.00
SM Stan Musial Uni A1 20.00 50.00
SS Sammy Sosa Bat 2 6.00 15.00
TH Todd Helton Bat 1 6.00 15.00
TS Tom Seaver Uni B2 10.00 25.00

2003 Topps Chrome Red Backs Relics

Randomly inserted into packs, these 20 cards are authentic game-used memorabilia attached to a card which was in 1951 Red Back design. These cards were issued in three different odds and we have notated those odds as well as what group the player belonged to in our checklist.

SERIES 2 BAT A ODDS 1:342 HOB/RET
SERIES 2 BAT B ODDS 1:383 HOB/RET
SERIES 2 JERSEY ODDS 1:49 HOB/RET
AD Adam Dunn Jsy 4.00 10.00
AJ Andruw Jones Jsy 4.00 10.00
AP Albert Pujols Bat B 8.00 20.00
AR Alex Rodriguez Jsy 6.00 15.00
AS Alfonso Soriano Bat A 6.00 15.00
CJ Chipper Jones Jsy 6.00 15.00
CS Curt Schilling Jsy 4.00 10.00
GA Garrett Anderson Bat A 6.00 15.00
JB Jeff Bagwell Jsy 4.00 10.00
MP Mike Piazza Jsy 6.00 15.00
MR Manny Ramirez Bat B 4.00 10.00
MS Mike Sweeney Jsy 4.00 10.00
NG Nomar Garciaparra Bat A 10.00 25.00
PB Pat Burrell Bat A 6.00 15.00
PM Pedro Martinez Jsy 4.00 10.00
RA Roberto Alomar Jsy 4.00 10.00
RJ Randy Johnson Jsy 6.00 15.00
SR Scott Rolen Bat A 6.00 15.00
TH Todd Helton Jsy 4.00 10.00
TKH Torii Hunter Jsy 4.00 10.00

2003 Topps Chrome Traded

These cards were issued at a stated rate of two per 2003 Topps Traded pack. Cards numbered 1 through 115 feature veterans who were traded while cards 116 through 120 feature managers. Cards numbered 121 through 165 featured prospects and cards 166 through 275 feature Rookie Cards. All of these cards were issued with a "T" prefix.

COMPLETE SET (275) 60.00 120.00
COMMON CARD (1-120) .30 .75
COMMON CARD (121-165) .40 1.00
COMMON CARD (166-275) .40 1.00
2 PER 2003 TOPPS TRADED HOBBY PACK
2 PER 2003 TOPPS TRADED HTA PACK
2 PER 2003 TOPPS TRADED RETAIL PACK
T1 Juan Pierre .30 .75
T2 Mark Grudzielanek .30 .75
T3 Tanyon Sturtze .30 .75
T4 Greg Vaughn .30 .75
T5 Greg Myers .30 .75
T6 Randall Simon .30 .75
T7 Todd Hundley .30 .75
T8 Marlon Anderson .30 .75
T9 Jeff Reboulet .30 .75
T10 Alex Sanchez .30 .75
T11 Mike Rivera .30 .75
T12 Todd Walker .30 .75
T13 Ray King .30 .75
T14 Shawn Estes .30 .75
T15 Gary Matthews Jr. .30 .75
T16 Jaret Wright .30 .75
T17 Edgardo Alfonzo .30 .75
T18 Omar Daal .30 .75
T19 Ryan Rupe .30 .75
T20 Tony Clark .30 .75
T21 Jeff Suppan .30 .75
T22 Mike Stanton .30 .75
T23 Ramon Martinez .30 .75
T24 Armando Rios .30 .75
T25 Johnny Estrada .30 .75
T26 Joe Girardi .30 .75
T27 Ivan Rodriguez .50 1.25
T28 Robert Fick .30 .75
T29 Rick White .30 .75
T30 Robert Person .30 .75
T31 Alan Benes .30 .75
T32 Chris Carpenter .30 .75
T33 Chris Widger .30 .75
T34 Travis Hafner .30 .75
T35 Mike Venafro .30 .75
T36 Jon Lieber .30 .75
T37 Orlando Hernandez .30 .75
T38 Aaron Myette .30 .75
T39 Paul Bako .30 .75
T40 Erubiel Durazo .30 .75
T41 Mark Guthrie .30 .75
T42 Steve Avery .30 .75
T43 Damian Jackson .30 .75
T44 Rey Ordonez .30 .75
T45 John Flaherty .30 .75
T46 Byung-Hyun Kim .30 .75
T47 Tom Goodwin .30 .75
T48 Elmer Dessens .30 .75
T49 Al Martin .30 .75
T50 Gene Kingsale .30 .75
T51 Lenny Harris .30 .75
T52 David Ortiz Sox .75 2.00
T53 Jose Lima .30 .75
T54 Mike Difelice .30 .75
T55 Jose Hernandez .30 .75
T56 Todd Zeile .30 .75
T57 Roberto Hernandez .30 .75
T58 Albie Lopez .30 .75
T59 Roberto Alomar .50 1.25
T60 Russ Ortiz .30 .75
T61 Brian Daubach .30 .75
T62 Carl Everett .30 .75
T63 Jeromy Burnitz .30 .75
T64 Mark Bellhorn .30 .75
T65 Ruben Sierra .30 .75
T66 Mike Fetters .30 .75
T67 Armando Benitez .30 .75
T68 Deivi Cruz .30 .75
T69 Jose Cruz Jr. .30 .75
T70 Jeremy Fikac .30 .75
T71 Jeff Kent .30 .75
T72 Andres Galarraga .30 .75
T73 Rickey Henderson .75 2.00
T74 Royce Clayton .30 .75
T75 Troy O'Leary .30 .75
T76 Ron Coomer .30 .75
T77 Greg Colbrunn .30 .75
T78 Wes Helms .30 .75
T79 Kevin Millwood .30 .75
T80 Damion Easley .30 .75
T81 Bobby Kielty .30 .75
T82 Keith Osik .30 .75
T83 Ramiro Mendoza .30 .75
T84 Shea Hillenbrand .30 .75
T85 Shannon Stewart .30 .75
T86 Eddie Perez .30 .75
T87 Ugueth Urbina .30 .75
T88 Orlando Palmeiro .30 .75
T89 Graeme Lloyd .30 .75
T90 John Vander Wal .30 .75
T91 Gary Bennett .30 .75
T92 Shane Reynolds .30 .75
T93 Steve Parris .30 .75
T94 Julio Lugo .30 .75
T95 John Halama .30 .75
T96 Carlos Baerga .30 .75
T97 Jim Parque .30 .75
T98 Mike Williams .30 .75
T99 Fred McGriff .50 1.25
T100 Kenny Rogers .30 .75
T101 Matt Herges .30 .75
T102 Jay Bell .30 .75
T103 Esteban Yan .30 .75
T104 Eric Owens .30 .75
T105 Aaron Fultz .30 .75
T106 Rey Sanchez .30 .75
T107 Jim Thome .50 1.25
T108 Aaron Boone .30 .75
T109 Raul Mondesi .30 .75
T110 Kenny Lofton .30 .75
T111 Jose Guillen .30 .75
T112 Aramis Ramirez .30 .75
T113 Sidney Ponson .30 .75
T114 Scott Williamson .30 .75
T115 Robin Ventura .30 .75
T116 Dusty Baker MG .30 .75
T117 Felipe Alou MG .30 .75
T118 Buck Showalter MG .30 .75
T119 Jack McKeon MG .30 .75
T120 Art Howe MG .30 .75
T121 Bobby Crosby PROS .40 1.00
T122 Adrian Gonzalez PROS .40 1.00
T123 Kevin Cash PROS .40 1.00
T124 Shin-Soo Choo PROS .40 1.00
T125 Chin-Feng Chen PROS 1.00 2.50
T126 Miguel Cabrera PROS 1.00 2.50
T127 Jason Young PROS .40 1.00
T128 Alex Herrera PROS .40 1.00
T129 Jason Dubois PROS .40 1.00
T130 Jeff Mathis PROS .40 1.00
T131 Casey Kotchman PROS .40 1.00
T132 Ed Rogers PROS .40 1.00
T133 Wilson Betemit PROS .40 1.00
T134 Jim Kavourias PROS .40 1.00
T135 Taylor Buchholz PROS .40 1.00
T136 Adam LaRoche PROS .40 1.00
T137 D.McPherson PROS .40 1.00
T138 Jesus Cota PROS .40 1.00
T139 Clint Nageotte PROS .40 1.00
T140 Boof Bonser PROS .40 1.00
T141 Walter Young PROS .40 1.00
T142 Joe Crede PROS .40 1.00
T143 Denny Bautista PROS .40 1.00
T144 Victor Diaz PROS .40 1.00
T145 Chris Narveson PROS .40 1.00
T146 Gabe Gross PROS .40 1.00
T147 Jimmy Journell PROS .40 1.00
T148 Rafael Soriano PROS .40 1.00
T149 Jerome Williams PROS .40 1.00
T150 Aaron Cook PROS .40 1.00
T151 An. Martinez PROS .40 1.00
T152 Scott Hairston PROS .40 1.00
T153 John Buck PROS .40 1.00
T154 Ryan Ludwick PROS .40 1.00
T155 Chris Bootcheck PROS .40 1.00
T156 John Rheinecker PROS .40 1.00
T157 Jason Lane PROS .40 1.00
T158 Shelley Duncan PROS .75 2.00
T159 Adam Wainwright PROS .40 1.00
T160 Jason Arnold PROS .40 1.00
T161 Jonny Gomes PROS .60 1.50
T162 James Loney PROS .50 1.25
T163 Mike Fontenot PROS .40 1.00
T164 Khalil Greene PROS 1.00 2.50
T165 Sean Burnett PROS .40 1.00
T166 David Martinez FY RC .40 1.00
T167 Felix Pie FY RC 4.00 10.00
T168 Joe Valentine FY RC .40 1.00
T169 Brandon Webb FY RC 3.00 8.00
T170 Matt Diaz FY RC .60 1.50
T171 Lew Ford FY RC .50 1.25
T172 Jeremy Griffiths FY RC .40 1.00
T173 Matt Hensley FY RC .40 1.00
T174 Charlie Manning FY RC .40 1.00
T175 Elizardo Ramirez FY RC .50 1.25
T176 Greg Aquino FY RC .40 1.00
T177 Felix Sanchez FY RC .40 1.00
T178 Kelly Shoppach FY RC .75 2.00
T179 Bubba Nelson FY RC .50 1.25
T180 Mike O'Keefe FY RC .40 1.00
T181 Hanley Ramirez FY RC 5.00 12.00
T182 T.Wellemeyer FY RC .40 1.00
T183 Dustin Moseley FY RC .40 1.00
T184 Eric Crozier FY RC .50 1.25
T185 Ryan Shealy FY RC 2.00 5.00
T186 Jer. Bonderman FY RC 3.00 8.00
T187 T.Story-Harden FY RC .40 1.00
T188 Dusty Brown FY RC .40 1.00
T189 Rob Hammock FY RC .40 1.00
T190 Jorge Piedra FY RC .50 1.25
T191 Chris De La Cruz FY RC .40 1.00
T192 Eli Whiteside FY RC .40 1.00
T193 Jason Kubel FY RC 1.25 3.00
T194 Jon Schuerholz FY RC .40 1.00
T195 St. Randolph FY RC .40 1.00
T196 Andy Sisco FY RC .40 1.00
T197 Sean Smith FY RC .50 1.25
T198 Jon-Mark Sprowl FY RC .40 1.00
T199 Matt Kata FY RC .40 1.00
T200 Robinson Cano FY RC 10.00 25.00
T201 Nook Logan FY RC .50 1.25
T202 Ben Francisco FY RC .40 1.00
T203 Arnie Munoz FY RC .40 1.00
T204 Ozzie Chavez FY RC .40 1.00
T205 Eric Riggs FY RC .50 1.25
T206 Beau Kemp FY RC .40 1.00
T207 Travis Wong FY RC .50 1.25
T208 Dustin Yount FY RC .50 1.25
T209 Brian McCann FY RC 6.00 15.00
T210 Wilton Reynolds FY RC .50 1.25
T211 Matt Bruback FY RC .40 1.00
T212 Andrew Brown FY RC .50 1.25
T213 Edgar Gonzalez FY RC .40 1.00
T214 Eider Torres FY RC .40 1.00
T215 Aquilino Lopez FY RC .40 1.00
T216 Bobby Basham FY RC .40 1.00
T217 Tim Olson FY RC .40 1.00
T218 Nathan Panther FY RC .40 1.00
T219 Bryan Grace FY RC .40 1.00
T220 Dusty Gomon FY RC .50 1.25
T221 Wil Ledezma FY RC .40 1.00
T222 Josh Willingham FY RC 1.00 2.50
T223 David Cash FY RC .40 1.00
T224 Oscar Villarreal FY RC .40 1.00
T225 Jeff Duncan FY RC .40 1.00
T226 Kade Johnson FY RC .40 1.00
T227 L.Steidlmayer FY RC .40 1.00
T228 Brandon Watson FY RC .40 1.00
T229 Jose Morales FY RC .40 1.00
T230 Mike Gallo FY RC .40 1.00
T231 Tyler Adamczyk FY RC .40 1.00
T232 Adam Stern FY RC .40 1.00
T233 Brennan King FY RC .40 1.00
T234 Dan Haren FY RC .75 2.00
T235 Mi. Hernandez FY RC .40 1.00
T236 Ben Fritz FY RC .40 1.00
T237 Clay Hensley FY RC .40 1.00
T238 Tyler Johnson FY RC .40 1.00
T239 Pete LaForest FY RC .40 1.00
T240 Tyler Martin FY RC .40 1.00
T241 J.D. Durbin FY RC .40 1.00
T242 Shane Victorino FY RC .75 2.00
T243 Rajai Davis FY RC .40 1.00
T244 Ismael Castro FY RC .40 1.00
T245 C.Wang FY RC 2.00 5.00
T246 Travis Ishikawa FY RC .75 2.00
T247 Corey Shafer FY RC .40 1.00
T248 G.Schneidmiller FY RC .40 1.00
T249 Dave Pember FY RC .40 1.00
T250 Keith Stamler FY RC .40 1.00
T251 Tyson Graham FY RC .40 1.00
T252 Ryan Cameron FY RC .40 1.00
T253 Eric Eckenstahler FY .40 1.00
T254 Ma. Peterson FY RC .40 1.00
T255 Dustin McGowan FY RC .50 1.25
T256 Pr. Redman FY RC .40 1.00
T257 Haj Turay FY RC .40 1.00
T258 Carlos Guzman FY RC .50 1.25
T259 Matt DeMarco FY RC .40 1.00
T260 Derek Michaelis FY RC .40 1.00
T261 Brian Burgamy FY RC .40 1.00
T262 Jay Sitzman FY RC .40 1.00
T263 Chris Fallon FY RC .40 1.00
T264 Mike Adams FY RC .40 1.00
T265 Clint Barmes FY RC 1.00 2.50
T266 Eric Reed FY RC .40 1.00
T267 Willie Eyre FY RC .40 1.00
T268 Carlos Duran FY RC .40 1.00
T269 Nick Trzesniak FY RC .40 1.00
T270 Ferdin Tejeda FY RC .40 1.00
T271 Mi. Garciaparra FY RC .40 1.00
T272 Michael Hinckley FY RC .50 1.25
T273 Br. Florence FY RC .40 1.00
T274 Trent Oeltjen FY RC .50 1.25
T275 Mike Neu FY RC .40 1.00

2003 Topps Chrome Traded Refractors

*REF 1-120: 2X TO 5X BASIC
*REF 121-165: 1.5X TO 4X BASIC
*REF 166-275: 1.5X TO 4X BASIC
STATED ODDS 1:12 HOB/RET, 1:4 HTA
T181 Hanley Ramirez FY 30.00 60.00
T245 Chien-Ming Wang FY 8.00 20.00

2003 Topps Chrome Traded Uncirculated X-Fractors

ONE PER TOPPS TRADED HTA BOX
STATED PRINT RUN 25 SERIAL #'d SETS
NO PRICING DUE TO SCARCITY

2004 Topps Chrome

This 233 card first series was released in January, 2004. A matching second series of 233 cards was released in May, 2004. This set was issued in four-card packs with an $3 SRP which came 20 packs to a box and 10 boxes to a case. The first 210 cards of the first series are veterans while the final 23 cards of the set feature first year cards. Please note that cards 221 through 233 were autographed by the featured players and those cards were issued to a stated rate of one in 21 hobby packs and one in 33 retail packs. In the second series cards numbered 234 through 246 feature autographs of the rookie pictured and those cards were inserted at a stated rate of one in 22 hobby packs and one in 35 retail packs. Bradley Sullivan (#234) was issued with either the correct back or an incorrect back numbered to 345 which consitituted about 20 percent of the total press run.

COMP.SERIES 1 w/o SP's (220) 40.00 80.00
COMP.SERIES 2 w/o SP's (220) 40.00 80.00
COMMON (1-210/257-466) .40 1.00
COMMON (211-220/247-256) .50 1.25
COMMON AU (221-233) 4.00 10.00
221-233 SERIES 1 ODDS 1:21 H, 1:33 R
234-246 SERIES 2 ODDS 1:22 H, 1:35 R
345 SULLIVAN ERR SHOULD BE NO.234
1 IN EVERY 5 SULLIVAN'S ARE ERR 345
4 IN EVERY 5 SULLIVAN'S ARE COR 234
SULLIVAN INFO PROVIDED BY TOPPS
1 Jim Thome .60 1.50
2 Reggie Sanders .40 1.00
3 Mark Kotsay .40 1.00
4 Edgardo Alfonzo .40 1.00
5 Tim Wakefield .40 1.00
6 Moises Alou .40 1.00
7 Jorge Julio .40 1.00
8 Bartolo Colon .40 1.00
9 Chan Ho Park .60 1.50
10 Ichiro Suzuki 1.50 4.00
11 Kevin Millwood .40 1.00
12 Preston Wilson .40 1.00
13 Tom Glavine .60 1.50
14 Junior Spivey .40 1.00
15 Marcus Giles .40 1.00
16 David Segui .40 1.00
17 Kevin Millar .40 1.00
18 Corey Patterson .40 1.00
19 Aaron Rowand .40 1.00
20 Derek Jeter 2.50 6.00
21 Luis Castillo .40 1.00
22 Manny Ramirez 1.00 2.50
23 Jay Payton .40 1.00
24 Bobby Higginson .40 1.00
25 Lance Berkman .60 1.50
26 Juan Pierre .40 1.00
27 Mike Mussina .60 1.50
28 Fred McGriff .60 1.50
29 Richie Sexson .40 1.00
30 Tim Hudson .60 1.50
31 Mike Piazza 1.00 2.50
32 Brad Radke .40 1.00
33 Jeff Weaver .40 1.00
34 Ramon Hernandez .40 1.00
35 David Bell .40 1.00
36 Randy Wolf .40 1.00
37 Jake Peavy .40 1.00
38 Tim Worrell .40 1.00
39 Gil Meche .40 1.00
40 Albert Pujols 2.50 6.00
41 Michael Young .40 1.00
42 Josh Phelps .40 1.00
43 Brendan Donnelly .40 1.00
44 Steve Finley .40 1.00
45 John Smoltz 1.00 2.50
46 Jay Gibbons .40 1.00
47 Trot Nixon .40 1.00
48 Carl Pavano .40 1.00
49 Frank Thomas 1.00 2.50
50 Mark Prior .60 1.50
51 Danny Graves .40 1.00
52 Milton Bradley .40 1.00
53 Kris Benson .40 1.00
54 Ryan Klesko .40 1.00
55 Mike Lowell .40 1.00
56 Geoff Blum .40 1.00
57 Michael Tucker .40 1.00
58 Paul Lo Duca .40 1.00
59 Vicente Padilla .40 1.00
60 Jacque Jones .40 1.00
61 Fernando Tatis .40 1.00
62 Ty Wigginton .40 1.00
63 Rich Aurilia .40 1.00
64 Andy Pettitte .60 1.50
65 Terrence Long .40 1.00
66 Cliff Floyd .40 1.00
67 Mariano Rivera 1.00 2.50
68 Kelvim Escobar .40 1.00
69 Marlon Byrd .40 1.00
70 Mark Mulder .40 1.00
71 Francisco Cordero .40 1.00
72 Carlos Guillen .40 1.00
73 Fernando Vina .40 1.00
74 Lance Carter .40 1.00
75 Hank Blalock .40 1.00
76 Jimmy Rollins .60 1.50
77 Francisco Rodriguez .60 1.50
78 Javy Lopez .40 1.00
79 Jerry Hairston Jr. .40 1.00
80 Andruw Jones .40 1.00
81 Rodrigo Lopez .40 1.00
82 Johnny Damon .60 1.50
83 Hee Seop Choi .40 1.00
84 Kazuhiro Sasaki .40 1.00
85 Danny Bautista .40 1.00
86 Matt Lawton .40 1.00
87 Juan Uribe .40 1.00
88 Rafael Furcal .40 1.00
89 Kyle Farnsworth .40 1.00
90 Jose Vidro .40 1.00
91 Luis Rivas .40 1.00
92 Hideo Nomo 1.00 2.50
93 Javier Vazquez .40 1.00
94 Al Leiter .40 1.00
95 Jose Valentin .40 1.00
96 Alex Cintron .40 1.00
97 Zach Day .40 1.00
98 Jorge Posada .60 1.50
99 C.C. Sabathia .60 1.50
100 Alex Rodriguez 1.50 4.00
101 Brad Penny .40 1.00
102 Brad Ausmus .40 1.00
103 Raul Ibanez .40 1.00
104 Mike Hampton .40 1.00
105 Adrian Beltre .40 1.00
106 Ramiro Mendoza .40 1.00
107 Rocco Baldelli .40 1.00
108 Esteban Loaiza .40 1.00
109 Russell Branyan .40 1.00
110 Todd Helton .60 1.50
111 Braden Looper .40 1.00
112 Octavio Dotel .40 1.00
113 Mike MacDougal .40 1.00
114 Cesar Izturis .40 1.00
115 Johan Santana 1.00 2.50
116 Jose Contreras .40 1.00
117 Placido Polanco .40 1.00
118 Jason Phillips .40 1.00
119 Orlando Hudson .40 1.00
120 Vernon Wells .40 1.00
121 Ben Grieve .40 1.00
122 Dave Roberts .40 1.00
123 Ismael Valdes .40 1.00
124 Eric Owens .40 1.00
125 Curt Schilling .60 1.50
126 Russ Ortiz .40 1.00
127 Mark Buehrle .60 1.50
128 Doug Mientkiewicz .40 1.00
129 Dmitri Young .40 1.00
130 Kazuhisa Ishii .40 1.00
131 A.J. Pierzynski .40 1.00
132 Brad Wilkerson .40 1.00
133 Joe McEwing .40 1.00
134 Alex Cora .40 1.00
135 Jose Cruz Jr. .40 1.00
136 Carlos Zambrano .60 1.50
137 Jeff Kent .40 1.00
138 Shigetoshi Hasegawa .40 1.00
139 Jarrod Washburn .40 1.00
140 Greg Maddux 1.50 4.00
141 Josh Beckett .60 1.50
142 Miguel Batista .40 1.00
143 Omar Vizquel .60 1.50
144 Alex Gonzalez .40 1.00
145 Billy Wagner .40 1.00
146 Brian Jordan .40 1.00
147 Wes Helms .40 1.00
148 Deivi Cruz .40 1.00
149 Alex Gonzalez .40 1.00
150 Jason Giambi .40 1.00
151 Erubiel Durazo .40 1.00
152 Mike Lieberthal .40 1.00
153 Jason Kendall .40 1.00
154 Xavier Nady .40 1.00
155 Kirk Rueter .40 1.00
156 Mike Cameron .40 1.00
157 Miguel Cairo .40 1.00
158 Woody Williams .40 1.00
159 Toby Hall .40 1.00
160 Bernie Williams .60 1.50
161 Darin Erstad .40 1.00
162 Matt Mantei .40 1.00
163 Shawn Chacon .40 1.00
164 Bill Mueller .40 1.00
165 Damian Miller .40 1.00
166 Tony Graffanino .40 1.00

167 Sean Casey .40 1.00
168 Brandon Phillips .40 1.00
169 Runelvys Hernandez .40 1.00
170 Adam Dunn .60 1.50
171 Carlos Lee .40 1.00
172 Juan Encarnacion .40 1.00
173 Angel Berroa .40 1.00
174 Desi Relaford .40 1.00
175 Joe Mays .40 1.00
176 Ben Sheets .40 1.00
177 Eddie Guardado .40 1.00
178 Rocky Biddle .40 1.00
179 Eric Gagne .40 1.00
180 Eric Chavez .40 1.00
181 Jason Michaels .40 1.00
182 Dustan Mohr .40 1.00
183 Kip Wells .40 1.00
184 Brian Lawrence .40 1.00
185 Bret Boone .40 1.00
186 Tino Martinez .60 1.50
187 Aubrey Huff .40 1.00
188 Kevin Mench .40 1.00
189 Tim Salmon .40 1.00
190 Carlos Delgado .40 1.00
191 John Lackey .40 1.00
192 Eric Byrnes .40 1.00
193 Luis Matos .40 1.00
194 Derek Lowe .40 1.00
195 Mark Grudzielanek .40 1.00
196 Tom Gordon .40 1.00
197 Matt Clement .40 1.00
198 Byung-Hyun Kim .40 1.00
199 Brandon Inge .40 1.00
200 Nomar Garciaparra 1.00 2.50
201 Frank Catalanotto .40 1.00
202 Cristian Guzman .40 1.00
203 Bo Hart .40 1.00
204 Jack Wilson .40 1.00
205 Ray Durham .40 1.00
206 Freddy Garcia .40 1.00
207 J.D. Drew .40 1.00
208 Orlando Cabrera .40 1.00
209 Roy Halladay 1.00 2.50
210 David Eckstein .40 1.00
211 Omar Falcon FY RC .50 1.25
212 Todd Self FY RC .50 1.25
213 David Murphy FY RC 1.25 3.00
214 Dioner Navarro FY RC .75 2.00
215 Marcus McBeth FY RC .50 1.25
216 Chris O'Riordan FY RC .50 1.25
217 Rodney Choy Foo FY RC .50 1.25
218 Tim Frend FY RC .50 1.25
219 Yadier Molina FY RC 3.00 8.00
220 Zach Duke FY RC .75 2.00
221 Anthony Lerew FY AU RC 6.00 15.00
222 B.Hawksworth FY AU RC 6.00 15.00
223 Brayan Pena FY AU RC 4.00 10.00
224 Craig Ansman FY AU RC 4.00 10.00
225 Jon Knott FY AU RC 4.00 10.00
226 Josh Labandeira FY AU RC 4.00 10.00
227 Khalid Ballouli FY AU RC 4.00 10.00
228 Kyle Davies FY AU RC 10.00 25.00
229 Matt Creighton FY AU RC 4.00 10.00
230 Mike Gosling FY AU RC 4.00 10.00
231 Nic Ungs FY AU RC 4.00 10.00
232 Zach Miner FY AU RC 10.00 25.00
233 Donald Levinski FY AU RC 4.00 10.00
234A Bradley Sullivan FY AU RC 6.00 15.00
234B B.Sullivan FY AU ERR 345 10.00 25.00
235 Carlos Quentin FY AU RC 10.00 25.00
236 Conor Jackson FY AU RC 6.00 15.00
237 Estee Harris FY AU RC 6.00 15.00
238 Jeffrey Allison FY AU RC 4.00 10.00
239 Kyle Sleeth FY AU RC 6.00 15.00
240 Matthew Moses FY AU RC 6.00 15.00
241 Tim Stauffer FY AU RC 4.00 10.00
242 Brad Snyder FY AU RC 5.00 12.00
243 Jason Hirsh FY AU RC 10.00 25.00
244 L.Milledge FY AU RC 20.00 50.00
245 Logan Kensing FY AU RC 4.00 10.00
246 Kory Casto FY AU RC 6.00 15.00
247 David Aardsma FY RC .50 1.25
248 Omar Quintanilla FY RC .50 1.25
249 Ervin Santana FY RC 1.25 3.00
250 Merkin Valdez FY RC .50 1.25
251 Vito Chiaravalloti FY RC .50 1.25
252 Travis Blackley FY RC .50 1.25
253 Chris Shelton FY RC .50 1.25
254 Rudy Guillen FY RC .50 1.25
255 Bobby Brownlie FY RC .50 1.25
256 Paul Maholm FY RC .75 2.00
257 Roger Clemens 1.25 3.00
258 Laynce Nix .40 1.00
259 Eric Hinske .40 1.00
260 Ivan Rodriguez .60 1.50
261 Brandon Webb .40 1.00
262 Jhonny Peralta .40 1.00
263 Adam Kennedy .40 1.00
264 Tony Batista .40 1.00
265 Jeff Suppan .40 1.00
266 Kenny Lofton .40 1.00
267 Scott Sullivan .40 1.00
268 Ken Griffey Jr. 1.50 4.00
269 Juan Rivera .40 1.00
270 Larry Walker .60 1.50
271 Todd Hollandsworth .40 1.00
272 Carlos Beltran .40 1.00
273 Carl Crawford .60 1.50
274 Karim Garcia .40 1.00
275 Jose Reyes .60 1.50
276 Brandon Duckworth .40 1.00
277 Brian Giles .40 1.00
278 J.T. Snow .40 1.00
279 Jamie Moyer .40 1.00
280 Julio Lugo .40 1.00
281 Mark Teixeira 1.00 2.50
282 Cory Lidle .40 1.00
283 Lyle Overbay .40 1.00
284 Troy Percival .40 1.00
285 Robby Hammock .40 1.00
286 Jason Johnson .40 1.00
287 Damian Rolls .40 1.00
288 Antonio Alfonseca .40 1.00
289 Tom Goodwin .40 1.00
290 Paul Konerko .60 1.50
291 D'Angelo Jimenez .40 1.00
292 Ben Broussard .40 1.00
293 Magglio Ordonez .60 1.50
294 Carlos Pena .60 1.50
295 Chad Fox .40 1.00
296 Jerome Robertson .40 1.00
297 Travis Hafner .40 1.00
298 Joe Randa .40 1.00
299 Brady Clark .40 1.00
300 Barry Zito .40 1.00
301 Ruben Sierra .40 1.00
302 Brett Myers .40 1.00
303 Oliver Perez .40 1.00
304 Benito Santiago .40 1.00
305 David Ross .40 1.00
306 Joe Nathan .40 1.00
307 Jim Edmonds .60 1.50
308 Matt Kata .40 1.00
309 Vinny Castilla .40 1.00
310 Marty Cordova .40 1.00
311 Aramis Ramirez .40 1.00
312 Carl Everett .40 1.00
313 Ryan Freel .40 1.00
314 Mark Bellhorn Sox .40 1.00
315 Joe Mauer 1.00 2.50
316 Tim Redding .40 1.00
317 Jeromy Burnitz .40 1.00
318 Miguel Cabrera 1.00 2.50
319 Ramon Nivar .40 1.00
320 Casey Blake .40 1.00
321 Adam LaRoche .40 1.00
322 Jermaine Dye .40 1.00
323 Jerome Williams .40 1.00
324 John Olerud .40 1.00
325 Scott Rolen .60 1.50
326 Bobby Kielty .40 1.00
327 Travis Lee .40 1.00
328 Jeff Cirillo .40 1.00
329 Scott Spiezio .40 1.00
330 Melvin Mora .40 1.00
331 Mike Timlin .40 1.00
332 Kerry Wood .40 1.00
333 Tony Womack .40 1.00
334 Jody Gerut .40 1.00
335 Morgan Ensberg .40 1.00
336 Odalis Perez .40 1.00
337 Michael Cuddyer .40 1.00
338 Jose Hernandez .40 1.00
339 LaTroy Hawkins .40 1.00
340 Marquis Grissom .40 1.00
341 Matt Morris .40 1.00
342 Juan Gonzalez .40 1.00
343 Jose Valverde .40 1.00
344 Joe Borowski .40 1.00
345 Josh Bard .40 1.00
346 Austin Kearns .40 1.00
347 Chin-Hui Tsao .40 1.00
348 Wil Ledezma .40 1.00
349 Aaron Guiel .40 1.00
350 Alfonso Soriano .40 1.00
351 Ted Lilly .40 1.00
352 Sean Burroughs .40 1.00
353 Rafael Palmeiro .60 1.50
354 Quinton McCracken .40 1.00
355 David Ortiz 1.00 2.50
356 Randall Simon .40 1.00
357 Wily Mo Pena .40 1.00
358 Brian Anderson .40 1.00
359 Corey Koskie .40 1.00
360 Keith Foulke Sox .40 1.00
361 Sidney Ponson .40 1.00
362 Gary Matthews Jr. .40 1.00
363 Herbert Perry .40 1.00
364 Shea Hillenbrand .40 1.00
365 Craig Biggio .60 1.50
366 Barry Larkin .60 1.50
367 Arthur Rhodes .40 1.00
368 Sammy Sosa 1.00 2.50
369 Joe Crede .40 1.00
370 Gary Sheffield .40 1.00
371 Coco Crisp .40 1.00
372 Torii Hunter .40 1.00
373 Derrek Lee .40 1.00
374 Adam Everett .40 1.00
375 Miguel Tejada .60 1.50
376 Jeremy Affeldt .40 1.00
377 Robin Ventura .40 1.00
378 Scott Podsednik .40 1.00
379 Matthew LeCroy .40 1.00
380 Vladimir Guerrero 1.00 2.50
381 Steve Karsay .40 1.00
382 Jeff Nelson .40 1.00
383 Chase Utley 1.00 2.50
384 Bobby Abreu .40 1.00
385 Josh Fogg .40 1.00
386 Trevor Hoffman .60 1.50
387 Matt Stairs .40 1.00
388 Edgar Martinez .60 1.50
389 Edgar Renteria .40 1.00
390 Chipper Jones 1.00 2.50
391 Eric Munson .40 1.00
392 Dewon Brazelton .40 1.00
393 John Thomson .40 1.00
394 Chris Woodward .40 1.00
395 Joe Kennedy .40 1.00
396 Reed Johnson .40 1.00
397 Johnny Estrada .40 1.00
398 Damian Moss .40 1.00
399 Victor Zambrano .40 1.00
400 Dontrelle Willis .40 1.00
401 Troy Glaus .40 1.00
402 Raul Mondesi .40 1.00
403 Jeff Davanon .40 1.00
404 Kurt Ainsworth .40 1.00
405 Pedro Martinez .60 1.50
406 Eric Karros .40 1.00
407 Billy Koch .40 1.00
408 Luis Gonzalez .40 1.00
409 Jack Cust .40 1.00
410 Mike Sweeney .40 1.00
411 Jason Bay .60 1.50
412 Mark Redman .40 1.00
413 Jason Jennings .40 1.00
414 Rondell White .40 1.00
415 Todd Hundley .40 1.00
416 Shannon Stewart .40 1.00
417 Jae Weong Seo .40 1.00
418 Livan Hernandez .40 1.00
419 Mark Ellis .40 1.00
420 Pat Burrell .40 1.00
421 Mark Loretta .40 1.00
422 Robb Nen .40 1.00
423 Joel Pineiro .40 1.00
424 Todd Walker .40 1.00
425 Jeremy Bonderman .40 1.00
426 A.J. Burnett .60 1.50
427 Greg Myers .40 1.00
428 Roy Oswalt .60 1.50
429 Carlos Baerga .40 1.00
430 Garret Anderson .40 1.00
431 Horacio Ramirez .40 1.00
432 Brian Roberts .40 1.00
433 Kevin Brown .40 1.00
434 Eric Milton .40 1.00
435 Ramon Vazquez .40 1.00
436 Alex Escobar .40 1.00
437 Alex Sanchez .40 1.00
438 Jeff Bagwell .60 1.50
439 Claudio Vargas .40 1.00
440 Shawn Green .40 1.00
441 Geoff Jenkins .40 1.00
442 David Wells .40 1.00
443 Nick Johnson .40 1.00
444 Jose Guillen .40 1.00
445 Scott Hatteberg .40 1.00
446 Phil Nevin .40 1.00
447 Jason Schmidt .40 1.00
448 Ricky Ledee .40 1.00
449 So Taguchi .40 1.00
450 Randy Johnson 1.00 2.50
451 Eric Young .40 1.00
452 Chone Figgins .40 1.00
453 Larry Bigbie .40 1.00
454 Scott Williamson .40 1.00
455 Ramon Martinez .40 1.00
456 Roberto Alomar .60 1.50
457 Ryan Dempster .40 1.00
458 Ryan Ludwick .40 1.00
459 Ramon Santiago .40 1.00
460 Jeff Conine .40 1.00
461 Brad Lidge .40 1.00
462 Ken Harvey .40 1.00
463 Guillermo Mota .40 1.00
464 Rick Reed .40 1.00
465 Armando Benitez .40 1.00
466 Wade Miller .40 1.00

2004 Topps Chrome Black Refractors

*BLACK 1-210/257-466: 1.5X TO 4X BASIC
*BLACK 211-220/247-256: 1.2X TO 3X BASIC
1-220 SERIES 1 ODDS 1:10 H, 1:20 R
247-466 SERIES 2 ODDS 1:19 H, 1:20 R
221-233 SERIES 1 ODDS 1:1527 H, 1:2480 R
234-246 SERIES 2 ODDS 1:1579 H, 1:2549 R
221-246 PRINT RUN 25 SERIAL #'d SETS
221-246 NO PRICING DUE TO SCARCITY

2004 Topps Chrome Gold Refractors

*GOLD 1-210/257-466: 1.25X TO 3X BASIC
*GOLD 211-220/247-256: 1X TO 2.5X BASIC
1-220 SERIES 1 ODDS 1:5 H, 1:10 R
247-466 SERIES 2 ODDS 1:9 H, 1:10 R
*GOLD AU 221-246: 2X TO 4X BASIC AU
221-233 SERIES 1 ODDS 1:759 H, 1:1208 R
234-246 SERIES 2 ODDS 1:790 H, 1:1324 R
221-246 PRINT RUN 50 SERIAL #'d SETS
232 Zach Miner FY AU 50.00 100.00
244 Lastings Milledge FY AU 150.00 250.00

2004 Topps Chrome Red X-Fractors

*RED XF 1-210/257-466: 3X TO 8X BASIC
*RED XF 211-220/247-256: 3X TO 8X BASIC
1-220 ONE PER SER.1 PARALLEL HOT PACK
247-466 1 PER SER.2 PARALLEL HOT PACK
ONE HOT PACK PER SEALED HOBBY BOX
1-220 STATED PRINT RUN 63 SETS
247-466 STATED PRINT RUN 61 SETS
1-220/247-466 ARE NOT SERIAL #'d
1-220/247-466 PRINT RUN GIVEN BY TOPPS
221-233 SERIES 1 ODDS 1:21,371 HOBBY
234-246 SERIES 2 ODDS 1:20,800 HOBBY
221-246 PRINT RUN 1 SERIAL #'d SET
221-246 NO PRICING DUE TO SCARCITY

2004 Topps Chrome Refractors

*REF 1-210/257-466: 1X TO 2.5X BASIC
*REF 211-220/247-256: .75X TO 2X BASIC
1-220 SERIES 1 ODDS 1:4 H/R
247-466 SERIES 2 ODDS 1:4 H/R
*REF AU 221-246: 1X TO 2.5X BASIC AU
221-233 SERIES 1 ODDS 1:380 H, 1:597 R
234-246 SERIES 2 ODDS 1:375 H, 1:680 R
221-246 PRINT RUN 100 SERIAL #'d SETS
232 Zach Miner FY AU 30.00 60.00
244 Lastings Milledge FY AU 90.00 150.00

2004 Topps Chrome Fashionably Great Relics

ONE RELIC PER SER.1 GU HOBBY PACK
GROUP A 1:59 SER.1 RETAIL
GROUP B 1:107 SER.1 RETAIL
AD Adam Dunn Jsy A 3.00 8.00
AJ Andruw Jones Uni A 4.00 10.00
AP Albert Pujols Jsy A 10.00 25.00
AR Alex Rodriguez Uni A 6.00 15.00
BM Brett Myers Jsy A 3.00 8.00
BW Billy Wagner Jsy B 3.00 8.00
CB Craig Biggio Uni A 4.00 10.00
CD Carlos Delgado Jsy A 3.00 8.00
CF Cliff Floyd Jsy A 3.00 8.00
CJ Chipper Jones Uni A 4.00 10.00
CS Curt Schilling Jsy A 4.00 10.00
DL Derek Lowe Uni B 3.00 8.00
EC Eric Chavez Uni B 3.00 8.00
FG Freddy Garcia Jsy A 3.00 8.00
FM Fred McGriff Jsy A 4.00 10.00
FT Frank Thomas Uni A 4.00 10.00
HB Hank Blalock Jsy A 3.00 8.00
IR Ivan Rodriguez Uni B 4.00 10.00
JB Jeff Bagwell Uni A 4.00 10.00
JBO Joe Borchard Jsy A 3.00 8.00
JO John Olerud Jsy A 3.00 8.00
JR Juan Rivera Jsy A 3.00 8.00
JS John Smoltz Uni A 4.00 10.00
JV Jose Vidro Jsy B 3.00 8.00
KB Kevin Brown Jsy B 3.00 8.00
MM Mark Mulder Uni A 3.00 8.00
MP Mike Piazza Uni A 6.00 15.00
MR Manny Ramirez Uni A 4.00 10.00
MS Mike Sweeney Uni A 3.00 8.00
NG Nomar Garciaparra Uni B 6.00 15.00
PM Pedro Martinez Jsy A 4.00 10.00
RP Rafael Palmeiro Jsy A 4.00 10.00
SS Sammy Sosa Jsy A 4.00 10.00
TH Tim Hudson Uni B 3.00 8.00
THO Trevor Hoffman Uni A 3.00 8.00
VW Vernon Wells Jsy B 3.00 8.00
WP Wily Mo Pena Jsy A 3.00 8.00

2004 Topps Chrome Handle With Care Bat Knob Relics

STATED PRINT RUN 5 SERIAL #'d SETS
1 OF 1 PRINT RUN 1 SERIAL #'d SET
NO PRICING DUE TO SCARCITY
RANDOM IN SERIES 1 HOBBY RELIC PACKS
AK Al Kaline
AP Albert Pujols
AR Alex Rodriguez
AS Alfonso Soriano
BR Brooks Robinson
CF Carlton Fisk
CY Carl Yastrzemski
FR Frank Robinson
GB George Brett
HK Harmon Killebrew
JB Johnny Bench
JG Jason Giambi
JT Jim Thome
LB Lance Berkman
LBR Lou Brock
LG Luis Gonzalez
MT Miguel Tejada
NG Nomar Garciaparra
PM Paul Molitor
RJ Reggie Jackson
RY Robin Yount
TH Torii Hunter
WB Wade Boggs
WM Willie Mays
WS Willie Stargell

2004 Topps Chrome Presidential First Pitch Seat Relics

SERIES 2 ODDS 1:15 BOX-LOADER HOBBY
SERIES 2 ODDS 1:633 HOBBY
STATED PRINT RUN 100 SETS
CARDS ARE NOT SERIAL-NUMBERED
PRINT RUN INFO PROVIDED BY TOPPS
BC Bill Clinton 20.00 50.00
CC Calvin Coolidge 10.00 25.00
DE Dwight Eisenhower 10.00 25.00
FR Franklin D. Roosevelt 15.00 40.00
GB George W. Bush 20.00 50.00
GF Gerald Ford 15.00 40.00
GHB George H.W. Bush 15.00 40.00
HH Herbert Hoover 10.00 25.00
HT Harry Truman 10.00 25.00
JK John F. Kennedy 20.00 50.00
LJ Lyndon B. Johnson 10.00 25.00
RN Richard Nixon 20.00 50.00
RR Ronald Reagan 30.00 60.00
WH Warren Harding 10.00 25.00
WT William Taft 10.00 25.00
WW Woodrow Wilson 10.00 25.00

2004 Topps Chrome Presidential Pastime Refractors

COMPLETE SET (42) 60.00 120.00
SERIES 2 ODDS 1:9 HOBBY
*X-FRACTOR p/r 26-43: 2X TO 5X BASIC
X-FRACTOR SER.2 ODDS 1:400 H, 1:791 R
X-F PRINT RUNS B/WN 1-43 COPIES PER
NO X-F PRICING ON QTY OF 25 OR LESS
PP1 George Washington 2.50 6.00
PP2 John Adams 1.50 4.00
PP3 Thomas Jefferson 2.50 6.00
PP4 James Madison 1.50 4.00
PP5 James Monroe 1.50 4.00
PP6 John Quincy Adams 1.50 4.00
PP7 Andrew Jackson 1.50 4.00
PP8 Martin Van Buren 1.50 4.00
PP9 William Harrison 1.50 4.00
PP10 John Tyler 1.50 4.00
PP11 James Polk 1.50 4.00
PP12 Zachary Taylor 1.50 4.00
PP13 Millard Fillmore 1.50 4.00
PP14 Franklin Pierce 1.50 4.00
PP15 James Buchanan 1.50 4.00
PP16 Abraham Lincoln 2.50 6.00
PP17 Andrew Johnson 1.50 4.00
PP18 Ulysses S. Grant 2.00 5.00
PP19 Rutherford B. Hayes 1.50 4.00
PP20 James Garfield 1.50 4.00
PP21 Chester Arthur 1.50 4.00
PP22 Grover Cleveland 1.50 4.00
PP23 Benjamin Harrison 1.50 4.00
PP24 William McKinley 1.50 4.00
PP25 Theodore Roosevelt 2.00 5.00
PP26 William Taft 1.50 4.00
PP27 Woodrow Wilson 1.50 4.00
PP28 Warren Harding 1.50 4.00
PP29 Calvin Coolidge 1.50 4.00
PP30 Herbert Hoover 1.50 4.00
PP31 Franklin D. Roosevelt 2.00 5.00
PP32 Harry Truman 1.50 4.00
PP33 Dwight Eisenhower 1.50 4.00
PP34 John F. Kennedy 2.00 5.00
PP35 Lyndon B. Johnson 1.50 4.00
PP36 Richard Nixon 2.00 5.00
PP37 Gerald Ford 2.00 5.00
PP38 Jimmy Carter 1.50 4.00
PP39 Ronald Reagan 5.00 12.00
PP40 George H.W. Bush 2.00 5.00
PP41 Bill Clinton 2.50 6.00
PP42 George W. Bush 2.50 6.00

2004 Topps Chrome Town Heroes Relics

SER.2 ODDS 1 PER HOBBY BOX-LOADER
SER.2 ODDS 1:48 RETAIL
AP Albert Pujols Bat 6.00 15.00
AR Alex Rodriguez Bat 6.00 15.00
BZ Barry Zito Uni 3.00 8.00
CJ Chipper Jones Jsy 4.00 10.00
EC Eric Chavez Uni 3.00 8.00
FT Frank Thomas Jsy 4.00 10.00
HN Hideo Nomo Jsy 4.00 10.00
JG Jason Giambi Uni 3.00 8.00
JR Jose Reyes Bat 3.00 8.00
KW Kerry Wood Jsy 3.00 8.00
LB Lance Berkman Jsy 3.00 8.00
MM Mark Mulder Uni 3.00 8.00
MP Mark Prior Bat 4.00 10.00
MR Manny Ramirez Bat 4.00 10.00
MT Miguel Tejada Bat 3.00 8.00
NG Nomar Garciaparra Bat 4.00 10.00
RH Rich Harden Uni 3.00 8.00
RP Rafael Palmeiro Jsy 4.00 10.00
SS Sammy Sosa Jsy 4.00 10.00
SST Shannon Stewart Jsy 3.00 8.00
TH Tim Hudson Uni 3.00 8.00

2004 Topps Chrome Traded

These cards were issued at a stated rate of two per 2004 Topps Traded pack. Cards numbered 1 through 65 feature veterans who were traded while cards 66 through 70 feature managers. Cards numbered 71 through 90 feature high draft picks, cards numbered 91 through 110 feature prospect and cards 111 through 220 feature Rookie Cards. All of these cards were issued with a "T" prefix.

COMPLETE SET (220) 60.00 120.00
COMMON CARD (1-70) .30 .75
COMMON CARD (71-90) .40 1.00
COMMON CARD (91-110) .40 1.00
COMMON CARD (111-220) .40 1.00
2 PER 2004 TOPPS TRADED HOBBY PACK
2 PER 2004 TOPPS TRADED HTA PACK
2 PER 2004 TOPPS TRADED RETAIL PACK
PLATE ODDS 1:1151 H, 1:1173 R, 1:327 HTA
PLATE PRINT RUN 1 SET PER COLOR
BLACK-CYAN-MAGENTA-YELLOW ISSUED
NO PLATE PRICING DUE TO SCARCITY
T1 Pokey Reese .30 .75
T2 Tony Womack .30 .75
T3 Richard Hidalgo .30 .75
T4 Juan Uribe .30 .75
T5 J.D. Drew .30 .75
T6 Alex Gonzalez .30 .75
T7 Carlos Guillen .30 .75
T8 Doug Mientkiewicz .30 .75
T9 Fernando Vina .30 .75
T10 Milton Bradley .30 .75
T11 Kelvim Escobar .30 .75
T12 Ben Grieve .30 .75
T13 Brian Jordan .30 .75
T14 A.J. Pierzynski .30 .75
T15 Billy Wagner .30 .75
T16 Terrence Long .30 .75
T17 Carlos Beltran .30 .75
T18 Carl Everett .30 .75
T19 Reggie Sanders .30 .75
T20 Javy Lopez .30 .75
T21 Jay Payton .30 .75
T22 Octavio Dotel .30 .75
T23 Eddie Guardado .30 .75
T24 Andy Pettitte .50 1.25
T25 Richie Sexson .30 .75
T26 Ronnie Belliard .30 .75
T27 Michael Tucker .30 .75
T28 Brad Fullmer .30 .75
T29 Freddy Garcia .30 .75
T30 Bartolo Colon .30 .75
T31 Larry Walker Cards .50 1.25
T32 Mark Kotsay .30 .75
T33 Jason Marquis .30 .75
T34 Dustan Mohr .30 .75
T35 Javier Vazquez .30 .75
T36 Nomar Garciaparra .75 2.00
T37 Tino Martinez .50 1.25
T38 Hee Seop Choi .30 .75
T39 Damian Miller .30 .75
T40 Jose Lima .30 .75
T41 Ty Wigginton .30 .75
T42 Raul Ibanez .30 .75
T43 Danys Baez .30 .75
T44 Tony Clark .30 .75
T45 Greg Maddux 1.25 3.00
T46 Victor Zambrano .30 .75
T47 Orlando Cabrera Sox .30 .75
T48 Jose Cruz Jr. .30 .75
T49 Kris Benson .30 .75
T50 Alex Rodriguez 1.25 3.00
T51 Steve Finley .30 .75
T52 Ramon Hernandez .30 .75
T53 Esteban Loaiza .30 .75
T54 Ugueth Urbina .30 .75
T55 Jeff Weaver .30 .75
T56 Flash Gordon .30 .75
T57 Jose Contreras .30 .75
T58 Paul Lo Duca .30 .75
T59 Junior Spivey .30 .75
T60 Curt Schilling .50 1.25
T61 Brad Penny .30 .75
T62 Braden Looper .30 .75
T63 Miguel Cairo .30 .75
T64 Juan Encarnacion .30 .75
T65 Miguel Batista .30 .75
T66 Terry Francona MG .30 .75
T67 Lee Mazzilli MG .30 .75
T68 Al Pedrique MG .30 .75
T69 Ozzie Guillen MG .30 .75
T70 Phil Garner MG .30 .75
T71 Matt Bush DP RC .60 1.50
T72 Homer Bailey DP RC .60 1.50
T73 Greg Golson DP RC .40 1.00
T74 Kyle Waldrop DP RC .40 1.00
T75 Richie Robnett DP RC .40 1.00
T76 Jay Rainville DP RC .40 1.00
T77 Bill Bray DP RC .40 1.00
T78 Philip Hughes DP RC 3.00 8.00
T79 Scott Elbert DP RC .40 1.00
T80 Josh Fields DP RC .60 1.50
T81 Justin Orenduff DP RC .60 1.50
T82 Dan Putnam DP RC .40 1.00
T83 Chris Nelson DP RC .40 1.00
T84 Blake DeWitt DP RC 1.50 4.00
T85 J.P. Howell DP RC .40 1.00
T86 Huston Street DP RC 1.00 2.50
T87 Kurt Suzuki DP RC 1.25 3.00
T88 Erick San Pedro DP RC .40 1.00
T89 Matt Tuiasosopo DP RC 1.00 2.50
T90 Matt Macri DP RC .60 1.50
T91 Chad Tracy PROS .40 1.00
T92 Scott Hairston PROS .40 1.00
T93 Jonny Gomes PROS .40 1.00
T94 Chin-Feng Chen PROS .40 1.00
T95 Chien-Ming Wang PROS 2.00 5.00
T96 Dustin McGowan PROS .40 1.00
T97 Chris Burke PROS .40 1.00
T98 Denny Bautista PROS .40 1.00
T99 Preston Larrison PROS .40 1.00
T100 Kevin Youkilis PROS .60 1.50
T101 John Maine PROS .60 1.50
T102 Guillermo Quiroz PROS .40 1.00
T103 Dave Krynzel PROS .40 1.00
T104 David Kelton PROS .40 1.00
T105 Edwin Encarnacion PROS .60 1.50
T106 Chad Gaudin PROS .40 1.00
T107 Sergio Mitre PROS .40 1.00
T108 Laynce Nix PROS .40 1.00
T109 David Parrish PROS .40 1.00
T110 Brandon Claussen PROS .40 1.00
T111 Frank Francisco FY RC .40 1.00
T112 Brian Dallimore FY RC .40 1.00
T113 Jim Crowell FY RC .40 1.00
T114 Andres Blanco FY RC .40 1.00
T115 Eduardo Villacis FY RC .40 1.00
T116 Kazuhito Tadano FY RC .40 1.00
T117 Aarom Baldiris FY RC .40 1.00
T118 Justin Germano FY RC .40 1.00
T119 Joey Gathright FY RC .40 1.00
T120 Franklyn Gracesqui FY RC .40 1.00
T121 Chin-Lung Hu FY RC .60 1.50
T122 Scott Olsen FY RC .40 1.00
T123 Tyler Davidson FY RC .40 1.00
T124 Fausto Carmona FY RC .60 1.50
T125 Tim Hutting FY RC .40 1.00
T126 Ryan Meaux FY RC .40 1.00
T127 Jon Connolly FY RC .40 1.00
T128 Hector Made FY RC .40 1.00
T129 Jamie Brown FY RC .40 1.00
T130 Paul McAnulty FY RC .40 1.00
T131 Chris Saenz FY RC .40 1.00
T132 Marland Williams FY RC .40 1.00
T133 Mike Huggins FY RC .40 1.00
T134 Jesse Crain FY RC .40 1.00
T135 Chad Bentz FY RC .40 1.00
T136 Kazuo Matsui FY RC .60 1.50
T137 Paul Maholm FY .60 1.50
T138 Brock Jacobsen FY RC .40 1.00
T139 Casey Daigle FY RC .40 1.00
T140 Nyjer Morgan FY RC .40 1.00
T141 Tom Mastny FY RC .40 1.00
T142 Kody Kirkland FY RC .40 1.00
T143 Jose Capellan FY RC .40 1.00
T144 Felix Hernandez FY RC 8.00 20.00
T145 Shawn Hill FY RC .40 1.00
T146 Danny Gonzalez FY RC .40 1.00
T147 Scott Dohmann FY RC .40 1.00
T148 Tommy Murphy FY RC .40 1.00
T149 Akinori Otsuka FY RC .40 1.00
T150 Miguel Perez FY RC .40 1.00
T151 Mike Rouse FY RC .40 1.00
T152 Ramon Ramirez FY RC .40 1.00
T153 Luke Hughes FY RC .40 1.00
T154 Howie Kendrick FY RC 3.00 8.00
T155 Ryan Budde FY RC .40 1.00
T156 Charlie Zink FY RC .40 1.00
T157 Warner Madrigal FY RC .40 1.00
T158 Jason Szuminski FY RC .40 1.00
T159 Chad Chop FY RC .40 1.00
T160 Shingo Takatsu FY RC .40 1.00
T161 Matt Lemanczyk FY RC .40 1.00
T162 Wardell Starling FY RC .40 1.00
T163 Nick Gorneault FY RC .40 1.00
T164 Scott Proctor FY RC .40 1.00
T165 Brooks Conrad FY RC .40 1.00
T166 Hector Gimenez FY RC .40 1.00
T167 Kevin Howard FY RC .40 1.00
T168 Vince Perkins FY RC .40 1.00
T169 Brock Peterson FY RC .40 1.00
T170 Chris Shelton FY RC .60 1.50
T171 Erick Aybar FY RC .60 1.50
T172 Paul Bacot FY RC .40 1.00
T173 Matt Capps FY RC .40 1.00
T174 Kory Casto FY .40 1.00
T175 Juan Cedeno FY RC .40 1.00
T176 Vito Chiaravalloti FY .40 1.00
T177 Alec Zumwalt FY RC .40 1.00
T178 J.J. Furmaniak FY RC .40 1.00
T179 Lee Gwaltney FY RC .40 1.00
T180 Donald Kelly FY RC .60 1.50
T181 Benji DeQuin FY RC .40 1.00
T182 Brant Colamarino FY RC .40 1.00
T183 Juan Gutierrez FY RC .40 1.00
T184 Carl Loadenthal FY RC .40 1.00
T185 Ricky Nolasco FY RC .60 1.50
T186 Jeff Salazar FY RC .40 1.00
T187 Rob Tejeda FY RC .40 1.00
T188 Alex Romero FY RC .40 1.00
T189 Yoann Torrealba FY RC .40 1.00
T190 Carlos Sosa FY RC .40 1.00
T191 Tim Bittner FY RC .40 1.00
T192 Chris Aguila FY RC .40 1.00
T193 Jason Frasor FY RC .40 1.00
T194 Reid Gorecki FY RC .40 1.00
T195 Dustin Nippert FY RC .40 1.00
T196 Javier Guzman FY RC .40 1.00
T197 Harvey Garcia FY RC .40 1.00
T198 Ivan Ochoa FY RC .40 1.00
T199 David Wallace FY RC .40 1.00
T200 Joel Zumaya FY RC 2.50 6.00

T201 Casey Kopitzke FY RC .40 1.00
T202 Lincoln Holdzkom FY RC .40 1.00
T203 Chad Santos FY RC .40 1.00
T204 Brian Pilkington FY RC .40 1.00
T205 Terry Jones FY RC .40 1.00
T206 Jerome Gamble FY RC .40 1.00
T207 Brad Eldred FY RC .40 1.00
T208 David Pauley FY RC .60 1.50
T209 Kevin Davidson FY RC .40 1.00
T210 Damaso Espino FY RC .40 1.00
T211 Tom Farmer FY RC .40 1.00
T212 Michael Mooney FY RC .40 1.00
T213 James Tomlin FY RC .40 1.00
T214 Greg Thissen FY RC .40 1.00
T215 Calvin Hayes FY RC .40 1.00
T216 Fernando Cortez FY RC .40 1.00
T217 Sergio Silva FY RC .40 1.00
T218 Jon de Vries FY RC .40 1.00
T219 Don Sutton FY RC .40 1.00
T220 Leo Nunez FY RC .40 1.00

2004 Topps Chrome Traded Blue Refractors

ODDS 1:4574 H, 1:4925 R, 1:1238 HTA
STATED PRINT RUN 1 SERIAL #'d SET
NO PRICING DUE TO SCARCITY

2004 Topps Chrome Traded Refractors

*REF 1-70: 2X TO 5X BASIC
*REF 71-90: 1.5X TO 4X BASIC
*REF 91-110: 1.5X TO 4X BASIC
*REF 111-220: 1.5X TO 4X BASIC
STATED ODDS 1:12 HOB/RET, 1:4 HTA
STATED PRINT RUN 355 SETS
CARDS ARE NOT SERIAL-NUMBERED
PRINT RUN INFO PROVIDED BY TOPPS

2004 Topps Chrome Traded X-Fractors

*XF 1-70: 8X TO 20X BASIC
*XF 91-110: 6X TO 15X BASIC
ONE XF PACK PER SEALED HTA BOX
ONE XF CARD PER XF PACK
STATED PRINT RUN 20 SERIAL #'d SETS
NO PRICING ON 71-90 DUE TO SCARCITY
NO PRICING ON 91-110 DUE TO SCARCITY

2005 Topps Chrome

This 234-card first series was released in January, 2005 while the 238-card second series was released in April, 2005. The cards were issued in four card hobby or retail packs with an $3 SRP which came 20 packs to a box and eight boxes to a case. Cards numbered 1-210 feature veteran players while cards 211-220 feature Rookie Cards and cards numbered 221-234 feature players in their first year with Topps who signed cards for this product. Cards numbered 221-234 were issued to a stated print run of 1771 sets (although these cards were not serial numbered) and were inserted at a stated rate of one in 28 hobby and one in 33 retail packs. In the second series, cards numbered 235 through 252 feature autographs and those cards were issued at a stated rate of one in two mini-boxes and one in 55 retail packs. In addition, these cards were issued to a stated print run of 1770 sets although these cards were not serial numbered.

COMP.SET w/o AU'S (440) 80.00 160.00
COMP.SERIES 1 w/o AU's (220) 40.00 80.00
COMP.SERIES 2 w/o AU's (220) 40.00 80.00
COMMON (1-210/253-467) .40 1.00
COMMON (211-220/468-472) .75 2.00
COMMON AU (221-252) 4.00 10.00
221-252 PRINT RUN PROVIDED BY TOPPS
EXCHANGE DEADLINE 05/31/07
1-234 PLATE ODDS 1:310 SER.1 HOBBY
235-252 PLATE ODDS 1:350 SER.2 MINI BOX
253-472 PLATE ODDS 1:29 SER.2 MINI BOX
PLATE PRINT RUN 1 SET PER COLOR
BLACK-CYAN-MAGENTA-YELLOW ISSUED
NO PLATE PRICING DUE TO SCARCITY
1 Alex Rodriguez 1.50 4.00
2 Placido Polanco .40 1.00
3 Torii Hunter .40 1.00
4 Lyle Overbay .40 1.00
5 Johnny Damon .60 1.50
6 Johnny Estrada .40 1.00
7 Rich Harden .40 1.00
8 Francisco Rodriguez .60 1.50
9 Jarrod Washburn .40 1.00
10 Sammy Sosa 1.00 2.50
11 Randy Wolf .40 1.00
12 Jason Bay .40 1.00
13 Tom Glavine .60 1.50
14 Michael Tucker .40 1.00
15 Brian Giles .40 1.00
16 Chad Tracy .40 1.00
17 Jim Edmonds .60 1.50
18 John Smoltz 1.00 2.50
19 Roy Halladay 1.00 2.50
20 Hank Blalock .40 1.00
21 Darin Erstad .40 1.00
22 Todd Walker .40 1.00
23 Mike Hampton .40 1.00
24 Mark Bellhorn .40 1.00
25 Jim Thome .60 1.50
26 Shingo Takatsu .40 1.00
27 Jody Gerut .40 1.00
28 Vinny Castilla .40 1.00
29 Luis Castillo .40 1.00
30 Ivan Rodriguez .60 1.50
31 Craig Biggio .60 1.50
32 Joe Randa .40 1.00
33 Adrian Beltre .40 1.00
34 Scott Podsednik .40 1.00
35 Cliff Floyd .40 1.00
36 Livan Hernandez .40 1.00
37 Eric Byrnes .40 1.00
38 Jose Acevedo .40 1.00
39 Jack Wilson .40 1.00
40 Gary Sheffield .40 1.00
41 Chan Ho Park .60 1.50
42 Carl Crawford .60 1.50
43 Shawn Estes .40 1.00
44 David Bell .40 1.00
45 Jeff DaVanon .40 1.00
46 Brandon Webb .60 1.50
47 Lance Berkman .60 1.50
48 Melvin Mora .40 1.00
49 David Ortiz 1.00 2.50
50 Andruw Jones .40 1.00
51 Chone Figgins .40 1.00
52 Danny Graves .40 1.00
53 Preston Wilson .40 1.00
54 Jeremy Bonderman .40 1.00
55 Carlos Guillen .40 1.00
56 Cesar Izturis .40 1.00
57 Kazuo Matsui .40 1.00
58 Jason Schmidt .40 1.00
59 Jason Marquis .40 1.00
60 Jose Vidro .40 1.00
61 Al Leiter .40 1.00
62 Javier Vazquez .40 1.00
63 Erubiel Durazo .40 1.00
64 Scott Spiezio .40 1.00
65 Scot Shields .40 1.00
66 Edgardo Alfonzo .40 1.00
67 Miguel Tejada .60 1.50
68 Francisco Cordero .40 1.00
69 Brett Myers .40 1.00
70 Curt Schilling .60 1.50
71 Matt Kata .40 1.00
72 Bartolo Colon .40 1.00
73 Rodrigo Lopez .40 1.00
74 Tim Wakefield .40 1.00
75 Frank Thomas 1.00 2.50
76 Jimmy Rollins .60 1.50
77 Barry Zito .40 1.00
78 Hideo Nomo 1.00 2.50
79 Brad Wilkerson .40 1.00
80 Adam Dunn .60 1.50
81 Derrek Lee .40 1.00
82 Joe Crede .40 1.00
83 Nate Robertson .40 1.00
84 John Thomson .40 1.00
85 Mike Sweeney .40 1.00
86 Kip Wells .40 1.00
87 Eric Gagne .40 1.00
88 Zach Day .40 1.00
89 Alex Sanchez .40 1.00
90 Bret Boone .40 1.00
91 Mark Loretta .40 1.00
92 Miguel Cabrera 1.00 2.50
93 Randy Winn .40 1.00
94 Adam Everett .40 1.00
95 Aubrey Huff .40 1.00
96 Kevin Mench .40 1.00
97 Frank Catalanotto .40 1.00
98 Flash Gordon .40 1.00
99 Scott Hatteberg .40 1.00
100 Albert Pujols 2.50 6.00
101 Jose Molina .40 1.00
Bengie Molina
102 Jason Johnson .40 1.00
103 Jay Gibbons .40 1.00
104 Byung-Hyun Kim .40 1.00
105 Joe Borowski .40 1.00
106 Mark Grudzielanek .40 1.00
107 Mark Buehrle .60 1.50
108 Paul Wilson .40 1.00
109 Ronnie Belliard .40 1.00
110 Reggie Sanders .40 1.00
111 Tim Redding .40 1.00
112 Brian Lawrence .40 1.00
113 Travis Hafner .40 1.00
114 Jose Hernandez .40 1.00
115 Ben Sheets .40 1.00
116 Johan Santana 1.00 2.50
117 Billy Wagner .40 1.00
118 Mariano Rivera 1.00 2.50
119 Steve Trachsel .40 1.00
120 Akinori Otsuka .40 1.00
121 Jose Valentin .40 1.00
122 Orlando Hernandez .40 1.00
123 Raul Ibanez .40 1.00
124 Mike Matheny .40 1.00
125 Vernon Wells .40 1.00
126 Jason Isringhausen .40 1.00
127 Jose Guillen .40 1.00
128 Danny Bautista .40 1.00
129 Marcus Giles .40 1.00
130 Javy Lopez .40 1.00
131 Kevin Millar .40 1.00
132 Kyle Farnsworth .40 1.00
133 Carl Pavano .40 1.00
134 Rafael Furcal .40 1.00
135 Casey Blake .40 1.00
136 Matt Holliday 1.00 2.50
137 Bobby Higginson .40 1.00
138 Adam Kennedy .40 1.00
139 Alex Gonzalez .40 1.00
140 Jeff Kent .40 1.00
141 Aaron Guiel .40 1.00
142 Shawn Green .40 1.00
143 Bill Hall .40 1.00
144 Shannon Stewart .40 1.00
145 Juan Rivera .40 1.00
146 Coco Crisp .40 1.00
147 Mike Mussina .60 1.50
148 Eric Chavez .40 1.00
149 Jon Lieber .40 1.00
150 Vladimir Guerrero 1.00 2.50
151 Alex Cintron .40 1.00
152 Luis Matos .40 1.00
153 Sidney Ponson .40 1.00
154 Trot Nixon .40 1.00
155 Greg Maddux 1.50 4.00
156 Edgar Renteria .40 1.00
157 Ryan Freel .40 1.00
158 Matt Lawton .40 1.00
159 Mark Prior .60 1.50
160 Josh Beckett .60 1.50
161 Ken Harvey .40 1.00
162 Angel Berroa .40 1.00
163 Juan Encarnacion .40 1.00
164 Wes Helms .40 1.00
165 Brad Radke .40 1.00
166 Phil Nevin .40 1.00
167 Mike Cameron .40 1.00
168 Billy Koch .40 1.00
169 Bobby Crosby .40 1.00
170 Mike Lieberthal .40 1.00
171 Rob Mackowiak .40 1.00
172 Sean Burroughs .40 1.00
173 J.T. Snow .40 1.00
174 Paul Konerko .60 1.50
175 Luis Gonzalez .40 1.00
176 John Lackey .40 1.00
177 Oliver Perez .40 1.00
178 Brian Roberts .40 1.00
179 Bill Mueller .40 1.00
180 Carlos Lee .40 1.00
181 Corey Patterson .40 1.00
182 Sean Casey .40 1.00
183 Cliff Lee .60 1.50
184 Jason Jennings .40 1.00
185 Dmitri Young .40 1.00
186 Juan Uribe .40 1.00
187 Andy Pettitte .60 1.50
188 Juan Gonzalez .40 1.00
189 Orlando Hudson .40 1.00
190 Jason Phillips .40 1.00
191 Braden Looper .40 1.00
192 Lew Ford .40 1.00
193 Mark Mulder .40 1.00
194 Bobby Abreu .40 1.00
195 Jason Kendall .40 1.00
196 Khalil Greene .40 1.00
197 A.J. Pierzynski .40 1.00
198 Tim Worrell .40 1.00
199 So Taguchi .40 1.00
200 Jason Giambi .40 1.00
201 Tony Batista .40 1.00
202 Carlos Zambrano .60 1.50
203 Trevor Hoffman .60 1.50
204 Odalis Perez .40 1.00
205 Jose Cruz Jr. .40 1.00
206 Michael Barrett .40 1.00
207 Chris Carpenter 1.00 2.50
208 Michael Young UER .60 1.50
Player sliding is Rod Barajas
209 Toby Hall .40 1.00
210 Woody Williams .40 1.00
211 Chris Denorfia FY RC .40 1.00
212 Darren Fenster FY RC .40 1.00
213 Elvys Quezada FY RC .40 1.00
214 Ian Kinsler FY RC 3.00 8.00
215 Matthew Lindstrom FY RC .40 1.00
216 Ryan Goleski FY RC .40 1.00
217 Ryan Sweeney FY RC .60 1.50
218 Sean Marshall FY RC 1.00 2.50
219 Steve Doetsch FY RC .40 1.00
220 Wade Robinson FY RC .40 1.00
221 Andre Ethier FY AU RC 40.00 80.00
222 Brandon Moss FY AU RC 8:00 20.00
223 Chadd Blasko FY AU RC 6.00 15.00
224 Chris Roberson FY AU RC 4.00 10.00
225 Chris Seddon FY AU RC 4.00 10.00
226 Ian Bladergroen FY AU RC 6.00 15.00
227 Jake Dittler FY AU 4.00 10.00
228 Jose Vaquedano FY AU RC 4.00 10.00
229 Jeremy West FY AU RC 6.00 15.00
230 Kole Strayhorn FY AU RC 4.00 10.00
231 Kevin West FY AU RC 4.00 10.00
232 Luis Ramirez FY AU RC 4.00 10.00
233 Melky Cabrera FY AU RC 6.00 15.00
234 Nate Schierholtz FY AU 4.00 10.00
235 Billy Butler FY AU RC 6.00 15.00
237 Chad Orvella FY AU RC 4.00 10.00
238 Chip Cannon FY AU RC 8.00 20.00
239 Eric Nielsen FY AU RC 4.00 10.00
240 Erik Cordier FY AU RC 4.00 10.00
241 Glen Perkins FY AU RC 8.00 20.00
242 Justin Verlander FY AU RC 50.00 100.00
243 Kevin Melillo FY AU RC 6.00 15.00
244 Landon Powell FY AU RC 6.00 15.00
245 Matt Campbell FY AU RC 4.00 10.00
246 Michael Rogers FY AU RC 4.00 10.00
247 Nate McLouth FY AU RC 8.00 20.00
248 Scott Mathieson FY AU RC 4.00 10.00
249 Shane Costa FY AU RC 4.00 10.00
250 Tony Giarratano FY AU RC 4.00 10.00
251 Tyler Pelland FY AU RC 6.00 15.00
252 Wes Swackhamer FY AU RC 4.00 10.00
253 Garret Anderson .40 1.00
254 Randy Johnson 1.00 2.50
255 Charles Thomas .40 1.00
256 Rafael Palmeiro .60 1.50
257 Kevin Youkilis .40 1.00
258 Freddy Garcia .40 1.00
259 Magglio Ordonez .60 1.50
260 Aaron Harang .40 1.00
261 Grady Sizemore .60 1.50
262 Chin-hui Tsao .40 1.00
263 Eric Munson .40 1.00
264 Juan Pierre .40 1.00
265 Brad Lidge .40 1.00
266 Brian Anderson .40 1.00
267 Todd Helton .60 1.50
268 Chad Cordero .40 1.00
269 Kris Benson .40 1.00
270 Brad Halsey .40 1.00
271 Jermaine Dye .40 1.00
272 Manny Ramirez 1.00 2.50
273 Adam Eaton .40 1.00
274 Brett Tomko .40 1.00
275 Bucky Jacobsen .40 1.00
276 Dontrelle Willis .40 1.00
277 B.J. Upton .60 1.50
278 Rocco Baldelli .40 1.00
279 Ryan Drese .40 1.00
280 Ichiro Suzuki 1.50 4.00
281 Brandon Lyon .40 1.00
282 Nick Green .40 1.00
283 Jerry Hairston Jr. .40 1.00
284 Mike Lowell .40 1.00
285 Kerry Wood .40 1.00
286 Omar Vizquel .60 1.50
287 Carlos Beltran .40 1.00
288 Carlos Pena .60 1.50
289 Jeff Weaver .40 1.00
290 Chad Moeller .40 1.00
291 Joe Mays .40 1.00
292 Termel Sledge .40 1.00
293 Richard Hidalgo .40 1.00
294 Justin Duchscherer .40 1.00
295 Eric Milton .40 1.00
296 Ramon Hernandez .40 1.00
297 Jose Reyes .60 1.50
298 Joel Pineiro .40 1.00
299 Matt Morris .40 1.00
300 John Halama .40 1.00
301 Gary Matthews Jr. .40 1.00
302 Ryan Madson .40 1.00
303 Mark Kotsay .40 1.00
304 Carlos Delgado .40 1.00
305 Casey Kotchman .40 1.00
306 Greg Aquino .40 1.00
307 LaTroy Hawkins .40 1.00
308 Jose Contreras .40 1.00
309 Ken Griffey Jr. 1.50 4.00
310 C.C. Sabathia .60 1.50
311 Brandon Inge .40 1.00
312 John Buck .40 1.00
313 Hee Seop Choi .40 1.00
314 Chris Capuano .40 1.00
315 Jesse Crain .40 1.00
316 Geoff Jenkins .40 1.00
317 Mike Piazza 1.00 2.50
318 Jorge Posada .60 1.50
319 Nick Swisher 1.00 2.50
320 Kevin Millwood .40 1.00
321 Mike Gonzalez .40 1.00
322 Jake Peavy .40 1.00
323 Dustin Hermanson .40 1.00
324 Jeremy Reed .40 1.00
325 Alfonso Soriano .60 1.50
326 Alexis Rios .60 1.50
327 David Eckstein .40 1.00
328 Shea Hillenbrand .40 1.00
329 Russ Ortiz .40 1.00
330 Kurt Ainsworth .40 1.00
331 Orlando Cabrera .40 1.00
332 Carlos Silva .40 1.00
333 Ross Gload .40 1.00
334 Josh Phelps .40 1.00
335 Mike Maroth .40 1.00
336 Guillermo Mota .40 1.00
337 Chris Burke .40 1.00
338 David DeJesus .40 1.00
339 Jose Lima .40 1.00
340 Cristian Guzman .40 1.00
341 Nick Johnson .40 1.00
342 Victor Zambrano .40 1.00
343 Rod Barajas .40 1.00
344 Damian Miller .40 1.00
345 Chase Utley .60 1.50
346 Sean Burnett .40 1.00
347 David Wells .40 1.00
348 Dustan Mohr .40 1.00
349 Bobby Madritsch .40 1.00
350 Reed Johnson .40 1.00
351 R.A. Dickey .40 1.00
352 Scott Kazmir 1.00 2.50
353 Tony Womack .40 1.00
354 Tomas Perez .40 1.00
355 Esteban Loaiza .40 1.00
356 Tomokazu Ohka .40 1.00
357 Ramon Ortiz .40 1.00
358 Richie Sexson .40 1.00
359 J.D. Drew .40 1.00
360 Barry Bonds 2.00 5.00
361 Aramis Ramirez .40 1.00
362 Wily Mo Pena .40 1.00
363 Jeromy Burnitz .40 1.00
364 Nomar Garciaparra 1.00 2.50
365 Brandon Backe .40 1.00
366 Derek Lowe .40 1.00
367 Doug Davis .40 1.00
368 Joe Mauer 1.00 2.50
369 Endy Chavez .40 1.00
370 Bernie Williams .60 1.50
371 Jason Michaels .40 1.00
372 Craig Wilson .40 1.00
373 Ryan Klesko .40 1.00
374 Ray Durham .40 1.00
375 Jose Lopez .40 1.00
376 Jeff Suppan .40 1.00
377 David Bush .40 1.00
378 Marlon Byrd .40 1.00
379 Roy Oswalt .60 1.50
380 Rondell White .40 1.00
381 Troy Glaus .40 1.00
382 Scott Hairston .40 1.00
383 Chipper Jones 1.00 2.50
384 Daniel Cabrera .40 1.00
385 Jon Garland .40 1.00
386 Austin Kearns .40 1.00
387 Jake Westbrook .40 1.00
388 Aaron Miles .40 1.00
389 Omar Infante .40 1.00
390 Paul Lo Duca .40 1.00
391 Morgan Ensberg .40 1.00
392 Tony Graffanino .40 1.00
393 Milton Bradley .40 1.00
394 Keith Ginter .40 1.00
395 Justin Morneau 1.00 2.50
396 Tony Armas Jr. .40 1.00
397 Kevin Brown .40 1.00
398 Marco Scutaro .40 1.00
399 Tim Hudson .60 1.50
400 Pat Burrell .40 1.00
401 Jeff Cirillo .40 1.00
402 Larry Walker .60 1.50
403 Dewon Brazelton .40 1.00
404 Shigetoshi Hasegawa .40 1.00
405 Octavio Dotel .40 1.00
406 Michael Cuddyer .40 1.00
407 Junior Spivey .40 1.00
408 Zack Greinke .60 1.50
409 Roger Clemens 1.25 3.00
410 Chris Shelton .40 1.00
411 Ugueth Urbina .40 1.00
412 Rafael Betancourt .40 1.00
413 Willie Harris .40 1.00
414 Keith Foulke .40 1.00
415 Larry Bigbie .40 1.00
416 Paul Byrd .40 1.00
417 Troy Percival .40 1.00
418 Pedro Martinez .60 1.50
419 Matt Clement .40 1.00
420 Ryan Wagner .40 1.00
421 Jeff Francis .40 1.00
422 Jeff Conine .40 1.00
423 Wade Miller .40 1.00
424 Gavin Floyd .40 1.00
425 Kazuhisa Ishii .40 1.00
426 Victor Santos .40 1.00
427 Jacque Jones .40 1.00
428 Hideki Matsui 1.50 4.00
429 Cory Lidle .40 1.00
430 Jose Castillo .40 1.00
431 Alex Gonzalez .40 1.00
432 Kirk Rueter .40 1.00
433 Jolbert Cabrera .40 1.00
434 Erik Bedard .40 1.00
435 Ricky Ledee .40 1.00
436 Mark Hendrickson .40 1.00
437 Laynce Nix .40 1.00
438 Jason Frasor .40 1.00
439 Kevin Gregg .40 1.00
440 Derek Jeter 2.50 6.00
441 Jaret Wright .40 1.00
442 Edwin Jackson .40 1.00
443 Moises Alou .40 1.00
444 Aaron Rowand .40 1.00
445 Kazuhito Tadano .40 1.00
446 Luis Gonzalez .40 1.00
447 A.J. Burnett .60 1.50
448 Jeff Bagwell .60 1.50
449 Brad Penny .40 1.00
450 Corey Koskie .40 1.00
451 Mark Ellis .40 1.00
452 Hector Luna .40 1.00
453 Miguel Olivo .40 1.00
454 Scott Rolen .60 1.50
455 Ricardo Rodriguez .40 1.00
456 Eric Hinske .40 1.00
457 Tim Salmon .40 1.00
458 Adam LaRoche .40 1.00
459 B.J. Ryan .40 1.00
460 Steve Finley .40 1.00
461 Joe Nathan .40 1.00
462 Vicente Padilla .40 1.00
463 Yadier Molina .60 1.50
464 Tino Martinez .60 1.50
465 Mark Teixeira 1.00 2.50
466 Kelvim Escobar .40 1.00
467 Pedro Feliz .40 1.00
468 Ryan Garko FY RC .40 1.00
469 Bobby Livingston FY RC .40 1.00
470 Yorman Bazardo FY RC .40 1.00
471 Mike Bourn FY RC 1.00 2.50
472 Andy LaRoche FY RC 2.00 5.00

2005 Topps Chrome Black Refractors

*BLACK 1-210/253-467: 1.5X TO 4X BASIC
*BLACK 211-220/468-472: 1.5X TO 4X BASIC
1-220 SER.1 ODDS 1:10 H, 1:20 R
253-472 SER.2 ODDS 1:1 MINI BOX, 1:36 R
1-220/253-472 PRINT RUN 225 #'d SETS
*BLACK AU 221-252: 1X TO 2.5X BASIC AU
221-234 SER.1 ODDS 1:250 H, 1:291 R
235-252 SER.2 ODDS 1:12 MINI BOX, 1:508 R
221-252 PRINT RUN 200 SERIAL #'d SETS
233 Melky Cabrera FY AU 15.00 40.00
242 Justin Verlander FY AU 125.00 250.00
247 Nate McLouth FY AU 50.00 100.00

2005 Topps Chrome Gold Super-Fractors

1-220 SER.1 ODDS 1:1234 HOBBY
235-252 SER.2 AU ODDS 1:1397 MINI BOXES
253-472 SER.2 ODDS 1:56 BOX LOADER
STATED PRINT RUN 1 SERIAL #'d SET
NO PRICING DUE TO SCARCITY

2005 Topps Chrome Red X-Fractors

*RED XF 1-210/253-467: 6X TO 15X BASIC
1-220 SER.1 ODDS 1:50 HOBBY
221-234 SER.1 AU ODDS 1:779 HOBBY
235-252 SER.2 AU ODDS 1:91 MINI BOX
235-252 SER.2 AU ODDS 1:4042 RETAIL
253-472 SER.2 ODDS 1:3 BOX LOADER
STATED PRINT RUN 25 SERIAL #'d SETS
211-252/468-472 NO PRICING AVAILABLE
360 Barry Bonds 30.00 80.00

2005 Topps Chrome Refractors

*REF 1-210/253-467: 1X TO 2.5X BASIC
*REF 211-220/468-472: 1X TO 2.5X BASIC
1-220 SER.1 ODDS 1:6 H, 1:4 R
253-472 SER.2 ODDS 2 PER MINI BOX, 1:5 R
*REF AU 221-252: .5X TO 1.2X BASIC AU
221-234 SER.1 AU ODDS 1:100 H, 1:118 R
235-252 SER.2 AU ODDS 1:5 MINI BOXES
235-252 SER.2 AU ODDS 1:199 RETAIL
221-252 PRINT RUN 500 SERIAL #'d SETS
233 Melky Cabrera FY AU 10.00 25.00
242 Justin Verlander FY AU 75.00 150.00
247 Nate McLouth FY AU 15.00 40.00

2005 Topps Chrome A-Rod Throwbacks

COMPLETE SET (4) 3.00 8.00
COMMON CARD (1-4) 1.25 3.00
SER.2 ODDS 2 PER MINI BOX, 1:5 R
*BLACK REF: 2X TO 5X BASIC
BLACK REF SER.2 ODDS 1:14 BOX LOADER
BLACK REF PRINT RUN 225 #'d SETS
GOLD SUPER SER.2 ODDS 1:2968 BOX LDR
GOLD SUPER PRINT RUN 1 #'d SET
NO GOLD SUPER PRICING AVAILABLE
*RED XF: 6X TO 15X BASIC
RED XF SER.2 ODDS 1:124 BOX LOADER
RED XF PRINT RUN 25 #'d SETS
*REFRACTOR: 1X TO 2.5X BASIC
REFRACTOR SER.2 ODDS 1:3 BOX LOADER
1 Alex Rodriguez 1994 1.25 3.00
2 Alex Rodriguez 1995 1.25 3.00
3 Alex Rodriguez 1996 1.25 3.00
4 Alex Rodriguez 1997 1.25 3.00

2005 Topps Chrome Dem Bums Autographs

SERIES 1 ODDS 1:1816 H, 1:7270 R
STATED PRINT RUN 50 SETS
CARDS ARE NOT SERIAL-NUMBERED
PRINT RUN INFO PROVIDED BY TOPPS
CE Carl Erskine 30.00 60.00
CL Clem Labine 30.00 60.00
DS Duke Snider 50.00 100.00
DZ Don Zimmer 30.00 60.00
JP Johnny Podres 30.00 60.00

2005 Topps Chrome the Game Relics

SER.1 GROUP A ODDS 1:15 BOX-LOADER
SER.1 GROUP B ODDS 1:2 BOX-LOADER
AR Alex Rodriguez Bat A 6.00 15.00
AS Alfonso Soriano Uni B 3.00 8.00
JB Jeff Bagwell Uni B 4.00 10.00
JP Jorge Posada Uni B 4.00 10.00
JS John Smoltz Uni B 4.00 10.00
MP Mark Prior Jsy B 4.00 10.00
MPI Mike Piazza Jsy B 4.00 10.00
MY Michael Young Bat A 3.00 8.00
SS Sammy Sosa Jsy B 4.00 10.00
TH Torii Hunter Jsy B 3.00 8.00
WB Wade Boggs Uni B 4.00 10.00

2005 Topps Chrome the Game Patch Relics

*3-COLOR ADD: ADD 20% PREMIUM
SER.1 ODDS 1:8 BOX-LOADER
STATED PRINT RUN 70 SETS
CARDS ARE NOT SERIAL-NUMBERED
PRINT RUN INFO PROVIDED BY TOPPS
AD1 Adam Dunn Pose 6.00 15.00
AD2 Adam Dunn Fielding 6.00 15.00
AP Albert Pujols 20.00 50.00
AR Alex Rodriguez 15.00 40.00
BB Bret Boone 6.00 15.00
CJ Chipper Jones 10.00 25.00
CS C.C. Sabathia 6.00 15.00
DW Dontrelle Willis 6.00 15.00
FT Frank Thomas 10.00 25.00
HN Hideo Nomo 10.00 25.00
JB Jeff Bagwell 10.00 25.00
JBE Josh Beckett 6.00 15.00
KI Kazuhisa Ishii 6.00 15.00
KW Kerry Wood 6.00 15.00
LB Lance Berkman 6.00 15.00
ML Mike Lowell 6.00 15.00
MO Magglio Ordonez 6.00 15.00
MPI Mike Piazza 10.00 25.00
MT Mark Teixeira 10.00 25.00
PL Paul Lo Duca 6.00 15.00
PM Pedro Martinez 10.00 25.00
SS Sammy Sosa 10.00 25.00
TG Troy Glaus 6.00 15.00
TH Todd Helton 10.00 25.00

2005 Topps Chrome Update

This 237-card set was released in January, 2006. This set was issued in four-card hobby and retail packs with an $3 SRP which came 24 packs per retail box with 20 retail boxes per case. The hobby boxes are actually two 10-count boxes which come eight full (or 16 mini) boxes to a case. Cards numbered 1-85 feature players who switched teams from when their regular Chrome card was printed. Cards numbered 86-105 feature leading prospects while cards numbered 106 through 216 feature players with their first year on Topps cards. Cards numbered 216 through 220 feature players who accomplished important feats during the 2005 season. Cards numbered 221 through 237 feature signed Rookie Cards. Those cards were inserted at differing odds depending on whether the player was a group A or a group B autograph.

COMPLETE SET (237) 200.00 300.00
COMP.SET w/o SP's (220) 40.00 80.00
COM (1-85/216-220) .30 .75
COMMON (86-105) .30 .75
COM (14/65/106-215) .30 .75
COMMON (196-215) .75 2.00
SEMIS 196-215 1.25 3.00
UNLISTED 196-215 2.00 5.00
COMMON AU (221-237) 4.00 10.00
221-237 GROUP A ODDS 1:25 H, 1:49 R
221-237 GROUP B ODDS 1:29 H, 1:57 R
1-220 PLATE ODDS 1:347 H
221-237 PLATE AU ODDS 1:4857 H
PLATE PRINT RUN 1 SET PER COLOR
BLACK-CYAN-MAGENTA-YELLOW ISSUED
NO PLATE PRICING DUE TO SCARCITY
1 Sammy Sosa .75 2.00
2 Jeff Francoeur .75 2.00
3 Tony Clark .30 .75
4 Michael Tucker .30 .75
5 Mike Matheny .30 .75
6 Eric Young .30 .75

7 Jose Valentin .30 .75
8 Matt Lawton .30 .75
9 Juan Rivera .30 .75
10 Shawn Green .30 .75
11 Aaron Boone .30 .75
12 Woody Williams .30 .75
13 Brad Wilkerson .30 .75
14 Anthony Reyes RC .50 1.25
15 Gustavo Chacin .30 .75
16 Michael Restovich .30 .75
17 Humberto Quintero .30 .75
18 Matt Ginter .30 .75
19 Scott Podsednik .30 .75
20 Byung-Hyun Kim .30 .75
21 Orlando Hernandez .30 .75
22 Mark Grudzielanek .30 .75
23 Jody Gerut .30 .75
24 Adrian Beltre .30 .75
25 Scott Schoeneweis .30 .75
26 Marlon Anderson .30 .75
27 Jason Vargas .30 .75
28 Claudio Vargas .30 .75
29 Jason Kendall .30 .75
30 Aaron Small .30 .75
31 Juan Cruz .30 .75
32 Placido Polanco .30 .75
33 Jorge Sosa .30 .75
34 John Olerud .30 .75
35 Ryan Langerhans .30 .75
36 Randy Winn .30 .75
37 Zach Duke .30 .75
38 Garrett Atkins .30 .75
39 Al Leiter .30 .75
40 Shawn Chacon .30 .75
41 Mark DeRosa .30 .75
42 Miguel Ojeda .30 .75
43 A.J. Pierzynski .30 .75
44 Carlos Lee .30 .75
45 LaTroy Hawkins .30 .75
46 Nick Green .30 .75
47 Shawn Estes .30 .75
48 Eli Marrero .30 .75
49 Jeff Kent .30 .75
50 Joe Randa .30 .75
51 Jose Hernandez .30 .75
52 Joe Blanton .30 .75
53 Huston Street .30 .75
54 Marlon Byrd .30 .75
55 Alex Sanchez .30 .75
56 Livan Hernandez .30 .75
57 Chris Young .50 1.25
58 Brad Eldred .30 .75
59 Terrence Long .30 .75
60 Phil Nevin .30 .75
61 Kyle Farnsworth .30 .75
62 Jon Lieber .30 .75
63 Antonio Alfonseca .30 .75
64 Tony Graffanino .30 .75
65 Tadahito Iguchi RC .50 1.25
66 Brad Thompson .30 .75
67 Jose Vidro .30 .75
68 Jason Phillips .30 .75
69 Carl Pavano .30 .75
70 Pokey Reese .30 .75
71 Jerome Williams .30 .75
72 Kazuhisa Ishii .30 .75
73 Felix Hernandez 1.25 3.00
74 Edgar Renteria .30 .75
75 Mike Myers .30 .75
76 Jeff Cirillo .30 .75
77 Endy Chavez .30 .75
78 Jose Guillen .30 .75
79 Ugueth Urbina .30 .75
80 Zach Day .30 .75
81 Javier Vazquez .30 .75
82 Willy Taveras .30 .75
83 Mark Mulder .30 .75
84 Vinny Castilla .30 .75
85 Russ Adams .30 .75
86 Homer Bailey PROS .30 .75
87 Ervin Santana PROS .30 .75
88 Bill Bray PROS .30 .75
89 Thomas Diamond PROS .30 .75
90 Trevor Plouffe PROS .30 .75
91 James Houser PROS .30 .75
92 Jake Stevens PROS .30 .75
93 Anthony Whittington PROS .30 .75
94 Philip Hughes PROS .50 1.25
95 Greg Golson PROS .30 .75
96 Paul Maholm PROS .30 .75
97 Carlos Quentin PROS .50 1.25
98 Dan Johnson PROS .30 .75
99 Mark Rogers PROS .30 .75
100 Neil Walker PROS .30 .75
101 Omar Quintanilla PROS .30 .75
102 Blake DeWitt PROS .50 1.25
103 Taylor Tankersley PROS .30 .75
104 David Murphy PROS .50 1.25
105 Chris Lambert PROS .30 .75
106 Drew Anderson FY RC .30 .75
107 Luis Hernandez FY RC .30 .75
108 Jim Burt FY RC .30 .75
109 Mike Morse FY RC .75 2.00
110 Elliot Johnson FY RC .30 .75
111 C.J. Smith FY RC .30 .75
112 Casey McGehee FY RC 1.00 2.50
113 Brian Miller FY RC .30 .75
114 Chris Vines FY RC .30 .75
115 D.J. Houlton FY RC .30 .75
116 Chuck Tiffany FY RC .75 2.00
117 Humberto Sanchez FY RC .50 1.25
118 Baltazar Lopez FY RC .30 .75
119 Russ Martin FY RC 1.25 3.00
120 Dana Eveland FY RC .30 .75
121 Johan Silva FY RC .30 .75
122 Adam Harben FY RC .30 .75
123 Brian Bannister FY RC .50 1.25
124 Adam Boeve FY RC .30 .75
125 Thomas Oldham FY RC .30 .75
126 Cody Haerther FY RC .30 .75
127 Dan Santin FY RC .30 .75
128 Daniel Haigwood FY RC .30 .75
129 Craig Tatum FY RC .30 .75
130 Martin Prado FY RC 2.00 5.00
131 Errol Simonitsch FY RC .30 .75
132 Lorenzo Scott FY RC .30 .75
133 Hayden Penn FY RC .30 .75
134 Heath Totten FY RC .30 .75
135 Nick Masset FY RC .30 .75
136 Pedro Lopez FY RC .30 .75
137 Ben Harrison FY .30 .75
138 Mike Spidale FY RC .30 .75
139 Jeremy Harts FY RC .30 .75
140 Danny Zell FY RC .30 .75
141 Kevin Collins FY RC .30 .75
142 Tony Arnerich FY RC .30 .75
143 Matt Albers FY RC .30 .75
144 Ricky Barrett FY RC .30 .75
145 Hernan Iribarren FY RC .30 .75
146 Sean Tracey FY RC .30 .75
147 Jerry Owens FY RC .30 .75
148 Steve Nelson FY RC .30 .75
149 Brandon McCarthy FY RC .50 1.25
150 David Shepard FY RC .30 .75
151 Steven Bondurant FY RC .30 .75
152 Billy Sadler FY RC .30 .75
153 Ryan Feierabend FY RC .30 .75
154 Stuart Pomeranz FY RC .30 .75
155 Shaun Marcum FY .75 2.00
156 Erik Schindewolf FY RC .30 .75
157 Stefan Bailie FY RC .30 .75
158 Mike Esposito FY RC UER .30 .75
Front photo is of a Kansas City Royal
159 Buck Coats FY RC .30 .75
160 Andy Sides FY RC .30 .75
161 Micah Schnurstein FY RC .30 .75
162 Jesse Gutierrez FY RC .30 .75
163 Jake Postlewait FY RC .30 .75
164 Willy Mota FY RC .30 .75
165 Ryan Speier FY RC .30 .75
166 Frank Mata FY RC .30 .75
167 Jair Jurrjens FY RC 1.50 4.00
168 Nick Touchstone FY RC .30 .75
169 Matthew Kemp FY RC 4.00 10.00
170 Vinny Rottino FY RC .30 .75
171 J.B. Thurmond FY RC .30 .75
172 Kelvin Pichardo FY RC .30 .75
173 Scott Mitchinson FY RC .30 .75
174 Darwinson Salazar FY RC .30 .75
175 George Kottaras FY RC .50 1.25
176 Kenny Durost FY RC .30 .75
177 Jonathan Sanchez FY RC 1.25 3.00
178 Brandon Moorhead FY RC .30 .75
179 Kennard Bibbs FY RC .30 .75
180 David Gassner FY RC .30 .75
181 Micah Furtado FY RC .30 .75
182 Ismael Ramirez FY RC .30 .75
183 Carlos Gonzalez FY RC 3.00 8.00
184 Brandon Sing FY RC .30 .75
185 Jason Motte FY RC .50 1.25
186 Chuck James FY RC .75 2.00
187 Andy Santana FY RC .30 .75
188 Manny Parra FY RC .75 2.00
189 Chris B.Young FY RC 1.25 3.00
190 Juan Senreiso FY RC .30 .75
191 Franklin Morales FY RC .50 1.25
192 Jared Gothreaux FY RC .30 .75
193 Jayce Tingler FY RC .30 .75
194 Matt Brown FY RC .30 .75
195 Frank Diaz FY RC .30 .75
196 Stephen Drew FY RC 4.00 10.00
197 Jered Weaver FY RC 3.00 8.00
198 Ryan Braun FY RC 8.00 20.00
199 John Mayberry Jr. FY RC 2.00 5.00
200 Aaron Thompson FY RC 1.25 3.00
201 Ben Copeland FY RC .75 2.00
202 Jacoby Ellsbury FY RC 5.00 12.00
203 Garrett Olson FY RC .75 2.00
204 Cliff Pennington FY RC .75 2.00
205 Colby Rasmus FY RC 4.00 10.00
206 Chris Volstad FY RC 2.00 5.00
207 Ricky Romero FY RC 1.25 3.00
208 Ryan Zimmerman FY RC 6.00 15.00
209 C.J. Henry FY RC 1.25 3.00
210 Nelson Cruz FY RC 3.00 8.00
211 Josh Wall FY RC 1.25 3.00
212 Nick Webber FY RC .75 2.00
213 Paul Kelly FY RC .75 2.00
214 Kyle Winters FY RC .75 2.00
215 Mitch Boggs FY RC .75 2.00
216 Craig Biggio HL .50 1.25
217 Greg Maddux HL 1.25 3.00
218 Bobby Abreu HL .30 .75
219 Alex Rodriguez HL 1.25 3.00
220 Trevor Hoffman HL .50 1.25
221 Trevor Bell FY AU A RC 6.00 15.00
222 Jay Bruce FY AU A RC 30.00 60.00
223 Travis Buck FY AU B RC 6.00 15.00
224 Cesar Carrillo FY AU B RC 6.00 15.00
225 Mike Costanzo FY AU A RC 8.00 20.00
226 Brent Cox FY AU A RC 4.00 10.00
227 Matt Garza FY AU A RC 10.00 25.00
228 Josh Geer FY AU A RC 4.00 10.00
229 Tyler Greene FY AU A RC 6.00 15.00
230 Eli Iorg FY AU A RC 4.00 10.00
231 Craig Italiano FY AU B RC 4.00 10.00
232 Beau Jones FY AU A RC 6.00 15.00
233 M.McCormick FY AU B RC 4.00 10.00
234 A.McCutchen FY AU B RC 20.00 50.00
235 Micah Owings FY AU B RC 8.00 20.00
236 Cesar Ramos FY AU B RC 4.00 10.00
237 Chaz Roe FY AU A RC 4.00 10.00

2005 Topps Chrome Update Refractors

*REF 1-85: 1.25X TO 3X BASIC
*REF 86-105: 1X TO 2.5X BASIC
*REF 14/65/106-215: 1X TO 2.5X BASIC
*REF 216-220: 2X TO 5X BASIC
1-220 ODDS 1:5 HOBBY, 1:5 RETAIL
*REF AU 221-237: .6X TO 1.5X BASIC AU
221-237 AU ODDS 1:53 H, 1:115 R
221-237 AU PRINT RUN 500 #'d SETS
198 Ryan Braun FY 30.00 60.00
222 Jay Bruce FY AU 50.00 100.00
223 Travis Buck FY AU 12.50 30.00
227 Matt Garza FY AU 15.00 40.00

2005 Topps Chrome Update Black Refractors

There have been several copies of card number 235 Micah Owings in existence that does not have the serial number on back. Furthermore, the backs are coated with an extra amount of gloss. The back also features "Black Refractor" written over what seems to be the text "Refractor". This is considered to have been a production error and recorded as card number 235B. There is no information on the print run on this variation.

*BLACK 1-85: 2X TO 5X BASIC
*BLACK 86-105: 2X TO 5X BASIC
*BLACK 14/65/106-215: 1.5X TO 4X BASIC
*BLACK 216-220: 2.5X TO 6X BASIC
1-220 ODDS 1:10 HOBBY, 1:19 RETAIL
1-220 PRINT RUN 250 #'d SETS
*BLACK AU 221-237: 1X TO 2.5X BASIC AU
221-237 AU ODDS 1:140 H, 1:279 R
221-237 AU PRINT RUN 200 #'d SETS
183 Carlos Gonzalez FY 40.00 80.00
198 Ryan Braun FY 50.00 100.00
222 Jay Bruce FY AU 125.00 250.00
223 Travis Buck FY AU 30.00 60.00
227 Matt Garza FY AU 20.00 50.00
235A Micah Owings FY AU 40.00 80.00
235B Micah Owings FY AU
No Serial Number

2005 Topps Chrome Update Gold Super-Fractors

1-220 ODDS 1:1482 HOBBY
221-237 AU ODDS 1:19,730 HOBBY
STATED PRINT RUN 1 SERIAL #'d SET
NO PRICING DUE TO SCARCITY

2005 Topps Chrome Update Red X-Fractors

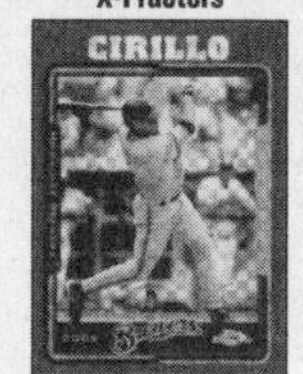

*RED 1-85: 4X TO 10X BASIC
*RED 86-105: 4X TO 10X BASIC
*RED 14/65/106-215: 5X TO 12X BASIC
*RED 216-220: 5X TO 12X BASIC
1-220 ODDS 1:5 HOBBY
1-220 PRINT RUN 65 #'d SETS
221-237 AU ODDS 1:766 HOBBY
221-237 AU PRINT RUN 25 #'d SETS
221-237 NO PRICING DUE TO SCARCITY
183 Carlos Gonzalez FY 100.00 175.00
198 Ryan Braun FY 100.00 200.00

2005 Topps Chrome Update Barry Bonds Home Run History

COMPLETE SET (29) 20.00 50.00
COMPLETE SERIES 1 (15) 12.50 30.00
COMPLETE SERIES 2 (14) 8.00 20.00
COMMON CARD 1.25 3.00
1-350 ODDS 1:12 HOBBY, 1:23 RETAIL
375-700 ODDS 1:6 HOBBY, 1:23 RETAIL
1-350 PLATE ODDS 1:347 H
375-700 PLATE ODDS 1:300 BOX LDR
PLATE PRINT RUN 1 SET PER COLOR
BLACK-CYAN-MAGENTA-YELLOW ISSUED
*REF: 1.25X TO 3X BASIC
1-350 REF ODDS 1:71 H, 1:141 R
375-700 REF ODDS 1:70 H, 1:350 R
375-700 REF PRINT RUN 500 #'d SETS
*BLACK REF: 2X TO 5X BASIC
1-350 BLACK REF.ODDS 1:178 H, 1:365 R
375-700 BLACK REF.ODDS 1:175 H, 1:950 R
BLACK REF.PRINT RUN 200 #'d SETS
*BLUE: 4X TO 10X BASIC
375-700 BLUE REF ODDS 1:300 RETAIL
BLUE REF.PRINT RUN 100 #'d SETS
1-350 GOLD SUPER ODDS 1:22,548 H
375-700 GOLD SUP.ODDS 1:1234 BOX LDR
GOLD SUPER.PRINT RUN 1 #'d SET
NO GOLD SUP.PRICING DUE TO SCARCITY
*RED X-F: 6X TO 15X BASIC
1-350 RED X-F ODDS 1:872 H
375-700 RED X-F ODDS 1:48 BOX LDR
RED X-F PRINT RUN 25 #'d SETS
1-350 ISSUED IN '05 CHROME UPDATE
375-700 ISSUED IN '06 CHROME

2006 Topps Chrome

This 355-card set was released in July, 2006. In a change from previous years, this chrome set was issued all in one series. The set was issued in four-card packs with an $3 SRP and those packs came 24 to a box and 10 boxes to a case. The first 252 cards in this set feature veterans while cards numbered 253-275 feature Award Winners, 276-330 feature rookies and 331-354 feature signed rookies. Card number 285 Kenji Johjima also comes in a signed version. The overall odds of securing a signed rookie card was stated to be one in fifteen hobby packs.

COMP.SET w/o AU's (330) 40.00 80.00
COMMON CARD (1-252) .25 .60
COMMON CARD (253-275) .15 .40
COMMON ROOKIE (276-330) .40 1.00
COMMON AUTO (285b/331-354) 4.00 10.00
AU 331-354 ODDS 1:15 HOBBY
JOHJIMA AU ODDS 1:1650 HOBBY
1-330 PLATES 1:25 HOBBY BOX LDR
331-354 AU PLATES 1:324 HOBBY BOX LDR
PLATE PRINT RUN 1 SET PER COLOR
BLACK-CYAN-MAGENTA-YELLOW ISSUED
NO PLATE PRICING DUE TO SCARCITY
1 Alex Rodriguez 1.00 2.50
2 Garrett Atkins .25 .60
3 Carl Crawford .40 1.00
4 Clint Barmes .25 .60
5 Tadahito Iguchi .25 .60
6 Brian Roberts .25 .60
7 Mickey Mantle UER 2.00 5.00
Distance of 1953 homer in cartoon is wrong
Highest seasonal home run total noted for wrong year
8 David Wright 1.00 2.50
9 Jeremy Reed .25 .60
10 Bobby Abreu .25 .60
11 Lance Berkman .40 1.00
12 Jonny Gomes .25 .60
13 Jason Marquis .25 .60
14 Chipper Jones .60 1.50
15 Jon Garland .25 .60
16 Brad Wilkerson .25 .60
17 Rickie Weeks .40 1.00
18 Jorge Posada .40 1.00
19 Greg Maddux 1.00 2.50
20 Jeff Francis .25 .60
21 Felipe Lopez .25 .60
22 Dan Johnson .25 .60
23 Manny Ramirez .60 1.50
24 Joe Mauer .60 1.50
25 Randy Winn .25 .60
26 Pedro Feliz .25 .60
27 Kenny Rogers .25 .60
28 Rocco Baldelli .25 .60
29 Nomar Garciaparra .60 1.50
30 Carlos Lee .25 .60
31 Tom Glavine .40 1.00
32 Craig Biggio .40 1.00
33 Steve Finley .25 .60
34 Eric Gagne .25 .60
35 Dallas McPherson .25 .60
36 Mark Kotsay .25 .60
37 Kerry Wood .25 .60
38 Huston Street .25 .60
39 Hank Blalock .25 .60
40 Brad Radke .25 .60
41 Chien-Ming Wang .40 1.00
42 Mark Buehrle .40 1.00
43 Andy Pettitte .40 1.00
44 Bernie Williams .40 1.00
45 Victor Martinez .40 1.00
46 Darin Erstad .25 .60
47 Gustavo Chacin .25 .60
48 Carlos Guillen .25 .60
49 Lyle Overbay .25 .60
50 Barry Bonds 1.25 3.00
51 Nook Logan .25 .60
52 Mark Teahen .25 .60
53 Mike Lamb .25 .60
54 Jayson Werth .40 1.00
55 Mariano Rivera .60 1.50
56 Julio Lugo .25 .60
57 Adam Dunn .40 1.00
58 Troy Percival .25 .60
59 Chad Tracy .25 .60
60 Edgar Renteria .25 .60
61 Jason Giambi .25 .60
62 Justin Morneau .60 1.50
63 Carlos Delgado .25 .60
64 John Buck .25 .60
65 Shannon Stewart .25 .60
66 Mike Cameron .25 .60
67 Richie Sexson .25 .60
68 Russ Adams .25 .60
69 Josh Beckett .40 1.00
70 Ryan Freel .25 .60
71 Victor Zambrano .25 .60
72 Ronnie Belliard .25 .60
73 Brian Giles .25 .60
74 Randy Wolf .25 .60
75 Robinson Cano .60 1.50
76 Joe Blanton .25 .60
77 Esteban Loaiza .25 .60
78 Troy Glaus .25 .60
79 Matt Clement .25 .60
80 Geoff Jenkins .25 .60
81 Roy Oswalt .40 1.00
82 A.J. Pierzynski .25 .60
83 Pedro Martinez .40 1.00
84 Roger Clemens * .75 2.00
85 Jack Wilson .25 .60
86 Mike Piazza .60 1.50
87 Paul Lo Duca .25 .60
88 Jeff Bagwell .40 1.00
89 Carlos Zambrano .40 1.00
90 Brandon Claussen .25 .60
91 Travis Hafner .25 .60
92 Chris Shelton .25 .60
93 Rafael Furcal .25 .60
94 Frank Thomas .60 1.50
95 Noah Lowry .25 .60
96 Jhonny Peralta .25 .60
97 Vernon Wells .25 .60
98 Jorge Cantu .25 .60
99 Willy Taveras .25 .60
100 Ivan Rodriguez .40 1.00
101 Jose Reyes .40 1.00
102 Barry Zito .25 .60
103 Mark Teixeira .60 1.50
104 Chone Figgins .25 .60
105 Todd Helton .40 1.00
106 Tim Wakefield .25 .60
107 Mike Maroth .25 .60
108 Johnny Damon .40 1.00
109 David DeJesus .25 .60
110 Ryan Klesko .25 .60
111 Nick Johnson .25 .60
112 Freddy Garcia .25 .60
113 Torii Hunter .25 .60
114 Mike Sweeney .25 .60
115 Scott Rolen .40 1.00
116 Jim Thome .40 1.00
117 Adam Kennedy .25 .60
118 Albert Pujols 1.50 4.00
119 Kazuo Matsui .25 .60
120 Zack Greinke .40 1.00
121 Jimmy Rollins .40 1.00
122 Edgardo Alfonzo .25 .60
123 Billy Wagner .25 .60
124 B.J. Ryan .25 .60
125 Orlando Hudson .25 .60
126 Preston Wilson .25 .60
127 Melvin Mora .25 .60
128 Alfonso Soriano .40 1.00
129 Javy Lopez .25 .60
130 Wilson Betemit .25 .60
131 Garret Anderson .25 .60
132 Jason Bay .25 .60
133 Adam LaRoche .25 .60
134 C.C. Sabathia .40 1.00
135 Bartolo Colon .25 .60
136 Ichiro Suzuki 1.00 2.50
137 Jim Edmonds .40 1.00
138 David Eckstein .25 .60
139 Cristian Guzman .25 .60
140 Jeff Kent .25 .60
141 Chris Capuano .25 .60
142 Cliff Floyd .25 .60
143 Zach Duke .25 .60
144 Matt Morris .25 .60
145 Jose Vidro .25 .60
146 David Wells .25 .60
147 John Smoltz .60 1.50
148 Felix Hernandez .60 1.50
149 Orlando Cabrera .25 .60
150 Mark Prior .40 1.00
151 Ted Lilly .25 .60
152 Michael Young .40 1.00
153 Livan Hernandez .25 .60
154 Yadier Molina .40 1.00
155 Eric Chavez .25 .60
156 Miguel Batista .25 .60
157 Ben Sheets .25 .60
158 Oliver Perez .25 .60
159 Doug Davis .25 .60
160 Andruw Jones .25 .60
161 Hideki Matsui .60 1.50
162 Reggie Sanders .25 .60
163 Joe Nathan .25 .60
164 John Lackey .25 .60
165 Matt Murton .25 .60
166 Grady Sizemore .40 1.00
167 Brad Thompson .25 .60
168 Kevin Millwood .25 .60
169 Orlando Hernandez .25 .60
170 Mark Mulder .25 .60
171 Chase Utley .60 1.50
172 Moises Alou .25 .60
173 Wily Mo Pena .25 .60
174 Brian McCann .25 .60
175 Jermaine Dye .25 .60
176 Ryan Madson .25 .60
177 Aramis Ramirez .25 .60
178 Khalil Greene .25 .60
179 Mike Hampton .25 .60
180 Mike Mussina .40 1.00
181 Rich Harden .25 .60
182 Woody Williams .25 .60
183 Chris Carpenter .60 1.50
184 Brady Clark .25 .60
185 Luis Gonzalez .25 .60
186 Raul Ibanez .40 1.00
187 Magglio Ordonez .40 1.00
188 Adrian Beltre .25 .60
189 Marcus Giles .25 .60
190 Odalis Perez .25 .60
191 Derek Jeter 1.50 4.00
192 Jason Schmidt .25 .60
193 Toby Hall .25 .60
194 Danny Haren .25 .60
195 Tim Hudson .40 1.00
196 Jake Peavy .25 .60
197 Casey Blake .25 .60
198 J.D. Drew .25 .60
199 Ervin Santana .25 .60
200 J.J. Hardy .25 .60
201 Austin Kearns .25 .60
202 Pat Burrell .25 .60
203 Jason Vargas .25 .60
204 Ryan Howard 1.00 2.50
205 Joe Crede .25 .60
206 Vladimir Guerrero .60 1.50
207 Roy Halladay .60 1.50
208 David Dellucci .25 .60
209 Brandon Webb .40 1.00
210 Ryan Church .25 .60
211 Miguel Tejada .40 1.00
212 Mark Loretta .25 .60
213 Kevin Youkilis .25 .60
214 Jon Lieber .25 .60
215 Miguel Cabrera .60 1.50
216 A.J. Burnett .40 1.00
217 David Bell .25 .60
218 Eric Byrnes .25 .60
219 Lance Niekro .25 .60
220 Shawn Green .25 .60
221 Ken Griffey Jr. 1.00 2.50
222 Johnny Estrada .25 .60
223 Omar Vizquel .40 1.00
224 Gary Sheffield .25 .60
225 Brad Halsey .25 .60
226 Aaron Cook .25 .60
227 David Ortiz .40 1.00
228 Scott Kazmir .40 1.00
229 Dustin McGowan .25 .60
230 Gregg Zaun .25 .60
231 Carlos Beltran .25 .60
232 Bob Wickman .25 .60
233 Brett Myers .25 .60
234 Casey Kotchman .25 .60
235 Jeff Francoeur .60 1.50
236 Paul Konerko .40 1.00
237 Juan Rivera .25 .60
238 Bobby Crosby .25 .60
239 Derrek Lee .25 .60
240 Curt Schilling .40 1.00
241 Jake Westbrook .25 .60
242 Dontrelle Willis .25 .60
243 Brad Lidge .25 .60
244 Randy Johnson .60 1.50
245 Nick Swisher .60 1.50
246 Johan Santana .60 1.50
247 Jeremy Bonderman .25 .60
248 Ramon Hernandez .25 .60
249 Mike Lowell .25 .60
250 Javier Vazquez .25 .60
251 Jose Contreras .25 .60
252 Aubrey Huff .25 .60
253 Kenny Rogers AW .15 .40
254 Mark Teixeira AW .40 1.00
255 Orlando Hudson AW .15 .40
256 Derek Jeter AW 1.00 2.50
257 Eric Chavez AW .15 .40
258 Torii Hunter AW .15 .40
259 Vernon Wells AW .15 .40
260 Ichiro Suzuki AW .60 1.50
261 Greg Maddux AW .60 1.50
262 Mike Matheny AW .15 .40
263 Derrek Lee AW .15 .40
264 Luis Castillo AW .15 .40
265 Omar Vizquel AW .25 .60
266 Mike Lowell AW .15 .40
267 Andruw Jones AW .15 .40
268 Jim Edmonds AW .25 .60
269 Bobby Abreu AW .15 .40
270 Bartolo Colon AW .15 .40
271 Chris Carpenter AW .40 1.00
272 Alex Rodriguez AW .60 1.50
273 Albert Pujols AW 1.00 2.50
274 Huston Street AW .15 .40
275 Ryan Howard AW .60 1.50
276 Chris Denorfia (RC) .40 1.00
277 John Van Benschoten (RC) .40 1.00
278 Russ Martin (RC) .60 1.50
279 Fausto Carmona (RC) .40 1.00
280 Freddie Bynum (RC) .40 1.00
281 Kelly Shoppach (RC) .40 1.00
282 Chris Demaria RC .40 1.00
283 Jordan Tata RC .40 1.00
284 Ryan Zimmerman (RC) 2.00 5.00
285a Kenji Johjima RC 1.00 2.50
285b Kenji Johjima AU 30.00 60.00
286 Ruddy Lugo (RC) .40 1.00
287 Tommy Murphy (RC) .40 1.00
288 Bobby Livingston (RC) .40 1.00
289 Anderson Hernandez (RC) .40 1.00
290 Brian Slocum (RC) .40 1.00
291 Sendy Rleal RC .40 1.00
292 Ryan Spilborghs (RC) .40 1.00
293 Brandon Fahey RC .40 1.00
294 Jason Kubel (RC) .40 1.00
295 James Loney (RC) .60 1.50
296 Jeremy Accardo RC .40 1.00
297 Fabio Castro RC .40 1.00
298 Matt Capps (RC) .40 1.00
299 Casey Janssen RC .40 1.00
300 Martin Prado (RC) .60 1.50
301 Ronny Paulino (RC) .40 1.00
302 Josh Barfield (RC) .40 1.00
303 Joel Zumaya (RC) 1.00 2.50
304 Matt Cain (RC) 1.00 2.50
305 Conor Jackson (RC) .60 1.50
306 Brian Anderson (RC) .40 1.00
307 Prince Fielder (RC) 1.50 4.00
308 Jeremy Hermida (RC) .40 1.00
309 Justin Verlander (RC) 3.00 8.00
310 Brian Bannister (RC) .40 1.00
311 Josh Willingham (RC) .40 1.00
312 John Rheinecker (RC) .40 1.00
313 Nick Markakis (RC) 1.00 2.50
314 Jonathan Papelbon (RC) 2.00 5.00
315 Mike Jacobs (RC) .40 1.00
316 Jose Capellan (RC) .40 1.00
317 Mike Napoli RC 1.25 3.00
318 Ricky Nolasco (RC) .40 1.00
319 Ben Johnson (RC) .40 1.00
320 Paul Maholm (RC) .40 1.00
321 Drew Meyer (RC) .40 1.00
322 Jeff Mathis (RC) .40 1.00
323 Fernando Nieve (RC) .40 1.00
324 John Koronka (RC) .40 1.00
325 Wil Nieves (RC) .40 1.00
326 Nate McLouth (RC) .40 1.00
327 Howie Kendrick (RC) 1.00 2.50
328 Sean Marshall (RC) .60 1.50
329 Brandon Watson (RC) .40 1.00
330 Skip Schumaker (RC) .40 1.00
331 Ryan Garko AU (RC) 4.00 10.00
332 Jason Bergmann AU RC 4.00 10.00
333 Chuck James AU (RC) 6.00 15.00
334 Adam Wainwright AU (RC) 10.00 25.00
335 Dan Ortmeier AU (RC) 4.00 10.00
336 Francisco Liriano AU (RC) 5.00 12.00
337 Craig Breslow AU RC 4.00 10.00
338 Darrell Rasner AU (RC) 4.00 10.00
339 Jason Botts AU (RC) 4.00 10.00
340 Ian Kinsler AU (RC) 10.00 25.00
341 Joey Devine AU RC 4.00 10.00
342 Miguel Perez AU (RC) 4.00 10.00
343 Scott Olsen AU (RC) 6.00 15.00
344 Tyler Johnson AU (RC) 4.00 10.00
345 Anthony Lerew AU (RC) 4.00 10.00
346 Nelson Cruz AU (RC) 10.00 25.00
347 Willie Eyre AU (RC) 4.00 10.00
348 Josh Johnson AU (RC) 12.50 30.00
349 Shaun Marcum AU (RC) 4.00 10.00
350 Dustin Nippert AU (RC) 4.00 10.00
351 Josh Wilson AU (RC) 4.00 10.00
352 Hanley Ramirez AU (RC) 10.00 25.00
353 Reggie Abercrombie AU (RC) 4.00 10.00
354 Dan Uggla AU (RC) 10.00 25.00

2006 Topps Chrome Refractors

*REF 1-275: .6X TO 1.5X BASIC
*REF 276-330: .6X TO 1.5X BASIC RC
1-330 STATED ODDS 1:4 H, 1:4 R
*REF AU 331-354: .5X TO 1.2X BASIC AU
331-354 AU ODDS 1:65 HOBBY
331-354 PRINT RUN 500 SERIAL #'d SETS
340 Ian Kinsler AU 25.00 60.00
346 Nelson Cruz AU 15.00 40.00
354 Dan Uggla AU 15.00 40.00

2006 Topps Chrome Black Refractors

*BLACK REF 1-275: 1.25X TO 3X BASIC
*BLACK REF 276-330: 1.25X TO 3X BASIC RC
1-330 STATED ODDS 1:6 H, 1:19 R
1-330 PRINT RUN 549 SERIAL #'d SETS
*BLK REF AU 331-354: .6X TO 1.5X BASIC AU
331-354 AU ODDS 1:162 HOBBY
331-354 PRINT RUN 200 SERIAL #'d SETS
340 Ian Kinsler AU 40.00 80.00
346 Nelson Cruz AU 20.00 50.00
348 Josh Johnson AU 60.00 120.00
354 Dan Uggla AU 20.00 50.00

2006 Topps Chrome Blue Refractors

*BLUE REF 1-275: 2X TO 5X BASIC
*BLUE REF 276-330: 2X TO 5X BASIC RC
STATED ODDS 1:8 RETAIL

2006 Topps Chrome Gold Super-Fractors

1-330 ODDS 1:97 HOBBY BOX LOADER
311-354 AU ODDS 1:1335 HOBBY BOX LDR
STATED PRINT RUN 1 SERIAL #'d SET
NO PRICING DUE TO SCARCITY

2006 Topps Chrome Red Refractors

*RED REF 1-275: 4X TO 10X BASIC
*RED REF 276-330: 3X TO 8X BASIC RC
1-330 ODDS 1:2 HOBBY BOX LOADER
1-330 PRINT RUN 90 SERIAL #'d SETS
331-354 AU ODDS 1:52 HOBBY BOX LOADER
331-354 AU PRINT RUN 25 SERIAL #'d SETS
NO AU PRICING DUE TO SCARCITY

2006 Topps Chrome X-Fractors

*X-FRAC: 1-275: 1.5X TO 4X BASIC
*X-FRAC: 276-330: 1.5X TO 4X BASIC RC
STATED ODDS 1:6 RETAIL

2006 Topps Chrome Declaration of Independence

COMPLETE SET (56)	60.00	120.00

STATED ODDS 1:7 H, 1:7 R
*REF: .5X TO 1.2X BASIC
REF ODDS 1:11 HOBBY, 1:44 RETAIL

AC Abraham Clark	1.25	3.00
AM Arthur Middleton	1.25	3.00
BF Benjamin Franklin	2.00	5.00
BG Button Gwinnett	1.25	3.00
BH Benjamin Harrison	1.25	3.00
BR Benjamin Rush	1.25	3.00
CB Carter Braxton	1.25	3.00
CC Charles Carroll	1.25	3.00
CR Caesar Rodney	1.25	3.00
EG Elbridge Gerry	1.25	3.00
ER Edward Rutledge	1.25	3.00
FH Francis Hopkinson	1.25	3.00
FL Francis Lewis	1.25	3.00
FLL Francis Lightfoot Lee	1.25	3.00
GC George Clymer	1.25	3.00
GR George Ross	1.25	3.00
GRE George Read	1.25	3.00
GT George Taylor	1.25	3.00
GW George Walton	1.25	3.00
GWY George Wythe	1.25	3.00
JA John Adams	1.25	3.00
JB Josiah Bartlett	1.25	3.00
JH John Hancock	1.25	3.00
JHA John Hart	1.25	3.00
JHE Joseph Hewes	1.25	3.00
JM John Morton	1.25	3.00
JP John Penn	1.25	3.00
JS James Smith	1.25	3.00
JW James Wilson	1.25	3.00
JWI John Witherspoon	1.25	3.00
LH Lyman Hall	1.25	3.00
LM Lewis Morris	1.25	3.00
MT Matthew Thornton	1.25	3.00
OW Oliver Wolcott	1.25	3.00
PL Philip Livingston	1.25	3.00
RHL Richard Henry Lee	1.25	3.00
RM Robert Morris	1.25	3.00
RS Roger Sherman	1.25	3.00
RST Richard Stockton	1.25	3.00
RTP Robert Treat Paine	1.25	3.00
SA Samuel Adams	1.25	3.00
SC Samuel Chase	1.25	3.00
SH Stephen Hopkins	1.25	3.00
SHU Samuel Huntington	1.25	3.00
TH Thomas Heyward Jr.	1.25	3.00
TJ Thomas Jefferson	2.00	5.00
TL Thomas Lynch Jr.	1.25	3.00
TM Thomas McKean	1.25	3.00
TN Thomas Nelson Jr.	1.25	3.00
TS Thomas Stone	1.25	3.00
WE William Ellery	1.25	3.00
WF William Floyd	1.25	3.00
WH William Hooper	1.25	3.00
WP William Paca	1.25	3.00
WW William Whipple	1.25	3.00
WWI William Williams	1.25	3.00
HDR1 Declaration of Independence	1.25	3.00

2006 Topps Chrome Mantle Home Run History

COMPLETE SET (59)	40.00	80.00
COMP.07TCH SET (13)	8.00	20.00
COMP.07TCH SET (29)	15.00	40.00
COMP.08TCH SET (17)	8.00	20.00
COMMON CARD (1-59)	1.00	2.50

STATED 06 ODDS 1:6 HOBBY, 1:23 RETAIL
STATED 07 ODDS 1:8 HOBBY, 1:24 RETAIL
06 PLATE ODDS 1:300 HOBBY BOX LOADER
07 PLATE ODDS 1:116 HOBBY BOX LOADER
08 PLATE ODDS 1:1971 HOBBY
PLATE PRINT RUN 1 SET PER COLOR
BLACK-CYAN-MAGENTA-YELLOW ISSUED
NO PLATE PRICING DUE TO SCARCITY
*REF: .75X TO 2X BASIC
06 REF ODDS 1:70 HOBBY, 1:350 RETAIL
07 REF ODDS 1:27 HOBBY, 1:71 RETAIL
08 REF ODDS 1:31 HOBBY
REF PRINT RUN 500 SERIAL #'d SETS
08 REF PRINT RUN 400 SER.#'d SETS
*BLACK REF: 2.5X TO 6X BASIC
BLACK ODDS 1:175 HOBBY, 1:950 RETAIL
BLACK PRINT RUN 200 SERIAL #'d SETS
*06-07 BLUE REF: 3X TO 8X BASIC
*08 BLUE REF: 2.5X TO 6X BASIC
06 BLUE ODDS 1:300 RETAIL
07 BLUE ODDS 1:72 RETAIL
06-07 BLUE PRINT RUN 100 SERIAL #'d SETS
08 BLUE PRINT RUN 200 SERIAL #'d SETS
*COPPER REF: 3X TO 8X BASIC
COPPER ODDS 1:117 HOBBY
STATED PRINT RUN 100 SERIAL #'d SETS
06 GOLD SF ODDS 1:1234 HOBBY BOX LDR
08 GOLD SF ODDS 1:7885 HOBBY
GOLD SF PRINT RUN 1 SERIAL #'d SET
NO GOLD SF PRICING DUE TO SCARCITY
*07 RED REF: 3X TO 8X BASIC
*08 RED REF: 12X TO 30X BASIC
08 RED REF ODDS 1:315 HOBBY
07 RED REF PRINT RUN 99 SER.#'d SETS
08 RED REF PRINT RUN 25 SER.#'d SETS
*RED XF: 12X TO 30X BASIC
RED XF ODDS 1:48 HOBBY BOX LOADER
RED XF PRINT RUN 25 SERIAL #'d SETS
*WHITE REF: 2.5X TO 6X BASIC
07 WHITE REF ODDS 1:67 HOBBY, 1:185 RETAIL
WHITE REF PRINT RUN 200 SER.#'d SETS

2006 Topps Chrome Rookie Logos

ONE PER UPDATE HOB.BOX LOADER
STATED PRINT RUN 599 SER.#'d SETS

1 Ben Zobrist	3.00	8.00
2 Shane Komine	2.00	5.00
3 Casey Janssen	1.25	3.00
4 Kevin Frandsen	1.25	3.00
5 John Rheinecker	1.25	3.00
6 Matt Kemp	6.00	15.00
7 Scott Mathieson	1.25	3.00
8 Jered Weaver	3.00	8.00
9 Joel Guzman	1.25	3.00
10 Anibal Sanchez	1.25	3.00
11 Melky Cabrera	2.00	5.00
12 Howie Kendrick	3.00	8.00
13 Cole Hamels	5.00	12.00
14 Willy Aybar	1.25	3.00
15 James Shields	4.00	10.00
16 Kevin Thompson	1.25	3.00
17 Jon Lester	5.00	12.00
18 Stephen Drew	3.00	8.00
19 Andre Ethier	5.00	12.00
20 Jordan Tata	1.25	3.00
21 Mike Napoli	4.00	10.00
22 Kason Gabbard	1.25	3.00
23 Lastings Milledge	1.25	3.00
24 Erick Aybar	1.25	3.00
25 Fausto Carmona	1.25	3.00
26 Russ Martin	2.00	5.00
27 David Pauley	1.25	3.00
28 Andy Marte	1.25	3.00
29 Carlos Quentin	2.00	5.00
30 Franklin Gutierrez	1.25	3.00
31 Taylor Buchholz	1.25	3.00
32 Josh Johnson	3.00	8.00
33 Chad Billingsley	2.00	5.00
34 Kendry Morales	3.00	8.00
35 Adam Loewen	1.25	3.00
36 Yusmeiro Petit	1.25	3.00
37 Matt Albers	1.25	3.00
38 John Maine	2.00	5.00
39 Josh Willingham	1.25	3.00
40 Taylor Tankersley	1.25	3.00
41 Pat Neshek	12.00	30.00
42 Francisco Rosario	1.25	3.00
43 Matt Smith	2.00	5.00
44 Jonathan Sanchez	3.00	8.00
45 Chris Demaria	1.25	3.00
46 Manuel Corpas	1.25	3.00
47 Kevin Reese	1.25	3.00
48 Brent Clevlen	2.00	5.00
49 Anderson Hernandez	1.25	3.00
50 Chris Roberson	1.25	3.00

2006 Topps Chrome Rookie Logos Refractors

STATED ODDS 1:25 UPD.HOB.BOX LDR
STATED PRINT RUN 25 SER. #'d SETS
NO PRICING DUE TO SCARCITY

2006 Topps Chrome United States Constitution

COMPLETE SET (42)	30.00	60.00

STATED ODDS 1:15 H, 1:15 R
*REF: .5X TO 1.2X BASIC
REF ODDS 1:9 HOBBY, 1:36 RETAIL

AB Abraham Baldwin	.75	2.00
AH Alexander Hamilton	.75	2.00
BF Benjamin Franklin	1.25	3.00
CCP Charles Cotesworth Pinckney	.75	2.00
CP Charles Pinckney	.75	2.00
DB David Brearly	.75	2.00
DC Daniel Carroll	.75	2.00
DJ Daniel of St. Thomas Jenifer	.75	2.00
GB Gunning Bedford Jr.	.75	2.00
GC George Clymer	.75	2.00
GM Gouverneur Morris	.75	2.00
GR George Read	.75	2.00
GW George Washington	1.25	3.00
HW Hugh Williamson	.75	2.00
JB John Blair	.75	2.00
JBR Jacob Broom	.75	2.00
JD Jonathan Dayton	.75	2.00
JDI John Dickinson	.75	2.00
JI Jared Ingersoll	.75	2.00
JL John Langdon	.75	2.00
JM James Madison	.75	2.00
JMC James McHenry	.75	2.00
JR John Rutledge	.75	2.00
JW James Wilson	.75	2.00
NG Nicholas Gilman	.75	2.00
NGO Nathaniel Gorham	.75	2.00
PB Pierce Butler	.75	2.00
RB Richard Bassett	.75	2.00
RDS Richard Dobbs Spaight	.75	2.00
RK Rufus King	.75	2.00
RM Robert Morris	.75	2.00
RS Roger Sherman	.75	2.00
TF Thomas Fitzsimons	.75	2.00
TM Thomas Mifflin	.75	2.00
WB William Blount	.75	2.00
WF William Few	.75	2.00
WJ William Samuel Johnson	.75	2.00
WL William Livingston	.75	2.00
WP William Paterson	.75	2.00
HDR1 United States Constitution	.75	2.00
HDR2	.75	2.00
HDR3	.75	2.00

2007 Topps Chrome

This 369-card set was released in July, 2007. The set was issued in both hobby and retail versions. The hobby packs consisted of four-card packs (with an $3 SRP) which came 24 packs to a box and 12 boxes to a case. Cards numbered 1-275 featured veterans while cards 276-330 featured rookies and cards 331-355 (and a featured signed Rookie Cards. The signed cards were inserted into packs at a stated rate of one in 16 hobby and one in 122 retail. In addition, the players in this set who were originally from Japan all were issued in American and Japanese versions and the Japanese cards were issued at a stated rate of one in 82 hobby packs.

COMP.SET w/o AU's (330)	40.00	80.00
COMMON CARD	.20	.50
COMMON ROOKIE	.40	1.00

JAPANESE VARIATION ODDS 1:82 H

COMMON AUTO	3.00	8.00

AUTO ODDS 1:16 HOBBY, 1:122 RETAIL
PRINT.PLATE ODDS 1:36 HOBBY BOX LDR
VAR.PLATES 1:1943 HOBBY BOX LDR
AU PLATES 1:343 HOBBY BOX LDR
PLATE PRINT RUN 1 SET PER COLOR
BLACK-CYAN-MAGENTA-YELLOW ISSUED
NO PLATE PRICING DUE TO SCARCITY
EXCHANGE DEADLINE 07/31/09

1 Nick Swisher	.50	1.25
2 Bobby Abreu	.20	.50
3 Edgar Renteria	.20	.50
4 Mickey Mantle	1.50	4.00
5 Preston Wilson	.20	.50
6 C.C. Sabathia	.30	.75
7 Julio Lugo	.20	.50
8 J.D. Drew	.20	.50
9 Jason Varitek	.50	1.25
10 Orlando Hernandez	.20	.50
11 Corey Patterson	.20	.50
12 Josh Bard	.20	.50
13 Gary Matthews	.20	.50
14 Jason Jennings	.20	.50
15 Bronson Arroyo	.20	.50
16 Andy Pettitte	.30	.75
17 Ervin Santana	.20	.50
18 Paul Konerko	.30	.75
19 Adam LaRoche	.20	.50
20 Jim.Edmonds	.30	.75
21 Derek Jeter	1.25	3.00
22 Aubrey Huff	.20	.50
23 Andre Ethier	.30	.75
24 Jeremy Sowers	.20	.50
25 Miguel Cabrera	.50	1.25
26 Carlos Lee	.20	.50
27 Mike Piazza	.50	1.25
28 Cole Hamels	.50	1.25
29 Mark Loretta	.20	.50
30 John Smoltz	.50	1.25
31 Dan Uggla	.30	.75
32 Lyle Overbay	.20	.50
33 Michael Barrett	.20	.50
34 Ivan Rodriguez	.30	.75
35 Jake Westbrook	.20	.50
36 Moises Alou	.20	.50
37 Jered Weaver	.30	.75
38 Lastings Milledge	.30	.75
39 Austin Kearns	.20	.50
40 Adam Loewen	.20	.50
41 Josh Barfield	.20	.50
42 Johan Santana	.50	1.25
43 Ian Kinsler	.30	.75
44 Mike Lowell	.20	.50
45 Scott Rolen	.30	.75
46 Chipper Jones	.50	1.25
47 Joe Crede	.20	.50
48 Rafael Furcal	.20	.50
49 Dave Bush	.20	.50
50 Marcus Giles	.20	.50
51 Joe Blanton	.20	.50
52 Dontrelle Willis	.20	.50
53 Scott Kazmir	.30	.75
54 Jeff Kent	.20	.50
55 Travis Hafner	.20	.50
56 Ryan Garko	.20	.50
57 Nick Markakis	.50	1.25
58 Michael Cuddyer	.20	.50
59 Jason Giambi	.20	.50
60 Chone Figgins	.20	.50
61 Carlos Delgado	.20	.50
62 Aramis Ramirez	.20	.50
63 Albert Pujols	1.25	3.00
64 Gary Sheffield	.20	.50
65 Adrian Gonzalez	.30	.75
66 Prince Fielder	.30	.75
67 Freddy Sanchez	.20	.50
68 Jack Wilson	.20	.50
69 Jake Peavy	.20	.50
70 Javier Vazquez	.20	.50
71 Todd Helton	.30	.75
72 Bill Hall	.20	.50
73 Jeremy Bonderman	.20	.50
74 Rocco Baldelli	.20	.50
75 Noah Lowry	.20	.50
76 Justin Verlander	.60	1.50
77 Mark Buehrle	.30	.75
78 Hank Blalock	.20	.50
79 Mark Teahen	.20	.50
80 Chien-Ming Wang	.30	.75
81 Roy Halladay	.50	1.25
82 Melvin Mora	.20	.50
83 Grady Sizemore	.30	.75
84 Matt Cain	.30	.75
85 Carl Crawford	.30	.75
86 Johnny Damon	.30	.75
87 Freddy Garcia	.20	.50
88 Ryan Shealy	.20	.50
89 Carlos Beltran	.20	.50
90 Chuck James	.20	.50
91 Ben Sheets	.20	.50
92 Mark Mulder	.20	.50
93 Carlos Quentin	.20	.50
94 Richie Sexson	.20	.50
95 Brian Schneider	.20	.50
96a Hideki Matsui	.50	1.25
96b Hideki Matsui Japanese	2.00	5.00
97 Robinson Tejeda	.20	.50
98 Scott Hatteberg	.20	.50
99 Jeff Francis	.20	.50
100 Robinson Cano	.50	1.25
101 Barry Zito	.20	.50
102 Reed Johnson	.20	.50
103 Chris Carpenter	.50	1.25
104 Chad Tracy	.20	.50
105 Anibal Sanchez	.20	.50
106 Brad Penny	.20	.50
107 David Wright	.75	2.00
108 Jimmy Rollins	.30	.75
109 Alfonso Soriano	.30	.75
110 Greg Maddux	.75	2.00
111 Curt Schilling	.30	.75
112 Stephen Drew	.20	.50
113 Matt Holliday	.50	1.25
114 Jorge Posada	.30	.75
115 Vladimir Guerrero	.50	1.25
116 Frank Thomas	.50	1.25
117 Jonathan Papelbon	.50	1.25
118 Manny Ramirez	.50	1.25
119 Magglio Ordonez	.30	.75
120 Joe Mauer	.50	1.25
121 Ryan Howard	.75	2.00
122 Chris Young	.20	.50
123 A.J. Burnett	.30	.75
124 Brian McCann	.20	.50
125 Juan Pierre	.20	.50
126 Jonny Gomes	.20	.50
127 Roger Clemens	.60	1.50
128 Chad Billingsley	.20	.50
129a Kenji Johjima	.50	1.25
129b Kenji Johjima Japanese	2.00	5.00
130 Brian Giles	.20	.50
131 Chase Utley	.50	1.25
132 Carl Pavano	.20	.50
133 Curtis Granderson	.30	.75
134 Sean Casey	.20	.50
135 Jon Garland	.20	.50
136 David Ortiz	.30	.75
137 Bobby Crosby	.20	.50
138 Conor Jackson	.20	.50
139 Tim Hudson	.30	.75
140 Rickie Weeks	.30	.75
141 Mark Prior	.30	.75
142 Ben Zobrist	.20	.50
143 Troy Glaus	.20	.50
144 Cliff Lee	.30	.75
145 Adrian Beltre	.20	.50
146 Endy Chavez	.20	.50
147 Ramon Hernandez	.20	.50
148 Chris Young	.20	.50
149 Jason Schmidt	.20	.50
150 Kevin Millwood	.20	.50
151 Placido Polanco	.20	.50
152 Torii Hunter	.20	.50
153 Roy Oswalt	.30	.75
154 Kelvim Escobar	.20	.50
155 Milton Bradley	.20	.50
156 Chris Capuano	.20	.50
157 Juan Encarnacion	.20	.50
158a Ichiro Suzuki	.75	2.00
158b Ichiro Suzuki Japanese	3.00	8.00
159 Matt Kemp	.30	.75
160 Matt Morris	.20	.50
161 Casey Blake	.20	.50
162 Josh Willingham	.20	.50
163 Nick Johnson	.20	.50
164 Khalil Greene	.20	.50
165 Tom Glavine	.30	.75
166 Jason Bay	.30	.75
167 Brandon Phillips	.20	.50
168 Jorge Cantu	.20	.50
169 Jeff Weaver	.20	.50
170 Melky Cabrera	.20	.50
171 Dan Haren	.20	.50
172 Jeff Francoeur	.50	1.25
173 Randy Wolf	.20	.50
174 Carlos Zambrano	.30	.75
175 Justin Morneau	.50	1.25
176 Takashi Saito	.20	.50
177 Victor Martinez	.30	.75
178 Felix Hernandez	.50	1.25
179 Paul LoDuca	.20	.50
180 Miguel Tejada	.30	.75
181 Mark Teixeira	.50	1.25
182 Pat Burrell	.20	.50
183 Mike Cameron	.20	.50
184 Josh Beckett	.30	.75
185 Francisco Liriano	.50	1.25
186 Ken Griffey Jr.	.75	2.00
187 Mike Mussina	.30	.75
188 Howie Kendrick	.20	.50
189 Ted Lilly	.20	.50
190 Mike Hampton	.20	.50
191 Jeff Suppan	.20	.50
192 Jose Reyes	.30	.75
193 Russell Martin	.20	.50
194 Jhonny Peralta	.20	.50
195 Raul Ibanez	.30	.75
196 Hanley Ramirez	.50	1.25
197 Kerry Wood	.20	.50
198 Gary Sheffield	.20	.50
199 David Dellucci	.20	.50
200 Xavier Nady	.20	.50
201 Michael Young	.30	.75
202 Kevin Youkilis	.20	.50
203 Aaron Harang	.20	.50
204 Matt Garza	.20	.50
205 Jim Thome	.30	.75
206 Jose Contreras	.20	.50
207 Tadahito Iguchi	.20	.50
208 Eric Chavez	.20	.50
209 Vernon Wells	.20	.50
210 Doug Davis	.20	.50
211 Andruw Jones	.20	.50
212 David Eckstein	.20	.50
213 J.J. Hardy	.20	.50
214 Orlando Hudson	.20	.50
215 Pedro Martinez	.30	.75
216 Brian Roberts	.20	.50
217 Brett Myers	.20	.50
218 Alex Rodriguez	.75	2.00
219 Kenny Rogers	.20	.50
220 Jason Kubel	.20	.50
221 Jermaine Dye	.20	.50
222 Bartolo Colon	.20	.50
223 Craig Biggio	.30	.75
224 Alex Rios	.30	.75
225 Adam Dunn	.30	.75
226 Anthony Reyes	.20	.50
227 Derrek Lee	.20	.50
228 Jeremy Hermida	.20	.50
229 Derek Lowe	.20	.50
230 Randy Winn	.20	.50
231 Brandon Webb	.30	.75
232 Jose Vidro	.20	.50
233 Erik Bedard	.20	.50
234 Jon Lieber	.20	.50
235 Wily Mo Pena	.20	.50
236 Kelly Johnson	.20	.50
237 David DeJesus	.20	.50
238 Andy Marte	.20	.50
239 Scott Olsen	.20	.50
240 Randy Johnson	.50	1.25
241 Nelson Cruz	.30	.75
242 Carlos Guillen	.20	.50
243 Brandon McCarthy	.20	.50
244 Garret Anderson	.20	.50
245 Mike Sweeney	.20	.50
246 Brian Bannister	.20	.50
247 Jose Guillen	.20	.50
248 Brad Wilkerson	.20	.50
249 Lance Berkman	.30	.75
250 Ryan Zimmerman	.30	.75
251 Garrett Atkins	.20	.50
252 Johan Santana	.50	1.25
253 Brandon Webb	.30	.75
254 Justin Verlander	.60	1.50
255 Hanley Ramirez	.50	1.25
256 Justin Morneau	.50	1.25
257 Ryan Howard	.75	2.00
258 Eric Chavez	.20	.50
259 Scott Rolen	.30	.75
260 Derek Jeter	1.25	3.00
261 Omar Vizquel	.30	.75
262 Mark Grudzielanek	.20	.50
263 Orlando Hudson	.20	.50
264 Mark Teixeira	.50	1.25
265 Albert Pujols	1.25	3.00
266 Ivan Rodriguez	.30	.75
267 Brad Ausmus	.20	.50
268 Torii Hunter	.20	.50
269 Mike Cameron	.20	.50
270 Ichiro Suzuki	.75	2.00
271 Carlos Beltran	.20	.50
272 Vernon Wells	.20	.50
273 Andruw Jones	.20	.50
274 Kenny Rogers	.20	.50
275 Greg Maddux	.75	2.00
276 Danny Putnam (RC)	.40	1.00
277 Chase Wright RC	1.00	2.50
278 Zach McClellan RC	.40	1.00
279 Jamie Vermilyea RC	.40	1.00
280 Felix Pie (RC)	.40	1.00
281 Phil Hughes (RC)	2.00	5.00
282 Jon Knott (RC)	.40	1.00
283 Micah Owings (RC)	.40	1.00
284 Devern Hansack RC	.40	1.00
285 Andy Cannizaro RC	.40	1.00
286 Lee Gardner (RC)	.40	1.00
287 Josh Hamilton (RC)	1.50	4.00
288a Angel Sanchez RC	.40	1.00
288b Angel Sanchez AU	3.00	8.00
289 J.D. Durbin (RC)	.40	1.00
290 Jaime Burke (RC)	.40	1.00
291 Joe Bisenius RC	.40	1.00
292 Rick Vanden Hurk RC	.40	1.00
293 Brian Barden RC	.40	1.00
294 Levale Speigner RC	.40	1.00
295 Kevin Cameron RC	.40	1.00
296 Don Kelly (RC)	.40	1.00
297a Hideki Okajima RC	2.00	5.00
297b Hideki Okajima Japanese	3.00	8.00
298 Andrew Miller RC	1.00	2.50
299 Delmon Young (RC)	.60	1.50
300 Vinny Rottino (RC)	.40	1.00
301 Philip Humber (RC)	.40	1.00
302 Drew Anderson RC	.40	1.00
303 Jerry Owens (RC)	.40	1.00
304 Jose Garcia RC	.40	1.00
305 Shane Youman RC	.40	1.00
306 Ryan Feierabend (RC)	.40	1.00
307 Mike Rabelo RC	.40	1.00
308 Josh Fields (RC)	.40	1.00
309 Jon Coutlangus (RC)	.40	1.00
310 Travis Buck (RC)	.40	1.00
311 Doug Slaten RC	.40	1.00
312 Ryan Braun RC	.40	1.00
313 Juan Salas (RC)	.40	1.00
314 Matt Lindstrom (RC)	.40	1.00
315 Cesar Jimenez RC	.40	1.00
316 Jay Marshall RC	.40	1.00
317 Jared Burton RC	.40	1.00
318 Juan Perez RC	.40	1.00
319 Elijah Dukes RC	.60	1.50
320 Juan Lara RC	.40	1.00
321 Justin Hampson (RC)	.40	1.00
322a Kei Igawa RC	1.00	2.50
322b Kei Igawa Japanese	2.00	5.00
323 Zack Segovia (RC)	.40	1.00
324 Alejandro De Aza RC	.60	1.50
325 Brandon Morrow RC	2.00	5.00
326 Gustavo Molina RC	.40	1.00
327 Joe Smith RC	.40	1.00
328 Jesus Flores RC	.40	1.00
329 Jeff Baker (RC)	.40	1.00
330a Daisuke Matsuzaka RC	4.00	10.00
330b Daisuke Matsuzaka Japanese	4.00	10.00
331 Troy Tulowitzki AU (RC)	10.00	25.00
332 John Danks AU RC	6.00	15.00
333 Kevin Kouzmanoff AU (RC)	3.00	8.00
334 David Murphy AU (RC)	3.00	8.00
335 Ryan Sweeney AU (RC)	3.00	8.00
336 Fred Lewis AU (RC)	4.00	10.00
337 Delwyn Young AU (RC)	3.00	8.00
338 Matt Chico AU (RC)	3.00	8.00
339 Miguel Montero AU (RC)	3.00	8.00
340 Shawn Riggans AU (RC)	3.00	8.00
341 Brian Stokes AU (RC)	3.00	8.00
342 Scott Moore AU (RC)	3.00	8.00
343 Adam Lind AU (RC)	4.00	10.00
344 Chris Narveson AU (RC)	3.00	8.00
345 Alex Gordon AU RC	8.00	20.00
346 Joaquin Arias AU (RC)	3.00	8.00
347 Brian Burres AU (RC)	3.00	8.00
348 Glen Perkins AU (RC)	3.00	8.00
349 Ubaldo Jimenez AU (RC)	10.00	25.00
350 Chris Stewart AU RC	3.00	8.00
351 Beltran Perez AU (RC)	3.00	8.00
352 Dennis Sarfate AU (RC)	3.00	8.00
353 Carlos Maldonado AU (RC)	3.00	8.00
354 Mitch Maier AU RC	3.00	8.00
355 Kory Casto AU (RC)	3.00	8.00
356 Juan Morillo AU (RC)	3.00	8.00
357 Hector Gimenez AU (RC)	3.00	8.00
358 Alexi Casilla AU RC	4.00	10.00
359 Michael Bourn AU (RC)	4.00	10.00
360 Sean Henn AU (RC)	3.00	8.00
361 Tim Gradoville AU RC	3.00	8.00
363 Oswaldo Navarro AU RC	3.00	8.00

2007 Topps Chrome Refractors

*REF: 1.2X TO 3X BASIC
REF ODDS 1:3 HOB,1:2 RET
*REF RC: .6X TO 1.5X BASIC RC
REF RC ODDS 1:3 HOB, 1:2 RET
*REF VAR: .5X TO 1.2X BASIC VARIATION
REF VAR ODDS 1:73 HOBBY
REF VAR PRINT RUN 500 SER.#'d SETS
*REF AU: .5X TO 1.2X BASIC AUTO
REF AU ODDS 1:71 HOB, 1:570 RET
REF AU PRINT RUN 500 SER.#'d SETS
EXCHANGE DEADLINE 07/31/09

349 Ubaldo Jimenez AU	12.50	30.00

2007 Topps Chrome Blue Refractors

*BLUE: 4X TO 10X BASIC
*BLUE RC: 2.5X TO 6X BASIC RC
STATED ODDS 1:6 RETAIL

2007 Topps Chrome Red Refractors

*RED REF: 4X TO 10X BASIC
*RED REF RC: 2.5X TO 6X BASIC RC
STATED ODDS 1:2 HOB.BOX LDR
STATED PRINT RUN 99 SER.#'d SETS
STATED VAR.ODDS 1:311 HOB.BOX LDR
STATED VAR.PRINT RUN 25 SER.#'d SETS
NO VARIATION PRICING AVAILABLE
STATED AU ODDS 1:55 HOB.BOX LDR
STATED AU PRINT RUN 25 SER.#'d SETS
NO AU PRICING AVAILABLE
EXCHANGE DEADLINE 07/31/09

2007 Topps Chrome White Refractors

*WHITE REF: 1.5X TO 4X BASIC
WHITE REF ODDS 1:6 HOB,1:23 RET
WHITE REF PRINT RUN 660 SER.#'d SETS
*WHITE REF RC: .75X TO 2X BASIC RC
WHITE REF RC ODDS 1:6 HOB, 1:23 RET
WHITE REF RC PRINT RUN 660 SER.#'d SETS
*WHITE REF VAR: .6X TO 1.5X BASIC VAR
WHITE REF VAR ODDS 1:932 HOBBY
WHITE REF VAR PRINT RUN 200 SER.#'d SETS
*WHITE REF AU: .75X TO 2X BASIC AUTO
WHITE REF AU ODDS 1:177 HOB, 1:1475 RET
WHITE REF AU PRINT RUN 200 SER.#'d SETS
EXCHANGE DEADLINE 07/31/09

297b Hideki Okajima Japanese	15.00	40.00
330b Daisuke Matsuzaka Japanese	15.00	40.00
349 Ubaldo Jimenez AU	20.00	50.00

2007 Topps Chrome SuperFractors

STATED ODDS 1:108 HOB.BOX LDR
STATED VAR.ODDS 1:7775 HOB.BOX LDR
STATED AU ODDS 1:1372 HOB.BOX LDR
STATED PRINT RUN 1 SER.#'d SET
NO PRICING DUE TO SCARCITY
EXCHANGE DEADLINE 07/31/09

2007 Topps Chrome X-Fractors

*X-F: 1.5X TO 4X BASIC
*X-F RC: 1.5X TO 4X BASIC RC
STATED ODDS 1:3 RETAIL

2007 Topps Chrome Generation Now

COMPLETE SET (41)	10.00	25.00
COMMON A.ETHIER	.75	2.00
COMMON R.HOWARD	1.25	3.00
COMMON N.MARKAKIS	.50	1.25
COMMON R.MARTIN	.30	.75
COMMON J.MORNEAU	.50	1.25
COMMON M.NAPOLI	.30	.75

COMMON H.RAMIREZ .50 1.25
COMMON N.SWISHER .30 .75
COMMON C.UTLEY .75 2.00
COMMON J.VERLANDER .75 2.00
COMMON C.WANG .75 2.00
COMMON JER.WEAVER .50 1.25
COMMON D.YOUNG .50 1.25
COMMON R.ZIMMERMAN .75 2.00
STATED ODDS 1:5 HOBBY,1:17 RETAIL
PLATE ODDS 1:116 HOB.BOXLOADER
PLATE PRINT RUN 1 SET PER COLOR
BLACK-CYAN-MAGENTA-YELLOW ISSUED
NO PLATE PRICING DUE TO SCARCITY
SUPERFRAC.PRINT RUN 1 SER.#'d SET
NO SUPERFRAC.PRICING DUE TO SCARCITY

2007 Topps Chrome Generation Now Refractors

*REF: 1X TO 2.5X BASIC
STATED ODDS 1:27 H, 1:71 R
STATED PRINT RUN 500 SER.#'d SETS

2007 Topps Chrome Generation Now Blue Refractors

*BLUE REF: 2.5X TO 6X BASIC
STATED ODDS 1:72 RETAIL
STATED PRINT RUN 100 SER.#'d SETS

2007 Topps Chrome Generation Now Red Refractors

*RED REF: 2.5X TO 6X BASIC
STATED ODDS
STATED PRINT RUN 99 SER.#'d SETS

2007 Topps Chrome Generation Now White Refractors

*WHITE REF: 1.25X TO 3X BASIC
STATED ODDS 1:67 HOBBY,1:185 RETAIL
STATED PRINT RUN 200 SER.#'d SETS

2007 Topps Chrome Mickey Mantle Story

COMMON MANTLE (1-40) .75 2.00
1-30 STATED ODDS 1:7 H, :23 R
46-55 STATED ODDS 1:20 HOBBY
1-30 PLATE ODDS 1:116 HOB.BOXLDR
46-55 PLATE ODDS 1:1971 HOBBY
PLATE PRINT RUN 1 SET PER COLOR
BLACK-CYAN-MAGENTA-YELLOW ISSUED
NO PLATE PRICING DUE TO SCARCITY
*REF: 1X TO 2.5X BASIC
1-30 REF.ODDS 1:27 H, 1:71 R
46-55 REF.ODDS 1:31 HOBBY
1-30 REF PRINT RUN 500 SER.#'d SETS
46-55 REF PRINT RUN 400 SER.#'d SETS
*07 BLUE REF: 2.5X TO 6X BASIC
*08 BLUE REF: 1.2X TO 3X BASIC
07 BLUE REF ODDS 1:72 RETAIL
07 BLUE REF PRINT RUN 100 SER.#'d SETS
08 BLUE REF PRINT RUN 200 SER.#'d SETS
*COPPER: 2.5X TO 6X BASIC
STATED ODDS 1:117 HOBBY
STATED PRINT RUN 100 SER.#'d SETS
*1-30 RED REF: 2.5X TO 6X BASIC
46-55 RED REF ODDS 1:315 HOBBY
1-30 RED REF 99 SER.#'d SETS
46-55 RED REF 25 SER.#'d SETS
NO 46-55 RED PRICING AVAILABLE
*WHITE REF: 1.2X TO 3X BASIC
WHITE REF.ODDS 1:67 HOBBY,1:185 RETAIL
WHITE REF PRINT RUN 200 SER.#'d SETS
46-55 SUP.FRAC. ODDS 1:7885
SUPERFRAC.PRINT RUN 1 SER.#'d SET
NO SUPERFRAC.PRICING DUE TO SCARCITY
1-30 ISSUED IN 07 TOPPS CHROME
46-55 ISSUED IN 08 TOPPS CHROME

2008 Topps Chrome

COMP.SET w/o AU's (220) 30.00 60.00
COMMON CARD .20 .50
COMMON ROOKIE .60 1.50
COMMON AUTO 4.00 10.00
AUTO ODDS 1:15 HOBBY
PRINT.PLATE ODDS 1:1896 HOBBY
AU PLATES 1:10,961 HOBBY
PLATE PRINT RUN 1 SET PER COLOR
BLACK-CYAN-MAGENTA-YELLOW ISSUED
NO PLATE PRICING DUE TO SCARCITY
EXCHANGE DEADLINE 6/30/2010
1 Alex Rodriguez .75 2.00
2 Barry Zito .20 .50
3 Scott Kazmir .30 .75
4 Stephen Drew .20 .50
5 Miguel Cabrera .50 1.25
6 Daisuke Matsuzaka .50 1.25
7 Mickey Mantle 1.50 4.00
8 Jimmy Rollins .30 .75
9 Joe Mauer .50 1.25
10 Cole Hamels .50 1.25
11 Yovani Gallardo .20 .50
12 Miguel Tejada .30 .75
13 Dontrelle Willis .20 .50
14 Orlando Cabrera .20 .50
15 Jake Peavy .20 .50
16 Erik Bedard .20 .50
17 Victor Martinez .30 .75
18 Chris Young .20 .50
19 Jose Reyes .30 .75
20 Mike Lowell .20 .50
21 Dan Uggla .30 .75
22 Garrett Atkins .20 .50
23 Felix Hernandez .50 1.25
24 Ivan Rodriguez .30 .75
25 Alex Rios .20 .50
26 Jason Bay .30 .75
27 Vladimir Guerrero .50 1.25
28 John Lackey .20 .50
29 Ryan Howard .60 1.50
30 Kevin Youkilis .30 .75
31 Justin Morneau .50 1.25
32 Johan Santana .50 1.25
33 Jeremy Hermida .20 .50
34 Andruw Jones .20 .50
35 Mike Cameron .20 .50
36 Jason Varitek .50 1.25
37 Tim Hudson .30 .75
38 Justin Upton .30 .75
39 Brad Penny .20 .50
40 Robinson Cano .50 1.25
41 Brandon Webb .30 .75
42 Magglio Ordonez .30 .75
43 Aaron Hill .20 .50
44 Alfonso Soriano .30 .75
45 Carlos Zambrano .30 .75
46 Ben Sheets .20 .50
47 Tim Lincecum .75 2.00
48 Phil Hughes .50 1.25
49 Scott Rolen .30 .75
50 John Maine .20 .50
51 Delmon Young .30 .75
52 Tadahito Iguchi .20 .50
53 Yunel Escobar .20 .50
54 Russell Martin .30 .75
55 Orlando Hudson .20 .50
56 Jim Edmonds .30 .75
57 Todd Helton .30 .75
58 Melky Cabrera .20 .50
59 Adrian Beltre .20 .50
60 Manny Ramirez .50 1.25
61 Gil Meche .20 .50
62 David DeJesus .20 .50
63 Roy Oswalt .30 .75
64 Mark Buehrle .30 .75
65 Hunter Pence .50 1.25
66 Dustin Pedroia .60 1.50
67 Roy Halladay .50 1.25
68 Rich Harden .20 .50
69 Jim Thome .30 .75
70 Akinori Iwamura .20 .50
71 Dan Haren .20 .50
72 Brandon Phillips .20 .50
73 Brett Myers .20 .50
74 James Loney .30 .75
75 C.C. Sabathia .30 .75
76 Jermaine Dye .20 .50
77 Carlos Ruiz .20 .50
78 Brian McCann .30 .75
79 Paul Konerko .30 .75
80 Jorge Posada .30 .75
81 Chien-Ming Wang .30 .75
82 Carlos Delgado .20 .50
83 Ichiro Suzuki .75 2.00
84 Elijah Dukes .20 .50
85 David Wright .60 1.50
86 Carl Crawford .30 .75
87 Mark Teixeira .50 1.25
88 Bobby Crosby .20 .50
89 Brian Roberts .20 .50
90 David Ortiz .30 .75
91 Derrek Lee .20 .50
92 Adam Dunn .30 .75
93 Fausto Carmona .20 .50
94 Grady Sizemore .30 .75
95 Jeff Francoeur .30 .75
96 Jered Weaver .20 .50
97 Troy Tulowitzki .50 1.25
98 Troy Glaus .30 .75
99 Nick Markakis .50 1.25
100 Lance Berkman .30 .75
101 Randy Johnson .50 1.25
102 Kenji Johjima .20 .50
103 Jarrod Saltalamacchia .20 .50
104 Matt Holliday .50 1.25
105 Travis Hafner .20 .50
106 Johnny Damon .30 .75
107 Alex Gordon .30 .75
108 Derek Lowe .20 .50
109 Nick Swisher .50 1.25
110 Aaron Harang .20 .50
111 Hanley Ramirez .50 1.25
112 Carlos Guillen .20 .50
113 Ryan Braun .60 1.50
114 Torii Hunter .20 .50
115 Joe Blanton .20 .50
116 Josh Hamilton .50 1.25
117 Pedro Martinez .30 .75
118 Hideki Matsui .50 1.25
119 Cameron Maybin .20 .50
120 Prince Fielder .30 .75
121 Derek Jeter 1.25 3.00
122 Chone Figgins .20 .50
123 Chase Utley .50 1.25
124 Jacoby Ellsbury .75 2.00
125 Freddy Sanchez .20 .50
126 Rocco Baldelli .20 .50
127 Tom Gorzelanny .20 .50
128 Adrian Gonzalez .30 .75
129 Geovany Soto .50 1.25
130 Bobby Abreu .20 .50
131 Albert Pujols 1.25 3.00
132 Chipper Jones .50 1.25
133 Jeremy Bonderman .20 .50
134 B.J. Upton .30 .75
135 Justin Verlander .60 1.50
136 Jeff Francis .20 .50
137 A.J. Burnett .20 .50
138 Travis Buck .20 .50
139 Vernon Wells .20 .50
140 Raul Ibanez .30 .75
141 Ryan Zimmerman .30 .75
142 John Smoltz .50 1.25
143 Carlos Lee .20 .50
144 Chris Young .20 .50
145 Francisco Liriano .20 .50
146 Curt Schilling .30 .75
147 Josh Beckett .30 .75
148 Aramis Ramirez .20 .50
149 Ronnie Belliard .20 .50
150 Homer Bailey .30 .75
151 Curtis Granderson .30 .75
152 Ken Griffey Jr. .75 2.00
153 Kazuo Matsui .20 .50
154 Brian Bannister .20 .50
155 Joba Chamberlain .30 .75
156 Tom Glavine .30 .75
157 Carlos Beltran .20 .50
158 Kelly Johnson .20 .50
159 Rich Hill .20 .50
160 Pat Burrell .20 .50
161 Asdrubal Cabrera .30 .75
162 Gary Sheffield .20 .50
163 Greg Maddux .60 1.50
164 Eric Chavez .20 .50
165 Chris Carpenter .50 1.25
166 Michael Young .30 .75
167 Carlos Pena .30 .75
168 Frank Thomas .50 1.25
169 Aaron Rowand .20 .50
170 Yadier Molina .30 .75
171 Luis Castillo .20 .50
172 Ryan Theriot .20 .50
173 Andre Ethier .30 .75
174 Casey Kotchman .20 .50
175 Rickie Weeks .30 .75
176 Milton Bradley .20 .50
177 Daniel Cabrera .20 .50
178 Jo-Jo Reyes .20 .50
179 Livan Hernandez .20 .50
180 Hideki Okajima .20 .50
181 Matt Kemp .30 .75
182 Jonny Gomes .20 .50
183 Billy Butler .20 .50
184 Adam LaRoche .20 .50
185 Brad Hawpe .20 .50
186 Paul Maholm .20 .50
187 Placido Polanco .20 .50
188 Noah Lowry .20 .50
189 Gregg Zaun .20 .50
190 Nate McLouth .20 .50
191 Edinson Volquez .20 .50
192 Jeff Niemann (RC) .60 1.50
193 Evan Longoria RC 3.00 8.00
194 Adam Jones .30 .75
195 Eugenio Velez RC .60 1.50
196 Joey Votto (RC) 2.50 6.00
197 Nick Blackburn RC 1.00 2.50
198 Harvey Garcia (RC) .60 1.50
199 Hiroki Kuroda RC 1.00 2.50
200 Elliot Johnson (RC) .60 1.50
201 Luis Mendoza (RC) .60 1.50
202 Alex Romero (RC) 1.00 2.50
203 Gregor Blanco (RC) .60 1.50
204 Rico Washington (RC) .60 1.50
205 Brian Bocock RC .60 1.50
206 Evan Meek RC .60 1.50
207 Stephen Holm RC .60 1.50
208 Matt Tupman RC .60 1.50
209 Fernando Hernandez RC .60 1.50
210 Randor Bierd RC .60 1.50
211 Blake DeWitt (RC) 1.50 4.00
212 Randy Wells RC 1.00 2.50
213 Wesley Wright RC .60 1.50
214 Clete Thomas RC 1.00 2.50
215 Kyle McClellan RC .60 1.50
216 Brian Bixler (RC) .60 1.50
217 Kazuo Fukumori RC 1.00 2.50
218 Burke Badenhop RC 1.00 2.50
219 Denard Span (RC) 1.00 2.50
220 Brian Bass (RC) .60 1.50
221 J.R. Towles AU RC 4.00 10.00
222 Felipe Paulino AU RC 4.00 10.00
223 Sam Fuld AU RC 10.00 25.00
224 Kevin Hart AU (RC) 4.00 10.00
225 Nyjer Morgan AU (RC) 4.00 10.00
226 Daric Barton AU (RC) 4.00 10.00
227 Armando Galarraga AU RC 8.00 20.00
228 Chin-Lung Hu AU (RC) 6.00 15.00
229 Clay Buchholz AU (RC) EXCH 10.00 25.00
230 Rich Thompson AU RC 4.00 10.00
231 Brian Barton AU RC 5.00 12.00
232 Ross Ohlendorf AU RC 4.00 10.00
233 Masahide Kobayashi AU RC 5.00 12.00
234 Callix Crabbe AU (RC) 4.00 10.00
235 Matt Tolbert AU RC 4.00 10.00
236 Jayson Nix AU (RC) 4.00 10.00
237 Johnny Cueto AU RC 10.00 25.00
238 Evan Meek AU RC 4.00 10.00
239 Randy Wells AU (RC) 6.00 15.00

2008 Topps Chrome Refractors

*REF: 1.2X TO 3X BASIC
REF ODDS 1:3 HOBBY
*REF RC: .6X TO 1.5X BASIC RC
REF RC ODDS 1:3 HOBBY
*REF AU: .5X TO 1.2X BASIC AUTO
REF AU ODDS 1:95 HOBBY
REF AU PRINT RUN 500 SER.#'d SETS
EXCHANGE DEADLINE 6/30/2010

2008 Topps Chrome Blue Refractors

*BLUE REF: 4X TO 10X BASIC
*BLUE REF RC: 1.2X TO 3X BASIC RC
*BLUE REF AU: .6X TO 1.5X BASIC AUTO
BLUE REF AU ODDS 1:230 HOBBY
BLUE REF AU PRINT RUN 200 SER.#'d SETS
EXCHANGE DEADLINE 6/30/2010
227 Armando Galarraga AU 20.00 50.00
228 Chin-Lung Hu AU 15.00 40.00
229 Clay Buchholz AU 20.00 50.00
231 Brian Barton AU 12.50 30.00
237 Johnny Cueto AU 20.00 50.00

2008 Topps Chrome Copper Refractors

*COPPER REF: 2X TO 5X BASIC
COPPER.REF ODDS 1:12 HOBBY
*COPPER REF RC: 1X TO 2.5X BASIC RC
REF RC ODDS 1:12 HOBBY
COPPER REF PRINT RUN 599 SER.#'d SETS
*COPPER REF AU: 1X TO 2.5X BASIC AUTO
COPPER REF AU ODDS 1:980 HOBBY
COPPER REF AU PRINT RUN 100 SER.#'d SETS
EXCHANGE DEADLINE 6/30/2010
227 Armando Galarraga AU 40.00 80.00
228 Chin-Lung Hu AU 40.00 80.00
229 Clay Buchholz AU 30.00 60.00
231 Brian Barton AU 30.00 60.00
233 Masahide Kobayashi AU 20.00 50.00
237 Johnny Cueto AU 30.00 60.00

2008 Topps Chrome Red Refractors

RED 1-220 ODDS 1:143 HOBBY
RED AU 221-239 ODDS 1:2185 HOBBY
STATED PRINT RUN 25 SER.#'d SETS
NO PRICING DUE TO SCARCITY

2008 Topps Chrome SuperFractors

SF 1-220 ODDS 1:3584 HOBBY
SF AU 221-239 ODDS 1:41,500 HOBBY
STATED PRINT RUN 1 SER.#'d SET
NO PRICING DUE TO SCARCITY

2008 Topps Chrome 50th Anniversary All Rookie Team

COMPLETE SET (23) 12.50 30.00
STATED ODDS 1:9 HOBBY
PRINTING PLATE ODDS 1:1971 HOBBY
PLATE PRINT RUN 1 SET PER COLOR
BLACK-CYAN-MAGENTA-YELLOW ISSUED
NO PLATE PRICING DUE TO SCARCITY
*REF: .75X TO 2X BASIC
REF ODDS 1:31 HOBBY
REF.PRINT RUN 400 SER.#'d SETS
*BLUE REF: 1.2X TO 3X BASIC
BLUE REF PRINT RUN 200 SER.#'d SETS
*COP.REF: 1X TO 2.5X BASIC
COP.REF ODDS 1:117 HOBBY
COP.REF PRINT RUN 100 SER.#'d SETS
RED.REF ODDS 1:315 HOBBY
RED PRINT RUN 25 SER.#'d SETS
NO RED PRICING DUE TO SCARCITY
SUPFRAC.ODDS 1:7885 HOBBY
SUPFRAC.PRINT RUN 1 SER.#'d SET
NO SUPFRAC.PRICING DUE TO SCARCITY
ARC1 Gary Sheffield .40 1.00
ARC2 Ivan Rodriguez .60 1.50
ARC3 Mike Piazza 1.00 2.50
ARC4 Manny Ramirez 1.00 2.50
ARC5 Chipper Jones 1.00 2.50
ARC6 Derek Jeter 2.50 6.00
ARC7 Andruw Jones .40 1.00
ARC8 Alfonso Soriano .60 1.50
ARC9 Jimmy Rollins .60 1.50
ARC10 Albert Pujols 2.50 6.00
ARC11 Ichiro Suzuki 1.50 4.00
ARC12 Mark Teixeira 1.00 2.50
ARC13 Matt Holliday 1.00 2.50
ARC14 Joe Mauer 1.00 2.50
ARC15 Prince Fielder .60 1.50
ARC16 Hideki Okajima .40 1.00
ARC17 Roy Oswalt .60 1.50
ARC18 Hunter Pence 1.00 2.50
ARC19 Nick Markakis 1.00 2.50
ARC20 Ryan Zimmerman .60 1.50
ARC21 Ryan Braun 1.25 3.00
ARC22 C.C. Sabathia .60 1.50
ARC23 Dustin Pedroia 1.25 3.00

2008 Topps Chrome Dick Perez

EXCLUSIVE TO WALMART PACKS
REF: .5X TO 1.2X
WMDPC1 Manny Ramirez 2.00 5.00
WMDPC2 Cameron Maybin .75 2.00
WMDPC3 Ryan Howard 2.50 6.00
WMDPC4 David Ortiz 1.25 3.00
WMDPC5 Tim Lincecum 3.00 8.00
WMDPC6 David Wright 2.50 6.00
WMDPC7 Mickey Mantle 3.00 8.00
WMDPC8 Joba Chamberlain 1.25 3.00
WMDPC9 Ichiro Suzuki 3.00 8.00
WMDPC10 Prince Fielder 1.25 3.00
WMDPC11 Jacoby Ellsbury 3.00 8.00
WMDPC12 Jake Peavy .75 2.00
WMDPC13 Miguel Cabrera 2.00 5.00
WMDPC14 Josh Beckett 1.25 3.00
WMDPC15 Jimmy Rollins 1.25 3.00
WMDPC16 Torii Hunter .75 2.00
WMDPC17 Alfonso Soriano 1.25 3.00
WMDPC18 Jose Reyes 1.25 3.00
WMDPC19 C.C. Sabathia 1.25 3.00
WMDPC20 Alex Rodriguez 3.00 8.00

2008 Topps Chrome T205

EXCLUSIVE TO TARGET PACKS
*REF: .5X TO 1.2X BASIC
TCCP1 Albert Pujols 5.00 12.00
TCCP2 Clay Buchholz 2.00 5.00
TCCP3 Matt Holliday 2.00 5.00
TCCP4 Luke Hochevar 1.25 3.00
TCCP5 Alex Rodriguez 3.00 8.00
TCCP6 Joey Votto 3.00 8.00
TCCP7 Chin-Lung Hu 1.25 3.00
TCCP8 Ryan Braun 2.50 6.00
TCCP9 Joba Chamberlain 1.25 3.00
TCCP10 Ryan Howard 2.50 6.00
TCCP11 Ichiro Suzuki 3.00 8.00
TCCP12 Steve Pearce 1.25 3.00
TCCP13 Vladimir Guerrero 2.00 5.00
TCCP14 Wladimir Balentien .75 2.00
TCCP15 David Ortiz 1.25 3.00
TCCP16 Jacoby Ellsbury 3.00 8.00
TCCP17 David Wright 2.50 6.00
TCCP18 Chase Utley 2.00 5.00
TCCP19 Manny Ramirez 2.00 5.00
TCCP20 Dan Haren .75 2.00
TCCP21 Nick Markakis 2.00 5.00
TCCP22 Grady Sizemore 1.25 3.00
TCCP23 Hanley Ramirez 2.00 5.00
TCCP24 Daisuke Matsuzaka 2.00 5.00
TCCP25 Troy Tulowitzki 2.00 5.00
TCCP26 Jose Reyes 1.25 3.00
TCCP27 Tim Lincecum 3.00 8.00
TCCP28 Prince Fielder 1.25 3.00
TCCP29 Alfonso Soriano 1.25 3.00
TCCP30 Andrew Miller .75 2.00

2008 Topps Chrome Trading Card History

COMPLETE SET (50) 30.00 60.00
STATED ODDS 1:9 HOBBY
PRINTING PLATE ODDS 1:1971 HOBBY
PLATE PRINT RUN 1 SET PER COLOR
BLACK-CYAN-MAGENTA-YELLOW ISSUED
NO PLATE PRICING DUE TO SCARCITY
*REF: .75X TO 2X BASIC
REF ODDS 1:31 HOBBY
REF.PRINT RUN 400 SER.#'d SETS
RED.REF ODDS 1:315 HOBBY
RED PRINT RUN 25 SER.#'d SETS
NO RED PRICING DUE TO SCARCITY
SUPFRAC.ODDS 1:7885 HOBBY
SUPFRAC.PRINT RUN 1 SER.#'d SET
NO SUPFRAC.PRICING DUE TO SCARCITY
TCHC1 Jacoby Ellsbury 1.50 4.00
TCHC2 Joba Chamberlain .60 1.50
TCHC3 Daisuke Matsuzaka 1.00 2.50
TCHC4 Prince Fielder .60 1.50
TCHC5 Alex Rodriguez 1.50 4.00
TCHC6 Mickey Mantle 2.50 6.00
TCHC7 Ryan Braun 1.25 3.00
TCHC8 Albert Pujols 2.50 6.00
TCHC9 Joe Mauer 1.00 2.50
TCHC10 Jose Reyes .60 1.50
TCHC11 Johan Santana 1.00 2.50
TCHC12 Hunter Pence 1.00 2.50
TCHC13 Hideki Okajima .40 1.00
TCHC14 Cameron Maybin .40 1.00
TCHC15 Tim Lincecum 1.50 4.00
TCHC16 Mark Teixeira 1.00 2.50
Jeff Francoeur
TCHC17 Justin Upton .60 1.50
TCHC18 Alfonso Soriano .60 1.50
TCHC19 Ichiro Suzuki 1.50 4.00
TCHC20 Grady Sizemore .60 1.50
TCHC21 Ryan Howard 1.25 3.00
TCHC22 David Wright 1.25 3.00
TCHC23 Jimmy Rollins .60 1.50
TCHC24 Ken Griffey Jr 1.50 4.00
TCHC25 Chipper Jones 1.00 2.50
TCHC26 Justin Verlander 1.25 3.00
TCHC27 Manny Ramirez 1.00 2.50
TCHC28 Chase Utley 1.00 2.50
TCHC29 Ivan Rodriguez .60 1.50
TCHC30 Josh Beckett .60 1.50
TCHC31 Vladimir Guerrero 1.00 2.50
TCHC32 Lance Berkman .60 1.50
TCHC33 Gary Sheffield .40 1.00
TCHC34 David Ortiz .60 1.50
TCHC35 Andruw Jones .40 1.00
TCHC36 Hideki Matsui 1.00 2.50
TCHC37 C.C. Sabathia .60 1.50
TCHC38 Magglio Ordonez .60 1.50
TCHC39 Pedro Martinez .60 1.50
TCHC40 Derek Jeter 2.50 6.00
TCHC41 Hanley Ramirez 1.00 2.50
TCHC42 Jake Peavy .40 1.00
TCHC43 Brandon Webb .60 1.50
TCHC44 Matt Holliday 1.00 2.50
TCHC45 Carlos Beltran .40 1.00
TCHC46 Troy Tulowitzki 1.00 2.50
TCHC47 Justin Morneau 1.00 2.50
TCHC48 Phil Hughes 1.00 2.50
TCHC49 Torii Hunter .40 1.00
TCHC50 Brad Hawpe .40 1.00

2008 Topps Chrome Trading Card History Blue Refractors

*BLUE REF: 1.2X TO 3X BASIC
STATED PRINT RUN 200 SER.#'d SETS
TCHC1 Jacoby Ellsbury 30.00 60.00

2008 Topps Chrome Trading Card History Copper Refractors

*COP.REF: 1X TO 2.5X BASIC
STATED ODDS 1:117 HOBBY
STATED PRINT RUN 100 SER.#'d SETS
TCHC1 Jacoby Ellsbury 20.00 50.00

2009 Topps Chrome

COMP.SET w/o AU's (220) 30.00 60.00
COMMON CARD .20 .50
COMMON ROOKIE .60 1.50
COMMON AUTO 4.00 10.00
AUTO ODDS 1:20 HOBBY
PRINT.PLATE ODDS 1:383 HOBBY
AU PLATES 1:5330 HOBBY
PLATE PRINT RUN 1 SET PER COLOR
BLACK-CYAN-MAGENTA-YELLOW ISSUED
NO PLATE PRICING DUE TO SCARCITY
1 Alex Rodriguez .75 2.00
2 Kerry Wood .20 .50
3 Dan Uggla .30 .75
4 Nate McLouth .20 .50
5 Brad Lidge .20 .50
6 Jon Lester .50 1.25
7 Mickey Mantle 1.50 4.00
8 Jason Giambi .20 .50
9 Mike Lowell .20 .50
10 Ken Griffey Jr. .75 2.00
11 Erick Aybar .20 .50
12 Stephen Drew .20 .50
13 Geoff Jenkins .20 .50
14 Aubrey Huff .20 .50
15 Kazuo Matsui .20 .50
16 David Ortiz .30 .75
17 Mariano Rivera .50 1.25
18 Jermaine Dye .20 .50
19 Rich Harden .20 .50
20 Brian McCann .30 .75
21 Brad Hawpe .20 .50
22 Justin Morneau .50 1.25
23 Akinori Iwamura .20 .50
24 David Wright .60 1.50
25 Garrett Atkins .20 .50
26 David DeJesus .20 .50
27 Francisco Liriano .20 .50
28 George Sherrill .20 .50
29 Hideki Matsui .50 1.25
30 Chris Young .20 .50
31 Kevin Youkilis .30 .75
32 Mark Teixeira .50 1.25
33 Roy Oswalt .30 .75
34 Orlando Hudson .20 .50
35 Vladimir Guerrero .50 1.25
36 Juan Pierre .20 .50
37 Carlos Delgado .20 .50
38 Tim Hudson .30 .75
39 Brandon Webb .30 .75
40 Alex Gordon .30 .75
41 Glen Perkins .20 .50
42 Kosuke Fukudome .50 1.25
43 Ian Stewart .20 .50
44a A.J. Pierzynski .20 .50
44b Barack Obama SP 6.00 15.00
45 Roy Halladay .50 1.25
46 Carlos Pena .30 .75
47 Evan Longoria .60 1.50
48 Matt Kemp .30 .75
49 CC Sabathia .30 .75
50 Yadier Molina .30 .75
51 James Shields .20 .50
52 Jeff Samardzija .30 .75
53 Rafael Furcal .20 .50
54 Cliff Lee .30 .75
55 Daniel Murphy RC 1.50 4.00
56 Randy Johnson .30 .75
57 Jon Garland .20 .50
58 Chien-Ming Wang .30 .75
59 Zack Greinke .30 .75
60 Tim Lincecum .75 2.00
61 Conor Jackson .20 .50
62 Chase Utley .50 1.25
63 Andy Sonnanstine .20 .50
64 Miguel Tejada .30 .75
65 Geovany Soto .30 .75
66 Jeremy Sowers .20 .50
67 Ian Kinsler .30 .75
68 Jay Bruce .20 .50
69 Max Scherzer .30 .75
70 Scott Rolen .30 .75
71 Justin Upton .30 .75
72 Xavier Nady .20 .50
73 Erik Bedard .20 .50
74 Chad Billingsley .20 .50
75 Ryan Braun .60 1.50
76 Pat Burrell .20 .50
77 Edgar Renteria .20 .50
78 Joe Crede .20 .50
79 Manny Ramirez .50 1.25
80 Carlos Zambrano .30 .75
81 Hunter Pence .30 .75
82 Grady Sizemore .30 .75
83 Brian Roberts .20 .50
84 Alex Rios .30 .75
85 Joe Saunders .20 .50
86 Albert Pujols 1.25 3.00
87 Derrek Lee .20 .50
88 Ichiro Suzuki .75 2.00
89 Javier Vazquez .20 .50
90 Johan Santana .50 1.25
91 Miguel Cabrera .50 1.25
92 Daisuke Matsuzaka .50 1.25
93 Chris Young .20 .50
94 Joe Mauer .50 1.25
95 Stephen Drew .20 .50
96 Justin Masterson .20 .50
97 Dustin Pedroia .60 1.50
98 Derek Jeter 1.25 3.00
99 John Smoltz .50 1.25
100 Jason Varitek .50 1.25
101 Jorge Posada .30 .75
102 Mark Buehrle .30 .75
103 Bobby Abreu .20 .50
104 Victor Martinez .30 .75
105 Jeff Francis .20 .50
106 Rickie Weeks .20 .50
107 Carlos Quentin .30 .75
108 Howie Kendrick .20 .50
109 Aramis Ramirez .20 .50
110 Jonathan Papelbon .30 .75
111 Dan Haren .20 .50
112 Barry Zito .20 .50
113 Magglio Ordonez .30 .75
114 Alfonso Soriano .30 .75
115 Todd Helton .30 .75
116 Troy Tulowitzki .50 1.25
117 Josh Beckett .30 .75
118 Andy Pettitte .30 .75
119 Hank Blalock .20 .50
120 Curtis Granderson .30 .75
121 Francisco Rodriguez .30 .75
122 Carlos Lee .20 .50
123 Gavin Floyd .20 .50
124 Joe Nathan .20 .50
125 Matt Holliday .50 1.25
126 Hanley Ramirez .50 1.25
127 Javier Valentin .20 .50
128 John Maine .20 .50
129 Jeremy Bonderman .20 .50
130 Nick Markakis .50 1.25
131 Troy Glaus .20 .50
132 Derek Lowe .20 .50
133 Lance Berkman .30 .75
134 Jered Weaver .30 .75
135 Chipper Jones .50 1.25
136 Prince Fielder .30 .75
137 Travis Hafner .20 .50
138 Joba Chamberlain .30 .75
139 Ryan Howard .60 1.50
140 Paul Konerko .30 .75
141 Kenji Johjima .20 .50
142 Yovani Gallardo .20 .50
143 Adrian Gonzalez .30 .75
144 Jimmy Rollins .30 .75
145 Nick Swisher .50 1.25
146 Felix Hernandez .50 1.25
147 Garret Anderson .20 .50
148 Russell Martin .20 .50
149 Jason Bay .30 .75
150 Fausto Carmona .20 .50
151 Matt Garza .20 .50
152 Matt Cain .30 .75
153 Ryan Freel .20 .50
154 Rocco Baldelli .20 .50
155 Scott Kazmir .20 .50
156 Alexei Ramirez .30 .75
157 Adam Dunn .30 .75
158 Johnny Damon .30 .75
159 Jake Peavy .20 .50
160 Jose Reyes .30 .75
161 Rick Ankiel .20 .50
162 Michael Young .30 .75

163 Robinson Cano .50 1.25
164 Ryan Zimmerman .30 .75
165 Jim Thome .30 .75
166 A.J. Burnett .30 .75
167 Joakim Soria .20 .50
168 J.D. Drew .20 .50
169 Cole Hamels .50 1.25
170 Jacoby Ellsbury .50 1.25
171 Travis Snider RC 1.00 2.50
172 Josh Outman RC 1.00 2.50
173 Dexter Fowler (RC) 1.00 2.50
174 Matt Tuiasosopo (RC) .60 1.50
175 Bobby Parnell RC 1.00 2.50
176 Jason Motte (RC) 1.00 2.50
177 James McDonald RC 1.50 4.00
178 Scott Lewis (RC) .60 1.50
179 George Kottaras (RC) .60 1.50
180 Phil Coke RC 1.00 2.50
181 Jordan Schafer (RC) 1.00 2.50
182 Joe Martinez RC 1.00 2.50
183 Trevor Crowe RC .60 1.50
184 Shairon Martis RC 1.00 2.50
185 Everth Cabrera RC 1.00 2.50
186 Trevor Cahill RC 1.50 4.00
187 Jesse Chavez RC .60 1.50
188 Josh Whitesell RC 1.00 2.50
189 Brian Duensing RC 1.00 2.50
190 Andrew Bailey RC 1.50 4.00
191 Ryan Perry RC 1.50 4.00
192 Brett Anderson RC 1.00 2.50
193 Ricky Romero (RC) 1.50 4.00
194 Elvis Andrus RC 1.00 2.50
195 Kenshin Kawakami RC 1.00 2.50
196 Colby Rasmus (RC) 1.50 4.00
197 David Patton RC 1.00 2.50
198 David Hernandez RC .60 1.50
199 David Freese RC 5.00 12.00
200 Rick Porcello RC 2.00 5.00
201 Fernando Martinez RC 1.50 4.00
202 Edwin Moreno (RC) .60 1.50
203 Koji Uehara RC 1.00 2.50
204 Jason Jaramillo (RC) .60 1.50
205 Ramiro Pena RC 1.00 2.50
206 Brad Nelson (RC) .60 1.50
207 Michael Hinckley (RC) .60 1.50
208 Ronald Belisario (RC) .60 1.50
209 Chris Jakubauskas RC 1.00 2.50
210 Hunter Jones RC 1.00 2.50
211 Walter Silva RC 1.00 2.50
212 Jordan Zimmermann RC .60 1.50
213 Andrew McCutchen (RC) 2.50 6.00
214 Gordon Beckham RC 5.00 12.00
215 Anthony Claggett RC 1.00 2.50
216 Mark Melancon RC .60 1.50
217 Brett Cecil RC .60 1.50
218 Derek Holland RC 1.00 2.50
219 Greg Golson (RC) .60 1.50
220 Bobby Scales RC 1.00 2.50
221 Jordan Schafer AU 5.00 12.00
222 Trevor Crowe AU 4.00 10.00
223 Ramiro Pena AU 6.00 15.00
224 Trevor Cahill AU 6.00 15.00
225 Ryan Perry AU 5.00 12.00
226 Brett Anderson AU 8.00 20.00
227 Elvis Andrus AU 10.00 25.00
229 Michael Bowden AU (RC) 5.00 12.00
230 David Freese AU 40.00 80.00
231 Nolan Reimold AU (RC) 8.00 20.00
233 Jason Jaramillo AU 4.00 10.00
234 Ricky Romero AU 8.00 20.00
235 Jordan Zimmermann AU 5.00 12.00
236 Derek Holland AU 6.00 15.00
237 George Kottaras AU 4.00 10.00
239 Sergio Escalona AU RC 4.00 10.00
240 Brian Duensing AU 5.00 12.00
241 Everth Cabrera AU 6.00 15.00
242 Andrew Bailey AU 6.00 15.00
243 Chris Jakubauskas AU 4.00 10.00
CL1 Checklist Card .20 .50
CL2 Checklist Card .20 .50
CL3 Checklist Card .20 .50
NNO1 Tommy Hanson AU RC 10.00 25.00
NNO2 Mark Melancon AU 6.00 15.00
NNO3 Will Venable AU RC 4.00 10.00

2009 Topps Chrome Refractors

*REF: 1X TO 2.5X BASIC
REF ODDS 1:3 HOBBY
*REF RC: .6X TO 1.5X BASIC RC
REF RC ODDS 1:3 HOBBY
*REF AU: .5X TO 1.2X BASIC AUTO
REF AU ODDS 1:47 HOBBY
REF AU PRINT RUN 499 SER.#'d SETS
44b Barack Obama 8.00 20.00

2009 Topps Chrome Blue Refractors

*BLUE REF: 2.5X TO 6X BASIC
BLUE REF ODDS 1:13 HOBBY
*BLUE REF RC: 1.2X TO 3X BASIC RC
BLUE REF RC ODDS 1:13 HOBBY
*BLUE REF AU: .6X TO 1.5X BASIC AU
BLUE REF AU ODDS 1:120 HOBBY
BLUE REF.PRINT RUN 199 SER.#'d SETS
44b Barack Obama 12.50 30.00
214 Gordon Beckham 30.00 60.00
230 David Freese AU 75.00 150.00
NNO3 Will Venable AU

2009 Topps Chrome Gold Refractors

*GOLD REF: 4X TO 10X BASIC
GOLD REF ODDS 1:50 HOBBY
*GOLD REF RC: 2X TO 5X BASIC RC
GOLD REF RC ODDS 1:50 HOBBY
GOLD AUTO ODDS 1:473 HOBBY
GOLD REF.PRINT RUN 50 SER.#'d SETS
44b Barack Obama 40.00 80.00
214 Gordon Beckham 60.00 120.00
221 Jordan Schafer AU
222 Trevor Crowe AU 12.50 30.00
223 Ramiro Pena AU 15.00 40.00
224 Trevor Cahill AU 40.00 80.00
225 Ryan Perry AU 12.50 30.00
226 Brett Anderson AU 60.00 120.00
227 Elvis Andrus AU 30.00 60.00
229 Michael Bowden AU 15.00 40.00
230 David Freese AU 200.00 400.00
231 Nolan Reimold AU 40.00 80.00
233 Jason Jaramillo AU 12.50 30.00
234 Ricky Romero AU 30.00 60.00
235 Jordan Zimmermann AU 12.50 30.00
236 Derek Holland AU 20.00 50.00
237 George Kottaras AU 12.50 30.00
239 Sergio Escalona AU 12.50 30.00
240 Brian Duensing AU 15.00 40.00
241 Everth Cabrera AU 20.00 50.00
242 Andrew Bailey AU 30.00 60.00
243 Chris Jakubauskas AU 12.50 30.00
NNO2 Mark Melancon AU
NNO3 Will Venable AU 12.50 30.00

2009 Topps Chrome Red Refractors

RED 1-220 ODDS 1:100 HOBBY
RED AU ODDS 1:924 HOBBY
STATED PRINT RUN 25 SER.#'d SETS
NO PRICING DUE TO SCARCITY

2009 Topps Chrome SuperFractors

SUPER 1-220 ODDS 1:1532 HOBBY
STATED PRINT RUN 1 SER.#'d SET
SUPER AU ODDS 1:21,320 HOBBY
NO PRICING DUE TO SCARCITY

2009 Topps Chrome X-Fractors

*X-F: 1.5X TO 4X BASIC
*X-F RC: .75X TO 2X BASIC RC
RANDOM INSERTS IN RETAIL PACKS

2009 Topps Chrome World Baseball Classic

STATED ODDS 1:4 HOBBY
PRINT.PLATE ODDS 1:383 HOBBY
PLATE PRINT RUN 1 SET PER COLOR
BLACK-CYAN-MAGENTA-YELLOW ISSUED
NO PLATE PRICING DUE TO SCARCITY
*REF: 1X TO 2.5X BASIC
REF ODDS 1:16 HOBBY
REF PRINT RUN 500 SER.#'d SETS
*BLUE REF: 1.5X TO 4X BASIC
BLUE REF ODDS 1:13 HOBBY
BLUE REF PRINT RUN 199 SER.#'d SETS
*GOLD REF: 2.5X TO 6X BASIC
GOLD REF ODDS 1:50 HOBBY
GOLD REF PRINT RUN 50 SER.#'d SETS
RED REF ODDS 1:100 HOBBY
RED REF PRINT RUN 25 SER.#'d SETS
NO RED REF PRICING AVAILABLE
SUPERFRAC ODDS 1:1532 HOBBY
SUPERFRAC PRINT RUN 1 SER.#'d SET
NO SUPERFRAC PRICING AVAILABLE
W1 Yu Darvish 4.00 10.00
W2 Yulieski Gourriel .40 1.00
W3 Yi-Chuan Lin .60 1.50
W4 Ichiro Suzuki 1.50 4.00
W5 Hung-Wen Chen .40 1.00
W6 Yuneski Maya .40 1.00
W7 Chih-Hsien Chiang 1.00 2.50
W8 Kenji Johjima .60 1.50
W9 Hanley Ramirez 1.00 2.50
W10 Chenhao Li .40 1.00
W11 Yoennis Cespedes 3.00 8.00
W12 Dae Ho Lee .40 1.00
W13 Alex Rodriguez 1.50 4.00
W14 Luis Durango .40 1.00
W15 Chipper Jones 1.00 2.50
W16 Dennis Neuman .40 1.00
W17 Carlos Lee .40 1.00
W18 Tae Kyun Kim .40 1.00
W19 Adrian Gonzalez .60 1.50
W20 Michel Enriquez .40 1.00
W21 Miguel Cabrera 1.00 2.50
W22 Hisashi Iwakuma .60 1.50
W23 Aroldis Chapman 1.50 4.00
W24 Daisuke Matsuzaka 1.00 2.50
W25 Chris Denorfia .40 1.00
W26 David Wright 1.25 3.00
W27 Alex Rios .60 1.50
W28 Michihiro Ogasawara .60 1.50
W29 Frederich Cepeda .60 1.50
W30 Chen-Chang Lee .60 1.50
W31 Shunsuke Watanabe .60 1.50
W32 Luca Panerati .40 1.00
W33 David Ortiz .60 1.50
W34 Tetsuya Yamaguchi .60 1.50
W35 Jin Young Lee .40 1.00
W36 Tom Stuifbergen .40 1.00
W37 Masahiro Tanaka 1.00 2.50
W38 Cheng-Ming Peng .60 1.50
W39 Yoshiyuki Ishihara .60 1.50
W40 Manuel Corpas .40 1.00
W41 Yi-Feng Kuo .40 1.00
W42 Ruben Tejada .40 1.00
W43 Kenley Jansen 1.00 2.50
W44 Shinnosuke Abe .60 1.50
W45 Shuichi Murata .60 1.50
W46 Yolexis Ulacia .40 1.00
W47 Yueh-Ping Lin .60 1.50
W48 James Beresford .40 1.00
W49 Justin Morneau 1.00 2.50
W50 Brad Harman .40 1.00
W51 Juan Carlos Sulbaran .40 1.00
W52 Ubaldo Jimenez .60 1.50
W53 Joel Naughton .40 1.00
W54 Rafael Diaz .40 1.00
W55 Russell Martin .40 1.00
W56 Concepcion Rodriguez .40 1.00
W57 Po Yu Lin .40 1.00
W58 Chih-Kang Kao .40 1.00
W59 Gregor Blanco .40 1.00
W60 Justin Erasmus .40 1.00
W61 Kosuke Fukudome 1.00 2.50
W62 Hiroyuki Nakajima .60 1.50
W63 Luke Hughes .60 1.50
W64 Sidney de Jong .40 1.00
W65 Greg Halman .60 1.50
W66 Seiichi Uchikawa .60 1.50
W67 Tao Bu .40 1.00
W68 Pedro Martinez .60 1.50
W69 Jingchao Wang .60 1.50
W70 Arquimedes Nieto .40 1.00
W71 Yang Yang .40 1.00
W72 Alex Liddi 1.25 3.00
W73 Fei Feng .40 1.00
W74 Pedro Lazo .40 1.00
W75 Magglio Ordonez .60 1.50
W76 Bryan Engelhardt .40 1.00
W77 Yen-Wen Kuo .40 1.00
W78 Norichika Aoki .60 1.50
W79 Jose Reyes .60 1.50
W80 Kanigan Xia .40 1.00
W81 Shin-Soo Choo .60 1.50
W82 Frank Catalanotto .40 1.00
W83 Ray Chang .40 1.00
W84 Nelson Cruz .60 1.50
W85 Fu-Te Ni .60 1.50
W86 Hein Robb .40 1.00
W87 Hyun-Soo Kim .40 1.00
W88 Tai-Chi Kuo .40 1.00
W89 Akinori Iwamura .40 1.00
W90 Chi-Hung Cheng .40 1.00
W91 Fujia Chu .40 1.00
W92 Gift Ngoepe .40 1.00
W93 Zhenwang Zhang .40 1.00
W94 Bernie Williams .60 1.50
W95 Dustin Pedroia 1.25 3.00
W96 Dylan Lindsay .60 1.50
W97 Max Ramirez .40 1.00
W98 Yadier Molina .60 1.50
W99 Phillippe Aumont 1.00 2.50
W100 Derek Jeter 2.50 6.00

2010 Topps Chrome

COMPLETE SET (220) 20.00 50.00
COMMON CARD (1-170) .20 .50
COMMON RC (171-220) .40 1.00
PRINTING PLATE ODDS 1:1592 HOBBY
PLATE PRINT RUN 1 SET PER COLOR
BLACK-CYAN-MAGENTA-YELLOW ISSUED
NO PLATE PRICING DUE TO SCARCITY
1 Prince Fielder .30 .75
2 Derrek Lee .20 .50
3 Clayton Kershaw .50 1.25
4 Bobby Abreu .20 .50
5 Johnny Cueto .20 .50
6 Dexter Fowler .20 .50
7 Mickey Mantle 1.50 4.00
8 Tommy Hanson .30 .75
9 Shane Victorino .30 .75
10 Adam Jones .30 .75
11 Zach Duke .20 .50
12 Victor Martinez .30 .75
13 Rick Porcello .20 .50
14 Josh Johnson .30 .75
15 Marco Scutaro .20 .50
16 Howie Kendrick .20 .50
17 Joey Votto .50 1.25
18 Zack Greinke .30 .75
19 John Lackey .30 .75
20 Manny Ramirez .50 1.25
21 CC Sabathia .30 .75
22 David Wright .60 1.50
23 Nick Swisher .50 1.25
24 Cole Hamels .50 1.25
25 Adrian Gonzalez .30 .75
26 Joe Saunders .20 .50
27 Tim Lincecum .75 2.00
28 Ken Griffey Jr. .75 2.00
29 J.A. Happ .30 .75
30 Ian Kinsler .30 .75
31 Carl Crawford .30 .75
32 Albert Pujols 1.25 3.00
33 Daniel Murphy .20 .50
34 Erick Aybar .20 .50
35 Andrew McCutchen .50 1.25
36 Gordon Beckham .20 .50
37 Jorge Posada .30 .75
38 Ichiro Suzuki .75 2.00
39 Vladimir Guerrero .50 1.25
40 Cliff Lee .30 .75
41 Freddy Sanchez .20 .50
42 Ryan Dempster .20 .50
43 Adam Wainwright .20 .50
44 Matt Holliday .50 1.25
45 Chone Figgins .20 .50
46 Tim Hudson .30 .75
47 Rich Harden .20 .50
48 Justin Upton .30 .75
49 Yunel Escobar .20 .50
50 Joe Mauer .50 1.25
51 Vernon Wells .20 .50
52 Miguel Tejada .30 .75
53 Denard Span .20 .50
54 Brandon Phillips .20 .50
55 Jason Bay .30 .75
56 Kendry Morales .20 .50
57 Josh Hamilton .50 1.25
58 Yovani Gallardo .20 .50
59 Adam Lind .30 .75
60 Nick Johnson .20 .50
61 Hideki Matsui .50 1.25
62 Pablo Sandoval .30 .75
63 James Shields .20 .50
64 Roy Halladay .50 1.25
65 Chris Coghlan .20 .50
66 Alexei Ramirez .20 .50
67 Josh Beckett .20 .50
68 Magglio Ordonez .30 .75
69 Matt Kemp .30 .75
70 Max Scherzer .20 .50
71 Curtis Granderson .20 .50
72 David Price .50 1.25
73 Lance Berkman .30 .75
74 Andre Ethier .30 .75
75 Mark Teixeira .50 1.25
76 Edwin Jackson .20 .50
77 Akinori Iwamura .20 .50
78 Placido Polanco .20 .50
79 Jair Jurrjens .20 .50
80 Stephen Drew .20 .50
81 Javier Vazquez .20 .50
82 Lyle Overbay .20 .50
83 Orlando Hudson .20 .50
84 Adam Dunn .30 .75
85 Kevin Youkilis .30 .75
86 Chase Utley .50 1.25
87 Elvis Andrus .30 .75
88 Scott Kazmir .20 .50
89 Brian McCann .30 .75
90 Alex Rios .20 .50
91 Wandy Rodriguez .20 .50
92 Felix Hernandez .50 1.25
93 Carlos Gonzalez .30 .75
94 Kosuke Fukudome .50 1.25
95 A.J. Burnett .20 .50
96 Nelson Cruz .30 .75
97 Luke Hochevar .20 .50
98 Francisco Liriano .20 .50
99 Chris Carpenter .50 1.25
100 Russell Martin .20 .50
101 Carlos Pena .30 .75
102 Jake Peavy .20 .50
103 Jose Lopez .20 .50
104 Todd Helton .30 .75
105 Mike Pelfrey .20 .50
106 Jacoby Ellsbury .50 1.25
107 Edinson Volquez .20 .50
108 Michael Young .30 .75
109 Dustin Pedroia .60 1.50
110 Chipper Jones .50 1.25
111 Brad Hawpe .20 .50
112 Justin Morneau .50 1.25
113 Hiroki Kuroda .20 .50
114 Robinson Cano .50 1.25
115 Torii Hunter .20 .50
116 Jimmy Rollins .30 .75
117 Delmon Young .30 .75
118 Matt Cain .30 .75
119 Ryan Zimmerman .30 .75
120 Johan Santana .50 1.25
121 Roy Oswalt .30 .75
122 Jay Bruce .30 .75
123 Ubaldo Jimenez .30 .75
124 Geovany Soto .30 .75
125 Jon Lester .50 1.25
126 Ryan Howard .60 1.50
127 Jayson Werth .30 .75
128 David Ortiz .30 .75
129 Dan Haren .20 .50
130 Daisuke Matsuzaka .50 1.25
131 Michael Bourn .20 .50
132 Michael Cuddyer .20 .50
133 Carlos Quentin .30 .75
134 Justin Verlander .60 1.50
135 Carlos Beltran .20 .50
136 Alfonso Soriano .30 .75
137 Ryan Braun .60 1.50
138 Carlos Zambrano .30 .75
139 Jose Reyes .30 .75
140 Koji Uehara .30 .75
141 Evan Longoria .60 1.50
142 Mark Buehrle .30 .75
143 Troy Tulowitzki .60 1.50
144 Alex Rodriguez .75 2.00
145 Chad Billingsley .20 .50
146 Shin-Soo Choo .30 .75
147 Mark Reynolds .20 .50
148 Jered Weaver .20 .50
149 Carlos Lee .20 .50
150 B.J. Upton .30 .75
151 Aaron Hill .20 .50
152 Nick Markakis .50 1.25
153 Hanley Ramirez .50 1.25
154 Alex Gordon .30 .75
155 Mike Napoli .30 .75
156 Miguel Cabrera .50 1.25
157 Grady Sizemore .30 .75
158 Aramis Ramirez .30 .75
159 Brandon Webb .20 .50
160 Gavin Floyd .20 .50
161 Yadier Molina .20 .50
162 Nate McLouth .20 .50
163 Dan Uggla .20 .50
164 Hunter Pence .30 .75
165 Derek Jeter 1.25 3.00
166 Brian Roberts .20 .50
167 Franklin Gutierrez .20 .50
168 Glen Perkins .20 .50
169 Matt Garza .20 .50
170 Raul Ibanez .30 .75
171 Eric Young Jr. (RC) .40 1.00
172 Bryan Anderson (RC) .40 1.00
173 Jon Link RC .40 1.00
174 Jason Heyward RC 2.50 6.00
175 Scott Sizemore RC .60 1.50
176 Mike Leake RC 1.25 3.00
177 Austin Jackson RC .60 1.50
178 Jon Jay RC .60 1.50
179 John Ely RC .60 1.50
180 Jason Donald RC .40 1.00
181 Tyler Colvin RC .60 1.50
182 Brennan Boesch RC 1.00 2.50
183 Esmil Rogers RC .40 1.00
184 Ike Davis RC 1.00 2.50
185 Andrew Cashner RC .40 1.00
186 Cole Gillespie RC .40 1.00
187 Luke Hughes (RC) .40 1.00
188 Alex Burnett RC .40 1.00
189 Wilson Ramos RC 1.00 2.50
190 Mike Stanton RC 1.50 4.00
191 Josh Donaldson RC .40 1.00
192 Chris Heisey RC .40 1.00
193 Lance Zawadzki RC .40 1.00
194 Cesar Valdez RC .40 1.00
195 Starlin Castro RC 1.50 4.00
196 Kevin Russo RC .40 1.00
197 Brandon Hicks RC .60 1.50
198 Carlos Santana RC 1.25 3.00
199 Allen Craig RC 1.00 2.50
200 Jenrry Mejia RC .60 1.50
201 Ruben Tejada RC .60 1.50
202 Drew Butera (RC) .40 1.00
203 Jesse English (RC) .40 1.00
204 Tyson Ross RC .40 1.00
205 Ian Desmond (RC) .60 1.50
206 Mike McCoy RC .40 1.00
207 Tommy Manzella (RC) .40 1.00
208 Kanekoa Texeira RC .40 1.00
209 Daniel McCutchen RC .60 1.50
210 Brian Matusz RC 1.00 2.50
211 Sergio Santos (RC) .40 1.00
212 Stephen Strasburg RC 2.50 6.00
213 Jake Arrieta RC .60 1.50
214 Ivan Nova RC 2.00 5.00
215 Kila Ka'aihue (RC) .60 1.50
216 Drew Storen RC .60 1.50
217 Hisanori Takahashi RC .60 1.50
218 Andy Oliver RC .40 1.00
219 Drew Stubbs RC 1.00 2.50
220 Wade Davis (RC) .40 1.00

2010 Topps Chrome Refractors

*REF VET: 1X TO 2.5X BASIC
*REF RC: 1X TO 2.5X BASIC RC
STATED ODDS 1:3 HOBBY

2010 Topps Chrome Blue Refractors

*BLUE VET: 3X TO 8X BASIC
*BLUE RC: 1.5X TO 4X BASIC RC
STATED ODDS 1:58 HOBBY
STATED PRINT RUN 199 SER.#'d SETS

2010 Topps Chrome Gold Refractors

*GOLD VET: 6X TO 15X BASIC
*GOLD RC: 3X TO 8X BASIC RC
STATED ODDS 1:224 HOBBY
STATED PRINT RUN 50 SER.#'d SETS

2010 Topps Chrome Orange Refractors

*ORANGE VET: 1.5X TO 4X BASIC
*ORANGE RC: 1.2X TO 3X BASIC RC
RANDOM INSERTS IN RETAIL PACKS

2010 Topps Chrome Purple Refractors

*PURPLE VET: 2.5X TO 6X BASIC
*PURPLE RC: 1.25X TO 3X BASIC RC
RANDOM INSERTS IN PACKS
STATED PRINT RUN 599 SER.#'d SETS

2010 Topps Chrome Red Refractors

STATED ODDS 1:370 HOBBY
STATED PRINT RUN 25 SER.#'d SETS
NO PRICING DUE TO SCARCITY

2010 Topps Chrome Superfractors

STATED ODDS 1:9265 HOBBY
STATED PRINT RUN 1 SER.#'d SET
NO PRICING DUE TO SCARCITY

2010 Topps Chrome X-Fractors

*X-F VET: 1.5X TO 4X BASIC
*X-F RC: 1.2X TO 3X BASIC RC
RANDOM INSERTS IN RETAIL PACKS

2010 Topps Chrome Rookie Autographs

STATED ODDS 1:20 HOBBY
PRINTING PLATE ODDS 1:11,078 HOBBY
PLATE PRINT RUN 1 SET PER COLOR
BLACK-CYAN-MAGENTA-YELLOW ISSUED
NO PLATE PRICING DUE TO SCARCITY
171 Eric Young Jr. 3.00 8.00
172 Bryan Anderson 3.00 8.00
173 Jon Link 3.00 8.00
174 Jason Heyward 20.00 50.00
175 Scott Sizemore 3.00 8.00
176 Mike Leake 5.00 12.00
177 Austin Jackson 6.00 15.00
178 Jon Jay 4.00 10.00
179 John Ely 3.00 8.00
181 Tyler Colvin 6.00 15.00
182 Brennan Boesch 6.00 15.00
183 Esmil Rogers 3.00 8.00
184 Ike Davis 8.00 20.00
186 Cole Gillespie 3.00 8.00
187 Luke Hughes 3.00 8.00
188 Alex Burnett 3.00 8.00
189 Wilson Ramos 5.00 12.00
190 Mike Stanton 20.00 50.00
191 Josh Donaldson 3.00 8.00
192 Chris Heisey 5.00 12.00
193 Lance Zawadzki 3.00 8.00
194 Cesar Valdez 3.00 8.00
195 Starlin Castro 20.00 50.00
196 Kevin Russo 3.00 8.00
197 Brandon Hicks 3.00 8.00
198 Carlos Santana 8.00 20.00
199 Allen Craig 6.00 15.00
200 Jenrry Mejia 4.00 10.00
201 Ruben Tejada 3.00 8.00
202 Drew Butera 3.00 8.00
203 Jesse English 3.00 8.00
204 Tyson Ross 3.00 8.00
205 Ian Desmond 4.00 10.00
206 Mike McCoy 3.00 8.00
207 Tommy Manzella 3.00 8.00
208 Kanekoa Texeira 3.00 8.00
209 Daniel McCutchen 3.00 8.00
210 Brian Matusz 8.00 20.00
211 Sergio Santos 3.00 8.00
212 Stephen Strasburg 100.00 200.00
214 Ivan Nova 12.50 30.00
215 Kila Ka'aihue 3.00 8.00
216 Drew Storen 4.00 10.00
217 Hisanori Takahashi 8.00 20.00
219 Drew Stubbs 6.00 15.00
220 Wade Davis 4.00 10.00

2010 Topps Chrome Rookie Autographs Refractors

*REF: .5X TO 1.2X BASIC
STATED ODDS 1:95 HOBBY
STATED PRINT RUN 499 SER.#'d SETS
174 Jason Heyward 40.00 80.00

2010 Topps Chrome Rookie Autographs Blue Refractors

*BLUE: .75X TO 2X BASIC
STATED ODDS 1:238 HOBBY
STATED PRINT RUN 199 SER.#'d SETS
174 Jason Heyward 60.00 120.00

2010 Topps Chrome Rookie Autographs Gold Refractors

*GOLD: 1.25X TO 3X BASIC
STATED ODDS 1:941 HOBBY
STATED PRINT RUN 50 SER.#'d SETS
174 Jason Heyward 100.00 200.00
177 Austin Jackson 30.00 60.00
178 Jon Jay 20.00 50.00
181 Tyler Colvin 40.00 80.00
189 Wilson Ramos 25.00 60.00
190 Mike Stanton 150.00 300.00
195 Starlin Castro 125.00 250.00
200 Jenrry Mejia 20.00 50.00
201 Ruben Tejada 20.00 50.00
212 Stephen Strasburg 300.00 500.00
214 Ivan Nova 60.00 150.00

2010 Topps Chrome Rookie Autographs Red Refractors

STATED ODDS 1:1881 HOBBY
STATED PRINT RUN 25 SER.#'d SETS
NO PRICING DUE TO SCARCITY

2010 Topps Chrome 206 Chrome

STATED ODDS 1:25 HOBBY
STATED PRINT RUN 999 SER.#'d SETS
*BLUE: .75X TO 2X BASIC
BLUE ODDS 1:125 HOBBY
BLUE PRINT RUN 199 SER.#'d SETS
*GOLD: 2.5X TO 6X BASIC
GOLD ODDS 1:497 HOBBY
GOLD PRINT RUN 50 SER.#'d SETS
PRINTING PLATE ODDS 1:1595 HOBBY
PLATE PRINT RUN 1 SER.#'d SET
NO PLATE PRICING DUE TO SCARCITY
RED ODDS 1:814 HOBBY
RED PRINT RUN 25 SER.#'d SETS
NO RED PRICING DUE TO SCARCITY
*REF: .5X TO 1.2X BASIC
REF.ODDS 1:50 HOBBY
REF.PRINT RUN 499 HOBBY
SUPERFRAC.ODDS 1:20,384 HOBBY
SUPERFRAC.PRINT RUN 1 SER.#'d SET
NO SUPERFRAC.PRICING AVAILABLE
TC1 Matt Holliday 1.50 4.00
TC2 Shane Victorino 1.00 2.50
TC3 Zack Greinke 1.00 2.50
TC4 Mike Leake 2.00 5.00
TC5 Justin Upton 1.00 2.50
TC6 Gordon Beckham 1.00 2.50
TC7 Yovani Gallardo .60 1.50
TC8 Martin Prado .60 1.50
TC9 Adrian Gonzalez 1.00 2.50
TC10 Justin Verlander 2.00 5.00
TC11 Pablo Sandoval 1.00 2.50
TC12 Josh Beckett 1.00 2.50
TC13 Matt Kemp 1.00 2.50
TC14 Mickey Mantle 5.00 12.00
TC15 Jorge Posada 1.00 2.50
TC16 Evan Longoria 2.00 5.00
TC17 Howie Kendrick .60 1.50
TC18 Joey Votto 1.50 4.00
TC19 Mark Teixeira 1.50 4.00
TC20 Alex Rodriguez 2.50 6.00
TC21 B.J. Upton 1.00 2.50
TC22 Troy Tulowitzki 1.50 4.00
TC23 Ian Kinsler 1.00 2.50
TC24 Brett Anderson 1.00 2.50
TC25 Roy Halladay 1.50 4.00
TC26 Cliff Lee 1.00 2.50
TC27 Ryan Braun 2.00 5.00
TC28 Jake Peavy .60 1.50
TC29 Neftali Feliz .60 1.50
TC30 Derek Jeter 4.00 10.00
TC31 Austin Jackson 1.00 2.50
TC32 Stephen Strasburg 4.00 10.00
TC33 Dan Haren .60 1.50
TC34 Hanley Ramirez 1.50 4.00
TC35 Victor Martinez 1.00 2.50
TC36 Stephen Drew .60 1.50
TC37 Adam Jones 1.00 2.50
TC38 Vladimir Guerrero 1.50 4.00
TC39 Jacoby Ellsbury 1.50 4.00
TC40 Joe Mauer 1.50 4.00
TC41 Rick Porcello .60 1.50
TC42 Albert Pujols 4.00 10.00
TC43 Francisco Liriano .60 1.50
TC44 Dan Uggla .60 1.50
TC45 Hideki Matsui 1.50 4.00
TC46 Tim Lincecum 2.50 6.00
TC47 Ryan Howard 2.00 5.00
TC48 Carl Crawford 1.00 2.50
TC49 Andrew McCutchen 1.50 4.00
TC50 Alfonso Soriano 1.00 2.50

2010 Topps Chrome National Chicle

STATED ODDS 1:25 HOBBY
STATED PRINT RUN 999 SER.#'d SETS
*BLUE: .75X TO 2X BASIC
BLUE ODDS 1:125 HOBBY
BLUE PRINT RUN 199 SER.#'d SETS
*GOLD: 2.5X TO 6X BASIC
GOLD ODDS 1:497 HOBBY
GOLD PRINT RUN 50 SER.#'d SETS
PRINTING PLATE ODDS 1:1595 HOBBY
PLATE PRINT RUN 1 SER.#'d SET
NO PLATE PRICING DUE TO SCARCITY
RED ODDS 1:814 HOBBY
RED PRINT RUN 25 SER.#'d SETS
NO RED PRICING DUE TO SCARCITY
*REF: .5X TO 1.2X BASIC
REF.ODDS 1:50 HOBBY
REF.PRINT RUN 499 HOBBY
SUPERFRAC.ODDS 1:20,384 HOBBY
SUPERFRAC.PRINT RUN 1 SER.#'d SET
NO SUPERFRAC.PRICING AVAILABLE
CC1 Albert Pujols 4.00 10.00
CC2 Grady Sizemore 1.00 2.50
CC3 Ichiro Suzuki 2.50 6.00
CC4 Daisuke Matsuzaka 1.50 4.00
CC5 James Loney 1.00 2.50
CC6 Tim Wakefield .60 1.50
CC7 Shane Victorino 1.00 2.50
CC8 Jacoby Ellsbury 1.50 4.00
CC9 Hunter Pence 1.00 2.50
CC10 Andy Pettitte 1.00 2.50
CC11 David Wright 2.00 5.00
CC12 Derek Jeter 4.00 10.00
CC13 Ryan Howard 2.00 5.00
CC14 Russell Martin .60 1.50
CC15 Michael Young 1.00 2.50
CC16 Johnny Damon 1.00 2.50
CC17 Robinson Cano 1.50 4.00
CC18 Adrian Gonzalez 1.00 2.50
CC19 Gordon Beckham 1.00 2.50
CC20 Aramis Ramirez .60 1.50
CC21 Alex Rodriguez 2.50 6.00
CC22 Johan Santana 1.50 4.00
CC23 Vladimir Guerrero 1.50 4.00
CC24 Nick Markakis 1.50 4.00
CC25 Justin Verlander 2.00 5.00
CC26 Adam Jones 1.00 2.50
CC27 Chone Figgins .60 1.50
CC28 Cole Hamels 1.50 4.00
CC29 Roy Oswalt 1.00 2.50
CC30 Ryan Braun 2.00 5.00
CC31 Alexei Ramirez .60 1.50
CC32 Adam Dunn 1.00 2.50
CC33 Pablo Sandoval 1.00 2.50
CC34 Todd Helton 1.00 2.50
CC35 Carlos Beltran .60 1.50
CC36 Ubaldo Jimenez 1.00 2.50
CC37 Tommy Hanson 1.00 2.50
CC38 Zack Greinke 1.00 2.50
CC39 Chris Coghlan .60 1.50
CC40 Chris Young .60 1.50
CC41 Jake Peavy .60 1.50
CC42 Dexter Fowler .60 1.50
CC43 Phil Hughes .60 1.50
CC44 Chase Utley 1.50 4.00
CC45 Ian Stewart .60 1.50
CC46 John Danks .60 1.50
CC47 Ichiro Suzuki 2.50 6.00
CC48 Lance Berkman 1.00 2.50
CC49 Ryan Zimmerman 1.00 2.50
CC50 Albert Pujols 4.00 10.00

2010 Topps Chrome Rookie Autographs Superfractors

STATED ODDS 1:44,314 HOBBY
STATED PRINT RUN 1 SER.#'d SETS
NO PRICING DUE TO SCARCITY

2010 Topps Chrome Target Exclusive Refractors

COMPLETE SET (5) 6.00 15.00
BC1 Stephen Strasburg 2.00 5.00
BC2 Starlin Castro 1.25 3.00
BC3 Jason Heyward 2.00 5.00
BC4 Mickey Mantle 2.50 6.00
BC5 Jackie Robinson .75 2.00

2010 Topps Chrome USA Baseball Autographs

STATED ODDS 1:287 HOBBY
USA1 Tyler Anderson 8.00 20.00
USA2 Matt Barnes 10.00 25.00
USA3 Jackie Bradley Jr. 15.00 40.00
USA4 Gerrit Cole 50.00 100.00
USA5 Alex Dickerson 10.00 25.00
USA6 Nolan Fontana 10.00 25.00
USA7 Sean Gilmartin 8.00 20.00
USA8 Sonny Gray 10.00 25.00
USA9 Brian Johnson 8.00 20.00
USA10 Andrew Maggi 8.00 20.00
USA11 Mike Mahtook 10.00 25.00
USA12 Scott McGough 10.00 25.00
USA13 Brad Miller 8.00 20.00
USA14 Brett Mooneyham 8.00 20.00
USA15 Peter O'Brien 8.00 20.00
USA16 Nick Ramirez 8.00 20.00
USA17 Noe Ramirez 8.00 20.00
USA19 Steve Rodriguez 8.00 20.00
USA20 George Springer 15.00 40.00
USA21 Kyle Winkler 8.00 20.00
USA22 Ryan Wright 8.00 20.00

2010 Topps Chrome Wal Mart Exclusive Refractors

COMPLETE SET (3) 6.00 15.00
ONE PER WAL MART VALUE PACK
WME1 Babe Ruth 2.00 5.00
WME2 Cal Ripken Jr. 3.00 8.00
WME3 Stephen Strasburg 2.00 5.00

2010 Topps Chrome Wrapper Redemption Autographs

STATED PRINT RUN 90 SER.#'d SETS
174 Jason Heyward 100.00 200.00
221 Buster Posey 300.00 500.00

2010 Topps Chrome Wrapper Redemption Refractors

COMPLETE SET (15) 20.00 50.00
*GREEN RC: .75X TO 2X BASIC
*GREEN VET: .75X TO 2X BASIC
GREEN PRINT RUN 599 SER.#'d SETS
174 Jason Heyward 6.00 15.00
176 Mike Leake 3.00 8.00
177 Austin Jackson 1.50 4.00
181 Tyler Colvin 1.50 4.00
184 Ike Davis 2.50 6.00

190 Mike Stanton 4.00 10.00
195 Starlin Castro 4.00 10.00
198 Carlos Santana 3.00 8.00
212 Stephen Strasburg 6.00 15.00
221 Buster Posey 10.00 25.00
222 Babe Ruth 6.00 15.00
223 Lou Gehrig 5.00 12.00
224 Jackie Robinson 2.50 6.00
225 Ty Cobb 4.00 10.00
226 Mickey Mantle 8.00 20.00

2011 Topps Chrome

COMPLETE SET (220) 20.00 50.00
COMMON CARD (1-169) .20 .50
COMMON RC (1-220)
PRINTING PLATE ODDS 1:718 HOBBY
PLATE PRINT RUN 1 SET PER COLOR
BLACK-CYAN-MAGENTA-YELLOW ISSUED
NO PLATE PRICING DUE TO SCARCITY
1 Buster Posey .60 1.50
2 Chipper Jones .50 1.25
3 Carl Crawford .30 .75
4 Andre Ethier .30 .75
5 David Wright .60 1.50
6 Zack Greinke .30 .75
7 Mickey Mantle 1.50 4.00
8 Andrew McCutchen .50 1.25
9 Prince Fielder .30 .75
10 Hanley Ramirez .50 1.25
11 Ryan Zimmerman .30 .75
12 David Ortiz .30 .75
13 Evan Longoria .60 1.50
14 Adam Dunn .30 .75
15 Tim Lincecum .50 1.25
16 Jason Heyward .60 1.50
17 Starlin Castro .50 1.25
18 Ian Kinsler .30 .75
19 Joey Votto .50 1.25
20 Derek Jeter 1.25 3.00
21 Carlos Ruiz .20 .50
22 Nick Markakis .50 1.25
23 Russell Martin .20 .50
24 Matt Kemp .30 .75
25 Adrian Gonzalez .30 .75
26 Dan Uggla .30 .75
27 Orlando Hudson .20 .50
28 Austin Jackson .20 .50
29 Phil Hughes .20 .50
30 Miguel Cabrera .50 1.25
31 Tommy Hunter .20 .50
32 Yadier Molina .30 .75
33 Danny Espinosa RC .40 1.00
34 Josh Beckett .30 .75
35 Chase Utley .50 1.25
36 Rafael Soriano .20 .50
37 Mike Leake .30 .75
38 Justin Upton .30 .75
39 Travis Wood .20 .50
40 Cliff Lee .50 1.25
41 Danny Valencia .30 .75
42 Mariano Rivera .50 1.25
43 Josh Johnson .30 .75
44 David Price .50 1.25
45 Ryan Howard .60 1.50
46 Billy Butler .20 .50
47 James Loney .30 .75
48 Jay Bruce .30 .75
49 Jonathan Papelbon .30 .75
50 Ichiro Suzuki .75 2.00
51 Gordon Beckham .30 .75
52 CC Sabathia .30 .75
53 Carlos Santana .50 1.25
54 Ryan Braun .60 1.50
55 Jon Lester .50 1.25
56 Gio Gonzalez .20 .50
57 John Jaso .20 .50
58 Jason Bay .30 .75
59 Joe Nathan .20 .50
60 Josh Hamilton .50 1.25
61 Yovani Gallardo .20 .50
62 Brian Wilson .50 1.25
63 Neil Walker .20 .50
64 Vernon Wells .20 .50
65 Jason Bartlett .20 .50
66 Neftali Feliz .20 .50
67 Aaron Hill .20 .50
68 Aroldis Chapman RC 1.25 3.00
69 Michael Young .30 .75
70 Robinson Cano .50 1.25
71 Colby Rasmus .50 1.25
72 Brian McCann .30 .75
73 James Shields .30 .75
74 Nelson Cruz .30 .75
75 Roy Halladay .50 1.25
76 Jose Bautista .30 .75
77 David DeJesus .20 .50
78 Sean Rodriguez .20 .50
79 Jonathan Sanchez .20 .50
80 Joe Mauer .50 1.25
81 Mat Latos .20 .50
82 Franklin Gutierrez .20 .50
83 Adam Jones .30 .75
84 Jorge Posada .30 .75
85 Mike Stanton .30 .75
86 Drew Stubbs .30 .75
87 Todd Helton .30 .75
88 Joakim Soria .20 .50
89 Gaby Sanchez .20 .50
90 Kevin Youkilis .30 .75
91 Alfonso Soriano .30 .75
92 Jake Peavy .20 .50
93 Pablo Sandoval .30 .75
94 Shane Victorino .30 .75
95 Cameron Maybin .20 .50
96 Hunter Pence .30 .75
97 Ubaldo Jimenez .30 .75
98 Heath Bell .20 .50
99 Kendry Morales .20 .50
100 Alex Rodriguez .75 2.00
101 Tim Hudson .30 .75
102 Jordan Zimmerman .20 .50
103 Shin-Soo Choo .30 .75
104 Matt Garza .20 .50
105 Felix Hernandez .50 1.25
106 Ike Davis .30 .75
107 Clayton Kershaw .50 1.25
108 Mike Morse .20 .50
109 Ricky Romero .20 .50
110 Carlos Gonzalez .30 .75
111 Marlon Byrd .20 .50
112 Carlos Pena .30 .75
113 Jayson Werth .30 .75
114 Carlos Beltran .20 .50
115 Justin Verlander .60 1.50
116 Clay Buchholz .30 .75
117 Jimmy Rollins .30 .75
118 Francisco Liriano .20 .50
119 Ryan Ludwick .20 .50
120 Stephen Strasburg 1.00 2.50
121 Chris Carpenter .50 1.25
122 Adam Lind .30 .75
123 B.J. Upton .30 .75
124 Jacoby Ellsbury .50 1.25
125 Roy Oswalt .30 .75
126 Johan Santana .50 1.25
127 Madison Bumgarner .20 .50
128 Matt Joyce .20 .50
129 Mark Reynolds .20 .50
130 Matt Holliday .50 1.25
131 Tyler Colvin .30 .75
132 Matt Cain .30 .75
133 Drew Storen .20 .50
134 Grady Sizemore .30 .75
135 Martin Prado .20 .50
136 C.J. Wilson .20 .50
137 Chris Young .20 .50
138 Jose Reyes .30 .75
139 Clayton Richard .20 .50
140 Mark Teixeira .50 1.25
141 Lance Berkman .30 .75
142 John Buck .20 .50
143 Brett Anderson .30 .75
144 Johnny Damon .30 .75
145 Rickie Weeks .30 .75
146 Brett Myers .20 .50
147 Chone Figgins .20 .50
148 Derrek Lee .20 .50
149 Ian Desmond .30 .75
150 Albert Pujols 1.25 3.00
151 Pedro Alvarez RC .60 1.50
152 Josh Thole .20 .50
153 Jonathan Broxton .20 .50
154 Justin Morneau .50 1.25
155 Tommy Hanson .30 .75
156 Cole Hamels .50 1.25
157 Angel Pagan .20 .50
158 Curtis Granderson .30 .75
159 Paul Konerko .30 .75
160 Troy Tulowitzki .50 1.25
161 Dustin Pedroia .60 1.50
162 Elvis Andrus .30 .75
163 Logan Morrison .20 .50
164 Jered Weaver .20 .50
165 Adrian Beltre .20 .50
166 Victor Martinez .30 .75
167 Chad Billingsley .30 .75
168 J.A. Happ .20 .50
169 Rafael Furcal .20 .50
170 Eric Hosmer RC 3.00 8.00
171 Tsuyoshi Nishioka RC 1.25 3.00
172 Brandon Belt RC 1.50 4.00
173 Freddie Freeman RC 1.50 4.00
174 Michael Pineda RC 1.25 3.00
175 Ben Revere RC .60 1.50
176 Brandon Beachy RC 1.00 2.50
177 Aneury Rodriguez RC .40 1.00
178 Mark Trumbo (RC) .60 1.50
179 Marcos Mateo RC .40 1.00
180 Hank Conger RC .60 1.50
181 Jake McGee (RC) .40 1.00
182 J.P. Arencibia (RC) .60 1.50
183 Jordan Walden RC .40 1.00
184 Eric Sogard RC .40 1.00
185 Matt Young RC .40 1.00
186 Domonic Brown (RC) 1.00 2.50
187 Scott Cousins RC .40 1.00
188 Alexi Ogando RC 1.00 2.50
189 Mike Nickeas (RC) .40 1.00
190 Ivan DeJesus RC .40 1.00
191 Andrew Cashner (RC) .40 1.00
192 Josh Lueke RC .40 1.00
193 Darwin Barney RC 1.25 3.00
194 Mason Tobin RC .40 1.00
195 Craig Kimbrel RC 1.00 2.50
196 Lance Pendleton RC .40 1.00
197 Julio Teheran RC 1.25 3.00
198 Eduardo Nunez RC .40 1.00
199 Pedro Beato RC .40 1.00
200 Jeremy Hellickson RC 1.25 3.00
201 Vinnie Pestano RC .40 1.00
202 Tom Wilhelmsen RC .40 1.00
203 Brett Wallace (RC) .40 1.00
204 Chris Pettit (RC) .40 1.00
205 Chris Sale RC .60 1.50
206 Brandon Kintzler RC .40 1.00
207 Alex Cobb RC .40 1.00
208 Michael Kohn RC .40 1.00
209 Cory Luebke RC .40 1.00
210 Pedro Strop (RC) .40 1.00
211 Jerry Sands RC 1.50 4.00
212 Dee Gordon RC 1.00 2.50
213 Joe Paterson RC .60 1.50
214 Brent Morel RC .40 1.00
215 Kyle Drabek RC .60 1.50
216 Zach Britton RC 1.00 2.50
217 Mike Minor (RC) .40 1.00
218 Hector Noesi RC .60 1.50
219 Carlos Peguero RC .60 1.50
220 Aaron Crow RC .60 1.50

2011 Topps Chrome Refractors

*REF VET: 1X TO 2.5X BASIC
*REF RC: .6X TO 1.5X BASIC RC
STATED ODDS 1:3 HOBBY

2011 Topps Chrome Atomic Refractors

*ATOMIC VET: 2X TO 5X BASIC
*ATOMIC RC: 1X TO 2.5X BASIC RC
STATED ODDS 1:19 HOBBY
STATED PRINT RUN 225 SER.#'d SETS
170 Eric Hosmer 15.00 40.00

2011 Topps Chrome Black Refractors

*BLACK VET: 4X TO 10X BASIC
*BLACK RC: 2X TO 5X BASIC RC
STATED ODDS 1:84 HOBBY
STATED PRINT RUN 100 SER.#'d SETS

2011 Topps Chrome Blue Refractors

*BLUE VET: 4X TO 10X BASIC
*BLUE RC: 2X TO 5X BASIC RC
STATED ODDS 1:57 HOBBY
STATED PRINT RUN 99 SER.#'d SETS
170 Eric Hosmer 20.00 50.00

2011 Topps Chrome Gold Canary Diamond Refractors

STATED ODDS 1:4220 HOBBY
STATED PRINT RUN 1 SER.#'d SET
NO PRICING DUE TO SCARCITY

2011 Topps Chrome Gold Refractors

*GOLD VET: 6X TO 15X BASIC
*GOLD RC: 3X TO 8X BASIC RC
STATED ODDS 1:111 HOBBY
STATED PRINT RUN 50 SER.#'d SETS
20 Derek Jeter 40.00 80.00
170 Eric Hosmer 50.00 100.00

2011 Topps Chrome Orange Refractors

*ORANGE VET: 1.5X TO 4X BASIC
*ORANGE RC: .75X TO 2X BASIC RC

2011 Topps Chrome Purple Refractors

*PURPLE VET: 2X TO 5X BASIC
*PURPLE RC: 1X TO 2.5X BASIC RC
STATED PRINT RUN 499 SER.#'d SETS
7 Mickey Mantle 12.50 30.00
170 Eric Hosmer 12.50 30.00

2011 Topps Chrome Red Refractors

STATED ODDS 1:167 HOBBY
STATED PRINT RUN 25 SER.#'d SETS
NO PRICING DUE TO SCARCITY

2011 Topps Chrome Sepia Refractors

*SEPIA VET: 4X TO 10X BASIC
*SEPIA RC: 2X TO 5X BASIC RC
STATED ODDS 1:43 HOBBY
STATED PRINT RUN 99 SER.#'d SETS
170 Eric Hosmer 20.00 50.00

2011 Topps Chrome Superfractors

STATED ODDS 1:4182 HOBBY
STATED PRINT RUN 1 SER.#'d SET
NO PRICING DUE TO SCARCITY

2011 Topps Chrome X-Fractors

*X-FRAC.VET: 1.5X TO 4X BASIC
*X-FRAC.RC: .75X TO 2X BASIC RC

2011 Topps Chrome Rookie Autographs

STATED ODDS 1:12 HOBBY
PRINTING PLATE ODDS 1:8217 HOBBY
PLATE PRINT RUN 1 SET PER COLOR
BLACK-CYAN-MAGENTA-YELLOW ISSUED
NO PLATE PRICING DUE TO SCARCITY
EXCHANGE DEADLINE 8/31/2014
33 Danny Espinosa 5.00 12.00
170 Eric Hosmer EXCH 90.00 150.00
171 Tsuyoshi Nishioka EXCH 50.00 100.00
172 Brandon Belt 10.00 25.00
173 Freddie Freeman EXCH 10.00 25.00
174 Michael Pineda 10.00 25.00
175 Ben Revere 4.00 10.00
176 Brandon Beachy 8.00 20.00
178 Mark Trumbo 8.00 20.00
181 Jake McGee 3.00 8.00
182 J.P. Arencibia 5.00 12.00
183 Jordan Walden 4.00 10.00
184 Eric Sogard 3.00 8.00
188 Alexi Ogando 4.00 10.00
190 Ivan DeJesus Jr. 3.00 8.00
191 Andrew Cashner 3.00 8.00
193 Darwin Barney 5.00 12.00
195 Craig Kimbrel 10.00 25.00
197 Julio Teheran 8.00 20.00
198 Eduardo Nunez 5.00 12.00
205 Chris Sale 5.00 12.00
207 Alex Cobb 3.00 8.00
214 Brent Morel 3.00 8.00
215 Kyle Drabek 4.00 10.00
216 Zach Britton 5.00 12.00
217 Mike Minor 5.00 12.00
218 Hector Noesi 5.00 12.00
219 Carlos Peguero 5.00 12.00
220 Aaron Crow 3.00 8.00

2011 Topps Chrome Rookie Autographs Refractors

*REF: .5X TO 1.2X BASIC
STATED ODDS 1:72 HOBBY
STATED PRINT RUN 499 SER.#'d SETS
EXCHANGE DEADLINE 8/31/2014
170 Eric Hosmer EXCH
171 Tsuyoshi Nishioka EXCH

2011 Topps Chrome Rookie Autographs Atomic Refractors

STATED ODDS 1:3310 HOBBY
STATED PRINT RUN 10 SER.#'d SETS
NO PRICING DUE TO SCARCITY
EXCHANGE DEADLINE 8/31/2014

2011 Topps Chrome Rookie Autographs Black Refractors

*BLACK REF: 1X TO 2.5X BASIC
STATED ODDS 1:328 HOBBY
STATED PRINT RUN 100 SER.#'d SETS
EXCHANGE DEADLINE 8/31/2014
170 Eric Hosmer EXCH 125.00 250.00
171 Tsuyoshi Nishioka EXCH

2011 Topps Chrome Rookie Autographs Blue Refractors

*BLUE REF: .75X TO 2X BASIC
STATED ODDS 1:181 HOBBY
STATED PRINT RUN 199 SER.#'d SETS
EXCHANGE DEADLINE 8/31/2014
170 Eric Hosmer EXCH
171 Tsuyoshi Nishioka EXCH

2011 Topps Chrome Rookie Autographs Gold Refractors

*GOLD REF: 1.2X TO 3X BASIC
STATED ODDS 1:694 HOBBY
STATED PRINT RUN 50 SER.#'d SETS
EXCHANGE DEADLINE 8/31/2014
170 Eric Hosmer EXCH 250.00 350.00
172 Brandon Belt 60.00 120.00
173 Freddie Freeman EXCH 60.00 120.00
188 Alexi Ogando 15.00 40.00

2011 Topps Chrome Rookie Autographs Red Refractors

STATED ODDS 1:1314 HOBBY
STATED PRINT RUN 25 SER.#'d SETS
NO PRICING DUE TO SCARCITY
EXCHANGE DEADLINE 8/31/2014

2011 Topps Chrome Rookie Autographs Sepia Refractors

*SEPIA REF: 1X TO 2.5X BASIC
STATED ODDS 1:350 HOBBY
STATED PRINT RUN 99 SER.#'d SETS
EXCHANGE DEADLINE 8/31/2014
170 Eric Hosmer EXCH 125.00 250.00
171 Tsuyoshi Nishioka EXCH

2011 Topps Chrome Rookie Autographs Superfractors

STATED ODDS 1:32,800 HOBBY
STATED PRINT RUN 1 SER.#'d SETS
NO PRICING DUE TO SCARCITY
EXCHANGE DEADLINE 8/31/2014

2011 Topps Chrome USA Baseball Autographs

EXCHANGE CARD ODDS 1:824 HOBBY
EXCHANGE DEADLINE 9/6/2012
PRINTING PLATE ODDS 1:230,000 HOBBY
PLATE PRINT RUN 1 SET PER COLOR
BLACK-CYAN-MAGENTA-YELLOW ISSUED
NO PLATE PRICING DUE TO SCARCITY
NNO Exchange Card 40.00 80.00

2011 Topps Chrome USA Baseball Autographs Refractors

EXCHANGE ODDS 1:1173 HOBBY
EXCHANGE DEADLINE 9/6/2012
NNO Exchange Card 50.00 100.00

2011 Topps Chrome USA Baseball Autographs Atomic Refractors

*ATOMIC REF: X TO X BASIC
EXCHANGE ODDS 1:25,600 HOBBY
EXCHANGE DEADLINE 9/6/2012

2011 Topps Chrome USA Baseball Autographs Blue Refractors

EXCHANGE ODDS 1:2397 HOBBY
EXCHANGE DEADLINE 9/6/2012
NNO Exchange Card 75.00 150.00

2011 Topps Chrome USA Baseball Autographs Gold Refractors

EXCHANGE ODDS 1:4900 HOBBY
EXCHANGE DEADLINE 9/6/2012
NNO Exchange Card 200.00 400.00

2011 Topps Chrome USA Baseball Autographs Red Refractors

EXCHANGE ODDS 1:57,725 HOBBY
NO PRICING DUE TO SCARCITY
EXCHANGE DEADLINE 9/6/2012

2011 Topps Chrome USA Baseball Autographs Superfractors

EXCHANGE ODDS 1:57,500 HOBBY
STATED PRINT RUN 1 SER.#'d SET
NO PRICING DUE TO SCARCITY
EXCHANGE DEADLINE 9/6/2012

2011 Topps Chrome USA Baseball Refractors

EXCHANGE CARD ODDS 1:964 HOBBY
STATED PRINT RUN 999 SER.#'d SETS
EXCHANGE DEADLINE 9/6/2012
PRINTING PLATE ODDS 1:230,000 HOBBY
PLATE PRINT RUN 1 SET PER COLOR
BLACK-CYAN-MAGENTA-YELLOW ISSUED
NO PLATE PRICING DUE TO SCARCITY
NNO Exchange Card 20.00 50.00

2011 Topps Chrome USA Baseball Blue Refractors

EXCHANGE ODDS 1:2025 HOBBY
EXCHANGE DEADLINE 9/6/2012
NNO Exchange Card 30.00 60.00

2011 Topps Chrome USA Baseball Gold Refractors

EXCHANGE ODDS 1:18,400 HOBBY
STATED PRINT RUN 50 SER.#'d SETS
EXCHANGE DEADLINE 9/6/2012
NNO Exchange Card 90.00 150.00

2011 Topps Chrome USA Baseball Red Refractors

EXCHANGE ODDS 1:184,000 HOBBY
NO PRICING DUE TO SCARCITY
EXCHANGE DEADLINE 9/6/2012

2011 Topps Chrome USA Baseball Superfractors

EXCHANGE ODDS 1:920,000 HOBBY
STATED PRINT RUN 1 SER.#'d SET
NO PRICING DUE TO SCARCITY
EXCHANGE DEADLINE 9/6/2012

2011 Topps Chrome Vintage Chrome

COMPLETE SET (50) 20.00 50.00
STATED ODDS 1:6 HOBBY
VC1 Buster Posey 1.00 2.50
VC2 Chipper Jones .75 2.00
VC3 Carl Crawford .50 1.25
VC4 David Wright 1.00 2.50
VC5 Prince Fielder .50 1.25
VC6 Hanley Ramirez .75 2.00
VC7 Ryan Zimmerman .50 1.25
VC8 David Ortiz .50 1.25
VC9 Evan Longoria 1.00 2.50
VC10 Tim Lincecum .75 2.00
VC11 Jason Heyward 1.00 2.50
VC12 Joey Votto .75 2.00
VC13 Derek Jeter 2.00 5.00
VC14 Matt Kemp .50 1.25
VC15 Adrian Gonzalez .50 1.25
VC16 Dan Uggla .50 1.25
VC17 Austin Jackson .30 .75
VC18 Starlin Castro .75 2.00
VC19 Chase Utley .75 2.00
VC20 David Price .75 2.00
VC21 Ryan Howard 1.00 2.50
VC22 Ichiro Suzuki 1.25 3.00
VC23 CC Sabathia .50 1.25
VC24 Ryan Braun 1.00 2.50
VC25 Josh Hamilton .75 2.00
VC26 Robinson Cano .75 2.00
VC27 Brian McCann .50 1.25
VC28 Nelson Cruz .50 1.25
VC29 Roy Halladay .75 2.00
VC30 Jose Bautista .50 1.25
VC31 Joe Mauer .75 2.00
VC32 Mike Stanton .50 1.25
VC33 Troy Tulowitzki .75 2.00
VC34 Kevin Youkilis .50 1.25
VC35 Miguel Cabrera .75 2.00
VC36 Alex Rodriguez 1.25 3.00
VC37 Felix Hernandez .75 2.00
VC38 Stephen Strasburg 1.50 4.00
VC39 Mark Teixeira .75 2.00
VC40 Albert Pujols 2.00 5.00
VC41 Carlos Gonzalez .50 1.25
VC42 Dustin Pedroia 1.00 2.50
VC43 Tsuyoshi Nishioka 1.00 2.50
VC44 Brandon Belt 1.25 3.00
VC45 Freddie Freeman 1.25 3.00
VC46 J.P. Arencibia .50 1.25
VC47 Domonic Brown .75 2.00
VC48 Aroldis Chapman 1.00 2.50
VC49 Jeremy Hellickson 1.00 2.50
VC50 Kyle Drabek .50 1.25

2006 Topps Co-Signers

This 120-card set was released in May, 2006. The set was issued only in six-card hobby packs with an $10 SRP. The packs came 12 to a box and 24 boxes to a case. Cards numbered 1-100 feature veteran players while cards numbered 101-120 feature signed cards of 2006 rookies.

COMP.SET w/o AU's (100) 15.00 40.00
COMMON CARD (1-100) .30 .75
101-120 GROUP A ODDS 1:2025
101-120 GROUP B ODDS 1:1625
101-120 GROUP C ODDS 1:920
101-120 GROUP D ODDS 1:81
101-120 GROUP E ODDS 1:270
101-120 GROUP F ODDS 1:68
101-120 GROUP G ODDS 1:12
101-120 GROUP A PRINT RUN 200 CARDS
101-120 GROUP B PRINT RUN 250 CARDS
101-120 GROUP C PRINT RUN 440 CARDS
A-C CARDS ARE NOT SERIAL NUMBERED
A-C PRINT RUNS PROVIDED BY TOPPS
1 Albert Pujols 2.00 5.00
2 Roger Clemens 1.00 2.50
3 Paul Konerko .50 1.25
4 Jeff Francoeur .75 2.00
5 Miguel Tejada .50 1.25
6 Curt Schilling .50 1.25
7 Mickey Mantle 2.50 6.00
8 Miguel Cabrera .75 2.00
9 Derrek Lee .30 .75
10 Jeff Kent .30 .75
11 Gary Sheffield .30 .75
12 Rich Harden .30 .75
13 Scott Rolen .50 1.25
14 David Wright 1.25 3.00
15 Troy Glaus .30 .75
16 Torii Hunter .30 .75
17 Nolan Ryan 2.00 5.00
18 Alfonso Soriano .50 1.25
19 Hank Blalock .30 .75
20 Chase Utley .75 2.00
21 Ryan Howard 1.25 3.00
22 Robinson Cano .75 2.00
23 Derek Jeter 2.00 5.00
24 Huston Street .30 .75
25 Jason Giambi .30 .75
26 Rafael Furcal .30 .75
27 Rickie Weeks .50 1.25
28 Ivan Rodriguez .50 1.25
29 Travis Hafner .30 .75
30 Greg Maddux 1.25 3.00
31 Andruw Jones .30 .75
32 Andy Pettitte .50 1.25
33 Scott Podsednik .30 .75
34 Francisco Rodriguez .50 1.25
35 Josh Beckett .50 1.25
36 Lance Berkman .50 1.25
37 Roy Oswalt .50 1.25
38 Pedro Martinez .50 1.25
39 Jimmy Rollins .50 1.25
40 Johan Santana .75 2.00
41 Randy Johnson .75 2.00
42 Mariano Rivera .75 2.00
43 Nick Johnson .30 .75
44 Josh Gibson .75 2.00
45 Shawn Green .30 .75
46 Adrian Beltre .30 .75
47 Johnny Damon .50 1.25
48 Joe Mauer .75 2.00
49 Todd Helton .50 1.25
50 Alex Rodriguez 1.25 3.00
51 Jake Peavy .30 .75
52 David Ortiz .50 1.25
53 Mark Buehrle .50 1.25
54 Eric Gagne .30 .75
55 Hideki Matsui .75 2.00
56 Bobby Abreu .30 .75
57 Victor Martinez .50 1.25
58 Brian Roberts .30 .75
59 Chipper Jones .75 2.00
60 Carlos Beltran .30 .75
61 Tim Hudson .50 1.25
62 Carlos Lee .30 .75
63 Barry Zito .30 .75
64 Moises Alou .30 .75
65 Mark Teixeira .75 2.00
66 Lyle Overbay .30 .75
67 Kerry Wood .30 .75
68 B.J. Ryan .30 .75
69 Jim Edmonds .50 1.25
70 Carlos Delgado .30 .75
71 Magglio Ordonez .50 1.25
72 Juan Pierre .30 .75
73 Manny Ramirez .75 2.00
74 Dontrelle Willis .30 .75
75 Ichiro Suzuki 1.25 3.00
76 Nomar Garciaparra .75 2.00
77 Zach Duke .30 .75
78 Chris Carpenter .75 2.00
79 A.J. Burnett .50 1.25
80 Scott Kazmir .50 1.25
81 Carl Crawford .50 1.25
82 Mark Prior .50 1.25
83 Adam Dunn .50 1.25
84 Justin Morneau .75 2.00
85 Morgan Ensberg .30 .75
86 Pat Burrell .30 .75
87 Paul Lo Duca .30 .75
88 Jason Bay .30 .75
89 Aubrey Huff .30 .75
90 Kevin Millwood .30 .75
91 Vernon Wells .30 .75
92 Javy Lopez .30 .75
93 Michael Young .50 1.25
94 Felix Hernandez .75 2.00
95 Ken Griffey Jr. 1.25 3.00
96 Bartolo Colon .30 .75
97 Billy Wagner .30 .75
98 Vladimir Guerrero .75 2.00
99 Jose Reyes .50 1.25
100 Barry Bonds 1.50 4.00
101 Anthony LeRew AU G (RC) 4.00 10.00
102 R.Zimm AU C/440 (RC) * 10.00 25.00
103 C.Hansen AU B/250 RC * 20.00 50.00
104 Francisco Liriano AU G (RC) 4.00 10.00
105 Jason Botts AU G (RC) 4.00 10.00
106 Josh Johnson AU G (RC) 8.00 20.00
107 Hanley Ramirez AU G (RC) 8.00 20.00
108 Adam Wainwright AU G (RC) 8.00 20.00
109 K.Johjima AU A/200 RC * 50.00 100.00
110 Dan Ortmeier AU G (RC) 4.00 10.00
111 Darrell Rasner AU G (RC) 4.00 10.00
112 Chuck James AU F (RC) 6.00 15.00
113 Nelson Cruz AU F (RC) 8.00 20.00
114 Hong-Chih Kuo AU E (RC) 15.00 40.00
115 Ryan Garko AU G (RC) 4.00 10.00
116 Reggie Abercrombie AU D (RC) 4.00 10.00
117 Ian Kinsler AU D (RC) 10.00 25.00
118 Joel Zumaya AU D (RC) 10.00 25.00
119 Willie Eyre AU D (RC) 4.00 10.00
120 Dan Uggla AU D (RC) 6.00 15.00

2006 Topps Co-Signers Changing Faces Blue

*BLUE: .75X TO 2X BASIC
STATED ODDS 1:11
STATED PRINT RUN 125 SERIAL #'d SETS

2006 Topps Co-Signers Changing Faces Bronze

*BRONZE: .75X TO 2X BASIC
STATED ODDS 1:9
STATED PRINT RUN 150 SERIAL #'d SETS

2006 Topps Co-Signers Changing Faces Gold

*GOLD: .75X TO 2X BASIC
STATED ODDS 1:12
STATED PRINT RUN 115 SERIAL #'d SETS

2006 Topps Co-Signers Changing Faces Red

*RED: .75X TO 2X BASIC
STATED ODDS 1:9
STATED PRINT RUN 150 SERIAL #'d SETS

2006 Topps Co-Signers Changing Faces Silver Blue

*SILVER BLUE: 1X TO 2.5X BASIC
STATED ODDS 1:18
STATED PRINT RUN 75 SERIAL #'d SETS

2006 Topps Co-Signers Changing Faces Silver Bronze

*SILVER BRONZE: .75X TO 2X BASIC
STATED ODDS 1:11
STATED PRINT RUN 125 SERIAL #'d SETS

2006 Topps Co-Signers Changing Faces Silver Gold

*SILVER GOLD: 1.25X TO 3X BASIC
STATED ODDS 1:27
STATED PRINT RUN 50 SERIAL #'d SETS

2006 Topps Co-Signers Changing Faces Silver Red

*SILVER RED: .75X TO 2X BASIC
STATED ODDS 1:14
STATED PRINT RUN 100 SERIAL #'d SETS

2006 Topps Co-Signers Changing Faces HyperSilver Blue

STATED ODDS 1:135
STATED PRINT RUN 10 SERIAL #'d SETS
NO PRICING DUE TO SCARCITY

2006 Topps Co-Signers Changing Faces HyperSilver Bronze

*HYPER BRONZE: 1X TO 2.5X BASIC
STATED ODDS 1:18
STATED PRINT RUN 75 SERIAL #'d SETS

2006 Topps Co-Signers Changing Faces HyperSilver Gold

STATED ODDS 1:270
STATED PRINT RUN 5 SERIAL #'d SETS
NO PRICING DUE TO SCARCITY

2006 Topps Co-Signers Changing Faces HyperSilver Red

*HYPER RED: 2X TO 5X BASIC
STATED ODDS 1:54
STATED PRINT RUN 25 SERIAL #'d SETS
NO BONDS PRICING DUE TO VOLATILITY

2006 Topps Co-Signers Dual Autographs

GROUP A ODDS 1:11,375
GROUP B ODDS 1:20,350
GROUP C ODDS 1:522
GROUP D ODDS 1:1013
GROUP E ODDS 1:2705
GROUP F ODDS 1:580
GROUP G ODDS 1:3223
GROUP H ODDS 1:2025
GROUP I ODDS 1:540
GROUP J ODDS 1:1352
GROUP K ODDS 1:1158
GROUP L ODDS 1:950
GROUP M ODDS 1:902
GROUP N ODDS 1:162
GROUP O ODDS 1:624
GROUP P ODDS 1:270
GROUP Q ODDS 1:68
GROUP R ODDS 1:90
GROUP S ODDS 1:29
GROUP A PRINT RUN 18 SETS
GROUP B PRINT RUN 20 SETS
GROUP C PRINT RUN 25 SETS
GROUP D PRINT RUN 50 SETS
GROUP E PRINT RUN 75 SETS
GROUP F PRINT RUN 100 SETS
GROUP G PRINT RUN 125 SETS
GROUP H PRINT RUN 200 SETS
GROUP I PRINT RUN 250 SETS
AROD/BONDS PRINT RUN 25 SERIAL #'d SETS
CARDS ARE NOT SERIAL NUMBERED
PRINT RUN INFO PROVIDED BY TOPPS
NO GROUP A-C PRICING DUE TO SCARCITY

Card	Low	High
CS1 Alex Rodriguez / Barry Bonds C/25		
CS2 David Wright / Alex Rodriguez C/25 *		
CS3 Victor Martinez / Kenji Johjima C/25 *		
CS4 Kenji Johjima / Felix Hernandez A/18 *		
CS5 David Ortiz / Manny Ramirez C/25 *		
CS6 Nolan Ryan / Roger Clemens C/25 *		
CS7 David Ortiz / Albert Pujols C/25 *		
CS8 Chipper Jones / Dale Murphy C/25 *		
CS9 Wade Boggs / Don Mattingly C/25 *		
CS10 Nolan Ryan / Felix Hernandez A/18 *		
CS11 Stan Musial / Albert Pujols B/20 *		
CS12 Robinson Cano / Rod Carew C/25 *		
CS13 Cal Ripken / Brooks Robinson C/25 *		
CS14 Dave Winfield / Johnny Damon C/25 *		
CS15 Prince Fielder / Ryan Zimmerman I/250 *	15.00	40.00
CS16 Cal Ripken / Ozzie Smith C/25 *		
CS17 Alex Rodriguez / Don Mattingly C/25 *		
CS18 Don Larsen / Yogi Berra C/25 *		
CS19 Mike Schmidt / Brooks Robinson C/25 *		
CS20 Ryan Zimmerman / Wade Boggs C/25 *		
CS21 Dwight Gooden / Keith Hernandez C/25 *		
CS22 Ryan Howard / Derrek Lee E/75 *	20.00	50.00
CS23 Jeff Mathis / Chris Snyder S	4.00	10.00
CS24 Dontrelle Willis / Miguel Cabrera C/25 *		
CS25 Ray Knight / Keith Hernandez F/100 *	10.00	25.00
CS26 Mike Schmidt / Chase Utley C/25 *		
CS27 Billy Wagner / Paul Lo Duca D/50 *	40.00	80.00
CS28 Tony Gwynn / Wade Boggs C/25 *		
CS29 Mike Schmidt / Ozzie Smith C/25 *		
CS30 Dwight Gooden / Darryl Strawberry D/50 *	20.00	50.00
CS31 Ryan Howard / Huston Street N	30.00	60.00
CS32 Mariano Rivera / Huston Street C/25 *		
CS33 Prince Fielder / Ryan Howard D/50 *	40.00	80.00
CS34 Robinson Cano / Chase Utley E/75 *	40.00	80.00
CS35 Johnny Podres / Duke Snider C/25 *		
CS36 David Justice / Chipper Jones C/25 *		
CS37 David Wright / Jose Reyes D/50 *	150.00	250.00
CS38 Jeff Mathis / Ryan Garko S	10.00	25.00
CS39 Brandon McCarthy / Pedro Lopez S	4.00	10.00
CS40 David Justice / Dale Murphy F/100 *	30.00	60.00
CS41 Dave Winfield / Gary Sheffield C/25 *		
CS42 Joe Mauer / Francisco Liriano Q	40.00	80.00
CS43 Jim Leyritz / Reggie Jackson C/25 *		
CS44 Ryan Zimmerman / David Wright F/100 *	60.00	120.00
CS45 Rick Rhoden / Dave Parker F/100 *	15.00	40.00
CS46 Jonathan Papelbon / Craig Breslow R	5.00	12.00
CS47 Ryan Zimmerman / Kenji Johjima C/25 *		
CS48 Dan Johnson / Prince Fielder F/100 *	15.00	40.00
CS49 Victor Martinez / Ryan Garko N	8.00	20.00
CS50 Ben Hendrickson / Anthony Reyes Q	6.00	15.00
CS51 Nelson Cruz / Prince Fielder F/100 *	20.00	50.00
CS52 Jonathan Papelbon / Anthony Reyes R	10.00	25.00
CS53 Ben Hendrickson / Rich Hill Q	6.00	15.00
CS54 Shin-Soo Choo / Kenji Johjima C/25 *		
CS55 Francisco Liriano / Johan Santana F/100 *	75.00	150.00
CS56 Brandon McCarthy / Zach Duke S	6.00	15.00
CS57 Josh Johnson / Scott Olsen S	10.00	25.00
CS58 Tommy John / Bob Welch K	6.00	15.00
CS59 Roy White / Joe Pepitone N	10.00	25.00
CS60 Cecil Fielder / Prince Fielder N	50.00	100.00
CS61 Andre Dawson / Derrek Lee C/25 *		
CS62 Conor Jackson / Ryan Howard Q	10.00	25.00
CS63 Dontrelle Willis / Zach Duke D/50 *	15.00	40.00
CS64 Mariano Rivera / Billy Wagner C/25 *		
CS65 Hong-Chih Kuo / Shin-Soo Choo Q	15.00	40.00
CS66 Jim Leyritz / Cecil Fielder G/125 *	20.00	50.00
CS67 Scott Kazmir / Francisco Liriano P	6.00	15.00
CS68 Scott Kazmir / Roy Oswalt D/50 *	6.00	15.00
CS69 Chuck James / Anthony LeRew S	6.00	15.00
CS70 Cecil Fielder / Ryan Howard I/250 *	30.00	60.00
CS71 Chien-Ming Wang / Hong-Chih Kuo C/25 *		
CS72 Shin-Soo Choo / Chien-Ming Wang D/50 *	100.00	175.00
CS73 Nelson Cruz / Jason Botts Q	6.00	15.00
CS74 Francisco Liriano / Ervin Santana S	6.00	15.00
CS75 Adam Wainwright / Anthony Reyes S	6.00	15.00
CS76 Scott Kazmir / Ervin Santana H/200 *	12.50	30.00
CS77 Robinson Cano / Gary Sheffield I/250 *	30.00	60.00
CS78 David Wright / Miguel Cabrera D/50 *	60.00	120.00
CS79 Dan Johnson / Conor Jackson P	6.00	15.00
CS80 Frank Tanana / Mickey Tettleton R	6.00	15.00
CS81 Andruw Jones / Chipper Jones J	30.00	60.00
CS82 Morgan Ensberg / Roy Oswalt M	6.00	15.00
CS83 Michael Young / Ozzie Smith O	15.00	40.00
CS84 Grady Sizemore / Nick Swisher L	10.00	25.00
CS85 Garrett Atkins / Clint Barmes N	6.00	15.00

2006 Topps Co-Signers Dual Cut Signatures

GROUP A ODDS 1:30,000
GROUP B ODDS 1:6800
GROUP C ODDS 1:43,000
GROUP D ODDS 1:21,000
GROUP E ODDS 1:1125
GROUP F ODDS 1:4450
GROUP G ODDS 1:875
GROUP H ODDS 1:3650
GROUP I ODDS 1:5150
GROUP J ODDS 1:1980
GROUP A PRINT RUN 1 SERIAL #'d SET
NO A-F PRICING DUE TO SCARCITY

Card	Low	High
GWTJ A.B. Chandler / Billy Herman H	60.00	120.00
ABCFF A.B. Chandler / Ford Frick A		
ABCJC A.B. Chandler / Jocko Conlon E		
ABCJJ A.B. Chandler / Judy Johnson B		
ABCLB A.B. Chandler / Lou Boudreau B		
ABCRF A.B. Chandler / Rick Ferrell B		
ABCWG A.B. Chandler / Warren Giles B		
ABCWH A.B. Chandler / Will Harridge G	125.00	200.00
AETE Albert Einstein / Thomas Edison A		
ALLA Al Lopez / Luke Appling E		
BDWH Bill Dickey / Waite Hoyt A		
BHJM Billy Herman / Joe McCarthy B		
BLHW Bob Lemon / Hoyt Wilhelm E		
BLJH Bob Lemon / Jim 'Catfish' Hunter G	100.00	175.00
BLJJ Buck Leonard / Judy Johnson J	125.00	200.00
BLJS Bob Lemon / Joe Sewell E		
BLLB Bob Lemon / Lou Boudreau I	75.00	150.00
BLRF Bob Lemon / Rick Ferrell G	75.00	150.00
BTGK Bill Terry / George Kelly E		
BTSM Bill Terry / Sal Maglie E		
BTTJ Bill Terry / Travis Jackson E		
BTTW Bill Terry / Ted Williams A		
CGFF Charles Gehringer / Frankie Frisch B		
CGHN Charles Gehringer / Hal Newhouser C		
CGRF Charles Gehringer / Rick Ferrell G	75.00	150.00
CHBH Charles Gehringer / Billy Herman G	75.00	150.00
CHWH Catfish Hunter / Waite Hoyt E		
DGGM David Ben Gurion / Golda Meir A		
EALB Earl Averill / Lou Boudreau F		
FCGW Frank Crosetti / Gene Woodling G	100.00	175.00
GWTJ George Washington / Thomas Jefferson A		
HGCG Hank Greenberg / Charles Gehringer A		
HKCG Harvey Kuenn / Charles Gehringer J	75.00	150.00
HKLB Harvey Kuenn / Lou Boudreau B		
HTBT Harry Truman / Bess Truman A		
HWHN Hoyt Wilhelm / Hal Newhouser B		
HWTL Hoyt Wilhelm / Ted Lyons B		
JCAB Jocko Conlon / Al Barlick B		
JFKRFK John F. Kennedy / Robert F. Kennedy A		
JSGW Joe Sewell / Gene Woodling E		
JSLA Joe Sewell / Luke Appling G	100.00	175.00
JSLB Joe Sewell / Lou Boudreau G	60.00	120.00
JSSC Joe Sewell / Stanley Coveleski F / Coveleski's name is spelled incorrectly		
LABH Luke Appling / Billy Herman E		
LBBH Lou Boudreau / Billy Herman B		
LBCG Lou Boudreau / Charles Gehringer F		
LBRF Lou Boudreau / Rick Ferrell B		
LWBT Lloyd Waner / Bill Terry E		
LWCG Lloyd Waner / Charles Gehringer G	75.00	150.00
LWWS Lloyd Waner / (Willie Stargell A		
MMRM Mickey Mantle / Roger Maris A		
MMTW Mickey Mantle / Ted Williams A		
RFJJ Rick Ferrell / Judy Johnson E		
RNGF Richard Nixon / Gerald Ford A		
RRNR Ronald Reagan / Nancy Reagan A		
SMHW Sal Maglie / Hoyt Wilhelm D		
TJBH Travis Jackson / Billy Herman E		
TJGK Travis Jackson / George Kelly E		

2006 Topps Co-Signers Solo Sigs

GROUP A ODDS 1:2528
GROUP B ODDS 1:1790
GROUP C ODDS 1:2025
GROUP D ODDS 1:2700
GROUP E ODDS 1:2025
GROUP F ODDS 1:2025
GROUP G ODDS 1:540
GROUP H ODDS 1:135
GROUP I ODDS 1:600
GROUP J ODDS 1:108
GROUP K ODDS 1:45
GROUP A PRINT RUN 20 SETS
GROUP B PRINT RUN 25 SETS
GROUP C PRINT RUN 50 SETS
GROUP D PRINT RUN 75 SETS
GROUP E PRINT RUN 100 SETS
GROUP F-G PRINT RUN 250 SETS
CARDS ARE NOT SERIAL NUMBERED
PRINT RUN INFO PROVIDED BY TOPPS
NO A-B PRICING DUE TO SCARCITY

Card	Low	High
AD Andre Dawson H	4.00	10.00
AK Al Kaline E/100 *	15.00	40.00
AP Albert Pujols A/20 *		
AR Alex Rodriguez A/20 *		
ARE Anthony Reyes K	6.00	15.00
CB Clint Barmes J	4.00	10.00
CBR Craig Breslow K	4.00	10.00
CF Cecil Fielder J	6.00	15.00
CJ Chipper Jones B/25 *		
CM Craig Monroe K	4.00	10.00
CR Cal Ripken A/20 *		
CS Chris Snyder K	4.00	10.00
CY Carl Yastrzemski B/25 *		
DJ Dan Johnson F/250 *	4.00	10.00
DL Don Larsen H	6.00	15.00
DLE Derrek Lee C/50 *	20.00	50.00
DM Don Mattingly C/50 *	60.00	120.00
DO David Ortiz B/25 *		
DS Darryl Strawberry J	6.00	15.00
DW David Wright D/75 *	40.00	80.00
DWI Dontrelle Willis H	6.00	15.00
ES Ervin Santana G/250 *	4.00	10.00
GC Gustavo Chacin K	4.00	10.00
HS Huston Street G/250 *	6.00	15.00
JC Jack Clark H	4.00	10.00
JD Johnny Damon B/25 *		
JM Jeff Mathis K	4.00	10.00
JMA Joe Mauer D/75 *	30.00	60.00
JP Jonathan Papelbon H	20.00	50.00
JS Johan Santana C/50 *	20.00	50.00
MC Miguel Cabrera B/25 *		
MR Mariano Rivera B/25 *		
MRA Manny Ramirez A/20 *		
NR Nolan Ryan A/20 *		
OS Ozzie Smith B/25 *		
PF Prince Fielder G/250 *	15.00	40.00
RC Robinson Cano J	12.50	30.00
RCL Roger Clemens A/20 *		
RH Ryan Howard E/100 *	40.00	80.00
RHI Rich Hill K	12.50	30.00
RJ Reggie Jackson B/25 *		
RR Rick Rhoden J	4.00	10.00
SK Scott Kazmir H	10.00	25.00
SO Scott Olsen K	4.00	10.00
SSC Shin-Soo Choo K	12.50	30.00
TG Tony Gwynn A/20 *		
VG Vladimir Guerrero A/20 *		
VM Victor Martinez C/50 *	12.50	30.00
YB Yogi Berra B/25 *		
ZD Zach Duke I	6.00	15.00

2007 Topps Co-Signers

This 127-card set was released in June, 2007. This set was issued in six-card packs which came 12 packs to a box; 12 boxes to a carton and two cartons to a case. Cards numbered 1-93 feature rookies; while cards 94-121 feature rookies. Cards numbered 96-100 came in both signed and unsigned versions and cards 101-121 were all signed by the player featured. The signed rookie cards were inserted at a stated rate of one in 28 and the signed rookie variation cards were inserted at a stated rate of one in 198.

Card	Low	High
COMP.SET w/o AU's (100)	12.50	30.00
COMMON CARD (1-92)	.25	.60
COMMON ROOKIE (93-100)	.30	.75
COMMON ROOKIE AU (96-121)	3.00	8.00

ROOKIE AUTO ODDS 1:28
ROOKIE AUTO VARIATION ODDS 1:198
PRINTING PLATE ODDS 1:705
PRINTING PLATE AUTO ODDS 1:21,168
PLATE PRINT RUN 1 SET PER COLOR
BLACK-CYAN-MAGENTA-SPOT-YELLOW ISSUED
NO PLATE PRICING DUE TO SCARCITY

Card	Low	High
1 Ryan Howard	1.00	2.50
2 Jered Weaver	.40	1.00
3 Brian McCann	.25	.60
4 Garrett Atkins	.25	.60
5 Travis Hafner	.25	.60
6 Jason Schmidt	.25	.60
7 Curtis Granderson	.40	1.00
8 Ben Sheets	.25	.60
9 Chien-Ming Wang	.40	1.00
10 Francisco Liriano	.60	1.50
11 Freddy Sanchez	.25	.60
12 Roy Oswalt	.40	1.00
13 Jim Edmonds	.40	1.00
14 Matt Cain	.40	1.00
15 Jake Peavy	.25	.60
16 Ryan Zimmerman	.40	1.00
17 Troy Glaus	.25	.60
18 Kenji Johjima	.60	1.50
19 Curt Schilling	.40	1.00
20 Alfonso Soriano	.40	1.00
21 Adam Dunn	.40	1.00
22 Hanley Ramirez	.60	1.50
23 Mark Teahen	.25	.60
24 Todd Helton	.40	1.00
25 Alex Rodriguez	1.00	2.50
26 Mike Mussina	.40	1.00
27 Jason Bay	.40	1.00
28 Carl Crawford	.40	1.00
29 Vernon Wells	.25	.60
30 Rich Harden	.25	.60
31 Justin Morneau	.60	1.50
32 Andre Ethier	.40	1.00
33 Ramon Hernandez	.25	.60
34 Erik Bedard	.25	.60
35 Vladimir Guerrero	.60	1.50
36 Stephen Drew	.25	.60
37 Felix Hernandez	.60	1.50
38 C.C. Sabathia	.40	1.00
39 Adrian Gonzalez	.40	1.00
40 Prince Fielder	.40	1.00
41 Carlos Delgado	.25	.60
42 Jimmy Rollins	.40	1.00
43 Raul Ibanez	.40	1.00
44 Jorge Cantu	.25	.60
45 Michael Young	.40	1.00
46 Austin Kearns	.25	.60
47 Ivan Rodriguez	.40	1.00
48 Mark Teixeira	.60	1.50
49 David Ortiz	.40	1.00
50 David Wright	1.00	2.50
51 Justin Verlander	.75	2.00
52 Nick Markakis	.60	1.50
53 Miguel Cabrera	.60	1.50
54 Lance Berkman	.40	1.00
55 Robinson Cano	.60	1.50
56 Jon Lieber	.25	.60
57 Andruw Jones	.25	.60
58 Dan Haren	.25	.60
59 Grady Sizemore	.40	1.00
60 Gary Sheffield	.25	.60
61 Paul Lo Duca	.25	.60
62 Cole Hamels	.60	1.50
63 Richie Sexson	.25	.60
64 David Eckstein	.25	.60
65 Carlos Zambrano	.40	1.00
66 Scott Kazmir	.40	1.00
67 Anthony Reyes	.25	.60
68 Mark Kotsay	.25	.60
69 Miguel Tejada	.40	1.00
70 Pedro Martinez	.40	1.00
71 Jack Wilson	.25	.60
72 Joe Mauer	.60	1.50
73 Brian Giles	.25	.60
74 Jonathan Papelbon	.60	1.50
75 Albert Pujols	1.50	4.00
76 Nick Swisher	.60	1.50
77 Bill Hall	.25	.60
78 Jose Contreras	.25	.60
79 David DeJesus	.25	.60
80 Bobby Abreu	.25	.60
81 John Smoltz	.60	1.50
82 Chipper Jones	.60	1.50
83 Mark Buehrle	.40	1.00
84 Josh Barfield	.25	.60
85 Derrek Lee	.25	.60
86 Jim Thome	.40	1.00
87 Kenny Rogers	.25	.60
88 Jeremy Sowers	.25	.60
89 Brandon Webb	.40	1.00
90 Roy Halladay	.60	1.50
91 Tadahito Iguchi	.25	.60
92 Jeff Kent	.25	.60
93 Johnny Damon	.40	1.00
94 Daisuke Matsuzaka RC	1.25	3.00
95 Kei Igawa RC	.75	2.00
96a Delmon Young (RC)	.50	1.25
96b Delmon Young AU	8.00	20.00
97a Jeff Baker (RC)	.30	.75
97b Jeff Baker AU	3.00	8.00
98a Michael Bourn (RC)	.30	.75
98b Michael Bourn AU	4.00	10.00
99a Ubaldo Jimenez (RC)	2.00	5.00
99b Ubaldo Jimenez AU	10.00	25.00
100a Andrew Miller RC	.75	2.00
100b Andrew Miller AU	10.00	25.00
101 Angel Sanchez AU RC	3.00	8.00
102 Troy Tulowitzki AU (RC)	12.50	30.00
103 Joaquin Arias AU (RC)	3.00	8.00
104 Beltran Perez AU (RC)	3.00	8.00
105 Josh Fields AU (RC)	4.00	10.00
106 Hector Gimenez AU (RC)	3.00	8.00
107 Kevin Kouzmanoff AU (RC)	4.00	10.00
108 Miguel Montero AU (RC)	3.00	8.00
109 Philip Humber AU (RC)	4.00	10.00
110 Jerry Owens AU (RC)	3.00	8.00
111 Shawn Riggans AU (RC)	3.00	8.00
112 Brian Stokes AU (RC)	3.00	8.00
113 Scott Moore AU (RC)	3.00	8.00
114 David Murphy AU (RC)	3.00	8.00
115 Mitch Maier AU RC	3.00	8.00
116 Adam Lind AU (RC)	4.00	10.00
117 Glen Perkins AU (RC)	4.00	10.00
118 Dennis Sarfate AU (RC)	3.00	8.00
119 Elijah Dukes AU RC	6.00	15.00
120 Josh Hamilton AU (RC)	12.50	30.00
121 Alex Gordon AU RC	6.00	15.00
122 Barry Bonds	3.00	8.00

2007 Topps Co-Signers Blue

*BLUE: .75X TO 2X BASIC
*BLUE RC: .5X TO 1.2X BASIC
*BLUE AUTO: .4X TO 1X BASIC
BASE/ROOKIE CARD ODDS 1:10
ROOKIE AUTO ODDS 1:104
BASE/RC PRINT RUN 250 SER.#'d SETS
RC AUTO PRINT RUN 225 SER.#'d SETS

2007 Topps Co-Signers Bronze

*BRONZE: .75X TO 2X BASIC
*BRONZE RC: .5X TO 1.2X BASIC
*BRONZE AUTO: .4X TO 1X BASIC
BASE/ROOKIE CARD ODDS 1:9
ROOKIE AUTO ODDS 1:94
BASE/RC PRINT RUN 275 SER.#'d SETS
RC AUTO PRINT RUN 250 SER.#'d SETS

2007 Topps Co-Signers Gold

*GOLD: .75X TO 2X BASIC
*GOLD RC: .5X TO 1.2X BASIC
*GOLD AUTO: .4X TO 1X BASIC
BASE/ROOKIE CARD ODDS 1:11
ROOKIE AUTO ODDS 1:117
BASE/RC PRINT RUN 225 SER.#'d SETS
RC AUTO PRINT RUN 200 SER.#'d SETS

2007 Topps Co-Signers Red

*RED: .75X TO 2X BASIC
*RED RC: .5X TO 1.2X BASIC
*RED AUTO: .4X TO 1X BASIC
BASE/ROOKIE CARD ODDS 1:9
ROOKIE AUTO ODDS 1:85
BASE/RC PRINT RUN 299 SER.#'d SETS
RC AUTO PRINT RUN 275 SER.#'d SETS

2007 Topps Co-Signers Hyper Plaid Silver

BASE/ROOKIE CARD ODDS 1:2490
ROOKIE AUTO ODDS 1:25,872
STATED PRINT RUN 1 SERIAL #'d SET
NO PRICING DUE TO SCARCITY

2007 Topps Co-Signers Hyper Silver Blue

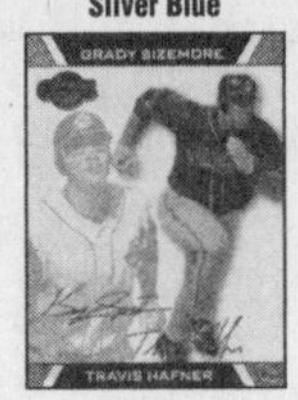

BASE/ROOKIE CARD ODDS 1:165
ROOKIE AUTO ODDS 1:938
BASE/ROOKIE PRINT RUN 15 SER.#'d SETS
ROOKIE AUTO PRINT RUN 25 SER.#'d SETS
NO PRICING DUE TO SCARCITY

2007 Topps Co-Signers Hyper Silver Bronze

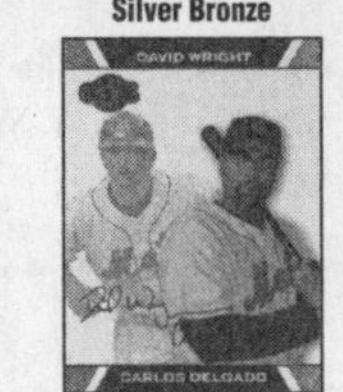

*HS BRONZE: 1.2X TO 3X BASIC
*HS BRONZE RC: 1.2X TO 3X BASIC
*HS BRONZE AUTO: .6X TO 1.5X BASIC
BASE/ROOKIE CARD ODDS 1:49
ROOKIE AUTO ODDS 1:468
STATED PRINT RUN 50 SER.#'d SETS

2007 Topps Co-Signers Hyper Silver Gold

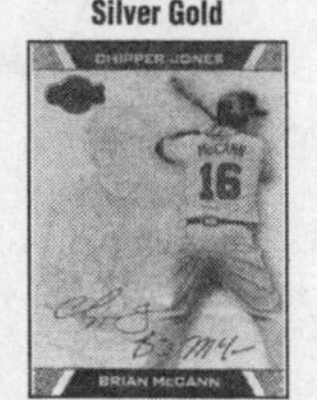

BASE/ROOKIE CARD ODDS 1:493
ROOKIE AUTO ODDS 1:4800
STATED PRINT RUN 5 SERIAL #'d SETS
NO PRICING DUE TO SCARCITY

2007 Topps Co-Signers Hyper Silver Red

*HS RED: 1X TO 2.5X BASIC
*HS RED RC: .75X TO 2X BASIC
*HS RED AUTO: .6X TO 1.5X BASIC
BASE/ROOKIE CARD ODDS 1:33
ROOKIE AUTO ODDS 1:312
STATED PRINT RUN 75 SER.#'d SETS

2007 Topps Co-Signers Silver Blue

*SIL BLUE: .75X TO 2X BASIC
*SIL BLUE RC: .5X TO 1.2X BASIC
*SIL BLUE AUTO: .5X TO 1.2X BASIC
BASE/ROOKIE CARD ODDS 1:17
ROOKIE AUTO ODDS 1:187
BASE/RC PRINT RUN 150 SER.#'d SETS
RC AUTO PRINT RUN 125 SER.#'d SETS

2007 Topps Co-Signers Silver Bronze

*SIL BRONZE: .75X TO 2X BASIC
*SIL BRONZE RC: .5X TO 1.2X BASIC
*SIL BRONZE AUTO: .5X TO 1.2X BASIC
BASE/ROOKIE CARD ODDS 1:14
ROOKIE AUTO ODDS 1:156
BASE/RC PRINT RUN 175 SER.#'d SETS
RC AUTO PRINT RUN 150 SER.#'d SETS

2007 Topps Co-Signers Silver Gold

*SIL GOLD: 1X TO 2.5X BASIC
*SIL GOLD RC: .75X TO 2X BASIC
*SIL GOLD AUTO: .5X TO 1.2X BASIC
BASE/ROOKIE CARD ODDS 1:20
ROOKIE AUTO ODDS 1:234
BASE/RC PRINT RUN 125 SER.#'d SETS
RC AUTO PRINT RUN 100 SER.#'d SETS

2007 Topps Co-Signers Silver Red

*SIL RED: .75X TO 2X BASIC
*SIL RED RC: .5X TO 1.2X BASIC
*SIL RED AUTO: .5X TO 1.2X BASIC
BASE/ROOKIE CARD ODDS 1:13
ROOKIE AUTO ODDS 1:134
BASE/RC PRINT RUN 199 SER.#'d SETS
RC AUTO PRINT RUN 175 SER.#'d SETS

2007 Topps Co-Signers Cut Signatures Dual

STATED ODDS 1:46,569
NO PRICING DUE TO SCARCITY
CM Chipper Jones
Mickey Mantle
DM Joe DiMaggio
Mickey Mantle
EM Dwight Eisenhower
Mickey Mantle
HM Ryan Howard
Mickey Mantle
JM Lyndon B. Johnson
Mickey Mantle
RM Alex Rodriguez
Mickey Mantle
SM Duke Snider
Mickey Mantle
TM Harry Truman
Mickey Mantle
WM David Wright
Mickey Mantle
ADM Abner Doubleday
Mickey Mantle

2007 Topps Co-Signers Dual Autographs

GROUP A ODDS 1:17
GROUP B ODDS 1:49
GROUP C ODDS 1:1646
GROUP D ODDS 1:2464
GROUP E ODDS 1:328
AH Garrett Atkins 6.00 15.00
Matt Holliday B
AI Matt Albers 4.00 10.00
Chris Iannetta A
AS Matt Albers 4.00 10.00
Brian Slocum A
BB Brian Bannister 10.00 25.00
Floyd Bannister A
BDE Erik Bedard 6.00 15.00
Zach Duke A
BG Jeremy Bonderman 10.00 25.00
{Curtis Granderson B
BS Jeff Baker 4.00 10.00
Jeff Salazar B
BV Jeremy Bonderman 15.00 40.00
Justin Verlander E
CC Melky Cabrera 30.00 60.00
Robinson Cano E
CJ Chris Carpenter 10.00 25.00
{Tyler Johnson E
CK Robinson Cano 15.00 40.00
Chuck Knoblach E
CM Fabio Castro 4.00 10.00
Scott Mathieson A
CW Miguel Cabrera 15.00 40.00
Dontrelle Willis B
CY Alberto Callaspo 8.00 20.00
Chris Young B
CZ Alberto Callaspo 5.00 12.00
Ben Zobrist A
GB Garrett Atkins 4.00 10.00
Clint Barmes B
GC Curtis Granderson 8.00 20.00
Melky Cabrera A
GM Hector Gimenez -4.00 10.00
Miguel Montero A
GS Dwight Gooden 15.00 40.00
Darryl Strawberry E
HH Bill Hall 10.00 25.00
J.J. Hardy A
HO Ryan Howard 50.00 100.00
David Ortiz E
IK Chris Iannetta 15.00 40.00
Matt Kemp A
IM Chris Iannetta 6.00 15.00
Miguel Montero A
JJ Andruw Jones 40.00 80.00
David Justice E
JS Ubaldo Jimenez 10.00 25.00
Dennis Sarfate A
JY Conor Jackson 6.00 15.00
Chris Young D
KA Howie Kendrick 10.00 25.00
Erick Aybar A
KF Kevin Kouzmanoff 6.00 15.00
Josh Fields B
KG Matt Kemp 8.00 20.00
Franklin Gutierrez A
KM Josh Kinney 4.00 10.00
Tom Mastny A
KMA Jeff Karstens 4.00 10.00
Scott Mathieson A
KZ Austin Kearns 10.00 25.00
Ryan Zimmerman A
LG Adam LaRoche 6.00 15.00
Tom Gorzelanny A
LK Francisco Liriano 10.00 25.00
Jim Kaat B
LL Tony Larussa 30.00 60.00
Jim Leyland E
LP Francisco Liriano 6.00 15.00
Jonathan Papelbon C
LV Francisco Liriano 12.50 30.00
Justin Verlander B
LY Adam Lind 6.00 15.00
Delwyn Young A
MB Nick Markakis 12.50 30.00
Brian Roberts B
MC Omar Minaya 40.00 80.00
Brian Cashman E
MCA Nick Markakis 8.00 20.00
Melky Cabrera B
MG Craig Monroe 12.50 30.00
Curtis Granderson A
MH John Maine 12.50 30.00
Philip Humber B
MM Lastings Milledge 12.50 30.00
{John Maine B
MMA David Murphy 4.00 10.00
Mitch Maier A
MP Andrew Miller 10.00 25.00
Glen Perkins B
MQ Nick Markakis 6.00 15.00
Carlos Quetin B
MS Justin Morneau 10.00 25.00
Nick Swisher B
MSL Tom Mastny 4.00 10.00
Brian Slocum A
MW Lastings Milledge 10.00 25.00
David Wright E
OB Jerry Owens 4.00 10.00
Mike Bourn B
PC Angel Pagan 6.00 15.00
Buck Coats A
PS Yusmeiro Petit 4.00 10.00
Anibal Sanchez A
PV Jonathan Papelbon 20.00 50.00
Justin Verlander B
SH Jonathan Sanchez 10.00 25.00
Brad Hennessey A
SM Freddy Sanchez 15.00 40.00
Joe Mauer E
SMA Chris Stewart 4.00 10.00
Carlos Maldonado A
SR Brian Stokes 4.00 10.00
Shawn Riggans A
VF Justin Verlander 50.00 100.00
Mark Fidrych B
VM John Van Benschoten 4.00 10.00
Scott Mathieson A
VP Jason Varitek 40.00 80.00
{Jorge Posada E
WC David Wright 40.00 80.00
Robinson Cano E
WS Dontrelle Willis 6.00 15.00
Anibal Sanchez E
YL Chris Young 6.00 15.00
Nook Logan B
YU Delmon Young 20.00 50.00
B.J. Upton E
ZG Ben Zobrist 5.00 12.00
Joel Guzman A

2007 Topps Co-Signers Moon Shots Autographs

STATED ODDS 1:339
AW Alfred Worden 50.00 100.00
BA Buzz Aldrin 125.00 250.00
CD Charles Duke 50.00 100.00
EM Edgar Mitchell 50.00 100.00
FH Fred Haise 60.00 120.00
RC Robert Crippen 50.00 100.00
RG Richard Gordon 50.00 100.00
SC Scott Carpenter 60.00 120.00
WC Walt Cunningham 50.00 100.00
WS Wally Schirra 75.00 150.00

2007 Topps Co-Signers Moon Shots Autographs Dual

STATED ODDS 1:1028
NO PRICING DUE TO SCARCITY

2007 Topps Co-Signers Solo Sigs

GROUP A ODDS 1:25
GROUP B ODDS 1:164
GROUP C ODDS 1:2464
GROUP D ODDS 1:9908
AH Aaron Hill A 5.00 12.00
AL Anthony Lerew B 4.00 10.00
AS Anibal Sanchez A 4.00 10.00
BB Boof Bonser A 4.00 10.00
CB Clint Barmes A 4.00 10.00
CH Cole Hamels A 10.00 25.00
CJ Chuck James A 4.00 10.00
CQ Carlos Quentin A 5.00 12.00
DH Dave Henderson A 4.00 10.00
DU Dan Uggla A 6.00 15.00
ES Ervin Santana B 4.00 10.00
FL Francisco Liriano A 4.00 10.00
FS Freddy Sanchez A 4.00 10.00
GA Garrett Atkins A 4.00 10.00
HK Howie Kendrick B 6.00 15.00
HM Hideki Matsui D
HR Hanley Ramirez A 6.00 15.00
JM Justin Morneau B 10.00 25.00
JS Jeremy Sowers A 4.00 10.00
MC Matt Cain A 5.00 12.00
MH Matt Holliday A 8.00 20.00
NM Nick Markakis A 8.00 20.00
RC Robinson Cano A 12.50 30.00
RG Ryan Garko A 4.00 10.00
RH Ryan Howard B 25.00 50.00
RR Rick Rhoden A 4.00 10.00
VG Vladimir Guerrero C 15.00 40.00
RCE Ronny Cedeno B 4.00 10.00

2007 Topps Co-Signers Tri-Signers

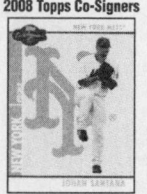

STATED ODDS 1:264
ANS J. Arias/O. Navarro/A. Sanchez 10.00 25.00
CPC M. Cabrera/W. M Pena/M. Cabrera 20.00 50.00
HLC B. Hennessey/J. Sanchez/M. Cain 15.00 40.00
JGK C. Jackson/R. Garko/H. Kendrick 15.00 40.00
JHS C. James/C. Hamels/J. Sowers 10.00 25.00
LNB F. Liriano/J. Nathan/B. Bonser 20.00 50.00
MAR J. Morneau/G. Atkins/B. Roberts 12.50 30.00
MLM J. Morneau/F. Liriano/M. Garza 30.00 60.00
MLP J. Morneau/F. Liriano/G. Perkins 10.00 25.00
MSG J. Morneau/N. Swisher/A. Gonzalez 15.00 40.00
MYT A. Miller/D. Young/T. Tulowitzki 15.00 40.00
OPV D. Ortiz/J. Papelbon/J. Varitek 100.00 175.00
OWH D. Ortiz/D. Wright/R. Howard 100.00 175.00
QJY C. Quentin/C. Jackson/C. Young 15.00 40.00
RCC A. Rodriguez/M. Cabrera/R. Cano 75.00 150.00
RWH A. Rodriguez/D. Wright/R. Howard 125.00 250.00
SHH H. Street/R. Harden/D. Haren 20.00 50.00
TPW T. Tankersley/Y. Petit/D. Willis 10.00 25.00
URW D. Uggla/H. Ramirez/D. Willis 20.00 50.00

2007 Topps Co-Signers Yankees Cut Signatures

A-ROD MANTLE ODDS 1:66,528
A-ROD DIMAGGIO ODDS 1:93,139
TRIPLE CUT SIG ODDS 1:232,848
PRINT RUNS B/WN 3-7 COPIES PER
NO PRICING DUE TO SCARCITY
YCS1 Alex Rodriguez
Mickey Mantle/7
YCS2 Alex Rodriguez
Joe DiMaggio/6
YCS3 Alex Rodriguez
Mickey Mantle
Joe DiMaggio/3

2008 Topps Co-Signers

COMP.SET w/o AU's (100) 12.50 30.00
COMMON CARD (1-95) .25 .60
COMMON RC (96-100) .60 1.50
AU RC VAR ODDS 1:315 HOBBY
COMMON AU RC 3.00 8.00
AU RC ODDS 1:22 HOBBY
PRINTING PLATE VET/RC ODDS 1:445
PRINTING PLATE AU RC VAR ODDS 1:29,736
PRINTING PLATE AU RC ODDS 1:5216
PLATE PRINT RUN 1 SET PER COLOR
5TH-BLACK-CYAN-MAGENTA-YELLOW ISSUED
NO PLATE PRICING DUE TO SCARCITY
1 Jacoby Ellsbury 1.00 2.50
2 Michael Young .40 1.00
3 Cameron Maybin .25 .60
4 Dmitri Young .25 .60
5 Grady Sizemore .40 1.00
6 Brandon Webb .40 1.00
7 Derrek Lee .25 .60
8 Jeff Francis .25 .60
9 Aaron Harang .25 .60
10 John Smoltz .60 1.50
11 Nick Markakis .60 1.50
12 Tom Gorzelanny .25 .60
13 Miguel Cabrera .60 1.50
14 Josh Beckett .40 1.00
15 Magglio Ordonez .40 1.00
16 Joe Mauer .60 1.50
17 Carl Crawford .40 1.00
18 Barry Zito .25 .60
19 Brad Penny .25 .60
20 C.C. Sabathia .40 1.00
21 Mark Buehrle .40 1.00
22 Carlos Lee .25 .60
23 Chipper Jones .60 1.50
24 Chase Utley .60 1.50
25 David Ortiz .40 1.00
26 Justin Morneau .60 1.50
27 Erik Bedard .25 .60
28 Greg Maddux .75 2.00
29 Joba Chamberlain .40 1.00
30 Vernon Wells .25 .60
31 Orlando Hudson .25 .60
32 Kevin Youkilis .40 1.00
33 Curtis Granderson .40 1.00
34 Chone Figgins .25 .60
35 Jorge Posada .40 1.00
36 Ken Griffey Jr. 1.00 2.50
37 Tim Hudson .40 1.00
38 Nick Swisher .60 1.50
39 Carlos Beltran .25 .60
40 Alex Gordon .40 1.00
41 Andre Ethier .40 1.00
42 Todd Helton .40 1.00
43 Miguel Tejada .40 1.00
44 Yadier Molina .40 1.00
45 Hanley Ramirez .60 1.50
46 Justin Verlander .75 2.00
47 Adam Dunn .40 1.00
48 Raul Ibanez .40 1.00
49 Scott Rolen .40 1.00
50 Alex Rodriguez 1.00 2.50
51 Garret Anderson .25 .60
52 Andruw Jones .25 .60
53 Matt Cain .25 .60
54 Daisuke Matsuzaka .60 1.50
55 Ichiro Suzuki 1.00 2.50
56 Scott Kazmir .40 1.00
57 Jeff Kent .25 .60
58 Aubrey Huff .25 .60
59 Justin Upton .40 1.00
60 Prince Fielder .40 1.00
61 Alex Rios .40 1.00
62 Alfonso Soriano .40 1.00
63 Paul Konerko .40 1.00
64 Matt Holliday .60 1.50
65 Felix Hernandez .60 1.50
66 Ivan Rodriguez .40 1.00
67 John Maine .25 .60
68 Roy Oswalt .40 1.00
69 Brian McCann .40 1.00
70 Albert Pujols 1.50 4.00
71 John Lackey .25 .60
72 Travis Hafner .25 .60
73 Gil Meche .25 .60
74 Ben Sheets .25 .60
75 Ryan Howard .75 2.00
76 Hideki Matsui .60 1.50
77 Mike Lowell .25 .60
78 Dan Haren .25 .60
79 Adrian Gonzalez .40 1.00
80 David Wright .75 2.00
81 Jason Bay .40 1.00
82 Carlos Zambrano .40 1.00
83 Johan Santana .60 1.50
84 David DeJesus .25 .60
85 Ryan Zimmerman .40 1.00
86 Bobby Abreu .25 .60
87 Richie Sexson .25 .60
88 Eric Chavez .25 .60
89 Derek Lowe .25 .60
90 Jake Peavy .25 .60
91 Joe Blanton .25 .60
92 Jermaine Dye .25 .60
93 Pedro Martinez .40 1.00
94 B.J. Upton .40 1.00
95 Vladimir Guerrero .60 1.50
96 Ross Ohlendorf RC 1.00 2.50
97 J.R. Towles RC 1.00 2.50
98 Jonathan Meloan RC 1.00 2.50
99a Chin-Lung Hu (RC) 1.00 2.50
99b Chin-Lung Hu AU 10.00 25.00
100a Clay Buchholz (RC) 1.50 4.00
100b Clay Buchholz AU 6.00 15.00
101 Willie Collazo AU RC 3.00 8.00
102 David Davidson AU RC 3.00 8.00
103 Joe Koshansky AU (RC) 3.00 8.00
104 Sam Fuld AU RC 6.00 15.00
105 Nyjer Morgan AU (RC) 3.00 8.00
106 Clint Sammons AU (RC) 3.00 8.00
107 Josh Anderson AU (RC) 3.00 8.00
108 Bronson Sardinha AU (RC) 3.00 8.00
109 Wladimir Balentien AU (RC) 3.00 8.00
110 Kevin Hart AU (RC) 3.00 8.00
111 Felipe Paulino AU RC 3.00 8.00
112 Rob Johnson AU (RC) 3.00 8.00

2008 Topps Co-Signers Hyper Plaid Blue

*HS BLUE VET: 1.2X TO 3X BASIC
STATED VET ODDS 1:32 HOBBY
VET PRINT RUN 50 SER.#'D SETS
*HS BLUE RC: 1.5X TO 4X BASIC
STATED RC ODDS 1:32 HOBBY
RC PRINT RUN 50 SER.#'D SETS
*HS BLUE AU: .5X TO 1.2X BASIC AU RC
STATED AU RC ODDS 1:540 HOBBY
AU PRINT RUN 50 SER.#'d SETS

2008 Topps Co-Signers Hyper Plaid Bronze

*HS BRONZE VET: 1X TO 2.5X BASIC
STATED VET ODDS 1:21 HOBBY
VET PRINT RUN 75 SER.#'D SETS
*HS BRONZE RC: 1X TO 2.5X BASIC
STATED RC ODDS 1:21 HOBBY
RC PRINT RUN 100 SER.#'D SETS
*HS BRONZE AU: .5X TO 1.2X BASIC AU RC
STATED AU RC ODDS 1:355 HOBBY
AU PRINT RUN 75 SER.#'d SETS

2008 Topps Co-Signers Hyper Plaid Gold

1-100 A/B ODDS 1:155 HOBBY
101-112 AUTO ODDS 1:3267 HOBBY
STATED PRINT RUN 10 SER.#'d SETS
NO PRICING DUE TO SCARCTIY
EXCHANGE DEADLINE 4/30/10

2008 Topps Co-Signers Hyper Plaid Green

1-100 A/B ODDS 1:63 HOBBY
101-112 AUTO ODDS 1:1130 HOBBY
STATED PRINT RUN 25 SER.#'d SETS
NO PRICING DUE TO SCARCTIY
EXCHANGE DEADLINE 4/30/10

2008 Topps Co-Signers Hyper Plaid Red

*HS RED VET: 1X TO 2.5X BASIC
STATED VET ODDS 1:16 HOBBY
VET PRINT RUN 100 SER.#'D SETS
*HS RED RC: 1X TO 2.5X BASIC
STATED RC ODDS 1:16 HOBBY
RC PRINT RUN 100 SER.#'D SETS
*HS RED AU: .4X TO 1X BASIC AU RC
STATED AU RC ODDS 1:264 HOBBY
AU PRINT RUN 100 SER.#'d SETS

2008 Topps Co-Signers Hyper Plaid Silver

1-100 A/B ODDS 1:1556 HOBBY
101-112 AUTO ODDS 1:24,780 HOBBY
STATED PRINT RUN 1 SER.#'d SET
NO PRICING DUE TO SCARCTIY
EXCHANGE DEADLINE 4/30/10

2008 Topps Co-Signers Silver Blue

*BLUE VET: .6X TO 1.5X BASIC
STATED VET ODDS 1:7 HOBBY
VET PRINT RUN 250 SER.#'D SETS
*BLUE RC: .6X TO 1.5X BASIC
STATED RC ODDS 1:7 HOBBY
RC PRINT RUN 250 SER.#'D SETS
*BLUE AU: .4X TO 1X BASIC AU RC
STATED AU RC ODDS 1:87 HOBBY
AU PRINT RUN 300 SER.#'d SETS

2008 Topps Co-Signers Silver Bronze

*BRONZE VET: .6X TO 1.5X BASIC
STATED VET ODDS 1:6 HOBBY
VET PRINT RUN 300 SER.#'D SETS
*BRONZE RC: .6X TO 1.5X BASIC
STATED RC ODDS 1:6 HOBBY
RC PRINT RUN 300 SER.#'D SETS
*BRONZE AU: .4X TO 1X BASIC AU RC
STATED AU RC ODDS 1:65 HOBBY
AU PRINT RUN 400 SER.#'d SETS

2008 Topps Co-Signers Silver Gold

*GOLD VET: .75X TO 2X BASIC
STATED VET ODDS 1:11 HOBBY
VET PRINT RUN 150 SER.#'D SETS
*GOLD RC: .75X TO 2X BASIC
STATED RC ODDS 1:11 HOBBY
RC PRINT RUN 150 SER.#'D SETS
*GOLD AU: .4X TO 1X BASIC AU RC
STATED AU RC ODDS 1:175 HOBBY
AU PRINT RUN 150 SER.#'d SETS

2008 Topps Co-Signers Silver Green

*GREEN VET: .75X TO 2X BASIC
STATED VET ODDS 1:8 HOBBY
VET PRINT RUN 200 SER.#'D SETS
*GREEN RC: .75X TO 2X BASIC
STATED RC ODDS 1:8 HOBBY
RC PRINT RUN 200 SER.#'D SETS
*GREEN AU: .4X TO 1X BASIC AU RC
STATED AU RC ODDS 1:131 HOBBY
AU PRINT RUN 200 SER.#'d SETS

2008 Topps Co-Signers Silver Red

*RED VET: .6X TO 1.5X BASIC
STATED VET ODDS 1:4 HOBBY
VET PRINT RUN 400 SER.#'d SETS
*RED RC: .6X TO 1.5X BASIC
STATED RC ODDS 1:4 HOBBY
RC PRINT RUN 400 SER.#'d SETS
*RED AU: .4X TO 1X BASIC AU RC
STATED AU RC ODDS 1:52 HOBBY
AU PRINT RUN 500 SER.#'d SETS

2008 Topps Co-Signers Cowhide Dual Signatures

STATED ODDS 1:29,736 HOBBY
STATED PRINT RUN 1 SER.#'d SET
NO PRICING DUE TO SCARCITY

2008 Topps Co-Signers Cut Signatures Dual

STATED ODDS 1:21,240 HOBBY
STATED PRINT RUN 1 SER.#'d SET
NO PRICING DUE TO SCARCITY

2008 Topps Co-Signers Cut Signatures Quad

STATED ODDS 1:237,600 HOBBY
STATED PRINT RUN 1 SER.#'d SET
NO PRICING DUE TO SCARCITY
MEMB Douglas MacArthur
Dwight Eisenhower
George Marshall
Omar Bradley
OHGM Barack Obama
Hillary Clinton
Rudy Giuliani
John McCain

2008 Topps Co-Signers Dual Autographs

GROUP A ODDS 1:23 HOBBY
GROUP B ODDS 1:39 HOBBY
GROUP C ODDS 1:101 HOBBY
GROUP D ODDS 1:443 HOBBY
GROUP E ODDS 1:3912 HOBBY
AC Jorge Arce 6.00 15.00
Ivan Calderon C
BA Josh Banks 4.00 10.00
Jeremy Accardo A
BB Daric Barton 10.00 25.00
Clay Buchholz A
BJ Erik Bedard 15.00 40.00
Adam Jones B
BM Bill Buck 4.00 10.00
Cameron Maybin B
BZ Jason Bartlett 8.00 20.00
Ben Zobrist A
CB Steve Cunningham 4.00 10.00
Shannon Briggs C
CC Robinson Cano 12.50 30.00
Asdrubal Cabrera A
CE Jack Cust 4.00 10.00
Mark Ellis A
CG Jerome Cochran 6.00 15.00
Curtis Granderson B
DB Chad Dawson 10.00 25.00
Andre Berto C
DD Juan Diaz 6.00 15.00
Julio Diaz C
DG Vic Darchinyan 4.00 10.00
Danny Green C
DR Chris Duncan 10.00 25.00
Brendan Ryan A
EH Bob Engle 10.00 25.00
Felix Hernandez B
FC Chone Figgins 6.00 15.00
Carl Crawford D
FH Jeff Francis 4.00 10.00
Jason Hirsh A
FJ Jeff Francis 6.00 15.00
Ubaldo Jimenez B
FP Sam Fuld 4.00 10.00
Felix Pie A
GS Tom Gorzelanny 4.00 10.00
Freddy Sanchez A
HC Felix Hernandez 12.50 30.00
Joba Chamberlain A
JA Brandon Jones 4.00 10.00
Josh Anderson A
JM Dave Jennings 6.00 15.00
Nick Markakis B
KA Roman Karmazin 6.00 15.00
Arthur Abraham C
KC Tim Kelly 6.00 15.00
Joba Chamberlain B
LG Don Lyle 4.00 10.00
Ryan Garko B
LH Andy LaRoche 10.00 25.00
Chin-Lung Hu B
MB Edison Miranda 4.00 10.00
O'Neil Bell C EXCH
MD Lastings Milledge 4.00 10.00
Elijah Dukes B
MM Andrew Miller 4.00 10.00
Cameron Maybin A
MP Joe Mason 6.00 15.00
Jonathan Papelbon B
MS Carlos Marmol 20.00 50.00
Geovany Soto A
MV Rafael Marquez 20.00 50.00
Israel Vasquez C
OB Garrett Olsen 4.00 10.00
Brian Burres A
PG Daniel Ponce de Leon 10.00 25.00
Joan Guzman C
PO Jonathan Papelbon 30.00 60.00
Hideki Okajima D
PP Samuel Peter 12.50 30.00
Aaron Pryor C
PS Steve Pearce 4.00 10.00
Freddy Sanchez A
RM Alex Rios 10.00 25.00
Nick Markakis B
RO Edwar Ramirez 6.00 15.00
Ross Ohlendorf A
RR Jimmy Rollins 40.00 80.00
Jose Reyes D
RW Jose Reyes 40.00 80.00
David Wright D
SC Brian Schneider 6.00 15.00
Ramon Castro A
SE Arthur Shorin 50.00 100.00
Michael Eisner E
SG Andy Sonnanstine 12.50 30.00
Matt Garza A
SP Geovany Soto 12.50 30.00
Felix Pie A
SZ Alex Smith 6.00 15.00
Ryan Zimmerman B
VC Joey Votto 15.00 40.00
Daric Barton B
WB David Wright 50.00 100.00
Ryan Braun D
WF Dontrelle Willis 15.00 40.00
Mark Fidrych D
BMP Ray Mancini 75.00 150.00
Kelly Pavlik E
CCC Martin Castillo 12.50 30.00
Julio Cesar Chavez Jr. C
CLC Joel Casamayor 10.00 25.00
Jose Luis Castillo C
FHO Prince Fielder 40.00 80.00
Ryan Howard D
HCA Josue Herrera 4.00 10.00
Fausto Carmona B
MMJ Juan Manuel Marquez 10.00 25.00
Chris John C
OBA Dan Ontiveros 4.00 10.00
Daric Barton B
PKS Glen Perkins 4.00 10.00
Kevin Slowey A

2008 Topps Co-Signers Quad Signers

STATED ODDS 1:1436 HOBBY
NO PRICING DUE TO SCARCITY
EXCHANGE DEADLINE 4/30/10

2008 Topps Co-Signers Solo Sigs

STATED ODDS 1:21 HOBBY
EXCHANGE DEADLINE 4/30/10
AA Arthur Abraham 6.00 15.00
AB Andre Berto 6.00 15.00
AP Aaron Pryor 10.00 25.00
AW Andre Ward 6.00 15.00
BS Bert Sugar EXCH 8.00 20.00
CD Chad Dawson 5.00 12.00
CJ Chris John 4.00 10.00
DP Daniel Ponce de Leon 5.00 12.00
EM Edison Miranda 6.00 15.00
FM Fernando Montiel 4.00 10.00
IC Ivan Calderon 6.00 15.00
IV Israel Vasquez 6.00 15.00
JA Jorge Arce 6.00 15.00
JC Joel Casamayor 6.00 15.00
JD Juan Diaz 6.00 15.00
JF Jeff Fenech 4.00 10.00
JG Joan Guzman 4.00 10.00
JM Juan Manuel Marquez 8.00 20.00
KP Kelly Pavlik 30.00 60.00
MC Martin Castillo 4.00 10.00
OB O'Neil Bell EXCH 4.00 10.00
RK Roman Karmazin 4.00 10.00
RM Rafael Marquez 6.00 15.00
SB Shannon Briggs 5.00 12.00
SC Steve Cunningham 4.00 10.00
SP Samuel Peter 6.00 15.00
TA Teddy Atlas 8.00 20.00
VD Vic Darchinyan 4.00 10.00
DAG Danny Green EXCH 4.00 10.00
JCC Julio Cesar Chavez Jr. EXCH 8.00 20.00
JLC Jose Luis Castillo 5.00 12.00
JUD Julio Diaz 4.00 10.00
RBBM Ray Mancini 30.00 60.00

2008 Topps Co-Signers Tri Signers

STATED ODDS 1:317 HOBBY
EXCHANGE DEADLINE 4/30/10
BHH Clay Buchholz 20.00 50.00
Phil Hughes
Felix Hernandez
CEC Asdrubal Cabrera 15.00 40.00
Yunel Escobar
Robinson Cano
CHC Joba Chamberlain 50.00 100.00
Phil Hughes
Melky Cabrera
GFH Tom Gorzelanny 10.00 25.00
Jeff Francis
Cole Hamels
HSY Josh Hamilton 20.00 50.00
Jarrod Saltalamacchia
Michael Young
MGY Cameron Maybin 10.00 25.00
Curtis Granderson
Chris Young
MHR Nick Markakis 20.00 50.00
Matt Holliday
Alex Rios
MRH Cameron Maybin 30.00 60.00
Hanley Ramirez
Jeremy Hermida EXCH
PBG Manny Parra 50.00 100.00
Ryan Braun
Yovani Gallardo EXCH
WZB David Wright 60.00 120.00
Ryan Zimmerman
Ryan Braun EXCH

2004 Topps Cracker Jack

This 250 card set was released in April, 2004. The set was issued in nine-card packs which came 20 packs to a box and 10 boxes to a case. Please note that many cards in this set were issued in shorter supply than others (we have notated those cards

with an SP) or have variation poses. In addition, to mirror the original Cracker Jack set the managers of the 2003 World Series were included as well as the Marlins Owner, Jeffrey Loria. In addition, to acknowledge the late trade of Alex Rodriguez to the Yankees a Rodriguez card in a Yankee uniform was a late addition to this set and was issued without a card number. In addition, 550 original cracker jacks were inserted into packs, those cards were issued at a stated rate of one in 2598 hobby and one in 3084 retail packs.

COMPLETE SET (250) 125.00 200.00
COMP.SET w/o SP's (200) 15.00 40.00
COMMON CARD .15 .40
COMMON RC .15 .40
COMMON SP 1.50 4.00
COMMON SP RC 1.50 4.00
SP STATED ODDS 1:3
SP CL: 1/3B/13/17/20/25B/35/50-51/60/80A
SP CL: 80B/87/95B/100/104B/108-109/126
SP CL: 140B/145/163/165-167/172/175/179
SP CL: 182/184/186/192-193/195-196/198
SP CL: 200/206/209-211214/216/220/224B
SP CL: 226/229B/232/236A-236B
VINT.BUYBACK ODDS 1:2598 H, 1:3084 R
550 TOTAL BUYBACKS SEEDED IN PACKS
BUYBACK PRINT RUN INFO FROM TOPPS
1 Jose Reyes SP 1.50 4.00
2 Edgar Renteria .15 .40
3A Albert Pujols Portrait 1.00 2.50
3B Albert Pujols Swinging SP 3.00 8.00
4 Garret Anderson .15 .40
5 Bobby Abreu .15 .40
6 Andruw Jones .15 .40
7 Jeff Kent .15 .40
8 Magglio Ordonez .25 .60
9 Kris Benson .15 .40
10 Luis Gonzalez .15 .40
11 Corey Patterson .15 .40
12 Connie Mack MG .15 .40
13 Vernon Wells SP 1.50 4.00
14 Jim Edmonds .25 .60
15 Bret Boone .15 .40
16 Travis Lee .15 .40
17 Alex Rodriguez Yanks SP 3.00 8.00
18 Erubiel Durazo .15 .40
19 Brett Myers .15 .40
20 Scott Rolen SP 2.00 5.00
21 Paul Lo Duca .15 .40
22 Geoff Jenkins .15 .40
23 Charles Comiskey .15 .40
24 Cliff Floyd .15 .40
25A Jim Thome Batting .25 .60
25B Jim Thome Fielding SP 2.00 5.00
26 Russ Ortiz .15 .40
27 Bill Mueller .15 .40
28 Kenny Lofton .15 .40
29 Jay Gibbons .15 .40
30 Ken Griffey Jr. .60 1.50
31 Jeff Bagwell .25 .60
32 Jose Lima .15 .40
33 Brad Radke .15 .40
34 Ramon Hernandez .15 .40
35 Brian Giles SP 1.50 4.00
36 Jeremy Bonderman .15 .40
37 Jerome Williams .15 .40
38 Rafael Palmeiro .25 .60
39 Scott Podsednik .15 .40
40 Rafael Furcal .15 .40
41 Roy Oswalt .25 .60
42 Orlando Hudson .15 .40
43 Todd Helton .25 .60
44 Kerry Wood .15 .40
45 Tom Glavine .25 .60
46 David Eckstein .15 .40
47 Trot Nixon .15 .40
48 Preston Wilson .15 .40
49 Bernie Williams .25 .60
50 Eric Gagne SP 1.50 4.00
51 Ichiro Suzuki SP 3.00 8.00
52 Juan Gonzalez .15 .40
53 Torii Hunter .15 .40
54 Bartolo Colon .15 .40
55A Dick Hoblitzel ERR .15 .40
55B Dick Hoblitzell COR .15 .40
56 Al Leiter .15 .40
57 Johnny Damon .25 .60
58 Larry Walker .25 .60
59 Brian Jordan .15 .40
60 Richie Sexson SP 1.50 4.00
61 Orlando Cabrera .15 .40
62 Jason Phillips .15 .40
63 Phil Nevin .15 .40
64 John Olerud .15 .40
65 Miguel Tejada .25 .60
66A Nap La Joie ERR .25 .60
66B Nap Lajoie COR .25 .60
67 C.C. Sabathia .25 .60
68 Ty Wigginton .15 .40
69 Troy Glaus .15 .40
70 Mike Piazza .40 1.00
71 Craig Biggio .25 .60
72 Cristian Guzman .15 .40
73 Dmitri Young .15 .40
74 Roger Clemens .50 1.25
75 Runelvys Hernandez .15 .40
76 Nomar Garciaparra .40 1.00
77 Mark Mulder .15 .40
78 Derek Lowe .15 .40
79 Paul Konerko .25 .60
80A Sammy Sosa SP 2.00 5.00
80B Felix Pie SP 2.00 5.00
81 Vladimir Guerrero .40 1.00
82 Xavier Nady .15 .40
83 Joel Pineiro .15 .40
84 Chipper Jones .40 1.00
85 Manny Ramirez .40 1.00
86A Burt Shotten ERR .15 .40
86B Burt Shotton COR UER .15 .40
Began his playing career in 1997; should be 1907
87 Raul Ibanez SP 1.50 4.00
88 Eric Chavez .15 .40
89 Frank Catalanotto .15 .40
90 Dontrelle Willis .15 .40
91 Roy Halladay .40 1.00
92 Jermaine Dye .15 .40
93 Jason Kendall .15 .40
94 Jacque Jones .15 .40
95A Gary Sheffield Braves .15 .40
95B Gary Sheffield Yanks SP 2.00 5.00
96 Mike Lieberthal .15 .40
97 Adam Dunn .25 .60
98 Carl Crawford .25 .60
99 Reggie Sanders .15 .40
100 Mark Prior SP 2.00 5.00
101 Luis Matos .15 .40
102 Barry Zito .15 .40
103 Randy Johnson .40 1.00
104A Kevin Brown .15 .40
104B Edwin Jackson SP 1.50 4.00
105 Pat Burrell .15 .40
106 Steve Finley .15 .40
107 Moises Alou .15 .40
108 David Ortiz SP 2.50 6.00
109 Austin Kearns SP 1.50 4.00
110 Carlos Beltran .15 .40
111 Shawn Green .15 .40
112 Javier Vazquez .15 .40
113 Hideo Nomo .40 1.00
114 Kazuhisa Ishii .15 .40
115 Corey Koskie .15 .40
116 Kevin Millwood .15 .40
117 Randy Wolf .15 .40
118 Darin Erstad .15 .40
119 Fernando Vina .15 .40
120 Pedro Martinez .25 .60
121 Melvin Mora .15 .40
122 Carl Everett .15 .40
123 Matt Morris .15 .40
124 Greg Maddux .60 1.50
125 Jason Schmidt .15 .40
126 Mark Teixeira SP 2.00 5.00
127 Randy Winn .15 .40
128 Rich Aurilia .15 .40
129 Vicente Padilla .15 .40
130 Tim Hudson .25 .60
131 Marlon Byrd .15 .40
132 Jae Weong Seo .15 .40
133 Branch Rickey MG .15 .40
134 A.J. Pierzynski .15 .40
135 Ryan Klesko .15 .40
136 Eric Hinske .15 .40
137 Mike Cameron .15 .40
138 Roberto Alomar .25 .60
139 Jarrod Washburn .15 .40
140A Curt Schilling D'backs .25 .60
140B Curt Schilling Sox SP 2.00 5.00
141 Omar Vizquel .25 .60
142 Mike Sweeney .15 .40
143 Wade Miller .15 .40
144 Jose Vidro .15 .40
145 Rich Harden SP 1.50 4.00
146 Eric Munson .15 .40
147 Lance Berkman .25 .60
148 Mark Buehrle .25 .60
149 Carlos Delgado .15 .40
150 Sean Burroughs .15 .40
151 Kevin Millar .15 .40
152 Frank Thomas .40 1.00
153 Adrian Beltre .15 .40
154 Shannon Stewart .15 .40
155 Johan Santana .40 1.00
156 Edgardo Alfonzo .15 .40
157 Jose Cruz Jr. .15 .40
158 Sidney Ponson .15 .40
159 Edgar Martinez .25 .60
160 Jamie Moyer .15 .40
161 Tony Batista .15 .40
162 Wes Helms .15 .40
163 Brandon Webb SP 1.50 4.00
164 Gil Meche .15 .40
165 Marcus Giles SP 1.50 4.00
166 Angel Berroa SP 1.50 4.00
167 Rocco Baldelli SP 1.50 4.00
168 Michael Young .15 .40
169 Esteban Loaiza .15 .40
170 Casey Blake .15 .40
171 Jody Gerut .15 .40
172 Bo Hart SP 1.50 4.00
173 Kelvim Escobar .15 .40
174 Aaron Guiel .15 .40
175 Javy Lopez SP 1.50 4.00
176 Aubrey Huff .15 .40
177 Hank Blalock .15 .40
178 Edwin Jackson .15 .40
179 Delmon Young SP 2.00 5.00
180 Bobby Jenks .15 .40
181 Felix Pie .15 .40
182 Jeremy Reed SP 1.50 4.00
183 Aaron Hill .25 .60
184 Casey Kotchman SP 1.50 4.00
185 Grady Sizemore .25 .60
186 Joe Mauer SP 2.00 5.00
187 Ryan Harvey .15 .40
188 Neal Cotts .15 .40
189 Victor Martinez .25 .60
190 Rene Reyes .15 .40
191 Eric Duncan .15 .40
192 B.J. Upton SP 2.00 5.00
193 Khalil Greene SP 2.00 5.00
194 Bobby Crosby .15 .40
195 Rickie Weeks SP 1.50 4.00
196 Zack Greinke SP 1.50 4.00
197 Laynce Nix .15 .40
198 Vito Chiaravalloti SP RC 1.50 4.00
199 Estee Harris RC .15 .40
200 Jon Knott SP RC 1.50 4.00
201 Dioner Navarro RC .25 .60
202 Craig Ansman RC .15 .40
203 Travis Blackley RC .15 .40
204 Yadier Molina RC 1.00 2.50
205 Rodney Choy Foo RC .15 .40
206 Kyle Sleeth SP RC 2.00 5.00
207 Jeff Allison RC .15 .40
208 Josh Labandeira RC .15 .40
209 Lastings Milledge SP RC 3.00 8.00
210 Rudy Guillen SP RC 2.00 5.00
211 Blake Hawksworth SP RC 2.00 5.00
212 David Aardsma RC .15 .40
213 Shawn Hill RC .15 .40
214 Erick Aybar SP RC 2.00 5.00
215 Ervin Santana RC .40 1.00
216 Tim Stauffer SP RC 2.00 5.00
217 Merkin Valdez RC .15 .40
218 Jack McKeon MG .15 .40
219 Jeff Conine .15 .40
220 Josh Beckett SP 1.50 4.00
221 Luis Castillo .15 .40
222 Mike Lowell .15 .40
223 Juan Pierre .15 .40
224A Ivan Rodriguez Marlins .25 .60
224B Ivan Rodriguez Tigers SP 2.00 5.00
225 A.J. Burnett .25 .60
226 Miguel Cabrera SP 2.00 5.00
227 Jeffrey Loria .15 .40
228 Joe Torre MG .25 .60
229A Jason Giambi Portrait .15 .40
229B Jason Giambi Fielding SP 1.50 4.00
230 Aaron Boone .15 .40
231 Jose Contreras .15 .40
232 Derek Jeter SP 3.00 8.00
233 Ruben Sierra .15 .40
234 Mike Mussina .25 .60
235 Mariano Rivera .40 1.00
236A Jorge Posada SP 2.00 5.00
236B Dioner Navarro SP 2.00 5.00
237 Alfonso Soriano .15 .40
NNO Alex Rodriguez Yanks 1.25 3.00
VB Vintage Buyback

2004 Topps Cracker Jack Mini

COMP.SET w/o SP's (200) 40.00 80.00
*MINI: .75X TO 2X BASIC
*MINI: .75X TO 2X BASIC RC
*MINI SP: .6X TO 1.5X BASIC SP
*MINI SP: .5X TO 1.2X BASIC SP RC
MINI STATED ODDS ONE PER PACK
MINI SP STATED ODDS 1:20
SP'S ARE SAME AS IN BASIC SET

2004 Topps Cracker Jack Mini Autographs

Luis Castillo did not return his cards in time for pack-out and those cards could be redeemed until March 31st, 2006.

STATED ODDS 1:258 HOBBY/RETAIL
SHEFFIELD PRINT RUN 50 CARDS
SHEFFIELD IS NOT SERIAL NUMBERED
SHEFFIELD INFO PROVIDED BY TOPPS
95 Gary Sheffield SP/50
112 Javier Vazquez 15.00 40.00
163 Brandon Webb 6.00 15.00
165 Marcus Giles 8.00 20.00
221 Luis Castillo 4.00 10.00
226 Miguel Cabrera 12.50 30.00

2004 Topps Cracker Jack Mini Blue

*BLUE: 4X TO 10X BASIC
*BLUE: 4X TO 10X BASIC RC
*BLUE SP: 1.25X TO 3X BASIC SP
*BLUE SP: 1X TO 2.5X BASIC SP RC
BLUE STATED ODDS 1:10
BLUE SP STATED ODDS 1:60
SP'S ARE SAME AS IN BASIC SET

2004 Topps Cracker Jack Mini Stickers

*STICKERS: .75X TO 2X BASIC
*STICKERS: .75X TO 2X BASIC RC
*SP STICKERS: .4X TO 1X BASIC SP
*SP STICKERS: .4X TO 1X BASIC SP RC
ONE PER SURPRISE PACK
SP ODDS 1:10 SURPRISE PACKS
SP'S ARE SAME AS IN BASIC SET

2004 Topps Cracker Jack Mini White

STATED ODDS 1:6189 HOB, 1:6413 RET
STATED PRINT RUN 1 SET
CARDS ARE NOT SERIAL-NUMBERED
PRINT RUN INFO PROVIDED BY TOPPS
NO PRICING DUE TO SCARCITY

2004 Topps Cracker Jack 1-2-3 Strikes You're Out Relics

GROUP A 1:5045 H, 1:5310 R SURPRISE
GROUP B 1:103 H, 1:109 R SURPRISE
GROUP C 1:177 H, 1:202 R SURPRISE
GROUP D 1:157 H, 1:191 R SURPRISE
BM Brett Myers Jsy C 3.00 8.00
BW Billy Wagner Jsy B 3.00 8.00
BZ Barry Zito Jsy B 3.00 8.00
CCS C.C. Sabathia Jsy C 3.00 8.00
CS Curt Schilling Jsy A 6.00 15.00
DL Derek Lowe Jsy B 3.00 8.00
EG Eric Gagne Jsy C 3.00 8.00
HN Hideo Nomo Jsy B 4.00 10.00
JB Josh Beckett Uni B 3.00 8.00
JS John Smoltz Jsy D 4.00 10.00
KB Kevin Brown Uni B 3.00 8.00
KM Kevin Millwood Jsy D 3.00 8.00
KW Kerry Wood Jsy C 3.00 8.00
MAM Mark Mulder Uni D 3.00 8.00
MM Mike Mussina Uni A 8.00 20.00
PM Pedro Martinez Jsy B 4.00 10.00
RH Rich Harden Jsy B 3.00 8.00
RJ Randy Johnson Jsy B 4.00 10.00

2004 Topps Cracker Jack Secret Surprise Signatures

Scott Rolen did not return his cards in time for pack-out and those cards could be redeemed until March 31st, 2006.

GROUP A 1:1448 H, 1:1657 R SURPRISE
GROUP B 1:481 H, 1:524 R SURPRISE
GROUP C 1:323 H, 1:368 R SURPRISE
GROUP D 1:372 H, 1:404 R SURPRISE
AH Aubrey Huff B 6.00 15.00
BG Brian Giles D 6.00 15.00
CF Cliff Floyd B 6.00 15.00
DM Dustin McGowan B 4.00 10.00
DW Dontrelle Willis A 10.00 25.00
FP Felix Pie C 10.00 25.00
JW Jerome Williams A 4.00 10.00
ML Mike Lamb C 4.00 10.00
MV Merkin Valdez B 6.00 15.00
SP Scott Podsednik D 10.00 25.00
SR Scott Rolen C 10.00 25.00

2004 Topps Cracker Jack Take Me Out to the Ballgame Relics

GROUP A 1:654 SURPRISE
GROUP B 1:645 H, 1:645 R SURPRISE
GROUP C 1:152 H, 1:194 R SURPRISE
GROUP D 1:131 H, 1:223 R SURPRISE
GROUP E 1:99 H, 1:125 R SURPRISE
GROUP F 1:201 H, 1:264 R SURPRISE
GROUP G 1:211 H, 1:297 R SURPRISE
GROUP H 1:190 H, 1:226 R SURPRISE
GROUP I 1:126 H, 1:154 R SURPRISE
GROUP J 1:149 H, 1:189 R SURPRISE
GROUP K 1:89 H, 1:93 R SURPRISE
AB Angel Berroa Bat I 3.00 8.00
AD Adam Dunn Jsy C 3.00 8.00
AP Albert Pujols Uni G 6.00 15.00
AP2 Albert Pujols Bat C 6.00 15.00
AR Alex Rodriguez Jsy H 4.00 10.00
AR2 A.Rodriguez Yanks Bat C 8.00 20.00
AS Alfonso Soriano Uni G 3.00 8.00
AS2 Alfonso Soriano Bat A 4.00 10.00
BA Bob Abreu Jsy E 3.00 8.00
BB1 Bret Boone Bat C 3.00 8.00
BB2 Bret Boone Jsy K 3.00 8.00
CB Craig Biggio Jsy E 4.00 10.00
CJ Chipper Jones Jsy K 4.00 10.00
EC Eric Chavez Uni F 3.00 8.00
GA Garrett Anderson Bat B 4.00 10.00
HB Hank Blalock Bat C 3.00 8.00
IR Ivan Rodriguez Bat D 4.00 10.00
JB Jeff Bagwell Uni E 4.00 10.00
JE Jim Edmonds Jsy E 3.00 8.00
JGA Jason Giambi Jsy C 3.00 8.00
JGH Jason Giambi Uni F 3.00 8.00
JL Javy Lopez Jsy E 3.00 8.00
JL2 Javy Lopez Bat A 4.00 10.00
JR Jose Reyes Jsy D 3.00 8.00
JRO Jimmy Rollins Jsy E 3.00 8.00
JT Jim Thome Jsy I 4.00 10.00
KW Kerry Wood Jsy G 3.00 8.00
LB Lance Berkman Bat F 3.00 8.00
LB2 Lance Berkman Jsy K 3.00 8.00
LG Luis Gonzalez Jsy B 4.00 10.00
LW Larry Walker Jsy J 3.00 8.00
MA Moises Alou Jsy J 3.00 8.00
MC Miguel Cabrera Bat H 4.00 10.00
MCT Mark Teixeira Jsy I 4.00 10.00
MG Marcus Giles Jsy E 3.00 8.00
MP Mike Piazza Jsy F 4.00 10.00
MR Manny Ramirez Uni C 4.00 10.00
MS Mike Sweeney Jsy A 4.00 10.00
MT Miguel Tejada Bat K 3.00 8.00
MY Michael Young Jsy D 3.00 8.00
NG Nomar Garciaparra Jsy B 6.00 15.00
NG2 Nomar Garciaparra Bat A 6.00 15.00
PB Pat Burrell Jsy E 3.00 8.00
PL Paul Lo Duca Uni D 3.00 8.00
RB Rocco Baldelli Bat H 3.00 8.00
RF Rafael Furcal Jsy J 3.00 8.00
SG Shawn Green Uni D 3.00 8.00
SG2 Shawn Green Bat C 3.00 8.00
SS Sammy Sosa Bat D 4.00 10.00
SS2 Sammy Sosa Jsy E 4.00 10.00
TG Troy Glaus Jsy I 3.00 8.00
TH Todd Helton Jsy K 4.00 10.00
TKH Torii Hunter Jsy B 4.00 10.00
VW Vernon Wells Jsy D 3.00 8.00

2005 Topps Cracker Jack

This 250-card set was released in April, 2004. These cards were issued in nine-card packs with a $3 SRP which came 20 packs to a box and 12 boxes to a case. There were random short prints sprinkled throughout the set and those cards are notated in our checklist as SP's and were issued to a stated rate of one in three.

COMPLETE SET (250) 100.00 200.00
COMP.SET w/o SP'S (200) 15.00 40.00
COMMON CARD .15 .40
COMMON RC .15 .40
COMMON SP .75 2.00
COMMON SP RC .75 2.00
SP STATED ODDS 1:3 HOBBY/RETAIL
SP CL: 1/3B/4/6/11/13/21/26/30/31/41/51
SP CL: 56/60B/71/75A/75B/84/85B/106/110
SP CL: 111/112/126/135A/135B/146/151/156
SP CL: 164B/166/176/181/186/191/196/201
SP CL: 211/216/221A/221B/225/226/228B
SP CL: 231/235/236A/236B
1 David Wright SP 3.00 8.00
2 Rafael Furcal .15 .40
3A Alex Rodriguez Portrait .60 1.50
3B Alex Rodriguez Fielding SP 3.00 8.00
4 Victor Martinez SP 1.25 3.00
5 Ken Griffey Jr. .60 1.50
6 Bobby Crosby SP .75 2.00
7 Ivan Rodriguez .25 .60
8 Darin Erstad .15 .40
9 Javy Lopez .15 .40
10 Brian Giles .15 .40
11 Aaron Rowand SP .75 2.00
12 Joe Torre MG .25 .60
13 Zack Greinke SP 1.25 3.00
14 Shannon Stewart .15 .40
15 Jack Wilson .15 .40
16 Jose Vidro .15 .40
17 Josh Beckett .25 .60
18 Barry Zito .15 .40
19 Bret Boone .15 .40
20 Greg Maddux .60 1.50
21 Carl Crawford SP 1.25 3.00
22 Mark Teixeira .40 1.00
23 Jason Schmidt .15 .40
24 Kazuhisa Ishii .15 .40
25 Mike Piazza .40 1.00
26 Daniel Cabrera SP .75 2.00
27 Mike Lieberthal .15 .40
28 Gil Meche .15 .40
29 Phil Nevin .15 .40
30 Adrian Beltre SP .75 2.00
31 Chipper Jones SP 2.00 5.00
32 Zach Day .15 .40
33 Ben Sheets .15 .40
34 Carlos Zambrano .25 .60
35 Melvin Mora .15 .40
36 Joe Mauer .40 1.00
37 Ken Harvey .15 .40
38 Bernie Williams .25 .60
39 Mike Maroth .15 .40
40 Eric Chavez .15 .40
41 Matt Lawton SP .75 2.00
42 Ray Durham .15 .40
43 Vernon Wells .15 .40
44 Mike Lowell .15 .40
45 Jim Thome .25 .60
46 Joel Pineiro .15 .40
47 Lance Berkman .25 .60
48 Ryan Klesko .15 .40
49 Adam Dunn .25 .60
50 Vladimir Guerrero .40 1.00
51 Eric Gagne SP .75 2.00
52 Richie Sexson .15 .40
53 Javier Vazquez .15 .40
54 Roy Oswalt .25 .60
55 Carlos Delgado .15 .40
56 John Buck SP .75 2.00
57 Kenny Rogers .15 .40
58 Sidney Ponson .15 .40
59 Vicente Padilla .15 .40
60A Mark Prior Leg Up .25 .60
60B Mark Prior Portrait SP 1.25 3.00
61 A.J. Pierzynski .15 .40
62 Aubrey Huff .15 .40
63 Shea Hillenbrand .15 .40
64 Carlos Guillen .15 .40
65 Lyle Overbay .15 .40
66 Al Leiter .15 .40
67 Eric Hinske .15 .40
68 Laynce Nix .15 .40
69 Scott Hairston .15 .40
70 Roger Clemens .50 1.25
71 Cesar Izturis SP .75 2.00
72 Shawn Green .15 .40
73 Marcus Giles .15 .40
74 Rafael Palmeiro .25 .60
75A Gary Sheffield SP .75 2.00
75B Melky Cabrera SP 2.00 5.00
76 Juan Pierre .15 .40
77 Pat Burrell .15 .40
78 Sean Burroughs .15 .40
79 Frank Thomas .40 1.00
80 Andruw Jones .15 .40
81 C.C. Sabathia .25 .60
82 Jeff Bagwell .25 .60
83 Tom Glavine .25 .60
84 Craig Wilson SP .75 2.00
85A Johan Santana Throwing .40 1.00
85B Johan Santana Portrait SP 2.00 5.00
86 Raul Ibanez .15 .40
87 Sean Casey .15 .40
88 Bucky Jacobsen .15 .40
89 B.J. Upton .25 .60
90 Bobby Abreu .15 .40
91 Geoff Jenkins .15 .40
92 Troy Glaus .15 .40
93 Dontrelle Willis .15 .40
94 Jose Lima .15 .40
95 Rocco Baldelli .15 .40
96 Aramis Ramirez .15 .40
97 Paul Lo Duca .15 .40
98 Torii Hunter .15 .40
99 Jay Payton .15 .40
100 Carlos Beltran .15 .40
101 Jarel Wright .15 .40
102 Jason Bay .15 .40
103 Cliff Floyd .15 .40
104 Mike Sweeney .15 .40
105 Sammy Sosa .40 1.00
106 Khalil Greene SP .75 2.00
107 David DeJesus .15 .40
108 Jermaine Dye .15 .40
109 Miguel Cabrera .40 1.00
110 Miguel Tejada SP 1.25 3.00
111 Johnny Estrada SP .75 2.00
112 Ronnie Belliard SP .75 2.00
113 Austin Kearns .15 .40
114 Erubiel Durazo .15 .40
115 Preston Wilson .15 .40
116 Hideo Nomo .40 1.00
117 Dmitri Young .15 .40
118 Jon Lieber .15 .40
119 Derrek Lee .15 .40
120 Todd Helton .25 .60
121 Omar Vizquel .25 .60
122 Wily Mo Pena .15 .40
123 J.D. Drew .15 .40
124 Matt Holliday .40 1.00
125 Ichiro Suzuki .60 1.50
126 Mark Buehrle SP 1.25 3.00
127 Barry Bonds .75 2.00
128 Jeff Kent .15 .40
129 Kerry Wood .15 .40
130 Mariano Rivera .40 1.00
131 Nick Johnson .15 .40
132 Randy Winn .15 .40
133 Phil Garner MG .15 .40
134 Jose Reyes .25 .60
135A Michael Young SP 1.25 3.00
135B Ian Kinsler SP 6.00 15.00
136 Jose Contreras .15 .40
137 Oliver Perez .15 .40
138 Roy Halladay .40 1.00
139 Kevin Millwood .15 .40
140 Jorge Posada .25 .60
141 Mike Cameron .15 .40
142 Edgardo Alfonzo .15 .40
143 Chris Shelton .15 .40
144 Luis Castillo .15 .40
145 Alfonso Soriano .25 .60
146 Ryan Drese SP .75 2.00
147 Mark Mulder .15 .40
148 Jason Giambi .15 .40
149 Travis Hafner .15 .40
150 Randy Johnson .40 1.00
151 Paul Konerko SP 1.25 3.00
152 Mike Mussina .25 .60
153 Brad Wilkerson .15 .40
154 Tim Hudson .25 .60
155 Garret Anderson .15 .40
156 Chase Utley SP 1.25 3.00
157 Jamie Moyer .15 .40
158 Scott Kazmir .40 1.00
159 Brett Myers .15 .40
160 Kazuo Matsui .15 .40
161 Orlando Hudson .15 .40
162 Luis Gonzalez .15 .40
163 Kevin Youkilis .15 .40
164A Jason Kendall .15 .40
164B Landon Powell SP .75 2.00
165 Hank Blalock .15 .40
166 Mark Loretta SP .75 2.00
167 Miguel Cairo .15 .40
168 Corey Patterson .15 .40
169 Victor Zambrano .15 .40
170 Magglio Ordonez .25 .60
171 J.T. Snow .15 .40
172 Randy Wolf .15 .40
173 Rich Harden .15 .40
174 Bartolo Colon .15 .40
175 Derek Jeter 1.00 2.50
176 Casey Kotchman SP .75 2.00
177 Val Majewski .15 .40
178 Grady Sizemore .25 .60
179 Rickie Weeks .25 .60
180 Robinson Cano .40 1.00
181 Nick Swisher SP 2.00 5.00
182 Ryan Howard .75 2.00
183 John Van Benschoten .15 .40
184 Delmon Young .40 1.00
185 Aaron Hill .15 .40
186 Chris Burke SP .75 2.00
187 Merkin Valdez .15 .40
188 Jeremy Reed .15 .40
189 Conor Jackson .25 .60
190 Mark Teahen .15 .40
191 Joey Gathright SP .75 2.00
192 Gavin Floyd .15 .40
193 Joe Blanton .15 .40
194 Jason Kubel .15 .40
195 Jeff Francis .15 .40
196 Angel Guzman SP .75 2.00
197 Dallas McPherson .15 .40
198 Melky Cabrera RC .40 1.00
199 Jake Dittler .15 .40
200 Elvys Quezada RC .15 .40
201 Ian Kinsler SP RC 6.00 15.00
202 Nate McLouth RC .25 .60
203 Chris Seddon RC .15 .40
204 Chad Orvella RC .15 .40
205 Ian Bladergroen RC .15 .40
206 James Jurries SP RC .75 2.00
207 Landon Powell RC .15 .40
208 Eric Nielsen RC .15 .40
209 Chris Roberson RC .15 .40
210 Andre Ethier RC 1.25 3.00
211 Chris Denorfia SP RC .75 2.00
212 Darren Fenster RC .15 .40
213 Jeremy West RC .15 .40
214 Sean Marshall RC .40 1.00
215 Ryan Sweeney RC .25 .60
216 Steve Doetsch SP RC .75 2.00
217 Kevin Melillo RC .15 .40
218 Chip Cannon RC .15 .40
219 Tony La Russa MG .25 .60
220 Chris Carpenter .40 1.00
221A Edgar Renteria Sox SP .75 2.00
221B Edgar Renteria Cards SP .75 2.00
222 Albert Pujols 1.00 2.50
223 Jim Edmonds .25 .60
224 Jason Marquis .15 .40
225 Scott Rolen SP 1.25 3.00
226 Larry Walker SP 1.25 3.00
227 Matt Morris .15 .40
228A Mike Matheny Giants .15 .40
228B Mike Matheny Cards SP .75 2.00
229 Jeremy Burnitz .15 .40
230 Terry Francona MG .25 .60
231 Johnny Damon SP 1.25 3.00
232 Keith Foulke .15 .40
233 Trot Nixon .15 .40
234 Manny Ramirez .40 1.00
235 David Ortiz SP 2.00 5.00
236A Pedro Martinez Sox SP 1.25 3.00
236B Pedro Martinez Mets SP 1.25 3.00
237 Curt Schilling .25 .60
238 Kevin Millar .15 .40
239 Bill Mueller .15 .40
240 Mark Bellhorn .15 .40
NNO Josh Beckett NNO SP 1.25 3.00

2005 Topps Cracker Jack Mini Blue

*BLUE: 8X TO 20X BASIC
*BLUE: 5X TO 12X BASIC RC
STATED ODDS 1:75 HOBBY/RETAIL
STATED PRINT RUN 50 SERIAL #'d SETS
1 David Wright 12.00 30.00
3B Alex Rodriguez Fielding 12.00 30.00
4 Victor Martinez 5.00 12.00
6 Bobby Crosby 3.00 8.00
11 Aaron Rowand 3.00 8.00
13 Zack Greinke 5.00 12.00
21 Carl Crawford 5.00 12.00
26 Daniel Cabrera 3.00 8.00
30 Adrian Beltre 3.00 8.00
31 Chipper Jones 8.00 20.00
41 Matt Lawton 3.00 8.00
51 Eric Gagne 3.00 8.00
56 John Buck 3.00 8.00
60A Mark Prior Leg Up 5.00 12.00
60B Mark Prior Portrait 5.00 12.00
71 Cesar Izturis 3.00 8.00
75A Gary Sheffield 3.00 8.00
75B Melky Cabrera 8.00 20.00
84 Craig Wilson 3.00 8.00
85B Johan Santana Portrait 8.00 20.00
106 Khalil Greene 3.00 8.00
110 Miguel Tejada 5.00 12.00
111 Johnny Estrada 3.00 8.00
112 Ronnie Belliard 3.00 8.00
126 Mark Buehrle 5.00 12.00
135A Michael Young 5.00 12.00
135B Ian Kinsler 25.00 60.00
146 Ryan Drese 3.00 8.00
151 Paul Konerko 5.00 12.00
156 Chase Utley 5.00 12.00
164B Landon Powell 3.00 8.00
166 Mark Loretta 3.00 8.00
176 Casey Kotchman 3.00 8.00
181 Nick Swisher 8.00 20.00
186 Chris Burke 3.00 8.00
191 Joey Gathright 3.00 8.00
196 Angel Guzman 3.00 8.00

201 Ian Kinsler 25.00 60.00
206 James Jurries 3.00 8.00
216 Steve Doetsch 3.00 8.00
221A Edgar Renteria Sox 3.00 8.00
221B Edgar Renteria Cards 3.00 8.00
225 Scott Rolen 5.00 12.00
226 Larry Walker 5.00 12.00
228B Mike Matheny Cards 3.00 8.00
231 Johnny Damon 5.00 12.00
235 David Ortiz 8.00 20.00
236A Pedro Martinez Sox 5.00 12.00
236B Pedro Martinez Mets 5.00 12.00
NNO Josh Beckett NNO 5.00 12.00

2005 Topps Cracker Jack Mini Grey

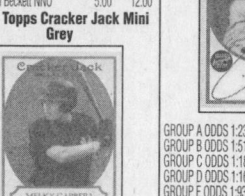

STATED ODDS 1:151 HOBBY, 1:150 RETAIL
STATED PRINT RUN 25 SERIAL #'d SETS
NO PRICING DUE TO SCARCITY

2005 Topps Cracker Jack Mini Red

COMP.SET w/o SP'S (200) 40.00 80.00
*RED: .75X TO 2X BASIC
*RED: .75X TO 2X BASIC RC
ONE PER PACK
*RED SP: .6X TO 1.5X BASIC SP
*RED SP: .5X TO 1.2X BASIC SP RC
SP STATED ODDS 1:20 HOBBY/RETAIL

2005 Topps Cracker Jack Mini Stickers

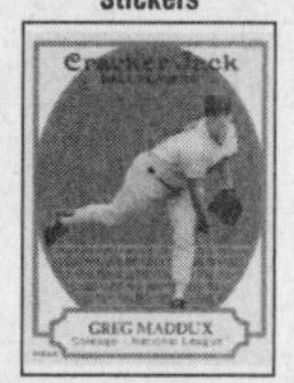

COMP.SET w/o SP'S (200) 40.00 80.00
*STICKER: .75X TO 2X BASIC
*STICKER: .75X TO 2X BASIC RC
ONE PER PACK
*STICKER SP: .6X TO 1.5X BASIC SP
*STICKER SP: .5X TO 1.2X BASIC SP RC
SP STATED ODDS 1:20 HOBBY/RETAIL

2005 Topps Cracker Jack Mini White

STATED ODDS 1:3763 HOB, 1:3813 RET
STATED PRINT RUN 1 SERIAL #'d SET
NO PRICING DUE TO SCARCITY

2005 Topps Cracker Jack 1-2-3 Strikes You're Out Mini Relics

STATED ODDS 1:204 HOBBY/RETAIL
BR Brad Radke Jsy 3.00 8.00
CS Curt Schilling Jsy 6.00 15.00
JB Josh Beckett Uni 3.00 8.00
JW Jaret Wright Jsy 3.00 8.00
RD Ryan Drese Jsy 3.00 8.00
RO Russ Ortiz Jsy 3.00 8.00

2005 Topps Cracker Jack Autographs

GROUP A ODDS 1:38,675 HOBBY/RETAIL
GROUP B ODDS 1:1864 HOBBY/RETAIL
GROUP A PRINT RUN 25 SERIAL #'d SETS
GROUP B PRINT RUN 50 SERIAL #'d SETS
NO GROUP A PRICING DUE TO SCARCITY
AR Alex Rodriguez B/50 250.00 500.00
BB Barry Bonds A/25
CC Carl Crawford B/50 30.00 60.00
CS C.C. Sabathia B/50 30.00 60.00
CW Craig Wilson B/50 15.00 40.00
DW David Wright B/50 125.00 200.00
EC Eric Chavez B/50 30.00 60.00
EG Eric Gagne B/50 40.00 80.00
GA Garret Anderson B/50 30.00 60.00
JS Johan Santana B/50 30.00 60.00

2005 Topps Cracker Jack Secret Surprise Mini Autographs

GROUP A ODDS 1:2328 HOBBY/RETAIL
GROUP B ODDS 1:517 HOBBY/RETAIL
GROUP C ODDS 1:1864 HOBBY/RETAIL
GROUP D ODDS 1:163 HOBBY/RETAIL
GROUP E ODDS 1:930 HOBBY/RETAIL
GROUP F ODDS 1:155 HOBBY/RETAIL
GROUP A PRINT RUN 100 COPIES PER
GROUP A ARE NOT SERIAL-NUMBERED
GROUP A PRINT RUN PROVIDED BY TOPPS
AG Angel Guzman F 4.00 10.00
AR Alex Rodriguez A/100 * 150.00 300.00
CC Carl Crawford D 10.00 25.00
CN Chris Nelson F 8.00 20.00
CS C.C. Sabathia D 15.00 40.00
CT Curtis Thigpen B 6.00 15.00
CW Craig Wilson D 4.00 10.00
DM Dallas McPherson A/100 * 10.00 25.00
DW David Wright D 20.00 50.00
EC Eric Chavez B 10.00 25.00
EG Eric Gagne D 8.00 20.00
GA Garret Anderson B 10.00 25.00
HB Hank Blalock D 6.00 15.00
JS Johan Santana B 15.00 40.00
KM Kevin Millar F 12.50 30.00
MK Mark Kotsay A/100 * 10.00 25.00
ML Mark Loretta A/100 * 10.00 25.00
MM Melvin Mora E 6.00 15.00
RR Richie Robnett F 6.00 15.00
SK Scott Kazmir C 10.00 25.00

2005 Topps Cracker Jack Take Me Out to the Ballgame Mini Relics

STATED ODDS 1:16 HOBBY/RETAIL
AB Adrian Beltre Bat 3.00 8.00
AB1 Angel Berroa Bat 3.00 8.00
AB2 Angel Berroa Uni 3.00 8.00
AD Adam Dunn Bat 3.00 8.00
AL Adam LaRoche Bat 3.00 8.00
AP Albert Pujols Jsy 8.00 20.00
AR Alex Rodriguez Bat 6.00 15.00
ARA Aramis Ramirez Bat 3.00 8.00
AS Alfonso Soriano Bat 3.00 8.00
BB Barry Bonds Uni 12.50 30.00
BC Bobby Cox Uni 3.00 8.00
BCR Bobby Crosby Bat 3.00 8.00
BK Bobby Kielty Bat 3.00 8.00
BS Benito Santiago Bat 4.00 10.00
BW Bernie Williams Uni 4.00 10.00
CB Carlos Beltran Bat 3.00 8.00
CBI Craig Biggio Uni 4.00 10.00
CC Coco Crisp Bat 3.00 8.00
CG Cristian Guzman Bat 3.00 8.00
CP Corey Patterson Bat 3.00 8.00
CT Charles Thomas Bat 3.00 8.00
DE Darin Erstad Bat 3.00 8.00
DM Doug Mientkiewicz Bat 3.00 8.00
DO David Ortiz Bat 4.00 10.00
DW Dontrelle Willis Bat 3.00 8.00
EC1 Eric Chavez Bat 3.00 8.00
EC2 Eric Chavez Uni 3.00 8.00
GS Gary Sheffield Bat 3.00 8.00
HB1 Hank Blalock Bat 3.00 8.00
HB2 Hank Blalock Uni 3.00 8.00
HB3 Hank Blalock Jsy 3.00 8.00
IR1 Ivan Rodriguez Bat 4.00 10.00
IR2 Ivan Rodriguez Jsy 4.00 10.00
JB Jeff Bagwell Uni 4.00 10.00
JE Johnny Estrada Jsy 3.00 8.00
JE1 Jim Edmonds Bat 3.00 8.00
JE2 Jim Edmonds Jsy 3.00 8.00
JG Jody Gerut Bat 3.00 8.00
JGI Jay Gibbons Bat 3.00 8.00
JGU Jose Guillen Bat 3.00 8.00
JJ Jacque Jones Bat 3.00 8.00
JK Jason Kendall Bat 3.00 8.00
JP1 Jorge Posada Bat 4.00 10.00
JP2 Jorge Posada Jsy 4.00 10.00
JR Jeremy Reed Bat 3.00 8.00
JT Jim Thome Bat 4.00 10.00
JTO Joe Torre Uni 6.00 15.00
KM Kevin Millar Bat 3.00 8.00
KME Kevin Mench Jsy 3.00 8.00
LB1 Lance Berkman Bat 3.00 8.00
LB2 Lance Berkman Jsy 3.00 8.00
LG Luis Gonzalez Bat 3.00 8.00
LN Laynce Nix Jsy 3.00 8.00
MC Miguel Cabrera Bat 4.00 10.00
MG Marcus Giles Bat 3.00 8.00
MK Mark Kotsay Bat 3.00 8.00
MM Melvin Mora Bat 3.00 8.00
MO Magglio Ordonez Bat 3.00 8.00
MP Mike Piazza Uni 4.00 10.00
MR Manny Ramirez Bat 4.00 10.00
MRE Mike Restovich Bat 3.00 8.00
MTE1 Miguel Tejada Uni 3.00 8.00
MTE2 Miguel Tejada Bat 3.00 8.00
MT1 Mark Teixeira Uni 4.00 10.00
MT2 Mark Teixeira Jsy 4.00 10.00
MT3 Mark Teixeira Bat 4.00 10.00
MY Michael Young Jsy 3.00 8.00
NG Nick Green Jsy 3.00 8.00
OV Omar Vizquel Bat 4.00 10.00
PK Paul Konerko Bat 3.00 8.00
PN Phil Nevin Bat 3.00 8.00
RB Ron Belliard Bat 3.00 8.00
RF Rafael Furcal Jsy 3.00 8.00
RK Ryan Klesko Jsy 3.00 8.00
RP Rafael Palmeiro Bat 4.00 10.00
RS Reggie Sanders Bat 3.00 8.00
SB Sean Burroughs Bat 3.00 8.00
SG Shawn Green Bat 3.00 8.00
TG Troy Glaus Bat 3.00 8.00
TH Todd Helton Bat 4.00 10.00
THU Torii Hunter Bat 3.00 8.00
VC Vinny Castilla Bat 3.00 8.00
VG Vladimir Guerrero Bat 4.00 10.00
VM Victor Martinez Bat 3.00 8.00

1996 Topps Gallery

The 1996 Topps Gallery set was issued in one series totalling 180 cards. The eight-card packs retailed for $3.00 each. The set is divided into five themes: Classics (1-90), New Editions (91-108), Modernists (109-126), Futurists (127-144) and Masters (145-180). Each theme features a different design on front, but the bulk of the set has full-bleed, color action shots. A Mickey Mantle Masterpiece was inserted into these packs at a rate of one every 48 packs. It is priced at the bottom of these listings.

COMPLETE SET (180) 20.00 40.00
1 Tom Glavine .30 .75
2 Carlos Baerga .20 .50
3 Dante Bichette .20 .50
4 Mark Langston .20 .50
5 Ray Lankford .20 .50
6 Moises Alou .20 .50
7 Marquis Grissom .20 .50
8 Ramon Martinez .20 .50
9 Steve Finley .20 .50
10 Todd Hundley .20 .50
11 Brady Anderson .20 .50
12 John Valentin .20 .50
13 Heathcliff Slocumb .20 .50
14 Ruben Sierra .20 .50
15 Jeff Conine .20 .50
16 Jay Buhner .20 .50
17 Sammy Sosa .50 1.25
18 Doug Drabek .20 .50
19 Jose Mesa .20 .50
20 Jeff King .20 .50
21 Mickey Tettleton .20 .50
22 Jeff Montgomery .20 .50
23 Alex Fernandez .20 .50
24 Greg Vaughn .20 .50
25 Chuck Finley .20 .50
26 Terry Steinbach .20 .50
27 Rod Beck .20 .50
28 Jack McDowell .20 .50
29 Mark Wohlers .20 .50
30 Len Dykstra .20 .50
31 Bernie Williams .30 .75
32 Travis Fryman .20 .50
33 Jose Canseco .30 .75
34 Ken Caminiti .20 .50
35 Devon White .20 .50
36 Bobby Bonilla .20 .50
37 Paul Sorrento .20 .50
38 Ryne Sandberg .75 2.00
39 Derek Bell .20 .50
40 Bobby Jones .20 .50
41 J.T. Snow .20 .50
42 Denny Neagle .20 .50
43 Tim Wakefield .20 .50
44 Andres Galarraga .20 .50
45 David Segui .20 .50
46 Lee Smith .20 .50
47 Mel Rojas .20 .50
48 John Franco .20 .50
49 Pete Schourek .20 .50
50 John Wetteland .20 .50
51 Paul Molitor .20 .50
52 Ivan Rodriguez .30 .75
53 Chris Hoiles .20 .50
54 Mike Greenwell .20 .50
55 Orel Hershiser .20 .50
56 Brian McRae .20 .50
57 Geronimo Berroa .20 .50
58 Craig Biggio .30 .75
59 David Justice .20 .50
60 Lance Johnson .20 .50
61 Andy Ashby .20 .50
62 Randy Myers .20 .50
63 Gregg Jefferies .20 .50
64 Kevin Appier .20 .50
65 Rick Aguilera .20 .50
66 Shane Reynolds .20 .50
67 John Smoltz .30 .75
68 Ron Gant .20 .50
69 Eric Karros .20 .50
70 Jim Thome .30 .75
71 Terry Pendleton .20 .50
72 Kenny Rogers .20 .50
73 Robin Ventura .20 .50
74 Dave Nilsson .20 .50
75 Brian Jordan .20 .50
76 Glenallen Hill .20 .50
77 Greg Colbrunn .20 .50
78 Roberto Alomar .30 .75
79 Rickey Henderson .50 1.25
80 Carlos Garcia .20 .50
81 Dean Palmer .20 .50
82 Mike Stanley .20 .50
83 Hal Morris .20 .50
84 Wade Boggs .30 .75
85 Chad Curtis .20 .50
86 Roberto Hernandez .20 .50
87 John Olerud .20 .50
88 Frank Castillo .20 .50
89 Rafael Palmeiro .30 .75
90 Trevor Hoffman .20 .50
91 Marty Cordova .20 .50
92 Hideo Nomo .50 1.25
93 Johnny Damon .30 .75
94 Bill Pulsipher .20 .50
95 Garret Anderson .20 .50
96 Ray Durham .20 .50
97 Ricky Bottalico .20 .50
98 Carlos Perez .20 .50
99 Troy Percival .20 .50
100 Chipper Jones .50 1.25
101 Esteban Loaiza .20 .50
102 John Mabry .20 .50
103 Jon Nunnally .20 .50
104 Andy Pettitte .30 .75
105 Lyle Mouton .20 .50
106 Jason Isringhausen .20 .50
107 Brian L.Hunter .20 .50
108 Quilvio Veras .20 .50
109 Jim Edmonds .20 .50
110 Ryan Klesko .20 .50
111 Pedro Martinez .30 .75
112 Joey Hamilton .20 .50
113 Vinny Castilla .20 .50
114 Alex Gonzalez .20 .50
115 Raul Mondesi .20 .50
116 Rondell White .20 .50
117 Dan Miceli .20 .50
118 Tom Goodwin .20 .50
119 Bret Boone .20 .50
120 Shawn Green .20 .50
121 Jeff Cirillo .20 .50
122 Rico Brogna .20 .50
123 Chris Gomez .20 .50
124 Ismael Valdes .20 .50
125 Javy Lopez .20 .50
126 Manny Ramirez .30 .75
127 Paul Wilson .20 .50
128 Billy Wagner .20 .50
129 Eric Owens .20 .50
130 Todd Greene .20 .50
131 Karim Garcia .20 .50
132 Jimmy Haynes .20 .50
133 Michael Tucker .20 .50
134 John Wasdin .20 .50
135 Brooks Kieschnick .20 .50
136 Alex Ochoa .20 .50
137 Ariel Prieto .20 .50
138 Tony Clark .20 .50
139 Mark Loretta .20 .50
140 Rey Ordonez .20 .50
141 Chris Snopek .20 .50
142 Roger Cedeno .20 .50
143 Derek Jeter 1.25 3.00
144 Jeff Suppan .20 .50
145 Greg Maddux .75 2.00
146 Ken Griffey Jr. .75 2.00
147 Tony Gwynn .60 1.50
148 Darren Daulton .20 .50
149 Will Clark .30 .75
150 Mo Vaughn .20 .50
151 Reggie Sanders .20 .50
152 Kirby Puckett .50 1.25
153 Paul O'Neill .30 .75
154 Tim Salmon .30 .75
155 Mark McGwire 1.25 3.00
156 Barry Bonds 1.25 3.00
157 Albert Belle .20 .50
158 Edgar Martinez .30 .75
159 Mike Mussina .30 .75
160 Cecil Fielder .20 .50
161 Kenny Lofton .20 .50
162 Randy Johnson .50 1.25
163 Juan Gonzalez .20 .50
164 Jeff Bagwell .30 .75
165 Joe Carter .20 .50
166 Mike Piazza .75 2.00
167 Eddie Murray .50 1.25
168 Cal Ripken 1.50 4.00
169 Barry Larkin .30 .75
170 Chuck Knoblauch .20 .50
171 Chili Davis .20 .50
172 Fred McGriff .30 .75
173 Matt Williams .20 .50
174 Roger Clemens 1.00 2.50
175 Frank Thomas .50 1.25
176 Dennis Eckersley .20 .50
177 Gary Sheffield .20 .50
178 David Cone .20 .50
179 Larry Walker .20 .50
180 Mark Grace .30 .75
NNO M. Mantle Masterpiece 8.00 20.00

1996 Topps Gallery Players Private Issue

Randomly inserted in packs at a rate of one in 12, this 180-card parallel is foil stamped. The backs are sequentially numbered 0-999, with the first 100 cards (numbers 0-99) sent to the players and the balance inserted in packs. Topps released a statement at the end of the 1996 season, claiming that they destroyed 400 sets.

*STARS: 6X TO 15X BASIC CARDS
*ROOKIES: 5X TO 12X BASIC CARDS
STATED ODDS 1:8

1996 Topps Gallery Expressionists

Randomly inserted in packs at a rate of one in 24, this 20-card set features leaders printed on triple foil stamped and texture embossed cards. Card backs contain a second photo and narrative about the player.

COMPLETE SET (20) 30.00 80.00
STATED ODDS 1:24
1 Mike Piazza 3.00 8.00
2 J.T. Snow .75 2.00
3 Ken Griffey Jr. 3.00 8.00
4 Kirby Puckett 2.00 5.00
5 Carlos Baerga .75 2.00
6 Chipper Jones 2.00 5.00
7 Hideo Nomo 2.00 5.00
8 Mark McGwire 5.00 12.00
9 Gary Sheffield .75 2.00
10 Randy Johnson 2.00 5.00
11 Ray Lankford .75 2.00
12 Sammy Sosa 2.00 5.00
13 Denny Martinez .75 2.00
14 Jose Canseco 1.25 3.00
15 Tony Gwynn 2.50 6.00
16 Edgar Martinez 1.25 3.00
17 Reggie Sanders .75 2.00
18 Andres Galarraga .75 2.00
19 Albert Belle .75 2.00
20 Barry Larkin 1.25 3.00

1996 Topps Gallery Photo Gallery

Randomly inserted in packs at a rate of one in 30, this 15-card set features top photography chronicling baseball's biggest stars and greatest moments from last year. Each double foil stamped card is printed on 24 pt. stock with customized designs to accentuate the photography.

COMPLETE SET (15) 30.00 80.00
STATED ODDS 1:30
PG1 Eddie Murray 2.50 6.00
PG2 Randy Johnson 2.50 6.00
PG3 Cal Ripken 8.00 20.00
PG4 Bret Boone 1.00 2.50
PG5 Frank Thomas 2.50 6.00
PG6 Jeff Conine 1.00 2.50
PG7 Johnny Damon 1.50 4.00
PG8 Roger Clemens 5.00 12.00
PG9 Albert Belle 1.00 2.50
PG10 Ken Griffey Jr. 4.00 10.00
PG11 Kirby Puckett 2.50 6.00
PG12 David Justice 1.00 2.50
PG13 Bobby Bonilla 1.00 2.50
PG14 Colorado Rockies 1.00 2.50
PG15 Atlanta Braves 1.00 2.50

1997 Topps Gallery Promos

This four-card set was distributed as a promotion for the 1997 Topps Gallery set and features color player pictures in four different frame designs with a player portrait, biographical, and career statistics on the backs.

COMPLETE SET (4) 4.00 10.00
PP1 Andruw Jones 1.25 3.00
PP2 Derek Jeter 2.50 6.00
PP3 Mike Piazza 1.50 4.00
PP4 Craig Biggio .40 1.00

1997 Topps Gallery

The 1997 Topps Gallery set was issued in one series totalling 180 cards. The eight-card packs retailed for $4.00 each. This hobby only set is divided into four themes: Veterans, Prospects, Rising Stars and Young Stars. Printed on 24-point card stock with a high-gloss film and etch stamped with one or more foils, each theme features a different design on front with a variety of informative statistics and revealing player text on the back.

COMPLETE SET (180) 20.00 50.00
1 Paul Molitor .20 .50
2 Devon White .20 .50
3 Andres Galarraga .20 .50
4 Cal Ripken 1.50 4.00
5 Tony Gwynn .60 1.50
6 Mike Stanley .20 .50
7 Orel Hershiser .20 .50
8 Jose Canseco .30 .75
9 Chili Davis .20 .50
10 Harold Baines .20 .50
11 Rickey Henderson .50 1.25
12 Darryl Strawberry .20 .50
13 Todd Worrell .20 .50
14 Cecil Fielder .20 .50
15 Gary Gaetti .20 .50
16 Bobby Bonilla .20 .50
17 Will Clark .30 .75
18 Kevin Brown .20 .50
19 Tom Glavine .30 .75
20 Wade Boggs .30 .75
21 Edgar Martinez .30 .75
22 Lance Johnson .20 .50
23 Gregg Jefferies .20 .50
24 Bip Roberts .20 .50
25 Tony Phillips .20 .50
26 Greg Maddux .75 2.00
27 Mickey Tettleton .20 .50
28 Terry Steinbach .20 .50
29 Ryne Sandberg .75 2.00
30 Wally Joyner .20 .50
31 Joe Carter .20 .50
32 Ellis Burks .20 .50
33 Fred McGriff .30 .75
34 Barry Larkin .30 .75
35 John Franco .20 .50
36 Rafael Palmeiro .30 .75
37 Mark McGwire 1.25 3.00
38 Ken Caminiti .20 .50
39 David Cone .20 .50
40 Julio Franco .20 .50
41 Roger Clemens 1.00 2.50
42 Barry Bonds 1.25 3.00
43 Dennis Eckersley .20 .50
44 Eddie Murray .50 1.25
45 Paul O'Neill .30 .75
46 Craig Biggio .30 .75
47 Roberto Alomar .30 .75
48 Mark Grace .30 .75
49 Matt Williams .20 .50
50 Jay Buhner .20 .50
51 John Smoltz .30 .75
52 Randy Johnson .50 1.25
53 Ramon Martinez .20 .50
54 Curt Schilling .20 .50
55 Gary Sheffield .20 .50
56 Jack McDowell .20 .50
57 Brady Anderson .20 .50
58 Dante Bichette .20 .50
59 Ron Gant .20 .50
60 Alex Fernandez .20 .50
61 Moises Alou .20 .50
62 Travis Fryman .20 .50
63 Dean Palmer .20 .50
64 Todd Hundley .20 .50
65 Jeff Brantley .20 .50
66 Bernard Gilkey .20 .50
67 Geronimo Berroa .20 .50
68 John Wetteland .20 .50
69 Robin Ventura .20 .50
70 Ray Lankford .20 .50
71 Kevin Appier .20 .50
72 Larry Walker .20 .50
73 Juan Gonzalez .20 .50
74 Jeff King .20 .50
75 Greg Vaughn .20 .50
76 Steve Finley .20 .50
77 Brian McRae .20 .50
78 Paul Sorrento .20 .50
79 Ken Griffey Jr. .75 2.00
80 Omar Vizquel .30 .75
81 Jose Mesa .20 .50
82 Albert Belle .20 .50
83 Glenallen Hill .20 .50
84 Sammy Sosa .50 1.25
85 Andy Benes .20 .50
86 David Justice .20 .50
87 Marquis Grissom .20 .50
88 John Olerud .20 .50
89 Tino Martinez .30 .75
90 Frank Thomas .50 1.25
91 Raul Mondesi .20 .50
92 Steve Trachsel .20 .50
93 Jim Edmonds .20 .50
94 Rusty Greer .20 .50
95 Joey Hamilton .20 .50
96 Ismael Valdes .20 .50
97 Dave Nilsson .20 .50
98 John Jaha .20 .50
99 Alex Gonzalez .20 .50
100 Javy Lopez .20 .50
101 Ryan Klesko .20 .50
102 Tim Salmon .30 .75
103 Bernie Williams .30 .75
104 Roberto Hernandez .20 .50
105 Chuck Knoblauch .20 .50
106 Mike Lansing .20 .50
107 Vinny Castilla .20 .50
108 Reggie Sanders .20 .50
109 Mo Vaughn .20 .50
110 Rondell White .20 .50
111 Ivan Rodriguez .30 .75
112 Mike Mussina .30 .75
113 Carlos Baerga .20 .50
114 Jeff Conine .20 .50
115 Jim Thome .30 .75
116 Manny Ramirez .30 .75
117 Kenny Lofton .20 .50
118 Wilson Alvarez .20 .50
119 Eric Karros .20 .50
120 Robb Nen .20 .50
121 Mark Wohlers .20 .50
122 Ed Sprague .20 .50
123 Pat Hentgen .20 .50
124 Juan Guzman .20 .50
125 Derek Bell .20 .50
126 Jeff Bagwell .30 .75
127 Eric Young .20 .50
128 John Valentin .20 .50
129 Al Martin UER .20 .50
Picture of Javy Lopez
130 Trevor Hoffman .20 .50
131 Henry Rodriguez .20 .50
132 Pedro Martinez .30 .75
133 Mike Piazza .75 2.00
134 Brian Jordan .20 .50
135 Jose Valentin .20 .50
136 Jeff Cirillo .20 .50
137 Chipper Jones .50 1.25
138 Ricky Bottalico .20 .50
139 Hideo Nomo .50 1.25
140 Troy Percival .20 .50
141 Rey Ordonez .20 .50
142 Edgar Renteria .20 .50
143 Luis Castillo .20 .50
144 Vladimir Guerrero .50 1.25
145 Jeff D'Amico .20 .50
146 Andruw Jones .30 .75
147 Darin Erstad .20 .50
148 Bob Abreu .30 .75
149 Carlos Delgado .20 .50
150 Jamey Wright .20 .50
151 Nomar Garciaparra .75 2.00
152 Jason Kendall .20 .50
153 Jermaine Allensworth .20 .50
154 Scott Rolen .30 .75
155 Rocky Coppinger .20 .50
156 Paul Wilson .20 .50
157 Garret Anderson .20 .50
158 Mariano Rivera .50 1.25
159 Ruben Rivera .20 .50
160 Andy Pettitte .30 .75
161 Derek Jeter 1.25 3.00
162 Neifi Perez .20 .50
163 Ray Durham .20 .50
164 James Baldwin .20 .50
165 Marty Cordova .20 .50
166 Tony Clark .20 .50
167 Michael Tucker .20 .50
168 Mike Sweeney .20 .50
169 Johnny Damon .30 .75
170 Jermaine Dye .20 .50
171 Alex Ochoa .20 .50
172 Jason Isringhausen .20 .50
173 Mark Grudzielanek .20 .50
174 Jose Rosado .20 .50
175 Todd Hollandsworth .20 .50
176 Alan Benes .20 .50
177 Jason Giambi .20 .50
178 Billy Wagner .20 .50
179 Justin Thompson .20 .50
180 Todd Walker .20 .50

1997 Topps Gallery Player's Private Issue

Randomly inserted in packs at a rate of one in 12, this 180-card set is a foil-stamped parallel version of the regular Topps Gallery set, limited to 250, with some of the cards sent to the players. The cards are spot UV coated on the photo only to allow for autographing.

*STARS: 6X TO 15X BASIC CARDS
STATED ODDS 1:12

1997 Topps Gallery Gallery of Heroes

Randomly inserted in packs at a rate of one in 36, this 10-card set features color player photos designed to command the attention paid to works hanging in art museums. The backs carry player information.

COMPLETE SET (10) 60.00 150.00
STATED ODDS 1:36
GH1 Derek Jeter 10.00 25.00
GH2 Chipper Jones 4.00 10.00
GH3 Frank Thomas 4.00 10.00
GH4 Ken Griffey Jr. 6.00 15.00
GH5 Cal Ripken 12.50 30.00
GH6 Mark McGwire 10.00 25.00
GH7 Mike Piazza 6.00 15.00
GH8 Jeff Bagwell 2.50 6.00
GH9 Tony Gwynn 5.00 12.00
GH10 Mo Vaughn 1.50 4.00

1997 Topps Gallery Peter Max Serigraphs

Randomly inserted in packs at a rate of one in 24, this 10-card set features painted renditions of ten superstars by the artist, Peter Max. The backs carry his commentary about the player.

COMPLETE SET (10) 30.00 80.00
STATED ODDS 1:24
*AUTOS: 8X TO 20X BASIC SERIGRAPHS
AUTOS RANDOM INSERTS IN PACKS
AUTOS STATED PRINT RUN 40 SETS
AU'S SIGNED BY MAX BENEATH UV COATING
1 Derek Jeter 12.50 30.00
2 Albert Belle .75 2.00
3 Ken Caminiti .75 2.00
4 Chipper Jones 2.00 5.00
5 Ken Griffey Jr. 3.00 8.00
6 Frank Thomas 2.00 5.00
7 Cal Ripken 6.00 15.00
8 Mark McGwire 5.00 12.00
9 Barry Bonds 5.00 12.00
10 Mike Piazza 3.00 8.00

1997 Topps Gallery Photo Gallery

Randomly inserted in packs at a rate of one in 24, this 16-card set features color photos of some of baseball's hottest stars and their most memorable moments. Each card is enhanced by customized designs and double foil-stamping.

COMPLETE SET (16) 40.00 100.00
STATED ODDS 1:24
PG1 John Wetteland 1.00 2.50
PG2 Paul Molitor 1.00 2.50
PG3 Eddie Murray 2.50 6.00
PG4 Ken Griffey Jr. 4.00 10.00
PG5 Chipper Jones 2.50 6.00
PG6 Derek Jeter 6.00 15.00
PG7 Frank Thomas 2.50 6.00
PG8 Mark McGwire 6.00 15.00
PG9 Kenny Lofton 1.00 2.50
PG10 Gary Sheffield 1.00 2.50
PG11 Mike Piazza 4.00 10.00
PG12 Vinny Castilla 1.00 2.50
PG13 Andres Galarraga 1.00 2.50
PG14 Andy Pettitte 1.50 4.00
PG15 Robin Ventura 1.00 2.50
PG16 Barry Larkin 1.50 4.00

1998 Topps Gallery

The 1998 Topps Gallery hobby-only set was issued in one series totalling 150 cards. The six-card packs retailed for $3.00 each. The set is divided by five subset groupings: Expressionists, Exhibitionists, Impressions, Portraits and Permanent Collection. Each theme features a different design with informative stats and text on each player.

COMPLETE SET (150) 20.00 50.00
1 Andruw Jones .30 .75
2 Fred McGriff .30 .75
3 Wade Boggs .30 .75
4 Pedro Martinez .30 .75
5 Matt Williams .20 .50
6 Wilson Alvarez .20 .50
7 Henry Rodriguez .20 .50
8 Jay Bell .20 .50
9 Marquis Grissom .20 .50
10 Darryl Kile .20 .50
11 Chuck Knoblauch .20 .50
12 Kenny Lofton .20 .50
13 Quinton McCracken .20 .50
14 Andres Galarraga .20 .50
15 Brian Jordan .20 .50
16 Mike Lansing .20 .50
17 Travis Fryman .20 .50
18 Tony Saunders .20 .50
19 Moises Alou .20 .50
20 Travis Lee .20 .50
21 Garret Anderson .20 .50
22 Ken Caminiti .20 .50
23 Pedro Astacio .20 .50
24 Ellis Burks .20 .50
25 Albert Belle .20 .50
26 Alan Benes .20 .50
27 Jay Buhner .20 .50
28 Derek Bell .20 .50
29 Jeromy Burnitz .20 .50
30 Kevin Appier .20 .50
31 Jeff Cirillo .20 .50
32 Bernard Gilkey .20 .50
33 David Cone .20 .50
34 Jason Dickson .20 .50
35 Jose Cruz Jr. .20 .50
36 Marty Cordova .20 .50
37 Ray Durham .20 .50
38 Jaret Wright .20 .50
39 Billy Wagner .20 .50
40 Roger Clemens 1.00 2.50
41 Juan Gonzalez .20 .50
42 Jeremi Gonzalez .20 .50
43 Mark Grudzielanek .20 .50
44 Tom Glavine .30 .75
45 Barry Larkin .30 .75
46 Lance Johnson .20 .50
47 Bobby Higginson .20 .50
48 Mike Mussina .30 .75
49 Al Martin .20 .50
50 Mark McGwire 1.25 3.00
51 Todd Hundley .20 .50
52 Ray Lankford .20 .50
53 Jason Kendall .20 .50
54 Javy Lopez .20 .50
55 Ben Grieve .20 .50
56 Randy Johnson .50 1.25
57 Jeff King .20 .50
58 Mark Grace .30 .75
59 Rusty Greer .20 .50
60 Greg Maddux .75 2.00
61 Jeff Kent .20 .50
62 Rey Ordonez .20 .50
63 Hideo Nomo .50 1.25
64 Charles Nagy .20 .50
65 Rondell White .20 .50
66 Todd Helton .30 .75
67 Jim Thome .30 .75
68 Denny Neagle .20 .50
69 Ivan Rodriguez .30 .75
70 Vladimir Guerrero .50 1.25
71 Jorge Posada .30 .75
72 J.T. Snow .20 .50
73 Reggie Sanders .20 .50
74 Scott Rolen .30 .75
75 Robin Ventura .20 .50
76 Mariano Rivera .50 1.25
77 Cal Ripken 1.50 4.00
78 Justin Thompson .20 .50
79 Mike Piazza .75 2.00
80 Kevin Brown .20 .50
81 Sandy Alomar Jr. .20 .50
82 Craig Biggio .30 .75
83 Vinny Castilla .20 .50
84 Eric Young .20 .50
85 Bernie Williams .30 .75
86 Brady Anderson .20 .50
87 Bobby Bonilla .20 .50
88 Tony Clark .20 .50
89 Dan Wilson .20 .50
90 John Wetteland .20 .50
91 Barry Bonds 1.25 3.00
92 Chan Ho Park .20 .50
93 Carlos Delgado .20 .50
94 David Justice .20 .50
95 Chipper Jones .50 1.25
96 Shawn Estes .20 .50
97 Jason Giambi .20 .50
98 Ron Gant .20 .50
99 John Olerud .20 .50
100 Frank Thomas .50 1.25
101 Jose Guillen .20 .50
102 Brad Radke .20 .50
103 Troy Percival .20 .50
104 John Smoltz .30 .75
105 Edgardo Alfonzo .20 .50
106 Dante Bichette .20 .50
107 Larry Walker .20 .50
108 John Valentin .20 .50
109 Roberto Alomar .30 .75
110 Mike Cameron .20 .50
111 Eric Davis .20 .50
112 Johnny Damon .30 .75
113 Darin Erstad .20 .50
114 Omar Vizquel .30 .75
115 Derek Jeter 1.25 3.00
116 Tony Womack .20 .50
117 Edgar Renteria .20 .50
118 Raul Mondesi .20 .50
119 Tony Gwynn .60 1.50
120 Ken Griffey Jr. .75 2.00
121 Jim Edmonds .20 .50
122 Brian Hunter .20 .50
123 Neifi Perez .20 .50
124 Dean Palmer .20 .50
125 Alex Rodriguez .75 2.00
126 Tim Salmon .30 .75
127 Curt Schilling .20 .50
128 Kevin Orie .20 .50
129 Andy Pettitte .30 .75
130 Gary Sheffield .20 .50
131 Jose Rosado .20 .50
132 Manny Ramirez .30 .75
133 Rafael Palmeiro .30 .75
134 Sammy Sosa .50 1.25
135 Jeff Bagwell .30 .75
136 Delino DeShields .20 .50
137 Ryan Klesko .20 .50
138 Mo Vaughn .20 .50
139 Steve Finley .20 .50
140 Nomar Garciaparra .75 2.00
141 Paul Molitor .20 .50
142 Pat Hentgen .20 .50
143 Eric Karros .20 .50
144 Bobby Jones .20 .50
145 Tino Martinez .30 .75
146 Matt Morris .20 .50
147 Livan Hernandez .20 .50
148 Edgar Martinez .30 .75
149 Paul O'Neill .30 .75
150 Checklist .20 .50

1998 Topps Gallery Gallery Proofs

Randomly inserted in packs at a rate of one in 34, this 150-card set is a parallel to the Topps Gallery base set. The set is sequentially numbered to 125.

*STARS: 10X TO 25X BASIC CARDS
STATED ODDS 1:34 HOBBY

1998 Topps Gallery Original Printing Plates

Randomly inserted in packs at a rate of one in 537, this 150-card set is a parallel to the Topps Gallery base set. Each player in this set has eight different plates, one for each of the four colors used in printing, front and back. Pricing for stars is unavailable due to scarcity.

STATED ODDS 1:537 HOBBY

1998 Topps Gallery Player's Private Issue

Randomly inserted in packs at a rate of one in 17, this 150-card set is a parallel to the Topps Gallery base set. The set is sequentially numbered to 250.

*STARS: 5X TO 12X BASIC CARDS
STATED ODDS 1:17 HOBBY

1998 Topps Gallery Player's Private Issue Auction

Seeded at a rate of one per pack, these standard-sized cards loosely parallel the far more scarce Player's Private Issue cards. Two glaring differences, however, are readily apparent: 1) The Auction cards are printed on thin paper stock (compared to the thick 20 pt board for PPI cards) and 2) The Auction card backs contain rules and guidelines for the auction promotion (compared to the normal statistics and player photo on the PPI cards). Collectors who obtained Auction cards were supposed to "bid" on a selection of ten different pieces of framed artwork (one for each of the following players: J.Gonzalez, M.McGwire, C.Ripken, M.Piazza, C.Jones, F.Thomas, D.Jeter, K.Griffey Jr., A.Rodriguez and N.Garciaparra). Bidding points were available in 25, 50, 75 and 100 point increments detailed at the top right corner of each Auction card back. Point totals were doubled, however, when the player featured on the Auction card was the same player actually being bid on. The auction period ran from July 4th, 1998 through October 16th, 1998. During that time period, collectors had to mail in their accumulated bid points and specify which of the ten pieces they were bidding upon. An "800" number was available for collectors to check upon the status of the current high bid, allowing them the opportunity to submit additional bid points prior to the October 16th closing date. Winners were notified 30 days after the closing date.

COMPLETE SET (150) 50.00 100.00
*STARS: .75X TO 2X BASIC CARDS

1998 Topps Gallery Awards Gallery

Randomly inserted in packs at a rate of one in 24, this 10-card set honors the achievements of the majors top stars.

COMPLETE SET (10) 25.00 60.00
STATED ODDS 1:24 HOBBY
AG1 Ken Griffey Jr. 4.00 10.00
AG2 Larry Walker 1.00 2.50
AG3 Roger Clemens 5.00 12.00
AG4 Pedro Martinez 1.50 4.00
AG5 Nomar Garciaparra 4.00 10.00
AG6 Scott Rolen 1.50 4.00
AG7 Frank Thomas 2.50 6.00
AG8 Tony Gwynn 3.00 8.00
AG9 Mark McGwire 6.00 15.00
AG10 Livan Hernandez 1.00 2.50

1998 Topps Gallery Gallery of Heroes

Randomly inserted in packs at a rate of one in 24, this 15-card set is an insert to the Topps Gallery base set. The fronts feature a translucent stain-glass design that helps showcase some of today's high performance players.

COMPLETE SET (15) 60.00 150.00
STATED ODDS 1:24 HOBBY
*JUMBOS: .3X TO .8X BASIC HEROES
ONE JUMBO PER HOBBY BOX
GH1 Ken Griffey Jr. 5.00 12.00
GH2 Derek Jeter 8.00 20.00
GH3 Barry Bonds 8.00 20.00
GH4 Alex Rodriguez 5.00 12.00
GH5 Frank Thomas 3.00 8.00
GH6 Nomar Garciaparra 5.00 12.00
GH7 Mark McGwire 8.00 20.00
GH8 Mike Piazza 5.00 12.00
GH9 Cal Ripken 10.00 25.00
GH10 Jose Cruz Jr. 1.25 3.00
GH11 Jeff Bagwell 2.00 5.00
GH12 Chipper Jones 3.00 8.00
GH13 Juan Gonzalez 1.25 3.00
GH14 Hideo Nomo 3.00 8.00
GH15 Greg Maddux 5.00 12.00

1998 Topps Gallery Photo Gallery

Randomly inserted in packs at a rate of one in 24, this 10-card set features a selection of top stars in riveting game action.

COMPLETE SET (10) 30.00 80.00
STATED ODDS 1:24 HOBBY
PG1 Alex Rodriguez 4.00 10.00
PG2 Frank Thomas 2.50 6.00
PG3 Derek Jeter 6.00 15.00
PG4 Cal Ripken 8.00 20.00
PG5 Ken Griffey Jr. 4.00 10.00
PG6 Mike Piazza 4.00 10.00
PG7 Nomar Garciaparra 4.00 10.00
PG8 Tim Salmon 1.50 4.00
PG9 Jeff Bagwell 1.50 4.00
PG10 Barry Bonds 6.00 15.00

1999 Topps Gallery Previews

This three-card standard-size set was released to preview the 1999 Topps Gallery set. The set features a regular design as well as a couple of the subsets involved in this set.

COMPLETE SET (3) 2.00 5.00
PP1 Scott Rolen 1.00 2.50
PP2 A.Galarraga MAS .60 1.50
PP3 Brad Fullmer ART .40 1.00

1999 Topps Gallery

The 1999 Topps Gallery set was issued in one series totalling 150 cards and was distributed in six-card packs for a suggested retail price of $3. The set features 100 veteran stars and 50 subset cards finely crafted and printed on 24-pt. stock, with serigraph textured frame, etched foil stamping, and spot UV finish. The set contains the following subsets: Masters (101-115), Artisans (116-127), and Apprentices (128-150). Rookie Cards inlcude Pat Burrell, Nick Johnson and Alfonso Soriano.

COMPLETE SET (150) 20.00 50.00
COMP.SET w/o SP's (100) 10.00 25.00
COMMON CARD (1-100) .10 .30
COMMON (101-150) .30 .75
1 Mark McGwire .75 2.00
2 Jim Thome .20 .50
3 Bernie Williams .20 .50
4 Larry Walker .20 .50
5 Juan Gonzalez .10 .30
6 Ken Griffey Jr. .50 1.25
7 Raul Mondesi .10 .30
8 Sammy Sosa .30 .75
9 Greg Maddux .50 1.25
10 Jeff Bagwell .20 .50
11 Vladimir Guerrero .30 .75
12 Scott Rolen .20 .50
13 Nomar Garciaparra .50 1.25
14 Mike Piazza .50 1.25
15 Travis Lee .10 .30
16 Carlos Delgado .10 .30
17 Darin Erstad .10 .30
18 David Justice .10 .30
19 Cal Ripken 1.00 2.50
20 Derek Jeter .75 2.00
21 Tony Clark .10 .30
22 Barry Larkin .20 .50
23 Greg Vaughn .10 .30
24 Jeff Kent .10 .30
25 Wade Boggs .20 .50
26 Andres Galarraga .10 .30
27 Ken Caminiti .10 .30
28 Jason Kendall .10 .30
29 Todd Helton .20 .50
30 Chuck Knoblauch .10 .30
31 Roger Clemens .60 1.50
32 Jeromy Burnitz .10 .30
33 Javy Lopez .10 .30
34 Roberto Alomar .20 .50
35 Eric Karros .10 .30
36 Ben Grieve .10 .30
37 Eric Davis .10 .30
38 Rondell White .10 .30
39 Dmitri Young .10 .30
40 Ivan Rodriguez .20 .50
41 Paul O'Neill .20 .50
42 Jeff Cirillo .10 .30
43 Kerry Wood .10 .30
44 Albert Belle .10 .30
45 Frank Thomas .30 .75
46 Manny Ramirez .20 .50
47 Tom Glavine .20 .50
48 Mo Vaughn .10 .30
49 Jose Cruz Jr. .10 .30
50 Sandy Alomar Jr. .10 .30
51 Edgar Martinez .20 .50
52 John Olerud .10 .30
53 Todd Walker .10 .30
54 Tim Salmon .20 .50
55 Derek Bell .10 .30
56 Matt Williams .10 .30
57 Alex Rodriguez .50 1.25
58 Rusty Greer .10 .30
59 Vinny Castilla .10 .30
60 Jason Giambi .10 .30
61 Mark Grace .20 .50
62 Jose Canseco .20 .50
63 Gary Sheffield .10 .30
64 Brad Fullmer .10 .30
65 Trevor Hoffman .10 .30
66 Mark Kotsay .10 .30
67 Mike Mussina .20 .50
68 Johnny Damon .20 .50
69 Tino Martinez .20 .50
70 Curt Schilling .10 .30
71 Jay Buhner .10 .30
72 Kenny Lofton .10 .30
73 Randy Johnson .30 .75
74 Kevin Brown .20 .50
75 Brian Jordan .10 .30
76 Craig Biggio .20 .50
77 Barry Bonds .75 2.00
78 Tony Gwynn .40 1.00
79 Jim Edmonds .10 .30
80 Shawn Green .10 .30
81 Todd Hundley .10 .30
82 Cliff Floyd .10 .30
83 Jose Guillen .10 .30
84 Dante Bichette .10 .30
85 Moises Alou .10 .30
86 Chipper Jones .30 .75
87 Ray Lankford .10 .30
88 Fred McGriff .20 .50
89 Rod Beck .10 .30
90 Dean Palmer .10 .30
91 Pedro Martinez .20 .50
92 Andruw Jones .20 .50
93 Robin Ventura .10 .30
94 Ugueth Urbina .10 .30
95 Orlando Hernandez .10 .30
96 Sean Casey .10 .30
97 Denny Neagle .10 .30
98 Troy Glaus .20 .50
99 John Smoltz .20 .50
100 Al Leiter .10 .30
101 Ken Griffey Jr. MAS 1.00 2.50
102 Frank Thomas MAS .60 1.50
103 Mark McGwire MAS 1.50 4.00
104 Sammy Sosa MAS .60 1.50
105 Chipper Jones MAS .60 1.50
106 Alex Rodriguez MAS 1.00 2.50
107 N.Garciaparra MAS 1.00 2.50
108 Juan Gonzalez MAS .30 .75
109 Derek Jeter MAS 1.50 4.00
110 Mike Piazza MAS 1.00 2.50
111 Barry Bonds MAS 1.50 4.00
112 Tony Gwynn MAS .75 2.00
113 Cal Ripken MAS 2.00 5.00
114 Greg Maddux MAS 1.00 2.50
115 Roger Clemens MAS 1.25 3.00
116 Brad Fullmer ART .30 .75
117 Kerry Wood ART .30 .75
118 Ben Grieve ART .30 .75
119 Todd Helton ART .40 1.00
120 Kevin Millwood ART .30 .75
121 Sean Casey ART .30 .75
122 V.Guerrero ART .60 1.50
123 Travis Lee ART .30 .75
124 Troy Glaus ART .40 1.00
125 Bartolo Colon ART .30 .75
126 Andruw Jones ART .40 1.00
127 Scott Rolen ART .40 1.00
128 A.Soriano APP RC 2.00 5.00
129 Nick Johnson APP RC .75 2.00
130 Matt Belisle APP RC .30 .75
131 Jorge Toca APP RC .30 .75
132 Masao Kida APP RC .30 .75
133 Carlos Pena APP RC .40 1.00
134 Adrian Beltre APP .30 .75
135 Eric Chavez APP .30 .75
136 Carlos Beltran APP .40 1.00
137 Alex Gonzalez APP .30 .75
138 Ryan Anderson APP .30 .75
139 Ruben Mateo APP .30 .75
140 Bruce Chen APP .30 .75
141 Pat Burrell APP RC 1.25 3.00
142 Michael Barrett APP .30 .75
143 Carlos Lee APP .30 .75
144 Mark Mulder APP RC 1.00 2.50
145 C.Freeman APP RC .30 .75
146 Gabe Kapler APP .30 .75
147 J.Encarnacion APP .30 .75
148 Jeremy Giambi APP .30 .75
149 Jason Tyner APP RC .30 .75
150 George Lombard APP .30 .75

1999 Topps Gallery Player's Private Issue

Randomly inserted in packs at the rate of one in 17, this 150-card set is parallel to the base set with a "Players Private Issue" foil stamp and sequentially numbered to 250.

*STARS 1-100: 8X TO 20X BASIC CARDS
*MASTERS 101-115: 4X TO 10X BASIC
*ARTISANS 116-127: 3X TO 8X BASIC
*APPRENTICES 128-150: 3X TO 8X BASIC
*APP.RC'S 128-150: 2X TO 5X BASIC
STATED ODDS 1:17

1999 Topps Gallery Press Plates

Randomly inserted in packs at the rate of one in 985, this set is parallel to the base set and are the actual four color printing plates from the 150 Gallery Baseball cards. Unlike the 1998 Gallery Plates, the card backs were not featured this year. No pricing is available on stars due to scarcity.

STATED ODDS 1:985

1999 Topps Gallery Autographs

Randomly inserted into packs at the rate of one in 209, this three-card set features color photos of three of baseball's top prospects printed on 24-point stock with the "Topps Certified Autograph" foil stamp logo.

COMPLETE SET (3) 40.00 80.00
STATED ODDS 1:209
GA1 Troy Glaus 6.00 15.00
GA2 Adrian Beltre 8.00 20.00
GA3 Eric Chavez 6.00 15.00

1999 Topps Gallery Awards Gallery

Randomly inserted into packs at the rate of one in 12, this 10-card set features color photos of the game's HR Champs, Cy Young award winners, RBI Leaders, MVP winnners, and Rookies of the year from 1998.

COMPLETE SET (10) 12.50 30.00
STATED ODDS 1:12
AG1 Kerry Wood .50 1.25
AG2 Ben Grieve .50 1.25
AG3 Roger Clemens 2.50 6.00
AG4 Tom Glavine .75 2.00
AG5 Juan Gonzalez .50 1.25
AG6 Sammy Sosa 1.25 3.00
AG7 Ken Griffey Jr. 2.00 5.00
AG8 Mark McGwire 3.00 8.00
AG9 Bernie Williams .75 2.00
AG10 Larry Walker .50 1.25

1999 Topps Gallery Exhibitions

Randomly inserted in packs at the rate of one in 48, this 20-card set features color photos of top players printed on textured 24-point card stock with the look and feel of brushstrokes on canvas.

COMPLETE SET (20) 80.00 200.00
STATED ODDS 1:48
E1 Sammy Sosa 3.00 8.00
E2 Mark McGwire 8.00 20.00
E3 Greg Maddux 5.00 12.00
E4 Roger Clemens 6.00 15.00
E5 Ben Grieve 1.25 3.00
E6 Kerry Wood 1.25 3.00
E7 Ken Griffey Jr. 5.00 12.00
E8 Tony Gwynn 4.00 10.00
E9 Cal Ripken 10.00 25.00
E10 Frank Thomas 3.00 8.00
E11 Jeff Bagwell 2.00 5.00
E12 Derek Jeter 8.00 20.00
E13 Alex Rodriguez 5.00 12.00
E14 Nomar Garciaparra 5.00 12.00
E15 Manny Ramirez 2.00 5.00
E16 Vladimir Guerrero 3.00 8.00
E17 Darin Erstad 1.25 3.00
E18 Scott Rolen 2.00 5.00
E19 Mike Piazza 5.00 12.00
E20 Andres Galarraga 1.25 3.00

1999 Topps Gallery Gallery of Heroes

Randomly inserted into packs at the rate of one in 24, this 10-card set features some of the game's top players depicted on clear Polycarbonate stock simulating the appearance of stained glass.

COMPLETE SET (10) 30.00 80.00
STATED ODDS 1:24
GH1 Mark McGwire 5.00 12.00
GH2 Sammy Sosa 2.00 5.00
GH3 Ken Griffey Jr. 3.00 8.00
GH4 Mike Piazza 3.00 8.00
GH5 Derek Jeter 5.00 12.00
GH6 Nomar Garciaparra 3.00 8.00
GH7 Kerry Wood .75 2.00
GH8 Ben Grieve .75 2.00
GH9 Chipper Jones 2.00 5.00
GH10 Alex Rodriguez 3.00 8.00

1999 Topps Gallery Heritage

Randomly inserted into packs at the rate of one in 12, this 20-card set features color photos of legendary stars printed on 24-point conventional card stock depicting the 1953 Topps design. This was one of the most popular insert sets issued in 1999 as hobbyists responded well to the gorgeous 1953 retro art. Interestingly, the back of the Aaron card was written as if it were 1953 while the modern players were written about their current accomplishments.

COMPLETE SET (20) 75.00 200.00
STATED ODDS 1:12
*PROOFS: .4X TO 1X BASIC HERITAGE
PROOFS STATED ODDS 1:48
TH1 Hank Aaron 12.50 30.00
TH2 Ben Grieve 3.00 8.00
TH3 Nomar Garciaparra 10.00 25.00
TH4 Roger Clemens 12.50 30.00
TH5 Travis Lee 3.00 8.00
TH6 Tony Gwynn 8.00 20.00
TH7 Alex Rodriguez 10.00 25.00
TH8 Ken Griffey Jr. 10.00 25.00
TH9 Derek Jeter 15.00 40.00
TH10 Sammy Sosa 6.00 15.00
TH11 Scott Rolen 4.00 10.00
TH12 Chipper Jones 6.00 15.00
TH13 Cal Ripken 20.00 50.00
TH14 Kerry Wood 4.00 8.00
TH15 Barry Bonds 15.00 40.00
TH16 Juan Gonzalez 4.00 8.00
TH17 Mike Piazza 10.00 25.00
TH18 Greg Maddux 10.00 25.00
TH19 Frank Thomas 6.00 15.00
TH20 Mark McGwire 20.00 50.00

1999 Topps Gallery Heritage Postcards

This seven-card postcard-sized set was issued by Topps in 1999. The set features superstar players painted by James Fiorentino.

COMPLETE SET (7) 15.00 40.00
1 Mark McGwire 2.00 5.00
2 Sammy Sosa 1.25 3.00
3 Roger Clemens 2.00 5.00
4 Mike Piazza 2.50 6.00
5 Cal Ripken 4.00 10.00
6 Derek Jeter 4.00 10.00
7 Ken Griffey Jr. 2.00 5.00

2000 Topps Gallery Pre-Production

This three card set was issued in a sealed cello pack to dealers and hobby media several weeks prior to the products release. The cards have a "PP" prefix so they can be differentiated from the regular cards.

COMPLETE SET (3) 2.50 6.00
PP1 Derek Jeter 1.60 4.00
PP2 Mark McGwire .75 2.00
PP3 Josh Hamilton 1.25 3.00

2000 Topps Gallery

The 2000 Topps Gallery product was released in early June, 2000 as a 150-card set. The set features 100 player cards, a 20-card Masters of the Game subset, and a 30-card Students of the Game subset. Please note that cards 101-150 were issued at a rate of one per pack. Each pack contained six cards and carried a suggested retail price of $3.00. Notable Rookie Cards include Bobby Bradley.

COMPLETE SET (150) 40.00 100.00
COMP.SET w/o SP's (100) 10.00 25.00
COMMON CARD (1-100) .10 .30
COMMON (101-150) .40 1.00
1 Nomar Garciaparra .50 1.25
2 Kevin Millwood .10 .30
3 Jay Bell .10 .30
4 Rusty Greer .10 .30
5 Bernie Williams .20 .50
6 Barry Larkin .20 .50
7 Carlos Beltran .10 .30
8 Damion Easley .10 .30
9 Magglio Ordonez .10 .30
10 Matt Williams .10 .30
11 Shannon Stewart .10 .30
12 Ray Lankford .10 .30
13 Vinny Castilla .10 .30
14 Miguel Tejada .10 .30
15 Craig Biggio .20 .50
16 Chipper Jones .30 .75
17 Albert Belle .10 .30

18 Doug Glanville .10 .30
19 Brian Giles .10 .30
20 Shawn Green .10 .30
21 Bret Boone .10 .30
22 Luis Gonzalez .10 .30
23 Carlos Delgado .10 .30
24 J.D. Drew .10 .30
25 Ivan Rodriguez .20 .50
26 Tino Martinez .20 .50
27 Erubiel Durazo .10 .30
28 Scott Rolen .20 .50
29 Gary Sheffield .10 .30
30 Manny Ramirez .20 .50
31 Luis Castillo .10 .30
32 Fernando Tatis .10 .30
33 Darin Erstad .10 .30
34 Tim Hudson .10 .30
35 Sammy Sosa .30 .75
36 Jason Kendall .10 .30
37 Todd Walker .10 .30
38 Orlando Hernandez .10 .30
39 Pokey Reese .10 .30
40 Mike Piazza .50 1.25
41 B.J. Surhoff .10 .30
42 Tony Gwynn .40 1.00
43 Kevin Brown .10 .30
44 Preston Wilson .10 .30
45 Kenny Lofton .10 .30
46 Rondell White .10 .30
47 Frank Thomas .30 .75
48 Neifi Perez .10 .30
49 Edgardo Alfonzo .05 .15
50 Ken Griffey Jr. .50 1.25
51 Barry Bonds .75 2.00
52 Brian Jordan .10 .30
53 Raul Mondesi .10 .30
54 Troy Glaus .10 .30
55 Curt Schilling .10 .30
56 Mike Mussina .20 .50
57 Brian Daubach .10 .30
58 Roger Clemens .60 1.50
59 Carlos Febles .10 .30
60 Todd Helton .20 .50
61 Mark Grace .20 .50
62 Randy Johnson .30 .75
63 Jeff Bagwell .20 .50
64 Tom Glavine .20 .50
65 Adrian Beltre .10 .30
66 Rafael Palmeiro .20 .50
67 Paul O'Neill .20 .50
68 Robin Ventura .10 .30
69 Ray Durham .10 .30
70 Mark McGwire .75 2.00
71 Greg Vaughn .10 .30
72 Javy Lopez .10 .30
73 Ryan Klesko .10 .30
74 Mike Lieberthal .10 .30
75 Cal Ripken 1.00 2.50
76 Juan Gonzalez .10 .30
77 Sean Casey .10 .30
78 Jermaine Dye .10 .30
79 John Olerud .10 .30
80 Jose Canseco .20 .50
81 Eric Karros .10 .30
82 Roberto Alomar .20 .50
83 Ben Grieve .10 .30
84 Greg Maddux .50 1.25
85 Pedro Martinez .20 .50
86 Tony Clark .10 .30
87 Richie Sexson .10 .30
88 Cliff Floyd .10 .30
89 Eric Chavez .10 .30
90 Andruw Jones .20 .50
91 Vladimir Guerrero .30 .75
92 Alex Gonzalez .10 .30
93 Jim Thome .20 .50
94 Bob Abreu .10 .30
95 Derek Jeter .75 2.00
96 Larry Walker .10 .30
97 Mike Hampton .10 .30
98 Mo Vaughn .10 .30
99 Jason Giambi .10 .30
100 Alex Rodriguez .50 1.25
101 Mark McGwire MAS 1.50 4.00
102 Sammy Sosa MAS .60 1.50
103 Alex Rodriguez MAS 1.00 2.50
104 Derek Jeter MAS 1.50 4.00
105 Greg Maddux MAS 1.00 2.50
106 Jeff Bagwell MAS .40 1.00
107 N.Garciaparra MAS 1.00 2.50
108 Mike Piazza MAS 1.00 2.50
109 Pedro Martinez MAS .40 1.00
110 Chipper Jones MAS .60 1.50
111 Randy Johnson MAS .60 1.50
112 Barry Bonds MAS 1.50 4.00
113 Ken Griffey Jr. MAS 1.00 2.50
114 Manny Ramirez MAS .40 1.00
115 Ivan Rodriguez MAS .40 1.00
116 Juan Gonzalez MAS .40 1.00
117 V.Guerrero MAS .60 1.50
118 Tony Gwynn MAS .75 2.00
119 Larry Walker MAS .40 1.00
120 Cal Ripken MAS 2.00 5.00
121 Josh Hamilton SG 1.00 2.50
122 Corey Patterson SG .40 1.00
123 Pat Burrell SG .40 1.00
124 Nick Johnson SG .40 1.00
125 Adam Piatt SG .40 1.00
126 Rick Ankiel SG .40 1.00
127 A.J. Burnett SG .40 1.00
128 Ben Petrick SG .40 1.00
129 Rafael Furcal SG .40 1.00
130 Alfonso Soriano SG .60 1.50
131 Dee Brown SG .40 1.00
132 Ruben Mateo SG .40 1.00
133 Pablo Ozuna SG .40 1.00
134 S.Burroughs SG UER .40 1.00
Eric Munson's bio on back
135 Mark Mulder SG .40 1.00
136 Jason Jennings SG .40 1.00
137 Eric Munson SG .40 1.00
138 Vernon Wells SG .40 1.00
139 Brett Myers SG RC .75 2.00
140 B.Christensen SG RC .40 1.00
141 Bobby Bradley SG RC .40 1.00
142 Ruben Salazar SG RC .40 1.00
143 R.Christianson SG RC .40 1.00
144 Corey Myers SG RC .40 1.00
145 Aaron Rowand SG RC 1.00 2.50
146 Julio Zuleta SG RC .40 1.00
147 Kurt Ainsworth SG RC .40 1.00
148 Scott Downs SG RC .40 1.00
149 Larry Bigbie SG RC .40 1.00
150 Chance Caple SG RC .40 1.00

2000 Topps Gallery Player's Private Issue

Randomly inserted into packs at one in 20, this 150-card set is a complete parallel of the Topps Gallery base set. Each card in the set is individually serial numbered to 250. The cards are serial numbered in gold foil on the back of the cards.

*STARS 1-100: 6X TO 15X BASIC CARDS
*MASTERS 101-120: 3X TO 8X BASIC
*STUDENTS 121-138: 1.5X TO 4X BASIC
*STUDENTS RC's 139-150: 2X TO 5X BASIC

2000 Topps Gallery Autographs

Randomly inserted into packs at one in 153, this insert set features autographed cards from five of the major league's top prospects. Card backs are numbered using the players initials.

BP Ben Petrick 4.00 10.00
CP Corey Patterson 4.00 10.00
RA Rick Ankiel 10.00 25.00
RM Ruben Mateo 4.00 10.00
VW Vernon Wells 6.00 15.00

2000 Topps Gallery Exhibits

Randomly inserted into packs at one in 18, this 30-card insert captures some of baseball's best on canvas texturing. Card backs carry a "GE" prefix.

COMPLETE SET (30) 125.00 300.00
GE1 Mark McGwire 8.00 20.00
GE2 Jeff Bagwell 2.00 5.00
GE3 Mike Piazza 5.00 12.00
GE4 Alex Rodriguez 5.00 12.00
GE5 Nomar Garciaparra 5.00 12.00
GE6 Ivan Rodriguez 2.00 5.00
GE7 Chipper Jones 3.00 8.00
GE8 Cal Ripken 10.00 25.00
GE9 Tony Gwynn 4.00 10.00
GE10 Jose Canseco 2.00 5.00
GE11 Albert Belle 1.25 3.00
GE12 Greg Maddux 5.00 12.00
GE13 Barry Bonds 8.00 20.00
GE14 Ken Griffey Jr. 5.00 12.00
GE15 Juan Gonzalez 1.25 3.00
GE16 Rickey Henderson 6.00 15.00
GE17 Craig Biggio 2.00 5.00
GE18 Vladimir Guerrero 3.00 8.00
GE19 Rey Ordonez 4.00 10.00
GE20 Roberto Alomar 2.00 5.00
GE21 Derek Jeter 8.00 20.00
GE22 Manny Ramirez 2.00 5.00
GE23 Shawn Green 1.25 3.00
GE24 Sammy Sosa 3.00 8.00
GE25 Larry Walker 1.25 3.00
GE26 Pedro Martinez 2.00 5.00
GE27 Randy Johnson 3.00 8.00
GE28 Pat Burrell 1.25 3.00
GE29 Josh Hamilton 3.00 8.00
GE30 Corey Patterson 1.25 3.00

2000 Topps Gallery Gallery of Heroes

Randomly inserted into packs at one in 24, this insert features ten celestial superstars on clear, die-cut polycarbonate stock, creating a stained glass effect. Card backs carry a "GH" prefix.

COMPLETE SET (10) 30.00 80.00
GH1 Alex Rodriguez 3.00 8.00
GH2 Chipper Jones 2.00 5.00
GH3 Pedro Martinez 1.25 3.00
GH4 Sammy Sosa 2.00 5.00
GH5 Mark McGwire 5.00 12.00
GH6 Nomar Garciaparra 3.00 8.00
GH7 Vladimir Guerrero 2.00 5.00
GH8 Ken Griffey Jr. 3.00 8.00
GH9 Mike Piazza 3.00 8.00
GH10 Derek Jeter 5.00 12.00

2000 Topps Gallery Heritage

Randomly inserted into packs at one in 12, this 20-card insert set was influenced by the 1954 Topps set, the set features many of baseball's elite players as illustrated artist renderings. Card backs carry a "TGH" prefix.

COMPLETE SET (20) 60.00 150.00
*PROOFS: .6X TO 1.5X BASIC HERITAGE
PROOFS STATED ODDS 1:27
TGH1 Mark McGwire 10.00 25.00
TGH2 Sammy Sosa 4.00 10.00
TGH3 Greg Maddux 6.00 15.00
TGH4 Mike Piazza 6.00 15.00
TGH5 Ivan Rodriguez 2.50 6.00
TGH6 Manny Ramirez 2.50 6.00
TGH7 Jeff Bagwell 2.50 6.00
TGH8 Sean Casey 1.50 4.00
TGH9 Orlando Hernandez 1.50 4.00
TGH10 Randy Johnson 4.00 10.00
TGH11 Pedro Martinez 2.50 6.00
TGH12 Vladimir Guerrero 4.00 10.00
TGH13 Shawn Green 1.50 4.00
TGH14 Ken Griffey Jr. 6.00 15.00
TGH15 Alex Rodriguez 6.00 15.00
TGH16 Nomar Garciaparra 6.00 15.00
TGH17 Derek Jeter 10.00 25.00
TGH18 Tony Gwynn 5.00 12.00
TGH19 Chipper Jones 4.00 10.00
TGH20 Cal Ripken 12.50 30.00

2000 Topps Gallery Proof Positive

Randomly insert into packs at one in 48, these ten cards couple one master of the game with one student of the game by way of positive and negative photography. Card backs carry a "P" prefix.

COMPLETE SET (10) 40.00 100.00
P1 Ken Griffey Jr. 4.00 10.00
Ruben Mateo
P2 Derek Jeter 6.00 15.00
Alfonso Soriano
P3 Mark McGwire 6.00 15.00
Pat Burrell
P4 Pedro Martinez 1.50 4.00
A.J.Burnett
P5 Alex Rodriguez 4.00 10.00
Rafael Furcal
P6 Sammy Sosa 2.50 6.00
Corey Patterson
P7 Randy Johnson 2.50 6.00
Rick Ankiel
P8 Chipper Jones 2.50 6.00
Adam Piatt
P9 Nomar Garciaparra 4.00 10.00
Pablo Ozuna
P10 Mike Piazza 4.00 10.00
Eric Munson

2001 Topps Gallery

This 150 card set was issued in six card packs with an SRP of $3. The packs were issued 24 packs to a box with eight boxes to a case. Cards numbered 102-150 were short printed in these ratios: Prospects from 102-141 were issued one every 2.5 packs, rookies from 102-141 were issued one every 3.5 packs and cards numbered 142-150 were issued one every five packs. Card number 50 was supposedly only available to people who could show their dealers that that was the only card they were missing for the set. However, a retail version of that card was issued so many collectors did not get to share in the surprise of finding out the missing card was Willie Mays. In addition, a special Ichiro card was randomly included in packs, these cards were good for either an American or a Japanese version of what would become card number 151. The deadline to receive the Mays HTA version was October 24th, 2001 while the Ichiro exchange deadline was June 30th, 2003.

COMPLETE SET (150) 50.00 80.00
COMP.SET w/o SP's (100) 15.00 40.00
COMMON (1-49/51-101) .20 .50
COMMON (102-150) 1.25 3.00
1 Darin Erstad .20 .50
2 Chipper Jones .50 1.25
3 Nomar Garciaparra .75 2.00
4 Fernando Vina .20 .50
5 Bartolo Colon .20 .50
6 Bobby Higginson .20 .50
7 Antonio Alfonseca .20 .50
8 Mike Sweeney .20 .50
9 Kevin Brown .20 .50
10 Jose Vidro .20 .50
11 Derek Jeter 1.25 3.00
12 Jason Giambi .20 .50
13 Pat Burrell .20 .50
14 Jeff Kent .20 .50
15 Alex Rodriguez .75 2.00
16 Rafael Palmeiro .30 .75
17 Garret Anderson .20 .50
18 Brad Fullmer .20 .50
19 Doug Glanville .20 .50
20 Mark Quinn .20 .50
21 Mo Vaughn .20 .50
22 Andruw Jones .30 .75
23 Pedro Martinez .30 .75
24 Ken Griffey Jr. .75 2.00
25 Roberto Alomar .30 .75
26 Dean Palmer .20 .50
27 Jeff Bagwell .30 .75
28 Jermaine Dye .20 .50
29 Chan Ho Park .20 .50
30 Vladimir Guerrero .50 1.25
31 Bernie Williams .30 .75
32 Ben Grieve .20 .50
33 Jason Kendall .20 .50
34 Barry Bonds 1.25 3.00
35 Jim Edmonds .20 .50
36 Ivan Rodriguez .30 .75
37 Javy Lopez .20 .50
38 J.T. Snow .20 .50
39 Erubiel Durazo .20 .50
40 Terrence Long .20 .50
41 Tim Salmon .30 .75
42 Greg Maddux .75 2.00
43 Sammy Sosa .50 1.25
44 Sean Casey .20 .50
45 Jeff Cirillo .20 .50
46 Juan Gonzalez .20 .50
47 Richard Hidalgo .20 .50
48 Shawn Green .20 .50
49 Jeromy Burnitz .20 .50
50 Willie Mays HTA 6.00 15.00
N.Y. Giants
50 Willie Mays RETAIL 15.00 40.00
S.F. Giants
51 David Justice .20 .50
52 Tim Hudson .20 .50
53 Brian Giles .20 .50
54 Robb Nen .20 .50
55 Fernando Tatis .20 .50
56 Tony Batista .20 .50
57 Pokey Reese .20 .50
58 Ray Durham .20 .50
59 Greg Vaughn .20 .50
60 Kazuhiro Sasaki .20 .50
61 Troy Glaus .20 .50
62 Rafael Furcal .20 .50
63 Magglio Ordonez .20 .50
64 Jim Thome .30 .75
65 Todd Helton .30 .75
66 Preston Wilson .20 .50
67 Moises Alou .20 .50
68 Gary Sheffield .20 .50
69 Geoff Jenkins .20 .50
70 Mike Piazza .75 2.00
71 Jorge Posada .30 .75
72 Bobby Abreu .20 .50
73 Phil Nevin .20 .50
74 John Olerud .20 .50
75 Mark McGwire 1.25 3.00
76 Jose Cruz Jr. .20 .50
77 David Segui .20 .50
78 Neifi Perez .20 .50
79 Omar Vizquel .30 .75
80 Rick Ankiel .20 .50
81 Randy Johnson .50 1.25
82 Albert Belle .20 .50
83 Frank Thomas .50 1.25
84 Manny Ramirez Sox .30 .75
85 Larry Walker .20 .50
86 Luis Castillo .20 .50
87 Johnny Damon .30 .75
88 Adrian Beltre .20 .50
89 Cristian Guzman .20 .50
90 Jay Payton .20 .50
91 Miguel Tejada .20 .50
92 Scott Rolen .30 .75
93 Ryan Klesko .20 .50
94 Edgar Martinez .30 .75
95 Fred McGriff .30 .75
96 Carlos Delgado .20 .50
97 Barry Zito .30 .75
98 Mike Lieberthal .20 .50
99 Trevor Hoffman .20 .50
100 Gabe Kapler .20 .50
101 Edgardo Alfonzo .20 .50
102 Corey Patterson 1.25 3.00
103 Alfonso Soriano 1.25 3.00
104 Keith Ginter 1.25 3.00
105 Keith Reed 1.25 3.00
106 Nick Johnson 1.25 3.00
107 Carlos Pena 1.25 3.00
108 Vernon Wells 1.25 3.00
109 Roy Oswalt 1.50 4.00
110 Alex Escobar 1.25 3.00
111 Adam Everett 1.25 3.00
112 Jimmy Rollins 1.25 3.00
113 Marcus Giles 1.25 3.00
114 Jack Cust 1.25 3.00
115 Chin-Feng Chen 1.25 3.00
116 Pablo Ozuna 1.25 3.00
117 Ben Sheets 1.25 3.00
118 Adrian Gonzalez 8.00 20.00
119 Ben Davis 1.25 3.00
120 Eric Valent 1.25 3.00
121 Scott Heard 1.25 3.00
122 David Parrish RC 1.25 3.00
123 Sean Burnett 1.25 3.00
124 Derek Thompson 1.25 3.00
125 Tim Christman RC 1.25 3.00
126 Mike Jacobs RC 3.00 8.00
127 Luis Montanez RC 1.25 3.00
128 Chris Bass RC 1.25 3.00
129 Will Smith RC 1.25 3.00
130 Justin Wayne RC 1.25 3.00
131 Shawn Fagan RC 1.25 3.00
132 Chad Petty RC 1.25 3.00
133 J.R. House 1.25 3.00
134 Joel Pineiro 1.25 3.00
135 Albert Pujols RC 20.00 50.00
136 Carmen Cali RC 1.25 3.00
137 Steve Smyth RC 1.25 3.00
138 John Lackey 1.25 3.00
139 Bob Keppel RC 1.25 3.00
140 Dominic Rich RC 1.25 3.00
141 Josh Hamilton 2.50 6.00
142 Nolan Ryan 2.50 6.00
143 Tom Seaver 1.50 4.00
144 Reggie Jackson 1.50 4.00
145 Johnny Bench 1.50 4.00
146 Warren Spahn 1.50 4.00
147 Brooks Robinson 1.50 4.00
148 Carl Yastrzemski 2.00 5.00
149 Al Kaline 1.50 4.00
150 Bob Feller 1.25 3.00
151A I. Suzuki English RC 6.00 15.00
151B I.Suzuki Japan RC 6.00 15.00

2001 Topps Gallery Press Plates

Randomly inserted into packs at one in 1347, this 150-card insert is a complete parallel of the base set. The set features the actual press plates used to make all of the 150-card base set. There are four colored press plates inserted for each player: black, cyan, magenta, and yellow.

NO PRICING DUE TO SCARCITY

2001 Topps Gallery Autographs

Inserted at overall odds of one in 232, these six cards feature cards signed by active professionals. All of these cards are all also the special painted cards for this product. Rick Ankiel did not return his cards in time for inclusion in this product. Those cards were redeemable until June 30, 2003.

GROUP A STATED ODDS 1:1066
GROUP B STATED ODDS 1:1144
GROUP C STATED ODDS 1:400
GAAG Adrian Gonzalez B 20.00 50.00
GAAR Alex Rodriguez A 60.00 120.00
GABB Barry Bonds A 50.00 100.00
GAIR Ivan Rodriguez A 40.00 80.00
GAPB Pat Burrell C 8.00 20.00
GARA R. Ankiel C EXCH 15.00 40.00

2001 Topps Gallery Bucks

Issued at a rate of one in 102, this "Buck" was good for $5 towards purchase of Topps Memorabilia.

1 Johnny Bench $5 2.00 5.00

2001 Topps Gallery Heritage

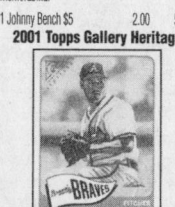

Inserted one per 12 packs, these 12 cards feature a mix of active and retired players in the design Topps used for their 1965 set.

COMPLETE SET (10) 30.00 60.00
GH1 Todd Helton 1.25 3.00
GH2 Greg Maddux 3.00 8.00
GH3 Pedro Martinez 1.25 3.00
GH4 Orlando Cepeda 1.25 3.00
GH5 Willie McCovey 1.25 3.00
GH6 Ken Griffey Jr. 3.00 8.00
GH7 Alex Rodriguez 3.00 8.00
GH8 Derek Jeter 5.00 12.00
GH9 Mark McGwire 5.00 12.00
GH10 Vladimir Guerrero 2.00 5.00

2001 Topps Gallery Heritage Game Jersey

Inserted at a rate of one in 133 packs, these five cards feature pieces of game-worn uniforms along with the Gallery Heritage design.

GHRGM Greg Maddux 10.00 25.00
GHRMR Mystery Jersey .40 1.00
GHROC Orlando Cepeda 6.00 15.00
GHRPM Pedro Martinez 10.00 25.00
GHRVG Vladimir Guerrero 10.00 25.00
GHRWM Willie McCovey 6.00 15.00

2001 Topps Gallery Heritage Game Jersey Autographs

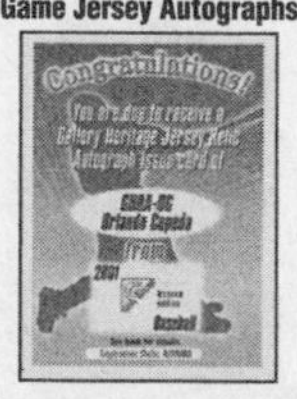

Issued at a rate of one in 16,313 these two cards feature not only the Heritage design and a game-worn jersey piece but they also feature an autograph by the featured player. Orlando Cepeda did not return his cards in time for inclusion in this set so those cards were redeemable until June 30, 2003. These cards are serial numbered to 25.

GHRAOC Orlando Cepeda
GHRAWM W.McCovey

2001 Topps Gallery Originals Game Bat

Issued at a rate of one per 133 packs these 15 cards feature game-used bat cards from 15 leading active hitters today. These cards display the genuine issue sticker. Sammy Sosa and Jason Giambi were the two players made available through the Mystery Exchange redemption cards.

GRAG Adrian Gonzalez 4.00 10.00
GRAJ Andruw Jones 6.00 15.00
GRBW Bernie Williams 6.00 15.00
GRDE Darin Erstad 4.00 10.00
GRJD Jermaine Dye 4.00 10.00
GRJG Jason Giambi 4.00 10.00
GRJK Jason Kendall 4.00 10.00
GRJFK Jeff Kent 4.00 10.00
GRMR1 Mystery Relic .40 1.00
GRMR2 Mystery Relic .40 1.00
GRPR Pokey Reese 4.00 10.00
GRPW Preston Wilson 4.00 10.00
GRRA Roberto Alomar 6.00 15.00
GRRP Rafael Palmeiro 6.00 15.00
GRRV Robin Ventura 4.00 10.00
GRSG Shawn Green 4.00 10.00
GRSS Sammy Sosa 6.00 15.00

2001 Topps Gallery Star Gallery

Issued at a rate of one in eight, these 10 cards feature some of the most popular players in the game.

COMPLETE SET (10) 15.00 40.00
SG1 Vladimir Guerrero 1.00 2.50
SG2 Alex Rodriguez 1.50 4.00
SG3 Derek Jeter 2.50 6.00
SG4 Nomar Garciaparra 1.50 4.00
SG5 Ken Griffey Jr. 1.50 4.00
SG6 Mark McGwire 2.50 6.00
SG7 Chipper Jones 1.00 2.50
SG8 Sammy Sosa 1.00 2.50
SG9 Barry Bonds 2.50 6.00
SG10 Mike Piazza 1.50 4.00

2002 Topps Gallery

This 200 card set was released in June, 2002. The set was issued in five-card packs, with an SRP of $3, which came packaged 24 packs to a box and eight boxes to a case. The first 150 cards of this set featured veterans while cards 151 through 190 featured rookies and cards 191-200 featured retired stars.

COMPLETE SET (200) 40.00 100.00
COMMON CARD (1-150) .20 .50
COMMON CARD (151-190) .40 1.00
COMMON CARD (191-200) .75 2.00
1 Jason Giambi .20 .50
2 Mark Grace .30 .75
3 Bret Boone .20 .50
4 Antonio Alfonseca .20 .50
5 Kevin Brown .20 .50
6 Cristian Guzman .20 .50
7 Magglio Ordonez .20 .50
8 Luis Gonzalez .20 .50
9 Jorge Posada .30 .75
10 Roberto Alomar .30 .75
11 Mike Sweeney .20 .50
12 Jeff Kent .20 .50
13 Matt Morris .20 .50
14 Alfonso Soriano .20 .50
15 Adam Dunn .20 .50
16 Neifi Perez .20 .50
17 Todd Walker .20 .50
18 J.D. Drew .20 .50
19 Eric Chavez .20 .50
20 Alex Rodriguez .75 2.00
21 Ray Lankford .20 .50
22 Roger Cedeno .20 .50
23 Chipper Jones .50 1.25
24 Josh Beckett .20 .50
25 Mike Piazza .75 2.00
26 Freddy Garcia .20 .50
27 Todd Helton .30 .75
28 Tino Martinez .30 .75
29 Kazuhiro Sasaki .20 .50
30 Curt Schilling .20 .50
31 Mark Buehrle .20 .50
32 John Olerud .20 .50
33 Brad Radke .20 .50
34 Steve Sparks .20 .50
35 Jason Tyner .20 .50
36 Jeff Shaw .20 .50
37 Mariano Rivera .50 1.25
38 Russ Ortiz .20 .50
39 Richard Hidalgo .20 .50
40 Carl Everett .20 .50
41 John Burkett .20 .50
42 Tim Hudson .20 .50
43 Mike Hampton .20 .50
44 Orlando Cabrera .20 .50
45 Barry Zito .20 .50
46 C.C. Sabathia .20 .50
47 Chan Ho Park .20 .50
48 Tom Glavine .30 .75
49 Aramis Ramirez .20 .50
50 Lance Berkman .20 .50
51 Al Leiter .20 .50
52 Phil Nevin .20 .50
53 Javier Vazquez .20 .50
54 Troy Glaus .20 .50
55 Tsuyoshi Shinjo .20 .50
56 Albert Pujols 1.00 2.50
57 John Smoltz .30 .75
58 Derek Jeter 1.25 3.00
59 Robb Nen .20 .50
60 Jason Kendall .20 .50
61 Eric Gagne .20 .50
62 Vladimir Guerrero .50 1.25
63 Corey Patterson .20 .50
64 Rickey Henderson .50 1.25
65 Jack Wilson .20 .50
66 Jason LaRue .20 .50
67 Sammy Sosa .50 1.25
68 Ken Griffey Jr. .75 2.00
69 Randy Johnson .50 1.25
70 Nomar Garciaparra .75 2.00
71 Ivan Rodriguez .30 .75
72 J.T. Snow .20 .50
73 Darryl Kile .20 .50
74 Andruw Jones .30 .75
75 Brian Giles .20 .50
76 Pedro Martinez .30 .75
77 Jeff Bagwell .30 .75
78 Rafael Palmeiro .30 .75
79 Ryan Dempster .20 .50
80 Jeff Cirillo .20 .50
81 Geoff Jenkins .20 .50
82 Brandon Duckworth .20 .50
83 Roger Clemens 1.00 2.50
84 Fred McGriff .30 .75
85 Hideo Nomo .50 1.25
86 Larry Walker .20 .50
87 Sean Casey .20 .50
88 Trevor Hoffman .20 .50
89 Robert Fick .20 .50
90 Armando Benitez .20 .50
91 Jeromy Burnitz .20 .50
92 Bernie Williams .30 .75
93 Carlos Delgado .20 .50
94 Troy Percival .20 .50
95 Nate Cornejo .20 .50
96 Derrek Lee .30 .75
97 Jose Ortiz .20 .50
98 Brian Jordan .20 .50
99 Jose Cruz Jr. .20 .50
100 Ichiro Suzuki 1.00 2.50
101 Jose Mesa .20 .50
102 Tim Salmon .30 .75
103 Bud Smith .20 .50
104 Paul LoDuca .20 .50
105 Juan Pierre .20 .50
106 Ben Grieve .20 .50
107 Russell Branyan .20 .50
108 Bob Abreu .20 .50
109 Moises Alou .20 .50
110 Richie Sexson .20 .50
111 Jerry Hairston Jr. .20 .50
112 Marlon Anderson .20 .50
113 Juan Gonzalez .20 .50
114 Craig Biggio .30 .75
115 Carlos Beltran .20 .50
116 Eric Milton .20 .50
117 Cliff Floyd .20 .50
118 Rich Aurilia .20 .50
119 Adrian Beltre .20 .50
120 Jason Bere .20 .50
121 Darin Erstad .20 .50
122 Ben Sheets .20 .50
123 Johnny Damon Sox .30 .75
124 Jimmy Rollins .20 .50
125 Shawn Green .20 .50
126 Greg Maddux .75 2.00
127 Mark Mulder .20 .50
128 Bartolo Colon .20 .50
129 Shannon Stewart .20 .50
130 Ramon Ortiz .20 .50
131 Kerry Wood .20 .50
132 Ryan Klesko .20 .50
133 Preston Wilson .20 .50
134 Roy Oswalt .20 .50
135 Rafael Furcal .30 .75
136 Eric Karros .20 .50
137 Nick Neugebauer .20 .50
138 Doug Mientkiewicz .20 .50
139 Paul Konerko .20 .50
140 Bobby Higginson .20 .50
141 Garret Anderson .20 .50
142 Wes Helms .20 .50
143 Brent Abernathy .20 .50
144 Scott Rolen .30 .75
145 Dmitri Young .20 .50
146 Jim Thome .30 .75
147 Raul Mondesi .20 .50
148 Pat Burrell .20 .50
149 Gary Sheffield .20 .50
150 Miguel Tejada .20 .50
151 Brandon Inge PROS .40 1.00
152 Carlos Pena PROS .40 1.00
153 Jason Lane PROS .40 1.00
154 Nathan Haynes PROS .40 1.00
155 Hank Blalock PROS .60 1.50
156 Juan Cruz PROS .40 1.00
157 Morgan Ensberg PROS .40 1.00

158 Sean Burroughs PROS .40 1.00
159 Ed Rogers PROS .40 1.00
160 Nick Johnson PROS .40 1.00
161 Orlando Hudson PROS .40 1.00
162 A.Martinez PROS RC .40 1.00
163 Jeremy Affeldt PROS .40 1.00
164 Brandon Claussen PROS .40 1.00
165 Deivis Santos PROS .40 1.00
166 Mike Rivera PROS .40 1.00
167 Carlos Silva PROS .40 1.00
168 Val Pascucci PROS .40 1.00
169 Xavier Nady PROS .40 1.00
170 David Espinosa PROS .40 1.00
171 Dan Phillips FYP RC .40 1.00
172 Tony Fontana FYP RC .40 1.00
173 Juan Silvestre FYP .40 1.00
174 Henry Pichardo FYP RC .40 1.00
175 Pablo Arias FYP RC .40 1.00
176 Brett Roneberg FYP RC .40 1.00
177 Chad Qualls FYP RC .60 1.50
178 Greg Sain FYP RC .40 1.00
179 Rene Reyes FYP RC .40 1.00
180 So Taguchi FYP RC .60 1.50
181 Dan Johnson FYP RC .75 2.00
182 J.Backsmeyer FYP RC .40 1.00
183 J.M. Gonzalez FYP RC .40 1.00
184 Jason Ellison FYP RC .60 1.50
185 Kazuhisa Ishii FYP RC .60 1.50
186 Joe Mauer FYP RC 4.00 10.00
187 James Shanks FYP RC .40 1.00
188 Kevin Cash FYP RC .40 1.00
189 J.J. Trujillo FYP RC .40 1.00
190 Jorge Padilla FYP RC .40 1.00
191 Nolan Ryan RET 2.50 6.00
192 George Brett RET 2.00 5.00
193 Ryne Sandberg RET 2.00 5.00
194 Robin Yount RET 1.00 2.50
195 Tom Seaver RET .75 2.00
196 Mike Schmidt RET 2.00 5.00
197 Frank Robinson RET .75 2.00
198 Harmon Killebrew RET 1.00 2.50
199 Kirby Puckett RET 1.00 2.50
200 Don Mattingly RET 2.00 5.00

2002 Topps Gallery Veteran Variation 1

Inserted at stated odds of one in 24, these 10 cards feature the most important players from the Gallery set featuring a variation from the regular issue cards. Since these were not announced until after the product went live, we have put the information about the variation next to the player's name.

1 Jason Giambi Solid Blue 1.00 2.50
20 Alex Rodriguez Grey Jsy 4.00 10.00
25 Mike Piazza Black Jsy 4.00 10.00
27 Todd Helton Solid Blue 1.50 4.00
56 Albert Pujols Red Hat 5.00 12.00
58 Derek Jeter Solid Blue 6.00 15.00
67 Sammy Sosa Black Bat 2.50 6.00
71 Ivan Rodriguez Blue Jsy 1.50 4.00
76 Pedro Martinez Red Shirt 1.50 4.00
100 Ichiro Suzuki Empty Dugout 5.00 12.00

2002 Topps Gallery Autographs

Issued at overall stated odds of one in 240, these 10 cards feature players who have added their signature to these painted cards. The players belong to three different groups and we have put that information about their group next to their name in our checklist.

GROUP A ODDS 1:815 HOB/RET
GROUP B ODDS 1:1017 HOB, 1:1023 RET
GROUP C ODDS 1:509 HOB/RET
GABBO Bret Boone A 10.00 25.00
GAJD J.D. Drew B 10.00 25.00
GAJL Jason Lane C 4.00 10.00
GAJP Jorge Posada A 20.00 50.00
GAJS Juan Silvestre C 4.00 10.00
GALB Lance Berkman A 12.50 30.00
GALG Luis Gonzalez B 10.00 25.00
GAMO Magglio Ordonez A 10.00 25.00
GASG Shawn Green A 10.00 25.00

2002 Topps Gallery Bucks

Inserted at stated odds of one in 27, this $5 buck could be used for redemption towards purchasing original Topps Gallery artwork.

NNO Nolan Ryan $5 3.00 8.00

2002 Topps Gallery Heritage

Inserted at stated odds of one in 12, these 25 cards feature drawings of players in the style of their Topps rookie card. We have put the year of the players "Topps" rookie card next to their name in our checklist.

COMPLETE SET (25) 50.00 120.00
GHAK Al Kaline 54 2.00 5.00
GHAR Alex Rodriguez 98 3.00 8.00
GHBR Brooks Robinson 57 1.25 3.00
GHBBO Bret Boone 93 1.25 3.00
GHCJ Chipper Jones 91 2.00 5.00
GHCY Carl Yastrzemski 60 3.00 8.00
GHGM Greg Maddux 87 3.00 8.00
GHJG Jason Giambi 91 1.25 3.00
GHKG Ken Griffey Jr. 89 3.00 8.00
GHLG Luis Gonzalez 91 1.25 3.00
GHMM Mark McGwire 85 6.00 15.00
GHMP Mike Piazza 93 3.00 8.00
GHMS Mike Schmidt 73 4.00 10.00
GHNR Nolan Ryan 68 5.00 12.00
GHPM Pedro Martinez 93 1.25 3.00
GHRA Roberto Alomar 88 1.25 3.00
GHRC Roger Clemens 85 4.00 10.00
GHRJ Reggie Jackson 69 1.25 3.00
GHRY Robin Yount 75 2.00 5.00
GHSG Shawn Green 92 1.25 3.00
GHSM Stan Musial 58 3.00 8.00
GHSS Sammy Sosa 90 2.00 5.00
GHTG Tony Gwynn 83 2.50 6.00
GHTS Tom Seaver 67 1.25 3.00
GHTSH Tsuyoshi Shinjo 01 1.25 3.00

2002 Topps Gallery Heritage Autographs

Inserted at stated odds of one in 13,595 hobby and one in 14,064 retail, these three cards feature authentic autographs of the featured players. These cards have a stated print run of 25 serial numbered sets and due to market scarcity, no pricing is provided for these cards.

GHALG Luis Gonzalez 91
GHASG Shawn Green 92
GHABBO Bret Boone 93

2002 Topps Gallery Heritage Uniform Relics

Inserted in packs at an overall stated rate of one in 85, these nine cards are a partial parallel to the Heritage insert set. Each card contains not only the player's photo but also a game-worn uniform piece. The players were broken up into two groups and we have notated the groups the player belonged to as well as their stated odds in our set information.

GROUP A ODDS 1:106 HOB/RET
GROUP B ODDS 1:424 HOB/RET
GHRAR Alex Rodriguez 98 A 8.00 20.00
GHRCJ Chipper Jones 91 B 6.00 15.00
GHRGM Greg Maddux 87 A 6.00 15.00
GHRLG Luis Gonzalez 91 A 4.00 10.00
GHRMP Mike Piazza 93 A 6.00 15.00
GHRPM Pedro Martinez 93 A 6.00 15.00
GHRTG Tony Gwynn 83 A 6.00 15.00
GHRTS Tsuyoshi Shinjo 01 A 4.00 10.00
GHRBBO Bret Boone 93 A 4.00 10.00

2002 Topps Gallery Original Bat Relics

Inserted at overall stated odds of one in 169, these 15 cards feature not only the player's photo featured but also a game-used bat piece.

GOAJ Andruw Jones 6.00 15.00
GOAP Albert Pujols 15.00 40.00
GOAR Alex Rodriguez 6.00 15.00
GOAS Alfonso Soriano 4.00 10.00
GOBW Bernie Williams 6.00 15.00
GOBBO Bret Boone 4.00 10.00
GOCD Carlos Delgado 4.00 10.00
GOCJ Chipper Jones 6.00 15.00
GOJC Jose Canseco 6.00 15.00
GOJG Juan Gonzalez 4.00 10.00
GOLG Luis Gonzalez 4.00 10.00
GOMP Mike Piazza 10.00 25.00
GOTG Tony Gwynn 8.00 20.00
GOTH Todd Helton 6.00 15.00
GOTM Tino Martinez 6.00 15.00

2003 Topps Gallery

This 200 card set was released in August, 2003. These cards were issued in four card packs with an $5 SRP which came 20 packs to a box and eight boxes to a case. Cards numbered 1 through 150 featured veterans while cards 151 through 167 featured first year cards, cards 168 through 190 featured leading prospects and cards numbered 191 through 200 featured legendary retired players. In addition, 20 variations (seeded at a stated rate of one in 20) were also included in this set.

COMP.SET w/o SP's (200) 40.00 100.00
COMMON (1-150/168-190) .20 .50
COMMON CARD (151-167) .25 .60
VARIATION STATED ODDS 1:20
COMMON CARD (191-200) .50 1.25
1 Jason Giambi .20 .50
1A Jason Giambi Blue Jsy 2.00 5.00
2 Miguel Tejada .20 .50
3 Mike Lieberthal .20 .50
4 Jason Kendall .20 .50
5 Robb Nen .20 .50
6 Freddy Garcia .20 .50
7 Scott Rolen .30 .75
8 Boomer Wells .20 .50
9 Rafael Palmeiro .30 .75
10 Garret Anderson .20 .50
11 Curt Schilling .20 .50
12 Greg Maddux .75 2.00
13 Rodrigo Lopez .20 .50
14 Nomar Garciaparra .75 2.00
14A N.Garciaparra Btg Glv 3.00 8.00
15 Kerry Wood .20 .50
16 Frank Thomas .50 1.25
17 Ken Griffey Jr. .75 2.00
18 Jim Thome .30 .75
19 Todd Helton .30 .75
20 Lance Berkman .20 .50
21 Robert Fick .20 .50
22 Kevin Brown .20 .50
23 Richie Sexson .20 .50
24 Eddie Guardado .20 .50
25 Vladimir Guerrero .50 1.25
26 Mike Piazza .75 2.00
27 Bernie Williams .30 .75
28 Eric Chavez .20 .50
29 Jimmy Rollins .20 .50
30 Ichiro Suzuki 1.00 2.50
30A I.Suzuki Black Sleeve 3.00 8.00
31 J.D. Drew .20 .50
32 Nick Johnson .20 .50
33 Shannon Stewart .20 .50
34 Tim Salmon .30 .75
35 Andruw Jones .30 .75
36 Jay Gibbons .20 .50
37 Johnny Damon .30 .75
38 Fred McGriff .30 .75
39 Carlos Lee .20 .50
40 Adam Dunn .20 .50
40A Adam Dunn Red Sleeve 2.00 5.00
41 Jason Jennings .20 .50
42 Mike Lowell .20 .50
43 Mike Sweeney .20 .50
44 Shawn Green .20 .50
45 Doug Mientkiewicz .20 .50
46 Bartolo Colon .20 .50
47 Edgardo Alfonzo .20 .50
48 Roger Clemens 1.00 2.50
49 Randy Wolf .20 .50
50 Alex Rodriguez .75 2.00
50A Alex Rodriguez Red Shirt 3.00 8.00
51 Vernon Wells .20 .50
52 Kenny Lofton .20 .50
53 Mariano Rivera .50 1.25
54 Brian Jordan .20 .50
55 Roberto Alomar .30 .75
56 Carlos Pena .20 .50
57 Moises Alou .20 .50
58 John Smoltz .30 .75
59 Adam Kennedy .20 .50
60 Randy Johnson .50 1.25
61 Mark Buehrle .20 .50
62 C.C. Sabathia .20 .50
63 Craig Biggio .30 .75
64 Eric Karros .20 .50
65 Jose Vidro .20 .50
66 Tim Hudson .20 .50
67 Trevor Hoffman .20 .50
68 Bret Boone .20 .50
69 Carl Crawford .20 .50
70 Derek Jeter 1.25 3.00
71 Troy Percival .20 .50
72 Gary Sheffield .20 .50
73 Rickey Henderson .50 1.25
74 Paul Konerko .20 .50
75 Larry Walker .20 .50
76 Pat Burrell .20 .50
77 Brian Giles .20 .50
78 Jeff Kent .20 .50
79 Kazuhiro Sasaki .20 .50
80 Chipper Jones .50 1.25
81 Darin Erstad .20 .50
82 Sean Casey .20 .50
83 Luis Gonzalez .20 .50
84 Roy Oswalt .20 .50
85 Dustan Mohr .20 .50
86 Al Leiter .20 .50
87 Mike Mussina .30 .75
88 Vicente Padilla .20 .50
89 Rich Aurilia .20 .50
90 Albert Pujols 1.00 2.50
91 John Olerud .20 .50
92 Ivan Rodriguez .30 .75
93 Eric Hinske .20 .50
94 Phil Nevin .20 .50
95 Barry Zito .20 .50
96 Armando Benitez .20 .50
97 Torii Hunter .20 .50
98 Paul Lo Duca .20 .50
99 Preston Wilson .20 .50
100 Sammy Sosa .50 1.25
100A Sammy Sosa Black Bat 2.00 5.00
101 Jarrod Washburn .20 .50
102 Steve Finley .20 .50
103 Cliff Floyd .20 .50
104 Mark Prior .30 .75
105 Austin Kearns .20 .50
106 Jeff Bagwell .30 .75
107 A.J. Pierzynski .20 .50
108 Pedro Martinez .30 .75
109 Orlando Cabrera .20 .50
110 Raul Mondesi .20 .50
111 Russ Ortiz .20 .50
112 Ruben Sierra .20 .50
113 Tino Martinez .30 .75
114 Manny Ramirez .30 .75
115 Troy Glaus .20 .50
116 Magglio Ordonez .20 .50
117 Omar Vizquel .30 .75
118 Carlos Beltran .20 .50
119 Jose Hernandez .20 .50
120 Javier Vazquez .20 .50
121 Jorge Posada .30 .75
122 Aramis Ramirez .20 .50
123 Jason Schmidt .20 .50
124 Jamie Moyer .20 .50
125 Jim Edmonds .20 .50
126 Aubrey Huff .20 .50
127 Carlos Delgado .20 .50
128 Junior Spivey .20 .50
129 Tom Glavine .30 .75
130 Marty Cordova .20 .50
131 Derek Lowe .20 .50
132 Ellis Burks .20 .50
133 Barry Bonds 1.25 3.00
134 Josh Beckett .20 .50
135 Raul Ibanez .20 .50
136 Kazuhisa Ishii .20 .50
137 Geoff Jenkins .20 .50
138 Eric Milton .20 .50
139 Mo Vaughn .20 .50
140 Mark Mulder .20 .50
141 Bobby Abreu .20 .50
142 Ryan Klesko .20 .50
143 Tsuyoshi Shinjo .20 .50
144 Jose Mesa .20 .50
145 Shea Hillenbrand .20 .50
146 Edgar Renteria .20 .50
147 Juan Gonzalez .20 .50
148 Edgar Martinez .30 .75
149 Matt Morris .20 .50
150 Alfonso Soriano .20 .50
150A Alfonso Soriano No Pad 2.00 5.00
151 Bryan Bullington FY RC .25 .60
151A B.Bullington Red Back FY 2.00 5.00
152 Andy Marte FY RC 2.00 5.00
152A A.Marte No Necklace FY 3.00 8.00
153 Brendan Harris FY RC .40 1.00
154 Juan Camacho FY RC .25 .60
155 Byron Gettis FY RC .25 .60
156 Daryl Clark FY RC .25 .60
157 J.D. Durbin FY RC .25 .60
158 Craig Brazell FY RC .25 .60
158A Craig Brazell Black Jsy 2.00 5.00
159 Jason Kubel FY RC 1.00 2.50
160 Br. Roberson FY RC .25 .60
161 Jose Contreras FY RC .60 1.50
162 Hanley Ramirez FY RC 2.00 5.00
163 Jaime Bubela FY RC .25 .60
164 Chris Duncan FY RC 2.50 6.00
165 Tyler Johnson FY RC .25 .60
166 Joey Gomes FY RC .25 .60
167 Ben Francisco FY RC .25 .60
168 Adam LaRoche PROS .20 .50
169 Tommy Whiteman PROS .20 .50
170 Trey Hodges PROS .20 .50
171 Fr. Rodriguez PROS .20 .50
172 Jason Arnold PROS .20 .50
173 Brett Myers PROS .20 .50
174 Rocco Baldelli PROS .20 .50
175 Adrian Gonzalez PROS .20 .50
176 Dontrelle Willis PROS .50 1.25
177 Walter Young PROS .20 .50
178 Marlon Byrd PROS .20 .50
179 Aaron Heilman PROS .20 .50
180 Casey Kotchman PROS .20 .50
181 Miguel Cabrera PROS .50 1.25
182 Hee Seop Choi PROS .20 .50
183 Drew Henson PROS .20 .50
184 Jose Reyes PROS .20 .50
185 Michael Cuddyer PROS .20 .50
186 Brandon Phillips PROS .20 .50
187 Victor Martinez PROS .30 .75
188 Joe Mauer PROS .50 1.25
189 Hank Blalock PROS .20 .50
190 Mark Teixeira PROS .30 .75
191 Willie Mays RET 1.50 4.00
192 George Brett RET 1.50 4.00
193 Tony Gwynn RET 1.00 2.50
194 Carl Yastrzemski RET 1.25 3.00
195 Nolan Ryan RET 2.00 5.00
196 Reggie Jackson RET .50 1.25
197 Mike Schmidt RET 1.50 4.00
198 Cal Ripken RET 2.50 6.00
199 Don Mattingly RET 1.50 4.00
200 Tom Seaver RET .50 1.25

2003 Topps Gallery Artist's Proofs

*AP 1-150/168-190: .75X TO 2X BASIC
*AP 151-167: .75X TO 2X BASIC
*AP 191-200: 1X TO 2.5X BASIC
ONE PER PACK
AP'S FEATURE SILVER HOLO-FOIL

2003 Topps Gallery Press Plates

STATED PRINT RUN 4 SERIAL #'d SETS
NO PRICING DUE TO SCARCITY

2003 Topps Gallery Bucks

Inserted at a stated rate of one in 41, this one "card" insert set featured a photo of Willie Mays along with a $5 gift certificate good for Topps product.

5 Willie Mays $5 2.00 5.00

2003 Topps Gallery Currency Collection Coin Relics

Inserted in each hobby box as a "box-topper" these 25 cards feature players from throughout the world along with a coin from their homeland.

AJ Andruw Jones 3.00 8.00
AP Albert Pujols 6.00 15.00
AS Alfonso Soriano 3.00 8.00
BA Bobby Abreu 3.00 8.00
BC Bartolo Colon 3.00 8.00
ER Edgar Renteria 3.00 8.00
FR Francisco Rodriguez 3.00 8.00
HC Hee Seop Choi 3.00 8.00
HN Hideo Nomo 4.00 10.00
IS Ichiro Suzuki 6.00 15.00
JR Jose Reyes 3.00 8.00
KI Kazuhisa Ishii 3.00 8.00
KS Kazuhiro Sasaki 3.00 8.00
LW Larry Walker 3.00 8.00
MO Magglio Ordonez 3.00 8.00
MR Manny Ramirez 3.00 8.00
MRI Mariano Rivera 4.00 10.00
OC Orlando Cabrera 3.00 8.00
OV Omar Vizquel 3.00 8.00
PM Pedro Martinez 3.00 8.00
RL Rodrigo Lopez 3.00 8.00
RM Raul Mondesi 3.00 8.00
SS Sammy Sosa 4.00 10.00
VG Vladimir Guerrero 4.00 10.00
VP Vicente Padilla 3.00 8.00

2003 Topps Gallery Heritage

STATED ODDS 1:10
AD Adam Dunn 1.25 3.00
AS Alfonso Soriano 1.25 3.00
BW Bernie Williams 2.00 5.00
CY Carl Yastrzemski 3.00 8.00
DJ Derek Jeter 5.00 12.00
DS Duke Snider 2.00 5.00
GB George Brett 3.00 8.00
HK Harmon Killebrew 2.00 5.00
HN Hideo Nomo 2.00 5.00
IR Ivan Rodriguez 2.00 5.00
IS Ichiro Suzuki 4.00 10.00
JC Jose Canseco 2.00 5.00
JT Jim Thome 2.00 5.00
KP Kirby Puckett 2.00 5.00
KR Jerry Koosman 6.00 15.00
Nolan Ryan
MJ Miguel Tejada 1.25 3.00
NG Nomar Garciaparra 3.00 8.00
RC Roger Clemens 4.00 10.00
RH Rickey Henderson 2.00 5.00
RJ Randy Johnson 2.00 5.00
SG Shawn Green 1.25 3.00
TG Tom Glavine 2.00 5.00
TGW Tony Gwynn 2.50 6.00
WB Wade Boggs 2.00 5.00
WM Willie Mays 4.00 10.00

2003 Topps Gallery Heritage Autograph Relics

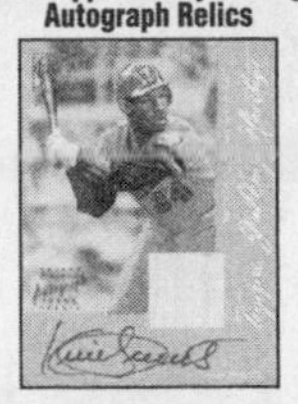

Randomly inserted into packs, these four cards feature not only a game-used memorabilia piece but also an authentic autograph of the featured player. Each of these cards were issued to a stated print run of 25 copies and no pricing is available due to market scarcity.

NO PRICING DUE TO SCARCITY
GB George Brett Bat
KP Kirby Puckett Bat
TG Tony Gwynn Jsy
WB Wade Boggs Uni

2003 Topps Gallery Heritage Relics

Inserted at varying odds depending what group the card belonged to, this 10 card set featured game-used memorabilia pieces of the featured player.

GROUP A ODDS 1:141
GROUP B ODDS 1:67
GB George Brett Bat A 10.00 25.00
HK Harmon Killebrew Bat A 10.00 25.00
HN Hideo Nomo Jsy A 6.00 15.00
JC Jose Canseco Bat B 4.00 10.00
KP Kirby Puckett Bat A 6.00 15.00
RC Roger Clemens Jsy A 6.00 15.00
RH Rickey Henderson Bat B 4.00 10.00
SG Shawn Green Jsy B 3.00 8.00
TG Tony Gwynn Jsy B 6.00 15.00
WB Wade Boggs Uni B 4.00 10.00

2003 Topps Gallery Originals Bat Relics

GROUP A ODDS 1:131
GROUP B ODDS 1:81
GROUP C ODDS 1:15
AD Adam Dunn C 3.00 8.00
AJ Andruw Jones C 4.00 10.00
AP Albert Pujols B 8.00 20.00
AR Alex Rodriguez C 6.00 15.00
AS Alfonso Soriano B 3.00 8.00
BB Bret Boone C 3.00 8.00
BW Bernie Williams C 4.00 10.00
CJ Chipper Jones C 4.00 10.00
CY Carl Yastrzemski A 8.00 20.00
DH Drew Henson B 3.00 8.00
FT Frank Thomas C 4.00 10.00
GS Gary Sheffield C 3.00 8.00
IR Ivan Rodriguez C 4.00 10.00
JM Joe Mauer A 8.00 20.00
JT Jim Thome C 4.00 10.00
LB Lance Berkman C 3.00 8.00
LG Luis Gonzalez A 4.00 10.00
MA Moises Alou B 3.00 8.00
MJ Miguel Tejada A 4.00 10.00
MO Magglio Ordonez C 3.00 8.00
MP Mike Piazza C 6.00 15.00
MR Manny Ramirez C 4.00 10.00
NG Nomar Garciaparra B 6.00 15.00
RA Roberto Alomar C 4.00 10.00
RH Rickey Henderson C 4.00 10.00
RP Rafael Palmeiro C 4.00 10.00
SG Shawn Green B 3.00 8.00
TG Tony Gwynn C 4.00 10.00
TH Todd Helton C 4.00 10.00
THU Torii Hunter A 4.00 10.00

2005 Topps Gallery

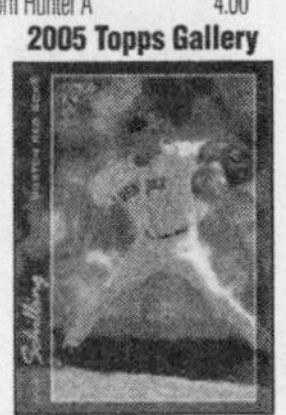

This 205-card set was released in January, 2005. The set was issued in five-card packs with an $10 SRP which came 20 packs to a box and 12 boxes to a case. Cards numbered 1-150 feature veterans while cards 151 through 170 feature players in their first year in Topps. Cards numbered 171 through 185 feature leading prospects while cards 186-195 feature retired players. Cards numbered 151 through 195 were issued at a stated rate of five per "mini-box" and there are some short print "variations" which came one in eight mini-boxes.

COMP.SET w/o SP'S (150) 30.00 60.00
COMMON CARD (1-150) .30 .75
COMMON CARD (151-170) .60 1.50
COMMON CARD (171-185) .60 1.50
COMMON CARD (186-195) .60 1.50
151-195 ODDS FIVE PER MINI-BOX
COMMON VARIATION 1.25 3.00
VARIATION ODDS 1:8 MINI-BOXES
VARIATION STATED PRINT RUN 517 SETS
VARIATIONS ARE NOT SERIAL-NUMBERED
PRINT RUN INFO PROVIDED BY TOPPS
VAR CL: 1/40/100/154-155/157/
VAR CL: 167-168/187
SEE BECKETT.COM FOR VARIATION INFO
PLATE ODDS 1:48 MINI-BOXES
PLATE PRINT RUN 1 SET PER COLOR
BLACK-CYAN-MAGENTA-YELLOW ISSUED
NO PLATE PRICING DUE TO SCARCITY
1A A.Rodriguez White Glv 1.25 3.00
1B A.Rodriguez Blk Glv SP 5.00 12.00
2 Eric Chavez .30 .75
3 Mike Piazza .75 2.00
4 Bret Boone .30 .75
5 Albert Pujols 2.00 5.00
6 Vernon Wells .30 .75
7 Andruw Jones .30 .75
8 Miguel Tejada .50 1.25
9 Johnny Damon .50 1.25
10 Nomar Garciaparra .75 2.00
11 Pat Burrell .30 .75
12 Bartolo Colon .30 .75
13 Johnny Estrada .30 .75
14 Luis Gonzalez .30 .75
15 Jay Gibbons .30 .75
16 Curt Schilling .50 1.25
17 Aramis Ramirez .30 .75
18 Frank Thomas .75 2.00
19 Adam Dunn .50 1.25
20 Sammy Sosa .75 2.00
21 Matt Lawton .30 .75
22 Preston Wilson UER .30 .75
Preston is listed as his own father in text
23 Carlos Pena .50 1.25
24 Josh Beckett .50 1.25
25 Carlos Beltran .30 .75
26 Juan Gonzalez .30 .75
27 Adrian Beltre .30 .75
28 Lyle Overbay .30 .75
29 Justin Morneau .75 2.00
30 Derek Jeter 2.00 5.00
31 Barry Zito .30 .75
32 Bobby Abreu .30 .75
33 Jason Bay .30 .75
34 Jose Reyes .50 1.25
35 Nick Johnson .30 .75
36 Lew Ford .30 .75
37 Scott Podsednik .30 .75
38 Rocco Baldelli .30 .75
39 Eric Hinske .30 .75
40A Ichiro Black Wall 1.25 3.00
40B Ichiro Writing on Wall SP 5.00 12.00
41 Larry Walker .50 1.25
42 Mark Teixeira .75 2.00
43 Khalil Greene .30 .75
44 Edgardo Alfonzo .30 .75
45 Javier Vazquez .30 .75
46 Cliff Floyd .30 .75
47 Geoff Jenkins .30 .75
48 Ken Griffey Jr. 1.25 3.00
49 Vinny Castilla .30 .75
50 Mark Prior .50 1.25
51 Jose Guillen .30 .75
52 J.D. Drew .30 .75
53 Rafael Palmeiro .50 1.25
54 Kevin Youkilis .30 .75
55 Derrek Lee .30 .75
56 Freddy Garcia .30 .75
57 Wily Mo Pena .30 .75
58 C.C. Sabathia .50 1.25
59 Craig Biggio .50 1.25
60 Ivan Rodriguez .50 1.25
61 Angel Berroa .30 .75
62 Ben Sheets .30 .75
63 Johan Santana .75 2.00
64 Al Leiter .30 .75
65 Bernie Williams .50 1.25
66 Bobby Crosby .30 .75
67 Jack Wilson .30 .75
68 A.J. Pierzynski .30 .75
69 Jimmy Rollins .50 1.25
70 Jason Giambi .30 .75
71 Tom Glavine .50 1.25
72 Kevin Brown .30 .75
73 B.J. Upton .50 1.25
74 Edgar Renteria .30 .75
75 Alfonso Soriano .50 1.25
76 Mike Lieberthal .30 .75
77 Kazuo Matsui .30 .75
78 Phil Nevin .30 .75
79 Shawn Green .30 .75
80 Miguel Cabrera .75 2.00
81 Todd Helton .50 1.25
82 Magglio Ordonez .50 1.25
83 Manny Ramirez .75 2.00
84 Bill Mueller .30 .75
85 Troy Glaus .30 .75
86 Richie Sexson .30 .75
87 Javy Lopez .30 .75
88 David Ortiz .75 2.00
89 Greg Maddux 1.25 3.00
90 Vladimir Guerrero .75 2.00
91 Jeromy Burnitz .30 .75
92 Jeff Kent .30 .75
93 Travis Hafner .30 .75

94 Mark Buehrle	.50	1.25
95 Paul Lo Duca	.30	.75
96 Roy Oswalt	.50	1.25
97 Torii Hunter	.30	.75
98 Gary Sheffield	.30	.75
99 Erubiel Durazo	.30	.75
100A J.Thome Kid's Shirt Blue	.50	1.25
100B J.Thome Kid's Shirt Red SP	2.00	5.00
101 Ken Harvey	.30	.75
102 Shannon Stewart	.30	.75
103 Dmitri Young	.30	.75
104 Kevin Millar	.30	.75
105 Kerry Wood	.30	.75
106 Paul Konerko	.50	1.25
107 Ronnie Belliard	.30	.75
108 Mike Lowell	.30	.75
109 Hee Seop Choi	.30	.75
110 Joe Mauer	.75	2.00
111 David Wright	1.25	3.00
112 Jorge Posada	.50	1.25
113 Tim Hudson	.50	1.25
114 Brian Giles	.30	.75
115 Jason Schmidt	.30	.75
116 Aubrey Huff	.30	.75
117 Hank Blalock	.30	.75
118 Jim Edmonds	.50	1.25
119 Raul Ibanez	.30	.75
120 Carlos Delgado	.30	.75
121 Craig Wilson	.30	.75
122 Ryan Klesko	.30	.75
123 Mark Mulder	.30	.75
124 Jose Vidro	.30	.75
125 Mike Sweeney	.30	.75
126 Lance Berkman	.50	1.25
127 Juan Pierre	.30	.75
128 Austin Kearns	.30	.75
129 Moises Alou	.30	.75
130 Garret Anderson	.30	.75
131 Pedro Martinez	.50	1.25
132 Melvin Mora	.30	.75
133 Marcus Giles	.30	.75
134 Corey Patterson	.30	.75
135 Carlos Lee	.30	.75
136 Sean Casey	.30	.75
137 Jody Gerut	.30	.75
138 Jose Valentin	.30	.75
139 Aaron Miles	.30	.75
140 Randy Johnson	.75	2.00
141 Carlos Guillen	.30	.75
142 Dontrelle Willis	.30	.75
143 Jeff Bagwell	.50	1.25
144 Jason Kendall	.30	.75
145 Mark Loretta	.30	.75
146 Scott Rolen	.50	1.25
147 Carl Crawford	.50	1.25
148 Michael Young	.50	1.25
149 Jermaine Dye	.30	.75
150 Chipper Jones	.75	2.00
151 Melky Cabrera FY RC	1.50	4.00
152 Chris Seddon FY RC	.60	1.50
153 Nate Schierholtz FY	.60	1.50
154A Ian Kinsler FY Green RC	5.00	12.00
154B Ian Kinsler FY Gold SP	10.00	25.00
155A B.Moss FY Black Hat RC	2.50	6.00
155B B.Moss FY Red Hat SP	5.00	12.00
156 Chadd Blasko FY RC	1.00	2.50
157A J.West FY Red Jsy RC	.60	1.50
157B J.West FY Navy Jsy SP	1.25	3.00
158 Sean Marshall FY RC	1.50	4.00
159 Ryan Sweeney FY RC	1.00	2.50
160 Matthew Lindstrom FY RC	.60	1.50
161 Ryan Goleski FY RC	.60	1.50
162 Brett Harper FY RC	.60	1.50
163 Chris Roberson FY RC	.60	1.50
164 Andre Ethier FY RC	5.00	12.00
165A I.Bladergroen FY Pose RC	.60	1.50
165B I.Bladergroen FY Swing SP	1.25	3.00
166 James Jurries FY RC	.60	1.50
167A Billy Butler FY Vest RC	3.00	8.00
167B B.Butler FY Black Uni SP	6.00	15.00
168A M.Rogers FY Ball/Air RC	.60	1.50
168B M.Rogers FY Ball/Hand SP	1.25	3.00
169 Tyler Clippard FY RC	4.00	10.00
170 Luis Ramirez FY RC	.60	1.50
171 Casey Kotchman PROS	.60	1.50
172 Chris Burke PROS	.60	1.50
173 Dallas McPherson PROS	.60	1.50
174 Edwin Jackson PROS	.60	1.50
175 Felix Hernandez PROS	2.50	6.00
176 Gavin Floyd PROS	.60	1.50
177 Guillermo Quiroz PROS	.60	1.50
178 Jason Kubel PROS	.60	1.50
179 Jeff Mathis PROS	1.00	2.50
180 Rickie Weeks PROS	1.00	2.50
181 Ryan Howard PROS	3.00	8.00
182 Franklin Gutierrez PROS	2.00	5.00
183 Jeremy Reed PROS	.60	1.50
184 Carlos Quentin PROS	1.00	2.50
185 Jeff Francis PROS	.60	1.50
186 Nolan Ryan RET	4.00	10.00
187A Hank Aaron RET w/o 755	3.00	8.00
187B Hank Aaron RET w/755 SP	6.00	15.00
188 Duke Snider RET	1.00	2.50
189 Mike Schmidt RET	3.00	8.00
190 Ernie Banks RET	1.50	4.00
191 Frank Robinson RET	1.00	2.50
192 Harmon Killebrew RET	1.50	4.00
193 Al Kaline RET	1.50	4.00
194 Rod Carew RET	1.00	2.50
195 Johnny Bench RET	1.50	4.00

2005 Topps Gallery Artist's Proof

*AP 1-150: 1X TO 2.5X BASIC
1-150 ODDS FIVE PER MINI-BOX
*AP 151-195: .75X TO 2X BASIC
151-195 ODDS 1:4 MINI-BOXES
151-195 STATED PRINT RUN 259 SETS
151-195 ARE NOT SERIAL-NUMBERED
*AP VAR: .75X TO 2X BASIC VAR
VARIATION ODDS 1:29 MINI-BOXES
VARIATION STATED PRINT RUN 130 SETS
VARIATIONS ARE NOT SERIAL-NUMBERED
PRINT RUN INFO PROVIDED BY TOPPS

2005 Topps Gallery Murray Olderman Sketches

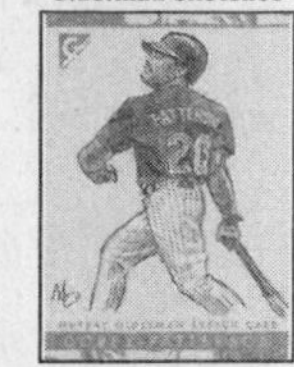

STATED ODDS 1:203 MINI-BOXES
STATED PRINT RUN 1 SERIAL #'d SET
NO PRICING DUE TO SCARCITY

2005 Topps Gallery Cut Signatures

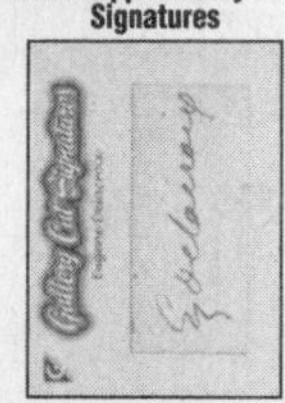

STATED ODDS 1:1376 MINI-BOXES
CARDS ARE SERIAL #'d AS 1 OF 1's
ACTUAL PRINT RUNS B/WN 1-7 COPIES PER
NO PRICING DUE TO SCARCITY
BW Benjamin West/1
ED Eugene Delacroix/1
FB Frederic Bartholdi/2
FC Frederic Church/1
FF Friz Freleng/1
FR Frederic Remington/1
GM Grandma Moses/1
JF James Earl Fraser/1
JM Joan Miro/2
JW James Whistler/1
MC Marc Chagall/2
ME Max Ernst/1
NR Norman Rockwell/2
PP Pablo Picasso/1
RK Rockwell Kent/1
SD Salvador Dali/2
TN Thomas Nast/7
WD Walt Disney/1

2005 Topps Gallery Gallo's Gallery

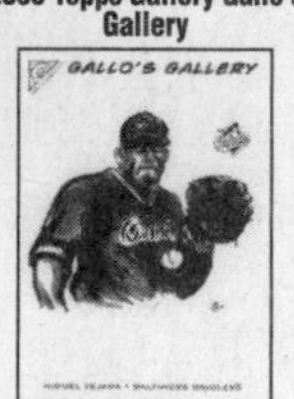

STATED ODDS 1:3 MINI-BOXES

AP Albert Pujols	6.00	15.00
AR Alex Rodriguez	4.00	10.00
AS Alfonso Soriano	1.50	4.00
CJ Chipper Jones	2.50	6.00
DJ Derek Jeter	6.00	15.00
HA Hank Aaron	5.00	12.00
HB Hank Blalock	1.00	2.50
IR Ivan Rodriguez	1.50	4.00
IS Ichiro Suzuki	4.00	10.00
JT Jim Thome	1.50	4.00
MP Mark Prior	1.50	4.00
MPI Mike Piazza	2.50	6.00
MS Mike Schmidt	5.00	12.00
MT Miguel Tejada	1.50	4.00
NG Nomar Garciaparra	2.50	6.00
NR Nolan Ryan	6.00	15.00
RJ Randy Johnson	2.50	6.00
SS Sammy Sosa	2.50	6.00
TH Todd Helton	1.50	4.00
VG Vladimir Guerrero	2.50	6.00

2005 Topps Gallery Heritage

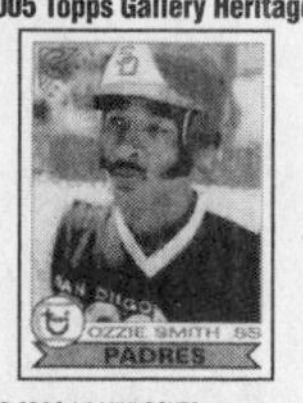

STATED ODDS 1:3 MINI-BOXES

AK Al Kaline 59 Thrill	3.00	8.00
AP Albert Pujols 01 TT	8.00	20.00
BG Bob Gibson 59	2.00	5.00
BR Brooks Robinson 72 Boy	2.00	5.00
CB Carlos Beltran 95 DP	1.25	3.00
CS Curt Schilling 90	2.00	5.00
DM Don Mattingly 84	6.00	15.00
DS Darryl Strawberry 84	1.25	3.00
DSN Duke Snider 59 Thrill	2.00	5.00
DW Dontrelle Willis 02 TT	1.25	3.00
EB Ernie Banks 54	3.00	8.00
FR Frank Robinson 57	2.00	5.00
GB George Brett 77 RB	6.00	15.00
HB Hank Blalock 01	1.25	3.00
IR Ivan Rodriguez 04	2.00	5.00
JB Johnny Bench 69	3.00	8.00
JC Jose Canseco 87	2.00	5.00
JP Jim Palmer 73 Boy	1.25	3.00
MS Mike Schmidt 83 SV	6.00	15.00
NR Nolan Ryan 90 HL	8.00	20.00
OS Ozzie Smith 79	5.00	12.00
RJ Alex Rodriguez Derek Jeter Kings of New York	8.00	20.00
RP Rafael Palmeiro 87	2.00	5.00
RR Frank Robinson Brooks Robinson 68 Bird Belters	2.00	5.00
TS Jim Thome Mike Schmidt South Philly Sluggers	6.00	15.00

2005 Topps Gallery Heritage Relics

STATED ODDS 1:8 MINI BOXES

AP Albert Pujols 01 TT Jsy	8.00	20.00
AR Alex Rodriguez 04 Bat	6.00	15.00
DM Don Mattingly 84 Bat	8.00	20.00
DS Darryl Strawberry 84 Bat	3.00	8.00
DW Dontrelle Willis 02 TT Jsy	3.00	8.00
GB George Brett 77 RB Bat	6.00	15.00
IR Ivan Rodriguez 04 Bat	4.00	10.00
JC Jose Canseco 87 Bat	4.00	10.00
NR Nolan Ryan 90 HL Jsy	10.00	25.00
OS Ozzie Smith 79 Bat	6.00	15.00

2005 Topps Gallery Heritage Relics Autographs

STATED ODDS 1:396 MINI-BOXES
STATED PRINT RUN 25 SERIAL #'d SETS
EXCHANGE DEADLINE 01/31/07
NO PRICING DUE TO SCARCITY
AR Alex Rodriguez 04 Bat
DM Don Mattingly 84 Bat
NR Nolan Ryan 90 HL Uni

2005 Topps Gallery Originals Relics

STATED ODDS 1:2 MINI-BOXES

AB Angel Berroa Bat	3.00	8.00
AP Albert Pujols Jsy	8.00	20.00
AR Alex Rodriguez Uni	6.00	15.00
AS Alfonso Soriano Bat	3.00	8.00
BU B.J. Upton Bat	4.00	10.00
BW Bernie Williams Bat	4.00	10.00
CJ Chipper Jones Jsy	4.00	10.00
DO David Ortiz Bat	4.00	10.00
DW Dontrelle Willis Jsy	3.00	8.00
FT Frank Thomas Bat	4.00	10.00
HB Hank Blalock Jsy	3.00	8.00
HBB Hank Blalock Bat	3.00	8.00
IR Ivan Rodriguez Bat	4.00	10.00
JB Jeff Bagwell Uni	4.00	10.00
JBE Josh Beckett Bat	3.00	8.00
JD Johnny Damon Bat	4.00	10.00
JG Jason Giambi Bat	3.00	8.00
JL Javy Lopez Bat	3.00	8.00
JR Jose Reyes Bat	3.00	8.00
KM Kazuo Matsui Bat	4.00	10.00
KW Kerry Wood Jsy	3.00	8.00
LB Lance Berkman Jsy	3.00	8.00
LN Laynce Nix Jsy	3.00	8.00
MC Miguel Cabrera Jsy	4.00	10.00
MG Marcus Giles Jsy	3.00	8.00
ML Mike Lowell Jsy	3.00	8.00
MP Mike Piazza Jsy	4.00	10.00
MPB Mike Piazza Bat	4.00	10.00
MPR Mark Prior Jsy	4.00	10.00
MR Manny Ramirez Bat	4.00	10.00
MT Mark Teixeira Jsy	4.00	10.00
MTE Miguel Tejada Bat	3.00	8.00
MY Michael Young Jsy	3.00	8.00
PM Pedro Martinez Jsy	4.00	10.00
RB Rocco Baldelli Bat	3.00	8.00
RD Ryan Drese Jsy	3.00	8.00
RH Rich Harden Uni	3.00	8.00
SS Sammy Sosa Jsy	4.00	10.00
TH Todd Helton Jsy	4.00	10.00
VG Vladimir Guerrero Bat	4.00	10.00

2005 Topps Gallery Penmanship Autographs

GROUP A ODDS 1:786 MINI-BOXES
GROUP B ODDS 1:132 MINI-BOXES
GROUP C ODDS 1:39 MINI-BOXES
GROUP D ODDS 1:39 MINI-BOXES
GROUP E ODDS 1:5 MINI-BOXES
GROUP A STATED PRINT RUN 25 SETS
GROUP A PRINT RUN PROVIDED BY TOPPS
NO GROUP A PRICING DUE TO SCARCITY
EXCHANGE DEADLINE 01/31/07

AH Aubrey Huff C	4.00	10.00
AR Alex Rodriguez A/25 *		
DM Dallas McPherson E	4.00	10.00
EC Eric Chavez D	6.00	15.00
FH Felix Hernandez E	10.00	25.00
JB Jason Bartlett E	4.00	10.00
JJ Justin Jones B	4.00	10.00
TB Taylor Buchholz E	4.00	10.00
VW Vernon Wells C	6.00	15.00

2003 Topps Gallery HOF

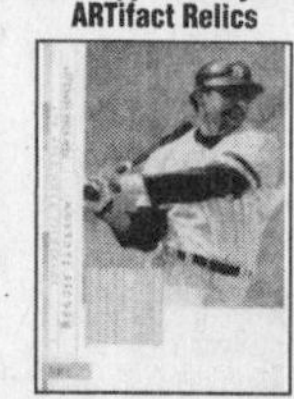

This set was released in April, 2003. Each card in the set was actually issued in different versions, some of each were easy to identify and others had far more subtle differences. This set was issued in five card packs with an $5 SRP. The packs were issued in 20 pack boxes which came six boxes to a case.

COMPLETE SET (74)	15.00	40.00
COMMON CARD (1-74)	.30	.75
COMMON VARIATION (1-74)	.60	1.50
1 Willie Mays Bleachers	1.25	3.00
1B Willie Mays Gold	2.50	6.00
2 Al Kaline Stripes	.60	1.50
2B Al Kaline No Stripes	1.25	3.00
3 Hank Aaron Black Hat	1.25	3.00
3B Hank Aaron Blue Hat	2.50	6.00
4 Carl Yastrzemski Black Ltr	1.00	2.50
4B Carl Yastrzemski Red Ltr	2.00	5.00
5 Luis Aparicio Wood Bat	.30	.75
5B Luis Aparicio Black Bat	.60	1.50
6 Sam Crawford Grey Uni	.30	.75
6B Sam Crawford Navy Uni	.60	1.50
7 Tom Lasorda Trees	.30	.75
7B Tom Lasorda Red	.60	1.50
8 John McGraw MG No Logo	.40	1.00
8B J.McGraw MG NY Logo	.75	2.00
9 Edd Roush White C	.30	.75
9B Edd Roush Red C	.60	1.50
10 Reggie Jackson Grass	.40	1.00
10B Reggie Jackson Red	.75	2.00
11 Catfish Hunter Yellow Jsy	.40	1.00
11B Catfish Hunter White Jsy	.75	2.00
12 Rob. Clemente White Uni	1.50	4.00
12B Rob. Clemente Yellow Uni	3.00	8.00
13 Eddie Collins Grey Uni	.30	.75
13B Eddie Collins Navy Uni	.60	1.50
14 Frankie Frisch Olive	.30	.75
14B Frankie Frisch Blue	.60	1.50
15 Nolan Ryan Leather Glv	1.50	4.00
15B Nolan Ryan Black Glv	3.00	8.00
16 Brooks Robinson Yellow	.40	1.00
16B Brooks Robinson Green	.75	2.00
17 Phil Niekro Black Hat	.30	.75
17B Phil Niekro Blue Hat	.60	1.50
18 Joe Cronin Blue Sleeve	.30	.75
18B Joe Cronin White Sleeve	.60	1.50
19 Joe Tinker White Hat	.30	.75
19B Joe Tinker Blue Hat	.60	1.50
20 Johnny Bench Day	.60	1.50
20B Johnny Bench Night	1.25	3.00
21 Harry Heilmann Day	.30	.75
21B Harry Heilmann Night	.60	1.50
22 Ernie Harwell BRD Red Tie	.30	.75
22B Ernie Harwell BRD Blue Tie	.60	1.50
23 Warren Spahn Patch	.40	1.00
23B Warren Spahn No Patch	.75	2.00
24 George Kelly Blue Bill	.30	.75
24B George Kelly Red Bill	.60	1.50
25 Phil Rizzuto Bleachers	.40	1.00
25B Phil Rizzuto Green	.75	2.00
26 Robin Roberts Day	.30	.75
26B Robin Roberts Night	.60	1.50
27 Ozzie Smith Red Sleeve	1.00	2.50
27B Ozzie Smith Blue Sleeve	2.00	5.00
28 Jim Palmer White Hat	.30	.75
28B Jim Palmer Black Hat	.60	1.50
29 Duke Snider No Patch	.40	1.00
29B Duke Snider Flag Patch	.75	2.00
30 Bob Feller White Uni	.30	.75
30B Bob Feller Grey Uni	.60	1.50
31 Buck Leonard Bleachers	.30	.75
31B Buck Leonard Red	.60	1.50
32 Kirby Puckett Wood Bat	.60	1.50
32B Kirby Puckett Black Bat	1.25	3.00
33 Monte Irvin Black Sleeve	.30	.75
33B Monte Irvin White Sleeve	.60	1.50
34 Chuck Klein Black Socks	.30	.75
34B Chuck Klein Red Socks	.60	1.50
35 Willie Stargell Yellow Uni	.40	1.00
35B Willie Stargell White Uni	.75	2.00
36 Juan Marichal Ballpark	.30	.75
36B Juan Marichal Gold	.60	1.50
37 Lou Brock Day	.40	1.00
37B Lou Brock Night	.75	2.00
38 Bucky Harris Black W	.30	.75
38B Bucky Harris Red W	.60	1.50
39 Bobby Doerr Ballpark	.30	.75
39B Bobby Doerr Red	.60	1.50
40 Lee MacPhail Blue Tie	.30	.75
40B Lee MacPhail Red Tie	.60	1.50
41 H.Manush Grey Sleeve	.30	.75
41B H.Manush Navy Sleeve	.60	1.50
42 George Brett Patch	1.25	3.00
42B George Brett No Patch	2.50	6.00
43 Harmon Killebrew Blue Hat	.60	1.50
43B Har. Killebrew Red Hat	1.25	3.00
44 Whitey Ford Day	.40	1.00
44B Whitey Ford Night	.75	2.00
45 Eddie Mathews Day	.60	1.50
45B Eddie Mathews Night	1.25	3.00
46 Gaylord Perry Leather Glv	.30	.75
46B Gaylord Perry Black Glv	.60	1.50
47 Red Schoendienst Stripes	.30	.75
47B R.Schoendienst No Stripes	.60	1.50
48 Earl Weaver MG Day	.30	.75
48B Earl Weaver MG Night	.60	1.50
49 Joe Morgan Day	.30	.75
49B Joe Morgan Night	.60	1.50
50 Mike Schmidt Grey Uni	1.25	3.00
50B Mike Schmidt White Uni	2.50	6.00
51 Willie McCovey Wood Bat	.30	.75
51B Willie McCovey Black Bat	.60	1.50
52 Stan Musial Day	1.00	2.50
52B Stan Musial Night	2.00	5.00
53 Don Sutton Ballpark	.30	.75
53B Don Sutton Gray	.60	1.50
54 Hank Greenberg w/Player	.60	1.50
54B H.Greenberg No Player	1.25	3.00
55 Robin Yount w/Player	.60	1.50
55B Robin Yount No Player	1.25	3.00
56 Tom Seaver Leather Glv	.40	1.00
56B Tom Seaver Black Glv	.75	2.00
57 Tony Perez Wood Bat	.30	.75
57B Tony Perez Black Bat	.60	1.50
58 George Sisler w/Ad	.30	.75
58B George Sisler No Ad	.60	1.50
59 Jim Bottomley White Hat	.30	.75
59B Jim Bottomley Red Hat	.60	1.50
60 Yogi Berra Leather Chest	.60	1.50
60B Yogi Berra Navy Chest	1.25	3.00
61 Fred Lindstrom Blue Bill	.30	.75
61B Fred Lindstrom Red Bill	.60	1.50
62 Napoleon Lajoie White Uni	.60	1.50
62B Nap. Lajoie Navy Uni	1.25	3.00
63 Frank Robinson Wood Bat	.40	1.00
63B Fr. Robinson Black Bat	.75	2.00
64 Carlton Fisk Red Ltr	.40	1.00
64B Carlton Fisk Black Ltr	.75	2.00
65 Orlando Cepeda Blue Sky	.30	.75
65B Orlando Cepeda Sunset	.60	1.50
66 Fergie Jenkins Leather Glv	.30	.75
66B Fergie Jenkins Black Glv	.60	1.50
67 Ernie Banks Day	.60	1.50
67B Ernie Banks Night	1.25	3.00
68 Bill Mazeroski No Sleeves	.40	1.00
68B Bill Mazeroski w/Sleeves	.75	2.00
69 Jim Bunning Grey Uni	.30	.75
69B Jim Bunning White Uni	.60	1.50
70 Rollie Fingers Day	.30	.75
70B Rollie Fingers Night	.60	1.50
71 Jimmie Foxx Black Sleeve	.60	1.50
71B Ji. Foxx White Sleeve	1.25	3.00
72 Rod Carew Red Btg Glv	.40	1.00
72B Rod Carew Blue Btg Glv	.75	2.00
73 Sparky Anderson Blue Sky	.30	.75
73B Sparky Anderson Yellow	.60	1.50
74 George Kell Red D	.30	.75
74B George Kell White D	.60	1.50

2003 Topps Gallery HOF Artist's Proofs

Inserted in packs at a rate of one per for basic cards and one in 20 for variations cards, this is a complete parallel of the Topps Gallery set. The Artist Proof cards can be differentiated by the presence of silver foil and those are also much heavier than the regular cards.

*ARTIST'S PROOFS: .75X TO 2X BASIC
*VARIATIONS: 2X TO 5X BASIC VAR

2003 Topps Gallery HOF Accent Mark Autographs

Issued at various odds depending on who signed the cards, these six cards featured authentic autographs of the featured HOFer. Each person signed a different amount of cards and we have notated the group of the signed card next to their name in our checklist.

GROUP A ODDS 1:3446
GROUP B ODDS 1:2074
GROUP C ODDS 1:1483
GROUP D ODDS 1:1149
GROUP E ODDS 1:941
GROUP F ODDS 1:545
ARTIST'S PROOFS ODDS 1:1723
ARTIST'S PROOFS PRINT RUN 25 #'d SETS
NO AP PRICING DUE TO SCARCITY
AP'S FEATURE SILVER HOLO-FOIL

BD Bobby Doerr B	15.00	40.00
LM Lee MacPhail D	15.00	40.00
RR Robin Roberts E	15.00	40.00
RS Red Schoendienst C	15.00	40.00
WS Warren Spahn F	15.00	40.00
YB Yogi Berra A	40.00	80.00

2003 Topps Gallery HOF ARTifact Relics

Inserted in packs at differing rates depending on what group the relic belongs to, this is a 57-card insert set featuring game-used relic pieces of various Hall of Famers. We have notated next to the player's name both the relic piece as well as what group the relic piece belonged to.

BAT GROUP A ODDS 1:1812
BAT GROUP B ODDS 1:469
BAT GROUP C ODDS 1:242
BAT GROUP D ODDS 1:111
BAT GROUP E ODDS 1:96
BAT GROUP F ODDS 1:28
BAT GROUP G ODDS 1:62
JSY/UNI GROUP A ODDS 1:1812
JSY/UNI GROUP B ODDS 1:2353
JSY/UNI GROUP C ODDS 1:728
JSY/UNI GROUP D ODDS 1:151
JSY/UNI GROUP E ODDS 1:145
ARTIST'S PROOFS BAT ODDS 1:345
ARTIST'S PROOFS JSY/UNI ODDS 1:967
ARTIST'S PROOFS PRINT RUN 25 #'d SETS
NO AP PRICING DUE TO SCARCITY
AP'S FEATURE SILVER HOLO-FOIL

AK Al Kaline Bat F	6.00	15.00
BD Bobby Doerr Jsy D	4.00	10.00
BH Bucky Harris Bat F	6.00	15.00
BR Babe Ruth Bat B	90.00	180.00
BRO Brooks Robinson Bat D	6.00	15.00
CF Carlton Fisk Bat G	6.00	15.00
CK Chuck Klein Bat F	6.00	15.00
CY Carl Yastrzemski Bat F	8.00	20.00
DS Duke Snider Bat F	6.00	15.00
DSU Don Sutton Bat D	4.00	10.00
EB Ernie Banks Uni B	15.00	40.00
EC Eddie Collins Bat B	15.00	40.00
EM Eddie Mathews Jsy A		
ER Edd Roush Bat B	12.50	30.00
FF Frankie Frisch Bat E	6.00	15.00
FR Frank Robinson Bat G	6.00	15.00
GB George Brett Jsy D	12.50	30.00
GK George Kelly Bat D	12.50	30.00
GP Gaylord Perry Uni E	4.00	10.00
GS George Sisler Bat F	6.00	15.00
HA Hank Aaron Bat F	10.00	25.00
HG Hank Greenberg Bat D	15.00	40.00
HH Harry Heilmann Bat B	8.00	20.00
HK Harmon Killebrew Jsy E	8.00	20.00
HM Heinie Manush Bat B	8.00	20.00
HW Honus Wagner Bat A		
HWI Hoyt Wilhelm Uni D	4.00	10.00
JB Jim Bottomley Bat E	12.50	30.00
JBE Johnny Bench Bat G	6.00	15.00
JF Jimmie Foxx Bat A		
JM Joe Morgan Bat E	4.00	10.00
JP Jim Palmer Jsy A		
JR Jackie Robinson Bat C	20.00	50.00
JT Joe Tinker Bat E	20.00	50.00
KP Kirby Puckett Bat E	8.00	20.00
LA Luis Aparicio Bat A		
LB Lou Brock Bat A		
LG Lou Gehrig Bat C	75.00	150.00
MS Mike Schmidt Uni E	12.50	30.00
NR Nolan Ryan Bat C	30.00	60.00
OC Orlando Cepeda Bat F	4.00	10.00
OS Ozzie Smith Bat E	8.00	20.00
PN Phil Niekro Uni D	4.00	10.00
PW Paul Waner Bat C	10.00	25.00
RCA Rod Carew Jsy E	6.00	15.00
RJ Reggie Jackson Bat F	6.00	15.00
RY Robin Yount Bat F	6.00	15.00
SA Sparky Anderson Uni A		
SC Sam Crawford Bat D	10.00	25.00
SM Stan Musial Bat D	12.50	30.00
TC Ty Cobb Bat C	60.00	120.00
TLA Tom Lasorda Jsy A		
TP Tony Perez Bat F	4.00	10.00
TS Tom Seaver Bat C	8.00	20.00
WM Willie Mays Jsy C	20.00	50.00
WMC Willie McCovey Bat F	4.00	10.00
WS Willie Stargell Jsy C	8.00	20.00

2003 Topps Gallery HOF ARTifact Relics Autographs

Inserted at different rates depending on which group the player belonged to, these 11 cards feature not only a game-used relic piece of the featured player but also an authentic autograph. We have notated next to the player's name not only what type of memorabilia piece but also what group the card belongs to.

GROUP A ODDS 1:3446
GROUP B ODDS 1:691
GROUP C ODDS 1:691
ARTIST'S PROOFS ODDS 1:941
ARTIST'S PROOFS PRINT RUN 25 #'d SETS
NO AP PRICING DUE TO SCARCITY
AP'S FEATURE SILVER HOLO-FOIL

AK Al Kaline Bat C	50.00	100.00
BD Bobby Doerr Jsy C	20.00	50.00
BRO Brooks Robinson Bat C	40.00	80.00
DS Duke Snider Bat B	40.00	80.00
HK Harmon Killebrew Jsy B	50.00	100.00
JM Joe Morgan Bat B	20.00	50.00
JP Jim Palmer Jsy A		
MS Mike Schmidt Uni B		
OC Orlando Cepeda Bat B		
RS Red Schoendienst Jsy A		
RY Robin Yount Bat A		

2003 Topps Gallery HOF Currency Connection Coin Relics

Issued as a box topper, these 12 cards feature not only a player but an authentic coin from a key point in their career.

STATED ODDS ONE PER BOX

BF B.Feller 1945 Dime B	6.00	15.00
BR B.Ruth 1916 Dime A	20.00	50.00
EB E.Banks 1958 Penny B	10.00	25.00
HG H.Greenberg 1945 Nickel B	10.00	25.00
JR J.Robinson 1946 Dime B	10.00	25.00
LG L.Gehrig 1938 Nickel A	15.00	40.00
OC O.Cepeda 1958 Penny B	6.00	15.00
SM S.Musial 1943 Penny B	15.00	40.00
TC T.Cobb 1909 Penny A	20.00	50.00
WM W.Mays 1958 Penny B	10.00	25.00
WMA W.Mays 1954 Nickel B	10.00	25.00
WMC W.McCovey 1959 Penny B	6.00	15.00

2003 Topps Gallery HOF Paint by Number Patch Relics

Inserted into packs at a stated rate of one in 1037, these 14 cards feature prime patch swatches of game-worn jerseys on specially designed art cards. These cards were issued to a stated print run of 25 serial numbered sets and no pricing is available due to market scarcity.

2011 Topps Gypsy Queen

COMPLETE SET (350)		
COMP.SET w/o SP's (300)	30.00	60.00
COMMON CARD (1-300)	.15	.40
COMMON RC (1-300)	.40	1.00
COMMON SP (301-350)	1.50	4.00
PLATE PRINT RUN 1 SET PER COLOR		
BLACK-CYAN-MAGENTA-YELLOW ISSUED		
NO PLATE PRICING DUE TO SCARCITY		
1 Ichiro Suzuki	.60	1.50
2 Roy Halladay	.40	1.00
3 Cole Hamels	.40	1.00
4 Jackie Robinson	.40	1.00
5 Tris Speaker	.25	.60
6 Frank Robinson	.25	.60
7 Jim Palmer	.15	.40
8 Troy Tulowitzki	.40	1.00
9 Scott Rolen	.25	.60
10 Jason Heyward	.50	1.25
11 Zack Greinke	.25	.60
12 Ryan Howard	.50	1.25
13 Joey Votto	.40	1.00
14 Brooks Robinson	.25	.60
15 Matt Kemp	.25	.60
16 Chris Carpenter	.40	1.00
17 Mark Teixeira	.40	1.00
18 Christy Mathewson	.40	1.00
19 Jon Lester	.40	1.00
20 Andre Dawson	.25	.60

Card	Low	High
21 David Wright	.50	1.25
22 Barry Larkin	.25	.60
23 Johnny Cueto	.15	.40
24 Chipper Jones	.40	1.00
25 Mel Ott	.40	1.00
26 Adrian Gonzalez	.25	.60
27 Roy Oswalt	.25	.60
28 Tony Gwynn	.40	1.00
29 Ty Cobb	.60	1.50
30 Hanley Ramirez	.40	1.00
31 Joe Mauer	.40	1.00
32 Carl Crawford	.25	.60
33 Ian Kinsler	.25	.60
34 Johan Santana	.40	1.00
35 Pee Wee Reese	.25	.60
36 Vladimir Guerrero	.40	1.00
37 Ryan Braun	.50	1.25
38 Walter Johnson	.40	1.00
39 Johnny Mize	.25	.60
40 George Sisler	.40	1.00
41 Matt Holliday	.40	1.00
42 Jose Reyes	.25	.60
43 Matt Cain	.25	.60
44 Bob Gibson	.25	.60
45 Carlos Gonzalez	.25	.60
46 Thurman Munson	.40	1.00
47 Jimmy Rollins	.25	.60
48 Roger Maris	.40	1.00
49 Honus Wagner	.40	1.00
50 Al Kaline	.40	1.00
51 Alex Rodriguez	.60	1.50
52 Carlos Santana	.40	1.00
53 Jimmie Foxx	.40	1.00
54 Frank Thomas	.40	1.00
55 Evan Longoria	.50	1.25
56 Mat Latos	.15	.40
57 David Ortiz	.25	.60
58 Dale Murphy	.40	1.00
59 Duke Snider	.25	.60
60 Rogers Hornsby	.25	.60
61 Robin Yount	.40	1.00
62 Red Schoendienst	.15	.40
63 Jimmie Foxx	.40	1.00
64 Josh Hamilton	.40	1.00
65 Babe Ruth	1.00	2.50
66 Sandy Koufax	1.25	3.00
67 Dave Winfield	.15	.40
68 Gary Carter	.15	.40
69 Kevin Youkilis	.25	.60
70 Rogers Hornsby	.25	.60
71 CC Sabathia	.25	.60
72 Justin Morneau	.40	1.00
73 Carl Yastrzemski	.40	1.00
74 Tom Seaver	.25	.60
75 Albert Pujols	1.00	2.50
76 Felix Hernandez	.40	1.00
77 Hunter Pence	.25	.60
78 Ryne Sandberg	.75	2.00
79 Andrew McCutchen	.40	1.00
80 Stephen Strasburg	.75	2.00
81 Nelson Cruz	.25	.60
82 Starlin Castro	.40	1.00
83 David Price	.40	1.00
84 Tim Lincecum	.40	1.00
85 Frank Robinson	.25	.60
86 Prince Fielder	.25	.60
87 Clayton Kershaw	.40	1.00
88 Robinson Cano	.40	1.00
89 Mickey Mantle	1.25	3.00
90 Derek Jeter	1.00	2.50
91 Josh Johnson	.25	.60
92 Mariano Rivera	.40	1.00
93 Victor Martinez	.25	.60
94 Buster Posey	.50	1.25
95 George Sisler	.40	1.00
96 Ubaldo Jimenez	.25	.60
97 Stan Musial	.60	1.50
98 Aroldis Chapman RC	1.25	3.00
99 Ozzie Smith	.60	1.50
100 Nolan Ryan	1.25	3.00
101 Ricky Nolasco	.15	.40
102 Jorge Posada	.25	.60
103 Magglio Ordonez	.25	.60
104 Lucas Duda RC	.60	1.50
105 Chris Carter	.15	.40
106 Ben Revere RC	.60	1.50
107 Brian Wilson	.40	1.00
108 Brett Wallace	.15	.40
109 Chris Volstad	.15	.40
110 Todd Helton	.25	.60
111 Jason Bay	.25	.60
112 Carlos Zambrano	.25	.60
113 Jose Bautista	.25	.60
114 Chris Coghlan	.15	.40
115 Jeremy Jeffress RC	.40	1.00
116 Jake Peavy	.15	.40
117 Dallas Braden	.15	.40
118 Mike Pelfrey	.15	.40
119 Brian Bogusevic (RC)	.40	1.00
120 Gaby Sanchez	.15	.40
121 Michael Cuddyer	.15	.40
122 Derrek Lee	.15	.40
123 Ted Lilly	.15	.40
124 J.J. Hardy	.15	.40
125 Francisco Liriano	.15	.40
126 Billy Butler	.15	.40
127 Rickie Weeks	.25	.60
128 Dan Haren	.15	.40
129 Aaron Hill	.15	.40
130 Will Venable	.15	.40
131 Cody Ross	.15	.40
132 David Murphy	.15	.40
133 Pablo Sandoval	.25	.60
134 Kelly Johnson	.15	.40
135 Ryan Dempster	.15	.40
136 Brett Myers	.15	.40
137 Ricky Romero	.15	.40
138 Yovani Gallardo	.15	.40
139 Raul Ibanez	.25	.60
140 Shaun Marcum	.15	.40
141 Brandon Inge	.15	.40
142 Max Scherzer	.15	.40
143 Carl Pavano	.15	.40
144 Jon Niese	.15	.40
145 Jason Bartlett	.15	.40
146 Melky Cabrera	.15	.40
147 Kurt Suzuki	.15	.40
148 Carlos Quentin	.15	.40
149 Adam Jones	.25	.60
150 Kosuke Fukudome	.40	1.00
151 Michael Young	.25	.60
152 Paul Maholm	.15	.40
153 Delmon Young	.25	.60
154 Dan Uggla	.25	.60
155 R.A. Dickey	.15	.40
156 Brennan Boesch	.25	.60
157 Ryan Ludwick	.15	.40
158 Madison Bumgarner	.15	.40
159 Ervin Santana	.15	.40
160 Miguel Montero	.15	.40
161 Aramis Ramirez	.15	.40
162 Cliff Lee	.40	1.00
163 Russell Martin	.15	.40
164 Cy Young	.40	1.00
165 Yadier Molina	.25	.60
166 Gordon Beckham	.25	.60
167 Cal Ripken Jr.	1.50	4.00
168 Alex Gordon	.25	.60
169 Orlando Hudson	.15	.40
170 Nick Swisher	.40	1.00
171 Manny Ramirez	.40	1.00
172 Ryan Zimmerman	.25	.60
173 Adam Dunn	.25	.60
174 Reggie Jackson	.25	.60
175 Edwin Jackson	.15	.40
176 Kendry Morales	.15	.40
177 Bernie Williams	.25	.60
178 Chone Figgins	.15	.40
179 Neil Walker	.15	.40
180 Alexei Ramirez	.15	.40
181 Lars Anderson	.25	.60
182 Bobby Abreu	.15	.40
183 Rafael Furcal	.15	.40
184 Gerardo Parra	.15	.40
185 Logan Morrison	.15	.40
186 Tommy Hunter	.15	.40
187 Lance Berkman	.25	.60
188 Chris Sale RC	.60	1.50
189 Mike Aviles	.15	.40
190 Jaime Garcia	.25	.60
191 Desmond Jennings RC	1.00	2.50
192 Jair Jurrjens	.15	.40
193 Carlos Beltran	.15	.40
194 Lorenzo Cain	.15	.40
195 Bronson Arroyo	.15	.40
196 Pat Burrell	.15	.40
197 Colby Rasmus	.40	1.00
198 Jayson Werth	.25	.60
199 James Shields	.15	.40
200 John Lackey	.15	.40
201 Travis Snider	.15	.40
202 Adam Wainwright	.25	.60
203 Brian Matusz	.40	1.00
204 Neftali Feliz	.15	.40
205 Chris Johnson	.15	.40
206 Torii Hunter	.15	.40
207 Kyle Drabek RC	.60	1.50
208 Mike Stanton	.25	.60
209 Tim Hudson	.25	.60
210 Aaron Rowand	.15	.40
211 Rollie Fingers	.15	.40
212 Miguel Tejada	.25	.60
213 Rick Porcello	.15	.40
214 Pedro Alvarez RC	.60	1.50
215 Trevor Cahill	.15	.40
216 Angel Pagan	.15	.40
217 Adrian Beltre	.15	.40
218 Austin Jackson	.15	.40
219 Casey McGehee	.15	.40
220 Tyler Colvin	.25	.60
221 Martin Prado	.15	.40
222 Heath Bell	.25	.60
223 Ivan Rodriguez	.25	.60
224 Drew Stubbs	.25	.60
225 Vernon Wells	.15	.40
226 Geovany Soto	.25	.60
227 Cameron Maybin	.15	.40
228 Ryan Kalish	.25	.60
229 Alex Gonzalez	.15	.40
230 Ian Desmond	.25	.60
231 Mark Reynolds	.15	.40
232 Jhonny Peralta	.15	.40
233 Yunesky Maya RC	.40	1.00
234 Sean Rodriguez	.15	.40
235 Johnny Bench	.40	1.00
236 Alex Rios	.25	.60
237 Roy Campanella	.40	1.00
238 Brandon Beachy RC	1.00	2.50
239 Josh Willingham	.15	.40
240 Fausto Carmona	.15	.40
241 Brian Roberts	.15	.40
242 Joba Chamberlain	.25	.60
243 Jim Thome	.25	.60
244 Scott Kazmir	.15	.40
245 Hank Conger RC	.60	1.50
246 A.J. Burnett	.25	.60
247 Matt Garza	.15	.40
248 Dustin Pedroia	.50	1.25
249 Jacoby Ellsbury	.40	1.00
250 Joe Saunders	.15	.40
251 Mark Buehrle	.25	.60
252 David DeJesus	.15	.40
253 Carlos Lee	.15	.40
254 Brandon Phillips	.15	.40
255 Barry Zito	.15	.40
256 Wade Davis	.15	.40
257 James Loney	.25	.60
258 Freddy Sanchez	.15	.40
259 Aubrey Huff	.15	.40
260 Marlon Byrd	.15	.40
261 Daniel Bard	.15	.40
262 Marco Scutaro	.15	.40
263 Johnny Damon	.25	.60
264 Jeremy Hellickson RC	1.25	3.00
265 Stephen Drew	.15	.40
266 Daric Barton	.15	.40
267 Jake Arrieta	.15	.40
268 Wandy Rodriguez	.15	.40
269 Curtis Granderson	.25	.60
270 Brad Lidge	.15	.40
271 John Danks	.15	.40
272 Felix Pie	.15	.40
273 Chad Billingsley	.15	.40
274 Jose Tabata	.25	.60
275 Ruben Tejada	.15	.40
276 Ian Stewart	.15	.40
277 Derek Lowe	.15	.40
278 Denard Span	.15	.40
279 Josh Thole	.15	.40
280 Jonathan Sanchez	.15	.40
281 Juan Pierre	.15	.40
282 B.J. Upton	.25	.60
283 Rick Ankiel	.15	.40
284 Jed Lowrie	.25	.60
285 Colby Lewis	.15	.40
286 Jason Kubel	.15	.40
287 Jorge De la Rosa	.15	.40
288 C.J. Wilson	.15	.40
289 Will Rhymes	.15	.40
290 Jake McGee (RC)	.40	1.00
291 Chris Young	.15	.40
292 Andre Ethier	.25	.60
293 Joakim Soria	.15	.40
294 Garrett Jones	.15	.40
295 Phil Hughes	.15	.40
296 Ty Cobb	.60	1.50
297 Grady Sizemore	.25	.60
298 Tris Speaker	.25	.60
299 Andruw Jones	.15	.40
300 Franklin Gutierrez	.15	.40
301 Alfonso Soriano SP	2.00	5.00
302 Brian McCann SP	2.00	5.00
303 Johnny Mize SP	2.00	5.00
304 Brian Duensing SP	1.50	4.00
305 Mark Ellis SP	1.50	4.00
306 Tommy Hanson SP	2.00	5.00
307 Danny Valencia SP	2.00	5.00
308 Kila Ka'aihue SP	1.50	4.00
309 Clay Buchholz SP	2.00	5.00
310 Jon Garland SP	1.50	4.00
311 Hisanori Takahashi SP	1.50	4.00
312 Justin Verlander SP	2.00	5.00
313 Mike Minor SP	1.50	4.00
314 Yonder Alonso RC SP	2.00	5.00
315 Jered Weaver SP	1.50	4.00
316 Lou Gehrig SP	4.00	10.00
317 Justin Upton SP	1.50	4.00
318 Hank Aaron SP	4.00	10.00
319 Elvis Andrus SP	2.00	5.00
320 Dexter Fowler SP	1.50	4.00
321 Brett Sinkbeil SP	1.50	4.00
322 Ike Davis SP	2.00	5.00
323 Shin-Soo Choo SP	2.50	6.00
324 Jay Bruce SP	2.00	5.00
325 Jason Castro SP	1.50	4.00
326 Chase Utley SP	2.50	6.00
327 Miguel Cabrera SP	2.50	6.00
328 Brett Anderson SP	2.00	5.00
329 Ian Kennedy SP	1.50	4.00
330 Brandon Morrow SP	1.50	4.00
331 Greg Halman RC SP	2.50	6.00
332 Ty Wigginton SP	1.50	4.00
333 Travis Wood SP	1.50	4.00
334 Nick Markakis SP	2.50	6.00
335 Freddie Freeman RC SP	5.00	12.00
336 Domonic Brown SP	2.50	6.00
337 Jason Vargas SP	1.50	4.00
338 Babe Ruth SP	5.00	12.00
339 Omar Infante SP	1.50	4.00
340 Miguel Olivo SP	1.50	4.00
341 Nyjer Morgan SP	1.50	4.00
342 Placido Polanco SP	1.50	4.00
343 Mitch Moreland SP	1.50	4.00
344 Josh Beckett SP	2.00	5.00
345 Erik Bedard SP	1.50	4.00
346 Shane Victorino SP	2.00	5.00
347 Konrad Schmidt RC SP	1.50	4.00
348 J.A. Happ SP	2.00	5.00
349 Xavier Nady SP	1.50	4.00
350 Carlos Pena SP	2.00	5.00

2011 Topps Gypsy Queen Framed Green

*GREEN: 1.2X TO 3X BASIC
*GREEN RC .5X TO 1.2X BASIC RC

2011 Topps Gypsy Queen Framed Paper

*PAPER: 1.5X TO 4X BASIC
*PAPER RC: .6X TO 1.5X BASIC RC
STATED PRINT RUN 999 SER.#'d SETS

2011 Topps Gypsy Queen Framed Stamp

STATED PRINT RUN 10 SER.#'d SETS
NO PRICING DUE TO SCARCITY

2011 Topps Gypsy Queen Mini

*MINI 1-300: 1.2X TO 3X BASIC
*MINI RC 1-300 .5X TO 1.2X BASIC
PLATE PRINT RUN 1 SET PER COLOR
BLACK-CYAN-MAGENTA-YELLOW ISSUED
NO PLATE PRICING DUE TO SCARCITY

Card	Low	High
1B Ichiro Suzuki SP	6.00	15.00
Swing follow through		
2B Roy Halladay SP	4.00	10.00
Facing right		
3B Cole Hamels SP	4.00	10.00
Arm back		
4B Jackie Robinson SP	4.00	10.00
Glove up		
5B Tris Speaker SP	2.50	6.00
Standing		
6B Frank Robinson SP	2.50	6.00
Portrait		
7B Jim Palmer SP	1.50	4.00
Portrait		
8B Troy Tulowitzki SP	4.00	10.00
Swinging		
9B Scott Rolen SP	2.50	6.00
Running		
10B Jason Heyward SP	5.00	12.00
Swinging		
11B Zack Greinke SP	2.50	6.00
White jersey		
12B Ryan Howard SP	5.00	12.00
Swing follow through		
13B Joey Votto SP	4.00	10.00
Running		
14B Brooks Robinson SP	2.50	6.00
Fielding		
15B Matt Kemp SP	2.50	6.00
Front leg up		
16B Chris Carpenter SP	4.00	10.00
Pitching		
17B Mark Teixeira SP	4.00	10.00
Swinging		
18B Christy Mathewson SP	4.00	10.00
With bat		
19B Jon Lester SP	4.00	10.00
Front leg up		
20B Andre Dawson SP	2.50	6.00
Cubs		
21B David Wright SP	5.00	12.00
Swinging		
22B Barry Larkin SP	2.00	5.00
Running		
23B Johnny Cueto SP	1.50	4.00
Pitching		
24B Chipper Jones SP	4.00	10.00
Swinging		
25B Mel Ott SP	4.00	10.00
Bat on shoulder		
26B Adrian Gonzalez SP	2.50	6.00
Running		
27B Roy Oswalt SP	2.50	6.00
Knee up		
28B Tony Gwynn SP	4.00	10.00
Pinstripe jersey		
29B Ty Cobb SP	6.00	15.00
With glove		
30B Hanley Ramirez SP	4.00	10.00
Swinging		
31B Joe Mauer SP	4.00	10.00
Blue jersey		
32B Carl Crawford SP	2.50	6.00
Bat on shoulder		
33B Ian Kinsler SP	2.50	6.00
Red jersey		
34B Johan Santana SP	4.00	10.00
Arm up		
35B Pee Wee Reese SP	2.50	6.00
With bat		
36B Vladimir Guerrero SP	4.00	10.00
Swinging		
37B Ryan Braun SP	5.00	12.00
Running		
38B Walter Johnson SP	4.00	10.00
Pitch follow through		
39B Johnny Mize SP	2.50	6.00
Yankees		
40B George Sisler SP	4.00	10.00
Bat on shoulder		
41B Matt Holliday SP	4.00	10.00
Swinging		
42B Jose Reyes SP	2.50	6.00
Swinging		
43B Matt Cain SP	2.50	6.00
Portrait		
44B Bob Gibson SP	2.50	6.00
Leg up		
45B Carlos Gonzalez SP	2.50	6.00
Front leg up		
46B Thurman Munson SP	4.00	10.00
Swing follow through		
47B Jimmy Rollins SP	2.50	6.00
Facing right		
48B Roger Maris SP	4.00	10.00
Cardinals		
49B Honus Wagner SP	4.00	10.00
With glove		
50B Al Kaline SP	3.00	8.00
With glove		
51B Alex Rodriguez SP	5.00	12.00
Running		
52B Carlos Santana SP	3.00	8.00
With bat		
53B Jimmie Foxx SP	3.00	8.00
Bat on left shoulder		
54B Frank Thomas SP	3.00	8.00
Facing left		
55B Evan Longoria SP	5.00	12.00
Running		
56B Mat Latos SP	1.25	3.00
Hands together		
57B David Ortiz SP	2.00	5.00
Front leg down		
58B Dale Murphy SP	3.00	8.00
Red jersey		
59B Duke Snider SP	2.00	5.00
Hands together		
60B Rogers Hornsby SP	2.00	5.00
Leaning on knee		
61B Robin Yount SP	3.00	8.00
Blue jersey		
62B Red Schoendienst SP	1.25	3.00
With ball		
63B Jimmie Foxx SP	3.00	8.00
Glove up		
64B Josh Hamilton SP	3.00	8.00
Blue jersey		
65B Babe Ruth SP	8.00	20.00
With bat		
66B Sandy Koufax SP	10.00	25.00
Hands together		
67B Dave Winfield SP	1.25	3.00
Swing follow through		
68B Gary Carter SP	1.25	3.00
Mets		
69B Kevin Youkilis SP	2.00	5.00
Facing left		
70B Rogers Hornsby SP	2.00	5.00
Giants		
71B CC Sabathia SP	2.00	5.00
No crowd in background		
72B Justin Morneau SP	4.00	10.00
Blue jersey		
73B Carl Yastrzemski SP	3.00	8.00
Bat up		
74B Tom Seaver SP	2.00	5.00
Arms up		
75B Albert Pujols SP	10.00	25.00
With bat		
76B Felix Hernandez SP	3.00	8.00
White jersey		
77B Hunter Pence SP	2.00	5.00
Facing right		
78B Ryne Sandberg SP	6.00	15.00
With bat		
79B Andrew McCutchen SP	4.00	10.00
Arms back		
80B Stephen Strasburg SP	8.00	20.00
37 showing on jersey		
81B Nelson Cruz SP	2.00	5.00
Red jersey		
82B Starlin Castro SP	3.00	8.00
Blue jersey		
83B David Price SP	3.00	8.00
Hands together		
84B Tim Lincecum SP	4.00	10.00
Black jersey		
85B Frank Robinson SP	2.00	5.00
Fielding		
86B Prince Fielder SP	2.50	6.00
Bat up		
87B Clayton Kershaw SP	4.00	10.00
Leg up		
88B Robinson Cano SP	3.00	8.00
Swinging		
89B Mickey Mantle SP	10.00	25.00
Bat up		
90B Derek Jeter SP	40.00	80.00
With bat		
91B Josh Johnson SP	2.00	5.00
Leg up		
92B Mariano Rivera SP	3.00	8.00
Arm up		
93B Victor Martinez SP	2.50	6.00
Facing right		
94B Buster Posey SP	5.00	12.00
With bat		
95B George Sisler SP	3.00	8.00
Both hands on bat		
96B Ubaldo Jimenez SP	2.00	5.00
Portrait		
97B Stan Musial SP	5.00	12.00
Facing left		
98B Aroldis Chapman SP	5.00	12.00
Portrait		
99B Ozzie Smith SP	5.00	12.00
With bat		
100B Nolan Ryan SP	12.00	30.00
Angels		
301 Alfonso Soriano	1.00	2.50
302 Brian McCann	1.00	2.50
303 Johnny Mize	1.00	2.50
304 Brian Duensing	.60	1.50
305 Mark Ellis	.60	1.50
306 Tommy Hanson	1.00	2.50
307 Danny Valencia	1.00	2.50
308 Kila Ka'aihue	.60	1.50
309 Clay Buchholz	1.00	2.50
310 Jon Garland	.60	1.50
311 Hisanori Takahashi	.60	1.50
312 Justin Verlander	2.00	5.00
313 Mike Minor	.60	1.50
314 Yonder Alonso	1.00	2.50
315 Jered Weaver	.60	1.50
316 Lou Gehrig	3.00	8.00
317 Justin Upton	1.00	2.50
318 Hank Aaron	3.00	8.00
319 Elvis Andrus	1.00	2.50
320 Dexter Fowler	.60	1.50
321 Brett Sinkbeil	.60	1.50
322 Ike Davis	1.00	2.50
323 Shin-Soo Choo	1.00	2.50
324 Jay Bruce	1.00	2.50
325 Jason Castro	.60	1.50
326 Chase Utley	1.50	4.00
327 Miguel Cabrera	1.50	4.00
328 Brett Anderson	1.00	2.50
329 Ian Kennedy	1.00	2.50
330 Brandon Morrow	.60	1.50
331 Greg Halman	1.00	2.50
332 Ty Wigginton	.60	1.50
333 Travis Wood	.60	1.50
334 Nick Markakis	1.50	4.00
335 Freddie Freeman	2.50	6.00
336 Domonic Brown	1.50	4.00
337 Jason Vargas	.60	1.50
338 Babe Ruth	4.00	10.00
339 Omar Infante	.60	1.50
340 Miguel Olivo	.60	1.50
341 Nyjer Morgan	.60	1.50
342 Placido Polanco	.60	1.50
343 Mitch Moreland	.60	1.50
344 Josh Beckett	1.00	2.50
345 Erik Bedard	.60	1.50
346 Shane Victorino	1.00	2.50
347 Konrad Schmidt	.60	1.50
348 J.A. Happ	1.00	2.50
349 Xavier Nady	.60	1.50
350 Carlos Pena	1.00	2.50

2011 Topps Gypsy Queen Mini Black

*BLACK: 2.5X TO 6X BASIC
*BLACK RC: 1X TO 2.5X BASIC

Card	Low	High
90 Derek Jeter	20.00	50.00
301 Alfonso Soriano	1.50	4.00
302 Brian McCann	1.50	4.00
303 Johnny Mize	1.50	4.00
304 Brian Duensing	1.00	2.50
305 Mark Ellis	1.00	2.50
306 Tommy Hanson	1.50	4.00
307 Danny Valencia	1.50	4.00
308 Kila Ka'aihue	1.00	2.50
309 Clay Buchholz	1.50	4.00
310 Jon Garland	1.00	2.50
311 Hisanori Takahashi	1.00	2,50
312 Justin Verlander	3.00	8.00
313 Mike Minor	1.00	2.50
314 Yonder Alonso	1.50	4.00
315 Jered Weaver	1.00	2.50
316 Lou Gehrig	5.00	12.00
317 Justin Upton	1.50	4.00
318 Hank Aaron	5.00	12.00
319 Elvis Andrus	1.50	4.00
320 Dexter Fowler	1.00	2.50
321 Brett Sinkbeil	1.00	2.50
322 Ike Davis	1.50	4.00
323 Shin-Soo Choo	1.50	4.00
324 Jay Bruce	1.50	4.00
325 Jason Castro	1.00	2.50
326 Chase Utley	2.50	6.00
327 Miguel Cabrera	2.50	6.00
328 Brett Anderson	1.50	4.00
329 Ian Kennedy	1.50	4.00
330 Brandon Morrow	1.00	2.50
331 Greg Halman	1.50	4.00
332 Ty Wigginton	1.00	2.50
333 Travis Wood	1.00	2.50
334 Nick Markakis	2.50	6.00
335 Freddie Freeman	4.00	10.00
336 Domonic Brown	2.50	6.00
337 Jason Vargas	1.00	2.50
338 Babe Ruth	6.00	15.00
339 Omar Infante	1.00	2.50
340 Miguel Olivo	1.00	2.50
341 Nyjer Morgan	1.00	2.50
342 Placido Polanco	1.00	2.50
343 Mitch Moreland	1.00	2.50
344 Josh Beckett	1.50	4.00
345 Erik Bedard	1.00	2.50
346 Shane Victorino	1.50	4.00
347 Konrad Schmidt	1.00	2.50
348 J.A. Happ	1.50	4.00
349 Xavier Nady	1.00	2.50
350 Carlos Pena	1.50	4.00

2011 Topps Gypsy Queen Mini Leather

STATED PRINT RUN 10 SER.#'d SETS
NO PRICING DUE TO SCARCITY

2011 Topps Gypsy Queen Mini Red Gypsy Queen Back

*RED: 1.5X TO 4X BASIC
*RED RC: .6X TO 1.5X BASIC

Card	Low	High
167 Cal Ripken Jr.	15.00	40.00
301 Alfonso Soriano	1.00	2.50
302 Brian McCann	1.00	2.50
303 Johnny Mize	1.00	2.50
304 Brian Duensing	.60	1.50
305 Mark Ellis	.60	1.50
306 Tommy Hanson	1.00	2.50
307 Danny Valencia	1.00	2.50
308 Kila Ka'aihue	.60	1.50
309 Clay Buchholz	1.00	2.50
310 Jon Garland	.60	1.50
311 Hisanori Takahashi	.60	1.50
312 Justin Verlander	2.00	5.00
313 Mike Minor	.60	1.50
314 Yonder Alonso	1.00	2.50
315 Jered Weaver	.60	1.50
316 Lou Gehrig	3.00	8.00
317 Justin Upton	1.00	2.50
318 Hank Aaron	3.00	8.00
319 Elvis Andrus	1.00	2.50
320 Dexter Fowler	.60	1.50
321 Brett Sinkbeil	.60	1.50
322 Ike Davis	1.00	2.50
323 Shin-Soo Choo	1.00	2.50
324 Jay Bruce	1.00	2.50
325 Jason Castro	.60	1.50
326 Chase Utley	1.50	4.00
327 Miguel Cabrera	1.50	4.00
328 Brett Anderson	1.00	2.50
329 Ian Kennedy	1.00	2.50
330 Brandon Morrow	.60	1.50
331 Greg Halman	1.00	2.50
332 Ty Wigginton	.60	1.50
333 Travis Wood	.60	1.50
334 Nick Markakis	1.50	4.00
335 Freddie Freeman	2.50	6.00
336 Domonic Brown	1.50	4.00
337 Jason Vargas	.60	1.50
338 Babe Ruth	4.00	10.00
339 Omar Infante	.60	1.50
340 Miguel Olivo	.60	1.50
341 Nyjer Morgan	.60	1.50
342 Placido Polanco	.60	1.50
343 Mitch Moreland	.60	1.50
344 Josh Beckett	1.00	2.50
345 Erik Bedard	.60	1.50
346 Shane Victorino	1.00	2.50
347 Konrad Schmidt	.60	1.50
348 J.A. Happ	1.00	2.50
349 Xavier Nady	.60	1.50
350 Carlos Pena	1.00	2.50

2011 Topps Gypsy Queen Mini Sepia

*SEPIA: 3X TO 8X BASIC
*SEPIA RC: 1.2X TO 3X BASIC RC
STATED PRINT RUN 99 SER.#'d SETS

Card	Low	High
1 Ichiro Suzuki	6.00	15.00
29 Ty Cobb	6.00	15.00
78 Ryne Sandberg	8.00	20.00
80 Stephen Strasburg	12.50	30.00
84 Tim Lincecum	6.00	15.00
90 Derek Jeter	20.00	50.00
98 Aroldis Chapman	10.00	25.00
296 Ty Cobb	6.00	15.00

2011 Topps Gypsy Queen Autographs

EXCHANGE DEADLINE 4/30/2014

Card	Low	High
AC Andrew Cashner	5.00	12.00
AK Al Kaline	20.00	50.00
AP Angel Pagan	6.00	15.00
AT Andres Torres	6.00	15.00
BC Brett Cecil	4.00	10.00
BR Brooks Robinson	20.00	50.00
CB Clay Buchholz	6.00	15.00
CR Cal Ripken Jr. EXCH	100.00	175.00
CS CC Sabathia EXCH	30.00	60.00
DB Domonic Brown	8.00	20.00
DD David DeJesus	4.00	10.00
DH Daniel Hudson	6.00	15.00
DO David Ortiz	20.00	50.00
EL Evan Longoria	15.00	40.00
FF Freddie Freeman	10.00	25.00
FR Frank Robinson	30.00	60.00
GB Gordon Beckham	6.00	15.00
GG Gio Gonzalez	6.00	15.00
HA Hank Aaron	300.00	500.00
JB Jose Bautista	12.50	30.00
JC Jason Castro	10.00	25.00
JH Josh Hamilton EXCH	30.00	60.00
JJA Jon Jay	5.00	12.00
JJ Josh Johnson	5.00	12.00
JT Josh Tomlin	5.00	12.00
MB Marlon Byrd	4.00	10.00
MS Mike Stanton	20.00	50.00
NC Nelson Cruz	6.00	15.00
NF Neftali Feliz	6.00	15.00
NM Nick Markakis	6.00	15.00
PS Pablo Sandoval	8.00	20.00
RH Roy Halladay EXCH	100.00	200.00
RN Ricky Nolasco	4.00	10.00
RS Ryne Sandberg	60.00	120.00
SK Sandy Koufax	400.00	600.00
SV Shane Victorino	8.00	20.00
TH Tommy Hunter	4.00	10.00
WV Will Venable	4.00	10.00
YA Yonder Alonso	10.00	25.00
ACH Aroldis Chapman	30.00	60.00
CSA Chris Sale	5.00	12.00
JHE Jason Heyward EXCH	20.00	50.00
RHA Ryan Howard	50.00	100.00
RSH Red Schoendienst	10.00	25.00

2011 Topps Gypsy Queen Dual Relic Autographs

STATED PRINT RUN 15 SER.#'d SETS
NO PRICING DUE TO SCARCITY
EXCHANGE DEADLINE 4/30/2014

2011 Topps Gypsy Queen Framed Mini Relic Autographs

STATED PRINT RUN 25 SER.#'d SETS
NO PRICING DUE TO SCARCITY
EXCHANGE DEADLINE 4/30/2014

2011 Topps Gypsy Queen Framed Mini Relics

Card	Low	High
BL Barry Larkin	4.00	10.00
BR Babe Ruth	75.00	150.00
CR Cal Ripken Jr.	10.00	25.00
CU Chase Utley	4.00	10.00
DJ Derek Jeter	10.00	25.00
DO David Ortiz	3.00	8.00
DU Dan Uggla	4.00	10.00
DW David Wright	4.00	10.00
EL Evan Longoria	4.00	10.00
FR Frank Robinson	4.00	10.00
JH Josh Hamilton	5.00	12.00
JR Jackie Robinson	12.50	30.00
LG Lou Gehrig	75.00	150.00
MC Miguel Cabrera	3.00	8.00
MH Matt Holliday	5.00	12.00
MK Matt Kemp	3.00	8.00
NR Nolan Ryan	15.00	40.00
OS Ozzie Smith	8.00	20.00
PF Prince Fielder	3.00	8.00
RC Robinson Cano	6.00	15.00
RH Ryan Howard	5.00	12.00
SM Stan Musial	12.50	30.00
TM Thurman Munson	12.50	30.00
RHE Rickey Henderson	8.00	20.00

2011 Topps Gypsy Queen Future Stars

Card	Low	High
COMPLETE SET (20)	10.00	25.00

PLATE PRINT RUN 1 SET PER COLOR
BLACK-CYAN-MAGENTA-YELLOW ISSUED
NO PLATE PRICING DUE TO SCARCITY
*MINI: .75X TO 2X BASIC

Card	Low	High
FS1 Brian Matusz	1.00	2.50
FS2 Kyle Drabek	.60	1.50
FS3 Yonder Alonso	.60	1.50
FS4 Freddie Freeman	1.50	4.00
FS5 Desmond Jennings	1.00	2.50
FS6 Trevor Cahill	.40	1.00
FS7 Ike Davis	.60	1.50
FS8 Jason Heyward	1.25	3.00
FS9 Starlin Castro	1.00	2.50
FS10 Phil Hughes	.40	1.00
FS11 Buster Posey	1.25	3.00
FS12 Neftali Feliz	.40	1.00

FS13 Stephen Strasburg 2.00 5.00
FS14 Mat Latos .40 1.00
FS15 Jose Tabata .60 1.50
FS16 David Price 1.00 2.50
FS17 Clay Buchholz .60 1.50
FS18 Aroldis Chapman 1.25 3.00
FS19 Gordon Beckham .60 1.50
FS20 Mike Stanton .60 1.50

2011 Topps Gypsy Queen Great Ones

COMPLETE SET (30) 20.00 50.00
PLATE PRINT RUN 1 SET PER COLOR
BLACK-CYAN-MAGENTA-YELLOW ISSUED
NO PLATE PRICING DUE TO SCARCITY
*MINI: .75X TO 2X BASIC
GO1 Andre Dawson .60 1.50
GO2 Babe Ruth 2.50 6.00
GO3 Bob Gibson .60 1.50
GO4 Brooks Robinson .60 1.50
GO5 Christy Mathewson 1.00 2.50
GO6 Frank Robinson .60 1.50
GO7 George Sisler 1.00 2.50
GO8 Jackie Robinson 1.00 2.50
GO9 Jim Palmer .40 1.00
GO10 Jimmie Foxx 1.00 2.50
GO11 Johnny Mize .60 1.50
GO12 Johnny Bench 1.00 2.50
GO13 Lou Gehrig 2.00 5.00
GO14 Mel Ott 1.00 2.50
GO15 Mickey Mantle 3.00 8.00
GO16 Nolan Ryan 3.00 8.00
GO17 Pee Wee Reese .60 1.50
GO18 Robin Yount 1.00 2.50
GO19 Rogers Hornsby .60 1.50
GO20 Rollie Fingers .40 1.00
GO21 Thurman Munson 1.00 2.50
GO22 Tom Seaver .60 1.50
GO23 Tris Speaker .60 1.50
GO24 Ty Cobb 1.50 4.00
GO25 Walter Johnson 1.00 2.50
GO26 Honus Wagner 1.00 2.50
GO27 Cy Young 1.00 2.50
GO28 Babe Ruth 2.50 6.00
GO29 Frank Robinson .60 1.50
GO30 Nolan Ryan 3.00 8.00

2011 Topps Gypsy Queen Gypsy Queens

COMPLETE SET (19) 30.00 60.00
*RED TAROT: .6X TO 1.5X BASIC
GQ1 Zenda 1.50 4.00
GQ2 Oriana 1.50 4.00
GQ3 Halaveni 1.50 4.00
GQ4 Keyseria 1.50 4.00
GQ5 Sonia 1.50 4.00
GQ6 Sheerah 1.50 4.00
GQ7 Kara 1.50 4.00
GQ8 Dianamara 1.50 4.00
GQ9 Kali 1.50 4.00
GQ10 Levitia 1.50 4.00
GQ11 Mahrya 1.50 4.00
GQ12 Adara 1.50 4.00
GQ13 Mirela 1.50 4.00
GQ14 Angelina 1.50 4.00
GQ15 Lavenia 1.50 4.00
GQ16 Stefumari 1.50 4.00
GQ17 Olga 1.50 4.00
GQ18 Hevalia 1.50 4.00
GQ19 Adamina 1.50 4.00

2011 Topps Gypsy Queen Gypsy Queens Autographs

GQA1 Zenda 8.00 20.00
GQA2 Oriana 8.00 20.00
GQA3 Halaveni 8.00 20.00
GQA4 Keyseria 8.00 20.00
GQA5 Sonia 8.00 20.00
GQA6 Sheerah 8.00 20.00
GQA7 Kara 8.00 20.00
GQA8 Dianamara 8.00 20.00
GQA9 Kali 8.00 20.00
GQA10 Levitia 8.00 20.00
GQA11 Mahrya 8.00 20.00
GQA12 Adara 8.00 20.00
GQA13 Mirela 8.00 20.00
GQA14 Angelina 8.00 20.00
GQA15 Lavenia 8.00 20.00
GQA16 Stefumari 8.00 20.00
GQA17 Olga 8.00 20.00
GQA18 Hevalia 8.00 20.00
GQA19 Adamina 8.00 20.00

2011 Topps Gypsy Queen Gypsy Queens Jewel Relics

GQR1 Zenda 12.50 30.00
GQR2 Oriana 12.50 30.00
GQR3 Halaveni 12.50 30.00
GQR4 Keyseria 12.50 30.00
GQR5 Sonia 12.50 30.00
GQR6 Sheerah 12.50 30.00
GQR7 Kara 12.50 30.00
GQR8 Dianamara 12.50 30.00
GQR9 Kali 12.50 30.00
GQR10 Levitia 12.50 30.00
GQR11 Mahrya 12.50 30.00
GQR12 Adara 12.50 30.00
GQR13 Mirela 12.50 30.00
GQR14 Angelina 12.50 30.00
GQR15 Lavenia 12.50 30.00
GQR16 Stefumari 12.50 30.00
GQR17 Olga 12.50 30.00
GQR18 Hevalia 12.50 30.00
GQR19 Adamina 12.50 30.00

2011 Topps Gypsy Queen Home Run Heroes

COMPLETE SET (25) 10.00 25.00
PLATE PRINT RUN 1 SET PER COLOR
BLACK-CYAN-MAGENTA-YELLOW ISSUED
NO PLATE PRICING DUE TO SCARCITY
*MINI: .75X TO 2X BASIC
HH1 Babe Ruth 2.50 6.00
HH2 Albert Pujols 2.50 6.00
HH3 Jose Bautista .60 1.50
HH4 Mark Teixeira 1.00 2.50
HH5 Carlos Pena .60 1.50
HH6 Ryan Howard 1.25 3.00
HH7 Miguel Cabrera 1.00 2.50
HH8 Prince Fielder .60 1.50
HH9 Alex Rodriguez 1.50 4.00
HH10 David Ortiz .60 1.50
HH11 Andruw Jones .40 1.00
HH12 Adrian Beltre .40 1.00
HH13 Manny Ramirez 1.00 2.50
HH14 Jim Thome .60 1.50
HH15 Troy Glaus .40 1.00
HH16 Andre Dawson .60 1.50
HH17 Frank Robinson .60 1.50
HH18 Jimmie Foxx 1.00 2.50
HH19 Johnny Mize .60 1.50
HH20 Johnny Bench 1.00 2.50
HH21 Lou Gehrig 2.00 5.00
HH22 Mel Ott 1.00 2.50
HH23 Mickey Mantle 3.00 8.00
HH24 Rogers Hornsby .60 1.50
HH25 Tris Speaker .60 1.50

2011 Topps Gypsy Queen Original Art Patches

STATED PRINT RUN 1 SER.#'d SET
NO PRICING DUE TO SCARCITY

2011 Topps Gypsy Queen Relic Autographs

STATED PRINT RUN 25 SER.#'d SETS
NO PRICING DUE TO SCARCITY
EXCHANGE DEADLINE 4/30/2014

2011 Topps Gypsy Queen Relics

AR Alex Rodriguez 5.00 12.00
BG Brett Gardner 3.00 8.00
CR Cal Ripken Jr. 8.00 20.00
DJ Derek Jeter 8.00 20.00
DO David Ortiz 3.00 8.00
DP Dustin Pedroia 4.00 10.00
HR Hanley Ramirez 3.00 8.00
JE Jacoby Ellsbury 3.00 8.00
JJ Josh Johnson 3.00 8.00
JP Jorge Posada 3.00 8.00
KF Kosuke Fukudome 3.00 8.00
KY Kevin Youkilis 3.00 8.00
PF Prince Fielder 3.00 8.00
RB Ryan Braun 4.00 10.00
RC Robinson Cano 5.00 12.00
RH Ryan Howard 4.00 10.00
SC Scott Rolen 3.00 8.00
TH Tommy Hanson 3.00 8.00
YM Yadier Molina 5.00 12.00
JWE Jayson Werth 3.00 8.00

2011 Topps Gypsy Queen Royal Wedding Jewel Relic

PWR Prince William 100.00 200.00
Kate Middleton

2011 Topps Gypsy Queen Sticky Fingers

SF1 Derek Jeter 2.50 6.00
SF2 Chase Utley 1.00 2.50
SF3 David Eckstein .40 1.00
SF4 Starlin Castro 1.00 2.50
SF5 Elvis Andrus .60 1.50
SF6 Mark Teixeira 1.00 2.50
SF7 Jose Reyes .60 1.50
SF8 Ivan Rodriguez .60 1.50
SF9 Brandon Phillips .40 1.00
SF10 David Wright 1.25 3.00
SF11 Hanley Ramirez 1.00 2.50
SF12 Orlando Hudson .40 1.00
SF13 Kevin Youkilis .60 1.50
SF14 Alcides Escobar .40 1.00
SF15 Jason Bartlett .40 1.00

2011 Topps Gypsy Queen Triple Relic Autographs

STATED PRINT RUN 10 SER.#'d SETS
NO PRICING DUE TO SCARCITY
EXCHANGE DEADLINE 4/30/2014

2011 Topps Gypsy Queen Wall Climbers

WC1 Torii Hunter .40 1.00
WC2 Mike Stanton .60 1.50
WC3 Nick Swisher 1.00 2.50
WC4 Denard Span .40 1.00
WC5 Rajai Davis .40 1.00
WC6 Ichiro Suzuki 1.50 4.00
WC7 Franklin Gutierrez .40 1.00
WC8 Michael Brantley .40 1.00
WC9 Jason Heyward 1.25 3.00
WC10 David DeJesus .40 1.00

2001 Topps Heritage

The 2001 Topps Heritage product was released in February 2001. Each pack contained eight cards and carried a $1.99 SRP. The base set features 407 cards. Please note that all low series cards 1-80, feature both red and black back variations and are in shorter supply than mid-series cards 81-310. Also, high series cards 311-407 are short-printed with an announced seeding ratio of 1:2 packs. Finally, the following mid-series cards were erroneously printed exclusively in black back format: 103, 159, 171, 176, 179, 188, 201, 212, 224 and 241. All told, a master set of all red and black variations consists of 487-cards (397 red backs and 90 black backs). Most collectors in pursuit of a 407-card complete set typically intermingle red and black back cards.

COMP.MASTER SET (487) 350.00 500.00
COMPLETE SET (407) 250.00 400.00
COMP.SET w/o SP's (230) 40.00 80.00
COMMON CARD (81-310) .20 .50
COMMON CARD (1-80) 1.00 2.50
COMMON (311-407) 2.00 5.00
1 Kris Benson 1.00 2.50
1 Kris Benson Black 1.00 2.50
2 Brian Jordan 1.00 2.50
2 Brian Jordan Black 1.00 2.50
3 Fernando Vina 1.00 2.50
3 Fernando Vina Black 1.00 2.50
4 Mike Sweeney 1.00 2.50
4 Mike Sweeney Black 1.00 2.50
5 Rafael Palmeiro 1.00 2.50
5 Rafael Palmeiro Black 1.00 2.50
6 Paul O'Neill 1.00 2.50
6 Paul O'Neill Black 1.00 2.50
7 Todd Helton 1.00 2.50
7 Todd Helton Black 1.00 2.50
8 Ramiro Mendoza 1.00 2.50
8 Ramiro Mendoza Black 1.00 2.50
9 Kevin Millwood 1.00 2.50
9 Kevin Millwood Black 1.00 2.50
10 Chuck Knoblauch 1.00 2.50
10 Chuck Knoblauch Black 1.00 2.50
11 Derek Jeter 4.00 10.00
11 Derek Jeter Black 4.00 10.00
12 A.Rodriguez Rangers 2.50 6.00
12 A.Rod Black Rangers 2.50 6.00
13 Geoff Jenkins 1.00 2.50
13 Geoff Jenkins Black 1.00 2.50
14 David Justice 1.00 2.50
14 David Justice Black 1.00 2.50
15 David Cone 1.00 2.50
15 David Cone Black 1.00 2.50
16 Andres Galarraga 1.00 2.50
16 Andres Galarraga Black 1.00 2.50
17 Garret Anderson 1.00 2.50
17 Garret Anderson Black 1.00 2.50
18 Roger Cedeno 1.00 2.50
18 Roger Cedeno Black 1.00 2.50
19 Randy Velarde 1.00 2.50
19 Randy Velarde Black 1.00 2.50
20 Carlos Delgado 1.00 2.50
20 Carlos Delgado Black 1.00 2.50
21 Quilvio Veras 1.00 2.50
21 Quilvio Veras Black 1.00 2.50
22 Jose Vidro 1.00 2.50
22 Jose Vidro Black 1.00 2.50
23 Corey Patterson 1.00 2.50
23 Corey Patterson Black 1.00 2.50
24 Jorge Posada 1.00 2.50
24 Jorge Posada Black 1.00 2.50
25 Eddie Perez 1.00 2.50
25 Eddie Perez Black 1.00 2.50
26 Jack Cust 1.00 2.50
26 Jack Cust Black 1.00 2.50
27 Sean Burroughs 1.00 2.50
27 Sean Burroughs Black 1.00 2.50
28 Randy Wolf 1.00 2.50
28 Randy Wolf Black 1.00 2.50
29 Mike Lamb 1.00 2.50
29 Mike Lamb Black 1.00 2.50
30 Rafael Furcal 1.00 2.50
30 Rafael Furcal Black 1.00 2.50
31 Barry Bonds 4.00 10.00
31 Barry Bonds Black 4.00 10.00
32 Tim Hudson 1.00 2.50
32 Tim Hudson Black 1.00 2.50
33 Tom Glavine 1.00 2.50
33 Tom Glavine Black 1.00 2.50
34 Javy Lopez 1.00 2.50
34 Javy Lopez Black 1.00 2.50
35 Aubrey Huff 1.00 2.50
35 Aubrey Huff Black 1.00 2.50
36 Wally Joyner 1.00 2.50
36 Wally Joyner Black 1.00 2.50
37 Magglio Ordonez 1.00 2.50
37 Magglio Ordonez Black 1.00 2.50
38 Matt Lawton 1.00 2.50
38 Matt Lawton Black 1.00 2.50
39 Mariano Rivera 1.50 4.00
39 Mariano Rivera Black 1.50 4.00
40 Andy Ashby 1.00 2.50
40 Andy Ashby Black 1.00 2.50
41 Mark Buehrle 1.00 2.50
41 Mark Buehrle Black 1.00 2.50
42 Esteban Loaiza 1.00 2.50
42 Esteban Loaiza Black 1.00 2.50
43 Mark Redman 1.00 2.50
43 Mark Redman Black 1.00 2.50
44 Mark Quinn 1.00 2.50
44 Mark Quinn Black 1.00 2.50
45 Tino Martinez 1.00 2.50
45 Tino Martinez Black 1.00 2.50
46 Joe Mays 1.00 2.50
46 Joe Mays Black 1.00 2.50
47 Walt Weiss 1.00 2.50
47 Walt Weiss Black 1.00 2.50
48 Roger Clemens 3.00 8.00
48 Roger Clemens Black 3.00 8.00
49 Greg Maddux 2.50 6.00
49 Greg Maddux Black 2.50 6.00
50 Richard Hidalgo 1.00 2.50
50 Richard Hidalgo Black 1.00 2.50
51 Orlando Hernandez 1.00 2.50
51 O.Hernandez Black 1.00 2.50
52 Chipper Jones 1.50 4.00
52 Chipper Jones Black 1.50 4.00
53 Ben Grieve 1.00 2.50
53 Ben Grieve Black 1.00 2.50
54 Jimmy Haynes 1.00 2.50
54 Jimmy Haynes Black 1.00 2.50
55 Ken Caminiti 1.00 2.50
55 Ken Caminiti Black 1.00 2.50
56 Tim Salmon 1.00 2.50
56 Tim Salmon Black 1.00 2.50
57 Andy Pettitte 1.00 2.50
57 Andy Pettitte Black 1.00 2.50
58 Darin Erstad 1.00 2.50
58 Darin Erstad Black 1.00 2.50
59 Marquis Grissom 1.00 2.50
59 Marquis Grissom Black 1.00 2.50
60 Raul Mondesi 1.00 2.50
60 Raul Mondesi Black 1.00 2.50
61 Bengie Molina 1.00 2.50
61 Bengie Molina Black 1.00 2.50
62 Miguel Tejada 1.00 2.50
62 Miguel Tejada Black 1.00 2.50
63 Jose Cruz Jr. 1.00 2.50
63 Jose Cruz Jr. Black 1.00 2.50
64 Billy Koch 1.00 2.50
64 Billy Koch Black 1.00 2.50
65 Troy Glaus 1.00 2.50
65 Troy Glaus Black 1.00 2.50
66 Cliff Floyd 1.00 2.50
66 Cliff Floyd Black 1.00 2.50
67 Tony Batista 1.00 2.50
67 Tony Batista Black 1.00 2.50
68 Jeff Bagwell 1.00 2.50
68 Jeff Bagwell Black 1.00 2.50
69 Billy Wagner 1.00 2.50
69 Billy Wagner Black 1.00 2.50
70 Eric Chavez 1.00 2.50
70 Eric Chavez Black 1.00 2.50
71 Troy Percival 1.00 2.50
71 Troy Percival Black 1.00 2.50
72 Andruw Jones 1.00 2.50
72 Andruw Jones Black 1.00 2.50
73 Shane Reynolds 1.00 2.50
73 Shane Reynolds Black 1.00 2.50
74 Barry Zito 1.00 2.50
74 Barry Zito Black 1.00 2.50
75 Roy Halladay 1.00 2.50
75 Roy Halladay Black 1.00 2.50
76 David Wells 1.00 2.50
76 David Wells Black 1.00 2.50
77 Jason Giambi 1.00 2.50
77 Jason Giambi Black 1.00 2.50
78 Scott Elarton 1.00 2.50
78 Scott Elarton Black 1.00 2.50
79 Moises Alou 1.00 2.50
79 Moises Alou Black 1.00 2.50
80 Adam Platt 1.00 2.50
80 Adam Platt Black 1.00 2.50
81 Wilton Veras .20 .50
82 Darryl Kile .25 .60
83 Johnny Damon .40 1.00
84 Tony Armas Jr. .20 .50
85 Ellis Burks .25 .60
86 Jamey Wright .20 .50
87 Jose Vizcaino .20 .50
88 Bartolo Colon .25 .60
89 Carmen Cali RC .20 .50
90 Kevin Brown .25 .60
91 Josh Hamilton .40 1.00
92 Jay Buhner .25 .60
93 Scott Pratt RC .20 .50
94 Alex Cora .20 .50
95 Luis Montanez RC .25 .60
96 Dmitri Young .25 .60
97 J.T. Snow .25 .60
98 Damion Easley .20 .50
99 Greg Norton .20 .50
100 Matt Wheatland .20 .50
101 Chin-Feng Chen .25 .60
102 Tony Womack .20 .50
103 Adam Kennedy Black .20 .50
104 J.D. Drew .25 .60
105 Carlos Febles .20 .50
106 Jim Thome .40 1.00
107 Danny Graves .20 .50
108 Dave Mlicki .20 .50
109 Ron Coomer .20 .50
110 James Baldwin .20 .50
111 Shaun Boyd RC .20 .50
112 Brian Bohanon .20 .50
113 Jacque Jones .25 .60
114 Alfonso Soriano .40 1.00
115 Tony Clark .20 .50
116 Terrence Long .20 .50
117 Todd Hundley .20 .50
118 Kazuhiro Sasaki .25 .60
119 Brian Sellier RC .20 .50
120 John Olerud .25 .60
121 Javier Vazquez .25 .60
122 Sean Burnett .20 .50
123 Matt LeCroy .20 .50
124 Erubiel Durazo .20 .50
125 Juan Encarnacion .20 .50
126 Pablo Ozuna .20 .50
127 Russ Ortiz .20 .50
128 David Segui .20 .50
129 Mark McGwire 1.50 4.00
130 Mark Grace .40 1.00
131 Fred McGriff .40 1.00
132 Carl Pavano .25 .60
133 Derek Thompson .20 .50
134 Shawn Green .25 .60
135 B.J. Surhoff .25 .60
136 Michael Tucker .20 .50
137 Jason Isringhausen .25 .60
138 Eric Milton .20 .50
139 Mike Stodolka .20 .50
140 Milton Bradley .25 .60
141 Curt Schilling .25 .60
142 Sandy Alomar Jr. .20 .50
143 Brent Mayne .20 .50
144 Todd Jones .20 .50
145 Charles Johnson .25 .60
146 Dean Palmer .25 .60
147 Masato Yoshii .20 .50
148 Edgar Renteria .25 .60
149 Joe Randa .25 .60
150 Adam Johnson .20 .50
151 Greg Vaughn .20 .50
152 Adrian Beltre .25 .60
153 Glenallen Hill .20 .50
154 David Parrish RC .20 .50
155 Neifi Perez .20 .50
156 Pete Harnisch .20 .50
157 Paul Konerko .25 .60
158 Dennys Reyes .20 .50
159 Jose Lima Black .20 .50
160 Eddie Taubensee .20 .50
161 Miguel Cairo .20 .50
162 Jeff Kent .25 .60
163 Dustin Hermanson .20 .50
164 Alex Gonzalez .20 .50
165 Hideo Nomo .60 1.50
166 Sammy Sosa .60 1.50
167 C.J. Nitkowski .20 .50
168 Cal Eldred .20 .50
169 Jeff Abbott .20 .50
170 Jim Edmonds .25 .60
171 Mark Mulder Black .25 .60
172 Dominic Rich RC .20 .50
173 Ray Lankford .25 .60
174 Danny Borrell RC .20 .50
175 Rick Aguilera .20 .50
176 S.Stewart Black .25 .60
177 Steve Finley .25 .60
178 Jim Parque .20 .50
179 Kevin Appier Black .25 .60
180 Adrian Gonzalez 1.25 3.00
181 Tom Goodwin .20 .50
182 Kevin Tapani .20 .50
183 Fernando Tatis .20 .50
184 Mark Grudzielanek .20 .50
185 Ryan Anderson .20 .50
186 Jeffrey Hammonds .20 .50
187 Corey Koskie .20 .50
188 Brad Fullmer Black .20 .50
189 Rey Sanchez .20 .50
190 Michael Barrett .20 .50
191 Rickey Henderson .60 1.50
192 Jermaine Dye .25 .60
193 Scott Brosius .25 .60
194 Matt Anderson .20 .50
195 Brian Buchanan .20 .50
196 Derrek Lee .40 1.00
197 Larry Walker .25 .60
198 Dan Moylan RC .20 .50
199 Vinny Castilla .25 .60
200 Ken Griffey Jr. 1.00 2.50
201 Matt Stairs Black .20 .50
202 Ty Howington .20 .50
203 Andy Benes .20 .50
204 Luis Gonzalez .25 .60
205 Brian Moehler .20 .50
206 Harold Baines .25 .60
207 Pedro Astacio .20 .50
208 Cristian Guzman .20 .50
209 Kip Wells .20 .50
210 Frank Thomas .60 1.50
211 Jose Rosado .20 .50
212 Vernon Wells Black .25 .60
213 Bobby Higginson .25 .60
214 Juan Gonzalez .25 .60
215 Omar Vizquel .40 1.00
216 Bernie Williams .40 1.00
217 Aaron Sele .20 .50
218 Shawn Estes .20 .50
219 Roberto Alomar .40 1.00
220 Rick Ankiel .20 .50
221 Josh Kalinowski .20 .50
222 David Bell .20 .50
223 Keith Foulke .25 .60
224 Craig Biggio Black .40 1.00
225 Josh Axelson RC .20 .50
226 Scott Williamson .20 .50
227 Ron Belliard .20 .50
228 Chris Singleton .25 .60
229 Alex Serrano RC .20 .50
230 Deivi Cruz .20 .50
231 Eric Munson .20 .50
232 Luis Castillo .20 .50
233 Edgar Martinez .40 1.00
234 Jeff Shaw .20 .50
235 Jeromy Burnitz .20 .50
236 Richie Sexson .25 .60
237 Will Clark .40 1.00
238 Ron Villone .20 .50
239 Kerry Wood .25 .60
240 Rich Aurilia .20 .50
241 Mo Vaughn Black .25 .60
242 Travis Fryman .25 .60
243 M. Ramirez Sox .40 1.00
244 Chris Stynes .20 .50
245 Ray Durham .25 .60
246 Juan Uribe RC .40 1.00
247 Juan Guzman .20 .50
248 Lee Stevens .20 .50
249 Devon White .25 .60
250 Kyle Lohse RC .40 1.00
251 Bryan Wolff .20 .50
252 Matt Galante RC .20 .50
253 Eric Young .25 .60
254 Freddy Garcia .25 .60
255 Jay Bell .25 .60
256 Steve Cox .20 .50
257 Torii Hunter .25 .60
258 Jose Canseco .40 1.00
259 Brad Ausmus .25 .60
260 Jeff Cirillo .20 .50
261 Brad Penny .20 .50
262 Antonio Alfonseca .20 .50
263 Russ Branyan .20 .50
264 Chris Morris RC .20 .50
265 John Lackey .25 .60
266 Justin Wayne RC .25 .60
267 Brad Radke .25 .60
268 Todd Stottlemyre .20 .50
269 Mark Loretta .20 .50
270 Matt Williams .25 .60
271 Kenny Lofton .25 .60
272 Jeff D'Amico .20 .50
273 Jamie Moyer .25 .60
274 Darren Dreifort .20 .50
275 Denny Neagle .20 .50
276 Orlando Cabrera .25 .60
277 Chuck Finley .25 .60
278 Miguel Batista .20 .50
279 Carlos Beltran .25 .60
280 Eric Karros .25 .60
281 Mark Kotsay .25 .60
282 Ryan Dempster .20 .50
283 Barry Larkin .40 1.00
284 Jeff Suppan .20 .50
285 Gary Sheffield .25 .60
286 Jose Valentin .20 .50
287 Robb Nen .25 .60
288 Chan Ho Park .25 .60
289 John Halama .20 .50
290 Steve Smyth RC .25 .60
291 Gerald Williams .20 .50
292 Preston Wilson .25 .60
293 Victor Hall RC .25 .60
294 Ben Sheets .40 1.00
295 Eric Davis .25 .60
296 Kirk Rueter .20 .50
297 Chad Petty RC .20 .50
298 Kevin Millar .25 .60
299 Marvin Benard .20 .50
300 Vladimir Guerrero .60 1.50
301 Livan Hernandez .25 .60
302 Travis Baptist RC .25 .60
303 Bill Mueller .25 .60
304 Mike Cameron .20 .50
305 Randy Johnson UER .60 1.50
Facsimile signature is Randall K. Johnson
306 Alan Mahaffey RC .20 .50
307 Timo Perez UER .20 .50
No facsimile autograph on card
308 Pokey Reese .20 .50
309 Ryan Rupe .20 .50
310 Carlos Lee .25 .60
311 Doug Glanville SP 2.00 5.00
312 Jay Payton SP 2.00 5.00
313 Troy O'Leary SP 2.00 5.00
314 Francisco Cordero SP 2.00 5.00
315 Rusty Greer SP 2.00 5.00
316 Cal Ripken SP 10.00 25.00
317 Ricky Ledee SP 2.00 5.00
318 Brian Daubach SP 2.00 5.00
319 Robin Ventura SP 2.00 5.00
320 Todd Zeile SP 2.00 5.00
321 Francisco Cordova SP 2.00 5.00
322 Henry Rodriguez SP 2.00 5.00
323 Pat Meares SP 2.00 5.00
324 Glendon Rusch SP 2.00 5.00
325 Keith Osik SP 2.00 5.00
326 Robert Keppel SP RC 2.00 5.00
327 Bobby Jones SP 2.00 5.00
328 Alex Ramirez SP 2.00 5.00
329 Robert Person SP 2.00 5.00
330 Ruben Mateo SP 2.00 5.00
331 Rob Bell SP 2.00 5.00
332 Carl Everett SP 2.00 5.00
333 Jason Schmidt SP 2.00 5.00
334 Scott Rolen SP 3.00 8.00
335 Jimmy Anderson SP 2.00 5.00
336 Bret Boone SP 2.00 5.00
337 Delino DeShields SP 2.00 5.00
338 Trevor Hoffman SP 2.00 5.00
339 Bob Abreu SP 2.00 5.00
340 Mike Williams SP 2.00 5.00
341 Mike Hampton SP 2.00 5.00
342 John Wetteland SP 2.00 5.00
343 Scott Erickson SP 2.00 5.00
344 Enrique Wilson SP 2.00 5.00
345 Tim Wakefield SP 2.00 5.00
346 Mike Lowell SP 2.00 5.00
347 Todd Pratt SP 2.00 5.00
348 Brook Fordyce SP 2.00 5.00
349 Benny Agbayani SP 2.00 5.00
350 Gabe Kapler SP 2.00 5.00
351 Sean Casey SP 2.00 5.00
352 Darren Oliver SP 2.00 5.00
353 Todd Ritchie SP 2.00 5.00
354 Kenny Rogers SP 2.00 5.00
355 Jason Kendall SP 2.00 5.00
356 John Vander Wal SP 2.00 5.00
357 Ramon Martinez SP 2.00 5.00
358 Edgardo Alfonzo SP 2.00 5.00
359 Phil Nevin SP 2.00 5.00
360 Albert Belle SP 2.00 5.00
361 Ruben Rivera SP 2.00 5.00
362 Pedro Martinez SP 3.00 8.00
363 Derek Lowe SP 2.00 5.00
364 Pat Burrell SP 2.00 5.00
365 Mike Mussina SP 3.00 8.00
366 Brady Anderson SP 2.00 5.00
367 Darren Lewis SP 2.00 5.00
368 Sidney Ponson SP 2.00 5.00
369 Adam Eaton SP 2.00 5.00
370 Eric Owens SP 2.00 5.00
371 Aaron Boone SP 2.00 5.00
372 Matt Clement SP 2.00 5.00
373 Derek Bell SP 2.00 5.00
374 Trot Nixon SP 2.00 5.00
375 Travis Lee SP 2.00 5.00
376 Mike Benjamin SP 2.00 5.00
377 Jeff Zimmerman SP 2.00 5.00
378 Mike Lieberthal SP 2.00 5.00
379 Rick Reed SP 2.00 5.00
380 N.Garciaparra SP 5.00 12.00
381 Omar Daal SP 2.00 5.00
382 Ryan Klesko SP 2.00 5.00
383 Rey Ordonez SP 2.00 5.00
384 Kevin Young SP 2.00 5.00
385 Rick Helling SP 2.00 5.00
386 Brian Giles SP 2.00 5.00
387 Tony Gwynn SP 4.00 10.00
388 Ed Sprague SP 2.00 5.00
389 J.R. House SP 2.00 5.00
390 Scott Hatteberg SP 2.00 5.00
391 John Valentin SP 2.00 5.00
392 Melvin Mora SP 2.00 5.00
393 Royce Clayton SP 2.00 5.00
394 Jeff Fassero SP 2.00 5.00
395 Manny Alexander SP 2.00 5.00
396 John Franco SP 2.00 5.00
397 Luis Alicea SP 2.00 5.00
398 Ivan Rodriguez SP 3.00 8.00
399 Kevin Jordan SP 2.00 5.00
400 Jose Offerman SP 2.00 5.00
401 Jeff Conine SP 2.00 5.00
402 Seth Etherton SP 2.00 5.00
403 Mike Bordick SP 2.00 5.00
404 Al Leiter SP 2.00 5.00
405 Mike Piazza SP 5.00 12.00
406 Armando Benitez SP 2.00 5.00
407 Warren Morris SP 2.00 5.00

2001 Topps Heritage Chrome

Randomly inserted into packs at one in 25 Hob/Ret, this 110-card insert is a partial parallel of the 2001 Topps Heritage base set. Each card was produced using Topps Chrome technology. Please note that each card is also individually serial numbered to 552.

STATED ODDS 1:25 HOB/RET
STATED PRINT RUN 552 SERIAL #'d SETS
CP1 Cal Ripken 60.00 150.00
CP2 Jim Thome 10.00 25.00
CP3 Derek Jeter 50.00 120.00
CP4 Andres Galarraga 8.00 20.00
CP5 Carlos Delgado 8.00 20.00
CP6 Roberto Alomar 10.00 25.00
CP7 Tom Glavine 10.00 25.00
CP8 Gary Sheffield 8.00 20.00
CP9 Mo Vaughn 8.00 20.00
CP10 Preston Wilson 8.00 20.00
CP11 Mike Mussina 10.00 25.00
CP12 Greg Maddux 25.00 60.00
CP13 Ivan Rodriguez 10.00 25.00
CP14 Al Leiter 8.00 20.00
CP15 Seth Etherton 8.00 20.00
CP16 Edgardo Alfonzo 8.00 20.00
CP17 Richie Sexson 8.00 20.00
CP18 Andruw Jones 10.00 25.00
CP19 Bartolo Colon 8.00 20.00
CP20 Darin Erstad 8.00 20.00
CP21 Kevin Brown 8.00 20.00
CP22 Mike Sweeney 8.00 20.00
CP23 Mike Piazza 25.00 60.00
CP24 Rafael Palmeiro 10.00 25.00
CP25 Terrence Long 8.00 20.00
CP26 Kazuhiro Sasaki 8.00 20.00
CP27 John Olerud 8.00 20.00
CP28 Mark McGwire 50.00 120.00
CP29 Fred McGriff 10.00 25.00
CP30 Todd Helton 10.00 25.00
CP31 Curt Schilling 8.00 20.00
CP32 Alex Rodriguez 25.00 60.00
CP33 Jeff Kent 8.00 20.00
CP34 Pat Burrell 8.00 20.00
CP35 Jim Edmonds 8.00 20.00
CP36 Mark Mulder 8.00 20.00
CP37 Troy Glaus 8.00 20.00
CP38 Jay Payton 8.00 20.00
CP39 Jermaine Dye 8.00 20.00
CP40 Larry Walker 8.00 20.00
CP41 Ken Griffey Jr. 25.00 60.00
CP42 Jeff Bagwell 10.00 25.00
CP43 Rick Ankiel 8.00 20.00
CP44 Mark Redman 8.00 20.00
CP45 Edgar Martinez 10.00 25.00
CP46 Mike Hampton 8.00 20.00
CP47 Manny Ramirez Sox 10.00 25.00
CP48 Ray Durham 8.00 20.00
CP49 Rafael Furcal 8.00 20.00
CP50 Sean Casey 8.00 20.00
CP51 Jose Canseco 10.00 25.00
CP52 Barry Bonds 50.00 120.00
CP53 Tim Hudson 8.00 20.00
CP54 Barry Zito 10.00 25.00
CP55 Chuck Finley 8.00 20.00
CP56 Magglio Ordonez 8.00 20.00
CP57 David Wells 8.00 20.00
CP58 Jason Giambi 8.00 20.00
CP59 Tony Gwynn 20.00 50.00
CP60 Vladimir Guerrero 15.00 40.00
CP61 Randy Johnson 15.00 40.00
CP62 Bernie Williams 10.00 25.00
CP63 Craig Biggio 10.00 25.00
CP64 Jason Kendall 8.00 20.00
CP65 Pedro Martinez 10.00 25.00
CP66 Mark Quinn 8.00 20.00
CP67 Frank Thomas 15.00 40.00

CP68 Nomar Garciaparra	25.00	60.00
CP69 Brian Giles	8.00	20.00
CP70 Shawn Green	8.00	20.00
CP71 Roger Clemens	30.00	80.00
CP72 Sammy Sosa	15.00	40.00
CP73 Juan Gonzalez	8.00	20.00
CP74 Orlando Hernandez	8.00	20.00
CP75 Chipper Jones	15.00	40.00
CP76 Josh Hamilton	15.00	40.00
CP77 Adam Johnson	8.00	20.00
CP78 Shaun Boyd	8.00	20.00
CP79 Alfonso Soriano	10.00	25.00
CP80 Derek Thompson	8.00	20.00
CP81 Adrian Gonzalez	50.00	120.00
CP82 Ryan Anderson	8.00	20.00
CP83 Corey Patterson	8.00	20.00
CP84 J.R. House	8.00	20.00
CP85 Sean Burroughs	8.00	20.00
CP86 Bryan Wolff	8.00	20.00
CP87 John Lackey	8.00	20.00
CP88 Ben Sheets	10.00	25.00
CP89 Timo Perez	8.00	20.00
CP90 Robert Keppel	8.00	20.00
CP91 Luis Montanez	8.00	20.00
CP92 Sean Burnett	8.00	20.00
CP93 Justin Wayne	8.00	20.00
CP94 Eric Munson	8.00	20.00
CP95 Steve Smyth	8.00	20.00
CP96 Matt Galante	8.00	20.00
CP97 Carmen Cali	8.00	20.00
CP98 Brian Sellier	8.00	20.00
CP99 David Parrish	8.00	20.00
CP100 Danny Borrell	8.00	20.00
CP101 Chad Petty	8.00	20.00
CP102 Dominic Rich	8.00	20.00
CP103 Josh Axelson	8.00	20.00
CP104 Alex Serrano	8.00	20.00
CP105 Juan Uribe	10.00	25.00
CP106 Travis Baptist	8.00	20.00
CP107 Alan Mahaffey	8.00	20.00
CP108 Kyle Lohse	10.00	25.00
CP109 Victor Hall	8.00	20.00
CP110 Scott Pratt	8.00	20.00

2001 Topps Heritage Autographs

Randomly inserted into packs at one in 142 HOB/RET, this 51-card insert set features authentic autographs from many of the Major League's top players. Please note that a few of the players packed out as exchange cards, and must be redeemed by 1/31/02. Due to the untimely passing of Eddie Mathews, please note the exchange card issued for him went unredeemed. In addition, Larry Doby's card was originally seeded in packs as exchange cards (of which carried a January 31st, 2002 deadline).

*RED INK: .75X TO 1.5X BASIC AU
RED INK ODDS 1:545 HOB, 1:546 RET
RED INK PRINT RUN 52 SERIAL #'d SETS

THAAH Aubrey Huff	20.00	50.00
THAAP Andy Pafko	50.00	100.00
THAAR Alex Rodriguez	150.00	300.00
THABB Barry Bonds	225.00	350.00
THABS Bobby Shantz	30.00	60.00
THABT Bobby Thomson	60.00	120.00
THACD Carlos Delgado	40.00	80.00
THACF Cliff Floyd	40.00	80.00
THACJ Chipper Jones	100.00	200.00
THACP Corey Patterson	15.00	40.00
THACS Curt Simmons	40.00	80.00
THADD Dom DiMaggio	100.00	200.00
THADG Dick Groat	50.00	100.00
THADS Duke Snider	150.00	250.00
THAES Enos Slaughter	60.00	120.00
THAFV Fernando Vina	15.00	40.00
THAGJ Geoff Jenkins	15.00	40.00
THAGM Gil McDougald	50.00	100.00
THAHB Hank Bauer	60.00	120.00
THAHS Hank Sauer	60.00	120.00
THAHW Hoyt Wilhelm	60.00	120.00
THAJG Joe Garagiola	50.00	100.00
THAJM Joe Mays	15.00	40.00
THAJS Johnny Sain	60.00	120.00
THAJV Jose Vidro	15.00	40.00
THAKB Kris Benson	15.00	40.00
THAMB Mark Buehrle	50.00	100.00
THAMI Monte Irvin	50.00	100.00
THAML Mike Lamb	15.00	40.00
THAML Matt Lawton	15.00	40.00
THAMM Minnie Minoso	60.00	120.00
THAMO Magglio Ordonez	20.00	50.00
THAMQ Mark Quinn	15.00	40.00
THAMR Mark Redman	15.00	40.00
THAMS Mike Sweeney	20.00	50.00
THAMV Mickey Vernon	30.00	60.00
THANG Nomar Garciaparra	150.00	250.00
THAPR Preacher Roe	75.00	150.00
THAPFR Phil Rizzuto	100.00	175.00
THARH Richard Hidalgo	15.00	40.00
THARR Robin Roberts	50.00	100.00
THARS Red Schoendienst	50.00	100.00
THARW Randy Wolf	15.00	40.00
THASPB Sean Burroughs	15.00	40.00
THATG Tom Glavine	60.00	120.00
THATH Todd Helton	50.00	100.00
THATL Terrence Long	15.00	40.00
THAVL Vernon Law	50.00	100.00
THAWM Willie Mays	200.00	300.00
THAWS Warren Spahn	75.00	150.00

2001 Topps Heritage Autographs Red Ink

Randomly inserted into packs at 1:545 Hobby and 1:546 Retail, this 52-card insert set is a complete parallel of the Heritage Autographs signed in red ink. Please note that each of these cards are individually serial numbered to 52. Also note Larry Doby and Eddie Mathews packed out as exchange cards with a redemption deadline of 1/31/02. Due to his unlimely death, the Eddie Mathews exchange card went unredeemed. The Willie Mays autograph cards come with or without serial numbering.

THAAP Andy Pafko	200.00	300.00
THACJ Chipper Jones	400.00	500.00
THAGM Gil McDougald	100.00	200.00
THAHS Hank Sauer	150.00	300.00
THAHW Hoyt Wilhelm	150.00	250.00
THAJG Joe Garagiola	150.00	300.00
THAJS Johnny Sain	100.00	200.00
THAMV Mickey Vernon	100.00	200.00
THAVL Vernon Law	150.00	300.00

2001 Topps Heritage AutoProofs

Randomly inserted at approximately 1 in every 5749 boxes, this card is an actual 1952 Topps Willie Mays card that was bought from the Topps Company, then individually autographed by Willie Mays, and distributed into packs. Please note that each card is individually serial numbered to 25.

NO PRICING DUE TO SCARCITY
AUTOPROOF IS A REAL '52 TOPPS CARD
AP1 Willie Mays '52T AU/25

2001 Topps Heritage Classic Renditions

Randomly inserted into packs at one in 5 Hobby, and one in 9 Retail, this 10-card insert set features artist drawn sketches of some of the best modern day ballplayers. Card backs carry a "CR" prefix.

COMPLETE SET (10)	8.00	20.00
CR1 Mark McGwire	1.50	4.00
CR2 Nomar Garciaparra	1.00	2.50
CR3 Barry Bonds	1.50	4.00
CR4 Sammy Sosa	.60	1.50
CR5 Chipper Jones	.60	1.50
CR6 Pat Burrell	.40	1.00
CR7 Frank Thomas	.60	1.50
CR8 Manny Ramirez	.40	1.00
CR9 Derek Jeter	1.50	4.00
CR10 Ken Griffey Jr.	1.00	2.50

2001 Topps Heritage Classic Renditions Autograph

Randomly inserted into packs at one in 19,710 Hobby, and 1:20,926 Retail, this three-card insert set is a partial parallel of the Classic Renditions insert. Each of these cards have been autographed by the given player and are individually serial numbered to 25. Due to market scarcify, no pricing is provided.

CRABB Barry Bonds
CRACJ Chipper Jones
CRANG Nomar Garciaparra

2001 Topps Heritage Clubhouse Collection

Randomly inserted into packs, this 22-card insert features game-used memorabilia cards from past and present stars. Included in the set are game-used bat and jersey cards. Please note that a numbered of the players have autographed 25 of each of these cards. Also note that a few of the cards packed out as exchange cards, and must have been redeemed by 01/31/02. Common Bat cards were inserted at a rate of 1:590 and Jersey cards at 1:798 Hobby/1:799 Retail. Dual Bat cards were inserted at 1:5701 Hobby/1:5772 Retail. Dual Jersey cards were inserted into packs at 1:28,744 Hobby/1:29,820 Retail. Autographed Bat cards were inserted at 1:19,710 Hobby/1:20,928 Retail, and Autographed Jerseys at 1:62,714 Hobby/1:83,712 Retail. Exchange cards - with a deadline of Janury 31st, 2002 - were seeded into packs for the following cards: Eddie Mathews Bat, Duke Snider Bat AU and Willie Mays Bat AU.

BB Barry Bonds Bat	40.00	80.00
CJ Chipper Jones Bat	20.00	50.00
DS Duke Snider Bat	20.00	50.00
EM Eddie Mathews Bat	20.00	50.00
FT Frank Thomas Jsy	20.00	50.00
FV Fernando Vina Bat	15.00	40.00
MM Minnie Minoso Jsy	15.00	40.00
RA Richie Ashburn Bat	20.00	50.00
RS Red Schoendienst Bat	15.00	40.00
SG Shawn Green Bat	15.00	40.00
SR Scott Rolen Bat	20.00	50.00
WM Willie Mays Bat	30.00	60.00
ADS Duke Snider Bat AU/25		
AMM Minnie Minoso		
Jsy AU/25		
ARS Red Schoendienst		
Bat AU/25		
AWM Willie Mays Bat AU/25		
DSSG Duke Snider	125.00	200.00
Shawn Green Bat/52		
EMCJ Eddie Mathews	100.00	200.00
Chipper Jones Bat/52		
MMFT Minnie Minoso	75.00	150.00
Frank Thomas Jsy/52		
RASR Richie Ashburn	125.00	200.00
Scott Rolen Bat/52		
RSFV Red Schoendienst	125.00	200.00
Fernando Vina Bat/52		
WMBB Willie Mays	200.00	350.00
Barry Bonds Bat/52		

2001 Topps Heritage Grandstand Glory

Randomly inserted into packs at 1:211 Hobby/Retail, this seven-card insert set features a swatch of original stadium seating. Card backs carry the player's initials as numbering.

JR Jackie Robinson	15.00	40.00
NF Nellie Fox	10.00	25.00
PR Phil Rizzuto	15.00	40.00
RA Richie Ashburn	10.00	25.00
RR Robin Roberts	10.00	25.00
WM Willie Mays	40.00	80.00
YB Yogi Berra	15.00	40.00

2001 Topps Heritage New Age Performers

Randomly inserted into packs at 1:8 Hobby, 1:15 Retail, this 15-card insert set features players that have become the superstars of the future. Card backs carry a "NAP" prefix.

COMPLETE SET (15)	20.00	50.00
NAP1 Mike Piazza	1.50	4.00
NAP2 Sammy Sosa	1.00	2.50
NAP3 Alex Rodriguez	1.50	4.00
NAP4 Barry Bonds	2.50	6.00
NAP5 Ken Griffey Jr.	1.50	4.00
NAP6 Chipper Jones	1.00	2.50
NAP7 Randy Johnson	1.00	2.50
NAP8 Derek Jeter	2.50	6.00
NAP9 Nomar Garciaparra	1.50	4.00
NAP10 Mark McGwire	2.50	6.00
NAP11 Jeff Bagwell	1.00	2.50
NAP12 Pedro Martinez	1.00	2.50
NAP13 Todd Helton	1.00	2.50
NAP14 Vladimir Guerrero	1.00	2.50
NAP15 Greg Maddux	1.50	4.00

2001 Topps Heritage Then and Now

Randomly inserted into Hobby packs at 1:8 and Retail packs at 1:15, this 10-card set pairs up modern day heroes with players from the past that compare statistically. Card backs carry a "TH" prefix.

COMPLETE SET (10)	15.00	30.00
TH1 Yogi Berra	1.25	3.00
Mike Piazza		
TH2 Duke Snider	.75	2.00
Sammy Sosa		
TH3 Willie Mays	1.50	4.00
Ken Griffey Jr.		
TH4 Phil Rizzuto	2.00	5.00
Derek Jeter		
TH5 Pee Wee Reese	1.25	3.00
Nomar Garciaparra		
TH6 Jackie Robinson	1.25	3.00
Alex Rodriguez		
TH7 Johnny Mize	2.00	5.00
Mark McGwire		
TH8 Bob Feller	.75	2.00
Pedro Martinez		
TH9 Robin Roberts	1.25	3.00
Greg Maddux		
TH10 Warren Spahn	.75	2.00
Randy Johnson		

2001 Topps Heritage Time Capsule

This unique set features swatches of fabric taken from actual combat uniforms from the 1952 Korean War. It's important to note that though these cards do indeed feature patches of vintage Korean War uniforms, they were not worn by the athlete featured on the card. Stated odds for the four single-player cards was 1:369. Unlike the other cards in this set, the lone dual-player Willie Mays-Ted Williams card is hand-numbered on back. Only 52 copies of this card were produced, and each is marked by hand on back in black pen "X/52". The stated odds for this dual-player card is 1:28,744 packs.

DN Don Newcombe	10.00	25.00
TW Ted Williams UER	40.00	80.00
Card says 525 career homers, Williams hit 521		
WF Whitey Ford	15.00	40.00
WM Willie Mays	40.00	80.00
WMTW Willie Mays	125.00	200.00
Ted Williams/52		

2002 Topps Heritage

Issued in early February 2002, this set was the second year that Topps used their Heritage brand and achieved success in the secondary market. These cards were issued in eight card packs which were packed 24 to a box and had a SRP of $3 per pack. The set consists of 440 cards with seven short prints among the low numbers as well as all cards from 364 through 446 as short prints. Those cards were all inserted at a rate of one in two packs. In addition, there was an unnannounced variation in which 10 cards were printed in both day and night versions. The night versions were also inserted into packs at a rate of one in two.

COMPLETE SET (440)	200.00	400.00
COMP.SET w/o SP's (350)	40.00	80.00
COMMON CARD (1-363)	.20	.50
COMMON SP (364-446)	2.00	5.00
1 Ichiro Suzuki SP	6.00	15.00
2 Darin Erstad	.25	.60
3 Rod Beck	.25	.60
4 Doug Mientkiewicz	.25	.60
5 Mike Sweeney	.25	.60
6 Roger Clemens	1.25	3.00
7 Jason Tyner	.20	.50
8 Alex Gonzalez	.20	.50
9 Eric Young	.20	.50
10 Randy Johnson	.60	1.50
10N Randy Johnson Night SP	3.00	8.00
11 Aaron Sele	.20	.50
12 Tony Clark	.20	.50
13 C.C. Sabathia	.25	.60
14 Melvin Mora	.25	.60
15 Tim Hudson	.25	.60
16 Ben Petrick	.20	.50
17 Tom Glavine	.40	1.00
18 Jason Lane	.25	.60
19 Larry Walker	.25	.60
20 Mark Mulder	.25	.60
21 Steve Finley	.25	.60
22 Bengie Molina	.20	.50
23 Rob Bell	.20	.50
24 Nathan Haynes	.20	.50
25 Rafael Furcal	.25	.60
25N Rafael Furcal Night SP	2.00	5.00
26 Mike Mussina	.40	1.00
27 Paul LoDuca	.25	.60
28 Torii Hunter	.25	.60
29 Carlos Lee	.25	.60
30 Jimmy Rollins	.25	.60
31 Arthur Rhodes	.20	.50
32 Ivan Rodriguez	.40	1.00
33 Wes Helms	.20	.50
34 Cliff Floyd	.25	.60
35 Julian Tavarez	.20	.50
36 Mark McGwire	1.50	4.00
37 Chipper Jones SP	3.00	8.00
38 Denny Neagle	.20	.50
39 Odalis Perez	.20	.50
40 Antonio Alfonseca	.20	.50
41 Edgar Renteria	.25	.60
42 Troy Glaus	.25	.60
43 Scott Brosius	.25	.60
44 Abraham Nunez	.20	.50
45 Jamey Wright	.20	.50
46 Bobby Bonilla	.25	.60
47 Ismael Valdes	.20	.50
48 Chris Reitsma	.20	.50
49 Neifi Perez	.20	.50
50 Juan Cruz	.20	.50
51 Kevin Brown	.25	.60
52 Ben Grieve	.20	.50
53 Alex Rodriguez SP	5.00	12.00
54 Charles Nagy	.20	.50
55 Reggie Sanders	.25	.60
56 Nelson Figueroa	.20	.50
57 Felipe Lopez	.20	.50
58 Bill Ortega	.20	.50
59 Jeffrey Hammonds	.25	.60
60 Johnny Estrada	.20	.50
61 Bob Wickman	.20	.50
62 Doug Glanville	.20	.50
63 Jeff Cirillo	.20	.50
63N Jeff Cirillo Night SP	2.00	5.00
64 Corey Patterson	.20	.50
65 Aaron Myette	.20	.50
66 Magglio Ordonez	.25	.60
67 Ellis Burks	.25	.60
68 Miguel Tejada	.25	.60
69 John Olerud	.25	.60
69N John Olerud Night SP	2.00	5.00
70 Greg Vaughn	.20	.50
71 Andy Pettitte	.40	1.00
72 Mike Matheny	.20	.50
73 Brandon Duckworth	.20	.50
74 Scott Schoeneweis	.20	.50
75 Mike Lowell	.25	.60
76 Einar Diaz	.20	.50
77 Tino Martinez	.40	1.00
78 Matt Williams	.25	.60
79 Jason Young RC	.40	1.00
80 Nate Cornejo	.20	.50
81 Andres Galarraga	.25	.60
82 Bernie Williams SP	3.00	8.00
83 Ryan Klesko	.25	.60
84 Dan Wilson	.20	.50
85 Henry Pichardo RC	.40	1.00
86 Ray Durham	.25	.60
87 Omar Daal	.20	.50
88 Derrek Lee	.40	1.00
89 Al Leiter	.25	.60
90 Darrin Fletcher	.20	.50
91 Josh Beckett	.25	.60
92 Johnny Damon	.40	1.00
92N Johnny Damon Night SP	3.00	8.00
93 Abraham Nunez	.20	.50
94 Ricky Ledee	.20	.50
95 Richie Sexson	.25	.60
96 Adam Kennedy	.20	.50
97 Raul Mondesi	.25	.60
98 John Burkett	.25	.60
99 Ben Sheets	.25	.60
99N Ben Sheets Night SP	2.00	5.00
100 Preston Wilson	.25	.60
100N Pr. Wilson Night SP	2.00	5.00
101 Boof Bonser	.20	.50
102 Shigetoshi Hasegawa	.25	.60
103 Carlos Febles	.20	.50
104 Jorge Posada SP	3.00	8.00
105 Michael Tucker	.20	.50
106 Roberto Hernandez	.25	.60
107 John Rodriguez RC	.40	1.00
108 Danny Graves	.20	.50
109 Rich Aurilia	.20	.50
110 Jon Lieber	.20	.50
111 Tim Hummel RC	.40	1.00
112 J.T. Snow	.25	.60
113 Kris Benson	.20	.50
114 Derek Jeter	1.50	4.00
115 John Franco	.25	.60
116 Matt Stairs	.20	.50
117 Ben Davis	.20	.50
118 Darryl Kile	.25	.60
119 Mike Peeples RC	.40	1.00
120 Kevin Tapani	.20	.50
121 Armando Benitez	.20	.50
122 Damian Miller	.20	.50
123 Jose Jimenez	.20	.50
124 Pedro Astacio	.20	.50
125 Marlyn Tisdale RC	.40	1.00
126 Deivi Cruz	.20	.50
127 Paul O'Neill	.40	1.00
128 Jermaine Dye	.25	.60
129 Marcus Giles	.25	.60
130 Mark Loretta	.20	.50
131 Garret Anderson	.25	.60
132 Todd Ritchie	.20	.50
133 Joe Crede	.25	.60
134 Kevin Millwood	.25	.60
135 Shane Reynolds	.20	.50
136 Mark Grace	.40	1.00
137 Shannon Stewart	.25	.60
138 Nick Neugebauer	.20	.50
139 Nic Jackson RC	.40	1.00
140 Robb Nen UER	.25	.60
Name spelled Rob on front		
141 Dmitri Young	.25	.60
142 Kevin Appier	.25	.60
143 Jack Cust	.20	.50
144 Andres Torres	.20	.50
145 Frank Thomas	.60	1.50
146 Jason Kendall	.25	.60
147 Greg Maddux	1.00	2.50
148 David Justice	.25	.60
149 Hideo Nomo	.60	1.50
150 Bret Boone	.25	.60
151 Wade Miller	.20	.50
152 Jeff Kent	.25	.60
153 Scott Williamson	.20	.50
154 Julio Lugo	.20	.50
155 Bobby Higginson	.25	.60
156 Geoff Jenkins	.20	.50
157 Darren Dreifort	.20	.50
158 Freddy Sanchez RC	1.25	3.00
159 Bud Smith	.20	.50
160 Phil Nevin	.25	.60
161 Cesar Izturis	.20	.50
162 Sean Casey	.25	.60
163 Jose Ortiz	.20	.50
164 Brent Abernathy	.20	.50
165 Kevin Young	.20	.50
166 Daryle Ward	.20	.50
167 Trevor Hoffman	.25	.60
168 Rondell White	.25	.60
169 Kip Wells	.20	.50
170 John Vander Wal	.20	.50
171 Jose Lima	.20	.50
172 Wilton Guerrero	.20	.50
173 Aaron Dean RC	.40	1.00
174 Rick Helling	.20	.50
175 Juan Pierre	.25	.60
176 Jay Bell	.25	.60
177 Craig House	.20	.50
178 David Bell	.20	.50
179 Pat Burrell	.25	.60
180 Eric Gagne	.25	.60
181 Adam Pettyjohn	.20	.50
182 Ugueth Urbina	.20	.50
183 Peter Bergeron	.20	.50
184 Adrian Gonzalez UER	.20	.50
Birthdate is wrong		
184N Adrian Gonzalez	2.00	5.00
Night SP UER		
Birthdate is wrong		
185 Damion Easley	.20	.50
186 Gookie Dawkins	.20	.50
187 Matt Lawton	.20	.50
188 Frank Catalanotto	.20	.50
189 David Wells	.25	.60
190 Roger Cedeno	.20	.50
191 Brian Giles	.25	.60
192 Julio Zuleta	.20	.50
193 Timo Perez	.20	.50
194 Billy Wagner	.25	.60
195 Craig Counsell	.20	.50
196 Bart Miadich	.20	.50
197 Gary Sheffield	.25	.60
198 Richard Hidalgo	.20	.50
199 Juan Uribe	.20	.50
200 Curt Schilling	.25	.60
201 Javy Lopez	.25	.60
202 Jimmy Haynes	.20	.50
203 Jim Edmonds	.25	.60
204 Pokey Reese	.20	.50
204N Pokey Reese Night SP	2.00	5.00
205 Matt Clement	.25	.60
206 Dean Palmer	.25	.60
207 Nick Johnson	.25	.60
208 Nate Espy RC	.40	1.00
209 Pedro Feliz	.20	.50
210 Aaron Rowand	.25	.60
211 Masato Yoshii	.20	.50
212 Jose Cruz Jr.	.20	.50
213 Paul Byrd	.20	.50
214 Mark Phillips RC	.40	1.00
215 Benny Agbayani	.20	.50
216 Frank Menechino	.20	.50
217 John Flaherty	.20	.50
218 Brian Boehringer	.20	.50
219 Todd Hollandsworth	.20	.50
220 Sammy Sosa SP	3.00	8.00
221 Steve Sparks	.20	.50
222 Homer Bush	.20	.50
223 Mike Hampton	.25	.60
224 Bobby Abreu	.25	.60
225 Barry Larkin	.40	1.00
226 Ryan Rupe	.20	.50
227 Bubba Trammell	.20	.50
228 Todd Zeile	.25	.60
229 Jeff Shaw	.20	.50
230 Alex Ochoa	.20	.50
231 Orlando Cabrera	.25	.60
232 Jeremy Giambi	.20	.50
233 Tomo Ohka	.20	.50
234 Luis Castillo	.20	.50
235 Chris Holt	.20	.50
236 Shawn Green	.25	.60
237 Sidney Ponson	.20	.50
238 Lee Stevens	.20	.50
239 Hank Blalock	.40	1.00
240 Randy Winn	.20	.50
241 Pedro Martinez	.40	1.00
242 Vinny Castilla	.25	.60
243 Steve Karsay	.20	.50
244 Barry Bonds SP	8.00	20.00
245 Jason Bere	.20	.50
246 Scott Rolen	.40	1.00
246N Scott Rolen Night SP	3.00	8.00
247 Ryan Kohlmeier	.20	.50
248 Kerry Wood	.25	.60
249 Aramis Ramirez	.25	.60
250 Lance Berkman	.25	.60
251 Omar Vizquel	.40	1.00
252 Juan Encarnacion	.20	.50
253 Does Not Exist		
254 David Segui	.20	.50
255 Brian Anderson	.20	.50
256 Jay Payton	.20	.50
257 Mark Grudzielanek	.20	.50
258 Jimmy Anderson	.20	.50
259 Eric Valent	.20	.50
260 Chad Durbin	.20	.50
261 Does Not Exist		
262 Alex Gonzalez	.20	.50
263 Scott Dunn	.20	.50
264 Scott Elarton	.20	.50
265 Tom Gordon	.20	.50
266 Moises Alou	.25	.60
267 Does Not Exist		
268 Does Not Exist		
269 Mark Buehrle	.25	.60
270 Jerry Hairston	.20	.50
271 Does Not Exist		
272 Luke Prokopec	.20	.50
273 Graeme Lloyd	.20	.50
274 Bret Prinz	.20	.50
275 Does Not Exist		
276 Chris Carpenter	.25	.60
277 Ryan Minor	.20	.50
278 Jeff D'Amico	.20	.50
279 Raul Ibanez	.20	.50
280 Joe Mays	.20	.50
281 Livan Hernandez	.25	.60
282 Robin Ventura	.25	.60
283 Gabe Kapler	.25	.60
284 Tony Batista	.20	.50
285 Ramon Hernandez	.20	.50
286 Craig Paquette	.20	.50
287 Mark Kotsay	.25	.60*
288 Mike Lieberthal	.25	.60
289 Joe Borchard	.20	.50
290 Cristian Guzman	.20	.50
291 Craig Biggio	.40	1.00
292 Joaquin Benoit	.20	.50
293 Ken Caminiti	.25	.60
294 Sean Burroughs	.20	.50
295 Eric Karros	.25	.60
296 Eric Chavez	.25	.60
297 LaTroy Hawkins	.20	.50
298 Alfonso Soriano	.25	.60
299 John Smoltz	.40	1.00
300 Adam Dunn	.25	.60
301 Ryan Dempster	.20	.50
302 Travis Hafner	.25	.60
303 Russell Branyan	.20	.50
304 Dustin Hermanson	.20	.50
305 Jim Thome	.40	1.00
306 Carlos Beltran	.25	.60
307 Jason Botts RC	.25	.60
308 David Cone	.25	.60
309 Ivanon Coffie	.20	.50
310 Brian Jordan	.25	.60
311 Todd Walker	.20	.50
312 Jeromy Burnitz	.25	.60
313 Tony Armas Jr.	.20	.50
314 Jeff Conine	.25	.60
315 Todd Jones	.20	.50
316 Roy Oswalt	.25	.60
317 Aubrey Huff	.25	.60
318 Josh Fogg	.20	.50
319 Jose Vidro	.20	.50
320 Jace Brewer	.20	.50
321 Mike Redmond	.20	.50
322 Noochie Varner RC	.40	1.00
323 Russ Ortiz	.20	.50
324 Edgardo Alfonzo	.20	.50
325 Ruben Sierra	.25	.60
326 Calvin Murray	.20	.50
327 Marlon Anderson	.20	.50
328 Albie Lopez	.20	.50
329 Chris Gomez	.20	.50
330 Fernando Tatis	.20	.50
331 Stubby Clapp	.20	.50
332 Rickey Henderson	.60	1.50
333 Brad Radke	.25	.60
334 Brent Mayne	.20	.50
335 Cory Lidle	.20	.50
336 Edgar Martinez	.40	1.00
337 Aaron Boone	.25	.60
338 Jay Witasick	.20	.50
339 Benito Santiago	.25	.60
340 Jose Mercedes	.20	.50
341 Fernando Vina	.20	.50
342 A.J. Pierzynski	.25	.60
343 Jeff Bagwell	.40	1.00
344 Brian Bohanon	.20	.50
345 Adrian Beltre	.25	.60
346 Troy Percival	.25	.60
347 Napoleon Calzado RC	.40	1.00
348 Ruben Rivera	.20	.50
349 Rafael Soriano	.20	.50
350 Damian Jackson	.20	.50
351 Joe Randa	.25	.60
352 Chan Ho Park	.25	.60
353 Dante Bichette	.25	.60
354 Bartolo Colon	.25	.60
355 Jason Bay RC	2.00	5.00
356 Shea Hillenbrand	.25	.60
357 Matt Morris	.25	.60
358 Brad Penny	.20	.50
359 Mark Quinn	.20	.50
360 Marquis Grissom	.25	.60
361 Henry Blanco	.20	.50
362 Billy Koch	.20	.50
363 Mike Cameron	.20	.50
364 Albert Pujols SP	6.00	15.00
365 Paul Konerko SP	2.00	5.00
366 Eric Milton SP	2.00	5.00
367 Nick Bierbrodt SP	2.00	5.00
368 Rafael Palmeiro SP	3.00	8.00
369 Jorge Padilla SP RC	2.00	5.00
370 Jason Giambi	2.00	5.00
Yankees SP		
Stats on back are Jeremy Giambi's		
371 Mike Piazza SP	5.00	12.00
372 Alex Cora SP	2.00	5.00
373 Todd Helton SP	3.00	8.00
374 Juan Gonzalez SP	2.00	5.00
375 Mariano Rivera SP	3.00	8.00
376 Jason LaRue SP	2.00	5.00
377 Tony Gwynn SP	4.00	10.00
378 Wilson Betemit SP	2.00	5.00
379 J.J. Trujillo SP RC	2.00	5.00
380 Brad Ausmus SP	2.00	5.00
381 Chris George SP	2.00	5.00
382 Jose Canseco SP	3.00	8.00
383 Ramon Ortiz SP	2.00	5.00
384 John Rocker SP	2.00	5.00
385 Rey Ordonez SP	2.00	5.00
386 Ken Griffey Jr. SP	5.00	12.00
387 Juan Pena SP	2.00	5.00
388 Michael Barrett SP	2.00	5.00
389 J.D. Drew SP	2.00	5.00
390 Corey Koskie SP	2.00	5.00
391 Vernon Wells SP	2.00	5.00
392 Juan Tolentino SP RC	2.00	5.00
393 Luis Gonzalez SP	2.00	5.00
394 Terrence Long SP	2.00	5.00
395 Travis Lee SP	2.00	5.00
396 Earl Snyder SP RC	2.00	5.00
397 Nomar Garciaparra SP	5.00	12.00
398 Jason Schmidt SP	2.00	5.00
399 David Espinosa SP	2.00	5.00
400 Steve Green SP	2.00	5.00
401 Jack Wilson SP	2.00	5.00
402 Chris Tritle SP RC	2.00	5.00
403 Angel Berroa SP	2.00	5.00
404 Josh Towers SP	2.00	5.00
405 Andruw Jones SP	3.00	8.00
406 Brent Butler SP	2.00	5.00
407 Craig Kuzmic SP	2.00	5.00
408 Derek Bell SP	2.00	5.00
409 Eric Glaser SP RC	2.00	5.00
410 Joel Pineiro SP	2.00	5.00
411 Alexis Gomez SP	2.00	5.00
412 Mike Rivera SP	2.00	5.00
413 Shawn Estes SP	2.00	5.00
414 Milton Bradley SP	2.00	5.00
415 Carl Everett SP	2.00	5.00
416 Kazuhiro Sasaki SP	2.00	5.00
417 Tony Fontana SP RC	2.00	5.00
418 Josh Pearce SP	2.00	5.00
419 Gary Matthews Jr. SP	2.00	5.00
420 Raymond Cabrera SP RC	2.00	5.00
421 Joe Kennedy SP	2.00	5.00
422 Jason Maule SP RC	2.00	5.00
423 Casey Fossum SP	2.00	5.00
424 Christian Parker SP	2.00	5.00
425 Laynce Nix SP RC	4.00	10.00
426 Byung-Hyun Kim SP	2.00	5.00
427 Freddy Garcia SP	2.00	5.00
428 Herbert Perry SP	2.00	5.00
429 Jason Marquis SP	2.00	5.00
430 Sandy Alomar Jr. SP	2.00	5.00
431 Roberto Alomar SP	3.00	8.00
432 Tsuyoshi Shinjo SP	2.00	5.00
433 Tim Wakefield SP	2.00	5.00
434 Robert Fick SP	2.00	5.00
435 Vladimir Guerrero SP	3.00	8.00
436 Jose Mesa SP	2.00	5.00
437 Scott Spiezio SP	2.00	5.00
438 Jose Hernandez SP	2.00	5.00
439 Jose Acevedo SP	2.00	5.00
440 Brian West SP RC	2.00	5.00
441 Barry Zito SP	2.00	5.00
442 Luis Maza SP	2.00	5.00
443 Marlon Byrd SP	2.00	5.00
444 A.J. Burnett SP	2.00	5.00
445 Dee Brown SP	2.00	5.00
446 Carlos Delgado SP	2.00	5.00

2002 Topps Heritage Chrome

Inserted into packs at stated odds of one in 29, these 100 cards feature the "Chrome" technology and have a stated print run of 553 copies.

THC1 Darin Erstad	4.00	10.00
THC2 Doug Mientkiewicz	4.00	10.00
THC3 Mike Sweeney	4.00	10.00
THC4 Roger Clemens	12.50	30.00
THC5 C.C. Sabathia	4.00	10.00
THC6 Tim Hudson	4.00	10.00
THC7 Jason Lane	4.00	10.00

THC8 Larry Walker 4.00 10.00
THC9 Mark Mulder 4.00 10.00
THC10 Mike Mussina 4.00 10.00
THC11 Paul LoDuca 4.00 10.00
THC12 Jimmy Rollins 4.00 10.00
THC13 Ivan Rodriguez 4.00 10.00
THC14 Mark McGwire 15.00 40.00
THC15 Edgar Renteria 4.00 10.00
THC16 Scott Brosius 4.00 10.00
THC17 Juan Cruz 4.00 10.00
THC18 Kevin Brown 4.00 10.00
THC19 Charles Nagy 4.00 10.00
THC20 Bill Ortega 4.00 10.00
THC21 Corey Patterson 4.00 10.00
THC22 Maggiio Ordonez 4.00 10.00
THC23 Brandon Duckworth 4.00 10.00
THC24 Scott Schoeneweis 4.00 10.00
THC25 Tino Martinez 4.00 10.00
THC26 Jason Young 4.00 10.00
THC27 Nate Cornejo 4.00 10.00
THC28 Ryan Klesko 4.00 10.00
THC29 Omar Daal 4.00 10.00
THC30 Raul Mondesi 4.00 10.00
THC31 Boof Bonser 4.00 10.00
THC32 Rich Aurilia 4.00 10.00
THC33 Jon Lieber 4.00 10.00
THC34 Tim Hummel 4.00 10.00
THC35 J.T. Snow 4.00 10.00
THC36 Derek Jeter 15.00 40.00
THC37 Darryl Kile 4.00 10.00
THC38 Armando Benitez 4.00 10.00
THC39 Marlyn Tisdale 4.00 10.00
THC40 Shannon Stewart 4.00 10.00
THC41 Nic Jackson 4.00 10.00
THC42 Robb Nen UER 4.00 10.00
First name misspelled Rob
THC43 Dmitri Young 4.00 10.00
THC44 Greg Maddux 10.00 25.00
THC45 Hideo Nomo 6.00 15.00
THC46 Bret Boone 4.00 10.00
THC47 Wade Miller 4.00 10.00
THC48 Jeff Kent 4.00 10.00
THC49 Freddy Sanchez 6.00 15.00
THC50 Bud Smith 4.00 10.00
THC51 Sean Casey 4.00 10.00
THC52 Brent Abernathy 4.00 10.00
THC53 Trevor Hoffman 4.00 10.00
THC54 Aaron Dean 4.00 10.00
THC55 Juan Pierre 4.00 10.00
THC56 Pat Burrell 4.00 10.00
THC57 Gookie Dawkins 4.00 10.00
THC58 Roger Cedeno 4.00 10.00
THC59 Brian Giles 4.00 10.00
THC60 Jim Edmonds 4.00 10.00
THC61 Dean Palmer 4.00 10.00
THC62 Nick Johnson 4.00 10.00
THC63 Nate Espy 4.00 10.00
THC64 Aaron Rowand 4.00 10.00
THC65 Mark Phillips 4.00 10.00
THC66 Mike Hampton 4.00 10.00
THC67 Bobby Abreu 4.00 10.00
THC68 Alex Ochoa 4.00 10.00
THC69 Shawn Green 4.00 10.00
THC70 Hank Blalock 4.00 10.00
THC71 Pedro Martinez 4.00 10.00
THC72 Ryan Kohlmeier 4.00 10.00
THC73 Kerry Wood 4.00 10.00
THC74 Aramis Ramirez 4.00 10.00
THC75 Lance Berkman 4.00 10.00
THC76 Scott Dunn 4.00 10.00
THC77 Moises Alou 4.00 10.00
THC78 Mark Buehrle 4.00 10.00
THC79 Jerry Hairston 4.00 10.00
THC80 Joe Borchard 4.00 10.00
THC81 Cristian Guzman 4.00 10.00
THC82 Sean Burroughs 4.00 10.00
THC83 Alfonso Soriano 4.00 10.00
THC84 Adam Dunn 4.00 10.00
THC85 Jim Thome 4.00 10.00
THC86 Jason Botts 4.00 10.00
THC87 Jeromy Burnitz 4.00 10.00
THC88 Roy Oswalt 4.00 10.00
THC89 Russ Ortiz 4.00 10.00
THC90 Marlon Anderson 4.00 10.00
THC91 Stubby Clapp 4.00 10.00
THC92 Rickey Henderson 6.00 15.00
THC93 Brad Radke 4.00 10.00
THC94 Jeff Bagwell 4.00 10.00
THC95 Troy Percival 4.00 10.00
THC96 Napoleon Calzado 4.00 10.00
THC97 Joe Randa 4.00 10.00
THC98 Chan Ho Park 4.00 10.00
THC99 Jason Bay 8.00 20.00
THC100 Mark Quinn 4.00 10.00

2002 Topps Heritage Classic Renditions

Inserted into packs at stated odds of one in 12, these 10 cards show how current players might look like if they played in their 1953 team uniforms. These cards are printed on grayback paper stock.

COMPLETE SET (10) 8.00 20.00
CR1 Kerry Wood .75 2.00
CR2 Brian Giles .75 2.00
CR3 Roger Cedeno .75 2.00
CR4 Jason Giambi .75 2.00
CR5 Albert Pujols 2.00 5.00
CR6 Mark Buehrle .75 2.00
CR7 Cristian Guzman .75 2.00
CR8 Jimmy Rollins .75 2.00
CR9 Jim Thome .75 2.00
CR10 Shawn Green .75 2.00

2002 Topps Heritage Classic Renditions Autographs

Partially paralleling the Classic Rendition set, these three cards were all autographed by the player and have a stated print run of 25 sets. Due to market scarcity, no pricing is provided for these cards.

CRABG Brian Giles
CRACG Cristian Guzman
CRAJR Jimmy Rollins

2002 Topps Heritage Clubhouse Collection

Inserted into packs at a rate for jersey cards of one in 332 and bat cards at a rate of one in 498, these 12 cards feature a mix of active and retired players with a memorabilia swatch.

CCAD Alvin Dark Bat 10.00 25.00
CCBB Barry Bonds Bat 40.00 80.00
CCCP Corey Patterson Bat 10.00 25.00
CCEM Eddie Mathews Jsy 15.00 40.00
CCGK George Kell Jsy 15.00 40.00
CCGM Greg Maddux Jsy 15.00 40.00
CCHS Hank Sauer Bat 10.00 25.00
CCJP Jorge Posada Bat 15.00 40.00
CCNG Nomar Garciaparra Bat 20.00 50.00
CCRA Rich Aurilia Bat 10.00 25.00
CCWM Willie Mays Bat 50.00 100.00
CCYB Yogi Berra Jsy 15.00 40.00

2002 Topps Heritage Clubhouse Collection Autographs

These four cards parallel the Clubhouse Collection insert set. These cards feature autographs from the noted players are are serial numbered to 25. Due to market scarcity, no pricing is provided for these players.

CCAAD Alvin Dark Bat
CCAGK George Kell Jsy
CCAWM Willie Mays Bat
CCAYB Yogi Berra Jsy

2002 Topps Heritage Clubhouse Collection Duos

Inserted into packs at stated odds of one in 5016, these six cards feature one current player and one 1953 franchise alum from that same team with a relic from each player. These cards have a stated print run of 53 serial numbered sets. Due to market scarcity, no pricing is provided for these cards.

CC2BP Yogi Berra Jsy 75.00 150.00
Jorge Posada Bat
CC2DA Alvin Dark Bat 50.00 100.00
Rich Aurilia Bat
CC2KR George Kell Jsy 75.00 150.00
Nomar Garciaparra Bat
CC2MB Willie Mays Bat 150.00 250.00
Barry Bonds Bat UER
Card states Bonds is Mays' godfather
It is the other way around
CC2SM Eddie Mathews Jsy 40.00 80.00
Greg Maddux Jsy
CC2SP Hank Sauer Bat 50.00 100.00
Corey Patterson Bat

2002 Topps Heritage Grandstand Glory

Inserted into packs at different rates depending on which grop the player is from, these 12 cards feature retired 1950's players along with an authentic relic from an historic 1950's stadium.

GROUP A STATED ODDS 1:4115
GROUP B STATED ODDS 1:531
GROUP C STATED ODDS 1:1576
GROUP D STATED ODDS 1:370
GROUP E STATED ODDS 1:483
GGBF Bob Feller E 10.00 25.00
GGBM Billy Martin B 10.00 25.00
GGBP Billy Pierce B 8.00 20.00
GGBS Bobby Shantz D 8.00 20.00
GGEW Early Wynn E 10.00 25.00
GGHN Hal Newhouser B 10.00 25.00
GGHS Hank Sauer C 8.00 20.00
GGRC Roy Campanella D 15.00 40.00
GGSP Satchel Paige A 40.00 80.00
GGTK Ted Kluszewski E 15.00 40.00
GGWF Whitey Ford D 10.00 25.00
GGWS Warren Spahn D 15.00 40.00

2002 Topps Heritage New Age Performers

Inserted into packs at stated odds of one in 15, these 15 cards feature powerhouse players whose accomplishments have cemented their names in major league history.

COMPLETE SET (15) 20.00 50.00
NA1 Luis Gonzalez .75 2.00
NA2 Mark McGwire 2.50 6.00
NA3 Barry Bonds 2.50 6.00
NA4 Ken Griffey Jr. 1.50 4.00
NA5 Ichiro Suzuki 2.00 5.00
NA6 Sammy Sosa 1.00 2.50
NA7 Andruw Jones .75 2.00
NA8 Derek Jeter 2.50 6.00
NA9 Todd Helton .75 2.00
NA10 Alex Rodriguez 1.50 4.00
NA11 Jason Giambi Yankees .75 2.00
NA12 Bret Boone .75 2.00
NA13 Roberto Alomar .75 2.00
NA14 Albert Pujols 2.00 5.00
NA15 Vladimir Guerrero 1.00 2.50

2002 Topps Heritage Real One Autographs

Inserted into packs at different odds depending on which group the player belongs to, this 28 card set features a mix of authentic autographs between active players and those who were active in the 1953 season. Please note that the group which each player belongs to is listed next to their name in our checklist. The Roger Clemens card has been signed in both blue and black, please let us know if any other players are signed in more than one color.

GROUP 1 STATED ODDS 1:346
GROUP 2 STATED ODDS 1:6363
GROUP 3 STATED ODDS 1:4908
GROUP 4 STATED ODDS 1:3196
GROUP 5 STATED ODDS 1:498
*RED INK: .75X TO 1.5X BASIC AUTO'S
RED INK ODDS 1:306
RED INK PRINT RUN 53 SERIAL #'d SETS
ROAC Andy Carey 1 15.00 40.00
ROAD Alvin Dark 1 30.00 60.00
ROAR Al Rosen 1 50.00 100.00
ROARO Alex Rodriguez 2 100.00 175.00
ROASC Al Schoendienst 1 30.00 60.00
ROBF Bob Feller 1 50.00 100.00
ROBG Brian Giles 5 10.00 25.00
ROBS Bobby Shantz 1 30.00 60.00
ROCG Cristian Guzman 5 6.00 15.00
RODD Dom DiMaggio 1 50.00 100.00
ROES Enos Slaughter 1 50.00 100.00
ROGK George Kell 1 40.00 80.00
ROGM Gil McDougald 1 50.00 100.00
ROHW Hoyt Wilhelm 1 50.00 100.00
ROJB Joe Black 1 30.00 60.00
ROJE Jim Edmonds 4 15.00 40.00
ROJP John Podres 1 30.00 60.00
ROMI Monte Irvin 1 30.00 60.00
ROOM Minnie Minoso 1 30.00 60.00
ROPR Phil Rizzuto 1 50.00 100.00
ROPRO Preacher Roe 1 30.00 60.00
RORB Ray Boone 1 50.00 100.00
RORF Roy Face 1 30.00 60.00
RORCL Roger Clemens 3 100.00 175.00
ROWF Whitey Ford 1 90.00 150.00
ROWM Willie Mays 1 150.00 250.00
ROWS Warren Spahn 1 60.00 120.00
ROYB Yogi Berra 1 90.00 150.00

2002 Topps Heritage Then and Now

Inserted into packs at stated odds of one in 15, these 10 cards feature a 1953 player as well as a current stand-out. These cards offer statistical comparisions in major stat categories and are printed in greyback paper stock.

COMPLETE SET (10) 12.50 30.00
TN1 Eddie Mathews 2.50 6.00
Barry Bonds
TN2 Al Rosen 1.50 4.00
Alex Rodriguez
TN3 Carl Furillo .75 2.00
Larry Walker
TN4 Minnie Minoso 2.00 5.00
Ichiro Suzuki
TN5 Richie Ashburn .75 2.00
Rich Aurilia
TN6 Al Rosen .75 2.00
Bret Boone
TN7 Duke Snider 1.00 2.50
Sammy Sosa
TN8 Al Rosen 1.50 4.00
Alex Rodriguez
TN9 Robin Roberts 1.00 2.50
Randy Johnson
TN10 Billy Pierce 1.00 2.50
Hideo Nomo

2003 Topps Heritage

This 430-card set, which was designed to honor the 1954 Topps set, was released in February, 2003. These cards were issued in five card packs with an $3 SRP. These packs were issued in 24 pack boxes which came eight boxes to a case. In addition, many cards in the set were issued in two varieties. A few cards were issued featuring either a logo used today or a scarcer version in which the logo was used in the 1954 set. In addition, some cards were printed with either the originally designed version or a black background. The black background version is the tougher of the two versions of each card. A few cards between 1 and 363 were produced in less quantities and all cards from 364 on up were short printed as well. In a nod to the 1954 set, Alex Rodriguez had both cards 1 and 250; just as Ted Williams had in the original 1954 Topps set.

COMPLETE SET (450) 175.00 300.00
COMP.SET w/o SP's (350) 40.00 80.00
COMMON CARD .20 .50
COMMON RC .40 1.00
COMMON SP 2.00 5.00
COMMON SP RC 2.00 5.00
1A Alex Rodriguez Red 1.00 2.50
1B Alex Rodriguez Black SP 5.00 12.00
2 Jose Cruz Jr. .20 .50
3 Ichiro Suzuki SP 6.00 15.00
4 Rich Aurilia .20 .50
5 Trevor Hoffman .25 .60
6A Brian Giles New Logo .25 .60
6B Brian Giles Old Logo SP 2.00 5.00
7A Albert Pujols Orange 1.25 3.00
7B Albert Pujols Black SP 6.00 15.00
8 Vicente Padilla .20 .50
9 Bobby Crosby .25 .60
10A Derek Jeter New Logo 1.50 4.00
10B Derek Jeter Old Logo SP 6.00 15.00
11A Pat Burrell New Logo .25 .60
11B Pat Burrell Old Logo SP 2.00 5.00
12 Armando Benitez .20 .50
13 Javier Vazquez .25 .60
14 Justin Morneau .25 .60
15 Doug Mientkiewicz .25 .60
16 Kevin Brown .25 .60
17 Alexis Gomez .20 .50
18A Lance Berkman Blue .25 .60
18B Lance Berkman Black SP 2.00 5.00
19 Adrian Gonzalez .20 .50
20A Todd Helton Green .40 1.00
20B Todd Helton Black SP 3.00 8.00
21 Carlos Pena .20 .50
22 Matt Lawton .20 .50
23 Elmer Dessens .20 .50
24 Hee Seop Choi .20 .50
25 Chris Duncan SP RC 5.00 12.00
26 Ugueth Urbina .20 .50
27A Rodrigo Lopez New Logo .20 .50
27B Ro. Lopez Old Logo SP 2.00 5.00
28 Damian Moss .20 .50
29 Steve Finley .25 .60
30A Sammy Sosa New Logo .60 1.50
30B S.Sosa Old Logo SP 3.00 8.00
31 Kevin Cash .20 .50
32 Kenny Rogers .25 .60
33 Ben Grieve .20 .50
34 Jason Simontacchi .20 .50
35 Shin-Soo Choo .20 .50
36 Freddy Garcia .25 .60
37 Jesse Foppert .20 .50
38 Tony LaRussa MG .25 .60
39 Mark Kotsay .25 .60
40 Barry Zito .25 .60
41 Josh Fogg .20 .50
42 Marlon Byrd .20 .50
43 Marcus Thames .20 .50
44 Al Leiter .25 .60
45 Michael Barrett .20 .50
46 Jake Peavy .25 .60
47 Dustan Mohr .20 .50
48 Alex Sanchez .20 .50
49 Chin-Feng Chen .25 .60
50A Kazuhisa Ishii Blue .25 .60
50B Kazuhisa Ishii Black SP 2.00 5.00
51 Carlos Beltran .25 .60
52 Franklin Gutierrez RC .40 1.00
53 Miguel Cabrera .60 1.50
54 Roger Clemens 1.25 3.00
55 Juan Cruz .20 .50
56 Jason Young .20 .50
57 Alex Herrera .20 .50
58 Aaron Boone .25 .60
59 Mark Buehrle .25 .60
60 Larry Walker .25 .60
61 Morgan Ensberg .25 .60
62 Barry Larkin .40 1.00
63 Joe Borchard .20 .50
64 Jason Dubois .20 .50
65 Shea Hillenbrand .25 .60
66 Jay Gibbons .20 .50
67 Vinny Castilla .25 .60
68 Jeff Mathis .20 .50
69 Curt Schilling .25 .60
70 Garret Anderson .25 .60
71 Josh Phelps .20 .50
72 Chan Ho Park .25 .60
73 Edgar Renteria .25 .60
74 Kazuhiro Sasaki .25 .60
75 Lloyd McClendon MG .20 .50
76 Jon Lieber .20 .50
77 Rolando Viera .20 .50
78 Jeff Conine .25 .60
79 Kevin Millwood .25 .60
80A Randy Johnson Green .60 1.50
80B Randy Johnson Black SP 5.00 12.00
81 Troy Percival .25 .60
82 Cliff Floyd .25 .60
83 Tony Graffanino .20 .50
84 Austin Kearns .20 .50
85 Manuel Ramirez SP RC 3.00 8.00
86 Jim Tracy MG .20 .50
87 Rondell White .25 .60
88 Trot Nixon .25 .60
89 Carlos Lee .25 .60
90 Mike Lowell .25 .60
91 Raul Ibanez .20 .50
92 Ricardo Rodriguez .20 .50
93 Ben Sheets .25 .60
94 Jason Perry SP RC 3.00 8.00
95 Mark Teixeira .40 1.00
96 Brad Fullmer .20 .50
97 Casey Kotchman .25 .60
98 Craig Counsell .20 .50
99 Jason Marquis .20 .50
100A N.Garciaparra New Logo 1.00 2.50
100B N.Garciaparra Old Logo SP 5.00 12.00
101 Ed Rogers .20 .50
102 Wilson Betemit .20 .50
103 Wayne Lydon RC .40 1.00
104 Jack Cust .20 .50
105 Derrek Lee .40 1.00
106 Jim Kavourias .20 .50
107 Joe Randa .25 .60
108 Taylor Buchholz .20 .50
109 Gabe Kapler .25 .60
110 Preston Wilson .25 .60
111 Craig Biggio .40 1.00
112 Paul Lo Duca .25 .60
113 Eddie Guardado .20 .50
114 Andres Galarraga .40 1.00
115 Edgardo Alfonzo .20 .50
116 Robin Ventura .25 .60
117 Jeremy Giambi .20 .50
118 Ray Durham .25 .60
119 Mariano Rivera .60 1.50
120 Jimmy Rollins .25 .60
121 Dennis Tankersley .20 .50
122 Jason Schmidt .25 .60
123 Bret Boone .25 .60
124 Josh Hamilton .40 1.00
125 Scott Rolen .40 1.00
126 Steve Cox .20 .50
127 Larry Bowa MG .25 .60
128 Adam LaRoche SP 2.00 5.00
129 Ryan Klesko .25 .60
130 Tim Hudson .25 .60
131 Brandon Claussen .20 .50
132 Craig Brazell SP RC 2.00 5.00
133 Grady Little MG .20 .50
134 Jarrod Washburn .20 .50
135 Lyle Overbay .20 .50
136 John Burkett .20 .50
137 Daryl Clark RC .40 1.00
138 Kirk Rueter .20 .50
139A Joe Mauer .60 1.50
Jake Mauer Green
139B Joe Mauer 4.00 10.00
Jake Mauer Black SP
140 Troy Glaus .25 .60
141 Trey Hodges SP 2.00 5.00
142 Dallas McPherson .25 .60
143 Art Howe MG .20 .50
144 Jesus Cota .20 .50
145 J.R. House .20 .50
146 Reggie Sanders .25 .60
147 Clint Nageotte .20 .50
148 Jim Edmonds .25 .60
149 Carl Crawford .25 .60
150A Mike Piazza Blue 1.00 2.50
150B Mike Piazza Black SP 5.00 12.00
151 Seung Song .20 .50
152 Roberto Hernandez .25 .60
153 Marquis Grissom .25 .60
154 Billy Wagner .25 .60
155 Josh Beckett .25 .60
156A R.Simon New Logo .20 .50
156B R.Simon Old Logo SP 2.00 5.00
157 Ben Broussard .20 .50
158 Russell Branyan .20 .50
159 Frank Thomas .60 1.50
160 Alex Escobar .20 .50
161 Mark Bellhorn .25 .60
162 Melvin Mora .25 .60
163 Andruw Jones .40 1.00
164 Danny Bautista .20 .50
165 Ramon Ortiz .20 .50
166 Wily Mo Pena .25 .60
167 Jose Jimenez .20 .50
168 Mark Redman .20 .50
169 Angel Berroa .20 .50
170 Andy Marte SP RC 5.00 12.00
171 Juan Gonzalez .25 .60
172 Fernando Vina .20 .50
173 Joel Pineiro .20 .50
174 Boof Bonser .20 .50
175 Bernie Castro SP RC 2.00 5.00
176 Bobby Cox MG .20 .50
177 Jeff Kent .25 .60
178 Oliver Perez .25 .60
179 Chase Utley .60 1.50
180 Mark Mulder .25 .60
181 Bobby Abreu .25 .60
182 Ramiro Mendoza .20 .50
183 Aaron Heilman .20 .50
184 A.J. Pierzynski .25 .60
185 Eric Gagne .25 .60
186 Kirk Saarloos .20 .50
187 Ron Gardenhire MG .20 .50
188 Dmitri Young .25 .60
189 Todd Zeile .25 .60
190A Jim Thome New Logo .40 1.00
190B Jim Thome Old Logo SP 3.00 8.00
191 Cliff Lee .60 1.50
192 Matt Morris .25 .60
193 Robert Fick .20 .50
194 C.C. Sabathia .25 .60
195 Alexis Rios .25 .60
196 D'Angelo Jimenez .20 .50
197 Edgar Martinez .40 1.00
198 Robb Nen .25 .60
199 Taggert Bozied .20 .50
200 Vladimir Guerrero SP 3.00 8.00
201 Walter Young SP 2.00 5.00
202 Brendan Harris RC .40 1.00
203 Mike Hargrove MG .20 .50
204 Vernon Wells .25 .60
205 Hank Blalock .25 .60
206 Mike Cameron .20 .50
207 Tony Batista .20 .50
208 Matt Williams .25 .60
209 Tony Womack .20 .50
210 R.Nivar-Martinez RC .40 1.00
211 Aaron Sele .20 .50
212 Mark Grace .40 1.00
213 Joe Crede .25 .60
214 Ryan Dempster .20 .50
215 Omar Vizquel .40 1.00
216 Juan Pierre .25 .60
217 Denny Bautista .20 .50
218 Chuck Knoblauch .25 .60
219 Eric Karros .25 .60
220 Victor Diaz .25 .60
221 Jacque Jones .25 .60
222 Jose Vidro .20 .50
223 Joe McEwing .20 .50
224 Nick Johnson .25 .60
225 Eric Chavez .25 .60
226 Jose Mesa .20 .50
227 Aramis Ramirez .25 .60
228 John Lackey .20 .50
229 David Bell .20 .50
230 John Olerud .25 .60
231 Tino Martinez .40 1.00
232 Randy Winn .20 .50
233 Todd Hollandsworth .20 .50
234 Ruddy Lugo RC .40 1.00
235 Carlos Delgado .25 .60
236 Chris Narveson .20 .50
237 Tim Salmon .40 1.00
238 Orlando Palmeiro .20 .50
239 Jeff Clark SP RC 2.00 5.00
240 Byung-Hyun Kim .25 .60
241 Mike Remlinger .20 .50
242 Johnny Damon .40 1.00
243 Corey Patterson .20 .50
244 Paul Konerko .25 .60
245 Danny Graves .20 .50
246 Ellis Burks .25 .60
247 Gavin Floyd .20 .50
248 Jaime Bubela RC .40 1.00
249 Sean Burroughs .20 .50
250 Alex Rodriguez SP 5.00 12.00
251 Gabe Gross .20 .50
252 Rafael Palmeiro .40 1.00
253 Dewon Brazelton .20 .50
254 Jimmy Journell .20 .50
255 Rafael Soriano .20 .50
256 Jerome Williams .20 .50
257 Xavier Nady .20 .50
258 Mike Williams .20 .50
259 Randy Wolf .20 .50
260A Miguel Tejada Orange .25 .60
260B Miguel Tejada Black SP 2.00 5.00
261 Juan Rivera .20 .50
262 Rey Ordonez .20 .50
263 Bartolo Colon .25 .60
264 Eric Milton .20 .50
265 Jeffrey Hammonds .20 .50
266 Odalis Perez .20 .50
267 Mike Sweeney .25 .60
268 Richard Hidalgo .20 .50
269 Alex Gonzalez .20 .50
270 Aaron Cook .20 .50
271 Earl Snyder .20 .50
272 Todd Walker .20 .50
273 Aaron Rowand .25 .60
274 Matt Clement .25 .60
275 Anastacio Martinez .20 .50
276 Mike Bordick .25 .60
277 John Smoltz .40 1.00
278 Scott Hairston .20 .50
279 David Eckstein .25 .60
280 Shannon Stewart .25 .60
281 Carl Everett .25 .60
282 Aubrey Huff .25 .60
283 Mike Mussina .40 1.00
284 Ruben Sierra .25 .60
285 Russ Ortiz .20 .50
286 Brian Lawrence .20 .50
287 Kip Wells .20 .50
288 Placido Polanco .20 .50
289 Ted Lilly .20 .50
290 Andy Pettitte .40 1.00
291 John Buck .20 .50
292 Orlando Cabrera .25 .60
293 Cristian Guzman .20 .50
294 Ruben Quevedo .20 .50
295 Cesar Izturis .20 .50
296 Ryan Ludwick .20 .50
297 Roy Oswalt .25 .60
298 Jason Stokes .20 .50
299 Mike Hampton .25 .60
300 Pedro Martinez .40 1.00
301 Nic Jackson .20 .50
302A Mag. Ordonez New Logo .25 .60
302B Mag. Ordonez Old Logo SP 2.00 5.00
303 Manny Ramirez .40 1.00
304 Jorge Julio .20 .50
305 Javy Lopez .25 .60
306 Roy Halladay .25 .60
307 Kevin Mench .20 .50
308 Jason Isringhausen .25 .60
309 Carlos Guillen .25 .60
310 Tsuyoshi Shinjo .25 .60
311 Phil Nevin .25 .60
312 Pokey Reese .20 .50
313 Jorge Padilla .20 .50
314 Jermaine Dye .25 .60
315 David Wells .25 .60
316 Mo Vaughn .25 .60
317 Bernie Williams .40 1.00
318 Michael Restovich .20 .50
319 Jose Hernandez .20 .50
320 Richie Sexson .25 .60
321 Daryle Ward .20 .50
322 Luis Castillo .20 .50
323 Rene Reyes .20 .50
324 Victor Martinez .40 1.00
325A Adam Dunn New Logo .25 .60
325B Adam Dunn Old Logo SP 2.00 5.00
326 Corwin Malone .20 .50
327 Kerry Wood .25 .60
328 Rickey Henderson .60 1.50
329 Marty Cordova .20 .50
330 Greg Maddux 1.00 2.50
331 Miguel Batista .20 .50
332 Chris Bootcheck .20 .50
333 Carlos Baerga .20 .50
334 Antonio Alfonseca .20 .50
335 Shane Halter .20 .50
336 Juan Encarnacion .20 .50
337 Tom Gordon .20 .50
338 Hideo Nomo .60 1.50
339 Torii Hunter .25 .60
340A Alfonso Soriano Yellow .25 .60
340B Alf. Soriano Black SP 2.00 5.00
341 Roberto Alomar .40 1.00
342 David Justice .25 .60
343 Mike Lieberthal .25 .60
344 Jeff Weaver .20 .50
345 Timo Perez .20 .50
346 Travis Lee .20 .50
347 Sean Casey .25 .60
348 Willie Harris .20 .50
349 Derek Lowe .25 .60
350 Tom Glavine .40 1.00
351 Eric Hinske .20 .50
352 Rocco Baldelli .25 .60
353 J.D. Drew .25 .60
354 Jamie Moyer .25 .60
355 Todd Linden .20 .50
356 Benito Santiago .25 .60
357 Brad Baker .20 .50
358 Alex Gonzalez .20 .50
359 Brandon Duckworth .20 .50
360 John Rheinecker .20 .50
361 Orlando Hernandez .25 .60
362 Pedro Astacio .20 .50
363 Brad Wilkerson .20 .50
364 David Ortiz SP 3.00 8.00
365 Geoff Jenkins SP 2.00 5.00
366 Brian Jordan SP 2.00 5.00
367 Paul Byrd SP 2.00 5.00
368 Jason Lane SP 2.00 5.00
369 Jeff Bagwell SP 3.00 8.00
370 Bobby Higginson SP 2.00 5.00
371 Juan Uribe SP 2.00 5.00
372 Lee Stevens SP 2.00 5.00
373 Jimmy Haynes SP 2.00 5.00
374 Jose Valentin SP 2.00 5.00
375 Ken Griffey Jr. SP 5.00 12.00
376 Barry Bonds SP 8.00 20.00
377 Gary Matthews Jr. SP 2.00 5.00
378 Gary Sheffield SP 2.00 5.00
379 Rick Helling SP 2.00 5.00
380 Junior Spivey SP 2.00 5.00
381 Francisco Rodriguez SP 2.00 5.00
382 Chipper Jones SP 3.00 8.00
383 Orlando Hudson SP 2.00 5.00
384 Ivan Rodriguez SP 3.00 8.00
385 Chris Snelling SP 2.00 5.00
386 Kenny Lofton SP 2.00 5.00
387 Eric Cyr SP 2.00 5.00
388 Jason Kendall SP 2.00 5.00
389 Marlon Anderson SP 2.00 5.00
390 Billy Koch SP 2.00 5.00
391 Shelley Duncan SP 5.00 12.00
392 Jose Reyes SP 2.00 5.00
393 Fernando Tatis SP 2.00 5.00
394 Michael Cuddyer SP 2.00 5.00
395 Mark Prior SP 3.00 8.00
396 Dontrelle Willis SP 3.00 8.00
397 Jay Payton SP 2.00 5.00
398 Brandon Phillips SP 2.00 5.00
399 Dustin Moseley SP RC 2.00 5.00
400 Jason Giambi SP 2.00 5.00
401 John Mabry SP 2.00 5.00
402 Ron Gant SP 2.00 5.00
403 J.T. Snow SP 2.00 5.00
404 Jeff Cirillo SP 2.00 5.00
405 Darin Erstad SP 2.00 5.00
406 Luis Gonzalez SP 2.00 5.00
407 Marcus Giles SP 2.00 5.00
408 Brian Daubach SP 2.00 5.00
409 Moises Alou SP 2.00 5.00

410 Raul Mondesi SP 2.00 5.00
411 Adrian Beltre SP 2.00 5.00
412 A.J. Burnett SP 2.00 5.00
413 Jason Jennings SP 2.00 5.00
414 Edwin Almonte SP 2.00 5.00
415 Fred McGriff SP 3.00 8.00
416 Tim Raines Jr. SP 2.00 5.00
417 Rafael Furcal SP 2.00 5.00
418 Erubiel Durazo SP 2.00 5.00
419 Drew Henson SP 2.00 5.00
420 Kevin Appier SP 2.00 5.00
421 Chad Tracy SP 2.00 5.00
422 Adam Wainwright SP 2.00 5.00
423 Choo Freeman SP 2.00 5.00
424 Sandy Alomar Jr. SP 2.00 5.00
425 Corey Koskie SP 2.00 5.00
426 Jeromy Burnitz SP 2.00 5.00
427 Jorge Posada SP 3.00 8.00
428 Jason Arnold SP 2.00 5.00
429 Brett Myers SP 2.00 5.00
430 Shawn Green SP 2.00 5.00

2003 Topps Heritage Chrome

Inserted at a stated rate of one in eight, this is a partial parallel to the basic Topps Heritage set. These cards feature Topps special Chrome technology and were printed to a stated print run of 1954 serial numbered sets.

THC1 Alex Rodriguez 4.00 10.00
THC2 Ichiro Suzuki 4.00 10.00
THC3 Brian Giles 1.50 4.00
THC4 Albert Pujols 5.00 12.00
THC5 Derek Jeter 6.00 15.00
THC6 Pat Burrell 1.50 4.00
THC7 Lance Berkman 1.50 4.00
THC8 Todd Helton 2.00 5.00
THC9 Chris Duncan 8.00 20.00
THC10 Rodrigo Lopez 1.50 4.00
THC11 Sammy Sosa 2.50 6.00
THC12 Barry Zito 1.50 4.00
THC13 Marlon Byrd 1.50 4.00
THC14 Al Leiter 1.50 4.00
THC15 Kazuhisa Ishii 1.50 4.00
THC16 Franklin Gutierrez 2.00 5.00
THC17 Roger Clemens 4.00 10.00
THC18 Mark Buehrle 1.50 4.00
THC19 Larry Walker 1.50 4.00
THC20 Curt Schilling 1.50 4.00
THC21 Garret Anderson 1.50 4.00
THC22 Randy Johnson 2.50 6.00
THC23 Cliff Floyd 1.50 4.00
THC24 Austin Kearns 1.50 4.00
THC25 Manuel Ramirez 1.50 4.00
THC26 Raul Ibanez 1.50 4.00
THC27 Jason Perry 2.00 5.00
THC28 Mark Teixeira 2.00 5.00
THC29 Nomar Garciaparra 2.50 6.00
THC30 Wayne Lydon 1.50 4.00
THC31 Preston Wilson 1.50 4.00
THC32 Paul Lo Duca 1.50 4.00
THC33 Edgardo Alfonzo 1.50 4.00
THC34 Jeremy Giambi 1.50 4.00
THC35 Mariano Rivera 2.50 6.00
THC36 Jimmy Rollins 1.50 4.00
THC37 Bret Boone 1.50 4.00
THC38 Scott Rolen 2.00 5.00
THC39 Adam LaRoche 1.50 4.00
40 Tim Hudson 1.50 4.00
THC41 Craig Brazell 1.50 4.00
THC42 Daryl Clark 1.50 4.00
THC43 Joe Mauer 2.50 6.00
Jake Mauer
THC44 Troy Glaus 1.50 4.00
THC45 Trey Hodges 1.50 4.00
THC46 Carl Crawford 1.50 4.00
THC47 Mike Piazza 2.50 6.00
THC48 Josh Beckett 1.50 4.00
THC49 Randall Simon 1.50 4.00
THC50 Frank Thomas 2.50 6.00
THC51 Andruw Jones 2.00 5.00
THC52 Andy Marte 5.00 12.00
THC53 Bernie Castro 1.50 4.00
THC54 Jim Thome 2.00 5.00
THC55 Alexis Rios 1.50 4.00
THC56 Vladimir Guerrero 2.50 6.00
THC57 Walter Young 1.50 4.00
THC58 Hank Blalock 1.50 4.00
THC59 Ramon Nivar-Martinez 1.50 4.00
THC60 Jacque Jones 1.50 4.00
THC61 Nick Johnson 1.50 4.00
THC62 Ruddy Lugo 1.50 4.00
THC63 Carlos Delgado 1.50 4.00
THC64 Jeff Clark 1.50 4.00
THC65 Johnny Damon 2.00 5.00
THC66 Jaime Bubela 1.50 4.00
THC67 Alex Rodriguez 4.00 40.00
THC68 Rafael Palmeiro 2.00 5.00
THC69 Miguel Tejada 1.50 4.00
THC70 Bartolo Colon 1.50 4.00
THC71 Mike Sweeney 1.50 4.00
THC72 John Smoltz 2.00 5.00
THC73 Shannon Stewart 1.50 4.00
THC74 Mike Mussina 2.00 5.00
THC75 Roy Oswalt 1.50 4.00
THC76 Pedro Martinez 2.00 5.00
THC77 Magglio Ordonez 1.50 4.00
THC78 Manny Ramirez 2.00 5.00
THC79 David Wells 1.50 4.00
THC80 Richie Sexson 1.50 4.00
THC81 Adam Dunn 1.50 4.00
THC82 Greg Maddux 4.00 10.00
THC83 Alfonso Soriano 1.50 4.00
THC84 Roberto Alomar 2.00 5.00
THC85 Derek Lowe 1.50 4.00
THC86 Tom Glavine 2.00 5.00
THC87 Jeff Bagwell 2.00 5.00
THC88 Ken Griffey Jr. 4.00 10.00
THC89 Barry Bonds 6.00 15.00
THC90 Gary Sheffield 1.50 4.00
THC91 Chipper Jones 2.50 6.00
THC92 Orlando Hudson 1.50 4.00
THC93 Jose Cruz Jr. 1.50 4.00
THC94 Mark Prior 2.00 5.00
THC95 Jason Giambi 1.50 4.00
THC96 Luis Gonzalez 1.50 4.00
THC97 Drew Henson 1.50 4.00
THC98 Cristian Guzman 1.50 4.00
THC99 Shawn Green 1.50 4.00
THC100 Jose Vidro 1.50 4.00

2003 Topps Heritage Clubhouse Collection Relics

Inserted at different odds depending on the relic, these 12 cards feature a mix of active and retire players and various game-used relics used during their career.

BAT A STATED ODDS 1:2569
BAT B STATED ODDS 1:2506
BAT C STATED ODDS 1:2464
BAT D STATED ODDS 1:1989
UNI A STATED ODDS 1:4223
UNI B STATED ODDS 1:1207
UNI C STATED ODDS 1:921
UNI D STATED ODDS 1:171
AD Adam Dunn Uni D 6.00 15.00
AK Al Kaline Bat D 12.50 30.00
AP Albert Pujols Uni D 8.00 20.00
AR Alex Rodriguez Uni D 8.00 20.00
CJ Chipper Jones Uni D 6.00 15.00
DS Duke Snider Uni A 15.00 40.00
EB Ernie Banks Bat C 12.50 30.00
EM Eddie Mathews Bat B 12.50 30.00
JG Jim Gilliam Uni B 6.00 15.00
KW Kerry Wood Uni D 6.00 15.00
SG Shawn Green Uni C 6.00 15.00
WM Willie Mays Bat A 20.00 50.00

2003 Topps Heritage Clubhouse Collection Autograph Relics

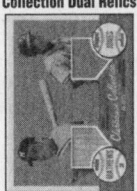

Inserted in packs at a stated rate of one in 15,424, these four cards feature not only a game used relic from the featured player but also an authentic autograph. These cards were issued to a stated print run of 25 serial numbered sets and no pricing is provided due to market scarcity.

AK Al Kaline Bat
DS Duke Snider Uni
EB Ernie Banks Bat
WM Willie Mays Bat

2003 Topps Heritage Clubhouse Collection Dual Relics

Issued at a stated rate of one in 9.521, these three cards feature game-used relics from both a legendary player and a current star of the same franchise. These cards were issued to a stated print run of 54 serial numbered sets.

BW Ernie Banks Bat
Kerry Wood Uni
MJ Eddie Mathews Bat
Chipper Jones Uni
SG Duke Snider Uni
Shawn Green Uni

2003 Topps Heritage Flashbacks

Inserted at a stated rate of one in 12, these 10 cards feature thrilling moments from the 1954 season.

COMPLETE SET 10) 8.00 20.00
F1 Willie Mays 2.00 5.00
F2 Yogi Berra 1.00 2.50
F3 Ted Kluszewski .75 2.00
F4 Stan Musial 1.50 4.00
F5 Hank Aaron 2.00 5.00
F6 Duke Snider .75 2.00
F7 Richie Ashburn .75 2.00
F8 Robin Roberts .75 2.00
F9 Mickey Vernon .75 2.00
F10 Don Larson .75 2.00

2003 Topps Heritage Flashbacks Autographs

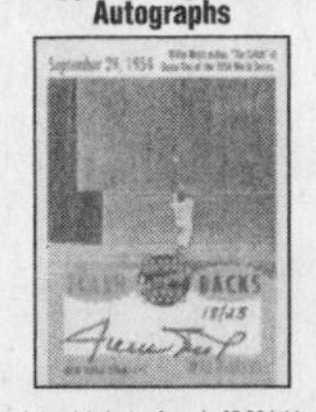

Inserted at a stated rate of one in 65,384 this card features an authentic autograph of Willie Mays. This card was issued to a stated print run of 25 serial numbered cards and no pricing is available due to market scarcity.

WM Willie Mays

2003 Topps Heritage Grandstand Glory Stadium Relics

Inserted at different odds depending on the group, these 12 cards feature a player photo along with a seat relic from any of nine historic ballparks involved in their career.

GROUP A ODDS 1:2804
GROUP B ODDS 1:514
GROUP C ODDS 1:1446
GROUP D ODDS 1:1356
GROUP E ODDS 1:654
GROUP F ODDS 1:214
AK Al Kaline F 8.00 20.00
AP Andy Pafko F 4.00 10.00
DG Dick Groat D 6.00 15.00
DS Duke Snider A 10.00 25.00
EB Ernie Banks C 10.00 25.00
EM Eddie Mathews F 6.00 15.00
PR Phil Rizzuto E 8.00 20.00
RA Richie Ashburn B 8.00 20.00
TK Ted Kluszewski B 8.00 20.00
WM Willie Mays B 15.00 40.00
WS Warren Spahn F 8.00 20.00
YB Yogi Berra E 10.00 25.00

2003 Topps Heritage New Age Performers

Issued at a stated rate of one in 15, these 15 cards feature prominent active players who have taken the game of baseball to new levels.

NA1 Mike Piazza 1.50 4.00
NA2 Ichiro Suzuki 2.00 5.00
NA3 Derek Jeter 2.50 6.00
NA4 Alex Rodriguez 1.50 4.00
NA5 Sammy Sosa 1.00 2.50
NA6 Jason Giambi .75 2.00
NA7 Vladimir Guerrero 1.00 2.50
NA8 Albert Pujols 2.00 5.00
NA9 Todd Helton .75 2.00
NA10 Nomar Garciaparra 1.50 4.00
NA11 Randy Johnson 1.00 2.50
NA12 Jim Thome .75 2.00
NA13 Barry Bonds 2.50 6.00
NA14 Miguel Tejada .75 2.00
NA15 Alfonso Soriano .75 2.00

2003 Topps Heritage Real One Autographs

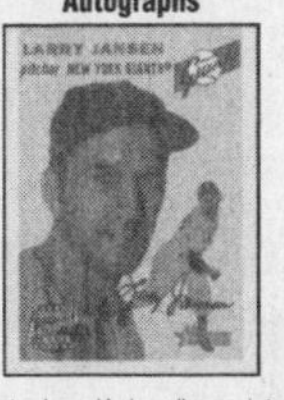

Inserted at various odds depending on what group the player belonged to, these cards feature authentic autographs from the featured player. Topps made an effort to secure autographs from every person who was still living that was in the 1954 Topps set. Hank Aaron, Yogi Berra and Johnny Sain did not return their cards in time for inclusion in this set and a collector could redeem these cards until February 28th, 2005. Sain never did sign his cards before his passing in November, 2006.

RETIRED ODDS 1:188
ACTIVE A ODDS 1:6168
ACTIVE B ODDS 1:1540
ACTIVE C ODDS 1:2802
*RED INK: 1X TO 2X BASIC RETIRED
*RED INK: .75X TO 1.5X BASIC ACTIVE A
*RED INK: .75X TO 1.5X BASIC ACTIVE B
*RED INK: .75X TO 1.5X BASIC ACTIVE C
RED INK STATED ODDS 1:696
RED INK PRINT RUN 54 SERIAL #'d SETS
AK Al Kaline 50.00 100.00
AP Andy Pafko 30.00 60.00
BR Bob Ross 10.00 25.00
BS Bill Skowron 15.00 40.00
BSH Bobby Shantz 15.00 40.00
BT Bob Talbot 10.00 25.00
BWE Bill Werle 10.00 25.00
CH Cal Hogue 10.00 25.00
CK Charlie Kress 10.00 25.00
CS Carl Scheib 12.50 30.00
DG Dick Groat 30.00 60.00
DK Dick Kryhoski 10.00 25.00
DL Don Lenhardt 10.00 25.00
DLU Don Lund 10.00 25.00
DS Duke Snider 50.00 100.00
EB Ernie Banks 75.00 150.00
EM Eddie Mayo 10.00 25.00
GH Gene Hermanski 10.00 25.00
HA Hank Aaron 200.00 350.00
HB Hank Bauer 15.00 40.00
JC Jose Cruz Jr. B 10.00 25.00
JP Joe Presko 10.00 25.00
JPO Johnny Podres 20.00 50.00
JR Jimmy Rollins C 15.00 40.00
JS Johnny Sain 15.00 40.00
Sain, due to ill health, never was able to sign cards for this product
JV Jose Vidro B 10.00 25.00
JW Jim Willis 10.00 25.00
LB Lance Berkman A 40.00 80.00
LJ Larry Jansen 15.00 40.00
LW Leroy Wheat 10.00 25.00
MB Matt Batts 10.00 25.00
MBL Mike Blyzka 10.00 25.00
MI Monte Irvin 30.00 60.00
MM Mickey Micelotta 10.00 25.00
MS Mike Sandlock 10.00 25.00
PP Paul Penson 10.00 25.00
PR Phil Rizzuto 30.00 60.00
PRO Preacher Roe 30.00 60.00
RF Roy Face 15.00 40.00
RM Ray Murray 10.00 25.00
TL Tom Lasorda 50.00 100.00
VL Vern Law 15.00 40.00
WF Whitey Ford 30.00 60.00
WM Willie Mays 150.00 250.00
YB Yogi Berra 50.00 100.00

2003 Topps Heritage Then and Now

Issued at a stated rate of one in 15, these 10 cards feature an 1954 star along with a current standout. The backs compare 10 league leaders of 1954 to the league leaders of 2002. Interestingly enough, Ted Kluszewski and Alex Rodriguez are on both the first two cards in this set.

COMPLETE SET (10) 12.50 30.00
TN1 Ted Kluszewski 1.50 4.00
Alex Rodriguez HR
TN2 Ted Kluszewski 1.50 4.00
Alex Rodriguez RBI
TN3 Willie Mays 2.50 6.00
Barry Bonds Batting
TN4 Don Mueller .75 2.00
Alfonso Soriano
TN5 Stan Musial 1.50 4.00
Garret Anderson
TN6 Minnie Minoso .75 2.00
Johnny Damon
TN7 Willie Mays 2.50 6.00
Barry Bonds Slugging
TN8 Duke Snider 1.50 4.00
Alex Rodriguez
TN9 Robin Roberts 1.00 2.50
Randy Johnson
TN10 Johnny Antonelli .75 2.00
Pedro Martinez

2004 Topps Heritage

This 495 card set was released in February, 2004. As this was the fourth year this set was issued, the cards were designed in the style of the 1955 Topps set. This set was issued in eight card packs which came 24 packs to a box and eight boxes to a case. This set features a mix of cards printed to standard amounts as well as various Short Prints and then even some variation short prints. Any type of short printed card was issued to a stated rate of one in two. We have delineated in our checklist what the various variations are. In addition, all cards from 398 through 475 are SP's.

COMPLETE SET (495) 200.00 350.00
COMP.SET w/o SP's (385) 30.00 60.00
COMMON CARD .20 .50
COMMON RC .30 .75
COMMON SP 2.00 5.00
COMMON SP RC 2.00 5.00
SP STATED ODDS 1:2
BASIC SP: 2/4/28/47/50/92/123/124/164
BASIC SP: 194/198/210/398-475
VARIATION SP: 1/8/10/30/40/49/60/70
VARIATION SP: 85/100/117/120/180/182
VARIATION SP: 200/213/250/311/342/361
SEE BECKETT.COM FOR VAR.DESCRIPTIONS
1A Jim Thome Fielding .30 .75
1B Jim Thome Hitting SP 3.00 8.00
2 Nomar Garciaparra SP 4.00 10.00
3 Aramis Ramirez .20 .50
4 Rafael Palmeiro SP 3.00 8.00
5 Danny Graves .20 .50
6 Casey Blake .20 .50
7 Juan Uribe .20 .50
8A Dmitri Young New Logo .20 .50
8B Dmitri Young Old Logo SP 2.00 5.00
9 Billy Wagner .20 .50
10A Jason Giambi Swinging .20 .50
10B Jason Giambi Btg Stance SP 2.00 5.00
11 Carlos Beltran .20 .50
12 Chad Hermansen .20 .50
13 B.J. Upton .40 1.00
14 Dustan Mohr .20 .50
15 Endy Chavez .20 .50
16 Cliff Floyd .20 .50
17 Bernie Williams .30 .75
18 Eric Chavez .20 .50
19 Chase Utley .50 1.25
20 Randy Johnson .60 1.50
21 Vernon Wells .20 .50
22 Juan Gonzalez .20 .50
23 Joe Kennedy .20 .50
24 Bengie Molina .20 .50
25 Carlos Lee .20 .50
26 Horacio Ramirez .20 .50
27 Anthony Acevedo RC .30 .75
28 Sammy Sosa SP 3.00 8.00
29 Jon Garland .20 .50
30A Adam Dunn Fielding .30 .75
30B Adam Dunn Hitting SP 2.00 5.00
31 Aaron Rowand .20 .50
32 Jody Gerut .20 .50
33 Chin-Hui Tsao .20 .50
34 Alex Sanchez .20 .50
35 A.J. Burnett .30 .75
36 Brad Ausmus .20 .50
37 Blake Hawksworth RC .30 .75
38 Francisco Rodriguez .30 .75
39 Alex Cintron .20 .50
40A Chipper Jones Pointing .60 1.50
40B Chipper Jones Fielding SP 3.00 8.00
41 Deivi Cruz .20 .50
42 Bill Mueller .20 .50
43 Joe Borowski .20 .50
44 Jimmy Haynes .20 .50
45 Mark Loretta .20 .50
46 Jerome Williams .20 .50
47 Gary Sheffield Yanks SP 3.00 8.00
48 Richard Hidalgo .20 .50
49A Jason Kendall New Logo .20 .50
49B Jason Kendall Old Logo SP 2.00 5.00
50 Ichiro Suzuki SP 5.00 12.00
51 Jim Edmonds .30 .75
52 Frank Catalanotto .20 .50
53 Jose Contreras .20 .50
54 Mo Vaughn .20 .50
55 Brendan Donnelly .20 .50
56 Luis Gonzalez .20 .50
57 Robert Fick .20 .50
58 Laynce Nix .20 .50
59 Johnny Damon .40 1.00
60A Magglio Ordonez Running .30 .75
60B Magglio Ordonez Hitting SP 2.00 5.00
61 Matt Clement .20 .50
62 Ryan Ludwick .20 .50
63 Luis Castillo .20 .50
64 Dave Crouthers RC .30 .75
65 Dave Berg .20 .50
66 Kyle Davies RC .30 .75
67 Tim Salmon .20 .50
68 Marcus Giles .20 .50
69 Marty Cordova .20 .50
70A Todd Helton White Jsy .40 1.00
70B Todd Helton Purple Jsy SP 3.00 8.00
71 Jeff Kent .20 .50
72 Michael Tucker .20 .50
73 Cesar Izturis .20 .50
74 Paul Quantrill .20 .50
75 Conor Jackson RC 2.00 5.00
76 Placido Polanco .20 .50
77 Adam Eaton .20 .50
78 Ramon Hernandez .20 .50
79 Edgardo Alfonzo .20 .50
80 Dioner Navarro RC .50 1.25
81 Woody Williams .20 .50
82 Rey Ordonez .20 .50
83 Randy Winn .20 .50
84 Casey Myers RC .30 .75
85A R.Choy Foo New Logo RC .30 .75
85B R.Choy Foo Old Logo SP 2.00 5.00
86 Ray Durham .20 .50
87 Sean Burroughs .20 .50
88 Tim Frend RC .30 .75
89 Shigetoshi Hasegawa .20 .50
90 Jeffrey Allison RC .30 .75
91 Orlando Hudson .20 .50
92 Matt Creighton SP RC .30 .75
93 Tim Worrell .20 .50
94 Kris Benson .20 .50
95 Mike Lieberthal .20 .50
96 David Wells .20 .50
97 Jason Phillips .20 .50
98 Bobby Cox MGR .20 .50
99 Johan Santana .60 1.50
100A Alex Rodriguez Hitting 1.00 2.50
100B Alex Rodriguez Throwing SP 4.00 10.00
101 John Vander Wal .20 .50
102 Orlando Cabrera .20 .50
103 Hideo Nomo .60 1.50
104 Todd Walker .20 .50
105 Jason Johnson .20 .50
106 Matt Mantei .20 .50
107 Jarrod Washburn .20 .50
108 Preston Wilson .20 .50
109 Carl Pavano .20 .50
110 Geoff Blum .20 .50
111 Eric Gagne .20 .50
112 Geoff Jenkins .20 .50
113 Joe Torre MG .30 .75
114 Jon Knott RC .30 .75
115 Hank Blalock .20 .50
116 John Olerud .20 .50
117A Pat Burrell New Logo .20 .50
117B Pat Burrell Old Logo SP 2.00 5.00
118 Aaron Boone .20 .50
119 Zach Day .20 .50
120A Frank Thomas New Logo .60 1.50
120B Frank Thomas Old Logo SP 3.00 8.00
121 Kyle Farnsworth .20 .50
122 Derek Lowe .20 .50
123 Zach Miner SP RC 3.00 8.00
124 Matthew Moses SP RC 3.00 8.00
125 Jesse Roman RC .30 .75
126 Josh Phelps .20 .50
127 Nic Ungs RC .30 .75
128 Dan Haren .20 .50
129 Kirk Rueter .20 .50
130 Jack McKeon MGR .20 .50
131 Keith Foulke .20 .50
132 Garrett Stephenson .20 .50
133 Wes Helms .20 .50
134 Raul Ibanez .20 .50
135 Morgan Ensberg .20 .50
136 Jay Payton .20 .50
137 Billy Koch .20 .50
138 Mark Grudzielanek .20 .50
139 Rodrigo Lopez .20 .50
140 Corey Patterson .20 .50
141 Troy Percival .20 .50
142 Shea Hillenbrand .20 .50
143 Brad Fullmer .20 .50
144 Ricky Nolasco RC .50 1.25
145 Mark Teixeira .50 1.25
146 Tydus Meadows RC .30 .75
147 Toby Hall .20 .50
148 Orlando Palmeiro .20 .50
149 Khalid Ballouli RC .30 .75
150 Grady Little MGR .20 .50
151 David Eckstein .20 .50
152 Kenny Perez RC .30 .75
153 Ben Grieve .20 .50
154 Ismael Valdes .20 .50
155 Bret Boone .20 .50
156 Jesse Foppert .20 .50
157 Vicente Padilla .20 .50
158 Bobby Abreu .20 .50
159 Scott Hatteberg .20 .50
160 Carlos Quentin RC 1.25 3.00
161 Anthony Lerew RC .30 .75
162 Lance Carter .20 .50
163 Robb Nen .20 .50
164 Zach Duke SP RC 4.00 10.00
165 Xavier Nady .20 .50
166 Kip Wells .20 .50
167 Kevin Millwood .20 .50
168 Jon Lieber .20 .50
169 Jose Reyes .30 .75
170 Eric Byrnes .20 .50
171 Paul Konerko .30 .75
172 Chris Lubanski .20 .50
173 Jae Weong Seo .20 .50
174 Corey Koskie .20 .50
175 Tim Stauffer RC .50 1.25
176 John Lackey .20 .50
177 Danny Bautista .20 .50
178 Shane Reynolds .20 .50
179 Jorge Julio .20 .50
180A Manny Ramirez New Logo .50 1.25
180B Manny Ramirez Old Logo SP 3.00 8.00
181 Alex Gonzalez .20 .50
182A Moises Alou New Logo .20 .50
182B Moises Alou Old Logo SP 2.00 5.00
183 Mark Buehrle .30 .75
184 Carlos Guillen .20 .50
185 Nate Cornejo .20 .50
186 Billy Traber .20 .50
187 Jason Jennings .20 .50
188 Eric Munson .20 .50
189 Braden Looper .20 .50
190 Juan Encarnacion .20 .50
191 Dusty Baker MGR .20 .50
192 Travis Lee .20 .50
193 Miguel Cairo .20 .50
194 Rich Aurilia SP 2.00 5.00
195 Tom Gordon .20 .50
196 Freddy Garcia .20 .50
197 Brian Lawrence .20 .50
198 Jorge Posada SP 3.00 8.00
199 Javier Vazquez .20 .50
200A Albert Pujols New Logo 1.25 3.00
200B Albert Pujols Old Logo SP 5.00 12.00
201 Victor Zambrano .20 .50
202 Eli Marrero .20 .50
203 Joel Pineiro .20 .50
204 Rondell White .20 .50
205 Craig Ansman RC .30 .75
206 Michael Young .20 .50
207 Carlos Baerga .20 .50
208 Andruw Jones .20 .50
209 Jerry Hairston Jr. .20 .50
210 Shawn Green SP 2.00 5.00
211 Ron Gardenhire MGR .20 .50
212 Darin Erstad .20 .50
213A Brandon Webb Glove Chest .20 .50
213B Brandon Webb Glove Out SP 2.00 5.00
214 Greg Maddux 1.00 2.50
215 Reed Johnson .20 .50
216 John Thomson .20 .50
217 Tino Martinez .40 1.00
218 Mike Cameron UER .20 .50
Card has facsimile autograph of Troy Cameron
219 Edgar Martinez .30 .75
220 Eric Young .20 .50
221 Reggie Sanders .20 .50
222 Randy Wolf .20 .50
223 Erubiel Durazo .20 .50
224 Mike Mussina .40 1.00
225 Tom Glavine .30 .75
226 Troy Glaus .20 .50
227 Oscar Villarreal .20 .50
228 David Segui .20 .50
229 Jeff Suppan .20 .50
230 Kenny Lofton .20 .50
231 Esteban Loaiza .20 .50
232 Felipe Lopez .20 .50
233 Matt Lawton .20 .50
234 Mark Bellhorn .20 .50
235 Wil Ledezma .20 .50
236 Todd Hollandsworth .20 .50
237 Octavio Dotel .20 .50
238 Darren Dreifort .20 .50
239 Paul Lo Duca .20 .50
240 Richie Sexson .20 .50
241 Doug Mientkiewicz .20 .50
242 Luis Rivas .20 .50
243 Claudio Vargas .20 .50
244 Mark Ellis .20 .50
245 Brett Myers .20 .50
246 Jake Peavy .20 .50
247 Marquis Grissom .20 .50
248 Armando Benitez .20 .50
249 Ryan Franklin .20 .50
250A Alfonso Soriano Throwing .20 .50
250B Alfonso Soriano Fielding SP 2.00 5.00
251 Tim Hudson .30 .75
252 Shannon Stewart .20 .50
253 A.J. Pierzynski .20 .50
254 Runelvys Hernandez .20 .50
255 Roy Oswalt .30 .75
256 Shawn Chacon .20 .50
257 Tony Graffanino .20 .50
258 Tim Wakefield .20 .50
259 Damian Miller .20 .50
260 Joe Crede .20 .50
261 Jason LaRue .20 .50
262 Jose Jimenez .20 .50
263 Juan Pierre .20 .50
264 Wade Miller .20 .50
265 Odalis Perez .20 .50
266 Eddie Guardado .20 .50
267 Rocky Biddle .20 .50
268 Jeff Nelson .20 .50
269 Terrence Long .20 .50
270 Ramon Ortiz .20 .50
271 Raul Mondesi .20 .50
272 Ugueth Urbina .20 .50
273 Jeromy Burnitz .20 .50
274 Brad Radke .20 .50
275 Jose Vidro .20 .50
276 Bobby Jenks .20 .50
277 Ty Wigginton .20 .50
278 Jose Guillen .20 .50
279 Delmon Young .30 .75
280 Brian Giles .20 .50
281 Jason Schmidt .20 .50
282 Nick Markakis .50 1.25
283 Felipe Alou MGR .20 .50
284 Carl Crawford .30 .75
285 Neifi Perez .20 .50
286 Miguel Tejada .30 .75
287 Victor Martinez .30 .75
288 Adam Kennedy .20 .50
289 Kerry Ligtenberg .20 .50
290 Scott Williamson .20 .50
291 Tony Womack .20 .50
292 Travis Hafner .20 .50
293 Bobby Crosby .20 .50
294 Chad Billingsley .20 .50
295 Russ Ortiz .20 .50
296 John Burkett .20 .50
297 Carlos Zambrano .30 .75
298 Randall Simon .20 .50
299 Juan Castro .20 .50
300 Mike Lowell .20 .50
301 Fred McGriff .20 .50
302 Glendon Rusch .20 .50
303 Sung Jung RC .30 .75
304 Rocco Baldelli .20 .50
305 Fernando Vina .20 .50
306 Gil Meche .20 .50
307 Jose Cruz Jr. .20 .50
308 Bernie Castro .20 .50
309 Scott Spiezio .20 .50
310 Paul Byrd .20 .50
311A Jay Gibbons New Logo .20 .50
311B Jay Gibbons Old Logo SP 2.00 5.00
312 Trot Nixon .20 .50
313 Chris O'Riordan RC .30 .75
314 Julio Lugo .20 .50
315 Ben Davis .20 .50
316 Mike Williams .20 .50
317 Trevor Hoffman .30 .75
318 Andy Pettitte .40 1.00
319 Orlando Hernandez .20 .50
320 Juan Rivera .20 .50
321 Elizardo Ramirez .20 .50
322 Junior Spivey .20 .50
323 Tony Batista .20 .50
324 Mike Remlinger .20 .50
325 Alex Gonzalez .20 .50
326 Aaron Hill .20 .50
327 Steve Finley .20 .50
328 Vinny Castilla .20 .50
329 Eric Duncan .20 .50
330 Mike Gosling RC .30 .75
331 Eric Hinske .20 .50
332 Scott Rolen .30 .75
333 Benito Santiago .20 .50
334 Jimmy Gobble .20 .50

335 Bobby Higginson .20 .50
336 Kelvim Escobar .20 .50
337 Mike DeJean .20 .50
338 Sidney Ponson .20 .50
339 Todd Self RC .30 .75
340 Jeff Cirillo .20 .50
341 Jimmy Rollins .30 .75
342A Barry Zito White Jsy .20 .50
342B Barry Zito Green Jsy SP 2.00 5.00
343 Felix Pie .20 .50
344 Matt Morris .20 .50
345 Kazuhiro Sasaki .20 .50
346 Jack Wilson .20 .50
347 Nick Johnson .20 .50
348 Wil Cordero .20 .50
349 Ryan Madson .20 .50
350 Torii Hunter .20 .50
351 Andy Ashby .20 .50
352 Aubrey Huff .20 .50
353 Brad Lidge .20 .50
354 Derrek Lee .40 1.00
355 Yadier Molina RC 2.00 5.00
356 Paul Wilson .20 .50
357 Omar Vizquel .30 .75
358 Rene Reyes .20 .50
359 Marlon Anderson .20 .50
360 Bobby Kielty .20 .50
361A Ryan Wagner New Logo .20 .50
361B Ryan Wagner Old Logo SP 2.00 5.00
362 Justin Morneau .20 .50
363 Shane Spencer .20 .50
364 David Bell .20 .50
365 Matt Stairs .20 .50
366 Joe Borchard .20 .50
367 Mark Redman .20 .50
368 Dave Roberts .20 .50
369 Desi Relaford .20 .50
370 Rich Harden .20 .50
371 Fernando Tatis .20 .50
372 Eric Karros .20 .50
373 Eric Milton .20 .50
374 Mike Sweeney .20 .50
375 Brian Daubach .20 .50
376 Brian Snyder .20 .50
377 Chris Reitsma .20 .50
378 Kyle Lohse .20 .50
379 Livan Hernandez .20 .50
380 Robin Ventura .20 .50
381 Jacque Jones .20 .50
382 Danny Kolb .20 .50
383 Casey Kotchman .20 .50
384 Cristian Guzman .20 .50
385 Josh Beckett .30 .75
386 Khalil Greene .30 .75
387 Greg Myers .20 .50
388 Francisco Cordero .20 .50
389 Donald Levinski RC .30 .75
390 Roy Halladay .50 1.25
391 J.D. Drew .20 .50
392 Jamie Moyer .20 .50
393 Ken Macha MGR .20 .50
394 Jeff Davanon .20 .50
395 Matt Kata .20 .50
396 Jack Cust .20 .50
397 Mike Timlin .20 .50
398 Zack Greinke SP 2.00 5.00
399 Byung-Hyun Kim SP 2.00 5.00
400 Kazuhisa Ishii SP 2.00 5.00
401 Brayan Pena SP RC 2.00 5.00
402 Garret Anderson SP 2.00 5.00
403 Kyle Sleeth SP RC 3.00 8.00
404 Javy Lopez SP 2.00 5.00
405 Damian Moss SP 2.00 5.00
406 David Ortiz SP 3.00 8.00
407 Pedro Martinez SP 3.00 8.00
408 Hee Seop Choi SP 2.00 5.00
409 Carl Everett SP 2.00 5.00
410 Dontrelle Willis SP 3.00 8.00
411 Ryan Harvey SP 2.00 5.00
412 Russell Branyan SP 2.00 5.00
413 Milton Bradley SP 2.00 5.00
414 Marcus McBeth SP RC 2.00 5.00
415 Carlos Pena SP 2.00 5.00
416 Ivan Rodriguez SP 3.00 8.00
417 Craig Biggio SP 3.00 8.00
418 Angel Berroa SP 2.00 5.00
419 Brian Jordan SP 2.00 5.00
420 Scott Podsednik SP 2.00 5.00
421 Omar Falcon SP RC 2.00 5.00
422 Joe Mays SP 2.00 5.00
423 Brad Wilkerson SP 2.00 5.00
424 Al Leiter SP 2.00 5.00
425 Derek Jeter SP 5.00 12.00
426 Mark Mulder SP 2.00 5.00
427 Marlon Byrd SP 2.00 5.00
428 David Murphy SP RC 3.00 8.00
429 Phil Nevin SP 2.00 5.00
430 J.T. Snow SP 2.00 5.00
431 Brad Sullivan SP RC 3.00 8.00
432 Bo Hart SP 2.00 5.00
433 Josh Labandeira SP RC 2.00 5.00
434 Chan Ho Park SP 2.00 5.00
435 Carlos Delgado SP 2.00 5.00
436 Curt Schilling Sox SP 3.00 8.00
437 John Smoltz SP 3.00 8.00
438 Luis Matos SP 2.00 5.00
439 Mark Prior SP 3.00 8.00
440 Roberto Alomar SP 3.00 8.00
441 Coco Crisp SP 2.00 5.00
442 Austin Kearns SP 2.00 5.00
443 Larry Walker SP 2.00 5.00
444 Neal Cotts SP 2.00 5.00
445 Jeff Bagwell SP 3.00 8.00
446 Adrian Beltre SP 2.00 5.00
447 Grady Sizemore SP 3.00 8.00
448 Keith Ginter SP 2.00 5.00
449 Vladimir Guerrero SP 3.00 8.00
450 Lyle Overbay SP 2.00 5.00
451 Rafael Furcal SP 2.00 5.00
452 Melvin Mora SP 2.00 5.00
453 Kerry Wood SP 2.00 5.00
454 Jose Valentin SP 2.00 5.00
455 Ken Griffey Jr. SP 4.00 10.00
456 Brandon Phillips SP 2.00 5.00
457 Miguel Cabrera SP 3.00 8.00
458 Edwin Jackson SP 2.00 5.00
459 Eric Owens SP 2.00 5.00
460 Miguel Batista SP 2.00 5.00
461 Mike Hampton SP 2.00 5.00
462 Kevin Millar SP 2.00 5.00
463 Bartolo Colon SP 2.00 5.00
464 Sean Casey SP 2.00 5.00
465 C.C. Sabathia SP 2.00 5.00
466 Rickie Weeks SP 2.00 5.00
467 Brad Penny SP 2.00 5.00
468 Mike MacDougal SP 2.00 5.00
469 Kevin Brown SP 2.00 5.00
470 Lance Berkman SP 2.00 5.00
471 Ben Sheets SP 2.00 5.00
472 Mariano Rivera SP 3.00 8.00
473 Mike Piazza SP 4.00 10.00
474 Ryan Klesko SP 2.00 5.00
475 Edgar Renteria SP 2.00 5.00

2004 Topps Heritage Chrome

COMPLETE SET (110) 150.00 250.00
STATED ODDS 1:7
STATED PRINT RUN 1955 SERIAL #'d SETS
THC1 Sammy Sosa 3.00 8.00
THC2 Nomar Garciaparra 3.00 8.00
THC3 Ichiro Suzuki 5.00 12.00
THC4 Rafael Palmeiro 2.00 5.00
THC5 Carlos Delgado 1.25 3.00
THC6 Troy Glaus 1.25 3.00
THC7 Jay Gibbons 1.25 3.00
THC8 Frank Thomas 3.00 8.00
THC9 Pat Burrell 1.25 3.00
THC10 Albert Pujols 8.00 20.00
THC11 Brandon Webb 1.25 3.00
THC12 Chipper Jones 3.00 8.00
THC13 Magglio Ordonez 2.00 5.00
THC14 Adam Dunn 2.00 5.00
THC15 Todd Helton 2.00 5.00
THC16 Jason Giambi 1.25 3.00
THC17 Alfonso Soriano 1.25 3.00
THC18 Barry Zito 1.25 3.00
THC19 Jim Thome 2.00 5.00
THC20 Alex Rodriguez 5.00 12.00
THC21 Hee Seop Choi 1.25 3.00
THC22 Pedro Martinez 2.00 5.00
THC23 Kerry Wood 1.25 3.00
THC24 Bartolo Colon 1.25 3.00
THC25 Austin Kearns 1.25 3.00
THC26 Ken Griffey Jr. 5.00 12.00
THC27 Coco Crisp 1.25 3.00
THC28 Larry Walker 2.00 5.00
THC29 Ivan Rodriguez 2.00 5.00
THC30 Dontrelle Willis 1.25 3.00
THC31 Miguel Cabrera 3.00 8.00
THC32 Jeff Bagwell 2.00 5.00
THC33 Lance Berkman 2.00 5.00
THC34 Shawn Green 1.25 3.00
THC35 Kevin Brown 1.25 3.00
THC36 Vladimir Guerrero 3.00 8.00
THC37 Mike Piazza 3.00 8.00
THC38 Derek Jeter 8.00 20.00
THC39 John Smoltz 3.00 8.00
40 Mark Prior 2.00 5.00
THC41 Gary Sheffield Yanks 1.25 3.00
THC42 Curt Schilling Sox 2.00 5.00
THC43 Randy Johnson 3.00 8.00
THC44 Luis Gonzalez 1.25 3.00
THC45 Andruw Jones 1.25 3.00
THC46 Greg Maddux 5.00 12.00
THC47 Tony Batista 1.25 3.00
THC48 Esteban Loaiza 1.25 3.00
THC49 Chin-Hui Tsao 1.25 3.00
THC50 Mike Lowell 1.25 3.00
THC51 Jeff Kent 1.25 3.00
THC52 Richie Sexson 1.25 3.00
THC53 Torii Hunter 1.25 3.00
THC54 Jose Vidro 1.25 3.00
THC55 Jose Reyes 2.00 5.00
THC56 Jimmy Rollins 2.00 5.00
THC57 Bret Boone 1.25 3.00
THC58 Rocco Baldelli 1.25 3.00
THC59 Hank Blalock 1.25 3.00
THC60 Rickie Weeks 1.25 3.00
THC61 Rodney Choy Foo 1.25 3.00
THC62 Zach Miner 2.00 5.00
THC63 Brayan Pena 1.25 3.00
THC64 David Murphy 3.00 8.00
THC65 Matt Creighton 1.25 3.00
THC66 Kyle Sleeth 1.25 3.00
THC67 Matthew Moses 2.00 5.00
THC68 Josh Labandeira 1.25 3.00
THC69 Grady Sizemore 2.00 5.00
THC70 Edwin Jackson 1.25 3.00
THC71 Marcus McBeth 1.25 3.00
THC72 Brad Sullivan 1.25 3.00
THC73 Zach Duke 2.00 5.00
THC74 Omar Falcon 1.25 3.00
THC75 Conor Jackson 8.00 20.00
THC76 Carlos Quentin 5.00 12.00
THC77 Craig Ansman 1.25 3.00
THC78 Mike Gosling 1.25 3.00
THC79 Kyle Davies 1.25 3.00
THC80 Anthony Lerew 1.25 3.00
THC81 Sung Jung 1.25 3.00
THC82 Dave Crouthers 1.25 3.00
THC83 Kenny Perez 1.25 3.00
THC84 Jeffrey Allison 1.25 3.00
THC85 Nic Ungs 1.25 3.00
THC86 Donald Levinski 1.25 3.00
THC87 Anthony Acevedo 1.25 3.00
THC88 Todd Self 1.25 3.00
THC89 Tim Frend 1.25 3.00
THC90 Tydus Meadows 1.25 3.00
THC91 Khalid Ballouli 1.25 3.00
THC92 Dioner Navarro 2.00 5.00
THC93 Casey Myers 1.25 3.00
THC94 Jon Knott 1.25 3.00
THC95 Tim Stauffer 2.00 5.00
THC96 Ricky Nolasco 2.00 5.00
THC97 Blake Hawksworth 1.25 3.00
THC98 Jesse Roman 1.25 3.00
THC99 Yadier Molina 8.00 20.00
THC100 Chris O'Riordan 1.25 3.00
THC101 Cliff Floyd 1.25 3.00
THC102 Nick Johnson 1.25 3.00
THC103 Edgar Martinez 2.00 5.00
THC104 Brett Myers 1.25 3.00
THC105 Francisco Rodriguez 2.00 5.00
THC106 Scott Rolen 2.00 5.00
THC107 Mark Teixeira 3.00 8.00
THC108 Miguel Tejada 2.00 5.00
THC109 Vernon Wells 1.25 3.00
THC110 Jerome Williams 1.25 3.00

2004 Topps Heritage Chrome Black Refractors

*BLACK REF: 2X TO 5X CHROME
*BLACK REF: 2X TO 5X CHROME RC YR
STATED ODDS 1:251
STATED PRINT RUN 55 SERIAL #'d SETS

2004 Topps Heritage Chrome Refractors

*REFRACTOR: .6X TO 1.5X CHROME
*REFRACTOR: .6X TO 1.5X CHROME RC YR
STATED ODDS 1:25
STATED PRINT RUN 555 SERIAL #'d SETS

2004 Topps Heritage Clubhouse Collection Relics

GROUP A ODDS 1:3037
GROUP B ODDS 1:4142
GROUP C ODDS 1:138
GROUP D ODDS 1:92
GROUP A STATED PRINT RUN 100 SETS
GROUP A PRINT RUN PROVIDED BY TOPPS
GROUP A ARE NOT SERIAL-NUMBERED
AD Adam Dunn Jsy D 3.00 8.00
AJ Andruw Jones Jsy C 4.00 10.00
AK Al Kaline Bat A 20.00 50.00
AP Albert Pujols Uni C 6.00 15.00
AR Alex Rodriguez Jsy C 4.00 10.00
AS Alfonso Soriano Uni D 3.00 8.00
BA Bobby Abreu Jsy D 3.00 8.00
BB Bret Boone Jsy D 3.00 8.00
BM Brett Myers Jsy D 3.00 8.00
BZ Barry Zito Uni C 3.00 8.00
CJ Chipper Jones Jsy D 4.00 10.00
CS C.C. Sabathia Jsy D 3.00 8.00
DS Duke Snider Bat A 15.00 40.00
EC Eric Chavez Uni D 3.00 8.00
EG Eric Gagne Uni D 3.00 8.00
FM Fred McGriff Bat C 4.00 10.00
GM Greg Maddux Jsy C 6.00 15.00
GS Gary Sheffield Uni D 3.00 8.00
HB Hank Blalock Jsy D 3.00 8.00
HK Harmon Killebrew Jsy C 10.00 25.00
IR Ivan Rodriguez Bat C 4.00 10.00
JD Johnny Damon Uni D 4.00 10.00
JG Jason Giambi Uni D 3.00 8.00
JL Javy Lopez Jsy D 3.00 8.00
JR Jimmy Rollins Jsy D 3.00 8.00
JRE Jose Reyes Jsy D 3.00 8.00
JS John Smoltz Jsy C 4.00 10.00
JT Jim Thome Bat D 4.00 10.00
KB Kevin Brown Uni D 3.00 8.00
KI Kazuhisa Ishii Uni D 3.00 8.00
KW Kerry Wood Jsy D 3.00 8.00
LB Lance Berkman Jsy C 3.00 8.00
LG Luis Gonzalez Jsy D 3.00 8.00
MG Marcus Giles Jsy C 3.00 8.00
MM Mark Mulder Uni D 3.00 8.00
MR Manny Ramirez Jsy C 4.00 10.00
MS Mike Sweeney Jsy D 3.00 8.00
MT Miguel Tejada Uni D 3.00 8.00
MTB Miguel Tejada Bat C 3.00 8.00
MTE Mark Teixeira Jsy D 4.00 10.00
NG Nomar Garciaparra Uni C 6.00 15.00
PL Paul Lo Duca Uni C 3.00 8.00
PM Pedro Martinez Jsy D 4.00 10.00
RB Rocco Baldelli Jsy D 3.00 8.00
RC Roger Clemens Uni D 6.00 15.00
RF Rafael Furcal Jsy D 3.00 8.00
RJ Randy Johnson Jsy C 4.00 10.00
SG Shawn Green Uni C 3.00 8.00
SM Stan Musial Bat A 30.00 60.00
SR Scott Rolen Uni B 4.00 10.00
SRB Scott Rolen Bat C 4.00 10.00
SS Sammy Sosa Jsy C 4.00 10.00
TG Troy Glaus Uni C 3.00 8.00
TH Tim Hudson Uni D 3.00 8.00
THU Torii Hunter Bat C 3.00 8.00
VW Vernon Wells Jsy C 3.00 8.00
WM Willie Mays Uni A 50.00 100.00
YB Yogi Berra Jsy A 20.00 50.00

2004 Topps Heritage Clubhouse Collection Autograph Relics

STATED ODDS 1:15,186
STATED PRINT RUN 25 SERIAL #'d SETS
NO PRICING DUE TO SCARCITY
AK Al Kaline Bat
DS Duke Snider Bat
EB Ernie Banks Uni
WM Willie Mays Uni

2004 Topps Heritage Clubhouse Collection Dual Relics

STATED ODDS 1:9244
STATED PRINT RUN 55 SERIAL #'d SETS
BC Yogi Berra Uni 75.00 150.00
Roger Clemens Uni
GS Shawn Green Jsy 75.00 150.00
Duke Snider Uni
MP Albert Pujols Jsy 150.00 250.00
Stan Musial Uni

2004 Topps Heritage Doubleheader

ONE PER SEALED HOBBY BOX
VINTAGE D-HEADERS RANDOMLY SEEDED
12 Alex Rodriguez 2.50 6.00
Nomar Garciaparra
34 Ichiro Suzuki 4.00 10.00
Albert Pujols
56 Sammy Sosa 4.00 10.00
Derek Jeter
78 Jim Thome 1.00 2.50
Adam Dunn
910 Jason Giambi 1.00 2.50
Ivan Rodriguez
1112 Todd Helton 1.00 2.50
Luis Gonzalez
1314 Jeff Bagwell 1.00 2.50
Lance Berkman
1516 Alfonso Soriano .60 1.50
Dontrelle Willis
1718 Mark Prior 1.50 4.00
Vladimir Guerrero
1920 Mike Piazza 2.00 5.00
Roger Clemens
2122 Randy Johnson 1.50 4.00
Curt Schilling
2324 Gary Sheffield 1.00 2.50
Pedro Martinez
2526 Carlos Delgado 1.00 2.50
Jimmy Rollins
2728 Andruw Jones .60 1.50
Chipper Jones
2930 Rocco Baldelli .60 1.50
Hank Blalock
NNO Vintage Buyback

2004 Topps Heritage Flashbacks

COMPLETE SET (10) 6.00 15.00
STATED ODDS 1:12
F1 Duke Snider .60 1.50
F2 Johnny Podres .40 1.00
F3 Don Newcombe .40 1.00
F4 Al Kaline 1.00 2.50
F5 Willie Mays 2.00 5.00
F6 Stan Musial 1.50 4.00
F7 Harmon Killebrew 1.00 2.50
F8 Herb Score .40 1.00
F9 Whitey Ford .60 1.50
F10 Robin Roberts .40 1.00

2004 Topps Heritage Flashbacks Autographs

STATED ODDS 1:30,373
STATED PRINT RUN 25 SERIAL #'d SETS
NO PRICING DUE TO SCARCITY
AK Al Kaline
NPS Don Newcombe
Johnny Podres
Duke Snider

2004 Topps Heritage Grandstand Glory Stadium Seat Relics

GROUP A ODDS 1:27,731
GROUP A ODDS 1:606
GROUP A STATED PRINT RUN 55 CARDS
GROUP A PRINT RUN PROVIDED BY TOPPS
GROUP A IS NOT SERIAL-NUMBERED
AK Al Kaline B 10.00 25.00
HK Harmon Killebrew B 10.00 25.00
SM Stan Musial B 15.00 40.00
WM Willie Mays A 90.00 150.00
WS Warren Spahn B 10.00 25.00
YB Yogi Berra B 10.00 25.00

2004 Topps Heritage New Age Performers

COMPLETE SET (15) 10.00 25.00
STATED ODDS 1:15
NA1 Jason Giambi .40 1.00
NA2 Ichiro Suzuki 1.50 4.00
NA3 Alex Rodriguez 1.50 4.00
NA4 Alfonso Soriano .40 1.00
NA5 Albert Pujols 2.50 6.00
NA6 Nomar Garciaparra 1.00 2.50
NA7 Mark Prior .60 1.50
NA8 Derek Jeter 2.50 6.00
NA9 Sammy Sosa 1.00 2.50
NA10 Carlos Delgado .40 1.00
NA11 Jim Thome .60 1.50
NA12 Todd Helton .60 1.50
NA13 Gary Sheffield .40 1.00
NA14 Vladimir Guerrero 1.00 2.50
NA15 Josh Beckett .60 1.50

2004 Topps Heritage Real One Autographs

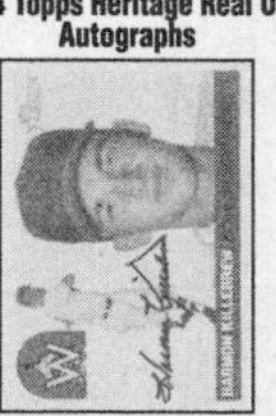

These autograph cards feature a mix of players who are active today; players who had cards in the 1955 Topps set and Stan Musial signing cards as if he were in the 1955 set. Scott Rolen did not return his cards in time for pack out and those exchange cards could be redeemed until February 28th, 2006.

STATED ODDS 1:230
STATED PRINT RUN 200 SETS
PRINT RUN INFO PROVIDED BY TOPPS
BASIC AUTOS ARE NOT SERIAL-NUMBERED
*RED INK: .75X TO 1.5X RETIRED
*RED INK MAYS: 1.25X TO 2X BASIC MAYS
*RED INK: .75X TO 1.5X ACTIVE
RED INK ODDS 1:835
RED INK PRINT RUN 55 #'d SETS
RED INK ALSO CALLED SPECIAL EDITION
AH Aubrey Huff 15.00 40.00
AK Al Kaline 50.00 100.00
BB Bob Borkowski 15.00 40.00
BC Billy Consolo 15.00 40.00
BG Bill Glynn 15.00 40.00
BK Bob Kline 15.00 40.00
BM Bob Milliken 15.00 40.00
BW Bill Wilson 20.00 50.00
CF Cliff Floyd 15.00 40.00
DN Don Newcombe 30.00 60.00
DP Duane Pillette 15.00 40.00
DS Duke Snider 50.00 100.00
DW Dontrelle Willis 15.00 40.00
EB Ernie Banks 70.00 120.00
FS Frank Smith 15.00 40.00
GA Gair Allie 15.00 40.00
HE Harry Elliott 15.00 40.00
HK Harmon Killebrew 60.00 120.00
HP Harry Perkowski 15.00 40.00
HV Corky Valentine 20.00 50.00
JG Johnny Gray 15.00 40.00
JP Jim Pearce 20.00 50.00
JPO Johnny Podres 30.00 60.00
LL Lou Limmer 30.00 60.00
ML Mike Lowell 15.00 40.00
MO Magglio Ordonez 15.00 40.00
SK Steve Kraly 30.00 60.00
SM Stan Musial 60.00 120.00
SR Scott Rolen 15.00 40.00
TK Thornton Kipper 20.00 50.00
TW Tom Wright 15.00 40.00
VT Jake Thies 20.00 50.00
WM Willie Mays 125.00 200.00
YB Yogi Berra 100.00 200.00

2004 Topps Heritage Then and Now

COMPLETE SET (6) 4.00 10.00
STATED ODDS 1:15
TN1 Willie Mays 2.00 5.00
Jim Thome
TN2 Al Kaline 2.50 6.00
Albert Pujols
TN3 Duke Snider .60 1.50
Carlos Delgado
TN4 Robin Roberts 1.00 2.50
Roy Halladay
TN5 Don Newcombe 1.00 2.50
Johan Santana
TN6 Herb Score .40 1.00
Kerry Wood

2005 Topps Heritage

This 495-card set was released in February, 2005. This set was issued in eight-card hobby/retail packs with an $3 SRP which came 24 packs to a box and eight boxes to a case. The 2005 version of Heritage honored the 1956 Topps set. Sprinkled throughout the set was a grouping of variation cards and other short printed cards. The Short print cards were issued at a stated rate of one in two hobby/retail packs.

COMPLETE SET (495) 250.00 400.00
COMP.SET w/o SP's (385) 30.00 60.00
COMMON CARD .20 .50
COMMON RC .20 .50
COMMON TEAM CARD .20 .50
COMMON SP 3.00 8.00
COMMON SP RC 3.00 8.00
SP STATED ODDS 1:2 HOBBY/RETAIL
BASIC SP: 5/20/30/31/33/79/101/110/130
BASIC SP: 135/260/292/398-475
VARIATION SP: 3/6/7/31/50/69/78/82/118
VARIATION SP: 125/135/155/261/273/286
VARIATION SP: 296/300/312/353/389
SEE BECKETT.COM FOR VAR.DESCRIPTIONS
1 Will Harridge .20 .50
2 Warren Giles .20 .50
3A Alfonso Soriano Fldg .30 .75
3B Alfonso Soriano Running SP 3.00 8.00
4 Mark Mulder .20 .50
5 Todd Helton SP 3.00 8.00
6A Jason Bay Black Cap .20 .50
6B Jason Bay Yellow Cap SP 3.00 8.00
7A Ichiro Suzuki Running .75 2.00
7B Ichiro Suzuki Crouch SP 4.00 10.00
8 Jim Tracy MG .20 .50
9 Gavin Floyd .20 .50
10 John Smoltz .50 1.25
11 Chicago Cubs TC .30 .75
12 Darin Erstad .20 .50
13 Chad Tracy .20 .50
14 Charles Thomas .20 .50
15 Miguel Tejada .30 .75
16 Andre Ethier RC 1.50 4.00
17 Jeff Francis .20 .50
18 Derrek Lee .20 .50
19 Juan Uribe .20 .50
20 Jim Edmonds SP 3.00 8.00
21 Kenny Lofton .20 .50
22 Brad Ausmus .20 .50
23 Jon Garland .20 .50
24 Edwin Jackson .20 .50
25 Joe Mauer .50 1.25
26 Wes Helms .20 .50
27 Brian Schneider .20 .50
28 Kazuo Matsui .20 .50
29 Flash Gordon .20 .50
30 Hideo Nomo SP 3.00 8.00
31A Albert Pujols Red Hat SP 5.00 12.00
31B Albert Pujols Blue Hat SP 5.00 12.00
32 Carl Crawford .30 .75
33 Vladimir Guerrero SP 3.00 8.00
34 Nick Green .20 .50
35 Jay Gibbons .20 .50
36 Kevin Youkilis .20 .50
37 Billy Wagner .20 .50
38 Terrence Long .20 .50
39 Kevin Mench .20 .50
40 Garret Anderson .20 .50
41 Reed Johnson .20 .50
42 Reggie Sanders .20 .50
43 Kirk Rueter .20 .50
44 Jay Payton .20 .50
45 Tike Redman .20 .50
46 Mike Lieberthal .20 .50
47 Damian Miller .20 .50
48 Zach Day .20 .50
49 Juan Rincon .20 .50
50A Jim Thome At Bat .30 .75
50B Jim Thome Fldg SP 3.00 8.00
51 Jose Guillen .20 .50
52 Richie Sexson .20 .50
53 Juan Cruz .20 .50
54 Byung-Hyun Kim .20 .50
55 Carlos Zambrano .30 .75
56 Carlos Lee .20 .50
57 Adam Dunn .30 .75
58 David Riske .20 .50
59 Carlos Guillen .20 .50
60 Larry Bowa MG .20 .50
61 Barry Bonds 1.00 2.50
62 Chris Woodward .20 .50
63 Matt DeSalvo RC .20 .50
64 Brian Stavisky RC .20 .50
65 Scot Shields .20 .50
66 J.D. Drew .20 .50
67 Erik Bedard .20 .50
68 Scott Williamson .20 .50
69A M.Prior New C on Cap .30 .75
69B M.Prior Old C on Cap SP 3.00 8.00
70 Ken Griffey Jr. .75 2.00
71 Kazuhito Tadano .20 .50
72 Philadelphia Phillies TC .20 .50
73 Jeremy Reed .20 .50
74 Ricardo Rodriguez .20 .50
75 Carlos Delgado .20 .50
76 Eric Milton .20 .50
77 Miguel Olivo .20 .50
78A E.Alfonzo No Socks .20 .50
78B E.Alfonzo Black Socks SP 3.00 8.00
79 Kazuhisa Ishii SP 3.00 8.00
80 Jason Giambi .20 .50
81 Cliff Floyd .20 .50
Facsimile autograph is Jeff Abbott
82A Torii Hunter Twins Cap .20 .50
82B Torii Hunter Wash Cap SP 3.00 8.00
83 Odalis Perez .20 .50
84 Scott Podsednik .20 .50
85 Cleveland Indians TC .20 .50
86 Jeff Suppan .20 .50
87 Ray Durham .20 .50
88 Tyler Clippard RC 1.25 3.00
89 Ryan Howard 1.00 2.50
90 Cincinnati Reds TC .20 .50
91 Bengie Molina .20 .50
92 Danny Bautista .20 .50
93 Eli Marrero .20 .50
94 Larry Bigbie .20 .50
95 Atlanta Braves TC .30 .75
96 Merkin Valdez .20 .50
97 Rocco Baldelli .20 .50
98 Woody Williams .20 .50
99 Jason Frasor .20 .50
100 Baltimore Orioles TC .20 .50
101 Ivan Rodriguez SP 3.00 8.00
102 Joe Kennedy .20 .50
103 Mike Lowell .20 .50
104 Armando Benitez .20 .50
105 Craig Biggio .30 .75
106 David DeJesus .20 .50
107 Adrian Beltre .20 .50
108 Phil Nevin .20 .50
109 Cristian Guzman .20 .50
110 Jorge Posada SP 3.00 8.00
111 Boston Red Sox TC .50 1.25
112 Jeff Mathis .30 .75
113 Bartolo Colon .20 .50
114 Alex Cintron .20 .50
115 Russ Ortiz .20 .50
116 Doug Mientkiewicz .20 .50
117 Placido Polanco .20 .50
118A M.Ordonez Black Uni .30 .75
118B M.Ordonez White Uni SP 3.00 8.00
119 Chris Seddon RC .20 .50
120 Bobby Abreu .20 .50
121 Pittsburgh Pirates TC .20 .50
122 Dallas McPherson .20 .50
123 Rodrigo Lopez .20 .50
124 Mark Bellhorn .20 .50
125A N.Garciaparra Red Cap .50 1.25
125B N.Garciaparra Blue Cap SP 3.00 8.00
126 Sean Casey .20 .50
127 Ronnie Belliard .20 .50
128 Tom Goodwin .20 .50
129 Preston Wilson .20 .50
130 Andruw Jones SP 3.00 8.00
131 Roberto Alomar .30 .75
132 John Buck .20 .50
133 Jason LaRue .20 .50
134 St. Louis Cardinals TC .30 .75
135A Alex Rodriguez Fldg SP 4.00 10.00
135B Alex Rodriguez At Bat SP 4.00 10.00
136 Nate Robertson .20 .50
137 Juan Pierre .20 .50
138 Morgan Ensberg .20 .50
139 Vinny Castilla .20 .50
140 Jake Dittler .20 .50
141 Chan Ho Park .30 .75

142 Felix Hernandez .75 2.00
143 Jason Isringhausen .20 .50
144 Dustan Mohr .20 .50
145 Khalil Greene .20 .50
146 Minnesota Twins TC .20 .50
147 Vicente Padilla .20 .50
148 Oliver Perez .20 .50
149 Brian Giles .20 .50
150 Shawn Green .20 .50
151 Matt Lawton .20 .50
152 Casey Blake .20 .50
153 Frank Thomas .50 1.25
154 Orlando Hernandez .20 .50
155A Eric Chavez Green Cap .20 .50
155B Eric Chavez Blue Cap SP 3.00 8.00
156 Chase Utley .30 .75
157 John Olerud .20 .50
158 Adam Eaton .20 .50
159 Josh Fogg .20 .50
160 Michael Tucker .20 .50
161 Kevin Brown .20 .50
162 Bobby Crosby .20 .50
163 Jason Schmidt .20 .50
164 Shannon Stewart .20 .50
165 Tony Womack .20 .50
166 Los Angeles Dodgers TC .20 .50
167 Franklin Gutierrez .60 1.50
168 Ted Lilly .20 .50
169 Mark Teixeira .50 1.25
170 Matt Morris .20 .50
171 Bucky Jacobsen .20 .50
172 Steve Doetsch RC .20 .50
173 Jeff Weaver .20 .50
174 Tony Graffanino .20 .50
175 Jeff Bagwell .30 .75
176 Carl Pavano .20 .50
177 Junior Spivey .20 .50
178 Carlos Silva .20 .50
179 Tim Redding .20 .50
180 Brett Myers .20 .50
181 Mike Mussina .30 .75
182 Richard Hidalgo .20 .50
183 Nick Johnson .20 .50
184 Lew Ford .20 .50
185 Barry Zito .20 .50
186 Jimmy Rollins .30 .75
187 Jack Wilson .20 .50
188 Chicago White Sox TC .20 .50
189 Guillermo Quiroz .20 .50
190 Mark Hendrickson .20 .50
191 Jeremy Bonderman .20 .50
192 Jason Jennings .20 .50
193 Paul Lo Duca .20 .50
194 A.J. Burnett .30 .75
195 Ken Harvey .20 .50
196 Geoff Jenkins .20 .50
197 Joe Mays .20 .50
198 Jose Vidro .20 .50
199 David Wright .75 2.00
200 Randy Johnson .50 1.25
201 Jeff DaVanon .20 .50
202 Paul Byrd .20 .50
203 David Ortiz .50 1.25
204 Kyle Farnsworth .20 .50
205 Keith Foulke .20 .50
206 Joe Crede .20 .50
207 Austin Kearns .20 .50
208 Jody Gerut .20 .50
209 Shawn Chacon .20 .50
210 Carlos Pena .30 .75
211 Luis Castillo .20 .50
212 Chris Denorfia RC .20 .50
213 Detroit Tigers TC .20 .50
214 Aubrey Huff .20 .50
215 Brad Fullmer .20 .50
216 Frank Catalanotto .20 .50
217 Raul Ibanez .20 .50
218 Ryan Klesko .20 .50
219 Octavio Dotel .20 .50
220 Rob Mackowiak .20 .50
221 Scott Hatteberg .20 .50
222 Pat Burrell .20 .50
223 Bernie Williams .30 .75
224 Kris Benson .20 .50
225 Eric Gagne .20 .50
226 San Francisco Giants TC .20 .50
227 Roy Oswalt .30 .75
228 Josh Beckett .30 .75
229 Lee Mazzilli MG .20 .50
230 Rickie Weeks .30 .75
231 Troy Glaus .20 .50
232 Chone Figgins .20 .50
233 John Thomson .20 .50
234 Trot Nixon .20 .50
235 Brad Penny .20 .50
236 Oakland A's TC .20 .50
237 Miguel Batista .20 .50
238 Ryan Drese .20 .50
239 Aaron Miles .20 .50
240 Randy Wolf .20 .50
241 Brian Lawrence .20 .50
242 A.J. Pierzynski .20 .50
243 Jamie Moyer .20 .50
244 Chris Carpenter .50 1.25
245 So Taguchi .20 .50
246 Rob Bell .20 .50
247 Francisco Cordero .20 .50
248 Tom Glavine .30 .75
249 Jermaine Dye .20 .50
250 Cliff Lee .30 .75
251 New York Yankees TC .50 1.25
252 Vernon Wells .20 .50
253 R.A. Dickey .20 .50
254 Larry Walker .30 .75
255 Randy Winn .20 .50
256 Pedro Feliz .20 .50
257 Mark Loretta .20 .50
258 Tim Worrell .20 .50
259 Kip Wells .20 .50
260 Cesar Izturis SP 3.00 8.00
261A Carlos Beltran Fldg .20 .50
261B Carlos Beltran At Bat SP 3.00 8.00
262 Juan Encarnacion .20 .50
263 Luis A. Gonzalez .20 .50
Facsimile autograph is of other Luis Gonzalez
264 Grady Sizemore .30 .75
265 Paul Wilson .20 .50
266 Mark Buehrle .30 .75
267 Todd Hollandsworth .20 .50
268 Orlando Cabrera .20 .50
269 Sidney Ponson .20 .50
270 Mike Hampton .20 .50
271 Luis Gonzalez .20 .50
Facsimile autographs is of other Luis Gonzalez
272 Brendan Donnelly .20 .50
273A Chipper Jones Slide .50 1.25
273B Chipper Jones Fldg SP 3.00 8.00
274 Brandon Webb .30 .75
275 Marty Cordova .20 .50
276 Greg Maddux .75 2.00
277 Jose Contreras .20 .50
278 Aaron Harang .20 .50
279 Coco Crisp .20 .50
280 Bobby Higginson .20 .50
281 Guillermo Mota .20 .50
282 Andy Pettitte .30 .75
283 Jeremy West RC .20 .50
284 Craig Brazell .20 .50
285 Eric Hinske .20 .50
286A Hank Blalock Hitting .20 .50
286B Hank Blalock Fldg SP 3.00 8.00
287 B.J. Upton .30 .75
288 Jason Marquis .20 .50
289 Matt Herges .20 .50
290 Ramon Hernandez .20 .50
291 Marlon Byrd .20 .50
292 Ryan Sweeney SP RC 3.00 8.00
293 Esteban Loaiza .20 .50
294 Al Leiter .20 .50
295 Alex Gonzalez .20 .50
296A J.Santana Twins Cap .50 1.25
296B J.Santana Wash Cap SP 3.00 8.00
297 Milton Bradley .20 .50
298 Mike Sweeney .20 .50
299 Wade Miller .20 .50
300A Sammy Sosa Hitting .50 1.25
300B Sammy Sosa Standing SP 3.00 8.00
301 Wily Mo Pena .20 .50
302 Tim Wakefield .20 .50
303 Rafael Palmeiro .30 .75
304 Rafael Furcal .20 .50
305 David Eckstein .20 .50
306 David Segui .20 .50
307 Kevin Millar .20 .50
308 Matt Clement .20 .50
309 Wade Robinson RC .20 .50
310 Brad Radke .20 .50
311 Steve Finley .20 .50
312A Lance Berkman Hitting .30 .75
312B Lance Berkman Fldg SP 3.00 8.00
313 Joe Randa .20 .50
314 Miguel Cabrera .50 1.25
315 Billy Koch .20 .50
316 Alex Sanchez .20 .50
317 Chin-Hui Tsao .20 .50
318 Omar Vizquel .30 .75
319 Ryan Freel .20 .50
320 LaTroy Hawkins .20 .50
321 Aaron Rowand .20 .50
322 Paul Konerko .30 .75
323 Joe Borowski .20 .50
324 Jarrod Washburn .20 .50
325 Jaret Wright .20 .50
326 Johnny Damon .30 .75
327 Corey Patterson .20 .50
328 Travis Hafner .20 .50
329 Shingo Takatsu .20 .50
330 Dmitri Young .20 .50
331 Matt Holliday .50 1.25
332 Jeff Kent .20 .50
333 Desi Relaford .20 .50
334 Jose Hernandez .20 .50
335 Lyle Overbay .20 .50
336 Jacque Jones .20 .50
337 Termel Sledge .20 .50
338 Victor Zambrano .20 .50
339 Gary Sheffield .20 .50
340 Brad Wilkerson .20 .50
341 Ian Kinsler RC 1.50 4.00
342 Jesse Crain .20 .50
343 Orlando Hudson .20 .50
344 Laynce Nix .20 .50
345 Jose Cruz Jr. .20 .50
346 Edgar Renteria .20 .50
347 Eddie Guardado .20 .50
348 Jerome Williams .20 .50
349 Trevor Hoffman .30 .75
350 Mike Piazza .50 1.25
351 Jason Kendall .20 .50
352 Kevin Millwood .20 .50
353A Tim Hudson Atl Cap .30 .75
353B Tim Hudson Milw Cap SP 3.00 8.00
354 Paul Quantrill .20 .50
355 Jon Lieber .20 .50
356 Braden Looper .20 .50
357 Chad Cordero .20 .50
358 Joe Nathan .20 .50
359 Doug Davis .20 .50
360 Ian Bladergroen RC .20 .50
361 Val Majewski .20 .50
362 Francisco Rodriguez .30 .75
363 Kelvim Escobar .20 .50
364 Marcus Giles .20 .50
365 Darren Fenster RC .20 .50
366 David Bell .20 .50
367 Shea Hillenbrand .20 .50
368 Manny Ramirez .50 1.25
369 Ben Broussard .20 .50
370 Luis Ramirez RC .20 .50
371 Dustin Hermanson .20 .50
372 Akinori Otsuka .20 .50
373 Chadd Blasko RC .30 .75
374 Delmon Young .50 1.25
375 Michael Young .30 .75
376 Bret Boone .20 .50
377 Jake Peavy .20 .50
378 Matthew Lindstrom RC .20 .50
379 Sean Burroughs .20 .50
380 Rich Harden .20 .50
381 Chris Roberson RC .20 .50
382 John Lackey .20 .50
383 Johnny Estrada .20 .50
384 Matt Rogelstad RC .20 .50
385 Toby Hall .20 .50
386 Adam LaRoche .20 .50
387 Bill Hall .20 .50
388 Tim Salmon .20 .50
389A Curt Schilling Throw .30 .75
389B Curt Schilling Glove Up SP 3.00 8.00
390 Michael Barrett .20 .50
391 Jose Acevedo .20 .50
392 Nate Schierholtz .20 .50
393 J.T. Snow Jr. .20 .50
394 Mark Redman .20 .50
395 Ryan Madson .20 .50
396 Kevin West RC .20 .50
397 Ramon Ortiz .20 .50
398 Derek Lowe SP 3.00 8.00
399 Kerry Wood SP 3.00 8.00
400 Derek Jeter SP 5.00 12.00
401 Livan Hernandez SP 3.00 8.00
402 Casey Kotchman SP 3.00 8.00
403 Chaz Lytle SP RC 3.00 8.00
404 Alexis Rios SP 3.00 8.00
405 Scott Spiezio SP 3.00 8.00
406 Craig Wilson SP 3.00 8.00
407 Felix Rodriguez SP 3.00 8.00
408 D'Angelo Jimenez SP 3.00 8.00
409 Rondell White SP 3.00 8.00
410 Shawn Estes SP 3.00 8.00
411 Troy Percival SP 3.00 8.00
412 Melvin Mora SP 3.00 8.00
413 Aramis Ramirez SP 3.00 8.00
414 Carl Everett SP 3.00 8.00
415 Elvys Quezada SP RC 3.00 8.00
416 Ben Sheets SP 3.00 8.00
417 Matt Stairs SP 3.00 8.00
418 Adam Everett SP 3.00 8.00
419 Jason Johnson SP 3.00 8.00
420 Billy Butler SP RC 4.00 10.00
421 Justin Morneau SP 3.00 8.00
422 Jose Reyes SP 3.00 8.00
423 Mariano Rivera SP 3.00 8.00
424 Jose Vaquedano SP RC 3.00 8.00
425 Gabe Gross SP 3.00 8.00
426 Scott Rolen SP 3.00 8.00
427 Ty Wigginton SP 3.00 8.00
428 James Jurries SP RC 3.00 8.00
429 Pedro Martinez SP 3.00 8.00
430 Mark Grudzielanek SP 3.00 8.00
431 Josh Phelps SP 3.00 8.00
432 Ryan Goleski SP RC 3.00 8.00
433 Mike Matheny SP 3.00 8.00
434 Bobby Kielty SP 3.00 8.00
435 Tony Batista SP 3.00 8.00
436 Corey Koskie SP 3.00 8.00
437 Brad Lidge SP 3.00 8.00
438 Dontrelle Willis SP 3.00 8.00
439 Angel Berroa SP 3.00 8.00
440 Jason Kubel SP 3.00 8.00
441 Roy Halladay SP 3.00 8.00
442 Brian Roberts SP 3.00 8.00
443 Bill Mueller SP 3.00 8.00
444 Adam Kennedy SP 3.00 8.00
445 Brandon Moss SP RC 3.00 8.00
446 Sean Burnett SP 3.00 8.00
447 Eric Byrnes SP 3.00 8.00
448 Matt Campbell SP RC 3.00 8.00
449 Ryan Webb SP RC 3.00 8.00
450 Jose Valentin SP 3.00 8.00
451 Jake Westbrook SP 3.00 8.00
452 Glen Perkins SP RC 3.00 8.00
453 Alex Gonzalez SP 3.00 8.00
454 Jeromy Burnitz SP 3.00 8.00
455 Zack Greinke SP 3.00 8.00
456 Sean Marshall SP RC 2.50 6.00
457 Erubiel Durazo SP 3.00 8.00
458 Michael Cuddyer SP 3.00 8.00
459 Hee Seop Choi SP 3.00 8.00
460 Melky Cabrera SP RC 4.00 10.00
461 Jerry Hairston Jr. SP 3.00 8.00
462 Moises Alou SP 3.00 8.00
463 Michael Rogers SP RC 3.00 8.00
464 Javy Lopez SP 3.00 8.00
465 Freddy Garcia SP 3.00 8.00
466 Brett Harper SP RC 3.00 8.00
467 Juan Gonzalez SP 3.00 8.00
468 Kevin Melillo SP RC 3.00 8.00
469 Todd Walker SP 3.00 8.00
470 C.C. Sabathia SP 3.00 8.00
471 Kole Strayhorn SP RC 3.00 8.00
472 Mark Kotsay SP 3.00 8.00
473 Javier Vazquez SP 3.00 8.00
474 Mike Cameron SP 3.00 8.00
475 Wes Swackhamer SP RC 3.00 8.00

2005 Topps Heritage White Backs

COMPLETE SET (220) 75.00 150.00
*WHITE BACKS: .75X TO 2X BASIC
SEE BECKETT.COM FOR FULL CHECKLIST

2005 Topps Heritage Chrome

STATED ODDS 1:7 HOBBY/RETAIL
STATED PRINT RUN 1956 SERIAL #'d SETS
THC1 Will Harridge 1.50 4.00
THC2 Warren Giles 1.50 4.00
THC3 Alex Rodriguez 6.00 15.00
THC4 Alfonso Soriano 2.50 6.00
THC5 Barry Bonds 8.00 20.00
THC6 Todd Helton 2.50 6.00
THC7 Kazuo Matsui 1.50 4.00
THC8 Garret Anderson 1.50 4.00
THC9 Mark Prior 2.50 6.00
THC10 Jim Thome 2.50 6.00
THC11 Jason Giambi 1.50 4.00
THC12 Ivan Rodriguez 2.50 6.00
THC13 Mike Lowell 1.50 4.00
THC14 Vladimir Guerrero 4.00 10.00
THC15 Adrian Beltre 1.50 4.00
THC16 Andruw Jones 1.50 4.00
THC17 Jose Vidro 1.50 4.00
THC18 Josh Beckett 2.50 6.00
THC19 Mike Sweeney 1.50 4.00
THC20 Sammy Sosa 4.00 10.00
THC21 Scott Rolen 2.50 6.00
THC22 Javy Lopez 1.50 4.00
THC23 Albert Pujols 10.00 25.00
THC24 Adam Dunn 2.50 6.00
THC25 Ken Griffey Jr. 6.00 15.00
THC26 Torii Hunter 1.50 4.00
THC27 Jorge Posada 2.50 6.00
THC28 Magglio Ordonez 2.50 6.00
THC29 Shawn Green 1.50 4.00
THC30 Frank Thomas 4.00 10.00
THC31 Barry Zito 1.50 4.00
THC32 David Ortiz 4.00 10.00
THC33 Pat Burrell 1.50 4.00
THC34 Luis Gonzalez 1.50 4.00
THC35 Chipper Jones 4.00 10.00
THC36 Hank Blalock 1.50 4.00
THC37 Rafael Palmeiro 2.50 6.00
THC38 Lance Berkman 2.50 6.00
THC39 Miguel Cabrera 4.00 10.00
THC40 Paul Konerko 2.50 6.00
THC41 Jeff Kent 1.50 4.00
THC42 Gary Sheffield 1.50 4.00
THC43 Mike Piazza 4.00 10.00
THC44 Bret Boone 1.50 4.00
THC45 Kerry Wood 1.50 4.00
THC46 Derek Jeter 10.00 25.00
THC47 Pedro Martinez 2.50 6.00
THC48 Jason Bay 1.50 4.00
THC49 Ichiro Suzuki 6.00 15.00
THC50 Miguel Tejada 2.50 6.00
THC51 Richie Sexson 1.50 4.00
THC52 Jeff Bagwell 2.50 6.00
THC53 Lew Ford 1.50 4.00
THC54 Randy Johnson 4.00 10.00
THC55 Carlos Beltran 1.50 4.00
THC56 Greg Maddux 6.00 15.00
THC57 Lyle Overbay 1.50 4.00
THC58 Michael Young 2.50 6.00
THC59 Curt Schilling 2.50 6.00
THC60 Jose Reyes 2.50 6.00
THC61 Dontrelle Willis 1.50 4.00
THC62 Nomar Garciaparra 4.00 10.00
THC63 Paul Lo Duca 1.50 4.00
THC64 Larry Walker 2.50 6.00
THC65 Andre Ethier 12.00 30.00
THC66 Matt DeSalvo 1.50 4.00
THC67 Brian Stavisky 1.50 4.00
THC68 Tyler Clippard 10.00 25.00
THC69 Chris Seddon 1.50 4.00
THC70 Steve Doetsch 1.50 4.00
THC71 Chris Denorfia 1.50 4.00
THC72 Jeremy West 1.50 4.00
THC73 Ryan Sweeney 2.50 6.00
THC74 Ian Kinsler 12.00 30.00
THC75 Ian Bladergroen 1.50 4.00
THC76 Darren Fenster 1.50 4.00
THC77 Luis Ramirez 1.50 4.00
THC78 Chadd Blasko 2.50 6.00
THC79 Matthew Lindstrom 1.50 4.00
THC80 Chris Roberson 1.50 4.00
THC81 Matt Rogelstad 1.50 4.00
THC82 Nate Schierholtz 1.50 4.00
THC83 Kevin West 1.50 4.00
THC84 Chaz Lytle 2.50 6.00
THC85 Elvys Quezada 1.50 4.00
THC86 Billy Butler 8.00 20.00
THC87 Jose Vaquedano 1.50 4.00
THC88 James Jurries 1.50 4.00
THC89 Ryan Goleski 1.50 4.00
THC90 Brandon Moss 6.00 15.00
THC91 Matt Campbell 1.50 4.00
THC92 Ryan Webb 1.50 4.00
THC93 Glen Perkins 1.50 4.00
THC94 Sean Marshall 4.00 10.00
THC95 Melky Cabrera 4.00 10.00
THC96 Michael Rogers 1.50 4.00
THC97 Brett Harper 1.50 4.00
THC98 Kevin Melillo 1.50 4.00
THC99 Kole Strayhorn 1.50 4.00
THC100 Wes Swackhamer 1.50 4.00
THC101 Rickie Weeks 2.50 6.00
THC102 Delmon Young 4.00 10.00
THC103 Kazuhito Tadano 1.50 4.00
THC104 Kazuhisa Ishii 1.50 4.00
THC105 David Wright 6.00 15.00
THC106 Eric Gagne 1.50 4.00
THC107 So Taguchi 1.50 4.00
THC108 B.J. Upton 2.50 6.00
THC109 Shingo Takatsu 1.50 4.00
THC110 Akinori Otsuka 1.50 4.00

2005 Topps Heritage Chrome Black Refractors

*BLACK REF: 4X TO 8X CHROME
*BLACK REF: 4X TO 8X CHROME RC YR
STATED ODDS 1:250 HOBBY/RETAIL
STATED PRINT RUN 56 SERIAL #'d SETS

2005 Topps Heritage Chrome Refractors

*REFRACTOR: .6X TO 1.5X CHROME
*REFRACTOR: .6X TO 1.5X CHROME RC YR
STATED ODDS 1:25 HOBBY/RETAIL
STATED PRINT RUN 556 SERIAL #'d SETS

2005 Topps Heritage 1956 Cuts

STATED ODDS 1:92,490 HOBBY
STATED PRINT RUN 1 SERIAL #'d SET
NO PRICING DUE TO SCARCITY
DE Dwight Eisenhower
ER Eleanor Roosevelt
EW Earl Warren
JH J. Edgar Hoover
RN Richard Nixon
ERI Capt. Edward V. Rickenbacker
JSA Jonas Salk

2005 Topps Heritage Clubhouse Collection Relics

GROUP A ODDS 1:291 H, 1:292 R
GROUP B ODDS 1:384 H, 1:387 R
GROUP C ODDS 1:1303 H, 1:1307 R
GROUP D ODDS 1:497 H, 1:499 R
GROUP E ODDS 1:384 H, 1:387 R
AK Al Kaline Bat A 8.00 20.00
AP Albert Pujols Bat B 8.00 20.00
AR Alex Rodriguez Bat D 6.00 15.00
AS Alfonso Soriano Bat C 3.00 8.00
BW Bernie Williams Bat A 4.00 10.00
DW Dontrelle Willis Jsy E 3.00 8.00
EB Ernie Banks Bat A 8.00 20.00
GS Gary Sheffield Bat B 3.00 8.00
HK Harmon Killebrew Bat A 8.00 20.00
LA Luis Aparicio Bat A 4.00 10.00
LB Lance Berkman Bat D 3.00 8.00
MC Miguel Cabrera Bat A 4.00 10.00
MR Manny Ramirez Jsy E 4.00 10.00
MT Miguel Tejada Bat B 3.00 8.00
RS Red Schoendienst Bat B 4.00 10.00

2005 Topps Heritage Clubhouse Collection Autograph Relics

STATED ODDS 1:12,216 H, 1:13,728 R
STATED PRINT RUN 25 SERIAL #'d SETS
NO PRICING DUE TO SCARCITY
AK Al Kaline Bat
EB Ernie Banks Bat
HK Harmon Killebrew Bat
LA Luis Aparicio Bat
RS Red Schoendienst Bat

2005 Topps Heritage Clubhouse Collection Dual Relics

STATED ODDS 1:9249 H, 1:9490 R
STATED PRINT RUN 56 SERIAL #'d SETS
BG Ernie Banks Bat 75.00 150.00
Nomar Garciaparra Bat
KR Al Kaline Bat 75.00 150.00
Ivan Rodriguez Bat
MP Stan Musial Jsy 125.00 200.00
Albert Pujols Jsy

2005 Topps Heritage Flashbacks

COMPLETE SET (10) 5.00 12.00
STATED ODDS 1:12 HOBBY/RETAIL
AK Al Kaline 1.00 2.50
BF Bob Feller .40 1.00
DL Don Larsen .40 1.00
DS Duke Snider .60 1.50
EB Ernie Banks 1.00 2.50
FR Frank Robinson .60 1.50
HA Hank Aaron 2.00 5.00
HS Herb Score .40 1.00
LA Luis Aparicio .40 1.00
SM Stan Musial 1.50 4.00

2005 Topps Heritage Flashbacks Autographs

STATED ODDS 1:6166 H, 1:6864 R
STATED PRINT RUN 25 SERIAL #'d SETS
NO PRICING DUE TO SCARCITY

2005 Topps Heritage Flashbacks Seat Relics

STATED ODDS 1:96 HOBBY/RETAIL
AK Al Kaline 6.00 15.00
BF Bob Feller 6.00 15.00
DL Don Larsen 6.00 15.00
DS Duke Snider 6.00 15.00
EB Ernie Banks 6.00 15.00
FR Frank Robinson 4.00 10.00
HA Hank Aaron 8.00 20.00
HS Herb Score 4.00 10.00
LA Luis Aparicio 4.00 10.00
SM Stan Musial 8.00 20.00

2005 Topps Heritage Flashbacks Autograph Seat Relics

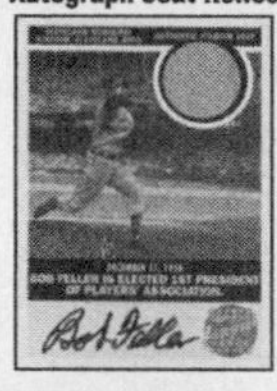

STATED ODDS 1:6166 H, 1:6864 R
STATED PRINT RUN 25 SERIAL #'d SETS
NO PRICING DUE TO SCARCITY

2005 Topps Heritage New Age Performers

COMPLETE SET (15) 10.00 25.00
STATED ODDS 1:15 HOBBY/RETAIL
1 Alfonso Soriano .60 1.50
2 Alex Rodriguez 1.50 4.00
3 Ichiro Suzuki 1.50 4.00
4 Albert Pujols 2.50 6.00
5 Vladimir Guerrero 1.00 2.50
6 Jim Thome .60 1.50
7 Derek Jeter 2.50 6.00
8 Sammy Sosa 1.00 2.50
9 Ivan Rodriguez .60 1.50
10 Manny Ramirez 1.00 2.50
11 Todd Helton .60 1.50
12 David Ortiz 1.00 2.50
13 Gary Sheffield .40 1.00
14 Nomar Garciaparra 1.00 2.50
15 Randy Johnson 1.00 2.50

2005 Topps Heritage Real One Autographs

STATED ODDS 1:333 H, 1:332 R
STATED PRINT RUN 200 SETS
PRINT RUN INFO PROVIDED BY TOPPS
BASIC AUTOS ARE NOT SERIAL-NUMBERED
*RED INK: .75X TO 1.5X BASIC
RED INK ODDS 1:1195 H, 1:1196 R
RED INK PRINT RUN 56 SERIAL #'d SETS
RED INK ALSO CALLED SPECIAL EDITION
AS Art Swanson 20.00 50.00
BF Bob Feller 40.00 80.00
BN Bob Nelson 20.00 50.00
BT Bill Tremel 20.00 50.00
CD Chuck Diering 20.00 50.00
DS Duke Snider 50.00 100.00
EB Ernie Banks 60.00 120.00
FM Fred Marsh 20.00 50.00
HA Hank Aaron 150.00 250.00
JA Joe Astroth 20.00 50.00
JB Jim Brady 20.00 50.00
JG Jim Greengrass 20.00 50.00
JM Jake Martin 20.00 50.00
JS Johnny Schmitz 20.00 50.00
JSA Jose Santiago 20.00 50.00
LP Laurin Pepper 20.00 50.00
LPO Leroy Powell 20.00 50.00
MI Monte Irvin 30.00 60.00
PM Paul Minner 20.00 50.00
RM Rudy Minarcin 20.00 50.00
SJ Spook Jacobs 20.00 50.00
WW Wally Westlake 20.00 50.00
YB Yogi Berra 60.00 120.00

2005 Topps Heritage Then and Now

COMPLETE SET (10) 5.00 12.00
STATED ODDS 1:15 HOBBY/RETAIL
TN1 Hank Aaron 2.00 5.00
Ichiro Suzuki
TN2 Don Newcombe .60 1.50
Curt Schilling
TN3 Robin Roberts .40 1.00
Livan Hernandez
TN4 Bob Friend .40 1.00
Livan Hernandez
TN5 Herb Score 1.00 2.50
Randy Johnson
TN6 Whitey Ford .40 1.00
Jake Peavy
TN7 Jimmy Piersall .40 1.00
Lyle Overbay
TN8 Clem Labine 1.00 2.50
Mariano Rivera
TN9 Billy Bruton .60 1.50
Carl Crawford
TN10 Ed Yost .40 1.00
Bob Abreu

2005 Topps Heritage Hawaii Trade Conference

ISSUED AT 05 HAWAII TRADE CONFERENCE
STATED PRINT RUN 100 SER. #'d SETS

2006 Topps Heritage

This 494-card set was released in February, 2006. This set, using the same design as the 1957 Topps baseball set, was issued in eight-card hobby and retail packs, both with an $3 SRP which came 24 packs to a box and eight boxes to a case. Card number 297, which was intended to be Alex Gordon had to be pulled from production as there was no approval to print that card as he had yet to participate in a major league game. In addition, cards numbered 265-352, with the curious exception of card #329 were short printed similar to the original 1957 Topps set in which those cards were issued in shorter quantities than the rest of the 57 set. A few variation and short prints were scattered around the rest of the set.

COMPLETE SET (494) 250.00 400.00
COMP.SET w/o SP's (384) 30.00 60.00
SP STATED ODDS 1:2 HOBBY/RETAIL
SP CL: 1/2/10/18/20B/23B/25/35/55
SP CL: 70/76/80B/91/95A/95B/99/106
SP CL: 123/127/165B/200B/212B/265-269
SP CL: 271-274/276-316/318-323/325A
SP CL: 325B/326-328/330-349/350A/350B
SP CL: 351-352/400/407/475B
VARIATION CL: 20/23/80/95/165/200
VARIATION CL: 212/325/350/475
TWO VERSIONS OF EACH VARIATION EXIST
SEE BECKETT.COM FOR VAR.DESCRIPTIONS
CARD 255 NOT INTENDED FOR RELEASE
COMP.SET EXCLUDES CARD 255 CUT OUT
1 David Ortiz SP 3.00 8.00
2 Mike Piazza SP 4.00 10.00
3 Daryle Ward .20 .50
4 Rafael Furcal .20 .50
5 Derek Lowe .20 .50
6 Eric Chavez .20 .50
7 Juan Uribe .20 .50
8 C.C. Sabathia .30 .75
9 Sean Casey .20 .50
10 Barry Bonds SP 5.00 12.00
11 Gary Sheffield .20 .50

12 Ted Lilly .20 .50
13 Lew Ford .20 .50
14 Tom Gordon .20 .50
15 Curt Schilling .30 .75
16 Jason Kendall .20 .50
17 Frank Catalanotto .20 .50
18 Pedro Martinez SP 3.00 8.00
19 David Dellucci .20 .50
20A A.Jones w/o Seats .20 .50
20B A.Jones w/Seats SP 3.00 8.00
21 Brad Halsey .20 .50
22 Vernon Wells .20 .50
23A D.Jeter Yellow/White Ltr 1.25 3.00
23B D.Jeter Blue Ltr SP 5.00 12.00
24 Todd Helton .30 .75
25 Randy Johnson SP 4.00 10.00
26 Jay Gibbons .20 .50
27 Joe Mays .20 .50
28 Paul Konerko .30 .75
29 Lyle Overbay .20 .50
30 Jorge Posada .30 .75
31 Brandon Webb .30 .75
32 Marcus Giles .20 .50
33 J.T. Snow .20 .50
34 Todd Walker .20 .50
35 Wily Mo Pena SP 3.00 8.00
36 Carlos Delgado .20 .50
37 David Wright .75 2.00
38 Shea Hillenbrand .20 .50
39 Daniel Cabrera .20 .50
40 Trevor Hoffman .30 .75
41 Matt Morris .20 .50
42 Mariano Rivera .50 1.25
43 Jeff Bagwell .30 .75
44 J.D. Drew .20 .50
45 Carl Pavano .20 .50
46 Placido Polanco .20 .50
47 Adrian Beltre .20 .50
48 J.D. Closser .20 .50
49 Paul Lo Duca .20 .50
50 Scott Rolen .30 .75
51 Bernie Williams .30 .75
52 Jose Guillen .20 .50
53 Aubrey Huff .20 .50
54 Greg Maddux .75 2.00
55 Derrek Lee SP 3.00 8.00
56 Hideki Matsui .50 1.25
57 Jose Bautista .50 1.25
58 Kyle Farnsworth .20 .50
59 Nate Robertson .20 .50
60 Sammy Sosa .50 1.25
61 Javier Vazquez .20 .50
62 Jeff Mathis .20 .50
63 Mark Buehrle .30 .75
64 Orlando Hernandez .20 .50
65 Brandon Claussen .20 .50
66 Miguel Batista .20 .50
67 Eddie Guardado .20 .50
68 Alex Gonzalez .20 .50
69 Kris Benson .20 .50
70 Bobby Abreu SP 3.00 8.00
71 Vinny Castilla .20 .50
72 Ben Broussard .20 .50
73 Travis Hafner .20 .50
74 Dmitri Young .20 .50
75 Alex S. Gonzalez .20 .50
76 Jason Bay SP 3.00 8.00
77 Charlton Jimerson .20 .50
78 Ryan Garko .20 .50
79 Lance Berkman .30 .75
80A T.Hudson Red/Blue Ltr .30 .75
80B T.Hudson Blue Ltr SP 3.00 8.00
81 Guillermo Mota .20 .50
82 Chris B. Young .20 .50
83 Brad Lidge .20 .50
84 A.J. Pierzynski .20 .50
85 Maicer Izturis .20 .50
86 Vladimir Guerrero .50 1.25
87 J.J. Hardy .20 .50
88 Cesar Izturis .20 .50
89 Mark Ellis .20 .50
90 Chipper Jones .50 1.25
91 Chris Snelling SP 3.00 8.00
92 Jose Reyes .30 .75
93 Mike Lieberthal .20 .50
94 Octavio Dotel .20 .50
95A A.Rodriguez Fielding SP 4.00 10.00
95B A.Rodriguez w/Bat SP 4.00 10.00
96 Brett Myers .20 .50
97 New York Yankees TC .30 .75
98 Ryan Klesko .20 .50
99 Brian Jordan SP 3.00 8.00
100 William Harridge .20 .50
Warren Giles
101 Adam Eaton .20 .50
102 Aaron Boone .20 .50
103 Alex Rios .30 .75
104 Andy Pettitte .30 .75
105 Barry Zito .20 .50
106 Bengie Molina SP 3.00 8.00
107 Austin Kearns .20 .50
108 Adam Everett .20 .50
109 A.J. Burnett .30 .75
110 Mark Prior .30 .75
111 Russ Ortiz .20 .50
112 Adam Dunn .30 .75
113 Byung-Hyun Kim
114 Atlanta Braves TC .20 .50
115 Carlos Silva .20 .50
116 Chad Cordero .20 .50
117 Chone Figgins .20 .50
118 Chris Reitsma .20 .50
119 Coco Crisp .20 .50
120 David DeJesus .20 .50
121 Chris Snyder .20 .50
122 Brad Eldred .20 .50
123 Humberto Cota SP 3.00 8.00
124 Erubiel Durazo .20 .50
125 Josh Beckett .30 .75
126 Kenny Lofton .20 .50
127 Joe Nathan SP 3.00 8.00
128 Bryan Bullington .20 .50
129 Jim Thome .30 .75
130 Shawn Green .20 .50
131 LaTroy Hawkins .20 .50
132 Mark Kotsay .20 .50
133 Matt Lawton .20 .50
134 Luis Castillo .20 .50
135 Michael Barrett .20 .50
136 Preston Wilson .20 .50
137 Orlando Cabrera .20 .50
138 Chuck James .20 .50
139 Raul Ibanez .30 .75
140 Frank Thomas .50 1.25
141 Orlando Hudson .20 .50
142 Scott Kazmir .30 .75
143 Steve Finley .20 .50
144 Danny Sandoval RC .20 .50
145 Javy Lopez .20 .50
146 Tony Giarratano .20 .50
147 Terrence Long .20 .50
148 Victor Martinez .30 .75
149 Toby Hall .20 .50
150 Fausto Carmona .20 .50
151 Tim Wakefield .30 .75
152 Troy Percival .30 .75
153 Chris Denorfia .20 .50
154 Junior Spivey .20 .50
155 Desi Relaford .20 .50
156 Francisco Liriano .50 1.25
157 Corey Koskie .20 .50
158 Chris Carpenter .50 1.25
159 Robert Andino RC .20 .50
160 Cliff Floyd .20 .50
161 Pittsburgh Pirates TC .20 .50
162 Anderson Hernandez .20 .50
163 Mike Maroth .20 .50
164 Aaron Rowand .20 .50
165A A.Pujols Grey Shirt 1.25 3.00
165B A.Pujols Red Shirt SP 5.00 12.00
166 David Bell .20 .50
167 Angel Berroa .20 .50
168 B.J. Ryan .20 .50
169 Bartolo Colon .20 .50
170 Hong-Chih Kuo .50 1.25
171 Cincinnati Reds TC .20 .50
172 Bill Mueller .20 .50
173 John Koronka .20 .50
174 Billy Wagner .20 .50
175 Zack Greinke .30 .75
176 Rick Short .20 .50
177 Yadier Molina .30 .75
178 Willy Taveras .20 .50
179 Wes Helms .20 .50
180 Wade Miller .20 .50
181 Luis Gonzalez .20 .50
182 Victor Zambrano .20 .50
183 Chicago Cubs TC .30 .75
184 Victor Santos .20 .50
185 Tyler Walker .20 .50
186 Bobby Crosby .20 .50
187 Trot Nixon .20 .50
188 Nick Johnson .20 .50
189 Nick Swisher .50 1.25
190 Brian Roberts .20 .50
191 Nomar Garciaparra .50 1.25
192 Oliver Perez .20 .50
193 Ramon Hernandez .20 .50
194 Randy Winn .20 .50
195 Ryan Church .20 .50
196 Ryan Wagner .20 .50
197 Todd Hollandsworth .20 .50
198 Detroit Tigers TC .20 .50
199 Tino Martinez .20 .50
200A R.Clemens On Mound .60 1.50
200B R.Clemens Red Shirt SP 4.00 10.00
201 Shawn Estes .20 .50
202 Justin Morneau .50 1.25
203 Jeff Francis .20 .50
204 Oakland Athletics TC .20 .50
205 Jeff Francoeur .50 1.25
206 C.J. Wilson .30 .75
207 Francisco Rodriguez .20 .50
208 Edgardo Alfonzo .20 .50
209 David Eckstein .20 .50
210 Cory Lidle .20 .50
211 Chase Utley .50 1.25
212A R.Baldelli Yellow/White Ltr .20 .50
212B R.Baldelli Blue Ltr SP 3.00 8.00
213 So Taguchi .20 .50
214 Philadelphia Phillies TC .20 .50
215 Brad Hawpe .20 .50
216 Walter Young .20 .50
217 Tom Gorzelanny .20 .50
218 Shaun Marcum .20 .50
219 Ryan Howard .75 2.00
220 Damian Jackson .20 .50
221 Craig Counsell .20 .50
222 Damian Miller .20 .50
223 Derrick Turnbow .20 .50
224 Hank Blalock .20 .50
225 Brayan Pena .20 .50
226 Grady Sizemore .30 .75
227 Ivan Rodriguez .30 .75
228 Jason Isringhausen .20 .50
229 Brian Fuentes .20 .50
230 Jason Phillips .20 .50
231 Jason Schmidt .20 .50
232 Javier Valentin .20 .50
233 Jeff Kent .20 .50
234 John Buck .20 .50
235 Mike Matheny .20 .50
236 Jorge Cantu .20 .50
237 Jose Castillo .20 .50
238 Kenny Rogers .20 .50
239 Kerry Wood .20 .50
240 Kevin Mench .20 .50
241 Tim Stauffer .20 .50
242 Eric Milton .20 .50
243 St. Louis Cardinals TC .30 .75
244 Shawn Chacon .20 .50
245 Mike Jacobs .20 .50
246 Ryan Dempster .20 .50
247 Todd Jones .20 .50
248 Tom Glavine .30 .75
249 Tony Graffanino .20 .50
250 Ichiro Suzuki .75 2.00
251 Baltimore Orioles TC .20 .50
252 Brad Radke .20 .50
253 Brad Wilkerson .20 .50
254 Carlos Lee .20 .50
255 Alex Gordon Cut Out 100.00 200.00
256 Gustavo Chacin .20 .50
257 Jermaine Dye .20 .50
258 Jose Mesa .20 .50
259 Julio Lugo .20 .50
260 Mark Redman .20 .50
261 Brandon Watson .20 .50
262 Pedro Feliz .20 .50
263 Esteban Loaiza .20 .50
264 Anthony Reyes .20 .50
265 Jose Contreras SP 3.00 8.00
266 Tadahito Iguchi SP 3.00 8.00
267 Mark Loretta SP 3.00 8.00
268 Ray Durham SP 3.00 8.00
269 Neifi Perez SP 3.00 8.00
270 Washington Nationals TC .20 .50
271 Troy Glaus SP 3.00 8.00
272 Matt Holliday SP 4.00 10.00
273 Kevin Millwood SP 3.00 8.00
274 Jon Lieber SP 3.00 8.00
275 Cleveland Indians TC .20 .50
276 Jeremy Reed SP 3.00 8.00
277 Garrett Atkins SP 3.00 8.00
278 Geoff Jenkins SP 3.00 8.00
279 Joey Gathright SP 3.00 8.00
280 Ben Sheets SP 3.00 8.00
281 Melvin Mora SP 3.00 8.00
282 Jonathan Papelbon SP 4.00 10.00
283 John Smoltz SP 3.00 8.00
284 Jake Peavy SP 3.00 8.00
285 Felix Hernandez SP 3.00 8.00
286 Alfonso Soriano SP 3.00 8.00
287 Bronson Arroyo SP 3.00 8.00
288 Adam LaRoche SP 3.00 8.00
289 Aramis Ramirez SP 3.00 8.00
290 Brad Hennessey SP 3.00 8.00
291 Conor Jackson SP 3.00 8.00
292 Rod Barajas SP 3.00 8.00
293 Chris R. Young SP 3.00 8.00
294 Jeremy Bonderman SP 3.00 8.00
295 Jack Wilson SP 3.00 8.00
296 Jay Payton SP 3.00 8.00
297 Danys Baez SP 3.00 8.00
298 Jose Lima SP 3.00 8.00
299 Luis A. Gonzalez SP 3.00 8.00
300 Mike Sweeney SP 3.00 8.00
301 Nelson Cruz SP 3.00 8.00
302 Eric Gagne SP 3.00 8.00
303 Juan Castro SP 3.00 8.00
304 Joe Mauer SP 3.00 8.00
305 Richie Sexson SP 3.00 8.00
306 Roy Oswalt SP 3.00 8.00
307 Rickie Weeks SP 3.00 8.00
308 Pat Borders SP 3.00 8.00
309 Mike Morse SP 3.00 8.00
310 Matt Stairs SP 3.00 8.00
311 Chad Tracy SP 3.00 8.00
312 Matt Cain SP 3.00 8.00
313 Mark Mulder SP 3.00 8.00
314 Mark Grudzielanek SP 3.00 8.00
315 Johnny Damon Yanks SP 4.00 10.00
316 Casey Kotchman SP 3.00 8.00
317 San Francisco Giants TC .20 .50
318 Chris Burke SP 3.00 8.00
319 Carl Crawford SP 3.00 8.00
320 Edgar Renteria SP 3.00 8.00
321 Chan Ho Park SP 3.00 8.00
322 Boston Red Sox TC SP 3.00 8.00
323 Robinson Cano SP 3.00 8.00
324 Los Angeles Dodgers TC .30 .75
325A M.Tejada w/Bat SP 3.00 8.00
325B M.Tejada Hand Up SP 3.00 8.00
326 Jimmy Rollins SP 3.00 8.00
327 Juan Pierre SP 3.00 8.00
328 Dan Johnson SP 3.00 8.00
329 Chicago White Sox TC .20 .50
330 Pat Burrell SP 3.00 8.00
331 Ramon Ortiz SP 3.00 8.00
332 Rondell White SP 3.00 8.00
333 David Wells SP 3.00 8.00
334 Michael Young SP 3.00 8.00
335 Mike Mussina SP 3.00 8.00
336 Moises Alou SP 3.00 8.00
337 Scott Podsednik SP 3.00 8.00
338 Rich Harden SP 3.00 8.00
339 Mark Teahen SP 3.00 8.00
340 Jacque Jones SP 3.00 8.00
341 Jason Giambi SP 3.00 8.00
342 Bill Hall SP 3.00 8.00
343 Jon Garland SP 3.00 8.00
344 Dontrelle Willis SP 3.00 8.00
345 Danny Haren SP 3.00 8.00
346 Brian Giles SP 3.00 8.00
347 Brad Penny SP 3.00 8.00
348 Brandon McCarthy SP 3.00 8.00
349 Chien-Ming Wang SP 4.00 10.00
350A T.Hunter Red/Blue Ltr SP 3.00 8.00
350B T.Hunter Blue Ltr SP 3.00 8.00
351 Yhency Brazoban SP 3.00 8.00
352 Rodrigo Lopez SP 3.00 8.00
353 Paul McAnulty .20 .50
354 Francisco Cordero .20 .50
355 Brandon Inge .20 .50
356 Jason Lane .20 .50
357 Brian Schneider .20 .50
358 Dustin Hermanson .20 .50
359 Eric Hinske .20 .50
360 Jarrod Washburn .20 .50
361 Jayson Werth .30 .75
362 Craig Breslow RC .20 .50
363 Jeff Weaver .20 .50
364 Jeromy Burnitz .20 .50
365 Jhonny Peralta .30 .75
366 Joe Crede .20 .50
367 Johan Santana .50 1.25
368 Jose Valentin .20 .50
369 Keith Foulke .20 .50
370 Larry Bigbie .20 .50
371 Manny Ramirez .50 1.25
372 Jim Edmonds .30 .75
373 Horacio Ramirez .20 .50
374 Garret Anderson .20 .50
375 Felipe Lopez .20 .50
376 Eric Byrnes .20 .50
377 Darin Erstad .20 .50
378 Carlos Zambrano .30 .75
379 Craig Biggio .30 .75
380 Darrell Rasner .20 .50
381 Dave Roberts .20 .50
382 Hanley Ramirez .50 1.25
383 Geoff Blum .20 .50
384 Joel Pineiro .20 .50
385 Kip Wells .20 .50
386 Kelvim Escobar .20 .50
387 John Patterson .20 .50
388 Jody Gerut .20 .50
389 Marshall McDougall .20 .50
390 Mike MacDougal .20 .50
391 Orlando Palmeiro .20 .50
392 Rich Aurilia .20 .50
393 Ronnie Belliard .20 .50
394 Rich Hill .20 .50
395 Scott Hatteberg .20 .50
396 Ryan Langerhans .20 .50
397 Richard Hidalgo .20 .50
398 Omar Vizquel .30 .75
399 Mike Lowell .20 .50
400 Astros Aces SP 3.00 8.00
Roy Oswalt
Roger Clemens
Andy Pettitte
401 Mike Cameron .20 .50
402 Matt Clement .20 .50
403 Miguel Cabrera .50 1.25
404 Milton Bradley .20 .50
405 Laynce Nix .20 .50
406 Rob Mackowiak .20 .50
407 White Sox Power Hitters SP 3.00 8.00
Jermaine Dye
Paul Konerko
408 Mark Teixeira .50 1.25
409 Brady Clark .20 .50
410 Johnny Estrada .20 .50
411 Juan Encarnacion .20 .50
412 Morgan Ensberg .20 .50
413 Nook Logan .20 .50
414 Phil Nevin .20 .50
415 Reggie Sanders .20 .50
416 Roy Halladay .50 1.25
417 Livan Hernandez .20 .50
418 Jose Vidro .20 .50
419 Shannon Stewart .20 .50
420 Brian Bruney .20 .50
421 Royce Clayton .20 .50
422 Chris Demaria RC .20 .50
423 Eduardo Perez .20 .50
424 Jeff Suppan .20 .50
425 Jaret Wright .20 .50
426 Joe Randa .20 .50
427 Bobby Kielty .20 .50
428 Jason Ellison .20 .50
429 Gregg Zaun .20 .50
430 Runelvys Hernandez .20 .50
431 Joe McEwing .20 .50
432 Jason LaRue .20 .50
433 Aaron Miles .20 .50
434 Adam Kennedy .20 .50
435 Ambiorix Burgos .20 .50
436 Armando Benitez .20 .50
437 Brad Ausmus .20 .50
438 Brandon Backe .20 .50
439 Brian James Anderson
440 Bruce Chen .20 .50
441 Carlos Guillen .20 .50
442 Casey Blake .20 .50
443 Chris Capuano .20 .50
444 Chris Duffy .20 .50
445 Chris Ray .20 .50
446 Clint Barmes .20 .50
447 Andrew Sisco .20 .50
448 Dallas McPherson .20 .50
449 Tanyon Sturtze .20 .50
450 Carlos Beltran .20 .50
451 Jason Vargas .20 .50
452 Ervin Santana .20 .50
453 Jason Marquis .20 .50
454 Juan Rivera .20 .50
455 Jake Westbrook .20 .50
456 Jason Johnson .20 .50
457 Joe Blanton .20 .50
458 Kevin Millar .20 .50
459 John Thomson .20 .50
460 J.P. Howell .20 .50
461 Justin Verlander 1.50 4.00
462 Kelly Johnson
463 Kyle Davies .20 .50
464 Lance Niekro .20 .50
465 Magglio Ordonez .30 .75
466 Melky Cabrera .30 .75
467 Nick Punto .20 .50
468 Paul Byrd .20 .50
469 Randy Wolf .20 .50
470 Ruben Gotay .20 .50
471 Ryan Madson .20 .50
472 Victor Diaz .20 .50
473 Xavier Nady .20 .50
474 Zach Duke .20 .50
475A H.Street Yellow/White Ltr .20 .50
475B H.Street Blue Ltr SP 3.00 8.00
476 Brad Thompson .20 .50
477 Jonny Gomes .20 .50
478 B.J. Upton .30 .75
479 Jamey Carroll .20 .50
480 Mike Hampton .20 .50
481 Tony Clark .20 .50
482 Antonio Alfonseca .20 .50
483 Justin Duchscherer .20 .50
484 Mike Timlin .20 .50
485 Joe Saunders .20 .50

2006 Topps Heritage Checklists

COMPLETE SET (5) .75 2.00
COMMON CARD (1-5) .20 .50
RANDOM INSERTS IN PACKS

2006 Topps Heritage Chrome

COMPLETE SET (109) 200.00 300.00
COMMON (1-102/104-110) 1.50 4.00
STATED ODDS 1:9 HOBBY, 1:10 RETAIL
STATED PRINT RUN 1957 SERIAL #'d SETS
CARD 103 DOES NOT EXIST
1 Rafael Furcal 1.25 3.00
2 C.C. Sabathia 2.00 5.00
3 Sean Casey 1.25 3.00
4 Gary Sheffield 1.25 3.00
5 William Harridge 1.25 3.00
Warren Giles
6 Curt Schilling 2.00 5.00
7 Jay Gibbons 1.25 3.00
8 Paul Konerko 2.00 5.00
9 Lyle Overbay 1.25 3.00
10 Jorge Posada 2.00 5.00
11 Todd Walker 1.25 3.00
12 Carlos Delgado 1.25 3.00
13 David Wright 5.00 12.00
14 Matt Morris 1.25 3.00
15 Mariano Rivera 3.00 8.00
16 Jeff Bagwell 2.00 5.00
17 Carl Pavano 1.25 3.00
18 Adrian Beltre 1.25 3.00
19 Scott Rolen 2.00 5.00
20 Aubrey Huff 1.25 3.00
21 Hideki Matsui 3.00 8.00
22 Andruw Jones 1.25 3.00
23 Sammy Sosa 3.00 8.00
24 Mark Buehrle 2.00 5.00
25 Orlando Hernandez 1.25 3.00
26 Travis Hafner 1.25 3.00
27 Vladimir Guerrero 3.00 8.00
28 Chipper Jones 3.00 8.00
29 Jose Reyes 2.00 5.00
30 Roger Clemens 4.00 10.00
31 Aaron Boone 1.25 3.00
32 Andy Pettitte 2.00 5.00
33 David DeJesus 1.25 3.00
34 Shawn Green 1.25 3.00
35 Luis Castillo 1.25 3.00
36 Frank Thomas 3.00 8.00
37 Javy Lopez 1.25 3.00
38 Victor Martinez 2.00 5.00
39 Tim Wakefield 1.25 3.00
40 Cliff Floyd 1.25 3.00
41 Bartolo Colon 1.25 3.00
42 Billy Wagner 1.25 3.00
43 Dmitri Young 1.25 3.00
44 Mark Prior 2.00 5.00
45 Nick Johnson 1.25 3.00
46 Brian Roberts 1.25 3.00
47 Nomar Garciaparra 3.00 8.00
48 Jorge Cantu 1.25 3.00
49 Jeff Francoeur 3.00 8.00
50 Barry Bonds 6.00 15.00
51 Francisco Rodriguez 2.00 5.00
52 Rocco Baldelli 1.25 3.00
53 Ryan Howard 5.00 12.00
54 Hank Blalock 1.25 3.00
55 Ivan Rodriguez 2.00 5.00
56 Jason Schmidt 1.25 3.00
57 Jeff Kent 1.25 3.00
58 Jose Castillo 1.25 3.00
59 Kerry Wood 1.25 3.00
60 Chase Utley 3.00 8.00
61 Shawn Chacon 1.25 3.00
62 Tom Glavine 2.00 5.00
63 Ichiro Suzuki 5.00 12.00
64 Carlos Lee 1.25 3.00
65 Jeff Weaver 1.25 3.00
66 Jeromy Burnitz 1.25 3.00
67 Jhonny Peralta 1.25 3.00
68 Johan Santana 3.00 8.00
69 Keith Foulke 1.25 3.00
70 Manny Ramirez 3.00 8.00
71 Jim Edmonds 2.00 5.00
72 Garret Anderson 1.25 3.00
73 Felipe Lopez 1.25 3.00
74 Craig Biggio 2.00 5.00
75 Ryan Langerhans 1.25 3.00
76 Mike Cameron 1.25 3.00
77 Matt Clement 1.25 3.00
78 Miguel Cabrera 3.00 8.00
79 Mark Teixeira 3.00 8.00
80 Johnny Estrada 1.25 3.00
81 Nook Logan 1.25 3.00
82 Livan Hernandez 1.25 3.00
83 Roy Halladay 3.00 8.00
84 Jose Vidro 1.25 3.00
85 Shannon Stewart 1.25 3.00
86 Brian Bruney 1.25 3.00
87 Jaret Wright 1.25 3.00
88 Gregg Zaun 1.25 3.00
89 Jason LaRue 1.25 3.00
90 Adam Kennedy 1.25 3.00
91 Armando Benitez 1.25 3.00
92 Chris Ray 1.25 3.00
93 Clint Barmes 1.25 3.00
94 Ervin Santana 1.25 3.00
95 Justin Verlander 10.00 25.00
96 Magglio Ordonez 2.00 5.00
97 Todd Helton 2.00 5.00
98 Zach Duke 1.25 3.00
99 Huston Street 1.25 3.00
100 Alex Rodriguez 5.00 12.00
101 Mike Hampton 1.25 3.00
102 Tony Clark 1.25 3.00
104 Barry Zito 1.25 3.00
105 Anderson Hernandez 1.25 3.00
106 B.J. Upton 1.25 3.00
107 Albert Pujols 8.00 20.00
108 Tim Hudson 2.00 5.00
109 Derek Jeter 8.00 20.00
110 Greg Maddux 5.00 12.00

2006 Topps Heritage Chrome Refractors

*CHROME REF: .6X TO 1.5X CHROME
STATED ODDS 1:33 HOBBY, 1:34 RETAIL
STATED PRINT RUN 557 SERIAL #'d SETS
CARD 103 DOES NOT EXIST

2006 Topps Heritage Chrome Black Refractors

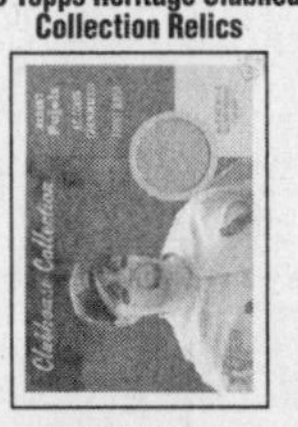

*BLACK: 6X TO 15X CHROME
STATED ODDS 1:328 HOBBY, 1:328 RETAIL
STATED PRINT RUN 57 SERIAL #'d SETS
CARD 103 DOES NOT EXIST

2006 Topps Heritage Clubhouse Collection Relics

GROUP A ODDS 1:3440 H, 1:3457 R
GROUP B ODDS 1:8164 H, 1:8232 R
GROUP C ODDS 1:1639 H, 1:1650 R
GROUP D ODDS 1:2928 H, 1:2935 R
GROUP E ODDS 1:4082 H, 1:4116 R
GROUP F ODDS 1:3404 H, 1:3426 R
GROUP G ODDS 1:487 H, 1:490 R
GROUP H ODDS 1:2583 H, 1:2600 R
GROUP I ODDS 1:206 H, 1:207 R
GROUP J ODDS 1:257 H, 1:255 R
GROUP K ODDS 1:1370 H, 1:1364 R
GROUP L ODDS 1:421 H, 1:419 R
OVERALL AU-RELIC ODDS 1:36 H, 1:36 R
GROUP A PRINT RUN 99 COPIES PER
GROUP B PRINT RUN 125 COPIES PER
GROUP A-B CARDS ARE NOT SERIAL #'d
A-B PRINT RUN INFO PROVIDED BY TOPPS
AD Adam Dunn Bat G 3.00 8.00
AJ Andruw Jones Uni G 4.00 10.00
AK Al Kaline Bat B/125 * 30.00 60.00
AP Albert Pujols Jsy I 8.00 20.00
AR Alex Rodriguez Bat A/99 * 40.00 80.00
AR2 Alex Rodriguez Jsy D 20.00 50.00
AS Alfonso Soriano Bat I 3.00 8.00
BB Barry Bonds Uni A/99 * 30.00 60.00
BM Bill Mazeroski Jsy A/99 * 50.00 100.00
BR Brian Roberts Bat I 3.00 8.00
BRO Brooks Robinson Bat A/99 * 15.00 40.00
BR2 Brian Roberts Jsy J 3.00 8.00
CB Clint Barmes Jsy J 3.00 8.00
CC Carl Crawford Bat I 3.00 8.00
CJ Conor Jackson Bat I 3.00 8.00
CS Curt Schilling Jsy C 4.00 10.00
DL Derrek Lee Bat I 4.00 10.00
DO David Ortiz Jsy C 4.00 10.00
DW David Wright Jsy L 4.00 10.00
DWI Dontrelle Willis Jsy J 3.00 8.00
EC Eric Chavez Uni L 3.00 8.00
EG Eric Gagne Jsy F 3.00 8.00
FJF Jeff Francis Jsy L 3.00 8.00
FR Frank Robinson Bat B/125 * 20.00 50.00
GS Gary Sheffield Bat I 3.00 8.00
JD Johnny Damon Bat E 4.00 10.00
JD2 Johnny Damon Jsy G 4.00 10.00
JE Jim Edmonds Jsy H 3.00 8.00
JP Jake Peavy Jsy J 3.00 8.00
JS Johan Santana Jsy J 4.00 10.00
KG Khalil Greene Jsy D 4.00 10.00
MC Miguel Cabrera Jsy G 4.00 10.00
ME Morgan Ensberg Bat I 3.00 8.00
MH Matt Holliday Bat I 4.00 10.00
MM Mickey Mantle Bat A/99 * 125.00 200.00
MMU Mark Mulder Uni K 3.00 8.00
MP Mike Piazza Bat C 6.00 15.00
MR Manny Ramirez Jsy C 4.00 10.00
MR2 Manny Ramirez Bat J 4.00 10.00
MT Miguel Tejada Uni I 3.00 8.00
MTE Mark Teixeira Jsy G 4.00 10.00
PM Pedro Martinez Jsy C 4.00 10.00
RC Robinson Cano Bat I 4.00 10.00
RW Rickie Weeks Bat G 3.00 8.00
SC Shin-Soo Choo Bat I 3.00 8.00
SM Stan Musial Bat A/99 * 15.00 40.00
TI Tadahito Iguchi Jsy J 3.00 8.00
VG Vladimir Guerrero Bat J 4.00 10.00

2006 Topps Heritage Clubhouse Collection Autograph Relics

STATED ODDS 1:16,400 H, 1:16,400 R
STATED PRINT RUN 25 SERIAL #'d SETS
EXCHANGE DEADLINE 02/28/08
NO PRICING DUE TO SCARCITY
2 Frank Robinson Jsy
3 Brooks Robinson Jsy
4 Al Kaline Jsy
6 Stan Musial Jsy

2006 Topps Heritage Clubhouse Collection Cut Signature Relic

STATED ODDS 1:963,072 HOBBY
STATED PRINT RUN 1 SERIAL #'d CARD
NO PRICING DUE TO SCARCITY
5 Mickey Mantle Bat

2006 Topps Heritage Clubhouse Collection Dual Relics

STATED ODDS 1:12,067 H, 1:12,067 R
STATED PRINT RUN 57 SERIAL #'d SETS
BR Brooks Robinson Bat 50.00 100.00
Brian Roberts Jsy
MP Stan Musial Bat 125.00 200.00
Albert Pujols Jsy
MR Mickey Mantle Bat 150.00 300.00
Alex Rodriguez Jsy

2006 Topps Heritage Flashbacks

COMPLETE SET (10) 10.00 25.00
STATED ODDS 1:12 HOBBY, 1:12 RETAIL
AK Al Kaline 1.00 2.50
BM Bill Mazeroski .60 1.50
BR Brooks Robinson .60 1.50
BRI Bobby Richardson .40 1.00
EB Ernie Banks 1.00 2.50
FR Frank Robinson .40 1.00
MM Mickey Mantle 3.00 8.00
SM Stan Musial 1.50 4.00
WF Whitey Ford .60 1.50
YB Yogi Berra 1.00 2.50

2006 Topps Heritage Flashbacks Autographs

STATED ODDS 1:16,400 H, 1:16,400 R
STATED PRINT RUN 25 SERIAL #'d SETS
NO PRICING DUE TO SCARCITY
BR Brooks Robinson
DS Duke Snider
EB Ernie Banks
FR Frank Robinson
SM Stan Musial

2006 Topps Heritage Flashbacks Autograph Seat Relics

STATED ODDS 1:16,400 H, 1:16,400 R
STATED PRINT RUN 25 SERIAL #'d SETS
NO PRICING DUE TO SCARCITY
BR Brooks Robinson
DS Duke Snider
EB Ernie Banks
FR Frank Robinson
SM Stan Musial

2006 Topps Heritage Flashbacks Seat Relics

GROUP A ODDS 1:14,607 H, 1:14,607 R
GROUP B ODDS 1:6225 H, 1:6175 R
GROUP C ODDS 1:721 H, 1:719 R
GROUP D ODDS 1:1711 H, 1:1703 R
GROUP E ODDS 1:308 H, 1:306 R
OVERALL AU-RELIC ODDS 1:36 H, 1:36 R
GROUP A PRINT RUN 140 COPIES
GROUP A CARD IS NOT SERIAL #'d
GROUP A PRINT RUN PROVIDED BY TOPPS
AK Al Kaline E 12.50 30.00
BM Bill Mazeroski B 10.00 25.00
BR Brooks Robinson E 6.00 15.00
BR Bobby Richardson C 10.00 25.00
EB Ernie Banks D 10.00 25.00
FR Frank Robinson E 4.00 10.00
MM Mickey Mantle E 20.00 50.00
SM Stan Musial A/140 * 40.00 80.00
WF Whitey Ford C 6.00 15.00
YB Yogi Berra C 10.00 25.00

2006 Topps Heritage New Age Performers

COMPLETE SET (15) 15.00 40.00
STATED ODDS 1:15 HOBBY, 1:15 RETAIL
AP Albert Pujols 2.50 6.00
AR Alex Rodriguez 1.50 4.00
BB Barry Bonds 2.00 5.00
CL Carlos Lee .40 1.00
DL Derrek Lee .40 1.00
DO David Ortiz .60 1.50
GM Mark Prior .60 1.50
GS Gary Sheffield .40 1.00
IS Ichiro Suzuki 1.50 4.00
MC Miguel Cabrera 1.00 2.50
MR Manny Ramirez 1.00 2.50
MT Mark Teixeira 1.00 2.50
PM Pedro Martinez .60 1.50
RC Roger Clemens 1.25 3.00
VG Vladimir Guerrero 1.00 2.50

2006 Topps Heritage Real One Autographs

Charley Thompson and Red Murff cards were originally seeded into packs as redemption cards with an exchange deadline of February 28th, 2008.

STATED ODDS 1:366 HOBBY, 1:366 RETAIL
STATED PRINT RUN 200 SETS
CARDS ARE NOT SERIAL-NUMBERED
PRINT RUN INFO PROVIDED BY TOPPS
*RED INK: .75X TO 1.5X BASIC
RED INK ODDS 1:1280 H, 1:1288 R
RED INK PRINT RUN 57 SERIAL #'d SETS
RED INK ALSO CALLED SPECIAL EDITION
EXCHANGE DEADLINE 02/28/08
BC Bob Chakales 20.00 50.00
BW Bob Wiesler 20.00 50.00
DK Don Kaiser 20.00 50.00
DR Dusty Rhodes 30.00 60.00
DS Duke Snider 50.00 100.00
EB Ernie Banks 75.00 150.00
EO Ernie Oravetz 20.00 50.00
EOB Eddie O'Brien 20.00 50.00
FR Frank Robinson 50.00 100.00
JAC Jackie Collum 20.00 50.00
JCR Jack Crimian 20.00 50.00
JD Jack Dittmer 20.00 50.00
JM Joe Margoneri 20.00 50.00
JP Jim Pyburn 20.00 50.00
JSM Jim Small 20.00 50.00
JSN Jerry Snyder UER 30.00 60.00
Photo is actually Ed Fitzgerald
KO Karl Olson 20.00 50.00
LK Lou Kretlow 20.00 50.00
MP Mel Parnell 30.00 60.00
NK Nellie King 20.00 50.00
PL Paul LaPalme 20.00 50.00
RN Ron Negray 20.00 50.00
SM Stan Musial 75.00 150.00
TB Tommy Byrne 30.00 60.00
WF Whitey Ford 50.00 100.00
WM Windy McCall 20.00 50.00
YB Yogi Berra 60.00 120.00

2006 Topps Heritage Real One Cut Signatures

STATED ODDS 1:481,536 HOBBY
STATED PRINT RUN 1 SERIAL #'d SET
NO PRICING DUE TO SCARCITY
MM Mickey Mantle
TW Ted Williams

2006 Topps Heritage Then and Now

COMPLETE SET (10) 10.00 25.00
STATED ODDS 1:15 HOBBY, 1:15 RETAIL
TN1 Mickey Mantle 3.00 8.00
Alex Rodriguez
TN2 Ted Williams .60 1.50
Michael Young
TN3 Mickey Mantle 3.00 8.00
Jason Giambi
TN4 Luis Aparicio .40 1.00
Chone Figgins
TN5 Ted Williams 2.50 6.00
Alex Rodriguez
TN6 Stan Musial 1.50 4.00
Derrek Lee
TN7 Stan Musial 1.50 4.00
Derrek Lee
TN8 Red Schoendienst .40 1.00
Derrek Lee
TN9 Johnny Podres 1.25 3.00
Roger Clemens
TN10 Clem Labine .40 1.00
Chad Cordero

2007 Topps Heritage

This 527-card set was released in March, 2007. This set was issued through both hobby and retail channels. The set was issued in eight-card hobby packs (with an $3 SRP) which came 24 packs to a box and 12 boxes to a case. Each pack also included a sealed piece of bubble gum. In the tradition of previous Heritage sets, this product honored the 1958 Topps set. In addition, in homage to the original 1958 set, some cards issued between 1-110 were issued in two varieties (a white and yellow letter version). Those yellow cards were inserted at a stated rate of one in six hobby or retail packs. Also, just like the original 1958 Topps set, there was no card #145 issued. In another long-standing Heritage tradition, many cards throughout the set were short-printed. Those short prints were inserted at a stated rate of one in two. In other tributes to the original 1958 sets, many multi-player cards and team checklist cards were inserted in the same card number as the original set and the set concludes with a 20-card All-Star set (476-495).

COMPLETE SET (527) 250.00 400.00
COMP.SET w/o SP's (384) 30.00 60.00
COMMON CARD .20 .50
COMMON RC .20 .50
COMMON TEAM CARD .20 .50
COMMON SP 2.50 6.00
SP STATED ODDS 1:2 HOBBY/RETAIL
SEE BECKETT.COM FOR SP CHECKLIST
COMMON YELLOW 2.00 5.00
YELLOW STATED ODDS 1:6 HOBBY/RETAIL
SEE BECKETT.COM FOR YELLOW CL
CARD 145 DOES NOT EXIST
1 David Ortiz .30 .75
2a Roger Clemens .60 1.50
2b Roger Clemens YT 3.00 8.00
3 David Wells .20 .50
4 Ronny Paulino SP 2.50 6.00
5 Derek Jeter SP 6.00 15.00
6 Felix Hernandez .50 1.25
7 Todd Helton .30 .75
8a David Eckstein .20 .50
8b David Eckstein YN 2.00 5.00
9 Craig Wilson .20 .50
10 John Smoltz .50 1.25
11a Rob Mackowiak .20 .50
11b Rob Mackowiak YT 2.00 5.00
12 Scott Hatteberg .20 .50
13a Wilfredo Ledezma SP 2.50 6.00
13b Wilfredo Ledezma YT 2.00 5.00
14 Bobby Abreu SP 2.50 6.00
15 Mike Stanton .20 .50
16 Wilson Betemit .20 .50
17 Darren Oliver .20 .50
18 Josh Beckett .30 .75
19 San Francisco Giants TC .20 .50
20a Robinson Cano .50 1.25
20b Robinson Cano YT 2.50 6.00
21 Matt Cain .30 .75
22 Jason Kendall SP 2.50 6.00
23a Mark Kotsay SP 2.50 6.00
23b Mark Kotsay YN 2.00 5.00
24a Yadier Molina .30 .75
24b Yadier Molina YN 2.00 5.00
25 Brad Penny .20 .50
26 Adrian Gonzalez .30 .75
27 Danny Haren .20 .50
28 Brian Giles .20 .50
29 Jose Lopez .20 .50
30a Ichiro Suzuki .75 2.00
30b Ichiro Suzuki YN 3.00 8.00
31 Beltran Perez SP (RC) 2.50 6.00
32 Brad Hawpe SP 2.50 6.00
33a Jim Thome .30 .75
33b Jim Thome YT 2.50 6.00
34 Mark DeRosa .20 .50
35a Woody Williams .20 .50
35b Woody Williams YT 2.00 5.00
36 Luis Gonzalez .20 .50
37 Billy Sadler (RC) .20 .50
38 Dave Roberts .20 .50
39 Mitch Maier RC .20 .50
40 Francisco Cordero SP 2.50 6.00
41 Anthony Reyes SP 2.50 6.00
42 Russell Martin .20 .50
43 Scott Proctor .20 .50
44 Washington Nationals TC .20 .50
45 Shane Victorino .20 .50
46a Joel Zumaya .30 .75
46b Joel Zumaya YN 2.50 6.00
47 Delmon Young (RC) .30 .75
48 Alex Rios .30 .75
49 Willy Taveras SP 2.50 6.00
50a Mark Buehrle SP 2.50 6.00
50b Mark Buehrle YT 2.00 5.00
51 Livan Hernandez .20 .50
52a Jason Bay .30 .75
52b Jason Bay YT 2.00 5.00
53a Jose Valentin .20 .50
53b Jose Valentin YN 2.00 5.00
54 Kevin Reese .20 .50
55 Felipe Lopez .20 .50
56 Ryan Sweeney (RC) .20 .50
57a Kelvim Escobar .20 .50
57b Kelvim Escobar YN 2.00 5.00
58a Nick Swisher SP 2.50 6.00
Oakland Athletics in small print
58b Nick Swisher YT 2.00 5.00
Oakland Athletics in large print
59 Kevin Millwood SP 2.50 6.00
60a Preston Wilson .20 .50
60b Preston Wilson YN 2.00 5.00
61a Mariano Rivera .50 1.25
61b Mariano Rivera YN 2.50 6.00
62 Josh Barfield .20 .50
63 Ryan Freel .20 .50
64 Tim Hudson .30 .75
65a Chris Narveson (RC) .20 .50
65b Chris Narveson YN (RC) 2.00 5.00
66 Matt Murton .20 .50
67 Melvin Mora SP 2.50 6.00
68 Jason Jennings SP 2.50 6.00
69 Emil Brown .20 .50
70a Magglio Ordonez .30 .75
70b Magglio Ordonez YN 2.00 5.00
71 Los Angeles Dodgers TC .20 .50
72 Ross Gload .20 .50
73 David Ross .20 .50
74 Juan Uribe .20 .50
75 Scott Podsednik .20 .50
76a Cole Hamels SP 3.00 8.00
76b Cole Hamels YT 2.50 6.00
77a Rafael Furcal SP 2.50 6.00
77b Rafael Furcal YT 2.00 5.00
78a Ryan Theriot .20 .50
78b Ryan Theriot YN 2.00 5.00
79a Corey Patterson .20 .50
79b Corey Patterson YT 2.00 5.00
80 Jered Weaver .30 .75
81a Stephen Drew .20 .50
81b Stephen Drew YT 2.50 6.00
82 Adam Kennedy .20 .50
83 Tony Gwynn Jr. .20 .50
84 Kazuo Matsui .20 .50
85a Omar Vizquel SP 3.00 8.00
85b Omar Vizquel YT 2.50 6.00
86 Fred Lewis SP (RC) 2.50 6.00
87a Shawn Chacon .20 .50
87b Shawn Chacon YN 2.00 5.00
88 Frank Catalanotto .20 .50
89 Orlando Hudson .20 .50
90 Pat Burrell .20 .50
91 David DeJesus .20 .50
92a David Wright .75 2.00
92b David Wright YN 3.00 8.00
93 Conor Jackson .20 .50
94 Xavier Nady SP 2.50 6.00
95 Bill Hall SP 2.50 6.00
96 Kip Wells .20 .50
97a Jeff Suppan .20 .50
97b Jeff Suppan YN 2.00 5.00
98a Ryan Zimmerman .30 .75
98b Ryan Zimmerman YN 2.50 6.00
99 Wes Helms .20 .50
100a Jose Contreras .20 .50
100b Jose Contreras YT 2.00 5.00
101a Miguel Cairo .20 .50
101b Miguel Cairo YN 2.00 5.00
102 Brian Roberts .20 .50
103 Carl Crawford SP 2.50 6.00
104 Mike Lamb SP 2.50 6.00
105 Mark Ellis .20 .50
106 Scott Rolen .30 .75
107 Garrett Atkins .20 .50
108a Hanley Ramirez .50 1.25
108b Hanley Ramirez YT 2.50 6.00
109 Trot Nixon .20 .50
110 Edgar Renteria .20 .50
111 Jeff Francis .20 .50
112 Marcus Thames SP 2.50 6.00
113 Brian Burres SP (RC) 2.50 6.00
114 Brian Schneider .20 .50
115 Jeremy Bonderman .20 .50
116 Ryan Madson .20 .50
117 Gerald Laird .20 .50
118 Roy Halladay .50 1.25
119 Victor Martinez .30 .75
120 Greg Maddux .75 2.00
121 Jay Payton SP 2.50 6.00
122 Jacque Jones SP 2.50 6.00
123 Juan Lara RC .20 .50
124 Derrick Turnbow .20 .50
125 Adam Everett .20 .50
126 Michael Cuddyer .20 .50
127 Gil Meche .20 .50
128 Willy Aybar .20 .50
129 Jerry Owens (RC) .20 .50
130 Manny Ramirez SP 3.00 8.00
131 Howie Kendrick SP 2.50 6.00
132 Byung-Hyun Kim .20 .50
133 Kevin Kouzmanoff (RC) .20 .50
134 Philadelphia Phillies TC .20 .50
135 Joe Blanton .20 .50
136 Ray Durham .20 .50
137 Luke Hudson .20 .50
138 Eric Byrnes .20 .50
139 Ryan Braun SP RC 2.50 6.00
140 Johnny Damon SP 3.00 8.00
141 Ambiorix Burgos .20 .50
142 Hideki Matsui .50 1.25
143 Josh Johnson .50 1.25
144 Miguel Cabrera .50 1.25
146 Delwyn Young (RC) .20 .50
147 Chuck James .20 .50
148 Morgan Ensberg .20 .50
149 Jose Vidro SP 2.50 6.00
150 Alex Rodriguez SP 5.00 12.00
151 Carlos Maldonado (RC) .20 .50
152 Jason Schmidt .20 .50
153 Alex Escobar .20 .50
154 Chris Gomez .20 .50
155 Endy Chavez .20 .50
156 Kris Benson .20 .50
157 Bronson Arroyo .20 .50
158 Cleveland Indians TC SP 2.50 6.00
159 Chris Ray SP 2.50 6.00
160 Richie Sexson .20 .50
161 Huston Street .20 .50
162 Kevin Youkilis .20 .50
163 Armando Benitez .20 .50
164 Vinny Rottino (RC) .20 .50
165 Garrett Anderson .20 .50
166 Todd Greene .20 .50
167 Brian Stokes SP (RC) 2.50 6.00
168 Albert Pujols SP 6.00 15.00
169 Todd Coffey .20 .50
170 Jason Michaels .20 .50
171 David Dellucci .20 .50
172 Eric Milton .20 .50
173 Austin Kearns .20 .50
174 Oakland Athletics TC .20 .50
175 Andy Cannizaro RC .20 .50
176 David Weathers SP 2.50 6.00
177 Jermaine Dye SP 2.50 6.00
178 Wily Mo Pena .20 .50
179 Chris Burke .20 .50
180 Jeff Weaver .20 .50
181 Edwin Encarnacion .20 .50
182 Jeremy Hermida .20 .50
183 Tim Wakefield .20 .50
184 Rich Hill .20 .50
185 Aaron Hill SP 2.50 6.00
186 Scot Shields SP 2.50 6.00
187 Randy Johnson .50 1.25
188 Dan Johnson .20 .50
189 Sean Marshall .20 .50
190 Marcus Giles .20 .50
191 Jonathan Broxton .20 .50
192 Mike Piazza .50 1.25
193 Carlos Quentin .20 .50
194 Derek Lowe SP 2.50 6.00
195 Russell Branyan SP 2.50 6.00
196 Jason Marquis .20 .50
197 Khalil Greene .20 .50
198 Ryan Dempster .20 .50
199 Ronnie Belliard .20 .50
200 Josh Fogg .20 .50
201 Carlos Lee .20 .50
202 Chris Denorfia .20 .50
203 Kendry Morales SP 3.00 8.00
204 Rafael Soriano SP 2.50 6.00
205 Brandon Phillips .20 .50
206 Andrew Miller RC .50 1.25
207 John Koronka .20 .50
208 Luis Castillo .20 .50
209 Angel Guzman .20 .50
210 Jim Edmonds .30 .75
211 Patrick Misch (RC) .75 2.00
212 Ty Wigginton SP 2.50 6.00
213 Brandon Inge SP 2.50 6.00
214 Royce Clayton .20 .50
215 Ben Broussard .20 .50
216 St. Louis Cardinals TC .20 .50
217 Mark Mulder .20 .50
218 Kenji Johjima .50 1.25
219 Joe Crede .20 .50
220 Shea Hillenbrand .20 .50
221 Josh Fields SP (RC) 2.50 6.00
222 Pat Neshek SP 3.00 8.00
223 Reed Johnson .20 .50
224 Mike Mussina .30 .75
225 Randy Winn .20 .50
226 Brian Rogers .20 .50
227 Juan Rivera .20 .50
228 Shawn Green .20 .50
229 Mike Napoli .30 .75
230 Chase Utley SP 3.00 8.00
231 John Nelson SP (RC) 2.50 6.00
232 Casey Blake .20 .50
233 Lyle Overbay .20 .50
234 Adam LaRoche .20 .50
235 Julio Lugo .20 .50
236 Johnny Estrada .20 .50
237 James Shields .20 .50
238 Jose Castillo .20 .50
239 Doug Davis SP 2.50 6.00
240 Jason Giambi SP 2.50 6.00
241 Mike Gonzalez .20 .50
242 Scott Downs .20 .50
243 Joe Inglett .20 .50
244 Matt Kemp .30 .75
245 Ted Lilly .20 .50
246 New York Yankees TC .50 1.25
247 Jamey Carroll .20 .50
248 Adam Wainwright SP 2.50 6.00
249 Matt Thornton SP 2.50 6.00
250 Alfonso Soriano .30 .75
251 Tom Gordon .20 .50
252 Dennis Sarfate (RC) .20 .50
253 Zach Duke .20 .50
254 Hank Blalock .20 .50
255 Johan Santana .50 1.25
256 Chicago White Sox TC .20 .50
257 Aaron Cook SP 2.50 6.00
258 Cliff Lee SP 2.50 6.00
259 Miguel Tejada .30 .75
260 Mike Lowell .20 .50
261 Ian Snell .20 .50
262 Jason Tyner .20 .50
263 Troy Tulowitzki (RC) 1.25 3.00
264 Ervin Santana .20 .50
265 Jon Lester .50 1.25
266 Andy Pettitte SP 3.00 8.00
267 A.J. Pierzynski SP 2.50 6.00
268 Rich Aurilia .20 .50
269 Phil Nevin .20 .50
270 Tom Glavine .30 .75
271 Chris Coste .20 .50
272 Moises Alou .20 .50
273 J.D. Drew .20 .50
274 Abraham Nunez .20 .50
275 Jorge Posada SP 3.00 8.00
276 Jeff Conine SP 2.50 6.00
277 Chad Cordero .20 .50
278 Nick Johnson .20 .50
279 Kevin Millar .20 .50
280 Mark Grudzielanek .20 .50
281 Chris Stewart RC .20 .50
282 Nate Robertson .20 .50
283 Drew Anderson RC .20 .50
284 Doug Mientkiewicz SP 2.50 6.00
285 Ken Griffey Jr. SP 4.00 10.00
286 Cory Sullivan .20 .50
287 Chris Carpenter .50 1.25
288 Gary Matthews .20 .50
289 Justin Verlander .60 1.50
Jeff Weaver
290 Vicente Padilla UER .20 .50
Vincente on front, Vicente on back
291 Chris Roberson .20 .50
292 Chris R. Young .20 .50
293 Ryan Garko SP 2.50 6.00
294 Miguel Batista SP 2.50 6.00
295 B.J. Upton .20 .50
296 Justin Verlander .60 1.50
297 Ben Zobrist .20 .50
298 Ben Sheets UER .20 .50
Listed as an San Diego Padre
299 Eric Chavez .20 .50
300 Scott Schoeneweis .20 .50
301 Placido Polanco .20 .50
302 Angel Sanchez SP RC 2.50 6.00
303 Freddy Sanchez SP 2.50 6.00
304 Magglio Ordonez .30 .75
Craig Monroe
305 A.J. Burnett .30 .75
306 Juan Perez RC .20 .50
307 Chris Britton .20 .50
308 Jon Garland .20 .50
309 Pedro Feliz .20 .50
310 Ryan Howard .75 2.00
311 Aaron Harang SP 2.50 6.00
312 Boston Red Sox TC SP 3.00 8.00
313 Chad Billingsley .20 .50
314 Chipper Jones .50 1.25
Bobby Cox MG
315 Bengie Molina .20 .50
316 Juan Pierre .20 .50
317 Luke Scott .20 .50
318 Javier Valentin .20 .50
319 Mark Loretta .20 .50
320 Kenny Lofton SP 2.50 6.00
321 Vladimir Guerrero 3.00 8.00
Ivan Rodriguez SP
322 Josh Willingham .20 .50
323 Lance Berkman .30 .75
324 Anibal Sanchez .20 .50
325 Maicer Izturis .20 .50
326 Brett Myers .20 .50
327 Chicago Cubs TC .20 .50
328 Francisco Liriano .50 1.25
329 Craig Monroe SP 2.50 6.00
330 Paul LoDuca SP 2.50 6.00
331 Steve Trachsel .20 .50
332 Bernie Williams .30 .75
333 Carlos Guillen .20 .50
334 Chien-Ming Wang .30 .75
Mike Mussina
335 Dave Bush .20 .50
336 Carlos Beltran .20 .50
337 Jason Isringhausen .20 .50
338 Todd Walker SP 2.50 6.00
339 Jarrod Washburn SP 2.50 6.00
340 Brandon Webb .30 .75
341 Pittsburgh Pirates TC .20 .50
342 Daryle Ward .20 .50
343 Chad Santos .20 .50
344 Brad Lidge .20 .50
345 Brad Ausmus .20 .50
346 Carlos Delgado .30 .75
347 Boone Logan SP 2.50 6.00
348 Jimmy Rollins SP 2.50 6.00
349 Orlando Hernandez .20 .50
350 Gary Sheffield .20 .50
351 Albert Pujols .30 .75
Chris Duncan
Jim Edmonds
Yadier Molina
352 Jake Peavy .20 .50
353 Jason Varitek .50 1.25
354 Freddy Garcia .20 .50
355 Matt Diaz .20 .50
356 Bernie Castro SP 2.50 6.00
357 Eric Stults SP RC 2.50 6.00
358 John Lackey .20 .50
359 Bobby Jenks .20 .50
360 Mark Teixeira .50 1.25
361 Jonathan Papelbon .50 1.25
362 Paul Konerko .30 .75
363 Erik Bedard .20 .50
364 Eliezer Alfonzo .20 .50
365 Fernando Rodney SP 2.50 6.00
366 Chris Duncan SP 2.50 6.00
367 Jose Diaz (RC) .20 .50
368 Travis Hafner .20 .50
369 Matt Capps .20 .50
370 Ivan Rodriguez .30 .75
371 David Murphy (RC) .20 .50
372 Carlos Zambrano .30 .75
373 Chris Iannetta .20 .50
374 Jose Mesa SP 2.50 6.00
375 Michael Young SP 2.50 6.00
376 Bill Bray .20 .50
377 Atlanta Braves TC .30 .75
378 Jeff Cirillo .20 .50
379 Barry Zito .30 .75
380 Clay Hensley .20 .50
381 J.J. Putz .20 .50
382 C.C. Sabathia .30 .75
383 Eduardo Perez SP 2.50 6.00
384 Scott Moore SP (RC) 2.50 6.00
385 Scott Olsen .20 .50
386 Ryan Howard .75 2.00
Chase Utley
387 Aaron Rowand .20 .50
388 Mike Rouse .20 .50
389 Alexis Gomez .20 .50
390 Brian McCann .20 .50
391 Ryan Shealy .20 .50
392 Shane Youman SP RC 2.50 6.00
393 Melky Cabrera SP 2.50 6.00
394 Jeremy Sowers .20 .50
395 Casey Janssen .20 .50
396 Travis Chick (RC) .20 .50
397 Detroit Tigers TC UER .20 .50
Listed as being in the National League
398 Reggie Abercrombie .20 .50
399 Ricky Nolasco .20 .50
400 Tadahito Iguchi .20 .50
401 Jose Reyes SP 2.50 6.00
402 Juan Encarnacion SP 2.50 6.00
403 Brandon Harper .20 .50
404 Torii Hunter .20 .50
405 Dan Uggla .30 .75
406 Orlando Cabrera .20 .50
407 Jose Capellan .20 .50
408 Baltimore Orioles TC .20 .50
409 Frank Thomas .50 1.25
410 Francisco Rodriguez SP 2.50 6.00
411 Ian Kinsler SP 3.00 8.00
412 Billy Wagner .20 .50
413 Andy Marte .20 .50
414 Mike Jacobs .20 .50
415 Raul Ibanez .30 .75
416 Jhonny Peralta .20 .50
417 Chris B. Young .20 .50
418 Albert Pujols .30 .75
Magglio Ordonez
419 Scott Kazmir SP 3.00 8.00
420 Norris Hopper SP 2.50 6.00
421 Chris Capuano .20 .50
422 Troy Glaus .20 .50
423 Roy Oswalt .30 .75
424 Grady Sizemore .30 .75
425 Chone Figgins .20 .50
426 Chad Tracy .20 .50
427 Brian Fuentes .20 .50
428 Cincinnati Reds TC SP 2.50 6.00
429 Ramon Hernandez SP 2.50 6.00
430 Mike Cameron .20 .50
431 Dontrelle Willis .20 .50
432 Josh Sharpless .20 .50
433 Adrian Beltre .20 .50
434 Curtis Granderson .30 .75
435 B.J. Ryan .20 .50
436 David Wright .75 2.00
Ryan Howard
437 Vernon Wells SP 2.50 6.00
438 Vladimir Guerrero SP 3.00 8.00
439 Jake Westbrook .20 .50
440 Chipper Jones .50 1.25
441 James Loney .30 .75
442 Nook Logan .20 .50
443 Oswaldo Navarro RC .20 .50
444 Joe Mauer .50 1.25
445 Miguel Montero (RC) .20 .50
446 Franklin Gutierrez SP 2.50 6.00
447 Mark Redman SP 2.50 6.00
448 Mike Rabelo RC .20 .50
449 Philip Humber (RC) .20 .50
450 Justin Morneau .50 1.25
451 Hector Gimenez (RC) .20 .50
452 Matt Holliday .50 1.25
453 Akinori Otsuka .20 .50
454 Prince Fielder .30 .75
455 Chien-Ming Wang SP 4.00 10.00
456 Shawn Riggans SP 2.50 6.00
457 John Maine .20 .50
458 Adam Lind (RC) .20 .50
459 Ubaldo Jimenez (RC) 1.25 3.00
460 Jaret Wright .20 .50
461 Cla Meredith .20 .50
462 Joaquin Arias (RC) .20 .50
463 Kenny Rogers .20 .50
464 Jose Garcia SP RC 2.50 6.00
465 Pedro Martinez SP 3.00 8.00
466 Jeff Salazar (RC) .20 .50
467 Glen Perkins .20 .50
468 Travis Ishikawa .20 .50
469 Joe Borowski .20 .50
470 Jeremy Brown .20 .50
471 Andre Ethier .30 .75
472 Taylor Tankersley .20 .50
473 Lastings Milledge SP 3.00 8.00
474 Brian Sanchez SP 2.50 6.00
475 Ozzie Guillen AS MG .20 .50
Phil Garner AS MG
476 Albert Pujols AS 1.25 3.00
477 David Ortiz AS .30 .75
478 Chase Utley AS .50 1.25
479 Mark Loretta AS .20 .50
480 David Wright AS .75 2.00
481 Alex Rodriguez AS .75 2.00
482 Edgar Renteria AS SP 2.50 6.00
483 Derek Jeter AS SP 5.00 12.00
484 Alfonso Soriano AS .30 .75
485 Vladimir Guerrero AS .50 1.25
486 Carlos Beltran AS .20 .50
487 Vernon Wells AS .20 .50
488 Jason Bay AS .30 .75
489 Ichiro Suzuki AS .75 2.00
490 Paul LoDuca AS .20 .50
491 Ivan Rodriguez AS SP 3.00 8.00
492 Brad Penny AS SP 2.50 6.00
493 Roy Halladay AS .50 1.25
494 Brian Fuentes AS .20 .50
495 Kenny Rogers AS .20 .50

2007 Topps Heritage Chrome

STATED ODDS 1:11 HOBBY, 1:12 RETAIL
STATED PRINT RUN 1958 SERIAL #'d SETS
THC1 David Ortiz 1.50 4.00
THC2 John Smoltz 2.50 6.00
THC3 San Francisco Giants TC 1.00 2.50
THC4 Brian Giles 1.00 2.50
THC5 Billy Sadler 1.00 2.50
THC6 Joel Zumaya 1.50 4.00
THC7 Felipe Lopez 1.00 2.50
THC8 Tim Hudson 1.50 4.00
THC9 David Ross 1.00 2.50
THC10 Adam Kennedy 1.00 2.50
THC11 David DeJesus 1.00 2.50
THC12 Jose Contreras 1.00 2.50
THC13 Trot Nixon 1.00 2.50
THC14 Roy Halladay 2.50 6.00
THC15 Gil Meche 1.00 2.50
THC16 Ray Durham 1.00 2.50
THC17 Delwyn Young 1.00 2.50
THC18 Endy Chavez 1.00 2.50
THC19 Vinny Rottino 1.00 2.50
THC20 Austin Kearns 1.00 2.50
THC21 Jeremy Hermida 1.00 2.50
THC22 Jonathan Broxton 1.00 2.50
THC23 Josh Fogg 1.00 2.50
THC24 Angel Guzman 1.00 2.50
THC25 Kenji Johjima 2.50 6.00
THC26 Juan Rivera 1.00 2.50
THC27 Johnny Estrada 1.00 2.50
THC28 Ted Lilly 1.00 2.50
THC29 Hank Blalock 1.00 2.50
THC30 Troy Tulowitzki 6.00 15.00
THC31 Moises Alou 1.00 2.50
THC32 Chris Stewart 1.00 2.50
THC33 Vicente Padilla 1.00 2.50
THC34 Eric Chavez 1.00 2.50
THC35 Jon Garland 1.00 2.50
THC36 Luke Scott 1.00 2.50
THC37 Brett Myers 1.00 2.50
THC38 Dave Bush 1.00 2.50
THC39 Brad Lidge 1.00 2.50
THC40 Jason Varitek 2.50 6.00
THC41 Paul Konerko 1.50 4.00
THC42 David Murphy 1.00 2.50
THC43 Clay Hensley 1.00 2.50
THC44 Alexis Gomez 1.00 2.50
THC45 Reggie Abercrombie 1.00 2.50
THC46 Jose Capellan 1.00 2.50
THC47 Jhonny Peralta 1.00 2.50
THC48 Chone Figgins 1.00 2.50
THC49 Curtis Granderson 1.50 4.00
THC50 Oswaldo Navarro 1.00 2.50
THC51 Matt Holliday 2.50 6.00
THC52 Cla Meredith 1.00 2.50
THC53 Jeremy Brown 1.00 2.50
THC54 Mark Loretta AS 1.00 2.50
THC55 Jason Bay AS 1.50 4.00
THC56 Roger Clemens 3.00 8.00
THC57 Rob Mackowiak 1.00 2.50
THC58 Robinson Cano 2.50 6.00
THC59 Jose Lopez 1.00 2.50
THC60 Dave Roberts 1.00 2.50
THC61 Delmon Young 1.50 4.00
THC62 Ryan Sweeney 1.00 2.50
THC63 Chris Narveson 1.00 2.50
THC64 Juan Uribe 1.00 2.50
THC65 Tony Gwynn Jr. 1.00 2.50
THC66 David Wright 4.00 10.00
THC67 Miguel Cairo 1.00 2.50
THC68 Edgar Renteria 1.00 2.50
THC69 Victor Martinez 1.50 4.00
THC70 Willy Aybar 1.00 2.50
THC71 Luke Hudson 1.00 2.50
THC72 Chuck James 1.00 2.50
THC73 Kris Benson 1.00 2.50
THC74 Garret Anderson 1.00 2.50
THC75 Oakland Athletics TC 1.00 2.50
THC76 Tim Wakefield 1.00 2.50
THC77 Mike Piazza 2.50 6.00
THC78 Carlos Lee 1.00 2.50
THC79 Jim Edmonds 1.50 4.00
THC80 Joe Crede 1.00 2.50
THC81 Shawn Green 1.00 2.50
THC82 James Shields 1.00 2.50
THC83 New York Yankees TC 2.50 6.00
THC84 Johan Santana 2.50 6.00
THC85 Ervin Santana 1.00 2.50
THC86 J.D. Drew 1.00 2.50
THC87 Nate Robertson 1.00 2.50
THC88 Chris Roberson 1.00 2.50
THC89 Scott Schoeneweis 1.00 2.50
THC90 Pedro Feliz 1.00 2.50
THC91 Javier Valentin 1.00 2.50
THC92 Chicago Cubs TC 1.00 2.50
THC93 Carlos Beltran 1.00 2.50
THC94 Brad Ausmus 1.00 2.50
THC95 Freddy Sanchez 1.00 2.50
THC96 Erik Bedard 1.00 2.50
THC97 Carlos Zambrano 1.50 4.00
THC98 J.J. Putz 1.00 2.50
THC99 Brian McCann 1.00 2.50
THC100 Ricky Nolasco 1.00 2.50
THC101 Baltimore Orioles TC 1.00 2.50
THC102 Chris B. Young 1.00 2.50
THC103 Chad Tracy 1.00 2.50
THC104 B.J. Ryan 1.00 2.50
THC105 Joe Mauer 2.50 6.00
THC106 Akinori Otsuka 1.00 2.50
THC107 Joaquin Arias 1.00 2.50
THC108 Andre Ethier 1.50 4.00
THC109 David Wright AS 4.00 10.00
THC110 Ichiro Suzuki AS 4.00 10.00

2007 Topps Heritage Chrome Refractors

*CHROME REF: 1X TO 2.5X
STATED ODDS 1:39 HOBBY, 1:40 RETAIL
STATED PRINT RUN 558 SERIAL #'d SETS

2007 Topps Heritage Chrome Black Refractors

STATED ODDS 1:383 HOBBY/RETAIL
STATED PRINT RUN 58 SERIAL #'d SETS
THC1 David Ortiz 20.00 50.00
THC2 John Smoltz 30.00 80.00
THC3 San Francisco Giants TC 12.00 30.00
THC4 Brian Giles 12.00 30.00
THC5 Billy Sadler 12.00 30.00
THC6 Joel Zumaya 20.00 50.00
THC7 Felipe Lopez 12.00 30.00
THC8 Tim Hudson 20.00 50.00
THC9 David Ross 12.00 30.00
THC10 Adam Kennedy 12.00 30.00
THC11 David DeJesus 12.00 30.00
THC12 Jose Contreras 12.00 30.00
THC13 Trot Nixon 12.00 30.00
THC14 Roy Halladay 30.00 80.00
THC15 Gil Meche 12.00 30.00
THC16 Ray Durham 12.00 30.00
THC17 Delwyn Young 12.00 30.00
THC18 Endy Chavez 12.00 30.00
THC19 Vinny Rottino 12.00 30.00
THC20 Austin Kearns 12.00 30.00
THC21 Jeremy Hermida 12.00 30.00
THC22 Jonathan Broxton 12.00 30.00
THC23 Josh Fogg 12.00 30.00
THC24 Angel Guzman 12.00 30.00
THC25 Kenji Johjima 30.00 80.00
THC26 Juan Rivera 12.00 30.00
THC27 Johnny Estrada 12.00 30.00
THC28 Ted Lilly 12.00 30.00
THC29 Hank Blalock 12.00 30.00
THC30 Troy Tulowitzki 80.00 200.00
THC31 Moises Alou 12.00 30.00
THC32 Chris Stewart 12.00 30.00
THC33 Vicente Padilla 12.00 30.00
THC34 Eric Chavez 12.00 30.00
THC35 Jon Garland 12.00 30.00
THC36 Luke Scott 12.00 30.00
THC37 Brett Myers 12.00 30.00
THC38 Dave Bush 12.00 30.00
THC39 Brad Lidge 12.00 30.00
THC40 Jason Varitek 30.00 80.00
THC41 Paul Konerko 20.00 50.00
THC42 David Murphy 12.00 30.00
THC43 Clay Hensley 12.00 30.00
THC44 Alexis Gomez 12.00 30.00
THC45 Reggie Abercrombie 12.00 30.00
THC46 Jose Capellan 12.00 30.00
THC47 Jhonny Peralta 12.00 30.00
THC48 Chone Figgins 12.00 30.00
THC49 Curtis Granderson 20.00 50.00
THC50 Oswaldo Navarro 12.00 30.00
THC51 Matt Holliday 30.00 80.00
THC52 Cla Meredith 12.00 30.00
THC53 Jeremy Brown 12.00 30.00
THC54 Mark Loretta AS 12.00 30.00
THC55 Jason Bay AS 20.00 50.00
THC56 Roger Clemens 40.00 100.00
THC57 Rob Mackowiak 12.00 30.00
THC58 Robinson Cano 30.00 80.00
THC59 Jose Lopez 12.00 30.00
THC60 Dave Roberts 12.00 30.00
THC61 Delmon Young 20.00 50.00
THC62 Ryan Sweeney 12.00 30.00
THC63 Chris Narveson 12.00 30.00
THC64 Juan Uribe 12.00 30.00
THC65 Tony Gwynn Jr. 12.00 30.00
THC66 David Wright 50.00 120.00
THC67 Miguel Cairo 12.00 30.00
THC68 Edgar Renteria 12.00 30.00
THC69 Victor Martinez 20.00 50.00
THC70 Willy Aybar 12.00 30.00
THC71 Luke Hudson 12.00 30.00
THC72 Chuck James 12.00 30.00
THC73 Kris Benson 12.00 30.00
THC74 Garret Anderson 12.00 30.00
THC75 Oakland Athletics TC 12.00 30.00
THC76 Tim Wakefield 12.00 30.00
THC77 Mike Piazza 30.00 80.00
THC78 Carlos Lee 12.00 30.00
THC79 Jim Edmonds 20.00 50.00
THC80 Joe Crede 12.00 30.00
THC81 Shawn Green 12.00 30.00
THC82 James Shields 12.00 30.00
THC83 New York Yankees TC 30.00 80.00
THC84 Johan Santana 30.00 80.00
THC85 Ervin Santana 12.00 30.00
THC86 J.D. Drew 12.00 30.00
THC87 Nate Robertson 12.00 30.00
THC88 Chris Roberson 12.00 30.00
THC89 Scott Schoeneweis 12.00 30.00
THC90 Pedro Feliz 12.00 30.00
THC91 Javier Valentin 12.00 30.00
THC92 Chicago Cubs TC 12.00 30.00
THC93 Carlos Beltran 12.00 30.00
THC94 Brad Ausmus 12.00 30.00
THC95 Freddy Garcia 12.00 30.00
THC96 Erik Bedard 12.00 30.00
THC97 Carlos Zambrano 20.00 50.00
THC98 J.J. Putz 12.00 30.00
THC99 Brian McCann 12.00 30.00
THC100 Ricky Nolasco 12.00 30.00
THC101 Baltimore Orioles TC 12.00 30.00
THC102 Chris B. Young 12.00 30.00
THC103 Chad Tracy 12.00 30.00
THC104 B.J. Ryan 12.00 30.00
THC105 Joe Mauer 30.00 80.00
THC106 Akinori Otsuka 12.00 30.00
THC107 Joaquin Arias 12.00 30.00
THC108 Andre Ethier 20.00 50.00
THC109 David Wright AS 50.00 120.00
THC110 Ichiro Suzuki AS 50.00 120.00

2007 Topps Heritage 1958 Cut Signature

STATED ODDS 1:403,200 HOBBY
STATED PRINT RUN 1 SER.#'d SET
NO PRICING DUE TO SCARCITY
MM Mickey Mantle
RM Roger Maris
TW Ted Williams

2007 Topps Heritage 1958 Home Run Champion

COMPLETE SET (42) 20.00 50.00
COMMON MANTLE .60 1.50
STATED ODDS 1:6 HOBBY, 1:6 RETAIL

2007 Topps Heritage Clubhouse Collection Relics

GROUP A ODDS 1:2425 HOBBY/RETAIL
GROUP B ODDS 1:202 HOBBY/RETAIL
GROUP C ODDS 1:67 HOBBY/RETAIL
GROUP D ODDS 1:808 HOBBY/RETAIL
AJP Albert Pujols Pants C 8.00 20.00
AK Al Kaline Bat C 8.00 20.00
ALR Anthony Reyes Jsy C 3.00 8.00
AR Alex Rodriguez Bat C 8.00 20.00
AW Adam Wainwright Jsy C 4.00 10.00
BR Brian Roberts Jsy B 3.00 8.00
BR Brooks Robinson Pants C 6.00 15.00
BS Ben Sheets Bat B 4.00 10.00
BU B.J. Upton Bat C 3.00 8.00
BW Billy Wagner Jsy C 3.00 8.00
BZ Barry Zito Pants D 3.00 8.00
CC Chris Carpenter Jsy C 3.00 8.00
CD Chris Duncan Jsy C 6.00 15.00
CJ Chipper Jones Jsy C 4.00 10.00
CJ Conor Jackson Bat B 3.00 8.00
CU Chase Utley Jsy B 8.00 20.00
DE David Eckstein Bat B 6.00 15.00
DM Doug Mientkiewicz Bat C 3.00 8.00
DO David Ortiz Jsy C 4.00 10.00
DS Duke Snider Pants C 6.00 15.00
DW David Wright Jsy A 12.50 30.00
DWW Dontrelle Willis Jsy C 3.00 8.00
DY Delmon Young Bat C 3.00 8.00
EC Eric Chavez Pants C 3.00 8.00
ER Edgar Renteria Bat C 3.00 8.00
ES Ervin Santana Jsy C 3.00 8.00
FL Francisco Liriano Jsy C 4.00 10.00
FR Frank Robinson Pants C 6.00 15.00
GS Gary Sheffield Bat C 3.00 8.00
HB Hank Blalock Jsy B 3.00 8.00
IR Ivan Rodriguez Jsy B 10.00 25.00
JBR Jose Reyes Jsy A 8.00 20.00
JD Johnny Damon Bat C 4.00 10.00
JM Justin Morneau Bat A 6.00 15.00
JP Juan Pierre Bat B 3.00 8.00
JR Jimmy Rollins Jsy C 3.00 8.00
JRP Jorge Posada Pants C 4.00 10.00
JS Jeff Suppan Jsy C 3.00 8.00
JSA Johan Santana Jsy C 4.00 10.00
JV Jose Vidro Bat B 3.00 8.00
JW Jeff Weaver Jsy C 3.00 8.00
LB Lance Berkman Jsy B 3.00 8.00
LG Luis Gonzalez Bat C 3.00 8.00
MA Moises Alou Bat C 3.00 8.00
MC Miguel Cabrera Bat B 4.00 10.00
MK Mark Kotsay Bat B 3.00 8.00
MM Melvin Mora Jsy C 3.00 8.00
MO Magglio Ordonez Bat C 3.00 8.00
MOT Miguel Tejada Pants C 3.00 8.00
MP Mike Piazza Bat B 6.00 15.00
MR Manny Ramirez Jsy C 4.00 10.00
MT Mark Teixeira Jsy B 4.00 10.00
NS Nick Swisher Jsy C 3.00 8.00
OV Omar Vizquel Bat C 4.00 10.00
PB Pat Burrell Bat B 3.00 8.00
PP Placido Polanco Bat B 10.00 25.00
RB Ronnie Belliard Bat B 3.00 8.00
RF Rafael Furcal Bat D 3.00 8.00
RH Ryan Howard Bat A 12.50 30.00
RS Richie Sexson Bat B 3.00 8.00
SM Stan Musial Pants B 12.50 30.00
TH Todd Helton Jsy B 4.00 10.00
TKH Torii Hunter Jsy B 3.00 8.00
VM Victor Martinez Jsy B 3.00 8.00
YB Yogi Berra Bat B 12.50 30.00
YM Yadier Molina Jsy B 10.00 25.00

2007 Topps Heritage Clubhouse Collection Relics Autographs

STATED ODDS 1:16,100 HOBBY
STATED ODDS 1:16,275 RETAIL
STATED PRINT RUN 25 SER.#'d SETS
NO PRICING DUE TO SCARCITY
BR Brooks Robinson Pants
DS Duke Snider Pants
FR Frank Robinson Pants
LA Luis Aparicio Bat
SM Stan Musial Pants
YB Yogi Berra Bat

2007 Topps Heritage Clubhouse Collection Relics Dual

STATED ODDS 1:13,900 HOBBY
STATED ODDS 1:14,000 RETAIL
STATED PRINT RUN 58 SER.#'d SETS
BR Yogi Berra Pants 125.00 250.00
Alex Rodriguez Pants
KR Al Kaline Bat 75.00 150.00
Ivan Rodriguez Bat
MP Stan Musial Pants 125.00 250.00
Albert Pujols Pants

2007 Topps Heritage Felt Logos

COMPLETE SET (13) 20.00 50.00
1 PER HOBBY BOX TOPPER
BOS Boston Red Sox 5.00 12.00
CHC Chicago Cubs 2.00 5.00
CHW Chicago White Sox 2.00 5.00
CIN Cincinnati Redlegs 2.00 5.00
KCA Kansas City Athletics 2.00 5.00
LAD Los Angeles Dodgers 2.00 5.00
NYY New York Yankees 5.00 12.00
PHI Philadelphia Phillies 2.00 5.00
PIT Pittsburgh Pirates 2.00 5.00
SFG San Francisco Giants 2.00 5.00
STL St. Louis Cardinals 2.00 5.00
WAS Washington Senators 2.00 5.00
BAL Baltimore Orioles 2.00 5.00

2007 Topps Heritage Flashbacks

COMPLETE SET (10) 5.00 12.00
STATED ODDS 1:12 HOBBY, 1:12 RETAIL
FB1 Al Kaline .75 2.00
FB2 Brooks Robinson .50 1.25
FB3 Red Schoendienst .30 .75
FB4 Warren Spahn .50 1.25
FB5 Stan Musial 1.25 3.00
FB6 Lew Burdette .30 .75
FB7 Eddie Yost .30 .75
FB8 Jim Bunning .30 .75
FB9 Richie Ashburn .50 1.25
FB10 Hoyt Wilhelm .30 .75

2007 Topps Heritage Flashbacks Autographs

STATED ODDS 1:19,500 HOBBY/RETAIL
STATED PRINT RUN 25 SER.#'d SETS
NO PRICING DUE TO SCARCITY
AK Al Kaline
BR Brooks Robinson
LA Luis Aparicio
RS Red Schoendienst
SM Stan Musial

2007 Topps Heritage Flashbacks Seat Relics

STATED ODDS 1:484 HOBBY, 1:484 RETAIL
AK Al Kaline 10.00 25.00
BR Brooks Robinson 10.00 25.00
EY Eddie Yost 8.00 20.00
HW Hoyt Wilhelm 8.00 20.00
JB Jim Bunning 10.00 25.00
RA Richie Ashburn 8.00 20.00
LB Lew Burdette 8.00 20.00
RS Red Schoendienst 8.00 20.00
SM Stan Musial 15.00 40.00
WS Warren Spahn 10.00 25.00

2007 Topps Heritage Flashbacks Seat Relics Autographs

STATED ODDS 1:19,500 HOBBY/RETAIL
STATED PRINT RUN 25 SER.#'d SETS
NO PRICING DUE TO SCARCITY
AK Al Kaline
BR Brooks Robinson
LA Luis Aparicio
RS Red Schoendienst
SM Stan Musial

2007 Topps Heritage Flashbacks Seat Relics Dual

STATED ODDS 1:82,544 HOBBY/RETAIL
STATED PRINT RUN 10 SER.#'d SETS
NO PRICING DUE TO SCARCITY
DS Duke Snider
HS Hank Sauer
SS Duke Snider
Hank Sauer

2007 Topps Heritage New Age Performers

COMPLETE SET (15) 10.00 25.00
STATED ODDS 1:15 HOBBY, 1:15 RETAIL
NP1 Ryan Howard 1.25 3.00
NP2 Alex Rodriguez 1.25 3.00
NP3 Alfonso Soriano .50 1.25
NP4 David Ortiz .50 1.25
NP5 Trevor Hoffman .50 1.25
NP6 Derek Jeter 2.00 5.00
NP7 Anibal Sanchez .30 .75
NP8 Roger Clemens 1.00 2.50
NP9 Johan Santana .75 2.00
NP10 Albert Pujols 2.00 5.00
NP11 Chipper Jones .75 2.00
NP12 Frank Thomas .75 2.00
NP13 Ivan Rodriguez .50 1.25
NP14 Ichiro Suzuki 1.25 3.00
NP15 Craig Biggio .50 1.25

2007 Topps Heritage Real One Autographs

STATED ODDS 1:327 HOBBY, 1:328 RETAIL
STATED PRINT RUN 200 SETS
CARDS ARE NOT SERIAL-NUMBERED
PRINT RUN INFO PROVIDED BY TOPPS
EXCHANGE DEADLINE 02/28/09
AK Al Kaline 60.00 120.00
BH Bob Henrich 20.00 50.00
BM Bobby Morgan 30.00 60.00
BP Buddy Pritchard 30.00 60.00
BR Brooks Robinson 60.00 120.00
BT Bill Taylor 20.00 50.00
BW Bill Wight 20.00 50.00
CR Charley Rabe 20.00 50.00
DM Dave Melton 20.00 50.00
DS Duke Snider 40.00 80.00
DW David Wright 90.00 150.00
DWW Dontrelle Willis 20.00 50.00
DY Delmon Young 10.00 25.00
DZ Don Zimmer 30.00 60.00
EN Ed Mayer 20.00 50.00
GK George Kell 20.00 50.00
HP Harding Peterson 12.50 30.00
JB Jim Bunning 40.00 80.00
JC Joe Caffie 30.00 60.00
JD Joe Durham 12.50 30.00
JL Joe Lonnett 30.00 60.00
JM Justin Morneau 20.00 50.00
JP Johnny Podres 50.00 100.00
LA Luis Aparicio 50.00 100.00
LM Lloyd Merritt 20.00 50.00
LS Lou Sleater 20.00 50.00
MB Milt Bolling 20.00 50.00
MEB Mack Burk 20.00 50.00
OH Orlando Hudson 20.00 50.00
PS Paul Smith 20.00 50.00
RC Ray Crone 30.00 60.00
RH Ryan Howard 30.00 60.00
RS Red Schoendienst 50.00 100.00
SP Stan Palys 20.00 50.00
TT Tim Thompson 20.00 50.00
CJD Jim Derrington 30.00 60.00

2007 Topps Heritage Real One Autographs Red Ink

STATED ODDS 1:1129 HOBBY/RETAIL
STATED PRINT RUN 58 SERIAL #'d SETS
RED INK ALSO CALLED SPECIAL EDITION
EXCHANGE DEADLINE 02/28/09
AK Al Kaline 125.00 250.00
BH Bob Henrich 50.00 100.00
BM Bobby Morgan 60.00 120.00
BP Buddy Pritchard 60.00 120.00
BR Brooks Robinson 75.00 150.00
BT Bill Taylor 60.00 120.00
BW Bill Wight 50.00 100.00
CH Chuck Harmon 50.00 100.00
CR Charley Rabe 50.00 100.00
DM Dave Melton 60.00 120.00
DS Duke Snider 100.00 200.00
DW David Wright 250.00 350.00
DY Delmon Young 20.00 50.00
DZ Don Zimmer 60.00 120.00
EN Ed Mayer 50.00 100.00
GK George Kell 30.00 60.00
HP Harding Peterson 30.00 60.00
JB Jim Bunning 75.00 150.00
JC Joe Caffie 60.00 120.00
JD Joe Durham 30.00 60.00
JL Joe Lonnett 50.00 100.00
JM Justin Morneau 50.00 100.00
JP Johnny Podres 90.00 150.00
LA Luis Aparicio 100.00 200.00
LM Lloyd Merritt 60.00 120.00
LS Lou Sleater 50.00 100.00
MB Milt Bolling 40.00 80.00
OH Orlando Hudson 50.00 100.00
PS Paul Smith 50.00 100.00
RC Ray Crone 40.00 80.00
RH Ryan Howard 30.00 120.00
RS Red Schoendienst 100.00 200.00
SP Stan Palys 50.00 100.00
TT Tim Thompson 40.00 80.00
CJD Jim Derrington 60.00 120.00
DWW Dontrelle Willis 50.00 100.00
MEB Mack Burk 50.00 100.00

2007 Topps Heritage Then and Now

COMPLETE SET (10) 8.00 20.00
STATED ODDS 1:15 HOBBY, 1:15 RETAIL
TN1 Frank Robinson 1.25 3.00
Ryan Howard
TN2 Mickey Mantle 2.50 6.00
David Ortiz
TN3 Ted Williams 2.00 5.00
Joe Mauer
TN4 Luis Aparicio .50 1.25
Jose Reyes
TN5 Lew Burdette .75 2.00
Johan Santana
TN6 Johnny Podres .30 .75
Aaron Harang
TN7 Richie Ashburn 1.25 3.00
Ichiro Suzuki
TN8 Stan Musial 1.25 3.00
Travis Hafner
TN9 Jim Bunning .30 .75
Anibal Sanchez
TN10 Warren Spahn .50 1.25
Chien-Ming Wang

2008 Topps Heritage

COMP.SET w/o SP's (425) 40.00 80.00
COMP.HN SET (220) 125.00 200.00
COMP.HN SET w/o SP's (150) 12.50 30.00
COMMON CARD .15 .40
COMMON RC .40 1.00
COMMON TEAM CARD .15 .40
COMMON GB SP .40 1.00
COMMON SP 2.50 6.00
SP STATED ODDS 1:3 HOBBY/RETAIL
HN SP ODDS 1:3 HOBBY/RETAIL
1 Vladimir Guerrero .40 1.00
2 Placido Polanco GB SP .40 1.00
3 Eric Byrnes GB SP .40 1.00
4 Mark Teixeira .40 1.00
5 Javier Vazquez GB SP .40 1.00
6 Jacoby Ellsbury .60 1.50
7 Joey Gathright GB SP .40 1.00
8 Philadelphia Phillies GB SP .40 1.00
9 Andre Ethier GB SP .60 1.50
10 Alex Rodriguez .60 1.50
11 Luke Scott SP 2.50 6.00
12 Curt Schilling GB SP .60 1.50
13 Billy Wagner GB SP .40 1.00
14 Gary Matthews GB SP .40 1.00
15 Sean Marshall .15 .40
16 Ichiro Suzuki GB SP 1.50 4.00
17 Jack Wilson .25 .60
Jason Bay
Freddy Sanchez
18 Dontrelle Willis GB SP .40 1.00
19 Josh Willingham .15 .40
20 Jeff Kent .15 .40
21 Troy Tulowitzki GB SP 1.00 2.50
22 Brian Fuentes GB SP .40 1.00
23 Robinson Cano GB SP 1.00 2.50
24 Felix Hernandez GB SP 1.00 2.50
25 Edwin Encarnacion .15 .40
26 Fausto Carmona .15 .40
27 Greg Maddux .50 1.25
28 Ivan Rodriguez GB SP .60 1.50
29 Joe Nathan .15 .40
30 Paul Konerko .25 .60
31 Nook Logan .15 .40
32 Derek Lowe .15 .40
33 Jose Lopez .15 .40
34 Magglio Ordonez .60 1.50
Curtis Granderson GB SP
35 Adam LaRoche GB SP .40 1.00
36 Kenny Lofton .15 .40
37 Matt Capps .15 .40
38 Mark Reynolds .15 .40
39 Joe Mauer .40 1.00
40 Tim Hudson GB SP .60 1.50
41 Kelvim Escobar GB SP .40 1.00
42 Jason Jennings GB SP .40 1.00
43 Victor Martinez .25 .60
44 Jason Kendall .15 .40
45 Chris Ray GB SP .40 1.00
46 Jason Bergmann .15 .40
47 Jason Marquis .15 .40
48 Baltimore Orioles .15 .40
49 Bill Hall GB SP .40 1.00
50 Ken Griffey Jr. .60 1.50
51 Chad Cordero .15 .40
52 Omar Vizquel GB SP .60 1.50
53 Jim Edmonds .25 .60
54 Justin Upton GB SP .60 1.50
55 Josh Beckett .25 .60
56 Jeff Francis .15 .40
57 Brad Lidge GB SP .40 1.00
58 Paul Lo Duca GB SP .40 1.00
59 John Patterson .15 .40
60 Andy Pettitte GB SP .60 1.50
61 Brendan Harris GB SP .40 1.00
62 Chris Young GB SP .40 1.00
63 Eric Chavez .15 .40
64 Francisco Rodriguez .25 .60
65 Jason Giambi GB SP .40 1.00
66 B.J. Ryan .15 .40
67 Rich Hill GB SP .40 1.00
68 Derek Jeter 1.00 2.50
69 San Francisco Giants GB SP .40 1.00
70 Carlos Guillen .15 .40
71 Trevor Hoffman GB SP .60 1.50
72 Zach Duke .15 .40
73 Dustin Pedroia .50 1.25
74 Dmitri Young .25 .60
Ryan Zimmerman
75 Cole Hamels .40 1.00
76 Carlos Delgado .15 .40
77 Jonathan Broxton .15 .40
78 Josh Hamilton GB SP 1.00 2.50
79 Mark Loretta GB SP .40 1.00
80 Grady Sizemore .25 .60
81 Torii Hunter GB SP .40 1.00
82 Carlos Beltran GB SP .40 1.00
83 Jason Isringhausen GB SP .40 1.00
84 Brad Penny GB SP .40 1.00
85 Jayson Werth .25 .60
86 Alex Gordon .25 .60
87 David DeJesus .15 .40
88 Clay Buchholz .40 1.00
89 Conor Jackson .15 .40
90 Hideki Matsui GB SP 1.00 2.50
91 Matt Garza GB SP .40 1.00
92 Phil Hughes GB SP 1.00 2.50
93 Mike Piazza .40 1.00
94 Chicago White Sox GB SP .40 1.00
95 Buddy Carlyle .15 .40
96 Mark DeRosa .15 .40
97 Brandon Webb .25 .60
98 Jon Garland GB SP .40 1.00
99 Mariano Rivera .40 1.00
100 Jack Cust .15 .40
101 Carlos Ruiz .15 .40
102 Moises Alou GB SP .40 1.00
103 Bengie Molina .15 .40
104 Adam Jones .25 .60
105 Alfonso Soriano .25 .60
106 Troy Glaus .25 .60
107 John Maine .15 .40
108 Pat Burrell .15 .40
109 David Eckstein .15 .40
110 Homer Bailey .25 .60
111 Cincinnati Reds .15 .40
112 Corey Hart .15 .40
113 Orlando Hernandez .15 .40
114 Orlando Cabrera .15 .40
115 Ryan Garko .15 .40
116 Wladimir Balentien GB SP (RC) .40 1.00
117 Daric Barton GB SP (RC) .40 1.00
118 Emilio Bonifacio RC 1.00 2.50
119 Lance Broadway (RC) .40 1.00
120 Jeff Clement (RC) .60 1.50
121 Dave Davidson RC .60 1.50
122 Ross Detwiler GB SP RC 1.00 2.50
123 Sam Fuld RC 1.25 3.00
124 Armando Galarraga RC .60 1.50
125 Harvey Garcia (RC) .40 1.00
126 Dan Giese GB SP (RC) .40 1.00
127 Alberto Gonzalez GB SP RC .60 1.50
128 Kevin Hart (RC) .40 1.00
129 Luke Hochevar GB SP RC .60 1.50
130 Chin-Lung Hu GB SP (RC) .60 1.50
131 Brandon Jones RC 1.00 2.50
132 Joe Koshansky (RC) .40 1.00
133 Radhames Liz RC .60 1.50
134 Donny Lucy (RC) .40 1.00
135 Mitch Stetter GB SP RC .60 1.50
136 Nyjer Morgan (RC) .40 1.00
137 Ross Ohlendorf RC .60 1.50
138 Steve Pearce RC .60 1.50
139 Jeff Ridgway RC .60 1.50
140 Bronson Sardinha (RC) .40 1.00
141 Seth Smith (RC) .40 1.00
142 Rich Thompson RC .60 1.50
143 Erick Threets (RC) .40 1.00
144 J.R. Towles RC .60 1.50
145 Eugenio Velez RC .40 1.00
146 Joey Votto (RC) 1.50 4.00
147 Alfonso Soriano .15 .40
Aramis Ramirez
Derrick Lee
148 Hunter Pence .40 1.00
149 Barry Zito .15 .40
150 Albert Pujols 2.50 6.00
151 Sammy Sosa .40 1.00
152 Brian Bannister .15 .40
153 Reggie Willits .15 .40
154 Bobby Abreu .15 .40
155 Johnny Damon GB SP .60 1.50
156 Brandon Webb .15 .40
Jake Peavy
157 Aramis Ramirez .15 .40
158 Aaron Cook .15 .40
159 David Weathers .15 .40
160 Jack Wilson .15 .40
161 Josh Fogg .15 .40
162 Garrett Atkins .15 .40
163 Brad Ausmus .15 .40
164 Gil Meche .15 .40
165 Jeff Francoeur .25 .60
166 Victor Martinez .25 .60
Travis Hafner
Grady Sizemore
167 Juan Pierre .15 .40
168 Rafael Furcal .15 .40
169 J.J. Hardy .15 .40
170 Nick Markakis .40 1.00
171 Delmon Young .25 .60
172 Oakland Athletics .15 .40
173 Ronny Paulino GB SP .40 1.00
174 Mike Cameron GB SP .40 1.00
175 Jeff Weaver GB SP .40 1.00
176 Preston Wilson GB SP .40 1.00
177 Robinson Tejeda GB SP .40 1.00
178 Adam Lind GB SP .40 1.00
179 Austin Kearns GB SP .40 1.00
180 Jorge Posada GB SP .60 1.50
181 Tadahito Iguchi .15 .40
182 Matt Cain .15 .40
183 Yuniesky Betancourt .15 .40
184 Bronson Arroyo .15 .40
185 Brad Hawpe GB SP .40 1.00
186 Rickie Weeks GB SP .60 1.50
187 Carlos Silva GB SP .40 1.00
188 Adrian Gonzalez .25 .60
189 Kenji Johjima .15 .40
190 Chris Duncan .15 .40
191 James Shields .15 .40
192 Akinori Iwamura .15 .40
193 David Murphy .15 .40
194 Alex Rios .25 .60
195 Carlos Quentin GB SP .40 1.00
196 Jose Valverde GB SP .40 1.00
197 Derrek Lee GB SP .40 1.00
198 Jerry Owens GB SP .40 1.00
199 Russell Martin .15 .40
200 Yovani Gallardo .15 .40
201a Johan Santana Twins .40 1.00
201b Johan Santana Mets 60.00 120.00
202 Nick Swisher .40 1.00
203 So Taguchi .15 .40
204 Justin Morneau .40 1.00
205 Milton Bradley .15 .40
206 Jake Westbrook .15 .40
207 Dave Roberts .15 .40
208 Billy Butler .15 .40
209 Lance Berkman .25 .60
210 J.J. Putz GB SP .40 1.00
211 Mike Sweeney GB SP .40 1.00
212 Andruw Jones .40 1.00
Chipper Jones
213 Ricky Nolasco .15 .40
214 Andy LaRoche .15 .40
215 Ray Durham .15 .40
216 Francisco Cordero .15 .40
217 Jered Weaver .15 .40
218 Rafael Soriano .15 .40
219 Orlando Hudson .15 .40
220 Mike Lowell .15 .40
221 Chris Snyder .15 .40
222 Cesar Izturis .15 .40
223 St. Louis Cardinals .15 .40
224 David Wright GB SP 1.25 3.00
225 Pedro Martinez GB SP .60 1.50
226 Rich Harden GB SP .40 1.00
227 Shane Victorino GB SP .40 1.00
228 Andrew Miller GB SP .40 1.00
229 Chris Young .15 .40
230 Andruw Jones .15 .40
231 Kevin Gregg SP 2.50 6.00
232 C.C. Sabathia .25 .60
233 Hanley Ramirez .40 1.00
234 Wandy Rodriguez .15 .40
235 Roy Oswalt .25 .60
236 Mark Grudzielanek .15 .40
237 Derek Jeter 1.00 2.50
Chien-Ming Wang
Robinson Cano
238 Todd Helton .25 .60
239 Zack Greinke .25 .60
240 Carlos Gomez .15 .40
241 Lastings Milledge .15 .40
242 Huston Street .15 .40
243 Dan Haren .15 .40
244 Carlos Pena .25 .60
245 Brad Wilkerson .15 .40
246 Roy Halladay .40 1.00
247 Dmitri Young .15 .40
248 Boston Red Sox .60 1.50
249 Jonathan Papelbon .25 .60
250 Felix Pie .15 .40
251 Alex Gonzalez .15 .40
252 Bobby Crosby .15 .40
253 Justin Ruggiano RC .60 1.50
254 Freddy Garcia .15 .40
255 Khalil Greene .15 .40
256 Rich Aurilia .15 .40
257 Jarrod Washburn .15 .40
258 B.J. Upton .25 .60
259 Michael Young .25 .60
260 Carlos Zambrano .25 .60
261 Livan Hernandez .15 .40
262 Chad Billingsley .40 1.00
Derek Lowe
Brad Penny GB SP
263 Melky Cabrera GB SP .40 1.00
264 Shannon Stewart GB SP .40 1.00
265 Aaron Rowand GB SP .40 1.00
266 Matt Morris GB SP .40 1.00
267 Xavier Nady GB SP .40 1.00
268 Jim Thome .25 .60
269 Horacio Ramirez .15 .40

270 Prince Fielder .25 .60
271 Andy Phillips .15 .40
272 Aaron Harang .15 .40
273 Josh Barfield .15 .40
274 Ubaldo Jimenez .25 .60
275 Anibal Sanchez .15 .40
276 Carlos Lee .15 .40
277 Mark Teahen .15 .40
278 Delwyn Young .15 .40
279 Kurt Suzuki .15 .40
280 Nate Schierholtz .15 .40
281 Raul Ibanez .25 .60
282 Jose Vidro .15 .40
283 Miguel Cabrera GB SP 1.00 2.50
284 Luis Gonzalez GB SP .40 1.00
285 Chad Billingsley GB SP .40 1.00
286 Tony Gwynn GB SP .40 1.00
287 Matt Kemp .25 .60
288 James Loney .25 .60
289 Brett Myers .15 .40
290 Nate McLouth .15 .40
291 Matt Chico .40 1.00
Jason Bergmann GB SP
292 Chad Tracy .15 .40
293 Edgar Renteria .15 .40
294 Jay Payton .15 .40
295 Josh Johnson .25 .60
296 Josh Banks (RC) .40 1.00
297 Bill Murphy (RC) .40 1.00
298 Ben Sheets .15 .40
299 Jose Reyes .25 .60
300 Chase Utley .40 1.00
301 Ronnie Belliard GB SP .40 1.00
302 Wily Mo Pena .15 .40
303 Tim Lincecum .60 1.50
304 Chicago Cubs .25 .60
305 John Lackey .15 .40
306 Stephen Drew .15 .40
307 Kelly Johnson .15 .40
308 Daisuke Matsuzaka .40 1.00
309 Craig Monroe .15 .40
310 Jerry Owens .15 .40
311 Jeff Suppan .15 .40
312 Tom Glavine .25 .60
313 Kei Igawa .15 .40
314 Mark Kotsay .15 .40
315 Jacque Jones SP 2.50 6.00
316 Melvin Mora .15 .40
317 Matt Holliday .40 1.00
Hanley Ramirez
318 Jarrod Saltalamacchia .15 .40
319 A.J. Burnett .25 .60
320 Casey Kotchman .15 .40
321 Randy Winn GB SP .40 1.00
322 Richie Sexson GB SP .40 1.00
323 Juan Encarnacion GB SP .40 1.00
324 Rick Ankiel GB SP .40 1.00
325 Dan Wheeler GB SP .40 1.00
326 Brian Roberts .15 .40
327 David Ortiz .25 .60
328 Garret Anderson .15 .40
329 Detroit Tigers .15 .40
330 Ty Wigginton GB SP .40 1.00
331 Travis Hafner .15 .40
332 Howie Kendrick GB SP .40 1.00
333 Kevin Kouzmanoff GB SP .40 1.00
334 Matt Holliday GB SP 1.00 2.50
335 Brandon Phillips GB SP .40 1.00
336 Ian Kinsler GB SP .60 1.50
337 Lyle Overbay GB SP .40 1.00
338 Justin Verlander GB SP 1.25 3.00
339 Ian Snell .15 .40
340 Hank Blalock .15 .40
341 Vernon Wells .15 .40
342 Matt Chico .15 .40
343 Tim Wakefield .15 .40
344 Michael Bourn .15 .40
345 Chris Carpenter .40 1.00
346 Daisuke Matsuzaka .40 1.00
Josh Beckett
347 Chuck James GB SP .40 1.00
348 Joba Chamberlain .25 .60
349 Erik Bedard .15 .40
350 Jimmy Rollins GB SP .60 1.50
351 Anthony Reyes .15 .40
352 Carl Crawford .25 .60
353 Jeremy Hermida .15 .40
354 Ervin Santana .15 .40
355 Edgar Gonzalez .15 .40
356 Yunel Escobar .15 .40
357 Yorvit Torrealba .15 .40
358 Hideki Okajima .15 .40
359 Paul Byrd .15 .40
360 Magglio Ordonez GB SP .60 1.50
361 Joe Borowski .15 .40
362 Clint Sammons (RC) .40 1.00
363 Chris Duffy .15 .40
364 Fred Lewis .15 .40
365 Adrian Beltre .15 .40
366 Alex Rodriguez BT .60 1.50
367 Troy Tulowitzki BT .40 1.00
368 Prince Fielder BT .25 .60
369 Clay Buchholz BT .40 1.00
370 Justin Verlander BT GB SP 1.25 3.00
371 Pedro Martinez BT GB SP .60 1.50
372 Ryan Howard BT GB SP 1.25 3.00
373 Ichiro Suzuki BT .60 1.50
374 Kenny Lofton BT .15 .40
375 Manny Ramirez BT .40 1.00
376 Randy Johnson .40 1.00
377 Chris Capuano .15 .40
378 Johnny Estrada .15 .40
379 Franklin Morales .15 .40
380 Ryan Howard .50 1.25
381 Casey Blake SP 2.50 6.00
382 Coco Crisp .15 .40
383 John Maine .15 .40
Willie Randolph MG
384 Jeremy Guthrie .15 .40
385 Geoff Jenkins .15 .40
386 Marlon Byrd .15 .40
387 Jeremy Bonderman .15 .40
388 Jason Varitek .40 1.00
389 Joe Girardi MG .25 .60
390 Ryan Braun .50 1.25
391 Ryan Zimmerman .25 .60
392 Mike Lowell .50 1.25
Kevin Youkilis
Dustin Pedroia
393 Pittsburgh Pirates .15 .40
394 Ryan Spilborghs .15 .40
395 Eric Gagne .15 .40
396 Joe Blanton .15 .40
397 Washington Nationals .15 .40
398 Ryan Church .15 .40
399 Ted Lilly .15 .40
400 Manny Ramirez .40 1.00
401 Chad Gaudin .15 .40
402 Dustin McGowan .15 .40
403 Scott Baker .15 .40
404 Franklin Gutierrez .15 .40
405 Dave Bush .15 .40
406 Aubrey Huff .15 .40
407 Jermaine Dye .15 .40
408 Chase Utley .40 1.00
Jimmy Rollins
409 Jon Lester SP 3.00 8.00
410 Mark Buehrle .25 .60
411 Sergio Mitre .15 .40
412 Jason Bartlett .15 .40
413 Edwin Jackson .15 .40
414 J.D. Drew .15 .40
415 Freddy Sanchez GB SP .40 1.00
416 Asdrubal Cabrera .25 .60
417 Nate Robertson .15 .40
418 Shaun Marcum .15 .40
419 Atlanta Braves .25 .60
420 Noah Lowry .15 .40
421 Jamie Moyer .15 .40
422 Michael Cuddyer .15 .40
423 Randy Wolf .15 .40
424 Juan Uribe .15 .40
425 Brian McCann .25 .60
426 Kyle Lohse SP 2.50 6.00
427 Doug Davis SP 2.50 6.00
428 Ian Snell 2.50 6.00
Matt Capps
Tom Gorzelanny
Paul Maholm SP
429 Miguel Batista SP 2.50 6.00
430 Chien-Ming Wang SP 4.00 10.00
431 Jeff Salazar SP 2.50 6.00
432 Yadier Molina SP 2.50 6.00
433 Adam Wainwright SP 2.50 6.00
434 Scott Kazmir SP 2.50 6.00
435 Adam Dunn SP 2.50 6.00
436 Ryan Freel SP 2.50 6.00
437 Jhonny Peralta SP 2.50 6.00
438 Kazuo Matsui SP 2.50 6.00
439 Daniel Cabrera .15 .40
440a John Smoltz .40 1.00
440b John Smoltz 50.00 100.00
Name misspelled Jon
441 Emil Brown SP 2.50 6.00
442 Gary Sheffield SP 2.50 6.00
443 Jake Peavy SP 3.00 8.00
444 Scott Rolen SP 3.00 8.00
445 Kason Gabbard SP 2.50 6.00
446 Aaron Hill SP 2.50 6.00
447 Felipe Lopez SP 2.50 6.00
448 Dan Uggla SP 2.50 6.00
449 Willy Taveras SP 2.50 6.00
450 Chipper Jones SP 3.00 8.00
451 Josh Anderson SP (RC) 3.00 8.00
452 Chris Young 3.00 8.00
Justin Upton
Eric Byrnes SP
453 Braden Looper SP 2.50 6.00
454 Brandon Inge SP 2.50 6.00
455 Brian Giles SP 2.50 6.00
456 Corey Patterson SP 2.50 6.00
457 Los Angeles Dodgers SP 3.00 8.00
458 Sean Casey SP 2.50 6.00
459 Pedro Feliz SP 2.50 6.00
460 Tom Gorzelanny .15 .40
461 Chone Figgins SP 2.50 6.00
462 Kyle Kendrick SP 2.50 6.00
463 Tony Pena SP 2.50 6.00
464 Marcus Giles SP 2.50 6.00
465 Augie Ojeda SP 2.50 6.00
466 Micah Owings SP 2.50 6.00
467 Ryan Theriot SP 2.50 6.00
468 Shawn Green SP 2.50 6.00
469 Frank Thomas SP 3.00 8.00
470 Lenny DiNardo SP 2.50 6.00
471 Jose Bautista SP 2.50 6.00
472 Manny Corpas SP 2.50 6.00
473 Kevin Millwood SP 2.50 6.00
474 Kevin Youkilis SP 2.50 6.00
475 Jose Contreras SP 2.50 6.00
476 Cleveland Indians .15 .40
477 Julio Lugo SP 2.50 6.00
478 Jason Bay .25 .60
479 Tony LaRussa AS MG SP 2.50 6.00
480 Jim Leyland AS MG SP 2.50 6.00
481 Derrek Lee AS SP 2.50 6.00
482 Justin Morneau AS SP 2.50 6.00
483 Orlando Hudson AS SP 2.50 6.00
484 Brian Roberts AS SP 2.50 6.00
485 Miguel Cabrera AS SP 3.00 8.00
486 Mike Lowell AS SP 2.50 6.00
487 J.J. Hardy AS SP 2.50 6.00
488 Carlos Guillen AS SP 2.50 6.00
489 Ken Griffey Jr. AS SP 4.00 10.00
490 Vladimir Guerrero AS SP 3.00 8.00
491 Alfonso Soriano AS SP 3.00 8.00
492 Ichiro Suzuki AS SP 4.00 10.00
493 Matt Holliday AS SP 3.00 8.00
494 Magglio Ordonez AS SP 3.00 8.00
495 Brian McCann AS SP 2.50 6.00
496 Victor Martinez AS SP 2.50 6.00
497 Brad Penny AS SP 2.50 6.00
498 Josh Beckett AS SP 3.00 8.00
499 Cole Hamels AS SP 3.00 8.00
500 Justin Verlander AS SP 3.00 8.00
501 John Danks .15 .40
502 Jamey Wright .15 .40
503 Johnny Cueto RC .60 1.50
504 Todd Wellemeyer .15 .40
505 Chase Headley .15 .40
506 Takashi Saito .15 .40
507 Skip Schumaker .15 .40
508 Tampa Bay Rays .15 .40
509 Marcus Thames .15 .40
510 Joe Saunders .15 .40
511 Jair Jurrjens .15 .40
512 Ryan Sweeney .15 .40
513 Darin Erstad .15 .40
514 Brandon Backe .40 1.00
515 Chris Volstad (RC) .40 1.00
516 Salomon Torres .15 .40
517 Brian Burres .15 .40
518 Brandon Boggs (RC) .60 1.50
519 Max Scherzer RC 1.25 3.00
520 Cliff Lee .25 .60
521 Angel Pagan .15 .40
522 Jason Kubel .15 .40
523 Jose Molina .40 1.00
524 Hiroki Kuroda RC .60 1.50
525 Matt Harrison (RC) .40 1.00
526 C.J. Wilson .15 .40
527 Robb Quinlan .15 .40
528 Darrell Rasner .40 1.00
529 Frank Catalanotto .40 1.00
530 Mike Mussina .25 .60
531 Ryan Doumit .40 1.00
532 Willie Bloomquist .40 1.00
533 Jonny Gomes .15 .40
534 Jesse Litsch .15 .40
535 Curtis Granderson .25 .60
536 A.J. Pierzynski .15 .40
537 Toronto Blue Jays .15 .40
538 Brian Buscher .40 1.00
539 Kelly Shoppach .40 1.00
540 Edinson Volquez .15 .40
541 Jon Rauch .40 1.00
542 Ramon Castro .40 1.00
543 Greg Smith RC .40 1.00
544 Sean Gallagher .15 .40
545 Justin Masterson RC 1.00 2.50
546 Milwaukee Brewers .15 .40
547 Jay Bruce (RC) 1.50 4.00
548 Glendon Rusch .15 .40
549 Jeremy Sowers .40 1.00
550 Ryan Dempster .15 .40
551 Clete Thomas RC .60 1.50
552 Jose Castillo .15 .40
553 Brandon Lyon .15 .40
554 Vicente Padilla .15 .40
555 Jeff Keppinger .15 .40
556 Colorado Rockies .15 .40
557 Dallas Braden .60 1.50
558 Adam Kennedy .15 .40
559 Luis Mendoza (RC) .40 1.00
560 Justin Duchscherer .15 .40
561 Mike Aviles RC .60 1.50
562 Jed Lowrie (RC) 1.00 2.50
563 Doug Mientkiewicz .40 1.00
564 Chris Burke .15 .40
565 Dana Eveland .15 .40
566 Bryan Lahair RC .40 1.00
567 Denard Span (RC) .60 1.50
568 Damion Easley .15 .40
569 Josh Fields .15 .40
570 Geovany Soto .40 1.00
571 Gerald Laird UER .15 .40
Pictured as rookie prospect
572 Bobby Jenks .15 .40
573 Andy Marte .15 .40
574 Mike Pelfrey .15 .40
575 Jerry Hairston .15 .40
576 Mike Lamb .15 .40
577 Ben Zobrist .15 .40
578 Carlos Gonzalez (RC) 1.00 2.50
579 Jose Guillen .40 1.00
580 Kosuke Fukudome RC 1.25 3.00
581 Gabe Kapler .40 1.00
582 Florida Marlins .15 .40
583 Ramon Vazquez .40 1.00
584 Wes Helms .40 1.00
585 Minnesota Twins .15 .40
586 Cody Ross .15 .40
587 Mike Napoli .25 .60
588 Alexi Casilla .15 .40
589 Emmanuel Burriss RC .60 1.50
590 Brian Wilson .40 1.00
591 Rod Barajas .15 .40
592 Mike Hampton .40 1.00
593 Nick Blackburn RC .60 1.50
594 Joe Mather RC .60 1.50
595 Clayton Kershaw RC 2.00 5.00
596 Cliff Floyd .40 1.00
597 Sidney Ponson .40 1.00
598 Brian Anderson .15 .40
599 Joe Inglett .15 .40
600 Miguel Tejada .25 .60
601 San Diego Padres .15 .40
602 Scott Hairston .40 1.00
603 Joel Pineiro .15 .40
604 Fernando Tatis .15 .40
605 Greg Reynolds RC .60 1.50
606 Brian Moehler .15 .40
607 Kevin Millar .40 1.00
608 Ben Francisco .15 .40
609 Troy Percival .15 .40
610 Kerry Wood .15 .40
611 Max Ramirez RC .40 1.00
612 Jeff Baker .15 .40
613 Houston Astros .15 .40
614 Russell Branyan .15 .40
615 Todd Jones .15 .40
616 Brian Schneider .15 .40
617 Gregorio Petit RC .60 1.50
618 Matt Diaz .15 .40
619 Blake DeWitt (RC) 1.00 2.50
620 Cristian Guzman .15 .40
621 Jeff Samardzija RC 1.25 3.00
622 John Baker (RC) .40 1.00
623 Eric Hinske .15 .40
624 Scott Olsen .15 .40
625 Greg Dobbs .15 .40
626 Carlos Marmol .60 1.50
627 Kansas City Royals .15 .40
628 Esteban German .15 .40
629 Dennis Sarfate .15 .40
630 Ryan Ludwick .15 .40
631 Mike Jacobs .15 .40
632 Tyler Yates .15 .40
633 Joel Hanrahan .25 .60
634 Manny Parra .15 .40
635 Maicer Izturis .15 .40
636 Juan Rivera .15 .40
637 Tim Redding .15 .40
638 Jose Arredondo RC .60 1.50
639 Mike Redmond .40 1.00
640 Joe Crede .15 .40
641 Omar Infante .15 .40
642 Nick Punto .15 .40
643 Jeff Mathis .15 .40
644 Andy Sonnanstine .15 .40
645 Masahide Kobayashi RC .60 1.50
646 Marco Scutaro .15 .40
647 Matt Macri (RC) .40 1.00
648 Ian Stewart SP 2.50 6.00
649 David Dellucci .40 1.00
650 Evan Longoria RC 2.00 5.00
651 Martin Prado .40 1.00
652 Glen Perkins .15 .40
653 Alfredo Amezaga .40 1.00
654 Brett Gardner (RC) 1.00 2.50
655 Angel Berroa .40 1.00
656 Pablo Sandoval RC 2.50 6.00
657 Jody Gerut .15 .40
658 Arizona Diamondbacks .15 4.00
659 Ryan Freel .40 1.00
660 Dioner Navarro .15 .40
661 Endy Chavez .40 1.00
662 Jorge Campillo .15 .40
663 Mark Ellis .15 .40
664 John Buck .15 .40
665 Texas Rangers .15 .40
666 Jason Michaels .15 .40
667 Chris Dickerson RC .60 1.50
668 Kevin Mench .15 .40
669 Aaron Miles .15 .40
670 Joakim Soria .15 .40
671 Chris Davis RC 1.00 2.50
672 Taylor Teagarden RC .60 1.50
673 Willy Aybar .15 .40
674 Paul Maholm .15 .40
675 Mike Gonzalez .15 .40
676 Seattle Mariners .15 .40
677 Ryan Langerhans SP 2.50 6.00
678 Alex Romero (RC) .60 1.50
679 Erick Aybar .15 .40
680 George Sherrill .15 .40
681 John Bowker (RC) .40 1.00
682 Zach Miner .40 1.00
683 Jorge Cantu .15 .40
684 Jo-Jo Reyes .15 .40
685 Ryan Raburn .15 .40
686 Gavin Floyd SP 2.50 6.00
687 Kevin Slowey SP 2.50 6.00
688 Gio Gonzalez SP (RC) 2.50 6.00
689 Eric Patterson SP 2.50 6.00
690 Jonathan Sanchez SP 2.50 6.00
691 Oliver Perez SP 2.50 6.00
692 John Lannan SP 2.50 6.00
693 Ramon Hernandez SP 2.50 6.00
694 Mike Fontenot SP 2.50 6.00
695 Ross Gload SP 2.50 6.00
696 Mark Sweeney SP 2.50 6.00
697 Nick Hundley SP (RC) 2.50 6.00
698 Kevin Correia SP 2.50 6.00
699 Jeremy Reed SP 2.50 6.00
700 Eddie Kunz SP RC 2.50 6.00
701 Miguel Montero SP 2.50 6.00
702 Gabe Gross SP 2.50 6.00
703 Matt Stairs SP 2.50 6.00
704 Kenny Rogers SP 2.50 6.00
705 Mark Hendrickson SP 2.50 6.00
706 Heath Bell SP 2.50 6.00
707 Wilson Betemit SP 2.50 6.00
708 Brandon Morrow SP 2.50 6.00
709 Brendan Ryan SP 2.50 6.00
710 Eric Hurley SP (RC) 2.50 6.00
711 Los Angeles Angels SP 2.50 6.00
712 Jack Hannahan SP 2.50 6.00
713 Seth McClung SP 2.50 6.00
714 New York Mets SP 2.50 6.00
715 Chris Perez SP RC 2.50 6.00
716 Clayton Richard SP (RC) 2.50 6.00
717 Jaime Garcia SP RC 2.50 6.00
718 Matt Joyce SP RC 3.00 8.00
719 Brad Ziegler SP RC 2.50 6.00
720 Ivan Ochoa (RC) .60 1.50

2008 Topps Heritage Black Back

*BLK BACK VET: .4X TO 1X BASIC
*BLK BACK RC: .4X TO 1X BASIC RC
RANDOM INSERTS IN PACKS

2008 Topps Heritage Chrome

1-100 ODDS 1:8 HOBBY, 1:18 RETAIL
1-100 INSERTED IN 08 HERITAGE
101-200 ODDS 1:6 HOBBY
101-200 INSERTED IN 08 TOPPS CHROME
201-300 ODDS 1:3 HOBBY
201-300 INSERTED IN 08 HERITAGE HN
STATED PRINT RUN 1959 SERIAL #'d SETS
C1 Hunter Pence 2.50 6.00
C2 Andre Ethier 2.00 5.00
C3 Curt Schilling 2.00 5.00
C4 Gary Matthews 1.50 4.00
C5 Dontrelle Willis 1.50 4.00
C6 Troy Tulowitzki 3.00 8.00
C7 Robinson Cano 3.00 8.00
C8 Felix Hernandez 3.00 8.00
C9 Josh Hamilton 2.00 5.00
C10 Justin Upton 1.50 4.00
C11 Brad Penny 1.50 4.00
C12 Hideki Matsui 2.50 6.00
C13 J.J. Putz 1.50 4.00
C14 Jorge Posada 2.00 5.00
C15 Albert Pujols 5.00 12.00
C16 Aaron Rowand 1.50 4.00
C17 Ronnie Belliard 1.50 4.00
C18 Rick Ankiel 1.50 4.00
C19 Ian Kinsler 2.00 5.00
C20 Justin Verlander 4.00 10.00
C21 Lyle Overbay 1.50 4.00
C22 Tim Hudson 2.50 6.00
C23 Ryan Zimmerman 2.00 5.00
C24 Ryan Braun 2.50 6.00
C25 Jimmy Rollins 2.00 5.00
C26 Kelvim Escobar 1.50 4.00
C27 Adam LaRoche 1.50 4.00
C28 Ivan Rodriguez 2.00 5.00
C29 Billy Wagner 1.50 4.00
C30 Ichiro Suzuki 3.00 8.00
C31 Chris Young 1.50 4.00
C32 Trevor Hoffman 2.50 6.00
C33 Torii Hunter 1.50 4.00
C34 Jason Isringhausen 1.50 4.00
C35 Jose Valverde 1.50 4.00
C36 Derrek Lee 1.25 3.00
C37 Rich Harden 1.50 4.00
C38 Andrew Miller 1.25 3.00
C39 Miguel Cabrera 3.00 8.00
C40 David Wright 2.50 6.00
C41 Brandon Phillips 1.50 4.00
C42 Magglio Ordonez 2.00 5.00
C43 Eric Byrnes 1.50 4.00
C44 John Smoltz 2.50 6.00
C45 Brandon Webb 2.00 5.00
C46 Barry Zito 1.50 4.00
C47 Sammy Sosa 3.00 8.00
C48 James Shields 1.50 4.00
C49 Alex Rios 2.50 6.00
C50 Matt Holliday 3.00 8.00
C51 Chris Young 1.50 4.00
C52 Roy Oswalt 2.50 6.00
C53 Matt Kemp 2.50 6.00
C54 Tim Lincecum 4.00 10.00
C55 Hanley Ramirez 2.50 6.00
C56 Vladimir Guerrero 2.50 6.00
C57 Mark Teixeira 3.00 8.00
C58 Fausto Carmona 1.50 4.00
C59 B.J. Ryan 1.50 4.00
C60 Manny Ramirez 2.50 6.00
C61 Carlos Delgado 1.50 4.00
C62 Matt Cain 1.50 4.00
C63 Brian Bannister 1.50 4.00
C64 Russell Martin 1.50 4.00
C65 Todd Helton 2.00 5.00
C66 Roy Halladay 4.00 10.00
C67 Lance Berkman 2.00 5.00
C68 John Lackey 1.50 4.00
C69 Daisuke Matsuzaka 2.00 5.00
C70 Joe Mauer 3.00 8.00
C71 Francisco Rodriguez 2.50 6.00
C72 Derek Jeter 5.00 12.00
C73 Homer Bailey 2.00 5.00
C74 Jonathan Papelbon 2.00 5.00
C75 Billy Butler 1.50 4.00
C76 B.J. Upton 2.00 5.00
C77 Ubaldo Jimenez 2.50 6.00
C78 Erik Bedard 1.50 4.00
C79 Jeff Kent 1.50 4.00
C80 Ken Griffey Jr. 3.00 8.00
C81 Josh Beckett 2.00 5.00
C82 Jeff Francis 1.50 4.00
C83 Grady Sizemore 2.00 5.00
C84 John Maine 1.50 4.00
C85 Cole Hamels 2.50 6.00
C86 Nick Markakis 3.00 8.00
C87 Ben Sheets 1.25 3.00
C88 Jose Reyes 2.00 5.00
C89 Vernon Wells 1.50 4.00
C90 Justin Morneau 3.00 8.00
C91 Brian McCann 2.00 5.00
C92 Jacoby Ellsbury 3.00 8.00
C93 Clay Buchholz 2.50 6.00
C94 Prince Fielder 1.50 4.00
C95 David Ortiz 1.50 4.00
C96 Joba Chamberlain 1.25 3.00
C97 Chien-Ming Wang 1.25 3.00
C98 Chipper Jones 2.00 5.00
C99 Chase Utley 2.50 6.00
C100 Alex Rodriguez 3.00 8.00
C101 Phil Hughes 2.50 6.00
C102 Hideki Okajima 1.50 4.00
C103 Chone Figgins 1.50 4.00
C104 Jose Vidro 1.50 4.00
C105 Johan Santana 3.00 8.00
C106 Paul Konerko 2.50 6.00
C107 Alfonso Soriano 2.00 5.00
C108 Kei Igawa 1.50 4.00
C109 Lastings Milledge 1.50 4.00
C110 Asdrubal Cabrera 2.50 6.00
C111 Brandon Jones 2.50 6.00
C112 Tom Gorzelanny 1.50 4.00
C113 Delmon Young 2.00 5.00
C114 Daric Barton 1.50 4.00
C115 David DeJesus 1.50 4.00
C116 Ryan Howard 2.50 6.00
C117 Tom Glavine 2.00 5.00
C118 Frank Thomas 2.50 6.00
C119 J.R. Towles 1.50 4.00
C120 Jeremy Bonderman 1.50 4.00
C121 Adrian Beltre 1.50 4.00
C122 Dan Haren 1.50 4.00
C123 Kazuo Matsui 1.50 4.00
C124 Joe Blanton 1.50 4.00
C125 Dan Uggla 2.00 5.00
C126 Stephen Drew 1.50 4.00
C127 Daniel Cabrera 1.50 4.00
C128 Jeff Clement 2.50 6.00
C129 Pedro Martinez 2.00 5.00
C130 Josh Anderson 1.50 4.00
C131 Orlando Hudson 1.50 4.00
C132 Jason Bay 2.50 6.00
C133 Eric Chavez 1.50 4.00
C134 Johnny Damon 2.00 5.00
C135 Lance Broadway 1.50 4.00
C136 Jake Peavy 1.25 3.00
C137 Carl Crawford 2.50 6.00
C138 Kenji Johjima 1.50 4.00
C139 Melky Cabrera 1.50 4.00
C140 Aaron Hill 1.50 4.00
C141 Carlos Lee 1.50 4.00
C142 Mark Buehrle 2.50 6.00
C143 Carlos Beltran 1.50 4.00
C144 Chin-Lung Hu 2.00 5.00
C145 C.C. Sabathia 2.50 6.00
C146 Dustin Pedroia 2.50 6.00
C147 Freddy Sanchez 1.50 4.00
C148 Kevin Youkilis 2.00 5.00
C149 Radhames Liz 2.00 5.00
C150 Jim Thome 2.00 5.00
C151 Greg Maddux 2.50 6.00
C152 Rich Hill 1.50 4.00
C153 Andy LaRoche 1.50 4.00
C154 Gil Meche 1.50 4.00
C155 Victor Martinez 2.50 6.00
C156 Mariano Rivera 2.50 6.00
C157 Kyle Kendrick 1.50 4.00
C158 Jarrod Saltalamacchia 1.50 4.00
C159 Tadahito Iguchi 1.50 4.00
C160 Eric Gagne 1.50 4.00
C161 Garrett Atkins 1.50 4.00
C162 Pat Burrell 1.50 4.00
C163 Akinori Iwamura 1.50 4.00
C164 Melvin Mora 1.50 4.00
C165 Joey Votto 4.00 10.00
C166 Brian Roberts 1.25 3.00
C167 Brett Myers 1.50 4.00
C168 Michael Young 2.50 6.00
C169 Adam Jones 2.50 6.00
C170 Carlos Zambrano 2.50 6.00
C171 Jeff Francoeur 2.00 5.00
C172 Brad Hawpe 1.50 4.00
C173 Andy Pettitte 2.00 5.00
C174 Ryan Garko 1.50 4.00
C175 Adrian Gonzalez 2.00 5.00
C176 Ted Lilly 1.50 4.00
C177 J.J. Hardy 1.50 4.00
C178 Jon Lester 3.00 8.00
C179 Carlos Pena 1.50 4.00
C180 Ross Detwiler 2.50 6.00
C181 Andruw Jones 1.50 4.00
C182 Gary Sheffield 1.50 4.00
C183 Dmitri Young 1.50 4.00
C184 Carlos Guillen 1.50 4.00
C185 Yovani Gallardo 1.50 4.00
C186 Alex Gordon 1.50 4.00
C187 Aaron Harang 1.50 4.00
C188 Travis Hafner 1.50 4.00
C189 Orlando Cabrera 1.50 4.00
C190 Bobby Abreu 1.50 4.00
C191 Randy Johnson 2.50 6.00
C192 Scott Kazmir 2.00 5.00
C193 Jason Varitek 2.50 6.00
C194 Mike Lowell 1.50 4.00
C195 A.J. Burnett 2.50 6.00
C196 Garret Anderson 1.50 4.00
C197 Chris Carpenter 4.00 10.00
C198 Jermaine Dye 1.50 4.00
C199 Luke Hochevar 1.50 4.00
C200 Steve Pearce 2.00 5.00
C201 Joe Saunders 1.50 4.00
C202 Cliff Lee 2.50 6.00
C203 Mike Mussina 2.50 6.00
C204 Ryan Dempster 1.50 4.00
C205 Edinson Volquez 1.50 4.00
C206 Justin Duchscherer 1.50 4.00
C207 Geovany Soto 2.50 6.00
C208 Brian Wilson 4.00 10.00
C209 Kerry Wood 1.50 4.00
C210 Kosuke Fukudome 2.50 6.00
C211 Cristian Guzman 1.50 4.00
C212 Ryan Ludwick 1.50 4.00
C213 Joe Crede 1.50 4.00
C214 Dioner Navarro 1.50 4.00
C215 Miguel Tejada 2.50 6.00
C216 Joakim Soria 1.50 4.00
C217 George Sherrill 1.50 4.00
C218 John Danks 1.50 4.00
C219 Jair Jurrjens 1.50 4.00
C220 Evan Longoria 4.00 10.00
C221 Hiroki Kuroda 2.00 5.00
C222 Greg Smith 1.50 4.00
C223 Dana Eveland 1.50 4.00
C224 Ryan Sweeney 1.50 4.00
C225 Mike Pelfrey 1.50 4.00
C226 Nick Blackburn 2.00 5.00
C227 Scott Olsen 1.50 4.00
C228 Manny Parra 1.50 4.00
C229 Tim Redding 1.50 4.00
C230 Paul Maholm 1.50 4.00
C231 Todd Wellemeyer 1.50 4.00
C232 Jesse Litsch 1.50 4.00
C233 Andy Sonnanstine 1.50 4.00
C234 Johnny Cueto 2.00 5.00
C235 Vicente Padilla 1.50 4.00
C236 Glen Perkins 1.50 4.00
C237 Brian Burres 1.50 4.00
C238 Jamey Wright 1.50 4.00
C239 Chase Headley 1.50 4.00
C240 Takashi Saito 1.50 4.00
C241 Skip Schumaker 1.50 4.00
C242 Curtis Granderson 2.50 6.00
C243 A.J. Pierzynski 1.50 4.00
C244 Jorge Cantu 1.50 4.00
C245 Maicer Izturis 1.50 4.00
C246 Kevin Mench 1.50 4.00
C247 Jason Kubel 1.50 4.00
C248 Rod Barajas 1.50 4.00
C249 Jed Lowrie 2.50 6.00
C250 Bobby Jenks 1.50 4.00
C251 Jonny Gomes 1.50 4.00
C252 Clete Thomas 2.00 5.00
C253 Eric Hinske 1.50 4.00
C254 Brett Gardner 3.00 8.00
C255 Denard Span 2.00 5.00
C256 Brian Anderson 1.50 4.00
C257 Troy Percival 1.50 4.00
C258 Darrell Rasner 1.50 4.00
C259 Willy Aybar 1.50 4.00
C260 John Bowker 1.50 4.00
C261 Marco Scutaro 1.50 4.00
C262 Adam Kennedy 1.50 4.00
C263 Nick Punto 1.50 4.00
C264 Mike Napoli 2.50 6.00
C265 Carlos Gonzalez 4.00 10.00
C266 Matt Macri 1.50 4.00
C267 Marcus Thames 1.50 4.00
C268 Ben Zobrist 1.50 4.00
C269 Mark Ellis 1.50 4.00
C270 Mike Aviles 2.00 5.00
C271 Angel Pagan 1.50 4.00
C272 Erick Aybar 1.50 4.00
C273 Todd Jones 1.50 4.00
C274 Brandon Boggs 2.50 6.00
C275 Mike Jacobs 1.50 4.00
C276 Mike Gonzalez 1.50 4.00
C277 Mike Lamb 1.50 4.00
C278 Robb Quinlan 1.50 4.00
C279 Salomon Torres 1.50 4.00
C280 Jose Castillo 1.50 4.00
C281 Damion Easley 1.50 4.00
C282 Jo-Jo Reyes 1.50 4.00
C283 Cody Ross 1.50 4.00
C284 Alexi Casilla 1.50 4.00
C285 Jerry Hairston
C286 Brandon Lyon 1.50 4.00
C287 Greg Dobbs 1.50 4.00
C288 Joel Pineiro 1.50 4.00
C289 Chris Davis 3.00 8.00
C290 Masahide Kobayashi 2.00 5.00
C291 Darin Erstad 1.50 4.00
C292 Matt Diaz 1.50 4.00
C293 Brian Schneider 1.50 4.00
C294 Gerald Laird 1.50 4.00
C295 Ben Francisco 1.50 4.00
C296 Brian Moehler 1.50 4.00
C297 Aaron Miles 1.50 4.00
C298 Max Scherzer 3.00 8.00
C299 C.J. Wilson 1.50 4.00
C300 Jay Bruce 3.00 8.00

2008 Topps Heritage Chrome Refractors

*CHROME REF: .6X TO 1.5X
1-100 ODDS 1:29 HOBBY, 1:59 RETAIL
1-100 INSERTED IN 08 TOPPS HERITAGE
101-200 ODDS 1:21 HOBBY
101-200 INSERTED IN 08 TOPPS CHROME
201-300 ODDS 1:11 HOBBY
201-300 INSERTED IN 08 HERITAGE HN
STATED PRINT RUN 559 SERIAL #'d SETS
C72 Derek Jeter 12.50 30.00
C100 Alex Rodriguez 12.50 30.00
C220 Evan Longoria 5.00 12.00

2008 Topps Heritage Chrome Refractors Black

1-100 ODDS 1:315 HOB,1:450 RET
1-100 INSERTED IN 08 TOPPS HERITAGE
101-200 ODDS 1:196 HOBBY
201-300 INSERTED IN 08 HERITAGE HN
201-300 ODDS 1:99 HOBBY
101-200 INSERTED IN 08 TOPPS CHROME
STATED PRINT RUN 59 SERIAL #'d SETS
C1 Hunter Pence 30.00 60.00
C2 Andre Ethier 20.00 50.00
C3 Curt Schilling 20.00 50.00
C4 Gary Matthews 20.00 50.00
C5 Dontrelle Willis 20.00 50.00
C6 Troy Tulowitzki 20.00 50.00
C7 Robinson Cano 20.00 50.00
C8 Felix Hernandez 20.00 50.00
C9 Josh Hamilton 50.00 100.00
C10 Justin Upton 20.00 50.00
C11 Brad Penny 20.00 50.00
C12 Hideki Matsui 30.00 60.00
C13 J.J. Putz 20.00 50.00
C14 Jorge Posada 20.00 50.00
C15 Albert Pujols 100.00 200.00
C16 Aaron Rowand 20.00 50.00
C17 Ronnie Belliard 20.00 50.00
C18 Rick Ankiel 20.00 50.00
C19 Ian Kinsler 20.00 50.00
C20 Justin Verlander 20.00 50.00
C21 Lyle Overbay 20.00 50.00
C22 Tim Hudson 20.00 50.00
C23 Ryan Zimmerman 20.00 50.00
C24 Ryan Braun 30.00 60.00
C25 Jimmy Rollins 20.00 50.00
C26 Kelvim Escobar 20.00 50.00
C27 Adam LaRoche 20.00 50.00
C28 Ivan Rodriguez 20.00 50.00
C29 Billy Wagner 20.00 50.00
C30 Ichiro Suzuki 60.00 120.00
C31 Chris Young 20.00 50.00
C32 Trevor Hoffman 20.00 50.00
C33 Torii Hunter 20.00 50.00
C34 Jason Isringhausen 20.00 50.00
C35 Jose Valverde 20.00 50.00
C36 Derrek Lee 20.00 50.00
C37 Rich Harden 20.00 50.00
C38 Andrew Miller 20.00 50.00
C39 Miguel Cabrera 20.00 50.00
C40 David Wright 40.00 80.00
C41 Brandon Phillips 20.00 50.00
C42 Magglio Ordonez 20.00 50.00
C43 Eric Byrnes 20.00 50.00
C44 John Smoltz 20.00 50.00
C45 Brandon Webb 20.00 50.00
C46 Barry Zito 20.00 50.00
C47 Sammy Sosa 20.00 50.00
C48 James Shields 20.00 50.00
C49 Alex Rios 20.00 50.00
C50 Matt Holliday 20.00 50.00
C51 Chris Young 20.00 50.00
C52 Roy Oswalt 20.00 50.00
C53 Matt Kemp 20.00 50.00
C54 Tim Lincecum 30.00 60.00

C55 Hanley Ramirez 20.00 50.00
C56 Vladimir Guerrero 20.00 50.00
C57 Mark Teixeira 20.00 50.00
C58 Fausto Carmona 20.00 50.00
C59 B.J. Ryan 20.00 50.00
C60 Manny Ramirez 20.00 50.00
C61 Carlos Delgado 20.00 50.00
C62 Matt Cain 20.00 50.00
C63 Brian Bannister 20.00 50.00
C64 Russell Martin 20.00 50.00
C65 Todd Helton 20.00 50.00
C66 Roy Halladay 20.00 50.00
C67 Lance Berkman 20.00 50.00
C68 John Lackey 20.00 50.00
C69 Daisuke Matsuzaka 40.00 80.00
C70 Joe Mauer 20.00 50.00
C71 Francisco Rodriguez 20.00 50.00
C72 Derek Jeter 60.00 120.00
C73 Homer Bailey 20.00 50.00
C74 Jonathan Papelbon 20.00 50.00
C75 Billy Butler 20.00 50.00
C76 B.J. Upton 20.00 50.00
C77 Ubaldo Jimenez 20.00 50.00
C78 Erik Bedard 20.00 50.00
C79 Jeff Kent 20.00 50.00
C80 Ken Griffey Jr. 60.00 120.00
C81 Josh Beckett 20.00 50.00
C82 Jeff Francis 20.00 50.00
C83 Grady Sizemore 20.00 50.00
C84 John Maine 20.00 50.00
C85 Cole Hamels 20.00 50.00
C86 Nick Markakis 20.00 50.00
C87 Ben Sheets 20.00 50.00
C88 Jose Reyes 20.00 50.00
C89 Vernon Wells 20.00 50.00
C90 Justin Morneau 20.00 50.00
C91 Brian McCann 20.00 50.00
C92 Jacoby Ellsbury 60.00 120.00
C93 Clay Buchholz 40.00 80.00
C94 Prince Fielder 30.00 60.00
C95 David Ortiz 30.00 60.00
C96 Joba Chamberlain 60.00 120.00
C97 Chien-Ming Wang 40.00 80.00
C98 Chipper Jones 20.00 50.00
C99 Chase Utley 20.00 50.00
C100 Alex Rodriguez 100.00 200.00
C101 Phil Hughes 20.00 50.00
C102 Hideki Okajima 12.50 30.00
C103 Chone Figgins 12.50 30.00
C104 Jose Vidro 12.50 30.00
C105 Johan Santana 20.00 50.00
C106 Paul Konerko 12.50 30.00
C107 Alfonso Soriano 15.00 40.00
C108 Kei Igawa 12.50 30.00
C109 Lastings Milledge 12.50 30.00
C110 Asdrubal Cabrera 12.50 30.00
C111 Brandon Jones 20.00 50.00
C112 Tom Gorzelanny 12.50 30.00
C113 Delmon Young 15.00 40.00
C114 Daric Barton 15.00 40.00
C115 David DeJesus 12.50 30.00
C116 Ryan Howard 60.00 120.00
C117 Tom Glavine 20.00 50.00
C118 Frank Thomas 20.00 50.00
C119 J.R. Towles 15.00 40.00
C120 Jeremy Bonderman 12.50 30.00
C121 Adrian Beltre 12.50 30.00
C122 Dan Haren 12.50 30.00
C123 Kazuo Matsui 12.50 30.00
C124 Joe Blanton 12.50 30.00
C125 Dan Uggla 12.50 30.00
C126 Stephen Drew 12.50 30.00
C127 Daniel Cabrera 12.50 30.00
C128 Jeff Clement 12.50 30.00
C129 Pedro Martinez 15.00 40.00
C130 Josh Anderson 12.50 30.00
C131 Orlando Hudson 12.50 30.00
C132 Jason Bay 12.50 30.00
C133 Eric Chavez 12.50 30.00
C134 Johnny Damon 12.50 30.00
C135 Lance Broadway 12.50 30.00
C136 Jake Peavy 15.00 40.00
C137 Carl Crawford 12.50 30.00
C138 Kenji Johjima 12.50 30.00
C139 Melky Cabrera 12.50 30.00
C140 Aaron Hill 12.50 30.00
C141 Carlos Lee 12.50 30.00
C142 Mark Buehrle 12.50 30.00
C143 Carlos Beltran 12.50 30.00
C144 Chin-Lung Hu 20.00 50.00
C145 C.C. Sabathia 12.50 30.00
C146 Dustin Pedroia 15.00 40.00
C147 Freddy Sanchez 12.50 30.00
C148 Kevin Youkilis 12.50 30.00
C149 Radhames Liz 15.00 40.00
C150 Jim Thome 15.00 40.00
C151 Greg Maddux 30.00 60.00
C152 Rich Hill 12.50 30.00
C153 Andy LaRoche 12.50 30.00
C154 Gil Meche 12.50 30.00
C155 Victor Martinez 12.50 30.00
C156 Mariano Rivera 20.00 50.00
C157 Kyle Kendrick 12.50 30.00
C158 Jarrod Saltalamacchia 12.50 30.00
C159 Tadahito Iguchi 12.50 30.00
C160 Eric Gagne 12.50 30.00
C161 Garrett Atkins 12.50 30.00
C162 Pat Burrell 12.50 30.00
C163 Akinori Iwamura 12.50 30.00
C164 Melvin Mora 12.50 30.00
C165 Joey Votto 15.00 40.00
C166 Brian Roberts 12.50 30.00
C167 Brett Myers 12.50 30.00
C168 Michael Young 12.50 30.00
C169 Adam Jones 12.50 30.00
C170 Carlos Zambrano 12.50 30.00
C171 Jeff Francoeur 15.00 40.00
C172 Brad Hawpe 12.50 30.00
C173 Andy Pettitte 15.00 40.00
C174 Ryan Garko 12.50 30.00
C175 Adrian Gonzalez 12.50 30.00
C176 Ted Lilly 12.50 30.00
C177 J.J. Hardy 12.50 30.00
C178 Jon Lester 15.00 40.00
C179 Carlos Pena 12.50 30.00
C180 Ross Detwiler 20.00 50.00
C181 Andruw Jones 12.50 30.00
C182 Gary Sheffield 12.50 30.00
C183 Dmitri Young 12.50 30.00
C184 Carlos Guillen 12.50 30.00
C185 Yovani Gallardo 12.50 30.00
C186 Alex Gordon 20.00 50.00
C187 Aaron Harang 12.50 30.00
C188 Travis Hafner 12.50 30.00
C189 Orlando Cabrera 12.50 30.00
C190 Bobby Abreu 12.50 30.00
C191 Randy Johnson 20.00 50.00
C192 Scott Kazmir 15.00 40.00
C193 Jason Varitek 20.00 50.00
C194 Mike Lowell 15.00 40.00
C195 A.J. Burnett 12.50 30.00
C196 Garret Anderson 12.50 30.00
C197 Chris Carpenter 12.50 30.00
C198 Jermaine Dye 12.50 30.00
C199 Luke Hochevar 15.00 40.00
C200 Steve Pearce 20.00 50.00
C201 Joe Saunders 12.50 30.00
C202 Cliff Lee 12.50 30.00
C203 Mike Mussina 12.50 30.00
C204 Ryan Dempster 12.50 30.00
C205 Edinson Volquez 12.50 30.00
C206 Justin Duchscherer 12.50 30.00
C207 Geovany Soto 12.50 30.00
C208 Brian Wilson 12.50 30.00
C209 Kerry Wood 12.50 30.00
C210 Kosuke Fukudome 20.00 50.00
C211 Cristian Guzman 12.50 30.00
C212 Ryan Ludwick 12.50 30.00
C213 Joe Crede 12.50 30.00
C214 Dioner Navarro 12.50 30.00
C215 Miguel Tejada 12.50 30.00
C216 Joakim Soria 12.50 30.00
C217 George Sherrill 12.50 30.00
C218 John Danks 12.50 30.00
C219 Jair Jurrjens 12.50 30.00
C220 Evan Longoria 60.00 120.00
C221 Hiroki Kuroda 15.00 40.00
C222 Greg Smith 12.50 30.00
C223 Dana Eveland 12.50 30.00
C224 Ryan Sweeney 12.50 30.00
C225 Mike Pelfrey 12.50 30.00
C226 Nick Blackburn 15.00 40.00
C227 Scott Olsen 12.50 30.00
C228 Manny Parra 12.50 30.00
C229 Tim Redding 12.50 30.00
C230 Paul Maholm 12.50 30.00
C231 Todd Wellemeyer 12.50 30.00
C232 Jesse Litsch 12.50 30.00
C233 Andy Sonnanstine 12.50 30.00
C234 Johnny Cueto 12.50 30.00
C235 Vicente Padilla 12.50 30.00
C236 Glen Perkins 12.50 30.00
C237 Brian Burres 12.50 30.00
C238 Jamey Wright 12.50 30.00
C239 Chase Headley 12.50 30.00
C240 Takashi Saito 20.00 50.00
C241 Skip Schumaker 12.50 30.00
C242 Curtis Granderson 12.50 30.00
C243 A.J. Pierzynski 12.50 30.00
C244 Jorge Cantu 12.50 30.00
C245 Maicer Izturis 12.50 30.00
C246 Kevin Mench 12.50 30.00
C247 Jason Kubel 12.50 30.00
C248 Rod Barajas 12.50 30.00
C249 Jed Lowrie 15.00 40.00
C250 Bobby Jenks 12.50 30.00
C251 Jonny Gomes 12.50 30.00
C252 Clete Thomas 15.00 40.00
C253 Eric Hinske 12.50 30.00
C254 Brett Gardner 15.00 40.00
C255 Denard Span 15.00 40.00
C256 Brian Anderson 12.50 30.00
C257 Troy Percival 12.50 30.00
C258 Darrell Rasner 12.50 30.00
C259 Willy Aybar 12.50 30.00
C260 John Bowker 12.50 30.00
C261 Marco Scutaro 12.50 30.00
C262 Adam Kennedy 12.50 30.00
C263 Nick Punto 12.50 30.00
C264 Mike Napoli 12.50 30.00
C265 Carlos Gonzalez 12.50 30.00
C266 Matt Macri 12.50 30.00
C267 Marcus Thames 12.50 30.00
C268 Ben Zobrist 12.50 30.00
C269 Mark Ellis 12.50 30.00
C270 Mike Aviles 15.00 40.00
C271 Angel Pagan 12.50 30.00
C272 Erick Aybar 12.50 30.00
C273 Todd Jones 12.50 30.00
C274 Brandon Boggs 12.50 30.00
C275 Mike Jacobs 12.50 30.00
C276 Mike Gonzalez 12.50 30.00
C277 Mike Lamb 12.50 30.00
C278 Robb Quinlan 12.50 30.00
C279 Salomon Torres 12.50 30.00
C280 Jose Castillo 12.50 30.00
C281 Damion Easley 12.50 30.00
C282 Jo-Jo Reyes 12.50 30.00
C283 Cody Ross 12.50 30.00
C284 Alexi Casilla 12.50 30.00
C285 Jerry Hairston 12.50 30.00
C286 Brandon Lyon 12.50 30.00
C287 Greg Dobbs 12.50 30.00
C288 Joel Pineiro 12.50 30.00
C289 Chris Davis 15.00 40.00
C290 Masahide Kobayashi 15.00 40.00
C291 Darin Erstad 12.50 30.00
C292 Matt Diaz 12.50 30.00
C293 Brian Schneider 12.50 30.00
C294 Gerald Laird 12.50 30.00
C295 Ben Francisco 12.50 30.00
C296 Brian Moehler 12.50 30.00
C297 Aaron Miles 12.50 30.00
C298 Max Scherzer 15.00 40.00
C299 C.J. Wilson 12.50 30.00
C300 Jay Bruce 20.00 50.00

2008 Topps Heritage 1959 Cut Signature

STATED ODDS 1:98,200 HOBBY
HN ODDS 1:65,000 HOBBY
STATED PRINT RUN 1 SER.#'d SET
NO PRICING DUE TO SCARCITY

2008 Topps Heritage 1959 Cut Signature Relics

STATED ODDS 1:100,000 HOBBY
STATED PRINT RUN 1 SER.#'d SET
NO PRICING DUE TO SCARCITY
EM Eddie Mathews HN
LB Lou Burdette HN
MM Mickey Mantle HN
RA Richie Ashburn HN

2008 Topps Heritage 2008 Flashbacks

COMPLETE SET (10) 6.00 15.00
STATED ODDS 1:12 HOBBY
FB1 Mark Teixeira 1.25 3.00
FB2 Tim Lincecum 2.00 5.00
FB3 Jon Lester 1.25 3.00
FB4 Ken Griffey Jr. 2.00 5.00
FB5 Kosuke Fukudome 1.50 4.00
FB6 Albert Pujols 3.00 8.00
FB7 Ichiro Suzuki 2.00 5.00
FB8 Felix Hernandez 1.25 3.00
FB9 Carlos Delgado .50 1.25
FB10 Josh Hamilton 1.25 3.00

2008 Topps Heritage Advertising Panels

ISSUED AS A BOX TOPPER
1 Bronson Arroyo .60 1.50
J.R. Towles
B.J. Ryan
2 Willy Aybar .40 1.00
Darrell Rasner
Troy Percival HN
3 Lance Berkman 1.00 2.50
Jeff Francoeur
Hanley Ramirez
4 Yuniesky Betancourt 1.50 4.00
Tim Lincecum
Jason Kendall
5 Brandon Boggs .60 1.50
Todd Jones
Erick Aybar HN
6 Lance Broadway .60 1.50
Russ Ohlendorf
Matt Capps
7 Jay Bruce 1.50 4.00
C.J. Wilson
Max Scherzer HN
8 Emmanuel Burriss .60 1.50
Tyler Yates
Clayton Richard HN
9 Alexi Casilla .40 1.00
Jerry Hairston
Brandon Lyon HN
10 Jose Castillo .40 1.00
Salomon Torres
Robb Quinlan HN
11 Eric Chavez .60 1.50
Zack Greinke
Josh Willingham
12 Chad Cordero .60 1.50
Kenji Johjima
Alfonso Soriano
13 Joe Crede .40 1.00
Ryan Ludwick
Cristian Guzman HN
14 Chicago Cubs 1.00 2.50
Tadahito Iguchi
Mariano Rivera
15 Johnny Cueto .60 1.50
Andy Sonnanstine
Jesse Litsch HN
16 Jack Cust 1.00 2.50
Aaron Harang
Vladimir Guerrero
17 Carlos Delgado .60 1.50
Lance Broadway
Russ Ohlendorf
18 Ryan Dempster .40 1.00
Edinson Volquez
Justin Duchscherer HN
19 Greg Dobbs 1.00 2.50
Joel Pineiro
Chris Davis HN
20 Stephen Drew .40 1.00
Joe Nathan
Bronson Arroyo
21 Damion Easley .40 1.00
JoJo Reyes
Cody Ross HN
22 Jim Edmonds .60 1.50
Horatio Ramirez
Brian Bannister
23 Dana Eveland .40 1.00
Ryan Sweeney
Mike Pelfrey HN
24 Josh Fields .60 1.50
Emmanuel Burriss
Tyler Yates HN
25 Jeff Francoeur 1.00 2.50
Hanley Ramirez
Josh Barfield
26 Armando Galarraga .60 1.50
Wandy Rodriguez
Wily Mo Pena
27 Brett Gardner 1.00 2.50
Eric Hinske
Clete Thomas HN
28 Carlos Gomez 1.00 2.50
Sammy Sosa
Russ Martin
29 Mike Gonzalez .60 1.50
Mike Jacobs
Brandon Boggs HN
30 Zack Greinke .60 1.50
Josh Willingham
Armando Galarraga
31 Mark Grudzielanek .60 1.50
Jim Thome
Joe Koshansky
32 J.J. Hardy 1.00 2.50
Alex Rios
Johan Santana
33 Kevin Hart .60 1.50
Radhames Liz
Jack Wilson
34 Eric Hinske .60 1.50
Clete Thomas
Jonny Gomes HN
35 Tadahito Iguchi 1.00 2.50
Mariano Rivera
Brandon Webb
36 Akinori Iwamura 1.50 4.00
Yuniesky Betancourt
Tim Lincecum
37 Randy Johnson 1.00 2.50
Brett Myers
Kenny Lofton BT
38 Andruw Jones .40 1.00
Stephen Drew
Joe Nathan
39 Todd Jones .40 1.00
Erick Aybar
Angel Pagan HN
40 Jair Jurrjens .40 1.00
John Danks
George Sherrill HN
41 Matt Kemp .60 1.50
Carlos Pena
Fausto Carmona
42 Adam Kennedy .60 1.50
Nick Punto
Mike Napoli HN
43 Gerald Laird UER .40 1.00
Brian Schneider
Matt Diaz HN
44 Cliff Lee .60 1.50
Mike Mussina
Ryan Dempster HN
45 Rhadhames Liz .40 1.00
Jack Wilson
Carlos Gomez
46 Greg Maddux 1.00 2.50
Carlos Ruiz
Nick Swisher
47 Sean Marshall .40 1.00
Craig Monroe
Aramis Ramirez
48 Victor Martinez .60 1.50
C.C. Sabathia
Carlos Delgado
49 Aaron Miles .40 1.00
Brian Moehler
Ben Francisco HN
50 Lastings Milledge .60 1.50
Dmitri Young
Ryan Zimmerman/Barry Zito
51 Bengie Molina .40 1.00
David Murphy
John Lackey
52 David Murphy .40 1.00
John Lackey
Buddy Carlyle
53 Mike Napoli .60 1.50
Carlos Gonzalez
Matt Macri HN
54 Dioner Navarro .40 1.00
Joe Crede
Ryan Ludwick HN
55 Russ Ohlendorf .60 1.50
Matt Capps
Chris Young
56 Scott Olsen .40 1.00
Manny Parra
Tim Redding HN
57 Manny Parra .40 1.00
Tim Redding
Paul Maholm HN
58 Hunter Pence 1.00 2.50
Carlos Guillen
David Weathers
59 Troy Percival .60 1.50
Brian Anderson
Denard Span HN
60 Glen Perkins .60 1.50
Vicente Padilla
Johnny Cueto HN
61 A.J. Pierzynski .40 1.00
Jorge Cantu
Matt Diaz HN
62 Joel Pineiro 1.00 2.50
Chris Davis
Masahide Kobayashi HN
63 Nick Punto .60 1.50
Mike Napoli
Carlos Gonzalez HN
64 Robb Quinlan .40 1.00
Mike Lamb
Mike Gonzalez HN
65 Hanley Ramirez 1.00 2.50
Josh Barfield
Chad Cordero
66 Horatio Ramirez 1.00 2.50
Brian Bannister
Manny Ramirez
67 Manny Ramirez 1.00 2.50
Randy Johnson
Brett Myers
68 Darrell Rasner .40 1.00
Troy Percival
Brian Anderson HN
69 Alex Rios 1.00 2.50
Johan Santana
Roy Halladay
70 Alex Rodriguez 1.50 4.00
Huston Street
Mark Grudzielanek
71 Carlos Ruiz 1.00 2.50
Nick Swisher
Kevin Hart
72 C.C. Sabathia .60 1.50
Carlos Delgado
Lance Broadway
73 Pablo Sandoval 2.50 6.00
Alex Romero
Ivan Ochoa HN
74 Johan Santana 1.00 2.50
Roy Halladay
Brad Wilkinson
75 Joe Saunders .60 1.50
Cliff Lee
Mike Mussina HN
76 Brian Schneider .40 1.00
Matt Diaz
Darin Erstad HN
77 Skip Schumaker .60 1.50
Curtis Granderson
A.J. Pierzynski HN
78 Marco Scutaro .40 1.00
Adam Kennedy
Nick Punto HN
79 George Sherrill .60 1.50
Joakim Soria
Miguel Tejada HN
80 James Shields .60 1.50
Nate McLouth
Rich Thompson
81 John Smoltz 1.00 2.50
Andruw Jones
Chipper Jones/Andruw Jones
82 Andy Sonnanstine .40 1.00
Jesse Litsch
Todd Wellemeyer HN
83 Sammy Sosa 1.00 2.50
Russ Martin
Mark Buehrle
84 Ryan Sweeney .60 1.50
Mike Pelfrey
Nick Blackburn HN
85 Nick Swisher 1.00 2.50
Kevin Hart
Rhadhames Liz
86 Mark Teixeira 1.00 2.50
John Smoltz
Andruw Jones/Chipper Jones
87 Marcus Thames .40 1.00
Ben Zobrist
Mark Ellis HN
88 Jim Thome .60 1.50
Joe Koshansky
Adrian Gonzalez
89 Salomon Torres .40 1.00
Rob Quinlan
Mike Lamb HN
90 J.R. Towles .60 1.50
B.J. Ryan
Roy Oswalt
91 Eugenio Velez .40 1.00
Akinori Iwamura
Yuniesky Betancourt
92 Edinson Volquez 1.00 2.50
Justin Duchscherer
Geovany Soto HN
93 Brad Wilkerson .40 1.00
Juan Pierre
Bengie Molina
94 Brian Wilson 1.00 2.50
Kerry Wood
Kosuke Fukudome HN
95 Jamey Wright .40 1.00
Brian Burres
Glen Perkins HN
96 Dmitri Young .60 1.50
Ryan Zimmerman
Barry Zito/Dmitri Young
97 Dmitri Young .40 1.00
Yovanni Gallardo
Chris Duncan
98 Barry Zito .40 1.00
Dmitri Young
Yovanni Gallardo
99 Ben Zobrist .60 1.50
Mark Ellis
Mike Aviles HN

2008 Topps Heritage Baseball Flashbacks

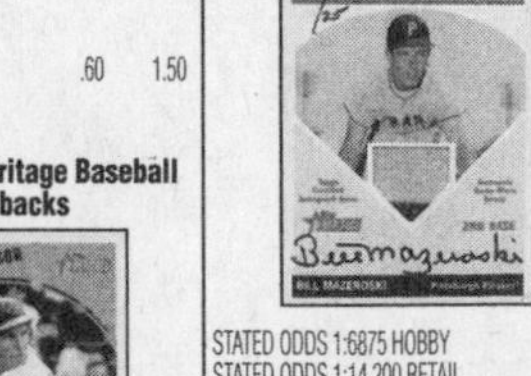

COMPLETE SET (10) 5.00 12.00
STATED ODDS 1:12 HOBBY,1:12 RETAIL
BF1 Minnie Minoso .50 1.25
BF2 Luis Aparicio .50 1.25
BF3 Ernie Banks 1.25 3.00
BF4 Bill Mazeroski .75 2.00
BF5 Bob Gibson .75 2.00
BF6 Frank Robinson .50 1.25
BF7 Brooks Robinson .75 2.00
BF8 Mickey Mantle 2.00 5.00
BF9 Orlando Cepeda .50 1.25
BF10 Eddie Mathews 1.25 3.00

2008 Topps Heritage Clubhouse Collection Relics

GROUP A ODDS 1:4100 H,1:7400 R
GROUP B ODDS 1:18,000 H,1:7800 R
GROUP C ODDS 1:90 H,1:182 R
GROUP D ODDS 1:54 H, 1:108 R
HN GROUP A ODDS 1:3600 HOBBY
HN GROUP B ODDS 1:74 HOBBY
HN GROUP C ODDS 1:55 HOBBY
NO HN GRP A PRICING AVAILABLE
AD Adam Dunn C 3.00 8.00
AG Alex Gordon HN C 4.00 10.00
AJ Andruw Jones C 3.00 8.00
AJ Andruw Jones HN B 3.00 8.00
AL Al Kaline HN A
AP Albert Pujols HN B 6.00 15.00
AR Aramis Ramirez C 3.00 8.00
AR Aramis Ramirez HN B 3.00 8.00
BA Bobby Abreu C 3.00 8.00
BD Blake DeWitt HN B 6.00 15.00
BG Bob Gibson A 30.00 60.00
BG Bob Gibson HN B 10.00 25.00
BM Bill Mazeroski HN B 10.00 25.00
BR Brooks Robinson HN B 10.00 25.00
BS Bill Skowron HN A
CAB Craig Biggio C 4.00 10.00
CB Carlos Beltran C 3.00 8.00
CB Carlos Beltran HN B 3.00 8.00
CC Carl Crawford C 3.00 8.00
CD Carlos Delgado C 3.00 8.00
CG Curtis Granderson HN C 3.00 8.00
CL Carlos Lee C 3.00 8.00
CL Carlos Lee HN B 3.00 8.00
DH Dan Haren HN C 3.00 8.00
DL Derrek Lee C 3.00 8.00
DL Derrek Lee HN B 3.00 8.00
DO David Ortiz C 4.00 10.00
DO David Ortiz HN B 4.00 10.00
DS Duke Snider HN A
DY Dmitri Young C 3.00 8.00
DY Dmitri Young HN B 3.00 8.00
EB Erik Bedard HN C 3.00 8.00
EC Eric Chavez C 3.00 8.00
FR Frank Robinson HN A
FT Frank Thomas C 4.00 10.00
FT Frank Thomas HN B 4.00 10.00
GA Garret Anderson D 3.00 8.00
HB Hank Blalock D 3.00 8.00
IR Ivan Rodriguez C 4.00 10.00
JB Jeremy Bonderman HN C 3.00 8.00
JD Johnny Damon C 3.00 8.00
JD Jermaine Dye HN C 3.00 8.00
JE Jim Edmonds D 3.00 8.00
JE Johnny Estrada HN C 3.00 8.00
JL Julio Lugo HN C 3.00 8.00
JP Jorge Posada C 4.00 10.00
JS John Smoltz D 4.00 10.00
JV Justin Verlander C 4.00 10.00
LA Luis Aparicio A 60.00 120.00
LB Lance Berkman D 3.00 8.00
MC Miguel Cabrera D 4.00 10.00
MM Minnie Minoso B 50.00 100.00
MM Mike Mussina D 3.00 8.00
MT Miguel Tejada D 3.00 8.00
MT Miguel Tejada HN B 3.00 8.00
NF Nellie Fox HN B 12.50 30.00
OC Orlando Cepeda HN A
PM Pedro Martinez D 4.00 10.00
PM Pedro Martinez HN B 3.00 8.00
RH Ryan Howard D 5.00 12.00
RO Roy Oswalt D 3.00 8.00
RO Roy Oswalt HN B 3.00 8.00
RR Robin Roberts HN B 8.00 20.00
RS Richie Sexson D 3.00 8.00
RS Darrell Rasner HN B 3.00 8.00
RZ Ryan Zimmerman D 4.00 10.00
RZ Ryan Zimmerman HN B 3.00 8.00
SG Shawn Green C 3.00 8.00
ST Steve Pearce HN C 3.00 8.00
TH Todd Helton C 4.00 10.00
TKH Torii Hunter D 3.00 8.00
TLH Travis Hafner D 3.00 8.00
WM Bill Mazeroski A 60.00 120.00
YB Yogi Berra A 60.00 120.00

2008 Topps Heritage Clubhouse Collection Relics Autographs

STATED ODDS 1:6875 HOBBY
STATED ODDS 1:14,200 RETAIL
HN ODDS 1:1815 HOBBY
STATED PRINT RUN 25 SER.#'d SETS
NO PRICING DUE TO SCARCITY
EXCHANGE DEADLINE 2/28/2010
HN EXCH DEADLINE 11/30/2010

2008 Topps Heritage Clubhouse Collection Relics Dual

STATED ODDS 1:5582 H,1:11,000 R
HN STATED ODDS 1:1900 HOBBY
HN PRINT RUN 59 SER.#'d SETS
AK Luis Aparicio 60.00 120.00
Paul Konerko
BL Ernie Banks 100.00 200.00
Derrek Lee
CL Orlando Cepeda 60.00 120.00
Fred Lewis HN
GE Bob Gibson 60.00 120.00
Jim Edmonds
KG Al Kaline 100.00 200.00
Curtis Granderson HN
MB Bill Mazeroski 60.00 120.00
Jason Bay
MH Minnie Minoso 60.00 120.00
Travis Hafner
RB Frank Robinson 50.00 100.00
Jay Bruce HN
SK Duke Snider 90.00 150.00
Clayton Kershaw HN
SR Bill Skowron 90.00 150.00
Darrell Rasner HN

2008 Topps Heritage Dick Perez

COMPLETE SET (10) 30.00 60.00
THREE PER $9.99 WALMART BOX
SIX PER $19.99 WALMART BOX
HDP1 Manny Ramirez 1.25 3.00
HDP2 Cameron Maybin .50 1.25
HDP3 Ryan Howard 1.50 4.00
HDP4 David Ortiz .75 2.00
HDP5 Tim Lincecum 2.00 5.00
HDP6 David Wright 1.50 4.00
HDP7 Mickey Mantle 2.50 6.00
HDP8 Joba Chamberlain .75 2.00
HDP9 Ichiro Suzuki 2.00 5.00
HDP10 Prince Fielder .75 2.00

2008 Topps Heritage Flashbacks Autographs

STATED ODDS 1:14,900 HOBBY
STATED ODDS 1:20,000 RETAIL
STATED PRINT RUN 25 SER.#'d SETS
NO PRICING DUE TO SCARCITY
EXCHANGE DEADLINE 2/28/10

2008 Topps Heritage Flashbacks Seat Relics

STATED ODDS 1:162 H,1:327 R
HN ODDS 1:3175 HOBBY
HN PRINT RUN 59 SER.#'d SETS
BG Bob Gibson 10.00 25.00
BR Brooks Robinson 10.00 25.00
DE Dwight D. Eisenhower HN 60.00 120.00
EB Ernie Banks 10.00 25.00
EM Eddie Mathews 10.00 25.00
FR Frank Robinson 8.00 20.00
LA Luis Aparicio 8.00 20.00
MM Minnie Minoso 8.00 20.00
MM Mickey Mantle 30.00 60.00
MO Motown HN 50.00 100.00
NK Nikita Khrushchev HN 60.00 120.00
OC Orlando Cepeda 8.00 20.00
WM Bill Mazeroski 10.00 25.00

2008 Topps Heritage Flashbacks Seat Relics Autographs

STATED ODDS 1:22,100 HOBBY
STATED ODDS 1:50,000 RETAIL
STATED PRINT RUN 25 SER.#'d SETS
NO PRICING DUE TO SCARCITY
EXCHANGE DEADLINE 2/28/10

2008 Topps Heritage Flashbacks Seat Relics Dual

STATED ODDS 1:55,000 HOBBY
STATED ODDS 1:40,000 RETAIL
STATED PRINT RUN 10 SER.#'d SETS
NO PRICING DUE TO SCARCITY

2008 Topps Heritage High Numbers Then and Now

COMPLETE SET (10) 6.00 15.00
STATED ODDS 1:12 HOBBY
TN1 Ernie Banks 1.25 3.00
Jimmy Rollins
TN2 Nellie Fox .75 2.00
Alex Rodriguez
TN3 Larry Sherry .50 1.25
Mike Lowell
TN4 Willie McCovey 1.50 4.00
Ryan Braun
TN5 Bob Allison 1.50 4.00
Dustin Pedroia
TN6 Del Crandall .50 1.25
Russ Martin
TN7 Luis Aparicio .50 1.25
Orlando Cabrera
TN8 Early Wynn .50 1.25
Alex Rodriguez
TN9 Early Wynn .50 1.25
Jake Peavy
TN10 Sam Jones .75 2.00
CC Sabathia

2008 Topps Heritage National Convention

1 Ted Williams
145 Bob Gibson
150 Mickey Mantle
310 Ernie Banks
496 Mickey Mantle

2008 Topps Heritage New Age Performers

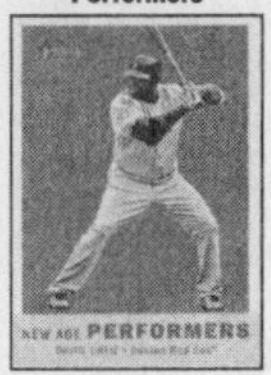

COMPLETE SET (15) 10.00 25.00
STATED ODDS 1:15 HOBBY,1:15 RETAIL
NAP1 Magglio Ordonez .75 2.00
NAP2 Ichiro Suzuki 2.00 5.00
NAP3 Matt Holliday 1.25 3.00
NAP4 Prince Fielder .75 2.00
NAP5 David Wright 1.50 4.00
NAP6 Jake Peavy .50 1.25
NAP7 Alex Rodriguez 2.00 5.00
NAP8 John Lackey .50 1.25
NAP9 Vladimir Guerrero 1.25 3.00
NAP10 Ryan Howard 1.50 4.00
NAP11 Brandon Webb .75 2.00
NAP12 Manny Ramirez 1.25 3.00
NAP13 Josh Beckett .75 2.00
NAP14 Jimmy Rollins .75 2.00
NAP15 David Ortiz .75 2.00

2008 Topps Heritage News Flashbacks

COMPLETE SET (10) 4.00 10.00
STATED ODDS 1:12 HOBBY,1:12 RETAIL
NF1 Alaska becomes the 49th state .60 1.50
NF2 The Day the Music Died .60 1.50
NF3 Castro becomes Prime Minister .60 1.50
NF4 The Dalai Lama flees to India .60 1.50
NF5 NASA astronauts .60 1.50
NF6 Nixon and Khrushchev .60 1.50
NF7 Hawaii becomes the 50th state .60 1.50
NF8 USSR's Luna 2 .60 1.50
NF9 In Cold Blood murders .60 1.50
NF10 Antarctic Treaty signed .60 1.50

2008 Topps Heritage Real One Autographs

STATED ODDS 1:247 H,1:495 R
HN ODDS 1:110 HOBBY
EXCHANGE DEADLINE 02/28/2010
HN EXCH DEADLINE 11/30/2010
AJ Al Jackson HN 15.00 40.00
AK Al Kaline HN 50.00 100.00
AR Aramis Ramirez 15.00 40.00
BB Bob Blaylock 20.00 50.00
BM Bob Martyn 15.00 40.00
BM Brian McCann HN 15.00 40.00
BMS Bill Skowron HN 20.00 50.00
BR Bill Renna 20.00 50.00
BS Bob Smith 20.00 50.00
BS Barney Schultz HN 15.00 40.00
BSP Bob Speake 10.00 25.00
CE Carl Erskine 10.00 25.00
CE Chuck Essegian HN 20.00 50.00
CG Curtis Granderson HN 15.00 40.00
CK Clayton Kershaw HN 20.00 50.00
CK Chuck King 30.00 60.00
DP Dustin Pedroia HN 40.00 80.00
DR Dusty Rhodes HN 15.00 40.00
DS Duke Snider HN 30.00 60.00
FL Fred Lewis HN 15.00 40.00
FR Frank Robinson HN 40.00 80.00
FS Freddy Sanchez EXCH 15.00 40.00
GEZ Gus Zernial 15.00 40.00
GS Geovany Soto HN 20.00 50.00
GZ George Zuverink 20.00 50.00
HL Hector Lopez HN 15.00 40.00
HP Herb Plews 20.00 50.00
JAB Jay Bruce HN 20.00 50.00
JB Jim Brosnan HN 20.00 50.00
JB Jim Bolger 20.00 50.00
JC Joba Chamberlain 75.00 150.00
JF Jack Fisher HN 10.00 25.00
JH Jay Hook HN 15.00 40.00
JK Jim Kaat HN 15.00 40.00
JO Johnny O'Brien 20.00 50.00
JP J.W. Porter 20.00 50.00
KL Ken Lehman 20.00 50.00
LA Luis Aparicio 20.00 50.00
LM Les Moss 10.00 25.00
LT Lee Tate 20.00 50.00
MB Mike Baxes 15.00 40.00
MIM Minnie Minoso EXCH 30.00 60.00
MM Morrie Martin 20.00 50.00
MW Maury Wills HN 10.00 25.00
OC Orlando Cepeda HN 20.00 50.00
PC Phil Clark 20.00 50.00
PG Pumpsie Green HN 20.00 50.00
RC Roger Craig HN 15.00 40.00
RH Russ Heman 20.00 50.00
RJ Randy Jackson 15.00 40.00
SP Scott Podsednik EXCH 20.00 50.00
TC Tom Carroll 20.00 50.00
TD Tommy Davis HN 12.50 30.00
TK Ted Kazanski 20.00 50.00
TQ Tom Qualters 20.00 50.00
VV Vito Valentinetti 15.00 40.00
WM Bill Mazeroski 30.00 60.00
YB Yogi Berra 60.00 120.00

2008 Topps Heritage Real One Autographs Dual

STATED ODDS 1:6869 HOBBY
HN ODDS 1:1850 HOBBY
STATED PRINT RUN 25 SER.#'d SETS
NO PRICING DUE TO SCARCITY
EXCHANGE DEADLINE 2/28/2010
EXCHANGE DEADLINE 11/30/2010

2008 Topps Heritage Real One Autographs Red Ink

*RED INK: .6X TO 1.5X BASIC
STATED ODDS 1:835 H,1:1650 R
HN ODDS 1:439 HOBBY
STATED PRINT RUN 59 SERIAL #'d SETS
RED INK ALSO CALLED SPECIAL EDITION
EXCHANGE DEADLINE 02/28/2010
HN EXCH DEADLINE 11/30/2010
CK Clayton Kershaw HN 40.00 80.00
DP Dustin Pedroia HN 75.00 150.00
DS Duke Snider HN 60.00 120.00
GS Geovany Soto HN 50.00 100.00
JAB Jay Bruce HN 60.00 120.00
JC Joba Chamberlain 200.00 300.00
MIM Minnie Minoso EXCH 60.00 120.00
RC Roger Craig HN 30.00 60.00
WM Bill Mazeroski 125.00 250.00

2008 Topps Heritage Rookie Performers

COMPLETE SET (15) 12.50 30.00
STATED ODDS 1:12 HOBBY
RP1 Clayton Kershaw 2.50 6.00
RP2 Mike Aviles .75 2.00
RP3 Armando Galarraga .75 2.00
RP4 Joey Votto 2.00 5.00
RP5 Kosuke Fukudome 1.50 4.00
RP6 Chris Davis 1.25 3.00
RP7 Jeff Samardzija 1.50 4.00
RP8 Carlos Gonzalez 1.25 3.00
RP9 Max Scherzer 1.50 4.00
RP10 Evan Longoria 2.50 6.00
RP11 Johnny Cueto .75 2.00
RP12 Hiroki Kuroda .75 2.00
RP13 John Bowker .50 1.25
RP14 Justin Masterson 1.25 3.00
RP15 Jay Bruce 2.00 5.00

2008 Topps Heritage T205 Mini

THREE PER $9.99 TARGET BOX
SIX PER $19.99 TARGET BOX
HTCP1 Albert Pujols 5.00 12.00
HTCP2 Clay Buchholz 3.00 8.00
HTCP3 Matt Holliday 2.00 5.00
HTCP4 Luke Hochevar 1.25 3.00
HTCP5 Alex Rodriguez 3.00 8.00
HTCP6 Joey Votto 3.00 8.00
HTCP7 Chin-Lung Hu 1.25 3.00
HTCP8 Ryan Braun 2.50 6.00
HTCP9 Joba Chamberlain 1.25 3.00
HTCP10 Ryan Howard 2.50 6.00
HTCP11 Ichiro Suzuki 3.00 8.00
HTCP12 Steve Pearce 1.25 3.00
HTCP13 Vladimir Guerrero 2.00 5.00
HTCP14 Wladimir Balentien .75 2.00
HTCP15 David Ortiz 1.25 3.00

2008 Topps Heritage Then and Now

COMPLETE SET (10) 6.00 15.00
STATED ODDS 1:15 HOBBY,1:15 RETAIL
TN1 Alex Rodriguez 2.00 5.00
Eddie Mathews
TN2 Alex Rodriguez 1.25 3.00
Ernie Banks
TN3 Magglio Ordonez .75 2.00
Orlando Cepeda
TN4 Jose Reyes .50 1.25
Luis Aparicio
TN5 David Ortiz 2.50 6.00
Mickey Mantle
TN6 Erik Bedard .50 1.25
Johnny Podres
TN7 Josh Beckett .75 2.00
Early Wynn
TN8 Ichiro Suzuki 2.00 5.00
Minnie Minoso
TN9 David Ortiz .75 2.00
Frank Robinson
TN10 Jake Peavy .50 1.25
Don Drysdale

2009 Topps Heritage

This set was released on February 27, 2009. The base set consists of 500 cards.

COMPLETE SET (733)
COMP.LO SET w/o VAR (425) 30.00 60.00
COMP.HI SET w/o VAR (220) 90.00 150.00
COMP.HI SET w/o SP's (185) 15.00 40.00
COMMON CARD (1-733) .15 .40
COMMON ROOKIE (1-733) .40 1.00
COMMON SP (426-500/586-720) 2.50 6.00
SP ODDS 1:3 HOBBY
1 Mark Buehrle .25 .60
2 Nyjer Morgan .15 .40
3 Casey Kotchman .15 .40
4 Edinson Volquez .15 .40
5 Andre Ethier .25 .60
6 Brandon Inge .15 .40
7 Tim Lincecum .60 1.50
Bruce Bochy
8 Gil Meche .15 .40
9 Brad Hawpe .15 .40
10 Hanley Ramirez .40 1.00
11 Ross Gload .15 .40
12 Jeremy Guthrie .15 .40
13 Garret Anderson .15 .40
14 Jeremy Sowers .15 .40
15a Dustin Pedroia .50 1.25
15b Dustin Pedroia SP VAR 60.00 120.00
Yankees Logo
16 Chris Perez .15 .40
17 Adam Lind .15 .40
18 Los Angeles Dodgers TC .15 .40
19 Stephen Drew .15 .40
20 Matt Capps .15 .40
21 Mike Napoli .15 .40
22 Khalil Greene .15 .40
23 Andy Sonnanstine .15 .40
24 Marco Scutaro .15 .40
25 Paul Konerko .25 .60
26 Miguel Tejada .25 .60
27 Nick Blackburn .15 .40
28 Nick Markakis .40 1.00
29 Johan Santana .40 1.00
30 Grady Sizemore .25 .60
31 Raul Ibanez .25 .60
32 Jay Bruce .25 .60
Johnny Cueto
33 Randy Johnson .25 .60
34 Ian Kinsler .25 .60
35 Andy Pettitte .25 .60
36 Lyle Overbay .15 .40
37 Jeff Francoeur .25 .60
38 Justin Duchscherer .15 .40
39 Mike Cameron .15 .40
40 Ryan Ludwick .25 .60
41 Dave Bush .15 .40
42 Pablo Sandoval (RC) 1.25 3.00
43 Washington Nationals TC .15 .40
44 Dana Eveland .15 .40
45 Jeff Keppinger .15 .40
46 Brandon Backe .15 .40
47 Ryan Theriot .15 .40
48 Vernon Wells .15 .40
49 Doug Davis .15 .40
50 Curtis Granderson .25 .60
51 Aaron Laffey .15 .40
52 Chris Young .15 .40
53 Adam Jones .25 .60
54 Jonathan Papelbon .25 .60
55 Nate McLouth .15 .40
56 Hunter Pence .25 .60
57 Scot Shields .25 .60
Francisco Rodriguez
58a Conor Jackson .15 .40
D'Backs
58b Conor Jackson 15.00 40.00
Rays
59 John Maine .15 .40
60 Ramon Hernandez .15 .40
61 Jorge De La Rosa .15 .40
62 Greg Maddux .50 1.25
63 Carlos Beltran .15 .40
64 Matt Harrison (RC) .40 1.00
65 Ivan Rodriguez .25 .60
66 Jesse Litsch .15 .40
67 Omar Vizquel .25 .60
68 Edwin Jackson .15 .40
69 Ray Durham .15 .40
70a Tom Glavine .25 .60
70b Tom Glavine UER 20.00 50.00
Name spelled Thom SP
71 Darin Erstad .15 .40
72 Detroit Tigers TC .15 .40
73 David Price RC 1.00 2.50
74 Marlon Byrd .15 .40
75 Ryan Garko .15 .40
76 Jered Weaver .15 .40
77 Kelly Shoppach .15 .40
78 Joe Saunders .15 .40
79 Carlos Pena .25 .60
80 Brian Wilson .40 1.00
81 Carlos Gonzalez .25 .60
82 Scott Baker .15 .40
83a Derek Jeter 1.00 2.50
83b Derek Jeter SP VAR 100.00 200.00
Red Sox Logo
84 Yadier Molina .25 .60
85 Justin Verlander .50 1.25
86 Jose Lopez .15 .40
87 Jarrod Washburn .15 .40
88 Russell Martin .15 .40
89 Garrett Olson .15 .40
90 Erick Aybar .15 .40
91 Kevin Millwood .15 .40
92 Jose Guillen .15 .40
93 Rickie Weeks .25 .60
94 Yovani Gallardo .15 .40
95 Aramis Ramirez .15 .40
96 Phil Hughes .25 .60
97 Kevin Kouzmanoff .15 .40
98 Shaun Marcum .15 .40
99 Lastings Milledge .15 .40
100 Jair Jurrjens .15 .40
101 Gio Gonzalez .15 .40
102a Adrian Gonzalez .25 .60
102b Adrian Gonzalez 20.00 50.00
Rangers Logo
103 Brad Lidge .15 .40
104 Chris Davis .15 .40
105 Brad Penny .15 .40
106 David Eckstein .15 .40
107 Jo-Jo Reyes .15 .40
108 John Buck .15 .40
109 Delmon Young .25 .60
110 Johnny Cueto .15 .40
111 Kevin Youkilis .25 .60
112 Scott Lewis (RC) .40 1.00
113 Brandon Moss .15 .40
114 Alexi Casilla .15 .40
115 Jonathan Papelbon .25 .60
Tim Wakefield
116 Emil Brown .15 .40
117 Michael Bowden (RC) .40 1.00
118 Chris Lambert (RC) .40 1.00
119 Wilkin Castillo RC .40 1.00
120 Fernando Perez (RC) .40 1.00
121 Angel Salome (RC) .40 1.00
122 Dexter Fowler (RC) .60 1.50
123 Will Venable RC .40 1.00
124 Jason Motte (RC) .60 1.50
125 Jesus Delgado RC .60 1.50
126 Alfredo Simon (RC) .60 1.50
127 Gaby Sanchez RC .60 1.50
128 Scott Elbert (RC) .40 1.00
129 James Parr (RC) .40 1.00
130 Greg Golson (RC) .40 1.00
131 Jonathon Niese RC .60 1.50
132 Mat Gamel RC 1.00 2.50
133 Luis Cruz RC .40 1.00
134 Phil Coke RC .60 1.50
135 Devon Lowery (RC) .40 1.00
136 Matt Tuiasosopo (RC) .40 1.00
137 Kila Ka'aihue (RC) .60 1.50
138 Andrew Carpenter RC .40 1.00
139 Jensen Lewis (RC) .40 1.00
140 Lou Marson (RC) .40 1.00
141 Wade LeBlanc RC .60 1.50
142 Juan Miranda RC .60 1.50
143 Alcides Escobar RC 1.00 2.50
144 Matt Antonelli RC .60 1.50
145 Jesse Chavez RC .40 1.00
146 Ramon Ramirez (RC) .40 1.00
147 Aaron Cunningham RC .40 1.00
148 Travis Snider RC .60 1.50
149 Adam Dunn .25 .60
150 John Danks .15 .40
151 San Francisco Giants TC .15 .40
152 Jorge Cantu .15 .40
153 Jacoby Ellsbury .40 1.00
154 Rich Aurilia .15 .40
155 Jeff Kent .15 .40
156 Salomon Torres .15 .40
157 Juan Uribe .15 .40
158 Gregor Blanco .15 .40
159 Shin-Soo Choo .25 .60
160 David Wright .60 1.50
Alex Rodriguez AS
161 Jose Valverde .15 .40
162 B.J. Upton .25 .60
163 Johnny Damon .25 .60
164 Cincinnati Reds TC .15 .40
165 Tim Lincecum .60 1.50
166 Carl Crawford .25 .60
167 Jeff Mathis .15 .40
168 Felipe Lopez .15 .40
169 Joe Nathan .15 .40
170 Brian McCann .25 .60
171 Matt Joyce .15 .40
172 Cameron Maybin .15 .40
173 Brandon Phillips .15 .40
174 Cleveland Indians TC .15 .40
175 Tim Redding .15 .40
176 Corey Patterson .15 .40
177 Joakim Soria .15 .40
178 Jhonny Peralta .15 .40
179 Daniel Murphy RC 1.00 2.50
180 Ryan Church .15 .40
181 Josh Johnson .25 .60
182 Carlos Zambrano .25 .60
183 Pittsburgh Pirates TC .15 .40
184 Boston Red Sox TC .25 .60
185 Kyle Kendrick .15 .40
186 Joel Zumaya .15 .40
187 Bronson Arroyo .15 .40
188 Joey Gathright .15 .40
189 Mike Gonzalez .15 .40
190 Luke Scott .15 .40
191 Jonathan Broxton .15 .40
192 Jeff Baker .15 .40
193 Brian Fuentes .15 .40
194 Pat Burrell .15 .40
195 Ryan Franklin .15 .40
196 Alex Gordon .25 .60
197 Orlando Hudson .15 .40
198 Chris Dickerson .15 .40
199 David Purcey .15 .40
200 Ken Griffey Jr. .60 1.50
201 Chad Tracy .15 .40
202 Troy Percival .15 .40
203 Chris Iannetta .15 .40
204 Baltimore Orioles TC .15 .40
205 Yunel Escobar .15 .40
206 Dan Haren .15 .40
207 Aubrey Huff .15 .40
208 Chicago White Sox TC .15 .40
209 Randy Wolf .15 .40
210 Ryan Zimmerman .25 .60
211 Manny Parra .15 .40
212 Manny Acta MG .15 .40
213 Dusty Baker MG .15 .40
214 Bruce Bochy MG .15 .40
215 Bobby Cox MG .15 .40
216 Terry Francona MG .25 .60
217 Joe Girardi MG .25 .60
218 Ozzie Guillen MG .15 .40
219 Bob Geren MG .15 .40
220 Tony La Russa MG .25 .60
221 Jim Leyland MG .15 .40
222 Charlie Manuel MG .15 .40
223 Lou Piniella MG .15 .40
224 John Russell MG .15 .40
225 Joe Torre MG .25 .60
226 Dave Trembley MG .15 .40
227 Eric Wedge MG .15 .40
228 Jeff Suppan .15 .40
229 Kaz Matsui .15 .40
230 Josh Beckett .40 1.00
Jon Lester
Daisuke Matsuzaka
231 Mark Reynolds .15 .40
232 Jay Payton .15 .40
233 Kerry Wood .15 .40
234 Juan Pierre .15 .40
235 Ryan Freel .15 .40
236 Ryan Feierabend .15 .40
237 Xavier Nady .15 .40
238 Ronny Paulino .15 .40
239 A.J. Burnett .25 .60
240 Orlando Cabrera .15 .40
241 Corey Hart .15 .40
242 St. Louis Cardinals TC .15 .40
243 Andy Marte .15 .40
244 Trevor Hoffman .25 .60
245 Carlos Guillen .15 .40
246 Brandon Jones .15 .40
247 Hideki Matsui .40 1.00
248 Henry Blanco .15 .40
249 Jon Lester .40 1.00
250a Albert Pujols 1.00 2.50
250b Albert Pujols SP VAR 100.00 200.00
All-Rookie Design
251 Manny Ramirez .40 1.00
252 Brian Bannister .15 .40
253 Alex Cintron .15 .40
254 Brandon Lyon .15 .40
255 Blake DeWitt .15 .40
256 Luis Castillo .15 .40
257 Mark Teixeira .40 1.00
258 Jack Wilson .15 .40
259 Kosuke Fukudome .40 1.00
260 Manny Ramirez .40 1.00
Andre Ethier
261 Scott Kazmir .15 .40
262 Mark Teahen .15 .40
263 Dioner Navarro .15 .40
264 Cole Hamels .40 1.00
265 Justin Upton .25 .60
266 Ricky Nolasco .15 .40
267 Hank Blalock .15 .40
268 John Lackey .15 .40
269 Jeremy Hermida .15 .40
270 Chien-Ming Wang .25 .60
271 Lance Berkman .25 .60
272 Scott Olsen .15 .40
273 Alex Rios .25 .60
274 Matt Garza .15 .40
275 Skip Schumaker .15 .40
276 Greg Smith .15 .40
277 Bobby Crosby .15 .40
278 Hiroki Kuroda .15 .40
279 Gary Matthews .15 .40
280 Tim Wakefield .15 .40
281 Mike Jacobs .15 .40
282 Chris Volstad .15 .40
283 Jeff Clement .15 .40
284 Max Scherzer .25 .60
285 Chase Headley .15 .40
286 Francisco Rodriguez .25 .60
287 Moises Alou .15 .40
288 Jeff Francis .15 .40
289 Carlos Delgado .15 .40
290 Jose Reyes .25 .60
291 Ubaldo Jimenez .25 .60
292 Kelly Shoppach .25 .60
Victor Martinez
293 Joe Blanton .15 .40
294 Mark DeRosa .25 .60
295 Casey Blake .15 .40
296 Mike Pelfrey .15 .40
297 Aaron Boone .15 .40
298 Aaron Cook .15 .40
299 Daric Barton .15 .40
300 Ryan Howard .50 1.25
301 Ty Wigginton .25 .60
302 Philadelphia Phillies TC .15 .40
303 Barry Zito .15 .40
304 Jake Peavy .15 .40
305 Alfonso Soriano .25 .60
306 Scott Linebrink .15 .40
307 Torii Hunter .15 .40
308 Zack Greinke .25 .60
309 Ryan Sweeney .15 .40
310 Mike Lowell .15 .40
311 Jason Marquis .15 .40
312 Aaron Rowand .15 .40
313 Brandon Morrow .25 .60
314 Edgar Renteria .15 .40
315 Mariano Rivera .40 1.00
316 Wilson Betemit .15 .40
317 Joey Votto .40 1.00
318 Evan Longoria .50 1.25
319 Mike Aviles .15 .40
320 Jay Bruce .25 .60
321 Denard Span .15 .40
322 David Murphy .15 .40
323 Geovany Soto .25 .60
324 John Lannan .15 .40
325 Brad Ziegler .15 .40
326 Ichiro Suzuki .60 1.50
327 Kyle Lohse .15 .40
328 Jesus Flores .15 .40
329 Edwin Encarnacion .15 .40
330 Franklin Gutierrez .15 .40
331 Troy Glaus .15 .40
332 David Ortiz .25 .60
333 Anibal Sanchez .15 .40
334 Jimmy Rollins .25 .60
335 Kelly Johnson .15 .40
336 Paul Byrd .15 .40
337 Akinori Iwamura .15 .40
338 Milton Bradley .15 .40
339 Miguel Olivo .15 .40
340 Ian Snell .15 .40
341 Vladimir Guerrero .40 1.00
342 Asdrubal Cabrera .25 .60
343 Clayton Kershaw .40 1.00
344 Rafael Furcal .15 .40
345 Aaron Harang .15 .40
346a Fred Lewis .15 .40
346b Fred Lewis UER 15.00 40.00
Randy Winn Pictured SP
347 Jack Cust .15 .40
348 Todd Helton .25 .60
349 Steve Pearce .15 .40
350 Javier Vazquez .15 .40
351 Ben Sheets .15 .40
352 Joey Votto .40 1.00
Edwin Encarnacion
Jay Bruce
353 Luke Hochevar .15 .40
354 Chris Snyder .15 .40
355 Rick Ankiel .15 .40
356 Emmanuel Burriss .15 .40
357 Vicente Padilla .15 .40
358 Yuniesky Betancourt .15 .40
359 Willy Taveras .15 .40
360 Gavin Floyd .15 .40
361 Gerald Laird .15 .40
362 Roy Oswalt .25 .60
363 Coco Crisp .15 .40
364 Felix Hernandez .40 1.00
365 Carlos Quentin .25 .60
366 Ervin Santana .15 .40
367 David DeJesus .15 .40
368 Aaron Miles .15 .40
369 B.J. Ryan .15 .40
370 Jason Giambi .15 .40
371 J.J. Putz .15 .40
372 Brian Schneider .15 .40
373 Andy LaRoche .15 .40
374 Tim Hudson .25 .60
375 Garrett Atkins .15 .40
376 James Shields .15 .40
377 Alex Rodriguez .60 1.50
378 J.J. Hardy .15 .40
379 Michael Young .25 .60
380 Prince Fielder .25 .60
381 Atlanta Braves TC .15 .40
382 Chone Figgins .15 .40
383 David Wright .50 1.25
384 Brian Giles .15 .40
385 Chase Utley WS .40 1.00
386 Eric Bruntlett WS .15 .40
387 Carlos Ruiz WS .15 .40
388 Ryan Howard WS .50 1.25
389 Jayson Werth WS .25 .60
390 B.J. Upton WS .25 .60
391 Brad Lidge .15 .40
392 Chad Cordero .15 .40
393 Ryan Doumit .15 .40
394 James Loney .25 .60
395 George Sherrill .15 .40
396 Gary Sheffield .15 .40
397 Chicago Cubs TC .15 .40
398 Rich Harden .15 .40
399 Scott Kazmir .40 1.00
David Price
James Shields
400 Magglio Ordonez .25 .60
401 Dan Uggla .25 .60
402 Adam LaRoche .15 .40
403 Taylor Teagarden .25 .60
404 Chris Young .15 .40
405 Robinson Cano .40 1.00
406 Dustin McGowan .15 .40
407a Randy Winn .15 .40
407b Randy Winn UER 15.00 40.00
Fred Lewis Pictured SP
408 Carlos Lee .15 .40
409 Kurt Suzuki .15 .40
410 Matt Cain .15 .40
411 Paul Bako .15 .40
412 Ted Lilly .15 .40
413 Kansas City Royals TC .15 .40
414 Miguel Cabrera .40 1.00
415 Jayson Werth .25 .60
416 J.C. Romero .15 .40
417 Martin Prado .15 .40
418 Armando Galarraga .15 .40
419 Brian Roberts .15 .40
420 Chipper Jones .40 1.00
421 Bengie Molina .15 .40
422 Matt Kemp .25 .60
423 Brian Buscher .15 .40
424 Erik Bedard .15 .40
425 Chad Billingsley .15 .40
426 Scott Rolen SP 2.00 5.00
427 Ben Francisco SP 2.50 6.00
428 Jermaine Dye SP 2.50 6.00
429 Dustin Pedroia 4.00 10.00
Ichiro Suzuki SP
430 Kevin Slowey SP 3.00 8.00
431 Jason Bartlett SP 2.50 6.00
432 Glen Perkins SP 2.50 6.00
433 Carlos Gomez SP 2.50 6.00
434 Jon Garland SP 2.50 6.00
435 Joe Crede SP 4.00 10.00
436 Billy Butler SP 2.50 6.00
437 Zach Duke SP 2.50 6.00
438 Chris Coste SP 2.50 6.00
439 Daisuke Matsuzaka SP 2.50 6.00
440 Elijah Dukes SP 2.50 6.00
441 Fausto Carmona SP 2.50 6.00
442 Joe Mauer SP 5.00 12.00
443 Marcus Thames SP 2.50 6.00
444 Mike Fontenot SP 2.50 6.00
445a John Smoltz 3.00 8.00
Atlanta Braves SP
445b John Smoltz 30.00 60.00
Boston Red Sox SP
446 Pedro Martinez SP 3.00 8.00
447 Adrian Beltre SP 2.50 6.00
448 Kevin Millar SP 2.50 6.00
449 Nick Swisher SP 6.00 15.00
450 Justin Morneau SP 5.00 12.00
451 Shane Victorino SP 2.50 6.00
452 Placido Polanco SP 2.50 6.00
453 Ryan Dempster SP 2.50 6.00
454 Frank Thomas SP 3.00 8.00
455 Dave Jauss 2.50 6.00
Juan Samuel
John Shelby CO SP
456 Brad Mills 2.50 6.00
John Farrell
Dave Magadan CO SP
457 Alan Trammell 2.50 6.00
Larry Rothschild
Matt Sinatro CO SP
458 Joey Cora 2.50 6.00
Harold Baines
Jeff Cox CO SP
459 Chris Speier 2.50 6.00
Billy Hatcher
Dick Pole CO SP
460 Jeff Datz 2.50 6.00
Luis Rivera
Carl Willis
Joel Skinner CO SP
461 Lloyd McClendon 2.50 6.00
Andy Van Slyke
Rafael Belliard CO SP
462 Jim Hickey 2.50 6.00
Steve Henderson
Tom Foley CO SP
463 Larry Bowa 2.50 6.00
Rick Honeycutt
Mariano Duncan
Bob Schaefer CO SP
464 Roger McDowell 2.50 6.00
Terry Pendleton
Chino Cadahia
Glenn Hubbard CO SP
465 Rob Thomson 2.50 6.00
Tony Pena
Kevin Long
Dave Eiland CO SP
466 Milt Thompson 2.50 6.00
Rich Dubee
Davey Lopes CO SP
467 Tony Beasley 2.50 6.00
Joe Kerrigan
Don Long CO SP
468 Dave Duncan 2.50 6.00
Hal McRae
Jose Oquendo
Dave McKay CO SP
469 Sandy Alomar Sr. 2.50 6.00
Howard Johnson
Dan Warthen CO SP
470 Randy St. Claire 2.50 6.00
Marquis Grissom
Jim Riggleman CO SP
471 Brad Ausmus SP 2.50 6.00
472 Melvin Mora SP 2.50 6.00
473 Austin Kearns SP 2.50 6.00
474 Josh Willingham SP 2.50 6.00
475 Derek Lowe SP 2.50 6.00
476 Nick Punto SP 2.50 6.00
477 A.J. Pierzynski SP 2.50 6.00
478 Troy Tulowitzki SP 5.00 12.00
479 CC Sabathia SP 3.00 8.00
480 Jorge Posada SP 3.00 8.00
481 Kevin Youkilis AS SP 3.00 8.00
482 Lance Berkman AS SP 3.00 8.00
483 Dustin Pedroia AS SP 4.00 10.00
484 Chase Utley AS SP 3.00 8.00
485 Alex Rodriguez AS SP 4.00 10.00
486 Chipper Jones AS SP 3.00 8.00
487 Derek Jeter AS SP 5.00 12.00
488a Hanley Ramirez AS 3.00 8.00
Florida Marlins SP
488b Hanley Ramirez AS 30.00 60.00
Boston Red Sox SP
489 Josh Hamilton AS SP 3.00 8.00
490 Ryan Braun AS SP 4.00 10.00
491 Manny Ramirez AS SP 3.00 6.00

492 Kosuke Fukudome AS SP 3.00 8.00
493 Ichiro Suzuki AS SP 4.00 10.00
494 Matt Holliday AS SP 5.00 12.00
495 Joe Mauer AS SP 5.00 12.00
496 Geovany Soto AS SP 3.00 8.00
497 Roy Halladay AS SP 6.00 15.00
498 Ben Sheets AS SP 2.50 6.00
499 Cliff Lee AS SP 3.00 8.00
500 Billy Wagner AS SP 2.50 6.00
501 Shane Robinson RC .40 1.00
502 Mat Latos RC 1.25 3.00
503 Aaron Poreda RC .40 1.00
504 Takashi Saito .15 .40
505 Adam Everett .15 .40
506 Adam Kennedy .15 .40
507 John Smoltz .40 1.00
508 Alex Cora .15 .40
509 Alfredo Aceves .25 .60
510 Alfredo Figaro RC .40 1.00
511 Andrew Bailey RC 1.00 2.50
512 Jhoulys Chacin RC .60 1.50
513 Andruw Jones .15 .40
514 Anthony Swarzak (RC) .40 1.00
515 Antonio Bastardo RC .40 1.00
516 Bartolo Colon .15 .40
517 Michael Saunders RC .60 1.50
518 Blake Hawksworth (RC) .40 1.00
519 Bud Norris RC .40 1.00
520 Bobby Scales RC .60 1.50
521 Nick Evans .15 .40
522 Brad Bergensen (RC) .40 1.00
523 Brad Mills RC
524 Brad Penny .15 .40
525 Braden Looper .15 .40
526 Brandon Lyon .15 .40
527 Brandon Wood .15 .40
528 Aaron Bates RC .40 1.00
529 Brett Cecil RC .40 1.00
530 Brett Gardner .15 .40
531 Brett Hayes (RC) .40 1.00
532 C.J. Wilson .15 .40
533 Carl Pavano .15 .40
534 Cesar Izturis .15 .40
535 Chad Qualls .15 .40
536 Marc Rzepczynski RC .60 1.50
537 Chris Gimenez RC .40 1.00
538 Chris Jakubauskas RC .60 1.50
539 Chris Perez .15 .40
540 Clay Zavada RC .60 1.50
541 Clayton Mortensen RC .40 1.00
542 Clayton Richard .15 .40
543 Cliff Floyd .15 .40
544 Coco Crisp .15 .40
545a Neftali Feliz RC 1.25 3.00
545b Neftali Feliz SP VAR 125.00 250.00
Black and White Photo
546 Craig Counsell .15 .40
547 Craig Stammen RC .40 1.00
548 Cristian Guzman .15 .40
549 Dallas Braden .25 .60
550 Daniel Bard RC .40 1.00
551 Jack Wilson .15 .40
552 Daniel Schlereth RC .40 1.00
553 David Aardsma .15 .40
554 David Eckstein .15 .40
555 David Freese RC 3.00 8.00
556 David Hernandez RC .40 1.00
557 David Huff RC .40 1.00
558 David Ross .15 .40
559 Delwyn Young .25 .60
560 Derek Holland RC .60 1.50
561 Derek Lowe .15 .40
562 Diory Hernandez RC .40 1.00
563a Pedro Martinez .25 .60
563b Pedro Martinez SP VAR 150.00 250.00
Black and White Photo
564 Emilio Bonifacio .15 .40
565 Endy Chavez .15 .40
566 Eric Byrnes .15 .40
567 Eric Hinske .15 .40
568 Everth Cabrera RC .60 1.50
569a Alex Rios .25 .60
569b Alex Rios SP VAR 75.00 150.00
Black and White Photo
570 Fernando Nieve .15 .40
571 Francisco Cervelli RC 1.00 2.50
572 Frank Catalanotto .15 .40
573 Fu-Te Ni RC .60 1.50
574 Gabe Kapler .15 .40
575 Scott Rolen .25 .60
576 Garrett Olson .15 .40
577 Adam LaRoche .15 .40
578 Gerardo Parra RC .60 1.50
579 George Sherrill .15 .40
580 Graham Taylor RC .60 1.50
581 Gregg Zaun .15 .40
582 Homer Bailey .15 .40
583 Garrett Jones .25 .60
584 Julio Lugo .15 .40
585 J.A. Happ .25 .60
586 J.J. Putz .15 .40
587 J.P. Howell .15 .40
588 Jake Fox .25 .60
589 Jamey Carroll .15 .40
590 Jarrett Hoffpauir (RC) .40 1.00
591 Felipe Lopez .15 .40
592 Cliff Lee .25 .60
593 Jason Giambi .15 .40
594 Jason Jaramillo (RC) .40 1.00
595 Jason Kubel .15 .40
596 Jason Marquis .15 .40
597 Jason Vargas .15 .40
598 Jeff Baker .15 .40
599 Jeff Francoeur .25 .60
600 Jeremy Reed .15 .40
601 Jerry Hairston .15 .40
602 Jesus Guzman RC .40 1.00
603 Jody Gerut .15 .40
604 Joe Crede .25 .60
605 Alex Gonzalez .15 .40
606 Joel Hanrahan .25 .60
607 John Mayberry Jr (RC) .40 1.00
608 Jon Garland .15 .40
609 Jonny Gomes .15 .40
610 Jordan Schafer (RC) .60 1.50
611 Victor Martinez .25 .60
612 Jose Contreras .15 .40
613 Josh Bard .15 .40
614 Josh Outman .25 .60
615 Juan Rivera .15 .40
616 Juan Uribe .15 .40
617 Julio Borbon RC .60 1.50
618 Jarrod Washburn .15 .40
619 Justin Masterson .15 .40
620 Kenshin Kawakami RC .60 1.50
621 Kevin Correia .15 .40
622 Kevin Gregg .15 .40
623 Kevin Millar .15 .40
624 Koji Uehara RC .60 1.50
625 Kris Medlen RC .60 1.50
626 Tim Redding .15 .40
627 Kyle Farnsworth .15 .40
628 Landon Powell (RC) .40 1.00
629 Lastings Milledge .15 .40
630 LaTroy Hawkins .15 .40
631 Laynce Nix .15 .40
632 Billy Wagner .15 .40
633 Tony Gwynn Jr. .15 .40
634 Mark Loretta .15 .40
635 Matt Diaz .15 .40
636 Ben Francisco .15 .40
637 Travis Ishikawa .15 .40
638 Matt Maloney (RC) .40 1.00
639 Scott Kazmir .15 .40
640 Melky Cabrera .15 .40
641 Micah Hoffpauir .15 .40
642 Micah Owings .15 .40
643 Mike Carp (RC) .60 1.50
644 Mike Hampton .15 .40
645 Mike Sweeney .15 .40
646 Milton Bradley .15 .40
647 Mitch Jones (RC) .40 1.00
648 Trevor Crowe RC .40 1.00
649 Ty Wigginton .25 .60
650 Jim Thome .25 .60
651 Nick Green .15 .40
652 Tyler Greene (RC) .40 1.00
653 Nyjer Morgan .15 .40
654 Omar Vizquel .25 .60
655 Omir Santos RC .40 1.00
656 Orlando Cabrera .15 .40
657 Vin Mazzaro RC .40 1.00
658 Pat Burrell .15 .40
659 Rafael Soriano .15 .40
660 Ramiro Pena RC .60 1.50
661 Freddy Sanchez .15 .40
662 Ramon Ramirez .15 .40
663 Wilkin Ramirez RC .40 1.00
664 Randy Wells .15 .40
665 Randy Wolf .15 .40
666 Rich Hill .15 .40
667 Willy Taveras .15 .40
668 Xavier Paul (RC) .40 1.00
669 Rocco Baldelli .15 .40
670 Ross Detwiler .15 .40
671 Ross Gload .15 .40
672 Aubrey Huff .15 .40
673 Yuniesky Betancourt .15 .40
674 Ryan Church .15 .40
675 Ryan Garko .15 .40
676 Ryan Perry RC 1.00 2.50
677 Ryan Sadowski RC .40 1.00
678 Ryan Spilborghs .15 .40
679 Scott Downs .15 .40
680 Scott Hairston .15 .40
681 Scott Olsen .15 .40
682 Scott Podsednik .15 .40
683 Bill Hall .15 .40
684 Sean O'Sullivan RC .40 1.00
685 Sean West (RC) .60 1.50
686 Aaron Hill SP 2.50 6.00
687 Adam Dunn SP 4.00 10.00
688 Andrew McCutchen SP (RC) 5.00 12.00
689 Ben Zobrist SP 2.50 6.00
690 Chris Tillman SP RC 4.00 10.00
691 Bobby Abreu SP 2.50 6.00
692 Brett Anderson SP RC 4.00 10.00
693 Chris Coghlan SP RC 3.00 8.00
694 Colby Rasmus SP (RC) 5.00 12.00
695 Elvis Andrus SP RC 3.00 8.00
696 Fernando Martinez SP RC 6.00 15.00
697 Garret Anderson SP 2.50 6.00
698 Gary Sheffield SP 2.50 6.00
699 Gordon Beckham SP RC 3.00 8.00
700 Huston Street SP 2.50 6.00
701 Ivan Rodriguez SP 3.00 8.00
702 Jason Bay SP 3.00 8.00
703 Jordan Zimmermann SP RC 2.50 6.00
704 Ken Griffey Jr. SP 4.00 10.00
705 Kendry Morales SP 2.50 6.00
706 Kyle Blanks SP RC 4.00 10.00
707 Tommy Hanson SP RC 3.00 8.00
708 Mark DeRosa SP 4.00 10.00
709 Matt Holliday SP 5.00 12.00
710 Matt LaPorta SP RC 3.00 8.00
711 Trevor Cahill SP RC 5.00 12.00
712 Nate McLouth SP 2.50 6.00
713 Trevor Hoffman SP 4.00 10.00
714 Nelson Cruz SP 4.00 10.00
715 Nolan Reimold SP (RC) 2.50 6.00
716 Orlando Hudson SP 2.50 6.00
717 Randy Johnson SP 3.00 8.00
718 Rick Porcello SP RC 2.50 6.00
719 Ricky Romero SP (RC) 5.00 12.00
720 Russell Branyan SP 2.50 6.00

2009 Topps Heritage Chrome

COMP.HIGH.SET (100) 100.00 200.00
1-100 STATED ODDS 1:6 HOBBY
101-200 STATED ODDS 1:3 HOBBY
STATED PRINT RUN 1960 SER.#'d SETS
C1 Manny Ramirez 2.50 6.00
C2 Andre Ethier 2.00 5.00
C3 Miguel Tejada 2.00 5.00
C4 Nick Markakis 3.00 8.00
C5 Johan Santana 2.50 6.00
C6 Grady Sizemore 2.00 5.00
C7 Ian Kinsler 2.00 5.00
C8 Ryan Ludwick 2.00 5.00
C9 Jonathan Papelbon 2.00 5.00
C10 Albert Pujols 5.00 12.00
C11 Carlos Beltran 1.50 4.00
C12 David Price 2.00 5.00
C13 Carlos Pena 2.00 5.00
C14 Derek Jeter 5.00 12.00
C15 Mark Teixeira 2.50 6.00
C16 Aramis Ramirez 1.50 4.00
C17 Dexter Fowler 2.00 5.00
C18 Brad Lidge 1.50 4.00
C19 Johnny Cueto 1.50 4.00
C20 David Wright 3.00 8.00
C21 Mat Gamel 2.50 6.00
C22 B.J. Upton 2.00 5.00
C23 Carl Crawford 2.00 5.00
C24 Mariano Rivera 3.00 8.00
C25 Scott Kazmir 1.25 3.00
C26 Vladimir Guerrero 2.50 6.00
C27 Clayton Kershaw 2.50 6.00
C28 Ben Sheets 1.50 4.00
C29 Rick Ankiel 1.25 3.00
C30 Nate McLouth 1.50 4.00
C31 Roy Oswalt 2.00 5.00
C32 Felix Hernandez 3.00 8.00
C33 Ervin Santana 1.50 4.00
C34 Prince Fielder 1.50 4.00
C35 Cole Hamels 2.50 6.00
C36 Jon Lester 3.00 8.00
C37 Kosuke Fukudome 2.50 6.00
C38 Justin Upton 2.00 5.00
C39 John Lackey 1.50 4.00
C40 Lance Berkman 2.00 5.00
C41 Chien-Ming Wang 1.50 4.00
C42 Alex Rios 2.50 6.00
C43 Carlos Delgado 1.50 4.00
C44 Jake Peavy 1.25 3.00
C45 Hanley Ramirez 2.50 6.00
C46 Alfonso Soriano 2.00 5.00
C47 Jimmy Rollins 2.00 5.00
C48 J.J. Hardy 1.50 4.00
C49 James Loney 2.00 5.00
C50 Ryan Howard 3.00 8.00
C51 Rich Harden 1.50 4.00
C52 Dan Uggla 2.50 6.00
C53 Miguel Cabrera 3.00 8.00
C54 Matt Kemp 1.50 4.00
C55 Russell Martin 1.25 3.00
C56 Chipper Jones 2.50 6.00
C57 Stephen Drew 1.50 4.00
C58 Randy Johnson 1.50 4.00
C59 Andy Pettitte 2.00 5.00
C60 Francisco Rodriguez 2.00 5.00
C61 Vernon Wells 1.50 4.00
C62 Ivan Rodriguez 2.00 5.00
C63 Joe Saunders 1.50 4.00
C64 Yadier Molina 2.00 5.00
C65 Ken Griffey Jr. 3.00 8.00
C66 Justin Verlander 4.00 10.00
C67 Edinson Volquez 1.50 4.00
C68 Phil Hughes 2.00 5.00
C69 Yovani Gallardo 1.50 4.00
C70 Jose Reyes 1.50 4.00
C71 Gio Gonzalez 1.50 4.00
C72 Adrian Gonzalez 2.00 5.00
C73 Chris Davis 1.50 4.00
C74 Brad Penny 1.50 4.00
C75 Dustin Pedroia 2.50 6.00
C76 Kevin Youkilis 2.00 5.00
C77 Angel Salome 1.50 4.00
C78 Kila Ka'aihue 2.00 5.00
C79 Lou Marson 1.50 4.00
C80 Ichiro Suzuki 3.00 8.00
C81 Alcides Escobar 3.00 8.00
C82 Travis Snider 1.25 3.00
C83 Adam Dunn 2.00 5.00
C84 Jacoby Ellsbury 2.50 6.00
C85 Jay Bruce 1.50 4.00
C86 Ryan Doumit 1.50 4.00
C87 Tim Lincecum 4.00 10.00
C88 Joe Nathan 1.50 4.00
C89 Brian McCann 2.00 5.00
C90 Evan Longoria 2.50 6.00
C91 Carlos Zambrano 2.50 6.00
C92 Pat Burrell 1.25 3.00
C93 Alex Gordon 2.00 5.00
C94 Ryan Zimmerman 2.00 5.00
C95 Carlos Quentin 2.00 5.00
C96 Xavier Nady 1.50 4.00
C97 Max Scherzer 2.00 5.00
C98 Hiroki Kuroda 1.50 4.00
C99 Carlos Lee 1.50 4.00
C100 Alex Rodriguez 3.00 8.00
CHR101 Chad Qualls 1.50 4.00
CHR102 Daniel Schlereth 1.50 4.00
CHR103 Derek Lowe 1.50 4.00
CHR104 Jason Giambi 1.50 4.00
CHR105 Jason Marquis 1.50 4.00
CHR106 Kevin Correia 1.50 4.00
CHR107 Koji Uehara 2.00 5.00
CHR108 Matt Diaz 1.50 4.00
CHR109 Melky Cabrera 1.50 4.00
CHR110 Milton Bradley 1.50 4.00
CHR111 Rafael Soriano 1.50 4.00
CHR112 Scott Downs 1.50 4.00
CHR113 David Aardsma 1.50 4.00
CHR114 Eric Byrnes 1.50 4.00
CHR115 Gerardo Parra 2.00 5.00
CHR116 Homer Bailey 1.50 4.00
CHR117 J.P. Howell 1.50 4.00
CHR118 Joe Crede 2.00 5.00
CHR119 John Mayberry Jr 1.50 4.00
CHR120 Josh Outman 2.00 5.00
CHR121 Lastings Milledge 1.50 4.00
CHR122 Mike Hampton 1.50 4.00
CHR123 Orlando Cabrera 1.50 4.00
CHR124 Randy Wells 1.50 4.00
CHR125 Michael Saunders 2.50 6.00
CHR126 Tony Gwynn Jr. 1.50 4.00
CHR127 Trevor Crowe 1.25 3.00
CHR128 Vin Mazzaro 1.50 4.00
CHR129 Andruw Jones 1.50 4.00
CHR130 Brad Penny 1.50 4.00
CHR131 Brandon Wood 1.50 4.00
CHR132 Cristian Guzman 1.50 4.00
CHR133 David Huff 1.50 4.00
CHR134 J.A. Happ 2.00 5.00
CHR135 Jason Kubel 1.50 4.00
CHR136 Ryan Garko 1.50 4.00
CHR137 Jose Contreras 1.50 4.00
CHR138 Juan Rivera 1.50 4.00
CHR139 Jhoulys Chacin 2.00 5.00
CHR140 Randy Wolf 1.50 4.00
CHR141 Aaron Hill 1.50 4.00
CHR142 Adam Dunn 2.00 5.00
CHR143 Andrew Bailey 2.50 6.00
CHR144 Andrew McCutchen 4.00 10.00
CHR145 Ben Zobrist 1.50 4.00
CHR146 Bobby Abreu 1.50 4.00
CHR147 Brett Anderson 2.50 6.00
CHR148 Chris Coghlan 2.50 6.00
CHR149 Colby Rasmus 3.00 8.00
CHR150 Elvis Andrus 2.00 5.00
CHR151 Fernando Martinez 4.00 10.00
CHR152 Garret Anderson 1.50 4.00
CHR153 Gary Sheffield 1.50 4.00
CHR154 Gordon Beckham 2.50 6.00
CHR155 Huston Street 1.50 4.00
CHR156 Ivan Rodriguez 2.00 5.00
CHR157 Jason Bay 2.00 5.00
CHR158 Jeff Francoeur 2.00 5.00
CHR159 Jordan Zimmermann 1.50 4.00
CHR160 Ken Griffey Jr. 3.00 8.00
CHR161 Kendry Morales 1.50 4.00
CHR162 Kyle Blanks 2.50 6.00
CHR163 Mark DeRosa 2.00 5.00
CHR164 Matt Holliday 3.00 8.00
CHR165 Matt LaPorta 2.50 6.00
CHR166 Nate McLouth 1.50 4.00
CHR167 Nelson Cruz 2.50 6.00
CHR168 Nolan Reimold 1.50 4.00
CHR169 Orlando Hudson 1.50 4.00
CHR170 Randy Johnson 2.00 5.00
CHR171 Rick Porcello 2.50 6.00
CHR172 Ricky Romero 3.00 8.00
CHR173 Russell Branyan 1.50 4.00
CHR174 Tommy Hanson 2.50 6.00
CHR175 Trevor Cahill 3.00 8.00
CHR176 Trevor Hoffman 2.50 6.00
CHR177 Aaron Poreda 1.50 4.00
CHR178 John Smoltz 2.50 6.00
CHR179 Brad Mills 1.50 4.00
CHR180 Brett Gardner 1.50 4.00
CHR181 Carl Pavano 1.50 4.00
CHR182 Daniel Bard 1.50 4.00
CHR183 David Hernandez 1.50 4.00
CHR184 Fu-Te Ni 1.50 4.00
CHR185 Jerry Hairston 1.50 4.00
CHR186 Jordan Schafer 2.00 5.00
CHR187 Julio Borbon 2.00 5.00
CHR188 Kris Medlen 2.00 5.00
CHR189 Micah Hoffpauir 1.50 4.00
CHR190 Nyjer Morgan 1.50 4.00
CHR191 Derek Holland 2.00 5.00
CHR192 Jack Wilson 1.50 4.00
CHR193 Cliff Lee 2.00 5.00
CHR194 Freddy Sanchez 1.50 4.00
CHR195 Pat Burrell 1.25 3.00
CHR196 Ryan Spilborghs 1.50 4.00
CHR197 Takashi Saito 1.50 4.00
CHR198 Bud Norris 1.50 4.00
CHR199 Chris Tillman 2.50 6.00
CHR200 Everth Cabrera 2.00 5.00

2009 Topps Heritage Chrome Refractors

*REF: .6X TO 1.5X BASIC INSERTS
1-100 STATED ODDS 1:23 HOBBY
101-200 STATED ODDS 1:11 HOBBY
STATED PRINT RUN 560 SER.#'d SETS

2009 Topps Heritage Chrome Refractors Black

1-100 STATED ODDS 1:255 HOBBY
101-200 STATED ODDS 1:102 HOBBY
STATED PRINT RUN 60 SER.#'d SETS
C1 Manny Ramirez 25.00 60.00
C2 Andre Ethier 15.00 40.00
C3 Miguel Tejada 15.00 40.00
C4 Nick Markakis 25.00 60.00
C5 Johan Santana 25.00 60.00
C6 Grady Sizemore 15.00 40.00
C7 Ian Kinsler 15.00 40.00
C8 Ryan Ludwick 15.00 40.00
C9 Jonathan Papelbon 15.00 40.00
C10 Albert Pujols 60.00 150.00
C11 Carlos Beltran 10.00 25.00
C12 David Price 25.00 60.00
C13 Carlos Pena 15.00 40.00
C14 Derek Jeter 60.00 150.00
C15 Mark Teixeira 25.00 60.00
C16 Aramis Ramirez 10.00 25.00
C17 Dexter Fowler 15.00 40.00
C18 Brad Lidge 10.00 25.00
C19 Johnny Cueto 10.00 25.00
C20 David Wright 30.00 80.00
C21 Mat Gamel 25.00 60.00
C22 B.J. Upton 15.00 40.00
C23 Carl Crawford 15.00 40.00
C24 Mariano Rivera 25.00 60.00
C25 Scott Kazmir 10.00 25.00
C26 Vladimir Guerrero 25.00 60.00
C27 Clayton Kershaw 25.00 60.00
C28 Ben Sheets 10.00 25.00
C29 Rick Ankiel 10.00 25.00
C30 Nate McLouth 10.00 25.00
C31 Roy Oswalt 15.00 40.00
C32 Felix Hernandez 25.00 60.00
C33 Ervin Santana 10.00 25.00
C34 Prince Fielder 15.00 40.00
C35 Cole Hamels 25.00 60.00
C36 Jon Lester 25.00 60.00
C37 Kosuke Fukudome 25.00 60.00
C38 Justin Upton 15.00 40.00
C39 John Lackey 10.00 25.00
C40 Lance Berkman 15.00 40.00
C41 Chien-Ming Wang 15.00 40.00
C42 Alex Rios 15.00 40.00
C43 Carlos Delgado 10.00 25.00
C44 Jake Peavy 10.00 25.00
C45 Hanley Ramirez 25.00 60.00
C46 Alfonso Soriano 15.00 40.00
C47 Jimmy Rollins 15.00 40.00
C48 J.J. Hardy 10.00 25.00
C49 James Loney 15.00 40.00
C50 Ryan Howard 30.00 80.00
C51 Rich Harden 10.00 25.00
C52 Dan Uggla 15.00 40.00
C53 Miguel Cabrera 25.00 60.00
C54 Matt Kemp 15.00 40.00
C55 Russell Martin 10.00 25.00
C56 Chipper Jones 25.00 60.00
C57 Stephen Drew 10.00 25.00
C58 Randy Johnson 15.00 40.00
C59 Andy Pettitte 15.00 40.00
C60 Francisco Rodriguez 15.00 40.00
C61 Vernon Wells 10.00 25.00
C62 Ivan Rodriguez 15.00 40.00
C63 Joe Saunders 10.00 25.00
C64 Yadier Molina 15.00 40.00
C65 Ken Griffey Jr. 40.00 100.00
C66 Justin Verlander 30.00 80.00
C67 Edinson Volquez 10.00 25.00
C68 Phil Hughes 15.00 40.00
C69 Yovani Gallardo 10.00 25.00
C70 Jose Reyes 15.00 40.00
C71 Gio Gonzalez 10.00 25.00
C72 Adrian Gonzalez 15.00 40.00
C73 Chris Davis 10.00 25.00
C74 Brad Penny 10.00 25.00
C75 Dustin Pedroia 30.00 80.00
C76 Kevin Youkilis 15.00 40.00
C77 Angel Salome 10.00 25.00
C78 Kila Ka'aihue 15.00 40.00
C79 Lou Marson 10.00 25.00
C80 Ichiro Suzuki 40.00 100.00
C81 Alcides Escobar 25.00 60.00
C82 Travis Snider 15.00 40.00
C83 Adam Dunn 15.00 40.00
C84 Jacoby Ellsbury 25.00 60.00
C85 Jay Bruce 15.00 40.00
C86 Ryan Doumit 10.00 25.00
C87 Tim Lincecum 40.00 100.00
C88 Joe Nathan 10.00 25.00
C89 Brian McCann 15.00 40.00
C90 Evan Longoria 30.00 80.00
C91 Carlos Zambrano 15.00 40.00
C92 Pat Burrell 10.00 25.00
C93 Alex Gordon 15.00 40.00
C94 Ryan Zimmerman 15.00 40.00
C95 Carlos Quentin 15.00 40.00
C96 Xavier Nady 10.00 25.00
C97 Max Scherzer 15.00 40.00
C98 Hiroki Kuroda 10.00 25.00
C99 Carlos Lee 10.00 25.00
C100 Alex Rodriguez 40.00 100.00
CHR101 Chad Qualls 10.00 25.00
CHR102 Daniel Schlereth 10.00 25.00
CHR103 Derek Lowe 10.00 25.00
CHR104 Jason Giambi 10.00 25.00
CHR105 Jason Marquis 10.00 25.00
CHR106 Kevin Correia 10.00 25.00
CHR107 Koji Uehara 15.00 40.00
CHR108 Matt Diaz 10.00 25.00
CHR109 Melky Cabrera 10.00 25.00
CHR110 Milton Bradley 10.00 25.00
CHR111 Rafael Soriano 10.00 25.00
CHR112 Scott Downs 10.00 25.00
CHR113 David Aardsma 10.00 25.00
CHR114 Eric Byrnes 10.00 25.00
CHR115 Gerardo Parra 15.00 40.00
CHR116 Homer Bailey 10.00 25.00
CHR117 J.P. Howell 10.00 25.00
CHR118 Joe Crede 15.00 40.00
CHR119 John Mayberry Jr 10.00 25.00
CHR120 Josh Outman 15.00 40.00
CHR121 Lastings Milledge 10.00 25.00
CHR122 Mike Hampton 10.00 25.00
CHR123 Orlando Cabrera 10.00 25.00
CHR124 Randy Wells 10.00 25.00
CHR125 Michael Saunders 15.00 40.00
CHR126 Tony Gwynn Jr. 10.00 25.00
CHR127 Trevor Crowe 10.00 25.00
CHR128 Vin Mazzaro 10.00 25.00
CHR129 Andruw Jones 10.00 25.00
CHR130 Brad Penny 10.00 25.00
CHR131 Brandon Wood 10.00 25.00
CHR132 Cristian Guzman 10.00 25.00
CHR133 David Huff 10.00 25.00
CHR134 J.A. Happ 15.00 40.00
CHR135 Jason Kubel 10.00 25.00
CHR136 Ryan Garko 10.00 25.00
CHR137 Jose Contreras 10.00 25.00
CHR138 Juan Rivera 10.00 25.00
CHR139 Jhoulys Chacin 15.00 40.00
CHR140 Randy Wolf 10.00 25.00
CHR141 Aaron Hill 10.00 25.00
CHR142 Adam Dunn 15.00 40.00
CHR143 Andrew Bailey 25.00 60.00
CHR144 Andrew McCutchen 40.00 100.00
CHR145 Ben Zobrist 10.00 25.00
CHR146 Bobby Abreu 10.00 25.00
CHR147 Brett Anderson 15.00 40.00
CHR148 Chris Coghlan 25.00 60.00
CHR149 Colby Rasmus 25.00 60.00
CHR150 Elvis Andrus 15.00 40.00
CHR151 Fernando Martinez 25.00 60.00
CHR152 Garret Anderson 10.00 25.00
CHR153 Gary Sheffield 10.00 25.00
CHR154 Gordon Beckham 30.00 80.00
CHR155 Huston Street 10.00 25.00
CHR156 Ivan Rodriguez 15.00 40.00
CHR157 Jason Bay 15.00 40.00
CHR158 Jeff Francoeur 15.00 40.00
CHR159 Jordan Zimmermann 10.00 25.00
CHR160 Ken Griffey Jr. 40.00 100.00
CHR161 Kendry Morales 10.00 25.00
CHR162 Kyle Blanks 15.00 40.00
CHR163 Mark DeRosa 15.00 40.00
CHR164 Matt Holliday 25.00 60.00
CHR165 Matt LaPorta 25.00 60.00
CHR166 Nate McLouth 10.00 25.00
CHR167 Nelson Cruz 15.00 40.00
CHR168 Nolan Reimold 10.00 25.00
CHR169 Orlando Hudson 10.00 25.00
CHR170 Randy Johnson 15.00 40.00
CHR171 Rick Porcello 30.00 80.00
CHR172 Ricky Romero 25.00 60.00
CHR173 Russell Branyan 10.00 25.00
CHR174 Tommy Hanson 30.00 80.00
CHR175 Trevor Cahill 25.00 60.00
CHR176 Trevor Hoffman 15.00 40.00
CHR177 Aaron Poreda 10.00 25.00
CHR178 John Smoltz 25.00 60.00
CHR179 Brad Mills 10.00 25.00
CHR180 Brett Gardner 10.00 25.00
CHR181 Carl Pavano 10.00 25.00
CHR182 Daniel Bard 10.00 25.00
CHR183 David Hernandez 10.00 25.00
CHR184 Fu-Te Ni 15.00 40.00
CHR185 Jerry Hairston 10.00 25.00
CHR186 Jordan Schafer 15.00 40.00
CHR187 Julio Borbon 15.00 40.00
CHR188 Kris Medlen 15.00 40.00
CHR189 Micah Hoffpauir 10.00 25.00
CHR190 Nyjer Morgan 10.00 25.00
CHR191 Derek Holland 15.00 40.00
CHR192 Jack Wilson 10.00 25.00
CHR193 Cliff Lee 15.00 40.00
CHR194 Freddy Sanchez 10.00 25.00
CHR195 Pat Burrell 10.00 25.00
CHR196 Ryan Spilborghs 10.00 25.00
CHR197 Takashi Saito 10.00 25.00
CHR198 Bud Norris 10.00 25.00
CHR199 Chris Tillman 15.00 40.00
CHR200 Everth Cabrera 15.00 40.00

2009 Topps Heritage 1960 Buybacks

STATED ODDS XXX
NO PRICING DUE TO SCARCITY

2009 Topps Heritage 1960 Cut Signatures

STATED ODDS XXX
STATED PRINT RUN 1 SER.#'d SETS
NO PRICING DUE TO SCARCITY

2009 Topps Heritage Advertising Panels

ISSUED AS BOX TOPPER
1 Garret Anderson .60 1.50
Brandon Backe
Shin Soo Choo
2 Matt Antonelli 1.50 4.00
David Wright
Alex Rodriguez
Alfredo Simon
3 Bronson Arroyo .40 1.00
Detroit Tigers TC
Matt Cain
4 Brandon Backe .60 1.50
Shin Soo Choo
Ozzie Guillen
5 Carlos Beltran .60 1.50
Andre Ethier
Kelly Shoppach
Victor Martinez
6 Brad Bergesen .60 1.50
Dallas Braden
Garrett Olson HN
7 Nick Blackburn .40 1.00
Scott Lewis
Ramon Ramirez
8 Aaron Boone .60 1.50
James Loney
Gerald Laird
9 Julio Borbon .60 1.50
Jarrett Hoffpauir
David Hernandez HN
10 Emil Brown .60 1.50
Scott Shields
Francisco Rodriguez
David Murphy
11 Pat Burrell .40 1.00
Brian Bannister
Jesus Flores
12 Mike Cameron .40 1.00
Ted Lilly
John Lackey
13 Mike Carp .60 1.50
Jody Gerut
Daniel Schlereth HN
14 Brett Cecil .40 1.00
Aubrey Huff
Mike Hampton HN
15 Shin-Soo Choo .60 1.50
Ozzie Guillen
Mike Aviles
16 Jeff Clement .40 1.00
Bronson Arroyo
Detroit Tigers TC
17 John Danks .60 1.50
Carlos Beltran
Andre Ethier
18 Jesus Delgado 1.00 2.50
Brian Wilson
Gary Mathews
19 Stephen Drew .40 1.00
Ryan Feirebrand
Andy Pettitte
20 Scott Elbert .40 1.00
Fernando Perez
Jeremy Guthrie
21 Yunel Escobar .60 1.50
Gaby Sanchez
Vernon Wells
22 Andre Ethier .60 1.50
Kelly Shoppach
Victor Martinez
Ronny Paulino
23 Cliff Floyd .40 1.00
Alfredo Figaro
Anthony Swarzak HN
24 Ryan Franklin .60 1.50
Emil Brown
Scott Shields
Francisco Rodriguez
25 David Freese 3.00 8.00
J.J. Putz
Juan Uribe HN
26 Jody Gerut .40 1.00
Daniel Schlereth
Brett Cecil HN
27 Ross Gload .60 1.50
Miguel Tejada
Matt Harrison
28 Khalil Greene 1.00 2.50
Cole Hamels
Juan Pierre
29 Jeremy Guthrie .40 1.00
Nick Blackburn
Scott Lewis
30 Scott Hairston .40 1.00
Orlando Cabrera
Matt Maloney HN
31 Bill Hall .40 1.00
Randy Wells
Kevin Gregg HN
32 Cole Hamels 1.00 2.50
Juan Pierre
Yunel Escobar
33 Mike Hampton .40 1.00
Jerry Hairston
Scott Downs HN
34 Dan Haren .40 1.00
John Danks
Carlos Beltran
35 Corey Hart .40 1.00
Aubrey Huff
Rich Aurilia
36 Brad Hawpe .60 1.50
Roy Oswalt
Mike Jacobs
37 David Hernandez .60 1.50
Brandon Lyon
Koji Uehara HN
38 Aubrey Huff .40 1.00
Mike Hampton
Jerry Hairston HN
39 Aubrey Huff .40 1.00
Rich Aurilia
Scott Baker
40 Mike Jacobs 1.00 2.50
Terry Francona
Jacoby Ellsbury
41 Scott Kazmir .40 1.00
Jeff Clement
Bronson Arroyo
42 John Lackey .40 1.00
Lyle Overbay
Chris Lambert
43 Aaron Laffey 1.00 2.50
Hanley Ramirez
Scott Olsen
44 Gerald Laird .60 1.50
Chien-Ming Wang
Corey Hart
45 Chris Lambert .60 1.50
Carlos Zambrano
Dave Tremblay
46 Ted Lilly .40 1.00
John Lackey
Lyle Overbay
47 James Loney .60 1.50
Gerald Laird
Chien-Ming Wang
48 Los Angeles Dodgers TC 1.00 2.50
Jesus Delgado
Brian Wilson
49 Matt Maloney .60 1.50
Julio Borbon
Jarret Hoffpauir HN
50 Hideki Matsui 1.00 2.50
Ty Wigginton
Vicente Padilla
51 John Mayberry Jr .40 1.00
David Aardsma
Scott Podsednik HN
52 Gil Meche 1.00 2.50
David Price
Luke Scott
53 Brad Mills .40 1.00
David Ross
Chris Perez HN
54 Daniel Murphy 1.00 2.50
Hideki Matsui
Ty Wigginton
55 Mike Napoli .60 1.50
David Wright
Matt Antonelli
56 Scott Olsen .60 1.50
Ryan Franklin
Emil Brown
57 Roy Oswalt .60 1.50
Mike Jacobs
Terry Francona
58 Josh Outman .60 1.50
Homer Bailey
Daniel Bard HN
59 Lyle Overbay .60 1.50
Chris Lambert
Carlos Zambrano
60 Vicente Padilla .60 1.50
Brad Hawpe
Roy Oswalt
61 Jon Papelbon .40 1.00
Tim Wakefield
Corey Patterson
Pat Burrell
62 Corey Patterson .40 1.00
Pat Burrell
Brian Bannister
63 Xavier Paul .40 1.00
John Mayberry Jr
David Aardsma HN
64 Chris Perez .60 1.50
Ramiro Pena
Rocco Baldelli HN
65 Fernando Perez .40 1.00
Jeremy Guthrie
Nick Blackburn
66 Juan Pierre .60 1.50
Yunel Escobar

Gaby Sanchez
67 Lou Piniella .40 1.00
Scott Kazmir
Jeff Clement
68 Aaron Poreda .40 1.00
Bill Hall
Randy Wells HN
69 David Price 1.00 2.50
Luke Scott
Jeff Suppan
70 Albert Pujols 2.50 6.00
Dan Haren
John Danks
71 Hanley Ramirez 1.00 2.50
Scott Olsen
Ryan Franklin
72 Tim Redding .40 1.00
Jamey Carroll
Endy Chavez
73 Jeremy Reed .40 1.00
Laynce Nix
Ryan Sadowski HN
74 Edgar Renteria .40 1.00
Brian Giles
Greg Smith
75 Gaby Sanchez .60 1.50
Vernon Wells
Ross Gload
76 Bobby Scales .60 1.50
Clay Zavada
Jason Jaramillo HN
77 Daniel Schlereth .40 1.00
Brett Cecil
Aubrey Huff HN
78 Kelly Shoppach .60 1.50
Victor Martinez
Ronny Paulino
Mike Gonzalez
79 John Smoltz .60 1.50
Mike Carp
Jody Gerut HN
80 Rafael Soriano .40 1.00
Ross Gload
Vin Mazzaro HN
81 Craig Stammen .60 1.50
John Smoltz
Mike Carp HN
82 Anthony Swarzak .40 1.00
C.J. Wilson
Derek Lowe HN
83 Miguel Tejada .60 1.50
Matt Harrison
James Parr
84 Detroit Tigers TC .40 1.00
Matt Cain
Jeff Francis
85 Dave Tremblay .40 1.00
Edgar Renteria
Brian Giles
86 Koji Uehara .60 1.50
Brad Bergesen
Dallas Braden HN
87 Juan Uribe .40 1.00
Rafael Soriano
Ross Gload HN
88 Jason Vargas .40 1.00
Eric Byrnes
Brad Mills HN
89 Chien-Ming Wang .60 1.50
Corey Hart
Aubrey Huff
90 Randy Wells .40 1.00
Kevin Gregg
J.P. Howell HN
91 Vernon Wells .60 1.50
Ross Gload
Miguel Tejada
92 Sean West .60 1.50
Melky Cabrera
Braden Looper HN
93 Ty Wigginton .60 1.50
Vicente Padilla
Brad Hawpe
94 Brian Wilson 1.00 2.50
Gary Mathews
Ubaldo Jimenez
95 Jack Wilson .40 1.00
Cincinnati Reds TC
Dustin McGowan
96 Kerry Wood .40 1.00
Scott Elbert
Fernando Perez
97 David Wright 1.50 4.00
Matt Antonelli
David Wright
Alex Rodriguez
98 Carlos Zambrano .60 1.50
Dave Tremblay
Edgar Renteria

2009 Topps Heritage Baseball Flashbacks

COMPLETE SET (10) 5.00 12.00
STATED ODDS 1:12 HOBBY
BF1 Mickey Mantle 1.50 4.00
BF2 Bill Mazeroski .75 2.00
BF3 Juan Marichal .50 1.25
BF4 Paul Richards .50 1.25
Hoyt Wilhelm
BF5 Luis Aparicio .50 1.25
BF6 Frank Robinson .75 2.00
BF7 Brooks Robinson .75 2.00
BF8 Ernie Banks 1.25 3.00
BF9 Mickey Mantle 1.50 4.00
BF10 Bobby Richardson .50 1.25

2009 Topps Heritage Clubhouse Collection Relics

GROUP A ODDS 1:219 HOBBY
GROUP B ODDS 1:52 HOBBY
GROUP C ODDS 1:97 HOBBY
HN ODDDS 1:26 HOBBY
AG Adrian Gonzalez HN 2.50 6.00
AJ Adam Jones HN 2.50 6.00
AR Aramis Ramirez Jsy 2.50 6.00
AR Aramis Ramirez HN 2.50 6.00
AS Alfonso Soriano HN 2.50 6.00
BM Brian McCann HN 2.50 6.00
BR Brooks Robinson HN 50.00 100.00
BU B.J. Upton Bat 2.50 6.00
CB Clay Buchholz Jsy 2.50 6.00
CB Chad Billingsley HN 2.50 6.00
CC Carl Crawford Uni 2.50 6.00
CH Cole Hamels HN 4.00 10.00
CJ Chipper Jones HN 4.00 10.00
CM Cameron Maybin Bat 2.50 6.00
CQ Carlos Quentin HN 2.50 6.00
CT Curtis Thigpen Jsy 2.50 6.00
CU Chase Utley Jsy 5.00 12.00
CU Chase Utley HN 5.00 12.00
DJ Dan Johnson Jsy 2.50 6.00
DP Dustin Pedroia Jsy 5.00 12.00
DS Duke Snider HN 20.00 50.00
DU Dan Uggla Jsy 2.50 6.00
DW Dontrelle Willis Jsy 2.50 6.00
DW David Wright HN 4.00 10.00
DWR David Wright Jsy 4.00 10.00
EB Ernie Banks HN 50.00 100.00
EL Evan Longoria HN 5.00 12.00
FH Felix Hernandez HN 4.00 10.00
FR Frank Robinson HN 40.00 80.00
GS Geovany Soto HN 4.00 10.00
HR Hanley Ramirez HN 2.50 6.00
IK Ian Kinsler HN 2.50 6.00
JB Jay Bruce HN 4.00 10.00
JD J.D. Drew Jsy 2.50 6.00
JL Jon Lester Jsy 4.00 10.00
JM Joe Mauer HN 4.00 10.00
JR Jimmy Rollins HN 4.00 10.00
JS Joakim Soria HN 2.50 6.00
JU Justin Upton HN 2.50 6.00
KFM Kevin Mench Jsy 2.50 6.00
KK Kenshin Kawakami HN 4.00 10.00
KM Kevin Millwood Jsy 2.50 6.00
KS Kurt Suzuki Bat 2.50 6.00
KU Koji Uehara HN 4.00 10.00
KY Kevin Youkilis Jsy 4.00 10.00
LM Lastings Milledge Bat 2.50 6.00
MH Matt Holliday HN 4.00 10.00
MM Mickey Mantle HN 60.00 120.00
MR Manny Ramirez Jsy 5.00 12.00
MT Miguel Tejada Bat 2.50 6.00
RB Rocco Baldelli Jsy 2.50 6.00
RB Ryan Braun HN 4.00 10.00
RH Ryan Howard HN 4.00 10.00
RM Roger Maris HN 50.00 100.00
SM Stan Musial HN 40.00 80.00
SP Scott Podsednik Jsy 2.50 6.00
TL Tim Lincecum HN 5.00 12.00
VW Vernon Wells Jsy 2.50 6.00
WM Willie McCovey HN 50.00 100.00
ALR Alexei Ramirez HN 2.50 6.00
BJU B.J. Upton HN 2.50 6.00
EVL Evan Longoria HN 5.00 12.00
JAB Jay Bruce HN 4.00 10.00
MIC Miguel Cabrera HN 4.00 10.00

2009 Topps Heritage Clubhouse Collection Relics Autographs

STATED ODDS 1:6150 HOBBY
HN STATED ODDS 1:2425 HOBBY
STATED PRINT RUN 25 SER.#'d SETS
NO PRICING DUE TO SCARCITY
EXCHANGE DEADLINE 2/28/2012

2009 Topps Heritage Clubhouse Collection Relics Dual

STATED ODDS 1:4800 HOBBY
HN STATED ODDS 1:2020 HOBBY
STATED PRINT RUN 60 SER.#'d SETS
BR Jay Bruce Bat 20.00 50.00
Frank Robinson Pants
HM Matt Holliday 90.00 150.00
Stan Musial HN
LM Tim Lincecum 60.00 120.00
Juan Marichal HN
MR Nick Markakis 60.00 120.00
Brooks Robinson HN
PM Albert Pujols Bat 100.00 200.00
Stan Musial Pants
PM Jorge Posada 90.00 150.00
Mickey Mantle HN
RM Alex Rodriguez Jsy 125.00 250.00
Mickey Mantle Jsy
SB Alfonso Soriano Bat 60.00 120.00
Ernie Banks Bat
SK Duke Snider 40.00 80.00
Matt Kemp HN
TM Mark Teixeira Bat 125.00 250.00
Mickey Mantle Jsy

2009 Topps Heritage Clubhouse Collection Relics Dual Autographs

STATED ODDS 1:10,200 HOBBY
HN STATED ODDS 1:6113 HOBBY
STATED PRINT RUN 10 SER.#'d SETS
NO PRICING DUE TO SCARCITY
EXCHANGE DEADLINE 2/28/2012

2009 Topps Heritage Flashback Autographs

STATED ODDS 1:12,400 HOBBY
STATED PRINT RUN 25 SER.#'d SETS
NO PRICING DUE TO SCARCITY
EXCHANGE DEADLINE 2/28/2012
BJ Ben Johnson
GM Gil McDougald
JG Johnny Groth
JH Jack Harshman
RW Red Wilson

2009 Topps Heritage Flashback Stadium Relics

STATED ODDS 1:383 HOBBY
HN STATED ODDS 1:925 HOBBY
AK Al Kaline 12.50 30.00
BM Bill Mazeroski 12.50 30.00
BR Brooks Robinson 15.00 40.00
BRI Bobby Richardson 12.50 30.00
CP Comiskey Park HN
EB Ernie Banks 15.00 40.00
EF Ebbets Field HN
FR Frank Robinson 10.00 25.00
LA Luis Aparicio 8.00 20.00
MM Mickey Mantle 20.00 50.00
MM2 Mickey Mantle 20.00 50.00
SM Stan Musial 12.50 30.00
SS Seals Stadium HN

2009 Topps Heritage Flashback Stadium Relics Autographs

STATED ODDS 1:12,300 HOBBY
STATED PRINT RUN 25 SER.#'d SETS
NO PRICING DUE TO SCARCITY
EXCHANGE DEADLINE 2/28/2012

2009 Topps Heritage Flashback Stadium Relics Dual

STATED ODDS 1:34,000 HOBBY
NO PRICING DUE TO SCARCITY
STATED PRINT RUN 10 SER.#'d SETS

2009 Topps Heritage High Number Flashbacks

COMPLETE SET (10) 5.00 12.00
STATED ODDS 1:12 HOBBY
FB01 Jonathan Sanchez .50 1.25
FB02 Jason Giambi .50 1.25
FB03 Randy Johnson .75 2.00
FB04 Ian Kinsler .75 2.00
FB05 Carl Crawford .75 2.00
FB06 Albert Pujols 3.00 8.00
FB07 Todd Helton .75 2.00
FB08 Mariano Rivera 1.25 3.00
FB09 Gary Sheffield .50 1.25
FB10 Ichiro Suzuki 2.00 5.00

2009 Topps Heritage High Number Rookie Performers

COMPLETE SET (15) 12.50 30.00
STATED ODDS 1:12 HOBBY
RP01 Colby Rasmus 1.50 4.00
RP02 Tommy Hanson 2.00 5.00
RP03 Andrew McCutchen 2.50 6.00
RP04 Rick Porcello 2.00 5.00
RP05 Nolan Reimold .60 1.50
RP06 Mat Latos 2.00 5.00
RP07 Gordon Beckham 2.00 5.00
RP08 Brett Anderson 1.00 2.50
RP09 Chris Coghlan 1.50 4.00
RP10 Jordan Zimmermann .60 1.50
RP11 Brad Bergesen .60 1.50
RP12 Elvis Andrus 1.00 2.50
RP13 Ricky Romero 1.50 4.00
RP14 Dexter Fowler 1.00 2.50
RP15 David Price 1.50 4.00

2009 Topps Heritage High Number Then and Now

COMPLETE SET (10) 5.00 12.00
STATED ODDS 1:12 HOBBY
TN01 Dustin Pedroia 1.25 3.00
Roger Maris
TN02 Jimmy Rollins 1.00 2.50
Ernie Banks
TN03 Adrian Beltre .60 1.50
Brooks Robinson
TN04 Michael Young .60 1.50
Ernie Banks
TN05 Ichiro Suzuki 1.50 4.00
Roger Maris
TN06 Grady Sizemore 1.00 2.50
Roger Maris
TN07 Albert Pujols 2.50 6.00
Roger Maris
TN08 David Wright 1.25 3.00
Brooks Robinson
TN09 Cole Hamels 1.00 2.50
Bobby Richardson
TN10 Torii Hunter 1.00 2.50
Roger Maris

2009 Topps Heritage Mayo

COMPLETE SET (10) 15.00 40.00
RANDOM INSERTS IN PACKS
AP Albert Pujols 5.00 12.00
AR Alex Rodriguez 3.00 8.00
ARI Alex Rios 1.25 3.00
AS Alfonso Soriano 1.25 3.00
CJ Chipper Jones 2.00 5.00
DM Daisuke Matsuzaka 2.00 5.00
DO David Ortiz 1.25 3.00
DP Dustin Pedroia 2.50 6.00
DW David Wright 2.50 6.00
EL Evan Longoria 2.50 6.00
GS Grady Sizemore 1.25 3.00
HR Hanley Ramirez 2.00 5.00
IS Ichiro Suzuki 3.00 8.00
JH Josh Hamilton 2.00 5.00
JS Johan Santana 2.00 5.00
MR Manny Ramirez 2.00 5.00
RB Ryan Braun 2.50 6.00
RH Ryan Howard 2.50 6.00
TL Tim Lincecum 3.00 8.00
VG Vladimir Guerrero 2.00 5.00

2009 Topps Heritage New Age Performers

COMPLETE SET (15) 12.50 30.00
STATED ODDS 1:15 HOBBY
NAP1 David Wright 1.50 4.00
NAP2 Manny Ramirez 1.25 3.00
NAP3 Mark Teixeira 1.25 3.00
NAP4 Josh Hamilton 1.25 3.00
NAP5 Chase Utley 1.25 3.00
NAP6 Tim Lincecum 2.00 5.00
NAP7 Stephen Drew .50 1.25
NAP8 Cliff Lee .75 2.00
NAP9 Carlos Quentin .75 2.00
NAP10 Ryan Braun 1.50 4.00
NAP11 Cole Hamels 1.25 3.00
NAP12 Dustin Pedroia 1.50 4.00
NAP13 Geovany Soto .75 2.00
NAP14 Scott Kazmir .50 1.25
NAP15 Evan Longoria 1.50 4.00

2009 Topps Heritage News Flashbacks

COMPLETE SET (10) 6.00 15.00
STATED ODDS 1:12 HOBBY
NF1 Aswan High Dam .50 1.25
NF2 Bathyscaphe Trieste .50 1.25
NF3 Weather Satellite - TIROS-1 .50 1.25
NF4 Civil Rights Act of 1960 .50 1.25
NF5 Fifty-Star Flag .50 1.25
NF6 USS Seadragon .50 1.25
NF7 Marshall Space Flight Center .50 1.25
NF8 Presidential Debate 1.00 2.50
NF9 John F. Kennedy 1.25 3.00
NF10 Polaris Missle .50 1.25

2009 Topps Heritage Real One Autographs

STATED ODDS 1:308 HOBBY
HN STATED ODDS 1:372 HOBBY
EXCHANGE DEADLINE 2/28/2012
AC Art Ceccarelli 10.00 25.00
AD Alvin Dark HN 30.00 60.00
AS Art Schult 10.00 25.00
BB Brian Barton HN 10.00 25.00
BG Buddy Gilbert 10.00 25.00
BJ Ben Johnson 10.00 25.00
BJ Bob Johnson HN 20.00 50.00
BR Bob Rush 10.00 25.00
BTH Bill Harris 10.00 25.00
CK Clayton Kershaw 30.00 60.00
CK Clayton Kershaw HN 30.00 60.00
CM Carl Mathias 10.00 25.00
CN Cal Neeman 10.00 25.00
CP Cliff Pennington HN 15.00 40.00
CR Curt Raydon 10.00 25.00
DB Dick Burwell HN 20.00 50.00
DG Dick Gray 10.00 25.00
DW Don Williams EXCH 10.00 25.00
FC Fausto Carmona 10.00 25.00
GB Gordon Beckham HN 60.00 120.00
GC Gio Gonzalez HN 15.00 40.00
GM Gil McDougald 10.00 25.00
IN Irv Noren 10.00 25.00
IN Irv Noren HN 20.00 50.00
JB Jay Bruce 10.00 25.00
JB Jay Bruce HN 10.00 25.00
JG Johnny Groth 15.00 40.00
JH Jack Harshman 20.00 50.00
JM Justin Masterson 10.00 25.00
JP Jim Proctor 10.00 25.00
JR John Romonosky 10.00 25.00
JS Joe Shipley 10.00 25.00
JSS Jake Striker 10.00 25.00
MB Milton Bradley HN 10.00 25.00
MG Mat Gamel 10.00 25.00
ML Mike Lee 10.00 25.00
NC Nelson Chittum 10.00 25.00
RI Raul Ibanez HN 20.00 50.00
RJW Red Wilson 10.00 25.00
RS Ron Samford 10.00 25.00
RW Ray Webster 10.00 25.00
SK Steve Korcheck 10.00 25.00
SL Stan Lopata 10.00 25.00
TP Taylor Phillips 10.00 25.00
TW Ted Wieand EXCH 10.00 25.00
WL Whitey Lockman 10.00 25.00
WT Wayne Terwilliger 10.00 25.00
BWI Bobby Wine HN 20.00 50.00

2009 Topps Heritage Real One Autographs Red Ink

STATED ODDS 1:514 HOBBY
HN STATED ODDS 1:623 HOBBY
STATED PRINT RUN 60 SER.#'d SETS
EXCHANGE DEADLINE 2/28/2012
AC Art Ceccarelli 12.50 30.00
AD Alvin Dark HN 40.00 80.00
AS Art Schult 12.50 30.00
BB Brian Barton HN 20.00 50.00
BG Buddy Gilbert 12.50 30.00
BJ Ben Johnson 12.50 30.00
BJ Bob Johnson HN 30.00 60.00
BR Bob Rush 12.50 30.00
BTH Bill Harris 12.50 30.00
CK Clayton Kershaw 75.00 150.00
CK Clayton Kershaw HN 75.00 150.00
CM Carl Mathias 12.50 30.00
CN Cal Neeman 12.50 30.00
CP Cliff Pennington HN 20.00 50.00
CR Curt Raydon 12.50 30.00
DB Dick Burwell HN 30.00 60.00
DG Dick Gray 12.50 30.00
DW Don Williams EXCH 12.50 30.00
FC Fausto Carmona 12.50 30.00
GB Gordon Beckham HN 100.00 200.00
GC Gio Gonzalez HN 30.00 60.00
GM Gil McDougald 12.50 30.00
IN Irv Noren 12.50 30.00
IN Irv Noren HN 30.00 60.00
JB Jay Bruce 15.00 40.00
JB Jay Bruce HN 15.00 40.00
JG Johnny Groth 20.00 50.00
JH Jack Harshman 30.00 60.00
JM Justin Masterson 12.50 30.00
JP Jim Proctor 12.50 30.00
JR John Romonosky 12.50 30.00
JS Joe Shipley 12.50 30.00
JSS Jake Striker 12.50 30.00
MB Milton Bradley HN 20.00 50.00
MG Mat Gamel 12.50 30.00
ML Mike Lee 12.50 30.00
NC Nelson Chittum 12.50 30.00
RI Raul Ibanez HN 30.00 60.00
RJW Red Wilson 12.50 30.00
RS Ron Samford 12.50 30.00
RW Ray Webster 12.50 30.00
SK Steve Korcheck 12.50 30.00
SL Stan Lopata 12.50 30.00
TP Taylor Phillips 12.50 30.00
TW Ted Wieand 12.50 30.00
WL Whitey Lockman 12.50 30.00
WT Wayne Terwilliger 12.50 30.00
BWI Bobby Wine HN 30.00 60.00

2009 Topps Heritage Real One Autographs Dual

STATED ODDS 1:2005 HOBBY
HN STATED ODDS 1:1200
STATED PRINT RUN 25 SER.#'d SETS
NO PRICING DUE TO SCARCITY
EXCHANGE DEADLINE 2/28/2012

2009 Topps Heritage Then and Now

COMPLETE SET (10) 10.00 25.00
STATED ODDS 1:15 HOBBY
TN1 Ernie Banks 1.50 4.00
Ryan Howard
TN2 Ernie Banks 1.50 4.00
Ryan Howard
TN3 Minnie Minoso 1.25 3.00
Chipper Jones
TN4 Luis Aparicio .50 1.25
Willy Taveras
TN5 Mickey Mantle .30 .75
Adam Dunn
TN6 Bob Friend 1.25 3.00
Johan Santana
TN7 Johnny Podres 2.00 5.00
Tim Lincecum
TN8 Bob Friend .75 2.00
Cliff Lee
TN9 Bob Friend 1.25 3.00
Roy Halladay
TN10 Whitey Ford .75 2.00
CC Sabathia

2009 Topps Heritage 1959 National Convention VIP

COMPLETE SET (5) 8.00 20.00
573A Mickey Mantle 4.00 10.00
Facing Left
573B Mickey Mantle 4.00 10.00
Facing Right
574 Roy Campanella 1.25 3.00
575 Jackie Robinson 1.25 3.00
576 Roger Maris 1.25 3.00

2010 Topps Heritage

COMP.SET w/o SPs (425) 30.00 60.00
COMMON CARD (1-425) .15 .40
COMMON RC (1-425) .40 1.00
DICE ODDS 1:72 HOBBY
COMMON NAME VAR (1-427) 30.00 60.00
61 CHASE ODDS 1:435 HOBBY
COMMON SP (426-500) 2.50 6.00
SP ODDS 1:3 HOBBY
1a Albert Pujols 1.00 2.50
1b Albert Pujols 6.00 15.00
Dice Back SP
1c Albert Pujols 50.00 100.00
All Black Nameplate SP
2a Joe Mauer .40 1.00
2b Joe Mauer 3.00 8.00
Dice Back SP
2c Joe Mauer 30.00 60.00
All Black Nameplate SP
3 Joe Blanton .15 .40
4 Delmon Young .25 .60
5 Kelly Shoppach .15 .40
6 Ronald Belisario .15 .40
7 Chicago White Sox .15 .40
8 Rajai Davis .15 .40
9 Aaron Harang .15 .40
10 Brian Roberts .15 .40
11 Adam Wainwright .25 .60
12 Geovany Soto .25 .60
13 Ramon Santiago .15 .40
14 Albert Callaspo .15 .40
15a Grady Sizemore .25 .60
15b Grady Sizemore 3.00 8.00
Dice Back SP
15c Grady Sizemore 30.00 60.00
Red-Green Nameplate SP
16 Clay Buchholz .25 .60
17 Checklist .15 .40
18 David Huff .15 .40
19a Alex Rodriguez .60 1.50
20 Cole Hamels .40 1.00
21 Orlando Cabrera .15 .40
22 Ross Ohlendorf .15 .40
23a Matt Kemp .25 .60
23b Matt Kemp 3.00 8.00
Dice Back SP
24 Andrew Bailey .15 .40
25 Juan Francisco .40 1.00
Jay Bruce
Joey Votto
26 Chris Tillman .15 .40
27 Mike Fontenot .15 .40
28 Melky Cabrera .15 .40
29 Reid Gorecki (RC) .60 1.50
30 Jayson Nix .15 .40
31 Bengie Molina .15 .40
32 Chris Carpenter .40 1.00
33 Jason Bay .25 .60
34 Fausto Carmona .15 .40
35 Gordon Beckham .25 .60
36 Glen Perkins .15 .40
37 Curtis Granderson .25 .60
38 Rafael Furcal .15 .40
39 Matt Carson (RC) .40 1.00
40 A.J. Burnett .25 .60
41 H. Ramirez/P. Sandoval/A. Pujols/T. Helton 1.00 2.50
42 J. Mauer/I. Suzuki/D. Jeter/M. Cabrera 1.00 2.50
43 A. Pujols/P. Fielder/R. Howard/M. Reynolds .25 .60
44 C. Pena/M. Teixeira/J. Bay/A. Hill .40 1.00
45 Carpenter/Lincecum/Jurrjens/Wainwright .40 1.00
46 Greinke/Hernandez/Halladay/Sabathia .25 .60
47 Wainwright/Carpenter/De La Rosa/Arroyo .40 1.00
48 Hernandez/Sabathia/Verlander/Beckett .50 1.25
49 Lincecum/Vazquez/Haren/Wainwright .60 1.50
50 Verlander/Greinke/Lester/Hernandez .50 1.25
51 Detroit Tigers .15 .40
52 Ronny Cedeno .15 .40
53 Jason Varitek .40 1.00
54 Daniel McCutchen RC .60 1.50
55a Pablo Sandoval .25 .60
55b Pablo Sandoval 30.00 60.00
Yellow-Green Nameplate SP
56a Jake Peavy .15 .40
56b Mickey Mantle SP 30.00 60.00
57 Billy Butler .15 .40
58 Ryan Dempster .15 .40
59 Neil Walker (RC) .60 1.50
60a Asdrubal Cabrera .25 .60
60b Babe Ruth SP 15.00 40.00
61a Ryan Church .15 .40
61b Roger Maris SP 20.00 50.00
62 Nick Markakis .40 1.00
63 Nick Blackburn .15 .40
64 Mark DeRosa .15 .40
65 Paul Konerko .25 .60
66 Daniel Ray Herrera .15 .40
67 Brandon Inge .25 .60
68 Josh Thole RC .60 1.50
69 Josh Beckett .25 .60
70 Lastings Milledge .15 .40
71 Robert Andino .15 .40
72 Matt Cain .25 .60
73 Nate McLouth .15 .40
74 Russell Martin .15 .40
75 Albert Pujols 1.00 2.50
David Wright
76 Jay Bruce .25 .60
77a J.A. Happ .25 .60
77b J.A. Happ 40.00 80.00
Orange-Blue Nameplate SP
78 Jayson Werth .25 .60
79 A.J. Pierzynski .15 .40
80 Michael Cuddyer .15 .40
81 Dustin Richardson RC .40 1.00
82a Justin Upton .25 .60
82b Justin Upton 3.00 8.00
Dice Back SP
83 Rick Porcello .15 .40
84 Garret Anderson .15 .40
85 Jeremy Guthrie .15 .40
86 Los Angeles Dodgers .25 .60
87 Juan Uribe .15 .40
88 Alfonso Soriano .25 .60
89 Martin Prado .15 .40
90 Gavin Floyd .15 .40
91 Colby Rasmus .40 1.00
92a Mark Teixeira .40 1.00
92b Mark Teixeira 3.00 8.00
Dice Back SP
93 Raul Ibanez .25 .60
94a Zack Greinke .25 .60
94b Zack Greinke 50.00 100.00
Yellow-Blue Nameplate SP
95 Miguel Cabrera .40 1.00
96 Randy Johnson .25 .60
97 Chris Dickerson .15 .40
98 Checklist .15 .40
99 Jed Lowrie .25 .60
100 Zach Duke .15 .40
101 Jhonny Peralta .15 .40
102 Nolan Reimold .25 .60
103 Jimmy Rollins .25 .60
104 Jorge Posada .25 .60
105 Tim Hudson .25 .60
106 Scott Hairston .15 .40
107 Rich Harden .15 .40
108 Jason Kubel .15 .40
109 Clayton Kershaw .40 1.00
110 Willy Taveras .15 .40
111 Brett Myers .15 .40
112 Adam Everett .15 .40
113 Jonathan Papelbon .25 .60
114 Buster Posey RC 5.00 12.00
115 Kerry Wood .15 .40
116 Jerry Hairston Jr. .15 .40
117 Adam Dunn .25 .60
118 Yadier Molina .25 .60
119 David DeJesus .25 .60
Alex Gordon
120a Chipper Jones .40 1.00
120b Chipper Jones 3.00 8.00
Dice Back SP
121 John Lackey .15 .40
122 Chicago Cubs .25 .60
123 Nick Punto .15 .40
124 Daniel Hudson RC .60 1.50
125 David Hernandez .15 .40
126 Garrett Jones .15 .40
127 Joel Pineiro .15 .40
128 Jacoby Ellsbury .40 1.00
129 Ian Desmond (RC) .60 1.50
130 James Loney .25 .60
131 Dave Trembley MG .15 .40
132 Ozzie Guillen MG .15 .40
133 Joe Girardi MG .25 .60
134 Jim Riggleman MG .15 .40
135 Dusty Baker MG .15 .40
136 Joe Torre MG .25 .60
137 Bobby Cox MG .15 .40
138 John Russell MG .15 .40
139 Tony LaRussa MG .25 .60
140 Jarrod Saltalamacchia .15 .40
141 Kosuke Fukudome .40 1.00
142 Mariano Rivera .40 1.00
143 David DeJesus .15 .40
144 Jon Niese .15 .40
145 Jair Jurrjens .15 .40
146 Josh Willingham .15 .40
147 Chris Pettit RC .40 1.00
148 Chris Getz .15 .40
149 Ryan Doumit .15 .40
150 Aaron Rowand .15 .40
151 Brad Kilby RC .40 1.00
152 Prince Fielder .25 .60
153 Scott Baker .15 .40
154 Shane Victorino .25 .60
155 Luis Valbuena .15 .40
156 Drew Stubbs RC 1.00 2.50
157 Mark Buehrle .25 .60
158 Josh Bard .15 .40
159 Baltimore Orioles .15 .40
160 Andy Pettitte .25 .60
161 Madison Bumgarner RC 1.00 2.50
162 Johnny Cueto .15 .40
163 Jeff Mathis .15 .40
164 Yunel Escobar .15 .40
165 Steve Pearce .15 .40
166 Ramon Hernandez .15 .40
167 San Francisco Giants .15 .40
168 Chris Coghlan .15 .40
169 Ted Lilly .15 .40
170 Alex Rios .25 .60
171 Justin Verlander .50 1.25
172 Michael Brantley RC .40 1.00
173 Dustin Pedroia .50 1.25
Jacoby Ellsbury
174 Craig Stammen .15 .40
175 Scott Rolen .25 .60
176 Howie Kendrick .15 .40
177 Trevor Cahill .15 .40
178 Matt Holliday .40 1.00
179a Chase Utley .40 1.00
179b Chase Utley 3.00 8.00
Dice Back SP
180 Robinson Cano .40 1.00
181 Paul Maholm .15 .40
182a Adam Jones .25 .60
182b Adam Jones 3.00 8.00
Dice Back SP
183 Felipe Lopez .15 .40
184 Kendry Morales .15 .40
185 John Danks .15 .40
186 Denard Span .15 .40
187 Nyjer Morgan .15 .40
188 Adrian Gonzalez .25 .60
189 Checklist .15 .40
190 Chad Billingsley .15 .40
191 Travis Hafner .15 .40
192 Gerald Laird .15 .40
193a Daisuke Matsuzaka .40 1.00
193b Daisuke Matsuzaka 2.50 6.00
Dice Back SP
194 Joey Votto .40 1.00
195 Jered Weaver .15 .40
196 Ryan Theriot .15 .40
197 Gio Gonzalez .15 .40
198 Chris Iannetta .15 .40
199 Mike Jacobs .15 .40
19b Alex Rodriguez 4.00 10.00
Dice Back SP
200 Javier Vasquez .15 .40
201 Josh Beckett .40 1.00
Johan Santana
202 Torii Hunter .15 .40
203 Juan Rivera .15 .40
204 Brandon Phillips .15 .40
205 Edwin Jackson .15 .40
206 Lance Berkman .25 .60
207 Gil Meche .15 .40
208 Jorge Cantu .15 .40
209 Eric Young Jr (RC) .40 1.00
210 Andre Ethier .25 .60
211 Rickie Weeks .25 .60
212 Omir Santos .15 .40
213 Mat Latos .15 .40
214 Tyler Colvin RC .60 1.50
215a Derek Jeter 1.00 2.50
215b Derek Jeter 6.00 15.00
Dice Back SP
215c Derek Jeter 50.00 100.00
Red-Yellow Nameplate
216 Carlos Pena .25 .60
217 Carlos Ruiz .15 .40
218 Jason Marquis .15 .40
219 Charlie Manuel MG .15 .40
220 Bruce Bochy MG .15 .40
221 Terry Francona MG .25 .60
222 Manny Acta MG .15 .40
223 Jim Leyland MG .15 .40
224 Bob Geren MG .15 .40
225 Mike Scioscia MG .15 .40
226 Ron Gardenhire MG .15 .40
227 Luis Castillo .15 .40
228 New York Mets .25 .60
229 Carlos Carrasco (RC) 1.00 2.50
230 Chone Figgins .15 .40
231 Johan Santana .40 1.00
232 Max Scherzer .15 .40
233a Ian Kinsler .25 .60
233b Ian Kinsler 3.00 8.00
Dice Back SP
234 Jeff Samardzija .15 .40
235 Will Venable .15 .40
236 Cristian Guzman .15 .40
237 Alexei Ramirez .15 .40
238 B.J. Upton .25 .60
239 Derek Lowe .15 .40
240 Elvis Andrus .25 .60
241 Joakim Soria .15 .40
242 Chase Headley .15 .40

243 Adam Lind .25 .60
244a Ichiro Suzuki .60 1.50
244b Ichiro Suzuki 4.00 10.00
Dice Back SP
245 Ryan Howard .50 1.25
246 Johnny Damon .25 .60
247 Casey Blake .15 .40
248 Kevin Millwood .15 .40
249 Cincinnati Reds .15 .40
250 Andrew McCutchen .40 1.00
Garrett Jones
251 Jarrod Washburn .15 .40
252 Dan Uggla .25 .60
253 Cliff Lee .25 .60
254 Chris Davis .15 .40
255 Jordan Zimmermann .15 .40
256 Pedro Feliz .15 .40
257 Carlos Quentin .25 .60
258 Derek Holland .15 .40
259 Jose Reyes .25 .60
260 Manny Ramirez .40 1.00
261 David Ortiz .25 .60
262 Andrew McCutchen .40 1.00
263 Brian Fuentes .15 .40
264 Nelson Cruz .25 .60
265 Dexter Fowler .15 .40
266 Carlos Beltran .15 .40
267 Michael Young .25 .60
268 Chris Young .15 .40
269 Edgar Renteria .15 .40
270 Vin Mazzaro .15 .40
271 Gary Sheffield .15 .40
272 Roy Oswalt .25 .60
273 Checklist .15 .40
274 Stephen Drew .15 .40
275 John Lannan .15 .40
276 Tyler Flowers RC .60 1.50
277 Coco Crisp .15 .40
278 Luis Durango RC .40 1.00
279 Erick Aybar .15 .40
280 Tobi Stoner RC .60 1.50
281 Cody Ross .15 .40
282 Koji Uehara .25 .60
283 Cleveland Indians .15 .40
284 Yovani Gallardo .15 .40
285 Wilkin Ramirez .15 .40
286 Roy Halladay .40 1.00
287 Juan Francisco RC .60 1.50
288 Carlos Zambrano .25 .60
289 Carl Crawford .25 .60
290 Joba Chamberlain .25 .60
291 Fernando Martinez .15 .40
292 Jhoulys Chacin .15 .40
293 Felix Hernandez .40 1.00
294 Josh Hamilton .40 1.00
295 Rick Ankiel .15 .40
296 Hiroki Kuroda .15 .40
297 Oakland Athletics .15 .40
298 Wade Davis (RC) .40 1.00
299 Derrek Lee .15 .40
300a Hanley Ramirez .40 1.00
300b Hanley Ramirez 3.00 8.00
Dice Back SP
301 Ryan Spilborghs .15 .40
302 Adrian Beltre .15 .40
303 James Shields .15 .40
304 Alex Gordon .25 .60
305 Brad Bergesen .15 .40
306 Lee Dominates .25 .60
307 Burnett Outduels Pedro .25 .60
308 Replay Gives AROD Homer .60 1.50
309 Damon Steals 2 Bags on 1 Pitch .25 .60
310 Utley Ties Reggie .40 1.00
311 Matsui Knocks in 6 .40 1.00
312 Matsui Named MVP .40 1.00
313 The Winners Celebrate .40 1.00
314 Hanley Ramirez .50 1.25
Evan Longoria
315 Brandon Webb .25 .60
316 Kevin Youkilis .25 .60
317 Brent Dlugach (RC) .40 1.00
318 Aubrey Huff .15 .40
319 John Maine .15 .40
320 Pittsburgh Pirates .15 .40
321 Aramis Ramirez .15 .40
322 Michael Dunn RC .40 1.00
323 Shin-Soo Choo .25 .60
324 Mike Pelfrey .15 .40
325 Brett Gardner .15 .40
326 Nick Johnson .15 .40
327 Henry Rodriguez RC .40 1.00
328 Joe Nathan .15 .40
329 Mike Napoli .25 .60
330 Jamie Moyer .15 .40
331 Kyle Blanks .15 .40
332 Ryan Langerhans .15 .40
333 Travis Snider .15 .40
334 Wandy Rodriguez .15 .40
335 Carlos Gonzalez .25 .60
336 Francisco Rodriguez .25 .60
337 Mark Buehrle .15 .40
Jake Peavy
338 Ryan Zimmerman .25 .60
339 Michael Bourn .15 .40
340 Magglio Ordonez .25 .60
341 Brandon Morrow .15 .40
342 Daniel Murphy .15 .40
343 Ricky Romero .15 .40
344 Homer Bailey .15 .40
345 Nick Swisher .40 1.00
346 Akinori Iwamura .15 .40
347 St. Louis Cardinals .25 .60
348 Julio Borbon .15 .40
349 Jose Guillen .15 .40
350 Scott Podsednik .15 .40
351 Bobby Crosby .15 .40
352 Ryan Ludwick .15 .40
353 Brett Cecil .15 .40
354 Minnesota Twins .15 .40
355 Ben Zobrist .15 .40
356 Dan Haren .15 .40
357 Vernon Wells .15 .40
358 Skip Schumaker .15 .40
359 Jose Lopez .15 .40
360a Vladimir Guerrero .40 1.00
360b Vladimir Guerrero 3.00 8.00
Dice Back SP
361 Checklist .15 .40
362 Brandon Allen (RC) .40 1.00
363 Joe Mauer .40 1.00
Roy Halladay
364 Todd Helton .25 .60
365 J.J. Hardy .15 .40
366a CC Sabathia .25 .60
366b CC Sabathia 50.00 100.00
Green-Yellow Nameplate SP
367 Yuniesky Betancourt .15 .40
368 Placido Polanco .15 .40
369 Josh Johnson .25 .60
370 Mark Reynolds .15 .40
371a Victor Martinez .25 .60
371b Victor Martinez 3.00 8.00
Dice Back SP
372 Ian Stewart .15 .40
373 Boston Red Sox .25 .60
374 Brad Hawpe .15 .40
375 Ricky Nolasco .15 .40
376 Marco Scutaro .15 .40
377 Troy Tulowitzki .40 1.00
378 Francisco Liriano .15 .40
379 Randy Wells .15 .40
380 Jeff Francoeur .25 .60
381 Mike Lowell .15 .40
382 Hunter Pence .25 .60
383 Tim Lincecum .60 1.50
Matt Cain
384 Scott Kazmir .15 .40
385 Hideki Matsui .40 1.00
386 Tim Wakefield .15 .40
387 Jeff Niemann .15 .40
388 John Smoltz .40 1.00
389 Franklin Gutierrez .15 .40
390 Matt LaPorta .40 1.00
391 Melvin Mora .15 .40
392 Jeremy Bonderman .15 .40
393a Ryan Braun .50 1.25
393b Ryan Braun 30.00 60.00
Blue-Orange Nameplate SP
394 Emilio Bonifacio .15 .40
395 Tommy Hanson .25 .60
396 Aaron Hill .15 .40
397 Micah Owings .15 .40
398 Jack Cust .15 .40
399 Jason Bartlett .15 .40
400 Brian McCann .25 .60
401 Babe Ruth BT 1.00 2.50
402 George Sisler BT .40 1.00
403 Jackie Robinson BT .40 1.00
404 Rogers Hornsby BT .25 .60
405 Lou Gehrig BT .75 2.00
406 Mickey Mantle BT 1.25 3.00
407 Ty Cobb BT .60 1.50
408 Christy Mathewson BT .40 1.00
409 Walter Johnson BT .40 1.00
410 Honus Wagner BT .40 1.00
411 Andy Pettitte 1.00 2.50
Jorge Posada
Derek Jeter
Mariano Rivera
412 Joe Saunders .15 .40
413 Andrew Miller .15 .40
414 Alcides Escobar .25 .60
415 Luke Hochevar .15 .40
416 Gerardo Parra .15 .40
417 Garrett Atkins .15 .40
418 Jim Thome .25 .60
419 Michael Saunders .15 .40
420 Justin Morneau .40 1.00
421 Dustin Pedroia .50 1.25
422 Dioner Navarro .15 .40
423 Checklist .15 .40
424 Chien-Ming Wang .25 .60
425 Marcus Thames .15 .40
426 David Price SP 3.00 8.00
427a David Wright SP 4.00 10.00
427b David Wright 30.00 60.00
Green-Yellow Nameplate SP
428 Tommy Manzella SP (RC) 2.50 6.00
429a Tim Lincecum SP 5.00 12.00
429b Tim Lincecum 5.00 12.00
Dice Back SP
430 Ken Griffey Jr. SP 4.00 10.00
431 Justin Masterson SP 2.50 6.00
432 Jermaine Dye SP 2.50 6.00
433 Casey McGehee SP 2.50 6.00
434 Brett Anderson SP 4.00 10.00
435 Matt Garza SP 2.50 6.00
436 Miguel Tejada SP 3.00 8.00
437 Checklist SP 2.50 6.00
438 Kurt Suzuki SP 2.50 6.00
439 Evan Longoria SP 3.00 8.00
440 Edinson Volquez SP 2.50 6.00
441 Doug Fister SP 2.50 6.00
442 Carlos Delgado SP 2.50 6.00
443 Philadelphia Phillies SP 2.50 6.00
444 Justin Duchscherer SP 2.50 6.00
445 Chris Volstad SP 2.50 6.00
446 Freddy Sanchez SP 2.50 6.00
447 Carlos Lee SP 2.50 6.00
448 Carlos Guillen SP 2.50 6.00
449 Hank Blalock SP 2.50 6.00
450 Ubaldo Jimenez SP 4.00 10.00
451 Derek Jeter 5.00 12.00
Jason Bartlett SP
452 Cliff Pennington SP 2.50 6.00
453 Miguel Montero SP 2.50 6.00
454 Corey Hart SP 2.50 6.00
455 Bronson Arroyo SP 2.50 6.00
456 Carlos Gomez SP 2.50 6.00
457 J.D. Drew SP 2.50 6.00
458 Kenshin Kawakami SP 3.00 8.00
459 Neftali Feliz SP 2.00 5.00
460 Bobby Abreu SP 2.50 6.00
461 Joe Maddon MG AS SP 2.50 6.00
462 Charlie Manuel MG AS SP 2.50 6.00
463a Mark Teixeira AS SP 3.00 8.00
463b Atlanta Braves SP 12.50 30.00
464 Albert Pujols AS SP 5.00 12.00
465 Aaron Hill AS SP 2.50 6.00
466 Chase Utley AS SP 3.00 8.00
467 Michael Young AS SP 3.00 8.00
468 David Wright AS SP 4.00 10.00
469 Derek Jeter AS SP 5.00 12.00
470 Hanley Ramirez AS SP 3.00 8.00
471 Jason Giambi SP 2.50 6.00
472 Ichiro Suzuki SP 4.00 10.00
473 Miguel Tejada SP 3.00 8.00
474 Alex Rodriguez SP 4.00 10.00
475 Justin Morneau SP 5.00 12.00
476 Dustin Pedroia SP 4.00 10.00
477 Albert Pujols SP 5.00 12.00
478 Jimmy Rollins SP 3.00 8.00
479 Ryan Howard SP 4.00 10.00
480 Cole Hamels SP 3.00 8.00
481 Manny Ramirez SP 3.00 8.00
482 Jermaine Dye SP 2.50 6.00
483 Mariano Rivera SP 5.00 12.00
484 Roy Oswalt SP 3.00 8.00
485 Matt Garza SP 2.50 6.00
486 Derek Jeter SP 5.00 12.00
487 Ichiro Suzuki AS SP 4.00 10.00
488 Raul Ibanez AS SP 3.00 8.00
489 Josh Hamilton AS SP 3.00 8.00
490 Shane Victorino AS SP 3.00 8.00
491 Jason Bay AS SP 3.00 8.00
492 Ryan Braun AS SP 4.00 10.00
493 Joe Mauer AS SP 3.00 8.00
494 Yadier Molina AS SP 3.00 8.00
495 Roy Halladay AS SP 5.00 12.00
496 Tim Lincecum AS SP 5.00 12.00
497 Mark Buehrle AS SP 4.00 10.00
498 Johan Santana AS SP 3.00 8.00
499 Mariano Rivera AS SP 5.00 12.00
500 Francisco Rodriguez AS SP 3.00 8.00

2010 Topps Heritage Chrome

COMPLETE SET (150) 125.00 250.00
1-100 STATED ODDS 1:5 HERITAGE HOBBY
101-150 ODDS 1:26 T.CHROME HOBBY
STATED PRINT RUN 1961 SER.#'d SETS
C1 Albert Pujols 5.00 12.00
C2 Joe Mauer 2.50 6.00
C3 Rajai Davis 1.50 4.00
C4 Adam Wainwright 2.00 5.00
C5 Grady Sizemore 2.00 5.00
C6 Alex Rodriguez 3.00 8.00
C7 Cole Hamels 2.50 6.00
C8 Matt Kemp 2.00 5.00
C9 Chris Tillman 1.50 4.00
C10 Reid Gorecki 2.00 5.00
C11 Chris Carpenter 2.50 6.00
C12 Jason Bay 2.00 5.00
C13 Gordon Beckham 2.00 5.00
C14 Curtis Granderson 2.00 5.00
C15 Daniel McCutchen 2.00 5.00
C16 Pablo Sandoval 2.00 5.00
C17 Jake Peavy 1.25 3.00
C18 Ryan Church 1.50 4.00
C19 Nick Markakis 2.50 6.00
C20 Josh Beckett 2.00 5.00
C21 Matt Cain 2.00 5.00
C22 Nate McLouth 1.50 4.00
C23 J.A. Happ 2.00 5.00
C24 Justin Upton 2.50 6.00
C25 Rick Porcello 1.50 4.00
C26 Mark Teixeira 2.50 6.00
C27 Raul Ibanez 2.00 5.00
C28 Zack Greinke 2.00 5.00
C29 Nolan Reimold 2.00 5.00
C30 Jimmy Rollins 2.00 5.00
C31 Jorge Posada 2.00 5.00
C32 Clayton Kershaw 2.50 6.00
C33 Buster Posey 12.00 30.00
C34 Adam Dunn 2.00 5.00
C35 Chipper Jones 2.50 6.00
C36 John Lackey 1.50 4.00
C37 Daniel Hudson 2.00 5.00
C38 Jacoby Ellsbury 2.50 6.00
C39 Mariano Rivera 2.50 6.00
C40 Jair Jurrjens 1.50 4.00
C41 Prince Fielder 1.50 4.00
C42 Shane Victorino 2.00 5.00
C43 Mark Buehrle 2.00 5.00
C44 Madison Bumgarner 2.50 6.00
C45 Yunel Escobar 1.50 4.00
C46 Chris Coghlan 1.50 4.00
C47 Justin Verlander 4.00 10.00
C48 Michael Brantley 1.50 4.00
C49 Matt Holliday 2.50 6.00
C50 Chase Utley 2.50 6.00
C51 Adam Jones 2.00 5.00
C52 Kendry Morales 1.50 4.00
C53 Denard Span 1.50 4.00
C54 Nyjer Morgan 1.50 4.00
C55 Adrian Gonzalez 2.00 5.00
C56 Daisuke Matsuzaka 2.00 5.00
C57 Joey Votto 2.50 6.00
C58 Jered Weaver 1.50 4.00
C59 Lance Berkman 2.00 5.00
C60 Andre Ethier 2.00 5.00
C61 Mat Latos 1.50 4.00
C62 Derek Jeter 5.00 12.00
C63 Johan Santana 2.50 6.00
C64 Max Scherzer 1.50 4.00
C65 Ian Kinsler 2.00 5.00
C66 Elvis Andrus 2.00 5.00
C67 Adam Lind 2.00 5.00
C68 Ichiro Suzuki 3.00 8.00
C69 Ryan Howard 2.50 6.00
C70 Dan Uggla 2.00 5.00
C71 Cliff Lee 2.00 5.00
C72 Andrew McCutchen 2.50 6.00
C73 Nelson Cruz 2.00 5.00
C74 Stephen Drew 1.25 3.00
C75 Koji Uehara 2.00 5.00
C76 Roy Halladay 2.50 6.00
C77 Felix Hernandez 2.50 6.00
C78 Josh Hamilton 2.50 6.00
C79 Hanley Ramirez 2.50 6.00
C80 Kevin Youkilis 2.00 5.00
C81 Kyle Blanks 1.50 4.00
C82 Ryan Zimmerman 2.00 5.00
C83 Ricky Romero 1.50 4.00
C84 Julio Borbon 1.50 4.00
C85 Ben Zobrist 1.50 4.00
C86 Vladimir Guerrero 2.50 6.00
C87 CC Sabathia 2.00 5.00
C88 Josh Johnson 2.00 5.00
C89 Mark Reynolds 1.50 4.00
C90 Troy Tulowitzki 3.00 8.00
C91 Hunter Pence 2.00 5.00
C92 Ryan Braun 2.50 6.00
C93 Tommy Hanson 2.00 5.00
C94 Aaron Hill 1.50 4.00
C95 Brian McCann 2.00 5.00
C96 David Wright 2.50 6.00
C97 Tim Lincecum 3.00 8.00
C98 Evan Longoria 2.50 6.00
C99 Ubaldo Jimenez 2.00 5.00
C100 Neftali Feliz 1.50 4.00
C101 Brian Roberts 1.50 4.00
C102 A.J. Burnett 2.00 5.00
C103 Ryan Dempster 1.50 4.00
C104 Russell Martin 1.50 4.00
C105 Jay Bruce 2.00 5.00
C106 Jayson Werth 2.00 5.00
C107 Michael Cuddyer 1.50 4.00
C108 Alfonso Soriano 2.00 5.00
C109 Martin Prado 1.50 4.00
C110 Miguel Cabrera 2.50 6.00
C111 Yadier Molina 2.00 5.00
C112 Kosuke Fukudome 2.50 6.00
C113 Andy Pettitte 2.00 5.00
C114 Johnny Cueto 1.50 4.00
C115 Alex Rios 2.00 5.00
C116 Howie Kendrick 1.50 4.00
C117 Robinson Cano 2.50 6.00
C118 Chad Billingsley 1.50 4.00
C119 Torii Hunter 1.50 4.00
C120 Brandon Phillips 1.50 4.00
C121 Carlos Pena 2.00 5.00
C122 Chone Figgins 1.50 4.00
C123 Alexei Ramirez 1.50 4.00
C124 Carlos Quentin 2.00 5.00
C125 Jose Reyes 2.00 5.00
C126 Manny Ramirez 2.50 6.00
C127 David Ortiz 2.00 5.00
C128 Carlos Beltran 1.50 4.00
C129 Michael Young 2.50 6.00
C130 Roy Oswalt 2.00 5.00
C131 Erick Aybar 1.50 4.00
C132 Yovani Gallardo 1.50 4.00
C133 Carlos Zambrano 2.00 5.00
C134 Carl Crawford 2.00 5.00
C135 Aramis Ramirez 1.50 4.00
C136 Shin-Soo Choo 1.50 4.00
C137 Wandy Rodriguez 1.50 4.00
C138 Magglio Ordonez 2.00 5.00
C139 Dan Haren 1.50 4.00
C140 Victor Martinez 2.00 5.00
C141 Ian Stewart 1.50 4.00
C142 Francisco Liriano 1.50 4.00
C143 Scott Kazmir 1.50 4.00
C144 Hideki Matsui 2.50 6.00
C145 Justin Morneau 2.50 6.00
C146 Dustin Pedroia 2.50 6.00
C147 David Price 2.50 6.00
C148 Ken Griffey Jr. 3.00 8.00
C149 Carlos Lee 1.50 4.00
C150 Bobby Abreu 1.50 4.00

2010 Topps Heritage Chrome Black Refractors

1-100 ODDS 1:255 HERITAGE HOBBY
101-150 ODDS 1:816 T.CHROME HOBBY
STATED PRINT RUN 61SER.#'d SETS
C1 Albert Pujols 50.00 120.00
C2 Joe Mauer 20.00 50.00
C3 Rajai Davis 8.00 20.00
C4 Adam Wainwright 12.00 30.00
C5 Grady Sizemore 12.00 30.00
C6 Alex Rodriguez 30.00 80.00
C7 Cole Hamels 20.00 50.00
C8 Matt Kemp 12.00 30.00
C9 Chris Tillman 8.00 20.00
C10 Reid Gorecki 12.00 30.00
C11 Chris Carpenter 20.00 50.00
C12 Jason Bay 12.00 30.00
C13 Gordon Beckham 12.00 30.00
C14 Curtis Granderson 12.00 30.00
C15 Daniel McCutchen 12.00 30.00
C16 Pablo Sandoval 12.00 30.00
C17 Jake Peavy 8.00 20.00
C18 Ryan Church 8.00 20.00
C19 Nick Markakis 20.00 50.00
C20 Josh Beckett 12.00 30.00
C21 Matt Cain 12.00 30.00
C22 Nate McLouth 8.00 20.00
C23 J.A. Happ 12.00 30.00
C24 Justin Upton 12.00 30.00
C25 Rick Porcello 8.00 20.00
C26 Mark Teixeira 20.00 50.00
C27 Raul Ibanez 12.00 30.00
C28 Zack Greinke 12.00 30.00
C29 Nolan Reimold 12.00 30.00
C30 Jimmy Rollins 12.00 30.00
C31 Jorge Posada 12.00 30.00
C32 Clayton Kershaw 20.00 50.00
C33 Buster Posey 80.00 200.00
C34 Adam Dunn 12.00 30.00
C35 Chipper Jones 20.00 50.00
C36 John Lackey 8.00 20.00
C37 Daniel Hudson 12.00 30.00
C38 Jacoby Ellsbury 20.00 50.00
C39 Mariano Rivera 20.00 50.00
C40 Jair Jurrjens 8.00 20.00
C41 Prince Fielder 12.00 30.00
C42 Shane Victorino 12.00 30.00
C43 Mark Buehrle 12.00 30.00
C44 Madison Bumgarner 20.00 50.00
C45 Yunel Escobar 8.00 20.00
C46 Chris Coghlan 8.00 20.00
C47 Justin Verlander 25.00 60.00
C48 Michael Brantley 8.00 20.00
C49 Matt Holliday 20.00 50.00
C50 Chase Utley 20.00 50.00
C51 Adam Jones 12.00 30.00
C52 Kendry Morales 8.00 20.00
C53 Denard Span 8.00 20.00
C54 Nyjer Morgan 8.00 20.00
C55 Adrian Gonzalez 12.00 30.00
C56 Daisuke Matsuzaka 20.00 50.00
C57 Joey Votto 20.00 50.00
C58 Jered Weaver 8.00 20.00
C59 Lance Berkman 12.00 30.00
C60 Andre Ethier 12.00 30.00
C61 Mat Latos 8.00 20.00
C62 Derek Jeter 50.00 120.00
C63 Johan Santana 20.00 50.00
C64 Max Scherzer 8.00 20.00
C65 Ian Kinsler 12.00 30.00
C66 Elvis Andrus 12.00 30.00
C67 Adam Lind 12.00 30.00
C68 Ichiro Suzuki 30.00 80.00
C69 Ryan Howard 25.00 60.00
C70 Dan Uggla 12.00 30.00
C71 Cliff Lee 12.00 30.00
C72 Andrew McCutchen 20.00 50.00
C73 Nelson Cruz 12.00 30.00
C74 Stephen Drew 8.00 20.00
C75 Koji Uehara 12.00 30.00
C76 Roy Halladay 20.00 50.00
C77 Felix Hernandez 20.00 50.00
C78 Josh Hamilton 20.00 50.00
C79 Hanley Ramirez 20.00 50.00
C80 Kevin Youkilis 12.00 30.00
C81 Kyle Blanks 8.00 20.00
C82 Ryan Zimmerman 12.00 30.00
C83 Ricky Romero 8.00 20.00
C84 Julio Borbon 8.00 20.00
C85 Ben Zobrist 8.00 20.00
C86 Vladimir Guerrero 20.00 50.00
C87 CC Sabathia 12.00 30.00
C88 Josh Johnson 12.00 30.00
C89 Mark Reynolds 8.00 20.00
C90 Troy Tulowitzki 20.00 50.00
C91 Hunter Pence 12.00 30.00
C92 Ryan Braun 25.00 60.00
C93 Tommy Hanson 12.00 30.00
C94 Aaron Hill 8.00 20.00
C95 Brian McCann 12.00 30.00
C96 David Wright 25.00 60.00
C97 Tim Lincecum 30.00 80.00
C98 Evan Longoria 25.00 60.00
C99 Ubaldo Jimenez 12.00 30.00
C100 Neftali Feliz 8.00 20.00
C101 Brian Roberts 8.00 20.00
C102 A.J. Burnett 12.00 30.00
C103 Ryan Dempster 8.00 20.00
C104 Russell Martin 8.00 20.00
C105 Jay Bruce 12.00 30.00
C106 Jayson Werth 12.00 30.00
C107 Michael Cuddyer 8.00 20.00
C108 Alfonso Soriano 12.00 30.00
C109 Martin Prado 8.00 20.00
C110 Miguel Cabrera 20.00 50.00
C111 Yadier Molina 12.00 30.00
C112 Kosuke Fukudome 20.00 50.00
C113 Andy Pettitte 12.00 30.00
C114 Johnny Cueto 8.00 20.00
C115 Alex Rios 12.00 30.00
C116 Howie Kendrick 8.00 20.00
C117 Robinson Cano 20.00 50.00
C118 Chad Billingsley 8.00 20.00
C119 Torii Hunter 8.00 20.00
C120 Brandon Phillips 8.00 20.00
C121 Carlos Pena 12.00 30.00
C122 Chone Figgins 8.00 20.00
C123 Alexei Ramirez 8.00 20.00
C124 Carlos Quentin 12.00 30.00
C125 Jose Reyes 12.00 30.00
C126 Manny Ramirez 20.00 50.00
C127 David Ortiz 12.00 30.00
C128 Carlos Beltran 8.00 20.00
C129 Michael Young 12.00 30.00
C130 Roy Oswalt 12.00 30.00
C131 Erick Aybar 8.00 20.00
C132 Yovani Gallardo 8.00 20.00
C133 Carlos Zambrano 12.00 30.00
C134 Carl Crawford 12.00 30.00
C135 Aramis Ramirez 8.00 20.00
C136 Shin-Soo Choo 12.00 30.00
C137 Wandy Rodriguez 8.00 20.00
C138 Magglio Ordonez 12.00 30.00
C139 Dan Haren 8.00 20.00
C140 Victor Martinez 12.00 30.00
C141 Ian Stewart 8.00 20.00
C142 Francisco Liriano 8.00 20.00
C143 Scott Kazmir 8.00 20.00
C144 Hideki Matsui 20.00 50.00
C145 Justin Morneau 20.00 50.00
C146 Dustin Pedroia 25.00 60.00
C147 David Price 20.00 50.00
C148 Ken Griffey Jr. 30.00 80.00
C149 Carlos Lee 8.00 20.00
C150 Bobby Abreu 8.00 20.00

2010 Topps Heritage Chrome Refractors

*REF: .6X TO 1.5X BASIC INSERTS
1-100 ODDS 1:18 HERITAGE HOBBY
101-150 ODDS 1:88 T.CHROME HOBBY
STATED PRINT RUN 561 SER.#'d SETS

2010 Topps Heritage Baseball Flashbacks

COMPLETE SET (10) 6.00 15.00
STATED ODDS 1:12 HOBBY
BF1 Roger Maris 1.25 3.00
BF2 Warren Spahn .75 2.00
BF3 Whitey Ford .75 2.00
BF4 Frank Robinson .75 2.00
BF5 Whitey Ford .75 2.00
BF6 Candlestick Park .50 1.25
BF7 Carl Yastrzemski 1.25 3.00
BF8 Luis Aparicio .50 1.25
BF9 Al Kaline 1.25 3.00
BF10 Angels .50 1.25
Senators

2010 Topps Heritage Chase 61 Dual Relic

STATED ODDS 1:192,300 HOBBY
STATED PRINT RUN 5 SER.#'d SETS
NO PRICING DUE TO SCARCITY
MM Mickey Mantle
Roger Maris

2010 Topps Heritage Chase 61 Triple Relic

STATED ODDS 1:192,300 HOBBY
STATED PRINT RUN 5 SER.#'d SETS
NO PRICING DUE TO SCARCITY
MMR Mickey Mantle
Roger Maris
Babe Ruth

2010 Topps Heritage Chase 61 Dual Cut Signature

STATED ODDS 1:577,000
STATED PRINT RUN 1 SER.#'d SET
NO PRICING DUE TO SCARCITY
MM Mickey Mantle
Roger Maris

2010 Topps Heritage Chase 61 Triple Cut Signature

STATED ODDS 1:577,000
STATED PRINT RUN 1 SER.#'d SET
NO PRICING DUE TO SCARCITY
MMR Mickey Mantle
Roger Maris
Babe Ruth

2010 Topps Heritage Clubhouse Collection Relics

STATED ODDS 1:29 HOBBY
AE Andre Ethier 3.00 8.00
AK Adam Kennedy 3.00 8.00
AL Adam Lind 3.00 8.00
AP Albert Pujols 10.00 25.00
AR Aramis Ramirez 3.00 8.00
AW Adam Wainwright 3.00 8.00
BJ Bobby Jenks 3.00 8.00
BW Billy Wagner 3.00 8.00
CB Clay Buchholz 3.00 8.00
CG Cristian Guzman 3.00 8.00
CH Cole Hamels 4.00 10.00
CM Carlos Marmol 3.00 8.00
CS CC Sabathia 4.00 10.00
CZ Carlos Zambrano 3.00 8.00
DH Dan Haren 3.00 8.00
DN Dioner Navarro 3.00 8.00
DO David Ortiz 3.00 8.00
DU Dan Uggla 3.00 8.00
EL Evan Longoria 4.00 10.00
EV Edinson Volquez 3.00 8.00
GB Gordon Beckham 5.00 12.00
GS Grady Sizemore 4.00 10.00
HK Hiroki Kuroda 3.00 8.00
JB Jason Bulger 3.00 8.00
JC Jose Contreras 3.00 8.00
JD Jermaine Dye 3.00 8.00
JF Jeff Francis 3.00 8.00
JL James Loney 3.00 8.00
JV Joey Votto 3.00 8.00
JW Jered Weaver 3.00 8.00
KJ Kenji Johjima 3.00 8.00
KM Kendry Morales 3.00 8.00
KW Kerry Wood 3.00 8.00
LB Lance Berkman 3.00 8.00
MB Mark Buehrle 3.00 8.00
ME Mark Ellis
MK Matt Kemp 3.00 8.00
MT Miguel Tejada 3.00 8.00
MY Michael Young 3.00 8.00
NM Nate McLouth 3.00 8.00
PK Paul Konerko 3.00 8.00
PS Pablo Sandoval 4.00 10.00
RB Rocco Baldelli 3.00 8.00
RD Ryan Dempster 3.00 8.00
RH Ryan Howard 4.00 10.00
RL Ryan Ludwick 3.00 8.00
RM Russell Martin
VG Vladimir Guerrero 3.00 8.00
AJP A.J. Pierzynski 3.00 8.00
ARA Alexei Ramirez 3.00 8.00
BWE Brandon Webb 3.00 8.00
CHE Chase Headley 3.00 8.00
HCK Hong-Chih Kuo 3.00 8.00
JCR Joe Crede 3.00 8.00
KMI Kevin Millwood 3.00 8.00
MTH Matt Thornton

2010 Topps Heritage Clubhouse Collection Dual Relics

STATED ODDS 1:6150 HOBBY
STATED PRINT RUN 61 SER.#'d SETS
AR Luis Aparicio 60.00 120.00
Alexei Ramirez
BM Brooks Robinson
Nick Markakis
MR Roger Maris 100.00 200.00
Alex Rodriguez
MT Mickey Mantle 100.00 200.00
Mark Teixeira
YB Carl Yastrzemski
Jason Bay
YE Carl Yastrzemski 150.00 300.00
Jacoby Ellsbury

2010 Topps Heritage Clubhouse Collection Relic Autographs

STATED ODDS 1:7900 HOBBY
STATED PRINT RUN 25 SER.#'d SETS
NO PRICING DUE TO SCARCITY

2010 Topps Heritage Clubhouse Collection Dual Relic Autographs

STATED ODDS 1:12,275 HOBBY
STATED PRINT RUN 10 SER.#'d SETS
NO PRICING DUE TO SCARCITY

2010 Topps Heritage Cut Signatures

STATED ODDS 1:285,000
STATED PRINT RUN 1 SER.#'d SET
NO PRICING DUE TO SCARCITY

2010 Topps Heritage Flashback Autographs

STATED ODDS 1:15,600 HOBBY
STATED PRINT RUN 25 SER.#'d SETS
NO PRICING DUE TO SCARCITY

2010 Topps Heritage Flashback Stadium Dual Relics

STATED ODDS 1:38,500 HOBBY
STATED PRINT RUN 10 SER.#'d SETS
NO PRICING DUE TO SCARCITY

2010 Topps Heritage Flashback Stadium Relic Autographs

STATED ODDS 1:15,600 HOBBY
STATED PRINT RUN 25 SER.#'d SETS
NO PRICING DUE TO SCARCITY

2010 Topps Heritage Flashback Stadium Relics

STATED ODDS 1:475 HOBBY
AK Al Kaline 12.50 30.00
BG Bob Gibson 12.50 30.00
EB Ernie Banks 15.00 40.00
FR Frank Robinson
JP Jim Piersall 12.50 30.00
LA Luis Aparicio 20.00 50.00
MM Mickey Mantle 50.00 100.00
RM Roger Maris 30.00 60.00
RS Brooks Robinson 10.00 25.00
SM Stan Musial 15.00 40.00

2010 Topps Heritage Framed Buyback Stamps

STATED ODDS 1:6074 HOBBY
STATED PRINT RUN 1 SER.#'d SET
NO PRICING DUE TO SCARCITY

2010 Topps Heritage Framed Dual Stamps

STATED ODDS 1:193 HOBBY
STATED PRINT RUN 50 SER.#'d SETS
AD Brett Anderson 6.00 15.00
Adam Dunn
AH Bronson Arroyo 4.00 10.00
Luke Hochevar
AP Garret Anderson 6.00 15.00
Andy Pettitte
BA Casey Blake 6.00 15.00
Elvis Andrus
BE Mark Buehrle 6.00 15.00
Yunel Escobar
BF Ryan Braun 12.00 30.00
Gavin Floyd
BG Jay Bruce 6.00 15.00
Curtis Granderson
BL Carlos Beltran 4.00 10.00
John Lackey
BT Marlon Byrd 6.00 15.00
Josh Thole
BU Kyle Blanks 6.00 15.00
B.J. Upton
CB Jorge Cantu 4.00 10.00
Scott Baker
CE Michael Cuddyer 6.00 15.00
Andre Either
CG Johnny Cueto 6.00 15.00
Zack Greinke
CH1 Miguel Cabrera 10.00 25.00
Felix Hernandez
CH2 Chris Coghlan 10.00 25.00
Felix Hernandez
CJ Miguel Cabrera 10.00 25.00
Garrett Jones
CK Matt Cain 6.00 15.00
Paul Konerko
CL Melky Cabrera 4.00 10.00
Mat Latos
CM Orlando Cabrera 6.00 15.00
Yadier Molina
CR Shin-Soo Choo 6.00 15.00
Francisco Rodriguez
DA Adam Dunn 6.00 15.00
Bobby Abreu
DF Zach Duke 6.00 15.00
Tyler Flowers
DG David DeJesus 6.00 15.00
Reid Gorecki
DI Johnny Damon 6.00 15.00
Raul Ibanez
DR Rajai Davis 4.00 10.00
Mark Reynolds
DY Ryan Dempster 6.00 15.00
Michael Young
EC Andre Either 10.00 25.00
Robinson Cano
FB Pedro Feliz 4.00 10.00
Adrian Beltre
FG Jeff Francouer 6.00 15.00
Carlos Guillen
GB Cristian Guzman 4.00 10.00
Chad Billingsley
GC Adrian Gonzalez 6.00 15.00
Carl Crawford
GF Matt Garza 6.00 15.00
Prince Fielder
GG Curtis Granderson 6.00 15.00
Adrian Gonzalez
GH Carlos Guillen 4.00 10.00
Rich Harden
GR Zack Greinke 10.00 25.00
Hanley Ramirez
GS Reid Gorecki 6.00 15.00
Joe Saunders
GW Vladimir Guerrero 12.00 30.00
David Wright
HA Orlando Hudson 4.00 10.00
Erick Aybar
HB Rich Harden 4.00 10.00
Marlon Byrd
HC J.A. Happ 10.00 25.00
Miguel Cabrera
HM Matt Holiday 10.00 25.00
Justin Morneau
HR Aaron Hill 6.00 15.00
Jimmy Rollins
HU Roy Halladay 6.00 15.00
Justin Upton
IL Raul Ibanez 10.00 25.00
Jon Lester
IU Ian Kinsler 10.00 25.00
Chase Utley

JL Jair Jurrjens 6.00 15.00
Adam Lind
JM Josh Johnson 6.00 15.00
Victor Martinez
JN Garrett Jones 4.00 10.00
Jeff Neimann
JO Ubaldo Jimenez 6.00 15.00
Magglio Ordonez
JZ Adam Jones 6.00 15.00
Ryan Zimmerman
KA Howie Kendrick 4.00 10.00
Bronson Arroyo
KD Jason Kubel 4.00 10.00
Stephen Drew
KJ Paul Konerko 6.00 15.00
Ubaldo Jimenez
KK Matt Kemp 6.00 15.00
Scott Kazmir
KM Scott Kazmir 4.00 10.00
Nate McLouth
KP Hiroki Kuroda 4.00 10.00
Chris Pettit
KQ Kenshin Kawakami 6.00 15.00
Carlos Quentin
KR Clayton Kershaw 10.00 25.00
Alexi Ramirez
LC Derek Lowe 4.00 10.00
Orlando Cabrera
LG Tim Lincecum 15.00 40.00
Matt Garza
LL Adam Lind 6.00 15.00
Felipe Lopez
LM Cliff Lee 10.00 25.00
Hideki Matsui
LT Mat Latos 4.00 10.00
Chris Tillman
LW Jon Lester 10.00 25.00
Jayson Werth
LZ Jose Lopez 4.00 10.00
Jordan Zimmermann
MB Kevin Millwood 4.00 10.00
Casey Blake
MD Yadier Molina 6.00 15.00
David DeJesus
ME Nate McLouth 10.00 25.00
Jacoby Ellsbury
MG Miguel Montero 15.00 40.00
Ken Griffey
ML Hideki Matsui 10.00 25.00
James Loney
MM Kendry Morales 10.00 25.00
Andrew McCutchen
MU Justin Morneau 10.00 25.00
Dan Uggla
MV Andrew McCutchen 12.00 30.00
Justin Verlander
NF Ricky Nolasco 4.00 10.00
Scott Feldman
NG Jeff Neimann 4.00 10.00
Cristian Guzman
NL Joe Nathan 4.00 10.00
Derek Lowe
OA Roy Oswalt 6.00 15.00
Brett Anderson
OO Magglio Ordonez 6.00 15.00
Roy Oswalt
OW David Ortiz 6.00 15.00
Brandon Webb
PB Dustin Pedroia 12.00 30.00
Carlos Beltran
PF Andy Pettitte 6.00 15.00
Pedro Feliz
PG Hunter Pence 6.00 15.00
Franklin Gutierrez
PR Mike Pelfrey 4.00 10.00
Dustin Richardson
PS David Price 10.00 25.00
Max Scherzer
QP Carlos Quentin 6.00 15.00
Gerardo Parra
RB Manny Ramirez 10.00 25.00
Gordon Beckham
RJ Hanley Ramirez 10.00 25.00
Adam Jones
RL Alex Rodriguez 15.00 40.00
Tim Lincecum
RM Dustin Richardson 6.00 15.00
Brian McCann
RR Jose Reyes 15.00 40.00
Alex Rodriguez
RT Mark Reynolds 10.00 25.00
Mark Teixeira
SB Ichiro Suzuki 15.00 40.00
Ryan Braun
SC Grady Sizemore 6.00 15.00
Johnny Cueto
SD Johan Santana 10.00 25.00
Rajai Davis
SG Pablo Sandoval 10.00 25.00
Vladimir Guerrero
SJ Denard Span 4.00 10.00
Jair Jurrjens
SK Kurt Suzuki 10.00 25.00
Clayton Kershaw
SY Nick Swisher 10.00 25.00
Eric Young Jr.
TD Ryan Theriot 6.00 15.00
Johnny Damon
TS Troy Tulowitzki 10.00 25.00
Grady Sizemore
TZ Chris Tillman 6.00 15.00
Carlos Zambrano
UC Koji Uehara 6.00 15.00
Jorge Cantu
UH Dan Uggla 6.00 15.00
Torii Hunter
UK Justin Upton 6.00 15.00
Ian Kinsler
UM B.J. Upton 6.00 15.00
Miguel Montero
UY Chase Utley 10.00 25.00
Kevin Youkilis
VH Justin Verlander 12.00 30.00
Ryan Howard
VM Joey Votto 10.00 25.00
Nick Markakis
VR Shane Victorino 6.00 15.00
Brian Roberts
WF Jered Weaver 4.00 10.00
Dexter Fowler
WL Jayson Werth 6.00 15.00
Jose Lopez
WR Brandon Webb 6.00 15.00
Nolan Reimold
YC Eric Young Jr. 4.00 10.00
Melky Cabrera
YH Michael Young 10.00 25.00
Matt Holliday
YT Kevin Youkilis 10.00 25.00
Troy Tulowitzki
ZL Ryan Zimmerman 12.00 30.00
Evan Longoria
ZO Carlos Zambrano 6.00 15.00
David Ortiz
ZU Jordan Zimmermann 6.00 15.00
Koji Uehara
AR1 Elvis Andrus 10.00 25.00
Colby Rasmus
AR2 Erick Aybar 4.00 10.00
Jorge De La Rosa
AV1 Bobby Abreu 4.00 10.00
Shane Victorino
AV2 Brandon Allen 4.00 10.00
Will Venable
BB1 Jason Bay 6.00 15.00
Lance Berkman
BB2 Adrian Beltre 4.00 10.00
Kyle Blanks
BB3 Chad Billingsley 4.00 10.00
Nick Blackburn
BH1 Scott Baker 4.00 10.00
Dan Haren
BH2 Gordon Beckham 6.00 15.00
Tommy Hanson
BM1 Jason Bartlett 6.00 15.00
Daniel McCutchen
BM2 Lance Berkman 10.00 25.00
Daisuke Matsuzaka
BP1 Josh Beckett 6.00 15.00
Hunter Pence
BP2 A.J. Burnett 6.00 15.00
Joel Pineiro
BV1 Nick Blackburn 10.00 25.00
Joey Votto
BV2 Billy Butler 4.00 10.00
Javier Vazquez
CD1 Robinson Cano 10.00 25.00
Carlos Delgado
CD2 Carl Crawford 6.00 15.00
Ryan Dempster
DB1 Jorge De La Rosa 4.00 10.00
Jason Bartlett
DB2 Carlos Delgado 4.00 10.00
Billy Butler
DS1 Mark Derosa 4.00 10.00
James Shields
DS2 Stephen Drew 4.00 10.00
CC Sabathia
EP1 Jacoby Ellsbury 60.00 150.00
Buster Posey
EP2 Yunel Escobar 4.00 10.00
Rick Porcello
FM1 Prince Fielder 6.00 15.00
Kendry Morales
FM2 Tyler Flowers 6.00 15.00
Daniel Murphy
FS1 Gavin Floyd 6.00 15.00
Alfonso Soriano
FS2 Dexter Fowler 4.00 10.00
Denard Span
FT1 Scott Feldman 4.00 10.00
Ryan Theriot
FT2 Chone Figgins 6.00 15.00
Miguel Tejada
GD1 Ken Griffey 15.00 40.00
Zach Duke
GD2 Franklin Gutierrez 4.00 10.00
Mark Derosa
HF1 Tommy Hanson 6.00 15.00
Chone Figgins
HF2 Luke Hochevar 6.00 15.00
Jeff Francoeur
HH1 Brad Hawpe 6.00 15.00
Daniel Hudson
HH2 Felix Hernandez 10.00 25.00
Orlando Hudson
HJ1 Josh Hamilton 10.00 25.00
Chipper Jones
HJ2 Daniel Hudson 6.00 15.00
Nick Johnson
HK1 Cole Hamels 10.00 25.00
Jason Kubel
HK2 Todd Helton 6.00 15.00
Howie Kendrick
HK3 Torii Hunter 6.00 15.00
Matt Kemp
HP1 Dan Haren 4.00 10.00
Placido Polanco
HP2 Ryan Howard 12.00 30.00
Dustin PedroiaRyan Howard
JS1 Derek Jeter 25.00 60.00
Pablo Sandoval
JS2 Nick Johnson 10.00 25.00
Nick Swisher
JS3 Chipper Jones 15.00 40.00
Ichiro Suzuki
LB1 John Lackey 6.00 15.00
Jay Bruce
LB2 Derrek Lee 4.00 10.00
Mark Buehrle
LB3 Felipe Lopez 6.00 15.00
A.J. Burnett
LR1 Evan Longoria 12.00 30.00
Jose Reyes
LR2 James Loney 6.00 15.00
Juan Rivera
MP1 Nick Markakis 10.00 25.00
David Price
MP2 Joe Mauer 25.00 60.00
Albert Pujols
MR1 Victor Martinez 10.00 25.00
Manny Ramirez
MR2 Daisuke Matsuzaka 10.00 25.00
Aramis Ramirez
MR3 Brian McCann 10.00 25.00
Mariano Rivera
MR4 Daniel Murphy 4.00 10.00
Ricky Romero
MW1 John Maine 4.00 10.00
Vernon Wells
MW2 Daniel McCutchen 6.00 15.00
Jered Weaver
PA1 Jake Peavy 4.00 10.00
Garret Anderson
PA2 Rick Porcello 4.00 10.00
Brandon Allen
PC1 Carlos Pena 6.00 15.00
Matt Cain
PC2 Joel Pineiro 6.00 15.00
Shin-Soo Choo
PJ1 Jorge Posada 6.00 15.00
Josh Johnson
PJ2 Albert Pujols 25.00 60.00
Derek Jeter
PM1 Chris Pettit 4.00 10.00
John Maine
PM2 Placido Polanco 4.00 10.00
Kevin Millwood
PP1 Gerardo Parra 4.00 10.00
Jake Peavy
PP2 Buster Posey 40.00 100.00
Jorge Posada
RH1 Alexi Ramirez 4.00 10.00
Brad Hawpe
RH2 Colby Rasmus 10.00 25.00
J.A. Happ
RK1 Nolan Reimold 6.00 15.00
Kenshin Kawakami
RK2 Ricky Romero 4.00 10.00
Hiroki Kuroda
RN1 Juan Rivera 4.00 10.00
Ricky Nolasco
RN2 Francisco Rodriguez 6.00 15.00
Joe Nathan
RP1 Aramis Ramirez 6.00 15.00
Carlos Pena
RP2 Brian Roberts 4.00 10.00
Mike Pelfrey
RS1 Mariano Rivera 10.00 25.00
Johan Santana
RS2 Jimmy Rollins 6.00 15.00
Kurt Suzuki
SH1 Max Scherzer 4.00 10.00
Aaron Hill
SH2 James Shields 10.00 25.00
Cole Hamels
SH3 Alfonso Soriano 10.00 25.00
Roy Halladay
SL1 CC Sabathia 4.00 10.00
Derrek Lee
SL2 Joe Saunders 6.00 15.00
Cliff Lee
TC1 Mark Teixeira 10.00 25.00
Chris Coghlan
TC2 Miguel Tejada 6.00 15.00
Michael Cuddyer
VB1 Javier Vazquez 6.00 15.00
Josh Beckett
VB2 Will Venable 6.00 15.00
Jason Bay
WH1 Vernon Wells 6.00 15.00
Todd Helton
WH2 David Wright 12.00 30.00
Josh Hamilton

2010 Topps Heritage Mantle Chase 61

COMPLETE SET (15) 30.00 60.00
COMMON MANTLE 3.00 8.00
RANDOM INSERTS IN TARGET PACKS
MM1 Mickey Mantle 3.00 8.00
MM2 Mickey Mantle 3.00 8.00
MM3 Mickey Mantle 3.00 8.00
MM4 Mickey Mantle 3.00 8.00
MM5 Mickey Mantle 3.00 8.00
MM6 Mickey Mantle 3.00 8.00
MM7 Mickey Mantle 3.00 8.00
MM8 Mickey Mantle 3.00 8.00
MM9 Mickey Mantle 3.00 8.00
MM10 Mickey Mantle 3.00 8.00
MM11 Mickey Mantle 3.00 8.00
MM12 Mickey Mantle 3.00 8.00
MM13 Mickey Mantle 3.00 8.00
MM14 Mickey Mantle 3.00 8.00
MM15 Mickey Mantle 3.00 8.00

2010 Topps Heritage Mantle Chase 61 Relics

FOUND IN TARGET PACKS
STATED PRINT RUN 7 SER.#'d SETS
NO PRICING DUE TO SCARCITY

2010 Topps Heritage Maris Chase 61

COMPLETE SET (15) 60.00 120.00
COMMON MARIS 5.00 12.00
RANDOM INSERTS IN WAL-MART PACKS
RM1 Roger Maris 5.00 12.00
RM2 Roger Maris 5.00 12.00
RM3 Roger Maris 5.00 12.00
RM4 Roger Maris 5.00 12.00
RM5 Roger Maris 5.00 12.00
RM6 Roger Maris 5.00 12.00
RM7 Roger Maris 5.00 12.00
RM8 Roger Maris 5.00 12.00
RM9 Roger Maris 5.00 12.00
RM10 Roger Maris 5.00 12.00
RM11 Roger Maris 5.00 12.00
RM12 Roger Maris 5.00 12.00
RM13 Roger Maris 5.00 12.00
RM14 Roger Maris 5.00 12.00
RM15 Roger Maris 5.00 12.00

2010 Topps Heritage Maris Chase 61 Relics

FOUND IN WAL-MART PACKS
STATED PRINT RUN 9 SER.#'d SETS
NO PRICING DUE TO SCARCITY

2010 Topps Heritage New Age Performers

COMPLETE SET (15) 15.00 40.00
STATED ODDS 1:15 HOBBY
NA1 Justin Upton .75 2.00
NA2 Jacoby Ellsbury 1.25 3.00
NA3 Gordon Beckham .75 2.00
NA4 Tommy Hanson .75 2.00
NA5 Hanley Ramirez 1.25 3.00
NA6 Joe Mauer 1.25 3.00
NA7 Ichiro Suzuki 2.00 5.00
NA8 Derek Jeter 3.00 8.00
NA9 Albert Pujols 3.00 8.00
NA10 Ryan Howard 1.50 4.00
NA11 Zack Greinke .75 2.00
NA12 Matt Kemp .75 2.00
NA13 Miguel Cabrera 1.25 3.00
NA14 Mariano Rivera 1.25 3.00
NA15 Prince Fielder .75 2.00

2010 Topps Heritage News Flashbacks

COMPLETE SET (10) 5.00 12.00
STATED ODDS 1:12 HOBBY
NF1 Peace Corps .50 1.25
NF2 John F. Kennedy 1.25 3.00
NF3 Ham the Chimp .50 1.25
NF4 Venera 1 .50 1.25
NF5 Hassan II .50 1.25
NF6 Twenty Third Amendment .50 1.25
NF7 Apollo Program Announce .50 1.25
NF8 Berlin Wall .50 1.25
NF9 Vostok 1 .50 1.25
NF10 Ty Cobb 1.25 3.00

2010 Topps Heritage Real One Autographs

STATED ODDS 1:357 HOBBY
AN Al Neiger 30.00 60.00
AR Al Rosen 20.00 50.00
BG Bob Gibson 30.00 60.00
BH Billy Harrell 20.00 50.00
BM Bobby Malkmus 30.00 60.00
BP Buster Posey 100.00 200.00
CB Collin Balester 20.00 50.00
CY Carl Yastrzemski
DK Danny Kravitz 20.00 50.00
DP Dustin Pedroia 20.00 50.00
DW David Wright
FR Frank Robinson 40.00 80.00
GB Gordon Beckham 15.00 40.00
GL Gene Leek 20.00 50.00
JB Jay Bruce 20.00 50.00
JB Julio Becquer 20.00 50.00
JC Jerry Casale 20.00 50.00
JD Joe DeMaestri 20.00 50.00
JG Joe Ginsberg 20.00 50.00
JJ Johnny James 30.00 60.00
JR Jim Rivera 20.00 50.00
JU Justin Upton 30.00 60.00
JW Jim Woods 20.00 50.00
LA Luis Aparicio 30.00 60.00
MH Matt Holliday
NG Ned Garver 20.00 50.00
RB Rocky Bridges 30.00 60.00
RB Reno Bertoia 20.00 50.00
RI Raul Ibanez 20.00 50.00
RL Ralph Lumenti 20.00 50.00
RS Ray Semproch 30.00 60.00
RS Red Schoendienst 30.00 60.00
RS R.C. Stevens 30.00 60.00
SM Stan Musial
TB Tom Borland 20.00 50.00
TB Tom Brewer 30.00 60.00
TL Ted Lepcio 20.00 50.00
WD Walt Dropo 20.00 50.00
BHA Bob Hale 20.00 50.00

2010 Topps Heritage Real One Autographs Red Ink

STATED ODDS 1:586 HOBBY
STATED PRINT RUN 61 SER.#'d SETS
AN Al Neiger 40.00 80.00
AR Al Rosen 30.00 60.00
BG Bob Gibson 60.00 120.00
BH Billy Harrell 30.00 60.00
BM Bobby Malkmus 40.00 80.00
BP Buster Posey 150.00 300.00
CB Collin Balester 30.00 60.00
CY Carl Yastrzemski
DK Danny Kravitz 30.00 60.00
DP Dustin Pedroia 30.00 60.00
DW David Wright
FR Frank Robinson 50.00 100.00
GB Gordon Beckham 40.00 80.00
GL Gene Leek 30.00 60.00
JB Julio Becquer 30.00 60.00
JB Jay Bruce 30.00 60.00
JC Jerry Casale 30.00 60.00
JD Joe DeMaestri 30.00 60.00
JG Joe Ginsberg 30.00 60.00
JJ Johnny James 40.00 80.00
JM Juan Marichal 50.00 100.00
JR Jim Rivera 30.00 60.00
JU Justin Upton 50.00 100.00
JW Jim Woods 30.00 60.00
LA Luis Aparicio 40.00 80.00
MH Matt Holliday
NG Ned Garver 30.00 60.00
RB Rocky Bridges 40.00 80.00
RB Reno Bertoia 30.00 60.00
RI Raul Ibanez 50.00 100.00
RL Ralph Lumenti 30.00 60.00
RS Red Schoendienst 40.00 80.00
RS Ray Semproch
RS R.C. Stevens 40.00 80.00
SM Stan Musial
TB Tom Borland 30.00 60.00
TB Tom Brewer 40.00 80.00
TL Ted Lepcio 30.00 60.00
WD Walt Dropo 30.00 60.00
BHA Bob Hale 30.00 60.00

2010 Topps Heritage Real One Dual Autographs

STATED ODDS 1:2414 HOBBY
STATED PRINT RUN 25 SER.#'d SETS
NO PRICING DUE TO SCARCITY

2010 Topps Heritage Ruth Chase 61

COMPLETE SET (15) 6.00 15.00
COMMON RUTH 1.25 3.00
RANDOM INSERTS IN HOBBY PACKS
BR1 Babe Ruth 1.25 3.00
BR2 Babe Ruth 1.25 3.00
BR3 Babe Ruth 1.25 3.00
BR4 Babe Ruth 1.25 3.00
BR5 Babe Ruth 1.25 3.00
BR6 Babe Ruth 1.25 3.00
BR7 Babe Ruth 1.25 3.00
BR8 Babe Ruth 1.25 3.00
BR9 Babe Ruth 1.25 3.00
BR10 Babe Ruth 1.25 3.00
BR11 Babe Ruth 1.25 3.00
BR12 Babe Ruth 1.25 3.00
BR13 Babe Ruth 1.25 3.00
BR14 Babe Ruth 1.25 3.00
BR15 Babe Ruth 1.25 3.00

2010 Topps Heritage Ruth Chase 61 Relics

STATED ODDS 1:13,110 HOBBY
STATED PRINT RUN 3 SER.#'d SETS
NO PRICING DUE TO SCARCITY

2010 Topps Heritage Team Stamp Panels

1 Anaheim Angels 1.25 3.00
Kendry Morales
Torii Hunter
Jered Weaver
2 Arizona Diamondbacks 2.00 5.00
Justin Upton
Mark Reynolds
Dan Haren
3 Atlanta Braves 3.00 8.00
Chipper Jones
Nate McLouth
Brian McCann
4 Baltimore Orioles 3.00 8.00
Adam Jones
Nick Markakis
5 Boston Red Sox 3.00 8.00
Kevin Youkilis
Dustin Pedroia
Daisuke Matsuzaka
6 Chicago Cubs 1.25 3.00
Alfonso Soriano
Derrek Lee
Carlos Zambrano
7 Chicago White Sox 1.25 3.00
Gordon Beckham
Mark Buehrle
Jake Peavy
8 Cincinnati Reds 3.00 8.00
Johnny Cueto
Jay Bruce
Joey Votto
9 Cleveland Indians 2.00 5.00
Grady Sizemore
Shin-Soo Choo
10 Colorado Rockies 3.00 8.00
Troy Tulowitzki
Ubaldo Jimenez
Todd Helton
11 Detroit Tigers 4.00 10.00
Justin Verlander
Rick Porcello
Miguel Cabrera
12 Florida Marlins 3.00 8.00
Hanley Ramirez
Dan Uggla
Josh Johnson
13 Houston Astros 2.00 5.00
Hunter Pence
Lance Berkman
Roy Oswalt
14 Kansas City Royals 2.00 5.00
Zack Greinke
Billy Butler
David DeJesus
15 Los Angeles Dodgers 2.00 5.00
Matt Kemp
Manny Ramirez
Andre Ethier
16 Milwaukee Brewers 2.00 5.00
Ryan Braun
Prince Fielder
17 Minnesota Twins 3.00 8.00
Joe Mauer
Justin Morneau
Joe Nathan
18 New York Mets 4.00 10.00
David Wright
Carlos Beltran
Johan Santana
19 New York Yankees 8.00 20.00
Derek Jeter
Alex Rodriguez
Mark Teixeira
20 Oakland Athletics 2.00 5.00
Brett Anderson
Rajai Davis
Kurt Suzuki
21 Philadelphia Phillies 4.00 10.00
Chase Utley
Ryan Howard
Jimmy Rollins
22 Pittsburgh Pirates 3.00 8.00
Andrew McCutchen
Zach Duke
23 San Diego Padres 2.00 5.00
Adrian Gonzalez
Will Venable
Kyle Blanks
24 San Francisco Giants 5.00 12.00
Pablo Sandoval
Tim Lincecum
25 Seattle Mariners 3.00 8.00
Ichiro Suzuki
Felix Hernandez
Ken Griffey Jr.
26 St. Louis Cardinals 8.00 20.00
Albert Pujols
Matt Holliday
27 Tampa Bay Rays 4.00 10.00
Evan Longoria
Carl Crawford
David Price
28 Texas Rangers 2.00 5.00
Josh Hamilton
Ian Kinsler
Michael Young
29 Toronto Blue Jays 2.00 5.00
Adam Lind
Aaron Hill
30 Washington Nationals 2.00 5.00
Ryan Zimmerman
Adam Dunn

2010 Topps Heritage Then and Now

STATED ODDS 1:15 HOBBY
TN1 Roger Maris 2.00 5.00
Albert Pujols
TN2 Roger Maris .75 2.00
Prince Fielder
TN3 Al Kaline 1.25 3.00
Joe Mauer
TN4 Luis Aparicio 1.25 3.00
Jacoby Ellsbury
TN5 Mickey Mantle 2.00 5.00
Adrian Gonzalez
TN6 Whitey Ford .75 2.00
Zack Greinke
TN7 Whitey Ford 1.50 4.00
Justin Verlander
TN8 Whitey Ford 1.25 3.00
Felix Hernandez
TN9 Whitey Ford 1.50 4.00
Justin Verlander
TN10 Whitey Ford 1.25 3.00
Roy Halladay

2011 Topps Heritage

COMP.SET w/o SP's (425) 40.00 80.00
COMMON CARD (1-425) .15 .40
COMMON ROOKIE (1-425) .40 1.00
COMPLETE J.ROB SET (10) 50.00 100.00
COMMON J.ROB SP (135-144) 5.00 12.00
STATED J.ROB ODDS 1:50 HOBBY
COMMON SP (426-500) 2.50 6.00
SP ODDS 1:3 HOBBY
1 Josh Hamilton .40 1.00
2 Francisco Cordero .15 .40
3 David Ortiz .25 .60
4 Ben Zobrist .15 .40
5 Clayton Kershaw .40 1.00
6 Brian Roberts .15 .40
7 Carlos Beltran .15 .40
8 John Danks .15 .40
9 Juan Uribe .15 .40
10 Andrew McCutchen .40 1.00
11 Joe Nathan .15 .40
12 Brad Mills MG .15 .40
13 Cliff Pennington .15 .40
14 Carlos Pena .25 .60
15 Fausto Carmona .15 .40
16 John Jaso .15 .40
17 Jayson Werth .25 .60
18 Albert Pujols 1.00 2.50
Ryan Braun
19 Jake McGee (RC) .40 1.00
20 Johnny Damon .25 .60
21 Carl Pavano .15 .40
22 San Diego Padres .15 .40
23 Carlos Lee .15 .40
24 Detroit Tigers .15 .40
25 Starlin Castro .40 1.00
26 Josh Thole .15 .40
27 Adam Kennedy .15 .40
28 Vernon Wells .15 .40
29 Terry Collins MG .15 .40
30 Chipper Jones .40 1.00
31 Ozzie Martinez RC .40 1.00
32 Russell Martin .15 .40
33 Barry Zito .15 .40
34 Ian Kinsler .25 .60
35 Stephen Strasburg .75 2.00
36 Mark Reynolds .15 .40
37 Derek Jeter 1.00 2.50
Robinson Cano
38 Coco Crisp .15 .40
39 Erick Aybar .15 .40
40 Pablo Sandoval .25 .60
41 Chris Valaika RC .40 1.00
42 Nelson Cruz .25 .60
43 Los Angeles Dodgers .25 .60
44 Justin Upton .25 .60
45 Evan Longoria .50 1.25
46 Cole Hamels .25 .60
47 Kosuke Fukudome .25 .60
48 CC Sabathia .25 .60
49 Jordan Brown (RC) .40 1.00
50 Albert Pujols 1.00 2.50
51 Josh Hamilton .40 1.00
Miguel Cabrera
Joe Mauer
Adrian Beltre
52 Carlos Gonzalez .40 1.00
Joey Votto
Omar Infante
Troy Tulowitzki
53 Jose Bautista .25 .60
Paul Konerko
Miguel Cabrera
Mark Teixeira
54 Albert Pujols 1.00 2.50
Adam Dunn
Joey Votto
55 Felix Hernandez .40 1.00
Clay Buchholz
David Price
Trevor Cahill
56 Josh Johnson .40 1.00
Adam Wainwright
Roy Halladay
Jaime Garcia
57 CC Sabathia .40 1.00
David Price
Jon Lester
58 Roy Halladay .40 1.00
Adam Wainwright
Ubaldo Jimenez
59 Jered Weaver .50 1.25
Felix Hernandez
Jon Lester
Justin Verlander
60 Tim Lincecum .40 1.00
Roy Halladay
Ubaldo Jimenez
Adam Wainwright
61 Milwaukee Brewers .15 .40
62 Brandon Inge .15 .40
63 Tommy Hanson .25 .60
64 Nick Markakis .40 1.00
65 Robinson Cano .40 1.00
66 Geovany Soto .25 .60
67 Zach Duke .15 .40
68 Travis Snider .15 .40
69 Cory Luebke RC .40 1.00
70 Justin Morneau .40 1.00
71 Jonathan Sanchez .15 .40
72 Jimmy Rollins .40 1.00
Chase Utley
73 Gordon Beckham .25 .60
74 Hanley Ramirez .40 1.00
75 Chris Tillman .15 .40
76 Freddie Freeman RC 1.50 4.00
77 Chase Utley .40 1.00
78 Matt LaPorta .15 .40
79 Jordan Zimmermann .15 .40
80 Jay Bruce .25 .60
81 Jason Varitek .40 1.00
82 Kevin Kouzmanoff .15 .40
83 Chris Carpenter .40 1.00
84 Denard Span .15 .40
85 Ike Davis .25 .60
86 Alex Presley RC 1.00 2.50
87 Manny Ramirez .40 1.00
88 Joe Girardi MG .25 .60
89 Jake Peavy .15 .40
90 Julio Borbon .15 .40
91 Gaby Sanchez .15 .40
92 Armando Galarraga .15 .40
93 Nick Swisher .40 1.00
94 R.A. Dickey .15 .40
95 Ryan Zimmerman .25 .60
96 Jered Weaver .15 .40
97 Grady Sizemore .25 .60
98 Minnesota Twins .15 .40
99 Brandon Snyder (RC) .40 1.00
100 David Price .40 1.00
101 Jacoby Ellsbury .40 1.00
102 Matt Capps .15 .40
103 Brandon Phillips .15 .40
104 Domonic Brown .40 1.00
105 Max Scherzer .15 .40
106 Yadier Molina .25 .60
107 Madison Bumgarner .15 .40
108 Matt Kemp .25 .60
109 Ted Lilly .15 .40
110 Mark Teixeira .40 1.00
111 Brad Lidge .15 .40
112 Luke Scott .15 .40
113 Chicago White Sox .15 .40
114 Kyle Drabek RC .60 1.50
115 Alfonso Soriano .25 .60
116 Gavin Floyd .15 .40
117 Alex Rios .25 .60
118 Skip Schumaker .15 .40
119 Scott Cousins RC .40 1.00
120 Bronson Arroyo .15 .40
121 Buck Showalter MG .15 .40
122 Trevor Cahill .15 .40
123 Aaron Hill .15 .40
124 Brian Duensing .15 .40
125A Vladimir Guerrero .40 1.00
125B Vladimir Guerrero SP 50.00 100.00
Listed as P on card back
126 James Shields .15 .40
127 Dallas Braden .15 .40
Trevor Cahill
128 Joel Pineiro .15 .40
129 Carlos Quentin .15 .40
130 Omar Infante .15 .40
131 Brett Sinkbeil RC .40 1.00
132 Los Angeles Angels .15 .40
133 Andres Torres .15 .40
134 Brett Cecil .15 .40
135A Babe Ruth 1.00 2.50
Babe As A Boy
135B Jackie Robinson 5.00 12.00
Displays Athletic Talents At An Early Age SP
136A Babe Ruth 1.00 2.50
Babe Joins Yanks
136B Jackie Robinson 5.00 12.00
Emerges As College Star SP
137A Babe Ruth 1.00 2.50
Babe And Mgr. Huggins
137B Jackie Robinson 5.00 12.00
Serves Three Years In The Army SP
138A Babe Ruth 1.00 2.50

The Famous Slugger
138B Jackie Robinson 5.00 12.00
Breaks The Game's Color Barrier SP
139A Babe Ruth 1.00 2.50
Babe Hits 60
139B Jackie Robinson 5.00 12.00
Takes ROY Honors, Then MVP SP
139C Joba Chamberlain SP 40.00 80.00
140A Babe Ruth 1.00 2.50
Gehrig And Ruth
140B Jackie Robinson 5.00 12.00
Wraps Up Hall Of Fame Career SP
141A Babe Ruth 1.00 2.50
Twilight Years
141B Jackie Robinson 5.00 12.00
Legacy Lives On SP
142A Babe Ruth 1.00 2.50
Coaching For The Dodgers
142B Jackie Robinson 5.00 12.00
Racks 'Em Up SP
143A Babe Ruth 1.00 2.50
Greatest Sports Hero
143B Jackie Robinson 5.00 12.00
Robinson Shines in the Fall SP
144A Babe Ruth 1.00 2.50
Farewell Speech
144B Jackie Robinson 5.00 12.00
The Resume SP
145 Dallas Braden .15 .40
146 Placido Polanco .15 .40
147 Joakim Soria .15 .40
148 Jonny Gomes .15 .40
149 Ryan Franklin .15 .40
150 Miguel Cabrera .40 1.00
151 Arthur Rhodes .15 .40
152 Jim Riggleman MG .15 .40
153 Marco Scutaro .15 .40
154 Brennan Boesch .25 .60
155 Brian Wilson .40 1.00
156 Hank Conger RC .60 1.50
157 Shane Victorino .25 .60
158 Atlanta Braves .15 .40
159 Joba Chamberlain .25 .60
160 Garrett Jones .15 .40
161 Bobby Jenks .15 .40
162 Alex Gordon .25 .60
163 Mark Teixeira .60 1.50
Alex Rodriguez
164 Jason Kendall .15 .40
165 Adam Jones .25 .60
166 Kevin Slowey .15 .40
167 Wilson Ramos .15 .40
168 Rajai Davis .15 .40
169 Curtis Granderson .25 .60
170 Aramis Ramirez .15 .40
171 Edinson Volquez .15 .40
172 Dusty Baker MG .15 .40
173 Jhonny Peralta .15 .40
174 Jon Garland .15 .40
175 Adam Dunn .25 .60
176 Chase Headley .15 .40
177 J.A. Happ .25 .60
178 A.J. Pierzynski .15 .40
179 Mat Latos .15 .40
180 Jim Thome .25 .60
181 Dillon Gee RC .60 1.50
182 Cody Ross .15 .40
183 Mike Pelfrey .15 .40
184 Kurt Suzuki .15 .40
185 Mariano Rivera .40 1.00
186 Rick Ankiel .15 .40
187 Jon Lester .40 1.00
188 Freddy Sanchez .15 .40
189 Heath Bell .25 .60
190 Todd Helton .25 .60
191 Ryan Dempster .15 .40
192 Florida Marlins .15 .40
193 Miguel Tejada .25 .60
194 Jordan Walden RC .40 1.00
195 Paul Konerko .25 .60
196 Jose Valverde .15 .40
197 Casey Blake .15 .40
198 Tony La Russa MG .25 .60
199 Aroldis Chapman RC 1.25 3.00
200 Derek Jeter 1.00 2.50
201 Josh Beckett .25 .60
202 Corey Hart .15 .40
203 Kevin Millwood .15 .40
204 Brian Bogusevic (RC) .40 1.00
205 Scott Rolen .25 .60
206 Washington Nationals .15 .40
207 C.J. Wilson .15 .40
208 Rickie Weeks .25 .60
209 Andrew Romine RC .40 1.00
210 Evan Meek .15 .40
211 Elvis Andrus .25 .60
Ian Kinsler
212 Roy Oswalt .25 .60
213 Angel Pagan .15 .40
214 Chris Sale RC .60 1.50
215 Asdrubal Cabrera .25 .60
216 David Aardsma .15 .40
217 Don Mattingly MG .75 2.00
218 Buster Posey .50 1.25
219 Jeremy Hellickson RC 1.25 3.00
220 Ryan Howard .50 1.25
221 Jeremy Guthrie .15 .40
222 Franklin Gutierrez .15 .40
223 Ryan Theriot .15 .40
224 Casey Coleman RC .40 1.00
225 Adrian Beltre .15 .40
226 San Francisco Giants .15 .40
227 Cliff Lee .40 1.00
228 Marlon Byrd .15 .40
229 Pedro Ciriaco RC .40 1.00
230 Francisco Liriano .15 .40
231 Chone Figgins .15 .40
232 Giants Win Opener HL .15 .40
Freddy Sanchez
233 Cain Dominates HL .25 .60
234 Rangers Retaliate HL .15 .40
Mitch Moreland
235 Bumgarner Baffles HL .15 .40
236 Giants Crush Rangers HL .15 .40

Edgar Renteria
237 Winners Celebrate HL .40 1.00
Tim Lincecum
238 Ichiro Suzuki .60 1.50
239 Brandon Beachy RC 1.00 2.50
240 Xavier Nady .15 .40
241 Josh Johnson .25 .60
242 Manny Acta MG .15 .40
243 A.J. Burnett .25 .60
244 Lars Anderson RC .60 1.50
245 Jason Bartlett .15 .40
246 Andrew Bailey .15 .40
247 Jonathan Lucroy .15 .40
248 Chris Johnson .15 .40
249 Vance Worley (RC) 1.50 4.00
250 Joe Mauer .40 1.00
251 Texas Rangers .15 .40
252 James McDonald .15 .40
253 Lou Marson .15 .40
254 Chris Carter .15 .40
255 Edwin Jackson .15 .40
256 Ruben Tejada .15 .40
257 Scott Kazmir .15 .40
258 Ryan Braun .50 1.25
259 Kelly Johnson .15 .40
260 Matt Cain .25 .60
261 Reid Brignac .15 .40
262 Ivan Rodriguez .25 .60
263 Josh Hamilton .40 1.00
Nelson Cruz
264 Jeff Niemann .15 .40
265 Derrek Lee .15 .40
266 Jose Ceda RC .40 1.00
267 B.J. Upton .25 .60
268 Ervin Santana .15 .40
269 Lance Berkman .25 .60
270 Ronny Cedeno .15 .40
271 Jeremy Jeffress RC .40 1.00
272 Delmon Young .25 .60
273 Chris Perez .15 .40
274 Will Venable .15 .40
275 Billy Butler .15 .40
276 Darwin Barney RC 1.25 3.00
277 Pedro Alvarez RC .25 .60
278 Derek Lowe .15 .40
279A Bengie Molina .15 .40
279B Bengie Molina SP
Birthday listed as July 20,1994
280 Hiroki Kuroda .15 .40
281 Eduardo Nunez RC .40 1.00
282 Aaron Harang .15 .40
283 Danny Valencia .25 .60
284 Jimmy Rollins .25 .60
285 Adam Wainwright .25 .60
286 Ozzie Guillen MG .15 .40
287 Neftali Feliz .15 .40
288 Mike Stanton .25 .60
289 Darren Ford RC .40 1.00
290 Ty Wigginton .15 .40
291 Bobby Cramer RC .40 1.00
292 Orlando Hudson .15 .40
293 Jonathon Niese .15 .40
294 Philadelphia Phillies .15 .40
295 Paul Maholm .15 .40
296 Ian Desmond .25 .60
297 Jonathan Broxton .15 .40
298 Jason Kubel .15 .40
299 Daniel Descalso RC .40 1.00
300 Carl Crawford .25 .60
301 Clay Buchholz .25 .60
302 Ramon Hernandez .15 .40
303 Daric Barton .15 .40
304 Brett Myers .15 .40
305 Mike Aviles .15 .40
306 David Ortiz .50 1.25
Dustin Pedroia
307 Jair Jurrjens .15 .40
308 Jason Bay .25 .60
309 Yonder Alonso RC .60 1.50
310 Andy Pettitte .25 .60
311 Derek Jeter IA 1.00 2.50
312 Roy Halladay IA .40 1.00
313 Jose Bautista IA .25 .60
314 Miguel Cabrera IA .40 1.00
315 CC Sabathia IA .25 .60
316 Joe Mauer IA .40 1.00
317 Ichiro Suzuki IA .60 1.50
318 Mark Teixeira IA .40 1.00
319 Tim Lincecum IA .40 1.00
320 Jason Heyward .50 1.25
321 Matt Mangini RC .40 1.00
322 Bruce Bochy MG .15 .40
323 Jon Jay .15 .40
324 Tommy Hunter .15 .40
325 Alexei Ramirez .15 .40
326 Gregory Infante RC .40 1.00
327 Jose Lopez .15 .40
328 Raul Ibanez .25 .60
329 Yovani Gallardo .15 .40
330 Mike Napoli .25 .60
331 Mike Leake .25 .60
332 Alcides Escobar .15 .40
333 Lucas Duda RC .60 1.50
334 Tampa Bay Rays .15 .40
335 Austin Jackson .15 .40
336 John Lackey .15 .40
337 Adam LaRoche .15 .40
338 Brett Gardner .15 .40
339 J.J. Hardy .15 .40
340 Chad Billingsley .15 .40
341 Lorenzo Cain .15 .40
342 Zack Greinke .25 .60
343 Bobby Abreu .15 .40
344 Fernando Salas (RC) .60 1.50
345 Dustin Pedroia .50 1.25
346 Felix Hernandez .40 1.00
347 Nyjer Morgan .15 .40
348 Eric Sogard RC .40 1.00
349 Jeremy Bonderman .15 .40
350 Joey Votto .40 1.00
351 Justin Morneau .40 1.00
Joe Mauer
352 Ricky Nolasco .15 .40
353 Neil Walker .15 .40

354 Hunter Pence .25 .60
355 Brian Matusz .40 1.00
356 Jose Bautista .25 .60
357 Brett Anderson .25 .60
358 Andre Ethier .25 .60
359 Carlos Zambrano .25 .60
360 Jorge Posada .25 .60
361 Randy Wolf .15 .40
362 Greg Halman RC .60 1.50
363 Nick Hundley .15 .40
364 Russell Branyan .15 .40
365 Howie Kendrick .15 .40
366 Rick Porcello .15 .40
367 Dan Uggla .25 .60
368 J.P. Arencibia .25 .60
369 Dan Haren .15 .40
370 Matt Holliday .40 1.00
371 Victor Martinez .25 .60
372 Jaime Garcia .25 .60
373 Carlos Gonzalez .25 .60
374 Charlie Manuel MG .15 .40
375 James Loney .25 .60
376 Phil Hughes .15 .40
377 Carlos Santana .40 1.00
378 Ubaldo Jimenez .25 .60
379 Travis Hafner .15 .40
380 Tim Hudson .25 .60
381 Orlando Cabrera .15 .40
382 Casey McGehee .15 .40
383 Daniel Hudson .15 .40
384 Oakland Athletics .15 .40
385 Mark Buehrle .25 .60
386 Michael Cuddyer .15 .40
387 Desmond Jennings RC 1.00 2.50
388 Rafael Soriano .15 .40
389 Ryan Doumit .15 .40
390 Albert Pujols AS 1.00 2.50
391 Martin Prado AS .15 .40
392A Ryan Zimmerman AS .25 .60
392B Ryan Zimmerman AS SP 100.00 200.00
.370 BA on card back
393 Hanley Ramirez AS .40 1.00
394 Ryan Braun AS .50 1.25
395 Matt Holliday AS .40 1.00
396 Carlos Gonzalez AS .25 .60
397 Brian McCann AS .25 .60
398 Joey Votto AS .40 1.00
399 Roy Halladay AS .40 1.00
400 Mark Teixeira .40 1.00
401 Matt Kemp .25 .60
Andre Ethier
402 David DeJesus .15 .40
403 Jonathan Papelbon .25 .60
404 Mark Trumbo (RC) .60 1.50
405 Gio Gonzalez .15 .40
406 Tyler Colvin .25 .60
407 Wade Davis .15 .40
408 Chris Coghlan .15 .40
409 Pittsburgh Pirates .15 .40
410 Juan Pierre .15 .40
411 Michael Young .25 .60
412 Colby Rasmus .40 1.00
413 Chris Young .15 .40
414 Jarrod Dyson RC .40 1.00
415 Dexter Fowler .15 .40
416 Jim Leyland MG .15 .40
417 Lucas May RC .40 1.00
418 Ian Stewart .15 .40
419 Wandy Rodriguez .15 .40
420 Miguel Montero .15 .40
421 Francisco Rodriguez .25 .60
422 Kendry Morales .15 .40
423 Brian Wilson .50 1.25
Buster Posey
424 Leo Nunez .15 .40
425 Kevin Youkilis .25 .60
426 Brent Morel SP RC 2.50 6.00
427 Will Rhymes SP 2.50 6.00
428 Josh Willingham SP 2.50 6.00
429 Tim Lincecum SP 3.00 8.00
430 Troy Tulowitzki SP 5.00 12.00
431 Welington Castillo SP (RC) 2.50 6.00
432 Michael Bourn SP 2.50 6.00
433 Kyle Davies SP 2.50 6.00
434 Carlos Ruiz SP 2.50 6.00
435 Huston Street SP 2.50 6.00
436 Jose Reyes SP 3.00 8.00
437 Adrian Gonzalez SP 3.00 8.00
438 Shaun Marcum SP 2.50 6.00
439 Stephen Drew SP 2.50 6.00
440 Ricky Romero SP 2.50 6.00
441 Jorge de la Rosa SP 2.50 6.00
442 Kevin Gregg SP 2.50 6.00
443 Brian McCann SP 3.00 8.00
444 Rafael Furcal SP 2.50 6.00
445 Prince Fielder SP 2.00 5.00
446 Carlos Marmol SP 3.00 8.00
447 Shin-Soo Choo SP 2.00 5.00
448 Clayton Richard SP 2.50 6.00
449 Elvis Andrus SP 3.00 8.00
450 Johnny Cueto SP 2.50 6.00
451 Ben Revere SP RC 3.00 8.00
452 Adam Lind SP 3.00 8.00
453 Roy Halladay SP 3.00 8.00
454 Jose Tabata SP 4.00 10.00
455 Joe Saunders SP 2.50 6.00
456 Jeff Keppinger SP 2.50 6.00
457 J.D. Drew SP 2.50 6.00
458 Ian Kennedy SP 4.00 10.00
459 John Buck SP 2.50 6.00
460 Justin Verlander SP 6.00 15.00
461 Russ Mitchell SP RC 2.50 6.00
462 Magglio Ordonez SP 3.00 8.00
463 Bob Geren MG SP 2.50 6.00
464 Johan Santana SP 3.00 8.00
465 Cincinnati Reds SP 2.50 6.00
466 Miguel Cabrera AS SP 3.00 8.00
467 Robinson Cano AS SP 3.00 8.00
468 Evan Longoria AS SP 4.00 10.00
469 Alexei Ramirez AS SP 2.50 6.00
470 Carl Crawford AS SP 3.00 8.00
471 Josh Hamilton AS SP 3.00 8.00
472 Jose Bautista AS SP 3.00 8.00
473 Joe Mauer AS SP 3.00 8.00

474 Vladimir Guerrero AS SP 3.00 8.00
475 Felix Hernandez AS SP 3.00 8.00
476 Baltimore Orioles SP 2.50 6.00
477 Yunel Escobar SP 2.50 6.00
478A David Wright SP 4.00 10.00
478B David Wright 75.00 150.00
Cincinnati Reds SP
479 Lucas Harrell SP (RC) 2.50 6.00
480 Aubrey Huff SP 2.50 6.00
481 Kila Ka'aihue SP 2.50 6.00
482 Ron Gardenhire MG SP 2.50 6.00
483 Trevor Hoffman SP 3.00 8.00
484 David Eckstein SP 2.50 6.00
485 Matt Garza SP 2.50 6.00
486 Martin Prado SP 2.50 6.00
487 Drew Stubbs SP 4.00 10.00
488 Koji Uehara SP 2.50 6.00
489 Brandon Morrow SP 2.50 6.00
490A Alex Rodriguez SP 5.00 12.00
490B Alex Rodriguez 60.00 120.00
Reverse Negative SP
491 Torii Hunter SP 2.50 6.00
492 Jason Castro SP 2.50 6.00
493 Josh Tomlin 2.50 6.00
Jeanmar Gomez
Felix Doubront
Jake Arrieta
Andy Oliver SP
494 Barry Enright RC 2.50 6.00
Mike Minor
Travis Wood
Alex Sanabia
Drew Storen SP
495 Andrew Cashner 4.00 10.00
Jonny Venters
Kenley Jansen
Jenrry Mejia
John Axford SP
496 Michael McKenry RC 4.00 10.00
Max St. Pierre
Chris Hatcher RC
Mike Nickeas
Steve Hill SP RC
497 Argenis Diaz 2.50 6.00
Brett Wallace
Brandon Hicks
Lance Zawadzki SP
498 Josh Bell 2.50 6.00
Danny Worth
Luke Hughes
Trevor Plouffe SP
499 Dayan Viciedo 2.50 6.00
Jason Donald
Steve Tolleson
Mitch Moreland SP
500 Peter Bourjos 3.00 8.00
Ryan Kalish
Daniel Nava
Chris Heisey
Logan Morrison SP

2011 Topps Heritage Blue Tint

110 Mark Teixeira 5.00 12.00
111 Brad Lidge 2.00 5.00
112 Luke Scott 2.00 5.00
113 Chicago White Sox 2.00 5.00
114 Kyle Drabek 3.00 8.00
115 Alfonso Soriano 3.00 8.00
116 Gavin Floyd 2.00 5.00
117 Alex Rios 3.00 8.00
118 Skip Schumaker 2.00 5.00
119 Scott Cousins 2.00 5.00
120 Bronson Arroyo 2.00 5.00
121 Buck Showalter MG 2.00 5.00
122 Trevor Cahill 2.00 5.00
123 Aaron Hill 2.00 5.00
124 Brian Duensing 2.00 5.00
125 Vladimir Guerrero 5.00 12.00
126 James Shields 2.00 5.00
127 Dallas Braden 2.00 5.00
Trevor Cahill
128 Joel Pineiro 2.00 5.00
129 Carlos Quentin 2.00 5.00
130 Omar Infante 2.00 5.00
131 Brett Sinkbeil 2.00 5.00
132 Los Angeles Angels 2.00 5.00
133 Andres Torres 2.00 5.00
134 Brett Cecil 2.00 5.00
135 Babe Ruth 6.00 15.00
Babe As A Boy
136 Babe Ruth 6.00 15.00
Babe Joins Yanks
137 Babe Ruth 6.00 15.00
Babe And Mgr. Huggins
138 Babe Ruth 6.00 15.00
The Famous Slugger
139A Babe Ruth 6.00 15.00
Babe Hits 60
139C Joba Chamberlain 30.00 60.00
140 Babe Ruth 6.00 15.00
Gehrig And Ruth
141 Babe Ruth 6.00 15.00
Twilight Years
142 Babe Ruth 6.00 15.00
Coaching For The Dodgers
143 Babe Ruth 6.00 15.00
Greatest Sports Hero
144 Babe Ruth 6.00 15.00
Farewell Speech
145 Dallas Braden 2.00 5.00
146 Placido Polanco 2.00 5.00
147 Joakim Soria 2.00 5.00
148 Jonny Gomes 2.00 5.00
149 Ryan Franklin 2.00 5.00
150 Miguel Cabrera 5.00 12.00
151 Arthur Rhodes 2.00 5.00
152 Jim Riggleman MG 2.00 5.00
153 Marco Scutaro 2.00 5.00
154 Brennan Boesch 3.00 8.00
155 Brian Wilson 5.00 12.00
156 Hank Conger 3.00 8.00
157 Shane Victorino 3.00 8.00
158 Atlanta Braves 2.00 5.00
160 Garrett Jones 2.00 5.00
161 Bobby Jenks 2.00 5.00
162 Alex Gordon 3.00 8.00
163 Mark Teixeira 8.00 20.00
Alex Rodriguez
164 Jason Kendall 2.00 5.00
165 Adam Jones 3.00 8.00
166 Kevin Slowey 2.00 5.00
167 Wilson Ramos 2.00 5.00
168 Rajai Davis 2.00 5.00
169 Curtis Granderson 3.00 8.00
170 Aramis Ramirez 2.00 5.00
171 Edinson Volquez 2.00 5.00
172 Dusty Baker MG 2.00 5.00
173 Jhonny Peralta 2.00 5.00
174 Jon Garland 2.00 5.00
175 Adam Dunn 3.00 8.00
176 Chase Headley 2.00 5.00
177 J.A. Happ 3.00 8.00
178 A.J. Pierzynski 2.00 5.00
179 Mat Latos 2.00 5.00
180 Jim Thome 3.00 8.00
181 Dillon Gee 3.00 8.00
182 Cody Ross 2.00 5.00
183 Mike Pelfrey 2.00 5.00
184 Kurt Suzuki 2.00 5.00
185 Mariano Rivera 5.00 12.00
186 Rick Ankiel 2.00 5.00
187 Jon Lester 5.00 12.00
188 Freddy Sanchez 2.00 5.00
189 Heath Bell 3.00 8.00
190 Todd Helton 3.00 8.00
191 Ryan Dempster 2.00 5.00
192 Florida Marlins 2.00 5.00
193 Miguel Tejada 3.00 8.00
194 Jordan Walden 2.00 5.00
195 Paul Konerko 3.00 8.00
196 Jose Valverde 2.00 5.00

2011 Topps Heritage Green Tint

110 Mark Teixeira 6.00 15.00
111 Brad Lidge 2.50 6.00
112 Luke Scott 2.50 6.00
113 Chicago White Sox 2.50 6.00
114 Kyle Drabek 4.00 10.00
115 Alfonso Soriano 4.00 10.00
116 Gavin Floyd 2.50 6.00
117 Alex Rios 4.00 10.00
118 Skip Schumaker 2.50 6.00
119 Scott Cousins 2.50 6.00
120 Bronson Arroyo 2.50 6.00
121 Buck Showalter MG 2.50 6.00
122 Trevor Cahill 2.50 6.00
123 Aaron Hill 2.50 6.00
124 Brian Duensing 2.50 6.00
125 Vladimir Guerrero 6.00 15.00
126 James Shields 2.50 6.00
127 Dallas Braden 2.50 6.00
Trevor Cahill
128 Joel Pineiro 2.50 6.00
129 Carlos Quentin 2.50 6.00
130 Omar Infante 2.50 6.00
131 Brett Sinkbeil 2.50 6.00
132 Los Angeles Angels 2.50 6.00
133 Andres Torres 2.50 6.00
134 Brett Cecil 2.50 6.00
135 Babe Ruth 8.00 20.00
Babe As A Boy
136 Babe Ruth 8.00 20.00
Babe Joins Yanks
137 Babe Ruth 8.00 20.00
Babe And Mgr. Huggins
138 Babe Ruth 8.00 20.00
The Famous Slugger
139A Babe Ruth 8.00 20.00
Babe Hits 60
139C Joba Chamberlain 30.00 60.00
140 Babe Ruth 8.00 20.00
Gehrig And Ruth
141 Babe Ruth 8.00 20.00
Twilight Years
142 Babe Ruth 8.00 20.00
Coaching For The Dodgers
143 Babe Ruth 8.00 20.00
Greatest Sports Hero
144 Babe Ruth 8.00 20.00
Farewell Speech
145 Dallas Braden 2.50 6.00
146 Placido Polanco 2.50 6.00
147 Joakim Soria 2.50 6.00
148 Jonny Gomes 2.50 6.00
149 Ryan Franklin 2.50 6.00
150 Miguel Cabrera 6.00 15.00
151 Arthur Rhodes 2.50 6.00
152 Jim Riggleman MG 2.50 6.00
153 Marco Scutaro 2.50 6.00
154 Brennan Boesch 4.00 10.00
155 Brian Wilson 6.00 15.00
156 Hank Conger 4.00 10.00
157 Shane Victorino 4.00 10.00
158 Atlanta Braves 2.50 6.00
160 Garrett Jones 2.50 6.00
161 Bobby Jenks 2.50 6.00
162 Alex Gordon 4.00 10.00
163 Mark Teixeira 20.00 50.00
Alex Rodriguez
164 Jason Kendall 2.50 6.00
165 Adam Jones 4.00 10.00
166 Kevin Slowey 2.50 6.00
167 Wilson Ramos 2.50 6.00
168 Rajai Davis 2.50 6.00
169 Curtis Granderson 4.00 10.00
170 Aramis Ramirez 2.50 6.00
171 Edinson Volquez 2.50 6.00
172 Dusty Baker MG 2.50 6.00
173 Jhonny Peralta 2.50 6.00
174 Jon Garland 2.50 6.00
175 Adam Dunn 4.00 10.00
176 Chase Headley 2.50 6.00
177 J.A. Happ 4.00 10.00
178 A.J. Pierzynski 2.50 6.00
179 Mat Latos 2.50 6.00
180 Jim Thome 4.00 10.00
181 Dillon Gee 4.00 10.00
182 Cody Ross 2.50 6.00
183 Mike Pelfrey 2.50 6.00
184 Kurt Suzuki 2.50 6.00
185 Mariano Rivera 6.00 15.00
186 Rick Ankiel 2.50 6.00
187 Jon Lester 6.00 15.00
188 Freddy Sanchez 2.50 6.00
189 Heath Bell 4.00 10.00
190 Todd Helton 4.00 10.00
191 Ryan Dempster 2.50 6.00
192 Florida Marlins 2.50 6.00
193 Miguel Tejada 4.00 10.00
194 Jordan Walden 2.50 6.00
195 Paul Konerko 4.00 10.00
196 Jose Valverde 2.50 6.00

2011 Topps Heritage Red Tint

110 Mark Teixeira 8.00 20.00
111 Brad Lidge 3.00 8.00
112 Luke Scott 3.00 8.00
113 Chicago White Sox 3.00 8.00
114 Kyle Drabek 5.00 12.00
115 Alfonso Soriano 5.00 12.00
116 Gavin Floyd 3.00 8.00
117 Alex Rios 5.00 12.00
118 Skip Schumaker 3.00 8.00
119 Scott Cousins 3.00 8.00
120 Bronson Arroyo 3.00 8.00
121 Buck Showalter MG 3.00 8.00
122 Trevor Cahill 3.00 8.00
123 Aaron Hill 3.00 8.00
124 Brian Duensing 3.00 8.00
125 Vladimir Guerrero 8.00 20.00
126 James Shields 3.00 8.00
127 Dallas Braden 3.00 8.00
Trevor Cahill
128 Joel Pineiro 3.00 8.00
129 Carlos Quentin 3.00 8.00
130 Omar Infante 3.00 8.00
131 Brett Sinkbeil 3.00 8.00
132 Los Angeles Angels 3.00 8.00
133 Andres Torres 3.00 8.00
134 Brett Cecil 3.00 8.00
135 Babe Ruth 8.00 20.00
Babe As A Boy
136 Babe Ruth 8.00 20.00
Babe Joins Yanks
137 Babe Ruth 8.00 20.00
Babe And Mgr. Huggins
138 Babe Ruth 8.00 20.00
The Famous Slugger
139A Babe Ruth 8.00 20.00
Babe Hits 60
139C Joba Chamberlain 30.00 60.00
140 Babe Ruth 8.00 20.00
Gehrig And Ruth
141 Babe Ruth 8.00 20.00
Twilight Years
142 Babe Ruth 8.00 20.00
Coaching For The Dodgers
143 Babe Ruth 8.00 20.00
Greatest Sports Hero
144 Babe Ruth 8.00 20.00
Farewell Speech
145 Dallas Braden 3.00 8.00
146 Placido Polanco 3.00 8.00
147 Joakim Soria 3.00 8.00
148 Jonny Gomes 3.00 8.00
149 Ryan Franklin 3.00 8.00
150 Miguel Cabrera 8.00 20.00
151 Arthur Rhodes 3.00 8.00
152 Jim Riggleman MG 3.00 8.00
153 Marco Scutaro 3.00 8.00
154 Brennan Boesch 5.00 12.00
155 Brian Wilson 8.00 20.00
156 Hank Conger 5.00 12.00
157 Shane Victorino 5.00 12.00
158 Atlanta Braves 3.00 8.00
160 Garrett Jones 3.00 8.00
161 Bobby Jenks 3.00 8.00
162 Alex Gordon 5.00 12.00
163 Mark Teixeira 12.00 30.00
Alex Rodriguez
164 Jason Kendall 3.00 8.00
165 Adam Jones 5.00 12.00
166 Kevin Slowey 3.00 8.00
167 Wilson Ramos 3.00 8.00
168 Rajai Davis 3.00 8.00
169 Curtis Granderson 5.00 12.00
170 Aramis Ramirez 3.00 8.00
171 Edinson Volquez 3.00 8.00
172 Dusty Baker MG 3.00 8.00
173 Jhonny Peralta 3.00 8.00
174 Jon Garland 3.00 8.00
175 Adam Dunn 5.00 12.00
176 Chase Headley 3.00 8.00
177 J.A. Happ 5.00 12.00
178 A.J. Pierzynski 3.00 8.00
179 Mat Latos 3.00 8.00
180 Jim Thome 5.00 12.00
181 Dillon Gee 5.00 12.00
182 Cody Ross 3.00 8.00
183 Mike Pelfrey 3.00 8.00
184 Kurt Suzuki 3.00 8.00
185 Mariano Rivera 8.00 20.00
186 Rick Ankiel 3.00 8.00
187 Jon Lester 8.00 20.00
188 Freddy Sanchez 3.00 8.00
189 Heath Bell 5.00 12.00
190 Todd Helton 5.00 12.00
191 Ryan Dempster 3.00 8.00
192 Florida Marlins 3.00 8.00
193 Miguel Tejada 5.00 12.00
194 Jordan Walden 3.00 8.00
195 Paul Konerko 5.00 12.00
196 Jose Valverde 3.00 8.00

2011 Topps Heritage 1962 Buybacks

RANDOMLY INSERTED BOX TOPPERS
NO PRICING DUE TO SCARCTITY

2011 Topps Heritage 62 Mint Coins

STATED ODDS 1:263 HOBBY
AO First American Orbits the Earth 15.00 40.00
BF Bob Feller 50.00 100.00
BR Brooks Robinson 40.00 80.00
CE U.S. Announces E. Against Cuba 12.50 30.00
CM Cuban Missile Crisis Begins 12.50 30.00
DS Duke Snider 30.00 60.00
EB Ernie Banks 15.00 40.00
ED Eric Davis 15.00 40.00
EK Ed Kranepool 20.00 50.00
FT Frank Thomas 20.00 50.00
GP Gaylord Perry 10.00 25.00
HK Harmon Killebrew 30.00 60.00
JM Jamie Moyer 12.50 30.00
JR Jackie Robinson 50.00 100.00
MM Mickey Mantle 60.00 120.00
NS U.S. Navy SEALs Are Activated 15.00 40.00
SF Sid Fernandez 10.00 25.00
WS Warren Spahn 50.00 100.00
DST Darryl Strawberry 10.00 25.00
WST Willie Stargell 12.50 30.00

2011 Topps Heritage Advertising Panels

ISSUED AS BOX TOPPER
1 Atlanta Braves .60 1.50
Tyler Colvin
Matt Capps
2 Chris Carter .40 1.00
Ben Zobrist
Billy Butler
3 Jose Cerda 1.50 4.00
Carlos Pena
Ichiro Suzuki
4 Joba Chamberlain 1.00 2.50
Colby Rasmus
Gavin Floyd
5 Johnny Damon .60 1.50
Rafael Soriano
Jered Weaver
6 John Danks .60 1.50
Adam Wainwright
Adam Kennedy
7 Brian Duensing .40 1.00
A.J. Pierzynski
Rick Ankiel
8 Ryan Howard 1.25 3.00
Jason Kendall
Leo Nunez
9 Gregory Infante 1.00 2.50
Felix Hernandez
Clay Buchholz
David Price
Trevor Cahill
Joey Votto AS
10 Derek Jeter 2.50 6.00
Robinson Cano
Travis Hafner
Gaby Sanchez
11 Clayton Kershaw 1.00 2.50
Ronny Cedeno
John Jaso
12 Victor Martinez .60 1.50
Zach Duke
Mark Trumbo
13 Kendry Morales 1.25 3.00
Brian Wilson
Buster Posey
Brett Cecil
14 Mike Napoli .60 1.50
Nick Markakis
Jonathan Lucroy
15 Ricky Nolasco .60 1.50
Geovany Soto
Wade Davis
16 Cliff Pennington .40 1.00
Brett Myers
Vernon Wells
17 Andy Pettitte .60 1.50
Ian Kinsler
B.J. Upton
18 Joel Pineiro .40 1.00
Marco Scutaro
Andrew Romine
19 Albert Pujols 2.50 6.00
Adam Dunn
Joey Votto
Derek Lowe
San Diego Padres
20 Hanley Ramirez 2.50 6.00
Ted Lilly
Babe Ruth Special
21 Scott Rolen 1.00 2.50
Rangers Retaliate
Mat Latos
22 Jimmy Rollins .60 1.50
Carlos Lee
Carlos Gonzalez
23 Cody Ross 1.00 2.50
Brandon Beachy
Bruce Bochy
24 Babe Ruth Special 2.50 6.00
Mark Buehrle
Armando Galarraga
25 CC Sabathia 1.00 2.50
David Price
Jon Lester
Joe Mauer
Francisco Cordero
26 Grady Sizemore .60 1.50
Chris Young
Buck Showalter
27 Brandon Snyder 2.50 6.00
Babe Ruth Special
Francisco Liriano
28 Jim Thome .60 1.50
Franklin Gutierrez
Ryan Theriot

2011 Topps Heritage Baseball Bucks

RANDOMLY INSERTED BOX TOPPER
BB1 Justin Upton 3.00 8.00
BB2 Miguel Montero 2.00 5.00
BB3 Daniel Hudson 2.00 5.00
BB4 Torii Hunter 2.00 5.00
BB5 Jered Weaver 2.00 5.00
BB6 Kendry Morales 2.00 5.00
BB7 Chipper Jones 5.00 12.00
BB8 Jason Heyward 6.00 15.00

BB9 Martin Prado 2.00 5.00
BB10 Adam Jones 3.00 8.00
BB11 Nick Markakis 5.00 12.00
BB12 Brian Roberts 2.00 5.00
BB13 David Ortiz 3.00 8.00
BB14 Victor Martinez 3.00 8.00
BB15 Clay Buchholz 3.00 8.00
BB16 Starlin Castro 5.00 12.00
BB17 Aramis Ramirez 2.00 5.00
BB18 Tyler Colvin 3.00 8.00
BB19 Manny Ramirez 5.00 12.00
BB20 Carlos Quentin 2.00 5.00
BB21 John Danks 2.00 5.00
BB22 Joey Votto 5.00 12.00
BB23 Brandon Phillips 2.00 5.00
BB24 Jay Bruce 3.00 8.00
BB25 Shin-Soo Choo 3.00 8.00
BB26 Grady Sizemore 3.00 8.00
BB27 Carlos Santana 5.00 12.00
BB28 Troy Tulowitzki 5.00 12.00
BB29 Ubaldo Jimenez 3.00 8.00
BB30 Carlos Gonzalez 3.00 8.00
BB31 Miguel Cabrera 5.00 12.00
BB32 Justin Verlander 6.00 15.00
BB33 Austin Jackson 2.00 5.00
BB34 Hanley Ramirez 5.00 12.00
BB35 Mike Stanton 3.00 8.00
BB36 Logan Morrison 2.00 5.00
BB37 Hunter Pence 3.00 8.00
BB38 Wandy Rodriguez 2.00 5.00
BB39 Brett Wallace 2.00 5.00
BB40 Lorenzo Cain 2.00 5.00
BB41 Billy Butler 2.00 5.00
BB42 Joakim Soria 2.00 5.00
BB43 Clayton Kershaw 5.00 12.00
BB44 Andre Ethier 3.00 8.00
BB45 Matt Kemp 3.00 8.00
BB46 Ryan Braun 6.00 15.00
BB47 Yovani Gallardo 2.00 5.00
BB48 Casey McGehee 2.00 5.00
BB49 Joe Mauer 5.00 12.00
BB50 Justin Morneau 5.00 12.00
BB51 Danny Valencia 3.00 8.00
BB52 David Wright 6.00 15.00
BB53 Johan Santana 5.00 12.00
BB54 Ike Davis 3.00 8.00
BB55 Derek Jeter 12.00 30.00
BB56 CC Sabathia 3.00 8.00
BB57 Alex Rodriguez 8.00 20.00
BB58 Trevor Cahill 2.00 5.00
BB59 Kurt Suzuki 2.00 5.00
BB60 Brett Anderson 3.00 8.00
BB61 Roy Halladay 5.00 12.00
BB62 Ryan Howard 6.00 15.00
BB63 Domonic Brown 5.00 12.00
BB64 Andrew McCutchen 5.00 12.00
BB65 Jose Tabata 3.00 8.00
BB66 Neil Walker 2.00 5.00
BB67 Adrian Gonzalez 3.00 8.00
BB68 Heath Bell 3.00 8.00
BB69 Mat Latos 2.00 5.00
BB70 Tim Lincecum 5.00 12.00
BB71 Brian Wilson 5.00 12.00
BB72 Pablo Sandoval 3.00 8.00
BB73 Buster Posey 6.00 15.00
BB74 Matt Cain 3.00 8.00
BB75 Cody Ross 2.00 5.00
BB76 Ichiro Suzuki 8.00 20.00
BB77 Felix Hernandez 5.00 12.00
BB78 Franklin Gutierrez 2.00 5.00
BB79 Albert Pujols 12.00 30.00
BB80 Adam Wainwright 3.00 8.00
BB81 Yadier Molina 3.00 8.00
BB82 Evan Longoria 6.00 15.00
BB83 David Price 5.00 12.00
BB84 Jeremy Hellickson 6.00 15.00
BB85 Josh Hamilton 5.00 12.00
BB86 Neftali Feliz 2.00 5.00
BB87 Elvis Andrus 3.00 8.00
BB88 Michael Young 3.00 8.00
BB89 Ian Kinsler 3.00 8.00
BB90 Nelson Cruz 3.00 8.00
BB91 Vernon Wells 2.00 5.00
BB92 Jose Bautista 3.00 8.00
BB93 Brandon Morrow 2.00 5.00
BB94 Ryan Zimmerman 3.00 8.00
BB95 Jordan Zimmermann 2.00 5.00
BB96 Ian Desmond 3.00 8.00

2011 Topps Heritage Baseball Flashbacks

COMPLETE SET (10) 6.00 15.00
STATED ODDS 1:12 HOBBY
BF1 Mickey Mantle 3.00 8.00
BF2 Brooks Robinson .60 1.50
BF3 Roger Maris 1.00 2.50
BF4 Robin Roberts .40 1.00
BF5 Carl Yastrzemski 1.00 2.50
BF6 Whitey Ford .60 1.50
BF7 Harmon Killebrew 1.00 2.50
BF8 Warren Spahn .60 1.50
BF9 Frank Robinson .60 1.50
BF10 Bob Gibson .60 1.50

2011 Topps Heritage Black

*BLACK: .75X TO 2X BASIC CHROME

2011 Topps Heritage Checklists

COMPLETE SET (6) 1.50 4.00
COMMON CHECKLIST .40 1.00

2011 Topps Heritage Chrome

HERITAGE ODDS 1:11 HOBBY
TOPPS CHROME ODDS 1:7 HOBBY
STATED PRINT RUN 1962 SER.#'d SETS
1-100 ISSUED IN TOPPS HERITAGE
101-200 ISSUED IN TOPPS CHROME
C1 Andrew McCutchen 2.50 6.00
C2 Joe Nathan 1.00 2.50
C3 Jake McGee 1.00 2.50
C4 Miguel Cabrera 2.50 6.00
C5 Starlin Castro 2.50 6.00
C6 Josh Thole 1.00 2.50
C7 Russell Martin 1.00 2.50
C8 Mark Reynolds 1.00 2.50
C9 Nelson Cruz 1.50 4.00
C10 Cole Hamels 2.50 6.00
C11 CC Sabathia 1.50 4.00
C12 Carlos Gonzalez 2.50 6.00
Joey Votto
Omar Infante
Troy Tulowitzki
C13 Jose Bautista 1.50 4.00
Paul Konerko
Miguel Cabrera
Mark Teixeira
C14 Jered Weaver 2.50 6.00
Felix Hernandez
Jon Lester
Justin Verlander
C15 Tim Lincecum 2.00 5.00
Roy Halladay
Ubaldo Jimenez
Adam Wainwright
C16 Tommy Hanson 1.50 4.00
C17 Travis Snider 1.00 2.50
C18 Jonathan Sanchez 1.00 2.50
C19 Ike Davis 1.50 4.00
C20 Nick Swisher 2.50 6.00
C21 Jacoby Ellsbury 2.50 6.00
C22 Brad Lidge 1.00 2.50
C23 Ryan Braun 2.50 6.00
C24 Kyle Drabek 1.50 4.00
C25 Bronson Arroyo 1.00 2.50
C26 Aaron Hill 1.00 2.50
C27 Omar Infante 1.00 2.50
C28 Babe Ruth 5.00 12.00
C29 Jonny Gomes 1.00 2.50
C30 Clay Buchholz 1.50 4.00
C31 Jhonny Peralta 1.00 2.50
C32 Mike Pelfrey 1.00 2.50
C33 Kurt Suzuki 1.00 2.50
C34 Paul Konerko 1.50 4.00
C35 Casey Blake 1.00 2.50
C36 Josh Beckett 1.50 4.00
C37 Corey Hart 1.00 2.50
C38 Kevin Millwood 1.00 2.50
C39 Evan Longoria 2.50 6.00
C40 Rickie Weeks 1.50 4.00
C41 Roy Oswalt 1.50 4.00
C42 Asdrubal Cabrera 1.50 4.00
C43 Don Mattingly 4.00 10.00
C44 Casey Coleman 1.00 2.50
C45 Adrian Beltre 1.00 2.50
C46 Cliff Lee 2.50 6.00
C47 Marlon Byrd 1.00 2.50
C48 Chone Figgins 1.00 2.50
C49 Giants Win Opener HL 1.00 2.50
C50 Giants Crush Rangers HL 1.00 2.50
C51 Xavier Nady 1.00 2.50
C52 Josh Johnson 1.50 4.00
C53 Chris Johnson 1.00 2.50
C54 Vance Worley 4.00 10.00
C55 Lou Marson 1.00 2.50
C56 Edwin Jackson 1.00 2.50
C57 Ruben Tejada 1.00 2.50
C58 Josh Hamilton 2.50 6.00
Nelson Cruz
C59 Delmon Young 1.50 4.00
C60 Will Venable 1.00 2.50
C61 Pedro Alvarez 1.50 4.00
C62 Hiroki Kuroda 1.00 2.50
C63 Neftali Feliz 1.00 2.50
C64 Mike Stanton 1.50 4.00
C65 Ty Wigginton 1.00 2.50
C66 Bobby Cramer 1.00 2.50
C67 Jason Kubel 1.00 2.50
C68 Daniel Descalso 1.00 2.50
C69 Ramon Hernandez 1.00 2.50
C70 Mike Aviles 1.00 2.50
C71 David Ortiz 2.50 6.00
Dustin Pedroia
C72 Jason Bay 1.50 4.00
C73 CC Sabathia 1.50 4.00
C74 Joe Mauer 2.50 6.00
C75 Tommy Hunter 1.00 2.50
C76 Alexei Ramirez 1.00 2.50
C77 Raul Ibanez 1.50 4.00
C78 Lucas Duda 1.50 4.00
C79 Chad Billingsley 1.00 2.50
C80 Bobby Abreu 1.00 2.50
C81 Fernando Salas 1.50 4.00
C82 Nyjer Morgan 1.00 2.50
C83 Justin Morneau 2.50 6.00
Joe Mauer
C84 Hunter Pence 1.50 4.00
C85 Jose Bautista 1.50 4.00
C86 Brett Anderson 1.50 4.00
C87 Carlos Zambrano 1.50 4.00
C88 Greg Halman 1.50 4.00
C89 Nick Hundley 1.00 2.50
C90 J.P. Arencibia 1.50 4.00
C91 Dan Haren 1.00 2.50
C92 James Loney 1.50 4.00
C93 Phil Hughes 1.00 2.50
C94 Ubaldo Jimenez 1.50 4.00
C95 Michael Cuddyer 1.00 2.50
C96 Desmond Jennings 2.50 6.00
C97 Ryan Doumit 1.00 2.50
C98 Mark Teixeira 2.50 6.00
C99 Lucas May 1.00 2.50
C100 Wandy Rodriguez 1.00 2.50
C101 Albert Pujols 5.00 12.00
Ryan Braun
C102 Derek Jeter 5.00 12.00
Robinson Cano
C103 Mark Teixeira 3.00 8.00
Alex Rodriguez
C104 Matt Kemp 1.50 4.00
Andre Ethier
C105 Derek Jeter 5.00 12.00
C106 Roy Halladay 2.50 6.00
C107 Jose Bautista 1.50 4.00
C108 Miguel Cabrera 2.50 6.00
C109 Ichiro Suzuki 3.00 8.00
C110 Mark Teixeira 2.50 6.00
C111 Tim Lincecum 2.00 5.00
C112 Cory Luebke 1.00 2.50
C113 Freddie Freeman 3.00 8.00
C114 Scott Cousins 1.00 2.50
C115 Hank Conger 1.50 4.00
C116 Jordan Walden 1.00 2.50
C117 Aroldis Chapman 2.50 6.00
C118 Chris Sale 1.50 4.00
C119 Jeremy Hellickson 2.50 6.00
C120 Brandon Beachy 2.00 5.00
C121 Eric Sogard 1.00 2.50
C122 Mark Trumbo 1.50 4.00
C123 Brent Morel 1.00 2.50
C124 Stephen Strasburg 4.00 10.00
C125 Gaby Sanchez 1.00 2.50
C126 Buster Posey 2.50 6.00
C127 Danny Valencia 1.50 4.00
C128 Jason Heyward 2.50 6.00
C129 Austin Jackson 1.00 2.50
C130 Neil Walker 1.00 2.50
C131 Jaime Garcia 1.50 4.00
C132 Jose Tabata 1.50 4.00
C133 Josh Hamilton 2.50 6.00
C134 David Ortiz 1.50 4.00
C135 Clayton Kershaw 2.50 6.00
C136 Carlos Beltran 1.00 2.50
C137 Carlos Pena 1.50 4.00
C138 Jayson Werth 1.50 4.00
C139 Vernon Wells 1.00 2.50
C140 Chipper Jones 2.50 6.00
C141 Ian Kinsler 1.50 4.00
C142 Pablo Sandoval 1.50 4.00
C143 Justin Upton 1.50 4.00
C144 Kosuke Fukudome 2.50 6.00
C145 Albert Pujols 5.00 12.00
C146 Nick Markakis 2.50 6.00
C147 Robinson Cano 2.50 6.00
C148 Justin Morneau 2.50 6.00
C149 Gordon Beckham 1.50 4.00
C150 Hanley Ramirez 2.50 6.00
C151 Chase Utley 2.50 6.00
C152 Jay Bruce 1.50 4.00
C153 Nelson Cruz 1.50 4.00
C154 Ryan Zimmerman 1.50 4.00
C155 Jered Weaver 1.00 2.50
C156 David Price 2.50 6.00
C157 Domonic Brown 2.50 6.00
C158 Madison Bumgarner 1.00 2.50
C159 Matt Kemp 1.50 4.00
C160 Mark Teixeira 2.50 6.00
C161 Alfonso Soriano 1.50 4.00
C162 Carlos Quentin 1.00 2.50
C163 Miguel Cabrera 2.50 6.00
C164 Adam Jones 1.50 4.00
C165 Curtis Granderson 1.50 4.00
C166 Adam Dunn 1.50 4.00
C167 Jim Thome 1.50 4.00
C168 Mariano Rivera 2.50 6.00
C169 Jon Lester 2.50 6.00
C170 Derek Jeter 5.00 12.00
C171 Ryan Howard 2.50 6.00
C172 Francisco Liriano 1.00 2.50
C173 Ichiro Suzuki 3.00 8.00
C174 Joe Mauer 2.50 6.00
C175 Ryan Braun 2.50 6.00
C176 Matt Cain 1.50 4.00
C177 Carl Crawford 1.50 4.00
C178 Zack Greinke 1.50 4.00
C179 Dustin Pedroia 2.50 6.00
C180 Felix Hernandez 2.50 6.00
C181 Joey Votto 2.50 6.00
C182 Andre Ethier 1.50 4.00
C183 Jorge Posada 1.50 4.00
C184 Dan Uggla 1.50 4.00
C185 Matt Holliday 2.50 6.00
C186 Victor Martinez 1.50 4.00
C187 Carlos Gonzalez 1.50 4.00
C188 Carlos Santana 2.50 6.00
C189 Kevin Youkilis 1.50 4.00
C190 Tim Lincecum 2.00 5.00
C191 Troy Tulowitzki 2.50 6.00
C192 Jose Reyes 1.50 4.00
C193 Adrian Gonzalez 1.50 4.00
C194 Brian McCann 1.50 4.00
C195 Prince Fielder 1.50 4.00
C196 Roy Halladay 2.50 6.00
C197 David Wright 2.50 6.00
C198 Martin Prado 1.00 2.50
C199 Drew Stubbs 1.50 4.00
C200 Alex Rodriguez 3.00 8.00

2011 Topps Heritage Chrome Refractors

*REF: .6X TO 1.5X BASIC CHROME
HERITAGE ODDS 1:137 HOBBY
TOPPS CHROME ODDS 1:22 HOBBY
STATED PRINT RUN 562 SER.#'d SETS
1-100 ISSUED IN TOPPS HERITAGE
101-200 ISSUED IN TOPPS CHROME

2011 Topps Heritage Chrome Black Refractors

HERITAGE ODDS 1:334 HOBBY
TOPPS CHROME ODDS 1:148 HOBBY
STATED PRINT RUN 62 SER.#'d SETS
1-100 ISSUED IN TOPPS HERITAGE
101-200 ISSUED IN TOPPS CHROME
C1 Andrew McCutchen 12.00 30.00
C2 Joe Nathan 8.00 20.00
C3 Jake McGee 8.00 20.00
C4 Miguel Cabrera 12.00 30.00
C5 Starlin Castro 12.00 30.00
C6 Josh Thole 8.00 20.00
C7 Russell Martin 8.00 20.00
C8 Mark Reynolds 8.00 20.00
C9 Nelson Cruz 10.00 25.00
C10 Cole Hamels 12.00 30.00
C11 CC Sabathia 10.00 25.00
C12 Carlos Gonzalez 12.00 30.00
Joey Votto
Omar Infante
Troy Tulowitzki
C13 Jose Bautista 8.00 20.00
Paul Konerko
Miguel Cabrera
Mark Teixeira
C14 Jered Weaver 15.00 40.00
Felix Hernandez
Jon Lester
Justin Verlander
C15 Tim Lincecum 15.00 40.00
Roy Halladay
Ubaldo Jimenez
Adam Wainwright
C16 Tommy Hanson 10.00 25.00
C17 Travis Snider 8.00 20.00
C18 Jonathan Sanchez 8.00 20.00
C19 Ike Davis 10.00 25.00
C20 Nick Swisher 12.00 30.00
C21 Jacoby Ellsbury 12.00 30.00
C22 Brad Lidge 8.00 20.00
C23 Ryan Braun 15.00 40.00
C24 Kyle Drabek 10.00 25.00
C25 Bronson Arroyo 8.00 20.00
C26 Aaron Hill 8.00 20.00
C27 Omar Infante 8.00 20.00
C28 Babe Ruth 30.00 80.00
C29 Jonny Gomes 8.00 20.00
C30 Clay Buchholz 10.00 25.00
C31 Jhonny Peralta 8.00 20.00
C32 Mike Pelfrey 8.00 20.00
C33 Kurt Suzuki 8.00 20.00
C34 Paul Konerko 10.00 25.00
C35 Casey Blake 8.00 20.00
C36 Josh Beckett 10.00 25.00
C37 Corey Hart 8.00 20.00
C38 Kevin Millwood 8.00 20.00
C39 Evan Longoria 15.00 40.00
C40 Rickie Weeks 10.00 25.00
C41 Roy Oswalt 10.00 25.00
C42 Asdrubal Cabrera 10.00 25.00
C43 Don Mattingly 25.00 60.00
C44 Casey Coleman 8.00 20.00
C45 Adrian Beltre 8.00 20.00
C46 Cliff Lee 12.00 30.00
C47 Marlon Byrd 8.00 20.00
C48 Chone Figgins 8.00 20.00
C49 Giants Win Opener HL 8.00 20.00
C50 Giants Crush Rangers HL 8.00 20.00
C51 Xavier Nady 8.00 20.00
C52 Josh Johnson 10.00 25.00
C53 Chris Johnson 8.00 20.00
C54 Vance Worley 30.00 80.00
C55 Lou Marson 8.00 20.00
C56 Edwin Jackson 8.00 20.00
C57 Ruben Tejada 8.00 20.00
C58 Josh Hamilton 12.00 30.00
Nelson Cruz
C59 Delmon Young 10.00 25.00
C60 Will Venable 8.00 20.00
C61 Pedro Alvarez 10.00 25.00
C62 Hiroki Kuroda 8.00 20.00
C63 Neftali Feliz 8.00 20.00
C64 Mike Stanton 10.00 25.00
C65 Ty Wigginton 8.00 20.00
C66 Bobby Cramer 8.00 20.00
C67 Jason Kubel 8.00 20.00
C68 Daniel Descalso 8.00 20.00
C69 Ramon Hernandez 8.00 20.00
C70 Mike Aviles 8.00 20.00
C71 David Ortiz 15.00 40.00
Dustin Pedroia
C72 Jason Bay 10.00 25.00
C73 CC Sabathia 10.00 25.00
C74 Joe Mauer 12.00 30.00
C75 Tommy Hunter 8.00 20.00
C76 Alexei Ramirez 8.00 20.00
C77 Raul Ibanez 10.00 25.00
C78 Lucas Duda 10.00 25.00
C79 Chad Billingsley 8.00 20.00
C80 Bobby Abreu 8.00 20.00
C81 Fernando Salas 12.00 30.00
C82 Nyjer Morgan 8.00 20.00
C83 Justin Morneau 12.00 30.00
Joe Mauer
C84 Hunter Pence 10.00 25.00
C85 Jose Bautista 8.00 20.00
C86 Brett Anderson 10.00 25.00
C87 Carlos Zambrano 10.00 25.00
C88 Greg Halman 8.00 20.00
C89 Nick Hundley 8.00 20.00
C90 J.P. Arencibia 10.00 25.00
C91 Dan Haren 8.00 20.00
C92 James Loney 10.00 25.00
C93 Phil Hughes 8.00 20.00
C94 Ubaldo Jimenez 10.00 25.00
C95 Michael Cuddyer 8.00 20.00
C96 Desmond Jennings 12.00 30.00
C97 Ryan Doumit 8.00 20.00
C98 Mark Teixeira 12.00 30.00
C99 Lucas May 8.00 20.00
C100 Wandy Rodriguez 8.00 20.00
C101 Albert Pujols 30.00 80.00
Ryan Braun
C102 Derek Jeter 30.00 80.00
Robinson Cano
C103 Mark Teixeira 25.00 60.00
Alex Rodriguez
C104 Matt Kemp 10.00 25.00
Andre Ethier
C105 Derek Jeter 30.00 80.00
C106 Roy Halladay 12.00 30.00
C107 Jose Bautista 8.00 20.00
C108 Miguel Cabrera 12.00 30.00
C109 Ichiro Suzuki 25.00 60.00
C110 Mark Teixeira 12.00 30.00
C111 Tim Lincecum 15.00 40.00
C112 Cory Luebke 8.00 20.00
C113 Freddie Freeman 20.00 50.00
C114 Scott Cousins 8.00 20.00
C115 Hank Conger 10.00 25.00
C116 Jordan Walden 8.00 20.00
C117 Aroldis Chapman 15.00 40.00
C118 Chris Sale 8.00 20.00
C119 Jeremy Hellickson 15.00 40.00
C120 Brandon Beachy 12.00 30.00
C121 Eric Sogard 8.00 20.00
C122 Mark Trumbo 10.00 25.00
C123 Brent Morel 8.00 20.00
C124 Stephen Strasburg 25.00 60.00
C125 Gaby Sanchez 8.00 20.00
C126 Buster Posey 15.00 40.00
C127 Danny Valencia 10.00 25.00
C128 Jason Heyward 15.00 40.00
C129 Austin Jackson 8.00 20.00
C130 Neil Walker 8.00 20.00
C131 Jaime Garcia 10.00 25.00
C132 Jose Tabata 10.00 25.00
C133 Josh Hamilton 12.00 30.00
C134 David Ortiz 10.00 25.00
C135 Clayton Kershaw 12.00 30.00
C136 Carlos Beltran 8.00 20.00
C137 Carlos Pena 10.00 25.00
C138 Jayson Werth 10.00 25.00
C139 Vernon Wells 8.00 20.00
C140 Chipper Jones 12.00 30.00
C141 Ian Kinsler 10.00 25.00
C142 Pablo Sandoval 10.00 25.00
C143 Justin Upton 10.00 25.00
C144 Kosuke Fukudome 12.00 30.00
C145 Albert Pujols 30.00 80.00
C146 Nick Markakis 12.00 30.00
C147 Robinson Cano 12.00 30.00
C148 Justin Morneau 12.00 30.00
C149 Gordon Beckham 10.00 25.00
C150 Hanley Ramirez 12.00 30.00
C151 Chase Utley 12.00 30.00
C152 Jay Bruce 10.00 25.00
C153 Nelson Cruz 8.00 20.00
C154 Ryan Zimmerman 10.00 25.00
C155 Jered Weaver 8.00 20.00
C156 David Price 12.00 30.00
C157 Domonic Brown 12.00 30.00
C158 Madison Bumgarner 8.00 20.00
C159 Matt Kemp 10.00 25.00
C160 Mark Teixeira 12.00 30.00
C161 Alfonso Soriano 10.00 25.00
C162 Carlos Quentin 8.00 20.00
C163 Miguel Cabrera 12.00 30.00
C164 Adam Jones 10.00 25.00
C165 Curtis Granderson 10.00 25.00
C166 Adam Dunn 10.00 25.00
C167 Jim Thome 10.00 25.00
C168 Mariano Rivera 12.00 30.00
C169 Jon Lester 12.00 30.00
C170 Derek Jeter 30.00 80.00
C171 Ryan Howard 15.00 40.00
C172 Francisco Liriano 8.00 20.00
C173 Ichiro Suzuki 25.00 60.00
C174 Joe Mauer 12.00 30.00
C175 Ryan Braun 15.00 40.00
C176 Matt Cain 10.00 25.00
C177 Carl Crawford 10.00 25.00
C178 Zack Greinke 10.00 25.00
C179 Dustin Pedroia 15.00 40.00
C180 Felix Hernandez 12.00 30.00
C181 Joey Votto 12.00 30.00
C182 Andre Ethier 10.00 25.00
C183 Jorge Posada 10.00 25.00
C184 Dan Uggla 10.00 25.00
C185 Matt Holliday 12.00 30.00
C186 Victor Martinez 10.00 25.00
C187 Carlos Gonzalez 10.00 25.00
C188 Carlos Santana 12.00 30.00
C189 Kevin Youkilis 10.00 25.00
C190 Tim Lincecum 15.00 40.00
C191 Troy Tulowitzki 12.00 30.00
C192 Jose Reyes 10.00 25.00
C193 Adrian Gonzalez 10.00 25.00
C194 Brian McCann 10.00 25.00
C195 Prince Fielder 8.00 20.00
C196 Roy Halladay 12.00 30.00
C197 David Wright 15.00 40.00
C198 Martin Prado 8.00 20.00
C199 Drew Stubbs 10.00 25.00
C200 Alex Rodriguez 25.00 60.00

2011 Topps Heritage Chrome Green Refractors

*GREEN REF: .75X TO 2X BASIC CHROME

2011 Topps Heritage Clubhouse Collection Dual Relic Autographs

STATED ODDS 1:14,883 HOBBY
STATED PRINT RUN 10 SER.#'d SETS
NO PRICING DUE TO SCARCITY
EXCHANGE DEADLINE 2/28/2014

2011 Topps Heritage Clubhouse Collection Dual Relics

STATED ODDS 1:7600 HOBBY
STATED PRINT RUN 62 SER.#'d SETS
FS Whitey Ford 40.00 80.00
CC Sabathia
GH Bob Gibson 50.00 100.00
Roy Halladay
KC Al Kaline 50.00 100.00
Miguel Cabrera
RV Frank Robinson 50.00 100.00
Joey Votto
RW Brooks Robinson 75.00 150.00
David Wright

2011 Topps Heritage Clubhouse Collection Relic Autographs

STATED ODDS 1:9,500 HOBBY
STATED PRINT RUN 25 SER.#'d SETS
NO PRICING DUE TO SCARCITY
EXCHANGE DEADLINE 2/28/2014

2011 Topps Heritage Clubhouse Collection Relics

STATED ODDS 1:29 HOBBY
AP Albert Pujols 10.00 25.00
AR Alex Rios 3.00 8.00
BG Brett Gardner 4.00 10.00
CB Carlos Beltran 3.00 8.00
CC Carl Crawford 3.00 8.00
CK Clayton Kershaw 3.00 8.00
CL Carlos Lee 3.00 8.00
CS Carlos Santana 4.00 10.00
CU Chase Utley 10.00 25.00
DU Dan Uggla 3.00 8.00
DW David Wright 4.00 10.00
EL Evan Longoria 4.00 10.00
FH Felix Hernandez 3.00 8.00
FL Francisco Liriano 3.00 8.00
GS Gaby Sanchez 3.00 8.00
HR Hanley Ramirez 3.00 8.00
ID Ike Davis 4.00 10.00
IK Ian Kinsler 3.00 8.00
IS Ichiro Suzuki 6.00 15.00
JB Jason Bartlett 3.00 8.00
JE Jacoby Ellsbury 4.00 10.00
JH Josh Hamilton 5.00 12.00
JJ Josh Johnson 3.00 8.00
JM Joe Mauer 6.00 15.00
JP Jorge Posada 4.00 10.00
JR Jose Reyes 3.00 8.00
JS Johan Santana 3.00 8.00
JT Jim Thome 6.00 15.00
JV Joey Votto 5.00 12.00
JW Jayson Werth 3.00 8.00
MC Miguel Cabrera 4.00 10.00
MR Manny Ramirez 3.00 8.00
MT Mark Teixeira 4.00 10.00
PF Prince Fielder 3.00 8.00
PP Placido Polanco 4.00 10.00
RB Ryan Braun 4.00 10.00
RC Robinson Cano 5.00 12.00
RH Ryan Howard 4.00 10.00
SR Scott Rolen 4.00 10.00
TT Troy Tulowitzki 3.00 8.00
VG Vladimir Guerrero 3.00 8.00
VM Victor Martinez 3.00 8.00
YM Yadier Molina 5.00 12.00
ZG Zack Greinke 3.00 8.00
CBU Clay Buchholz 3.00 8.00
JBA Jason Bay 3.00 8.00
JMO Justin Morneau 3.00 8.00
JTA Jose Tabata 4.00 10.00
JWI Josh Willingham 3.00 8.00
MRE Mark Reynolds 3.00 8.00

2011 Topps Heritage Cut Signatures

STATED ODDS 1:238,000 HOBBY
STATED PRINT RUN 1 SER.#'d SET
NO PRICING DUE TO SCARCITY

2011 Topps Heritage Flashback Autographs

STATED ODDS 1:19,000 HOBBY
STATED PRINT RUN 25 SER.#'d SETS
NO PRICING DUE TO SCARCITY
EXCHANGE DEADLINE 2/28/2014

2011 Topps Heritage Flashback Stadium Dual Relics

STATED ODDS 1:45,000 HOBBY
STATED PRINT RUN 10 SER.#'d SETS
NO PRICING DUE TO SCARCITY

2011 Topps Heritage Flashback Stadium Relic Autographs

STATED ODDS 1:19,000 HOBBY
STATED PRINT RUN 25 SER.#'d SETS
NO PRICING DUE TO SCARCITY
EXCHANGE DEADLINE 2/28/2014

2011 Topps Heritage Flashback Stadium Relics

STATED ODDS 1:1175 HOBBY
AK Al Kaline 15.00 40.00
BG Roger Maris 20.00 50.00
BM Bill Mazeroski 15.00 40.00
BR Brooks Robinson 10.00 25.00
FR Luis Aparicio 10.00 25.00
FT Frank Thomas 12.50 30.00
HK Harmon Killebrew 10.00 25.00
HW Hoyt Wilhelm 10.00 25.00
MM Mickey Mantle 20.00 50.00
RR Robin Roberts 10.00 25.00

2011 Topps Heritage Framed Dual Stamps

STATED ODDS 1:211 HOBBY
STATED PRINT RUN 62 SER.#'d SETS
1 Bobby Abreu 6.00 15.00
Cole Hamels
2 Brett Anderson 6.00 15.00
Vernon Wells
3 Elvis Andrus 6.00 15.00
Curtis Granderson
4 Bronson Arroyo 8.00 20.00
Brad Lidge
5 Jason Bartlett 8.00 20.00
Adam Wainwright
6 Daric Barton 6.00 15.00
Carl Pavano
7 Jose Bautista 6.00 15.00
Clay Buchholz
8 Gordon Beckham 6.00 15.00
Howie Kendrick
9 Heath Bell 6.00 15.00
Alex Rios
10 Adrian Beltre 6.00 15.00
Denard Span
11 Chad Billingsley 10.00 25.00
Kendry Morales
12 Michael Bourn 8.00 20.00
Francisco Liriano
13 Dallas Braden 6.00 15.00
Will Venable
14 Ryan Braun 10.00 25.00
Gaby Sanchez
15 Domonic Brown 6.00 15.00
Stephen Drew
16 Jay Bruce 6.00 15.00
Miguel Cabrera
17 Clay Buchholz 8.00 20.00
Yovani Gallardo
18 Billy Butler 6.00 15.00
Brett Gardner
19 Marlon Byrd 6.00 15.00
Mat Latos
20 Miguel Cabrera 10.00 25.00
Ryan Zimmerman
21 Trevor Cahill 8.00 20.00
Jose Tabata
22 Matt Cain 15.00 40.00
Evan Longoria
23 Robinson Cano 8.00 20.00
Ian Desmond
24 Matt Capps 12.50 30.00
Adam Jones
25 Chris Carpenter 10.00 25.00
Felix Hernandez
26 Starlin Castro 10.00 25.00
Francisco Cordero
27 Shin-Soo Choo 12.50 30.00
Logan Morrison
28 Chris Coghlan 8.00 20.00
Carlos Marmol
29 Tyler Colvin 6.00 15.00
Edwin Jackson
30 Francisco Cordero 6.00 15.00
Mike Napoli
31 Carl Crawford 8.00 20.00
Aaron Hill
32 Nelson Cruz 6.00 15.00
Brett Myers
33 Michael Cuddyer 10.00 25.00
Omar Infante
34 John Danks 8.00 20.00
Jorge Posada
35 Ike Davis 15.00 40.00
Dan Uggla
36 Ryan Dempster 6.00 15.00
Chris Young
37 Ian Desmond 6.00 15.00
Ben Zobrist
38 Stephen Drew 8.00 20.00
Roy Halladay
39 Adam Dunn 8.00 20.00
Adrian Beltre
40 Jacoby Ellsbury 12.50 30.00
Colby Rasmus
41 Andre Ethier 6.00 15.00
Wandy Rodriguez
42 Neftali Feliz 8.00 20.00
Alfonso Soriano
43 Prince Fielder 10.00 25.00
Corey Hart
44 Yovani Gallardo 6.00 15.00
Carl Crawford
45 Jaime Garcia 10.00 25.00
Jim Thome
46 Brett Gardner 10.00 25.00
Miguel Tejada
47 Matt Garza 6.00 15.00
Jayson Werth
48 Adrian Gonzalez 10.00 25.00
Jonathan Papelbon
49 Carlos Gonzalez 8.00 20.00
Trevor Cahill
50 Gio Gonzalez 6.00 15.00
Andre Ethier
51 Curtis Granderson 12.50 30.00
Buster Posey
52 Vladimir Guerrero 8.00 20.00
Justin Morneau
53 Franklin Gutierrez 6.00 15.00
Juan Pierre
54 Roy Halladay 8.00 20.00
Daric Barton
55 Cole Hamels 8.00 20.00
Danny Valencia
56 Josh Hamilton 12.50 30.00
Hanley Ramirez
57 Tommy Hanson 8.00 20.00
Vladimir Guerrero
58 Dan Haren 6.00 15.00
Franklin Gutierrez

59 Corey Hart 8.00 20.00
Yadier Molina
60 Chase Headley 6.00 15.00
Josh Johnson
61 Felix Hernandez 8.00 20.00
Matt Kemp
62 Jason Heyward 8.00 20.00
Chase Headley
63 Aaron Hill 6.00 15.00
Kelly Johnson
64 Matt Holliday 12.50 30.00
David Price
65 Ryan Howard 12.50 30.00
Ichiro Suzuki
66 Daniel Hudson 6.00 15.00
James Shields
67 Tim Hudson 10.00 25.00
Adam Lind
68 Aubrey Huff 15.00 40.00
Ike Davis
69 Phil Hughes 6.00 15.00
Torii Hunter
70 Torii Hunter 8.00 20.00
Casey McGehee
71 Omar Infante 15.00 40.00
Dustin Pedroia
72 Austin Jackson 8.00 20.00
Mariano Rivera
73 Edwin Jackson 6.00 15.00
Michael Bourn
74 Jon Jay
Derek Lowe
75 Derek Jeter 20.00 50.00
B.J. Upton
76 Ubaldo Jimenez 8.00 20.00
Angel Pagan
77 Josh Johnson 6.00 15.00
Ian Kinsler
78 Kelly Johnson 6.00 15.00
Ivan Rodriguez
79 Adam Jones 10.00 25.00
Chris Coghlan
80 Chipper Jones 30.00 60.00
Robinson Cano
81 Jair Jurrjens 8.00 20.00
Nick Markakis
82 Matt Kemp 8.00 20.00
John Lackey
83 Howie Kendrick 6.00 15.00
David Ortiz
84 Clayton Kershaw 10.00 25.00
Jimmy Rollins
85 Ian Kinsler 10.00 25.00
Rafael Soriano
86 Paul Konerko 8.00 20.00
Manny Ramirez
87 John Lackey 10.00 25.00
Tommy Hanson
88 Mat Latos 6.00 15.00
Matt Holliday
89 Cliff Lee 10.00 25.00
Kevin Youkilis
90 Derrek Lee 6.00 15.00
C.J. Wilson
91 Jon Lester 12.50 30.00
Andres Torres
92 Brad Lidge 6.00 15.00
Bobby Abreu
93 Tim Lincecum 12.50 30.00
Carlos Ruiz
94 Adam Lind 8.00 20.00
Carlos Quentin
95 Francisco Liriano 10.00 25.00
Justin Verlander
96 James Loney 30.00 60.00
Alex Rodriguez
97 Evan Longoria 30.00 60.00
Derek Jeter
98 Derek Lowe 10.00 25.00
Joey Votto
99 Nick Markakis 12.50 30.00
Adrian Gonzalez
100 Carlos Marmol 6.00 15.00
Barry Zito
101 Victor Martinez 6.00 15.00
Jay Bruce
102 Brian Matusz 10.00 25.00
Dallas Braden
103 Joe Mauer 12.50 30.00
Kurt Suzuki
104 Brian McCann 8.00 20.00
Aubrey Huff
105 Andrew McCutchen 10.00 25.00
Max Scherzer
106 Casey McGehee 6.00 15.00
Derrek Lee
107 Jenrry Mejia 6.00 15.00
Brian Roberts
108 Yadier Molina 8.00 20.00
Jason Bartlett
109 Miguel Montero 6.00 15.00
Brett Wallace
110 Kendry Morales 8.00 20.00
Brandon Morrow
111 Justin Morneau 12.50 30.00
Pablo Sandoval
112 Logan Morrison 8.00 20.00
Drew Stubbs
113 Brandon Morrow 8.00 20.00
Jonathan Sanchez
114 Brett Myers 6.00 15.00
Daniel Hudson
115 Mike Napoli 8.00 20.00
CC Sabathia
116 David Ortiz 15.00 40.00
Joakim Soria
117 Roy Oswalt 10.00 25.00
Jaime Garcia
118 Angel Pagan 12.50 30.00
Michael Cuddyer
119 Jonathan Papelbon 12.50 30.00
Delmon Young
120 Carl Pavano 8.00 20.00
Grady Sizemore
121 Dustin Pedroia 15.00 40.00
Brian Wilson
122 Mike Pelfrey 8.00 20.00
Domonic Brown
123 Hunter Pence 10.00 25.00
Josh Hamilton
124 Andy Pettitte 15.00 40.00
Mark Teixeira
125 Brandon Phillips 10.00 25.00
Johan Santana
126 Juan Pierre 6.00 15.00
Jon Jay
127 Jorge Posada 10.00 25.00
Tyler Colvin
128 Buster Posey 15.00 40.00
Clayton Kershaw
129 Martin Prado 8.00 20.00
Elvis Andrus
130 David Price 10.00 25.00
Andy Pettitte
131 Albert Pujols 20.00 50.00
Matt Garza
132 Carlos Quentin 8.00 20.00
Bronson Arroyo
133 Alexei Ramirez 6.00 15.00
Mike Pelfrey
134 Aramis Ramirez 6.00 15.00
Michael Young
135 Hanley Ramirez 12.50 30.00
Nick Swisher
136 Manny Ramirez 15.00 40.00
Cliff Lee
137 Colby Rasmus 12.50 30.00
Adam Dunn
138 Jose Reyes 10.00 25.00
Jose Bautista
139 Mark Reynolds 8.00 20.00
Andrew McCutchen
140 Alex Rios 8.00 20.00
Victor Martinez
141 Mariano Rivera 10.00 25.00
Dan Haren
142 Brian Roberts 6.00 15.00
Heath Bell
143 Alex Rodriguez 15.00 40.00
Jair Jurrjens
144 Ivan Rodriguez 10.00 25.00
Jose Reyes
145 Wandy Rodriguez 6.00 15.00
Billy Butler
146 Jimmy Rollins 20.00 50.00
Tim Lincecum
147 Ricky Romero 6.00 15.00
Jered Weaver
148 Carlos Ruiz 6.00 15.00
Martin Prado
149 CC Sabathia 20.00 50.00
Albert Pujols
150 Gaby Sanchez 6.00 15.00
Ricky Romero
151 Jonathan Sanchez 10.00 25.00
Nelson Cruz
152 Pablo Sandoval 15.00 40.00
Chris Carpenter
153 Carlos Santana 8.00 20.00
Jon Lester
154 Ervin Santana 8.00 20.00
Shin-Soo Choo
155 Johan Santana 8.00 20.00
Miguel Montero
156 Max Scherzer 15.00 40.00
Jason Heyward
157 Luke Scott 8.00 20.00
Mike Stanton
158 James Shields 6.00 15.00
Chad Billingsley
159 Grady Sizemore 8.00 20.00
Alexei Ramirez
160 Joakim Soria 6.00 15.00
Ervin Santana
161 Alfonso Soriano 8.00 20.00
Prince Fielder
162 Rafael Soriano 6.00 15.00
Mark Reynolds
163 Denard Span 10.00 25.00
Carlos Santana
164 Mike Stanton 12.50 30.00
Matt Capps
165 Drew Stubbs 10.00 25.00
Gordon Beckham
166 Ichiro Suzuki 10.00 25.00
Justin Upton
167 Kurt Suzuki 8.00 20.00
Gio Gonzalez
168 Nick Swisher 10.00 25.00
Brian Matusz
169 Jose Tabata 8.00 20.00
Phil Hughes
170 Mark Teixeira 10.00 25.00
Ryan Dempster
171 Miguel Tejada 15.00 40.00
Joe Mauer
172 Jim Thome 8.00 20.00
Brett Anderson
173 Andres Torres 12.50 30.00
Jacoby Ellsbury
174 Troy Tulowitzki 8.00 20.00
Hunter Pence
175 Dan Uggla 12.50 30.00
Matt Cain
176 B.J. Upton 6.00 15.00
Brian McCann
177 Justin Upton 8.00 20.00
Roy Oswalt
178 Chase Utley 8.00 20.00
Luke Scott
179 Danny Valencia 10.00 25.00
Tim Hudson
180 Will Venable 8.00 20.00
Troy Tulowitzki
181 Justin Verlander 8.00 20.00
Shane Victorino
182 Shane Victorino 8.00 20.00
John Danks
183 Joey Votto 10.00 25.00
Austin Jackson
184 Adam Wainwright 12.50 30.00
Rickie Weeks
185 Neil Walker 10.00 25.00
James Loney
186 Brett Wallace 10.00 25.00
Ryan Braun
187 Jered Weaver 6.00 15.00
Brandon Phillips
188 Rickie Weeks 8.00 20.00
Neftali Feliz
189 Vernon Wells 8.00 20.00
Ryan Howard
190 Jayson Werth 12.50 30.00
David Wright
191 Brian Wilson 12.50 30.00
Aramis Ramirez
192 C.J. Wilson 10.00 25.00
Carlos Gonzalez
193 David Wright 12.50 30.00
Starlin Castro
194 Kevin Youkilis 20.00 50.00
Chipper Jones
195 Chris Young 6.00 15.00
Marlon Byrd
196 Delmon Young 10.00 25.00
Neil Walker
197 Michael Young 6.00 15.00
Ubaldo Jimenez
198 Ryan Zimmerman 6.00 15.00
Jenrry Mejia
199 Barry Zito 10.00 25.00
Chase Utley
200 Ben Zobrist 8.00 20.00
Paul Konerko

2011 Topps Heritage Jackie Robinson Special Memorabilia

COMMON ROBINSON 40.00 80.00
STATED ODDS 1:1777 HOBBY
STATED PRINT RUN 42 SER.#'d SETS
135 Jackie Robinson 40.00 80.00
136 Jackie Robinson 40.00 80.00
137 Jackie Robinson 40.00 80.00
138 Jackie Robinson 40.00 80.00
139 Jackie Robinson 40.00 80.00
140 Jackie Robinson 40.00 80.00
141 Jackie Robinson 40.00 80.00
142 Jackie Robinson 40.00 80.00
143 Jackie Robinson 40.00 80.00
144 Jackie Robinson 40.00 80.00

2011 Topps Heritage New Age Performers

COMPLETE SET (15) 15.00 40.00
STATED ODDS 1:15 HOBBY
NAP1 Cliff Lee 1.25 3.00
NAP2 Jim Thome .75 2.00
NAP3 Josh Hamilton 1.25 3.00
NAP4 Roy Halladay 1.25 3.00
NAP5 Miguel Cabrera 1.25 3.00
NAP6 Ubaldo Jimenez .75 2.00
NAP7 Joey Votto 1.25 3.00
NAP8 CC Sabathia .75 2.00
NAP9 David Price 1.25 3.00
NAP10 Alex Rodriguez 2.00 5.00
NAP11 Evan Longoria 1.50 4.00
NAP12 Carlos Gonzalez .75 2.00
NAP13 Robinson Cano 1.25 3.00
NAP14 Felix Hernandez 1.25 3.00
NAP15 Albert Pujols 3.00 8.00

2011 Topps Heritage News Flashbacks

COMPLETE SET (10) 4.00 10.00
STATED ODDS 1:12 HOBBY
NF1 Cuban Missile Crisis Begins .40 1.00
NF2 Glenn First To Orbit Earth .40 1.00
NF3 Mona Lisa Exhibited in U.S. .40 1.00
NF4 U.S. Embargo Against Cuba .40 1.00
NF5 U.S. Navy SEALs Are Activated .40 1.00
NF6 Dodger Stadium Opens Its Doors .40 1.00
NF7 Mariner 2 Encounters Venus .40 1.00
NF8 New York Mets Join the NL .60 1.50
NF9 Jamaica Ends British Rule .40 1.00
NF10 Robinson In Cooperstown 1.00 2.50

2011 Topps Heritage Real One Autographs

STATED ODDS 1:303
EXCHANGE DEADLINE 2/28/2014
AD Art Ditmar 12.50 30.00
AJ David Wright 30.00 60.00
AK Al Kaline 60.00 120.00
BC Bob Cerv 10.00 25.00
BG Bob Gibson 50.00 100.00
BP Bill Pierce 10.00 25.00
BR Brooks Robinson 50.00 100.00
DB Don Buddin 10.00 25.00
DD Dan Dobbek 10.00 25.00
DG Dick Gernert 10.00 25.00
DH Dave Hillman 10.00 25.00
EB Ernie Banks 50.00 100.00
EL Evan Longoria 60.00 120.00
EY Eddie Yost 10.00 25.00
FT Frank Thomas 12.50 30.00
HA Hank Aaron EXCH 300.00 500.00
HB Howie Bedell 10.00 25.00
HN Hal Naragon 10.00 25.00
HR Hanley Ramirez EXCH 10.00 25.00
HS Hal Stowe 15.00 40.00
JA Jim Archer 10.00 25.00
JD Jim Donohue 10.00 25.00
JH Joe Hicks 12.50 30.00
LP Leo Posada 10.00 25.00
MK Marty Kutyna 10.00 25.00
MS Mike Stanton 20.00 50.00
NC Neil Chrisley 10.00 25.00
RR Ray Rippelmeyer 10.00 25.00
SC Starlin Castro 30.00 60.00
SK Sandy Koufax EXCH 500.00 700.00
SM Stan Musial 125.00 250.00
TP Tom Parsons 10.00 25.00
TW Ted Wills 10.00 25.00
DGI Don Gile 10.00 25.00
EBO Ed Bouchee 10.00 25.00
GWI Gordon Windhorn 12.50 30.00
JDE John DeMerit 12.50 30.00

2011 Topps Heritage Real One Autographs Red Ink

*RED: 5.X TO 1.2X BASIC
STATED ODDS 1:700 HOBBY
STATED PRINT RUN 62 SER.#'d SETS
HA Hank Aaron EXCH
HR Hanley Ramirez EXCH
SK Sandy Koufax EXCH
SM Stan Musial 150.00 300.00

2011 Topps Heritage Real One Dual Autographs

STATED ODDS 1:2989 HOBBY
STATED PRINT RUN 25 SER.#'d SETS
NO PRICING DUE TO SCARCITY
EXCHANGE DEADLINE 2/28/2014
BC Ernie Banks
Starlin Castro
GS Bob Gibson
Stephen Strasburg EXCH
GW Dick Gernert
Brett Wallace
KJ Al Kaline
Austin Jackson
MU Stan Musial
Chase Utley
RL Brooks Robinson
Evan Longoria
RS Frank Robinson
Mike Stanton
TW Frank Thomas
David Wright
WP Ted Wills
Jonathan Papelbon
YR Eddie Yost
Juan Rivera

2011 Topps Heritage Then and Now

COMPLETE SET (10) 8.00 20.00
STATED ODDS 1:15 HOBBY
TN1 Harmon Killebrew .60 1.50
Jose Bautista
TN2 Frank Robinson 1.00 2.50
Miguel Cabrera
TN3 Frank Robinson 1.00 2.50
Josh Hamilton
TN4 Luis Aparicio .40 1.00
Juan Pierre
TN5 Mickey Mantle .60 1.50
Prince Fielder
TN6 Robin Roberts 1.00 2.50
Felix Hernandez
TN7 Bob Gibson .60 1.50
Jered Weaver
TN8 Juan Marichal .60 1.50
CC Sabathia
TN9 Warren Spahn 1.00 2.50
Roy Halladay
TN10 Bob Gibson 1.00 2.50
Roy Halladay

2011 Topps Heritage Triple Stamp Box Topper

RANDOMLY INSERTED BOX TOPPER
TSBL1 Jered Weaver 1.50 4.00
Torii Hunter
Dan Haren
TSBL2 Stephen Drew 2.50 6.00
Justin Upton
Miguel Montero
TSBL3 Brian McCann 5.00 12.00
Jason Heyward
Martin Prado
TSBL4 Brian Matusz 4.00 10.00
Adam Jones
Nick Markakis
TSBL5 Dustin Pedroia 5.00 12.00
David Ortiz
Jon Lester
TSBL6 Alfonso Soriano 4.00 10.00
Starlin Castro
Carlos Marmol
TSBL7 Alex Rios 2.50 6.00
Gordon Beckham
Alexei Ramirez
TSBL8 Brandon Phillips 4.00 10.00
Joey Votto
Jay Bruce
TSBL9 Shin-Soo Choo 2.50 6.00
Carlos Santana
Grady Sizemore
TSBL10 Troy Tulowitzki 4.00 10.00
Carlos Gonzalez
Ubaldo Jimenez
TSBL11 Justin Verlander 5.00 12.00
Miguel Cabrera
Austin Jackson
TSBL12 Mike Stanton 4.00 10.00
Hanley Ramirez
Josh Johnson
TSBL13 Michael Bourn 2.50 6.00
Hunter Pence
Wandy Rodriguez
TSBL14 Billy Butler 1.50 4.00
Lorenzo Cain
Joakim Soria
TSBL15 Andre Ethier 4.00 10.00
Clayton Kershaw
Matt Kemp
TSBL16 Prince Fielder 2.50 6.00
Ryan Braun
Yovani Gallardo
TSBL17 Justin Morneau 4.00 10.00
Joe Mauer
Francisco Liriano
TSBL18 Johan Santana 5.00 12.00
David Wright
Jose Reyes
TSBL19 Robinson Cano 10.00 25.00
Derek Jeter
CC Sabathia
TSBL20 Brett Anderson 2.50 6.00
Trevor Cahill
Gio Gonzalez
TSBL21 Ryan Howard 5.00 12.00
Roy Halladay
Chase Utley
TSBL22 Jose Tabata 4.00 10.00
Andrew McCutchen
Neil Walker
TSBL23 Mat Latos 2.50 6.00
Chase Headley
Heath Bell
TSBL24 Tim Lincecum 4.00 10.00
Buster Posey
Brian Wilson
TSBL25 Felix Hernandez 6.00 15.00
Ichiro Suzuki
Franklin Gutierrez
TSBL26 Matt Holliday 10.00 25.00
Albert Pujols
Adam Wainwright
TSBL27 David Price 5.00 12.00
Evan Longoria
B.J. Upton
TSBL28 Nelson Cruz 4.00 10.00
Josh Hamilton
Ian Kinsler
TSBL29 Jose Bautista 2.50 6.00
Ricky Romero
Brandon Morrow
TSBL30 Jayson Werth 2.50 6.00
Ryan Zimmerman
Ian Desmond

2011 Topps Lineage

COMPLETE SET (200) 15.00 40.00
COMMON CARD (1-200) .12 .30
COMMON ROOKIE (1-200) .25 .60
PRINTING PLATE ODDS 1:925 HOBBY
PLATE PRINT RUN 1 SET PER COLOR
BLACK-CYAN-MAGENTA-YELLOW ISSUED
NO PLATE PRICING DUE TO SCARCITY
1 Sandy Koufax 1.00 2.50
2 Derek Jeter .75 2.00
3 Jimmie Foxx .30 .75
4 Buster Posey .40 1.00
5 Felix Hernandez .30 .75
6 Carlos Beltran .20 .50
7 Mickey Mantle 1.00 2.50
8 Francisco Liriano .12 .30
9 Matt Holliday .30 .75
10 Jim Palmer .12 .30
11 Ryan Zimmerman .20 .50
12 Elvis Andrus .20 .50
13 Cal Ripken Jr. 1.25 3.00
14 Kendry Morales .12 .30
15 Curtis Granderson .20 .50
16 Walter Johnson .30 .75
17 Billy Butler .12 .30
18 Brett Anderson .20 .50
19 Larry Walker .20 .50
20 Justin Morneau .30 .75
21 Edinson Volquez .12 .30
22 Johan Santana .30 .75
23 Carlos Zambrano .20 .50
24 Tsuyoshi Nishioka RC .75 2.00
25 Whitey Ford .20 .50
26 Grady Sizemore .20 .50
27 George Sisler .30 .75
28 Aramis Ramirez .12 .30
29 Chris Sale RC .40 1.00
30 Chase Utley .30 .75
31 Jeremy Hellickson RC .75 2.00
32 Jon Lester .30 .75
33 Tony Perez .12 .30
34 Kyle Drabek RC .40 1.00
35 Hanley Ramirez .30 .75
36 Michael Young .20 .50
37 Justin Upton .20 .50
38 Chris Carpenter .30 .75
39 Ricky Romero .12 .30
40 Stan Musial .50 1.25
41 Vladimir Guerrero .30 .75
42 Jackie Robinson .30 .75
43 Victor Martinez .20 .50
44 Jay Bruce .20 .50
45 Ryan Howard .40 1.00
46 Logan Morrison .12 .30
47 Lance Berkman .20 .50
48 Carlton Fisk .20 .50
49 Matt Kemp .20 .50
50 Lou Gehrig .60 1.50
51 Hunter Pence .20 .50
52 Andre Dawson .20 .50
53 Mike Schmidt .50 1.25
54 Alfonso Soriano .20 .50
55 Nolan Ryan 1.00 2.50
56 Shane Victorino .20 .50
57 Willie McCovey .20 .50
58 Gordon Beckham .20 .50
59 Duke Snider .20 .50
60 Reggie Jackson .20 .50
61 Zach Britton RC .60 1.50
62 Adrian Beltre .12 .30
63 Ubaldo Jimenez .20 .50
64 Joe Morgan .12 .30
65 Josh Johnson .20 .50
66 Andrew McCutchen .30 .75
67 Nelson Cruz .20 .50
68 Alexei Ramirez .12 .30
69 Jayson Werth .20 .50
70 Carlos Santana .30 .75
71 Kurt Suzuki .12 .30
72 Rickie Weeks .20 .50
73 Kosuke Fukudome .30 .75
74 Brooks Robinson .20 .50
75 Alex Rodriguez .50 1.25
76 Roberto Alomar .20 .50
77 David Wright .40 1.00
78 Dan Uggla .20 .50
79 Carl Crawford .20 .50
80 Troy Tulowitzki .30 .75
81 Andruw Jones .12 .30
82 Ike Davis .20 .50
83 Adam Wainwright .20 .50
84 Clayton Kershaw .30 .75
85 Al Kaline .30 .75
86 Carlos Gonzalez .20 .50
87 David Ortiz .20 .50
88 David Price .30 .75
89 Eddie Murray .30 .75
90 Tris Speaker .20 .50
91 Brent Morel RC .25 .60
92 Clay Buchholz .20 .50
93 Roy Oswalt .20 .50
94 John Smoltz .30 .75
95 Johnny Mize .20 .50
96 Jason Bay .20 .50
97 Aaron Hill .12 .30
98 Evan Longoria .40 1.00
99 Honus Wagner .30 .75
100 Babe Ruth .75 2.00
101 Madison Bumgarner .12 .30
102 Cole Hamels .30 .75
103 Joey Votto .30 .75
104 Miguel Montero .12 .30
105 Ty Cobb .50 1.25
106 Cy Young .30 .75
107 Chad Billingsley .12 .30
108 Hank Aaron .60 1.50
109 Mat Latos .12 .30
110 Thurman Munson .30 .75
111 Neil Walker .12 .30
112 Johnny Cueto .12 .30
113 Trevor Cahill .12 .30
114 Dustin Pedroia .40 1.00
115 Chipper Jones .30 .75
116 Pedro Alvarez RC .20 .50
117 Torii Hunter .12 .30
118 Todd Helton .20 .50
119 Matt Cain .20 .50
120 Ichiro Suzuki .50 1.25
121 Roy Halladay .30 .75
122 Paul O'Neill .20 .50
123 Andre Ethier .20 .50
124 Franklin Gutierrez .12 .30
125 Mark Teixeira .30 .75
126 Shin-Soo Choo .20 .50
127 Orlando Hudson .12 .30
128 Vernon Wells .12 .30
129 Jason Heyward .40 1.00
130 Joe Mauer .30 .75
131 Carlos Lee .12 .30
132 Nick Markakis .30 .75
133 Zack Greinke .20 .50
134 John Danks .12 .30
135 Tim Lincecum .30 .75
136 Starlin Castro .30 .75
137 Johnny Bench .30 .75
138 Prince Fielder .20 .50
139 Michael Pineda RC .75 2.00
140 Albert Belle .12 .30
141 Ozzie Smith .50 1.25
142 Dan Haren .12 .30
143 Miguel Cabrera .30 .75
144 Roy Campanella .30 .75
145 Adrian Gonzalez .20 .50
146 Freddie Freeman RC 1.00 2.50
147 Ryan Braun .40 1.00
148 Aroldis Chapman RC .75 2.00
149 Kevin Youkilis .20 .50
150 Robinson Cano .30 .75
151 Johnny Damon .20 .50
152 David DeJesus .12 .30
153 B.J. Upton .20 .50
154 Fergie Jenkins .12 .30
155 Bob Gibson .20 .50
156 Austin Jackson .12 .30
157 Wandy Rodriguez .12 .30
158 Monte Irvin .12 .30
159 Yonder Alonso RC .40 1.00
160 Stephen Strasburg .60 1.50
161 Luis Aparicio .12 .30
162 Brandon Belt RC 1.00 2.50
163 Jered Weaver .12 .30
164 Brandon Beachy RC .60 1.50
165 Jose Reyes .20 .50
166 Yovani Gallardo .12 .30
167 Corey Hart .12 .30
168 Delmon Young .20 .50
169 Cliff Lee .30 .75
170 Tom Seaver .20 .50
171 Ryne Sandberg .60 1.50
172 Jose Bautista .20 .50
173 Adam Dunn .20 .50
174 Adam Jones .20 .50
175 CC Sabathia .20 .50
176 Miguel Tejada .20 .50
177 Phil Hughes .12 .30
178 Albert Pujols .75 2.00
179 Jake McGee (RC) .25 .60
180 Marlon Byrd .12 .30
181 Frank Thomas .30 .75
182 Frank Robinson .20 .50
183 Brian McCann .20 .50
184 Josh Hamilton .30 .75
185 Ian Kinsler .20 .50
186 Mel Ott .30 .75
187 Justin Verlander .40 1.00
188 Daniel Hudson .12 .30
189 Jaime Garcia .20 .50
190 Bert Blyleven .12 .30
191 Johnny Bench .30 .75
192 Willie McCovey .20 .50
193 Joe Morgan .12 .30
194 Cal Ripken Jr 1.25 3.00
195 Chipper Jones .30 .75
196 Ichiro Suzuki .50 1.25
197 Andre Dawson .20 .50
198 Andruw Jones .12 .30
199 CC Sabathia .20 .50
200 Tom Seaver .20 .50

2011 Topps Lineage Canary Diamond Refractors

STATED ODDS 1:3702 HOBBY
STATED PRINT RUN 1 SER.#'d SET
NO PRICING DUE TO SCARCITY

2011 Topps Lineage Diamond Anniversary Refractors

The cards in this 200 card base set parallel feature a foil board front and a Topps Diamond Anniversary logo.

*VET REF: 1.5X TO 4X BASIC
*RC REF: .75X TO 2X BASIC
STATED ODDS 1:4 HOBBY

2011 Topps Lineage Diamond Anniversary Platinum Refractors

The cards in this 200 card base set parallel feature a "glittering" or "sparkling" effect on the front of the card along with Topps Diamond Anniversary logo.

*VET PLAT.REF: 1.5X TO 4X BASIC
*RC PLAT.REF: .75X TO 2X BASIC
STATED ODDS 1:4 HOBBY

2011 Topps Lineage 1952 Autographs

GROUP A ODDS 1:38 HOBBY
GROUP B ODDS 1:131 HOBBY
GROUP D ODDS 1:327 HOBBY
GROUP C ODDS 1:397 HOBBY
GOLD CANARY ODDS 1:771 HOBBY
GOLD CANARY PRINT RUN 10 SER.#'d SETS
NO GOLD CANARY PRICING AVAILABLE
EXCHANGE DEADLINE 7/31/2014
52ABL Brandon League 3.00 8.00
52ABP Buster Posey 40.00 80.00
52ACB Clay Buchholz 6.00 15.00
52ACM Charlie Morton 4.00 10.00
52ADD David DeJesus 3.00 8.00
52AFF Freddie Freeman 15.00 40.00
52AFR Fernando Rodney 3.00 8.00
52AGS Gaby Sanchez 10.00 25.00
52AID Ike Davis 8.00 20.00
52AJB John Buck 3.00 8.00

52AJG Jonny Gomes 3.00 8.00
52AJM Jason Motte 4.00 10.00
52ALM Logan Morrison 6.00 15.00
52AMB Madison Bumgarner 8.00 20.00
52AMH Matt Harrison 3.00 8.00
52AMM Michael Morse 5.00 12.00
52AMS Mike Stanton 12.50 30.00
52ARZ Ryan Zimmerman 8.00 20.00
52ASV Shane Victorino 12.50 30.00
52ATW Ty Wigginton 3.00 8.00
52AUJ Ubaldo Jimenez 10.00 25.00
52AMBY Marlon Byrd 4.00 10.00

2011 Topps Lineage 1975 Mini

COMPLETE SET (200) 250.00 350.00
*MINI VET: 2X TO 5X BASIC
*MINI RC: 1X TO 2.5X BASIC RC
STATED ODDS 1:4 HOBBY

2011 Topps Lineage 1975 Mini Relics

GROUP A ODDS 1:28 HOBBY
GROUP B ODDS 1:331 HOBBY
GROUP C ODDS 1:6500 HOBBY
GOLD CANARY ODDS 1:747 HOBBY
GOLD CANARY PRINT RUN 10 SER.#'d SETS
NO GOLD CANARY PRICING AVAILABLE
AB Adrian Beltre 3.00 8.00
AD Andre Dawson 8.00 20.00
AE Andre Ethier 4.00 10.00
AJ Austin Jackson 3.00 8.00
AK Al Kaline 12.50 30.00
AM Andrew McCutchen 5.00 12.00
AP Albert Pujols 12.50 30.00
AR Aramis Ramirez 3.00 8.00
AS Alfonso Soriano 3.00 8.00
BG Bob Gibson 15.00 40.00
BP Buster Posey 8.00 20.00
BR Brooks Robinson 10.00 25.00
BU B.J. Upton 3.00 8.00
CC Chris Carpenter 3.00 8.00
CF Carlton Fisk 12.50 30.00
CJ Chipper Jones 5.00 12.00
CK Clayton Kershaw 4.00 10.00
CL Carlos Lee 3.00 8.00
CR Cal Ripken Jr. 12.50 30.00
DO David Ortiz 4.00 10.00
DP David Price 4.00 10.00
DS Duke Snider 10.00 25.00
DU Dan Uggla 4.00 10.00
DW David Wright 4.00 10.00
EA Elvis Andrus 4.00 10.00
EL Evan Longoria 4.00 10.00
EM Eddie Murray 8.00 20.00
EV Edinson Volquez 3.00 8.00
FH Felix Hernandez 4.00 10.00
FJ Fergie Jenkins 12.50 30.00
FT Frank Thomas 30.00 60.00
GS Grady Sizemore 3.00 8.00
HA Hank Aaron 20.00 50.00
HW Honus Wagner 100.00 200.00
ID Ike Davis 4.00 10.00
IK Ian Kinsler 4.00 10.00
IS Ichiro Suzuki 10.00 25.00
JB Jay Bruce 4.00 10.00
JC Johnny Cueto 4.00 10.00
JH Jason Heyward 4.00 10.00
JJ Josh Johnson 3.00 8.00
JP Jim Palmer 10.00 25.00
JU Justin Upton 3.00 8.00
JV Joey Votto 6.00 15.00
JW Jayson Werth 4.00 10.00
KF Kosuke Fukudome 3.00 8.00
KY Kevin Youkilis 4.00 10.00
MB Madison Bumgarner 4.00 10.00
MC Matt Cain 4.00 10.00
MK Matt Kemp 3.00 8.00
MM Mickey Mantle 100.00 200.00
MO Mel Ott 12.50 30.00
MS Mike Schmidt 20.00 50.00
NC Nelson Cruz 4.00 10.00
NR Nolan Ryan 20.00 50.00
OS Ozzie Smith 8.00 20.00
PF Prince Fielder 4.00 10.00
RB Ryan Braun 4.00 10.00
RC Roy Campanella 12.50 30.00
RJ Reggie Jackson 10.00 25.00
RR Ricky Romero 4.00 10.00
RZ Ryan Zimmerman 4.00 10.00
SC Starlin Castro 5.00 12.00
SK Sandy Koufax 100.00 200.00
SM Stan Musial 20.00 50.00
SS Stephen Strasburg 20.00 50.00
SV Shane Victorino 4.00 10.00
TH Todd Helton 4.00 10.00
TL Tim Lincecum 8.00 20.00
TP Tony Perez 10.00 25.00
VM Victor Martinez 4.00 10.00
VW Vernon Wells 3.00 8.00
WF Whitey Ford 20.00 50.00
WM Willie McCovey Jsy 10.00 25.00
WR Wandy Rodriguez 3.00 8.00
YG Yovani Gallardo 4.00 10.00
ABE Albert Belle 6.00 15.00
ADU Adam Dunn 4.00 10.00
ARA Alexei Ramirez 4.00 10.00
ARO Alex Rodriguez 6.00 15.00
BMC Brian McCann 4.00 10.00
BRU Babe Ruth 100.00 200.00
CBU Clay Buchholz 4.00 10.00
CBE Carlos Beltran 4.00 10.00
CCS CC Sabathia 4.00 10.00
CGO Carlos Gonzalez 5.00 12.00
DPE Dustin Pedroia 8.00 20.00
JBA Jose Bautista 10.00 25.00
JBE Johnny Bench 15.00 40.00
JBY Jason Bay 4.00 10.00
JMA Joe Mauer 5.00 12.00
JMI Johnny Mize 12.50 30.00
JRE Jose Reyes 5.00 12.00
JSM John Smoltz 4.00 10.00
JVE Justin Verlander 6.00 15.00
JWE Jered Weaver 3.00 8.00
MBY Marlon Byrd 3.00 8.00
MCA Miguel Cabrera 5.00 12.00
WM2 Willie McCovey Bat 10.00 25.00

2011 Topps Lineage 3-D

COMPLETE SET (25) 30.00 60.00
STATED ODDS 1:12 HOBBY
*BLACK: 2.5X TO 6X BASIC
STATED BLACK ODDS 1:446 HOBBY
STATED RED ODDS 1:30,873 HOBBY
RED PRINT RUN 1 SER.#'d SET
BLACK PRINT RUN 99 SER.#'d SETS
NO RED PRICING DUE TO SCARCITY
T3D1 Ichiro Suzuki 2.50 6.00
T3D2 Buster Posey 2.00 5.00
T3D3 Ryan Howard 2.00 5.00
T3D4 Mark Teixeira 1.50 4.00
T3D5 Joe Mauer 1.50 4.00
T3D6 Ryan Braun 2.00 5.00
T3D7 Carlos Gonzalez 1.00 2.50
T3D8 Joey Votto 1.50 4.00
T3D9 Adrian Gonzalez 1.00 2.50
T3D10 Alex Rodriguez 2.50 6.00
T3D11 David Wright 2.00 5.00
T3D12 Carl Crawford 1.00 2.50
T3D13 Miguel Cabrera 1.50 4.00
T3D14 Chase Utley 1.50 4.00
T3D15 Evan Longoria 2.00 5.00
T3D16 Jason Heyward 2.00 5.00
T3D17 Kendry Morales .60 1.50
T3D18 Shin-Soo Choo 1.00 2.50
T3D19 Hanley Ramirez 1.50 4.00
T3D20 Josh Hamilton 1.50 4.00
T3D21 Justin Upton 1.00 2.50
T3D22 Troy Tulowitzki 1.50 4.00
T3D23 Hunter Pence 1.00 2.50
T3D24 Derek Jeter 4.00 10.00
T3D25 Albert Pujols 4.00 10.00

2011 Topps Lineage 60th Anniversary Jumbo Relic Patches

STATED ODDS 1:5923 HOBBY
STATED PRINT RUN 5 SER.#'d SETS
NO PRICING DUE TO SCARCITY

2011 Topps Lineage 60th Anniversary Jumbo Relics

STATED ODDS 1:1190 HOBBY
STATED PRINT RUN 25 SER.#'d SETS
NO PRICING DUE TO SCARCITY

2011 Topps Lineage Autographs

GROUP A ODDS 1:38 HOBBY
GROUP B-C ODDS 1:131 HOBBY
GROUP D ODDS 1:1810 HOBBY
GOLD CANARY ODDS 1:771 HOBBY
GOLD CANARY PRINT RUN 10 SER.#'d SETS
NO GOLD CANARY PRICING AVAILABLE
EXCHANGE DEADLINE 7/31/2014
AD Al Dark 10.00 25.00
AK Al Kaline EXCH 40.00 80.00
AM Andrew McCutchen 8.00 20.00
AS Al Schoendienst 15.00 40.00
BA Bob Addis EXCH 8.00 20.00
BB Bob Borkowski 8.00 20.00
BD Bob Del Greco 12.50 30.00
BF Bob Friend 10.00 25.00
BK Bob Kelly 12.50 30.00
BK Bob Kuzava 12.50 30.00
BM Bobby Morgan 10.00 25.00
BP Billy Pierce 10.00 25.00
BS Bobby Shantz 10.00 25.00
CB Cloyd Boyer 10.00 25.00
CC Cliff Chambers 12.50 30.00
CD Chuck Diering 6.00 15.00
CE Carl Erskine
CS Charlie Silvera 10.00 25.00
DC Del Crandall 12.50 30.00
DG Dick Groat 12.50 30.00
DH Daniel Hudson 4.00 10.00
DL Don Lenhardt 12.50 30.00
DP Duane Pillette EXCH 10.00 25.00
EE Ed Erautt 8.00 20.00
ER Eddie Robinson 8.00 20.00
EY Eddie Yost 8.00 20.00
FC Fausto Carmona 4.00 10.00
FJ Fergie Jenkins 30.00 60.00
GC Gil Coan 8.00 20.00
GH Grady Hatton EXCH 10.00 25.00
GS George Spencer EXCH 6.00 15.00
GZ George Zuverink 10.00 25.00
HA Hank Aaron EXCH
HJ Howie Judson 10.00 25.00
HP Harry Perkowski EXCH 6.00 15.00
ID Ivan Delock 10.00 25.00
IK Ian Kinsler 5.00 12.00
IN Irv Noren 10.00 25.00
JA Joe Astroth 8.00 20.00
JC Jerry Coleman 10.00 25.00
JD Joe DeMaestri 10.00 25.00
JG Johnny Groth 10.00 25.00
JM Joe Morgan EXCH 30.00 60.00
JP Joe Presko 10.00 25.00
JP Johnny Pesky EXCH
JS John Smoltz EXCH 30.00 60.00
LB Lou Brissie 10.00 25.00
LS Lou Sleater 6.00 15.00
MB Matt Batts EXCH 8.00 20.00
MG Myron Ginsberg EXCH 10.00 25.00
MI Monte Irvin 12.50 30.00
NG Ned Garver 10.00 25.00
NR Nolan Ryan EXCH 100.00 175.00
PS Pablo Sandoval 5.00 12.00
RA Roberto Alomar EXCH 30.00 60.00
RB Rocky Bridges EXCH 12.50 30.00
RJ Randy Jackson 8.00 20.00
RS Roy Smalley 10.00 25.00
SK Sandy Koufax EXCH
TL Ted Lepcio 8.00 20.00
VL Vern Law 10.00 25.00
VT Virgil Trucks 12.50 30.00
WT Wayne Terwilliger 12.50 30.00
WW Wally Westlake EXCH 10.00 25.00
BMI Bob Miller 8.00 20.00
CSI Curt Simmons 12.50 30.00
DGE Dick Gernert 10.00 25.00
JAN John Antonelli 10.00 25.00
JGA Joe Garagiola 40.00 80.00
RBR Ralph Branca 30.00 60.00
RH1 Roy Halladay EXCH 60.00 120.00
RSI Roy Sievers 10.00 25.00
SMU Stan Musial 75.00 150.00
TBA Tony Bartirome 8.00 20.00

2011 Topps Lineage Cloth Stickers

COMMON CARD .50 1.25
SEMISTARS .75 2.00
UNLISTED STARS 1.25 3.00
STATED ODDS 1:12 HOBBY
TCS1 Sandy Koufax 4.00 10.00
TCS2 Derek Jeter 3.00 8.00
TCS3 Buster Posey 1.50 4.00
TCS4 Felix Hernandez 1.25 3.00
TCS5 Mickey Mantle 4.00 10.00
TCS6 Cal Ripken Jr. 5.00 12.00
TCS7 Whitey Ford .75 2.00
TCS8 George Sisler 1.25 3.00
TCS9 Hanley Ramirez 1.25 3.00
TCS10 Stan Musial 2.00 5.00
TCS11 Jackie Robinson 1.25 3.00
TCS12 Ryan Howard 1.50 4.00
TCS13 Lou Gehrig 2.50 6.00
TCS14 Hunter Pence .75 2.00
TCS15 Mike Schmidt 2.00 5.00
TCS16 Nolan Ryan 4.00 10.00
TCS17 Duke Snider .75 2.00
TCS18 Reggie Jackson .75 2.00
TCS19 Alex Rodriguez 2.00 5.00
TCS20 David Wright 1.50 4.00
TCS21 Carl Crawford .75 2.00
TCS22 Troy Tulowitzki 1.25 3.00
TCS23 Victor Martinez .75 2.00
TCS24 Al Kaline 1.25 3.00
TCS25 Carlos Gonzalez .75 2.00
TCS26 Eddie Murray 1.25 3.00
TCS27 Tris Speaker .75 2.00
TCS28 Evan Longoria 1.50 4.00
TCS29 Honus Wagner 1.25 3.00
TCS30 Babe Ruth 3.00 8.00
TCS31 Joey Votto 1.25 3.00
TCS32 Ty Cobb 2.00 5.00
TCS33 Cy Young 1.25 3.00
TCS34 Hank Aaron 2.50 6.00
TCS35 Chipper Jones 1.25 3.00
TCS36 Ichiro Suzuki 2.00 5.00
TCS37 Roy Halladay 1.25 3.00
TCS38 Jason Heyward 1.50 4.00
TCS39 Joe Mauer 1.25 3.00
TCS40 Tim Lincecum 1.25 3.00
TCS41 Johnny Bench 1.25 3.00
TCS42 Miguel Cabrera 1.25 3.00
TCS43 Adrian Gonzalez .75 2.00
TCS44 Ryan Braun 1.50 4.00
TCS45 Robinson Cano 1.25 3.00
TCS46 Bob Gibson .75 2.00
TCS47 Tom Seaver .75 2.00
TCS48 Ryne Sandberg 2.50 6.00
TCS49 Albert Pujols 3.00 8.00
TCS50 Josh Hamilton 1.25 3.00

2011 Topps Lineage Giants

COMPLETE SET (20) 60.00 120.00
ONE PER HOBBY BOX TOPPER
TG1 Albert Pujols 6.00 15.00
TG2 Buster Posey 3.00 8.00
TG3 Jason Heyward 3.00 8.00
TG4 Joe Mauer 2.50 6.00
TG5 Derek Jeter 6.00 15.00
TG6 Roy Halladay 2.50 6.00
TG7 Joey Votto 2.50 6.00
TG8 Ichiro Suzuki 4.00 10.00
TG9 Miguel Cabrera 2.50 6.00
TG10 Mike Stanton 1.50 4.00
TG11 Adrian Gonzalez 1.50 4.00
TG12 Josh Hamilton 2.50 6.00
TG13 Evan Longoria 3.00 8.00
TG14 Tim Lincecum 2.50 6.00
TG15 David Wright 3.00 8.00
TG16 Ryan Braun 3.00 8.00
TG17 Hanley Ramirez 2.50 6.00
TG18 Troy Tulowitzki 2.50 6.00
TG19 Carlos Santana 2.50 6.00
TG20 Vladimir Guerrero 2.50 6.00

2011 Topps Lineage Giants Relics

STATED ODDS 1:24 HOBBY BOXES
STATED PRINT RUN 64 SER.#'d SETS
TG1 Albert Pujols 50.00 100.00
TG2 Buster Posey 30.00 60.00
TG3 Jason Heyward 12.50 30.00
TG4 Joe Mauer 12.50 30.00
TG5 Derek Jeter 50.00 100.00
TG6 Roy Halladay 15.00 40.00
TG7 Joey Votto 20.00 50.00
TG8 Ichiro Suzuki 15.00 40.00
TG9 Miguel Cabrera 15.00 40.00
TG10 Mike Stanton 10.00 25.00
TG11 Adrian Gonzalez 15.00 40.00
TG12 Josh Hamilton 15.00 40.00
TG13 Evan Longoria 15.00 40.00
TG14 Tim Lincecum 15.00 40.00
TG15 David Wright 10.00 25.00
TG16 Ryan Braun 10.00 25.00
TG17 Hanley Ramirez 6.00 15.00
TG18 Troy Tulowitzki 10.00 25.00
TG19 Carlos Santana 15.00 40.00
TG20 Vladimir Guerrero 12.50 30.00

2011 Topps Lineage Rookies

COMPLETE SET (19) 8.00 20.00
STATED ODDS 1:6 HOBBY
TR1 Freddie Freeman 1.50 4.00
TR2 Chris Sale .60 1.50
TR3 Brent Morel .40 1.00
TR4 Aroldis Chapman 1.25 3.00
TR5 Jeremy Hellickson 1.25 3.00
TR6 Jake McGee .40 1.00
TR7 Kyle Drabek .60 1.50
TR8 Craig Kimbrel 3.00 8.00
TR9 Mike Minor .40 1.00
TR10 Zach Britton 1.00 2.50
TR11 Brandon Belt 1.50 4.00
TR12 Brandon Beachy 1.00 2.50
TR13 Michael Pineda 1.25 3.00
TR14 Tsuyoshi Nishioka 1.25 3.00
TR16 Hank Conger .60 1.50
TR17 Domonic Brown 1.00 2.50
TR18 J.P. Arencibia .60 1.50
TR19 Corey Luebke .40 1.00
TR20 Brett Wallace .40 1.00

2011 Topps Lineage Stand-Ups

COMPLETE SET (25) 50.00 100.00
STATED ODDS 1:12 HOBBY
TS1 Jose Bautista 1.25 3.00
TS2 Ryan Zimmerman 1.25 3.00
TS3 Albert Pujols 5.00 12.00
TS4 Felix Hernandez 2.00 5.00
TS5 Tim Lincecum 2.00 5.00
TS6 Ryan Howard 2.50 6.00
TS7 Mariano Rivera 2.00 5.00
TS8 Jason Heyward 2.50 6.00
TS9 Ryan Braun 2.50 6.00
TS10 Hunter Pence 1.25 3.00
TS11 Miguel Cabrera 2.00 5.00
TS12 Adam Dunn 1.25 3.00
TS13 Kevin Youkilis 1.25 3.00
TS14 Joey Votto 2.00 5.00
TS15 Carlos Gonzalez 1.25 3.00
TS16 Mike Stanton 1.25 3.00
TS17 Matt Kemp 1.25 3.00
TS18 Joe Mauer 2.00 5.00
TS19 Alex Rodriguez 3.00 8.00
TS20 Roy Halladay 2.00 5.00
TS21 Brooks Robinson 1.25 3.00
TS22 Hank Aaron 4.00 10.00
TS23 Mickey Mantle 6.00 15.00
TS24 Juan Marichal .75 2.00
TS25 Sandy Koufax 6.00 15.00

2011 Topps Lineage Venezuelan

COMPLETE SET (25) 10.00 25.00
STATED ODDS 1:12 HOBBY
TV1 Derek Jeter 3.00 8.00
TV2 Buster Posey 1.50 4.00
TV3 Felix Hernandez 1.25 3.00
TV4 Ryan Zimmerman .75 2.00
TV5 Chris Carpenter 1.25 3.00
TV6 Josh Johnson .75 2.00
TV7 Andrew McCutchen 1.25 3.00
TV8 Carlos Santana 1.25 3.00
TV9 David Wright 1.50 4.00
TV10 Troy Tulowitzki 1.25 3.00
TV11 Clayton Kershaw 1.25 3.00
TV12 David Price 1.25 3.00
TV13 Chipper Jones 1.25 3.00
TV14 Ichiro Suzuki 2.00 5.00
TV15 Mark Teixeira 1.25 3.00
TV16 Jason Heyward 1.50 4.00
TV17 Joe Mauer 1.25 3.00
TV18 Starlin Castro 1.25 3.00
TV19 Adrian Gonzalez .75 2.00
TV20 Ryan Braun 1.50 4.00
TV21 Cliff Lee 1.25 3.00
TV22 Jose Bautista .75 2.00
TV23 Adam Dunn .75 2.00
TV24 Albert Pujols 3.00 8.00
TV25 Ian Kinsler .75 2.00

2011 Topps Marquee

COMPLETE SET (100) 60.00 120.00
COMMON CARD (1-100) .40 1.00
COMMON RC (1-100) .40 1.00
1 Ryan Braun 1.25 3.00
2 Juan Marichal .40 1.00
3 Cliff Lee 1.00 2.50
4 Christy Mathewson 1.00 2.50
5 Ozzie Smith 1.50 4.00
6 Robinson Cano 1.00 2.50
7 Mark Teixeira 1.00 2.50
8 Jim Palmer .40 1.00
9 Jered Weaver .40 1.00
10 Rogers Hornsby .60 1.50
11 Albert Pujols 2.50 6.00
12 Bob Gibson .60 1.50
13 Dustin Pedroia 1.25 3.00
14 Ryan Zimmerman .60 1.50
15 Nolan Ryan 3.00 8.00
16 Brandon Phillips .40 1.00
17 Starlin Castro 1.00 2.50
18 George Sisler 1.00 2.50
19 Lou Gehrig 2.00 5.00
20 CC Sabathia .60 1.50
21 Brian Wilson 1.00 2.50
22 Justin Verlander 1.25 3.00
23 Jon Lester 1.00 2.50
24 Pee Wee Reese .60 1.50
25 Joey Votto 1.00 2.50
26 Ichiro Suzuki 1.50 4.00
27 Mariano Rivera 1.00 2.50
28 Carlos Gonzalez .60 1.50
29 Chipper Jones 1.00 2.50
30 Cy Young 1.00 2.50
31 Mickey Mantle 3.00 8.00
32 Tony Gwynn 1.00 2.50
33 Tris Speaker .60 1.50
34 Thurman Munson 1.00 2.50
35 Jason Heyward 1.25 3.00
36 Babe Ruth 2.50 6.00
37 Prince Fielder .60 1.50
38 Cal Ripken Jr. 4.00 10.00
39 Cole Hamels 1.00 2.50
40 Joe Morgan .40 1.00
41 Justin Morneau 1.00 2.50
42 Michael Pineda RC 1.25 3.00
43 Stan Musial 1.50 4.00
44 Hanley Ramirez 1.00 2.50
45 Jackie Robinson 1.00 2.50
46 Derek Jeter 2.50 6.00
47 Frank Robinson .60 1.50
48 Ty Cobb 1.50 4.00
49 Whitey Ford .60 1.50
50 Ian Kinsler .60 1.50
51 Kevin Youkilis .60 1.50
52 Matt Kemp .60 1.50
53 Miguel Cabrera 1.00 2.50
54 Tom Seaver .60 1.50
55 Ryan Howard 1.25 3.00
56 Andre Ethier .60 1.50
57 Matt Holliday 1.00 2.50
58 Josh Johnson .60 1.50
59 Ryne Sandberg 2.00 5.00
60 Zach Britton RC 1.00 2.50
61 Jose Bautista .60 1.50
62 Mel Ott 1.00 2.50
63 Zack Greinke .60 1.50
64 Sandy Koufax 3.00 8.00
65 Mike Schmidt 1.50 4.00
66 Ubaldo Jimenez .60 1.50
67 Clayton Kershaw 1.00 2.50
68 Adrian Gonzalez .60 1.50
69 Nelson Cruz .60 1.50
70 Alex Rodriguez 1.50 4.00
71 Shin-Soo Choo .60 1.50
72 Willie McCovey .60 1.50
73 Eddie Murray 1.00 2.50
74 Justin Upton .60 1.50
75 Duke Snider .60 1.50
76 David Wright 1.25 3.00
77 Hank Aaron 2.00 5.00
78 Roy Campanella 1.00 2.50
79 Jose Reyes .60 1.50
80 Evan Longoria 1.25 3.00
81 David Price 1.00 2.50
82 Tim Lincecum 1.00 2.50
83 Reggie Jackson .60 1.50
84 Johnny Mize .60 1.50
85 Roberto Alomar .60 1.50
86 Carlos Santana 1.00 2.50
87 Brandon Belt RC 1.50 4.00
88 Josh Hamilton 1.00 2.50
89 Buster Posey 1.25 3.00
90 Joe DiMaggio 2.50 6.00
91 Troy Tulowitzki 1.00 2.50
92 Brett Anderson .60 1.50
93 Johnny Bench 1.00 2.50
94 Chase Utley 1.00 2.50
95 Roy Halladay 1.00 2.50
96 Carl Crawford .60 1.50
97 Honus Wagner 1.00 2.50
98 Felix Hernandez 1.00 2.50
99 Joe Mauer 1.00 2.50
100 Brooks Robinson .60 1.50

2011 Topps Marquee Blue

*BLUE: .6X TO 1.5X BASIC
*BLUE RC: .6X TO 1.5X BASIC
STATED ODDS 1:3 HOBBY
STATED PRINT RUN 299 SER.#'d SETS

2011 Topps Marquee Copper

*COPPER: .6X TO 1.5X BASIC
*COPPER RC: .6X TO 1.5X BASIC
STATED ODDS 1:3 HOBBY
STATED PRINT RUN 199 SER.#'d SETS

2011 Topps Marquee Gold

*GOLD: 1X TO 2.5X BASIC
*GOLD RC: 1X TO 2.5X BASIC
STATED ODDS 1:6 HOBBY
STATED PRINT RUN 99 SER.#'d SETS

2011 Topps Marquee Red

STATED ODDS 1:568 HOBBY
STATED PRINT RUN 1 SER.#'d SET
NO PRICING DUE TO SCARCITY

2011 Topps Marquee Acclaimed Impressions Dual Relic Autographs Gold

STATED ODDS 1:178 HOBBY
STATED PRINT RUN 5 SER.#'d SETS
NO PRICING DUE TO SCARCITY
EXCHANGE DEADLINE 9/30/2014

2011 Topps Marquee Acclaimed Impressions Dual Relic Autographs Red

STATED ODDS 1:888 HOBBY
STATED PRINT RUN 1 SER.#'d SET
NO PRICING DUE TO SCARCITY
EXCHANGE DEADLINE 9/30/2014

2011 Topps Marquee Acclaimed Impressions Triple Relic Autographs

STATED ODDS 1:15 HOBBY
PRINT RUNS B/WN 10-606 COPIES PER
EXCHANGE DEADLINE 9/30/2014
AIT1 Tony Gwynn/10
AIT2 Jason Heyward/20
AIT3 Drew Stubbs/606 6.00 15.00
AIT4 Neftali Feliz/470 6.00 15.00
AIT5 Tommy Hanson/50 15.00 40.00
AIT6 Jose Tabata/470 6.00 15.00
AIT7 Trevor Cahill/70 6.00 15.00
AIT8 Fergie Jenkins/20
AIT9 Clayton Kershaw/20
AIT10 Felix Hernandez/20
AIT11 Heath Bell/150 6.00 15.00
AIT12 Ian Kinsler EXCH 10.00 25.00
AIT13 Josh Johnson/50 10.00 25.00
AIT14 Ryan Zimmerman/50 15.00 40.00
AIT15 Tom Seaver EXCH
AIT16 Ubaldo Jimenez/20
AIT17 Steve Garvey/156 10.00 25.00
AIT18 Nelson Cruz/70 10.00 25.00
AIT19 Shane Victorino/70 20.00 50.00
AIT20 Brett Anderson/350 6.00 15.00
AIT21 Evan Longoria/10
AIT22 Adam Jones/50 20.00 50.00
AIT23 Torii Hunter/20
AIT24 Matt Kemp/20
AIT25 Josh Hamilton/20
AIT26 Martin Prado/250 8.00 20.00
AIT27 Clay Buchholz/50 10.00 25.00
AIT28 Austin Jackson/150 8.00 20.00
AIT29 Justin Upton/50 15.00 40.00
AIT30 Andrew McCutchen/150 12.50 30.00
AIT31 Chris Coghlan/250 6.00 15.00
AIT32 Billy Butler EXCH 10.00 25.00
AIT33 Brandon Phillips/50 12.50 30.00

2011 Topps Marquee Acclaimed Impressions Triple Relic Autographs Gold

STATED ODDS 1:344 HOBBY
STATED PRINT RUN 5 SER.#'d SETS
NO PRICING DUE TO SCARCITY
EXCHANGE DEADLINE 9/30/2014

2011 Topps Marquee Acclaimed Impressions Triple Relic Autographs Red

STATED ODDS 1:1722 HOBBY
STATED PRINT RUN 1 SER.#'d SET
NO PRICING DUE TO SCARCITY
EXCHANGE DEADLINE 9/30/2014

2011 Topps Marquee Gametime Mementos Quad Relic Autographs

STATED ODDS 1:227 HOBBY
PRINT RUNS B/WN 10-20 COPIES PER
NO PRICING DUE TO SCARCITY
EXCHANGE DEADLINE 9/30/2014

2011 Topps Marquee Gametime Mementos Quad Relics Gold

STATED ODDS 1:41 HOBBY
PRINT RUN B/WN 5-25 COPIES PER
NO PRICING DUE TO SCARCITY

2011 Topps Marquee Gametime Mementos Quad Relics Red

*RED: .4X TO 1X BASIC
STATED ODDS 1:32 HOBBY
PRINT RUNS B/WN 125-150 COPIES PER

2011 Topps Marquee Monumental Markings Autographs

STATED ODDS 1:5 HOBBY
PRINT RUNS B/WN 10-600 COPIES PER
NO PRICING ON QTY 25 OR LESS
EXCHANGE DEADLINE 9/30/2014
AC Aroldis Chapman EXCH 10.00 25.00
AE Andre Ethier/20
AG Adrian Gonzalez/20
AP Albert Pujols EXCH 200.00 300.00
BA Brett Anderson/570 4.00 10.00
BB Brandon Belt/570 12.50 30.00
BL Barry Larkin EXCH
BM Brian McCann/20
BR Brooks Robinson EXCH
CC Carl Crawford EXCH
CK Clayton Kershaw/20
CR Colby Rasmus/570 5.00 12.00
DP Dustin Pedroia EXCH 20.00 50.00
DS Drew Stubbs/570 6.00 15.00
EA Elvis Andrus/75 8.00 20.00
EL Evan Longoria EXCH
FF Freddie Freeman/185 10.00 25.00
FJ Fergie Jenkins/20
GF George Foster EXCH 10.00 25.00
HA Hank Aaron EXCH
HB Heath Bell/190 5.00 12.00
ID Ike Davis/75 10.00 25.00
IK Ian Kinsler
JB Jay Bruce/75 10.00 25.00
JH Jeremy Hellickson/185 12.50 30.00
JH Josh Hamilton/20
JJ Josh Johnson/20
JM Juan Marichal/20
JP Jim Palmer EXCH
JT Jose Tabata/570 6.00 15.00
JW Jered Weaver/20
KD Kyle Drabek/75 6.00 15.00
ML Mat Latos EXCH 6.00 15.00
MP Michael Pineda/570 10.00 25.00
MP Manny Pacquiao 200.00 300.00
MS Mike Schmidt EXCH 50.00 100.00
NF Neftali Feliz/75 6.00 15.00
OS Ozzie Smith EXCH
PS Pablo Sandoval/75 10.00 25.00
RB Ryan Braun/20
RH Roy Halladay/10
RZ Ryan Zimmerman/20
SC Starlin Castro/75 20.00 50.00
SK Sandy Koufax/10
TC Trevor Cahill/75 10.00 25.00
TG Tony Gwynn EXCH
ZB Zach Britton/75 6.00 15.00
AOG Alexi Ogando/570 5.00 12.00
APA Angel Pagan/570 6.00 15.00
BGI Bob Gibson/10
BJU B.J. Upton EXCH 8.00 20.00
BPO Buster Posey/20
BWA Brett Wallace/570 4.00 10.00
CBU Clay Buchholz/20
CKI Craig Kimbrel/570 10.00 25.00
CYO Chris Young/75 6.00 15.00
DST Drew Storen/600 6.00 15.00
ESA Ervin Santana/300 5.00 12.00
FCA Fausto Carmona/300 4.00 10.00
FMA Fernando Martinez/600 5.00 12.00
JCU Johnny Cueto/75 8.00 20.00
JFR Jeff Francis/570 4.00 10.00
JHE Jason Heyward EXCH
JJE Jeremy Jeffress/600 4.00 10.00
MBU Madison Bumgarner EXCH 15.00 40.00
MHO Matt Holliday EXCH
MST Mike Stanton EXCH
MSZ Max Scherzer/185 12.50 30.00
NWK Neil Walker/185 8.00 20.00
PON Paul O'Neill/75 15.00 40.00
RED Red Schoendienst/75 15.00 40.00
THA Tommy Hanson EXCH
THU Torii Hunter/20
TRO Tyson Ross/600 4.00 10.00
UJI Ubaldo Jimenez/20

2011 Topps Marquee Monumental Markings Autographs Gold

STATED ODDS 1:135 HOBBY
PRINT RUN B/WN 5-50 COPIES PER
NO PRICING ON QTY 5
EXCHANGE DEADLINE 9/30/2014
MP Manny Pacquiao/50 250.00 400.00

2011 Topps Marquee Monumental Markings Autographs Dual

STATED ODDS 1:152 HOBBY
STATED PRINT RUN 15 SER.#'d SETS
NO PRICING DUE TO SCARCITY
EXCHANGE DEADLINE 9/30/2014

2011 Topps Marquee Museum Collection Autographs

STATED ODDS 1:48 HOBBY
STATED PRINT RUN 10 SER.#'d SETS
NO PRICING DUE TO SCARCITY
EXCHANGE DEADLINE 9/30/2014

2011 Topps Marquee Titanic Threads

STATED ODDS 1:6 HOBBY
STATED PRINT RUN 99 SER.#'d SETS
TTJR1 Mike Schmidt 15.00 40.00
TTJR2 Derek Jeter 20.00 50.00
TTJR3 Nolan Ryan 40.00 80.00
TTJR4 Evan Longoria 10.00 25.00
TTJR5 Joe DiMaggio 125.00 250.00
TTJR6 Rickey Henderson 12.50 30.00
TTJR7 Mickey Mantle 100.00 200.00
TTJR8 Ichiro Suzuki 20.00 50.00
TTJR9 Albert Pujols 12.50 30.00
TTJR10 Hank Aaron 50.00 100.00
TTJR11 Sandy Koufax 75.00 150.00
TTJR12 Roy Halladay 12.50 30.00
TTJR13 Stan Musial 30.00 60.00
TTJR14 Bob Gibson 12.50 30.00
TTJR15 Felix Hernandez 8.00 20.00
TTJR16 Tony Gwynn 8.00 20.00
TTJR17 Johnny Bench 10.00 25.00
TTJR18 Rollie Fingers 6.00 15.00
TTJR19 Carlton Fisk 10.00 25.00
TTJR20 Reggie Jackson 12.50 30.00
TTJR21 Fergie Jenkins 12.50 30.00
TTJR22 Al Kaline 10.00 25.00
TTJR23 Juan Marichal 10.00 25.00
TTJR24 Willie McCovey 10.00 25.00
TTJR25 Eddie Murray 12.50 30.00
TTJR26 Tony Perez 10.00 25.00
TTJR27 Gaylord Perry 10.00 25.00
TTJR28 Red Schoendienst 10.00 25.00
TTJR29 Tom Seaver 10.00 25.00
TTJR30 Ozzie Smith 15.00 40.00
TTJR31 Roy Campanella 30.00 60.00
TTJR32 Johnny Mize 15.00 40.00
TTJR33 Mel Ott 20.00 50.00
TTJR34 Roberto Alomar 10.00 25.00
TTJR35 Albert Belle 8.00 20.00
TTJR36 Andre Dawson 8.00 20.00
TTJR37 Steve Garvey 10.00 25.00
TTJR38 Paul Molitor 8.00 20.00
TTJR39 Paul O'Neill 12.50 30.00
TTJR40 Cal Ripken Jr. 12.50 30.00
TTJR41 Frank Robinson 10.00 25.00
TTJR42 John Smoltz 8.00 20.00
TTJR43 Frank Thomas 10.00 25.00
TTJR44 Jered Weaver 6.00 15.00
TTJR45 Torii Hunter 6.00 15.00
TTJR46 Hunter Pence 6.00 15.00
TTJR47 Trevor Cahill 6.00 15.00
TTJR48 Kyle Drabek 6.00 15.00
TTJR49 Martin Prado 6.00 15.00
TTJR50 Chipper Jones 12.50 30.00
TTJR51 Jason Heyward 8.00 20.00
TTJR52 Ryan Braun 10.00 25.00
TTJR53 Prince Fielder 8.00 20.00
TTJR54 Adam Wainwright 10.00 25.00
TTJR55 Starlin Castro 15.00 40.00
TTJR56 Aramis Ramirez 6.00 15.00
TTJR57 Justin Upton 6.00 15.00
TTJR58 Stephen Drew 6.00 15.00
TTJR59 Andre Ethier 6.00 15.00
TTJR60 Matt Kemp 10.00 25.00
TTJR61 Clayton Kershaw 12.50 30.00
TTJR62 Tim Lincecum 12.50 30.00
TTJR63 Pablo Sandoval 8.00 20.00
TTJR64 Brian Wilson 10.00 25.00
TTJR65 Shin-Soo Choo 10.00 25.00
TTJR66 Carlos Santana 6.00 15.00
TTJR67 Grady Sizemore 6.00 15.00
TTJR68 Michael Pineda 8.00 20.00
TTJR69 Carlos Beltran 6.00 15.00
TTJR70 David Wright 8.00 20.00
TTJR71 Jose Reyes 10.00 25.00
TTJR72 Robinson Cano 12.50 30.00
TTJR73 Hanley Ramirez 6.00 15.00
TTJR74 Josh Johnson 6.00 15.00
TTJR75 Ryan Zimmerman 8.00 20.00
TTJR76 Zach Britton 6.00 15.00
TTJR77 Alex Rodriguez 15.00 40.00
TTJR79 Heath Bell 6.00 15.00
TTJR80 Cliff Lee 15.00 40.00
TTJR81 Ryan Howard 10.00 25.00
TTJR84 Nelson Cruz 6.00 15.00
TTJR85 Ian Kinsler 6.00 15.00
TTJR86 Jeremy Hellickson 12.50 30.00
TTJR88 Adrian Gonzalez 8.00 20.00
TTJR89 Josh Beckett 6.00 15.00
TTJR90 Carl Crawford 6.00 15.00
TTJR91 Joey Votto 10.00 25.00
TTJR92 Brandon Phillips 6.00 15.00
TTJR93 Troy Tulowitzki 10.00 25.00
TTJR94 Carlos Gonzalez 8.00 20.00
TTJR95 Billy Butler 8.00 20.00
TTJR96 Miguel Cabrera 8.00 20.00
TTJR97 Justin Verlander 12.50 30.00
TTJR98 Justin Morneau 8.00 20.00
TTJR99 Carlos Quentin 6.00 15.00
TTJR100 Mark Teixeira 10.00 25.00
TTJR102 Jay Bruce 6.00 15.00
TTJR103 Johnny Cueto 6.00 15.00
TTJR104 Drew Stubbs 6.00 15.00
TTJR105 Edwin Encarnacion 6.00 15.00
TTJR106 Vladimir Guerrero 8.00 20.00
TTJR107 A.J. Pierzynski 6.00 15.00
TTJR108 Asdrubal Cabrera 6.00 15.00
TTJR109 Mark Buehrle 8.00 20.00
TTJR110 Jimmy Rollins 10.00 25.00
TTJR111 Alex Gordon 10.00 25.00

TTJR112 Michael Young 6.00 15.00
TTJR113 Fausto Carmona 6.00 15.00
TTJR114 Carlos Marmol 6.00 15.00
TTJR115 B.J. Upton 6.00 15.00

2011 Topps Marquee Titanic Threads Gold

STATED ODDS 1:52 HOBBY
STATED PRINT RUN 10 SER.#'d SETS
NO PRICING DUE TO SCARCITY

2011 Topps Marquee Titanic Threads Red

*RED: .4X TO 1X BASIC
STATED ODDS 1:28 HOBBY
STATED PRINT RUN 50 SER.#'d SETS

2010 Topps National Chicle

COMPLETE SET (329) 125.00 250.00
COMP.SET w/o SP's (275) 15.00 40.00
COMMON CARD (1-275) .15 .40
COMMON RC (256-275) .40 1.00
COMMON SP (276-329) 2.00 5.00
SP ODDS 1:4 HOBBY
PRINTING PLATE ODDS 1:300 HOBBY
PLATE PRINT RUN 1 SET PER COLOR
BLACK-CYAN-MAGENTA-YELLOW ISSUED
NO PLATE PRICING DUE TO SCARCITY
1 Albert Pujols 1.00 2.50
2 Grady Sizemore .25 .60
3 Ichiro Suzuki .60 1.50
4 Daisuke Matsuzaka .40 1.00
5 Prince Fielder .25 .60
6 Joba Chamberlain .25 .60
7 Joe Mauer .40 1.00
8 Jason Bartlett .15 .40
9 Brandon Webb .25 .60
10 Manny Ramirez .40 1.00
11 CC Sabathia .25 .60
12 Raul Ibanez .25 .60
13 Dan Uggla .25 .60
14 Mariano Rivera .40 1.00
15 Brad Hawpe .15 .40
16 James Loney .25 .60
17 Ken Griffey Jr. .60 1.50
18 Josh Johnson .25 .60
19 Jay Bruce .25 .60
20 David DeJesus .15 .40
21 J.A. Happ .25 .60
22 Tim Wakefield .15 .40
23 Shane Victorino .25 .60
24 Kevin Kouzmanoff .15 .40
25 Aaron Hill .15 .40
26 Rick Porcello .15 .40
27 Jacoby Ellsbury .40 1.00
28 Andrew McCutchen .40 1.00
29 Hunter Pence .25 .60
30 Michael Cuddyer .15 .40
31 Jayson Werth .25 .60
32 Andy Pettitte .25 .60
33 Evan Longoria .50 1.25
34 David Wright .50 1.25
35 Justin Morneau .40 1.00
36 Derek Jeter 1.00 2.50
37 Ryan Howard .50 1.25
38 Russell Martin .15 .40
39 Michael Young .25 .60
40 Johnny Damon .25 .60
41 Carlos Pena .25 .60
42 Robinson Cano .40 1.00
43 Ian Kinsler .25 .60
44 Jason Bay .25 .60
45 Adam Lind .25 .60
46 Kevin Youkilis .25 .60
47 Brandon Inge .25 .60
48 Jason Kubel .15 .40
49 Adrian Gonzalez .25 .60
50 David Ortiz .25 .60
51 Joey Votto .40 1.00
52 Nick Swisher .40 1.00
53 Marco Scutaro .15 .40
54 Yunel Escobar .15 .40
55 Carl Crawford .25 .60
56 B.J. Upton .25 .60
57 Kosuke Fukudome .40 1.00
58 Matt Cain .25 .60
59 Wandy Rodriguez .15 .40
60 J.J. Hardy .15 .40
61 Gordon Beckham .25 .60
62 Chad Billingsley .15 .40
63 Aramis Ramirez .15 .40
64 Alex Rodriguez .60 1.50
65 Clayton Kershaw .40 1.00
66 Johan Santana .40 1.00
67 Mark Buehrle .25 .60
68 Vladimir Guerrero .40 1.00
69 Jose Reyes .25 .60
70 Cliff Lee .25 .60
71 Miguel Cabrera .40 1.00
72 Jorge Posada .25 .60
73 Nick Markakis .40 1.00
74 Ryan Zimmerman .25 .60
75 Kendry Morales .15 .40
76 Victor Martinez .25 .60
77 Carlos Lee .15 .40
78 Bobby Abreu .15 .40
79 Russell Branyan .15 .40
80 Jermaine Dye .15 .40
81 Hideki Matsui .40 1.00
82 Josh Beckett .25 .60
83 Brian Roberts .15 .40
84 Hanley Ramirez .40 1.00
85 Justin Verlander .50 1.25
86 Adam Jones .25 .60
87 Ted Lilly .15 .40
88 Jorge Cantu .15 .40
89 Chone Figgins .15 .40
90 Miguel Tejada .25 .60
91 Asdrubal Cabrera .25 .60
92 Cole Hamels .40 1.00
93 Roy Oswalt .25 .60
94 Nyjer Morgan .15 .40
95 Ryan Braun .50 1.25
96 Derrek Lee .15 .40
97 Matt Kemp .25 .60
98 Troy Tulowitzki .40 1.00
99 Alexei Ramirez .15 .40
100 Adam Dunn .25 .60
101 Torii Hunter .15 .40
102 Adam Wainwright .25 .60
103 Pablo Sandoval .25 .60
104 Justin Upton .25 .60
105 Mark Reynolds .15 .40
106 Todd Helton .25 .60
107 Mark Teixeira .40 1.00
108 Josh Hamilton .40 1.00
109 Nelson Cruz .25 .60
110 Curtis Granderson .25 .60
111 Paul Konerko .25 .60
112 Dustin Pedroia .50 1.25
113 Billy Butler .15 .40
114 Felix Hernandez .40 1.00
115 Lance Berkman .25 .60
116 Carlos Beltran .15 .40
117 Jason Marquis .15 .40
118 Ubaldo Jimenez .25 .60
119 Jose Lopez .15 .40
120 Tommy Hanson .25 .60
121 Yovani Gallardo .15 .40
122 Roy Halladay .40 1.00
123 Brian McCann .25 .60
124 Carlos Zambrano .25 .60
125 Luis Castillo .15 .40
126 Melky Cabrera .15 .40
127 Kyle Blanks .15 .40
128 Michael Bowden .15 .40
129 Nolan Reimold .25 .60
130 Elvis Andrus .25 .60
131 David Price .40 1.00
132 Bengie Molina .15 .40
133 Andrew Bailey .15 .40
134 Felix Pie .15 .40
135 Chris Carpenter .40 1.00
136 Julio Borbon .15 .40
137 Zack Greinke .25 .60
138 Scott Kazmir .15 .40
139 Yadier Molina .25 .60
140 Javier Vazquez .15 .40
141 Brett Anderson .25 .60
142 Colby Rasmus .40 1.00
143 Chris Coghlan .15 .40
144 Jhoulys Chacin .15 .40
145 Kurt Suzuki .15 .40
146 Scott Feldman .15 .40
147 Jon Lester .40 1.00
148 Chris Young .15 .40
149 Trevor Cahill .15 .40
150 Zach Duke .15 .40
151 Michael Bourn .15 .40
152 Rick Ankiel .15 .40
153 Alex Gordon .25 .60
154 Derek Lowe .15 .40
155 Vernon Wells .15 .40
156 Luke Scott .15 .40
157 Jimmy Rollins .25 .60
158 Stephen Drew .15 .40
159 Kenshin Kawakami .25 .60
160 Jonathan Sanchez .15 .40
161 Juan Pierre .15 .40
162 Jonathan Papelbon .25 .60
163 Erick Aybar .15 .40
164 Andre Ethier .25 .60
165 Jed Lowrie .25 .60
166 Duke Snider .25 .60
167 Ryan Ludwick .15 .40
168 Jake Peavy .15 .40
169 Denard Span .15 .40
170 Jair Jurrjens .15 .40
171 Mike Cameron .15 .40
172 Gavin Floyd .15 .40
173 Jonathan Broxton .15 .40
174 Marlon Byrd .15 .40
175 Dexter Fowler .15 .40
176 Aaron Rowand .15 .40
177 Koji Uehara .25 .60
178 Joel Pineiro .15 .40
179 Carlos Quentin .25 .60
180 Freddy Sanchez .15 .40
181 John Maine .15 .40
182 Neftali Feliz .15 .40
183 Nate McLouth .15 .40
184 Phil Hughes .15 .40
185 Travis Snider .15 .40
186 Alfonso Soriano .25 .60
187 Joe Saunders .15 .40
188 Rich Harden .15 .40
189 Mat Gamel .15 .40
190 Orlando Hudson .15 .40
191 Chase Utley .40 1.00
192 J.D. Drew .15 .40
193 Marc Rzepczynski .15 .40
194 Tim Lincecum .60 1.50
195 Alex Rios .25 .60
196 Will Venable .15 .40
197 Dan Haren .15 .40
198 Michael Saunders .15 .40
199 Trevor Crowe .15 .40
200 Chipper Jones .40 1.00
201 A.J. Burnett .25 .60
202 Ian Stewart .15 .40
203 Edinson Volquez .15 .40
204 Carlos Gonzalez .25 .60
205 John Danks .15 .40
206 Hank Greenberg .40 1.00
207 Johnny Bench .40 1.00
208 Luis Aparicio .15 .40
209 Juan Marichal .15 .40
210 Robin Yount .40 1.00
211 Jim Palmer .15 .40
212 Ozzie Smith .60 1.50
213 Paul Molitor .40 1.00
214 Warren Spahn .25 .60
215 Orlando Cepeda .15 .40
216 Bob Gibson .25 .60
217 Frank Robinson .25 .60
218 Carlton Fisk .25 .60
219 Eddie Murray .40 1.00
220 Dale Murphy .40 1.00
221 Dennis Eckersley .15 .40
222 Lou Brock .25 .60
223 Carl Yastrzemski .40 1.00
224 Al Kaline .40 1.00
225 Mike Schmidt .60 1.50
226 Phil Rizzuto .25 .60
227 Rogers Hornsby .25 .60
228 Pee Wee Reese .25 .60
229 Lou Gehrig .75 2.00
230 Jimmie Foxx .40 1.00
231 Honus Wagner .40 1.00
232 Roy Campanella .40 1.00
233 Mel Ott .40 1.00
234 Tris Speaker .25 .60
235 Jackie Robinson .40 1.00
236 George Sisler .40 1.00
237 Thurman Munson .40 1.00
238 Johnny Mize .25 .60
239 Walter Johnson .40 1.00
240 Cy Young .40 1.00
241 Christy Mathewson .40 1.00
242 Mickey Mantle 1.25 3.00
243 Stan Musial .60 1.50
244 Eddie Mathews .40 1.00
245 Whitey Ford .25 .60
246 Willie McCovey .25 .60
247 Reggie Jackson .25 .60
248 Tom Seaver .25 .60
249 Nolan Ryan 1.25 3.00
250 Joe Morgan .15 .40
251 Richie Ashburn .25 .60
252 Duke Snider .25 .60
253 Ryne Sandberg .75 2.00
254 Ernie Banks .40 1.00
255 Babe Ruth 1.00 2.50
256 Tyler Flowers RC .60 1.50
257 Madison Bumgarner RC 1.00 2.50
258 Gordon Beckham .25 .60
259 Henry Rodriguez RC .40 1.00
260 Drew Stubbs RC 1.00 2.50
261 Kevin Richardson (RC) .40 1.00
262 Reid Gorecki (RC) .60 1.50
263 Eric Young Jr. (RC) .40 1.00
264 Josh Thole RC .60 1.50
265 Neil Walker (RC) .60 1.50
266 Carlos Carrasco (RC) 1.00 2.50
267 Tobi Stoner RC .60 1.50
268 Luis Durango RC .40 1.00
269 Tommy Manzella (RC) .40 1.00
270 Adam Moore RC .40 1.00
271 Brent Dlugach (RC) .40 1.00
272 Michael Brantley RC .40 1.00
273 Juan Francisco RC .60 1.50
274 Ian Desmond (RC) .60 1.50
275 Buster Posey RC 4.00 10.00
276 Babe Ruth SP 5.00 12.00
277 Rogers Hornsby SP 2.00 5.00
278 Pee Wee Reese SP 2.00 5.00
279 Lou Gehrig SP 4.00 10.00
280 Jimmie Foxx SP 2.50 6.00
281 Honus Wagner SP 2.50 6.00
282 Roy Campanella SP 2.50 6.00
283 Mel Ott SP 2.50 6.00
284 Tris Speaker SP 1.25 3.00
285 Jackie Robinson SP 2.50 6.00
286 George Sisler SP 2.50 6.00
287 Ty Cobb SP 3.00 8.00
288 Thurman Munson SP 2.50 6.00
289 Johnny Mize SP 2.00 5.00
290 Walter Johnson SP 2.50 6.00
291 Cy Young SP 2.50 6.00
292 Christy Mathewson SP 2.50 6.00
293 Mickey Mantle SP 6.00 15.00
294 Stan Musial SP 3.00 8.00
295 Eddie Mathews SP 2.50 6.00
296 Ernie Banks SP 2.50 6.00
297 Ryne Sandberg SP 4.00 10.00
298 Joe Morgan SP 2.00 5.00
299 Reggie Jackson SP 2.00 5.00
300 Ian Desmond SP 3.00 8.00
301 Albert Pujols SP 5.00 12.00
302 Ichiro Suzuki SP 3.00 8.00
303 Alex Rodriguez SP 3.00 8.00
304 Ryan Howard SP 2.50 6.00
305 Lance Berkman SP 2.00 5.00
306 Chipper Jones SP 2.50 6.00
307 Manny Ramirez SP 2.50 6.00
308 Dustin Pedroia SP 2.50 6.00
309 Ryan Zimmerman SP 2.00 5.00
310 Joe Mauer SP 2.50 6.00
311 Buster Posey SP 8.00 20.00
312 Tyler Flowers SP 3.00 8.00
313 Madison Bumgarner SP 2.00 5.00
314 Adam Moore SP 2.00 5.00
315 Henry Rodriguez SP 1.25 3.00
316 Drew Stubbs SP 3.00 8.00
317 Kevin Richardson SP 2.00 5.00
318 Reid Gorecki SP 2.00 5.00
319 Eric Young Jr. SP 2.00 5.00
320 Josh Thole SP 2.00 5.00
321 Neil Walker SP 3.00 8.00
322 Carlos Carrasco SP 2.50 6.00
323 Tobi Stoner SP 2.00 5.00
324 Matt Carson SP 2.00 5.00
325 Tommy Manzella SP 2.00 5.00
326 Michael Dunn SP RC 1.25 3.00
327 Brent Dlugach SP 2.00 5.00
328 Michael Brantley SP 2.00 5.00
329 Juan Francisco SP 2.00 5.00

2010 Topps National Chicle Artist's Proof Signatures

STATED ODDS 1:120 HOBBY
STATED PRINT RUN 10 SER.#'d SETS
CARDS FEATURE ARTIST SIGNATURES
NO PRICING DUE TO SCARCITY

2010 Topps National Chicle Bazooka Back

*1-275 BAZOOKA: 2X TO 5X BASIC
*1-275 BAZOOKA RC: .75X TO 2X BASIC
1-275 BAZOOKA ODDS 1:8 HOBBY
*276-329 BAZOOKA: .5X TO 1.2X BASIC
276-329 BAZOOKA ODDS 1:100 HOBBY

2010 Topps National Chicle Cowhide

STATED ODDS 1:1200 HOBBY
STATED PRINT RUN 1 SER.#'d SET
NO PRICING DUE TO SCARCITY

2010 Topps National Chicle National Chicle Back

*1-275 NATIONAL: 1.2X TO 3X BASIC
*1-275 NATIONAL RC: .5X TO 1.2X BASIC
1-275 NATIONAL ODDS 1:4 HOBBY
*276-329 NATIONAL: .4X TO 1X BASIC
276-329 NATIONAL ODDS 1:50 HOBBY

2010 Topps National Chicle Umbrella Black Back

STATED ODDS 1:82 HOBBY
STATED PRINT RUN 25 SER.#'d SETS
NO PRICING DUE TO SCARCITY

2010 Topps National Chicle Autographs

GROUP A ODDS 1:15 HOBBY
GROUP B ODDS 1:594 HOBBY
PRINTING PLATE ODDS 1:3671 HOBBY
PLATE PRINT RUN 1 SET PER COLOR
BLACK-CYAN-MAGENTA-YELLOW ISSUED
NO PLATE PRICING DUE TO SCARCITY
AB Andrew Bailey A 4.00 10.00
BD Brent Dlugach A 3.00 8.00
CC Carlos Carrasco A 3.00 8.00
CR Colby Rasmus B 20.00 50.00
CY Carl Yastrzemski B 30.00 60.00
DS Denard Span A 4.00 10.00
GB Gordon Beckham B 30.00 60.00
HR Henry Rodriguez A 3.00 8.00
ID Ian Desmond A 4.00 10.00
JB Jason Bartlett A 3.00 8.00
JF Juan Francisco A 4.00 10.00
JT Josh Thole A 4.00 10.00
KU Koji Uehara A 5.00 12.00
LD Luis Durango A 3.00 8.00
MB Madison Bumgarner A 8.00 20.00
NF Neftali Feliz A 4.00 10.00
NM Nate McLouth A 3.00 8.00
NW Neil Walker A 3.00 8.00
PS Pablo Sandoval A 6.00 15.00
RH Ryan Howard B 30.00 60.00
RP Rick Porcello B 12.50 30.00
SM Stan Musial B 60.00 120.00
TH Tommy Hanson B 8.00 20.00
TM Tommy Manzella A 3.00 8.00
TS Tobi Stoner A 3.00 8.00
DST Drew Stubbs A 5.00 12.00
MBR Michael Brantley A 4.00 10.00

2010 Topps National Chicle Autographs Bazooka Back

*BAZOOKA: .5X TO 1.2X BASIC
STATED ODDS 1:188 HOBBY
STATED PRINT RUN 99 SER.#'d SETS

2010 Topps National Chicle Autographs National Chicle Back

*NATIONAL: .5X TO 1.2X BASIC
STATED ODDS 1:126 HOBBY
STATED PRINT RUN 199 SER.#'d SETS
GROUP B/199 AUTOS DO NOT EXIST

2010 Topps National Chicle Autographs Umbrella Black Back

STATED ODDS 1:745 HOBBY
STATED PRINT RUN 25 SER.#'d SETS
NO PRICING DUE TO SCARCITY

2010 Topps National Chicle Autographs Umbrella Red Back

STATED ODDS 1:15,623 HOBBY
STATED PRINT RUN 1 SER.#'d SET
NO PRICING DUE TO SCARCITY

2010 Topps National Chicle Autographs Dual

STATED ODDS 1:1586 HOBBY
STATED PRINT RUN 25 SER.#'d SETS
NO PRICING DUE TO SCARCITY

2010 Topps National Chicle Cabinet

COMPLETE SET (25) 75.00 150.00
BR Babe Ruth 6.00 15.00
CM Christy Mathewson 2.50 6.00
CY Cy Young 2.50 6.00
EM Eddie Mathews 2.50 6.00
GS George Sisler 2.50 6.00
HW Honus Wagner 2.50 6.00
JF Jimmie Foxx 2.50 6.00
JM Johnny Mize 1.50 4.00
JR Jackie Robinson 2.50 6.00
LG Lou Gehrig 5.00 12.00
MM Mickey Mantle 8.00 20.00
MO Mel Ott 2.50 6.00
NR Nolan Ryan 8.00 20.00
RC Roy Campanella 2.50 6.00
RH Rogers Hornsby 1.50 4.00
RJ Reggie Jackson 1.50 4.00
SM Stan Musial 4.00 10.00
TC Ty Cobb 4.00 10.00
TM Thurman Munson 2.50 6.00
TS Tris Speaker 1.50 4.00
WF Whitey Ford 1.50 4.00
WJ Walter Johnson 2.50 6.00
CYA Carl Yastrzemski 2.50 6.00
PWR Pee Wee Reese 1.50 4.00
TSE Tom Seaver 1.50 4.00

2010 Topps National Chicle Cabinet Artist Signatures

RANDOM BOX TOPPER INSERTS
STATED PRINT RUN 50 SER.#'d SETS
CARDS FEATURE ARTIST SIGNATURES
BR Babe Ruth 20.00 50.00
Dave Hobrecht AU
CM Christy Mathewson
Jeff Zachowski AU
CY Cy Young 8.00 20.00
Monty Sheldon AU
EM Eddie Mathews 8.00 20.00
Paul Lempa AU
GS George Sisler
Chris Felix AU
HW Honus Wagner
Don Higgins AU
JF Jimmie Foxx 12.50 30.00
Monty Sheldon AU
JM Johnny Mize
Jason Davies AU
JR Jackie Robinson
Brian Kong AU
LG Lou Gehrig 20.00 50.00
Jason Davies AU
MM Mickey Mantle 30.00 60.00
Jason Davies AU
MO Mel Ott
Dave Hobrecht AU
NR Nolan Ryan 20.00 50.00
Paul Lempa AU
RC Roy Campanella 10.00 25.00
Monty Sheldon AU
RH Rogers Hornsby 12.50 30.00
Monty Sheldon AU
RJ Reggie Jackson 10.00 25.00
Brian Kong AU
SM Stan Musial 12.50 30.00
Monty Sheldon AU
TC Ty Cobb 12.50 30.00
Dave Hobrecht AU
TM Thurman Munson 12.50 30.00
Paul Lempa AU
TS Tris Speaker 10.00 25.00
Mike Kupka AU
WF Whitey Ford 8.00 20.00
Jason Davies AU
WJ Walter Johnson 15.00 40.00
Mike Kupka AU
CYA Carl Yastrzemski 8.00 20.00
Paul Lempa AU
PWR Pee Wee Reese 10.00 25.00
Mike Kupka AU
TSE Tom Seaver 10.00 25.00
Paul Lempa AU

2010 Topps National Chicle Relics

GROUP A ODDS 1:156 HOBBY
GROUP B ODDS 1:65 HOBBY
GROUP C ODDS 1:2061 HOBBY
AE Andre Ethier A 3.00 8.00
AP Albert Pujols B 6.00 15.00
AR Alex Rodriguez A 6.00 15.00
AS Alfonso Soriano B 3.00 8.00
BR Babe Ruth C 60.00 120.00
CB Carlos Beltran B 3.00 8.00
CJ Chipper Jones A 4.00 10.00
CR Colby Rasmus B 5.00 12.00
DM Dale Murphy B 5.00 12.00
DO David Ortiz B 3.00 8.00
DP Dustin Pedroia B 3.00 8.00
EA Elvis Andrus B 3.00 8.00
EL Evan Longoria B 4.00 10.00
EM Eddie Murray A 4.00 10.00
HG Hank Greenberg A 10.00 25.00
JC Joba Chamberlain B 3.00 8.00
JH Josh Hamilton A 3.00 8.00
JM Justin Morneau B 3.00 8.00
KF Kosuke Fukudome B 3.00 8.00
LG Lou Gehrig C 50.00 100.00
MM Mickey Mantle C 60.00 120.00
MR Manny Ramirez B 4.00 10.00
MT Mark Teixeira B 4.00 10.00
NM Nick Markakis B 3.00 8.00
NR Nolan Ryan A 10.00 25.00
NS Nick Swisher B 3.00 8.00
OS Ozzie Smith A 4.00 10.00
PF Prince Fielder B 3.00 8.00
PH Phil Hughes B 3.00 8.00
PM Paul Molitor A 4.00 10.00
PR Phil Rizzuto A 5.00 12.00
PS Pablo Sandoval B 4.00 10.00
RC Robinson Cano B 4.00 10.00
TM Thurman Munson B 5.00 12.00
VG Vladimir Guerrero B 3.00 8.00
WF Whitey Ford A 6.00 15.00
JPA Jim Palmer A 4.00 10.00
PWR Pee Wee Reese A 5.00 12.00

2010 Topps National Chicle Relics Bazooka Back

*BAZOOKA: .5X TO 1.2X BASIC
STATED ODDS 1:174 HOBBY
STATED PRINT RUN 99 SER.#'d SETS
GROUP C/99 RELICS DO NOT EXIST

2010 Topps National Chicle Relics National Chicle Back

*NATIONAL: .5X TO 1.2X BASIC
STATED ODDS 1:87 HOBBY
STATED PRINT RUN 199 SER.#'d SETS
GROUP C/199 RELICS DO NOT EXIST

2010 Topps National Chicle Relics Umbrella Black Back

STATED ODDS 1:668 HOBBY
STATED PRINT RUN 25 SER.#'d SETS
NO PRICING DUE TO SCARCITY

2010 Topps National Chicle Relics Umbrella Red Back

STATED ODDS 1:11,607 HOBBY
STATED PRINT RUN 1 SER.#'d SET
NO PRICING DUE TO SCARCITY

2010 Topps National Chicle Umbrella Red Back

STATED ODDS 1:1200 HOBBY
STATED PRINT RUN 1 SER.#'d SET
NO PRICING DUE TO SCARCITY

1998 Topps Opening Day

This 165-card set is a parallel version of basic 1998 Topps cards and features 110 cards from Series 1 and 55 cards from Series 2. Cards were issued in special retail seven-card "Opening Day" packs carrying an SRP of $0.99. The cards are an exact parallel of the 1998 Topps base cards except, of course, for the bold Opening Day foil logo on front and the different numbering on back.

COMPLETE SET (165) 30.00 50.00
*OPEN.DAY: .75X TO 2X BASIC TOPPS
ISSUED IN OPENING DAY PACKS

1999 Topps Opening Day

This 165-card set is a parallel version of basic 1999 Topps cards. Cards were issued in special retail seven-card "Opening Day" packs carrying an SRP of $0.99. The cards are an exact parallel of the 1999 Topps base cards except, of course, for the bold Opening Day foil logo on front and the different numbering on back. A Hank Aaron autograph card was inserted one every 29,462 packs.

COMPLETE SET (165) 15.00 40.00
*OPEN.DAY: .75X TO 2X BASIC TOPPS
ISSUED IN OPENING DAY PACKS
AARON AUTO STATED ODDS 1:29,642
1 Hank Aaron 1.00 2.50
NNO Hank Aaron AU 175.00 350.00

1999 Topps Opening Day Oversize

Randomly inserted one per retail box of 1999 Topps Opening Day base set, this three-card set features color player photos printed on 4 1/2" by 3 1/4" cards.

COMPLETE SET (3) 4.00 8.00
1 Sammy Sosa .50 1.25
2 Mark McGwire 1.25 3.00
3 Ken Griffey Jr. .75 2.00

2000 Topps Opening Day

The Topps Opening Day set was released in March, 2000 as a retail only 165-card set that featured 153 player cards, 10 Memorable Moments, 1 Hank Aaron 1954 reprint, and 1 checklist. Each pack contained seven cards and carried a suggested retail price of .99.

COMPLETE SET (165) 15.00 40.00
*OPEN.DAY: .75X TO 2X BASIC TOPPS
ISSUED IN OPENING DAY PACKS
UER 110 AARON '54 REPRINT #'d 128
NO MM VARIATIONS IN OPENING DAY

2000 Topps Opening Day Autographs

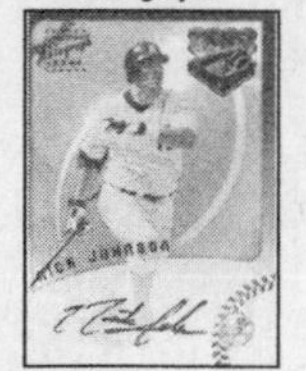

Randomly inserted in packs, this insert set features autographs of five major league players. There were three levels of autographs. Level A were inserted into packs at one in 4207, Level B were inserted at one in 48074, Level C were inserted at one in 6280. Card backs carry an "ODA" prefix.

GROUP A STATED ODDS 1:4207
GROUP B STATED ODDS 1:48074
GROUP C STATED ODDS 1:6280
ODA1 Edgardo Alfonzo A 15.00 40.00
ODA2 Wade Boggs A 40.00 80.00
ODA3 Robin Ventura A 15.00 40.00
ODA4 Josh Hamilton B 10.00 25.00
ODA5 Vernon Wells C 15.00 40.00

2001 Topps Opening Day

The 2001 Topps Opening Day product packed out in early March, 2001 and offers a 165-card base set. The base set features 150 Veteran players (1-150), four Prospects (151-154), 10 Golden Moments cards (155-164), and one checklist card (165). Each pack contained seven cards, and carries a suggested retail price of 1.99.

COMPLETE SET (165) 15.00 40.00
*OPEN.DAY: .75X TO 2X BASIC TOPPS
ISSUED IN OPENING DAY PACKS

2001 Topps Opening Day Autographs

Randomly inserted into packs, this 4-card insert set features authentic autographs from four of the Major League's top players. The set is broken down into four groups: Group A is Chipper Jones (1:31,680), Group B is Todd Helton (1:15,020), Group C is Magglio Ordonez (1:10,004), and Group D is Corey Patterson (1:5,940). Card backs carry an "ODA" prefix followed by the player's initials.

GROUP A ODDS 1:31,680
GROUP B ODDS 1:15,020
GROUP C ODDS 1:10,004
GROUP D ODDS 1:5,940
ODACJ Chipper Jones A 60.00 120.00
ODACP Corey Patterson D 15.00 30.00
ODAMO Magglio Ordonez C 15.00 30.00
ODATH Todd Helton B 25.00 50.00

2001 Topps Opening Day Stickers

Randomly inserted into packs at approximately one in two, this 30-card insert features stickers of all 30 Major League Franchises. Card backs are not numbered and are listed below in alphabetical order for convenience.

COMPLETE SET (30) 2.50 6.00
COMMON TEAM (1-30) .08 .25

2002 Topps Opening Day

Released in early 2002, this 165 card set, which was issued in seven-card packs is a partial parallel of the 2002 Topps set. These cards all have an opening day logo on the front. The Barry Bonds card issued at card numbered 73 only featured the 73 home run logo. Unlike the regular set, this was the only version of that card issued.

COMPLETE SET (165) 15.00 40.00
*OPEN.DAY: .75X TO X2 BASIC TOPPS
ISSUED IN OPENING DAY PACKS

2002 Topps Opening Day Autographs

Randomly inserted into packs, these three cards feature autographs of players in the Opening Day set. These cards were all inserted at differening odds and we have notated that information next to the player's name.

GROUP A STATED ODDS 1:6069
GROUP B STATED ODDS 1:3036
GROUP C STATED ODDS 1:2014
NO PRICING DUE TO SCARCITY
ODABS Ben Sheets B
ODAGJ Geoff Jenkins A
ODANJ Nick Johnson C

2003 Topps Opening Day

This 165-card set was issued in February, 2003. These cards were issued in six card packs which came 22 packs to a box and 20 boxes to a case. These cards can be notated by the special Topps Opening Day logo printed on the front.

COMPLETE SET (165) 15.00 40.00
*OPEN.DAY: .75X TO 2X BASIC TOPPS
ISSUED IN OPENING DAY PACKS

2003 Topps Opening Day Stickers

Issued one per pack, these 72 cards partially parallel the Opening Day set. Each of the fronts is designed exactly as the basic 2003 Topps card.

*OD STICKERS: 1.5X TO 4X BASIC TOPPS
ONE PER PACK

2003 Topps Opening Day Autographs

Inserted at different odds depending on which group the players were assigned to, these cards feature authentic autographs of the featured players.

GROUP A ODDS 1:10,623
GROUP B ODDS 1:3539
GROUP C ODDS 1:2654

Card	Low	High
JD Johnny Damon B	15.00	40.00
LB Lance Berkman A	20.00	50.00
RF Rafael Furcal C	10.00	25.00

2004 Topps Opening Day

This 165-card set, which is a mini-parallel to the basic Topps set was released in February, 2004. The set was issued in six card packs which came 36 packs to a box and 20 boxes to a case. Each of these cards have a special "Opening Day" logo embossed on them.

Card	Low	High
COMPLETE SET (165)	15.00	40.00

*OPEN.DAY 1-165: .75X TO 2X BASIC TOPPS
ISSUED IN OPENING DAY PACKS

2004 Topps Opening Day Autographs

STATED ODDS 1:629

Card	Low	High
AT Andres Torres	6.00	15.00
DW Dontrelle Willis	15.00	40.00
JD Jeff Duncan	6.00	15.00
JW Jerome Williams	6.00	15.00
RH Rich Harden	10.00	25.00
RW Ryan Wagner	6.00	15.00

2005 Topps Opening Day

This 165-card set was released early in 2005. The set features a mix of players from either series of the 2005 basic Topps set with the only difference being an opening day logo on the card.

Card	Low	High
COMPLETE SET (165)	15.00	40.00
COMMON CARD (1-165)	.15	.40
ISSUED IN OPENING DAY PACKS		
1 Alex Rodriguez	.60	1.50
2 Placido Polanco	.15	.40
3 Torii Hunter	.15	.40
4 Lyle Overbay	.15	.40
5 Johnny Damon	.25	.60
6 Mike Cameron	.15	.40
7 Ichiro Suzuki	.60	1.50
8 Francisco Rodriguez	.25	.60
9 Bobby Crosby	.15	.40
10 Sammy Sosa	.40	1.00
11 Randy Wolf	.15	.40
12 Jason Bay	.15	.40
13 Mike Lieberthal	.15	.40
14 Paul Konerko	.25	.60
15 Brian Giles	.15	.40
16 Luis Gonzalez	.15	.40
17 Jim Edmonds	.25	.60
18 Carlos Lee	.15	.40
19 Corey Patterson	.15	.40
20 Hank Blalock	.15	.40
21 Sean Casey	.15	.40
22 Dmitri Young	.15	.40
23 Mark Mulder	.15	.40
24 Bobby Abreu	.15	.40
25 Jim Thome	.25	.60
26 Jason Kendall	.15	.40
27 Jason Giambi	.15	.40
28 Vinny Castilla	.15	.40
29 Tony Batista	.15	.40
30 Ivan Rodriguez	.25	.60
31 Craig Biggio	.25	.60
32 Chris Carpenter	.40	1.00
33 Adrian Beltre	.15	.40
34 Scott Podsednik	.15	.40
35 Cliff Floyd	.15	.40
36 Chad Tracy	.15	.40
37 John Smoltz	.40	1.00
38 Shingo Takatsu	.15	.40
39 Jack Wilson	.15	.40
40 Gary Sheffield	.15	.40
41 Lance Berkman	.25	.60
42 Carl Crawford	.25	.60
43 Carlos Guillen	.15	.40
44 David Bell	.15	.40
45 Kazuo Matsui	.15	.40
46 Jason Schmidt	.15	.40
47 Jason Marquis	.15	.40
48 Melvin Mora	.15	.40
49 David Ortiz	.40	1.00
50 Andruw Jones	.15	.40
51 Miguel Tejada	.25	.60
52 Bartolo Colon	.15	.40
53 Derrek Lee	.15	.40
54 Eric Gagne	.15	.40
55 Miguel Cabrera	.40	1.00
56 Travis Hafner	.15	.40
57 Jose Valentin	.15	.40
58 Mark Prior	.25	.60
59 Phil Nevin	.15	.40
60 Jose Vidro	.15	.40
61 Khalil Greene	.15	.40
62 Carlos Zambrano	.25	.60
63 Erubiel Durazo	.15	.40
64 Michael Young UER Player sliding is Rod Barajas	.25	.60
65 Woody Williams	.15	.40
66 Edgardo Alfonzo	.15	.40
67 Troy Glaus	.15	.40
68 Garret Anderson	.15	.40
69 Richie Sexson	.15	.40
70 Curt Schilling	.25	.60
71 Randy Johnson	.40	1.00
72 Chipper Jones	.40	1.00
73 J.D. Drew	.15	.40
74 Russ Ortiz	.15	.40
75 Frank Thomas	.40	1.00
76 Jimmy Rollins	.25	.60
77 Barry Zito	.15	.40
78 Rafael Palmeiro	.25	.60
79 Brad Wilkerson	.15	.40
80 Adam Dunn	.25	.60
81 Doug Mientkiewicz	.15	.40
82 Manny Ramirez	.40	1.00
83 Pedro Martinez	.25	.60
84 Moises Alou	.15	.40
85 Mike Sweeney	.15	.40
86 Boston Red Sox WC	.40	1.00
87 Matt Clement	.15	.40
88 Nomar Garciaparra	.40	1.00
89 Magglio Ordonez	.25	.60
90 Bret Boone	.15	.40
91 Mark Loretta	.15	.40
92 Jose Contreras	.15	.40
93 Randy Winn	.15	.40
94 Austin Kearns	.15	.40
95 Ken Griffey Jr.	.60	1.50
96 Jake Westbrook	.15	.40
97 Kazuhito Tadano	.15	.40
98 C.C. Sabathia	.25	.60
99 Todd Helton	.25	.60
100 Albert Pujols	1.00	2.50
101 Jose Molina Bengie Molina	.15	.40
102 Aaron Miles	.15	.40
103 Mike Lowell	.15	.40
104 Paul Lo Duca	.15	.40
105 Juan Pierre	.15	.40
106 Dontrelle Willis	.15	.40
107 Jeff Bagwell	.25	.60
108 Carlos Beltran	.25	.60
109 Ronnie Belliard	.15	.40
110 Roy Oswalt	.25	.60
111 Zack Greinke	.25	.60
112 Steve Finley	.15	.40
113 Kazuhisa Ishii	.15	.40
114 Justin Morneau	.40	1.00
115 Ben Sheets	.15	.40
116 Johan Santana	.40	1.00
117 Billy Wagner	.15	.40
118 Mariano Rivera	.40	1.00
119 Corey Koskie	.15	.40
120 Akinori Otsuka	.15	.40
121 Joe Mauer	.40	1.00
122 Jacque Jones	.15	.40
123 Joe Nathan	.15	.40
124 Nick Johnson	.15	.40
125 Vernon Wells	.15	.40
126 Mike Piazza	.40	1.00
127 Jose Guillen	.15	.40
128 Jose Reyes	.25	.60
129 Marcus Giles	.15	.40
130 Javy Lopez	.15	.40
131 Kevin Millar	.15	.40
132 Jorge Posada	.25	.60
133 Carl Pavano	.15	.40
134 Bernie Williams	.25	.60
135 Kerry Wood	.15	.40
136 Matt Holliday	.40	1.00
137 Kevin Brown	.15	.40
138 Derek Jeter	1.00	2.50
139 Barry Bonds	.75	2.00
140 Jeff Kent	.15	.40
141 Mark Kotsay	.15	.40
142 Shawn Green	.15	.40
143 Tim Hudson	.25	.60
144 Shannon Stewart	.15	.40
145 Pat Burrell	.15	.40
146 Gavin Floyd	.15	.40
147 Mike Mussina	.25	.60
148 Eric Chavez	.15	.40
149 Jon Lieber	.15	.40
150 Vladimir Guerrero	.40	1.00
151 Vicente Padilla	.15	.40
152 Ryan Klesko	.15	.40
153 Jake Peavy	.15	.40
154 Scott Rolen	.25	.60
155 Greg Maddux	.60	1.50
156 Edgar Renteria	.15	.40
157 Larry Walker	.25	.60
158 Scott Kazmir	.40	1.00
159 B.J. Upton	.25	.60
160 Mark Teixeira	.40	1.00
161 Ken Harvey	.15	.40
162 Alfonso Soriano	.25	.60
163 Carlos Delgado	.15	.40
164 Alexis Rios	.25	.60
165 Checklist	.15	.40

2005 Topps Opening Day Chrome Refractors

Card	Low	High
1 Albert Pujols	4.00	10.00
2 Alex Rodriguez	2.50	6.00
3 Ivan Rodriguez	1.00	2.50
4 Jim Thome	1.00	2.50
5 Sammy Sosa	1.50	4.00
6 Vladimir Guerrero	1.50	4.00
7 Alfonso Soriano	1.00	2.50
8 Ichiro Suzuki	2.50	6.00
9 Derek Jeter	4.00	10.00
10 Chipper Jones	1.50	4.00

2005 Topps Opening Day Autographs

GROUP A ODDS 1:852
GROUP B ODDS 1:1192
EXCHANGE DEADLINE 02/28/07

Card	Low	High
AH Aaron Hill B	4.00	10.00
AW Anthony Whittington A	4.00	10.00
CC Chad Cordero A	6.00	15.00
OQ Omar Quintanilla B	6.00	15.00
PM Paul Maholm A	4.00	10.00

2005 Topps Opening Day MLB Game Worn Jersey Collection

RANDOM INSERTS IN TARGET RETAIL

Card	Low	High
37 Vladimir Guerrero	3.00	8.00
38 Albert Pujols	6.00	15.00
39 Torii Hunter	2.00	5.00
40 Alfonso Soriano	2.00	5.00
41 Bobby Abreu	2.00	5.00
42 Moises Alou	2.00	5.00
43 Sean Burroughs	2.00	5.00
44 Shannon Stewart	2.00	5.00
45 Troy Glaus	2.00	5.00
46 Fernando Vina	2.00	5.00
47 Dan Wilson	2.00	5.00
48 Paul Konerko	2.00	5.00
49 Jimmy Rollins	2.00	5.00
50 Livan Hernandez	2.00	5.00
51 Sean Casey	2.00	5.00
52 Paul LoDuca	2.00	5.00
53 Richie Sexson	2.00	5.00
54 Aubrey Huff	2.00	5.00

2006 Topps Opening Day

This 165-card set was released in March, 2006. This set was issued six-card hobby and retail packs with an 99 cent SRP which came 36 packs to a box and 20 boxes to a case. Cards numbered 1-134 feature veterans while cards 135-164 feature players who qualified for the rookie card status in 2006.

Card	Low	High
COMPLETE SET (165)	15.00	40.00
COMMON CARD (1-165)	.15	.40
OVERALL PLATE SER.1 ODDS 1:246 HTA		
PLATE PRINT RUN 1 SET PER COLOR		
BLACK-CYAN-MAGENTA-YELLOW ISSUED		
NO PLATE PRICING DUE TO SCARCITY		
1 Alex Rodriguez	.60	1.50
2 Jhonny Peralta	.15	.40
3 Garrett Atkins	.15	.40
4 Vernon Wells	.15	.40
5 Carl Crawford	.25	.60
6 Josh Beckett	.25	.60
7 Mickey Mantle	1.25	3.00
8 Willy Taveras	.15	.40
9 Ivan Rodriguez	.25	.60
10 Clint Barmes	.15	.40
11 Jose Reyes	.25	.60
12 Travis Hafner	.15	.40
13 Tadahito Iguchi	.15	.40
14 Barry Zito	.15	.40
15 Brian Roberts	.15	.40
16 David Wright	.60	1.50
17 Mark Teixeira	.25	.60
18 Roy Halladay	.40	1.00
19 Scott Rolen	.25	.60
20 Bobby Abreu	.15	.40
21 Lance Berkman	.25	.60
22 Moises Alou	.15	.40
23 Chone Figgins	.15	.40
24 Aaron Rowand	.15	.40
25 Chipper Jones	.40	1.00
26 Johnny Damon	.25	.60
27 Matt Clement	.15	.40
28 Nick Johnson	.15	.40
29 Freddy Garcia	.15	.40
30 Jon Garland	.15	.40
31 Torii Hunter	.15	.40
32 Mike Sweeney	.15	.40
33 Mike Lieberthal	.15	.40
34 Rafael Furcal	.15	.40
35 Brad Wilkerson	.15	.40
36 Brad Penny	.15	.40
37 Jorge Cantu	.15	.40
38 Paul Konerko	.25	.60
39 Rickie Weeks	.25	.60
40 Jorge Posada	.25	.60
41 Albert Pujols	1.00	2.50
42 Zack Greinke	.25	.60
43 Jimmy Rollins	.25	.60
44 Mark Prior	.25	.60
45 Greg Maddux	.60	1.50
46 Jeff Francis	.15	.40
47 Felipe Lopez	.15	.40
48 Dan Johnson	.15	.40
49 B.J. Ryan	.15	.40
50 Manny Ramirez	.40	1.00
51 Melvin Mora	.15	.40
52 Javy Lopez	.15	.40
53 Garret Anderson	.15	.40
54 Jason Bay	.15	.40
55 Joe Mauer	.40	1.00
56 C.C. Sabathia	.25	.60
57 Bartolo Colon	.15	.40
58 Ichiro Suzuki	.60	1.50
59 Andruw Jones	.15	.40
60 Rocco Baldelli	.15	.40
61 Jeff Kent	.15	.40
62 Cliff Floyd	.15	.40
63 John Smoltz	.40	1.00
64 Shawn Green	.15	.40
65 Nomar Garciaparra	.40	1.00
66 Miguel Cabrera	.40	1.00
67 Vladimir Guerrero	.40	1.00
68 Gary Sheffield	.15	.40
69 Jake Peavy	.15	.40
70 Carlos Lee	.15	.40
71 Tom Glavine	.25	.60
72 Craig Biggio	.25	.60
73 Steve Finley	.15	.40
74 Adrian Beltre	.15	.40
75 Eric Gagne	.15	.40
76 Aubrey Huff	.15	.40
77 Livan Hernandez	.15	.40
78 Scott Podsednik	.15	.40
79 Todd Helton	.25	.60
80 Kerry Wood	.15	.40
81 Randy Johnson	.40	1.00
82 Huston Street	.15	.40
83 Pedro Martinez	.25	.60
84 Roger Clemens	.50	1.25
85 Hank Blalock	.15	.40
86 Carlos Beltran	.25	.60
87 Chien-Ming Wang	.25	.60
88 Rich Harden	.15	.40
89 Mike Mussina	.25	.60
90 Mark Buehrle	.25	.60
91 Michael Young	.25	.60
92 Mark Mulder	.15	.40
93 Khalil Greene	.15	.40
94 Johan Santana	.40	1.00
95 Andy Pettitte	.25	.60
96 Derek Jeter	1.00	2.50
97 Jack Wilson	.15	.40
98 Ben Sheets	.15	.40
99 Miguel Tejada	.25	.60
100 Barry Bonds	.75	2.00
101 Dontrelle Willis	.15	.40
102 Curt Schilling	.25	.60
103 Jose Contreras	.15	.40
104 Jeremy Bonderman	.15	.40
105 David Ortiz	.25	.60
106 Lyle Overbay	.15	.40
107 Robinson Cano	.40	1.00
108 Tim Hudson	.25	.60
109 Paul Lo Duca	.15	.40
110 Mariano Rivera	.40	1.00
111 Derrek Lee	.15	.40
112 Morgan Ensberg	.15	.40
113 Wily Mo Pena	.15	.40
114 Roy Oswalt	.25	.60
115 Adam Dunn	.25	.60
116 Hideki Matsui	.40	1.00
117 Pat Burrell	.15	.40
118 Jason Schmidt	.15	.40
119 Alfonso Soriano	.25	.60
120 Aramis Ramirez	.15	.40
121 Jason Giambi	.15	.40
122 Orlando Hernandez	.15	.40
123 Magglio Ordonez	.25	.60
124 Troy Glaus	.15	.40
125 Carlos Delgado	.15	.40
126 Kevin Millwood	.15	.40
127 Shannon Stewart	.15	.40
128 Luis Castillo	.15	.40
129 Jim Edmonds	.25	.60
130 Richie Sexson	.15	.40
131 Dmitri Young	.15	.40
132 Russ Adams	.15	.40
133 Nick Swisher	.40	1.00
134 Jermaine Dye	.15	.40
135 Anderson Hernandez (RC)	.15	.40
136 Justin Huber (RC)	.15	.40
137 Jason Botts (RC)	.15	.40
138 Jeff Mathis (RC)	.15	.40
139 Ryan Garko (RC)	.15	.40
140 Charlton Jimerson (RC)	.15	.40
141 Chris Denorfia (RC)	.15	.40
142 Anthony Reyes (RC)	.15	.40
143 Bryan Bullington (RC)	.15	.40
144 Chuck James (RC)	.15	.40
145 Danny Sandoval RC	.15	.40
146 Walter Young (RC)	.15	.40
147 Fausto Carmona (RC)	.15	.40
148 Francisco Liriano (RC)	.40	1.00
149 Hong-Chih Kuo (RC)	.40	1.00
150 Joe Saunders (RC)	.15	.40
151 John Koronka (RC)	.15	.40
152 Robert Andino RC	.15	.40
153 Shaun Marcum (RC)	.15	.40
154 Tom Gorzelanny (RC)	.15	.40
155 Craig Breslow RC	.15	.40
156 Chris Demaria RC	.15	.40
157 Bryan Pena (RC)	.15	.40
158 Rich Hill (RC)	.15	.40
159 Rick Short (RC)	.15	.40
160 Darrell Rasner (RC)	.15	.40
161 C.J. Wilson (RC)	.25	.60
162 Brandon Watson (RC)	.15	.40
163 Paul McAnulty (RC)	.15	.40
164 Marshall McDougall (RC)	.15	.40
165 Checklist	.15	.40

2006 Topps Opening Day Red Foil

*RED FOIL: 3X TO 8X BASIC
*RED FOIL: 3X TO 8X BASIC RC
STATED ODDS 1:8 HOBBY, 1:11 RETAIL
STATED PRINT RUN 2006 SERIAL #'d SETS

2006 Topps Opening Day Autographs

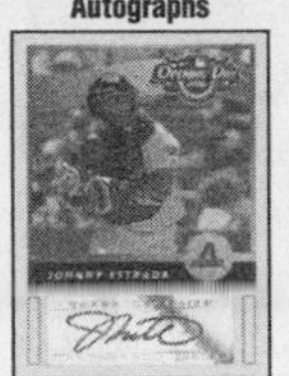

GROUP A ODDS 1:10928 H, 1:11668 R
GROUP B ODDS 1:3491 H, 1:3491 R
GROUP C ODDS 1:978 H, 1:1185 R

Card	Low	High
BE Brad Eldred B	4.00	10.00
EM Eli Marrero C	4.00	10.00
JE Johnny Estrada A	6.00	15.00
MK Mark Kotsay B	6.00	15.00
TH Toby Hall C	4.00	10.00
VZ Victor Zambrano C	4.00	10.00

2006 Topps Opening Day Sports Illustrated For Kids

Card	Low	High
COMPLETE SET (25)	4.00	10.00
STATED ODDS 1:1		
1 Vladimir Guerrero	.60	1.50
2 Marcus Giles	.25	.60
3 Michael Young	.40	1.00
4 Derek Jeter	1.50	4.00
5 Barry Bonds	1.25	3.00
6 Ivan Rodriguez	.40	1.00
7 Miguel Cabrera	.60	1.50
8 Jim Edmonds	.40	1.00
9 Jack Wilson	.25	.60
10 Khalil Greene	.25	.60
11 Miguel Tejada	.40	1.00
12 Eric Chavez	.25	.60
13 Shannon Stewart	.25	.60
14 Julio Lugo	.25	.60
15 Andruw Jones	.25	.60
16 Nick Johnson Randy Johnson	.60	1.50
17 Tadahito Iguchi Ivan Rodriguez	.40	1.00
18 Roy Oswalt Jose Reyes	.40	1.00
19 Manny Ramirez Ronnie Belliard	.60	1.50
20 Todd Helton Khalil Greene	.25	.60
21 David Ortiz Dontrelle Willis	.40	1.00
22 Ichiro Suzuki Johnny Damon	1.00	2.50
23 Craig Biggio Jack Wilson	.40	1.00
24 Brian Roberts Richie Sexson	.25	.60
25 Chipper Jones Marcus Giles	.60	1.50

2007 Topps Opening Day

This 220-card set was released in March, 2007. This set was issued in six-card packs, with an 99 cent SRP, which came 36 packs to a box and 20 boxes to a case. The Derek Jeter (#46) card, which featured Mickey Mantle and President George W Bush in the regular Topps set; did not feature either personage in the background.

Card	Low	High
COMPLETE SET (220)	20.00	50.00
COMMON CARD (1-220)	.15	.40
COMMON RC	.15	.40
OVERALL PLATE ODDS 1:370 HOBBY		
PLATE PRINT RUN 1 SET PER COLOR		
BLACK-CYAN-MAGENTA-YELLOW ISSUED		
NO PLATE PRICING DUE TO SCARCITY		
1 Bobby Abreu	.15	.40
2 Mike Piazza	.40	1.00
3 Jake Westbrook	.15	.40
4 Zach Duke	.15	.40
5 David Wright	.60	1.50
6 Adrian Gonzalez	.25	.60
7 Mickey Mantle	1.25	3.00
8 Bill Hall	.15	.40
9 Robinson Cano	.40	1.00
10 Dontrelle Willis	.15	.40
11 J.D. Drew	.15	.40
12 Paul Konerko	.25	.60
13 Austin Kearns	.15	.40
14 Mike Lowell	.15	.40
15 Magglio Ordonez	.25	.60
16 Rafael Furcal	.15	.40
17 Matt Cain	.25	.60
18 Craig Monroe	.15	.40
19 Matt Holliday	.20	.50
20 Edgar Renteria	.15	.40
21 Mark Buehrle	.25	.60
22 Carlos Quentin	.15	.40
23 C.C. Sabathia	.25	.60
24 Nick Markakis	.40	1.00
25 Chipper Jones	.40	1.00
26 Jason Giambi	.15	.40
27 Barry Zito	.15	.40
28 Jake Peavy	.15	.40
29 Hank Blalock	.15	.40
30 Johnny Damon	.25	.60
31 Chad Tracy	.15	.40
32 Nick Swisher	.40	1.00
33 Willy Taveras	.15	.40
34 Chuck James	.15	.40
35 Carlos Delgado	.15	.40
36 Livan Hernandez	.15	.40
37 Freddy Garcia	.15	.40
38 Bronson Arroyo	.15	.40
39 Jack Wilson	.15	.40
40 Dan Uggla	.25	.60
41 Chris Carpenter	.40	1.00
42 Jorge Posada	.25	.60
43 Joe Mauer	.25	.60
44 Corey Patterson	.15	.40
45 Chien-Ming Wang	.25	.60
46 Derek Jeter	1.00	2.50
47 Carlos Beltran	.25	.60
48 Jim Edmonds	.25	.60
49 Jeremy Sowers	.15	.40
50 Randy Johnson	.40	1.00
51 Jered Weaver	.25	.60
52 Josh Barfield	.15	.40
53 Scott Rolen	.25	.60
54 Ryan Shealy	.15	.40
55 Freddy Sanchez	.15	.40
56 Javier Vazquez	.15	.40
57 Jeremy Bonderman	.15	.40
58 Miguel Cabrera	.40	1.00
59 Kazuo Matsui	.15	.40
60 Curt Schilling	.25	.60
61 Alfonso Soriano	.25	.60
62 Orlando Hernandez	.15	.40
63 Joe Blanton	.15	.40
64 Aramis Ramirez	.15	.40
65 Ben Sheets	.15	.40
66 Jimmy Rollins	.25	.60
67 Mark Loretta	.15	.40
68 Cole Hamels	.40	1.00
69 Albert Pujols	1.00	2.50
70 Moises Alou	.15	.40
71 Mark Teahen	.15	.40
72 Roy Halladay	.40	1.00
73 Cory Sullivan	.15	.40
74 Frank Thomas	.40	1.00
75 Ryan Howard	.60	1.50
76 Rocco Baldelli	.15	.40
77 Manny Ramirez	.40	1.00
78 Ray Durham	.15	.40
79 Gary Sheffield	.15	.40
80 Jay Gibbons	.15	.40
81 Todd Helton	.25	.60
82 Gary Matthews	.15	.40
83 Brandon Inge	.15	.40
84 Jonathan Papelbon	.40	1.00
85 John Smoltz	.40	1.00
86 Chone Figgins	.15	.40
87 Hideki Matsui	.40	1.00
88 Carlos Lee	.15	.40
89 Jose Reyes	.25	.60
90 Lyle Overbay	.15	.40
91 Johan Santana	.40	1.00
92 Ian Kinsler	.25	.60
93 Scott Kazmir	.25	.60
94 Hanley Ramirez	.40	1.00
95 Greg Maddux	.60	1.50
96 Johnny Estrada	.15	.40
97 B.J. Upton	.15	.40
98 Francisco Liriano	.40	1.00
99 Chase Utley	.40	1.00
100 Preston Wilson	.15	.40
101 Marcus Giles	.15	.40
102 Jeff Kent	.15	.40
103 Grady Sizemore	.25	.60
104 Ken Griffey	.60	1.50
105 Garret Anderson	.15	.40
106 Brian McCann	.15	.40
107 Jon Garland	.15	.40
108 Troy Glaus	.15	.40
109 Brandon Webb	.25	.60
110 Jason Schmidt	.15	.40
111 Ramon Hernandez	.15	.40
112 Justin Morneau	.40	1.00
113 Mike Cameron	.15	.40
114 Andruw Jones	.15	.40
115 Russell Martin	.15	.40
116 Vernon Wells	.15	.40
117 Orlando Hudson	.15	.40
118 Derek Lowe	.15	.40
119 Alex Rodriguez	.60	1.50
120 Chad Billingsley	.25	.60
121 Kenji Johjima	.40	1.00
122 Nick Johnson	.15	.40
123 Dan Haren	.15	.40
124 Mark Teixeira	.40	1.00
125 Jeff Francoeur	.40	1.00
126 Ted Lilly	.15	.40
127 Jhonny Peralta	.15	.40
128 Aaron Harang	.15	.40
129 Ryan Zimmerman	.25	.60
130 Jermaine Dye	.15	.40
131 Orlando Cabrera	.15	.40
132 Juan Pierre	.15	.40
133 Brian Giles	.15	.40
134 Jason Bay	.25	.60
135 David Ortiz	.25	.60
136 Chris Capuano	.15	.40
137 Carlos Zambrano	.25	.60
138 Luis Gonzalez	.15	.40
139 Jeff Weaver	.15	.40
140 Lance Berkman	.25	.60
141 Raul Ibanez	.15	.40
142 Jim Thome	.25	.60
143 Jose Contreras	.15	.40
144 David Eckstein	.15	.40
145 Adam Dunn	.25	.60
146 Alex Rios	.15	.40
147 Garrett Atkins	.15	.40
148 A.J. Burnett	.25	.60
149 Jeremy Hermida	.15	.40
150 Conor Jackson	.15	.40
151 Adrian Beltre	.15	.40
152 Torii Hunter	.15	.40
153 Andrew Miller RC	.40	1.00
154 Ichiro Suzuki	.60	1.50
155 Mark Redman	.15	.40
156 Paul LoDuca	.15	.40
157 Xavier Nady	.15	.40
158 Stephen Drew	.15	.40
159 Eric Chavez	.15	.40
160 Pedro Martinez	.25	.60
161 Derrek Lee	.15	.40
162 David DeJesus	.15	.40
163 Troy Tulowitzki (RC)	1.00	2.50
164 Vinny Rottino (RC)	.15	.40
165 Phillip Humber (RC)	.15	.40
166 Jerry Owens (RC)	.15	.40
167 Ubaldo Jimenez (RC)	1.00	2.50
168 Michael Young	.25	.60
169 Ryan Braun RC	.15	.40
170 Kevin Kouzmanoff (RC)	.15	.40
171 Oswaldo Navarro RC	.15	.40
172 Miguel Montero (RC)	.15	.40
173 Roy Oswalt	.25	.60
174 Shane Youman RC	.15	.40
175 Josh Fields (RC)	.15	.40
176 Adam Lind (RC)	.15	.40
177 Miguel Tejada	.25	.60
178 Delwyn Young (RC)	.15	.40
179 Scott Moore (RC)	.15	.40
180 Fred Lewis (RC)	.25	.60
181 Glen Perkins (RC)	.15	.40
182 Vladimir Guerrero	.40	1.00
183 Drew Anderson RC	.15	.40
184 Jeff Salazar (RC)	.15	.40
185 Tom Gordon	.15	.40
186 The Bird	.15	.40
187 Justin Verlander	.50	1.25
188 Delmon Young (RC)	.25	.60
189 Homer	.15	.40
190 Wally the Green Monster	.15	.40
191 Southpaw	.15	.40
192 Dinger	.15	.40
193 Carl Crawford	.25	.60
194 Slider	.15	.40
195 Gapper	.15	.40
196 Paws	.15	.40
197 Billy the Marlin	.15	.40
198 Ivan Rodriguez	.25	.60
199 Slugger	.15	.40
200 Junction Jack	.15	.40
201 Bernie Brewer	.15	.40
202 Travis Hafner	.15	.40
203 Stomper	.15	.40
204 Mr. Met	.15	.40
205 The Moose	.15	.40
206 Phillie Phanatic	.15	.40
207 Prince Fielder	.25	.60
208 Julio Lugo	.15	.40
209 Pirate Parrot	.15	.40
210 Joel Zumaya	.25	.60
211 Swinging Friar	.15	.40
212 Jay Payton	.15	.40
213 Lou Seal	.15	.40
214 Fredbird	.15	.40
215 Screech	.15	.40
216 TC Bear	.15	.40
217 Andre Ethier	.25	.60
218 Ervin Santana	.15	.40
219 Melvin Mora	.15	.40
220 Checklist	.15	.40

2007 Topps Opening Day Gold

Card	Low	High
COMPLETE SET (219)	75.00	150.00

*GOLD: 1.2X TO 3X BASIC
*GOLD: 1.2X TO 3X BASIC RC
STATED ODDS APPX. 1 PER HOBBY PACK
STATED PRINT RUN 2007 SERIAL #'d SETS

2007 Topps Opening Day Autographs

STATED ODDS 1:965 HOBBY, 1:965 RETAIL

Card	Low	High
EF Emiliano Fruto	10.00	25.00
HK Howie Kendrick	20.00	50.00
JM Juan Morillo	6.00	15.00
JT Jordan Tata		
MC Matt Cain	5.00	12.00
MK Matt Kemp	10.00	25.00
MN Mike Napoli		
OH Orlando Hudson	10.00	25.00
RM Rob Mackowiak		
SS Shannon Stewart	6.00	15.00

2007 Topps Opening Day Diamond Stars

Card	Low	High
COMPLETE SET (25)	6.00	15.00
STATED ODDS 1:4 HOBBY, 1:4 RETAIL		
DS1 Ryan Howard	1.00	2.50
DS2 Alfonso Soriano	.40	1.00
DS3 Alex Rodriguez	1.00	2.50

DS4 David Ortiz .40 1.00
DS5 Raul Ibanez .40 1.00
DS6 Matt Holliday .60 1.50
DS7 Delmon Young .40 1.00
DS8 Derrick Turnbow .25 .60
DS9 Freddy Sanchez .25 .60
DS10 Troy Glaus .25 .60
DS11 A.J. Pierzynski .25 .60
DS12 Dontrelle Willis .25 .60
DS13 Justin Morneau .60 1.50
DS14 Jose Reyes .40 1.00
DS15 Derek Jeter 1.50 4.00
DS16 Ivan Rodriguez .40 1.00
DS17 Jay Payton .25 .60
DS18 Adrian Gonzalez .40 1.00
DS19 David Eckstein .25 .60
DS20 Chipper Jones .60 1.50
DS21 Aramis Ramirez .25 .60
DS22 David Wright 1.00 2.50
DS23 Mark Teixeira .60 1.50
DS24 Stephen Drew .25 .60
DS25 Ichiro Suzuki 1.00 2.50

2007 Topps Opening Day Movie Gallery

STATED ODDS 1:6 HOBBY
NNO Alex Rodriguez .15 .40

2007 Topps Opening Day Puzzle

COMPLETE SET (28) 6.00 15.00
STATED ODDS 1:3 HOBBY, 1:3 RETAIL
P1 Adam Dunn .40 1.00
P2 Adam Dunn .40 1.00
P3 Miguel Tejada .40 1.00
P4 Miguel Tejada .40 1.00
P5 Hanley Ramirez .60 1.50
P6 Hanley Ramirez .60 1.50
P7 Johan Santana .60 1.50
P8 Johan Santana .60 1.50
P9 Brandon Webb .40 1.00
P10 Brandon Webb .40 1.00
P11 David Wright 1.00 2.50
P12 David Wright 1.00 2.50
P13 Alex Rodriguez 1.00 2.50
P14 Alex Rodriguez 1.00 2.50
P15 Ryan Howard 1.00 2.50
P16 Ryan Howard 1.00 2.50
P17 Albert Pujols 1.50 4.00
P18 Albert Pujols 1.50 4.00
P19 Andruw Jones .25 .60
P20 Andruw Jones .25 .60
P21 Alfonso Soriano .40 1.00
P22 Alfonso Soriano .40 1.00
P23 Vladimir Guerrero .60 1.50
P24 Vladimir Guerrero .60 1.50
P25 David Ortiz .40 1.00
P26 David Ortiz .40 1.00
P27 Ichiro Suzuki 1.00 2.50
P28 Ichiro Suzuki 1.00 2.50

2008 Topps Opening Day

COMPLETE SET (220) 15.00 40.00
COMMON CARD (1-194) .12 .30
COMMON RC (195-220) .20 .50
OVERALL PLATE ODDS 1:546 HOBBY
PLATE PRINT RUN 1 SET PER COLOR
BLACK-CYAN-MAGENTA-YELLOW ISSUED
NO PLATE PRICING DUE TO SCARCITY
1 Alex Rodriguez .50 1.25
2 Barry Zito .12 .30
3 Jeff Suppan .12 .30
4 Placido Polanco .12 .30
5 Scott Kazmir .20 .50
6 Ivan Rodriguez .20 .50
7 Mickey Mantle 1.00 2.50
8 Stephen Drew .12 .30
9 Ken Griffey Jr. .50 1.25
10 Miguel Cabrera .30 .75
11 Yorvit Torrealba .12 .30
12 Daisuke Matsuzaka .30 .75
13 Kyle Kendrick .12 .30
14 Jimmy Rollins .20 .50
15 Joe Mauer .30 .75
16 Cole Hamels .30 .75
17 Yovani Gallardo .12 .30
18 Miguel Tejada .20 .50
19 Corey Hart .12 .30
20 Nick Markakis .30 .75
21 Zack Greinke .20 .50
22 Orlando Cabrera .12 .30
23 Jake Peavy .12 .30
24 Erik Bedard .12 .30
25 Trevor Hoffman .20 .50
26 Derrek Lee .12 .30
27 Hank Blalock .12 .30
28 Victor Martinez .20 .50
29 Chris Young .12 .30
30 Jose Reyes .20 .50
31 Mike Lowell .12 .30
32 Curtis Granderson .20 .50
33 Dan Uggla .20 .50
34 Mike Piazza .30 .75
35 Garrett Atkins .12 .30
36 Felix Hernandez .30 .75
37 Alex Rios .20 .50
38 Mark Reynolds .12 .30
39 Jason Bay .20 .50
40 Josh Beckett .20 .50
41 Jack Cust .12 .30
42 Vladimir Guerrero .30 .75
43 Marcus Giles .12 .30
44 Kenny Lofton .12 .30
45 John Lackey .12 .30
46 Ryan Howard .40 1.00
47 Kevin Youkilis .20 .50
48 Gary Sheffield .12 .30
49 Justin Morneau .30 .75
50 Albert Pujols .75 2.00
51 Ubaldo Jimenez .20 .50
52 Johan Santana .30 .75
53 Chuck James .12 .30
54 Jeremy Hermida .12 .30
55 Andruw Jones .12 .30
56 Jason Varitek .30 .75
57 Tim Hudson .20 .50
58 Justin Upton .20 .50
59 Brad Penny .12 .30
60 Robinson Cano .30 .75
61 Johnny Estrada .12 .30
62 Brandon Webb .20 .50
63 Chris Duncan .12 .30
64 Aaron Hill .12 .30
65 Alfonso Soriano .20 .50
66 Carlos Zambrano .20 .50
67 Ben Sheets .12 .30
68 Andy LaRoche .12 .30
69 Tim Lincecum .50 1.25
70 Phil Hughes .40 1.00
71 Magglio Ordonez .20 .50
72 Scott Rolen .20 .50
73 John Maine .12 .30
74 Delmon Young .20 .50
75 Chase Utley .30 .75
76 Jose Valverde .12 .30
77 Tadahito Iguchi .12 .30
78 Checklist .12 .30
79 Russell Martin .12 .30
80 B.J. Upton .20 .50
81 Orlando Hudson .12 .30
82 Jim Edmonds .20 .50
83 J.J. Hardy .12 .30
84 Todd Helton .20 .50
85 Melky Cabrera .12 .30
86 Adrian Beltre .12 .30
87 Manny Ramirez .30 .75
88 Rafael Furcal .12 .30
89 Gil Meche .12 .30
90 Grady Sizemore .20 .50
91 Jeff Kent .12 .30
92 David DeJesus .12 .30
93 Lyle Overbay .12 .30
94 Moises Alou .12 .30
95 Frank Thomas .30 .75
96 Ryan Garko .12 .30
97 Kevin Kouzmanoff .12 .30
98 Roy Oswalt .20 .50
99 Mark Buehrle .20 .50
100 David Ortiz .20 .50
101 Hunter Pence .30 .75
102 David Wright .40 1.00
103 Dustin Pedroia .40 1.00
104 Roy Halladay .30 .75
105 Derek Jeter .75 2.00
106 Casey Blake .12 .30
107 Rich Harden .12 .30
108 Shane Victorino .12 .30
109 Richie Sexson .12 .30
110 Jim Thome .20 .50
111 Akinori Iwamura .12 .30
112 Dan Haren .12 .30
113 Jose Contreras .12 .30
114 Jonathan Papelbon .20 .50
115 Prince Fielder .20 .50
116 Dan Johnson .12 .30
117 Dmitri Young .12 .30
118 Brandon Phillips .12 .30
119 Brett Myers .12 .30
120 James Loney .20 .50
121 C.C. Sabathia .20 .50
122 Jermaine Dye .12 .30
123 Aubrey Huff .12 .30
124 Carlos Ruiz .12 .30
125 Hanley Ramirez .30 .75
126 Edgar Renteria .12 .30
127 Mark Loretta .12 .30
128 Brian McCann .20 .50
129 Paul Konerko .20 .50
130 Jorge Posada .20 .50
131 Chien-Ming Wang .20 .50
132 Jose Vidro .12 .30
133 Carlos Delgado .12 .30
134 Kelvim Escobar .12 .30
135 Pedro Martinez .20 .50
136 Jeremy Guthrie .12 .30
137 Ramon Hernandez .12 .30
138 Ian Kinsler .20 .50
139 Ichiro Suzuki .50 1.25
140 Garret Anderson .12 .30
141 Tom Gorzelanny .12 .30
142 Bobby Crosby .12 .30
143 Jeff Francoeur .20 .50
144 Josh Hamilton .30 .75
145 Mark Teixeira .30 .75
146 Fausto Carmona .12 .30
147 Alex Gordon .20 .50
148 Nick Swisher .30 .75
149 Justin Verlander .40 1.00
150 Pat Burrell .12 .30
151 Chris Carpenter .30 .75
152 Matt Holliday .30 .75
153 Adam Dunn .20 .50
154 Curt Schilling .20 .50
155 Kelly Johnson .12 .30
156 Aaron Rowand .12 .30
157 Brian Roberts .12 .30
158 Bobby Abreu .12 .30
159 Carlos Beltran .12 .30
160 Lance Berkman .20 .50
161 Gary Matthews .12 .30
162 Jeff Francis .12 .30
163 Vernon Wells .12 .30
164 Dontrelle Willis .12 .30
165 Travis Hafner .12 .30
166 Brian Bannister .12 .30
167 Carlos Pena .20 .50
168 Raul Ibanez .20 .50
169 Aramis Ramirez .12 .30
170 Eric Byrnes .12 .30
171 Greg Maddux .40 1.00
172 John Smoltz .30 .75
173 Jarrod Saltalamacchia .12 .30
174 Hideki Okajima .20 .50
175 Javier Vazquez .12 .30
176 Aaron Harang .12 .30
177 Jhonny Peralta .12 .30
178 Carlos Lee .12 .30
179 Ryan Braun .40 1.00
180 Torii Hunter .12 .30
181 Hideki Matsui .30 .75
182 Eric Chavez .12 .30
183 Freddy Sanchez .12 .30
184 Adrian Gonzalez .20 .50
185 Bengie Molina .12 .30
186 Kenji Johjima .12 .30
187 Carl Crawford .20 .50
188 Chipper Jones .30 .75
189 Chris Young .12 .30
190 Michael Young .20 .50
191 Troy Glaus .20 .50
192 Ryan Zimmerman .20 .50
193 Brian Giles .12 .30
194 Troy Tulowitzki .30 .75
195 Chin-Lung Hu (RC) .30 .75
196 Seth Smith (RC) .20 .50
197 Wladimir Balentien (RC) .20 .50
198 Rich Thompson RC .30 .75
199 Radhames Liz RC .30 .75
200 Ross Detwiler RC .50 1.25
201 Sam Fuld RC .60 1.50
202 Clint Sammons (RC) .20 .50
203 Ross Ohlendorf RC .30 .75
204 Jonathan Albaladejo RC .30 .75
205 Brandon Jones RC .50 1.25
206 Steve Pearce RC .30 .75
207 Kevin Hart (RC) .20 .50
208 Luke Hochevar RC .30 .75
209 Troy Patton (RC) .20 .50
210 Josh Anderson (RC) .20 .50
211 Clay Buchholz (RC) .50 1.25
212 Joe Koshansky (RC) .20 .50
213 Bronson Sardinha (RC) .20 .50
214 Emilio Bonifacio RC .50 1.25
215 Daric Barton (RC) .20 .50
216 Lance Broadway (RC) .20 .50
217 Jeff Clement (RC) .30 .75
218 Joey Votto (RC) .75 2.00
219 J.R. Towles RC .30 .75
220 Nyjer Morgan (RC) .20 .50

2008 Topps Opening Day Gold

COMPLETE SET (220) 50.00 100.00
*GOLD VET: 1X TO 2.5X BASIC
*GOLD RC: 1X TO 2.5X BASIC RC
STATED ODDS APPX. ONE PER PACK
STATED PRINT RUN 2199 SERIAL #'d SETS
7 Mickey Mantle 3.00 8.00

2008 Topps Opening Day Autographs

GROUP A ODDS 1:359
GROUP B ODDS 1:7800
AAL Adam Lind A 6.00 15.00
AL Anthony Lerew A 6.00 15.00
GP Glen Perkins A 3.00 8.00
JAB Jason Bartlett A 3.00 8.00
JB Jeff Baker A 3.00 8.00
JCB Jason Botts B 6.00 15.00
JRB John Buck A 3.00 8.00
KG Kevin Gregg A 5.00 12.00
NS Nate Schierholtz A 5.00 12.00

2008 Topps Opening Day Flapper Cards

COMPLETE SET (18) 6.00 15.00
STATED ODDS 1:8
AP Albert Pujols 1.50 4.00
AR Alex Rodriguez 1.00 2.50
CJ Chipper Jones .60 1.50
DJ Derek Jeter 1.50 4.00
DM Daisuke Matsuzaka .60 1.50
DO David Ortiz .40 1.00
DW David Wright .75 2.00
GM Greg Maddux .75 2.00
IS Ichiro Suzuki 1.00 2.50
JB Josh Beckett .40 1.00
JR Jose Reyes .40 1.00
KG Ken Griffey Jr 1.00 2.50
MM Mickey Mantle 1.50 4.00
MR Manny Ramirez .60 1.50
PF Prince Fielder .40 1.00
RC Roger Clemens .75 2.00
RH Ryan Howard .75 2.00
VG Vladimir Guerrero .60 1.50

2008 Topps Opening Day Puzzle

COMPLETE SET (28) 5.00 12.00
STATED ODDS 1:3
P1 Matt Holliday .50 1.25
P2 Matt Holliday .50 1.25
P3 Vladimir Guerrero .50 1.25
P4 Vladimir Guerrero .50 1.25
P5 Jose Reyes .30 .75
P6 Jose Reyes .30 .75
P7 Josh Beckett .30 .75
P8 Josh Beckett .30 .75
P9 Albert Pujols 1.25 3.00
P10 Albert Pujols 1.25 3.00
P11 Alex Rodriguez .75 2.00
P12 Alex Rodriguez .75 2.00
P13 Jake Peavy .20 .50
P14 Jake Peavy .20 .50
P15 David Ortiz .30 .75
P16 David Ortiz .30 .75
P17 Ryan Howard .60 1.50
P18 Ryan Howard .60 1.50
P19 Ichiro Suzuki .75 2.00
P20 Ichiro Suzuki .75 2.00
P21 Hanley Ramirez .50 1.25
P22 Hanley Ramirez .50 1.25
P23 Grady Sizemore .30 .75
P24 Grady Sizemore .30 .75
P25 David Wright .60 1.50
P26 David Wright .60 1.50
P27 Alex Rios .30 .75
P28 Alex Rios .30 .75

2008 Topps Opening Day Tattoos

STATED ODDS 1:12
AB Atlanta Braves .60 1.50
AD Arizona Diamondbacks .60 1.50
BB Bernie Brewer .60 1.50
BM Billy the Marlin .60 1.50
BRS Boston Red Sox .60 1.50
CC Chicago Cubs .60 1.50
CI Cleveland Indians .60 1.50
CR Cincinnati Reds .60 1.50
CWS Chicago White Sox .60 1.50
FB Fredbird .60 1.50
FM Florida Marlins .60 1.50
JJ Junction Jack .60 1.50
LAA Los Angeles Angels .60 1.50
LS Lou Seal .60 1.50
MM Mr. Met .60 1.50
NYM New York Mets .60 1.50
NYY New York Yankees .60 1.50
PIP Pirate Parrot .60 1.50
PP Phillie Phanatic .60 1.50
PW Paws .60 1.50
SF Swinging Friar .60 1.50
SFG San Francisco Giants .60 1.50
SL Slider .60 1.50
ST Stomper .60 1.50
TB TC Bear .60 1.50
TBJ Toronto Blue Jays .60 1.50
TDR Tampa Bay Rays .60 1.50
TM The Moose .60 1.50
TR Texas Rangers .60 1.50
WM Wally the Green Monster .60 1.50

2010 Topps Opening Day

COMPLETE SET (220) 15.00 40.00
COMMON CARD (1-205/220) .12 .30
COMMON RC (206-219) .20 .50
OVERALL PLATE ODDS 1:2119 HOBBY
PLATE PRINT RUN 1 SET PER COLOR
BLACK-CYAN-MAGENTA-YELLOW ISSUED
NO PLATE PRICING DUE TO SCARCITY
1 Prince Fielder .20 .50
2 Derrek Lee .12 .30
3 Clayton Kershaw .30 .75
4 Orlando Cabrera .12 .30
5 Ted Lilly .12 .30
6 Bobby Abreu .12 .30
7 Mickey Mantle 1.00 2.50
8 Johnny Cueto .12 .30
9 Dexter Fowler .12 .30
10 Felipe Lopez .12 .30
11 Tommy Hanson .20 .50
12 Cristian Guzman .12 .30
13 Shane Victorino .20 .50
14 John Maine .12 .30
15 Adam Jones .20 .50
16 Aubrey Huff .12 .30
17 Victor Martinez .20 .50
18 Rick Porcello .12 .30
19 Garret Anderson .12 .30
20 Josh Johnson .20 .50
21 Marco Scutaro .12 .30
22 Howie Kendrick .12 .30
23 Joey Votto .30 .75
24 Jorge De La Rosa .12 .30
25 Zack Greinke .20 .50
26 Eric Young Jr .12 .30
27 Billy Butler .12 .30
28 John Lackey .12 .30
29 Manny Ramirez .30 .75
30 CC Sabathia .20 .50
31 Kyle Blanks .12 .30
32 David Wright .40 1.00
33 Kevin Millwood .12 .30
34 Nick Swisher .30 .75
35 Matt LaPorta .30 .75
36 Brandon Inge .20 .50
37 Cole Hamels .30 .75
38 Adrian Gonzalez .20 .50
39 Joe Saunders .12 .30
40 Kenshin Kawakami .20 .50
41 Tim Lincecum .50 1.25
42 Ken Griffey Jr. .50 1.25
43 Ian Kinsler .20 .50
44 Ivan Rodriguez .20 .50
45 Carl Crawford .20 .50
46 Jon Garland .12 .30
47 Albert Pujols .75 2.00
48 Daniel Murphy .12 .30
49 Scott Hairston .12 .30
50 Justin Masterson .12 .30
51 Andrew McCutchen .30 .75
52 Gordon Beckham .20 .50
53 David DeJesus .12 .30
54 Jorge Posada .20 .50
55 Brett Anderson .20 .50
56 Ichiro Suzuki .50 1.25
57 Hank Blalock .12 .30
58 Vladimir Guerrero .30 .75
59 Cliff Lee .20 .50
60 Freddy Sanchez .12 .30
61 Ryan Dempster .12 .30
62 Adam Wainwright .20 .50
63 Matt Holliday .30 .75
64 Chone Figgins .12 .30
65 Tim Hudson .20 .50
66 Rich Harden .12 .30
67 Justin Upton .20 .50
68 Yunel Escobar .12 .30
69 Joe Mauer .30 .75
70 Jeff Niemann .12 .30
71 Vernon Wells .12 .30
72 Miguel Tejada .20 .50
73 Denard Span .12 .30
74 Brandon Phillips .12 .30
75 Jason Bay .20 .50
76 Kendry Morales .12 .30
77 Josh Hamilton .30 .75
78 Yovani Gallardo .12 .30
79 Adam Lind .20 .50
80 Nick Johnson .12 .30
81 Coco Crisp .12 .30
82 Jeff Francoeur .20 .50
83 Hideki Matsui .30 .75
84 Will Venable .12 .30
85 Adrian Beltre .12 .30
86 Pablo Sandoval .20 .50
87 Mat Latos .12 .30
88 James Shields .12 .30
89 Roy Halladay UER 2.50 6.00
90 Chris Coghlan .12 .30
91 Colby Rasmus .30 .75
92 Alexei Ramirez .12 .30
93 Josh Beckett .20 .50
94 Kelly Shoppach .12 .30
95 Magglio Ordonez .20 .50
96 Matt Kemp .20 .50
97 Max Scherzer .12 .30
98 Curtis Granderson .20 .50
99 David Price .30 .75
100 Neftali Feliz .12 .30
101 Ian Stewart .12 .30
102 Ricky Romero .12 .30
103 Barry Zito .12 .30
104 Lance Berkman .20 .50
105 Andre Ethier .20 .50
106 Mark Teixeira .30 .75
107 Bengie Molina .12 .30
108 Edwin Jackson .12 .30
109 Akinori Iwamura .12 .30
110 Jermaine Dye .12 .30
111 Jair Jurrjens .12 .30
112 Stephen Drew .12 .30
113 Carlos Delgado .12 .30
114 Mark DeRosa .12 .30
115 Kurt Suzuki .12 .30
116 Javier Vazquez .12 .30
117 Lyle Overbay .12 .30
118 Orlando Hudson .12 .30
119 Adam Dunn .20 .50
120 Kevin Youkilis .20 .50
121 Ben Zobrist .12 .30
122 Chase Utley .30 .75
123 Jack Cust .12 .30
124 Gerald Laird .12 .30
125 Elvis Andrus .20 .50
126 Jason Kubel .12 .30
127 Scott Kazmir .12 .30
128 Ryan Doumit .12 .30
129 Brian McCann .20 .50
130 Jim Thome .20 .50
131 Alex Rios .20 .50
132 Jered Weaver .12 .30
133 Carlos Lee .12 .30
134 Mark Buehrle .20 .50
135 Chipper Jones .30 .75
136 Robinson Cano .30 .75
137 Mark Reynolds .12 .30
138 David Ortiz .20 .50
139 Carlos Gonzalez .20 .50
140 Torii Hunter .12 .30
141 Nick Markakis .30 .75
142 Jose Reyes .20 .50
143 Johnny Damon .20 .50
144 Roy Oswalt .20 .50
145 Alfonso Soriano .20 .50
146 Jimmy Rollins .20 .50
147 Matt Garza .12 .30
148 Michael Cuddyer .12 .30
149 Rick Ankiel .12 .30
150 Miguel Cabrera .30 .75
151 Mike Napoli .20 .50
152 Josh Willingham .12 .30
153 Chris Carpenter .30 .75
154 Paul Konerko .20 .50
155 Jake Peavy .12 .30
156 Nate McLouth .12 .30
157 Daisuke Matsuzaka .30 .75
158 Brad Hawpe .12 .30
159 Johan Santana .30 .75
160 Grady Sizemore .20 .50
161 Chad Billingsley .12 .30
162 Corey Hart .12 .30
163 A.J. Burnett .20 .50
164 Kosuke Fukudome .30 .75
165 Justin Verlander .40 1.00
166 Jayson Werth .20 .50
167 Matt Cain .20 .50
168 Carlos Pena .20 .50
169 Hunter Pence .20 .50
170 Russell Martin .12 .30
171 Carlos Quentin .20 .50
172 Jacoby Ellsbury .30 .75
173 Todd Helton .20 .50
174 Derek Jeter .75 2.00
175 Dan Haren .12 .30
176 Nelson Cruz .20 .50
177 Jose Lopez .12 .30
178 Carlos Zambrano .20 .50
179 Hanley Ramirez .30 .75
180 Aaron Hill .12 .30
181 Ubaldo Jimenez .20 .50
182 Brian Roberts .12 .30
183 Jon Lester .30 .75
184 Ryan Braun .40 1.00
185 Jay Bruce .20 .50
186 Aramis Ramirez .12 .30
187 Dustin Pedroia .40 1.00
188 Troy Tulowitzki .30 .75
189 Justin Morneau .30 .75
190 Jorge Cantu .12 .30
191 Scott Rolen .20 .50
192 B.J. Upton .20 .50
193 Yadier Molina .20 .50
194 Alex Rodriguez .50 1.25
195 Felix Hernandez .30 .75
196 Raul Ibanez .20 .50
197 Travis Snider .12 .30
198 Brandon Webb .20 .50
199 Ryan Howard .40 1.00
200 Michael Young .20 .50
201 Rajai Davis .12 .30
202 Ryan Zimmerman .20 .50
203 Carlos Beltran .12 .30
204 Evan Longoria .40 1.00
205 Dan Uggla .20 .50
206 Brandon Allen (RC) .20 .50
207 Buster Posey RC 3.00 8.00
208 Drew Stubbs RC .50 1.25
209 Madison Bumgarner RC .50 1.25
210 Reid Gorecki (RC) .30 .75
211 Wade Davis (RC) .20 .50
212 Neil Walker (RC) .30 .75
213 Ian Desmond (RC) .30 .75
214 Josh Thole RC .30 .75
215 Chris Pettit RC .20 .50
216 Daniel McCutchen RC .30 .75
217 Daniel Hudson RC .30 .75
218 Michael Brantley RC .20 .50
219 Tyler Flowers RC .30 .75
220 Checklist .12 .30

2010 Topps Opening Day Blue

*GOLD VET: 1.5X TO 4X BASIC
*GOLD RC: 1.2X TO 3X BASIC RC
STATED ODDS 1:5 HOBBY
STATED PRINT RUN 2010 SERIAL #'d SETS
207 Buster Posey 20.00 50.00

2010 Topps Opening Day Attax

COMPLETE SET (25) 10.00 25.00
STATED ODDS 1:6 HOBBY
ODTA1 Tim Lincecum 1.50 4.00
ODTA2 Ichiro Suzuki 1.50 4.00
ODTA3 Miguel Cabrera 1.00 2.50
ODTA4 Ryan Braun 1.25 3.00
ODTA5 Zack Greinke .60 1.50
ODTA6 Alex Rodriguez 1.50 4.00
ODTA7 Albert Pujols 2.50 6.00
ODTA8 Evan Longoria 1.25 3.00
ODTA9 Roy Halladay 1.00 2.50
ODTA10 Ryan Howard 1.25 3.00
ODTA11 Josh Beckett .60 1.50
ODTA12 Hanley Ramirez 1.00 2.50
ODTA13 Lance Berkman .60 1.50
ODTA14 Dan Haren .40 1.00
ODTA15 Joe Mauer 1.00 2.50
ODTA16 Adrian Gonzalez .60 1.50
ODTA17 Vladimir Guerrero 1.00 2.50
ODTA18 Felix Hernandez 1.00 2.50
ODTA19 Matt Kemp .60 1.50
ODTA20 Mariano Rivera 1.00 2.50
ODTA21 Grady Sizemore .60 1.50
ODTA22 Nick Markakis 1.00 2.50
ODTA23 CC Sabathia .60 1.50
ODTA24 Ian Kinsler .60 1.50
ODTA25 David Wright 1.25 3.00

2010 Topps Opening Day Autographs

STATED ODDS 1:746 HOBBY
AC Aaron Cunningham 4.00 10.00
CP Cliff Pennington 4.00 10.00
CV Chris Volstad 4.00 10.00
DS Denard Span 8.00 20.00
EV Eugenio Velez
GP Gerardo Parra 5.00 12.00
MT Matt Tolbert 8.00 20.00
RR Ricky Romero
DSC Daniel Schlereth 6.00 15.00

2010 Topps Opening Day Mascots

COMPLETE SET (25) 6.00 15.00
STATED ODDS 1:4 HOBBY
M1 Baxter the Bobcat .40 1.00
M2 Homer the Brave .40 1.00
M3 The Oriole Bird .40 1.00
M4 Wally the Green Monster .40 1.00
M5 Southpaw .40 1.00
M6 Gapper .40 1.00
M7 Slider .40 1.00
M8 Dinger .40 1.00
M9 Paws .40 1.00
M10 Billy the Marlin .40 1.00
M11 Junction Jack .40 1.00
M12 Sluggerrr .40 1.00
M13 Bernie Brewer .40 1.00
M14 TC the Bear .40 1.00
M15 Mr. Met .40 1.00
M16 Stomper .40 1.00
M17 Phillie Phanatic .40 1.00
M18 The Pirate Parrot .40 1.00
M19 The Swinging Friar .40 1.00
M20 Mariner Moose .40 1.00
M21 Fredbird .40 1.00
M22 Raymond .40 1.00
M23 Rangers Captain .40 1.00
M24 ACE .40 1.00
M25 Screech the Eagle .40 1.00

2010 Topps Opening Day Superstar Celebrations

COMPLETE SET (10) 4.00 10.00
STATED ODDS 1:9 HOBBY
SC1 Ryan Braun .75 2.00
SC2 Mark Buehrle .40 1.00
SC3 Alex Rodriguez 1.00 2.50
SC4 Ichiro Suzuki 1.00 2.50
SC5 Ryan Zimmerman .40 1.00
SC6 Colby Rasmus .60 1.50
SC7 Andre Ethier .40 1.00
SC8 Michael Young .40 1.00
SC9 Evan Longoria .75 2.00
SC10 Aramis Ramirez .25 .60

2010 Topps Opening Day Topps Town Stars

COMPLETE SET (25) 5.00 12.00
STATED ODDS 1:3 HOBBY
TTS1 Vladimir Guerrero .50 1.25
TTS2 Justin Upton .30 .75
TTS3 Chipper Jones .50 1.25
TTS4 Nick Markakis .50 1.25
TTS5 David Ortiz .30 .75
TTS6 Alfonso Soriano .30 .75
TTS7 Jake Peavy .20 .50
TTS8 Jay Bruce .30 .75
TTS9 Grady Sizemore .30 .75
TTS10 Troy Tulowitzki .50 1.25
TTS11 Miguel Cabrera .50 1.25
TTS12 Hanley Ramirez .50 1.25
TTS13 Hunter Pence .30 .75
TTS14 Zack Greinke .30 .75
TTS15 Manny Ramirez .50 1.25
TTS16 Prince Fielder .30 .75
TTS17 Joe Mauer .50 1.25
TTS18 David Wright .60 1.50
TTS19 Mark Teixeira .50 1.25
TTS20 Evan Longoria .60 1.50
TTS21 Ryan Howard .60 1.50
TTS22 Albert Pujols 1.25 3.00
TTS23 Adrian Gonzalez .30 .75
TTS24 Tim Lincecum .75 2.00
TTS25 Ichiro Suzuki .75 2.00

2010 Topps Opening Day Where'd You Go Bazooka Joe

COMPLETE SET (10) 5.00 12.00
WBJ1 David Wright .75 2.00
WBJ2 Ryan Howard .75 2.00
WBJ3 Miguel Cabrera .60 1.50
WBJ4 Albert Pujols 1.50 4.00
WBJ5 CC Sabathia .40 1.00
WBJ6 Prince Fielder .40 1.00
WBJ7 Evan Longoria .75 2.00
WBJ8 Chipper Jones .60 1.50
WBJ9 Grady Sizemore .40 1.00
WBJ10 Ian Kinsler .40 1.00

2011 Topps Opening Day

COMPLETE SET (220) 15.00 40.00
COMMON CARD (1-220) .12 .30
COMMON RC (1-220) .20 .50
OVERALL PLATE ODDS 1:2660
PLATE PRINT RUN 1 SET PER COLOR
BLACK-CYAN-MAGENTA-YELLOW ISSUED
NO PLATE PRICING DUE TO SCARCITY
1 Carlos Gonzalez .20 .50
2 Shin-Soo Choo .20 .50
3 Jon Lester .30 .75
4 Jason Kubel .12 .30
5 David Wright .40 1.00
6 Aramis Ramirez .12 .30
7 Mickey Mantle 1.00 2.50
8 Hanley Ramirez .30 .75
9 Michael Cuddyer .12 .30
10 Joey Votto .30 .75
11 Jaime Garcia .20 .50
12 Neil Walker .12 .30
13 Carl Crawford .20 .50
14 Ben Zobrist .12 .30
15 David Price .30 .75
16 Max Scherzer .12 .30
17 Ryan Dempster .12 .30
18 Justin Upton .20 .50
19 Carlos Marmol .20 .50
20 Mariano Rivera .30 .75
21 Martin Prado .12 .30
22 Hunter Pence .20 .50
23 Chris Johnson .12 .30
24 Andrew Cashner .12 .30
25 Johan Santana .30 .75
26 Gaby Sanchez .12 .30
27 Andrew McCutchen .30 .75
28 Edinson Volquez .12 .30
29 Jonathan Papelbon .20 .50
30 Alex Rodriguez .50 1.25
31 Chris Sale RC .30 .75
32 James McDonald .12 .30
33 Kyle Drabek RC .30 .75
34 Jair Jurrjens .12 .30
35 Vladimir Guerrero .30 .75
36 Daniel Descalso RC .20 .50
37 Tim Hudson .20 .50
38 Mike Stanton .20 .50
39 Kurt Suzuki .12 .30
40 CC Sabathia .20 .50
41 Aubrey Huff .12 .30
42 Greg Halman RC .30 .75
43 Jered Weaver .12 .30
44 Omar Infante .12 .30
45 Desmond Jennings RC .50 1.25
46 Yadier Molina .20 .50
47 Phil Hughes .12 .30
48 Paul Konerko .20 .50

49 Yonder Alonso RC	.30	.75
50 Albert Pujols	.75	2.00
51 Ben Revere RC	.30	.75
52 Placido Polanco	.12	.30
53 Bronson Arroyo	.12	.30
54 Ian Stewart	.12	.30
55 Cliff Lee	.30	.75
56 Brian Bogusevic (RC)	.20	.50
57 Zack Greinke	.20	.50
58 Howie Kendrick	.12	.30
59 Russell Martin	.12	.30
60 Aroldis Chapman RC	.60	1.50
61 Jason Bay	.20	.50
62 Mat Latos	.12	.30
63 Manny Ramirez	.30	.75
64 Miguel Tejada	.20	.50
65 Mike Stanton	.20	.50
66 Brett Anderson	.20	.50
67 Johnny Cueto	.12	.30
68 Jeremy Jeffress RC	.12	.30
69 Lance Berkman	.20	.50
70 Freddie Freeman RC	.75	2.00
71 Jon Niese	.12	.30
72 Ricky Romero	.12	.30
73 David Aardsma	.12	.30
74 Fausto Carmona	.12	.30
75 Buster Posey	.40	1.00
76 Chris Perez	.12	.30
77 Koji Uehara	.12	.30
78 Garrett Jones	.12	.30
79 Heath Bell	.20	.50
80 Jeremy Hellickson RC	.60	1.50
81 Jay Bruce	.20	.50
82 Brennan Boesch	.20	.50
83 Daniel Hudson	.12	.30
84 Brian Matusz	.30	.75
85 Carlos Santana	.30	.75
86 Stephen Strasburg	.60	1.50
87 Brandon Morrow	.12	.30
88 Carl Pavano	.12	.30
89 Pablo Sandoval	.20	.50
90 Chase Utley	.30	.75
91 Andres Torres	.12	.30
92 Nick Markakis	.30	.75
93 Aaron Hill	.12	.30
94 Jimmy Rollins	.20	.50
95 Josh Johnson	.20	.50
96 James Shields	.12	.30
97 Mike Napoli	.20	.50
98 Angel Pagan	.12	.30
99 Clay Buchholz	.20	.50
100 Miguel Cabrera	.30	.75
101 Brian Wilson	.30	.75
102 Carlos Ruiz	.12	.30
103 Jose Bautista	.20	.50
104 Victor Martinez	.20	.50
105 Roy Oswalt	.20	.50
106 Todd Helton	.20	.50
107 Scott Rolen	.20	.50
108 Jonathan Sanchez	.12	.30
109 Mark Buehrle	.20	.50
110 Ichiro Suzuki	.50	1.25
111 Nelson Cruz	.20	.50
112 Andre Ethier	.20	.50
113 Wandy Rodriguez	.12	.30
114 Ervin Santana	.12	.30
115 Starlin Castro	.30	.75
116 Torii Hunter	.12	.30
117 Tyler Colvin	.20	.50
118 Rafael Soriano	.12	.30
119 Alexei Ramirez	.12	.30
120 Roy Halladay	.30	.75
121 John Danks	.12	.30
122 Rickie Weeks	.20	.50
123 Stephen Drew	.12	.30
124 Clayton Kershaw	.30	.75
125 Adam Dunn	.20	.50
126 Brian Duensing	.12	.30
127 Nick Swisher	.30	.75
128 Andrew Bailey	.12	.30
129 Ike Davis	.20	.50
130 Justin Morneau	.30	.75
131 Chris Carpenter	.30	.75
132 Miguel Montero	.12	.30
133 Alex Rios	.20	.50
134 Ian Desmond	.20	.50
135 David Ortiz	.20	.50
136 Gaby Sanchez	.12	.30
137 Joel Pineiro	.12	.30
138 Chris Young	.12	.30
139 Michael Young	.20	.50
140 Derek Jeter	.75	2.00
141 Brent Morel RC	.20	.50
142 C.J. Wilson	.12	.30
143 Jeremy Guthrie	.12	.30
144 Brett Gardner	.12	.30
145 Ubaldo Jimenez	.20	.50
146 Gavin Floyd	.12	.30
147 Josh Hamilton	.30	.75
148 Kevin Youkilis	.20	.50
149 Tommy Hanson	.20	.50
150 Matt Cain	.20	.50
151 Adam Wainwright	.20	.50
152 Mark Reynolds	.12	.30
153 Kendry Morales	.12	.30
154 Dan Haren	.12	.30
155 Cole Hamels	.30	.75
156 Ryan Zimmerman	.20	.50
157 Adam Lind	.20	.50
158 Brian McCann	.20	.50
159 Dan Uggla	.20	.50
160 Carlos Lee	.12	.30
161 Jose Tabata	.20	.50
162 Gordon Beckham	.20	.50
163 Chad Billingsley	.12	.30
164 Grady Sizemore	.20	.50
165 Carlos Zambrano	.20	.50
166 Ian Kinsler	.20	.50
167 Geovany Soto	.20	.50
168 Tim Lincecum	.30	.75
169 Felix Hernandez	.30	.75
170 Logan Morrison	.12	.30
171 Yovani Gallardo	.12	.30
172 Jorge Posada	.20	.50
173 Joakim Soria	.12	.30
174 Buster Posey	.40	1.00
175 Adam Jones	.20	.50
176 Jason Heyward	.40	1.00
177 Magglio Ordonez	.20	.50
178 Joe Mauer	.30	.75
179 Prince Fielder	.20	.50
180 Colby Rasmus	.30	.75
181 Josh Beckett	.20	.50
182 Troy Tulowitzki	.30	.75
183 Jacoby Ellsbury	.30	.75
184 Austin Jackson	.12	.30
185 Billy Butler	.12	.30
186 Evan Longoria	.40	1.00
187 Brandon Phillips	.12	.30
188 Justin Verlander	.40	1.00
189 B.J. Upton	.20	.50
190 Elvis Andrus	.20	.50
191 Corey Hart	.12	.30
192 Dustin Pedroia	.40	1.00
193 Trevor Cahill	.12	.30
194 Delmon Young	.20	.50
195 Shaun Marcum	.12	.30
196 Brian Roberts	.12	.30
197 Kelly Johnson	.12	.30
198 Adrian Gonzalez	.20	.50
199 Francisco Liriano	.12	.30
200 Robinson Cano	.30	.75
201 Madison Bumgarner	.12	.30
202 Mike Leake	.20	.50
203 Neftali Feliz	.12	.30
204 Carlos Beltran	.12	.30
205 Carlos Quentin	.12	.30
206 Rafael Furcal	.12	.30
207 Kosuke Fukudome	.30	.75
208 Matt Kemp	.20	.50
209 Shane Victorino	.20	.50
210 Drew Stubbs	.20	.50
211 Ricky Nolasco	.12	.30
212 Vernon Wells	.12	.30
213 Matt Holliday	.30	.75
214 Bobby Abreu	.12	.30
215 Mark Teixeira	.30	.75
216 Jose Reyes	.20	.50
217 Andy Pettitte	.20	.50
218 Ryan Howard	.40	1.00
219 Matt Garza	.12	.30
220 Alfonso Soriano	.20	.50

2011 Topps Opening Day Blue

*BLUE VET: 3X TO 8X BASIC
*BLUE RC: 1.5X TO 4X BASIC RC
STATED ODDS 1:5
STATED PRINT RUN 2011 SER.#'d SETS

2011 Topps Opening Day Autographs

STATED ODDS 1:480

CC Chris Carter	10.00	25.00
CM Casey McGehee	6.00	15.00
DM Dustin Moseley	10.00	25.00
HK Howie Kendrick	8.00	20.00
JG Justin Germano	8.00	20.00
JM Jose Mijares	8.00	20.00
PH Philip Humber	6.00	15.00
TB Taylor Buchholz	4.00	10.00
JMO Jose Morales	6.00	15.00
JVE Jonathan Van Every	8.00	20.00

2011 Topps Opening Day Mascots

COMPLETE SET (25)	12.50	30.00
STATED ODDS 1:4		
M1 Arizona Diamondbacks	.60	1.50
M2 Atlanta Braves	.60	1.50
M3 Baltimore Orioles	.60	1.50
M4 Wally the Green Monster	.60	1.50
M5 Chicago White Sox	.60	1.50
M6 Gapper	.60	1.50
M7 Slider	.60	1.50
M8 Dinger	.60	1.50
M9 Paws	.60	1.50
M10 Billy the Marlin	.60	1.50
M11 Junction Jack	.60	1.50
M12 Kansas City Royals	.60	1.50
M13 Bernie Brewer	.60	1.50
M14 TC	.60	1.50
M15 Mr. Met	.60	1.50
M16 Oakland Athletics	.60	1.50
M17 Phillie Phanatic	.60	1.50
M18 Pirate Parrot	.60	1.50
M19 Swinging Friar	.60	1.50
M20 Mariner Moose	.60	1.50
M21 Fredbird	.60	1.50
M22 Raymond	.60	1.50
M23 Rangers Captain	.60	1.50
M24 Toronto Blue Jays	.60	1.50
M25 Screech	.60	1.50

2011 Topps Opening Day Presidential First Pitch

COMPLETE SET (10)	4.00	10.00
STATED ODDS 1:6		
PFP1 Barack Obama	1.00	2.50
PFP2 Harry Truman	.40	1.00
PFP3 Calvin Coolidge	.40	1.00
PFP4 Ronald Reagan	.75	2.00
PFP5 Richard Nixon	.40	1.00
PFP6 Woodrow Wilson	.40	1.00
PFP7 George W. Bush	.75	2.00
PFP8 George W. Bush	.75	2.00
PFP9 John F. Kennedy	.75	2.00
PFP10 Barack Obama	1.00	2.50

2011 Topps Opening Day Spot the Error

COMPLETE SET (10)	4.00	10.00
STATED ODDS 1:6		
1 Mark Teixeira	.50	1.25
2 Jason Heyward	.60	1.50
3 Jose Bautista	.30	.75
4 Chase Utley	.50	1.25
5 David Ortiz	.30	.75
6 Ubaldo Jimenez	.30	.75
7 David Wright	.60	1.50
8 Hanley Ramirez	.50	1.25
9 Buster Posey	.60	1.50
10 Derek Jeter	1.25	3.00

2011 Topps Opening Day Stadium Lights

COMPLETE SET (10)	4.00	10.00
STATED ODDS 1:9		
UL1 Joe Mauer	.60	1.50
UL2 Troy Tulowitzki	.60	1.50
UL3 Robinson Cano	.60	1.50
UL4 Alex Rodriguez	1.00	2.50
UL5 Miguel Cabrera	.60	1.50
UL6 Chase Utley	.60	1.50
UL7 Pedro Alvarez	.40	1.00
UL8 Adrian Gonzalez	.40	1.00
UL9 Jason Heyward	.75	2.00
UL10 Ryan Braun	.75	2.00

2011 Topps Opening Day Stars

COMPLETE SET (10)	5.00	12.00
STATED ODDS 1:12		
ODS1 Roy Halladay	.60	1.50
ODS2 Carlos Gonzalez	.40	1.00
ODS3 Alex Rodriguez	1.00	2.50
ODS4 Josh Hamilton	.60	1.50
ODS5 Miguel Cabrera	.60	1.50
ODS6 CC Sabathia	.40	1.00
ODS7 Joe Mauer	.60	1.50
ODS8 Joey Votto	.60	1.50
ODS9 David Price	.60	1.50
ODS10 Albert Pujols	1.50	4.00

2011 Topps Opening Day Superstar Celebrations

COMPLETE SET (25)	5.00	12.00
STATED ODDS 1:4		
SC1 Jason Heyward	.50	1.25
SC2 Buster Posey	.50	1.25
SC3 David Ortiz	.25	.60
SC4 Jay Bruce	.25	.60
SC5 Ubaldo Jimenez	.25	.60
SC6 Evan Longoria	.50	1.25
SC7 Jim Thome	.25	.60
SC8 Vladimir Guerrero	.40	1.00
SC9 Nick Markakis	.40	1.00
SC10 Carlos Pena	.25	.60
SC11 Jimmy Rollins	.25	.60
SC12 Matt Garza	.15	.40
SC13 Albert Pujols	1.00	2.50
SC14 David Wright	.50	1.25
SC15 Alex Rodriguez	.60	1.50
SC16 Jose Reyes	.25	.60
SC17 Prince Fielder	.25	.60
SC18 Derek Jeter	1.00	2.50
SC19 Bobby Abreu	.15	.40
SC20 Ichiro Suzuki	.60	1.50
SC21 Matt Holliday	.50	1.25
SC22 Cliff Lee	.40	1.00
SC23 Ryan Braun	.50	1.25
SC24 Troy Tulowitzki	.40	1.00
SC25 Matt Kemp	.25	.60

2011 Topps Opening Day Topps Town Codes

COMPLETE SET (25)	8.00	20.00
TTOD1 Clayton Kershaw	.60	1.50
TTOD2 Hunter Pence	.40	1.00
TTOD3 Trevor Cahill	.25	.60
TTOD4 Jose Bautista	.40	1.00
TTOD5 Jon Lester	.60	1.50
TTOD6 Matt Holliday	.60	1.50
TTOD7 Carlos Marmol	.40	1.00
TTOD8 Justin Upton	.40	1.00
TTOD9 Jered Weaver	.25	.60
TTOD10 Tim Lincecum	.60	1.50
TTOD11 Logan Morrison	.25	.60
TTOD12 Ike Davis	.40	1.00
TTOD13 Ian Desmond	.40	1.00
TTOD14 Brian Matusz	.60	1.50
TTOD15 Justin Morneau	.60	1.50
TTOD16 Jose Tabata	.40	1.00
TTOD17 Ian Kinsler	.40	1.00
TTOD18 Desmond Jennings	.60	1.50
TTOD19 Martin Prado	.25	.60
TTOD20 Alex Rodriguez	1.00	2.50
TTOD21 Austin Jackson	.25	.60
TTOD22 Carlos Ruiz	.25	.60
TTOD23 Gordon Beckham	.40	1.00
TTOD24 Jay Bruce	.40	1.00
TTOD25 Derek Jeter	1.50	4.00

2004 Topps Originals Signature

This 1179-card set was released in July, 2004. The set was released in one-card packs with an $50 SRP which came six packs to a box and 4 boxes to a case. All of the cards used in the set were original Topps cards which Topps bought back and the players signed. All of the players signed one copy of each of their rookie cards.

ONE AUTO PER PACK
PRINT RUNS B/WN 1-339 COPIES PER
NO PRICING ON QTY OF 14 OR LESS

AD1 Andre Dawson 77/1		
AD2 Andre Dawson 79/3		
AD3 Andre Dawson 80/27	15.00	40.00
AD4 Andre Dawson 81/37	10.00	25.00
AD5 Andre Dawson 82/55	10.00	25.00
AD6 Andre Dawson 83/47	10.00	25.00
AD7 Andre Dawson 84/25	15.00	40.00
AD8 Andre Dawson 85/22	15.00	40.00
AD9 Andre Dawson 86/24	15.00	40.00
AD10 Andre Dawson 88/9		
AH1 Al Hrabosky 71/1		
AH2 Al Hrabosky 74/2		
AH3 Al Hrabosky 75/1		
AH4 Al Hrabosky 76/5		
AH5 Al Hrabosky 77/5		
AH6 Al Hrabosky 78/20	12.50	30.00
AH7 Al Hrabosky 79/40	10.00	25.00
AH8 Al Hrabosky 80/61	10.00	25.00
AH9 Al Hrabosky 81/38	6.00	15.00
AH10 Al Hrabosky 82/62	6.00	15.00
AH11 Al Hrabosky 89 Sr./20	10.00	25.00
AK1 Al Kaline 54/1		
AK2 Al Kaline 59/1		
AK3 Al Kaline 60/1		
AK4 Al Kaline 60 AS/1		
AK5 Al Kaline 61/3		
AK6 Al Kaline 62/3		
AK7 Al Kaline 62 AS/2		
AK8 Al Kaline 64/4		
AK9 Al Kaline 66/1		
AK10 Al Kaline 67/18	60.00	120.00
AK11 Al Kaline 68/6		
AK12 Al Kaline 69/7		
AK13 Al Kaline 70/3		
AK14 Al Kaline 71/7		
AK15 Al Kaline 72/11		
AK16 Al Kaline 73/25	50.00	100.00
AK17 Al Kaline 74/11		
AK18 Al Kaline 75 HL/1		
AO1 Al Oliver 69/1		
AO2 Al Oliver 74/2		
AO3 Al Oliver 75/2		
AO4 Al Oliver 76/2		
AO5 Al Oliver 78/3		
AO6 Al Oliver 79/42	10.00	25.00
AO7 Al Oliver 80/6		
AO8 Al Oliver 81/54	6.00	15.00
AO9 Al Oliver 82/45	6.00	15.00
AO10 Al Oliver 83/50	6.00	15.00
AO11 Al Oliver 84/51	6.00	15.00
AO12 Al Oliver 85/46	6.00	15.00
AO13 Al Oliver 86/44	6.00	15.00
AT1 Alan Trammell 79/12		
AT2 Alan Trammell 80/17	20.00	50.00
AT3 Alan Trammell 81/26	12.50	30.00
AT4 Alan Trammell 82/40	10.00	25.00
AT5 Alan Trammell 83/21	15.00	40.00
AT6 Alan Trammell 84/57	10.00	25.00
AT7 Alan Trammell 85/39	10.00	25.00
AT8 Alan Trammell 86/23	15.00	40.00
AT9 Alan Trammell 87/15	15.00	40.00
AV1 Andy Van Slyke 84/1		
AV2 Andy Van Slyke 85/35	20.00	50.00
AV3 Andy Van Slyke 86/37	15.00	40.00
AV4 Andy Van Slyke 87/178	10.00	25.00
AV5 Andy Van Slyke 87 TR/130	10.00	25.00
BB1 Buddy Bell 73/1		
BB2 Buddy Bell 75/1		
BB3 Buddy Bell 76/1		
BB4 Buddy Bell 78/3		
BB5 Buddy Bell 79/135	6.00	15.00
BB6 Buddy Bell 80/10		
BB7 Buddy Bell 81/11		
BB8 Buddy Bell 82/34	8.00	20.00
BB9 Buddy Bell 83/83	4.00	10.00
BB10 Buddy Bell 84/22	10.00	25.00
BB11 Buddy Bell 85/13		
BB12 Buddy Bell 86/32	8.00	20.00
BBL1 Bert Blyleven 71/1		
BBL2 Bert Blyleven 75/1		
BBL3 Bert Blyleven 76/4		
BBL4 Bert Blyleven 79/45	15.00	40.00
BBL5 Bert Blyleven 80/12		
BBL6 Bert Blyleven 81/29	12.50	30.00
BBL7 Bert Blyleven 82 NNO/51	15.00	40.00
BBL8 Bert Blyleven 83/41	10.00	25.00
BBL9 Bert Blyleven 84/10		
BBL10 Bert Blyleven 85/40	10.00	25.00
BBL11 Bert Blyleven 86/62	10.00	25.00
BBL12 Bert Blyleven 87/54	10.00	25.00
BC1 Bert Campaneris 65/1		
BC2 Bert Campaneris 72/5		
BC3 Bert Campaneris 74/1		
BC4 Bert Campaneris 78/2		
BC5 Bert Campaneris 79/107	6.00	15.00
BC6 Bert Campaneris 80/6		
BC7 Bert Campaneris 84/28	8.00	20.00
BD1 Bucky Dent 74/1		
BD2 Bucky Dent 78/1		
BD3 Bucky Dent 79/14		
BD4 Bucky Dent 80/9		
BD5 Bucky Dent 81/16	15.00	40.00
BD6 Bucky Dent 82/49	10.00	25.00
BD7 Bucky Dent 83/92	4.00	10.00
BD8 Bucky Dent 84/63	6.00	15.00
BD9 Bucky Dent 90 MG/10		
BG1 Bob Grich 71/1		
BG2 Bob Grich 79/29	10.00	25.00
BG3 Bob Grich 80/70	6.00	15.00
BG4 Bob Grich 81/14		
BG5 Bob Grich 82/45	6.00	15.00
BG6 Bob Grich 83/85	4.00	10.00
BG7 Bob Grich 84/57	6.00	15.00
BG8 Bob Grich 85/36	6.00	15.00
BG9 Bob Grich 86/13		
BH1 Bob Horner 79/1		
BH2 Bob Horner 80/14		
BH3 Bob Horner 81/11		
BH4 Bob Horner 82/21	15.00	40.00
BH5 Bob Horner 83/69	6.00	15.00
BH6 Bob Horner 84/63	10.00	25.00
BH7 Bob Horner 85/15	15.00	40.00
BH8 Bob Horner 86/118	6.00	15.00
BH9 Bob Horner 87/38	10.00	25.00
BJ1 Bo Jackson 86 TR/1		
BJ2 Bo Jackson 87/100	30.00	60.00
BJA1 Brook Jacoby 85/1		
BJA2 Brook Jacoby 86/133	4.00	10.00
BJA3 Brook Jacoby 87/191	4.00	10.00
BJA4 Brook Jacoby 88/9		
BM1 Bill Madlock 74/1		
BM2 Bill Madlock 75/7		
BM3 Bill Madlock 76/4		
BM4 Bill Madlock 79/6		
BM5 Bill Madlock 80/11		
BM6 Bill Madlock 81/11		
BM7 Bill Madlock 82/26	8.00	20.00
BM8 Bill Madlock 83/55	6.00	15.00
BM9 Bill Madlock 84/69	4.00	10.00
BM10 Bill Madlock 85/60	6.00	15.00
BM11 Bill Madlock 86/63	6.00	15.00
BM12 Bill Madlock 87/42	6.00	15.00
BP1 Boog Powell 62/1		
BP2 Boog Powell 64/4		
BP3 Boog Powell 65/7		
BP4 Boog Powell 66/4		
BP5 Boog Powell 67/3		
BP6 Boog Powell 69/5		
BP7 Boog Powell 70/6		
BP8 Boog Powell 72/13		
BP9 Boog Powell 73/17	20.00	50.00
BP10 Boog Powell 74/7		
BP11 Boog Powell 75/19	20.00	50.00
BP12 Boog Powell 76/6		
BP13 Boog Powell 77/15	20.00	50.00
BR1 Brooks Robinson 57/1		
BR2 Brooks Robinson 59/1		
BR3 Brooks Robinson 60/2		
BR4 Brooks Robinson 61/1		
BR5 Brooks Robinson 69/6		
BR6 Brooks Robinson 69 AS/2		
BR7 Brooks Robinson 70/8		
BR8 Brooks Robinson 70 AS/3		
BR9 Brooks Robinson 72/6		
BR10 Brooks Robinson 73/14		
BR11 Brooks Robinson 74/20	50.00	100.00
BR12 Brooks Robinson 75/10		
BR13 Brooks Robinson 76/17	50.00	100.00
BR14 Brooks Robinson 77/13		
BS1 Bret Saberhagen 85/1		
BS2 Bret Saberhagen 86/23	15.00	40.00
BS3 Bret Saberhagen 87/230	6.00	15.00
BSU1 Bruce Sutter 77/1		
BSU2 Bruce Sutter 78/5		
BSU3 Bruce Sutter 79/8		
BSU4 Bruce Sutter 80/9		
BSU5 Bruce Sutter 81/11		
BSU6 Bruce Sutter 82/111	10.00	25.00
BSU7 Bruce Sutter 83/45	15.00	40.00
BSU8 Bruce Sutter 84/24	30.00	60.00
BSU9 Bruce Sutter 85/19	30.00	60.00
BSU10 Bruce Sutter 86/78	10.00	25.00
BSU11 Bruce Sutter 87/36	15.00	40.00
BU1 Bill Buckner 70/1		
BU2 Bill Buckner 74/5		
BU3 Bill Buckner 75/1		
BU4 Bill Buckner 76/1		
BU5 Bill Buckner 78/1		
BU6 Bill Buckner 79/11		
BU7 Bill Buckner 80/8		
BU8 Bill Buckner 81/39	10.00	25.00
BU9 Bill Buckner 82/38	10.00	25.00
BU10 Bill Buckner 83/47	10.00	25.00
BU11 Bill Buckner 84/31	12.50	30.00
BU12 Bill Buckner 84 TR/24	15.00	40.00
BU13 Bill Buckner 85/80	6.00	15.00
BU14 Bill Buckner 86/63	10.00	25.00
BW1 Bob Watson 69/1		
BW2 Bob Watson 74/1		
BW3 Bob Watson 79/77	6.00	15.00
BW4 Bob Watson 80/8		
BW5 Bob Watson 81/16	10.00	25.00
BW6 Bob Watson 82/23	10.00	25.00
BW7 Bob Watson 83/93	4.00	10.00
BW8 Bob Watson 84/64	6.00	15.00
BW9 Bob Watson 85/68	4.00	10.00
CF1 Cecil Fielder 86/1		
CF2 Cecil Fielder 87/208	6.00	15.00
CF3 Cecil Fielder 88/26	12.50	30.00
CF4 Cecil Fielder 89/16	15.00	40.00
CFI1 Carlton Fisk 72/1		
CFI2 Carlton Fisk 78/3		
CFI3 Carlton Fisk 79/24	40.00	80.00
CFI4 Carlton Fisk 80/32	30.00	60.00
CFI5 Carlton Fisk 81/15		
CFI6 Carlton Fisk 82/30	20.00	50.00
CG1 Cesar Geronimo 71/1		
CG2 Cesar Geronimo 74/1		
CG3 Cesar Geronimo 79/28	10.00	25.00
CG4 Cesar Geronimo 80/11		
CG5 Cesar Geronimo 81/21	10.00	25.00
CG6 Cesar Geronimo 82/52	6.00	15.00
CG7 Cesar Geronimo 83/67	4.00	10.00
CG8 Cesar Geronimo 84/70	4.00	10.00
CH1 Charlie Hough 72/1		
CH2 Charlie Hough 83/19	10.00	25.00
CH3 Charlie Hough 84/50	6.00	15.00
CH4 Charlie Hough 85/57	6.00	15.00
CH5 Charlie Hough 86/66	4.00	10.00
CH6 Charlie Hough 87/46	6.00	15.00
CH7 Charlie Hough 88/19	10.00	25.00
CH8 Charlie Hough 91 TR/70	4.00	10.00
CH9 Charlie Hough 92/25	10.00	25.00
CH10 Charlie Hough 94/8		
CL1 Carney Lansford 79/1		
CL2 Carney Lansford 80/12		
CL3 Carney Lansford 81/184	4.00	10.00
CL4 Carney Lansford 82/6		
CL5 Carney Lansford 83/40	6.00	15.00
CL6 Carney Lansford 85/35	8.00	20.00
CL7 Carney Lansford 86/76	4.00	10.00
CLE1 Chet Lemon 76/1		
CLE2 Chet Lemon 78/3		
CLE3 Chet Lemon 79/24	12.50	30.00
CLE4 Chet Lemon 80/16	12.50	30.00
CLE5 Chet Lemon 81/12		
CLE6 Chet Lemon 82/23	10.00	25.00
CLE7 Chet Lemon 83/35	8.00	20.00
CLE8 Chet Lemon 84/42	6.00	15.00
CLE9 Chet Lemon 85/32	8.00	20.00
CLE10 Chet Lemon 86/136	4.00	10.00
CLE11 Chet Lemon 87/27	8.00	20.00
CR1 Cal Ripken 82/1		
CR2 Cal Ripken 84/10		
CR3 Cal Ripken 85/15		
CR4 Cal Ripken 86/74	60.00	120.00
CS1 Cory Snyder 85 OLY/1		
CS2 Cory Snyder 87/291	4.00	10.00
CS3 Cory Snyder 91/39	6.00	15.00
CS4 Cory Snyder 91 TR/8		
CS5 Cory Snyder 93/8		
CS6 Cory Snyder 93 Gold/8		
CS7 Cory Snyder 94/10		
CY1 Carl Yastrzemski 60/1		
CY2 Carl Yastrzemski 78/3		
CY3 Carl Yastrzemski 79/2		
CY4 Carl Yastrzemski 80/60	50.00	100.00
CY5 Carl Yastrzemski 81/35	60.00	120.00
DC1 Dave Concepcion 71/1		
DC2 Dave Concepcion 75/2		
DC3 Dave Concepcion 76/1		
DC4 Dave Concepcion 78/3		
DC5 Dave Concepcion 79/3		
DC6 Dave Concepcion 80/21	20.00	50.00
DC7 Dave Concepcion 81/8		
DC8 Dave Concepcion 82/43	10.00	25.00
DC9 Dave Concepcion 83/34	12.50	30.00
DC10 Dave Concepcion 84/24	15.00	40.00
DC11 Dave Concepcion 85/41	10.00	25.00
DC12 Dave Concepcion 86/69	6.00	15.00
DD1 Darren Daulton 86/1		
DD2 Darren Daulton 87/269	4.00	10.00
DD3 Darren Daulton 90/8		
DD4 Darren Daulton 92/32	8.00	20.00
DD5 Darren Daulton 94/17	10.00	25.00
DD6 Darren Daulton 96/22	10.00	25.00
DDE1 Doug DeCinces 75/1		
DDE2 Doug DeCinces 79/38	10.00	25.00
DDE3 Doug DeCinces 80/24	12.50	30.00
DDE4 Doug DeCinces 81/24	10.00	25.00
DDE5 Doug DeCinces 82/42	6.00	15.00
DDE6 Doug DeCinces 83/75	4.00	10.00
DDE7 Doug DeCinces 84/19	10.00	25.00
DDE8 Doug DeCinces 85/54	6.00	15.00
DDE9 Doug DeCinces 86/74	4.00	10.00
DE1 Dennis Eckersley 76/1		
DE2 Dennis Eckersley 78/10		
DE3 Dennis Eckersley 79/44	30.00	60.00
DE4 Dennis Eckersley 80/40	30.00	60.00
DE5 Dennis Eckersley 81/9		
DEV1 Darrell Evans 70/1		
DEV2 Darrell Evans 74/5		
DEV3 Darrell Evans 75/3		
DEV4 Darrell Evans 78/2		
DEV5 Darrell Evans 79/19	12.50	30.00
DEV6 Darrell Evans 80/5		
DEV7 Darrell Evans 81/15	10.00	25.00
DEV8 Darrell Evans 82/25	10.00	25.00
DEV9 Darrell Evans 83/63	6.00	15.00
DEV10 Darrell Evans 84/81	4.00	10.00
DEV11 Darrell Evans 85/48	6.00	15.00
DEV12 Darrell Evans 86/82	4.00	10.00
DG1 Dwight Gooden 85/1		
DG2 Dwight Gooden 86/16	15.00	40.00
DG3 Dwight Gooden 87/52	10.00	25.00
DG4 Dwight Gooden 89/19	15.00	40.00
DJ1 David Justice 90 DB/69	6.00	15.00
DJ2 David Justice 90 TR/1		
DJ3 David Justice 93/32	12.50	30.00
DK1 Dave Kingman 72/1		
DK2 Dave Kingman 79/9		
DK3 Dave Kingman 80/8		
DK4 Dave Kingman 81/25	15.00	40.00
DK5 Dave Kingman 82/5		
DK6 Dave Kingman 83/32	12.50	30.00
DK7 Dave Kingman 86/25	15.00	40.00
DL1 Davey Lopes 73/1		
DL2 Davey Lopes 76/1		
DL3 Davey Lopes 78/1		
DL4 Davey Lopes 79/71	6.00	15.00
DL5 Davey Lopes 80/19	12.50	30.00
DL6 Davey Lopes 81/12		
DL7 Davey Lopes 82/17	10.00	25.00
DL8 Davey Lopes 83/65	6.00	15.00
DL9 Davey Lopes 84/15	10.00	25.00
DL10 Davey Lopes 85/24	10.00	25.00
DL11 Davey Lopes 86/40	6.00	15.00
DL12 Davey Lopes 01 MG/67	4.00	10.00
DL13 Davey Lopes 02 MG/19	10.00	25.00
DM1 Don Mattingly 84/1		
DM2 Don Mattingly 85/16		
DM3 Don Mattingly 87/84	50.00	100.00
DMU1 Dale Murphy 77/1		
DMU2 Dale Murphy 79/38	30.00	60.00
DMU3 Dale Murphy 80/11		
DMU4 Dale Murphy 82/1		
DMU5 Dale Murphy 83/10		
DMU6 Dale Murphy 84/29	20.00	50.00
DMU7 Dale Murphy 85/18	30.00	60.00
DMU8 Dale Murphy 86/25	30.00	60.00
DMU9 Dale Murphy 87/91	10.00	25.00
DMU10 Dale Murphy 88/11		
DMU11 Dale Murphy 89/14		
DP1 Dave Parker 74/1		
DP2 Dave Parker 75/2		
DP3 Dave Parker 79/6		
DP4 Dave Parker 80/9		
DP5 Dave Parker 81/19	15.00	40.00
DP6 Dave Parker 82/73	6.00	15.00
DP7 Dave Parker 83/30	12.50	30.00
DP8 Dave Parker 84/14		
DP9 Dave Parker 85/45	10.00	25.00
DP10 Dave Parker 86/29	12.50	30.00
DP11 Dave Parker 87/12		
DP12 Dave Parker 88/11		
DS1 Duke Snider 52/1		
DS2 Duke Snider 58/3		
DS3 Duke Snider 59/4		
DS4 Duke Snider 60/2		
DS5 Duke Snider 61/13		
DS6 Duke Snider 62/4		
DS7 Duke Snider 63/4		
DS8 Duke Snider 64/18	60.00	120.00
DSE1 Dave Stieb 80/1		
DSE2 Dave Stieb 81/21	15.00	40.00
DSE3 Dave Stieb 82/34	12.50	30.00
DSE4 Dave Stieb 83/70	6.00	15.00
DSE5 Dave Stieb 84/20	15.00	40.00
DSE6 Dave Stieb 85/55	10.00	25.00
DSE7 Dave Stieb 86/69	6.00	15.00
DSE8 Dave Stieb 87/75	6.00	15.00
DSE9 Dave Stieb 88/11		
DSR1 Darryl Strawberry 84/1		
DSR2 Darryl Strawberry 85/32	12.50	30.00
DSR3 Darryl Strawberry 86/24	15.00	40.00
DSR4 Darryl Strawberry 87/183	6.00	15.00
DSR5 Darryl Strawberry 87 AS/110	6.00	15.00
DSW1 Dave Stewart 82/1		
DSW2 Dave Stewart 83/41	6.00	15.00
DSW3 Dave Stewart 84/60	6.00	15.00
DSW4 Dave Stewart 85/24	10.00	25.00
DSW5 Dave Stewart 86/53	6.00	15.00
DSW6 Dave Stewart 87/171	4.00	10.00
EB1 Ernie Banks 54/1		
EB2 Ernie Banks 58 AS/1		
EB3 Ernie Banks 59/1		
EB4 Ernie Banks 59 AS/1		
EB5 Ernie Banks 60/2		
EB6 Ernie Banks 61/2		
EB7 Ernie Banks 61 MVP/7		
EB8 Ernie Banks 62/3		
EB9 Ernie Banks 64/5		
EB10 Ernie Banks 66/7		
EB11 Ernie Banks 67/4		
EB12 Ernie Banks 68/7		
EB13 Ernie Banks 69/7		
EB14 Ernie Banks 70/2		
ED1 Eric Davis 85/1		
ED2 Eric Davis 86/13		
ED3 Eric Davis 87/336	6.00	15.00
EW1 Earl Weaver 69 MG/1		
EW2 Earl Weaver 72 MG/1		
EW3 Earl Weaver 74 MG/1		
EW4 Earl Weaver 78 MG/52	10.00	25.00
EW5 Earl Weaver 83 MG/38	6.00	15.00
EW6 Earl Weaver 85 TR MG/12		
EW7 Earl Weaver 86 MG/107	4.00	10.00
EW8 Earl Weaver 87 MG/175	4.00	10.00
FJ1 Fergie Jenkins 66/1		
FJ2 Fergie Jenkins 68/2		
FJ3 Fergie Jenkins 70/1		
FJ4 Fergie Jenkins 71/1		
FJ5 Fergie Jenkins 72/4		
FJ6 Fergie Jenkins 76/10		
FJ7 Fergie Jenkins 77/11		
FJ8 Fergie Jenkins 78/17	20.00	50.00
FJ9 Fergie Jenkins 79/9		
FJ10 Fergie Jenkins 80/37	15.00	40.00
FJ11 Fergie Jenkins 81/32	12.50	30.00
FJ12 Fergie Jenkins 82/65	10.00	25.00
FJ13 Fergie Jenkins 83/22	15.00	40.00
FJ14 Fergie Jenkins 84/42	10.00	25.00
FR1 Frank Robinson 57/1		
FR2 Frank Robinson 63/1		
FR3 Frank Robinson 65/1		
FR4 Frank Robinson 69/4		
FR5 Frank Robinson 71/2		
FR6 Frank Robinson 72/16	40.00	80.00
FR7 Frank Robinson 73/4		
FR8 Frank Robinson 74/4		
FR9 Frank Robinson 75/1		
FR10 Frank Robinson 83 MG/13		
FR11 Frank Robinson 84 MG/3		
FV1 Frank Viola 83/1		
FV2 Frank Viola 84/1		
FV3 Frank Viola 85/25	15.00	40.00
FV4 Frank Viola 86/99	6.00	15.00
FV5 Frank Viola 87/209	6.00	15.00
FV6 Frank Viola 88/10		
GB1 George Bell 82/1		
GB2 George Bell 84/67	4.00	10.00
GB3 George Bell 85/32	8.00	20.00

GB4 George Bell 86/46	6.00	15.00
GB5 George Bell 87/204	4.00	10.00
GBR1 George Brett 75/1		
GBR2 George Brett 79/16		
GBR3 George Brett 80/9		
GBR4 George Brett 81/19	90.00	150.00
GBR5 George Brett 82/6		
GC1 Gary Carter 75/1		
GC2 Gary Carter 78/9		
GC3 Gary Carter 79/21	20.00	50.00
GC4 Gary Carter 80/24	20.00	50.00
GC5 Gary Carter 81/22	15.00	40.00
GC6 Gary Carter 82/12		
GC7 Gary Carter 83/2		
GC8 Gary Carter 84/9		
GF1 George Foster 71/1		
GF2 George Foster 74/5		
GF3 George Foster 75/3		
GF4 George Foster 76/1		
GF5 George Foster 78/3		
GF6 George Foster 79/20	12.50	30.00
GF7 George Foster 80/7		
GF8 George Foster 81/10		
GF9 George Foster 82/14		
GF10 George Foster 83/39	6.00	15.00
GF11 George Foster 84/112	4.00	10.00
GF12 George Foster 85/76	4.00	10.00
GF13 George Foster 86/64	6.00	15.00
GL1 Greg Luzinski 71/1		
GL2 Greg Luzinski 72/5		
GL3 Greg Luzinski 75/6		
GL4 Greg Luzinski 76/1		
GL5 Greg Luzinski 78/5		
GL6 Greg Luzinski 79/14		
GL7 Greg Luzinski 80/21	20.00	50.00
GL8 Greg Luzinski 81/11		
GL9 Greg Luzinski 82/34	12.50	30.00
GL10 Greg Luzinski 83/75	6.00	15.00
GL11 Greg Luzinski 84/85	6.00	15.00
GL12 Greg Luzinski 85/92	6.00	15.00
GM1 Gary Matthews Sr. 73/1		
GM2 Gary Matthews Sr. 82/10		
GM3 Gary Matthews Sr. 83/20	10.00	25.00
GM4 Gary Matthews Sr. 84/43	6.00	15.00
GM5 Gary Matthews Sr. 85/39	6.00	15.00
GM6 Gary Matthews Sr. 86/38	6.00	15.00
GM7 Gary Matthews Sr. 87/82	4.00	10.00
GM8 Gary Matthews Sr. 88/30	8.00	20.00
HA1 Hank Aaron 54/1		
HA2 Hank Aaron 58 AS/2		
HA3 Hank Aaron 59/1		
HA4 Hank Aaron 60 AS/1		
HA5 Hank Aaron 61/1		
HA6 Hank Aaron 61 MVP/1		
HA7 Hank Aaron 62 AS/1		
HA8 Hank Aaron 65/1		
HA9 Hank Aaron 68/1		
HA10 Hank Aaron 69/1		
HA11 Hank Aaron 70/6		
HA12 Hank Aaron 70 AS/3		
HA13 Hank Aaron 71/3		
HA14 Hank Aaron 72/2		
HA15 Hank Aaron 73/8		
HA16 Hank Aaron 75/5		
HA17 Hank Aaron 75 HL/1		
HA18 Hank Aaron 76/12		
HB1 Harold Baines 81/1		
HB2 Harold Baines 82/31	12.50	30.00
HB3 Harold Baines 83/19	15.00	40.00
HB4 Harold Baines 84/5		
HB5 Harold Baines 85/97	6.00	15.00
HB6 Harold Baines 86/93	6.00	15.00
HB7 Harold Baines 87/115	6.00	15.00
HK1 Harmon Killebrew 55/1		
HK2 Harmon Killebrew 60/1		
HK3 Harmon Killebrew 61/1		
HK4 Harmon Killebrew 62/2		
HK5 Harmon Killebrew 64/2		
HK6 Harmon Killebrew 66/2		
HK7 Harmon Killebrew 68/2		
HK8 Harmon Killebrew 68 AS/2		
HK9 Harmon Killebrew 69/5		
HK10 Harmon Killebrew 70/3		
HK11 Harmon Killebrew 71/3		
HK12 Harmon Killebrew 72/12		
HK13 Harmon Killebrew 73/4		
HK14 Harmon Killebrew 74/6		
HK15 Harmon Killebrew 75/9		
HR1 Harold Reynolds 86/1		
HR2 Harold Reynolds 87/255	6.00	15.00
JA1 Jim Abbott 88 TR/339	10.00	25.00
JA2 Jim Abbott 89/1		
JA3 Jim Abbott 90 DB/50	15.00	40.00
JB1 Jesse Barfield 82/1		
JB2 Jesse Barfield 83/45	6.00	15.00
JB3 Jesse Barfield 84/12		
JB4 Jesse Barfield 85/60	6.00	15.00
JB5 Jesse Barfield 86/37	6.00	15.00
JB6 Jesse Barfield 87/180	4.00	10.00
JB7 Jesse Barfield 88/10		
JBE1 Johnny Bench 68/1		
JBE2 Johnny Bench 79/14		
JBE3 Johnny Bench 80/10		
JBE4 Johnny Bench 81/8		
JBE5 Johnny Bench 82/16	40.00	80.00
JBE6 Johnny Bench 83/2		
JC1 John Candelaria 76/1		
JC2 John Candelaria 79/77	10.00	25.00
JC3 John Candelaria 80/8		
JC4 John Candelaria 81/19	15.00	40.00
JC5 John Candelaria 82/42	10.00	25.00
JC6 John Candelaria 83/77	6.00	15.00
JC7 John Candelaria 84/18	15.00	40.00
JC8 John Candelaria 85/61	10.00	25.00
JC9 John Candelaria 86/36	10.00	25.00
JC10 John Candelaria 87/13		
JCA1 Jose Canseco 86 TR/1		
JCA2 Jose Canseco 87/99	20.00	50.00
JCR1 Joe Carter 85/1		
JCR2 Joe Carter 86/24	30.00	60.00
JCR3 Joe Carter 87/23	30.00	60.00
JCR4 Joe Carter 90/2		
JCU1 Jose Cruz Sr. 72/1		
JCU2 Jose Cruz Sr. 74/2		
JCU3 Jose Cruz Sr. 76/1		
JCU4 Jose Cruz Sr. 78/5		
JCU5 Jose Cruz Sr. 79/7		
JCU6 Jose Cruz Sr. 80/14		
JCU7 Jose Cruz Sr. 81/14		
JCU8 Jose Cruz Sr. 82/28	8.00	20.00
JCU9 Jose Cruz Sr. 83/102	4.00	10.00
JCU10 Jose Cruz Sr. 84/67	4.00	10.00
JCU11 Jose Cruz Sr. 85/68	4.00	10.00
JCU12 Jose Cruz Sr. 86/31	8.00	20.00
JK1 Jimmy Key 85/1		
JK2 Jimmy Key 86/21	15.00	40.00
JK3 Jimmy Key 87/263	6.00	15.00
JK4 Jimmy Key 88/15	15.00	40.00
JK5 Jimmy Key 92/37	10.00	25.00
JK6 Jimmy Key 94/11		
JKR1 John Kruk 86 TR/1		
JKR2 John Kruk 87/214	10.00	25.00
JKR3 John Kruk 92/22	30.00	60.00
JKR4 John Kruk 93/13		
JL1 Jim Leyritz 90 TR/1		
JL2 Jim Leyritz 91/38	6.00	15.00
JL3 Jim Leyritz 93/49	6.00	15.00
JL4 Jim Leyritz 94/16	10.00	25.00
JL5 Jim Leyritz 95/14		
JL6 Jim Leyritz 97/62	6.00	15.00
JL7 Jim Leyritz 98/20	10.00	25.00
JL8 Jim Leyritz 99/124	4.00	10.00
JL9 Jim Leyritz 00/40	6.00	15.00
JM1 Jack McDowell 88 TR/1		
JM2 Jack McDowell 89/36	6.00	15.00
JM3 Jack McDowell 90 TR/61	6.00	15.00
JM4 Jack McDowell 91/33	8.00	20.00
JM5 Jack McDowell 92/38	6.00	15.00
JM6 Jack McDowell 93/27	8.00	20.00
JM7 Jack McDowell 94/3		
JM8 Jack McDowell 95/9		
JM9 Jack McDowell 96/15	10.00	25.00
JM10 Jack McDowell 97/27	8.00	20.00
JMO1 Joe Morgan 65/1		
JMO2 Joe Morgan 74/2		
JMO3 Joe Morgan 75/1		
JMO4 Joe Morgan 76/5		
JMO5 Joe Morgan 77/6		
JMO6 Joe Morgan 78/3		
JMO7 Joe Morgan 79/4		
JMO8 Joe Morgan 80/12		
JMO9 Joe Morgan 81/32	12.50	30.00
JMO10 Joe Morgan 82/18	15.00	40.00
JMO11 Joe Morgan 83/49	10.00	25.00
JMO12 Joe Morgan 83 TR/4		
JMO13 Joe Morgan 84/73	6.00	15.00
JMO14 Joe Morgan 85/40	10.00	25.00
JP1 Jim Palmer 66/1		
JP2 Jim Palmer 79/4		
JP3 Jim Palmer 80/33	15.00	40.00
JP4 Jim Palmer 81/23	15.00	40.00
JP5 Jim Palmer 82/24	15.00	40.00
JP6 Jim Palmer 83/7		
JP7 Jim Palmer 84/9		
JR1 Jim Rice 75/1		
JR2 Jim Rice 76/2		
JR3 Jim Rice 77/4		
JR4 Jim Rice 78/3		
JR5 Jim Rice 79/6		
JR6 Jim Rice 80/9		
JR7 Jim Rice 81/123	10.00	25.00
JR8 Jim Rice 82/24	15.00	40.00
JR9 Jim Rice 83/71	10.00	25.00
JR10 Jim Rice 84/12		
JRU1 Joe Rudi 69/1		
JRU2 Joe Rudi 72/2		
JRU3 Joe Rudi 73/9		
JRU4 Joe Rudi 74/6		
JRU5 Joe Rudi 75/7		
JRU6 Joe Rudi 76/4		
JRU7 Joe Rudi 77/7		
JRU8 Joe Rudi 78/14		
JRU9 Joe Rudi 79/24	12.50	30.00
JRU10 Joe Rudi 80/45	10.00	25.00
JRU11 Joe Rudi 82/26	8.00	20.00
JRU12 Joe Rudi 83/75	4.00	10.00
KB1 Kevin Bass 79/1		
KB2 Kevin Bass 84/71	4.00	10.00
KB3 Kevin Bass 85/30	8.00	20.00
KB4 Kevin Bass 86/44	6.00	15.00
KB5 Kevin Bass 87/74	4.00	10.00
KB6 Kevin Bass 90 TR/35	8.00	20.00
KG1 Ken Griffey Sr. 74/1		
KG2 Ken Griffey Sr. 75/2		
KG3 Ken Griffey Sr. 76/2		
KG4 Ken Griffey Sr. 79/3		
KG5 Ken Griffey Sr. 80/15	20.00	50.00
KG6 Ken Griffey Sr. 81/11		
KG7 Ken Griffey Sr. 82/18	15.00	40.00
KG8 Ken Griffey Sr. 83/70	6.00	15.00
KG9 Ken Griffey Sr. 84/64	10.00	25.00
KG10 Ken Griffey Sr. 85/32	12.50	30.00
KG11 Ken Griffey Sr. 86 TR/32	12.50	30.00
KGI1 Kirk Gibson 81/1		
KGI2 Kirk Gibson 82/35	12.50	30.00
KGI3 Kirk Gibson 83/35	12.50	30.00
KGI4 Kirk Gibson 84/5		
KGI5 Kirk Gibson 85/44	10.00	25.00
KGI6 Kirk Gibson 86/44	10.00	25.00
KGI7 Kirk Gibson 87/65	10.00	25.00
KGI8 Kirk Gibson 89/14		
KGI9 Kirk Gibson 90/12		
KGU1 Kelly Gruber 87/1		
KGU2 Kelly Gruber 88/77	4.00	10.00
KGU3 Kelly Gruber 89/44	6.00	15.00
KGU4 Kelly Gruber 90/86	4.00	10.00
KGU5 Kelly Gruber 91/52	6.00	15.00
KGU6 Kelly Gruber 92/55	6.00	15.00
KGU7 Kelly Gruber 93/26	8.00	20.00
KGU8 Kelly Gruber 93 Gold/9		
KH1 Keith Hernandez 75/1		
KH2 Keith Hernandez 79/8		
KH3 Keith Hernandez 80/38	15.00	40.00
KH4 Keith Hernandez 81/19	15.00	40.00
KH5 Keith Hernandez 82/156	6.00	15.00
KH6 Keith Hernandez 83/17	15.00	40.00
KH7 Keith Hernandez 84/4		
KH8 Keith Hernandez 86/7		
KS1 Kevin Seitzer 87 TR/1		
KS2 Kevin Seitzer 88/88	4.00	10.00
KS3 Kevin Seitzer 89/39	6.00	15.00
KS4 Kevin Seitzer 90/18	10.00	25.00
KS5 Kevin Seitzer 91/39	6.00	15.00
KS6 Kevin Seitzer 92/49	6.00	15.00
KS7 Kevin Seitzer 92 Gold/2		
KS8 Kevin Seitzer 92 TR/9		
KS9 Kevin Seitzer 93/38	6.00	15.00
KS10 Kevin Seitzer 94/22	10.00	25.00
KS11 Kevin Seitzer 95/16	10.00	25.00
KS12 Kevin Seitzer 96/9		
KS13 Kevin Seitzer 97/24	10.00	25.00
KT1 Kent Tekulve 76/1		
KT2 Kent Tekulve 78/2		
KT3 Kent Tekulve 79/14		
KT4 Kent Tekulve 80/6		
KT5 Kent Tekulve 81/17	15.00	40.00
KT6 Kent Tekulve 82/36	10.00	25.00
KT7 Kent Tekulve 83/52	10.00	25.00
KT8 Kent Tekulve 84/71	6.00	15.00
KT9 Kent Tekulve 85/43	10.00	25.00
KT10 Kent Tekulve 86/57	10.00	25.00
KT11 Kent Tekulve 87/32	12.50	30.00
KT12 Kent Tekulve 88/20	15.00	40.00
LA1 Luis Aparicio 56/1		
LA2 Luis Aparicio 60/1		
LA3 Luis Aparicio 61/3		
LA4 Luis Aparicio 62/2		
LA5 Luis Aparicio 63/3		
LA6 Luis Aparicio 66/3		
LA7 Luis Aparicio 67/2		
LA8 Luis Aparicio 68/14		
LA9 Luis Aparicio 69/49	15.00	40.00
LA10 Luis Aparicio 70/2		
LA11 Luis Aparicio 71/1		
LA12 Luis Aparicio 72/15	20.00	50.00
LA13 Luis Aparicio 73/3		
LA14 Luis Aparicio 74/3		
LB1 Lou Brock 62/1		
LB2 Lou Brock 66/1		
LB3 Lou Brock 68/2		
LB4 Lou Brock 70/20	40.00	80.00
LB5 Lou Brock 71/3		
LB6 Lou Brock 72/3		
LB7 Lou Brock 73/4		
LB8 Lou Brock 74/5		
LB9 Lou Brock 75/9		
LB10 Lou Brock 76/5		
LB11 Lou Brock 77/11		
LB12 Lou Brock 78/11		
LB13 Lou Brock 79/27	30.00	60.00
LD1 Leon Durham 81/1		
LD2 Leon Durham 82/51	6.00	15.00
LD3 Leon Durham 83/52	6.00	15.00
LD4 Leon Durham 84/151	4.00	10.00
LD5 Leon Durham 85/2		
LD6 Leon Durham 86/19	10.00	25.00
LD7 Leon Durham 87/87	4.00	10.00
LDY1 Len Dykstra 86/1		
LDY2 Len Dykstra 87/200	6.00	15.00
LDY3 Len Dykstra 88/30	12.50	30.00
LDY4 Len Dykstra 89/17	15.00	40.00
LDY5 Len Dykstra 92/7		
LS1 Lee Smith 82/1		
LS2 Lee Smith 83/39	10.00	25.00
LS3 Lee Smith 84/6		
LS4 Lee Smith 85/9		
LS5 Lee Smith 86/29	12.50	30.00
LS6 Lee Smith 87/237	6.00	15.00
LS7 Lee Smith 88/27	12.50	30.00
LS8 Lee Smith 92/12		
LT1 Luis Tiant 65/1		
LT2 Luis Tiant 68/16	20.00	50.00
LT3 Luis Tiant 70/9		
LT4 Luis Tiant 71/2		
LT5 Luis Tiant 73/12		
LT6 Luis Tiant 74/19	20.00	50.00
LT7 Luis Tiant 75/10		
LT8 Luis Tiant 76/3		
LT9 Luis Tiant 77/3		
LT10 Luis Tiant 78/6		
LT11 Luis Tiant 79/22	12.50	30.00
LT12 Luis Tiant 80/23	12.50	30.00
LT13 Luis Tiant 81/20	10.00	25.00
LT14 Luis Tiant 82/51	6.00	15.00
LT15 Luis Tiant 83/58	6.00	15.00
MB1 Mike Boddicker 81/1		
MB2 Mike Boddicker 84/56	6.00	15.00
MB3 Mike Boddicker 85/139	4.00	10.00
MB4 Mike Boddicker 86/66	4.00	10.00
MB5 Mike Boddicker 87/88	4.00	10.00
MF1 Mark Fidrych 77/1		
MF2 Mark Fidrych 78/3		
MF3 Mark Fidrych 79/74	20.00	50.00
MF4 Mark Fidrych 80/16	40.00	80.00
MF5 Mark Fidrych 81/11		
MR1 Mickey Rivers 72/1		
MR2 Mickey Rivers 79/35	10.00	25.00
MR3 Mickey Rivers 80/14		
MR4 Mickey Rivers 81/13		
MR5 Mickey Rivers 82/49	6.00	15.00
MR6 Mickey Rivers 83/79	4.00	10.00
MR7 Mickey Rivers 84/91	4.00	10.00
MR8 Mickey Rivers 85/34	8.00	20.00
MS1 Mike Schmidt 73/1		
MS2 Mike Schmidt 80/100	30.00	60.00
MSC1 Mike Scott 80/1		
MSC2 Mike Scott 81/6		
MSC3 Mike Scott 82/32	8.00	20.00
MSC4 Mike Scott 83/55	6.00	15.00
MSC5 Mike Scott 84/28	8.00	20.00
MSC6 Mike Scott 86/73	4.00	10.00
MSC7 Mike Scott 87/36	6.00	15.00
MSC8 Mike Scott 88/21	10.00	25.00
MT1 Paul Molitor Alan Trammell 78/1		
MW1 Mookie Wilson 81/1		
MW2 Mookie Wilson 82/20	15.00	40.00
MW3 Mookie Wilson 83/41	10.00	25.00
MW4 Mookie Wilson 84/11		
MW5 Mookie Wilson 85/51	10.00	25.00
MW6 Mookie Wilson 86/47	10.00	25.00
MW7 Mookie Wilson 87/67	6.00	15.00
MW8 Mookie Wilson 88/12		
NR1 Nolan Ryan 68/1		
NR2 Nolan Ryan 80/10		
NR3 Nolan Ryan 81/13		
NR4 Nolan Ryan 82/11		
NR5 Nolan Ryan 83/23	100.00	175.00
NR6 Nolan Ryan 84/20	100.00	175.00
NR7 Nolan Ryan 85/4		
NR8 Nolan Ryan 86/20	100.00	175.00
OH1 Orel Hershiser 85/1		
OH2 Orel Hershiser 86/23	30.00	60.00
OH3 Orel Hershiser 87/218	10.00	25.00
OH4 Orel Hershiser 88/9		
OS1 Ozzie Smith 79/1		
OS2 Ozzie Smith 81/28	50.00	100.00
OS3 Ozzie Smith 82/27	50.00	100.00
OS4 Ozzie Smith 83/6		
OS5 Ozzie Smith 84/19	60.00	120.00
OS6 Ozzie Smith 85/16	60.00	120.00
OS7 Ozzie Smith 86/3		
PI1 Pete Incaviglia 86 TR/1		
PI2 Pete Incaviglia 87/311	4.00	10.00
PM1 Paul Molitor 79/15	50.00	100.00
PM2 Paul Molitor 80/26	40.00	80.00
PM3 Paul Molitor 81/12		
PM4 Paul Molitor 82/32	20.00	50.00
PM5 Paul Molitor 83/14		
PO1 Paul O'Neill 88/1		
PO2 Paul O'Neill 89/24	30.00	60.00
PO3 Paul O'Neill 90/18	30.00	60.00
PO4 Paul O'Neill 91/24	30.00	60.00
PO5 Paul O'Neill 97/33	20.00	50.00
RC1 Rod Carew 67/1		
RC2 Rod Carew 70/10		
RC3 Rod Carew 78/2		
RC4 Rod Carew 79/29	30.00	60.00
RC5 Rod Carew 80/10		
RC6 Rod Carew 81/21	30.00	60.00
RC7 Rod Carew 82/18	30.00	60.00
RC8 Rod Carew 84/9		
RCE1 Ron Cey 72/1		
RCE2 Ron Cey 75/4		
RCE3 Ron Cey 79/55	10.00	25.00
RCE4 Ron Cey 80/8		
RCE5 Ron Cey 81/16	10.00	25.00
RCE6 Ron Cey 82/34	8.00	20.00
RCE7 Ron Cey 83/87	4.00	10.00
RCE8 Ron Cey 83 TR/68	4.00	10.00
RCE9 Ron Cey 84/15	10.00	25.00
RCE10 Ron Cey 85/19	10.00	25.00
RCE11 Ron Cey 86/43	6.00	15.00
RD1 Ron Darling 85/1		
RD2 Ron Darling 86/12		
RD3 Ron Darling 87/224	6.00	15.00
RD4 Ron Darling 93/13		
RDI1 Rob Dibble 89/1		
RDI2 Rob Dibble 90/31	8.00	20.00
RDI3 Rob Dibble 91/62	6.00	15.00
RDI4 Rob Dibble 92/56	6.00	15.00
RDI5 Rob Dibble 92 Gold/17	10.00	25.00
RDI6 Rob Dibble 93/47	6.00	15.00
RDI7 Rob Dibble 94/37	6.00	15.00
RF1 Rollie Fingers 69/1		
RF2 Rollie Fingers 78/6		
RF3 Rollie Fingers 79/52	15.00	40.00
RF4 Rollie Fingers 80/15	20.00	50.00
RF5 Rollie Fingers 81/18	15.00	40.00
RF6 Rollie Fingers 82/8		
RG1 Rich Gossage 73/1		
RG2 Rich Gossage 74/6		
RG3 Rich Gossage 76/3		
RG4 Rich Gossage 78/2		
RG5 Rich Gossage 79/11		
RG6 Rich Gossage 80/15	20.00	50.00
RG7 Rich Gossage 81/21	10.00	25.00
RG8 Rich Gossage 82/30	12.50	30.00
RG9 Rich Gossage 83/34	12.50	30.00
RG10 Rich Gossage 84/90	6.00	15.00
RG11 Rich Gossage 85/7		
RG12 Rich Gossage 86/30	12.50	30.00
RGU1 Ron Guidry 76/1		
RGU2 Ron Guidry 78/9		
RGU3 Ron Guidry 79/10		
RGU4 Ron Guidry 80/22	20.00	50.00
RGU5 Ron Guidry 81/104	6.00	15.00
RGU6 Ron Guidry 82/53	10.00	25.00
RGU7 Ron Guidry 83/46	10.00	25.00
RGU8 Ron Guidry 84/40	10.00	25.00
RGU9 Ron Guidry 85/50	10.00	25.00
RGU10 Ron Guidry 86/15	15.00	40.00
RJ1 Reggie Jackson 69/1		
RJ2 Reggie Jackson 73/3		
RJ3 Reggie Jackson 75/1		
RJ4 Reggie Jackson 76/2		
RJ5 Reggie Jackson 79/2		
RJ6 Reggie Jackson 80/7		
RJ7 Reggie Jackson 81/12		
RJ8 Reggie Jackson 82/21	50.00	100.00
RJ9 Reggie Jackson 83/14		
RJ10 Reggie Jackson 84/3		
RJ11 Reggie Jackson 85/17	40.00	80.00
RJ12 Reggie Jackson 86/17	40.00	80.00
RK1 Ron Kittle 84/1		
RK2 Ron Kittle 85/86	4.00	10.00
RK3 Ron Kittle 86/55	6.00	15.00
RK4 Ron Kittle 87/201	4.00	10.00
RKN1 Ray Knight 78/1		
RKN2 Ray Knight 79/10		
RKN3 Ray Knight 80/5		
RKN4 Ray Knight 81/7		
RKN5 Ray Knight 82/25	15.00	40.00
RKN6 Ray Knight 83/36	10.00	25.00
RKN7 Ray Knight 84/26	12.50	30.00
RKN8 Ray Knight 85/68	6.00	15.00
RKN9 Ray Knight 86/80	6.00	15.00
RKN10 Ray Knight 87 TR/90	6.00	15.00
RM1 Reggie Smith 67/1		
RM2 Reggie Smith 69/1		
RM3 Reggie Smith 73/7		
RM4 Reggie Smith 74/4		
RM5 Reggie Smith 75/2		
RM6 Reggie Smith 76/3		
RM7 Reggie Smith 77/2		
RM8 Reggie Smith 79/15	12.50	30.00
RM9 Reggie Smith 80/16	12.50	30.00
RM10 Reggie Smith 81/14		
RM11 Reggie Smith 82/32	8.00	20.00
RM12 Reggie Smith 83/48	6.00	15.00
RS1 Ryne Sandberg 83/1		
RS2 Ryne Sandberg 84/37	50.00	100.00
RS3 Ryne Sandberg 85/4		
RS4 Ryne Sandberg 86/1		
RS5 Ryne Sandberg 87/32	50.00	100.00
RS6 Ryne Sandberg 88/6		
RS7 Ryne Sandberg 89/9		
RS8 Ryne Sandberg 92/10		
RSA1 Ron Santo 61/1		
RSA2 Ron Santo 67/2		
RSA3 Ron Santo 68/6		
RSA4 Ron Santo 69/2		
RSA5 Ron Santo 70/1		
RSA6 Ron Santo 70 AS/1		
RSA7 Ron Santo 71/2		
RSA8 Ron Santo 72/2		
RSA9 Ron Santo 72 IA/3		
RSA10 Ron Santo 73/13		
RSA11 Ron Santo 74/2		
RSA12 Ron Santo 74 TR/1		
RSA13 Ron Santo 75/12		
RU1 Rick Sutcliffe 80/1		
RU2 Rick Sutcliffe 81/9		
RU3 Rick Sutcliffe 82/53	6.00	15.00
RU4 Rick Sutcliffe 83/43	6.00	15.00
RU5 Rick Sutcliffe 84/33	8.00	20.00
RU6 Rick Sutcliffe 85/82	4.00	10.00
RU7 Rick Sutcliffe 86/10		
RU8 Rick Sutcliffe 87/19	10.00	25.00
RY1 Robin Yount 75/1		
RY2 Robin Yount 77/1		
RY3 Robin Yount 78/3		
RY4 Robin Yount 79/1		
RY5 Robin Yount 80/18	50.00	100.00
RY6 Robin Yount 81/23	50.00	100.00
RY7 Robin Yount 82/11		
RY8 Robin Yount 83/2		
RY9 Robin Yount 84/15	50.00	100.00
RY10 Robin Yount 85/5		
RY11 Robin Yount 86/21	50.00	100.00
SA1 Sparky Anderson 59/1		
SA2 Sparky Anderson 60/2		
SA3 Sparky Anderson 74 MG/3		
SA4 Sparky Anderson 78 MG/6		
SA5 Sparky Anderson 83 MG/67	6.00	15.00
SA6 Sparky Anderson 84 MG/97	6.00	15.00
SA7 Sparky Anderson 85 MG/73	6.00	15.00
SA8 Sparky Anderson 86 MG/6		
SF1 Sid Fernandez 85/1		
SF2 Sid Fernandez 86/18	15.00	40.00
SF3 Sid Fernandez 87/211	6.00	15.00
SF4 Sid Fernandez 93/20	15.00	40.00
SG1 Steve Garvey 71/1		
SG2 Steve Garvey 75/1		
SG3 Steve Garvey 76/4		
SG4 Steve Garvey 79/26	15.00	40.00
SG5 Steve Garvey 80/5		
SG6 Steve Garvey 81/10		
SG7 Steve Garvey 82/122	6.00	15.00
SG8 Steve Garvey 83/19	15.00	40.00
SG9 Steve Garvey 84/32	12.50	30.00
SG10 Steve Garvey 85/129	6.00	15.00
SM1 Stan Musial 58 AS/15	150.00	250.00
SM2 Stan Musial 59/1		
SM3 Stan Musial 60/5		
SM4 Stan Musial 61/13		
SM5 Stan Musial 62/16	150.00	250.00
SM6 Stan Musial 63/1		
SS1 Steve Sax 82/1		
SS2 Steve Sax 83/34	8.00	20.00
SS3 Steve Sax 84/14		
SS4 Steve Sax 85/33	8.00	20.00
SS5 Steve Sax 86/45	6.00	15.00
SS6 Steve Sax 87/215	4.00	10.00
SS7 Steve Sax 88/10		
SY1 Steve Yeager 73/1		
SY2 Steve Yeager 74/1		
SY3 Steve Yeager 76/1		
SY4 Steve Yeager 78/18	12.50	30.00
SY5 Steve Yeager 79/23	12.50	30.00
SY6 Steve Yeager 80/10		
SY7 Steve Yeager 81/12		
SY8 Steve Yeager 82/18	10.00	25.00
SY9 Steve Yeager 83/80	4.00	10.00
SY10 Steve Yeager 84/15	10.00	25.00
SY11 Steve Yeager 85/4		
SY12 Steve Yeager 86/47	6.00	15.00
SY13 Steve Yeager 86 TR/100	4.00	10.00
TB1 Tom Brunansky 82/1		
TB2 Tom Brunansky 83/27	8.00	20.00
TB3 Tom Brunansky 84/62	6.00	15.00
TB4 Tom Brunansky 85/13		
TB5 Tom Brunansky 86/28	8.00	20.00
TB6 Tom Brunansky 87/193	4.00	10.00
TB7 Tom Brunansky 88/18	10.00	25.00
TB8 Tom Brunansky 90/8		
TF1 Tony Fernandez 85/1		
TF2 Tony Fernandez 86/41	6.00	15.00
TF3 Tony Fernandez 87/228	4.00	10.00
TF4 Tony Fernandez 88/10		
TF5 Tony Fernandez 90/11		
TG1 Tony Gwynn 83/1		
TG2 Tony Gwynn 84/95	30.00	60.00
TG3 Tony Gwynn 85/4		
TH1 Tom Herr 80/1		
TH2 Tom Herr 81/22	10.00	25.00
TH3 Tom Herr 82/42	6.00	15.00
TH4 Tom Herr 83/80	4.00	10.00
TH5 Tom Herr 84/30	8.00	20.00
TH6 Tom Herr 85/17	10.00	25.00
TH7 Tom Herr 86/28	8.00	20.00
TH8 Tom Herr 87/134	4.00	10.00
TM1 Tim McCarver 62/1		
TM2 Tim McCarver 76/5		
TM3 Tim McCarver 77/8		
TM4 Tim McCarver 78/12		
TM5 Tim McCarver 79/22	12.50	30.00
TM6 Tim McCarver 80/4		
TO1 Tony Oliva 63/1		
TO2 Tony Oliva 68/1		
TO3 Tony Oliva 69/4		
TO4 Tony Oliva 69 AS/1		
TO5 Tony Oliva 70/9		
TO6 Tony Oliva 71/2		
TO7 Tony Oliva 72/5		
TO8 Tony Oliva 73/18	20.00	50.00
TO9 Tony Oliva 74/11		
TO10 Tony Oliva 75/10		
TO11 Tony Oliva 76/1		
TR1 Tim Raines 81/1		
TR2 Tim Raines 82/43	10.00	25.00
TR3 Tim Raines 83/26	12.50	30.00
TR4 Tim Raines 84/10		
TR5 Tim Raines 85/43	10.00	25.00
TR6 Tim Raines 86/21	15.00	40.00
TR7 Tim Raines 87/211	6.00	15.00
TS1 Tom Seaver 67/1		
TS2 Tom Seaver 79/44	40.00	80.00
TS3 Tom Seaver 80/9		
TS4 Tom Seaver 81/16	40.00	80.00
TS5 Tom Seaver 82/25	40.00	80.00
TS6 Tom Seaver 83/4		
TS7 Tom Seaver 85/6		
TW1 Tim Wallach 82/1		
TW2 Tim Wallach 83/49	6.00	15.00
TW3 Tim Wallach 84/13		
TW4 Tim Wallach 85/46	6.00	15.00
TW5 Tim Wallach 86/44	6.00	15.00
TW6 Tim Wallach 87/197	4.00	10.00
VB1 Vida Blue 70/1		
VB2 Vida Blue 72/1		
VB3 Vida Blue 75/1		
VB4 Vida Blue 78/10		
VB5 Vida Blue 79/21	12.50	30.00
VB6 Vida Blue 80/10		
VB7 Vida Blue 81/227	4.00	10.00
VB8 Vida Blue 82/53	6.00	15.00
VB9 Vida Blue 83/45	6.00	15.00
VC1 Vince Coleman 85 TR/1		
VC2 Vince Coleman 87/299	6.00	15.00
VC3 Vince Coleman 88/34	12.50	30.00
VC4 Vince Coleman 91 TR/23	15.00	40.00
WB1 Wade Boggs 83/1		
WB2 Wade Boggs 84/20	40.00	80.00
WB3 Wade Boggs 85/25	40.00	80.00
WB4 Wade Boggs 86/9		
WB5 Wade Boggs 87/45	30.00	60.00
WF1 Whitey Ford 53/1		
WF2 Whitey Ford 58/1		
WF3 Whitey Ford 59/3		
WF4 Whitey Ford 60/5		
WF5 Whitey Ford 61/6		
WF6 Whitey Ford 62/5		
WF7 Whitey Ford 62 AS/2		
WF8 Whitey Ford 62 WS/3		
WF9 Whitey Ford 63/1		
WF10 Whitey Ford 65/1		
WF11 Whitey Ford 66/9		
WF12 Whitey Ford 67/13		
WH1 Whitey Herzog 57/1		
WH2 Whitey Herzog 61/13		
WH3 Whitey Herzog 62/1		
WH4 Whitey Herzog 83 MG/63	6.00	15.00
WH5 Whitey Herzog 84 MG/85	4.00	10.00
WH6 Whitey Herzog 85 MG/75	4.00	10.00
WH7 Whitey Herzog 86 MG/66	4.00	10.00
WH8 Whitey Herzog 87 MG/29	8.00	20.00
WH9 Whitey Herzog 88 MG/35	8.00	20.00
WJ1 Wally Joyner 86 TR/1		
WJ2 Wally Joyner 87/335	6.00	15.00
WJ3 Wally Joyner 94/14		
WM1 Willie Mays 52/1		
WM2 Willie Mays 60/1		
WM3 Willie Mays 61/3		
WM4 Willie Mays 61 MVP/4		
WM5 Willie Mays 62/1		
WM6 Willie Mays 62 AS/3		
WM7 Willie Mays 69/1		
WM8 Willie Mays 70/2		
WM9 Willie Mays 72/25	200.00	350.00
WM10 Willie Mays 72 IA/5		
WM11 Willie Mays 73/5		
WMC1 Willie McGee 83/1		
WMC2 Willie McGee 84/66	6.00	15.00
WMC3 Willie McGee 85/44	10.00	25.00
WMC4 Willie McGee 86/24	15.00	40.00
WMC5 Willie McGee 87/117	6.00	15.00
WW1 Walt Weiss 88 TR/1		
WW2 Walt Weiss 89/34	8.00	20.00
WW3 Walt Weiss 91/30	8.00	20.00
WW4 Walt Weiss 92/71	4.00	10.00
WW5 Walt Weiss 93/10		
WW6 Walt Weiss 94/21	10.00	25.00
WW7 Walt Weiss 97/49	6.00	15.00
WW8 Walt Weiss 98 Rockies/23	10.00	25.00
WW9 Walt Weiss 98 Braves/21	10.00	25.00
WW10 Walt Weiss 99/40	6.00	15.00
WW11 Walt Weiss 01/51	6.00	15.00
YB1 Yogi Berra 52/1		
YB2 Yogi Berra 59/1		
YB3 Yogi Berra 60/1		
YB4 Yogi Berra 61/2		
YB5 Yogi Berra 62/3		
YB6 Yogi Berra 64 MG/3		
YB7 Yogi Berra 65 CO/1		
YB8 Yogi Berra 73 MG/5		
YB9 Yogi Berra 74 MG/6		
YB10 Yogi Berra 85 MG/27	40.00	80.00

2002 Topps Pristine

This 210 card set was issued in October, 2002. This set was issued in eight card packs with an $40 SRP which came five packs to a box and six boxes to a case. The first 140 cards feature active veterans stars while cards 141-150 feature retired greats and cards numbered 151-210 feature three different versions of each rookie. Each rookie has a common version, a uncommon version which has a print run of 1999 serial numbered sets and a rare version which has a stated print run of 799 serial numbered sets.

COMMON CARD (1-140)	.50	1.25
COMMON CARD (141-150)	.75	2.00
COMMON C CARD (151-210)	.50	1.25
COMMON U CARD (151-210)	1.00	2.50
COMMON R CARD (151-210)	1.50	4.00
1 Alex Rodriguez	2.00	5.00
2 Carlos Delgado	.50	1.25
3 Jimmy Rollins	.50	1.25
4 Jason Kendall	.50	1.25
5 John Olerud	.50	1.25
6 Albert Pujols	2.50	6.00
7 Curt Schilling	.50	1.25
8 Gary Sheffield	.50	1.25
9 Johnny Damon Sox	.75	2.00
10 Ichiro Suzuki	2.50	6.00
11 Pat Burrell	.50	1.25
12 Garret Anderson	.50	1.25
13 Andruw Jones	.75	2.00
14 Kerry Wood	.50	1.25
15 Kenny Lofton	.50	1.25
16 Adam Dunn	.50	1.25
17 Juan Pierre	.50	1.25
18 Josh Beckett	.50	1.25
19 Roy Oswalt	.50	1.25
20 Derek Jeter	3.00	8.00
21 Jose Vidro	.50	1.25
22 Richie Sexson	.50	1.25
23 Mike Sweeney	.50	1.25
24 Jeff Kent	.50	1.25
25 Jason Giambi	.50	1.25
26 Bret Boone	.50	1.25
27 J.D. Drew	.50	1.25
28 Shannon Stewart	.50	1.25
29 Miguel Tejada	.50	1.25
30 Barry Bonds	3.00	8.00
31 Randy Johnson	1.25	3.00
32 Pedro Martinez	.75	2.00
33 Maggilo Ordonez	.50	1.25
34 Todd Helton	.75	2.00
35 Craig Biggio	.75	2.00
36 Shawn Green	.50	1.25
37 Vladimir Guerrero	1.25	3.00
38 Mo Vaughn	.50	1.25
39 Alfonso Soriano	.50	1.25
40 Barry Zito	.50	1.25
41 Aramis Ramirez	.50	1.25
42 Ryan Klesko	.50	1.25
43 Ruben Sierra	.50	1.25
44 Tino Martinez	.75	2.00
45 Toby Hall	.50	1.25
46 Ivan Rodriguez	.75	2.00
47 Raul Mondesi	.50	1.25
48 Carlos Pena	.50	1.25
49 Darin Erstad	.50	1.25
50 Sammy Sosa	1.25	3.00
51 Bartolo Colon	.50	1.25
52 Robert Fick	.50	1.25
53 Cliff Floyd	.50	1.25
54 Brian Jordan	.50	1.25
55 Torii Hunter	.50	1.25
56 Roberto Alomar	.75	2.00
57 Roger Clemens	2.50	6.00
58 Mark Mulder	.50	1.25
59 Brian Giles	.50	1.25
60 Mike Piazza	2.00	5.00
61 Rich Aurilia	.50	1.25
62 Freddy Garcia	.50	1.25
63 Jim Edmonds	.50	1.25
64 Eric Hinske	.50	1.25
65 Vicente Padilla	.50	1.25
66 Javier Vazquez	.50	1.25
67 Cristian Guzman	.50	1.25
68 Paul Lo Duca	.50	1.25
69 Bobby Abreu	.50	1.25
70 Nomar Garciaparra	2.00	5.00
71 Troy Glaus	.50	1.25
72 Chipper Jones	1.25	3.00
73 Scott Rolen	.75	2.00
74 Lance Berkman	.50	1.25
75 C.C. Sabathia	.50	1.25
76 Bernie Williams	.75	2.00
77 Rafael Palmeiro	.75	2.00
78 Phil Nevin	.50	1.25
79 Kazuhiro Sasaki	.50	1.25
80 Eric Chavez	.50	1.25
81 Jorge Posada	.75	2.00
82 Edgardo Alfonzo	.50	1.25
83 Geoff Jenkins	.50	1.25
84 Preston Wilson	.50	1.25
85 Jim Thome	.75	2.00
86 Frank Thomas	1.25	3.00
87 Jeff Bagwell	.75	2.00
88 Greg Maddux	2.00	5.00
89 Mark Prior	.75	2.00
90 Larry Walker	.50	1.25
91 Luis Gonzalez	.50	1.25
92 Tim Hudson	.50	1.25
93 Tsuyoshi Shinjo	.50	1.25
94 Juan Gonzalez	.50	1.25
95 Shea Hillenbrand	.50	1.25
96 Paul Konerko	.50	1.25
97 Tom Glavine	.75	2.00
98 Marty Cordova	.50	1.25
99 Moises Alou	.50	1.25
100 Ken Griffey Jr.	2.00	5.00
101 Hank Blalock	.75	2.00
102 Matt Morris	.50	1.25
103 Robb Nen	.50	1.25
104 Mike Cameron	.50	1.25
105 Mark Buehrle	.50	1.25
106 Sean Burroughs	.50	1.25
107 Orlando Cabrera	.50	1.25
108 Jeromy Burnitz	.50	1.25
109 Juan Uribe	.50	1.25
110 Eric Milton	.50	1.25
111 Carlos Lee	.50	1.25
112 Jose Mesa	.50	1.25
113 Morgan Ensberg	.50	1.25
114 Derek Lowe	.50	1.25
115 Juan Cruz	.50	1.25
116 Mike Lieberthal	.50	1.25
117 Armando Benitez	.50	1.25
118 Vinny Castilla	.50	1.25
119 Russ Ortiz	.50	1.25
120 Mike Lowell	.50	1.25
121 Corey Patterson	.50	1.25
122 Mike Mussina	.75	2.00
123 Rafael Furcal	.50	1.25
124 Mark Grace	.75	2.00
125 Ben Sheets	.50	1.25
126 John Smoltz	.75	2.00
127 Fred McGriff	.75	2.00
128 Nick Johnson	.50	1.25
129 J.T. Snow	.50	1.25
130 Jeff Cirillo	.50	1.25
131 Trevor Hoffman	.50	1.25
132 Kevin Brown	.50	1.25
133 Mariano Rivera	1.25	3.00
134 Marlon Anderson	.50	1.25
135 Al Leiter	.50	1.25
136 Doug Mientkiewicz	.50	1.25
137 Eric Karros	.50	1.25
138 Bobby Higginson	.50	1.25
139 Sean Casey	.50	1.25
140 Troy Percival	.50	1.25
141 Willie Mays	2.50	6.00
142 Carl Yastrzemski	2.00	5.00
143 Stan Musial	2.00	5.00
144 Harmon Killebrew	1.25	3.00
145 Mike Schmidt	2.50	6.00
146 Duke Snider	.75	2.00
147 Brooks Robinson	.75	2.00
148 Frank Robinson	.75	2.00
149 Nolan Ryan	3.00	8.00
150 Reggie Jackson	.75	2.00
151 Joe Mauer C RC	5.00	12.00
152 Joe Mauer U	8.00	20.00
153 Joe Mauer R	12.50	30.00
154 Colt Griffin C RC	.50	1.25
155 Colt Griffin U	1.00	2.50
156 Colt Griffin R	1.50	4.00
157 Jason Simontacchi C RC	.50	1.25
158 Jason Simontacchi U	1.00	2.50
159 Jason Simontacchi R	1.50	4.00

160 Casey Kotchman C RC 1.25 3.00
161 Casey Kotchman U 2.50 6.00
162 Casey Kotchman R 4.00 10.00
163 Greg Sain C RC .50 1.25
164 Greg Sain U 1.00 2.50
165 Greg Sain R 1.50 4.00
166 David Wright C RC 12.50 30.00
167 David Wright U 20.00 50.00
168 David Wright R 30.00 60.00
169 Scott Hairston C RC .75 2.00
170 Scott Hairston U 1.50 4.00
171 Scott Hairston R 2.50 6.00
172 Rolando Viera C RC .60 1.25
173 Rolando Viera U 1.00 2.50
174 Rolando Viera R 1.50 4.00
175 Tyrell Godwin C RC .50 1.25
176 Tyrell Godwin U 1.00 2.50
177 Tyrell Godwin R 1.50 4.00
178 Jesus Cota C RC .50 1.25
179 Jesus Cota U 1.00 2.50
180 Jesus Cota R 1.50 4.00
181 Dan Johnson C RC 1.25 3.00
182 Dan Johnson U 2.50 6.00
183 Dan Johnson R 4.00 10.00
184 Mario Ramos C RC .50 1.25
185 Mario Ramos U 1.00 2.50
186 Mario Ramos R 1.50 4.00
187 Jason Dubois C RC .75 2.00
188 Jason Dubois U 1.50 4.00
189 Jason Dubois R 2.50 6.00
190 Jonny Gomes C RC 1.50 4.00
191 Jonny Gomes U 3.00 8.00
192 Jonny Gomes R 5.00 12.00
193 Chris Snelling C RC .60 1.50
194 Chris Snelling U 1.25 3.00
195 Chris Snelling R 2.00 5.00
196 Hansel Izquierdo C RC .50 1.25
197 Hansel Izquierdo U 1.00 2.50
198 Hansel Izquierdo R 1.50 4.00
199 So Taguchi C RC .75 2.00
200 So Taguchi U 1.50 4.00
201 So Taguchi R 2.50 6.00
202 Kazuhisa Ishii C RC .75 2.00
203 Kazuhisa Ishii U 1.50 4.00
204 Kazuhisa Ishii R 2.50 6.00
205 Jorge Padilla C RC .50 1.25
206 Jorge Padilla U 1.00 2.50
207 Jorge Padilla R 1.50 4.00
208 Earl Snyder C RC .50 1.25
209 Earl Snyder U 1.00 2.50
210 Earl Snyder R 1.50 4.00

2002 Topps Pristine Gold Refractors

Inserted one per hobby box, this is a parallel of the regular set. Each card has a stated print run of 70 serial numbered sets.

*GOLD 1-140: 2.5X TO 6X BASIC
*GOLD 141-150: 2.5X TO 6X BASIC
*GOLD C 151-210: 4X TO 10X BASIC C
*GOLD U 151-210: 2X TO 5X BASIC U
*GOLD R 151-210: 1.25X TO 3X BASIC R
166 David Wright C 125.00 250.00
167 David Wright U 125.00 250.00
168 David Wright R 125.00 250.00

2002 Topps Pristine Refractors

Issued at different odds depending on the card number, these cards parallel the regular pristine set. The veterans and retired players were issued to a stated print run of 149 serial numbered sets. The rookie cards were issued to stated print runs of 1999 for the common versions, 799 for the uncommon versions and 149 for the rare version.

*REFRACTORS 1-140: 1.5X TO 4X
*REFRACTORS 141-150: 1.5X TO 4X
1-150 STATED ODDS 1:4
*REFRACTORS C 151-210: 1X TO 2.5X
COMMON 151-210 STATED ODDS 1:2
*REFRACTORS U 151-210: .75X TO 2X
UNCOMMON 151-210 STATED ODDS 1:5
*REFRACTORS R 151-210: .75X TO 2X
RARE 151-210 STATED ODDS 1:27
166 David Wright C 40.00 80.00
167 David Wright U 50.00 100.00
168 David Wright R 60.00 120.00

2002 Topps Pristine Fall Memories

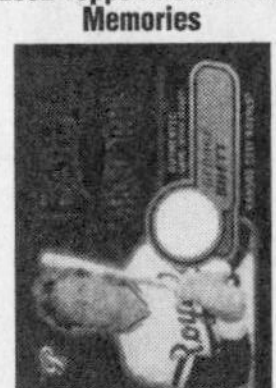

Issued at different odds depending on which group the insert card belonged to, these cards feature players who had participated in post-season play and a piece of game-used memorabilia pertaining to that player. We have listed the stated print run information for that player as well as what type of memorabilia next to the player's name in our checklist.

GROUP A ODDS 1:21
GROUP B ODDS 1:8
GROUP C ODDS 1:49
GROUP A PRINT RUN 425 SERIAL #'d SETS
GROUP B PRINT RUN 1000 SERIAL #'d SETS
GROUP C PRINT RUN 1600 SERIAL #'d SETS
AJ Andruw Jones Uni B 4.00 10.00
AS Alfonso Soriano Bat B 3.00 8.00
BB Barry Bonds Bat A 15.00 40.00
BW Bernie Williams Bat B 4.00 10.00
CJ Chipper Jones Bat A 6.00 15.00
CS Curt Schilling Jsy B 3.00 8.00
EM Eddie Murray Bat A 6.00 15.00
GB George Brett Jsy B 12.50 30.00
GS Gary Sheffield Bat C 3.00 8.00
JB Johnny Bench Jsy B 6.00 15.00
JP Jorge Posada Bat B 4.00 10.00
KP Kirby Puckett Bat A 6.00 15.00
LG Luis Gonzalez Bat B 3.00 8.00
MG Mark Grace Bat A 6.00 15.00
RJ Reggie Jackson Bat A 6.00 15.00
SG Shawn Green Bat A 4.00 10.00
TG Tom Glavine Jsy B 4.00 10.00
TH Todd Helton Jsy B 4.00 10.00
TM Tino Martinez Bat A 6.00 15.00
WM Willie Mays Jsy A 15.00 40.00

2002 Topps Pristine In the Gap

Inserted at a stated rate of one in 12 for group A cards and one in five for group B cards, these 30 cards feature players along with a game-used memorabilia piece. We have notated next to the player's name not only what type of memorabilia but also what grouping they belonged to.

GROUP A ODDS 1:12
GROUP B ODDS 1:5
GROUP A PRINT RUN 425 SERIAL #'d SETS
GROUP B PRINT RUN 1000 SERIAL #'d SETS
AD Adam Dunn Jsy B 3.00 8.00
AJ Andruw Jones Jsy B 4.00 10.00
AP Albert Pujols Uni B 8.00 20.00
AR Alex Rodriguez Bat A 6.00 15.00
ARA Aramis Ramirez Bat A 4.00 10.00
AS Alfonso Soriano Bat A 4.00 10.00
BB Bret Boone Bat B 3.00 8.00
BBO Barry Bonds Uni B 12.50 30.00
BW Bernie Williams Bat A 6.00 15.00
CD Carlos Delgado Bat A 4.00 10.00
DE Darin Erstad Bat A 4.00 10.00
EC Eric Chavez Bat A 4.00 10.00
IR Ivan Rodriguez Bat A 6.00 15.00
JE Jim Edmonds Jsy B 3.00 8.00
JK Jeff Kent Jsy B 3.00 8.00
LB Lance Berkman Bat A 4.00 10.00
LW Larry Walker Jsy B 3.00 8.00
MP Mike Piazza Bat A 6.00 15.00
NG Nomar Garciaparra Bat A 6.00 15.00
PL Paul Lo Duca Bat A 4.00 10.00
PW Preston Wilson Jsy B 3.00 8.00
RA Roberto Alomar Bat B 4.00 10.00
RH Rickey Henderson Bat A 6.00 15.00
RK Ryan Klesko Bat A 4.00 10.00
RP Rafael Palmeiro Bat A 6.00 15.00
TG Tony Gwynn Jsy B 6.00 15.00
TH Todd Helton Bat B 4.00 10.00
TS Tsuyoshi Shinjo Bat B 3.00 8.00
WB Wade Boggs Uni B 4.00 10.00
WBE Wilson Betemit Bat B 3.00 8.00

2002 Topps Pristine Patches

Inserted at stated odds of one in 126, these 25 cards feature game-used patches of the featured player. Each of these cards were issued to a stated print run of 25 serial numbered sets and no pricing is provided due to scarcity.

AD Adam Dunn
AJ Andruw Jones
AP Albert Pujols
AR Alex Rodriguez
BB Bret Boone
BBO Barry Bonds
CD Carlos Delgado
CJ Chipper Jones
CS Curt Schilling
DM Don Mattingly
EC Eric Chavez
FT Frank Thomas
GB George Brett
GM Greg Maddux
KS Kazuhiro Sasaki
LW Larry Walker
MP Mike Piazza
NG Nomar Garciaparra
PM Pedro Martinez
RP Rafael Palmeiro
SR Scott Rolen
TG Tony Gwynn
TGL Tom Glavine
TH Todd Helton
WB Wade Boggs

2002 Topps Pristine Personal Endorsements

Inserted at different odds depending on the group the player belonged to, these cards feature authentic player autographs on a clear acrylic like card surface. We have notated what group the player belongs to next to their name in our checklist.

GROUP A ODDS 1:396
GROUP B ODDS 1:63
GROUP C ODDS 1:79
GROUP D ODDS 1:33
GROUP E ODDS 1:9
GROUP F ODDS 1:53
AP Albert Pujols A 175.00 250.00
BB Barry Bonds E 40.00 80.00
BS Ben Sheets B 8.00 20.00
CG Cristian Guzman C 4.00 10.00
CK Casey Kotchman E 6.00 15.00
CM Corwin Malone E 4.00 10.00
DB Dewon Brazelton D 4.00 10.00
GF Gavin Floyd D 6.00 15.00
IG Irvin Guzman E 30.00 50.00
JD Johnny Damon Sox B 15.00 40.00
JL Jason Lane E 6.00 15.00
JR Jimmy Rollins C 8.00 20.00
JS Juan Silvestre E 4.00 10.00
KB Kenny Baugh F 4.00 10.00
KI Kazuhisa Ishii A 15.00 40.00
LB Lance Berkman B 12.50 30.00
MT Marcus Thames E 4.00 10.00
NN Nick Neugebauer E 4.00 10.00
OH Orlando Hudson D 4.00 10.00
RA Roberto Alomar B 12.50 30.00
ST So Taguchi B 12.50 30.00

2002 Topps Pristine Popular Demand

Inserted at a stated print run of one in four, these 20 cards feature some of the leading players in the game along with a game-used memorabilia piece. Each card was issued to a stated print run of 1000 serial numbered sets.

AD Adam Dunn Jsy 3.00 8.00
AP Albert Pujols Jsy 8.00 20.00
AR Alex Rodriguez Bat 6.00 15.00
BB Bret Boone Jsy 3.00 8.00
BBO Barry Bonds Uni 12.50 30.00
CD Carlos Delgado Uni 3.00 8.00
CJ Chipper Jones Jsy 6.00 15.00
CS Curt Schilling Jsy 3.00 8.00
DM Don Mattingly Jsy 15.00 40.00
FT Frank Thomas Jsy 6.00 15.00
IR Ivan Rodriguez Uni 4.00 10.00
JB Jeff Bagwell Jsy 4.00 10.00
LW Larry Walker Jsy 3.00 8.00
MP Mike Piazza Jsy 6.00 15.00
NG Nomar Garciaparra Jsy 6.00 15.00
RA Roberto Alomar Jsy 4.00 10.00
SG Shawn Green Jsy 3.00 8.00
TG Tony Gwynn Jsy 6.00 15.00
TH Todd Helton Jsy 4.00 10.00
WB Wade Boggs Jsy 4.00 10.00

2002 Topps Pristine Portions

Issued at different odds depending on which group the insert card belonged to, these cards feature some leading players along with a piece of game-used memorabilia pertaining to that player. We have listed the stated print run information for that player as well as what type of memorabilia next to the player's name in our checklist.

GROUP A ODDS 1:21
GROUP B ODDS 1:4
GROUP C ODDS 1:33
GROUP A PRINT RUN 425 SERIAL #'d SETS
GROUP B PRINT RUN 1000 SERIAL #'d SETS
GROUP C PRINT RUN 2400 SERIAL #'d SETS
AD Adam Dunn Bat B 4.00 10.00
AP Albert Pujols Uni B 8.00 20.00
AR Alex Rodriguez Jsy B 6.00 15.00
BB Bret Boone Jsy B 4.00 10.00
BBO Barry Bonds Uni C 8.00 20.00
CB Craig Biggio Jsy B 6.00 15.00
CD Carlos Delgado Jsy B 4.00 10.00
CF Cliff Floyd Jsy B 4.00 10.00
CG Cristian Guzman Jsy B 3.00 8.00
EM Edgar Martinez Bat A 6.00 15.00
GM Greg Maddux Jsy A 6.00 15.00
IR Ivan Rodriguez Bat A 6.00 15.00
JB Jeff Bagwell Uni A 6.00 15.00
JP Jorge Posada Bat A 6.00 15.00
KS Kazuhiro Sasaki Jsy A 6.00 15.00
LB Lance Berkman Bat A 6.00 15.00
LD Paul Lo Duca Jsy B 4.00 10.00
MM Mike Mussina Uni B 6.00 15.00
MO Magglio Ordonez Jsy B 4.00 10.00
MP Mike Piazza Bat A 6.00 15.00
NG Nomar Garciaparra Jsy B 6.00 15.00
NJ Nick Johnson Bat B 4.00 10.00
NR Nolan Ryan Uni B 20.00 50.00
RA Roberto Alomar Bat A 6.00 15.00
RD Ryan Dempster Jsy D 0.00 0.00
RF Rafael Furcal Jsy B 4.00 10.00
RP Rafael Palmeiro Jsy B 6.00 15.00
TH Todd Helton Jsy B 6.00 15.00

2003 Topps Pristine

This 190 card pack was issued in special eight-card packs, which actually came as a few packs within a large pack. Each pack contained a mix of cards from the base set as well as an encased special. In the basic set, cards numbered 1 through 95 featured veterans, cards numbered 96 through 100 featured retired greats and cards 101 through 190 featured rookies. Each of the rookies were issued in three forms as "Common", "Uncommon" or "Rare". The "Uncommon" rookies were issued to a stated print run of 1499 serial numbered sets while the "rare" rookies were issued to a stated print run of 499 serial numbered sets.

COMMON CARD (1-100) .60 1.50
COMMON C (101-190) .50 1.25
C 101-190 APPX. 2X EASIER THAN 1-100
COMMON U (101-190) 1.00 2.50
UNCOMMON 101-190 STATED ODDS 1:2
UNCOMMON PRINT 1499 SERIAL #'d SETS
COMMON R (101-190) 2.00 5.00
RARE 101-190 STATED ODDS 1:6
RARE PRINT RUN 499 SERIAL #'d SETS
1 Pedro Martinez 1.00 2.50
2 Derek Jeter 4.00 10.00
3 Alex Rodriguez 2.50 6.00
4 Miguel Tejada .60 1.50
5 Nomar Garciaparra 2.50 6.00
6 Austin Kearns .60 1.50
7 Jose Vidro .60 1.50
8 Bret Boone .60 1.50
9 Scott Rolen 1.00 2.50
10 Mike Sweeney .60 1.50
11 Jason Schmidt .60 1.50
12 Alfonso Soriano .60 1.50
13 Tim Hudson .60 1.50
14 A.J. Pierzynski .60 1.50
15 Lance Berkman .60 1.50
16 Frank Thomas 1.50 4.00
17 Gary Sheffield .60 1.50
18 Jarrod Washburn .60 1.50
19 Hideo Nomo 1.50 4.00
20 Barry Zito .60 1.50
21 Kevin Millwood .60 1.50
22 Matt Morris .60 1.50
23 Carl Crawford .60 1.50
24 Carlos Delgado .60 1.50
25 Mike Piazza 2.50 6.00
26 Brad Radke .60 1.50
27 Richie Sexson .60 1.50
28 Kevin Brown .60 1.50
29 Carlos Beltran .60 1.50
30 Curt Schilling .60 1.50
31 Chipper Jones 1.50 4.00
32 Paul Konerko .60 1.50
33 Larry Walker .60 1.50
34 Jeff Bagwell 1.00 2.50
35 Jason Giambi .60 1.50
36 Mark Mulder .60 1.50
37 Vicente Padilla .60 1.50
38 Kris Benson .60 1.50
39 Bernie Williams 1.00 2.50
40 Jim Thome 1.00 2.50
41 Roger Clemens 3.00 8.00
42 Roberto Alomar 1.00 2.50
43 Torii Hunter .60 1.50
44 Bobby Abreu .60 1.50
45 Jeff Kent .60 1.50
46 Roy Oswalt .60 1.50
47 Bartolo Colon .60 1.50
48 Greg Maddux 2.50 6.00
49 Tom Glavine 1.00 2.50
50 Sammy Sosa 1.50 4.00
51 Ichiro Suzuki 3.00 8.00
52 Mark Prior 1.00 2.50
53 Manny Ramirez 1.00 2.50
54 Andruw Jones 1.00 2.50
55 Randy Johnson 1.50 4.00
56 Garret Anderson .60 1.50
57 Roy Halladay .60 1.50
58 Rafael Palmeiro 1.00 2.50
59 Rocco Baldelli .60 1.50
60 Albert Pujols 3.00 8.00
61 Edgar Renteria .60 1.50
62 John Olerud .60 1.50
63 Rich Aurilia .60 1.50
64 Ryan Klesko .60 1.50
65 Brian Giles .60 1.50
66 Eric Chavez .60 1.50
67 Jorge Posada 1.00 2.50
68 Cliff Floyd .60 1.50
69 Vladimir Guerrero 1.50 4.00
70 Cristian Guzman .60 1.50
71 Raul Ibanez .60 1.50
72 Paul Lo Duca .60 1.50
73 A.J. Burnett .60 1.50
74 Ken Griffey Jr. 2.50 6.00
75 Mark Buehrle .60 1.50
76 Moises Alou .60 1.50
77 Adam Dunn .60 1.50
78 Tony Batista .60 1.50
79 Troy Glaus .60 1.50
80 Luis Gonzalez .60 1.50
81 Shea Hillenbrand .60 1.50
82 Kerry Wood .60 1.50
83 Magglio Ordonez .60 1.50
84 Omar Vizquel 1.00 2.50
85 Bobby Higginson .60 1.50
86 Mike Lowell .60 1.50
87 Runelvys Hernandez .60 1.50
88 Shawn Green .60 1.50
89 Erubiel Durazo .60 1.50
90 Pat Burrell .60 1.50
91 Todd Helton 1.00 2.50
92 Jim Edmonds .60 1.50
93 Aubrey Huff .60 1.50
94 Eric Hinske .60 1.50
95 Barry Bonds 4.00 10.00
96 Willie Mays 3.00 8.00
97 Bo Jackson 1.50 4.00
98 Carl Yastrzemski 2.50 6.00
99 Don Mattingly 3.00 8.00
100 Gary Carter 1.00 2.50
101 Jose Contreras C RC .75 2.00
102 Jose Contreras U 1.50 4.00
103 Jose Contreras R 3.00 8.00
104 Dan Haren C RC .75 2.00
105 Dan Haren U 1.50 4.00
106 Dan Haren R 3.00 8.00
107 Michel Hernandez C RC .50 1.25
108 Michel Hernandez U 1.00 2.50
109 Michel Hernandez R 2.00 5.00
110 Bobby Basham C RC .50 1.25
111 Bobby Basham U 1.00 2.50
112 Bobby Basham R 2.00 5.00
113 Bryan Bullington C RC .50 1.25
114 Bryan Bullington U 1.00 2.50
115 Bryan Bullington R 2.00 5.00
116 Bernie Castro C RC .50 1.25
117 Bernie Castro U 1.00 2.50
118 Bernie Castro R 2.00 5.00
119 Chien-Ming Wang C RC 1.00 2.50
120 Chien-Ming Wang U 5.00 12.00
121 Chien-Ming Wang R 8.00 20.00
122 Eric Crozier C RC .50 1.25
123 Eric Crozier U 1.00 2.50
124 Eric Crozier R 2.00 5.00
125 Mi. Garciaparra C RC .50 1.25
126 Michael Garciaparra U 1.00 2.50
127 Michael Garciaparra R 2.00 5.00
128 Joey Gomes C RC .50 1.25
129 Joey Gomes U 1.00 2.50
130 Joey Gomes R 2.00 5.00
131 Wil Ledezma C RC .50 1.25
132 Wil Ledezma U 1.00 2.50
133 Wil Ledezma R 2.00 5.00
134 Branden Florence C RC .50 1.25
135 Branden Florence U 1.00 2.50
136 Branden Florence R 2.00 5.00
137 Jeremy Bonderman C RC 2.00 5.00
138 Jeremy Bonderman U 4.00 10.00
139 Jeremy Bonderman R 8.00 20.00
140 Travis Ishikawa C RC .75 2.00
141 Travis Ishikawa U 1.50 4.00
142 Travis Ishikawa R 3.00 8.00
143 Ben Francisco C RC .50 1.25
144 Ben Francisco U 1.00 2.50
145 Ben Francisco R 2.00 5.00
146 Jason Kubel C RC 1.00 2.50
147 Jason Kubel U 2.00 5.00
148 Jason Kubel R 4.00 10.00
149 Tyler Martin C RC .50 1.25
150 Tyler Martin U 1.00 2.50
151 Tyler Martin R 2.00 5.00
152 Jason Perry C RC .50 1.25
153 Jason Perry U 1.00 2.50
154 Jason Perry R 2.00 5.00
155 Ryan Shealy C RC 2.00 5.00
156 Ryan Shealy U 3.00 8.00
157 Ryan Shealy R 6.00 15.00
158 Hanley Ramirez C RC 2.50 6.00
159 Hanley Ramirez U 5.00 12.00
160 Hanley Ramirez R 10.00 25.00
161 Rajai Davis C RC .50 1.25
162 Rajai Davis U 1.00 2.50
163 Rajai Davis R 2.00 5.00
164 Gary Schneidmiller C RC .50 1.25
165 Gary Schneidmiller U 1.00 2.50
166 Gary Schneidmiller R 2.00 5.00
167 Haj Turay C RC .50 1.25
168 Haj Turay U 1.00 2.50
169 Haj Turay R 2.00 5.00
170 Kevin Youkilis C RC 1.25 3.00
171 Kevin Youkilis U 2.50 6.00
172 Kevin Youkilis R 5.00 12.00
173 Shane Bazzell C RC .50 1.25
174 Shane Bazzell U 1.00 2.50
175 Shane Bazzell R 2.00 5.00
176 Elizardo Ramirez C RC .50 1.25
177 Elizardo Ramirez U 1.00 2.50
178 Elizardo Ramirez R 2.00 5.00
179 Robinson Cano C RC 5.00 12.00
180 Robinson Cano U 10.00 25.00
181 Robinson Cano R 20.00 50.00
182 Nook Logan C RC .50 1.25
183 Nook Logan U 1.00 2.50
184 Nook Logan R 2.00 5.00
185 Dustin McGowan C RC .50 1.25
186 Dustin McGowan U 1.00 2.50
187 Dustin McGowan R 2.00 5.00
188 Ryan Howard C RC 6.00 15.00
189 Ryan Howard U 8.00 20.00
190 Ryan Howard R 15.00 40.00

2003 Topps Pristine Gold Refractors

*GOLD 1-95: 2.5X TO 6X BASIC
*GOLD 96-100: 2.5X TO 6X BASIC
*GOLD C 101-190: 4X TO 10X BASIC C
*GOLD U 101-190: 2X TO 5X BASIC U
*GOLD R 101-190: 1X TO 2.5X BASIC R
ONE PER SEALED HOBBY BOX
STATED PRINT RUN 69 SERIAL #'d SETS
119 Chien-Ming Wang C 30.00 60.00
120 Chien-Ming Wang U 30.00 60.00
121 Chien-Ming Wang R 30.00 60.00
188 Ryan Howard C 50.00 100.00
189 Ryan Howard U 50.00 100.00
190 Ryan Howard R 50.00 100.00

2003 Topps Pristine Plates

STATED ODDS 1:83
STATED PRINT RUN 4 SETS
BLACK, CYAN, MAGENTA AND YELLOW EXIST
NO PRICING DUE TO SCARCITY

2003 Topps Pristine Refractors

*REFRACTORS 1-95: 2X TO 5X BASIC
*REFRACTORS 96-100: 2X TO 5X BASIC
REFRACTORS 1-100 ODDS 1:8
REFRACTORS 1-100 PRINT RUN 99 #'d SETS
*REFRACTORS C 101-190: .75X TO 2X
COMMON 101-190 PRINT RUN 1599 #'d SETS
*REFRACTORS U 101-190: .75X TO 2X
UNCOMMON 101-190 ODDS 1:6
UNCOMMON 101-190 PRINT 499 #'d SETS
*REFRACTORS R 101-190: .75X TO 2X
RARE 101-190 ODDS 1:27
RARE 101-190 PRINT RUN 99 #'d SETS
119 Chien-Ming Wang C 6.00 15.00
120 Chien-Ming Wang U 8.00 20.00
121 Chien-Ming Wang R 15.00 40.00
179 Robinson Cano C 8.00 20.00
180 Robinson Cano U 15.00 40.00
181 Robinson Cano R 40.00 80.00
188 Ryan Howard C 15.00 40.00
189 Ryan Howard U 20.00 50.00
190 Ryan Howard R 40.00 80.00

2003 Topps Pristine Bonds Jersey Relics

REFRACTOR ODDS 1:787
REFRACTOR PRINT RUN 25 SERIAL #'d SETS
NO REFRACTOR PRICING DUE TO SCARCITY
BB Barry Bonds BB 15.00 40.00
GG Barry Bonds GG 15.00 40.00
HR Barry Bonds HR 15.00 40.00
MVP Barry Bonds MVP 15.00 40.00

2003 Topps Pristine Bonds Dual Relics

REFRACTOR STATED ODDS 1:787
REFRACTOR PRINT RUN 25 SERIAL #'d SETS
NO REFRACTOR PRICING DUE TO SCARCITY
BJ Barry Bonds Jsy / Randy Johnson Jsy 20.00 50.00
BM Willie Mays Jsy / Barry Bonds Jsy 60.00 120.00
BR Alex Rodriguez Jsy / Barry Bonds Jsy 20.00 50.00
BT Miguel Tejada Bat / Barry Bonds Bat 20.00 50.00

2003 Topps Pristine Bomb Squad Relics

GROUP A ODDS 1:3
GROUP B ODDS 1:5
GROUP C ODDS 1:9
REFRACTOR ODDS 1:59
REFRACTOR PRINT RUN 25 SERIAL #'d SETS
NO REFRACTOR PRICING DUE TO SCARCITY
AD Adam Dunn Jsy A 3.00 8.00
AJ Andruw Jones Bat B 6.00 15.00
AP1 Albert Pujols Bat A 8.00 20.00
AP2 Albert Pujols Uni B 10.00 25.00
AR1 Alex Rodriguez Bat C 4.00 10.00
AR2 Alex Rodriguez Jsy A 4.00 10.00
AS Alfonso Soriano Uni A 3.00 8.00
BB Barry Bonds Jsy B 10.00 25.00
CC Carl Crawford Bat C 3.00 8.00
CF Cliff Floyd Bat B 4.00 10.00
CJ Chipper Jones Bat B 6.00 15.00
DE1 Darin Erstad Uni B 4.00 10.00
DE2 Darin Erstad Jsy B 4.00 10.00
EC1 Eric Chavez Gray Uni A 3.00 8.00
EC2 Eric Chavez White Uni A 3.00 8.00
FT Frank Thomas Bat C 4.00 10.00
GA1 Garret Anderson Bat A 3.00 8.00
GA2 Garret Anderson Uni B 4.00 10.00
GB1 George Brett Jsy A 8.00 20.00
GB2 George Brett Bat B 8.00 20.00
GC Gary Carter Bat C 3.00 8.00
GS Gary Sheffield Bat A 3.00 8.00
HB Hank Blalock Bat B 4.00 10.00
JAG Juan Gonzalez Jsy B 4.00 10.00
JB Johnny Bench Bat A 4.00 10.00
JG Jason Giambi Bat A 3.00 8.00
JK Jeff Kent Bat B 4.00 10.00
JRB Jeff Bagwell Bat B 6.00 15.00
JT Jim Thome Bat B 6.00 15.00
LB1 Lance Berkman Jsy C 3.00 8.00
LB2 Lance Berkman Bat C 3.00 8.00
LG Luis Gonzalez Jsy B 4.00 10.00
MO Magglio Ordonez Jsy A 3.00 8.00
MO1 Moises Alou Uni A 3.00 8.00
MO2 Moises Alou Bat B 4.00 10.00
MP Mike Piazza Jsy B 6.00 15.00
MR Manny Ramirez Bat A 4.00 10.00
MS1 Mike Schmidt Bat A 8.00 20.00
MS2 Mike Schmidt Uni A 8.00 20.00
MT Miguel Tejada Bat B 4.00 10.00
NG1 Nomar Garciaparra Bat B 6.00 15.00
NG2 Nomar Garciaparra Jsy B 6.00 15.00
RH Rickey Henderson Bat B 6.00 15.00
RP Rafael Palmeiro Jsy B 6.00 15.00
SG Shawn Green Bat B 4.00 10.00
SS1 Sammy Sosa Bat B 6.00 15.00
SS2 Sammy Sosa Jsy A 4.00 10.00
TG1 Troy Glaus Bat A 3.00 8.00
TG2 Troy Glaus Uni B 4.00 10.00
TH Todd Helton Bat B 6.00 15.00
TS Tim Salmon Uni B 6.00 15.00
VG1 Vladimir Guerrero Jsy A 4.00 10.00
VG2 Vladimir Guerrero Bat A 4.00 10.00

2003 Topps Pristine Borders Relics

REFRACTOR ODDS 1:210
REFRACTOR PRINT RUN 25 SERIAL #'d SETS
NO REFRACTOR PRICING DUE TO SCARCITY
AJ Andruw Jones Uni 4.00 10.00
AP Albert Pujols Jsy 8.00 20.00
AS Alfonso Soriano Bat 3.00 8.00
BW Bernie Williams Bat 4.00 10.00
CC Chin Feng Chen Jsy 15.00 40.00
CG Cristian Guzman Bat 3.00 8.00
IR Ivan Rodriguez Bat 4.00 10.00
KI Kazuhisa Ishii Jsy 3.00 8.00
MO Magglio Ordonez Jsy 3.00 8.00
MR Manny Ramirez Jsy 4.00 10.00
MT Miguel Tejada Bat 3.00 8.00
PM Pedro Martinez Jsy 4.00 10.00
SS Sammy Sosa Jsy 4.00 10.00
TS Tsuyoshi Shinjo Bat 3.00 8.00
VG Vladimir Guerrero Jsy 4.00 10.00

2003 Topps Pristine Corners Relics

STATED ODDS 1:12
REFRACTOR ODDS 1:285
REFRACTOR PRINT RUN 25 SERIAL #'d SETS
NO REFRACTOR PRICING DUE TO SCARCITY
AS Edgardo Alfonzo Bat / J.T. Snow Bat 4.00 10.00
BK Sean Burroughs Jsy / Ryan Klesko Bat 4.00 10.00
BM Adrian Beltre Bat / Fred McGriff Bat 4.00 10.00
BT David Bell Bat / Jim Thome Bat 6.00 15.00
CD Eric Chavez Bat / Erubiel Durazo Bat 4.00 10.00
GS Troy Glaus Jsy / Scott Spiezio Jsy 4.00 10.00
KM Corey Koskie Bat / Doug Mientkiewicz Bat 4.00 10.00
RM Scott Rolen Bat / Tino Martinez Bat 10.00 25.00
TP Mark Teixeira Bat / Rafael Palmeiro Bat 6.00 15.00
VG Robin Ventura Bat / Jason Giambi Bat 4.00 10.00
WG Matt Williams Bat / Mark Grace Bat 6.00 15.00

2003 Topps Pristine Factor Bat Relics

STATED ODDS 1:9
REFRACTOR ODDS 1:210
REFRACTOR PRINT RUN 25 SERIAL #'d SETS
NO REFRACTOR PRICING DUE TO SCARCITY
AD Adam Dunn 3.00 8.00
AR Alex Rodriguez 4.00 10.00
AS Alfonso Soriano 3.00 8.00
DE Darin Erstad 3.00 8.00
JG Jason Giambi 3.00 8.00
LB Lance Berkman 3.00 8.00
MO Magglio Ordonez 3.00 8.00
MP Mike Piazza 6.00 15.00
MR Manny Ramirez 4.00 10.00
NG Nomar Garciaparra 6.00 15.00
SS Sammy Sosa 4.00 10.00
TG Troy Glaus 3.00 8.00
TH Todd Helton 4.00 10.00
TKH Torii Hunter 3.00 8.00
VG Vladimir Guerrero 4.00 10.00

2003 Topps Pristine Mini

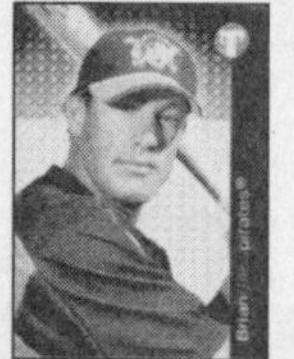

VETERAN STATED ODDS 1:8
ROOKIE STATED ODDS 1:16
AK Austin Kearns V 1.25 3.00
AR Alex Rodriguez V 4.00 10.00
AS Alfonso Soriano V 1.25 3.00
BB Barry Bonds V 6.00 15.00
BC Bernie Castro R 1.25 3.00
BG Brian Giles V 1.25 3.00
BPB Bryan Bullington R 1.25 3.00
BWB Bobby Basham R 1.25 3.00
CW Chien-Ming Wang R 5.00 12.00
DH Dan Haren R 2.00 5.00
DJ Derek Jeter V 6.00 15.00
DM Dustin McGowan R 1.50 4.00
EC Eric Chavez V 1.25 3.00
ELC Eric Crozier R 1.50 4.00
ER Elizardo Ramirez R 1.50 4.00
IS Ichiro Suzuki V 5.00 12.00
JB Jeremy Bonderman R 4.00 10.00
JC Jose Contreras R 2.00 5.00
JG Jason Giambi V 1.25 3.00
JJK Jason Kubel R 3.00 8.00
JK Jeff Kent V 1.25 3.00
JT Jim Thome V 1.50 4.00
KY Kevin Youkilis R 3.00 8.00
MH Michel Hernandez R 1.25 3.00
MJP Mike Piazza V 4.00 10.00
MO Magglio Ordonez V 1.25 3.00
MP Mark Prior V 1.50 4.00
MT Miguel Tejada V 1.25 3.00
NG Nomar Garciaparra V 4.00 10.00
NL Nook Logan R 1.50 4.00
RB Rocco Baldelli V 1.25 3.00
RC Roger Clemens V 5.00 12.00
RD Rajai Davis R 1.25 3.00
RH Ryan Howard R 15.00 40.00
RJC Robinson Cano R 10.00 25.00
RS Ryan Shealy R 4.00 10.00
SS Sammy Sosa V 2.50 6.00
TM Tyler Martin R 1.25 3.00
VG Vladimir Guerrero V 2.50 6.00
WL Wil Ledezma R 1.25 3.00

2003 Topps Pristine Mini Autograph

STATED ODDS 1:636
STATED PRINT RUN 100 CARDS
PRINT RUN INFO PROVIDED BY TOPPS
CARD IS NOT SERIAL-NUMBERED
RC Roger Clemens/100 * 60.00 120.00

2003 Topps Pristine Personal Endorsements

STATED ODDS 1:5
GOLD STATED ODDS 1:184
GOLD PRINT RUN 25 SERIAL #'d SETS
NO GOLD PRICING DUE TO SCARCITY
AB Andrew Brown 6.00 15.00
BM Brett Myers 6.00 15.00
DE David Eckstein 12.50 30.00
FS Felix Sanchez 4.00 10.00
FV Fernando Vina 4.00 10.00
JG Jay Gibbons 4.00 10.00
JP Josh Phelps 4.00 10.00
KH Ken Harvey 4.00 10.00
KS Kelly Shoppach 6.00 15.00
LF Lew Ford 6.00 15.00
ML Mike Lowell 6.00 15.00
MS Mike Sweeney 6.00 15.00
PK Paul Konerko 10.00 25.00
RJH Rich Harden 10.00 25.00
RYC Ryan Church 6.00 15.00
SR Scott Rolen 6.00 15.00
VM Victor Martinez 4.00 10.00

2003 Topps Pristine Primary Elements Patch Relics

STATED ODDS 1:45
STATED PRINT RUN 50 SETS
CARDS ARE NOT SERIAL-NUMBERED
PRINT RUN INFO PROVIDED BY TOPPS
NO PRICING DUE TO SCARCITY
REFRACTOR ODDS 1:224
REFRACTOR PRINT RUN 10 SERIAL #'d SETS
NO REFRACTOR PRICING DUE TO SCARCITY

2004 Topps Pristine

This 190-card set was released in October, 2004. The set was issued, in what has been traditional for this product, in a pack within a pack concept. The "full" pack, is an eight card pack with an $30 SRP which came five packs to a box and six boxes to a case. Cards numbered 1 through 100 feature veterans while cards 101 through 190 feature three cards each of the same rookie with decreasing print runs for each card. The Common Rookie Cards were printed in the approximate same print run as the veterans while the uncommon cards were issued to a stated rate of one in two with a stated print run of 999 serial numbered sets and the rare rookies were issued with a stated print run of 499 serial numbered sets and were issued at a stated rate of one in four. There are some reports that the #168 and #169 Chris Saenz cards were never produced.

COMMON CARD (1-100) .50 1.25
COMMON C (101-190) .50 1.25
C 101-190 APPROX.EQUAL TO 1-100
COMMON U (101-190) .75 2.00
UNCOMMON 101-190 STATED ODDS 1:2
UNCOMMON 101-190 PRINT RUN 999 #'d SETS
COMMON R (101-190) 1.25 3.00
RARE 101-190 STATED ODDS 1:4
RARE 101-190 PRINT RUN 499 #'d SETS
OVERALL PLATES ODDS 1:52 HOBBY
PLATE PRINT RUN 1 SET PER COLOR
BLACK-CYAN-MAGENTA-YELLOW ISSUED
NO PLATE PRICING DUE TO SCARCITY
1 Jim Thome .75 2.00
2 Ryan Klesko .50 1.25
3 Ichiro Suzuki 2.00 5.00
4 Rocco Baldelli .50 1.25
5 Vernon Wells .50 1.25
6 Javier Vazquez .50 1.25
7 Billy Wagner .50 1.25
8 Jose Reyes .75 2.00
9 Lance Berkman .75 2.00
10 Alex Rodriguez 2.00 5.00
11 Pat Burrell .50 1.25
12 Mark Mulder .50 1.25
13 Mike Piazza 1.25 3.00
14 Miguel Cabrera 1.25 3.00
15 Larry Walker .75 2.00
16 Carlos Lee .50 1.25
17 Mark Prior .50 1.25
18 Pedro Martinez .75 2.00
19 Melvin Mora .50 1.25
20 Sammy Sosa 1.25 3.00
21 Bartolo Colon .50 1.25
22 Luis Gonzalez .50 1.25
23 Marcus Giles .50 1.25
24 Ken Griffey Jr. 2.00 5.00
25 Ivan Rodriguez .75 2.00
26 Carlos Beltran .50 1.25
27 Geoff Jenkins .50 1.25
28 Nick Johnson .50 1.25
29 Gary Sheffield .50 1.25
30 Alfonso Soriano .50 1.25
31 Scott Rolen .75 2.00
32 Garret Anderson .50 1.25
33 Richie Sexson .50 1.25
34 Curt Schilling .75 2.00
35 Greg Maddux 2.00 5.00
36 Adam Dunn .75 2.00
37 Preston Wilson .50 1.25
38 Josh Beckett .75 2.00
39 Roy Oswalt .75 2.00
40 Derek Jeter 3.00 8.00
41 Jason Kendall .50 1.25
42 Bret Boone .50 1.25
43 Torii Hunter .50 1.25
44 Roy Halladay 1.25 3.00
45 Edgar Renteria .50 1.25
46 Troy Glaus .50 1.25
47 Chipper Jones 1.25 3.00
48 Manny Ramirez 1.25 3.00
49 C.C. Sabathia .75 2.00
50 Albert Pujols 3.00 8.00
51 Randy Wolf .50 1.25
52 Eric Chavez .50 1.25
53 Kevin Brown .50 1.25
54 Cliff Floyd .50 1.25
55 Jeff Bagwell .75 2.00
56 Frank Thomas 1.25 3.00
57 David Ortiz 1.25 3.00
58 Rafael Palmeiro .75 2.00
59 Randy Johnson 1.25 3.00
60 Vladimir Guerrero 1.25 3.00
61 Carlos Delgado .50 1.25
62 Hank Blalock .50 1.25
63 Jim Edmonds .75 2.00
64 Jason Schmidt .50 1.25
65 Mike Lieberthal .50 1.25
66 Tim Hudson .75 2.00
67 Jorge Posada .75 2.00
68 Jose Vidro .50 1.25
69 Eric Gagne .50 1.25
70 Roger Clemens 1.50 4.00
71 Mike Lowell .50 1.25
72 Dontrelle Willis .50 1.25
73 Austin Kearns .50 1.25
74 Kerry Wood .50 1.25
75 Miguel Tejada .75 2.00
76 Bobby Abreu .50 1.25
77 Edgar Martinez .75 2.00
78 Joe Mauer 1.25 3.00
79 Mike Sweeney .50 1.25
80 Jason Giambi .50 1.25
81 Mark Teixeira 1.25 3.00
82 Aubrey Huff .50 1.25
83 Brian Giles .50 1.25
84 Barry Zito .50 1.25
85 Mike Mussina .75 2.00
86 Brandon Webb .50 1.25
87 Andruw Jones .50 1.25
88 Javy Lopez .50 1.25
89 Bill Mueller .50 1.25
90 Scott Podsednik .50 1.25
91 Moises Alou .50 1.25
92 Esteban Loaiza .50 1.25
93 Magglio Ordonez .75 2.00
94 Jeff Kent .50 1.25
95 Todd Helton .75 2.00
96 Juan Pierre .50 1.25
97 Jody Gerut .50 1.25
98 Angel Berroa .50 1.25
99 Shawn Green .50 1.25
100 Nomar Garciaparra 1.25 3.00
101 David Aardsma C RC .50 1.25
102 David Aardsma U .75 2.00
103 David Aardsma R 1.25 3.00
104 Erick Aybar C RC .75 2.00
105 Erick Aybar U 1.25 3.00
106 Erick Aybar R 2.00 5.00
107 Chad Bentz C RC .50 1.25
108 Chad Bentz U .75 2.00
109 Chad Bentz R 1.25 3.00
110 Travis Blackley C RC .50 1.25
111 Travis Blackley U .75 2.00
112 Travis Blackley R 1.25 3.00
113 Bobby Brownlie C RC .50 1.25
114 Bobby Brownlie U .75 2.00
115 Bobby Brownlie R 1.25 3.00
116 Alberto Callaspo C RC 1.25 3.00
117 Alberto Callaspo U 2.00 5.00
118 Alberto Callaspo R 3.00 8.00
119 Kazuo Matsui C RC .75 2.00
120 Kazuo Matsui U 1.25 3.00
121 Kazuo Matsui R 2.00 5.00
122 Jesse Crain C RC .50 1.25
123 Jesse Crain U .75 2.00
124 Jesse Crain R 1.25 3.00
125 Howie Kendrick C RC 8.00 20.00
126 Howie Kendrick U 12.00 30.00
127 Howie Kendrick R 20.00 50.00
128 Blake Hawksworth C RC .50 1.25
129 Blake Hawksworth U .75 2.00
130 Blake Hawksworth R 1.25 3.00
131 Conor Jackson C RC 3.00 8.00
132 Conor Jackson U 5.00 12.00
133 Conor Jackson R 8.00 20.00
134 Paul Maholm C RC .50 1.25
135 Paul Maholm U 1.25 3.00
136 Paul Maholm R 2.00 5.00
137 Lastings Milledge C RC 3.00 8.00
138 Lastings Milledge U 5.00 12.00
139 Lastings Milledge R 8.00 20.00
140 Matt Moses C RC .75 2.00
141 Matt Moses U 1.25 3.00
142 Matt Moses R 2.00 5.00
143 David Murphy C RC 1.25 3.00
144 David Murphy U 2.00 5.00
145 David Murphy R 3.00 8.00
146 Dioner Navarro C RC .75 2.00
147 Dioner Navarro U 1.25 3.00
148 Dioner Navarro R 2.00 5.00
149 Dustin Nippert C RC .50 1.25
150 Dustin Nippert U .75 2.00
151 Dustin Nippert R 1.25 3.00
152 Vito Chiaravalloti C RC .50 1.25
153 Vito Chiaravalloti U .75 2.00
154 Vito Chiaravalloti R 1.25 3.00
155 Akinori Otsuka C RC .50 1.25
156 Akinori Otsuka U .75 2.00
157 Akinori Otsuka R 1.25 3.00
158 Casey Daigle C RC .50 1.25
159 Casey Daigle U .75 2.00
160 Casey Daigle R 1.25 3.00
161 Carlos Quentin C RC 2.00 5.00
162 Carlos Quentin U 3.00 8.00
163 Carlos Quentin R 5.00 12.00
164 Omar Quintanilla C RC .50 1.25
165 Omar Quintanilla U .75 2.00
166 Omar Quintanilla R 1.25 3.00
167 Chris Saenz C RC .50 1.25
168 Chris Saenz U .75 2.00
169 Chris Saenz R 1.25 3.00
170 Ervin Santana C RC 1.25 3.00
171 Ervin Santana U 2.00 5.00
172 Ervin Santana R 3.00 8.00
173 Chris Shelton C RC .50 1.25
174 Chris Shelton U .75 2.00
175 Chris Shelton R 1.25 3.00
176 Kyle Sleeth C RC .50 1.25
177 Kyle Sleeth U .75 2.00
178 Kyle Sleeth R 1.25 3.00
179 Brad Snyder C RC .50 1.25
180 Brad Snyder U .75 2.00
181 Brad Snyder R 1.25 3.00
182 Tim Stauffer C RC .75 2.00
183 Tim Stauffer U 1.25 3.00
184 Tim Stauffer R 2.00 5.00
185 Shingo Takatsu C RC .50 1.25
186 Shingo Takatsu U .75 2.00
187 Shingo Takatsu R 1.25 3.00
188 Merkin Valdez C RC .50 1.25
189 Merkin Valdez U .75 2.00
190 Merkin Valdez R 1.25 3.00

2004 Topps Pristine Gold Refractors

*GOLD 1-100: 2.5X TO 6X BASIC
*GOLD C 101-190: 2.5X TO 6X BASIC
*GOLD U 101-190: 1.5X TO 4X BASIC
*GOLD R 101-190: 1X TO 2.5X BASIC
ONE PER SEALED HOBBY BOX
STATED PRINT RUN 41 SERIAL #'d SETS

2004 Topps Pristine Refractors

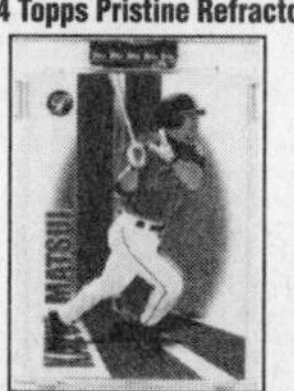

*REFRACTORS 1-100: 2.5X TO 6X BASIC
1-100 STATED ODDS 1:11
1-100 PRINT RUN 49 SERIAL #'d SETS
*REFRACTORS C 101-190: .6X TO 1.5X BASIC
COMMON 101-190 RANDOM IN PACKS
COMMON 101-190 PRINT RUN 999 #'d SETS
*REFRACTORS U 101-190: .6X TO 1.5X BASIC
UNCOMMON 101-190 ODDS 1:5
UNCOMMON 101-190 PRINT RUN 399 #'d SETS
*REFRACTORS R 101-190: 1X TO 2.5X BASIC
RARE 101-190 ODDS 1:35
RARE 101-190 PRINT RUN 49 #'d SETS

2004 Topps Pristine 1-2-3 Triple Relics

STATED ODDS 1:171
*REFRACTOR: X TO X BASIC
REFRACTOR ODDS 1:686
REFRACTOR PRINT RUN 25 #'d SETS
B = 'S BAT; J = 'S JSY
BOS Johnny Damon Bat 20.00 50.00
Bill Mueller Jsy
Nomar Garciaparra Jsy
CHC Mark Grudzielanek Bat 15.00 40.00
Alex Gonzalez Bat
Sammy Sosa Bat
NYY Kenny Lofton Bat 20.00 50.00
Derek Jeter Bat
Alex Rodriguez Bat

2004 Topps Pristine Fantasy Favorites Relics

*REFRACTOR: 2X TO 5X BASIC
REFRACTOR STATED ODDS 1:59
REFRACTOR PRINT RUN 25 #'d SETS
AB Angel Berroa Bat 2.00 5.00
AJ Andruw Jones Jsy 3.00 8.00
AP Albert Pujols Jsy 6.00 15.00
AR Alex Rodriguez Bat 4.00 10.00
BB Bret Boone Jsy 2.00 5.00
BW Brandon Webb Uni 2.00 5.00
CD Carlos Delgado Jsy 2.00 5.00
CJ Chipper Jones Jsy 4.00 10.00
CK Corey Koskie Bat 2.00 5.00
DJ Derek Jeter Bat 10.00 25.00
EG Eric Gagne Jsy 2.00 5.00
FT Frank Thomas Jsy 4.00 10.00
JB Jeff Bagwell Uni 3.00 8.00
JD Johnny Damon Bat 3.00 8.00
JR Jimmy Rollins Jsy 2.00 5.00
JT Jim Thome Uni 3.00 8.00
JV Jose Vidro Bat 2.00 5.00
KL Kenny Lofton Bat 2.00 5.00
KW Kerry Wood Jsy 2.00 5.00
LW Larry Walker Jsy 2.00 5.00
MA Moises Alou Jsy 2.00 5.00
MG Mark Grudzielanek Bat 2.00 5.00
MP Mark Prior Jsy 3.00 8.00
MPI Mike Piazza Jsy 4.00 10.00
MT Mark Teixeira Bat 3.00 8.00
NG Nomar Garciaparra Jsy 4.00 10.00
PM Pedro Martinez Jsy 3.00 8.00
PW Preston Wilson Jsy 2.00 5.00
RB Rocco Baldelli Bat 2.00 5.00
RF Rafael Furcal Bat 2.00 5.00
RFJ Rafael Furcal Jsy 2.00 5.00
SG Shawn Green Jsy 2.00 5.00
TH Tim Hudson Jsy 2.00 5.00
THE Todd Helton Jsy 3.00 8.00
VG Vladimir Guerrero Bat 4.00 10.00

2004 Topps Pristine Going Going Gone Bat Relics

GROUP A ODDS 1:6
GROUP B ODDS 1:11
*REFRACTOR: 2X TO 5X BASIC
REFRACTOR STATED ODDS 1:93
REFRACTOR PRINT RUN 25 #'d SETS
AD Adam Dunn B 2.00 5.00
AP Albert Pujols A 6.00 15.00
AR Alex Rodriguez A 4.00 10.00
AS Alfonso Soriano A 2.00 5.00
BB Bret Boone A 2.00 5.00
CJ Chipper Jones A 4.00 10.00
DO David Ortiz B 4.00 10.00
FT Frank Thomas B 4.00 10.00
JG Juan Gonzalez A 2.00 5.00
JJ Jacque Jones A 2.00 5.00
JK Jeff Kent A 2.00 5.00
JT Jim Thome A 3.00 8.00
LB Lance Berkman A 2.00 5.00
LG Luis Gonzalez A 2.00 5.00
MO Magglio Ordonez A 2.00 5.00
MP Mike Piazza B 4.00 10.00
MR Manny Ramirez B 3.00 8.00
RK Ryan Klesko B 2.00 5.00
SR Scott Rolen A 3.00 8.00
SS Sammy Sosa A 4.00 10.00
VG Vladimir Guerrero A 4.00 10.00
VW Vernon Wells A 2.00 5.00

2004 Topps Pristine Key Acquisition Bat Relics

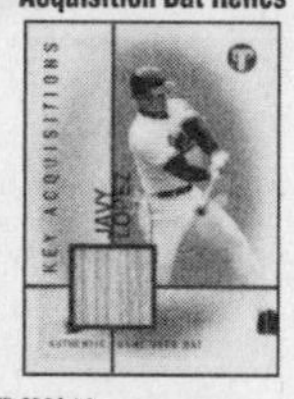

STATED ODDS 1:8
*REFRACTOR: 2X TO 5X BASIC
REFRACTOR ODDS 1:256
REFRACTOR PRINT RUN 25 #'d SETS
AR Alex Rodriguez 4.00 10.00
AS Alfonso Soriano 2.00 5.00
GS Gary Sheffield 2.00 5.00
HC Hee Seop Choi 2.00 5.00
IR Ivan Rodriguez 3.00 8.00
JG Juan Gonzalez 2.00 5.00
JL Javy Lopez 2.00 5.00
VG Vladimir Guerrero 4.00 10.00

2004 Topps Pristine Mini

STATED ODDS 1:5
AO Akinori Otsuka R .60 1.50
AP Albert Pujols V 4.00 10.00
AR Alex Rodriguez V 2.50 6.00
BH Blake Hawksworth R .60 1.50
CJ Chipper Jones V 1.50 4.00
CJA Conor Jackson R 4.00 10.00
DA David Aardsma R .60 1.50
DJ Derek Jeter V 4.00 10.00
DM David Murphy R 1.50 4.00
DN Dioner Navarro R 1.00 2.50
DW Dontrelle Willis V .60 1.50
EA Erick Aybar R 1.00 2.50
HK Howie Kendrick R 10.00 25.00
IS Ichiro Suzuki V 2.50 6.00
JG Jason Giambi V .60 1.50
JT Jim Thome V 1.00 2.50
KM Kazuo Matsui R 1.00 2.50
KS Kyle Sleeth R .60 1.50
KW Kerry Wood V .60 1.50
LM Lastings Milledge R 4.00 10.00
MM Matt Moses R 1.00 2.50
MP Mark Prior V 1.00 2.50
MPI Mike Piazza V 1.50 4.00
MV Merkin Valdez R .60 1.50
NG Nomar Garciaparra V 1.50 4.00
SS Sammy Sosa V 1.50 4.00
ST Shingo Takatsu R .60 1.50
TS Tim Stauffer R 1.00 2.50
VC Vito Chiaravalloti R .60 1.50
VG Vladimir Guerrero V 1.50 4.00

2004 Topps Pristine Mini Relics

STATED ODDS 1:51
STATED PRINT RUN 100 SETS
CARDS ARE NOT SERIAL-NUMBERED
PRINT RUN INFO PROVIDED BY TOPPS
AP Albert Pujols Jsy 10.00 25.00
CJ Chipper Jones Jsy 6.00 15.00
EG Eric Gagne Jsy 3.00 8.00
JB Jeff Bagwell Uni 5.00 12.00
KW Kerry Wood Jsy 3.00 8.00
MP Mark Prior Jsy 5.00 12.00
NG Nomar Garciaparra Jsy 6.00 15.00
PM Pedro Martinez Jsy 5.00 12.00
PW Preston Wilson Jsy 3.00 8.00
MPI Mike Piazza Jsy 6.00 15.00

2004 Topps Pristine Patch Place Relics

GROUP A ODDS 1:30
GROUP B ODDS 1:34
REFRACTOR STATED ODDS 1:155
REFRACTOR PRINT RUN 10 #'d SETS
NO REFPRICING DUE TO SCARCITY
LISTED PRICES ARE SINGLE COLOR PATCH
*MULTI-COLOR: ADD 100% PREMIUM
AD Adam Dunn A 4.00 10.00
AJ Andruw Jones A 6.00 15.00
AK Austin Kearns A 4.00 10.00
AP Albert Pujols B 15.00 40.00
BB Bret Boone B 4.00 10.00
BZ Barry Zito A 4.00 10.00
CC Chin-Feng Chen A 20.00 50.00
CD Carlos Delgado A 4.00 10.00
CJ Chipper Jones B 6.00 15.00
DW Dontrelle Willis A 6.00 15.00
EG Eric Gagne A 4.00 10.00
FT Frank Thomas A 6.00 15.00
JB Jeff Bagwell B 6.00 15.00
JBE Josh Beckett B 4.00 10.00
JR Jose Reyes A 4.00 10.00
JS John Smoltz A 6.00 15.00
KW Kerry Wood A 4.00 10.00
LC Luis Castillo A 4.00 10.00
LG Luis Gonzalez B 4.00 10.00
ML Mike Lowell A 4.00 10.00
MP Mark Prior B 6.00 15.00
MPI Mike Piazza B 6.00 15.00
NG Nomar Garciaparra A 6.00 15.00
PL Paul Lo Duca A 4.00 10.00
PM Pedro Martinez B 6.00 15.00
PW Preston Wilson A 4.00 10.00
RB Rocco Baldelli A 4.00 10.00
RF Rafael Furcal A 4.00 10.00
RJ Randy Johnson B 6.00 15.00
SG Shawn Green A 4.00 10.00
SS Sammy Sosa A 6.00 15.00
TH Tim Hudson A 4.00 10.00
THE Todd Helton B 6.00 15.00

2004 Topps Pristine Personal Endorsements

GROUP A ODDS 1:39
GROUP B ODDS 1:41
GROUP C ODDS 1:7
GOLD STATED ODDS 1:73
GOLD PRINT RUN 25 SERIAL #'d SETS
NO GOLD PRICING DUE TO SCARCITY
AH Aubrey Huff C 4.00 10.00
AR Alex Rodriguez A 60.00 120.00
BC Bobby Crosby C 4.00 10.00
BM Brett Myers A 6.00 15.00
BW Brandon Webb B 4.00 10.00
CJ Conor Jackson C 8.00 20.00
CL Chris Lubanski C 4.00 10.00
DA David Aardsma C 6.00 15.00
DM Dustin McGowan C 4.00 10.00
DY Delmon Young A 10.00 25.00
EH Estee Harris C 6.00 15.00
ES Ervin Santana C 10.00 25.00
GA Garret Anderson A 6.00 15.00
GS Gary Sheffield A 15.00 40.00
GSI Grady Sizemore C 10.00 25.00
HB Hank Blalock B 6.00 15.00
IR Ivan Rodriguez A 15.00 40.00
JF Jennie Finch A 100.00 175.00
JM Joe Mauer B 30.00 60.00
JP Jorge Posada A 15.00 40.00
JV Javier Vazquez A 6.00 15.00
LB Lance Berkman A 10.00 25.00
MC Miguel Cabrera B 10.00 25.00
MG Marcus Giles A 6.00 15.00
SP Scott Podsednik B 10.00 25.00
VC Vito Chiaravalloti C 4.00 10.00
VG Vladimir Guerrero A 20.00 50.00
WM Willie Mays A 125.00 200.00

2004 Topps Pristine Two of a Kind Dual Autographs

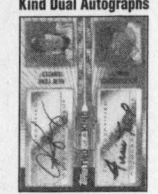

STATED ODDS 1:3705
STATED PRINT RUN 13 SERIAL #'d CARDS
AROD/CANSECO NOT SER.#'d
NO PRICING DUE TO SCARCITY
RM Alex Rodriguez
Willie Mays
RC Alex Rodriguez
Jose Canseco

2005 Topps Pristine

This 210-card set was released in October, 2005. The set was issued in eight-card packs which came as a multi-pack concept. Cards numbered 1-100 feature active veterans while cards 101 through 130 feature Rookie Cards. Cards numbered 131 through 180 feature game-used cards of veterans while cards 181 through 205 feature signed cards of players (Most of whom are Rookies or Prospects). Cards numbered 206 through 210 feature both an autograph and a game-worn jersey piece. Cards numbered 131 through 180 were issued to a stated print run of 500 serial numbered sets and were issued to stated odds of one in three. Cards numbered 181 through 205 were issued at stated odds of one in 22 and were issued to a stated print run of 100 serial numbered sets. Cards numbered 206 through 210 were issued at a stated rate of one in 219 and those cards were issued to a stated print run of 49 serial numbered sets. A couple of players did not return their cards in time for pack-out and those cards could be exchanged until October 31, 2007.

COMMON CARD (1-100) .40 1.00
COMMON RC (101-130) .40 1.00
COMMON GU (131-180) 2.00 5.00
GU 131-180 STATED ODDS 1:3
GU 131-180 PRINT RUN 500 #'d SETS
COMMON AU (181-205) 12.50 30.00
COMMON FY AU (181-205) 10.00 25.00
AU 181-205 STATED ODDS 1:22
AU 181-205 PRINT RUN 100 #'d SETS
AU-GU 206-210 STATED ODDS 1:219
AU-GU 206-210 PRINT RUN 49 #'d SETS
AU-GU 206-210 EXCH.DEADLINE 10/31/07
OVERALL PLATE ODDS 1:53 HOBBY
PLATE PRINT RUN 1 SET PER COLOR
BLACK-CYAN-MAGENTA-YELLOW ISSUED
NO PLATE PRICING DUE TO SCARCITY
1 Alex Rodriguez 1.50 4.00
2 Jake Peavy .40 1.00
3 Bobby Crosby .40 1.00
4 J.D. Drew .40 1.00
5 Scott Rolen .60 1.50
6 Bobby Abreu .40 1.00
7 Ken Griffey Jr. 1.50 4.00
8 Jeremy Bonderman .40 1.00
9 Mike Sweeney .40 1.00
10 Mark Prior .60 1.50
11 Tim Hudson .60 1.50
12 Clint Barmes .40 1.00
13 Jeff Bagwell .60 1.50
14 Andruw Jones .40 1.00
15 Carlos Delgado .40 1.00
16 Rocco Baldelli .40 1.00
17 Adam Dunn .60 1.50
18 Greg Maddux 1.50 4.00
19 Torii Hunter .40 1.00
20 Miguel Tejada .60 1.50
21 Lyle Overbay .40 1.00
22 Craig Wilson .40 1.00
23 Scott Kazmir 1.00 2.50
24 Alex Rios .60 1.50
25 Ichiro Suzuki 1.50 4.00
26 Jorge Posada .60 1.50
27 Jose Reyes .60 1.50
28 Hank Blalock .40 1.00
29 Troy Glaus .40 1.00
30 Todd Helton .60 1.50
31 Javy Lopez .40 1.00
32 Barry Zito .40 1.00
33 Jimmy Rollins .60 1.50
34 Mark Loretta .40 1.00
35 Richie Sexson .40 1.00
36 Nick Johnson .40 1.00
37 Ivan Rodriguez .60 1.50
38 Jeff Kent .40 1.00
39 Jake Westbrook .40 1.00
40 Carlos Beltran .60 1.50
41 Rich Harden .40 1.00
42 Joe Mauer 1.00 2.50
43 Luis Gonzalez .40 1.00
44 Frank Thomas 1.00 2.50
45 Michael Young .60 1.50
46 Jason Schmidt .40 1.00
47 Eric Chavez .40 1.00
48 Vinny Castilla .40 1.00
49 John Smoltz 1.00 2.50
50 Barry Bonds 2.00 5.00
51 Jim Edmonds .60 1.50
52 Edgar Renteria .40 1.00

53 Jose Vidro .40 1.00
54 Chipper Jones 1.00 2.50
55 Curt Schilling .60 1.50
56 Victor Martinez .60 1.50
57 Josh Beckett .60 1.50
58 Derrek Lee .40 1.00
59 Shawn Green .40 1.00
60 Roger Clemens 1.25 3.00
61 Orlando Cabrera .40 1.00
62 Mike Piazza 1.00 2.50
63 Gary Sheffield .40 1.00
64 Carl Crawford .60 1.50
65 Johan Santana 1.00 2.50
66 Oliver Perez .40 1.00
67 Manny Ramirez 1.00 2.50
68 Paul Konerko .60 1.50
69 Preston Wilson .40 1.00
70 Sammy Sosa 1.00 2.50
71 Eric Gagne .40 1.00
72 Geoff Jenkins .40 1.00
73 Magglio Ordonez .60 1.50
74 Kerry Wood .40 1.00
75 Albert Pujols 2.50 6.00
76 Roy Halladay 1.00 2.50
77 Aubrey Huff .40 1.00
78 Nomar Garciaparra 1.00 2.50
79 Brian Roberts .40 1.00
80 Randy Johnson 1.00 2.50
81 Pat Burrell .40 1.00
82 Brian Giles .40 1.00
83 Mike Mussina .60 1.50
84 Mark Teixeira 1.00 2.50
85 Pedro Martinez .60 1.50
86 Jason Bay .40 1.00
87 Mark Buehrle .60 1.50
88 Rafael Furcal .40 1.00
89 Juan Pierre .40 1.00
90 Jim Thome .60 1.50
91 Ben Sheets .40 1.00
92 Alfonso Soriano .60 1.50
93 Adrian Beltre .40 1.00
94 Miguel Cabrera 1.00 2.50
95 Derek Jeter 2.50 6.00
96 Vernon Wells .40 1.00
97 Lance Berkman .60 1.50
98 Hideki Matsui 1.50 4.00
99 David Ortiz 1.00 2.50
100 Vladimir Guerrero 1.00 2.50
101 Justin Verlander FY RC 8.00 20.00
102 Billy Butler FY RC 2.00 5.00
103 Wladimir Balentien FY RC .60 1.50
104 Jeremy West FY RC .40 1.00
105 Philip Humber FY RC 1.00 2.50
106 Tyler Pelland FY RC .40 1.00
107 Andy LaRoche FY RC 2.00 5.00
108 Hernan Iribarren FY RC .40 1.00
109 Luke Scott FY RC 1.00 2.50
110 Landon Powell FY RC .40 1.00
111 Alexander Smit FY RC .40 1.00
112 Ryan Garko FY RC .40 1.00
113 Bear Bay FY RC .40 1.00
114 Ian Bladergroen FY RC .40 1.00
115 Manny Parra FY RC 1.00 2.50
116 Andy Sides FY RC .40 1.00
117 Travis Chick FY RC .40 1.00
118 Stefan Bailie FY RC .40 1.00
119 Chuck Tiffany FY RC 1.00 2.50
120 Buck Coats FY RC .40 1.00
121 Jeff Niemann FY RC 1.00 2.50
122 Jake Postlewait FY RC .40 1.00
123 Matt Campbell FY RC .40 1.00
124 Kevin Melillo FY RC .40 1.00
125 Mike Morse FY RC 1.00 2.50
126 Anthony Reyes FY RC .60 1.50
127 Casey McGehee FY RC 1.25 3.00
128 Cody Haerther FY RC .40 1.00
129 Brandon McCarthy FY RC .60 1.50
130 Glen Perkins FY RC .40 1.00
131 Moises Alou Bat 2.00 5.00
132 Nomar Garciaparra Bat 4.00 10.00
133 Scott Rolen Jsy 3.00 8.00
134 Miguel Tejada Uni 2.00 5.00
135 Alex Rodriguez Bat 6.00 15.00
136 Michael Young Jsy 2.00 5.00
137 Tim Hudson Uni 2.00 5.00
138 Troy Glaus Bat 2.00 5.00
139 Eric Chavez Uni 2.00 5.00
140 David Ortiz Bat 3.00 8.00
141 Andruw Jones Jsy 3.00 8.00
142 Richie Sexson Bat 2.00 5.00
143 Jim Thome Bat 3.00 8.00
144 Javy Lopez Bat 2.00 5.00
145 Lance Berkman Jsy 2.00 5.00
146 Gary Sheffield Bat 2.00 5.00
147 Dontrelle Willis Jsy 2.00 5.00
148 Curt Schilling Jsy 3.00 8.00
149 Jorge Posada Jsy 3.00 8.00
150 Vladimir Guerrero Bat 4.00 10.00
151 Adam Dunn Jsy 2.00 5.00
152 Ryan Drese Jsy 2.00 5.00
153 Hank Blalock Uni 2.00 5.00
154 Kerry Wood Jsy 2.00 5.00
155 Alfonso Soriano Bat 2.00 5.00
156 Aramis Ramirez Bat 2.00 5.00
157 Mark Mulder Uni 2.00 5.00
158 Paul Konerko Bat 2.00 5.00
159 Jim Edmonds Jsy 2.00 5.00
160 Roger Clemens Jsy 5.00 12.00
161 Mariano Rivera Jsy 4.00 10.00
162 Rafael Palmeiro Bat 3.00 8.00
163 Mark Teixeira Bat 3.00 8.00
164 Eric Gagne Jsy 2.00 5.00
165 Sammy Sosa Bat 4.00 10.00
166 Brett Myers Jsy 2.00 5.00
167 Kazuhisa Ishii Uni 2.00 5.00
168 Ken Harvey Bat 2.00 5.00
169 Johnny Estrada Jsy 2.00 5.00
170 Todd Helton Jsy 3.00 8.00
171 Rich Harden Jsy 2.00 5.00
172 Johnny Damon Bat 3.00 8.00
173 Manny Ramirez Bat 3.00 8.00
174 Benito Santiago Bat 2.00 5.00
175 Albert Pujols Jsy 6.00 15.00
176 Chipper Jones Jsy 4.00 10.00
177 Miguel Cabrera Bat 3.00 8.00
178 Jeff Bagwell Uni 3.00 8.00
179 Ivan Rodriguez Jsy 3.00 8.00
180 Mike Piazza Uni 4.00 10.00
181 Chip Cannon FY AU RC 15.00 40.00
182 Erik Cordier FY AU RC 10.00 25.00
183 Billy Butler FY AU 50.00 80.00
184 C.J. Smith FY AU RC 10.00 25.00
185 Alfonso Soriano AU 12.50 30.00
186 Bobby Livingston FY AU RC 10.00 25.00
187 Wladimir Balentien FY AU 15.00 40.00
188 Mike Morse FY AU 10.00 25.00
189 W.Swackhamer FY AU RC 10.00 25.00
190 Justin Verlander FY AU 30.00 60.00
191 Jake Postlewait FY AU 10.00 25.00
192 Michael Rogers FY AU RC 10.00 25.00
193 Matt Campbell FY AU 10.00 25.00
194 Eric Nielsen FY AU RC 10.00 25.00
195 Gary Sheffield AU 20.00 50.00
196 Glen Perkins FY AU 15.00 40.00
197 Kevin Melillo FY AU 10.00 25.00
198 Chad Orvella FY AU RC 10.00 25.00
199 Jeff Niemann FY AU 10.00 25.00
200 Alex Rodriguez AU 100.00 175.00
201 Brian Stavisky FY AU RC 10.00 25.00
202 Brian Miller FY AU RC 10.00 25.00
203 Landon Powell FY AU 15.00 40.00
204 Philip Humber FY AU 15.00 40.00
205 Mariano Rivera AU 60.00 120.00
207 Nolan Ryan AU Jsy 60.00 120.00
208 Albert Pujols AU Jsy 175.00 350.00
209 Stan Musial AU Bat 60.00 120.00

2005 Topps Pristine Die Cut Red

*DC RED 1-100: 2.5X TO 6X BASIC
*DC RED 101-130: 1.5X TO 4X BASIC
1-130 ODDS 1:2 HOBBY BOXES
1-130 PRINT RUN 66 SERIAL #'d SETS
GU 131-180 ODDS 1:59 HOBBY BOXES
AU 181-205 ODDS 1:117 HOBBY BOXES
AU-GU 206-210 ODDS 1:595 HOBBY BOXES
AU-GU 206-210 EXCH.DEADLINE 10/31/07
131-210 PRINT RUN 3 SERIAL #'d SETS
181-210 NO PRICING DUE TO SCARCITY

2005 Topps Pristine Uncirculated Bronze

*BRZ 1-100: 1.5X TO 4X BASIC
*BRZ 101-130: 1X TO 2.5X BASIC
1-130 STATED ODDS 1:2
1-130 PRINT RUN 375 SERIAL #'d SETS
*BRZ 131-180: .6X TO 1.5X BASIC
GU 131-180 STATED ODDS 1:11
GU 131-180 PRINT RUN 100 SERIAL #'d SETS
AU 181-205 STATED ODDS 1:121
AU 181-205 PRINT RUN 18 SERIAL #'d SETS
AU-GU 206-210 STATED ODDS 1:3482
AU-GU 206-210 PRINT RUN 10 #'d SETS
AU-GU 206-210 EXCH.DEADLINE 10/31/07
181-205 NO PRICING DUE TO SCARCITY

2005 Topps Pristine Doubles Act Autographs

GROUP A ODDS 1:579
GROUP B ODDS 1:8705
STATED PRINT RUN 5 SERIAL #'d SETS
NO PRICING DUE TO SCARCITY
EXCHANGE DEADLINE 10/31/07

2005 Topps Pristine Fielder's Choice Glove Relics

STATED ODDS 1:139
STATED PRINT RUN 9 SERIAL #'d SETS
NO PRICING DUE TO SCARCITY

2005 Topps Pristine In the Name Letter Patch Relics

STATED ODDS 1:803
STATED PRINT RUN 1 SERIAL #'d SET
ONE CARD MADE FOR EACH LETTER
NO PRICING DUE TO SCARCITY

2005 Topps Pristine Personal Endorsements Common

STATED ODDS 1:6
STATED PRINT RUN 497 SERIAL #'d SETS
UNCIRCULATED ODDS 1:916
UNCIRCULATED PRINT RUN 3 #'d SETS
NO UNCIRC PRICING DUE TO SCARCITY

BB Billy Butler 15.00 40.00
BJ Blake Johnson 4.00 10.00
BL Bobby Livingston 4.00 10.00
CJS C.J. Smith 4.00 10.00
CO Chad Orvella 4.00 10.00
GP Glen Perkins 6.00 15.00
JF Josh Fields 6.00 15.00
JPH J.P. Howell 4.00 10.00
JS Jeremy Sowers 6.00 15.00
JV Justin Verlander 30.00 60.00
LC Lance Cormier 4.00 10.00
LH Livan Hernandez 6.00 15.00
LP Landon Powell 6.00 15.00
MB Milton Bradley 6.00 15.00
MR Mike Rodriguez 4.00 10.00
MRO Mark Rogers 4.00 10.00
PH Philip Humber 6.00 15.00
SE Scott Elbert 4.00 10.00
TS Termel Sledge 4.00 10.00
ZJ Zach Jackson 4.00 10.00

2005 Topps Pristine Personal Endorsements Uncommon

STATED ODDS 1:18
STATED PRINT RUN 247 SERIAL #'d SETS
UNCIRCULATED ODDS 1:1451
UNCIRCULATED PRINT RUN 3 #'d SETS
NO UNCIRC PRICING DUE TO SCARCITY
AB Aaron Boone 6.00 15.00
BB Billy Butler 20.00 50.00
BL Bobby Livingston 4.00 10.00
CC Chip Cannon 5.00 12.00
CE Carl Erskine 6.00 15.00
CW Craig Wilson 4.00 10.00
DO David Ortiz 20.00 50.00
DW David Wright 15.00 40.00
DZ Don Zimmer 10.00 25.00
HK Harmon Killebrew 20.00 50.00
JB Jason Bay 6.00 15.00
MB Matt Bush 6.00 15.00
ML Mark Loretta 4.00 10.00

2005 Topps Pristine Personal Endorsements Rare

STATED ODDS 1:95
STATED PRINT RUN 97 SERIAL #'d SETS
UNCIRCULATED ODDS 1:3072
UNCIRCULATED PRINT RUN 3 #'d SETS
NO UNCIRC PRICING DUE TO SCARCITY
AS Alfonso Soriano 10.00 25.00
EB Ernie Banks 30.00 60.00
GA Garret Anderson 10.00 25.00
MR Mariano Rivera 60.00 120.00
SM Stan Musial 30.00 60.00
TS Tom Seaver 15.00 40.00

2005 Topps Pristine Personal Endorsements Scarce

STATED ODDS 1:1226
STATED PRINT RUN 22 SERIAL #'d SETS
UNCIRCULATED ODDS 1:10,466
UNCIRCULATED PRINT RUN 3 #'d SETS
NO PRICING DUE TO SCARCITY
EXCHANGE DEADLINE 10/31/07
AP Albert Pujols

2005 Topps Pristine Personal Pieces Common Relics

STATED ODDS 1:3
STATED PRINT RUN 425 SERIAL #'d SETS
HAFNER PRINT RUN 400 SERIAL #'d CARDS
UNCIRCULATED ODDS 1:363
UNCIRCULATED PRINT RUN 3 #'d SETS
NO UNCIRC PRICING DUE TO SCARCITY
AB Adrian Beltre Bat 2.00 5.00
AD Adam Dunn Bat 2.00 5.00
AJ Andruw Jones Bat 3.00 8.00
AP Albert Pujols Jsy 6.00 15.00
AS Alfonso Soriano Bat 2.00 5.00
BC Bobby Crosby Bat 2.00 5.00
BJU B.J. Upton Bat 2.00 5.00
BM Brett Myers Jsy 2.00 5.00
BR Brad Radke Jsy 2.00 5.00
BW Bernie Williams Bat 3.00 8.00
BZ Barry Zito Uni 2.00 5.00
CG Cristian Guzman Bat 2.00 5.00
CJ Chipper Jones Bat 4.00 10.00
CS Curt Schilling Jsy 3.00 8.00
EC Eric Chavez Uni 2.00 5.00
ER Edgar Renteria Bat 2.00 5.00
FT Frank Thomas Jsy 4.00 10.00
GS Gary Sheffield Bat 2.00 5.00
HB Hank Blalock Jsy 2.00 5.00
JB Jeff Bagwell Jsy 3.00 8.00
JDD J.D. Drew Jsy 2.00 5.00
JE Jim Edmonds Jsy 2.00 5.00
JES Johnny Estrada Jsy 2.00 5.00
JG Jason Giambi Uni 2.00 5.00
JGI Jay Gibbons Bat 2.00 5.00
JL Javy Lopez Bat 2.00 5.00
JT Jim Thome Jsy 3.00 8.00
KM Kevin Millar Bat 2.00 5.00
KW Kerry Wood Jsy 2.00 5.00
LB Lance Berkman Jsy 2.00 5.00
LN Laynce Nix Jsy 2.00 5.00
ML Mark Loretta Bat 2.00 5.00
MLO Mike Lowell Jsy 2.00 5.00
MM Mark Mulder Uni 2.00 5.00
MP Mike Piazza Uni 4.00 10.00
MPR Mark Prior Jsy 3.00 8.00
MR Manny Ramirez Bat 3.00 8.00
MRI Mariano Rivera Jsy 4.00 10.00
MT Miguel Tejada Uni 2.00 5.00
MTE Mark Teixeira Jsy 3.00 8.00
PM Pedro Martinez Jsy 3.00 8.00
RB Ronnie Belliard Bat 2.00 5.00
RC Roger Clemens Jsy 5.00 12.00
SG Shawn Green Bat 2.00 5.00
SR Scott Rolen Jsy 3.00 8.00
TH Todd Helton Jsy 3.00 8.00
THA Travis Hafner Bat/400 2.00 5.00
THU Tim Hudson Uni 2.00 5.00
VG Vladimir Guerrero Bat 4.00 10.00
VM Victor Martinez Bat 2.00 5.00

2005 Topps Pristine Personal Pieces Uncommon Relics

STATED ODDS 1:11
STATED PRINT RUN 200 SERIAL #'d SETS
UNCIRCULATED ODDS 1:726
UNCIRCULATED PRINT RUN 3 #'d SETS
NO UNCIRC PRICING DUE TO SCARCITY
AB Adrian Beltre Bat 2.00 5.00
AJ Andruw Jones Bat 3.00 8.00
AP Albert Pujols Jsy 6.00 15.00
AR Alex Rodriguez Jsy 6.00 15.00
AS Alfonso Soriano Uni 2.00 5.00
CB Carlos Beltran Jsy 2.00 5.00
CJ Chipper Jones Jsy 4.00 10.00
CS Curt Schilling Jsy 3.00 8.00
DO David Ortiz Jsy 4.00 10.00
EG Eric Gagne Jsy 2.00 5.00
IR Ivan Rodriguez Jsy 3.00 8.00
JE Jim Edmonds Jsy 2.00 5.00
JP Jorge Posada Uni 3.00 8.00
JT Jim Thome Jsy 3.00 8.00
MC Miguel Cabrera Jsy 3.00 8.00
MM Mark Mulder Uni 2.00 5.00
MO Magglio Ordonez Bat 2.00 5.00
MP Mike Piazza Jsy 4.00 10.00
MR Manny Ramirez Jsy 3.00 8.00
MRI Mariano Rivera Jsy 4.00 10.00
RC Roger Clemens Jsy 5.00 12.00
SR Scott Rolen Jsy 3.00 8.00
SS Sammy Sosa Bat 4.00 10.00
TG Troy Glaus Bat 2.00 5.00
TH Torii Hunter Jsy 2.00 5.00

2005 Topps Pristine Personal Pieces Rare Relics

STATED ODDS 1:72
STATED PRINT RUN 75 SERIAL #'d SETS
UNCIRCULATED ODDS 1:1801
UNCIRCULATED PRINT RUN 3 #'d SETS
NO UNCIRC PRICING DUE TO SCARCITY
AP Albert Pujols Jsy 12.50 30.00
AR Alex Rodriguez Jsy 12.50 30.00
BB Barry Bonds AS Jsy * 40.00 80.00
CB Carlos Beltran Jsy 4.00 10.00
EG Eric Gagne Jsy 4.00 10.00
JD Johnny Damon Jsy 6.00 15.00
PM Pedro Martinez Jsy 6.00 15.00
RC Roger Clemens Jsy 10.00 25.00
TH Todd Helton Jsy 6.00 15.00
VG Vladimir Guerrero Jsy 6.00 15.00

2005 Topps Pristine Personal Pieces Scarce Relics

STATED ODDS 1:1088
STATED PRINT RUN 10 SERIAL #'d SETS
UNCIRCULATED ODDS 1:3731
UNCIRCULATED PRINT RUN 3 #'d SETS
NO PRICING DUE TO SCARCITY
AP Albert Pujols Jsy
AR Alex Rodriguez Jsy
BB Barry Bonds AS Jsy *
RC Roger Clemens Jsy
VG Vladimir Guerrero Jsy

2005 Topps Pristine Power Core Bat Knob Relics

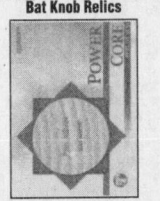

STATED ODDS 1:69
PRINT RUNS B/WN 3-10 COPIES PER
NO PRICING DUE TO SCARCITY

2005 Topps Pristine Power Stick Bat Knob Relics

STATED ODDS 1:395
STATED PRINT RUN 1 SERIAL #'d SET
NO PRICING DUE TO SCARCITY

2005 Topps Pristine Selective Swatch Letter-Number Patch Relics

OVERALL SELECTIVE SWATCH ODDS 1:768
STATED PRINT RUN 1 SERIAL #'d SET
NO PRICING DUE TO SCARCITY

2005 Topps Pristine Selective Swatch Logo Patch Relics

OVERALL SELECTIVE SWATCH ODDS 1:768
STATED PRINT RUN 1 SERIAL #'d SET
NO PRICING DUE TO SCARCITY

2005 Topps Pristine Legends

This 140-card set was released in August, 2005. The set was issued in eight-card hobby packs with an $30 SRP which came five packs per box and six boxes per case. The set was also issued in eight-card retail packs with an $30 SRP which came one pack per case. Cards numbered 1-100 feature common retired veterans. Cards numbered 101-125, which were inserted at a stated rate of four in five packs, feature players in college photos and were printed to a stated print run of 1999 serial numbered sets. Cards numbered 126 through 135 feature Negro League greats, were issued at a stated rate of one in seven, and were issued to a stated print run of 999 serial numbered sets. Cards numbered 136-140 feature players during their Little League days and were issued at a stated rate of one in 26. Those cards were issued to a stated print run of 499 serial numbered sets.

COMP. SET w/o SP's (100) 60.00 120.00
COMMON C (1-100) .40 1.00
COMMON U (101-125) .75 2.00
101-125 ODDS 4:5 HOBBY/RETAIL
101-125 PRINT RUN 1999 #'d SETS
101-125 ARE COLLEGE YEARS CARDS
COMMON R (126-135) 1.00 2.50
126-135 ODDS 1:7 HOBBY/RETAIL
126-135 PRINT RUN 999 #'d SETS
126-135 ARE NEGRO LEAGUE CARDS
COMMON S (136-140) 1.25 3.00
136-140 ODDS 1:26 HOBBY/RETAIL
136-140 PRINT RUN 499 #'d SETS
136-140 ARE LITTLE LEAGUE CARDS
OVERALL PLATE ODDS 1:82 HOBBY
PLATE PRINT RUN 1 SET PER COLOR
BLACK-CYAN-MAGENTA-YELLOW ISSUED
NO PLATE PRICING DUE TO SCARCITY
1 Vida Blue C .40 1.00
2 Bert Blyleven C .40 1.00
3 Joe Carter C .40 1.00
4 Bill Buckner C .40 1.00
5 Luis Aparicio C .40 1.00
6 Ernie Banks C 1.00 2.50
7 Wade Boggs C .60 1.50
8 George Brett C 2.00 5.00
9 Lou Brock C .60 1.50
10 Rod Carew C .60 1.50
11 Gary Carter C .40 1.00
12 Andre Dawson C .60 1.50
13 Dennis Eckersley C .40 1.00
14 Rollie Fingers C .40 1.00
15 Steve Garvey C .40 1.00
16 Dwight Gooden C .40 1.00
17 Goose Gossage C .40 1.00
18 Ron Guidry C .40 1.00
19 Keith Hernandez C .40 1.00
20 Charlie Hough C .40 1.00
21 Bo Jackson C 1.00 2.50
22 Monte Irvin C .40 1.00
23 Reggie Jackson C 1.00 2.50
24 Ferguson Jenkins C .40 1.00
25 Ralph Kiner C .40 1.00
26 Juan Marichal C .40 1.00
27 Stan Musial C 1.50 4.00
28 Tony Oliva C .40 1.00
29 Jim Palmer C .40 1.00
30 Dave Parker C .40 1.00
31 Gaylord Perry C .40 1.00
32 Jimmy Piersall C .40 1.00
33 Johnny Podres C .40 1.00
34 Brooks Robinson C .60 1.50
35 Frank Robinson C .60 1.50
36 Nolan Ryan C 2.50 6.00
37 Tom Seaver C .60 1.50
38 Ozzie Smith C 1.50 4.00
39 Duke Snider C .60 1.50
40 Bobby Thomson C .60 1.50
41 Carl Yastrzemski C 1.25 3.00
42 Maury Wills C .40 1.00
43 Robin Yount C 1.00 2.50
44 Matt Williams C .60 1.50
45 Orel Hershiser C .40 1.00
46 Tim McCarver C .40 1.00
47 Don Newcombe C .40 1.00
48 Paul O'Neill C .60 1.50
49 Al Kaline C 1.00 2.50
50 Harmon Killebrew C 1.00 2.50
51 Dave Kingman C .40 1.00
52 Ken Griffey Sr. C .40 1.00
53 George Foster C .40 1.00
54 Mark Fidrych C .40 1.00
55 Orlando Cepeda C .40 1.00
56 Don Larsen C .40 1.00
57 Bill Madlock C .40 1.00
58 Dale Murphy C .40 1.00
59 Graig Nettles C .40 1.00
60 Phil Niekro C .40 1.00
61 Al Oliver C .40 1.00
62 Harold Reynolds C .40 1.00
63 Bobby Richardson C .40 1.00
64 Mike Scott C .40 1.00
65 Dave Stewart C .40 1.00
66 Rick Sutcliffe C .40 1.00
67 Bruce Sutter C .40 1.00
68 Luis Tiant C .40 1.00
69 Bob Watson C .40 1.00
70 Walt Weiss C .40 1.00
71 Don Zimmer C .40 1.00
72 Tommy John C .40 1.00
73 Ray Knight C .40 1.00
74 Jack Morris C .40 1.00
75 Mickey Rivers C .40 1.00
76 Lee Smith C .40 1.00
77 Darryl Strawberry C .40 1.00
78 Dave Justice C 1.00 2.50
79 Wally Joyner C .40 1.00
80 Jimmy Key C .40 1.00
81 John Kruk C .40 1.00
82 Greg Luzinski C .40 1.00
83 Mookie Wilson C .40 1.00
84 Wilbur Wood C .40 1.00
85 Tim Raines C .40 1.00
86 Jim Rice C .40 1.00
87 Tony Armas C .40 1.00
88 Harold Baines C .40 1.00
89 Bucky Dent C .40 1.00
90 Darrell Evans C .40 1.00
91 Cecil Fielder C .40 1.00
92 Jose Cruz C .40 1.00
93 Dave Concepcion C .40 1.00
94 Ron Cey C .40 1.00
95 Davey Lopes C .40 1.00
96 Boog Powell C .40 1.00
97 Buddy Bell C .40 1.00
98 George Bell C .40 1.00
99 Bert Campaneris C .40 1.00
100 Chet Lemon C .40 1.00
101 Bo Jackson U 2.00 5.00
102 Will Clark U 1.25 3.00
103 Cecil Fielder U .75 2.00
104 Ron Cey U .75 2.00
105 Tony Gwynn U 2.50 6.00
106 Orel Hershiser U .75 2.00
107 Jimmy Key U .75 2.00
108 Paul Molitor U 2.00 5.00
109 Pete Incaviglia U .75 2.00
110 Wally Joyner U .75 2.00
111 Dave Kingman U .75 2.00
112 Ron Guidry U .75 2.00
113 Ron Darling U .75 2.00
114 Mookie Wilson U .75 2.00
115 Reggie Jackson U 2.00 5.00
116 Walt Weiss U .75 2.00
117 Joe Carter U .75 2.00
118 Cory Snyder U .75 2.00
119 Dave Winfield U .75 2.00
120 Terry Steinbach U .75 2.00
121 Matt Williams U 1.25 3.00
122 Ozzie Smith U 3.00 8.00
123 Jack McDowell U .75 2.00
124 Bob Horner U .75 2.00
125 Don Kessinger U .75 2.00
126 Minnie Minoso R 1.00 2.50
127 Josh Gibson R 2.50 6.00
128 Buck O'Neil R 1.00 2.50
129 Monte Irvin R 1.00 2.50
130 Jim Gilliam R 1.00 2.50
131 Josh Gibson R 2.50 6.00
132 Ernie Banks R 2.50 6.00
133 Don Newcombe R 1.00 2.50
134 Josh Gibson R 2.50 6.00
135 Josh Gibson R 2.50 6.00
136 Gary Carter S 1.25 3.00
137 Bo Jackson S 3.00 8.00
138 George Brett S 6.00 15.00
139 Joe Carter S 1.25 3.00
140 Nolan Ryan S 8.00 20.00

2005 Topps Pristine Legends Refractors

*REF 1-100: 1X TO 2.5X BASIC
1-100 ONE PER PACK
1-100 PRINT RUN 549 SERIAL #'d SETS
*REF 101-125: 1X TO 2.5X BASIC
101-125 ODDS 1:13 HOBBY/RETAIL
101-125 PRINT RUN 199 SERIAL #'d SETS
*REF 126-135: 1X TO 2.5X BASIC
126-135 ODDS 1:64 HOBBY/RETAIL
126-135 PRINT RUN 99 SERIAL #'d SETS
136-140 ODDS 1:514 HOBBY, 1:480 RETAIL
136-140 PRINT RUN 25 SERIAL #'d SETS
136-140 NO PRICING DUE TO SCARCITY

2005 Topps Pristine Legends Gold Die Cut Refractors

*GOLD DC 1-100: 2X TO 5X BASIC
*GOLD DC 101-125: 1.25X TO 3X BASIC
*GOLD DC 126-135: 1X TO 2.5X BASIC
*GOLD DC 136-140: .6X TO 1.5X BASIC
ONE PER SEALED HOBBY BOX
STATED PRINT RUN 65 SERIAL #'d SETS

2005 Topps Pristine Legends SuperFractors

STATED ODDS 1:455 HOBBY, 1:480 RETAIL
STATED PRINT RUN 1 SERIAL #'d SET
NO PRICING DUE TO SCARCITY

2005 Topps Pristine Legends Celebrity Threads

STATED ODDS 1:18 HOBBY/RETAIL
REFRACTOR ODDS 1:1284 H, 1:1440 R
REF PRINT RUN 25 SERIAL #'d SETS
NO REF PRICING DUE TO SCARCITY
EP Elvis Presley Shirt 30.00 60.00
MM Marilyn Monroe Dress 40.00 80.00

2005 Topps Pristine Legends Leading Indicators Relics

GROUP A ODDS 1:210 HOBBY/RETAIL
GROUP B ODDS 1:71 HOBBY/RETAIL
GROUP C ODDS 1:7 HOBBY/RETAIL
GROUP D ODDS 1:20 HOBBY/RETAIL
GROUP E ODDS 1:8 HOBBY/RETAIL
GROUP A PRINT RUN 99 SERIAL #'d SETS
REF GROUP A ODDS 1:14,550 HOBBY

REF GROUP B ODDS 1:111 HOBBY/RETAIL
REF A PRINT RUN 1 SERIAL #'d SET
REF B PRINT RUN 25 SERIAL #'d SETS
NO REF PRICING DUE TO SCARCITY

AD Andre Dawson Bat C	3.00	8.00
AK Al Kaline Bat C	4.00	10.00
BF Bob Feller Uni D	4.00	10.00
CF Cecil Fielder Bat C	3.00	8.00
CY Carl Yastrzemski Bat C	6.00	15.00
DBM Dale Murphy Bat C	4.00	10.00
DK Dave Kingman Bat C	3.00	8.00
DM Don Mattingly Bat D	6.00	15.00
DP Dave Parker Bat E	3.00	8.00
DS Darryl Strawberry Bat C	3.00	8.00
GF George Foster Bat C	3.00	8.00
GP Gaylord Perry Jsy E	3.00	8.00
JR Jim Rice Bat B	3.00	8.00
LB Lou Brock Bat A/99	6.00	15.00
MS Mike Scott Jsy E	3.00	8.00
MW Maury Wills Bat A/99	4.00	10.00
NR Nolan Ryan Jsy C	6.00	15.00
PO Paul O'Neill Bat E	4.00	10.00
RC Rod Carew Bat C	4.00	10.00
RM Roger Maris Bat B	15.00	40.00
TG Tony Gwynn Jsy E	4.00	10.00
TO Tony Oliva Bat D	3.00	8.00
TR Tim Raines Uni C	3.00	8.00
TR2 Tim Raines Bat C	3.00	8.00
TS Tom Seaver Jsy A/99	6.00	15.00
WB Wade Boggs Bat E	4.00	10.00

2005 Topps Pristine Legends Personal Endorsements

GROUP A ODDS 1:40 HOBBY/RETAIL
GROUP B ODDS 1:16 HOBBY/RETAIL
GROUP C ODDS 1:9 HOBBY/RETAIL
GOLD ODDS 1:85 HOBBY/RETAIL
GOLD PRINT RUN 25 SERIAL #'d SETS
NO GOLD PRICING DUE TO SCARCITY

AD Andre Dawson A	6.00	15.00
AK Al Kaline A	15.00	40.00
BB Bert Blyleven B	4.00	10.00
BG Bobby Grich C	4.00	10.00
BJ Bo Jackson A	30.00	60.00
BR Brooks Robinson A	10.00	25.00
CF Carlton Fisk A	10.00	25.00
CR Cal Ripken A	60.00	120.00
CY Carl Yastrzemski A	20.00	50.00
DE Dennis Eckersley A	6.00	15.00
DL Don Larsen B	4.00	10.00
DS Duke Snider A	15.00	40.00
DWE Darrell Evans C	4.00	10.00
EW Earl Weaver C	4.00	10.00
GB George Brett A	30.00	60.00
GC Gary Carter B	4.00	10.00
GF George Foster C	4.00	10.00
GG Goose Gossage B	10.00	25.00
GN Graig Nettles B	4.00	10.00
JA Jim Abbott C	4.00	10.00
JAP Jimmy Piersall B	6.00	15.00
JM Jack McDowell C	4.00	10.00
JO Jesse Orosco C	4.00	10.00
JP Jim Palmer A	6.00	15.00
KH Keith Hernandez A	6.00	15.00
LA Luis Aparicio B	6.00	15.00
NR Nolan Ryan A	50.00	100.00
RD Ron Darling B	4.00	10.00
RJ Reggie Jackson A	15.00	40.00
RY Robin Yount A	15.00	40.00
SM Stan Musial A	20.00	50.00

2005 Topps Pristine Legends Signature Marks

STATED ODDS 1:4850 HOBBY
STATED PRINT RUN 1 SERIAL #'d SET
NO PRICING DUE TO SCARCITY

2005 Topps Pristine Legends Title Threads Relics

GROUP A ODDS 1:66 HOBBY/RETAIL
GROUP B ODDS 1:9 HOBBY/RETAIL
GROUP C ODDS 1:6 HOBBY/RETAIL
REFRACTOR ODDS 1:111 HOBBY/RETAIL
REF PRINT RUN 25 SERIAL #'d SETS
NO REF PRICING DUE TO SCARCITY

BD Bucky Dent Uni B	3.00	8.00
CS Cesar Geronimo Bat C	3.00	8.00
DJ Dave Justice Uni A	4.00	10.00
DS Darryl Strawberry Bat B	3.00	8.00
EK Ed Kranepool Uni C	3.00	8.00
GC Gary Carter Bat C	3.00	8.00
GF George Foster Bat B	3.00	8.00
GG Goose Gossage Uni C	3.00	8.00
GN Graig Nettles Uni C	3.00	8.00
JC Joe Carter Bat B	3.00	8.00
JK Jimmy Key Uni C	3.00	8.00
JP Jim Palmer Uni B	3.00	8.00
KG Ken Griffey Sr. Bat B	3.00	8.00
LD Len Dykstra Bat B	3.00	8.00
MI Monte Irvin Bat B	3.00	8.00
MW Mookie Wilson Uni B	3.00	8.00
OC Orlando Cepeda Jsy C	3.00	8.00
OH Orel Hershiser Jsy A	3.00	8.00
PO Paul O'Neill Uni C	3.00	8.00
RF Rollie Fingers Uni C	3.00	8.00
TM Tim McCarver Uni C	3.00	8.00
WB Wade Boggs Uni C	4.00	10.00
WH Willie Horton Jsy B	3.00	8.00

2005 Topps Pristine Legends Valuable Performance Relics

GROUP A ODDS 1:7275 HOBBY
GROUP B ODDS 1:6 HOBBY/RETAIL
GROUP C ODDS 1:12 HOBBY/RETAIL
GROUP A PRINT RUN 9 SERIAL #'d CARDS
NO GROUP A PRICING DUE TO SCARCITY
REF GROUP A ODDS 1:43,650 HOBBY
REF GROUP B ODDS 1:128 H, 1:125 R
REF A PRINT RUN 1 SERIAL #'d SET
REF B PRINT RUN 25 SERIAL #'d SETS
NO REF PRICING DUE TO SCARCITY

AD Andre Dawson Uni C	3.00	8.00
CF Cecil Fielder Bat B	3.00	8.00
CR Cal Ripken Bat B	8.00	20.00
CY Carl Yastrzemski Bat B	4.00	10.00
DBM Don Mattingly Uni C	6.00	15.00
DE Dennis Eckersley Jsy C	3.00	8.00
DM Dale Murphy Bat B	4.00	10.00
DP Dave Parker Uni C	3.00	8.00
FR Frank Robinson Bat B	3.00	8.00
HK Harmon Killebrew Bat B	4.00	10.00
JC Jose Canseco Bat B	4.00	10.00
JM Joe Morgan Bat B	3.00	8.00
JR Jim Rice Bat B	3.00	8.00
KH Keith Hernandez Bat B	3.00	8.00
MS Mike Schmidt Bat C	6.00	15.00
RC Roberto Clemente Bat A/9		
RJ Reggie Jackson Bat B	4.00	10.00
RY Robin Yount Bat B	4.00	10.00
SG Steve Garvey Bat B	3.00	8.00
SM Stan Musial Bat B	6.00	15.00
YB Yogi Berra Bat B	4.00	10.00

2003 Topps Retired Signature

This 110-card set was released in July, 2003. The set was issued in five card packs with an $30 SRP which came five packs to a box and six boxes to a case.

COMPLETE SET (110)	100.00	200.00
1 Willie Mays	2.50	6.00
2 Tony Perez	.50	1.25
3 Tom Seaver	.75	2.00
4 Johnny Bench	1.25	3.00
5 Rod Carew	.75	2.00
6 Red Schoendienst	.50	1.25
7 Phil Rizzuto	.75	2.00
8 Ozzie Smith	2.00	5.00
9 Maury Wills	.50	1.25
10 Hank Aaron	2.50	6.00
11 Jim Palmer	.50	1.25
12 Jose Cruz Sr.	.50	1.25
13 Dave Parker	.50	1.25
14 Don Sutton	.50	1.25
15 Brooks Robinson	.75	2.00
16 Bo Jackson	1.25	3.00
17 Andre Dawson	.50	1.25
18 Fergie Jenkins	.50	1.25
19 George Foster	.50	1.25
20 George Brett	2.50	6.00
21 Jerry Koosman	.50	1.25
22 John Kruk	.50	1.25
23 Kent Tekulve	.50	1.25
24 Lee Smith	.50	1.25
25 Nolan Ryan	3.00	8.00
26 Paul O'Neill	.50	1.25
27 Rich Gossage	.50	1.25
28 Ron Santo	.50	1.25
29 Tom Lasorda	.50	1.25
30 Tony Gwynn	1.50	4.00
31 Vida Blue	.50	1.25
32 Whitey Herzog	.50	1.25
33 Willie McGee	.50	1.25
34 Bill Mazeroski	.50	1.25
35 Al Kaline	1.25	3.00
36 Bobby Richardson	.50	1.25
37 Carlton Fisk	.75	2.00
38 Darrell Evans	.50	1.25
39 Dave Concepcion	.50	1.25
40 Cal Ripken	4.00	10.00
41 Dwight Evans	.75	2.00
42 Earl Weaver	.50	1.25
43 Fred Lynn	.50	1.25
44 Greg Luzinski	.50	1.25
45 Duke Snider	.75	2.00
46 Hank Bauer	.50	1.25
47 Jim Rice	.50	1.25
48 Johnny Sain	.50	1.25
49 Lenny Dykstra	.50	1.25
50 Mike Schmidt	2.50	6.00
51 Orlando Cepeda	.50	1.25
52 Ralph Kiner	.50	1.25
53 Robin Roberts	.50	1.25
54 Ron Guidry	.50	1.25
55 Steve Garvey	.50	1.25
56 Tony Oliva	.50	1.25
57 Whitey Ford	.75	2.00
58 Willie McCovey	.50	1.25
59 Phil Niekro	.50	1.25
60 Stan Musial	2.00	5.00
61 Rollie Fingers	.50	1.25
62 Robin Yount	1.25	3.00
63 Alan Trammell	.50	1.25
64 Bill Buckner	.50	1.25
65 Bob Feller	.50	1.25
66 Bruce Sutter	.50	1.25
67 Dale Murphy	.75	2.00
68 Dennis Eckersley	.50	1.25
69 Don Newcombe	.50	1.25
70 Don Mattingly	2.50	6.00
71 Dwight Gooden	.50	1.25
72 Frank Robinson	.75	2.00
73 Gary Carter	.50	1.25
74 Graig Nettles	.50	1.25
75 Harmon Killebrew	1.25	3.00
76 Jim Bunning	.50	1.25
77 Joe Morgan	.50	1.25
78 Joe Rudi	.50	1.25
79 Jose Canseco	.75	2.00
80 Ernie Banks	1.25	3.00
81 Luis Aparicio	.50	1.25
82 Luis Tiant	.50	1.25
83 Mark Fidrych	.50	1.25
84 Kirk Gibson	.50	1.25
85 Lou Brock	.75	2.00
86 Juan Marichal	.50	1.25
87 Monte Irvin	.50	1.25
88 Paul Molitor	.50	1.25
89 Tommy John	.50	1.25
90 Warren Spahn	.75	2.00
91 Wade Boggs	.75	2.00
92 Reggie Jackson	.75	2.00
93 Kirby Puckett	1.25	3.00
94 Boog Powell	.75	2.00
95 Carl Yastrzemski	2.00	5.00
96 Bobby Thomson	.50	1.25
97 Bill Skowron	.50	1.25
98 Bill Madlock	.50	1.25
99 Sparky Anderson	.50	1.25
100 Yogi Berra	1.25	3.00
101 Bobby Doerr	.50	1.25
102 Gaylord Perry	.50	1.25
103 George Kell	.50	1.25
104 Harold Reynolds	.50	1.25
105 Joe Carter	.50	1.25
106 Johnny Podres	.50	1.25
107 Ron Cey	.50	1.25
108 Tim McCarver	.50	1.25
109 Tug McGraw	.50	1.25
110 Don Larsen	.50	1.25

2003 Topps Retired Signature Black

*BLACK: 2.5X TO 6X BASIC
STATED ODDS 1:8
STATED PRINT RUN 99 SERIAL #'d SETS

2003 Topps Retired Signature Autographs

Inserted at a stated rate of one per pack, these 120 cards feature signatures from some of the most famous retired players. These cards were signed in different ratios and we have notated the insert odds as well as what group the player belonged to in our checklist.

ONE AUTOGRAPH PER PACK
A-B PRINT RUNS PROVIDED BY TOPPS
GROUPS A-B ARE NOT SERIAL-NUMBERED
NO GROUP A PRICING DUE TO SCARCITY

AD Andre Dawson D	10.00	25.00
AK Al Kaline C	20.00	50.00
AT Alan Trammell E	10.00	25.00
BB Bert Blyleven F	12.50	30.00
BBU Bill Buckner C	12.50	30.00
BD Bobby Doerr C	20.00	50.00
BF Bob Feller F	12.50	30.00
BGR Bobby Grich C	12.50	30.00
BH Bob Horner C	20.00	50.00
BJ Bo Jackson C	50.00	100.00
BM Bill Madlock G	4.00	10.00
BMA Bill Mazeroski C	15.00	40.00
BP Boog Powell G	6.00	15.00
BR Bobby Richardson G	6.00	15.00
BRO Brooks Robinson B/75	125.00	200.00
BS Bill Skowron G	6.00	15.00
BSA Bret Saberhagen C	20.00	50.00
BSU Bruce Sutter E	10.00	25.00
BT Bobby Thomson D	10.00	25.00
BW Bob Watson C	12.50	30.00
CF Carlton Fisk C	30.00	60.00
CR Cal Ripken A/25		
CY Carl Yastrzemski C	60.00	120.00
DE Darrell Evans F	4.00	10.00
DEC Dennis Eckersley C	20.00	50.00
DEV Dwight Evans B/78	125.00	200.00
DG Dwight Gooden C	20.00	50.00
DL Don Larsen G	6.00	15.00
DM Dale Murphy C	30.00	60.00
DN Don Newcombe C	12.50	30.00
DON Don Mattingly B/81	125.00	250.00
DP Dave Parker C	20.00	50.00
DS Dave Stieb C	20.00	50.00
DSN Duke Snider B/75	125.00	200.00
DSU Don Sutton C	20.00	50.00
EB Ernie Banks A/24		
EW Earl Weaver G	6.00	15.00
FJ Fergie Jenkins D	10.00	25.00
FL Fred Lynn C	20.00	50.00
FR Frank Robinson C	30.00	60.00
GB George Brett A/25		
GC Gary Carter B/77	90.00	150.00
GF George Foster G	10.00	25.00
GK George Kell C	10.00	25.00
GL Greg Luzinski D	10.00	25.00
GN Graig Nettles G	6.00	15.00
GP Gaylord Perry C	12.50	30.00
HA Hank Aaron A/30		
HB Harold Baines F	6.00	15.00
HBA Hank Bauer C	20.00	50.00
HK Harmon Killebrew B/76	150.00	250.00
HR Harold Reynolds C	12.50	30.00
JA Jim Abbott E	6.00	15.00
JB Jim Bunning B/76	125.00	200.00
JBE Johnny Bench C	40.00	80.00
JC Joe Carter C	20.00	50.00
JCA Jose Canseco C	30.00	60.00
JCR Jose Cruz Sr. D	6.00	15.00
JK Jerry Koosman C	12.50	30.00
JKR John Kruk C	20.00	50.00
JM Joe Morgan C	20.00	50.00
JMA Juan Marichal C	20.00	50.00
JP Jim Palmer C	30.00	60.00
JPI Jim Piersall G	6.00	15.00
JPO Johnny Podres G	6.00	15.00
JR Jim Rice C	15.00	40.00
JRU Joe Rudi F	4.00	10.00
KG Kirk Gibson C	20.00	50.00
KGR Ken Griffey Sr. C	20.00	50.00
KP Kirby Puckett B/75		
KT Kent Tekulve C	20.00	50.00
LA Luis Aparicio G	10.00	25.00
LB Lou Brock B/76	60.00	120.00
LD Lenny Dykstra D	10.00	25.00
LP Lance Parrish G	6.00	15.00
LS Lee Smith E	6.00	15.00
LT Luis Tiant G	6.00	15.00
MF Mark Fidrych D	20.00	50.00
MI Monte Irvin C	30.00	60.00
MS Mike Schmidt B/83	150.00	250.00
MW Maury Wills F	6.00	15.00
NR Nolan Ryan B/77	200.00	300.00
OC Orlando Cepeda B/75	125.00	200.00
OS Ozzie Smith C	50.00	100.00
PM Paul Molitor C	20.00	50.00
PN Phil Niekro D	10.00	25.00
PO Paul O'Neill C	30.00	60.00
PR Phil Rizzuto B/77	125.00	200.00
RCA Rod Carew C	30.00	60.00
RCE Ron Cey F	4.00	10.00
RF Rollie Fingers C	10.00	25.00
RG Rich Gossage C	12.50	30.00
RGU Ron Guidry D	10.00	25.00
RJ Reggie Jackson C	50.00	100.00
RK Ralph Kiner B/80	125.00	200.00
RR Robin Roberts C	10.00	25.00
RS Red Schoendienst B/83	125.00	200.00
RSA Ron Santo G	12.50	30.00
RY Robin Yount A/25		
SA Sparky Anderson C	12.50	30.00
SG Steve Garvey D	10.00	25.00
SM Stan Musial A/28		
TG Tony Gwynn A/25		
TJ Tommy John C	12.50	30.00
TL Tom Lasorda B/76	90.00	150.00
TM Tim McCarver C	20.00	50.00
TMC Tug McGraw D	20.00	50.00
TO Tony Oliva C	10.00	25.00
TP Tony Perez C	15.00	40.00
TPE Terry Pendleton D	6.00	15.00
TS Tom Seaver C	40.00	80.00
VB Vida Blue E	4.00	10.00
WB Wade Boggs B/77	125.00	200.00
WF Whitey Ford C	30.00	60.00
WH Whitey Herzog D	10.00	25.00
WM Willie Mays A/25		
WMC Willie McCovey C	30.00	60.00
WMG Willie McGee D	10.00	25.00
WS Warren Spahn F	20.00	50.00
YB Yogi Berra A/25		

2003 Topps Retired Signature Autographs Refractors

STATED ODDS 1:27
STATED PRINT RUN 25 SERIAL #'d SETS
NO PRICING DUE TO SCARCITY

2004 Topps Retired Signature

This 110-card set was released in September, 2004. The set was issued in four card packs (of which one card was autographed) with an $30 SRP which came five packs to a box and six boxes to a case.

COMPLETE SET (110)	75.00	150.00
COMMON CARD (1-110)	.40	1.00
1 Willie Mays	2.00	5.00
2 Tony Gwynn	1.00	2.50
3 Dale Murphy	.60	1.50
4 Lenny Dykstra	.40	1.00
5 Johnny Bench	1.00	2.50
6 Bill Buckner	.40	1.00
7 Ferguson Jenkins	.40	1.00
8 George Brett	2.00	5.00
9 Ralph Kiner	.60	1.50
10 Ernie Banks	1.00	2.50
11 Hal McRae	.40	1.00
12 Lou Brock	.60	1.50
13 Keith Hernandez	.40	1.00
14 Jose Canseco	.60	1.50
15 Whitey Ford	.60	1.50
16 Dave Kingman	.40	1.00
17 Tim Raines	.40	1.00
18 Paul O'Neill	.60	1.50
19 Lou Whitaker	.40	1.00
20 Mike Schmidt	1.50	4.00
21 Wally Joyner	.40	1.00
22 Kirk Gibson	.40	1.00
23 Ryne Sandberg	2.00	5.00
24 Luis Tiant	.40	1.00
25 Al Kaline	1.00	2.50
26 Brooks Robinson	.60	1.50
27 Don Zimmer	.40	1.00
28 Nolan Ryan	3.00	8.00
29 Maury Wills	.40	1.00
30 Stan Musial	1.50	4.00
31 Garry Maddox	.40	1.00
32 Tom Brunansky	.40	1.00
33 Don Mattingly	2.00	5.00
34 Earl Weaver	.40	1.00
35 Bobby Grich	.40	1.00
36 Orlando Cepeda	.40	1.00
37 Alan Trammell	.40	1.00
38 Al Hrabosky	.40	1.00
39 Dave Lopes	.40	1.00
40 Rod Carew	.60	1.50
41 Robin Yount	1.00	2.50
42 Dwight Gooden	.40	1.00
43 Andre Dawson	.60	1.50
44 Hank Aaron	2.00	5.00
45 Norm Cash	.40	1.00
46 Reggie Jackson	.60	1.50
47 Jim Rice	.60	1.50
48 Carlton Fisk	.60	1.50
49 Dave Parker	.40	1.00
50 Cal Ripken	4.00	10.00
51 Roy Face	.40	1.00
52 Bob Gibson	.60	1.50
53 Jimmy Key	.40	1.00
54 Al Oliver	.40	1.00
55 Don Larsen	.40	1.00
56 Tom Seaver	.60	1.50
57 Tony Armas	.40	1.00
58 Dave Stieb	.40	1.00
59 Will Clark	.60	1.50
60 Duke Snider	.60	1.50
61 Cesar Geronimo	.40	1.00
62 Ron Kittle	.40	1.00
63 Ron Santo	.60	1.50
64 Mickey Rivers	.40	1.00
65 Jim Piersall	.40	1.00
66 Ron Swoboda	.40	1.00
67 Kent Hrbek	.40	1.00
68 Dennis Eckersley	.40	1.00
69 Greg Luzinski	.40	1.00
70 Harmon Killebrew	1.00	2.50
71 Ron Guidry	.40	1.00
72 Steve Garvey	.40	1.00
73 Andy Van Slyke	.40	1.00
74 Goose Gossage	.40	1.00
75 Ozzie Smith	1.50	4.00
76 Richie Allen	.40	1.00
77 Vida Blue	.40	1.00
78 Tony Oliva	.40	1.00
79 Darryl Strawberry	.40	1.00
80 Frank Robinson	.60	1.50
81 Bruce Sutter	.40	1.00
82 Dave Concepcion	.40	1.00
83 Darrell Evans	.40	1.00
84 Jack Morris	.40	1.00
85 Bo Jackson	1.00	2.50
86 Orel Hershiser	.40	1.00
87 Rob Dibble	.40	1.00
88 Wade Boggs	.60	1.50
89 Fernando Valenzuela	.40	1.00
90 Jim Palmer	.40	1.00
91 George Foster	.40	1.00
92 Mike Scott	.40	1.00
93 Paul Molitor	1.00	2.50
94 Gary Carter	.40	1.00
95 Bobby Richardson	.40	1.00
96 Rollie Fingers	.40	1.00
97 Tim McCarver	.40	1.00
98 John Candelaria	.40	1.00
99 Dave Winfield	.40	1.00
100 Yogi Berra	1.00	2.50
101 Bill Madlock	.40	1.00
102 Jack McDowell	.40	1.00
103 Luis Aparicio	.40	1.00
104 Graig Nettles	.40	1.00
105 Dave Stewart	.40	1.00
106 Darren Daulton	.40	1.00
107 Gary Gaetti	.40	1.00
108 Tony Fernandez	.40	1.00
109 Buddy Bell	.40	1.00
110 Carl Yastrzemski	1.00	2.50

2004 Topps Retired Signature Black

*BLACK: 2.5X TO 6X BASIC
STATED ODDS 1:7
STATED PRINT RUN 99 SERIAL #'d SETS

2004 Topps Retired Signature Autographs

GROUP A ODDS 1:675
GROUP B ODDS 1:338
GROUP C ODDS 1:82
GROUP D ODDS 1:25
GROUP E ODDS 1:8
GROUP F ODDS 1:46
GROUP G ODDS 1:2
GROUP H ODDS 1:33
GROUP A PRINT RUN 25 SETS
GROUP B PRINT RUN 50 SETS
GROUP C PRINT RUN 75 SETS
GROUP A-C ARE NOT SERIAL-NUMBERED
A-C PRINT RUNS PROVIDED BY TOPPS
OVERALL PRESS PLATE ODDS 1:222
PLATE PRINT RUN 1 SET PER COLOR
BLACK-CYAN-MAGENTA-YELLOW ISSUED
NO PLATE PRICING DUE TO SCARCITY

AH Al Hrabosky E	4.00	10.00
AO Al Oliver G	6.00	15.00
AT Alan Trammell E	6.00	15.00
BB Bill Buckner G	6.00	15.00
BBE Buddy Bell E	6.00	15.00
BD Bucky Dent E	6.00	15.00
BG Bob Gibson C	60.00	120.00
BGR Bobby Grich G	4.00	10.00
BM Bill Madlock G	4.00	10.00
BR Bobby Richardson G	6.00	15.00
BRO Brooks Robinson C	75.00	150.00
BS Bruce Sutter G	10.00	25.00
CF Carlton Fisk D	20.00	50.00
CG Cesar Geronimo E	6.00	15.00
CR Cal Ripken A	300.00	500.00
CY Carl Yastrzemski A	175.00	300.00
DD Darren Daulton G	4.00	10.00
DE Darrell Evans G	4.00	10.00
DEC Dennis Eckersley E	10.00	25.00
DG Dwight Gooden C	60.00	120.00
DL Davey Lopes F	4.00	10.00
DM Don Mattingly C	125.00	200.00
DMU Dale Murphy G	10.00	25.00
DP Dave Parker E	6.00	15.00
DS Darryl Strawberry D	20.00	50.00
DSN Duke Snider B	125.00	200.00
DST Dave Stieb G	4.00	10.00
DZ Don Zimmer D	15.00	40.00
EB Ernie Banks B	125.00	200.00
EW Earl Weaver G	6.00	15.00
FJ Ferguson Jenkins G	6.00	15.00
FR Frank Robinson D	30.00	60.00
GC Gary Carter D	20.00	50.00
GF George Foster E	4.00	10.00
GG Goose Gossage E	6.00	15.00
GL Greg Luzinski E	6.00	15.00
GN Graig Nettles G	6.00	15.00
HA Hank Aaron B	200.00	350.00
JB Johnny Bench C	100.00	175.00
JC John Candelaria D	10.00	25.00
JCA Jose Canseco D	20.00	50.00
JK Jimmy Key G	6.00	15.00
JM Jack McDowell G	4.00	10.00
JP Jim Piersall E	6.00	15.00
KG Kirk Gibson E	6.00	15.00
LT Luis Tiant G	4.00	10.00
MS Mike Schmidt C	125.00	200.00
MW Maury Wills G	4.00	10.00
NR Nolan Ryan A	250.00	400.00
OC Orlando Cepeda G	6.00	15.00
OH Orel Hershiser E	12.50	30.00
OS Ozzie Smith C	60.00	120.00
PM Paul Molitor D	15.00	40.00
PO Paul O'Neill D	20.00	50.00
RC Rod Carew E	15.00	40.00
RD Rob Dibble E	4.00	10.00
RF Rollie Fingers E	6.00	15.00
RFA Roy Face H	10.00	25.00
RK Ralph Kiner D	20.00	50.00
RKI Ron Kittle G	4.00	10.00
RS Ron Swoboda G	4.00	10.00
RSA Ryne Sandberg D	40.00	80.00
RSN Ron Santo G	15.00	40.00
RY Robin Yount A	175.00	300.00
SM Stan Musial B	150.00	250.00
TA Tony Armas G	4.00	10.00
TB Tom Brunansky G	10.00	25.00
TF Tony Fernandez E	6.00	15.00
TG Tony Gwynn C	60.00	120.00
TO Tony Oliva E	10.00	25.00
TS Tom Seaver C	75.00	150.00
VB Vida Blue G	4.00	10.00
WB Wade Boggs D	40.00	80.00
WF Whitey Ford C	100.00	175.00
WJ Wally Joyner G	4.00	10.00
YB Yogi Berra C	125.00	200.00

2004 Topps Retired Signature Autographs Refractors

STATED ODDS 1:36
STATED PRINT RUN 25 SERIAL #'d SETS

AH Al Hrabosky	30.00	60.00
AO Al Oliver	40.00	80.00
AT Alan Trammell	40.00	80.00
BB Bill Buckner	40.00	80.00
BBE Buddy Bell	30.00	60.00
BD Bucky Dent	30.00	60.00
BG Bob Gibson	60.00	120.00
BGR Bobby Grich	30.00	60.00
BM Bill Madlock	30.00	60.00
BR Bobby Richardson	40.00	80.00
BRO Brooks Robinson	60.00	120.00
BS Bruce Sutter	60.00	120.00
CF Carlton Fisk	60.00	120.00
CG Cesar Geronimo	40.00	80.00
CR Cal Ripken	300.00	500.00
CY Carl Yastrzemski	150.00	250.00
DD Darren Daulton	30.00	60.00
DE Darrell Evans	30.00	60.00
DEC Dennis Eckersley	40.00	80.00
DG Dwight Gooden	40.00	80.00
DL Davey Lopes	30.00	60.00
DM Don Mattingly	175.00	300.00
DMU Dale Murphy	60.00	120.00
DP Dave Parker	40.00	80.00
DS Darryl Strawberry	40.00	80.00
DSN Duke Snider	60.00	120.00
DST Dave Stieb	40.00	80.00
DZ Don Zimmer	40.00	80.00
EB Ernie Banks	150.00	250.00
EW Earl Weaver	30.00	60.00
FJ Ferguson Jenkins	40.00	80.00
FR Frank Robinson	60.00	120.00
GC Gary Carter	60.00	120.00
GF George Foster	30.00	60.00
GG Goose Gossage	40.00	80.00
GL Greg Luzinski	30.00	60.00
GN Graig Nettles	40.00	80.00
HA Hank Aaron	350.00	600.00
JB Johnny Bench	75.00	150.00
JC John Candelaria	40.00	80.00
JCA Jose Canseco	60.00	120.00
JK Jimmy Key	40.00	80.00
JM Jack McDowell	30.00	60.00
JP Jim Piersall	30.00	60.00
KG Kirk Gibson	40.00	80.00
LT Luis Tiant	30.00	60.00
MS Mike Schmidt	175.00	300.00
MW Maury Wills	40.00	80.00
NR Nolan Ryan	300.00	500.00
OC Orlando Cepeda	60.00	120.00
OH Orel Hershiser	40.00	80.00
OS Ozzie Smith	125.00	200.00
PM Paul Molitor	40.00	80.00
PO Paul O'Neill	40.00	80.00
RC Rod Carew	60.00	120.00
RD Rob Dibble	30.00	60.00
RF Rollie Fingers	40.00	80.00
RFA Roy Face	40.00	80.00
RK Ralph Kiner	40.00	80.00
RKI Ron Kittle	30.00	60.00
RS Ron Swoboda	40.00	80.00
RSA Ryne Sandberg	125.00	200.00
RSN Ron Santo	100.00	200.00
RY Robin Yount	150.00	250.00
SM Stan Musial	200.00	350.00
TA Tony Armas	30.00	60.00
TB Tom Brunansky	30.00	60.00
TF Tony Fernandez	30.00	60.00
TG Tony Gwynn	125.00	200.00
TO Tony Oliva	30.00	60.00
TS Tom Seaver	75.00	150.00
VB Vida Blue	30.00	60.00
WB Wade Boggs	75.00	150.00
WF Whitey Ford	75.00	150.00
WJ Wally Joyner	30.00	60.00
YB Yogi Berra	75.00	150.00

2004 Topps Retired Signature Co-Signers

STATED ODDS 1:675
STATED PRINT RUN 25 SERIAL #'d SETS
NO PRICING DUE TO SCARCITY

2005 Topps Retired Signature

This 110-card set was released in September, 2005. The set was issued in four-card packs (of which one card was an autograph), with an $30 SRP which came five packs to a box and six boxes to a case.

PLATE ODDS 1:126 HOBBY, 1:127 RETAIL
PLATE PRINT RUN 1 SET PER COLOR
BLACK-CYAN-MAGENTA-YELLOW ISSUED
NO PLATE PRICING DUE TO SCARCITY

1 Josh Gibson	2.00	5.00
2 Andre Dawson	1.25	3.00
3 Al Kaline	2.00	5.00
4 Andy Van Slyke	.75	2.00
5 Brett Butler	.75	2.00
6 Bob Gibson	1.25	3.00
7 Bo Jackson	2.00	5.00
8 Carlton Fisk	1.25	3.00
9 Chuck Knoblauch	.75	2.00
10 Cal Ripken	8.00	20.00

11 Carl Yastrzemski 2.50 6.00
12 Tom Niedenfuer .75 2.00
13 Dennis Eckersley .75 2.00
14 Darryl Strawberry .75 2.00
15 Dwight Gooden .75 2.00
16 Davey Johnson .75 2.00
17 Don Mattingly 4.00 10.00
18 Dave Winfield .75 2.00
19 Don Zimmer .75 2.00
20 Ernie Banks 2.00 5.00
21 George Brett 4.00 10.00
22 Gary Carter .75 2.00
23 Gregg Jefferies .75 2.00
24 Harold Baines .75 2.00
25 Ryne Sandberg 4.00 10.00
26 Howard Johnson .75 2.00
27 Jim Abbott .75 2.00
28 Johnny Bench 2.00 5.00
29 Jay Buhner .75 2.00
30 Johnny Podres .75 2.00
31 Jose Canseco 1.25 3.00
32 Keith Hernandez .75 2.00
33 Lou Brock Cubs 1.25 3.00
34 Lou Whitaker .75 2.00
35 Mark Fidrych .75 2.00
36 Orlando Cepeda .75 2.00
37 Ozzie Smith 3.00 8.00
38 Paul O'Neill 1.25 3.00
39 Reggie Jackson 2.00 5.00
40 Sid Fernandez .75 2.00
41 Tony Gwynn 2.50 6.00
42 Tim Raines .75 2.00
43 Tom Seaver 1.25 3.00
44 Vida Blue .75 2.00
45 Brady Anderson .75 2.00
46 Bob Brenly .75 2.00
47 Bob Feller .75 2.00
48 Bill Mazeroski 1.25 3.00
49 Brooks Robinson 1.25 3.00
50 Harmon Killebrew 2.00 5.00
51 Bob Welch .75 2.00
52 Carl Erskine .75 2.00
53 Dale Murphy .75 2.00
54 Denny McLain .75 2.00
55 Dave Magadan .75 2.00
56 Duke Snider 1.25 3.00
57 Ed Kranepool .75 2.00
58 Frank Robinson 1.25 3.00
59 Jesus Alou .75 2.00
60 Joe Girardi 1.25 3.00
61 John Kruk .75 2.00
62 Jimmy Leyland MG .75 2.00
63 Juan Marichal .75 2.00
64 Johnny Pesky .75 2.00
65 Jesse Orosco .75 2.00
66 Ken Singleton .75 2.00
67 Matty Alou .75 2.00
68 Monte Irvin .75 2.00
69 Matt Williams 1.25 3.00
70 Pedro Guerrero .75 2.00
71 Ron Blomberg .75 2.00
72 Rod Carew 1.25 3.00
73 Rafael Santana .75 2.00
74 Ralph Kiner .75 2.00
75 Wade Boggs 1.25 3.00
76 Roger Craig .75 2.00
77 Robin Yount 2.00 5.00
78 Steve Carlton .75 2.00
79 Shawon Dunston .75 2.00
80 Steve Garvey .75 2.00
81 Stan Musial 3.00 8.00
82 Travis Fryman .75 2.00
83 Tito Fuentes .75 2.00
84 Mike Cuellar .75 2.00
85 Roberto Clemente 5.00 12.00
86 Whitey Ford 1.25 3.00
87 Yogi Berra 2.00 5.00
88 Atlee Hammaker .75 2.00
89 Bill Freehan .75 2.00
90 Brian Cashman GM .75 2.00
91 Bobby Richardson .75 2.00
92 Bob Boone .75 2.00
93 Charlie Hough .75 2.00
94 Glenn Hubbard .75 2.00
95 Grady Little MG .75 2.00
96 Jimmy Piersall .75 2.00
97 Jim Frey MG .75 2.00
98 Jerry Grote .75 2.00
99 Jim Leyritz .75 2.00
100 Nolan Ryan 5.00 12.00
101 Jim Kaat .75 2.00
102 Joe Pepitone .75 2.00
103 J.R. Richard .75 2.00
104 John Candelaria .75 2.00
105 Moose Skowron .75 2.00
106 Rick Cerone .75 2.00
107 Ron Santo 1.25 3.00
108 Rick Dempsey .75 2.00
109 Roy White .75 2.00
110 Tippy Martinez .75 2.00

2005 Topps Retired Signature Black

*BLACK: 2X TO 5X BASIC
STATED ODDS 1:9 HOBBY, 1:11 RETAIL
STATED PRINT RUN 54 SERIAL #'d SETS

2005 Topps Retired Signature Foilboard

STATED ODDS 1:497 HOBBY, 1:528 RETAIL
STATED PRINT RUN 1 SERIAL #'d SET
NO PRICING DUE TO SCARCITY

2005 Topps Retired Signature Gold

*GOLD: .5X TO 1.2X BASIC
STATED ODDS 1:2 HOBBY/RETAIL
STATED PRINT RUN 500 SERIAL #'d SETS

2005 Topps Retired Signature Autographs

GROUP A ODDS 1:205 HOBBY/RETAIL
GROUP B ODDS 1:35 HOBBY, 1:34 RETAIL
GROUP C ODDS 1:65 HOBBY, 1:64 RETAIL
GROUP D ODDS 1:11 HOBBY/RETAIL
GROUP E ODDS 1:149 HOBBY/RETAIL
GROUP F ODDS 1:5 HOBBY/RETAIL
GROUP G ODDS 1:16 HOBBY/RETAIL
GROUP H ODDS 1:64 HOBBY/RETAIL
GROUP I ODDS 1:4 HOBBY/RETAIL
GROUP J ODDS 1:6 HOBBY/RETAIL
GROUP A PRINT RUNS B/WN 24-35 PER
GROUP B PRINT RUNS B/WN 60-70 PER
GROUP C PRINT RUNS B/WN 170-175 PER
GROUP D PRINT RUN 220 SETS
A-D ARE NOT SERIAL-NUMBERED
A-D PRINT RUNS PROVIDED BY TOPPS
AU PLATE ODDS 1:121 HOBBY
AU PLATE PRINT RUN 1 SET PER COLOR
BLACK-CYAN-MAGENTA-YELLOW ISSUED
NO AU PLATE PRICING DUE TO SCARCITY
AD Andre Dawson D/220 * 10.00 25.00
AH Atlee Hammaker I 4.00 10.00
AK Al Kaline D/220 * 20.00 50.00
AY Anthony Young H 4.00 10.00
BA Brady Anderson F 6.00 15.00
BAF Bill Freehan I 6.00 15.00
BB Brett Butler F 6.00 15.00
BC Brian Cashman GM B/70 * 50.00 100.00
BCR Bobby Richardson F 6.00 15.00
BD Bob Dernier F 10.00 25.00
BEB Bob Brenly F 6.00 15.00
BF Bob Feller D/220 * 15.00 40.00
BG Bob Gibson A/35 *
BJ Bo Jackson B/70 * 75.00 150.00
BM Bill Mazeroski B/70 * 12.50 30.00
BR Brooks Robinson D/220 * 20.00 50.00
BRB Bob Boone F 6.00 15.00
BW Bob Welch F 6.00 15.00
CDH Charlie Hayes F 4.00 10.00
CE Carl Erskine D/220 * 10.00 25.00
CF Carlton Fisk C/170 * 15.00 40.00
CH Charlie Hough I 4.00 10.00
CR Cal Ripken B/70 * 150.00 250.00
CY Carl Yastrzemski B/70 * 60.00 120.00
DBM Dale Murphy F 10.00 25.00
DDM Denny McLain F 15.00 40.00
DES Darryl Strawberry B/70 * 20.00 50.00
DG Dwight Gooden F 6.00 15.00
DJ Davey Johnson B/70 * 15.00 40.00
DJM Dave Magadan F 4.00 10.00
DLB Daryl Boston J 4.00 10.00
DM Don Mattingly B/70 * 75.00 150.00
DS Duke Snider C/170 * 40.00 80.00
DW Dave Winfield B/70 * 30.00 60.00
DZ Don Zimmer D/220 * 10.00 25.00
EB Ernie Banks A/35 *
EK Ed Kranepool F 6.00 15.00
FR Frank Robinson B/70 * 30.00 60.00
GB George Brett B/70 * 75.00 150.00
GC Gary Carter D/220 * 10.00 25.00
GH Glenn Hubbard I 4.00 10.00
GJ Gregg Jefferies F 4.00 10.00
GL Grady Little MG I 4.00 10.00
HB Harold Baines F 6.00 15.00
HJ Howard Johnson D/220 * 6.00 15.00
HK Harmon Killebrew B/70 * 75.00 150.00
JA Jesus Alou F 6.00 15.00
JAA Jim Abbott F 6.00 15.00
JAP Jimmy Piersall J 6.00 15.00
All of these cards were issued without the Topps certification
JB Johnny Bench A/35 *
JC Jose Canseco D/220 * 20.00 50.00
JCB Jay Buhner D/220 * 10.00 25.00
JF Jim Frey MG I 4.00 10.00
JG Jerry Grote I 4.00 10.00
JJL Jim Leyritz I 4.00 10.00
JJP Johnny Podres B/70 * 20.00 50.00
JK John Kruk D/220 * 6.00 15.00
JL Jimmy Leyland MG J 4.00 10.00
JLK Jim Kaat I 6.00 15.00
JM Juan Marichal D/220 * 10.00 25.00
JMP Johnny Pesky F 10.00 25.00
JO Jesse Orosco F 4.00 10.00
JP Joe Pepitone J 6.00 15.00
JR J.R. Richard I 6.00 15.00
JRC John Candelaria I 4.00 10.00
JRL Jim Lonborg I 4.00 10.00
KH Keith Hernandez D/220 * 10.00 25.00
KS Ken Singleton G 6.00 15.00
LB Lou Brock Cubs F 15.00 40.00
LW Lou Whitaker C/175 * 15.00 40.00
MA Matty Alou F 6.00 15.00
MC Mike Cuellar J 6.00 15.00
MI Monte Irvin B/70 * 10.00 25.00
MS Moose Skowron I 6.00 15.00
MW Matt Williams B/70 * 20.00 50.00
NR Nolan Ryan A/35 *
OC Orlando Cepeda D/220 * 10.00 25.00
OS Ozzie Smith B/70 * 50.00 100.00
PG Pedro Guerrero F 6.00 15.00
PO Paul O'Neill B/70 * 30.00 60.00
RB Ron Blomberg D/220 * 6.00 15.00
RC Rick Cerone I 4.00 10.00
RCC Rod Carew B/70 * 30.00 60.00
RD Ron Darling I 6.00 15.00
REG Ron Gant D/220 * 20.00 50.00
RES Ron Santo I 15.00 40.00
RFS Rafael Santana G 4.00 10.00
RG Rusty Greer B/70 * 15.00 40.00
RJ Reggie Jackson B/60 * 75.00 150.00
RK Ralph Kiner D/220 * 20.00 50.00
RKD Rob Dibble D/220 * 6.00 15.00
RLC Roger Craig G 6.00 15.00
RRD Rick Dempsey I 4.00 10.00
RS Ryne Sandberg C/170 * 40.00 80.00
RW Roy White J 4.00 10.00
RY Robin Yount B/70 * 60.00 120.00
SC Steve Carlton D/220 * 20.00 50.00
SD Shawon Dunston D/220 * 10.00 25.00
SF Sid Fernandez D/220 * 6.00 15.00
SG Steve Garvey F 10.00 25.00
SM Stan Musial A/35 *
TDF Travis Fryman F 6.00 15.00
TF Tito Fuentes D/220 * 10.00 25.00
TG Tony Gwynn B/70 * 60.00 120.00
TH Toby Harrah G 4.00 10.00
TL Tony LaRussa D/220 * 10.00 25.00
TM Tippy Martinez J 4.00 10.00
TN Tom Niedenfuer E 6.00 15.00
TR Tim Raines B/70 * 20.00 50.00
TS Tom Seaver A/24 *
VB Vida Blue D/220 * 6.00 15.00
WB Wade Boggs C/170 * 20.00 50.00
WF Whitey Ford A/35 *
YB Yogi Berra A/35 *
ZS Zane Smith G 4.00 10.00

2005 Topps Retired Signature Autographs Refractors

GROUP A ODDS 1:788 HOBBY/RETAIL
GROUP B ODDS 1:21 HOBBY/RETAIL
GROUP A PRINT RUN 10 SERIAL #'d SETS
GROUP B PRINT RUN 25 SERIAL #'d SETS
NO GROUP A PRICING DUE TO SCARCITY
AD Andre Dawson B/25 30.00 60.00
AH Atlee Hammaker B/25 20.00 50.00
AK Al Kaline B/25 75.00 150.00
AY Anthony Young B/25 20.00 50.00
BA Brady Anderson B/25 30.00 60.00
BAF Bill Freehan B/25 30.00 60.00
BB Brett Butler B/25 30.00 60.00
BC Brian Cashman GM B/25 60.00 120.00
BCR Bobby Richardson B/25 30.00 60.00
BD Bob Dernier B/25 30.00 60.00
BEB Bob Brenly B/25 30.00 60.00
BF Bob Feller B/25 50.00 100.00
BG Bob Gibson A/10
BJ Bo Jackson B/25 75.00 150.00
BM Bill Mazeroski B/25 20.00 50.00
BR Brooks Robinson B/25 50.00 100.00
BRB Bob Boone B/25 30.00 60.00
BW Bob Welch B/25 30.00 60.00
CDH Charlie Hayes B/25 20.00 50.00
CE Carl Erskine B/25 30.00 60.00
CF Carlton Fisk B/25 30.00 60.00
CH Charlie Hough B/25 20.00 50.00
CR Cal Ripken B/25 250.00 400.00
CY Carl Yastrzemski B/25 125.00 200.00
DBM Dale Murphy B/25 50.00 100.00
DDM Denny McLain B/25 60.00 150.00
DES Darryl Strawberry B/25 30.00 60.00
DG Dwight Gooden B/25 30.00 60.00
DJ Davey Johnson B/25 20.00 50.00
DJM Dave Magadan B/25 20.00 50.00
DLB Daryl Boston B/25 20.00 50.00
DM Don Mattingly B/25 125.00 200.00
DS Duke Snider B/25 75.00 150.00
DW Dave Winfield B/25 50.00 100.00
DZ Don Zimmer B/25 30.00 60.00
EB Ernie Banks A/10
EK Ed Kranepool B/25 30.00 60.00
FR Frank Robinson B/25 50.00 100.00
GB George Brett B/25
GC Gary Carter B/25 30.00 60.00
GH Glenn Hubbard B/25 20.00 50.00
GJ Gregg Jefferies B/25 20.00 50.00
GL Grady Little MG B/25 20.00 50.00
HB Harold Baines B/25 30.00 60.00
HJ Howard Johnson B/25 20.00 50.00
HK Harmon Killebrew B/25 100.00 200.00
JA Jesus Alou B/25 30.00 60.00
JAA Jim Abbott B/25 30.00 60.00
JAP Jimmy Piersall B/25 30.00 60.00
JB Johnny Bench A/10
JC Jose Canseco B/25 75.00 150.00
JCB Jay Buhner B/25 30.00 60.00
JF Jim Frey MG B/25 20.00 50.00
JG Jerry Grote B/25 20.00 50.00
JJL Jim Leyritz B/25 20.00 50.00
JJP Johnny Podres B/25 30.00 60.00
JK John Kruk B/25 30.00 60.00
JL Jimmy Leyland MG B/25 20.00 50.00
JLK Jim Kaat B/25 30.00 60.00
JM Juan Marichal B/25 30.00 60.00
JMP Johnny Pesky B/25 50.00 100.00
JO Jesse Orosco B/25 20.00 50.00
JP Joe Pepitone B/25 30.00 60.00
JR J.R. Richard B/25 30.00 60.00
JRC John Candelaria B/25 20.00 50.00
JRL Jim Lonborg B/25 20.00 50.00
KH Keith Hernandez B/25 30.00 60.00
KS Ken Singleton B/25 30.00 60.00
LB Lou Brock Cubs B/25 50.00 100.00
LW Lou Whitaker B/25 30.00 60.00
MA Matty Alou B/25 30.00 60.00
MC Mike Cuellar B/25 30.00 60.00
MI Monte Irvin B/25 40.00 100.00
MS Moose Skowron B/25 30.00 60.00
MW Matt Williams B/25 30.00 60.00
NR Nolan Ryan A/10
OC Orlando Cepeda B/25 30.00 60.00
OS Ozzie Smith B/25
PG Pedro Guerrero B/25 30.00 60.00
PO Paul O'Neill B/25 50.00 100.00
RB Ron Blomberg B/25 20.00 50.00
RC Rick Cerone B/25 20.00 50.00
RCC Rod Carew B/25 50.00 100.00
RD Ron Darling B/25 30.00 60.00
REG Ron Gant B/25 30.00 60.00
RES Ron Santo B/25 75.00 150.00
RFS Rafael Santana B/25 20.00 50.00
RG Rusty Greer B/25 20.00 50.00
RJ Reggie Jackson B/25 75.00 150.00
RK Ralph Kiner B/25 50.00 100.00
RKD Rob Dibble B/25 20.00 50.00
RLC Roger Craig B/25 30.00 60.00
RRD Rick Dempsey B/25 20.00 50.00
RS Ryne Sandberg B/25 100.00 175.00
RW Roy White B/25 20.00 50.00
RY Robin Yount B/25 75.00 150.00
SC Steve Carlton B/25 50.00 100.00
SD Shawon Dunston B/25 30.00 60.00
SF Sid Fernandez B/25 20.00 50.00
SG Steve Garvey B/25 50.00 100.00
SM Stan Musial A/10
TDF Travis Fryman B/25 50.00 100.00
TF Tito Fuentes B/25 30.00 60.00
TG Tony Gwynn B/25
TH Toby Harrah B/25 20.00 50.00
TL Tony LaRussa B/25 30.00 60.00
TM Tippy Martinez B/25 20.00 50.00
TN Tom Niedenfuer B/25 30.00 60.00
TR Tim Raines B/25 30.00 60.00
TS Tom Seaver B/25 125.00 200.00
VB Vida Blue B/25 20.00 50.00
WB Wade Boggs B/25 50.00 100.00
WF Whitey Ford A/10
YB Yogi Berra A/10
ZS Zane Smith B/25 20.00 50.00

2005 Topps Retired Signature Co-Signers

GROUP A ODDS 1:6295 H, 1:6192 R
GROUP B ODDS 1:224 HOBBY/RETAIL
GROUP A PRINT RUN 9 SERIAL #'d SETS
GROUP B PRINT RUN 49 SERIAL #'d SETS
NO GROUP A PRICING DUE TO SCARCITY
REFRACTOR ODDS 1:9443 H, 1:12,384 R
REFRACTOR PRINT RUN 1 SERIAL #'d SET
NO REF PRICING DUE TO SCARCITY
BF Johnny Bench / Carlton Fisk B/49 75.00 150.00
BJ Barry Bonds / Reggie Jackson A/9
BS Wade Boggs / Ryne Sandberg B/49 75.00 150.00
GF Bob Gibson / Whitey Ford B/49 60.00 120.00
MS Stan Musial / Duke Snider B/49 100.00 175.00
SR Tom Seaver / Nolan Ryan B/49 200.00 350.00

2006 Topps Sterling

This 200-card set was releasedin November, 2006. The set was issued in a special "cherry wood player specific box" which had three base cards plus an autographed relic or relic card of the featured player,. In addition, each box had an mystery pack with either an cut signature or an framed parallel card of the featured player. These "boxes" had an $250 SRP and were issued 10 to a case. Each base card in this set had a stated print run of 250 serial numbered sets.

B.BONDS (1-19) 5.00 12.00
B.BONDS ODDS 1:10
M.MANTLE (20-39) 6.00 15.00
M.MANTLE ODDS 1:10
J.GIBSON (40-43) 12.50 30.00
J.GIBSON ODDS 1:191
R.HENDERSON (44-53) 4.00 10.00
R.HENDERSON ODDS 1:22
T.WILLIAMS (54-62) 5.00 12.00
T.WILLIAMS ODDS 1:27
R.CLEMENTE (63-67) 10.00 25.00
R.CLEMENTE ODDS 1:40
N.RYAN (68-77) 8.00 20.00
N.RYAN ODDS 1:20
C.RIPKEN (78-96) 8.00 20.00
C.RIPKEN ODDS 1:10
S.MUSIAL (97-101) 4.00 10.00
S.MUSIAL ODDS 1:40
R.JACKSON (102-106) 4.00 10.00
R.JACKSON ODDS 1:40
J.BENCH (107-111) 4.00 10.00
J.BENCH ODDS 1:43
G.BRETT (112-121) 4.00 10.00
G.BRETT ODDS 1:20
D.MATTINGLY (122-131) 5.00 12.00
D.MATTINGLY ODDS 1:20
R.MARIS (132-136) 5.00 12.00
R.MARIS ODDS 1:40
R.CAREW (137-146) 4.00 10.00
R.CAREW ODDS 1:20
Y.BERRA (147-151) 4.00 10.00
Y.BERRA ODDS 1:40
M.SCHMIDT (152-156) 4.00 10.00
M.SCHMIDT ODDS 1:40
C.YASTRZEMSKI (157-175) 4.00 10.00
C.YASTRZEMSKI ODDS 1:10
T.GWYNN (176-185) 4.00 10.00
T.GWYNN ODDS 1:20
R.SANDBERG (186-190) 4.00 10.00
R.SANDBERG ODDS 1:40
O.SMITH (191-200) 4.00 10.00
O.SMITH ODDS 1:20
STATED PRINT RUN 250 SER.#'d SETS

2006 Topps Sterling Framed Burgundy

B.BONDS (1-19) 30.00 60.00
M.MANTLE (20-39) 50.00 100.00
J.GIBSON (40-43) 30.00 60.00
R.HENDERSON (44-53) 20.00 50.00
T.WILLIAMS (54-62) 30.00 60.00
R.CLEMENTE (63-67) 40.00 80.00
N.RYAN (68-77) 75.00 150.00
C.RIPKEN (78-96) 75.00 150.00
S.MUSIAL (97-101) 20.00 50.00
R.JACKSON (102-106) 20.00 50.00
J.BENCH (107-111) 20.00 50.00
G.BRETT (112-121) 30.00 60.00
D.MATTINGLY (122-131) 30.00 60.00
R.MARIS (132-136) 30.00 60.00
R.CAREW (137-146) 10.00 25.00
Y.BERRA (147-151) 20.00 50.00
M.SCHMIDT (152-156) 20.00 50.00
C.YASTRZEMSKI (157-175) 20.00 50.00
T.GWYNN (176-185 20.00 50.00
R.SANDBERG (186-190) 20.00 50.00
O.SMITH (191-200) 20.00 50.00
RANDOM INSERTS IN BONUS PACKS
STATED PRINT RUN 10 SER.#'d SETS

2006 Topps Sterling Framed Cherry Wood

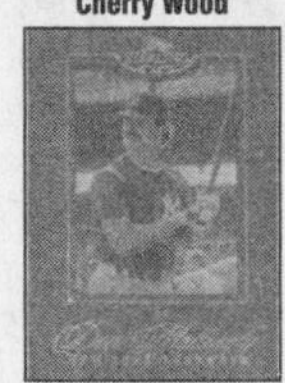

RANDOM INSERTS IN BONUS PACKS
STATED PRINT RUN 1 SER.#'d SET
NO PRICING DUE TO SCARCITY

2006 Topps Sterling Framed Silver

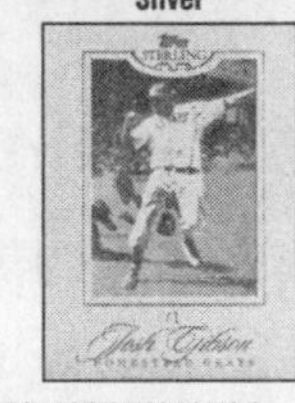

RANDOM INSERTS IN BONUS PACKS
STATED PRINT RUN 1 SER.#'d SET
NO PRICING DUE TO SCARCITY

2006 Topps Sterling Framed White

*FRAMED WHITE: .6X TO 1.5X BASIC
RANDOM INSERTS IN BONUS PACKS
STATED PRINT RUN 50 SER.#'d SETS

2006 Topps Sterling Baseball Cut Signatures

OVERALL CUT SIGNATURE ODDS 1:5
AK Al Kaline 30.00 60.00
BF Bob Feller 15.00 40.00
BG Bob Gibson 30.00 60.00
BR Brooks Robinson 20.00 50.00
CF Carlton Fisk 30.00 60.00
CY Carl Yastrzemski
DE Dennis Eckersley
DS Duke Snider 30.00 60.00
DW Dave Winfield
EB Ernie Banks
EM Eddie Murray
EW Earl Weaver 15.00 40.00
FR Frank Robinson
GC Gary Carter 30.00 60.00
GK George Kell 12.50 30.00
GP Gaylord Perry 15.00 40.00
HK Harmon Killebrew 40.00 80.00
JB Johnny Bench
JM Juan Marichal
JMO Joe Morgan 15.00 40.00
JP Jim Palmer 15.00 40.00
LA Luis Aparicio 15.00 40.00
LB Lou Brock 20.00 50.00
MI Monte Irvin 15.00 40.00
MS Mike Schmidt
NR Nolan Ryan
OC Orlando Cepeda 15.00 40.00
OS Ozzie Smith
PM Paul Molitor
PN Phil Niekro 15.00 40.00
RC Rod Carew 20.00 50.00
RF Rollie Fingers 15.00 40.00
RJ Reggie Jackson
RK Ralph Kiner 20.00 50.00
RR Robin Roberts 20.00 50.00
RS Ryne Sandberg 40.00 80.00
RSH Red Schoendienst 20.00 50.00
RY Robin Yount 30.00 60.00
SA Sparky Anderson 15.00 40.00
SC Steve Carlton
SM Stan Musial
TP Tony Perez
TS Tom Seaver
WB Wade Boggs
WF Whitey Ford
YB Yogi Berra

2006 Topps Sterling Career Stats Relics

OVERALL AU/GU ODDS 1:3
STATED PRINT RUN 10 SERIAL #'d SETS
NO PRICING DUE TO SCARCITY
PRIME PRINT RUN 1 SERIAL #'d SET
NO PRIME PRICING DUE TO SCARCITY
STER.SIL. PRINT RUN 1 SER. #'d SET
NO STER.SIL. PRICING DUE TO SCARCITY
SS PRIME PRINT RUN 1 SER.#'d SET
NO SS PRIME PRICING DUE TO SCARCITY

2006 Topps Sterling Career Stats Relics Autographs

OVERALL AU/GU ODDS 1:3
STATED PRINT RUN 10 SERIAL #'d SETS
NO PRICING DUE TO SCARCITY
PRIME PRINT RUN 1 SERIAL #'d SET
NO PRIME PRICING DUE TO SCARCITY
STER.SIL. PRINT RUN 1 SER. #'d SET
NO STER.SIL. PRICING DUE TO SCARCITY
SS PRIME PRINT RUN 1 SER.#'d SET
NO SS PRIME PRICING DUE TO SCARCITY

2006 Topps Sterling Cut from the Same Cloth Signatures

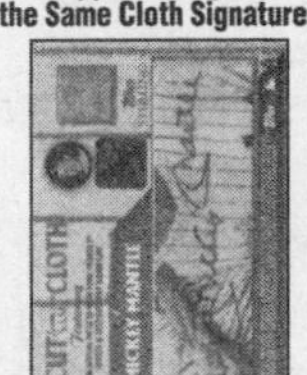

OVERALL CUT SIGNATURES ODDS 1:5
PRINT RUNS B/WN 1-5 COPIES PER
NO PRICING DUE TO SCARCITY

2006 Topps Sterling Cut Signatures

OVERALL CUT SIGNATURE ODDS 1:5
67 Lloyd Waner 75.00 150.00
68 Sal Maglie 40.00 80.00
69 Waite Hoyt 40.00 80.00
70 Warren Spahn 75.00 150.00
72 A.B. Chandler 40.00 80.00
73 Al Barlick 40.00 80.00
74 Bill Dickey 60.00 120.00
75 Bill Terry 15.00 40.00
76 Billy Herman 30.00 60.00
77 Bob Lemon 10.00 25.00
78 Buck Leonard 12.50 30.00
79 Charles Gehringer 60.00 120.00
82 Hoyt Wilhelm 40.00 80.00
83 Catfish Hunter 50.00 100.00
84 Joe Sewell 40.00 80.00
85 Judy Johnson 40.00 80.00
86 Carl Hubbell 50.00 100.00
87 Lou Boudreau 40.00 80.00
88 Luke Appling 40.00 80.00
89 Ray Dandridge 40.00 80.00
90 Rick Ferrell 30.00 60.00
91 Stan Coveleski 40.00 80.00
92 Willie Stargell 75.00 150.00

2006 Topps Sterling Moments Relics

B.BONDS 30.00 80.00
M.MANTLE 3 or 4 RELIC 150.00 250.00
M.MANTLE 5 or 6 RELIC 300.00 600.00
J.GIBSON 250.00 500.00
R.HENDERSON 30.00 80.00
T.WILLIAMS 60.00 150.00
R.CLEMENTE 100.00 200.00
N.RYAN 60.00 150.00
C.RIPKEN 40.00 80.00
S.MUSIAL 30.00 80.00
R.JACKSON 25.00 60.00
J.BENCH 25.00 60.00
G.BRETT 25.00 60.00
R.MARIS 50.00 120.00
Y.BERRA 30.00 80.00
M.SCHMIDT 25.00 60.00
C.YASTRZEMSKI 20.00 50.00
T.GWYNN 25.00 60.00
R.SANDBERG 25.00 60.00
OVERALL AU/GU ODDS 1:3
STATED PRINT RUN 10 SER.#'d SETS
PRIME PRIME RUN 1 SER.#'d SET
NO PRIME PRICING DUE TO SCARCITY

2006 Topps Sterling Moments Relics Autographs

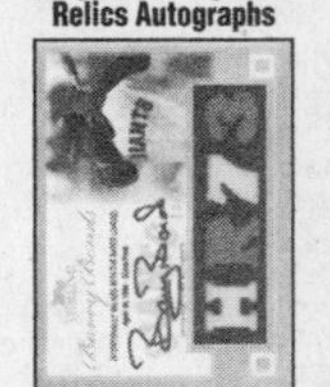

R.HENDERSON 75.00 150.00
N.RYAN 150.00 300.00
C.RIPKEN 150.00 300.00
S.MUSIAL 90.00 150.00
R.JACKSON 75.00 150.00
J.BENCH 75.00 150.00
G.BRETT 75.00 150.00
D.MATTINGLY 75.00 150.00
R.CAREW 40.00 80.00
Y.BERRA 90.00 150.00
M.SCHMIDT 75.00 150.00
C.YASTRZEMSKI 60.00 120.00
T.GWYNN 50.00 100.00
R.SANDBERG 75.00 150.00
O.SMITH 50.00 100.00
OVERALL AU-GU ODDS 1:3
STATED PRINT RUN 10 SERIAL #'d SETS
NO BONDS PRICING DUE TO SCARCITY
PRIME PRINT RUN 1 SER.#'d SET
NO PRIME PRICING DUE TO SCARCITY

2007 Topps Sterling

This 254-card set was released in December, 2007. The set was issued in "box" form which consisted of a player specific wood box and a mystery pack which also pertained to the player one recieved in the wood box. Each full box had five total cards in them and those boxes came five per carton and two cartons per full case.

COMMON MANTLE (1-24) 5.00 12.00
COMMON BONDS (25-48) 5.00 12.00
COMMON ICHIRO (49-56) 4.00 10.00
COMMON YAZ (57-64) 3.00 8.00
COMMON WRIGHT (65-76) 3.00 8.00
COMMON CLEMENTE (77-81) 6.00 15.00
COMMON SANTANA (82-89) 3.00 8.00
COMMON MORNEAU (90-101) 3.00 8.00
COMMON R.JACKSON (102-109) 3.00 8.00
COMMON CLEMENS (110-117) 4.00 10.00
COMMON T.WILLIAMS (118-122) 5.00 12.00
COMMON BERRA (123-130) 3.00 8.00
COMMON MATSUI (131-135) 3.00 8.00
COMMON HOWARD (136-143) 3.00 8.00
COMMON GWYNN (144-151) 3.00 8.00
COMMON ORTIZ (152-159) 2.50 6.00

COMMON SEAVER (160-167) 2.50 6.00
COMMON PUJOLS (168-175) 4.00 10.00
COMMON MUSIAL (176-183) 3.00 8.00
COMMON WANG (184-191) 5.00 12.00
COMMON SANDBERG (192-199) 4.00 10.00
COMMON N.RYAN (200-207) 8.00 20.00
COMMON B.GIBSON (208-215) 2.50 6.00
COMMON MARIS (216-220) 3.00 8.00
COMMON M.RAMIREZ (221-228) 3.00 8.00
COMMON SCHMIDT (229-236) 4.00 10.00
COMMON A.ROD (237-244) 3.00 8.00
COMMON MATSUZAKA (245-249) 6.00 15.00
COMMON DIMAGGIO (250-254) 4.00 10.00
THREE BASE CARDS PER BOX
STATED PRINT RUN 250 SER.#'d SETS
1 Mickey Mantle 5.00 12.00
2 Mickey Mantle 5.00 12.00
3 Mickey Mantle 5.00 12.00
4 Mickey Mantle 5.00 12.00
5 Mickey Mantle 5.00 12.00
6 Mickey Mantle 5.00 12.00
7 Mickey Mantle 5.00 12.00
8 Mickey Mantle 5.00 12.00
9 Mickey Mantle 5.00 12.00
10 Mickey Mantle 5.00 12.00
11 Mickey Mantle 5.00 12.00
12 Mickey Mantle 5.00 12.00
13 Mickey Mantle 5.00 12.00
14 Mickey Mantle 5.00 12.00
15 Mickey Mantle 5.00 12.00
16 Mickey Mantle 5.00 12.00
17 Mickey Mantle 5.00 12.00
18 Mickey Mantle 5.00 12.00
19 Mickey Mantle 5.00 12.00
20 Mickey Mantle 5.00 12.00
21 Mickey Mantle 5.00 12.00
22 Mickey Mantle 5.00 12.00
23 Mickey Mantle 5.00 12.00
24 Mickey Mantle 5.00 12.00
25 Barry Bonds 5.00 12.00
26 Barry Bonds 5.00 12.00
27 Barry Bonds 5.00 12.00
28 Barry Bonds 5.00 12.00
29 Barry Bonds 5.00 12.00
30 Barry Bonds 5.00 12.00
31 Barry Bonds 5.00 12.00
32 Barry Bonds 5.00 12.00
33 Barry Bonds 5.00 12.00
34 Barry Bonds 5.00 12.00
35 Barry Bonds 5.00 12.00
36 Barry Bonds 5.00 12.00
37 Barry Bonds 5.00 12.00
38 Barry Bonds 5.00 12.00
39 Barry Bonds 5.00 12.00
40 Barry Bonds 5.00 12.00
41 Barry Bonds 5.00 12.00
42 Barry Bonds 5.00 12.00
43 Barry Bonds 5.00 12.00
44 Barry Bonds 5.00 12.00
45 Barry Bonds 5.00 12.00
46 Barry Bonds 5.00 12.00
47 Barry Bonds 5.00 12.00
48 Barry Bonds 5.00 12.00
49 Ichiro Suzuki 4.00 10.00
50 Ichiro Suzuki 4.00 10.00
51 Ichiro Suzuki 4.00 10.00
52 Ichiro Suzuki 4.00 10.00
53 Ichiro Suzuki 4.00 10.00
54 Ichiro Suzuki 4.00 10.00
55 Ichiro Suzuki 4.00 10.00
56 Ichiro Suzuki 4.00 10.00
57 Carl Yastrzemski 3.00 8.00
58 Carl Yastrzemski 3.00 8.00
59 Carl Yastrzemski 3.00 8.00
60 Carl Yastrzemski 3.00 8.00
61 Carl Yastrzemski 3.00 8.00
62 Carl Yastrzemski 3.00 8.00
63 Carl Yastrzemski 3.00 8.00
64 Carl Yastrzemski 3.00 8.00
65 David Wright 3.00 8.00
66 David Wright 3.00 8.00
67 David Wright 3.00 8.00
68 David Wright 3.00 8.00
69 David Wright 3.00 8.00
70 David Wright 3.00 8.00
71 David Wright 3.00 8.00
72 David Wright 3.00 8.00
73 David Wright 3.00 8.00
74 David Wright 3.00 8.00
75 David Wright 3.00 8.00
76 David Wright 3.00 8.00
77 Roberto Clemente 6.00 15.00
78 Roberto Clemente 6.00 15.00
79 Roberto Clemente 6.00 15.00
80 Roberto Clemente 6.00 15.00
81 Roberto Clemente 6.00 15.00
82 Johan Santana 3.00 8.00
83 Johan Santana 3.00 8.00
84 Johan Santana 3.00 8.00
85 Johan Santana 3.00 8.00
86 Johan Santana 3.00 8.00
87 Johan Santana 3.00 8.00
88 Johan Santana 3.00 8.00
89 Johan Santana 3.00 8.00
90 Justin Morneau 3.00 8.00
91 Justin Morneau 3.00 8.00
92 Justin Morneau 3.00 8.00
93 Justin Morneau 3.00 8.00
94 Justin Morneau 3.00 8.00
95 Justin Morneau 3.00 8.00
96 Justin Morneau 3.00 8.00
97 Justin Morneau 3.00 8.00
98 Justin Morneau 3.00 8.00
99 Justin Morneau 3.00 8.00
100 Justin Morneau 3.00 8.00
101 Justin Morneau 3.00 8.00
102 Reggie Jackson 3.00 8.00
103 Reggie Jackson 3.00 8.00
104 Reggie Jackson 3.00 8.00
105 Reggie Jackson 3.00 8.00
106 Reggie Jackson 3.00 8.00
107 Reggie Jackson 3.00 8.00
108 Reggie Jackson 3.00 8.00
109 Reggie Jackson 3.00 8.00
110 Roger Clemens 4.00 10.00
111 Roger Clemens 4.00 10.00
112 Roger Clemens 4.00 10.00
113 Roger Clemens 4.00 10.00
114 Roger Clemens 4.00 10.00
115 Roger Clemens 4.00 10.00
116 Roger Clemens 4.00 10.00
117 Roger Clemens 4.00 10.00
118 Ted Williams 5.00 12.00
119 Ted Williams 5.00 12.00
120 Ted Williams 5.00 12.00
121 Ted Williams 5.00 12.00
122 Ted Williams 5.00 12.00
123 Yogi Berra 3.00 8.00
124 Yogi Berra 3.00 8.00
125 Yogi Berra 3.00 8.00
126 Yogi Berra 3.00 8.00
127 Yogi Berra 3.00 8.00
128 Yogi Berra 3.00 8.00
129 Yogi Berra 3.00 8.00
130 Yogi Berra 3.00 8.00
131 Hideki Matsui 3.00 8.00
132 Hideki Matsui 3.00 8.00
133 Hideki Matsui 3.00 8.00
134 Hideki Matsui 3.00 8.00
135 Hideki Matsui 3.00 8.00
136 Ryan Howard 3.00 8.00
137 Ryan Howard 3.00 8.00
138 Ryan Howard 3.00 8.00
139 Ryan Howard 3.00 8.00
140 Ryan Howard 3.00 8.00
141 Ryan Howard 3.00 8.00
142 Ryan Howard 3.00 8.00
143 Ryan Howard 3.00 8.00
144 Tony Gwynn 3.00 8.00
145 Tony Gwynn 3.00 8.00
146 Tony Gwynn 3.00 8.00
147 Tony Gwynn 3.00 8.00
148 Tony Gwynn 3.00 8.00
149 Tony Gwynn 3.00 8.00
150 Tony Gwynn 3.00 8.00
151 Tony Gwynn 3.00 8.00
152 David Ortiz 2.50 6.00
153 David Ortiz 2.50 6.00
154 David Ortiz 2.50 6.00
155 David Ortiz 2.50 6.00
156 David Ortiz 2.50 6.00
157 David Ortiz 2.50 6.00
158 David Ortiz 2.50 6.00
159 David Ortiz 2.50 6.00
160 Tom Seaver 2.50 6.00
161 Tom Seaver 2.50 6.00
162 Tom Seaver 2.50 6.00
163 Tom Seaver 2.50 6.00
164 Tom Seaver 2.50 6.00
165 Tom Seaver 2.50 6.00
166 Tom Seaver 2.50 6.00
167 Tom Seaver 2.50 6.00
168 Albert Pujols 4.00 10.00
169 Albert Pujols 4.00 10.00
170 Albert Pujols 4.00 10.00
171 Albert Pujols 4.00 10.00
172 Albert Pujols 4.00 10.00
173 Albert Pujols 4.00 10.00
174 Albert Pujols 4.00 10.00
175 Albert Pujols 4.00 10.00
176 Stan Musial 3.00 8.00
177 Stan Musial 3.00 8.00
178 Stan Musial 3.00 8.00
179 Stan Musial 3.00 8.00
180 Stan Musial 3.00 8.00
181 Stan Musial 3.00 8.00
182 Stan Musial 3.00 8.00
183 Stan Musial 3.00 8.00
184 Chien-Ming Wang 5.00 12.00
185 Chien-Ming Wang 5.00 12.00
186 Chien-Ming Wang 5.00 12.00
187 Chien-Ming Wang 5.00 12.00
188 Chien-Ming Wang 5.00 12.00
189 Chien-Ming Wang 5.00 12.00
190 Chien-Ming Wang 5.00 12.00
191 Chien-Ming Wang 5.00 12.00
192 Ryne Sandberg 4.00 10.00
193 Ryne Sandberg 4.00 10.00
194 Ryne Sandberg 4.00 10.00
195 Ryne Sandberg 4.00 10.00
196 Ryne Sandberg 4.00 10.00
197 Ryne Sandberg 4.00 10.00
198 Ryne Sandberg 4.00 10.00
199 Ryne Sandberg 4.00 10.00
200 Nolan Ryan 8.00 20.00
201 Nolan Ryan 8.00 20.00
202 Nolan Ryan 8.00 20.00
203 Nolan Ryan 8.00 20.00
204 Nolan Ryan 8.00 20.00
205 Nolan Ryan 8.00 20.00
206 Nolan Ryan 8.00 20.00
207 Nolan Ryan 8.00 20.00
208 Bob Gibson 2.50 6.00
209 Bob Gibson 2.50 6.00
210 Bob Gibson 2.50 6.00
211 Bob Gibson 2.50 6.00
212 Bob Gibson 2.50 6.00
213 Bob Gibson 2.50 6.00
214 Bob Gibson 2.50 6.00
215 Bob Gibson 2.50 6.00
216 Roger Maris 3.00 8.00
217 Roger Maris 3.00 8.00
218 Roger Maris 3.00 8.00
219 Roger Maris 3.00 8.00
220 Roger Maris 3.00 8.00
221 Manny Ramirez 3.00 8.00
222 Manny Ramirez 3.00 8.00
223 Manny Ramirez 3.00 8.00
224 Manny Ramirez 3.00 8.00
225 Manny Ramirez 3.00 8.00
226 Manny Ramirez 3.00 8.00
227 Manny Ramirez 3.00 8.00
228 Manny Ramirez 3.00 8.00
229 Mike Schmidt 4.00 10.00
230 Mike Schmidt 4.00 10.00
231 Mike Schmidt 4.00 10.00
232 Mike Schmidt 4.00 10.00
233 Mike Schmidt 4.00 10.00
234 Mike Schmidt 4.00 10.00
235 Mike Schmidt 4.00 10.00
236 Mike Schmidt 4.00 10.00
237 Alex Rodriguez 3.00 8.00
238 Alex Rodriguez 3.00 8.00
239 Alex Rodriguez 3.00 8.00
240 Alex Rodriguez 3.00 8.00
241 Alex Rodriguez 3.00 8.00
242 Alex Rodriguez 3.00 8.00
243 Alex Rodriguez 3.00 8.00
244 Alex Rodriguez 3.00 8.00
245 Daisuke Matsuzaka RC 6.00 15.00
246 Daisuke Matsuzaka RC 6.00 15.00
247 Daisuke Matsuzaka RC 6.00 15.00
248 Daisuke Matsuzaka RC 6.00 15.00
249 Daisuke Matsuzaka RC 6.00 15.00
250 Joe DiMaggio 4.00 10.00
251 Joe DiMaggio 4.00 10.00
252 Joe DiMaggio 4.00 10.00
253 Joe DiMaggio 4.00 10.00
254 Joe DiMaggio 4.00 10.00

2007 Topps Sterling Framed Burgundy

COMMON MANTLE (1-24) 20.00 50.00
COMMON BONDS (25-48) 12.50 30.00
COMMON ICHIRO (49-56) 12.50 30.00
COMMON YAZ (57-64) 12.50 30.00
COMMON WRIGHT (65-76) 10.00 25.00
COMMON CLEMENTE (77-81) 20.00 50.00
COMMON SANTANA (82-89) 8.00 20.00
COMMON MORNEAU (90-101) 6.00 15.00
COMMON R.JACKSON (102-109) 10.00 25.00
COMMON CLEMENS (110-117) 10.00 25.00
COMMON T.WILLIAMS (118-122) 12.50 30.00
COMMON BERRA (123-130) 6.00 15.00
COMMON MATSUI (131-135) 8.00 20.00
COMMON HOWARD (136-143) 10.00 25.00
COMMON GWYNN (144-151) 20.00 50.00
COMMON ORTIZ (152-159) 6.00 15.00
COMMON SEAVER (160-167) 8.00 20.00
COMMON PUJOLS (168-175) 12.50 30.00
COMMON MUSIAL (176-183) 10.00 25.00
COMMON WANG (184-191) 15.00 40.00
COMMON SANDBERG (192-199) 12.50 30.00
COMMON N.RYAN (200-207) 30.00 60.00
COMMON B.GIBSON (208-215) 8.00 20.00
COMMON MARIS (216-220) 12.50 30.00
COMMON M.RAMIREZ (221-228) 6.00 15.00
COMMON SCHMIDT (229-236) 15.00 40.00
COMMON A.ROD (237-244) 20.00 50.00
COMMON MATSUZAKA (245-249) 20.00 50.00
COMMON DIMAGGIO (250-254) 15.00 40.00
RANDOMLY INSERTED IN MYSTERY PACKS
STATED PRINT RUN 14 SER.#'d SETS

2007 Topps Sterling Framed Cherry Wood

RANDOM INSERTS IN MYSTERY PACKS
STATED PRINT RUN 1 SER.#'d SET
NO PRICING DUE TO SCARCITY

2007 Topps Sterling Framed Gold

COMMON MANTLE (1-24) 40.00 80.00
COMMON BONDS (25-48) 30.00 60.00
COMMON ICHIRO (49-56) 20.00 50.00
COMMON YAZ (57-64) 15.00 40.00
COMMON WRIGHT (65-76) 15.00 40.00
COMMON CLEMENTE (77-81) 30.00 60.00
COMMON SANTANA (82-89) 10.00 25.00
COMMON MORNEAU (90-101) 6.00 15.00
COMMON R.JACKSON (102-109) 12.50 30.00
COMMON CLEMENS (110-117) 12.50 30.00
COMMON T.WILLIAMS (118-122) 15.00 40.00
COMMON BERRA (123-130) 10.00 25.00
COMMON MATSUI (131-135) 15.00 40.00
COMMON HOWARD (136-143) 12.50 30.00
COMMON GWYNN (144-151) 30.00 60.00
COMMON ORTIZ (152-159) 8.00 20.00
COMMON SEAVER (160-167) 10.00 25.00
COMMON PUJOLS (168-175) 20.00 50.00
COMMON MUSIAL (176-183) 12.50 30.00
COMMON WANG (184-191) 30.00 60.00
COMMON SANDBERG (192-199) 15.00 40.00
COMMON N.RYAN (200-207) 30.00 60.00
COMMON B.GIBSON (208-215) 12.50 30.00
COMMON MARIS (216-220) 12.50 30.00
COMMON M.RAMIREZ (221-228) 8.00 20.00
COMMON SCHMIDT (229-236) 20.00 50.00
COMMON A.ROD (237-244) 20.00 50.00
COMMON MATSUZAKA (245-249) 30.00 60.00
COMMON DIMAGGIO (250-254) 20.00 50.00
RANDOMLY INSERTED IN MYSTERY PACKS
STATED PRINT RUN 9 SER.#'d SETS

2007 Topps Sterling Career Stats Relics Five

COMMON MANTLE 100.00 175.00
COMMON BONDS 30.00 60.00
COMMON ICHIRO 75.00 150.00
COMMON YAZ 30.00 60.00
COMMON WRIGHT 40.00 80.00
COMMON CLEMENTE 90.00 150.00
COMMON MORNEAU 12.50 30.00
COMMON CLEMENS 20.00 50.00
COMMON T.WILLIAMS 75.00 150.00
COMMON MATSUI 50.00 100.00
COMMON HOWARD 30.00 60.00
COMMON ORTIZ 20.00 50.00
COMMON PUJOLS 30.00 60.00
COMMON WANG 40.00 80.00
COMMON RYAN 50.00 100.00
COMMON GIBSON 20.00 50.00
COMMON MARIS 50.00 100.00
COMMON M.RAMIREZ 15.00 40.00
COMMON SCHMIDT 40.00 80.00
COMMON A.ROD 60.00 120.00
COMMON MATSUZAKA 60.00 120.00
COMMON DIMAGGIO 60.00 120.00
RANDOM INSERTS IN BOXES
OVERALL ONE AUTO OR MEM PER BOX
STATED PRINT RUN 10 SER.#'d SETS
NO BERRA,GWYNN PRICING
NO SEAVER,SANDBERG PRICING

2007 Topps Sterling Career Stats Relics Five Sterling Silver

RANDOM INSERTS IN BOXES
OVERALL ONE AUTO OR MEM PER BOX
OVERALL ONE OF ONE RELICS 1:10 BOXES
STATED PRINT RUN ONE SER.#'d SET
NO PRICING DUE TO SCARCITY

2007 Topps Sterling Career Stats Relics Quad

COMMON MANTLE 100.00 175.00
COMMON BONDS 20.00 50.00
COMMON ICHIRO 60.00 120.00
COMMON YAZ 30.00 60.00
COMMON CLEMENTE 90.00 150.00
COMMON SANTANA 15.00 40.00
COMMON CLEMENS 15.00 40.00
COMMON T.WILLIAMS 75.00 150.00
COMMON MATUSI 40.00 80.00
COMMON ORTIZ 15.00 40.00
COMMON SEAVER 30.00 60.00
COMMON PUJOLS 20.00 50.00
COMMON GIBSON 20.00 50.00
COMMON MARIS 50.00 100.00
COMMON SCHMIDT 40.00 80.00
COMMON MATSUZAKA 60.00 120.00
COMMON DIMAGGIO 60.00 120.00
RANDOM INSERTS IN BOXES
OVERALL ONE AUTO OR MEM PER BOX
STATED PRINT RUN 10 SER.#'d SETS
NO WRIGHT,MORNEAU,JACKSON PRICING
NO HOWARD,MUSIAL,WANG PRICING
NO SANDBERG PRICING

2007 Topps Sterling Career Stats Relics Quad Sterling Silver

RANDOM INSERTS IN BOXES
OVERALL ONE AUTO OR MEM PER BOX
OVERALL ONE OF ONE RELICS 1:10 BOXES
STATED PRINT RUN ONE SER.#'d SET
NO PRICING DUE TO SCARCITY

2007 Topps Sterling Career Stats Relics Six

COMMON MANTLE 100.00 200.00
COMMON BONDS 30.00 60.00
COMMON ICHIRO 75.00 150.00
COMMON D.WRIGHT 40.00 80.00
COMMON CLEMENTE 100.00 200.00
COMMON SANTANA 20.00 50.00
COMMON MORNEAU 12.50 30.00
COMMON R.JACKSON 30.00 60.00
COMMON CLEMENS 20.00 50.00
COMMON T.WILLIAMS 100.00 200.00
COMMON MATSUI 50.00 100.00
COMMON ORTIZ 20.00 50.00
COMMON PUJOLS 40.00 80.00
COMMON WANG 50.00 100.00
COMMON SANDBERG 20.00 50.00
COMMON RYAN 50.00 100.00
COMMON MARIS 50.00 100.00
COMMON M.RAMIREZ 20.00 50.00
COMMON SCHMIDT 40.00 80.00
COMMON AROD 75.00 150.00
COMMON MATSUZAKA 75.00 150.00
COMMON DIMAGGIO 75.00 150.00
RANDOM INSERTS IN BOXES
OVERALL ONE AUTO OR MEM PER BOX
STATED PRINT RUN 10 SER.#'d SETS
NO YAZ,BERRA,GWYNN PRICING
NO MUSIAL OR GIBSON PRICING

2007 Topps Sterling Career Stats Relics Six Sterling Silver

RANDOM INSERTS IN BOXES
OVERALL ONE AUTO OR MEM PER BOX
OVERALL ONE OF ONE RELICS 1:10 BOXES
STATED PRINT RUN ONE SER.#'d SET
NO PRICING DUE TO SCARCITY

2007 Topps Sterling Career Stats Relics Triple

COMMON MANTLE 90.00 150.00
COMMON BONDS 20.00 50.00
COMMON ICHIRO 60.00 120.00
COMMON D.WRIGHT 30.00 60.00
COMMON CLEMENTE 75.00 150.00
COMMON MORNEAU 10.00 25.00
COMMON CLEMENS 15.00 40.00
COMMON T.WILLIAMS 50.00 100.00
COMMON BERRA 30.00 60.00
COMMON MATSUI 30.00 60.00
COMMON ORTIZ 15.00 40.00
COMMON SEAVER 20.00 50.00
COMMON PUJOLS 20.00 50.00
COMMON MUSIAL 30.00 60.00
COMMON GIBSON 15.00 40.00
COMMON MARIS 40.00 80.00
COMMON SCHMIDT 40.00 80.00
COMMON MATSUZAKA 60.00 120.00
COMMON DIMAGGIO 60.00 120.00
RANDOM INSERTS IN BOXES
OVERALL ONE AUTO OR MEM PER BOX
STATED PRINT RUN 10 SER.#'d SETS
NO YAZ,JACKSON,GWYNN PRICING
NO SANDBERG,RYAN PRICING

2007 Topps Sterling Career Stats Relics Triple Sterling Silver

RANDOM INSERTS IN BOXES
OVERALL ONE AUTO OR MEM PER BOX
OVERALL ONE OF ONE RELICS 1:10 BOXES
STATED PRINT RUN ONE SER.#'d SET
NO PRICING DUE TO SCARCITY

2007 Topps Sterling Career Stats Relics Autographs Quad

COMMON YAZ 50.00 100.00
COMMON D.WRIGHT 75.00 150.00
COMMON SANTANA 30.00 60.00
COMMON MORNEAU 20.00 50.00
COMMON R.JACKSON 40.00 80.00
COMMON R.CLEMENS 60.00 120.00
COMMON Y.BERRA 60.00 120.00
COMMON R.HOWARD 50.00 100.00
COMMON T.GWYNN 60.00 120.00
COMMON ORTIZ 50.00 100.00
COMMON T.SEAVER 40.00 80.00
COMMON PUJOLS 175.00 300.00
COMMON MUSIAL 60.00 120.00
COMMON WANG 150.00 250.00
COMMON SANDBERG 60.00 120.00
COMMON RYAN 75.00 150.00
COMMON GIBSON 30.00 60.00
COMMON M.RAMIREZ 40.00 80.00
COMMON SCHMIDT 40.00 80.00
COMMON AROD 175.00 300.00
RANDOM INSERTS IN BOXES
OVERALL ONE AUTO OR MEM PER BOX
STATED PRINT RUN 10 SER.#'d SETS
NO MATSUI PRICING DUE TO SCARCITY

2007 Topps Sterling Career Stats Relics Autographs Quad Sterling Silver

RANDOM INSERTS IN BOXES
OVERALL ONE AUTO OR MEM PER BOX
OVERALL ONE OF ONE AUTO 1:10 BOXES
STATED PRINT RUN ONE SER.#'d SET
NO PRICING DUE TO SCARCITY

2007 Topps Sterling Career Stats Relics Autographs Triple

COMMON BONDS 175.00 300.00
COMMON YAZ 40.00 80.00
COMMON D.WRIGHT 60.00 120.00
COMMON SANTANA 20.00 50.00
COMMON MORNEAU 20.00 50.00
COMMON R.JACKSON 30.00 60.00
COMMON R.CLEMENS 60.00 120.00
COMMON Y.BERRA 50.00 100.00
COMMON R.HOWARD 50.00 100.00
COMMON T.GWYNN 50.00 100.00
COMMON ORTIZ 40.00 80.00
COMMON T.SEAVER 40.00 80.00
COMMON PUJOLS 175.00 300.00
COMMON MUSIAL 50.00 100.00
COMMON WANG 150.00 250.00
COMMON SANDBERG 50.00 100.00
COMMON RYAN 60.00 120.00
COMMON GIBSON 30.00 60.00
COMMON M.RAMIREZ 30.00 60.00
COMMON SCHMIDT 40.00 80.00
COMMON AROD 175.00 300.00
RANDOM INSERTS IN BOXES
OVERALL ONE AUTO OR MEM PER BOX
STATED PRINT RUN 10 SER.#'d SETS

2007 Topps Sterling Career Stats Relics Autographs Triple Sterling Silver

RANDOM INSERTS IN BOXES
OVERALL ONE AUTO OR MEM PER BOX
OVERALL ONE OF ONE AUTO 1:10 BOXES
STATED PRINT RUN ONE SER.#'d SET
NO PRICING DUE TO SCARCITY

2007 Topps Sterling Moments Relics Eight

COMMON MANTLE 275.00 375.00
COMMON BONDS 150.00 250.00
COMMON MATSUI 75.00 150.00
COMMON ORTIZ 40.00 80.00
RANDOM INSERTS IN BOXES
OVERALL ONE AUTO OR MEM PER BOX
STATED PRINT RUN 10 SER.#'d SETS
NO PRICING ON MOST DUE TO SCARCITY

2007 Topps Sterling Moments Relics Eight Sterling Silver

RANDOM INSERTS IN BOXES
OVERALL ONE AUTO OR MEM PER BOX
OVERALL ONE OF ONE RELICS 1:10 BOXES
STATED PRINT RUN ONE SER.#'d SET
NO PRICING DUE TO SCARCITY

2007 Topps Sterling Moments Relics Five

COMMON MANTLE 100.00 175.00
COMMON BONDS 30.00 60.00
COMMON ICHIRO 75.00 150.00
COMMON YAZ 30.00 60.00
COMMON WRIGHT 40.00 80.00
COMMON CLEMENTE 90.00 150.00
COMMON MORNEAU 12.50 30.00
COMMON CLEMENS 20.00 50.00
COMMON T.WILLIAMS 75.00 150.00
COMMON MATSUI 50.00 100.00
COMMON HOWARD 30.00 60.00
COMMON ORTIZ 20.00 50.00
COMMON PUJOLS 30.00 60.00
COMMON WANG 40.00 80.00
COMMON RYAN 50.00 100.00
COMMON GIBSON 20.00 50.00
COMMON MARIS 50.00 100.00
COMMON M.RAMIREZ 15.00 40.00
COMMON SCHMIDT 40.00 80.00
COMMON A.ROD 60.00 120.00
COMMON MATSUZAKA 60.00 120.00
COMMON DIMAGGIO 60.00 120.00
RANDOM INSERTS IN BOXES
OVERALL ONE AUTO OR MEM PER BOX
STATED PRINT RUN 10 SER.#'d SETS
NO JOHAN,SEAVER,MUSIAL PRICING

2007 Topps Sterling Moments Relics Five Sterling Silver

RANDOM INSERTS IN BOXES
OVERALL ONE AUTO OR MEM PER BOX
OVERALL ONE OF ONE RELICS 1:10 BOXES
STATED PRINT RUN ONE SER.#'d SET
NO PRICING DUE TO SCARCITY

2007 Topps Sterling Moments Relics Quad

COMMON MANTLE 100.00 175.00
COMMON BONDS 20.00 50.00
COMMON ICHIRO 60.00 120.00
COMMON YAZ 30.00 60.00
COMMON CLEMENTE 90.00 150.00
COMMON SANTANA 15.00 40.00
COMMON CLEMENS 15.00 40.00
COMMON T.WILLIAMS 75.00 150.00
COMMON MATUSI 40.00 80.00
COMMON ORTIZ 15.00 40.00
COMMON SEAVER 30.00 60.00
COMMON PUJOLS 20.00 50.00
COMMON GIBSON 20.00 50.00
COMMON MARIS 50.00 100.00
COMMON SCHMIDT 40.00 80.00
COMMON MATSUZAKA 60.00 120.00
COMMON DIMAGGIO 60.00 120.00
RANDOM INSERTS IN BOXES
OVERALL ONE AUTO OR MEM PER BOX
STATED PRINT RUN 10 SER.#'d SETS
NO WRIGHT,MORNEAU,BERRA PRICING
NO GWYNN OR MUSIAL PRICING

2007 Topps Sterling Moments Relics Quad Sterling Silver

RANDOM INSERTS IN BOXES
OVERALL ONE AUTO OR MEM PER BOX
OVERALL ONE OF ONE RELICS 1:10 BOXES
STATED PRINT RUN ONE SER.#'d SET
NO PRICING DUE TO SCARCITY

2007 Topps Sterling Moments Relics Six

COMMON MANTLE 100.00 200.00
COMMON BONDS 30.00 60.00
COMMON ICHIRO 75.00 150.00
COMMON D.WRIGHT 40.00 100.00
COMMON CLEMENTE 100.00 200.00
COMMON SANTANA 20.00 50.00
COMMON MORNEAU 12.50 30.00
COMMON R.JACKSON 30.00 60.00
COMMON CLEMENS 20.00 50.00
COMMON T.WILLIAMS 100.00 200.00
COMMON MATSUI 50.00 100.00
COMMON ORTIZ 20.00 50.00
COMMON PUJOLS 40.00 80.00
COMMON WANG 50.00 100.00
COMMON SANDBERG 20.00 50.00
COMMON RYAN 50.00 100.00
COMMON MARIS 50.00 100.00
COMMON M.RAMIREZ 20.00 50.00
COMMON SCHMIDT 40.00 80.00
COMMON AROD 75.00 150.00
COMMON MATSUZAKA 75.00 150.00
COMMON DIMAGGIO 75.00 150.00
RANDOM INSERTS IN BOXES
OVERALL ONE AUTO OR MEM PER BOX
STATED PRINT RUN 10 SER.#'d SETS
NO HOWARD PRICING

2007 Topps Sterling Moments Relics Six Sterling Silver

RANDOM INSERTS IN BOXES
OVERALL ONE AUTO OR MEM PER BOX
OVERALL ONE OF ONE RELICS 1:10 BOXES
STATED PRINT RUN ONE SER.#'d SET
NO PRICING DUE TO SCARCITY

2007 Topps Sterling Moments Relics Triple

COMMON MANTLE 90.00 150.00
COMMON BONDS 20.00 50.00
COMMON ICHIRO 60.00 120.00
COMMON D.WRIGHT 30.00 60.00
COMMON CLEMENTE 75.00 150.00
COMMON MORNEAU 10.00 25.00
COMMON CLEMENS 15.00 40.00
COMMON T.WILLIAMS 50.00 100.00
COMMON BERRA 30.00 60.00
COMMON MATSUI 30.00 60.00
COMMON ORTIZ 15.00 40.00
COMMON SEAVER 20.00 50.00
COMMON PUJOLS 20.00 50.00
COMMON MUSIAL 30.00 60.00
COMMON GIBSON 15.00 40.00
COMMON MARIS 40.00 80.00
COMMON SCHMIDT 40.00 80.00
COMMON MATSUZAKA 60.00 120.00
COMMON DIMAGGIO 60.00 120.00
RANDOM INSERTS IN BOXES
OVERALL ONE AUTO OR MEM PER BOX
STATED PRINT RUN 10 SER.#'d SETS
NO JACKSON OR GWYNN PRICING

2007 Topps Sterling Moments Relics Triple Sterling Silver

RANDOM INSERTS IN BOXES
OVERALL ONE AUTO OR MEM PER BOX
OVERALL ONE OF ONE RELICS 1:10 BOXES
STATED PRINT RUN ONE SER.#'d SET
NO PRICING DUE TO SCARCITY

2007 Topps Sterling Moments Relics Autographs Eight

COMMON M.RAMIREZ 60.00 120.00
RANDOM INSERTS IN BOXES
OVERALL ONE AUTO OR MEM PER BOX
STATED PRINT RUN 10 SER.#'d SETS
NO PRICING ON MOST DUE TO SCARCITY

2007 Topps Sterling Moments Relics Autographs Eight Sterling Silver

RANDOM INSERTS IN BOXES
OVERALL ONE AUTO OR MEM PER BOX
OVERALL ONE OF ONE AUTO 1:10 BOXES
STATED PRINT RUN ONE SER.#'d SET
NO PRICING DUE TO SCARCITY

2007 Topps Sterling Moments Relics Autographs Quad

COMMON YAZ 50.00 100.00
COMMON D.WRIGHT 75.00 150.00
COMMON SANTANA 30.00 60.00
COMMON MORNEAU 20.00 50.00
COMMON R.JACKSON 40.00 80.00
COMMON R.CLEMENS 60.00 120.00
COMMON Y.BERRA 60.00 120.00
COMMON R.HOWARD 50.00 100.00
COMMON T.GWYNN 60.00 120.00
COMMON ORTIZ 50.00 100.00
COMMON T.SEAVER 40.00 80.00
COMMON PUJOLS 175.00 300.00
COMMON MUSIAL 60.00 120.00
COMMON WANG 150.00 250.00
COMMON SANDBERG 60.00 120.00
COMMON RYAN 75.00 150.00
COMMON GIBSON 30.00 60.00
COMMON M.RAMIREZ 40.00 80.00
COMMON SCHMIDT 40.00 80.00
COMMON AROD 175.00 300.00
RANDOM INSERTS IN BOXES
OVERALL ONE AUTO OR MEM PER BOX
STATED PRINT RUN 10 SER.#'d SETS
NO BONDS PRICING DUE TO SCARCITY

2007 Topps Sterling Moments Relics Autographs Quad Sterling Silver

RANDOM INSERTS IN BOXES
OVERALL ONE AUTO OR MEM PER BOX
OVERALL ONE OF ONE AUTO 1:10 BOXES
STATED PRINT RUN ONE SER.#'d SET
NO PRICING DUE TO SCARCITY

2007 Topps Sterling Moments Relics Autographs Triple

COMMON BONDS 175.00 300.00
COMMON YAZ 40.00 80.00
COMMON D.WRIGHT 60.00 120.00
COMMON SANTANA 20.00 50.00
COMMON MORNEAU 20.00 50.00

COMMON R.JACKSON 30.00 60.00
COMMON R.CLEMENS 60.00 120.00
COMMON Y.BERRA 50.00 100.00
COMMON R.HOWARD 50.00 100.00
COMMON T.GWYNN 50.00 100.00
COMMON ORTIZ 40.00 80.00
COMMON T.SEAVER 40.00 80.00
COMMON PUJOLS 175.00 300.00
COMMON MUSIAL 50.00 100.00
COMMON WANG 150.00 250.00
COMMON SANDBERG 50.00 100.00
COMMON RYAN 60.00 120.00
COMMON GIBSON 30.00 60.00
COMMON M.RAMIREZ 30.00 60.00
COMMON SCHMIDT 40.00 80.00
COMMON AROD 175.00 300.00
RANDOM INSERTS IN BOXES
OVERALL ONE AUTO OR MEM PER BOX
STATED PRINT RUN 10 SER.#'d SETS

2007 Topps Sterling Moments Relics Autographs Triple Sterling Silver

RANDOM INSERTS IN BOXES
OVERALL ONE AUTO OR MEM PER BOX
OVERALL ONE OF ONE AUTO 1:10 BOXES
STATED PRINT RUN ONE SER.#'d SET
NO PRICING DUE TO SCARCITY

2007 Topps Sterling Stardom Relics Eight

COMMON MANTLE 275.00 375.00
COMMON BONDS 150.00 250.00
COMMON MATSUI 75.00 150.00
COMMON ORTIZ 40.00 80.00
RANDOM INSERTS IN BOXES
OVERALL ONE AUTO OR MEM PER BOX
STATED PRINT RUN 10 SER.#'d SETS
NO PRICING ON MOST DUE TO SCARCITY

2007 Topps Sterling Stardom Relics Eight Sterling Silver

RANDOM INSERTS IN BOXES
OVERALL ONE AUTO OR MEM PER BOX
OVERALL ONE OF ONE RELICS 1:10 BOXES
STATED PRINT RUN ONE SER.#'d SET
NO PRICING DUE TO SCARCITY

2007 Topps Sterling Stardom Relics Five

COMMON MANTLE 100.00 175.00
COMMON BONDS 30.00 60.00
COMMON ICHIRO 75.00 150.00
COMMON YAZ 30.00 60.00
COMMON WRIGHT 40.00 80.00
COMMON CLEMENTE 90.00 150.00
COMMON MORNEAU 12.50 30.00
COMMON CLEMENS 20.00 50.00
COMMON T.WILLIAMS 75.00 150.00
COMMON MATSUI 50.00 100.00
COMMON HOWARD 30.00 60.00
COMMON ORTIZ 20.00 50.00
COMMON PUJOLS 30.00 60.00
COMMON WANG 40.00 80.00
COMMON RYAN 50.00 100.00
COMMON GIBSON 20.00 50.00
COMMON MARIS 50.00 100.00
COMMON M.RAMIREZ 15.00 40.00
COMMON SCHMIDT 40.00 80.00
COMMON A.ROD 60.00 120.00
COMMON MATSUZAKA 60.00 120.00
COMMON DIMAGGIO 60.00 120.00
RANDOM INSERTS IN BOXES
OVERALL ONE AUTO OR MEM PER BOX
STATED PRINT RUN 10 SER.#'d SETS
NO JOHAN,JACKSON,BERRA PRICING

2007 Topps Sterling Stardom Relics Five Sterling Silver

RANDOM INSERTS IN BOXES
OVERALL ONE AUTO OR MEM PER BOX
OVERALL ONE OF ONE RELICS 1:10 BOXES
STATED PRINT RUN ONE SER.#'d SET
NO PRICING DUE TO SCARCITY

2007 Topps Sterling Stardom Relics Quad

COMMON MANTLE 100.00 175.00
COMMON BONDS 20.00 50.00
COMMON ICHIRO 60.00 120.00
COMMON YAZ 30.00 60.00
COMMON CLEMENTE 90.00 150.00
COMMON SANTANA 15.00 40.00
COMMON CLEMENS 15.00 40.00
COMMON T.WILLIAMS 75.00 150.00
COMMON MATUSI 40.00 80.00
COMMON ORTIZ 15.00 40.00
COMMON SEAVER 30.00 60.00
COMMON PUJOLS 20.00 50.00
COMMON GIBSON 20.00 50.00
COMMON MARIS 50.00 100.00
COMMON SCHMIDT 40.00 80.00
COMMON MATSUZAKA 60.00 120.00
COMMON DIMAGGIO 60.00 120.00
RANDOM INSERTS IN BOXES
OVERALL ONE AUTO OR MEM PER BOX
STATED PRINT RUN 10 SER.#'d SETS
NO BERRA,HOWARD,GWYNN PRICING
NO WANG,SANDBERG, AROD PRICING

2007 Topps Sterling Stardom Relics Quad Sterling Silver

RANDOM INSERTS IN BOXES
OVERALL ONE AUTO OR MEM PER BOX
OVERALL ONE OF ONE RELICS 1:10 BOXES
STATED PRINT RUN ONE SER.#'d SET
NO PRICING DUE TO SCARCITY

2007 Topps Sterling Stardom Relics Six

COMMON MANTLE 100.00 200.00
COMMON BONDS 30.00 60.00
COMMON ICHIRO 75.00 150.00
COMMON D.WRIGHT 40.00 100.00
COMMON CLEMENTE 100.00 200.00
COMMON SANTANA 20.00 50.00
COMMON MORNEAU 12.50 30.00
COMMON R.JACKSON 30.00 60.00
COMMON CLEMENS 20.00 50.00
COMMON T.WILLIAMS 100.00 200.00
COMMON MATSUI 50.00 100.00
COMMON ORTIZ 20.00 50.00
COMMON PUJOLS 40.00 80.00
COMMON WANG 50.00 100.00
COMMON SANDBERG 20.00 50.00
COMMON RYAN 50.00 100.00
COMMON MARIS 50.00 100.00
COMMON M.RAMIREZ 20.00 50.00
COMMON SCHMIDT 40.00 80.00
COMMON AROD 75.00 150.00
COMMON MATSUZAKA 75.00 150.00
COMMON DIMAGGIO 75.00 150.00
RANDOM INSERTS IN BOXES
OVERALL ONE AUTO OR MEM PER BOX
STATED PRINT RUN 10 SER.#'d SETS
NO HOWARD PRICING

2007 Topps Sterling Stardom Relics Six Sterling Silver

RANDOM INSERTS IN BOXES
OVERALL ONE AUTO OR MEM PER BOX
OVERALL ONE OF ONE RELICS 1:10 BOXES
STATED PRINT RUN ONE SER.#'d SET
NO PRICING DUE TO SCARCITY

2007 Topps Sterling Stardom Relics Triple

COMMON MANTLE 90.00 150.00
COMMON BONDS 20.00 50.00
COMMON ICHIRO 60.00 120.00
COMMON D.WRIGHT 30.00 60.00
COMMON CLEMENTE 75.00 150.00
COMMON MORNEAU 10.00 25.00
COMMON CLEMENS 15.00 40.00
COMMON T.WILLIAMS 50.00 100.00
COMMON BERRA 30.00 60.00
COMMON MATSUI 30.00 60.00
COMMON ORTIZ 15.00 40.00
COMMON SEAVER 20.00 50.00
COMMON PUJOLS 20.00 50.00
COMMON MUSIAL 30.00 60.00
COMMON GIBSON 15.00 40.00
COMMON MARIS 40.00 80.00
COMMON SCHMIDT 40.00 80.00
COMMON MATSUZAKA 60.00 120.00
COMMON DIMAGGIO 60.00 120.00
RANDOM INSERTS IN BOXES
OVERALL ONE AUTO OR MEM PER BOX
STATED PRINT RUN 10 SER.#'d SETS
NO YAZ OR RYAN PRICING

2007 Topps Sterling Stardom Relics Triple Sterling Silver

RANDOM INSERTS IN BOXES
OVERALL ONE AUTO OR MEM PER BOX
OVERALL ONE OF ONE RELICS 1:10 BOXES
STATED PRINT RUN ONE SER.#'d SET
NO PRICING DUE TO SCARCITY

2007 Topps Sterling Stardom Relics Autographs Eight

COMMON M.RAMIREZ 60.00 120.00
RANDOM INSERTS IN BOXES
OVERALL ONE AUTO OR MEM PER BOX
STATED PRINT RUN 10 SER.#'d SETS
NO PRICING ON MOST DUE TO SCARCITY

2007 Topps Sterling Stardom Relics Autographs Eight Sterling Silver

RANDOM INSERTS IN BOXES
OVERALL ONE AUTO OR MEM PER BOX
OVERALL ONE OF ONE AUTO 1:10 BOXES
STATED PRINT RUN ONE SER.#'d SET
NO PRICING DUE TO SCARCITY

2007 Topps Sterling Stardom Relics Autographs Quad

COMMON YAZ 50.00 100.00
COMMON D.WRIGHT 75.00 150.00
COMMON SANTANA 30.00 60.00
COMMON MORNEAU 20.00 50.00
COMMON R.JACKSON 40.00 80.00
COMMON R.CLEMENS 60.00 120.00
COMMON Y.BERRA 60.00 120.00
COMMON R.HOWARD 50.00 100.00
COMMON T.GWYNN 60.00 120.00
COMMON ORTIZ 50.00 100.00
COMMON T.SEAVER 40.00 80.00
COMMON PUJOLS 175.00 300.00
COMMON MUSIAL 60.00 120.00
COMMON WANG 150.00 250.00
COMMON SANDBERG 60.00 120.00
COMMON RYAN 75.00 150.00
COMMON GIBSON 30.00 60.00
COMMON M.RAMIREZ 40.00 80.00
COMMON SCHMIDT 40.00 80.00
COMMON AROD 175.00 300.00
RANDOM INSERTS IN BOXES
OVERALL ONE AUTO OR MEM PER BOX
STATED PRINT RUN 10 SER.#'d SETS
NO BONDS OR MATSUI PRICING

2007 Topps Sterling Stardom Relics Autographs Quad Sterling Silver

RANDOM INSERTS IN BOXES
OVERALL ONE AUTO OR MEM PER BOX
OVERALL ONE OF ONE AUTO 1:10 BOXES
STATED PRINT RUN ONE SER.#'d SET
NO PRICING DUE TO SCARCITY

2007 Topps Sterling Stardom Relics Autographs Triple

COMMON BONDS 175.00 300.00
COMMON YAZ 40.00 80.00
COMMON D.WRIGHT 60.00 120.00
COMMON SANTANA 20.00 50.00
COMMON MORNEAU 20.00 50.00
COMMON R.JACKSON 30.00 60.00
COMMON R.CLEMENS 60.00 120.00
COMMON Y.BERRA 50.00 100.00
COMMON R.HOWARD 50.00 100.00
COMMON T.GWYNN 50.00 100.00
COMMON ORTIZ 40.00 80.00
COMMON T.SEAVER 40.00 80.00
COMMON PUJOLS 175.00 300.00
COMMON MUSIAL 50.00 100.00
COMMON WANG 150.00 250.00
COMMON SANDBERG 50.00 100.00
COMMON RYAN 60.00 120.00
COMMON GIBSON 30.00 60.00
COMMON M.RAMIREZ 30.00 60.00
COMMON SCHMIDT 40.00 80.00
COMMON AROD 175.00 300.00
RANDOM INSERTS IN BOXES
OVERALL ONE AUTO OR MEM PER BOX
STATED PRINT RUN 10 SER.#'d SETS

2007 Topps Sterling Stardom Relics Autographs Triple Sterling Silver

RANDOM INSERTS IN BOXES
OVERALL ONE AUTO OR MEM PER BOX
OVERALL ONE OF ONE AUTO 1:10 BOXES
STATED PRINT RUN ONE SER.#'d SET
NO PRICING DUE TO SCARCITY

2008 Topps Sterling

This set was released on December 24, 2008. The base set consists of 282 cards.

COMMON MANTLE (1-4) 5.00 12.00
COMMON RUTH (5-8) 6.00 15.00
COMMON OTT (9-12) 2.00 5.00
COMMON BENCH (13-23) 3.00 8.00
COMMON FOXX (24-27) 2.50 6.00
COMMON MURRAY (28-38) 2.00 5.00
COMMON J.ROBINSON (39-42) 3.00 8.00
COMMON SNIDER (43-53) 2.50 6.00
COMMON GIBSON (54-64) 2.50 6.00
COMMON BERRA (65-75) 3.00 8.00
COMMON MUSIAL (76-86) 4.00 10.00
COMMON HORNSBY (87-90) 2.50 6.00
COMMON SEAVER (91-101) 2.50 6.00
COMMON FORD (102-112) 2.50 6.00
COMMON MARIS (124-127) 2.50 6.00
COMMON MUNSON (128-131) 2.50 6.00
COMMON PALMER (132-142) 2.00 5.00
COMMON R.JACKSON (143-153) 2.50 6.00
COMMON SCHMIDT (154-164) 2.50 6.00
COMMON YAZ (165-175) 2.50 6.00
COMMON MATTINGLY (176-186) 3.00 8.00
COMMON CAMPANELLA (187-190) 2.00 5.00
COMMON RYAN (191-201) 6.00 15.00
COMMON COBB (213-216) 3.00 8.00
COMMON YOUNT (217-227) 2.50 6.00
COMMON RIPKEN (228-231) 5.00 12.00
COMMON GEHRIG (232-235) 4.00 10.00
COMMON CLEMENTE (236-239) 5.00 12.00
COMMON SANDBERG (240-250) 3.00 8.00
COMMON T.WILLIAMS (251-254) 3.00 8.00
COMMON F.ROBINSON (255-265) 2.00 5.00
COMMON T.GWYNN (266-276) 2.50 6.00
COMMON BANKS (277-287) 3.00 8.00
COMMON WAGNER (288-291) 2.50 6.00
COMMON MOLITOR (296-308) 2.50 6.00
THREE BASE CARDS PER PACK
STATED PRINT RUN 250 SER.#'d SETS

2008 Topps Sterling Framed Burgundy

COMMON MANTLE (1-4) 30.00 60.00
COMMON RUTH (5-8) 40.00 80.00
COMMON OTT (9-12) 12.50 30.00
COMMON BENCH (13-23) 15.00 40.00
COMMON FOXX (24-27) 12.50 30.00
COMMON MURRAY (28-38) 15.00 40.00
COMMON J.ROBINSON (39-42) 20.00 50.00
COMMON SNIDER (43-53) 10.00 25.00
COMMON GIBSON (54-64) 12.50 30.00
COMMON BERRA (65-75) 20.00 50.00
COMMON MUSIAL (76-86) 12.50 30.00
COMMON HORNSBY (87-90) 10.00 25.00
COMMON SEAVER (91-101) 12.50 30.00
COMMON FORD (102-112) 10.00 25.00
COMMON MARIS (124-127) 20.00 50.00
COMMON MUNSON (128-131) 12.50 30.00
COMMON PALMER (132-142) 10.00 25.00
COMMON R.JACKSON (143-153) 12.50 30.00
COMMON SCHMIDT (154-164) 12.50 30.00
COMMON YAZ (165-175) 12.50 30.00
COMMON MATTINGLY (176-186) 20.00 50.00
COMMON CAMPANELLA (187-190) 12.50 30.00
COMMON RYAN (191-201) 50.00 100.00
COMMON COBB (213-216) 40.00 80.00
COMMON YOUNT (217-227) 15.00 40.00
COMMON RIPKEN (228-231) 60.00 120.00
COMMON GEHRIG (232-235) 20.00 50.00
COMMON CLEMENTE (236-239) 40.00 80.00
COMMON SANDBERG (240-250) 12.50 30.00
COMMON T.WILLIAMS (251-254) 20.00 50.00
COMMON F.ROBINSON (255-265) 10.00 25.00
COMMON T.GWYNN (266-276) 20.00 50.00
COMMON BANKS (277-287) 20.00 50.00
COMMON WAGNER (288-291) 10.00 25.00
COMMON MOLITOR (296-308) 10.00 25.00
RANDOMLY INSERTED IN MYSTERY PACKS
STATED PRINT RUN 10 SER.#'d SETS

2008 Topps Sterling Framed Cherry Wood

RANDOM INSERTS IN MYSTERY PACKS
STATED PRINT RUN 1 SER.#'d SET
NO PRICING DUE TO SCARCITY

2008 Topps Sterling Framed Gold

COMMON MANTLE (1-4) 60.00 120.00
COMMON RUTH (5-8) 75.00 150.00
COMMON OTT (9-12) 30.00 60.00
COMMON BENCH (13-23) 30.00 60.00
COMMON FOXX (24-27) 40.00 80.00
COMMON MURRAY (28-38) 20.00 50.00
COMMON J.ROBINSON (39-42) 30.00 60.00
COMMON SNIDER (43-53) 20.00 50.00
COMMON GIBSON (54-64) 20.00 50.00
COMMON BERRA (65-75) 30.00 60.00
COMMON MUSIAL (76-86) 20.00 50.00
COMMON HORNSBY (87-90) 15.00 40.00
COMMON SEAVER (91-101) 15.00 40.00
COMMON FORD (102-112) 12.50 30.00
COMMON MARIS (124-127) 30.00 60.00
COMMON MUNSON (128-131) 30.00 60.00
COMMON PALMER (132-142) 20.00 50.00
COMMON R.JACKSON (143-153) 40.00 80.00
COMMON SCHMIDT (154-164) 30.00 60.00
COMMON YAZ (165-175) 20.00 50.00
COMMON MATTINGLY (176-186) 50.00 100.00
COMMON CAMPANELLA (187-190) 15.00 40.00
COMMON RYAN (191-201) 100.00 200.00
COMMON COBB (213-216) 50.00 100.00
COMMON YOUNT (217-227) 20.00 50.00
COMMON RIPKEN (228-231) 100.00 175.00
COMMON GEHRIG (232-235) 40.00 80.00
COMMON CLEMENTE (236-239) 75.00 150.00
COMMON SANDBERG (240-250) 40.00 80.00
COMMON T.WILLIAMS (251-254) 30.00 60.00
COMMON F.ROBINSON (255-265) 20.00 50.00
COMMON T.GWYNN (266-276) 30.00 60.00
COMMON BANKS (277-287) 40.00 80.00
COMMON WAGNER (288-291) 30.00 60.00
COMMON MOLITOR (296-308) 30.00 60.00
RANDOMLY INSERTED IN MYSTERY PACKS
STATED PRINT RUN 5 SER.#'d SETS

2008 Topps Sterling Framed Sterling Silver

RANDOM INSERTS IN MYSTERY PACKS
STATED PRINT RUN 1 SER.#'d SET
NO PRICING DUE TO SCARCITY

2008 Topps Sterling Framed White

COMMON MANTLE (1-4) 10.00 25.00
COMMON RUTH (5-8) 10.00 25.00
COMMON OTT (9-12) 6.00 15.00
COMMON BENCH (13-23) 5.00 12.00
COMMON FOXX (24-27) 4.00 10.00
COMMON MURRAY (28-38) 4.00 10.00
COMMON J.ROBINSON (39-42) 6.00 15.00
COMMON SNIDER (43-53) 4.00 10.00
COMMON GIBSON (54-64) 5.00 12.00
COMMON BERRA (65-75) 5.00 12.00
COMMON MUSIAL (76-86) 6.00 15.00
COMMON HORNSBY (87-90) 4.00 10.00
COMMON SEAVER (91-101) 4.00 10.00
COMMON FORD (102-112) 4.00 10.00
COMMON MARIS (124-127) 5.00 12.00
COMMON MUNSON (128-131) 5.00 12.00
COMMON PALMER (132-142) 4.00 10.00
COMMON R.JACKSON (143-153) 4.00 10.00
COMMON SCHMIDT (154-164) 4.00 10.00
COMMON YAZ (165-175) 4.00 10.00
COMMON MATTINGLY (176-186) 4.00 10.00
COMMON CAMPANELLA (187-190) 4.00 10.00
COMMON RYAN (191-201) 10.00 25.00
COMMON COBB (213-216) 6.00 15.00
COMMON YOUNT (217-227) 5.00 12.00
COMMON RIPKEN (228-231) 20.00 50.00
COMMON GEHRIG (232-235) 8.00 20.00
COMMON CLEMENTE (236-239) 12.50 30.00
COMMON SANDBERG (240-250) 5.00 12.00
COMMON T.WILLIAMS (251-254) 6.00 15.00
COMMON F.ROBINSON (255-265) 4.00 10.00
COMMON T.GWYNN (266-276) 6.00 15.00
COMMON BANKS (277-287) 6.00 15.00
COMMON WAGNER (288-291) 5.00 12.00
COMMON MOLITOR (296-308) 4.00 10.00
RANDOMLY INSERTED IN MYSTERY PACKS
STATED PRINT RUN 50 SER.#'d SETS

2008 Topps Sterling Career Stats Relics Five

COMMON MANTLE 75.00 150.00
COMMON RUTH 300.00 400.00
COMMON OTT 50.00 100.00
COMMON BENCH 20.00 50.00
COMMON FOXX 50.00 100.00
COMMON J.ROBINSON 40.00 80.00
COMMON MUSIAL 20.00 50.00
COMMON HORNSBY 40.00 80.00
COMMON SEAVER 15.00 40.00
COMMON MARIS 50.00 100.00
COMMON MUNSON 30.00 60.00
COMMON R.JACKSON 20.00 50.00
COMMON YAZ 20.00 50.00
COMMON CAMPANELLA 30.00 60.00
COMMON RYAN 50.00 100.00
COMMON COBB 100.00 175.00
COMMON RIPKEN 100.00 175.00
COMMON GEHRIG 150.00 250.00
COMMON CLEMENTE 60.00 120.00
COMMON T.WILLIAMS 60.00 120.00
COMMON F.ROBINSON 15.00 40.00
COMMON T.GWYNN 20.00 50.00
COMMON BANKS 30.00 60.00
COMMON WAGNER 100.00 200.00
OVERALL ONE AUTO OR MEM PER BOX
STATED PRINT RUN 10 SER.#'d SETS
5CS1 Mickey Mantle 75.00 150.00
5CS2 Mickey Mantle 75.00 150.00
5CS3 Babe Ruth 300.00 400.00
5CS4 Babe Ruth 300.00 400.00
5CS5 Mel Ott 50.00 100.00
5CS6 Mel Ott 50.00 100.00
5CS7 Johnny Bench 20.00 50.00
5CS8 Johnny Bench 20.00 50.00
5CS9 Johnny Bench 20.00 50.00
5CS10 Johnny Bench 20.00 50.00
5CS11 Jimmie Foxx 50.00 100.00
5CS12 Jimmie Foxx 50.00 100.00
5CS13 Jackie Robinson 40.00 80.00
5CS14 Jackie Robinson 40.00 80.00
5CS15 Stan Musial 20.00 50.00
5CS16 Stan Musial 20.00 50.00
5CS17 Stan Musial 20.00 50.00
5CS18 Stan Musial 20.00 50.00
5CS19 Rogers Hornsby 40.00 80.00
5CS20 Rogers Hornsby 40.00 80.00
5CS21 Tom Seaver 15.00 40.00
5CS22 Tom Seaver 15.00 40.00
5CS23 Tom Seaver 15.00 40.00
5CS24 Tom Seaver 15.00 40.00
5CS29 Roger Maris 50.00 100.00
5CS30 Roger Maris 50.00 100.00
5CS31 Thurman Munson 30.00 60.00
5CS32 Thurman Munson 30.00 60.00
5CS33 Reggie Jackson 20.00 50.00
5CS34 Reggie Jackson 20.00 50.00
5CS35 Reggie Jackson 20.00 50.00
5CS36 Reggie Jackson 20.00 50.00
5CS37 Carl Yastrzemski 20.00 50.00
5CS38 Carl Yastrzemski 20.00 50.00
5CS39 Carl Yastrzemski 20.00 50.00
5CS40 Carl Yastrzemski 20.00 50.00
5CS41 Roy Campanella 30.00 60.00
5CS42 Roy Campanella 30.00 60.00
5CS43 Nolan Ryan 50.00 100.00
5CS44 Nolan Ryan 50.00 100.00
5CS45 Nolan Ryan 50.00 100.00
5CS46 Nolan Ryan 50.00 100.00
5CS51 Ty Cobb 100.00 175.00
5CS52 Ty Cobb 100.00 175.00
5CS53 Cal Ripken 100.00 175.00
5CS54 Lou Gehrig 150.00 250.00
5CS55 Lou Gehrig 150.00 250.00
5CS56 Roberto Clemente 60.00 120.00
5CS57 Roberto Clemente 60.00 120.00
5CS58 Ted Williams 60.00 120.00
5CS59 Ted Williams 60.00 120.00
5CS60 Frank Robinson 15.00 40.00
5CS61 Frank Robinson 15.00 40.00
5CS62 Frank Robinson 15.00 40.00
5CS63 Frank Robinson 15.00 40.00
5CS64 Tony Gwynn 20.00 50.00
5CS65 Tony Gwynn 20.00 50.00
5CS66 Tony Gwynn 20.00 50.00
5CS67 Tony Gwynn 20.00 50.00
5CS68 Ernie Banks 30.00 60.00
5CS69 Ernie Banks 30.00 60.00
5CS70 Ernie Banks 30.00 60.00
5CS71 Ernie Banks 30.00 60.00
5CS72 Honus Wagner 100.00 200.00
5CS73 Honus Wagner 100.00 200.00

2008 Topps Sterling Career Stats Relics Five Sterling Silver

RANDOM INSERTS IN BOXES
OVERALL ONE AUTO OR MEM PER BOX
STATED PRINT RUN 1 SER.#'d SET
NO PRICING DUE TO SCARCITY

2008 Topps Sterling Career Stats Relics Quad

COMMON MANTLE 75.00 150.00
COMMON RUTH 200.00 350.00
COMMON OTT 50.00 100.00
COMMON BENCH 20.00 50.00
COMMON FOXX 40.00 80.00
COMMON J.ROBINSON 60.00 120.00
COMMON MUSIAL 30.00 60.00
COMMON HORNSBY 50.00 100.00
COMMON SEAVER 15.00 40.00
COMMON MARIS 50.00 100.00
COMMON MUNSON 30.00 60.00
COMMON R.JACKSON 15.00 40.00
COMMON YAZ 15.00 40.00
COMMON CAMPANELLA 30.00 60.00
COMMON COBB 75.00 150.00
COMMON RIPKEN 90.00 150.00
COMMON GEHRIG 100.00 250.00
COMMON CLEMENTE 60.00 120.00
COMMON T.WILLIAMS 40.00 80.00
COMMON F.ROBINSON 15.00 40.00
COMMON T.GWYNN 15.00 40.00
COMMON WAGNER 100.00 200.00
OVERALL ONE AUTO OR MEM PER BOX
STATED PRINT RUN 10 SER.#'d SETS
NO RYAN PRICING AVAILABLE
4CS1 Mickey Mantle 75.00 150.00
4CS2 Mickey Mantle 75.00 150.00
4CS3 Babe Ruth 200.00 350.00
4CS4 Babe Ruth 200.00 350.00
4CS5 Mel Ott 50.00 100.00
4CS6 Mel Ott 50.00 100.00
4CS7 Johnny Bench 20.00 50.00
4CS9 Johnny Bench 20.00 50.00
4CS11 Jimmie Foxx 40.00 80.00
4CS12 Jimmie Foxx 40.00 80.00
4CS13 Jackie Robinson 60.00 120.00
4CS14 Jackie Robinson 60.00 120.00
4CS15 Stan Musial 30.00 60.00
4CS16 Stan Musial 30.00 60.00
4CS17 Stan Musial 30.00 60.00
4CS19 Rogers Hornsby 50.00 100.00
4CS20 Rogers Hornsby 50.00 100.00
4CS21 Tom Seaver 15.00 40.00
4CS22 Tom Seaver 15.00 40.00
4CS23 Tom Seaver 15.00 40.00
4CS24 Tom Seaver 15.00 40.00
4CS29 Roger Maris 50.00 100.00
4CS30 Roger Maris 50.00 100.00
4CS31 Thurman Munson 30.00 60.00
4CS32 Thurman Munson 30.00 60.00
4CS34 Reggie Jackson 15.00 40.00
4CS35 Reggie Jackson 15.00 40.00
4CS36 Reggie Jackson 15.00 40.00
4CS40 Carl Yastrzemski 15.00 40.00
4CS41 Roy Campanella 30.00 60.00
4CS42 Roy Campanella 30.00 60.00
4CS46 Nolan Ryan
4CS54 Ty Cobb 75.00 150.00
4CS55 Ty Cobb 75.00 150.00
4CS56 Cal Ripken 90.00 150.00
4CS57 Lou Gehrig 100.00 250.00
4CS58 Lou Gehrig 100.00 250.00
4CS59 Roberto Clemente 60.00 120.00
4CS60 Roberto Clemente 60.00 120.00
4CS61 Ted Williams 40.00 80.00
4CS62 Ted Williams 40.00 80.00
4CS63 Frank Robinson 15.00 40.00
4CS64 Frank Robinson 15.00 40.00
4CS66 Frank Robinson 15.00 40.00
4CS67 Tony Gwynn 15.00 40.00
4CS68 Tony Gwynn 15.00 40.00
4CS69 Tony Gwynn 15.00 40.00
4CS70 Tony Gwynn 15.00 40.00
4CS77 Honus Wagner 100.00 200.00
4CS78 Honus Wagner 100.00 200.00

2008 Topps Sterling Career Stats Relics Six

COMMON MANTLE 100.00 200.00
COMMON RUTH 250.00 400.00
COMMON OTT 50.00 100.00
COMMON BENCH 20.00 50.00
COMMON FOXX 50.00 100.00
COMMON MURRAY 20.00 50.00
COMMON J.ROBINSON 50.00 100.00
COMMON SNIDER 30.00 60.00
COMMON GIBSON 20.00 50.00
COMMON BERRA 30.00 60.00
COMMON MUSIAL 30.00 60.00
COMMON HORNSBY 40.00 80.00
COMMON SEAVER 20.00 50.00
COMMON FORD 20.00 50.00
COMMON MARIS 60.00 120.00
COMMON MUNSON 40.00 80.00
COMMON PALMER 12.50 30.00
COMMON R.JACKSON 20.00 50.00
COMMON SCHMIDT 20.00 50.00
COMMON YAZ 20.00 50.00
COMMON MATTINGLY 40.00 80.00
COMMON CAMPANELLA 30.00 60.00
COMMON RYAN 30.00 60.00
COMMON COBB 150.00 250.00
COMMON YOUNT 20.00 50.00
COMMON RIPKEN 75.00 150.00
COMMON GEHRIG 175.00 300.00
COMMON CLEMENTE 75.00 150.00
COMMON SANDBERG 20.00 50.00
COMMON T.WILLIAMS 75.00 150.00
COMMON F.ROBINSON 20.00 50.00
COMMON T.GWYNN 20.00 50.00
COMMON BANKS 20.00 50.00
COMMON WAGNER 150.00 250.00
OVERALL ONE AUTO OR MEM PER BOX
STATED PRINT RUN 10 SER.#'d SETS
6CS1 Mickey Mantle 100.00 200.00
6CS2 Mickey Mantle 100.00 200.00
6CS3 Babe Ruth 250.00 400.00
6CS4 Babe Ruth 250.00 400.00
6CS5 Mel Ott 50.00 100.00
6CS6 Mel Ott 50.00 100.00
6CS7 Johnny Bench 20.00 50.00
6CS8 Johnny Bench 20.00 50.00
6CS9 Jimmie Foxx 50.00 100.00
6CS10 Jimmie Foxx 50.00 100.00
6CS11 Eddie Murray 20.00 50.00
6CS12 Jackie Robinson 50.00 100.00
6CS13 Jackie Robinson 50.00 100.00
6CS14 Duke Snider 30.00 60.00
6CS15 Bob Gibson 20.00 50.00
6CS16 Yogi Berra 30.00 60.00
6CS17 Stan Musial 30.00 60.00
6CS18 Stan Musial 30.00 60.00
6CS19 Rogers Hornsby 40.00 80.00
6CS20 Rogers Hornsby 40.00 80.00
6CS21 Tom Seaver 20.00 50.00
6CS22 Tom Seaver 20.00 50.00
6CS23 Whitey Ford 20.00 50.00
6CS26 Roger Maris 60.00 120.00
6CS27 Roger Maris 60.00 120.00
6CS28 Thurman Munson 40.00 80.00
6CS29 Thurman Munson 40.00 80.00
6CS30 Jim Palmer 12.50 30.00
6CS31 Reggie Jackson 20.00 50.00
6CS32 Reggie Jackson 20.00 50.00
6CS33 Mike Schmidt 20.00 50.00
6CS34 Carl Yastrzemski 20.00 50.00
6CS35 Carl Yastrzemski 20.00 50.00
6CS36 Don Mattingly 40.00 80.00
6CS37 Roy Campanella 30.00 60.00
6CS38 Roy Campanella 30.00 60.00
6CS39 Nolan Ryan 30.00 60.00
6CS40 Nolan Ryan 30.00 60.00
6CS41 Nolan Ryan 30.00 60.00
6CS42 Nolan Ryan 30.00 60.00
6CS43 Nolan Ryan 30.00 60.00
6CS44 Nolan Ryan 30.00 60.00
6CS51 Ty Cobb 150.00 250.00
6CS52 Ty Cobb 150.00 250.00
6CS53 Robin Yount 20.00 50.00
6CS54 Cal Ripken 75.00 150.00
6CS55 Cal Ripken 75.00 150.00
6CS56 Lou Gehrig 175.00 300.00
6CS57 Lou Gehrig 175.00 300.00
6CS58 Roberto Clemente 75.00 150.00
6CS59 Roberto Clemente 75.00 150.00
6CS60 Ryne Sandberg 20.00 50.00
6CS61 Ted Williams 75.00 150.00
6CS62 Ted Williams 75.00 150.00
6CS63 Frank Robinson 20.00 50.00
6CS64 Frank Robinson 20.00 50.00
6CS65 Tony Gwynn 20.00 50.00
6CS66 Tony Gwynn 20.00 50.00
6CS67 Ernie Banks 20.00 50.00
6CS68 Ernie Banks 20.00 50.00
6CS69 Ernie Banks 20.00 50.00
6CS70 Ernie Banks 20.00 50.00
6CS71 Ernie Banks 20.00 50.00
6CS72 Honus Wagner 150.00 250.00
6CS73 Honus Wagner 150.00 250.00

2008 Topps Sterling Career Stats Relics Triple

COMMON MANTLE 60.00 120.00
COMMON RUTH 250.00 350.00
COMMON OTT 40.00 80.00
COMMON FOXX 40.00 80.00
COMMON J.ROBINSON 40.00 80.00
COMMON GIBSON 40.00 80.00
COMMON MARIS 40.00 80.00
COMMON MUNSON 50.00 100.00
COMMON CAMPANELLA 20.00 50.00
COMMON COBB 75.00 150.00
COMMON RIPKEN 90.00 150.00
COMMON GEHRIG 150.00 250.00
COMMON CLEMENTE 50.00 100.00
COMMON T.WILLIAMS 40.00 80.00
COMMON WAGNER 90.00 150.00
OVERALL ONE AUTO OR MEM PER BOX
STATED PRINT RUN 10 SER.#'d SETS
3CS1 Mickey Mantle 60.00 120.00
3CS2 Mickey Mantle 60.00 120.00
3CS3 Mickey Mantle 60.00 120.00
3CS4 Babe Ruth 250.00 350.00
3CS5 Babe Ruth 250.00 350.00
3CS6 Babe Ruth 250.00 350.00
3CS7 Mel Ott 40.00 80.00
3CS8 Mel Ott 40.00 80.00
3CS9 Mel Ott 40.00 80.00
3CS13 Jimmie Foxx 40.00 80.00
3CS14 Jimmie Foxx 40.00 80.00
3CS15 Jimmie Foxx 40.00 80.00
3CS16 Jackie Robinson 40.00 80.00
3CS17 Jackie Robinson 40.00 80.00
3CS18 Jackie Robinson 40.00 80.00
3CS22 Rogers Hornsby 40.00 80.00
3CS23 Rogers Hornsby 40.00 80.00
3CS24 Rogers Hornsby 40.00 80.00
3CS31 Roger Maris 40.00 80.00
3CS32 Roger Maris 40.00 80.00
3CS33 Roger Maris 40.00 80.00
3CS34 Thurman Munson 50.00 100.00
3CS35 Thurman Munson 50.00 100.00
3CS36 Thurman Munson 50.00 100.00
3CS43 Roy Campanella 20.00 50.00
3CS44 Roy Campanella 20.00 50.00
3CS45 Roy Campanella 20.00 50.00
3CS54 Ty Cobb 75.00 150.00
3CS55 Ty Cobb 75.00 150.00
3CS56 Ty Cobb 75.00 150.00
3CS57 Cal Ripken 90.00 150.00
3CS58 Lou Gehrig 150.00 250.00
3CS59 Lou Gehrig 150.00 250.00
3CS60 Lou Gehrig 150.00 250.00
3CS61 Roberto Clemente 50.00 100.00
3CS62 Roberto Clemente 50.00 100.00
3CS63 Roberto Clemente 50.00 100.00
3CS64 Ted Williams 40.00 80.00
3CS65 Ted Williams 40.00 80.00
3CS66 Ted Williams 40.00 80.00
3CS77 Honus Wagner 90.00 150.00
3CS78 Honus Wagner 90.00 150.00
3CS79 Honus Wagner 90.00 150.00

2008 Topps Sterling Career Stats Relics Autographs Quad

COMMON BENCH 40.00 80.00
COMMON MURRAY 30.00 60.00
COMMON SNIDER 30.00 60.00
COMMON GIBSON 30.00 60.00
COMMON BERRA 50.00 100.00
COMMON MUSIAL 50.00 100.00
COMMON SEAVER 30.00 60.00
COMMON FORD 40.00 80.00
COMMON PALMER 20.00 50.00
COMMON R.JACKSON 40.00 80.00
COMMON SCHMIDT 40.00 80.00
COMMON YAZ 40.00 80.00
COMMON MATTINGLY 50.00 100.00
COMMON RYAN 75.00 150.00
COMMON YOUNT 30.00 60.00
COMMON RIPKEN 100.00 200.00
COMMON SANDBERG 40.00 80.00
COMMON F.ROBINSON 20.00 50.00
COMMON T.GWYNN 40.00 80.00
COMMON BANKS 60.00 120.00
COMMON MOLITOR 30.00 60.00
OVERALL ONE AUTO OR MEM PER BOX
STATED PRINT RUN 10 SER.#'d SETS
4CSA1 Johnny Bench 40.00 80.00
4CSA2 Johnny Bench 40.00 80.00
4CSA3 Johnny Bench 40.00 80.00
4CSA4 Eddie Murray 30.00 60.00
4CSA5 Eddie Murray 30.00 60.00
4CSA6 Eddie Murray 30.00 60.00
4CSA7 Eddie Murray 30.00 60.00
4CSA8 Eddie Murray 30.00 60.00
4CSA9 Eddie Murray 30.00 60.00
4CSA10 Eddie Murray 30.00 60.00
4CSA11 Eddie Murray 30.00 60.00
4CSA12 Eddie Murray 30.00 60.00
4CSA13 Eddie Murray 30.00 60.00
4CSA15 Eddie Murray 30.00 60.00
4CSA16 Duke Snider 30.00 60.00
4CSA17 Duke Snider 30.00 60.00
4CSA18 Duke Snider 30.00 60.00
4CSA19 Duke Snider 30.00 60.00

4CSA20 Duke Snider	30.00	60.00
4CSA21 Duke Snider	30.00	60.00
4CSA22 Duke Snider	30.00	60.00
4CSA23 Duke Snider	30.00	60.00
4CSA24 Duke Snider	30.00	60.00
4CSA25 Duke Snider	30.00	60.00
4CSA26 Duke Snider	30.00	60.00
4CSA27 Bob Gibson	30.00	60.00
4CSA28 Bob Gibson	30.00	60.00
4CSA29 Bob Gibson	30.00	60.00
4CSA30 Bob Gibson	30.00	60.00
4CSA31 Bob Gibson	30.00	60.00
4CSA32 Bob Gibson	30.00	60.00
4CSA33 Bob Gibson	30.00	60.00
4CSA34 Bob Gibson	30.00	60.00
4CSA35 Bob Gibson	30.00	60.00
4CSA36 Bob Gibson	30.00	60.00
4CSA37 Bob Gibson	30.00	60.00
4CSA38 Bob Gibson	30.00	60.00
4CSA39 Yogi Berra	50.00	100.00
4CSA40 Yogi Berra	50.00	100.00
4CSA41 Yogi Berra	50.00	100.00
4CSA42 Yogi Berra	50.00	100.00
4CSA43 Yogi Berra	50.00	100.00
4CSA44 Yogi Berra	50.00	100.00
4CSA45 Yogi Berra	50.00	100.00
4CSA46 Yogi Berra	50.00	100.00
4CSA47 Yogi Berra	50.00	100.00
4CSA48 Yogi Berra	50.00	100.00
4CSA49 Yogi Berra	50.00	100.00
4CSA50 Stan Musial	50.00	100.00
4CSA51 Stan Musial	50.00	100.00
4CSA52 Stan Musial	50.00	100.00
4CSA53 Stan Musial	50.00	100.00
4CSA54 Tom Seaver	30.00	60.00
4CSA55 Tom Seaver	30.00	60.00
4CSA56 Tom Seaver	30.00	60.00
4CSA57 Whitey Ford	40.00	80.00
4CSA58 Whitey Ford	40.00	80.00
4CSA59 Whitey Ford	40.00	80.00
4CSA60 Whitey Ford	40.00	80.00
4CSA61 Whitey Ford	40.00	80.00
4CSA62 Whitey Ford	40.00	80.00
4CSA63 Whitey Ford	40.00	80.00
4CSA64 Whitey Ford	40.00	80.00
4CSA65 Whitey Ford	40.00	80.00
4CSA66 Whitey Ford	40.00	80.00
4CSA67 Whitey Ford	40.00	80.00
4CSA68 Whitey Ford	40.00	80.00
4CSA73 Jim Palmer	20.00	50.00
4CSA74 Jim Palmer	20.00	50.00
4CSA75 Jim Palmer	20.00	50.00
4CSA76 Jim Palmer	20.00	50.00
4CSA77 Jim Palmer	20.00	50.00
4CSA78 Jim Palmer	20.00	50.00
4CSA79 Jim Palmer	20.00	50.00
4CSA80 Jim Palmer	20.00	50.00
4CSA81 Jim Palmer	20.00	50.00
4CSA82 Jim Palmer	20.00	50.00
4CSA83 Jim Palmer	20.00	50.00
4CSA84 Reggie Jackson	40.00	80.00
4CSA85 Reggie Jackson	40.00	80.00
4CSA86 Reggie Jackson	40.00	80.00
4CSA87 Mike Schmidt	40.00	80.00
4CSA88 Mike Schmidt	40.00	80.00
4CSA89 Mike Schmidt	40.00	80.00
4CSA90 Mike Schmidt	40.00	80.00
4CSA91 Mike Schmidt	40.00	80.00
4CSA92 Mike Schmidt	40.00	80.00
4CSA93 Mike Schmidt	40.00	80.00
4CSA94 Mike Schmidt	40.00	80.00
4CSA95 Mike Schmidt	40.00	80.00
4CSA96 Mike Schmidt	40.00	80.00
4CSA97 Mike Schmidt	40.00	80.00
4CSA98 Mike Schmidt	40.00	80.00
4CSA99 Carl Yastrzemski	40.00	80.00
4CSA100 Carl Yastrzemski	40.00	80.00
4CSA101 Carl Yastrzemski	40.00	80.00
4CSA102 Don Mattingly	50.00	100.00
4CSA103 Don Mattingly	50.00	100.00
4CSA104 Don Mattingly	50.00	100.00
4CSA105 Don Mattingly	50.00	100.00
4CSA106 Don Mattingly	50.00	100.00
4CSA107 Don Mattingly	50.00	100.00
4CSA108 Don Mattingly	50.00	100.00
4CSA109 Don Mattingly	50.00	100.00
4CSA110 Don Mattingly	50.00	100.00
4CSA111 Don Mattingly	50.00	100.00
4CSA112 Don Mattingly	50.00	100.00
4CSA113 Nolan Ryan	75.00	150.00
4CSA114 Nolan Ryan	75.00	150.00
4CSA117 Robin Yount	30.00	60.00
4CSA118 Robin Yount	30.00	60.00
4CSA119 Robin Yount	30.00	60.00
4CSA120 Robin Yount	30.00	60.00
4CSA121 Robin Yount	30.00	60.00
4CSA122 Robin Yount	30.00	60.00
4CSA123 Robin Yount	30.00	60.00
4CSA124 Robin Yount	30.00	60.00
4CSA125 Robin Yount	30.00	60.00
4CSA126 Robin Yount	30.00	60.00
4CSA127 Robin Yount	30.00	60.00
4CSA128 Cal Ripken	100.00	200.00
4CSA129 Ryne Sandberg	40.00	80.00
4CSA130 Ryne Sandberg	40.00	80.00
4CSA131 Ryne Sandberg	40.00	80.00
4CSA132 Ryne Sandberg	40.00	80.00
4CSA133 Ryne Sandberg	40.00	80.00
4CSA134 Ryne Sandberg	40.00	80.00
4CSA135 Ryne Sandberg	40.00	80.00
4CSA136 Ryne Sandberg	40.00	80.00
4CSA137 Ryne Sandberg	40.00	80.00
4CSA138 Ryne Sandberg	40.00	80.00
4CSA139 Ryne Sandberg	40.00	80.00
4CSA140 Frank Robinson	20.00	50.00
4CSA141 Frank Robinson	20.00	50.00
4CSA142 Frank Robinson	20.00	50.00
4CSA143 Frank Robinson	20.00	50.00
4CSA144 Tony Gwynn	40.00	80.00
4CSA145 Tony Gwynn	40.00	80.00
4CSA146 Tony Gwynn	40.00	80.00
4CSA147 Ernie Banks	60.00	120.00
4CSA148 Ernie Banks	60.00	120.00
4CSA149 Paul Molitor	30.00	60.00
4CSA150 Paul Molitor	30.00	60.00
4CSA153 Paul Molitor	30.00	60.00
4CSA155 Paul Molitor	30.00	60.00
4CSA157 Paul Molitor	30.00	60.00
4CSA160 Paul Molitor	30.00	60.00

2008 Topps Sterling Career Stats Relics Autographs Triple

COMMON BENCH	40.00	80.00
COMMON MURRAY	30.00	60.00
COMMON SNIDER	30.00	60.00
COMMON GIBSON	40.00	80.00
COMMON BERRA	40.00	80.00
COMMON SEAVER	30.00	60.00
COMMON FORD	40.00	80.00
COMMON PALMER	20.00	50.00
COMMON R.JACKSON	30.00	60.00
COMMON SCHMIDT	40.00	80.00
COMMON YAZ	30.00	60.00
COMMON MATTINGLY	60.00	120.00
COMMON RYAN	75.00	150.00
COMMON YOUNT	30.00	60.00
COMMON RIPKEN	125.00	250.00
COMMON SANDBERG	40.00	80.00
COMMON T.GWYNN	50.00	100.00
COMMON BANKS	40.00	80.00
COMMON MOLITOR	30.00	60.00

OVERALL ONE AUTO OR MEM PER BOX
STATED PRINT RUN 10 SER.#'d SETS

3CSA3 Johnny Bench	40.00	80.00
3CSA4 Johnny Bench	40.00	80.00
3CSA5 Eddie Murray	30.00	60.00
3CSA6 Eddie Murray	30.00	60.00
3CSA13 Eddie Murray	30.00	60.00
3CSA14 Eddie Murray	30.00	60.00
3CSA15 Eddie Murray	30.00	60.00
3CSA16 Duke Snider	30.00	60.00
3CSA17 Duke Snider	30.00	60.00
3CSA21 Duke Snider	30.00	60.00
3CSA23 Duke Snider	30.00	60.00
3CSA24 Duke Snider	30.00	60.00
3CSA28 Bob Gibson	40.00	80.00
3CSA29 Bob Gibson	40.00	80.00
3CSA31 Bob Gibson	40.00	80.00
3CSA34 Bob Gibson	40.00	80.00
3CSA37 Bob Gibson	40.00	80.00
3CSA40 Yogi Berra	40.00	80.00
3CSA42 Yogi Berra	40.00	80.00
3CSA43 Yogi Berra	40.00	80.00
3CSA45 Yogi Berra	40.00	80.00
3CSA47 Yogi Berra	40.00	80.00
3CSA48 Yogi Berra	40.00	80.00
3CSA49 Yogi Berra	40.00	80.00
3CSA54 Tom Seaver	30.00	60.00
3CSA56 Tom Seaver	30.00	60.00
3CSA59 Whitey Ford	40.00	80.00
3CSA61 Whitey Ford	40.00	80.00
3CSA64 Whitey Ford	40.00	80.00
3CSA66 Whitey Ford	40.00	80.00
3CSA72 Jim Palmer	20.00	50.00
3CSA74 Jim Palmer	20.00	50.00
3CSA76 Jim Palmer	20.00	50.00
3CSA77 Jim Palmer	20.00	50.00
3CSA78 Jim Palmer	20.00	50.00
3CSA82 Jim Palmer	20.00	50.00
3CSA86 Reggie Jackson	30.00	60.00
3CSA89 Mike Schmidt	40.00	80.00
3CSA92 Mike Schmidt	40.00	80.00
3CSA93 Mike Schmidt	40.00	80.00
3CSA98 Mike Schmidt	40.00	80.00
3CSA102 Carl Yastrzemski	30.00	60.00
3CSA103 Don Mattingly	60.00	120.00
3CSA105 Don Mattingly	60.00	120.00
3CSA106 Don Mattingly	60.00	120.00
3CSA108 Don Mattingly	60.00	120.00
3CSA110 Don Mattingly	60.00	120.00
3CSA114 Don Mattingly	60.00	120.00
3CSA115 Nolan Ryan	75.00	150.00
3CSA118 Robin Yount	30.00	60.00
3CSA120 Robin Yount	30.00	60.00
3CSA121 Robin Yount	30.00	60.00
3CSA124 Robin Yount	30.00	60.00
3CSA125 Robin Yount	30.00	60.00
3CSA128 Cal Ripken	125.00	250.00
3CSA130 Ryne Sandberg	40.00	80.00
3CSA133 Ryne Sandberg	40.00	80.00
3CSA136 Ryne Sandberg	40.00	80.00
3CSA139 Ryne Sandberg	40.00	80.00
3CSA140 Ryne Sandberg	40.00	80.00
3CSA146 Tony Gwynn	50.00	100.00
3CSA148 Ernie Banks	40.00	80.00
3CSA157 Paul Molitor	30.00	60.00
3CSA158 Paul Molitor	30.00	60.00
3CSA159 Paul Molitor	30.00	60.00

2008 Topps Sterling Moments Relics Five

COMMON MANTLE	75.00	150.00
COMMON RUTH	300.00	400.00
COMMON OTT	50.00	100.00
COMMON BENCH	20.00	50.00
COMMON FOXX	50.00	100.00
COMMON J.ROBINSON	40.00	80.00
COMMON MUSIAL	20.00	50.00
COMMON HORNSBY	40.00	80.00
COMMON SEAVER	15.00	40.00
COMMON MARIS	50.00	100.00
COMMON MUNSON	30.00	60.00
COMMON R.JACKSON	20.00	50.00
COMMON YAZ	20.00	50.00
COMMON CAMPANELLA	30.00	60.00
COMMON RYAN	50.00	100.00
COMMON COBB	100.00	175.00
COMMON RIPKEN	100.00	175.00
COMMON GEHRIG	150.00	250.00
COMMON CLEMENTE	60.00	120.00
COMMON T.WILLIAMS	60.00	120.00
COMMON F.ROBINSON	15.00	40.00
COMMON T.GWYNN	20.00	50.00
COMMON BANKS	30.00	60.00
COMMON WAGNER	100.00	200.00

OVERALL ONE AUTO OR MEM PER BOX
STATED PRINT RUN 10 SER.#'d SETS

5SM1 Mickey Mantle	75.00	150.00
5SM2 Mickey Mantle	75.00	150.00
5SM3 Babe Ruth	300.00	400.00
5SM4 Babe Ruth	300.00	400.00
5SM5 Mel Ott	50.00	100.00
5SM6 Mel Ott	50.00	100.00
5SM7 Johnny Bench	20.00	50.00
5SM8 Johnny Bench	20.00	50.00
5SM9 Johnny Bench	20.00	50.00
5SM10 Johnny Bench	20.00	50.00
5SM11 Johnny Bench	20.00	50.00
5SM12 Jimmie Foxx	50.00	100.00
5SM13 Jimmie Foxx	50.00	100.00
5SM14 Jackie Robinson	40.00	80.00
5SM15 Jackie Robinson	40.00	80.00
5SM16 Stan Musial	20.00	50.00
5SM17 Stan Musial	20.00	50.00
5SM18 Stan Musial	20.00	50.00
5SM19 Stan Musial	20.00	50.00
5SM20 Stan Musial	20.00	50.00
5SM21 Rogers Hornsby	40.00	80.00
5SM22 Rogers Hornsby	40.00	80.00
5SM23 Tom Seaver	15.00	40.00
5SM24 Tom Seaver	15.00	40.00
5SM25 Tom Seaver	15.00	40.00
5SM26 Tom Seaver	15.00	40.00
5SM27 Tom Seaver	15.00	40.00
5SM33 Roger Maris	50.00	100.00
5SM34 Roger Maris	50.00	100.00
5SM35 Thurman Munson	30.00	60.00
5SM36 Thurman Munson	30.00	60.00
5SM37 Reggie Jackson	20.00	50.00
5SM38 Reggie Jackson	20.00	50.00
5SM39 Reggie Jackson	20.00	50.00
5SM40 Reggie Jackson	20.00	50.00
5SM41 Reggie Jackson	20.00	50.00
5SM42 Carl Yastrzemski	20.00	50.00
5SM43 Carl Yastrzemski	20.00	50.00
5SM44 Carl Yastrzemski	20.00	50.00
5SM45 Carl Yastrzemski	20.00	50.00
5SM46 Carl Yastrzemski	20.00	50.00
5SM47 Roy Campanella	30.00	60.00
5SM48 Roy Campanella	30.00	60.00
5SM51 Nolan Ryan	50.00	100.00
5SM52 Nolan Ryan	50.00	100.00
5SM58 Ty Cobb	100.00	175.00
5SM59 Ty Cobb	100.00	175.00
5SM60 Cal Ripken	100.00	175.00
5SM61 Lou Gehrig	150.00	250.00
5SM62 Lou Gehrig	150.00	250.00
5SM63 Roberto Clemente	60.00	120.00
5SM64 Roberto Clemente	60.00	120.00
5SM65 Ted Williams	60.00	120.00
5SM66 Ted Williams	60.00	120.00
5SM67 Frank Robinson	15.00	40.00
5SM68 Frank Robinson	15.00	40.00
5SM69 Frank Robinson	15.00	40.00
5SM70 Frank Robinson	15.00	40.00
5SM71 Frank Robinson	15.00	40.00
5SM72 Tony Gwynn	20.00	50.00
5SM73 Tony Gwynn	20.00	50.00
5SM74 Tony Gwynn	20.00	50.00
5SM75 Tony Gwynn	20.00	50.00
5SM76 Tony Gwynn	20.00	50.00
5SM77 Ernie Banks	30.00	60.00
5SM78 Ernie Banks	30.00	60.00
5SM79 Ernie Banks	30.00	60.00
5SM80 Ernie Banks	30.00	60.00
5SM81 Ernie Banks	30.00	60.00
5SM82 Honus Wagner	100.00	200.00
5SM83 Honus Wagner	100.00	200.00

2008 Topps Sterling Moments Relics Quad

COMMON MANTLE	75.00	150.00
COMMON RUTH	200.00	350.00
COMMON OTT	50.00	100.00
COMMON BENCH	20.00	50.00
COMMON FOXX	40.00	80.00
COMMON J.ROBINSON	60.00	120.00
COMMON MUSIAL	30.00	60.00
COMMON HORNSBY	50.00	100.00
COMMON SEAVER	15.00	40.00
COMMON MARIS	50.00	100.00
COMMON MUNSON	30.00	60.00
COMMON R.JACKSON	15.00	40.00
COMMON YAZ	15.00	40.00
COMMON CAMPANELLA	30.00	60.00
COMMON COBB	75.00	150.00
COMMON RIPKEN	90.00	150.00
COMMON GEHRIG	100.00	250.00
COMMON CLEMENTE	60.00	120.00
COMMON T.WILLIAMS	40.00	80.00
COMMON F.ROBINSON	15.00	40.00
COMMON T.GWYNN	15.00	40.00
COMMON WAGNER	100.00	200.00

OVERALL ONE AUTO OR MEM PER BOX
STATED PRINT RUN 10 SER.#'d SETS
NO BANKS PRICING AVAILABLE

4SM1 Mickey Mantle	75.00	150.00
4SM2 Mickey Mantle	75.00	150.00
4SM3 Babe Ruth	200.00	350.00
4SM4 Babe Ruth	200.00	350.00
4SM5 Mel Ott	50.00	100.00
4SM6 Mel Ott	50.00	100.00
4SM8 Johnny Bench	20.00	50.00
4SM10 Johnny Bench	20.00	50.00
4SM13 Jimmie Foxx	40.00	80.00
4SM14 Jimmie Foxx	40.00	80.00
4SM15 Jackie Robinson	60.00	120.00
4SM16 Jackie Robinson	60.00	120.00
4SM17 Stan Musial	30.00	60.00
4SM19 Stan Musial	30.00	60.00
4SM20 Stan Musial	30.00	60.00
4SM23 Rogers Hornsby	50.00	100.00
4SM24 Rogers Hornsby	50.00	100.00
4SM27 Tom Seaver	15.00	40.00
4SM29 Tom Seaver	15.00	40.00
4SM37 Roger Maris	50.00	100.00
4SM38 Roger Maris	50.00	100.00
4SM39 Thurman Munson	30.00	60.00
4SM40 Thurman Munson	30.00	60.00
4SM41 Reggie Jackson	15.00	40.00
4SM42 Reggie Jackson	15.00	40.00
4SM43 Reggie Jackson	15.00	40.00
4SM45 Reggie Jackson	15.00	40.00
4SM46 Reggie Jackson	15.00	40.00
4SM48 Carl Yastrzemski	15.00	40.00
4SM50 Carl Yastrzemski	15.00	40.00
4SM51 Carl Yastrzemski	15.00	40.00
4SM52 Carl Yastrzemski	15.00	40.00
4SM53 Roy Campanella	30.00	60.00
4SM54 Roy Campanella	30.00	60.00
4SM65 Ty Cobb	75.00	150.00
4SM66 Ty Cobb	75.00	150.00
4SM67 Cal Ripken	90.00	150.00
4SM68 Lou Gehrig	100.00	250.00
4SM69 Lou Gehrig	100.00	250.00
4SM70 Roberto Clemente	60.00	120.00
4SM71 Roberto Clemente	60.00	120.00
4SM72 Ted Williams	40.00	80.00
4SM73 Ted Williams	40.00	80.00
4SM74 Frank Robinson	15.00	40.00
4SM76 Frank Robinson	15.00	40.00
4SM78 Frank Robinson	15.00	40.00
4SM79 Frank Robinson	15.00	40.00
4SM82 Tony Gwynn	15.00	40.00
4SM83 Tony Gwynn	15.00	40.00
4SM84 Tony Gwynn	15.00	40.00
4SM89 Ernie Banks		
4SM92 Honus Wagner	100.00	200.00
4SM93 Honus Wagner	100,00	200.00

2008 Topps Sterling Moments Relics Six

COMMON MANTLE	100.00	200.00
COMMON RUTH	250.00	400.00
COMMON OTT	50.00	100.00
COMMON BENCH	20.00	50.00
COMMON FOXX	50.00	100.00
COMMON MURRAY	20.00	50.00
COMMON J.ROBINSON	50.00	100.00
COMMON SNIDER	30.00	60.00
COMMON GIBSON	20.00	50.00
COMMON BERRA	30.00	60.00
COMMON MUSIAL	30.00	60.00
COMMON HORNSBY	40.00	80.00
COMMON SEAVER	20.00	50.00
COMMON FORD	20.00	50.00
COMMON MARIS	60.00	120.00
COMMON MUNSON	40.00	80.00
COMMON PALMER	12.50	30.00
COMMON R.JACKSON	20.00	50.00
COMMON SCHMIDT	20.00	50.00
COMMON YAZ	20.00	50.00
COMMON MATTINGLY	40.00	80.00
COMMON CAMPANELLA	30.00	60.00
COMMON RYAN	30.00	60.00
COMMON COBB	150.00	250.00
COMMON YOUNT	20.00	50.00
COMMON RIPKEN	75.00	150.00
COMMON GEHRIG	175.00	300.00
COMMON CLEMENTE	75.00	150.00
COMMON SANDBERG	20.00	50.00
COMMON T.WILLIAMS	75.00	150.00
COMMON F.ROBINSON	20.00	50.00
COMMON T.GWYNN	20.00	50.00
COMMON BANKS	20.00	50.00
COMMON WAGNER	150.00	250.00
COMMON MOLITOR	20.00	50.00

OVERALL ONE AUTO OR MEM PER BOX
STATED PRINT RUN 10 SER.#'d SETS

6SM1 Mickey Mantle	100.00	200.00
6SM2 Babe Ruth	250.00	400.00
6SM3 Mel Ott	50.00	100.00
6SM4 Johnny Bench	20.00	50.00
6SM5 Johnny Bench	20.00	50.00
6SM6 Johnny Bench	20.00	50.00
6SM7 Jimmie Foxx	50.00	100.00
6SM8 Eddie Murray	20.00	50.00
6SM9 Jackie Robinson	50.00	100.00
6SM10 Duke Snider	30.00	60.00
6SM11 Bob Gibson	20.00	50.00
6SM12 Yogi Berra	30.00	60.00
6SM13 Stan Musial	30.00	60.00
6SM14 Stan Musial	30.00	60.00
6SM15 Stan Musial	30.00	60.00
6SM16 Rogers Hornsby	40.00	80.00
6SM17 Tom Seaver	20.00	50.00
6SM18 Tom Seaver	20.00	50.00
6SM19 Tom Seaver	20.00	50.00
6SM20 Whitey Ford	20.00	50.00
6SM24 Roger Maris	60.00	120.00
6SM25 Thurman Munson	40.00	80.00
6SM26 Jim Palmer	12.50	30.00
6SM27 Reggie Jackson	20.00	50.00
6SM28 Reggie Jackson	20.00	50.00
6SM29 Reggie Jackson	20.00	50.00
6SM30 Mike Schmidt	20.00	50.00
6SM31 Carl Yastrzemski	20.00	50.00
6SM32 Carl Yastrzemski	20.00	50.00
6SM33 Carl Yastrzemski	20.00	50.00
6SM34 Don Mattingly	40.00	80.00
6SM35 Roy Campanella	30.00	60.00
6SM36 Nolan Ryan	30.00	60.00
6SM37 Nolan Ryan	30.00	60.00
6SM38 Nolan Ryan	30.00	60.00
6SM39 Nolan Ryan	30.00	60.00
6SM40 Nolan Ryan	30.00	60.00
6SM41 Nolan Ryan	30.00	60.00
6SM42 Nolan Ryan	30.00	60.00
6SM43 Nolan Ryan	30.00	60.00
6SM44 Nolan Ryan	30.00	60.00
6SM45 Nolan Ryan	30.00	60.00
6SM46 Nolan Ryan	30.00	60.00
6SM47 Nolan Ryan	30.00	60.00
6SM48 Nolan Ryan	30.00	60.00
6SM60 Ty Cobb	150.00	250.00
6SM61 Robin Yount	20.00	50.00
6SM62 Cal Ripken	75.00	150.00
6SM63 Lou Gehrig	175.00	300.00
6SM64 Roberto Clemente	75.00	150.00
6SM65 Ryne Sandberg	20.00	50.00
6SM66 Ted Williams	75.00	150.00
6SM67 Frank Robinson	20.00	50.00
6SM68 Frank Robinson	20.00	50.00
6SM69 Frank Robinson	20.00	50.00
6SM70 Tony Gwynn	20.00	50.00
6SM71 Tony Gwynn	20.00	50.00
6SM72 Tony Gwynn	20.00	50.00
6SM73 Ernie Banks	20.00	50.00
6SM74 Ernie Banks	20.00	50.00
6SM75 Ernie Banks	20.00	50.00
6SM76 Ernie Banks	20.00	50.00
6SM77 Ernie Banks	20.00	50.00
6SM78 Ernie Banks	20.00	50.00
6SM79 Ernie Banks	20.00	50.00
6SM80 Ernie Banks	20.00	50.00
6SM81 Ernie Banks	20.00	50.00
6SM82 Ernie Banks	20.00	50.00
6SM83 Ernie Banks	20.00	50.00
6SM84 Honus Wagner	150.00	250.00
6SM88 Paul Molitor	20.00	50.00

2008 Topps Sterling Moments Relics Triple

COMMON MANTLE	60.00	120.00
COMMON RUTH	250.00	350.00
COMMON OTT	40.00	80.00
COMMON FOXX	40.00	80.00
COMMON J.ROBINSON	40.00	80.00
COMMON HORNSBY	40.00	80.00
COMMON MARIS	40.00	80.00
COMMON MUNSON	50.00	100.00
COMMON CAMPANELLA	20.00	50.00
COMMON COBB	75.00	150.00
COMMON RIPKEN	90.00	150.00
COMMON GEHRIG	150.00	250.00
COMMON CLEMENTE	50.00	100.00
COMMON T.WILLIAMS	40.00	80.00
COMMON WAGNER	90.00	150.00

OVERALL ONE AUTO OR MEM PER BOX
STATED PRINT RUN 10 SER.#'d SETS
NO SEAVER PRICING AVAILABLE

3SM1 Mickey Mantle	60.00	120.00
3SM2 Mickey Mantle	60.00	120.00
3SM3 Mickey Mantle	60.00	120.00
3SM4 Babe Ruth	250.00	350.00
3SM5 Babe Ruth	250.00	350.00
3SM6 Babe Ruth	250.00	350.00
3SM7 Mel Ott	40.00	80.00
3SM8 Mel Ott	40.00	80.00
3SM9 Mel Ott	40.00	80.00
3SM14 Jimmie Foxx	40.00	80.00
3SM15 Jimmie Foxx	40.00	80.00
3SM16 Jimmie Foxx	40.00	80.00
3SM17 Jackie Robinson	40.00	80.00
3SM18 Jackie Robinson	40.00	80.00
3SM19 Jackie Robinson	40.00	80.00
3SM24 Rogers Hornsby	40.00	80.00
3SM25 Rogers Hornsby	40.00	80.00
3SM26 Rogers Hornsby	40.00	80.00
3SM27 Tom Seaver		
3SM35 Roger Maris	40.00	80.00
3SM36 Roger Maris	40.00	80.00
3SM37 Roger Maris	40.00	80.00
3SM38 Thurman Munson	50.00	100.00
3SM39 Thurman Munson	50.00	100.00
3SM40 Thurman Munson	50.00	100.00
3SM49 Roy Campanella	20.00	50.00
3SM50 Roy Campanella	20.00	50.00
3SM51 Roy Campanella	20.00	50.00
3SM62 Ty Cobb	75.00	150.00
3SM63 Ty Cobb	75.00	150.00
3SM64 Ty Cobb	75.00	150.00
3SM65 Cal Ripken	90.00	150.00
3SM66 Lou Gehrig	150.00	250.00
3SM67 Lou Gehrig	150.00	250.00
3SM68 Lou Gehrig	150.00	250.00
3SM69 Roberto Clemente	50.00	100.00
3SM70 Roberto Clemente	50.00	100.00
3SM71 Roberto Clemente	50.00	100.00
3SM72 Ted Williams	40.00	80.00
3SM73 Ted Williams	40.00	80.00
3SM74 Ted Williams	40.00	80.00
3SM90 Honus Wagner	90.00	150.00
3SM91 Honus Wagner	90.00	150.00
3SM92 Honus Wagner	90.00	150.00

2008 Topps Sterling Moments Relics Autographs Eight

COMMON BENCH	60.00	120.00
COMMON MURRAY	60.00	120.00
COMMON SNIDER	50.00	100.00
COMMON GIBSON	40.00	80.00
COMMON BERRA	75.00	150.00
COMMON MUSIAL	75.00	150.00
COMMON SEAVER	40.00	80.00
COMMON FORD	50.00	100.00
COMMON PALMER	30.00	60.00
COMMON R.JACKSON	40.00	80.00
COMMON SCHMIDT	60.00	120.00
COMMON YAZ	75.00	150.00
COMMON MATTINGLY	75.00	150.00
COMMON RYAN	100.00	175.00
COMMON YOUNT	60.00	120.00
COMMON RIPKEN	100.00	200.00
COMMON SANDBERG	60.00	120.00
COMMON F.ROBINSON	50.00	100.00
COMMON T.GWYNN	75.00	150.00
COMMON BANKS	75.00	150.00
COMMON MOLITOR	50.00	100.00

OVERALL ONE AUTO OR MEM PER BOX
STATED PRINT RUN 10 SER.#'d SETS

8SMA1 Johnny Bench	60.00	120.00
8SMA2 Johnny Bench	60.00	120.00
8SMA3 Eddie Murray	60.00	120.00
8SMA4 Duke Snider	50.00	100.00
8SMA5 Duke Snider	50.00	100.00
8SMA6 Bob Gibson	40.00	80.00
8SMA7 Yogi Berra	75.00	150.00
8SMA8 Stan Musial	75.00	150.00
8SMA9 Stan Musial	75.00	150.00
8SMA10 Tom Seaver	40.00	80.00
8SMA11 Tom Seaver	40.00	80.00
8SMA12 Whitey Ford	50.00	100.00
8SMA14 Jim Palmer	30.00	60.00
8SMA15 Jim Palmer	30.00	60.00
8SMA16 Reggie Jackson	40.00	80.00
8SMA17 Mike Schmidt	60.00	120.00
8SMA18 Carl Yastrzemski	75.00	150.00
8SMA19 Carl Yastrzemski	75.00	150.00
8SMA20 Don Mattingly	75.00	150.00
8SMA21 Nolan Ryan	100.00	175.00
8SMA23 Robin Yount	60.00	120.00
8SMA24 Robin Yount	60.00	120.00
8SMA25 Cal Ripken	100.00	200.00
8SMA26 Ryne Sandberg	60.00	120.00
8SMA27 Ryne Sandberg	60.00	120.00
8SMA28 Frank Robinson	50.00	100.00
8SMA29 Tony Gwynn	75.00	150.00
8SMA30 Ernie Banks	75.00	150.00
8SMA31 Paul Molitor	50.00	100.00

2008 Topps Sterling Moments Relics Autographs Quad

COMMON BENCH	40.00	80.00
COMMON MURRAY	30.00	60.00
COMMON SNIDER	30.00	60.00
COMMON GIBSON	30.00	60.00
COMMON BERRA	50.00	100.00
COMMON MUSIAL	50.00	100.00
COMMON SEAVER	30.00	60.00
COMMON FORD	40.00	80.00
COMMON PALMER	20.00	50.00
COMMON R.JACKSON	40.00	80.00
COMMON SCHMIDT	40.00	80.00
COMMON YAZ	40.00	80.00
COMMON MATTINGLY	50.00	100.00
COMMON RYAN	75.00	150.00
COMMON YOUNT	30.00	60.00
COMMON RIPKEN	100.00	200.00
COMMON SANDBERG	40.00	80.00
COMMON F.ROBINSON	20.00	50.00
COMMON T.GWYNN	40.00	80.00
COMMON BANKS	60.00	120.00
COMMON MOLITOR	30.00	60.00

OVERALL ONE AUTO OR MEM PER BOX
STATED PRINT RUN 10 SER.#'d SETS

4SMA1 Johnny Bench	40.00	80.00
4SMA2 Johnny Bench	40.00	80.00
4SMA3 Johnny Bench	40.00	80.00
4SMA4 Eddie Murray	30.00	60.00
4SMA5 Eddie Murray	30.00	60.00
4SMA6 Eddie Murray	30.00	60.00
4SMA7 Eddie Murray	30.00	60.00
4SMA8 Eddie Murray	30.00	60.00
4SMA9 Eddie Murray	30.00	60.00
4SMA10 Eddie Murray	30.00	60.00
4SMA11 Eddie Murray	30.00	60.00
4SMA12 Eddie Murray	30.00	60.00
4SMA13 Eddie Murray	30.00	60.00
4SMA14 Eddie Murray	30.00	60.00
4SMA15 Eddie Murray	30.00	60.00
4SMA16 Eddie Murray	30.00	60.00
4SMA17 Eddie Murray	30.00	60.00
4SMA18 Duke Snider	30.00	60.00
4SMA19 Duke Snider	30.00	60.00
4SMA20 Duke Snider	30.00	60.00
4SMA21 Duke Snider	30.00	60.00
4SMA22 Duke Snider	30.00	60.00
4SMA23 Duke Snider	30.00	60.00
4SMA24 Duke Snider	30.00	60.00
4SMA25 Duke Snider	30.00	60.00
4SMA26 Duke Snider	30.00	60.00
4SMA27 Duke Snider	30.00	60.00
4SMA28 Duke Snider	30.00	60.00
4SMA29 Duke Snider	30.00	60.00
4SMA30 Duke Snider	30.00	60.00
4SMA31 Duke Snider	30.00	60.00
4SMA32 Bob Gibson	30.00	60.00
4SMA33 Bob Gibson	30.00	60.00
4SMA34 Bob Gibson	30.00	60.00
4SMA35 Bob Gibson	30.00	60.00
4SMA36 Bob Gibson	30.00	60.00
4SMA37 Bob Gibson	30.00	60.00
4SMA38 Bob Gibson	30.00	60.00
4SMA39 Bob Gibson	30.00	60.00
4SMA40 Bob Gibson	30.00	60.00
4SMA41 Bob Gibson	30.00	60.00
4SMA42 Bob Gibson	30.00	60.00
4SMA43 Bob Gibson	30.00	60.00
4SMA44 Bob Gibson	30.00	60.00
4SMA45 Bob Gibson	30.00	60.00
4SMA46 Yogi Berra	50.00	100.00
4SMA47 Yogi Berra	50.00	100.00
4SMA48 Yogi Berra	50.00	100.00
4SMA49 Yogi Berra	50.00	100.00
4SMA50 Yogi Berra	50.00	100.00
4SMA51 Yogi Berra	50.00	100.00
4SMA52 Yogi Berra	50.00	100.00
4SMA53 Yogi Berra	50.00	100.00
4SMA54 Yogi Berra	50.00	100.00
4SMA55 Yogi Berra	50.00	100.00
4SMA56 Yogi Berra	50.00	100.00
4SMA57 Yogi Berra	50.00	100.00
4SMA58 Yogi Berra	50.00	100.00
4SMA59 Yogi Berra	50.00	100.00
4SMA60 Stan Musial	50.00	100.00
4SMA61 Stan Musial	50.00	100.00
4SMA62 Stan Musial	50.00	100.00
4SMA63 Tom Seaver	30.00	60.00
4SMA64 Tom Seaver	30.00	60.00
4SMA65 Tom Seaver	30.00	60.00
4SMA66 Whitey Ford	40.00	80.00
4SMA67 Whitey Ford	40.00	80.00
4SMA68 Whitey Ford	40.00	80.00
4SMA69 Whitey Ford	40.00	80.00
4SMA70 Whitey Ford	40.00	80.00
4SMA71 Whitey Ford	40.00	80.00
4SMA72 Whitey Ford	40.00	80.00
4SMA73 Whitey Ford	40.00	80.00
4SMA74 Whitey Ford	40.00	80.00
4SMA75 Whitey Ford	40.00	80.00
4SMA76 Whitey Ford	40.00	80.00
4SMA77 Whitey Ford	40.00	80.00
4SMA78 Whitey Ford	40.00	80.00
4SMA79 Whitey Ford	40.00	80.00
4SMA84 Jim Palmer	20.00	50.00
4SMA85 Jim Palmer	20.00	50.00
4SMA86 Jim Palmer	20.00	50.00
4SMA87 Jim Palmer	20.00	50.00
4SMA88 Jim Palmer	20.00	50.00
4SMA89 Jim Palmer	20.00	50.00
4SMA90 Jim Palmer	20.00	50.00
4SMA91 Jim Palmer	20.00	50.00
4SMA92 Jim Palmer	20.00	50.00
4SMA93 Jim Palmer	20.00	50.00
4SMA94 Jim Palmer	20.00	50.00
4SMA95 Jim Palmer	20.00	50.00
4SMA96 Jim Palmer	20.00	50.00
4SMA97 Jim Palmer	20.00	50.00
4SMA98 Reggie Jackson	40.00	80.00
4SMA99 Reggie Jackson	40.00	80.00
4SMA100 Reggie Jackson	40.00	80.00
4SMA101 Mike Schmidt	40.00	80.00
4SMA102 Mike Schmidt	40.00	80.00
4SMA103 Mike Schmidt	40.00	80.00
4SMA104 Mike Schmidt	40.00	80.00
4SMA105 Mike Schmidt	40.00	80.00
4SMA106 Mike Schmidt	40.00	80.00
4SMA107 Mike Schmidt	40.00	80.00
4SMA108 Mike Schmidt	40.00	80.00
4SMA109 Mike Schmidt	40.00	80.00
4SMA110 Mike Schmidt	40.00	80.00
4SMA111 Mike Schmidt	40.00	80.00
4SMA112 Mike Schmidt	40.00	80.00
4SMA113 Mike Schmidt	40.00	80.00
4SMA114 Mike Schmidt	40.00	80.00
4SMA115 Carl Yastrzemski	40.00	80.00
4SMA116 Carl Yastrzemski	40.00	80.00
4SMA117 Carl Yastrzemski	40.00	80.00
4SMA118 Don Mattingly	50.00	100.00
4SMA119 Don Mattingly	50.00	100.00
4SMA120 Don Mattingly	50.00	100.00
4SMA121 Don Mattingly	50.00	100.00
4SMA122 Don Mattingly	50.00	100.00
4SMA123 Don Mattingly	50.00	100.00
4SMA124 Don Mattingly	50.00	100.00
4SMA125 Don Mattingly	50.00	100.00
4SMA126 Don Mattingly	50.00	100.00
4SMA127 Don Mattingly	50.00	100.00
4SMA128 Don Mattingly	50.00	100.00
4SMA129 Don Mattingly	50.00	100.00
4SMA130 Don Mattingly	50.00	100.00
4SMA131 Don Mattingly	50.00	100.00
4SMA132 Nolan Ryan	75.00	150.00
4SMA133 Nolan Ryan	75.00	150.00
4SMA135 Robin Yount	30.00	60.00
4SMA136 Robin Yount	30.00	60.00
4SMA137 Robin Yount	30.00	60.00
4SMA138 Robin Yount	30.00	60.00
4SMA139 Robin Yount	30.00	60.00
4SMA140 Robin Yount	30.00	60.00
4SMA141 Robin Yount	30.00	60.00
4SMA142 Robin Yount	30.00	60.00
4SMA143 Robin Yount	30.00	60.00
4SMA144 Robin Yount	30.00	60.00
4SMA145 Robin Yount	30.00	60.00
4SMA146 Robin Yount	30.00	60.00
4SMA147 Robin Yount	30.00	60.00
4SMA148 Robin Yount	30.00	60.00
4SMA149 Cal Ripken	100.00	200.00
4SMA150 Cal Ripken	100.00	200.00
4SMA151 Ryne Sandberg	40.00	80.00
4SMA152 Ryne Sandberg	40.00	80.00
4SMA153 Ryne Sandberg	40.00	80.00
4SMA154 Ryne Sandberg	40.00	80.00
4SMA155 Ryne Sandberg	40.00	80.00
4SMA156 Ryne Sandberg	40.00	80.00
4SMA157 Ryne Sandberg	40.00	80.00
4SMA158 Ryne Sandberg	40.00	80.00
4SMA159 Ryne Sandberg	40.00	80.00
4SMA160 Ryne Sandberg	40.00	80.00
4SMA161 Ryne Sandberg	40.00	80.00
4SMA162 Ryne Sandberg	40.00	80.00
4SMA163 Ryne Sandberg	40.00	80.00
4SMA164 Ryne Sandberg	40.00	80.00
4SMA165 Frank Robinson	20.00	50.00
4SMA166 Frank Robinson	20.00	50.00
4SMA167 Frank Robinson	20.00	50.00
4SMA168 Tony Gwynn	40.00	80.00
4SMA169 Tony Gwynn	40.00	80.00
4SMA170 Tony Gwynn	40.00	80.00
4SMA171 Ernie Banks	60.00	120.00
4SMA172 Ernie Banks	60.00	120.00
4SMA174 Paul Molitor	30.00	60.00
4SMA176 Paul Molitor	30.00	60.00
4SMA177 Paul Molitor	30.00	60.00
4SMA178 Paul Molitor	30.00	60.00
4SMA180 Paul Molitor	30.00	60.00

2008 Topps Sterling Moments Relics Autographs Triple

COMMON BENCH	40.00	80.00
COMMON MURRAY	30.00	60.00
COMMON SNIDER	30.00	60.00
COMMON GIBSON	40.00	80.00
COMMON BERRA	40.00	80.00
COMMON MUSIAL	50.00	100.00
COMMON SEAVER	30.00	60.00
COMMON FORD	40.00	80.00
COMMON PALMER	20.00	50.00
COMMON R.JACKSON	30.00	60.00
COMMON SCHMIDT	40.00	80.00
COMMON YAZ	30.00	60.00
COMMON MATTINGLY	60.00	120.00
COMMON RYAN	75.00	150.00
COMMON YOUNT	30.00	60.00
COMMON RIPKEN	125.00	250.00
COMMON SANDBERG	40.00	80.00
COMMON F.ROBINSON	20.00	50.00
COMMON T.GWYNN	50.00	100.00
COMMON BANKS	40.00	80.00
COMMON MOLITOR	30.00	60.00

OVERALL ONE AUTO OR MEM PER BOX
STATED PRINT RUN 10 SER.#'d SETS

3SMA2 Johnny Bench	40.00	80.00
3SMA6 Eddie Murray	30.00	60.00
3SMA7 Eddie Murray	30.00	60.00
3SMA10 Eddie Murray	30.00	60.00
3SMA11 Eddie Murray	30.00	60.00
3SMA16 Eddie Murray	30.00	60.00
3SMA17 Eddie Murray	30.00	60.00
3SMA20 Duke Snider	30.00	60.00
3SMA21 Duke Snider	30.00	60.00
3SMA26 Duke Snider	30.00	60.00
3SMA27 Duke Snider	30.00	60.00
3SMA28 Duke Snider	30.00	60.00
3SMA34 Bob Gibson	40.00	80.00
3SMA37 Bob Gibson	40.00	80.00
3SMA39 Bob Gibson	40.00	80.00
3SMA40 Bob Gibson	40.00	80.00
3SMA42 Bob Gibson	40.00	80.00
3SMA43 Bob Gibson	40.00	80.00
3SMA47 Yogi Berra	40.00	80.00
3SMA48 Yogi Berra	40.00	80.00
3SMA49 Yogi Berra	40.00	80.00
3SMA52 Yogi Berra	40.00	80.00
3SMA58 Stan Musial	50.00	100.00
3SMA60 Stan Musial	50.00	100.00
3SMA62 Tom Seaver	30.00	60.00
3SMA64 Tom Seaver	30.00	60.00
3SMA67 Whitey Ford	40.00	80.00
3SMA68 Whitey Ford	40.00	80.00
3SMA71 Whitey Ford	40.00	80.00
3SMA75 Whitey Ford	40.00	80.00
3SMA76 Whitey Ford	40.00	80.00
3SMA77 Whitey Ford	40.00	80.00
3SMA85 Jim Palmer	20.00	50.00
3SMA89 Jim Palmer	20.00	50.00
3SMA90 Jim Palmer	20.00	50.00
3SMA93 Jim Palmer	20.00	50.00
3SMA94 Jim Palmer	20.00	50.00
3SMA97 Reggie Jackson	30.00	60.00
3SMA101 Reggie Jackson	30.00	60.00
3SMA102 Mike Schmidt	40.00	80.00
3SMA105 Mike Schmidt	40.00	80.00
3SMA106 Mike Schmidt	40.00	80.00
3SMA109 Mike Schmidt	40.00	80.00
3SMA111 Mike Schmidt	40.00	80.00
3SMA112 Mike Schmidt	40.00	80.00
3SMA115 Carl Yastrzemski	30.00	60.00
3SMA116 Carl Yastrzemski	30.00	60.00
3SMA123 Don Mattingly	60.00	120.00
3SMA126 Don Mattingly	60.00	120.00
3SMA127 Don Mattingly	60.00	120.00
3SMA130 Don Mattingly	60.00	120.00
3SMA132 Don Mattingly	60.00	120.00
3SMA133 Nolan Ryan	75.00	150.00
3SMA136 Robin Yount	30.00	60.00
3SMA138 Robin Yount	30.00	60.00
3SMA139 Robin Yount	30.00	60.00
3SMA141 Robin Yount	30.00	60.00
3SMA143 Robin Yount	30.00	60.00
3SMA145 Robin Yount	30.00	60.00
3SMA146 Robin Yount	30.00	60.00
3SMA148 Cal Ripken	125.00	250.00
3SMA149 Ryne Sandberg	40.00	80.00
3SMA154 Ryne Sandberg	40.00	80.00
3SMA156 Ryne Sandberg	40.00	80.00

3SMA161 Ryne Sandberg 40.00 80.00
3SMA163 Frank Robinson 20.00 50.00
3SMA165 Frank Robinson 20.00 50.00
3SMA170 Tony Gwynn 50.00 100.00
3SMA172 Ernie Banks 40.00 80.00
3SMA174 Paul Molitor 30.00 60.00
3SMA176 Paul Molitor 30.00 60.00

2008 Topps Sterling Stardom Relics Five

COMMON MANTLE 75.00 150.00
COMMON RUTH 300.00 400.00
COMMON OTT 50.00 100.00
COMMON BENCH 20.00 50.00
COMMON FOXX 50.00 100.00
COMMON J.ROBINSON 40.00 80.00
COMMON MUSIAL 20.00 50.00
COMMON HORNSBY 40.00 80.00
COMMON SEAVER 15.00 40.00
COMMON MARIS 50.00 100.00
COMMON MUNSON 30.00 60.00
COMMON R.JACKSON 20.00 50.00
COMMON YAZ 20.00 50.00
COMMON CAMPANELLA 30.00 60.00
COMMON RYAN 50.00 100.00
COMMON COBB 100.00 175.00
COMMON RIPKEN 100.00 175.00
COMMON GEHRIG 150.00 250.00
COMMON CLEMENTE 60.00 120.00
COMMON T.WILLIAMS 60.00 120.00
COMMON F.ROBINSON 15.00 40.00
COMMON T.GWYNN 20.00 50.00
COMMON BANKS 30.00 60.00
COMMON WAGNER 100.00 200.00
OVERALL ONE AUTO OR MEM PER BOX
STATED PRINT RUN 10 SER.#'d SETS
5SS1 Mickey Mantle 75.00 150.00
5SS2 Mickey Mantle 75.00 150.00
5SS3 Babe Ruth 300.00 400.00
5SS4 Babe Ruth 300.00 400.00
5SS5 Mel Ott 50.00 100.00
5SS6 Mel Ott 50.00 100.00
5SS7 Johnny Bench 20.00 50.00
5SS8 Johnny Bench 20.00 50.00
5SS9 Johnny Bench 20.00 50.00
5SS10 Johnny Bench 20.00 50.00
5SS11 Johnny Bench 20.00 50.00
5SS12 Jimmie Foxx 50.00 100.00
5SS13 Jimmie Foxx 50.00 100.00
5SS14 Jackie Robinson 40.00 80.00
5SS15 Jackie Robinson 40.00 80.00
5SS16 Stan Musial 20.00 50.00
5SS17 Stan Musial 20.00 50.00
5SS18 Stan Musial 20.00 50.00
5SS19 Stan Musial 20.00 50.00
5SS20 Stan Musial 20.00 50.00
5SS21 Rogers Hornsby 40.00 80.00
5SS22 Rogers Hornsby 40.00 80.00
5SS23 Tom Seaver 15.00 40.00
5SS24 Tom Seaver 15.00 40.00
5SS25 Tom Seaver 15.00 40.00
5SS26 Tom Seaver 15.00 40.00
5SS27 Tom Seaver 15.00 40.00
5SS33 Roger Maris 50.00 100.00
5SS34 Roger Maris 50.00 100.00
5SS35 Thurman Munson 30.00 60.00
5SS36 Thurman Munson 30.00 60.00
5SS37 Reggie Jackson 20.00 50.00
5SS38 Reggie Jackson 20.00 50.00
5SS39 Reggie Jackson 20.00 50.00
5SS40 Reggie Jackson 20.00 50.00
5SS41 Reggie Jackson 20.00 50.00
5SS42 Carl Yastrzemski 20.00 50.00
5SS43 Carl Yastrzemski 20.00 50.00
5SS44 Carl Yastrzemski 20.00 50.00
5SS45 Carl Yastrzemski 20.00 50.00
5SS46 Carl Yastrzemski 20.00 50.00
5SS47 Roy Campanella 30.00 60.00
5SS48 Roy Campanella 30.00 60.00
5SS49 Nolan Ryan 50.00 100.00
5SS50 Nolan Ryan 50.00 100.00
5SS51 Nolan Ryan 50.00 100.00
5SS52 Nolan Ryan 50.00 100.00
5SS53 Nolan Ryan 50.00 100.00
5SS59 Ty Cobb 100.00 175.00
5SS60 Ty Cobb 100.00 175.00
5SS61 Cal Ripken 100.00 175.00
5SS62 Lou Gehrig 150.00 250.00
5SS63 Lou Gehrig 150.00 250.00
5SS64 Roberto Clemente 60.00 120.00
5SS65 Roberto Clemente 60.00 120.00
5SS66 Ted Williams 60.00 120.00
5SS67 Ted Williams 60.00 120.00
5SS68 Frank Robinson 15.00 40.00
5SS69 Frank Robinson 15.00 40.00
5SS70 Frank Robinson 15.00 40.00
5SS71 Frank Robinson 15.00 40.00
5SS72 Frank Robinson 15.00 40.00
5SS73 Tony Gwynn 20.00 50.00
5SS74 Tony Gwynn 20.00 50.00
5SS75 Tony Gwynn 20.00 50.00
5SS76 Tony Gwynn 20.00 50.00
5SS77 Ernie Banks 30.00 60.00
5SS78 Ernie Banks 30.00 60.00
5SS79 Ernie Banks 30.00 60.00
5SS80 Ernie Banks 30.00 60.00
5SS81 Ernie Banks 30.00 60.00
5SS82 Honus Wagner 100.00 200.00
5SS83 Honus Wagner 100.00 200.00

2008 Topps Sterling Stardom Relics Quad

COMMON MANTLE 75.00 150.00
COMMON RUTH 200.00 350.00
COMMON OTT 50.00 100.00
COMMON BENCH 20.00 50.00
COMMON FOXX 40.00 80.00
COMMON J.ROBINSON 60.00 120.00
COMMON MUSIAL 30.00 60.00
COMMON HORNSBY 50.00 100.00
COMMON SEAVER 15.00 40.00
COMMON MARIS 50.00 100.00
COMMON MUNSON 30.00 60.00
COMMON R.JACKSON 15.00 40.00
COMMON YAZ 15.00 40.00
COMMON CAMPANELLA 30.00 60.00
COMMON COBB 75.00 150.00
COMMON RIPKEN 90.00 150.00
COMMON GEHRIG 100.00 250.00
COMMON CLEMENTE 60.00 120.00
COMMON T.WILLIAMS 40.00 80.00
COMMON F.ROBINSON 15.00 40.00
COMMON T.GWYNN 15.00 40.00
COMMON WAGNER 100.00 200.00
OVERALL ONE AUTO OR MEM PER BOX
STATED PRINT RUN 10 SER.#'d SETS
NO RYAN PRICING AVAILABLE
4SS1 Mickey Mantle 75.00 150.00
4SS2 Mickey Mantle 75.00 150.00
4SS3 Babe Ruth 200.00 350.00
4SS4 Babe Ruth 200.00 350.00
4SS5 Mel Ott 50.00 100.00
4SS6 Mel Ott 50.00 100.00
4SS7 Johnny Bench 20.00 50.00
4SS8 Johnny Bench 20.00 50.00
4SS10 Johnny Bench 20.00 50.00
4SS11 Johnny Bench 20.00 50.00
4SS12 Jimmie Foxx 40.00 80.00
4SS13 Jimmie Foxx 40.00 80.00
4SS14 Jackie Robinson 60.00 120.00
4SS15 Jackie Robinson 60.00 120.00
4SS16 Stan Musial 30.00 60.00
4SS17 Stan Musial 30.00 60.00
4SS19 Stan Musial 30.00 60.00
4SS21 Stan Musial 30.00 60.00
4SS22 Rogers Hornsby 50.00 100.00
4SS23 Rogers Hornsby 50.00 100.00
4SS24 Tom Seaver 15.00 40.00
4SS27 Tom Seaver 15.00 40.00
4SS35 Roger Maris 50.00 100.00
4SS36 Roger Maris 50.00 100.00
4SS37 Thurman Munson 30.00 60.00
4SS38 Thurman Munson 30.00 60.00
4SS41 Reggie Jackson 15.00 40.00
4SS42 Reggie Jackson 15.00 40.00
4SS44 Carl Yastrzemski 15.00 40.00
4SS46 Carl Yastrzemski 15.00 40.00
4SS47 Carl Yastrzemski 15.00 40.00
4SS48 Carl Yastrzemski 15.00 40.00
4SS49 Carl Yastrzemski 15.00 40.00
4SS50 Roy Campanella 30.00 60.00
4SS51 Roy Campanella 30.00 60.00
4SS53 Nolan Ryan
4SS63 Ty Cobb 75.00 150.00
4SS64 Ty Cobb 75.00 150.00
4SS65 Cal Ripken 90.00 150.00
4SS66 Lou Gehrig 100.00 250.00
4SS67 Lou Gehrig 100.00 250.00
4SS68 Roberto Clemente 60.00 120.00
4SS69 Roberto Clemente 60.00 120.00
4SS70 Ted Williams 40.00 80.00
4SS71 Ted Williams 40.00 80.00
4SS72 Frank Robinson 15.00 40.00
4SS74 Frank Robinson 15.00 40.00
4SS76 Frank Robinson 15.00 40.00
4SS78 Tony Gwynn 15.00 40.00
4SS81 Tony Gwynn 15.00 40.00
4SS82 Tony Gwynn 15.00 40.00
4SS87 Honus Wagner 100.00 200.00
4SS88 Honus Wagner 100.00 200.00

2008 Topps Sterling Stardom Relics Six

COMMON MANTLE 100.00 200.00
COMMON RUTH 250.00 400.00
COMMON OTT 50.00 100.00
COMMON BENCH 20.00 50.00
COMMON FOXX 50.00 100.00
COMMON MURRAY 20.00 50.00
COMMON J.ROBINSON 50.00 100.00
COMMON SNIDER 30.00 60.00
COMMON GIBSON 20.00 50.00
COMMON BERRA 30.00 60.00
COMMON MUSIAL 30.00 60.00
COMMON HORNSBY 40.00 80.00
COMMON SEAVER 20.00 50.00
COMMON FORD 20.00 50.00
COMMON MARIS 60.00 120.00
COMMON MUNSON 40.00 80.00
COMMON PALMER 12.50 30.00
COMMON R.JACKSON 20.00 50.00
COMMON SCHMIDT 20.00 50.00
COMMON YAZ 20.00 50.00
COMMON MATTINGLY 40.00 80.00
COMMON CAMPANELLA 30.00 60.00
COMMON RYAN 30.00 60.00
COMMON COBB 150.00 250.00
COMMON YOUNT 20.00 50.00
COMMON RIPKEN 75.00 150.00
COMMON GEHRIG 175.00 300.00
COMMON CLEMENTE 75.00 150.00
COMMON SANDBERG 20.00 50.00
COMMON T.WILLIAMS 75.00 150.00
COMMON F.ROBINSON 20.00 50.00
COMMON T.GWYNN 20.00 50.00
COMMON BANKS 20.00 50.00
COMMON WAGNER 150.00 250.00
COMMON MOLITOR 20.00 50.00
OVERALL ONE AUTO OR MEM PER BOX
STATED PRINT RUN 10 SER.#'d SETS
6SS1 Mickey Mantle 100.00 200.00
6SS2 Babe Ruth 250.00 400.00
6SS3 Mel Ott 50.00 100.00
6SS4 Johnny Bench 20.00 50.00
6SS5 Johnny Bench 20.00 50.00
6SS6 Johnny Bench 20.00 50.00
6SS7 Johnny Bench 20.00 50.00
6SS8 Jimmie Foxx 50.00 100.00
6SS9 Eddie Murray 20.00 50.00
6SS10 Jackie Robinson 50.00 100.00
6SS11 Duke Snider 30.00 60.00
6SS12 Bob Gibson 20.00 50.00
6SS13 Yogi Berra 30.00 60.00
6SS14 Stan Musial 30.00 60.00
6SS15 Stan Musial 30.00 60.00
6SS16 Stan Musial 30.00 60.00
6SS17 Stan Musial 30.00 60.00
6SS18 Rogers Hornsby 40.00 80.00
6SS19 Tom Seaver 20.00 50.00
6SS20 Tom Seaver 20.00 50.00
6SS21 Tom Seaver 20.00 50.00
6SS22 Tom Seaver 20.00 50.00
6SS23 Whitey Ford 20.00 50.00
6SS28 Roger Maris 60.00 120.00
6SS29 Thurman Munson 40.00 80.00
6SS30 Jim Palmer 12.50 30.00
6SS31 Reggie Jackson 20.00 50.00
6SS32 Reggie Jackson 20.00 50.00
6SS33 Reggie Jackson 20.00 50.00
6SS34 Reggie Jackson 20.00 50.00
6SS35 Mike Schmidt 20.00 50.00
6SS36 Carl Yastrzemski 20.00 50.00
6SS37 Carl Yastrzemski 20.00 50.00
6SS38 Carl Yastrzemski 20.00 50.00
6SS39 Carl Yastrzemski 20.00 50.00
6SS40 Don Mattingly 40.00 80.00
6SS41 Roy Campanella 30.00 60.00
6SS42 Nolan Ryan 30.00 60.00
6SS43 Nolan Ryan 30.00 60.00
6SS44 Nolan Ryan 30.00 60.00
6SS45 Nolan Ryan 30.00 60.00
6SS46 Nolan Ryan 30.00 60.00
6SS47 Nolan Ryan 30.00 60.00
6SS48 Nolan Ryan 30.00 60.00
6SS49 Nolan Ryan 30.00 60.00
6SS50 Nolan Ryan 30.00 60.00
6SS60 Ty Cobb 150.00 250.00
6SS61 Robin Yount 20.00 50.00
6SS62 Cal Ripken 75.00 150.00
6SS63 Lou Gehrig 175.00 300.00
6SS64 Roberto Clemente 75.00 150.00
6SS65 Ryne Sandberg 20.00 50.00
6SS66 Ted Williams 75.00 150.00
6SS67 Frank Robinson 20.00 50.00
6SS68 Frank Robinson 20.00 50.00
6SS69 Frank Robinson 20.00 50.00
6SS70 Frank Robinson 20.00 50.00
6SS71 Tony Gwynn 20.00 50.00
6SS72 Tony Gwynn 20.00 50.00
6SS73 Tony Gwynn 20.00 50.00
6SS74 Tony Gwynn 20.00 50.00
6SS75 Ernie Banks 20.00 50.00
6SS76 Ernie Banks 20.00 50.00
6SS77 Ernie Banks 20.00 50.00
6SS78 Ernie Banks 20.00 50.00
6SS79 Ernie Banks 20.00 50.00
6SS80 Ernie Banks 20.00 50.00
6SS81 Ernie Banks 20.00 50.00
6SS82 Ernie Banks 20.00 50.00
6SS83 Ernie Banks 20.00 50.00
6SS84 Honus Wagner 150.00 250.00
6SS87 Paul Molitor 20.00 50.00
6SS94 Paul Molitor 20.00 50.00

2008 Topps Sterling Stardom Relics Triple

COMMON MANTLE 60.00 120.00
COMMON RUTH 250.00 350.00
COMMON OTT 40.00 80.00
COMMON FOXX 40.00 80.00
COMMON J.ROBINSON 40.00 80.00
COMMON HORNSBY 40.00 80.00
COMMON MARIS 40.00 80.00
COMMON MUNSON 50.00 100.00
COMMON CAMPANELLA 20.00 50.00
COMMON COBB 75.00 150.00
COMMON RIPKEN 90.00 150.00
COMMON GEHRIG 150.00 250.00
COMMON CLEMENTE 50.00 100.00
COMMON T.WILLIAMS 40.00 80.00
COMMON WAGNER 90.00 150.00
OVERALL ONE AUTO OR MEM PER BOX
STATED PRINT RUN 10 SER.#'d SETS
NO RYAN PRICING AVAILABLE
3SS1 Mickey Mantle 60.00 120.00
3SS2 Mickey Mantle 60.00 120.00
3SS3 Mickey Mantle 60.00 120.00
3SS4 Babe Ruth 250.00 350.00
3SS5 Babe Ruth 250.00 350.00
3SS6 Babe Ruth 250.00 350.00
3SS7 Mel Ott 40.00 80.00
3SS8 Mel Ott 40.00 80.00
3SS9 Mel Ott 40.00 80.00
3SS14 Jimmie Foxx 40.00 80.00
3SS15 Jimmie Foxx 40.00 80.00
3SS16 Jimmie Foxx 40.00 80.00
3SS17 Jackie Robinson 40.00 80.00
3SS18 Jackie Robinson 40.00 80.00
3SS19 Jackie Robinson 40.00 80.00
3SS24 Rogers Hornsby 40.00 80.00
3SS25 Rogers Hornsby 40.00 80.00
3SS26 Rogers Hornsby 40.00 80.00
3SS35 Roger Maris 40.00 80.00
3SS36 Roger Maris 40.00 80.00
3SS37 Roger Maris 40.00 80.00
3SS38 Thurman Munson 50.00 100.00
3SS39 Thurman Munson 50.00 100.00
3SS40 Thurman Munson 50.00 100.00
3SS49 Roy Campanella 20.00 50.00
3SS50 Roy Campanella 20.00 50.00
3SS51 Roy Campanella 20.00 50.00
3SS52 Nolan Ryan
3SS60 Ty Cobb 75.00 150.00
3SS61 Ty Cobb 75.00 150.00
3SS62 Ty Cobb 75.00 150.00
3SS63 Cal Ripken 90.00 150.00
3SS64 Lou Gehrig 150.00 250.00
3SS65 Lou Gehrig 150.00 250.00
3SS66 Lou Gehrig 150.00 250.00
3SS67 Roberto Clemente 50.00 100.00
3SS68 Roberto Clemente 50.00 100.00
3SS69 Roberto Clemente 50.00 100.00
3SS70 Ted Williams 40.00 80.00
3SS71 Ted Williams 40.00 80.00
3SS72 Ted Williams 40.00 80.00
3SS85 Honus Wagner 90.00 150.00
3SS86 Honus Wagner 90.00 150.00
3SS87 Honus Wagner 90.00 150.00

2008 Topps Sterling Stardom Relics Autographs Eight

COMMON BENCH 60.00 120.00
COMMON MURRAY 60.00 120.00
COMMON SNIDER 50.00 100.00
COMMON GIBSON 40.00 80.00
COMMON BERRA 75.00 150.00
COMMON MUSIAL 75.00 150.00
COMMON SEAVER 40.00 80.00
COMMON FORD 50.00 100.00
COMMON PALMER 30.00 60.00
COMMON R.JACKSON 40.00 80.00
COMMON SCHMIDT 60.00 120.00
COMMON YAZ 75.00 150.00
COMMON MATTINGLY 75.00 150.00
COMMON RYAN 100.00 175.00
COMMON YOUNT 60.00 120.00
COMMON RIPKEN 100.00 200.00
COMMON SANDBERG 60.00 120.00
COMMON F.ROBINSON 50.00 100.00
COMMON T.GWYNN 75.00 150.00
COMMON BANKS 75.00 150.00
COMMON MOLITOR 50.00 100.00
OVERALL ONE AUTO OR MEM PER BOX
STATED PRINT RUN 10 SER.#'d SETS
8SSA1 Johnny Bench 60.00 120.00
8SSA2 Johnny Bench 60.00 120.00
8SSA3 Eddie Murray 60.00 120.00
8SSA4 Duke Snider 50.00 100.00
8SSA5 Bob Gibson 40.00 80.00
8SSA6 Bob Gibson 40.00 80.00
8SSA7 Yogi Berra 75.00 150.00
8SSA8 Stan Musial 75.00 150.00
8SSA9 Stan Musial 75.00 150.00
8SSA10 Tom Seaver 40.00 80.00
8SSA11 Whitey Ford 50.00 100.00
8SSA14 Jim Palmer 30.00 60.00
8SSA15 Reggie Jackson 40.00 80.00
8SSA16 Mike Schmidt 60.00 120.00
8SSA17 Carl Yastrzemski 75.00 150.00
8SSA18 Carl Yastrzemski 75.00 150.00
8SSA19 Don Mattingly 75.00 150.00
8SSA20 Don Mattingly 75.00 150.00
8SSA21 Nolan Ryan 100.00 175.00
8SSA23 Robin Yount 60.00 120.00
8SSA24 Cal Ripken 100.00 200.00
8SSA25 Ryne Sandberg 60.00 120.00
8SSA26 Frank Robinson 50.00 100.00
8SSA27 Frank Robinson 50.00 100.00
8SSA28 Tony Gwynn 75.00 150.00
8SSA29 Tony Gwynn 75.00 150.00
8SSA30 Ernie Banks 75.00 150.00
8SSA31 Paul Molitor 50.00 100.00

2008 Topps Sterling Stardom Relics Autographs Quad

COMMON BENCH 40.00 80.00
COMMON MURRAY 30.00 60.00
COMMON SNIDER 30.00 60.00
COMMON GIBSON 30.00 60.00
COMMON BERRA 50.00 100.00
COMMON MUSIAL 50.00 100.00
COMMON SEAVER 30.00 60.00
COMMON FORD 40.00 80.00
COMMON PALMER 20.00 50.00
COMMON R.JACKSON 40.00 80.00
COMMON SCHMIDT 40.00 80.00
COMMON YAZ 40.00 80.00
COMMON MATTINGLY 50.00 100.00
COMMON RYAN 75.00 150.00
COMMON YOUNT 30.00 60.00
COMMON RIPKEN 100.00 200.00
COMMON SANDBERG 40.00 80.00
COMMON F.ROBINSON 20.00 50.00
COMMON T.GWYNN 40.00 80.00
COMMON BANKS 60.00 120.00
COMMON MOLITOR 30.00 60.00
OVERALL ONE AUTO OR MEM PER BOX
STATED PRINT RUN 10 SER.#'d SETS
4SSA1 Johnny Bench 40.00 80.00
4SSA2 Johnny Bench 40.00 80.00
4SSA3 Johnny Bench 40.00 80.00
4SSA4 Johnny Bench 40.00 80.00
4SSA5 Johnny Bench 40.00 80.00
4SSA6 Johnny Bench 40.00 80.00
4SSA7 Eddie Murray 30.00 60.00
4SSA8 Eddie Murray 30.00 60.00
4SSA9 Eddie Murray 30.00 60.00
4SSA10 Eddie Murray 30.00 60.00
4SSA11 Eddie Murray 30.00 60.00
4SSA12 Eddie Murray 30.00 60.00
4SSA13 Eddie Murray 30.00 60.00
4SSA14 Eddie Murray 30.00 60.00
4SSA15 Eddie Murray 30.00 60.00
4SSA16 Eddie Murray 30.00 60.00
4SSA17 Eddie Murray 30.00 60.00
4SSA18 Eddie Murray 30.00 60.00
4SSA19 Duke Snider 30.00 60.00
4SSA20 Duke Snider 30.00 60.00
4SSA21 Duke Snider 30.00 60.00
4SSA22 Duke Snider 30.00 60.00
4SSA23 Duke Snider 30.00 60.00
4SSA24 Duke Snider 30.00 60.00
4SSA25 Duke Snider 30.00 60.00
4SSA26 Duke Snider 30.00 60.00
4SSA27 Duke Snider 30.00 60.00
4SSA28 Duke Snider 30.00 60.00
4SSA29 Duke Snider 30.00 60.00
4SSA30 Duke Snider 30.00 60.00
4SSA31 Bob Gibson 30.00 60.00
4SSA32 Bob Gibson 30.00 60.00
4SSA33 Bob Gibson 30.00 60.00
4SSA34 Bob Gibson 30.00 60.00
4SSA35 Bob Gibson 30.00 60.00
4SSA36 Bob Gibson 30.00 60.00
4SSA37 Bob Gibson 30.00 60.00
4SSA38 Bob Gibson 30.00 60.00
4SSA39 Bob Gibson 30.00 60.00
4SSA40 Bob Gibson 30.00 60.00
4SSA41 Bob Gibson 30.00 60.00
4SSA42 Bob Gibson 30.00 60.00
4SSA43 Yogi Berra 50.00 100.00
4SSA44 Yogi Berra 50.00 100.00
4SSA45 Yogi Berra 50.00 100.00
4SSA46 Yogi Berra 50.00 100.00
4SSA47 Yogi Berra 50.00 100.00
4SSA48 Yogi Berra 50.00 100.00
4SSA49 Yogi Berra 50.00 100.00
4SSA50 Yogi Berra 50.00 100.00
4SSA51 Yogi Berra 50.00 100.00
4SSA52 Yogi Berra 50.00 100.00
4SSA53 Yogi Berra 50.00 100.00
4SSA54 Yogi Berra 50.00 100.00
4SSA55 Stan Musial 50.00 100.00
4SSA56 Stan Musial 50.00 100.00
4SSA57 Stan Musial 50.00 100.00
4SSA58 Stan Musial 50.00 100.00
4SSA59 Stan Musial 50.00 100.00
4SSA60 Tom Seaver 30.00 60.00
4SSA61 Tom Seaver 30.00 60.00
4SSA62 Tom Seaver 30.00 60.00
4SSA63 Tom Seaver 30.00 60.00
4SSA64 Tom Seaver 30.00 60.00
4SSA65 Whitey Ford 40.00 80.00
4SSA66 Whitey Ford 40.00 80.00
4SSA67 Whitey Ford 40.00 80.00
4SSA68 Whitey Ford 40.00 80.00
4SSA69 Whitey Ford 40.00 80.00
4SSA70 Whitey Ford 40.00 80.00
4SSA71 Whitey Ford 40.00 80.00
4SSA72 Whitey Ford 40.00 80.00
4SSA73 Whitey Ford 40.00 80.00
4SSA74 Whitey Ford 40.00 80.00
4SSA75 Whitey Ford 40.00 80.00
4SSA76 Whitey Ford 40.00 80.00
4SSA82 Jim Palmer 20.00 50.00
4SSA83 Jim Palmer 20.00 50.00
4SSA84 Jim Palmer 20.00 50.00
4SSA85 Jim Palmer 20.00 50.00
4SSA86 Jim Palmer 20.00 50.00
4SSA87 Jim Palmer 20.00 50.00
4SSA88 Jim Palmer 20.00 50.00
4SSA89 Jim Palmer 20.00 50.00
4SSA90 Jim Palmer 20.00 50.00
4SSA91 Jim Palmer 20.00 50.00
4SSA92 Jim Palmer 20.00 50.00
4SSA93 Jim Palmer 20.00 50.00
4SSA94 Reggie Jackson 40.00 80.00
4SSA95 Reggie Jackson 40.00 80.00
4SSA96 Reggie Jackson 40.00 80.00
4SSA97 Reggie Jackson 40.00 80.00
4SSA98 Reggie Jackson 40.00 80.00
4SSA99 Reggie Jackson 40.00 80.00
4SSA100 Mike Schmidt 40.00 80.00
4SSA101 Mike Schmidt 40.00 80.00
4SSA102 Mike Schmidt 40.00 80.00
4SSA103 Mike Schmidt 40.00 80.00
4SSA104 Mike Schmidt 40.00 80.00
4SSA105 Mike Schmidt 40.00 80.00
4SSA106 Mike Schmidt 40.00 80.00
4SSA107 Mike Schmidt 40.00 80.00
4SSA108 Mike Schmidt 40.00 80.00
4SSA109 Mike Schmidt 40.00 80.00
4SSA110 Mike Schmidt 40.00 80.00
4SSA111 Mike Schmidt 40.00 80.00
4SSA112 Carl Yastrzemski 40.00 80.00
4SSA113 Carl Yastrzemski 40.00 80.00
4SSA114 Carl Yastrzemski 40.00 80.00
4SSA115 Carl Yastrzemski 40.00 80.00
4SSA116 Carl Yastrzemski 40.00 80.00
4SSA117 Don Mattingly 50.00 100.00
4SSA118 Don Mattingly 50.00 100.00
4SSA119 Don Mattingly 50.00 100.00
4SSA120 Don Mattingly 50.00 100.00
4SSA121 Don Mattingly 50.00 100.00
4SSA122 Don Mattingly 50.00 100.00
4SSA123 Don Mattingly 50.00 100.00
4SSA124 Don Mattingly 50.00 100.00
4SSA125 Don Mattingly 50.00 100.00
4SSA126 Don Mattingly 50.00 100.00
4SSA127 Don Mattingly 50.00 100.00
4SSA128 Don Mattingly 50.00 100.00
4SSA129 Nolan Ryan 75.00 150.00
4SSA132 Robin Yount 30.00 60.00
4SSA133 Robin Yount 30.00 60.00
4SSA134 Robin Yount 30.00 60.00
4SSA135 Robin Yount 30.00 60.00
4SSA136 Robin Yount 30.00 60.00
4SSA137 Robin Yount 30.00 60.00
4SSA138 Robin Yount 30.00 60.00
4SSA139 Robin Yount 30.00 60.00
4SSA140 Robin Yount 30.00 60.00
4SSA141 Robin Yount 30.00 60.00
4SSA142 Robin Yount 30.00 60.00
4SSA143 Cal Ripken 100.00 200.00
4SSA144 Cal Ripken 100.00 200.00
4SSA145 Ryne Sandberg 40.00 80.00
4SSA146 Ryne Sandberg 40.00 80.00
4SSA147 Ryne Sandberg 40.00 80.00
4SSA148 Ryne Sandberg 40.00 80.00
4SSA149 Ryne Sandberg 40.00 80.00
4SSA150 Ryne Sandberg 40.00 80.00
4SSA151 Ryne Sandberg 40.00 80.00
4SSA152 Ryne Sandberg 40.00 80.00
4SSA153 Ryne Sandberg 40.00 80.00
4SSA154 Ryne Sandberg 40.00 80.00
4SSA155 Ryne Sandberg 40.00 80.00
4SSA156 Ryne Sandberg 40.00 80.00
4SSA157 Frank Robinson 20.00 50.00
4SSA158 Frank Robinson 20.00 50.00
4SSA159 Frank Robinson 20.00 50.00
4SSA160 Frank Robinson 20.00 50.00
4SSA161 Frank Robinson 20.00 50.00
4SSA162 Frank Robinson 20.00 50.00
4SSA163 Tony Gwynn 40.00 80.00
4SSA164 Tony Gwynn 40.00 80.00
4SSA165 Tony Gwynn 40.00 80.00
4SSA166 Tony Gwynn 40.00 80.00
4SSA167 Tony Gwynn 40.00 80.00
4SSA168 Tony Gwynn 40.00 80.00
4SSA169 Ernie Banks 60.00 120.00
4SSA170 Ernie Banks 60.00 120.00
4SSA173 Paul Molitor 30.00 60.00
4SSA176 Paul Molitor 30.00 60.00

2008 Topps Sterling Stardom Relics Autographs Triple

COMMON BENCH 40.00 80.00
COMMON MURRAY 30.00 60.00
COMMON SNIDER 30.00 60.00
COMMON GIBSON 40.00 80.00
COMMON BERRA 40.00 80.00
COMMON MUSIAL 50.00 100.00
COMMON SEAVER 30.00 60.00
COMMON FORD 40.00 80.00
COMMON PALMER 20.00 50.00
COMMON R.JACKSON 30.00 60.00
COMMON SCHMIDT 40.00 80.00
COMMON YAZ 30.00 60.00
COMMON MATTINGLY 60.00 120.00
COMMON RYAN 75.00 150.00
COMMON YOUNT 30.00 60.00
COMMON RIPKEN 125.00 250.00
COMMON SANDBERG 40.00 80.00
COMMON F.ROBINSON 20.00 50.00
COMMON T.GWYNN 50.00 100.00
COMMON BANKS 40.00 80.00
OVERALL ONE AUTO OR MEM PER BOX
STATED PRINT RUN 10 SER.#'d SETS
3SSA1 Johnny Bench 40.00 80.00
3SSA9 Eddie Murray 30.00 60.00
3SSA11 Eddie Murray 30.00 60.00
3SSA12 Eddie Murray 30.00 60.00
3SSA14 Eddie Murray 30.00 60.00
3SSA16 Eddie Murray 30.00 60.00
3SSA21 Duke Snider 30.00 60.00
3SSA24 Duke Snider 30.00 60.00
3SSA26 Duke Snider 30.00 60.00
3SSA28 Duke Snider 30.00 60.00
3SSA30 Duke Snider 30.00 60.00
3SSA34 Bob Gibson 40.00 80.00
3SSA40 Bob Gibson 40.00 80.00
3SSA41 Bob Gibson 40.00 80.00
3SSA45 Yogi Berra 40.00 80.00
3SSA49 Yogi Berra 40.00 80.00
3SSA51 Yogi Berra 40.00 80.00
3SSA53 Yogi Berra 40.00 80.00
3SSA54 Yogi Berra 40.00 80.00
3SSA59 Stan Musial 50.00 100.00
3SSA62 Stan Musial 50.00 100.00
3SSA63 Tom Seaver 30.00 60.00
3SSA65 Tom Seaver 30.00 60.00
3SSA71 Whitey Ford 40.00 80.00
3SSA73 Whitey Ford 40.00 80.00
3SSA76 Whitey Ford 40.00 80.00
3SSA77 Whitey Ford 40.00 80.00
3SSA79 Whitey Ford 40.00 80.00
3SSA89 Jim Palmer 20.00 50.00
3SSA91 Jim Palmer 20.00 50.00
3SSA94 Jim Palmer 20.00 50.00
3SSA97 Jim Palmer 20.00 50.00
3SSA101 Reggie Jackson 30.00 60.00
3SSA103 Reggie Jackson 30.00 60.00
3SSA107 Reggie Jackson 30.00 60.00
3SSA111 Mike Schmidt 40.00 80.00
3SSA113 Mike Schmidt 40.00 80.00
3SSA114 Mike Schmidt 40.00 80.00
3SSA115 Mike Schmidt 40.00 80.00
3SSA119 Mike Schmidt 40.00 80.00
3SSA120 Carl Yastrzemski 30.00 60.00
3SSA125 Carl Yastrzemski 30.00 60.00
3SSA128 Don Mattingly 60.00 120.00
3SSA129 Don Mattingly 60.00 120.00
3SSA134 Don Mattingly 60.00 120.00
3SSA135 Don Mattingly 60.00 120.00
3SSA139 Nolan Ryan 75.00 150.00
3SSA142 Robin Yount 30.00 60.00
3SSA148 Robin Yount 30.00 60.00
3SSA149 Robin Yount 30.00 60.00
3SSA153 Cal Ripken 125.00 250.00
3SSA155 Ryne Sandberg 40.00 80.00
3SSA156 Ryne Sandberg 40.00 80.00
3SSA158 Ryne Sandberg 40.00 80.00
3SSA159 Ryne Sandberg 40.00 80.00
3SSA162 Ryne Sandberg 40.00 80.00
3SSA163 Ryne Sandberg 40.00 80.00
3SSA165 Ryne Sandberg 40.00 80.00
3SSA168 Frank Robinson 20.00 50.00
3SSA171 Frank Robinson 20.00 50.00
3SSA176 Tony Gwynn 50.00 100.00
3SSA178 Tony Gwynn 50.00 100.00
3SSA179 Tony Gwynn 50.00 100.00
3SSA180 Ernie Banks 40.00 80.00

2009 Topps Sterling

COMMON CARD .75 2.00
THREE BASE CARDS PER BOX
STATED PRINT RUN 250 SER.#'d SETS
1 Babe Ruth 5.00 12.00
2 Bob Feller .75 2.00
3 Orlando Cepeda .75 2.00
4 Curt Schilling 1.25 3.00
5 Mickey Mantle 6.00 15.00
6 Joey Votto 2.00 5.00
7 Koji Uehara RC 1.25 3.00
8 Mel Ott 2.00 5.00
9 Miguel Cabrera 2.00 5.00
10 Prince Fielder 1.25 3.00
11 Jose Reyes 1.25 3.00
12 Carlos Beltran .75 2.00
13 David Price RC 2.00 5.00
14 Tommy Hanson RC 2.50 6.00
15 Roger Maris 2.00 5.00
16 Roger Maris 2.00 5.00
17 Mike Schmidt 3.00 8.00
18 Lou Gehrig 4.00 10.00
19 Ozzie Smith 3.00 8.00
20 Reggie Jackson 1.25 3.00
21 Reggie Jackson 1.25 3.00
22 Reggie Jackson 1.25 3.00
23 Tim Lincecum 3.00 8.00
24 Warren Spahn 1.25 3.00
25 Duke Snider 1.25 3.00
26 Yogi Berra 2.00 5.00
27 Ty Cobb 3.00 8.00
28 Stan Musial 3.00 8.00
29 Jimmie Foxx 2.00 5.00
30 Jimmie Foxx 2.00 5.00
31 Rick Porcello RC 2.50 6.00
32 Dwight Gooden .75 2.00
33 Ichiro Suzuki 3.00 8.00
34 CC Sabathia 1.25 3.00
35 Willie McCovey 1.25 3.00
36 Albert Pujols 5.00 12.00
37 Gary Sheffield .75 2.00
38 Cal Ripken Jr. 8.00 20.00
39 Daisuke Matsuzaka 2.00 5.00
40 Gary Carter .75 2.00
41 Josh Hamilton 2.00 5.00
42 Joe Mauer 2.00 5.00
43 Pedro Martinez 1.25 3.00
44 Whitey Ford 1.25 3.00
45 Johnny Damon 1.25 3.00
46 Frank Thomas 2.00 5.00
47 Dale Murphy 2.00 5.00
48 George Sisler 1.25 3.00
49 Roger Clemens 2.50 6.00
50 Lou Brock 1.25 3.00
51 Paul Molitor 2.00 5.00
52 David Ortiz 1.25 3.00
53 Tris Speaker 1.25 3.00
54 Tris Speaker 1.25 3.00
55 Carl Yastrzemski 3.00 8.00
56 Nolan Ryan 6.00 15.00
57 Nolan Ryan 6.00 15.00
58 Nolan Ryan 6.00 15.00
59 Eddie Mathews 2.00 5.00
60 Joe Morgan .75 2.00
61 Honus Wagner 2.00 5.00
62 Andre Dawson 1.25 3.00
63 Justin Morneau 2.00 5.00
64 Manny Ramirez 2.00 5.00
65 Manny Ramirez 2.00 5.00
66 Manny Ramirez 2.00 5.00
67 Vladimir Guerrero 2.00 5.00
68 Hanley Ramirez 2.00 5.00
69 Ryan Braun 2.50 6.00
70 Dan Haren .75 2.00
71 Dave Winfield .75 2.00
72 Robin Yount 2.00 5.00
73 Ryne Sandberg 4.00 10.00
74 Johnny Mize 1.25 3.00
75 Johnny Mize 1.25 3.00
76 Johnny Mize 1.25 3.00
77 Don Mattingly 4.00 10.00
78 Ivan Rodriguez 1.25 3.00
79 Ralph Kiner 1.25 3.00
80 Steve Garvey .75 2.00
81 Carlos Delgado .75 2.00
82 Dustin Pedroia 2.50 6.00
83 Hank Greenberg 2.00 5.00
84 Al Kaline 2.00 5.00
85 Fergie Jenkins .75 2.00
86 David Wright 2.50 6.00
87 Frank Robinson 1.25 3.00
88 Brandon Webb 1.25 3.00
89 Colby Rasmus (RC) 2.00 5.00
90 Alfonso Soriano 1.25 3.00
91 Jackie Robinson 2.00 5.00
92 Lance Berkman 1.25 3.00
93 Chase Utley 2.00 5.00
94 Mark Teixeira 2.00 5.00
95 Mike Piazza 2.00 5.00
96 Johan Santana 2.00 5.00
97 Rogers Hornsby 1.25 3.00
98 Rogers Hornsby 1.25 3.00
99 Dennis Eckersley .75 2.00
100 Evan Longoria 2.50 6.00
101 Bob Gibson 1.25 3.00
102 Tom Seaver 1.25 3.00
103 Tony Gwynn 2.00 5.00
104 Johnny Bench 2.00 5.00
105 Carlton Fisk 1.25 3.00
106 Ernie Banks 2.00 5.00
107 Mariano Rivera 2.00 5.00
108 Tony Perez .75 2.00
109 Roy Campanella 2.00 5.00
110 Francisco Rodriguez 1.25 3.00
111 Luis Aparicio .75 2.00
112 Monte Irvin .75 2.00
113 Zack Greinke 1.25 3.00
114 Jim Thome 1.25 3.00
115 Jimmy Piersall .75 2.00
116 Eddie Murray 2.00 5.00
117 Jim Palmer .75 2.00
118 Carl Erskine .75 2.00
119 Juan Marichal .75 2.00
120 Joba Chamberlain 1.25 3.00
121 Chipper Jones 2.00 5.00
122 Johnny Podres .75 2.00
123 Wade Boggs 1.25 3.00
124 Michael Young 1.25 3.00
125 Steve Carlton .75 2.00
126 Ryan Howard 2.50 6.00
127 Jay Bruce 1.25 3.00
128 Alex Rodriguez 3.00 8.00
129 Alex Rodriguez 3.00 8.00
130 Alex Rodriguez 3.00 8.00

2009 Topps Sterling Career Chronicles Relics Quad

OVERALL MEM ODDS 1:1
STATED PRINT RUN 25 SER.#'d SETS
ALL VARIATIONS PRICED EQUALLY
10 PRINT RUN 10 SER.#'d SETS
NO 10 PRICING DUE TO SCARCITY
SS PRINT RUN 1 SER.#'d SET
NO SS PRICING DUE TO SCARCITY
1 Babe Ruth 200.00 400.00
2 Ichiro Suzuki 30.00 60.00
3 Ichiro Suzuki 30.00 60.00
4 Jackie Robinson 40.00 80.00
5 Jackie Robinson 40.00 80.00
6 Cal Ripken Jr. 30.00 60.00
7 Cal Ripken Jr. 30.00 60.00
8 David Ortiz 8.00 20.00
9 David Ortiz 8.00 20.00
10 Vladimir Guerrero 8.00 20.00
11 Vladimir Guerrero 8.00 20.00
12 Reggie Jackson 15.00 40.00
13 Reggie Jackson 15.00 40.00
14 Prince Fielder 10.00 25.00
15 Prince Fielder 10.00 25.00
16 Chase Utley 15.00 40.00
17 Chase Utley 15.00 40.00
18 Francisco Rodriguez 8.00 20.00
19 Francisco Rodriguez 8.00 20.00
20 Lou Brock 15.00 40.00
21 Lou Brock 15.00 40.00
22 Carl Yastrzemski 12.50 30.00
23 Carl Yastrzemski 12.50 30.00
24 Jimmie Foxx 20.00 50.00
25 Jimmie Foxx 20.00 50.00
26 Eddie Mathews 15.00 40.00
27 Eddie Mathews 15.00 40.00
28 Yogi Berra 20.00 50.00
29 Yogi Berra 20.00 50.00
30 Mike Schmidt 12.50 30.00
31 Mike Schmidt 12.50 30.00
32 Tim Lincecum 20.00 50.00
33 Tim Lincecum 20.00 50.00
34 Mark Teixeira 10.00 25.00
35 Mark Teixeira 10.00 25.00
36 Ernie Banks 12.50 30.00
37 Ernie Banks 12.50 30.00
38 Joe Morgan 8.00 20.00
39 Joe Morgan 8.00 20.00
40 Al Kaline 15.00 40.00
41 Al Kaline 15.00 40.00
42 Carlos Beltran 8.00 20.00
43 Carlos Beltran 8.00 20.00
44 Mel Ott 20.00 50.00
45 Mickey Mantle 60.00 120.00
46 Mickey Mantle 60.00 120.00
47 Albert Pujols 20.00 50.00
48 Albert Pujols 20.00 50.00
49 Chipper Jones 12.50 30.00
50 Chipper Jones 12.50 30.00
51 Daisuke Matsuzaka 10.00 25.00
52 Daisuke Matsuzaka 10.00 25.00
53 Carlos Delgado 8.00 20.00
54 Carlos Delgado 8.00 20.00
55 Joba Chamberlain 10.00 25.00
56 Joba Chamberlain 10.00 25.00
57 Dennis Eckersley 8.00 20.00
58 Dennis Eckersley 8.00 20.00
59 Luis Aparicio 10.00 25.00
60 Luis Aparicio 10.00 25.00
61 CC Sabathia 10.00 25.00
62 CC Sabathia 10.00 25.00
63 Evan Longoria 12.50 30.00
64 Evan Longoria 12.50 30.00
65 Honus Wagner 60.00 120.00
66 Ryan Howard 15.00 40.00
67 Ryan Howard 15.00 40.00
68 Mariano Rivera 15.00 40.00
69 Mariano Rivera 15.00 40.00
70 Ty Cobb 50.00 100.00
71 Nolan Ryan 30.00 60.00
72 Nolan Ryan 30.00 60.00

73 Lou Gehrig 100.00 175.00
74 Dale Murphy 20.00 50.00
75 Dale Murphy 20.00 50.00
76 Eddie Murray 12.50 30.00
77 Eddie Murray 12.50 30.00
78 Don Mattingly 15.00 40.00
79 Don Mattingly 15.00 40.00
80 Johnny Bench 10.00 25.00
81 Johnny Bench 10.00 25.00
82 Joe Mauer 15.00 40.00
83 Joe Mauer 15.00 40.00
84 Dave Winfield 10.00 25.00
85 Dave Winfield 10.00 25.00
86 David Wright 10.00 25.00
87 David Wright 10.00 25.00
88 Carlton Fisk 10.00 25.00
89 Carlton Fisk 10.00 25.00
90 Frank Robinson 8.00 20.00
91 Frank Robinson 8.00 20.00
92 Johan Santana 8.00 20.00
93 Johan Santana 8.00 20.00
94 Duke Snider 12.50 30.00
95 Duke Snider 12.50 30.00
96 Bob Gibson 10.00 25.00
97 Bob Gibson 10.00 25.00
98 Tom Seaver 10.00 25.00
99 Tom Seaver 10.00 25.00
100 Warren Spahn 15.00 40.00
101 Warren Spahn 15.00 40.00
102 Paul Molitor 10.00 25.00
103 Paul Molitor 10.00 25.00
104 Orlando Cepeda 8.00 20.00
105 Orlando Cepeda 8.00 20.00
106 Roger Maris 30.00 60.00
107 Roger Maris 30.00 60.00
108 Tris Speaker 30.00 60.00
109 Manny Ramirez 12.50 30.00
110 Manny Ramirez 12.50 30.00
111 Hank Greenberg 20.00 50.00
112 Hank Greenberg 20.00 50.00
113 Rogers Hornsby 20.00 50.00
114 Tony Gwynn 15.00 40.00
115 Tony Gwynn 15.00 40.00
116 Ozzie Smith 20.00 50.00
117 Ozzie Smith 20.00 50.00
118 Stan Musial 15.00 40.00
119 Stan Musial 15.00 40.00
120 George Sisler 30.00 60.00
121 Roy Campanella 15.00 40.00
122 Roy Campanella 15.00 40.00
123 Jim Palmer 10.00 25.00
124 Jim Palmer 10.00 25.00
125 Ryan Braun 10.00 25.00
126 Ryan Braun 10.00 25.00
127 Johnny Mize 10.00 25.00
128 Johnny Mize 10.00 25.00
129 Ryne Sandberg 12.50 30.00
130 Ryne Sandberg 12.50 30.00
131 Robin Yount 12.50 30.00
132 Robin Yount 12.50 30.00
133 Juan Marichal 8.00 20.00
134 Juan Marichal 8.00 20.00
135 Alex Rodriguez 30.00 60.00
136 Alex Rodriguez 30.00 60.00

2009 Topps Sterling Career Chronicles Relics Triple

OVERALL MEM ODDS 1:1
STATED PRINT RUN 25 SER.#'d SETS
ALL VARIATIONS PRICED EQUALLY
10 PRINT RUN 10 SER.#'d SETS
NO 10 PRICING DUE TO SCARCITY
SS PRINT RUN 1 SER.#'d SET
NO SS PRICING DUE TO SCARCITY
1 Babe Ruth 150.00 300.00
2 Babe Ruth 150.00 300.00
3 Babe Ruth 150.00 300.00
4 Ichiro Suzuki 20.00 50.00
5 Ichiro Suzuki 20.00 50.00
6 Ichiro Suzuki 20.00 50.00
7 Jackie Robinson 30.00 60.00
8 Jackie Robinson 30.00 60.00
9 Jackie Robinson 30.00 60.00
10 Cal Ripken Jr. 20.00 50.00
11 Cal Ripken Jr. 20.00 50.00
12 Cal Ripken Jr. 20.00 50.00
13 David Ortiz 6.00 15.00
14 David Ortiz 6.00 15.00
15 David Ortiz 6.00 15.00
16 Vladimir Guerrero 6.00 15.00
17 Vladimir Guerrero 6.00 15.00
18 Vladimir Guerrero 6.00 15.00
19 Reggie Jackson 12.50 30.00
20 Reggie Jackson 12.50 30.00
21 Reggie Jackson 12.50 30.00
22 Prince Fielder 10.00 25.00
23 Prince Fielder 10.00 25.00
24 Chase Utley 15.00 40.00
25 Chase Utley 15.00 40.00
26 Francisco Rodriguez 8.00 20.00
27 Francisco Rodriguez 8.00 20.00
28 Lou Brock 15.00 40.00
29 Lou Brock 15.00 40.00
30 Carl Yastrzemski 10.00 25.00
31 Carl Yastrzemski 10.00 25.00
32 Carl Yastrzemski 10.00 25.00
33 Jimmie Foxx 20.00 50.00
34 Jimmie Foxx 20.00 50.00
35 Eddie Mathews 15.00 40.00
36 Eddie Mathews 15.00 40.00
37 Yogi Berra 15.00 40.00
38 Yogi Berra 15.00 40.00
39 Yogi Berra 15.00 40.00
40 Mike Schmidt 10.00 25.00
41 Mike Schmidt 10.00 25.00
42 Mike Schmidt 10.00 25.00
43 Tim Lincecum 15.00 40.00
44 Tim Lincecum 15.00 40.00
45 Tim Lincecum 15.00 40.00
46 Mark Teixeira 10.00 25.00
47 Mark Teixeira 10.00 25.00
48 Ernie Banks 10.00 25.00
49 Ernie Banks 10.00 25.00
50 Ernie Banks 10.00 25.00
51 Joe Morgan 8.00 20.00
52 Joe Morgan 8.00 20.00
53 Al Kaline 15.00 40.00
54 Al Kaline 15.00 40.00
55 Carlos Beltran 8.00 20.00
56 Carlos Beltran 8.00 20.00
57 Mel Ott 15.00 40.00
58 Mel Ott 15.00 40.00
59 Mel Ott 15.00 40.00
60 Mickey Mantle 50.00 100.00
61 Mickey Mantle 50.00 100.00
62 Mickey Mantle 50.00 100.00
63 Albert Pujols 15.00 40.00
64 Albert Pujols 15.00 40.00
65 Albert Pujols 15.00 40.00
66 Chipper Jones 12.50 30.00
67 Chipper Jones 12.50 30.00
68 Daisuke Matsuzaka 8.00 20.00
69 Daisuke Matsuzaka 8.00 20.00
70 Daisuke Matsuzaka 8.00 20.00
71 Carlos Delgado 8.00 20.00
72 Carlos Delgado 8.00 20.00
73 Joba Chamberlain 8.00 20.00
74 Joba Chamberlain 8.00 20.00
75 Joba Chamberlain 8.00 20.00
76 Dennis Eckersley 8.00 20.00
77 Dennis Eckersley 8.00 20.00
78 Luis Aparicio 10.00 25.00
79 Luis Aparicio 10.00 25.00
80 CC Sabathia 10.00 25.00
81 CC Sabathia 10.00 25.00
82 Evan Longoria 12.50 30.00
83 Evan Longoria 12.50 30.00
84 Honus Wagner 60.00 120.00
85 Honus Wagner 60.00 120.00
86 Honus Wagner 60.00 120.00
87 Ryan Howard 12.50 30.00
88 Ryan Howard 12.50 30.00
89 Ryan Howard 12.50 30.00
90 Mariano Rivera 12.50 30.00
91 Mariano Rivera 12.50 30.00
92 Mariano Rivera 12.50 30.00
93 Ty Cobb 40.00 80.00
94 Ty Cobb 40.00 80.00
95 Ty Cobb 40.00 80.00
96 Nolan Ryan 20.00 50.00
97 Nolan Ryan 20.00 50.00
98 Nolan Ryan 20.00 50.00
99 Lou Gehrig 75.00 150.00
100 Lou Gehrig 75.00 150.00
101 Lou Gehrig 75.00 150.00
102 Dale Murphy 15.00 40.00
103 Dale Murphy 15.00 40.00
104 Dale Murphy 15.00 40.00
105 Eddie Murray 12.50 30.00
106 Eddie Murray 12.50 30.00
107 Don Mattingly 12.50 30.00
108 Don Mattingly 12.50 30.00
109 Don Mattingly 12.50 30.00
110 Johnny Bench 10.00 25.00
111 Johnny Bench 10.00 25.00
112 Johnny Bench 10.00 25.00
113 Joe Mauer 15.00 40.00
114 Joe Mauer 15.00 40.00
115 Dave Winfield 10.00 25.00
116 Dave Winfield 10.00 25.00
117 David Wright 10.00 25.00
118 David Wright 10.00 25.00
119 Carlton Fisk 10.00 25.00
120 Carlton Fisk 10.00 25.00
121 Frank Robinson 6.00 15.00
122 Frank Robinson 6.00 15.00
123 Frank Robinson 6.00 15.00
124 Johan Santana 8.00 20.00
125 Johan Santana 8.00 20.00
126 Duke Snider 12.50 30.00
127 Duke Snider 12.50 30.00
128 Bob Gibson 8.00 20.00
129 Bob Gibson 8.00 20.00
130 Bob Gibson 8.00 20.00
131 Tom Seaver 8.00 20.00
132 Tom Seaver 8.00 20.00
133 Tom Seaver 8.00 20.00
134 Warren Spahn 15.00 40.00
135 Warren Spahn 15.00 40.00
136 Paul Molitor 10.00 25.00
137 Paul Molitor 10.00 25.00
138 Orlando Cepeda 8.00 20.00
139 Orlando Cepeda 8.00 20.00
140 Roger Maris 30.00 60.00
141 Roger Maris 30.00 60.00
142 Roger Maris 30.00 60.00
143 Tris Speaker 20.00 50.00
144 Tris Speaker 20.00 50.00
145 Tris Speaker 20.00 50.00
146 Manny Ramirez 10.00 25.00
147 Manny Ramirez 10.00 25.00
148 Manny Ramirez 10.00 25.00
149 Hank Greenberg 20.00 50.00
150 Hank Greenberg 20.00 50.00
151 Rogers Hornsby 15.00 40.00
152 Rogers Hornsby 15.00 40.00
153 Rogers Hornsby 15.00 40.00
154 Tony Gwynn 15.00 40.00
155 Tony Gwynn 15.00 40.00
156 Ozzie Smith 15.00 40.00
157 Ozzie Smith 15.00 40.00
158 Ozzie Smith 15.00 40.00
159 Stan Musial 12.50 30.00
160 Stan Musial 12.50 30.00
161 Stan Musial 12.50 30.00
162 George Sisler 20.00 40.00
163 George Sisler 20.00 50.00
164 George Sisler 20.00 50.00
165 Roy Campanella 12.50 30.00
166 Roy Campanella 12.50 30.00
167 Roy Campanella 12.50 30.00
168 Jim Palmer 10.00 25.00
169 Jim Palmer 10.00 25.00
170 Ryan Braun 10.00 25.00
171 Ryan Braun 10.00 25.00
172 Johnny Mize 10.00 25.00
173 Johnny Mize 10.00 25.00
174 Ryne Sandberg 10.00 25.00
175 Ryne Sandberg 10.00 25.00
176 Ryne Sandberg 10.00 25.00
177 Robin Yount 12.50 30.00
178 Robin Yount 12.50 30.00
179 Juan Marichal 8.00 20.00
180 Juan Marichal 8.00 20.00
181 Alex Rodriguez 20.00 50.00
182 Alex Rodriguez 20.00 50.00
183 Alex Rodriguez 20.00 50.00

2010 Topps Sterling

COMMON CARD .75 2.00
COMMON RC 1.50 4.00
THREE BASE CARDS PER BOX
STATED PRINT RUN 250 SER.#'d SETS
1 Honus Wagner 2.00 5.00
2 Babe Ruth 5.00 12.00
3 Babe Ruth 5.00 12.00
4 Lou Gehrig 4.00 10.00
5 Christy Mathewson 2.00 5.00
6 Starlin Castro RC 6.00 15.00
7 Mickey Mantle 6.00 15.00
8 Carl Yastrzemski 2.00 5.00
9 Clayton Kershaw 2.00 5.00
10 Cal Ripken Jr. 8.00 20.00
11 Willie McCovey 1.25 3.00
12 Johnny Podres .75 2.00
13 Curt Schilling 1.25 3.00
14 Ernie Banks 2.00 5.00
15 Thurman Munson 2.00 5.00
16 Reggie Jackson 1.25 3.00
17 Reggie Jackson 1.25 3.00
18 Reggie Jackson 1.25 3.00
19 Tony Gwynn 2.00 5.00
20 Mike Schmidt 3.00 8.00
21 Ian Kinsler 1.25 3.00
22 Jason Heyward 5.00 12.00
23 Wade Boggs 1.25 3.00
24 Ryan Braun 2.50 6.00
25 Eddie Mathews 2.00 5.00
26 Chase Utley 2.00 5.00
27 Manny Ramirez 2.00 5.00
28 Manny Ramirez 2.00 5.00
29 Manny Ramirez 2.00 5.00
30 Ty Cobb 3.00 8.00
31 Ty Cobb 3.00 8.00
32 Steve Carlton .75 2.00
33 Steve Carlton .75 2.00
34 Frank Thomas 2.00 5.00
35 Hank Greenberg 2.00 5.00
36 Red Schoendienst .75 2.00
37 Stephen Strasburg RC 10.00 25.00
38 Fergie Jenkins .75 2.00
39 Roy Campanella 2.00 5.00
40 Mel Ott 2.00 5.00
41 Brooks Robinson 1.25 3.00
42 Jackie Robinson 2.00 5.00
43 Larry Walker 1.25 3.00
44 Juan Marichal .75 2.00
45 Bob Gibson 1.25 3.00
46 Duke Snider 1.25 3.00
47 Kevin Youkilis 1.25 3.00
48 Mike Piazza 2.00 5.00
49 Mike Piazza 2.00 5.00
50 Albert Pujols 5.00 12.00
51 Ichiro Suzuki 3.00 8.00
52 Robin Yount 2.00 5.00
53 Ozzie Smith 3.00 8.00
54 Ozzie Smith 3.00 8.00
55 Tim Lincecum 3.00 8.00
56 Paul Molitor 2.00 5.00
57 Paul Molitor 2.00 5.00
58 Rickey Henderson 2.00 5.00
59 Rickey Henderson 2.00 5.00
60 Joe Mauer 2.00 5.00
61 Willie Stargell 1.25 3.00
62 Joe Morgan .75 2.00
63 Johnny Mize 1.25 3.00
64 Johnny Mize 1.25 3.00
65 Johnny Mize 1.25 3.00
66 Whitey Ford 1.25 3.00
67 Carlton Fisk 1.25 3.00
68 Carlton Fisk 1.25 3.00
69 Harmon Killebrew 2.00 5.00
70 Jimmie Foxx 2.00 5.00
71 Jimmie Foxx 2.00 5.00
72 Bernie Williams 1.25 3.00
73 Justin Upton 1.25 3.00
74 Dale Murphy 2.00 5.00
75 Alex Rodriguez 3.00 8.00
76 Alex Rodriguez 3.00 8.00
77 Alex Rodriguez 3.00 8.00
78 Al Kaline 2.00 5.00
79 Justin Morneau 2.00 5.00
80 Yogi Berra 2.00 5.00
81 Dennis Eckersley .75 2.00
82 David Ortiz 1.25 3.00
83 Barry Larkin 1.25 3.00
84 Chipper Jones 2.00 5.00
85 Cy Young 2.00 5.00
86 Roberto Alomar 1.25 3.00
87 Tris Speaker 1.25 3.00
88 Eddie Murray 2.00 5.00
89 Adrian Gonzalez 1.25 3.00
90 Roger Maris 2.00 5.00
91 Roger Maris 2.00 5.00
92 Vladimir Guerrero 2.00 5.00
93 Vladimir Guerrero 2.00 5.00
94 Vladimir Guerrero 2.00 5.00
95 Pee Wee Reese 1.25 3.00
96 Robin Roberts .75 2.00
97 Johnny Bench 2.00 5.00
98 Josh Hamilton 2.00 5.00
99 Robinson Cano 2.00 5.00
100 Stan Musial 3.00 8.00
101 Dave Winfield .75 2.00
102 Dave Winfield .75 2.00
103 Mike Stanton RC 6.00 15.00
104 Orlando Cepeda .75 2.00
105 Evan Longoria 2.50 6.00
106 Dustin Pedroia 2.50 6.00
107 Luis Aparicio .75 2.00
108 Catfish Hunter .75 2.00
109 Bill Mazeroski 1.25 3.00
110 Frank Robinson 1.25 3.00
111 Frank Robinson 1.25 3.00
112 Phil Rizzuto 1.25 3.00
113 Prince Fielder 1.25 3.00
114 Gary Carter .75 2.00
115 Ryne Sandberg 4.00 10.00
116 Andre Ethier 1.25 3.00
117 Mark Teixeira 2.00 5.00
118 Mark Teixeira 2.00 5.00
119 Victor Martinez 1.25 3.00
120 George Sisler 2.00 5.00
121 Rod Carew 1.25 3.00
122 CC Sabathia 1.25 3.00
123 Craig Biggio 1.25 3.00
124 David Wright 2.50 6.00
125 Ryan Howard 2.50 6.00
126 Miguel Cabrera 2.00 5.00
127 Don Mattingly 4.00 10.00
128 Bob Feller .75 2.00
129 Rogers Hornsby 1.25 3.00
130 Rogers Hornsby 1.25 3.00
131 Greg Maddux 2.50 6.00
132 Greg Maddux 2.50 6.00
133 Ralph Kiner 1.25 3.00
134 Roy Halladay 2.00 5.00
135 Walter Johnson 2.00 5.00
136 Warren Spahn 1.25 3.00
137 Andre Dawson 1.25 3.00
138 Andre Dawson 1.25 3.00
139 Tom Seaver 1.25 3.00
140 Tom Seaver 1.25 3.00
141 Tom Seaver 1.25 3.00
142 Mariano Rivera 2.00 5.00
143 Hanley Ramirez 2.00 5.00
144 Ubaldo Jimenez 1.25 3.00
145 Jim Palmer .75 2.00
146 Monte Irvin .75 2.00
147 Nolan Ryan 6.00 15.00
148 Nolan Ryan 6.00 15.00
149 Nolan Ryan 6.00 15.00
150 Nolan Ryan 6.00 15.00

2010 Topps Sterling Framed Burgundy

OVERALL PARALLEL ODDS 1:1
STATED PRINT RUN 10 SER.#'d SETS
NO PRICING DUE TO SCARCITY

2010 Topps Sterling Framed Cherry Wood

OVERALL PARALLEL ODDS 1:1
STATED PRINT RUN 1 SER.#'d SET
NO PRICING DUE TO SCARCITY

2010 Topps Sterling Framed Gold

OVERALL PARALLEL ODDS 1:1
STATED PRINT RUN 5 SER.#'d SETS
NO PRICING DUE TO SCARCITY

2010 Topps Sterling Framed Sterling Silver

OVERALL PARALLEL ODDS 1:1
STATED PRINT RUN 1 SER.#'d SET
NO PRICING DUE TO SCARCITY

2010 Topps Sterling Framed Suede

OVERALL PARALLEL ODDS 1:1
STATED PRINT RUN 3 SER.#'d SETS
NO PRICING DUE TO SCARCITY

2010 Topps Sterling Framed White

*WHITE VET: .75X TO 2X BASIC
*WHITE RC: .5X TO 1.2X BASIC RC
OVERALL PARALLEL ODDS 1:1
STATED PRINT RUN 50 SER.#'d SETS

2010 Topps Sterling Career Chronicles Relics Five

OVERALL MEM ODDS 1:1
STATED PRINT RUN 25 SER.#'d SETS
ALL VARIATIONS PRICED EQUALLY
10 PRINT RUN 10 SER.#'d SETS
NO 10 PRICING DUE TO SCARCITY
SS PRINT RUN 1 SER.#'d SET
NO SS PRICING DUE TO SCARCITY
CCR1 Ryan Braun 10.00 25.00
CCR2 Ryan Braun 10.00 25.00
CCR3 Harmon Killebrew 20.00 50.00
CCR4 Harmon Killebrew 20.00 50.00
CCR5 Wade Boggs 12.50 30.00
CCR6 Evan Longoria 12.50 30.00
CCR7 Mickey Mantle 60.00 120.00
CCR8 Mickey Mantle 60.00 120.00
CCR9 Cal Ripken Jr. 30.00 60.00
CCR10 Cal Ripken Jr. 30.00 60.00
CCR11 Yogi Berra 15.00 40.00
CCR12 Yogi Berra 15.00 40.00
CCR13 Roy Halladay 15.00 40.00
CCR14 Roy Halladay 15.00 40.00
CCR15 Joe Mauer 12.50 30.00
CCR16 Joe Mauer 12.50 30.00
CCR17 Rogers Hornsby 20.00 50.00
CCR18 Hank Greenberg 20.00 50.00
CCR19 Albert Pujols 30.00 60.00
CCR20 Albert Pujols 30.00 60.00
CCR21 George Sisler 15.00 40.00
CCR22 George Sisler 15.00 40.00
CCR23 Jackie Robinson 30.00 60.00
CCR24 Jackie Robinson 30.00 60.00
CCR25 Manny Ramirez 15.00 40.00
CCR26 Jimmie Foxx 20.00 50.00
CCR27 Carl Yastrzemski 15.00 40.00
CCR28 Carl Yastrzemski 15.00 40.00
CCR29 Hanley Ramirez 12.50 30.00
CCR30 Hanley Ramirez 12.50 30.00
CCR31 Stan Musial 30.00 60.00
CCR32 Stan Musial 30.00 60.00
CCR33 Nolan Ryan 30.00 60.00
CCR34 Nolan Ryan 30.00 60.00
CCR35 Ty Cobb 60.00 120.00
CCR36 Pee Wee Reese 20.00 50.00
CCR37 Reggie Jackson 12.50 30.00
CCR38 Reggie Jackson 12.50 30.00
CCR39 Mike Schmidt 20.00 50.00
CCR40 Jim Palmer 10.00 25.00
CCR41 Miguel Cabrera 10.00 25.00
CCR42 Whitey Ford 15.00 40.00
CCR43 Honus Wagner 50.00 100.00
CCR44 Honus Wagner 50.00 100.00
CCR45 Frank Robinson 10.00 25.00
CCR46 Roy Campanella 20.00 50.00
CCR47 Alex Rodriguez 15.00 40.00
CCR48 Kevin Youkilis 12.50 30.00
CCR49 Mel Ott 20.00 50.00
CCR50 Tom Seaver 15.00 40.00
CCR51 Warren Spahn 12.50 30.00
CCR52 Roger Maris 30.00 60.00
CCR53 Tim Lincecum 15.00 40.00
CCR54 Tim Lincecum 15.00 40.00
CCR55 Johnny Mize 12.50 30.00
CCR56 Johnny Mize 12.50 30.00
CCR57 Lou Gehrig 75.00 150.00
CCR58 Lou Gehrig 75.00 150.00
CCR59 Ichiro Suzuki 40.00 80.00
CCR60 Ichiro Suzuki 40.00 80.00

2010 Topps Sterling Career Chronicles Relics Five 10

OVERALL MEM ODDS 1:1
STATED PRINT RUN 10 SER.#'d SETS
NO PRICING DUE TO SCARCITY

2010 Topps Sterling Career Chronicles Relics Five Sterling Silver

OVERALL MEM ODDS 1:1
STATED PRINT RUN 1 SER.#'d SET
NO PRICING DUE TO SCARCITY

2010 Topps Sterling Career Chronicles Relics Quad

OVERALL MEM ODDS 1:1
STATED PRINT RUN 25 SER.#'d SETS
ALL VARIATIONS PRICED EQUALLY
10 PRINT RUN 10 SER.#'d SETS
NO 10 PRICING DUE TO SCARCITY
SS PRINT RUN 1 SER.#'d SET
NO SS PRICING DUE TO SCARCITY
CCR1 Ryan Braun 8.00 20.00
CCR2 Ryan Braun 8.00 20.00
CCR3 Harmon Killebrew 15.00 40.00
CCR4 Harmon Killebrew 15.00 40.00
CCR5 Wade Boggs 10.00 25.00
CCR6 Evan Longoria 10.00 25.00
CCR7 Mickey Mantle 50.00 100.00
CCR8 Mickey Mantle 50.00 100.00
CCR9 Cal Ripken Jr. 20.00 50.00
CCR10 Cal Ripken Jr. 20.00 50.00
CCR11 Yogi Berra 12.50 30.00
CCR12 Yogi Berra 12.50 30.00
CCR13 Roy Halladay 12.50 30.00
CCR14 Roy Halladay 12.50 30.00
CCR15 Joe Mauer 10.00 25.00
CCR16 Joe Mauer 10.00 25.00
CCR17 Rogers Hornsby 15.00 40.00
CCR18 Hank Greenberg 15.00 40.00
CCR19 Albert Pujols 20.00 50.00
CCR20 Albert Pujols 20.00 50.00
CCR21 George Sisler 12.50 30.00
CCR22 George Sisler 12.50 30.00
CCR23 Jackie Robinson 20.00 50.00
CCR24 Jackie Robinson 20.00 50.00
CCR25 Manny Ramirez 12.50 30.00
CCR26 Jimmie Foxx 15.00 40.00
CCR27 Carl Yastrzemski 12.50 30.00
CCR28 Carl Yastrzemski 12.50 30.00
CCR29 Hanley Ramirez 10.00 25.00
CCR30 Hanley Ramirez 10.00 25.00
CCR31 Stan Musial 20.00 50.00
CCR32 Stan Musial 20.00 50.00
CCR33 Nolan Ryan 20.00 50.00
CCR34 Nolan Ryan 20.00 50.00
CCR35 Ty Cobb 40.00 80.00
CCR36 Pee Wee Reese 15.00 40.00
CCR37 Reggie Jackson 10.00 25.00
CCR38 Reggie Jackson 10.00 25.00
CCR39 Mike Schmidt 15.00 40.00
CCR40 Jim Palmer 8.00 20.00
CCR41 Miguel Cabrera 8.00 20.00
CCR42 Whitey Ford 12.50 30.00
CCR43 Honus Wagner 40.00 80.00
CCR44 Honus Wagner 40.00 80.00
CCR45 Frank Robinson 8.00 20.00
CCR46 Roy Campanella 15.00 40.00
CCR47 Alex Rodriguez 12.50 30.00
CCR48 Kevin Youkilis 10.00 25.00
CCR49 Mel Ott 15.00 40.00
CCR50 Tom Seaver 12.50 30.00
CCR51 Warren Spahn 10.00 25.00
CCR52 Roger Maris 20.00 50.00
CCR53 Tim Lincecum 12.50 30.00
CCR54 Tim Lincecum 12.50 30.00
CCR55 Johnny Mize 10.00 25.00
CCR56 Johnny Mize 10.00 25.00
CCR57 Lou Gehrig 60.00 120.00
CCR58 Lou Gehrig 60.00 120.00
CCR59 Ichiro Suzuki 30.00 60.00
CCR60 Ichiro Suzuki 30.00 60.00

2010 Topps Sterling Career Chronicles Relics Quad 10

OVERALL MEM ODDS 1:1
STATED PRINT RUN 10 SER.#'d SETS
NO PRICING DUE TO SCARCITY

2010 Topps Sterling Career Chronicles Relics Quad Sterling Silver

OVERALL MEM ODDS 1:1
STATED PRINT RUN 1 SER.#'d SET
NO PRICING DUE TO SCARCITY

2010 Topps Sterling Career Chronicles Relics Triple

OVERALL MEM ODDS 1:1
STATED PRINT RUN 25 SER.#'d SETS
ALL VARIATIONS PRICED EQUALLY
10 PRINT RUN 10 SER.#'d SETS
NO 10 PRICING DUE TO SCARCITY
SS PRINT RUN 1 SER.#'d SET
NO SS PRICING DUE TO SCARCITY
CCR1 Ryan Braun 8.00 20.00
CCR2 Ryan Braun 8.00 20.00
CCR3 Harmon Killebrew 15.00 40.00
CCR4 Harmon Killebrew 15.00 40.00
CCR5 Wade Boggs 10.00 25.00
CCR6 Evan Longoria 10.00 25.00
CCR7 Mickey Mantle 50.00 100.00
CCR8 Mickey Mantle 50.00 100.00
CCR9 Cal Ripken Jr. 20.00 50.00
CCR10 Cal Ripken Jr. 20.00 50.00
CCR11 Yogi Berra 12.50 30.00
CCR12 Yogi Berra 12.50 30.00
CCR13 Roy Halladay 12.50 30.00
CCR14 Roy Halladay 12.50 30.00
CCR15 Joe Mauer 10.00 25.00
CCR16 Joe Mauer 10.00 25.00
CCR17 Rogers Hornsby 15.00 40.00
CCR18 Hank Greenberg 15.00 40.00
CCR19 Albert Pujols 20.00 50.00
CCR20 Albert Pujols 20.00 50.00
CCR21 George Sisler 12.50 30.00
CCR22 George Sisler 12.50 30.00
CCR23 Jackie Robinson 20.00 50.00
CCR24 Jackie Robinson 20.00 50.00
CCR25 Manny Ramirez 12.50 30.00
CCR26 Jimmie Foxx 15.00 40.00
CCR27 Carl Yastrzemski 12.50 30.00
CCR28 Carl Yastrzemski 12.50 30.00
CCR29 Hanley Ramirez 10.00 25.00
CCR30 Hanley Ramirez 10.00 25.00
CCR31 Stan Musial 20.00 50.00
CCR32 Stan Musial 20.00 50.00
CCR33 Nolan Ryan 20.00 50.00
CCR34 Nolan Ryan 20.00 50.00
CCR35 Ty Cobb 40.00 80.00
CCR36 Pee Wee Reese 15.00 40.00
CCR37 Reggie Jackson 10.00 25.00
CCR38 Reggie Jackson 10.00 25.00
CCR39 Mike Schmidt 15.00 40.00
CCR40 Jim Palmer 8.00 20.00
CCR41 Miguel Cabrera 8.00 20.00
CCR42 Whitey Ford 12.50 30.00
CCR43 Honus Wagner 40.00 80.00
CCR44 Honus Wagner 40.00 80.00
CCR45 Frank Robinson 8.00 20.00
CCR46 Roy Campanella 15.00 40.00
CCR47 Alex Rodriguez 12.50 30.00
CCR48 Kevin Youkilis 10.00 25.00
CCR49 Mel Ott 15.00 40.00
CCR50 Tom Seaver 12.50 30.00
CCR51 Warren Spahn 10.00 25.00
CCR52 Roger Maris 20.00 50.00
CCR53 Tim Lincecum 12.50 30.00
CCR54 Tim Lincecum 12.50 30.00
CCR55 Johnny Mize 10.00 25.00
CCR56 Johnny Mize 10.00 25.00
CCR57 Lou Gehrig 60.00 120.00
CCR58 Lou Gehrig 60.00 120.00
CCR59 Ichiro Suzuki 30.00 60.00
CCR60 Ichiro Suzuki 30.00 60.00

2010 Topps Sterling Career Chronicles Relics Triple 10

OVERALL MEM ODDS 1:1
STATED PRINT RUN 10 SER.#'d SETS
NO PRICING DUE TO SCARCITY

2010 Topps Sterling Career Chronicles Relics Triple Sterling Silver

OVERALL MEM ODDS 1:1
STATED PRINT RUN 1 SER.#'d SET
NO PRICING DUE TO SCARCITY

2010 Topps Sterling Legendary Leather Relics Five

OVERALL MEM ODDS 1:1
STATED PRINT RUN 25 SER.#'d SETS
ALL VARIATIONS PRICED EQUALLY
10 PRINT RUN 10 SER.#'d SETS
NO 10 PRICING DUE TO SCARCITY
SS PRINT RUN 1 SER.#'d SET
NO SS PRICING DUE TO SCARCITY
LLR1 Babe Ruth 125.00 250.00
LLR2 Babe Ruth 125.00 250.00
LLR3 Mike Schmidt 20.00 50.00
LLR4 Mike Schmidt 20.00 50.00
LLR5 Joe Mauer 12.50 30.00
LLR6 Rickey Henderson 40.00 80.00
LLR7 Mickey Mantle 60.00 120.00
LLR8 Mickey Mantle 60.00 120.00
LLR9 Mark Teixeira 12.50 30.00
LLR10 Mark Teixeira 12.50 30.00
LLR11 Carl Yastrzemski 15.00 40.00
LLR12 Carl Yastrzemski 15.00 40.00
LLR13 David Wright 15.00 40.00
LLR14 David Wright 15.00 40.00
LLR15 Bob Gibson 15.00 40.00
LLR16 Bob Gibson 15.00 40.00
LLR17 Pee Wee Reese 20.00 50.00
LLR18 Pee Wee Reese 20.00 50.00
LLR19 Luis Aparicio 10.00 25.00
LLR20 Luis Aparicio 10.00 25.00
LLR21 Roberto Alomar 30.00 60.00
LLR22 Roberto Alomar 30.00 60.00
LLR23 Ernie Banks 12.50 30.00
LLR24 Rogers Hornsby 20.00 50.00
LLR25 Greg Maddux 15.00 40.00
LLR26 Greg Maddux 15.00 40.00
LLR27 Yogi Berra 15.00 40.00
LLR28 Johnny Bench 20.00 50.00
LLR29 Alex Rodriguez 15.00 40.00
LLR30 Dave Winfield 10.00 25.00
LLR31 Tony Gwynn 15.00 40.00
LLR32 Tony Gwynn 15.00 40.00
LLR33 Robinson Cano 15.00 40.00
LLR34 Robinson Cano 15.00 40.00
LLR35 Duke Snider 20.00 50.00
LLR36 Duke Snider 20.00 50.00
LLR37 Barry Larkin 10.00 25.00
LLR38 Barry Larkin 10.00 25.00
LLR39 Evan Longoria 12.50 30.00
LLR40 Evan Longoria 12.50 30.00
LLR41 Joe Morgan 10.00 25.00
LLR42 Roy Campanella 20.00 50.00
LLR43 Craig Biggio 12.50 30.00
LLR44 Craig Biggio 12.50 30.00
LLR45 Brooks Robinson 12.50 30.00
LLR46 Brooks Robinson 12.50 30.00
LLR47 Eddie Murray 12.50 30.00
LLR48 Thurman Munson 20.00 50.00
LLR49 Don Mattingly 20.00 50.00
LLR50 Don Mattingly 20.00 50.00
LLR51 Andre Dawson 12.50 30.00
LLR52 Andre Dawson 12.50 30.00
LLR53 Al Kaline 15.00 40.00
LLR54 Al Kaline 15.00 40.00
LLR55 Albert Pujols 30.00 60.00
LLR56 Albert Pujols 30.00 60.00
LLR57 Ichiro Suzuki 40.00 80.00
LLR58 Ichiro Suzuki 40.00 80.00
LLR59 Ozzie Smith 30.00 60.00
LLR60 Phil Rizzuto 20.00 50.00

2010 Topps Sterling Legendary Leather Relics Five 10

OVERALL MEM ODDS 1:1
STATED PRINT RUN 10 SER.#'d SETS
NO PRICING DUE TO SCARCITY

2010 Topps Sterling Legendary Leather Relics Five Sterling Silver

OVERALL MEM ODDS 1:1
STATED PRINT RUN 1 SER.#'d SET
NO PRICING DUE TO SCARCITY

2010 Topps Sterling Legendary Leather Relics Quad

OVERALL MEM ODDS 1:1
STATED PRINT RUN 25 SER.#'d SETS
ALL VARIATIONS PRICED EQUALLY
10 PRINT RUN 10 SER.#'d SETS
NO 10 PRICING DUE TO SCARCITY
SS PRINT RUN 1 SER.#'d SET
NO SS PRICING DUE TO SCARCITY
LLR1 Babe Ruth 100.00 200.00
LLR2 Babe Ruth 100.00 200.00
LLR3 Mike Schmidt 15.00 40.00
LLR4 Mike Schmidt 15.00 40.00
LLR5 Joe Mauer 10.00 25.00
LLR6 Rickey Henderson 30.00 60.00
LLR7 Mickey Mantle 50.00 100.00
LLR8 Mickey Mantle 50.00 100.00
LLR9 Mark Teixeira 10.00 25.00
LLR10 Mark Teixeira 10.00 25.00
LLR11 Carl Yastrzemski 12.50 30.00
LLR12 Carl Yastrzemski 12.50 30.00
LLR13 David Wright 12.50 30.00
LLR14 David Wright 12.50 30.00
LLR15 Bob Gibson 12.50 30.00
LLR16 Bob Gibson 12.50 30.00
LLR17 Johnny Bench
LLR18 Pee Wee Reese 15.00 40.00
LLR19 Luis Aparicio 8.00 20.00
LLR20 Luis Aparicio 8.00 20.00
LLR21 Roberto Alomar 20.00 50.00
LLR22 Roberto Alomar 20.00 50.00
LLR23 Ernie Banks 10.00 25.00
LLR24 Rogers Hornsby 15.00 40.00
LLR25 Greg Maddux 12.50 30.00
LLR26 Greg Maddux 12.50 30.00
LLR27 Yogi Berra 12.50 30.00
LLR28 Mike Piazza 30.00 60.00
LLR29 Alex Rodriguez 12.50 30.00
LLR30 Dave Winfield 8.00 20.00
LLR31 Tony Gwynn 12.50 30.00
LLR32 Tony Gwynn 12.50 30.00
LLR33 Robinson Cano 12.50 30.00
LLR34 Robinson Cano 12.50 30.00
LLR35 Duke Snider 15.00 40.00
LLR36 Duke Snider 15.00 40.00
LLR37 Barry Larkin 8.00 20.00
LLR38 Barry Larkin 8.00 20.00
LLR39 Evan Longoria 10.00 25.00
LLR40 Evan Longoria 10.00 25.00
LLR41 Joe Morgan 8.00 20.00
LLR42 Roy Campanella 15.00 40.00
LLR43 Craig Biggio 10.00 25.00
LLR44 Craig Biggio 10.00 25.00
LLR45 Brooks Robinson 10.00 25.00
LLR46 Brooks Robinson 10.00 25.00
LLR47 Eddie Murray 10.00 25.00
LLR48 Thurman Munson 15.00 40.00
LLR49 Don Mattingly 15.00 40.00
LLR50 Don Mattingly 15.00 40.00
LLR51 Andre Dawson 10.00 25.00
LLR52 Andre Dawson 10.00 25.00
LLR53 Al Kaline 12.50 30.00
LLR54 Honus Wagner 40.00 80.00
LLR55 Albert Pujols 20.00 50.00
LLR56 Albert Pujols 20.00 50.00
LLR57 Ichiro Suzuki 30.00 60.00
LLR58 Ichiro Suzuki 30.00 60.00
LLR59 Ozzie Smith 20.00 50.00
LLR60 Phil Rizzuto 15.00 40.00

2010 Topps Sterling Legendary Leather Relics Quad 10

OVERALL MEM ODDS 1:1
STATED PRINT RUN 10 SER.#'d SETS
NO PRICING DUE TO SCARCITY

2010 Topps Sterling Legendary Leather Relics Quad Sterling Silver

OVERALL MEM ODDS 1:1
STATED PRINT RUN 1 SER.#'d SET
NO PRICING DUE TO SCARCITY

2010 Topps Sterling Legendary Leather Relics Triple

OVERALL MEM ODDS 1:1
STATED PRINT RUN 25 SER.#'d SETS
ALL VARIATIONS PRICED EQUALLY
10 PRINT RUN 10 SER.#'d SETS
NO 10 PRICING DUE TO SCARCITY
SS PRINT RUN 1 SER.#'d SET
NO SS PRICING DUE TO SCARCITY
LLR1 Babe Ruth 100.00 200.00
LLR2 Babe Ruth 100.00 200.00
LLR3 Mike Schmidt 15.00 40.00
LLR4 Mike Schmidt 15.00 40.00
LLR5 Joe Mauer 10.00 25.00
LLR6 Rickey Henderson 30.00 60.00
LLR7 Mickey Mantle 50.00 100.00

LLR8 Mickey Mantle 50.00 100.00
LLR9 Mark Teixeira 10.00 25.00
LLR10 Mark Teixeira 10.00 25.00
LLR11 Carl Yastrzemski 12.50 30.00
LLR12 Carl Yastrzemski 12.50 30.00
LLR13 David Wright 12.50 30.00
LLR14 David Wright 12.50 30.00
LLR15 Bob Gibson 12.50 30.00
LLR16 Bob Gibson 12.50 30.00
LLR17 Johnny Bench
LLR18 Pee Wee Reese 15.00 40.00
LLR19 Luis Aparicio 8.00 20.00
LLR20 Luis Aparicio 8.00 20.00
LLR21 Roberto Alomar 20.00 50.00
LLR22 Roberto Alomar 20.00 50.00
LLR23 Ernie Banks 10.00 25.00
LLR24 Rogers Hornsby 15.00 40.00
LLR25 Greg Maddux 12.50 30.00
LLR26 Greg Maddux 12.50 30.00
LLR27 Yogi Berra 12.50 30.00
LLR28 Mike Piazza 30.00 60.00
LLR29 Alex Rodriguez 12.50 30.00
LLR30 Dave Winfield 8.00 20.00
LLR31 Tony Gwynn 12.50 30.00
LLR32 Tony Gwynn 12.50 30.00
LLR33 Robinson Cano 12.50 30.00
LLR34 Robinson Cano 12.50 30.00
LLR35 Duke Snider 15.00 40.00
LLR36 Duke Snider 15.00 40.00
LLR37 Barry Larkin 8.00 20.00
LLR38 Barry Larkin 8.00 20.00
LLR39 Evan Longoria 10.00 25.00
LLR40 Evan Longoria 10.00 25.00
LLR41 Joe Morgan 8.00 20.00
LLR42 Roy Campanella 15.00 40.00
LLR43 Craig Biggio 10.00 25.00
LLR44 Craig Biggio 10.00 25.00
LLR45 Brooks Robinson 10.00 25.00
LLR46 Brooks Robinson 10.00 25.00
LLR47 Eddie Murray 10.00 25.00
LLR48 Thurman Munson 15.00 40.00
LLR49 Don Mattingly 15.00 40.00
LLR50 Don Mattingly 15.00 40.00
LLR51 Andre Dawson 10.00 25.00
LLR52 Andre Dawson 10.00 25.00
LLR53 Al Kaline 12.50 30.00
LLR54 Al Kaline 12.50 30.00
LLR55 Albert Pujols 20.00 50.00
LLR56 Albert Pujols 20.00 50.00
LLR57 Ichiro Suzuki 30.00 60.00
LLR58 Ichiro Suzuki 30.00 60.00
LLR59 Ozzie Smith 20.00 50.00
LLR60 Phil Rizzuto 15.00 40.00

2010 Topps Sterling Legendary Leather Relics Triple 10

OVERALL MEM ODDS 1:1
STATED PRINT RUN 10 SER.#'d SETS
NO PRICING DUE TO SCARCITY

2010 Topps Sterling Sterling Stats Relics Six

OVERALL MEM ODDS 1:1
STATED PRINT RUN 25 SER.#'d SETS
ALL VARIATIONS PRICED EQUALLY
10 PRINT RUN 10 SER.#'d SETS
NO 10 PRICING DUE TO SCARCITY
SS PRINT RUN 1 SER.#'d SET
NO SS PRICING DUE TO SCARCITY
SSR1 Stephen Strasburg
SSR2 Stephen Strasburg
SSR3 Babe Ruth 125.00 250.00
SSR4 Babe Ruth 125.00 250.00
SSR5 Rickey Henderson 40.00 80.00
SSR6 Rickey Henderson 40.00 80.00
SSR7 Cal Ripken Jr. 30.00 60.00
SSR8 Cal Ripken Jr. 30.00 60.00
SSR9 George Sisler 50.00 100.00
SSR10 George Sisler 50.00 100.00
SSR11 Al Kaline 15.00 40.00
SSR12 Al Kaline 15.00 40.00
SSR13 Carl Yastrzemski 15.00 40.00
SSR14 Carl Yastrzemski 15.00 40.00
SSR15 Dale Murphy 12.50 30.00
SSR16 Dale Murphy 12.50 30.00
SSR17 Honus Wagner 50.00 100.00
SSR18 Honus Wagner 50.00 100.00
SSR19 Craig Biggio 12.50 30.00
SSR20 Craig Biggio 12.50 30.00
SSR21 Johnny Mize 12.50 30.00
SSR22 Johnny Mize 12.50 30.00
SSR23 Ryan Braun 10.00 25.00
SSR24 Ryan Braun 10.00 25.00
SSR25 Manny Ramirez 15.00 40.00
SSR26 Manny Ramirez 15.00 40.00
SSR27 Alex Rodriguez 15.00 40.00
SSR28 Alex Rodriguez 15.00 40.00
SSR29 Carlton Fisk 12.50 30.00
SSR30 Carlton Fisk 12.50 30.00
SSR31 Lou Gehrig 75.00 150.00
SSR32 Lou Gehrig 75.00 150.00
SSR33 Ozzie Smith 30.00 60.00
SSR34 Ozzie Smith 30.00 60.00
SSR35 Hank Greenberg 20.00 50.00
SSR36 Hank Greenberg 20.00 50.00
SSR37 Roy Campanella 20.00 50.00
SSR38 Roy Campanella 20.00 50.00
SSR39 Ernie Banks 20.00 50.00
SSR40 Ernie Banks 20.00 50.00
SSR41 Jackie Robinson 30.00 60.00
SSR42 Jackie Robinson 30.00 60.00
SSR43 Phil Rizzuto 20.00 50.00
SSR44 Phil Rizzuto 20.00 50.00
SSR45 Harmon Killebrew 20.00 50.00
SSR46 Harmon Killebrew 20.00 50.00
SSR47 Yogi Berra 15.00 40.00
SSR48 Yogi Berra 15.00 40.00
SSR49 Tom Seaver 15.00 40.00
SSR50 Tom Seaver 15.00 40.00
SSR51 Rogers Hornsby 40.00 80.00
SSR52 Rogers Hornsby 40.00 80.00
SSR53 Dustin Pedroia 20.00 50.00
SSR54 Dustin Pedroia 20.00 50.00
SSR55 Reggie Jackson 12.50 30.00
SSR56 Reggie Jackson 12.50 30.00
SSR57 Miguel Cabrera 10.00 25.00
SSR58 Miguel Cabrera 10.00 25.00
SSR59 Mel Ott 20.00 50.00
SSR60 Mel Ott 20.00 50.00
SSR61 Roger Maris 30.00 60.00
SSR62 Roger Maris 30.00 60.00
SSR63 Prince Fielder 8.00 20.00
SSR64 Prince Fielder 8.00 20.00
SSR65 Eddie Murray 12.50 30.00
SSR66 Eddie Murray 12.50 30.00
SSR67 Johnny Bench 12.50 30.00
SSR68 Johnny Bench 12.50 30.00
SSR69 Frank Robinson 10.00 25.00
SSR70 Frank Robinson 10.00 25.00
SSR71 Greg Maddux 15.00 40.00
SSR72 Greg Maddux 15.00 40.00
SSR73 Ty Cobb 60.00 120.00
SSR74 Ty Cobb 60.00 120.00
SSR75 Mike Schmidt 20.00 50.00
SSR76 Mike Schmidt 20.00 50.00
SSR77 Warren Spahn 40.00 80.00
SSR78 Warren Spahn 40.00 80.00
SSR79 Bob Gibson 15.00 40.00
SSR80 Bob Gibson 15.00 40.00
SSR81 Mark Teixeira 12.50 30.00
SSR82 Mark Teixeira 12.50 30.00
SSR83 Andre Dawson 12.50 30.00
SSR84 Andre Dawson 12.50 30.00
SSR85 Ryan Howard 15.00 40.00
SSR86 Ryan Howard 15.00 40.00
SSR87 Brooks Robinson 12.50 30.00
SSR88 Brooks Robinson 12.50 30.00
SSR89 Joe Morgan 10.00 25.00
SSR90 Joe Morgan 10.00 25.00
SSR91 Roy Halladay 15.00 40.00
SSR92 Roy Halladay 15.00 40.00
SSR93 Stan Musial 30.00 60.00
SSR94 Stan Musial 30.00 60.00
SSR95 Evan Longoria 12.50 30.00
SSR96 Evan Longoria 12.50 30.00
SSR97 Nolan Ryan 30.00 60.00
SSR98 Nolan Ryan 30.00 60.00
SSR99 Chase Utley 20.00 50.00
SSR100 Chase Utley 20.00 50.00
SSR101 Pee Wee Reese 20.00 50.00
SSR102 Pee Wee Reese 20.00 50.00
SSR103 Jim Palmer 10.00 25.00
SSR104 Jim Palmer 10.00 25.00
SSR105 Dave Winfield 10.00 25.00
SSR106 Dave Winfield 10.00 25.00
SSR107 David Ortiz 8.00 20.00
SSR108 David Ortiz 8.00 20.00
SSR109 Hanley Ramirez 12.50 30.00
SSR110 Hanley Ramirez 12.50 30.00
SSR111 Thurman Munson 20.00 50.00
SSR112 Thurman Munson 20.00 50.00
SSR113 David Wright 15.00 40.00
SSR114 David Wright 15.00 40.00
SSR115 Tim Lincecum 15.00 40.00
SSR116 Tim Lincecum 15.00 40.00
SSR117 Chipper Jones 15.00 40.00
SSR118 Chipper Jones 15.00 40.00
SSR119 Wade Boggs 12.50 30.00
SSR120 Wade Boggs 12.50 30.00
SSR121 Don Mattingly 50.00 100.00
SSR122 Don Mattingly 50.00 100.00
SSR123 Vladimir Guerrero 8.00 20.00
SSR124 Vladimir Guerrero 8.00 20.00
SSR125 Jimmie Foxx 20.00 50.00
SSR126 Jimmie Foxx 20.00 50.00
SSR127 CC Sabathia 8.00 20.00
SSR128 CC Sabathia 8.00 20.00
SSR129 Tony Gwynn 15.00 40.00
SSR130 Tony Gwynn 15.00 40.00
SSR131 Ryne Sandberg
SSR132 Ryne Sandberg
SSR133 Mariano Rivera 15.00 40.00
SSR134 Mariano Rivera 15.00 40.00
SSR135 Duke Snider 20.00 50.00
SSR136 Duke Snider 20.00 50.00
SSR137 Whitey Ford 15.00 40.00
SSR138 Whitey Ford 15.00 40.00
SSR139 Jason Heyward 20.00 50.00
SSR140 Jason Heyward 20.00 50.00

2011 Topps Stickers

COMMON CARD (1-309) .05 .15
COMMON FOIL (286-294) .12 .30
1 Luke Scott .05 .15
2 Adam Jones .10 .25
3 Nick Markakis .15 .40
4 Mark Reynolds .05 .15
5 J.J. Hardy .05 .15
6 Brian Roberts .05 .15
7 Derrek Lee .05 .15
8 Vladimir Guerrero .15 .40
9 Brian Matusz .15 .40
10 Carl Crawford .10 .25
11 Jacoby Ellsbury .15 .40
12 J.D. Drew .05 .15
13 Kevin Youkilis .10 .25
14 Jed Lowrie .10 .25
15 Dustin Pedroia .20 .50
16 Adrian Gonzalez .10 .25
17 David Ortiz .10 .25
18 Jon Lester .15 .40
19 Brett Gardner .05 .15
20 Curtis Granderson .10 .25
21 Nick Swisher .15 .40
22 Alex Rodriguez .25 .60
23 Derek Jeter .40 1.00
24 Robinson Cano .15 .40
25 Mark Teixeira .15 .40
26 Jorge Posada .10 .25
27 CC Sabathia .10 .25
28 Johnny Damon .10 .25
29 B.J. Upton .10 .25
30 Ben Zobrist .05 .15
31 Evan Longoria .20 .50
32 Reid Brignac .05 .15
33 Sean Rodriguez .05 .15
34 Casey Kotchman .05 .15
35 Sam Fuld .05 .15
36 David Price .15 .40
37 Juan Rivera .05 .15
38 Rajai Davis .05 .15
39 Edwin Encarnacion .05 .15
40 Jose Bautista .10 .25
41 Yunel Escobar .05 .15
42 Aaron Hill .05 .15
43 Adam Lind .10 .25
44 J.P. Arencibia .10 .25
45 Brandon Morrow .05 .15
46 Juan Pierre .05 .15
47 Alex Rios .10 .25
48 Carlos Quentin .05 .15
49 Adam Dunn .10 .25
50 Alexei Ramirez .05 .15
51 Gordon Beckham .10 .25
52 Paul Konerko .10 .25
53 A.J. Pierzynski .05 .15
54 Mark Buehrle .10 .25
55 Michael Brantley .05 .15
56 Grady Sizemore .10 .25
57 Shin-Soo Choo .10 .25
58 Travis Hafner .05 .15
59 Asdrubal Cabrera .10 .25
60 Orlando Cabrera .05 .15
61 Matt LaPorta .05 .15
62 Carlos Santana .15 .40
63 Fausto Carmona .05 .15
64 Alex Avila .05 .15
65 Austin Jackson .05 .15
66 Magglio Ordonez .10 .25
67 Brandon Inge .05 .15
68 Jhonny Peralta .05 .15
69 Brennan Boesch .10 .25
70 Miguel Cabrera .15 .40
71 Victor Martinez .10 .25
72 Justin Verlander .20 .50
73 Alex Gordon .10 .25
74 Melky Cabrera .05 .15
75 Jeff Francoeur .10 .25
76 Mike Moustakas .15 .40
77 Alcides Escobar .05 .15
78 Chris Getz .05 .15
79 Eric Hosmer .50 1.25
80 Billy Butler .05 .15
81 Luke Hochevar .05 .15
82 Delmon Young .10 .25
83 Denard Span .05 .15
84 Michael Cuddyer .05 .15
85 Danny Valencia .10 .25
86 Jason Kubel .05 .15
87 Tsuyoshi Nishioka .20 .50
88 Justin Morneau .15 .40
89 Joe Mauer .15 .40
90 Francisco Liriano .05 .15
91 Vernon Wells .05 .15
92 Torii Hunter .05 .15
93 Bobby Abreu .05 .15
94 Maicer Izturis .05 .15
95 Erick Aybar .05 .15
96 Howie Kendrick .05 .15
97 Kendrys Morales .05 .15
98 Jeff Mathis .05 .15
99 Jered Weaver .05 .15
100 Josh Willingham .05 .15
101 Coco Crisp .05 .15
102 David DeJesus .05 .15
103 Kevin Kouzmanoff .05 .15
104 Cliff Pennington .05 .15
105 Mark Ellis .05 .15
106 Daric Barton .05 .15
107 Kurt Suzuki .05 .15
108 Brett Anderson .10 .25
109 Carlos Peguero .10 .25
110 Franklin Gutierrez .05 .15
111 Ichiro Suzuki .25 .60
112 Chone Figgins .05 .15
113 Brendan Ryan .05 .15
114 Jack Wilson .05 .15
115 Jack Cust .05 .15
116 Miguel Olivo .05 .15
117 Felix Hernandez .15 .40
118 Josh Hamilton .15 .40
119 Julio Borbon .05 .15
120 Nelson Cruz .10 .25
121 Adrian Beltre .05 .15
122 Elvis Andrus .10 .25
123 Ian Kinsler .10 .25
124 Mitch Moreland .05 .15
125 Michael Young .10 .25
126 Neftali Feliz .05 .15
127 Baltimore Orioles .05 .15
309 San Francisco Giants
128 New York Yankees .10 .25
305 Houston Astros
129 Toronto Blue Jays .05 .15
298 Detroit Tigers
130 Cleveland Indians .05 .15
303 Philadelphia Phillies
131 Kansas City Royals .05 .15
306 Pittsburgh Pirates
132 Los Angeles Angels .05 .15
299 Minnesota Twins
133 Seattle Mariners .05 .15
307 Arizona Diamondbacks
134 Atlanta Braves .05 .15
296 Tampa Bay Rays
135 New York Mets .10 .25
295 Boston Red Sox
136 Washington Nationals .05 .15
302 Florida Marlins
137 Cincinnati Reds .05 .15
306 Los Angeles Dodgers
138 Milwaukee Brewers .05 .15
301 Texas Rangers
139 St. Louis Cardinals .05 .15
297 Chicago White Sox
140 Colorado Rockies .05 .15
300 Oakland Athletics
141 San Diego Padres .05 .15
304 Chicago Cubs
142 Martin Prado .05 .15
143 Nate McLouth .05 .15
144 Jason Heyward .20 .50
145 Chipper Jones .15 .40
146 Alex Gonzalez .05 .15
147 Dan Uggla .10 .25
148 Freddie Freeman .25 .60
149 Brian McCann .10 .25
150 Tim Hudson .10 .25
151 Logan Morrison .05 .15
152 Chris Coghlan .05 .15
153 Mike Stanton .10 .25
154 Wes Helms .05 .15
155 Hanley Ramirez .15 .40
156 Omar Infante .05 .15
157 Gaby Sanchez .05 .15
158 John Buck .05 .15
159 Josh Johnson .10 .25
160 Jason Bay .10 .25
161 Angel Pagan .05 .15
162 Carlos Beltran .05 .15
163 David Wright .20 .50
164 Jose Reyes .10 .25
165 Daniel Murphy .05 .15
166 Ike Davis .10 .25
167 Josh Thole .05 .15
168 Johan Santana .15 .40
169 Raul Ibanez .10 .25
170 Shane Victorino .10 .25
171 Ben Francisco .05 .15
172 Placido Polanco .05 .15
173 Jimmy Rollins .10 .25
174 Chase Utley .15 .40
175 Ryan Howard .20 .50
176 Carlos Ruiz .05 .15
177 Roy Halladay .15 .40
178 Mike Morse .05 .15
179 Rick Ankiel .05 .15
180 Jayson Werth .10 .25
181 Lance Nix .05 .15
182 Ryan Zimmerman .10 .25
183 Ian Desmond .10 .25
184 Adam LaRoche .05 .15
185 Ivan Rodriguez .10 .25
186 Jordan Zimmermann .05 .15
187 Alfonso Soriano .10 .25
188 Marlon Byrd .05 .15
189 Kosuke Fukudome .15 .40
190 Aramis Ramirez .05 .15
191 Starlin Castro .15 .40
192 Blake DeWitt .05 .15
193 Carlos Pena .10 .25
194 Geovany Soto .10 .25
195 Matt Garza .05 .15
196 Jonny Gomes .05 .15
197 Drew Stubbs .10 .25
198 Jay Bruce .10 .25
199 Scott Rolen .10 .25
200 Paul Janish .05 .15
201 Brandon Phillips .05 .15
202 Joey Votto .15 .40
203 Ramon Hernandez .05 .15
204 Aroldis Chapman .20 .50
205 Carlos Lee .05 .15
206 Michael Bourn .05 .15
207 Hunter Pence .10 .25
208 Chris Johnson .05 .15
209 Clint Barmes .05 .15
210 Bill Hall .05 .15
211 Brett Wallace .05 .15
212 Humberto Quintero .05 .15
213 Wandy Rodriguez .05 .15
214 Ryan Braun .20 .50
215 Carlos Gomez .05 .15
216 Corey Hart .05 .15
217 Casey McGehee .05 .15
218 Yuniesky Betancourt .05 .15
219 Rickie Weeks .10 .25
220 Prince Fielder .10 .25
221 Jonathan Lucroy .05 .15
222 Zack Greinke .10 .25
223 Jose Tabata .10 .25
224 Andrew McCutchen .15 .40
225 Garrett Jones .05 .15
226 Pedro Alvarez .10 .25
227 Ronny Cedeno .05 .15
228 Neil Walker .05 .15
229 Lyle Overbay .05 .15
230 Chris Snyder .05 .15
231 James McDonald .05 .15
232 Matt Holliday .15 .40
233 Colby Rasmus .15 .40
234 Lance Berkman .10 .25
235 David Freese .10 .25
236 Ryan Theriot .05 .15
237 Skip Schumaker .05 .15
238 Albert Pujols .40 1.00
239 Yadier Molina .10 .25
240 Adam Wainwright .10 .25
241 Xavier Nady .05 .15
242 Chris Young .05 .15
243 Justin Upton .10 .25
244 Melvin Mora .05 .15
245 Stephen Drew .05 .15
246 Kelly Johnson .05 .15
247 Juan Miranda .05 .15
248 Miguel Montero .05 .15
249 Daniel Hudson .05 .15
250 Carlos Gonzalez .10 .25
251 Dexter Fowler .05 .15
252 Seth Smith .05 .15
253 Ty Wigginton .05 .15
254 Troy Tulowitzki .15 .40
255 Jonathan Herrera .05 .15
256 Todd Helton .10 .25
257 Chris Iannetta .05 .15
258 Ubaldo Jimenez .10 .25
259 Jerry Sands .25 .60
260 Matt Kemp .10 .25
261 Andre Ethier .10 .25
262 Casey Blake .05 .15
263 Rafael Furcal .05 .15
264 Juan Uribe .05 .15
265 James Loney .10 .25
266 Dee Gordon .15 .40
267 Clayton Kershaw .15 .40
268 Ryan Ludwick .05 .15
269 Cameron Maybin .05 .15
270 Will Venable .05 .15
271 Chase Headley .05 .15
272 Jason Bartlett .05 .15
273 Orlando Hudson .05 .15
274 Anthony Rizzo .10 .25
275 Nick Hundley .05 .15
276 Mat Latos .05 .15
277 Mark DeRosa .05 .15
278 Andres Torres .05 .15
279 Cody Ross .05 .15
280 Pablo Sandoval .10 .25
281 Miguel Tejada .10 .25
282 Freddy Sanchez .05 .15
283 Aubrey Huff .05 .15
284 Buster Posey .20 .50
285 Tim Lincecum .15 .40
286 Hank Aaron FOIL .60 1.50
287 Babe Ruth FOIL .75 2.00
288 Stan Musial FOIL .50 1.25
289 Joe DiMaggio FOIL .75 2.00
290 Mike Schmidt FOIL .50 1.25
291 Jackie Robinson FOIL .30 .75
292 Lou Gehrig FOIL .60 1.50
293 Roy Campanella FOIL .30 .75
294 Sandy Koufax FOIL 1.00 2.50

2009 Topps Ticket to Stardom

COMP.SET w/o RCs (200) 12.50 30.00
COMMON CARD (1-200) .12 .30
COMMON RC (1-200) .25 .60
COMMON RC (201-225) 1.25 3.00
201-225 RC ODDS 1:45 HOBBY
201-225 RC PRINT RUN 199 SER.#'d SETS
PRINTING PLATE ODDS 1:240 HOBBY
PLATE PRINT RUN 1 SET PER COLOR
BLACK-CYAN-MAGENTA-YELLOW ISSUED
NO PLATE PRICING DUE TO SCARCITY
1 Albert Pujols .75 2.00
2 Ichiro Suzuki .50 1.25
3 Aubrey Huff .12 .30
4 Kevin Youkilis .20 .50
5 David Wright .40 1.00
6 Ryan Howard .40 1.00
7 Jimmy Rollins .20 .50
8 Justin Morneau .30 .75
9 Joe Saunders .12 .30
10 David DeJesus .12 .30
11 Grady Sizemore .20 .50
12 Brian Roberts .12 .30
13 Alex Rodriguez .50 1.25
14 Alex Rios .20 .50
15 Brad Hawpe .12 .30
16 Gary Matthews Jr. .12 .30
17 Glen Perkins .12 .30
18 Erick Aybar .12 .30
19 Manny Ramirez .30 .75
20 Kosuke Fukudome .30 .75
21 David Ortiz .20 .50
22 Hunter Pence .20 .50
23 Edgar Renteria .12 .30
24 Ken Griffey Jr. .50 1.25
25 Joe Mauer .30 .75
26 Adrian Gonzalez .20 .50
27 Brian McCann .20 .50
28 Paul Konerko .20 .50
29 Francisco Liriano .12 .30
30 Pat Burrell .12 .30
31 Stephen Drew .12 .30
32 Chris Young .12 .30
33 Carlos Pena .20 .50
34 Rich Harden .12 .30
35 Felix Hernandez .30 .75
36 Geoff Jenkins .12 .30
37 Kenji Johjima .20 .50
38 Yovani Gallardo .12 .30
39 Max Scherzer .20 .50
40 Joe Crede .20 .50
41 Miguel Tejada .20 .50
42 Nick Swisher .30 .75
43 Tim Lincecum .50 1.25
44 Mat Latos RC .75 2.00
45 Alex Gordon .20 .50
46 Jeff Francoeur .20 .50
47 Jay Bruce .20 .50
48 George Sherrill .12 .30
49 Zack Greinke .20 .50
50 Jeremy Guthrie .12 .30
51 Chris Young .12 .30
52 Melvin Mora .12 .30
53 Tim Wakefield .12 .30
54 Victor Martinez .20 .50
55 Nick Markakis .30 .75
56 Carlos Zambrano .20 .50
57 Ryan Garko .12 .30
58 Hideki Okajima .12 .30
59 Ubaldo Jimenez .20 .50
60 Justin Verlander .40 1.00
61 Brad Penny .12 .30
62 Cameron Maybin .12 .30
63 Milton Bradley .12 .30
64 Hideki Matsui .30 .75
65 Jorge Cantu .12 .30
66 Jose Contreras .12 .30
67 Jon Lester .30 .75
68 Torii Hunter .12 .30
69 Jermaine Dye .12 .30
70 Roy Halladay .30 .75
71 Carlos Marmol .20 .50
72 Kerry Wood .12 .30
73 Josh Fields .12 .30
74 Evan Longoria .40 1.00
75 Andrew McCutchen (RC) 1.00 2.50
76 Freddy Sanchez .12 .30
77 Mike Cameron .12 .30
78 Josh Hamilton .30 .75
79 A.J. Pierzynski .12 .30
80 Scott Rolen .20 .50
81 Joey Votto .30 .75
82 Brandon Inge .12 .30
83 Vernon Wells .12 .30
84 Armando Galarraga .12 .30
85 Mark Teixeira .30 .75
86 Austin Kearns .12 .30
87 Jason Giambi .12 .30
88 Kevin Millwood .12 .30
89 Josh Willingham .12 .30
90 Ryan Braun .40 1.00
91 Chris Davis .12 .30
92 Erik Bedard .12 .30
93 Prince Fielder .20 .50
94 Kurt Suzuki .12 .30
95 Ryan Doumit .12 .30
96 Bill Hall .12 .30
97 Jack Wilson .12 .30
98 Tim Hudson .20 .50
99 Paul Maholm .12 .30
100 Adrian Beltre .12 .30
101 Curtis Granderson .20 .50
102 Travis Hafner .12 .30
103 Edinson Volquez .12 .30
104 Mike Lowell .12 .30
105 Justin Upton .20 .50
106 Eric Chavez .12 .30
107 Bobby Abreu .12 .30
108 Joba Chamberlain .20 .50
109 Gary Sheffield .12 .30
110 Chad Billingsley .12 .30
111 Carlos Beltran .12 .30
112 Rickie Weeks .20 .50
113 Jeremy Hermida .12 .30
114 Bronson Arroyo .12 .30
115 Mark Buehrle .20 .50
116 Jorge Posada .20 .50
117 Derrek Lee .12 .30
118 Dustin Pedroia .40 1.00
119 Javier Vazquez .12 .30
120 Derek Jeter .75 2.00
121 Johan Santana .30 .75
122 J.J. Hardy .12 .30
123 Miguel Cabrera .30 .75
124 Daisuke Matsuzaka .30 .75
125 Geovany Soto .20 .50
126 Jason Varitek .30 .75
127 Magglio Ordonez .20 .50
128 Carlos Quentin .20 .50
129 Brandon Webb .20 .50
130 Jonathan Papelbon .20 .50
131 Josh [illegible] .20 .50
132 Dan Haren .12 .30
133 Alfonso Soriano .20 .50
134 Yadier Molina .20 .50
135 John Maine .12 .30
136 Todd Helton .20 .50
137 Troy Tulowitzki .30 .75
138 Luis Castillo .12 .30
139 Andy Pettitte .20 .50
140 Hank Blalock .12 .30
141 Jeremy Sowers .12 .30
142 Nate McLouth .12 .30
143 Carlos Lee .12 .30
144 Gavin Floyd .12 .30
145 Joe Nathan .12 .30
146 Matt Holliday .30 .75
147 Hanley Ramirez .30 .75
148 Akinori Iwamura .12 .30
149 Jeremy Bonderman .12 .30
150 Johnny Damon .20 .50
151 Derek Lowe .12 .30
152 Matt Kemp .20 .50
153 Troy Glaus .12 .30
154 Fausto Carmona .12 .30
155 Jered Weaver .12 .30
156 Orlando Hudson .12 .30
157 Garret Anderson .12 .30
158 Jason Bay .20 .50
159 Lance Berkman .20 .50
160 Randy Johnson .20 .50
161 Chipper Jones .30 .75
162 Conor Jackson .12 .30
163 Adam Dunn .20 .50
164 Jake Peavy .12 .30
165 Vladimir Guerrero .30 .75
166 Jacoby Ellsbury .30 .75
167 Cole Hamels .30 .75
168 J.D. Drew .12 .30
169 Cliff Lee .20 .50
170 Russell Martin .12 .30
171 Derek Holland RC .40 1.00
172 Joakim Soria .12 .30
173 Dan Uggla .20 .50
174 Carlos Delgado .12 .30
175 Jose Reyes .20 .50
176 Chase Utley .30 .75
177 Alexei Ramirez .20 .50
178 Roy Oswalt .20 .50
179 Matt Garza .12 .30
180 Matt Cain .12 .30
181 Chien-Ming Wang .20 .50
182 Gordon Beckham RC 3.00 8.00
183 Johnny Cueto .12 .30
184 Ryan Freel .12 .30
185 James Shields .12 .30
186 Rick Ankiel .12 .30
187 A.J. Burnett .20 .50
188 Adam Jones .20 .50
189 Jim Thome .20 .50
190 Andy Sonnanstine .12 .30
191 Ryan Zimmerman .20 .50
192 Jon Garland .12 .30
193 Robinson Cano .30 .75
194 Michael Young .20 .50
195 Xavier Nady .12 .30
196 B.J. Upton .20 .50
197 Ian Kinsler .20 .50
198 Scott Kazmir .12 .30
199 CC Sabathia .20 .50
200 Justin Masterson .12 .30
201 Colby Rasmus (RC) 3.00 8.00
202 Jordan Schafer (RC) 2.00 5.00
203 Ryan Perry RC 3.00 8.00
204 Brett Anderson RC 2.00 5.00
205 David Hernandez RC 1.25 3.00
206 Brian Duensing RC 2.00 5.00
207 Rick Porcello RC 4.00 10.00
208 Koji Uehara RC 2.00 5.00
209 Trevor Crowe RC 1.25 3.00
210 Andrew Bailey RC 3.00 8.00
211 David Price RC 3.00 8.00
212 Travis Snider RC 2.00 5.00
213 David Patton RC 2.00 5.00
214 Dexter Fowler (RC) 2.00 5.00
215 Phil Coke RC 2.00 5.00
216 Bobby Parnell RC 2.00 5.00
217 Ricky Romero (RC) 3.00 8.00
218 Everth Cabrera RC 2.00 5.00
219 Bobby Scales RC 2.00 5.00
220 Michael Bowden (RC) 1.25 3.00
221 Jordan Zimmermann RC 1.25 3.00
222 Fernando Martinez RC 3.00 8.00
223 David Freese RC 10.00 25.00
224 Elvis Andrus RC 2.00 5.00
225 Kenshin Kawakami RC 2.00 5.00

2009 Topps Ticket to Stardom Blue

*BLUE VET 1-200: 2X TO 5X BASIC
*BLUE RC 1-200: 1X TO 2.5X BASIC RC
*BLUE RC 201-225: .5X TO 1.2X BASIC RC
STATED ODDS 1:10
STATED PRINT RUN 99 SER.#'d SETS
182 Gordon Beckham 5.00 12.00

2009 Topps Ticket to Stardom Gold

*GOLD VET 1-200: 2.5X TO 6X BASIC
*GOLD RC 1-200: 1.2X TO 3X BASIC RC
*GOLD RC 201-225: .6X TO 1.5X BASIC RC
STATED ODDS 1:20 HOBBY
STATED PRINT RUN 50 SER.#'d SETS
182 Gordon Beckham 12.00 30.00

2009 Topps Ticket to Stardom Perforated

*GOLD VET 1-200: 1.2X TO 3X BASIC
*GOLD RC 1-200: .6X TO 1.5X BASIC RC
*GOLD RC 201-225: .3X TO .8X BASIC RC
STATED ODDS 1:1 HOBBY
182 Gordon Beckham 4.00 10.00

2009 Topps Ticket to Stardom Red

STATED ODDS 1:960 HOBBY
STATED PRINT RUN 1 SER.#'d SET
NO PRICING DUE TO SCARCITY

2009 Topps Ticket to Stardom Autograph Relics

GROUP A ODDS 1:23 HOBBY
GROUP B ODDS 1:503 HOBBY
GROUP A PRINT RUN 489 SER.#'d SETS
GROUP B PRINT RUN [illegible] SER.#'d SETS
AE Andre Ethier A 12.50 30.00
BD Blake DeWitt A 5.00 12.00
CJ Chipper Jones B 50.00 100.00
CK Clayton Kershaw A 8.00 20.00
DP Dustin Pedroia A 20.00 50.00
DW David Wright B 20.00 50.00
EL Evan Longoria A 30.00 60.00
ES Ervin Santana A 4.00 10.00
GA Garrett Atkins A 4.00 10.00
JB Jay Bruce A 10.00 25.00
JC Joba Chamberlain A 10.00 25.00
JM Justin Masterson A 5.00 12.00
JW Jayson Werth A 12.50 30.00
MB Michael Bowden A 10.00 25.00
MC Matt Cain A 8.00 20.00
MG Mat Gamel A 6.00 15.00
ML Mike Lowell B 30.00 60.00
NS Nick Swisher A 10.00 25.00
RH Ryan Howard B 50.00 100.00
SK Scott Kazmir A 5.00 12.00
TT Troy Tulowitzki A 8.00 20.00
UJ Ubaldo Jimenez A 12.50 30.00
VG Vladimir Guerrero B 20.00 50.00
CAJ Conor Jackson A 4.00 10.00
JCC Johnny Cueto A 5.00 12.00

2009 Topps Ticket to Stardom Autograph Relics Gold

STATED ODDS 1:864 HOBBY
STATED PRINT RUN 10 SER.#'d SETS
NO PRICING DUE TO SCARCITY

2009 Topps Ticket to Stardom Autograph Relics Red

STATED ODDS 1:8645 HOBBY
STATED PRINT RUN 1 SER.#'d SET
NO PRICING DUE TO SCARCITY

2009 Topps Ticket to Stardom Autograph Relics Dual

GROUP A ODDS 1:601 HOBBY
GROUP B ODDS 1:3329 HOBBY
GROUP A PRINT RUN 39 SER.#'d SETS
GROUP B PRINT RUN 14 SER.#'d SETS
NO GROUP B PRICING DUE TO SCARCITY
AGCY Adrian Gonzalez 30.00 60.00
Chris Young A
ARDW Alex Rodriguez
David Wright B
BUCP B.J. Upton 20.00 50.00
Carlos Pena A
CKMK Clayton Kershaw 20.00 50.00
Matt Kemp A
CPEL Carlos Pena 60.00 120.00
Evan Longoria A
EDRD Elijah Dukes
Ross Detwiler B
ELMH Evan Longoria 50.00 100.00
{Matt Holliday A
ESJW Ervin Santana
Jered Weaver B
MGJH Mat Gamel 10.00 25.00
{J.J. Hardy A
MGPF Mat Gamel 40.00 80.00
{Prince Fielder A
MLJP Mike Lowell 20.00 50.00
{Jonathan Papelbon A
NMJG Nick Markakis 15.00 40.00
Jeremy Guthrie A
RCJC Robinson Cano 30.00 60.00
Joba Chamberlain A
RHDW Ryan Howard
{David Wright B
RHSV Ryan Howard
Shane Victorino B

2009 Topps Ticket to Stardom Autograph Relics Dual Gold

STATED ODDS 1:1441 HOBBY
STATED PRINT RUN 10 SER.#'d SETS
NO PRICING DUE TO SCARCITY

2009 Topps Ticket to Stardom Autograph Relics Dual Red

STATED ODDS 1:14,409 HOBBY
STATED PRINT RUN 1 SER.#'d SET
NO PRICING DUE TO SCARCITY

2009 Topps Ticket to Stardom Big Ticket

STATED ODDS 1:8 HOBBY
*BLUE: .75X TO 2X BASIC
BLUE ODDS 1:57 HOBBY
BLUE PRINT RUN 99 SER.#'d SETS
*GOLD: 1X TO 2.5X BASIC
GOLD ODDS 1:112 HOBBY
GOLD PRINT RUN 50 SER.#'d SETS
RED ODDS 1:5403 HOBBY
RED PRINT RUN 1 SER.#'d SET
NO RED PRICING DUE TO SCARCITY
PRINTING PLATE ODDS 1:1350 HOBBY
PLATE PRINT RUN 1 SET PER COLOR
BLACK-CYAN-MAGENTA-YELLOW ISSUED
NO PLATE PRICING DUE TO SCARCITY
BT1 Ichiro Suzuki 1.25 3.00
BT2 Josh Hamilton .75 2.00
BT3 Ryan Braun 1.00 2.50
BT4 Albert Pujols 2.00 5.00
BT5 David Wright 1.00 2.50
BT6 Dustin Pedroia 1.00 2.50
BT7 Jose Reyes .50 1.25
BT8 Grady Sizemore .50 1.25
BT9 Tim Lincecum 1.25 3.00
BT10 Alex Rodriguez 1.25 3.00
BT11 Lance Berkman .50 1.25
BT12 Miguel Cabrera .75 2.00
BT13 Brandon Webb .50 1.25
BT14 Hanley Ramirez .75 2.00
BT15 CC Sabathia .50 1.25

2009 Topps Ticket to Stardom Opening Day Ticket Subs

STATED ODDS 1:120 HOBBY
PRINT RUNS B/WN 22-262 COPIES PER
NO HALLADAY PRICING AVAILABLE
AG Alex Gordon/50 8.00 20.00
AP Albert Pujols/55 30.00 60.00
AS Alfonso Soriano/50 10.00 25.00
BW Brandon Webb/50 12.50 30.00
CQ Carlos Quentin/78 4.00 10.00
DM Daisuke Matsuzaka/30 40.00 80.00
DW David Wright/107 15.00 40.00
EL Evan Longoria/50 15.00 40.00
GS Grady Sizemore/50 10.00 25.00
HR Hanley Ramirez/50 8.00 20.00
JB Jay Bruce/50 20.00 50.00
JH Josh Hamilton/50 30.00 60.00
JM Justin Morneau/50 8.00 20.00
JP Jake Peavy/50 8.00 20.00
KJ Kenji Johjima/262 6.00 15.00
LB Lance Berkman/50 15.00 40.00
MC Miguel Cabrera/55 10.00 25.00
MH Matt Holliday/52 12.50 30.00
MR Manny Ramirez/54 10.00 25.00
MT Mark Teixeira/50 20.00 50.00
NM Nick Markakis/50 12.50 30.00
PF Prince Fielder/99 10.00 25.00
RH Roy Halladay/22
RZ Ryan Zimmerman/100 12.50 30.00
TH Todd Helton/50 8.00 20.00
TL Tim Lincecum/50 10.00 25.00
VG Vladimir Guerrero/76 6.00 15.00
NMM Nate McLouth/41 4.00 10.00
RHH Ryan Howard/102 12.50 30.00

2009 Topps Ticket to Stardom Seasoned Vets

STATED ODDS 1:12 HOBBY
*BLUE: .75X TO 2X BASIC
BLUE ODDS 1:57 HOBBY
BLUE PRINT RUN 99 SER.#'d SETS
*GOLD: 1X TO 2.5X BASIC
GOLD ODDS 1:112 HOBBY
GOLD PRINT RUN 50 SER.#'d SETS
RED ODDS 1:5403 HOBBY
RED PRINT RUN 1 SER.#'d SET
NO RED PRICING DUE TO SCARCITY
PRINTING PLATE ODDS 1:1350 HOBBY
PLATE PRINT RUN 1 SET PER COLOR
BLACK-CYAN-MAGENTA-YELLOW ISSUED
NO PLATE PRICING DUE TO SCARCITY
SV1 Alex Rodriguez 1.25 3.00
SV2 David Wright 1.00 2.50
SV3 Manny Ramirez .75 2.00
SV4 Albert Pujols 2.00 5.00
SV5 Ryan Howard 1.00 2.50
SV6 Vladimir Guerrero .75 2.00
SV7 Alfonso Soriano .50 1.25
SV8 Magglio Ordonez .50 1.25
SV9 Ryan Braun 1.00 2.50
SV10 David Ortiz .50 1.25

2009 Topps Ticket to Stardom Ticket Stubs

RANDOM INSERTS IN PACKS
PRINT RUNS B/WN 16-110 COPIES PER
NO KURT SUZUKI PRICING AVAILABLE
TS1 Alex Rodriguez/110 10.00 25.00
TS2 Adrian Gonzalez/110 4.00 10.00
TS3 Carlos Beltran/110
TS4 Chad Billingsley/105 4.00 10.00
TS5 David Wright/110 5.00 12.00
TS6 Felix Hernandez/110 8.00 20.00
TS7 Ichiro Suzuki/110 8.00 20.00
TS8 Andre Ethier/110 5.00 12.00
TS9 Albert Pujols/110 20.00 50.00
TS10 Blake DeWitt/107 12.50 30.00
TS11 Brandon Webb/110 4.00 10.00
TS12 Alexei Ramirez/110 10.00 25.00
TS13 Chris Young/110 4.00 10.00
TS14 Carlos Delgado/110
TS15 Brian Fuentes/110
TS16 Grady Sizemore/110 4.00 10.00
TS17 Johan Santana/110 10.00 25.00
TS18 Kevin Kouzmanoff/110
TS19 Manny Ramirez/105 4.00 10.00
TS20 Prince Fielder/110 5.00 12.00
TS21 Ryan Howard/110 8.00 20.00
TS22 Todd Helton/110
TS23 Jose Reyes/110 10.00 25.00
TS24 Robinson Cano/110 4.00 10.00
TS25 Vladimir Guerrero/110 5.00 12.00
TS26 Evan Longoria/63 12.50 30.00
TS27 Jake Peavy/110
TS28 Nick Markakis/59 10.00 25.00
TS29 Alex Rios/102
TS30 Jon Lester/102 10.00 25.00
TS31 Chipper Jones/110 6.00 15.00
TS32 Josh Hamilton/110 4.00 10.00
TS33 Troy Glaus/110
TS34 Prince Fielder/110 5.00 12.00
TS35 Jarrod Saltalamacchia/110
TS36 Joey Votto/110 4.00 10.00
TS37 Kyle Lohse/110
TS38 Michael Young/110 3.00 8.00
TS39 J.J. Hardy/110
TS40 Travis Hafner/110 3.00 8.00
TS41 Adrian Beltre/53 8.00 20.00
TS42 Erick Aybar/110
TS43 Bobby Crosby/110 3.00 8.00
TS44 Miguel Cabrera/110 6.00 15.00
TS45 Fred Lewis/110 4.00 10.00
TS46 Chris Davis/110
TS47 Garrett Atkins/110 3.00 8.00
TS48 Jack Cust/110
TS49 Russell Martin/110 4.00 10.00
TS50 Adam Wainwright/110 6.00 15.00
TS51 Cristian Guzman/110
TS52 Corey Hart/110 4.00 10.00
TS53 Kurt Suzuki/110 5.00 12.00
TS54 Geovany Soto/79 3.00 8.00
TS55 Ryan Ludwick/110
TS56 Travis Buck/110 6.00 15.00
TS57 Justin Duchscherer/110 4.00 10.00
TS58 Daric Barton/110 8.00 20.00
TS59 Tim Lincecum/110 8.00 20.00
TS60 Rick Ankiel/110
TS61 Ryan Braun/110
TS62 Joba Chamberlain/110 6.00 15.00
TS63 Trevor Hoffman/110
TS64 Chone Figgins/110
TS65 Jermaine Dye/110
TS66 Troy Tulowitzki/110
TS67 Brian Giles/110
TS68 Nate McLouth/110 4.00 10.00
TS69 Matt Kemp/110
TS70 John Lackey/110 3.00 8.00
TS71 Rick Ankiel/110 4.00 10.00
TS72 Ryan Braun/110 5.00 12.00
TS73 Jose Reyes/110 10.00 25.00
TS74 Prince Fielder/110 4.00 10.00
TS75 Nate McLouth/110 3.00 8.00
TS76 Kurt Suzuki/16
TS77 Kevin Kouzmanoff/110
TS78 Justin Duchscherer/110 3.00 8.00
TS79 J.J. Hardy/110 3.00 8.00
TS80 Chris Young/110 3.00 8.00
TS81 Chad Billingsley/105 4.00 10.00
TS82 David Wright/110 4.00 10.00
TS83 Felix Hernandez/110 8.00 20.00
TS84 Daric Barton/110 6.00 15.00
TS85 Ichiro Suzuki/110 20.00 50.00
TS86 Blake DeWitt/106 12.50 30.00
TS87 Jarrod Saltalamacchia/110 3.00 8.00
TS88 Erick Aybar/95 4.00 10.00
TS89 Albert Pujols/110 10.00 25.00
TS90 Corey Hart/110 3.00 8.00
TS91 Adam Wainwright/110 8.00 20.00
TS92 Chris Davis/110 3.00 8.00
TS93 Carlos Delgado/110 5.00 12.00
TS94 Kevin Kouzmanoff/110 3.00 8.00
TS95 Trevor Hoffman/110
TS96 Jose Reyes/110 8.00 20.00
TS97 Russell Martin/110 4.00 10.00
TS98 Felix Hernandez/110 6.00 15.00
TS99 Adrian Gonzalez/110 3.00 8.00
TS100 Ichiro Suzuki/110 8.00 20.00

2009 Topps Ticket to Stardom Ticket Stubs Gold

RANDOM INSERTS IN PACKS
STATED PRINT RUN 10 SER.#'d SETS
NO PRICING DUE TO SCARCITY

2009 Topps Ticket to Stardom Ticket Stubs Red

RANDOM INSERTS IN PACKS
STATED PRINT RUN 1 SER.#'d SET
NO PRICING DUE TO SCARCITY

2009 Topps Ticket to Stardom Ticket Stubs Plus Memorabilia

STATED ODDS 1:22 HOBBY
PRINT RUNS B/WN 33-239 COPIES PER
TSP1 David Wright/224 6.00 15.00
TSP2 Bobby Crosby/239 3.00 8.00
TSP3 Albert Pujols/239 10.00 25.00
TSP4 Chad Billingsley/225 3.00 8.00
TSP5 Blake DeWitt/228 8.00 20.00
TSP6 Carlos Beltran/239 6.00 15.00
TSP7 Ichiro Suzuki/225 10.00 25.00
TSP8 Michael Young/224 3.00 8.00
TSP9 Nate McLouth/239 5.00 12.00
TSP10 Kevin Kouzmanoff/224 3.00 8.00
TSP11 Ryan Braun/224 5.00 12.00
TSP12 Josh Hamilton/239 6.00 15.00
TSP13 Robinson Cano/224 8.00 20.00
TSP14 Trevor Hoffman/224 5.00 12.00
TSP15 Eric Chavez/225 3.00 8.00
TSP16 Adrian Gonzalez/224 3.00 8.00
TSP17 Nick Swisher/224 5.00 12.00
TSP18 Manny Ramirez/239 6.00 15.00
TSP19 Troy Glaus/160 4.00 10.00
TSP20 Jermaine Dye/151 3.00 8.00
TSP21 Magglio Ordonez/90 8.00 20.00
TSP22 Rich Harden/225 3.00 8.00
TSP23 Alex Rodriguez/33 20.00 50.00
TSP24 Greg Maddux/79 10.00 25.00
TSP25 Hanley Ramirez/90 6.00 15.00
TSP26 Ryan Zimmerman/81 6.00 15.00
TSP27 Conor Jackson/81 8.00 20.00
TSP28 Ubaldo Jimenez/79 3.00 8.00
TSP29 Alfonso Soriano/79 3.00 8.00
TSP30 Aramis Ramirez/79 3.00 8.00
TSP31 Travis Buck/224 3.00 8.00
TSP32 Brian McCann/79 3.00 8.00
TSP33 Hunter Pence/79 3.00 8.00
TSP34 Clayton Kershaw/79 5.00 12.00
TSP35 Daisuke Matsuzaka/45 20.00 50.00
TSP36 Ichiro Suzuki/225 10.00 25.00
TSP37 Cliff Lee/63 8.00 20.00
TSP38 Derrek Lee/77 10.00 25.00
TSP39 Ichiro Suzuki/225 10.00 25.00
TSP40 Adrian Gonzalez/161 3.00 8.00
TSP41 Bobby Crosby/224 3.00 8.00
TSP42 Jack Cust/239 3.00 8.00
TSP43 Ichiro Suzuki/225 15.00 40.00
TSP44 Adrian Gonzalez/224 3.00 8.00
TSP45 Kevin Kouzmanoff/224 3.00 8.00
TSP46 Josh Hamilton/225 6.00 15.00
TSP47 Brian Giles/224 4.00 10.00
TSP48 Travis Buck/224 3.00 8.00
TSP49 Hanley Ramirez/110 6.00 15.00
TSP50 Miguel Tejada/110 3.00 8.00
TSP51 Jose Reyes/110 10.00 25.00
TSP52 Pedro Martinez/110 6.00 15.00
TSP53 Geovany Soto/110 4.00 10.00
TSP54 Bernie Williams/110 5.00 12.00
TSP55 Jonathan Sanchez/110 4.00 10.00
TSP56 J.C. Romero/110 5.00 12.00
TSP57 Michel Enriquez/110 10.00 25.00
TSP58 Yulieski Gourriel/110 4.00 10.00
TSP59 Yoennis Cespedes/110 12.50 30.00
TSP60 Frederich Cepeda/110 10.00 25.00
TSP61 Jimmy Rollins/110 8.00 20.00
TSP62 Roy Oswalt/110 8.00 20.00
TSP63 Adam Dunn/110 4.00 10.00
TSP64 Kosuke Fukudome/90 10.00 25.00
TSP65 Yu Darvish/90 125.00 250.00
TSP66 Masahiro Tanaka/90 20.00 50.00
TSP67 Shinnosuke Abe/90 10.00 25.00
TSP68 Norichika Aoki/90 15.00 40.00
TSP69 Kwang-Hyun Kim/90 5.00 12.00
TSP70 Tae Kyun Kim/90 10.00 25.00
TSP71 Jin Young Lee/90 3.00 8.00
TSP72 Shin-Soo Choo/90 15.00 40.00

2009 Topps Ticket to Stardom Ticket Stubs Plus Memorabilia Gold

STATED ODDS 1:313 HOBBY
STATED PRINT RUN 10 SER.#'d SETS
NO PRICING DUE TO SCARCITY

2009 Topps Ticket to Stardom Ticket Stubs Plus Memorabilia Red

STATED ODDS 1:3000 HOBBY
STATED PRINT RUN 1 SER.#'d SET
NO PRICING DUE TO SCARCITY

2009 Topps Ticket to Stardom Ticket Stubs Plus Memorabilia Dual

STATED ODDS 1:22 HOBBY
PRINT RUNS B/WN 14-239 COPIES PER
NO PRICING ON QTY 15 OR LESS
TSP1 Ichiro Suzuki/239 12.50 30.00
TSP2 Ichiro Suzuki/228 12.50 30.00
TSP3 Ichiro Suzuki/36 20.00 50.00
TSP4 David Wright/239 8.00 20.00
TSP5 David Wright/239 8.00 20.00
TSP6 David Wright/228 8.00 20.00
TSP7 David Wright/15
TSP8 Howie Kendrick/224 3.00 8.00
TSP9 Corey Hart/224 4.00 10.00
TSP10 Mike Napoli/224 5.00 12.00
TSP11 Jake Peavy/61 5.00 12.00
TSP12 J.J. Hardy/239 3.00 8.00
TSP13 J.J. Hardy/228 3.00 8.00
TSP14 J.J. Hardy/72 4.00 10.00
TSP15 Josh Hamilton/224 8.00 20.00
TSP16 Michael Young/224 3.00 8.00
TSP17 Robinson Cano/224 10.00 25.00
TSP18 Vladimir Guerrero/228 4.00 10.00
TSP19 Vladimir Guerrero/27 6.00 15.00
TSP20 Travis Buck/224 4.00 10.00
TSP21 Prince Fielder/239 5.00 12.00
TSP22 Prince Fielder/228 5.00 12.00
TSP23 Prince Fielder/14
TSP24 Eric Chavez/224 4.00 10.00
TSP25 Jose Reyes/239 12.50 30.00
TSP26 Jose Reyes/210 12.50 30.00
TSP27 Trevor Hoffman/224 6.00 15.00
TSP28 Troy Glaus/161 5.00 12.00
TSP29 Jack Cust/235 4.00 10.00
TSP30 Russell Martin/223 5.00 12.00
TSP31 Jake Peavy/116 4.00 10.00
TSP32 Alex Rios/180 12.50 30.00
TSP33 Matt Kemp/239 4.00 10.00
TSP34 Matt Kemp/40 6.00 15.00
TSP35 Nick Markakis/59 8.00 20.00
TSP36 Johnny Damon/85 8.00 20.00
TSP37 Bobby Crosby/224 4.00 10.00
TSP38 James Loney/79 6.00 15.00
TSP39 Carlos Delgado/81 6.00 15.00
TSP40 Conor Jackson/81 10.00 25.00
TSP41 Aaron Rowand/79 4.00 10.00
TSP42 Ryan Braun/126 6.00 15.00
TSP43 Kosuke Fukudome/90 12.50 30.00
TSP44 Chin-Lung Hu/77 5.00 12.00
TSP45 Wladimir Balentien/239 3.00 8.00
TSP46 Wladimir Balentien/228 3.00 8.00
TSP47 Wladimir Balentien/185 4.00 10.00
TSP48 Adrian Beltre/53 8.00 20.00
TSP49 Kevin Kouzmanoff/239 4.00 10.00
TSP50 Kevin Kouzmanoff/228 4.00 10.00
TSP51 Kevin Kouzmanoff/200 4.00 10.00
TSP52 Kevin Kouzmanoff/154 4.00 10.00
TSP53 Bobby Crosby/224 4.00 10.00
TSP54 Trevor Hoffman/162 6.00 15.00
TSP55 Wladimir Balentien/224 3.00 8.00
TSP56 Jack Cust/239 4.00 10.00
TSP57 Jack Cust/89 5.00 12.00
TSP58 Eric Chavez/239 4.00 10.00
TSP59 Eric Chavez/75 5.00 12.00
TSP60 Wladimir Balentien/228 3.00 8.00
TSP61 Wladimir Balentien/28 5.00 12.00
TSP62 Travis Buck/224 4.00 10.00
TSP63 Daric Barton/224 4.00 10.00

2009 Topps Ticket to Stardom Ticket Stubs Plus Memorabilia Dual Gold

STATED ODDS 1:352 HOBBY
STATED PRINT RUN 10 SER.#'d SETS
NO PRICING DUE TO SCARCITY

2009 Topps Ticket to Stardom Ticket Stubs Plus Memorabilia Dual Red

STATED ODDS 1:3450 HOBBY
STATED PRINT RUN 10 SER.#'d SETS
NO PRICING DUE TO SCARCITY

2009 Topps Ticket to Stardom Ticket To Stardom

STATED ODDS 1:4 HOBBY
*BLUE: .75X TO 2X BASIC
BLUE ODDS 1:57 HOBBY
BLUE PRINT RUN 99 SER.#'d SETS
*GOLD: 1X TO 2.5X BASIC
GOLD ODDS 1:112 HOBBY
GOLD PRINT RUN 50 SER.#'d SETS
RED ODDS 1:5403 HOBBY
RED PRINT RUN 1 SER.#'d SET
NO RED PRICING DUE TO SCARCITY
PRINTING PLATE ODDS 1:1350 HOBBY
PLATE PRINT RUN 1 SET PER COLOR
BLACK-CYAN-MAGENTA-YELLOW ISSUED
NO PLATE PRICING DUE TO SCARCITY
TTS1 David Price 1.00 2.50
TTS2 Travis Snider .60 1.50
TTS3 Colby Rasmus 1.00 2.50
TTS4 Cameron Maybin .40 1.00
TTS5 Matt Kemp .60 1.50
TTS6 Jay Bruce .60 1.50
TTS7 Prince Fielder .60 1.50
TTS8 Joba Chamberlain .60 1.50
TTS9 Grady Sizemore .60 1.50
TTS10 Evan Longoria 1.25 3.00
TTS11 Joe Mauer 1.00 2.50
TTS12 Joey Votto 1.00 2.50
TTS13 Nick Markakis 1.00 2.50
TTS14 Jacoby Ellsbury 1.00 2.50
TTS15 Kenshin Kawakami .60 1.50

2011 Topps Tier One

COMMON CARD (1-100) .60 1.50
COMMON RC (1-100) .60 1.50
STATED PRINT RUN 799 SER.#'d SETS
1 Joe DiMaggio 4.00 10.00
2 Derek Jeter 4.00 10.00
3 Babe Ruth 4.00 10.00
4 Lou Gehrig 3.00 8.00
5 Ty Cobb 2.50 6.00
6 Stan Musial 2.50 6.00
7 Mickey Mantle 5.00 12.00
8 Ryan Braun 2.00 5.00
9 Roger Maris 1.50 4.00
10 Albert Pujols 4.00 10.00
11 Luis Aparicio .60 1.50
12 Starlin Castro 1.50 4.00
13 Alex Rodriguez 2.50 6.00
14 Justin Verlander 2.00 5.00
15 Thurman Munson 1.50 4.00
16 Cliff Lee 1.50 4.00
17 Matt Holliday 1.50 4.00
18 Clayton Kershaw 1.50 4.00
19 Tony Gwynn 1.50 4.00
20 Frank Robinson 1.00 2.50
21 Paul O'Neill 1.00 2.50
22 Jim Palmer .60 1.50
23 Don Mattingly 3.00 8.00
24 Rickey Henderson 1.50 4.00
25 Matt Kemp 1.00 2.50
26 Chipper Jones 1.50 4.00
27 Juan Marichal .60 1.50
28 Bert Blyleven .60 1.50
29 Mark Teixeira 1.50 4.00
30 Johnny Mize 1.00 2.50
31 Dustin Pedroia 2.00 5.00
32 Sandy Koufax 5.00 12.00
33 Eddie Murray 1.50 4.00
34 Nolan Ryan 5.00 12.00
35 Frank Thomas 1.50 4.00
36 Michael Pineda RC 2.00 5.00
37 Jose Reyes 1.00 2.50
38 Buster Posey 2.00 5.00
39 Roy Campanella 1.50 4.00
40 Mel Ott 1.50 4.00
41 Tom Seaver 1.00 2.50
42 Jackie Robinson 1.50 4.00
43 Prince Fielder 1.00 2.50
44 Hank Aaron 3.00 8.00
45 Bob Gibson 1.00 2.50
46 Ryne Sandberg 3.00 8.00
47 Duke Snider 1.00 2.50
48 Joe Morgan .60 1.50
49 Tim Lincecum 1.50 4.00
50 Walter Johnson 1.50 4.00
51 Ichiro Suzuki 2.50 6.00
52 Cole Hamels 1.50 4.00
53 Zach Britton RC 1.50 4.00
54 Carl Crawford 1.00 2.50
55 Johnny Bench 1.50 4.00
56 Adrian Gonzalez 1.00 2.50
57 Paul Konerko 1.00 2.50
58 Anthony Rizzo RC 1.00 2.50
59 Felix Hernandez 1.50 4.00
60 Jimmie Foxx 1.50 4.00
61 Troy Tulowitzki 1.50 4.00
62 Jay Bruce 1.00 2.50
63 Mariano Rivera 1.50 4.00
64 Roberto Alomar 1.00 2.50
65 Willie McCovey 1.00 2.50
66 Ryan Howard 2.00 5.00
67 Mike Moustakas RC 1.50 4.00
68 Andre Dawson 1.00 2.50
69 Jose Bautista 1.00 2.50
70 Rogers Hornsby 1.00 2.50
71 Ozzie Smith 2.50 6.00
72 Carlton Fisk 1.00 2.50
73 Hunter Pence 1.00 2.50
74 Justin Upton 1.00 2.50
75 Robinson Cano 1.50 4.00
76 Brian Wilson 1.50 4.00
77 CC Sabathia 1.00 2.50
78 Hanley Ramirez 1.50 4.00
79 David Ortiz 1.00 2.50
80 Cal Ripken Jr. 6.00 15.00
81 Barry Larkin 1.00 2.50
82 Roy Halladay 1.50 4.00
83 Tris Speaker 1.00 2.50
84 David Wright 2.00 5.00
85 Brooks Robinson 1.00 2.50
86 Paul Molitor 1.50 4.00
87 Andrew McCutchen 1.50 4.00
88 Reggie Jackson 1.00 2.50
89 Evan Longoria 2.00 5.00
90 Christy Mathewson 1.50 4.00
91 Pee Wee Reese 1.00 2.50
92 Dustin Ackley RC 2.50 6.00
93 Carlos Gonzalez 1.00 2.50
94 Ryan Zimmerman 1.00 2.50
95 Mike Schmidt 2.50 6.00
96 Miguel Cabrera 1.50 4.00
97 Joe Mauer 1.50 4.00
98 Josh Hamilton 1.50 4.00
99 Honus Wagner 1.50 4.00
100 Eric Hosmer RC 5.00 12.00

2011 Topps Tier One Black

*BLACK VET: 1X TO 2.5X BASIC VET
*BLACK RC: 1X TO 2.5X BASIC RC
STATED ODDS 1:11 BOXES
STATED PRINT RUN 50 SER.#'d SETS

2011 Topps Tier One Blue

*BLUE VET: .75X TO 2X BASIC VET
*BLUE RC: .75X TO 2X BASIC RC
STATED ODDS 1:6 BOXES
STATED PRINT RUN 199 SER.#'d SETS

2011 Topps Tier One Gold

STATED PRINT RUN 1 SER.#'d SET
NO PRICING DUE TO SCARCITY

2011 Topps Tier One Purple

STATED ODDS 1:258 BOXES
STATED PRINT RUN 25 SER.#'d SETS
NO PRICING DUE TO SCARCITY

2011 Topps Tier One Crowd Pleaser Autographs

OVERALL AUTO ODDS 2:1 BOXES
PRINT RUNS B/WN 50-699 COPIES PER
GOLD STATED ODDS 1:18 BOXES
GOLD STATED PRINT RUN 25 SER.#'d SETS
NO GOLD PRICING DUE TO SCARCITY
EXCHANGE DEADLINE 11/30/2014
AB Albert Belle/75 20.00 50.00
AE Andre Ethier EXCH 20.00 50.00
AJ Adam Jones/75 15.00 40.00
AK Al Kaline/50 40.00 80.00
AL Adam Lind/649 3.00 8.00
AP Angel Pagan/499 3.00 8.00
AR Aramis Ramirez/50 6.00 15.00
BB Bert Blyleven/50 15.00 40.00
BG Brett Gardner EXCH 10.00 25.00
BM Brian McCann/50 20.00 50.00
BP Brandon Phillips/75 12.50 30.00
CB Clay Buchholz/50 8.00 20.00
CC Carl Crawford EXCH 10.00 25.00
CG Carlos Gonzalez EXCH 10.00 25.00
CJ Chipper Jones/50 50.00 100.00
CK Clayton Kershaw/75 30.00 60.00
CL Cliff Lee EXCH 30.00 60.00
CY Chris Young/75 4.00 10.00
DM Don Mattingly/50 50.00 100.00
DP Dustin Pedroia/50 15.00 40.00
EA Elvis Andrus/50 5.00 12.00
EM Edgar Martinez/75 30.00 60.00
ES Ervin Santana/549 4.00 10.00
FJ Fergie Jenkins/50 15.00 40.00
GF George Foster/50 12.50
GG Gio Gonzalez/699 3.00 8.00
HR Hanley Ramirez/50 10.00 25.00
IK Ian Kinsler EXCH 10.00 25.00
JB Jay Bruce/75 10.00 25.00
JC Johnny Cueto/699 4.00 10.00
JJ Josh Johnson/50 10.00 25.00
JM Joe Morgan EXCH 20.00 50.00
JP Jhonny Peralta/699 4.00 10.00
JW Jered Weaver/50 10.00 25.00
LA Luis Aparicio EXCH 15.00 40.00
MC Matt Cain EXCH 15.00 40.00
MG Matt Garza/75 8.00 20.00
MK Matt Kemp/75 20.00 50.00
ML Mat Latos EXCH 8.00 20.00
OS Ozzie Smith EXCH 30.00 60.00
PM Paul Molitor/50 15.00 40.00
PO Paul O'Neill/75 15.00 40.00
PS Pablo Sandoval/699 6.00 15.00
RA Roberto Alomar/50 30.00 60.00
RB Ryan Braun EXCH 30.00 60.00
RN Ricky Nolasco/699 3.00 8.00
RS Ryne Sandberg/50 40.00 80.00
RZ Ryan Zimmerman/75 12.50 30.00
TC Trevor Cahill/699 4.00 10.00
UJ Ubaldo Jimenez/50 10.00 25.00
WM Willie McCovey/50 40.00
BBU Billy Butler EXCH 10.00 25.00
BJU B.J. Upton/75 8.00 20.00
IKN Ian Kennedy EXCH 5.00 12.00
RED Red Schoendienst/75 12.50 30.00

2011 Topps Tier One Cut Signatures

STATED ODDS 1:1030 BOXES
STATED PRINT RUN 1 SER.#'d SET
NO PRICING DUE TO SCARCITY
EXHANGE DEADLINE 11/30/2014

2011 Topps Tier One Dual Autographs

STATED ODDS 1:69 BOXES
STATED PRINT RUN 25 SER.#'d SETS
NO PRICING DUE TO SCARCITY
EXCHANGE DEADLINE 11/30/2014

2011 Topps Tier One On The Rise Autographs

OVERALL AUTO ODDS 2:1 BOXES
PRINT RUNS B/WN 99-999 COPIES PER
GOLD STATED ODDS 1:18 BOXES
GOLD STATED PRINT RUN 25 SER.#'d SETS
NO GOLD PRICING DUE TO SCARCITY
EXCHANGE DEADLINE 11/30/2014
AC Alex Cobb/999 3.00 8.00
AJ Austin Jackson/99 6.00 15.00
AM Andrew McCutchen/99 12.50 30.00
AO Alexi Ogando/999 4.00 10.00
AR Anthony Rizzo/999 5.00 12.00
AW Alex White/999 3.00 8.00
BB Brandon Belt/699 10.00 25.00
BC Brandon Crawford/999 5.00 12.00
BG Brandon Guyer/999 3.00 8.00
BH Brad Hand/999 3.00 8.00
BM Brent Morel/699 3.00 8.00
BW Brett Wallace/399 4.00 10.00
CC Carlos Carrasco/999 3.00 8.00
CJ Chris Johnson/699 3.00 8.00
CK Craig Kimbrel/699 10.00 25.00
CP Carlos Peguero/999 3.00 8.00
CR Colby Rasmus/349 4.00 10.00
CS Carlos Santana/399 6.00 15.00
DA Dustin Ackley/399 15.00 40.00
DC David Cooper/999 3.00 8.00
DD Danny Duffy/999 3.00 8.00
DG Dee Gordon/999 6.00 15.00
DH Daniel Hudson/699 3.00 8.00
DS Drew Storen/699 4.00 10.00
DV Danny Valencia/999 4.00 10.00
EH Eric Hosmer/399 30.00 60.00
EN Eduardo Nunez/999 5.00 12.00
ES Eric Sogard/999 3.00 8.00
ET Eric Thames/999 3.00 8.00
FF Freddie Freeman/99 20.00 50.00
FM Fernando Martinez/499 3.00 8.00
GS Gaby Sanchez/399 3.00 8.00
HN Hector Noesi/999 4.00 10.00
JH Jason Heyward/99 20.00 50.00
JI Jose Iglesias/499 6.00 15.00
JS Jordan Schafer/999 4.00 10.00
JT Josh Thole/999 3.00 8.00
JZ Jordan Zimmermann/999 3.00 8.00
LF Logan Forsythe/999 3.00 8.00
MB Madison Bumgarner/99 15.00 40.00
MM Mike Minor/699 4.00 10.00
MP Michael Pineda/99 15.00 40.00
MS Mike Stanton EXCH 20.00 50.00
MT Mark Trumbo/399 10.00 25.00
RT Ruben Tejada/699 4.00 10.00
SC Starlin Castro/99 20.00 50.00
TC Tyler Colvin/999 3.00 8.00
TR Tyson Ross/999 3.00 8.00
ZB Zach Britton/99 15.00 40.00
ACH Aroldis Chapman/99 12.50 30.00
ACR Allen Craig/999 6.00 15.00
BBE Brandon Beachy/999 6.00 15.00
CSA Chris Sale/599 3.00 8.00
DGE Dillon Gee/999 4.00 10.00
JHE Jeremy Hellickson EXCH 12.50 30.00
MSC Max Scherzer EXCH 4.00 10.00

2011 Topps Tier One Prodigious Patches

STATED ODDS 1:103 BOXES
STATED PRINT RUN 10 SER.#'d SETS
NO PRICING DUE TO SCARCITY
EXHANGE DEADLINE 11/30/2014

2011 Topps Tier One Top Shelf Relics

OVERALL RELIC ODDS 1:1 BOXES
STATED PRINT RUN 399 SER.#'d SETS
EXCHANGE DEADLINE 9/30/2014
TSR1 Ichiro Suzuki 8.00 20.00
TSR2 Roberto Alomar 4.00 10.00
TSR3 Thurman Munson 12.50 30.00
TSR4 Carlton Fisk 4.00 10.00
TSR5 Joe DiMaggio 20.00 50.00
TSR6 Jimmie Foxx 10.00 25.00
TSR7 Rogers Hornsby 10.00 25.00
TSR8 Ryan Braun 4.00 10.00
TSR9 Roy Campanella 6.00 15.00
TSR10 Roy Halladay 6.00 15.00
TSR11 Johnny Mize 8.00 20.00
TSR12 Aramis Ramirez 3.00 8.00
TSR13 Pee Wee Reese 5.00 12.00
TSR14 George Sisler 8.00 20.00
TSR15 Tris Speaker 10.00 25.00
TSR16 Babe Ruth 50.00 100.00
TSR17 Carl Crawford 3.00 8.00
TSR18 Ian Kinsler 3.00 8.00
TSR19 Johnny Bench 6.00 15.00
TSR20 Reggie Jackson 4.00 10.00
TSR21 Carlos Beltran 4.00 10.00
TSR22 Ty Cobb 30.00 60.00
TSR23 Joey Votto 5.00 12.00
TSR24 Jose Reyes 4.00 10.00
TSR25 Cole Hamels 4.00 10.00
TSR26 Rickey Henderson EXCH 15.00 40.00
TSR27 Lou Gehrig 40.00 80.00
TSR28 Jered Weaver 3.00 8.00
TSR29 Paul Molitor 4.00 10.00
TSR30 Tim Lincecum 6.00 15.00
TSR31 David Wright 4.00 10.00
TSR32 Jacoby Ellsbury 4.00 10.00
TSR33 Sandy Koufax 30.00 60.00
TSR34 Dustin Pedroia 4.00 10.00
TSR35 Eddie Murray 4.00 10.00
TSR36 Mickey Mantle 40.00 80.00
TSR37 Stan Musial 10.00 25.00
TSR38 Ubaldo Jimenez 3.00 8.00
TSR39 Paul O'Neill 4.00 10.00
TSR40 Willie McCovey 6.00 15.00
TSR41 Brian McCann 3.00 8.00
TSR42 Albert Pujols 10.00 25.00
TSR43 Don Mattingly 8.00 20.00
TSR44 Hank Aaron 12.50 30.00
TSR45 Brooks Robinson 5.00 12.00
TSR46 Ryne Sandberg EXCH 6.00 15.00
TSR47 Tom Seaver 5.00 12.00
TSR48 Willie Mays 12.50 30.00
TSR49 Chipper Jones 5.00 12.00
TSR50 Cal Ripken Jr. 10.00 25.00

2011 Topps Tier One Top Shelf Relics Dual

STATED ODDS 1:6 BOXES
STATED PRINT RUN 99 SER.#'d SETS
EXCHANGE DEADLINE 9/30/2014
TSR1 Ichiro Suzuki 10.00 25.00
TSR2 Roberto Alomar 10.00 25.00
TSR3 Thurman Munson 12.50 30.00
TSR4 Carlton Fisk 4.00 10.00
TSR5 Joe DiMaggio 40.00 80.00
TSR6 Jimmie Foxx 12.50 30.00
TSR7 Rogers Hornsby 12.50 30.00
TSR8 Ryan Braun 5.00 12.00
TSR9 Roy Campanella 8.00 20.00
TSR10 Roy Halladay 6.00 15.00
TSR11 Johnny Mize 10.00 25.00
TSR12 Aramis Ramirez 4.00 10.00
TSR13 Pee Wee Reese 10.00 25.00
TSR14 George Sisler 10.00 25.00
TSR15 Tris Speaker 12.50 30.00
TSR16 Babe Ruth 75.00 150.00
TSR17 Carl Crawford 6.00 15.00
TSR18 Ian Kinsler 4.00 10.00
TSR19 Johnny Bench 10.00 25.00
TSR20 Reggie Jackson 8.00 20.00
TSR21 Carlos Beltran 4.00 10.00
TSR22 Ty Cobb 30.00 60.00
TSR23 Joey Votto 6.00 15.00
TSR24 Jose Reyes 6.00 15.00
TSR25 Cole Hamels 8.00 20.00
TSR26 Rickey Henderson EXCH 40.00 80.00
TSR27 Lou Gehrig 50.00 100.00
TSR28 Jered Weaver 4.00 10.00
TSR29 Paul Molitor 6.00 15.00
TSR30 Tim Lincecum 8.00 20.00
TSR31 David Wright 5.00 12.00
TSR32 Jacoby Ellsbury 10.00 25.00
TSR33 Sandy Koufax 30.00 60.00
TSR34 Dustin Pedroia 8.00 20.00
TSR35 Eddie Murray 8.00 20.00
TSR36 Mickey Mantle 50.00 100.00
TSR37 Stan Musial 15.00 40.00
TSR38 Ubaldo Jimenez 4.00 10.00
TSR39 Paul O'Neill 6.00 15.00
TSR40 Willie McCovey 6.00 15.00
TSR41 Brian McCann 5.00 12.00
TSR42 Albert Pujols 12.50 30.00
TSR43 Don Mattingly 15.00 40.00
TSR44 Hank Aaron 15.00 40.00
TSR45 Brooks Robinson 12.50 30.00
TSR46 Ryne Sandberg EXCH 10.00 25.00
TSR47 Tom Seaver 8.00 20.00
TSR48 Willie Mays 20.00 50.00
TSR49 Chipper Jones 10.00 25.00
TSR50 Cal Ripken Jr. 12.50 30.00

2011 Topps Tier One Top Shelf Relics Triple

STATED ODDS 1:21 BOXES
STATED PRINT RUN 25 SER.#'d SETS
NO PRICING DUE TO SCARCITY
EXHANGE DEADLINE 11/30/2014

2011 Topps Tier One Top Tier Autographs

STATED ODDS 1:13 BOXES
PRINT RUNS B/WN 99-199 COPIES PER
PACQUIAO NOT SERIAL NUMBERED
GOLD STATED ODDS 1:120 BOXES
GOLD PRINT RUN B/WN 10-25 COPIES PER
NO GOLD PRICING DUE TO SCARCITY
EXCHANGE DEADLINE 11/30/2014
AG Adrian Gonzalez/99 20.00 50.00
AP Albert Pujols EXCH 200.00 400.00
BG Bob Gibson/99 20.00 50.00
CF Carlton Fisk/99 15.00 40.00
EL Evan Longoria/99 30.00 60.00
FH Felix Hernandez/99 20.00 50.00
FR Frank Robinson/99 30.00 60.00
HA Hank Aaron EXCH 150.00 250.00
JB Johnny Bench/99 30.00 60.00
JH Josh Hamilton/99 20.00 50.00
MC Miguel Cabrera EXCH 20.00 50.00
MP Manny Pacquiao 150.00 300.00
MS Mike Schmidt/99 40.00 80.00
NR Nolan Ryan EXCH 100.00 175.00
PF Prince Fielder EXCH 30.00 60.00
RH Rickey Henderson/99 100.00 175.00
RH Roy Halladay EXCH 60.00 120.00
RJ Reggie Jackson/99 40.00 80.00
SK Sandy Koufax/199 175.00 350.00
SM Stan Musial/99 50.00 100.00
TG Tony Gwynn/99 30.00 60.00

2011 Topps Tier One Triple Autographs

STATED ODDS 1:515 BOXES
STATED PRINT RUN 10 SER.#'d SETS
NO PRICING DUE TO SCARCITY
EXCHANGE DEADLINE 11/30/2014

2002 Topps Total

This 990 card set was issued in June, 2002. These cards were issued in 10 card packs which came 36 packs to a box and six boxes to a case. Each card was numbered not only in a numerical sequence but also in a team sequence.

COMPLETE SET (990) 75.00 150.00
1 Joe Mauer RC 5.00 12.00
2 Derek Jeter .75 2.00
3 Shawn Green .10 .30
4 Vladimir Guerrero .30 .75
5 Mike Piazza .50 1.25
6 Brandon Duckworth .07 .20
7 Aramis Ramirez .10 .30
8 Josh Barfield RC 1.00 2.50
9 Troy Glaus .10 .30
10 Sammy Sosa .30 .75
11 Rod Barajas .07 .20
12 Tsuyoshi Shinjo .10 .30
13 Larry Bigbie .07 .20
14 Tino Martinez .20 .50
15 Craig Biggio .20 .50
16 Anastacio Martinez RC .15 .40
17 John McDonald .07 .20
18 Kyle Kane RC .08 .25
19 Aubrey Huff .10 .30
20 Juan Cruz .07 .20
21 Doug Creek .07 .20
22 Luther Hackman .07 .20
23 Rafael Furcal .10 .30
24 Andres Torres .07 .20
25 Jason Giambi .10 .30
26 Jose Paniagua .07 .20
27 Jose Offerman .07 .20
28 Alex Arias .07 .20
29 J.M. Gold .07 .20
30 Jeff Bagwell .20 .50
31 Brent Cookson .07 .20
32 Kelly Wunsch .07 .20
33 Larry Walker .10 .30
34 Luis Gonzalez .10 .30
35 John Franco .10 .30
36 Roy Oswalt .10 .30
37 Tom Glavine .20 .50
38 C.C. Sabathia .10 .30
39 Jay Gibbons .07 .20
40 Wilson Betemit .07 .20
41 Tony Armas Jr. .07 .20
42 Mo Vaughn .10 .30
43 Gerard Oakes RC .15 .40
44 Dmitri Young .10 .30
45 Tim Salmon .20 .50
46 Barry Zito .10 .30
47 Adrian Gonzalez .07 .20
48 Joe Davenport .07 .20
49 Adrian Hernandez .07 .20
50 Randy Johnson .30 .75
52 Adam Pettyjohn .07 .20
53 Alex Escobar .07 .20
54 Stevenson Agosto RC .08 .25
55 Omar Daal .07 .20
56 Mike Buddie .07 .20
57 Dave Williams .07 .20
58 Marquis Grissom .10 .30
59 Pat Burrell .10 .30
60 Mark Prior .20 .50
61 Mike Bynum .07 .20
62 Mike Hill RC .15 .40
63 Brandon Backe RC .20 .50
64 Dan Wilson .07 .20
65 Nick Johnson .10 .30
66 Jason Grimsley .07 .20
67 Russ Johnson .07 .20
68 Todd Walker .07 .20
69 Kyle Farnsworth .07 .20
70 Ben Broussard .07 .20
71 Garrett Guzman RC .15 .40
72 Terry Mulholland .07 .20
73 Tyler Houston .07 .20
74 Jace Brewer .07 .20
75 Chris Baker RC .15 .40
76 Frank Catalanotto .07 .20
77 Mike Redmond .07 .20
78 Matt Wise .07 .20
79 Fernando Vina .07 .20
80 Kevin Brown .10 .30
81 Grant Balfour .07 .20
82 Clint Nageotte RC .20 .50
83 Jeff Tam .07 .20
84 Steve Trachsel .07 .20
85 Tomo Ohka .07 .20
86 Keith McDonald .07 .20
87 Jose Ortiz .07 .20

88 Rusty Greer .10 .30
89 Jeff Suppan .07 .20
90 Moises Alou .10 .30
91 Juan Encarnacion .07 .20
92 Tyler Yates RC .15 .40
93 Scott Strickland .07 .20
94 Brent Butler .07 .20
95 Jon Rauch .07 .20
96 Brian Mallette RC .08 .25
97 Joe Randa .10 .30
98 Cesar Crespo .07 .20
99 Felix Rodriguez .07 .20
100 Chipper Jones .30 .75
101 Victor Martinez .30 .75
102 Danny Graves .07 .20
103 Brandon Berger .07 .20
104 Carlos Garcia .07 .20
105 Alfonso Soriano .10 .30
106 Allan Simpson RC .08 .25
107 Brad Thomas .07 .20
108 Devon White .10 .30
109 Scott Chiasson .07 .20
110 Cliff Floyd .10 .30
111 Scott Williamson .07 .20
112 Julio Zuleta .07 .20
113 Terry Adams .07 .20
114 Zach Day .07 .20
115 Ben Grieve .07 .20
116 Mark Ellis .07 .20
117 Bobby Jenks RC .60 1.50
118 LaTroy Hawkins .07 .20
119 Tim Raines Jr. .07 .20
120 Juan Uribe .07 .20
121 Bob Scanlan .07 .20
122 Brad Nelson RC .15 .40
123 Adam Johnson .07 .20
124 Raul Casanova .07 .20
125 Jeff D'Amico .07 .20
126 Aaron Cook RC .15 .40
127 Alan Benes .07 .20
128 Mark Little .07 .20
129 Randy Wolf .07 .20
130 Phil Nevin .10 .30
131 Guillermo Mota .07 .20
132 Nick Neugebauer .07 .20
133 Pedro Borbon Jr. .07 .20
134 Doug Mientkiewicz .10 .30
135 Edgardo Alfonzo .07 .20
136 Dustan Mohr .07 .20
137 Dan Reichert .07 .20
138 Dewon Brazelton .07 .20
139 Orlando Cabrera .10 .30
140 Todd Hollandsworth .07 .20
141 Darren Dreifort .07 .20
142 Jose Valentin .07 .20
143 Josh Kalinowski .07 .20
144 Randy Keisler .07 .20
145 Bret Boone .10 .30
146 Roosevelt Brown .07 .20
147 Brent Abernathy .07 .20
148 Jorge Julio .07 .20
149 Alex Gonzalez .07 .20
150 Juan Pierre .10 .30
151 Roger Cedeno .07 .20
152 Javier Vazquez .10 .30
153 Armando Benitez .07 .20
154 Dave Burba .07 .20
155 Brad Penny .07 .20
156 Ryan Jensen .07 .20
157 Jeromy Burnitz .10 .30
158 Matt Childers RC .15 .40
159 Wilmy Caceres .07 .20
160 Roger Clemens .60 1.50
161 Jamie Cerda RC .15 .40
162 Jason Christiansen .07 .20
163 Pokey Reese .07 .20
164 Ivanon Coffie .07 .20
165 Joaquin Benoit .07 .20
166 Mike Matheny .07 .20
167 Eric Cammack .07 .20
168 Alex Graman .07 .20
169 Brook Fordyce .07 .20
170 Mike Lieberthal .10 .30
171 Giovanni Carrara .07 .20
172 Antonio Perez .07 .20
173 Fernando Tatis .07 .20
174 Jason Bay RC 2.00 5.00
175 Jason Botts RC .20 .50
176 Danys Baez .07 .20
177 Shea Hillenbrand .10 .30
178 Jack Cust .07 .20
179 Clay Bellinger .07 .20
180 Roberto Alomar .20 .50
181 Graeme Lloyd .07 .20
182 Clint Weibl RC .08 .25
183 Royce Clayton .07 .20
184 Ben Davis .07 .20
185 Brian Adams RC .08 .25
186 Jack Wilson .07 .20
187 David Coggin .07 .20
188 Derrick Turnbow .07 .20
189 Vladimir Nunez .07 .20
190 Mariano Rivera .30 .75
191 Wilson Guzman .07 .20
192 Michael Barrett .07 .20
193 Corey Patterson .07 .20
194 Luis Sojo .07 .20
195 Scott Elarton .07 .20
196 Charles Thomas RC .15 .40
197 Ricky Bottalico .07 .20
198 Wilfredo Rodriguez .07 .20
199 Ricardo Rincon .07 .20
200 John Smoltz .20 .50
201 Travis Miller .07 .20
202 Ben Weber .07 .20
203 T.J. Tucker .07 .20
204 Terry Shumpert .07 .20
205 Bernie Williams .20 .50
206 Russ Ortiz .07 .20
207 Nate Rolison .07 .20
208 Jose Cruz Jr. .07 .20
209 Bill Ortega .07 .20
210 Carl Everett .10 .30
211 Luis Lopez .07 .20
212 Brian Wolfe RC .15 .40
213 Doug Davis .07 .20
214 Troy Mattes .07 .20
215 Al Leiter .10 .30
216 Joe Mays .07 .20
217 Bobby Smith .07 .20
218 J.J. Trujillo RC .15 .40
219 Hideo Nomo .30 .75
220 Jimmy Rollins .10 .30
221 Bobby Seay .07 .20
222 Mike Thurman .07 .20
223 Bartolo Colon .10 .30
224 Jesus Sanchez .07 .20
225 Ray Durham .10 .30
226 Juan Diaz .07 .20
227 Lee Stevens .07 .20
228 Ben Howard RC .15 .40
229 James Mouton .07 .20
230 Paul Quantrill .07 .20
231 Randy Knorr .07 .20
232 Abraham Nunez .07 .20
233 Mike Fetters .07 .20
234 Mario Encarnacion .07 .20
235 Jeremy Fikac .07 .20
236 Travis Lee .07 .20
237 Bob File .07 .20
238 Pete Harnisch .07 .20
239 Randy Galvez RC .15 .40
240 Geoff Goetz .07 .20
241 Gary Glover .07 .20
242 Troy Percival .10 .30
243 Len Dinardo RC .15 .40
244 Jonny Gomes RC 1.00 2.50
245 Jesus Medrano RC .15 .40
246 Rey Ordonez .07 .20
247 Juan Gonzalez .10 .30
248 Jose Guillen .10 .30
249 Franklyn German RC .15 .40
250 Mike Mussina .20 .50
251 Ugueth Urbina .07 .20
252 Melvin Mora .10 .30
253 Gerald Williams .07 .20
254 Jared Sandberg .07 .20
255 Darrin Fletcher .07 .20
256 A.J. Pierzynski .10 .30
257 Lenny Harris .07 .20
258 Blaine Neal .07 .20
259 Denny Neagle .07 .20
260 Jason Hart .07 .20
261 Henry Mateo .07 .20
262 Rheal Cormier .07 .20
263 Luis Terrero .07 .20
264 Shigetoshi Hasegawa .10 .30
265 Bill Haselman .07 .20
266 Scott Hatteberg .07 .20
267 Adam Hyzdu .07 .20
268 Mike Williams .07 .20
269 Marlon Anderson .07 .20
270 Bruce Chen .07 .20
271 Eli Marrero .07 .20
272 Jimmy Haynes .07 .20
273 Bronson Arroyo .10 .30
274 Kevin Jordan .07 .20
275 Rick Helling .07 .20
276 Mark Loretta .07 .20
277 Dustin Hermanson .07 .20
278 Pablo Ozuna .07 .20
279 Keto Anderson RC .15 .40
280 Jermaine Dye .10 .30
281 Will Smith .07 .20
282 Brian Daubach .07 .20
283 Eric Hinske .07 .20
284 Joe Jiannetti RC .15 .40
285 Chan Ho Park .10 .30
286 Curtis Legendre RC .15 .40
287 Jeff Reboulet .07 .20
288 Scott Rolen .20 .50
289 Chris Richard .07 .20
290 Eric Chavez .10 .30
291 Scot Shields .07 .20
292 Donnie Sadler .07 .20
293 Dave Veres .07 .20
294 Craig Counsell .07 .20
295 Armando Reynoso .07 .20
296 Kyle Lohse .07 .20
297 Arthur Rhodes .07 .20
298 Sidney Ponson .07 .20
299 Trevor Hoffman .10 .30
300 Kerry Wood .10 .30
301 Danny Bautista .07 .20
302 Scott Sauerbeck .07 .20
303 Johnny Estrada .07 .20
304 Mike Timlin .07 .20
305 Orlando Hernandez .10 .30
306 Tony Clark .07 .20
307 Tomas Perez .07 .20
308 Marcus Giles .10 .30
309 Mike Bordick .10 .30
310 Jorge Posada .20 .50
311 Jason Conti .07 .20
312 Kevin Millar .10 .30
313 Paul Shuey .07 .20
314 Jake Mauer RC .15 .40
315 Luke Hudson .07 .20
316 Angel Berroa .07 .20
317 Fred Bastardo RC .15 .40
318 Shawn Estes .07 .20
319 Andy Ashby .07 .20
320 Ryan Klesko .10 .30
321 Kevin Appier .10 .30
322 Juan Pena .07 .20
323 Alex Herrera .07 .20
324 Robb Nen .10 .30
325 Orlando Hudson .07 .20
326 Lyle Overbay .07 .20
327 Ben Sheets .10 .30
328 Mike DiFelice .07 .20
329 Pablo Arias RC .15 .40
330 Mike Sweeney .10 .30
331 Rick Ankiel .07 .20
332 Tomas De La Rosa .07 .20
333 Kazuhisa Ishii RC .20 .50
334 Jose Reyes .20 .50
335 Jeremy Giambi .07 .20
336 Jose Mesa .07 .20
337 Ralph Roberts RC .15 .40
338 Jose Nunez .07 .20
339 Curt Schilling .10 .30
340 Sean Casey .10 .30
341 Bob Wells .07 .20
342 Carlos Beltran .10 .30
343 Alexis Gomez .07 .20
344 Brandon Claussen .07 .20
345 Buddy Groom .07 .20
346 Mark Phillips RC .15 .40
347 Francisco Cordova .07 .20
348 Joe Oliver .07 .20
349 Danny Patterson .07 .20
350 Joel Pineiro .07 .20
351 J.R. House .07 .20
352 Benny Agbayani .07 .20
353 Jose Vidro .07 .20
354 Reed Johnson RC .40 1.00
355 Mike Lowell .10 .30
356 Scott Schoeneweis .07 .20
357 Brian Jordan .10 .30
358 Steve Finley .10 .30
359 Randy Choate .07 .20
360 Jose Lima .07 .20
361 Miguel Olivo .07 .20
362 Kenny Rogers .10 .30
363 David Justice .10 .30
364 Brandon Knight .07 .20
365 Joe Kennedy .07 .20
366 Eric Valent .07 .20
367 Nelson Cruz .07 .20
368 Brian Giles .10 .30
369 Charles Gipson RC .08 .25
370 Juan Pena .07 .20
371 Mark Redman .07 .20
372 Billy Koch .07 .20
373 Ted Lilly .07 .20
374 Craig Paquette .07 .20
375 Kevin Jarvis .07 .20
376 Scott Erickson .07 .20
377 Josh Paul .07 .20
378 Darwin Cubillan .07 .20
379 Nelson Figueroa .07 .20
380 Darin Erstad .10 .30
381 Jeremy Hill RC .15 .40
382 Elvin Nina .07 .20
383 David Wells .10 .30
384 Jay Caligiuri RC .15 .40
385 Freddy Garcia .10 .30
386 Damian Miller .07 .20
387 Bobby Higginson .10 .30
388 Alejandro Giron RC .15 .40
389 Ivan Rodriguez .20 .50
390 Ed Rogers .07 .20
391 Andy Benes .07 .20
392 Matt Blank .07 .20
393 Ryan Vogelsong .07 .20
394 Kelly Ramos RC .08 .25
395 Eric Karros .10 .30
396 Bobby J. Jones .07 .20
397 Omar Vizquel .20 .50
398 Matt Perisho .07 .20
399 Delino DeShields .07 .20
400 Carlos Hernandez .07 .20
401 Derrek Lee .20 .50
402 Kirk Rueter .07 .20
403 David Wright RC 5.00 12.00
404 Paul LoDuca .10 .30
405 Brian Schneider .07 .20
406 Milton Bradley .10 .30
407 Daryle Ward .07 .20
408 Cody Ransom .07 .20
409 Fernando Rodney .07 .20
410 John Suomi RC .15 .40
411 Joe Girardi .07 .20
412 Demetrius Heath RC .15 .40
413 John Foster RC .15 .40
414 Doug Glanville .07 .20
415 Ryan Kohlmeier .07 .20
416 Mike Matthews .07 .20
417 Craig Wilson .07 .20
418 Jay Witasick .07 .20
419 Jay Payton .07 .20
420 Andruw Jones .20 .50
421 Benji Gil .07 .20
422 Jeff Liefer .07 .20
423 Kevin Young .07 .20
424 Richie Sexson .10 .30
425 Cory Lidle .07 .20
426 Shane Halter .07 .20
427 Jesse Foppert RC .20 .50
428 Jose Molina .07 .20
429 Nick Alvarez RC .15 .40
430 Brian L. Hunter .07 .20
431 Cliff Bartosh RC .15 .40
432 Junior Spivey .07 .20
433 Eric Good RC .15 .40
434 Chin-Feng Chen .10 .30
435 T.J. Mathews .07 .20
436 Rich Rodriguez .07 .20
437 Bobby Abreu .10 .30
438 Joe McEwing .07 .20
439 Michael Tucker .07 .20
440 Preston Wilson .10 .30
441 Mike MacDougal .07 .20
442 Shannon Stewart .10 .30
443 Bob Howry .07 .20
444 Mike Benjamin .07 .20
445 Erik Hiljus .07 .20
446 Ryan Gripp RC .15 .40
447 Jose Vizcaino .07 .20
448 Shawn Wooten .07 .20
449 Steve Kent RC .15 .40
450 Ramiro Mendoza .07 .20
451 Jake Westbrook .07 .20
452 Joe Lawrence .07 .20
453 Jae Seo .07 .20
454 Ryan Fry RC .15 .40
455 Darren Lewis .07 .20
456 Brad Wilkerson .07 .20
457 Gustavo Chacin RC .40 1.00
458 Adrian Brown .07 .20
459 Mike Cameron .07 .20
460 Bud Smith .07 .20
461 Derrick Lewis .07 .20
462 Derek Lowe .10 .30
463 Matt Williams .10 .30
464 Jason Jennings .07 .20
465 Albie Lopez .07 .20
466 Felipe Lopez .07 .20
467 Luke Allen .07 .20
468 Brian Anderson .07 .20
469 Matt Riley .07 .20
470 Ryan Dempster .07 .20
471 Matt Ginter .07 .20
472 David Ortiz .30 .75
473 Cole Barthel RC .08 .25
474 Damian Jackson .07 .20
475 Andy Van Hekken .07 .20
476 Doug Brocail .07 .20
477 Denny Hocking .07 .20
478 Sean Douglass .07 .20
479 Eric Owens .07 .20
480 Ryan Ludwick .07 .20
481 Todd Pratt .07 .20
482 Aaron Sele .07 .20
483 Edgar Renteria .10 .30
484 Raymond Cabrera RC .15 .40
485 Brandon Lyon .07 .20
486 Chase Utley 1.00 2.50
487 Robert Fick .07 .20
488 Wilfredo Cordero .07 .20
489 Octavio Dotel .07 .20
490 Paul Abbott .07 .20
491 Jason Kendall .10 .30
492 Jarrod Washburn .07 .20
493 Dane Sardinha .07 .20
494 Jung Bong .07 .20
495 J.D. Drew .10 .30
496 Jason Schmidt .10 .30
497 Mike Magnante .07 .20
498 Jorge Padilla RC .15 .40
499 Eric Gagne .10 .30
500 Todd Helton .20 .50
501 Jeff Weaver .07 .20
502 Alex Sanchez .07 .20
503 Ken Griffey Jr. .50 1.25
504 Abraham Nunez .07 .20
505 Reggie Sanders .10 .30
506 Casey Kotchman RC .40 1.00
507 Jim Mann .07 .20
508 Matt LeCroy .07 .20
509 Frank Castillo .07 .20
510 Geoff Jenkins .07 .20
511 Jayson Durocher RC .08 .25
512 Ellis Burks .10 .30
513 Aaron Fultz .07 .20
514 Hiram Bocachica .07 .20
515 Nate Espy RC .15 .40
516 Placido Polanco .07 .20
517 Kerry Ligtenberg .07 .20
518 Doug Nickle .07 .20
519 Ramon Ortiz .07 .20
520 Greg Swindell .07 .20
521 J.J. Davis .07 .20
522 Sandy Alomar Jr. .07 .20
523 Chris Carpenter .10 .30
524 Vance Wilson .07 .20
525 Nomar Garciaparra .50 1.25
526 Jim Mecir .07 .20
527 Taylor Buchholz RC .20 .50
528 Brent Mayne .07 .20
529 John Rodriguez RC .20 .50
530 David Segui .07 .20
531 Nate Cornejo .07 .20
532 Gil Heredia .07 .20
533 Esteban Loaiza .07 .20
534 Pat Mahomes .07 .20
535 Matt Morris .10 .30
536 Todd Stottlemyre .07 .20
537 Brian Lesher .07 .20
538 Arturo McDowell .07 .20
539 Felix Diaz .07 .20
540 Mark Mulder .10 .30
541 Kevin Frederick RC .15 .40
542 Andy Fox .07 .20
543 Dionys Cesar RC .08 .25
544 Justin Miller .07 .20
545 Keith Osik .07 .20
546 Shane Reynolds .07 .20
547 Mike Myers .07 .20
548 Raul Chavez RC .08 .25
549 Joe Nathan .10 .30
550 Ryan Anderson .07 .20
551 Jason Marquis .07 .20
552 Marty Cordova .07 .20
553 Kevin Tapani .07 .20
554 Jimmy Anderson .07 .20
555 Pedro Martinez .20 .50
556 Rocky Biddle .07 .20
557 Alex Ochoa .07 .20
558 D'Angelo Jimenez .07 .20
559 Wilkin Ruan .07 .20
560 Terrence Long .07 .20
561 Mark Lukasiewicz .07 .20
562 Jose Santiago .07 .20
563 Brad Fullmer .07 .20
564 Corky Miller .07 .20
565 Matt White .07 .20
566 Mark Grace .20 .50
567 Raul Ibanez .07 .20
568 Josh Towers .07 .20
569 Juan M. Gonzalez RC .15 .40
570 Brian Buchanan .07 .20
571 Ken Harvey .07 .20
572 Jeffrey Hammonds .07 .20
573 Wade Miller .07 .20
574 Elpidio Guzman .07 .20
575 Kevin Olsen .07 .20
576 Austin Kearns .07 .20
577 Tim Kalita RC .15 .40
578 David Dellucci .07 .20
579 Alex Gonzalez .07 .20
580 Joe Orloski RC .15 .40
581 Gary Matthews Jr. .07 .20
582 Ryan Mills .07 .20
583 Erick Almonte .07 .20
584 Jeremy Affeldt .07 .20
585 Chris Tritle RC .08 .25
586 Michael Cuddyer .07 .20
587 Kris Foster .07 .20
588 Russell Branyan .07 .20
589 Darren Oliver .07 .20
590 Freddie Money RC .15 .40
591 Carlos Lee .10 .30
592 Tim Wakefield .10 .30
593 Bubba Trammell .07 .20
594 John Koronka RC .40 1.00
595 Geoff Blum .07 .20
596 Darryl Kile .10 .30
597 Neifi Perez .07 .20
598 Torii Hunter .10 .30
599 Luis Castillo .07 .20
600 Mark Buehrle .10 .30
601 Jeff Zimmerman .07 .20
602 Mike DeJean .07 .20
603 Julio Lugo .07 .20
604 Chad Hermansen .07 .20
605 Keith Foulke .10 .30
606 Lance Davis .07 .20
607 Jeff Austin RC .15 .40
608 Brandon Inge .07 .20
609 Orlando Merced .07 .20
610 Johnny Damon Sox .20 .50
611 Doug Henry .07 .20
612 Adam Kennedy .07 .20
613 Wiki Gonzalez .07 .20
614 Brian West RC .15 .40
615 Andy Pettitte .20 .50
616 Chone Figgins RC .60 1.50
617 Matt Lawton .07 .20
618 Paul Rigdon .07 .20
619 Keith Lockhart .07 .20
620 Tim Redding .07 .20
621 John Parrish .07 .20
622 Homer Bush .07 .20
623 Todd Greene .07 .20
624 David Eckstein .10 .30
625 Greg Montalbano RC .15 .40
626 Joe Beimel .07 .20
627 Adrian Beltre .10 .30
628 Charles Nagy .07 .20
629 Cristian Guzman .07 .20
630 Toby Hall .07 .20
631 Jose Hernandez .07 .20
632 Jose Macias .10 .30
633 Jaret Wright .07 .20
634 Steve Parris .07 .20
635 Gene Kingsale .07 .20
636 Tim Worrell .07 .20
637 Billy Martin .07 .20
638 Jovanny Cedeno .07 .20
639 Curtis Leskanic .07 .20
640 Tim Hudson .10 .30
641 Juan Castro .07 .20
642 Rafael Soriano .07 .20
643 Juan Rincon .07 .20
644 Mark DeRosa .07 .20
645 Carlos Pena .07 .20
646 Robin Ventura .10 .30
647 Odalis Perez .07 .20
648 Damion Easley .07 .20
649 Benito Santiago .10 .30
650 Alex Rodriguez .50 1.25
651 Aaron Rowand .10 .30
652 Alex Cora .07 .20
653 Bobby Kielty .07 .20
654 Jose Rodriguez RC .15 .40
655 Herbert Perry .07 .20
656 Jeff Urban .07 .20
657 Paul Bako .07 .20
658 Shane Spencer .07 .20
659 Pat Hentgen .07 .20
660 Jeff Kent .10 .30
661 Mark McLemore .07 .20
662 Chuck Knoblauch .10 .30
663 Blake Stein .07 .20
664 Brett Roneberg RC .15 .40
665 Josh Phelps .07 .20
666 Byung-Hyun Kim .10 .30
667 Dave Martinez .07 .20
668 Mike Maroth .07 .20
669 Shawn Chacon .07 .20
670 Billy Wagner .10 .30
671 Luis Alicea .07 .20
672 Sterling Hitchcock .07 .20
673 Adam Piatt .07 .20
674 Ryan Franklin .07 .20
675 Luke Prokopec .07 .20
676 Alfredo Amezaga .07 .20
677 Gookie Dawkins .07 .20
678 Eric Byrnes .07 .20
679 Barry Larkin .20 .50
680 Albert Pujols .60 1.50
681 Edwards Guzman .07 .20
682 Jason Bere .07 .20
683 Adam Everett .07 .20
684 Greg Colbrunn .07 .20
685 Brandon Puffer RC .15 .40
686 Mark Kotsay .10 .30
687 Willie Bloomquist .10 .30
688 Hank Blalock .20 .50
689 Travis Hafner .10 .30
690 Lance Berkman .10 .30
691 Joe Crede .10 .30
692 Chuck Finley .10 .30
693 John Grabow .07 .20
694 Randy Winn .07 .20
695 Mike James .07 .20
696 Kris Benson .07 .20
697 Bret Prinz .07 .20
698 Jeff Williams .07 .20
699 Eric Munson .07 .20
700 Mike Hampton .10 .30
701 Ramon E. Martinez .07 .20
702 Hansel Izquierdo RC .15 .40
703 Nathan Haynes .07 .20
704 Eddie Taubensee .07 .20
705 Esteban German .07 .20
706 Ross Gload .07 .20
707 Matt Merricks RC .15 .40
708 Chris Piersoll RC .08 .25
709 Seth Greisinger .07 .20
710 Ichiro Suzuki .60 1.50
711 Cesar Izturis .07 .20
712 Brad Cresse .07 .20
713 Carl Pavano .10 .30
714 Steve Sparks .07 .20
715 Dennis Tankersley .07 .20
716 Kelvim Escobar .07 .20
717 Jason LaRue .07 .20
718 Corey Koskie .07 .20
719 Vinny Castilla .10 .30
720 Tim Drew .07 .20
721 Chin-Hui Tsao .10 .30
722 Paul Byrd .07 .20
723 Alex Cintron .07 .20
724 Orlando Palmeiro .07 .20
725 Ramon Hernandez .07 .20
726 Mark Johnson .07 .20
727 B.J. Ryan .07 .20
728 Wendell Magee .07 .20
729 Michael Coleman .07 .20
730 Mario Ramos RC .15 .40
731 Mike Stanton .07 .20
732 Dee Brown .07 .20
733 Brad Ausmus .10 .30
734 Napoleon Calzado RC .15 .40
735 Woody Williams .07 .20
736 Paxton Crawford .07 .20
737 Jason Karnuth .07 .20
738 Michael Restovich .07 .20
739 Ramon Castro .07 .20
740 Magglio Ordonez .10 .30
741 Tom Gordon .07 .20
742 Mark Grudzielanek .07 .20
743 Jaime Moyer .10 .30
744 Marlyn Tisdale RC .15 .40
745 Steve Kline .07 .20
746 Adam Eaton .07 .20
747 Eric Glaser RC .15 .40
748 Sean DePaula .07 .20
749 Greg Norton .07 .20
750 Steve Reed .07 .20
751 Ricardo Aramboles .07 .20
752 Matt Mantei .07 .20
753 Gene Stechschulte .07 .20
754 Chuck McElroy .07 .20
755 Barry Bonds .75 2.00
756 Matt Anderson .07 .20
757 Yorvit Torrealba .07 .20
758 Jason Standridge .07 .20
759 Desi Relaford .07 .20
760 Jolbert Cabrera .07 .20
761 Chris George .07 .20
762 Erubiel Durazo .07 .20
763 Paul Konerko .10 .30
764 Tike Redman .07 .20
765 Chad Ricketts RC .08 .25
766 Roberto Hernandez .07 .20
767 Mark Lewis .07 .20
768 Livan Hernandez .10 .30
769 Carlos Brackley RC .15 .40
770 Kazuhiro Sasaki .10 .30
771 Bill Hall .10 .30
772 Nelson Castro RC .15 .40
773 Eric Milton .07 .20
774 Tom Davey .07 .20
775 Todd Ritchie .07 .20
776 Seth Etherton .07 .20
777 Chris Singleton .07 .20
778 Robert Averette RC .08 .25
779 Robert Person .07 .20
780 Fred McGriff .20 .50
781 Richard Hidalgo .07 .20
782 Kris Wilson .07 .20
783 John Rocker .10 .30
784 Justin Kaye .07 .20
785 Glendon Rusch .07 .20
786 Greg Vaughn .07 .20
787 Mike Lamb .07 .20
788 Greg Myers .07 .20
789 Nate Field RC .15 .40
790 Jim Edmonds .10 .30
791 Olmedo Saenz .07 .20
792 Jason Johnson .07 .20
793 Mike Lincoln .07 .20
794 Todd Coffey RC .15 .40
795 Jesus Sanchez .07 .20
796 Aaron Myette .07 .20
797 Tony Womack .07 .20
798 Chad Kreuter .07 .20
799 Brady Clark .07 .20
800 Adam Dunn .10 .30
801 Jacque Jones .10 .30
802 Kevin Millwood .10 .30
803 Mike Rivera .07 .20
804 Jim Thome .20 .50
805 Jeff Conine .10 .30
806 Elmer Dessens .07 .20
807 Randy Velarde .07 .20
808 Carlos Delgado .10 .30
809 Steve Karsay .07 .20
810 Casey Fossum .07 .20
811 J.C. Romero .07 .20
812 Chris Truby .07 .20
813 Tony Graffanino .07 .20
814 Wascar Serrano .07 .20
815 Delvin James .07 .20
816 Pedro Feliz .07 .20
817 Damian Rolls .07 .20
818 Scott Linebrink .07 .20
819 Rafael Palmeiro .20 .50
820 Javy Lopez .10 .30
821 Larry Barnes .07 .20
822 Brian Lawrence .07 .20
823 Scotty Layfield RC .15 .40
824 Jeff Cirillo .07 .20
825 Willis Roberts .07 .20
826 Rich Harden RC 1.25 3.00
827 Chris Snelling RC .25 .60
828 Gary Sheffield .10 .30
829 Jeff Heaverlo .07 .20
830 Matt Clement .10 .30
831 Rich Garces .07 .20
832 Rondell White .10 .30
833 Henry Pichardo RC .15 .40
834 Aaron Boone .10 .30
835 Ruben Sierra .10 .30
836 Deivis Santos .07 .20
837 Tony Batista .07 .20
838 Rob Bell .07 .20
839 Frank Thomas .30 .75
840 Jose Silva .07 .20
841 Dan Johnson RC .40 1.00
842 Steve Cox .07 .20
843 Jose Acevedo .07 .20
844 Jay Bell .10 .30
845 Mike Sirotka .07 .20
846 Garret Anderson .10 .30
847 James Shanks RC .15 .40
848 Trot Nixon .10 .30
849 Keith Ginter .07 .20
850 Tim Spooneybarger .07 .20
851 Matt Stairs .07 .20
852 Chris Stynes .07 .20
853 Marvin Benard .07 .20
854 Raul Mondesi .10 .30
855 Jeremy Owens .07 .20
856 Jon Garland .10 .30
857 Mitch Meluskey .07 .20
858 Chad Durbin .07 .20
859 John Burkett .07 .20
860 Jon Switzer RC .15 .40
861 Peter Bergeron .07 .20
862 Jesus Colome .07 .20
863 Todd Hundley .07 .20
864 Ben Petrick .07 .20
865 So Taguchi RC .20 .50
866 Ryan Drese .07 .20
867 Mike Trombley .07 .20
868 Rick Reed .07 .20
869 Mark Teixeira .30 .75
870 Corey Thurman RC .15 .40
871 Brian Roberts .10 .30
872 Mike Timlin .07 .20
873 Chris Reitsma .07 .20
874 Jeff Fassero .07 .20
875 Carlos Valderrama .07 .20
876 John Lackey .07 .20
877 Travis Fryman .10 .30
878 Ismael Valdes .07 .20
879 Rick White .07 .20
880 Edgar Martinez .20 .50
881 Dean Palmer .10 .30
882 Matt Allegra RC .15 .40
883 Greg Sain RC .15 .40
884 Carlos Silva .07 .20
885 Jose Valverde RC .15 .40
886 Dernell Stenson .07 .20
887 Todd Van Poppel .07 .20
888 Wes Anderson .07 .20
889 Bill Mueller .10 .30
890 Morgan Ensberg .10 .30
891 Marcus Thames .07 .20
892 Adam Walker RC .15 .40
893 John Halama .07 .20
894 Frank Menechino .07 .20
895 Greg Maddux .50 1.25
896 Gary Bennett .07 .20
897 Mauricio Lara RC .15 .40
898 Mike Young .30 .75
899 Travis Phelps .07 .20
900 Rich Aurilia .07 .20
901 Henry Blanco .07 .20
902 Carlos Febles .07 .20
903 Scott MacRae .07 .20
904 Lou Merloni .07 .20
905 Dicky Gonzalez .07 .20
906 Jeff DaVanon .07 .20
907 A.J. Burnett .10 .30
908 Einar Diaz .07 .20
909 Julio Franco .10 .30
910 John Olerud .10 .30
911 Mark Hamilton RC .15 .40
912 David Riske .07 .20
913 Jason Tyner .07 .20
914 Britt Reames .07 .20
915 Vernon Wells .10 .30
916 Eddie Perez .07 .20
917 Edwin Almonte RC .15 .40
918 Enrique Wilson .07 .20
919 Chris Gomez .07 .20
920 Jayson Werth .07 .20
921 Jeff Nelson .07 .20
922 Freddy Sanchez RC .75 2.00
923 John Vander Wal .07 .20
924 Chad Qualls RC .20 .50
925 Gabe White .07 .20
926 Chad Harville .07 .20
927 Ricky Gutierrez .07 .20
928 Carlos Guillen .10 .30
929 B.J. Surhoff .10 .30
930 Chris Woodward .07 .20
931 Ricardo Rodriguez .07 .20
932 Jimmy Gobble RC .15 .40
933 Jon Lieber .07 .20
934 Craig Kuzmic RC .15 .40
935 Eric Young .07 .20
936 Greg Zaun .07 .20
937 Miguel Batista .07 .20
938 Danny Wright .07 .20
939 Todd Zeile .10 .30
940 Chad Zerbe .07 .20
941 Jason Young RC .08 .25
942 Ronnie Belliard .07 .20
943 John Ennis RC .15 .40
944 John Flaherty .07 .20
945 Jerry Hairston Jr. .07 .20
946 Al Levine .07 .20
947 Antonio Alfonseca .07 .20
948 Brian Moehler .07 .20
949 Calvin Murray .07 .20
950 Nick Bierbrodt .07 .20
951 Sun Woo Kim .07 .20
952 Noochie Varner RC .15 .40
953 Luis Rivas .07 .20
954 Donnie Bridges .07 .20
955 Ramon Vazquez .07 .20
956 Luis Garcia .07 .20
957 Mark Quinn .07 .20
958 Armando Rios .07 .20
959 Chad Fox .07 .20
960 Hee Seop Choi .07 .20
961 Turk Wendell .07 .20
962 Adam Roller RC .15 .40
963 Grant Roberts .07 .20
964 Ben Molina .07 .20
965 Juan Rivera .07 .20
966 Matt Kinney .07 .20
967 Rod Beck .07 .20
968 Xavier Nady .07 .20
969 Masato Yoshii .07 .20
970 Miguel Tejada .10 .30
971 Danny Kolb .07 .20
972 Mike Remlinger .07 .20
973 Ray Lankford .10 .30
974 Ryan Minor .07 .20
975 J.T. Snow .10 .30
976 Brad Radke .10 .30
977 Jason Lane .10 .30
978 Jamey Wright .07 .20
979 Tom Goodwin .07 .20
980 Erik Bedard .10 .30
981 Gabe Kapler .10 .30
982 Brian Reith .07 .20
983 Nic Jackson RC .15 .40
984 Kurt Ainsworth .07 .20
985 Jason Isringhausen .10 .30
986 Willie Harris .07 .20
987 David Cone .10 .30
988 Bob Wickman .07 .20
989 Wes Helms .07 .20
990 Josh Beckett .10 .30

2002 Topps Total Award Winners

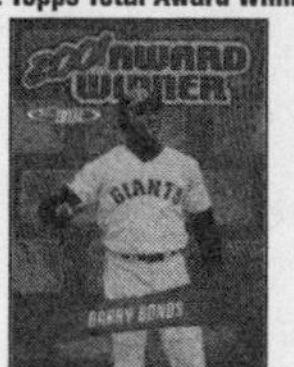

Issued at a stated rate of one in six, these 30 cards honored players who have won major awards during their career.

COMPLETE SET (30) 15.00 40.00
AW1 Ichiro Suzuki 1.50 4.00
AW2 Albert Pujols 1.50 4.00
AW3 Barry Bonds 2.00 5.00
AW4 Ichiro Suzuki 1.50 4.00
AW5 Randy Johnson .75 2.00
AW6 Roger Clemens 1.50 4.00
AW7 Jason Giambi A's .30 .75
AW8 Bret Boone .30 .75
AW9 Troy Glaus .30 .75
AW10 Alex Rodriguez 1.25 3.00
AW11 Juan Gonzalez .30 .75
AW12 Ichiro Suzuki 1.50 4.00
AW13 Jorge Posada .50 1.25
AW14 Edgar Martinez .50 1.25
AW15 Todd Helton .50 1.25
AW16 Jeff Kent .30 .75
AW17 Albert Pujols 1.50 4.00
AW18 Rich Aurilia .30 .75
AW19 Barry Bonds 2.00 5.00
AW20 Luis Gonzalez .30 .75
AW21 Sammy Sosa .75 2.00
AW22 Mike Piazza 1.25 3.00
AW23 Mike Hampton .30 .75
AW24 Ruben Sierra .30 .75
AW25 Matt Morris .30 .75
AW26 Curt Schilling .30 .75
AW27 Alex Rodriguez 1.25 3.00
AW28 Barry Bonds 2.00 5.00
AW29 Jim Thome .50 1.25
AW30 Barry Bonds 2.00 5.00

2002 Topps Total Production

Issued at a stated rate of one in 12, these 10 cards feature players who are among the best in the game in producing large offensive numbers.

COMPLETE SET (10) 8.00 20.00
TP1 Alex Rodriguez 1.25 3.00
TP2 Barry Bonds 2.00 5.00
TP3 Ichiro Suzuki 1.50 4.00
TP4 Edgar Martinez .50 1.25
TP5 Jason Giambi .50 1.25
TP6 Todd Helton .50 1.25
TP7 Nomar Garciaparra 1.25 3.00
TP8 Vladimir Guerrero .75 2.00
TP9 Sammy Sosa .75 2.00
TP10 Chipper Jones .75 2.00

2002 Topps Total Team Checklists

Seeded at a rate of approximately two in every three packs, these 30 cards feature team checklists for the 990-card Topps Total set. The card fronts are identical to the corresponding basic issue Topps Total cards. But the card backs feature a checklist of players (unlike basic issue cards of which feature statistics and career information on the specific player pictured on front). In addition, unlike basic issue Topps Total cards, these Team Checklist cards do not feature glossy coating on front and back.

COMPLETE SET (30) 4.00 10.00
TTC1 Troy Glaus .07 .20
TTC2 Randy Johnson .20 .50
TTC3 Chipper Jones .20 .50
TTC4 Scott Erickson .07 .20
TTC5 Nomar Garciaparra .30 .75
TTC6 Sammy Sosa .20 .50
TTC7 Magglio Ordonez .07 .20
TTC8 Ken Griffey Jr. .30 .75
TTC9 Jim Thome .10 .30
TTC10 Todd Helton .10 .30
TTC11 Bobby Higginson .07 .20
TTC12 Josh Beckett .07 .20
TTC13 Jeff Bagwell .10 .30
TTC14 Mike Sweeney .07 .20
TTC15 Shawn Green .07 .20
TTC16 Geoff Jenkins .07 .20
TTC17 Cristian Guzman .07 .20
TTC18 Vladimir Guerrero .20 .50
TTC19 Mike Piazza .30 .75
TTC20 Derek Jeter .50 1.25
TTC21 Eric Chavez .07 .20
TTC22 Pat Burrell .07 .20
TTC23 Brian Giles .07 .20
TTC24 Phil Nevin .07 .20
TTC25 Ichiro Suzuki .40 1.00
TTC26 Barry Bonds .50 1.25
TTC27 J.D. Drew .07 .20
TTC28 Carlos Delgado .07 .20
TTC29 Toby Hall .07 .20
TTC30 Alex Rodriguez

2002 Topps Total Topps

Inserted in packs at a stated rate of one in three, these 50 cards feature some of the leading players in the game.

COMPLETE SET (50) 20.00 50.00
TT1 Roberto Alomar .50 1.25
TT2 Moises Alou .30 .75
TT3 Jeff Bagwell .50 1.25
TT4 Lance Berkman .30 .75

TT5 Barry Bonds 2.00 5.00
TT6 Bret Boone .30 .75
TT7 Kevin Brown .30 .75
TT8 Eric Chavez .30 .75
TT9 Roger Clemens 1.50 4.00
TT10 Carlos Delgado .30 .75
TT11 Cliff Floyd .30 .75
TT12 Nomar Garciaparra 1.25 3.00
TT13 Jason Giambi .30 .75
TT14 Brian Giles .30 .75
TT15 Troy Glaus .30 .75
TT16 Tom Glavine .50 1.25
TT17 Luis Gonzalez .30 .75
TT18 Juan Gonzalez .30 .75
TT19 Shawn Green .30 .75
TT20 Ken Griffey Jr. 1.25 3.00
TT21 Vladimir Guerrero .75 2.00
TT22 Jorge Posada .50 1.25
TT23 Todd Helton .50 1.25
TT24 Tim Hudson .30 .75
TT25 Derek Jeter 2.00 5.00
TT26 Randy Johnson .75 2.00
TT27 Andruw Jones .50 1.25
TT28 Chipper Jones .75 2.00
TT29 Jeff Kent .30 .75
TT30 Greg Maddux 1.25 3.00
TT31 Edgar Martinez .50 1.25
TT32 Pedro Martinez .50 1.25
TT33 Magglio Ordonez .30 .75
TT34 Rafael Palmeiro .50 1.25
TT35 Mike Piazza 1.25 3.00
TT36 Albert Pujols 1.50 4.00
TT37 Aramis Ramirez .30 .75
TT38 Mariano Rivera .75 2.00
TT39 Alex Rodriguez 1.25 3.00
TT40 Ivan Rodriguez .50 1.25
TT41 Curt Schilling .30 .75
TT42 Gary Sheffield .30 .75
TT43 Sammy Sosa .75 2.00
TT44 Ichiro Suzuki 1.50 4.00
TT45 Miguel Tejada .30 .75
TT46 Frank Thomas .75 2.00
TT47 Jim Thome .50 1.25
TT48 Larry Walker .30 .75
TT49 Bernie Williams .50 1.25
TT50 Kerry Wood .30 .75

2003 Topps Total

For the second straight year, Topps issued this 990 card set which was designed to be a comprehensive look at who was in the majors at the time of issue. This set was released in May, 2003. This set was issued in 10 card packs with an 99 cent SRP which came 36 packs to a box and 6 boxes to a case.

COMPLETE SET (990) 100.00 200.00
COMMON CARD (1-990) .07 .20
COMMON RC .08 .25
1 Brent Abernathy .07 .20
2 Bobby Hill .07 .20
3 Victor Martinez .12 .30
4 Chip Ambres .07 .20
5 Matt Anderson .07 .20
6 Ricardo Aramboles .07 .20
7 Carlos Pena .12 .30
8 Aaron Guiel .07 .20
9 Luke Allen .07 .20
10 Francisco Rodriguez .12 .30
11 Jason Marquis .07 .20
12 Edwin Almonte .07 .20
13 Grant Balfour .07 .20
14 Adam Piatt .07 .20
15 Andy Phillips .07 .20
16 Adrian Beltre .07 .20
17 Brandon Backe .07 .20
18 Dave Berg .07 .20
19 Brett Myers .07 .20
20 Brian Meadows .07 .20
21 Chin-Feng Chen .07 .20
22 Blake Williams .07 .20
23 Josh Bard .07 .20
24 Josh Beckett .12 .30
25 Tommy Whiteman .07 .20
26 Matt Childers .07 .20
27 Adam Everett .07 .20
28 Mike Bordick .07 .20
29 Antonio Alfonseca .07 .20
30 Doug Creek .07 .20
31 J.D. Drew .07 .20
32 Milton Bradley .07 .20
33 David Wells .07 .20
34 Vance Wilson .07 .20
35 Jeff Fassero .07 .20
36 Sandy Alomar Jr. .07 .20
37 Ryan Vogelsong .07 .20
38 Roger Clemens .25 .60
39 Juan Gonzalez .07 .20
40 Dustin Hermanson .07 .20
41 Andy Ashby .07 .20
42 Adam Hyzdu .07 .20
43 Ben Broussard .07 .20
44 Ryan Klesko .07 .20
45 Chris Buglovsky FY RC .15 .40
46 Bud Smith .07 .20
47 Aaron Boone .07 .20
48 Cliff Floyd .07 .20
49 Alex Cora .07 .20
50 Curt Schilling .12 .30
51 Michael Cuddyer .07 .20
52 Joe Valentine FY RC .15 .40
53 Carlos Guillen .07 .20
54 Angel Berroa .07 .20
55 Eli Marrero .07 .20
56 A.J. Burnett .12 .30
57 Oliver Perez .07 .20
58 Matt Morris .07 .20
59 Valerio De Los Santos .07 .20
60 Austin Kearns .07 .20
61 Darren Dreifort .07 .20
62 Jason Standridge .07 .20
63 Carlos Silva .07 .20
64 Moises Alou .07 .20
65 Jason Anderson .07 .20
66 Russell Branyan .07 .20
67 B.J. Ryan .07 .20
68 Cory Aldridge .07 .20
69 Ellis Burks .07 .20
70 Troy Glaus .07 .20
71 Kelly Wunsch .07 .20
72 Brad Wilkerson .07 .20
73 Jayson Durocher .07 .20
74 Tony Fiore .07 .20
75 Brian Giles .07 .20
76 Billy Wagner .07 .20
77 Neifi Perez .07 .20
78 Jose Valverde .07 .20
79 Brent Butler .07 .20
80 Mario Ramos .07 .20
81 Kerry Robinson .07 .20
82 Brent Mayne .07 .20
83 Sean Casey .07 .20
84 Danys Baez .07 .20
85 Chase Utley .20 .50
86 Jared Sandberg .07 .20
87 Terrence Long .07 .20
88 Kevin Walker .07 .20
89 Royce Clayton .07 .20
90 Shea Hillenbrand .07 .20
91 Brad Lidge .07 .20
92 Shawn Chacon .07 .20
93 Kenny Rogers .07 .20
94 Chris Snelling .07 .20
95 Omar Vizquel .12 .30
96 Joe Borchard .07 .20
97 Matt Belisle .07 .20
98 Steve Smyth .07 .20
99 Raul Mondesi .07 .20
100 Chipper Jones .20 .50
101 Victor Alvarez .07 .20
102 J.M. Gold .07 .20
103 Willis Roberts .07 .20
104 Eddie Guardado .07 .20
105 Brad Voyles .07 .20
106 Bronson Arroyo .07 .20
107 Juan Castro .07 .20
108 Dan Plesac .07 .20
109 Ramon Castro .07 .20
110 Tim Salmon .07 .20
111 Gene Kingsale .07 .20
112 J.D. Closser .07 .20
113 Mark Buehrle .12 .30
114 Steve Karsay .07 .20
115 Cristian Guerrero .07 .20
116 Brad Ausmus .07 .20
117 Cristian Guzman .07 .20
118 Dan Wilson .07 .20
119 Jake Westbrook .07 .20
120 Manny Ramirez .20 .50
121 Jason Giambi .07 .20
122 Bob Wickman .07 .20
123 Aaron Cook .07 .20
124 Alfredo Amezaga .07 .20
125 Corey Thurman .07 .20
126 Brandon Puffer .07 .20
127 Hee Seop Choi .07 .20
128 Javier Vazquez .07 .20
129 Carlos Valderrama .07 .20
130 Jerome Williams .07 .20
131 Wilson Betemit .07 .20
132 Luke Prokopec .07 .20
133 Esteban Yan .07 .20
134 Brandon Berger .07 .20
135 Bill Hall .07 .20
136 LaTroy Hawkins .07 .20
137 Nate Cornejo .07 .20
138 Jim Mecir .07 .20
139 Joe Crede .07 .20
140 Andres Galarraga .07 .20
141 Reggie Sanders .07 .20
142 Joey Eischen .07 .20
143 Mike Timlin .07 .20
144 Jose Cruz Jr. .07 .20
145 Wes Helms .07 .20
146 Brian Roberts .07 .20
147 Bret Prinz .07 .20
148 Brian Hunter .07 .20
149 Chad Hermansen .07 .20
150 Andruw Jones .07 .20
151 Kurt Ainsworth .07 .20
152 Cliff Bartosh .07 .20
153 Kyle Lohse .07 .20
154 Brian Jordan .07 .20
155 Coco Crisp .07 .20
156 Tomas Perez .07 .20
157 Keith Foulke .07 .20
158 Chris Carpenter .20 .50
159 Mike Remlinger .07 .20
160 Dewon Brazelton .07 .20
161 Brook Fordyce .07 .20
162 Rusty Greer .07 .20
163 Scott Downs .07 .20
164 Jason Dubois .07 .20
165 David Coggin .07 .20
166 Mike DeJean .07 .20
167 Carlos Hernandez .07 .20
168 Matt Williams .07 .20
169 Rheal Cormier .07 .20
170 Duaner Sanchez .07 .20
171 Craig Counsell .07 .20
172 Edgar Martinez .12 .30
173 Zack Greinke .12 .30
174 Pedro Feliz .07 .20
175 Randy Choate .07 .20
176 Jon Garland .07 .20
177 Keith Ginter .07 .20
178 Carlos Febles .07 .20
179 Kerry Wood .07 .20
180 Jack Cust .07 .20
181 Koyie Hill .07 .20
182 Ricky Gutierrez .07 .20
183 Ben Grieve .07 .20
184 Scott Eyre .07 .20
185 Jason Isringhausen .07 .20
186 Gookie Dawkins .07 .20
187 Roberto Alomar .12 .30
188 Eric Junge .07 .20
189 Carlos Beltran .07 .20
190 Denny Hocking .07 .20
191 Jason Schmidt .07 .20
192 Cory Lidle .07 .20
193 Rob Mackowiak .07 .20
194 Charlton Jimerson RC .15 .40
195 Darin Erstad .07 .20
196 Jason Davis .07 .20
197 Luis Castillo .07 .20
198 Juan Encarnacion .07 .20
199 Jeffrey Hammonds .07 .20
200 Nomar Garciaparra .20 .50
201 Ryan Christianson .07 .20
202 Robert Person .07 .20
203 Damian Moss .07 .20
204 Chris Richard .07 .20
205 Todd Hundley .07 .20
206 Paul Bako .07 .20
207 Adam Kennedy .07 .20
208 Scott Hatteberg .07 .20
209 Andy Pratt .07 .20
210 Ken Griffey Jr. .30 .75
211 Chris George .07 .20
212 Lance Niekro .07 .20
213 Greg Colbrunn .07 .20
214 Herbert Perry .07 .20
215 Cody Ransom .07 .20
216 Craig Biggio .12 .30
217 Miguel Batista .07 .20
218 Alex Escobar .07 .20
219 Willie Harris .07 .20
220 Scott Strickland .07 .20
221 Felix Rodriguez .07 .20
222 Torii Hunter .07 .20
223 Tyler Houston .07 .20
224 Darrell May .07 .20
225 Benito Santiago .07 .20
226 Ryan Dempster .07 .20
227 Andy Fox .07 .20
228 Jung Bong .07 .20
229 Jose Macias .07 .20
230 Shannon Stewart .07 .20
231 Buddy Groom .07 .20
232 Eric Valent .07 .20
233 Scott Schoenweis .07 .20
234 Corey Hart .07 .20
235 Brett Tomko .07 .20
236 Shane Bazzell RC .15 .40
237 Tim Hummel .07 .20
238 Matt Stairs .07 .20
239 Pete Munro .07 .20
240 Ismael Valdes .07 .20
241 Brian Fuentes .07 .20
242 Cesar Izturis .07 .20
243 Mark Bellhorn .07 .20
244 Geoff Jenkins .07 .20
245 Derek Jeter .50 1.25
246 Anderson Machado .07 .20
247 Dave Roberts .07 .20
248 Jaime Cerda .07 .20
249 Woody Williams .07 .20
250 Vernon Wells .07 .20
251 Jon Lieber .07 .20
252 Franklyn German .07 .20
253 David Segui .07 .20
254 Freddy Garcia .07 .20
255 James Baldwin .07 .20
256 Tony Alvarez .07 .20
257 Walter Young .07 .20
258 Alex Herrera .07 .20
259 Robert Fick .07 .20
260 Rob Bell .07 .20
261 Ben Petrick .07 .20
262 Dee Brown .07 .20
263 Mike Bacsik .07 .20
264 Corey Patterson .07 .20
265 Marvin Benard .07 .20
266 Eddie Rogers .07 .20
267 Elio Serrano .07 .20
268 D'Angelo Jimenez .07 .20
269 Adam Johnson .07 .20
270 Gregg Zaun .07 .20
271 Nick Johnson .07 .20
272 Geoff Goetz .07 .20
273 Ryan Drese .07 .20
274 Eric Dubose .07 .20
275 Barry Zito .07 .20
276 Mike Crudale .07 .20
277 Paul Byrd .07 .20
278 Eric Gagne .07 .20
279 Aramis Ramirez .07 .20
280 Ray Durham .07 .20
281 Tony Graffanino .07 .20
282 Jeremy Guthrie .07 .20
283 Erik Bedard .07 .20
284 Vince Faison .07 .20
285 Bobby Kielty .07 .20
286 Francis Beltran .07 .20
287 Alexis Gomez .07 .20
288 Vladimir Guerrero .20 .50
289 Kevin Appier .07 .20
290 Gil Meche .07 .20
291 Marquis Grissom .07 .20
292 John Burkett .07 .20
293 Vinny Castilla .07 .20
294 Tyler Walker .07 .20
295 Shane Halter .07 .20
296 Geronimo Gil .07 .20
297 Eric Hinske .07 .20
298 Adam Dunn .12 .30
299 Mike Kinkade .07 .20
300 Mark Prior .12 .30
301 Corey Koskie .07 .20
302 David Dellucci .07 .20
303 Todd Helton .12 .30
304 Greg Miller .07 .20
305 Delvin James .07 .20
306 Humberto Cota .07 .20
307 Aaron Harang .07 .20
308 Jeremy Hill .07 .20
309 Billy Koch .07 .20
310 Brandon Claussen .07 .20
311 Matt Ginter .07 .20
312 Jason Lane .07 .20
313 Ben Weber .07 .20
314 Alan Benes .07 .20
315 Matt Walbeck .07 .20
316 Danny Graves .07 .20
317 Jason Johnson .07 .20
318 Jason Grimsley .07 .20
319 Steve Kline .07 .20
320 Johnny Damon .12 .30
321 Jay Gibbons .07 .20
322 J.J. Putz .07 .20
323 Stephen Randolph RC .15 .40
324 Bobby Higginson .07 .20
325 Kazuhisa Ishii .07 .20
326 Carlos Lee .07 .20
327 J.R. House .07 .20
328 Mark Loretta .07 .20
329 Mike Matheny .07 .20
330 Ben Diggins .07 .20
331 Seth Etherton .07 .20
332 Eli Whiteside FY RC .15 .40
333 Juan Rivera .07 .20
334 Jeff Conine .07 .20
335 John McDonald .07 .20
336 Erik Hiljus .07 .20
337 David Eckstein .07 .20
338 Jeff Bagwell .12 .30
339 Matt Holliday .20 .50
340 Jeff Liefer .07 .20
341 Greg Myers .07 .20
342 Scott Sauerbeck .07 .20
343 Omar Infante .07 .20
344 Ryan Langerhans .07 .20
345 Abraham Nunez .07 .20
346 Mike MacDougal .07 .20
347 Travis Phelps .07 .20
348 Terry Shumpert .07 .20
349 Alex Rodriguez .30 .75
350 Bobby Seay .07 .20
351 Ichiro Suzuki .30 .75
352 Brandon Inge .07 .20
353 Jack Wilson .07 .20
354 John Ennis .07 .20
355 Jamal Strong .07 .20
356 Jason Jennings .07 .20
357 Jeff Kent .07 .20
358 Scott Chiasson .07 .20
359 Jeremy Griffiths RC .15 .40
360 Paul Konerko .12 .30
361 Jeff Austin .07 .20
362 Todd Van Poppel .07 .20
363 Sun Woo Kim .07 .20
364 Jerry Hairston Jr. .07 .20
365 Tony Torcato .07 .20
366 Arthur Rhodes .07 .20
367 Jose Jimenez .07 .20
368 Matt LeCroy .07 .20
369 Curtis Leskanic .07 .20
370 Ramon Vazquez .07 .20
371 Joe Randa .07 .20
372 John Franco .07 .20
373 Bobby Estalella .07 .20
374 Craig Wilson .07 .20
375 Michael Young .07 .20
376 Mark Ellis .07 .20
377 Joe Mauer .20 .50
378 Checklist 1 .07 .20
379 Jason Kendall .07 .20
380 Checklist 2 .07 .20
381 Alex Gonzalez .07 .20
382 Tom Gordon .07 .20
383 John Buck .07 .20
384 Shigetoshi Hasegawa .07 .20
385 Scott Stewart .07 .20
386 Luke Hudson .07 .20
387 Todd Jones .07 .20
388 Fred McGriff .12 .30
389 Mike Sweeney .07 .20
390 Marlon Anderson .07 .20
391 Terry Adams .07 .20
392 Mark DeRosa .07 .20
393 Doug Mientkiewicz .07 .20
394 Miguel Cairo .07 .20
395 Jamie Moyer .07 .20
396 Jose Leon .07 .20
397 Matt Clement .07 .20
398 Bengie Molina .07 .20
399 Marcus Thames .07 .20
400 Nick Bierbrodt .07 .20
401 Tim Kalita .07 .20
402 Corwin Malone .07 .20
403 Jesse Orosco .07 .20
404 Brandon Phillips .07 .20
405 Eric Cyr .07 .20
406 Jason Michaels .07 .20
407 Julio Lugo .07 .20
408 Gabe Kapler .07 .20
409 Mark Mulder .07 .20
410 Adam Eaton .07 .20
411 Ken Harvey .07 .20
412 Jolbert Cabrera .07 .20
413 Eric Milton .07 .20
414 Josh Hall RC .15 .40
415 Bob File .07 .20
416 Brett Evert .07 .20
417 Ron Chiavacci .07 .20
418 Jorge De La Rosa .07 .20
419 Quinton McCracken .07 .20
420 Luther Hackman .07 .20
421 Gary Knotts .07 .20
422 Kevin Brown .07 .20
423 Jeff Cirillo .07 .20
424 Damaso Marte .07 .20
425 Chan Ho Park .12 .30
426 Nathan Haynes .07 .20
427 Matt Lawton .07 .20
428 Mike Stanton .07 .20
429 Bernie Williams .12 .30
430 Kevin Jarvis .07 .20
431 Joe McEwing .07 .20
432 Mark Kotsay .07 .20
433 Juan Cruz .07 .20
434 Russ Ortiz .07 .20
435 Jeff Nelson .07 .20
436 Alan Embree .07 .20
437 Miguel Tejada .12 .30
438 Kirk Saarloos .07 .20
439 Cliff Lee .12 .30
440 Ryan Ludwick .07 .20
441 Derrek Lee .07 .20
442 Bobby Abreu .07 .20
443 Dustan Mohr .07 .20
444 Nook Logan RC .20 .50
445 Seth McClung .07 .20
446 Miguel Olivo .07 .20
447 Henry Blanco .07 .20
448 Seung Song .07 .20
449 Kris Wilson .07 .20
450 Xavier Nady .07 .20
451 Corky Miller .07 .20
452 Jim Thome .12 .30
453 George Lombard .07 .20
454 Rey Ordonez .07 .20
455 Deivis Santos .07 .20
456 Mike Myers .07 .20
457 Edgar Renteria .07 .20
458 Braden Looper .07 .20
459 Guillermo Mota .07 .20
460 Scott Rolen .12 .30
461 Lance Berkman .12 .30
462 Jeff Heaverlo .07 .20
463 Ramon Hernandez .07 .20
464 Jason Simontacchi .07 .20
465 So Taguchi .07 .20
466 Dave Veres .07 .20
467 Shane Loux .07 .20
468 Rodrigo Lopez .07 .20
469 Bubba Trammell .07 .20
470 Scott Sullivan .07 .20
471 Mike Mussina .12 .30
472 Ramon Ortiz .07 .20
473 Lyle Overbay .07 .20
474 Mike Lowell .07 .20
475 Al Martin .07 .20
476 Larry Bigbie .07 .20
477 Rey Sanchez .07 .20
478 Magglio Ordonez .12 .30
479 Rondell White .07 .20
480 Jay Witasick .07 .20
481 Jimmy Rollins .12 .30
482 Mike Maroth .07 .20
483 Alejandro Machado .07 .20
484 Nick Neugebauer .07 .20
485 Victor Zambrano .07 .20
486 Travis Lee .07 .20
487 Bobby Bradley .07 .20
488 Marcus Giles .07 .20
489 Steve Trachsel .07 .20
490 Derek Lowe .07 .20
491 Hideo Nomo .20 .50
492 Brad Hawpe .07 .20
493 Jesus Medrano .07 .20
494 Rick Ankiel .07 .20
495 Pasqual Coco .07 .20
496 Michael Barrett .07 .20
497 Joe Beimel .07 .20
498 Marty Cordova .07 .20
499 Aaron Sele .07 .20
500 Sammy Sosa .20 .50
501 Ivan Rodriguez .12 .30
502 Keith Osik .07 .20
503 Hank Blalock .07 .20
504 Hiram Bocachica .07 .20
505 Junior Spivey .07 .20
506 Edgardo Alfonzo .07 .20
507 Alex Graman .07 .20
508 J.J. Davis .07 .20
509 Roger Cedeno .07 .20
510 Joe Roa .07 .20
511 Wily Mo Pena .07 .20
512 Eric Munson .07 .20
513 Arnie Munoz RC .15 .40
514 Albie Lopez .07 .20
515 Andy Pettitte .12 .30
516 Jim Edmonds .12 .30
517 Jeff Davanon .07 .20
518 Aaron Myette .07 .20
519 C.C. Sabathia .12 .30
520 Gerardo Garcia .07 .20
521 Brian Schneider .07 .20
522 Wes Obermueller .07 .20
523 John Mabry .07 .20
524 Casey Fossum .07 .20
525 Toby Hall .07 .20
526 Denny Neagle .07 .20
527 Willie Bloomquist .07 .20
528 A.J. Pierzynski .07 .20
529 Bartolo Colon .07 .20
530 Chad Harville .07 .20
531 Blaine Neal .07 .20
532 Luis Terrero .07 .20
533 Reggie Taylor .07 .20
534 Melvin Mora .07 .20
535 Tino Martinez .07 .20
536 Peter Bergeron .07 .20
537 Jorge Padilla .07 .20
538 Oscar Villarreal RC .15 .40
539 David Weathers .07 .20
540 Mike Lamb .07 .20
541 Greg Norton .07 .20
542 Michael Tucker .07 .20
543 Ben Kozlowski .07 .20
544 Alex Sanchez .07 .20
545 Trey Lunsford .07 .20
546 Abraham Nunez .07 .20
547 Mike Lincoln .07 .20
548 Orlando Hernandez .07 .20
549 Kevin Mench .07 .20
550 Garret Anderson .07 .20
551 Kyle Farnsworth .07 .20
552 Kevin Olsen .07 .20
553 Joel Pineiro .07 .20
554 Jorge Julio .07 .20
555 Jose Mesa .07 .20
556 Jorge Posada .12 .30
557 Jose Ortiz .07 .20
558 Mike Tonis .07 .20
559 Gabe White .07 .20
560 Rafael Furcal .07 .20
561 Matt Franco .07 .20
562 Trey Hodges .07 .20
563 Esteban German .07 .20
564 Josh Fogg .07 .20
565 Fernando Tatis .07 .20
566 Alex Cintron .07 .20
567 Grant Roberts .07 .20
568 Gene Stechschulte .07 .20
569 Rafael Palmeiro .12 .30
570 Mike Hampton .07 .20
571 Ben Davis .07 .20
572 Dean Palmer .07 .20
573 Jerrod Riggan .07 .20
574 Nate Frese .07 .20
575 Josh Phelps .07 .20
576 Freddie Bynum .07 .20
577 Morgan Ensberg .07 .20
578 Juan Rincon .07 .20
579 Kazuhiro Sasaki .07 .20
580 Yorvit Torrealba .07 .20
581 Tim Wakefield .07 .20
582 Sterling Hitchcock .07 .20
583 Craig Paquette .07 .20
584 Kevin Millwood .07 .20
585 Damian Rolls .07 .20
586 Brad Baisley .07 .20
587 Kyle Snyder .07 .20
588 Paul Quantrill .07 .20
589 Trot Nixon .07 .20
590 J.T. Snow .07 .20
591 Kevin Young .07 .20
592 Tomo Ohka .07 .20
593 Brian Boehringer .07 .20
594 Danny Patterson .07 .20
595 Jeff Tam .07 .20
596 Anastacio Martinez .07 .20
597 Rod Barajas .07 .20
598 Octavio Dotel .07 .20
599 Jason Tyner .07 .20
600 Gary Sheffield .07 .20
601 Ruben Quevedo .07 .20
602 Jay Payton .07 .20
603 Mo Vaughn .07 .20
604 Pat Burrell .07 .20
605 Fernando Vina .07 .20
606 Wes Anderson .07 .20
607 Alex Gonzalez .07 .20
608 Ted Lilly .07 .20
609 Nick Punto .07 .20
610 Ryan Madson .07 .20
611 Odalis Perez .07 .20
612 Chris Woodward .07 .20
613 John Olerud .07 .20
614 Brad Cresse .07 .20
615 Chad Zerbe .07 .20
616 Brad Penny .07 .20
617 Barry Larkin .12 .30
618 Brandon Duckworth .07 .20
619 Brad Radke .07 .20
620 Troy Brohawn .07 .20
621 Juan Pierre .07 .20
622 Rick Reed .07 .20
623 Omar Daal .07 .20
624 Jose Hernandez .07 .20
625 Greg Maddux .30 .75
626 Henry Mateo .07 .20
627 Kip Wells .07 .20
628 Kevin Cash .07 .20
629 Wil Ledezma FY RC .15 .40
630 Luis Gonzalez .07 .20
631 Jason Conti .07 .20
632 Ricardo Rincon .07 .20
633 Mike Bynum .07 .20
634 Mike Redmond .07 .20
635 Chance Caple .07 .20
636 Chris Widger .07 .20
637 Michael Restovich .07 .20
638 Mark Grudzielanek .07 .20
639 Brandon Larson .07 .20
640 Rocco Baldelli .07 .20
641 Javy Lopez .07 .20
642 Rene Reyes .07 .20
643 Orlando Merced .07 .20
644 Jason Phillips .07 .20
645 Luis Ugueto .07 .20
646 Ron Calloway .07 .20
647 Josh Paul .07 .20
648 Todd Greene .07 .20
649 Joe Girardi .12 .30
650 Todd Ritchie .07 .20
651 Kevin Millar Sox .07 .20
652 Shawn Wooten .07 .20
653 David Riske .07 .20
654 Luis Rivas .07 .20
655 Roy Halladay .20 .50
656 Travis Driskill .07 .20
657 Ricky Ledee .07 .20
658 Timo Perez .07 .20
659 Fernando Rodney .07 .20
660 Trevor Hoffman .12 .30
661 Pat Hentgen .07 .20
662 Bret Boone .07 .20
663 Ryan Jensen .07 .20
664 Ricardo Rodriguez .07 .20
665 Jeremy Lambert .07 .20
666 Troy Percival .07 .20
667 Jon Rauch .07 .20
668 Mariano Rivera .20 .50
669 Jason LaRue .07 .20
670 J.C. Romero .07 .20
671 Cody Ross .07 .20
672 Eric Byrnes .07 .20
673 Paul Lo Duca .07 .20
674 Brad Fullmer .07 .20
675 Cliff Politte .07 .20
676 Justin Miller .07 .20
677 Nic Jackson .07 .20
678 Kris Benson .07 .20
679 Carl Sadler .07 .20
680 Joe Nathan .07 .20
681 Julio Santana .07 .20
682 Wade Miller .07 .20
683 Josh Pearce .07 .20
684 Tony Armas Jr. .07 .20
685 Al Leiter .07 .20
686 Raul Ibanez .12 .30
687 Danny Bautista .07 .20
688 Travis Hafner .07 .20
689 Carlos Zambrano .12 .30
690 Pedro Martinez .12 .30
691 Ramon Santiago .07 .20
692 Felipe Lopez .07 .20
693 David Ross .07 .20
694 Chone Figgins .07 .20
695 Antonio Osuna .07 .20
696 Jay Powell .07 .20
697 Ryan Church .07 .20
698 Alexis Rios .12 .30
699 Tanyon Sturtze .07 .20
700 Turk Wendell .07 .20
701 Richard Hidalgo .07 .20
702 Joe Mays .07 .20
703 Jorge Sosa .07 .20

704 Eric Karros .07 .20
705 Steve Finley .07 .20
706 Sean Smith FY RC .20 .50
707 Jeremy Giambi .07 .20
708 Scott Hodges .07 .20
709 Vicente Padilla .07 .20
710 Erubiel Durazo .07 .20
711 Aaron Rowand .07 .20
712 Dennis Tankersley .07 .20
713 Rick Bauer .07 .20
714 Tim Olson FY RC .15 .40
715 Jeff Urban .07 .20
716 Steve Sparks .07 .20
717 Glendon Rusch .07 .20
718 Ricky Stone .07 .20
719 Benji Gil .07 .20
720 Pete Walker .07 .20
721 Tim Worrell .07 .20
722 Michael Tejera .07 .20
723 David Kelton .07 .20
724 Britt Reames .07 .20
725 John Stephens .07 .20
726 Mark McLemore .07 .20
727 Jeff Zimmerman .07 .20
728 Checklist 3 .07 .20
729 Andres Torres .07 .20
730 Checklist 4 .07 .20
731 Johan Santana .20 .50
732 Dane Sardinha .07 .20
733 Rodrigo Rosario .07 .20
734 Frank Thomas .20 .50
735 Tom Glavine .12 .30
736 Doug Mirabelli .07 .20
737 Juan Uribe .07 .20
738 Ryan Anderson .07 .20
739 Sean Burroughs .07 .20
740 Eric Chavez .07 .20
741 Enrique Wilson .07 .20
742 Elmer Dessens .07 .20
743 Marlon Byrd .07 .20
744 Brendan Donnelly .07 .20
745 Gary Bennett .07 .20
746 Roy Oswalt .12 .30
747 Andy Van Hekken .07 .20
748 Jesus Colome .07 .20
749 Erick Almonte .07 .20
750 Frank Catalanotto .07 .20
751 Kenny Lofton .07 .20
752 Carlos Delgado .07 .20
753 Ryan Franklin .07 .20
754 Wilkin Ruan .07 .20
755 Kelvim Escobar .07 .20
756 Tim Drew .07 .20
757 Jarrod Washburn .07 .20
758 Runelvys Hernandez .07 .20
759 Cory Vance .07 .20
760 Doug Glanville .07 .20
761 Ryan Rupe .07 .20
762 Jermaine Dye .07 .20
763 Mike Cameron .07 .20
764 Scott Erickson .07 .20
765 Richie Sexson .07 .20
766 Jose Vidro .07 .20
767 Brian West .07 .20
768 Shawn Estes .07 .20
769 Brian Tallet .07 .20
770 Larry Walker .12 .30
771 Josh Hamilton .20 .50
772 Orlando Hudson .07 .20
773 Justin Morneau .20 .50
774 Ryan Bukvich .07 .20
775 Mike Gonzalez .07 .20
776 Tsuyoshi Shinjo .07 .20
777 Matt Mantei .07 .20
778 Jimmy Journell .07 .20
779 Brian Lawrence .07 .20
780 Mike Lieberthal .07 .20
781 Scott Mullen .07 .20
782 Zach Day .07 .20
783 John Thomson .07 .20
784 Ben Sheets .07 .20
785 Damon Minor .07 .20
786 Jose Valentin .07 .20
787 Armando Benitez .07 .20
788 Jamie Walker RC .10 .25
789 Preston Wilson .07 .20
790 Josh Wilson .07 .20
791 Phil Nevin .07 .20
792 Roberto Hernandez .07 .20
793 Mike Williams .07 .20
794 Jake Peavy .07 .20
795 Paul Shuey .07 .20
796 Chad Bradford .07 .20
797 Bobby Jenks .07 .20
798 Sean Douglass .07 .20
799 Damian Miller .07 .20
800 Mark Wohlers .07 .20
801 Ty Wigginton .07 .20
802 Alfonso Soriano .12 .30
803 Randy Johnson .20 .50
804 Placido Polanco .07 .20
805 Drew Henson .07 .20
806 Tony Womack .07 .20
807 Pokey Reese .07 .20
808 Albert Pujols .50 1.25
809 Henri Stanley .07 .20
810 Mike Rivera .07 .20
811 John Lackey .07 .20
812 Brian Wright FY RC .15 .40
813 Eric Good .07 .20
814 Dernell Stenson .07 .20
815 Kirk Rueter .07 .20
816 Todd Zeile .07 .20
817 Brad Thomas .07 .20
818 Shawn Sedlacek .07 .20
819 Garrett Stephenson .07 .20
820 Mark Teixeira .20 .50
821 Tim Hudson .12 .30
822 Mike Koplove .07 .20
823 Chris Reitsma .07 .20
824 Rafael Soriano .07 .20
825 Ugueth Urbina .07 .20
826 Lance Carter .07 .20
827 Colin Young .07 .20
828 Pat Strange .07 .20
829 Juan Pena .07 .20
830 Joe Thurston .07 .20
831 Shawn Green .07 .20
832 Pedro Astacio .07 .20
833 Danny Wright .07 .20
834 Wes O'Brien FY RC .15 .40
835 Luis Lopez .07 .20
836 Randall Simon .07 .20
837 Jaret Wright .07 .20
838 Jayson Werth .07 .20
839 Endy Chavez .07 .20
840 Checklist 5 .07 .20
841 Chad Paronto .07 .20
842 Randy Winn .07 .20
843 Sidney Ponson .07 .20
844 Robin Ventura .07 .20
845 Rich Aurilia .07 .20
846 Joaquin Benoit .07 .20
847 Barry Bonds .40 1.00
848 Carl Crawford .12 .30
849 Jeromy Burnitz .07 .20
850 Orlando Cabrera .07 .20
851 Luis Vizcaino .07 .20
852 Randy Wolf .07 .20
853 Todd Walker .07 .20
854 Jeremy Affeldt .07 .20
855 Einar Diaz .07 .20
856 Carl Everett .07 .20
857 Wiki Gonzalez .07 .20
858 Mike Paradis .07 .20
859 Travis Harper .07 .20
860 Mike Piazza .20 .50
861 Will Ohman .07 .20
862 Eric Young .07 .20
863 Jason Grabowski .07 .20
864 Rett Johnson RC .15 .40
865 Aubrey Huff .07 .20
866 John Smoltz .20 .50
867 Mickey Callaway .07 .20
868 Joe Kennedy .07 .20
869 Tim Redding .07 .20
870 Colby Lewis .07 .20
871 Salomon Torres .07 .20
872 Marco Scutaro .07 .20
873 Tony Batista .07 .20
874 Dmitri Young .07 .20
875 Scott Williamson .07 .20
876 Scott Spiezio .07 .20
877 John Webb .07 .20
878 Jose Acevedo .07 .20
879 Kevin Orie .07 .20
880 Jacque Jones .07 .20
881 Ben Francisco FY RC .15 .40
882 Bobby Basham FY RC .15 .40
883 Corey Shafer FY RC .15 .40
884 J.D. Durbin FY RC .15 .40
885 Chien-Ming Wang FY RC 1.50 4.00
886 Adam Stern FY RC .10 .25
887 Wayne Lydon FY RC .15 .40
888 Derell McCall FY RC .15 .40
889 Jon Nelson FY RC .20 .50
890 Willie Eyre FY RC .15 .40
891 R.Nivar-Martinez FY RC .15 .40
892 Adrian Myers FY RC .10 .25
893 Jamie Athas FY RC .15 .40
894 Ismael Castro FY RC .20 .50
895 David Martinez FY RC .15 .40
896 Terry Tiffee FY RC .15 .40
897 Nathan Panther FY RC .15 .40
898 Kyle Roat FY RC .15 .40
899 Kason Gabbard FY RC .15 .40
900 Hanley Ramirez FY RC 2.00 5.00
901 Bryan Grace FY RC .15 .40
902 B.J. Barns FY RC .15 .40
903 Greg Bruso FY RC .15 .40
904 Mike Neu FY RC .15 .40
905 Dustin Yount FY RC .20 .50
906 Shane Victorino FY RC .40 1.00
907 Brian Burgamy FY RC .15 .40
908 Beau Kemp FY RC .15 .40
909 David Corrente FY RC .15 .40
910 Dexter Cooper FY RC .15 .40
911 Chris Colton FY RC .15 .40
912 David Cash FY RC .15 .40
913 Bernie Castro FY RC .15 .40
914 Luis Hodge FY RC .15 .40
915 Jeff Clark FY RC .15 .40
916 Jason Kubel FY RC .40 1.00
917 T.J. Bohn FY RC .15 .40
918 Luke Steidlmayer FY RC .15 .40
919 Matthew Peterson FY RC .15 .40
920 Darrell Rasner FY RC .15 .40
921 Scott Tyler FY RC .20 .50
922 G.Schneidmiller FY RC .15 .40
923 Gregor Blanco FY RC .15 .40
924 Ryan Cameron FY RC .15 .40
925 Wilfredo Rodriguez FY .07 .20
926 Rajai Davis FY RC .15 .40
927 E.Bastida-Martinez FY RC .15 .40
928 Chris Duncan FY RC 1.50 4.00
929 Dave Pember FY RC .15 .40
930 Branden Florence FY RC .15 .40
931 Eric Eckenstahler FY .07 .20
932 Hong-Chih Kuo FY RC 2.00 5.00
933 Il Kim FY RC .15 .40
934 Mi. Garciaparra FY RC .15 .40
935 Kip Bouknight FY RC .20 .50
936 Gary Harris FY RC .15 .40
937 Derry Hammond FY RC .15 .40
938 Joey Gomes FY RC .15 .40
939 Donnie Hood FY RC .20 .50
940 Clay Hensley FY RC .15 .40
941 David Pahucki FY RC .15 .40
942 Wilton Reynolds FY RC .15 .40
943 Michael Hinckley FY RC .20 .50
944 Josh Willingham FY RC .40 1.00
945 Pete LaForest FY RC .15 .40
946 Pete Smart FY RC .15 .40
947 Jay Sitzman FY RC .15 .40
948 Mark Malaska FY RC .15 .40
949 Mike Gallo FY RC .15 .40
950 Matt Diaz FY RC .30 .75
951 Brennan King FY RC .15 .40
952 Ryan Howard FY RC 8.00 20.00
953 Daryl Clark FY RC .15 .40
954 Dayton Buller FY RC .15 .40
955 Rylan Reed FY RC .15 .40
956 Chris Booker FY .07 .20
957 Brandon Watson FY RC .15 .40
958 Matt DeMarco FY RC .15 .40
959 Doug Waechter FY RC .20 .50
960 Callix Crabbe FY RC .20 .50
961 Jairo Garcia FY RC .20 .50
962 Jason Perry FY RC .20 .50
963 Eric Riggs FY RC .20 .50
964 Travis Ishikawa FY RC .30 .75
965 Simon Pond FY RC .15 .40
966 Manuel Ramirez FY RC .20 .50
967 Tyler Johnson FY RC .15 .40
968 Jaime Bubela FY RC .15 .40
969 Haj Turay FY RC .10 .25
970 Tyson Graham FY RC .15 .40
971 David DeJesus FY RC .30 .75
972 Franklin Gutierrez FY RC .40 1.00
973 Craig Brazell FY RC .15 .40
974 Keith Stamler FY RC .15 .40
975 Jemel Spearman FY RC .15 .40
976 Ozzie Chavez FY RC .15 .40
977 Nick Trzesniak FY RC .15 .40
978 Bill Simon FY RC .15 .40
979 Matthew Hagen FY RC .15 .40
980 Chris Kroski FY RC .15 .40
981 Prentice Redman FY RC .15 .40
982 Kevin Randel FY RC .15 .40
983 Tho. Story-Harden FY RC .15 .40
984 Brian Shackelford FY RC .15 .40
985 Mike Adams FY RC .15 .40
986 Brian McCann FY RC 2.00 5.00
987 Mike McNutt FY RC .15 .40
988 Aron Weston FY RC .15 .40
989 Dustin Moseley FY RC .15 .40
990 Bryan Bullington FY RC .15 .40

2003 Topps Total Silver

*SILVER: 1X TO 2.5X BASIC
*SILVER RC'S: 1X TO 2.5X BASIC
STATED ODDS 1:1
885 Chien-Ming Wang FY 4.00 10.00
952 Ryan Howard FY 12.50 30.00

2003 Topps Total Award Winners

COMPLETE SET (30) 15.00 40.00
STATED ODDS 1:12
AW1 Barry Zito .30 .75
AW2 Randy Johnson .75 2.00
AW3 Miguel Tejada .30 .75
AW4 Barry Bonds 2.00 5.00
AW5 Sammy Sosa .75 2.00
AW6 Barry Bonds 2.00 5.00
AW7 Mike Piazza 1.25 3.00
AW8 Todd Helton .50 1.25
AW9 Jeff Kent .30 .75
AW10 Edgar Renteria .30 .75
AW11 Scott Rolen .50 1.25
AW12 Vladimir Guerrero .75 2.00
AW13 Mike Hampton .30 .75
AW14 Jason Giambi .30 .75
AW15 Alfonso Soriano .30 .75
AW16 Alex Rodriguez 1.25 3.00
AW17 Eric Chavez .30 .75
AW18 Jorge Posada .50 1.25
AW19 Bernie Williams .50 1.25
AW20 Magglio Ordonez .30 .75
AW21 Garret Anderson .30 .75
AW22 Manny Ramirez .50 1.25
AW23 Jason Jennings .30 .75
AW24 Eric Hinske .30 .75
AW25 Billy Koch .30 .75
AW26 John Smoltz .50 1.25
AW27 Alex Rodriguez 1.25 3.00
AW28 Barry Bonds 2.00 5.00
AW29 Tony La Russa MG .30 .75
AW30 Mike Scioscia MG .30 .75

2003 Topps Total Production

COMPLETE SET (10) 6.00 15.00
STATED ODDS 1:18
TP1 Barry Bonds 2.00 5.00
TP2 Manny Ramirez .50 1.25
TP3 Albert Pujols 1.50 4.00
TP4 Jason Giambi .30 .75
TP5 Magglio Ordonez .30 .75
TP6 Lance Berkman .30 .75
TP7 Todd Helton .50 1.25
TP8 Miguel Tejada .30 .75
TP9 Sammy Sosa .75 2.00
TP10 Alex Rodriguez 1.25 3.00

2003 Topps Total Signatures

STATED ODDS 1:176
TSBP Brandon Phillips 4.00 10.00
TSEM Eli Marrero 4.00 10.00
TSMB Marlon Byrd 4.00 10.00
TSMT Marcus Thames 4.00 10.00
TSTT Tony Torcato 4.00 10.00

2003 Topps Total Team Checklists

COMPLETE SET (30) 6.00 15.00
1 Troy Glaus .10 .30
2 Randy Johnson .30 .75
3 Greg Maddux .50 1.25
4 Jay Gibbons .10 .30
5 Nomar Garciaparra .50 1.25
6 Sammy Sosa .30 .75
7 Paul Konerko .10 .30
8 Ken Griffey Jr. .50 1.25
9 Omar Vizquel .20 .50
10 Todd Helton .20 .50
11 Carlos Pena .10 .30
12 Mike Lowell .10 .30
13 Lance Berkman .10 .30
14 Mike Sweeney .10 .30
15 Shawn Green .10 .30
16 Richie Sexson .10 .30
17 Torii Hunter .10 .30
18 Vladimir Guerrero .30 .75
19 Mike Piazza .50 1.25
20 Jason Giambi .10 .30
21 Eric Chavez .10 .30
22 Jim Thome .20 .50
23 Brian Giles .10 .30
24 Ryan Klesko .10 .30
25 Barry Bonds .75 2.00
26 Ichiro Suzuki .60 1.50
27 Albert Pujols .60 1.50
28 Carl Crawford .10 .30
29 Alex Rodriguez .50 1.25
30 Carlos Delgado .10 .30

2003 Topps Total Team Logo Stickers

COMPLETE SET (3) 2.00 5.00
STATED ODDS 1:24
1 Anaheim Angels .75 2.00
Arizona Diamondbacks
Atlanta Braves
Baltimore Orioles
Boston Red Sox
Chicago Cubs
Chicago White Sox
Cincinnati Reds
Cleveland Indians
Colorado Rockies
2 Detroit Tigers .75 2.00
Florida Marlins
Houston Astros
Kansas City Royals
Los Angeles Dodgers
Milwaukee Brewers
Minnesota Twins
Montreal Expos
New York Mets
New York Yankees
3 Oakland Athletics .75 2.00
Philadelphia Phillies
Pittsburgh Pirates
San Diego Padres
San Francisco Giants
Seattle Mariners
St. Louis Cardinals
Tampa Bay Devil Rays
Texas Rangers
Toronto Blue Jays

2003 Topps Total Topps

COMPLETE SET (50) 15.00 40.00
STATED ODDS 1:7
TT1 Ichiro Suzuki 1.50 4.00
TT2 Alex Rodriguez 1.25 3.00
TT3 Barry Bonds 2.00 5.00
TT4 Jason Giambi .30 .75
TT5 Troy Glaus .30 .75
TT6 Greg Maddux 1.25 3.00
TT7 Albert Pujols 1.50 4.00
TT8 Randy Johnson .75 2.00
TT9 Chipper Jones .75 2.00
TT10 Magglio Ordonez .30 .75
TT11 Jim Thome .50 1.25
TT12 Jeff Kent .30 .75
TT13 Curt Schilling .30 .75
TT14 Alfonso Soriano .30 .75
TT15 Rafael Palmeiro .50 1.25
TT16 Carlos Delgado .30 .75
TT17 Torii Hunter .30 .75
TT18 Pat Burrell .30 .75
TT19 Adam Dunn .30 .75
TT20 Roberto Alomar .50 1.25
TT21 Eric Chavez .30 .75
TT22 Derek Jeter 1.50 4.00
TT23 Nomar Garciaparra 1.25 3.00
TT24 Lance Berkman .30 .75
TT25 Jim Edmonds .30 .75
TT26 Todd Helton .50 1.25
TT27 Sammy Sosa .75 2.00
TT28 Phil Nevin .30 .75
TT29 Andruw Jones .50 1.25
TT30 Barry Zito .30 .75
TT31 Richie Sexson .30 .75
TT32 Ken Griffey Jr. 1.25 3.00
TT33 Gary Sheffield .30 .75
TT34 Shawn Green .30 .75
TT35 Mike Sweeney .30 .75
TT36 Mike Lowell .30 .75
TT37 Larry Walker .30 .75
TT38 Manny Ramirez .50 1.25
TT39 Miguel Tejada .30 .75
TT40 Mike Piazza 1.25 3.00
TT41 Scott Rolen .50 1.25
TT42 Brian Giles .30 .75
TT43 Garret Anderson .30 .75
TT44 Vladimir Guerrero .75 2.00
TT45 Bartolo Colon .30 .75
TT46 Jorge Posada .50 1.25
TT47 Ivan Rodriguez .50 1.25
TT48 Ryan Klesko .30 .75
TT49 Jose Vidro .30 .75
TT50 Pedro Martinez .50 1.25

2004 Topps Total

This 880-card set was released in May, 2004. This set was issued in 10 card packs with an $1 SRP which came 36 packs to box and six boxes to a case. Cards numbered 781 through 875 feature Rookie Cards while cards numbered 876 through 880 are checklists.

COMPLETE SET (880) 75.00 150.00
COMMON CARD (1-880) .10 .30
COMMON RC .10 .30
OVERALL PRESS PLATES ODDS 1:159
PLATES PRINT RUN 1 #'d SET PER COLOR
PLATES: BLACK, CYAN, MAGENTA & YELLOW
NO PLATES PRICING DUE TO SCARCITY
1 Kevin Brown .12 .30
2 Mike Mordecai .12 .30
3 Seung Song .12 .30
4 Mike Maroth .12 .30
5 Mike Lieberthal .12 .30
6 Billy Koch .12 .30
7 Mike Stanton .12 .30
8 Brad Penny .12 .30
9 Brooks Kieschnick .12 .30
10 Carlos Delgado .12 .30
11 Brady Clark .12 .30
12 Ramon Martinez .12 .30
13 Dan Wilson .12 .30
14 Guillermo Mota .12 .30
15 Trevor Hoffman .20 .50
16 Tony Batista .12 .30
17 Rusty Greer .12 .30
18 David Weathers .12 .30
19 Horacio Ramirez .12 .30
20 Aubrey Huff .12 .30
21 Casey Blake .12 .30
22 Ryan Bukvich .12 .30
23 Garrett Atkins .12 .30
24 Jose Contreras .12 .30
25 Chipper Jones .30 .75
26 Neifi Perez .12 .30
27 Scott Linebrink .12 .30
28 Matt Kinney .12 .30
29 Michael Restovich .12 .30
30 Scott Rolen .20 .50
31 John Franco .12 .30
32 Toby Hall .12 .30
33 Wily Mo Pena .12 .30
34 Dennis Tankersley .12 .30
35 Robb Nen .12 .30
36 Jose Valverde .12 .30
37 Chin-Feng Chen .12 .30
38 Gary Knotts .12 .30
39 Mark Sweeney .12 .30
40 Bret Boone .12 .30
41 Josh Phelps .12 .30
42 Jason LaRue .12 .30
43 Tim Redding .12 .30
44 Greg Myers .12 .30
45 Darin Erstad .12 .30
46 Kip Wells .12 .30
47 Matt Ford .12 .30
48 Jerome Williams .12 .30
49 Brian Meadows .12 .30
50 Albert Pujols .75 2.00
51 Kirk Saarloos .12 .30
52 Scott Eyre .12 .30
53 John Flaherty .12 .30
54 Rafael Soriano .12 .30
55 Shea Hillenbrand .12 .30
56 Kyle Farnsworth .12 .30
57 Nate Cornejo .12 .30
58 Julian Tavarez .12 .30
59 Ryan Vogelsong .12 .30
60 Ryan Klesko .12 .30
61 Luke Hudson .12 .30
62 Justin Morneau .12 .30
63 Frank Catalanotto .12 .30
64 Derrick Turnbow .12 .30
65 Marcus Giles .12 .30
66 Mark Mulder .12 .30
67 Matt Anderson .12 .30
68 Mike Matheny .12 .30
69 Brian Lawrence .12 .30
70 Bobby Abreu .12 .30
71 Damian Moss .12 .30
72 Richard Hidalgo .12 .30
73 Mark Kotsay .12 .30
74 Mike Cameron .12 .30
75 Troy Glaus .12 .30
76 Matt Holliday .30 .75
77 Byung-Hyun Kim .12 .30
78 Aaron Sele .12 .30
79 Danny Graves .12 .30
80 Barry Zito .12 .30
81 Matt LeCroy .12 .30
82 Jason Isringhausen .12 .30
83 Colby Lewis .12 .30
84 Franklyn German .12 .30
85 Luis Matos .12 .30
86 Mike Timlin .12 .30
87 Miguel Batista .12 .30
88 John McDonald .12 .30
89 Joey Eischen .12 .30
90 Mike Mussina .20 .50
91 Jack Wilson .12 .30
92 Aaron Cook .12 .30
93 John Parrish .12 .30
94 Jose Valentin .12 .30
95 Johnny Damon .20 .50
96 Pat Burrell .12 .30
97 Brendan Donnelly .12 .30
98 Lance Carter .12 .30
99 Omar Daal .12 .30
100 Ichiro Suzuki .50 1.25
101 Robin Ventura .12 .30
102 Brian Shouse .12 .30
103 Kevin Jarvis .12 .30
104 Jason Young .12 .30
105 Moises Alou .12 .30
106 Wes Obermueller .12 .30
107 David Segui .12 .30
108 Mike MacDougal .12 .30
109 John Buck .12 .30
110 Gary Sheffield .12 .30
111 Yorvit Torrealba .12 .30
112 Matt Kata .12 .30
113 David Bell .12 .30
114 Juan Gonzalez .12 .30
115 Kelvim Escobar .12 .30
116 Ruben Sierra .12 .30
117 Todd Wellemeyer .12 .30
118 Jamie Walker .12 .30
119 Will Cunnane .12 .30
120 Cliff Floyd .12 .30
121 Aramis Ramirez .12 .30
122 Damaso Marte .12 .30
123 Juan Castro .12 .30
124 Chris Woodward .12 .30
125 Andruw Jones .12 .30
126 Ben Weber .12 .30
127 Dee Brown .12 .30
128 Steve Reed .12 .30
129 Gabe Kapler .12 .30
130 Miguel Cabrera .30 .75
131 Billy McMillon .12 .30
132 Julio Mateo .12 .30
133 Preston Wilson .12 .30
134 Tony Clark .12 .30
135 Carlos Lee .12 .30
136 Carlos Baerga .12 .30
137 Mike Crudale .12 .30
138 David Ross .12 .30
139 Josh Fogg .12 .30
140 Dmitri Young .12 .30
141 Cliff Lee .20 .50
142 Mike Lowell .12 .30
143 Jason Lane .12 .30
144 Pedro Feliz .12 .30
145 Ken Griffey Jr. .50 1.25
146 Dustin Hermanson .12 .30
147 Scott Hodges .12 .30
148 Aquilino Lopez .12 .30
149 Wes Helms .12 .30
150 Jason Giambi .12 .30
151 Erasmo Ramirez .12 .30
152 Sean Burroughs .12 .30
153 J.T. Snow .12 .30
154 Eddie Guardado .12 .30
155 C.C. Sabathia .20 .50
156 Kyle Lohse .12 .30
157 Roberto Hernandez .12 .30
158 Jason Simontacchi .12 .30
159 Tim Spooneybarger .12 .30
160 Alfonso Soriano .12 .30
161 Mike Gonzalez .12 .30
162 Alex Cora .12 .30
163 Kevin Gryboski .12 .30
164 Mike Lincoln .12 .30
165 Luis Castillo .12 .30
166 Odalis Perez .12 .30
167 Alex Sanchez .12 .30
168 Rob Mackowiak .12 .30
169 Francisco Rodriguez .20 .50
170 Roy Oswalt .20 .50
171 Omar Infante .12 .30
172 Ryan Jensen .12 .30
173 Ben Broussard .12 .30
174 Mark Hendrickson .12 .30
175 Manny Ramirez .30 .75
176 Rob Bell .12 .30
177 Adam Everett .12 .30
178 Chris George .12 .30
179 Ronnie Belliard .12 .30
180 Eric Gagne .12 .30
181 Scott Schoeneweis .12 .30
182 Kris Benson .12 .30
183 Amaury Telemaco .12 .30
184 John Riedling .12 .30
185 Juan Pierre .12 .30
186 Ramon Ortiz .12 .30
187 Luis Rivas .12 .30
188 Larry Bigbie .12 .30
189 Robby Hammock .12 .30
190 Geoff Jenkins .12 .30
191 Chad Cordero .12 .30
192 Mark Ellis .12 .30
193 Mark Loretta .12 .30
194 Ryan Drese .12 .30
195 Lance Berkman .20 .50
196 Kevin Appier .12 .30
197 Kiko Calero .12 .30
198 Mickey Callaway .12 .30
199 Chase Utley .30 .75
200 Nomar Garciaparra .30 .75
201 Kevin Cash .12 .30
202 Ramiro Mendoza .12 .30
203 Shane Reynolds .12 .30
204 Chris Spurling .12 .30
205 Aaron Guiel .12 .30
206 Mark DeRosa .12 .30
207 Adam Kennedy .12 .30
208 Andy Pettitte .20 .50
209 Rafael Palmeiro .20 .50
210 Luis Gonzalez .12 .30
211 Ryan Franklin .12 .30
212 Bob Wickman .12 .30
213 Ron Calloway .12 .30
214 Jae Weong Seo .12 .30
215 Kazuhisa Ishii .12 .30
216 Sterling Hitchcock .12 .30
217 Jimmy Gobble .12 .30
218 Chad Moeller .12 .30
219 Jake Peavy .12 .30
220 John Smoltz .30 .75
221 Donovan Osborne .12 .30
222 David Wells .12 .30
223 Brad Lidge .12 .30
224 Carlos Zambrano .20 .50
225 Kerry Wood .12 .30
226 Alex Cintron .12 .30
227 Javier A. Lopez .12 .30
228 Jeremy Griffiths .12 .30
229 Jon Garland .12 .30
230 Curt Schilling .20 .50
231 Alex Scott Gonzalez .12 .30
232 Jay Gibbons .12 .30
233 Aaron Miles .12 .30
234 Mike Gallo .12 .30
235 Johan Santana .30 .75
236 Jose Guillen .12 .30
237 Jeff Conine .12 .30
238 Matt Roney .12 .30
239 Desi Relaford .12 .30
240 Frank Thomas .30 .75
241 Danny Patterson .12 .30
242 Kevin Mench .12 .30
243 Mike Redmond .12 .30
244 Jeff Suppan .12 .30
245 Carl Everett .12 .30
246 Jack Cressend .12 .30
247 Matt Mantei .12 .30
248 Enrique Wilson .12 .30
249 Craig Counsell .12 .30
250 Mark Prior .20 .50
251 Jared Sandberg .12 .30
252 Scott Strickland .12 .30
253 Lew Ford .12 .30
254 Hee Seop Choi .12 .30
255 Jason Phillips .12 .30
256 Jason Jennings .12 .30
257 Todd Pratt .12 .30
258 Matt Herges .12 .30
259 Kerry Ligtenberg .12 .30
260 Austin Kearns .12 .30
261 Jay Witasick .12 .30
262 Tony Armas Jr. .12 .30
263 Tom Martin .12 .30
264 Oliver Perez .12 .30
265 Jorge Posada .20 .50
266 Jason Boyd .12 .30
267 Ben Hendrickson .12 .30
268 Reggie Sanders .12 .30
269 Julio Lugo .12 .30
270 Pedro Martinez .20 .50
271 Kyle Snyder .12 .30
272 Felipe Lopez .12 .30
273 Kevin Millar .12 .30
274 Travis Hafner .12 .30
275 Magglio Ordonez .20 .50
276 Marlon Byrd .12 .30
277 Scott Spiezio .12 .30
278 Mark Corey .12 .30
279 Tim Salmon .12 .30
280 Alex Gonzalez .12 .30
281 Marquis Grissom .12 .30
282 Miguel Olivo .12 .30
283 Orlando Hudson .12 .30
284 Rondell White .12 .30
285 Jermaine Dye .12 .30
286 Paul Shuey .12 .30
287 Brandon Inge .12 .30
288 B.J. Surhoff .12 .30
289 Edgar Gonzalez .12 .30
290 Angel Berroa .12 .30
291 Claudio Vargas .12 .30
292 Cesar Izturis .12 .30
293 Brandon Phillips .12 .30
294 Jeff Duncan .12 .30
295 Randy Wolf .12 .30
296 Barry Larkin .20 .50
297 Felix Rodriguez .12 .30
298 Robb Quinlan .12 .30
299 Brian Jordan .12 .30
300 Dontrelle Willis .12 .30
301 Doug Davis .12 .30
302 Ricky Stone .12 .30
303 Travis Harper .12 .30
304 Jaret Wright .12 .30
305 Edgardo Alfonzo .12 .30
306 Quinton McCracken .12 .30
307 Jason Bay .20 .50
308 Joe Randa .12 .30
309 Steve Sparks .12 .30
310 Roy Halladay .30 .75
311 Antonio Alfonseca .12 .30
312 Michael Cuddyer .12 .30
313 John Patterson .12 .30
314 Chris Widger .12 .30
315 Shigetoshi Hasegawa .12 .30
316 Tim Wakefield .12 .30
317 Scott Hatteberg .12 .30
318 Mike Remlinger .12 .30
319 Jose Vizcaino .12 .30
320 Rocco Baldelli .12 .30
321 David Riske .12 .30
322 Steve Karsay .12 .30
323 Peter Bergeron .12 .30
324 Jeff Weaver .12 .30
325 Larry Walker .20 .50
326 Jack Cust .12 .30
327 Bo Hart .12 .30
328 Rod Beck .12 .30
329 Jose Acevedo .12 .30
330 Hank Blalock .12 .30
331 Tom Gordon .12 .30
332 Brian Fuentes .12 .30
333 Tomas Perez .12 .30
334 Lenny Harris .12 .30
335 Matt Morris .12 .30
336 Jeremi Gonzalez .12 .30
337 David Eckstein .12 .30
338 Aaron Rowand .12 .30
339 Rick Bauer .12 .30
340 Jim Edmonds .20 .50
341 Joe Borowski .12 .30
342 Eric DuBose .12 .30

343 D'Angelo Jimenez .12 .30
344 Tomo Ohka .12 .30
345 Victor Zambrano .12 .30
346 Joe McEwing .12 .30
347 Jorge Sosa .12 .30
348 Keith Ginter .12 .30
349 A.J. Pierzynski .12 .30
350 Mike Sweeney .12 .30
351 Shawn Chacon .12 .30
352 Matt Clement .12 .30
353 Vance Wilson .12 .30
354 Benito Santiago .12 .30
355 Eric Hinske .12 .30
356 Vladimir Guerrero .30 .75
357 Kenny Rogers .12 .30
358 Travis Lee .12 .30
359 Jay Powell .12 .30
360 Phil Nevin .12 .30
361 Willie Harris .12 .30
362 Ty Wigginton .12 .30
363 Chad Fox .12 .30
364 Junior Spivey .12 .30
365 Brandon Webb .12 .30
366 Brett Myers .12 .30
367 Alexis Gomez .12 .30
368 Dave Roberts .12 .30
369 LaTroy Hawkins .12 .30
370 Kevin Millwood .12 .30
371 Brian Schneider .12 .30
372 Blaine Neal .12 .30
373 Jeromy Burnitz .12 .30
374 Ted Lilly .12 .30
375 Shawn Green .12 .30
376 Carlos Pena .20 .50
377 Gil Meche .12 .30
378 Jeff Bagwell .20 .50
379 Alex Escobar .12 .30
380 Erubiel Durazo .12 .30
381 Cristian Guzman .12 .30
382 Rocky Biddle .12 .30
383 Craig Wilson .12 .30
384 Rey Sanchez .12 .30
385 Russ Ortiz .12 .30
386 Freddy Garcia .12 .30
387 Luis Vizcaino .12 .30
388 David Ortiz .30 .75
389 Jose Molina .12 .30
390 Edgar Martinez .20 .50
391 Nate Bump .12 .30
392 Brent Mayne .12 .30
393 Ray King .12 .30
394 Paul Wilson .12 .30
395 Melvin Mora .12 .30
396 Morgan Ensberg .12 .30
397 Ramon Hernandez .12 .30
398 Juan Rincon .12 .30
399 Ron Mahay .12 .30
400 Jeff Kent .12 .30
401 Cal Eldred .12 .30
402 Mike Ditelice .12 .30
403 Valerio De Los Santos .12 .30
404 Steve Finley .12 .30
405 Trot Nixon .12 .30
406 Akinori Otsuka RC .12 .30
407 Ryan Freel .12 .30
408 Ray Durham .12 .30
409 Aaron Heilman .12 .30
410 Edgar Renteria .12 .30
411 Mike Hampton .12 .30
412 Kirk Rueter .12 .30
413 Jim Mecir .12 .30
414 Brian Roberts .12 .30
415 Paul Konerko .20 .50
416 Reed Johnson .12 .30
417 Roger Clemens .40 1.00
418 Coco Crisp .12 .30
419 Carlos Hernandez .12 .30
420 Scott Podsednik .12 .30
421 Miguel Cairo .12 .30
422 Abraham Nunez .12 .30
423 Endy Chavez .12 .30
424 Eric Munson .12 .30
425 Torii Hunter .12 .30
426 Ben Howard .12 .30
427 Chris Gomez .12 .30
428 Francisco Cordero .12 .30
429 Jeffrey Hammonds .12 .30
430 Shannon Stewart .12 .30
431 Einar Diaz .12 .30
432 Eric Byrnes .12 .30
433 Marty Cordova .12 .30
434 Matt Ginter .12 .30
435 Victor Martinez .20 .50
436 Geronimo Gil .12 .30
437 Grant Balfour .12 .30
438 Ramon Vazquez .12 .30
439 Jose Cruz Jr. .12 .30
440 Orlando Cabrera .12 .30
441 Joe Kennedy .12 .30
442 Scott Williamson .12 .30
443 Troy Percival .12 .30
444 Derrek Lee .12 .30
445 Runelvys Hernandez .12 .30
446 Mark Grudzielanek .12 .30
447 Trey Hodges .12 .30
448 Jimmy Haynes .12 .30
449 Eric Milton .12 .30
450 Todd Helton .20 .50
451 Greg Zaun .12 .30
452 Woody Williams .12 .30
453 Todd Walker .12 .30
454 Juan Cruz .12 .30
455 Fernando Vina .12 .30
456 Omar Vizquel .20 .50
457 Roberto Alomar .20 .50
458 Bill Hall .12 .30
459 Juan Rivera .12 .30
460 Tom Glavine .20 .50
461 Ramon Castro .12 .30
462 Cory Vance .12 .30
463 Dan Miceli .12 .30
464 Lyle Overbay .12 .30
465 Craig Biggio .20 .50
466 Ricky Ledee .12 .30
467 Michael Barrett .12 .30
468 Jason Anderson .12 .30
469 Matt Stairs .12 .30
470 Jarrod Washburn .12 .30
471 Todd Hundley .12 .30
472 Grant Roberts .12 .30
473 Randy Winn .12 .30
474 Pat Hentgen .12 .30
475 Jose Vidro .12 .30
476 Tony Torcato .12 .30
477 Jeremy Affeldt .12 .30
478 Carlos Guillen .12 .30
479 Paul Quantrill .12 .30
480 Rafael Furcal .12 .30
481 Adam Melhuse .12 .30
482 Jerry Hairston Jr. .12 .30
483 Adam Bernero .12 .30
484 Terrence Long .12 .30
485 Paul Lo Duca .12 .30
486 Corey Koskie .12 .30
487 John Lackey .12 .30
488 Chad Zerbe .12 .30
489 Vinny Castilla .12 .30
490 Corey Patterson .12 .30
491 John Olerud .12 .30
492 Josh Bard .12 .30
493 Darren Dreifort .12 .30
494 Jason Standridge .12 .30
495 Ben Sheets .12 .30
496 Jose Castillo .12 .30
497 Jay Payton .12 .30
498 Rob Bowen .12 .30
499 Bobby Higginson .12 .30
500 Alex Rodriguez Yanks .50 1.25
501 Octavio Dotel .12 .30
502 Rheal Cormier .12 .30
503 Felix Heredia .12 .30
504 Dan Wright .12 .30
505 Michael Young .12 .30
506 Wilfredo Ledezma .12 .30
507 Sun Woo Kim .12 .30
508 Michael Tejera .12 .30
509 Herbert Perry .12 .30
510 Esteban Loaiza .12 .30
511 Alan Embree .12 .30
512 Ben Davis .12 .30
513 Greg Colbrunn .12 .30
514 Josh Hall .12 .30
515 Raul Ibanez .12 .30
516 Jason Kershner .12 .30
517 Corky Miller .12 .30
518 Jason Marquis .12 .30
519 Roger Cedeno .12 .30
520 Adam Dunn .20 .50
521 Paul Byrd .12 .30
522 Sandy Alomar Jr. .12 .30
523 Salomon Torres .12 .30
524 John Halama .12 .30
525 Mike Piazza .30 .75
526 Buddy Groom .12 .30
527 Adrian Beltre .12 .30
528 Chad Harville .12 .30
529 Javier Vazquez .12 .30
530 Jody Gerut .12 .30
531 Elmer Dessens .12 .30
532 B.J. Ryan .12 .30
533 Chad Durbin .12 .30
534 Doug Mirabelli .12 .30
535 Bernie Williams .20 .50
536 Jeff DaVanon .12 .30
537 Dave Berg .12 .30
538 Geoff Blum .12 .30
539 John Thomson .12 .30
540 Jeremy Bonderman .12 .30
541 Jeff Zimmerman .12 .30
542 Derek Lowe .12 .30
543 Scot Shields .12 .30
544 Michael Tucker .12 .30
545 Tim Hudson .20 .50
546 Ryan Ludwick .12 .30
547 Rick Reed .12 .30
548 Placido Polanco .12 .30
549 Tony Graffanino .12 .30
550 Garret Anderson .12 .30
551 Timo Perez .12 .30
552 Jesus Colome .12 .30
553 R.A. Dickey .12 .30
554 Tim Worrell .12 .30
555 Jason Kendall .12 .30
556 Tom Goodwin .12 .30
557 Joaquin Benoit .12 .30
558 Stephen Randolph .12 .30
559 Miguel Tejada .20 .50
560 A.J. Burnett .20 .50
561 Ben Diggins .12 .30
562 Kent Mercker .12 .30
563 Zach Day .12 .30
564 Antonio Perez .12 .30
565 Jason Schmidt .12 .30
566 Armando Benitez .12 .30
567 Denny Neagle .12 .30
568 Eric Eckenstahler .12 .30
569 Chan Ho Park .20 .50
570 Carlos Beltran .12 .30
571 Brett Tomko .12 .30
572 Henry Mateo .12 .30
573 Ken Harvey .12 .30
574 Matt Lawton .12 .30
575 Mariano Rivera .30 .75
576 Darrell May .12 .30
577 Jamie Moyer .12 .30
578 Paul Bako .12 .30
579 Cory Lidle .12 .30
580 Jacque Jones .12 .30
581 Jolbert Cabrera .12 .30
582 Jason Grimsley .12 .30
583 Danny Kolb .12 .30
584 Billy Wagner .12 .30
585 Rich Aurilia .12 .30
586 Vicente Padilla .12 .30
587 Oscar Villarreal .12 .30
588 Rene Reyes .12 .30
589 Jon Lieber .12 .30
590 Nick Johnson .12 .30
591 Bobby Crosby .12 .30
592 Steve Trachsel .12 .30
593 Brian Boehringer .12 .30
594 Juan Uribe .12 .30
595 Bartolo Colon .12 .30
596 Bobby Hill .12 .30
597 Chris Shelton RC .12 .30
598 Carl Pavano .12 .30
599 Kurt Ainsworth .12 .30
600 Derek Jeter .75 2.00
601 Doug Mientkiewicz .12 .30
602 Orlando Palmeiro .12 .30
603 J.C. Romero .12 .30
604 Scott Sullivan .12 .30
605 Brad Radke .12 .30
606 Fernando Rodney .12 .30
607 Jim Brower .12 .30
608 Josh Towers .12 .30
609 Brad Fullmer .12 .30
610 Jose Reyes .20 .50
611 Ryan Wagner .12 .30
612 Joe Mays .12 .30
613 Jung Bong .12 .30
614 Curtis Leskanic .12 .30
615 Al Leiter .12 .30
616 Wade Miller .12 .30
617 Keith Foulke Sox .12 .30
618 Casey Fossum .12 .30
619 Craig Monroe .12 .30
620 Hideo Nomo .30 .75
621 Bob File .12 .30
622 Steve Kline .12 .30
623 Bobby Kielty .12 .30
624 Dewon Brazelton .12 .30
625 Eric Chavez .12 .30
626 Chris Carpenter .30 .75
627 Alexis Rios .20 .50
628 Jason Davis .12 .30
629 Jose Jimenez .12 .30
630 Vernon Wells .12 .30
631 Kenny Lofton .12 .30
632 Chad Bradford .12 .30
633 Brad Wilkerson .12 .30
634 Pokey Reese .12 .30
635 Richie Sexson .12 .30
636 Chin-Hui Tsao .12 .30
637 Eli Marrero .12 .30
638 Chris Reitsma .12 .30
639 Daryle Ward .12 .30
640 Mark Teixeira .30 .75
641 Corwin Malone .12 .30
642 Adam Eaton .12 .30
643 Jimmy Rollins .20 .50
644 Brian Anderson .12 .30
645 Bill Mueller .12 .30
646 Jake Westbrook .12 .30
647 Bengie Molina .12 .30
648 Jorge Julio .12 .30
649 Billy Traber .12 .30
650 Randy Johnson .30 .75
651 Javy Lopez .12 .30
652 Doug Glanville .12 .30
653 Jeff Cirillo .12 .30
654 Tino Martinez .20 .50
655 Mark Buehrle .20 .50
656 Jason Michaels .12 .30
657 Damian Rolls .12 .30
658 Rosman Garcia .12 .30
659 Scott Hairston .12 .30
660 Carl Crawford .20 .50
661 Livan Hernandez .12 .30
662 Danny Bautista .12 .30
663 Brad Ausmus .12 .30
664 Juan Acevedo .12 .30
665 Sean Casey .12 .30
666 Josh Beckett .20 .50
667 Milton Bradley .12 .30
668 Braden Looper .12 .30
669 Paul Abbott .12 .30
670 Joel Pineiro .12 .30
671 Luis Terrero .12 .30
672 Rodrigo Lopez .12 .30
673 Joe Crede .12 .30
674 Mike Koplove .12 .30
675 Brian Giles .12 .30
676 Jeff Nelson .12 .30
677 Russell Branyan .12 .30
678 Mike DeJean .12 .30
679 Brian Daubach .12 .30
680 Ellis Burks .12 .30
681 Ryan Dempster .12 .30
682 Cliff Politte .12 .30
683 Brian Reith .12 .30
684 Scott Stewart .12 .30
685 Allan Simpson .12 .30
686 Shawn Estes .12 .30
687 Jason Johnson .12 .30
688 Wil Cordero .12 .30
689 Kelly Stinnett .12 .30
690 Jose Lima .12 .30
691 Gary Bennett .12 .30
692 T.J. Tucker .12 .30
693 Shane Spencer .12 .30
694 Chris Hammond .12 .30
695 Raul Mondesi .12 .30
696 Xavier Nady .12 .30
697 Cody Ransom .12 .30
698 Ron Villone .12 .30
699 Brook Fordyce .12 .30
700 Sammy Sosa .30 .75
701 Terry Adams .12 .30
702 Ricardo Rincon .12 .30
703 Tike Redman .12 .30
704 Chris Stynes .12 .30
705 Mark Redman .12 .30
706 Juan Encarnacion .12 .30
707 Jhonny Peralta .12 .30
708 Denny Hocking .12 .30
709 Ivan Rodriguez .20 .50
710 Jose Hernandez .12 .30
711 Brandon Duckworth .12 .30
712 Dave Burba .12 .30
713 Joe Nathan .12 .30
714 Dan Smith .12 .30
715 Karim Garcia .12 .30
716 Arthur Rhodes .12 .30
717 Shawn Wooten .12 .30
718 Ramon Santiago .12 .30
719 Luis Ugueto .12 .30
720 Danys Baez .12 .30
721 Alfredo Amezaga PROS .12 .30
722 Sidney Ponson .12 .30
723 Joe Mauer PROS .30 .75
724 Jesse Foppert PROS .12 .30
725 Todd Greene .12 .30
726 Dan Haren PROS .12 .30
727 Brandon Larson PROS .12 .30
728 Bobby Jenks PROS .12 .30
729 Grady Sizemore PROS .20 .50
730 Ben Grieve .12 .30
731 Khalil Greene PROS .20 .50
732 Chad Gaudin PROS .12 .30
733 Johnny Estrada PROS .12 .30
734 Joe Valentine PROS .12 .30
735 Tim Raines Jr. PROS .12 .30
736 Brandon Claussen PROS .12 .30
737 Sam Marsonek PROS .12 .30
738 Delmon Young PROS .20 .50
739 David Dellucci .12 .30
740 Sergio Mitre PROS .12 .30
741 Nick Neugebauer PROS .12 .30
742 Laynce Nix PROS .12 .30
743 Joe Thurston PROS .12 .30
744 Ryan Langerhans PROS .12 .30
745 Pete LaForest PROS .12 .30
746 Arnie Munoz PROS .12 .30
747 Rickie Weeks PROS .12 .30
748 Neal Cotts PROS .12 .30
749 Jonny Gomes PROS .12 .30
750 Jim Thome .20 .50
751 Jon Rauch PROS .12 .30
752 Edwin Jackson PROS .12 .30
753 Ryan Madson PROS .12 .30
754 Andrew Good PROS .12 .30
755 Eddie Perez .12 .30
756 Joe Borchard PROS .12 .30
757 Jeremy Guthrie PROS .12 .30
758 Jose Mesa .12 .30
759 Doug Waechter PROS .12 .30
760 J.D. Drew .12 .30
761 Adam LaRoche PROS .12 .30
762 Rich Harden PROS .12 .30
763 Justin Speier .12 .30
764 Todd Zeile .12 .30
765 Turk Wendell .12 .30
766 Mark Bellhorn Sox .12 .30
767 Mike Jackson .12 .30
768 Chone Figgins .12 .30
769 Mike Neu .12 .30
770 Greg Maddux .50 1.25
771 Frank Menechino .12 .30
772 Alec Zumwalt RC .12 .30
773 Eric Young .12 .30
774 Dustan Mohr .12 .30
775 Shane Halter .12 .30
776 Brian Buchanan .12 .30
777 So Taguchi .12 .30
778 Eric Karros .12 .30
779 Ramon Nivar .12 .30
780 Marlon Anderson .12 .30
781 Brayan Pena FY RC .12 .30
782 Chris O'Riordan FY RC .12 .30
783 Dioner Navarro FY RC .20 .50
784 Alberto Callaspo FY RC .30 .75
785 Hector Gimenez FY RC .12 .30
786 Yadier Molina FY RC .75 2.00
787 Kevin Richardson FY RC .12 .30
788 Brian Pilkington FY RC .12 .30
789 Adam Greenberg FY RC .12 .30
790 Ervin Santana FY RC .30 .75
791 Brant Colamarino FY RC .12 .30
792 Ben Himes FY RC .12 .30
793 Todd Self FY RC .12 .30
794 Brad Vericker FY RC .12 .30
795 Donald Kelly FY RC .20 .50
796 Brock Jacobsen FY RC .12 .30
797 Brock Peterson FY RC .12 .30
798 Carlos Sosa FY RC .12 .30
799 Chad Chop FY RC .12 .30
800 Matt Moses FY RC .20 .50
801 Chris Aguila FY RC .12 .30
802 David Murphy FY RC .30 .75
803 Don Sutton FY RC .12 .30
804 Jereme Milons FY RC .12 .30
805 Jon Coutlangus FY RC .12 .30
806 Greg Thissen FY RC .12 .30
807 Jose Capellan FY RC .12 .30
808 Chad Santos FY RC .12 .30
809 Wardell Starling FY RC .12 .30
810 Kevin Kouzmanoff FY RC .75 2.00
811 Kevin Davidson FY RC .12 .30
812 Michael Mooney FY RC .12 .30
813 Rodney Choy Foo FY RC .12 .30
814 Reid Gorecki FY RC .12 .30
815 Rudy Guillen FY RC .12 .30
816 Harvey Garcia FY RC .12 .30
817 Warner Madrigal FY RC .12 .30
818 Kenny Perez FY RC .12 .30
819 Joaquin Arias FY RC .30 .75
820 Benji DeQuin FY RC .12 .30
821 Lastings Milledge FY RC .75 2.00
822 Blake Hawksworth FY RC .12 .30
823 Estee Harris FY RC .12 .30
824 Bobby Brownlie FY RC .12 .30
825 Wanell Severino FY RC .12 .30
826 Bobby Madritsch FY .12 .30
827 Travis Hanson FY RC .12 .30
828 Brandon Medders FY RC .12 .30
829 Kevin Howard FY RC .12 .30
830 Brian Steffek FY RC .12 .30
831 Terry Jones FY RC .12 .30
832 Anthony Acevedo FY RC .12 .30
833 Kory Casto FY RC .12 .30
834 Brooks Conrad FY RC UER .12 .30
Anthony Acevedo Pictured on front
835 Juan Gutierrez FY RC .12 .30
836 Charlie Zink FY RC .12 .30
837 David Aardsma FY RC .12 .30
838 Carl Loadenthal FY RC .12 .30
839 Donald Levinski FY RC .12 .30
840 Dustin Nippert FY RC .12 .30
841 Calvin Hayes FY RC .12 .30
842 Felix Hernandez FY RC 2.50 6.00
843 Tyler Davidson FY RC .12 .30
844 George Sherrill FY RC .12 .30
845 Craig Ansman FY RC .12 .30
846 Jeff Allison FY RC .12 .30
847 Tommy Murphy FY RC .12 .30
848 Jerome Gamble FY RC .12 .30
849 Jesse English FY RC .12 .30
850 Alex Romero FY RC .12 .30
851 Joel Zumaya FY RC .75 2.00
852 Carlos Quentin FY RC .50 1.25
853 Jose Valdez FY RC .12 .30
854 J.J. Furmaniak FY RC .12 .30
855 Juan Cedeno FY RC .12 .30
856 Kyle Sleeth FY RC .12 .30
857 Josh Labandeira FY RC .12 .30
858 Lee Gwaltney FY RC .12 .30
859 Lincoln Holdzkom FY RC .12 .30
860 Ivan Ochoa FY RC .12 .30
861 Luke Anderson FY RC .12 .30
862 Conor Jackson FY RC .75 2.00
863 Matt Capps FY RC .12 .30
864 Merkin Valdez FY RC .12 .30
865 Paul Bacot FY RC .12 .30
866 Erick Aybar FY RC .20 .50
867 Scott Proctor FY RC .12 .30
868 Tim Stauffer FY RC .20 .50
869 Matt Creighton FY RC .12 .30
870 Zach Miner FY RC .20 .50
871 Danny Gonzalez FY RC .12 .30
872 Tom Farmer FY RC .12 .30
873 John Santor FY RC .12 .30
874 Logan Kensing FY RC .12 .30
875 Vito Chiaravalloti FY RC .12 .30
876 Checklist .12 .30
877 Checklist .12 .30
878 Checklist .12 .30
879 Checklist .12 .30
880 Checklist .12 .30

2004 Topps Total Silver

*PARALLEL: 1X TO 2.5X BASIC
*PARALLEL RC's: 1X TO 2.5X BASIC RC's
ONE PER PACK

2004 Topps Total Award Winners

COMPLETE SET (30) 12.50 30.00
STATED ODDS 1:12
OVERALL PRESS PLATES ODDS 1:159
PLATES PRINT RUN 1 #'d SET PER COLOR
PLATES: BLACK, CYAN, MAGENTA & YELLOW
NO PLATES PRICING DUE TO SCARCITY
AW1 Roy Halladay CY .75 2.00
AW2 Eric Gagne CY .30 .75
AW3 Alex Rodriguez MVP 1.25 3.00
AW4 Albert Pujols POY 2.00 5.00
AW5 Alex Rodriguez POY 1.25 3.00
AW6 Jorge Posada SS .50 1.25
AW7 Javy Lopez SS .30 .75
AW8 Carlos Delgado SS .30 .75
AW9 Todd Helton SS .50 1.25
AW10 Bret Boone SS .30 .75
AW11 Jose Vidro SS .30 .75
AW12 Bill Mueller SS .30 .75
AW13 Mike Lowell SS .30 .75
AW14 Alex Rodriguez SS 1.25 3.00
AW15 Edgar Renteria SS .30 .75
AW16 Garret Anderson SS .30 .75
AW17 Albert Pujols SS 2.00 5.00
AW18 Manny Ramirez SS .75 2.00
AW19 Vernon Wells SS .30 .75
AW20 Gary Sheffield SS .30 .75
AW21 Edgar Martinez SS .50 1.25
AW22 Mike Hampton SS .30 .75
AW23 Angel Berroa ROY .30 .75
AW24 Dontrelle Willis ROY .30 .75
AW25 Keith Foulke Rolaids .30 .75
AW26 Eric Gagne Rolaids .30 .75
AW27 Alex Rodriguez HA 1.25 3.00
AW28 Albert Pujols HA 2.00 5.00
AW29 Tony Pena MG .30 .75
AW30 Jack McKeon MG .30 .75

2004 Topps Total Production

COMPLETE SET (10) 6.00 15.00
STATED ODDS 1:18
OVERALL PRESS PLATES ODDS 1:159
PLATES PRINT RUN 1 #'d SET PER COLOR
PLATES: BLACK, CYAN, MAGENTA & YELLOW
NO PLATES PRICING DUE TO SCARCITY
TP1 Alex Rodriguez 1.25 3.00
TP2 Albert Pujols 2.00 5.00
TP3 Sammy Sosa .75 2.00
TP4 Carlos Delgado .30 .75
TP5 Gary Sheffield .30 .75
TP6 Manny Ramirez .75 2.00
TP7 Jim Thome .50 1.25
TP8 Todd Helton .50 1.25
TP9 Garret Anderson .30 .75
TP10 Nomar Garciaparra .75 2.00

2004 Topps Total Signatures

STATED ODDS 1:414
BC Brandon Claussen 4.00 10.00
GB Grant Balfour 4.00 10.00
JJ Jimmy Journell 4.00 10.00
LB Larry Bigbie 6.00 15.00
TB Toby Hall 4.00 10.00

2004 Topps Total Team Checklists

COMPLETE SET (30) 6.00 15.00
STATED ODDS 1:4
OVERALL PRESS PLATES ODDS 1:159
PLATES PRINT RUN 1 #'d SET PER COLOR
PLATES: BLACK, CYAN, MAGENTA & YELLOW
NO PLATES PRICING DUE TO SCARCITY
TTC1 Garret Anderson .12 .30
TTC2 Randy Johnson .30 .75
TTC3 Chipper Jones .30 .75
TTC4 Miguel Tejada .20 .50
TTC5 Nomar Garciaparra .30 .75
TTC6 Mark Prior .20 .50
TTC7 Magglio Ordonez .20 .50
TTC8 Ken Griffey Jr. .50 1.25
TTC9 C.C. Sabathia .20 .50
TTC10 Todd Helton .20 .50
TTC11 Ivan Rodriguez .20 .50
TTC12 Dontrelle Willis .12 .30
TTC13 Roger Clemens .40 1.00
TTC14 Mike Sweeney .12 .30
TTC15 Shawn Green .12 .30
TTC16 Geoff Jenkins .12 .30
TTC17 Torii Hunter .12 .30
TTC18 Jose Vidro .12 .30
TTC19 Mike Piazza .30 .75
TTC20 Alex Rodriguez .50 1.25
TTC21 Eric Chavez .12 .30
TTC22 Jim Thome .20 .50
TTC23 Jason Kendall .12 .30
TTC24 Brian Giles .12 .30
TTC25 Jason Schmidt .12 .30
TTC26 Ichiro Suzuki .50 1.25
TTC27 Albert Pujols .75 2.00
TTC28 Aubrey Huff .12 .30
TTC29 Hank Blalock .12 .30
TTC30 Carlos Delgado .12 .30

2004 Topps Total Topps

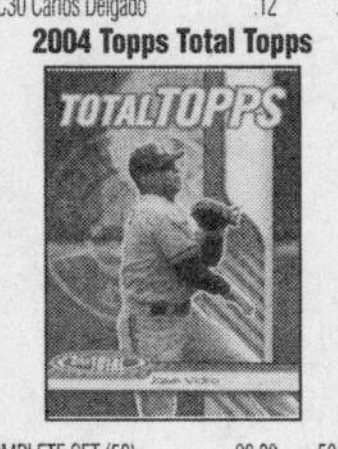

COMPLETE SET (50) 20.00 50.00
STATED ODDS 1:7
OVERALL PRESS PLATES ODDS 1:159
PLATES PRINT RUN 1 SERIAL #'d SET
NO PLATES PRICING DUE TO SCARCITY
TT1 Derek Jeter 2.00 5.00
TT2 Jose Reyes .50 1.25
TT3 Miguel Tejada .50 1.25
TT4 Larry Walker .50 1.25
TT5 Frank Thomas .75 2.00
TT6 Carlos Delgado .30 .75
TT7 Vernon Wells .30 .75
TT8 Jeff Bagwell .50 1.25
TT9 Jason Giambi .30 .75
TT10 Mike Lowell .30 .75
TT11 Shannon Stewart .30 .75
TT12 Mike Piazza .75 2.00
TT13 Todd Helton .50 1.25
TT14 Austin Kearns .30 .75
TT15 Jim Edmonds .50 1.25
TT16 Jose Vidro .30 .75
TT17 Andruw Jones .30 .75
TT18 Gary Sheffield .30 .75
TT19 Eric Chavez .30 .75
TT20 Magglio Ordonez .50 1.25
TT21 Geoff Jenkins .30 .75
TT22 Ken Griffey Jr. 1.25 3.00
TT23 Jeff Kent .30 .75
TT24 Jorge Posada .50 1.25
TT25 Albert Pujols 2.00 5.00
TT26 Javy Lopez .30 .75
TT27 Alfonso Soriano .30 .75
TT28 Brian Giles .30 .75
TT29 Mike Sweeney .30 .75
TT30 Miguel Cabrera .75 2.00
TT31 Luis Gonzalez .30 .75
TT32 Scott Rolen .50 1.25
TT33 Jim Thome .50 1.25
TT34 Garret Anderson .30 .75
TT35 Vladimir Guerrero .75 2.00
TT36 Shawn Green .30 .75
TT37 Hank Blalock .30 .75
TT38 Marcus Giles .30 .75
TT39 Torii Hunter .30 .75
TT40 Sammy Sosa .75 2.00
TT41 Nomar Garciaparra .75 2.00
TT42 Bobby Abreu .30 .75
TT43 Richie Sexson .30 .75
TT44 Manny Ramirez .75 2.00
TT45 Troy Glaus .30 .75
TT46 Preston Wilson .30 .75
TT47 Ivan Rodriguez .50 1.25
TT48 Ichiro Suzuki 1.25 3.00
TT49 Chipper Jones .75 2.00
TT50 Alex Rodriguez 1.25 3.00

2005 Topps Total

This massive 770-card set lays claim to the most comprehensive selection of players for any product issued in 2005 with just over 950 athletes featured. The set is structured with veterans as 1-575, dual-player veterans 576-690, prospects 691-720, "First

Year" minor leaguers 721-765 and checklists 766-770. Oddly enough, card 666 (a number feared by some as the sign of the devil) is a single player card featuring Red Sox closer Keith Foulke - indicating a serious dislike for the Red Sox by whomever at Topps was responsible for constructing the checklist. The set was issued within 10-card packs carrying an affordable SRP of $1.00. Each box contained 36 packs. The actual printing plates used to create each card (barring the checklists) were cut up and seeded into packs. Black, Cyan, Magenta and Yellow plates were produced, each labeled as a 1 of 1. In a move deemed about as popular as bad breath by most collectors, the plates for the card backs were incorporated alongside the far more popular card fronts - harkening back to the card back plates issued eight years earlier in forgettable products such as New Pinnacle. Though these plates are too scarce to price for individual stars, most common fronts can be had between $15-$40 per and back between $8-$25 per.

COMPLETE SET (770) 75.00 150.00
COMMON (1-575/666) .10 .30
COMMON CARD (576-690) .10 .30
COM (269/588/691-765) .10 .30
COMMON CL (766-770) .10 .30
OVERALL PLATE ODDS 1:85 HOBBY
PLATE PRINT RUN 1 SET PER COLOR
BLACK-CYAN-MAGENTA-YELLOW ISSUED
FRONT AND BACK PLATES PRODUCED
NO PLATE PRICING DUE TO SCARCITY
1 Rafael Furcal .12 .30
2 Tony Clark .12 .30
3 Hideki Matsui .50 1.25
4 Zach Day .12 .30
5 Garret Anderson .12 .30
6 B.J. Surhoff .12 .30
7 Trevor Hoffman .20 .50
8 Kenny Lofton .12 .30
9 Ross Gload .12 .30
10 Jorge Cantu .12 .30
11 Joel Pineiro .12 .30
12 Alex Cintron .12 .30
13 Mike Matheny .12 .30
14 Rod Barajas .12 .30
15 Ray Durham .12 .30
16 Danys Baez .12 .30
17 Brian Schneider .12 .30
18 Tike Redman .12 .30
19 Ricardo Rodriguez .12 .30
20 Mike Sweeney .12 .30
21 Greg Myers .12 .30
22 Chone Figgins .12 .30
23 Brian Lawrence .12 .30
24 Joe Nathan .12 .30
25 Placido Polanco .12 .30
26 Yadier Molina .20 .50
27 Gary Bennett .12 .30
28 Yorvit Torrealba .12 .30
29 Javier Valentin .12 .30
30 Jason Giambi .12 .30
31 Brandon Claussen .12 .30
32 Miguel Olivo .12 .30
33 Josh Bard .12 .30
34 Ramon Hernandez .12 .30
35 Geoff Jenkins .12 .30
36 Bobby Kielty .12 .30
37 Luis A. Gonzalez .12 .30
38 Benito Santiago .12 .30
39 Brandon Inge .12 .30
40 Mark Prior .20 .50
41 Mike Lieberthal .12 .30
42 Toby Hall .12 .30
43 Brad Ausmus .12 .30
44 Damian Miller .12 .30
45 Mark Kotsay .12 .30
46 John Buck .12 .30
47 Oliver Perez .12 .30
48 Matt Morris .12 .30
49 Raul Chavez .12 .30
50 Randy Johnson .30 .75
51 Dave Bush .12 .30
52 Jose Macias .12 .30
53 Paul Wilson .12 .30
54 Wilfredo Ledezma .12 .30
55 J.D. Drew .12 .30
56 Pedro Martinez .20 .50
57 Josh Towers .12 .30
58 Jamie Moyer .12 .30
59 Scott Elarton .12 .30
60 Ken Griffey Jr. .50 1.25
61 Steve Trachsel .12 .30
62 Bubba Crosby .12 .30
63 Michael Barrett .12 .30
64 Odalis Perez .12 .30
65 B.J. Upton .20 .50
66 Eric Bruntlett .12 .30
67 Victor Zambrano .12 .30
68 Brandon League .12 .30
69 Carlos Silva .12 .30
70 Lyle Overbay .12 .30
71 Runelvys Hernandez .12 .30
72 Brad Penny .12 .30
73 Ty Wigginton .12 .30
74 Orlando Hudson .12 .30
75 Roy Oswalt .20 .50
76 Jason LaRue .12 .30
77 Ismael Valdez .12 .30
78 Calvin Pickering .12 .30
79 Bill Hall .12 .30
80 Carl Crawford .20 .50
81 Tomas Perez .12 .30
82 Joe Kennedy .12 .30
83 Chris Woodward .12 .30
84 Jason Lane .12 .30
85 Steve Finley .12 .30
86 Jeff Francis .12 .30

87 Felipe Lopez .12 .30
88 Chan Ho Park .20 .50
89 Joe Crede .12 .30
90 Jose Vidro .12 .30
91 Casey Kotchman .12 .30
92 Brandon Backe .12 .30
93 Mike Hampton .12 .30
94 Ryan Dempster .12 .30
95 Wily Mo Pena .12 .30
96 Matt Holliday .30 .75
97 A.J. Pierzynski .12 .30
98 Jason Jennings .12 .30
99 Eli Marrero .12 .30
100 Carlos Beltran .12 .30
101 Scott Kazmir .30 .75
102 Kenny Rogers .12 .30
103 Roy Halladay .30 .75
104 Alex Cora .12 .30
105 Richie Sexson .12 .30
106 Ben Sheets .12 .30
107 Bartolo Colon .12 .30
108 Eddie Perez .12 .30
109 Vicente Padilla .12 .30
110 Sammy Sosa .30 .75
111 Mark Ellis .12 .30
112 Woody Williams .12 .30
113 Todd Greene .12 .30
114 Nook Logan .12 .30
115 Francisco Rodriguez .20 .50
116 Miguel Batista .12 .30
117 Livan Hernandez .12 .30
118 Chris Aguila .12 .30
119 Coco Crisp .12 .30
120 Jose Reyes .20 .50
121 Ricky Ledee .12 .30
122 Brad Radke .12 .30
123 Carlos Guillen .12 .30
124 Paul Bako .12 .30
125 Tom Glavine .20 .50
126 Chad Moeller .12 .30
127 Mark Buehrle .20 .50
128 Casey Blake .12 .30
129 Juan Rivera .12 .30
130 Preston Wilson .12 .30
131 Nate Robertson .12 .30
132 Julio Franco .12 .30
133 Derek Lowe .12 .30
134 Rob Bell .12 .30
135 Javy Lopez .12 .30
136 Javier Vazquez .12 .30
137 Desi Relaford .12 .30
138 Danny Graves .12 .30
139 Josh Fogg .12 .30
140 Bobby Crosby .12 .30
141 Ramon Castro .12 .30
142 Jerry Hairston Jr. .12 .30
143 Morgan Ensberg .12 .30
144 Brandon Webb .20 .50
145 Jack Wilson .12 .30
146 Bill Mueller .12 .30
147 Troy Glaus .12 .30
148 Armando Benitez .12 .30
149 Adam LaRoche .12 .30
150 Hank Blalock .12 .30
151 Ryan Franklin .12 .30
152 Kevin Millwood .12 .30
153 Jason Marquis .12 .30
154 Dewon Brazelton .12 .30
155 Al Leiter .12 .30
156 Garrett Atkins .12 .30
157 Todd Walker .12 .30
158 Kris Benson .12 .30
159 Eric Milton .12 .30
160 Bret Boone .12 .30
161 Matt LeCroy .12 .30
162 Chris Widger .12 .30
163 Ruben Gotay .12 .30
164 Craig Monroe .12 .30
165 Travis Hafner .12 .30
166 Vance Wilson .12 .30
167 Jason Grabowski .12 .30
168 Tim Salmon .12 .30
169 Henry Blanco .12 .30
170 Josh Beckett .20 .50
171 Jake Westbrook .12 .30
172 Paul Lo Duca .12 .30
173 Julio Lugo .12 .30
174 Juan Cruz .12 .30
175 Mark Mulder .12 .30
176 Juan Castro .12 .30
177 Damion Easley .12 .30
178 LaTroy Hawkins .12 .30
179 Jon Lieber .12 .30
180 Vernon Wells .12 .30
181 Jeff DaVanon .12 .30
182 Dustan Mohr .12 .30
183 Ryan Freel .12 .30
184 Doug Davis .12 .30
185 Sean Casey .12 .30
186 Robb Quinlan .12 .30
187 J.D. Closser .12 .30
188 Tim Wakefield .12 .30
189 Brian Jordan .12 .30
190 Adam Dunn .20 .50
191 Antonio Perez .12 .30
192 Brett Tomko .12 .30
193 John Flaherty .12 .30
194 Michael Cuddyer .12 .30
195 Ronnie Belliard .12 .30
196 Tony Womack .12 .30
197 Jason Johnson .12 .30
198 Victor Santos .12 .30
199 Danny Haren .12 .30
200 Derek Jeter .75 2.00
201 Brian Anderson .12 .30
202 Carlos Pena .20 .50
203 Jaret Wright .12 .30
204 Paul Byrd .12 .30
205 Shannon Stewart .12 .30
206 Chris Carpenter .30 .75
207 Matt Stairs .12 .30
208 Brad Hawpe .12 .30
209 Bobby Higginson .12 .30
210 Torii Hunter .12 .30
211 Shawn Green .12 .30
212 Todd Hollandsworth .12 .30
213 Scott Erickson .12 .30
214 C.C. Sabathia .20 .50
215 Mike Mussina .20 .50
216 Jason Kendall .12 .30
217 Todd Pratt .12 .30
218 Danny Kolb .12 .30
219 Tony Armas .12 .30
220 Edgar Renteria .12 .30
221 Dave Roberts .12 .30
222 Luis Rivas .12 .30
223 Adam Everett .12 .30
224 Jeff Cirillo .12 .30
225 Orlando Hernandez .12 .30
226 Ken Harvey .12 .30
227 Corey Patterson .12 .30
228 Humberto Cota .12 .30
229 A.J. Burnett .20 .50
230 Roger Clemens .40 1.00
231 Joe Randa .12 .30
232 David Dellucci .12 .30
233 Troy Percival .12 .30
234 Dustin Hermanson .12 .30
235 Eric Gagne .12 .30
236 Terry Tiffee .12 .30
237 Tony Graffanino .12 .30
238 Jayson Werth .20 .50
239 Mark Sweeney .12 .30
240 Chipper Jones .30 .75
241 Aramis Ramirez .12 .30
242 Frank Catalanotto .12 .30
243 Mike Maroth .12 .30
244 Kelvim Escobar .12 .30
245 Bobby Abreu .12 .30
246 Kyle Lohse .12 .30
247 Jason Isringhausen .12 .30
248 Jose Lima .12 .30
249 Adrian Gonzalez .20 .50
250 Alex Rodriguez .50 1.25
251 Ramon Ortiz .12 .30
252 Frank Menechino .12 .30
253 Keith Ginter .12 .30
254 Kip Wells .12 .30
255 Dmitri Young .12 .30
256 Craig Biggio .20 .50
257 Ramon E. Martinez .12 .30
258 Jason Bartlett .12 .30
259 Brad Lidge .12 .30
260 Brian Giles .12 .30
261 Luis Terrero .12 .30
262 Miguel Ojeda .12 .30
263 Rich Harden .12 .30
264 Jacque Jones .12 .30
265 Marcus Giles .12 .30
266 Carlos Zambrano .20 .50
267 Michael Tucker .12 .30
268 Wes Obermueller .12 .30
269 Pete Orr RC .20 .50
270 Jim Thome .20 .50
271 Omar Vizquel .20 .50
272 Jose Valentin .12 .30
273 Juan Uribe .12 .30
274 Doug Mirabelli .12 .30
275 Jeff Kent .20 .50
276 Brad Wilkerson .12 .30
277 Chris Burke .12 .30
278 Endy Chavez .12 .30
279 Richard Hidalgo .12 .30
280 John Smoltz .30 .75
281 Jarrod Washburn .12 .30
282 Larry Bigbie .12 .30
283 Edgardo Alfonzo .12 .30
284 Cliff Lee .20 .50
285 Carlos Lee .12 .30
286 Olmedo Saenz .12 .30
287 Tomo Ohka .12 .30
288 Ruben Sierra .12 .30
289 Nick Swisher .30 .75
290 Frank Thomas .30 .75
291 Aaron Cook .12 .30
292 Cody McKay .12 .30
293 Hee-Seop Choi .12 .30
294 Carl Pavano .12 .30
295 Scott Rolen .20 .50
296 Matt Kata .12 .30
297 Terrence Long .12 .30
298 Jimmy Gobble .12 .30
299 Jason Repko .12 .30
300 Manny Ramirez .30 .75
301 Dan Wilson .12 .30
302 Jhonny Peralta .12 .30
303 John Mabry .12 .30
304 Adam Melhuse .12 .30
305 Kerry Wood .12 .30
306 Ryan Langerhans .12 .30
307 Antonio Alfonseca .12 .30
308 Marco Scutaro .12 .30
309 Jamey Carroll .12 .30
310 Lance Berkman .20 .50
311 Willie Harris .12 .30
312 Phil Nevin .12 .30
313 Gregg Zaun .12 .30
314 Michael Ryan .12 .30
315 Zack Greinke .20 .50
316 Ted Lilly .12 .30
317 David Eckstein .12 .30
318 Tony Torcato .12 .30
319 Rob Mackowiak .12 .30
320 Mark Teixeira .30 .75
321 Jason Phillips .12 .30
322 Jeremy Reed .12 .30
323 Bengie Molina .12 .30
324 Termel Sledge .12 .30
325 Justin Morneau .30 .75
326 Sandy Alomar Jr. .12 .30
327 Jon Garland .12 .30
328 Jay Payton .12 .30
329 Tino Martinez .20 .50
330 Jason Bay .12 .30
331 Jeff Conine .12 .30
332 Shawn Chacon .12 .30
333 Angel Berroa .12 .30
334 Reggie Sanders .12 .30
335 Kevin Brown .12 .30
336 Brady Clark .12 .30
337 Casey Fossum .12 .30
338 Raul Ibanez .12 .30
339 Derrek Lee .12 .30
340 Victor Martinez .20 .50
341 Kazuhisa Ishii .12 .30
342 Royce Clayton .12 .30
343 Trot Nixon .12 .30
344 Eric Young .12 .30
345 Aubrey Huff .12 .30
346 Brett Myers .12 .30
347 Joey Gathright .12 .30
348 Mark Grudzielanek .12 .30
349 Scott Spiezio .12 .30
350 Eric Chavez .12 .30
351 Einar Diaz .12 .30
352 Dallas McPherson .12 .30
353 John Thomson .12 .30
354 Neifi Perez .12 .30
355 Larry Walker .20 .50
356 Billy Wagner .12 .30
357 Mike Cameron .12 .30
358 Jimmy Rollins .20 .50
359 Kevin Mench .12 .30
360 Joe Mauer .30 .75
361 Jose Molina .12 .30
362 Joe Borchard .12 .30
363 Kevin Cash .12 .30
364 Jay Gibbons .12 .30
365 Khalil Greene .12 .30
366 Justin Leone .12 .30
367 Eddie Guardado .12 .30
368 Mike Lamb .12 .30
369 Matt Riley .12 .30
370 Luis Gonzalez .12 .30
371 Alfredo Amezaga .12 .30
372 J.J. Hardy .12 .30
373 Hector Luna .12 .30
374 Greg Aquino .12 .30
375 Jim Edmonds .20 .50
376 Joe Blanton .12 .30
377 Russell Branyan .12 .30
378 J.T. Snow .12 .30
379 Magglio Ordonez .20 .50
380 Rafael Palmeiro .20 .50
381 Andruw Jones .12 .30
382 David DeJesus .12 .30
383 Marquis Grissom .12 .30
384 Bobby Hill .12 .30
385 Kazuo Matsui .12 .30
386 Mark Loretta .12 .30
387 Chris Shelton .12 .30
388 Johnny Estrada .12 .30
389 Adam Hyzdu .12 .30
390 Nomar Garciaparra .30 .75
391 Mark Teahen .12 .30
392 Chris Capuano .12 .30
393 Ben Broussard .12 .30
394 Daniel Cabrera .12 .30
395 Jeremy Bonderman .12 .30
396 Darin Erstad .12 .30
397 Alex S. Gonzalez .12 .30
398 Kevin Millar .12 .30
399 Freddy Garcia .12 .30
400 Alfonso Soriano .20 .50
401 Koyie Hill .12 .30
402 Omar Infante .12 .30
403 Alex Gonzalez .12 .30
404 Pat Burrell .12 .30
405 Wes Helms .12 .30
406 Junior Spivey .12 .30
407 Joe Mays .12 .30
408 Jason Stanford .12 .30
409 Gil Meche .12 .30
410 Tim Hudson .20 .50
411 Chase Utley .20 .50
412 Matt Clement .12 .30
413 Nick Green .12 .30
414 Jose Vizcaino .12 .30
415 Ryan Klesko .12 .30
416 Vinny Castilla .12 .30
417 Brian Roberts .12 .30
418 Geronimo Gil .12 .30
419 Gary Matthews .12 .30
420 Jeff Weaver .12 .30
421 Jerome Williams .12 .30
422 Andy Pettitte .20 .50
423 Randy Wolf .12 .30
424 D'Angelo Jimenez .12 .30
425 Moises Alou .12 .30
426 Eric Byrnes .12 .30
427 Mark Redman .12 .30
428 Jermaine Dye .12 .30
429 Cory Lidle .12 .30
430 Jason Schmidt .12 .30
431 Jason W. Smith .12 .30
432 Jose Castillo .12 .30
433 Pokey Reese .12 .30
434 Matt Lawton .12 .30
435 Jose Guillen .12 .30
436 Craig Counsell .12 .30
437 Jose Hernandez .12 .30
438 Braden Looper .12 .30
439 Scott Hatteberg .12 .30
440 Gary Sheffield .12 .30
441 Gabe Gross .12 .30
442 Chris Gomez .12 .30
443 Dontrelle Willis .12 .30
444 Jamey Wright .12 .30
445 Rocco Baldelli .12 .30
446 Bernie Williams .20 .50
447 Sean Burroughs .12 .30
448 Willie Bloomquist .12 .30
449 Luis Castillo .12 .30
450 Mike Piazza .30 .75
451 Ryan Drese .12 .30
452 Pedro Feliz .12 .30
453 Horacio Ramirez .12 .30
454 Luis Matos .12 .30
455 Craig Wilson .12 .30
456 Russ Ortiz .12 .30
457 Xavier Nady .12 .30
458 Hideo Nomo .30 .75
459 Miguel Cairo .12 .30
460 Mike Lowell .20 .50
461 Corky Miller .12 .30
462 Bobby Madritsch .12 .30
463 Jose Contreras .12 .30
464 Johnny Damon .20 .50
465 Miguel Cabrera .30 .75
466 Eric Hinske .12 .30
467 Marlon Byrd .12 .30
468 Aaron Miles .12 .30
469 Ramon Vazquez .12 .30
470 Michael Young .20 .50
471 Alex Sanchez .12 .30
472 Shea Hillenbrand .12 .30
473 Jeff Bagwell .20 .50
474 Erik Bedard .12 .30
475 Jake Peavy .12 .30
476 Jody Gerut .12 .30
477 Randy Winn .12 .30
478 Kevin Youkilis .12 .30
479 Eric Dubose .12 .30
480 David Wright .50 1.25
481 Wilson Valdez .12 .30
482 Cliff Floyd .12 .30
483 Jose Mesa .12 .30
484 Doug Mientkiewicz .12 .30
485 Jorge Posada .20 .50
486 Sidney Ponson .12 .30
487 Dave Krynzel .12 .30
488 Octavio Dotel .12 .30
489 Matt Treanor .12 .30
490 Johan Santana .30 .75
491 John Patterson .12 .30
492 So Taguchi .12 .30
493 Carl Everett .12 .30
494 Jason Dubois .12 .30
495 Albert Pujols .75 2.00
496 Kirk Rueter .12 .30
497 Geoff Blum .12 .30
498 Juan Encarnacion .12 .30
499 Mark Hendrickson .12 .30
500 Barry Bonds .60 1.50
501 Cesar Izturis .12 .30
502 David Wells .12 .30
503 Jorge Julio .12 .30
504 Cristian Guzman .12 .30
505 Juan Pierre .12 .30
506 Adam Eaton .12 .30
507 Nick Johnson .12 .30
508 Mike Redmond .12 .30
509 Daryle Ward .12 .30
510 Adrian Beltre .12 .30
511 Laynce Nix .12 .30
512 Reed Johnson .12 .30
513 Jeremy Affeldt .12 .30
514 R.A. Dickey .12 .30
515 Alex Rios .20 .50
516 Orlando Palmeiro .12 .30
517 Mark Bellhorn .12 .30
518 Adam Kennedy .12 .30
519 Curtis Granderson .20 .50
520 Todd Helton .20 .50
521 Aaron Boone .12 .30
522 Milton Bradley .12 .30
523 Timo Perez .12 .30
524 Jeff Suppan .12 .30
525 Austin Kearns .12 .30
526 Charles Thomas .12 .30
527 Bronson Arroyo .12 .30
528 Roger Cedeno .12 .30
529 Russ Adams .12 .30
530 Barry Zito .20 .50
531 Bob Wickman .12 .30
532 Deivi Cruz .12 .30
533 Mariano Rivera .30 .75
534 J.J. Davis .12 .30
535 Greg Maddux .50 1.25
536 Ryan Vogelsong .12 .30
537 Josh Phelps .12 .30
538 Scott Hairston .12 .30
539 Vladimir Guerrero .30 .75
540 Ivan Rodriguez .20 .50
541 David Newhan .12 .30
542 David Bell .12 .30
543 Lew Ford .12 .30
544 Grady Sizemore .20 .50
545 David Ortiz .30 .75
546 Jose Cruz Jr. .12 .30
547 Aaron Rowand .12 .30
548 Marcus Thames .12 .30
549 Scott Podsednik .12 .30
550 Ichiro Suzuki .50 1.25
551 Eduardo Perez .12 .30
552 Chris Snyder .12 .30
553 Corey Koskie .12 .30
554 Miguel Tejada .20 .50
555 Orlando Cabrera .12 .30
556 Rondell White .12 .30
557 Wade Miller .12 .30
558 Rodrigo Lopez .12 .30
559 Chad Tracy .12 .30
560 Paul Konerko .20 .50
561 Wil Cordero .12 .30
562 John McDonald .12 .30
563 Jason Ellison .12 .30
564 Jason Michaels .12 .30
565 Melvin Mora .12 .30
566 Ryan Church .12 .30
567 Ryan Ludwick .12 .30
568 Erubiel Durazo .12 .30
569 Noah Lowry .12 .30
570 Curt Schilling .20 .50
571 Esteban Loaiza .12 .30
572 Freddy Sanchez .12 .30
573 Rich Aurilia .12 .30
574 Travis Lee .12 .30
575 Nick Punto .12 .30
576 Jason Christiansen .12 .30
Kevin Correia
577 Brad Baker .12 .30
Tim Redding
578 Terry Adams .12 .30
Gavin Floyd
579 Seth Etherton .12 .30
Dan Meyer
580 Justin Lehr .12 .30
Derrick Turnbow
581 Mike Gosling .12 .30
Brad Halsey
582 Jim Mecir .12 .30
Logan Kensing
583 Brad Hennessey .12 .30
Jeff Fassero
584 Jon Adkins .12 .30
Felix Diaz
585 Jesse Crain .12 .30
Juan Rincon
586 Jamie Cerda .12 .30
Nate Field
587 Bartolome Fortunato .12 .30
Jae Weong Seo
588 Steve Schmoll RC .12 .30
Yhency Brazoban
589 Ugueth Urbina .12 .30
Jamie Walker
590 Jorge De Paula .12 .30
Scott Proctor
591 Jason Davis .12 .30
Bob Howry
592 Tim Worrell .12 .30
Pedro Liriano
593 Jose Acevedo .12 .30
Kent Mercker
594 Chris Hammond .12 .30
Scott Linebrink
595 Fernando Nieve .12 .30
John Franco
596 Randy Flores .12 .30
Mike Lincoln
597 Joe Borowski .12 .30
Sergio Mitre
598 Lance Carter .12 .30
Jesus Colome
599 John Halama .12 .30
Lenny DiNardo
600 Chad Bradford .12 .30
Kiko Calero
601 David Aardsma .12 .30
Jim Brower
602 Geoff Geary .12 .30
Ryan Madson
603 Brian Moehler .12 .30
Nate Bump
604 Chin-Hui Tsao .12 .30
Ryan Speier
605 Ryan Wagner .12 .30
Aaron Harang
606 Steve Kline .12 .30
Rick Bauer
607 Lance Cormier .12 .30
Randy Choate
608 Jon Leicester .12 .30
Todd Wellemeyer
609 Vinnie Chulk .12 .30
Jason Frasor
610 Scott Dohmann .12 .30
Brian Fuentes
611 Steve Colyer .12 .30
Roberto Hernandez
612 Ian Snell .12 .30
Salomon Torres
613 Cal Eldred .30 .75
Adam Wainwright
614 Ryan Bukvich .12 .30
Doug Brocail
615 J.J. Putz .12 .30
Aaron Sele
616 Bruce Chen .12 .30
Todd Williams
617 David Weathers .12 .30
Ben Weber
618 Dennys Reyes .12 .30
Rudy Seanez
619 Tim Harikkala .12 .30
Ricardo Rincon
620 Shawn Camp .12 .30
Denny Bautista
621 Javier A. Lopez .12 .30
Allan Simpson
622 Mike Remlinger .12 .30
Glendon Rusch
623 Roman Colon .12 .30
Kevin Gryboski
624 Tom Martin .12 .30
Chris Reitsma
625 Chad Qualls .12 .30
Dan Wheeler
626 Tommy Phelps .12 .30
Matt Wise
627 Scott Schoeneweis .12 .30
Justin Speier
628 Francisco Cordero .12 .30
Frank Francisco
629 Rafael Soriano .12 .30
Matt Thornton
630 Mike Stanton .12 .30
Steve Karsay
631 Mike MacDougal .12 .30
Scott Sullivan
632 Brian Bruney .12 .30
Oscar Villarreal
633 Mike Adams .12 .30
Ricky Bottalico
634 Eddy Rodriguez .12 .30
Dave Borkowski
635 Rafael Betancourt .12 .30
David Riske
636 Jorge De La Rosa .12 .30
Gary Glover
637 Matt Perisho .12 .30
Ben Howard
638 Jeff Bajenaru .12 .30
Luis Vizcaino
639 Ron Mahay .12 .30
Erasmo Ramirez
640 John Grabow .12 .30
Mike Gonzalez
641 J.C. Romero .12 .30
Matt Guerrier
642 Carlos Hernandez .12 .30
Brandon Duckworth UER
Tim Redding is referred to in the Hernandez informational blurb
643 Travis Harper .12 .30
Seth McClung
644 Matt Herges .12 .30
Tyler Walker
645 Kelly Wunsch .12 .30
Elmer Dessens
646 Mark Malaska .12 .30
Mike Myers
647 Kyle Farnsworth .12 .30
Gary Knotts
648 Justin Duchscherer .12 .30
Jairo Garcia
649 Aaron Rakers .12 .30
Steve Reed
650 Tom Gordon .12 .30
Paul Quantrill
651 Brandon Lyon .12 .30
Shawn Estes
652 Pete Walker .12 .30
Gustavo Chacin
653 John Lackey .12 .30
Scot Shields
654 Doug Waechter .12 .30
Trever Miller
655 Luis Ayala .12 .30
Chad Cordero
656 Ron Villone .12 .30
Julio Mateo
657 Matt Mantei .12 .30
Blaine Neal
658 Damaso Marte .12 .30
Cliff Politte
659 Joe Valentine .12 .30
Luke Hudson
660 Todd Jones .12 .30
John Riedling
661 Heath Bell .20 .50
Aaron Heilman
662 Darrell May .12 .30
Akinori Otsuka
663 Joey Eischen .12 .30
Joe Horgan
664 Andy Sisco .12 .30
Mike Wood
665 Alan Embree .12 .30
Mike Timlin
666 Keith Foulke .12 .30
667 Rheal Cormier .12 .30
Aaron Fultz
668 Jake Woods .12 .30
Kevin Gregg
669 Matt Ginter .12 .30
Franklyn German
670 Scott Eyre .12 .30
Merkin Valdez
671 Brian Meadows .12 .30
Rick White
672 Guillermo Mota .12 .30
Tim Spooneybarger
673 Jason Grimsley .12 .30
B.J. Ryan
674 Neal Cotts .12 .30
Shingo Takatsu
675 Mike DeJean .12 .30
Felix Heredia
676 Matt Belisle .12 .30
Josh Hancock
677 Jon Rauch .12 .30
T.J. Tucker
678 Nick Regilio .12 .30
Brian Shouse
679 Julian Tavarez .12 .30
Ray King
680 Chad Fox .12 .30
Michael Wuertz
681 Jorge Sosa .12 .30
Adam Bernero
682 Jose Valverde .12 .30
Mike Koplove
683 Arthur Rhodes .12 .30
Scott Sauerbeck
684 Felix Rodriguez .12 .30
Tanyon Sturtze
685 Giovanni Carrara .12 .30
Duaner Sanchez
686 Mike Gallo .12 .30
Chad Harville
687 Mike Johnston .12 .30
Sean Burnett
688 Jeff Nelson .12 .30
Shigetoshi Hasegawa
689 Claudio Vargas .12 .30
Antonio Osuna
690 Brendan Donnelly .12 .30
Esteban Yan
691 Jeff Mathis .20 .50
Ervin Santana
692 Clint Everts .12 .30
Bill Bray
693 Jason Kubel .12 .30
Trevor Plouffe
694 Jake Stevens .20 .50
Andy Marte
695 Aaron Hill .20 .50
Chad Gaudin
696 Carlos Quentin .20 .50
Jesus Cota
697 Thomas Diamond .20 .50
Chris Young
698 Omar Quintanilla .12 .30
Dan Johnson
699 John Maine .12 .30
Val Majewski
700 James Houser .12 .30
Jonny Gomes
701 David Murphy .20 .50
Hanley Ramirez
702 Chris Lambert .12 .30
Rick Ankiel
703 Felix Pie .12 .30
Angel Guzman
704 Fred Lewis .20 .50
Nate Schierholtz
705 Arnie Munoz .20 .50
Gio Gonzalez
706 Felix Hernandez .50 1.25
Travis Blackley
707 Ray Olmedo .20 .50
Edwin Encarnacion UER
Photos Reversed
708 Tim Stauffer .12 .30
Justin Germano
709 Jeremy Guthrie .20 .50
Jeremy Sowers
710 Jorge Cortes .20 .50
Tom Gorzelanny
711 Taylor Tankersley .12 .30
Eric Reed
712 Neil Walker .12 .30
Paul Maholm
713 Willy Taveras .30 .75
Luke Scott RC
714 Ryan Howard .60 1.50
Greg Golson
715 Blake DeWitt .20 .50
Edwin Jackson
716 Huston Street .12 .30
Dan Putnam
717 Rickie Weeks .20 .50
Mark Rogers
718 Robinson Cano .30 .75
Philip Hughes
719 Kyle Waldrop .12 .30
Jay Rainville
720 Craig Brazell .12 .30
Yusmeiro Petit
721 Baltazar Lopez RC .12 .30
Matt Brown RC
722 Daryl Thompson RC .12 .30
Ender Chavez RC
723 Dan Uggla RC 6.00 15.00
Erik Schindewolf RC
724 Ismael Ramirez RC .12 .30
Jayce Tingler RC
725 Tony Giarratano RC .12 .30
Eulogio de la Cruz RC
726 Matt Campbell RC .12 .30
Shane Costa RC
727 Martin Prado RC .75 2.00
Bill McCarthy RC
728 Ian Kinsler RC 1.00 2.50
Juan Senreiso RC UER
Kinsler photo is Edinson Volquez
729 Luis Ramirez RC .12 .30
Lorenzo Scott RC
730 Chris Seddon RC .12 .30
Elliot Johnson RC
731 Craig Tatum RC .12 .30
Javon Moran RC
732 Stuart Pomeranz RC .20 .50
Jason Motte RC
733 Jose Vaquedano RC .12 .30
Stefan Bailie RC
734 Matt Albers RC .12 .30
Wade Robinson RC
735 Matt DeSalvo RC .30 .75
Melky Cabrera RC
736 Brian Stavisky RC .12 .30
Landon Powell RC
737 Scott Mathieson RC .50 1.25
Scott Mitchinson RC
738 Sean Marshall RC .30 .75
Bear Bay RC
739 Brandon McCarthy RC .20 .50
Pedro Lopez RC
740 Alexander Smit RC .12 .30
Ricky Barrett RC
741 Matt Rogelstad RC .12 .30
Ryan Feierabend RC
742 Nate McLouth RC .20 .50
Adam Boeve RC
743 Kevin Melillo RC .12 .30
Michael Rogers RC
744 Matthew Kemp RC 1.50 4.00
Heath Totten RC
745 Jai Miller RC .12 .30
Tony Arnerich RC
746 Tyler Pelland RC .12 .30
Jesse Gutierrez RC
747 Jeremy West RC .12 .30
Willy Mota RC
748 Ryan Goleski RC .12 .30
Ryan Garko RC
749 Bryan Triplett RC .12 .30
Jared Gothreaux RC
750 Kevin West RC .12 .30
Glen Perkins RC
751 Mike Esposito RC .12 .30
Zach Parker RC
752 Ryan Sweeney RC .20 .50
Brian Miller RC
753 Casey McGehee RC .40 1.00
Buck Coats RC
754 Mike Bourn RC .30 .75
Kelvin Pichardo RC
755 Mike Morse RC .30 .75
Bobby Livingston RC
756 Wes Swackhamer RC .20 .50
Brendan Ryan RC
757 Micah Furtado RC .12 .30
Nick Masset RC
758 Peeter Ramos RC .20 .50
George Kottaras RC
759 Elvys Quezada RC .12 .30
T.J. Beam RC
760 Dana Eveland RC .12 .30
Travis Hinton RC
761 James Jurries RC .12 .30
Chris Vines RC
762 Humberto Sanchez RC 2.50 6.00
Justin Verlander RC
763 Philip Humber RC .30 .75
Shawn Bowman RC
764 Pat Misch RC .12 .30
J.B. Thurmond RC
765 Christian Colonel RC .12 .30
Neil Wilson RC
766 Checklist 1 .10 .30
767 Checklist 2 .10 .30
768 Checklist 3 .10 .30
769 Checklist 4 .10 .30
770 Checklist 5 .10 .30

2005 Topps Total Domination

*DOMINATION: .75X TO 2X BASIC
STATED ODDS 1:10 H 1:10 R
CL: 40/50/56/60/100/110/147/150/180/190
CL: 200/230/250/260/270/290/300/345/350
CL: 400/465/490/495/500/510/520/540/545
CL: 575/580

2005 Topps Total Domination Autograph

STATED ODDS 1:494,640 H, 1,257,760 R
STATED PRINT RUN 10 CARDS
NO PRICING DUE TO SCARCITY
EXCHANGE DEADLINE 05/31/07

2005 Topps Total Silver

*SILVER 1-575/666: 1X TO 2.5X BASIC
*SILVER 576-690: 1X TO 2.5X BASIC
*SILVER 269/691-765: 1X TO 2.5X BASIC
*SILVER 766-770: 1X TO 2.5X BASIC
ONE PER PACK

2005 Topps Total Award Winners

COMPLETE SET (30) 12.50 30.00
STATED ODDS 1:10 H, 1:10 R
OVERALL INSERT PLATE ODDS 1:726 H
PLATE PRINT RUN 1 SET PER COLOR
BLACK-CYAN-MAGENTA-YELLOW ISSUED
FRONT AND BACK PLATES PRODUCED
NO PLATE PRICING DUE TO SCARCITY
AW1 Barry Bonds MVP 1.50 4.00
AW2 Vladimir Guerrero MVP .75 2.00
AW3 Roger Clemens CY 1.00 2.50
AW4 Johan Santana CY .75 2.00
AW5 Jason Bay ROY .30 .75
AW6 Bobby Crosby ROY .30 .75
AW7 Eric Gagne Rolaids .30 .75
AW8 Mariano Rivera Rolaids .75 2.00
AW9 Albert Pujols SS 2.00 5.00
AW10 Mark Teixeira SS .75 2.00
AW11 Mark Loretta SS .30 .75
AW12 Alfonso Soriano SS .50 1.25
AW13 Jack Wilson SS .30 .75
AW14 Miguel Tejada SS .50 1.25
AW15 Adrian Beltre SS .30 .75
AW16 Melvin Mora SS .30 .75
AW17 Barry Bonds SS 1.50 4.00
AW18 Jim Edmonds SS .50 1.25
AW19 Bobby Abreu SS .30 .75
AW20 Manny Ramirez SS .75 2.00
AW21 Gary Sheffield SS .30 .75
AW22 Vladimir Guerrero SS .75 2.00
AW23 Johnny Estrada SS .30 .75
AW24 Victor Martinez SS .50 1.25
AW25 Ivan Rodriguez SS .50 1.25
AW26 Livan Hernandez SS .30 .75
AW27 David Ortiz SS .75 2.00
AW28 Bobby Cox MG .30 .75
AW29 Buck Showalter MG .30 .75
AW30 Barry Bonds Aaron Award 1.50 4.00

2005 Topps Total Production

COMPLETE SET (10) 6.00 15.00
STATED ODDS 1:15 H, 1:15 R
OVERALL INSERT PLATE ODDS 1:726 H
PLATE PRINT RUN 1 SET PER COLOR
BLACK-CYAN-MAGENTA-YELLOW ISSUED
FRONT AND BACK PLATES PRODUCED
NO PLATE PRICING DUE TO SCARCITY
AB Adrian Beltre .30 .75
AP Albert Pujols 2.00 5.00
AR Alex Rodriguez 1.25 3.00
AS Alfonso Soriano .50 1.25
BB Barry Bonds 1.50 4.00
JT Jim Thome .50 1.25
MR Manny Ramirez .75 2.00
MT Miguel Tejada .50 1.25
TH Todd Helton .50 1.25
VG Vladimir Guerrero .75 2.00

2005 Topps Total Signatures

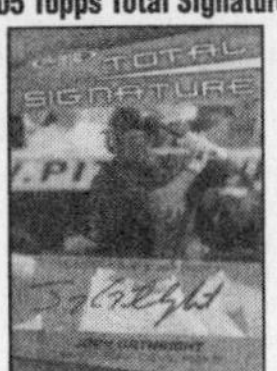

GROUP A ODDS 1:4849 H, 1:5484 R
GROUP B ODDS 1:608 H, 1:697 R
GROUP C ODDS 1:974 H, 1:1117 R
OVERALL AU PLATE ODDS 1:19,024 HOBBY
AU PLATE PRINT RUN 1 SET PER COLOR
BLACK-CYAN-MAGENTA-YELLOW ISSUED
NO AU PLATE PRICING DUE TO SCARCITY
EXCHANGE DEADLINE 05/31/07
BB Brian Bruney B 4.00 10.00
BM Brett Myers A
DW David Wright B 30.00 60.00
JG Joey Gathright B 4.00 10.00
RC Robinson Cano B 15.00 40.00
TT Terry Tiffee C 4.00 10.00
ZG Zack Greinke C 12.50 30.00

2005 Topps Total Team Checklists

COMPLETE SET (30) 6.00 15.00
STATED ODDS 1:4 H, 1:4 R
1 Luis Gonzalez .12 .30
2 John Smoltz .30 .75
3 Miguel Tejada .20 .50
4 David Ortiz .30 .75
5 Kerry Wood .12 .30
6 Frank Thomas .30 .75
7 Adam Dunn .20 .50
8 Victor Martinez .20 .50
9 Todd Helton .20 .50
10 Ivan Rodriguez .20 .50
11 Miguel Cabrera .30 .75
12 Roger Clemens .40 1.00
13 Zack Greinke .20 .50
14 Vladimir Guerrero .30 .75
15 Eric Gagne .12 .30
16 Ben Sheets .12 .30
17 Johan Santana .30 .75
18 Carlos Beltran .12 .30
19 Alex Rodriguez .50 1.25
20 Eric Chavez .12 .30
21 Jim Thome .20 .50
22 Jason Bay .12 .30
23 Brian Giles .12 .30
24 Barry Bonds .60 1.50
25 Ichiro Suzuki .50 1.25
26 Albert Pujols .75 2.00
27 Carl Crawford .20 .50
28 Alfonso Soriano .20 .50
29 Roy Halladay .30 .75
30 Jose Vidro .12 .30

2005 Topps Total Topps

COMPLETE SET (20) 12.50 30.00
STATED ODDS 1:15 H, 1:15 R
OVERALL INSERT PLATE ODDS 1:726 H
PLATE PRINT RUN 1 SET PER COLOR
BLACK-CYAN-MAGENTA-YELLOW ISSUED
FRONT AND BACK PLATES PRODUCED
NO PLATE PRICING DUE TO SCARCITY
AB Adrian Beltre .30 .75
AP Albert Pujols 2.00 5.00
AR Alex Rodriguez 1.25 3.00
AS Alfonso Soriano .50 1.25
BB Barry Bonds 1.50 4.00
CB Carlos Beltran .30 .75
DJ Derek Jeter 2.00 5.00
EC Eric Chavez .30 .75
GM Greg Maddux 1.25 3.00
IR Ivan Rodriguez .50 1.25
JS Johan Santana .75 2.00
JT Jim Thome .50 1.25
MP Mike Piazza .75 2.00
MR Manny Ramirez .75 2.00
MT Miguel Tejada .50 1.25
RC Roger Clemens 1.00 2.50
RJ Randy Johnson .75 2.00
SS Sammy Sosa .75 2.00
TH Todd Helton .50 1.25
VG Vladimir Guerrero .75 2.00

2001 Topps Tribute

This hobby-only product was released in mid-December 2001, and featured a 90-card base set that honors Hall of Fame caliber players like Babe Ruth and Mickey Mantle. Each pack contained four-cards, and carried a suggested retail price of 40.00.

COMPLETE SET (90) 100.00 200.00
PSA-GRADED MANTLE EXCH ODDS 1:170
M.MANTLE REPURCHASED ODDS 1:426
J.ROBINSON REPURCHASED ODDS 1:426
T.WILLIAMS REPURCHASED ODDS 1:426
EXCHANGE DEADLINE 11/30/03
1 Pee Wee Reese 2.50 6.00
2 Babe Ruth 8.00 20.00
3 Ralph Kiner 2.00 5.00
4 Brooks Robinson 2.00 5.00
5 Don Sutton 2.00 5.00
6 Carl Yastrzemski 4.00 10.00
7 Roger Maris 2.50 6.00
8 Andre Dawson 2.00 5.00
9 Luis Aparicio 2.00 5.00
10 Wade Boggs 2.00 5.00
11 Johnny Bench 2.50 6.00
12 Ernie Banks 2.50 6.00
13 Thurman Munson 2.50 6.00
14 Harmon Killebrew 2.50 6.00
15 Ted Kluszewski 2.00 5.00
16 Bob Feller 2.00 5.00
17 Mike Schmidt 5.00 12.00
18 Warren Spahn 2.00 5.00
19 Jim Palmer 2.00 5.00
20 Don Mattingly 5.00 12.00
21 Willie Mays 5.00 12.00
22 Gil Hodges 2.50 6.00
23 Juan Marichal 2.00 5.00
24 Robin Yount 2.50 6.00
25 Nolan Ryan Angels 6.00 15.00
26 Dave Winfield 2.00 5.00
27 Hank Greenberg 2.50 6.00
28 Honus Wagner 3.00 8.00
29 Nolan Ryan Rangers 6.00 15.00
30 Phil Niekro 2.00 5.00
31 Robin Roberts 2.00 5.00
32 Casey Stengel Yankees 2.00 5.00
33 Willie McCovey 2.00 5.00
34 Roy Campanella 2.50 6.00
35 Rollie Fingers A's 2.00 5.00
36 Tom Seaver 2.00 5.00
37 Jackie Robinson 2.50 6.00
38 Hank Aaron Braves 5.00 12.00
39 Bob Gibson 2.00 5.00
40 Carlton Fisk Red Sox 2.00 5.00
41 Hank Aaron Brewers 5.00 12.00
42 George Brett 5.00 12.00
43 Orlando Cepeda 2.00 5.00
44 Red Schoendienst 2.00 5.00
45 Don Drysdale 2.00 5.00
46 Mel Ott 2.50 6.00
47 Casey Stengel Mets 2.50 6.00
48 Al Kaline 2.50 6.00
49 Reggie Jackson 2.00 5.00
50 Tony Perez 2.00 5.00
51 Ozzie Smith 4.00 10.00
52 Billy Martin 2.00 5.00
53 Bill Dickey 2.00 5.00
54 Catfish Hunter 2.00 5.00
55 Duke Snider 2.00 5.00
56 Dale Murphy 2.00 5.00
57 Bobby Doerr 2.00 5.00
58 Earl Averill UER 2.00 5.00
Card pictures Earl Averill Jr.
59 Carlton Fisk White Sox 2.00 5.00
60 Tom Lasorda 2.00 5.00
61 Lou Gehrig 5.00 12.00
62 Enos Slaughter 2.00 5.00
63 Jim Bunning 2.00 5.00
64 Rollie Fingers Brewers 2.00 5.00
65 Frank Robinson Reds 2.00 5.00
66 Earl Weaver 2.00 5.00
67 Eddie Mathews 2.50 6.00
68 Kirby Puckett 2.50 6.00
69 Phil Rizzuto 2.50 6.00
70 Lou Brock 2.00 5.00
71 Walt Alston 2.00 5.00
72 Billy Pierce 2.00 5.00
73 Joe Morgan 2.00 5.00
74 Roberto Clemente 6.00 15.00
75 Whitey Ford 2.00 5.00
76 Richie Ashburn 2.00 5.00
77 Elston Howard 2.00 5.00
78 Gary Carter 2.00 5.00
79 Carl Hubbell 2.00 5.00
80 Yogi Berra 2.50 6.00
81 Ken Boyer 2.00 5.00
82 Nolan Ryan Astros 6.00 15.00
83 Bill Mazeroski 2.00 5.00
84 Dizzy Dean 2.50 6.00
85 Nellie Fox 2.00 5.00
86 Stan Musial 4.00 10.00
87 Steve Carlton 2.00 5.00
88 Willie Stargell 2.00 5.00
89 Hal Newhouser 2.00 5.00
90 Frank Robinson Orioles 2.00 5.00
NNO Mickey Mantle
PSA Redemption

2001 Topps Tribute Dual Relics

This two-card set features relic cards of Casey Stengel and Frank Robinson. Each card was issued at 1:860 packs.

CSYM Casey Stengel Jsy-Jsy 75.00 150.00
FRRO Frank Robinson Bat-Jsy 50.00 100.00

2001 Topps Tribute Franchise Figures Relics

This 19-card set features relic cards of franchise players from teams past. Please note that these cards were broken into two groups: Group A were inserted at a rate of 1:106, while, Group B were inserted at 1:34. Card backs carry a "RM" prefix.

GROUP A STATED ODDS 1:50
GROUP B STATED ODDS 1:106
AL Walt Alston Jsy 40.00 80.00
Tommy Lasorda Jsy A
CD Gary Carter 40.00 80.00
Andre Dawson B
FY Carlton Fisk 75.00 150.00
Carl Yastrzemski A
JM Reggie Jackson 75.00 150.00
Billy Martin B
KG Al Kaline 75.00 150.00
Hank Greenberg A
MM Thurman Munson Jsy 150.00 250.00
Don Mattingly Jsy A
PK Kirby Puckett 75.00 150.00
Harmon Killebrew A
RG Babe Ruth 400.00 700.00
Lou Gehrig A
RR Brooks Robinson Bat 60.00 120.00
Frank Robinson Uni A
AFF Luis Aparicio 60.00 120.00
Nellie Fox
Carlton Fisk A
HDB Bill Dickey Jsy 125.00 200.00
Elston Howard Bat
Yogi Berra Jsy A
HSS Gil Hodges Bat 125.00 250.00
Casey Stengel Bat
Tom Seaver Jsy A
MCS Bill Mazeroski 150.00 250.00
Roberto Clemente
Willie Stargell A
MMA Dale Murphy 125.00 200.00
Eddie Mathews
Hank Aaron A
MMC Willie Mays Jsy 125.00 200.00
Willie McCovey Bat
Orlando Cepeda Jsy A
RSC Pee Wee Reese 75.00 150.00
Duke Snider
Roy Campanella A
SAC Mike Schmidt Jsy 75.00 150.00
Richie Ashburn Bat
Steve Carlton Uni A
BPKRM Johnny Bench 150.00 250.00
Tony Perez
Ted Kluszewski
Frank Robinson
Joe Morgan A
SBSM Ozzie Smith 75.00 150.00
Lou Brock
Red Schoendienst
Stan Musial A

2001 Topps Tribute Game Bat Relics

This 31-card set features bat relic cards of classic players like George Brett and Hank Aaron. Please note that these cards were broken into two groups: Group 1 were inserted at a rate of 1:2, while, Group 2 were inserted at 1:35. Card backs carry a "RB" prefix.

GROUP 1 STATED ODDS 1:2
GROUP 2 STATED ODDS 1:35
BAT LOGO AND STENCIL CUT-OUT SAME QTY
BAT LOGO AND STENCIL CUT-OUT SAME VALUE
RBAK Al Kaline 1 10.00 25.00
RBBM Billy Martin 1 15.00 40.00
RBBR Babe Ruth 2 75.00 150.00
RBBRO B.Robinson 1 10.00 25.00
RBCFR C.Fisk Red Sox 1 10.00 25.00
RBCFW C.Fisk W.Sox 1 10.00 25.00
RBCS Casey Stengel 1 10.00 25.00
RBCY Carl Yastrzemski 1 20.00 50.00
RBDM Don Mattingly 1 20.00 50.00
RBFRR F.Robinson Reds 1 10.00 25.00
RBGB George Brett 1 15.00 40.00
RBGH Gil Hodges 1 15.00 40.00
RBHA H.Aaron Braves 1 20.00 50.00
RBHAB Hank Aaron Brewers 1 20.00 50.00
RBHG Hank Greenberg 1 20.00 50.00
RBHK Harmon Killebrew 1 10.00 25.00
RBHW Honus Wagner 1 75.00 150.00
RBJR Jackie Robinson 1
RBKB Ken Boyer 1 6.00 15.00
RBLA Luis Aparicio 1 6.00 15.00
RBLB Lou Brock 1 10.00 25.00
RBLG Lou Gehrig 1 75.00 150.00
RBOS Ozzie Smith 1 10.00 25.00
RBPWR P.W.Reese 1 10.00 25.00
RBRA Richie Ashburn 1 10.00 25.00
RBRC Roy Campanella 1 10.00 25.00
RBRCL R.Clemente 1 40.00 80.00
RBRJ Reggie Jackson 1 10.00 25.00
RBRM Roger Maris 1 20.00 50.00
RBTM T.Munson 1 10.00 25.00
RBWM Willie McCovey 1 10.00 25.00

2001 Topps Tribute Game Patch-Number Relics

This 23-card set features swatches of actual game-used jersey patches. These cards were issued into packs at 1:61. Card backs carry a "RPN" prefix.

RPNBD Bill Dickey 150.00 250.00
RPNBDO Bobby Doerr 90.00 150.00
RPNCY Carl Yastrzemski 125.00 250.00
RPNDM Don Mattingly 150.00 250.00
RPNDW Dave Winfield 90.00 150.00
RPNEM Eddie Mathews 125.00 200.00
RPNGB George Brett 125.00 200.00
RPNHK Harmon Killebrew 125.00 200.00
RPNJB Johnny Bench 125.00 200.00
RPNJM Juan Marichal 90.00 150.00
RPNJP Jim Palmer 90.00 150.00
RPNKB Kirby Puckett 125.00 200.00
RPNLB Lou Brock 125.00 200.00
RPNMS Mike Schmidt 150.00 300.00
RPNNRA N.Ryan Angels 250.00 500.00
RPNNRH N.Ryan Astros 250.00 500.00
RPNNRR Nolan Ryan Rgr 250.00 500.00
RPNRS Red Schoendienst 90.00 150.00
RPNRY Robin Yount 125.00 200.00
RPNTL Tom Lasorda 90.00 150.00
RPNWA Walt Alston 90.00 150.00
RPNWB Wade Boggs 125.00 200.00
RPNYB Yogi Berra 125.00 200.00

2001 Topps Tribute Game Worn Relics

This 39-card set features swatches of actual game-used jerseys. These cards were issued into packs in two different groups: Group 1 (1:282), and Group 2 (1:13) packs. Card backs carry a "RJ" prefix.

GROUP 1 STATED ODDS 1:282
GROUP 2 STATED ODDS 1:13
GROUP 3 STATED ODDS 1:42
GROUP 4 STATED ODDS 1:12
GROUP 5 STATED ODDS 1:9
OVERALL STATED ODDS 1:2
RJBD Bill Dickey 5 12.50 30.00
RJBDO Bobby Doerr 2 12.50 30.00
RJCS Casey Stengel 5 12.50 30.00
RJCY C.Yastrzemski White 3 15.00 40.00
RJCYA C.Yastrzemski Gray 3 15.00 40.00
RJDD Dizzy Dean Uni 4 20.00 50.00
RJDM Don Mattingly 2 15.00 40.00
RJDW Dave Winfield 2 8.00 20.00
RJEB E.Banks White 2 12.50 30.00
RJEM Eddie Mathews 2 12.50 30.00
RJEBA E.Banks Gray 2 12.50 30.00
RJFR Frank Robinson 2 12.50 30.00
RJGB George Brett 2 15.00 40.00
RJHK H.Killebrew 2 12.50 30.00
RJJB J.Bench White 2 12.50 30.00
RJJP Jim Palmer White 2 8.00 20.00
RJJR Jackie Robinson 1 200.00 350.00
RJJBE Johnny Bench Gray 2 12.50 30.00
RJJMG Juan Marichal 2 8.00 20.00
RJJPA Jim Palmer Gray 2 8.00 20.00
RJKP Kirby Puckett 2 12.50 30.00
RJLB Lou Brock 2 12.50 30.00
RJMSB M.Schmidt Blue 2 15.00 40.00
RJMSW M.Schmidt White 2 15.00 40.00
RJNF Nellie Fox 2 12.50 30.00
RJNRA N.Ryan Angels 2 30.00 60.00
RJNRH N.Ryan Astros 2 30.00 60.00
RJNRR N.Ryan Rangers 2 30.00 60.00
RJRS R.Schoendienst 2 8.00 20.00
RJRY Robin Yount 2 12.50 30.00
RJSC Steve Carlton 2 8.00 20.00
RJSM Stan Musial 2 20.00 50.00
RJTL Tom Lasorda 4 8.00 20.00
RJWA Walt Alston 4 12.50 30.00
RJWB Wade Boggs 2 12.50 30.00
RJWMF W.Mays Gray 2 15.00 40.00
RJWMW W.Mays White 2 15.00 40.00
RJWST Willie Stargell 2 12.50 30.00
RJYB Yogi Berra 2 12.50 30.00

2001 Topps Tribute Tri-Relic

This one-card set features a tri-relic card of Nolan Ryan. This card was issued at 1:1292. Card backs carry a "NR" prefix.

NRAAR Nolan Ryan

2002 Topps Tribute

This 90 card set was released in November, 2002. These cards were issued in five card packs which came six packs to a box and four boxes to a case. Each of these packs had an SRP of $50 per pack.

COMPLETE SET (90) 60.00 120.00
1 Hank Aaron 4.00 10.00
2 Rogers Hornsby 2.00 5.00
3 Bobby Thomson 1.50 4.00
4 Eddie Collins 1.50 4.00
5 Joe Carter 1.50 4.00
6 Jim Palmer 1.50 4.00
7 Willie Mays 4.00 10.00
8 Willie Stargell 1.50 4.00
9 Vida Blue 1.50 4.00
10 Whitey Ford 1.50 4.00
11 Bob Gibson 1.50 4.00
12 Nellie Fox 2.00 5.00
13 Napoleon Lajoie 2.00 5.00
14 Frankie Frisch 1.50 4.00
15 Nolan Ryan 5.00 12.00
16 Brooks Robinson 1.50 4.00
17 Kirby Puckett 2.00 5.00
18 Fergie Jenkins 1.50 4.00
19 Edd Roush 1.50 4.00
20 Honus Wagner 3.00 8.00
21 Richie Ashburn 1.50 4.00
22 Bob Feller 1.50 4.00
23 Joe Morgan 1.50 4.00
24 Orlando Cepeda 1.50 4.00
25 Steve Garvey 1.50 4.00
26 Hank Greenberg 2.00 5.00
27 Stan Musial 3.00 8.00
28 Sam Crawford 1.50 4.00
29 Jim Rice 1.50 4.00
30 Hack Wilson 1.50 4.00
31 Lou Brock 1.50 4.00
32 Mickey Vernon 1.50 4.00
33 Chuck Klein 1.50 4.00
34 Tony Gwynn 2.50 6.00
35 Duke Snider 1.50 4.00
36 Ryne Sandberg 4.00 10.00
37 Johnny Bench 2.00 5.00
38 Sam Rice 1.50 4.00
39 Lou Gehrig 4.00 10.00
40 Robin Yount 2.00 5.00
41 Don Sutton 1.50 4.00
42 Jim Bottomley 1.50 4.00
43 Billy Herman 1.50 4.00
44 Zach Wheat 1.50 4.00
45 Juan Marichal 1.50 4.00
46 Bert Blyleven 1.50 4.00
47 Jackie Robinson 2.00 5.00
48 Gil Hodges 1.50 4.00
49 Mike Schmidt 4.00 10.00
50 Dale Murphy 1.50 4.00
51 Phil Rizzuto 1.50 4.00
52 Ty Cobb 3.00 8.00
53 Andre Dawson 1.50 4.00
54 Fred Lindstrom 1.50 4.00
55 Roy Campanella 2.00 5.00
56 Don Larsen 1.50 4.00
57 Harry Heilmann 1.50 4.00
58 Catfish Hunter 1.50 4.00
59 Frank Robinson 1.50 4.00
60 Bill Mazeroski 1.50 4.00
61 Roger Maris 2.00 5.00
62 Dave Winfield 1.50 4.00
63 Warren Spahn 1.50 4.00
64 Babe Ruth 6.00 15.00
65 Ernie Banks 2.00 5.00
66 Wade Boggs 1.50 4.00
67 Carl Yastrzemski 3.00 8.00
68 Ron Santo 1.50 4.00
69 Dennis Martinez 1.50 4.00
70 Yogi Berra 2.00 5.00
71 Paul Waner 1.50 4.00
72 George Brett 4.00 10.00
73 Eddie Mathews 2.00 5.00
74 Bill Dickey 1.50 4.00
75 Carlton Fisk 1.50 4.00
76 Thurman Munson 2.00 5.00
77 Reggie Jackson 1.50 4.00
78 Phil Niekro 1.50 4.00
79 Luis Aparicio 1.50 4.00
80 Steve Carlton 1.50 4.00
81 Tris Speaker 1.50 4.00
82 Johnny Mize 1.50 4.00
83 Tom Seaver 1.50 4.00
84 Heinie Manush 1.50 4.00
85 Tommy John 1.50 4.00
86 Joe Cronin 1.50 4.00
87 Don Mattingly 4.00 10.00
88 Kirk Gibson 1.50 4.00
89 Bo Jackson 2.00 5.00
90 Mel Ott 2.00 5.00

2002 Topps Tribute First Impressions

Inserted into packs at a stated rate of one in 16, this is a parallel to the Topps Tribute set. Each of these cards were printed to a stated print run which matched the player's major league debut season. For those players who debuted in 1925 or before, no pricing is provided due to market scarcity.

1 Hank Aaron/54 25.00 60.00
2 Rogers Hornsby/15
3 Bobby Thomson/46 12.50 30.00
4 Eddie Collins/6
5 Joe Carter/83 6.00 15.00
6 Jim Palmer/65 10.00 25.00
7 Willie Mays/51 25.00 60.00
8 Willie Stargell/62 10.00 25.00
9 Vida Blue/69 8.00 20.00
10 Whitey Ford/50 12.50 30.00
11 Bob Gibson/59 10.00 25.00
12 Nellie Fox/47 20.00 50.00
13 Napoleon Lajoie/96 8.00 20.00
14 Frankie Frisch/19
15 Nolan Ryan/66 25.00 60.00
16 Brooks Robinson/55 10.00 25.00
17 Kirby Puckett/84 8.00 20.00
18 Fergie Jenkins/65 10.00 25.00
19 Edd Roush/13
20 Honus Wagner/97 12.50 30.00
21 Richie Ashburn/48 12.50 30.00
22 Bob Feller/36 12.50 30.00
23 Joe Morgan/63 10.00 25.00
24 Orlando Cepeda/58 10.00 25.00
25 Steve Garvey/69 8.00 20.00
26 Hank Greenberg/30 20.00 50.00
27 Stan Musial/41 25.00 60.00
28 Sam Crawford/99 6.00 15.00
29 Jim Rice/74 8.00 20.00
30 Hack Wilson/23
31 Lou Brock/61 10.00 25.00
32 Mickey Vernon/39 12.50 30.00
33 Chuck Klein/28 15.00 40.00
34 Tony Gwynn/82 10.00 25.00
35 Duke Snider/47 12.50 30.00
36 Ryne Sandberg/81 30.00 60.00
37 Johnny Bench/67 10.00 25.00
38 Sam Rice/15
39 Lou Gehrig/23
40 Robin Yount/74 10.00 25.00
41 Don Sutton/66 8.00 20.00
42 Jim Bottomley/22
43 Billy Herman/31 15.00 40.00
44 Zach Wheat/9
45 Juan Marichal/60 10.00 25.00
46 Bert Blyleven/70 8.00 20.00
47 Jackie Robinson/47 15.00 40.00
48 Gil Hodges/43 12.50 30.00
49 Mike Schmidt/72 20.00 50.00
50 Dale Murphy/76 20.00 50.00
51 Phil Rizzuto/41 12.50 30.00
52 Ty Cobb/5
53 Andre Dawson/76 8.00 20.00
54 Fred Lindstrom/24
55 Roy Campanella/48 15.00 40.00
56 Don Larsen/53 10.00 25.00
57 Harry Heilmann/14
58 Catfish Hunter/65 10.00 25.00
59 Frank Robinson/56 10.00 25.00
60 Bill Mazeroski/56 10.00 25.00
61 Roger Maris/57 12.50 30.00
62 Dave Winfield/73 8.00 20.00
63 Warren Spahn/42 12.50 30.00
64 Babe Ruth/14
65 Ernie Banks/53 12.50 30.00
66 Wade Boggs/82 6.00 15.00
67 Carl Yastrzemski/61 20.00 50.00
68 Ron Santo/60 10.00 25.00
69 Dennis Martinez/76 8.00 20.00
70 Yogi Berra/46 15.00 40.00
71 Paul Waner/26 15.00 40.00
72 George Brett/73 20.00 50.00
73 Eddie Mathews/52 20.00 50.00
74 Bill Dickey/28 15.00 40.00
75 Carlton Fisk/69 8.00 20.00
76 Thurman Munson/69 10.00 25.00
77 Reggie Jackson/67 8.00 20.00
78 Phil Niekro/64 10.00 25.00
79 Luis Aparicio/56 10.00 25.00
80 Steve Carlton/65 10.00 25.00
81 Tris Speaker/7
82 Johnny Mize/36 12.50 30.00
83 Tom Seaver/67 8.00 20.00
84 Heinie Manush/23
85 Tommy John/53 10.00 25.00
86 Joe Cronin/26 15.00 40.00
87 Don Mattingly/82 15.00 40.00
88 Kirk Gibson/79 8.00 20.00
89 Bo Jackson/86 8.00 20.00
90 Mel Ott/26 20.00 50.00

2002 Topps Tribute Lasting Impressions

Inserted into packs at a stated rate of one in 13, this is a parallel to the Topps Tribute set. Each of these cards were printed to a stated print run which matched the player's major league final season. For those players who retired in 1925 or before (or 2001 or later), no pricing is provided due to market scarcity.

1 Hank Aaron/76 20.00 50.00
2 Rogers Hornsby/37 15.00 40.00
3 Bobby Thomson/60 10.00 25.00
4 Eddie Collins/30 15.00 40.00
5 Joe Carter/98 6.00 15.00
6 Jim Palmer/84 6.00 15.00
7 Willie Mays/73 20.00 50.00
8 Willie Stargell/82 6.00 15.00
9 Vida Blue/86 6.00 15.00
10 Whitey Ford/67 8.00 20.00
11 Bob Gibson/75 8.00 20.00
12 Nellie Fox/65 20.00 50.00
13 Napoleon Lajoie/16
14 Frankie Frisch/37 12.50 30.00
15 Nolan Ryan/93 20.00 50.00
16 Brooks Robinson/77 8.00 20.00
17 Kirby Puckett/95 8.00 20.00
18 Fergie Jenkins/83 6.00 15.00
19 Edd Roush/31 15.00 40.00
20 Honus Wagner/17
21 Richie Ashburn/62 10.00 25.00
22 Bob Feller/56 10.00 25.00
23 Joe Morgan/84 6.00 15.00
24 Orlando Cepeda/74 8.00 20.00
25 Steve Garvey/87 6.00 15.00
26 Hank Greenberg/47 15.00 40.00
27 Stan Musial/63 20.00 50.00
28 Sam Crawford/17
29 Jim Rice/89 6.00 15.00
30 Hack Wilson/34 15.00 40.00
31 Lou Brock/79 8.00 20.00
32 Mickey Vernon/60 10.00 25.00
33 Chuck Klein/44 12.50 30.00
34 Tony Gwynn/1
35 Duke Snider/64 10.00 25.00
36 Ryne Sandberg/97 30.00 60.00
37 Johnny Bench/83 8.00 20.00
38 Sam Rice/34 15.00 40.00
39 Lou Gehrig/39 30.00 80.00
40 Robin Yount/93 8.00 20.00
41 Don Sutton/88 6.00 15.00
42 Jim Bottomley/37 12.50 30.00
43 Billy Herman/47 12.50 30.00
44 Zach Wheat/27 15.00 40.00
45 Juan Marichal/75 8.00 20.00
46 Bert Blyleven/92 6.00 15.00
47 Jackie Robinson/56 12.50 30.00
48 Gil Hodges/63 10.00 25.00
49 Mike Schmidt/89 20.00 50.00
50 Dale Murphy/93 20.00 50.00
51 Phil Rizzuto/56 10.00 25.00
52 Ty Cobb/28 30.00 80.00
53 Andre Dawson/96 6.00 15.00
54 Fred Lindstrom/36 12.50 30.00
55 Roy Campanella/57 12.50 30.00
56 Don Larsen/67 8.00 20.00

57 Harry Heilmann/32 15.00 40.00
58 Catfish Hunter/79 8.00 20.00
59 Frank Robinson/76 8.00 20.00
60 Bill Mazeroski/72 8.00 20.00
61 Roger Maris/68 10.00 25.00
62 Dave Winfield/95 6.00 15.00
63 Warren Spahn/65 10.00 25.00
64 Babe Ruth/35 30.00 80.00
65 Ernie Banks/71 10.00 25.00
66 Wade Boggs/99 6.00 15.00
67 Carl Yastrzemski/83 12.50 30.00
68 Don Sutton/74 8.00 20.00
69 Dennis Martinez/98 6.00 15.00
70 Yogi Berra/65 12.50 30.00
71 Paul Waner/45 12.50 30.00
72 George Brett/93 20.00 50.00
73 Eddie Mathews/68 20.00 50.00
74 Bill Dickey/46 12.50 30.00
75 Carlton Fisk/93 6.00 15.00
76 Thurman Munson/79 10.00 25.00
77 Reggie Jackson/87 6.00 15.00
78 Phil Niekro/87 6.00 15.00
79 Luis Aparicio/73 8.00 20.00
80 Steve Carlton/88 6.00 15.00
81 Tris Speaker/28 15.00 40.00
82 Johnny Mize/53 10.00 25.00
83 Tom Seaver/86 6.00 15.00
84 Heinie Manush/39 12.50 30.00
85 Tommy John/89 6.00 15.00
86 Joe Cronin/45 12.50 30.00
87 Don Mattingly/95 15.00 40.00
88 Kirk Gibson/95 6.00 15.00
89 Bo Jackson/94 8.00 20.00
90 Mel Ott/47 15.00 40.00

2002 Topps Tribute The Catch Dual Relic

Inserted into packs at a stated rate of one in 1023, this card features relics from players involved in Willie Mays' legendary catch during the 1954 World Series when he ran down a well hit ball by Vic Wertz.

JSY NUMBER ODDS 1:3161
JSY NUMBER PRINT RUN 24 #'d CARDS
NO JSY NUM.PRICING DUE TO SCARCITY
*SEASON: .6X TO 1.2X BASIC DUAL RELIC
SEASON ODDS 1:1391
SEASON PRINT RUN 54 SERIAL #'d CARDS
MW Vic Wertz Bat 150.00 300.00
Willie Mays Glove

2002 Topps Tribute Marks of Excellence Autograph

Inserted into packs at a stated rate of one in 61, these six cards feature players who signed cards honoring their signature moment.

DL Don Larsen 20.00 50.00
LB Lou Brock 20.00 50.00
MS Mike Schmidt 60.00 120.00
SC Steve Carlton 20.00 50.00
SM Stan Musial 60.00 120.00
WS Warren Spahn 40.00 80.00

2002 Topps Tribute Marks of Excellence Autograph Relics

Inserted in packs at a stated rate of one in 61, these six cards feature game-used memorabilia pieces honoring players and their signature moment.

BR Brooks Robinson Bat 40.00 80.00
DM Don Mattingly Jsy 30.00 60.00
DS Duke Snider Uni 40.00 80.00
FJ Fergie Jenkins Jsy 20.00 50.00
JP Jim Palmer Uni 20.00 50.00
RY Robin Yount Uni 40.00 80.00

2002 Topps Tribute Matching Marks Dual Relics

Inserted into packs at an overall stated rate of one in 11, these 22 cards feature two players and a game-used memorabilia piece from each of them.

GROUP A ODDS 1:134
GROUP B ODDS 1:368
GROUP C ODDS 1:123
GROUP D ODDS 1:43
GROUP E ODDS 1:105
GROUP F ODDS 1:82
GROUP G ODDS 1:31
AR Hank Aaron Bat 250.00 400.00
Babe Ruth Bat A
BB Wade Boggs Jsy 20.00 50.00
George Brett Jsy C
BF Johnny Bench Bat 30.00 60.00
Carlton Fisk Bat A
BM Vida Blue Jsy 6.00 15.00
Dennis Martinez Jsy G
BMA George Brett Jsy 75.00 150.00
Don Mattingly Jsy A
BS Bert Blyleven Jsy 8.00 20.00
Don Sutton Jsy C
GA Hank Greenberg Bat 60.00 120.00
Richie Ashburn Bat A
GH Steve Garvey Bat 10.00 25.00
Gil Hodges Bat D
JS Fergie Jenkins Jsy 20.00 50.00
Tom Seaver Jsy B
MA Willie Mays Uni 150.00 250.00
Hank Aaron Bat A
NS Phil Niekro Uni 8.00 20.00
Tom Seaver Uni G
PJ Jim Palmer Jsy 10.00 25.00
Tommy John Jsy D
RJ Frank Robinson Uni 30.00 60.00
Reggie Jackson Bat A
RS Nolan Ryan Jsy 75.00 150.00
Tom Seaver Jsy A
SB Tris Speaker Bat 200.00 300.00
George Brett Bat A
SBA Ron Santo Bat 10.00 25.00
Ernie Banks Bat D
SM Duke Snider Bat 50.00 100.00
Willie Mays Uni A
SR Willie Stargell Uni 8.00 20.00
Jim Rice Uni E
WY Dave Winfield Bat 15.00 40.00
Carl Yastrzemski Bat D
WYO Dave Winfield Uni 8.00 20.00
Robin Yount Uni F
YK Carl Yastrzemski Bat 50.00 100.00
Chuck Klein Bat A
YP Robin Yount Uni 30.00 60.00
Kirby Puckett Uni A

2002 Topps Tribute Memorable Materials

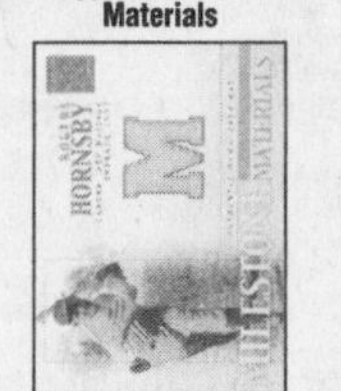

Inserted into packs at different rates depending on what group and game-used memorabilia piece, these 22 cards feature players from the tribute set as well as a memorabilia piece. We have notated next to the player's name what group this memorabilia piece belongs to.

BAT GROUP A ODDS 1:11,592
BAT GROUP B ODDS 1:6
JSY/UNI GROUP A ODDS 1:246
JSY/UNI GROUP B ODDS 1:12
BJ Bo Jackson Jsy B 10.00 25.00
BM Bill Mazeroski Uni B 8.00 20.00
BT Bobby Thomson Bat B 8.00 20.00
CF Carlton Fisk Bat B 10.00 25.00
CK Chuck Klein Bat B 15.00 40.00
CY Carl Yastrzemski Uni B 12.50 30.00
DM Don Mattingly Jsy B 15.00 40.00
GB George Brett Jsy B 15.00 40.00
HA Hank Aaron Bat B 15.00 40.00
HW Hack Wilson Bat B 30.00 60.00
JC Joe Carter Bat B 8.00 20.00
JM Joe Morgan Bat B 8.00 20.00
JR Jackie Robinson Bat B 20.00 50.00
KG Kirk Gibson Bat B 8.00 20.00
KP Kirby Puckett Bat B 15.00 40.00
LG Lou Gehrig Bat A
NR Nolan Ryan Jsy A 20.00 50.00
PR Phil Rizzuto Bat B 10.00 25.00
RC Roy Campanella Bat B 15.00 40.00
RJ Reggie Jackson Bat B 10.00 25.00
RM Roger Maris Bat B 40.00 80.00
TM Thurman Munson Bat B 20.00 50.00

2002 Topps Tribute Memorable Materials Jersey Number

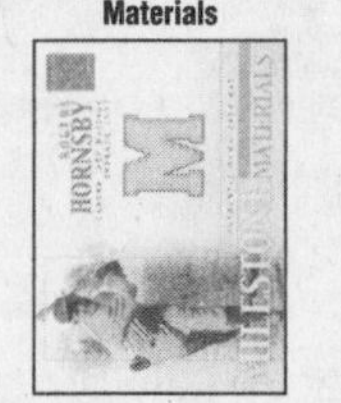

Inserted into packs at a different rate depending on whether it is a bat or a uniform piece, this is a parallel to the Memorable Materials insert set. Each of these cards are issued to a stated print run matching the uniform number that the player wore during his career. For cards with less than 40 cards printed, no pricing is provided due to market scarcity.

BAT STATED ODDS 1:208
JSY/UNI STATED ODDS 1:644
BJ Bo Jackson Jsy/16
BM Bill Mazeroski Uni/9
BT Bobby Thomson Bat/23
CF Carlton Fisk Bat/27
CK Chuck Klein Bat/1
CY Carl Yastrzemski Uni/27 UER
Yaz jersey number is actually 8
DM Don Mattingly Jsy/23
GB George Brett Jsy/5
HA Hank Aaron Bat/44 50.00 120.00
HW Hack Wilson Bat/1
JC Joe Carter Bat/29
JM Joe Morgan Bat/8
JR Jackie Robinson Bat/42 50.00 120.00
KG Kirk Gibson Bat/23
KP Kirby Puckett Bat/34
LG Lou Gehrig Bat/4
NR Nolan Ryan Jsy/34
PR Phil Rizzuto Bat/10
RC Roy Campanella Bat/39
RJ Reggie Jackson Bat/44 25.00 60.00
RM Roger Maris Bat/9
TM Thurman Munson Bat/15

2002 Topps Tribute Memorable Materials Season

Inserted into packs at a different rate depending on whether it is a bat or a uniform piece, this is a parallel to the Memorable Materials insert set. Each of these cards are issued to a stated print run matching the most memorable season that the player had during his career. For cards with less than 40 cards printed, no pricing is provided due to market scarcity.

BAT STATED ODDS 1:72
JSY/UNI STATED ODDS 1:152
BJ Bo Jackson Jsy/89 30.00 80.00
BM Bill Mazeroski Uni/60 15.00 40.00
BT Bobby Thomson Bat/51 15.00 40.00
CF Carlton Fisk Bat/75 15.00 40.00
CK Chuck Klein Bat/33
CY Carl Yastrzemski Uni/75 UER 20.00 50.00
Card commemorates 1967 season
DM Don Mattingly Jsy/87 25.00 60.00
GB George Brett Jsy/83 30.00 80.00
HA Hank Aaron Bat/74 30.00 80.00
HW Hack Wilson Bat/30
JC Joe Carter Bat/93 12.50 30.00
JM Joe Morgan Bat/76 12.50 30.00
JR Jackie Robinson Bat/47 40.00 100.00
KG Kirk Gibson Bat/88 12.50 30.00
KP Kirby Puckett Bat/91 25.00 60.00
LG Lou Gehrig Bat/39
NR Nolan Ryan Jsy/91 30.00 80.00
PR Phil Rizzuto Bat/50 20.00 50.00
RC Roy Campanella Bat/55 30.00 80.00
RJ Reggie Jackson Bat/77 15.00 40.00
RM Roger Maris Bat/61 60.00 150.00
TM Thurman Munson Bat/76 30.00 80.00

2002 Topps Tribute Milestone Materials

Inserted at different stated odds depending on whether it is a bat or a jersey/uniform piece, these 50 cards feature game-used memorabilia from the feature player's career.

BAT STATED ODDS 1:4
JSY/UNI STATED ODDS 1:5
AD Andre Dawson Jsy 6.00 15.00
BD Bill Dickey Uni 10.00 25.00
BF Bob Feller Bat 15.00 40.00
BG Bob Gibson Uni 8.00 20.00
BH Billy Herman Uni 6.00 15.00
BR Babe Ruth Bat 150.00 250.00
BRO Brooks Robinson Bat 10.00 25.00
CH Catfish Hunter Jsy 8.00 20.00
DM Dale Murphy Jsy 8.00 20.00
DS Duke Snider Uni 8.00 20.00
EB Ernie Banks Uni 10.00 25.00
EC Eddie Collins Bat 75.00 150.00
EM Eddie Mathews Jsy 10.00 25.00
ER Edd Roush Bat 15.00 40.00
FF Frankie Frisch Bat 10.00 25.00
FL Fred Lindstrom Uni 10.00 25.00
FR Frank Robinson Bat 10.00 25.00
HH Harry Heilmann Bat 10.00 25.00
HM Heinie Manush Bat 15.00 40.00
HW Honus Wagner Bat 75.00 150.00
JB Johnny Bench Jsy 10.00 25.00
JBO Jim Bottomley Bat 15.00 40.00
JC Joe Cronin Bat 10.00 25.00
JM Johnny Mize Uni 8.00 20.00
JMA Juan Marichal Jsy 6.00 15.00
JP Jim Palmer Uni 6.00 15.00
LA Luis Aparicio Bat 8.00 20.00
LG Lou Gehrig Bat 100.00 175.00
MO Mel Ott Bat 30.00 60.00
MV Mickey Vernon Bat 8.00 20.00
NF Nellie Fox Uni 10.00 25.00
NL Napoleon Lajoie Bat 90.00 150.00
NR Nolan Ryan Jsy 12.50 30.00
OC Orlando Cepeda Jsy 6.00 15.00
PW Paul Waner Bat 15.00 40.00
RH Rogers Hornsby Bat 30.00 60.00
RJ Reggie Jackson Jsy 8.00 20.00
RS Ryne Sandberg Bat 10.00 25.00
RY Robin Yount Uni 10.00 25.00
SC Sam Crawford Bat 15.00 40.00
SR Sam Rice Bat 30.00 60.00
TC Ty Cobb Bat 75.00 150.00
TS Tom Seaver Jsy 8.00 20.00
TSP Tris Speaker Bat 75.00 150.00
WB Wade Boggs Uni 8.00 20.00
WF Whitey Ford Uni 8.00 20.00
WM Willie Mays Uni 20.00 50.00
WS Willie Stargell Uni 8.00 20.00
YB Yogi Berra Jsy 10.00 25.00
ZW Zach Wheat Bat 15.00 40.00

2002 Topps Tribute Milestone Materials Jersey Number

Inserted into packs at a different rate depending on whether it is a bat or a uniform piece, this is a parallel to the Milestone Materials insert set. Each of these cards are issued to a stated print run matching the uniform number that the player wore during his career. For cards with less than 40 cards printed, no pricing is provided due to market scarcity.

BAT STATED ODDS 1:443
JSY/UNI STATED ODDS 1:148
AD Andre Dawson Jsy/8
BD Bill Dickey Uni/8
BF Bob Feller Bat/19
BG Bob Gibson Uni/45 20.00 50.00
BH Billy Herman Uni/2
BR Babe Ruth Bat/3
BRO Brooks Robinson Bat/5
CH Catfish Hunter Jsy/27
DM Dale Murphy Jsy/3
DS Duke Snider Uni/4
EB Ernie Banks Uni/14
EC Eddie Collins Bat/1
EM Eddie Mathews Jsy/41 25.00 60.00
ER Edd Roush Bat/1
FF Frankie Frisch Bat/3
FL Fred Lindstrom Uni/3
FR Frank Robinson Bat/20
HH Harry Heilmann Bat/1
HM Heinie Manush Bat/3
HW Honus Wagner Bat/33
JB Johnny Bench Jsy/5
JBO Jim Bottomley Bat/4
JC Joe Cronin Bat/4
JM Johnny Mize Uni/36
JMA Juan Marichal Jsy/27
JP Jim Palmer Uni/22
LA Luis Aparicio Bat/11
LG Lou Gehrig Bat/4
MO Mel Ott Bat/4
MV Mickey Vernon Bat/3
NF Nellie Fox Uni/2
NL Napoleon Lajoie Bat/1
NR Nolan Ryan Jsy/34
OC Orlando Cepeda Jsy/30
PW Paul Waner Bat/9
RH Rogers Hornsby Bat/9
RJ Reggie Jackson Jsy/44 20.00 50.00
RS Ryne Sandberg Bat/23
RY Robin Yount Uni/19
SC Sam Crawford Bat/1
SR Sam Rice Bat/1
TC Ty Cobb Bat/1
TS Tom Seaver Jsy/41 20.00 50.00
TSP Tris Speaker Bat/1
WB Wade Boggs Uni/26
WF Whitey Ford Uni/16
WM Willie Mays Uni/24
WS Willie Stargell Uni/8
YB Yogi Berra Jsy/8
ZW Zach Wheat Bat/1

2002 Topps Tribute Milestone Materials Season

Inserted into packs at a different rate depending on whether it is a bat or a uniform piece, this is a parallel to the Memorable Materials insert set. Each of these cards are issued to a stated print run matching the most memorable season that the player had during his career. For cards with less than 40 cards printed, no pricing is provided due to market scarcity.

BAT STATED ODDS 1:73
JSY/UNI STATED ODDS 1:41
AD Andre Dawson Jsy/95 12.50 30.00
BD Bill Dickey Uni/46 25.00 60.00
BF Bob Feller Bat/54 25.00 60.00
BG Bob Gibson Uni/74 15.00 40.00
BH Billy Herman Uni/47 15.00 40.00
BR Babe Ruth Bat/34
BRO Brooks Robinson Bat/74 20.00 50.00
CH Catfish Hunter Jsy/79 15.00 40.00
DM Dale Murphy Jsy/91 20.00 50.00
DS Duke Snider Uni/63 20.00 50.00
EB Ernie Banks Uni/70 20.00 50.00
EC Eddie Collins Bat/25
EM Eddie Mathews Jsy/67 20.00 50.00
ER Edd Roush Bat/31
FF Frankie Frisch Bat/35
FL Fred Lindstrom Uni/36
FR Frank Robinson Bat/71 20.00 50.00
HH Harry Heilmann Bat/32
HM Heinie Manush Bat/39
HW Honus Wagner Bat/14
JB Johnny Bench Jsy/80 20.00 50.00
JBO Jim Bottomley Bat/36
JC Joe Cronin Bat/45 25.00 60.00
JM Johnny Mize Uni/50 20.00 50.00
JMA Juan Marichal Jsy/7
JP Jim Palmer Uni/82 12.50 30.00
LA Luis Aparicio Bat/73 15.00 40.00
LG Lou Gehrig Bat/37
MO Mel Ott Bat/45 60.00 150.00
MV Mickey Vernon Bat/56 20.00 50.00
NF Nellie Fox Uni/41 40.00 100.00
NL Napoleon Lajoie Bat/14
NR Nolan Ryan Jsy/89 40.00 100.00
OC Orlando Cepeda Jsy/73 12.50 30.00
PW Paul Waner Bat/42 40.00 100.00
RH Rogers Hornsby Bat/37
RJ Reggie Jackson Jsy/84 15.00 40.00
RS Ryne Sandberg Bat/93 30.00 80.00
RY Robin Yount Uni/92 15.00 40.00
SC Sam Crawford Bat/16
SR Sam Rice Bat/34
TC Ty Cobb Bat/27
TS Tom Seaver Jsy/81 15.00 40.00
TSP Tris Speaker Bat/25
WB Wade Boggs Uni/99 15.00 40.00
WF Whitey Ford Uni/62 20.00 50.00
WM Willie Mays Uni/69 40.00 100.00
WS Willie Stargell Uni/80 15.00 40.00
YB Yogi Berra Jsy/61 25.00 60.00
ZW Zach Wheat Bat/25

2002 Topps Tribute Pastime Patches

Inserted into packs at a stated overall rate of one in 92, these 12 cards feature game-worn patch relic cards of these baseball legends.

*LOGO PATCHES: 2.5X VALUE
GROUP A ODDS 1:184
GROUP B ODDS 1:184
OVERALL ODDS 1:92
BD Bill Dickey B 125.00 200.00
CY Carl Yastrzemski B 125.00 200.00
DM Don Mattingly A 100.00 200.00
DW Dave Winfield A 60.00 120.00
EM Eddie Mathews A 75.00 150.00
GB George Brett A 125.00 200.00
JB Johnny Bench B 75.00 150.00
JP Jim Palmer B 75.00 150.00
KP Kirby Puckett B 75.00 150.00
RY Robin Yount B 75.00 150.00
WB Wade Boggs B 75.00 150.00
NRR Nolan Ryan B 150.00 250.00

2002 Topps Tribute Signature Cuts

Inserted into packs at a stated rate of one in 9936, these four cards feature cut autographs of four of baseball's most legendary figures. According to Topps, each of these cards were issued to a print run of two cards.

BR Babe Ruth
JR Jackie Robinson
LG Lou Gehrig
TC Ty Cobb

2009 Topps Tribute

COMPLETE SET (100) 100.00 200.00
COMMON CARD (1-100) .60 1.50
COMMON RC (1-100) 1.00 2.50
PRINTING PLATE ODDS 1:91 HOBBY
PLATE PRINT RUN 1 SET PER COLOR
BLACK-CYAN-MAGENTA-YELLOW ISSUED
NO PLATE PRICING DUE TO SCARCITY
1 Babe Ruth 4.00 10.00
2 Christy Mathewson 1.50 4.00
3 Don Zimmer .60 1.50
4 Nolan Ryan 5.00 12.00
5 Dennis Eckersley .60 1.50
6 Carl Yastrzemski 2.50 6.00
7 Mickey Mantle 5.00 12.00
8 Tony Perez .60 1.50
9 Cal Ripken Jr. 6.00 15.00
10 Derek Jeter 4.00 10.00
11 Wade Boggs 1.00 2.50
12 Tom Seaver 1.00 2.50
13 Willie McCovey 1.00 2.50
14 Walter Johnson 1.50 4.00
15 Steve Garvey .60 1.50
16 George Sisler 1.00 2.50
17 Joe Morgan .60 1.50
18 Don Larsen .60 1.50
19 Reggie Jackson 1.00 2.50
20 Thurman Munson 1.50 4.00
21 Howard Johnson .60 1.50
22 Johnny Bench 1.50 4.00
23 Bo Jackson 1.50 4.00
24 Ray Knight .60 1.50
25 Cy Young 1.50 4.00
26 Bruce Sutter .60 1.50
27 Mike Schmidt 2.50 6.00
28 Roy Campanella 1.50 4.00
29 John Smoltz 1.50 4.00
30 Bob Gibson 1.00 2.50
31 Roy Halladay 1.50 4.00
32 Tris Speaker 1.00 2.50
33 Tony Gwynn 1.50 4.00
34 Whitey Ford 1.00 2.50
35 Carlos Beltran .60 1.50
36 Manny Ramirez 1.50 4.00
37 Frank Thomas 1.50 4.00
38 Honus Wagner 1.50 4.00
39 Josh Beckett 1.00 2.50
40 Hanley Ramirez 1.50 4.00
41 Ty Cobb 2.50 6.00
42 Darryl Strawberry .60 1.50
43 Stan Musial 2.50 6.00
44 Duke Snider 1.00 2.50
45 Rollie Fingers .60 1.50
46 Juan Marichal .60 1.50
47 Eddie Mathews 1.50 4.00
48 Paul Molitor 1.50 4.00
49 Pee Wee Reese 1.00 2.50
50 Ryan Howard 2.00 5.00
51 Johnny Podres .60 1.50
52 Randy Johnson 1.00 2.50
53 Rogers Hornsby 1.00 2.50
54 Dwight Gooden .60 1.50
55 Ryne Sandberg 3.00 8.00
56 Robin Yount 1.50 4.00
57 Greg Maddux 2.00 5.00
58 Jackie Robinson 1.50 4.00
59 Adrian Gonzalez 1.00 2.50
60 Jim Palmer .60 1.50
61 David Wright 2.00 5.00
62 Ernie Banks 1.50 4.00
63 Chipper Jones 1.50 4.00
64 Gary Carter .60 1.50
65 Aramis Ramirez .60 1.50
66 Jimmie Foxx 1.50 4.00
67 Joe Mauer 1.50 4.00
68 Ozzie Smith 2.50 6.00
69 George Kell .60 1.50
70 Derrek Lee .60 1.50
71 Hank Greenberg 1.50 4.00
72 Joey Votto 1.50 4.00
73 Mel Ott 1.50 4.00
74 Clayton Kershaw 1.50 4.00
75 Josh Hamilton 1.50 4.00
76 Tommy Hanson RC 3.00 8.00
77 Alex Rodriguez 2.50 6.00
78 Andre Dawson 1.00 2.50
79 Johnny Mize 1.00 2.50
80 Sal Bando .60 1.50
81 Justin Morneau 1.50 4.00
82 Keith Hernandez .60 1.50
83 Lou Gehrig 3.00 8.00
84 Dustin Pedroia 2.00 5.00
85 Mark Teixeira 1.50 4.00
86 Jay Bruce 1.00 2.50
87 Chase Utley 1.50 4.00
88 Lance Berkman 1.00 2.50
89 Frank Robinson 1.00 2.50
90 Matt LaPorta RC 2.50 6.00
91 Albert Pujols 4.00 10.00
92 Mike Piazza 1.50 4.00
93 Robin Roberts .60 1.50
94 Evan Longoria 2.00 5.00
95 Ryan Braun 2.00 5.00
96 Rick Porcello RC 3.00 8.00
97 CC Sabathia 1.00 2.50
98 Brooks Robinson 1.00 2.50
99 Ichiro Suzuki 2.50 6.00
100 Ken Griffey Jr. 2.50 6.00

2009 Topps Tribute Black

*BLACK: .75X TO 2X BASIC
*BLACK RC: .6X TO 1.5X BASIC RC
STATED ODDS 1:4 HOBBY
STATED PRINT RUN 99 SER.#'d SETS

2009 Topps Tribute Blue

*BLUE: .5X TO 1.2X BASIC
*BLUE RC: .5X TO 1.2X BASIC RC
RANDOM INSERTS IN PACKS
STATED PRINT RUN 219 SER.#'d SETS

2009 Topps Tribute Gold

*GOLD: 1.5X TO 4X BASIC
*GOLD RC: .75X TO 2X BASIC RC
STATED ODDS 1:8 HOBBY
STATED PRINT RUN 50 SER.#'d SETS

2009 Topps Tribute Red

STATED ODDS 1:368 HOBBY
STATED PRINT RUN 1 SER.#'d SET
NO PRICING DUE TO SCARCITY

2009 Topps Tribute A Cut Above the Rest Cut Signatures

STATED PRINT RUN 1 SER.#'d SET
NO PRICING DUE TO SCARCITY
MO Mel Ott
TS Tris Speaker

2009 Topps Tribute Autograph Relics

STATED ODDS 1:7 HOBBY
STATED PRINT RUN 99 SER.#'d SETS
ALL VARIATIONS PRICED EQUALLY
JH Josh Hamilton 12.50 30.00
JM Juan Marichal 10.00 25.00
TS Tom Seaver 15.00 40.00
AD1 Andre Dawson 15.00 40.00
AD2 Andre Dawson 15.00 40.00
CC1 Carl Crawford 12.50 30.00
CC2 Carl Crawford 12.50 30.00
CK1 Clayton Kershaw 12.50 30.00
CK2 Clayton Kershaw 12.50 30.00
CK3 Clayton Kershaw 12.50 30.00
CK4 Clayton Kershaw 12.50 30.00
DP1 Dustin Pedroia 30.00 60.00
DP2 Dustin Pedroia 30.00 60.00
DP3 Dustin Pedroia 30.00 60.00
DP4 Dustin Pedroia 30.00 60.00
DS1 Duke Snider 12.50 30.00
DS2 Duke Snider 12.50 30.00
DS3 Duke Snider 12.50 30.00
DS4 Duke Snider 12.50 30.00
DW1 David Wright 20.00 50.00
DW2 David Wright 20.00 50.00
DW3 David Wright 20.00 50.00
DW4 David Wright 20.00 50.00
EL1 Evan Longoria 20.00 50.00
EL2 Evan Longoria 20.00 50.00
EL3 Evan Longoria 20.00 50.00
EL4 Evan Longoria 20.00 50.00
GC1 Gary Carter 8.00 20.00
GC2 Gary Carter 8.00 20.00
GC3 Gary Carter 8.00 20.00
GC4 Gary Carter 8.00 20.00
JB1 Jay Bruce 10.00 25.00
JB2 Jay Bruce 10.00 25.00
JB3 Jay Bruce 10.00 25.00
JB4 Jay Bruce 10.00 25.00
JP1 Johnny Podres 8.00 20.00
JP2 Johnny Podres 8.00 20.00
KH1 Keith Hernandez 6.00 15.00
KH2 Keith Hernandez 6.00 15.00
KH3 Keith Hernandez 6.00 15.00
KH4 Keith Hernandez 6.00 15.00
ML1 Matt LaPorta 12.50 30.00
RB1 Ryan Braun 15.00 40.00
RB2 Ryan Braun 15.00 40.00
RB3 Ryan Braun 15.00 40.00
RB4 Ryan Braun 15.00 40.00
RP1 Rick Porcello 12.50 30.00
RP2 Rick Porcello 12.50 30.00
RP3 Rick Porcello 12.50 30.00
RP4 Rick Porcello 12.50 30.00
SB1 Sal Bando 6.00 15.00
SB2 Sal Bando 6.00 15.00
SB3 Sal Bando 6.00 15.00
SB4 Sal Bando 6.00 15.00
TH1 Tommy Hanson 12.50 30.00
TH2 Tommy Hanson 12.50 30.00

2009 Topps Tribute Autograph Relics Black

*BLACK: .5X TO 1.2X BASIC
OVERALL ODDS 1:10 HOBBY
STATED PRINT RUN 50 SER.#'d SETS

2009 Topps Tribute Autograph Relics Blue

*BLUE: .4X TO 1X BASIC
OVERALL ODDS 1:7 HOBBY
STATED PRINT RUN 75 SER.#'d SETS

2009 Topps Tribute Autograph Relics Gold

OVERALL ODDS 1:19 HOBBY
STATED PRINT RUN 25 SER.#'d SETS
NO PRICING DUE TO SCARCITY

2009 Topps Tribute Autograph Relics Red

OVERALL ODDS 1:472 HOBBY
STATED PRINT RUN 1 SER.#'d SET
NO PRICING DUE TO SCARCITY

2009 Topps Tribute Autograph Dual Relics

STATED ODDS 1:21 HOBBY
STATED PRINT RUN 99 SER.#'d SETS
ALL VARIATIONS PRICED EQUALLY
AI Akinori Iwamura 8.00 20.00
AR Aramis Ramirez 8.00 20.00
BJ Bo Jackson 30.00 60.00
DG Dwight Gooden 10.00 25.00
DP Dustin Pedroia 20.00 50.00
DS Duke Snider 15.00 40.00
DS Darryl Strawberry 10.00 25.00
DW David Wright 20.00 50.00
EL Evan Longoria 20.00 50.00
GC Gary Carter 10.00 25.00
JB Jay Bruce 10.00 25.00
MC Melky Cabrera 6.00 15.00
PF Prince Fielder 15.00 40.00
RP Rick Porcello 12.50 30.00
DW2 David Wright 20.00 50.00
EL2 Evan Longoria 20.00 50.00
RC1 Robinson Cano 15.00 40.00
RC2 Robinson Cano 15.00 40.00

2009 Topps Tribute Autograph Dual Relics Black

*BLACK: .5X TO 1.2X BASIC
OVERALL ODDS 1:10 HOBBY
STATED PRINT RUN 50 SER.#'d SETS

2009 Topps Tribute Autograph Dual Relics Blue

*BLUE: .4X TO 1X BASIC
OVERALL ODDS 1:7 HOBBY
STATED PRINT RUN 75 SER.#'d SETS

2009 Topps Tribute Autograph Dual Relics Gold

OVERALL ODDS 1:19 HOBBY
STATED PRINT RUN 25 SER.#'d SETS
NO PRICING DUE TO SCARCITY

2009 Topps Tribute Autograph Dual Relics Red

OVERALL ODDS 1:472 HOBBY
STATED PRINT RUN 1 SER.#'d SET
NO PRICING DUE TO SCARCITY

2009 Topps Tribute Autograph Triple Relics

STATED ODDS 1:75 HOBBY
STATED PRINT RUN 99 SER.#'d SETS
AP Albert Pujols 125.00 250.00
CJ Chipper Jones 30.00 60.00
DM Don Mattingly 30.00 60.00
DW David Wright 20.00 50.00
RH Ryan Howard 30.00 60.00

2009 Topps Tribute Autograph Triple Relics Black

*BLACK: .5X TO 1.2X BASIC
OVERALL ODDS 1:10 HOBBY
STATED PRINT RUN 50 SER.#'d SETS

2009 Topps Tribute Autograph Triple Relics Blue

*BLUE: .4X TO 1X BASIC
OVERALL ODDS 1:7 HOBBY
STATED PRINT RUN 75 SER.#'d SETS

2009 Topps Tribute Autograph Triple Relics Gold

OVERALL ODDS 1:19 HOBBY
STATED PRINT RUN 25 SER.#'d SETS
NO PRICING DUE TO SCARCITY

2009 Topps Tribute Autograph Triple Relics Red

OVERALL ODDS 1:472 HOBBY
STATED PRINT RUN 1 SER.#'d SET
NO PRICING DUE TO SCARCITY

2009 Topps Tribute Franchise Tribute Dual Relic Autographs

STATED ODDS 1:147 HOBBY
STATED PRINT RUN 25 SER.#'d SETS
NO PRICING DUE TO SCARCITY

2009 Topps Tribute Franchise Tribute Dual Relic Autographs Red
STATED ODDS 1:3500 HOBBY
STATED PRINT RUN 1 SER.#'d SET
NO PRICING DUE TO SCARCITY

2009 Topps Tribute Franchise Tribute Quad Relic Autographs
STATED ODDS 1:1521 HOBBY
STATED PRINT RUN 1 SER.#'d SET
NO PRICING DUE TO SCARCITY

2009 Topps Tribute Franchise Tribute Quad Relic Autographs Red
STATED ODDS 1:6998 HOBBY
STATED PRINT RUN 1 SER.#'d SET
NO PRICING DUE TO SCARCITY

2009 Topps Tribute Franchise Tribute Quad Relics
STATED ODDS 1:1521 HOBBY
STATED PRINT RUN 5 SER.#'d SETS
NO PRICING DUE TO SCARCITY

2009 Topps Tribute Franchise Tribute Quad Relics Red
STATED ODDS 1:6998 HOBBY
STATED PRINT RUN 1 SER.#'d SET
NO PRICING DUE TO SCARCITY

2009 Topps Tribute Jumbo Dual Relics
STATED ODDS 1:147 HOBBY
STATED PRINT RUN 25 SER.#'d SETS
NO PRICING DUE TO SCARCITY

2009 Topps Tribute Jumbo Dual Relics Red
STATED ODDS 1:3500 HOBBY
STATED PRINT RUN 1 SER.#'d SET
NO PRICING DUE TO SCARCITY

2009 Topps Tribute Relics
STATED ODDS 1:8 HOBBY
STATED PRINT RUN 99 SER.#'d SETS
1 Babe Ruth 60.00 120.00
4 Nolan Ryan 12.50 30.00
6 Carl Yastrzemski 5.00 12.00
7 Mickey Mantle 50.00 100.00
9 Cal Ripken Jr. 10.00 25.00
12 Tom Seaver 8.00 20.00
18 Don Larsen 4.00 10.00
19 Reggie Jackson 6.00 15.00
20 Thurman Munson 8.00 20.00
22 Johnny Bench 5.00 12.00
23 Bo Jackson 8.00 20.00
27 Mike Schmidt 6.00 15.00
28 Roy Campanella 8.00 20.00
30 Bob Gibson 5.00 12.00
33 Tony Gwynn 5.00 12.00
34 Whitey Ford 8.00 20.00
36 Manny Ramirez 4.00 10.00
40 Hanley Ramirez 3.00 8.00
41 Ty Cobb 20.00 50.00
44 Duke Snider 5.00 12.00
46 Juan Marichal 3.00 8.00
47 Eddie Mathews 6.00 15.00
49 Pee Wee Reese 6.00 15.00
50 Ryan Howard 5.00 12.00
58 Jackie Robinson 20.00 50.00
61 David Wright 6.00 15.00
63 Chipper Jones 5.00 12.00
67 Joe Mauer 5.00 12.00
68 Ozzie Smith 5.00 12.00
72 Joey Votto 4.00 10.00
74 Clayton Kershaw 3.00 8.00
75 Josh Hamilton 4.00 10.00
76 Tommy Hanson 5.00 12.00
77 Alex Rodriguez 10.00 25.00
81 Justin Morneau 5.00 12.00
83 Lou Gehrig 60.00 120.00
84 Dustin Pedroia 4.00 10.00
85 Mark Teixeira 6.00 15.00
87 Chase Utley 5.00 12.00
88 Lance Berkman 3.00 8.00
91 Albert Pujols 6.00 15.00
92 Mike Piazza 6.00 15.00
94 Evan Longoria 5.00 12.00
95 Ryan Braun 4.00 10.00
96 Rick Porcello 3.00 8.00
97 CC Sabathia 3.00 8.00
99 Ichiro Suzuki 12.50 30.00

2009 Topps Tribute Relics Black
*BLACK: .5X TO 1.2X BASIC
STATED ODDS 1:11 HOBBY
STATED PRINT RUN 50 SER.#'d SETS

2009 Topps Tribute Relics Blue
*BLUE: .4X TO 1X BASIC
STATED ODDS 1:8 HOBBY
STATED PRINT RUN 75 SER.#'d SETS

2009 Topps Tribute Relics Gold
OVERALL ODDS 1:22 HOBBY
STATED PRINT RUN 25 SER.#'d SETS
NO PRICING DUE TO SCARCITY

2009 Topps Tribute Relics Red
OVERALL ODDS 1:555 HOBBY
STATED PRINT RUN 1 SER.#'d SET
NO PRICING DUE TO SCARCITY

2009 Topps Tribute Relics Dual
STATED ODDS 1:25 HOBBY
STATED PRINT RUN 99 SER.#'d SETS
1 Babe Ruth 75.00 150.00
9 Cal Ripken Jr. 12.50 30.00
19 Reggie Jackson 6.00 15.00
22 Johnny Bench 6.00 15.00
27 Mike Schmidt 10.00 25.00
33 Tony Gwynn 6.00 15.00
36 Manny Ramirez 5.00 12.00
41 Ty Cobb 40.00 80.00
44 Duke Snider 6.00 15.00
50 Ryan Howard 6.00 15.00
61 David Wright 6.00 15.00
76 Tommy Hanson 5.00 12.00
94 Evan Longoria 5.00 12.00
95 Ryan Braun 5.00 12.00
99 Ichiro Suzuki 12.50 30.00

2009 Topps Tribute Relics Dual Black
*BLACK: .5X TO 1.2X BASIC
STATED ODDS 1:11 HOBBY
STATED PRINT RUN 50 SER.#'d SETS

2009 Topps Tribute Relics Dual Blue
*BLUE: .4X TO 1X BASIC
STATED ODDS 1:8 HOBBY
STATED PRINT RUN 75 SER.#'d SETS

2009 Topps Tribute Relics Dual Gold
OVERALL ODDS 1:22 HOBBY
STATED PRINT RUN 25 SER.#'d SETS
NO PRICING DUE TO SCARCITY

2009 Topps Tribute Relics Dual Red
OVERALL ODDS 1:555 HOBBY
STATED PRINT RUN 1 SER.#'d SET
NO PRICING DUE TO SCARCITY

2009 Topps Tribute Relics Triple
STATED ODDS 1:75 HOBBY
STATED PRINT RUN 99 SER.#'d SETS
1 Babe Ruth 150.00 300.00
7 Mickey Mantle 60.00 120.00
58 Jackie Robinson 20.00 50.00
77 Alex Rodriguez 12.50 30.00
91 Albert Pujols 12.50 30.00

2009 Topps Tribute Relics Triple Black
*BLACK: .5X TO 1.2X BASIC
STATED ODDS 1:11 HOBBY
STATED PRINT RUN 50 SER.#'d SETS

2009 Topps Tribute Relics Triple Blue
*BLUE: .4X TO 1X BASIC
STATED ODDS 1:8 HOBBY
STATED PRINT RUN 75 SER.#'d SETS

2009 Topps Tribute Relics Triple Gold
OVERALL ODDS 1:22 HOBBY
STATED PRINT RUN 25 SER.#'d SETS
NO PRICING DUE TO SCARCITY

2009 Topps Tribute Relics Triple Red
OVERALL ODDS 1:555 HOBBY
STATED PRINT RUN 1 SER.#'d SET
NO PRICING DUE TO SCARCITY

2010 Topps Tribute

COMPLETE SET (100) 100.00 200.00
COMMON CARD (1-75) .60 1.50
COMMON CARD (75-90) .60 1.50
COMMON CARD (91-100) .60 1.50
PRINTING PLATE ODDS 1:161 HOBBY
PLATE PRINT RUN 1 SET PER COLOR
BLACK-CYAN-MAGENTA-YELLOW ISSUED
NO PLATE PRICING DUE TO SCARCITY
1 Babe Ruth 4.00 10.00
2 Walter Johnson 1.50 4.00
3 Ty Cobb 2.50 6.00
4 Tris Speaker 1.00 2.50
5 Thurman Munson 1.50 4.00
6 Roy Campanella 1.50 4.00
7 Rogers Hornsby 1.00 2.50
8 Orlando Cepeda .60 1.50
9 Jackie Robinson 1.50 4.00
10 Mel Ott 1.50 4.00
11 Johnny Mize 1.00 2.50
12 Jimmie Foxx 1.50 4.00
13 Honus Wagner 1.50 4.00
14 Pee Wee Reese 1.00 2.50
15 Christy Mathewson 1.50 4.00
16 Carlton Fisk 1.00 2.50
17 Yogi Berra 1.50 4.00
18 Lou Gehrig 3.00 8.00
19 Jim Bunning .60 1.50
20 Reggie Jackson 1.00 2.50
21 Tony Gwynn 1.50 4.00
22 Al Kaline 1.50 4.00
23 Roger Maris 1.50 4.00
24 Harmon Killebrew 1.50 4.00
25 Eddie Mathews 1.50 4.00
26 Willie McCovey 1.00 2.50
27 Joe Morgan .60 1.50
28 Eddie Murray 1.50 4.00
29 Jim Palmer .60 1.50
30 Tony Perez .60 1.50
31 Gaylord Perry .60 1.50
32 Phil Rizzuto 1.00 2.50
33 Robin Roberts .60 1.50
34 Brooks Robinson 1.00 2.50
35 Nolan Ryan 5.00 12.00
36 Ryne Sandberg 3.00 8.00
37 Mike Schmidt 2.50 6.00
38 Red Schoendienst .60 1.50
39 Tom Seaver 1.00 2.50
40 Ozzie Smith 2.50 6.00
41 Warren Spahn 1.00 2.50
42 Willie Stargell 1.00 2.50
43 Stan Musial 2.50 6.00
44 Cy Young 1.50 4.00
45 Bob Gibson 1.00 2.50
46 Dizzy Dean .60 1.50
47 Frank Robinson 1.00 2.50
48 Hank Greenberg 1.50 4.00
49 Johnny Bench 1.50 4.00
50 Mickey Mantle 5.00 12.00
51 Albert Pujols 4.00 10.00
52 Ichiro Suzuki 2.50 6.00
53 Alex Rodriguez 2.50 6.00
54 Prince Fielder 1.00 2.50
55 Joe Mauer 1.50 4.00
56 Tim Lincecum 2.50 6.00
57 Hanley Ramirez 1.50 4.00
58 Chase Utley 1.50 4.00
59 Roy Halladay 1.50 4.00
60 Adrian Gonzalez 1.00 2.50
61 Manny Ramirez 1.50 4.00
62 Chipper Jones 1.50 4.00
63 Grady Sizemore 1.00 2.50
64 Mariano Rivera 1.50 4.00
65 Miguel Cabrera 1.50 4.00
66 Johan Santana 1.50 4.00
67 Ryan Braun 2.00 5.00
68 Zack Greinke 1.00 2.50
69 Ryan Howard 2.00 5.00
70 Dustin Pedroia 2.00 5.00
71 Ian Kinsler 1.00 2.50
72 Evan Longoria 2.00 5.00
73 David Wright 2.00 5.00
74 Vladimir Guerrero 1.50 4.00
75 Derek Jeter 4.00 10.00
76 Lou Gehrig T205 3.00 8.00
77 Ichiro Suzuki T205 2.50 6.00
78 Jackie Robinson T205 1.50 4.00
79 Cy Young T205 1.50 4.00
80 Derek Jeter T205 4.00 10.00
81 Ty Cobb T205 2.50 6.00
82 Mickey Mantle T205 5.00 12.00
83 Nolan Ryan T205 5.00 12.00
84 Joe Mauer T205 1.50 4.00
85 Honus Wagner T205 1.50 4.00
86 Frank Robinson T205 1.00 2.50
87 Albert Pujols T205 4.00 10.00
88 Tim Lincecum T205 2.50 6.00
89 Babe Ruth T205 4.00 10.00
90 Tom Seaver T205 1.00 2.50
91 Hatfields vs. McCoys 1.00 2.50
92 David vs. Goliath 1.00 2.50
93 Moby Dick vs. Captain Ahab 1.00 2.50
94 Billy the Kid vs. Pat Garrett 1.00 2.50
95 John F. Kennedy vs Richard Nixon 1.50 4.00
96 Barack Obama vs John McCain 2.00 5.00
97 Abraham Lincoln vs Jefferson Davis 1.50 4.00
98 Montagues vs Capulets 1.00 2.50
99 USA vs. Russia 1.00 2.50
100 Tortoise vs The Hare 1.00 2.50

2010 Topps Tribute Black
*BLACK: .75X TO 2X BASIC
STATED ODDS 1:7 HOBBY
STATED PRINT RUN 99 SER.#'d SETS

2010 Topps Tribute Black and White
*BW: .75X TO 2X BASIC
STATED ODDS 1:7 HOBBY
STATED PRINT RUN 99 SER.#'d SETS

2010 Topps Tribute Blue
*BLUE: .5X TO 1.2X BASIC
RANDOM INSERTS IN PACKS
STATED PRINT RUN 399 SER.#'d SETS

2010 Topps Tribute Gold
*GOLD: 1.2X TO 3X BASIC
STATED ODDS 1:13 HOBBY
STATED PRINT RUN 50 SER.#'d SETS

2010 Topps Tribute Red
STATED ODDS 1:656 HOBBY
STATED PRINT RUN 1 SER.#'d SET
NO PRICING DUE TO SCARCITY

2010 Topps Tribute Autograph Relics
STATED ODDS 1:35 HOBBY
STATED PRINT RUN 99 SER.#'d SETS
EXCH DEADLINE 7/31/2013
SAME PLAYER VERSIONS EQUALLY PRICED
AH Aaron Hill 5.00 12.00
AI Akinori Iwamura 5.00 12.00
AJ Adam Jones 8.00 20.00
BM Bengie Molina 6.00 15.00
BMC Brian McCann 10.00 25.00
CF Chone Figgins 5.00 12.00
CP Carlos Pena 8.00 20.00
CS Curt Schilling 10.00 25.00
JHE Jason Heyward 60.00 120.00
JL Jon Lester 15.00 40.00
MCA Miguel Cabrera 15.00 40.00
MK Matt Kemp EXCH 12.50 30.00
ML Mat Latos 10.00 25.00
NM Nick Markakis EXCH 8.00 20.00
OC Orlando Cabrera 5.00 12.00
PF Prince Fielder 10.00 25.00
RK Ralph Kiner 12.50 30.00
SS Stephen Strasburg EXCH 100.00 200.00
TH Tommy Hanson 10.00 25.00
TL Tony LaRussa 12.50 30.00
AD1 Andre Dawson 10.00 25.00
AD2 Andre Dawson 10.00 25.00
AD3 Andre Dawson 10.00 25.00
AD4 Andre Dawson 10.00 25.00
BC1 Bobby Cox 20.00 50.00
BC2 Bobby Cox 20.00 50.00
BM2 Bengie Molina 6.00 15.00
CK1 Clayton Kershaw 8.00 20.00
CK2 Clayton Kershaw 8.00 20.00
CK3 Clayton Kershaw 8.00 20.00
CK4 Clayton Kershaw 8.00 20.00
CL1 Cliff Lee 15.00 40.00
CL2 Cliff Lee 15.00 40.00
CL3 Cliff Lee 15.00 40.00
CL4 Cliff Lee 15.00 40.00
DG01 Dwight Gooden 8.00 20.00
DG02 Dwight Gooden 8.00 20.00
DP1 Dustin Pedroia 15.00 40.00
DP2 Dustin Pedroia 15.00 40.00
DP3 Dustin Pedroia 15.00 40.00
DP4 Dustin Pedroia 15.00 40.00
DSN1 Duke Snider 12.50 30.00
DS1 Darryl Strawberry 10.00 25.00
DS2 Darryl Strawberry 10.00 25.00
DSN2 Duke Snider 12.50 30.00
DSN3 Duke Snider 12.50 30.00
GC1 Gary Carter 10.00 25.00
GC2 Gary Carter 10.00 25.00
GS1 Gary Sheffield 6.00 15.00
GS2 Gary Sheffield 6.00 15.00
GS3 Gary Sheffield 6.00 15.00
GS4 Gary Sheffield 6.00 15.00
JG1 Joe Girardi 20.00 50.00
JG2 Joe Girardi 20.00 50.00
JH1 Josh Hamilton 15.00 40.00
JH2 Josh Hamilton 15.00 40.00
JH3 Josh Hamilton 15.00 40.00
JH4 Josh Hamilton 15.00 40.00
MK2 Matt Kemp EXCH 12.50 30.00
MK3 Matt Kemp EXCH 12.50 30.00
MK4 Matt Kemp EXCH 12.50 30.00
MS1 Max Scherzer 8.00 20.00
MS2 Max Scherzer 8.00 20.00
MS3 Max Scherzer 8.00 20.00
MS4 Max Scherzer 8.00 20.00
NM2 Nick Markakis 8.00 20.00
NM3 Nick Markakis 8.00 20.00
NM4 Nick Markakis 8.00 20.00
OC2 Orlando Cabrera 5.00 12.00
PS1 Pablo Sandoval 10.00 25.00
PS2 Pablo Sandoval 10.00 25.00
PS3 Pablo Sandoval 10.00 25.00
PS4 Pablo Sandoval 10.00 25.00
RC1 Robinson Cano 20.00 50.00
RC2 Robinson Cano 20.00 50.00
RC3 Robinson Cano 20.00 50.00
RC4 Robinson Cano 20.00 50.00
RP1 Rick Porcello 6.00 15.00
RP2 Rick Porcello 6.00 15.00
RP3 Rick Porcello 6.00 15.00
RP4 Rick Porcello 6.00 15.00
RZ1 Ryan Zimmerman 10.00 25.00
RZ2 Ryan Zimmerman 10.00 25.00
RZ3 Ryan Zimmerman 10.00 25.00
RZ4 Ryan Zimmerman 10.00 25.00
ST1 Starlin Castro 30.00 60.00
ST2 Starlin Castro 30.00 60.00
ST3 Starlin Castro 30.00 60.00
ST4 Starlin Castro 30.00 60.00
TL2 Tony LaRussa 12.50 30.00
TT1 Troy Tulowitzki 15.00 40.00
TT2 Troy Tulowitzki 15.00 40.00
TT3 Troy Tulowitzki 15.00 40.00
TT4 Troy Tulowitzki 15.00 40.00
ADU1 Adam Dunn 8.00 20.00
ADU2 Adam Dunn 8.00 20.00
ADU3 Adam Dunn 8.00 20.00
ADU4 Adam Dunn 8.00 20.00
DG03 Dwight Gooden 8.00 20.00
DSN4 Duke Snider 12.50 30.00

2010 Topps Tribute Autograph Relics Black
*BLACK: .5X TO 1.2X BASIC
STATED ODDS 1:11 HOBBY
STATED PRINT RUN 50 SER.#'d SETS
EXCH DEADLINE 7/31/2013

2010 Topps Tribute Autograph Relics Blue
*BLUE: .4X TO 1X BASIC
STATED ODDS 1:7 HOBBY
STATED PRINT RUN 75 SER.#'d SETS
EXCH DEADLINE 7/31/2013

2010 Topps Tribute Autograph Relics Gold
STATED ODDS 1:21 HOBBY
STATED PRINT RUN 25 SER.#'d SETS
NO PRICING DUE TO SCARCITY
EXCH DEADLINE 7/31/2010

2010 Topps Tribute Autograph Relics Red
STATED ODDS 1:514 HOBBY
STATED PRINT RUN 1 SER.#'d SET
NO PRICING DUE TO SCARCITY
EXCH DEADLINE 7/31/2010

2010 Topps Tribute Autograph Dual Relics
STATED ODDS 1:35 HOBBY
STATED PRINT RUN 99 SER.#'d SETS
COMPLETE SET (19)
AJ Adam Jones 8.00 20.00
DO David Ortiz 15.00 40.00
DW David Wright 20.00 50.00
EL Evan Longoria 20.00 50.00
GB Gordon Beckham 10.00 25.00
GC Gary Carter 10.00 25.00
GK George Kell 10.00 25.00
JH Josh Hamilton 12.50 30.00
JH Jason Heyward 60.00 120.00
JU Justin Upton 12.50 30.00
MH Matt Holliday 15.00 40.00
MK Matt Kemp EXCH 10.00 25.00
PF Prince Fielder 12.50 30.00
RB Ryan Braun 15.00 40.00
RP Rick Porcello 6.00 15.00
SS Stephen Strasburg EXCH 125.00 250.00
TH Tommy Hanson 12.50 30.00
TT Troy Tulowitzki 8.00 20.00
WM Willie McCovey 20.00 50.00

2010 Topps Tribute Autograph Dual Relics Black
*BLACK: .5X TO 1.2X BASIC
STATED ODDS 1:11 HOBBY
STATED PRINT RUN 50 SER.#'d SETS
EXCH DEADLINE 7/31/2013

2010 Topps Tribute Autograph Dual Relics Blue
*BLUE: .4X TO 1X BASIC
STATED ODDS 1:7 HOBBY
STATED PRINT RUN 75 SER.#'d SETS
EXCH DEADLINE 7/31/2013

2010 Topps Tribute Autograph Dual Relics Gold
STATED ODDS 1:21 HOBBY
STATED PRINT RUN 25 SER.#'d SETS
NO PRICING DUE TO SCARCITY
EXCH DEADLINE 7/31/2013

2010 Topps Tribute Autograph Dual Relics Red
STATED ODDS 1:514 HOBBY
STATED PRINT RUN 1 SER.#'d SET
NO PRICING DUE TO SCARCITY
EXCH DEADLINE 7/31/2013

2010 Topps Tribute Autograph Triple Relics
GROUP A ODDS 1:73 HOBBY
GROUP B ODDS 1:262 HOBBY
STATED PRINT RUN 99 SER.#'d SETS
EXCH DEADLINE 7/31/2013
AP Albert Pujols 125.00 250.00
AR Alex Rodriguez 100.00 200.00
CR Cal Ripken 50.00 100.00
DS Duke Snider 12.50 30.00
DW David Wright 15.00 40.00
EL Evan Longoria 15.00 40.00
HR Hanley Ramirez 12.50 30.00
MC Miguel Cabrera 20.00 50.00
MK Matt Kemp EXCH 8.00 20.00
MR Manny Ramirez 30.00 60.00
NM Nick Markakis 8.00 20.00
RC Robinson Cano 30.00 60.00
RC Rod Carew 15.00 40.00
RH Ryan Howard 30.00 60.00
VG Vladimir Guerrero 15.00 40.00

2010 Topps Tribute Autograph Triple Relics Black
*BLACK: .5X TO 1.2X BASIC
STATED ODDS 1:11 HOBBY
STATED PRINT RUN 50 SER.#'d SETS
EXCH DEADLINE 7/31/2013

2010 Topps Tribute Autograph Triple Relics Blue
*BLUE: .4X TO 1X BASIC
STATED ODDS 1:7 HOBBY
STATED PRINT RUN 75 SER.#'d SETS
EXCH DEADLINE 7/31/2013

2010 Topps Tribute Autograph Triple Relics Gold
STATED ODDS 1:21 HOBBY
STATED PRINT RUN 25 SER.#'d SETS
NO PRICING DUE TO SCARCITY
EXCH DEADLINE 7/31/2010

2010 Topps Tribute Autograph Triple Relics Red
STATED ODDS 1:514 HOBBY
STATED PRINT RUN 1 SER.#'d SET
NO PRICING DUE TO SCARCITY
EXCH DEADLINE 7/31/2010

2010 Topps Tribute Buyback Relics
STATED ODDS 1:167 HOBBY
PRINT RUNS B/WN 10-50 COPIES PER
NO PRICING ON QTY 25 OR LESS
AP Albert Pujols 15.00 40.00
2003 Topps Tribute Contemporary/50
BG Bob Gibson
2002 Topps Tribute Milestones/25
BR Babe Ruth 60.00 120.00
2003 Topps Tribute Contemporary/35
CF Carlton Fisk
2002 Topps Tribute Milestones/25
CK Bill Dickey
2002 Topps Tribute Milestones/10
CK Chuck Klein
2002 Topps Tribute Milestones/10
CY Carl Yastrzemski
2002 Topps Tribute Milestones/10
EM Eddie Mathews
2002 Topps Tribute Milestones/10
FR Frank Robinson
2002 Topps Tribute Milestones/25
HA Hank Aaron 20.00 50.00
2003 Topps Tribute Contemporary/45
JB Johnny Bench
2002 Topps Tribute Milestones/10
JM Johnny Mize
2002 Topps Tribute Milestones/15
NL Nap Lajoie
2002 Topps Tribute Milestones/10
RM Roger Maris
2002 Topps Tribute Milestones/25
RS Ryne Sandberg
2002 Topps Tribute Milestones/25
RY Robin Yount
2002 Topps Tribute Milestones/10
SC Sam Crawford
2002 Topps Tribute Milestones/25
WF Whitey Ford
2002 Topps Tribute Milestones/10
ZW Zach Wheat
2002 Topps Tribute Milestones/10

2010 Topps Tribute Relics
STATED ODDS 1:7 HOBBY
STATED PRINT RUN 99 SER.#'d SETS
AD Adrian Gonzalez 4.00 10.00
AK Al Kaline 10.00 25.00
AP Albert Pujols 10.00 25.00
AR Alex Rodriguez 6.00 15.00
BD Bobby Doerr 8.00 20.00
BF Bob Feller 6.00 15.00
BG Bob Gibson 6.00 15.00
BL Bob Lemon 5.00 12.00
BM Bill Mazeroski 10.00 25.00
BR Brooks Robinson 6.00 15.00
BS Bruce Sutter 6.00 15.00
BW Billy Williams 4.00 10.00
CF Carlton Fisk 5.00 12.00
CH Catfish Hunter 4.00 10.00
CJ Chipper Jones 8.00 20.00
CS CC Sabathia 6.00 15.00
CU Chase Utley 5.00 12.00
CY Carl Yastrzemski 8.00 20.00
DE Dennis Eckersley 3.00 8.00
DJ Derek Jeter 10.00 25.00
DJ2 Derek Jeter 10.00 25.00
DJ3 Derek Jeter 10.00 25.00
DJ4 Derek Jeter 10.00 25.00
DS Don Sutton 4.00 10.00
DW David Wright 6.00 15.00
EB Ernie Banks 6.00 15.00
EL Evan Longoria 5.00 12.00
EM Eddie Mathews 12.50 30.00
ES Enos Slaughter 8.00 20.00
EW Early Wynn 6.00 15.00
FJ Fergie Jenkins 4.00 10.00
FR Frank Robinson 4.00 10.00
GC Gary Carter 4.00 10.00
GK George Kell 4.00 10.00
GP Gaylord Perry 3.00 8.00
HG Hank Greenberg 10.00 25.00
HK Harmon Killebrew 8.00 20.00
HN Hal Newhouser 4.00 10.00
HR Hanley Ramirez 3.00 8.00
HW Hoyt Wilhelm 5.00 12.00
IS Ichiro Suzuki 12.50 30.00
JB Johnny Bench 8.00 20.00
JF Jimmie Foxx 12.50 30.00
JM Juan Marichal 4.00 10.00
JR Jackie Robinson 12.50 30.00
LA Luis Aparicio 4.00 10.00
LG Lou Gehrig 40.00 80.00
MC Miguel Cabrera 5.00 12.00
MI Monte Irvin 6.00 15.00
MM Mickey Mantle 50.00 100.00
MO Mel Ott 10.00 25.00
MR Mariano Rivera 8.00 20.00
MS Mike Schmidt 12.50 30.00
MT Mark Teixeira 6.00 15.00
NR Nolan Ryan 10.00 25.00
OC Orlando Cepeda 3.00 8.00
OS Ozzie Smith 6.00 15.00
PF Prince Fielder 4.00 10.00
PM Paul Molitor 5.00 12.00
PN Phil Niekro 3.00 8.00
PR Phil Rizzuto 6.00 15.00
RA Richie Ashburn 8.00 20.00
RB Ryan Braun 4.00 10.00
RC Rod Carew 4.00 10.00
RF Rick Ferrell 8.00 20.00
RH Rogers Hornsby 12.50 30.00
RJ Reggie Jackson 8.00 20.00
RK Ralph Kiner 6.00 15.00
RM Roger Maris 20.00 50.00
RR Robin Roberts 8.00 20.00
RS Ryne Sandberg 6.00 15.00
RY Robin Yount 8.00 20.00
SC Steve Carlton 6.00 15.00
SM Stan Musial 10.00 25.00
TC Ty Cobb 30.00 60.00
TG Tony Gwynn 6.00 15.00
TL Tim Lincecum 8.00 20.00
TM Thurman Munson 12.50 30.00
TP Tony Perez 4.00 10.00
TS Tom Seaver 6.00 15.00
VG Vladimir Guerrero 4.00 10.00
WM Willie McCovey 5.00 12.00
WS Warren Spahn 8.00 20.00
BRU Babe Ruth 60.00 120.00
EMU Eddie Murray 4.00 10.00
HWA Honus Wagner 40.00 80.00
JBU Jim Bunning 4.00 10.00
JMA Joe Mauer 6.00 15.00
JMI Johnny Mize 6.00 15.00
JMO Joe Morgan 4.00 10.00
JPI Jimmy Piersall 8.00 20.00
LBR Lou Brock 6.00 15.00
MRA Manny Ramirez 5.00 12.00
RCA Roy Campanella 12.50 30.00
RFI Rollie Fingers 3.00 8.00
RHO Ryan Howard 6.00 15.00
RSC Red Schoendienst 4.00 10.00
TSP Tris Speaker 15.00 40.00
WST Willie Stargell 8.00 20.00

2010 Topps Tribute Relics Black
*BLACK: .5X TO 1.2X BASIC
STATED ODDS 1:10 HOBBY
STATED PRINT RUN 50 SER.#'d SETS

2010 Topps Tribute Relics Blue
*BLUE: .4X TO 1X BASIC
STATED ODDS 1:7 HOBBY
STATED PRINT RUN 75 SER.#'d SETS

2010 Topps Tribute Relics Gold
STATED ODDS 1:20 HOBBY
STATED PRINT RUN 25 SER.#'d SETS
NO PRICING DUE TO SCARCITY

2010 Topps Tribute Relics Red
STATED ODDS 1:505 HOBBY
STATED PRINT RUN 1 SER.#'d SET
NO PRICING DUE TO SCARCITY

2010 Topps Tribute Relics Dual
STATED ODDS 1:7 HOBBY
STATED PRINT RUN 99 SER.#'d SETS
AR Alex Rodriguez 10.00 25.00
CF Carlton Fisk 6.00 15.00
CS CC Sabathia 5.00 12.00
DJ Derek Jeter 12.50 30.00
DP Dustin Pedroia 6.00 15.00
DW David Wright 8.00 20.00
JB Johnny Bench 6.00 15.00
JE Jacoby Ellsbury 10.00 25.00
JP Jorge Posada 5.00 12.00
KY Kevin Youkilis 5.00 12.00
MR Mariano Rivera 8.00 20.00
MS Mike Schmidt 10.00 25.00
MT Mark Teixeira 6.00 15.00
NR Nolan Ryan 10.00 25.00
OS Ozzie Smith 6.00 15.00
RA Richie Ashburn 10.00 25.00
RB Ryan Braun 4.00 10.00
RH Ryan Howard 6.00 15.00
TG Tony Gwynn 4.00 10.00
VM Victor Martinez 4.00 10.00
JPA Jim Palmer

2010 Topps Tribute Relics Dual Black
*BLACK: .5X TO 1.2X BASIC
STATED ODDS 1:10 HOBBY
STATED PRINT RUN 50 SER.#'d SETS

2010 Topps Tribute Relics Dual Blue
*BLUE: .4X TO 1X BASIC
STATED ODDS 1:7 HOBBY
STATED PRINT RUN 75 SER.#'d SETS

2010 Topps Tribute Relics Dual Gold
STATED ODDS 1:20 HOBBY
STATED PRINT RUN 25 SER.#'d SETS
NO PRICING DUE TO SCARCITY

2010 Topps Tribute Relics Dual Red
STATED ODDS 1:505 HOBBY
STATED PRINT RUN 1 SER.#'d SET
NO PRICING DUE TO SCARCITY

2010 Topps Tribute Relics Triple
STATED ODDS 1:7 HOBBY
STATED PRINT RUN 99 SER.#'d SETS
BM Bobby Murcer
CR Cal Ripken 10.00 25.00
DJ Derek Jeter 15.00 40.00
JM Justin Morneau 5.00 12.00
PM Paul Molitor 5.00 12.00
RA Richie Ashburn 12.50 30.00
RG Reggie Jackson 4.00 10.00
RP Rick Porcello 4.00 10.00
RY Robin Yount 8.00 20.00
TG Tony Gwynn 5.00 12.00
TM Thurman Munson 12.50 30.00

2010 Topps Tribute Relics Triple Black
*BLACK: .5X TO 1.2X BASIC
STATED ODDS 1:10 HOBBY
STATED PRINT RUN 50 SER.#'d SETS

2010 Topps Tribute Relics Triple Blue
*BLUE: .4X TO 1X BASIC
STATED ODDS 1:7 HOBBY
STATED PRINT RUN 75 SER.#'d SETS

2010 Topps Tribute Relics Triple Gold
STATED ODDS 1:20 HOBBY
STATED PRINT RUN 25 SER.#'d SETS
NO PRICING DUE TO SCARCITY

2010 Topps Tribute Relics Triple Red
STATED ODDS 1:505 HOBBY
STATED PRINT RUN 1 SER.#'d SET
NO PRICING DUE TO SCARCITY

2011 Topps Tribute
COMPLETE SET (100) 200.00 300.00
COMMON CARD (1-100) .60 1.50

PLATES RANDOMLY INSERTED
PLATE PRINT RUN 1 SET PER COLOR
BLACK-CYAN-MAGENTA-YELLOW ISSUED
NO PLATE PRICING DUE TO SCARCITY

1 Babe Ruth 4.00 10.00
2 Cy Young 1.50 4.00
3 Joe Mauer 1.50 4.00
4 Honus Wagner 1.50 4.00
5 Justin Morneau 1.50 4.00
6 Nolan Ryan 5.00 12.00
7 David Wright 2.00 5.00
8 Evan Longoria 2.00 5.00
9 Troy Tulowitzki 1.50 4.00
10 Mark Teixeira 1.50 4.00
11 Stan Musial 2.50 6.00
12 Sandy Koufax 5.00 12.00
13 Ryan Howard 2.00 5.00
14 Joey Votto 1.50 4.00
15 Carlos Gonzalez 1.00 2.50
16 Roy Halladay 1.50 4.00
17 Brooks Robinson 1.00 2.50
18 Hoyt Wilhelm .60 1.50
19 Walter Johnson 1.50 4.00
20 Eddie Murray 1.50 4.00
21 Stephen Strasburg 3.00 8.00
22 Lou Gehrig 3.00 8.00
23 Derek Jeter 4.00 10.00
24 Rod Carew 1.00 2.50
25 Felix Hernandez 1.50 4.00
26 Robin Yount 1.50 4.00
27 Jason Heyward 2.00 5.00
28 Hanley Ramirez 1.50 4.00
29 Fergie Jenkins .60 1.50
30 Mickey Mantle 5.00 12.00
31 Josh Hamilton 1.50 4.00
32 Al Kaline 1.50 4.00
33 Hank Greenberg 1.50 4.00
34 Miguel Cabrera 1.50 4.00
35 Jackie Robinson 1.50 4.00
36 Cal Ripken Jr. 6.00 15.00
37 Bob Feller .60 1.50
38 Ryne Sandberg 3.00 8.00
39 Dizzy Dean .60 1.50
40 Catfish Hunter .60 1.50
41 Harmon Killebrew 1.50 4.00
42 Goose Gossage .60 1.50
43 Bill Mazeroski 1.00 2.50
44 Bob Gibson 1.00 2.50
45 Johnny Mize 1.00 2.50
46 Tom Seaver 1.00 2.50
47 Jim Bunning .60 1.50
48 CC Sabathia 1.00 2.50
49 Rogers Hornsby 1.00 2.50
50 Adam Wainwright 1.00 2.50
51 Thurman Munson 1.50 4.00
52 Albert Pujols 4.00 10.00
53 Willie Stargell 1.00 2.50
54 Tony Gwynn 1.50 4.00
55 Whitey Ford 1.00 2.50
56 Pee Wee Reese 1.00 2.50
57 Frank Robinson 1.00 2.50
58 Roy Campanella 1.50 4.00
59 Robin Roberts .60 1.50
60 George Sisler 1.50 4.00
61 Alex Rodriguez 2.50 6.00
62 Ozzie Smith 2.50 6.00
63 Jered Weaver .60 1.50
64 Lou Brock 1.00 2.50
65 Bobby Doerr .60 1.50
66 Josh Johnson 1.00 2.50
67 David Ortiz 1.00 2.50
68 Johan Santana 1.50 4.00
69 Buster Posey 2.00 5.00
70 Ubaldo Jimenez 1.00 2.50
71 Duke Snider 1.00 2.50
72 Josh Beckett 1.00 2.50
73 Vladimir Guerrero 1.50 4.00
74 Justin Verlander 2.00 5.00
75 Mike Schmidt 2.50 6.00
76 Chipper Jones 1.50 4.00
77 Jim Palmer .60 1.50
78 Ryan Braun 2.00 5.00
79 Tim Lincecum 1.50 4.00
80 Vernon Wells .60 1.50
81 Joe Morgan .60 1.50
82 David Price 1.50 4.00
83 Jon Lester 1.50 4.00
84 Reggie Jackson 1.00 2.50
85 Christy Mathewson 1.50 4.00
86 Prince Fielder 1.00 2.50
87 Johnny Bench 1.50 4.00
88 Tris Speaker 1.00 2.50
89 Juan Marichal .60 1.50
90 Ichiro Suzuki 2.50 6.00
91 Warren Spahn 1.00 2.50
92 Yogi Berra 1.50 4.00
93 Willie McCovey 1.00 2.50
94 Cliff Lee 1.50 4.00
95 Mel Ott 1.50 4.00
96 Ty Cobb 2.50 6.00
97 Rollie Fingers .60 1.50
98 Chase Utley 1.50 4.00
99 Early Wynn .60 1.50
100 Hank Aaron 3.00 8.00

2011 Topps Tribute Black

STATED ODDS 1:41 HOBBY
STATED PRINT RUN 10 SER.#'d SETS
NO PRICING DUE TO SCARCITY

2011 Topps Tribute Blue

*BLUE: .6X TO 1.5X BASIC
RANDOM INSERTS IN PACKS
STATED PRINT RUN 199 SER.#'d SETS

2011 Topps Tribute Gold

*GOLD: 1.5X TO 4X BASIC
STATED ODDS 1:7 HOBBY
STATED PRINT RUN 50 SER.#'d SETS

2011 Topps Tribute Green

*GREEN: 1X TO 2.5X BASIC
STATED ODDS 1:5 HOBBY
STATED PRINT RUN 75 SER.#'d SETS

2011 Topps Tribute Red

STATED ODDS 1:329 HOBBY
STATED PRINT RUN 1 SER.#'d SET
NO PRICING DUE TO SCARCITY

2011 Topps Tribute 2010 Rookies Book

STATED ODDS 1:3472 HOBBY
STATED PRINT RUN 9 SER.#'d SETS
NO PRICING DUE TO SCARCITY

RTBC1 Carlos Santana
Stephen Strasburg
Mike Stanton
Buster Posey
Danny Valencia
Starlin Castro
Neftali Feliz
Austin Jackson
Jason Heyward
Domonic Brown

2011 Topps Tribute 2010 Rookies Book Red

STATED ODDS 1:31,248 HOBBY
STATED PRINT RUN 1 SER.#'d SET
NO PRICING DUE TO SCARCITY

2011 Topps Tribute Autograph Dual Relics

STATED ODDS 1:23 HOBBY
STATED PRINT RUN 99 SER.#'d SETS
EXCHANGE DEADLINE 3/31/2014

BP Buster Posey 40.00 80.00
BR Brooks Robinson 15.00 40.00
CB Clay Buchholz 10.00 25.00
DW David Wright 15.00 40.00
EB Ernie Banks 30.00 60.00
EL Evan Longoria 15.00 40.00
FR Frank Robinson 15.00 40.00
JR Jim Rice 10.00 25.00
MM Mike Mussina 12.50 30.00
NG Nomar Garciaparra 20.00 50.00
RH Ryan Howard 20.00 50.00
RS Ryne Sandberg 30.00 60.00
WF Whitey Ford 30.00 60.00
WM Willie McCovey 20.00 50.00
YB Yogi Berra EXCH 40.00 80.00

2011 Topps Tribute Autograph Dual Relics Black

STATED ODDS 1:77 HOBBY
STATED PRINT RUN 5 SER.#'d SETS
NO PRICING DUE TO SCARCITY

2011 Topps Tribute Autograph Dual Relics Gold

STATED ODDS 1:22 HOBBY
STATED PRINT RUN 20 SER.#'d SETS
NO PRICING DUE TO SCARCITY

2011 Topps Tribute Autograph Dual Relics Green

*GREEN: .4X TO 1X BASIC
STATED ODDS 1:6 HOBBY
STATED PRINT RUN 75 SER.#'d SETS
EXCHANGE DEADLINE 3/31/2014

2011 Topps Tribute Autograph Dual Relics Red

STATED ODDS 1:386 HOBBY
STATED PRINT RUN 1 SER.#'d SET
NO PRICING DUE TO SCARCITY

2011 Topps Tribute Autograph Relics

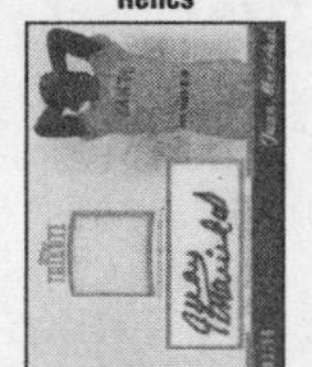

STATED ODDS 1:6 HOBBY
RC AU RELIC ODDS 1:110 HOBBY
STATED PRINT RUN 99 SER.#'d SETS
EXCHANGE DEADLINE 3/31/2014

AB Albert Belle 15.00 40.00
AC Aroldis Chapman EXCH 30.00 60.00
AK Al Kaline 20.00 50.00
BL Barry Larkin 20.00 50.00
BP Buster Posey 50.00 100.00
BW Bernie Williams 40.00 80.00
CR Cal Ripken Jr. 60.00 120.00
CS Curt Schilling 15.00 40.00
CU Chase Utley 30.00 60.00
CY Carl Yastrzemski 30.00 60.00
DC David Cone 10.00 25.00
DE Dennis Eckersley 10.00 25.00
DM Don Mattingly 30.00 60.00
DW Dave Winfield 12.50 30.00
EB Ernie Banks 30.00 60.00
FF Freddie Freeman EXCH 30.00 60.00
FT Frank Thomas 20.00 50.00
HR Hanley Ramirez 10.00 25.00
JH Josh Hamilton 15.00 40.00
JM Joe Morgan 12.50 30.00
JR Jim Rice 12.50 30.00
JS John Smoltz 15.00 40.00
MI Monte Irvin EXCH 10.00 25.00
MR Manny Ramirez 15.00 40.00
PO Paul O'Neill 15.00 40.00
RA Roberto Alomar 12.50 30.00
RB Ryan Braun 15.00 40.00
RC Robinson Cano 20.00 50.00
RG Ron Guidry 10.00 25.00
SK Sandy Koufax 200.00 350.00
TG Tony Gwynn 15.00 40.00
AB2 Albert Belle 15.00 40.00
AD1 Andre Dawson 10.00 25.00
BP2 Buster Posey 40.00 80.00
CBU Clay Buchholz 10.00 25.00
DM1 Dale Murphy 15.00 40.00
DS1 Duke Snider 15.00 40.00
DS2 Duke Snider 15.00 40.00
DW1 David Wright 10.00 25.00
DW2 David Wright 10.00 25.00
FJ1 Fergie Jenkins 12.50 30.00
GC1 Gary Carter 10.00 25.00
JHE Jason Heyward 40.00 80.00
JMA Juan Marichal 10.00 25.00
JS2 John Smoltz 15.00 40.00
MMC Mike Mussina 12.50 30.00
MS1 Mike Stanton 15.00 40.00
MS2 Mike Stanton 15.00 40.00
OC1 Orlando Cepeda 10.00 25.00
OC2 Orlando Cepeda 10.00 25.00
PO2 Paul O'Neill 15.00 40.00
RA2 Roberto Alomar 12.50 30.00
RA3 Roberto Alomar 12.50 30.00
RG2 Ron Guidry 10.00 25.00
RH1 Ryan Howard 15.00 40.00
RH2 Ryan Howard 15.00 40.00
RK1 Ralph Kiner 12.50 30.00
RK2 Ralph Kiner 12.50 30.00
TP1 Tony Perez EXCH 10.00 25.00
YA1 Yonder Alonso 10.00 25.00
YA2 Yonder Alonso 10.00 25.00
CBU2 Clay Buchholz 10.00 25.00
JHEL Jeremy Hellickson EXCH 20.00 50.00

2011 Topps Tribute Autograph Relics Black

STATED ODDS 1:77 HOBBY
RC AU RELIC ODDS 1:2083 HOBBY
STATED PRINT RUN 5 SER.#'d SETS
NO PRICING DUE TO SCARCITY

2011 Topps Tribute Autograph Relics Gold

STATED ODDS 1:22 HOBBY
RC AU RELIC ODDS 1:548 HOBBY
STATED PRINT RUN 20 SER.#'d SETS
NO PRICING DUE TO SCARCITY

2011 Topps Tribute Autograph Relics Green

*GREEN: .4X TO 1X BASIC
STATED ODDS 1:6 HOBBY
RC AU RELIC ODDS 1:145 HOBBY
STATED PRINT RUN 75 SER.#'d SETS
EXCHANGE DEADLINE 3/31/2014

2011 Topps Tribute Autograph Relics Red

STATED ODDS 1:386 HOBBY
RC AU RELIC ODDS 1:10,416 HOBBY
STATED PRINT RUN 1 SER.#'d SET
NO PRICING DUE TO SCARCITY

2011 Topps Tribute Autograph Triple Relics

STATED ODDS 1:34 HOBBY
STATED PRINT RUN 99 SER.#'d SETS
COMPLETE SET (63)

AP Albert Pujols 125.00 250.00
AR Alex Rodriguez 100.00 200.00
HA Hank Aaron 125.00 250.00
MR Mariano Rivera 75.00 150.00
NR Nolan Ryan 60.00 120.00
OS Ozzie Smith 30.00 60.00
RH Ryan Howard 30.00 60.00
RJ Reggie Jackson EXCH 30.00 60.00
TS Tom Seaver 20.00 50.00
CCS CC Sabathia 30.00 60.00

2011 Topps Tribute Autograph Triple Relics Black

STATED ODDS 1:77 HOBBY
STATED PRINT RUN 5 SER.#'d SETS
NO PRICING DUE TO SCARCITY

2011 Topps Tribute Autograph Triple Relics Gold

STATED ODDS 1:22 HOBBY
STATED PRINT RUN 20 SER.#'d SETS
NO PRICING DUE TO SCARCITY

2011 Topps Tribute Autograph Triple Relics Green

*GREEN: .4X TO 1X BASIC
STATED ODDS 1:6 HOBBY
STATED PRINT RUN 75 SER.#'d SETS
EXCHANGE DEADLINE 3/31/2014

2011 Topps Tribute Autograph Triple Relics Red

STATED ODDS 1:386 HOBBY
STATED PRINT RUN 1 SER.#'d SET
NO PRICING DUE TO SCARCITY

2011 Topps Tribute Cut Signatures

STATED ODDS 1:3125 HOBBY
STATED PRINT RUN 1 SER.#'d SET
NO PRICING DUE TO SCARCITY

2011 Topps Tribute Dual Relics

STATED ODDS 1:7 HOBBY
STATED PRINT RUN 99 SER.#'d SETS

AB Albert Belle 4.00 10.00
AD Andre Dawson 4.00 10.00
AK Al Kaline 10.00 25.00
BD Bobby Doerr 6.00 15.00
BR Babe Ruth 75.00 150.00
CF Carlton Fisk 8.00 20.00
CR Cal Ripken Jr. 12.50 30.00
CY Carl Yastrzemski 10.00 25.00
DM Don Mattingly 12.50 30.00
DW Dave Winfield 5.00 12.00
EM Eddie Mathews 10.00 25.00
FR Frank Robinson 5.00 12.00
FT Frank Thomas 10.00 25.00
GS George Sisler 10.00 25.00
HA Hank Aaron 20.00 50.00
HG Hank Greenberg 10.00 25.00
HK Harmon Killebrew 10.00 25.00
HW Honus Wagner 50.00 100.00
JB Johnny Bench 8.00 20.00
JF Jimmie Foxx 15.00 40.00
JM Johnny Mize 8.00 20.00
JP Jim Palmer EXCH 8.00 20.00
JR Jackie Robinson 20.00 50.00
JS John Smoltz 5.00 12.00
LG Lou Gehrig 60.00 120.00
MM Mickey Mantle 50.00 100.00
MP Mike Piazza 6.00 15.00
MS Mike Schmidt 8.00 20.00
NR Nolan Ryan 15.00 40.00
OC Orlando Cepeda 8.00 20.00
OS Ozzie Smith 8.00 20.00
PR Phil Rizzuto 10.00 25.00
RA Roberto Alomar 8.00 20.00
RC Roy Campanella 10.00 25.00
RH Rogers Hornsby 12.50 30.00
RJ Reggie Jackson 8.00 20.00
RM Roger Maris 30.00 60.00
RR Robin Roberts EXCH 10.00 25.00
RS Ryne Sandberg 10.00 25.00
RY Robin Yount 6.00 15.00
SK Sandy Koufax 50.00 100.00
SM Stan Musial 15.00 40.00
TC Ty Cobb 30.00 60.00
TG Tony Gwynn 6.00 15.00
TM Thurman Munson 12.50 30.00
TP Tony Perez 4.00 10.00
TS Tris Speaker 12.50 30.00
WF Whitey Ford 10.00 25.00
WS Warren Spahn 10.00 25.00
YB Yogi Berra 10.00 25.00
BRO Brooks Robinson 10.00 25.00
DMU Dale Murphy 6.00 15.00
EMU Eddie Murray 5.00 12.00
RCA Rod Carew 6.00 15.00
TSE Tom Seaver 6.00 15.00
WST Willie Stargell 10.00 25.00

2011 Topps Tribute Dual Relics Black

STATED ODDS 1:81 HOBBY
STATED PRINT RUN 1 SER.#'d SET
NO PRICING DUE TO SCARCITY

2011 Topps Tribute Dual Relics Gold

STATED ODDS 1:23 HOBBY
STATED PRINT RUN 20 SER.#'d SETS
NO PRICING DUE TO SCARCITY

2011 Topps Tribute Dual Relics Green

*GREEN: .4X TO 1X BASIC
STATED ODDS 1:5 HOBBY
STATED PRINT RUN 75 SER.#'d SETS

2011 Topps Tribute Dual Relics Red

STATED ODDS 1:401 HOBBY
STATED PRINT RUN 1 SER.#'d SET
NO PRICING DUE TO SCARCITY

2011 Topps Tribute Pastime Patches Dual

STATED ODDS 1:55 HOBBY
STATED PRINT RUN 24 SER.#'d SETS
NO PRICING DUE TO SCARCITY

2011 Topps Tribute Pastime Patches Dual Red

STATED ODDS 1:1302 HOBBY
STATED PRINT RUN 1 SER.#'d SET
NO PRICING DUE TO SCARCITY

2011 Topps Tribute Quad Relics

STATED ODDS 1:34 HOBBY
STATED PRINT RUN 99 SER.#'d SETS

AR Alex Rodriguez 10.00 25.00
BG Bob Gibson 8.00 20.00
DJ Derek Jeter 12.50 30.00
IS Ichiro Suzuki 20.00 50.00
JV Joey Votto 10.00 25.00
MO Mel Ott 12.50 30.00
NR Nolan Ryan 20.00 50.00
RH Roy Halladay 15.00 40.00
RH Ryan Howard 10.00 25.00
SS Stephen Strasburg 20.00 50.00

2011 Topps Tribute Quad Relics Black

STATED ODDS 1:81 HOBBY
STATED PRINT RUN 1 SER.#'d SET
NO PRICING DUE TO SCARCITY

2011 Topps Tribute Quad Relics Gold

STATED ODDS 1:23 HOBBY
STATED PRINT RUN 20 SER.#'d SETS
NO PRICING DUE TO SCARCITY

2011 Topps Tribute Quad Relics Green

*GREEN: .4X TO 1X BASIC
STATED ODDS 1:5 HOBBY
STATED PRINT RUN 75 SER.#'d SETS

2011 Topps Tribute Quad Relics Red

STATED ODDS 1:401 HOBBY
STATED PRINT RUN 1 SER.#'d SET
NO PRICING DUE TO SCARCITY

2011 Topps Tribute Roll Call Book

STATED ODDS 1:363 HOBBY
STATED PRINT RUN 9 SER.#'d SETS
NO PRICING DUE TO SCARCITY

2011 Topps Tribute Roll Call Book Red

STATED ODDS 1:3125 HOBBY
STATED PRINT RUN 1 SER.#'d SET
NO PRICING DUE TO SCARCITY

2011 Topps Tribute Tribute to the Stars Dual Autographs

STATED ODDS 1:38 HOBBY
STATED PRINT RUN 74 SER.#'d SETS

DR Andre Dawson 12.50 30.00
Jim Rice
DS Andre Dawson 50.00 100.00
Ryne Sandberg
GC Dwight Gooden 20.00 50.00
Gary Carter
HU Ryan Howard 60.00 120.00
Chase Utley
KZ George Kell 12.50 30.00
Ryan Zimmerman
LH Nelson Cruz 50.00 100.00
Josh Hamilton
MH Dale Murphy 60.00 120.00
Jason Heyward
MP Brian Matusz 12.50 30.00
Jim Palmer
PM Albert Pujols 200.00 400.00
Stan Musial
PS Johnny Podres 30.00 60.00
Duke Snider
SG Darryl Strawberry 20.00 50.00
Dwight Gooden
PSA Buster Posey 50.00 100.00
Carlos Santana

2011 Topps Tribute Tribute to the Stars Dual Autographs Gold

STATED ODDS 1:119 HOBBY
STATED PRINT RUN 25 SER.#'d SETS
NO PRICING DUE TO SCARCITY

2011 Topps Tribute Tribute to the Stars Dual Autographs Red

STATED ODDS 1:2604 HOBBY
STATED PRINT RUN 1 SER.#'d SET
NO PRICING DUE TO SCARCITY

2011 Topps Tribute Tribute to the Stars Triple Autographs

STATED ODDS 1:124 HOBBY
STATED PRINT RUN 24 SER.#'d SETS

SRC Ozzie Smith 50.00 100.00
Hanley Ramirez
Starlin Castro
FFM Johnny Podres 50.00 100.00
Whitey Ford
Juan Marichal
HCR Phil Hughes 150.00 250.00
Robinson Cano
Mariano Rivera
JDS Fergie Jenkins 100.00 200.00
Andre Dawson
Ryne Sandberg
PKL David Price 50.00 100.00
Clayton Kershaw
Jon Lester
PSM Buster Posey 60.00 120.00
Carlos Santana
Brian McCann
PSN Johnny Podres 150.00 300.00
Duke Snider
Don Newcombe
SBH Mike Stanton 75.00 150.00
Domonic Brown
Jason Heyward
SGH Darryl Strawberry 50.00 100.00
Dwight Gooden
Gary Carter
UHV Chase Utley 100.00 200.00
Ryan Howard
Shane Victorino
WAB Vernon Wells 60.00 120.00
Roberto Alomar
Jose Bautista
YMB Robin Yount 75.00 150.00
Paul Molitor
Ryan Braun

2011 Topps Tribute Tribute to the Stars Triple Autographs Red

STATED ODDS 1:2604 HOBBY
STATED PRINT RUN 1 SER.#'d SET
NO PRICING DUE TO SCARCITY

2011 Topps Tribute Triple Relics

STATED ODDS 1:23 HOBBY
STATED PRINT RUN 99 SER.#'d SETS

AB Albert Belle 5.00 12.00
AP Albert Pujols 20.00 50.00
CR Cal Ripken Jr. 20.00 50.00
DJ Derek Jeter 15.00 40.00
DM Don Mattingly 10.00 25.00
DW Dave Winfield 6.00 15.00
HA Hank Aaron 20.00 50.00
HK Harmon Killebrew 12.50 30.00
JB Johnny Bench 10.00 25.00
JS John Smoltz 6.00 15.00
LG Lou Gehrig 75.00 150.00
MR Mariano Rivera 10.00 25.00
RS Ryne Sandberg 10.00 25.00
TG Tony Gwynn 10.00 25.00
TS Tom Seaver 8.00 20.00

2011 Topps Tribute Triple Relics Black

STATED ODDS 1:81 HOBBY
STATED PRINT RUN 1 SER.#'d SET
NO PRICING DUE TO SCARCITY

2011 Topps Tribute Triple Relics Gold

STATED ODDS 1:23 HOBBY
STATED PRINT RUN 20 SER.#'d SETS
NO PRICING DUE TO SCARCITY

2011 Topps Tribute Triple Relics Green

*GREEN: .4X TO 1X BASIC
STATED ODDS 1:5 HOBBY
STATED PRINT RUN 75 SER.#'d SETS

2011 Topps Tribute Triple Relics Red

STATED ODDS 1:401 HOBBY
STATED PRINT RUN 1 SER.#'d SET
NO PRICING DUE TO SCARCITY

2003 Topps Tribute Contemporary

This 110 card set was released in August, 2003. These cards were issued in five card packs with an $50 SRP which came six packs to a box and four boxes to a case. Cards numbered 1-90 feature veterans and cards 91-100 feature rookies. Cards numbered 101 through 110 also feature rookies, but those cards are signed and were issued to a stated print run of 499 serial numbered sets and these cards were inserted at a stated rate of one in seven. Jose Contreras did not return his cards in time for inclusion in this product and those cards could be redeemed until August 31, 2005.

COMMON CARD (1-90) .75 2.00
COMMON CARD (91-100) .75 2.00
COMMON CARD (101-110) 4.00 10.00
1 Jim Thome 1.00 2.50
2 Edgardo Alfonzo .75 2.00
3 Edgar Martinez 1.00 2.50
4 Scott Rolen 1.00 2.50
5 Eric Hinske .75 2.00
6 Mark Mulder .75 2.00
7 Jason Giambi .75 2.00
8 Bernie Williams 1.00 2.50
9 Cliff Floyd .75 2.00
10 Ichiro Suzuki 3.00 8.00
11 Pat Burrell .75 2.00
12 Garret Anderson .75 2.00
13 Gary Sheffield .75 2.00
14 Johnny Damon 1.00 2.50
15 Kerry Wood .75 2.00
16 Bartolo Colon .75 2.00
17 Adam Dunn .75 2.00
18 Omar Vizquel 1.00 2.50
19 Todd Helton 1.00 2.50
20 Nomar Garciaparra 2.50 6.00
21 A.J. Burnett .75 2.00
22 Craig Biggio 1.00 2.50
23 Carlos Beltran .75 2.00
24 Kazuhisa Ishii .75 2.00
25 Vladimir Guerrero 1.50 4.00
26 Roberto Alomar 1.00 2.50
27 Roger Clemens 3.00 8.00
28 Tim Hudson .75 2.00
29 Brian Giles .75 2.00
30 Barry Bonds 4.00 10.00
31 Jim Edmonds .75 2.00
32 Rafael Palmeiro 1.00 2.50
33 Francisco Rodriguez .75 2.00
34 Andruw Jones 1.00 2.50
35 Shea Hillenbrand .75 2.00
36 Moises Alou .75 2.00
37 Luis Gonzalez .75 2.00
38 Darin Erstad .75 2.00
39 John Smoltz 1.00 2.50
40 Derek Jeter 4.00 10.00
41 Aubrey Huff .75 2.00
42 Eric Chavez .75 2.00
43 Doug Mientkiewicz .75 2.00
44 Lance Berkman .75 2.00
45 Josh Beckett .75 2.00
46 Austin Kearns .75 2.00
47 Frank Thomas 1.50 4.00
48 Pedro Martinez 1.00 2.50
49 Tim Salmon .75 2.00
50 Alex Rodriguez 2.50 6.00
51 Ryan Klesko .75 2.00
52 Tom Glavine 1.00 2.50
53 Shawn Green .75 2.00
54 Jeff Kent .75 2.00
55 Carlos Pena .75 2.00
56 Paul Konerko .75 2.00
57 Troy Glaus .75 2.00
58 Manny Ramirez 1.00 2.50
59 Jason Jennings .75 2.00
60 Randy Johnson 1.50 4.00
61 Ivan Rodriguez 1.00 2.50
62 Roy Oswalt .75 2.00
63 Kevin Brown .75 2.00
64 Jose Vidro .75 2.00
65 Jorge Posada 1.00 2.50
66 Mike Piazza 2.50 6.00
67 Bret Boone .75 2.00
68 Carlos Delgado .75 2.00
69 Jimmy Rollins .75 2.00
70 Alfonso Soriano .75 2.00
71 Greg Maddux 2.50 6.00
72 Mark Prior 1.00 2.50
73 Jeff Bagwell 1.00 2.50
74 Richie Sexson .75 2.00
75 Sammy Sosa 1.50 4.00
76 Curt Schilling .75 2.00
77 Mike Sweeney .75 2.00
78 Torii Hunter .75 2.00
79 Larry Walker .75 2.00
80 Miguel Tejada .75 2.00
81 Rich Aurilia .75 2.00
82 Bobby Abreu .75 2.00
83 Phil Nevin .75 2.00
84 Rodrigo Lopez .75 2.00
85 Chipper Jones 1.50 4.00
86 Ken Griffey Jr. 2.50 6.00
87 Mike Lowell .75 2.00
88 Magglio Ordonez .75 2.00
89 Barry Zito .75 2.00
90 Albert Pujols 3.00 8.00
91 Corey Shafer FY RC .75 2.00
92 Dan Haren FY RC 1.25 3.00
93 Jeremy Bonderman FY RC 3.00 8.00
94 Branden Florence FY RC .75 2.00
95 E.Bastida-Martinez FY RC .75 2.00
96 Brian Wright FY RC .75 2.00
97 Elizardo Ramirez FY RC 1.25 3.00
98 Mi.Garciaparra FY RC .75 2.00
99 Clay Hensley FY RC .75 2.00
100 Bobby Basham FY RC .75 2.00
101 Jose Contreras FY AU RC 8.00 20.00
102 Br. Bullington FY AU RC 4.00 10.00
103 Joey Gomes FY AU RC 4.00 10.00
104 Craig Brazell FY AU RC 4.00 10.00
105 Andy Marte FY AU RC 30.00 60.00
106 Han. Ramirez FY AU RC 50.00 100.00
107 Ryan Shealy FY AU RC 12.50 30.00
108 Daryl Clark FY AU RC 4.00 10.00
109 Tyler Johnson FY AU RC 4.00 10.00
110 Ben Francisco FY AU RC 4.00 10.00

2003 Topps Tribute Contemporary Gold

Card 101 (Jose Contreras) was issued in packs in the form of an exchange card with a redemption deadline of August 31st, 2005.

STATED PRINT RUN 25 SERIAL #'d SETS
NO PRICING DUE TO SCARCITY

2003 Topps Tribute Contemporary Red

*RED 1-90: .6X TO 1.5X BASIC CARDS
*RED 91-100: .75X TO 2X BASIC CARDS
1-100 PRINT RUN 225 SERIAL #'d SETS
*RED 101-110: .6X TO 1.5X BASIC
101-110 PRINT RUN 99 SERIAL #'d SETS
106 Hanley Ramirez FY AU 50.00 100.00

2003 Topps Tribute Contemporary Bonds Tribute Relics

*RED BONDS: .6X TO 1.5X BASIC BONDS
RED BONDS PRINT RUN 50 #'d SETS
GOLD BONDS PRINT RUN 1 #'d SET
NO GOLD PRICING DUE TO SCARCITY
DB Barry Bonds Bat-Jsy 20.00 50.00
SB Barry Bonds Jsy 15.00 40.00
TB Barry Bonds Bat-Cap-Jsy 40.00 80.00

2003 Topps Tribute Contemporary Bonds Tribute 40-40 Club Relics

NO GOLD PRICING DUE TO SCARCITY
CBR Jose Canseco Uni 40.00 80.00
Barry Bonds Uni
Alex Rodriguez Uni
CBRG Jose Canseco Uni
Barry Bonds Uni
Alex Rodriguez Uni Gold/1
CBRR Jose Canseco Uni 60.00 120.00
Barry Bonds Uni
Alex Rodriguez Uni Red/50

2003 Topps Tribute Contemporary Bonds Tribute 600 HR Club Relics

*RED 600: .6X TO 1.5X BASIC
RED 600 PRINT RUN 50 SERIAL #'d SETS
GOLD PRINT RUN 1 SERIAL #'d SET
NO GOLD PRICING DUE TO SCARCITY
BB Barry Bonds Bat 15.00 40.00
BR Babe Ruth Bat 75.00 150.00
HA Hank Aaron Bat 15.00 40.00
WM Willie Mays Uni 20.00 50.00

2003 Topps Tribute Contemporary Bonds Tribute 600 HR Club Double Relics

*RED 600 DOUBLE: .6X TO 1.5X BASIC
RED 600 DOUBLE PRINT RUN 50 #'d SETS
GOLD 600 DOUBLE PRINT 1 SERIAL #'d SET
NO GOLD PRICING DUE TO SCARCITY
BA Barry Bonds Bat 50.00 100.00
Hank Aaron Bat
BM Barry Bonds Bat 50.00 100.00
Willie Mays Uni
RB Babe Ruth Bat 125.00 200.00
Barry Bonds Bat

2003 Topps Tribute Contemporary Bonds Tribute 600 HR Club Quad Relics

PRINT RUNS B/WN 1-50 COPIES PER
NO GOLD/RED PRICING DUE TO SCARCITY
HR Babe Ruth Bat 300.00 500.00
Willie Mays Uni
Hank Aaron Bat
Barry Bonds Bat/50
HRG Babe Ruth Bat
Willie Mays Uni
Hank Aaron Bat
Barry Bonds Bat Gold/1
HRR Babe Ruth Bat
Willie Mays Uni

Hank Aaron Bat
Barry Bonds Bat Red/25

2003 Topps Tribute Contemporary Matching Marks Dual Relics

*RED MARKS: .6X TO 1.5X BASIC
RED MARKS PRINT RUN 50 SERIAL #'d SETS
GOLD MARKS PRINT RUN 1 SERIAL #'d SET
NO GOLD PRICING DUE TO SCARCITY
AP Roberto Alomar Bat 6.00 15.00
Rafael Palmeiro Bat
BG Jeff Bagwell Uni 6.00 15.00
Juan Gonzalez Bat
BP Barry Bonds Bat 15.00 40.00
Rafael Palmeiro Bat
GR Nomar Garciaparra Jsy 10.00 25.00
Alex Rodriguez Jsy
HR Rickey Henderson Bat 6.00 15.00
Manny Ramirez Bat
MG Fred McGriff Bat 4.00 10.00
Juan Gonzalez Bat
MP Fred McGriff Bat 6.00 15.00
Rafael Palmeiro Bat
PA Rafael Palmeiro Bat 6.00 15.00
Roberto Alomar Uni
PH Rafael Palmeiro Bat 6.00 15.00
Rickey Henderson Bat
PS Rafael Palmeiro Uni 6.00 15.00
Sammy Sosa Bat
RP Manny Ramirez Jsy 10.00 25.00
Mike Piazza Uni
SB Sammy Sosa Bat 6.00 15.00
Jeff Bagwell Uni
SG Alfonso Soriano Uni 6.00 15.00
Vladimir Guerrero Bat

2003 Topps Tribute Contemporary Memorable Materials Relics

*RED MEM: .6X TO 1.5X BASIC
RED MEM PRINT RUN 50 SERIAL #'d SETS
GOLD MEM PRINT RUN 1 SERIAL #'d SET
NO GOLD PRICING DUE TO SCARCITY
AJ Andruw Jones Jsy 6.00 15.00
AP Albert Pujols Jsy 10.00 25.00
AR Alex Rodriguez Jsy 8.00 20.00
AS Alfonso Soriano Uni 4.00 10.00
BB Barry Bonds Jsy 15.00 40.00
CR Cal Ripken Bat 20.00 50.00
GM Greg Maddux Jsy 6.00 15.00
JG Jason Giambi Jsy 4.00 10.00
JG2 Jason Giambi Bat 4.00 10.00
KW Kerry Wood Jsy 4.00 10.00
LG Luis Gonzalez Bat 4.00 10.00
MT Miguel Tejada Bat 4.00 10.00
RH Rickey Henderson Uni 6.00 15.00
SG Shawn Green Jsy 4.00 10.00
SS Sammy Sosa Bat 6.00 15.00
SS2 Sammy Sosa Jsy 6.00 15.00
TG Troy Glaus Uni 4.00 10.00
TH Torii Hunter Jsy 4.00 10.00
VG Vladimir Guerrero Bat 6.00 15.00

2003 Topps Tribute Contemporary Milestone Materials Relics

*RED MILE: .6X TO 1.5X BASIC
RED MILE PRINT RUN 50 SERIAL #'d SETS
GOLD PRINT RUN 1 SERIAL #'d SET
NO GOLD PRICING DUE TO SCARCITY
AR Alex Rodriguez Jsy 8.00 20.00
BB1 Barry Bonds 1500 RBI Uni 10.00 25.00
BB2 Barry Bonds 1500 Runs Uni 10.00 25.00
BB3 Barry Bonds 2000 Hits Uni 10.00 25.00
BB4 Barry Bonds 500 2B Uni 10.00 25.00
BB5 Barry Bonds 600 HR Uni 10.00 25.00
CJ Chipper Jones Jsy 6.00 15.00
FM1 Fred McGriff Cubs Bat 4.00 10.00
FM2 Fred McGriff 2000 Hits Bat 4.00 10.00
FM3 Fred McGriff 400 HR Bat 4.00 10.00
FT Frank Thomas Jsy 6.00 15.00
JB1 Jeff Bagwell Jsy 4.00 10.00
JB2 Jeff Bagwell Uni 4.00 10.00
JG1 Juan Gonzalez Indians Bat 3.00 8.00
JG2 Juan Gonzalez Rgr Bat 3.00 8.00
MP1 Mike Piazza Bat 6.00 15.00
MP2 Mike Piazza Uni 6.00 15.00
MR1 Manny Ramirez Bat 4.00 10.00
MR2 Manny Ramirez Jsy 4.00 10.00
NG Nomar Garciaparra Jsy 10.00 25.00
RA Roberto Alomar Uni 6.00 15.00
RH1 R.Henderson Mets Bat 4.00 10.00
RH2 R.Henderson Sox Bat 4.00 10.00
RH3 R.Henderson A's Bat 4.00 10.00
RH4 R.Henderson 3000 Hits Bat 4.00 10.00
RH5 R.Henderson 500 2B Bat 4.00 10.00
RP1 R.Palmeiro 1500 RBI Jsy 4.00 10.00
RP2 R.Palmeiro 2500 Hits Bat 4.00 10.00
RP3 R.Palmeiro 500 HR Uni 4.00 10.00
RP4 R.Palmeiro 500 2B Bat 4.00 10.00
SS1 Sammy Sosa 1250 RBI Jsy 6.00 15.00
SS2 Sammy Sosa 2000 Hits Jsy 6.00 15.00
SS3 Sammy Sosa Bat 6.00 15.00
TH Todd Helton Jsy 6.00 15.00
VG Vladimir Guerrero Bat 6.00 15.00

2003 Topps Tribute Contemporary Modern Marks Autographs

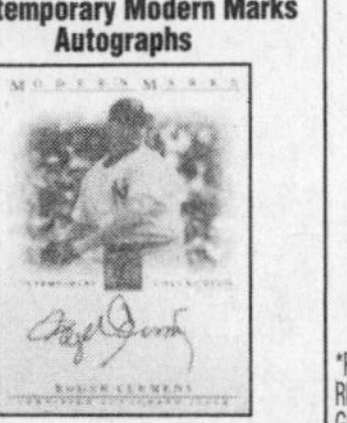

Inserted at a stated rate of one in 19, these nine cards feature authentic autographs from current major leaguers.

STATED ODDS 1:19
*RED MARKS: .5X TO 1.2X BASIC
RED MARKS STATED ODDS 1:38
RED MARKS PRINT RUN 99 SERIAL #'d SETS
GOLD MARKS STATED ODDS 1:149
GOLD MARKS PRINT RUN 25 SERIAL #'d SETS
NO GOLD PRICING DUE TO SCARCITY
CF Cliff Floyd 6.00 15.00
EH Eric Hinske 6.00 15.00
LB Lance Berkman 10.00 25.00
MO Magglio Ordonez 6.00 15.00
MS Mike Sweeney 6.00 15.00
PK Paul Konerko 10.00 25.00
PL Paul Lo Duca 6.00 15.00
RC Roger Clemens 40.00 80.00
TH Torii Hunter 10.00 25.00

2003 Topps Tribute Contemporary Perennial All-Star Relics

*RED AS: .6X TO 1.5X BASIC
RED AS PRINT RUN 50 SERIAL #'d SETS
GOLD AS PRINT RUN 1 SERIAL #'d SET
NO GOLD PRICING DUE TO SCARCITY
AR Alex Rodriguez Jsy 8.00 20.00
BB Barry Bonds Uni 10.00 25.00
BS Benito Santiago Bat 4.00 10.00
BW Bernie Williams Bat 6.00 15.00
CB Craig Biggio Uni 6.00 15.00
CJ Chipper Jones Jsy 6.00 15.00
CS Curt Schilling Jsy 4.00 10.00
CM Edgar Martinez Bat 6.00 15.00
FT Frank Thomas Bat 6.00 15.00
GM Greg Maddux Jsy 6.00 15.00
GS Gary Sheffield Bat 4.00 10.00
IR Ivan Rodriguez Bat 6.00 15.00
JS John Smoltz Uni 6.00 15.00
LW Larry Walker Bat 4.00 10.00
MM Mike Mussina Uni 6.00 15.00
MP Mike Piazza Bat 6.00 15.00
MR Manny Ramirez Bat 6.00 15.00
PM Pedro Martinez Jsy 6.00 15.00
RA Roberto Alomar Bat 6.00 15.00
RC Roger Clemens Uni 8.00 20.00
RH Rickey Henderson Bat 6.00 15.00
SS Sammy Sosa Bat 6.00 15.00

2003 Topps Tribute Contemporary Performance Double Relics

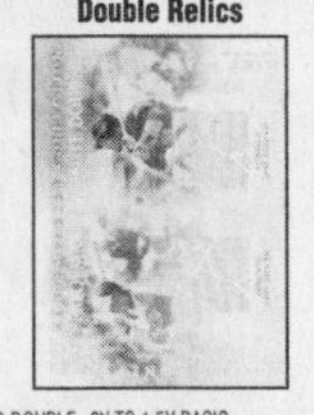

*RED DOUBLE: .6X TO 1.5X BASIC
RED DOUBLE PRINT RUN 50 #'d SETS
GOLD DOUBLE PRINT RUN 1 #'d SET
NO GOLD PRICING DUE TO SCARCITY
RAMDOM INSERTS IN PACKS
BJ Barry Bonds Uni 10.00 25.00
Chipper Jones Bat
CM Roger Clemens Uni 15.00 40.00
Greg Maddux Jsy
GG Luis Gonzalez Bat 4.00 10.00
Troy Glaus Uni
JP Chipper Jones Bat 8.00 20.00
Mike Piazza Bat
MM Pedro Martinez Jsy 8.00 20.00
Greg Maddux Uni
PR Mike Piazza Uni 8.00 20.00
Ivan Rodriguez Bat
PS Mike Piazza Bat 8.00 20.00
Benito Santiago Bat
PW Albert Pujols Jsy 10.00 25.00
Kerry Wood Jsy
RG Alex Rodriguez Jsy 15.00 40.00
Nomar Garciaparra Jsy
RR Cal Ripken Bat 30.00 60.00
Alex Rodriguez Jsy
RT Alex Rodriguez Jsy 8.00 20.00
Miguel Tejada Bat
SA Alfonso Soriano Uni 6.00 15.00
Roberto Alomar Uni
SG Sammy Sosa Bat 6.00 15.00
Juan Gonzalez Bat
ZJ Barry Zito Uni 6.00 15.00
Randy Johnson Uni

2003 Topps Tribute Contemporary Performance Triple Relics

*RED TRIPLE: .6X TO 1.5X BASIC
RED TRIPLE PRINT RUN 50 #'d SETS
GOLD TRIPLE PRINT RUN 1 #'d SET
NO GOLD PRICING DUE TO SCARCITY
BMP Barry Bonds Uni 15.00 40.00
Fred McGriff Bat
Rafael Palmeiro Jsy
CMJ Roger Clemens Uni 15.00 40.00
Greg Maddux Jsy
Randy Johnson Jsy
RPH Manny Ramirez Jsy 15.00 40.00
Mike Piazza Uni
Rickey Henderson Bat
SPM Sammy Sosa Bat 12.50 30.00
Rafael Palmeiro Bat
Fred McGriff Bat
STB Sammy Sosa Jsy 12.50 30.00
Frank Thomas Jsy
Jeff Bagwell Jsy

2003 Topps Tribute Contemporary Team Double Relics

*RED DOUBLE: .6X TO 1.5X BASIC
RED DOUBLE PRINT RUN 50 #'d SETS
GOLD DOUBLE PRINT RUN 1 #'d SET
NO GOLD PRICING DUE TO SCARCITY
BB Craig Biggio Jsy 6.00 15.00
Jeff Bagwell Uni
GR Nomar Garciaparra Jsy 10.00 25.00
Manny Ramirez Jsy
IN Kazuhisa Ishii Jsy 10.00 25.00
Hideo Nomo Jsy
MS Greg Maddux Jsy 20.00 50.00
John Smoltz Jsy
RP Alex Rodriguez Jsy 8.00 20.00
Rafael Palmeiro Bat
WH Larry Walker Jsy 6.00 15.00
Todd Helton Jsy

2003 Topps Tribute Contemporary Team Triple Relics

*RED TRIPLE: .6X TO 1.5X BASIC
RED TRIPLE PRINT RUN 50 SERIAL #'d SETS
GOLD PRINT RUN 1 SERIAL #'d SET
NO GOLD PRICING DUE TO SCARCITY
ASP Moises Alou Bat 12.50 30.00
Sammy Sosa Jsy
Corey Patterson Bat
BBB Craig Biggio Uni 10.00 25.00
Lance Berkman Bat
Jeff Bagwell Uni
CTM Eric Chavez Uni 10.00 25.00
Miguel Tejada Jsy
Mark Mulder Uni
GRM Nomar Garciaparra Jsy 15.00 40.00
Manny Ramirez Jsy
Pedro Martinez Jsy
HZM Tim Hudson Uni 10.00 25.00
Barry Zito Uni
Mark Mulder Uni
JSJ Andruw Jones Jsy 12.50 30.00
Gary Sheffield Bat
Chipper Jones Jsy
MHM Joe Mauer Bat 12.50 30.00
Torii Hunter Jsy
Doug Mientkiewicz Bat
MOB Edgar Martinez Jsy 10.00 25.00
John Olerud Bat
Bret Boone Jsy
PER Albert Pujols Bat 15.00 40.00
Jim Edmonds Jsy
Scott Rolen Bat
RBT Alex Rodriguez Bat 12.50 30.00
Hank Blalock Bat
Mark Teixeira Bat
RGP Alex Rodriguez Jsy 12.50 30.00
Juan Gonzalez Bat
Rafael Palmeiro Jsy
SGV Alfonso Soriano Bat 10.00 25.00
Jason Giambi Bat
Robin Ventura Bat
TBB Jim Thome Jsy 10.00 25.00
Marlon Byrd Jsy
Pat Burrell Jsy
TOK Frank Thomas Jsy 12.50 30.00
Magglio Ordonez Jsy
Paul Konerko Jsy

2003 Topps Tribute Contemporary Tribute to the Stars Dual Relics

*RED DUAL: .6X TO 1.5X BASIC
RED DUAL PRINT RUN 50 #'d SETS
GOLD DUAL PRINT RUN 1 SERIAL #'d SET
NO GOLD PRICING DUE TO SCARCITY
AD Adam Dunn Bat-Jsy 6.00 15.00
AJ Andruw Jones Bat-Jsy 6.00 15.00
AP Albert Pujols Bat-Uni 15.00 40.00
AR Alex Rodriguez Bat-Jsy 12.50 30.00
AS Alfonso Soriano Bat-Uni 6.00 15.00
BB Barry Bonds Bat-Uni 20.00 50.00
CJ Chipper Jones Bat-Jsy 6.00 15.00
EC Eric Chavez Bat-Uni 6.00 15.00
FT Frank Thomas Bat-Jsy 6.00 15.00
GA Garret Anderson Bat-Uni 6.00 15.00
GM Greg Maddux Bat-Uni 8.00 20.00
JT Jim Thome Bat-Jsy 6.00 15.00
LB Lance Berkman Bat-Jsy 6.00 15.00
LW Larry Walker Bat-Jsy 6.00 15.00
MP Mike Piazza Bat-Uni 8.00 20.00
NG Nomar Garciaparra Bat-Jsy 15.00 40.00
PB Pat Burrell Bat-Jsy 6.00 15.00
RA Roberto Alomar Bat-Uni 6.00 15.00
RH Rickey Henderson Bat-Uni 6.00 15.00
RP Rafael Palmeiro Bat-Jsy 6.00 15.00
SS Sammy Sosa Bat-Jsy 6.00 15.00
TG Troy Glaus Bat-Uni 6.00 15.00
TH Todd Helton Bat-Jsy 6.00 15.00
VG Vladimir Guerrero Bat-Jsy 6.00 15.00
THU Torii Hunter Bat-Jsy 6.00 15.00

2003 Topps Tribute Contemporary Tribute to the Stars Patchworks Dual Relics

STATED ODDS 1:34
STATED PRINT RUN 50 SERIAL #'d SETS
AP Albert Pujols 50.00 100.00
AR Alex Rodriguez 30.00 60.00
AR2 Alex Rodriguez Blue 30.00 60.00
BB Barry Bonds 50.00 100.00
CJ Chipper Jones 15.00 40.00
CS Curt Schilling 10.00 25.00
FT Frank Thomas 15.00 40.00
GM Greg Maddux 20.00 50.00
JB Jeff Bagwell 15.00 40.00
KW Kerry Wood 10.00 25.00
LG Luis Gonzalez 10.00 25.00
MR Manny Ramirez 15.00 40.00
NG Nomar Garciaparra 20.00 50.00
PM Pedro Martinez 15.00 40.00
RJ Randy Johnson 15.00 40.00
RP Rafael Palmeiro 15.00 40.00
SG Shawn Green 10.00 25.00
SS Sammy Sosa 15.00 40.00
TH Todd Helton 15.00 40.00
THU Torii Hunter 10.00 25.00

2003 Topps Tribute Contemporary World Series Relics

*RED WS: .6X TO 1.5X BASIC
RED WS PRINT RUN 50 SERIAL #'d SETS
GOLD WS PRINT RUN 1 SERIAL #'d SET
NO GOLD PRICING DUE TO SCARCITY
MR•Mariano Rivera Jsy 6.00 15.00
TG•Troy Glaus Uni 4.00 10.00

2003 Topps Tribute Contemporary World Series Double Relics

*RED WS DOUBLE: .6X TO 1.5X BASIC
RED WS DOUBLE PRINT RUN 50 #'d SETS
GOLD WS DOUBLE PRINT RUN 1 #'d SET
NO GOLD PRICING DUE TO SCARCITY
BG Barry Bonds Uni 15.00 40.00
Troy Glaus Uni
LP John Lackey Uni 4.00 10.00
Troy Percival Uni
PC Mike Piazza Bat 15.00 40.00
Roger Clemens Uni
PP Jorge Posada Bat 10.00 25.00
Andy Pettitte Jsy
SJ Curt Schilling Jsy 6.00 15.00
Randy Johnson Jsy
WG Bernie Williams Bat 6.00 15.00
Luis Gonzalez Bat
WO Bernie Williams Bat 6.00 15.00
Paul O'Neill Bat

2003 Topps Tribute Contemporary World Series Triple Relics

*RED WS TRIPLE: .6X TO 1.5X BASIC
RED WS TRIPLE PRINT RUN 50 #'d SETS
GOLD WS TRIPLE PRINT RUN 1 #'d SET
NO GOLD PRICING DUE TO SCARCITY
EGS Darin Erstad Uni 10.00 25.00
Troy Glaus Uni
Tim Salmon Uni
LGP John Lackey Uni 6.00 15.00
Troy Glaus Bat
Troy Percival Uni

2004 Topps Tribute HOF

This 80-card set was released in January, 2005. The set was issued in five card packs with an $50 SRP which came six packs to a box and four boxes to a case. Each pack contained either a game-used card or some other special card. This set was highlighted by the insertion of a 'cut signature' of just about every Hall of Famer all of which were issued to a stated print run of one serial numbered set.

COMPLETE SET (80) 75.00 150.00
COMMON CARD (1-80) .75 2.00
1 Willie Mays 4.00 10.00
2 Richie Ashburn 1.25 3.00
3 Babe Ruth 5.00 12.00
4 Lou Gehrig 4.00 10.00
5 Carl Yastrzemski 2.00 5.00
6 Fergie Jenkins .75 2.00
7 Cool Papa Bell 1.25 3.00
8 Johnny Bench 2.00 5.00
9 Satchel Paige 2.00 5.00
10 Ty Cobb 3.00 8.00
11 Robin Roberts .75 2.00
12 Eddie Mathews 2.00 5.00
13 Tom Seaver 1.25 3.00
14 Kirby Puckett 2.00 5.00
15 Stan Musial 3.00 8.00
16 Ralph Kiner 1.25 3.00
17 Reggie Jackson 1.25 3.00
18 Walter Johnson 1.25 3.00
19 Phil Niekro .75 2.00
20 Mike Schmidt 3.00 8.00
21 Brooks Robinson 1.25 3.00
22 Jimmie Foxx 2.00 5.00
23 Nellie Fox 1.25 3.00
24 Joe Morgan .75 2.00
25 Cy Young 1.25 3.00
26 Hank Greenberg 2.00 5.00
27 Josh Gibson 2.00 5.00
28 Robin Yount 2.00 5.00
29 Hoyt Wilhelm .75 2.00
30 Yogi Berra 2.00 5.00
31 Rollie Fingers .75 2.00
32 Gaylord Perry .75 2.00
33 Ozzie Smith 3.00 8.00
34 Jim Palmer .75 2.00
35 Harmon Killebrew 2.00 5.00
36 Bob Feller .75 2.00
37 Chuck Klein .75 2.00
38 Mordecai Brown .75 2.00
39 Napoleon Lajoie 1.25 3.00
40 Al Kaline 2.00 5.00
41 Paul Molitor 2.00 5.00
42 Jackie Robinson 2.00 5.00
43 Mel Ott 2.00 5.00
44 Hank Aaron 4.00 10.00
45 Rod Carew 1.25 3.00
46 Rogers Hornsby 1.25 3.00
47 Bob Gibson 1.25 3.00
48 Juan Marichal .75 2.00
49 Bill Mazeroski 1.25 3.00
50 Roberto Clemente 5.00 12.00
51 Willie McCovey 1.25 3.00
52 Red Schoendienst .75 2.00
53 Nolan Ryan 6.00 15.00
54 Dennis Eckersley .75 2.00
55 Monte Irvin .75 2.00
56 George Kell .75 2.00
57 Gary Carter .75 2.00
58 Tony Perez .75 2.00
59 Carlton Fisk 1.25 3.00
60 Duke Snider 1.25 3.00
61 Bobby Doerr .75 2.00
62 John McGraw 1.25 3.00
63 George Sisler .75 2.00
64 Orlando Cepeda .75 2.00
65 Earl Weaver .75 2.00
66 Roy Campanella 2.00 5.00
67 Tris Speaker 1.25 3.00
68 Sparky Anderson .75 2.00
69 Willie Stargell 1.25 3.00
70 Honus Wagner 2.00 5.00
71 Lou Brock 1.25 3.00
72 Whitey Ford 1.25 3.00
73 George Brett 4.00 10.00
74 Luis Aparicio .75 2.00
75 Ernie Banks 2.00 5.00
76 Jim Bunning .75 2.00
77 Warren Spahn 1.25 3.00
78 Catfish Hunter .75 2.00
79 Pee Wee Reese 1.25 3.00
80 Frank Robinson 1.25 3.00

2004 Topps Tribute HOF Gold

*GOLD p/r 80-99: 1.25X TO 3X BASIC
*GOLD p/r 50-79: 1.5X TO 4X BASIC
*GOLD p/r 36-49: 2X TO 5X BASIC
GROUP A ODDS 1:2714
GROUP B ODDS 1:74
GROUP C ODDS 1:38
GROUP D ODDS 1:14
GROUP A PRINT RUNS B/WN 1-4 PER
GROUP B PRINT RUNS B/WN 36-56 PER
GROUP C PRINT RUNS B/WN 62-79 PER
GROUP D PRINT RUNS B/WN 80-99 PER
NO PRICING ON QTY OF 4 OR LESS

2004 Topps Tribute HOF Cooperstown Classmates Dual Cut Signatures

STATED ODDS 1:10,854
STATED PRINT RUN 1 SERIAL #'d SET
NO PRICING DUE TO SCARCITY
DT Bill Dickey
Bill Terry
GC Hank Greenberg
Joe Cronin
RC Babe Ruth
Ty Cobb
WS Hoyt Wilhelm
Enos Slaughter

2004 Topps Tribute HOF Cooperstown Classmates Dual Relics

GROUP A ODDS 1:4342
GROUP B ODDS 1:229
GROUP C ODDS 1:122
GROUP A PRINT RUN 5 SERIAL #'d SETS
GROUP B PRINT RUN 50 SERIAL #'d SETS
GROUP C PRINT RUN 75 SERIAL #'d SETS
NO GROUP A PRICING DUE TO SCARCITY
*GOLD: .6X TO 1.5X BASIC C
*GOLD: .5X TO 1.2X BASIC B
GOLD STATED ODDS 1:201
GOLD PRINT RUN 25 SERIAL #'d SETS
GOLD OTT/FOXX PRINT RUN 1 #'d CARD
GOLD RUTH/COBB PRINT RUN 1 #'d CARD
NO GOLD OTT/FOXX, RUTH/COBB PRICING
BY Johnny Bench Uni 30.00 60.00
Carl Yastrzemski Uni C
CR Orlando Cep Bat 30.00 60.00
Nolan Ryan Jsy C
KK Chuck Klein Bat 30.00 60.00
Al Kaline Bat C
ME Paul Molitor Bat 10.00 25.00
Dennis Eckersley Uni C
MP Joe Morgan Bat 10.00 25.00
Jim Palmer Uni C
MR Juan Marichal Uni 20.00 50.00
Brooks Robinson Bat B
OF Mel Ott Bat
Jimmie Foxx Bat A
PC Gaylord Perry Uni 20.00 50.00
Rod Carew Uni B
RB Nolan Ryan Uni 40.00 80.00
George Brett Uni B
RC Babe Ruth Bat
Ty Cobb Uni A
SK Duke Snider Bat 40.00 80.00
Al Kaline Uni B

2004 Topps Tribute HOF Relics

GROUP A ODDS 1:118
GROUP B ODDS 1:36
GROUP C ODDS 1:22
GROUP D ODDS 1:6
GROUP E ODDS 1:5
GROUP F ODDS 1:6
GROUP G ODDS 1:4
GROUP A PRINT RUNS B/WN 20-85 PER
GROUP B PRINT RUNS B/WN 100-175 PER
GROUP C PRINT RUNS B/WN 200-455 PER
A-C PRINT RUNS PROVIDED BY TOPPS
GROUP A-C ARE NOT SERIAL-NUMBERED
AK Al Kaline Uni B/125 * 10.00 25.00
AKB Al Kaline Bat D 6.00 15.00
BG Bob Gibson Uni E 6.00 15.00
BR Babe Ruth Bat B/163 * 100.00 175.00
BRO Brooks Robinson Bat E 6.00 15.00
CF Carlton Fisk Wall C/300 * 15.00 40.00
CK Chuck Klein Bat B/107 * 10.00 25.00
CY C.Yastrzemski Wall C/300 * 20.00 50.00
CYU Carl Yastrzemski Uni E 8.00 20.00
DS Duke Snider Bat E 6.00 15.00
EW Earl Weaver Jsy A/25 * 10.00 25.00
FR Frank Robinson O's Uni E 4.00 10.00
FRA F.Robinson Angels Uni D 4.00 10.00
FRB Frank Robinson Bat D 4.00 10.00
GB George Brett Uni F 8.00 20.00
GBB George Brett Bat D 8.00 20.00
GC G.Carter Mets Jsy C/200 * 6.00 15.00
GCU Gary Carter Expos Uni D 4.00 10.00
GS George Sisler Bat C/455 * 10.00 25.00
HA Hank Aaron Bat D 15.00 40.00
HG Hank Greenberg Bat E 10.00 25.00
HK H.Killebrew Bat B/135 * 15.00 40.00
HW Honus Wagner Bat B/118 * 75.00 150.00
JB J.Bench w/Glv Uni C/250 * 10.00 25.00
JB2 J.Bench w/o Glv Uni G 6.00 15.00
JF Jimmie Foxx Bat A/25 * 100.00 175.00
JM Joe Morgan Bat E 4.00 10.00
JMA Juan Marichal Uni B/125 * 6.00 15.00
JP J.Palmer Arm Up Uni F 4.00 10.00
JP2 J.Palmer Arm Down Uni F 4.00 10.00
JR Jackie Robinson Bat G 10.00 25.00
KP Kirby Puckett Jsy B/175 * 10.00 25.00
KPB Kirby Puckett Bat G 6.00 15.00
LBB Lou Brock Bat E 6.00 15.00
LG Lou Gehrig Bat A/52 * 175.00 300.00
MO Mel Ott Bat A/25 * 60.00 120.00
MS Mike Schmidt Jsy A/50 * 15.00 40.00
MSB Mike Schmidt Bat G 8.00 20.00
NR Nolan Ryan Rgr Uni F 12.50 30.00
NRA N.Ryan Angels Uni C/425 * 15.00 40.00
NRJ Nolan Ryan Astros Jsy F 12.50 30.00
OC Orl Cepeda Bat B/100 * 6.00 15.00
OS Ozzie Smith Bat F 6.00 15.00
PM Paul Molitor Jsy G 4.00 10.00
PMB Paul Molitor Bat D 4.00 10.00
RC Roberto Clemente Bat E 30.00 60.00
RH Rogers Hornsby Bat D 15.00 40.00
RJ R.Jackson Jsy B/110 * 10.00 25.00
RJB R.Jackson Bat C/200 * 10.00 25.00
RY Robin Yount Uni A/50 * 15.00 40.00
SM Stan Musial Jsy G 10.00 25.00
TC Ty Cobb Uni A/20 *
TCB Ty Cobb Bat D 40.00 80.00
TS Tom Seaver Uni D 6.00 15.00
TSP Tris Speaker Bat A/85 * 100.00 175.00
WF Whitey Ford Uni A/50 * 15.00 40.00
WM1 Willie Mays Glove B/110 * 100.00 175.00
WM2 Willie Mays Giants Bat D 15.00 40.00
WM3 Willie Mays Mets Bat D 15.00 40.00
WM4 Willie Mays Uni Gray F 15.00 40.00
WM5 Willie Mays Uni White G 15.00 40.00

2004 Topps Tribute HOF Relics Gold

*GOLD: 1.25X TO 3X GROUP E-G
*GOLD: 1.25X TO 3X GROUP D
*GOLD: .75X TO 2X GROUP C
*GOLD: .75X TO 2X GROUP B
*GOLD: .6X TO 1.5X GROUP A p/r 50-85
*GOLD: .5X TO 1.2X GROUP A p/r 20-25
STATED ODDS 1:33
STATED PRINT RUN 25 SERIAL #'d SETS
E.WEAVER PRINT RUN 1 SERIAL #'d CARD
J.FOXX PRINT RUN 1 SERIAL #'d CARD
M.OTT PRINT RUN 1 SERIAL #'d CARD
T.COBB UNI PRINT RUN 1 SERIAL #'d CARD
W.FORD PRINT RUN 15 SERIAL #'d CARDS
NO PRICING ON QTY OF 15 OR LESS
BR Babe Ruth Bat 175.00 300.00
CY Carl Yastrzemski Wall 40.00 100.00
GB George Brett Uni 30.00 80.00
GBB George Brett Bat 30.00 80.00
HA Hank Aaron Bat 40.00 100.00
HW Honus Wagner Bat 75.00 150.00
JR Jackie Robinson Bat 40.00 100.00
KP Kirby Puckett Jsy 25.00 60.00
KPB Kirby Puckett Bat 25.00 60.00
MS Mike Schmidt Jsy 30.00 80.00
MSB Mike Schmidt Bat 30.00 80.00
NRA Nolan Ryan Angels Uni 40.00 100.00
OS Ozzie Smith Bat 25.00 60.00
RC Roberto Clemente Bat 75.00 150.00
RH Rogers Hornsby Bat 30.00 80.00
SM Stan Musial Jsy 40.00 100.00
TCB Ty Cobb Bat 75.00 150.00
TSP Tris Speaker Bat 100.00 175.00
WF Whitey Ford Uni/15 40.00 100.00
WM1 Willie Mays Glove 200.00 350.00
WM2 Willie Mays Giants Bat 40.00 100.00
WM3 Willie Mays Mets Bat 40.00 100.00
WM4 Willie Mays Uni Gray 40.00 100.00
WM5 Willie Mays Uni White 40.00 100.00

2004 Topps Tribute HOF Relics Autographs

GROUP A ODDS 1:835
GROUP B ODDS 1:120
GROUP A PRINT RUN 55 SERIAL #'d SETS
GROUP B PRINT RUN 95 SERIAL #'d SETS
GOLD STATED ODDS 1:1888
GOLD PRINT RUN 5 SERIAL #'d SETS
NO GOLD PRICING DUE TO SCARCITY

AKB Al Kaline Bat B 30.00 60.00
BRO Brooks Robinson Bat B 30.00 60.00
CYU Carl Yastrzemski Uni B 40.00 80.00
EW Earl Weaver Jsy A 15.00 40.00
NRJ Nolan Ryan Jsy B 75.00 150.00

2004 Topps Tribute HOF Relics Jersey Patch

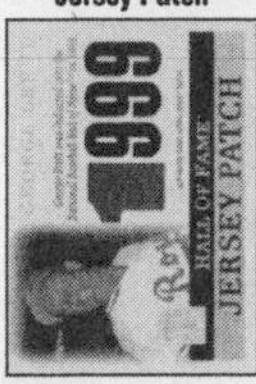

*3-COLOR PATCH: ADD 20% PREMIUM
GROUP A ODDS 1:172
GROUP B ODDS 1:114
GROUP A PRINT RUNS B/WN 10-50 PER
GROUP B PRINT RUN 100 SERIAL #'d SETS
NO PRICING ON QTY OF 17 OR LESS
*GOLD p/r 25: .75X TO 2X BASIC p/r 100
*GOLD p/r 25: .6X TO 1.5X BASIC p/r 50
GOLD STATED ODDS 1:251
GOLD PRINT RUNS B/WN 1-25 COPIES PER
NO GOLD PRICING ON QTY OF 10 OR LESS

DE Dennis Eckersley A/50 15.00 40.00
FR Frank Robinson A/39 30.00 60.00
GB George Brett A/50 20.00 50.00
LB Lou Brock A/17
MS Mike Schmidt Swing B 20.00 50.00
MS2 Mike Schmidt Stance B 20.00 50.00
NR Nolan Ryan B 30.00 60.00
OS Ozzie Smith A/10
RC Rod Carew B 15.00 40.00
RJ Reggie Jackson A/50 20.00 50.00
RY Robin Yount A/50 20.00 50.00

2004 Topps Tribute HOF Signature Cuts Cooperstown

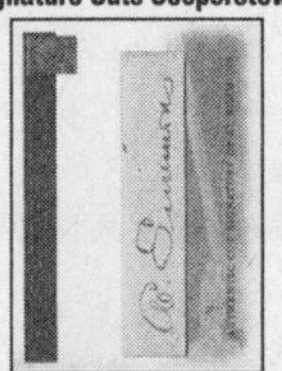

STATED ODDS 1:244
STATED PRINT RUN 1 SERIAL #'d SET
NO PRICING DUE TO SCARCITY

2004 Topps Tribute HOF Signature Cuts Personalities

STATED ODDS 1:1034
STATED PRINT RUN 1 SERIAL #'d SET
NO PRICING DUE TO SCARCITY

2004 Topps Tribute HOF Signature Cuts Personalities Dual

STATED ODDS 1:4824
STATED PRINT RUN 1 SERIAL #'d SET
NO PRICING DUE TO SCARCITY

2003 Topps Tribute Perennial All-Star

This 50 card set was released in February, 2003. These cards were issued in five card packs with an $50 SRP. These packs were issued in six pack boxes which came four boxes to a case. These cards honored players who made at least five trips to the All-Star game during their career.

COMPLETE SET (50) 40.00 100.00

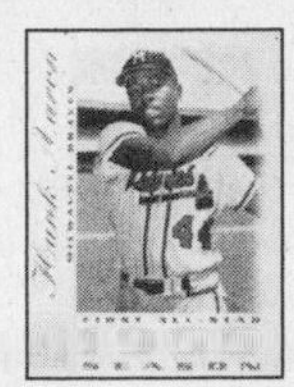

1 Willie Mays 4.00 10.00
2 Don Mattingly 4.00 10.00
3 Hoyt Wilhelm 1.50 4.00
4 Hank Aaron 4.00 10.00
5 Hank Greenberg 2.00 5.00
6 Johnny Bench 2.00 5.00
7 Duke Snider 1.50 4.00
8 Carl Yastrzemski 3.00 8.00
9 Jim Palmer 1.50 4.00
10 Roberto Clemente 5.00 12.00
11 Mike Schmidt 4.00 10.00
12 Joe Cronin 1.50 4.00
13 Lou Brock 1.50 4.00
14 Orlando Cepeda 1.50 4.00
15 Bill Mazeroski 1.50 4.00
16 Whitey Ford 1.50 4.00
17 Rod Carew 1.50 4.00
18 Joe Morgan 1.50 4.00
19 Luis Aparicio 1.50 4.00
20 Nolan Ryan 5.00 12.00
21 Bobby Doerr 1.50 4.00
22 Dale Murphy 1.50 4.00
23 Bob Feller 1.50 4.00
24 Paul Molitor 1.50 4.00
25 Tom Seaver 1.50 4.00
26 Ozzie Smith 3.00 8.00
27 Stan Musial 3.00 8.00
28 Willie McCovey 1.50 4.00
29 Gary Carter 1.50 4.00
30 Reggie Jackson 1.50 4.00
31 Gaylord Perry 1.50 4.00
32 George Brett 4.00 10.00
33 Robin Roberts 1.50 4.00
34 Wade Boggs 1.50 4.00
35 Cal Ripken 6.00 15.00
36 Carlton Fisk 1.50 4.00
37 Al Kaline 2.00 5.00
38 Kirby Puckett 2.00 5.00
39 Phil Rizzuto
40 Willie Stargell 1.50 4.00
41 Harmon Killebrew 2.00 5.00
42 Red Schoendienst 1.50 4.00
43 Tony Gwynn 2.50 6.00
44 Ralph Kiner 1.50 4.00
45 Yogi Berra 2.00 5.00
46 Catfish Hunter 1.50 4.00
47 Frank Robinson 1.50 4.00
48 Ernie Banks 2.00 5.00
49 Warren Spahn 1.50 4.00
50 Brooks Robinson 1.50 4.00

2003 Topps Tribute Perennial All-Star Gold

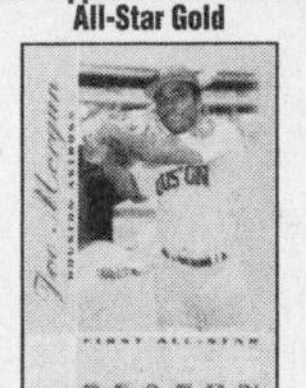

This is a parallel to the Topps Tribute set. These cards were issued at different rates depending on what group the card was issued from. We have notated that information next to the player's name in our checklist.

*GOLD p/r 81-86: 1.5X TO 4X BASIC
*GOLD p/r 66-80: 2X TO 5X BASIC
*GOLD p/r 51-65: 2.5X TO 6X BASIC
*GOLD p/r 36-50: 3X TO 8X BASIC
*GOLD p/r 26-35: 4X TO 10X BASIC
GROUP A ODDS 1:106
GROUP B ODDS 1:49
GROUP C ODDS 1:38

2003 Topps Tribute Perennial All-Star Relics

This 65-card insert set was inserted at various odds depending on what type of relic and what group the card belonged to. We have notated the group, the odds for the group as well as the relic in our checklist.

BAT GROUP A ODDS 1:556
BAT GROUP B ODDS 1:
BAT GROUP C ODDS 1:276
BAT GROUP D ODDS 1:61
BAT GROUP E ODDS 1:158
BAT GROUP F ODDS 1:23
BAT GROUP G ODDS 1:111
BAT GROUP H ODDS 1:46
BAT GROUP I ODDS 1:85
BAT GROUP J ODDS 1:16
BAT GROUP K ODDS 1:18
BAT GROUP L ODDS 1:31
BAT GROUP M ODDS 1:50
BAT GROUP N ODDS 1:46
BAT GROUP O ODDS 1:21
BAT GROUP P ODDS 1:37
JSY/UNI GROUP A ODDS 1:368
JSY/UNI GROUP B ODDS 1:148
JSY/UNI GROUP C ODDS 1:92
JSY/UNI GROUP D ODDS 1:185
JSY/UNI GROUP E ODDS 1:69
JSY/UNI GROUP F ODDS 1:55
JSY/UNI GROUP G ODDS 1:79
JSY/UNI GROUP H ODDS 1:61
JSY/UNI GROUP I ODDS 1:55
JSY/UNI GROUP J ODDS 1:25
JSY/UNI GROUP K ODDS 1:46
JSY/UNI GROUP L ODDS 1:43
JSY/UNI GROUP M ODDS 1:21
JSY/UNI GROUP N ODDS 1:8
JSY/UNI GROUP O ODDS 1:29
JSY/UNI GROUP P ODDS 1:10

AD Andre Dawson Bat F 8.00 20.00
AK Al Kaline Bat E 12.50 30.00
BD Bobby Doerr Jsy N 6.00 15.00
BF Bob Feller Bat I 6.00 15.00
BM Bill Mazeroski Uni C 10.00 25.00
BR Babe Ruth Bat J 90.00 180.00
BRO Brooks Robinson Bat J 8.00 20.00
CF Carlton Fisk Bat J 8.00 20.00
CH Catfish Hunter Jsy B 10.00 25.00
CRB Cal Ripken Bat P 15.00 40.00
CY Carl Yastrzemski Jsy E 15.00 40.00
DD Dizzy Dean Uni E 20.00 50.00
DM Dale Murphy Jsy A 12.50 30.00
DMA Don Mattingly Jsy L 12.50 30.00
DN Don Newcombe Bat K 6.00 15.00
DSN Duke Snider Bat F 10.00 25.00
EB Ernie Banks Bat M 8.00 20.00
EM Eddie Mathews Jsy K 8.00 20.00
FR Frank Robinson Uni G 8.00 20.00
GB George Brett Jsy M 12.50 30.00
GC Gary Carter Jsy I 6.00 15.00
HA Hank Aaron Bat O 30.00 60.00
HG Hank Greenberg Bat D 20.00 50.00
HK Harmon Killebrew Jsy J 8.00 20.00
HW Honus Wagner Bat B 100.00 200.00
HWI Hoyt Wilhelm Uni N 6.00 15.00
JBE Johnny Bench Uni F 12.50 30.00
JCR Joe Cronin Bat N 6.00 15.00
JF Jimmie Foxx Bat F 20.00 50.00
JMI Johnny Mize Uni D 15.00 40.00
JMO Joe Morgan Bat K 6.00 15.00
JP Jim Palmer Uni N 6.00 15.00
JR Jackie Robinson Bat L 20.00 50.00
KP Kirby Puckett Jsy N 8.00 20.00
LA Luis Aparicio Bat C 8.00 20.00
LB Lou Brock Bat A 12.50 30.00
LBU Lou Brock Uni H 8.00 20.00
LG Lou Gehrig Bat F 100.00 200.00
MO Mel Ott Bat D 12.50 30.00
MS Mike Schmidt Uni P 8.00 20.00
NL Nap Lajoie Bat D 90.00 150.00
NR Nolan Ryan Rangers Uni O 30.00 60.00
NRA Nolan Ryan Astros Jsy F 20.00 50.00
OC Orlando Cepeda Jsy C 8.00 20.00
OS Ozzie Smith Uni J 8.00 20.00
PM Paul Molitor Bat K 6.00 15.00
PR Phil Rizzuto Bat H 10.00 25.00
RC Roberto Clemente Bat L 30.00 60.00
RCA Roy Campanella Bat F 10.00 25.00
RH Rogers Hornsby Bat G 20.00 50.00
RJ Reggie Jackson Bat O 8.00 20.00
ROD Rod Carew Jsy N 8.00 20.00
RS Red Schoendienst Bat H 6.00 15.00
SM Stan Musial Bat J 15.00 40.00
TC Ty Cobb Bat F 60.00 120.00
TG Tony Gwynn Jsy P 6.00 15.00
TM Thurman Munson Jsy M 12.50 30.00
TS Tris Speaker Bat A 100.00 175.00
TSE Tom Seaver Jsy A 12.50 30.00
WB Wade Boggs Uni C 10.00 25.00
WF Whitey Ford Uni B 10.00 25.00
WM Willie Mays Bat K 15.00 40.00
WMC Willie McCovey Bat J 6.00 15.00
WST Willie Stargell Uni B 10.00 25.00
YB Yogi Berra Jsy A 20.00 50.00

2003 Topps Tribute Perennial All-Star Patch Relics

Inserted at a stated rate of one in 123, these 15 cards feature premium relics from prestigious retired talents. These game-worn uniform patch relic cards display a unique design featuring the player, his relic and the site of an All-Star appearance. These cards were issued to a stated print run of 30 serial numbered sets.

CR Cal Ripken 175.00 300.00
CY Carl Yastrzemski 125.00 200.00
DMU Dale Murphy 40.00 80.00
GB George Brett 150.00 250.00
GC Gary Carter 20.00 50.00
HK Harmon Killebrew 60.00 120.00
JM Joe Morgan 20.00 50.00
MS Mike Schmidt 150.00 250.00
NR Nolan Ryan Rangers 150.00 250.00
NRA Nolan Ryan Astros 150.00 250.00
OS Ozzie Smith 125.00 200.00
TG Tony Gwynn 75.00 150.00
WB Wade Boggs 40.00 80.00
WM Willie McCovey 20.00 50.00
WS Willie Stargell 40.00 80.00

2003 Topps Tribute Perennial All-Star Signing

Issued at a stated rate of one in 34, these cards feature not only a game-used relic from the player's career but also an authentic signature of the featured player.

GOLD STATED ODDS 1:201
GOLD PRINT RUN 25 SERIAL #'d SETS
NO GOLD PRICING DUE TO SCARCITY

AD Andre Dawson Bat 15.00 40.00
AK Al Kaline Bat 40.00 80.00
DM Dale Murphy Jsy 15.00 40.00
DMA Don Mattingly Jsy 60.00 120.00

DSN Duke Snider Bat 30.00 60.00
GC Gary Carter Jsy 15.00 40.00
JP Jim Palmer Uni 15.00 40.00
LB Lou Brock Uni 30.00 60.00
MS Mike Schmidt Uni 60.00 120.00
OC Orlando Cepeda Jsy 15.00 40.00
TG Tony Gwynn Jsy 50.00 100.00

2003 Topps Tribute Perennial All-Star 1st Class Cut Relics

Inserted at a stated rate of one in 7461, these seven cards feature autograph cuts from among the most legendary figures in the game. On back each card is an authentic USPS stamp of the featured player. Each of these cards is a true 1 of 1 and is stamped as such on back.

2003 Topps Tribute Perennial All-Star Memorable Match-Up Relics

Issued at a stated rate of one in 41, these 10 cards feature two all stars who appeared in the same all-star game along with a game-used relic from each of their career. These cards were issued to a stated print run of 150 serial numbered sets.

GOLD STATED ODDS 1:245
GOLD PRINT RUN 25 SERIAL #'d SETS
NO GOLD PRICING DUE TO SCARCITY

BF Johnny Bench Bat 20.00 50.00
 Carlton Fisk Bat
BG Wade Boggs Bat 20.00 50.00
 Tony Gwynn Bat
BS George Brett Jsy 20.00 50.00
 Mike Schmidt Uni
CM Gary Carter Jsy 40.00 80.00
 Don Mattingly Jsy
KA Harmon Killebrew Jsy 60.00 120.00
 Hank Aaron Bat
MJ Willie Mays Bat 50.00 100.00
 Reggie Jackson Bat
PG Kirby Puckett Bat 20.00 50.00
 Tony Gwynn Bat
YB Carl Yastrzemski Jsy 40.00 80.00
 Johnny Bench Bat
YBR Carl Yastrzemski Jsy 20.00 50.00
 Lou Brock Bat

2003 Topps Tribute World Series

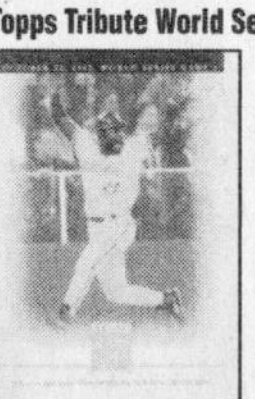

This 150 card set was released in October, 2003. The set was issued in four card packs with an $50 SRP which came six packs to a box and four boxes to a case. Cards numbered 1 through 130 feature players from a year in which their team participated in a World Series while cards 131 through 150 is a Fall Classic sub set featuring key moments in World Series history.

COMMON CARD (1-130) 1.50 4.00
COMMON CARD (131-150) 1.50 4.00
1 Willie Mays 54 4.00 10.00
2 Gary Carter 86 1.50 4.00
3 Yogi Berra 47 2.00 5.00
4 Dennis Eckersley 88 1.50 4.00
5 Willie McCovey 62 1.50 4.00
6 Willie Stargell 71 1.50 4.00
7 Mike Schmidt 80 4.00 10.00
8 Robin Yount 82 2.00 5.00
9 Bucky Harris 24 1.50 4.00
10 Carl Yastrzemski 67 3.00 8.00
11 Lenny Dykstra 86 1.50 4.00
12 Boog Powell 66 1.50 4.00
13 Bill Lee 75 1.50 4.00
14 Lou Brock 64 1.50 4.00
15 Bob Friend 60 1.50 4.00
16 Hank Greenberg 34 2.00 5.00
17 Maury Wills 59 1.50 4.00
18 Tom Lasorda 77 1.50 4.00
19 Moose Skowron 55 1.50 4.00
20 Frank Robinson 61 1.50 4.00
21 Rollie Fingers 72 1.50 4.00
22 Doug DeCinces 79 1.50 4.00
23 Eric Davis 90 1.50 4.00
24 Johnny Podres 53 1.50 4.00
25 Darrell Evans 84 1.50 4.00
26 Ron Cey 74 1.50 4.00
27 Ray Knight 86 1.50 4.00
28 Don Larsen 55 1.50 4.00
29 Harold Baines 90 1.50 4.00
30 Brooks Robinson 66 1.50 4.00
31 Wade Boggs 86 1.50 4.00
32 Joe Morgan 72 1.50 4.00
33 Kirk Gibson 84 1.50 4.00
34 Tommy John 77 1.50 4.00
35 Monte Irvin 51 1.50 4.00
36 Goose Gossage 78 1.50 4.00
37 Tug McGraw 73 1.50 4.00
38 Walt Weiss 88 1.50 4.00
39 Bill Madlock 79 1.50 4.00
40 Juan Marichal 62 1.50 4.00
41 Willie McGee 82 1.50 4.00
42 Joe Cronin 33 1.50 4.00
43 Paul Blair 66 1.50 4.00
44 Norm Cash 59 1.50 4.00
45 Ken Griffey 75 1.50 4.00
46 Bret Saberhagen 85 1.50 4.00
47 Don Sutton 74 1.50 4.00
48 Kirby Puckett 87 2.00 5.00
49 Keith Hernandez 82 1.50 4.00
50 George Brett 80 4.00 10.00
51 Bobby Richardson 57 1.50 4.00
52 Jose Canseco 88 1.50 4.00
53 Greg Luzinski 80 1.50 4.00
54 Bill Mazeroski 60 1.50 4.00
55 Red Schoendienst 46 1.50 4.00
56 Graig Nettles 76 1.50 4.00
57 Jerry Koosman 69 1.50 4.00
58 Tony Perez 70 1.50 4.00
59 Jim Rice 86 1.50 4.00
60 Duke Snider 49 1.50 4.00
61 David Justice 91 1.50 4.00
62 Johnny Sain 48 1.50 4.00
63 Chuck Klein 35 1.50 4.00
64 Sparky Anderson 70 1.50 4.00
65 Alan Trammell 84 1.50 4.00
66 Willie Wilson 80 1.50 4.00
67 Hoyt Wilhelm 54 1.50 4.00
68 Joe Pepitone 63 1.50 4.00
69 Darren Daulton 93 1.50 4.00
70 Tom Seaver 69 1.50 4.00
71 Catfish Hunter 72 1.50 4.00
72 Tim McCarver 64 1.50 4.00
73 Dave Parker 79 1.50 4.00
74 Earl Weaver 69 1.50 4.00
75 Ted Kluszewski 59 1.50 4.00
76 John Kruk 93 1.50 4.00
77 Dwight Evans 75 1.50 4.00
78 Ron Darling 86 1.50 4.00
79 Tony Oliva 65 1.50 4.00
80 Johnny Bench 70 2.00 5.00
81 Sam Crawford 07 1.50 4.00
82 Steve Yeager 74 1.50 4.00
83 Paul Molitor 82 1.50 4.00
84 Bert Campaneris 72 1.50 4.00
85 Mickey Rivers 76 1.50 4.00
86 Vince Coleman 87 1.50 4.00
87 Kent Tekulve 79 1.50 4.00
88 Dwight Gooden 86 1.50 4.00
89 Whitey Herzog 82 1.50 4.00
90 Whitey Ford 50 1.50 4.00
91 Warren Spahn 48 1.50 4.00
92 Fred Lynn 75 1.50 4.00
93 Joe Tinker 06 1.50 4.00
94 Bill Buckner 74 1.50 4.00
95 Bob Feller 48 1.50 4.00
96 Hank Bauer 49 1.50 4.00
97 Joe Rudi 72 1.50 4.00
98 Steve Sax 81 1.50 4.00
99 Bruce Sutter 82 1.50 4.00
100 Nolan Ryan 69 5.00 12.00
101 Bobby Thomson 51 1.50 4.00
102 Bob Watson 81 1.50 4.00
103 Vida Blue 72 1.50 4.00
104 Robin Roberts 50 1.50 4.00
105 Orlando Cepeda 62 1.50 4.00
106 Jim Bottomley 26 1.50 4.00
107 Heinie Manush 33 1.50 4.00
108 Jim Gilliam 53 1.50 4.00
109 Dave Concepcion 70 1.50 4.00
110 Al Kaline 68 2.00 5.00
111 Howard Johnson 84 1.50 4.00
112 Phil Rizzuto 41 1.50 4.00
113 Steve Garvey 74 1.50 4.00
114 George Foster 72 1.50 4.00
115 Carlton Fisk 75 1.50 4.00
116 Don Newcombe 49 1.50 4.00
117 Lance Parrish 84 1.50 4.00
118 Reggie Jackson 73 1.50 4.00
119 Luis Aparicio 59 1.50 4.00
120 Jim Palmer 66 1.50 4.00
121 Ron Guidry 77 1.50 4.00
122 Frankie Frisch 21 1.50 4.00
123 Chet Lemon 84 1.50 4.00
124 Cecil Cooper 75 1.50 4.00
125 Harmon Killebrew 65 2.00 5.00
126 Luis Tiant 75 1.50 4.00
127 John McGraw 05 1.50 4.00
128 Paul O'Neill 90 1.50 4.00
129 Jack Clark 85 1.50 4.00
130 Stan Musial 42 3.00 8.00
131 Mike Schmidt FC 4.00 10.00
132 Kirby Puckett FC 2.00 5.00
133 Carlton Fisk FC 1.50 4.00
134 Bill Mazeroski FC 1.50 4.00
135 Johnny Podres FC 1.50 4.00
136 Robin Yount FC 2.00 5.00
137 David Justice FC 1.50 4.00
138 Bobby Thomson FC 1.50 4.00
139 Joe Carter FC 1.50 4.00
140 Reggie Jackson FC 1.50 4.00
141 Kirk Gibson FC 1.50 4.00
142 Whitey Ford FC 1.50 4.00
143 Don Larsen FC 1.50 4.00
144 Duke Snider FC 1.50 4.00
145 Carl Yastrzemski FC 3.00 8.00
146 Johnny Bench FC 2.00 5.00
147 Lou Brock FC 1.50 4.00
148 Ted Kluszewski FC 1.50 4.00
149 Jim Palmer FC 1.50 4.00
150 Willie Mays FC 4.00 10.00

2003 Topps Tribute World Series Gold

*GOLD 1-130: 1.5X TO 4X BASIC
*GOLD 131-150: 1.5X TO 4X BASIC
STATED PRINT RUN 100 SERIAL #'d SETS

2003 Topps Tribute World Series Fall Classic Cuts

STATED ODDS 1:3437
STATED PRINT RUN 1 SERIAL #'d SET
NO PRICING DUE TO SCARCITY

2003 Topps Tribute World Series Memorable Match-Up Relics

STATED ODDS 1:28
PRINT RUNS B/WN 9-88 COPIES PER
NO PRICING ON QTY OF 19 OR LESS

AM Sparky Anderson Uni 15.00 40.00
 Billy Martin Uni/76
AS Luis Aparicio Bat 20.00 50.00
 Duke Snider Bat/59
CR Eddie Collins Bat
 Edd Roush Bat/19
EG Dennis Eckersley Uni 15.00 40.00
 Kirk Gibson Bat/88
FS Whitey Ford Uni 40.00 80.00
 Duke Snider Bat/52
GF Hank Greenberg Bat 75.00 150.00
 Frankie Frisch Bat/34
GK Hank Greenberg Bat 75.00 150.00
 Chuck Klein Bat/35
KB Al Kaline Uni 40.00 80.00
 Lou Brock Bat/68
MF Bill Mazeroski Jsy 40.00 80.00
 Whitey Ford Uni/64
PR Phil Rizzuto Bat 75.00 150.00
 Willie Mays Uni/51
RBE Brooks Robinson Bat 40.00 80.00
 Johnny Bench Bat/70
RS Frank Robinson Bat 20.00 50.00
 Tom Seaver Uni/69
SB Mike Schmidt Uni 50.00 100.00
 George Brett Uni/80
SP Willie Stargell Bat 15.00 40.00
 Jim Palmer Jsy/79
SRI Mike Schmidt Uni 75.00 150.00
 Cal Ripken Uni/83
SY Ozzie Smith Bat 20.00 50.00
 Robin Yount Jsy/82
TG Alan Trammell Jsy 40.00 80.00
 Tony Gwynn Bat/84
WB Mookie Wilson Bat 20.00 50.00
 Bill Buckner Jsy/86
WC Honus Wagner Bat
 Ty Cobb Bat/9

2003 Topps Tribute World Series Pastime Patches

STATED ODDS 1:146
STATED PRINT RUN 15 SERIAL #'d SETS
NO PRICING DUE TO SCARCITY

2003 Topps Tribute World Series Signature Relics

GROUP A ODDS 1:218
GROUP B ODDS 1:94
GROUP C ODDS 1:9
GROUP D ODDS 1:12
GOLD STATED ODDS 1:88
GOLD PRINT RUN 25 SERIAL #'d SETS
NO GOLD PRICING DUE TO SCARCITY

AK Al Kaline Uni C 20.00 50.00
AT Alan Trammell Jsy C 15.00 40.00
BR Brooks Robinson Bat A 40.00 80.00
DJ David Justice Uni B 20.00 50.00
DN Don Newcombe Bat A 20.00 50.00
EW Earl Weaver Jsy D 20.00 50.00
JC Joe Carter Bat C 10.00 25.00
JP Jim Palmer Jsy D 15.00 40.00
KG Kirk Gibson Bat C 15.00 40.00
MS Moose Skowron Bat C 15.00 40.00
MW Maury Wills Jsy D 10.00 25.00
MWI Mookie Wilson Bat B 15.00 40.00
SA Sparky Anderson Uni C 20.00 50.00
SG Steve Garvey Bat C 10.00 25.00
WF Whitey Ford Uni C 30.00 60.00

2003 Topps Tribute World Series Subway Fan Fare Tokens

ONE PER BOX

BM Billy Martin 6.00 15.00
DJ David Justice 4.00 10.00
DL Don Larsen 4.00 10.00
DN Don Newcombe 4.00 10.00
DS Duke Snider 6.00 15.00
HB Hank Bauer 4.00 10.00
JP Johnny Podres 4.00 10.00
MS Moose Skowron 4.00 10.00
PO Paul O'Neill 6.00 15.00
PR Phil Rizzuto 6.00 15.00
WF Whitey Ford 6.00 15.00
YB Yogi Berra 8.00 20.00

2003 Topps Tribute World Series Team Tribute Relics

GROUP A ODDS 1:436
GROUP B ODDS 1:7
GROUP A PRINT RUN 25 SERIAL #'d SETS
GROUP B PRINT RUN 275 SERIAL #'d SETS
NO GROUP A PRICING DUE TO SCARCITY

CM Orlando Cepeda Bat 12.50 30.00
 Juan Marichal Uni B
CPM Dave Concepcion Bat 20.00 50.00
 Tony Perez Uni
 Joe Morgan Uni B
CYG Ron Cey Bat 12.50 30.00
 Steve Yeager Bat
 Steve Garvey Bat B
EC Dennis Eckersley Jsy 10.00 25.00
 Jose Canseco Jsy B
FB Whitey Ford Uni
 Yogi Berra Jsy A
FPG George Foster Bat 15.00 40.00
 Tony Perez Uni
 Ken Griffey Sr. Bat B
GB Lou Gehrig Bat
 Babe Ruth Bat A
GT Kirk Gibson Bat 10.00 25.00
 Alan Trammell Jsy B
HCD Keith Hernandez Bat 12.50 30.00
 Gary Carter Uni
 Lenny Dykstra Bat B
HJ Catfish Hunter Jsy 12.50 30.00
 Reggie Jackson Bat B
KCA Al Kaline Uni 15.00 40.00
 Norm Cash Bat B
MM Willie Mays Uni 30.00 80.00
 Willie McCovey Bat B
OSD Paul O'Neill Bat 15.00 40.00
 Chris Sabo Bat
 Eric Davis Bat B
SB Bret Saberhagen Jsy 15.00 40.00
 George Brett Bat B
SMC Ozzie Smith Uni 25.00 60.00
 Willie McGee Bat
 Vince Coleman Bat B
SPM Willie Stargell Bat 15.00 40.00
 Dave Parker Jsy
 Bill Madlock Bat B
SR Moose Skowron Bat
 Bobby Richardson Bat A
SRK Tom Seaver Uni 15.00 40.00
 Nolan Ryan Bat
 Jerry Koosman Jsy B
TA Alan Trammell Jsy 10.00 25.00

Sparky Anderson Uni B
YLK Carl Yastrzemski Jsy 20.00 50.00
Fred Lynn Jsy
Carlton Fisk Bat B
YM Robin Yount Jsy 15.00 40.00
Paul Molitor Bat B

2003 Topps Tribute World Series Tribute Relics

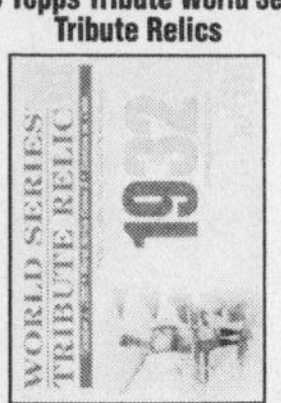

GROUP A ODDS 1:41
GROUP B ODDS 1:3
GROUP A PRINT RUN 50 SERIAL #'d SETS
GROUP B PRINT RUN 425 SERIAL #'d SETS
GOLD STATED ODDS 1:25
GOLD PRINT RUN 25 SERIAL #'d SETS
NO GOLD PRICING DUE TO SCARCITY
BH Bucky Harris Bat B 12.50 30.00
BM Bill Mazeroski Uni B 6.00 15.00
BMA Billy Martin Uni B 6.00 15.00
BR Babe Ruth Bat B 100.00 175.00
BT Bobby Thomson Bat B 4.00 10.00
CF Carlton Fisk Bat-Wall B 20.00 50.00
CH Catfish Hunter Jsy B 6.00 15.00
CK Chuck Klein Bat B 6.00 15.00
CR Cal Ripken Uni B 20.00 50.00
CY Carl Yastrzemski Jsy B 15.00 40.00
ER Edd Roush Bat A 20.00 50.00
FF Frankie Frisch Bat B 30.00 60.00
FR Frank Robinson Bat B 6.00 15.00
GB George Brett Uni B 10.00 25.00
HA Hank Aaron Bat A 100.00 175.00
HB Hank Bauer Bat A 20.00 50.00
HG Hank Greenberg Bat A 40.00 80.00
HK Harmon Killebrew Uni B 15.00 40.00
HM Heinie Manush Bat A 20.00 50.00
HW Honus Wagner Bat A 150.00 250.00
JB Jim Bottomley Bat A 20.00 50.00
JBE Johnny Bench Uni B 10.00 25.00
JC Jose Canseco Jsy B 6.00 15.00
JF Jimmie Foxx Bat A 60.00 120.00
JM Juan Marichal Uni B 4.00 10.00
JR Jackie Robinson Bat B 20.00 50.00
JT Joe Tinker Bat B 20.00 50.00
KP Kirby Puckett Bat B 10.00 25.00
LB Lou Brock Bat B 6.00 15.00
LG Lou Gehrig Bat A 150.00 250.00
MS Mike Schmidt Uni B 10.00 25.00
NC Norm Cash Jsy A 30.00 60.00
OC Orlando Cepeda Bat A 20.00 50.00
OS Ozzie Smith Uni B 10.00 25.00
RC Roberto Clemente Bat A 75.00 150.00
RH Rogers Hornsby Bat B 15.00 40.00
RJ Reggie Jackson Bat B 6.00 15.00
RM Roger Maris Bat A 50.00 100.00
RS Red Schoendienst Bat B 6.00 15.00
RY Robin Yount Jsy B 10.00 25.00
SC Sam Crawford Bat A 20.00 50.00
SM Stan Musial Bat B 15.00 40.00
TC Ty Cobb Uni B 75.00 150.00
TG Tony Gwynn Uni B 10.00 25.00
TK Ted Kluszewski Uni B 6.00 15.00
TM Thurman Munson Bat B 12.50 30.00
TS Tom Seaver Uni B 6.00 15.00
TSP Tris Speaker Bat A 100.00 175.00
WB Wade Boggs Bat B 6.00 15.00
WM Willie Mays Uni B 20.00 50.00
WMC Willie McCovey Uni B 4.00 10.00
WS Willie Stargell Uni A 20.00 50.00
YB Yogi Berra Uni B 10.00 25.00

2003 Topps Tribute World Series Tribute Autograph Relics

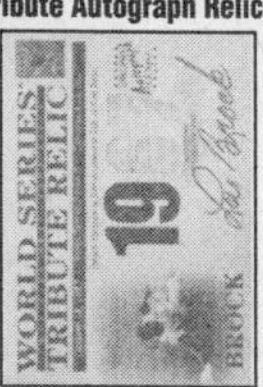

STATED ODDS 1:55
GOLD STATED ODDS 1:163
GOLD PRINT RUN 25 SERIAL #'d SETS
NO GOLD PRICING DUE TO SCARCITY
BM Bill Mazeroski Jsy 30.00 60.00
BT Bobby Thomson Bat 15.00 40.00
CF Carlton Fisk Bat-Wall 100.00 200.00
HK Harmon Killebrew Uni 30.00 60.00
JC Jose Canseco Jsy 30.00 60.00
LB Lou Brock Bat 30.00 60.00
MS Mike Schmidt Uni 60.00 120.00
WM Willie Mays Uni 250.00 400.00

2006 Topps Triple Threads

This 120-card set was released in April, 2006. The set was release solely through the hobby in six-card packs with an $80 SRP which came two packs to a box and 18 boxes to a case. The first 100-cards are a mix of veteran players and retired greats. With the exception of Don Mattingly, all of the retired players pictured are in the Hall of Fame. Cards numbered 101-120 feature younger players who both signed these cards and had some game-used memorabilia included on the card. These cards were issued to a stated print run of 225 serial numbered cards.

1-100 THREE PER PACK
101-120 ODDS 1:7 MINI
101-120 PRINT RUN 225 SERIAL #'d SETS
OVERALL 1-100 PLATE ODDS 1:80 MINI
PLATE PRINT RUN 1 SET PER COLOR
BLACK-CYAN-MAGENTA-YELLOW ISSUED
NO PLATE PRICING DUE TO SCARCITY
1 Hideki Matsui 2.00 5.00
2 Josh Gibson HOF 2.00 5.00
3 Roger Clemens 2.50 6.00
4 Paul Konerko 1.25 3.00
5 Brooks Robinson HOF 1.25 3.00
6 Stan Musial HOF 3.00 8.00
7 Dontrelle Willis .75 2.00
8 Yogi Berra HOF 2.00 5.00
9 John Smoltz 2.00 5.00
10 Brian Roberts .75 2.00
11 Gary Sheffield .75 2.00
12 Wade Boggs HOF 1.25 3.00
13 Alex Rodriguez 3.00 8.00
14 Ernie Banks HOF 2.00 5.00
15 Ichiro Suzuki 3.00 8.00
16 Whitey Ford HOF 1.25 3.00
17 Vladimir Guerrero 2.00 5.00
18 Tadahito Iguchi .75 2.00
19 Robin Yount HOF 2.00 5.00
20 Jason Schmidt .75 2.00
21 Roberto Clemente HOF 6.00 15.00
22 Andruw Jones .75 2.00
23 Don Mattingly 4.00 10.00
24 Joe Mauer 2.00 5.00
25 Barry Bonds 4.00 10.00
26 Johnny Damon 1.25 3.00
27 Chris Carpenter 2.00 5.00
28 Garret Anderson .75 2.00
29 Scott Rolen 1.25 3.00
30 Tim Hudson 1.25 3.00
31 Dave Winfield HOF .75 2.00
32 Steve Carlton HOF .75 2.00
33 Miguel Tejada 1.25 3.00
34 Nolan Ryan HOF 5.00 12.00
35 Mark Buehrle 1.25 3.00
36 Travis Hafner .75 2.00
37 Rickie Weeks 1.25 3.00
38 Sammy Sosa 2.00 5.00
39 Carlos Beltran .75 2.00
40 Todd Helton 1.25 3.00
41 Tom Seaver HOF 1.25 3.00
42 Ted Williams HOF 5.00 12.00
43 Alfonso Soriano 1.25 3.00
44 Reggie Jackson HOF 1.25 3.00
45 Pedro Martinez 1.25 3.00
46 Randy Johnson 2.00 5.00
47 Ted Williams HOF UER 5.00 12.00
Lifetime stats double his real career stats
48 Torii Hunter .75 2.00
49 Manny Ramirez 2.00 5.00
50 George Brett HOF 4.00 10.00
51 Chipper Jones 2.00 5.00
52 Nomar Garciaparra 2.00 5.00
53 Richie Sexson .75 2.00
54 David Ortiz 1.25 3.00
55 Derek Jeter 5.00 12.00
56 Mickey Mantle HOF 6.00 15.00
57 Michael Young 1.25 3.00
58 Aramis Ramirez .75 2.00
59 Bartolo Colon .75 2.00
60 Troy Glaus .75 2.00
61 Carlos Delgado .75 2.00
62 Mike Sweeney .75 2.00
63 Jorge Cantu .75 2.00
64 Mike Mussina 1.25 3.00
65 Hank Blalock .75 2.00
66 Frank Robinson HOF .75 2.00
67 Carl Yastrzemski HOF 3.00 8.00
68 Adam Dunn 1.25 3.00
69 Eric Chavez .75 2.00
70 Curt Schilling 1.25 3.00
71 Jeff Francoeur 2.00 5.00
72 C.C. Sabathia 1.25 3.00
73 Roy Oswalt 1.25 3.00
74 Carlos Lee .75 2.00
75 Barry Zito .75 2.00
76 Derrek Lee .75 2.00
77 Greg Maddux 3.00 8.00
78 Ivan Rodriguez 1.25 3.00
79 Jeff Kent .75 2.00
80 Gary Carter HOF .75 2.00
81 Jose Reyes 1.25 3.00
82 Johan Santana 2.00 5.00
83 Magglio Ordonez 1.25 3.00
84 Mark Prior 1.25 3.00
85 Johnny Bench HOF 2.00 5.00
86 Vernon Wells .75 2.00
87 Mark Mulder .75 2.00
88 Cal Ripken 8.00 20.00
89 Mark Teixeira 2.00 5.00
90 Miguel Cabrera 2.00 5.00
91 Duke Snider HOF 1.25 3.00
92 Jason Giambi .75 2.00
93 Albert Pujols 5.00 12.00
94 Carl Crawford 1.25 3.00
95 Jim Edmonds 1.25 3.00
96 Jose Contreras .75 2.00
97 Victor Martinez 1.25 3.00
98 Jeremy Bonderman .75 2.00
99 Lance Berkman 1.25 3.00
100 Rocco Baldelli .75 2.00
101 Zach Duke AU J-J 10.00 25.00
102 Felix Hernandez AU J-J 15.00 40.00
103 Dan Johnson AU J-J 6.00 15.00
104 Brandon McCarthy AU J-J 10.00 25.00
105 Huston Street AU J-J 10.00 25.00
106 Robinson Cano AU J-J 12.50 30.00
107 Jason Bay AU J-J 10.00 25.00
108 Ryan Howard AU B-B 30.00 60.00
109 Ervin Santana AU J-J 6.00 15.00
110 Rich Harden AU J-J 6.00 15.00
111 Aaron Hill AU J-J 6.00 15.00
112 David Wright AU J-J 30.00 60.00
113 Rich Hill AU J-J (RC) 15.00 40.00
114 Nelson Cruz AU J-J (RC) 8.00 20.00
115 Francisco Liriano AU J-J (RC) 6.00 15.00
116 Hong-Chih Kuo AU J-J (RC) 30.00 60.00
117 Ryan Garko AU J-J (RC) 10.00 25.00
118 Craig Hansen AU J-J RC 20.00 50.00
119 Shin-Soo Choo AU J-J (RC) 6.00 15.00
120 Darrell Rasner AU J-J (RC) 6.00 15.00

2006 Topps Triple Threads White Whale Prospect-Rookie Printing Plate

OVERALL WHALE PLATE ODDS 1:400 MINI
STATED PRINT RUN 1 SERIAL #'d SET
NO PRICING DUE TO SCARCITY

2006 Topps Triple Threads Emerald

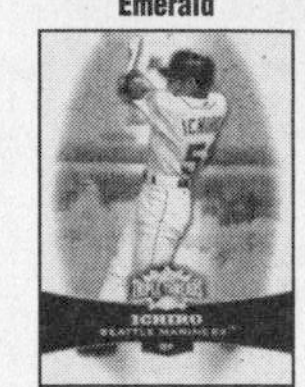

*EMERALD 1-100: .75X TO 2X BASIC
1-100 ODDS 1:4 MINI
1-100 PRINT RUN 99 SERIAL #'d SETS
*EMERALD 101-112: .5X TO 1.2X BASIC AU
*EMERALD 113-120: .5X TO 1.2X BASIC AU
101-120 AU ODDS 1:21 MINI
101-120 AU PRINT RUN 75 SERIAL #'d SETS

2006 Topps Triple Threads Gold

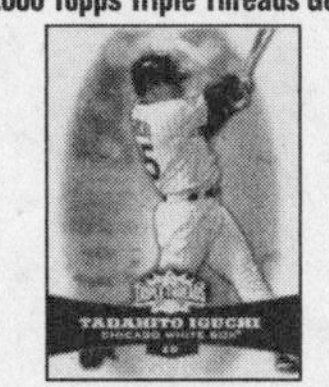

*GOLD 1-100: 1.25X TO 3X BASIC
1-100 ODDS 1:7 MINI
1-100 PRINT RUN 50 SERIAL #'d SETS
*GOLD 101-112: .6X TO 1.5X BASIC AU
*GOLD 113-120: .6X TO 1.5X BASIC AU
101-120 AU ODDS 1:32 MINI
101-120 AU PRINT RUN 50 SERIAL #'d SETS
116 Hong-Chih Kuo AU J-J 75.00 150.00
118 Craig Hansen AU J-J 30.00 60.00

2006 Topps Triple Threads Platinum

1-100 ODDS 1:322 MINI
101-120 AU ODDS 1:1598 MINI
STATED PRINT RUN 1 SERIAL #'d SET
NO PRICING DUE TO SCARCITY

2006 Topps Triple Threads Sapphire

*SAPHIRE 1-100: 2X TO 5X BASIC
1-100 ODDS 1:13 MINI
1-100 PRINT RUN 25 SERIAL #'d SETS
101-120 AU ODDS 1:63 MINI
101-120 AU PRINT RUN 25 SERIAL #'d SETS
101-120 NO PRICING DUE TO SCARCITY

2006 Topps Triple Threads Sepia

*SEPIA 1-100: .6X TO 1.5X BASIC
1-100 ODDS 1:3 MINI
1-100 PRINT RUN 150 SERIAL #'d SETS
*SEPIA 101-112: .4X TO 1X BASIC AU
*SEPIA 113-120: .4X TO 1X BASIC AU
101-120 AU ODDS 1:13 MINI
101-120 AU PRINT RUN 125 SERIAL #'d SETS

2006 Topps Triple Threads Heroes

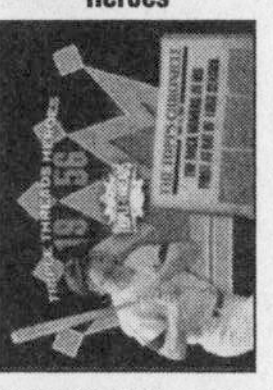

COMM.T.WILL (1-5/42;1-5/47) 5.00 12.00
COMMON MANTLE (1-10) 6.00 15.00
COMMON F.ROB (1-10) .75 2.00
COMMON YAZ (1-10) 3.00 8.00
ONE BASIC OR DIE CUT HEROES PER PACK
*DIE CUT: 1X TO 2.5X BASIC
DIE CUT ODDS 1:16 MINI
DIE CUT PRINT RUN 50 SERIAL #'d SETS

2006 Topps Triple Threads Heroes Autograph

STATED ODDS 1:524 MINI
STATED PRINT RUN 3 SERIAL #'d SETS
NO PRICING DUE TO SCARCITY

2006 Topps Triple Threads Heroes Cut Signature

STATED ODDS 1:10,122 MINI
STATED PRINT RUN 1 SERIAL #'d SET
NO PRICING DUE TO SCARCITY
MM Mickey Mantle
42TW Ted Williams 1942
47TW Ted Williams 1947

2006 Topps Triple Threads Heroes Co-Signer

STATED ODDS 1:10,122 MINI
STATED PRINT RUN 3 SERIAL #'d CARDS
NO PRICING DUE TO SCARCITY
RY Frank Robinson
Carl Yastrzemski

2006 Topps Triple Threads Heroes Triple Signed Hide

STATED ODDS 1:15,183 MINI
STATED PRINT RUN 1 SERIAL #'d SET
NO PRICING DUE TO SCARCITY
MRY Mickey Mantle Cut
Frank Robinson
Carl Yastrzemski
WRY Ted Williams Cut
Frank Robinson
Carl Yastrzemski

2006 Topps Triple Threads Heroes Quad Signer

STATED ODDS 1:10,122 MINI
STATED PRINT RUN 1 SERIAL #'d CARD
NO PRICING DUE TO SCARCITY
QS Mickey Mantle Cut
Ted Williams Cut
Frank Robinson
Carl Yastrzemski

2006 Topps Triple Threads Relic

STATED ODDS 1:7 MINI
STATED PRINT RUN 18 SERIAL #'d SETS
*GOLD: .5X TO 1.2X BASIC
GOLD ODDS 1:15 MINI
GOLD PRINT RUN 9 SERIAL #'d SETS
PLATINUM ODDS 1:43 MINI
PLATINUM PRINT RUN 3 SERIAL #'d SETS
NO PLATINUM PRICING DUE TO SCARCITY
1 Adam Dunn RBI 10.00 25.00
PT-PT-J
2 Adam Dunn CIN 10.00 25.00
PT-PT-PT
3 Adrian Beltre LAD 10.00 25.00
B-B-B
4 Adrian Beltre SEA 10.00 25.00
B-B-B
5 Al Kaline GOLD GLOVE 40.00 80.00
B-B-B
6 Al Kaline HOF 40.00 80.00
B-B-B
7 Al Kaline DET 40.00 80.00
B-B-B
8 Albert Pujols STL 30.00 60.00
J-PT-J
9 Albert Pujols 300 BAT AVG 30.00 60.00
J-J-J
10 Albert Pujols MVP 30.00 60.00
H-J-P
11 Albert Pujols ROY 30.00 60.00
J-J-J
12 Alex Rodriguez NYY 60.00 120.00
J-J-J
13 Alex Rodriguez #13 40.00 80.00
J-J-J
14 Alex Rodriguez MVP 50.00 100.00
J-B-J
15 Alex Rodriguez 400 50.00 100.00
B-B-J
16 Alex Rodriguez SEA 40.00 80.00
B-H-B
17 Alex Rodriguez 40/40 40.00 80.00
H-B-J
18 Alex Rodriguez TEX 50.00 100.00
PT-PT-PT
19 Alex Rodriguez GOLD GLOVE 40.00 80.00
J-PT-J
20 Alex Rodriguez MVP 50.00 100.00
J-B-J
21 Alfonso Soriano NYY 10.00 25.00
B-P-P
22 Alfonso Soriano TEX 10.00 25.00
P-B-S
23 Andruw Jones GOLD GLOVE 15.00 40.00
PT-PT-PT
24 Andruw Jones ATL 15.00 40.00
PT-J-PT
25 Andy Pettitte ACE 15.00 40.00
J-PT-J
26 Andy Pettitte HOU 15.00 40.00
J-J-J
27 Aramis Ramirez CHC 10.00 25.00
B-B-B
28 B.J. Upton MLB 10.00 25.00
B-B-B
29 Barry Bonds 40/40 40.00 80.00
B-B-B
30 Barry Bonds MVP 40.00 80.00
B-B-B
31 Barry Bonds PIT 40.00 80.00
B-B-B
32 Barry Bonds 700 40.00 80.00
ST-ST-ST
33 Barry Bonds SFG 40.00 80.00
P-B-P
34 Barry Bonds 700 40.00 80.00
P-B-P
35 Barry Bonds #25 40.00 80.00
P-B-P
36 Barry Bonds 7MVP 40.00 80.00
P-B-P
37 Barry Zito OAK 10.00 25.00
PT-P-PT
38 Barry Zito CY YOUNG 10.00 25.00
P-PT-P
39 Ben Sheets USA 10.00 25.00
B-B-B
40 Bill Mazeroski PIT 15.00 40.00
B-B-B
41 Bob Feller HOF 15.00 40.00
P-P-P
42 Bobby Abreu PHI 10.00 25.00
J-J-J
43 Bobby Cox ATL 10.00 25.00
J-P-J
44 Bobby Doerr BOS 10.00 25.00
B-B-B
45 Brad Lidge HOU 10.00 25.00
J-J-J
46 Brian Giles SDP 10.00 25.00
B-B-B
47 Brian Roberts BAL 10.00 25.00
J-B-J
48 Cal Ripken CAL 40.00 80.00
J-B-J
49 Cal Ripken MVP 40.00 80.00
J-P-BS
50 Cal Ripken BAL 40.00 80.00
J-B-P
51 Carl Yastrzemski YAZ 30.00 60.00
J-B-J
52 Carl Yastrzemski MVP 30.00 60.00
J-P-J
53 Carl Yastrzemski BOS 30.00 60.00
B-J-S
54 Carlos Beltran ROY 10.00 25.00
B-B-B
55 Carlos Beltran NYM 10.00 25.00
J-PT-J
56 Carlos Delgado RBI 10.00 25.00
B-B-B
57 Carlton Fisk BOS 15.00 40.00
P-B-P
58 Carlton Fisk HOF 15.00 40.00
P-P-P
59 Carlton Fisk CWS 15.00 40.00
P-P-P
60 Chipper Jones MVP 30.00 60.00
J-PT-J
61 Chipper Jones 300 BAT AVG 30.00 60.00
PT-PT-PT
62 Chipper Jones ATL 30.00 60.00
PT-B-PT
63 Chris Carpenter STL 15.00 40.00
J-J-J
64 Craig Biggio HBP 15.00 40.00
J-B-J
65 Craig Biggio HOU 15.00 40.00
J-P-J
66 Curt Schilling World Series 10.00 25.00
J-PT-J
67 Curt Schilling ACE 10.00 25.00
PT-J-H
68 Curt Schilling World Series 15.00 40.00
J-J-J
69 Curt Schilling BOS 15.00 40.00
J-J-J
70 Dale Murphy ATL 15.00 40.00
B-B-B
71 Darryl Strawberry NYM 10.00 25.00
J-B-J
72 Darryl Strawberry ROY 10.00 25.00
B-J-B
73 Dave Winfield GOLD GLOVE 10.00 25.00
J-PT-P
74 Dave Winfield NYY 10.00 25.00
P-J-P
75 Dave Winfield HOF 10.00 25.00
B-B-B
76 David Ortiz RBI 15.00 40.00
J-PT-J
77 David Ortiz BOS 15.00 40.00
J-J-J
78 David Ortiz MIN 10.00 25.00
B-B-B
79 Derrek Lee CHC 15.00 40.00
J-J-J
80 Don Mattingly NYY 30.00 60.00
J-B-P
81 Don Mattingly #23 30.00 60.00
J-J-J
82 Don Mattingly MVP 30.00 60.00
J-P-P
83 Dontrelle Willis ROY 10.00 25.00
PT-PT-PT
84 Dontrelle Willis FLA 10.00 25.00
PT-PT-PT
85 Duke Snider HOF 15.00 40.00
P-P-P
86 Dwight Gooden Dr.K 10.00 25.00
J-J-J
87 Dwight Gooden ROY 10.00 25.00
J-J-J
88 Eric Chavez OAK 10.00 25.00
P-P-P
89 Ernie Banks CHC 20.00 50.00
P-P-P
90 Ernie Banks 2MVP 20.00 50.00
P-B-P
91 Ernie Banks 512 20.00 50.00
P-P-P
92 Frank Robinson 586 15.00 40.00
B-B-B
93 Frank Robinson MVP 15.00 40.00
P-P-P
94 Frankie Frisch HOF 20.00 50.00
B-B-B
95 Gary Carter NYM 10.00 25.00
B-PT-B
96 Gary Sheffield NYY 10.00 25.00
B-B-B
97 Gary Sheffield RBI 10.00 25.00
B-B-B
98 George Brett KC5 40.00 80.00
PT-H-B
99 George Brett MVP 40.00 80.00
PT-PT-PT
100 Greg Maddux CHC 40.00 80.00
PT-B-PT
101 Hank Blalock TEX 10.00 25.00
J-PT-J
102 Hank Greenberg HOF 60.00 120.00
B-B-B
103 Hank Greenberg DET 60.00 120.00
B-B-B
104 Hideki Matsui NYY 40.00 80.00
J-PT-J
105 Hideki Matsui MLB 40.00 80.00
J-J-J
106 Hideki Matsui RBI 40.00 80.00
J-J-J
107 Ichiro Suzuki SEA 60.00 120.00
J-J-J
108 Ichiro Suzuki ROY 60.00 120.00
J-J-J
109 Ichiro Suzuki 262 60.00 120.00
B-B-B
110 Ivan Rodriguez GOLD GLOVE 10.00 25.00
J-J-PT
111 Ivan Rodriguez DET 10.00 25.00
J-PT-J
112 Ivan Rodriguez FLA 10.00 25.00
J-J-J
113 Ivan Rodriguez TEX 10.00 25.00
PT-PT-PT
114 Jake Peavy SDP 10.00 25.00
J-J-J
115 Javy Lopez BAL 10.00 25.00
J-J-J
116 Jeff Bagwell HOU 15.00 40.00
P-J-P
117 Jim Edmonds STL 10.00 25.00
J-PT-J
118 Jim Thome PHI 15.00 40.00
PT-P-PT
119 Joe Mauer MIN 10.00 25.00
J-J-J
120 Joe Torre STL 10.00 25.00
J-PT-J
121 Johan Santana CY YOUNG 15.00 40.00
J-J-J
122 Johan Santana MIN 15.00 40.00
J-J-J
123 Johnny Bench ROY 30.00 60.00
P-B-P
124 Johnny Bench CIN 30.00 60.00
P-P-P
125 Johnny Damon BOS 15.00 40.00
J-B-PT
126 Jon Garland World Series 10.00 25.00
P-P-P
127 Jon Garland CWS 10.00 25.00
P-P-P
128 Jorge Posada NYY 15.00 40.00
P-B-P
129 Jorge Posada RBI 15.00 40.00
P-P-P
130 Jose Canseco ROY 40.00 80.00
J-PT-P
131 Jose Reyes NYM 10.00 25.00
J-J-J
132 Juan Marichal SFG 10.00 25.00
J-J-J
133 Kerry Wood ROY 10.00 25.00
PT-J-PT
134 Kerry Wood CHC 10.00 25.00
PT-PT-PT
135 Lance Berkman MLB 10.00 25.00
J-PT-J
136 Lance Berkman HOU 10.00 25.00
PT-J-PT
137 Lloyd Waner HOF 40.00 80.00
B-B-B
138 Lloyd Waner PIT 40.00 80.00
B-B-B
139 Lou Brock HOF 15.00 40.00
B-B-B
140 Manny Ramirez RBI 15.00 40.00
J-B-J
141 Manny Ramirez BOS 15.00 40.00
J-J-J
142 Mariano Rivera NYY 30.00 60.00
J-J-J
143 Mariano Rivera SAV 30.00 60.00
J-J-J
144 Mark Buehrle CWS 10.00 25.00
P-FG-P
145 Mark Mulder OAK 10.00 25.00
PT-PT-PT
146 Mark Mulder STL 10.00 25.00
P-P-P
147 Mark Prior CHC 10.00 25.00
J-J-J
148 Mark Teixeira TEX 15.00 40.00
J-PT-J
149 Michael Young TEX 10.00 25.00
J-PT-J
150 Michael Young BAT CROWN 10.00 25.00
J-J-J
151 Mickey Mantle NYY 200.00 350.00
ST-SH-ST
152 Mickey Mantle 536 200.00 350.00
P-J-P
153 Mickey Mantle HOF 200.00 350.00
J-B-P
154 Mickey Mantle NY7 200.00 350.00
P-P-P
155 Mickey Mantle 3MVP 200.00 350.00
B-B-B
156 Miguel Cabrera FLA 15.00 40.00
J-B-J
157 Miguel Tejada #10 10.00 25.00
P-P-P
158 Miguel Tejada RBI 10.00 25.00
P-B-P
159 Miguel Tejada BAL 10.00 25.00
P-P-P
160 Miguel Tejada MVP 10.00 25.00
P-B-P
161 Mike Mussina NYY 15.00 40.00
P-P-P
162 Mike Mussina ACE 15.00 40.00
P-P-P
163 Mike Piazza LAD 40.00 80.00
H-B-H
164 Mike Piazza NYM 40.00 80.00
PT-J-PT
165 Mike Piazza #31 30.00 60.00
J-PT-J
166 Mike Schmidt 548 30.00 60.00
B-PT-H
167 Mike Schmidt HOF 30.00 60.00
H-S-B
168 Mike Schmidt MVP 30.00 60.00
PT-H-B
169 Monte Irvin HOF 15.00 40.00
B-B-B
170 Morgan Ensberg HOU 10.00 25.00
J-J-J
171 Nolan Ryan HOF 40.00 80.00
J-P-J
172 Nolan Ryan HOU 40.00 80.00
P-B-P
173 Nolan Ryan TEX 40.00 80.00
J-PT-J
174 Nolan Ryan 324 40.00 80.00
J-J-J
175 Wade Boggs WS 15.00 40.00
B-J-B
176 Ozzie Smith GOLD GLOVE 20.00 50.00
B-J-S
177 Ozzie Smith HOF 20.00 50.00
B-S-B
178 Pat Burrell PHI 10.00 25.00
B-PT-B
179 Paul Konerko WS 10.00 25.00
P-PT-P
180 Paul Konerko RBI 10.00 25.00
P-B-P
181 Paul Konerko CWS 10.00 25.00
PT-B-P
182 Paul Molitor HOF 10.00 25.00
J-PT-P
183 Pedro Martinez 3CY 15.00 40.00
PT-PT-PT
184 Pedro Martinez NYM 15.00 40.00
J-B-J
185 Pedro Martinez ACE 15.00 40.00
J-B-J
186 Randy Johnson Triple Crown 15.00 40.00
P-B-J
187 Randy Johnson 5CY 15.00 40.00
P-P-P
188 Reggie Jackson OCT 20.00 50.00
B-B-B
189 Reggie Jackson 563 20.00 50.00
B-PT-B
190 Rickey Henderson NYY 30.00 60.00
B-B-B
191 Rickey Henderson OAK 30.00 60.00
J-P-S
192 Rickey Henderson MVP 30.00 60.00
S-P-S
193 Rickey Henderson 130 30.00 60.00
J-PT-J
194 Rickie Weeks MLB 10.00 25.00
B-B-B
195 Rickie Weeks MIL 10.00 25.00
B-B-B
196 Roberto Clemente 3000 HITS 100.00 175.00
B-P-B
197 Roberto Clemente MVP 100.00 175.00
P-B-P
198 Robin Yount 2MVP 30.00 60.00
J-H-J
199 Rod Carew ROY 15.00 40.00
B-B-B
200 Roger Clemens 7CY 30.00 60.00
J-J-J
201 Roger Clemens CY YOUNG 30.00 60.00
J-J-J
202 Roger Clemens ERA 30.00 60.00
J-J-J
203 Roger Clemens HOU 30.00 60.00
J-J-J
204 Roger Clemens NYY 30.00 60.00

J-H-J
205 Roger Clemens CY 30.00 60.00
J-J-J
206 Roy Halladay CY YOUNG 10.00 25.00
J-J-J
207 Roy Oswalt 20W 10.00 25.00
J-PT-J
208 Roy Oswalt HOU 10.00 25.00
J-J-J
209 Ryne Sandberg HOF 40.00 80.00
B-B-B
210 Ryne Sandberg MVP 40.00 80.00
B-B-B
211 Sammy Sosa 500 30.00 60.00
J-J-B
212 Sammy Sosa BAL 30.00 60.00
J-J-J
213 Sammy Sosa MVP 30.00 60.00
PT-J-PT
214 Sammy Sosa CHC 30.00 60.00
J-J-J
215 Sammy Sosa 500 30.00 60.00
J-J-J
216 Scott Rolen ROY 15.00 40.00
J-B-J
217 Scott Rolen STL 15.00 40.00
J-PT-J
218 Sean Burroughs SDP 10.00 25.00
B-J-B
219 Stan Musial 3MVP 30.00 60.00
P-P-P
220 Steve Carlton PHI 10.00 25.00
P-P-P
221 Steve Carlton 4CY 10.00 25.00
P-S-P
222 Steve Carlton 329 10.00 25.00
P-P-P
223 Steve Garvey MVP 10.00 25.00
B-B-B
224 Tadahito Iguchi CWS 10.00 25.00
B-J-B
225 Ted Williams 0.406 150.00 250.00
B-B-B
226 Ted Williams 521 150.00 250.00
B-B-B
227 Tim Hudson ATL 10.00 25.00
P-P-P
228 Tim Hudson OAK 10.00 25.00
J-P-J
229 Todd Helton GOLD GLOVE 15.00 40.00
PT-PT-PT
230 Todd Helton 300 BAT AVG 15.00 40.00
PT-J-PT
231 Todd Helton COL 15.00 40.00
PT-J-PT
232 Tom Seaver 311 15.00 40.00
P-P-P
233 Tony Gwynn SDP 30.00 60.00
PT-B-PT
234 Tony Gwynn 300 BAT AVG 30.00 60.00
J-J-J
235 Tony Gwynn 3000 HITS 30.00 60.00
J-B-J
236 Torii Hunter GOLD GLOVE 10.00 25.00
J-PT-J
237 Torii Hunter MIN 10.00 25.00
PT-PT-PT
238 Travis Hafner CLE 10.00 25.00
J-J-J
239 Vladimir Guerrero MVP 20.00 50.00
B-PT-B
240 Vladimir Guerrero RBI 20.00 50.00
PT-B-PT
241 Wade Boggs 3000 HITS 15.00 40.00
B-H-S
242 Willie Stargell HOF 15.00 40.00
P-P-P
243 Willie Stargell PIT 15.00 40.00
P-B-H
244 Willie Stargell POP 15.00 40.00
P-B-P
245 Willy Taveras HOU 10.00 25.00
J-J-J

2006 Topps Triple Threads Relic Autograph

STATED ODDS 1:14 MINI
STATED PRINT RUN 18 SERIAL #'d SETS
*GOLD: .5X TO 1.2X BASIC
GOLD ODDS 1:27 MINI
GOLD PRINT RUN 9 SERIAL #'d SETS
PLATINUM ODDS 1:81 MINI
PLATINUM PRINT RUN 3 SERIAL #'d SETS
NO PLATINUM PRICING DUE TO SCARCITY
1 Albert Pujols MVP 300.00 500.00
J-P-J
2 Albert Pujols ROY 300.00 500.00
PT-PT-PT
3 Albert Pujols STL 300.00 500.00
PT-B-PT
4 Alex Rodriguez MVP 150.00 300.00
J-B-J
5 Alex Rodriguez 40/40 150.00 300.00
J-B-H
6 Alex Rodriguez MVP 150.00 300.00
PT-PT-PT
7 Derrek Lee CHC 25.00 60.00
P-B-P
8 Barry Bonds 700 250.00 400.00
B-J-J
9 Ben Sheets MIL 15.00 40.00
B-B-B
10 Ben Sheets USA 15.00 40.00
B-B-B
11 Brad Lidge HOU 15.00 40.00
J-J-J
12 Brad Lidge Pitcher-Ball 15.00 40.00
J-PT-J
13 Cal Ripken BAL 125.00 200.00
P-B-BS
14 Cal Ripken HIT 125.00 200.00
J-J-J
15 Cal Ripken MVP 125.00 200.00
J-P-J
16 Carl Yastrzemski BOS 60.00 120.00
S-B-J
17 Carl Yastrzemski MVP 60.00 120.00
J-S-J
18 Carl Yastrzemski YAZ 60.00 120.00
J-J-B
19 Chase Utley PHI 25.00 60.00
J-J-J
20 Chase Utley RBI 25.00 60.00
J-PT-J
21 C.Wang Chinese 600.00 1000.00
J-PT-J
22 Chien-Ming Wang ERA 300.00 500.00
J-J-J
23 Chien-Ming Wang NYY 300.00 500.00
J-PT-J
24 C.Wang Pitcher-Ball 300.00 500.00
J-J-J
25 Chris Carpenter CY 60.00 120.00
J-J-J
26 Chris Carpenter STL 60.00 120.00
J-PT-J
27 Clint Barmes COL 10.00 25.00
J-PT-J
28 Clint Barmes MLB 10.00 25.00
J-J-J
29 Conor Jackson 1ST 25.00 60.00
B-B-B
30 Conor Jackson ARI 25.00 60.00
B-B-B
31 David Ortiz BOS 50.00 100.00
J-PT-J
32 Don Mattingly #23 60.00 120.00
J-PT-P
33 Don Mattingly MVP 60.00 120.00
J-B-P
34 Don Mattingly NYY 60.00 120.00
J-B-J
35 Duke Snider LAD 30.00 80.00
P-P-P
36 Duke Snider World Series 30.00 80.00
P-P-P
37 Ernie Banks CHC 75.00 150.00
P-P-P
38 Frank Robinson MVP 25.00 60.00
B-B-B
39 Frank Robinson CIN 25.00 60.00
P-B-P
40 Frank Robinson Triple Crown 25.00 60.00
B-P-B
41 Garrett Atkins 3RD 10.00 25.00
B-B-B
42 Garrett Atkins COL 10.00 25.00
B-B-B
43 Derrek Lee BAT 25.00 60.00
J-J-J
44 Derrek Lee LEE 25.00 60.00
J-J-J
45 Derrek Lee OPS 25.00 60.00
J-J-J
46 J.J. Hardy MIL 40.00 80.00
B-B-B
47 J.J. Hardy SS6 40.00 80.00
B-B-B
48 Jake Peavy ERA 25.00 60.00
J-J-J
49 Jake Peavy SDP 25.00 60.00
J-PT-J
50 Jeff Francis COL 10.00 25.00
J-PT-J
51 Jeff Francis Pitcher-Ball 10.00 25.00
P-P-P
52 Joe Mauer MIN 30.00 60.00
J-J-J
53 Joe Mauer RBI 30.00 60.00
J-J-J
54 Joey Devine ATL 15.00 40.00
J-J-J
55 J.Devine Pitcher-Ball 15.00 40.00
J-J-J
56 Johan Santana CY 40.00 80.00
PT-PT-J
57 Johan Santana ERA 40.00 80.00
J-J-J
58 Johan Santana MIN 40.00 80.00
J-J-J
59 Johan Santana Strikeouts 40.00 80.00
J-J-J
60 Johnny Bench CIN 50.00 100.00
P-B-P
61 Johnny Bench MVP 50.00 100.00
P-P-P
62 Johnny Bench ROY 50.00 100.00
P-B-P
63 Johnny Damon BOS 50.00 100.00
J-J-P
64 Jonny Gomes MLB 15.00 40.00
J-PT-J
65 Jonny Gomes RBI 15.00 40.00
J-J-J
66 Jose Reyes MLB 20.00 50.00
PT-J-PT
67 Jose Reyes NYM 20.00 50.00
J-B-J
68 Justin Morneau 1ST 15.00 40.00
B-B-B
69 Justin Morneau MIN 15.00 40.00
B-B-B
70 Lou Brock 938 25.00 60.00
B-B-B
71 Lou Brock 3 Stars 25.00 60.00
B-PT-B
72 Lou Brock HOF 25.00 60.00
B-B-B
73 Lou Brock STL 25.00 60.00
PT-B-B
74 Manny Ramirez BOS 50.00 100.00
J-PT-J
75 Mariano Rivera 0.81 125.00 200.00
J-PT-J
76 Mark Prior CHC 15.00 40.00
J-PT-J
77 Miguel Cabrera #24 30.00 80.00
J-PT-J
78 Miguel Cabrera FLA 30.00 80.00
B-J-B
79 Miguel Cabrera 300 30.00 80.00
J-J-J
80 Miguel Cabrera RBI 30.00 80.00
B-J-PT
81 Mike Schmidt HOF 50.00 100.00
PT-B-H
82 Mike Schmidt MVP 50.00 100.00
B-H-S
83 Mike Schmidt PHI 50.00 100.00
PT-PT-PT
84 Morgan Ensberg 3 Stars 15.00 40.00
J-J-J
85 Morgan Ensberg HOU 15.00 40.00
J-PT-J
86 Nick Swisher OAK 15.00 40.00
B-B-B
87 Nick Swisher RBI 15.00 40.00
B-B-B
88 Nolan Ryan HOF 75.00 150.00
P-B-P
89 Nolan Ryan TEX 75.00 150.00
J-PT-J
90 Nolan Ryan 7 NO NO 75.00 150.00
J-PT-J
91 Zach Duke PIT 15.00 40.00
J-J-J
92 Zach Duke WIN 15.00 40.00
J-J-J
93 Ozzie Smith Gold Glove 50.00 100.00
B-J-S
94 Ozzie Smith HOF 50.00 100.00
B-H-P
95 Ozzie Smith STL 50.00 100.00
H-J-P
96 Pedro Martinez NYM 75.00 150.00
J-PT-J
97 Robin Yount HOF 25.00 60.00
PT-PT-PT
98 Robin Yount MIL 25.00 60.00
J-B-J
99 Robin Yount MVP 25.00 60.00
J-J-J
100 Rod Carew BAT 20.00 50.00
B-B-B
101 Rod Carew MIN 20.00 50.00
B-B-B
102 Rod Carew MVP 20.00 50.00
B-B-B
103 Rod Carew ROY 20.00 50.00
B-B-B
104 Roger Clemens CY 125.00 200.00
J-J-J
105 Roger Clemens CY 125.00 200.00
J-J-H
106 Ryan Langerhans ATL 20.00 50.00
B-B-B
107 Ryan Langerhans RBI 20.00 50.00
B-B-B
108 Ryne Sandberg CHC 50.00 100.00
B-B-B
109 Ryne Sandberg HOF 50.00 100.00
S-B-S
110 Ryne Sandberg MVP 50.00 100.00
B-B-B
111 Scott Kazmir ERA 15.00 40.00
J-PT-J
112 Scott Kazmir Pitcher-Ball 15.00 40.00
J-PT-J
113 Stan Musial 3 Stars 60.00 120.00
P-B-P
114 Stan Musial MVP 60.00 120.00
B-P-B
115 Stan Musial STL 60.00 120.00
B-P-B
116 Steve Carlton 329 15.00 40.00
P-P-P
117 Steve Carlton CY 15.00 40.00
P-P-P
118 Steve Carlton PHI 15.00 40.00
P-P-P
119 Steve Garvey LAD 20.00 50.00
B-B-B
120 Steve Garvey MVP 20.00 50.00
B-B-B
121 Tony Gwynn 300 50.00 100.00
PT-PT-PT
122 Tony Gwynn HIT 50.00 100.00
PT-PT-PT
123 Tony Gwynn SDP 50.00 100.00
J-PT-J
124 Travis Hafner CLE 25.00 60.00
J-PT-J
125 Travis Hafner RBI 25.00 60.00
J-J-J
126 Victor Martinez CLE 15.00 40.00
J-J-J
127 Victor Martinez RBI 15.00 40.00
J-J-J
128 Wade Boggs BAT 25.00 60.00
B-S-B
129 Wade Boggs BOS 25.00 60.00
B-J-H
130 Wade Boggs RBI 25.00 60.00
B-S-H

2006 Topps Triple Threads Relic Combos

STATED ODDS 1:7 MINI
STATED PRINT RUN 18 SERIAL #'d SETS
*GOLD: .5X TO 1.2X BASIC
GOLD ODDS 1:14 MINI
GOLD PRINT RUN 9 SERIAL #'d SETS
PLATINUM ODDS 1:42 MINI
PLATINUM PRINT RUN 3 SERIAL #'d SETS
NO PLATINUM PRICING DUE TO SCARCITY
1 Albert Pujols Jsy 60.00 120.00
Alex Rodriguez Patch
Barry Bonds Pants 300
2 Alex Rodriguez Jsy 60.00 120.00
Barry Bonds Jsy
Albert Pujols Jsy 300
3 Albert Pujols Pants 40.00 80.00
Alex Rodriguez Bat
Manny Ramirez Jsy 300
4 Albert Pujols Jsy 90.00 150.00
Barry Bonds Cap
Ted Williams Bat 300
5 Alex Rodriguez Bat 50.00 100.00
Barry Bonds Pants
Chipper Jones Jsy 300
6 Alex Rodriguez Jsy 60.00 120.00
Roberto Clemente Pants
Barry Bonds Pants 300
7 Alex Rodriguez Jsy 50.00 100.00
Vladimir Guerrero Cap
Ichiro Suzuki Jsy 300
8 Alex Rodriguez Bat 50.00 100.00
Stan Musial Pants
Ted Williams Bat 300
9 Andruw Jones Cap 15.00 40.00
Alfonso Soriano Cleats
Vladimir Guerrero Cap 300
10 Barry Bonds Bat 75.00 150.00
Ichiro Suzuki Jsy
Roberto Clemente Bat 300
11 Barry Bonds Bat 50.00 100.00
Lloyd Waner Bat
Roberto Clemente Bat 300
12 Barry Bonds Bat 30.00 60.00
Manny Ramirez Cleats
Andruw Jones Btg Glv 300
13 Barry Bonds Pants 50.00 100.00
Manny Ramirez Jsy
Ted Williams Bat 300
14 Barry Bonds Pants 75.00 150.00
Roberto Clemente Bat
Willie Stargell Cap 300
15 Carl Yastrzemski Cleats 30.00 60.00
Paul Molitor Cleats
Manny Ramirez Cleats 300
16 Don Mattingly Jsy 30.00 60.00
Paul Molitor Cleats
Wade Boggs Bat 300
17 Don Mattingly Jsy 30.00 60.00
Rod Carew Bat
Tony Gwynn Jsy 300
18 Gary Sheffield Pants 15.00 40.00
Vladimir Guerrero Patch
Ivan Rodriguez Patch 300
19 Hank Greenberg Bat 75.00 150.00
Stan Musial Bat
Ted Williams Bat 300
20 Ichiro Suzuki Jsy 50.00 100.00
Chipper Jones Patch
Barry Bonds Pants 300
21 Ichiro Suzuki Jsy 150.00 250.00
Ted Williams Bat
Roberto Clemente Pants 300
22 Joe Morgan Cap 15.00 40.00
Paul Molitor Cleats
Gary Carter Cap 300
23 Manny Ramirez Jsy 40.00 80.00
Vladimir Guerrero Bat
Roberto Clemente Pants 300
24 Mike Piazza Btg Glv 30.00 60.00
Paul Molitor Btg Glv
Rickey Henderson Btg Glv 300
25 Napoleon Lajoie Bat 75.00 150.00
Stan Musial Bat
Ted Williams Bat 300
26 Paul Molitor Cap 15.00 40.00
Andruw Jones Cap
Robin Yount Cap 300
27 Paul Molitor Cleats 15.00 40.00
Andruw Jones Cleats
Alfonso Soriano Cleats 300
28 Reggie Jackson Patch 20.00 50.00
Vladimir Guerrero Patch
Andruw Jones Patch 300
29 Rickey Henderson Cleats 30.00 60.00
Wade Boggs Cleats
Tony Gwynn Cleats 300
30 Roberto Clemente Bat 75.00 150.00
Ted Williams Bat
Tony Gwynn Bat 300
31 Stan Musial Bat 50.00 100.00
Ted Williams Bat
Tony Gwynn Bat 300
32 Ted Williams Bat 75.00 150.00
Ichiro Suzuki Jsy
Wade Boggs Bat 300
33 Albert Pujols Jsy 150.00 250.00
Ted Williams Bat
Mickey Mantle Jsy 300
34 Andruw Jones Cap 20.00 50.00
George Brett Cap
Chipper Jones Cap 300
35 Greg Maddux Patch 30.00 60.00
Nolan Ryan Bat
Steve Carlton Pants 300
36 Greg Maddux Patch 20.00 50.00
Steve Carlton Pants
Tom Seaver Pants 300
37 Nolan Ryan Jsy 20.00 50.00
Steve Carlton Cleats
Tom Seaver Bat 300
38 Nolan Ryan Jsy 40.00 80.00
Tom Seaver Cap
Roger Clemens Jsy 300
39 Roger Clemens Cap 40.00 80.00
Nolan Ryan Jsy
Tom Seaver Cap 300
40 Barry Bonds Bat 30.00 60.00
Rickey Henderson Cleats
Tony Gwynn Cleats 300
41 Cal Ripken Pants 40.00 80.00
Carl Yastrzemski Jsy
Paul Molitor Jsy 3000
42 Cal Ripken Pants 60.00 120.00
George Brett Bat
Roberto Clemente Pants 3000
43 Cal Ripken Pants 40.00 80.00
George Brett Bat
Tony Gwynn Cleats 3000
44 Cal Ripken Jsy 30.00 60.00
Paul Molitor Patch
Rickey Henderson Jsy 3000
45 Cal Ripken Jsy 30.00 60.00
Paul Molitor Jsy
Tony Gwynn Jsy 3000
46 George Brett Bat 40.00 80.00
Cal Ripken Pants
Rod Carew Bat 3000
47 George Brett Bat 40.00 80.00
Cal Ripken Pants
Rod Carew Patch 3000
48 George Brett Bat 20.00 50.00
Robin Yount Jsy
Rod Carew Bat 3000
49 George Brett Bat [illegible] [illegible]
Rod Carew Patch
Stan Musial Bat 3000
50 George Brett Bat 30.00 60.00
Tony Gwynn Jsy
Wade Boggs Bat 3000
51 Paul Molitor Cap 20.00 50.00
Robin Yount Jsy
Wade Boggs Jsy 3000
52 Paul Waner Bat 40.00 80.00
Rickey Henderson Cleats
Stan Musial Pants 3000
53 Paul Waner Bat 30.00 60.00
Rickey Henderson Pants
Wade Boggs Bat 3000
54 Paul Waner Bat 15.00 40.00
Rod Carew Bat
Wade Boggs Bat 3000
55 Rickey Henderson Jsy 30.00 60.00
Stan Musial Bat
Wade Boggs Bat 3000
56 Roberto Clemente Pants 50.00 100.00
Robin Yount Cap
Rod Carew Bat 3000
57 Roberto Clemente Pants 50.00 100.00
Robin Yount Cap
Tony Gwynn Cleats 3000
58 Roberto Clemente Bat 50.00 100.00
Stan Musial Bat
Tony Gwynn Bat 3000
59 Rod Carew Jsy 20.00 50.00
Stan Musial Pants
Tony Gwynn Jsy 3000
60 Stan Musial Pants 20.00 50.00
Tony Gwynn Jsy
Wade Boggs Patch 3000
61 Wade Boggs Bat 20.00 50.00
Wade Boggs Bat
Wade Boggs Bat 3000
62 Barry Bonds Bat 100.00 175.00
Mickey Mantle Bat
Frank Robinson Bat 500
63 Barry Bonds Suit 200.00 350.00
Ted Williams Bat
Mickey Mantle Suit 500
64 Barry Bonds Bat 40.00 80.00
Frank Robinson Pants
Reggie Jackson Bat 500
65 Barry Bonds Pants 30.00 60.00
Frank Robinson Bat
Harmon Killebrew Jsy 500
66 Frank Robinson Bat 40.00 80.00
Barry Bonds Pants
Mike Schmidt Jsy 500
67 Frank Robinson Bat 100.00 175.00
Harmon Killebrew Bat
Mickey Mantle Bat 500
68 Josh Gibson Model Bat 200.00 350.00
Barry Bonds Pants
Mickey Mantle Patch 500
69 Josh Gibson Model Bat 125.00 200.00
Barry Bonds Jsy
Ted Williams Bat 500
70 Mike Schmidt Bat 30.00 60.00
Harmon Killebrew Jsy
Reggie Jackson Bat 500
71 Dave Winfield Jsy 15.00 40.00
Vladimir Guerrero Bat
Reggie Jackson Jsy ANA
72 Rod Carew Bat 15.00 40.00
Reggie Jackson Jsy
Vladimir Guerrero Bat ANA
73 Andruw Jones Cleats 30.00 60.00
Chipper Jones Patch
Jeff Francoeur Jsy ATL
74 Bobby Cox Patch 20.00 50.00
Andruw Jones Cleats
Chipper Jones Jsy ATL
75 Chipper Jones Patch 40.00 80.00
Greg Maddux Patch
Andruw Jones Patch ATL
76 Brian Roberts Jsy 15.00 40.00
Sammy Sosa Jsy
Miguel Tejada Pants BAL
77 Brooks Robinson Bat 40.00 80.00
Cal Ripken Pants
Jim Palmer Cap BAL
78 Brooks Robinson Bat 15.00 40.00
Jim Palmer Jsy
Frank Robinson Bat BAL
79 Cal Ripken Pants 30.00 60.00
Brooks Robinson Bat
Miguel Tejada Pants BAL
80 Cal Ripken Pants 30.00 60.00
Frank Robinson Bat
Sammy Sosa Jsy BAL
81 Frank Robinson Bat 20.00 50.00
Reggie Jackson Jsy
Brooks Robinson Bat BAL
82 Jim Palmer Jsy 15.00 40.00
Frank Robinson Bat
Reggie Jackson Jsy BAL
83 Jim Palmer Pants 30.00 60.00
Reggie Jackson Jsy
Sammy Sosa Jsy BAL
84 Jim Palmer Pants 15.00 40.00
Sammy Sosa Bat
Miguel Tejada Pants BAL
85 Miguel Tejada Pants 30.00 60.00
Brian Roberts Jsy
Cal Ripken Pants BAL
86 Reggie Jackson Jsy 30.00 60.00
Frank Robinson Bat
Sammy Sosa Jsy BAL
87 Bobby Doerr Bat 75.00 150.00
Carl Yastrzemski Cleats
Ted Williams Bat BOS
88 Carl Yastrzemski Cleats 30.00 60.00
David Ortiz Jsy
Manny Ramirez Cleats BOS
89 Carl Yastrzemski Pants 75.00 150.00
Ted Williams Bat
David Ortiz Jsy BOS
90 Carl Yastrzemski Jsy 75.00 150.00
Ted Williams Bat
Manny Ramirez Cleats BOS
91 Curt Schilling Jsy 15.00 40.00
David Ortiz Jsy
Johnny Damon Jsy BOS
92 Curt Schilling Patch 15.00 40.00
David Ortiz Bat
Manny Ramirez Jsy BOS
93 Curt Schilling Jsy 15.00 40.00
Manny Ramirez Jsy
Johnny Damon Jsy BOS
94 David Ortiz Bat 15.00 40.00
Johnny Damon Pants
Manny Ramirez Bat BOS
95 Johnny Damon Bat 40.00 80.00
Manny Ramirez Jsy
Ted Williams Bat BOS
96 Manny Ramirez Cleats 30.00 60.00
David Ortiz Jsy
Pedro Martinez Patch BOS
97 Manny Ramirez Jsy 60.00 120.00
Ted Williams Bat
David Ortiz Jsy BOS
98 Pedro Martinez Cleats 30.00 60.00
Roger Clemens Cap
Manny Ramirez Cleats BOS
99 Greg Maddux Jsy 50.00 100.00
Randy Johnson Jsy
Roger Clemens Jsy C*Y
100 Johan Santana Jsy 20.00 50.00
Pedro Martinez Cleats
Roger Clemens Jsy C*Y
101 Roger Clemens Jsy 50.00 100.00
Roger Clemens Jsy
Roger Clemens Jsy C*Y
102 Roger Clemens Jsy 75.00 150.00
Roger Clemens Jsy
Roger Clemens Jsy C*Y
103 Randy Johnson Cap 30.00 60.00
Curt Schilling Jsy
Roger Clemens Cap World Series
104 Derrek Lee Jsy 15.00 40.00
Aramis Ramirez Bat
Mark Prior Jsy CHC
105 Derrek Lee Jsy 40.00 80.00
Ryne Sandberg Bat
Sammy Sosa Jsy CHC
106 Ernie Banks Pants 40.00 80.00
Ryne Sandberg Bat
Derrek Lee Jsy CHC
107 Ernie Banks Pants 40.00 80.00
Ryne Sandberg Bat
Sammy Sosa Jsy CHC
108 Greg Maddux Jsy 50.00 100.00
Ryne Sandberg Bat
Ernie Banks Pants CHC
109 Mark Prior Jsy 30.00 60.00
Kerry Wood Patch
Greg Maddux Jsy CHC
110 Sammy Sosa Jsy 40.00 80.00
Ernie Banks Pants
Derrek Lee Jsy CHC
111 Frank Robinson Pants 20.00 50.00
Joe Morgan Cap
Johnny Bench Pants CIN
112 Johnny Bench Pants 20.00 50.00
Frank Robinson Bat
Tom Seaver Cap CIN
113 Johnny Bench Pants 20.00 50.00
Tom Seaver Cap
Joe Morgan Jsy CIN
114 Jermaine Dye Pants 15.00 40.00
Scott Podsednik Bat
Tadahito Iguchi Jsy CWS
115 Jim Thome Bat 30.00 60.00
Paul Konerko Pants
Tadahito Iguchi Bat CWS
116 Jon Garland Pants 15.00 40.00
Scott Podsednik Bat
Mark Buehrle Pants CWS
117 Jon Garland Pants 15.00 40.00
Tadahito Iguchi Jsy
Mark Buehrle Pants CWS
118 Paul Konerko Pants 30.00 60.00
Sammy Sosa Bat
Carlton Fisk Pants CWS
119 Paul Konerko Pants 15.00 40.00
Tadahito Iguchi Jsy
Jermaine Dye Pants CWS
120 Al Kaline Bat 50.00 100.00
Ivan Rodriguez Jsy
Hank Greenberg Bat DET
121 Greg Maddux Btg Glv 30.00 60.00
Johan Santana Jsy
Roger Clemens Jsy ERA
122 Juan Marichal Jsy 30.00 60.00
Nolan Ryan Pants
Roger Clemens Pants ERA
123 Nolan Ryan Pants 30.00 60.00
Randy Johnson Jsy
Whitey Ford Bat ERA
124 Cal Ripken Jsy 40.00 80.00
Ozzie Smith Bat
Mike Schmidt Jsy Gold Glove
125 Mike Schmidt Bat 40.00 80.00
Cal Ripken Pants
Ozzie Smith Bat Gold Glove
126 Al Kaline Bat 30.00 60.00
Frank Robinson Pants
Paul Waner Bat HOF
127 Al Kaline Bat 30.00 60.00
Harmon Killebrew Pants
Frank Robinson Bat HOF
128 Al Kaline Bat 100.00 175.00
Mickey Mantle Pants
Reggie Jackson Jsy HOF
129 Al Kaline Bat 40.00 80.00
Reggie Jackson Bat
Stan Musial Bat HOF
130 Al Kaline Bat 30.00 60.00
Robin Yount Jsy
Paul Waner Bat HOF
131 Barry Bonds Pants 30.00 60.00
Chipper Jones Patch
Manny Ramirez Wristband OPS
132 Bob Feller Pants 20.00 50.00
Juan Marichal Jsy
Nolan Ryan Jsy HOF
133 Bob Feller Pants 15.00 40.00
Whitey Ford Bat
Steve Carlton Pants HOF
134 Bobby Doerr Bat 40.00 80.00
Ted Williams Bat
Wade Boggs Bat HOF
135 Brooks Robinson Bat 30.00 60.00
Ozzie Smith Bat
Ryne Sandberg Bat HOF
136 Carl Yastrzemski Cleats 30.00 60.00
George Brett Bat
Paul Molitor Cleats HOF
137 Carlton Fisk Bat 20.00 50.00
Carl Yastrzemski Jsy
Wade Boggs Bat HOF
138 Joe Morgan Cap 30.00 60.00
George Brett Cap
Mike Schmidt Cap HOF
139 Yogi Berra Glv 20.00 50.00
Carlton Fisk Bat
Gary Carter Cap HOF
140 Andy Pettitte Jsy 20.00 50.00
Nolan Ryan Pants
Brad Lidge Jsy HOU
141 Andy Pettitte Jsy 20.00 50.00
Nolan Ryan Bat
Randy Johnson Pants HOU
142 Andy Pettitte Jsy 30.00 60.00
Nolan Ryan Pants
Roger Clemens Jsy HOU
143 Andy Pettitte Jsy 15.00 40.00
Randy Johnson Pants
Brad Lidge Jsy HOU
144 Andy Pettitte Jsy 30.00 60.00
Roy Oswalt Jsy
Roger Clemens Jsy HOU
145 Brad Lidge Jsy 15.00 40.00
Roy Oswalt Jsy
Andy Pettitte Jsy HOU
146 Craig Biggio Patch 20.00 50.00
Jeff Bagwell Cap
Lance Berkman Patch HOU
147 Nolan Ryan Pants 50.00 100.00
Roger Clemens Jsy
Randy Johnson Pants HOU
148 Roger Clemens Jsy 20.00 50.00
Brad Lidge Jsy
Andy Pettitte Jsy HOU
149 Roger Clemens Jsy 20.00 50.00
Randy Johnson Pants
Andy Pettitte Jsy HOU
150 Ichiro Suzuki Jsy 100.00 175.00
Hideki Matsui Jsy
Ichiro Suzuki Jsy JPN
151 Ichiro Suzuki Bat 100.00 175.00
Hideki Matsui Jsy
Kaz Matsui Bat JPN
152 Ichiro Suzuki Jsy 100.00 175.00
Tadahito Iguchi Jsy
Hideki Matsui Jsy JPN
153 Eric Gagne Patch 20.00 50.00
Mike Piazza Bat
Duke Snider Pants LAD
154 Gary Sheffield Pants 15.00 40.00
Rickie Weeks Bat
Paul Molitor Jsy MIL
155 Paul Molitor Pants 20.00 50.00
Gary Sheffield Pants
Robin Yount Patch MIL
156 Robin Yount Bat 15.00 40.00
Paul Molitor Jsy
Rickie Weeks Bat MIL
157 Harmon Killebrew Pants 20.00 50.00
Rod Carew Bat
Johan Santana Jsy MIN
158 Harmon Killebrew Pants 20.00 50.00
Torii Hunter Jsy
Rod Carew Bat MIN
159 Johan Santana Jsy 15.00 40.00
Joe Mauer Jsy
Torii Hunter Jsy MIN
160 Paul Molitor Pants 30.00 60.00
Rod Carew Bat
Harmon Killebrew Bat MIN
161 Albert Pujols Jsy 75.00 150.00
Ichiro Suzuki Jsy
Barry Bonds Pants MVP
162 Alex Rodriguez Jsy 50.00 100.00
Barry Bonds Pants
George Brett Patch MVP
163 Alex Rodriguez Jsy 125.00 200.00
Barry Bonds Pants
Mickey Mantle Jsy MVP
164 Alex Rodriguez Jsy 150.00 250.00
Ichiro Suzuki Jsy
Mickey Mantle Jsy MVP
165 Alex Rodriguez Bat 50.00 100.00
Reggie Jackson Bat
Yogi Berra Bat MVP
166 Alex Rodriguez Jsy 175.00 300.00
Ted Williams Bat
Mickey Mantle Pants MVP
167 Alex Rodriguez Jsy 60.00 120.00
Yogi Berra Bat
Don Mattingly Pants MVP
168 Alex Rodriguez Cleats 50.00 100.00
Barry Bonds Bat
Don Mattingly Pants MVP
169 Alex Rodriguez Cleats 40.00 80.00
Cal Ripken Pants
Miguel Tejada Pants MVP
170 Barry Bonds Bat 40.00 80.00
Harmon Killebrew Jsy
Reggie Jackson Bat MVP
171 Barry Bonds Bat 75.00 150.00
Roberto Clemente Pants
Willie Stargell Bat MVP
172 Barry Bonds Pants 60.00 120.00
Alex Rodriguez Jsy
Albert Pujols Cap MVP
173 Barry Bonds Pants 75.00 150.00
Cal Ripken Jsy
Mickey Mantle Pants MVP
174 Barry Bonds Pants 75.00 150.00
Josh Gibson Model Bat
Albert Pujols Jsy MVP
175 Barry Bonds Pants 50.00 100.00
Vladimir Guerrero Bat
Ichiro Suzuki Jsy MVP
176 Brooks Robinson Bat 30.00 60.00

George Brett Bat
Mike Schmidt Bat MVP
177 Cal Ripken Bat 100.00 175.00
Barry Bonds Bat
Ichiro Suzuki Bat MVP
178 Cal Ripken Jsy 50.00 100.00
Don Mattingly Jsy
George Brett Bat MVP
179 Cal Ripken Pants 50.00 100.00
George Brett Bat
Don Mattingly Jsy MVP
180 Cal Ripken Jsy 50.00 100.00
Mike Schmidt Bat
Don Mattingly Jsy MVP
181 Cal Ripken Pants 50.00 100.00
Roger Clemens Jsy
Don Mattingly Pants MVP
182 Chipper Jones Patch 40.00 80.00
Dale Murphy Bat
Don Mattingly Pants MVP
183 Don Mattingly Jsy 125.00 200.00
Mickey Mantle Pants
Reggie Jackson Bat MVP
184 George Brett Bat 30.00 60.00
Johnny Bench Pants
Mike Schmidt Bat MVP
185 George Brett Bat 30.00 60.00
Johnny Bench Bat
Mike Schmidt Bat HIT
186 Ichiro Suzuki Bat 150.00 250.00
Barry Bonds Pants
Mickey Mantle Bat MVP
187 Ivan Rodriguez Pants 15.00 40.00
Vladimir Guerrero Bat
Miguel Tejada Pants MVP
188 Ivan Rodriguez Pants 20.00 50.00
Yogi Berra Jsy
Johnny Bench Pants MVP
189 Ivan Rodriguez Pants 20.00 50.00
Yogi Berra Fld Glv
Johnny Bench Pants MVP
190 Johnny Bench Pants 40.00 80.00
Mike Piazza Bat
Yogi Berra Pants MVP
191 Mickey Mantle Bat 200.00 350.00
Barry Bonds Pants
Ted Williams Bat MVP
192 Mickey Mantle Pants 175.00 300.00
Ichiro Suzuki Jsy
Roberto Clemente Pants MVP
193 Mickey Mantle Jsy 125.00 200.00
Roberto Clemente Pants
Stan Musial Pants MVP
194 Mickey Mantle Jsy 100.00 200.00
Ted Williams Bat
Roberto Clemente Pants MVP
195 Mickey Mantle Pants 60.00 120.00
Vladimir Guerrero Bat
Roberto Clemente Pants MVP
196 Miguel Tejada Pants 20.00 50.00
Reggie Jackson Bat
Rickey Henderson Pants MVP
197 Reggie Jackson Bat 30.00 60.00
Alex Rodriguez Jsy
Yogi Berra Bat MVP
198 Roberto Clemente Bat 125.00 200.00
Mickey Mantle Bat
Barry Bonds Bat MVP
199 Buck O'Neil Bat 150.00 250.00
Josh Gibson Model Bat
Monte Irvin Bat N*L
200 Carlos Beltran Jsy 20.00 50.00
Carlos Delgado Bat
David Wright Jsy NYM
201 Carlos Beltran Jsy 15.00 40.00
Carlos Delgado Bat
Jose Reyes Jsy NYM
202 Carlos Beltran Jsy 20.00 50.00
David Wright Jsy
Pedro Martinez Jsy NYM
203 Darryl Strawberry Bat 15.00 40.00
Dwight Gooden Jsy
Gary Carter Bat NYM
204 David Wright Jsy 40.00 80.00
Carlos Beltran Patch
Mike Piazza Jsy NYM
205 David Wright Bat 40.00 80.00
Mike Piazza Patch
Jose Reyes Bat NYM
206 Jose Reyes Jsy 15.00 40.00
Kaz Matsui Bat
David Wright Jsy NYM
207 Alex Rodriguez Jsy 150.00 250.00
Don Mattingly Jsy
Mickey Mantle Jsy NYY
208 Alex Rodriguez Jsy 50.00 100.00
Hideki Matsui Jsy
Joe Torre Pants NYY
209 Alex Rodriguez Jsy 150.00 250.00
Hideki Matsui Jsy
Mickey Mantle Pants NYY
210 Don Mattingly Jsy 75.00 150.00
Mickey Mantle Jsy
Roger Clemens Jsy NYY
211 Hideki Matsui Jsy 50.00 100.00
Gary Sheffield Bat
Alex Rodriguez Jsy NYY
212 Hideki Matsui Jsy 40.00 80.00
Gary Sheffield Bat
Jorge Posada Jsy NYY
213 Jorge Posada Jsy 30.00 60.00
Roger Clemens Jsy
Mike Mussina Pants NYY
214 Mickey Mantle Jsy 150.00 250.00
Whitey Ford Bat
Yogi Berra Fld Glv NYY
215 Mike Mussina Pants 30.00 60.00
Whitey Ford Bat
Roger Clemens Jsy NYY
216 Roger Clemens Jsy 150.00 250.00
Mickey Mantle Pants
Alex Rodriguez Jsy NYY
217 Wade Boggs Cleats 15.00 40.00
Joe Torre Pants
Alfonso Soriano Cleats NYY
218 Barry Zito Pants 15.00 40.00
Mark Mulder Patch
Tim Hudson Jsy OAK
219 Jose Canseco Jsy 20.00 50.00
Reggie Jackson Bat
Rickey Henderson Cleats OAK
220 Mark Mulder Pants 15.00 40.00
Miguel Tejada Pants
Tim Hudson Pants OAK
221 Bob Abreu Jsy 15.00 40.00
Pat Burrell Bat
Jim Thome Patch PHI
222 Curt Schilling Cap 20.00 50.00
Mike Schmidt Bat
Steve Carlton Pants PHI
223 Mike Schmidt Bat 20.00 50.00
Pat Burrell Bat
Scott Rolen Bat PHI
224 Barry Bonds Bat 100.00 175.00
Roberto Clemente Bat
Josh Gibson Model Bat PIT
225 Paul Waner Bat 75.00 150.00
Roberto Clemente Pants
Lloyd Waner Bat PIT
226 Willie Stargell Pants 60.00 120.00
Bill Mazeroski Bat
Roberto Clemente Pants PIT
227 Albert Pujols Pants 30.00 60.00
Carlos Beltran Bat
Dontrelle Willis Patch ROY
228 Albert Pujols Bat 50.00 100.00
Dontrelle Willis Patch
Ichiro Suzuki Bat ROY
229 Cal Ripken Jsy 40.00 80.00
Albert Pujols Pants
Dontrelle Willis Jsy ROY
230 Cal Ripken Jsy 30.00 60.00
Carlton Fisk Bat
Tom Seaver Pants ROY
231 Cal Ripken Pants 30.00 60.00
Rod Carew Bat
Carlton Fisk Pants ROY
232 Cal Ripken Pants 30.00 60.00
Rod Carew Bat
Carlton Fisk Pants 300
233 Jeff Bagwell Cap 30.00 60.00
Albert Pujols Bat
Mike Piazza Cap ROY
234 Mike Piazza Bat 30.00 60.00
Jeff Bagwell Pants
Scott Rolen Jsy ROY
235 Rickey Henderson Cleats 30.00 60.00
Steve Garvey Bat
Tony Gwynn Jsy SDP
236 Adrian Beltre Bat 50.00 100.00
Ichiro Suzuki Jsy
Alex Rodriguez Bat SEA
237 Ichiro Suzuki Jsy 50.00 100.00
Alex Rodriguez Bat
Randy Johnson Cap SEA
238 Barry Bonds Pants 40.00 80.00
Juan Marichal Jsy
Moises Alou Bat SFG
239 Juan Marichal Jsy 15.00 40.00
Monte Irvin Bat
Moises Alou Bat SFG
240 Moises Alou Bat 30.00 60.00
Monte Irvin Bat
Barry Bonds Jsy SFG
241 Albert Pujols Jsy 50.00 100.00
Frankie Frisch Bat
Stan Musial Pants STL
242 Albert Pujols Jsy 30.00 60.00
Mark Mulder Pants
Scott Rolen Jsy STL
243 Scott Rolen Jsy 40.00 80.00
Jim Edmonds Jsy
Albert Pujols Jsy STL
244 Stan Musial Pants 40.00 80.00
Ozzie Smith Bat
Albert Pujols Pants STL
245 Alex Rodriguez Cleats 20.00 50.00
Ivan Rodriguez Patch
Alfonso Soriano Cleats TEX
246 Alex Rodriguez Jsy 20.00 50.00
Mark Teixeira Jsy
Alfonso Soriano Pants TEX
247 Alex Rodriguez Cleats 30.00 60.00
Nolan Ryan Jsy
Alfonso Soriano Cleats TEX
248 Alfonso Soriano Pants 15.00 40.00
Hank Blalock Jsy
Mark Teixeira Jsy TEX
249 Alfonso Soriano Cleats 15.00 40.00
Hank Blalock Jsy
Michael Young Jsy TEX
250 Mark Teixeira Jsy 15.00 40.00
Alfonso Soriano Cleats
Michael Young Jsy TEX

2006 Topps Triple Threads Relic Combos Autograph

STATED ODDS 1:59 MINI
STATED PRINT RUN 18 SERIAL #'d SETS
*GOLD: .5X TO 1.2X BASIC
GOLD ODDS 1:116 MINI
GOLD PRINT RUN 9 SERIAL #'d SETS
PLATINUM ODDS 1:353 MINI
PLATINUM PRINT RUN 3 SERIAL #'d SETS
NO PLATINUM PRICING DUE TO SCARCITY
1 Albert Pujols Jsy 400.00 800.00
Barry Bonds Jsy
Alex Rodriguez Jsy MVP
2 Felix Hernandez Jsy 100.00 200.00
Alex Rodriguez Jsy
Shin-Soo Choo Jsy SEA
3 Nolan Ryan Jsy 175.00 350.00
Roger Clemens Jsy
Felix Hernandez Jsy ERA
4 Johnny Damon Bat 150.00 300.00
Alex Rodriguez Jsy
Robinson Cano Pants NYY
5 Manny Ramirez Jsy 100.00 200.00
Carl Yastrzemski Jsy
David Ortiz Jsy BOS
6 Michael Young Jsy 125.00 250.00
Cal Ripken Jsy
Ozzie Smith Cleats SS6
7 Brian Roberts Jsy 100.00 200.00
Cal Ripken Jsy
Frank Robinson Bat BAL
8 Stan Musial Pants 100.00 200.00
Ozzie Smith Bat
Lou Brock Bat HOF
9 Ozzie Smith Cleats 100.00 200.00
Stan Musial Pants
Lou Brock Bat STL
10 Tony Gwynn Jsy 100.00 200.00
Stan Musial Pants
Rod Carew Patch HOF
11 Brooks Robinson Pants 100.00 200.00
Cal Ripken Jsy
Brian Roberts Jsy BAL
12 Rod Carew Patch 60.00 120.00
Robin Yount Jsy
Paul Molitor Jsy HOF
13 Derrek Lee Jsy 100.00 200.00
Ryne Sandberg Bat
Mark Prior Jsy CHC
14 Chien-Ming Wang Jsy 125.00 250.00
Steve Carlton Pants
Dontrelle Willis Patch Pitcher
15 Brad Lidge Jsy 100.00 200.00
Mariano Rivera Jsy
Huston Street Jsy SAV
16 Morgan Ensberg Jsy 60.00 120.00
Wade Boggs Bat
David Wright Jsy 3RD
17 Ben Sheets Jsy 40.00 80.00
Steve Carlton Pants
Felix Hernandez Jsy Pitcher
18 Victor Martinez Jsy 75.00 150.00
Johnny Bench Pants
Joe Mauer Jsy RBI
19 David Wright Jsy 60.00 120.00
Mike Schmidt Bat
Aaron Hill Jsy 3RD
20 Chase Utley Jsy 150.00 300.00
Mike Schmidt Cleats
Ryan Howard Bat PHI
21 Felix Hernandez Jsy 40.00 80.00
Steve Carlton Pants
Brandon McCarthy Jsy Pitcher
22 David Wright Jsy 40.00 80.00
Miguel Cabrera Jsy
Jason Bay Jsy RBI
23 Robinson Cano Pants 200.00 400.00
Don Mattingly Jsy
Chien-Ming Wang Jsy NYY
24 Justin Morneau Bat 75.00 150.00
Don Mattingly Jsy
Travis Hafner Jsy 1ST
25 Steve Garvey Bat 50.00 100.00
Don Mattingly Jsy
Dan Johnson Jsy 1ST
26 Travis Hafner Patch 50.00 100.00
Miguel Cabrera Jsy
Jason Bay Jsy RBI
27 Ben Sheets Jsy 50.00 100.00
Johan Santana Jsy
Jake Peavy Jsy Pitcher
28 Ervin Santana Jsy 30.00 60.00
Johan Santana Jsy
Ben Sheets Bat Pitcher
29 Chris Carpenter Jsy 40.00 80.00
Johan Santana Jsy
Rich Harden Jsy Pitcher
30 Zach Duke Jsy 30.00 60.00
Johan Santana Jsy
Brandon McCarthy Jsy Pitcher

2006 Topps Triple Threads White Whale Relic

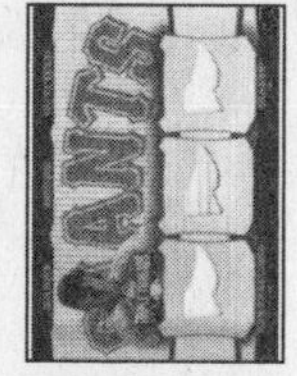

STATED ODDS 1:56 MINI
STATED PRINT RUN 1 SERIAL #'d SET
NO PRICING DUE TO SCARCITY

2006 Topps Triple Threads White Whale Relic Combos

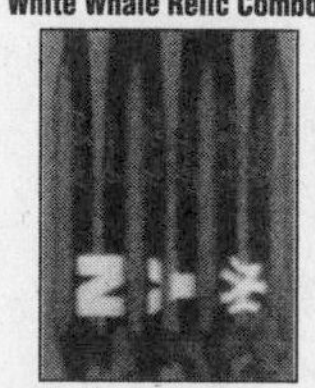

STATED ODDS 1:130 MINI
STATED PRINT RUN 1 SERIAL #'d SET
NO PRICING DUE TO SCARCITY

2006 Topps Triple Threads White Whale Autograph Relic Printing Plate

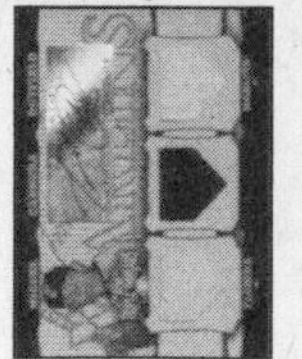

STATED ODDS 1:56 MINI
STATED PRINT RUN 1 SERIAL #'d SET
NO PRICING DUE TO SCARCITY

2006 Topps Triple Threads White Whale Autograph Relic Printing Plate Combos

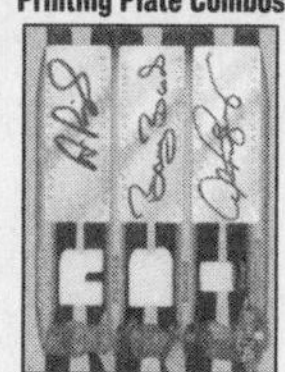

STATED ODDS 1:131 MINI
STATED PRINT RUN 1 SERIAL #'d SET
NO PRICING DUE TO SCARCITY

2007 Topps Triple Threads

This 204-card set was released in June, 2007. This set was issued in three-card mini-boxes with an $65 SRP. Those mini-boxes came two to an display box which came nine boxes to a carton and two cartons to a case. Cards numbered 1-125 feature veterans, while the rest of the set features either just game-used relic cards or game-used relic cards with an autograph as well.

COMP.SET w/o AU's (125) 125.00 200.00
COMMON CARD (1-125) .40 1.00
1-125 STATED PRINT RUN 1350 SER.#'d SETS
COMMON JSY AU 5.00 12.00
126-189 JSY AU ODDS 1:9 MINI
126-189 JSY AU VARIATION ODDS 1:38 MINI
126-189 JSY AU PRINT RUN 99 SER.#'d SETS
TEAM INITIAL DIECUTS ARE VARIATIONS
OVERALL 1-125 PLATE ODDS 1:113 MINI
PLATE PRINT RUN 1 SET PER COLOR
BLACK-CYAN-MAGENTA-YELLOW ISSUED
NO PLATE PRICING DUE TO SCARCITY
1 Alex Rodriguez 1.50 4.00
2 Barry Zito .40 1.00
3 Corey Patterson .40 1.00
4 Roberto Clemente 3.00 8.00
5 David Wright 1.50 4.00
6 Dontrelle Willis .40 1.00
7 Mickey Mantle 3.00 8.00
8 Adam Dunn .60 1.50
9 Richie Ashburn .60 1.50
10 Ryan Howard 1.50 4.00
11 Miguel Tejada .60 1.50
12 Ernie Banks 1.00 2.50
13 Ken Griffey Jr. 1.50 4.00
14 Johnny Bench 1.00 2.50
15 Ichiro Suzuki 1.50 4.00
16 Gil Meche .40 1.00
17 Kazuo Matsui .40 1.00
18 Matt Holliday 1.00 2.50
19 Juan Pierre .40 1.00
20 Yogi Berra 1.00 2.50
21 Bill Hall .40 1.00
22 Wade Boggs .60 1.50
23 Jason Bay .60 1.50
24 Troy Glaus .40 1.00
25 Paul Konerko .60 1.50
26 Rod Carew .60 1.50
27 Jay Gibbons .40 1.00
28 Frank Thomas 1.00 2.50
29 Joe Mauer 1.00 2.50
30 Carlos Beltran .60 1.50
31 Frank Robinson .40 1.00
32 Bobby Abreu .40 1.00
33 Roy Oswalt .60 1.50
34 Edgar Renteria .40 1.00
35 Magglio Ordonez .60 1.50
36 Mike Piazza 1.00 2.50
37 Trevor Hoffman .60 1.50
38 Eddie Mathews 1.00 2.50
39 Albert Pujols 2.50 6.00
40 Dennis Eckersley .40 1.00
41 Andruw Jones .40 1.00
42 Alfonso Soriano .60 1.50
43 Bob Feller .40 1.00
44 J.D. Drew .40 1.00
45 Jason Schmidt .40 1.00
46 Vladimir Guerrero 1.00 2.50
47 Reggie Jackson .60 1.50
48 Lance Berkman .60 1.50
49 Michael Young .60 1.50
50 Carlton Fisk .60 1.50
51 Brandon Webb .60 1.50
52 Adrian Beltre .40 1.00
53 Hideki Matsui 1.00 2.50
54 Bronson Arroyo .40 1.00
55 Tony Gwynn 1.00 2.50
56 Ray Durham .40 1.00
57 Garrett Atkins .40 1.00
58 Nolan Ryan 2.50 6.00
59 Daisuke Matsuzaka RC 1.50 4.00
60 Todd Helton .60 1.50
61 Carl Crawford .60 1.50
62 Jake Peavy .40 1.00
63 Rafael Furcal .40 1.00
64 Joe Morgan .40 1.00
65 Greg Maddux 1.50 4.00
66 Luis Aparicio .40 1.00
67 Derrek Lee .40 1.00
68 Johnny Damon .60 1.50
69 Mike Lowell .40 1.00
70 Roger Maris 1.00 2.50
71 Vernon Wells .40 1.00
72 Monte Irvin .40 1.00
73 Jermaine Dye .40 1.00
74 Miguel Cabrera 1.00 2.50
75 Barry Bonds 2.00 5.00
76 Stan Musial 1.50 4.00
77 Derek Lowe .40 1.00
78 Don Mattingly 2.00 5.00
79 Lyle Overbay .40 1.00
80 Chien-Ming Wang .60 1.50
81 Carlos Zambrano .60 1.50
82 Kei Igawa RC 1.00 2.50
83 Cole Hamels 1.00 2.50
84 Gary Sheffield .40 1.00
85 Nick Johnson .40 1.00
86 Brooks Robinson .60 1.50
87 Curt Schilling .60 1.50
88 Ryne Sandberg 2.00 5.00
89 Mike Cameron .40 1.00
90 Mike Schmidt 1.50 4.00
91 Chris Carpenter 1.00 2.50
92 Scott Rolen .60 1.50
93 Rocco Baldelli .40 1.00
94 C.C. Sabathia .60 1.50
95 Jeff Francis .40 1.00
96 Ozzie Smith 1.50 4.00
97 Aramis Ramirez .40 1.00
98 Aaron Harang .40 1.00
99 Duke Snider .60 1.50
100 David Ortiz .60 1.50
101 Raul Ibanez .60 1.50
102 Bruce Sutter .40 1.00
103 Gary Matthews .40 1.00
104 Chipper Jones 1.00 2.50
105 Craig Biggio .60 1.50
106 Roy Halladay 1.00 2.50
107 Hoyt Wilhelm .40 1.00
108 Manny Ramirez 1.00 2.50
109 Randy Johnson 1.00 2.50
110 Carl Yastrzemski 1.50 4.00
111 Mark Teixeira 1.00 2.50
112 Derek Jeter 2.50 6.00
113 Stephen Drew .40 1.00
114 Darryl Strawberry .40 1.00
115 Travis Hafner .40 1.00
116 Torii Hunter .40 1.00
117 Jim Edmonds .60 1.50
118 John Smoltz 1.00 2.50
119 Bo Jackson 1.00 2.50
120 Roger Clemens 1.25 3.00
121 Pedro Martinez .60 1.50
122 Rickey Henderson 1.00 2.50
123 Ivan Rodriguez .60 1.50
124 Robin Yount 1.00 2.50
125 Johan Santana 1.00 2.50
126a Robinson Cano Jsy AU 12.50 30.00
126b Robinson Cano Jsy AU 12.50 30.00
127a Jose Reyes Jsy AU 12.50 30.00
127b Jose Reyes Jsy AU 12.50 30.00
128a Justin Morneau Jsy AU 10.00 25.00
128b Justin Morneau Jsy AU 10.00 25.00
129a Curtis Granderson Jsy AU 12.50 30.00
129b Curtis Granderson Jsy AU 12.50 30.00
130a Justin Verlander Jsy AU 20.00 50.00
130b Justin Verlander Jsy AU 20.00 50.00
131 Prince Fielder Jsy AU 30.00 60.00
132a Ryan Zimmerman Jsy AU 10.00 25.00
132b Ryan Zimmerman Jsy AU 10.00 25.00
133 Mike Napoli Jsy AU 10.00 25.00
134 Melky Cabrera Jsy AU 10.00 25.00
135 Jonathan Papelbon Jsy AU 15.00 40.00
136a Nick Markakis Jsy AU 10.00 25.00
136b Nick Markakis Jsy AU 10.00 25.00
137 B.J. Upton Jsy AU 12.50 30.00
138a Joel Zumaya Jsy AU 10.00 25.00
138b Joel Zumaya Jsy AU 10.00 25.00
140 Nick Swisher Jsy AU 10.00 25.00
141 Andre Ethier Jsy AU 10.00 25.00
142a Jered Weaver Jsy AU 8.00 20.00
142b Jered Weaver Jsy AU 8.00 20.00
143 Matt Cain Jsy AU 12.50 30.00
144 Lastings Milledge Jsy AU 8.00 20.00
145 Brian McCann Jsy AU 15.00 40.00
146 Shin-Soo Choo Jsy AU 6.00 15.00
147a Dan Uggla Jsy AU 6.00 15.00
147b Dan Uggla Jsy AU 6.00 15.00
148 Hanley Ramirez Jsy AU 10.00 25.00
149 Russell Martin Jsy AU 15.00 40.00
150 Francisco Liriano Jsy AU 6.00 15.00
151 Anthony Reyes Jsy AU 5.00 12.00
152 Josh Barfield Jsy AU 6.00 15.00
153 Anibal Sanchez Jsy AU 5.00 12.00
154 Jeremy Hermida Jsy AU 5.00 12.00
155 Kendry Morales Jsy AU 5.00 12.00
156 Matt Kemp Jsy AU 12.50 30.00
157 Freddy Sanchez Jsy AU 6.00 15.00
158 Howie Kendrick Jsy AU 8.00 20.00
159 Scott Thorman Jsy AU 6.00 15.00
160 Franklin Gutierrez Bat AU 6.00 15.00
161 Jason Bartlett Jsy AU 6.00 15.00
162 Chris Duncan Jsy AU 20.00 50.00
163 Maicer Izturis Jsy AU 5.00 12.00
164 Jason Botts Jsy AU 5.00 12.00
165 Tony Gwynn Jr. Jsy AU 15.00 40.00
166 Jorge Cantu Jsy AU 5.00 12.00
167 Adam Jones Jsy AU 15.00 40.00
168 Edinson Volquez Jsy AU 40.00 80.00
169 Joey Gathright Jsy AU 5.00 12.00
170 Carlos Marmol Jsy AU 8.00 20.00
171 Ben Zobrist Jsy AU 6.00 15.00
172 Josh Willingham Jsy AU 5.00 12.00
173 Brad Thompson Jsy AU 10.00 25.00
174a Chris Ray Jsy AU 6.00 15.00
174b Ervin Santana Jsy AU 6.00 15.00
175 Ronny Paulino Jsy AU 5.00 12.00
176 Tyler Johnson Jsy AU 5.00 12.00
177 J.J. Hardy Jsy AU 12.50 30.00
178 Adrian Gonzalez Jsy AU 12.50 30.00
179 Scott Kazmir Jsy AU 6.00 15.00
180 Juan Morillo Jsy AU (RC) 5.00 12.00
181a Shawn Riggans JSY AU (RC) 5.00 12.00
181b Shawn Riggans JSY AU (RC) 5.00 12.00
182 Brian Stokes JSY AU (RC) 5.00 12.00
183 Delmon Young JSY AU (RC) 12.50 30.00
184a Troy Tulowitzki JSY AU (RC) 20.00 50.00
184b Troy Tulowitzki JSY AU (RC) 20.00 50.00
185 Adam Lind JSY AU (RC) 6.00 15.00
186 David Murphy JSY AU (RC) 6.00 15.00
187a Philip Humber JSY AU (RC) 6.00 15.00
187b Philip Humber JSY AU (RC) 6.00 15.00
188a Andrew Miller JSY AU RC 15.00 40.00
188b Andrew Miller JSY AU RC 15.00 40.00
189a Glen Perkins JSY AU (RC) 5.00 12.00
189b Glen Perkins JSY AU (RC) 5.00 12.00

2007 Topps Triple Threads Emerald

*EMERALD 1-125: .75X TO 2X BASIC
1-125 ODDS 1:2 MINI
1-125 PRINT RUN 239 SERIAL #'d SETS
*EMERALD AUTO: .5X TO 1.2X BASIC AU
*EMERALD VAR AUTO: .5X TO 1.2X BASIC AU VAR
126-189 AU ODDS 1:18 MINI
126-189 AU VARIATION ODDS 1:75 MINI
126-189 AU PRINT RUN 50 SERIAL #'d SETS
TEAM INITIAL DIECUTS ARE VARIATIONS
168 Edinson Volquez Jsy AU 75.00 150.00

2007 Topps Triple Threads Gold

*GOLD 1-125: 1.25X TO 3X BASIC
1-125 ODDS 1:5 MINI
1-125 PRINT RUN 99 SERIAL #'d SETS
*GOLD AUTO: .75X TO 2X BASIC AU
*GOLD VAR AUTO: .75X TO 2X BASIC AU VAR
126-189 AU ODDS 1:35 MINI
126-189 AU VARIATION ODDS 1:149 MINI
126-189 AU PRINT RUN 25 SERIAL #'d SETS
TEAM INITIAL DIECUTS ARE VARIATIONS
168 Edinson Volquez Jsy AU 175.00 300.00

2007 Topps Triple Threads Platinum

1-125 ODDS 1:454 MINI
1-125 PRINT RUN 1 SERIAL #'d SET
126-189 AU ODDS 1:1219 MINI
126-189 AU VARIATION ODDS 1:4878 MINI
126-189 AU PRINT RUN 1 SERIAL #'d SET
TEAM INITIAL DIECUTS ARE VARIATIONS
NO PRICING DUE TO SCARCITY

2007 Topps Triple Threads Sapphire

*SAPPHIRE 1-125: 3X TO 8X BASIC
1-125 ODDS 1:19 MINI
1-125 PRINT RUN 25 SERIAL #'d SETS
126-189 JSY AU ODDS 1:88 MINI
126-189 JSY AU VAR.ODDS 1:372 MINI
126-189 AU PRINT RUN 10 SERIAL #'d SETS
TEAM INITIAL DIECUTS ARE VARIATIONS
NO SAPPHIRE JSY AUTO PRICING AVAILABLE

2007 Topps Triple Threads Sepia

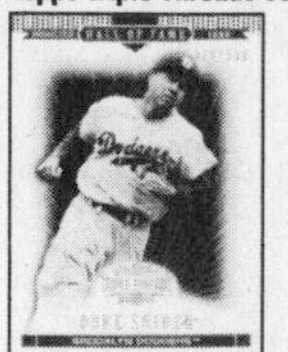

*SEPIA 1-125: .5X TO 1.2X BASIC
1-125 PRINT RUN 559 SERIAL #'d SETS
*SEPIA AUTO: .5X TO 1.2X BASIC AU
*SEPIA VAR AUTO: .5X TO 1.2X BASIC AU VAR
126-189 AU ODDS 1:12 MINI
126-189 AU VAR.ODDS 1:50 MINI
126-189 AU PRINT RUN 75 SERIAL #'d SETS
TEAM INITIAL DIECUTS ARE VARIATIONS
168 Edinson Volquez Jsy AU 40.00 80.00

2007 Topps Triple Threads White Whale Printing Plate

126-189 JSY AU ODDS 1:333 MINI
126-189 JSY AU VAR.ODDS 1:1330 MINI
STATED PRINT RUN 1 SERIAL #'d SET
TEAM INITIAL DIECUTS ARE VARIATIONS
NO PRICING DUE TO SCARCITY

2007 Topps Triple Threads All-Star Triple Patches

STATED ODDS 1:97 MINI
STATED PRINT RUN 9 SER.#'d SETS

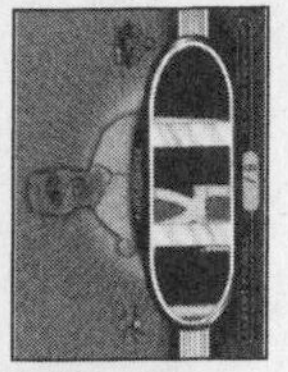

NO PRICING DUE TO SCARCITY
LOGO MAN ODDS 1:879 MINI
LOGO MAN PRINT RUN 1 SER.#'d SET
NO LOGO MAN PRICING DUE TO SCARCITY
PLATINUM ODDS 1:879 MINI
PLATINUM PRINT RUN 1 SER.#'d SET
NO PLATINUM PRICING DUE TO SCARCITY

2007 Topps Triple Threads Bat-Barrels

STATED ODDS 1:1729 MINI
STATED PRINT RUN 1 SER.#'d SET
NO PRICING DUE TO SCARCITY

2007 Topps Triple Threads Cut Above

STATED ODDS 1:10,717 MINI
STATED PRINT RUN 1 SER.#'d SET
NO PRICING DUE TO SCARCITY
JD Joe DiMaggio
MM Mickey Mantle
RC Roberto Clemente
RM Roger Maris
TW Ted Williams

2007 Topps Triple Threads Relics

STATED ODDS 1:11 MINI
STATED PRINT RUN 36 SER.#'d SETS
PLATINUM ODDS 1:373 MINI
PLATINUM PRINT RUN 1 SER.#'d SET
NO PLATINUM PRICING DUE TO SCARCITY
SAPPHIRE ODDS 1:125 MINI
SAPPHIRE PRINT RUN 3 SER.#'d SETS
NO SAPPHIRE PRICING DUE TO SCARCITY
*SEPIA: .4X TO 1X BASIC
SEPIA ODDS 1:14 MINI
SEPIA PRINT RUN 27 SER.#'d SETS
ALL DC VARIATIONS PRICED EQUALLY
1 Carl Yastrzemski 12.50 30.00
2 Carl Yastrzemski 12.50 30.00
3 Carl Yastrzemski 12.50 30.00
4 Roberto Clemente 75.00 150.00
5 Roberto Clemente 75.00 150.00
6 Roberto Clemente 75.00 150.00
7 Roberto Clemente 75.00 150.00
8 Roberto Clemente 75.00 150.00
9 Roberto Clemente 75.00 150.00
10 Alex Rodriguez 25.00 60.00
11 Alex Rodriguez 25.00 60.00
12 Alex Rodriguez 25.00 60.00
13 Alex Rodriguez 25.00 60.00
14 Alex Rodriguez 25.00 60.00
15 Alex Rodriguez 25.00 60.00
16 Ryan Howard 20.00 50.00
17 Ryan Howard 20.00 50.00
18 Ryan Howard 20.00 50.00
19 David Wright 20.00 50.00
20 David Wright 20.00 50.00
21 David Wright 20.00 50.00
22 Chien-Ming Wang 75.00 150.00
23 Chien-Ming Wang 75.00 150.00
24 Chien-Ming Wang 75.00 150.00
25 Ichiro Suzuki 60.00 120.00
26 Ichiro Suzuki 60.00 120.00
27 Ichiro Suzuki 60.00 120.00
28 Hideki Matsui 25.00 60.00
29 Hideki Matsui 25.00 60.00
30 Hideki Matsui 25.00 60.00
31 Luis Aparicio 8.00 20.00
32 Luis Aparicio 8.00 20.00
33 Luis Aparicio 8.00 20.00
34 Joe DiMaggio 50.00 100.00
35 Joe DiMaggio 50.00 100.00
36 Joe DiMaggio 50.00 100.00
37 Ted Williams 50.00 100.00
38 Ted Williams 50.00 100.00
39 Ted Williams 50.00 100.00
40 Mickey Mantle 50.00 100.00
41 Mickey Mantle 50.00 100.00
42 Mickey Mantle 50.00 100.00
43 Mickey Mantle 50.00 100.00
44 Mickey Mantle 50.00 100.00
45 Mickey Mantle 50.00 100.00
46 Mickey Mantle 50.00 100.00
47 Mickey Mantle 50.00 100.00
48 Mickey Mantle 50.00 100.00
49 David Ortiz 12.50 30.00
50 David Ortiz 12.50 30.00
51 David Ortiz 12.50 30.00
52 Albert Pujols 25.00 60.00
53 Albert Pujols 25.00 60.00
54 Albert Pujols 25.00 60.00
55 Justin Morneau 10.00 25.00
56 Justin Morneau 10.00 25.00
57 Justin Morneau 10.00 25.00
58 Nolan Ryan 25.00 60.00
59 Nolan Ryan 25.00 60.00
60 Nolan Ryan 25.00 60.00
61 Nolan Ryan 25.00 60.00
62 Nolan Ryan 25.00 60.00
63 Nolan Ryan 25.00 60.00
64 Manny Ramirez 10.00 25.00
65 Manny Ramirez 10.00 25.00
66 Manny Ramirez 10.00 25.00
67 Roger Maris 50.00 100.00

68 Roger Maris 50.00 100.00
69 Roger Maris 50.00 100.00
70 Daisuke Matsuzaka 10.00 25.00
71 Daisuke Matsuzaka 10.00 25.00
72 Daisuke Matsuzaka 10.00 25.00
73 Brian Cashman 8.00 20.00
74 Brian Cashman 8.00 20.00
75 Brian Cashman 8.00 20.00
76 Ernie Banks 20.00 50.00
77 Ernie Banks 20.00 50.00
78 Ernie Banks 20.00 50.00
79 Stan Musial 25.00 60.00
80 Stan Musial 25.00 60.00
81 Stan Musial 25.00 60.00
82 Duke Snider 12.50 30.00
83 Duke Snider 12.50 30.00
84 Duke Snider 12.50 30.00
85 Yogi Berra 20.00 50.00
86 Yogi Berra 20.00 50.00
87 Yogi Berra 20.00 50.00
88 Harmon Killebrew 15.00 40.00
89 Harmon Killebrew 15.00 40.00
90 Harmon Killebrew 15.00 40.00
91 Joe Mauer 8.00 20.00
92 Joe Mauer 8.00 20.00
93 Joe Mauer 8.00 20.00
94 Alfonso Soriano 10.00 25.00
95 Alfonso Soriano 10.00 25.00
96 Alfonso Soriano 10.00 25.00
97 Reggie Jackson 15.00 40.00
98 Reggie Jackson 15.00 40.00
99 Reggie Jackson 15.00 40.00
100 Reggie Jackson 15.00 40.00
101 Reggie Jackson 15.00 40.00
102 Reggie Jackson 15.00 40.00
103 Vladimir Guerrero 10.00 25.00
104 Vladimir Guerrero 10.00 25.00
105 Vladimir Guerrero 10.00 25.00
106 Pedro Martinez 10.00 25.00
107 Pedro Martinez 10.00 25.00
108 Pedro Martinez 10.00 25.00
109 Roger Clemens 12.50 30.00
110 Roger Clemens 12.50 30.00
111 Roger Clemens 12.50 30.00
112 Randy Johnson 10.00 25.00
113 Randy Johnson 10.00 25.00
114 Randy Johnson 10.00 25.00
115 Don Mattingly 15.00 40.00
116 Don Mattingly 15.00 40.00
117 Don Mattingly 15.00 40.00
118 Bill Dickey 20.00 50.00
119 Bill Dickey 20.00 50.00
120 Bill Dickey 20.00 50.00
121a Barry Bonds 60.00 120.00
121b Bruce Sutter 10.00 25.00
122a Barry Bonds 60.00 120.00
122b Bruce Sutter 10.00 25.00
123a Barry Bonds 60.00 120.00
123b Bruce Sutter 10.00 25.00
124 John F. Kennedy 150.00 250.00
125 John F. Kennedy 150.00 250.00
126 John F. Kennedy 150.00 250.00
127 Johnny Bench 12.50 30.00
128 Johnny Bench 12.50 30.00
129 Johnny Bench 12.50 30.00
130 Mark Teixeira 8.00 20.00
131 Mark Teixeira 8.00 20.00
132 Mark Teixeira 8.00 20.00
133 Johan Santana 15.00 40.00
134 Johan Santana 15.00 40.00
135 Johan Santana 15.00 40.00
136 Alex Rodriguez 25.00 60.00
137 Alex Rodriguez 25.00 60.00
138 Alex Rodriguez 25.00 60.00
139 Brooks Robinson 12.50 30.00
140 Brooks Robinson 12.50 30.00
141 Brooks Robinson 12.50 30.00
142 Rickey Henderson 12.50 30.00
143 Rickey Henderson 12.50 30.00
144 Rickey Henderson 12.50 30.00
145 Ozzie Smith 20.00 50.00
146 Ozzie Smith 20.00 50.00
147 Ozzie Smith 20.00 50.00
148 Chipper Jones 12.50 30.00
149 Chipper Jones 12.50 30.00
150 Chipper Jones 12.50 30.00

2007 Topps Triple Threads Relics Emerald

*EMERALD: .5X TO 1.2X BASIC
STATED ODDS 1:21 MINI
STATED PRINT RUN 18 SER.#'d SETS
ALL DC VARIATIONS PRICED EQUALLY
4 Roberto Clemente 75.00 150.00
40 Mickey Mantle 50.00 100.00
121a Barry Bonds 60.00 120.00
124 John F. Kennedy 150.00 250.00

2007 Topps Triple Threads Relics Gold

*GOLD: .6X TO 1.5X BASIC
STATED ODDS 1:42 MINI
STATED PRINT RUN 9 SER.#'d SETS
ALL DC VARIATIONS PRICED EQUALLY
4 Roberto Clemente 100.00 175.00
25 Ichiro Suzuki 150.00 300.00
79 Stan Musial 40.00 80.00
118 Bill Dickey 30.00 60.00
121a Barry Bonds 60.00 120.00
124 John F. Kennedy 150.00 250.00
145 Ozzie Smith 30.00 60.00

2007 Topps Triple Threads Relics Autographs

STATED ODDS 1:18 MINI
STATED PRINT RUN 18 SER.#'d SETS
*GOLD: .5X TO 1.2X BASIC
GOLD ODDS 1:34 MINI
GOLD PRINT RUN 9 SER.#'d SETS
PLATINUM ODDS 1:472 MINI
PLATINUM PRINT RUN 1 SER.#'d SET
NO PLATINUM PRICING DUE TO SCARCITY
SAPPHIRE ODDS 1:104 MINI
SAPPHIRE PRINT RUN 3 SER.#'d SETS
NO SAPPHIRE PRICING DUE TO SCARCITY
WHITE WHALE ODDS 1:118 MINI
WHITE WHALE PRINT RUN 1 SER.#'d SET
NO WHITE WHALE PRICING DUE TO SCARCITY
ALL DC VARIATIONS PRICED EQUALLY
1 Alex Rodriguez 125.00 250.00
2 Alex Rodriguez 125.00 250.00
3 Alex Rodriguez 125.00 250.00
4 Chien-Ming Wang 300.00 400.00
5 Chien-Ming Wang 300.00 400.00
6 Chien-Ming Wang 300.00 400.00
7 David Ortiz 50.00 100.00
8 David Ortiz 50.00 100.00
9 David Ortiz 50.00 100.00
10 Manny Ramirez 60.00 120.00
11 Manny Ramirez 60.00 120.00
12 Manny Ramirez 60.00 120.00
13 Johnny Damon 30.00 60.00
14 Johnny Damon 30.00 60.00
15 Johnny Damon 30.00 60.00
16 Miguel Tejada 20.00 50.00
17 Miguel Tejada 20.00 50.00
18 Miguel Tejada 20.00 50.00
19 Carl Crawford 20.00 50.00
20 Carl Crawford 20.00 50.00
21 Carl Crawford 20.00 50.00
22 Johan Santana 10.00 25.00
23 Johan Santana 10.00 25.00
24 Johan Santana 10.00 25.00
25 Francisco Liriano 20.00 50.00
26 Francisco Liriano 20.00 50.00
27 Francisco Liriano 20.00 50.00
28 Bob Feller 40.00 80.00
29 Bob Feller 40.00 80.00
30 Bob Feller 40.00 80.00
31 Vladimir Guerrero 40.00 80.00
32 Vladimir Guerrero 40.00 80.00
33 Vladimir Guerrero 40.00 80.00
34 Ernie Banks 100.00 200.00
35 Ernie Banks 100.00 200.00
36 Ernie Banks 100.00 200.00
37 Yogi Berra 60.00 120.00
38 Yogi Berra 60.00 120.00
39 Yogi Berra 60.00 120.00
40 Nolan Ryan 100.00 200.00
41 Nolan Ryan 100.00 200.00
42 Nolan Ryan 100.00 200.00
43 Ozzie Smith 40.00 80.00
44 Ozzie Smith 40.00 80.00
45 Ozzie Smith 40.00 80.00
46 David Wright 50.00 100.00
47 David Wright 50.00 100.00
48 David Wright 50.00 100.00
49 Albert Pujols 200.00 350.00
50 Albert Pujols 200.00 350.00
51 Albert Pujols 200.00 350.00
52 Ryan Howard 50.00 100.00
53 Ryan Howard 50.00 100.00
54 Ryan Howard 50.00 100.00
55 Don Mattingly 50.00 100.00
56 Don Mattingly 50.00 100.00
57 Don Mattingly 50.00 100.00
58 Brooks Robinson 30.00 60.00
59 Brooks Robinson 30.00 60.00
60 Brooks Robinson 30.00 60.00
61 Robin Yount 30.00 60.00
62 Robin Yount 30.00 60.00
63 Robin Yount 30.00 60.00
64 Mike Schmidt 60.00 120.00
65 Mike Schmidt 60.00 120.00
66 Mike Schmidt 60.00 120.00
67 Carl Yastrzemski 50.00 100.00
68 Carl Yastrzemski 50.00 100.00
69 Carl Yastrzemski 50.00 100.00
70 Wade Boggs 30.00 60.00
71 Wade Boggs 30.00 60.00
72 Wade Boggs 30.00 60.00
73 Andre Dawson 30.00 60.00
74 Andre Dawson 30.00 60.00
75 Andre Dawson 30.00 60.00
76 Reggie Jackson 40.00 80.00
77 Reggie Jackson 40.00 80.00
78 Reggie Jackson 40.00 80.00
79 Miguel Cabrera 30.00 60.00
80 Miguel Cabrera 30.00 60.00
81 Miguel Cabrera 30.00 60.00
82 Tom Seaver 40.00 80.00
83 Tom Seaver 40.00 80.00
84 Tom Seaver 40.00 80.00
85 Ralph Kiner 30.00 60.00
86 Ralph Kiner 30.00 60.00
87 Ralph Kiner 30.00 60.00
88 Chipper Jones 50.00 100.00
89 Chipper Jones 50.00 100.00
90 Chipper Jones 50.00 100.00
91 Andruw Jones 10.00 25.00
92 Andruw Jones 10.00 25.00
93 Andruw Jones 10.00 25.00
94 Dontrelle Willis 20.00 50.00
95 Dontrelle Willis 20.00 50.00
96 Dontrelle Willis 20.00 50.00
97 Bob Gibson 30.00 60.00
98 Bob Gibson 30.00 60.00
99 Bob Gibson 30.00 60.00
100 Johnny Bench 40.00 80.00
101 Johnny Bench 40.00 80.00
102 Johnny Bench 40.00 80.00
103 Joe Morgan 20.00 50.00
104 Joe Morgan 20.00 50.00
105 Joe Morgan 20.00 50.00
106 Ryne Sandberg 50.00 100.00
107 Ryne Sandberg 50.00 100.00
108 Ryne Sandberg 50.00 100.00
109 Dwight Gooden 20.00 50.00
110 Dwight Gooden 20.00 50.00
111 Dwight Gooden 20.00 50.00
112 Johnny Podres 20.00 50.00
113 Johnny Podres 20.00 50.00
114 Johnny Podres 20.00 50.00
115 Monte Irvin 10.00 25.00
116 Monte Irvin 10.00 25.00
117 Monte Irvin 10.00 25.00
118 Orlando Cepeda 20.00 50.00
119 Orlando Cepeda 20.00 50.00
120 Orlando Cepeda 20.00 50.00
121 Bo Jackson 60.00 120.00
122 Bo Jackson 60.00 120.00
123 Bo Jackson 60.00 120.00
124 Gary Sheffield 20.00 50.00
125 Gary Sheffield 20.00 50.00
126 Gary Sheffield 20.00 50.00
127 Tom Glavine 40.00 80.00
128 Tom Glavine 40.00 80.00
129 Tom Glavine 40.00 80.00
130 Tony LaRussa 20.00 50.00
131 Tony LaRussa 20.00 50.00
132 Tony LaRussa 20.00 50.00
133 Jim Leyland 20.00 50.00
134 Jim Leyland 20.00 50.00
135 Jim Leyland 20.00 50.00
136 Joe Torre 40.00 80.00
137 Joe Torre 40.00 80.00
138 Joe Torre 40.00 80.00
139 Gary Carter 30.00 60.00
140 Gary Carter 30.00 60.00
141 Gary Carter 30.00 60.00
142 Roy Oswalt 20.00 50.00
143 Roy Oswalt 20.00 50.00
144 Roy Oswalt 20.00 50.00
145 Carlos Delgado 20.00 50.00
146 Carlos Delgado 20.00 50.00
147 Carlos Delgado 20.00 50.00
148 Jason Varitek 40.00 80.00
149 Jason Varitek 40.00 80.00
150 Jason Varitek 40.00 80.00
151 Bobby Abreu 20.00 50.00
152 Bobby Abreu 20.00 50.00
153 Bobby Abreu 20.00 50.00
154 Juan Marichal 20.00 50.00
155 Juan Marichal 20.00 50.00
156 Juan Marichal 20.00 50.00
157 Frank Robinson 30.00 60.00
158 Frank Robinson 30.00 60.00
159 Frank Robinson 30.00 60.00
160 Jorge Posada 50.00 100.00
161 Jorge Posada 50.00 100.00
162 Jorge Posada 50.00 100.00
163 Luis Aparicio 20.00 50.00
164 Luis Aparicio 20.00 50.00
165 Luis Aparicio 20.00 50.00
166 Carlton Fisk 30.00 60.00
167 Carlton Fisk 30.00 60.00
168 Carlton Fisk 30.00 60.00
169 Dale Murphy 75.00 150.00
170 Dale Murphy 75.00 150.00
171 Dale Murphy 75.00 150.00
172 Mark Teixeira 30.00 60.00
173 Mark Teixeira 30.00 60.00
174 Mark Teixeira 30.00 60.00
175 Darryl Strawberry 20.00 50.00
176 Darryl Strawberry 20.00 50.00
177 Darryl Strawberry 20.00 50.00
178 Justin Morneau 30.00 60.00
179 Justin Morneau 30.00 60.00
180 Justin Morneau 30.00 60.00

2007 Topps Triple Threads Relics Autographs Gold

*GOLD: .5X TO 1.2X BASIC
STATED ODDS 1:34 MINI
STATED PRINT RUN 9 SER.#'d SETS
ALL DC VARIATIONS PRICED EQUALLY
34 Ernie Banks 100.00 200.00
37 Yogi Berra 60.00 120.00
49 Albert Pujols 250.00 350.00
52 Ryan Howard 100.00 150.00
88 Chipper Jones 75.00 150.00
121 Bo Jackson 150.00 250.00

2007 Topps Triple Threads Relics Combos

STATED ODDS 1:16 MINI
STATED PRINT RUN 36 SER.#'d SETS
*EMERALD: .5X TO 1.2X BASIC
EMERALD ODDS 1:31 MINI
EMERALD PRINT RUN 18 SER.#'d SETS
GOLD ODDS 1:62 MINI
GOLD PRINT RUN 9 SER.#'d SETS
NO GOLD PRICING DUE TO SCARCITY
PLATINUM ODDS 1:558 MINI
PLATINUM PRINT RUN 1 SER.#'d SET
NO PLATINUM PRICING DUE TO SCARCITY
SAPPHIRE ODDS 1:186 MINI
SAPPHIRE PRINT RUN 3 SER.#'d SETS
NO SAPPHIRE PRICING DUE TO SCARCITY
*SEPIA: .4X TO 1X BASIC
SEPIA ODDS 1:21 MINI
SEPIA PRINT RUN 27 SER.#'d SETS
WHITE WHALE RANDOMLY INSERTED
WHITE WHALE PRINT RUN 1 SER.#'d SET
NO WHITE WHALE PRICING DUE TO SCARCITY
1 Albert Pujols 20.00 50.00
Manny Ramirez
David Ortiz
2 Albert Pujols 20.00 50.00
Pedro Martinez
Vladimir Guerrero
3 Ivan Rodriguez 30.00 60.00
Carlos Delgado
Roberto Clemente
4 Roberto Clemente 30.00 60.00
Bernie Williams
Carlos Beltran
5 Jose Reyes 8.00 20.00
Alfonso Soriano
Miguel Tejada
6 Carl Crawford 8.00 20.00
Jose Reyes
Juan Pierre
7 Hideki Matsui 40.00 80.00
Ichiro
So Taguchi
8 Miguel Cabrera 12.50 30.00
Johan Santana
Bobby Abreu
9 Alex Rodriguez 30.00 60.00
Mariano Rivera
Hideki Matsui
10 Reggie Jackson 30.00 60.00
Alex Rodriguez
Don Mattingly
11 Yogi Berra 30.00 60.00
Don Mattingly
Reggie Jackson
12 David Ortiz 12.50 30.00
Wade Boggs
Manny Ramirez
13 David Ortiz 12.50 30.00
Manny Ramirez
Pedro Martinez
14 Miguel Tejada 10.00 25.00
Eddie Murray
Brooks Robinson
15 Joe Mauer 15.00 40.00
Justin Morneau
Johan Santana
16 Harmon Killebrew 20.00 50.00
Joe Mauer
Justin Morneau
17 Justin Verlander 12.50 30.00
Ivan Rodriguez
Joel Zumaya
18 Barry Zito 8.00 20.00
Dennis Eckersley
Huston Street
19 Reggie Jackson 10.00 25.00
Rod Carew
Vladimir Guerrero
20 Vladimir Guerrero 12.50 30.00
Pedro Martinez
Moises Alou
21 Michael Young 12.50 30.00
Mark Teixeira
Alex Rodriguez
22 Edgar Martinez 30.00 60.00
Ichiro
Alex Rodriguez
23 David Wright 12.50 30.00
Carlos Delgado
Jose Reyes
24 Jose Reyes 15.00 40.00
Pedro Martinez
David Wright
25 Jose Reyes 15.00 40.00
Carlos Beltran
David Wright
26 Ryan Howard 30.00 60.00
Chase Utley
Jimmy Rollins
27 Jeff Francoeur 15.00 40.00
Chipper Jones
Brian McCann
28 John Smoltz 20.00 50.00
Tom Glavine
Greg Maddux
29 Chipper Jones 15.00 40.00
Jeff Francoeur
Andruw Jones
30 Nolan Ryan 20.00 50.00
Pedro Martinez
Tom Seaver
31 Mike Schmidt 15.00 40.00
Jim Thome
Ryan Howard
32 Stan Musial 30.00 60.00
Albert Pujols
Ozzie Smith
33 Albert Pujols 15.00 40.00
David Eckstein
Jim Edmonds
34 Lance Berkman 12.50 30.00
Roy Oswalt
Craig Biggio
35 Roger Clemens 15.00 40.00
Roy Oswalt
Nolan Ryan
36 Frank Robinson 20.00 50.00
Joe Morgan
Johnny Bench
37 Paul Molitor 15.00 40.00
Prince Fielder
Robin Yount
38 Ernie Banks 20.00 50.00
Alfonso Soriano
Ryne Sandberg
39 Andre Ethier 8.00 20.00
Matt Kemp
Jered Weaver
40 Chien-Ming Wang 50.00 100.00
Alex Rodriguez
Mariano Rivera
41 Albert Pujols 20.00 50.00
Ichiro
Vladimir Guerrero
42 Albert Pujols 40.00 80.00
Alex Rodriguez
Ichiro
43 Ryan Howard 15.00 40.00
Justin Morneau
Albert Pujols
44 Albert Pujols 50.00 100.00
Roberto Clemente
Ichiro
45 Albert Pujols 100.00 200.00
Roberto Clemente
Mickey Mantle
46 Joe DiMaggio 100.00 150.00
Mickey Mantle
Alex Rodriguez
47 Ted Williams 150.00 250.00
Joe DiMaggio
Mickey Mantle
48 Roberto Clemente 75.00 150.00
Mickey Mantle
Reggie Jackson
49 Stan Musial 50.00 100.00
Roberto Clemente
Frank Robinson
50 Albert Pujols 60.00 120.00
Johnny Bench
Mickey Mantle
51 Carl Yastrzemski 100.00 150.00
Ted Williams
Mickey Mantle
52 Brandon Webb 12.50 30.00
Tom Seaver
Johan Santana
53 Roger Clemens 15.00 40.00
Dwight Gooden
Pedro Martinez
54 Johan Santana 12.50 30.00
Greg Maddux
Roger Clemens
55 Johan Santana 12.50 30.00
Pedro Martinez
Roger Clemens
56 Randy Johnson 12.50 30.00
Roger Clemens
Tom Glavine
57 Justin Verlander 20.00 50.00
Ryan Howard
Ichiro
58 Dontrelle Willis 8.00 20.00
Carlos Beltran
Jason Bay
59 Albert Pujols 20.00 50.00
Scott Rolen
Ryan Howard
60 Roberto Clemente 125.00 200.00
Joe DiMaggio
Mickey Mantle
61 Stan Musial 60.00 120.00
Ernie Banks
Mickey Mantle
62 Mike Schmidt 15.00 40.00
Joe Morgan
Johnny Bench
63 George Brett 30.00 60.00
Robin Yount
Ozzie Smith
64 Albert Pujols 30.00 60.00
Ichiro
Rod Carew
65 Alfonso Soriano 60.00 120.00
Mickey Mantle
Alex Rodriguez
66 Don Mattingly 20.00 50.00
Wade Boggs
Tony Gwynn
67 Rod Carew 10.00 25.00
Vladimir Guerrero
Garret Anderson
68 Tony Gwynn 20.00 50.00
Wade Boggs
George Brett
69 Vladimir Guerrero 15.00 40.00
Alfonso Soriano
Bobby Abreu
70 Darryl Strawberry 12.50 30.00
Carlos Beltran
Howard Johnson
71 Jim Thome 12.50 30.00
Manny Ramirez
Frank Thomas
72 Mickey Mantle 60.00 120.00
Mike Piazza
Mike Schmidt
73 Carl Yastrzemski 20.00 50.00
Alex Rodriguez
Dave Winfield
74 Johan Santana 12.50 30.00
Pedro Martinez
Roger Clemens
75 Greg Maddux 30.00 60.00
Nolan Ryan
Tom Seaver
76 Bob Gibson 20.00 50.00
Dwight Gooden
Greg Maddux
77 Roberto Clemente 30.00 60.00
Reggie Jackson
Manny Ramirez
78 Johnny Podres 10.00 25.00
Don Larsen
Lew Burdette
79 Ichiro 30.00 60.00
Kenji Johjima
Tadahito Iguchi
80 Paul Molitor 10.00 25.00
Jimmy Rollins
Chase Utley
81 Gary Carter 30.00 60.00
Paul Lo Duca
Mike Piazza
82 George Brett 30.00 60.00
Alex Rodriguez
David Wright
83 Hoyt Wilhelm 20.00 50.00
Phil Niekro
Tim Wakefield
84 Franklin D. Roosevelt 40.00 80.00
Harry S. Truman
Dwight D. Eisenhower
85 Ichiro 20.00 50.00
Eric Chavez
Torii Hunter
86 Richard Nixon 60.00 120.00
Ronald Reagan
George W. Bush
87 John Smoltz 8.00 20.00
Carlos Delgado
Edgar Martinez
88 Manny Ramirez 12.50 30.00
Vladimir Guerrero
David Ortiz
89 Livan Hernandez 10.00 25.00
Orel Hershiser
Willie Stargell
90 David Ortiz 15.00 40.00
Ryan Howard
Albert Pujols
91 Chien-Ming Wang 40.00 80.00
Johan Santana
Jon Garland
92 Deion Sanders 15.00 40.00
Bo Jackson
Brian Jordan
93 Franklin D. Roosevelt 75.00 150.00
John F. Kennedy
Bill Clinton
94 Vladimir Guerrero 30.00 60.00
Ichiro
Vernon Wells
95 Jim Thome 10.00 25.00
Jermaine Dye
Paul Konerko
96 A.J. Pierzynski 8.00 20.00
Kelvim Escobar
Josh Paul
97 Joe Carter 15.00 40.00
Rickey Henderson
Paul Molitor
98 Kirk Gibson 8.00 20.00
Dennis Eckersley
99 Luis Castillo 8.00 20.00
Moises Alou
Mark Prior
100 Mookie Wilson 20.00 50.00
Ray Knight
Bill Buckner

2007 Topps Triple Threads Relics Combos Autographs

STATED ODDS 1:94 MINI
STATED PRINT RUN 36 SER.#'d SETS
EMERALD: .5X TO 1.2X BASIC
EMERALD ODDS 1:185 MINI
EMERALD PRINT RUN 18 SER.#'d SETS
GOLD ODDS 1:371 MINI
GOLD PRINT RUN 9 SER.#'d SETS
NO GOLD PRICING DUE TO SCARCITY
PLATINUM ODDS 1:2996 MINI
PLATINUM PRINT RUN 1 SER.#'d SET
NO PLATINUM PRICING DUE TO SCARCITY
SAPPHIRE ODDS 1:1145 MINI
SAPPHIRE PRINT RUN 3 SER.#'d SETS
NO SAPPHIRE PRICING DUE TO SCARCITY
*SEPIA: .4X TO 1X BASIC
SEPIA ODDS 1:129 MINI
SEPIA PRINT RUN 27 SER.#'d SETS
WHITE WHALE ODDS 1:1219 MINI
WHITE WHALE PRINT RUN 1 SER.#'d SET
NO WHITE WHALE PRICING DUE TO SCARCITY
1 Brooks Robinson 60.00 120.00
Robin Yount
Johnny Bench
2 Reggie Jackson 60.00 120.00
Joe Morgan
Ryne Sandberg
3 Tom Seaver 125.00 200.00
Bob Gibson
Nolan Ryan
4 Albert Pujols 175.00 350.00
Alex Rodriguez
Vladimir Guerrero
5 Tom Seaver 75.00 150.00
Roger Clemens
Dwight Gooden
6 Johan Santana 150.00 250.00
Tom Glavine
Roger Clemens
7 Alex Rodriguez 150.00 300.00
Chien-Ming Wang
Don Mattingly
8 Ryan Howard 75.00 150.00
Mike Schmidt
Bobby Abreu
9 Ryan Howard 200.00 300.00
David Ortiz
Albert Pujols
10 Alex Rodriguez 125.00 250.00
David Wright
Jose Reyes
11 Miguel Cabrera 60.00 120.00
Manny Ramirez
David Ortiz
12 Justin Verlander 150.00 300.00
Jered Weaver
Chien-Ming Wang
13 Ralph Kiner 60.00 120.00
Duke Snider
Yogi Berra
14 Ryan Howard 100.00 200.00
Alex Rodriguez
Andruw Jones
15 Adam Lind 12.50 30.00
Brian Stokes
David Murphy
16 Andrew Miller 15.00 40.00
Brian Stokes
Glen Perkins
17 Shawn Riggans 20.00 50.00
Troy Tulowitzki
Andrew Miller
18 Glen Perkins 20.00 50.00
Lastings Milledge
Troy Tulowitzki

2007 Topps Triple Threads Relics Combos Double

STATED ODDS 1:31 MINI
STATED PRINT RUN 36 SER.#'d SETS
*EMERALD: .4X TO 1X BASIC
EMERALD ODDS 1:62 MINI
EMERALD PRINT RUN 18 SER.#'d SETS
GOLD ODDS 1:125 MINI
PLATINUM ODDS 1:1140 MINI
PLATINUM PRINT RUN 1 SER.#'d SET
GOLD PRINT RUN 9 SER.#'d SETS
NO GOLD PRICING DUE TO SCARCITY
NO PLATINUM PRICING DUE TO SCARCITY
SAPPHIRE ODDS 1:372 MINI
SAPPHIRE PRINT RUN 3 SER.#'d SETS
NO SAPPHIRE PRICING DUE TO SCARCITY
*SEPIA: .4X TO 1X BASIC
SEPIA ODDS 1:42 MINI
SEPIA PRINT RUN 27 SER.#'d SETS
1 Mickey Mantle 200.00 300.00
Joe DiMaggio
2 Alex Rodriguez 125.00 175.00
Chien-Ming Wang
Johnny Damon
Manny Ramirez
David Ortiz
Jason Varitek
3 David Wright 30.00 60.00
Carlos Beltran
Tom Glavine
Chipper Jones
Andruw Jones
John Smoltz
4 David Wright 30.00 60.00
5 Albert Pujols 50.00 100.00
6 Chien-Ming Wang 100.00 200.00
7 David Wright 30.00 60.00
Ryan Howard
8 Alex Rodriguez 50.00 100.00
9 Ryan Howard 40.00 80.00
10 Ichiro Suzuki 75.00 150.00
11 Albert Pujols 30.00 60.00
Pedro Martinez
David Ortiz
Vladimir Guerrero
Manny Ramirez
Alfonso Soriano
12 Ichiro 100.00 200.00
So Taguchi
Hideki Matsui
Kazuo Matsui
Tadahito Iguchi
Kenji Johjima
13 Roberto Clemente 75.00 150.00
Ivan Rodriguez
Carlos Beltran
Bernie Williams
Carlos Delgado
Javy Lopez
14 Johan Santana 40.00 80.00
Miguel Cabrera
Bobby Abreu
Omar Vizquel
Ozzie Guillen
Luis Aparicio
15 Mickey Mantle 250.00 500.00
Joe DiMaggio
Ted Williams
Ernie Banks
Yogi Berra
Stan Musial
16 Mickey Mantle 250.00 350.00
Albert Pujols
Vladimir Guerrero
Roberto Clemente
Joe DiMaggio
Ted Williams
17 Mickey Mantle 200.00 300.00
Alex Rodriguez
Don Mattingly
Yogi Berra
Chien-Ming Wang
Reggie Jackson
18 Carl Yastrzemski 40.00 80.00
Manny Ramirez
David Ortiz
Pedro Martinez
Johnny Damon
Carlton Fisk
19 Justin Morneau 50.00 100.00
Torii Hunter
Joe Mauer
Johan Santana
Francisco Liriano
Harmon Killebrew
20 Justin Verlander 50.00 100.00
Joel Zumaya
Curtis Granderson
Magglio Ordonez
Ivan Rodriguez
Kenny Rogers
21 Nick Swisher 60.00 120.00
Huston Street
Reggie Jackson
Barry Zito
Jose Canseco

Dennis Eckersley
22 Vladimir Guerrero 20.00 50.00
Rod Carew
Jered Weaver
Reggie Jackson
Garret Anderson
Francisco Rodriguez
23 Vladimir Guerrero 30.00 60.00
Pedro Martinez
Moises Alou
Gary Carter
Andre Dawson
Randy Johnson
24 Nolan Ryan 50.00 100.00
Mark Teixeira
Michael Young
Alex Rodriguez
Ivan Rodriguez
Hank Blalock
25 Kenji Johjima 60.00 120.00
Ichiro
Alex Rodriguez
Randy Johnson
Edgar Martinez
Richie Sexson
26 David Wright 60.00 120.00
Jose Reyes
Carlos Beltran
Pedro Martinez
Tom Glavine
Carlos Delgado
27 David Eckstein 50.00 100.00
Albert Pujols
Chris Carpenter
Stan Musial
Ozzie Smith
Jim Edmonds
28 Nolan Ryan 100.00 200.00
Andy Pettitte
Roger Clemens
Roy Oswalt
Lance Berkman
Craig Biggio
29 Ryan Howard 125.00 175.00
Chase Utley
Mike Schmidt
Jimmy Rollins
Richie Ashburn
Steve Carlton
30 Jeff Francoeur 60.00 120.00
Brian McCann
Chipper Jones
Andruw Jones
John Smoltz
Tim Hudson
31 Alfonso Soriano 40.00 80.00
Ernie Banks
Ryne Sandberg
Kerry Wood
Mark Prior
Andre Dawson
32 David Wright 40.00 80.00
Justin Morneau
Ryan Howard
Chien-Ming Wang
Chase Utley
Jose Reyes
33 David Ortiz 30.00 60.00
34 Roger Maris 125.00 175.00
Stan Musial
Roberto Clemente
Ernie Banks
Johnny Bench
Carl Yastrzemski
35 Albert Pujols 50.00 100.00
Jim Edmonds
Scott Rolen
Ivan Rodriguez
Kenny Rogers
Magglio Ordonez
36 Derrek Lee 40.00 80.00
Juan Pierre
Greg Maddux
Paul Konerko
Jermaine Dye
Jim Thome
37 David Wright 12.50 30.00
Paul Lo Duca
Jose Reyes
Alex Rodriguez
Jason Giambi
Johnny Damon
38 Joe Mauer 30.00 60.00
Freddy Sanchez
Robinson Cano
Miguel Cabrera
Albert Pujols
Miguel Tejada
39 Ryan Howard 40.00 80.00
David Ortiz
Albert Pujols
Alfonso Soriano
Lance Berkman
Jermaine Dye
40 Ryan Howard 40.00 80.00
Albert Pujols
David Ortiz
Lance Berkman
Justin Morneau
Andruw Jones
41 Johan Santana 30.00 60.00
Roy Oswalt
Chris Carpenter
Brandon Webb
Roy Halladay
C.C. Sabathia
42 Chien-Ming Wang 50.00 100.00
Johan Santana
Jon Garland
Randy Johnson
Kenny Rogers
Freddy Garcia
43 Johan Santana 30.00 60.00
Aaron Harang
Jake Peavy
John Smoltz
Carlos Zambrano
Jeremy Bonderman
44 Jeff Suppan 30.00 60.00
Roy Oswalt
Albert Pujols
Placido Polanco
Paul Konerko
David Ortiz
45 Orlando Cepeda 50.00 100.00
Monte Irvin
Bobby Thomson
Duke Snider
Johnny Podres
Don Zimmer
46 Ryne Sandberg 40.00 80.00
Wade Boggs
Dennis Eckersley
Paul Molitor
Gary Carter
Eddie Murray
47 Jermaine Dye 30.00 60.00
Paul Konerko
A.J. Pierzynski
Craig Biggio
Lance Berkman
Morgan Ensberg
48 Roger Clemens 40.00 80.00
Randy Johnson
Greg Maddux
Curt Schilling
Pedro Martinez
John Smoltz
49 David Wright 125.00 175.00
Brooks Robinson
George Brett
Mike Schmidt
Alex Rodriguez
Eddie Mathews
50 Alfonso Soriano 40.00 80.00
Bobby Abreu
Carlos Beltran
Vladimir Guerrero
Alex Rodriguez
Preston Wilson

2007 Topps Triple Threads Triple Signed Hide

STATED ODDS 1:13,396 MINI
STATED PRINT RUN 1 SER.#'d SET
NO PRICING DUE TO SCARCITY
MPR Mickey Mantle
Albert Pujols
Alex Rodriguez
MRW Mickey Mantle
Alex Rodriguez
David Wright
RWP Alex Rodriguez
David Wright
Albert Pujols
WRO Ted Williams
Manny Ramirez
David Ortiz

2008 Topps Triple Threads

COMMON CARD (1-145) .40 1.00
1-145 PRINT RUN 1350 SER.#'d SETS
COMMON JSY AU RC (146-170) 4.00 10.00
JSY AU RC ODDS 1:11 MINI
JSY AU RC VAR.ODDS 1:20 MINI
JSY AU RC PRINT RUN 99 SER.#'d SETS
TEAM INITIAL DIECUTS ARE VARIATIONS
COMMON JSY AU (171-220) 4.00 10.00
JSY AU ODDS 1:11 MINI
JSY AU VAR.ODDS 1:20 MINI
JSY AU PRINT RUN 99 SER.#'d SETS
TEAM INITIAL DIECUTS ARE VARIATIONS
COMMON CARD (221-251) .40 1.00
221-251 PRINT RUN 1350 SER.#'d SETS
COMMON ROOKIE (221-251) .40 1.00
221-251 RC PRINT RUN 1350 SER.#'d SETS
OVERALL 1-145 PLATE ODDS 1:116 MINI
OVERALL 221-251 PLATE ODDS 1:116 MINI
PLATE PRINT RUN 1 SET PER COLOR
BLACK-CYAN-MAGENTA-YELLOW ISSUED
NO PLATE PRICING DUE TO SCARCITY
1 David Wright 1.25 3.00
2 Nolan Ryan 3.00 8.00
3 Johnny Damon .60 1.50
4 Joe Mauer 1.00 2.50
5 Francisco Rodriguez .60 1.50
6 Carlos Beltran .40 1.00
7 Mickey Mantle 3.00 8.00
8 Brian Roberts .40 1.00
9 Lou Gehrig 2.00 5.00
10 Babe Ruth 2.50 6.00
11 Ryne Sandberg 2.00 5.00
12 Bob Gibson .60 1.50
13 Greg Maddux 1.25 3.00
14 Jered Weaver .40 1.00
15 Johnny Bench 1.00 2.50
16 Magglio Ordonez .60 1.50
17 Carl Yastrzemski 1.50 4.00
18 Derek Jeter 2.50 6.00
19 Gil Meche .40 1.00
20 Hanley Ramirez 1.00 2.50
21 Edgar Martinez .60 1.50
22 Steve Carlton .40 1.00
23 C.C. Sabathia .60 1.50
24 Chase Utley 1.00 2.50
25 Francisco Cordero .40 1.00
26 Mark Ellis .40 1.00
27 Jeff Kent .40 1.00
28 Brian Fuentes .40 1.00
29 Johan Santana 1.00 2.50
30 Ichiro 1.50 4.00
31 Ken Griffey Jr. 1.50 4.00
32 Steve Garvey .40 1.00
33 Rafael Furcal .40 1.00
34 Chipper Jones 1.00 2.50
35 Roberto Clemente 2.00 5.00
36 Rich Harden .40 1.00
37 Cy Young 1.00 2.50
38 Albert Pujols 2.50 6.00
39 Dontrelle Willis .40 1.00
40 Mark Teixeira 1.00 2.50
41 Daisuke Matsuzaka 1.00 2.50
42 Harmon Killebrew 1.00 2.50
43 Darryl Strawberry .40 1.00
44 Eric Chavez .40 1.00
45 Don Larsen .40 1.00
46 Huston Street .40 1.00
47 Jake Peavy .40 1.00
48 Prince Fielder .60 1.50
49 Garret Anderson .40 1.00
50 Matt Holliday 1.00 2.50
51 Travis Buck .40 1.00
52 Ben Sheets .40 1.00
53 George Brett 2.00 5.00
54 Dmitri Young .40 1.00
55 Phil Rizzuto .60 1.50
56 Jimmy Rollins .60 1.50
57 Manny Ramirez 1.00 2.50
58 Ozzie Smith 1.50 4.00
59 Dale Murphy .60 1.50
60 Bobby Crosby .40 1.00
61 Trevor Hoffman .60 1.50
62 Chien-Ming Wang .60 1.50
63 Jose Reyes .60 1.50
64 Vladimir Guerrero 1.00 2.50
65 Vida Blue .40 1.00
66 Rod Carew .60 1.50
67 Aaron Rowand .40 1.00
68 Hong-Chih Kuo .40 1.00
69 Mike Schmidt 1.50 4.00
70 Rogers Hornsby .60 1.50
71 Alex Rodriguez 1.50 4.00
72 Roger Maris 1.00 2.50
73 Travis Hafner .40 1.00
74 Tom Glavine .60 1.50
75 Pat Burrell .40 1.00
76 Pedro Martinez .60 1.50
77 Joba Chamberlain .60 1.50
78 Jason Varitek 1.00 2.50
79 Hideo Nomo 1.00 2.50
80 Frank Thomas 1.00 2.50
81 Rollie Fingers .40 1.00
82 Carl Crawford .60 1.50
83 Bobby Jenks .40 1.00
84 Victor Martinez .60 1.50
85 Ernie Banks 1.00 2.50
86 Josh Beckett .60 1.50
87 Jose Valverde .40 1.00
88 Reggie Jackson .60 1.50
89 Duke Snider .60 1.50
90 Mike Lowell .40 1.00
91 Dom DiMaggio .40 1.00
92 Torii Hunter .40 1.00
93 Alfonso Soriano .60 1.50
94 Justin Morneau 1.00 2.50
95 Carlos Delgado .40 1.00
96 Ty Cobb 1.50 4.00
97 Andruw Jones .40 1.00
98 Yogi Berra 1.00 2.50
99 Joe DiMaggio 2.50 6.00
100 Willie Randolph .40 1.00
101 Miguel Cabrera 1.00 2.50
102 Grady Sizemore .60 1.50
103 Michael Young .60 1.50
104 Wade Boggs .60 1.50
105 Goose Gossage .40 1.00
106 Robin Roberts .40 1.00
107 Brooks Robinson .60 1.50
108 Jim Palmer .40 1.00
109 Jorge Posada .60 1.50
110 Keith Hernandez .40 1.00
111 Ivan Rodriguez .60 1.50
112 Carlos Lee .40 1.00
113 John Lackey .40 1.00
114 Alex Rios .60 1.50
115 Carlton Fisk .60 1.50
116 Gary Matthews .40 1.00
117 Billy Martin .60 1.50
118 Paul Molitor 1.00 2.50
119 Hideki Matsui 1.00 2.50
120 Al Kaline 1.00 2.50
121 Takashi Saito .40 1.00
122 Stan Musial 1.50 4.00
123 Ryan Howard 1.25 3.00
124 Whitey Ford .60 1.50
125 John Smoltz 1.00 2.50
126 Roy Oswalt .60 1.50
127 Jim Thome .60 1.50
128 Tony Gwynn 1.00 2.50
129 Dennis Eckersley .40 1.00
130 Ted Williams 2.50 6.00
131 Justin Verlander 1.25 3.00
132 David Ortiz .60 1.50
133 Tom Gordon .40 1.00
134 Tom Seaver .60 1.50
135 Red Schoendienst .40 1.00
136 Johnny Podres .40 1.00
137 Paul Konerko .60 1.50
138 Robin Yount 1.00 2.50
139 Todd Helton .60 1.50
140 Frank Robinson .40 1.00
141 J.J. Putz .40 1.00
142 Jackie Robinson 1.00 2.50
143 Brandon Webb .60 1.50
144 Eddie Murray 1.00 2.50
145 Freddy Sanchez .40 1.00
146 Josh Anderson Jsy AU (RC) 5.00 12.00
147a Daric Barton Jsy AU (RC) 5.00 12.00
147b Daric Barton Jsy AU (RC) 5.00 12.00
148 Steve Pearce Jsy AU RC 6.00 15.00
149 Chin-Lung Hu Jsy AU (RC) 20.00 50.00
150a Clay Buchholz Jsy AU (RC) 10.00 25.00
150b Clay Buchholz Jsy AU (RC) 10.00 25.00
151a J.R. Towles Jsy AU RC 6.00 15.00
151b J.R. Towles Jsy AU RC 6.00 15.00
152 Brandon Jones Jsy AU RC 5.00 12.00
153 Lance Broadway Jsy AU (RC) 6.00 15.00
154a Nyjer Morgan Jsy AU (RC) 5.00 12.00
154b Nyjer Morgan Jsy AU (RC) 4.00 10.00
155a Ross Ohlendorf Jsy AU RC 5.00 12.00
155b Ross Ohlendorf Jsy AU RC 5.00 12.00
156 Chris Seddon Jsy AU (RC) 4.00 10.00
157 Jonathan Albaladejo Jsy AU RC 5.00 12.00
158a Seth Smith Jsy AU (RC) 4.00 10.00
158b Seth Smith Jsy AU (RC) 4.00 10.00
159a Kevin Hart Jsy AU (RC) 5.00 12.00
159b Kevin Hart Jsy AU (RC) 5.00 12.00
160 Bill White Jsy AU RC 5.00 12.00
161 Wladimir Balentien Jsy AU (RC) 5.00 12.00
162a Justin Ruggiano Jsy AU RC 4.00 10.00
162b Justin Ruggiano Jsy AU RC 4.00 10.00
163a Clint Sammons Jsy AU (RC) 5.00 12.00
163b Clint Sammons Jsy AU (RC) 5.00 12.00
164 Rich Thompson Jsy AU RC 5.00 12.00
165 Dave Davidson Jsy AU RC 4.00 10.00
166 Troy Patton Jsy AU (RC) 5.00 12.00
167 Joe Koshansky Jsy AU (RC) 5.00 12.00
168a Colt Morton Jsy AU RC 5.00 12.00
168b Colt Morton Jsy AU RC 5.00 12.00
169 Armando Galarraga Jsy AU RC 12.50 30.00
170a Sam Fuld Jsy AU RC 60.00 120.00
170b Sam Fuld Jsy AU RC 60.00 120.00
171 Dustin Moseley Bat AU 4.00 10.00
172 Tim Lincecum Jsy AU 50.00 100.00
173a Ryan Braun Jsy AU 40.00 80.00
173b Ryan Braun Jsy AU 40.00 80.00
174 Phil Hughes Jsy AU 15.00 40.00
175a Joba Chamberlain Jsy AU 12.50 30.00
175b Joba Chamberlain Jsy AU 12.50 30.00
176 Hunter Pence Jsy AU 12.50 30.00
177a Fausto Carmona Jsy AU 5.00 12.00
177b Fausto Carmona Jsy AU 5.00 12.00
178a Ubaldo Jimenez Jsy AU 12.50 30.00
178b Ubaldo Jimenez Jsy AU 12.50 30.00
179a Cameron Maybin Jsy AU 6.00 15.00
179b Cameron Maybin Jsy AU 6.00 15.00
180a Adam Jones Jsy AU 15.00 40.00
180b Adam Jones Jsy AU 15.00 40.00
181a Brian Bannister Jsy AU 5.00 12.00
181b Brian Bannister Jsy AU 5.00 12.00
182a Jarrod Saltalamacchia Jsy AU 6.00 15.00
182b Jarrod Saltalamacchia Jsy AU 6.00 15.00
183 Alex Gordon Jsy AU 10.00 25.00
184a Russell Martin Jsy AU 10.00 25.00
184b Russell Martin Jsy AU 10.00 25.00
185 John Maine Jsy AU 10.00 25.00
186a Hideki Okajima Jsy AU 12.50 30.00
186b Hideki Okajima Jsy AU 12.50 30.00
187a Curtis Granderson Jsy AU 15.00 40.00
187b Curtis Granderson Jsy AU 15.00 40.00
188 Delmon Young Jsy AU 5.00 12.00
189a Jo-Jo Reyes Jsy AU 5.00 12.00
189b Jo-Jo Reyes Jsy AU 5.00 12.00
190 Yovani Gallardo Jsy AU 8.00 20.00
191a Ryan Zimmerman Jsy AU 10.00 25.00
191b Ryan Zimmerman Jsy AU 10.00 25.00
192 Jeremy Guthrie Jsy AU 8.00 20.00
193a Dan Uggla Jsy AU 8.00 20.00
193b Dan Uggla Jsy AU 8.00 20.00
194a Andre Ethier Jsy AU 20.00 50.00
194b Andre Ethier Jsy AU 20.00 50.00
195a Chris Young Jsy AU 6.00 15.00
195b Chris Young Jsy AU 6.00 15.00
196a Elijah Dukes Jsy AU 5.00 12.00
196b Elijah Dukes Jsy AU 5.00 12.00
197a Nick Markakis Jsy AU 12.50 30.00
197b Nick Markakis Jsy AU 12.50 30.00
198a Melky Cabrera Jsy AU 8.00 20.00
198b Melky Cabrera Jsy AU 8.00 20.00
199 Cole Hamels Jsy AU 10.00 25.00
200 James Loney Jsy AU 10.00 25.00
201a Kevin Slowey Jsy AU 8.00 20.00
201b Kevin Slowey Jsy AU 8.00 20.00
202 Carlos Marmol Jsy AU 8.00 20.00
203a Akinori Iwamura Jsy AU 10.00 25.00
203b Akinori Iwamura Jsy AU 10.00 25.00
204 Adrian Gonzalez Jsy AU 12.50 30.00
205a Brandon Phillips Jsy AU 10.00 25.00
205b Brandon Phillips Jsy AU 10.00 25.00
206 J.J. Hardy Jsy AU 10.00 25.00
207a Tom Gorzelanny Jsy AU 4.00 10.00
207b Tom Gorzelanny Jsy AU 4.00 10.00
208a Matt Cain Jsy AU 12.50 30.00
208b Matt Cain Jsy AU 12.50 30.00
209a Matt Capps Jsy AU 5.00 12.00
209b Matt Capps Jsy AU 5.00 12.00
210a Jeff Francis Jsy AU 5.00 12.00
210b Jeff Francis Jsy AU 5.00 12.00
211 Brian McCann Jsy AU 10.00 25.00
212 Matt Garza Jsy AU 8.00 20.00
213a Robinson Cano Jsy AU 20.00 50.00
213b Robinson Cano Jsy AU 20.00 50.00
214 Felix Hernandez Jsy AU 10.00 25.00
215 Yunel Escobar Jsy AU 8.00 20.00
216a Francisco Liriano Jsy AU 8.00 20.00
216b Francisco Liriano Jsy AU 8.00 20.00
217a Rich Hill Jsy AU 5.00 12.00
217b Rich Hill Jsy AU 5.00 12.00
218a Taylor Buchholz Jsy AU 4.00 10.00
218b Taylor Buchholz Jsy AU 4.00 10.00
219 Asdrubal Cabrera Jsy AU 5.00 12.00
220a Lastings Milledge Jsy AU 5.00 12.00
220b Lastings Milledge Jsy AU 5.00 12.00
221 Honus Wagner 1.00 2.50
222 Walter Johnson 1.00 2.50
223 Thurman Munson 1.00 2.50
224 Roy Campanella 1.00 2.50
225 George Sisler .60 1.50
226 Pee Wee Reese .60 1.50
227 Johnny Mize .60 1.50
228 Jimmie Foxx 1.00 2.50
229 Tris Speaker .60 1.50
230 Christy Mathewson 1.00 2.50
231 Mel Ott 1.00 2.50
232 Ralph Kiner .60 1.50
233 Joey Votto (RC) 1.50 4.00
234 Hiroki Kuroda RC .60 1.50
235 John Bowker (RC) .40 1.00
236 Lance Berkman .60 1.50
237 Aaron Harang .40 1.00
238 B.J. Upton .60 1.50
239 Zack Greinke .60 1.50
240 Cal Ripken Jr. 4.00 10.00
241 Justin Upton .60 1.50
242 Roy Halladay 1.00 2.50
243 Orlando Hudson .40 1.00
244 Scott Kazmir .60 1.50
245 Matt Kemp .60 1.50
246 Mark Buehrle .60 1.50
247 Adam Dunn .60 1.50
248 Erik Bedard .40 1.00
249 Carlos Zambrano .60 1.50
250 Jeff Francoeur .60 1.50
251 Brad Penny .40 1.00

2008 Topps Triple Threads Black

*BLACK 1-145: 3X TO 8X BASIC
*BLACK 221-251: 3X TO 8X BASIC
1-145/221-251 ODDS 1:16 MINI
1-145/221-251 PNT RUN 30 SER.#'d SETS

2008 Topps Triple Threads Emerald

*EMERALD 1-145: .6X TO 1.5X BASIC
*EMERALD 221-251: .6X TO 1.5X BASIC
1-145/221-251 ODDS 1:2 MINI
1-145/221-251 PNT RUN 240 SER.#'d SETS
*EMERALD AUTO: .5X TO 1.2X BASIC AU
*EMERALD VAR AU: .5X TO 1.2X BASIC AU
146-220 AU ODDS 1:22 MINI
146-220 AU VAR.ODDS 1:39 MINI
146-220 AU PRINT RUN 50 SERIAL #'d SETS
TEAM INITIAL DIECUTS ARE VARIATIONS

2008 Topps Triple Threads Gold

*GOLD 1-145: 1X TO 2.5X BASIC
*GOLD 221-251: 1X TO 2.5X BASIC
1-145/221-251 ODDS 1:5 MINI
1-145/221-251 PNT RUN 99 SER.#'d SETS
*GOLD AUTO: .6X TO 1.5X BASIC AU
*GOLD VAR AU: .6X TO 1.5X BASIC AU
146-220 AU ODDS 1:43 MINI
146-220 AU VAR.ODDS 1:77 MINI
146-220 AU PRINT RUN 25 SERIAL #'d SETS
TEAM INITIAL DIECUTS ARE VARIATIONS

2008 Topps Triple Threads Platinum

1-145 ODDS 1:461 MINI
221-251 ODDS 1:461 MINI
STATED PRINT RUN 1 SER.#'d SET
NO PRICING DUE TO SCARCITY
146-220 AU ODDS 1:1080 MINI
146-220 AU VARIATION ODDS 1:1945 MINI
146-220 AU PRINT RUN 1 SERIAL #'d SET
TEAM INITIAL DIECUTS ARE VARIATIONS
NO PRICING DUE TO SCARCITY

2008 Topps Triple Threads Sapphire

*SAPPHIRE 1-145: 3X TO 8X BASIC
*SAPPHIRE 221-251: 3X TO 8X BASIC
1-145/221-251 ODDS 1:19 MINI
1-145/221-251 PNT RUN 25 SER.#'d SETS
146-220 JSY AU ODDS 1:107 MINI
146-220 JSY AU VAR.ODDS 1:190 MINI
146-220 AU PRINT RUN 10 SERIAL #'d SETS
TEAM INITIAL DIECUTS ARE VARIATIONS
NO SAPPHIRE JSY AUTO PRICING AVAILABLE

2008 Topps Triple Threads Sepia

*SEPIA 1-145: .5X TO 1.2X BASIC
*SEPIA 221-251: .5X TO 1.2X BASIC
1-145/221-251 RANDOMLY INSERTED
1-145/221-251 PNT RUN 525 SER.#'d SETS
*SEPIA AUTO: .4X TO 1X BASIC AU
*SEPIA VAR AU: .4X TO 1X BASIC AU
146-220 AU ODDS 1:15 MINI
146-220 AU VAR.ODDS 1:26 MINI
146-220 AU PRINT RUN 75 SERIAL #'d SETS
TEAM INITIAL DIECUTS ARE VARIATIONS

2008 Topps Triple Threads White Whale Printing Plates

VERSION A ODDS 1:267 MINI
VERSION B ODDS 1:157 MINI
VERSION C ODDS 1:457 MINI
TEAM INITIALS ODDS 1:477 MINI
STATED PRINT RUN 1 SER.#'d SET
NO PRICING DUE TO SCARCITY

2008 Topps Triple Threads All-Star Triple Patches

STATED ODDS 1:171 MINI
STATED PRINT RUN 9 SER.#'d SETS
NO PRICING DUE TO SCARCITY
STATED LOGO ODDS 1:1588 MINI
STATED PRINT RUN 1 SER.#'d SETS
NO PRICING DUE TO SCARCITY
STATED PLATINUM ODDS 1:1588 MINI
STATED PRINT RUN 1 SER.#'d SETS
NO PRICING DUE TO SCARCITY

2008 Topps Triple Threads Bat Barrels

STATED ODDS 1:2358 MINI
STATED PRINT RUN 1 SER.#'d SET
NO PRICING DUE TO SCARCITY

2008 Topps Triple Threads Cut Above

STATED ODDS 1:7781 MINI
STATED PRINT RUN 1 SER.#'d SET
NO PRICING DUE TO SCARCITY

2008 Topps Triple Threads Cut Above Presidential

GROUP A ODDS 1:8646 MINI
GROUP B ODDS 1:77,814 MINI
STATED PRINT RUN 1 SER.#'d SET
NO PRICING DUE TO SCARCITY

2008 Topps Triple Threads Jumbo Plus Relics

STATED ODDS 1:1080 MINI
STATED PRINT RUN 3 SER.#'d SETS
NO PRICING DUE TO SCARCITY
PLATINUM ODDS 1:3112 MINI
PLATINUM PRINT RUN 1 SER.#'d SET
NO PRICING DUE TO SCARCITY

2008 Topps Triple Threads Letter Plus Relics

STATED ODDS 1:1080 MINI
STATED PRINT RUN 3 SER.#'d SETS
NO PRICING DUE TO SCARCITY
PLATINUM ODDS 1:3112 MINI
PLATINUM PRINT RUN 1 SER.#'d SET
NO PRICING DUE TO SCARCITY

2008 Topps Triple Threads Relics

STATED ODDS 1:10 MINI
STATED PRINT RUN 36 SER.#'d SETS
*EMERALD: .5X TO 1.2X BASIC
EMERALD ODDS 1:19 MINI
EMERALD PRINT RUN 18 SER.#'d SETS
NO 226-240 EMERALD PRICING
*GOLD: .6X TO 1.5X BASIC
GOLD ODDS 1:38 MINI
GOLD PRINT RUN 9 SER.#'d SETS
NO 226-240 GOLD PRICING
PLATINUM ODDS 1:334 MINI
PLATINUM PRINT RUN 1 SER.#'d SET
NO PLATINUM PRICING DUE TO SCARCITY
SAPPHIRE ODDS 1:111 MINI
SAPPHIRE PRINT RUN 3 SER.#'d SETS
NO SAPPHIRE PRICING DUE TO SCARCITY
*SEPIA: .4X TO 1X BASIC
SEPIA ODDS 1:13 MINI
SEPIA PRINT RUN 27 SER.#'d SETS
ALL DC VARIATIONS PRICED EQUALLY
1 David Wright 15.00 40.00
2 David Wright 15.00 40.00
3 David Wright 15.00 40.00
4 Alex Rodriguez 20.00 50.00
5 Alex Rodriguez 20.00 50.00
6 Alex Rodriguez 20.00 50.00
7 Mickey Mantle 60.00 120.00
8 Mickey Mantle 60.00 120.00
9 Mickey Mantle 60.00 120.00
10 Duke Snider 12.50 30.00
11 Duke Snider 12.50 30.00
12 Duke Snider 12.50 30.00
13 Carlton Fisk 10.00 25.00
14 Carlton Fisk 10.00 25.00
15 Carlton Fisk 10.00 25.00
16 Ichiro Suzuki 20.00 50.00
17 Ichiro Suzuki 20.00 50.00
18 Ichiro Suzuki 20.00 50.00
19 Wade Boggs 10.00 25.00
20 Wade Boggs 10.00 25.00
21 Wade Boggs 10.00 25.00
22 Chien-Ming Wang 6.00 15.00
23 Chien-Ming Wang 6.00 15.00
24 Chien-Ming Wang 6.00 15.00
25 Alfonso Soriano 8.00 20.00
26 Alfonso Soriano 8.00 20.00
27 Alfonso Soriano 8.00 20.00
28 Ernie Banks 12.50 30.00
29 Ernie Banks 12.50 30.00
30 Ernie Banks 12.50 30.00
31 Jimmy Rollins 8.00 20.00
32 Jimmy Rollins 8.00 20.00
33 Jimmy Rollins 8.00 20.00
34 Bob Gibson 10.00 25.00
35 Bob Gibson 10.00 25.00
36 Bob Gibson 10.00 25.00
37 Brooks Robinson 15.00 40.00
38 Brooks Robinson 15.00 40.00
39 Brooks Robinson 40.00 80.00
40 Joe DiMaggio 50.00 100.00
41 Joe DiMaggio 50.00 100.00
42 Joe DiMaggio 30.00 60.00
43 Hideo Nomo 20.00 50.00
44 Hideo Nomo 20.00 50.00
45 Hideo Nomo 20.00 50.00
46 Ted Williams 30.00 60.00
47 Ted Williams 30.00 60.00
48 Ted Williams 30.00 60.00
49 David Ortiz 8.00 20.00
50 David Ortiz 8.00 20.00
51 David Ortiz 8.00 20.00
52 Frank Robinson 12.50 30.00
53 Frank Robinson 12.50 30.00
54 Frank Robinson 12.50 30.00
55 Tony Gwynn 15.00 40.00
56 Tony Gwynn 15.00 40.00
57 Tony Gwynn 30.00 60.00
58 Jose Reyes 12.50 30.00
59 Jose Reyes 12.50 30.00
60 Jose Reyes 12.50 30.00
61 Roger Maris 30.00 60.00
62 Roger Maris 30.00 60.00
63 Roger Maris 30.00 60.00
64 Mike Schmidt 15.00 40.00
65 Mike Schmidt 15.00 40.00
66 Mike Schmidt 15.00 40.00
67 Eddie Murray 10.00 25.00
68 Eddie Murray 10.00 25.00
69 Eddie Murray 10.00 25.00
70 Johnny Bench 12.50 30.00
71 Johnny Bench 12.50 30.00
72 Johnny Bench 12.50 30.00
73 Roberto Clemente 40.00 80.00
74 Roberto Clemente 40.00 80.00
75 Roberto Clemente 40.00 80.00
76 Steve Carlton 8.00 20.00
77 Steve Carlton 8.00 20.00
78 Steve Carlton 8.00 20.00
79 Grady Sizemore 10.00 25.00
80 Grady Sizemore 10.00 25.00
81 Grady Sizemore 10.00 25.00
82 Robin Yount 10.00 25.00
83 Robin Yount 10.00 25.00
84 Robin Yount 10.00 25.00
85 Hanley Ramirez 8.00 20.00
86 Hanley Ramirez 8.00 20.00
87 Hanley Ramirez 8.00 20.00
88 Al Kaline 12.50 30.00
89 Al Kaline 12.50 30.00
90 Al Kaline 12.50 30.00
91 Vladimir Guerrero 8.00 20.00
92 Vladimir Guerrero 8.00 20.00
93 Vladimir Guerrero 8.00 20.00
94 George Kell 10.00 25.00
95 George Kell 10.00 25.00
96 George Kell 10.00 25.00
97 Reggie Jackson 10.00 25.00
98 Reggie Jackson 10.00 25.00
99 Reggie Jackson 10.00 25.00
100 Tom Seaver 12.50 30.00
101 Tom Seaver 12.50 30.00
102 Tom Seaver 12.50 30.00
103 Johan Santana 8.00 20.00
104 Johan Santana 8.00 20.00
105 Johan Santana 8.00 20.00
106 Jason Varitek 10.00 25.00
107 Jason Varitek 10.00 25.00
108 Jason Varitek 10.00 25.00
109 Ryan Howard 10.00 25.00
110 Ryan Howard 10.00 25.00
111 Ryan Howard 10.00 25.00
112 Manny Ramirez 8.00 20.00
113 Manny Ramirez 8.00 20.00
114 Manny Ramirez 8.00 20.00
115 Miguel Cabrera 8.00 20.00
116 Miguel Cabrera 8.00 20.00
117 Miguel Cabrera 8.00 20.00
118 Jorge Posada 8.00 20.00
119 Jorge Posada 8.00 20.00
120 Jorge Posada 8.00 20.00
121 Nolan Ryan 20.00 50.00
122 Nolan Ryan 20.00 50.00
123 Nolan Ryan 20.00 50.00
124 Paul Molitor 8.00 20.00
125 Paul Molitor 8.00 20.00
126 Paul Molitor 8.00 20.00
127 Chipper Jones 10.00 25.00
128 Chipper Jones 10.00 25.00
129 Chipper Jones 10.00 25.00
130 Carl Yastrzemski 15.00 40.00
131 Carl Yastrzemski 15.00 40.00
132 Carl Yastrzemski 15.00 40.00
133 Whitey Ford 15.00 40.00
134 Whitey Ford 15.00 40.00
135 Whitey Ford 15.00 40.00
136 Yogi Berra 20.00 50.00
137 Yogi Berra 20.00 50.00
138 Yogi Berra 40.00 80.00
139 Albert Pujols 20.00 50.00
140 Albert Pujols 20.00 50.00
141 Albert Pujols 15.00 40.00
142 Jim Palmer 8.00 20.00
143 Jim Palmer 8.00 20.00
144 Jim Palmer 8.00 20.00
145 Harmon Killebrew 20.00 50.00
146 Harmon Killebrew 20.00 50.00
147 Harmon Killebrew 20.00 50.00
148 Ozzie Smith 10.00 25.00
149 Ozzie Smith 10.00 25.00
150 Ozzie Smith 10.00 25.00
151 Stan Musial 15.00 40.00
152 Stan Musial 15.00 40.00
153 Stan Musial 15.00 40.00
154 Ryne Sandberg 12.50 30.00
155 Ryne Sandberg 12.50 30.00
156 Ryne Sandberg 12.50 30.00
157 Matt Holliday 8.00 20.00
158 Matt Holliday 8.00 20.00
159 Matt Holliday 8.00 20.00
160 Carlos Beltran 8.00 20.00
161 Carlos Beltran 8.00 20.00
162 Carlos Beltran 8.00 20.00
163 Prince Fielder 8.00 20.00
164 Prince Fielder 8.00 20.00
165 Prince Fielder 8.00 20.00
166 Ivan Rodriguez 8.00 20.00
167 Ivan Rodriguez 8.00 20.00
168 Ivan Rodriguez 8.00 20.00
169 Victor Martinez 8.00 20.00
170 Victor Martinez 8.00 20.00
171 Victor Martinez 8.00 20.00
172 Justin Verlander 8.00 20.00
173 Justin Verlander 8.00 20.00
174 Justin Verlander 8.00 20.00
175 Reggie Jackson 10.00 25.00
176 Reggie Jackson 10.00 25.00
177 Reggie Jackson 20.00 50.00
178 Alfonso Soriano 8.00 20.00
179 Alfonso Soriano 8.00 20.00
180 Alfonso Soriano 8.00 20.00
181 Prince Fielder 8.00 20.00
182 Prince Fielder 8.00 20.00
183 Prince Fielder 8.00 20.00
184 Ichiro Suzuki 20.00 50.00
185 Ichiro Suzuki 20.00 50.00
186 Ichiro Suzuki 20.00 50.00
187 David Wright 15.00 40.00
188 David Wright 15.00 40.00
189 David Wright 15.00 40.00
190 Eddie Murray 10.00 25.00
191 Eddie Murray 10.00 25.00
192 Eddie Murray 10.00 25.00
193 Manny Ramirez 8.00 20.00
194 Manny Ramirez 8.00 20.00
195 Manny Ramirez 8.00 20.00
196 Mike Schmidt 15.00 40.00
197 Mike Schmidt 15.00 40.00
198 Mike Schmidt 15.00 40.00
199 Johnny Bench 12.50 30.00
200 Johnny Bench 12.50 30.00
201 Johnny Bench 12.50 30.00
202 Matt Holliday 8.00 20.00
203 Matt Holliday 8.00 20.00
204 Matt Holliday 8.00 20.00
205 Alex Rodriguez 20.00 50.00
206 Alex Rodriguez 20.00 50.00
207 Alex Rodriguez 20.00 50.00
208 Jose Reyes 12.50 30.00
209 Jose Reyes 12.50 30.00
210 Jose Reyes 12.50 30.00
211 Jimmy Rollins 8.00 20.00
212 Jimmy Rollins 8.00 20.00
213 Jimmy Rollins 8.00 20.00
214 David Ortiz 8.00 20.00
215 David Ortiz 8.00 20.00
216 David Ortiz 8.00 20.00
217 Robin Yount 10.00 25.00
218 Robin Yount 10.00 25.00
219 Robin Yount 10.00 25.00
220 Nolan Ryan 20.00 50.00
221 Nolan Ryan 20.00 50.00
222 Nolan Ryan 20.00 50.00
223 Ryan Howard 10.00 25.00
224 Ryan Howard 10.00 25.00
225 Ryan Howard 10.00 25.00
226 John F. Kennedy 150.00 200.00
227 Ty Cobb 100.00 200.00
228 Jimmie Foxx 40.00 80.00
229 Rogers Hornsby 40.00 80.00
230 George Sisler 15.00 40.00
231 Mel Ott 60.00 120.00
232 Jackie Robinson 60.00 120.00
233 Tris Speaker 40.00 80.00
234 Honus Wagner 150.00 250.00
235 Lou Gehrig 100.00 150.00
236 Pee Wee Reese 12.50 30.00
237 Roy Campanella 30.00 60.00
238 Johnny Mize 10.00 25.00
239 Thurman Munson 30.00 60.00
240 Babe Ruth 350.00 450.00

2008 Topps Triple Threads Relics Platinum

STATED ODDS 1:727 MINI
STATED PRINT RUN 1 SER.#'d SET
NO PRICING DUE TO SCARCITY

2008 Topps Triple Threads Relics Sapphire

STATED ODDS 1:241 MINI
STATED PRINT RUN 3 SER.#'d SETS
NO PRICING DUE TO SCARCITY

2008 Topps Triple Threads Relics Autographs

STATED ODDS 1:25 MINI
STATED PRINT RUN 18 SER.#'d SETS
*GOLD: .5X TO 1.2X BASIC

GOLD ODDS 1:50 MINI
GOLD PRINT RUN 9 SER.#'d SETS
PLATINUM ODDS 1:447 MINI
PLATINUM PRINT RUN 1 SER.#'d SET
NO PLATINUM PRICING DUE TO SCARCITY
SAPPHIRE ODDS 1:149 MINI
SAPPHIRE PRINT RUN 3 SER.#'d SETS
NO SAPPHIRE PRICING DUE TO SCARCITY
WHITE WHALE ODDS 1:111 MINI
WHITE WHALE PRINT RUN 1 SER.#'d SET
NO WHITE WHALE PRICING DUE TO SCARCITY
ALL DC VARIATIONS PRICED EQUALLY
1 Prince Fielder 30.00 60.00
2 Prince Fielder 30.00 60.00
3 Prince Fielder 30.00 60.00
4 Vladimir Guerrero 30.00 60.00
5 Vladimir Guerrero 30.00 60.00
6 Vladimir Guerrero 30.00 60.00
7 Bob Gibson 30.00 60.00
8 Bob Gibson 30.00 60.00
9 Bob Gibson 30.00 60.00
10 Chien-Ming Wang 90.00 150.00
11 Chien-Ming Wang 90.00 150.00
12 Chien-Ming Wang 90.00 150.00
13 Johnny Podres 20.00 50.00
14 Johnny Podres 20.00 50.00
15 Johnny Podres 20.00 50.00
16 Frank Robinson 20.00 50.00
17 Frank Robinson 20.00 50.00
18 Frank Robinson 20.00 50.00
19 Robin Yount 30.00 60.00
20 Robin Yount 30.00 60.00
21 Robin Yount 30.00 60.00
22 David Ortiz 40.00 80.00
23 David Ortiz 40.00 80.00
24 David Ortiz 40.00 80.00
25 Chipper Jones 60.00 120.00
26 Chipper Jones 60.00 120.00
27 Chipper Jones 60.00 120.00
28 Cal Ripken Jr. 150.00 250.00
29 Cal Ripken Jr. 150.00 200.00
30 Cal Ripken Jr. 150.00 200.00
31 Carlton Fisk 20.00 50.00
32 Carlton Fisk 20.00 50.00
33 Carlton Fisk 20.00 50.00
34 Jason Varitek 30.00 60.00
35 Jason Varitek 30.00 60.00
36 Jason Varitek 30.00 60.00
37 Ernie Banks 60.00 120.00
38 Ernie Banks 60.00 120.00
39 Ernie Banks 60.00 120.00
40 Harmon Killebrew 60.00 120.00
41 Harmon Killebrew 60.00 120.00
42 Harmon Killebrew 60.00 120.00
43 Travis Hafner 20.00 50.00
44 Travis Hafner 20.00 50.00
45 Travis Hafner 20.00 50.00
46 Manny Ramirez 50.00 100.00
47 Manny Ramirez 50.00 100.00
48 Manny Ramirez 50.00 100.00
49 Tony Gwynn 30.00 60.00
50 Tony Gwynn 30.00 60.00
51 Tony Gwynn 30.00 60.00
52 Alfonso Soriano 20.00 50.00
53 Alfonso Soriano 20.00 50.00
54 Alfonso Soriano 20.00 50.00
55 Carl Yastrzemski 60.00 120.00
56 Carl Yastrzemski 60.00 120.00
57 Carl Yastrzemski 60.00 120.00
58 Jim Palmer 20.00 50.00
59 Jim Palmer 20.00 50.00
60 Jim Palmer 20.00 50.00
61 Jimmy Rollins 30.00 60.00
62 Jimmy Rollins 30.00 60.00
63 Jimmy Rollins 30.00 60.00
64 Frank Thomas 50.00 100.00
65 Frank Thomas 50.00 100.00
66 Frank Thomas 50.00 100.00
67 Brooks Robinson 30.00 60.00
68 Brooks Robinson 30.00 60.00
69 Brooks Robinson 30.00 60.00
70 Dom DiMaggio 20.00 50.00
71 Dom DiMaggio 20.00 50.00
72 Dom DiMaggio 20.00 50.00
73 George Kell 30.00 60.00
74 George Kell 30.00 60.00
75 George Kell 30.00 60.00
76 Wade Boggs 20.00 50.00
77 Wade Boggs 20.00 50.00
78 Wade Boggs 20.00 50.00
79 Johan Santana 40.00 80.00
80 Johan Santana 40.00 80.00
81 Johan Santana 40.00 80.00
82 Jose Reyes 30.00 60.00
83 Jose Reyes 30.00 60.00
84 Jose Reyes 30.00 60.00
85 Hanley Ramirez 30.00 60.00
86 Hanley Ramirez 30.00 60.00
87 Hanley Ramirez 30.00 60.00
88 Johnny Bench 40.00 80.00
89 Johnny Bench 40.00 80.00
90 Johnny Bench 40.00 80.00
91 Mike Lowell 20.00 50.00
92 Mike Lowell 20.00 50.00
93 Mike Lowell 20.00 50.00
94 Tom Seaver 30.00 60.00
95 Tom Seaver 30.00 60.00
96 Tom Seaver 30.00 60.00
97 John Smoltz 40.00 80.00
98 John Smoltz 40.00 80.00
99 John Smoltz 40.00 80.00
100 Ozzie Smith 30.00 60.00
101 Ozzie Smith 30.00 60.00
102 Ozzie Smith 30.00 60.00
103 Duke Snider 30.00 60.00
104 Duke Snider 30.00 60.00
105 Duke Snider 30.00 60.00
106 Steve Carlton 20.00 50.00
107 Steve Carlton 20.00 50.00
108 Steve Carlton 20.00 50.00
109 Jorge Posada 20.00 50.00
110 Jorge Posada 20.00 50.00
111 Jorge Posada 20.00 50.00
112 Andruw Jones 20.00 50.00
113 Andruw Jones 20.00 50.00
114 Andruw Jones 20.00 50.00
115 Reggie Jackson 50.00 100.00
116 Reggie Jackson 50.00 100.00
117 Reggie Jackson 50.00 100.00
118 C.C. Sabathia 40.00 80.00
119 C.C. Sabathia 40.00 80.00
120 C.C. Sabathia 40.00 80.00
121 Jim Thome 30.00 60.00
122 Jim Thome 30.00 60.00
123 Jim Thome 30.00 60.00
124 Mike Schmidt 30.00 60.00
125 Mike Schmidt 30.00 60.00
126 Mike Schmidt 30.00 60.00
127 Yogi Berra 50.00 100.00
128 Yogi Berra 50.00 100.00
129 Yogi Berra 50.00 100.00
130 Dontrelle Willis 20.00 50.00
131 Dontrelle Willis 20.00 50.00
132 Dontrelle Willis 20.00 50.00
133 Nolan Ryan 75.00 150.00
134 Nolan Ryan 75.00 150.00
135 Nolan Ryan 75.00 150.00
136 Goose Gossage 30.00 60.00
137 Goose Gossage 30.00 60.00
138 Goose Gossage 30.00 60.00
139 Al Kaline 30.00 60.00
140 Al Kaline 30.00 60.00
141 Al Kaline 30.00 60.00
142 David Wright 50.00 100.00
143 David Wright 50.00 100.00
144 David Wright 50.00 100.00
145 Miguel Cabrera 30.00 60.00
146 Miguel Cabrera 30.00 60.00
147 Miguel Cabrera 30.00 60.00
148 Ryne Sandberg 40.00 80.00
149 Ryne Sandberg 40.00 80.00
150 Ryne Sandberg 40.00 80.00
151 Tom Glavine 30.00 60.00
152 Tom Glavine 30.00 60.00
153 Tom Glavine 30.00 60.00
154 Paul Molitor 30.00 60.00
155 Paul Molitor 30.00 60.00
156 Paul Molitor 30.00 60.00
157 Eddie Murray 30.00 60.00
158 Eddie Murray 30.00 60.00
159 Eddie Murray 30.00 60.00
160 Justin Verlander 40.00 80.00
161 Justin Verlander 40.00 80.00
162 Justin Verlander 40.00 80.00
163 Dale Murphy 50.00 100.00
164 Dale Murphy 50.00 100.00
165 Dale Murphy 50.00 100.00
166 Whitey Ford 30.00 60.00
167 Whitey Ford 30.00 60.00
168 Whitey Ford 30.00 60.00
169 Matt Holliday 20.00 50.00
170 Matt Holliday 20.00 50.00
171 Matt Holliday 20.00 50.00
172 Albert Pujols 250.00 500.00
173 Albert Pujols 250.00 500.00
174 Albert Pujols 250.00 500.00
175 Stan Musial 50.00 100.00
176 Stan Musial 50.00 100.00
177 Stan Musial 50.00 100.00
178 Ryan Howard 50.00 100.00
179 Ryan Howard 50.00 100.00
180 Ryan Howard 50.00 100.00
181 Johnny Cueto 10.00 25.00
182 Johnny Cueto 10.00 25.00
183 Johnny Cueto 10.00 25.00
184 Evan Longoria 100.00 175.00
185 Evan Longoria 100.00 175.00
186 Evan Longoria 100.00 175.00

2008 Topps Triple Threads Relics Autographs Sapphire

STATED ODDS 1:149 MINI
STATED PRINT RUN 3 SER.#'d SETS
NO PRICING DUE TO SCARCITY

2008 Topps Triple Threads Relics Autographs White Whale Printing Plates

STATED ODDS 1:111 MINI
STATED PRINT RUN 1 SER.#'d SET
NO PRICING DUE TO SCARCITY

2008 Topps Triple Threads Relics Combos

STATED ODDS 1:20 MINI
STATED PRINT RUN 36 SER.#'d SETS
EMERALD ODDS 1:41 MINI
EMERALD PRINT RUN 18 SER.#'d SETS
NO EMERALD PRICING AVAILABLE
GOLD ODDS 1:81 MINI
GOLD PRINT RUN 9 SER.#'d SETS
NO GOLD PRICING AVAILABLE
PLATINUM ODDS 1:727 MINI
PLATINUM PRINT RUN 1 SER.#'d SET
NO PLATINUM PRICING AVAILABLE
SAPPHIRE ODDS 1:241 MINI
SAPPHIRE PRINT RUN 3 SER.#'d SETS
NO SAPPHIRE PRICING AVAILABLE
*SEPIA: 4X TO 1X BASIC COMBO
SEPIA ODDS 1:27 MINI
SEPIA PRINT RUN 27 SER.#'d SETS
1 Alex Rodriguez 20.00 50.00
David Wright
Ryan Howard
2 Mickey Mantle 200.00 300.00
Ted Williams
Joe DiMaggio
3 Ted Williams 40.00 80.00
Carl Yastrzemski
Manny Ramirez
4 Magglio Ordonez 12.50 30.00
Ichiro Suzuki
Placido Polanco
5 Alex Rodriguez 20.00 50.00
Prince Fielder
Ryan Howard
6 Alex Rodriguez 20.00 50.00
Matt Holliday
Magglio Ordonez
7 Jose Reyes 8.00 20.00
Juan Pierre
Hanley Ramirez
8 Chien-Ming Wang 20.00 50.00
Alex Rodriguez
Mariano Rivera
9 Jake Peavy 10.00 25.00
Scott Kazmir
Johan Santana
10 Joe DiMaggio 75.00 150.00
Roberto Clemente
Mickey Mantle
11 Mark Buehrle 10.00 25.00
Justin Verlander
Clay Buchholz
12 Magglio Ordonez 15.00 40.00
Al Kaline
Curtis Granderson
13 Russ Martin 8.00 20.00
Andruw Jones
Rafael Furcal
14 Jason Varitek 8.00 20.00
Jorge Posada
Ivan Rodriguez
15 Yogi Berra 100.00 200.00
Mickey Mantle
Roger Maris
16 Gary Matthews 8.00 20.00
Vladimir Guerrero
Torii Hunter
17 Troy Tulowitzki 10.00 25.00
Matt Holliday
Todd Helton
18 Roberto Clemente 50.00 100.00
Carl Yastrzemski
Reggie Jackson
19 Ernie Banks 15.00 40.00
Alfonso Soriano
Ryne Sandberg
20 Mickey Mantle 60.00 120.00
Albert Pujols
Roberto Clemente
21 Lance Berkman 8.00 20.00
Carlos Lee
Hunter Pence
22 Alex Gordon 12.50 30.00
Ryan Braun
Ryan Zimmerman
23 Mickey Mantle 75.00 150.00
Alex Rodriguez
Ted Williams
24 Justin Morneau 15.00 40.00
Harmon Killebrew
Joe Mauer
25 Trevor Hoffman 20.00 50.00
Dennis Eckersley
Mariano Rivera
26 Jose Reyes 20.00 50.00
David Wright
John Maine
27 Daisuke Matsuzaka 40.00 80.00
Ichiro Suzuki
Hideki Matsui
28 Stan Musial 75.00 150.00
Albert Pujols
Rogers Hornsby
29 Vince DiMaggio 60.00 120.00
Joe DiMaggio
Dom DiMaggio
30 Mike Schmidt 20.00 50.00
George Brett
Steve Carlton
31 Nick Markakis 15.00 40.00
Brooks Robinson
Brian Roberts
32 Prince Fielder 15.00 40.00
Paul Molitor
Ryan Braun
33 Tim Lincecum 30.00 60.00
Joba Chamberlain
Brian Bannister
34 Andruw Jones 10.00 25.00
Ryan Howard
Prince Fielder
35 Manny Ramirez 30.00 60.00
Alex Rodriguez
David Ortiz
36 Jim Palmer 15.00 40.00
Pedro Martinez
Tom Seaver
37 Ichiro Suzuki 20.00 50.00
Todd Helton
Albert Pujols
38 Pedro Martinez 10.00 25.00
Roy Oswalt
Greg Maddux
39 Yogi Berra 75.00 150.00
Joe DiMaggio
Phil Rizzuto
40 Ernie Banks 40.00 80.00
Roberto Clemente
Carl Yastrzemski
41 Justin Morneau 10.00 25.00
Ryan Howard
Prince Fielder
42 Alex Gordon 10.00 25.00
George Brett
Brian Bannister
43 Ryan Howard 20.00 50.00
Albert Pujols
Manny Ramirez
44 Alex Rodriguez 20.00 50.00
Vladimir Guerrero
Prince Fielder
45 Randy Johnson 20.00 50.00
Nolan Ryan
Hideo Nomo
46 Rollie Fingers 15.00 40.00
Reggie Jackson
Vida Blue
47 Roberto Clemente 75.00 150.00
Ichiro Suzuki
Mickey Mantle
48 Brooks Robinson 20.00 50.00
Jim Palmer
Frank Robinson
49 Reggie Jackson 10.00 25.00
Steve Garvey
Willie Randolph
50 David Ortiz 30.00 60.00
Ted Williams
Manny Ramirez
51 Mickey Mantle 75.00 150.00
Alex Rodriguez
Joe DiMaggio
52 Duke Snider 15.00 40.00
Russ Martin
Steve Garvey
53 Ichiro Suzuki 10.00 25.00
Alfonso Soriano
Carlos Beltran
54 Chase Utley 12.50 30.00
Dan Uggla
Dustin Pedroia
55 Jose Reyes 8.00 20.00
Jimmy Rollins
Hanley Ramirez
56 Jimmy Rollins 30.00 60.00
Joe DiMaggio
Chase Utley
57 Johnny Bench 10.00 25.00
Ivan Rodriguez
Carlton Fisk
58 Pedro Martinez 15.00 40.00
Nolan Ryan
Johan Santana
59 Jose Reyes 15.00 40.00
Ozzie Smith
Jimmy Rollins
60 Jimmy Rollins 12.50 30.00
Jake Peavy
Ryan Braun
61 Alex Rodriguez 12.50 30.00
C.C. Sabathia
Dustin Pedroia
62 Delmon Young 15.00 40.00
Alex Rodriguez
Justin Upton
63 Alex Rodriguez 20.00 50.00
Frank Thomas
Jim Thome
64 Roger Maris 100.00 200.00
Mickey Mantle
Harmon Killebrew
65 Carlos Beltran 8.00 20.00
Chipper Jones
Jose Reyes
66 Jimmy Rollins 8.00 20.00
Matt Holliday
Prince Fielder
67 Alex Rodriguez 10.00 25.00
Magglio Ordonez
Vladimir Guerrero
68 Jake Peavy 8.00 20.00
Brandon Webb
Brad Penny
69 C.C. Sabathia 10.00 25.00
Josh Beckett
John Lackey
70 Ryan Braun 10.00 25.00
Troy Tulowitzki
Hunter Pence
71 Dustin Pedroia 10.00 25.00
Delmon Young
Brian Bannister
72 Victor Martinez 10.00 25.00
Grady Sizemore
Travis Hafner
73 Magglio Ordonez 10.00 25.00
Ichiro Suzuki
Vladimir Guerrero
74 Dan Uggla 8.00 20.00
Hanley Ramirez
Cameron Maybin
75 Ichiro Suzuki 30.00 60.00
Daisuke Matsuzaka
Akinori Iwamura
76 Jason Varitek 12.50 30.00
Alex Rodriguez
Chase Utley
77 Tris Speaker 20.00 50.00
Manny Ramirez
Travis Hafner
78 Eddie Mathews 40.00 80.00
Chipper Jones
Dale Murphy
79 Mike Schmidt 12.50 30.00
Ryan Howard
Richie Ashburn
80 Jimmy Rollins 10.00 25.00
Ryan Howard
Chase Utley
81 Matt Holliday 8.00 20.00
Carlos Beltran
Carlos Lee
82 Vladimir Guerrero 10.00 25.00
Magglio Ordonez
Ichiro Suzuki
83 Andruw Jones 8.00 20.00
Jeff Francoeur
Carlos Beltran
84 Grady Sizemore 15.00 40.00
Ichiro Suzuki
Torii Hunter
85 Stan Musial 30.00 60.00
Carl Yastrzemski
Ted Williams
86 Alex Rodriguez 20.00 50.00
Alex Rodriguez
Alex Rodriguez
87 Chipper Jones 12.50 30.00
Brian McCann
Jeff Francoeur
88 Nolan Ryan 60.00 120.00
Nolan Ryan
Nolan Ryan
89 David Ortiz 8.00 20.00
Paul Molitor
Edgar Martinez
90 Alex Rodriguez 20.00 50.00
Albert Pujols
Manny Ramirez
91 Randy Johnson 20.00 50.00
Luis Gonzalez
Mariano Rivera
92 Goose Gossage 20.00 50.00
George Brett
Billy Martin
93 Fausto Carmona 8.00 20.00
Joba Chamberlain
Grady Sizemore
94 Brian Giles 8.00 20.00
Matt Holliday
Michael Barrett
95 Franklin D. Roosevelt 40.00 80.00
Harry S Truman
John F. Kennedy
96 George Bush 50.00 100.00
Ronald Reagan
George W. Bush
97 William H. Taft 40.00 80.00
Woodrow Wilson
Warren G. Harding
98 Johnny Damon 10.00 25.00
Chipper Jones
Matt Holliday
99 David Ortiz 10.00 25.00
Jose Reyes
Alfonso Soriano
100 Adrian Beltre 10.00 25.00
Albert Pujols
Placido Polanco
101 Joe DiMaggio 200.00 300.00
Lou Gehrig
Mickey Mantle
102 Ty Cobb 250.00 350.00
Babe Ruth
Honus Wagner
103 Roy Campanella 30.00 60.00
Thurman Munson
Johnny Bench
104 Pee Wee Reese 40.00 80.00
Jackie Robinson
Roy Campanella
105 Roberto Clemente 75.00 150.00
Honus Wagner
Ralph Kiner
106 Johnny Mize 50.00 100.00
Mel Ott
Rogers Hornsby
107 Reggie Jackson 30.00 60.00
Thurman Munson
Billy Martin
108 Jimmie Foxx 100.00 175.00
Lou Gehrig
Mel Ott
109 Roger Maris 250.00 350.00
Babe Ruth
Mickey Mantle
110 Honus Wagner 200.00 300.00
Ty Cobb
Tris Speaker
111 Jimmie Foxx 30.00 60.00
Manny Ramirez
Ted Williams

2008 Topps Triple Threads Relics Combos Autographs

STATED ODDS 1:97 MINI
STATED PRINT RUN 36 SER.#'d SETS
EMERALD ODDS 1:193 MINI
EMERALD PRINT RUN 18 SER.#'d SETS
NO EMERALD PRICING AVAILABLE
GOLD ODDS 1:387 MINI
GOLD PRINT RUN 9 SER.#'d SETS
NO GOLD PRICING AVAILABLE
PLATINUM ODDS 1:3383 MINI
PLAT.PRINT RUN 1 SER.#'d SET
NO PLAT.PRICING AVAILABLE
SAPPHIRE ODDS 1:1179 MINI
SAPP.PRINT RUN 3 SER.#'d SETS
NO SAPP.PRICING AVAILABLE
*SEPIA: 4X TO 1X BASIC
SEPIA ODDS 1:129 MINI
SEPIA PRINT RUN 27 SER.#'d SETS
WHITE WHALE ODDS 1:674 MINI
WHITE WHALE PRINT RUN 1 SER.#'d SET
NO WHITE WHALE PRICING AVAILABLE
1 Jose Reyes 50.00 100.00
Ozzie Smith
Hanley Ramirez
2 Albert Pujols 125.00 250.00
Manny Ramirez
Vladimir Guerrero
3 Keith Hernandez 50.00 100.00
Mike Schmidt
Dale Murphy
4 Frank Robinson 100.00 200.00
Carl Yastrzemski
Harmon Killebrew
5 Bob Gibson 60.00 120.00
Tom Seaver
Steve Carlton
6 Harmon Killebrew 60.00 120.00
Rod Carew
Brooks Robinson
7 David Wright 150.00 300.00
Ryan Howard
Albert Pujols
8 Prince Fielder 60.00 120.00
Eddie Murray
Ryan Howard
9 Nolan Ryan 125.00 250.00
George Brett
Robin Yount
10 Johnny Bench 60.00 120.00
Ivan Rodriguez
Carlton Fisk
11 Yogi Berra 75.00 150.00
Whitey Ford
Jorge Posada
12 Tony Gwynn 60.00 120.00
Dale Murphy
Darryl Strawberry
13 Mike Lowell 60.00 120.00
Manny Ramirez
David Ortiz
14 Joba Chamberlain 125.00 250.00
Jorge Posada
Chien-Ming Wang
15 Jeff Francis 30.00 60.00
Taylor Buchholz
Ubaldo Jimenez
16 Melky Cabrera 20.00 50.00
Ross Ohlendorf
Robinson Cano
17 Dan Uggla 15.00 40.00
Chris Seddon
Hanley Ramirez
18 Alex Gordon 30.00 60.00
Evan Longoria
Ryan Zimmerman
19 Chris Young 12.50 30.00
Melky Cabrera
Lastings Milledge
20 Rich Hill 12.50 30.00
Johnny Cueto
Tom Gorzelanny
21 Dustin Moseley 15.00 40.00
Francisco Liriano
Felix Hernandez
22 Hanley Ramirez 15.00 40.00
James Loney
J.J. Hardy
23 Armando Galarraga 12.50 30.00
Fausto Carmona
Troy Patton

2008 Topps Triple Threads Relics Combos Double

STATED ODDS 1:41 MINI
STATED PRINT RUN 36 SER.#'d SETS
EMERALD ODDS 1:81 MINI
EMERALD PRINT RUN 18 SER.#'d SETS
NO EMERALD PRICING AVAILABLE
GOLD ODDS 1:162 MINI
GOLD PRINT RUN 9 SER.#'d SETS
NO GOLD PRICING AVAILABLE
PLATINUM ODDS 1:1496 MINI
PLAT.PRINT RUN 1 SER.#'d SET
NO PLAT.PRICING AVAILABLE
SAPPHIRE ODDS 1:486 MINI
SAPP.PRINT RUN 3 SER.#'d SETS
NO SAPP.PRICING AVAILABLE
*SEPIA: 4X TO 1X BASIC
SEPIA ODDS 1:54 MINI
SEPIA PRINT RUN 27 SER.#'d SETS
1 Joe DiMaggio 125.00 250.00
Mickey Mantle
Roger Maris
Roberto Clemente
Ted Williams
Tris Speaker
2 Ty Cobb 250.00 350.00
Rogers Hornsby
Joe DiMaggio
Ted Williams
Tony Gwynn
Ichiro Suzuki
3 Troy Tulowitzki 30.00 60.00
Chipper Jones
Troy Tulowitzki
Kelly Johnson
Troy Tulowitzki
Edgar Renteria
4 Albert Pujols 60.00 120.00
Bob Gibson
Rogers Hornsby
Stan Musial
Ozzie Smith
Red Schoendienst
5 Ryan Howard 40.00 80.00
Albert Pujols
Prince Fielder
Vladimir Guerrero
Alex Rodriguez
David Ortiz
6 Tom Seaver 60.00 120.00
Nolan Ryan
Steve Carlton
Dennis Eckersley
Jim Palmer
Whitey Ford
7 Jose Reyes 30.00 60.00
Hanley Ramirez
Jimmy Rollins
Carl Crawford
Brian Roberts
Ichiro Suzuki
8 Russell Martin 30.00 60.00
Brian McCann
Jorge Posada
Mike Piazza
Carlton Fisk
Yogi Berra
9 Joe DiMaggio/Mickey Mantle 100.00 200.00
10 Joe DiMaggio 100.00 200.00
Mickey Mantle
Roger Maris
Billy Martin
Phil Rizzuto
Whitey Ford
11 Frank Robinson 75.00 150.00
Carl Yastrzemski
Roberto Clemente
Mickey Mantle
Ted Williams
Harmon Killebrew
12 Roy Oswalt 20.00 50.00
Peter Munro
Kirk Saarloos
Brad Lidge
Octavio Dotel
Billy Wagner
13 Mickey Mantle 75.00 150.00
Joe DiMaggio
Ted Williams
David Wright
Ryan Howard
Alex Rodriguez
14 Alex Rodriguez 50.00 100.00
Hideki Matsui
Jorge Posada
Johnny Damon
Chien-Ming Wang
Joba Chamberlain
15 Akinori Iwamura 50.00 100.00
Kenji Johjima
Hideki Matsui
Hideki Okajima
Kaz Matsui
Ichiro Suzuki
16 Russell Martin 20.00 50.00
Jason Bay
Erik Bedard
Rich Harden
Justin Morneau
Shawn Hill
17 Carlos Beltran 30.00 60.00
David Wright
Carlos Delgado
Jose Reyes
Pedro Martinez
John Maine
18 Travis Hafner 20.00 50.00
Victor Martinez
Grady Sizemore
C.C. Sabathia
Fausto Carmona
Bob Feller
19 Brooks Robinson 20.00 50.00
Jim Palmer
Eddie Murray
Brian Roberts
Nick Markakis
Melvin Mora
20 David Ortiz 40.00 80.00
Jason Varitek
Josh Beckett
Manny Ramirez
Mike Lowell
Hideki Okajima
21 Jose Vidro 40.00 80.00
Alex Rodriguez
Ichiro Suzuki
J.J. Putz
Edgar Martinez
Kenji Johjima
22 Alex Rodriguez 30.00 60.00
C.C. Sabathia
Dustin Pedroia
Jimmy Rollins
Jake Peavy
Ryan Braun
23 Mickey Mantle 150.00 250.00
24 Joe DiMaggio 60.00 120.00
25 Roberto Clemente 60.00 120.00
26 Carlos Lee 30.00 60.00
Roy Oswalt
Lance Berkman
Hunter Pence
Nolan Ryan
Kaz Matsui
27 Jimmy Rollins 30.00 60.00
Mike Schmidt
Chase Utley
Cole Hamels
Robin Roberts
Ryan Howard
28 Johnny Podres 40.00 80.00
Whitey Ford
Bob Gibson
Frank Robinson
Brooks Robinson
Roberto Clemente
29 Ted Williams 50.00 100.00
30 Justin Morneau 50.00 100.00
Rod Carew
Francisco Liriano
Joe Mauer
Delmon Young
Harmon Killebrew
31 Justin Morneau 30.00 60.00
Ryan Howard
Albert Pujols
Prince Fielder
Carlos Delgado
Mark Teixeira
32 Magglio Ordonez 50.00 100.00
Al Kaline
Ivan Rodriguez
Curtis Granderson
Ty Cobb
Gary Sheffield
33 Carlton Fisk 20.00 50.00
Jim Thome
Jermaine Dye
Mark Buehrle
Paul Konerko
Luis Aparicio
34 Keith Hernandez 20.00 50.00
Dwight Gooden
Darryl Strawberry
David Wright
Pedro Martinez
Jose Reyes
35 Chipper Jones 30.00 60.00
John Smoltz
Brian McCann
Jeff Francoeur
Mark Teixeira
Tom Glavine
36 Alex Rodriguez 40.00 80.00
Jorge Posada
Johnny Damon
David Ortiz
Manny Ramirez
Jason Varitek
37 Roger Maris/Mickey Mantle 200.00 300.00
38 Ichiro Suzuki 40.00 80.00
39 Albert Pujols 30.00 60.00
40 Robin Yount 30.00 60.00
Paul Molitor
Rollie Fingers
Prince Fielder
Ryan Braun
Ben Sheets
41 Nolan Ryan 30.00 60.00
Alex Rodriguez
Ivan Rodriguez
Ian Kinsler
Michael Young
Hank Blalock
42 Vladimir Guerrero 20.00 50.00
John Lackey
Jered Weaver
Garret Anderson
Torii Hunter
Gary Matthews
43 Tim Lincecum 20.00 50.00
Rich Aurilia
Barry Zito
Eric Chavez
Mark Ellis
Bobby Crosby
44 Russell Martin 20.00 50.00
Rafael Furcal
Andruw Jones
Matt Kemp
Jeff Kent
Hong-Chih Kuo
45 David Wright 30.00 60.00
Carlos Beltran
Jose Reyes
Ryan Howard
Jimmy Rollins
Chase Utley
46 Chien-Ming Wang 40.00 80.00
47 Ichiro Suzuki 30.00 60.00
Alex Rodriguez
Magglio Ordonez
David Ortiz
Ivan Rodriguez
Vladimir Guerrero
48 Manny Ramirez 30.00 60.00
David Ortiz
Mike Lowell
Travis Hafner
Victor Martinez

Grady Sizemore
49 Matt Holliday 20.00 50.00
Todd Helton
Troy Tulowitzki
Orlando Hudson
Stephen Drew
Chris Young
50 Manny Ramirez 30.00 60.00
David Ortiz
Mike Lowell
Matt Holliday
Todd Helton
Troy Tulowitzki
51 Alex Rodriguez/Mickey Mantle 40.00 80.00
52 Albert Pujols 30.00 60.00
Vladimir Guerrero
Manny Ramirez
David Ortiz
Pedro Martinez
Alfonso Soriano
53 Joe DiMaggio 450.00 650.00
Ty Cobb
Babe Ruth
Lou Gehrig
Ted Williams
Mickey Mantle
54 George Sisler 100.00 200.00
Rogers Hornsby
Jimmie Foxx
Mel Ott
Johnny Mize
Pee Wee Reese
55 Jackie Robinson 100.00 200.00
Duke Snider
Roy Campanella
Phil Rizzuto
Mickey Mantle
Yogi Berra

2008 Topps Triple Threads Relics Combos Double Autographs

STATED ODDS 1:4323 MINI
STATED PRINT RUN 3 SER.#'d SETS
NO PRICING DUE TO SCARCITY

2008 Topps Triple Threads Relics Pairs Rookie-Stars Autographs

STATED ODDS 1:160 MINI
STATED PRINT RUN 50 SER.#'d SETS
GLD ODDS 1:322 MINI
GLD.PRINT RUN 25 SER.#'d SETS
NO GLD.PRICING AVAILABLE
PLAT.ODDS 1:7781 MINI
PLAT.PRINT RUN 1 SER.#'d SET
NO PLAT.PRICING AVAILABLE
SAP.ODDS 1:802 MINI
SAP.PRINT RUN 10 SER.#'d SETS
NO SAP.PRICING AVAILABLE
1 Steve Pearce 10.00 25.00
Nyjer Morgan
2 Cameron Maybin 12.50 30.00
Curtis Granderson
3 Melky Cabrera 20.00 50.00
Robinson Cano
4 Lastings Milledge 10.00 25.00
Elijah Dukes
5 Rich Hill 10.00 25.00
Sam Fuld
6 J.R. Towles 10.00 25.00
Jarrod Saltalamacchia
7 Clay Buchholz 20.00 50.00
Fausto Carmona
8 Ryan Braun 30.00 60.00
Ryan Zimmerman
9 Phil Hughes 30.00 60.00
Joba Chamberlain
10 Brandon Phillips 12.50 30.00
Homer Bailey

2008 Topps Triple Threads Relics X Autographs Gold

STATED ODDS 1:3890 MINI
STATED PRINT RUN 10 SER.#'d SETS
NO PRICING DUE TO SCARCITY
PLATINUM STATED ODDS 1:38,907 MINI
PLAT.PRINT RUN 1 SER.#'d SET
NO PLAT.PRICING DUE TO SCARCITY
SAPPHIRE STATED ODDS 1:7781 MINI
SAPP.PRINT RUN 5 SER.#'d SETS
NO SAPP.PRICING DUE TO SCARCITY
1 Daisuke Matsuzaka
2 John Elway

2008 Topps Triple Threads Triple Signed Hide

STATED ODDS 1:15,562 MINI
STATED PRINT RUN 1 SER.#'d SET
NO PRICING DUE TO SCARCITY

2008 Topps Triple Threads XXIV Legends Relics

STATED ODDS 1:15,562 MINI
NO PRICING DUE TO SCARCITY

2009 Topps Triple Threads

COMMON CARD (1-100) .40 1.00
1-100 PRINT RUN 1350 SER.#'d SETS
COMMON JSY AU RC (101-138) 6.00 15.00
JSY AU RC PRINT RUN 99 SER.#'d SETS
COMMON JSY AU (101-121) 6.00 15.00
JSY AU ODDS 1:11 MINI
JSY AU PRINT RUN 99 SER.#'d SETS
OVERALL 1-100 PLATE ODDS 1:97 MINI
OVERALL 101-138 PLATE ODDS 1:255 MINI
PLATE PRINT RUN 1 SET PER COLOR
BLACK-CYAN-MAGENTA-YELLOW ISSUED
NO PLATE PRICING DUE TO SCARCITY
1 Justin Upton .60 1.50
2 Brian McCann .60 1.50
3 Babe Ruth 2.50 6.00
4 Alfonso Soriano .60 1.50
5 Albert Pujols 2.50 6.00
6 Edinson Volquez .40 1.00
7 Todd Helton .60 1.50
8 Hanley Ramirez 1.00 2.50
9 Mickey Mantle 3.00 8.00
10 Manny Ramirez 1.00 2.50
11 Francisco Liriano .40 1.00
12 Lou Gehrig 2.00 5.00
13 Carlos Delgado .40 1.00
14 Walter Johnson 1.00 2.50
15 Alex Rodriguez 1.50 4.00
16 Ryan Howard 1.25 3.00
17 Nate McLouth .40 1.00
18 Cy Young 1.00 2.50
19 Ichiro Suzuki 1.50 4.00
20 Jorge Posada .60 1.50
21 Scott Kazmir .40 1.00
22 Michael Young .60 1.50
23 Brandon Webb .60 1.50
24 George Sisler .60 1.50
25 Chipper Jones 1.00 2.50
26 Adam Jones .60 1.50
27 David Ortiz .60 1.50
28 Geovany Soto .60 1.50
29 Tony Gwynn 1.00 2.50
30 Victor Martinez .60 1.50
31 Jose Lopez .40 1.00
32 Lance Berkman .60 1.50
33 Russell Martin .40 1.00
34 Cal Ripken 4.00 10.00
35 Dan Haren .40 1.00
36 Jose Reyes .60 1.50
37 Rogers Hornsby .60 1.50
38 Mark Teixeira 1.00 2.50
39 Ernie Banks 1.00 2.50
40 Jimmy Rollins .60 1.50
41 Jake Peavy .40 1.00
42 Jackie Robinson 1.00 2.50
43 B.J. Upton .60 1.50
44 Roy Halladay 1.00 2.50
45 Jimmie Foxx 1.00 2.50
46 Randy Johnson .60 1.50
47 Mel Ott 1.00 2.50
48 Carlos Lee .40 1.00
49 Nick Markakis 1.00 2.50
50 Dustin Pedroia 1.25 3.00
51 Nolan Ryan 3.00 8.00
52 Matt Cain .40 1.00
53 Grady Sizemore .60 1.50
54 Christy Mathewson 1.00 2.50
55 Miguel Cabrera 1.00 2.50
56 Roy Campanella 1.00 2.50
57 Prince Fielder .60 1.50
58 Ty Cobb 1.50 4.00
59 Carlos Beltran .40 1.00
60 Pee Wee Reese .60 1.50
61 A.J. Burnett .60 1.50
62 Carl Crawford .60 1.50
63 Chase Utley 1.00 2.50
64 Adrian Gonzalez .60 1.50
65 Thurman Munson 1.00 2.50
66 Felix Hernandez 1.00 2.50
67 Chris Carpenter 1.00 2.50
68 Carl Yastrzemski 1.50 4.00
69 Ian Kinsler .60 1.50
70 Vernon Wells .40 1.00
71 Matt Holliday 1.00 2.50
72 Tris Speaker .60 1.50
73 Roy Oswalt .60 1.50
74 Ozzie Smith 1.50 4.00
75 Daisuke Matsuzaka 1.00 2.50
76 David Wright 1.25 3.00
77 Kosuke Fukudome 1.00 2.50
78 Johan Santana 1.00 2.50
79 Curtis Granderson .60 1.50
80 Johnny Mize .60 1.50
81 Derek Jeter 2.50 6.00
82 Vladimir Guerrero 1.00 2.50
83 Dan Uggla .60 1.50
84 Hank Greenberg 1.00 2.50
85 Justin Morneau 1.00 2.50
86 CC Sabathia .60 1.50
87 Mike Schmidt 1.50 4.00
88 Cole Hamels 1.00 2.50
89 Alex Rios .60 1.50
90 Ryne Sandberg 2.00 5.00
91 Ryan Ludwick .60 1.50
92 Tim Lincecum 1.50 4.00
93 Honus Wagner 1.00 2.50
94 Carlos Quentin .60 1.50
95 Alexei Ramirez .60 1.50
96 Joe Mauer 1.00 2.50
97 Bob Gibson .60 1.50
98 Reggie Jackson .60 1.50
99 Carlos Zambrano .60 1.50
100 Stan Musial 1.50 4.00
101 Ryan Braun Jsy AU 15.00 40.00
102 Jay Bruce Jsy AU 10.00 25.00
103 Fausto Carmona Jsy AU 6.00 15.00
104 Matt Kemp Jsy AU 15.00 40.00
105 Cameron Maybin Jsy AU 8.00 20.00
106 Johnny Cueto Jsy AU 6.00 15.00
107 Josh Hamilton Jsy AU 12.50 30.00
108 Ubaldo Jimenez Jsy AU 40.00 80.00
109 Geovany Soto Jsy AU 10.00 25.00
110 Jon Lester Jsy AU 15.00 40.00
111 Clayton Kershaw Jsy AU 12.50 30.00
112 Luke Hochevar Jsy AU 6.00 15.00
113 Evan Longoria Jsy AU 30.00 60.00
114 Justin Masterson Jsy AU 10.00 25.00
115 Blake DeWitt Jsy AU 6.00 15.00
116 Daniel Murphy Jsy AU RC 10.00 25.00
117 Chad Billingsley Jsy AU 8.00 20.00
118 Dustin Pedroia Jsy AU 20.00 50.00
119 Hunter Pence Jsy AU 10.00 25.00
120 Joakim Soria Jsy AU 8.00 20.00
121 Justin Upton Jsy AU 20.00 50.00
122 Fernando Martinez Jsy AU RC 10.00 25.00
123 Nolan Reimold Jsy AU (RC) 15.00 40.00
124 Mat Gamel Jsy AU RC 10.00 25.00
125 Michael Bowden Jsy AU (RC) 6.00 15.00
126 Derek Holland Jsy AU RC 10.00 25.00
127 Elvis Andrus Jsy AU RC 12.50 30.00
128 Trevor Cahill Jsy AU RC 8.00 20.00
129 Ryan Perry Jsy AU RC 8.00 20.00
130 Jordan Zimmermann Jsy AU RC 8.00 20.00
131 Tommy Hanson Jsy AU RC 50.00 100.00
132 David Price Jsy AU RC 15.00 40.00
133 Colby Rasmus Jsy AU (RC) 15.00 40.00
134 Rick Porcello Jsy AU RC 30.00 60.00
135 Brett Anderson Jsy AU RC 8.00 20.00
136 Koji Uehara Jsy AU RC 30.00 60.00
137 Lou Marson Jsy AU (RC) 6.00 15.00
138 Matt Tolbert Jsy AU 6.00 15.00

2009 Topps Triple Threads Emerald

*EMERALD 1-100: .6X TO 1.5X BASIC
1-100 ODDS 1:2 MINI
1-100 PRINT RUN 240 SER.#'d SETS
*EMERALD JSY AU: .4X TO 1X BASIC
EMERALD JSY AU ODDS 1:21 MINI
EM.JSY AU PRINT RUN 50 SER.#'d SETS

2009 Topps Triple Threads Gold

*GOLD 1-100: 1X TO 2.5X BASIC
1-100 ODDS 1:4 MINI
1-100 PRINT RUN 99 SER.#'d SETS
GOLD JSY AU ODDS 1:41 MINI
GOLD JSY AU PRINT RUN 25 SER.#'d SETS
NO GOLD JSY AU PRICING AVAILABLE

2009 Topps Triple Threads Platinum

1-100 ODDS 1:387 MINI
1-100 PRINT RUN 1 SER.#'d SET
101-138 ODDS 1:1006 MINI
101-138 PRINT RUN 1 SER.#'d SET
NO PRICING DUE TO SCARCITY

2009 Topps Triple Threads Sapphire

1-100 ODDS 1:16 MINI
1-100 PRINT RUN 25 SER.#'d SETS
101-138 ODDS 1:102 MINI
101-138 PRINT RUN 10 SER.#'d SETS
NO PRICING DUE TO SCARCITY

2009 Topps Triple Threads Wood

STATED ODDS 1:1006 MINI
101-138 PRINT RUN 1 SER.#'d SET
NO PRICING DUE TO SCARCITY

2009 Topps Triple Threads All-Star Jumbo Sleeve Patches

STATED ODDS 1:610 MINI
STATED PRINT RUN 1 SER.#'d SET
NO PRICING DUE TO SCARCITY

2009 Topps Triple Threads All-Star Triple Patches

STATED ODDS 1:67 MINI
STATED PRINT RUN 9 SER.#'d SETS
NO PRICING DUE TO SCARCITY

2009 Topps Triple Threads All-Star Triple Patches Platinum

STATED ODDS 1:610 MINI
STATED PRINT RUN 1 SER.#'d SET
NO PRICING DUE TO SCARCITY

2009 Topps Triple Threads Bat Barrels

STATED ODDS 1:2482 MINI
STATED PRINT RUN 1 SER.#'d SET
NO PRICING DUE TO SCARCITY

2009 Topps Triple Threads Bat Knobs

STATED ODDS 1:3722 MINI
STATED PRINT RUN 1 SER.#'d SET
NO PRICING DUE TO SCARCITY

2009 Topps Triple Threads Camelot Relic

STATED ODDS 1:2481 MINI
STATED PRINT RUN 5 SER.#'d SETS
NO PRICING DUE TO SCARCITY
KEN John F. Kennedy
Robert F. Kennedy
Edward M. Kennedy

2009 Topps Triple Threads Cut Above

STATED ODDS 1:3722 MINI
STATED PRINT RUN 1 SER.#'d SET
NO PRICING DUE TO SCARCITY

2009 Topps Triple Threads Cut Above Dual

STATED ODDS 1:12,408 MINI
STATED PRINT RUN 1 SER.#'d SET
NO PRICING DUE TO SCARCITY

2009 Topps Triple Threads Cut Above Presidential

STATED ODDS 1:3722 MINI
STATED PRINT RUN 1 SER.#'d SET
NO PRICING DUE TO SCARCITY

2009 Topps Triple Threads Cut Above Triple

RANDOMLY INSERTED IN MINI PACKS
STATED PRINT RUN 1 SER.#'d SET
NO PRICING DUE TO SCARCITY

2009 Topps Triple Threads Jumbo Patch Combos

STATED ODDS 1:3722 MINI
STATED PRINT RUN 1 SER.#'d SETS
NO PRICING DUE TO SCARCITY

2009 Topps Triple Threads Jumbo Plus Relics

STATED ODDS 1:886 MINI
STATED PRINT RUN 3 SER.#'d SETS
NO PRICING DUE TO SCARCITY

2009 Topps Triple Threads Jumbo Plus Relics Platinum

STATED ODDS 1:2482 MINI
STATED PRINT RUN 1 SER.#'d SET
NO PRICING DUE TO SCARCITY

2009 Topps Triple Threads Legend Relics

STATED ODDS 1:72 MINI
STATED PRINT RUN 36 SER.#'d SETS
1 Babe Ruth 175.00 350.00
2 Rogers Hornsby 50.00 100.00
3 Pee Wee Reese 10.00 25.00
4 Lou Gehrig 150.00 250.00
5 Jimmie Foxx 30.00 60.00
6 Honus Wagner 100.00 175.00
7 Roy Campanella 20.00 50.00
8 Mickey Mantle 100.00 175.00
9 Mel Ott 40.00 80.00
10 Tris Speaker 40.00 80.00
11 Jackie Robinson 40.00 80.00
12 George Sisler 20.00 50.00
13 Ty Cobb 90.00 150.00
14 Thurman Munson 20.00 50.00
15 Johnny Mize 20.00 50.00

2009 Topps Triple Threads Legend Relics Emerald

STATED ODDS 1:144 MINI
STATED PRINT RUN 18 SER.#'d SETS
NO PRICING DUE TO SCARCITY

2009 Topps Triple Threads Legend Relics Gold

STATED ODDS 1:286 MINI
STATED PRINT RUN 9 SER.#'d SETS
NO PRICING DUE TO SCARCITY

2009 Topps Triple Threads Legend Relics Platinum

STATED ODDS 1:2481 MINI
STATED PRINT RUN 1 SER.#'d SET
NO PRICING DUE TO SCARCITY

2009 Topps Triple Threads Legend Relics Sapphire

STATED ODDS 1:886 MINI
STATED PRINT RUN 3 SER.#'d SETS
NO PRICING DUE TO SCARCITY

2009 Topps Triple Threads Legend Relics Sepia

*SEPIA: .4X TO 1X BASIC
STATED ODDS 1:96 MINI
STATED PRINT RUN 27 SER.#'d SETS

2009 Topps Triple Threads Letter Number Logo

STATED ODDS 1:3722 MINI
STATED PRINT RUN 1 SER.#'d SET
NO PRICING DUE TO SCARCITY

2009 Topps Triple Threads Letter Plus Relics

STATED ODDS 1:866 MINI
STATED PRINT RUN 3 SER.#'d SETS
NO PRICING DUE TO SCARCITY

2009 Topps Triple Threads Letter Plus Relics Platinum

STATED ODDS 1:2482 MINI
STATED PRINT RUN 1 SER.#'d SET
NO PRICING DUE TO SCARCITY

2009 Topps Triple Threads Relic Autographs

STATED ODDS 1:13 MINI
STATED PRINT RUN 18 SER.#'d SETS
ALL DC VARIATIONS PRICED EQUALLY
1 David Wright 30.00 60.00
2 David Wright 30.00 60.00
3 David Wright 30.00 60.00
4 David Ortiz 30.00 60.00
5 David Ortiz 30.00 60.00
6 David Ortiz 30.00 60.00
7 Jose Reyes 30.00 60.00
8 Jose Reyes 30.00 60.00
9 Jose Reyes 30.00 60.00
10 Zack Greinke 20.00 50.00
11 Zack Greinke 20.00 50.00
12 Zack Greinke 20.00 50.00
13 Miguel Cabrera 20.00 50.00
14 Miguel Cabrera 20.00 50.00
15 Miguel Cabrera 20.00 50.00
16 Matt Cain 10.00 25.00
17 Matt Cain 10.00 25.00
18 Matt Cain 10.00 25.00
19 Robinson Cano 20.00 50.00
20 Robinson Cano 20.00 50.00
21 Robinson Cano 20.00 50.00
22 Andre Ethier 12.50 30.00
23 Andre Ethier 12.50 30.00
24 Andre Ethier 12.50 30.00
25 Curtis Granderson 20.00 50.00
26 Curtis Granderson 20.00 50.00
27 Curtis Granderson 20.00 50.00
28 Manny Ramirez 100.00 200.00
29 Manny Ramirez 100.00 200.00
30 Manny Ramirez 100.00 200.00
31 Nick Markakis 12.50 30.00
32 Nick Markakis 12.50 30.00
33 Nick Markakis 12.50 30.00
34 Vladimir Guerrero 40.00 80.00
35 Vladimir Guerrero 40.00 80.00
36 Vladimir Guerrero 40.00 80.00
37 Matt Holliday 15.00 40.00
38 Matt Holliday 15.00 40.00
39 Matt Holliday 15.00 40.00
40 Ryan Howard 50.00 100.00
41 Ryan Howard 50.00 100.00
42 Ryan Howard 50.00 100.00
43 Chipper Jones 40.00 80.00
44 Chipper Jones 40.00 80.00
45 Chipper Jones 40.00 80.00
46 Scott Kazmir 10.00 25.00
47 Scott Kazmir 10.00 25.00
48 Scott Kazmir 10.00 25.00
49 Joba Chamberlain 20.00 50.00
50 Joba Chamberlain 20.00 50.00
51 Joba Chamberlain 20.00 50.00
52 Alfonso Soriano 15.00 40.00
53 Alfonso Soriano 15.00 40.00
54 Alfonso Soriano 15.00 40.00
55 Nick Swisher 20.00 50.00
56 Nick Swisher 20.00 50.00
57 Nick Swisher 20.00 50.00
58 Prince Fielder 30.00 60.00
59 Prince Fielder 30.00 60.00
60 Prince Fielder 30.00 60.00
61 Ryan Zimmerman 20.00 50.00
62 Ryan Zimmerman 20.00 50.00
63 Ryan Zimmerman 20.00 50.00
64 Johnny Podres 20.00 50.00
65 Johnny Podres 20.00 50.00
66 Johnny Podres 20.00 50.00
67 George Kell 20.00 50.00
68 George Kell 20.00 50.00
69 George Kell 20.00 50.00
70 Gary Carter 30.00 60.00
71 Gary Carter 30.00 60.00
72 Gary Carter 30.00 60.00
73 Whitey Ford 40.00 80.00
74 Whitey Ford 40.00 80.00
75 Whitey Ford 40.00 80.00
76 Bob Gibson 30.00 60.00
77 Bob Gibson 30.00 60.00
78 Bob Gibson 30.00 60.00
79 Juan Marichal 20.00 50.00
80 Juan Marichal 20.00 50.00
81 Juan Marichal 20.00 50.00
82 Duke Snider 30.00 60.00
83 Duke Snider 30.00 60.00
84 Duke Snider 30.00 60.00
85 Robin Yount 20.00 50.00
86 Robin Yount 20.00 50.00
87 Robin Yount 20.00 50.00
88 Jim Palmer 15.00 40.00
89 Jim Palmer 15.00 40.00
90 Jim Palmer 15.00 40.00
91 Bo Jackson 40.00 80.00
92 Bo Jackson 40.00 80.00
93 Bo Jackson 40.00 80.00
94 Don Larsen 30.00 60.00
95 Don Larsen 30.00 60.00
96 Don Larsen 30.00 60.00
97 Tony Gwynn 40.00 80.00
98 Tony Gwynn 40.00 80.00
99 Tony Gwynn 40.00 80.00
100 Brian McCann 15.00 40.00
101 Brian McCann 15.00 40.00
102 Brian McCann 15.00 40.00
103 Shane Victorino 40.00 80.00
104 Shane Victorino 40.00 80.00
105 Shane Victorino 40.00 80.00
106 Adrian Gonzalez 12.50 30.00
107 Adrian Gonzalez 12.50 30.00
108 Adrian Gonzalez 12.50 30.00
109 Garrett Atkins 8.00 20.00
110 Garrett Atkins 8.00 20.00
111 Garrett Atkins 8.00 20.00
112 Carl Yastrzemski 40.00 80.00
113 Carl Yastrzemski 40.00 80.00
114 Carl Yastrzemski 40.00 80.00
115 Carlos Delgado 15.00 40.00
116 Carlos Delgado 15.00 40.00
117 Carlos Delgado 15.00 40.00
118 Jason Varitek 20.00 50.00
119 Jason Varitek 20.00 50.00
120 Jason Varitek 20.00 50.00
121 Tom Seaver 40.00 80.00
122 Tom Seaver 40.00 80.00
123 Tom Seaver 40.00 80.00
124 Rich Harden 12.50 30.00
125 Rich Harden 12.50 30.00
126 Rich Harden 12.50 30.00
127 Aramis Ramirez 15.00 40.00
128 Aramis Ramirez 15.00 40.00
129 Aramis Ramirez 15.00 40.00
130 Chien-Ming Wang 90.00 150.00
131 Chien-Ming Wang 90.00 150.00
132 Chien-Ming Wang 90.00 150.00
133 Jayson Werth 20.00 50.00
134 Jayson Werth 20.00 50.00
135 Jayson Werth 20.00 50.00
136 Jonathan Papelbon 12.50 30.00
137 Jonathan Papelbon 12.50 30.00
138 Jonathan Papelbon 12.50 30.00
139 Alex Rodriguez 125.00 250.00
140 Alex Rodriguez 125.00 250.00
141 Alex Rodriguez 125.00 250.00
142 Johnny Bench 40.00 80.00
143 Johnny Bench 40.00 80.00
144 Johnny Bench 40.00 80.00
145 Mark Teixeira 90.00 150.00
146 Mark Teixeira 90.00 150.00
147 Mark Teixeira 90.00 150.00
148 Dan Haren 10.00 25.00
149 Dan Haren 10.00 25.00
150 Dan Haren 10.00 25.00
151 Ernie Banks 40.00 80.00
152 Ernie Banks 40.00 80.00
153 Ernie Banks 40.00 80.00
154 Lance Berkman 15.00 40.00
155 Lance Berkman 15.00 40.00
156 Lance Berkman 15.00 40.00
157 Cal Ripken 100.00 200.00
158 Cal Ripken 100.00 200.00
159 Cal Ripken 100.00 200.00
160 Paul Molitor 30.00 60.00
161 Paul Molitor 30.00 60.00
162 Paul Molitor 30.00 60.00
163 Mike Lowell 15.00 40.00
164 Mike Lowell 15.00 40.00
165 Mike Lowell 15.00 40.00
166 Dan Uggla 8.00 20.00
167 Dan Uggla 8.00 20.00
168 Dan Uggla 8.00 20.00
169 Aaron Hill 12.50 30.00
170 Aaron Hill 12.50 30.00
171 Aaron Hill 12.50 30.00
172 Johnny Damon 90.00 150.00
173 Johnny Damon 90.00 150.00
174 Johnny Damon 90.00 150.00

2009 Topps Triple Threads Relic Autographs Gold

*GOLD: .5X TO 1.2X BASIC
STATED ODDS 1:25 MINI
STATED PRINT RUN 9 SER.#'d SETS
ALL DC VARIATIONS PRICED EQUALLY

2009 Topps Triple Threads Relic Autographs Platinum

STATED ODDS 1:222 HOBBY MINI
STATED PRINT RUN 1 SER.#'d SET
NO PRICING DUE TO SCARCITY

2009 Topps Triple Threads Relic Autographs Sapphire

STATED ODDS 1:74 MINI
STATED PRINT RUN 3 SER.#'d SET
NO PRICING DUE TO SCARCITY

2009 Topps Triple Threads Relic Autographs White Whale Printing Plates

STATED ODDS 1:56 MINI
STATED PRINT RUN 1 SER.#'d SET
NO PRICING DUE TO SCARCITY

2009 Topps Triple Threads Relic Autographs Wood

STATED ODDS 1:222 HOBBY MINI
STATED PRINT RUN 1 SER.#'d SET
NO PRICING DUE TO SCARCITY

2009 Topps Triple Threads Relic Autographs Pairs

STATED ODDS 1:730 MINI
STATED PRINT RUN 18 SER.#'d SETS
NO PRICING DUE TO SCARCITY
1 Dustin Pedroia
Ryan Howard
2 Ryan Howard
Alex Rodriguez
3 David Wright
Alex Rodriguez

2009 Topps Triple Threads Relic Autographs Pairs Gold

STATED ODDS 1:1490 MINI
STATED PRINT RUN 9 SER.#'d SETS
NO PRICING DUE TO SCARCITY

2009 Topps Triple Threads Relic Autographs Pairs Platinum

STATED ODDS 1:12,408 MINI
STATED PRINT RUN 1 SER.#'d SET
NO PRICING DUE TO SCARCITY

2009 Topps Triple Threads Relic Autographs Pairs Sapphire

STATED ODDS 1:4136 MINI
STATED PRINT RUN 3 SER.#'d SETS
NO PRICING DUE TO SCARCITY

2009 Topps Triple Threads Relic Combo Autographs

STATED ODDS 1:51 MINI
STATED PRINT RUN 36 SER.#'d SETS
1 Geovany Soto 15.00 40.00
Brian McCann
Russell Martin
2 Hanley Ramirez 30.00 60.00
Jose Reyes
Miguel Tejada
3 Johnny Cueto 12.50 30.00
Carlos Silva
Joakim Soria
4 Roy Halladay 50.00 100.00
Brandon Webb
Chien-Ming Wang
5 Manny Ramirez 75.00 150.00
Matt Kemp
Ryan Howard
Andre Ethier
6 Frank Robinson 40.00 80.00
Jim Palmer
Eddie Murray
7 Scott Kazmir 30.00 60.00
Joba Chamberlain
Jon Lester
8 Ryan Howard 150.00 300.00
Albert Pujols
Miguel Cabrera
9 Reggie Jackson 125.00 250.00
Alex Rodriguez
Robinson Cano
10 Paul Molitor 60.00 120.00
Robin Yount
Ryan Braun
11 Jon Lester 30.00 60.00
Justin Masterson
Jonathan Papelbon
12 Jay Bruce 12.50 30.00
Josh Hamilton
Hunter Pence
13 David Ortiz 40.00 80.00
Jason Varitek
Jonathan Papelbon
14 Duke Snider 60.00 120.00
Manny Ramirez
Matt Kemp
15 Brian Roberts 50.00 100.00
Dustin Pedroia
Robinson Cano
16 Alfonso Soriano 40.00 80.00
Aramis Ramirez
Ryne Sandberg
17 David Wright 150.00 250.00
Hanley Ramirez
Albert Pujols
18 Scott Kazmir 40.00 80.00
Evan Longoria
David Price
19 Mark Teixeira 175.00 350.00
Robinson Cano
Alex Rodriguez
20 Jonathan Papelbon 20.00 50.00
Joakim Soria
Joe Nathan
21 Torii Hunter 40.00 80.00
Vladimir Guerrero
Reggie Jackson

2009 Topps Triple Threads Relic Combo Autographs Emerald

STATED ODDS 1:102 MINI
STATED PRINT RUN 18 SER.#'d SETS
NO PRICING DUE TO SCARCITY

2009 Topps Triple Threads Relic Combo Autographs Gold

STATED ODDS 1:205 MINI
STATED PRINT RUN 9 SER.#'d SETS
NO PRICING DUE TO SCARCITY

2009 Topps Triple Threads Relic Combo Autographs Platinum

STATED ODDS 1:1861 MINI
STATED PRINT RUN 1 SER.#'d SET
NO PRICING DUE TO SCARCITY

2009 Topps Triple Threads Relic Combo Autographs Sapphire

STATED ODDS 1:621 MINI
STATED PRINT RUN 3 SER.#'d SETS
NO PRICING DUE TO SCARCITY

2009 Topps Triple Threads Relic Combo Autographs Sepia

*SEPIA: .4X TO 1X BASIC
STATED ODDS 1:68 MINI
STATED PRINT RUN 27 SER.#'d SETS

2009 Topps Triple Threads Relic Combo Autographs White Whale Printing Plates

STATED ODDS 1:456 MINI
STATED PRINT RUN 1 SER.#'d SET
NO PRICING DUE TO SCARCITY

2009 Topps Triple Threads Relic Combo Autographs Wood

STATED ODDS 1:1861 MINI
STATED PRINT RUN 1 SER.#'d SET
NO PRICING DUE TO SCARCITY

2009 Topps Triple Threads Relic Combo Double Autographs

STATED ODDS 1:4136 MINI
STATED PRINT RUN 3 SER.#'d SETS
NO PRICING DUE TO SCARCITY

2009 Topps Triple Threads Relic Combo Double Autographs Platinum

STATED ODDS 1:12,408 MINI
STATED PRINT RUN 1 SER.#'d SET
NO PRICING DUE TO SCARCITY

2009 Topps Triple Threads Relic Combos

STATED ODDS 1:24 MINI
STATED PRINT RUN 36 SER.#'d SETS
1 Tom Seaver 20.00 50.00
Nolan Ryan
Johan Santana
2 Ryan Howard 40.00 80.00
Mike Schmidt
Chase Utley
3 Jorge Posada 50.00 100.00
Mickey Mantle
Mark Teixeira
4 Josh Beckett 12.50 30.00
Jon Lester
John Smoltz
5 Jose Reyes 20.00 50.00
Gary Carter
David Wright
6 Albert Pujols 12.50 30.00
Miguel Cabrera
Ryan Howard
7 Ryne Sandberg 15.00 40.00
Mike Schmidt
Ozzie Smith
8 Daisuke Matsuzaka 30.00 60.00
Ichiro Suzuki
Hideki Matsui
9 Kenshin Kawakami 30.00 60.00
Daisuke Matsuzaka
Koji Uehara
10 Manny Ramirez 10.00 25.00
Carlos Beltran
Alfonso Soriano
11 Josh Hamilton 8.00 20.00
Ian Kinsler
Michael Young
12 Grady Sizemore 12.50 30.00
Josh Hamilton
Ichiro Suzuki
13 Hanley Ramirez 8.00 20.00
Jimmy Rollins
Jose Reyes
14 Dustin Pedroia 10.00 25.00
Ryne Sandberg
Ian Kinsler
15 Evan Longoria 15.00 40.00
Alex Rodriguez
Chipper Jones
16 Manny Ramirez 12.50 30.00
Albert Pujols

Ryan Howard
17 Jim Thome 8.00 20.00
Manny Ramirez
Gary Sheffield
18 Mickey Mantle 350.00 450.00
Babe Ruth
Lou Gehrig
19 Stan Musial
Duke Snider
Frank Robinson
20 Mickey Mantle 50.00 100.00
Frank Robinson
Carl Yastrzemski
21 Pee Wee Reese 40.00 80.00
Jackie Robinson
Roy Campanella
22 Carlos Beltran 10.00 25.00
Carlos Delgado
David Wright
23 Ryan Zimmerman 12.50 30.00
David Wright
Evan Longoria
24 Joe Mauer 12.50 30.00
Johnny Bench
Brian McCann
25 Ryan Howard 12.50 30.00
Alex Rodriguez
David Wright
26 Tim Lincecum 12.50 30.00
Jake Peavy
Brandon Webb
27 Kevin Youkilis 10.00 25.00
David Ortiz
Jason Varitek
28 Russell Martin 10.00 25.00
Manny Ramirez
Matt Kemp
29 Geovany Soto 10.00 25.00
Ryan Braun
Hanley Ramirez
30 Albert Pujols 12.50 30.00
Ryan Howard
Hanley Ramirez
31 Adrian Gonzalez 10.00 25.00
Jimmy Rollins
David Wright
32 Cal Ripken 30.00 60.00
Alex Rodriguez
Chipper Jones
33 Ernie Banks 12.50 30.00
Ozzie Smith
Hanley Ramirez
34 Adrian Gonzalez 10.00 25.00
Tony Gwynn
Jake Peavy
35 Ernie Banks 20.00 50.00
Ozzie Smith
Cal Ripken
36 Chase Utley 20.00 50.00
Jimmy Rollins
Ryan Howard
37 Reggie Jackson 15.00 40.00
Reggie Jackson
Reggie Jackson
38 Nolan Ryan 30.00 60.00
Nolan Ryan
Nolan Ryan
39 Prince Fielder 12.50 30.00
Albert Pujols
Lance Berkman
40 Jorge Cantu 10.00 25.00
Joakim Soria
Edgar Gonzalez
41 Felix Hernandez 12.50 30.00
Magglio Ordonez
Miguel Cabrera
42 Jimmy Rollins 8.00 20.00
Roy Oswalt
Adam Dunn
43 Dae Ho Lee 12.50 30.00
Jin Young Lee
Shin-Soo Choo
44 Phillippe Aumont 30.00 60.00
Aroldis Chapman
Dylan Lindsay
45 Frederich Cepeda 8.00 20.00
Yulieski Gourriel
Yoennis Cespedes
46 Ichiro Suzuki 60.00 120.00
Yu Darvish
Norichika Aoki

2009 Topps Triple Threads Relic Combos Emerald

STATED ODDS 1:47 MINI
STATED PRINT RUN 18 SER.#'d SETS
NO PRICING DUE TO SCARCITY

2009 Topps Triple Threads Relic Combos Gold

STATED ODDS 1:94 MINI
STATED PRINT RUN 9 SER.#'d SETS
NO PRICING DUE TO SCARCITY

2009 Topps Triple Threads Relic Combos Platinum

STATED ODDS 1:666 MINI
STATED PRINT RUN 1 SER.#'d SET
NO PRICING DUE TO SCARCITY

2009 Topps Triple Threads Relic Combos Sapphire

STATED ODDS 1:280 MINI
STATED PRINT RUN 3 SER.#'d SETS
NO PRICING DUE TO SCARCITY

2009 Topps Triple Threads Relic Combos Sepia

*SEPIA: .4X TO 1X BASIC
STATED ODDS 1:32 MINI
STATED PRINT RUN 27 SER.#'d SETS
1 Tom Seaver 20.00 50.00
Nolan Ryan
Johan Santana
2 Ryan Howard 40.00 80.00
Mike Schmidt
Chase Utley
3 Jorge Posada 50.00 100.00
Mickey Mantle
Mark Teixeira
4 Josh Beckett 12.50 30.00
Jon Lester
John Smoltz
5 Jose Reyes 20.00 50.00
Gary Carter
David Wright
6 Albert Pujols 12.50 30.00
Miguel Cabrera
Ryan Howard
7 Ryne Sandberg 15.00 40.00
Mike Schmidt
Ozzie Smith
8 Daisuke Matsuzaka 30.00 60.00
Ichiro Suzuki
Hideki Matsui
9 Kenshin Kawakami 30.00 60.00
Daisuke Matsuzaka
Koji Uehara
10 Manny Ramirez 10.00 25.00
Carlos Beltran
Alfonso Soriano
11 Josh Hamilton 8.00 20.00
Ian Kinsler
Michael Young
12 Grady Sizemore 12.50 30.00
Josh Hamilton
Ichiro Suzuki
13 Hanley Ramirez 8.00 20.00
Jimmy Rollins
Jose Reyes
14 Dustin Pedroia 10.00 25.00
Ryne Sandberg
Ian Kinsler
15 Evan Longoria 15.00 40.00
Alex Rodriguez
Chipper Jones
16 Manny Ramirez 12.50 30.00
Albert Pujols
Ryan Howard
17 Jim Thome 8.00 20.00
Manny Ramirez
Gary Sheffield
18 Mickey Mantle 350.00 450.00
Babe Ruth
Lou Gehrig
19 Stan Musial
Duke Snider
Frank Robinson
20 Mickey Mantle 50.00 100.00
Frank Robinson
Carl Yastrzemski
21 Pee Wee Reese 40.00 80.00
Jackie Robinson
Roy Campanella
22 Carlos Beltran 10.00 25.00
Carlos Delgado
David Wright
23 Ryan Zimmerman 12.50 30.00
David Wright
Evan Longoria
24 Joe Mauer 12.50 30.00
Johnny Bench
Brian McCann
25 Ryan Howard 12.50 30.00
Alex Rodriguez
David Wright
26 Tim Lincecum 12.50 30.00
Jake Peavy
Brandon Webb
27 Kevin Youkilis 10.00 25.00
David Ortiz
Jason Varitek
28 Russell Martin 10.00 25.00
Manny Ramirez
Matt Kemp
29 Geovany Soto 10.00 25.00
Ryan Braun
Hanley Ramirez
30 Albert Pujols 12.50 30.00
Ryan Howard
Hanley Ramirez
31 Adrian Gonzalez 10.00 25.00
Jimmy Rollins
David Wright
32 Cal Ripken 30.00 60.00
Alex Rodriguez
Chipper Jones
33 Ernie Banks 12.50 30.00
Ozzie Smith
Hanley Ramirez
34 Adrian Gonzalez 10.00 25.00
Tony Gwynn
Jake Peavy
35 Ernie Banks 20.00 50.00
Ozzie Smith
Cal Ripken
36 Chase Utley 20.00 50.00
Jimmy Rollins
Ryan Howard
37 Reggie Jackson 15.00 40.00
Reggie Jackson
Reggie Jackson
38 Nolan Ryan 30.00 60.00
Nolan Ryan
Nolan Ryan
39 Prince Fielder 12.50 30.00
Albert Pujols
Lance Berkman
40 Jorge Cantu 10.00 25.00
Joakim Soria
Edgar Gonzalez
41 Felix Hernandez 12.50 30.00
Magglio Ordonez
Miguel Cabrera
42 Jimmy Rollins 8.00 20.00
Roy Oswalt
Adam Dunn
43 Dae Ho Lee 12.50 30.00
Jin Young Lee
Shin-Soo Choo
44 Phillippe Aumont 30.00 60.00
Aroldis Chapman
Dylan Lindsay
45 Frederich Cepeda 8.00 20.00
Yulieski Gourriel
Yoennis Cespedes
46 Ichiro Suzuki 60.00 120.00
Yu Darvish
Norichika Aoki

2009 Topps Triple Threads Relic Combos Double

STATED ODDS 1:90 MINI
STATED PRINT RUN 36 SER.#'d SETS
1 Mike Schmidt 30.00 60.00
Ryan Howard
2 Yulieski Gourriel 75.00 150.00
Yu Darvish
3 Ryan Howard 20.00 50.00
4 Dustin Pedroia 15.00 40.00
5 Ryan Howard 15.00 40.00
Dustin Pedroia
6 Cal Ripken 30.00 60.00
Alex Rodriguez
7 Jake Peavy 12.50 30.00
Tim Lincecum
8 Ichiro 30.00 60.00
Daisuke Matsuzaka
9 Manny Ramirez 20.00 50.00
Alfonso Soriano
Ryan Howard
Evan Longoria
Carlos Quentin
Vladimir Guerrero
10 Mariano Rivera 30.00 60.00
Jonathan Papelbon
Trevor Hoffman
Joe Nathan
Francisco Rodriguez
Dennis Eckersley
11 Alex Rodriguez 20.00 50.00
Evan Longoria
Kevin Youkilis
Alex Rios
Nick Markakis
Wade Boggs
12 Albert Pujols 40.00 80.00
David Wright
Hanley Ramirez
Alex Rodriguez
Josh Hamilton
Evan Longoria

2009 Topps Triple Threads Relic Combos Double Emerald

STATED ODDS 1:179 MINI
STATED PRINT RUN 18 SER.#'d SETS
NO PRICING DUE TO SCARCITY

2009 Topps Triple Threads Relic Combos Double Gold

STATED ODDS 1:361 MINI
STATED PRINT RUN 9 SER.#'d SETS
NO PRICING DUE TO SCARCITY

2009 Topps Triple Threads Relic Combos Double Platinum

STATED ODDS 1:3102 MINI
STATED PRINT RUN 1 SER.#'d SET
NO PRICING DUE TO SCARCITY

2009 Topps Triple Threads Relic Combos Double Sapphire

STATED ODDS 1:1128 MINI
STATED PRINT RUN 3 SER.#'d SETS
NO PRICING DUE TO SCARCITY

2009 Topps Triple Threads Relic Combos Double Sepia

*SEPIA: .4X TO 1X BASIC
STATED ODDS 1:120 MINI
STATED PRINT RUN 27 SER.#'d SETS

2009 Topps Triple Threads Relics

STATED ODDS 1:10 MINI
STATED PRINT RUN 36 SER.#'d SETS
ALL DC VARIATIONS PRICED EQUALLY
1 Tim Lincecum 12.50 30.00
2 Tim Lincecum 12.50 30.00
3 Tim Lincecum 12.50 30.00
4 David Wright 10.00 25.00
5 David Wright 10.00 25.00
6 David Wright 10.00 25.00
7 Albert Pujols 20.00 50.00
8 Albert Pujols 20.00 50.00
9 Albert Pujols 20.00 50.00
10 Alex Rodriguez 15.00 40.00
11 Alex Rodriguez 15.00 40.00
12 Alex Rodriguez 15.00 40.00
13 David Ortiz 10.00 25.00
14 David Ortiz 10.00 25.00
15 David Ortiz 10.00 25.00
16 Manny Ramirez 12.50 30.00
17 Manny Ramirez 12.50 30.00
18 Manny Ramirez 12.50 30.00
19 Ichiro Suzuki 20.00 50.00
20 Ichiro Suzuki 20.00 50.00
21 Ichiro Suzuki 20.00 50.00
22 Vladimir Guerrero 6.00 15.00
23 Vladimir Guerrero 6.00 15.00
24 Vladimir Guerrero 6.00 15.00
25 Ryan Braun 10.00 25.00
26 Ryan Braun 10.00 25.00
27 Ryan Braun 10.00 25.00
28 Chipper Jones 10.00 25.00
29 Chipper Jones 10.00 25.00
30 Chipper Jones 10.00 25.00
31 Evan Longoria 12.50 30.00
32 Evan Longoria 12.50 30.00
33 Evan Longoria 12.50 30.00
34 Dustin Pedroia 8.00 20.00
35 Dustin Pedroia 8.00 20.00
36 Dustin Pedroia 8.00 20.00
37 Alfonso Soriano 6.00 15.00
38 Alfonso Soriano 6.00 15.00
39 Alfonso Soriano 6.00 15.00
40 Miguel Cabrera 8.00 20.00
41 Miguel Cabrera 8.00 20.00
42 Miguel Cabrera 8.00 20.00
43 Nick Markakis 8.00 20.00
44 Nick Markakis 8.00 20.00
45 Nick Markakis 8.00 20.00
46 Josh Hamilton 8.00 20.00
47 Josh Hamilton 8.00 20.00
48 Josh Hamilton 8.00 20.00
49 Jose Reyes 8.00 20.00
50 Jose Reyes 8.00 20.00
51 Jose Reyes 8.00 20.00
52 Bob Gibson 10.00 25.00
53 Bob Gibson 10.00 25.00
54 Bob Gibson 10.00 25.00
55 Frank Robinson 10.00 25.00
56 Frank Robinson 10.00 25.00
57 Frank Robinson 10.00 25.00
58 Paul Molitor 10.00 25.00
59 Paul Molitor 10.00 25.00
60 Paul Molitor 10.00 25.00
61 Tom Seaver 10.00 25.00
62 Tom Seaver 10.00 25.00
63 Tom Seaver 10.00 25.00
64 Gary Carter 12.50 30.00
65 Gary Carter 12.50 30.00
66 Gary Carter 12.50 30.00
67 Stan Musial 15.00 40.00
68 Stan Musial 15.00 40.00
69 Stan Musial 15.00 40.00
70 Ryne Sandberg 15.00 40.00
71 Ryne Sandberg 15.00 40.00
72 Ryne Sandberg 15.00 40.00
73 Carl Yastrzemski 10.00 25.00
74 Carl Yastrzemski 10.00 25.00
75 Carl Yastrzemski 10.00 25.00
76 Duke Snider 12.50 30.00
77 Duke Snider 12.50 30.00
78 Duke Snider 12.50 30.00
79 Whitey Ford 15.00 40.00
80 Whitey Ford 15.00 40.00
81 Whitey Ford 15.00 40.00
82 Mike Schmidt 15.00 40.00
83 Mike Schmidt 15.00 40.00
84 Mike Schmidt 15.00 40.00
85 Daisuke Matsuzaka 10.00 25.00
86 Daisuke Matsuzaka 10.00 25.00
87 Daisuke Matsuzaka 10.00 25.00
88 Grady Sizemore 6.00 15.00
89 Grady Sizemore 6.00 15.00
90 Grady Sizemore 6.00 15.00
91 Chase Utley 12.50 30.00
92 Chase Utley 12.50 30.00
93 Chase Utley 12.50 30.00
94 Josh Beckett 8.00 20.00
95 Josh Beckett 8.00 20.00
96 Josh Beckett 8.00 20.00
97 Hanley Ramirez 8.00 20.00
98 Hanley Ramirez 8.00 20.00
99 Hanley Ramirez 8.00 20.00
100 Johan Santana 8.00 20.00
101 Johan Santana 8.00 20.00
102 Johan Santana 8.00 20.00
103 Ryan Howard 12.50 30.00
104 Ryan Howard 12.50 30.00
105 Ryan Howard 12.50 30.00
106 Bo Jackson 10.00 25.00
107 Bo Jackson 10.00 25.00
108 Bo Jackson 10.00 25.00
109 Carlos Quentin 6.00 15.00
110 Carlos Quentin 6.00 15.00
111 Carlos Quentin 6.00 15.00
112 Hideki Matsui 15.00 40.00
113 Hideki Matsui 15.00 40.00
114 Hideki Matsui 15.00 40.00
115 Rickey Henderson 50.00 100.00
116 Rickey Henderson 50.00 100.00
117 Rickey Henderson 50.00 100.00

2009 Topps Triple Threads Relics Emerald

*EMERALD: .5X TO 1.2X BASIC
STATED ODDS 1:19 MINI
STATED PRINT RUN 18 SER.#'d SETS
ALL DC VARIATIONS PRICED EQUALLY

2009 Topps Triple Threads Relics Gold

*GOLD: .6X TO 1.5X BASIC
STATED ODDS 1:37 MINI
STATED PRINT RUN 9 SER.#'d SETS
ALL DC VARIATIONS PRICED EQUALLY

2009 Topps Triple Threads Relics Platinum

STATED ODDS 1:332 MINI
STATED PRINT RUN 1 SER.#'d SET
NO PRICING DUE TO SCARCITY

2009 Topps Triple Threads Relics Sapphire

STATED ODDS 1:111 MINI
STATED PRINT RUN 3 SER.#'d SETS
NO PRICING DUE TO SCARCITY

2009 Topps Triple Threads Relics Sepia

*SEPIA: .4X TO 1X BASIC
STATED ODDS 1:13 MINI
STATED PRINT RUN 27 SER.#'d SETS
ALL DC VARIATIONS PRICED EQUALLY

2009 Topps Triple Threads Rookie-Rising Stars Relic Autograph Pairs

STATED ODDS 1:258 MINI
STATED PRINT RUN 18 SER.#'d SETS
NO PRICING DUE TO SCARCITY

2009 Topps Triple Threads Rookie-Rising Stars Relic Autograph Pairs Gold

STATED ODDS 1:510 MINI
STATED PRINT RUN 9 SER.#'d SETS
NO PRICING DUE TO SCARCITY

2009 Topps Triple Threads Rookie-Rising Stars Relic Autograph Pairs Platinum

STATED ODDS 1:12,408 MINI
STATED PRINT RUN 1 SER.#'d SET
NO PRICING DUE TO SCARCITY

2009 Topps Triple Threads Rookie-Rising Stars Relic Autograph Pairs Sapphire

STATED ODDS 1:1283 MINI
STATED PRINT RUN 3 SER.#'d SETS
NO PRICING DUE TO SCARCITY

2009 Topps Triple Threads WBC Dual Patch Logo

STATED ODDS 1:1772 MINI
STATED PRINT RUN 1 SER.#'d SET
NO PRICING DUE TO SCARCITY

2009 Topps Triple Threads WBC Relic Autographs

STATED ODDS 1:178 MINI
STATED PRINT RUN 36 SER.#'d SETS
BCAR1 Miguel Tejada 8.00 20.00
BCAR2 Jose Reyes 20.00 50.00
BCAR3 Geovany Soto 10.00 25.00
BCAR4 David Wright 50.00 100.00
BCAR5 Roy Oswalt 12.50 30.00
BCAR6 Miguel Cabrera 30.00 60.00

2009 Topps Triple Threads WBC Relic Autographs Emerald

STATED ODDS 1:358 HOBBY
STATED PRINT RUN 18 SER.#'d SETS
NO PRICING DUE TO SCARCITY

2009 Topps Triple Threads WBC Relic Autographs Gold

STATED ODDS 1:730 HOBBY
STATED PRINT RUN 9 SER.#'d SETS
NO PRICING DUE TO SCARCITY

2009 Topps Triple Threads WBC Relic Autographs Platinum

STATED ODDS 1:6204 HOBBY
STATED PRINT RUN 1 SER.#'d SET
NO PRICING DUE TO SCARCITY

2009 Topps Triple Threads WBC Relic Autographs Sapphire

STATED ODDS 1:2068 HOBBY
STATED PRINT RUN 3 SER.#'d SETS
NO PRICING DUE TO SCARCITY

2009 Topps Triple Threads WBC Relic Autographs Sepia

*SEPIA: .4X TO 1X BASIC
STATED ODDS 1:239 MINI
STATED PRINT RUN 27 SER.#'d SETS

2009 Topps Triple Threads WBC Relic Autographs White Whale Printing Plates

STATED ODDS 1:1551 HOBBY
STATED PRINT RUN 1 SER.#'d SET
NO PRICING DUE TO SCARCITY

2009 Topps Triple Threads WBC Relic Autographs Wood

STATED ODDS 1:6204 HOBBY
STATED PRINT RUN 1 SER.#'d SET
NO PRICING DUE TO SCARCITY

2009 Topps Triple Threads WBC Triple Patches

STATED ODDS 1:179 MINI
STATED PRINT RUN 1 SER.#'d SET
NO PRICING DUE TO SCARCITY

2009 Topps Triple Threads WBC Triple Patches Platinum

STATED ODDS 1:1772 MINI
STATED PRINT RUN 1 SER.#'d SET
NO PRICING DUE TO SCARCITY

2009 Topps Triple Threads XXIV Legends Relics

STATED ODDS 1:7445 MINI
STATED PRINT RUN 18 SER.#'d SETS
NO PRICING DUE TO SCARCITY

2009 Topps Triple Threads XXIV Relics

STATED ODDS 1:144 MINI
STATED PRINT RUN 18 SER.#'d SETS
NO PRICING DUE TO SCARCITY

2009 Topps Triple Threads XXIV Relics Gold

STATED ODDS 1:287 MINI
STATED PRINT RUN 9 SER.#'d SETS
NO PRICING DUE TO SCARCITY

2009 Topps Triple Threads XXIV Relics Platinum

STATED ODDS 1:2482 MINI
STATED PRINT RUN 1 SER.#'d SET
NO PRICING DUE TO SCARCITY

2009 Topps Triple Threads XXIV Relics Sapphire

STATED ODDS 1:886 MINI
STATED PRINT RUN 3 SER.#'d SETS
NO PRICING DUE TO SCARCITY

2010 Topps Triple Threads

COMMON CARD (1-120) .40 1.00
1-120 PRINT RUN 1350 SER.#'d SETS
COMMON JSY AU RC (121-189) 6.00 15.00
JSY AU RC ODDS 1:12 HOBBY
JSY AU RC PRINT RUN 99 SER.#'d SETS
COMMON JSY AU (121-189) 6.00 15.00
JSY AU ODDS 1:12 HOBBY
JSY AU PRINT RUN 99 SER.#'d SETS
EXCHANGE DEADLINE 9/30/2013
OVERALL 1-120 PLATE ODDS 1:110 HOBBY
PLATE PRINT RUN 1 SET PER COLOR
BLACK-CYAN-MAGENTA-YELLOW ISSUED
NO PLATE PRICING DUE TO SCARCITY
1 Chipper Jones 1.00 2.50
2 Harmon Killebrew 1.00 2.50
3 Robin Roberts .40 1.00
4 Mark Teixeira 1.00 2.50
5 Todd Helton .60 1.50
6 Roy Halladay 1.00 2.50
7 Albert Pujols 2.50 6.00
8 Ryan Braun 1.25 3.00
9 Ryne Sandberg 2.00 5.00
10 Tony Perez .40 1.00
11 Jose Reyes .60 1.50
12 Al Kaline 1.00 2.50
13 Dustin Pedroia 1.25 3.00
14 Warren Spahn .60 1.50
15 Jacoby Ellsbury 1.00 2.50
16 Carl Yastrzemski 1.00 2.50
17 Jake Peavy .40 1.00
18 Carl Crawford .60 1.50
19 Reggie Jackson .60 1.50
20 Brian McCann .60 1.50
21 Ichiro Suzuki 1.50 4.00
22 Miguel Cabrera 1.00 2.50
23 Brooks Robinson .60 1.50
24 Ty Cobb 1.50 4.00
25 Christy Mathewson 1.00 2.50
26 Johnny Bench 1.00 2.50
27 Ozzie Smith 1.50 4.00
28 Bob Feller .40 1.00
29 Ken Griffey Jr. 1.50 4.00
30 Josh Hamilton .60 1.50
31 Adrian Gonzalez .60 1.50
32 Derek Jeter 2.50 6.00
33 Johnny Mize .60 1.50
34 Victor Martinez .60 1.50
35 Steve Carlton .40 1.00
36 Babe Ruth 2.50 6.00
37 Hunter Pence .60 1.50
38 Honus Wagner 1.00 2.50
39 Jorge Posada .60 1.50
40 Adam Dunn .60 1.50
41 Johan Santana 1.00 2.50
42 Andre Ethier .60 1.50
43 Phil Rizzuto .60 1.50
44 Justin Upton .60 1.50
45 Prince Fielder .60 1.50
46 Dave Winfield .40 1.00
47 Josh Beckett .60 1.50
48 Jackie Robinson 1.00 2.50
49 Walter Johnson 1.00 2.50
50 CC Sabathia .60 1.50
51 Ralph Kiner .60 1.50
52 Cole Hamels 1.00 2.50
53 Mark Buehrle .60 1.50
54 Ian Kinsler .60 1.50
55 Yogi Berra 1.00 2.50
56 Bobby Doerr .40 1.00
57 Roy Campanella 1.00 2.50
58 Alfonso Soriano .60 1.50
59 Tom Seaver .60 1.50
60 Hanley Ramirez 1.00 2.50
61 Mariano Rivera 1.00 2.50
62 Cy Young 1.00 2.50
63 Jimmie Foxx 1.00 2.50
64 Jim Palmer .40 1.00
65 Mickey Mantle 3.00 8.00
66 Pee Wee Reese .60 1.50
67 Justin Verlander 1.25 3.00
68 Zack Greinke .60 1.50
69 Jimmy Rollins .60 1.50
70 Felix Hernandez 1.00 2.50
71 Nolan Ryan 3.00 8.00
72 Ryan Howard 1.25 3.00
73 Manny Ramirez 1.00 2.50
74 Lou Brock .60 1.50
75 Mike Schmidt 1.50 4.00
76 Grady Sizemore .60 1.50
77 Alex Rodriguez 1.50 4.00
78 Joe Morgan .40 1.00
79 Eddie Mathews 1.00 2.50
80 Hideki Matsui 1.00 2.50
81 Mel Ott 1.00 2.50
82 Rogers Hornsby .60 1.50
83 Tris Speaker .60 1.50
84 Vladimir Guerrero 1.00 2.50
85 Evan Longoria 1.25 3.00
86 Dan Haren .40 1.00
87 Willie McCovey .60 1.50
88 Lou Gehrig 2.00 5.00
89 Tim Lincecum 1.50 4.00
90 Justin Morneau 1.00 2.50
91 Kevin Youkilis .60 1.50
92 B.J. Upton .60 1.50
93 Rickey Henderson 1.00 2.50
94 Roy Oswalt .60 1.50
95 Chase Utley .60 1.50
96 Lance Berkman .60 1.50
97 Matt Kemp .60 1.50
98 Dale Murphy 1.00 2.50
99 George Sisler 1.00 2.50
100 Nick Markakis 1.00 2.50
101 Thurman Munson 1.00 2.50
102 Dan Uggla .60 1.50
103 Matt Holliday .60 1.50
104 Bill Mazeroski .60 1.50
105 Joe Mauer 1.00 2.50
106 Chris Carpenter 1.00 2.50
107 David Wright 1.25 3.00
108 Ron Guidry .40 1.00
109 Roger Maris 1.00 2.50
110 Aaron Hill .40 1.00
111 Torii Hunter .40 1.00
112 Ubaldo Jimenez .60 1.50
113 Aramis Ramirez .40 1.00
114 Whitey Ford .60 1.50
115 Andrew McCutchen 1.00 2.50
116 Hank Greenberg 1.00 2.50
117 Dizzy Dean .40 1.00
118 Mark Fidrych .40 1.00
119 Bob Gibson .60 1.50
120 Johnny Damon .60 1.50
121 Pablo Sandoval Jsy AU 12.50 30.00
122 Denard Span Jsy AU EXCH 6.00 15.00
123 Colby Rasmus Jsy AU 10.00 25.00
124 Carlos Gomez Jsy AU EXCH 8.00 20.00
125 Tommy Hanson Jsy AU 20.00 50.00
126 Rick Porcello Jsy AU 10.00 25.00
128 Adam Jones Jsy AU 12.50 30.00
129 Gordon Beckham Jsy AU 20.00 50.00
130 Elvis Andrus Jsy AU 10.00 25.00
131 Adam Lind Jsy AU 6.00 15.00
132 Chris Young Jsy AU 6.00 15.00
134 Chris Coghlan Jsy AU 8.00 20.00
135 Alcides Escobar Jsy AU 12.50 30.00
136 Nelson Cruz Jsy AU 10.00 25.00
137 Neftali Feliz Jsy AU 12.50 30.00
139 Jason Heyward Jsy AU RC 75.00 150.00
140 Austin Jackson Jsy AU RC 30.00 60.00
141 Scott Sizemore Jsy AU RC 8.00 20.00
142 Clayton Kershaw Jsy AU 15.00 40.00
143 Ike Davis Jsy AU RC 20.00 50.00
144 Josh Johnson Jsy AU 12.50 30.00
146 Andre Ethier Jsy AU 15.00 40.00
147 Starlin Castro Jsy AU RC 20.00 50.00
148 J.A. Happ Jsy AU EXCH 10.00 25.00
149 Ian Kinsler Jsy AU EXCH 8.00 20.00
150 Will Venable Jsy AU 8.00 20.00
151 Chris Volstad Jsy AU 6.00 15.00
152 Drew Stubbs Jsy AU RC 15.00 40.00
153 Chris Getz Jsy AU 6.00 15.00
155 Daniel McCutchen Jsy AU RC 8.00 20.00
157 Andrew McCutchen Jsy AU 15.00 40.00
158 Daniel Murphy Jsy AU 6.00 15.00
159 Howie Kendrick Jsy AU 8.00 20.00
160 Billy Butler Jsy AU 12.50 30.00
162 Jenrry Mejia Jsy AU RC 12.50 30.00
163 Trevor Cahill Jsy AU 8.00 20.00
164 Wade Davis Jsy AU (RC) 8.00 20.00
165 Manny Parra Jsy AU EXCH 6.00 15.00
166 Drew Storen Jsy AU RC 10.00 25.00
167 Brian Matusz Jsy AU RC 15.00 40.00
169 Eric Young Jr. Jsy AU (RC) 8.00 20.00
171 Stephen Strasburg Jsy AU RC 100.00 200.00
171 Alexei Ramirez Jsy AU 6.00 15.00
178 Casey McGehee Jsy AU 8.00 20.00
182 Mark Reynolds Jsy AU 8.00 20.00
186 Mike Stanton Jsy AU RC 40.00 80.00
188 Carlos Santana Jsy AU RC 15.00 40.00
189 Michael Brantley Jsy AU RC 6.00 15.00

2010 Topps Triple Threads Emerald

*EMERALD 1-120: .6X TO 1.5X BASIC
1-120 ODDS 1:2 MINI
1-120 PRINT RUN 240 SER.#'d SETS
*EMERALD JSY AU: .4X TO 1X BASIC
EMERALD JSY AU ODDS 1:22 MINI
EM.JSY AU PRINT RUN 50 SER.#'d SETS

2010 Topps Triple Threads Gold

*GOLD 1-120: 1X TO 2.5X BASIC
1-120 ODDS 1:5 MINI
1-120 PRINT RUN 99 SER.#'d SETS
121-189 ODDS 1:44 HOBBY
121-189 PRINT RUN 25 SER.#'d SETS
NO 121-189 PRICING DUE TO SCARCITY

2010 Topps Triple Threads Platinum

1-120 ODDS 1:441 HOBBY
121-189 ODDS 1:1080 HOBBY
STATED PRINT RUN 1 SER.#'d SET
NO PRICING DUE TO SCARCITY

2010 Topps Triple Threads Sapphire

1-120 ODDS 1:18 HOBBY
1-120 PRINT RUN 25 SER.#'d SETS
121-189 ODDS 1:110 HOBBY
121-189 PRINT RUN 10 SER.#'d SETS
NO PRICING DUE TO SCARCITY

2010 Topps Triple Threads Sepia

*SEPIA 1-120: .5X TO 1.2X BASIC
1-120 RANDOMLY INSERTED
1-120 PRINT RUN 525 SER.#'d SETS
*SEPIA JSY AU: .4X TO 1X BASIC
SEPIA JSY AU ODDS 1:15 MINI
SEP.JSY AU PRINT RUN 75 SER.#'d SETS

2010 Topps Triple Threads White Whale Printing Plates

STATED ODDS 1:275 MINI
STATED PRINT RUN 1 SER.#'d SET
NO PRICING DUE TO SCARCITY

2010 Topps Triple Threads Wood

STATED ODDS 1:1080 MINI
STATED PRINT RUN 1 SER.#'d SET
NO PRICING DUE TO SCARCITY

2010 Topps Triple Threads All-Star Jumbo Patches

STATED ODDS 1:88 MINI
STATED PRINT RUN 9 SER.#'d SETS
NO PRICING DUE TO PRICING

2010 Topps Triple Threads All-Star Jumbo Patches Platinum

STATED ODDS 1:806 MINI
STATED PRINT RUN 1 SER.#'d SET
NO PRICING DUE TO PRICING

2010 Topps Triple Threads All-Star Jumbo Sleeve Patches

STATED ODDS 1:806 MINI
STATED PRINT RUN 1 SER.#'d SET
NO PRICING DUE TO SCARCITY

2010 Topps Triple Threads All-Star Jumbo Team Patches

STATED ODDS 1:819 MINI
STATED PRINT RUN 1 SER.#'d SET
NO PRICING DUE TO SCARCITY

2010 Topps Triple Threads All-Star Laundry Tags

STATED ODDS 1:941 MINI
STATED PRINT RUN 1 SER.#'d SET
NO PRICING DUE TO SCARCITY

2010 Topps Triple Threads Autograph Relic Combos

STATED ODDS 1:98 MINI
STATED PRINT RUN 36 SER.#'d SETS
ARC1 David Wright 60.00 120.00
Mike Schmidt
Ryan Zimmerman
ARC2 Albert Pujols 150.00 300.00
Prince Fielder
Ryan Howard
ARC3 Aaron Hill 30.00 60.00
Robinson Cano
Dustin Pedroia
ARC4 Jason Heyward 40.00 80.00
Adam Jones
Justin Upton
ARC5 Whitey Ford 125.00 250.00
Mariano Rivera
Yogi Berra
ARC6 Evan Longoria 50.00 100.00
Gordon Beckham
Miguel Cabrera
ARC7 David Price 50.00 100.00
Jon Lester
CC Sabathia
ARC8 Rick Porcello 30.00 60.00
Miguel Cabrera
Johnny Damon
ARC9 Jason Varitek 40.00 80.00
Curt Schilling
David Ortiz
ARC10 Matt Holliday 60.00 120.00
Ryan Braun
David Wright
ARC11 John Lackey 30.00 60.00
Jon Lester
Jonathan Papelbon
ARC12 Andre Dawson 40.00 80.00

Gary Carter
Vladimir Guerrero
ARC13 Jason Heyward 75.00 150.00
Brian McCann
Dale Murphy
ARC14 Ryan Howard 200.00 400.00
Alex Rodriguez
Albert Pujols
ARC15 Alex Rodriguez 75.00 150.00
David Ortiz
Manny Ramirez

2010 Topps Triple Threads Autograph Relic Combos Emerald

STATED ODDS 1:195 MINI
STATED PRINT RUN 18 SER.#'d SETS
NO PRICING DUE TO SCARCITY

2010 Topps Triple Threads Autograph Relic Combos Gold

STATED ODDS 1:391 MINI
STATED PRINT RUN 9 SER.#'d SETS
NO PRICING DUE TO SCARCITY

2010 Topps Triple Threads Autograph Relic Combos Platinum

STATED ODDS 1:3629 MINI
STATED PRINT RUN 1 SER.#'d SET
NO PRICING DUE TO SCARCITY

2010 Topps Triple Threads Autograph Relic Combos Sapphire

STATED ODDS 1:1181 MINI
STATED PRINT RUN 3 SER.#'d SETS
NO PRICING DUE TO SCARCITY

2010 Topps Triple Threads Autograph Relic Combos Sepia

*SEPIA: .4X TO 1X BASIC
STATED ODDS 1:130 MINI
STATED PRINT RUN 27 SER.#'d SETS

2010 Topps Triple Threads Autograph Relic Combos White Whale Printing Plates

STATED ODDS 1:891 MINI
STATED PRINT RUN 1 SER.#'d SET
NO PRICING DUE TO SCARCITY

2010 Topps Triple Threads Autograph Relic Combos Wood

STATED ODDS 1:3629 MINI
STATED PRINT RUN 1 SER.#'d SET
NO PRICING DUE TO SCARCITY

2010 Topps Triple Threads Autograph Relic Combos Double

STATED ODDS 1:2822 MINI
STATED PRINT RUN 3 SER.#'d SETS
NO PRICING DUE TO SCARCITY

2010 Topps Triple Threads Autograph Relic Combos Double Platinum

STATED ODDS 1:8466 MINI
STATED PRINT RUN 1 SER.#'d SET
NO PRICING DUE TO SCARCITY

2010 Topps Triple Threads Autograph MLB Die Cut Relics

STATED ODDS 1:10 MINI
STATED PRINT RUN 18 SER.#'d SETS
ALL DC VARIATIONS PRICED EQUALLY
AD Adam Dunn 12.50 30.00
AD Andre Dawson 40.00 80.00
AG Adrian Gonzalez 8.00 20.00
AP Albert Pujols 200.00 300.00
AR Alex Rodriguez 100.00 175.00
BM Brian McCann 15.00 40.00
BS Bruce Sutter 15.00 40.00
BZ Ben Zobrist 15.00 40.00
CB Chad Billingsley 12.50 30.00
CC Carl Crawford 12.50 30.00
CF Chone Figgins 8.00 20.00
CL Cliff Lee 30.00 60.00
CP Carlos Pena 8.00 20.00
CS CC Sabathia 50.00 100.00
CY Carl Yastrzemski 30.00 60.00
DG Dwight Gooden 20.00 50.00
DM Dale Murphy 40.00 80.00
DO David Ortiz 15.00 40.00
DS Duke Snider 30.00 60.00
DW David Wright 40.00 80.00
EL Evan Longoria 40.00 80.00
FT Frank Thomas 75.00 150.00
GC Gary Carter 20.00 50.00
GK George Kell 15.00 40.00
HR Hanley Ramirez 12.50 30.00
JD Johnny Damon 30.00 60.00
JH Josh Hamilton 20.00 50.00
JH Jason Heyward 75.00 150.00
JL Jon Lester 30.00 60.00
JM Joe Morgan 20.00 50.00
MC Miguel Cabrera 20.00 50.00
MH Matt Holliday 20.00 50.00
MK Matt Kemp 10.00 25.00
MR Manny Ramirez 50.00 100.00
MT Miguel Tejada 8.00 20.00
NS Nick Swisher 30.00 60.00
PF Prince Fielder 12.50 30.00
RB Ryan Braun 20.00 50.00
RC Robinson Cano 30.00 60.00
RH Ryan Howard 40.00 80.00
RK Ralph Kiner 30.00 60.00
RZ Ryan Zimmerman 20.00 50.00
SM Stan Musial 60.00 120.00
SS Stephen Strasburg 150.00 250.00
SV Shane Victorino 30.00 60.00
VW Vernon Wells 10.00 25.00
WF Whitey Ford 30.00 60.00
CSC Curt Schilling 15.00 40.00
DWI Dave Winfield 30.00 60.00
MRI Mariano Rivera 100.00 175.00

2010 Topps Triple Threads Autograph MLB Die Cut Relics Gold

*GOLD: .5X TO 1.2X BASIC
STATED ODDS 1:19 MINI
STATED PRINT RUN 9 SER.#'d SETS
ALL DC VARIATIONS PRICED EQUALLY

2010 Topps Triple Threads Autograph Relics

STATED ODDS 1:10 MINI
STATED PRINT RUN 18 SER.#'d SETS
ALL DC VARIATIONS PRICED EQUALLY
AR1 Cliff Lee 30.00 60.00
AR2 Cliff Lee 30.00 60.00
AR3 Cliff Lee 30.00 60.00
AR4 Duke Snider 30.00 60.00
AR5 Duke Snider 30.00 60.00
AR6 Duke Snider 30.00 60.00
AR7 Gary Carter 20.00 50.00
AR8 Gary Carter 20.00 50.00
AR9 Gary Carter 20.00 50.00
AR10 Robinson Cano 30.00 60.00
AR11 Robinson Cano 30.00 60.00
AR12 Robinson Cano 30.00 60.00
AR13 Prince Fielder 12.50 30.00
AR14 Prince Fielder 12.50 30.00
AR15 Prince Fielder 12.50 30.00
AR16 Ryan Howard 60.00 120.00
AR17 Ryan Howard 60.00 120.00
AR18 Ryan Howard 60.00 120.00
AR19 Alex Rodriguez 100.00 175.00
AR20 Alex Rodriguez 100.00 175.00
AR21 Alex Rodriguez 100.00 175.00
AR22 Josh Hamilton 20.00 50.00
AR23 Josh Hamilton 20.00 50.00
AR24 Josh Hamilton 20.00 50.00
AR25 Chad Billingsley 12.50 30.00
AR26 Chad Billingsley 12.50 30.00
AR27 Chad Billingsley 12.50 30.00
AR28 Dustin Pedroia 15.00 40.00
AR29 Dustin Pedroia 15.00 40.00
AR30 Dustin Pedroia 15.00 40.00
AR31 Manny Ramirez 50.00 100.00
AR32 Manny Ramirez 50.00 100.00
AR33 Manny Ramirez 50.00 100.00
AR34 CC Sabathia 30.00 60.00
AR35 CC Sabathia 30.00 60.00
AR36 CC Sabathia 30.00 60.00
AR37 Jon Lester 30.00 60.00
AR38 Jon Lester 30.00 60.00
AR39 Jon Lester 30.00 60.00
AR40 Curt Schilling 15.00 40.00
AR41 Curt Schilling 15.00 40.00
AR42 Curt Schilling 15.00 40.00
AR43 Ryan Braun 30.00 60.00
AR44 Ryan Braun 30.00 60.00
AR45 Ryan Braun 30.00 60.00
AR46 David Wright 40.00 80.00
AR47 David Wright 40.00 80.00
AR48 David Wright 40.00 80.00
AR49 B.J. Upton 12.50 30.00
AR50 B.J. Upton 12.50 30.00
AR51 B.J. Upton 12.50 30.00
AR52 David Ortiz 15.00 40.00
AR53 David Ortiz 15.00 40.00
AR54 David Ortiz 15.00 40.00
AR55 Frank Thomas 60.00 120.00
AR56 Frank Thomas 60.00 120.00
AR57 Frank Thomas 60.00 120.00
AR58 Dave Winfield 30.00 60.00
AR59 Dave Winfield 30.00 60.00
AR60 Dave Winfield 30.00 60.00
AR61 John Lackey 20.00 50.00
AR62 John Lackey 20.00 50.00
AR63 John Lackey 20.00 50.00
AR64 Evan Longoria 40.00 80.00
AR65 Evan Longoria 40.00 80.00
AR66 Evan Longoria 40.00 80.00
AR67 Adam Dunn 12.50 30.00
AR68 Adam Dunn 12.50 30.00
AR69 Adam Dunn 12.50 30.00
AR70 Joe Morgan 20.00 50.00
AR71 Joe Morgan 20.00 50.00
AR72 Joe Morgan 20.00 50.00
AR73 Matt Cain 12.50 30.00
AR74 Matt Cain 12.50 30.00
AR75 Matt Cain 12.50 30.00
AR76 Dale Murphy 40.00 80.00
AR77 Dale Murphy 40.00 80.00
AR78 Dale Murphy 40.00 80.00
AR79 Whitey Ford 30.00 60.00
AR80 Whitey Ford 30.00 60.00
AR81 Whitey Ford 30.00 60.00
AR82 Michael Young 10.00 25.00
AR83 Michael Young 10.00 25.00
AR84 Michael Young 10.00 25.00
AR85 Matt Holliday 20.00 50.00
AR86 Matt Holliday 20.00 50.00
AR87 Matt Holliday 20.00 50.00
AR88 Ozzie Smith 30.00 60.00
AR89 Ozzie Smith 30.00 60.00
AR90 Ozzie Smith 30.00 60.00
AR91 Barry Larkin 40.00 80.00
AR92 Barry Larkin 40.00 80.00
AR93 Barry Larkin 40.00 80.00
AR94 Aramis Ramirez 8.00 20.00
AR95 Aramis Ramirez 8.00 20.00
AR96 Aramis Ramirez 8.00 20.00
AR97 Hanley Ramirez 12.50 30.00
AR98 Hanley Ramirez 12.50 30.00
AR99 Hanley Ramirez 12.50 30.00
AR100 Mariano Rivera 100.00 175.00
AR101 Mariano Rivera 100.00 175.00
AR102 Mariano Rivera 100.00 175.00
AR103 Reggie Jackson 50.00 100.00
AR104 Reggie Jackson 50.00 100.00
AR105 Reggie Jackson 50.00 100.00
AR106 Nolan Ryan 100.00 175.00
AR107 Nolan Ryan 100.00 175.00
AR108 Nolan Ryan 100.00 175.00
AR109 Torii Hunter 15.00 40.00
AR110 Torii Hunter 15.00 40.00
AR111 Torii Hunter 15.00 40.00
AR112 Albert Pujols 200.00 300.00
AR113 Albert Pujols 200.00 300.00
AR114 Albert Pujols 200.00 300.00
AR115 Shane Victorino 30.00 60.00
AR116 Shane Victorino 30.00 60.00
AR117 Shane Victorino 30.00 60.00
AR118 Justin Verlander 30.00 60.00
AR119 Justin Verlander 30.00 60.00
AR120 Justin Verlander 30.00 60.00
AR121 Miguel Cabrera 20.00 50.00
AR122 Miguel Cabrera 20.00 50.00
AR123 Miguel Cabrera 20.00 50.00
AR124 Adrian Gonzalez 12.50 30.00
AR125 Adrian Gonzalez 12.50 30.00
AR126 Adrian Gonzalez 12.50 30.00
AR127 Chone Figgins 8.00 20.00
AR128 Chone Figgins 8.00 20.00
AR129 Chone Figgins 8.00 20.00
AR130 Nick Swisher 30.00 60.00
AR131 Nick Swisher 30.00 60.00
AR132 Nick Swisher 30.00 60.00
AR133 Phil Hughes 20.00 50.00
AR134 Phil Hughes 20.00 50.00
AR135 Phil Hughes 20.00 50.00
AR136 Aaron Hill 10.00 25.00
AR137 Aaron Hill 10.00 25.00
AR138 Aaron Hill 10.00 25.00
AR139 Johnny Damon 30.00 60.00
AR140 Johnny Damon 30.00 60.00
AR141 Johnny Damon 30.00 60.00
AR142 Miguel Tejada 8.00 20.00
AR143 Miguel Tejada 8.00 20.00
AR144 Miguel Tejada 8.00 20.00
AR145 Vernon Wells 10.00 25.00
AR146 Vernon Wells 10.00 25.00
AR147 Vernon Wells 10.00 25.00
AR148 George Kell 15.00 40.00
AR149 George Kell 15.00 40.00
AR150 George Kell 15.00 40.00
AR151 Carlos Pena 8.00 20.00
AR152 Carlos Pena 8.00 20.00
AR153 Carlos Pena 8.00 20.00
AR154 Andre Dawson 40.00 80.00
AR155 Andre Dawson 40.00 80.00
AR156 Andre Dawson 40.00 80.00
AR157 Dwight Gooden 20.00 50.00
AR158 Dwight Gooden 20.00 50.00
AR159 Dwight Gooden 20.00 50.00
AR160 Ralph Kiner 30.00 60.00
AR161 Ralph Kiner 30.00 60.00
AR162 Ralph Kiner 30.00 60.00
AR163 Bobby Murcer 50.00 100.00
AR164 Bobby Murcer 50.00 100.00
AR165 Bobby Murcer 50.00 100.00
AR166 Tony Perez 30.00 60.00
AR167 Tony Perez 30.00 60.00
AR168 Tony Perez 30.00 60.00
AR169 Rich Harden 8.00 20.00
AR170 Rich Harden 8.00 20.00
AR171 Rich Harden 8.00 20.00
AR172 Joba Chamberlain 12.50 30.00
AR173 Joba Chamberlain 12.50 30.00
AR174 Joba Chamberlain 12.50 30.00
AR175 Cal Ripken Jr. 150.00 250.00
AR176 Cal Ripken Jr. 150.00 250.00
AR177 Cal Ripken Jr. 150.00 250.00
AR178 Carl Yastrzemski 30.00 60.00
AR179 Carl Yastrzemski 30.00 60.00
AR180 Carl Yastrzemski 30.00 60.00
AR181 Bruce Sutter 15.00 40.00
AR182 Bruce Sutter 15.00 40.00
AR183 Bruce Sutter 15.00 40.00
AR184 Stan Musial 60.00 120.00
AR185 Stan Musial 60.00 120.00
AR186 Stan Musial 60.00 120.00
AR187 Frank Robinson 20.00 50.00
AR188 Frank Robinson 20.00 50.00
AR189 Frank Robinson 20.00 50.00
AR190 Ryan Zimmerman 20.00 50.00
AR191 Ryan Zimmerman 20.00 50.00
AR192 Ryan Zimmerman 20.00 50.00
AR193 Felix Hernandez 40.00 80.00
AR194 Felix Hernandez 40.00 80.00
AR195 Felix Hernandez 40.00 80.00
AR196 Carl Crawford 12.50 30.00
AR197 Carl Crawford 12.50 30.00
AR198 Carl Crawford 12.50 30.00
AR199 Raul Ibanez 20.00 50.00
AR200 Raul Ibanez 20.00 50.00
AR201 Raul Ibanez 20.00 50.00
AR202 Brian McCann 15.00 40.00
AR203 Brian McCann 15.00 40.00
AR204 Brian McCann 15.00 40.00
AR205 Matt Garza 12.50 30.00
AR206 Matt Garza 12.50 30.00
AR207 Matt Garza 12.50 30.00
AR208 Chipper Jones 50.00 100.00
AR209 Chipper Jones 50.00 100.00
AR210 Chipper Jones 50.00 100.00
AR211 Jason Heyward 75.00 150.00
AR212 Jason Heyward 75.00 150.00
AR213 Jason Heyward 75.00 150.00
AR214 Stephen Strasburg 150.00 250.00
AR215 Stephen Strasburg 150.00 250.00
AR216 Stephen Strasburg 150.00 250.00
AR217 Al Kaline 30.00 60.00
AR218 Al Kaline 30.00 60.00
AR219 Al Kaline 30.00 60.00
AR220 Ryne Sandberg 40.00 80.00
AR221 Ryne Sandberg 40.00 80.00
AR222 Ryne Sandberg 40.00 80.00
AR226 Ivan Rodriguez 40.00 80.00
AR227 Ivan Rodriguez 40.00 80.00
AR228 Ivan Rodriguez 40.00 80.00
AR229 Alfonso Soriano 12.50 30.00
AR230 Alfonso Soriano 12.50 30.00
AR231 Alfonso Soriano 12.50 30.00
AR232 Ben Zobrist 15.00 40.00
AR233 Ben Zobrist 15.00 40.00
AR234 Ben Zobrist 15.00 40.00
AR235 Roberto Alomar 60.00 120.00
AR236 Roberto Alomar 60.00 120.00
AR237 Roberto Alomar 60.00 120.00
AR238 Tony Gwynn 30.00 60.00
AR239 Tony Gwynn 30.00 60.00
AR240 Tony Gwynn 30.00 60.00
AR241 Mike Schmidt 30.00 60.00
AR242 Mike Schmidt 30.00 60.00
AR243 Mike Schmidt 30.00 60.00
AR244 Matt Kemp 15.00 40.00
AR245 Matt Kemp 15.00 40.00
AR246 Matt Kemp 15.00 40.00
AR247 Johnny Bench 30.00 60.00
AR248 Johnny Bench 30.00 60.00
AR249 Johnny Bench 30.00 60.00
AR250 Ernie Banks 40.00 80.00
AR251 Ernie Banks 40.00 80.00
AR252 Ernie Banks 40.00 80.00
AR262 Ron Santo 40.00 80.00
AR263 Ron Santo 40.00 80.00
AR264 Ron Santo 40.00 80.00
AR265 Hunter Pence 12.50 30.00
AR266 Hunter Pence 12.50 30.00
AR267 Hunter Pence 12.50 30.00
AR274 Carlton Fisk 20.00 50.00
AR275 Carlton Fisk 20.00 50.00
AR276 Carlton Fisk 20.00 50.00
AR280 Shin-Soo Choo 20.00 50.00
AR281 Shin-Soo Choo 20.00 50.00
AR282 Shin-Soo Choo 20.00 50.00
AR283 Bernie Williams 60.00 120.00
AR284 Bernie Williams 60.00 120.00
AR285 Bernie Williams 60.00 120.00

2010 Topps Triple Threads Autograph Relics Gold

*GOLD: .5X TO 1.2X BASIC
STATED ODDS 1:19 MINI
STATED PRINT RUN 9 SER.#'d SETS
ALL DC VARIATIONS PRICED EQUALLY

2010 Topps Triple Threads Legend Relics

STATED ODDS 1:49 MINI
STATED PRINT RUN 36 SER.#'d SETS
RL1 Yogi Berra 20.00 50.00
RL2 Roy Campanella 20.00 50.00
RL3 Ty Cobb 60.00 120.00
RL4 Nolan Ryan 30.00 60.00
RL5 Johnny Bench 12.50 30.00
RL6 Jim Palmer 12.50 30.00
RL7 Whitey Ford 12.50 30.00
RL8 Jimmie Foxx 40.00 80.00
RL9 Lou Gehrig 100.00 175.00
RL10 Bob Gibson 20.00 50.00
RL11 Hank Greenberg 30.00 60.00
RL12 Rogers Hornsby 40.00 80.00
RL13 Ralph Kiner 15.00 40.00
RL14 Mickey Mantle 100.00 175.00
RL15 Roger Maris 50.00 100.00
RL16 Eddie Mathews 20.00 50.00
RL17 Johnny Mize 12.50 30.00
RL18 Thurman Munson 15.00 40.00
RL19 Stan Musial 30.00 60.00
RL20 Frank Robinson 12.50 30.00
RL21 Mel Ott 30.00 60.00
RL22 Pee Wee Reese 20.00 50.00
RL23 Phil Rizzuto 15.00 40.00
RL24 Jackie Robinson 30.00 60.00
RL25 Babe Ruth 350.00 500.00
RL26 Tom Seaver 12.50 30.00
RL27 George Sisler 30.00 60.00
RL28 Warren Spahn 20.00 50.00
RL29 Tris Speaker 20.00 50.00
RL30 Honus Wagner 75.00 150.00

2010 Topps Triple Threads Legend Relics Emerald

STATED ODDS 1:98 MINI
STATED PRINT RUN 18 SER.#'d SETS
NO PRICING DUE TO SCARCITY

2010 Topps Triple Threads Legend Relics Gold

STATED ODDS 1:196 MINI
STATED PRINT RUN 9 SER.#'d SETS
NO PRICING DUE TO SCARCITY

2010 Topps Triple Threads Legend Relics Platinum

STATED ODDS 1:1752 MINI
STATED PRINT RUN 1 SER.#'d SET
NO PRICING DUE TO SCARCITY

2010 Topps Triple Threads Legend Relics Sapphire

STATED ODDS 1:591 MINI
STATED PRINT RUN 3 SER.#'d SETS
NO PRICING DUE TO SCARCITY

2010 Topps Triple Threads Legend Relics Sepia

*SEPIA: .4X TO 1X BASIC
STATED ODDS 1:66 MINI
STATED PRINT RUN 27 SER.#'d SETS

2010 Topps Triple Threads Logoman Patches

STATED ODDS 1:806 MINI
STATED PRINT RUN 1 SER.#'d SET
NO PRICING DUE TO SCARCITY

2010 Topps Triple Threads MLB Die Cut Relics

STATED ODDS 1:10 MINI
STATED PRINT RUN 36 SER.#'d SETS
ALL DC VARIATIONS PRICED EQUALLY
AG Adrian Gonzalez 6.00 15.00
AK Al Kaline 15.00 40.00
CF Carlton Fisk 6.00 15.00
CJ Chipper Jones 12.50 30.00
CR Cal Ripken Jr. 20.00 50.00
CS Curt Schilling 6.00 15.00
CU Chase Utley 15.00 40.00
DJ Derek Jeter 30.00 60.00
DW David Wright 15.00 40.00
EL Evan Longoria 12.50 30.00
HR Hanley Ramirez 6.00 15.00
KY Kevin Youkilis 6.00 15.00
MC Miguel Cabrera 8.00 20.00
MR Manny Ramirez 12.50 30.00
MT Mark Teixeira 12.50 30.00
OC Orlando Cepeda 6.00 15.00
PF Prince Fielder 6.00 15.00
PM Paul Molitor 8.00 20.00
RH Rickey Henderson 30.00 60.00
RH Roy Halladay 15.00 40.00
SC Steve Carlton 8.00 20.00
TG Tony Gwynn 12.50 30.00
WS Willie Stargell 15.00 40.00
DWI Dave Winfield 8.00 20.00
SSC Shin-Soo Choo 10.00 25.00

2010 Topps Triple Threads MLB Die Cut Relics Emerald

*EMERALD: .5X TO 1.2X BASIC
STATED ODDS 1:19 MINI
STATED PRINT RUN 18 SER.#'d SETS
ALL DC VARIATIONS PRICED EQUALLY

2010 Topps Triple Threads MLB Die Cut Relics Gold

*GOLD: .6X TO 1.5X BASIC
STATED ODDS 1:38 MINI
STATED PRINT RUN 9 SER.#'d SETS
ALL DC VARIATIONS PRICED EQUALLY

2010 Topps Triple Threads MLB Die Cut Relics Platinum

STATED ODDS 1:339 HOBBY
STATED PRINT RUN 1 SER.#'d SET
NO PRICING DUE TO SCARCITY

2010 Topps Triple Threads MLB Die Cut Relics Sapphire

STATED ODDS 1:112 HOBBY
STATED PRINT RUN 3 SER.#'d SETS
NO PRICING DUE TO SCARCITY

2010 Topps Triple Threads MLB Die Cut Relics Sepia

*SEPIA: .4X TO 1X BASIC
STATED ODDS 1:13 MINI
STATED PRINT RUN 27 SER.#'d SETS
ALL DC VARIATIONS PRICED EQUALLY

2010 Topps Triple Threads Relic Combos

STATED ODDS 1:25 MINI
STATED PRINT RUN 36 SER.#'d SETS
RC1 Joe Mauer 20.00 50.00
Harmon Killebrew
Justin Morneau
RC2 Mariano Rivera 20.00 50.00
Jorge Posada
Andy Pettitte
RC3 Tim Lincecum 12.50 30.00
Roy Halladay
Johan Santana
RC4 Albert Pujols 30.00 60.00
Bob Gibson
Stan Musial
RC5 Cal Ripken Jr. 40.00 80.00
Frank Robinson
Jim Palmer
RC6 Willie McCovey 12.50 30.00
Pablo Sandoval
Monte Irvin
RC7 Miguel Cabrera 10.00 25.00
Mark Teixeira
Justin Morneau
RC8 Evan Longoria 12.50 30.00
David Wright
Ryan Zimmerman
RC9 Chase Utley 10.00 25.00
Ryne Sandberg
Ian Kinsler
RC10 Hanley Ramirez 40.00 80.00
Cal Ripken Jr.
Troy Tulowitzki
RC11 Hideki Matsui 30.00 60.00
Ichiro Suzuki
Daisuke Matsuzaka
RC12 David Wright 8.00 20.00
Aramis Ramirez
Pablo Sandoval
RC13 Jason Heyward 30.00 60.00
Chipper Jones
Brian McCann
RC14 Hunter Pence 10.00 25.00
Ryan Braun
Matt Holliday
RC15 Ryne Sandberg 20.00 50.00
Ernie Banks
Andre Dawson
RC16 Brian McCann 30.00 60.00
Joe Mauer
Jorge Posada
RC17 Carl Crawford 20.00 50.00
Rickey Henderson
Jacoby Ellsbury
RC18 Joe Mauer
Dustin Pedroia
Alex Rodriguez
RC19 Zack Greinke 10.00 25.00
Cliff Lee
CC Sabathia
RC20 Ryan Braun
Hanley Ramirez
Ryan Howard
RC21 Ichiro Suzuki 40.00 80.00
Cal Ripken Jr.
Frank Robinson
RC22 Rickey Henderson 40.00 80.00
Rickey Henderson
Rickey Henderson
RC23 Adrian Gonzalez 8.00 20.00
Ryan Zimmerman
Jimmy Rollins
RC24 Justin Morneau 10.00 25.00
Dustin Pedroia
Alex Rodriguez
RC25 Andre Dawson 15.00 40.00
Gary Carter
Vladimir Guerrero
RC26 Johnny Bench 20.00 50.00
Joe Mauer
Carlton Fisk
RC27 Ron Guidry
Whitey Ford
Andy Pettitte
RC28 Chipper Jones 12.50 30.00
Jorge Posada
Lance Berkman
RC29 Mike Stanton 30.00 60.00
Stephen Strasburg
Jason Heyward
RC30 Adam Jones 10.00 25.00
Brian Roberts
Nick Markakis
RC31 Mickey Mantle 250.00 400.00
Babe Ruth
Roger Maris
RC32 Mark Reynolds 8.00 20.00
Justin Upton
Stephen Drew
RC33 David Wright 20.00 50.00
Gary Carter
Jason Bay
RC34 Vladimir Guerrero 8.00 20.00
David Ortiz
Manny Ramirez
RC35 Chase Utley 30.00 60.00
Ryan Howard
Jason Werth
RC36 Tim Lincecum 15.00 40.00
Pablo Sandoval
Matt Cain
RC37 Nelson Cruz 30.00 60.00
Josh Hamilton
Ian Kinsler
RC38 Ivan Rodriguez 12.50 30.00
Ivan Rodriguez
Ivan Rodriguez
RC39 Albert Pujols 15.00 40.00
Hanley Ramirez
Alex Rodriguez
RC40 Josh Hamilton 10.00 25.00
Adrian Gonzalez
Joe Mauer
RC41 Alex Rodriguez 12.50 30.00
Joe Mauer
Justin Upton
RC42 Jose Reyes 12.50 30.00
Dustin Pedroia
Ichiro Suzuki
RC43 Al Kaline 60.00 120.00
Ty Cobb
George Kell
RC44 Albert Pujols 15.00 40.00
Ryan Howard
Prince Fielder
RC45 Mark Teixeira 10.00 25.00
Miguel Cabrera
Alex Rodriguez
RC46 Mike Schmidt 20.00 50.00
Willie Stargell
Johnny Bench
RC47 Harmon Killebrew 20.00 50.00
Carl Yastrzemski
Frank Robinson
RC48 Felix Hernandez 8.00 20.00
CC Sabathia
Justin Verlander
RC49 Catfish Hunter
Ron Guidry
Andy Pettitte
RC50 Mariano Rivera 8.00 20.00
Curt Schilling
Cole Hamels
RC51 Nolan Ryan 30.00 60.00
Nolan Ryan
Nolan Ryan
RC52 Shane Victorino 8.00 20.00
Jose Reyes
Jimmy Rollins
RC53 Prince Fielder 8.00 20.00
Justin Morneau
Vladimir Guerrero
RC54 Justin Verlander 12.50 30.00
Rick Porcello
Jim Bunning
RC55 Josh Beckett 10.00 25.00
Jon Lester
John Lackey
RC56 Troy Tulowitzki 10.00 25.00
Jimmy Rollins
Hanley Ramirez
RC57 Justin Upton 12.50 30.00
Ichiro Suzuki
Grady Sizemore
RC58 CC Sabathia 15.00 40.00
Zack Greinke
Felix Hernandez
RC59 Mariano Rivera 15.00 40.00
Dennis Eckersley
Goose Gossage
RC60 Alex Rodriguez 20.00 50.00
Alex Rodriguez
Alex Rodriguez

2010 Topps Triple Threads Relic Combos Emerald

STATED ODDS 1:49 MINI
STATED PRINT RUN 18 SER.#'d SETS
NO PRICING DUE TO SCARCITY

2010 Topps Triple Threads Relic Combos Gold

STATED ODDS 1:98 MINI
STATED PRINT RUN 9 SER.#'d SETS
NO PRICING DUE TO SCARCITY

2010 Topps Triple Threads Relic Combos Platinum

STATED ODDS 1:891 MINI
STATED PRINT RUN 1 SER.#'d SET
NO PRICING DUE TO SCARCITY

2010 Topps Triple Threads Relic Combos Sapphire

STATED ODDS 1:294 MINI
STATED PRINT RUN 3 SER.#'d SETS
NO PRICING DUE TO SCARCITY

2010 Topps Triple Threads Relic Combos Sepia

*SEPIA: .4X TO 1X BASIC
STATED ODDS 1:33 MINI
STATED PRINT RUN 27 SER.#'d SETS

2010 Topps Triple Threads Relic Combos Double

STATE ODDS 1:82 MINI
STATED PRINT RUN 36 SER.#'d SETS
RDC1 Albert Pujols 40.00 80.00
Joe Mauer
RDC2 Albert Pujols 30.00 60.00
Alex Rodriguez
RDC3 Ralph Kiner 50.00 100.00
Hank Greenberg
Eddie Mathews
Harmon Killebrew
Willie McCovey
Frank Robinson
RDC4 Albert Pujols 50.00 100.00
Ryan Howard
Matt Holliday
Gary Carter
Mike Schmidt
Dale Murphy
RDC5 Ryan Howard 20.00 50.00
Matt Holliday
Albert Pujols
CC Sabathia
Josh Beckett
David Ortiz
RDC6 Miguel Cabrera 20.00 50.00
Justin Morneau
Kendry Morales
Ryan Howard
Albert Pujols
Prince Fielder
RDC7 Alex Rodriguez 20.00 50.00
Joe Mauer
Torii Hunter
Ryan Howard
Albert Pujols
Manny Ramirez
RDC8 Tim Lincecum 20.00 50.00
Roy Halladay
Johan Santana
Zack Greinke
Felix Hernandez
CC Sabathia
RDC9 Justin Upton 20.00 50.00
Ryan Braun
Hunter Pence
Matt Kemp
Andrew McCutchen
Jason Heyward
RDC10 Joe Mauer 40.00 80.00
Jorge Posada
Ivan Rodriguez
Carlton Fisk
Johnny Bench
Yogi Berra
RDC11 Adrian Gonzlez 20.00 50.00
Ryan Zimmerman
Jimmy Rollins
Matt Kemp
Shane Victorino
Yadier Molina
RDC12 Joe Mauer 75.00 150.00
Mark Teixeira
Evan Longoria
Ichiro Suzuki
Adam Jones
Torii Hunter
RDC13 Andre Dawson 75.00 150.00
Rickey Henderson
Goose Gossage
Cal Ripken Jr.
Tony Gwynn
Bruce Sutter
RDC14 Frank Robinson 20.00 50.00
Frank Robinson
RDC15 Lou Brock 20.00 50.00
Rickey Henderson
Jacoby Ellsbury
Carl Crawford
Jose Reyes
Jimmy Rollins
RDC16 Tim Lincecum 30.00 60.00
Zack Greinke
Steve Carlton
Johan Santana
Tom Seaver
Whitey Ford
RDC17 Catfish Hunter 20.00 50.00
Thurman Munson
RDC18 Ryan Howard 40.00 80.00
Prince Fielder
Albert Pujols
Harmon Killebrew
Ralph Kiner
Frank Robinson

2010 Topps Triple Threads Relic Combos Double Emerald

STATED ODDS 1:163 MINI
STATED PRINT RUN 18 SER.#'d SETS
NO PRICING DUE TO SCARCITY

2010 Topps Triple Threads Relic Combos Double Gold

STATED ODDS 1:328 MINI
STATED PRINT RUN 9 SER.#'d SETS
NO PRICING DUE TO SCARCITY

2010 Topps Triple Threads Relic Combos Double Platinum

STATED ODDS 1:2822 MINI
STATED PRINT RUN 1 SER.#'d SET
NO PRICING DUE TO SCARCITY

2010 Topps Triple Threads Relic Combos Double Sapphire

STATED ODDS 1:996 MINI
STATED PRINT RUN 3 SER.#'d SETS
NO PRICING DUE TO SCARCITY

2010 Topps Triple Threads Relic Combos Double Sepia

*SEPIA: .4X TO 1X BASIC
STATED ODDS 1:109 MINI
STATED PRINT RUN 27 SER.#'d SETS

2010 Topps Triple Threads Relics

STATED ODDS 1:10 MINI
STATED PRINT RUN 36 SER.#'d SETS
ALL DC VARIATIONS PRICED EQUALLY
R1 Albert Pujols 30.00 60.00
R2 Albert Pujols 30.00 60.00
R3 Albert Pujols 30.00 60.00
R4 Chase Utley 12.50 30.00
R5 Chase Utley 12.50 30.00
R6 Chase Utley 12.50 30.00

R7 Ichiro Suzuki 30.00 60.00
R8 Ichiro Suzuki 30.00 60.00
R9 Ichiro Suzuki 30.00 60.00
R10 Grady Sizemore 6.00 15.00
R11 Grady Sizemore 6.00 15.00
R12 Grady Sizemore 6.00 15.00
R13 Mark Teixeira 12.50 30.00
R14 Mark Teixeira 12.50 30.00
R15 Mark Teixeira 12.50 30.00
R16 Shin-Soo Choo 10.00 25.00
R17 Shin-Soo Choo 10.00 25.00
R18 Shin-Soo Choo 10.00 25.00
R22 Hanley Ramirez 6.00 15.00
R23 Hanley Ramirez 6.00 15.00
R24 Hanley Ramirez 6.00 15.00
R25 Evan Longoria 12.50 30.00
R26 Evan Longoria 12.50 30.00
R27 Evan Longoria 12.50 30.00
R28 David Wright 12.50 30.00
R29 David Wright 12.50 30.00
R30 David Wright 12.50 30.00
R31 Hunter Pence 6.00 15.00
R32 Hunter Pence 6.00 15.00
R33 Hunter Pence 6.00 15.00
R34 Joe Mauer 15.00 40.00
R35 Joe Mauer 15.00 40.00
R36 Joe Mauer 15.00 40.00
R37 Rickey Henderson 30.00 60.00
R38 Rickey Henderson 30.00 60.00
R39 Rickey Henderson 30.00 60.00
R40 Al Kaline 15.00 40.00
R41 Al Kaline 15.00 40.00
R42 Al Kaline 15.00 40.00
R43 Catfish Hunter 12.50 30.00
R44 Catfish Hunter 12.50 30.00
R45 Catfish Hunter 12.50 30.00
R46 Dave Winfield 8.00 20.00
R47 Dave Winfield 8.00 20.00
R48 Dave Winfield 8.00 20.00
R49 Carlton Fisk 6.00 15.00
R50 Carlton Fisk 6.00 15.00
R51 Carlton Fisk 6.00 15.00
R52 Curt Schilling 6.00 15.00
R53 Curt Schilling 6.00 15.00
R54 Curt Schilling 6.00 15.00
R58 Mike Schmidt 12.50 30.00
R58 Mike Schmidt 12.50 30.00
R59 Mike Schmidt 12.50 30.00
R61 Steve Carlton 8.00 20.00
R62 Steve Carlton 8.00 20.00
R63 Steve Carlton 8.00 20.00
R64 Orlando Cepeda 6.00 15.00
R65 Orlando Cepeda 6.00 15.00
R65 Orlando Cepeda 6.00 15.00
R67 Prince Fielder 6.00 15.00
R68 Prince Fielder 6.00 15.00
R69 Prince Fielder 6.00 15.00
R70 Ryne Sandberg 12.50 30.00
R71 Ryne Sandberg 12.50 30.00
R72 Ryne Sandberg 12.50 30.00
R73 Tony Gwynn 12.50 30.00
R74 Tony Gwynn 12.50 30.00
R75 Tony Gwynn 12.50 30.00
R75 Willie Stargell 15.00 40.00
R77 Willie Stargell 15.00 40.00
R78 Willie Stargell 15.00 40.00
R79 Miguel Cabrera 8.00 20.00
R80 Miguel Cabrera 8.00 20.00
R81 Miguel Cabrera 8.00 20.00
R82 George Kell 8.00 20.00
R83 George Kell 8.00 20.00
R84 George Kell 8.00 20.00
R85 Cal Ripken Jr. 20.00 50.00
R86 Cal Ripken Jr. 20.00 50.00
R87 Cal Ripken Jr. 20.00 50.00
R88 Joe Morgan 10.00 25.00
R89 Joe Morgan 10.00 25.00
R90 Joe Morgan 10.00 25.00
R91 Chipper Jones 12.50 30.00
R92 Chipper Jones 12.50 30.00
R93 Chipper Jones 12.50 30.00
R94 Paul Molitor 8.00 20.00
R95 Paul Molitor 8.00 20.00
R96 Paul Molitor 8.00 20.00
R97 Phil Niekro 8.00 20.00
R98 Phil Niekro 8.00 20.00
R99 Phil Niekro 8.00 20.00
R100 Manny Ramirez 12.50 30.00
R101 Manny Ramirez 12.50 30.00
R102 Manny Ramirez 12.50 30.00
R103 Kevin Youkilis 6.00 15.00
R104 Kevin Youkilis 6.00 15.00
R105 Kevin Youkilis 6.00 15.00
R106 Josh Beckett 8.00 20.00
R107 Josh Beckett 8.00 20.00
R108 Josh Beckett 8.00 20.00
R109 Victor Martinez 6.00 15.00
R110 Victor Martinez 6.00 15.00
R111 Victor Martinez 6.00 15.00
R112 Adam Dunn 8.00 20.00
R113 Adam Dunn 8.00 20.00
R114 Adam Dunn 8.00 20.00
R115 Justin Morneau 10.00 25.00
R116 Justin Morneau 10.00 25.00
R117 Justin Morneau 10.00 25.00
R118 Roy Halladay 15.00 40.00
R119 Roy Halladay 15.00 40.00
R120 Roy Halladay 15.00 40.00
R121 Andrew McCutchen 10.00 25.00
R122 Andrew McCutchen 10.00 25.00
R123 Andrew McCutchen 10.00 25.00
R124 Ryan Zimmerman 8.00 20.00
R125 Ryan Zimmerman 8.00 20.00
R126 Ryan Zimmerman 8.00 20.00
R127 Adrian Gonzalez 6.00 15.00
R128 Adrian Gonzalez 6.00 15.00
R129 Adrian Gonzalez 6.00 15.00
R130 Derek Jeter 30.00 60.00
R131 Derek Jeter 30.00 60.00
R132 Derek Jeter 30.00 60.00
R136 Reggie Jackson 15.00 40.00
R137 Reggie Jackson 15.00 40.00
R138 Reggie Jackson 15.00 40.00
R139 Monte Irvin 15.00 40.00
R140 Monte Irvin 15.00 40.00
R141 Monte Irvin 15.00 40.00

2010 Topps Triple Threads Relics Emerald

*EMERALD: .5X TO 1.2X BASIC
STATED ODDS 1:19 MINI
STATED PRINT RUN 18 SER.#'d SETS
ALL DC VARIATIONS PRICED EQUALLY

2010 Topps Triple Threads Relics Gold

*GOLD: .6X TO 1.5X BASIC
STATED ODDS 1:38 MINI
STATED PRINT RUN 9 SER.#'d SETS
ALL DC VARIATIONS PRICED EQUALLY

2010 Topps Triple Threads Relics Platinum

STATED ODDS 1:339 MINI
STATED PRINT RUN 1 SER.#'d SET
NO PRICING DUE TO SCARCITY

2010 Topps Triple Threads Relics Sapphire

STATED ODDS 1:112 MINI
STATED PRINT RUN 3 SER.#'d SETS
NO PRICING DUE TO SCARCITY

2010 Topps Triple Threads Relics Sepia

*SEPIA: .4X TO 1X BASIC
STATED ODDS 1:13 MINI
STATED PRINT RUN 27 SER.#'d SETS
ALL DC VARIATIONS PRICED EQUALLY

2010 Topps Triple Threads Rookie Rising Stars Autograph Relic Pairs

STATED ODDS 1:176 MINI
STATED PRINT RUN 50 SER.#'d SETS
RRARP1 Stephen Strasburg 150.00 250.00
Josh Johnson
RRARP2 Jason Heyward 100.00 200.00
Tommy Hanson
RRARP3 Gordon Beckham 20.00 50.00
Chris Coghlan
RRARP4 Justin Upton 20.00 50.00
Adam Jones
RRARP5 Rick Porcello 20.00 50.00
Max Scherzer
RRARP6 Stephen Strasburg 175.00 350.00
Jason Heyward

2010 Topps Triple Threads Rookie Rising Stars Autograph Relic Pairs Gold

STATED ODDS 1:353 MINI
STATED PRINT RUN 25 SER.#'d SETS
NO PRICING DUE TO SCARCITY

2010 Topps Triple Threads Rookie Rising Stars Autograph Relic Pairs Platinum

STATED ODDS 1:8466 MINI
STATED PRINT RUN 1 SER.#'d SET
NO PRICING DUE TO SCARCITY

2010 Topps Triple Threads Rookie Rising Stars Autograph Relic Pairs Sapphire

STATED ODDS 1:876 MINI
STATED PRINT RUN 10 SER.#'d SETS
NO PRICING DUE TO SCARCITY

2010 Topps Triple Threads XXIV Legend Relics

STATED ODDS 1:10,159 MINI
STATED PRINT RUN 18 SER.#'d SETS
NO PRICING DUE TO SCARCITY
XXIVL1 Frank Robinson
XXIVL2 Rickey Henderson
XXIVL3 Mickey Mantle
XXIVL4 Thurman Munson
XXIVL5 Ty Cobb

2010 Topps Triple Threads XXIV Relics

STATED ODDS 1:163 MINI
STATED PRINT RUN 18 SER.#'d SETS
NO PRICING DUE TO SCARCITY

2010 Topps Triple Threads XXIV Relics Gold

STATED ODDS 1:328 MINI
STATED PRINT RUN 9 SER.#'d SETS
NO PRICING DUE TO SCARCITY

2010 Topps Triple Threads XXIV Relics Platinum

STATED ODDS 1:2822 MINI
STATED PRINT RUN 1 SER.#'d SET
NO PRICING DUE TO SCARCITY

2010 Topps Triple Threads XXIV Relics Sapphire

STATED ODDS 1:996 MINI
STATED PRINT RUN 3 SER.#'d SETS
NO PRICING DUE TO SCARCITY

2011 Topps Triple Threads

COMP.SET w/o AU's (100) 40.00 80.00
COMMON CARD (1-100) .30 .75
1-100 PRINT RUN 1500 SER.#'d SETS
COMMON JSY AU RC (101-150) 5.00 12.00
JSY AU RC ODDS 1:11 HOBBY
JSY AU RC PRINT RUN 99 SER.#'d SETS
COMMON JSY AU (101-150) 5.00 12.00
JSY AU ODDS 1:11 HOBBY
JSY AU PRINT RUN 99 SER.#'d SETS
EXCHANGE DEADLINE 9/30/2014
OVERALL 1-100 PLATE ODDS 1:126 HOBBY
PLATE PRINT RUN 1 SET PER COLOR
BLACK-CYAN-MAGENTA-YELLOW ISSUED
NO PLATE PRICING DUE TO SCARCITY
1 Ryan Braun 1.00 2.50
2 Johnny Mize .50 1.25
3 Bert Blyleven .30 .75
4 Lou Gehrig 1.50 4.00
5 Albert Pujols 2.00 5.00
6 Cliff Lee .75 2.00
7 Mickey Mantle 2.50 6.00
8 Cal Ripken Jr. 3.00 8.00
9 Dustin Pedroia 1.00 2.50
10 Nolan Ryan 2.50 6.00
11 Duke Snider .50 1.25
12 Shin-Soo Choo .50 1.25
13 Hanley Ramirez .75 2.00
14 Eddie Murray .75 2.00
15 Josh Hamilton .75 2.00
16 Chase Utley .75 2.00
17 Willie McCovey .50 1.25
18 Roy Campanella .75 2.00
19 Matt Kemp .50 1.25
20 Victor Martinez .50 1.25
21 Ozzie Smith 1.25 3.00
22 Kevin Youkilis .50 1.25
23 Evan Longoria 1.00 2.50
24 Reggie Jackson .50 1.25
25 Jason Heyward 1.00 2.50
26 Ty Cobb 1.25 3.00
27 Babe Ruth 2.00 5.00
28 Clayton Kershaw .75 2.00
29 Andrew McCutchen .75 2.00
30 Justin Verlander 1.00 2.50
31 Joe Morgan .30 .75
32 Carl Crawford .50 1.25
33 Johnny Bench .75 2.00
34 Robinson Cano .75 2.00
35 Mike Stanton .50 1.25
36 Honus Wagner .75 2.00
37 Troy Tulowitzki .75 2.00
38 Jackie Robinson .75 2.00
39 Ryan Zimmerman .50 1.25
40 Carlos Gonzalez .50 1.25
41 Ichiro Suzuki 1.25 3.00
42 Mike Schmidt 1.25 3.00
43 Carlton Fisk .50 1.25
44 Mark Teixeira .75 2.00
45 Tim Lincecum .75 2.00
46 Hank Aaron 1.50 4.00
47 Buster Posey 1.00 2.50
48 Jim Palmer .30 .75
49 David Wright 1.00 2.50
50 Mel Ott .75 2.00
51 Brooks Robinson .50 1.25
52 Ryan Howard 1.00 2.50
53 Joe Mauer .75 2.00
54 Josh Johnson .50 1.25
55 Stan Musial 1.25 3.00
56 Derek Jeter 2.00 5.00
57 Ryne Sandberg 1.50 4.00
58 Pee Wee Reese .50 1.25
59 Bob Gibson .50 1.25
60 Carlos Santana .75 2.00
61 Jose Reyes .50 1.25
62 Paul Molitor .75 2.00
63 Frank Robinson .50 1.25
64 Darryl Strawberry .30 .75
65 Adrian Gonzalez .50 1.25
66 Christy Mathewson .75 2.00
67 Roy Halladay .75 2.00
68 Andre Dawson .50 1.25
69 George Sisler .75 2.00
70 Joey Votto .75 2.00
71 Roger Maris .75 2.00
72 Jimmie Foxx .75 2.00
73 Prince Fielder .50 1.25
74 Roberto Alomar .50 1.25
75 CC Sabathia .50 1.25
76 Rogers Hornsby .50 1.25
77 Ian Kinsler .50 1.25
78 Rickey Henderson .75 2.00
79 Andre Ethier .50 1.25
80 Thurman Munson .75 2.00
81 Matt Holliday .75 2.00
82 Walter Johnson .75 2.00
83 Jon Lester .75 2.00
84 Tom Seaver .50 1.25
85 Starlin Castro .75 2.00
86 Joe DiMaggio 2.00 5.00
87 Felix Hernandez .75 2.00
88 Monte Irvin .30 .75
89 Cy Young .75 2.00
90 Barry Larkin .50 1.25
91 Tony Gwynn .75 2.00
92 Mariano Rivera .75 2.00
93 Clay Buchholz .50 1.25
94 John Smoltz .75 2.00
95 Alex Rodriguez 1.25 3.00
96 Tris Speaker .50 1.25
97 Miguel Cabrera .75 2.00
98 Whitey Ford .50 1.25
99 Justin Morneau .75 2.00
100 Sandy Koufax 2.50 6.00
101 Buster Posey Bat AU 30.00 60.00
102 Gordon Beckham Jsy AU 6.00 15.00
103 Jay Bruce Bat AU 10.00 25.00
104 Danny Valencia Bat AU 8.00 20.00
105 Neftali Feliz Jsy AU 10.00 25.00
106 Jose Tabata Jsy AU 6.00 15.00
107 Carlos Santana Jsy AU 10.00 25.00
108 Pablo Sandoval Jsy AU 10.00 25.00
109 Mitch Moreland Bat AU 8.00 20.00
110 Gio Gonzalez Jsy AU 6.00 15.00
111 Brett Wallace Bat AU 6.00 15.00
112 Chris Sale Jsy AU RC 6.00 15.00
113 Kyle Drabek Jsy AU RC 6.00 15.00
114 Starlin Castro Jsy AU 20.00 50.00
115 Austin Jackson Jsy AU 8.00 20.00
116 Max Scherzer Jsy AU 6.00 15.00
117 Aroldis Chapman Jsy AU RC 15.00 40.00
118 Andrew McCutchen Jsy AU 12.50 30.00
119 Zach Britton Jsy AU RC 10.00 25.00
120 Madison Bumgarner JSY AU EXCH 12.5030.00
121 Mike Stanton Jsy AU 15.00 40.00
122 Jason Heyward Jsy AU EXCH 20.00 50.00
123 Freddie Freeman Bat AU RC 20.00 50.00
124 Logan Morrison Bat AU 8.00 20.00
125 Brandon Belt Jsy AU RC 20.00 50.00
126 Brett Anderson Jsy AU 5.00 12.00
127 Michael Pineda Jsy AU RC 15.00 40.00
128 Drew Stubbs Jsy AU 6.00 15.00
129 Elvis Andrus Jsy AU 12.50 30.00
130 Colby Rasmus Jsy AU 6.00 15.00
131 Chris Coghlan Jsy AU 5.00 12.00
132 Tommy Hanson Jsy AU EXCH 8.00 20.00
133 Clayton Kershaw Jsy AU 20.00 50.00
134 Brent Morel Jsy AU RC 5.00 12.00
135 Jaime Garcia Jsy AU 12.50 30.00
136 Eric Hosmer Jsy AU RC EXCH 50.00 100.00
137 Jeremy Hellickson Jsy AU RC 12.50 30.00
138 Pedro Alvarez Jsy AU RC 8.00 20.00
139 Gaby Sanchez Jsy AU 5.00 12.00
140 J.P. Arencibia Bat AU 8.00 20.00
141 Neil Walker Jsy AU 8.00 20.00
143 Jordan Zimmerman Bat AU 5.00 12.00
144 Ian Desmond Jsy AU 5.00 12.00
145 Rick Porcello Jsy AU 6.00 15.00
146 Daniel Bard Jsy AU 10.00 25.00
147A Alcides Escobar Jsy AU 5.00 12.00
147B Hank Conger Jsy AU RC EXCH 5.00 12.00
148 Brett Gardner Bat AU 15.00 40.00
149 Ike Davis Jsy AU 10.00 25.00
150 Carlos Gonzalez Jsy AU 12.50 30.00

2011 Topps Triple Threads Emerald

*EMERALD 1-100: .6X TO 1.5X BASIC
1-100 ODDS 1:3 MINI
1-100 PRINT RUN 249 SER.#'d SETS
*EMERALD JSY AU: .4X TO 1X BASIC
EMERALD JSY AU ODDS 1:21 MINI
EM.JSY AU PRINT RUN 50 SER.#'d SETS
EXCHANGE DEADLINE 9/30/2014

2011 Topps Triple Threads Gold

*GOLD 1-100: .75X TO 2X BASIC
1-100 ODDS 1:6 MINI
1-100 PRINT RUN 99 SER.#'d SETS
101-150 ODDS 1:41 HOBBY
101-150 PRINT RUN 25 SER.#'d SETS
NO 101-150 PRICING DUE TO SCARCITY
EXCHANGE DEADLINE 9/30/2014

2011 Topps Triple Threads Platinum

1-100 STATED ODDS 1:502 MINI
101-150 STATED ODDS 1:1005 MINI
STATED PRINT RUN 1 SER.#'d SET
NO PRICING DUE TO SCARCITY
EXCHANGE DEADLINE 9/30/2014

2011 Topps Triple Threads Sapphire

1-100 STATED ODDS 1:20 MINI
1-100 PRINT RUN 25 SER.#'d SETS
101-150 STATED ODDS 1:101 MINI
101-150 PRINT RUN 10 SER.#'d SETS
NO PRICING DUE TO SCARCITY
EXCHANGE DEADLINE 9/30/2014

2011 Topps Triple Threads Sepia

*SEPIA 1-100: .5X TO 1.2X BASIC
1-100 RANDOMLY INSERTED
1-100 PRINT RUN 625 SER.#'d SETS
*SEPIA JSY AU: .4X TO 1X BASIC
SEPIA JSY AU ODDS 1:14 MINI
SEP.JSY AU PRINT RUN 75 SER.#'d SETS
EXCHANGE DEADLINE 9/30/2014

2011 Topps Triple Threads White Whale Printing Plates

STATED ODDS 1:251 MINI
STATED PRINT RUN 1 SER.#'d SET
NO PRICING DUE TO SCARCITY
EXCHANGE DEADLINE 9/30/2014

2011 Topps Triple Threads Wood

STATED ODDS 1:1005 MINI
STATED PRINT RUN 1 SER.#'d SET
NO PRICING DUE TO SCARCITY
EXCHANGE DEADLINE 9/30/2014

2011 Topps Triple Threads All-Star Jumbo Laundry Tag

STATED ODDS 1:690 MINI
STATED PRINT RUN 1 SER.#'d SET
NO PRICING DUE TO SCARCITY

2011 Topps Triple Threads All-Star Jumbo Sleeve Patches

STATED ODDS 1:778 MINI
STATED PRINT RUN 1 SER.#'d SET
NO PRICING DUE TO SCARCITY

2011 Topps Triple Threads All-Star Jumbo Sleeve Team Patches

STATED ODDS 1:754 MINI
STATED PRINT RUN 1 SER.#'d SET
NO PRICING DUE TO SCARCITY

2011 Topps Triple Threads All-Star MLB Logo Patch

STATED ODDS 1:680 MINI
STATED PRINT RUN 1 SER.#'d SET
NO PRICING DUE TO SCARCITY

2011 Topps Triple Threads All-Star Patches

STATED ODDS 1:80 MINI
STATED PRINT RUN 9 SER.#'d SETS
NO PRICING DUE TO SCARCITY

2011 Topps Triple Threads All-Star Patches Platinum

STATED ODDS 1:689 MINI
STATED PRINT RUN 1 SER.#'d SET
NO PRICING DUE TO SCARCITY

2011 Topps Triple Threads Autograph Relic Combos

STATED ODDS 1:93 MINI
STATED PRINT RUN 36 SER.#'d SETS
EXCHANGE DEADLINE 9/30/2014
ARC1 Roberto Alomar 50.00 100.00
Chase Utley
Robinson Cano
ARC2 Johnny Bench 75.00 150.00
Joe Mauer
Buster Posey
ARC3 Larry Walker 20.00 50.00
Carlos Gonzalez
Ubaldo Jimenez
ARC4 Mike Schmidt 75.00 150.00
Alex Rodriguez
Evan Longoria
ARC5 Willie McCovey 60.00 120.00
Ryan Howard
Prince Fielder
ARC6 Ryne Sandberg 40.00 80.00
Dustin Pedroia
Ian Kinsler
ARC7 David Wright 60.00 120.00
Ryan Zimmerman
Chipper Jones
ARC8 Nolan Ryan 75.00 150.00
Roy Halladay
Felix Hernandez
ARC9 Rickey Henderson 50.00 100.00
Carl Crawford
Brett Gardner
ARC10 Sandy Koufax 250.00 350.00
Clayton Kershaw
Aroldis Chapman
ARC11 Ryan Braun 50.00 100.00
Zack Greinke
Prince Fielder
ARC12 Stan Musial 50.00 100.00
Matt Holliday
Colby Rasmus
ARC13 Ryne Sandberg 50.00 100.00
Andre Dawson
Starlin Castro
ARC14 Darryl Strawberry 30.00 60.00
Jason Heyward
Chris Young
ARC15 Bob Gibson 30.00 60.00
Felix Hernandez
Josh Johnson

2011 Topps Triple Threads Autograph Relic Combos Emerald

STATED ODDS 1:186 MINI
STATED PRINT RUN 18 SER.#'d SETS
NO PRICING DUE TO SCARCITY
EXCHANGE DEADLINE 9/30/2014

2011 Topps Triple Threads Autograph Relic Combos Gold

STATED ODDS 1:371 MINI
STATED PRINT RUN 9 SER.#'d SETS
NO PRICING DUE TO SCARCITY
EXCHANGE DEADLINE 9/30/2014

2011 Topps Triple Threads Autograph Relic Combos Platinum

STATED ODDS 1:3447 MINI
STATED PRINT RUN 1 SER.#'d SET
NO PRICING DUE TO SCARCITY
EXCHANGE DEADLINE 9/30/2014

2011 Topps Triple Threads Autograph Relic Combos Sapphire

STATED ODDS 1:1122 MINI
STATED PRINT RUN 3 SER.#'d SETS
NO PRICING DUE TO SCARCITY
EXCHANGE DEADLINE 9/30/2014

2011 Topps Triple Threads Autograph Relic Combos Sepia

*SEPIA: .4X TO 1X BASIC
STATED ODDS 1:124 MINI
STATED PRINT RUN 27 SER.#'d SETS
EXCHANGE DEADLINE 9/30/2014

2011 Topps Triple Threads Autograph Relic Combos White What Printing Plates

STATED ODDS 1:846 MINI
STATED PRINT RUN 1 SER.#'d SET
NO PRICING DUE TO SCARCITY
EXCHANGE DEADLINE 9/30/2014

2011 Topps Triple Threads Autograph Relic Combos Wood

STATED ODDS 1:3447 MINI
STATED PRINT RUN 1 SER.#'d SET
NO PRICING DUE TO SCARCITY
EXCHANGE DEADLINE 9/30/2014

2011 Topps Triple Threads Autograph Relic Combos Double

STATED ODDS 1:2681 HOBBY
STATED PRINT RUN 3 SER.#'d SETS
NO PRICING DUE TO SCARCITY
EXCHANGE DEADLINE 9/30/2014

2011 Topps Triple Threads Autograph Relic Combos Double Platinum

STATED ODDS 1:8043 HOBBY
STATED PRINT RUN 1 SER.#'d SET
NO PRICING DUE TO SCARCITY
EXCHANGE DEADLINE 9/30/2014

2011 Topps Triple Threads Flashback Relics

STATED ODDS 1:56 MINI
STATED PRINT RUN 36 SER.#'d SETS
TTFR1 Mickey Mantle 100.00 200.00
TTFR2 Frank Robinson 12.50 30.00
TTFR3 Babe Ruth 175.00 350.00
TTFR4 Ozzie Smith 20.00 50.00
TTFR5 Nolan Ryan 40.00 80.00
TTFR6 Tony Gwynn 15.00 40.00
TTFR7 Mike Schmidt 15.00 40.00
TTFR8 Paul Molitor 12.50 30.00
TTFR9 Brooks Robinson 15.00 40.00
TTFR10 Hank Aaron 40.00 80.00
TTFR11 Willie McCovey 12.50 30.00
TTFR12 Stan Musial 20.00 50.00
TTFR13 Cal Ripken Jr. 30.00 60.00
TTFR14 Roger Maris 40.00 80.00
TTFR15 Reggie Jackson 12.50 30.00
TTFR16 Ryne Sandberg 15.00 40.00
TTFR17 Carlton Fisk 12.50 30.00
TTFR18 Jackie Robinson 30.00 60.00
TTFR19 Rickey Henderson 30.00 60.00
TTFR20 Johnny Bench 12.50 30.00
TTFR21 Lou Gehrig 100.00 200.00
TTFR22 Al Kaline 15.00 40.00
TTFR23 Ty Cobb 50.00 100.00
TTFR24 Rogers Hornsby 30.00 60.00
TTFR25 Sandy Koufax 75.00 150.00

2011 Topps Triple Threads Flashback Relics Emerald

STATED ODDS 1:112 MINI
STATED PRINT RUN 18 SER.#'d SETS
NO PRICING DUE TO SCARCITY

2011 Topps Triple Threads Flashback Relics Platinum

STATED ODDS 1:2010 MINI
STATED PRINT RUN 1 SER.#'d SET
NO PRICING DUE TO SCARCITY

2011 Topps Triple Threads Flashback Relics Sapphire

STATED ODDS 1:680 MINI
STATED PRINT RUN 3 SER.#'d SETS
NO PRICING DUE TO SCARCITY

2011 Topps Triple Threads Flashback Relics Sepia

*SEPIA: .4X TO 1X BASIC
STATED ODDS 1:75 MINI
STATED PRINT RUN 27 SER.#'d SETS

2011 Topps Triple Threads Jumbo Letter Number Logo

STATED ODDS 1:4825 MINI
STATED PRINT RUN 1 SER.#'d SET
NO PRICING DUE TO SCARCITY

2011 Topps Triple Threads Jumbo Patch Combos

STATED ODDS 1:4825 MINI
STATED PRINT RUN 1 SER.#'d SET
NO PRICING DUE TO SCARCITY

2011 Topps Triple Threads Jumbo Plus Relic Autographs

STATED ODDS 1:1027 MINI
STATED PRINT RUN 3 SER.#'d SETS
NO PRICING DUE TO SCARCITY
EXCANGE DEADLINE 9/30/2013

2011 Topps Triple Threads Jumbo Plus Relic Autographs Platinum

STATED ODDS 1:3016 MINI
STATED PRINT RUN 1 SER.#'d SET
NO PRICING DUE TO SCARCITY
EXCANGE DEADLINE 9/30/2013

2011 Topps Triple Threads Jumbo Plus Relics

STATED ODDS 1:1072 MINI
STATED PRINT RUN 3 SER.#'d SETS
NO PRICING DUE TO SCARCITY

2011 Topps Triple Threads Jumbo Plus Relics Platinum

STATED ODDS 1:3016 MINI
STATED PRINT RUN 1 SER.#'d SET
NO PRICING DUE TO SCARCITY

2011 Topps Triple Threads Legend Relics

STATED ODDS 1:94 MINI
STATED PRINT RUN 36 SER.#'d SETS
TTRL1 Ty Cobb 30.00 60.00
TTRL2 Brooks Robinson 12.50 30.00
TTRL3 Babe Ruth 150.00 300.00
TTRL4 Mike Schmidt 10.00 25.00
TTRL5 Joe DiMaggio 60.00 120.00
TTRL6 Johnny Bench 10.00 25.00
TTRL7 Mickey Mantle 75.00 150.00
TTRL8 Jackie Robinson 20.00 50.00
TTRL9 Jim Palmer 10.00 25.00
TTRL10 Lou Gehrig 75.00 150.00
TTRL11 Roy Campanella 12.50 30.00
TTRL12 Bob Gibson 10.00 25.00
TTRL13 Willie McCovey 10.00 25.00
TTRL14 Stan Musial 15.00 40.00
TTRL15 Hank Aaron 30.00 60.00

2011 Topps Triple Threads Legend Relics Emerald

STATED ODDS 1:186 MINI
STATED PRINT RUN 18 SER.#'d SETS
NO PRICING DUE TO SCARCITY

2011 Topps Triple Threads Legend Relics Gold

STATED ODDS 1:371 MINI
STATED PRINT RUN 9 SER.#'d SETS
NO PRICING DUE TO SCARCITY

2011 Topps Triple Threads Legend Relics Platinum

STATED ODDS 1:3127 MINI
STATED PRINT RUN 1 SER.#'d SET
NO PRICING DUE TO SCARCITY

2011 Topps Triple Threads Legend Relics Sapphire

STATED ODDS 1:1149 MINI
STATED PRINT RUN 3 SER.#'d SETS
NO PRICING DUE TO SCARCITY

2011 Topps Triple Threads Legend Relics Sepia

*SEPIA: .4X TO 1X BASIC
STATED ODDS 1:124 MINI
STATED PRINT RUN 27 SER.#'D SETS

2011 Topps Triple Threads Letter Plus Relic Autographs

STATED ODDS 1:1026 MINI
STATED PRINT RUN 3 SER.#'d SETS
NO PRICING DUE TO SCARCITY
EXCANGE DEADLINE 9/30/2013

2011 Topps Triple Threads Letter Plus Relic Autographs Platinum

STATED ODDS 1:3016 MINI
STATED PRINT RUN 1 SER.#'d SET
NO PRICING DUE TO SCARCITY
EXCANGE DEADLINE 9/30/2013

2011 Topps Triple Threads Letter Plus Relics

STATED ODDS 1:1072 MINI
STATED PRINT RUN 3 SER.#'d SETS
NO PRICING DUE TO SCARCITY

2011 Topps Triple Threads Letter Plus Relics Platinum

STATED ODDS 1:3016 MINI
STATED PRINT RUN 1 SER.#'d SET
NO PRICING DUE TO SCARCITY

2011 Topps Triple Threads Presidential Cut Above Relic Autographs

STATED ODDS 1:8043 MINI
STATED PRINT RUN 1 SER.#'d SET
NO PRICING DUE TO SCARCITY
EXCHANGE DEADLINE 9/30/2014

2011 Topps Triple Threads Relic Autographs

STATED ODDS 1:11 MINI
STATED PRINT RUN 18 SER.#'d SETS
ALL DC VARIATIONS PRICED EQUALLY
NO PRICING ON PLAYERS W/ONE DC VERSION
EXCHANGE DEADLINE 9/30/2014
TTAR1 Sandy Koufax
TTAR2 Hank Aaron
TTAR3 Joe Mauer
TTAR4 Ubaldo Jimenez 10.00 25.00
TTAR5 Ubaldo Jimenez 10.00 25.00
TTAR6 Andre Dawson 15.00 40.00
TTAR7 Andre Dawson 15.00 40.00
TTAR8 Chase Utley
TTAR9 Aroldis Chapman 40.00 80.00
TTAR10 Aroldis Chapman 40.00 80.00
TTAR11 Aroldis Chapman 40.00 80.00
TTAR12 Aroldis Chapman 40.00 80.00
TTAR13 Elvis Andrus 10.00 25.00
TTAR14 Johnny Cueto 8.00 20.00
TTAR15 Jay Bruce 15.00 40.00
TTAR16 Jeremy Hellickson 15.00 40.00
TTAR17 Andrew McCutchen 15.00 40.00
TTAR18 Rickey Henderson
TTAR19 Alex Rodriguez
TTAR20 George Foster
TTAR21 George Foster
TTAR22 Frank Thomas
TTAR23 Casey McGehee
TTAR24 Casey McGehee
TTAR25 Casey McGehee
TTAR26 Casey McGehee
TTAR28 Justin Upton 12.50 30.00
TTAR29 Justin Upton 12.50 30.00
TTAR30 Luis Aparicio 12.50 30.00
TTAR31 Luis Aparicio 12.50 30.00
TTAR32 Juan Marichal 20.00 50.00
TTAR33 Juan Marichal 20.00 50.00
TTAR34 Carlos Santana 10.00 25.00
TTAR35 Carlos Santana 10.00 25.00
TTAR36 Carlos Santana 10.00 25.00
TTAR37 Carlos Santana 10.00 25.00
TTAR38 Carlos Santana 10.00 25.00
TTAR39 Stan Musial
TTAR40 Tommy Hanson 8.00 20.00
TTAR41 Tommy Hanson 8.00 20.00
TTAR42 Tommy Hanson 8.00 20.00
TTAR43 Tommy Hanson 8.00 20.00
TTAR44 Roberto Alomar 30.00 60.00
TTAR45 Roberto Alomar 30.00 60.00
TTAR46 Elvis Andrus 10.00 25.00
TTAR47 Elvis Andrus 10.00 25.00
TTAR48 Elvis Andrus 10.00 25.00
TTAR49 Elvis Andrus 10.00 25.00
TTAR50 Max Scherzer 8.00 20.00
TTAR51 Max Scherzer 8.00 20.00
TTAR52 Max Scherzer 8.00 20.00
TTAR53 Max Scherzer 8.00 20.00
TTAR54 Jose Bautista 15.00 40.00
TTAR55 Jose Bautista 15.00 40.00
TTAR56 Jose Bautista 15.00 40.00
TTAR57 Jose Bautista 15.00 40.00
TTAR58 Joe Morgan 10.00 25.00
TTAR59 Joe Morgan 10.00 25.00
TTAR60 Matt Garza 10.00 25.00
TTAR61 Matt Garza 10.00 25.00
TTAR62 Matt Garza 10.00 25.00
TTAR63 Matt Garza 10.00 25.00
TTAR64 Don Mattingly
TTAR65 Frank Robinson
TTAR66 Josh Johnson 8.00 20.00
TTAR67 Josh Johnson 8.00 20.00
TTAR68 Josh Johnson 8.00 20.00
TTAR69 Josh Johnson 8.00 20.00
TTAR70 Red Schoendienst 20.00 50.00
TTAR71 Red Schoendienst 20.00 50.00
TTAR72 Red Schoendienst 20.00 50.00
TTAR73 Jason Heyward 30.00 60.00
TTAR74 Jason Heyward 30.00 60.00
TTAR75 Eddie Murray
TTAR76 Dustin Pedroia 30.00 60.00
TTAR77 Dustin Pedroia 30.00 60.00
TTAR78 Duke Snider 30.00 60.00
TTAR79 Duke Snider 30.00 60.00
TTAR80 Pablo Sandoval 12.50 30.00
TTAR81 Pablo Sandoval 12.50 30.00
TTAR82 Pablo Sandoval 12.50 30.00
TTAR83 Pablo Sandoval 12.50 30.00
TTAR84 Pablo Sandoval 12.50 30.00
TTAR85 Angel Pagan 8.00 20.00
TTAR86 Angel Pagan 8.00 20.00
TTAR87 Angel Pagan 8.00 20.00
TTAR88 Angel Pagan 8.00 20.00
TTAR89 Angel Pagan 8.00 20.00
TTAR90 Brian McCann 15.00 40.00
TTAR91 Brian McCann 15.00 40.00
TTAR92 Brian McCann 15.00 40.00
TTAR93 Cal Ripken Jr.
TTAR94 Robinson Cano 20.00 50.00
TTAR95 Robinson Cano 20.00 50.00
TTAR96 Aramis Ramirez 8.00 20.00
TTAR97 Aramis Ramirez 8.00 20.00
TTAR98 Aramis Ramirez 8.00 20.00
TTAR99 Steve Garvey 20.00 50.00
TTAR100 Steve Garvey 20.00 50.00
TTAR101 David Wright 30.00 60.00
TTAR102 David Wright 30.00 60.00
TTAR103 John Smoltz 40.00 80.00
TTAR104 John Smoltz 40.00 80.00
TTAR105 Brooks Robinson 30.00 60.00
TTAR106 Brooks Robinson 30.00 60.00
TTAR107 Prince Fielder 20.00 50.00
TTAR108 Prince Fielder 20.00 50.00
TTAR109 Trevor Cahill 8.00 20.00
TTAR110 Trevor Cahill 8.00 20.00
TTAR111 Trevor Cahill 8.00 20.00
TTAR112 Trevor Cahill 8.00 20.00
TTAR113 Trevor Cahill 8.00 20.00
TTAR114 Carlton Fisk
TTAR115 Carlton Fisk
TTAR116 Evan Longoria
TTAR117 Tim Hudson 15.00 40.00
TTAR118 Tim Hudson 15.00 40.00
TTAR119 Nick Markakis 15.00 40.00
TTAR120 Nick Markakis 15.00 40.00
TTAR121 Nick Markakis 15.00 40.00
TTAR122 Nick Markakis 15.00 40.00
TTAR123 Nolan Ryan
TTAR124 Josh Hamilton 30.00 60.00

TTAR125 Josh Hamilton 30.00 60.00
TTAR126 Larry Walker
TTAR127 Larry Walker
TTAR128 Roy Halladay
TTAR129 Ozzie Smith 15.00 40.00
TTAR130 Ozzie Smith 15.00 40.00
TTAR131 Vernon Wells 8.00 20.00
TTAR132 Vernon Wells 8.00 20.00
TTAR133 Billy Butler 8.00 20.00
TTAR134 Billy Butler 8.00 20.00
TTAR135 Billy Butler 8.00 20.00
TTAR136 Billy Butler 8.00 20.00
TTAR137 Reggie Jackson
TTAR138 Ryan Zimmerman 12.50 30.00
TTAR139 Ryan Zimmerman 12.50 30.00
TTAR140 Ryan Zimmerman 12.50 30.00
TTAR141 Miguel Cabrera 30.00 60.00
TTAR142 Miguel Cabrera 30.00 60.00
TTAR143 Jim Palmer 30.00 60.00
TTAR144 Jim Palmer 30.00 60.00
TTAR145 Adrian Gonzalez 30.00 60.00
TTAR146 Adrian Gonzalez 30.00 60.00
TTAR147 Andrew McCutchen 15.00 40.00
TTAR148 Andrew McCutchen 15.00 40.00
TTAR149 Andrew McCutchen 15.00 40.00
TTAR150 Andrew McCutchen 15.00 40.00
TTAR151 Neftali Feliz 12.50 30.00
TTAR152 Neftali Feliz 12.50 30.00
TTAR153 Neftali Feliz 12.50 30.00
TTAR154 Neftali Feliz 12.50 30.00
TTAR155 Neftali Feliz 12.50 30.00
TTAR156 Johnny Bench
TTAR157 Vladimir Guerrero
TTAR158 Nelson Cruz 10.00 25.00
TTAR159 Nelson Cruz 10.00 25.00
TTAR160 Nelson Cruz 10.00 25.00
TTAR161 Nelson Cruz 10.00 25.00
TTAR162 Jonathan Papelbon 10.00 25.00
TTAR163 Jonathan Papelbon 10.00 25.00
TTAR164 Tom Seaver
TTAR165 Buster Posey 50.00 100.00
TTAR166 Buster Posey 50.00 100.00
TTAR167 Gordon Beckham 10.00 25.00
TTAR168 Gordon Beckham 10.00 25.00
TTAR169 Gordon Beckham 10.00 25.00
TTAR170 Paul Molitor 15.00 40.00
TTAR171 Paul Molitor 15.00 40.00
TTAR172 Mike Stanton 20.00 50.00
TTAR173 Mike Stanton 20.00 50.00
TTAR174 Mike Stanton 20.00 50.00
TTAR175 Jeremy Hellickson 15.00 40.00
TTAR176 Jeremy Hellickson 15.00 40.00
TTAR177 Jeremy Hellickson 15.00 40.00
TTAR178 Jeremy Hellickson 15.00 40.00
TTAR179 Ryne Sandberg
TTAR180 Joey Votto 20.00 50.00
TTAR181 Joey Votto 20.00 50.00
TTAR182 Cliff Lee 40.00 80.00
TTAR183 Cliff Lee 40.00 80.00
TTAR184 Ian Kinsler 12.50 30.00
TTAR185 Ian Kinsler 12.50 30.00
TTAR186 Ian Kinsler 12.50 30.00
TTAR187 Ian Kinsler 12.50 30.00
TTAR188 Adam Jones 12.50 30.00
TTAR189 Adam Jones 12.50 30.00
TTAR190 Adam Jones 12.50 30.00
TTAR191 Adam Jones 12.50 30.00
TTAR192 Barry Larkin
TTAR193 Barry Larkin
TTAR194 Carl Crawford
TTAR195 Carl Crawford
TTAR196 Manny Pacquiao 250.00 350.00
TTAR197 Manny Pacquiao 250.00 350.00
TTAR198 Manny Pacquiao 250.00 350.00
TTAR199 Bob Gibson
TTAR200 Tony Gwynn
TTAR201 Ryan Howard 30.00 60.00
TTAR202 Ryan Howard 30.00 60.00
TTAR203 Austin Jackson 12.50 30.00
TTAR204 Austin Jackson 12.50 30.00
TTAR205 Austin Jackson 12.50 30.00
TTAR206 Austin Jackson 12.50 30.00
TTAR207 Dan Haren
TTAR208 Dan Haren
TTAR209 Dan Uggla 15.00 40.00
TTAR210 Dan Uggla 15.00 40.00
TTAR211 Paul O'Neill 30.00 60.00
TTAR212 Paul O'Neill 30.00 60.00
TTAR213 Paul O'Neill 30.00 60.00
TTAR214 Shane Victorino 15.00 40.00
TTAR215 Shane Victorino 15.00 40.00
TTAR216 Shane Victorino 15.00 40.00
TTAR217 Shane Victorino 15.00 40.00
TTAR218 Starlin Castro 20.00 50.00
TTAR219 Starlin Castro 20.00 50.00
TTAR220 Starlin Castro 20.00 50.00
TTAR221 Starlin Castro 20.00 50.00
TTAR222 Starlin Castro 20.00 50.00
TTAR223 Johnny Cueto 8.00 20.00
TTAR224 Johnny Cueto 8.00 20.00
TTAR225 Johnny Cueto 8.00 20.00
TTAR226 Johnny Cueto 8.00 20.00
TTAR227 Willie McCovey
TTAR228 Fergie Jenkins 15.00 40.00
TTAR229 Fergie Jenkins 15.00 40.00
TTAR230 Andre Ethier 10.00 25.00
TTAR231 Andre Ethier 10.00 25.00
TTAR232 Andre Ethier 10.00 25.00
TTAR233 Andre Ethier 10.00 25.00
TTAR234 Bert Blyleven 15.00 40.00
TTAR235 Bert Blyleven 15.00 40.00
TTAR236 Bert Blyleven 15.00 40.00
TTAR237 Hanley Ramirez 8.00 20.00
TTAR238 Hanley Ramirez 8.00 20.00
TTAR239 Rick Porcello 8.00 20.00
TTAR240 Rick Porcello 8.00 20.00
TTAR241 Rick Porcello 8.00 20.00
TTAR242 Rick Porcello 8.00 20.00
TTAR243 Albert Belle 30.00 60.00
TTAR244 Albert Belle 30.00 60.00
TTAR245 Albert Belle 30.00 60.00
TTAR246 B.J. Upton 8.00 20.00
TTAR247 B.J. Upton 8.00 20.00
TTAR248 B.J. Upton 8.00 20.00
TTAR249 B.J. Upton 8.00 20.00
TTAR250 Matt Holliday 30.00 60.00
TTAR251 Matt Holliday 30.00 60.00
TTAR252 Al Kaline 30.00 60.00
TTAR253 Al Kaline 30.00 60.00
TTAR254 Adam Lind 8.00 20.00
TTAR255 Adam Lind 8.00 20.00
TTAR256 Adam Lind 8.00 20.00
TTAR257 Adam Lind 8.00 20.00
TTAR258 Adam Lind 8.00 20.00
TTAR259 Mike Schmidt
TTAR260 Jay Bruce 15.00 40.00
TTAR261 Jay Bruce 15.00 40.00
TTAR262 Jay Bruce 15.00 40.00
TTAR263 Jay Bruce 15.00 40.00
TTAR264 Heath Bell 8.00 20.00
TTAR265 Heath Bell 8.00 20.00
TTAR266 Heath Bell 8.00 20.00
TTAR267 Heath Bell 8.00 20.00
TTAR268 Darryl Strawberry 30.00 60.00
TTAR269 Darryl Strawberry 30.00 60.00
TTAR270 Albert Pujols

2011 Topps Triple Threads Relic Autographs Gold

*GOLD: .5X TO 1.2X BASIC
STATED ODDS 1:21 MINI
STATED PRINT RUN 9 SER.#'d SETS
ALL DC VARIATIONS PRICED EQUALLY
NO PRICING ON MANY DUE TO SCARCITY
EXCHANGE DEADLINE 9/30/2014

2011 Topps Triple Threads Relic Combos

STATED ODDS 1:24 MINI
STATED PRINT RUN 36 SER.#'d SETS
TTRC1 Alex Rodriguez 20.00 50.00
Derek Jeter
Robinson Cano
TTRC2 Hanley Ramirez 10.00 25.00
Troy Tulowitzki
Jose Reyes
TTRC3 Albert Pujols 20.00 50.00
Joey Votto
Miguel Cabrera
TTRC4 Carl Crawford 8.00 20.00
Adrian Gonzalez
Dustin Pedroia
TTRC5 Evan Longoria 10.00 25.00
David Wright
Ryan Zimmerman
TTRC6 Jason Heyward 12.50 30.00
Chipper Jones
Brian McCann
TTRC7 Tim Lincecum 20.00 50.00
Buster Posey
Matt Cain
TTRC8 Ryan Howard 15.00 40.00
Chase Utley
Jimmy Rollins
TTRC9 Andrew McCutchen 8.00 20.00
Justin Upton
Matt Kemp
TTRC10 Josh Hamilton 12.50 30.00
Ian Kinsler
Nelson Cruz
TTRC11 Jon Lester 6.00 15.00
CC Sabathia
David Price
TTRC12 Josh Hamilton 10.00 25.00
Ryan Braun
Carlos Gonzalez
TTRC13 Roy Halladay 20.00 50.00
Cliff Lee
Cole Hamels
TTRC14 Mike Stanton 12.50 30.00
Hanley Ramirez
Josh Johnson
TTRC15 Ichiro Suzuki 10.00 25.00
Felix Hernandez
Chone Figgins
TTRC16 Joe Mauer 12.50 30.00
Buster Posey
Brian McCann
TTRC17 Justin Verlander 15.00 40.00
Miguel Cabrera
Victor Martinez
TTRC18 Shin-Soo Choo 8.00 20.00
Carlos Santana
Grady Sizemore
TTRC19 Carlos Gonzalez 6.00 15.00
Troy Tulowitzki
Ubaldo Jimenez
TTRC20 Robinson Cano 10.00 25.00
Dustin Pedroia
Ian Kinsler
TTRC21 Clayton Kershaw 8.00 20.00
Jon Lester
David Price
TTRC22 Aroldis Chapman 12.50 30.00
Joey Votto
Brandon Phillips
TTRC23 Joe Mauer 10.00 25.00
Justin Morneau
Francisco Liriano
TTRC24 Mike Stanton 10.00 25.00
Jason Heyward
Pedro Alvarez
TTRC25 Mariano Rivera 10.00 25.00
CC Sabathia
Phil Hughes
TTRC26 David Wright 10.00 25.00
Jose Reyes
Ike Davis
TTRC27 Albert Pujols 15.00 40.00
Matt Holliday
Colby Rasmus
TTRC28 Brett Anderson 6.00 15.00
Trevor Cahill
Gio Gonzalez
TTRC29 Jose Bautista 10.00 25.00
Brandon Morrow
Kyle Drabek
TTRC30 Roy Halladay 12.50 30.00
Tim Lincecum
Felix Hernandez
TTRC31 Larry Walker 12.50 30.00
Justin Morneau
Joey Votto
TTRC32 Carlton Fisk 10.00 25.00
Jorge Posada
Buster Posey
TTRC33 Reggie Jackson 12.50 30.00
Darryl Strawberry
Carlos Beltran
TTRC34 Willie McCovey 8.00 20.00
Ryan Howard
Prince Fielder
TTRC35 Juan Marichal 15.00 40.00
Tim Lincecum
Matt Cain
TTRC36 Luis Aparicio 10.00 25.00
Jose Reyes
Elvis Andrus
TTRC37 Joe Morgan 12.50 30.00
Roberto Alomar
Robinson Cano
TTRC38 Eddie Murray 8.00 20.00
Mark Teixeira
Chipper Jones
TTRC39 Roy Campanella 15.00 40.00
Thurman Munson
Joe Mauer
TTRC40 Babe Ruth 175.00 350.00
Joe DiMaggio
Mickey Mantle
TTRC41 Brooks Robinson 10.00 25.00
Evan Longoria
Ryan Zimmerman
TTRC42 Duke Snider 12.50 30.00
Andre Ethier
Matt Kemp
TTRC43 Nolan Ryan 15.00 40.00
Felix Hernandez
Ubaldo Jimenez
TTRC44 Ryne Sandberg 15.00 40.00
Starlin Castro
Aramis Ramirez
TTRC45 Mike Schmidt 15.00 40.00
Alex Rodriguez
Evan Longoria
TTRC46 Tom Seaver 10.00 25.00
Edinson Volquez
Johnny Cueto
TTRC47 Ozzie Smith 15.00 40.00
Derek Jeter
Jimmy Rollins
TTRC48 Ty Cobb 40.00 80.00
Ichiro Suzuki
Robinson Cano
TTRC49 Jimmie Foxx 20.00 50.00
Albert Pujols
Ryan Howard
TTRC50 Sandy Koufax 30.00 60.00
Clayton Kershaw
David Price
TTRC51 Andre Dawson 8.00 20.00
Jason Heyward
Carlos Gonzalez
TTRC52 Cal Ripken Jr. 20.00 50.00
Derek Jeter
Troy Tulowitzki
TTRC53 Bob Gibson 12.50 30.00
Adam Wainwright
Chris Carpenter
TTRC54 Tony Gwynn 12.50 30.00
Ichiro Suzuki
Carlos Gonzalez
TTRC55 Rickey Henderson 15.00 40.00
Carl Crawford
Andrew McCutchen
TTRC56 Barry Larkin 8.00 20.00
Hanley Ramirez
Troy Tulowitzki
TTRC57 Paul Molitor 12.50 30.00
Ryan Braun
Prince Fielder
TTRC58 Stan Musial 10.00 25.00
Matt Holliday
Colby Rasmus
TTRC59 Whitey Ford 15.00 40.00
CC Sabathia
Mariano Rivera
TTRC60 Joe DiMaggio 75.00 150.00
Hank Aaron
Sandy Koufax

2011 Topps Triple Threads Relic Combos Emerald

STATED ODDS 1:47 MINI
STATED PRINT RUN 18 SER.#'d SETS
NO PRICING DUE TO SCARCITY

2011 Topps Triple Threads Relic Combos Gold

STATED ODDS 1:371 MINI
STATED PRINT RUN 9 SER.#'d SETS
NO PRICING DUE TO SCARCITY

2011 Topps Triple Threads Relic Combos Platinum

STATED ODDS 1:846 MINI
STATED PRINT RUN 1 SER.#'d SET
NO PRICING DUE TO SCARCITY

2011 Topps Triple Threads Relic Combos Sapphire

STATED ODDS 1:279 MINI
STATED PRINT RUN 3 SER.#'d SETS
NO PRICING DUE TO SCARCITY

2011 Topps Triple Threads Relic Combos Sepia

*SEPIA: .4X TO 1X BASIC
STATED ODDS 1:31 MINI
STATED PRINT RUN 27 SER.#'d SETS

2011 Topps Triple Threads Relic Combos Double

STATED ODDS 1:78 MINI
STATED PRINT RUN 27 SER.#'d SETS
RDC1 Honus Wagner 75.00 150.00
Ozzie Smith
Cal Ripken Jr.
Derek Jeter
Hanley Ramirez
Troy Tulowitzki
RDC2 Josh Hamilton 20.00 50.00
Joey Votto
RDC3 Mickey Mantle 175.00 350.00
Frank Robinson
Hank Aaron
Babe Ruth
Mel Ott
Stan Musial
RDC4 Jered Weaver 20.00 50.00
Jon Lester
Felix Hernandez
Roy Halladay
Tim Lincecum
Ubaldo Jimenez
RDC5 Jose Bautista 30.00 60.00
Miguel Cabrera
Josh Hamilton
Albert Pujols
Joey Votto
Carlos Gonzalez
RDC6 Roy Halladay 20.00 50.00
Felix Hernandez
RDC7 Austin Jackson 20.00 50.00
Carlos Santana
Jason Heyward
Buster Posey
Mike Stanton
Starlin Castro
RDC8 Chase Utley 40.00 80.00
Dustin Pedroia
Robinson Cano
Jackie Robinson
Ryne Sandberg
Joe Morgan
RDC9 Pablo Sandoval 100.00 200.00
Madison Bumgarner
Tim Lincecum
Buster Posey
Matt Cain
Brian Wilson
RDC10 Jimmie Foxx 100.00 200.00
Stan Musial
Joe DiMaggio
Mickey Mantle
Mike Schmidt
Roy Campanella
RDC11 Steve Garvey 60.00 120.00
Duke Snider
Sandy Koufax
Clayton Kershaw
Andre Ethier
Matt Kemp
RDC12 Joe DiMaggio 100.00 200.00
Derek Jeter
RDC13 Reggie Jackson 40.00 80.00
Willie McCovey
Hank Aaron
Albert Pujols
Josh Hamilton
Ryan Howard
RDC14 Jim Palmer 50.00 100.00
Tom Seaver
Nolan Ryan
Sandy Koufax
Bob Gibson
Whitey Ford
RDC15 Nolan Ryan 60.00 120.00
Tom Seaver
Darryl Strawberry
David Wright
Johan Santana
Jose Reyes
RDC16 Starlin Castro 20.00 50.00
Carlos Gonzalez
Buster Posey
David Price
Jose Bautista
Clay Buchholz
RDC17 Kevin Youkilis 30.00 60.00
Dustin Pedroia
Adrian Gonzalez
Carl Crawford
David Ortiz
Jacoby Ellsbury
RDC18 Bob Gibson 40.00 80.00
Nolan Ryan
Sandy Koufax
Aroldis Chapman
Justin Verlander
Ubaldo Jimenez

2011 Topps Triple Threads Relic Combos Double Emerald

STATED ODDS 1:155 MINI
STATED PRINT RUN 18 SER.#'d SETS
NO PRICING DUE TO SCARCITY

2011 Topps Triple Threads Relic Combos Double Gold

STATED ODDS 1:311 MINI
STATED PRINT RUN 9 SER.#'d SETS
NO PRICING DUE TO SCARCITY

2011 Topps Triple Threads Relic Combos Double Platinum

STATED ODDS 1:2681 MINI
STATED PRINT RUN 1 SER.#'d SET
NO PRICING DUE TO SCARCITY

2011 Topps Triple Threads Relic Combos Double Sapphire

STATED ODDS 1:946 MINI
STATED PRINT RUN 3 SER.#'d SETS
NO PRICING DUE TO SCARCITY

2011 Topps Triple Threads Relic Combos Double Sepia

*SEPIA: .4X TO 1X BASIC
STATED ODDS 1:103 MINI
STATED PRINT RUN 27 SER.#'d SETS

2011 Topps Triple Threads Relic Paris

STATED ODDS 1:468 MINI
STATED PRINT RUN 18 SER.#'d SETS
NO PRICING DUE TO SCARCITY
EXCHANGE DEADLINE 9/30/2014

2011 Topps Triple Threads Relic Paris Gold

STATED ODDS 1:946 MINI
STATED PRINT RUN 9 SER.#'d SETS
NO PRICING DUE TO SCARCITY
EXCHANGE DEADLINE 9/30/2014

2011 Topps Triple Threads Relic Paris Platinum

STATED ODDS 1:8043 MINI
STATED PRINT RUN 1 SER.#'d SET
NO PRICING DUE TO SCARCITY
EXCHANGE DEADLINE 9/30/2014

2011 Topps Triple Threads Relic Paris Sapphire

STATED ODDS 1:2681 MINI
STATED PRINT RUN 3 SER.#'d SETS
NO PRICING DUE TO SCARCITY
EXCHANGE DEADLINE 9/30/2014

2011 Topps Triple Threads Relics

STATED ODDS 1:11 MINI
STATED PRINT RUN 36 SER.#'d SETS
ALL DC VARIATIONS PRICED EQUALLY
TTR1 Derek Jeter 30.00 60.00
TTR2 Derek Jeter 30.00 60.00
TTR3 Derek Jeter 30.00 60.00
TTR4 Derek Jeter 30.00 60.00
TTR5 Ichiro Suzuki 12.50 30.00
TTR6 Ichiro Suzuki 12.50 30.00
TTR7 Ichiro Suzuki 12.50 30.00
TTR8 Ichiro Suzuki 12.50 30.00
TTR9 Carlos Gonzalez 5.00 12.00
TTR10 Carlos Gonzalez 5.00 12.00
TTR11 Carlos Gonzalez 5.00 12.00
TTR12 Carlos Gonzalez 5.00 12.00
TTR13 Roy Halladay 10.00 25.00
TTR14 Roy Halladay 10.00 25.00
TTR15 Roy Halladay 10.00 25.00
TTR16 Roy Halladay 10.00 25.00
TTR17 Starlin Castro 10.00 25.00
TTR18 Starlin Castro 10.00 25.00
TTR19 Starlin Castro 10.00 25.00
TTR20 Starlin Castro 10.00 25.00
TTR21 CC Sabathia 8.00 20.00
TTR22 CC Sabathia 8.00 20.00
TTR23 CC Sabathia 8.00 20.00
TTR24 Jose Bautista 6.00 15.00
TTR25 Jose Bautista 6.00 15.00
TTR26 Jose Bautista 6.00 15.00
TTR27 Jose Bautista 6.00 15.00
TTR28 Tim Lincecum 12.50 30.00
TTR29 Tim Lincecum 12.50 30.00
TTR30 Tim Lincecum 12.50 30.00
TTR31 Tim Lincecum 12.50 30.00
TTR32 Mark Teixeira 6.00 15.00
TTR33 Mark Teixeira 6.00 15.00
TTR34 Mark Teixeira 6.00 15.00
TTR35 Mark Teixeira 6.00 15.00
TTR36 Josh Johnson 5.00 12.00
TTR37 Josh Johnson 5.00 12.00
TTR38 Josh Johnson 5.00 12.00
TTR39 Josh Johnson 5.00 12.00
TTR40 Shin-Soo Choo 6.00 15.00
TTR41 Shin-Soo Choo 6.00 15.00
TTR42 Shin-Soo Choo 6.00 15.00
TTR43 Ryan Howard 8.00 20.00
TTR44 Ryan Howard 8.00 20.00
TTR45 Ryan Howard 8.00 20.00
TTR46 Ryan Howard 8.00 20.00
TTR47 Dustin Pedroia 10.00 25.00
TTR48 Dustin Pedroia 10.00 25.00
TTR49 Dustin Pedroia 10.00 25.00
TTR50 Dustin Pedroia 10.00 25.00
TTR51 Evan Longoria 6.00 15.00
TTR52 Evan Longoria 6.00 15.00
TTR53 Evan Longoria 6.00 15.00
TTR54 Evan Longoria 6.00 15.00
TTR55 Justin Morneau 6.00 15.00
TTR56 Justin Morneau 6.00 15.00
TTR57 Justin Morneau 6.00 15.00
TTR58 Hanley Ramirez 5.00 12.00
TTR59 Hanley Ramirez 5.00 12.00
TTR60 Hanley Ramirez 5.00 12.00
TTR61 Hanley Ramirez 5.00 12.00
TTR62 Alex Rodriguez 10.00 25.00
TTR63 Alex Rodriguez 10.00 25.00
TTR64 Alex Rodriguez 10.00 25.00
TTR65 Alex Rodriguez 10.00 25.00
TTR66 Joe Mauer 6.00 15.00
TTR67 Joe Mauer 6.00 15.00
TTR68 Joe Mauer 6.00 15.00
TTR69 Joe Mauer 6.00 15.00
TTR70 Joey Votto 8.00 20.00
TTR71 Joey Votto 8.00 20.00
TTR72 Joey Votto 8.00 20.00
TTR73 Joey Votto 8.00 20.00
TTR74 Chase Utley 8.00 20.00
TTR75 Chase Utley 8.00 20.00
TTR76 Chase Utley 8.00 20.00
TTR77 Prince Fielder 8.00 20.00
TTR78 Prince Fielder 8.00 20.00
TTR79 Prince Fielder 8.00 20.00
TTR80 Prince Fielder 8.00 20.00
TTR81 Robinson Cano 12.50 30.00
TTR82 Robinson Cano 12.50 30.00
TTR83 Robinson Cano 12.50 30.00
TTR84 Robinson Cano 12.50 30.00
TTR85 Carlos Santana 5.00 12.00
TTR86 Carlos Santana 5.00 12.00
TTR87 Carlos Santana 5.00 12.00
TTR88 Hunter Pence 6.00 15.00
TTR89 Hunter Pence 6.00 15.00
TTR90 Hunter Pence 6.00 15.00
TTR91 Kevin Youkilis 6.00 15.00
TTR92 Kevin Youkilis 6.00 15.00
TTR93 Kevin Youkilis 6.00 15.00
TTR94 David Wright 8.00 20.00
TTR95 David Wright 8.00 20.00
TTR96 David Wright 8.00 20.00
TTR97 David Wright 8.00 20.00
TTR98 Jon Lester 6.00 15.00
TTR99 Jon Lester 6.00 15.00
TTR100 Jon Lester 6.00 15.00
TTR101 Justin Upton 5.00 12.00
TTR102 Justin Upton 5.00 12.00
TTR103 Justin Upton 5.00 12.00
TTR104 Justin Upton 5.00 12.00
TTR105 Matt Holliday 6.00 15.00
TTR106 Matt Holliday 6.00 15.00
TTR107 Matt Holliday 6.00 15.00
TTR108 Miguel Cabrera 8.00 20.00
TTR109 Miguel Cabrera 8.00 20.00
TTR110 Miguel Cabrera 8.00 20.00
TTR111 Miguel Cabrera 8.00 20.00
TTR112 Jose Reyes 6.00 15.00
TTR113 Jose Reyes 6.00 15.00
TTR114 Jose Reyes 6.00 15.00
TTR115 Josh Hamilton 10.00 25.00
TTR116 Josh Hamilton 10.00 25.00
TTR117 Josh Hamilton 10.00 25.00
TTR118 Josh Hamilton 10.00 25.00
TTR119 Jason Heyward 8.00 20.00
TTR120 Jason Heyward 8.00 20.00
TTR121 Jason Heyward 8.00 20.00
TTR122 Matt Kemp 6.00 15.00
TTR123 Matt Kemp 6.00 15.00
TTR124 Matt Kemp 6.00 15.00
TTR125 Albert Pujols 15.00 40.00
TTR126 Albert Pujols 15.00 40.00
TTR127 Albert Pujols 15.00 40.00
TTR128 Felix Hernandez 6.00 15.00
TTR129 Felix Hernandez 6.00 15.00
TTR130 Felix Hernandez 6.00 15.00
TTR131 Felix Hernandez 6.00 15.00
TTR132 Ryan Braun 10.00 25.00
TTR133 Ryan Braun 10.00 25.00
TTR134 Ryan Braun 10.00 25.00
TTR135 Ryan Braun 10.00 25.00
TTR136 Troy Tulowitzki 8.00 20.00
TTR137 Troy Tulowitzki 8.00 20.00
TTR138 Troy Tulowitzki 8.00 20.00

2011 Topps Triple Threads Relics Emerald

*EMERALD: .5X TO 1.2X BASIC
STATED ODDS 1:21 MINI
STATED PRINT RUN 18 SER.#'d SETS
ALL DC VARIATIONS EQUALLY PRICED

2011 Topps Triple Threads Relics Gold

*EMERALD: .6X TO 1.5X BASIC
STATED ODDS 1:41 MINI
STATED PRINT RUN 9 SER.#'d SETS
ALL DC VARIATIONS EQUALLY PRICED

2011 Topps Triple Threads Relics Platinum

STATED ODDS 1:362 MINI
STATED PRINT RUN 1 SER.#'d SET
NO PRICING DUE TO SCARCITY

2011 Topps Triple Threads Relics Sapphire

STATED ODDS 1:121 MINI
STATED PRINT RUN 3 SER.#'d SETS
NO PRICING DUE TO SCARCITY

2011 Topps Triple Threads Relics Sepia

*SEPIA: .4X TO 1X BASIC
STATED ODDS 1:14 MINI
STATED PRINT RUN 27 SER.#'d SETS
ALL DC VARIATIONS EQUALLY PRICED

2011 Topps Triple Threads Rookie Phenom Relic Paris

STATED ODDS 1:168 MINI
STATED PRINT RUN 50 SER.#'d SETS
EXCHANGE DEADLINE 9/30/2014
RFPP1 Aroldis Chapman 30.00 60.00
Chris Sale
RFPP2 Buster Posey 40.00 80.00
Neftali Feliz
RFPP3 Andrew McCutchen 30.00 60.00
Pedro Alvarez
RFPP4 Jason Heyward 50.00 100.00
Freddie Freeman
RFPP5 Mike Stanton 30.00 60.00
Logan Morrison
RFPP6 Starlin Castro 30.00 60.00
Elvis Andrus

2011 Topps Triple Threads Rookie Phenom Relic Paris Gold

STATED ODDS 1:337 MINI
STATED PRINT RUN 25 SER.#'d SETS
NO PRICING DUE TO SCARCITY
EXCHANGE DEADLINE 9/30/2014

2011 Topps Triple Threads Rookie Phenom Relic Paris Platinum

STATED ODDS 1:8043 MINI
STATED PRINT RUN 1 SER.#'d SET
NO PRICING DUE TO SCARCITY
EXCHANGE DEADLINE 9/30/2014

2011 Topps Triple Threads Rookie Phenom Relic Paris Sapphire

STATED ODDS 1:832 MINI
STATED PRINT RUN 10 SER.#'d SETS
NO PRICING DUE TO SCARCITY
EXCHANGE DEADLINE 9/30/2014

2011 Topps Triple Threads Unity Relic Autographs

STATED ODDS 1:6 MINI
STATED PRINT RUN 99 SER.#'d SETS
EXCHANGE DEADLINE 9/30/2014
UAR1 Martin Prado 4.00 10.00
UAR2 Chipper Jones 20.00 50.00
UAR3 Brian McCann 10.00 25.00
UAR4 Tim Hudson 6.00 15.00
UAR5 Mike Minor 5.00 12.00
UAR6 Jason Heyward 12.50 30.00
UAR7 Mike Minor 5.00 12.00
UAR8 Tommy Hanson 4.00 10.00
UAR9 Martin Prado 4.00 10.00
UAR10 Colby Rasmus 4.00 10.00
UAR11 Matt Holliday 15.00 40.00
UAR12 David Freese 30.00 60.00
UAR13 Ozzie Smith 20.00 50.00
UAR14 Colby Rasmus 4.00 10.00
UAR15 Jon Jay 5.00 12.00
UAR16 Jason Motte 8.00 20.00
UAR17 Allen Craig 12.50 30.00
UAR18 Jon Jay 5.00 12.00
UAR19 Marlon Byrd 4.00 10.00
UAR20 Andrew Cashner 4.00 10.00
UAR21 Randy Wells 4.00 10.00
UAR22 Marlon Byrd 4.00 10.00
UAR23 Aramis Ramirez 4.00 10.00
UAR24 Starlin Castro 12.50 30.00
UAR25 Marlon Byrd 4.00 10.00
UAR26 Tyler Colvin 4.00 10.00
UAR27 Andrew Cashner 4.00 10.00
UAR28 Pablo Sandoval 6.00 15.00
UAR29 Freddy Sanchez 5.00 12.00
UAR30 Cody Ross 5.00 12.00
UAR31 Pablo Sandoval 6.00 15.00
UAR32 Buster Posey 20.00 50.00
UAR33 Matt Cain 6.00 15.00
UAR34 Cody Ross 5.00 12.00
UAR35 Freddy Sanchez 5.00 12.00
UAR36 Brian Wilson 15.00 40.00
UAR37 Chris Coghlan 4.00 10.00
UAR38 Ricky Nolasco 4.00 10.00
UAR39 Logan Morrison 4.00 10.00
UAR40 Mike Stanton 12.50 30.00
UAR41 Hanley Ramirez 8.00 20.00
UAR42 Josh Johnson 5.00 12.00
UAR43 Gaby Sanchez 4.00 10.00
UAR44 Chris Coghlan 4.00 10.00
UAR45 Logan Morrison 4.00 10.00
UAR46 Angel Pagan 4.00 10.00
UAR47 Josh Thole 4.00 10.00
UAR48 Ike Davis 6.00 15.00
UAR49 Angel Pagan 4.00 10.00
UAR50 David Wright 12.50 30.00
UAR51 Darryl Strawberry 10.00 25.00
UAR52 Angel Pagan 4.00 10.00
UAR53 Josh Thole 4.00 10.00
UAR54 Jon Niese 5.00 12.00
UAR55 Jose Tabata 4.00 10.00
UAR56 Garrett Jones 4.00 10.00
UAR57 Neil Walker 5.00 12.00
UAR58 Jose Tabata 4.00 10.00
UAR59 Andrew McCutchen 8.00 20.00
UAR60 Pedro Alvarez 6.00 15.00
UAR61 Garrett Jones 4.00 10.00
UAR62 Neil Walker 5.00 12.00
UAR63 Daniel McCutchen 4.00 10.00
UAR64 Craig Gentry 6.00 15.00
UAR65 Elvis Andrus 6.00 15.00
UAR66 Ian Kinsler 10.00 25.00
UAR67 Josh Hamilton 15.00 40.00
UAR68 Mitch Moreland 5.00 12.00
UAR69 Neftali Feliz 6.00 15.00
UAR70 Nelson Cruz 10.00 25.00
UAR71 Mitch Moreland 5.00 12.00
UAR72 Derek Holland
UAR73 Chris Heisey 8.00 20.00
UAR74 Johnny Cueto 4.00 10.00
UAR75 Edinson Volquez 4.00 10.00
UAR76 Jay Bruce 10.00 25.00
UAR77 Johnny Cueto 4.00 10.00
UAR78 Aroldis Chapman 10.00 25.00
UAR79 Drew Stubbs 5.00 12.00
UAR80 Edinson Volquez 4.00 10.00
UAR81 Travis Wood 4.00 10.00
UAR82 Scott Sizemore 4.00 10.00
UAR83 Jhonny Peralta 5.00 12.00
UAR84 Ryan Perry 4.00 10.00
UAR85 Austin Jackson 5.00 12.00
UAR86 Daniel Schlereth 4.00 10.00
UAR87 Max Scherzer 6.00 15.00
UAR88 Austin Jackson 5.00 12.00
UAR89 Rick Porcello 5.00 12.00
UAR90 Jhonny Peralta 5.00 12.00
UAR91 Torii Hunter 5.00 12.00
UAR92 Kendrys Morales 4.00 10.00
UAR93 Jered Weaver 6.00 15.00
UAR94 Vernon Wells 4.00 10.00
UAR95 Kendrys Morales 4.00 10.00
UAR96 Jordan Walden 4.00 10.00
UAR97 Torii Hunter 5.00 12.00
UAR98 Hank Conger 4.00 10.00
UAR99 Dan Haren 5.00 12.00

2011 Topps Triple Threads Unity Relic Autographs Emerald

*EMERALD: .5X TO 1.2X BASIC
STATED ODDS 1:11 MINI
STATED PRINT RUN 50 SER.#'d SETS
EXCHANGE DEADLINE 9/30/2014

2011 Topps Triple Threads Unity Relic Autographs Gold

*GOLD: .5X TO 1.2X BASIC
STATED ODDS 1:21 MINI
STATED PRINT RUN 25 SER.#'d SETS
NO PRICING ON MOST DUE SCARCITY
EXCHANGE DEADLINE 9/30/2014

2011 Topps Triple Threads Unity Relic Autographs Platinum

STATED ODDS 1:503 MINI
STATED PRINT RUN 1 SER.#'d SET
NO PRICING DUE TO SCARCITY
EXCHANGE DEADLINE 9/30/2014

2011 Topps Triple Threads Unity Relic Autographs Sapphire

STATED ODDS 1:51 MINI
STATED PRINT RUN 10 SER.#'d SETS
NO PRICING DUE TO SCARCITY
EXCHANGE DEADLINE 9/30/2014

2011 Topps Triple Threads Unity Relic Autographs Sepia

*SEPIA: .4X TO 1X BASIC
STATED ODDS 1:7 MINI
STATED PRINT RUN 75 SER.#'d SETS
EXCHANGE DEADLINE 9/30/2014

2011 Topps Triple Threads Unity Relics

STATED ODDS 1:6 MINI
STATED PRINT RUN 36 SER.#'d SETS
USR1 Derek Jeter 10.00 25.00
USR2 Reggie Jackson 6.00 15.00
USR3 Mickey Mantle 30.00 60.00
USR4 Reggie Jackson 6.00 15.00
USR5 Babe Ruth 60.00 120.00
USR6 Joe DiMaggio 30.00 60.00
USR7 Lou Gehrig 50.00 100.00
USR8 Joe DiMaggio 30.00 60.00
USR9 Mariano Rivera 5.00 12.00
USR10 Torii Hunter 4.00 10.00
USR11 Kendrys Morales 4.00 10.00
USR12 Jered Weaver 4.00 10.00
USR13 Torii Hunter 4.00 10.00
USR14 Nolan Ryan 12.50 30.00
USR15 Reggie Jackson 6.00 15.00
USR16 Torii Hunter 4.00 10.00
USR17 Nolan Ryan 12.50 30.00
USR18 Reggie Jackson 6.00 15.00
USR19 Nolan Ryan 12.50 30.00
USR20 Joe Morgan 4.00 10.00
USR21 Hunter Pence 4.00 10.00
USR22 Nolan Ryan 12.50 30.00
USR23 Joe Morgan 4.00 10.00
USR24 Lance Berkman 4.00 10.00
USR25 Nolan Ryan 12.50 30.00
USR26 Joe Morgan 4.00 10.00
USR27 Hunter Pence 4.00 10.00
USR28 Rickey Henderson 15.00 40.00
USR29 Reggie Jackson 6.00 15.00
USR30 Brett Anderson 4.00 10.00
USR31 Rickey Henderson 15.00 40.00
USR32 Reggie Jackson 6.00 15.00
USR33 Rollie Fingers 4.00 10.00
USR34 Rickey Henderson 15.00 40.00
USR35 Rollie Fingers 4.00 10.00
USR36 Kurt Suzuki 4.00 10.00

USR37 Vernon Wells 4.00 10.00
USR38 Paul Molitor 5.00 12.00
USR39 Aaron Hill 4.00 10.00
USR40 Roberto Alomar 6.00 15.00
USR41 Roy Halladay 5.00 12.00
USR42 Jose Bautista 4.00 10.00
USR43 Roberto Alomar 6.00 15.00
USR44 Roy Halladay 5.00 12.00
USR45 Jose Bautista 4.00 10.00
USR46 Hank Aaron 12.50 30.00
USR47 Chipper Jones 6.00 15.00
USR48 Brian McCann 4.00 10.00
USR49 Hank Aaron 12.50 30.00
USR50 John Smoltz 4.00 10.00
USR51 Jason Heyward 4.00 10.00
USR52 Hank Aaron 12.50 30.00
USR53 Tommy Hanson 4.00 10.00
USR54 Jason Heyward 4.00 10.00
USR55 Paul Molitor 5.00 12.00
USR56 Ryan Braun 6.00 15.00
USR57 Prince Fielder 4.00 10.00
USR58 Paul Molitor 5.00 12.00
USR59 Ryan Braun 6.00 15.00
USR60 Prince Fielder 4.00 10.00
USR61 Paul Molitor 5.00 12.00
USR62 Ryan Braun 6.00 15.00
USR63 Yovani Gallardo 4.00 10.00
USR64 Ozzie Smith 6.00 15.00
USR65 Matt Holliday 4.00 10.00
USR66 Bob Gibson 6.00 15.00
USR67 Stan Musial 10.00 25.00
USR68 Albert Pujols 10.00 25.00
USR69 Rogers Hornsby 15.00 40.00
USR70 Albert Pujols 10.00 25.00
USR71 Adam Wainwright 4.00 10.00
USR72 Johnny Mize 6.00 15.00
USR73 Starlin Castro 4.00 10.00
USR74 Fergie Jenkins 5.00 12.00
USR75 Ryne Sandberg 8.00 20.00
USR76 Andre Dawson 4.00 10.00
USR77 Starlin Castro 4.00 10.00
USR78 Ryne Sandberg 8.00 20.00
USR79 Aramis Ramirez 4.00 10.00
USR80 Alfonso Soriano 4.00 10.00
USR81 Fergie Jenkins 5.00 12.00
USR82 Jackie Robinson
USR83 Duke Snider 6.00 15.00
USR84 Clayton Kershaw 4.00 10.00
USR85 Sandy Koufax 30.00 60.00
USR86 Andre Ethier 4.00 10.00
USR87 Roy Campanella 8.00 20.00
USR88 Matt Kemp 4.00 10.00
USR89 Clayton Kershaw 4.00 10.00
USR90 Andre Ethier 4.00 10.00
USR91 Juan Marichal 4.00 10.00
USR92 Brian Wilson 6.00 15.00
USR93 Matt Cain 4.00 10.00
USR94 Willie McCovey 4.00 10.00
USR95 Tim Lincecum 6.00 15.00
USR96 Buster Posey 6.00 15.00
USR97 Willie McCovey 4.00 10.00
USR98 Tim Lincecum 6.00 15.00
USR99 Buster Posey 6.00 15.00
USR100 Carlos Santana 4.00 10.00
USR101 Shin-Soo Choo 5.00 12.00
USR102 Roberto Alomar 6.00 15.00
USR103 Grady Sizemore 4.00 10.00
USR104 Roberto Alomar 6.00 15.00
USR105 Albert Belle 5.00 12.00
USR106 Carlos Santana 4.00 10.00
USR107 Grady Sizemore 4.00 10.00
USR108 Albert Belle 5.00 12.00
USR109 Alex Rodriguez 6.00 15.00
USR110 Ichiro Suzuki 12.50 30.00
USR111 Felix Hernandez 4.00 10.00
USR112 Alex Rodriguez 6.00 15.00
USR113 Ichiro Suzuki 12.50 30.00
USR114 Felix Hernandez 4.00 10.00
USR115 Alex Rodriguez 6.00 15.00
USR116 Ichiro Suzuki 12.50 30.00
USR117 Felix Hernandez 4.00 10.00
USR118 Hanley Ramirez 4.00 10.00
USR119 Josh Johnson 4.00 10.00
USR120 Logan Morrison 4.00 10.00
USR121 Mike Stanton 5.00 12.00
USR122 Hanley Ramirez 4.00 10.00
USR123 Josh Johnson 4.00 10.00
USR124 Mike Stanton 5.00 12.00
USR125 Hanley Ramirez 4.00 10.00
USR126 Logan Morrison 4.00 10.00
USR127 Darryl Strawberry 4.00 10.00
USR128 Tom Seaver 5.00 12.00
USR129 Johan Santana 4.00 10.00
USR130 David Wright 6.00 15.00
USR131 Nolan Ryan 12.50 30.00
USR132 Jose Reyes 6.00 15.00
USR133 Tom Seaver 5.00 12.00
USR134 Jose Reyes 6.00 15.00
USR135 Darryl Strawberry 4.00 10.00
USR136 Nick Markakis 4.00 10.00
USR137 Eddie Murray 5.00 12.00
USR138 Adam Jones 4.00 10.00
USR139 Jim Palmer 4.00 10.00
USR140 Cal Ripken Jr. 12.50 30.00
USR141 Brooks Robinson 6.00 15.00
USR142 Frank Robinson 4.00 10.00
USR143 Brian Roberts 4.00 10.00
USR144 Brian Matusz 4.00 10.00
USR145 Mat Latos 4.00 10.00
USR146 Heath Bell 4.00 10.00
USR147 Tony Gwynn 6.00 15.00
USR148 Tony Gwynn 6.00 15.00
USR149 Ozzie Smith 6.00 15.00
USR150 Willie McCovey 4.00 10.00
USR151 Mat Latos 4.00 10.00
USR152 Tony Gwynn 6.00 15.00
USR153 Heath Bell 4.00 10.00
USR154 Mike Schmidt 6.00 15.00
USR155 Roy Halladay 5.00 12.00
USR156 Jimmy Rollins 4.00 10.00
USR157 Ryan Howard 5.00 12.00
USR158 Mike Schmidt 6.00 15.00
USR159 Chase Utley 4.00 10.00
USR160 Roy Halladay 5.00 12.00
USR161 Ryan Howard 5.00 12.00
USR162 Chase Utley 4.00 10.00
USR163 Andrew McCutchen 4.00 10.00
USR164 Jose Tabata 4.00 10.00
USR165 Pedro Alvarez 4.00 10.00
USR166 Honus Wagner 40.00 80.00
USR167 Andrew McCutchen 4.00 10.00
USR168 Jose Tabata 4.00 10.00
USR169 Andrew McCutchen 4.00 10.00
USR170 Jose Tabata 4.00 10.00
USR171 Pedro Alvarez 4.00 10.00
USR172 Michael Young 4.00 10.00
USR173 Nelson Cruz 4.00 10.00
USR174 Ian Kinsler 4.00 10.00
USR175 Nolan Ryan 12.50 30.00
USR176 Josh Hamilton 5.00 12.00
USR177 Alex Rodriguez 6.00 15.00
USR178 Vladimir Guerrero 4.00 10.00
USR179 Josh Hamilton 5.00 12.00
USR180 Ian Kinsler 4.00 10.00
USR181 Evan Longoria 4.00 10.00
USR182 David Price 4.00 10.00
USR183 B.J. Upton 4.00 10.00
USR184 Evan Longoria 4.00 10.00
USR185 David Price 4.00 10.00
USR186 B.J. Upton 4.00 10.00
USR187 Evan Longoria 4.00 10.00
USR188 David Price 4.00 10.00
USR189 Jeremy Hellickson 4.00 10.00
USR190 Nomar Garciaparra 6.00 15.00
USR191 David Ortiz 4.00 10.00
USR192 Kevin Youkilis 4.00 10.00
USR193 Jimmie Foxx 12.50 30.00
USR194 Jon Lester 4.00 10.00
USR195 Dustin Pedroia 4.00 10.00
USR196 Manny Ramirez 5.00 12.00
USR197 Carlton Fisk 5.00 12.00
USR198 Jacoby Ellsbury
USR199 Barry Larkin 6.00 15.00
USR200 Jay Bruce 4.00 10.00
USR201 Johnny Cueto 4.00 10.00
USR202 Johnny Bench 6.00 15.00
USR203 Joey Votto 5.00 12.00
USR204 Tom Seaver 5.00 12.00
USR205 Frank Robinson 4.00 10.00
USR206 Joe Morgan 4.00 10.00
USR207 Aroldis Chapman 5.00 12.00
USR208 Matt Holliday 4.00 10.00
USR209 Ubaldo Jimenez 4.00 10.00
USR210 Troy Tulowitzki 4.00 10.00
USR211 Larry Walker 4.00 10.00
USR212 Carlos Gonzalez 4.00 10.00
USR213 Todd Helton 4.00 10.00
USR214 Ubaldo Jimenez 4.00 10.00
USR215 Troy Tulowitzki 4.00 10.00
USR216 Larry Walker 4.00 10.00
USR217 Justin Verlander 6.00 15.00
USR218 Miguel Cabrera 4.00 10.00
USR219 Al Kaline 10.00 25.00
USR220 Ty Cobb 30.00 60.00
USR221 Miguel Cabrera 4.00 10.00
USR222 Al Kaline 10.00 25.00
USR223 Austin Jackson 4.00 10.00
USR224 Miguel Cabrera 4.00 10.00
USR225 Justin Verlander 6.00 15.00
USR226 Francisco Liriano 4.00 10.00
USR227 Joe Mauer 4.00 10.00
USR228 Justin Morneau 5.00 12.00
USR229 Bert Blyleven 5.00 12.00
USR230 Joe Mauer 4.00 10.00
USR231 Justin Morneau 5.00 12.00
USR232 Joe Nathan
USR233 Joe Mauer 4.00 10.00
USR234 Justin Morneau 5.00 12.00
USR235 Luis Aparicio 5.00 12.00
USR236 Gordon Beckham 4.00 10.00
USR237 John Danks 4.00 10.00
USR238 Carlton Fisk 5.00 12.00
USR239 Mark Buehrle 4.00 10.00
USR240 Paul Konerko 4.00 10.00
USR241 Alex Rios 4.00 10.00
USR242 Carlos Quentin 4.00 10.00
USR243 Alexei Ramirez 4.00 10.00
USR244 Justin Upton 4.00 10.00
USR245 Stephen Drew 4.00 10.00
USR246 Kelly Johnson 4.00 10.00
USR247 Justin Upton 4.00 10.00
USR248 Stephen Drew 4.00 10.00
USR249 Chris Young 4.00 10.00
USR250 Justin Upton 4.00 10.00
USR251 Stephen Drew 4.00 10.00
USR252 Miguel Montero 4.00 10.00
USR253 Stephen Strasburg 8.00 20.00
USR254 Ryan Zimmerman 4.00 10.00
USR255 Jayson Werth 4.00 10.00
USR256 Stephen Strasburg 8.00 20.00
USR257 Ryan Zimmerman 4.00 10.00
USR258 Jayson Werth 4.00 10.00
USR259 Stephen Strasburg 8.00 20.00
USR260 Ryan Zimmerman 4.00 10.00
USR261 Carl Crawford 4.00 10.00
USR262 Zack Greinke 4.00 10.00
USR263 Billy Butler 4.00 10.00
USR264 Joakim Soria 4.00 10.00
USR265 Billy Butler 4.00 10.00
USR266 Joakim Soria 4.00 10.00
USR267 Alex Gordon 4.00 10.00
USR268 Billy Butler 4.00 10.00
USR269 Joakim Soria 4.00 10.00
USR270 Alex Gordon 4.00 10.00

2011 Topps Triple Threads Unity Relics Emerald

*EMERALD: .5X TO 1.2X BASIC
STATED ODDS 1:11 MINI
STATED PRINT RUN 18 SER.#'d SETS
ALL VERSIONS EQUALLY PRICED
SOME NOT PRICED DUE TO SCARCITY

2011 Topps Triple Threads Unity Relics Gold

*GOLD: .6X TO 1.5X BASIC
STATED ODDS 1:21 MINI
STATED PRINT RUN 9 SER.#'d SETS
ALL VERSIONS EQUALLY PRICED
SOME NOT PRICED DUE TO SCARCITY

2011 Topps Triple Threads Unity Relics Platinum

STATED ODDS 1:186 MINI
STATED PRINT RUN 1 SER.#'d SET
NO PRICING DUE TO SCARCITY

2011 Topps Triple Threads Unity Relics Sapphire

STATED ODDS 1:62 MINI
STATED PRINT RUN 3 SER.#'d SETS
NO PRICING DUE TO SCARCITY

2011 Topps Triple Threads Unity Relics Sepia

*SEPIA: .4X TO 1X BASIC
STATED ODDS 1:7 MINI
STATED PRINT RUN 27 SER.#'d SETS

2005 Topps Turkey Red

This 330-card set was released in August, 2005. The set was issued in eight-card packs with a $4 SRP which came 24 packs to a box and eight boxes to a case. Interspersed throughout the set are both short prints and reprinted cards of some of the great players in the original set. The SP's were issued at a stated rate of one in four. Cards numbered 271 through 300 feature Rookie Cards while cards 301 through 315 feature retired greats.

COMPLETE SET (330) 200.00 300.00
COMP.SET w/o SP's (275) 20.00 50.00
COMMON CARD (1-270) .15 .40
COMMON SP (1-270) 3.00 8.00
COMMON REPRINT .30 .75
COMMON RC (271-300) .25 .60
COMMON RET (301-315) .30 .75
VAR CL: 1/5/10/16/75/83/100/102/120/125
VAR CL: 130/160/225/230/270
TWO VERSIONS OF EACH VARIATION EXIST
1A B.Bonds Grey Uni SP 6.00 15.00
1B B.Bonds White Uni .75 2.00
2 Michael Young .25 .60
3 Jim Edmonds .25 .60
4 Cliff Floyd .15 .40
5A R.Clemens Blue Sky SP 4.00 10.00
5B R.Clemens Yellow Sky SP 4.00 10.00
6 Hal Chase REP .30 .75
7 Shannon Stewart .15 .40
8 Fred Clarke REP .30 .75
9 Travis Hafner .15 .40
10A S.Sosa w/Name SP 3.00 8.00
10B S.Sosa w/o Name SP 3.00 8.00
11 Jermaine Dye .15 .40
12 Lyle Overbay .15 .40
13 Oliver Perez .15 .40
14 Red Dooin REP .30 .75
15 Kid Elberfeld REP .30 .75
16A M.Piazza Blue Uni SP 3.00 8.00
16B M.Piazza Pinstripe .40 1.00
17 Bret Boone .15 .40
18 Hughie Jennings REP .30 .75
19 Jeff Francis .15 .40
20 Manny Ramirez SP 3.00 8.00
21 Russ Ortiz .15 .40
22 Carlos Zambrano .25 .60
23 Luis Castillo .15 .40
24 David DeJesus .15 .40
25 Carlos Beltran SP 3.00 8.00
26 Doug Davis .15 .40
27 Bobby Abreu .15 .40
28 Rich Harden SP 3.00 8.00
29 Brian Giles .15 .40
30 Richie Sexson SP 3.00 8.00
31 Nick Johnson .15 .40
32 Roy Halladay .40 1.00
33 Andy Pettitte .25 .60
34 Miguel Cabrera .40 1.00
35 Jeff Kent .15 .40
36 Chone Figgins .15 .40
37 Carlos Lee .15 .40
38 Greg Maddux .60 1.50
39 Preston Wilson .15 .40
40 Chipper Jones .40 1.00
41 Coco Crisp .15 .40
42 Adam Dunn .25 .60
43 Out At Second M.Tejada CL .25 .60
44 Sheffield At Bat CL .15 .40
45 Play At the Plate J.Lopez CL .15 .40
46 Rolen Diggin' In CL .25 .60
47 Helton With the Slap Tag CL .25 .60
48 Clemens Bringing Heat CL .50 1.25
49 A Close Play J.Rollins CL .25 .60
50 Ichiro At Bat CL .60 1.50
51 Can of Corn C.Floyd CL .15 .40
52 Pulling String J.Santana CL .40 1.00
53 Mark Teixeira .25 .60
54 Chris Carpenter .40 1.00
55 Roy Oswalt SP 3.00 8.00
56 Casey Kotchman .15 .40
57 Torii Hunter .15 .40
58 Jose Reyes .25 .60
59 Wily Mo Pena SP 3.00 8.00
60 Magglio Ordonez SP 3.00 8.00
61 Aaron Miles .15 .40
62 Dallas McPherson .15 .40
63 Javy Lopez .15 .40
64 Luis Gonzalez .15 .40
65 David Ortiz .40 1.00
66 Jorge Posada .25 .60
67 Xavier Nady .15 .40
68 Larry Walker .25 .60
69 Mark Loretta .15 .40
70 Jim Thome SP 3.00 8.00
71 Livan Hernandez .15 .40
72 Garrett Atkins .15 .40
73 Milton Bradley .15 .40
74 B.J. Upton .25 .60
75A I.Suzuki w/Name SP 4.00 10.00
75B I.Suzuki w/o Name SP 4.00 10.00
76 Aramis Ramirez .15 .40
77 Eric Milton .15 .40
78 Troy Glaus SP 3.00 8.00
79 David Newhan .15 .40
80 Delmon Young .40 1.00
81 Justin Morneau .40 1.00
82 Ramon Ortiz .15 .40
83A E.Chavez Blue Sky .15 .40
83B E.Chavez Purple Sky SP 3.00 8.00
84 Sean Burroughs .15 .40
85 Scott Rolen SP 3.00 8.00
86 Rocco Baldelli .15 .40
87 Joe Mauer SP 4.00 10.00
88 Tony Womack .15 .40
89 Ken Griffey Jr. .60 1.50
90 Alfonso Soriano SP 3.00 8.00
91 Paul Konerko .25 .60
92 Guillermo Mota .15 .40
93 Lance Berkman .25 .60
94 Mark Buehrle .25 .60
95 Matt Clement .15 .40
96 Melvin Mora .15 .40
97 Khalil Greene .15 .40
98 David Wright .60 1.50
99 Jack Wilson .15 .40
100A A.Rodriguez w/Bat SP 4.00 10.00
100B A.Rodriguez w/Glove SP 4.00 10.00
101 Joe Nathan .15 .40
102A A.Beltre Grey Uni SP 3.00 8.00
102B A.Beltre White Uni .15 .40
103 Mike Sweeney .15 .40
104 Brad Lidge .15 .40
105 Shawn Green .15 .40
106 Miguel Tejada SP 3.00 8.00
107 Derrek Lee .15 .40
108 Eric Hinske .15 .40
109 Eric Byrnes .15 .40
110 Hideki Matsui SP 3.00 8.00
111 Tom Glavine .25 .60
112 Jimmy Rollins .25 .60
113 Ryan Drese .15 .40
114 Josh Beckett .25 .60
115 Curt Schilling SP 3.00 8.00
116 Jeremy Bonderman .15 .40
117 Kazuo Matsui .15 .40
118 Chase Utley .25 .60
119 Troy Percival .15 .40
120A V.Guerrero w/Bat SP 3.00 8.00
120B V.Guerrero w/Glove SP 3.00 8.00
121 Gary Sheffield .15 .40
122 Jeromy Burnitz .15 .40
123 Javier Vazquez .15 .40
124 Kevin Millar .15 .40
125A R.Johnson Blue Sky .40 1.00
125B R.Johnson Purple Sky SP 3.00 8.00
126 Pat Burrell .15 .40
127 Jason Schmidt .15 .40
128 Jose Vidro .15 .40
129 Kip Wells .15 .40
130A I.Rodriguez w/Cap .25 .60
130B I.Rodriguez w/Helmet SP 3.00 8.00
131 C.C. Sabathia .25 .60
132 Carlos Delgado SP 3.00 8.00
133 Bartolo Colon .15 .40
134 Andruw Jones .15 .40
135 Kerry Wood .15 .40
136 Sidney Ponson .15 .40
137 Eric Gagne .15 .40
138 Rickie Weeks .15 .40
139 Mariano Rivera .40 1.00
140 Bobby Crosby .15 .40
141 Jamie Moyer .15 .40
142 Corey Koskie .15 .40
143 John Smoltz .40 1.00
144 Frank Thomas .40 1.00
145 Cristian Guzman .15 .40
146 Paul Lo Duca .15 .40
147 Geoff Jenkins .15 .40
148 Nick Swisher .40 1.00
149 Jason Bay SP 3.00 8.00
150 Albert Pujols SP 6.00 15.00
151 Edwin Jackson .15 .40
152 Carl Crawford .25 .60
153 Mark Mulder .15 .40
154 Rafael Palmeiro .25 .60
155 Pedro Martinez SP 3.00 8.00
156 Jake Westbrook .15 .40
157 Sean Casey .15 .40
158 Aaron Rowand .15 .40
159 J.D. Drew .15 .40
160A J.Sant Glove on Knee SP 3.00 8.00
160B J.Santana Throwing SP 3.00 8.00
161 Gavin Floyd .15 .40
162 Vernon Wells .15 .40
163 Aubrey Huff .15 .40
164 Jeff Bagwell .25 .60
165 Boomer Wells .15 .40
166 Brad Penny .15 .40
167 Austin Kearns .15 .40
168 Mike Mussina .25 .60
169 Randy Wolf .15 .40
170 Tim Hudson SP 3.00 8.00
171 Casey Blake .15 .40
172 Edgar Renteria .15 .40
173 Ben Sheets .15 .40
174 Kevin Brown .15 .40
175 Nomar Garciaparra SP 3.00 8.00
176 Armando Benitez .15 .40
177 Jody Gerut .15 .40
178 Craig Biggio .25 .60
179 Omar Vizquel .25 .60
180 Jake Peavy .15 .40
181 Gustavo Chacin SP 3.00 8.00
182 Johnny Damon .25 .60
183 Mike Lieberthal .15 .40
184 Felix Hernandez SP 6.00 15.00
185 Zach Day SP 3.00 8.00
186 Matt Cain .15 .40
187 Erubiel Durazo .15 .40
188 Zack Greinke .25 .60
189 Matt Morris .15 .40
190 Billy Wagner .15 .40
191 Al Leiter .15 .40
192 Miguel Olivo .15 .40
193 Jose Capellan SP 3.00 8.00
194 Adam Eaton .15 .40
195 Steven White SP RC 3.00 8.00
196 Joe Randa .15 .40
197 Richard Hidalgo .15 .40
198 Orlando Cabrera .15 .40
199 Joel Guzman SP 3.00 8.00
200 Garret Anderson .15 .40
201 Endy Chavez .15 .40
202 Andy Marte .25 .60
203 Jose Guillen .15 .40
204 Victor Martinez .25 .60
205 Johnny Estrada .15 .40
206 Damian Miller .15 .40
207 Ken Harvey .15 .40
208 Ronnie Belliard .15 .40
209 Chan Ho Park .25 .60
210 Laynce Nix .15 .40
211 Lew Ford .15 .40
212 Moises Alou .15 .40
213 Kris Benson .15 .40
214 Mike Gonzalez SP 3.00 8.00
215 Chris Burke .15 .40
216 Juan Pierre .15 .40
217 Phil Nevin .15 .40
218 Jerry Hairston Jr. .15 .40
219 Jeremy Reed .15 .40
220 Scott Kazmir SP 3.00 8.00
221 Mike Maroth .15 .40
222 Alex Rios .25 .60
223 Esteban Loaiza .15 .40
224 Termel Sledge .15 .40
225A M.Prior Blue Sky SP 3.00 8.00
225B M.Prior Yellow Sky SP 3.00 8.00
226 Hank Blalock .15 .40
227 Craig Wilson .15 .40
228 Cesar Izturis .15 .40
229 Dmitri Young .15 .40
230A D.Jeter Blue Sky SP 6.00 15.00
230B D.Jeter Purple Sky SP 6.00 15.00
231 Mark Kotsay .15 .40
232 Darin Erstad .15 .40
233 Brandon Backe SP 3.00 8.00
234 Mike Lowell .15 .40
235 Scott Podsednik .15 .40
236 Michael Barrett .15 .40
237 Chad Tracy .15 .40
238 David Dellucci .15 .40
239 Brady Clark .15 .40
240 Jorge Cantu .15 .40
241 Wil Ledezma .15 .40
242 Morgan Ensberg .15 .40
243 Omar Infante .15 .40
244 Corey Patterson .15 .40
245 Matt Holliday .40 1.00
246 Vinny Castilla .15 .40
247 Jason Bartlett .15 .40
248 Noah Lowry .15 .40
249 Huston Street .15 .40
250 Russell Branyan .15 .40
251 Juan Uribe .15 .40
252 Larry Bigbie .15 .40
253 Grady Sizemore .25 .60
254 Pedro Feliz .15 .40
255 Brad Wilkerson .15 .40
256 Brandon Inge .15 .40
257 Dewon Brazelton .15 .40
258 Rodrigo Lopez .15 .40
259 Jacque Jones .15 .40
260 Jason Giambi .15 .40
261 Clint Barmes .15 .40
262 Willy Taveras .15 .40
263 Marcus Giles .15 .40
264 Joe Blanton .15 .40
265 John Thomson .15 .40
266 Steve Finley SP 3.00 8.00
267 Kevin Millwood .15 .40
268 David Eckstein .15 .40
269 Barry Zito .15 .40
270A T.Helton Purple Sky SP 3.00 8.00
270B T.Helton Yellow Sky SP 3.00 8.00
271 Landon Powell RC .25 .60
272 Justin Verlander RC 5.00 12.00
273 Wes Swackhamer RC .25 .60
274 Wladimir Balentien RC .40 1.00
275 Philip Humber RC .60 1.50
276 Kevin Melillo RC .25 .60
277 Billy Butler RC 1.25 3.00
278 Michael Rogers RC .25 .60
279 Bobby Livingston RC .25 .60
280 Glen Perkins RC .25 .60
281 Mike Bourn RC .60 1.50
282 Tyler Pelland RC .25 .60
283 Jeremy West RC .25 .60
284 Brandon McCarthy RC .40 1.00
285 Ian Kinsler RC 2.00 5.00
286 Chris Roberson RC .25 .60
287 Melky Cabrera RC .60 1.50
288 Ryan Sweeney RC .40 1.00
289 Chip Cannon RC .25 .60
290 Andy LaRoche RC 1.25 3.00
291 Chuck Tiffany RC .60 1.50
292 Ian Bladergroen RC .25 .60
293 Bear Bay RC .25 .60
294 Hernan Iribarren RC .25 .60
295 Stuart Pomeranz RC .25 .60
296 Luke Scott RC .60 1.50
297 Chuck James RC .60 1.50
298 Kennard Bibbs RC .25 .60
299 Steven Bondurant RC .25 .60
300 Thomas Oldham RC .25 .60
301 Nolan Ryan RET 2.00 5.00
302 Reggie Jackson RET .75 2.00
303 Tom Seaver RET .50 1.25
304 Al Kaline RET .75 2.00
305 Cal Ripken RET 3.00 8.00
306 Josh Gibson RET .75 2.00
307 Frank Robinson RET .50 1.25
308 Duke Snider RET .50 1.25
309 Wade Boggs RET .50 1.25
310 Tony Gwynn RET 1.00 2.50
311 Carl Yastrzemski RET 1.00 2.50
312 Ryne Sandberg RET 1.50 4.00
313 Gary Carter RET .30 .75
314 Brooks Robinson RET .50 1.25
315 Ernie Banks RET .75 2.00

2005 Topps Turkey Red Black

*BLACK 1-270: 5X TO 12X BASIC
*BLACK 1-270: .75X TO 2X BASIC SP
*BLACK 1-270: 4X TO 10X BASIC REP
*BLACK 271-300: 3X TO 8X BASIC
*BLACK 301-315: 2.5X TO 6X BASIC
STATED ODDS 1:20 HOBBY/RETAIL
STATED PRINT RUN 142 SETS
CARDS ARE NOT SERIAL-NUMBERED
PRINT RUN INFO PROVIDED BY TOPPS
THERE ARE NO SP'S IN THIS SET
1A Barry Bonds Grey Uni 20.00 50.00
1B Barry Bonds White Uni 20.00 50.00
5A Roger Clemens Blue Sky 8.00 20.00
10A Sammy Sosa w/Name 5.00 12.00
10B Sammy Sosa w/o Name 5.00 12.00
16A Mike Piazza Blue Uni 5.00 12.00
20 Manny Ramirez 3.00 8.00
25 Carlos Beltran 2.00 5.00
28 Rich Harden 2.00 5.00
30 Richie Sexson 2.00 5.00
52 Pulling String J.Santana CL 3.00 8.00
55 Roy Oswalt 2.00 5.00
59 Wily Mo Pena 2.00 5.00
60 Magglio Ordonez 2.00 5.00
70 Jim Thome 3.00 8.00
75A Ichiro Suzuki w/Name 10.00 25.00
75B Ichiro Suzuki w/o Name 10.00 25.00
78 Troy Glaus 2.00 5.00
83B Eric Chavez Purple Sky 2.00 5.00
85 Scott Rolen 3.00 8.00
87 Joe Mauer 3.00 8.00
90 Alfonso Soriano 2.00 5.00
102A Adrian Beltre Grey Uni 2.00 5.00
106 Miguel Tejada 2.00 5.00
110 Hideki Matsui 8.00 20.00
115 Curt Schilling 2.00 5.00
120A Vladimir Guerrero w/Bat 5.00 12.00
120B Vladimir Guerrero w/Glove 5.00 12.00
125B Randy Johnson Purple Sky 5.00 12.00
130B Ivan Rodriguez w/Helmet 3.00 8.00
132 Carlos Delgado 2.00 5.00
149 Jason Bay 2.00 5.00
150 Albert Pujols 10.00 25.00
155 Pedro Martinez 3.00 8.00
160A J.Santana Glove on Knee 5.00 12.00
160B J.Santana Throwing 5.00 12.00
170 Tim Hudson 2.00 5.00
175 Nomar Garciaparra 5.00 12.00
181 Gustavo Chacin 2.00 5.00
184 Felix Hernandez 8.00 20.00
185 Zach Day 2.00 5.00
193 Jose Capellan 2.00 5.00
195 Steven White 2.00 5.00
199 Joel Guzman 2.00 5.00
214 Mike Gonzalez 2.00 5.00
220 Scott Kazmir 2.00 5.00
225A Mark Prior Blue Sky 3.00 8.00
225B Mark Prior Yellow Sky 3.00 8.00
230A Derek Jeter Blue Sky 15.00 40.00
230B Derek Jeter Purple Sky 15.00 40.00
233 Brandon Backe 2.00 5.00
266 Steve Finley 2.00 5.00
270A Todd Helton Purple Sky 3.00 8.00
270B Todd Helton Yellow Sky 3.00 8.00

2005 Topps Turkey Red Gold

*GOLD 1-270: 12X TO 30X BASIC
*GOLD 1-270: 2X TO 5X BASIC SP
*GOLD 1-270: 10X TO 25X BASIC REP
*GOLD 271-300: 6X TO 15X BASIC
*GOLD 301-315: 5X TO 12X BASIC
STATED ODDS 1:59 HOBBY/RETAIL
STATED PRINT RUN 50 SERIAL #'d SETS
1A Barry Bonds Grey Uni 75.00 150.00
1B Barry Bonds White Uni 75.00 150.00
10A Sammy Sosa w/Name 12.50 30.00
10B Sammy Sosa w/o Name 12.50 30.00
16A Mike Piazza Blue Uni 8.00 20.00
20 Manny Ramirez 8.00 20.00
25 Carlos Beltran 5.00 12.00
28 Rich Harden 5.00 12.00
30 Richie Sexson 5.00 12.00
52 Pulling String J.Santana CL 8.00 20.00
55 Roy Oswalt 5.00 12.00
59 Wily Mo Pena 5.00 12.00
60 Magglio Ordonez 5.00 12.00
70 Jim Thome 8.00 20.00
75A Ichiro Suzuki w/Name 30.00 60.00
75B Ichiro Suzuki w/o Name 30.00 60.00
78 Troy Glaus 5.00 12.00
83B Eric Chavez Purple Sky 5.00 12.00
85 Scott Rolen 8.00 20.00
87 Joe Mauer 8.00 20.00
90 Alfonso Soriano 5.00 12.00
102A Adrian Beltre Grey Uni 5.00 12.00
106 Miguel Tejada 5.00 12.00
110 Hideki Matsui 20.00 50.00
115 Curt Schilling 5.00 12.00
120A Vladimir Guerrero w/Bat 12.50 30.00
120B Vladimir Guerrero w/Glove 12.50 30.00
125B Randy Johnson Purple Sky 12.50 30.00
130B Ivan Rodriguez w/Helmet 8.00 20.00
132 Carlos Delgado 5.00 12.00
149 Jason Bay 5.00 12.00
150 Albert Pujols 30.00 60.00
155 Pedro Martinez 8.00 20.00
160A J.Santana Glove on Knee 8.00 20.00
160B J.Santana Throwing 8.00 20.00
170 Tim Hudson 5.00 12.00
175 Nomar Garciaparra 12.50 30.00
181 Gustavo Chacin 5.00 12.00
184 Felix Hernandez 20.00 50.00
185 Zach Day 5.00 12.00
193 Jose Capellan 5.00 12.00
195 Steven White 5.00 12.00
199 Joel Guzman 5.00 12.00
214 Mike Gonzalez 5.00 12.00
220 Scott Kazmir 5.00 12.00
225A Mark Prior Blue Sky 8.00 20.00
225B Mark Prior Yellow Sky 8.00 20.00
230A Derek Jeter Blue Sky 50.00 100.00
230B Derek Jeter Purple Sky 50.00 100.00
233 Brandon Backe 5.00 12.00
270A Todd Helton Purple Sky 8.00 20.00
270B Todd Helton Yellow Sky 8.00 20.00
305 Cal Ripken RET 50.00 100.00

2005 Topps Turkey Red Red

*RED 1-270: 1X TO 2.5X BASIC
*RED 1-270: .2X TO .5X BASIC SP
*RED 1-270: .75X TO 2X BASIC REP
*RED 271-300: 1.2X TO 3X BASIC
*RED 301-315: .75X TO 2X BASIC
ONE RED OR OTHER PARALLEL PER PACK
THERE ARE NO SP'S IN THIS SET
10A Sammy Sosa w/Name 1.00 2.50
10B Sammy Sosa w/o Name 1.00 2.50
16A Mike Piazza Blue Uni 1.00 2.50
20 Manny Ramirez .60 1.50
25 Carlos Beltran .40 1.00
28 Rich Harden .40 1.00
30 Richie Sexson .40 1.00
52 Pulling String J.Santana CL 1.00 2.50
55 Roy Oswalt .40 1.00
59 Wily Mo Pena .40 1.00
60 Magglio Ordonez .40 1.00
70 Jim Thome .60 1.50
78 Troy Glaus .40 1.00
83B Eric Chavez Purple Sky .40 1.00
85 Scott Rolen .60 1.50
87 Joe Mauer 1.00 2.50
90 Alfonso Soriano .40 1.00
102B Adrian Beltre White Uni .40 1.00
106 Miguel Tejada .40 1.00
115 Curt Schilling .60 1.50
120A Vladimir Guerrero w/Bat 1.00 2.50
120B Vladimir Guerrero w/Glove 1.00 2.50
125B Randy Johnson Purple Sky 1.00 2.50
130B Ivan Rodriguez w/Helmet .60 1.50
132 Carlos Delgado .40 1.00
149 Jason Bay .40 1.00
155 Pedro Martinez .60 1.50
160A J.Santana Glove on Knee 1.00 2.50
160B J.Santana Throwing 1.00 2.50
170 Tim Hudson .40 1.00
175 Nomar Garciaparra 1.00 2.50
181 Gustavo Chacin .40 1.00
185 Zach Day .40 1.00
193 Jose Capellan .40 1.00
195 Steven White .40 1.00
199 Joel Guzman .40 1.00
214 Mike Gonzalez .40 1.00
220 Scott Kazmir .40 1.00
225A Mark Prior Blue Sky .60 1.50
225B Mark Prior Yellow Sky .60 1.50
233 Brandon Backe .40 1.00
266 Steve Finley .40 1.00
270A Todd Helton Purple Sky .60 1.50
270B Todd Helton Yellow Sky .60 1.50

2005 Topps Turkey Red Suede

STATED ODDS 1:2955 H, 1:3072 R
STATED PRINT RUN 1 SERIAL #'d SET
NO PRICING DUE TO SCARCITY

2005 Topps Turkey Red White

*WHITE 1-270: 2X TO 5X BASIC
*WHITE 1-270: .3X TO .8X BASIC SP
*WHITE 1-270: 1.5X TO 4X BASIC REP
*WHITE 271-300: 1X TO 2.5X BASIC
*WHITE 301-315: 1.5X TO 4X BASIC
STATED ODDS 1:4 HOBBY/RETAIL
THERE ARE NO SP'S IN THIS SET
10A Sammy Sosa w/Name 2.00 5.00
10B Sammy Sosa w/o Name 2.00 5.00
16A Mike Piazza Blue Uni 2.00 5.00
20 Manny Ramirez 1.25 3.00
25 Carlos Beltran .75 2.00
28 Rich Harden .75 2.00
30 Richie Sexson .75 2.00
52 Pulling String J.Santana CL 2.00 5.00
55 Roy Oswalt .75 2.00
59 Wily Mo Pena .75 2.00
60 Magglio Ordonez .75 2.00
70 Jim Thome 1.25 3.00
75A Ichiro Suzuki w/Name 4.00 10.00
75B Ichiro Suzuki w/o Name 4.00 10.00
78 Troy Glaus .75 2.00
83B Eric Chavez Purple Sky .75 2.00
85 Scott Rolen 1.25 3.00
87 Joe Mauer 2.00 5.00
90 Alfonso Soriano .75 2.00
102A Adrian Beltre Grey Uni .75 2.00
106 Miguel Tejada .75 2.00
110 Hideki Matsui 3.00 8.00
115 Curt Schilling 1.25 3.00
120A Vladimir Guerrero w/Bat 2.00 5.00
120B Vladimir Guerrero w/Glove 2.00 5.00
125B Randy Johnson Purple Sky 2.00 5.00
130B Ivan Rodriguez w/Helmet 1.25 3.00

132 Carlos Delgado .75 2.00
149 Jason Bay .75 2.00
150 Albert Pujols 4.00 10.00
155 Pedro Martinez 1.25 3.00
160A J.Santana Glove on Knee 2.00 5.00
160B J.Santana Throwing 2.00 5.00
170 Tim Hudson .75 2.00
175 Nomar Garciaparra 2.00 5.00
181 Gustavo Chacin .75 2.00
184 Felix Hernandez 4.00 10.00
185 Zach Day .75 2.00
193 Jose Capellan .75 2.00
195 Steven White .75 2.00
199 Joel Guzman .75 2.00
214 Mike Gonzalez .75 2.00
220 Scott Kazmir .75 2.00
225A Mark Prior Blue Sky 1.25 3.00
225B Mark Prior Yellow Sky 1.25 3.00
230A Derek Jeter Blue Sky 4.00 10.00
230B Derek Jeter Purple Sky 4.00 10.00
233 Brandon Backe .75 2.00
266 Steve Finley .75 2.00
270A Todd Helton Purple Sky 1.25 3.00
270B Todd Helton Yellow Sky 1.25 3.00

2005 Topps Turkey Red Autographs

GROUP A ODDS 1:6495 H, 1:6262 R
GROUP B ODDS 1:1280 H, 1:4372 R
GROUP C ODDS 1:106 H, 1:1037 R
GROUP D ODDS 1:1270 H, 1:2714 R
GROUP E ODDS 1:816 H, 1:3024 R
GROUP A PRINT RUNS B/WN 17-67 PER
GROUP B PRINT RUNS B/WN 142-192 PER
GROUP A-B ARE NOT SERIAL-NUMBERED
A-B PRINT RUNS PROVIDED BY TOPPS
NO GROUP A PRICING DUE TO SCARCITY
EXCHANGE DEADLINE 08/31/07
AR Alex Rodriguez A/42 *
AS A.Soriano B/142 * 10.00 25.00
BJ Blake Johnson C 4.00 10.00
BM Brett Myers A/67 *
CC Carl Crawford A/17 *
CN Chris Nelson C 4.00 10.00
DO David Ortiz C 20.00 50.00
DP Dustin Pedroia C 20.00 50.00
EG Eric Gagne B/142 * 15.00 40.00
GS Gary Sheffield C 10.00 25.00
JF Josh Fields C 6.00 15.00
JG Jody Gerut D 4.00 10.00
JJ Jason Jaramillo C 4.00 10.00
JPH J.P. Howell C 4.00 10.00
JS Jeremy Sowers C 6.00 15.00
MB Matt Bush A/17 *
MK Mark Kotsay A/17 *
MRO Mike Rodriguez E 4.00 10.00
SE Scott Elbert C 6.00 15.00
ZJ Zach Jackson C 4.00 10.00
ZP Zach Parker C 4.00 10.00

2005 Topps Turkey Red Autographs Black

*GROUP B: .6X TO 1.5X BASIC
BONDS ODDS 1:344,256 H
GROUP A ODDS 1:18,119 H, 1:20,032 R
GROUP B ODDS 1:574 H, 1:1809 R
BONDS PRINT RUN 1 SERIAL #'d CARD
GROUP A PRINT RUN 5 SERIAL #'d SETS
GROUP B PRINT RUN 99 SERIAL #'d SETS
NO BONDS PRICING DUE TO SCARCITY
NO GROUP A PRICING DUE TO SCARCITY
EXCHANGE DEADLINE 08/31/07

2005 Topps Turkey Red Autographs Gold

BONDS ODDS 1:344,256 H
GROUP A ODDS 1:46,437 H, 1:60,096 R
GROUP B ODDS 1:3742 H, 1:3840 R
BONDS PRINT RUN 1 SERIAL #'d CARD
GROUP A PRINT RUN 2 SERIAL #'d SETS
GROUP B PRINT RUN 25 SERIAL #'d SETS
NO PRICING DUE TO SCARCITY
EXCHANGE DEADLINE 08/31/07

2005 Topps Turkey Red Autographs Red

*GROUP B: .4X TO 1X BASIC
BONDS ODDS 1:344,256 H
GROUP A ODDS 1:5935 H, 1:6048 R
GROUP B ODDS 1:153 H, 1:1943R
BONDS PRINT RUN 1 SERIAL #'d CARD
GROUP A PRINT RUN 15 SERIAL #'d SETS
GROUP B PRINT RUN 300 SERIAL #'d SETS
NO BONDS PRICING DUE TO SCARCITY
NO GROUP A PRICING DUE TO SCARCITY
EXCHANGE DEADLINE 08/31/07

2005 Topps Turkey Red Autographs Suede

STATED ODDS 1:40,632 H, 1:60,096 R
STATED PRINT RUN 1 SERIAL #'d SET
NO PRICING DUE TO SCARCITY
EXCHANGE DEADLINE 08/31/07

2005 Topps Turkey Red Autographs White

*GROUP B: .5X TO 1.2X BASIC
BONDS ODDS 1:344,256 H
GROUP A ODDS 1:9563 H, 1:9072 R
GROUP B ODDS 1:242 H, 1:1536 R
BONDS PRINT RUN 1 SERIAL #'d CARD
GROUP A PRINT RUN 10 SERIAL #'d SETS
GROUP B PRINT RUN 200 SERIAL #'d SETS
NO BONDS PRICING DUE TO SCARCITY
NO GROUP A PRICING DUE TO SCARCITY
EXCHANGE DEADLINE 08/31/07

2005 Topps Turkey Red B-18 Blankets

STATED ODDS 1:2 JUMBO
SP STATED ODDS 1:6 JUMBO
REPURCHASED ODDS 1:165 JUMBO
AR1 Alex Rodriguez Blue SP 10.00 25.00
AR2 Alex Rodriguez Green 6.00 15.00
AS1 Alfonso Soriano Red SP 6.00 15.00
AS2 Alfonso Soriano White 4.00 10.00
BB1 Barry Bonds Red SP 15.00 40.00
BB2 Barry Bonds White 10.00 25.00
CS1 Curt Schilling Red SP 6.00 15.00
CS2 Curt Schilling White 4.00 10.00
DJ1 Derek Jeter Blue SP 10.00 25.00
DJ2 Derek Jeter Green 6.00 15.00
IS1 Ichiro Suzuki Green SP 10.00 25.00
IS2 Ichiro Suzuki White 6.00 15.00
RC1 Roger Clemens Purple SP 10.00 25.00
RC2 Roger Clemens White 6.00 15.00
TH1 Todd Helton Green SP 6.00 15.00
TH2 Todd Helton White 4.00 10.00
NNO Repurchased B-18 Blanket

2005 Topps Turkey Red Cabinet

STATED ODDS 1:2 JUMBO
SP STATED ODDS 1:30 JUMBO
SP STATED PRINT RUNS 118 COPIES PER
SP'S ARE NOT SERIAL-NUMBERED
SP PRINT RUNS PROVIDED BY TOPPS
SP'S HAVE ADVERTISEMENTS ON BACK
REPURCHASED ODDS 1:211 JUMBO
AP Albert Pujols 8.00 20.00
AR1 Alex Rodriguez w/Bat 5.00 12.00
AR2 A.Rod w/Glove SP/118 * 6.00 15.00
BB1 Barry Bonds At Bat SP/118 * 8.00 20.00
BB2 Barry Bonds On Steps 6.00 15.00
GB George W. Bush 3.00 8.00
GW George Washington 3.00 8.00
JS Johan Santana 3.00 8.00
JT Jim Thome 2.00 5.00
MP Mike Piazza 3.00 8.00
MR Manny Ramirez 3.00 8.00
MT Miguel Tejada 2.00 5.00
RJ Randy Johnson 3.00 8.00
SR Scott Rolen 2.00 5.00
SS Sammy Sosa 3.00 8.00
WT William Howard Taft 3.00 8.00
NNO Repurchased T-3 Cabinet

2005 Topps Turkey Red Cabinet Auto Relics

GROUP A ODDS 1:2869 JUMBO
GROUP B ODDS 1:202 JUMBO
GROUP C ODDS 1:67 JUMBO
GROUP D ODDS 1:101 JUMBO
GROUP E ODDS 1:9 JUMBO
GROUP A PRINT RUN 5 SERIAL #'d SETS
GROUP B PRINT RUN 25 SERIAL #'d SETS
GROUP C PRINT RUN 75 SERIAL #'d SETS
GROUP D PRINT RUN 150 SERIAL #'d SETS
GROUP E PRINT RUN 450 SERIAL #'d SETS
NO GROUP A-B PRICING DUE TO SCARCITY
EXCHANGE DEADLINE 08/31/07
AR Alex Rodriguez Bat B/25
BB Barry Bonds Jsy A/5
BM Brett Myers Jsy D/150 15.00 40.00
CC Carl Crawford Bat E/450 10.00 25.00
DO David Ortiz Bat C/75 60.00 120.00
EG Eric Gagne Jsy C/75 60.00 120.00
GS Gary Sheffield Bat B/25
JG Jody Gerut Bat E/450 6.00 15.00
MB Matt Bush Jsy E/450 10.00 25.00
MK Mark Kotsay Bat E/450 10.00 25.00

2005 Topps Turkey Red Cut Signatures

STATED ODDS 1:86,064 HOBBY
STATED PRINT RUN 1 SERIAL #'d SET
NO PRICING DUE TO SCARCITY
DE Dwight D. Eisenhower
FR Franklin D. Roosevelt
TR Theodore Roosevelt
WT William Howard Taft

2005 Topps Turkey Red Relics

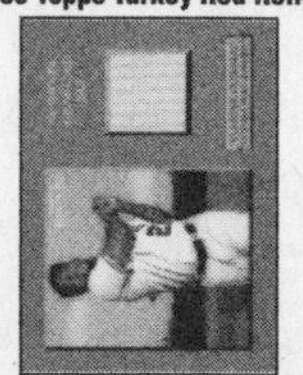

GROUP A ODDS 1:2550 H, 1:2560 R
GROUP B ODDS 1:1776 H, 1:1781 R
GROUP C ODDS 1:1383 H, 1:1398 R
GROUP D ODDS 1:349 H, 1:1202 R
GROUP E ODDS 1:208 H, 1:577 R
GROUP F ODDS 1:65 H, 1:200 R
GROUP G ODDS 1:172 H, 1:427 R
GROUP H ODDS 1:52 H, 1:102 R
AB Adrian Beltre Bat C 4.00 10.00
AP Albert Pujols Bat E 6.00 15.00
AR Alex Rodriguez Uni D 5.00 12.00
AR2 Alex Rodriguez Bat G 4.00 10.00
AS Alfonso Soriano Bat H 2.00 5.00
BB Barry Bonds Pants D 8.00 20.00
CB Carlos Beltran Bat E 3.00 8.00
CJ Chipper Jones Jsy H 3.00 8.00
CS Curt Schilling Jsy F 3.00 8.00
DO David Ortiz Jsy F 3.00 8.00
GS Gary Sheffield Bat H 2.00 5.00
HB Hank Blalock Bat F 2.00 5.00
JB Jeff Bagwell Uni H 3.00 8.00
JD Johnny Damon Bat G 3.00 8.00
JD2 Johnny Damon Jsy E 4.00 10.00
JT Jim Thome Bat F 3.00 8.00
LW Larry Walker Bat B 6.00 15.00
MC Miguel Cabrera Jsy H 3.00 8.00
ML Mike Lowell Jsy H 2.00 5.00
MM Mark Mulder Uni F 2.00 5.00
MO Magglio Ordonez Bat F 2.00 5.00
MP Mike Piazza Uni A 6.00 15.00
MPR Mark Prior Jsy B 6.00 15.00
MR Manny Ramirez Jsy D 4.00 10.00
MT Miguel Tejada Uni F 2.00 5.00
MTE Mark Teixeira Bat G 3.00 8.00
RC Roger Clemens Bat A 8.00 20.00
RC2 Roger Clemens Jsy E 5.00 12.00
RP Rafael Palmeiro Bat F 3.00 8.00
SS Sammy Sosa Bat C 6.00 15.00
TH Todd Helton Jsy H 3.00 8.00
VG Vladimir Guerrero Bat H 3.00 8.00

2005 Topps Turkey Red Relics Black

*BLACK: 1.25X TO 3X BASIC F-H
*BLACK: 1X TO 2.5X BASIC D-E
*BLACK: .6X TO 1.5X BASIC A-C
STATED ODDS 1:608 H, 1:614 R
STATED PRINT RUN 50 SERIAL #'d SETS

2005 Topps Turkey Red Relics Gold

STATED ODDS 1:1217 H, 1:1218 R
STATED PRINT RUN 25 SERIAL #'d SETS
NO PRICING DUE TO SCARCITY

2005 Topps Turkey Red Relics Red

*RED: .75X TO 2X BASIC F-H
*RED: .6X TO 1.5X BASIC D-E

*RED: .4X TO 1X BASIC A-C
STATED ODDS 1:295 H, 1:341 R
STATED PRINT RUN 99 SERIAL #'d SETS

2005 Topps Turkey Red Relics Suede

STATED ODDS 1:38,251 H, 1:36,288 R
STATED PRINT RUN 1 SERIAL #'d SET
NO PRICING DUE TO SCARCITY

2005 Topps Turkey Red Relics White

*WHITE: 1X TO 2.5X BASIC F-H
*WHITE: .75X TO 2X BASIC D-E
*WHITE: .5X TO 1.2X BASIC A-C
STATED ODDS 1:377 H, 1:417 R
STATED PRINT RUN 75 SERIAL #'d SETS

2006 Topps Turkey Red

This 330-card set was released in September, 2006. These cards were issued in eight-card packs with an $4 SRP which came 24 packs to a box and eight boxes to a case. This set was numbered in continuation of the Topps Turkey Red set issued in 2005. Interspersed throughout the set were some short printed cards as well as some players printed with both their original team and their current team. The short prints were issued at stated odds of one in four hobby or retail packs. Subsets in this product include Checklists (571-580); Retired Players (581-590) and 2006 Rookies (591-630).

COMPLETE SET (330) 150.00 250.00
COMP.SET w/o SP's (275) 15.00 40.00
COMMON CARD (316-580) .15 .40
COMMON SP (316-580) 3.00 8.00
SP STATED ODDS 1:4 HOBBY, 1:4 RETAIL
SEE BECKETT.COM FOR SP CHECKLIST
COMMON CL (571-580) .07 .20
COMMON RET (581-590) .30 .75
COMMON RC (591-630) .40 1.00
OVERALL PLATE ODDS 1:477 H
PLATE PRINT RUN 1 SET PER COLOR
BLACK-CYAN-MAGENTA-YELLOW ISSUED
NO PLATE PRICING DUE TO SCARCITY
316A Alex Rodriguez Yanks .60 1.50
316B Alex Rodriguez Rangers SP 4.00 10.00
316C Alex Rodriguez M's SP 4.00 10.00
317 Jeff Francoeur SP 3.00 8.00
318 Shawn Green .15 .40
319 Daniel Cabrera .15 .40
320 Craig Biggio .25 .60
321 Jeremy Bonderman .15 .40
322 Mark Kotsay .15 .40
323 Cliff Floyd .15 .40
324 Jimmy Rollins .25 .60
325A Magglio Ordonez Tigers .25 .60
325B Magglio Ordonez White Sox SP 3.00 8.00
326 C.C. Sabathia .25 .60
327 Oliver Perez .15 .40
328 Orlando Hudson .15 .40
329 Chris Ray .15 .40
330 Manny Ramirez .40 1.00
331 Paul Konerko .25 .60
332 Joe Mauer SP 3.00 8.00
333 Jorge Posada .25 .60
334 Mark Ellis .15 .40
335 A.J. Burnett .25 .60
336 Mike Sweeney .15 .40
337 Shannon Stewart .15 .40
338 Jake Peavy SP 3.00 8.00
339A Carlos Delgado Mets SP 3.00 8.00
339B Carlos Delgado Blue Jays SP 3.00 8.00
340 Brian Roberts .15 .40
341 Dontrelle Willis .15 .40
342 Aaron Rowand .15 .40
343A Richie Sexson M's .15 .40
343B Richie Sexson Brewers SP 3.00 8.00
344 Chris Carpenter .40 1.00
345 Carlos Zambrano .25 .60
346 Nomar Garciaparra .40 1.00
347 Carlos Lee .15 .40
348A Preston Wilson Astros .15 .40
348B Preston Wilson Marlins SP 3.00 8.00
349 Mariano Rivera .40 1.00
350 Ichiro Suzuki SP 4.00 10.00
351A Mike Piazza Padres .40 1.00
351B Mike Piazza Mets SP 3.00 8.00
352 Jason Schmidt .15 .40
353 Jeff Weaver .15 .40
354 Rocco Baldelli .15 .40
355 Adam Dunn .25 .60
356 Jeromy Burnitz .15 .40
357 Chris Shelton SP 3.00 8.00
358 Chone Figgins SP 3.00 8.00
359 Javier Vazquez .15 .40
360 Chipper Jones .40 1.00
361 Frank Thomas .40 1.00
362 Mark Loretta .15 .40
363 Hideki Matsui .40 1.00
364 J.J. Hardy SP 3.00 8.00
365 Todd Helton .25 .60
366 Reggie Sanders .15 .40
367 Jay Gibbons .15 .40
368 Johnny Estrada .15 .40
369 Grady Sizemore .25 .60
370 Jim Thome .25 .60
371 Ivan Rodriguez .25 .60
372 Jason Bay .15 .40
373 Carl Crawford .25 .60
374 Adrian Beltre .15 .40
375 Derrek Lee SP 3.00 8.00
376 Miguel Olivo .15 .40
377 Roy Oswalt .25 .60
378 Coco Crisp .15 .40
379 Moises Alou .15 .40
380 Kevin Millwood .15 .40
381 Mark Grudzielanek .15 .40
382 Justin Morneau .40 1.00
383 Austin Kearns .15 .40
384 Brad Penny .15 .40
385 Troy Glaus .15 .40
386 Cliff Lee .25 .60
387 Armando Benitez .15 .40
388 Clint Barmes .15 .40
389 Orlando Cabrera .15 .40
390 Jim Edmonds SP 3.00 8.00
391 Jermaine Dye .15 .40
392 Morgan Ensberg SP 3.00 8.00
393 Paul LoDuca .15 .40
394 Eric Chavez .15 .40
395 Greg Maddux SP 4.00 10.00
396 Jack Wilson .15 .40
397 Omar Vizquel .25 .60
398 Joe Nathan .15 .40
399 Bobby Abreu .15 .40
400 Barry Bonds SP 6.00 15.00
401 Gary Sheffield .15 .40
402 John Patterson .15 .40
403 J.D. Drew .15 .40
404 Bruce Chen .15 .40
405 Johnny Damon SP 3.00 8.00
406 Aubrey Huff .15 .40
407 Mark Mulder .15 .40
408 Jamie Moyer .15 .40
409 Carlos Guillen .15 .40
410 Andruw Jones SP 3.00 8.00
411 Jhonny Peralta SP 3.00 8.00
412 Doug Davis .15 .40
413 Aaron Miles .15 .40
414 Jon Lieber .15 .40
415 Aaron Hill .15 .40
416 Josh Beckett SP 3.00 8.00
417 Bobby Crosby .15 .40
418 Noah Lowry SP 3.00 8.00
419 Sidney Ponson .15 .40
420 Luis Castillo .15 .40
421 Brad Wilkerson .15 .40
422 Felix Hernandez SP 3.00 8.00
423 Vinny Castilla .15 .40
424 Tom Glavine .25 .60
425 Vladimir Guerrero .40 1.00
426 Javy Lopez .15 .40
427 Ronnie Belliard .15 .40
428 Dmitri Young .15 .40
429 Johan Santana .40 1.00
430A David Ortiz Red Sox SP 3.00 8.00
430B David Ortiz Twins SP 3.00 8.00
431 Ben Sheets .15 .40
432 Matt Holliday .40 1.00
433 Brian McCann .15 .40
434 Joe Blanton .15 .40
435 Sean Casey .15 .40
436 Brad Lidge .15 .40
437 Chad Tracy .15 .40
438 Brett Myers .15 .40
439 Matt Morris .15 .40
440 Brian Giles .15 .40
441 Zach Duke .15 .40
442 Jose Lopez .15 .40
443 Kris Benson .15 .40
444 Jose Reyes SP 3.00 8.00
445 Travis Hafner .15 .40
446 Orlando Hernandez .15 .40
447 Edgar Renteria .15 .40
448 Scott Podsednik .15 .40
449 Nick Swisher SP 3.00 8.00
450 Derek Jeter SP 6.00 15.00
451 Scott Kazmir SP 3.00 8.00
452 Hank Blalock .15 .40
453 Jake Westbrook .15 .40
454 Miguel Cabrera .40 1.00
455A Ken Griffey Jr. Reds .60 1.50
455B Ken Griffey Jr. M's SP 4.00 10.00
456 Rafael Furcal .15 .40
457 Lance Berkman .25 .60
458 Aramis Ramirez .15 .40
459A Xavier Nady Mets .15 .40
459B Xavier Nady Padres SP 3.00 8.00
460A Randy Johnson Yanks .40 1.00
460B Randy Johnson Astros SP 3.00 8.00
461 Khalil Greene .15 .40
462 Bartolo Colon .15 .40
463 Mike Lowell .15 .40
464 David DeJesus .15 .40
465 Ryan Howard SP 4.00 10.00
466 Tim Salmon SP 3.00 8.00
467 Mark Buehrle SP 3.00 8.00
468 Curtis Granderson .25 .60
469 Kerry Wood .15 .40
470 Miguel Tejada .25 .60
471 Geoff Jenkins .15 .40
472 Jeremy Reed .15 .40
473 David Eckstein .15 .40
474 Lyle Overbay .15 .40
475 Michael Young .25 .60
476A Nick Johnson Nats SP 3.00 8.00
476B Nick Johnson Yanks SP 3.00 8.00
477 Carlos Beltran .15 .40
478 Huston Street .15 .40
479 Brandon Webb .25 .60
480 Phil Nevin .15 .40
481 Ryan Madson SP 3.00 8.00
482 Jason Giambi .15 .40
483 Angel Berroa .15 .40
484 Casey Blake .15 .40
485 Pat Burrell .15 .40
486 B.J. Ryan .15 .40
487 Torii Hunter .15 .40
488 Garret Anderson .15 .40
489 Chase Utley SP 3.00 8.00
490 Matt Murton .15 .40
491 Rich Harden .15 .40
492 Garrett Atkins .15 .40
493 Tadahito Iguchi SP 3.00 8.00
494 Jarrod Washburn .15 .40
495 Carl Everett .15 .40
496 Kameron Loe .15 .40
497 Jorge Cantu SP 3.00 8.00
498 Chris Young .15 .40
499 Marcus Giles .15 .40
500 Albert Pujols 1.00 2.50
501A Alfonso Soriano Nats SP 3.00 8.00
501B Alfonso Soriano Yanks SP 3.00 8.00
502 Randy Winn .15 .40
503 Roy Halladay .40 1.00
504 Victor Martinez .25 .60
505 Pedro Martinez .25 .60
506 Rickie Weeks .25 .60
507 Dan Johnson .15 .40
508A Tim Hudson Braves .25 .60
508B Tim Hudson A's SP 3.00 8.00
509 Mark Prior .25 .60
510 Melvin Mora .15 .40
511 Matt Clement .15 .40
512 Brandon Inge .15 .40
513 Mike Mussina .25 .60
514 Mike Cameron .15 .40
515 Barry Zito .15 .40
516 Luis Gonzalez .15 .40
517 Jose Castillo .15 .40
518 Andy Pettitte .25 .60
519 Wily Mo Pena .15 .40
520 Billy Wagner .15 .40
521 Ervin Santana SP 3.00 8.00
522 Juan Pierre .15 .40
523 Dan Haren .15 .40
524 Adrian Gonzalez SP 3.00 8.00
525 Robinson Cano .40 1.00
526 Jeff Kent .15 .40
527 Cory Sullivan .15 .40
528 Joe Crede SP 3.00 8.00
529 John Smoltz .40 1.00
530 David Wright .60 1.50
531 Chad Cordero .15 .40
532 Scott Rolen SP 3.00 8.00
533 Edwin Jackson .15 .40
534 Doug Mientkiewicz .15 .40
535 Mark Teixeira SP 3.00 8.00
536 Kelvim Escobar .15 .40
537 Alex Rios .25 .60
538 Jose Vidro .15 .40
539 Alex Gonzalez .15 .40
540 Yadier Molina .25 .60
541 Ronny Cedeno SP 3.00 8.00
542 Mark Hendrickson .15 .40
543 Russ Adams .15 .40
544 Chris Capuano .15 .40
545 Raul Ibanez .25 .60
546 Vicente Padilla .15 .40
547 Chris Duffy .15 .40
548 Bengie Molina .15 .40
549 Chien-Ming Wang .25 .60
550 Curt Schilling .25 .60
551 Craig Wilson .15 .40
552 Mike Lieberthal .15 .40
553 Kazuo Matsui .15 .40
554 Jeff Francis .15 .40
555 Brady Clark .15 .40
556 Willy Taveras .15 .40
557 Mike Maroth .15 .40
558 Bernie Williams .25 .60
559 Edwin Encarnacion .15 .40
560 Vernon Wells .15 .40
561A Livan Hernandez Nats .15 .40
561B Livan Hernandez Giants SP 3.00 8.00
562 Kenny Rogers .15 .40
563 Steve Finley .15 .40
564 Trot Nixon .15 .40
565 Jonny Gomes SP 3.00 8.00
566 Brandon Phillips .15 .40
567 Shawn Chacon .15 .40
568 Dave Bush .15 .40
569 Jose Guillen .15 .40
570 Gustavo Chacin .15 .40
571 A.Rod Safe at the Plate CL .30 .75
572 Pujols At Bat CL .50 1.25
573 Bonds On Deck CL .40 1.00
574 Breaking Up Two CL .07 .20
575 Conference On The Mound CL .20 .50
576 Touch Em All CL .30 .75
577 Avoiding The Runner CL .07 .20
578 Bunting The Runner Over CL .07 .20
579 In The Hole CL .12 .30
580 Jeter Steals Third CL .50 1.25
581 Nolan Ryan RET 2.00 5.00
582 Cal Ripken RET 3.00 8.00
583 Carl Yastrzemski RET 1.25 3.00
584 Duke Snider RET .50 1.25
585 Tom Seaver RET .50 1.25
586 Mickey Mantle RET 2.50 6.00
587 Jim Palmer RET .30 .75
588 Gary Carter RET .30 .75
589 Stan Musial RET 1.25 3.00
590 Luis Aparicio RET .30 .75
591 Prince Fielder (RC) 1.50 4.00
592 Conor Jackson (RC) .60 1.50
593 Jeremy Hermida (RC) .40 1.00
594 Jeff Mathis (RC) .40 1.00
595 Alay Soler RC .40 1.00
596 Ryan Spilborghs (RC) .40 1.00
597 Chuck James (RC) .40 1.00
598 Josh Barfield (RC) .40 1.00
599 Ian Kinsler (RC) 1.25 3.00
600 Val Majewski (RC) .40 1.00
601 Brian Slocum (RC) .40 1.00
602 Matt Kemp (RC) 2.00 5.00
603 Nate McLouth (RC) .40 1.00
604 Sean Marshall (RC) .60 1.50
605 Brian Bannister (RC) .40 1.00
606 Ryan Zimmerman (RC) 2.00 5.00
607 Kendry Morales (RC) 1.00 2.50
608 Jonathan Papelbon (RC) 2.00 5.00
609 Matt Cain (RC) 1.00 2.50
610 Anderson Hernandez (RC) .40 1.00
611 Jose Capellan (RC) .40 1.00
612 Lastings Milledge (RC) .40 1.00
613 Francisco Liriano (RC) 1.00 2.50
614 Hanley Ramirez (RC) 1.00 2.50
615 Brian Anderson (RC) .40 1.00
616 Reggie Abercrombie (RC) .40 1.00
617 Erick Aybar (RC) .40 1.00
618 James Loney (RC) .60 1.50
619 Joel Zumaya (RC) 1.00 2.50
620 Travis Ishikawa (RC) .40 1.00
621 Jason Kubel (RC) .40 1.00
622 Drew Meyer (RC) .40 1.00
623 Kenji Johjima RC 1.00 2.50
624 Fausto Carmona (RC) .40 1.00
625 Nick Markakis (RC) 1.00 2.50
626 John Rheinecker (RC) .40 1.00
627 Melky Cabrera (RC) .60 1.50
628 Michael Pelfrey RC 1.00 2.50
629 Dan Uggla (RC) 1.00 2.50
630 Justin Verlander (RC) 3.00 8.00

2006 Topps Turkey Red Black

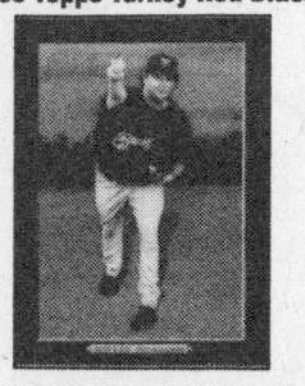

*BLACK 316-580: 4X TO 10X BASIC
*BLACK 316-580: .6X TO 1.5X BASIC SP
*BLACK 581-590: 2X TO 5X BASIC RET
*BLACK 591-630: 1.25X TO 3X BASIC ROOKIE
STATED ODDS 1:20 HOBBY/RETAIL
THERE ARE NO SP'S IN THIS SET

2006 Topps Turkey Red Gold

COMMON CARD (316-580) 5.00 12.00
COMMON CL (571-580) 3.00 8.00
COMMON RET (581-590) 5.00 12.00
COMMON ROOKIE (591-630) 6.00 15.00
STATED ODDS 1:60 HOBBY/RETAIL
THERE ARE NO SP'S IN THIS SET
316A Alex Rodriguez Yanks 20.00 50.00
316B Alex Rodriguez Rangers 20.00 50.00
316C Alex Rodriguez M's 20.00 50.00
317 Jeff Francoeur 12.00 30.00
318 Shawn Green 5.00 12.00
319 Daniel Cabrera 5.00 12.00
320 Craig Biggio 8.00 20.00
321 Jeremy Bonderman 5.00 12.00
322 Mark Kotsay 5.00 12.00
323 Cliff Floyd 5.00 12.00
324 Jimmy Rollins 8.00 20.00
325A Magglio Ordonez Tigers 8.00 20.00
325B Magglio Ordonez White Sox 8.00 20.00
326 C.C. Sabathia 8.00 20.00
327 Oliver Perez 5.00 12.00
328 Orlando Hudson 5.00 12.00
329 Chris Ray 5.00 12.00
330 Manny Ramirez 12.00 30.00
331 Paul Konerko 8.00 20.00
332 Joe Mauer 12.00 30.00
333 Jorge Posada 8.00 20.00
334 Mark Ellis 5.00 12.00
335 A.J. Burnett 8.00 20.00
336 Mike Sweeney 5.00 12.00
337 Shannon Stewart 5.00 12.00
338 Jake Peavy 5.00 12.00
339A Carlos Delgado Mets 5.00 12.00
339B Carlos Delgado Blue Jays 5.00 12.00
340 Brian Roberts 5.00 12.00
341 Dontrelle Willis 5.00 12.00
342 Aaron Rowand 5.00 12.00
343A Richie Sexson M's 5.00 12.00
343B Richie Sexson Brewers 5.00 12.00
344 Chris Carpenter 12.00 30.00
345 Carlos Zambrano 8.00 20.00
346 Nomar Garciaparra 12.00 30.00
347 Carlos Lee 5.00 12.00
348A Preston Wilson Astros 5.00 12.00
348B Preston Wilson Marlins 5.00 12.00
349 Mariano Rivera 12.00 30.00
350 Ichiro Suzuki 20.00 50.00
351A Mike Piazza Padres 12.00 30.00
351B Mike Piazza Mets 12.00 30.00
352 Jason Schmidt 5.00 12.00
353 Jeff Weaver 5.00 12.00
354 Rocco Baldelli 5.00 12.00
355 Adam Dunn 8.00 20.00
356 Jeromy Burnitz 5.00 12.00
357 Chris Shelton 5.00 12.00
358 Chone Figgins 5.00 12.00
359 Javier Vazquez 5.00 12.00
360 Chipper Jones 12.00 30.00
361 Frank Thomas 12.00 30.00
362 Mark Loretta 5.00 12.00
363 Hideki Matsui 12.00 30.00
364 J.J. Hardy 5.00 12.00
365 Todd Helton 8.00 20.00
366 Reggie Sanders 5.00 12.00
367 Jay Gibbons 5.00 12.00
368 Johnny Estrada 5.00 12.00
369 Grady Sizemore 8.00 20.00
370 Jim Thome 8.00 20.00
371 Ivan Rodriguez 8.00 20.00
372 Jason Bay 5.00 12.00
373 Carl Crawford 8.00 20.00
374 Adrian Beltre 5.00 12.00
375 Derrek Lee 5.00 12.00
376 Miguel Olivo 5.00 12.00
377 Roy Oswalt 8.00 20.00
378 Coco Crisp 5.00 12.00
379 Moises Alou 5.00 12.00

380 Kevin Millwood 5.00 12.00
381 Mark Grudzielanek 5.00 12.00
382 Justin Morneau 12.00 30.00
383 Austin Kearns 5.00 12.00
384 Brad Penny 5.00 12.00
385 Troy Glaus 5.00 12.00
386 Cliff Lee 8.00 20.00
387 Armando Benitez 5.00 12.00
388 Clint Barmes 5.00 12.00
389 Orlando Cabrera 5.00 12.00
390 Jim Edmonds 8.00 20.00
391 Jermaine Dye 5.00 12.00
392 Morgan Ensberg 5.00 12.00
393 Paul LoDuca 5.00 12.00
394 Eric Chavez 5.00 12.00
395 Greg Maddux 20.00 50.00
396 Jack Wilson 5.00 12.00
397 Omar Vizquel 8.00 20.00
398 Joe Nathan 5.00 12.00
399 Bobby Abreu 5.00 12.00
400 Barry Bonds 25.00 60.00
401 Gary Sheffield 5.00 12.00
402 John Patterson 5.00 12.00
403 J.D. Drew 5.00 12.00
404 Bruce Chen 5.00 12.00
405 Johnny Damon 8.00 20.00
406 Aubrey Huff 5.00 12.00
407 Mark Mulder 5.00 12.00
408 Jamie Moyer 5.00 12.00
409 Carlos Guillen 5.00 12.00
410 Andruw Jones 5.00 12.00
411 Jhonny Peralta 5.00 12.00
412 Doug Davis 5.00 12.00
413 Aaron Miles 5.00 12.00
414 Jon Lieber 5.00 12.00
415 Aaron Hill 5.00 12.00
416 Josh Beckett 8.00 20.00
417 Bobby Crosby 5.00 12.00
418 Noah Lowry 5.00 12.00
419 Sidney Ponson 5.00 12.00
420 Luis Castillo 5.00 12.00
421 Brad Wilkerson 5.00 12.00
422 Felix Hernandez 12.00 30.00
423 Vinny Castilla 5.00 12.00
424 Tom Glavine 8.00 20.00
425 Vladimir Guerrero 12.00 30.00
426 Javy Lopez 5.00 12.00
427 Ronnie Belliard 5.00 12.00
428 Dmitri Young 5.00 12.00
429 Johan Santana 12.00 30.00
430A David Ortiz Red Sox 8.00 20.00
430B David Ortiz Twins 8.00 20.00
431 Ben Sheets 5.00 12.00
432 Matt Holliday 12.00 30.00
433 Brian McCann 5.00 12.00
434 Joe Blanton 5.00 12.00
435 Sean Casey 5.00 12.00
436 Brad Lidge 5.00 12.00
437 Chad Tracy 5.00 12.00
438 Brett Myers 5.00 12.00
439 Matt Morris 5.00 12.00
440 Brian Giles 5.00 12.00
441 Zach Duke 5.00 12.00
442 Jose Lopez 5.00 12.00
443 Kris Benson 5.00 12.00
444 Jose Reyes 8.00 20.00
445 Travis Hafner 5.00 12.00
446 Orlando Hernandez 5.00 12.00
447 Edgar Renteria 5.00 12.00
448 Scott Podsednik 5.00 12.00
449 Nick Swisher 12.00 30.00
450 Derek Jeter 30.00 80.00
451 Scott Kazmir 8.00 20.00
452 Hank Blalock 5.00 12.00
453 Jake Westbrook 5.00 12.00
454 Miguel Cabrera 12.00 30.00
455A Ken Griffey Jr. Reds 20.00 50.00
455B Ken Griffey Jr. M's 20.00 50.00
456 Rafael Furcal 5.00 12.00
457 Lance Berkman 8.00 20.00
458 Aramis Ramirez 5.00 12.00
459A Xavier Nady Mets 5.00 12.00
459B Xavier Nady Padres 5.00 12.00
460A Randy Johnson Yanks 12.00 30.00
460B Randy Johnson Astros 12.00 30.00
461 Khalil Greene 5.00 12.00
462 Bartolo Colon 5.00 12.00
463 Mike Lowell 5.00 12.00
464 David DeJesus 5.00 12.00
465 Ryan Howard 20.00 50.00
466 Tim Salmon 5.00 12.00
467 Mark Buehrle 8.00 20.00
468 Curtis Granderson 8.00 20.00
469 Kerry Wood 5.00 12.00
470 Miguel Tejada 8.00 20.00
471 Geoff Jenkins 5.00 12.00
472 Jeremy Reed 5.00 12.00
473 David Eckstein 5.00 12.00
474 Lyle Overbay 5.00 12.00
475 Michael Young 8.00 20.00
476A Nick Johnson Nats 5.00 12.00
476B Nick Johnson Yanks 5.00 12.00
477 Carlos Beltran 5.00 12.00
478 Huston Street 5.00 12.00
479 Brandon Webb 8.00 20.00
480 Phil Nevin 5.00 12.00
481 Ryan Madson 5.00 12.00
482 Jason Giambi 5.00 12.00
483 Angel Berroa 5.00 12.00
484 Casey Blake 5.00 12.00
485 Pat Burrell 5.00 12.00
486 B.J. Ryan 5.00 12.00
487 Torii Hunter 5.00 12.00
488 Garret Anderson 5.00 12.00
489 Chase Utley 12.00 30.00
490 Matt Murton 5.00 12.00
491 Rich Harden 5.00 12.00
492 Garrett Atkins 5.00 12.00
493 Tadahito Iguchi 5.00 12.00
494 Jarrod Washburn 5.00 12.00
495 Carl Everett 5.00 12.00
496 Kameron Loe 5.00 12.00
497 Jorge Cantu 5.00 12.00
498 Chris Young 5.00 12.00
499 Marcus Giles 5.00 12.00
500 Albert Pujols 30.00 80.00
501A Alfonso Soriano Nats 8.00 20.00
501B Alfonso Soriano Yanks 8.00 20.00
502 Randy Winn 5.00 12.00
503 Roy Halladay 12.00 30.00
504 Victor Martinez 8.00 20.00
505 Pedro Martinez 8.00 20.00
506 Rickie Weeks 8.00 20.00
507 Dan Johnson 5.00 12.00
508A Tim Hudson Braves 8.00 20.00
508B Tim Hudson A's 8.00 20.00
509 Mark Prior 8.00 20.00
510 Melvin Mora 5.00 12.00
511 Matt Clement 5.00 12.00
512 Brandon Inge 5.00 12.00
513 Mike Mussina 8.00 20.00
514 Mike Cameron 5.00 12.00
515 Barry Zito 5.00 12.00
516 Luis Gonzalez 5.00 12.00
517 Jose Castillo 5.00 12.00
518 Andy Pettitte 8.00 20.00
519 Wily Mo Pena 5.00 12.00
520 Billy Wagner 5.00 12.00
521 Ervin Santana 5.00 12.00
522 Juan Pierre 5.00 12.00
523 Dan Haren 5.00 12.00
524 Adrian Gonzalez 8.00 20.00
525 Robinson Cano 12.00 30.00
526 Jeff Kent 5.00 12.00
527 Cory Sullivan 5.00 12.00
528 Joe Crede 5.00 12.00
529 John Smoltz 12.00 30.00
530 David Wright 20.00 50.00
531 Chad Cordero 5.00 12.00
532 Scott Rolen 8.00 20.00
533 Edwin Jackson 5.00 12.00
534 Doug Mientkiewicz 5.00 12.00
535 Mark Teixeira 12.00 30.00
536 Kelvim Escobar 5.00 12.00
537 Alex Rios 8.00 20.00
538 Jose Vidro 5.00 12.00
539 Alex Gonzalez 5.00 12.00
540 Yadier Molina 8.00 20.00
541 Ronny Cedeno 5.00 12.00
542 Mark Hendrickson 5.00 12.00
543 Russ Adams 5.00 12.00
544 Chris Capuano 5.00 12.00
545 Raul Ibanez 8.00 20.00
546 Vicente Padilla 5.00 12.00
547 Chris Duffy 5.00 12.00
548 Bengie Molina 5.00 12.00
549 Chien-Ming Wang 8.00 20.00
550 Curt Schilling 8.00 20.00
551 Craig Wilson 5.00 12.00
552 Mike Lieberthal 5.00 12.00
553 Kazuo Matsui 5.00 12.00
554 Jeff Francis 5.00 12.00
555 Brady Clark 5.00 12.00
556 Willy Taveras 5.00 12.00
557 Mike Maroth 5.00 12.00
558 Bernie Williams 8.00 20.00
559 Edwin Encarnacion 5.00 12.00
560 Vernon Wells 5.00 12.00
561A Livan Hernandez Nats 5.00 12.00
561B Livan Hernandez Giants 5.00 12.00
562 Kenny Rogers 5.00 12.00
563 Steve Finley 5.00 12.00
564 Trot Nixon 5.00 12.00
565 Jonny Gomes 5.00 12.00
566 Brandon Phillips 5.00 12.00
567 Shawn Chacon 5.00 12.00
568 Dave Bush 5.00 12.00
569 Jose Guillen 5.00 12.00
570 Gustavo Chacin 5.00 12.00
571 A.Rod Safe at the Plate CL 12.00 30.00
572 Pujols At Bat CL 20.00 50.00
573 Bonds On Deck CL 15.00 40.00
574 Breaking Up Two CL 3.00 8.00
575 Conference On The Mound CL 8.00 20.00
576 Touch Em All CL 12.00 30.00
577 Avoiding The Runner CL 3.00 8.00
578 Bunting The Runner Over CL 3.00 8.00
579 In The Hole CL 5.00 12.00
580 Jeter Steals Third CL 20.00 50.00
581 Nolan Ryan 30.00 80.00
582 Cal Ripken 50.00 120.00
583 Carl Yastrzemski 20.00 50.00
584 Duke Snider 8.00 20.00
585 Tom Seaver 8.00 20.00
586 Mickey Mantle 40.00 100.00
587 Jim Palmer 5.00 12.00
588 Gary Carter 5.00 12.00
589 Stan Musial 20.00 50.00
590 Luis Aparicio 5.00 12.00
591 Prince Fielder 25.00 60.00
592 Conor Jackson 10.00 25.00
593 Jeremy Hermida 6.00 15.00
594 Jeff Mathis 6.00 15.00
595 Alay Soler 6.00 15.00
596 Ryan Spilborghs 6.00 15.00
597 Chuck James 6.00 15.00
598 Josh Barfield 6.00 15.00
599 Ian Kinsler 20.00 50.00
600 Val Majewski 6.00 15.00
601 Brian Slocum 6.00 15.00
602 Matt Kemp 30.00 80.00
603 Nate McLouth 6.00 15.00
604 Sean Marshall 10.00 25.00
605 Brian Bannister 6.00 15.00
606 Ryan Zimmerman 30.00 80.00
607 Kendry Morales 15.00 40.00
608 Jonathan Papelbon 30.00 80.00
609 Matt Cain 15.00 40.00
610 Anderson Hernandez 6.00 15.00
611 Jose Capellan 6.00 15.00
612 Lastings Milledge 6.00 15.00
613 Francisco Liriano 15.00 40.00
614 Hanley Ramirez 15.00 40.00
615 Brian Anderson 6.00 15.00
616 Reggie Abercrombie 6.00 15.00
617 Erick Aybar 6.00 15.00
618 James Loney 10.00 25.00
619 Joel Zumaya 15.00 40.00
620 Travis Ishikawa 6.00 15.00
621 Jason Kubel 6.00 15.00
622 Drew Meyer 6.00 15.00
623 Kenji Johjima 15.00 40.00
624 Fausto Carmona 6.00 15.00
625 Nick Markakis 15.00 40.00
626 John Rheinecker 6.00 15.00
627 Melky Cabrera 10.00 25.00
628 Michael Pelfrey 15.00 40.00
629 Dan Uggla 15.00 40.00
630 Justin Verlander 50.00 120.00

2006 Topps Turkey Red Red

*RED 316-580: 1X TO 2X BASIC
*RED 316-580: .2X TO .5X BASIC SP
*RED 581-590: .5X TO 1.2X BASIC RET
*RED 591-630: .6X TO 1.5X BASIC ROOKIE
ONE RED OR OTHER PARALLEL PER PACK
THERE ARE NO SP'S IN THIS SET

2006 Topps Turkey Red Suede

STATED ODDS 1:1910 HOBBY
STATED PRINT RUN 1 SERIAL #'d SET
NO PRICING DUE TO SCARCITY

2006 Topps Turkey Red White

*WHITE 316-580: 2X TO 5X BASIC
*WHITE 316-580: .25X TO .6X BASIC SP
*WHITE 581-590: .6X TO 1.5X BASIC RET
*WHITE 591-630: .75X TO 2X BASIC ROOKIE
STATED ODDS 1:4 HOBBY/RETAIL
THERE ARE NO SP'S IN THIS SET

2006 Topps Turkey Red Autographs

GROUP A ODDS 1:870 H, 1:880 R
GROUP B ODDS 1:165 H, 1:170 R
EXCHANGE DEADLINE 09/30/08
BM Brian McCann B 10.00 25.00
BMC Brandon McCarthy B 4.00 10.00
CB Clint Barmes B 4.00 10.00
CJ Chipper Jones A 40.00 80.00
DJ Dan Johnson B 4.00 10.00
DL Derrek Lee A 15.00 40.00
DW David Wright A 60.00 120.00
GA Garrett Atkins B 4.00 10.00
JB Josh Barfield B 6.00 15.00
JG Jonny Gomes A 15.00 40.00
KJ Kenji Johjima A 30.00 60.00
MC Miguel Cabrera A 30.00 60.00
MM Mike Morse B 4.00 10.00
PL Paul LoDuca A 15.00 40.00
RC Robinson Cano A 50.00 100.00
RH Ryan Howard A 60.00 120.00
RO Roy Oswalt A 15.00 40.00

2006 Topps Turkey Red Autographs Black

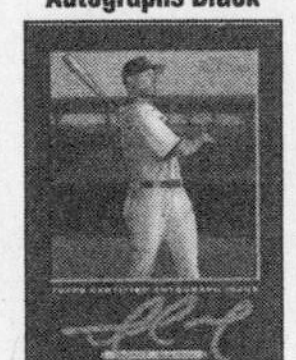

*BLACK GROUP B: .6X TO 1.5X BASIC
GROUP A ODDS 1:6000 H, 1:6200 R
GROUP B ODDS 1:1185 H, 1:1200 R
GROUP A PRINT RUN 15 SERIAL #'d SETS
GROUP B PRINT RUN 99 SERIAL #'d SETS
NO GROUP A PRICING DUE TO SCARCITY
EXCHANGE DEADLINE 09/30/08

2006 Topps Turkey Red Autographs Gold

GROUP A ODDS 1:17,000 H, 1:21,000 R
GROUP B ODDS 1:4500 H, 1:4600 R
GROUP A PRINT RUN 5 SERIAL #'d SETS
GROUP B PRINT RUN 25 SERIAL #'d SETS
NO PRICING DUE TO SCARCITY
EXCHANGE DEADLINE 09/30/08

2006 Topps Turkey Red Autographs Red

*RED GROUP A: .4X TO 1X BASIC
*RED GROUP B: .4X TO 1X BASIC
GROUP A ODDS 1:1800 H, 1:1850 R
GROUP B ODDS 1:245 H, 1:250 R
GROUP A PRINT RUN 50 SERIAL #'d SETS
GROUP B PRINT RUN 475 SERIAL #'d SETS
EXCHANGE DEADLINE 09/30/08
DW David Wright A/50 60.00 120.00
KJ Kenji Johjima A/50 40.00 80.00
MC Miguel Cabrera A/50 20.00 50.00
PL Paul LoDuca A/50 12.50 30.00

2006 Topps Turkey Red Autographs Suede

STATED ODDS 1:28,300 HOBBY
STATED PRINT RUN 1 SERIAL #'d SET
NO PRICING DUE TO SCARCITY
EXCHANGE DEADLINE 09/30/08

2006 Topps Turkey Red Autographs White

*WHITE GROUP B: .5X TO 1.2X BASIC
GROUP A ODDS 1:3600 H, 1:3800 R
GROUP B ODDS 1:585 H, 1:600 R
GROUP A PRINT RUN 25 SERIAL #'d SETS
GROUP B PRINT RUN 200 SERIAL #'d SETS
NO GROUP A PRICING DUE TO SCARCITY
EXCHANGE DEADLINE 09/30/08

2006 Topps Turkey Red B-18 Blankets

STATED ODDS 1:2 JUMBO
REPURCHASED ODDS 1:159 JUMBO
AR1 Alex Rodriguez White 5.00 12.00
AR2 Alex Rodriguez Blue 5.00 12.00
BB1 Barry Bonds White 6.00 15.00
BB2 Barry Bonds Red 6.00 15.00
DL1 Derrek Lee White 1.25 3.00
DL2 Derrek Lee Red 1.25 3.00
DO1 David Ortiz White 2.00 5.00
DO2 David Ortiz Orange 2.00 5.00
HM1 Hideki Matsui White 3.00 8.00
HM2 Hideki Matsui Blue 3.00 8.00
IS1 Ichiro Suzuki White 5.00 12.00
IS2 Ichiro Suzuki Green 5.00 12.00
KJ1 Kenji Johjima White 3.00 8.00
KJ2 Kenji Johjima Green 3.00 8.00
MM1 Mickey Mantle White 10.00 25.00
MM2 Mickey Mantle Blue 10.00 25.00
MR1 Manny Ramirez White 3.00 8.00
MR2 Manny Ramirez Orange 3.00 8.00
VG1 Vladimir Guerrero White 3.00 8.00
VG2 Vladimir Guerrero Green 3.00 8.00
NNO Repurchased B-18 Blanket

2006 Topps Turkey Red Cabinet

STATED ODDS 1:2 JUMBO
REPURCHASED ODDS 1:4340 JUMBO
SUEDE ODDS 1:634 JUMBO
SUEDE PRINT RUN 1 SERIAL #'d SET
NO SUEDE PRICING DUE TO SCARCITY
AJ Andruw Jones 6.00 15.00
AP Albert Pujols 12.50 30.00
AR Alex Rodriguez 10.00 25.00
AS Alfonso Soriano 4.00 10.00
BB Barry Bonds 10.00 25.00
CC Carl Crawford 4.00 10.00
CCA Chris Carpenter 4.00 10.00
CD Carlos Delgado 4.00 10.00
CY Carl Yastrzemski 10.00 25.00
DJ Derek Jeter 12.50 30.00
DL Derrek Lee 4.00 10.00
DO David Ortiz 6.00 15.00
DS Duke Snider 6.00 15.00
DW David Wright 10.00 25.00
FL Francisco Liriano 6.00 15.00
GC Gary Carter 4.00 10.00
HM Hideki Matsui 6.00 15.00
IR Ivan Rodriguez 6.00 15.00
IS Ichiro Suzuki 10.00 25.00
JB Josh Barfield 4.00 10.00
JBE Josh Beckett 4.00 10.00
JC Jorge Cantu 4.00 10.00
JD Johnny Damon 6.00 15.00
JF Jeff Francoeur 6.00 15.00
JG Jonny Gomes 4.00 10.00
JP Jake Peavy 4.00 10.00
JPA Jonathan Papelbon 10.00 25.00
JR Jimmy Rollins 4.00 10.00
JS Johan Santana 6.00 15.00
JT Jim Thome 6.00 15.00
KG Ken Griffey Jr. 10.00 25.00
MM Mickey Mantle 30.00 60.00
MP Mike Piazza 6.00 15.00
NG Nomar Garciaparra 6.00 15.00
NJ Nick Johnson 4.00 10.00
NM Nick Markakis 6.00 15.00
NR Nolan Ryan 15.00 40.00
PF Prince Fielder 6.00 15.00
PM Pedro Martinez 6.00 15.00
RH Ryan Howard 10.00 25.00
RJ Randy Johnson 6.00 15.00
TG Troy Glaus 4.00 10.00
NNO Repurchased T-3 Cabinet

2006 Topps Turkey Red Cabinet Auto Relics

STATED ODDS 1:86 JUMBO
NO PRICING DUE TO SCARCITY
EXCHANGE DEADLINE 09/30/08
BM Brian McCann Bat
CB Clint Barmes Jsy
CJO Chipper Jones Jsy
DL Derrek Lee Jsy
DW David Wright Jsy
NS Nick Swisher Bat
PL Paul LoDuca Jsy
RC Robinson Cano Bat
RO Roy Oswalt Jsy

2006 Topps Turkey Red Cabinet Auto Relics Suede

STATED ODDS 1:1730 JUMBO
STATED PRINT RUN 1 SERIAL #'d SET
NO PRICING DUE TO SCARCITY
EXCHANGE DEADLINE 09/30/08

2006 Topps Turkey Red Cabinet Auto Relics Dual

STATED ODDS 1:1368 JUMBO
NO PRICING DUE TO SCARCITY
EXCHANGE DEADLINE 09/30/08
HL Ryan Howard Bat
Derrek Lee Jsy
RB Alex Rodriguez Jsy
Barry Bonds Pants
WC David Wright Jsy
Robinson Cano Bat

2006 Topps Turkey Red Cabinet Auto Relics Dual Suede

STATED ODDS 1:6520 JUMBO
STATED PRINT RUN 1 SERIAL #'d SET
NO PRICING DUE TO SCARCITY

2006 Topps Turkey Red Relics

GROUP A ODDS 1:330 H, 1:335 R
GROUP B ODDS 1:205 H, 1:211 R
GROUP C-D ODDS 1:50 H, 1:54 R
GROUP E ODDS 1:88 H, 1:88 R
AJ Andruw Jones Jsy D 3.00 8.00
AP Albert Pujols Jsy D 8.00 20.00
APE Andy Pettitte Jsy B 3.00 8.00
AR Alex Rodriguez Jsy C 8.00 20.00
BL Brad Lidge Jsy C 3.00 8.00
BR Brian Roberts Jsy E 3.00 8.00
BW Bernie Williams Pants C 3.00 8.00
CB Carlos Beltran Jsy C 3.00 8.00
CBA Clint Barmes Jsy A 3.00 8.00
CC Chris Carpenter Jsy D 3.00 8.00
CD Carlos Delgado Bat A 3.00 8.00
CJ Chipper Jones Jsy C 5.00 12.00
DL Derrek Lee Jsy B 3.00 8.00
DO David Ortiz Jsy D 5.00 12.00
DW David Wright Jsy C 6.00 15.00
DWI Dontrelle Willis Jsy D 3.00 8.00
EC Eric Chavez Pants D 3.00 8.00
HB Hank Blalock Jsy D 3.00 8.00
HM Hideki Matsui Jsy C 5.00 12.00
IS Ichiro Suzuki Jsy A 8.00 20.00
JC Jose Contreras Jsy D 3.00 8.00
JD Johnny Damon Bat A 3.00 8.00
JE Jim Edmonds Jsy C 3.00 8.00
JF Jeff Francoeur Jsy E 5.00 12.00
JG Jon Garland Pants D 3.00 8.00
JH Jeremy Hermida Bat A 3.00 8.00
JM Joe Mauer Jsy E 3.00 8.00
JR Jose Reyes Jsy C 3.00 8.00
JS Johan Santana Jsy B 3.00 8.00
LB Lance Berkman Jsy D 3.00 8.00
MC Miguel Cabrera Jsy C 3.00 8.00
ME Morgan Ensberg Jsy E 3.00 8.00
MM Mike Mussina Pants B 3.00 8.00
MP Mike Piazza Bat A 5.00 12.00
MR Manny Ramirez Pants E 3.00 8.00
MRI Mariano Rivera Jsy C 5.00 12.00
MT Mark Teixeira Jsy D 3.00 8.00
MY Michael Young Jsy C 3.00 8.00
PK Paul Konerko Pants C 3.00 8.00
PL Paul LoDuca Jsy D 3.00 8.00
PM Pedro Martinez Jsy C 3.00 8.00
RC Robinson Cano Bat C 5.00 12.00
RH Ryan Howard Bat A 8.00 20.00
RHA Roy Halladay Jsy E 3.00 8.00
RIH Rich Harden Jsy C 3.00 8.00
RO Roy Oswalt Jsy B 3.00 8.00
TH Torii Hunter Jsy E 3.00 8.00
VG Vladimir Guerrero Jsy D 5.00 12.00

2006 Topps Turkey Red Relics Black

*BLACK: .75X TO 2X BASIC
STATED ODDS 1:485 H, 1:500 R
STATED PRINT RUN 50 SERIAL #'d SETS

2006 Topps Turkey Red Relics Gold

STATED ODDS 1:975 H, 1:1000 R
STATED PRINT RUN 25 SERIAL #'d SETS
NO PRICING DUE TO SCARCITY

2006 Topps Turkey Red Relics Red

*RED: .5X TO 1.2X BASIC
STATED ODDS 1:160 H, 1:170 R
STATED PRINT RUN 150 SERIAL #'d SETS

2006 Topps Turkey Red Relics Suede

STATED ODDS 1:13,250 HOBBY
STATED PRINT RUN 1 SERIAL #'d SET
NO PRICING DUE TO SCARCITY

2006 Topps Turkey Red Relics White

*WHITE: .6X TO 1.5X BASIC
STATED ODDS 1:245 H, 1:250 R
STATED PRINT RUN 99 SERIAL #'d SETS

2007 Topps Turkey Red

This 200-card set was released in September, 2007. The set was issued in both retail and hobby versions. The hobby packs consisted of eight cards (with an $4 SRP) which came 24 packs to a box and eight boxes to a case. Some of the cards in this set were either short printed or had an ad back variation. Both the SP's, which are explicitly noted in our checklist and the cards with the ad backs were inserted into packs at a stated rate of one in four hobby or retail packs.

COMPLETE SET (200) 150.00 200.00
COMP.SET w/o SP's (150) 12.50 30.00
COMMON CARD (1-186) .12 .30
COMMON RC (1-186) .15 .40
COMMON SP (1-186) 2.50 6.00
SP ODDS 1:4 HOBBY, 1:4 RETAIL
COMMON AD BACK (1-186) 2.50 6.00
AD BACK ODDS 1:4 HOBBY, 1:4 RETAIL
1 Ryan Howard .50 1.25
1b Ryan Howard Ad Back SP 4.00 10.00
2 Dontrelle Willis .12 .30
3 Matt Cain .20 .50
4 John Maine .12 .30
5 Cole Hamels .30 .75
6 Corey Patterson .12 .30
7 Mickey Mantle SP 10.00 25.00
8 Servin Up Strikes Johan Santana CL .30 .75
9 Josh Beckett .20 .50
10 Jimmy Rollins .20 .50
11 Kenji Johjima .30 .75
12 Orlando Hernandez .12 .30
13 Jorge Posada Play at the Plate CL .20 .50
14 Ivan Rodriguez .20 .50
15 Ichiro Suzuki .50 1.25
15b Ichiro Suzuki Ad Back SP 4.00 10.00
16 Stand Up Double Ken Griffey CL .50 1.25
17 Stephen Drew .12 .30
18 B.J. Upton .12 .30
19 Mickey Mantle 1.00 2.50
20 Alex Rodriguez .50 1.25
20b Alex Rodriguez Ad Back SP 4.00 10.00
21 Adam Dunn .20 .50
22 Adam Lind SP (RC) 2.50 6.00
23 Adrian Gonzalez .20 .50
24 Akinori Iwamura RC .40 1.00
25 Albert Pujols .75 2.00
25b Albert Pujols Ad Back SP 4.00 10.00
26 Frank Thomas .30 .75
27 Roy Halladay .30 .75
28 Alejandro De Aza RC .25 .60
29 Alex Gordon RC .50 1.25
30 Barry Bonds .60 1.50
31 Andrew Miller RC .40 1.00
32 Andruw Jones .12 .30
33 Kurt Suzuki SP (RC) 2.50 6.00
34 Mickey Mantle 1.00 2.50
35 Andy Pettitte .20 .50
36 Tadahito Iguchi .12 .30
37 Edgar Renteria .12 .30
38 Tim Hudson .20 .50
39 Micah Owings (RC) .15 .40
40 Chipper Jones .30 .75
40b Chipper Jones Ad Back SP 3.00 8.00
41 Barry Zito .12 .30
42 Dice-K Daisuke Matsuzaka CL .50 1.25
43 Jarrod Saltalamacchia SP (RC) 2.50 6.00
44 Bill Hall .12 .30
45 Billy Butler (RC) .25 .60
46 Billy Wagner .12 .30
47 Rich Harden SP 2.50 6.00
48 Prince Albert Albert Pujols CL .75 2.00
49 Brandon Inge .12 .30
50 Jason Giambi .12 .30
51 Brandon Webb .20 .50
52 Brandon Wood (RC) .15 .40
53 Swiping Second Carl Crawford CL .20 .50
54 Brian Giles .12 .30
55 Josh Hamilton (RC) .60 1.50
56 Chase Utley Ad Back SP 3.00 8.00
57 Miguel Montero (RC) .15 .40
58 Carl Crawford .20 .50
59 Carlos Beltran .12 .30
60 Mariano Rivera .30 .75
61 Carlos Delgado .12 .30
62 Carlos Lee SP 2.50 6.00
63 Carlos Zambrano SP 2.50 6.00
64 Miguel Tejada .20 .50
65 Mike Cameron .12 .30
66 Chase Utley SP 3.00 8.00
67 Chase Wright RC .40 1.00
68 Chien-Ming Wang .20 .50
69 Nick Swisher .30 .75
70 David Wright .50 1.25
71 Mike Piazza SP 3.00 8.00
72 Chris Carpenter .30 .75
73 Mark Buehrle SP 2.50 6.00
74 Torii Hunter SP 2.50 6.00
75 Tyler Clippard (RC) .25 .60
76 Nick Markakis .30 .75
77 Mickey Mantle 1.00 2.50
78 Curt Schilling .20 .50
79 Curtis Granderson .20 .50
80 Craig Biggio .20 .50
81 Juan Pierre .12 .30
82 Dallas Braden SP RC 2.50 6.00
83 Dan Haren SP 3.00 8.00
84 Dan Uggla .20 .50
85 Danny Putnam (RC) .15 .40
86 David DeJesus .12 .30
87 David Eckstein .12 .30
88 Tim Lincecum RC 2.50 6.00
89 Johnny Damon SP 2.50 6.00
90 Justin Morneau .30 .75
91 Delmon Young (RC) .25 .60
92 Homer Bailey (RC) .25 .60
93 Carlos Gomez RC .25 .60
94 Josh Fields SP (RC) 2.50 6.00
95 Derek Jeter .75 2.00
95b Derek Jeter Ad Back SP 6.00 15.00
96 Derek Lee .12 .30
97 Don Kelly (RC) .15 .40
98 Doug Slaten RC .15 .40
99 Dustin Moseley .12 .30
100 Gary Sheffield .12 .30
101 Orlando Hudson SP 2.50 6.00
102 Elijah Dukes RC .25 .60
103 Eric Byrnes SP 2.50 6.00
104 Eric Chavez .12 .30
105 Phil Hughes (RC) .75 2.00
105b Phil Hughes Ad Back SP (RC) 4.00 10.00
106 Felix Hernandez SP 2.50 6.00
106b Felix Hernandez Ad Back SP 2.50 6.00
107 Mickey Mantle 1.00 2.50
108 Felix Pie (RC) .15 .40
109 The Captain Derek Jeter CL .75 2.00
110 Daisuke Matsuzaka RC .60 1.50

110b Daisuke Matsuzaka Ad Back SP RC 6.00 15.00
111 Francisco Rodriguez .20 .50
112 Ramon Hernandez .12 .30
113 Randy Johnson .30 .75
114 Gary Matthews .12 .30
115 Prince Fielder .20 .50
116 Vladdy Goes Yard Vladimir Guerrero CL .30 .75
117 Mickey Mantle 1.00 2.50
118 Hideki Matsui .20 .50
119 Hideki Okajima RC .75 2.00
120 Manny Ramirez .30 .75
121 Hunter Pence SP (RC) 6.00 15.00
122 Roy Oswalt .20 .50
123 Josh Willingham SP 2.50 6.00
124 Tom Gordon SP 2.50 6.00
125 Michael Young .20 .50
126 J.D. Drew .12 .30
127 Ryan Zimmerman .20 .50
128 James Shields SP 3.00 8.00
129 Jack Wilson .12 .30
130 David Ortiz .20 .50
130b David Ortiz Ad Back SP 3.00 8.00
131 Jose Jose Jose Jose Jose Reyes CL .20 .50
132 Jamie Vermilyea RC .15 .40
133 Jason Bay .20 .50
134 Scott Kazmir SP 2.50 6.00
135 Jason Isringhausen SP 3.00 8.00
136 Jason Marquis SP 2.50 6.00
137 Jason Schmidt .12 .30
138 Shawn Green .12 .30
139 Jeff Francoeur SP 3.00 8.00
140 Alfonso Soriano .20 .50
141 Kevin Kouzmanoff (RC) .15 .40
142 Jered Weaver .20 .50
143 Todd Helton SP 2.50 6.00
144 Jermaine Dye .12 .30
145 Jim Thome .20 .50
146 Tom Glavine SP 2.50 6.00
147 Joe Mauer .30 .75
148 Joe Nathan .12 .30
149 Joe Smith RC .15 .40
150 Ken Griffey Jr. .50 1.25
150b Ken Griffey Jr. Ad Back SP 4.00 10.00
151 Grady Sizemore .20 .50
152 Sammy Sosa SP 3.00 8.00
153 Andy LaRoche (RC) .15 .40
154 Travis Buck (RC) .15 .40
155 Alex Rios .20 .50
156 Travis Hafner .12 .30
157 Jake Peavy .12 .30
158 Jeff Kent .12 .30
159 Johan Santana .30 .75
159b Johan Santana Ad Back SP 2.50 6.00
160 Ivan Rodriguez .20 .50
161 Trevor Hoffman .20 .50
162 Troy Glaus .12 .30
163 Troy Tulowitzki (RC) 1.00 2.50
164 Jorge Posada .20 .50
165 Kei Igawa SP RC 3.00 8.00
166 Jose Reyes .20 .50
167 Mickey Mantle 1.00 2.50
168 Hit Streak Chase Utley CL .30 .75
169 Justin Verlander .40 1.00
170 Hanley Ramirez .30 .75
171 Kelly Johnson SP 2.50 6.00
172 Kelvin Jimenez RC .15 .40
173 Roger Clemens .40 1.00
174 Khalil Greene SP 2.50 6.00
175 Lance Berkman .20 .50
176 Turning Two Hanley Ramirez CL .30 .75
177 Kyle Kendrick RC .40 1.00
178 Magglio Ordonez .20 .50
179 Marcus Giles SP 2.50 6.00
180 Miguel Cabrera .30 .75
180b Miguel Cabrera Ad Back SP 2.50 6.00
181 Mark Teahen .12 .30
182 Mark Teixeira SP 2.50 6.00
183 Matt Chico SP (RC) 2.50 6.00
184 Matt Holliday .30 .75
185 Vladimir Guerrero .30 .75
185b Vladimir Guerrero Ad Back SP 3.00 8.00
186 Yovani Gallardo (RC) .40 1.00

2007 Topps Turkey Red Chrome

STATED ODDS 1:4 HOBBY,1:7 RETAIL
STATED PRINT RUN 1999 SER.#'d SETS
SKIP NUMBERED SET
1 Ryan Howard 4.00 10.00
2 Dontrelle Willis 1.00 2.50
4 John Maine 1.00 2.50
5 Cole Hamels 2.50 6.00
9 Josh Beckett 1.50 4.00
11 Kenji Johjima 2.50 6.00
12 Orlando Hernandez 1.00 2.50
15 Ichiro Suzuki 4.00 10.00
17 Stephen Drew 1.00 2.50
20 Alex Rodriguez 4.00 10.00
21 Adam Dunn 1.50 4.00
24 Akinori Iwamura 2.50 6.00
25 Albert Pujols 6.00 15.00
29 Alex Gordon 3.00 8.00
30 Barry Bonds 5.00 12.00
31 Andrew Miller 2.50 6.00
32 Andruw Jones 1.00 2.50
34 Mickey Mantle 8.00 20.00
35 Andy Pettitte 1.50 4.00
36 Tadahito Iguchi 1.00 2.50
39 Micah Owings 1.00 2.50
40 Chipper Jones 2.50 6.00
41 Barry Zito 1.00 2.50
45 Billy Butler 1.50 4.00
46 Billy Wagner 1.00 2.50
51 Brandon Webb 1.50 4.00
52 Brandon Wood 1.00 2.50
55 Josh Hamilton 4.00 10.00
59 Carlos Beltran 1.00 2.50
60 Mariano Rivera 2.50 6.00
61 Carlos Delgado 1.00 2.50
64 Miguel Tejada 1.50 4.00
68 Chien-Ming Wang 1.50 4.00
70 David Wright 4.00 10.00
72 Chris Carpenter 2.50 6.00
75 Tyler Clippard 1.50 4.00
76 Nick Markakis 2.50 6.00
77 Mickey Mantle 8.00 20.00
81 Juan Pierre 1.00 2.50
84 Dan Uggla 1.50 4.00
85 Danny Putnam 1.00 2.50
87 David Eckstein 1.00 2.50
88 Tim Lincecum 15.00 40.00
90 Justin Morneau 2.50 6.00
91 Delmon Young 1.50 4.00
93 Carlos Gomez 1.50 4.00
95 Derek Jeter 6.00 15.00
96 Derek Lee 1.00 2.50
97 Don Kelly 1.00 2.50
98 Doug Slaten 1.00 2.50
99 Dustin Moseley 1.00 2.50
100 Gary Sheffield 1.00 2.50
102 Elijah Dukes 1.50 4.00
104 Eric Chavez 1.00 2.50
105 Phil Hughes 5.00 12.00
107 Mickey Mantle 8.00 20.00
108 Felix Pie 1.00 2.50
110 Daisuke Matsuzaka 4.00 10.00
111 Francisco Rodriguez 1.50 4.00
113 Randy Johnson 2.50 6.00
114 Gary Matthews 1.00 2.50
115 Prince Fielder 1.50 4.00
117 Mickey Mantle 8.00 20.00
119 Hideki Okajima 5.00 12.00
120 Manny Ramirez 2.50 6.00
122 Roy Oswalt 1.50 4.00
125 Michael Young 1.50 4.00
126 J.D. Drew 1.00 2.50
127 Ryan Zimmerman 1.50 4.00
130 David Ortiz 1.50 4.00
133 Jason Bay 1.50 4.00
137 Jason Schmidt 1.00 2.50
140 Alfonso Soriano 1.50 4.00
141 Kevin Kouzmanoff 1.00 2.50
142 Jered Weaver 1.50 4.00
144 Jermaine Dye 1.00 2.50
147 Joe Mauer 2.50 6.00
149 Joe Smith 1.00 2.50
150 Ken Griffey Jr. 4.00 10.00
151 Grady Sizemore 1.50 4.00
154 Travis Buck 1.00 2.50
155 Alex Rios 1.50 4.00
158 Jeff Kent 1.00 2.50
159 Johan Santana 2.50 6.00
160 Ivan Rodriguez 1.50 4.00
162 Troy Glaus 1.00 2.50
163 Troy Tulowitzki 6.00 15.00
166 Jose Reyes 1.50 4.00
167 Mickey Mantle 8.00 20.00
169 Justin Verlander 3.00 8.00
170 Hanley Ramirez 2.50 6.00
172 Kelvin Jimenez 1.00 2.50
173 Roger Clemens 3.00 8.00
175 Lance Berkman 1.50 4.00
177 Kyle Kendrick 2.50 6.00
178 Magglio Ordonez 1.50 4.00
180 Miguel Cabrera 2.50 6.00
181 Mark Teahen 1.00 2.50
185 Vladimir Guerrero 2.50 6.00
186 Yovani Gallardo 2.50 6.00

2007 Topps Turkey Red Chrome Refractors

*CHROME REF: .5X TO 1.2X BASIC CHROME
STATED ODDS 1:8 HOBBY,1:16 RETAIL
STATED PRINT RUN 999 SER.#'d SETS
SKIP NUMBERED SET

2007 Topps Turkey Red Chrome Black Refractors

*BLACK REF: 1X TO 2.5X BASIC CHROME
STATED ODDS 1:43 HOBBY
STATED PRINT RUN 99 SER.#'d SETS
SKIP NUMBERED SET

2007 Topps Turkey Red Cabinet

STATED ODDS 1:2 HOB.BOXLOADER
AD Adam Dunn 2.00 5.00
AG Alex Gordon 4.00 10.00
AI Akinori Iwamura 3.00 8.00
AJ Andruw Jones 1.25 3.00
AP Albert Pujols 8.00 20.00
AR Alex Rodriguez 5.00 12.00

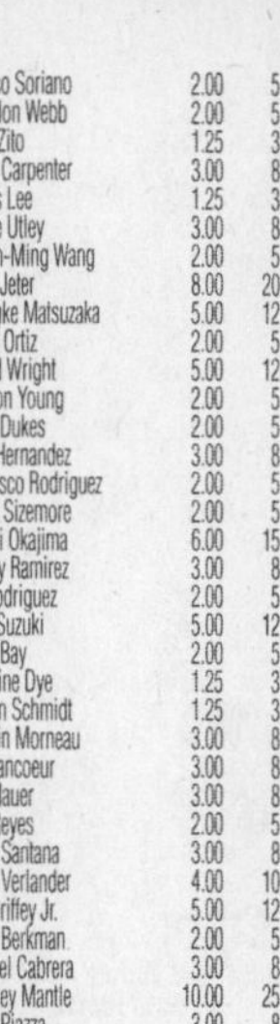

AS Alfonso Soriano 2.00 5.00
BW Brandon Webb 2.00 5.00
BZ Barry Zito 1.25 3.00
CC Chris Carpenter 3.00 8.00
CL Carlos Lee 1.25 3.00
CU Chase Utley 3.00 8.00
CW Chien-Ming Wang 2.00 5.00
DJ Derek Jeter 8.00 20.00
DM Daisuke Matsuzaka 5.00 12.00
DO David Ortiz 2.00 5.00
DW David Wright 5.00 12.00
DY Delmon Young 2.00 5.00
ED Elijah Dukes 2.00 5.00
FH Felix Hernandez 3.00 8.00
FR Francisco Rodriguez 2.00 5.00
GS Grady Sizemore 2.00 5.00
HO Hideki Okajima 6.00 15.00
HR Hanley Ramirez 3.00 8.00
IR Ivan Rodriguez 2.00 5.00
IS Ichiro Suzuki 5.00 12.00
JB Jason Bay 2.00 5.00
JD Jermaine Dye 1.25 3.00
JDS Jason Schmidt 1.25 3.00
JEM Justin Morneau 3.00 8.00
JF Jeff Francoeur 3.00 8.00
JM Joe Mauer 3.00 8.00
JR Jose Reyes 2.00 5.00
JS Johan Santana 3.00 8.00
JV Justin Verlander 4.00 10.00
KG Ken Griffey Jr. 5.00 12.00
LB Lance Berkman 2.00 5.00
MC Miguel Cabrera 3.00 8.00
MM Mickey Mantle 10.00 25.00
MP Mike Piazza 3.00 8.00
MR Manny Ramirez 3.00 8.00
MT Miguel Tejada 2.00 5.00
MY Michael Young 2.00 5.00
NM Nick Markakis 3.00 8.00
PF Prince Fielder 2.00 5.00
RC Roger Clemens 4.00 10.00
RH Ryan Howard 5.00 12.00
RZ Ryan Zimmerman 2.00 5.00
SD Stephen Drew 1.25 3.00
TT Troy Tulowitzki 8.00 20.00
VG Vladimir Guerrero 3.00 8.00

2007 Topps Turkey Red Cabinet Dick Perez Autographs

STATED ODDS 1:14 HOB.BOXLOADER
STATED PRINT RUN 25 SER.#'d SETS
CARDS FEATURE DICK PEREZ AUTO
NO PRICING DUE TO SCARCITY

2007 Topps Turkey Red Chromographs

GROUP A ODDS 1:3700 HOBBY/RETAIL
GROUP B ODDS 1:292 HOBBY/RETAIL
GROUP C ODDS 1:194 HOBBY/RETAIL
GROUP D ODDS 1:177 HOBBY/RETAIL
NO GROUP A PRICING AVAILABLE
EXCH DEADLINE 9/30/2009
AG Alex Gordon D 10.00 25.00
AK Austin Kearns D 4.00 10.00
AR Alex Rodriguez A
BJ Bobby Jenks C 10.00 25.00
BW Brad Wilkerson B 3.00 8.00
CAH Clay Hensley C 3.00 8.00
CG Curtis Granderson B 30.00 60.00
CH Cole Hamels C 8.00 20.00
CJ Chuck James B 4.00 10.00
DE Darin Erstad B 4.00 10.00
DU Dan Uggla D 6.00 15.00
DW David Wright A
EC Eric Chavez B 6.00 15.00
FP Felix Pie C 6.00 15.00
GS Gary Sheffield A
HCK Hong-Chih Kuo C 6.00 15.00
HR Hanley Ramirez C 12.50 30.00
JB Jason Bay A
JD Johnny Damon A
JM John Maine C 10.00 25.00
JP Jake Peavy A
JZ Joel Zumaya D 6.00 15.00
LM Lastings Milledge D 6.00 15.00
MC Melky Cabrera D 10.00 25.00
MG Mike Gonzalez C 3.00 8.00
NM Nick Markakis D 6.00 15.00
NR Nate Robertson C 6.00 15.00
PL Paul LoDuca B 4.00 10.00
RC Robinson Cano B 15.00 40.00
RH Ryan Howard A
RJH Rich Hill D 4.00 10.00
RM Rob Mackowiak B 3.00 8.00
RNM Russell Martin D 10.00 25.00
SC Sean Casey B 10.00 25.00
SP Scott Podsednik B 3.00 8.00
SV Shane Victorino C 15.00 40.00
TG Tony Gwynn Jr. B 6.00 15.00
WN Wil Nieves B 6.00 15.00

2007 Topps Turkey Red Presidents

COMPLETE SET (43) 60.00 150.00
STATED ODDS 1:12 HOBBY, 1:12 RETAIL
TRP1 George Washington 2.00 5.00
TRP2 John Adams 1.50 4.00

TRP3 Thomas Jefferson 1.50 4.00
TRP4 James Madison 1.50 4.00
TRP5 James Monroe 1.50 4.00
TRP6 John Quincy Adams 1.50 4.00
TRP7 Andrew Jackson 1.50 4.00
TRP8 Martin Van Buren 1.50 4.00
TRP9 William H. Harrison 1.50 4.00
TRP10 John Tyler 1.50 4.00
TRP11 James K. Polk 1.50 4.00
TRP12 Zachary Taylor 1.50 4.00
TRP13 Millard Fillmore 1.50 4.00
TRP14 Franklin Pierce 1.50 4.00
TRP15 James Buchanan 1.50 4.00
TRP16 Abraham Lincoln 2.00 5.00
TRP17 Andrew Johnson 1.50 4.00
TRP18 Ulysses S. Grant 1.50 4.00
TRP19 Rutherford B. Hayes 1.50 4.00
TRP20 James Garfield 1.50 4.00
TRP21 Chester A. Arthur 1.50 4.00
TRP22 Grover Cleveland 1.50 4.00
TRP23 Benjamin Harrison 1.50 4.00
TRP24 Grover Cleveland 1.50 4.00
TRP25 William McKinley 1.50 4.00
TRP26 Theodore Roosevelt 1.50 4.00
TRP27 William H. Taft 1.50 4.00
TRP28 Woodrow Wilson 1.50 4.00
TRP29 Warren G. Harding 1.50 4.00
TRP30 Calvin Coolidge 1.50 4.00
TRP31 Herbert Hoover 1.50 4.00
TRP32 Franklin D. Roosevelt 1.50 4.00
TRP33 Harry S. Truman 1.50 4.00
TRP34 Dwight D. Eisenhower 1.50 4.00
TRP35 John F. Kennedy 2.00 5.00
TRP36 Lyndon B. Johnson 1.50 4.00
TRP37 Richard Nixon 1.50 4.00
TRP38 Gerald Ford 1.50 4.00
TRP39 Jimmy Carter 1.50 4.00
TRP40 Ronald Reagan 2.00 5.00
TRP41 George H. W. Bush 2.00 5.00
TRP42 Bill Clinton 2.00 5.00
TRP43 George W. Bush 2.00 5.00

2007 Topps Turkey Red Relics

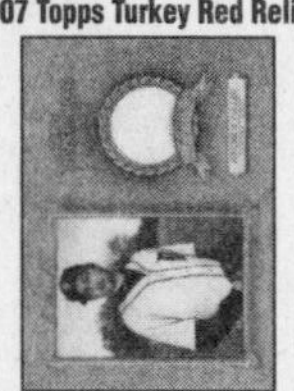

GROUP A ODDS 1:13,000 HOBBY/RETAIL
GROUP B ODDS 1:211 HOBBY/RETAIL
GROUP C ODDS 1:58 HOBBY/RETAIL
GROUP D ODDS 1:155 HOBBY/RETAIL
GROUP E ODDS 1:65 HOBBY/RETAIL
GROUP F ODDS 1:80 HOBBY/RETAIL
GROUP G ODDS 1:53 HOBBY/RETAIL
AB Adrian Beltre Bat D 3.00 8.00
AD Adam Dunn Jsy C 3.00 8.00
AH Aaron Harang Bat D 3.00 8.00
AJ1 Andruw Jones Jsy B 4.00 10.00
AJ2 Andruw Jones Bat F 3.00 8.00
AM Andrew Miller Jsy G 3.00 8.00
ANB Angel Berroa Bat F 3.00 8.00
AS Alfonso Soriano Bat C 4.00 10.00
BB Barry Bonds Bat B 12.50 30.00
BC Bobby Crosby Pants C 3.00 8.00
BJR B.J. Ryan Jsy C 3.00 8.00
BR Brian Roberts Jsy B 5.00 12.00
BS Brian Stokes Jsy E 3.00 8.00
BT Brad Thompson Jsy E 3.00 8.00
BW Brandon Webb Pants B 5.00 12.00
BZ Ben Zobrist Bat B 4.00 10.00
CB1 Carlos Beltran Jsy G 3.00 8.00
CB2 Carlos Beltran Bat B 4.00 10.00
CC Coco Crisp Bat C 3.00 8.00
CD Carlos Delgado Bat B 5.00 12.00
CH Cole Hamels Jsy D 5.00 12.00
CJ Chipper Jones Jsy C 4.00 10.00
CJC Chris Carpenter Jsy C 3.00 8.00
CL Carlos Lee Bat B 4.00 10.00
CR Chris Ray Jsy E 3.00 8.00
CS C.C. Sabathia Jsy E 3.00 8.00
DM Daisuke Matsuzaka Jsy A
DN Dioner Navarro Bat C 3.00 8.00
DO David Ortiz Bat C 4.00 10.00
DR Darrell Rasner Jsy E 3.00 8.00
DU Dan Uggla Jsy C 3.00 8.00
DW David Wright Jsy D 6.00 15.00
DWA Daryle Ward Bat G 3.00 8.00
DWW Dontrelle Willis Jsy G 3.00 8.00
DY Delmon Young Bat C 3.00 8.00
ES Ervin Santana Jsy C 3.00 8.00
GP Glen Perkins Jsy C 3.00 8.00
HB Hank Blalock Jsy C 3.00 8.00
HR Hanley Ramirez Bat B 5.00 12.00
IR Ivan Rodriguez Pants D 4.00 10.00
IS Ichiro Suzuki Bat B 8.00 20.00
JB Josh Beckett Bat G 3.00 8.00
JC Jorge Cantu Bat C 3.00 8.00
JD Jermaine Dye Pants B 5.00 12.00
JE Jim Edmonds Jsy C 3.00 8.00
JF Jeff Francoeur Bat B 6.00 15.00
JG Jon Garland Pants G 3.00 8.00
JH Josh Hamilton Bat G 4.00 10.00
JK Jeff Kent Bat B 4.00 10.00
JM Justin Morneau Bat C 3.00 8.00
JP Josh Paul Bat D 3.00 8.00
JPM Joe Mauer Jsy C 4.00 10.00
JR Jose Reyes Jsy E 3.00 8.00
JRB Jason Bay Jsy B 4.00 10.00
JS John Smoltz Jsy C 4.00 10.00
JV2 Jason Varitek Bat D 4.00 10.00
JW Jered Weaver JsyB 5.00 12.00
JZ Joel Zumaya Jsy D 3.00 8.00
KM Kaz Matsui Bat D 3.00 8.00
LB Lance Berkman Jsy G 3.00 8.00
LC Luis Castillo Bat C 3.00 8.00
MC Melky Cabrera Bat C 3.00 8.00
ME Morgan Ensberg Jsy E 3.00 8.00
MG Marcus Giles Jsy F 3.00 8.00
MJC Miguel Cairo Bat C 3.00 8.00
MM Mickey Mantle Bat B 60.00 120.00
MP Mike Piazza Bat D 5.00 12.00
MR Manny Ramirez Jsy F 4.00 10.00
MT Miguel Tejada Pants C 3.00 8.00
MY Michael Young Jsy C 3.00 8.00
NM Nick Markakis Bat B 6.00 15.00
NP Neifi Perez Bat G 3.00 8.00
NS Nick Swisher Pants E 3.00 8.00
PM Pedro Martinez Bat C 3.00 8.00
PP Placido Polanco Bat D 3.00 8.00
RB1 Rocco Baldelli Jsy F 3.00 8.00
RB2 Rocco Baldelli Bat C 3.00 8.00
RH Ryan Howard Jsy B 10.00 25.00
RJH Rich Hill Jsy F 3.00 8.00
RK Ryan Klesko Bat C 3.00 8.00
RS Reggie Sanders Bat C 3.00 8.00
RZ Ryan Zimmerman Bat C 5.00 12.00
SR Scott Rolen Jsy F 3.00 8.00
SS Sammy Sosa Bat E 4.00 10.00
ST So Taguchi Bat C 3.00 8.00
TB Travis Buck Jsy F 3.00 8.00
TH Travis Hafner Jsy B 5.00 12.00
TI Tadahito Iguchi Jsy C 3.00 8.00
TJ Tyler Johnson Pants C 3.00 8.00
VG Vladimir Guerrero Jsy B 5.00 12.00
VW Vernon Wells Jsy B 5.00 12.00

2007 Topps Turkey Red Silks

STATED ODDS 1:85 HOBBY
STATED PRINT RUN 99 SER.#'d SETS
AD Adam Dunn 6.00 15.00
AI Akinori Iwamura 8.00 20.00
AIR Alex Rios 8.00 20.00
AP Albert Pujols 30.00 60.00
AR Alex Rodriguez 30.00 60.00
AS Alfonso Soriano 10.00 25.00
BB Billy Butler 12.50 30.00
BLB Barry Bonds 20.00 50.00
CH Cole Hamels 10.00 25.00
CJ Chipper Jones 12.50 30.00
CS C.C. Sabathia 8.00 20.00
CY Adrian Gonzalez 6.00 15.00
DH Dan Haren 6.00 15.00
DJ Derek Jeter 20.00 50.00
DM Daisuke Matsuzaka 12.50 30.00
DO David Ortiz 12.50 30.00
DU Dan Uggla 8.00 20.00
DW David Wright 12.50 30.00
DWW Dontrelle Willis 6.00 15.00
EB Erik Bedard 8.00 20.00
GS Grady Sizemore 10.00 25.00
HP Hunter Pence 15.00 40.00
HR Hanley Ramirez 8.00 20.00
IS Ichiro Suzuki 20.00 50.00
JAS John Smoltz 12.50 30.00
JB Josh Beckett 10.00 25.00
JBR Jose Reyes 12.50 30.00
JD Jermaine Dye 6.00 15.00
JH J.J. Hardy 6.00 15.00
JL John Lackey 6.00 15.00
JM Justin Morneau 6.00 15.00
JP Jake Peavy 10.00 25.00
JR Jimmy Rollins 12.50 30.00
JRB Jason Bay 6.00 15.00
JS Johan Santana 15.00 40.00
JV Justin Verlander 10.00 25.00
KG Ken Griffey Jr. 20.00 50.00
MAR Manny Ramirez 10.00 25.00
MH Matt Holliday 12.50 30.00
MM Mickey Mantle 60.00 120.00
MO Magglio Ordonez 15.00 40.00
MR Mark Reynolds 10.00 25.00
MT Mark Teixeira 8.00 20.00
NS Nick Swisher 8.00 20.00
PF Prince Fielder 15.00 40.00
RH Ryan Howard 20.00 50.00
RM Russell Martin 8.00 20.00
RZ Ryan Zimmerman 8.00 20.00
TH Torii Hunter 6.00 15.00
VG Vladimir Guerrero 8.00 20.00

2009 Topps Uncirculated Autographs

ISSUED AS EXCHANGE REPLACEMENTS
1 Andre Dawson 8.00 20.00
2 Lou Piniella 8.00 20.00
3 Clay Buchholz 5.00 12.00
5 Adam Lind 5.00 12.00
6 Carlos Pena 5.00 12.00
7 Prince Fielder 8.00 20.00
8 Robinson Cano 20.00 50.00
9 Darryl Strawberry 8.00 20.00

2009 Topps Unique

COMP.SET w/o RC's (150) 12.50 30.00
COMMON CARD (1-150) .20 .50
COMMON ROOKIE (151-200) .75 2.00
RC PRINT RUN 2699 SER.#'d SETS
1 Nick Markakis .50 1.25
2 Geovany Soto .30 .75
3 Brandon Phillips .20 .50
4 Torii Hunter .20 .50
5 Jay Bruce .30 .75
6 Cliff Lee .30 .75
7 Jose Reyes .30 .75
8 Justin Masterson .20 .50
9 Jermaine Dye .20 .50
10 Ryan Braun .60 1.50
11 Ubaldo Jimenez .30 .75
12 Carlos Lee .20 .50
13 Alex Rodriguez .75 2.00
14 Jon Lester .50 1.25
15 Chipper Jones .50 1.25
16 Justin Morneau .50 1.25
17 Dan Haren .20 .50
18 Andre Ethier .30 .75
19 Felix Hernandez .50 1.25
20 Grady Sizemore .30 .75
21 Rick Ankiel .20 .50
22 Ryan Dempster .20 .50
23 Justin Verlander .60 1.50
24 Chase Utley .50 1.25
25 David Wright .60 1.50
26 Matt Cain .20 .50
27 Brad Hawpe .20 .50
28 John Lackey .20 .50
29 Roy Oswalt .30 .75
30 Alfonso Soriano .30 .75
31 Braden Looper .20 .50
32 Jayson Werth .30 .75
33 Edinson Volquez .20 .50
34 Matt Kemp .30 .75
35 Adam Jones .30 .75
36 Joba Chamberlain .30 .75
37 Jason Giambi .20 .50
38 Chris Carpenter .50 1.25
39 Jim Thome .30 .75
40 Daisuke Matsuzaka .50 1.25
41 Kevin Millwood .20 .50
42 Francisco Liriano .20 .50
43 Joey Votto .50 1.25
44 Aramis Ramirez .20 .50
45 Hanley Ramirez .50 1.25
46 Johan Santana .50 1.25
47 Hank Blalock .20 .50
48 Joe Saunders .20 .50
49 Carlos Quentin .30 .75
50 Ryan Howard .60 1.50
51 Aaron Rowand .20 .50
52 Aaron Cook .20 .50
53 Curtis Granderson .30 .75
54 Max Scherzer .30 .75
55 Manny Ramirez .50 1.25
56 Carlos Delgado .20 .50
57 Garrett Atkins .20 .50
58 Josh Johnson .30 .75
59 Gary Sheffield .20 .50
60 Victor Martinez .30 .75
61 Miguel Tejada .30 .75
62 Roy Halladay .50 1.25
63 Kevin Kouzmanoff .20 .50
64 Javier Vazquez .20 .50
65 Joe Mauer .50 1.25
66 Lance Berkman .30 .75
67 Ryan Zimmerman .30 .75
68 Ryan Ludwick .30 .75
69 Randy Johnson .30 .75
70 Jimmy Rollins .30 .75
71 A.J. Burnett .30 .75
72 Adrian Beltre .20 .50
73 Nelson Cruz .30 .75
74 Bobby Abreu .20 .50
75 Miguel Cabrera .50 1.25
76 Chad Billingsley .30 .75
77 Freddy Sanchez .20 .50
78 Scott Kazmir .20 .50
79 Magglio Ordonez .30 .75
80 Brandon Webb .30 .75
81 Hunter Pence .30 .75
82 Adam Dunn .30 .75
83 Dan Uggla .30 .75
84 Jair Jurrjens .20 .50
85 Prince Fielder .30 .75
86 Melvin Mora .20 .50
87 Jason Bay .30 .75
88 Clayton Kershaw .50 1.25
89 Akinori Iwamura .20 .50
90 Zack Greinke .30 .75
91 Yunel Escobar .20 .50
92 Russell Martin .20 .50
93 Derrek Lee .20 .50
94 Mike Pelfrey .20 .50
95 Tim Lincecum .75 2.00
96 Carlos Pena .30 .75
97 Justin Upton .30 .75
98 Denard Span .20 .50
99 Paul Konerko .20 .50
100 Albert Pujols 1.25 3.00
101 Kurt Suzuki .20 .50
102 Corey Hart .20 .50
103 Aubrey Huff .20 .50
104 Scott Rolen .20 .50
105 Ken Griffey Jr. .75 2.00
106 Stephen Drew .20 .50
107 Carlos Beltran .30 .75
108 Dustin Pedroia .60 1.50
109 Derek Jeter 1.25 3.00
110 Carl Crawford .30 .75
111 Carlos Zambrano .30 .75
112 Yovani Gallardo .30 .75
113 Raul Ibanez .30 .75
114 Vernon Wells .20 .50
115 Vladimir Guerrero .50 1.25
116 Adam LaRoche .20 .50
117 Carlos Guillen .20 .50
118 Todd Helton .30 .75
119 Brian McCann .30 .75
120 Jake Peavy .20 .50
121 David Ortiz .30 .75
122 Mark Buehrle .30 .75
123 CC Sabathia .30 .75
124 Jorge Cantu .20 .50
125 Ichiro Suzuki .75 2.00
126 Josh Hamilton .50 1.25
127 Nate McLouth .20 .50
128 B.J. Upton .30 .75
129 Alex Gordon .30 .75
130 Cole Hamels .50 1.25
131 Josh Beckett .30 .75
132 James Shields .20 .50
133 Alexei Ramirez .30 .75
134 Kosuke Fukudome .50 1.25
135 Adrian Gonzalez .30 .75
136 Ian Kinsler .30 .75
137 Johnny Cueto .20 .50
138 Jacoby Ellsbury .50 1.25
139 Jorge Posada .30 .75
140 Alex Rios .30 .75
141 Matt Holliday .50 1.25
142 Michael Young .30 .75
143 Robinson Cano .50 1.25
144 Mike Lowell .20 .50
145 Evan Longoria .60 1.50
146 John Maine .20 .50
147 Jose Lopez .20 .50
148 Aaron Hill .20 .50
149 Garret Anderson .20 .50
150 Mark Teixeira .50 1.25
151 Fernando Martinez RC 1.50 4.00
152 David Hernandez RC .60 1.50
153 Chris Coghlan RC 1.50 4.00
154 Brett Anderson RC 1.00 2.50
155 Tyler Greene (RC) .60 1.50
156 Michael Bowden (RC) .60 1.50
157 Wilkin Ramirez RC .60 1.50
158 Trevor Cahill RC 1.50 4.00
159 Dexter Fowler (RC) 1.00 2.50
160 Bud Norris RC .60 1.50
161 Francisco Cervelli RC 1.50 4.00
162 Brett Cecil RC .60 1.50
163 Mat Latos RC 2.00 5.00
164 Derek Holland RC 1.00 2.50
165 Mat Gamel RC 1.50 4.00
166 Kenshin Kawakami RC 1.00 2.50
167 Matt LaPorta RC 1.50 4.00
168 Kris Medlen RC 1.00 2.50
169 Gerardo Parra RC 1.00 2.50
170 Josh Outman RC 1.00 2.50
171 Trevor Crowe RC .60 1.50
172 Ryan Perry RC 1.50 4.00
173 Colby Rasmus (RC) 1.50 4.00
174 Rick Porcello RC 2.00 5.00
175 Nolan Reimold (RC) .60 1.50
176 David Price RC 1.50 4.00
177 Omir Santos RC .60 1.50
178 Ricky Romero (RC) 1.50 4.00
179 Jordan Schafer (RC) 1.00 2.50
180 Anthony Swarzak (RC) .60 1.50
181 Travis Snider RC 1.00 2.50
182 Koji Uehara RC 1.00 2.50
183 Jesus Guzman RC .60 1.50
184 Sean West (RC) 1.00 2.50
185 Neftali Feliz RC 2.00 5.00
186 Vin Mazzaro RC .60 1.50
187 Gordon Beckham RC 2.00 5.00
188 Jordan Zimmermann RC .60 1.50
189 Chris Tillman RC 1.00 2.50
190 Tommy Hanson RC 2.00 5.00
191 Josh Reddick RC 1.00 2.50
192 Michael Saunders RC 1.00 2.50
193 Alfredo Aceves RC 1.00 2.50
194 Kyle Blanks RC 1.00 2.50
195 Elvis Andrus RC 1.00 2.50
196 Andrew McCutchen (RC) 2.50 6.00
197 Will Venable RC .60 1.50
198 David Huff RC .60 1.50
199 Aaron Bates RC .60 1.50
200 Jhoulys Chacin RC 1.00 2.50

2009 Topps Unique Bronze

*BRONZE VET: 2X TO 5X BASIC VET
*BRONZE RC: .75X TO 2X BASIC RC
STATED PRINT RUN 99 SER.#'d SETS
187 Gordon Beckham 12.00 30.00

2009 Topps Unique Gold

STATED PRINT RUN 25 SER.#'d SETS
NO PRICING DUE TO SCARCITY

2009 Topps Unique Platinum

STATED PRINT RUN 1 SER.#'d SET
NO PRICING DUE TO SCARCITY

2009 Topps Unique Red

*RED VET: .75X TO 2X BASIC VET
*RED RC: .5X TO 1.2X BASIC RC
STATED PRINT RUN 1199 SER.#'d SETS

2009 Topps Unique Alone at the Top

*BRONZE: .6X TO 1.5X BASIC
BRONZE PRINT RUN 99 SER.#'d SETS
GOLD PRINT RUN 25 SER.#'d SETS
NO GOLD PRICING AVAILABLE
PLATINUM PRINT RUN 1 SER.#'d SET
NO PLATINUM PRICING AVAILABLE
AT01 Chipper Jones 1.00 2.50
AT02 Albert Pujols 2.50 6.00
AT03 Hanley Ramirez 1.00 2.50
AT04 Ryan Howard 1.25 3.00
AT05 Adam Dunn .60 1.50
AT06 Willy Taveras .40 1.00
AT07 Johan Santana 1.00 2.50
AT08 Tim Lincecum 1.50 4.00
AT09 Francisco Rodriguez .60 1.50
AT10 Roy Halladay 1.00 2.50

2009 Topps Unique Authentic Tag

STATED PRINT RUN 1 SER.#'d SET
NO PRICING DUE TO SCARCITY

2009 Topps Unique Barrels

STATED PRINT RUN 1 SER.#'d SET
NO PRICING DUE TO SCARCITY

2009 Topps Unique Bat Barrel Autographs

STATED PRINT RUN 1 SER.#'d SET
NO PRICING DUE TO SCARCITY

2009 Topps Unique Bat Knob Autographs
STATED PRINT RUN 1 SER.#'d SET
NO PRICING DUE TO SCARCITY

2009 Topps Unique Dual Distinction Relics
STATED PRINT RUN 99 SER.#'d SETS
BF Ryan Braun 6.00 15.00
Prince Fielder
BP Lance Berkman 4.00 10.00
Hunter Pence
CL Matt Cain 6.00 15.00
Tim Lincecum
CP Miguel Cabrera 10.00 25.00
Albert Pujols
EP Jacoby Ellsbury 10.00 25.00
Dustin Pedroia
GH Vladimir Guerrero 4.00 10.00
Torii Hunter
GP Adrian Gonzalez 8.00 20.00
Albert Pujols
HB Roy Halladay 4.00 10.00
Josh Beckett
HK Josh Hamilton 4.00 10.00
Ian Kinsler
HU Ryan Howard 15.00 40.00
Chase Utley
IM Ichiro Suzuki 12.50 30.00
Daisuke Matsuzaka
JM Chipper Jones 4.00 10.00
Brian McCann
KR Matt Kemp 5.00 12.00
Manny Ramirez
LC Evan Longoria 6.00 15.00
Carl Crawford
MJ Nick Markakis 12.50 30.00
Adam Jones
MM Joe Mauer 8.00 20.00
Justin Morneau
OY David Ortiz 4.00 10.00
Kevin Youkilis
PR Jorge Posada 20.00 50.00
Mariano Rivera
RU Hanley Ramirez 4.00 10.00
Dan Uggla
SH Johan Santana 5.00 12.00
Cole Hamels
SR Alfonso Soriano 4.00 10.00
Aramis Ramirez
SS Grady Sizemore 8.00 20.00
Ichiro Suzuki
TR Mark Teixeira 10.00 25.00
Alex Rodriguez
VP Justin Verlander 5.00 12.00
Rick Porcello
WR David Wright 4.00 10.00
Jose Reyes

2009 Topps Unique Jumbo Patches
PRINT RUNS B/WN 13-40 COPIES PER
NO PRICING ON QTY 22 OR LESS
PRICING FOR NON-PREMIUM PATCHES
AR Anthony Reyes/20
BM Brian McCann/40 8.00 20.00
CL Che-Hsuan Lin/40 30.00 60.00
CQ Carlos Quentin/15
CS CC Sabathia/40 60.00 120.00
CU Chase Utley
DC David Cortes
DE Damaso Espino/40 5.00 12.00
DU Dan Uggla/35 50.00 100.00
FC Francisco Cervelli/40 5.00 12.00
FH Felix Hernandez/40 40.00 80.00
GS Grady Sizemore/13
HR Hein Robb/14
JE Justin Erasmus/40 5.00 12.00
JH Josh Hamilton/15
JM Joe Mauer/15
JR Jimmy Rollins/20
JU Justin Upton
JW Jered Weaver/13
MC Mike Costanzo
MH Matt Holliday
MO Magglio Ordonez/22
MT Mark Teixeira/40 30.00 60.00
NM Nick Markakis/15
RA Rick Ankiel/40 8.00 20.00
RD Ryan Doumit/15
RH Ryan Howard/15
RJ Randy Johnson/30 20.00 50.00
RL Ryan Ludwick/40 50.00 100.00
TH Todd Helton/15
TL Tim Lincecum/20
YC Yurendell de Caster/40
YG Yovani Gallardo
CSM Curt Smith/40 8.00 20.00
HJR Hyun-Jin Ryu/40 5.00 12.00
HRA Hanley Ramirez/15
JRE Jose Reyes/15
JWE Jeff Weaver/40 15.00 40.00
MCO Manuel Corpas/40
MO2 Magglio Ordonez/40 30.00 60.00

2009 Topps Unique Presidential Plates
PLATINUM PRINT RUN 1 SER.#'d SET
NO PLATINUM PRICING AVAILABLE
PP1 George Washington 40.00 80.00
PP2 John Adams 20.00 50.00
PP3 Thomas Jefferson 100.00 200.00
PP4 James Madison 15.00 40.00
PP5 James Monroe 15.00 40.00
PP6 John Quincy Adams 15.00 40.00
PP7 Andrew Jackson 30.00 60.00
PP8 Martin Van Buren 15.00 40.00
PP9 William Henry Harrison 15.00 40.00
PP10 John Tyler 15.00 40.00
PP11 James K. Polk 15.00 40.00
PP12 Zachary Taylor 15.00 40.00
PP13 Millard Fillmore 15.00 40.00
PP14 Franklin Pierce 15.00 40.00
PP15 James Buchanan 15.00 40.00
PP16 Abraham Lincoln 60.00 120.00
PP17 Andrew Johnson 15.00 40.00
PP18 Ulysses S. Grant 20.00 50.00
PP19 Rutherford B. Hayes 15.00 40.00
PP20 James A. Garfield 15.00 40.00
PP21 Chester A. Arthur 30.00 60.00
PP22 Grover Cleveland 15.00 40.00
PP23 Benjamin Harrison 15.00 40.00
PP24 Grover Cleveland 15.00 40.00
PP25 William McKinley 15.00 40.00
PP26 Theodore Roosevelt 20.00 50.00
PP27 William Howard Taft 15.00 40.00
PP28 Woodrow Wilson 20.00 50.00
PP29 Warren G. Harding 30.00 60.00
PP30 Calvin Coolidge 15.00 40.00
PP31 Herbert Hoover
PP32 Franklin D. Roosevelt 20.00 50.00
PP33 Harry S Truman 20.00 50.00
PP34 Dwight D. Eisenhower 20.00 50.00
PP35 John F. Kennedy 30.00 100.00
PP36 Lyndon B. Johnson 20.00 50.00
PP37 Richard Nixon 20.00 50.00
PP38 Gerald R. Ford 15.00 40.00
PP39 Jimmy Carter
PP40 Ronald Reagan 20.00 50.00
PP41 George Bush 20.00 50.00
PP42 Bill Clinton 20.00 50.00
PP43 George W. Bush 20.00 50.00
PP44 Barack Obama 40.00 80.00

2009 Topps Unique Primetime Patches
PRINT RUNS B/WN 20-99 COPIES PER
NO PRICING ON QTY 25 OR LESS
PRICING FOR NON-PREMIUM PATCHES
PTP1 Adam Dunn/99 4.00 10.00
PTP2 Adrian Beltre/99 4.00 10.00
PTP3 Albert Pujols/99 12.50 30.00
PTP4 Alex Gordon/99 10.00 25.00
PTP5 Alex Rodriguez/20
PTP6 Alex Rodriguez/99 8.00 20.00
PTP7 Andrew Miller/99 4.00 10.00
PTP8 Anthony Reyes/75 5.00 12.00
PTP9 B.J. Upton
PTP10 Barry Zito/99 4.00 10.00
PTP11 Brad Lidge/99 4.00 10.00
PTP12 Brett Myers/99 4.00 10.00
PTP13 Carlos Beltran/99 6.00 15.00
PTP14 Carlos Delgado/75 8.00 20.00
PTP15 Carlos Zambrano/25
PTP16 CC Sabathia/99 4.00 10.00
PTP17 Chase Utley/50 20.00 50.00
PTP18 Chipper Jones/99 6.00 15.00
PTP19 David Ortiz/99 4.00 10.00
PTP20 Edinson Volquez/99 4.00 10.00
PTP21 Ervin Santana/75 4.00 10.00
PTP22 Freddy Sanchez/99 4.00 10.00
PTP23 Hank Blalock/99 4.00 10.00
PTP24 Hideki Okajima/50 8.00 20.00
PTP25 Howie Kendrick/99 4.00 10.00
PTP26 Ian Kinsler/99 4.00 10.00
PTP27 Ivan Rodriguez/99 5.00 12.00
PTP28 J.D. Drew/50 4.00 10.00
PTP29 J.J. Hardy/75 4.00 10.00
PTP30 Jacoby Ellsbury/75 12.50 30.00
PTP31 Jason Giambi/75 4.00 10.00
PTP32 Jim Thome
PTP33 Jim Thome/75 5.00 12.00
PTP34 Jim Thome
PTP35 Joey Votto/99 8.00 20.00
PTP36 John Smoltz/99 5.00 12.00
PTP37 Johnny Damon/75 5.00 12.00
PTP38 Jorge Posada/75 10.00 25.00
PTP39 Jose Reyes/99 5.00 12.00
PTP40 Josh Hamilton/99 5.00 12.00
PTP41 Kevin Millwood/99 4.00 10.00
PTP42 Kevin Youkilis/75 6.00 15.00
PTP43 Lance Berkman/99 4.00 10.00
PTP44 Magglio Ordonez/99 6.00 15.00
PTP45 Manny Ramirez/99 5.00 12.00
PTP46 Mark Teixeira/75 8.00 20.00
PTP47 Matt Holliday/75 4.00 10.00
PTP48 Michael Young/99 4.00 10.00
PTP49 Miguel Cabrera/99 5.00 12.00
PTP50 Miguel Tejada/99 4.00 10.00
PTP51 Mike Lowell/99 4.00 10.00
PTP52 Mike Napoli/99 6.00 15.00
PTP53 Pablo Sandoval/75 30.00 60.00
PTP54 Pat Burrell/99 4.00 10.00
PTP55 Pedro Martinez/99 5.00 12.00
PTP56 Phil Hughes/75 5.00 12.00
PTP57 Prince Fielder/75 6.00 15.00
PTP58 Rafael Furcal/99 4.00 10.00
PTP59 Robinson Cano/50 6.00 15.00
PTP60 Rocco Baldelli/99 4.00 10.00
PTP61 Roy Oswalt/99 4.00 10.00
PTP62 Scott Rolen/99 5.00 12.00
PTP63 Todd Helton/99 4.00 10.00
PTP64 Torii Hunter/99 4.00 10.00
PTP65 Trevor Hoffman/75 4.00 10.00
PTP66 Vernon Wells/75 4.00 10.00
PTP67 Victor Martinez/99 5.00 12.00
PTP68 Vladimir Guerrero/99 4.00 10.00
PTP69 Wladimir Balentien/99 4.00 10.00
PTP70 Yovani Gallardo/99 5.00 12.00
PTP71 Anthony Reyes/50 5.00 12.00
PTP72 Carlos Delgado/50 10.00 25.00
PTP73 Jason Giambi/50 4.00 10.00
PTP74 Jim Thome/50 5.00 12.00
PTP75 Jim Thome
PTP76 Johnny Damon/50 5.00 12.00
PTP77 Mark Teixeira/50 8.00 20.00
PTP78 Pablo Sandoval/50 30.00 60.00
PTP79 Prince Fielder/50 6.00 15.00
PTP80 Albert Pujols/50 20.00 50.00
PTP81 Andrew Miller/50 5.00 12.00
PTP82 Brett Myers/50 5.00 12.00
PTP83 Carlos Beltran/50 8.00 20.00
PTP84 Edinson Volquez/50 5.00 12.00
PTP85 Freddy Sanchez/50 5.00 12.00
PTP86 Josh Hamilton/50 6.00 15.00
PTP87 Miguel Cabrera/50 6.00 15.00
PTP88 Mike Lowell/50 5.00 12.00
PTP89 Mike Napoli/50 8.00 20.00
PTP90 Vladimir Guerrero/50 5.00 12.00
PTP91 Adrian Beltre/99 4.00 10.00
PTP92 Barry Zito/99 4.00 10.00
PTP93 David Ortiz/99 4.00 10.00
PTP94 Hank Blalock/99 4.00 10.00
PTP95 Ivan Rodriguez/99 5.00 12.00
PTP96 Jose Reyes/99 5.00 12.00
PTP97 Magglio Ordonez/99 6.00 15.00
PTP98 Michael Young/99 4.00 10.00
PTP99 Miguel Tejada/99 4.00 10.00
PTP100 Pedro Martinez/99 5.00 12.00
PTP101 Rocco Baldelli/99 4.00 10.00
PTP102 Roy Oswalt/99 4.00 10.00
PTP103 Scott Rolen/99 5.00 12.00
PTP104 Wladimir Balentien/99 4.00 10.00
PTP105 Kevin Millwood/99 4.00 10.00
PTP106 Kevin Millwood/50 5.00 12.00
PTP107 Torii Hunter/99 4.00 10.00
PTP108 Torii Hunter/99 4.00 10.00
PTP109 Adam Dunn/99 4.00 10.00
PTP110 Adam Dunn/99 4.00 10.00
PTP111 Adam Dunn/99 4.00 10.00
PTP112 Chipper Jones/99 6.00 15.00
PTP113 Chipper Jones/99 6.00 15.00
PTP114 Chipper Jones/99 6.00 15.00
PTP115 Lance Berkman/99 4.00 10.00
PTP116 Lance Berkman/99 4.00 10.00
PTP117 Lance Berkman/99 4.00 10.00
PTP118 Todd Helton/99 4.00 10.00
PTP119 Todd Helton/99 4.00 10.00
PTP120 Todd Helton/99 4.00 10.00

2009 Topps Unique Solo Shot Relics
STATED PRINT RUN 275 SER.#'d SETS
AG Adrian Gonzalez 3.00 8.00
AP Albert Pujols 6.00 15.00
AR Alex Rodriguez 8.00 20.00
AS Alfonso Soriano 3.00 8.00
CJ Chipper Jones 4.00 10.00
CU Chase Utley 5.00 12.00
DO David Ortiz 3.00 8.00
DW David Wright 5.00 12.00
EL Evan Longoria 5.00 12.00
GS Grady Sizemore 3.00 8.00
HR Hanley Ramirez 4.00 10.00
IS Ichiro Suzuki 8.00 20.00
JH Josh Hamilton 3.00 8.00
JM Joe Mauer 4.00 10.00
JR Jimmy Rollins 4.00 10.00
MC Miguel Cabrera 3.00 8.00
MH Matt Holliday 5.00 12.00
MR Manny Ramirez 5.00 12.00
MT Mark Teixeira 10.00 25.00
NM Nick Markakis 5.00 12.00
PF Prince Fielder 3.00 8.00
RB Ryan Braun 4.00 10.00
RH Ryan Howard 6.00 15.00
VG Vladimir Guerrero 3.00 8.00
JMO Justin Morneau 3.00 8.00

2009 Topps Unique Solo Shots Autographs
AE Andre Ethier 10.00 25.00
AG Adrian Gonzalez 10.00 25.00
AL Adam Lind 3.00 8.00
CB Chad Billingsley 4.00 10.00
CG Curtis Granderson 8.00 20.00
DP David Price 8.00 20.00
DU Dan Uggla 4.00 10.00
GB Gordon Beckham 20.00 50.00
JB Jay Bruce 10.00 25.00
JC Johnny Cueto 4.00 10.00
JJ Josh Johnson 3.00 8.00
JU Justin Upton
MB Milton Bradley 3.00 8.00
MC Melky Cabrera 8.00 20.00
MK Matt Kemp 8.00 20.00
MS Max Scherzer 3.00 8.00
NM Nick Markakis 12.50 30.00
PH Phil Hughes 6.00 15.00
RB Ryan Braun 15.00 40.00
RC Ryan Church 3.00 8.00
RH Rich Hill 3.00 8.00
RI Raul Ibanez 10.00 25.00
RP Rick Porcello 15.00 40.00
TL Tim Lincecum 60.00 120.00
ZG Zack Greinke 10.00 25.00
DPE Dustin Pedroia 12.50 30.00
JCH Joba Chamberlain 10.00 25.00
JCU Jack Cust 3.00 8.00
MCA Matt Cain 6.00 15.00

2009 Topps Unique Unique Unis
*BRONZE: .6X TO 1.5X BASIC
BRONZE PRINT RUN 99 SER.#'d SETS
GOLD PRINT RUN 25 SER.#'d SETS
NO GOLD PRICING AVAILABLE
PLATINUM PRINT RUN 1 SER.#'d SET
NO PLATINUM PRICING AVAILABLE
UU01 Chipper Jones 1.00 2.50
UU02 Ryan Braun 1.25 3.00
UU03 Alexei Ramirez .60 1.50
UU04 Andrew McCutchen 1.50 4.00
UU05 Ben Sheets .40 1.00
UU06 Jermaine Dye .40 1.00
UU07 Prince Fielder .60 1.50
UU08 Evan Longoria 1.25 3.00
UU09 Jason Giambi .40 1.00
UU10 Jose Reyes .60 1.50
UU11 Curtis Granderson .60 1.50
UU12 Jason Bay .60 1.50
UU13 Jimmy Rollins .60 1.50
UU14 Justin Verlander 1.25 3.00
UU15 Roy Halladay 1.00 2.50
UU16 David Wright 1.25 3.00
UU17 Carl Crawford .60 1.50
UU18 Gil Meche .40 1.00
UU19 Kevin Youkilis .60 1.50
UU20 Ryan Zimmerman .60 1.50

2009 Topps Unique Unparalled Performances
*BRONZE: .6X TO 1.5X BASIC
BRONZE PRINT RUN 99 SER.#'d SETS
GOLD PRINT RUN 25 SER.#'d SETS
NO GOLD PRICING AVAILABLE
PLATINUM PRINT RUN 1 SER.#'d SET
NO PLATINUM PRICING AVAILABLE
UP01 Ian Kinsler .60 1.50
UP02 Carlos Delgado .40 1.00
UP03 Randy Johnson .60 1.50
UP04 Alex Rodriguez 1.50 4.00
UP05 Orlando Hudson .40 1.00
UP06 Carl Crawford .60 1.50
UP07 Mariano Rivera 1.00 2.50
UP08 Alfonso Soriano .60 1.50
UP09 Dexter Fowler .60 1.50
UP10 Fernando Tatis .40 1.00
UP11 Adam LaRoche .40 1.00
UP12 Raul Ibanez .60 1.50
UP13 Carlos Beltran .40 1.00
UP14 James Loney .60 1.50
UP15 Bronson Arroyo .40 1.00
UP16 Aaron Hill .40 1.00
UP17 Jeremy Hermida .40 1.00
UP18 Randy Johnson .60 1.50
UP19 Micah Owings .40 1.00
UP20 Johnny Cueto .40 1.00

2009 Topps World Baseball Classic Box Set
COMPLETE SET (55) 10.00 25.00
1 Yu Darvish 2.00 5.00
2 Derek Jeter 1.25 3.00
3 Ryan Braun .60 1.50
4 Michel Enriquez .20 .50
5 Phillippe Aumont .50 1.25
6 Yulieski Gourriel .20 .50
7 Shinnosuke Abe .30 .75
8 Hanley Ramirez .50 1.25
9 Daisuke Matsuzaka .50 1.25
10 Justin Erasmus .20 .50
11 Frank Catalanotto .20 .50
12 Travis Blackley .20 .50
13 Alex Rodriguez .75 2.00
14 Brian McCann .30 .75
15 Arquimedes Nieto .20 .50
16 Joakim Soria .20 .50
17 Justin Morneau .50 1.25
18 Geovany Soto .30 .75
19 Alex Liddi .60 1.50
20 Cheng-Min Peng .30 .75
21 Luke Hughes .20 .50
22 Manuel Corpas .20 .50
23 Chipper Jones .50 1.25
24 Drew Naylor .20 .50
25 Jimmy Rollins .30 .75
26 Kosuke Fukudome .50 1.25
27 Jose Reyes .30 .75
28 David Wright .60 1.50
29 Ichiro Suzuki .75 2.00
30 Carlos Lee .20 .50
31 Joey Votto .50 1.25
32 Jin Young Lee .20 .50
33 Jonathan Sanchez .20 .50
34 Lenny DiNardo .20 .50
35 Miguel Cabrera .50 1.25
36 Rick VanDeHurk .20 .50
37 David Ortiz .30 .75
38 Jason Bay .30 .75
39 Dylan Lindsay .30 .75
40 Chris Denorfia .20 .50
41 Bernie Williams .30 .75
42 Akinori Iwamura .20 .50
43 Pedro Martinez .30 .75
44 Gift Ngoepe .20 .50
45 Chenhao Li .20 .50
46 Roy Oswalt .30 .75
47 Dustin Pedroia .60 1.50
48 Tao Bu .20 .50
49 Greg Halman .30 .75
50 Adrian Gonzalez .30 .75
51 Carlos Beltran .20 .50
52 Pedro Lazo .20 .50
53 Jorge Cantu .20 .50
54 Kenji Johjima .30 .75
55 Fu-Te Ni .30 .75

2008 UD A Piece of History
COMPLETE SET (200) 15.00 40.00
COMMON CARD (1-100) .20 .50
COMMON ROOKIE (101-150) .40 1.00
COMMON HM (151-200) .20 .50
1 Brandon Webb .30 .75
2 Dan Haren .20 .50
3 Justin Upton .30 .75
4 Chris B. Young .20 .50
5 Mark Teixeira .50 1.25
6 Jeff Francoeur .30 .75
7 John Smoltz .50 1.25
8 Tom Glavine .30 .75
9 Brian McCann .30 .75
10 Chipper Jones .50 1.25
11 Erik Bedard .20 .50
12 Nick Markakis .50 1.25
13 Josh Beckett .30 .75
14 David Ortiz .30 .75
15 Manny Ramirez .50 1.25
16 Dustin Pedroia .60 1.50
17 Grady Sizemore .30 .75
18 Jonathan Papelbon .30 .75
19 Daisuke Matsuzaka .50 1.25
20 Curt Schilling .30 .75
21 Alfonso Soriano .30 .75
22 Aramis Ramirez .20 .50
23 Carlos Zambrano .30 .75
24 Nick Swisher .50 1.25
25 Jim Thome .30 .75
26 Ken Griffey Jr. .75 2.00
27 Adam Dunn .30 .75
28 Aaron Harang .20 .50
29 Matt Holliday .50 1.25
30 Troy Tulowitzki .50 1.25
31 Todd Helton .30 .75
32 Magglio Ordonez .30 .75
33 Justin Verlander .60 1.50
34 Miguel Cabrera .50 1.25
35 Gary Sheffield .20 .50
36 Ivan Rodriguez .30 .75
37 Dontrelle Willis .20 .50
38 Hanley Ramirez .50 1.25
39 Andrew Miller .20 .50
40 Lance Berkman .30 .75
41 Roy Oswalt .30 .75
42 Carlos Lee .20 .50
43 Hunter Pence .50 1.25
44 Alex Gordon .30 .75
45 Mark Teahen .20 .50
46 Torii Hunter .20 .50
47 Vladimir Guerrero .50 1.25
48 Victor Martinez .30 .75
49 Andruw Jones .20 .50
50 James Loney .30 .75
51 Russell Martin .20 .50
52 Jeff Kent .20 .50
53 Ryan Braun .60 1.50
54 Prince Fielder .30 .75
55 Joe Mauer .50 1.25
56 Justin Morneau .50 1.25
57 Delmon Young .30 .75
58 Jose Reyes .30 .75
59 David Wright .60 1.50
60 Carlos Beltran .20 .50
61 Johan Santana .50 1.25
62 Pedro Martinez .30 .75
63 Alex Rodriguez .75 2.00
64 Derek Jeter 1.25 3.00
65 Hideki Matsui .50 1.25
66 Robinson Cano .50 1.25
67 Joba Chamberlain .30 .75
68 Phil Hughes .50 1.25
69 Mariano Rivera .50 1.25
70 Rich Harden .20 .50
71 Joe Blanton .20 .50
72 Cole Hamels .50 1.25
73 Ryan Howard .60 1.50
74 Jimmy Rollins .30 .75
75 Chase Utley .50 1.25
76 Jason Bay .30 .75
77 Freddy Sanchez .20 .50
78 Jake Peavy .20 .50
79 Greg Maddux .60 1.50
80 Trevor Hoffman .30 .75
81 Barry Zito .20 .50
82 Tim Lincecum .75 2.00
83 Travis Hafner .20 .50
84 C.C. Sabathia .30 .75
85 Felix Hernandez .50 1.25
86 Ichiro Suzuki .75 2.00
87 Troy Glaus .30 .75
88 Albert Pujols 1.25 3.00
89 Chris Carpenter .50 1.25
90 Scott Kazmir .30 .75
91 Carl Crawford .30 .75
92 B.J. Upton .30 .75
93 Michael Young .30 .75
94 Josh Hamilton .50 1.25
95 Vernon Wells .20 .50
96 Alex Rios .30 .75
97 Scott Rolen .30 .75
98 Frank Thomas .50 1.25
99 Chad Cordero .20 .50
100 Ryan Zimmerman .30 .75
101 Emilio Bonifacio RC 1.00 2.50
102 Bill Murphy (RC) .40 1.00
103 Billy Buckner (RC) .40 1.00
104 Brandon Jones RC 1.00 2.50
105 Clint Sammons (RC) .40 1.00
106 Clay Buchholz (RC) 1.00 2.50
107 Kevin Hart (RC) .40 1.00
108 Lance Broadway (RC) .40 1.00
109 Donny Lucy (RC) .40 1.00
110 Heath Phillips RC .60 1.50
111 Ryan Hanigan RC .60 1.50
112 Joey Votto (RC) 1.50 4.00
113 Joe Koshansky (RC) .40 1.00
114 Josh Newman RC .60 1.50
115 Seth Smith (RC) .40 1.00
116 Harvey Garcia (RC) .40 1.00
117 Chris Seddon (RC) .40 1.00
118 Josh Anderson (RC) .40 1.00
119 Troy Patton (RC) .40 1.00
120 Felipe Paulino RC .60 1.50
121 J.R. Towles RC .60 1.50
122 Luke Hochevar RC .60 1.50
123 Chin-Lung Hu (RC) .60 1.50
124 Jonathan Meloan RC .60 1.50
125 Sam Fuld RC 1.25 3.00
126 Mitch Stetter RC .60 1.50
127 Jose Morales (RC) .40 1.00
128 Carlos Muniz RC .60 1.50
129 Alberto Gonzalez RC .60 1.50
130 Ian Kennedy RC 1.00 2.50
131 Ross Ohlendorf RC .60 1.50
132 Jonathan Albaladejo RC .60 1.50
133 Daric Barton (RC) .40 1.00
134 Jerry Blevins RC .60 1.50
135 Dave Davidson RC .60 1.50
136 Nyjer Morgan (RC) .40 1.00
137 Steve Pearce RC .60 1.50
138 Colt Morton RC .60 1.50
139 Eugenio Velez RC .40 1.00
140 Erick Threets (RC) .40 1.00
141 Bronson Sardinha (RC) .40 1.00
142 Wladimir Balentien (RC) .40 1.00
143 Jeff Clement (RC) .60 1.50
144 Rob Johnson (RC) .40 1.00
145 Jeff Ridgway RC .60 1.50
146 Justin Ruggiano RC .60 1.50
147 Luis Mendoza (RC) .40 1.00
148 Bill White RC .40 1.00
149 Ross Detwiler RC 1.00 2.50
150 Justin Maxwell RC .40 1.00
151 Fall of the Berlin Wall .20 .50
152 Wright Brothers 1st Flight .20 .50
153 Signing of Declaration of Independence .20 .50
154 Columbus Discovers America .20 .50
155 First Space Shuttle launch .20 .50
156 Hawaii becomes 50th state .20 .50
157 Statue of Liberty given to U.S. .20 .50
158 Gettysburg Address .20 .50
159 Completion Transcontinental Railroad .20 .50
160 Opening of Panama Canal .20 .50
161 U.S. enters World War 1 .20 .50
162 Treaty of Versailes .20 .50
163 Television invented .20 .50
164 Geneva Summit .20 .50
165 Woodstock .20 .50
166 Invention of Cotton Gin .20 .50
167 Eiffel Tower .20 .50
168 Suez Canal opens .20 .50
169 New York City Subway opens .20 .50
170 Polio Vaccine invented .20 .50
171 Bell X-1 Breaks Sound Barrier .20 .50
172 USS Enterprise Aircraft Carrier laun .20 .50
173 Hubble Telescope launches .20 .50
174 N.A.T.O. created .20 .50
175 Sputnik launched by Russia .20 .50
176 U.S.S.R. Crumbles .20 .50
177 Boston Tea Party .20 .50
178 Paul Revere's Ride .20 .50
179 Civil Rights Act Passes .20 .50
180 Hindenburg blows up .20 .50
181 Franklin discovers electricity .20 .50
182 Creation of the Internet .20 .50
183 1st World's Fair - 1851 London .20 .50
184 Pope John Paul II .20 .50
185 1st Heart Transplant .20 .50
186 California Gold Rush .20 .50
187 Creation of the personal computer .20 .50
188 Louisiana Purchase .20 .50
189 1st Dictionary published .20 .50
190 Steam Engine invented .20 .50
191 History of Nobel Prize .20 .50
192 Liberty Bell .20 .50
193 International Space Station .20 .50
194 Human Genome Project .20 .50
195 The Supreme Court .20 .50
196 Lewis and Clark .20 .50
197 Battle of the Alamo .20 .50
198 The creation of baseball .20 .50
199 Juan Ponce De Leon .20 .50
200 Jamestown - 1607 .20 .50

2008 UD A Piece of History Blue
RANDOM INSERTS IN PACKS
STATED PRINT RUN 25 SER.#'d SETS
NO PRICING DUE TO SCARCITY

2008 UD A Piece of History Gold
*GOLD 1-100: 1.5X TO 4X BASIC 1-100
*GOLD RC 101-150: 1.5X TO 4X BASIC RC
*GOLD HM 151-200: 1.5X TO 4X BASIC HM
RANDOM INSERTS IN PACKS
STATED PRINT RUN 75 SER.#'d SETS

2008 UD A Piece of History Red
*RED 1-100: 1X TO 2.5X BASIC 1-100
*RED RC 101-150: 1X TO 2.5X BASIC RC
*RED HM 151-200: 1X TO 2.5X BASIC HM
RANDOM INSERTS IN PACKS
STATED PRINT RUN 149 SER.#'d SETS

2008 UD A Piece of History Silver
*SILVER 1-100: .6X TO 1.5X BASIC 1-100
*SILVER RC 101-150: .6X TO 1.5X BASIC RC
*SILVER HM 151-200: .6X TO 1.5X BASIC HM
RANDOM INSERTS IN PACKS

2008 UD A Piece of History Rookie Autographs
OVERALL AU ODDS 1:16
PRINT RUNS B/W 50-499 COPIES PER
101 Emilio Bonifacio/499 15.00 40.00
102 Bill Murphy/499 3.00 8.00
103 Billy Buckner/149 4.00 10.00
104 Brandon Jones/499 3.00 8.00
105 Clint Sammons/499 3.00 8.00
106 Clay Buchholz/199 8.00 20.00
107 Kevin Hart/499 3.00 8.00
108 Lance Broadway/99 4.00 10.00
111 Ryan Hanigan/499 3.00 8.00
112 Joey Votto/50 20.00 50.00
113 Joe Koshansky/499 3.00 8.00
114 Josh Newman/499 3.00 8.00
115 Seth Smith/499 3.00 8.00
116 Harvey Garcia/499 3.00 8.00
117 Chris Seddon/459 3.00 8.00
118 Josh Anderson/499 3.00 8.00
119 Troy Patton/499 4.00 10.00
120 Felipe Paulino/499 3.00 8.00
121 J.R. Towles/499 4.00 10.00
122 Luke Hochevar/99
123 Chin-Lung Hu/99 12.50 30.00
124 Jonathan Meloan/99
127 Jose Morales/499 3.00 8.00
129 Alberto Gonzalez/499 4.00 10.00
130 Ian Kennedy/199 6.00 15.00
131 Ross Ohlendorf/499 4.00 10.00
132 Jonathan Albaladejo/499 3.00 8.00
133 Daric Barton/99 4.00 10.00
134 Jerry Blevins/499 3.00 8.00
135 Dave Davidson/499 3.00 8.00
136 Nyjer Morgan/499 3.00 8.00
137 Steve Pearce/499 4.00 10.00
138 Colt Morton/499 3.00 8.00
139 Eugenio Velez/499 3.00 8.00
141 Bronson Sardinha/499 3.00 8.00
142 Wladimir Balentien/199 4.00 10.00
144 Rob Johnson/499 3.00 8.00
146 Justin Ruggiano/499 3.00 8.00
147 Luis Mendoza/499 3.00 8.00
148 Bill White/499 3.00 8.00
149 Ross Detwiler/499 3.00 8.00
150 Justin Maxwell/499 4.00 10.00

2008 UD A Piece of History Rookie Autographs Blue
*BLUE: .6X TO 1.5X BASIC
OVERALL AU ODDS 1:16
PRINT RUNS B/WN 15-50 COPIES PER
NO PRICING ON QTY 25 OR LESS

2008 UD A Piece of History Rookie Autographs Copper
OVERALL AUTO ODDS 1:16
PRINT RUNS B/WN 5-10 COPIES PER
NO PRICING DUE TO SCARCITY

2008 UD A Piece of History Rookie Autographs Gold
*GOLD: .6X TO 1.5X BASIC
OVERALL AU ODDS 1:16
PRINT RUNS B/WN 20-75 COPIES PER
NO PRICING ON QTY 25 OR LESS
106 Clay Buchholz/50 15.00 40.00

2008 UD A Piece of History Rookie Autographs Red
*RED: .6X TO 1.5X BASIC
OVERALL AU ODDS 1:16
PRINT RUNS B/WN 25-99 COPIES PER
NO PRICING ON QTY 25 OR LESS

2008 UD A Piece of History Rookie Autographs Silver
OVERALL AUTO ODDS 1:16
PRINT RUNS B/WN 10-25 COPIES PER
NO PRICING DUE TO SCARCITY

2008 UD A Piece of History A Piece of Hollywood Memorablia
STATED ODDS 1:16
1 Amanda Bynes 6.00 15.00
Sydney White Costume
2 Mel Gibson 5.00 12.00
We Were Soldiers Shirt
3 Brad Pitt 5.00 12.00
Spy Game Shirt
4 George Clooney 4.00 10.00
3 Kings Army Jacket
5 Denzell Washington 4.00 10.00
Courage Under Fire Jacket
6 Jamie Foxx 4.00 10.00
Ray Shirt
7 Kevin Costner 5.00 12.00
JFK Shirt
8 Jack Nicholson 5.00 12.00
A Few Good Men Shirt
9 Mike Myers 6.00 15.00
Austin Powers Pants
10 Dana Carvey 6.00 15.00
Wayne's World Hockey Jersey
11 Phillip Seymour Hoffman 4.00 10.00
Capote Sweater
12 Jim Carrey 4.00 10.00
Bruce Almighty Shirt
13 Scarlett Johanson 6.00 15.00
Nanny Diaries T-Shirt
14 Demi Moore 4.00 10.00
GI Jane Jacket
15 Christopher Reeve 12.50 30.00
Superman 3 Cape
16 Mel Gibson 20.00 50.00
We Were Soldiers Shoes SP
17 Denzel Washington 40.00 80.00
Courage Under Fire Hat SP
18 Jim Carrey 4.00 10.00
Bruce Almighty Pants
19 George Clooney 4.00 10.00
3 Kings Army Pants
20 Scarlett Johanson 10.00 25.00
Nanny Diaries Undershirt SP
21 Phillip Seymour Hoffman 4.00 10.00
Capote Jacket
22 Denzell Washington 4.00 10.00
Courage Under Fire Army Pants
23 Mel Gibson 5.00 12.00
We Were Soldiers Pants
24 Woody Harrelson 4.00 10.00
Kingpin Jacket
25 Robin Williams 4.00 10.00
Birdcage Shirt
26 Jennifer Garner 5.00 12.00
Time of Your Life Pajamas
27 Tom Cruise 6.00 15.00
A Few Good Men Shirt

2008 UD A Piece of History Box Score Memories
RANDOM INSERTS IN PACKS
STATED PRINT RUN 699 SER.#'d SETS
*BLUE: .6X TO 1.5X BASIC
BLUE RANDOMLY INSERTED
BLUE PRINT RUN 75 SER.#'d SETS
*COPPER: .6X TO 1.5X BASIC
COPPER RANDOMLY INSERTED
COPPER PRINT RUN 99 SER.#'d SETS
*RED: .5X TO 1.2X BASIC
RED RANDOMLY INSERTED
RED PRINT RUN 149 SER.#'d SETS
SILVER RANDOMLY INSERTED
SILVER PRINT RUN 25 SER.#'d SETS
NO SILVER PRICING DUE TO SCARCITY
BSM1 Chris B. Young .50 1.25
BSM2 Stephen Drew .50 1.25
BSM3 Chipper Jones 1.25 3.00
BSM4 Mark Teixeira 1.25 3.00
BSM5 Jeff Francoeur .75 2.00
BSM6 David Ortiz .75 2.00
BSM7 Dustin Pedroia 1.50 4.00
BSM8 Manny Ramirez 1.25 3.00
BSM9 Mike Lowell .50 1.25
BSM10 Alfonso Soriano .75 2.00
BSM11 Aramis Ramirez .50 1.25
BSM12 Jim Thome .75 2.00
BSM13 Ken Griffey Jr. 2.00 5.00
BSM14 Adam Dunn .75 2.00
BSM15 Grady Sizemore .75 2.00
BSM16 Travis Hafner .50 1.25
BSM17 Victor Martinez .75 2.00
BSM18 Matt Holliday 1.25 3.00
BSM19 Todd Helton .75 2.00
BSM20 Troy Tulowitzki 1.25 3.00
BSM21 Ivan Rodriguez .75 2.00
BSM22 Miguel Cabrera 1.50 4.00
BSM23 Magglio Ordonez .75 2.00
BSM24 Hanley Ramirez 1.25 3.00
BSM25 Hunter Pence 1.25 3.00
BSM26 Lance Berkman .75 2.00
BSM27 Carlos Lee .50 1.25
BSM28 Alex Gordon .75 2.00
BSM29 Vladimir Guerrero 1.25 3.00
BSM30 Andruw Jones .50 1.25
BSM31 Jeff Kent .50 1.25
BSM32 Ryan Braun 1.50 4.00
BSM33 Prince Fielder .75 2.00
BSM34 Joe Mauer 1.25 3.00
BSM35 Justin Morneau 1.25 3.00
BSM36 David Wright 1.50 4.00
BSM37 Carlos Beltran .50 1.25
BSM38 Jose Reyes .75 2.00
BSM39 Derek Jeter 3.00 8.00
BSM40 Alex Rodriguez 2.00 5.00
BSM41 Hideki Matsui 1.25 3.00
BSM42 Bobby Abreu .50 1.25
BSM43 Chase Utley 1.25 3.00
BSM44 Ryan Howard 1.50 4.00
BSM45 Jimmy Rollins .75 2.00
BSM46 Jason Bay .75 2.00
BSM47 Khalil Greene .50 1.25
BSM48 Ichiro Suzuki 2.00 5.00
BSM49 Albert Pujols 3.00 8.00
BSM50 Frank Thomas 1.25 3.00

2008 UD A Piece of History Box Score Memories Jersey Red
OVERALL GU ODDS 1:8
BSM1 Chris B. Young 3.00 8.00

BSM2 Stephen Drew 3.00 8.00
BSM3 Chipper Jones 3.00 8.00
BSM4 Mark Teixeira 3.00 8.00
BSM5 Jeff Francoeur 3.00 8.00
BSM6 David Ortiz 4.00 10.00
BSM7 Dustin Pedroia 3.00 8.00
BSM8 Manny Ramirez 3.00 8.00
BSM10 Alfonso Soriano 3.00 8.00
BSM11 Aramis Ramirez 3.00 8.00
BSM12 Jim Thome 3.00 8.00
BSM16 Travis Hafner 3.00 8.00
BSM17 Victor Martinez 3.00 8.00
BSM18 Matt Holliday 3.00 8.00
BSM19 Todd Helton 3.00 8.00
BSM20 Troy Tulowitzki 3.00 8.00
BSM21 Ivan Rodriguez 3.00 8.00
BSM23 Magglio Ordonez 3.00 8.00
BSM24 Hanley Ramirez 3.00 8.00
BSM25 Hunter Pence 4.00 10.00
BSM26 Lance Berkman 3.00 8.00
BSM27 Carlos Lee 3.00 8.00
BSM28 Alex Gordon 4.00 10.00
BSM29 Vladimir Guerrero 3.00 8.00
BSM31 Jeff Kent 3.00 8.00
BSM33 Prince Fielder 4.00 10.00
BSM34 Joe Mauer 3.00 8.00
BSM35 Justin Morneau 3.00 8.00
BSM37 Carlos Beltran 3.00 8.00
BSM38 Jose Reyes 3.00 8.00
BSM39 Derek Jeter 8.00 20.00
BSM40 Alex Rodriguez 6.00 15.00
BSM42 Bobby Abreu 3.00 8.00
BSM45 Jimmy Rollins 3.00 8.00
BSM46 Jason Bay 3.00 8.00
BSM47 Khalil Greene 3.00 8.00
BSM49 Albert Pujols 6.00 15.00
BSM50 Frank Thomas 4.00 10.00

2008 UD A Piece of History Box Score Memories Jersey Blue

OVERALL GU ODDS 1:8
STATED PRINT RUN 25 SER.#'D SETS
NO PRICING DUE TO SCARCITY

2008 UD A Piece of History Box Score Memories Jersey Gold

*GOLD: .5X TO 1.2X BASIC
OVERALL GU ODDS 1:8
STATED PRINT RUN 75 SER.#'d SETS
BSM14 Adam Dunn 4.00 10.00
BSM15 Grady Sizemore 4.00 10.00
BSM22 Miguel Cabrera 4.00 10.00
BSM32 Ryan Braun 6.00 15.00
BSM43 Chase Utley 4.00 10.00

2008 UD A Piece of History Box Score Memories Jersey Gold Patch

OVERALL GU ODDS 1:8
STATED PRINT RUN 25 SER.#'D SETS
NO PRICING DUE TO SCARCITY

2008 UD A Piece of History Box Score Memories Jersey Autographs

OVERALL AUTO ODDS 1:16
PRINT RUNS B/WN 10-99 COPIES PER
NO PRICING ON QTY 25 OR LESS
BSM1 Chris B. Young/99
BSM2 Stephen Drew/10
BSM3 Chipper Jones/25
BSM5 Jeff Francoeur/99 12.50 30.00
BSM10 Alfonso Soriano/15
BSM11 Aramis Ramirez/99 10.00 25.00
BSM12 Jim Thome/10
BSM13 Ken Griffey Jr./25
BSM14 Adam Dunn/25
BSM16 Travis Hafner/50 6.00 15.00
BSM17 Victor Martinez/99 6.00 15.00
BSM18 Matt Holliday/25
BSM20 Troy Tulowitzki/99 10.00 25.00
BSM22 Miguel Cabrera/10
BSM24 Hanley Ramirez/50 12.50 30.00
BSM25 Hunter Pence/10
BSM26 Lance Berkman/10
BSM27 Carlos Lee/99 10.00 25.00
BSM28 Alex Gordon/25
BSM30 Andruw Jones/15
BSM32 Ryan Braun/25
BSM33 Prince Fielder/15
BSM34 Joe Mauer/10
BSM39 Derek Jeter/25
BSM46 Jason Bay/99 6.00 15.00
BSM47 Khalil Greene/15
BSM50 Frank Thomas/10

2008 UD A Piece of History Cut From the Same Cloth

RANDOM INSERTS IN PACKS
STATED PRINT RUN 799 SER.#'d SETS
BLUE RANDOMLY INSERTED
BLUE PRINT RUN 25 SER.#'d SETS
NO BLUE PRICING DUE TO SCARCITY
*PEWTER: .6X TO 1.5X BASIC
PEWTER RANDOMLY INSERTED
PEWTER PRINT RUN 75 SER.#'d SETS
*RED: .6X TO 1.5X BASIC
RED RANDOMLY INSERTED
RED PRINT RUN 99 SER.#'d SETS
*SILVER: .5X TO 1.2X BASIC
SILVER RANDOMLY INSERTED
SILVER PRINT RUN 149 SER.#'d SETS
BB Jeremy Bonderman .40 1.00
Joe Blanton
BP A.J. Burnett .40 1.00
Jake Peavy
BR Carlos Beltran .60 1.50
Jose Reyes
BS Mark Buehrle 1.00 2.50
Johan Santana
BV Mark Buehrle 1.25 3.00
Justin Verlander
BZ Ryan Zimmerman 1.25 3.00
Ryan Braun
CB Carlos Beltran .40 1.00
Carlos Beltran
CH Trevor Hoffman .60 1.50
Chad Cordero
CS Curt Schilling .60 1.50
Curt Schilling
DD Johnny Damon .60 1.50
Johnny Damon
FT Frank Thomas 1.00 2.50
Frank Thomas
GD Ken Griffey Jr. .60 1.50
Adam Dunn
GM Greg Maddux 1.25 3.00
Greg Maddux
GO Magglio Ordonez .60 1.50
Curtis Granderson
GT Ken Griffey Jr. 1.50 4.00
Frank Thomas
HH Todd Helton 1.00 2.50
Matt Holliday
HJ Matt Holliday 1.00 2.50
Andruw Jones
HL Francisco Liriano 1.00 2.50
Cole Hamels
HM Greg Maddux .60 1.50
Tim Hudson
HP Jake Peavy .40 1.00
Dan Haren
HS John Smoltz .60 1.50
Tim Hudson
HY Michael Young .60 1.50
J.J. Hardy
HZ Carlos Zambrano .60 1.50
Felix Hernandez
JB Josh Beckett .60 1.50
Josh Beckett
JD Jason Varitek 1.00 2.50
Daisuke Matsuzaka
JH Andruw Jones .40 1.00
Torii Hunter
JS Randy Johnson 1.00 2.50
Johan Santana
JT Jim Thome .60 1.50
Jim Thome
JY Derek Jeter .60 1.50
Michael Young
JZ Chipper Jones 1.00 2.50
Ryan Zimmerman
KS Johan Santana 1.00 2.50
Scott Kazmir
LF Derrek Lee .60 1.50
Prince Fielder
MA Joe Mauer 1.00 2.50
Russell Martin
MJ Mariano Rivera 1.00 2.50
Jonathan Papelbon
MK Justin Morneau 1.00 2.50
Jason Kubel
MM Victor Martinez .60 1.50
Joe Mauer
MS Curt Schilling 1.00 2.50
Daisuke Matsuzaka
OF David Ortiz .60 1.50
Prince Fielder
OG Carlos Guillen .60 1.50
Magglio Ordonez
OP David Ortiz 2.50 6.00
Albert Pujols
OR Manny Ramirez .60 1.50
David Ortiz
OV Jason Varitek .60 1.50
David Ortiz
PG Vladimir Guerrero 2.50 6.00
Albert Pujols
PH Roy Halladay .40 1.00
Jake Peavy
PM Pedro Martinez .60 1.50
Pedro Martinez
PO Roy Oswalt .40 1.00
Jake Peavy
PS Curt Schilling .60 1.50
Jonathan Papelbon
PV Jason Varitek 1.00 2.50
Jorge Posada
RJ Randy Johnson 1.00 2.50
Randy Johnson
RL Derrek Lee .40 1.00
Aramis Ramirez
RP BJ Ryan .60 1.50
Jonathan Papelbon
RR Jose Reyes 1.00 2.50
Hanley Ramirez
RU Jimmy Rollins 1.00 2.50
Chase Utley
SH Travis Hafner .60 1.50
Grady Sizemore
SL Francisco Liriano 1.00 2.50
Johan Santana
SM Pedro Martinez .60 1.50
Curt Schilling
TR Roy Halladay .60 1.50
Tim Hudson
UU Chase Utley 1.00 2.50
Dan Uggla
VR Manny Ramirez 1.00 2.50
Jason Varitek
WS C.C. Sabathia .60 1.50
Dontrelle Willis

2008 UD A Piece of History Cut From the Same Cloth Dual Jersey

OVERALL GU ODDS 1:8
PRINT RUNS B/WN 33-99 COPIES PER
BB Jeremy Bonderman 4.00 10.00
Joe Blanton/99
BP A.J. Burnett 5.00 12.00
Jake Peavy/99
BR Carlos Beltran 5.00 12.00
Jose Reyes/99
BS Mark Buehrle 6.00 15.00
Johan Santana/99
BV Mark Buehrle 6.00 15.00
Justin Verlander/33
BZ Ryan Zimmerman 8.00 20.00
Ryan Braun/99
CB Carlos Beltran 4.00 10.00
Carlos Beltran/70
CH Trevor Hoffman 4.00 10.00
Chad Cordero/99
CS Curt Schilling 5.00 12.00
Curt Schilling/99
DD Johnny Damon 4.00 10.00
Johnny Damon/99
FT Frank Thomas 6.00 15.00
Frank Thomas/99
GM Greg Maddux 8.00 20.00
Greg Maddux/99
GO Magglio Ordonez 5.00 12.00
Curtis Granderson/99
HH Todd Helton 5.00 12.00
Matt Holliday/99
HJ Matt Holliday 5.00 12.00
Andruw Jones/99
HL Francisco Liriano 5.00 12.00
Cole Hamels/99
HM Greg Maddux 8.00 20.00
Tim Hudson/99
HP Jake Peavy 5.00 12.00
Dan Haren/99
HS John Smoltz 5.00 12.00
Tim Hudson/99
HY Michael Young 4.00 10.00
J.J. Hardy/99
HZ Carlos Zambrano 5.00 12.00
Felix Hernandez/99
JB Josh Beckett 5.00 12.00
Josh Beckett/99
JD Jason Varitek 10.00 25.00
Daisuke Matsuzaka/99
JH Andruw Jones 4.00 10.00
Torii Hunter/99
JS Randy Johnson 6.00 15.00
Johan Santana/99
JT Jim Thome 5.00 12.00
Jim Thome/99
JY Derek Jeter 12.50 30.00
Michael Young/99
JZ Chipper Jones 5.00 12.00
Ryan Zimmerman/99
LF Derrek Lee 6.00 15.00
Prince Fielder/99
MA Joe Mauer 5.00 12.00
Russell Martin/99
MJ Mariano Rivera 8.00 20.00
Jonathan Papelbon/99
MK Justin Morneau 5.00 12.00
Jason Kubel/99
MM Victor Martinez 5.00 12.00
Joe Mauer/99
MS Curt Schilling 10.00 25.00
Daisuke Matsuzaka/99
OF David Ortiz 6.00 15.00
Prince Fielder/99
OG Carlos Guillen 5.00 12.00
Magglio Ordonez/99
OP David Ortiz 12.50 30.00
Albert Pujols/99
OR Manny Ramirez 8.00 20.00
David Ortiz/99
OV Jason Varitek 8.00 20.00
David Ortiz/99
PG Vladimir Guerrero 10.00 25.00
Albert Pujols/99
PH Roy Halladay 5.00 12.00
Jake Peavy/99
PM Pedro Martinez 5.00 12.00
Pedro Martinez/99
PO Roy Oswalt 5.00 12.00
Jake Peavy/99
PS Curt Schilling 5.00 12.00
Jonathan Papelbon/99
PV Jason Varitek 6.00 15.00
Jorge Posada/99
RJ Randy Johnson 6.00 15.00
Randy Johnson/99
RL Derrek Lee 4.00 10.00
Aramis Ramirez/99
RP BJ Ryan 5.00 12.00
Jonathan Papelbon/99
RR Jose Reyes 5.00 12.00
Hanley Ramirez/99
RU Jimmy Rollins 5.00 12.00
Chase Utley/99
SH Travis Hafner 5.00 12.00
Grady Sizemore/99
SL Francisco Liriano 6.00 15.00
Johan Santana/99
SM Pedro Martinez 5.00 12.00
Curt Schilling/99
TR Tim Hudson 4.00 10.00
Roy Halladay/99
UU Chase Utley 5.00 12.00
Dan Uggla/99
VR Manny Ramirez 8.00 20.00
Jason Varitek/99
WS C.C. Sabathia 4.00 10.00
Dontrelle Willis/99

2008 UD A Piece of History Franchise History

RANDOM INSERTS IN PACKS
STATED PRINT RUN 699 SER.#'d SETS
*BLUE: .6X TO 1.5X BASIC
BLUE RANDOMLY INSERTED
BLUE PRINT RUN 75 SER.#'d SETS
*COPPER: .6X TO 1.5X BASIC
COPPER RANDOMLY INSERTED
COPPER PRINT RUN 99 SER.#'d SETS
*RED: .5X TO 1.2X BASIC
RED RANDOMLY INSERTED
RED PRINT RUN 149 SER.#'d SETS
SILVER RANDOMLY INSERTED
SILVER PRINT RUN 25 SER.#'d SETS
NO SILVER PRICING DUE TO SCARCITY
FH1 Justin Upton .75 2.00
FH2 Randy Johnson 1.25 3.00
FH3 Mark Teixeira 1.25 3.00
FH4 John Smoltz 1.25 3.00
FH5 Chipper Jones 1.25 3.00
FH6 Jonathan Papelbon .75 2.00
FH7 Manny Ramirez 1.25 3.00
FH8 Daisuke Matsuzaka 1.25 3.00
FH9 Josh Beckett .75 2.00
FH10 David Ortiz .75 2.00
FH11 Alfonso Soriano .75 2.00
FH12 Jim Thome .75 2.00
FH13 Adam Dunn .75 2.00
FH14 Ken Griffey Jr. 2.00 5.00
FH15 C.C. Sabathia .75 2.00
FH16 Grady Sizemore .75 2.00
FH17 Travis Hafner .50 1.25
FH18 Matt Holliday .75 2.00
FH19 Troy Tulowitzki .75 2.00
FH20 Magglio Ordonez .75 2.00
FH21 Ivan Rodriguez .75 2.00
FH22 Miguel Cabrera 1.25 3.00
FH23 Hanley Ramirez 1.25 3.00
FH24 Hunter Pence 1.25 3.00
FH25 Lance Berkman .75 2.00
FH26 Vladimir Guerrero 1.25 3.00
FH27 Andruw Jones .50 1.25
FH28 Prince Fielder .75 2.00
FH29 Ryan Braun 1.50 4.00
FH30 Joe Mauer 1.25 3.00
FH31 Carlos Beltran .50 1.25
FH32 Pedro Martinez .75 2.00
FH33 Johan Santana 1.25 3.00
FH34 Jose Reyes .75 2.00
FH35 David Wright 1.50 4.00
FH36 Joba Chamberlain .75 2.00
FH37 Hideki Matsui 1.25 3.00
FH38 Alex Rodriguez 2.00 5.00
FH39 Derek Jeter 3.00 8.00
FH40 Jimmy Rollins .75 2.00
FH41 Ryan Howard 1.50 4.00
FH42 Chase Utley 1.25 3.00
FH43 Greg Maddux 1.50 4.00
FH44 Jake Peavy .50 1.25
FH45 Trevor Hoffman .75 2.00
FH46 Ichiro Suzuki 2.00 5.00
FH47 Felix Hernandez 1.25 3.00
FH48 Albert Pujols 3.00 8.00
FH49 Frank Thomas 1.25 3.00
FH50 Vernon Wells .50 1.25

2008 UD A Piece of History Franchise History Jersey Red

OVERALL GU ODDS 1:8
FH1 Justin Upton 4.00 10.00
FH2 Randy Johnson 4.00 10.00
FH3 Mark Teixeira 3.00 8.00
FH4 John Smoltz 3.00 8.00
FH5 Chipper Jones 3.00 8.00
FH6 Jonathan Papelbon 3.00 8.00
FH7 Manny Ramirez 3.00 8.00
FH8 Daisuke Matsuzaka 6.00 15.00
FH9 Josh Beckett 3.00 8.00
FH10 David Ortiz 4.00 10.00
FH11 Alfonso Soriano 3.00 8.00
FH12 Jim Thome 3.00 8.00
FH13 Adam Dunn 3.00 8.00
FH14 Ken Griffey Jr. 5.00 12.00
FH15 C.C. Sabathia 3.00 8.00
FH16 Grady Sizemore 3.00 8.00
FH17 Travis Hafner 3.00 8.00
FH18 Matt Holliday 3.00 8.00
FH19 Troy Tulowitzki 3.00 8.00
FH20 Magglio Ordonez 3.00 8.00
FH21 Ivan Rodriguez 3.00 8.00
FH22 Miguel Cabrera 3.00 8.00
FH23 Hanley Ramirez 3.00 8.00
FH24 Hunter Pence 4.00 10.00
FH25 Lance Berkman 3.00 8.00
FH26 Vladimir Guerrero 3.00 8.00
FH27 Andruw Jones 3.00 8.00
FH28 Prince Fielder 4.00 10.00
FH29 Ryan Braun 5.00 12.00
FH30 Joe Mauer 3.00 8.00
FH31 Carlos Beltran 3.00 8.00
FH32 Pedro Martinez 3.00 8.00
FH33 Johan Santana 4.00 10.00
FH34 Jose Reyes 3.00 8.00
FH36 Joba Chamberlain 3.00 8.00
FH38 Alex Rodriguez 6.00 15.00
FH39 Derek Jeter 8.00 20.00
FH40 Jimmy Rollins 3.00 8.00
FH42 Chase Utley 3.00 8.00
FH43 Greg Maddux 5.00 12.00
FH44 Jake Peavy 3.00 8.00
FH45 Trevor Hoffman 3.00 8.00
FH47 Felix Hernandez 3.00 8.00
FH48 Albert Pujols 6.00 15.00
FH49 Frank Thomas 4.00 10.00
FH50 Vernon Wells 3.00 8.00

2008 UD A Piece of History Franchise History Jersey Blue

OVERALL GU ODDS 1:8
STATED PRINT RUN 25 SER.#'D SETS
NO PRICING DUE TO SCARCITY

2008 UD A Piece of History Franchise History Jersey Gold

*GOLD: .5X TO 1.2X BASIC
OVERALL GU ODDS 1:8
STATED PRINT RUN 99 SER.#'d SETS

2008 UD A Piece of History Franchise History Jersey Gold Patch

OVERALL GU ODDS 1:8
STATED PRINT RUN 25 SER.#'D SETS
NO PRICING DUE TO SCARCITY

2008 UD A Piece of History Franchise History Jersey Autographs

OVERALL AUTO ODDS 1:16
PRINT RUNS B/WN 5-99 COPIES PER
NO PRICING ON QTY 25 OR LESS
FH1 Justin Upton/25
FH3 Mark Teixeira/10
FH5 Chipper Jones/25
FH6 Jonathan Papelbon/99 12.50 30.00
FH8 Daisuke Matsuzaka/15
FH9 Josh Beckett/10
FH11 Alfonso Soriano/15
FH12 Jim Thome/10
FH13 Adam Dunn/25
FH14 Ken Griffey Jr./25
FH17 Travis Hafner/50 6.00 15.00
FH18 Matt Holliday/25
FH19 Troy Tulowitzki/50 12.50 30.00
FH21 Ivan Rodriguez/5
FH22 Miguel Cabrera/10
FH23 Hanley Ramirez/50 12.50 30.00
FH24 Hunter Pence/10
FH25 Lance Berkman/10
FH27 Andruw Jones/15
FH28 Prince Fielder/15
FH29 Ryan Braun/25
FH30 Joe Mauer/10
FH36 Joba Chamberlain/20
FH39 Derek Jeter/24
FH44 Jake Peavy/10
FH45 Trevor Hoffman/10
FH47 Felix Hernandez/75 12.50 30.00
FH48 Albert Pujols/5
FH49 Frank Thomas/10

2008 UD A Piece of History Franchise Members Triple

RANDOM INSERTS IN PACKS
STATED PRINT RUN 799 SER.#'d SETS
BLUE RANDOMLY INSERTED
BLUE PRINT RUN 25 SER.#'d SETS
NO BLUE PRICING DUE TO SCARCITY
*PEWTER: .6X TO 1.5X BASIC
PEWTER RANDOMLY INSERTED
PEWTER PRINT RUN 75 SER.#'d SETS
*RED: .6X TO 1.5X BASIC
RED RANDOMLY INSERTED
RED PRINT RUN 99 SER.#'d SETS
*SILVER: .5X TO 1.2X BASIC
SILVER RANDOMLY INSERTED
SILVER PRINT RUN 149 SER.#'d SETS
1 John Smoltz .60 1.50
Tim Hudson
Tom Glavine
2 Josh Beckett 1.00 2.50
Daisuke Matsuzaka
Curt Schilling
3 David Ortiz .60 1.50
Manny Ramirez
Jason Varitek
4 Ken Griffey Jr. 1.50 4.00
Frank Thomas
Jim Thome
5 Grady Sizemore .60 1.50
Travis Hafner
Victor Martinez
6 Matt Holliday 1.00 2.50
Carlos Lee
Jason Bay
7 Carlos Guillen 1.00 2.50
Magglio Ordonez
Miguel Cabrera
8 Roy Oswalt .40 1.00
Jake Peavy
Dan Haren
9 Jered Weaver 1.00 2.50
Vladimir Guerrero
Casey Kotchman
10 Russell Martin 1.00 2.50
Joe Mauer
Brian McCann
11 Prince Fielder .60 1.50
Ryan Braun
JJ Hardy
12 Joe Mauer 1.00 2.50
Justin Morneau
Joe Nathan
13 Johan Santana 1.00 2.50
Pedro Martinez
Billy Wagner
14 Derek Jeter 2.50 6.00
Jose Reyes
Hanley Ramirez
15 Derek Jeter 2.50 6.00
Robinson Cano
Jason Giambi
16 Jake Peavy .40 1.00
Greg Maddux
Trevor Hoffman
17 Felix Hernandez 1.25 3.00
Justin Verlander
Rich Harden
18 Chris Carpenter 1.00 2.50
Randy Johnson
Cole Hamels
19 Albert Pujols 2.50 6.00
Troy Glaus
Chris Duncan
20 Roy Halladay .60 1.50
A.J. Burnett
Vernon Wells

2008 UD A Piece of History Franchise Members Triple Jersey

OVERALL GU ODDS 1:8
STATED PRINT RUN 99 SER.#'d SETS
1 John Smoltz 5.00 12.00
Tim Hudson
Tom Glavine
2 Josh Beckett 12.50 30.00
Daisuke Matsuzaka
Curt Schilling
3 David Ortiz 10.00 25.00
Manny Ramirez
Jason Varitek
5 Grady Sizemore 5.00 12.00
Travis Hafner
Victor Martinez
6 Matt Holliday 5.00 12.00
Carlos Lee
Jason Bay
7 Carlos Guillen 5.00 12.00
Magglio Ordonez
Miguel Cabrera
8 Roy Oswalt 5.00 12.00
Jake Peavy
Dan Haren
9 Jered Weaver 5.00 12.00
Vladimir Guerrero
Casey Kotchman
10 Russell Martin 5.00 12.00
Joe Mauer
Brian McCann
11 Prince Fielder 8.00 20.00
Ryan Braun
JJ Hardy
12 Joe Mauer 5.00 12.00
Justin Morneau
Joe Nathan
13 Johan Santana 6.00 15.00
Pedro Martinez
Billy Wagner
14 Derek Jeter 12.50 30.00
Jose Reyes
Hanley Ramirez
15 Derek Jeter 15.00 40.00
Robinson Cano
Jason Giambi
16 Jake Peavy 8.00 20.00
Greg Maddux
Trevor Hoffman
17 Felix Hernandez 5.00 12.00
Justin Verlander
Rich Harden
18 Chris Carpenter 6.00 15.00
Randy Johnson
Cole Hamels
19 Albert Pujols 10.00 25.00
Troy Glaus
Chris Duncan
20 Roy Halladay 4.00 10.00
A.J. Burnett
Vernon Wells

2008 UD A Piece of History Franchise Members Quad

RANDOM INSERTS IN PACKS
STATED PRINT RUN 799 SER.#'d SETS
BLUE RANDOMLY INSERTED
BLUE PRINT RUN 25 SER.#'d SETS
NO BLUE PRICING DUE TO SCARCITY
*PEWTER: .6X TO 1.5X BASIC
PEWTER RANDOMLY INSERTED
PEWTER PRINT RUN 75 SER.#'d SETS
*RED: .6X TO 1.5X BASIC
RED RANDOMLY INSERTED
RED PRINT RUN 99 SER.#'d SETS
*SILVER: .5X TO 1.2X BASIC
SILVER RANDOMLY INSERTED
SILVER PRINT RUN 149 SER.#'d SETS
1 Derek Jeter 2.50 6.00
Johnny Damon
Jorge Posada
Jason Giambi
2 Daisuke Matsuzaka 1.00 2.50
Josh Beckett
Jonathan Papelbon
Curt Schilling
3 Jose Reyes 1.00 2.50
Carlos Beltran
Carlos Delgado
Johan Santana
4 Jeff Francoeur 1.00 2.50
Brian McCann
Mark Teixeira
Chipper Jones
5 Prince Fielder .60 1.50
Rickie Weeks
Ryan Braun
JJ Hardy
6 Ken Griffey Jr. .60 1.50
Adam Dunn
Brandon Phillips
Aaron Harang
7 Justin Verlander 1.25 3.00
Joel Zumaya
Jeremy Bonderman
Dontrelle Willis
8 Jim Thome 1.00 2.50
David Ortiz
Frank Thomas
Gary Sheffield
9 Jake Peavy .40 1.00
Greg Maddux
Mark Prior
Chris Young
10 Brandon Webb 1.00 2.50
Dan Haren
Randy Johnson
Conor Jackson
11 Eric Chavez .40 1.00
Bobby Crosby
Rich Harden
Huston Street
12 Felix Hernandez 1.00 2.50
Erik Bedard
Adrian Beltre
Kenji Johjima
13 Chone Figgins 1.00 2.50
Vladimir Guerrero
Torii Hunter
Garret Anderson
14 Jose Reyes 2.50 6.00
Rafael Furcal
Derek Jeter
Jhonny Peralta
15 Ken Griffey Jr. 1.50 4.00
Jim Edmonds
Andruw Jones
Carlos Beltran
16 Ivan Rodriguez 1.00 2.50
Jason Varitek
Joe Mauer
Jorge Posada
17 Hanley Ramirez 1.00 2.50
Dan Uggla
Josh Willingham
Jeremy Hermida
18 Johan Santana 1.00 2.50
Cole Hamels
C.C. Sabathia
Francisco Liriano
19 Prince Fielder .60 1.50
Lance Berkman
Derrek Lee
Conor Jackson
20 Rafael Furcal .60 1.50
Matt Kemp
Andruw Jones
Jeff Kent

2008 UD A Piece of History Franchise Members Quad Jersey

OVERALL GU ODDS 1:8
STATED PRINT RUN 99 SER.#'d SETS
1 Derek Jeter 20.00 50.00
Johnny Damon
Jorge Posada
Jason Giambi
2 Daisuke Matsuzaka 15.00 40.00
Josh Beckett
Jonathan Papelbon
Curt Schilling
3 Jose Reyes 6.00 15.00
Carlos Beltran
Carlos Delgado
Johan Santana
4 Jeff Francoeur 5.00 12.00
Brian McCann
Mark Teixeira
Chipper Jones
5 Prince Fielder 8.00 20.00
Rickie Weeks
Ryan Braun
JJ Hardy
7 Justin Verlander 5.00 12.00
Joel Zumaya
Jeremy Bonderman
Dontrelle Willis
8 Jim Thome 6.00 15.00
David Ortiz
Frank Thomas
Gary Sheffield
9 Jake Peavy 8.00 20.00
Greg Maddux
Mark Prior
Chris Young
10 Brandon Webb 6.00 15.00
Dan Haren
Randy Johnson
Conor Jackson
11 Eric Chavez 4.00 10.00
Bobby Crosby
Rich Harden
Huston Street
12 Felix Hernandez 5.00 12.00
Erik Bedard
Adrian Beltre
Kenji Johjima
13 Chone Figgins 5.00 12.00
Vladimir Guerrero
Torii Hunter
Garret Anderson
14 Jose Reyes 12.50 30.00
Rafael Furcal
Derek Jeter
Jhonny Peralta
16 Ivan Rodriguez 6.00 15.00
Jason Varitek
Joe Mauer
Jorge Posada
18 Johan Santana 6.00 15.00
Cole Hamels
C.C. Sabathia
Francisco Liriano
19 Prince Fielder 6.00 15.00
Lance Berkman
Derrek Lee
Conor Jackson
20 Rafael Furcal 4.00 10.00
Matt Kemp
Andruw Jones
Jeff Kent

2008 UD A Piece of History Stadium Scenes

RANDOM INSERTS IN PACKS
STATED PRINT RUN 699 SER.#'d SETS
*BLUE: .6X TO 1.5X BASIC
BLUE RANDOMLY INSERTED
BLUE PRINT RUN 75 SER.#'d SETS
*COPPER: .6X TO 1.5X BASIC
COPPER RANDOMLY INSERTED
COPPER PRINT RUN 99 SER.#'d SETS
*RED: .5X TO 1.2X BASIC
RED RANDOMLY INSERTED
RED PRINT RUN 149 SER.#'d SETS
SILVER RANDOMLY INSERTED
SILVER PRINT RUN 25 SER.#'d SETS
NO SILVER PRICING DUE TO SCARCITY
SS1 Randy Johnson 1.25 3.00
SS2 Justin Upton .75 2.00
SS3 Mark Teixeira 1.25 3.00
SS4 Chipper Jones 1.25 3.00
SS5 John Smoltz 1.25 3.00
SS6 David Ortiz .75 2.00
SS7 Josh Beckett .75 2.00
SS8 Daisuke Matsuzaka 1.25 3.00
SS9 Manny Ramirez 1.25 3.00
SS10 Jonathan Papelbon .75 2.00
SS11 Alfonso Soriano .75 2.00
SS12 Kerry Wood .50 1.25
SS13 Derrek Lee .50 1.25
SS14 Jim Thome .75 2.00
SS15 Ken Griffey Jr. 2.00 5.00
SS16 Adam Dunn .75 2.00
SS17 Grady Sizemore .75 2.00
SS18 Travis Hafner .50 1.25
SS19 Victor Martinez .75 2.00
SS20 C.C. Sabathia .75 2.00
SS21 Miguel Cabrera 1.25 3.00
SS22 Justin Verlander 1.50 4.00
SS23 Ivan Rodriguez .75 2.00
SS24 Magglio Ordonez .75 2.00
SS25 Lance Berkman .75 2.00
SS26 Roy Oswalt .75 2.00
SS27 Vladimir Guerrero 1.25 3.00
SS28 Andruw Jones .50 1.25
SS29 Rickie Weeks .50 1.25
SS30 Ryan Braun 1.50 4.00
SS31 Prince Fielder .75 2.00
SS32 Joe Mauer 1.25 3.00
SS33 Pedro Martinez .75 2.00
SS34 Jose Reyes .75 2.00
SS35 David Wright 1.50 4.00
SS36 Johan Santana 1.25 3.00
SS37 Derek Jeter 3.00 8.00
SS38 Alex Rodriguez 2.00 5.00
SS39 Hideki Matsui 1.25 3.00
SS40 Joba Chamberlain .75 2.00
SS41 Cole Hamels 1.25 3.00
SS42 Chase Utley 1.25 3.00
SS43 Ryan Howard 1.50 4.00
SS44 Jimmy Rollins .75 2.00
SS45 Jake Peavy .50 1.25
SS46 Greg Maddux 1.50 4.00
SS47 Felix Hernandez 1.25 3.00
SS48 Ichiro Suzuki 2.00 5.00
SS49 Albert Pujols 3.00 8.00
SS50 Frank Thomas 1.25 3.00

2008 UD A Piece of History Stadium Scenes Jersey Red

OVERALL GU ODDS 1:8
SS1 Randy Johnson 4.00 10.00
SS2 Justin Upton 4.00 10.00
SS3 Mark Teixeira 3.00 8.00
SS4 Chipper Jones 3.00 8.00
SS5 John Smoltz 3.00 8.00
SS6 David Ortiz 4.00 10.00
SS7 Josh Beckett 3.00 8.00
SS8 Daisuke Matsuzaka 6.00 15.00
SS9 Manny Ramirez 3.00 8.00
SS10 Jonathan Papelbon 3.00 8.00
SS11 Alfonso Soriano 3.00 8.00
SS12 Kerry Wood 3.00 8.00
SS13 Derrek Lee 3.00 8.00
SS14 Jim Thome 3.00 8.00
SS15 Ken Griffey Jr. 5.00 12.00

SS16 Adam Dunn 3.00 8.00
SS18 Travis Hafner 3.00 8.00
SS19 Victor Martinez 3.00 8.00
SS20 C.C. Sabathia 3.00 8.00
SS21 Miguel Cabrera 3.00 8.00
SS22 Justin Verlander 3.00 8.00
SS23 Ivan Rodriguez 3.00 8.00
SS24 Magglio Ordonez 3.00 8.00
SS25 Lance Berkman 3.00 8.00
SS26 Roy Oswalt 3.00 8.00
SS27 Vladimir Guerrero 3.00 8.00
SS28 Andruw Jones 3.00 8.00
SS29 Rickie Weeks 3.00 8.00
SS30 Ryan Braun 5.00 12.00
SS31 Prince Fielder 4.00 10.00
SS32 Joe Mauer 3.00 8.00
SS33 Pedro Martinez 3.00 8.00
SS34 Jose Reyes 3.00 8.00
SS36 Johan Santana 4.00 10.00
SS37 Derek Jeter 8.00 20.00
SS38 Alex Rodriguez 6.00 15.00
SS40 Joba Chamberlain 8.00 20.00
SS41 Cole Hamels 3.00 8.00
SS42 Chase Utley 3.00 8.00
SS44 Jimmy Rollins 3.00 8.00
SS45 Jake Peavy 3.00 8.00
SS46 Greg Maddux 5.00 12.00
SS47 Felix Hernandez 3.00 8.00
SS49 Albert Pujols 6.00 15.00
SS50 Frank Thomas 4.00 10.00

2008 UD A Piece of History Stadium Scenes Jersey Blue

OVERALL GU ODDS 1:8
STATED PRINT RUN 25 SER.#'D SETS
NO PRICING DUE TO SCARCITY

2008 UD A Piece of History Stadium Scenes Jersey Gold

*GOLD: .5X TO 1.2X BASIC
OVERALL GU ODDS 1:8
STATED PRINT RUN 99 SER.#'d SETS

2008 UD A Piece of History Stadium Scenes Jersey Gold Patch

OVERALL GU ODDS 1:8
STATED PRINT RUN 25 SER.#'D SETS
NO PRICING DUE TO SCARCITY

2008 UD A Piece of History Stadium Scenes Jersey Autographs

OVERALL AUTO ODDS 1:16
PRINT RUNS B/WN 10-99 COPIES PER
NO PRICING ON QTY 25 OR LESS
SS2 Justin Upton/25
SS3 Mark Teixeira/10
SS4 Chipper Jones/25
SS7 Josh Beckett/10
SS8 Daisuke Matsuzaka/15
SS10 Jonathan Papelbon/99 12.50 30.00
SS11 Alfonso Soriano/15
SS12 Kerry Wood/99 6.00 15.00
SS13 Derrek Lee/25
SS14 Jim Thome/10
SS15 Ken Griffey Jr./25
SS16 Adam Dunn/25
SS18 Travis Hafner/50 6.00 15.00
SS19 Victor Martinez/99 6.00 15.00
SS21 Miguel Cabrera/10
SS22 Justin Verlander/15
SS25 Lance Berkman/10
SS26 Roy Oswalt/25
SS28 Andruw Jones/25
SS29 Rickie Weeks/50 6.00 15.00
SS30 Ryan Braun/25
SS31 Prince Fielder/15
SS32 Joe Mauer/10
SS37 Derek Jeter/25
SS40 Joba Chamberlain/20
SS41 Cole Hamels/25
SS45 Jake Peavy/10
SS47 Felix Hernandez/75 12.50 30.00
SS50 Frank Thomas/10

2008 UD A Piece of History Timeless Moments

RANDOM INSERTS IN PACKS
STATED PRINT RUN 699 SER.#'d SETS
*BLUE: .6X TO 1.5X BASIC
BLUE RANDOMLY INSERTED
BLUE PRINT RUN 75 SER.#'d SETS
*COPPER: .6X TO 1.5X BASIC
COPPER RANDOMLY INSERTED
COPPER PRINT RUN 99 SER.#'d SETS
*RED: .5X TO 1.2X BASIC
RED RANDOMLY INSERTED
RED PRINT RUN 149 SER.#'d SETS
SILVER RANDOMLY INSERTED
SILVER PRINT RUN 25 SER.#'d SETS
NO SILVER PRICING DUE TO SCARCITY
1 Randy Johnson 1.25 3.00
2 Dan Haren .50 1.25
3 John Smoltz 1.25 3.00
4 Chipper Jones 1.25 3.00
5 Mark Teixeira 1.25 3.00
6 David Ortiz .75 2.00
7 Dustin Pedroia 1.50 4.00
8 Josh Beckett .75 2.00
9 Curt Schilling .75 2.00
10 Daisuke Matsuzaka 1.25 3.00
11 Alfonso Soriano .75 2.00
12 Carlos Zambrano .75 2.00
13 Jim Thome .75 2.00
14 Ken Griffey Jr. 2.00 5.00
15 Adam Dunn .75 2.00
16 Grady Sizemore .75 2.00
17 C.C. Sabathia .75 2.00
18 Troy Tulowitzki 1.25 3.00
19 Matt Holliday 1.25 3.00
20 Justin Verlander 1.50 4.00
21 Ivan Rodriguez .75 2.00
22 Hanley Ramirez 1.25 3.00
23 Alex Gordon .75 2.00
24 Vladimir Guerrero 1.25 3.00
25 Jeff Kent .50 1.25
26 Nomar Garciaparra 1.25 3.00
27 Prince Fielder .75 2.00
28 Joe Mauer 1.25 3.00
29 Justin Morneau 1.25 3.00
30 Jose Reyes .75 2.00
31 David Wright 1.50 4.00
32 Pedro Martinez .75 2.00
33 Johan Santana 1.25 3.00
34 Joba Chamberlain .75 2.00
35 Derek Jeter 3.00 8.00
36 Alex Rodriguez 2.00 5.00
37 Hideki Matsui 1.25 3.00
38 Ryan Howard 1.50 4.00
39 Chase Utley 1.25 3.00
40 Jimmy Rollins .75 2.00
41 Cole Hamels 1.25 3.00
42 Jake Peavy .50 1.25
43 Greg Maddux 1.50 4.00
44 Phil Hughes 1.25 3.00
45 Felix Hernandez 1.25 3.00
46 Ichiro Suzuki 2.00 5.00
47 Albert Pujols 3.00 8.00
48 Chris Carpenter 1.25 3.00
49 Frank Thomas 1.25 3.00
50 Vernon Wells .50 1.25

2008 UD A Piece of History Timeless Moments Jersey

OVERALL GU ODDS 1:8
1 Randy Johnson 4.00 10.00
2 Dan Haren 3.00 8.00
3 John Smoltz 3.00 8.00
5 Mark Teixeira 3.00 8.00
6 David Ortiz 4.00 10.00
7 Dustin Pedroia 3.00 8.00
8 Josh Beckett 3.00 8.00
9 Curt Schilling 3.00 8.00
10 Daisuke Matsuzaka 6.00 15.00
11 Alfonso Soriano 3.00 8.00
12 Carlos Zambrano 3.00 8.00
13 Jim Thome 3.00 8.00
17 C.C. Sabathia 3.00 8.00
18 Troy Tulowitzki 3.00 8.00
19 Matt Holliday 3.00 8.00
20 Justin Verlander 3.00 8.00
21 Ivan Rodriguez 3.00 8.00
22 Hanley Ramirez 3.00 8.00
23 Alex Gordon 4.00 10.00
24 Vladimir Guerrero 3.00 8.00
25 Jeff Kent 3.00 8.00
27 Prince Fielder 4.00 10.00
28 Joe Mauer 3.00 8.00
29 Justin Morneau 3.00 8.00
30 Jose Reyes 3.00 8.00
32 Pedro Martinez 3.00 8.00
33 Johan Santana 4.00 10.00
34 Joba Chamberlain 8.00 20.00
35 Derek Jeter 8.00 20.00
36 Alex Rodriguez 6.00 15.00
39 Chase Utley 3.00 8.00
40 Jimmy Rollins 3.00 8.00
41 Cole Hamels 3.00 8.00
42 Jake Peavy 3.00 8.00
43 Greg Maddux 5.00 12.00
44 Phil Hughes 4.00 10.00
45 Felix Hernandez 3.00 8.00
47 Albert Pujols 6.00 15.00
48 Chris Carpenter 3.00 8.00
49 Frank Thomas 4.00 10.00
50 Vernon Wells 3.00 8.00

2008 UD A Piece of History Timeless Moments Jersey Blue

OVERALL GU ODDS 1:8
STATED PRINT RUN 25 SER.#'D SETS
NO PRICING DUE TO SCARCITY

2008 UD A Piece of History Timeless Moments Jersey Gold

*GOLD: .5X TO 1.2X BASIC
OVERALL GU ODDS 1:8
STATED PRINT RUN 99 SER.#'d SETS

2008 UD A Piece of History Timeless Moments Jersey Gold Patch

OVERALL GU ODDS 1:8
STATED PRINT RUN 25 SER.#'D SETS
NO PRICING DUE TO SCARCITY

2008 UD A Piece of History Timeless Moments Autographs

OVERALL AUTO ODDS 1:16
PRINT RUNS B/WN 5-75 COPIES PER
NO PRICING ON QTY 25 OR LESS
2 Dan Haren/50 6.00 15.00
4 Chipper Jones/25
5 Mark Teixeira/10
8 Josh Beckett/10
10 Daisuke Matsuzaka/15
11 Alfonso Soriano/15
13 Jim Thome/10
14 Ken Griffey Jr./25
15 Adam Dunn/25
18 Troy Tulowitzki/50 12.50 30.00
19 Matt Holliday/25
20 Justin Verlander/15
22 Hanley Ramirez/50
23 Alex Gordon/25
27 Prince Fielder/15
28 Joe Mauer/10
29 Justin Morneau/5
34 Joba Chamberlain/50 100.00 150.00
35 Derek Jeter/25
41 Cole Hamels/25
42 Jake Peavy/10
44 Phil Hughes/50 15.00 40.00
45 Felix Hernandez/75 12.50 30.00
47 Albert Pujols/5
49 Frank Thomas/10

2009 UD A Piece of History

This set was released on April 8, 2009. The base set consists of 199 cards.

COMPLETE SET (200) 20.00 50.00
COMMON CARD .20 .50
COMMON ROOKIE .40 1.00
1 Brandon Webb .30 .75
2 Randy Johnson .30 .75
3 Dan Haren .20 .50
4 Adam Dunn .30 .75
5 Chipper Jones .50 1.25
6 John Smoltz .50 1.25
7 Tom Glavine .30 .75
8 Brian Roberts .20 .50
9 Nick Markakis .50 1.25
10 Josh Beckett .30 .75
11 David Ortiz .30 .75
12 Daisuke Matsuzaka .50 1.25
13 Jacoby Ellsbury .50 1.25
14 Jonathan Papelbon .30 .75
15 Alfonso Soriano .30 .75
16 Derrek Lee .20 .50
17 Kosuke Fukudome .50 1.25
18 Carlos Zambrano .30 .75
19 Aramis Ramirez .20 .50
20 Rich Harden .20 .50
21 Carlos Quentin .20 .50
22 Jim Thome .30 .75
23 Ken Griffey Jr. .75 2.00
24 Jay Bruce .30 .75
25 Edinson Volquez .20 .50
26 Brandon Phillips .20 .50
27 Victor Martinez .30 .75
28 Grady Sizemore .30 .75
29 Travis Hafner .30 .75
30 Matt Holliday .50 1.25
31 Troy Tulowitzki .50 1.25
32 Garrett Atkins .20 .50
33 Miguel Cabrera .50 1.25
34 Magglio Ordonez .30 .75
35 Justin Verlander .60 1.50
36 Hanley Ramirez .30 .75
37 Dan Uggla .30 .75
38 Lance Berkman .30 .75
39 Carlos Lee .20 .50
40 Kevin Youkilis .20 .50
41 Miguel Tejada .30 .75
42 Alex Gordon .30 .75
43 Zack Greinke .30 .75
44 Mark Teixeira .50 1.25
45 Vladimir Guerrero .50 1.25
46 Torii Hunter .20 .50
47 Manny Ramirez .50 1.25
48 Russell Martin .30 .75
49 Matt Kemp .30 .75
50 Clayton Kershaw .50 1.25
51 CC Sabathia .30 .75
52 Corey Hart .20 .50
53 Prince Fielder .30 .75
54 Ryan Braun .60 1.50
55 Joe Mauer .50 1.25
56 Justin Morneau .50 1.25
57 Jose Reyes .30 .75
58 David Wright .60 1.50
59 Johan Santana .50 1.25
60 Carlos Beltran .20 .50
61 Pedro Martinez .30 .75
62 Alex Rodriguez .75 2.00
63 Derek Jeter 1.25 3.00
64 Chien-Ming Wang .30 .75
65 Hideki Matsui .50 1.25
66 Joba Chamberlain .30 .75
67 Mariano Rivera .50 1.25
68 Xavier Nady .20 .50
69 Frank Thomas .50 1.25
70 Jason Giambi .20 .50
71 Chase Utley .50 1.25
72 Ryan Howard .60 1.50
73 Jimmy Rollins .30 .75
74 Ryan Doumit .20 .50
75 Nate McLouth .20 .50
76 Adrian Gonzalez .30 .75
77 Chris Young
78 Jake Peavy .20 .50
79 Brian Giles .20 .50
80 Tim Lincecum .75 2.00
81 Matt Cain .20 .50
82 Felix Hernandez .50 1.25
83 Ichiro Suzuki .75 2.00
84 Erik Bedard .20 .50
85 Ryan Ludwick .30 .75
86 Albert Pujols 1.25 3.00
87 Chris Carpenter .50 1.25
88 Rick Ankiel .20 .50
89 B.J. Upton .30 .75
90 Evan Longoria .60 1.50
91 Scott Kazmir .20 .50
92 Carl Crawford .30 .75
93 Josh Hamilton .50 1.25
94 Ian Kinsler .30 .75
95 Michael Young .30 .75
96 Roy Halladay .50 1.25
97 Vernon Wells .20 .50
98 Alex Rios .30 .75
99 Ryan Zimmerman .30 .75
100 Lastings Milledge .20 .50
101 David Price RC 1.00 2.50
102 Conor Gillaspie RC 1.00 2.50
103 Josh Roenicke RC .40 1.00
104 Jeff Baisley RC .40 1.00
105 Alfredo Aceves RC .60 1.50
106 Matt Antonelli (RC) .60 1.50
107 Michael Bowden (RC) .40 1.00
108 Josh Whitesell RC .60 1.50
109 Wilkin Castillo RC .40 1.00
110 Francisco Cervelli RC 1.00 2.50
111 Phil Coke RC .60 1.50
112 Luis Cruz RC .40 1.00
113 Jesus Delgado RC .60 1.50
114 Scott Elbert (RC) .40 1.00
115 Alcides Escobar RC 1.00 2.50
116 Dexter Fowler (RC) .60 1.50
117 Mat Gamel RC 1.00 2.50
118 Josh Geer (RC) .40 1.00
119 Greg Golson (RC) .40 1.00
120 Kila Ka'aihue (RC) .60 1.50
121 Chris Lambert (RC) .40 1.00
122 Wade LeBlanc RC .60 1.50
123 Scott Lewis (RC) .40 1.00
124 Lou Marson (RC) .40 1.00
125 Shairon Martis RC .60 1.50
126 James McDonald RC .60 1.50
127 Juan Miranda RC .60 1.50
128 Luke Montz RC .40 1.00
129 Jonathon Niese RC .60 1.50
130 Josh Outman RC .60 1.50
131 James Parr (RC) .40 1.00
132 Dusty Ryan RC .40 1.00
133 Angel Salome (RC) .40 1.00
134 Travis Snider RC .60 1.50
135 Matt Tuiasosopo (RC) .40 1.00
136 Will Venable RC .40 1.00
137 Aaron Cunningham RC .40 1.00
138 George Kottaras (RC) .40 1.00
139 Devon Lowery (RC) .40 1.00
140 Jose Mijares RC 1.00 2.50
141 Jason Motte (RC) .60 1.50
142 Bobby Parnell RC .60 1.50
143 Fernando Perez (RC) .40 1.00
144 Jason Pridie (RC) .40 1.00
145 Ramon Ramirez (RC) .40 1.00
146 Justin Thomas (RC) .40 1.00
147 Luis Valbuena RC .60 1.50
148 Gaby Sanchez RC .60 1.50
149 Mike Hinckley (RC) .40 1.00
150 Mitch Talbot (RC) .40 1.00
151 Star Spangled Banner .20 .50
152 Dwight D. Eisenhower .20 .50
153 First Atomic Submarine Launched .20 .50
154 Alaska Becomes 49th State .20 .50
155 I Have A Dream Speech .20 .50
156 18th Amendment Adopted .20 .50
157 Discovery of Penicillin .20 .50
158 Germany Leaves League of Nations .20 .50
159 Attack on Pearl Harbor .20 .50
160 U.S.A. Enters World War II .20 .50
161 D-Day Invasion .20 .50
162 NATO Organized .20 .50
163 1970 Earth Day .20 .50
164 1989 San Francisco Earthquake .20 .50
165 Warsaw Pact .20 .50
166 NAFTA .20 .50
167 Boy Scouts of America Launches .20 .50
168 New Zealand Pioneers Women's Voting Rights .20 .50
169 First Moving Assembly Line .20 .50
170 Hollywood Sign Debuts .20 .50
171 Taj Mahal Completed .20 .50
172 United States Constitution Signed .20 .50
173 Empire State Building Built .20 .50
174 Golden Gate Bridge Completed .20 .50
175 Smallpox Eradicated .20 .50
176 Elevator Invented .20 .50
177 Microwave Oven Invented .20 .50
178 E-Mail Invented .20 .50
179 Eiffel Tower Erected .20 .50
180 Pilgrims Land at Plymouth Rock .20 .50
181 First Photograph Taken .20 .50
182 First Anesthetic Used .20 .50
183 First Kentucky Derby .20 .50
184 Brooklyn Bridge Completed .20 .50
185 X-Ray Invented .20 .50
186 Pluto Recategorized as Dwarf Planet .20 .50
187 Mount Rushmore Finished .20 .50
188 Thanksgiving Adopted as Holiday .20 .50
189 Chicago Cubs .20 .50
190 Baseball Hall of Fame Opens .20 .50
191 National League Established .20 .50
192 Olympic Games Begin .20 .50
193 Voyager 2 .20 .50
194 New Orleans Founded .20 .50
195 Discovery of New York .20 .50
196 Debut of New York Times .20 .50
197 Republican Party Founded .20 .50
198 City of Boston Founded .20 .50
199 Introduction of EURO Currency .20 .50
200 Czechoslavakia Splits in Two .20 .50

2009 UD A Piece of History Blue

*BLUE VET 1-100: .75X TO 2X BASIC
*BLUE RC 101-150: .6X TO 1.5X BASIC
*BLUE HIST.151-200: .75X TO 2X BASIC
RANDOM INSERTS IN PACKS
STATED PRINT RUN 299 SER.#'d SETS

2009 UD A Piece of History Gold

*GOLD VET 1-100: 2X TO 5X BASIC
*GOLD RC 101-150: 1X TO 2.5X BASIC
*GOLD HIST.151-200: 1.2X TO 3X BASIC
RANDOM INSERTS IN PACKS
STATED PRINT RUN 50 SER.#'d SETS

2009 UD A Piece of History Green

*GRN VET 1-100: 1.5X TO 4X BASIC
*GRN RC 101-150: .75X TO 2X BASIC
*GRN.HIST.151-200: 1X TO 2.5X BASIC
RANDOM INSERTS IN PACKS
STATED PRINT RUN 150 SER.#'d SETS

2009 UD A Piece of History Red

*RED VET 1-100: .6X TO 1.5X BASIC
*RED RC 101-150: .5X TO 1.2X BASIC
*RED.HIST.151-200: .6X TO 1.5X BASIC
RANDOM INSERTS IN PACKS

2009 UD A Piece of History Rookie Autographs Blue

*BLUE: .5X TO 1.2X BASIC
OVERALL AUTO ODDS 1:16
STATED PRINT RUN 99 SER.#'d SETS
EXCHANGE DEADLINE 3/16/2011
120 Kila Ka'aihue 6.00 15.00
125 Shairon Martis 5.00 12.00

2009 UD A Piece of History Rookie Autographs Green

COMPLETE SET (30)
OVERALL AUTO ODDS 1:16
STATED PRINT RUN 25 SER.#'d SETS
NO PRICING DUE TO SCARCITY
EXCHANGE DEADLINE 3/16/2011

2009 UD A Piece of History Rookie Autographs Violet

OVERALL AUTO ODDS 1:16
EXCHANGE DEADLINE 3/16/2011
101 David Price 15.00 40.00
102 Conor Gillaspie 6.00 15.00
104 Jeff Baisley 3.00 8.00
106 Matt Antonelli 3.00 8.00
107 Michael Bowden 10.00 25.00
110 Francisco Cervelli 6.00 15.00
111 Phil Coke 5.00 12.00
112 Luis Cruz 3.00 8.00
113 Jesus Delgado 3.00 8.00
116 Dexter Fowler 10.00 25.00
117 Mat Gamel 8.00 20.00
118 Josh Geer 4.00 10.00
119 Greg Golson 3.00 8.00
120 Kila Ka'aihue 5.00 12.00
121 Chris Lambert 3.00 8.00
122 Wade LeBlanc 3.00 8.00
124 Lou Marson 5.00 12.00
125 Shairon Martis 3.00 8.00
126 James McDonald 8.00 20.00
127 Juan Miranda 5.00 12.00
128 Luke Montz 3.00 8.00
130 Josh Outman 3.00 8.00
131 James Parr 3.00 8.00
133 Angel Salome 4.00 10.00
134 Travis Snider 15.00 40.00
135 Matt Tuiasosopo 4.00 10.00
137 Aaron Cunningham 3.00 8.00
138 George Kottaras
143 Fernando Perez 4.00 10.00
148 Gaby Sanchez 5.00 12.00

2009 UD A Piece of History A Piece of Hollywood

STATED ODDS 1:16
POHAS Arnold Schwarzenegger 20.00 50.00
POHBA Ben Affleck 0.00 0.00
POHBL Bruce Lee 30.00 60.00
POHBS Ben Stiller 3.00 8.00
POHDB Drew Barrymore 6.00 15.00
POHDW Denzel Washington 6.00 15.00
POHHB Humphrey Bogart
POHHJ John Hurt 3.00 8.00
POHHL Heath Ledger 12.50 30.00
POHHU John Hurt 3.00 8.00
POHJH John Hurt 3.00 8.00
POHMM Mike Myers 3.00 8.00
POHRM Rachel McAdams 8.00 20.00
POHSA Adam Sandler 4.00 10.00
POHSB Ben Stiller 3.00 8.00
POHSG Sidney Greenstreet 5.00 12.00
POHSP Sean Penn 4.00 10.00
POHST Ben Stiller 3.00 8.00
POHTH Tom Hanks 5.00 12.00
POHWD Denzel Washington 6.00 15.00
POHWF Will Ferrell 4.00 10.00
POHWS Will Smith 30.00 60.00

2009 UD A Piece of History Box Score Memories

RANDOM INSERTS IN PACKS
STATED PRINT RUN 999 SER.#'d SETS
*BLACK: .5X TO 1.2X BASIC
BLACK RANDOMLY INSERTED
BLACK PRINT RUN 149 SER.#'d SETS
*BLUE: 1.5X TO 4X BASIC
BLUE RANDOMLY INSERTED
BLUE PRINT RUN 25 SER.#'d SETS
*RED: .75X TO 2X BASIC
RED RANDOMLY INSERTED
RED PRINT RUN 75 SER.#'d SETS
*TURQUOISE: .6X TO 1.5X BASIC
TURQUOISE RANDOMLY INSERTED
TURQUOISE PRINT RUN 99 SER.#'d SETS
BSMCD Carlos Delgado .40 1.00
BSMCF Chone Figgins .40 1.00
BSMCJ Chipper Jones 1.00 2.50
BSMCL Carlos Lee .40 1.00
BSMDL Derrek Lee .40 1.00
BSMDO David Ortiz .60 1.50
BSMDU Dan Uggla .60 1.50
BSMGS Gary Sheffield .40 1.00
BSMHR Hanley Ramirez 1.00 2.50
BSMJD Johnny Damon .60 1.50
BSMJF Jeff Francoeur .60 1.50
BSMJH Jeremy Hermida .40 1.00
BSMJM Justin Morneau 1.00 2.50
BSMKG Khalil Greene .40 1.00
BSMMM Melvin Mora .40 1.00
BSMMR Manny Ramirez 1.00 2.50
BSMNM Nick Markakis 1.00 2.50
BSMPB Pat Burrell .40 1.00
BSMPK Paul Konerko .60 1.50
BSMRB Ryan Braun 1.25 3.00
BSMRF Rafael Furcal .40 1.00
BSMRW Rickie Weeks .60 1.50
BSMTH Travis Hafner .40 1.00
BSMVM Victor Martinez .60 1.50
BSMYE Yunel Escobar .40 1.00

2009 UD A Piece of History Box Score Memories Jersey

OVERALL MEM ODDS 1:16
BSMCD Carlos Delgado 3.00 8.00
BSMCF Chone Figgins 3.00 8.00
BSMCJ Chipper Jones 4.00 10.00
BSMCL Carlos Lee 3.00 8.00
BSMDL Derrek Lee 3.00 8.00
BSMDO David Ortiz 3.00 8.00
BSMDU Dan Uggla 3.00 8.00
BSMGS Gary Sheffield 3.00 8.00
BSMHR Hanley Ramirez 4.00 10.00
BSMJD Johnny Damon 3.00 8.00
BSMJF Jeff Francoeur 3.00 8.00
BSMJH Jeremy Hermida 3.00 8.00
BSMJM Justin Morneau 3.00 8.00
BSMKG Khalil Greene 3.00 8.00
BSMMM Melvin Mora 3.00 8.00
BSMMR Manny Ramirez 4.00 10.00
BSMNM Nick Markakis 4.00 10.00
BSMPB Pat Burrell 4.00 10.00
BSMPK Paul Konerko 3.00 8.00
BSMRB Ryan Braun 4.00 10.00
BSMRF Rafael Furcal 3.00 8.00
BSMRW Rickie Weeks 3.00 8.00
BSMTH Travis Hafner 3.00 8.00
BSMVM Victor Martinez 3.00 8.00
BSMYE Yunel Escobar 3.00 8.00

2009 UD A Piece of History Box Score Memories Jersey Red

*RED: .4X TO 1X BASIC
OVERALL MEM ODDS 1:16
STATED PRINT RUN 180 SER.#'d SETS

2009 UD A Piece of History Cut From The Same Cloth

RANDOM INSERTS IN PACKS
STATED PRINT RUN 999 SER.#'d SETS
*GOLD: .75X TO 2X BASIC
GOLD RANDOMLY INSERTED
GOLD PRINT RUN 75 SER.#'d SETS
*GREEN: .5X TO 1.2X BASIC
GREEN RANDOMLY INSERTED
GREEN PRINT RUN 149 SER.#'d SETS
*PURPLE: 1.5X TO 4X BASIC
PURPLE RANDOMLY INSERTED
PURPLE PRINT RUN 25 SER.#'d SETS
*RED: .6X TO 1.5X BASIC
RED RANDOMLY INSERTED
RED PRINT RUN 99 SER.#'d SETS
CSCAH Josh Hamilton .40 1.00
Rick Ankiel
CSCBC Josh Beckett .60 1.50
Joba Chamberlain
CSCBH Lance Berkman 1.00 2.50
Josh Hamilton
CSCBS Carlos Beltran .60 1.50
Grady Sizemore
CSCGB Ken Griffey Jr. .60 1.50
Jay Bruce
CSCGO Vladimir Guerrero 1.00 2.50
David Ortiz
CSCHF Ryan Howard .60 1.50
Prince Fielder
CSCHV Felix Hernandez 1.00 2.50
Edinson Volquez
CSCIC Ichiro Suzuki .60 1.50
Carl Crawford
CSCJK Randy Johnson .40 1.00
Scott Kazmir
CSCJT Derek Jeter 2.50 6.00
Troy Tulowitzki
CSCMG Justin Morneau 1.00 2.50
Adrian Gonzalez
CSCMM Joe Mauer .40 1.00
Russell Martin
CSCMS Pedro Martinez 1.00 2.50
Johan Santana
CSCOL Roy Oswalt 1.50 4.00
Tim Lincecum
CSCPC Albert Pujols 1.00 2.50
Miguel Cabrera
CSCPE Dustin Pedroia 1.25 3.00
Jacoby Ellsbury
CSCPW Jake Peavy .40 1.00
Brandon Webb
CSCQB Carlos Quentin 1.25 3.00
Ryan Braun
CSCRH Manny Ramirez 1.00 2.50
Matt Holliday
CSCRP Francisco Rodriguez .60 1.50
Jonathan Papelbon
CSCRR Jose Reyes .60 1.50
Jimmy Rollins
CSCRW Alex Rodriguez 1.50 4.00
David Wright
CSCSR Alfonso Soriano 1.00 2.50
Hanley Ramirez
CSCTJ Mark Teixeira 1.00 2.50
Chipper Jones
CSCUK Chase Utley .60 1.50
Ian Kinsler
CSCUU B.J. Upton .60 1.50
Justin Upton
CSCWL David Wright 1.25 3.00
Evan Longoria
CSCWM Chien-Ming Wang 1.00 2.50
Daisuke Matsuzaka
CSCZS Carlos Zambrano .60 1.50
CC Sabathia

2009 UD A Piece of History Franchise History

RANDOM INSERTS IN PACKS
STATED PRINT RUN 999 SER.#'d SETS
*BLACK: .5X TO 1.2X BASIC
BLACK RANDOMLY INSERTED
BLACK PRINT RUN 149 SER.#'d SETS
*BLUE: 1.5X TO 4X BASIC
BLUE RANDOMLY INSERTED
BLUE PRINT RUN 25 SER.#'d SETS
*RED: .75X TO 2X BASIC
RED RANDOMLY INSERTED
RED PRINT RUN 75 SER.#'d SETS
*TURQUOISE: .6X TO 1.5X BASIC
TURQUOISE RANDOMLY INSERTED
TURQUOISE PRINT RUN 99 SER.#'d SETS
FHAP Albert Pujols 2.50 6.00
FHBC Bobby Crosby .40 1.00
FHBM Brian McCann .60 1.50
FHBR Brian Roberts .40 1.00
FHCH Cole Hamels 1.00 2.50
FHCL Carlos Lee .40 1.00
FHDJ Derek Jeter 2.50 6.00
FHDL Derrek Lee .40 1.00
FHDU Dan Uggla .60 1.50
FHFL Francisco Liriano .60 1.50
FHHE Todd Helton .60 1.50
FHJH Josh Hamilton 1.00 2.50
FHJR Jose Reyes .60 1.50
FHJV Jason Varitek 1.00 2.50
FHKG Khalil Greene .40 1.00
FHMO Magglio Ordonez .60 1.50
FHPF Prince Fielder .60 1.50
FHPK Paul Konerko .60 1.50
FHRH Roy Halladay 1.00 2.50
FHRJ Randy Johnson .60 1.50
FHRM Russell Martin .40 1.00
FHSK Scott Kazmir .40 1.00
FHTH Travis Hafner .40 1.00
FHTL Tim Lincecum 1.50 4.00
FHZG Zack Greinke .60 1.50

2009 UD A Piece of History Franchise History Jersey

OVERALL MEM ODDS 1:16
FHAP Albert Pujols 6.00 15.00
FHBC Bobby Crosby 3.00 8.00
FHBM Brian McCann 3.00 8.00
FHBR Brian Roberts 3.00 8.00
FHCH Cole Hamels 6.00 15.00
FHCL Carlos Lee 3.00 8.00
FHDJ Derek Jeter 8.00 20.00
FHDL Derrek Lee 3.00 8.00
FHDU Dan Uggla 3.00 8.00
FHFL Francisco Liriano 3.00 8.00
FHHE Todd Helton 4.00 10.00
FHJR Jose Reyes 4.00 10.00
FHJV Jason Varitek 3.00 8.00
FHKG Khalil Greene 3.00 8.00
FHMO Magglio Ordonez 3.00 8.00
FHPF Prince Fielder 3.00 8.00
FHPK Paul Konerko 3.00 8.00
FHRH Roy Halladay 3.00 8.00
FHRM Russell Martin 3.00 8.00
FHSK Scott Kazmir 3.00 8.00
FHTH Travis Hafner 3.00 8.00
FHTL Tim Lincecum 5.00 12.00
FHZG Zack Greinke 4.00 10.00

2009 UD A Piece of History Franchise History Jersey Red

*RED: .4X TO 1X BASIC
OVERALL MEM ODDS 1:16
STATED PRINT RUN 180 SER.#'d SETS

2009 UD A Piece of History Franchise Members Quad

RANDOM INSERTS IN PACKS
STATED PRINT RUN 999 SER.#'d SETS
*GOLD: .75X TO 2X BASIC
GOLD RANDOMLY INSERTED
GOLD PRINT RUN 75 SER.#'d SETS
*GREEN: .5X TO 1.2X BASIC
GREEN RANDOMLY INSERTED
GREEN PRINT RUN 149 SER.#'d SETS
*PURPLE: 1.5X TO 4X BASIC
PURPLE RANDOMLY INSERTED
PURPLE PRINT RUN 25 SER.#'d SETS
*RED: .6X TO 1.5X BASIC
RED RANDOMLY INSERTED
RED PRINT RUN 99 SER.#'d SETS
FMBLTO Lance Berkman .60 1.50
Carlos Lee
Miguel Tejada
Roy Oswalt
FMFGHW Chone Figgins 1.00 2.50
Vladimir Guerrero
Torii Hunter
Reggie Willits
FMGTDQ Gavin Floyd .60 1.50
Jim Thome
Jermaine Dye
Carlos Quentin
FMJRCR Derek Jeter 2.50 6.00
Alex Rodriguez
Joba Chamberlain
Mariano Rivera
FMKCLU Scott Kazmir 1.25 3.00
Carl Crawford
Evan Longoria
B.J. Upton
FMOCGG Magglio Ordonez 1.00 2.50
Miguel Cabrera
Carlos Guillen
Curtis Granderson
FMOYPD David Ortiz 1.25 3.00
Kevin Youkilis
Dustin Pedroia
J.D. Drew
FMRWBS Jose Reyes .60 1.50
David Wright
Carlos Beltran
Johan Santana
FMSHMG Grady Sizemore .60 1.50
Travis Hafner
Victor Martinez
Ryan Garko
FMSLRS Alfonso Soriano .40 1.00
Derrek Lee
Aramis Ramirez
Geovany Soto

2009 UD A Piece of History Franchise Members Trio

RANDOM INSERTS IN PACKS
STATED PRINT RUN 999 SER.#'d SETS
*GOLD: .75X TO 2X BASIC
GOLD RANDOMLY INSERTED
GOLD PRINT RUN 75 SER.#'d SETS
*GREEN: .5X TO 1.2X BASIC
GREEN RANDOMLY INSERTED
GREEN PRINT RUN 149 SER.#'d SETS
*PURPLE: 1.5X TO 4X BASIC
PURPLE RANDOMLY INSERTED
PURPLE PRINT RUN 25 SER.#'d SETS
*RED: .6X TO 1.5X BASIC
RED RANDOMLY INSERTED
RED PRINT RUN 99 SER.#'d SETS
FMBML Josh Beckett 1.00 2.50
Daisuke Matsuzaka
Jon Lester
FMFBS Prince Fielder .60 1.50
Ryan Braun
Jeff Suppan
FMGYG Brian Giles .60 1.50
Chris Young
Adrian Gonzalez
FMHKY Josh Hamilton 1.00 2.50
Ian Kinsler
Michael Young
FMJEM Chipper Jones 1.00 2.50
Yunel Escobar
Brian McCann
FMJRM Derek Jeter 2.50 6.00
Alex Rodriguez
Hideki Matsui
FMPAL Albert Pujols .40 1.00
Rick Ankiel
Ryan Ludwick
FMRUH Hanley Ramirez .60 1.50
Dan Uggla
Jeremy Hermida
FMRWB Jose Reyes .60 1.50
David Wright
Carlos Beltran
FMURH Chase Utley 1.25 3.00
Jimmy Rollins
Ryan Howard

2009 UD A Piece of History Stadium Scenes

RANDOM INSERTS IN PACKS
STATED PRINT RUN 999 SER.#'d SETS
*BLACK: .5X TO 1.2X BASIC
BLACK RANDOMLY INSERTED
BLACK PRINT RUN 149 SER.#'d SETS
*BLUE: 1.5X TO 4X BASIC
BLUE RANDOMLY INSERTED
BLUE PRINT RUN 25 SER.#'d SETS
*RED: .75X TO 2X BASIC
RED RANDOMLY INSERTED
RED PRINT RUN 75 SER.#'d SETS
*TURQUOISE: .6X TO 1.5X BASIC
TURQUOISE RANDOMLY INSERTED
TURQUOISE PRINT RUN 99 SER.#'d SETS
SSAL Adam LaRoche .40 1.00
SSCC Chris Carpenter 1.00 2.50
SSCD Carlos Delgado .40 1.00
SSCG Curtis Granderson .60 1.50
SSCO Chad Cordero .40 1.00
SSCY Chris Young .40 1.00
SSDL Derrek Lee .40 1.00
SSDM Daisuke Matsuzaka 1.00 2.50
SSEC Eric Chavez .40 1.00
SSJC Johnny Cueto .40 1.00
SSJF Jeff Francoeur .40 1.00
SSJM Joe Mauer 1.00 2.50
SSJP Jorge Posada .60 1.50
SSLB Lance Berkman .60 1.50
SSMB Mark Buehrle .60 1.50
SSMR Mark Reynolds .60 1.50

SSNM Nick Markakis	1.00	2.50
SSRB Rocco Baldelli	.40	1.00
SSRG Ryan Garko	.40	1.00
SSRH Roy Halladay	1.00	2.50
SSRM Russell Martin	.40	1.00
SSRW Rickie Weeks	.60	1.50
SSTL Tim Lincecum	1.50	4.00
SSVG Vladimir Guerrero	1.00	2.50
SSZG Zack Greinke	.60	1.50

2009 UD A Piece of History Stadium Scenes Jersey

OVERALL MEM ODDS 1:16

SSAL Adam LaRoche	3.00	8.00
SSCC Chris Carpenter	3.00	8.00
SSCD Carlos Delgado	3.00	8.00
SSCG Curtis Granderson	3.00	8.00
SSCO Chad Cordero	3.00	8.00
SSCY Chris Young	3.00	8.00
SSDL Derrek Lee	3.00	8.00
SSDM Daisuke Matsuzaka	6.00	15.00
SSEC Eric Chavez	3.00	8.00
SSJC Johnny Cueto	3.00	8.00
SSJF Jeff Francoeur	3.00	8.00
SSJM Joe Mauer	3.00	8.00
SSJP Jorge Posada	3.00	8.00
SSLB Lance Berkman	3.00	8.00
SSMB Mark Buehrle	3.00	8.00
SSMR Mark Reynolds	3.00	8.00
SSNM Nick Markakis	4.00	10.00
SSRB Rocco Baldelli	3.00	8.00
SSRH Roy Halladay	3.00	8.00
SSRM Russell Martin	3.00	8.00
SSRW Rickie Weeks	3.00	8.00
SSTL Tim Lincecum	5.00	12.00
SSVG Vladimir Guerrero	3.00	8.00
SSZG Zack Greinke	4.00	10.00

2009 UD A Piece of History Stadium Scenes Jersey Red

*RED: .4X TO 1X BASIC
OVERALL MEM ODDS 1:16
STATED PRINT RUN 180 SER.#'d SETS

2009 UD A Piece of History Stadium Scenes Patch

STATED PRINT RUN 35 SER.#'d SETS

SSAL Adam LaRoche	6.00	15.00
SSCC Chris Carpenter	6.00	15.00
SSCD Carlos Delgado	6.00	15.00
SSCG Curtis Granderson		
SSCO Chad Cordero	6.00	15.00
SSCY Chris Young	6.00	15.00
SSDL Derrek Lee	10.00	25.00
SSDM Daisuke Matsuzaka		
SSEC Eric Chavez	6.00	15.00
SSJF Jeff Francoeur	12.50	30.00
SSJM Joe Mauer		
SSJP Jorge Posada		
SSLB Lance Berkman		
SSMB Mark Buehrle	6.00	15.00
SSMR Mark Reynolds	6.00	15.00
SSNM Nick Markakis	15.00	40.00
SSRB Rocco Baldelli		
SSRG Ryan Garko		
SSRH Roy Halladay	15.00	40.00
SSRM Russell Martin	10.00	25.00
SSRW Rickie Weeks	6.00	15.00
SSTL Tim Lincecum		
SSVG Vladimir Guerrero		
SSZG Zack Greinke	6.00	15.00

2009 UD A Piece of History Timeless Moments

RANDOM INSERTS IN PACKS
STATED PRINT RUN 999 SER.#'d SETS
*BLACK: .5X TO 1.2X BASIC
BLACK RANDOMLY INSERTED
BLACK PRINT RUN 149 SER.#'d SETS
*BLUE: 1.5X TO 4X BASIC
BLUE RANDOMLY INSERTED
BLUE PRINT RUN 25 SER.#'d SETS
*RED: .75X TO 2X BASIC
RED RANDOMLY INSERTED
RED PRINT RUN 75 SER.#'d SETS
*TURQUOISE: .6X TO 1.5X BASIC
TURQUOISE RANDOMLY INSERTED
TURQUOISE PRINT RUN 99 SER.#'d SETS

TMAP Albert Pujols	2.50	6.00
TMBR Brian Roberts	.40	1.00
TMCH Cole Hamels	1.00	2.50
TMDL Derek Lowe	.40	1.00
TMDO David Ortiz	.60	1.50
TMDW Dontrelle Willis	.40	1.00
TMEL Evan Longoria	1.25	3.00
TMEV Edinson Volquez	.40	1.00
TMFT Frank Thomas	1.00	2.50
TMJB Jay Bruce	.60	1.50
TMJD Jermaine Dye	.40	1.00
TMJH Josh Hamilton	1.00	2.50
TMJL Jon Lester	1.00	2.50
TMJP Jonathan Papelbon	.60	1.50
TMJV Joey Votto	1.00	2.50
TMKG Ken Griffey Jr.	1.50	4.00
TMMB Mark Buehrle	.60	1.50
TMML Mike Lowell	.40	1.00
TMPE Jake Peavy	.40	1.00
TMRB Ryan Braun	1.25	3.00
TMRJ Randy Johnson	.60	1.50
TMSK Scott Kazmir	.40	1.00
TMSM John Smoltz	1.00	2.50
TMTG Tom Glavine	.60	1.50

2009 UD A Piece of History Timeless Moments Jersey

OVERALL MEM ODDS 1:16

TMAP Albert Pujols	6.00	15.00
TMBR Brian Roberts	3.00	8.00
TMCH Cole Hamels	6.00	15.00
TMDO David Ortiz	3.00	8.00
TMEL Evan Longoria	10.00	25.00
TMEV Edinson Volquez	3.00	8.00
TMFT Frank Thomas	8.00	20.00
TMJB Jay Bruce	5.00	12.00
TMJD Jermaine Dye	3.00	8.00
TMJH Josh Hamilton	4.00	10.00
TMJL Jon Lester	3.00	8.00
TMJP Jonathan Papelbon	4.00	10.00
TMJV Joey Votto	4.00	10.00
TMKG Ken Griffey Jr.	6.00	15.00
TMMB Mark Buehrle	3.00	8.00
TMML Mike Lowell	3.00	8.00
TMPE Jake Peavy	3.00	8.00
TMRB Ryan Braun	4.00	10.00
TMRJ Randy Johnson	3.00	8.00
TMSK Scott Kazmir	3.00	8.00
TMSM John Smoltz	3.00	8.00
TMTG Tom Glavine	4.00	10.00

2009 UD A Piece of History Timeless Moments Jersey Red

*RED: .4X TO 1X BASIC
OVERALL MEM ODDS 1:16
STATED PRINT RUN 180 SER.#'d SETS

2007 UD Black

COMMON JSY AU (1-42)	12.50	30.00
1-42 PRINT RUNS B/WN 16-75 COPIES PER		
NO PRICING ON QTY 25 OR LESS		
COMMON AU RC (43-72)	10.00	25.00
43-72 PRINT RUN 99 SER.#'d SETS		
EXCHANGE DEADLINE 11/26/2009		
AUTO PRINTING PLATES RANDOMLY INSERTED		
PLATE PRINT RUN 1 SET PER COLOR		
BLACK-CYAN-MAGENTA-YELLOW ISSUED		
NO PLATE PRICING DUE TO SCARCITY		
1 Brandon Webb Jsy AU/75	20.00	50.00
2 Tim Hudson Jsy AU/75	20.00	50.00
3 Cal Ripken Jr. Jsy AU/75	100.00	175.00
4 Nick Markakis Jsy AU/35	30.00	60.00
5 David Ortiz Jsy AU/52	60.00	120.00
6 Jonathan Papelbon Jsy AU/75	30.00	60.00
7 Coco Crisp Jsy AU/43	15.00	40.00
8 Derrek Lee Jsy AU/75	20.00	50.00
9 Paul Konerko Jsy AU/75	15.00	40.00
10 Adam Dunn Jsy AU/75	20.00	50.00
11 Ken Griffey Jr. Jsy AU/75	50.00	100.00
12 Travis Hafner Jsy AU/75	30.00	60.00
13 Victor Martinez Jsy AU/75	15.00	40.00
14 Garrett Atkins Jsy AU/75	12.50	30.00
15 Justin Verlander Jsy AU/75	40.00	80.00
16 Jeremy Bonderman Jsy AU/75	12.50	30.00
17 Curtis Granderson Jsy AU/75	10.00	25.00
18 Hanley Ramirez Jsy AU/75	20.00	50.00
19 Dan Uggla Jsy AU/75	12.50	30.00
20 Lance Berkman Jsy AU/75	30.00	60.00
21 Mark Teahen Jsy AU/75	12.50	30.00
22 John Lackey Jsy AU/75	12.50	30.00
23 Howie Kendrick Jsy AU/75	15.00	40.00
24 Russell Martin Jsy AU/75	20.00	50.00
25 Prince Fielder Jsy AU/75	30.00	60.00
26 Torii Hunter Jsy AU/75	12.50	30.00
27 Justin Morneau Jsy AU/75	20.00	50.00
28 John Maine Jsy AU/75	20.00	50.00
29 Derek Jeter Jsy AU/16		
30 Dan Haren Jsy AU/75	12.50	30.00
31 Eric Chavez Jsy AU/75	12.50	30.00
32 Cole Hamels Jsy AU/75	30.00	60.00
33 Jason Bay Jsy AU/75	15.00	40.00
34 Adrian Gonzalez Jsy AU/75	30.00	60.00
35 Chris Young Jsy AU/75	15.00	40.00
36 Matt Cain Jsy AU/75	15.00	40.00
37 Felix Hernandez Jsy AU/75	20.00	50.00
38 Chris Duncan Jsy AU/75	15.00	40.00
39 B.J. Upton Jsy AU/75	20.00	50.00
40 Ian Kinsler Jsy AU/75	20.00	50.00
41 Roy Halladay Jsy AU/75	50.00	100.00
42a Chad Cordero Jsy AU/75	12.50	30.00
42b Chad Cordero Jsy AU/52	12.50	30.00
43 Adam Lind AU (RC)	10.00	25.00
44 Akinori Iwamura AU RC	50.00	100.00
45 Alex Gordon AU RC	12.50	30.00
46 Andy LaRoche AU (RC)	15.00	40.00
47 Billy Butler AU (RC)	30.00	60.00
48 David Murphy AU (RC)	10.00	25.00
49 Brandon Wood AU (RC)	12.50	30.00
50 Carlos Gomez AU RC	20.00	50.00
51 Chase Headley AU (RC)	15.00	40.00
52 Curtis Thigpen AU (RC)	10.00	25.00
53 Joba Chamberlain AU RC	60.00	120.00
54 Delmon Young AU (RC)	10.00	25.00
55 Felix Pie AU (RC)	12.50	30.00
56 Homer Bailey AU (RC)	20.00	50.00
57 Hunter Pence AU (RC)	40.00	80.00
58 Josh Hamilton AU (RC)	40.00	80.00
59 Kei Igawa AU RC	40.00	80.00
60 Kevin Slowey AU (RC)	20.00	50.00
61 Kurt Suzuki AU (RC)	12.50	30.00
62 Mark Reynolds AU RC	40.00	80.00
63 Daisuke Matsuzaka AU RC	125.00	250.00
64 Justin Upton AU RC	30.00	60.00
65 Phil Hughes AU (RC)	15.00	40.00
66 Ryan Braun AU (RC)	50.00	100.00
67 Ryan Sweeney AU (RC)	10.00	25.00
68 Sean Gallagher AU (RC)	10.00	25.00
69 Tim Lincecum AU RC	175.00	350.00
70 Travis Buck AU (RC)	10.00	25.00
71 Troy Tulowitzki AU (RC)	40.00	80.00
72 Yovani Gallardo AU (RC)	12.50	30.00

2007 UD Black Gold Spectrum

RANDOM INSERTS IN PACKS
STATED PRINT RUN 10 SER.#'d SETS
NO PRICING DUE TO SCARCITY
EXCHANGE DEADLINE 11/26/2009

2007 UD Black Natural Pearl

RANDOM INSERTS IN PACKS
STATED PRINT RUN 1 SER.#'d SET
NO PRICING DUE TO SCARCITY
EXCHANGE DEADLINE 11/26/2009

2007 UD Black August Patch Autographs

RANDOM INSERTS IN PACKS
PRINT RUNS B/WN 4-25 COPIES PER
NO PRICING DUE TO SCARCITY
GOLD SPEC.PRINT RUN 5 SER.#'d SETS
NO GOLD PRICING DUE TO SCARCITY
NAT.PEARL PRINT RUN 1 SER.#'d SET
NO PEARL PRICING DUE TO SCARCITY
EXCHANGE DEADLINE 11/26/2009

2007 UD Black Bat Barrel Autographs

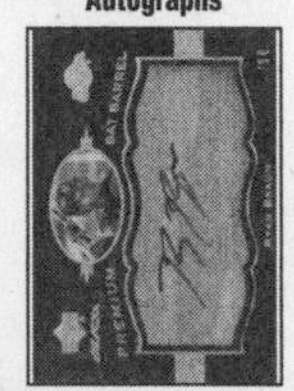

RANDOM INSERTS IN PACKS
PRINT RUNS B/WN 25-50 COPIES PER
GOLD SPEC.PRINT RUN 10 SER.#'d SETS
NO GOLD PRICING DUE TO SCARCITY
NAT.PEARL PRINT RUN 1 SER.#'d SET
NO PEARL PRICING DUE TO SCARCITY
EXCHANGE DEADLINE 11/26/2009

AD Adam Dunn	15.00	40.00
AE Andre Ethier	30.00	60.00
AI Akinori Iwamura	10.00	25.00
AL Andy LaRoche	10.00	25.00
BO Jeremy Bonderman	12.50	30.00
BU B.J. Upton	10.00	25.00
CC Carl Crawford	10.00	25.00
CL Carlos Lee	15.00	40.00
CR Cal Ripken Jr./25		
DJ Derek Jeter	100.00	200.00
DL Derrek Lee	15.00	40.00
DY Delmon Young	10.00	25.00
GA Garrett Atkins	10.00	25.00
HB Homer Bailey	15.00	40.00
HK Howie Kendrick	12.50	30.00
HR Hanley Ramirez	15.00	40.00
HU Torii Hunter	12.50	30.00
IK Ian Kinsler	20.00	50.00
JB Jason Bay	40.00	80.00
JH Josh Hamilton	40.00	80.00
JL John Lackey	12.50	30.00
JM Joe Mauer	40.00	80.00
KG Ken Griffey Jr.	100.00	150.00
KJ Kelly Johnson	12.50	30.00
MO Justin Morneau	15.00	40.00
MT Mark Teixeira	15.00	40.00
RB Ryan Braun	50.00	100.00
RM Russell Martin	20.00	50.00
TH Travis Hafner	20.00	50.00
TT Troy Tulowitzki	50.00	100.00

2007 UD Black Exclusive Eight Autographs

RANDOM INSERTS IN PACKS
STATED PRINT RUN 3 SER.#'d SETS
NO PRICING DUE TO SCARCITY
GOLD SPEC.PRINT RUN 2 SER.#'d SETS
NO GOLD PRICING DUE TO SCARCITY
NAT.PEARL PRINT RUN 1 SER.#'d SET
NO PEARL PRICING DUE TO SCARCITY
EXCHANGE DEADLINE 11/26/2009

2007 UD Black Game Day Box Score Autographs

RANDOM INSERTS IN PACKS
STATED PRINT RUN 50 SER.#'d SETS
GOLD SPEC. PRINT RUN 10 SER.#'d SETS
NO GOLD PRICING DUE TO SCARCITY
NAT.PEARL PRINT RUN 1 SER.#'d SET
NO PEARL PRICING DUE TO SCARCITY
EXCHANGE DEADLINE 11/26/2009

AE Andre Ethier	15.00	40.00
AG Adrian Gonzalez	8.00	20.00
AH Aaron Harang	6.00	15.00
AI Akinori Iwamura	20.00	50.00
AL Adam LaRoche	6.00	15.00
AM Andrew Miller	10.00	25.00
AR Aaron Rowand	6.00	15.00
BA Bronson Arroyo	10.00	25.00
BB Billy Butler	10.00	25.00
BP Brandon Phillips	6.00	15.00
BS Ben Sheets	6.00	15.00
CC Coco Crisp	6.00	15.00
CG Curtis Granderson	10.00	25.00
CH Cole Hamels	12.50	30.00
CY Chris Young	6.00	15.00
DH Dan Haren	8.00	20.00
DL Derrek Lee	10.00	25.00
DW Dontrelle Willis	6.00	15.00
DY Delmon Young	10.00	25.00
FC Fausto Carmona	10.00	25.00
FL Fred Lewis	6.00	15.00
GM Greg Maddux	40.00	80.00
GO Alex Gordon	10.00	25.00
HP Hunter Pence	30.00	60.00
JB Joe Blanton	6.00	15.00
JM John Maine	10.00	25.00
JN Joe Nathan	6.00	15.00
JV Justin Verlander	30.00	60.00
KG Ken Griffey Jr.	40.00	80.00
KI Kei Igawa	15.00	40.00
KJ Kelly Johnson	6.00	15.00
LI Francisco Liriano	6.00	15.00
MC Matt Cain	6.00	15.00
MH Matt Holliday	20.00	50.00
MM Melvin Mora	6.00	15.00
NS Nick Swisher	10.00	25.00
PH Phil Hughes	30.00	60.00
RB Ryan Braun	20.00	50.00
RZ Ryan Zimmerman	15.00	40.00
TB Travis Buck	6.00	15.00
TH Tim Hudson	10.00	25.00
TL Tim Lincecum	60.00	120.00

2007 UD Black Game Day Lineup Autographs

RANDOM INSERTS IN PACKS
STATED PRINT RUN 50 SER.#'d SETS
GOLD SPEC. PRINT RUN 10 SER.#'d SETS
NO GOLD PRICING DUE TO SCARCITY
NAT.PEARL PRINT RUN 1 SER.#'d SET
NO PEARL PRICING DUE TO SCARCITY
EXCHANGE DEADLINE 11/26/2009

AE Andre Ethier	15.00	40.00
AG Adrian Gonzalez	8.00	20.00
AH Aaron Harang	6.00	15.00
AI Akinori Iwamura	20.00	50.00
AL Adam LaRoche	6.00	15.00
AM Andrew Miller	10.00	25.00
AR Aaron Rowand	6.00	15.00
BA Bronson Arroyo	10.00	25.00
BB Billy Butler	10.00	25.00
BP Brandon Phillips	6.00	15.00
BS Ben Sheets	6.00	15.00
CC Coco Crisp	6.00	15.00
CG Curtis Granderson	10.00	25.00
CH Cole Hamels	12.50	30.00
CY Chris Young	6.00	15.00
DH Dan Haren	8.00	20.00
DL Derrek Lee	10.00	25.00
DW Dontrelle Willis	6.00	15.00
DY Delmon Young	10.00	25.00
FC Fausto Carmona	10.00	25.00
FL Fred Lewis	6.00	15.00
GM Greg Maddux	40.00	80.00
GO Alex Gordon	10.00	25.00
HP Hunter Pence	30.00	60.00
JB Joe Blanton	6.00	15.00
JM John Maine	10.00	25.00
JN Joe Nathan	6.00	15.00
JV Justin Verlander	30.00	60.00
KG Ken Griffey Jr.	50.00	100.00
KI Kei Igawa	15.00	40.00
KJ Kelly Johnson	6.00	15.00
LI Francisco Liriano	6.00	15.00
MC Matt Cain	6.00	15.00
MH Matt Holliday	20.00	50.00
MM Melvin Mora	6.00	15.00
NS Nick Swisher	6.00	25.00
PH Phil Hughes	30.00	60.00
RB Ryan Braun	20.00	50.00
RZ Ryan Zimmerman	15.00	40.00
TB Travis Buck	6.00	15.00
TH Tim Hudson	10.00	25.00
TL Tim Lincecum	60.00	120.00

2007 UD Black Game Day Ticket Autographs

RANDOM INSERTS IN PACKS
PRINT RUNS B/WN 15-50 COPIES PER
NO PRICING ON QTY OF 15
GOLD SPEC. PRINT RUN 10 SER.#'d SETS
NO GOLD PRICING DUE TO SCARCITY
NAT.PEARL PRINT RUN 1 SER.#'d SET
NO PEARL PRICING DUE TO SCARCITY
EXCHANGE DEADLINE 11/26/2009

AE Andre Ethier	15.00	40.00
AG Adrian Gonzalez	8.00	20.00
AH Aaron Harang	6.00	15.00
AI Akinori Iwamura	10.00	25.00
AL Adam LaRoche	6.00	15.00
AM Andrew Miller	10.00	25.00
AR Aaron Rowand	6.00	15.00
BA Bronson Arroyo	10.00	25.00
BB Billy Butler	10.00	25.00
BP Brandon Phillips	6.00	15.00
BS Ben Sheets	6.00	15.00
CC Coco Crisp	6.00	15.00
CG Curtis Granderson	10.00	25.00
CH Cole Hamels	12.50	30.00
CY Chris Young	6.00	15.00
DH Dan Haren	8.00	20.00
DL Derrek Lee	10.00	25.00
DW Dontrelle Willis	6.00	15.00
DY Delmon Young	10.00	25.00
FC Fausto Carmona	10.00	25.00
FL Fred Lewis	6.00	15.00
GM Greg Maddux	40.00	80.00
GO Alex Gordon	10.00	25.00
HP Hunter Pence	30.00	60.00
JB Joe Blanton	6.00	15.00
JM John Maine/15		
JN Joe Nathan	6.00	15.00
JV Justin Verlander	15.00	40.00
KG Ken Griffey Jr./15		
KI Kei Igawa	15.00	40.00
KJ Kelly Johnson	6.00	15.00
LI Francisco Liriano	6.00	15.00
MC Matt Cain	6.00	15.00
MH Matt Holliday	20.00	50.00
MM Melvin Mora	6.00	15.00
NS Nick Swisher	6.00	25.00
PH Phil Hughes	30.00	60.00
RB Ryan Braun	20.00	50.00
RZ Ryan Zimmerman	15.00	40.00
TB Travis Buck	6.00	15.00
TH Tim Hudson	10.00	25.00
TL Tim Lincecum	60.00	120.00

2007 UD Black Illustrious Dual Autographs

RANDOM INSERTS IN PACKS
PRINT RUNS B/WN 15-25 COPIES PER
NO PRICING DUE TO SCARCITY
GOLD SPEC.PRINT RUN 15 SER.#'d SETS
NO GOLD PRICING DUE TO SCARCITY
NAT.PEARL PRINT RUN 1 SER.#'d SET
NO PEARL PRICING DUE TO SCARCITY
EXCHANGE DEADLINE 11/26/2009

2007 UD Black Illustrious Dual Materials Autographs

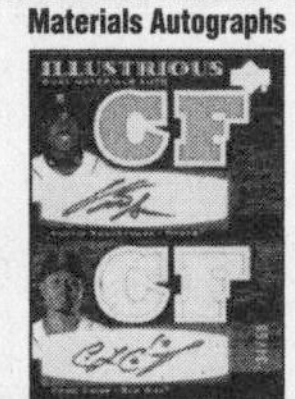

RANDOM INSERTS IN PACKS
PRINT RUNS B/WN 15-50 COPIES PER
NO PRICING ON QTY 15
EXCHANGE DEADLINE 11/26/2009

CI Eric Chavez Akinori Iwamura	20.00	50.00
CK Carl Crawford Scott Kazmir	15.00	40.00
CP Coco Crisp Jonathan Papelbon	20.00	50.00
GB Alex Gordon Ryan Braun	20.00	50.00
GC Curtis Granderson Coco Crisp	20.00	50.00
GH Ken Griffey Jr. Josh Hamilton/15		
GY Adrian Gonzalez Chris Young	12.50	30.00
HH Dan Haren Rich Harden	12.50	30.00
HM Aaron Harang John Maine	12.50	30.00
HW Jeremy Hermida Dontrelle Willis	12.50	30.00
JJ Justin Morneau Jason Bay	20.00	50.00
LC Tim Lincecum Matt Cain	60.00	120.00
LK John Lackey Howie Kendrick	20.00	50.00
LP Carlos Lee Hunter Pence	30.00	60.00
MM Russell Martin Victor Martinez	8.00	20.00
NH Joe Nathan Torii Hunter	12.50	30.00
NM Nick Markakis Melvin Mora	12.50	30.00
RG Aaron Rowand Brian Giles	12.50	30.00
RJ Cal Ripken Jr. Derek Jeter/15		
SB Huston Street Joe Blanton	12.50	30.00
TA Troy Tulowitzki Garrett Atkins	15.00	40.00
UW Dan Uggla Josh Willingham	12.50	30.00
UY B.J. Upton Delmon Young	12.50	30.00
ZB Joel Zumaya Jeremy Bonderman	15.00	40.00

2007 UD Black Illustrious Dual Patch Autographs

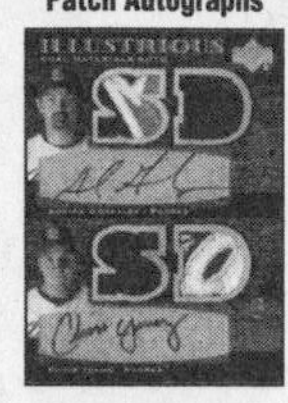

RANDOM INSERTS IN PACKS
PRINT RUNS B/WN 5-15 COPIES PER
NO PRICING DUE TO SCARCITY
EXCHANGE DEADLINE 11/26/2009

2007 UD Black Lustrous Autographs

RANDOM INSERTS IN PACKS
PRINT RUNS B/WN 15-50 COPIES PER
NO PRICING ON QTY 15
GOLD SPEC. PRINT RUN 10 SER.#'d SETS
NO GOLD PRICING DUE TO SCARCITY
NAT.PEARL PRINT RUN 1 SER.#'d SET
NO PEARL PRICING DUE TO SCARCITY
EXCHANGE DEADLINE 11/26/2009

AG Alex Gordon	10.00	25.00
BB Billy Butler	10.00	25.00
BU B.J. Upton	6.00	15.00
CC Carl Crawford	6.00	15.00
CH Cole Hamels	12.50	30.00
CR Cal Ripken Jr./15		
DJ Derek Jeter	75.00	150.00
DL Derrek Lee	10.00	25.00
DU Dan Uggla	6.00	15.00
DW Dontrelle Willis	6.00	15.00
GA Garrett Atkins	6.00	15.00
GR Khalil Greene	10.00	25.00
HA Josh Hamilton	20.00	50.00
HP Hunter Pence	30.00	60.00
HR Hanley Ramirez	10.00	25.00
HS Huston Street	6.00	15.00
IK Ian Kinsler	15.00	40.00
JB Jason Bay	10.00	25.00
JF Jeff Francis	6.00	15.00
JH Jeremy Hermida	6.00	15.00
JL Jon Lester	15.00	40.00
JN Joe Nathan	6.00	15.00
JV Justin Verlander	30.00	60.00
KE Howie Kendrick	10.00	25.00
KG Ken Griffey Jr.	50.00	100.00
KI Kei Igawa	15.00	40.00
LA John Lackey	6.00	15.00
MO Justin Morneau	10.00	25.00
MY Michael Young	6.00	15.00
PA Jonathan Papelbon	20.00	50.00
PF Prince Fielder	20.00	50.00
PH Phil Hughes	30.00	60.00
PK Paul Konerko	10.00	25.00
RM Russell Martin	10.00	25.00
RO Roy Oswalt	10.00	25.00
RT Ryan Theriot	10.00	25.00
RW Rickie Weeks	6.00	15.00
RZ Ryan Zimmerman	8.00	20.00
SA Jarrod Saltalamacchia	10.00	25.00
SK Scott Kazmir	8.00	20.00
TH Torii Hunter	6.00	15.00
VW Vernon Wells	6.00	15.00

2007 UD Black Lustrous Materials Autographs

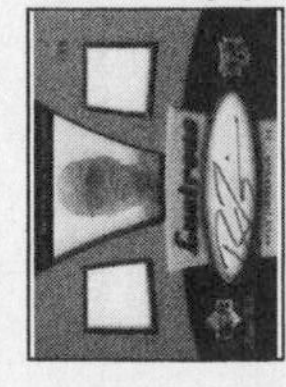

RANDOM INSERTS IN PACKS
PRINT RUNS B/WN 33-50 COPIES PER
GOLD SPEC. PRINT RUN 10 SER.#'d SETS
NO GOLD PRICING DUE TO SCARCITY
NAT.PEARL PRINT RUN 1 SER.#'d SET
NO PEARL PRICING DUE TO SCARCITY
EXCHANGE DEADLINE 11/26/2009

AD Adam Dunn/50	6.00	15.00
AE Andre Ethier/50	15.00	40.00
BO Jeremy Bonderman/50	10.00	25.00
BU B.J. Upton/50	10.00	25.00
CA Melky Cabrera/50	6.00	15.00
CC Carl Crawford/50	6.00	15.00
CL Carlos Lee/50	6.00	15.00
CO Chad Cordero/50	6.00	15.00
CP Coco Crisp/50	6.00	15.00
CR Cal Ripken Jr./50	100.00	150.00
DH Dan Haren/50	8.00	20.00
DJ Derek Jeter/50	100.00	150.00
DL Derrek Lee/50	10.00	25.00
DU Dan Uggla/50	6.00	15.00
DW Dontrelle Willis/50	6.00	15.00
DY Delmon Young/50	10.00	25.00
FH Felix Hernandez/50	20.00	50.00
GR Khalil Greene/50	6.00	15.00
HR Hanley Ramirez/33	10.00	25.00
HS Huston Street/50	6.00	15.00
IK Ian Kinsler/50	10.00	25.00
JB Jason Bay/50	12.50	30.00
JH Jeremy Hermida/50	6.00	15.00
JM Joe Mauer/50	30.00	60.00
JN Joe Nathan/50	6.00	15.00
JV Justin Verlander/50	30.00	60.00
JW Josh Willingham/50	6.00	15.00
JZ Joel Zumaya/50	10.00	25.00
KE Howie Kendrick/50	10.00	25.00
KG Ken Griffey Jr./50	60.00	120.00
KM Kendry Morales/50	6.00	15.00
MC Matt Cain/50	10.00	25.00
MM Melvin Mora/50	6.00	15.00
MP Mike Pelfrey/50	6.00	15.00
NM Nick Markakis/50	15.00	40.00
PA Jonathan Papelbon/50	20.00	50.00
PF Prince Fielder/50	30.00	60.00
RW Rickie Weeks/50	6.00	15.00
RZ Ryan Zimmerman/50	15.00	40.00
SD Stephen Drew/50	10.00	25.00
TH Torii Hunter/50	10.00	25.00
VW Vernon Wells/50	10.00	25.00

2007 UD Black Pride of a Nation Autographs

RANDOM INSERTS IN PACKS
PRINT RUNS B/WN 25-75 COPIES PER
NO PRICING ON QTY 25
GOLD SPEC.PRINT RUN 10 SER.#'d SETS
NO GOLD PRICING DUE TO SCARCITY
NAT.PEARL PRINT RUN 1 SER.#'d SET
NO PEARL PRICING DUE TO SCARCITY
PRINTING PLATES RANDOMLY INSERTED
PLATE PRINT RUN 1 SET PER COLOR
BLACK-CYAN-MAGENTA-YELLOW ISSUED
NO PLATE PRICING DUE TO SCARCITY
EXCHANGE DEADLINE 11/26/2009

AH Aaron Harang	10.00	25.00
AL Adam LaRoche	10.00	25.00
AR Aaron Rowand	10.00	25.00
BO Jeremy Bonderman	12.50	30.00
BP Brandon Phillips	10.00	25.00
CA Carl Crawford	12.50	30.00
CC Coco Crisp	15.00	40.00
CG Curtis Granderson	20.00	50.00
CL Carlos Lee	20.00	50.00
CR Cal Ripken Jr./25		
DH Dan Haren	10.00	25.00
DL Derrek Lee	15.00	40.00
DU Dan Uggla	10.00	25.00
DW Dontrelle Willis	12.50	30.00
EC Eric Chavez	12.50	30.00
FH Felix Hernandez	30.00	60.00
FT Frank Thomas	30.00	60.00
HR Hanley Ramirez	20.00	50.00
JB Jason Bay	20.00	50.00
JL John Lackey	10.00	25.00
JM John Maine	15.00	40.00
LB Lance Berkman	10.00	25.00
MM Melvin Mora	10.00	25.00
MO Justin Morneau	20.00	50.00
PF Prince Fielder	30.00	60.00
RM Russell Martin	12.50	30.00
RO Roy Oswalt	15.00	40.00
SK Scott Kazmir	12.50	30.00
VM Victor Martinez	15.00	40.00

2007 UD Black Prodigious Autographs

RANDOM INSERTS IN PACKS
PRINT RUNS B/WN 50-75 COPIES PER
GOLD SPEC. PRINT RUN 25 SER.#'d SETS
NO GOLD PRICING DUE TO SCARCITY
NAT.PEARL PRINT RUN 1 SER.#'d SET
NO PEARL PRICING DUE TO SCARCITY
EXCHANGE DEADLINE 11/26/2009
AE Andre Ethier/75 12.50 30.00
AG Adrian Gonzalez/75 12.50 30.00
AH Aaron Harang/75 6.00 15.00
AI Akinori Iwamura/75 20.00 50.00
AL Adam LaRoche/75 6.00 15.00
AR Aaron Rowand/50 6.00 15.00
BB Billy Butler/75 10.00 25.00
BE Josh Beckett/50 30.00 60.00
BP Brandon Phillips/50 6.00 15.00
BS Ben Sheets/50 6.00 15.00
BU B.J. Upton/75 6.00 15.00
CA Carl Crawford/75 6.00 15.00
CC Coco Crisp/50 6.00 15.00
CG Curtis Granderson/50 10.00 25.00
CH Cole Hamels/50 12.50 30.00
CO Chad Cordero/50 6.00 15.00
CR Cal Ripken Jr./75 50.00 100.00
CY Chris Young/50 6.00 15.00
DH Dan Haren/75 6.00 15.00
DM Daisuke Matsuzaka/75 200.00 400.00
DU Dan Uggla/75 6.00 15.00
DY Delmon Young/75 10.00 25.00
FP Felix Pie/75 10.00 25.00
GA Garrett Atkins/75 6.00 15.00
GO Alex Gordon/75 10.00 25.00
GP Glen Perkins/75 6.00 15.00
HB Homer Bailey/75 10.00 25.00
HK Howie Kendrick/50 20.00 50.00
HP Hunter Pence/75 20.00 50.00
HS Huston Street/50 6.00 15.00
JB Jeremy Bonderman/75 10.00 25.00
JE Johnny Estrada/75 6.00 15.00
JH Josh Hamilton/50 20.00 50.00
JL John Lackey/50 6.00 15.00
JM John Maine/50 10.00 25.00
JP Jonathan Papelbon/75 15.00 40.00
JS Joakim Soria/75 10.00 25.00
JV Justin Verlander/50 30.00 60.00
JW Josh Willingham/50 6.00 15.00
KE Kelvim Escobar/50 6.00 15.00
KI Kei Igawa/75 15.00 40.00
KJ Kelly Johnson/50 6.00 15.00
LE Jon Lester/75 10.00 25.00
MC Matt Cain/75 6.00 15.00
MH Matt Holliday/75 10.00 25.00
MM Melvin Mora/50 6.00 15.00
MO Justin Morneau/75 10.00 25.00
NM Nick Markakis/75 10.00 25.00
NS Nick Swisher/75 10.00 25.00
PK Paul Konerko/50 10.00 25.00
RB Ryan Braun/75 15.00 40.00
RH Rich Harden/50 6.00 15.00
RM Russell Martin/75 10.00 25.00
RZ Ryan Zimmerman/75 15.00 40.00
SK Scott Kazmir/75 8.00 20.00
SM Sergio Mitre/50 6.00 15.00
TH Tim Hudson/75 10.00 25.00
TL Tim Lincecum/75 60.00 120.00
VM Victor Martinez/75 10.00 25.00
YG Yovani Gallardo/50 10.00 25.00

2007 UD Black Prodigious Materials Autographs

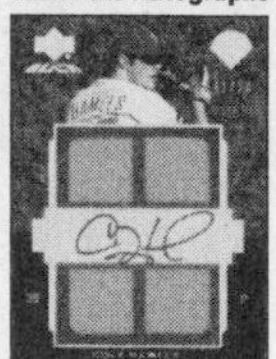

RANDOM INSERTS IN PACKS
PRINT RUNS B/WN 35-50 COPIES PER
GOLD SPEC. PRINT RUN 10 SER.#'d SETS
NO GOLD PRICING DUE TO SCARCITY
NAT.PEARL PRINT RUN 1 SER.#'d SET
NO PEARL PRICING DUE TO SCARCITY
EXCHANGE DEADLINE 11/26/2009
AD Adam Dunn 10.00 25.00
AE Andre Ethier 15.00 40.00
AL Adam LaRoche 10.00 25.00
AR Aaron Rowand 10.00 25.00
BO Jeremy Bonderman 10.00 25.00
BP Brandon Phillips 6.00 15.00
BU B.J. Upton 10.00 25.00
CC Coco Crisp 10.00 25.00
CD Chris Duncan 15.00 40.00
CH Cole Hamels 20.00 50.00
CL Cliff Lee 12.50 30.00
CR Carl Crawford 10.00 25.00
CY Chris Young 10.00 25.00
DH Dan Haren 6.00 15.00
DU Dan Uggla 10.00 25.00
DW Dontrelle Willis 10.00 25.00
FH Felix Hernandez 20.00 50.00
GA Garrett Atkins 6.00 15.00
HA Josh Hamilton 20.00 50.00
HK Hong-Chih Kuo 40.00 80.00
HR Hanley Ramirez 10.00 25.00
HS Huston Street 6.00 15.00
IK Ian Kinsler 10.00 25.00
JB Joe Blanton 6.00 15.00
JH Jeremy Hermida 6.00 15.00
JL Jon Lester 15.00 40.00
JN Joe Nathan 6.00 15.00
JS Johan Santana 20.00 50.00
JV Justin Verlander 30.00 60.00
JZ Joel Zumaya 10.00 25.00
KE Howie Kendrick 10.00 25.00
KW Kerry Wood 10.00 25.00
MO Justin Morneau 15.00 40.00
MT Mark Teixeira 15.00 40.00
PA Jonathan Papelbon 8.00 20.00
RI Cal Ripken Jr./35 50.00 100.00
RW Rickie Weeks 6.00 15.00
SK Scott Kazmir 8.00 20.00
SR Scott Rolen 10.00 25.00
TF Miguel Tejada 10.00 25.00
TG Tom Glavine 20.00 50.00
VW Vernon Wells 10.00 25.00

2007 UD Black Prominent Numbers Autographs

RANDOM INSERTS IN PACKS
PRINT RUNS B/WN 1-58 COPIES PER
NO PRICING ON QTY 25 OR LESS
GOLD SPEC. PRINT RUN 10 SER.#'d SETS
NO GOLD PRICING DUE TO SCARCITY
NAT.PEARL PRINT RUN 1 SER.#'d SET
NO PEARL PRICING DUE TO SCARCITY
EXCHANGE DEADLINE 11/26/2009
AE Andre Ethier/16
AH Aaron Harang/39 6.00 15.00
AI Akinori Iwamura/1
AL Adam LaRoche/25
BB Billy Butler/21
BL Joe Blanton/55 6.00 15.00
BU B.J. Upton/2
CA Chris Carpenter/22
CC Carl Crawford/13
CG Curtis Granderson/28 20.00 50.00
CH Cole Hamels/35 20.00 50.00
CR Cal Ripken Jr./8
CY Chris Young/32 10.00 25.00
DJ Derek Jeter/2
DY Delmon Young/26 10.00 25.00
FH Felix Hernandez/34 20.00 50.00
GA Garrett Atkins/27 10.00 25.00
HK Howie Kendrick/47 6.00 15.00
HR Hanley Ramirez/2
HS Huston Street/20
IK Ian Kinsler/5
JB Jason Bay/38 10.00 25.00
JE Johnny Estrada/33 6.00 15.00
JM Justin Morneau/33 10.00 25.00
JN Joe Nathan/36 6.00 15.00
JP Jonathan Papelbon/58 15.00 40.00
JV Justin Verlander/35 30.00 60.00
JZ Joel Zumaya/54 6.00 15.00
MA John Maine/33 10.00 25.00
MB Michael Bourn/45 6.00 15.00
MC Matt Cain/18
MH Matt Holliday/5
MM Melvin Mora/6
MT Miguel Tejada/3
NM Nick Markakis/21
NS Nick Swisher/18
PK Paul Konerko/14
RH Rich Harden/40 6.00 15.00
RM Russell Martin/55 15.00 40.00
RW Rickie Weeks/23
RZ Ryan Zimmerman/11
SK Scott Kazmir/19

2007 UD Black Triptych Triple Autographs

RANDOM INSERTS IN PACKS
STATED PRINT RUN 15 SER.#'d SETS
NO PRICING DUE TO SCARCITY
GOLD SPEC.PRINT RUN 5 SER.#'d SETS
NO GOLD PRICING DUE TO SCARCITY
NAT.PEARL PRINT RUN 1 SER.#'d SET
NO PEARL PRICING DUE TO SCARCITY
EXCHANGE DEADLINE 11/26/2009

2004 UD Legends Timeless Teams

This 300-card set was released in September, 2004. The set was issued in six card packs with an $5 SRP which came 18 packs to a box and 20 boxes to a case.

COMPLETE SET (300) 20.00 50.00
COMMON CARD (1-300) .15 .40
1 Bob Gibson 64 .25 .60
2 Lou Brock MM 64 .25 .60
3 Ray Washburn 64 .15 .40
4 Tim McCarver 64 .15 .40
5 Harmon Killebrew 65 .40 1.00
6 Jim Kaat 65 .15 .40
7 Jim Perry 65 .15 .40
8 Mudcat Grant 65 .15 .40
9 Boog Powell 66 .15 .40
10 Brooks Robinson 66 .25 .60
11 Frank Robinson MM 66 .25 .60
12 Jim Palmer 66 .15 .40
13 Carl Yastrzemski MM 67 .40 1.00
14 Jim Lonborg 67 .15 .40
15 George Scott 67 .15 .40
16 Sparky Lyle 67 .15 .40
17 Rico Petrocelli 67 .15 .40
18 Bob Gibson 67 .25 .60
19 Julian Javier 67 .15 .40
20 Lou Brock 67 .25 .60
21 Orlando Cepeda 67 .15 .40
22 Ray Washburn 67 .15 .40
23 Steve Carlton 67 .15 .40
24 Tim McCarver 67 .15 .40
25 Al Kaline 68 .40 1.00
26 Bill Freehan 68 .15 .40
27 Denny McLain MM 68 .15 .40
28 Dick McAuliffe 68 .15 .40
29 Jim Northrup 68 .15 .40
30 John Hiller 68 .15 .40
31 Mickey Lolich MM 68 .15 .40
32 Mickey Stanley 68 .15 .40
33 Willie Horton 68 .15 .40
34 Bob Gibson MM 68 .25 .60
35 Julian Javier 68 .15 .40
36 Lou Brock 68 .25 .60
37 Orlando Cepeda 68 .15 .40
38 Steve Carlton 68 .15 .40
39 Boog Powell 69 .15 .40
40 Brooks Robinson 69 .25 .60
41 Davey Johnson 69 .15 .40
42 Merv Rettenmund 69 .15 .40
43 Eddie Watt 69 .15 .40
44 Frank Robinson 69 .25 .60
45 Jim Palmer 69 .15 .40
46 Mike Cuellar 69 .15 .40
47 Paul Blair 69 .15 .40
48 Pete Richert 69 .15 .40
49 Ellie Hendricks 69 .15 .40
50 Billy Williams 69 .15 .40
51 Randy Hundley 69 .15 .40
52 Ernie Banks 69 .40 1.00
53 Fergie Jenkins 69 .15 .40
54 Jim Hickman 69 .15 .40
55 Ken Holtzman 69 .15 .40
56 Ron Santo MM 69 .25 .60
57 Ed Kranepool 69 .15 .40
58 Jerry Koosman MM 69 .15 .40
59 Nolan Ryan 69 1.25 3.00
60 Tom Seaver 69 .25 .60
61 Boog Powell 70 .15 .40
62 Brooks Robinson MM 70 .25 .60
63 Davey Johnson 70 .15 .40
64 Merv Rettenmund 70 .15 .40
65 Eddie Watt 70 .15 .40
66 Frank Robinson 70 .25 .60
67 Jim Palmer 70 .15 .40
68 Mike Cuellar 70 .15 .40
69 Paul Blair 70 .15 .40
70 Pete Richert 70 .15 .40
71 Ellie Hendricks 70 .15 .40
72 Al Kaline 72 .40 1.00
73 Bill Freehan 72 .15 .40
74 Dick McAuliffe 72 .15 .40
75 Jim Northrup 72 .15 .40
76 John Hiller 72 .15 .40
77 Mickey Lolich 72 .15 .40
78 Mickey Stanley 72 .15 .40
79 Willie Horton 72 .15 .40
80 Bert Campaneris 72 .15 .40
81 Blue Moon Odom MM 72 .15 .40
82 Sal Bando 72 .15 .40
83 Joe Rudi 72 .15 .40
84 Ken Holtzman 72 .15 .40
85 Billy North 73 .15 .40
86 Blue Moon Odom 73 .15 .40
87 Gene Tenace 73 .15 .40
88 Manny Trillo 73 .15 .40
89 Dick Green 73 .15 .40
90 Rollie Fingers 73 .15 .40
91 Sal Bando 73 .15 .40
92 Vida Blue 73 .15 .40
93 Bill Buckner 74 .15 .40
94 Davey Lopes 74 .15 .40
95 Don Sutton 74 .15 .40
96 Al Downing MM 74 .15 .40
97 Ron Cey 74 .15 .40
98 Steve Garvey 74 .15 .40
99 Tommy John 74 .15 .40
100 Bert Campaneris 74 .15 .40
101 Billy North 74 .15 .40
102 Joe Rudi MM 74 .15 .40
103 Sal Bando 74 .15 .40
104 Vida Blue 74 .15 .40
105 Carl Yastrzemski 75 .40 1.00
106 Carlton Fisk MM 75 .25 .60
107 Cecil Cooper 75 .15 .40
108 Dwight Evans 75 .15 .40
109 Fred Lynn 75 .15 .40
110 Jim Rice 75 .25 .60
111 Luis Tiant 75 .15 .40
112 Rick Burleson 75 .15 .40
113 Rico Petrocelli 75 .15 .40
114 Pedro Borbon 75 .15 .40
115 Dave Concepcion 75 .15 .40
116 Don Gullett 75 .15 .40
117 George Foster 75 UER .15 .40
Career triples total is wrong
118 Joe Morgan MM 75 .15 .40
119 Johnny Bench 75 .40 1.00
120 Rawly Eastwick 75 .15 .40
121 Sparky Anderson 75 .15 .40
122 Tony Perez 75 .15 .40
123 Billy Williams 75 .15 .40
124 Gene Tenace 75 .15 .40
125 Jim Perry 75 .15 .40
126 Vida Blue 75 .15 .40
127 Pedro Borbon 76 .15 .40
128 Dave Concepcion 76 .15 .40
129 Don Gullett 76 .15 .40
130 George Foster 76 .15 .40
131 Joe Morgan 76 .15 .40
132 Johnny Bench MM 76 .40 1.00
133 Ken Griffey Sr. 76 .15 .40
134 Rawly Eastwick 76 .15 .40
135 Tony Perez 76 .15 .40
136 Bill Russell 77 .15 .40
137 Burt Hooton 77 .15 .40
138 Davey Lopes 77 .15 .40
139 Don Sutton 77 .15 .40
140 Dusty Baker 77 .15 .40
141 Steve Yeager 77 .15 .40
142 Ron Cey 77 .15 .40
143 Steve Garvey MM 77 .15 .40
144 Tommy John 77 .15 .40
145 Bucky Dent 77 .15 .40
146 Chris Chambliss 77 .15 .40
147 Ed Figueroa 77 .15 .40
148 Graig Nettles 77 .15 .40
149 Lou Piniella 77 .15 .40
150 Roy White 77 .15 .40
151 Don Gullett 77 .15 .40
152 Sparky Lyle 77 .15 .40
153 Brian Doyle 78 .15 .40
154 Bucky Dent MM 78 .15 .40
155 Chris Chambliss 78 .15 .40
156 Ed Figueroa 78 .15 .40
157 Graig Nettles 78 .15 .40
158 Lou Piniella 78 .15 .40
159 Roy White 78 .15 .40
160 Rich Gossage 78 .15 .40
161 Sparky Lyle 78 .15 .40
162 Bobby Grich 79 .15 .40
163 Brian Downing 79 .15 .40
164 Dan Ford 79 .15 .40
165 Nolan Ryan 79 1.25 3.00
166 Dave Concepcion 79 .15 .40
167 George Foster 79 .15 .40
168 Johnny Bench 79 .40 1.00
169 Ray Knight 79 .15 .40
170 Tom Seaver 79 .25 .60
171 Bert Blyleven 79 .15 .40
172 Bill Madlock 79 .15 .40
173 Dave Parker MM 79 .15 .40
174 Phil Garner 79 .15 .40
175 Bill Russell 80 .15 .40
176 Steve Yeager 80 .15 .40
177 Don Sutton 80 .15 .40
178 Dusty Baker 80 .15 .40
179 Jerry Reuss 80 .15 .40
180 Mickey Hatcher 80 .15 .40
181 Pedro Guerrero 80 .15 .40
182 Ron Cey 80 .15 .40
183 Steve Garvey 80 .15 .40
184 Rudy May 80 .15 .40
185 Brian Doyle 80 .15 .40
186 Bucky Dent 80 .15 .40
187 Jim Kaat 80 .15 .40
188 Lou Piniella 80 .15 .40
189 Luis Tiant 80 .15 .40
190 Tommy John 80 .15 .40
191 Bake McBride 80 .15 .40
192 Bob Boone 80 .15 .40
193 Dickie Noles MM 80 .15 .40
194 Manny Trillo 80 .15 .40
195 Mike Schmidt 80 .60 1.50
196 Sparky Lyle 80 .15 .40
197 Steve Carlton 80 .15 .40
198 Steve Yeager 81 .15 .40
199 Burt Hooton 81 .15 .40
200 Dusty Baker 81 .15 .40
201 Jerry Reuss 81 .15 .40
202 Mike Scioscia 81 .15 .40
203 Pedro Guerrero 81 .15 .40
204 Ron Cey 81 .15 .40
205 Steve Garvey 81 .15 .40
206 Alejandro Pena 81 .15 .40
207 Steve Sax 81 .15 .40
208 Cecil Cooper 81 .15 .40
209 Gorman Thomas 81 .15 .40
210 Paul Molitor 81 .40 1.00
211 Robin Yount 81 .40 1.00
212 Rollie Fingers 81 .15 .40
213 Don Money 81 .15 .40
214 Rudy May 81 .15 .40
215 Bucky Dent 81 .15 .40
216 Dave Winfield 81 .15 .40
217 Lou Piniella 81 .15 .40
218 Rich Gossage 81 .15 .40
219 Tommy John 81 .15 .40
220 Cecil Cooper 82 .15 .40
221 Gorman Thomas 82 .15 .40
222 Paul Molitor MM 82 .40 1.00
223 Robin Yount 82 .40 1.00
224 Don Money 82 .15 .40
225 Cal Ripken MM 83 1.50 4.00
226 Dan Ford 83 .15 .40
227 Jim Palmer 83 .15 .40
228 John Shelby 83 .15 .40
229 Alan Trammell 84 .15 .40
230 Chet Lemon 84 .15 .40
231 Howard Johnson 84 .15 .40
232 Jack Morris MM 84 .15 .40
233 Kirk Gibson 84 .15 .40
234 Lou Whitaker 84 .15 .40
235 Sparky Anderson 84 .15 .40
236 Dave Winfield 85 .15 .40
237 Don Mattingly 85 .75 2.00
238 Ken Griffey Sr. 85 .15 .40
239 Phil Niekro 85 .15 .40
240 Yogi Berra 85 .40 1.00
241 Bill Buckner MM 86 .15 .40
242 Bruce Hurst 86 .15 .40
243 Dave Henderson 86 .15 .40
244 Dwight Evans 86 .15 .40
245 Jim Rice 86 .25 .60
246 Tom Seaver 86 .25 .60
247 Wade Boggs 86 .25 .60
248 Bob Boone 86 .15 .40
249 Bobby Grich 86 .15 .40
250 Brian Downing 86 .15 .40
251 Don Sutton 86 .15 .40
252 Terry Forster 86 .15 .40
253 Rick Burleson 86 .15 .40
254 Wally Joyner MM 86 .15 .40
255 Darryl Strawberry 86 .15 .40
256 Dwight Gooden 86 .15 .40
257 Gary Carter 86 .15 .40
258 Jesse Orosco MM 86 .15 .40
259 Keith Hernandez 86 .15 .40
260 Lenny Dykstra 86 .15 .40
261 Mookie Wilson 86 .15 .40
262 Ray Knight 86 .15 .40
263 Wally Backman 86 .15 .40
264 Sid Fernandez 86 .15 .40
265 Alan Trammell 87 .15 .40
266 Dan Petry 87 .15 .40
267 Chet Lemon 87 .15 .40
268 Sparky Anderson 87 .15 .40
269 Jack Morris 87 .15 .40
270 Kirk Gibson 87 .15 .40
271 Lou Whitaker 87 .15 .40
272 Bert Blyleven 87 .15 .40
273 Kent Hrbek MM 87 .15 .40
274 Kirby Puckett 87 .40 1.00
275 Alejandro Pena 88 .15 .40
276 Jesse Orosco 88 .15 .40
277 John Shelby 88 .15 .40
278 Kirk Gibson MM 88 .15 .40
279 Mickey Hatcher 88 .15 .40
280 Mike Scioscia 88 .15 .40
281 Steve Sax 88 .15 .40
282 Darryl Strawberry 88 .15 .40
283 Dwight Gooden 88 .15 .40
284 Gary Carter 88 .15 .40
285 Howard Johnson 88 .15 .40
286 Keith Hernandez 88 .15 .40
287 Lenny Dykstra 88 .15 .40
288 Mookie Wilson 88 .15 .40
289 Wally Backman 88 .15 .40
290 Sid Fernandez 88 .15 .40
291 Jack Morris 91 .15 .40
292 Kent Hrbek 91 .15 .40
293 Kirby Puckett MM 91 .40 1.00
294 Dave Winfield MM 92 .15 .40
295 Jack Morris 92 .15 .40
296 Joe Carter 92 .15 .40
297 Don Mattingly MM 95 .75 2.00
298 Paul O'Neill 95 .25 .60
299 Jack McDowell 95 .15 .40
300 Wade Boggs 95 .25 .60

2004 UD Legends Timeless Teams Bronze

*BRONZE: X TO X BASIC
RANDOM INSERTS IN RETAIL PACKS
STATED PRINT RUN 50 SERIAL #'d SETS

2004 UD Legends Timeless Teams Gold

STATED ODDS 1:360
STATED PRINT RUN 5 SERIAL #'d SETS
NO PRICING DUE TO SCARCITY

2004 UD Legends Timeless Teams Autographs

OVERALL AU PARALLEL ODDS 1:9
SP PRINT RUNS B/WN 25-100 COPIES PER
SP'S ARE NOT SERIAL-NUMBERED
SP PRINT RUNS PROVIDED BY UD
EXCHANGE DEADLINE 08/19/07
ASTERISK ='s SOME LIVE/SOME EXCH
1 Bob Gibson 64 SP/50 12.50 30.00
2 Lou Brock MM 64 SP/75 * 10.00 25.00
3 Ray Washburn 64 4.00 10.00
4 Tim McCarver 64 6.00 15.00
5 Harmon Killebrew 65 20.00 50.00
6 Jim Kaat 65 6.00 15.00
7 Jim Perry 65 4.00 10.00
8 Mudcat Grant 65 6.00 15.00
9 Boog Powell 66 6.00 15.00
10 Brooks Robinson 66 10.00 25.00
11 F.Robinson MM 66 SP/35 15.00 40.00
12 Jim Palmer 66 SP/50 12.50 30.00
13 C.Yastrzemski MM 67 SP/25 40.00 80.00
14 Jim Lonborg 67 4.00 10.00
15 George Scott 67 4.00 10.00
16 Sparky Lyle 67 * 4.00 10.00
17 Rico Petrocelli 67 4.00 10.00
18 Bob Gibson 67 SP/35 15.00 40.00
19 Julian Javier 67 4.00 10.00
20 Lou Brock 67 SP/60 12.50 30.00
21 Orlando Cepeda 67 SP/50 8.00 20.00
22 Ray Washburn 67 4.00 10.00
23 Steve Carlton 67 SP/25 10.00 25.00
24 Tim McCarver 67 6.00 15.00
25 Al Kaline 68 * 12.50 30.00
26 Bill Freehan 68 6.00 15.00
27 Denny McLain MM 68 6.00 15.00
28 Dick McAuliffe 68 4.00 10.00
29 Jim Northrup 68 6.00 15.00
30 John Hiller 68 4.00 10.00
31 Mickey Lolich MM 68 6.00 15.00
32 Mickey Stanley 68 4.00 10.00
33 Willie Horton 68 4.00 10.00
34 Bob Gibson MM 68 SP/25 15.00 40.00
35 Julian Javier 68 4.00 10.00
36 Lou Brock 68 SP/50 12.50 30.00
37 Orlando Cepeda 68 SP/25 10.00 25.00
38 Steve Carlton 68 SP/35 10.00 25.00
39 Boog Powell 69 6.00 15.00
40 Brooks Robinson 69 SP/100 10.00 25.00
41 Davey Johnson 69 4.00 10.00
42 Merv Rettenmund 69 4.00 10.00
43 Eddie Watt 69 4.00 10.00
44 Frank Robinson 69 SP/25 15.00 40.00
45 Jim Palmer 69 SP/25 15.00 40.00
46 Mike Cuellar 69 4.00 10.00
47 Paul Blair 69 4.00 10.00
48 Pete Richert 69 4.00 10.00
49 Ellie Hendricks 69 4.00 10.00
50 Billy Williams 69 SP/75 10.00 25.00
51 Randy Hundley 69 6.00 15.00
52 Ernie Banks 69 SP/50 20.00 50.00
53 Fergie Jenkins 69 6.00 15.00
54 Jim Hickman 69 6.00 15.00
55 Ken Holtzman 69 6.00 15.00
56 Ron Santo MM 69 12.50 30.00
57 Ed Kranepool 69 4.00 10.00
58 Jerry Koosman MM 69 6.00 15.00
59 Nolan Ryan 69 SP/50
60 Tom Seaver 69 SP/50 15.00 40.00
61 Boog Powell 70 6.00 15.00
62 B.Robinson MM 70 SP/35 15.00 40.00
63 Davey Johnson 70 4.00 10.00
64 Merv Rettenmund 70 4.00 10.00
65 Eddie Watt 70 4.00 10.00
66 Frank Robinson 70 SP/50 12.50 30.00
67 Jim Palmer 70 SP/75 10.00 25.00
68 Mike Cuellar 70 4.00 10.00
69 Paul Blair 70 4.00 10.00
70 Pete Richert 70 4.00 10.00
71 Ellie Hendricks 70 4.00 10.00
72 Al Kaline 72 * 12.50 30.00
73 Bill Freehan 72 6.00 15.00
74 Dick McAuliffe 72 4.00 10.00
75 Jim Northrup 72 6.00 15.00
76 John Hiller 72 4.00 10.00
77 Mickey Lolich 72 6.00 15.00
78 Mickey Stanley 72 4.00 10.00
79 Willie Horton 72 4.00 10.00
80 Bert Campaneris 72 4.00 10.00
81 Blue Moon Odom MM 72 4.00 10.00
83 Joe Rudi 72 6.00 15.00
84 Ken Holtzman 72 6.00 15.00
85 Billy North 73 4.00 10.00
86 Blue Moon Odom 73 4.00 10.00
87 Gene Tenace 73 4.00 10.00
88 Manny Trillo 73 4.00 10.00
89 Dick Green 73 4.00 10.00
90 Rollie Fingers 73 6.00 15.00
91 Sal Bando 73 4.00 10.00
92 Vida Blue 73 4.00 10.00
93 Bill Buckner 74 * 6.00 15.00
94 Davey Lopes 74 4.00 10.00
95 Don Sutton 74 6.00 15.00
96 Al Downing MM 74 4.00 10.00
97 Ron Cey 74 SP/25 6.00 15.00
98 Steve Garvey 74 SP/25 15.00 40.00
99 Tommy John 74 SP/25 6.00 15.00
100 Bert Campaneris 74 6.00 15.00
101 Billy North 74 4.00 10.00
102 Joe Rudi MM 74 4.00 10.00
103 Sal Bando 74 4.00 10.00
104 Vida Blue 74 SP/100 * 4.00 10.00
105 Carl Yastrzemski 75 SP/50 30.00 60.00
106 Carlton Fisk MM 75 SP/100 10.00 25.00
107 Cecil Cooper 75 SP/75 6.00 15.00
108 Dwight Evans 75 SP/75 10.00 25.00
109 Fred Lynn 75 4.00 10.00
112 Rick Burleson 75 4.00 10.00
113 Rico Petrocelli 75 4.00 10.00
114 Pedro Borbon 75 4.00 10.00
116 Don Gullett 75 4.00 10.00
117 George Foster 75 SP/50 5.00 12.00
118 Joe Morgan MM 75 SP/25 10.00 25.00
119 Johnny Bench 75 SP/85 20.00 50.00
120 Rawly Eastwick 75 4.00 10.00
121 Sparky Anderson 75 6.00 15.00
122 Tony Perez 75 10.00 25.00
123 Billy Williams 75 SP/50 12.50 30.00
124 Gene Tenace 75 4.00 10.00
125 Jim Perry 75 4.00 10.00
126 Vida Blue 75 SP/75 4.00 10.00
127 Pedro Borbon 76 4.00 10.00
129 Don Gullett 76 4.00 10.00
130 George Foster 76 SP/35 6.00 15.00
131 Joe Morgan 76 SP/50 8.00 20.00
132 J.Bench MM 76 SP/50 30.00 60.00
133 Ken Griffey Sr. 76 6.00 15.00
134 Rawly Eastwick 76 4.00 10.00
135 Tony Perez 76 10.00 25.00
136 Bill Russell 77 4.00 10.00
137 Burt Hooton 77 4.00 10.00
138 Davey Lopes 77 4.00 10.00
139 Don Sutton 77 6.00 15.00
142 Ron Cey 77 SP/35 6.00 15.00
143 Steve Garvey MM 77 SP/35 15.00 40.00
144 Tommy John 77 SP/35 6.00 15.00
145 Bucky Dent 77 SP/75 6.00 15.00
146 Chris Chambliss 77 4.00 10.00
147 Ed Figueroa 77 4.00 10.00
148 Graig Nettles 77 6.00 15.00
149 Lou Piniella 77 SP/25 6.00 15.00
150 Roy White 77 4.00 10.00
151 Don Gullett 77 4.00 10.00
152 Sparky Lyle 77 * 4.00 10.00
153 Brian Doyle 78 4.00 10.00
154 Bucky Dent MM 78 SP/75 6.00 15.00
155 Chris Chambliss 78 4.00 10.00
156 Ed Figueroa 78 4.00 10.00
157 Graig Nettles 78 6.00 15.00
158 Lou Piniella 78 SP/35 6.00 15.00
159 Roy White 78 4.00 10.00
160 Rich Gossage 78 10.00 25.00
161 Sparky Lyle 78 * 4.00 10.00
162 Bobby Grich 79 4.00 10.00
163 Brian Downing 79 4.00 10.00
164 Dan Ford 79 4.00 10.00
165 Nolan Ryan 79 SP/25 75.00 150.00
167 George Foster 79 SP/25 6.00 15.00
168 Johnny Bench 79 SP/25 40.00 80.00
169 Ray Knight 79 4.00 10.00
170 Tom Seaver 79 SP/35 20.00 50.00
171 Bert Blyleven 79 * 10.00 25.00
172 Bill Madlock 79 6.00 15.00
173 Dave Parker MM 79 6.00 15.00
174 Phil Garner 79 6.00 15.00
175 Bill Russell 80 4.00 10.00
176 Steve Yeager 80 4.00 10.00
177 Don Sutton 80 SP/50 8.00 20.00
178 Dusty Baker 80 6.00 15.00
179 Jerry Reuss 80 4.00 10.00
180 Mickey Hatcher 80 4.00 10.00
181 Pedro Guerrero 80 4.00 10.00
182 Ron Cey 80 SP/50 5.00 12.00
183 Steve Garvey 80 SP/50 12.50 30.00
184 Rudy May 80 4.00 10.00
185 Brian Doyle 80 4.00 10.00
186 Bucky Dent 80 SP/60 8.00 20.00
187 Jim Kaat 80 6.00 15.00
188 Lou Piniella 80 SP/50 5.00 12.00
189 Luis Tiant 80 4.00 10.00
190 Tommy John 80 SP/50 5.00 12.00
191 Bake McBride 80 6.00 15.00
192 Bob Boone 80 6.00 15.00
193 Dickie Noles MM 80 4.00 10.00
194 Manny Trillo 80 4.00 10.00
195 Mike Schmidt 80 SP/50
196 Sparky Lyle 80 4.00 10.00
197 Steve Carlton 80 SP/50 8.00 20.00
198 Steve Yeager 81 4.00 10.00
199 Burt Hooton 81 4.00 10.00
201 Jerry Reuss 81 4.00 10.00
202 Mike Scioscia 81 10.00 25.00
203 Pedro Guerrero 81 4.00 10.00
204 Ron Cey 81 SP/75 4.00 10.00
205 Steve Garvey 81 SP/75 10.00 25.00
206 Alejandro Pena 81 4.00 10.00
207 Steve Sax 81 SP/100 4.00 10.00
208 Cecil Cooper 81 SP/85 6.00 15.00
210 Paul Molitor 81 SP/25 10.00 25.00
211 Robin Yount 81 SP/25
212 Rollie Fingers 81 6.00 15.00
213 Don Money 81 4.00 10.00
214 Rudy May 81 4.00 10.00
215 Bucky Dent 81 SP/25 10.00 25.00
216 Dave Winfield 81 SP/50 12.50 30.00
217 Lou Piniella 81 SP/75 4.00 10.00
218 Rich Gossage 81 10.00 25.00
219 Tommy John 81 SP/75 4.00 10.00
220 Cecil Cooper 82 6.00 15.00
222 Paul Molitor MM 82 SP/50 8.00 20.00
223 Robin Yount 82 SP/50 30.00 60.00
224 Don Money 82 4.00 10.00
225 Cal Ripken MM 83 SP/50 150.00 250.00
226 Dan Ford 83 4.00 10.00
227 Jim Palmer 83 SP/35 15.00 40.00
228 John Shelby 83 4.00 10.00
229 Alan Trammell 84 6.00 15.00
230 Chet Lemon 84 4.00 10.00
231 Howard Johnson 84 4.00 10.00
232 Jack Morris MM 84 SP/35 10.00 25.00
233 Kirk Gibson 84 6.00 15.00
234 Lou Whitaker 84 SP/100 6.00 15.00
235 Sparky Anderson 84 * 6.00 15.00
236 Dave Winfield 85 SP/25 15.00 40.00
237 Don Mattingly 85 SP/50 30.00 60.00
238 Ken Griffey Sr. 85 6.00 15.00
239 Phil Niekro 85 6.00 15.00
240 Yogi Berra 85 SP/47 UER 30.00 60.00
Front says 1978 instead of 1985
241 Bill Buckner MM 86 6.00 15.00
242 Bruce Hurst 86 6.00 15.00
243 Dave Henderson 86 6.00 15.00
244 Dwight Evans 86 SP/50 12.50 30.00
246 Tom Seaver 86 SP/25 20.00 50.00
247 Wade Boggs 86 SP/50 15.00 40.00
248 Bob Boone 86 6.00 15.00
249 Bobby Grich 86 4.00 10.00
250 Brian Downing 86 4.00 10.00
251 Don Sutton 86 SP/75 6.00 15.00
252 Terry Forster 86 4.00 10.00
253 Rick Burleson 86 4.00 10.00
254 Wally Joyner MM 86 6.00 15.00
255 Darryl Strawberry 86 10.00 25.00
256 Dwight Gooden 86 6.00 15.00
257 Gary Carter 86 SP/75 6.00 15.00
258 Jesse Orosco MM 86 10.00 25.00
259 Keith Hernandez 86 6.00 15.00
260 Lenny Dykstra 86 6.00 15.00
261 Mookie Wilson 86 6.00 15.00
262 Ray Knight 86 4.00 10.00
263 Wally Backman 86 4.00 10.00
264 Sid Fernandez 86 6.00 15.00
265 Alan Trammell 87 6.00 15.00
266 Dan Petry 87 4.00 10.00
267 Chet Lemon 87 4.00 10.00
268 Sparky Anderson 87 6.00 15.00
269 Jack Morris 87 SP/25 10.00 25.00
270 Kirk Gibson 87 6.00 15.00
271 Lou Whitaker 87 SP/50 8.00 20.00
272 Bert Blyleven 87 * 4.00 10.00
273 Kent Hrbek MM 87 6.00 15.00
274 Kirby Puckett 87 SP/25 60.00 120.00
275 Alejandro Pena 88 4.00 10.00
276 Jesse Orosco 88 4.00 10.00
277 John Shelby 88 4.00 10.00
278 Kirk Gibson MM 88 SP/50 8.00 20.00
279 Mickey Hatcher 88 4.00 10.00
280 Mike Scioscia 88 6.00 15.00
281 Steve Sax 88 4.00 10.00
282 Darryl Strawberry 88 10.00 25.00
283 Dwight Gooden 88 6.00 15.00
284 Gary Carter 88 SP/50 8.00 20.00
285 Howard Johnson 88 4.00 10.00
286 Keith Hernandez 88 6.00 15.00
287 Lenny Dykstra 88 6.00 15.00
288 Mookie Wilson 88 6.00 15.00
289 Wally Backman 88 4.00 10.00
291 Jack Morris 91 SP/50 8.00 20.00
292 Kent Hrbek 91 6.00 15.00
293 Kirby Puckett MM 91 SP/50 60.00 120.00
294 D.Winfield MM 92 SP/35 15.00 40.00
295 Jack Morris 92 SP/75 6.00 15.00
296 Joe Carter 92 SP/100 6.00 15.00
297 Don Mattingly MM 95 SP/25 40.00 80.00
298 Paul O'Neill 95 * 10.00 25.00
299 Jack McDowell 95 4.00 10.00
300 Wade Boggs 95 SP/75 12.50 30.00

2004 UD Legends Timeless Teams Autographs Gold

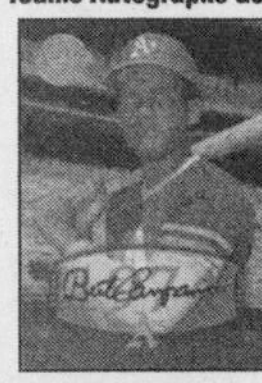

OVERALL AU PARALLEL ODDS 1:9
STATED PRINT RUN 5 SERIAL #'d SETS
NO PRICING DUE TO SCARCITY

2004 UD Legends Timeless Teams Autographs Platinum

STATED PRINT RUN 1 SERIAL #'d SET
NO PRICING DUE TO SCARCITY

2004 UD Legends Timeless Teams Legendary Combo Cuts

OVERALL FOLD-OPEN CARD ODDS 1:360
STATED PRINT RUN 1 SERIAL #'d SET
NO PRICING DUE TO SCARCITY

2004 UD Legends Timeless Teams Legendary Combo Signatures

OVERALL FOLD-OPEN CARD ODDS 1:360
STATED PRINT RUN 10 SERIAL #'d SETS
NO PRICING DUE TO SCARCITY

2004 UD Legends Timeless Teams Legendary Signatures Dual

OVERALL DUAL/TRIPLE SIG ODDS 1:90
PRINT RUNS B/WN 25-150 COPIES PER
EXCHANGE DEADLINE 08/19/07

BC Lou Brock 30.00 60.00
Orlando Cepeda/75
BJ Lou Brock 15.00 40.00
Julian Javier/150
BM Wade Boggs 75.00 150.00
Don Mattingly/50
BO Vida Blue 15.00 40.00
Blue Moon Odom/150
BW Ernie Banks 60.00 120.00
Billy Williams/25
CB Steve Carlton 15.00 40.00
Bob Boone/150
CG Ron Cey 15.00 40.00
Steve Garvey/150
CH Gary Carter 15.00 40.00
Keith Hernandez/150
CW Joe Carter
Dave Winfield/25
DD Bucky Dent 15.00 40.00
Brian Doyle/150
FR Fred Lynn 20.00 50.00
Jim Rice/150
GA Kirk Gibson 15.00 40.00
Sparky Anderson/150
GB Bob Gibson 40.00 80.00
Lou Brock/50
GC Dwight Gooden 15.00 40.00
Gary Carter/150
GM Bob Gibson 30.00 60.00
Tim McCarver/50
HJ Ken Holtzman 15.00 40.00
Fergie Jenkins/150
HK Keith Hernandez 15.00 40.00
Ray Knight/150
JH Fergie Jenkins 15.00 40.00
Randy Hundley/150
JS Tommy John 15.00 40.00
Don Sutton/150
KH Al Kaline 20.00 50.00
Willie Horton/150
KK Harmon Killebrew 30.00 60.00
Jim Kaat/150
LM Mickey Lolich 20.00 50.00
Denny McLain/75
MB Joe Morgan 50.00 100.00
Johnny Bench/25
MF Denny McLain 15.00 40.00
Bill Freehan/150
NC Graig Nettles 15.00 40.00
Chris Chambliss/150
OM Paul O'Neill 60.00 120.00
Don Mattingly/75
PC Jim Palmer 15.00 40.00
Mike Cuellar/150
PF Tony Perez 20.00 50.00
George Foster/150
PH Kirby Puckett
Kent Hrbek/50
PN Lou Piniella 15.00 40.00
Graig Nettles/150
PR Jim Palmer 15.00 40.00
Merv Rettenmund/150
RL Bill Russell 10.00 25.00
Davey Lopes/150
RR Brooks Robinson 40.00 80.00
Frank Robinson/50
RS Nolan Ryan 200.00 300.00
Tom Seaver/25
SD Steve Garvey 15.00 40.00
Davey Lopes/150
SG Darryl Strawberry 20.00 50.00
Dwight Gooden/150
SY Don Sutton 15.00 40.00
Steve Yeager/150
TF Luis Tiant 30.00 60.00
Carlton Fisk/50
WB Mookie Wilson 15.00 40.00
Bill Buckner/150
WT Lou Whitaker 30.00 60.00
Alan Trammell/75
YM Robin Yount 60.00 120.00
Paul Molitor/50
YP Carl Yastrzemski 40.00 80.00
Rico Petrocelli/50

2004 UD Legends Timeless Teams Legendary Signatures Triple

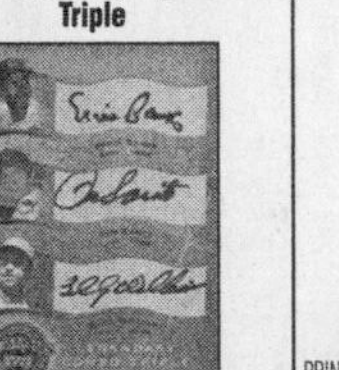

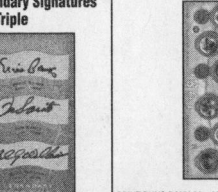

OVERALL DUAL/TRIPLE AU ODDS 1:90
PRINT RUNS B/WN 25-75 COPIES PER
EXCHANGE DEADLINE 08/19/07

BCM Johnny Bench 60.00 120.00
Dave Concepcion
Joe Morgan/25 EXCH
BOM Wade Boggs 100.00 175.00
Paul O'Neill
Don Mattingly/50
BRB Sal Bando 20.00 50.00
Joe Rudi
Vida Blue/75
BSW Ernie Banks 125.00 200.00
Ron Santo
Billy Williams/25
CDK Gary Carter 30.00 60.00
Lenny Dykstra
Ray Knight/50
CND Chris Chambliss 30.00 60.00
Graig Nettles
Bucky Dent/50
ERL Dwight Evans 100.00 175.00
Jim Rice
Fred Lynn/50
GBC Steve Garvey 40.00 80.00
Dusty Baker
Ron Cey/50
GBM Bob Gibson 50.00 100.00
Lou Brock
Tim McCarver/25
GDR Bobby Grich 125.00 200.00
Brian Downing
Nolan Ryan/25
GHS Kirk Gibson 40.00 80.00
Mickey Hatcher
Mike Scioscia/75
GMP Phil Garner 30.00 60.00
Bill Madlock
Dave Parker/50
HHS Jim Hickman 40.00 80.00
Ken Holtzman
Ron Santo/75
HSJ Burt Hooton 30.00 60.00
Don Sutton
Tommy John/50
JHH Fergie Jenkins 30.00 60.00
Randy Hundley
Ken Holtzman/75
KKP Harmon Killebrew 50.00 100.00
Jim Kaat
Jim Perry/50
KPG Jim Kaat 30.00 60.00
Jim Perry
Mudcat Grant/75 EXCH
KSR Jerry Koosman 250.00 350.00
Tom Seaver
Nolan Ryan/25
MHP Jack Morris 60.00 120.00
Kent Hrbek
Kirby Puckett/50
MLF Denny McLain 30.00 60.00
Mickey Lolich
Bill Freehan/50
NKH Jim Northrup 40.00 80.00
Al Kaline
Willie Horton/75
PBH Kirby Puckett 60.00 120.00
Bert Blyleven
Kent Hrbek/50
PCR Jim Palmer 20.00 50.00
Mike Cuellar
Pete Richert/75
PPW Jim Palmer 30.00 60.00
Boog Powell
Earl Weaver/75
RPR Frank Robinson 50.00 100.00
Boog Powell
Brooks Robinson/50
RWP Cal Ripken 200.00 300.00
Earl Weaver
Jim Palmer/25
SCB Mike Schmidt 100.00 175.00
Steve Carlton
Bob Boone/50
SGS Steve Sax 30.00 60.00
Pedro Guerrero
Mike Scioscia/75
STM Mike Schmidt
Manny Trillo
Bake McBride/50
TWA Alan Trammell 40.00 80.00
Lou Whitaker
Sparky Anderson/50
YCT Robin Yount 60.00 120.00
Cecil Cooper
Gorman Thomas/50 EXCH
YFT Carl Yastrzemski 100.00 175.00
Carlton Fisk
Luis Tiant/25
YMT Robin Yount 75.00 150.00
Paul Molitor
Gorman Thomas/75 EXCH

2004 UD Legends Timeless Teams Team Terrific GU Team Logo

PRINT RUNS B/WN 30-100 COPIES PER
*BRAND LOGO p/r 35-41: .5X TO 1.2X TEAM
BRAND LOGO PRINT RUN B/WN 10-41 PER
NO BRAND LOGO PRICING ON QTY OF 10
*HAT LOGO p/r 82: .4X TO 1X TEAM
*HAT LOGO p/r 50: .5X TO 1.2X TEAM
HAT LOGO PRINT RUN B/WN 15-82 PER
NO HAT LOGO PRICING ON QTY OF 15
LEAGUE LOGO PRINT RUN B/WN 5-15 PER
NO LEAGUE LOGO PRICING AVAILABLE
STATS PRINT RUN B/WN 1-5 COPIES PER
NO STATS PRICING AVAILABLE
OVERALL FOLD-OPEN CARD ODDS 1:360

BO Boog Powell Bat 50.00 100.00
Brooks Robinson Bat
Cal Ripken Bat
Davey Johnson Bat
Frank Robinson Bat
Paul Blair Bat/85
BR Carl Yastrzemski Bat 40.00 80.00
Carlton Fisk Bat
Dwight Evans Bat
Fred Lynn Bat
Jim Rice Bat
Rico Petrocelli Bat/85
CR Dave Concepcion Bat 50.00 100.00
George Foster Bat
Joe Morgan Bat
Johnny Bench Bat
Ken Griffey Sr. Bat
Tony Perez Bat/31
LD Bill Russell Bat 30.00 60.00
Davey Lopes Bat
Dusty Baker Bat
Ron Cey Bat
Steve Garvey Bat
Steve Yeager Bat/42
MB Cecil Cooper Jsy/Pants 20.00 50.00
Don Money Bat
Paul Molitor Bat
Robin Yount Bat
Rollie Fingers Jsy
Sal Bando Bat/100
NM Darryl Strawberry Bat 20.00 50.00
Gary Carter Bat
Keith Hernandez Bat
Lenny Dykstra Bat
Mookie Wilson Bat
Ray Knight Bat/85
NY Babe Ruth Bat
Don Mattingly Bat
Joe DiMaggio Bat
Lou Gehrig Jsy/Pants
Mickey Mantle Bat
Yogi Berra Bat/30
OA Bert Campaneris Bat 15.00 40.00
Billy North Bat
Billy Williams Bat
Gene Tenace Bat
Joe Rudi Jsy
Sal Bando Bat/100
SC Bob Gibson Jsy 40.00 80.00
Lou Brock Bat
Orlando Cepeda Bat
Stan Musial Bat
Steve Carlton Bat
Tim McCarver Bat/100

2007 UD Masterpieces

COMPLETE SET (90) 15.00 40.00
COMMON CARD (1-90) .25 .60
COMMON ROOKIE (1-90) .25 .60
PRINTING PLATES RANDOMLY INSERTED
PLATE PRINT RUN 1 SET PER COLOR
BLACK-CYAN-MAGENTA-YELLOW ISSUED
NO PLATE PRICING DUE TO SCARCITY

1 Babe Ruth 1.50 4.00
2 Babe Ruth 1.50 4.00
3 Bobby Thomson .40 1.00
4 Bill Mazeroski .40 1.00
5 Carlton Fisk .40 1.00
6 Kirk Gibson .25 .60
7 Don Larsen .25 .60
8 Lou Gehrig 1.25 3.00
9 Roger Maris .60 1.50
10 Cal Ripken Jr. 2.50 6.00
11 Bucky Dent .25 .60
12 Ryan Howard 1.00 2.50
13 Brooks Robinson .40 1.00
14 David Ortiz .40 1.00
15 Hideki Matsui .60 1.50
16 Roger Clemens .75 2.00
17 Sandy Koufax 2.00 5.00
18 Reggie Jackson .40 1.00
19 Ozzie Smith 1.00 2.50
20 Ty Cobb 1.00 2.50
21 Walter Johnson .60 1.50
22 Babe Ruth 1.50 4.00
23 Roy Campanella .60 1.50
24 Jackie Robinson .60 1.50
25 Carl Yastrzemski 1.00 2.50
26 Sandy Koufax 2.00 5.00
27 Daisuke Matsuzaka RC 1.00 2.50
28 Kei Igawa RC .60 1.50
29 Ken Griffey Jr. 1.00 2.50
30 Derek Jeter 1.50 4.00
31 David Ortiz .40 1.00
32 Vladimir Guerrero .60 1.50
33 Chase Utley .60 1.50
34 Troy Tulowitzki (RC) 1.50 4.00
35 Joe Mauer .60 1.50
36 Travis Hafner .25 .60
37 Miguel Cabrera .60 1.50
38 Albert Pujols 1.50 4.00
39 Frank Thomas .60 1.50
40 Mike Piazza .60 1.50
41 Josh Hamilton 1.00 2.50
42 Tony Gwynn 2.50 6.00
Cal Ripken Jr.
43 Ichiro Suzuki 1.00 2.50
44 Hideki Matsui .60 1.50
45 Ken Griffey Jr. 1.00 2.50
46 Michael Jordan 1.50 4.00
47 John F. Kennedy 1.00 2.50
48 Randy Johnson .60 1.50
49 Albert Pujols 1.50 4.00
50 Carlos Beltran .25 .60
51 Delmon Young (RC) .40 1.00
52 Johan Santana .60 1.50
53 Cal Ripken Jr. 2.50 6.00
54 Yogi Berra .60 1.50
Jackie Robinson
55 Cal Ripken Jr. 2.50 6.00
56 Hanley Ramirez .60 1.50
57 Victor Martinez .40 1.00
58 Cole Hamels .60 1.50
59 Bobby Doerr .25 .60
60 Bruce Sutter .25 .60
61 Jason Bay .40 1.00
62 Luis Aparicio .25 .60
63 Stephen Drew .25 .60
64 Jered Weaver .40 1.00
65 Alex Gordon RC .75 2.00
66 Howie Kendrick .25 .60
67 Ryan Zimmerman .40 1.00
68 Akinori Iwamura RC .60 1.50
69 Chien-Ming Wang .40 1.00
70 David Wright 1.00 2.50
71 Ryan Howard 1.00 2.50
72 Alex Rodriguez 1.00 2.50
73 Justin Morneau .60 1.50
74 Andrew Miller RC .60 1.50
75 Richard Nixon .60 1.50
76 Bill Clinton 1.00 2.50
77 Phil Hughes (RC) 1.25 3.00
78 Tom Glavine .40 1.00
79 Chipper Jones .60 1.50
80 Craig Biggio .40 1.00
81 Chris Chambliss .25 .60
82 Tim Lincecum RC 4.00 10.00
83 Billy Butler (RC) .40 1.00
84 Andy LaRoche (RC) .25 .60
85 1969 New York Mets .25 .60
86 2004 Boston Red Sox 1.00 2.50
87 Roberto Clemente 2.00 5.00
88 Chase Utley .60 1.50
89 Reggie Jackson .40 1.00
90 Curt Schilling .40 1.00

2007 UD Masterpieces Artists Proof

RANDOM INSERTS IN PACKS
STATED PRINT RUN 1 SER.#'d SET
NO PRICING DUE TO SCARCITY

2007 UD Masterpieces Black Linen

*BLACK VET: 1.5X TO 4X BASIC
*BLACK RC: 1.5X TO 4X BASIC
RANDOM INSERTS IN PACKS
STATED PRINT RUN 99 SER.#'d SETS

1 Babe Ruth 5.00 12.00
2 Babe Ruth 5.00 12.00
10 Cal Ripken Jr. 15.00 40.00
17 Sandy Koufax 12.50 30.00
22 Babe Ruth 5.00 12.00
26 Sandy Koufax 12.50 30.00
27 Daisuke Matsuzaka 12.50 30.00
29 Ken Griffey Jr. 6.00 15.00
30 Derek Jeter 15.00 40.00
40 Mike Piazza 6.00 15.00
42 Tony Gwynn 15.00 40.00
Cal Ripken Jr.
43 Ichiro Suzuki 6.00 15.00
45 Ken Griffey Jr. 6.00 15.00
46 Michael Jordan 15.00 40.00
53 Cal Ripken Jr. 15.00 40.00
55 Cal Ripken Jr. 15.00 40.00
69 Chien-Ming Wang 12.50 30.00

2007 UD Masterpieces Blue Steel

*BLUE STEEL VET: 1.5X TO 4X BASIC
*BLUE STEEL RC: 1.5X TO 4X BASIC
RANDOM INSERTS IN PACKS
STATED PRINT RUN 50 SER.#'d SETS

1 Babe Ruth 5.00 12.00
2 Babe Ruth 5.00 12.00
10 Cal Ripken Jr. 15.00 40.00
17 Sandy Koufax 12.50 30.00
22 Babe Ruth 5.00 12.00
26 Sandy Koufax 12.50 30.00
27 Daisuke Matsuzaka 12.50 30.00
29 Ken Griffey Jr. 6.00 15.00
30 Derek Jeter 15.00 40.00
40 Mike Piazza 6.00 15.00
42 Tony Gwynn 15.00 40.00
Cal Ripken Jr.
43 Ichiro Suzuki 6.00 15.00
45 Ken Griffey Jr. 6.00 15.00
46 Michael Jordan 15.00 40.00
53 Cal Ripken Jr. 15.00 40.00
55 Cal Ripken Jr. 15.00 40.00
69 Chien-Ming Wang 12.50 30.00

2007 UD Masterpieces Bronze Ore

RANDOM INSERTS IN PACKS
STATED PRINT RUN 1 SER.#'d SET
NO PRICING DUE TO SCARCITY

2007 UD Masterpieces Celestial Blue

RANDOM INSERTS IN PACKS
STATED PRINT RUN 1 SER.#'d SET
NO PRICING DUE TO SCARCITY

2007 UD Masterpieces Deep Blue Linen

*DEEP BLUE VET: 1.5X TO 4X BASIC
*DEEP BLUE RC: 1.5X TO 4X BASIC
RANDOM INSERTS IN PACKS
STATED PRINT RUN 75 SER.#'d SETS

1 Babe Ruth 5.00 12.00
2 Babe Ruth 5.00 12.00
10 Cal Ripken Jr. 15.00 40.00
17 Sandy Koufax 12.50 30.00
22 Babe Ruth 5.00 12.00
26 Sandy Koufax 12.50 30.00
27 Daisuke Matsuzaka 12.50 30.00
29 Ken Griffey Jr. 6.00 15.00
30 Derek Jeter 15.00 40.00
40 Mike Piazza 6.00 15.00
42 Tony Gwynn 15.00 40.00
Cal Ripken Jr.
43 Ichiro Suzuki 6.00 15.00
45 Ken Griffey Jr. 6.00 15.00
46 Michael Jordan 15.00 40.00
53 Cal Ripken Jr. 15.00 40.00
55 Cal Ripken Jr. 15.00 40.00
69 Chien-Ming Wang 12.50 30.00

2007 UD Masterpieces Green Linen

*GREEN VET: .75X TO 2X BASIC
*GREEN RC: .75X TO 2X BASIC
STATED ODDS 1:6 H, 1:48 R, 1:48 BLASTER

2007 UD Masterpieces Hades

*HADES VET: 1.5X TO 4X BASIC
*HADES RC: 1.5X TO 4X BASIC
RANDOM INSERTS IN PACKS
STATED PRINT RUN 50 SER.#'d SETS

1 Babe Ruth 5.00 12.00
2 Babe Ruth 5.00 12.00
10 Cal Ripken Jr. 15.00 40.00
17 Sandy Koufax 12.50 30.00
22 Babe Ruth 5.00 12.00
26 Sandy Koufax 12.50 30.00
29 Ken Griffey Jr. 6.00 15.00
30 Derek Jeter 15.00 40.00
40 Mike Piazza 6.00 15.00
42 Tony Gwynn 15.00 40.00
Cal Ripken Jr.
43 Ichiro Suzuki 6.00 15.00
45 Ken Griffey Jr. 6.00 15.00
46 Michael Jordan 15.00 40.00
53 Cal Ripken Jr. 15.00 40.00
55 Cal Ripken Jr. 15.00 40.00
69 Chien-Ming Wang 12.50 30.00

2007 UD Masterpieces Ionised

*IONISED VET: 1.5X TO 4X BASIC
*IONISED RC: 1.5X TO 4X BASIC
RANDOM INSERTS IN PACKS
STATED PRINT RUN 50 SER.#'d SETS

1 Babe Ruth 5.00 12.00
2 Babe Ruth 5.00 12.00
10 Cal Ripken Jr. 15.00 40.00
17 Sandy Koufax 12.50 30.00
22 Babe Ruth 5.00 12.00
26 Sandy Koufax 12.50 30.00
29 Ken Griffey Jr. 6.00 15.00
30 Derek Jeter 15.00 40.00
40 Mike Piazza 6.00 15.00
42 Tony Gwynn 15.00 40.00
Cal Ripken Jr.
43 Ichiro Suzuki 6.00 15.00
45 Ken Griffey Jr. 6.00 15.00
46 Michael Jordan 15.00 40.00
53 Cal Ripken Jr. 15.00 40.00
55 Cal Ripken Jr. 15.00 40.00
69 Chien-Ming Wang 12.50 30.00

2007 UD Masterpieces Persian Blue Linen

RANDOM INSERTS IN PACKS
STATED PRINT RUN 1 SER.#'d SET
NO PRICING DUE TO SCARCITY

2007 UD Masterpieces Pinot Red

*PINOT RED VET: 1.5X TO 4X BASIC
*PINOT RED RC: 1.5X TO 4X BASIC
RANDOM INSERTS IN PACKS
STATED PRINT RUN 75 SER.#'d SETS

1 Babe Ruth 5.00 12.00
2 Babe Ruth 5.00 12.00
10 Cal Ripken Jr. 15.00 40.00
17 Sandy Koufax 12.50 30.00
22 Babe Ruth 5.00 12.00
26 Sandy Koufax 12.50 30.00
29 Ken Griffey Jr. 6.00 15.00
30 Derek Jeter 15.00 40.00
40 Mike Piazza 6.00 15.00
42 Tony Gwynn 15.00 40.00
Cal Ripken Jr.
43 Ichiro Suzuki 6.00 15.00
45 Ken Griffey Jr. 6.00 15.00
46 Michael Jordan 15.00 40.00
53 Cal Ripken Jr. 15.00 40.00
55 Cal Ripken Jr. 15.00 40.00
69 Chien-Ming Wang 12.50 30.00

2007 UD Masterpieces Red Linen

RANDOM INSERTS IN PACKS
STATED PRINT RUN 1 SER.#'d SET
NO PRICING DUE TO SCARCITY

2007 UD Masterpieces Rusted

*RUSTED VET: 1.5X TO 4X BASIC
*RUSTED RC: 1.5X TO 4X BASIC
RANDOM INSERTS IN PACKS
STATED PRINT RUN 50 SER.#'d SETS

1 Babe Ruth 5.00 12.00
2 Babe Ruth 5.00 12.00
10 Cal Ripken Jr. 15.00 40.00
17 Sandy Koufax 12.50 30.00
22 Babe Ruth 5.00 12.00
26 Sandy Koufax 12.50 30.00
29 Ken Griffey Jr. 6.00 15.00
30 Derek Jeter 15.00 40.00
40 Mike Piazza 6.00 15.00
42 Tony Gwynn 15.00 40.00
Cal Ripken Jr.
43 Ichiro Suzuki 6.00 15.00
45 Ken Griffey Jr. 6.00 15.00
46 Michael Jordan 15.00 40.00
53 Cal Ripken Jr. 15.00 40.00
55 Cal Ripken Jr. 15.00 40.00
69 Chien-Ming Wang 12.50 30.00

2007 UD Masterpieces Serious Black

*SER.BLACK VET: 1.5X TO 4X BASIC
*SER.BLACK RC: 1.5X TO 4X BASIC
RANDOM INSERTS IN PACKS
STATED PRINT RUN 99 SER.#'d SETS

1 Babe Ruth 5.00 12.00
2 Babe Ruth 5.00 12.00
10 Cal Ripken Jr. 15.00 40.00
17 Sandy Koufax 12.50 30.00
22 Babe Ruth 5.00 12.00
26 Sandy Koufax 12.50 30.00
29 Ken Griffey Jr. 6.00 15.00
30 Derek Jeter 15.00 40.00
40 Mike Piazza 6.00 15.00
42 Tony Gwynn 15.00 40.00
Cal Ripken Jr.
43 Ichiro Suzuki 6.00 15.00
45 Ken Griffey Jr. 6.00 15.00
46 Michael Jordan 15.00 40.00
53 Cal Ripken Jr. 15.00 40.00
55 Cal Ripken Jr. 15.00 40.00
69 Chien-Ming Wang 12.50 30.00

2007 UD Masterpieces Urban Gray

RANDOM INSERTS IN PACKS
STATED PRINT RUN 1 SER.#'d SET
NO PRICING DUE TO SCARCITY

2007 UD Masterpieces Windsor Green

*WIN.GREEN VET: .75X TO 2X BASIC
*WIN.GREEN RC: .75X TO 2X BASIC
STATED ODDS 1:9 H, 1:72 R, 1:750 BLASTER

2007 UD Masterpieces 5x7 Box Topper

STATED ODDS ONE PER HOBBY BOX

MP1 Cal Ripken Jr. 6.00 15.00
MP2 Ken Griffey Jr. 5.00 12.00
MP3 Derek Jeter 6.00 15.00
MP4 Sandy Koufax 6.00 15.00
MP5 Babe Ruth 6.00 15.00
MP6 Lou Gehrig 6.00 15.00
MP7 Travis Hafner 3.00 8.00
MP8 Victor Martinez 3.00 8.00
MP9 Jered Weaver 3.00 8.00
MP10 Phil Hughes 4.00 10.00
MP11 Bobby Doerr 4.00 10.00
MP12 Billy Butler 3.00 8.00
MP13 Andy LaRoche 3.00 8.00
MP14 Josh Hamilton 6.00 15.00
MP15 Reggie Jackson 4.00 10.00
MP16 Hanley Ramirez 3.00 8.00
MP17 Don Larsen 4.00 10.00
MP18 Ken Griffey Jr. 5.00 12.00
MP19 Jason Bay 3.00 8.00
MP20 Daisuke Matsuzaka 5.00 12.00

2007 UD Masterpieces 5x7 Box Topper Signatures

STATED ODDS APPX.ONE PER HOBBY CASE
NO PRICING DUE TO SCARCITY
EXCHANGE DEADLINE 10/10/2009

2007 UD Masterpieces Captured on Canvas

STATED ODDS 1:6 H, 1:24 R, 1:1500 BLAST
BRONZE RANDOMLY INSERTED
BRONZE PRINT RUN 1 SER.#'d SET
NO BRONZE PRICING AVAILABLE
FOR.GREEN RANDOMLY INSERTED
FOR.GREEN PRINT RUN 1 SER.#'d SET
NO FOR.GREEN PRICING AVAILABLE

AB Adrian Beltre 3.00 8.00
AD Adam Dunn 3.00 8.00
AI Akinori Iwamura 4.00 10.00
AJ Andruw Jones 3.00 8.00
AP Albert Pujols 6.00 15.00
BA Bobby Abreu 3.00 8.00
BC Bobby Crosby 3.00 8.00
BE Carlos Beltran 3.00 8.00
BG Brian Giles 3.00 8.00

BL Brad Lidge 3.00 8.00
BO Jeremy Bonderman 3.00 8.00
BR Brian Roberts 3.00 8.00
BS Ben Sheets 3.00 8.00
CA Chris Carpenter 3.00 8.00
CB Craig Biggio 4.00 10.00
CC Carl Crawford 3.00 8.00
CD Carlos Delgado 3.00 8.00
CF Carlton Fisk 4.00 10.00
CJ Chipper Jones 4.00 10.00
CL Carlos Lee 3.00 8.00
CR Coco Crisp 3.00 8.00
CS C.C. Sabathia 4.00 10.00
CU Chase Utley 4.00 10.00
CY Carl Yastrzemski 4.00 10.00
DJ Derek Jeter 8.00 20.00
DL Derrek Lee 3.00 8.00
DM Don Mattingly 6.00 15.00
DO David Ortiz 4.00 10.00
DR J.D. Drew 3.00 8.00
DW Dontrelle Willis 3.00 8.00
EB Erik Bedard 3.00 8.00
EC Eric Chavez 3.00 8.00
EG Eric Gagne 3.00 8.00
FH Felix Hernandez 3.00 8.00
FL Francisco Liriano 4.00 10.00
GA Garrett Atkins 3.00 8.00
GL Tom Glavine 4.00 10.00
GR Khalil Greene 4.00 10.00
GS Grady Sizemore 4.00 10.00
HA Roy Halladay 3.00 8.00
HB Hank Blalock 3.00 8.00
HE Todd Helton 3.00 8.00
HR Hanley Ramirez 3.00 8.00
HS Huston Street 3.00 8.00
IR Ivan Rodriguez 3.00 8.00
JA Jason Bay 3.00 8.00
JB Josh Beckett 3.00 8.00
JH J.J. Hardy 4.00 10.00
JK Jason Kendall 3.00 8.00
JM Joe Mauer 3.00 8.00
JN Joe Nathan 3.00 8.00
JP Jake Peavy 3.00 8.00
JR Jose Reyes 4.00 10.00
JS John Smoltz 4.00 10.00
JV Jason Varitek 4.00 10.00
JW Jered Weaver 3.00 8.00
KG Ken Griffey Jr. 6.00 15.00
LB Lance Berkman 3.00 8.00
MA Daisuke Matsuzaka 8.00 20.00
MC Miguel Cabrera 3.00 8.00
MG Marcus Giles 3.00 8.00
MH Matt Holliday 6.00 15.00
MO Magglio Ordonez 3.00 8.00
MR Mariano Rivera 4.00 10.00
MT Miguel Tejada 3.00 8.00
MY Michael Young 3.00 8.00
PA Jonathan Papelbon 6.00 15.00
RA Manny Ramirez 3.00 8.00
RB Rocco Baldelli 3.00 8.00
RC Roger Clemens 6.00 15.00
RH Rich Harden 3.00 8.00
RI Cal Ripken Jr. 8.00 20.00
RJ Randy Johnson 3.00 8.00
RO Roy Oswalt 4.00 10.00
RW Rickie Weeks 3.00 8.00
RZ Ryan Zimmerman 4.00 10.00
SA Johan Santana 4.00 10.00
SC Curt Schilling 3.00 8.00
SH Gary Sheffield 4.00 10.00
SK Scott Kazmir 3.00 8.00
SR Scott Rolen 4.00 10.00
TE Mark Teixeira 4.00 10.00
TG Tony Gwynn 4.00 10.00
TH Tim Hudson 3.00 8.00
TR Travis Hafner 3.00 8.00
VG Vladimir Guerrero 4.00 10.00
VM Victor Martinez 3.00 8.00
WC Will Clark 6.00 15.00

2007 UD Masterpieces Original Paintings

RANDOM INSERTS IN PACKS
EACH PAINTING IS A ONE-OF-ONE
EXCHANGE DEADLINE 10/10/2009

2007 UD Masterpieces Stroke of Genius Signatures

STATED ODDS 1:18 H, 1:2500 R, 1:2500 BLAST
WIN.GREEN RANDOMLY INSERTED
WIN.GREEN PRINT RUN 1 SER.#'d SET
NO WIN.GREEN PRICING AVAILABLE
PRINTING PLATES RANDOMLY INSERTED
PLATE PRINT RUN 1 SET PER COLOR
BLACK-CYAN-MAGENTA-YELLOW ISSUED
NO PLATE PRICING DUE TO SCARCITY
EXCHANGE DEADLINE 10/10/2009
AD Adam Dunn
AG Adrian Gonzalez 10.00 25.00
AI Akinori Iwamura
AJ Andruw Jones
AK Al Kaline 10.00 25.00
AL Andy LaRoche 4.00 10.00
BA Bronson Arroyo 6.00 15.00
BB Billy Butler 10.00 25.00
BO Boof Bonser 3.00 8.00
BR Brooks Robinson 10.00 25.00
BS Ben Sheets 3.00 8.00
BU B.J. Upton 4.00 10.00
CD Chris Duffy 3.00 8.00
CF Chone Figgins 3.00 8.00
CH Cole Hamels 10.00 25.00
CL Carlos Lee
CQ Carlos Quentin 6.00 15.00
DH Dan Haren 4.00 10.00
DJ Derek Jeter 125.00 250.00
DM Don Mattingly
DO David Ortiz 20.00 50.00
DU Dan Uggla 3.00 8.00
DW Dontrelle Willis 6.00 15.00
DY Delmon Young
EC Eric Chavez 3.00 8.00
FH Felix Hernandez
FT Frank Thomas
GO Alex Gordon 8.00 20.00
GP Glen Perkins 3.00 8.00
GW Tony Gwynn
HA Justin Hampson 3.00 8.00
HI Rich Hill 4.00 10.00
HK Howie Kendrick 4.00 10.00
HP Hunter Pence 15.00 40.00
HR Hanley Ramirez 10.00 25.00
HS Huston Street 4.00 10.00
HU Torii Hunter 10.00 25.00
IK Ian Kinsler 6.00 15.00
JA Jason Bay 8.00 20.00
JB Jeff Baker 3.00 8.00
JH Josh Hamilton 12.50 30.00
JM Joe Mauer
JP Jonathan Papelbon 15.00 40.00
JT Jim Thome 30.00 60.00
JU Justin Morneau 6.00 15.00
JV Justin Verlander 20.00 50.00
JW Jered Weaver 8.00 20.00
JZ Joel Zumaya 4.00 10.00
KE Austin Kearns 3.00 8.00
KI Kei Igawa
KK Kevin Kouzmanoff 4.00 10.00
LE Cliff Lee 12.50 30.00
LI Adam Lind 3.00 8.00
MB Michael Bourn 3.00 8.00
MC Matt Cain 10.00 25.00
MO Micah Owings 4.00 10.00
MS Mike Schmidt 20.00 50.00
NR Nolan Ryan
PS Phil Hughes 8.00 20.00
RA Aramis Ramirez 4.00 10.00
RC Roger Clemens 30.00 60.00
RH Rich Harden 3.00 8.00
RO Roy Oswalt 6.00 15.00
RW Rickie Weeks
RZ Ryan Zimmerman 6.00 15.00
SD Stephen Drew 6.00 15.00
SH Sean Henn 3.00 8.00
SK Scott Kazmir 12.50 30.00
SO Jeremy Sowers 3.00 8.00
TG Tom Glavine
TI Tim Hudson 5.00 12.00
TL Tim Lincecum 60.00 120.00
TR Travis Hafner 10.00 25.00
TT Troy Tulowitzki 15.00 40.00
VG Vladimir Guerrero
VM Victor Martinez 5.00 12.00
WB Wade Boggs
WC Will Clark
XN Xavier Nady 3.00 8.00

2008 UD Masterpieces

COMPLETE SET (120) 60.00 120.00
COMP.SET w/o SPs (90) 12.50 30.00
COMMON CARD (1-90) .20 .50
COMMON ROOKIE (1-90) .40 1.00
COMMON SP (91-120) .50 1.25
SP ODDS 1:2 HOBBY
1 Brandon Webb .30 .75
2 Justin Upton .30 .75
3 Randy Johnson .50 1.25
4 Chipper Jones .50 1.25
5 Max Scherzer RC 1.25 3.00
6 Mark Teixeira .50 1.25
7 Evan Longoria RC 2.00 5.00
8 Jim Palmer .20 .50
9 Brooks Robinson .30 .75
10 Nick Markakis .50 1.25
11 Carl Yastrzemski .75 2.00
12 Wade Boggs .30 .75
13 Curt Schilling .30 .75
14 Daisuke Matsuzaka .50 1.25
15 David Ortiz .30 .75
16 Jonathan Papelbon .30 .75
17 Manny Ramirez .50 1.25
18 Alfonso Soriano .30 .75
19 Ryne Sandberg 1.00 2.50
20 Carlos Zambrano .30 .75
21 Derrek Lee .20 .50
22 Kosuke Fukudome RC 1.25 3.00
23 Jim Thome .30 .75
24 Adam Dunn .30 .75
25 Joe Morgan .20 .50
26 Grady Sizemore .30 .75
27 Victor Martinez .30 .75
28 Travis Hafner .20 .50
29 Troy Tulowitzki .50 1.25
30 Matt Holliday .50 1.25
31 Todd Helton .30 .75
32 Justin Verlander .60 1.50
33 Asdrubal Cabrera .30 .75
34 Gary Sheffield .20 .50
35 Magglio Ordonez .30 .75
36 Miguel Cabrera .50 1.25
37 Hanley Ramirez .50 1.25
38 Lance Berkman .30 .75
39 Roy Oswalt .30 .75
40 Alex Gordon .30 .75
41 Vladimir Guerrero .50 1.25
42 Andruw Jones .20 .50
43 Chin-Lung Hu (RC) .60 1.50
44 James Loney .30 .75
45 Hunter Pence .50 1.25
46 Robin Yount .50 1.25
47 Prince Fielder .30 .75
48 Ryan Braun .60 1.50
49 Harmon Killebrew .50 1.25
50 Joe Mauer .50 1.25
51 Justin Morneau .50 1.25
52 Ken Griffey Jr. .75 2.00
53 Carlos Beltran .20 .50
54 David Wright .60 1.50
55 Johan Santana .50 1.25
56 Jose Reyes .30 .75
57 Pedro Martinez .30 .75
58 Ian Kennedy RC 1.00 2.50
59 Jay Bruce (RC) 1.50 4.00
60 Whitey Ford .30 .75
61 Mariano Rivera .50 1.25
62 Alex Rodriguez .75 2.00
63 Hideki Matsui .50 1.25
64 Joba Chamberlain .30 .75
65 Jorge Posada .30 .75
66 Robinson Cano .50 1.25
67 Eric Chavez .20 .50
68 Rich Harden .20 .50
69 Chase Utley .50 1.25
70 Jimmy Rollins .30 .75
71 Ryan Howard .60 1.50
72 Bill Mazeroski .30 .75
73 Freddy Sanchez .20 .50
74 Luke Hochevar RC .60 1.50
75 Tony Gwynn .50 1.25
76 Greg Maddux .60 1.50
77 Jake Peavy .20 .50
78 Barry Zito .20 .50
79 Russell Martin .20 .50
80 Tim Lincecum .75 2.00
81 Ichiro Suzuki .75 2.00
82 Felix Hernandez .50 1.25
83 Ozzie Smith .75 2.00
84 Jason Varitek .50 1.25
85 Chris Carpenter .50 1.25
86 Carl Crawford .30 .75
87 Michael Young .30 .75
88 Frank Thomas .50 1.25
89 Roy Halladay .50 1.25
90 Ryan Zimmerman .30 .75
91 Eddie Murray SP 1.25 3.00
92 Cal Ripken Jr. SP 5.00 12.00
93 Frank Robinson SP .50 1.25
94 Ryne Sandberg SP 2.50 6.00
95 Warren Spahn SP .75 2.00
96 Ernie Banks SP 1.25 3.00
97 Carlton Fisk SP .75 2.00
98 Johnny Bench SP 1.25 3.00
99 Ken Griffey Jr. SP 2.00 5.00
100 Al Kaline SP 1.25 3.00
101 Cal Ripken Jr. SP 5.00 12.00
102 Nolan Ryan SP 4.00 10.00
103 Jack Morris SP .50 1.25
104 Rod Carew SP .75 2.00
105 Tom Seaver SP .75 2.00
106 Don Mattingly SP 2.50 6.00
107 Lou Brock SP .75 2.00
108 Joe DiMaggio SP 3.00 8.00
109 Derek Jeter SP 3.00 8.00
110 Yogi Berra SP 1.25 3.00
111 Reggie Jackson SP .75 2.00
112 Mike Schmidt SP 2.00 5.00
113 Steve Carlton SP .50 1.25
114 Willie Stargell SP .75 2.00
115 Roberto Clemente SP 2.50 6.00
116 Albert Pujols SP 3.00 8.00
117 Stan Musial SP 2.00 5.00
118 Bob Gibson SP .75 2.00
119 Dave Winfield SP .50 1.25
120 Joe Carter SP .50 1.25

2008 UD Masterpieces Framed Black

*BLK 1-90: 1X TO 2.5X BASIC
*BLK RC 1-90: .5X TO 1.2X BASIC
*BLK SP 91-120: .5X TO 1.2X BASIC
APPX.ODDS 1:3 HOBBY
7 Evan Longoria 3.00 8.00
92 Cal Ripken Jr. 8.00 20.00
101 Cal Ripken Jr. 8.00 20.00
102 Nolan Ryan 5.00 12.00

2008 UD Masterpieces Framed Blue 125

*BLUE 1-90: 2X TO 5X BASIC
*BLUE RC 1-90: 1X TO 2.5X BASIC
*BLUE SP 91-120: 1X TO 2.5X BASIC
RANDOM INSERTS IN PACKS
PRINT RUN 125 SER.#'d SETS
7 Evan Longoria 6.00 15.00
92 Cal Ripken Jr. 20.00 50.00
101 Cal Ripken Jr. 20.00 50.00
102 Nolan Ryan 10.00 25.00

2008 UD Masterpieces Framed Blue 50

*BLUE 1-90: 2.5X TO 6X BASIC
*BLUE RC 1-90: 1.2X TO 3X BASIC
*BLUE SP 91-120: 1.2X TO 3X BASIC
RANDOM INSERTS IN PACKS
PRINT RUN 50 SER.#'d SETS
7 Evan Longoria 8.00 20.00
92 Cal Ripken Jr. 25.00 60.00
101 Cal Ripken Jr. 25.00 60.00
102 Nolan Ryan 12.00 30.00

2008 UD Masterpieces Framed Blue 5

RANDOM INSERTS IN PACKS
STATED PRINT RUN 5 SER.#'d SETS
NO PRICING DUE TO SCARCITY

2008 UD Masterpieces Framed Brown 100

*BRN 1-90: 2X TO 5X BASIC
*BRN RC 1-90: 1X TO 2.5X BASIC
*BRN SP 91-120: 1X TO 2.5X BASIC
RANDOM INSERTS IN PACKS
PRINT RUN 100 SER.#'d SETS
7 Evan Longoria 6.00 15.00
92 Cal Ripken Jr. 20.00 50.00
101 Cal Ripken Jr. 20.00 50.00
102 Nolan Ryan 10.00 25.00

2008 UD Masterpieces Framed Green 75

*GRN 1-90: 2X TO 5X BASIC
*GRN RC 1-90: 1X TO 2.5X BASIC
*GRN SP 91-120: 1X TO 2.5X BASIC
RANDOM INSERTS IN PACKS
PRINT RUN 75 SER.#'d SETS
7 Evan Longoria 6.00 15.00
92 Cal Ripken Jr. 20.00 50.00
101 Cal Ripken Jr. 20.00 50.00
102 Nolan Ryan 10.00 25.00

2008 UD Masterpieces Framed Red

*RED 1-90: 1.2X TO 3X BASIC
*RED RC 1-90: .6X TO 1.5X BASIC
*RED SP 91-120: .6X TO 1.5X BASIC
APPX.ODDS 1:12 HOBBY
7 Evan Longoria 4.00 10.00
92 Cal Ripken Jr. 10.00 25.00
101 Cal Ripken Jr. 10.00 25.00
102 Nolan Ryan 8.00 20.00

2008 UD Masterpieces Framed Red 1

RANDOM INSERTS IN PACKS
STATED PRINT RUN 1 SER.#'d SET
NO PRICING DUE TO SCARCITY

2008 UD Masterpieces Framed Silver 25

RANDOM INSERTS IN PACKS
STATED PRINT RUN 25 SER.#'d SETS
NO PRICING DUE TO SCARCITY

2008 UD Masterpieces Captured on Canvas

OVERALL MEM ODDS 1:12
AJ Andruw Jones 3.00 8.00
AP Albert Pujols 6.00 15.00
AR Alex Rodriguez 8.00 20.00
BE Carlos Beltran 3.00 8.00
BH Bill Hall 3.00 8.00
BM Brian McCann 3.00 8.00
BP Brandon Phillips 4.00 10.00
BR Brian Roberts 5.00 12.00
BS Ben Sheets 3.00 8.00
BU B.J. Upton 3.00 8.00
CA Matt Cain 3.00 8.00
CB Chad Billingsley 3.00 8.00
CC Chris Carpenter 3.00 8.00
CD Chris Duncan 3.00 8.00
CF Carlton Fisk 3.00 8.00
CH Cole Hamels 3.00 8.00
CJ Chipper Jones 3.00 8.00
CL Carlos Lee 3.00 8.00
CR Cal Ripken Jr. 40.00 80.00
CS C.C. Sabathia 4.00 10.00
CW Rod Carew 3.00 8.00
CZ Carlos Zambrano 3.00 8.00
DJ Derek Jeter 10.00 25.00
DL Derrek Lee 3.00 8.00
DM Don Mattingly 6.00 15.00
DO David Ortiz 3.00 8.00
DU Dan Uggla 3.00 8.00
DW Dontrelle Willis 3.00 8.00
EB Erik Bedard 3.00 8.00
EC Eric Chavez 3.00 8.00
EM Eddie Murray 3.00 8.00
FH Felix Hernandez 3.00 8.00
FR Francisco Rodriguez 3.00 8.00
FS Freddy Sanchez 3.00 8.00
FT Frank Thomas 4.00 10.00
GA Garrett Atkins 3.00 8.00
GL Tom Glavine 5.00 12.00
GM Greg Maddux 8.00 20.00
GR Ken Griffey Jr. 6.00 15.00
GS Gary Sheffield 3.00 8.00
HK Howie Kendrick 3.00 8.00
HR Hanley Ramirez 3.00 8.00
HU Torii Hunter 3.00 8.00
IR Ivan Rodriguez 3.00 8.00
JB Josh Beckett 3.00 8.00
JE Derek Jeter 10.00 25.00
JF Jeff Francoeur 3.00 8.00
JL John Lackey 3.00 8.00
JM Joe Mauer 3.00 8.00
JO Kelly Johnson 3.00 8.00
JP Jake Peavy 3.00 8.00
JR Jose Reyes 4.00 10.00
JS Johan Santana 3.00 8.00
JT Jim Thome 3.00 8.00
JV Jason Varitek 5.00 12.00
JW Jered Weaver 3.00 8.00
KG Khalil Greene 3.00 8.00
KJ Kenji Johjima 3.00 8.00
KY Kevin Youkilis 3.00 8.00
LB Lance Berkman 3.00 8.00
MC Miguel Cabrera 3.00 8.00
MM Mark Mulder 3.00 8.00
MO Justin Morneau 3.00 8.00
MR Manny Ramirez 4.00 10.00
MT Mark Teixeira 3.00 8.00
MY Michael Young 3.00 8.00
NM Nick Markakis 6.00 15.00
NR Nolan Ryan 15.00 40.00
PA Jonathan Papelbon 4.00 10.00
PF Prince Fielder 3.00 8.00
PM Pedro Martinez 3.00 8.00
PO Jorge Posada 3.00 8.00
RA Aramis Ramirez 3.00 8.00
RB Ryan Braun 10.00 25.00
RC Roger Clemens
RH Rich Harden 3.00 8.00
RJ Randy Johnson 3.00 8.00
RO Roy Oswalt 3.00 8.00
RY Nolan Ryan 15.00 40.00
RZ Ryan Zimmerman 3.00 8.00
SC Curt Schilling 3.00 8.00
TG Tony Gwynn
TH Travis Hafner 3.00 8.00
VE Justin Verlander 3.00 8.00
VG Vladimir Guerrero 3.00 8.00
VM Victor Martinez 3.00 8.00
VW Vernon Wells 3.00 8.00
WI Josh Willingham 3.00 8.00
YB Yogi Berra
YE Yunel Escobar

2008 UD Masterpieces Captured on Canvas Autographs

OVERALL AUTO ODDS 1:12
EXCH DEADLINE 9/15/2010
BH Bill Hall 4.00 10.00
BM Brian McCann 6.00 15.00
BP Brandon Phillips 8.00 20.00
BU B.J. Upton 10.00 25.00
CA Matt Cain 10.00 25.00
CB Chad Billingsley 10.00 25.00
CH Cole Hamels 40.00 80.00
CJ Chipper Jones 40.00 80.00
CL Carlos Lee 8.00 20.00
CR Cal Ripken Jr. 150.00 250.00
CW Rod Carew 10.00 25.00
DJ Derek Jeter 90.00 150.00
DL Derrek Lee 6.00 15.00
DM Don Mattingly 20.00 50.00
DU Dan Uggla 6.00 15.00
FH Felix Hernandez 15.00 40.00
GR Ken Griffey Jr. 90.00 150.00
HR Hanley Ramirez 15.00 40.00
JB Josh Beckett 20.00 50.00
JE Derek Jeter 90.00 150.00
JF Jeff Francoeur 8.00 20.00
JO Kelly Johnson 4.00 10.00
KY Kevin Youkilis EXCH 15.00 40.00
LB Lance Berkman 10.00 25.00
MC Miguel Cabrera 40.00 80.00
PA Jonathan Papelbon 12.50 30.00
RA Aramis Ramirez 6.00 15.00
RH Rich Harden 4.00 10.00
RZ Ryan Zimmerman 8.00 20.00
TG Tony Gwynn 30.00 60.00
WI Josh Willingham 6.00 15.00

2008 UD Masterpieces Stroke of Genius Signatures

OVERALL AUTO ODDS 1:12
EXCH DEADLINE 9/15/2010
AE Andre Ethier 10.00 25.00
AG Adrian Gonzalez 10.00 25.00
AH Aaron Harang
AL Adam LaRoche 3.00 8.00
AR Aramis Ramirez 6.00 15.00
BC Clay Buchholz 8.00 20.00
BH Bill Hall 4.00 10.00
BM Brian McCann 10.00 25.00
BP Brandon Phillips 5.00 12.00
BS Bill Skowron 6.00 15.00
BU B.J. Upton 10.00 25.00
CB Chad Billingsley 8.00 20.00
CF Chone Figgins 4.00 10.00
CH Cole Hamels 20.00 50.00
CR Cal Ripken Jr. 100.00 175.00
CY Chris B. Young 6.00 15.00
DC Daniel Cabrera 3.00 8.00
EE Edwin Encarnacion 3.00 8.00
EL Evan Longoria 60.00 120.00
EV Edinson Volquez 8.00 20.00
FC Fausto Carmona 4.00 10.00
GF Gavin Floyd 5.00 12.00
GJ Geoff Jenkins 10.00 25.00
GL Tom Glavine
GN Graig Nettles 5.00 12.00
GP Glen Perkins 3.00 8.00
HR Hanley Ramirez 10.00 25.00
HU Chin-Lung Hu 12.50 30.00
IA Ian Kinsler 5.00 12.00
JA James Loney 4.00 10.00
JB Joe Blanton 3.00 8.00
JC Jack Cust 3.00 8.00
JF Jeff Francoeur
JG Jeremy Guthrie 10.00 25.00
JK John Kruk 10.00 25.00
JN Joe Nathan 4.00 10.00
JO Josh Hamilton 30.00 60.00
JT J.R. Towles 6.00 15.00
JW Josh Willingham 4.00 10.00
KJ Kelly Johnson 3.00 8.00
KY Kevin Youkilis 8.00 20.00
LE Jon Lester 12.50 30.00
LH Luke Hochevar 5.00 12.00
MA John Maine 4.00 10.00
MC Matt Cain 4.00 10.00
MK Matt Kemp 10.00 25.00
MS Max Scherzer 8.00 20.00
NA Nick Adenhart 10.00 25.00
NB Nick Blackburn 8.00 20.00
NL Noah Lowry 3.00 8.00
NS Nick Swisher 5.00 12.00
PK Paul Konerko 10.00 25.00
RH Rich Hill 3.00 8.00
RM Russell Martin EXCH 20.00 50.00
TG Tom Gorzelanny 3.00 8.00
TT Troy Tulowitzki
WB Wladimir Balentien 8.00 20.00
XN Xavier Nady 5.00 12.00
YG Yovani Gallardo 6.00 15.00

2004 UD Yankees Classics

This 90-card set was released in January, 2005. The set was issued in eight-card hobby and retail packs with an $5 SRP. The cards came 24 packs to a box and 16 boxes to a case.

COMPLETE SET (90) 10.00 25.00
COMMON CARD (1-85) .15 .40
COMMON CARD 86-90 .40 1.00
1 Bill Skowron .15 .40
2 Bob Cerv .15 .40
3 Bobby Murcer .15 .40
4 Bobby Richardson .15 .40
5 Brian Doyle .15 .40
6 Bucky Dent .15 .40
7 Chris Chambliss .15 .40
8 Clete Boyer .15 .40
9 Dave Kingman .15 .40
10 Dave Righetti .15 .40
11 Dave Winfield .15 .40
12 David Cone .15 .40
13 Red Ruffing .15 .40
14 Dock Ellis .15 .40
15 Don Baylor .15 .40
16 Don Larsen .15 .40
17 Don Mattingly .75 2.00
18 Dwight Gooden .15 .40
19 Ed Figueroa .15 .40
20 Joe Torre .25 .60
21 Darryl Strawberry .15 .40
22 Horace Clarke .15 .40
23 Gaylord Perry .15 .40
24 Phil Linz .15 .40
25 Gil McDougald .15 .40
26 Goose Gossage .15 .40
27 Graig Nettles .15 .40
28 Hank Bauer .15 .40
29 Jack Clark .15 .40
30 Don Gullett .15 .40
31 Jim Abbott .15 .40
32 Jim Bouton .15 .40
33 Jim Kaat .15 .40
34 Jim Leyritz .15 .40
35 Jim Wynn .15 .40
36 Jimmy Key .15 .40
37 Joe Niekro .15 .40
38 Joe Pepitone .15 .40
39 John Wetteland .15 .40
40 Ken Griffey Sr. .15 .40
41 Felipe Alou .15 .40
42 Kevin Maas .15 .40
43 Lindy McDaniel .15 .40
44 Lou Piniella .15 .40
45 Luis Tiant .15 .40
46 Mel Stottlemyre .15 .40
47 Mickey Rivers .15 .40
48 Oscar Gamble .15 .40
49 Pat Dobson .15 .40
50 Paul O'Neil .25 .60
51 Phil Niekro .15 .40
52 Phil Rizzuto .25 .60
53 Doc Medich .15 .40
54 Rick Cerone .15 .40
55 Ron Blomberg .15 .40
56 Ron Guidry .15 .40
57 Roy White .15 .40
58 Rudy May .15 .40
59 Sam McDowell .15 .40
60 Sparky Lyle .15 .40
61 Steve Balboni .15 .40
62 Steve Sax .15 .40
63 Jerry Coleman .15 .40
64 Tom Tresh .15 .40
65 Tommy John .15 .40
66 Tony Kubek .15 .40
67 Wade Boggs .25 .60
68 Whitey Ford .25 .60
69 Willie Randolph .15 .40
70 Yogi Berra .40 1.00
71 Babe Ruth 1.00 2.50
72 Bill Dickey .15 .40
73 Billy Martin .25 .60
74 Bob Meusel .15 .40
75 Casey Stengel .25 .60
76 Elston Howard .15 .40
77 Catfish Hunter .15 .40
78 Joe DiMaggio 1.00 2.50
79 Lefty Gomez .15 .40
80 Lou Gehrig .75 2.00
81 Mickey Mantle 1.25 3.00
82 Miller Huggins .15 .40
83 Roger Maris .40 1.00
84 Thurman Munson .40 1.00
85 Tony Lazzeri .15 .40
86 Yankee Stadium .40 1.00
87 Times Square .40 1.00
88 Central Park .40 1.00
89 Empire State Building .40 1.00
90 Statue of Liberty .40 1.00

2004 UD Yankees Classics Bronze

*BRONZE: 4X TO 10X BASIC
OVERALL PARALLEL ODDS 1:78 HOBBY
STATED PRINT RUN 99 SERIAL #'d SETS

2004 UD Yankees Classics Gold

*GOLD: 8X TO 20X BASIC
OVERALL PARALLEL ODDS 1:78 HOBBY
STATED PRINT RUN 30 SERIAL #'d SETS

2004 UD Yankees Classics Mitchell and Ness Jersey Redemption

STATED ODDS 1:384
PRINT RUNS B/WN 40-99 COPIES PER
EXCHANGE DEADLINE 01/05/08
1 Babe Ruth/40 250.00 400.00
2 Bill Dickey/75 75.00 150.00
3 Billy Martin/99 125.00 200.00
4 Bobby Murcer/99 125.00 200.00
5 Bucky Dent/92 60.00 120.00
6 Casey Stengel/65 75.00 150.00
7 Catfish Hunter/92 75.00 150.00
8 Chris Chambliss/99 60.00 120.00
9 Don Larsen/75 75.00 150.00
10 Don Mattingly/92 125.00 200.00
11 Elston Howard/88 60.00 120.00
12 Goose Gossage/92 60.00 120.00
13 Graig Nettles/99 60.00 120.00
14 Joe DiMaggio/55 150.00 250.00
15 Lefty Gomez/81 60.00 120.00
16 Lou Gehrig/40 150.00 250.00
17 Lou Piniella/92 60.00 120.00
18 Mickey Mantle/50 175.00 300.00
19 Moose Skowron/85 60.00 120.00
20 Phil Rizzuto/40 75.00 150.00
21 Roy White/50 60.00 120.00
22 Roger Maris/92 150.00 250.00
23 Ron Guidry/99 60.00 120.00
24 Sparky Lyle/99 60.00 120.00
25 Thurman Munson/91 125.00 200.00
26 Tony Kubek/75
27 Tony Lazzeri/79 60.00 120.00
28 Whitey Ford/43 125.00 200.00
29 Willie Randolph/92 60.00 120.00
30 Yogi Berra/50 125.00 200.00

2004 UD Yankees Classics Mitchell and Ness Pennants

ONE PER BOX W/CARD
PRINT RUNS B/WN 1-2000 COPIES PER
ITEMS ARE NOT SERIAL-NUMBERED
QTY PRODUCED LISTED ON CARD BACK
NO PRICING ON QTY OF 23 OR LESS
LISTED PRICES = PENNANT/CARD COMBO
*SEPARATE CARD: .08X TO .2X COMBO
*SEPARATE PENNANT: .3X TO .8X COMBO
1 1923 World Series/23
1D 1923 World Series/1
2 1927 World Series/1927 10.00 25.00
2D 1927 World Series/96 15.00 40.00
3 1928 World Series/1928 10.00 25.00
3D 1928 World Series/96 15.00 40.00
4 1932 World Series/1932 10.00 25.00
4D 1932 World Series/96 15.00 40.00
5 1936 World Series/36 20.00 50.00
5D 1936 World Series/1
6 1937 World Series/1937 10.00 25.00
6D 1937 World Series/96 15.00 40.00
7 1938 World Series/38 20.00 50.00
7D 1938 World Series/1
8 1939 World Series/1939 10.00 25.00
8D 1939 World Series/96 15.00 40.00
9 1941 World Series/41 20.00 50.00
9D 1941 World Series/2
10 1943 World Series/1943 10.00 25.00
10D 1943 World Series/97 15.00 40.00
11 1947 World Series/1947 10.00 25.00
11D 1947 World Series/97 15.00 40.00
12 1949 World Series/49 20.00 50.00
12D 1949 World Series/2
13 1950 World Series/1950 10.00 25.00
13D 1950 World Series/97 15.00 40.00
14 1951 World Series/51 20.00 50.00
14D 1951 World Series/2
15 1952 World Series/1952 10.00 25.00
15D 1952 World Series/97 15.00 40.00
16 1953 World Series/53 20.00 50.00
16D 1953 World Series/2
17 1956 World Series/1956 10.00 25.00
17D 1956 World Series/97 15.00 40.00
18 1958 World Series/1958 10.00 25.00
18D 1958 World Series/97 15.00 40.00
19 1961 World Series/61 20.00 50.00
19D 1961 World Series/3
20 1962 World Series/62 20.00 50.00
20D 1962 World Series/3
21 1977 World Series/77 15.00 40.00
21D 1977 World Series/3
22 1978 World Series/78 15.00 40.00
22D 1978 World Series/3
23 1996 World Series/1996 10.00 25.00
23D 1996 World Series/99 15.00 40.00
24 1998 World Series/1998 10.00 25.00
24D 1998 World Series/99 15.00 40.00
25 1999 World Series/1999 10.00 25.00
25D 1999 World Series/99 15.00 40.00
26 2000 World Series/2000 10.00 25.00
26D 2000 World Series/100 15.00 40.00
MM56 M.Mantle 56 MVP/7
MM56D M.Mantle 56 MVP/1
MM57 M.Mantle 57 MVP/1957 15.00 40.00
MM57D M.Mantle 57 MVP/97 30.00 60.00
MM62 Mi.Mantle 62 MVP/1962 15.00 40.00
MM62D M.Mantle 62 MVP/98 30.00 60.00

2004 UD Yankees Classics Scripts

OVERALL AUTO ODDS 1:8
SP INFO PROVIDED BY UPPER DECK
1 Bill Skowron 6.00 15.00
2 Bob Cerv 4.00 10.00
3 Bobby Murcer 20.00 50.00
4 Bobby Richardson 10.00 25.00
5 Brian Doyle 4.00 10.00
6 Bucky Dent 10.00 25.00
7 Chris Chambliss 6.00 15.00
8 Clete Boyer 6.00 15.00

9 Dave Kingman 4.00 10.00
10 Dave Righetti 6.00 15.00
11 Dave Winfield SP 20.00 50.00
12 David Cone 6.00 15.00
14 Dock Ellis 6.00 15.00
15 Don Baylor SP 10.00 25.00
16 Don Larsen SP 10.00 25.00
17 Don Mattingly SP 50.00 100.00
18 Dwight Gooden 6.00 15.00
19 Ed Figueroa 4.00 10.00
20 Joe Torre SP 125.00 200.00
21 Darryl Strawberry 10.00 25.00
23 Gaylord Perry 12.50 30.00
24 Phil Linz 6.00 15.00
25 Gil McDougald 6.00 15.00
26 Goose Gossage 10.00 25.00
27 Graig Nettles 6.00 15.00
28 Hank Bauer 6.00 15.00
29 Jack Clark 6.00 15.00
31 Jim Abbott 10.00 25.00
32 Jim Bouton 6.00 15.00
33 Jim Kaat 6.00 15.00
34 Jim Leyritz SP 10.00 25.00
35 Jim Wynn 6.00 15.00
36 Jimmy Key 6.00 15.00
37 Joe Niekro 4.00 10.00
38 Joe Pepitone 6.00 15.00
39 John Wetteland 10.00 25.00
40 Ken Griffey Sr. 6.00 15.00
42 Kevin Maas 6.00 15.00
43 Lindy McDaniel 6.00 15.00
44 Lou Piniella SP 10.00 25.00
45 Luis Tiant 6.00 15.00
46 Mel Stottlemyre 10.00 25.00
47 Mickey Rivers 6.00 15.00
48 Oscar Gamble 4.00 10.00
49 Pat Dobson 4.00 10.00
50 Paul O'Neil SP 15.00 40.00
51 Phil Niekro 10.00 25.00
52 Phil Rizzuto SP 20.00 50.00
53 Doc Medich 4.00 10.00
54 Rick Cerone 4.00 10.00
55 Ron Blomberg 6.00 15.00
56 Ron Guidry 10.00 25.00
57 Roy White 6.00 15.00
58 Rudy May 4.00 10.00
59 Sam McDowell 4.00 10.00
60 Sparky Lyle 6.00 15.00
61 Steve Balboni 6.00 15.00
62 Steve Sax 4.00 10.00
63 Jerry Coleman 6.00 15.00
64 Tom Tresh 6.00 15.00
65 Tommy John 6.00 15.00
66 Tony Kubek SP/70 * 400.00 550.00
67 Wade Boggs SP 20.00 50.00
68 Whitey Ford SP 20.00 50.00
69 Willie Randolph SP 10.00 25.00
70 Yogi Berra SP 20.00 50.00

2004 UD Yankees Classics Scripts Dual

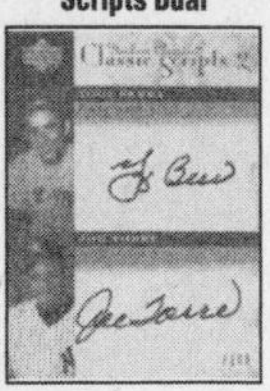

OVERALL AUTO ODDS 1:8
STATED PRINT RUN 100 SERIAL #'d SETS
EXCHANGE DEADLINE 01/06/08
AK Jim Abbott 30.00 60.00
Jim Kaat
BF Yogi Berra 100.00 175.00
Whitey Ford
BG Don Baylor 30.00 60.00
Ken Griffey Sr.
BH Yogi Berra 60.00 120.00
Joe Torre
BL Yogi Berra 75.00 150.00
Don Larsen
BM Don Mattingly 100.00 175.00
Wade Boggs
BN Clete Boyer 30.00 60.00
Graig Nettles
CB Chris Chambliss 30.00 60.00
Ron Blomberg
CG David Cone 40.00 80.00
Dwight Gooden
CL David Cone 60.00 120.00
Don Larsen
CN Chris Chambliss 30.00 60.00
Graig Nettles
CS Darryl Strawberry
David Cone
DN Bucky Dent 30.00 60.00
Graig Nettles
ED Dock Ellis 20.00 50.00
Pat Dobson
FG Ed Figueroa 30.00 60.00
Ron Guidry
FL Whitey Ford 75.00 150.00
Don Larsen
GL Goose Gossage 30.00 60.00
Sparky Lyle
KA Jimmy Key 30.00 60.00
Jim Abbott
KC Dave Kingman
Jack Clark
KJ Jim Kaat 30.00 60.00
Tommy John
KR Tony Kubek 60.00 120.00
Bobby Richardson
MB Bobby Murcer 40.00 80.00
Hank Bauer
MC Don Mattingly 50.00 100.00
Jack Clark
MM Kevin Maas 50.00 100.00
Don Mattingly
MP Bobby Murcer 40.00 80.00
Lou Piniella
MW Don Mattingly 75.00 150.00
Dave Winfield
NB Graig Nettles 40.00 80.00
Wade Boggs
OL Paul O'Neil 40.00 80.00
Jim Leyritz
PS Joe Pepitone 30.00 60.00
Bill Skowron
RC Dave Righetti 30.00 60.00
Rick Cerone
RM Phil Rizzuto 60.00 120.00
Gil McDougald
RW Mickey Rivers 30.00 60.00
Roy White
SC Bill Skowron 30.00 60.00
Bob Cerv
SD Steve Sax 20.00 50.00
Brian Doyle
SG Darryl Strawberry 40.00 80.00
Dwight Gooden
WM Bobby Murcer 40.00 80.00
Roy White

2004 UD Yankees Classics Scripts Triple

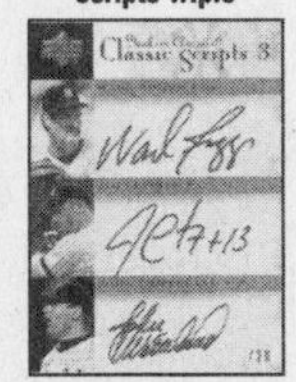

OVERALL AUTO ODDS 1:8
STATED PRINT RUN 20 SERIAL #'d SETS
EXCHANGE DEADLINE 01/05/08
NO PRICING DUE TO SCARCITY

2004 UD Yankees Classics Scripts Quad

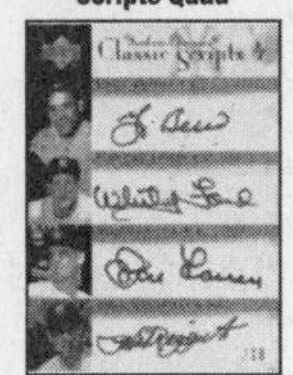

STATED PRINT RUN 10 SERIAL #'d SETS
EXCHANGE DEADLINE 01/05/08
NO PRICING DUE TO SCARCITY

2004 UD Yankees Classics Scripts Quad Cut

STATED ODDS 1:154,000 HOBBY
STATED PRINT RUN 1 SERIAL #'d SET
EXCHANGE DEADLINE 01/05/08
NO PRICING DUE TO SCARCITY

2001 Ultimate Collection

This product was released in mid-January 2002, and featured a 120-card base set that was broken up into tiers as follows: 90 Base Veterans, 10 Prospects numbered to 1000, 10 Prospects numbered to 750, and 10 Prospects numbered to 250. Exchange cards were seeded into packs for signed cards of Mark Prior and Mark Teixiera.

COMMON CARD (1-90) 1.50 4.00
COMMON CARD (91-100) 4.00 10.00
COMMON (101-110) 4.00 10.00
COMMON CARD (111-120) 6.00 15.00
1 Troy Glaus 1.50 4.00
2 Darin Erstad 1.50 4.00
3 Jason Giambi 1.50 4.00
4 Barry Zito 1.50 4.00
5 Tim Hudson 1.50 4.00
6 Miguel Tejada 1.50 4.00
7 Carlos Delgado 1.50 4.00
8 Shannon Stewart 1.50 4.00
9 Greg Vaughn 1.50 4.00
10 Toby Hall 1.50 4.00
11 Roberto Alomar 1.50 4.00
12 Juan Gonzalez 1.50 4.00
13 Jim Thome 1.50 4.00
14 Edgar Martinez 1.50 4.00
15 Freddy Garcia 1.50 4.00
16 Bret Boone 1.50 4.00
17 Kazuhiro Sasaki 1.50 4.00
18 Cal Ripken 8.00 20.00
19 Tim Raines Jr. 1.50 4.00
20 Alex Rodriguez 4.00 10.00
21 Ivan Rodriguez 1.50 4.00
22 Rafael Palmeiro 1.50 4.00
23 Pedro Martinez 1.50 4.00
24 Nomar Garciaparra 4.00 10.00
25 Manny Ramirez Sox 1.50 4.00
26 Hideo Nomo 2.50 6.00
27 Mike Sweeney 1.50 4.00
28 Carlos Beltran 1.50 4.00
29 Tony Clark 1.50 4.00
30 Dean Palmer 1.50 4.00
31 Doug Mientkiewicz 1.50 4.00
32 Cristian Guzman 1.50 4.00
33 Corey Koskie 1.50 4.00
34 Frank Thomas 2.50 6.00
35 Magglio Ordonez 1.50 4.00
36 Jose Canseco 1.50 4.00
37 Roger Clemens 5.00 12.00
38 Derek Jeter 6.00 15.00
39 Bernie Williams 1.50 4.00
40 Mike Mussina 1.50 4.00
41 Tino Martinez 1.50 4.00
42 Jeff Bagwell 1.50 4.00
43 Lance Berkman 1.50 4.00
44 Roy Oswalt 2.50 6.00
45 Chipper Jones 2.50 6.00
46 Greg Maddux 4.00 10.00
47 Andruw Jones 1.50 4.00
48 Tom Glavine 1.50 4.00
49 Richie Sexson 1.50 4.00
50 Jeromy Burnitz 1.50 4.00
51 Ben Sheets 1.50 4.00
52 Mark McGwire 6.00 15.00
53 Matt Morris 1.50 4.00
54 Jim Edmonds 1.50 4.00
55 J.D. Drew 1.50 4.00
56 Sammy Sosa 2.50 6.00
57 Fred McGriff 1.50 4.00
58 Kerry Wood 1.50 4.00
59 Randy Johnson 2.50 6.00
60 Luis Gonzalez 1.50 4.00
61 Curt Schilling 1.50 4.00
62 Shawn Green 1.50 4.00
63 Kevin Brown 1.50 4.00
64 Gary Sheffield 1.50 4.00
65 Vladimir Guerrero 2.50 6.00
66 Barry Bonds 6.00 15.00
67 Jeff Kent 1.50 4.00
68 Rich Aurilia 1.50 4.00
69 Cliff Floyd 1.50 4.00
70 Charles Johnson 1.50 4.00
71 Josh Beckett 1.50 4.00
72 Mike Piazza 4.00 10.00
73 Edgardo Alfonzo 1.50 4.00
74 Robin Ventura 1.50 4.00
75 Tony Gwynn 3.00 8.00
76 Ryan Klesko 1.50 4.00
77 Phil Nevin 1.50 4.00
78 Scott Rolen 1.50 4.00
79 Bobby Abreu 1.50 4.00
80 Jimmy Rollins 1.50 4.00
81 Brian Giles 1.50 4.00
82 Jason Kendall 1.50 4.00
83 Aramis Ramirez 1.50 4.00
84 Ken Griffey Jr. 4.00 10.00
85 Adam Dunn 1.50 4.00
86 Sean Casey 1.50 4.00
87 Barry Larkin 1.50 4.00
88 Larry Walker 1.50 4.00
89 Mike Hampton 1.50 4.00
90 Todd Helton 1.50 4.00
91 Ken Harvey T1 4.00 10.00
92 Bill Ortega T1 RC 4.00 10.00
93 Juan Diaz T1 RC 4.00 10.00
94 Greg Miller T1 RC 4.00 10.00
95 Brandon Berger T1 RC 4.00 10.00
96 Brandon Lyon T1 RC 4.00 10.00
97 Jay Gibbons T1 RC 6.00 15.00
98 Rob Mackowiak T1 RC 6.00 15.00
99 Erick Almonte T1 RC 4.00 10.00
100 J.Middlebrook T1 RC 4.00 10.00
101 Johnny Estrada T2 RC 6.00 15.00
102 Juan Uribe T2 RC 6.00 15.00
103 Travis Hafner T2 RC 12.50 30.00
104 M.Ensberg T2 RC 6.00 15.00
105 Mike Rivera T2 RC 4.00 10.00
106 Josh Towers T2 RC 6.00 15.00
107 A.Hernandez T2 RC 4.00 10.00
108 Rafael Soriano T2 RC 4.00 10.00
109 Jackson Melian T2 RC 4.00 10.00
110 Wilkin Ruan T2 RC 4.00 10.00
111 Albert Pujols T3 RC 300.00 600.00
112 T.Shinjo T3 RC 10.00 25.00
113 B.Duckworth T3 RC 6.00 15.00
114 Juan Cruz T3 RC 6.00 15.00
115 D.Brazelton T3 RC 6.00 15.00
116 Mark Prior T3 AU RC 20.00 50.00
117 Mark Teixeira T3 AU RC 200.00 300.00
118 Wilson Betemit T3 RC 10.00 25.00
119 Bud Smith T3 RC 6.00 15.00
120 I.Suzuki T3 AU RC 1800.00 2200.00

2001 Ultimate Collection Game Jersey

These cards feature swatches of actual game-used jerseys from various major league stars. Game Jersey cards (including Copper, Silver and Gold parallel versions) were cumulatively issued into packs at 1:2. Each card is serial-numbered to 150.

COPPER PRINT RUN 24 SERIAL #'d SETS
NO COPPER PRICING DUE TO SCARCITY
GOLD PRINT RUN 15 SERIAL #'d SETS
NO GOLD PRICING DUE TO SCARCITY
SILVER PRINT RUN 20 SERIAL #'d SETS
NO SILVER PRICING DUE TO SCARCITY
UAJ Andruw Jones 10.00 25.00
UAP Albert Pujols 60.00 120.00
UAR Alex Rodriguez 10.00 25.00
UBB Barry Bonds 15.00 40.00
UBW Bernie Williams 10.00 25.00
UCD Carlos Delgado 6.00 15.00
UCJ Chipper Jones 10.00 25.00
UCR Cal Ripken 20.00 50.00
UDE Darin Erstad 6.00 15.00
UFT Frank Thomas 10.00 25.00
UGM Greg Maddux 10.00 25.00
UGS Gary Sheffield 6.00 15.00
UIR Ivan Rodriguez 10.00 25.00
UJAG Jason Giambi 6.00 15.00
UJB Jeff Bagwell 10.00 25.00
UJC Jose Canseco 10.00 25.00
UJG Juan Gonzalez 6.00 15.00
UKG Ken Griffey Jr. 10.00 25.00
ULG Luis Gonzalez 6.00 15.00
ULW Larry Walker 6.00 15.00
UMO Magglio Ordonez 6.00 15.00
UMP Mike Piazza 10.00 25.00
URA Roberto Alomar 10.00 25.00
URC Roger Clemens 10.00 25.00
URJ Randy Johnson 10.00 25.00
USG Shawn Green 6.00 15.00
USR Scott Rolen 10.00 25.00
USS Sammy Sosa 10.00 25.00
UTG Tony Gwynn 10.00 25.00
UTH Todd Helton 10.00 25.00

2001 Ultimate Collection Ichiro Ball

This five-card insert set features game-used ball cards from the 2001 Rookie of the Year, Ichiro Suzuki. There is a Base, Copper, Silver, Gold and Autographed version. Card backs carry a "BB" prefix. Print runs are listed in our checklist. The signed Ichiro Ball card was available via an exchange card seeded into packs. The redemption date for the exchange card was February, 25th, 2004.

BI Ichiro Suzuki AU/25
IA Ichiro Suzuki SP 15.00 40.00
IG Ichiro Suzuki Gold/25
IH I.Suzuki Copper/150 30.00 60.00
IS I.Suzuki Silver/50 40.00 80.00

2001 Ultimate Collection Ichiro Base

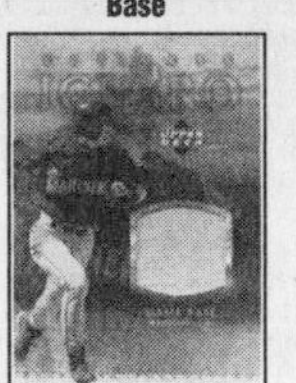

This five-card insert set features game-used base cards from the 2001 Rookie of the Year, Ichiro Suzuki. There is a Base, Copper, Silver, Gold and Autographed version. Card backs carry a "U" preifx. Print runs are listed in our checklist. The autograph card was seeded into packs in the form of an exchange card of which carried a redemption deadline of 02/25/04.

SUI Ichiro Suzuki AU/25
UIA Ichiro Suzuki 15.00 40.00
UIC Ichiro Suzuki Copper/150 40.00 80.00
UIG Ichiro Suzuki Gold/25
UIS Ichiro Suzuki Silver/50 30.00 60.00

2001 Ultimate Collection Ichiro Bat

This five-card insert set features game-used bat cards from the 2001 Rookie of the Year, Ichiro Suzuki. There is a Base, Copper, Silver, Gold and Autographed version. Card backs carry a "B" prefix.. Print runs are listed in our checklist. The autographed card was seeded into packs in the form of an exchange card of which carried a redemption deadline of 02/25/04.

BIA I.Suzuki Away SP 15.00 40.00
BIC I.Suzuki Home SP 20.00 50.00
BIG I.Suzuki Gold/200 60.00 120.00
BIS I.Suzuki Silver/250 60.00 120.00
SBI Ichiro Suzuki AU/50 1500.00 3500.00

2001 Ultimate Collection Ichiro Batting Glove

This two-card insert set features game-used batting glove cards from the 2001 Rookie of the Year, Ichiro Suzuki. There are two versions available, Base and Gold. Cards carry a "BG" prefix. Print runs are listed in our checklist.

BGI Ichiro Suzuki/75 175.00 300.00
BGIG Ichiro Suzuki Gold/25

2001 Ultimate Collection Ichiro Fielders Glove

Randomly inserted into Ultimate Collection packs, these two cards feature swatches of Ichiro Suzuki gloves. The cards are printed to different amounts and we have listed those cards in our checklist.

FGI Ichiro Suzuki/75 175.00 300.00
FGIG Ichiro Suzuki Gold/25

2001 Ultimate Collection Ichiro Jersey

This five-card insert set features game-used jersey cards from the 2001 Rookie of the Year, Ichiro Suzuki. There is a Base, Copper, Silver, Gold and Autographed version. Card backs carry a "J" prefix. Print runs listed in our checklist. The autographed card was seeded into packs in the form of an exchange card of which carried a redemption deadline of 02/25/04.

JIA Ichiro Suzuki Away 20.00 50.00
JIG I.Suzuki Gold/200 60.00 120.00
JIH I.Suzuki Home SP 40.00 80.00
JIS I.Suzuki Silver/250 50.00 100.00
SJI Ichiro Suzuki AU/50 1500.00 3500.00

2001 Ultimate Collection Magic Numbers Game Jersey

These cards feature swatches of actual game-used jerseys from various major league stars. They were issued into packs at 1:2. Card backs carry a "MN" prefix.

GAME JERSEY CUMULATIVE ODDS 1:2
STATED PRINT RUN 150 SERIAL #'d SETS
*RED: .75X TO 2X BASIC MAGIC NUMBERS
RED PRINT RUN 30 SERIAL #'d SETS
NO RED PUJOLS PRICING AVAILABLE
COPPER PRINT RUN 24 SERIAL #'d SETS
NO COPPER PRICING DUE TO SCARCITY
SILVER PRINT RUN 20 SERIAL #'d SETS
NO SILVER PRICING DUE TO SCARCITY
GOLD PRINT RUN 15 SERIAL #'d SETS
NO GOLD PRICING DUE TO SCARCITY
MNG Tony Gwynn 10.00 25.00
MNAJ Andruw Jones 10.00 25.00
MNAP Albert Pujols 75.00 125.00
MNAR Alex Rodriguez 10.00 25.00
MNBB Barry Bonds 15.00 40.00
MNBW Bernie Williams 10.00 25.00
MNCD Carlos Delgado 6.00 15.00
MNCJ Chipper Jones 10.00 25.00
MNCR Cal Ripken 20.00 50.00
MNDE Darin Erstad 6.00 15.00
MNFT Frank Thomas 10.00 25.00
MNGM Greg Maddux 10.00 25.00
MNGS Gary Sheffield 6.00 15.00
MNIR Ivan Rodriguez 10.00 25.00
MNJAG Jason Giambi 6.00 15.00
MNJB Jeff Bagwell 10.00 25.00
MNJC Jose Canseco 10.00 25.00
MNJG Juan Gonzalez 6.00 15.00
MNKG Ken Griffey Jr. 10.00 25.00
MNLG Luis Gonzalez 6.00 15.00
MNLW Larry Walker 6.00 15.00
MNMO Magglio Ordonez 6.00 15.00
MNMP Mike Piazza 10.00 25.00
MNRA Roberto Alomar 10.00 25.00
MNRC Roger Clemens 10.00 25.00
MNRJ Randy Johnson 10.00 25.00
MNSG Shawn Green 6.00 15.00
MNSR Scott Rolen 10.00 25.00
MNSS Sammy Sosa 10.00 25.00
MNTH Todd Helton 10.00 25.00

2001 Ultimate Collection Signatures

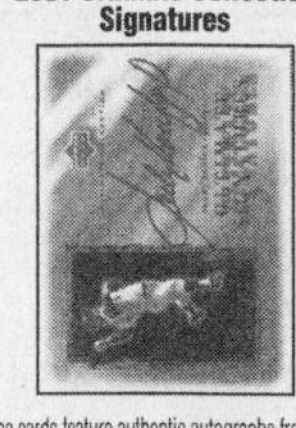

These cards feature authentic autographs from various major league stars. They were issued into packs at 1:4. Card backs carry the player's initials as numbering. Please note that there were only 150 sets produced. The following players cards were seeded into packs as exchange cards with a redemption deadline of 02/25/04: Cal Ripken, Edgar Martinez, Ken Griffey Jr. and Tom Glavine.

*COPPER: .75X TO 1.5X BASIC SIG
COPPER PRINT RUN 70 SERIAL #'d SETS
GOLD PRINT RUN 15 SERIAL #'d SETS
NO GOLD PRICING DUE TO SCARCITY
SILVER PRINT RUN 24 SERIAL #'d SETS
NO SILVER PRICING DUE TO SCARCITY
AR Alex Rodriguez 50.00 100.00
BAB Barry Bonds 100.00 175.00
CD Carlos Delgado 10.00 25.00
CF Carlton Fisk 15.00 40.00
CR Cal Ripken 75.00 150.00
DS Duke Snider 15.00 40.00
EB Ernie Banks 20.00 50.00
EM Edgar Martinez 20.00 50.00
FT Frank Thomas 20.00 50.00
GS Gary Sheffield 15.00 40.00
IR Ivan Rodriguez 20.00 50.00
JAG Jason Giambi 10.00 25.00
JT Jim Thome 20.00 50.00
KG Ken Griffey Jr. 60.00 120.00
KP Kirby Puckett 50.00 100.00
LG Luis Gonzalez 10.00 25.00
RA Roberto Alomar 15.00 40.00
RC Roger Clemens 50.00 100.00
RK Ryan Klesko 10.00 25.00
RY Robin Yount 30.00 60.00
SK Sandy Koufax 200.00 350.00
SS Sammy Sosa 50.00 100.00
TG Tony Gwynn 40.00 80.00
TGL Tom Glavine 20.00 50.00
TP Tony Perez 10.00 25.00
TS Tom Seaver 15.00 40.00

2002 Ultimate Collection

This 120 card set was released in late December, 2002. These cards were issued in five card packs which came four packs to a box and four boxes to a case with an SRP of approximately $100 per pack. Card numbered 61 through 120 featured Rookie Cards with cards numbered 110 through 120 being autographed by the player. The cards between 61 and 110 were issued to a stated print run of 500 serial numbered sets while cards numbered 111 through 113 were issued to a stated print run of 300 serial numbered sets and cards numbered 114 through 120 were issued to a stated print run of 550 serial numbered sets. One hundred Mark McGwire Priority Signing exchange cards were randomly seeded in to packs (at a believed odds of 1:1000 packs). The bearer of the card was allowed to send in one item of his or her choice to Upper Deck for McGwire to sign.

COMMON CARD (1-60) 1.50 4.00
COMMON CARD (61-110) 4.00 10.00
61-110 PRINT RUN 550 SERIAL #'d SETS
COMMON CARD (111-113) 6.00 15.00
COMMON CARD (114-120) 6.00 15.00
1 Troy Glaus 1.50 4.00
2 Luis Gonzalez 1.50 4.00
3 Curt Schilling 1.50 4.00
4 Randy Johnson 2.50 6.00
5 Andruw Jones 1.50 4.00
6 Greg Maddux 4.00 10.00
7 Chipper Jones 2.50 6.00
8 Gary Sheffield 1.50 4.00
9 Cal Ripken 8.00 20.00
10 Manny Ramirez 1.50 4.00
11 Pedro Martinez 1.50 4.00
12 Nomar Garciaparra 4.00 10.00
13 Sammy Sosa 2.50 6.00
14 Kerry Wood 1.50 4.00
15 Mark Prior 2.50 6.00
16 Magglio Ordonez 1.50 4.00
17 Frank Thomas 2.50 6.00
18 Adam Dunn 1.50 4.00
19 Ken Griffey Jr. 4.00 10.00
20 Jim Thome 1.50 4.00
21 Larry Walker 1.50 4.00
22 Todd Helton 1.50 4.00
23 Nolan Ryan 6.00 15.00
24 Jeff Bagwell 1.50 4.00
25 Roy Oswalt 1.50 4.00
26 Lance Berkman 1.50 4.00
27 Mike Sweeney 1.50 4.00
28 Shawn Green 1.50 4.00
29 Hideo Nomo 2.50 6.00
30 Torii Hunter 1.50 4.00
31 Vladimir Guerrero 2.50 6.00
32 Tom Seaver 1.50 4.00
33 Mike Piazza 4.00 10.00
34 Roberto Alomar 1.50 4.00
35 Derek Jeter 6.00 15.00
36 Alfonso Soriano 1.50 4.00
37 Jason Giambi 1.50 4.00
38 Roger Clemens 5.00 12.00
39 Mike Mussina 1.50 4.00
40 Bernie Williams 1.50 4.00
41 Joe DiMaggio 5.00 12.00
42 Mickey Mantle 10.00 25.00
43 Miguel Tejada 1.50 4.00
44 Eric Chavez 1.50 4.00
45 Barry Zito 1.50 4.00
46 Pat Burrell 1.50 4.00
47 Jason Kendall 1.50 4.00
48 Brian Giles 1.50 4.00
49 Barry Bonds 6.00 15.00
50 Ichiro Suzuki 5.00 12.00
51 Stan Musial 4.00 10.00
52 J.D. Drew 1.50 4.00
53 Scott Rolen 1.50 4.00
54 Albert Pujols 5.00 12.00
55 Mark McGwire 6.00 15.00
56 Alex Rodriguez 4.00 10.00
57 Ivan Rodriguez 1.50 4.00
58 Juan Gonzalez 1.50 4.00
59 Rafael Palmeiro 1.50 4.00
60 Carlos Delgado 1.50 4.00
61 Jose Valverde UR RC 4.00 10.00
62 Doug Devore UR RC 4.00 10.00
63 John Ennis UR RC 4.00. 10.00
64 Joey Dawley UR RC 4.00 10.00
65 Trey Hodges UR RC 4.00 10.00
66 Mike Mahoney UR 4.00 10.00
67 Aaron Cook UR RC 4.00 10.00
68 Rene Reyes UR RC 4.00 10.00
69 Mark Corey UR RC 4.00 10.00
70 Hansel Izquierdo UR RC 4.00 10.00
71 Brandon Puffer UR RC 4.00 10.00
72 Jeriome Robertson UR RC 4.00 10.00
73 Jose Diaz UR RC 4.00 10.00
74 David Ross UR RC 4.00 10.00
75 Jayson Durocher UR RC 4.00 10.00
76 Eric Good UR RC 4.00 10.00
77 Satoru Komiyama UR RC 4.00 10.00
78 Tyler Yates UR RC 4.00 10.00
79 Eric Junge UR RC 4.00 10.00
80 Anderson Machado UR RC 4.00 10.00
81 Adrian Burnside UR RC 4.00 10.00
82 Ben Howard UR RC 4.00 10.00
83 Clay Condrey UR RC 4.00 10.00
84 Nelson Castro UR RC 4.00 10.00
85 So Taguchi UR RC 6.00 15.00
86 Mike Crudale UR RC 4.00 10.00
87 Scotty Layfield UR RC 4.00 10.00
88 Steve Bechler UR RC 4.00 10.00
89 Travis Driskill UR RC 4.00 10.00
90 Howie Clark UR RC 4.00 10.00
91 Josh Hancock UR RC 5.00 12.00
92 Jorge De La Rosa UR RC 4.00 10.00
93 Anastacio Martinez UR RC 4.00 10.00
94 Brian Tallet UR RC 4.00 10.00
95 Carl Sadler UR RC 4.00 10.00
96 Cliff Lee UR RC 50.00 100.00
97 Josh Bard UR RC 4.00 10.00
98 Wes Obermueller UR RC 4.00 10.00
99 Juan Brito UR RC 4.00 10.00
100 Aaron Guiel UR RC 4.00 10.00
101 Jeremy Hill UR RC 4.00 10.00
102 Kevin Frederick UR RC 4.00 10.00
103 Nate Field UR RC 4.00 10.00
104 Julio Mateo UR RC 4.00 10.00
105 Chris Snelling UR RC 5.00 12.00
106 Felix Escalona UR RC 4.00 10.00
107 Reynaldo Garcia UR RC 4.00 10.00
108 Mike Smith UR RC 4.00 10.00
109 Ken Huckaby UR RC 4.00 10.00
110 Kevin Cash UR RC 4.00 10.00
111 Kazuhisa Ishii UR AU RC 15.00 40.00
112 Fr. Sanchez UR AU RC 15.00 40.00
113 J.Simontacchi UR AU RC 6.00 15.00
114 Jorge Padilla UR AU RC 6.00 15.00
115 Kirk Saarloos UR AU RC 6.00 15.00
116 Ro. Rosario UR AU RC 6.00 15.00
117 Oliver Perez UR AU RC 15.00 40.00
118 Mi. Asencio UR AU RC 6.00 15.00
119 Fr. German UR AU RC 6.00 15.00
120 Jaime Cerda UR AU RC 6.00 15.00

2002 Ultimate Collection Game Jersey Tier 1

Randomly inserted into packs, these 21 cards were issued to a stated print run of 99 serial numbered sets. These cards can be differentiated from the other game jersey as they have a "JB" numbering prefix as well as featuring batting images and the swatches are on the right side.

AD Adam Dunn 6.00 15.00
AJ Andruw Jones 10.00 25.00
AR Alex Rodriguez 10.00 25.00
AS Alfonso Soriano 6.00 15.00
CJ Chipper Jones 10.00 25.00
CR Cal Ripken 15.00 40.00
IR Ivan Rodriguez 10.00 25.00
IS Ichiro Suzuki 20.00 50.00
JD Joe DiMaggio 50.00 100.00
JG Jason Giambi 6.00 15.00
KG Ken Griffey Jr. 10.00 25.00
KI Kazuhisa Ishii 10.00 25.00
MC Mark McGwire 40.00 80.00
MM Mickey Mantle 75.00 150.00
MP Mike Piazza 10.00 25.00
MR Manny Ramirez 10.00 25.00
PM Pedro Martinez 10.00 25.00
PR Mark Prior 6.00 15.00
RC Roger Clemens 10.00 25.00

RJ Randy Johnson 10.00 25.00
SS Sammy Sosa 10.00 25.00

2002 Ultimate Collection Game Jersey Tier 1 Gold

Randomly inserted into packs, this is a parallel to the Tier 1 set. These cards have a stated print run of 50 serial numbered sets.

*TIER 1 GOLD: .75X TO 1.5X TIER 1 JSY

2002 Ultimate Collection Game Jersey Tier 2

Randomly inserted into packs, these 21 cards were issued to a stated print run of 99 serial numbered sets. These cards can be differentiated from the other game jersey as they have a "JF" numbering prefix as well as featuring fielding images and the swatches are on the left side.

*TIER 2: .4X TO 1X TIER 1 JSY

2002 Ultimate Collection Game Jersey Tier 2 Gold

Randomly inserted into packs, this is a parallel to the Tier 1 set. These cards have a stated print run of 30 serial numbered sets.

*TIER 2 GOLD: .75X TO 2X TIER JSY

2002 Ultimate Collection Game Jersey Tier 3

Randomly inserted into packs, these 21 cards were issued to a stated print run of 199 serial numbered sets. These cards can be differentiated from the other game jersey as they have a "JP" numbering prefix as well as featuring profile images and the swatches are on the right side.

*TIER 3: .3X TO .8X TIER 1 JSY

2002 Ultimate Collection Game Jersey Tier 4

Randomly inserted into packs, these 21 cards were issued to a stated print run of 199 serial numbered sets. These cards can be differentiated from the other game jersey as they have a "JR" numbering prefix as well as featuring running images and the swatches are on the left side.

*TIER 4: .3X TO .8X TIER 1 JSY

2002 Ultimate Collection Patch Card

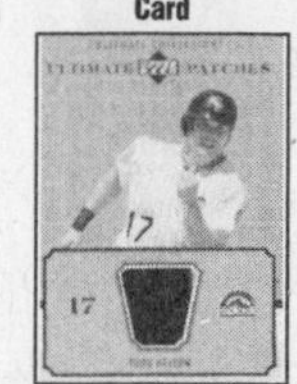

Randomly inserted into packs, these 10 cards featue game-used patch swatched of the feature player. Each of these cards were issued to a stated print run of 100 serial numbered sets.

*3-COLOR PATCH: 1X TO 1.5X HI COLUMN
CJ Chipper Jones 20.00 50.00
IR Ivan Rodriguez 20.00 50.00
IS Ichiro Suzuki 75.00 150.00
KI Kazuhisa Ishii 20.00 50.00
LG Luis Gonzalez 15.00 40.00
MM Mark McGwire 75.00 150.00
MP Mark Prior 12.50 30.00
SG Shawn Green 15.00 40.00
SS Sammy Sosa 20.00 50.00
TH Todd Helton 20.00 50.00

2002 Ultimate Collection Patch Card Double

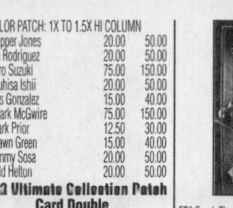

Randomly inserted into packs, these nine cards feature two game-used patch swatches of the featured players and were printed to a stated print run of 100 serial numbered sets.

DE J.D. Drew 20.00 50.00
  Jim Edmonds
GC Jason Giambi 50.00 100.00
  Roger Clemens
IG Ichiro Suzuki 75.00 150.00
  Ken Griffey Jr.
JS Randy Johnson 40.00 80.00
  Curt Schilling
MG Greg Maddux 50.00 100.00
  Tom Glavine
MS Mark McGwire 125.00 200.00
  Sammy Sosa
PA Mike Piazza 50.00 100.00
  Roberto Alomar
RG Alex Rodriguez 50.00 100.00
  Juan Gonzalez
RM Manny Ramirez 40.00 80.00
  Pedro Martinez

2002 Ultimate Collection Patch Card Double Gold

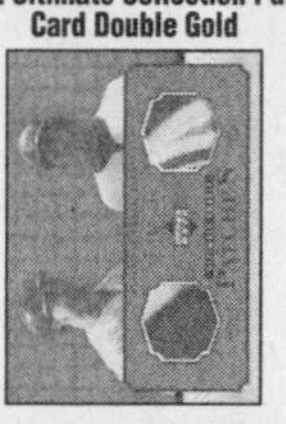

Randomly inserted into packs, these cards parallel the Patch Card Double insert set are were issued to a stated print run of 50 serial numbered sets. Please note that a card featuring Mickey Mantle and Joe DiMaggio was issued to a stated print run of 13 serial numbered sets and is not priced due to market scarcity.

*GOLD: .75X TO 1.5X BASIC PATCH
MD Mickey Mantle
  Joe DiMaggio/13

2002 Ultimate Collection Signatures Tier 1

Randomly inserted into packs, these 19 cards feature signatures of some of the leading players in baseball. As the cards are signed to a differing amount of signatures, we have notated that information next to their name in our checklist.

GOLD PRINT RUN 25 SERIAL #'d SETS
NO GOLD PRICING DUE TO SCARCITY
AD1 Adam Dunn/125 20.00 50.00
AR1 Alex Rodriguez/329 50.00 100.00
BG1 Brian Giles/220 8.00 20.00
BZ1 Barry Zito/199 12.50 30.00
CD1 Carlos Delgado/95 12.50 30.00
CR1 Cal Ripken/75 100.00 200.00
GS1 Gary Sheffield/95 20.00 50.00
JD1 J.D. Drew/220 8.00 20.00
JG1 Jason Giambi/295 8.00 20.00
JK1 Jason Kendall/220 8.00 20.00
JT1 Jim Thome/90 30.00 60.00
KG1 Ken Griffey Jr./195 60.00 120.00
LB1 Lance Berkman/179 12.50 30.00
LG1 Luis Gonzalez/199 8.00 20.00
MP1 Mark Prior/160 10.00 25.00
PB1 Pat Burrell/95 12.50 30.00
RA1 Roberto Alomar/155 20.00 50.00
RC1 Roger Clemens/320 50.00 100.00
SR1 Scott Rolen/160 12.50 30.00

2002 Ultimate Collection Signatures Tier 2

Randomly inserted into packs, these 16 cards feature signatures of some of the leading players in baseball. As the cards are signed to a differing amount of signatures, we have notated that information next to their name in our checklist.

GOLD PRINT RUN 10 SERIAL #'d SETS
NO GOLD PRICING DUE TO SCARCITY
AJ2 Andruw Jones/51 30.00 60.00
AR2 Alex Rodriguez/75 60.00 120.00
BZ2 Barry Zito/70 20.00 50.00
DS2 Duke Snider/51 30.00 60.00

FT2 Frank Thomas/51 40.00 80.00
JB2 Jeff Bagwell/51 40.00 80.00
JG2 Jason Giambi/50 20.00 50.00
KG2 Ken Griffey Jr./30 75.00 150.00
KP2 Kirby Puckett/75 50.00 100.00
KW2 Kerry Wood/51 30.00 60.00
LB2 Lance Berkman/85 20.00 50.00
LG2 Luis Gonzalez/70 12.50 30.00
MP2 Mark Prior/60 15.00 40.00
SR2 Scott Rolen/60 30.00 60.00
TG2 Tony Gwynn/51 50.00 100.00
TH2 Todd Helton/51 30.00 60.00

2002 Ultimate Collection Signed Excellence

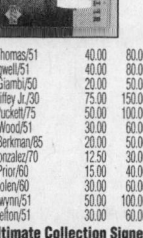

Randomly inserted into packs, these 20 cards feature signed cards of Upper Deck Spokespeople. Most of the cards were issued to a stated print run of 100 or fewer cards. Mark McGwire added a 583 HR notation to some of his signatures.

*MCGWIRE 583 HR: 1X TO 1.5X HI COLUMN
I1 Ichiro Suzuki/56 1000.00 2000.00
I2 Ichiro Suzuki/51 1000.00 2000.00
I3 Ichiro Suzuki/23
I4 Ichiro Suzuki/12
I5 Ichiro Suzuki Batting 400.00 600.00
I6 Ichiro Suzuki Throwing 400.00 600.00
MM1 Mark McGwire/70 175.00 300.00
MM2 Mark McGwire/65 175.00 300.00
MM3 Mark McGwire A's/49 175.00 300.00
MM4 Mark McGwire/25
MM5 Mark McGwire Standing 175.00 300.00
MM6 Mark McGwire Waving 175.00 300.00
MM7 Mark McGwire A's Fldg 175.00 300.00
SS1 Sammy Sosa/66 50.00 100.00
SS2 Sammy Sosa/64 50.00 100.00
SS3 Sammy Sosa/54 50.00 100.00
SS4 Sammy Sosa/21
SS5 Sammy Sosa Running 50.00 100.00
SS6 Sammy Sosa Holding Bat 50.00 100.00
SS7 Sammy Sosa Throwing 50.00 100.00

2002 Ultimate Collection Signed Excellence Gold

Randomly inserted into packs, these cards partially parallel the Signed Excellence insert set and were printed to a stated print run of 1 serial numbered sets. Due to market scarcity, no pricing is provided for these cards.

I4 Ichiro Suzuki
MM4 Mark McGwire
SS4 Sammy Sosa

2003 Ultimate Collection

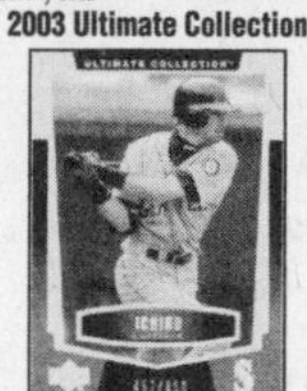

This 180 card set was released in very early January, 2004. The set was issued in four card packs with an $100 SRP which came four packs to a box and four boxes to a case. Cards numbered 1-84 feature veterans and were issued to a stated print run of 850 serial numbered sets. Cards 85-117 are Tier 1 Rookie Cards and were issued to a stated print run of 625 serial numbered sets. Cards numbered 118 through 140 are Tier 2 Rookie Cards and were issued to a stated print run of 399 serial numbered sets. Cards numbered 141 through 158 are Tier 3 Rookie Cards and were issued to a stated print run of 250 serial numbered sets. Cards numbered 159 through 168 are Tier 4 Rookie Cards and were issued to a stated print run of 100 serial numbered sets. Cards numbered 169 through 180 were each signed and inserted into packs at slightly different odds.

COMMON CARD (1-84) 1.25 3.00
1-84 STATED ODDS TWO PER PACK
COMMON CARD (85-117) 2.00 5.00
COMMON CARD (118-140) 2.00 5.00
118-140 PRINT RUN 399 SERIAL #'d SETS
COMMON CARD (141-158) 2.50 6.00
COMMON CARD (159-168) 5.00 12.00
159-168 PRINT RUN 100 SERIAL #'d SETS
85-168 STATED ODDS ONE PER PACK
COMMON CARD (169-174) 6.00 15.00
169-174 AND ULT.SIG.OVERALL ODDS 1:4
COMMON CARD (175-180) 6.00 15.00
175-180 AND BUYBACK OVERALL ODDS 1:8
169-180 PRINT RUN 250 SERIAL #'d SETS
MATSUI PART LIVE/ PART EXCH
EXCHANGE DEADLINE 12/17/06
1 Ichiro Suzuki 4.00 10.00
2 Ken Griffey Jr. 3.00 8.00
3 Sammy Sosa 2.00 5.00
4 Jason Giambi 1.25 3.00
5 Mike Piazza 3.00 8.00
6 Derek Jeter 4.00 10.00
7 Randy Johnson 2.00 5.00
8 Barry Bonds 5.00 12.00
9 Carlos Delgado 1.25 3.00
10 Mark Prior 2.00 5.00
11 Vladimir Guerrero 2.00 5.00
12 Alfonso Soriano 1.25 3.00
13 Jim Thome 2.00 5.00
14 Pedro Martinez 2.00 5.00
15 Nomar Garciaparra 3.00 8.00
16 Chipper Jones 2.00 5.00
17 Rocco Baldelli 1.25 3.00
18 Dontrelle Willis 2.00 5.00
19 Garret Anderson 1.25 3.00
20 Jeff Bagwell 2.00 5.00
21 Jim Edmonds 1.25 3.00
22 Rickey Henderson 2.00 5.00
23 Torii Hunter 1.25 3.00
24 Tom Glavine 2.00 5.00
25 Hideo Nomo 2.00 5.00
26 Luis Gonzalez 1.25 3.00
27 Alex Rodriguez 3.00 8.00
28 Albert Pujols 4.00 10.00
29 Manny Ramirez 2.00 5.00
30 Rafael Palmeiro 2.00 5.00
31 Bernie Williams 2.00 5.00
32 Curt Schilling 1.25 3.00
33 Roger Clemens 4.00 10.00
34 Andruw Jones 2.00 5.00
35 J.D. Drew 1.25 3.00
36 Kerry Wood 1.25 3.00
37 Scott Rolen 2.00 5.00
38 Darin Erstad 1.25 3.00
39 Joe DiMaggio 3.00 8.00
40 Magglio Ordonez 1.25 3.00
41 Todd Helton 2.00 5.00
42 Barry Zito 1.25 3.00
43 Mickey Mantle 6.00 15.00
44 Miguel Tejada 1.25 3.00
45 Troy Glaus 1.25 3.00
46 Kazuhisa Ishii 1.25 3.00
47 Adam Dunn 1.25 3.00
48 Ted Williams 4.00 10.00
49 Mike Mussina 2.00 5.00
50 Ivan Rodriguez 2.00 5.00
51 Jacque Jones 1.25 3.00
52 Stan Musial 3.00 8.00
53 Mariano Rivera 2.00 5.00
54 Larry Walker 1.25 3.00
55 Aaron Boone 1.25 3.00
56 Hank Blalock 1.25 3.00
57 Rich Harden 2.00 5.00
58 Lance Berkman 1.25 3.00
59 Eric Chavez 1.25 3.00
60 Carlos Beltran 1.25 3.00
61 Roy Oswalt 1.25 3.00
62 Moises Alou 1.25 3.00
63 Nolan Ryan 5.00 12.00
64 Jeff Kent 1.25 3.00
65 Roberto Alomar 2.00 5.00
66 Runelvys Hernandez 1.25 3.00
67 Roy Halladay 1.25 3.00
68 Tim Hudson 1.25 3.00
69 Tom Seaver 2.00 5.00
70 Edgardo Alfonzo 1.25 3.00
71 Andy Pettitte 2.00 5.00
72 Preston Wilson 1.25 3.00
73 Frank Thomas 2.00 5.00
74 Jerome Williams 1.25 3.00
75 Shawn Green 1.25 3.00
76 David Wells 1.25 3.00
77 John Smoltz 2.00 5.00
78 Jorge Posada 2.00 5.00
79 Marlon Byrd 1.25 3.00
80 Austin Kearns 1.25 3.00
81 Bret Boone 1.25 3.00
82 Rafael Furcal 1.25 3.00
83 Jay Gibbons 1.25 3.00
84 Shane Reynolds 1.25 3.00
85 Nate Bland UR T1 RC 2.00 5.00
86 Willie Eyre UR T1 RC 2.00 5.00
87 Jeremy Guthrie UR T1 2.00 5.00
88 Jeremy Wedel UR T1 RC 2.00 5.00
89 Jhonny Peralta UR T1 3.00 8.00
90 Luis Ayala UR T1 RC 2.00 5.00
91 Michael Hessman UR T1 RC 2.00 5.00
92 Michael Nakamura UR T1 RC 2.00 5.00
93 Nook Logan UR T1 RC 3.00 8.00
94 Rett Johnson UR T1 RC 2.00 5.00
95 Josh Hall UR T1 RC 2.00 5.00
96 Julio Manon UR T1 RC 2.00 5.00
97 Heath Bell UR T1 RC 2.00 5.00
98 Ian Ferguson UR T1 RC 2.00 5.00
99 Jason Gilfillan UR T1 RC 2.00 5.00
100 Jason Roach UR T1 RC 2.00 5.00
101 Jason Shiell UR T1 RC 2.00 5.00
102 Termel Sledge UR T1 RC 2.00 5.00
103 Phil Seibel UR T1 RC 2.00 5.00
104 Jeff Duncan UR T1 RC 2.00 5.00
105 Mike Neu UR T1 RC 2.00 5.00
106 Colin Porter UR T1 RC 2.00 5.00
107 David Matranga UR T1 RC 2.00 5.00
108 Aaron Looper UR T1 RC 2.00 5.00
109 Jeremy Bonderman UR T1 RC 6.00 15.00
110 Miguel Ojeda UR T1 RC 2.00 5.00
111 Chad Cordero UR T1 RC 4.00 10.00
112 Shane Bazzell UR T1 RC 2.00 5.00
113 Tim Olson UR T1 RC 2.00 5.00
114 Michel Hernandez UR T1 RC 2.00 5.00
115 Chien-Ming Wang UR T1 RC 10.00 25.00
116 Josh Stewart UR T1 RC 2.00 5.00
117 Clint Barmes UR T1 RC 2.00 5.00
118 Craig Brazell UR T2 RC 2.00 5.00
119 Josh Willingham UR T2 RC 4.00 10.00
120 Brent Hoard UR T2 RC 2.00 5.00
121 Francisco Rosario UR T2 RC 2.00 5.00
122 Rick Roberts UR T2 RC 2.00 5.00
123 Geoff Geary UR T2 RC 2.00 5.00
124 Edgar Gonzalez UR T2 RC 2.00 5.00
125 Kevin Correia UR T2 RC 2.00 5.00
126 Ryan Cameron UR T2 RC 2.00 5.00
127 Beau Kemp UR T2 RC 2.00 5.00
128 Tommy Phelps UR T2 2.00 5.00
129 Mark Malaska UR T2 RC 2.00 5.00
130 Kevin Ohme UR T2 RC 2.00 5.00
131 Humberto Quintero UR T2 RC 2.00 5.00
132 Aquilino Lopez UR T2 RC 2.00 5.00
133 Andrew Brown UR T2 RC 3.00 8.00
134 Wilfredo Ledezma UR T2 RC 2.00 5.00
135 Luis De Los Santos UR T2 2.00 5.00
136 Garrett Atkins UR T2 2.00 5.00
137 Fernando Cabrera UR T2 RC 2.00 5.00
138 D.J. Carrasco UR T2 RC 2.00 5.00
139 Alfredo Gonzalez UR T2 RC 2.00 5.00
140 Alex Prieto UR T2 RC 2.00 5.00
141 Matt Kata UR T3 RC 2.50 6.00
142 Chris Capuano UR T3 RC 6.00 15.00
143 Bobby Madritsch UR T3 RC 2.50 6.00
144 Greg Jones UR T3 RC 2.50 6.00
145 Pete Zoccolillo UR T3 RC 2.50 6.00
146 Chad Gaudin UR T3 RC 2.50 6.00
147 Neomar Garcia UR T3 RC 2.50 6.00
148 Gerald Laird UR T3 2.50 6.00
149 Danny Garcia UR T3 RC 2.50 6.00
150 Stephen Randolph UR T3 RC 2.50 6.00
151 Pete LaForest UR T3 RC 2.50 6.00
152 Brian Sweeney UR T3 RC 2.50 6.00
153 Aaron Miles UR T3 RC 4.00 10.00
154 Jorge DePaula UR T3 UER 2.50 6.00
  Real name is Julio DePaula
155 Graham Koonce UR T3 RC 2.50 6.00
156 Tom Gregorio UR T3 RC 2.50 6.00
157 Javier A. Lopez UR T3 RC 2.50 6.00
158 Oscar Villarreal UR T3 RC 2.50 6.00
159 Prentice Redman UR T4 RC 5.00 12.00
160 Francisco Cruceta UR T4 RC 5.00 12.00
161 Guillermo Quiroz UR T4 RC 5.00 12.00
162 Jeremy Griffiths UR T4 RC 5.00 12.00
163 Lew Ford UR T4 RC 8.00 20.00
164 Rob Hammock UR T4 RC 5.00 12.00
165 Todd Wellemeyer UR T4 RC 5.00 12.00
166 Ryan Wagner UR T4 RC 5.00 12.00
167 Edwin Jackson UR T4 RC 8.00 20.00
168 Dan Haren UR T4 RC 8.00 20.00
169 Hideki Matsui AU RC 250.00 350.00
170 Jose Contreras AU RC 20.00 50.00
171 Delmon Young AU RC 25.00 60.00
172 Rickie Weeks AU RC 30.00 60.00
173 Brandon Webb AU RC 15.00 40.00
174 Bo Hart AU RC 6.00 15.00
175 Rocco Baldelli YS AU 10.00 25.00
176 Jose Reyes YS AU 10.00 25.00
177 Dontrelle Willis YS AU 6.00 15.00
178 Bobby Hill YS AU 6.00 15.00
179 Jae Weong Seo YS AU 10.00 25.00
180 Jesse Foppert YS AU 6.00 15.00

2003 Ultimate Collection Gold

*GOLD ACTIVE 1-84: 1.25X TO 3X BASIC
*GOLD RETIRED 1-84: 1.25X TO 3X BASIC
1-84 PRINT RUN 50 SERIAL #'d SETS
*GOLD 84-117: .75X TO 2X BASIC
84-117 PRINT RUN 50 SERIAL #'d SETS
*GOLD 118-140: .75X TO 2X BASIC
118-140 PRINT RUN 35 SERIAL #'d SETS
*GOLD 141-158: .75X TO 2X BASIC
141-158 PRINT RUN 25 SERIAL #'d SETS
159-168 PRINT RUN 10 SERIAL #'d SETS
159-168 NO PRICING DUE TO SCARCITY
169-174 AU PRINT RUN 25 SERIAL #'d SETS
169-174 AU NO PRICING DUE TO SCARCITY
175-180 AU PRINT RUN 25 SERIAL #'d SETS
175-180 AU NO PRICING DUE TO SCARCITY
115 Chien-Ming Wang UR T1 30.00 60.00

2003 Ultimate Collection Buybacks

These 231 cards, which were randomly inserted into packs, feature mainly 2003 cards (with a smattering of earlier year cards) from varying Upper Deck products which UD bought back and had the player signed. Please note that for cards with print runs of 15 or fewer copies pricing is not provided due to scarity of market evidence.

BUYBACKS & YS 175-180 OVERALL ODDS 1:8
1 Rocco Baldelli 03 UDA Blue/10
2 Rocco Baldelli 03 UDA Red/10
3 Hank Blalock 02-3 SUP/10
4 Hank Blalock 02-3 SUP/35 15.00 40.00
5 Hank Blalock 03 40M/25 20.00 50.00
6 Hank Blalock 03 GF/25 20.00 50.00
7 Hank Blalock 03 MVP/10
8 Hank Blalock 03 Patch/25 20.00 50.00
9 Hank Blalock 03 SPA/20 20.00 50.00
10 Hank Blalock 03 SPA/25 20.00 50.00
11 Hank Blalock 03 UD/10
12 Hank Blalock 03 VIN/25 20.00 50.00
61 Luis Gonzalez 03 40M HR/25 20.00 50.00
66 Luis Gonzalez 03 Patch/17 20.00 50.00
68 Luis Gonzalez 03 SPA/25 20.00 50.00
69 Luis Gonzalez 03 SWS/15
70 Luis Gonzalez 03 UDA/15
71 Luis Gonzalez 03 VIN/25 20.00 50.00
72 K.Griffey Jr. 02-3 SUP/75 50.00 100.00
73 K.Griffey 02-3 SUP Spok/50 50.00 100.00
74 K.Griffey Jr. 03 40M/50 50.00 100.00
75 K.Griffey 03 40M HR824/50 50.00 100.00
76 K.Griffey 03 40M HR825/50 50.00 100.00
77 K.Griffey 03 40M HR829/50 50.00 100.00
78 K.Griffey Jr. 03 40M T40/50 50.00 100.00
79 K.Griffey Jr. 03 GF/50 50.00 100.00
80 K.Griffey Jr. 03 GF GF/3
81 K.Griffey Jr. 03 GF w/Oswalt/9
82 K.Griffey Jr. 03 HON/50 50.00 100.00
83 K.Griffey Jr. 03 HON SP/30 60.00 120.00
84 K.Griffey Jr. 03 Patch/75 50.00 100.00
85 K.Griffey Jr. 03 PB/75 50.00 100.00
86 K.Griffey Jr. 03 SPA/50 50.00 100.00
87 K.Griffey Jr. 03 SPA/75 50.00 100.00
88 K.Griffey Jr. 03 SPx/75 50.00 100.00
89 K.Griffey Jr. 03 SWS/75 50.00 100.00
90 K.Griffey Jr. 03 UD MP2/3
91 K.Griffey Jr. 03 UD MP4/3
92 K.Griffey Jr. 03 UD MP7/3
93 K.Griffey Jr. 03 UD MP26/3
94 K.Griffey Jr. 03 UDA/75 50.00 100.00
95 K.Griffey Jr. 03 VIN/50 50.00 100.00
96 Torii Hunter 03 40M/18 20.00 50.00
97 Torii Hunter 03 40M Flag/7
98 Torii Hunter 03 MVP/1
99 Torii Hunter 03 Patch/25 20.00 50.00
100 Torii Hunter 03 PB/50 15.00 40.00
101 Torii Hunter 03 PB Red/5
102 Torii Hunter 03 SPA/4
103 Torii Hunter 03 UD/10
104 Torii Hunter 03 UDA/5
105 Torii Hunter 03 VIN/25 20.00 50.00
118 Austin Kearns 03 40M/33 15.00 40.00
126 Matsui 03 40M NR/20 250.00 500.00
127 H.Mat 03 40M FlagNR/20 250.00 500.00
128 H.Mat 03 GFw/Pedro/18 250.00 500.00
129 Hideki Matsui 03 MVP/12
130 Hideki Matsui 03 PB/17 250.00 500.00
131 Hideki Matsui 03 PB Red/6
132 Hideki Matsui 03 UD/25 250.00 500.00
133 Hideki Matsui 03 UD LS Jsy/4
134 Hideki Matsui 03 UD MP/3
135 Hideki Matsui 03 VIN/25 250.00 500.00
143 Stan Musial 02 SPLC/30 40.00 80.00
144 Stan Musial 02 WSH/25
145 Stan Musial 03 PB/50 30.00 60.00
146 Stan Musial 03 PB Red/15
147 Stan Musial 03 SWSC/37 40.00 80.00
148 Stan Musial 03 UD MP/3
149 Stan Musial 03 UDA/9
150 Stan Musial 03 VIN/50 30.00 60.00
186 Sammy Sosa 02-3 SUP/25 50.00 100.00
194 Sammy Sosa 03 PB/25 50.00 100.00
195 Sammy Sosa 03 SPA/25 50.00 100.00
196 Sammy Sosa 03 UD/7
197 Sammy Sosa 03 UD LS Jsy/5
198 Sammy Sosa 03 UD MP/3
199 Sammy Sosa 03 UDA/17 50.00 100.00
200 Sammy Sosa 03 UDA Blue/10
201 Sammy Sosa 03 UDA Red/10
202 Sammy Sosa 03 VIN/25 50.00 100.00
203 Mark Teixeira 03 40M/50 15.00 40.00
204 Mark Teixeira 03 40M Rain/15
205 Mark Teixeira 03 Patch/50 15.00 40.00
206 Mark Teixeira 03 SPA RA/25 20.00 50.00
207 Mark Teixeira 03 SWS/23 20.00 50.00
208 Mark Teixeira 03 UD/25 20.00 50.00
209 Mark Teixeira 03 UDA/15
210 Mark Teixeira 03 VIN/25 20.00 50.00

2003 Ultimate Collection Dual Jersey

STATED PRINT RUN 50 SERIAL #'d SETS
*GOLD: .75X TO 1.5X BASIC
GOLD PRINT RUN 25 SERIAL #'d SETS
OVERALL GU ODDS 3:4
ALL ARE DUAL JSY UNLESS NOTED
AH Alfonso Soriano Jsy 20.00 50.00
  Hideki Matsui Jsy
AI Albert Pujols Jsy 30.00 60.00
  Ichiro Suzuki Jsy
BK Jeff Bagwell Jsy 10.00 25.00
  Jeff Kent Jsy
CA Chipper Jones Jsy 10.00 25.00
  Andruw Jones Jsy
CJ Carlos Delgado Jsy 6.00 15.00
  Jason Giambi Jsy
DE J.D. Drew Jsy 6.00 15.00
  Jim Edmonds Jsy
DG Carlos Delgado Jsy 10.00 25.00
  Vladimir Guerrero Jsy
DM Joe DiMaggio Pants 175.00 300.00
  Mickey Mantle Jsy/Pants
DP Carlos Delgado Jsy 10.00 25.00
  Rafael Palmeiro Jsy
DW Joe DiMaggio Jsy/Pants 100.00 175.00
  Ted Williams Jsy
GB Shawn Green Jsy 6.00 15.00
  Kevin Brown Jsy
GD Ken Griffey Jr. Jsy 15.00 40.00
  Adam Dunn Jsy
GE Troy Glaus Jsy 6.00 15.00
  Darin Erstad Jsy
GP Ken Griffey Jr. Jsy 15.00 40.00
  Rafael Palmeiro Jsy
GR Nomar Garciaparra Jsy 15.00 40.00
  Alex Rodriguez Jsy
GS Vladimir Guerrero Jsy 10.00 25.00
  Sammy Sosa Jsy
HJ Torii Hunter Jsy 6.00 15.00
  Jacque Jones Jsy
HZ Roy Halladay Jsy 6.00 15.00
  Barry Zito Jsy
IG Ichiro Suzuki Jsy 30.00 60.00
  Ken Griffey Jr. Jsy
IN Ichiro Suzuki Jsy 40.00 80.00
  Hideo Nomo Jsy
IS Ichiro Suzuki Jsy 30.00 60.00
  Sammy Sosa Jsy
JF Andruw Jones Jsy 10.00 25.00
  Rafael Furcal Jsy
JM Jorge Posada Jsy 15.00 40.00
  Mike Piazza Jsy
MC Greg Maddux Jsy 15.00 40.00
  Roger Clemens Jsy
MW Mickey Mantle Jsy/Pants 150.00 250.00
  Ted Williams Jsy
NI Hideo Nomo Jsy 15.00 40.00
  Kazuhusa Ishii Jsy
NM Hideo Nomo Jsy 30.00 60.00
  Hideki Matsui Jsy
PC Pedro Martinez Jsy 15.00 40.00
  Roger Clemens Jsy
PM Andy Pettitte Jsy 10.00 25.00
  Mike Mussina Jsy
PS Mark Prior Jsy 10.00 25.00
  Sammy Sosa Jsy
RM Manny Ramirez Jsy 10.00 25.00
  Pedro Martinez Jsy
RP Alex Rodriguez Jsy 10.00 25.00
  Rafael Palmeiro Jsy
SA Scott Rolen Jsy 20.00 50.00
  Albert Pujols Jsy
SB Alfonso Soriano Jsy 10.00 25.00
  Bernie Williams Jsy
SJ Curt Schilling Jsy 10.00 25.00
  Randy Johnson Jsy
SM John Smoltz Jsy 15.00 40.00
  Greg Maddux Jsy
TB Mark Teixeira Jsy 10.00 25.00
  Hank Blalock Jsy
TH Jim Thome Jsy 10.00 25.00
  Todd Helton Jsy
TR Miguel Tejada Jsy 10.00 25.00
  Alex Rodriguez Jsy
WL Dontrelle Willis Jsy 10.00 25.00
  Mike Lowell Jsy
YW Delmon Young Pants 15.00 40.00
  Rickie Weeks Jsy

2003 Ultimate Collection Dual Patch

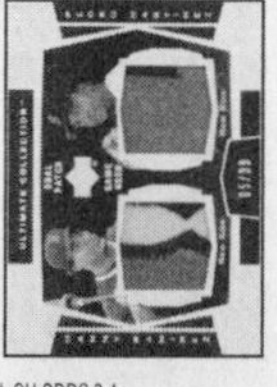

OVERALL GU ODDS 3:4
PRINT RUNS B/WN 14-99 COPIES PER
NO PRICING ON QTY OF 14 OR LESS
AI Albert Pujols 125.00 200.00
  Ichiro Suzuki/99
AM Andy Pettitte 30.00 60.00
  Mike Mussina/99
BK Jeff Bagwell 20.00 50.00
  Jeff Kent/99
CA Chipper Jones 20.00 50.00
  Andruw Jones/99
CV Carlos Delgado 20.00 50.00
  Vladimir Guerrero/99
DE J.D. Drew 15.00 40.00
  Jim Edmonds/99
DG Carlos Delgado 15.00 40.00
  Jason Giambi/99
DP Carlos Delgado
  Rafael Palmeiro/14
GB Shawn Green 15.00 40.00
  Kevin Brown/99
GD Ken Griffey Jr. 30.00 60.00
  Adam Dunn/99
GE Troy Glaus 15.00 40.00
  Darin Erstad/99
GP Ken Griffey Jr.
  Rafael Palmeiro/14
GR Nomar Garciaparra 50.00 100.00
  Alex Rodriguez/99
GS Vladimir Guerrero 20.00 50.00
  Sammy Sosa/99
HJ Torii Hunter 15.00 40.00
  Jacque Jones/83
HZ Roy Halladay 15.00 40.00
  Barry Zito/99
IG Ichiro Suzuki 60.00 120.00
  Ken Griffey Jr./99
IN Ichiro Suzuki 75.00 150.00
  Hideo Nomo/99
IS Ichiro Suzuki 60.00 120.00
  Sammy Sosa/99
JF Andruw Jones 20.00 50.00
  Rafael Furcal/99
JG John Smoltz 30.00 60.00
  Greg Maddux/99
MC Greg Maddux 40.00 80.00
  Roger Clemens/75
NI Hideo Nomo 50.00 100.00
  Kazuhisa Ishii/63
PM Jorge Posada 30.00 60.00
  Mike Piazza/73
PS Mark Prior 20.00 50.00
  Sammy Sosa/99
RM Manny Ramirez 20.00 50.00
  Pedro Martinez/99
SA Scott Rolen 50.00 100.00
  Albert Pujols/99
SB Alfonso Soriano 40.00 80.00
  Bernie Williams/21
SJ Curt Schilling 20.00 50.00
  Randy Johnson/99
SM Alfonso Soriano 40.00 80.00
  Hideki Matsui/99
TB Mark Teixeira 20.00 50.00
  Hank Blalock/99
TH Jim Thome 20.00 50.00
  Todd Helton/99
TR Miguel Tejada 30.00 60.00
  Alex Rodriguez/99
WL Dontrelle Willis 20.00 50.00
  Mike Lowell/85
YW Delmon Young 50.00 100.00
  Rickie Weeks/28

2003 Ultimate Collection Dual Patch Gold

*GOLD: .6X TO 1.2X BASIC PATCH p/r 63-99
*GOLD: .5X TO 1X BASIC PATCH p/r 21-28
OVERALL GU ODDS 3:4
STATED PRINT RUN 35 SERIAL #'d SETS
DIMAGGIO/WILLIAMS PRINT RUN 1 #'d CARD
SORIANO/MATSUI PRINT RUN 15 #'d CARDS
NO PRICING ON QTY OF 15 OR LESS

DP Carlos Delgado 30.00 60.00
Rafael Palmeiro
DW Joe DiMaggio
Ted Williams/1
GP Ken Griffey Jr. 40.00 80.00
Rafael Palmeiro
NM Hideo Nomo 125.00 200.00
Hideki Matsui
PR Pedro Martinez 40.00 80.00
Roger Clemens
RP Alex Rodriguez 40.00 80.00
Rafael Palmeiro

2003 Ultimate Collection Signatures

ULT.SIG. & AU RC OVERALL ODDS 1:4
PRINT RUNS B/WN 30-350 COPIES PER
GRIFFEY/MATSUI PART LIVE/ PART EXCH.
EXCHANGE DEADLINE 12/17/06

AP1 Albert Pujols w/Glove/40 175.00 250.00
AP2 Albert Pujols w/Bat/35 175.00 250.00
AR1 Alex Rodriguez/75 60.00 120.00
AR2 Alex Rodriguez/60 60.00 120.00
BG1 Bob Gibson Arm Up/299 12.50 30.00
BG2 Bob Gibson Stance/199 12.50 30.00
CD1 Carlos Delgado Hitting/150 12.50 30.00
CR1 Cal Ripken w/Helmet/85 75.00 150.00
CR2 Cal Ripken Fielding/85 75.00 150.00
CY1 Carl Yastrzemski w/Bat/199 40.00 80.00
DY1 Delmon Young Run/300 30.00 60.00
DY2 Delmon Young w/Bat/300 30.00 60.00
EG1 Eric Gagne Arm Down/350 20.00 50.00
GC1 Gary Carter Hitting/199 20.00 50.00
GM1 Greg Maddux New Uni/250 40.00 80.00
GM2 G.Maddux Retro Uni/140 50.00 100.00
HM1 H.Matsui w/Glove/250 175.00 300.00
HM2 H.Matsui Throwing/240 175.00 300.00
IS1 I.Suzuki w/Shades/199 500.00 600.00
IS2 Ichiro Suzuki Running/99 500.00 600.00
JG1 Jason Giambi Torso/35 20.00 50.00
JG2 J.Giambi Open Swing/35 20.00 50.00
KG1 Ken Griffey Jr. Hitting/350 30.00 60.00
KG2 Ken Griffey Jr. w/Bat/350 30.00 60.00
KW1 K.Wood Black Glv/170 20.00 50.00
KW2 K.Wood Brown Glv/85 30.00 60.00
MP1 Mark Prior w/Glove/299 12.50 30.00
MP2 Mark Prior Arm Up/225 12.50 30.00
NG1 N.Garciaparra/125 50.00 100.00
NG2 N.Garciaparra Hitting/180 50.00 100.00
NR1 Nolan Ryan Blue Uni/85 75.00 150.00
NR2 Nolan Ryan White Uni/75 75.00 150.00
OS1 Ozzie Smith Hitting/199 30.00 60.00
RC1 R.Clemens Glove Out/70 75.00 150.00
RC2 R.Clemens Arm Up/30 100.00 175.00
RJ1 R.Johnson Stripe Uni/75 50.00 100.00
RJ2 R.Johnson Black Uni/50 60.00 120.00
RS1 R.Sandberg Blue Uni/240 30.00 60.00
RS2 R.Sandberg Stripe Uni/200 30.00 60.00
RW1 R.Weeks White Uni/300 12.50 30.00
RW2 R.Weeks Red Uni/300 12.50 30.00
TS1 Tom Seaver Arms Up/75 20.00 50.00
TS2 Tom Seaver Arm Down/60 20.00 50.00
VG1 V.Guerrero Smiling/75 30.00 60.00
VG2 V.Guerrero Hitting/50 40.00 80.00

2003 Ultimate Collection Signatures Gold

ULT.SIG. & AU RC OVERALL ODDS 1:4
STATED PRINT RUN 25 SERIAL #'d SETS

AP Albert Pujols w/Glove 175.00 250.00
AR Alex Rodriguez 100.00 200.00
BG Bob Gibson Arm Up 30.00 60.00
CD Carlos Delgado Hitting 30.00 60.00
CR Cal Ripken w/Helmet 175.00 300.00
CY Carl Yastrzemski w/Bat 75.00 150.00
DY Delmon Young Run
EG Eric Gagne Arm Down 50.00 100.00
GC Gary Carter Hitting 50.00 100.00
GM Greg Maddux New Uni 150.00 250.00
HM H.Matsui w/Glove 175.00 300.00
IS Ichiro Suzuki w/Shades 600.00 1200.00
JG Jason Giambi Torso 30.00 60.00
KG Ken Griffey Jr. Hitting 60.00 120.00
KW K.Wood Black Glv 50.00 100.00
MP Mark Prior w/Glove 30.00 60.00
NG N.Garciaparra 60.00 120.00
NR Nolan Ryan Blue Uni 125.00 200.00
OS Ozzie Smith Hitting 75.00 150.00
RC R.Clemens Glove Out 150.00 250.00
RJ R.Johnson Stripe Uni 75.00 150.00
RS R.Sandberg Blue Uni 75.00 150.00
RW R.Weeks White Uni 40.00 80.00
TS Tom Seaver Arms Up 30.00 60.00
VG V.Guerrero Smiling 50.00 100.00

2003 Ultimate Collection Game Jersey Tier 1

STATED PRINT RUN 99 SERIAL #'d SETS
COPPER PRINT RUN 10 SERIAL #'d SETS
NO COPPER PRICING DUE TO SCARCITY
*GOLD p/r 75: .4X TO 1X BASIC
*GOLD MATSUI p/r 55: .6X TO 1.5X BASIC
*GOLD p/r 51: .6X TO 1.5X BASIC
*GOLD p/r 44-48: .75X TO 2X BASIC
*GOLD p/r 25-35: 1X TO 2.5X BASIC
*GOLD p/r 17-24: 1.25X TO 3X BASIC
GOLD PRINT RUNS B/WN 1-75 COPIES PER
NO GOLD PRICING ON QTY OF 15 OR LESS
OVERALL GU ODDS 3:4

AD Adam Dunn Red Jsy 4.00 10.00
AJ Andruw Jones w/Bat 6.00 15.00
AP Albert Pujols Running 10.00 25.00
AR Alex Rodriguez Throw 8.00 20.00
AS Alfonso Soriano No Glv 4.00 10.00
BW Bernie Williams White Jsy 6.00 15.00
BZ Barry Zito Green Jsy 4.00 10.00
CD Carlos Delgado Blue Jsy 4.00 10.00
CJ Chipper Jones No Bat 6.00 15.00
CS Curt Schilling Arm Up 4.00 10.00
DW Dontrelle Willis Black Jsy 6.00 15.00
DY Delmon Young Throw 6.00 15.00
FT Frank Thomas Black Jsy 6.00 15.00
GM Greg Maddux White Jsy 8.00 20.00
GS Gary Sheffield Throw 4.00 10.00
HM Hideki Matsui Ball Toss 20.00 50.00
HN Hideo Nomo Gray Jsy 10.00 25.00
IS Ichiro Suzuki Gray Jsy 30.00 60.00
JE Jim Edmonds White Jsy 4.00 10.00
JG Jason Giambi No Bat 4.00 10.00
JR Jose Reyes Throw 4.00 10.00
JT Jim Thome Red Jsy 6.00 15.00
KG Ken Griffey Jr. Gray Jsy 10.00 25.00
KI Kazuhisa Ishii Arms Up 4.00 10.00
KW Kerry Wood Pitching 4.00 10.00
MI Mike Piazza Mask On 8.00 20.00
MM Mike Mussina Blue Jsy 6.00 15.00
MP Mark Prior Pitching 6.00 15.00
MR Manny Ramirez Red Jsy 6.00 15.00
MT Miguel Tejada White Jsy 4.00 10.00
PB Pat Burrell Running 4.00 10.00
RB Rocco Baldelli Batting 4.00 10.00
RC Roger Clemens White Jsy 10.00 25.00
RF Rafael Furcal Fielding 4.00 10.00
RJ Randy Johnson White Jsy 6.00 15.00
RW Rickie Weeks Bat Up 5.00 12.00
SG Shawn Green White Jsy 4.00 10.00
SS Sammy Sosa Running 6.00 15.00
TG Tom Glavine Black Jsy 6.00 15.00
TH Torii Hunter Running 4.00 10.00
TR Troy Glaus Dirty Jsy 4.00 10.00
VG Vladimir Guerrero w/Bat 6.00 15.00

2003 Ultimate Collection Game Jersey Tier 2

STATED PRINT RUN 75 SERIAL #'d SETS
COPPER PRINT RUN 10 SERIAL #'d SETS
NO COPPER PRICING DUE TO SCARCITY
*GOLD p/r 75: .4X TO 1X BASIC
*GOLD MATSUI p/r 55: .6X TO 1.5X BASIC
*GOLD p/r 51: .6X TO 1.5X BASIC
*GOLD p/r 44-48: .75X TO 2X BASIC
*GOLD p/r 25-35: 1X TO 2.5X BASIC
*GOLD p/r 17-24: 1.25X TO 3X BASIC
GOLD PRINT RUNS B/WN 1-75 COPIES PER
NO GOLD PRICING ON QTY OF 15 OR LESS
OVERALL GU ODDS 3:4

AD2 Adam Dunn Swing 4.00 10.00
AJ2 Andruw Jones w/Glv 6.00 15.00
AP2 Albert Pujols Batting 10.00 25.00
AR2 Alex Rodriguez Running 8.00 20.00
AS2 Alfonso Soriano w/Glv 4.00 10.00
BW2 Bernie Williams Gray Jsy 6.00 15.00
BZ2 Barry Zito Gray Jsy 4.00 10.00
CD2 Carlos Delgado Gray Jsy 4.00 10.00
CJ2 Chipper Jones w/Bat 6.00 15.00
CS2 Curt Schilling Arm Down 4.00 10.00
DW Dontrelle Willis Gray Jsy 6.00 15.00
DY2 Delmon Young w/Ball 8.00 20.00
FT2 Frank Thomas White Jsy 6.00 15.00
GM2 Greg Maddux Blue Jsy 8.00 20.00
GS2 Gary Sheffield Batting 4.00 10.00
HM2 Hideki Matsui w/Bat 20.00 50.00
HN2 Hideo Nomo Blue Jsy 10.00 25.00
IS2 Ichiro Suzuki w/Bat 30.00 60.00
JE2 Jim Edmonds Gray Jsy 4.00 10.00
JG2 Jason Giambi w/Bat 4.00 10.00
JR2 Jose Reyes Walking 4.00 10.00
JT2 Jim Thome White Jsy 6.00 15.00
KG2 Ken Griffey Jr. Red Jsy 10.00 25.00
KI2 Kazuhisa Ishii Arms Down 4.00 10.00
KW2 Kerry Wood Standing 4.00 10.00
MI2 Mike Piazza w/Bat 8.00 20.00
MM2 Mike Mussina Gray Jsy 6.00 15.00
MP2 Mark Prior Hitting 6.00 15.00
MR2 Manny Ramirez Gray Jsy 6.00 15.00
MT2 Miguel Tejada Green Jsy 4.00 10.00
PB2 Pat Burrell Swinging 4.00 10.00
RB2 Rocco Baldelli Running 4.00 10.00
RC2 Roger Clemens Blue Jsy 10.00 25.00
RF2 Rafael Furcal Running 4.00 10.00
RJ2 Randy Johnson Black Jsy 6.00 15.00
RW2 Rickie Weeks Bat Forward 5.00 12.00
SG2 Shawn Green Gray Jsy 4.00 10.00
SS2 Sammy Sosa Batting 6.00 15.00
TG2 Tom Glavine Orange Jsy 6.00 15.00
TH2 Torii Hunter Swinging 4.00 10.00
TR2 Troy Glaus Clean Jsy 4.00 10.00
VG2 Vladimir Guerrero Point Up 6.00 15.00

2003 Ultimate Collection Game Patch

STATED PRINT RUN 99 SERIAL #'d SETS
SORIANO PRINT RUN 42 SERIAL #'d CARDS
*COPPER: .6X TO 1.2X BASIC p/r 99
*COPPER: .6X TO 1.2X BASIC p/r 42
COPPER PRINT RUN 35 SERIAL #'d SETS
*GOLD: .75X TO 1.5X BASIC p/r 99
*GOLD: .75X TO 1.5X BASIC p/r 42
GOLD PRINT RUN 25 SERIAL #'d SETS
OVERALL GU ODDS 3:4

AD Adam Dunn 10.00 25.00
AJ Andruw Jones 15.00 40.00
AP Albert Pujols 25.00 60.00
AR Alex Rodriguez 20.00 50.00
AS Alfonso Soriano/42 10.00 25.00
BW Bernie Williams 15.00 40.00
BZ Barry Zito 10.00 25.00
CD Carlos Delgado 10.00 25.00
CJ Chipper Jones 15.00 40.00
CS Curt Schilling 10.00 25.00
DW Dontrelle Willis 15.00 40.00
DY Delmon Young 10.00 25.00
FT Frank Thomas 15.00 40.00
GM Greg Maddux 20.00 50.00
HM Hideki Matsui 40.00 100.00
HN Hideo Nomo 20.00 50.00
IS Ichiro Suzuki 50.00 120.00
JE Jim Edmonds 10.00 25.00
JG Jason Giambi 10.00 25.00
JR Jose Reyes 10.00 25.00
JT Jim Thome 15.00 40.00
KG Ken Griffey Jr. 25.00 60.00
KI Kazuhisa Ishii 10.00 25.00
KW Kerry Wood 10.00 25.00
MI Mike Piazza 20.00 50.00
MM Mike Mussina 15.00 40.00
MP Mark Prior 15.00 40.00
MR Manny Ramirez 15.00 40.00
MT Miguel Tejada 10.00 25.00
PB Pat Burrell 10.00 25.00
RB Rocco Baldelli 10.00 25.00
RC Roger Clemens 25.00 60.00
RF Rafael Furcal 10.00 25.00
RH Roy Halladay 10.00 25.00
RJ Randy Johnson 15.00 40.00
RW Rickie Weeks 15.00 40.00
SG Shawn Green 10.00 25.00
SS Sammy Sosa 15.00 40.00
TG Tom Glavine 15.00 40.00
TH Torii Hunter 10.00 25.00
TR Troy Glaus 10.00 25.00
VG Vladimir Guerrero 15.00 40.00

2003 Ultimate Collection Ultimate Signatures Koufax

STATED PRINT RUN 75 SER.#'d SETS
GOLD PRINT RUN 5 SER.#'d SETS
NO GOLD PRICING DUE TO SCARCITY
PLATINUM PRINT RUN 25 SER.#'d SETS
NO PLATINUM PRICING AVAILABLE

SK Sandy Koufax 125.00 300.00

2004 Ultimate Collection

This 222 card set was released in January, 2005. The set was issued in four card packs with an $100 SRP which came four packs to a box and four boxes to a case. Cards numbered 1-42 feature retired veterans while cards 43 through 126 feature active veterans. Cards numbered 127 through 222 feature rookies either grouped by tiers or signed cards. A few players did not return their autographs in time for insertion and those autographs had an exchange date of December 28, 2007.

COMMON CARD (1-42) .75 2.00
COMMON CARD (43-126) .75 2.00
1-126 STATED ODDS TWO PER PACK
1-126 PRINT RUN 675 SERIAL #'d CARDS
COMMON CARD (127-168) 1.00 2.50
127-209/222 STATED ODDS 3:4 PACKS
127-168 PRINT RUN 525 SERIAL #'d SETS
COMMON CARD (169-194) 1.50 4.00
169-194 PRINT RUN 299 SERIAL #'d SETS
COMMON (195-209/222) 2.00 5.00
195-209/222 PRINT RUN 199 SER.#'d SETS
COMMON AUTO (210-221) 10.00 25.00
210-221 STATED ODDS 1:10
210-221 PRINT RUN 75 SERIAL #'d SETS
EXCHANGE DEADLINE 12/28/07

1 Al Kaline 2.00 5.00
2 Billy Williams .75 2.00
3 Bob Feller .75 2.00
4 Bob Gibson 1.25 3.00
5 Bob Lemon .75 2.00
6 Bobby Doerr .75 2.00
7 Brooks Robinson 1.25 3.00
8 Cal Ripken 8.00 20.00
9 Catfish Hunter .75 2.00
10 Eddie Mathews 2.00 5.00
11 Enos Slaughter .75 2.00
12 Ernie Banks 2.00 5.00
13 Fergie Jenkins .75 2.00
14 Gaylord Perry .75 2.00
15 Harmon Killebrew 2.00 5.00
16 Jim Bunning .75 2.00
17 Joe DiMaggio 5.00 12.00
18 Joe Morgan .75 2.00
19 Juan Marichal .75 2.00
20 Lou Brock 1.25 3.00
21 Luis Aparicio .75 2.00
22 Mickey Mantle 6.00 15.00
23 Mike Schmidt 3.00 8.00
24 Monte Irvin .75 2.00
25 Nolan Ryan 6.00 15.00
26 Pee Wee Reese 1.25 3.00
27 Phil Niekro .75 2.00
28 Phil Rizzuto 1.25 3.00
29 Ralph Kiner 1.25 3.00
30 Richie Ashburn 1.25 3.00
31 Robin Roberts .75 2.00
32 Robin Yount 2.00 5.00
33 Rod Carew 1.25 3.00
34 Rollie Fingers .75 2.00
35 Stan Musial 3.00 8.00
36 Ted Williams 5.00 12.00
37 Tom Seaver 1.25 3.00
38 Warren Spahn 1.25 3.00
39 Whitey Ford 1.25 3.00
40 Willie McCovey 1.25 3.00
41 Willie Stargell 1.25 3.00
42 Yogi Berra 2.00 5.00
43 Adrian Beltre .75 2.00
44 Albert Pujols 5.00 12.00
45 Alex Rodriguez 3.00 8.00
46 Alfonso Soriano .75 2.00
47 Andruw Jones .75 2.00
48 Andy Pettitte 1.25 3.00
49 Aubrey Huff .75 2.00
50 Barry Larkin 1.25 3.00
51 Ben Sheets .75 2.00
52 Bernie Williams 1.25 3.00
53 Bobby Abreu .75 2.00
54 Brad Penny .75 2.00
55 Bret Boone .75 2.00
56 Brian Giles .75 2.00
57 Carlos Beltran .75 2.00
58 Carlos Delgado .75 2.00
59 Carlos Guillen .75 2.00
60 Carlos Lee .75 2.00
61 Carlos Zambrano 1.25 3.00
62 Chipper Jones 2.00 5.00
63 Craig Biggio 1.25 3.00
64 Craig Wilson .75 2.00
65 Curt Schilling 1.25 3.00
66 David Ortiz 2.00 5.00
67 Derek Jeter 5.00 12.00
68 Eric Chavez .75 2.00
69 Eric Gagne .75 2.00
70 Frank Thomas 2.00 5.00
71 Garret Anderson .75 2.00
72 Gary Sheffield .75 2.00
73 Greg Maddux 3.00 8.00
74 Hank Blalock .75 2.00
75 Hideki Matsui 3.00 8.00
76 Ichiro Suzuki 3.00 8.00
77 Ivan Rodriguez 1.25 3.00
78 J.D. Drew .75 2.00
79 Jake Peavy .75 2.00
80 Jason Schmidt .75 2.00
81 Jeff Bagwell 1.25 3.00
82 Jeff Kent .75 2.00
83 Jim Thome 1.25 3.00
84 Joe Mauer 2.00 5.00
85 Johan Santana 2.00 5.00
86 Jose Reyes 1.25 3.00
87 Jose Vidro .75 2.00
88 Ken Griffey Jr. 3.00 8.00
89 Kerry Wood .75 2.00
90 Larry Walker Cards 1.25 3.00
91 Luis Gonzalez .75 2.00
92 Lyle Overbay .75 2.00
93 Magglio Ordonez 1.25 3.00
94 Manny Ramirez 2.00 5.00
95 Mark Mulder .75 2.00
96 Mark Prior 1.25 3.00
97 Mark Teixeira 2.00 5.00
98 Melvin Mora .75 2.00
99 Michael Young .75 2.00
100 Miguel Cabrera 2.00 5.00
101 Miguel Tejada 1.25 3.00
102 Mike Lowell .75 2.00
103 Mike Piazza 2.00 5.00
104 Mike Sweeney .75 2.00
105 Nomar Garciaparra 2.00 5.00
106 Oliver Perez .75 2.00
107 Pedro Martinez 1.25 3.00
108 Preston Wilson .75 2.00
109 Rafael Palmeiro 1.25 3.00
110 Randy Johnson 2.00 5.00
111 Roger Clemens 2.50 6.00
112 Roy Halladay 2.00 5.00
113 Roy Oswalt 1.25 3.00
114 Sammy Sosa 2.00 5.00
115 Scott Podsednik .75 2.00
116 Scott Rolen 1.25 3.00
117 Shawn Green .75 2.00
118 Tim Hudson 1.25 3.00
119 Todd Helton 1.25 3.00
120 Tom Glavine 1.25 3.00
121 Torii Hunter .75 2.00
122 Travis Hafner .75 2.00
123 Troy Glaus .75 2.00
124 Vernon Wells .75 2.00
125 Victor Martinez 1.25 3.00
126 Vladimir Guerrero 2.00 5.00
127 Aarom Baldiris UR T1 RC 1.00 2.50
128 Alfredo Simon UR T1 RC 1.00 2.50
129 Andres Blanco UR T1 RC 1.00 2.50
130 Jeff Bajenaru UR T1 RC 1.00 2.50
131 Bart Fortunato UR T1 RC 1.00 2.50
132 B.Medders UR T1 RC 1.00 2.50
133 Brian Dallimore UR T1 RC 1.00 2.50
134 Carlos Hines UR T1 RC 1.00 2.50
135 Carlos Vasquez UR T1 RC 1.00 2.50
136 Casey Daigle UR T1 RC 1.00 2.50
137 Chad Bentz UR T1 RC 1.00 2.50
138 Chris Aguila UR T1 RC 1.00 2.50
139 Chris Saenz UR T1 RC 1.00 2.50
140 Chris Shelton UR T1 RC 1.00 2.50
141 Colby Miller UR T1 RC 1.00 2.50
142 Dave Crouthers UR T1 RC 1.00 2.50
143 David Aardsma UR T1 RC 1.00 2.50
144 Dennis Sarfate UR T1 RC 1.00 2.50
145 Donnie Kelly UR T1 RC 1.50 4.00
146 Eddy Rodriguez UR T1 RC 1.00 2.50
147 Eduardo Villacis UR T1 RC 1.00 2.50
148 Edwardo Sierra UR T1 RC 1.00 2.50
149 Edwin Moreno UR T1 RC 1.00 2.50
150 Kyle Denney UR T1 RC 1.00 2.50
151 Evan Rust UR T1 RC 1.00 2.50
152 Fernando Nieve UR T1 RC 1.00 2.50
153 Frank Francisco UR T1 RC 1.00 2.50
154 Frank Gracesqui UR T1 RC 1.00 2.50
155 Freddy Guzman UR T1 RC 1.00 2.50
156 Greg Dobbs UR T1 RC 1.00 2.50
157 Hector Gimenez UR T1 RC 1.00 2.50
158 Jason Alfaro UR T1 RC 1.00 2.50
159 Jake Woods UR T1 RC 1.00 2.50
160 Andy Green UR T1 RC 1.00 2.50
161 Jason Bartlett UR T1 RC 3.00 8.00
162 Jason Frasor UR T1 RC 1.00 2.50
163 Jeff Bennett UR T1 RC 1.00 2.50
164 Jerome Gamble UR T1 RC 1.00 2.50
165 Jerry Gil UR T1 RC 1.00 2.50
166 Joe Hietpas UR T1 RC 1.00 2.50
167 Jorge Sequea UR T1 RC 1.00 2.50
168 Jorge Vasquez UR T1 RC 1.00 2.50
169 Josh Labandeira UR T2 RC 1.50 4.00
170 Justin Germano UR T2 RC 1.50 4.00
171 Justin Hampson UR T2 RC 1.50 4.00
172 Chris Young UR T2 RC 10.00 25.00
173 Justin Knoedler UR T2 RC 1.50 4.00
174 Justin Lehr UR T2 RC 1.50 4.00
175 Justin Leone UR T2 RC 1.50 4.00
176 Kaz Tadano UR T2 RC 1.50 4.00
177 Kevin Cave UR T2 RC 1.50 4.00
178 Linc Holdzkom UR T2 RC 1.50 4.00
179 Mike Rose UR T2 RC 1.50 4.00
180 Luis Gonzalez UR T2 RC 1.50 4.00
181 Mariano Gomez UR T2 RC 1.50 4.00
182 Rene Rivera UR T2 RC 1.50 4.00
183 Michael Wuertz UR T2 RC 1.50 4.00
184 Mike Gosling UR T2 RC 1.50 4.00
185 Mike Johnston UR T2 RC 1.50 4.00
186 Mike Rouse UR T2 RC 1.50 4.00
187 Nick Regilio UR T2 RC 1.50 4.00
188 Onil Joseph UR T2 RC 1.50 4.00
189 Orl Rodriguez UR T2 RC 1.50 4.00
190 Phil Stockman UR T2 RC 1.50 4.00
191 Renyel Pinto UR T2 RC 1.50 4.00
192 Roberto Novoa UR T2 RC 1.50 4.00
193 Roman Colon UR T2 RC 1.50 4.00
194 Ronald Belisario UR T2 RC 1.50 4.00
195 Ronny Cedeno UR T3 RC 2.00 5.00
196 Ryan Meaux UR T3 RC 2.00 5.00
197 Ryan Wing UR T3 RC 2.00 5.00
198 Scott Dohmann UR T3 RC 2.00 5.00
199 Joey Gathright UR T3 RC 2.00 5.00
200 Shawn Camp UR T3 RC 2.00 5.00
201 Shawn Hill UR T3 RC 2.00 5.00
202 Steve Andrade UR T3 RC 2.00 5.00
203 Tim Bausher UR T3 RC 2.00 5.00
204 Tim Bittner UR T3 RC 2.00 5.00
205 Brad Halsey UR T3 RC 2.00 5.00
206 William Bergolla UR T3 RC 2.00 5.00
207 Kameron Loe UR T3 RC 2.00 5.00
208 Jesse Crain UR T3 RC 2.00 5.00
209 Scott Kazmir UR T3 RC 10.00 25.00
210 Akinori Otsuka AU RC 20.00 50.00
211 Chris Oxspring AU RC 10.00 25.00
212 Ian Snell AU RC 15.00 40.00
213 John Gall AU RC 15.00 40.00
214 Jose Capellan AU RC 10.00 25.00
215 Yadier Molina AU RC 50.00 80.00
216 Merkin Valdez AU RC 10.00 25.00
218 Rusty Tucker AU RC 15.00 40.00
219 Scott Proctor AU RC 15.00 40.00
220 Sean Henn AU RC 10.00 25.00
221 Shingo Takatsu AU RC 15.00 40.00
222 Kazuo Matsui UR T3 RC 3.00 8.00

2004 Ultimate Collection Gold

*GOLD 1-42: 1.25X TO 3X BASIC
*GOLD 43-126: 1.25X TO 3X BASIC
*GOLD 127-168: 1X TO 2.5X BASIC
*GOLD 169-194: .6X TO 1.5X BASIC
OVERALL PARALLEL ODDS 1:4
1-194 PRINT RUN 50 SERIAL #'d SETS
195-209/222 PRINT RUN 25 SER.#'d SETS
AU 210-221 PRINT RUN 15 SERIAL #'d SETS
195-222 NO PRICING DUE TO SCARCITY
EXCHANGE DEADLINE 12/28/07

2004 Ultimate Collection Platinum

OVERALL PARALLEL ODDS 1:4
1-126 PRINT RUN 10 SERIAL #'d SETS
AU 210-221 PRINT RUN 1 SERIAL #'d SET
NO PRICING DUE TO SCARCITY
EXCHANGE DEADLINE 12/28/07

2004 Ultimate Collection Rainbow

OVERALL PARALLEL ODDS 1:4
STATED PRINT RUN 1 SERIAL #'d SET
NO PRICING DUE TO SCARCITY

2004 Ultimate Collection Achievement Materials

OVERALL GAME-USED ODDS 1:4
PRINT RUNS B/WN 9-99 COPIES PER
NO PRICING ON QTY OF 9

BG Bob Gibson Jsy/68 6.00 15.00
BR Brooks Robinson Jsy/64 8.00 20.00
CA Roy Campanella Pants/51 10.00 25.00
CL Roger Clemens Jsy/63 12.50 30.00
CR Cal Ripken Pants/82 20.00 50.00
CY Carl Yastrzemski Jsy/67 12.50 30.00
DD Don Drysdale Pants/51 10.00 25.00
DJ Derek Jeter Jsy/96 12.50 30.00
DM Don Mattingly Jsy/85 10.00 25.00
EB Ernie Banks Jsy/58 10.00 25.00
EM Eddie Murray Jsy/77 6.00 15.00
FR Frank Robinson Pants/66 4.00 10.00
GB George Brett Jsy/80 10.00 25.00
GM Greg Maddux Jsy/92 10.00 25.00
HK Harmon Killebrew Jsy/69 6.00 15.00
JB Johnny Bench Jsy/68 6.00 15.00
JD Joe DiMaggio Pants/39 50.00 100.00
JP Jim Palmer Jsy/34 6.00 15.00
JR Jackie Robinson Jsy/47 30.00 60.00
KG Ken Griffey Jr. Jsy/97 10.00 25.00
MA Mickey Mantle Pants/56 125.00 200.00
MC Willie McCovey Jsy/59 8.00 20.00
MP Mike Piazza Jsy/93 10.00 25.00
MS Mike Schmidt Jsy/80 10.00 25.00
OC Orlando Cepeda Jsy/58 5.00 12.00
PM Pedro Martinez Jsy/87 6.00 15.00
RC Rob Clemente Pants/66 50.00 100.00
RJ Randy Johnson Jsy/57 6.00 15.00
RM Roger Maris Jsy/61 30.00 60.00
RO Rod Carew Jsy/49 8.00 20.00
RS Ryne Sandberg Jsy/84 15.00 40.00
RY Robin Yount Jsy/82 6.00 15.00
SC Steve Carlton Pants/72 4.00 10.00
SS Sammy Sosa Jsy/75 6.00 15.00
TC Ty Cobb Pants/9
TM Thurman Munson Pants/70 6.00 15.00
TS Tom Seaver Jsy/69 6.00 15.00
TW Ted Williams Jsy/42 40.00 80.00
WS Warren Spahn Jsy/9
YB Yogi Berra Jsy/51 10.00 25.00

2004 Ultimate Collection All-Stars Signatures

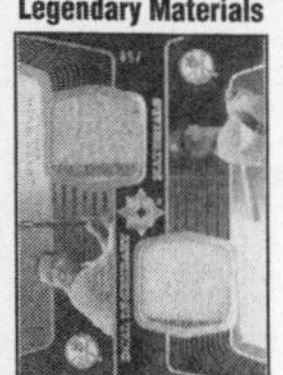

OVERALL AU ODDS 1:4
PRINT RUNS B/WN 1-24 COPIES PER
NO PRICING ON QTY OF 12 OR LESS
EXCHANGE DEADLINE 12/28/07

AK Al Kaline/15
BD Bobby Doerr/9
BF Bob Feller/8
BG Bob Gibson/8
BR Brooks Robinson/15 30.00 60.00
CB Carlos Beltran/1
CL Roger Clemens/10
CR Cal Ripken/19 150.00 250.00
CY Carl Yastrzemski/18 40.00 80.00
DJ Derek Jeter/6
DM Don Mattingly/6
DS Duke Snider/8
FT Frank Thomas/5
HB Hank Blalock/2
HK Harmon Killebrew/11
JB Jeff Bagwell/4
JC Joe Carter/5
JM Joe Morgan/10
JP Jim Palmer/6
KG Ken Griffey Jr./12
KW Kerry Wood/1
LA Luis Aparicio/10
MC Miguel Cabrera/1
MP Mark Prior/1
MR Manny Ramirez/8
MS Mike Schmidt/12
NG Nomar Garciaparra/5
NR Nolan Ryan/8
OS Ozzie Smith/15 40.00 80.00
RC Rod Carew/18 20.00 50.00
RP Rafael Palmeiro/4
RS Ryne Sandberg/10
SM Stan Musial/24 40.00 80.00
TH Todd Helton/5
VG Vladimir Guerrero/5
WC Will Clark/6
WF Whitey Ford/8
WM Willie McCovey/6

2004 Ultimate Collection Dual Game Patch

*OVERALL 4-COLOR: ADD 20% PREMIUM
*OVERALL 5+ COLOR: ADD 50% PREMIUM
*LOGO PATCH: ADD 50% PREMIUM
OVERALL PATCH ODDS 1:4
STATED PRINT RUN 25 SERIAL #'d SETS

BB Carlos Beltran 20.00 50.00
Jeff Bagwell
BC Josh Beckett 20.00 50.00
Miguel Cabrera
BG Lou Brock 40.00 80.00
Tony Gwynn
BM Yogi Berra
Roger Maris
BS George Brett 60.00 120.00
Mike Schmidt
BT Hank Blalock 20.00 50.00
Mark Teixeira
CG Rod Carew 20.00 50.00
Tony Gwynn
CP Gary Carter 20.00 50.00
Mike Piazza
CR Eric Chavez 20.00 50.00
Scott Rolen
FB Carlton Fisk 20.00 50.00
Johnny Bench
FR Bob Feller 50.00 100.00
Nolan Ryan
GC Mark Grace 20.00 50.00
Will Clark
GG Ken Griffey Jr. 40.00 80.00
Ken Griffey Sr.
GM Bob Gibson 40.00 80.00
Stan Musial
GS Mark Grace 50.00 100.00
Ryne Sandberg
HF Catfish Hunter 20.00 50.00
Rollie Fingers
JC Randy Johnson 40.00 80.00
Roger Clemens
JJ Andruw Jones 20.00 50.00
Chipper Jones
JM Derek Jeter 75.00 150.00
Hideki Matsui
KC Harmon Killebrew 30.00 60.00
Rod Carew
KM Harmon Killebrew 30.00 60.00
Willie McCovey
KS Ken Griffey Jr. 40.00 80.00
Sammy Sosa
LS Fred Lynn 60.00 120.00
Ichiro Suzuki
MG Greg Maddux 20.00 50.00
Tom Glavine
MJ Eddie Mathews 40.00 80.00
Chipper Jones
MM Hideki Matsui
Kazuo Matsui
MY Paul Molitor 20.00 50.00
Robin Yount
PC Rafael Palmeiro 20.00 50.00
Will Clark
PR Albert Pujols 30.00 60.00
Scott Rolen
RC Nolan Ryan 50.00 100.00
Roger Clemens
RM Cal Ripken 125.00 200.00
Eddie Murray
RP Cal Ripken 75.00 150.00
Jim Palmer
RR Jackie Robinson 150.00 250.00
Pee Wee Reese
RS Nolan Ryan 50.00 100.00
Tom Seaver
RT Cal Ripken 40.00 80.00
Miguel Tejada
SB Jim Bunning 40.00 80.00
Mike Schmidt
SM Curt Schilling 30.00 60.00
Pedro Martinez
ST Mike Schmidt 40.00 80.00
Jim Thome
WM Dave Winfield 40.00 80.00
Don Mattingly
WP Kerry Wood 15.00 40.00
Mark Prior
WS Billy Williams 20.00 50.00
Sammy Sosa
YR Carl Yastrzemski 40.00 80.00
Jim Rice

2004 Ultimate Collection Dual Legendary Materials

OVERALL GAME-USED ODDS 1:4
STATED PRINT RUN 50 SERIAL #'d SETS

BM Ernie Banks Jsy 20.00 50.00
Willie McCovey Jsy
BR Babe Ruth Pants 250.00 400.00
Roger Maris Jsy
CB Roy Campanella Pants 20.00 50.00
Yogi Berra Jsy

CM Roberto Clemente Pants 60.00 120.00
Thurman Munson Pants
CS Roy Campanella Pants 20.00 50.00
Duke Snider Pants
DM Joe DiMaggio Pants 150.00 250.00
Mickey Mantle Pants
DW Joe DiMaggio Pants 90.00 180.00
Ted Williams Jsy
FD Bob Feller Jsy 20.00 50.00
Don Drysdale Pants
MB Thurman Munson Pants 20.00 50.00
Yogi Berra Jsy
MC Mickey Mantle Pants 125.00 200.00
Roberto Clemente Pants
MM Mickey Mantle Pants 150.00 250.00
Roger Maris Jsy
MW Mickey Mantle Pants 150.00 250.00
Ted Williams Jsy
RB Ernie Banks Jsy 40.00 80.00
Jackie Robinson Jsy
RC Jackie Robinson Jsy 40.00 80.00
Roy Campanella Pants
RD Babe Ruth Pants 250.00 400.00
Joe DiMaggio Pants
RM Babe Ruth Pants 300.00 500.00
Mickey Mantle Pants
RP Jackie Robinson Jsy 50.00 100.00
Satchel Paige Pants
RW Roberto Clemente Pants 60.00 120.00
Ted Williams Jsy
WM Eddie Mathews Pants 75.00 150.00
Ted Williams Jsy

2004 Ultimate Collection Dual Materials

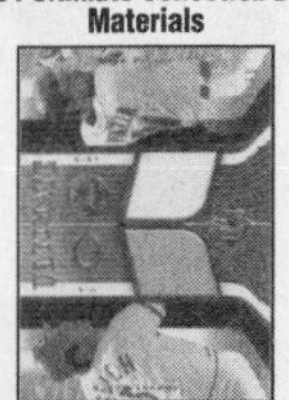

OVERALL GAME-USED ODDS 1:4
STATED PRINT RUN 60 SERIAL #'d SETS
BC Brooks Robinson Jsy 40.00 80.00
Cal Ripken Pants
BM Thurman Munson Jsy
Yogi Berra Jsy
BP Johnny Bench Jsy 15.00 40.00
Mike Piazza Jsy
BS George Brett Jsy 30.00 60.00
Mike Schmidt Jsy
CK Rod Carew Jsy 15.00 40.00
Harmon Killebrew Jsy
CM Will Clark Jsy 15.00 40.00
Willie McCovey Jsy
ER Ernie Banks Jsy 30.00 60.00
Ryne Sandberg Jsy
GS Sammy Sosa Jsy 15.00 40.00
Ken Griffey Jr. Jsy
JC Randy Johnson Jsy 20.00 50.00
Roger Clemens Jsy
JM Derek Jeter Jsy 30.00 60.00
Don Mattingly Jsy
MB Thurman Munson Pants
Johnny Bench Jsy
MC Don Mattingly Jsy 20.00 50.00
Will Clark Jsy
MP Joe Mauer Jsy 10.00 25.00
Mark Prior Jsy
MR Bill Mazeroski Jsy 40.00 80.00
Jackie Robinson Jsy
MT Kazuo Matsui Jsy 15.00 40.00
Shingo Takatsu Jsy
MY Paul Molitor Jsy 15.00 40.00
Robin Yount Jsy
PR Albert Pujols Jsy 20.00 50.00
Manny Ramirez Jsy
RC Nolan Ryan Jsy 30.00 60.00
Roger Clemens Jsy
RP Ivan Rodriguez Jsy 10.00 25.00
Mike Piazza Jsy
RR Brooks Robinson Jsy 15.00 40.00
Frank Robinson Pants
RT Roy Campanella Pants 15.00 40.00
Thurman Munson Pants
SG Ichiro Suzuki Jsy 30.00 60.00
Ken Griffey Jr. Jsy
SP Ben Sheets Jsy 6.00 15.00
Mark Prior Jsy
SR Duke Snider Pants 15.00 40.00
Pee Wee Reese Jsy
SS Sammy Sosa Jsy 30.00 60.00
Ryne Sandberg Jsy
TS Jim Thome Jsy 20.00 50.00
Mike Schmidt Jsy
WM Dave Winfield Jsy 15.00 40.00
Don Mattingly Jsy
WP Kerry Wood Jsy 6.00 15.00
Mark Prior Jsy
WR Kerry Wood Jsy 20.00 50.00
Nolan Ryan Jsy
YR Carl Yastrzemski Jsy 20.00 50.00
Manny Ramirez Jsy

2004 Ultimate Collection Dual Materials Signature

STATED PRINT RUN 25 SERIAL #'d SETS
BANKS/SANTO PRINT RUN 12 #'d CARDS
NO BANKS/SANTO PRICING AVAILABLE
EXCHANGE DEADLINE 12/28/07
AB Luis Aparicio Jsy 50.00 100.00
Ernie Banks Jsy
BB Hank Blalock Jsy 40.00 80.00
Wade Boggs Jsy
BC Brooks Robinson Jsy 175.00 300.00
Cal Ripken Jsy
BF Carlton Fisk Jsy 50.00 100.00
Johnny Bench Jsy
BG Carlos Beltran Jsy 100.00 175.00
Ken Griffey Jr. Jsy
BJ Derek Jeter Jsy 175.00 300.00
Yogi Berra Jsy
BM Brian Giles Jsy 30.00 60.00
Marcus Giles Jsy
BP Johnny Bench Jsy 125.00 200.00
Mike Piazza Jsy
BR Jim Bunning Jsy 30.00 60.00
Robin Roberts Jsy
BS Brooks Robinson Jsy
Scott Rolen Jsy
BT Hank Blalock Jsy 40.00 80.00
Mark Teixeira Jsy
CB Eric Chavez Jsy 30.00 60.00
Hank Blalock Jsy
CC Roger Clemens Jsy 100.00 175.00
Steve Carlton Pants EXCH
CJ Randy Johnson Jsy 250.00 400.00
Roger Clemens Jsy
CK Rod Carew Jsy 60.00 120.00
Harmon Killebrew Jsy
CL Miguel Cabrera Jsy 40.00 80.00
Willie McCovey Jsy
CM Carlos Beltran Jsy 75.00 150.00
Miguel Cabrera Jsy
CR Eric Chavez Jsy
Scott Rolen Jsy EXCH
DD Derek Jeter Jsy 200.00 350.00
Don Mattingly Jsy
DG Don Sutton Jsy 30.00 60.00
Gaylord Perry Jsy
DJ Dave Parker Jsy 60.00 120.00
Jim Rice Jsy
DS Andre Dawson Jsy 60.00 120.00
Ryne Sandberg Jsy
DW Andre Dawson Pants 30.00 60.00
Billy Williams Jsy
ER Ernie Banks Jsy 125.00 200.00
Ryne Sandberg Jsy
FC Bob Feller Jsy 40.00 80.00
Rocky Colavito Jsy
FR Bob Feller Jsy 125.00 200.00
Nolan Ryan Jsy
GB Brooks Robinson Jsy 75.00 150.00
George Brett Jsy
GG Ken Griffey Sr. Jsy 125.00 200.00
Ken Griffey Jr. Jsy
GM George Brett Jsy 125.00 200.00
Mike Schmidt Jsy
GP Ken Griffey Jr. Jsy 125.00 200.00
Rafael Palmeiro Jsy
GR Greg Maddux Jsy 200.00 350.00
Roger Clemens Jsy
GS Eric Gagne Jsy 40.00 80.00
John Smoltz Jsy
JB Fergie Jenkins Pants 60.00 120.00
Ernie Banks Pants
JC Randy Johnson Jsy 75.00 150.00
Steve Carlton Pants EXCH
JD Johnny Podres Jsy 30.00 60.00
Don Sutton Jsy
JG Randy Johnson Jsy 175.00 300.00
Ken Griffey Jr. Jsy
JM Chipper Jones Jsy 100.00 175.00
Dale Murphy Jsy
JP Fergie Jenkins Pants 30.00 60.00
Jim Palmer Jsy
JR Derek Jeter Jsy 350.00 600.00
Cal Ripken Jsy
KG Harmon Killebrew Jsy 125.00 250.00
Ken Griffey Jr. Jsy
KN Kerry Wood Jsy 125.00 200.00
Nolan Ryan Jsy
KT Scott Kazmir Jsy 40.00 80.00
Shingo Takatsu Jsy
LB Don Larsen Pants 150.00 250.00
Yogi Berra Pants
MB Joe Morgan Jsy 50.00 100.00
Johnny Bench Jsy
MC Don Mattingly Jsy 75.00 150.00
Will Clark Jsy
MH Mark Mulder Jsy 40.00 80.00
Tim Hudson Jsy
MP Joe Mauer Jsy 75.00 150.00
Mark Prior Jsy
MS Bill Mazeroski Jsy 75.00 150.00
Ryne Sandberg Jsy
MW Mark Grace Jsy 40.00 80.00
Will Clark Jsy
MY Paul Molitor Jsy 75.00 150.00
Robin Yount Jsy
NR Nolan Ryan Jsy 250.00 400.00
Roger Clemens Jsy
OR David Ortiz Jsy 125.00 200.00
Manny Ramirez Jsy
OS Ozzie Smith Jsy 100.00 175.00
Stan Musial Jsy
PC Rafael Palmeiro Jsy 50.00 100.00
Will Clark Jsy
PN Gaylord Perry Jsy 30.00 60.00
Phil Niekro Jsy
PS Duke Snider Pants 40.00 80.00
Johnny Podres Jsy
RB Bill Mazeroski Jsy 40.00 80.00
Rod Carew Jsy
RC Brooks Robinson Jsy 40.00 80.00
Eric Chavez Jsy
RM Cal Ripken Jsy 200.00 350.00
Eddie Murray Jsy
RP Brooks Robinson Jsy 40.00 80.00
Jim Palmer Jsy
RR Brooks Robinson Jsy 40.00 80.00
Frank Robinson Jsy
RS Robin Roberts Jsy 30.00 60.00
Steve Carlton Pants EXCH
RT Cal Ripken Pants 175.00 300.00
Miguel Tejada Jsy
RW Jose Reyes Jsy
David Wright Jsy EXCH
SB Ernie Banks Jsy
Ron Santo Jsy/12
SC Mike Schmidt Jsy 75.00 150.00
Steve Carlton Pants EXCH
SF Ben Sheets Jsy 30.00 60.00
Bob Feller Jsy
SG Bruce Sutter Jsy 40.00 80.00
Eric Gagne Jsy
SO Ben Sheets Jsy 30.00 60.00
Roy Oswalt Jsy
SP Ben Sheets Jsy 30.00 60.00
Mark Prior Jsy
SR Brooks Robinson Jsy 125.00 200.00
Mike Schmidt Jsy
SS Ben Sheets Jsy 50.00 100.00
Tom Seaver Jsy
TB Brian Giles Jsy 40.00 80.00
Tony Gwynn Jsy
TC Mark Teixeira Jsy 40.00 80.00
Miguel Cabrera Jsy
WM Dave Winfield Jsy 100.00 175.00
Don Mattingly Jsy
WO Willie McCovey Jsy 40.00 80.00
Orlando Cepeda Jsy
WP Kerry Wood Jsy
Mark Prior Jsy
WW Will Clark Jsy 40.00 80.00
Willie McCovey Jsy
YR Carl Yastrzemski Jsy 100.00 175.00
Manny Ramirez Jsy
YW Delmon Young Jsy
Rickie Weeks Jsy

2004 Ultimate Collection Game Materials

OVERALL GAME-USED ODDS 1:4
STATED PRINT RUN 99 SERIAL #'d SETS
AK Al Kaline Jsy 6.00 15.00
AP Albert Pujols Jsy 10.00 25.00
BF Bob Feller Jsy 4.00 10.00
BG Bob Gibson Jsy 6.00 15.00
BM Bill Mazeroski Jsy 6.00 15.00
BR Brooks Robinson Jsy 6.00 15.00
CF Carlton Fisk Pants 6.00 15.00
CL Roger Clemens Jsy 10.00 25.00
CR Cal Ripken Jsy 20.00 50.00
CY Carl Yastrzemski Jsy 10.00 25.00
DD Don Drysdale Pants 6.00 15.00
DJ Derek Jeter Jsy 12.50 30.00
DM Don Mattingly Jsy 10.00 25.00
DS Duke Snider Pants 6.00 15.00
DW Dave Winfield Jsy 4.00 10.00
EB Ernie Banks Jsy 6.00 15.00
ED Eddie Mathews Pants 6.00 15.00
EM Eddie Murray Jsy 6.00 15.00
FR Frank Robinson Pants 4.00 10.00
GB George Brett Jsy 10.00 25.00
HK Harmon Killebrew Jsy 6.00 15.00
IS Ichiro Suzuki Jsy 30.00 60.00
JB Johnny Bench Jsy 6.00 15.00
JP Jim Palmer Jsy 4.00 10.00
JR Jackie Robinson Jsy 20.00 50.00
KG Ken Griffey Jr. Jsy 10.00 25.00
KW Kerry Wood Jsy 4.00 10.00
LB Lou Brock Jsy 6.00 15.00
MA Juan Marichal Jsy 6.00 15.00
MP Mark Prior Jsy 6.00 15.00
MS Mike Schmidt Jsy 10.00 25.00
OS Ozzie Smith Jsy 10.00 25.00
PI Mike Piazza Jsy 10.00 25.00
PM Paul Molitor Jsy 4.00 10.00
RC Rod Carew Jsy 6.00 15.00
RJ Randy Johnson Jsy 6.00 15.00
RM Roger Maris Jsy 20.00 50.00
RS Ryne Sandberg Jsy 15.00 40.00
RY Robin Yount Jsy 6.00 15.00
SC Steve Carlton Pants 4.00 10.00
SM Stan Musial Jsy 15.00 40.00
TC Ty Cobb Pants 50.00 100.00
TG Tony Gwynn Jsy 10.00 25.00
TM Thurman Munson Pants 6.00 15.00
TS Tom Seaver Jsy 6.00 15.00
WB Wade Boggs Jsy 6.00 15.00
WC Will Clark Jsy 6.00 15.00
WM Willie McCovey Jsy 6.00 15.00
WS Warren Spahn Jsy 6.00 15.00
WS Willie Stargell Jsy 6.00 15.00

2004 Ultimate Collection Game Materials Signatures

OVERALL AUTO/GAME-USED ODDS 1:4
STATED PRINT RUN 50 SERIAL #'d SETS
TEJADA A's PRINT RUN 34 SER.#'d CARDS
EXCHANGE DEADLINE 12/28/07
AD Andre Dawson Cubs Jsy 15.00 40.00
AD1 Andre Dawson Expos Jsy 15.00 40.00
AK Al Kaline Jsy 30.00 60.00
AS Alfonso Soriano Jsy 20.00 50.00
BE Josh Beckett Jsy 20.00 50.00
BF Bob Feller Jsy 15.00 40.00
BG Bob Gibson Jsy 20.00 50.00
BM Bill Mazeroski Jsy 20.00 50.00
BR Brooks Robinson Jsy 20.00 50.00
BS Ben Sheets Blue Jsy 15.00 40.00
BS1 Ben Sheets White Jsy 15.00 40.00
BU Jim Bunning Jsy 15.00 40.00
BW Billy Williams Jsy 15.00 40.00
CA Miguel Cabrera Jsy 20.00 50.00
CB Carlos Beltran Jsy 15.00 40.00
CF Carlton Fisk R.Sox Jsy 20.00 50.00
CF1 Carlton Fisk W.Sox Jsy 20.00 50.00
CJ Chipper Jones Jsy 30.00 60.00
CL R.Clemens Astros Jsy 60.00 120.00
CL1 R.Clemens Yanks Jsy 60.00 120.00
CL2 R.Clemens Sox Jsy 60.00 120.00
CO R.Colavito Tigers Jsy 40.00 80.00
CO1 R.Colavito Indians Jsy 40.00 80.00
CR Cal Ripken Jsy 125.00 200.00
CY Carl Yastrzemski Jsy 40.00 80.00
DE Dennis Eckersley Sox Jsy 15.00 40.00
DE1 Dennis Eckersley A's Jsy 15.00 40.00
DJ Derek Jeter Jsy 125.00 200.00
DM Dale Murphy Jsy 20.00 50.00
DO Don Mattingly Jsy 40.00 80.00
DS Don Sutton Jsy 15.00 40.00
DW D.Winfield Yanks Jsy 20.00 50.00
DW1 D.Winfield Padres Jsy 20.00 50.00
DY Delm Young D-Rays Jsy 20.00 50.00
DY1 Delmon Young USA Jsy 20.00 50.00
EB Ernie Banks Jsy 30.00 60.00
EC Eric Chavez Jsy 15.00 40.00
EG Eric Gagne Jsy 15.00 40.00
EM Eddie Murray O's Jsy 50.00 100.00
FJ Fergie Jenkins Pants 15.00 40.00
FR Frank Robinson O's Jsy 20.00 50.00
FR1 Frank Robinson Reds Jsy 20.00 50.00
FT Frank Thomas Jsy 40.00 80.00
GB George Brett Jsy 50.00 100.00
GC Gary Carter Expos Jsy 15.00 40.00
GC1 Gary Carter Mets Jsy 15.00 40.00
GM Greg Maddux Cubs Jsy 75.00 150.00
GM1 Greg Maddux Braves Jsy 75.00 150.00
GP Gaylord Perry Indians Jsy 10.00 25.00
GP1 Gaylord Perry Giants Jsy 10.00 25.00
HB Hank Blalock Jsy 15.00 40.00
HE Todd Helton Jsy 20.00 50.00
HK Harmon Killebrew Jsy 40.00 80.00
JB Johnny Bench Jsy 30.00 60.00
JC Joe Carter Pants 15.00 40.00
JE Jeff Bagwell Jsy 30.00 60.00
JM Joe Mauer Blue Jsy 40.00 80.00
JM1 Joe Mauer White Jsy 40.00 80.00
JP Jim Palmer Jsy 15.00 40.00
JR Jim Rice Jsy 15.00 40.00
JS John Smoltz Jsy 30.00 60.00
JU Juan Marichal Jsy 15.00 40.00
KG Ken Griffey Jr. Reds Jsy 60.00 120.00
KG1 Ken Griffey Jr. M's Jsy 60.00 120.00
KW Kerry Wood Jsy 20.00 50.00
LB Lou Brock Cards Jsy 20.00 50.00
LB1 Lou Brock Cubs Jsy 20.00 50.00
MC Willie McCovey Jsy 20.00 50.00
MG Mark Grace Jsy 20.00 50.00
ML Mike Lowell Jsy 10.00 25.00
MO Joe Morgan Jsy 15.00 40.00
MP Mark Prior Cubs Jsy 15.00 40.00
MP1 Mark Prior USA Jsy 15.00 40.00
MR Manny Ramirez Jsy 40.00 80.00
MS Mike Schmidt Jsy 50.00 100.00
MT Mark Teixeira Jsy 12.50 30.00
MU Mark Mulder Jsy 15.00 40.00
NG N.Garciaparra Cubs Jsy 60.00 120.00
NG1 N. Garciaparra Sox Jsy 60.00 120.00
NR Nolan Ryan Rgr Jsy 60.00 120.00
NR1 Nolan Ryan Angels Jsy 60.00 120.00
NR2 Nolan Ryan Astros Jsy 60.00 120.00
NR3 Nolan Ryan Mets Jsy 60.00 120.00
OC Orl Cepeda Giants Jsy 15.00 40.00
OC1 Orl Cepeda Cards Jsy 15.00 40.00
OS Ozzie Smith Jsy 30.00 60.00
PI Mike Piazza Mets Jsy 75.00 150.00
PI1 Mike Piazza Dodgers Jsy 75.00 150.00
PM Paul Molitor Brewers Jsy 15.00 40.00
PM1 Paul Molitor Twins Jsy 15.00 40.00
PM2 Paul Molitor Jays Jsy 15.00 40.00
PO Johnny Podres Jsy 15.00 40.00
RC Rod Carew Twins Jsy 20.00 50.00
RC1 Rod Carew Angels Pants 20.00 50.00
RF R.Fingers Brewers Pants 15.00 40.00
RF1 Rollie Fingers A's Pants 15.00 40.00
RG Ron Guidry Jsy 20.00 50.00
RJ R.Johnson D'backs Jsy 60.00 120.00
RJ1 Randy Johnson M's Jsy 60.00 120.00
RO Roy Oswalt Jsy 15.00 40.00
RP Rafael Palmeiro Jsy 30.00 60.00
RR Robin Roberts Jsy 15.00 40.00
RS Red Schoendienst Jsy 15.00 40.00
RW Rickie Weeks Brewers Jsy 15.00 40.00
RW1 Rickie Weeks USA Jsy 15.00 40.00
SA Ryne Sandberg Jsy 50.00 100.00
SN D.Snider Brooklyn Pants 20.00 50.00
SN1 Duke Snider L.A. Pants
TE Miguel Tejada O's Jsy
TE1 Miguel Tejada A's Jsy/34 20.00 50.00
TG Tony Gwynn Jsy 30.00 60.00
TH Tim Hudson Jsy 20.00 50.00
TP Tony Perez Jsy 20.00 50.00
TS Tom Seaver Mets Jsy 30.00 60.00
TS1 Tom Seaver Reds Jsy 30.00 60.00
VG Vladimir Guerrero Jsy 40.00 80.00
WB Wade Boggs Sox Jsy 30.00 60.00
WB1 Wade Boggs Yanks Jsy 30.00 60.00
WC Will Clark Giants Jsy 20.00 50.00
WC1 Will Clark Cards Jsy 20.00 50.00
WC2 Will Clark Rgr Jsy 20.00 50.00
WC3 Will Clark O's Jsy 20.00 50.00

2004 Ultimate Collection Game Patch

*3-COLOR PATCH: ADD 20% PREMIUM
*4-COLOR PATCH: ADD 50% PREMIUM
*5+ COLOR PATCH: ADD 100% PREMIUM
*LOGO PATCH: ADD 150% PREMIUM
OVERALL PATCH ODDS 1:4
PRINT RUNS B/WN 10-75 COPIES PER
NO PRICING ON QTY OF 10
AK Al Kaline/21 40.00 80.00
AP Albert Pujols/75 20.00 50.00
AS Alfonso Soriano/75 6.00 15.00
BA Jeff Bagwell/75 10.00 25.00
BE Josh Beckett/75 6.00 15.00
BF Bob Feller/75 15.00 40.00
BM Bill Mazeroski/55 20.00 50.00
BR Brooks Robinson/75 15.00 40.00
BS Ben Sheets/75 6.00 15.00
BU Jim Bunning/66 15.00 40.00
BW Bernie Williams/75 10.00 25.00
CA Miguel Cabrera/75 10.00 25.00
CB Carlos Beltran/75 6.00 15.00
CF Carlton Fisk R.Sox/18 30.00 60.00
CF1 Carlton Fisk W.Sox/10
CH Catfish Hunter/75 15.00 40.00
CJ Chipper Jones/75 10.00 25.00
CL Roger Clemens/75 15.00 40.00
CO1 Rocky Colavito/75 50.00 100.00
CR Cal Ripken/75 30.00 60.00
CS Curt Schilling/75 10.00 25.00
CY Carl Yastrzemski/75 15.00 40.00
DJ Derek Jeter/75 20.00 50.00
DM Don Mattingly/75 20.00 50.00
DW Dave Winfield/75 10.00 25.00
EC Eric Chavez/75 6.00 15.00
EM Eddie Mathews/17 40.00 80.00
GB George Brett/75 20.00 50.00
GC Gary Carter/75 10.00 25.00
GL Troy Glaus/75 6.00 15.00
GM Greg Maddux Cubs/75 12.50 30.00
GM1 Greg Maddux Braves/75 12.50 30.00
GS Gary Sheffield/75 6.00 15.00
HB Hank Blalock/75 6.00 15.00
HK Harmon Killebrew/75 15.00 40.00
HM Hideki Matsui/44 50.00 100.00
IR Ivan Rodriguez/75 10.00 25.00
IS Ichiro Suzuki/75 60.00 120.00
JB Johnny Bench/75 15.00 40.00
JD Joe DiMaggio/75 150.00 300.00
JM Joe Mauer/75 8.00 20.00
JP Jim Palmer/75 10.00 25.00
JT Jim Thome/75
KG Ken Griffey Jr./75 15.00 40.00
KM Kazuo Matsui/75 15.00 40.00
KW Kerry Wood/75 6.00 15.00
LB Lou Brock/75 15.00 40.00
MA Juan Marichal/75 15.00 40.00
MO Joe Morgan/75 10.00 25.00
MP Mark Prior/75 10.00 25.00
MR Manny Ramirez/75 10.00 25.00
MS Mike Schmidt/75 20.00 50.00
MT Mark Teixeira/75 10.00 25.00
MU Eddie Murray/75 15.00 40.00
NF Nellie Fox/55 60.00 120.00
NR Nolan Ryan Rgr/51 20.00 50.00
NR1 Nolan Ryan Astros/75 20.00 50.00
NR2 Nolan Ryan Angels/75 20.00 50.00
OS Ozzie Smith/75 15.00 40.00
PE Pedro Martinez/75 10.00 25.00
PI Mike Piazza/75 12.50 30.00
PM Paul Molitor/75 10.00 25.00
PO Johnny Podres/75 10.00 25.00
RB Roberto Clemente/75 125.00 200.00
RC Rod Carew Angels/75 15.00 40.00
RG Ron Guidry/75 15.00 40.00
RJ Randy Johnson D'backs/75 10.00 25.00
RJ1 Randy Johnson M's/75 10.00 25.00
RO Rod Carew Twins/75 15.00 40.00
RP Rafael Palmeiro/75 10.00 25.00
RS Ryne Sandberg/75 20.00 50.00
RY Robin Yount/75 10.00 25.00
SM Stan Musial/75 40.00 80.00
SP Warren Spahn/62 30.00 60.00
SR Scott Rolen/75 10.00 25.00
SS Sammy Sosa/75 10.00 25.00
TE Miguel Tejada/75 6.00 15.00
TG Tony Gwynn/75 12.50 30.00
TH Todd Helton/75 10.00 25.00
TM Thurman Munson/75 15.00 40.00
TS Tom Seaver/75 15.00 40.00
VG Vladimir Guerrero/75 10.00 25.00
WB Wade Boggs/75 10.00 25.00
WC Will Clark Giants/75 15.00 40.00
WC1 Will Clark Rgr/75 15.00 40.00
WI Billy Williams/75 10.00 25.00
WM Willie McCovey/75 15.00 40.00
WS Willie Stargell/75 15.00 40.00
YB Yogi Berra/75 15.00 40.00

2004 Ultimate Collection Game Patch Signature

*4-COLOR PATCH: ADD 20% PREMIUM
*5+ COLOR PATCH: ADD 50% PREMIUM
*LOGO PATCH: ADD 100% PREMIUM
OVERALL AUTO/GAME-USED ODDS 1:4
STATED PRINT RUN 30 SERIAL #'d SETS
C.FISK PRINT RUN 10 SERIAL #'d CARDS
NO C.FISK PRICING DUE TO SCARCITY
EXCHANGE DEADLINE 12/28/07
AD Andre Dawson 20.00 50.00
AK Al Kaline 75.00 150.00
BG Bob Gibson 30.00 60.00
BR Brooks Robinson 30.00 60.00
BS Ben Sheets 20.00 50.00
CB Carlos Beltran 20.00 50.00
CF Carlton Fisk/10
CR Cal Ripken 150.00 250.00
CY Carl Yastrzemski 50.00 100.00
DJ Derek Jeter 150.00 250.00
DM Don Mattingly 50.00 100.00
EB Ernie Banks 40.00 80.00
EC Eric Chavez 20.00 50.00
EM Eddie Murray 40.00 80.00
FR Frank Robinson 60.00 120.00
GB George Brett 60.00 120.00
GM Greg Maddux 100.00 200.00
HB Hank Blalock 20.00 50.00
HK Harmon Killebrew 50.00 100.00
JB Johnny Bench 60.00 120.00
JM Joe Mauer 50.00 100.00
JP Jim Palmer 20.00 50.00
JR Jim Rice 20.00 50.00
KG Ken Griffey Jr. 100.00 200.00
KW Kerry Wood
MA Juan Marichal 20.00 50.00
MC Miguel Cabrera 30.00 60.00
MP Mark Prior 20.00 50.00
MS Mike Schmidt 60.00 120.00
MT Mark Teixeira 30.00 60.00
MU Mark Mulder 20.00 50.00
NR Nolan Ryan 100.00 200.00
OC Ozzie Smith 10.00 00.00
PI Mike Piazza 100.00 175.00
PM Paul Molitor 20.00 50.00
RC Rod Carew 30.00 60.00
RJ Randy Johnson 75.00 150.00
RO Roy Oswalt 20.00 50.00
RS Ryne Sandberg 75.00 150.00
RY Robin Yount 40.00 80.00
SC Red Schoendienst 20.00 50.00
SM Stan Musial 50.00 100.00
TG Tony Gwynn 40.00 80.00
TS Tom Seaver 40.00 80.00
WB Wade Boggs 40.00 80.00
WC Will Clark 30.00 60.00

2004 Ultimate Collection Legendary Materials

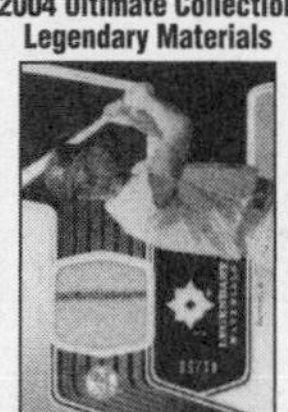

OVERALL GAME-USED ODDS 1:4
STATED PRINT RUN 50 SERIAL #'d SETS
BF Bob Feller Jsy 5.00 12.00
BR Babe Ruth Pants 175.00 300.00
CA Roy Campanella Pants 10.00 25.00
DD Don Drysdale Pants 10.00 25.00
DS Duke Snider Jsy 8.00 20.00
EB Ernie Banks Jsy 10.00 25.00
EM Eddie Mathews Pants 10.00 25.00
JD Joe DiMaggio Pants 50.00 100.00
JR Jackie Robinson Jsy 30.00 60.00
MM Mickey Mantle Pants 125.00 200.00
RC Roberto Clemente Jsy 50.00 100.00
RM Roger Maris Jsy 30.00 60.00
SM Stan Musial Jsy 15.00 40.00
SP Satchel Paige Pants 30.00 60.00
TC Ty Cobb Pants 60.00 120.00
TM Thurman Munson Pants 10.00 25.00
TW Ted Williams Jsy 40.00 80.00
WM Willie McCovey Jsy 8.00 20.00
YB Yogi Berra Jsy 10.00 25.00

2004 Ultimate Collection Loyalty Signature Materials

OVERALL AUTO/GAME-USED ODDS 1:4
PRINT RUNS B/WN 17-23 COPIES PER
BR Brooks Robinson Jsy/23 30.00 60.00
CR Cal Ripken Pants/21 150.00 250.00
CY Carl Yastrzemski Jsy/23 50.00 100.00
EB Ernie Banks Jsy/19 50.00 100.00
GB George Brett Jsy/21 60.00 120.00
HK Harmon Killebrew Jsy/21 50.00 100.00
JB Johnny Bench Jsy/17
MS Mike Schmidt Jsy/18 60.00 120.00
RY Robin Yount Jsy/20 40.00 80.00
TG Tony Gwynn Jsy/20 40.00 80.00

2004 Ultimate Collection Signature Numbers Patch

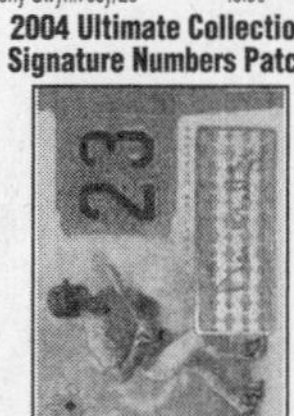

*4-COLOR PATCH: ADD 20% PREMIUM
*5+ COLOR PATCH: ADD 50% PREMIUM
*LOGO PATCH: ADD 100% PREMIUM
OVERALL AUTO/GAME-USED ODDS 1:4
PRINT RUNS B/WN 1-51 COPIES PER
NO PRICING ON QTY OF 14 OR LESS
EXCHANGE DEADLINE 12/28/07
BF Bob Feller/19 30.00 60.00
BM Bill Mazeroski/9
BU Jim Bunning/14
BW Billy Williams/26 20.00 50.00
CR Cal Ripken/8
CY Carl Yastrzemski/8
DJ Derek Jeter/2
DM Don Mattingly/23 60.00 120.00
DW Dave Winfield/23 30.00 60.00
EB Ernie Banks/14
EG Eric Gagne/38 20.00 50.00
GB George Brett/5
GM Greg Maddux/31
JB Johnny Bench/5
JP Jim Palmer/22 20.00 50.00
KG Ken Griffey Jr./30 75.00 150.00
LB Lou Brock/20 30.00 60.00
MA Juan Marichal/27
MC Miguel Cabrera/24 30.00 60.00
MG Mark Grace/17
MP Mark Prior/22 20.00 50.00
MS Mike Schmidt/20 60.00 120.00
MT Mark Teixeira/23 30.00 60.00
NR Nolan Ryan/30
OS Ozzie Smith/1
PI Mike Piazza/31 100.00 175.00
RC Rod Carew/29
RJ Randy Johnson/51 60.00 120.00
RO Roy Oswalt/44 15.00 40.00
RS Ryne Sandberg/23 75.00 150.00
RY Robin Yount/10 60.00 100.00
SM Stan Musial/6
TE Miguel Tejada/10
TG Tony Gwynn/19
VG Vladimir Guerrero/27 50.00 100.00
WB Wade Boggs/26 40.00 80.00
WC Will Clark/22
WM Willie McCovey/44 20.00 50.00
YB Yogi Berra/8

2004 Ultimate Collection Signatures

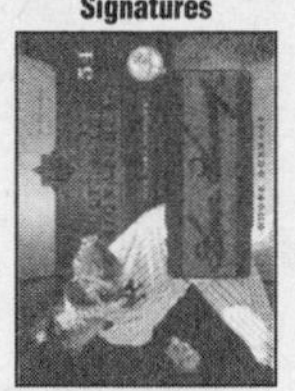

PRINT RUNS B/WN 6-99 COPIES PER
NO PRICING ON QTY OF 6
*GOLD p/r 25: .6X TO 1.5X BASIC p/r 69-99
GOLD PRINT RUNS B/WN 10-25 PER
NO GOLD PRICING ON QTY OF 10
OVERALL AUTO ODDS 1:4
PLATINUM: PREMIUM AU ODDS 1:20
PLATINUM PRINT RUN 1 SERIAL #'d SET
NO PLATINUM PRICING DUE TO SCARCITY
EXCHANGE DEADLINE 12/28/07
AD Andre Dawson/25 10.00 25.00
AK Al Kaline/25 30.00 60.00
AK1 Al Kaline/25
AO Akinori Otsuka/99 15.00 40.00
AR Al Rosen/99 10.00 25.00
BB Bret Boone/25
BD Bobby Doerr/99 10.00 25.00
BE Johnny Bench/25
BF Bob Feller/25 15.00 40.00
BF1 Bob Feller/25
BG Brian Giles/99 6.00 15.00
BI Craig Biggio/25 20.00 50.00
BL Bert Blyleven/99 10.00 25.00
BM Bill Mazeroski/25 20.00 50.00
BR Brooks Robinson Btg/25 30.00 60.00
BR1 Brooks Robinson Fldg/25
BS Ben Sheets/99 10.00 25.00
BW Billy Williams/25 15.00 40.00
CA Steve Carlton Right/25
CB Carlos Beltran/25 15.00 40.00
CC Carl Crawford/99 6.00 15.00
CL Roger Clemens/25
CP Corey Patterson/99 6.00 15.00
CR Cal Ripken/25 125.00 200.00
CW Rod Carew/25 20.00 50.00
CY Carl Yastrzemski/25 40.00 80.00
CZ Carlos Zambrano/99
DC David Cone/99 10.00 25.00
DE Dennis Eckersley/25 15.00 40.00
DG Dwight Gooden/99 10.00 25.00
DJ Derek Jeter/25
DM Dale Murphy/99 12.50 30.00
DN Don Newcombe/25 10.00 25.00
DO Don Mattingly/25
DP Dave Parker/25 10.00 25.00
DS Don Sutton/25
DW Dave Winfield/25 15.00 40.00
DY Delmon Young/99 12.50 30.00
EC Eric Chavez/25 15.00 40.00
EG Eric Gagne/25 20.00 50.00
FH Frank Howard/99 6.00 15.00
FL Fred Lynn/25 10.00 25.00
GB George Brett/25
GF George Foster/25 10.00 25.00
GG Goose Gossage/99 6.00 15.00
GI Bob Gibson/25 20.00 50.00
GK George Kell/99 15.00 40.00
GM Greg Maddux/25 75.00 150.00
GN Graig Nettles/99 10.00 25.00
GP Gaylord Perry/25 15.00 40.00
GR Mark Grace/99 15.00 40.00
HB Hank Blalock/25 15.00 40.00
HK H.Killebrew w/Bat/25 40.00 80.00
HK1 H.Killebrew Swing/25 40.00 80.00
HU Tim Hudson/25
JB Jim Bunning/99 10.00 25.00
JK Jim Kaat/99 10.00 25.00
JM Joe Mauer/99 40.00 80.00
JP Jim Palmer Knee Up/99 10.00 25.00
JP1 Jim Palmer Thigh Up/25 15.00 40.00
JR Jose Reyes/99
JS Jason Schmidt/99 10.00 25.00
KG Ken Griffey Sr./69 10.00 25.00
KG2 Ken Griffey Jr./25
KH Keith Hernandez/99 10.00 25.00
KP Kirby Puckett/25 50.00 100.00
LA Luis Aparicio R.Sox/25 10.00 25.00
LA1 Luis Aparicio W.Sox/25 10.00 25.00
LT Luis Tiant/99 6.00 15.00
MC M.Cabrera Swing/99 12.50 30.00
MC1 M.Cabrera Drop Bat/25 20.00 50.00
MG Marcus Giles/99 6.00 15.00
MI Monte Irvin/25 10.00 25.00
ML Mike Lowell/99 6.00 15.00
MM Mark Mulder/99 10.00 25.00
MO Joe Morgan/25 15.00 40.00
MP Mark Prior/25 15.00 40.00
MS Mike Schmidt/25
MT Mark Teixeira/25 20.00 50.00
MU Stan Musial/25 40.00 80.00
MW Maury Wills/25 10.00 25.00
NG Nomar Garciaparra/25 60.00 120.00
NR Nolan Ryan/6
OC Orlando Cepeda/25 10.00 25.00
OS Ozzie Smith/25 30.00 60.00

PI Mike Piazza/25	60.00	120.00
PN Phil Niekro/25		
PO Johnny Podres/99	10.00	25.00
RC Rocky Colavito/99	20.00	50.00
RF Rollie Fingers Brewers/25	10.00	25.00
RF1 Rollie Fingers A's/25	10.00	25.00
RG Ron Guidry/25	20.00	50.00
RI Jim Rice/25		
RJ Randy Johnson/25	60.00	120.00
RK Ralph Kiner B/W/25	20.00	50.00
RK1 Ralph Kiner Color/25	20.00	50.00
RO Roy Oswalt/99	10.00	25.00
RR Robin Roberts/25	15.00	40.00
RR1 Robin Roberts/25		
RS Red Schoendienst/25	15.00	40.00
RW Rickie Weeks/99	10.00	25.00
RY Ryne Sandberg/25	50.00	100.00
SA Ron Santo/99	15.00	40.00
SC Sean Casey/99	10.00	25.00
SL Sparky Lyle/99	6.00	15.00
SM John Smoltz/25	30.00	60.00
SN Duke Snider/25	20.00	50.00
ST Shingo Takatsu/99	10.00	25.00
SU Bruce Sutter/99	12.50	30.00
TH Travis Hafner/99	10.00	25.00
TP Tony Perez/25	15.00	40.00
TS Tom Seaver/25	30.00	60.00
VG Vladimir Guerrero/25	30.00	60.00
VM Victor Martinez/99	10.00	25.00
WB Wade Boggs/25	30.00	60.00
WC Will Clark/25	20.00	50.00
WF Whitey Ford/25	20.00	50.00
YB Yogi Berra/25	30.00	60.00

2004 Ultimate Collection Signatures Dual

OVERALL AUTO ODDS 1:4
STATED PRINT RUN 25 SERIAL #'d SETS
EXCHANGE DEADLINE 12/28/07

BB Hank Blalock	40.00	80.00
Wade Boggs		
BC Carlos Beltran	75.00	150.00
Miguel Cabrera		
BG Carlos Beltran		
Ken Griffey Jr.		
BP Johnny Bench		
Mike Piazza		
BR Jim Bunning		
Robin Roberts		
BS George Brett	125.00	200.00
Mike Schmidt		
BT Hank Blalock	40.00	80.00
Mark Teixeira		
CB Eric Chavez	30.00	60.00
Hank Blalock		
CJ Randy Johnson	250.00	400.00
Roger Clemens		
CL Miguel Cabrera	40.00	80.00
Mike Lowell		
CR Brooks Robinson	40.00	80.00
Eric Chavez		
DW Andre Dawson	30.00	60.00
Billy Williams		
EF Dennis Eckersley	30.00	60.00
Rollie Fingers		
FR Bob Feller	125.00	200.00
Nolan Ryan		
GC Mark Grace	40.00	80.00
Will Clark		
GG Brian Giles	30.00	60.00
Marcus Giles		
GK Harmon Killebrew	125.00	250.00
Ken Griffey Jr.		
GS Eric Gagne	60.00	120.00
John Smoltz		
IC Monte Irvin	30.00	60.00
Orlando Cepeda		
JC Randy Johnson	75.00	150.00
Steve Carlton		
JM Derek Jeter	250.00	400.00
Don Mattingly		
JP Fergie Jenkins	30.00	60.00
Jim Palmer		
JT Fergie Jenkins	30.00	60.00
Luis Tiant		
KG Ken Griffey Sr.	125.00	200.00
Ken Griffey Jr.		
KK Al Kaline	60.00	120.00
Harmon Killebrew		
MC Don Mattingly	75.00	150.00
Will Clark		
MH Mark Mulder	40.00	80.00
Tim Hudson		
MK Bill Mazeroski		
Ralph Kiner		
MP Joe Mauer	50.00	100.00
Mark Prior		
NS Don Newcombe	30.00	60.00
Don Sutton		
PN Gaylord Perry	30.00	60.00
Phil Niekro		
PR Dave Parker	40.00	80.00
Jim Rice		
PS Ben Sheets	30.00	60.00
Mark Prior		
RJ Cal Ripken	350.00	600.00
Derek Jeter		
RM Cal Ripken		
Eddie Murray		
RP Brooks Robinson	50.00	100.00
Jim Palmer		
SF Ben Sheets	30.00	60.00
Bob Feller		
SG Bruce Sutter	40.00	80.00
Eric Gagne		
SO Ben Sheets	30.00	60.00
Roy Oswalt		
SP Don Sutton	30.00	60.00
Gaylord Perry		
TC Mark Teixeira	40.00	80.00
Miguel Cabrera		
VM Vladimir Guerrero	50.00	100.00
Miguel Cabrera		
WS Billy Williams	40.00	80.00
Ron Santo		

2004 Ultimate Collection Stat Patch

*3-COLOR PATCH: ADD 20% PREMIUM
*4-COLOR PATCH: ADD 50% PREMIUM
*5+ COLOR PATCH: ADD 100% PREMIUM
*LOGO PATCH: ADD 150% PREMIUM
OVERALL PATCH ODDS 1:4
PRINT RUNS B/WN 4-66 COPIES PER
NO PRICING ON QTY OF 14 OR LESS

AP Albert Pujols/43	30.00	60.00
AP1 Albert Pujols/51	20.00	50.00
AS Alfonso Soriano/39	8.00	20.00
AS1 Alfonso Soriano/43	8.00	20.00
BE Johnny Bench/45	30.00	60.00
BG Bob Gibson/13		
BM Bill Mazeroski/11		
CB Carlos Beltran/29	10.00	25.00
CB1 Carlos Beltran/41	8.00	20.00
CF Carlton Fisk/17	15.00	40.00
CJ Chipper Jones/45	12.50	30.00
CL1 Roger Clemens Sox/24	20.00	50.00
CL2 Roger Clemens Yanks/7		
CR Cal Ripken/34	50.00	100.00
CR1 Cal Ripken/47	40.00	80.00
CY Carl Yastrzemski/44	20.00	50.00
DD Don Drysdale/25	40.00	80.00
DJ Derek Jeter/32	40.00	80.00
DJ1 Derek Jeter/24	40.00	80.00
DM Don Mattingly/35	40.00	80.00
DW Dave Winfield/37	12.50	30.00
EG Eric Gagne/55	8.00	20.00
EM Eddie Murray/19		
GB George Brett/20	40.00	80.00
GB1 George Brett/30		
GM Greg Maddux Braves/4		
GM1 Greg Maddux Cubs/20	20.00	50.00
GM2 Greg Maddux Cubs/49	15.00	40.00
HB Hank Blalock/29	10.00	25.00
HK Harmon Killebrew/49	30.00	60.00
HM Hideki Matsui/31	60.00	120.00
IR Ivan Rodriguez/35	15.00	40.00
IR1 Ivan Rodriguez/25	15.00	40.00
IS Ichiro Suzuki/56	60.00	120.00
IS1 Ichiro Suzuki/13		
JB Jeff Bagwell/47	12.50	30.00
JM Juan Marichal/26	15.00	40.00
JM1 Juan Marichal/10		
JP Jim Palmer/10		
JP1 Jim Palmer/23	15.00	40.00
JR Jim Rice/15	15.00	40.00
JR1 Jim Rice/46	12.50	30.00
JS John Smoltz/24	15.00	40.00
JS1 John Smoltz/55	12.50	30.00
JT Jim Thome/52	12.50	30.00
KG Ken Griffey Jr./56		
KG1 Ken Griffey Jr./10		
KW Kerry Wood/14		
KW1 Kerry Wood/20	10.00	25.00
MA Pedro Martinez/23	15.00	40.00
MP Mark Prior/18	20.00	50.00
MR Manny Ramirez/45	12.50	30.00
MS Mike Schmidt/48	30.00	60.00
MS1 Mike Schmidt/4		
MT Miguel Tejada/34	10.00	25.00
NR Nolan Ryan/9		
NR1 Nolan Ryan/22		
NR2 Nolan Ryan/7		
PI Mike Piazza/40	15.00	40.00
PM Paul Molitor/39	12.50	30.00
PN Phil Niekro Wins/23	15.00	40.00
PN1 Phil Niekro CG/23	15.00	40.00
RJ Randy Johnson/20	15.00	40.00
RO Jackie Robinson/19	150.00	250.00
RP Rafael Palmeiro/47	12.50	30.00
RS Ryne Sandberg/40	30.00	60.00
RS1 Ryne Sandberg/19	50.00	100.00
RY Robin Yount/49		
SP Warren Spahn/13		
SR Scott Rolen/31	15.00	40.00
SS Sammy Sosa/6		
SS1 Sammy Sosa/66	10.00	25.00
TG Tony Gwynn/56	15.00	40.00
TG1 Tony Gwynn/25	20.00	50.00
TM Thurman Munson/20	40.00	80.00
TS Tom Seaver/25	30.00	60.00
TS1 Tom Seaver/7		
VG Vladimir Guerrero/44	12.50	30.00
VG1 Vladimir Guerrero/40	12.50	30.00
WC Will Clark/35	30.00	60.00
WS Willie Stargell/48	20.00	50.00

2004 Ultimate Collection Super Patch

*3-COLOR PATCH: ADD 20% PREMIUM
*4-COLOR PATCH: ADD 50% PREMIUM
*5+ COLOR PATCH: ADD 100% PREMIUM
*LOGO PATCH: ADD 150% PREMIUM
OVERALL PATCH ODDS 1:4
PRINT RUNS B/WN 4-20 COPIES PER
NO PRICING ON QTY OF 4

AK Al Kaline/20		
AP Albert Pujols/20	60.00	120.00
CL Roger Clemens/20	30.00	60.00
CR Cal Ripken/20	75.00	150.00
CY Carl Yastrzemski/15	50.00	100.00
DJ Derek Jeter/20		
DM Don Mattingly/20	50.00	100.00
DW Dave Winfield/20	15.00	40.00
EM Eddie Murray/20	40.00	80.00
GB George Brett/20	50.00	100.00
GM Greg Maddux/20	40.00	80.00
HK Harmon Killebrew/20	40.00	80.00
HM Hideki Matsui/20	60.00	120.00
IS Ichiro Suzuki/20	125.00	200.00
JB Johnny Bench/20	40.00	80.00
JP Jim Palmer/20	15.00	40.00
KG Ken Griffey Jr./20	40.00	80.00
KW Kerry Wood/20	12.50	30.00
LB Lou Brock/20	30.00	60.00
MP Mark Prior/20	20.00	50.00
MR Manny Ramirez/20		
MS Mike Schmidt/20	50.00	100.00
NR Nolan Ryan/20	50.00	100.00
OS Ozzie Smith/20	40.00	80.00
PI Mike Piazza/20	40.00	80.00
PM Paul Molitor/20	15.00	40.00
RC Rod Carew/20	30.00	60.00
RS Ryne Sandberg/20	50.00	100.00
RY Robin Yount/20	40.00	80.00
SC Red Schoendienst/20	15.00	40.00
SS Sammy Sosa/20	20.00	50.00
TG Tony Gwynn/20	40.00	80.00
TS Tom Seaver/20	30.00	60.00
VG Vladimir Guerrero/20	30.00	60.00
WB Wade Boggs/20		
WC Will Clark Giants/20	30.00	60.00
WC1 Will Clark Rgr/4		

2005 Ultimate Collection

COMMON CARD (1-100)	.75	2.00
1-100 APPX ODDS 3:2 PACKS		
1-100 PRINT RUN 475 SERIAL #'d SETS		
COMMON CARD (101-142)	1.00	2.50
101-142 APPX. ODDS 1:3		
101-142 PRINT RUN 275 SERIAL #'d SETS		
COMMON CARD (143-237)	1.00	2.50
COMMON RC (143-237)	1.00	2.50
143-237 STATED ODDS 3:4 PACKS		
143-237 PRINT RUN 275 SERIAL #'d SETS		
COMMON AU (238-242)	10.00	25.00
238-242 OVERALL AU ODDS 1:4		
238-242 PRINT RUN 99 SERIAL #'d SETS		
1 A.J. Burnett	1.25	3.00
2 Adam Dunn	1.25	3.00
3 Adrian Beltre	.75	2.00
4 Albert Pujols	5.00	12.00
5 Alex Rodriguez	3.00	8.00
6 Alfonso Soriano	1.25	3.00
7 Andruw Jones	.75	2.00
8 Andy Pettitte	1.25	3.00
9 Aramis Ramirez	.75	2.00
10 Aubrey Huff	.75	2.00
11 Ben Sheets	.75	2.00
12 Bobby Abreu	.75	2.00
13 Bobby Crosby	.75	2.00
14 Chris Carpenter	2.00	5.00
15 Brian Giles	.75	2.00
16 Brian Roberts	.75	2.00
17 Carl Crawford	1.25	3.00
18 Carlos Beltran	.75	2.00
19 Carlos Delgado	.75	2.00
20 Carlos Zambrano	1.25	3.00
21 Chipper Jones	2.00	5.00
22 Corey Patterson	.75	2.00
23 Craig Biggio	1.25	3.00
24 Curt Schilling	1.25	3.00
25 Dallas McPherson	.75	2.00
26 David Ortiz	2.00	5.00
27 David Wright	3.00	8.00
28 Delmon Young	2.00	5.00
29 Derek Jeter	5.00	12.00
30 Derrek Lee	.75	2.00
31 Dontrelle Willis	.75	2.00
32 Eric Chavez	.75	2.00
33 Eric Gagne	.75	2.00
34 Francisco Rodriguez	1.25	3.00
35 Gary Sheffield	.75	2.00
36 Greg Maddux	3.00	8.00
37 Hank Blalock	.75	2.00
38 Hideki Matsui	3.00	8.00
39 Ichiro Suzuki	3.00	8.00
40 Ivan Rodriguez	1.25	3.00
41 J.D. Drew	.75	2.00
42 Jake Peavy	.75	2.00
43 Jason Bay	.75	2.00
44 Jason Schmidt	.75	2.00
45 Jeff Bagwell	1.25	3.00
46 Jeff Kent	.75	2.00
47 Jeremy Bonderman	.75	2.00
48 Jim Edmonds	1.25	3.00
49 Jim Thome	1.25	3.00
50 Joe Mauer	2.00	5.00
51 Johan Santana	2.00	5.00
52 John Smoltz	2.00	5.00
53 Johnny Damon	1.25	3.00
54 Jose Reyes	1.25	3.00
55 Jose Vidro	.75	2.00
56 Josh Beckett	1.25	3.00
57 Justin Morneau	2.00	5.00
58 Ken Griffey Jr.	3.00	8.00
59 Kerry Wood	.75	2.00
60 Khalil Greene	.75	2.00
61 Lance Berkman	1.25	3.00
62 Larry Walker	1.25	3.00
63 Luis Gonzalez	.75	2.00
64 Manny Ramirez	2.00	5.00
65 Mark Buehrle	1.25	3.00
66 Mark Mulder	.75	2.00
67 Mark Prior	1.25	3.00
68 Mark Teixeira	2.00	5.00
69 Michael Young	1.25	3.00
70 Miguel Cabrera	2.00	5.00
71 Miguel Tejada	1.25	3.00
72 Mike Mussina	1.25	3.00
73 Mike Piazza	2.00	5.00
74 Moises Alou	.75	2.00
75 Nomar Garciaparra	2.00	5.00
76 Oliver Perez	.75	2.00
77 Pat Burrell	.75	2.00
78 Paul Konerko	1.25	3.00
79 Pedro Feliz	.75	2.00
80 Pedro Martinez	1.25	3.00
81 Randy Johnson	2.00	5.00
82 Richie Sexson	.75	2.00
83 Rickie Weeks	1.25	3.00
84 Roger Clemens	2.50	6.00
85 Roy Halladay	2.00	5.00
86 Roy Oswalt	1.25	3.00
87 Sammy Sosa	2.00	5.00
88 Scott Kazmir	2.00	5.00
89 Scott Rolen	1.25	3.00
90 Shawn Green	.75	2.00
91 Tim Hudson	1.25	3.00
92 Todd Helton	1.25	3.00
93 Tom Glavine	1.25	3.00
94 Torii Hunter	.75	2.00
95 Travis Hafner	.75	2.00
96 Troy Glaus	.75	2.00
97 Vernon Wells	.75	2.00
98 Victor Martinez	1.25	3.00
99 Vladimir Guerrero	2.00	5.00
100 Zack Greinke	1.25	3.00
101 Al Kaline RET	2.50	6.00
102 Babe Ruth RET	6.00	15.00
103 Bo Jackson RET	2.50	6.00
104 Bob Gibson RET	1.50	4.00
105 Brooks Robinson RET	1.50	4.00
106 Cal Ripken RET	10.00	25.00
107 Carl Yastrzemski RET	3.00	8.00
108 Carlton Fisk RET	1.50	4.00
109 Catfish Hunter RET	1.00	2.50
110 Christy Mathewson RET	2.50	6.00
111 Cy Young RET	1.50	4.00
112 Don Mattingly RET	5.00	12.00
113 Eddie Mathews RET	1.50	4.00
114 Eddie Murray RET	2.50	6.00
115 Gary Carter RET	1.00	2.50
116 Harmon Killebrew RET	2.50	6.00
117 Jim Palmer RET	1.00	2.50
118 Jimmie Foxx RET	1.50	4.00
119 Joe DiMaggio RET	6.00	15.00
120 Johnny Bench RET	2.50	6.00
121 Lefty Grove RET	1.00	2.50
122 Lou Gehrig RET	5.00	12.00
123 Mel Ott RET	2.50	6.00
124 Reggie Jackson RET	2.50	6.00
125 Mike Schmidt RET	5.00	12.00
126 Nolan Ryan RET	6.00	15.00
127 Ozzie Smith RET	4.00	10.00
128 Paul Molitor RET	2.50	6.00
129 Pee Wee Reese RET	1.50	4.00
130 Robin Yount RET	2.50	6.00
131 Ryne Sandberg RET	5.00	12.00
132 Ted Williams RET	5.00	12.00
133 Thurman Munson RET	1.50	4.00
134 Tom Seaver RET	1.50	4.00
135 Tony Gwynn RET	3.00	8.00
136 Wade Boggs RET	1.50	4.00
137 Walter Johnson RET	1.50	4.00
138 Warren Spahn RET	1.50	4.00
139 Will Clark RET	1.50	4.00
140 Willie McCovey RET	1.50	4.00
141 Willie Stargell RET	1.50	4.00
142 Yogi Berra RET	2.50	6.00
143 Ambiorix Burgos UP RC	1.00	2.50
144 Ambiorix Concepcion UP RC	1.00	2.50
145 Anibal Sanchez UP RC	5.00	12.00
146 Bill McCarthy UP RC	1.00	2.50
147 Brian Burres UP RC	1.00	2.50
148 Carlos Ruiz UP RC	1.00	2.50
149 Casey Rogowski UP RC	1.50	4.00
150 Chris Resop UP RC	1.00	2.50
151 Chris Roberson UP RC	1.00	2.50
152 Chris Seddon UP RC	1.00	2.50
153 Colter Bean UP RC	1.00	2.50
154 Dae-Sung Koo UP RC	1.00	2.50
155 Danny Rueckel UP RC	1.00	2.50
156 Dave Gassner UP RC	1.00	2.50
157 Ryan Howard UP	5.00	12.00
158 D.J. Houlton UP RC	1.00	2.50
159 Derek Wathan UP RC	1.00	2.50
160 Devon Lowery UP RC	1.00	2.50
161 Enrique Gonzalez UP RC	1.00	2.50
162 Erick Threets UP RC	1.00	2.50
163 Eude Brito UP RC	1.00	2.50
164 Francisco Butto UP RC	1.00	2.50
165 Franquelis Osoria UP RC	1.00	2.50
166 Garrett Jones UP RC	1.50	4.00
167 Geovany Soto UP RC	5.00	12.00
168 Ismael Ramirez UP RC	1.00	2.50
169 Jared Gothreaux UP RC	1.00	2.50
170 Jason Hammel UP RC	1.00	2.50
171 Jeff Housman UP RC	1.00	2.50
172 Jeff Miller UP RC	1.00	2.50
173 Jeff Francoeur UP	2.50	6.00
174 John Hattig UP RC	1.00	2.50
175 Jorge Campillo UP RC	1.00	2.50
176 Juan Morillo UP RC	1.00	2.50
177 Justin Wechsler UP RC	1.00	2.50
178 Keiichi Yabu UP RC	1.00	2.50
179 Kendry Morales UP RC	2.50	6.00
180 Luis Hernandez UP RC	1.00	2.50
181 Luis Mendoza UP RC	1.00	2.50
182 Luis Pena UP RC	1.00	2.50
183 Luis O.Rodriguez UP RC	1.00	2.50
184 Luke Scott UP RC	2.50	6.00
185 Marcos Carvajal UP RC	1.00	2.50
186 Mark Woodyard UP RC	1.00	2.50
187 Matt Smith UP RC	1.00	2.50
188 Matthew Lindstrom UP RC	1.00	2.50
189 Miguel Negron UP RC	1.50	4.00
190 Mike Morse UP RC	2.50	6.00
191 Nate McLouth UP RC	1.50	4.00
192 Nick Masset UP RC	1.00	2.50
193 Paulino Reynoso UP RC	1.00	2.50
194 Pedro Lopez UP RC	1.00	2.50
195 Pete Orr UP RC	1.50	4.00
196 Randy Messenger UP RC	1.00	2.50
197 Randy Williams UP RC	1.00	2.50
198 Raul Tablado UP RC	1.00	2.50
199 Ronny Paulino UP RC	1.50	4.00
200 Russ Rohlicek UP RC	1.00	2.50
201 Russell Martin UP RC	4.00	10.00
202 Scott Baker UP RC	1.50	4.00
203 Scott Munter UP RC	1.00	2.50
204 Sean Thompson UP RC	1.00	2.50
205 Sean Tracey UP RC	1.00	2.50
206 Steve Schmoll UP RC	1.00	2.50
207 Tony Pena UP RC	1.00	2.50
208 Travis Bowyer UP RC	1.00	2.50
209 Ubaldo Jimenez UP RC	3.00	8.00
210 Wladimir Balentien UP RC	1.50	4.00
211 Yorman Bazardo UP RC	1.00	2.50
212 Yuniesky Betancourt UP RC	4.00	10.00
213 Adam Shabala UP RC	1.00	2.50
214 Brandon McCarthy UP RC	1.50	4.00
215 Chad Orvella UP RC	1.00	2.50
216 Jermaine Van Buren UP	1.00	2.50
217 Anthony Reyes UP RC	1.50	4.00
218 Dana Eveland UP RC	1.00	2.50
219 Brian Anderson UP RC	1.50	4.00
220 Hayden Penn UP RC	1.00	2.50
221 Chris Denorfia UP RC	1.00	2.50
222 Joel Peralta UP RC	1.00	2.50
223 Ryan Garko UP RC	1.00	2.50
224 Felix Hernandez UP	4.00	10.00
225 Mark McLemore UP RC	1.00	2.50
226 Melky Cabrera UP RC	2.50	6.00
227 Nelson Cruz UP RC	4.00	10.00
228 Norihiro Nakamura UP RC	1.00	2.50
229 Oscar Robles UP RC	1.00	2.50
230 Rick Short UP RC	1.00	2.50
231 Ryan Zimmerman UP RC	8.00	20.00
232 Ryan Speier UP RC	1.00	2.50
233 Ryan Spilborghs UP RC	2.50	6.00
234 Shane Costa UP RC	1.00	2.50
235 Zach Duke UP	1.00	2.50
236 Tony Giarratano UP RC	1.00	2.50
237 Jeff Niemann UP RC	2.50	6.00
238 Stephen Drew AU RC	100.00	200.00
239 Justin Verlander AU RC	150.00	300.00
240 Prince Fielder AU RC	250.00	500.00
241 Philip Humber AU RC	40.00	80.00
242 Tadahito Iguchi AU RC	60.00	120.00

2005 Ultimate Collection Silver

*SILVER 1-100: .75X TO 2X BASIC
*SILVER 101-142: .75X TO 2X BASIC
*SILVER 143-237: .75X TO 2X BASIC
*SILVER 143-237: .75X TO 2X BASIC RC
APPROXIMATE ODDS 1:3 PACKS
STATED PRINT RUN 50 SERIAL #'d SETS

2005 Ultimate Collection Baseball Stars Signatures

OVERALL AUTO ODDS 1:4
PRINT RUNS B/WN 5-25 COPIES PER
NO PRICING ON QTY OF 10 OR LESS
NO RC YR PRICING ON QTY OF 25 OR LESS
EXCHANGE DEADLINE 01/10/09

AB Adrian Beltre/15	12.50	30.00
AD Adam Dunn/10		
AN Andruw Jones/10		
AP Albert Pujols/5		
AR Aramis Ramirez/20	10.00	25.00
BC Bobby Crosby/15	12.50	30.00
BE Johnny Bench/10		
BG Brian Giles/15	12.50	30.00
BJ Bo Jackson/10		
BL Barry Larkin/15	30.00	60.00
BO Jeremy Bonderman/25	10.00	25.00
BR Brian Roberts/25	10.00	25.00
BS Ben Sheets/15	12.50	30.00
BU B.J. Upton/25	10.00	25.00
CA Rod Carew/10		
CB Craig Biggio/15	20.00	50.00
CC Carl Crawford/25	10.00	25.00
CF Carlton Fisk/10		
CJ Chipper Jones/10		
CO Coco Crisp/25	20.00	50.00
CS Curt Schilling/5		
CZ Carlos Zambrano/20	10.00	25.00
DA Andre Dawson/15	12.50	30.00
DG Dwight Gooden/25	10.00	25.00
DJ Derek Jeter/5		
DO David Ortiz/10		
DW Dontrelle Willis/15	20.00	50.00
EC Eric Chavez/15	12.50	30.00
EG Eric Gagne/10		
FH Felix Hernandez/5		
GC Gary Carter/10		
GR Khalil Greene/15	20.00	50.00
HA Roy Halladay/10		
HB Hank Blalock/15	12.50	30.00
HU Torii Hunter/15	12.50	30.00
JA Reggie Jackson/5		
JB Jason Bay/25	10.00	25.00
JD J.D. Drew/10		
JK Jeff Kent/10		
JM Justin Morneau/25	10.00	25.00
JN Jeff Niemann/25		
JO Joe Mauer/15	40.00	80.00
JP Jake Peavy/20	15.00	40.00
JR Jose Reyes/20	10.00	25.00
JV Jose Vidro/20	6.00	15.00
KG Ken Griffey Jr./25	50.00	100.00
KH Keith Hernandez/15	12.50	30.00
LE Derrek Lee/5		
MA Don Mattingly/10		
MC Miguel Cabrera/15	20.00	50.00
MM Mark Mulder/15	12.50	30.00
MP Mark Prior/10		
MS Mike Schmidt/10		
MT Mark Teixeira/15	20.00	50.00
MY Michael Young/20	10.00	25.00
NG Nomar Garciaparra/10		
NR Nolan Ryan/5		
OS Ozzie Smith/10		
PF Prince Fielder/5		
PH Philip Humber/25		
PM Paul Molitor/15	12.50	30.00
RC Roger Clemens/5		
RF Rafael Furcal/20	10.00	25.00
RH Rich Harden/25	10.00	25.00
RJ Randy Johnson/5		
RO Roy Oswalt/15	12.50	30.00
RS Ryne Sandberg/10		
RW Rickie Weeks/15	12.50	30.00
RY Robin Yount/10		
SD Stephen Drew/15		
SK Scott Kazmir/25	10.00	25.00
SM John Smoltz/15	40.00	80.00
SP Scott Podsednik/25	15.00	40.00
TE Miguel Tejada/5		
TG Tony Gwynn/10		
TH Tim Hudson/15	15.00	40.00
TI Tadahito Iguchi/20		
TR Travis Hafner/25	10.00	25.00
VE Justin Verlander/25		
VG Vladimir Guerrero/5		
VM Victor Martinez/25	10.00	25.00
WB Wade Boggs/10		
WC Will Clark/15	20.00	50.00
WP Wily Mo Pena/25	10.00	25.00
WR David Wright/15	50.00	100.00
ZG Zack Greinke/25	8.00	20.00

2005 Ultimate Collection Hurlers Materials

OVERALL GAME-USED ODDS 1:4
STATED PRINT RUN 20 SERIAL #'d SETS
*PATCH p/r 21-25: .6X TO 1.5X BASIC
OVERALL PATCH ODDS 1:4
PATCH PRINT RUN B/WN 2-25 PER
NO PATCH PRICING ON QTY OF 12 OR LESS

AB A.J. Burnett Jsy	4.00	10.00
BE Josh Beckett Jsy	4.00	10.00
BL Brad Lidge Jsy	4.00	10.00
BM Brett Myers Jsy	4.00	10.00
BO Jeremy Bonderman Jsy	4.00	10.00
BS Ben Sheets Jsy	4.00	10.00
CA Chris Carpenter Jsy	6.00	15.00
CC C.C. Sabathia Jsy	4.00	10.00
CP Carl Pavano Jsy	4.00	10.00
CS Curt Schilling Jsy	6.00	15.00
CZ Carlos Zambrano Jsy	4.00	10.00
DG Dwight Gooden Jsy	4.00	10.00
DH Danny Haren Jsy	4.00	10.00
DL Derek Lowe Jsy	4.00	10.00
DW Dontrelle Willis Jsy	4.00	10.00
EG Eric Gagne Jsy	4.00	10.00
FH Felix Hernandez Jsy	12.50	30.00
FR Francisco Rodriguez Jsy	4.00	10.00
GF Gavin Floyd Jsy	4.00	10.00
GM Greg Maddux Jsy	12.50	30.00
GP Gaylord Perry Jsy	4.00	10.00
HA Roy Halladay Jsy	4.00	10.00
HO Trevor Hoffman Jsy	6.00	15.00
JB Joe Blanton Jsy	4.00	10.00
JF Jeff Francis Jsy	4.00	10.00
JP Jake Peavy Jsy	4.00	10.00
JS Johan Santana Jsy	6.00	15.00
JW Jake Westbrook Jsy	4.00	10.00
KF Keith Foulke Jsy	4.00	10.00
KW Kerry Wood Jsy	4.00	10.00
LH Livan Hernandez Jsy	4.00	10.00
MA Matt Cain Jsy	15.00	40.00
MC Matt Clement Jsy	4.00	10.00
MM Mark Mulder Jsy	4.00	10.00
MP Mark Prior Jsy	6.00	15.00
MU Mike Mussina Jsy	6.00	15.00
NR1 Nolan Ryan Angels Jsy	15.00	40.00
NR2 Nolan Ryan Rgr Jsy	15.00	40.00
OP Odalis Perez Jsy	4.00	10.00
PE Oliver Perez Jsy	4.00	10.00
PM Pedro Martinez Jsy	6.00	15.00
RC Roger Clemens Jsy	12.50	30.00
RH Rich Harden Jsy	4.00	10.00
RJ Randy Johnson Jsy	8.00	20.00
RO Roy Oswalt Jsy	4.00	10.00
SK Scott Kazmir Jsy	4.00	10.00
SM John Smoltz Jsy	8.00	20.00
TG Tom Glavine Jsy	6.00	15.00
TH Tim Hudson Jsy	4.00	10.00
TW Tim Wakefield Jsy	10.00	25.00

2005 Ultimate Collection Hurlers Signature Materials

STATED PRINT RUN 20 SERIAL #'d SETS
PATCH PRINT RUN 10 SERIAL #'d SETS
NO PATCH PRICING DUE TO SCARCITY
OVERALL AU-GU ODDS 1:4
EXCHANGE DEADLINE 01/12/09

BE Josh Beckett Jsy	20.00	50.00
BL Brad Lidge Jsy	15.00	40.00
BM Brett Myers Jsy	6.00	15.00
BO Jeremy Bonderman Jsy	10.00	25.00
BS Ben Sheets Jsy	10.00	25.00
CA Chris Carpenter Jsy	20.00	50.00
CZ Carlos Zambrano Jsy	10.00	25.00
DH Danny Haren Jsy	6.00	15.00
DW Dontrelle Willis Jsy	15.00	40.00
EG Eric Gagne Jsy	10.00	25.00
FH Felix Hernandez Jsy	60.00	120.00
FR Francisco Rodriguez Jsy	10.00	25.00
GF Gavin Floyd Jsy	6.00	15.00
GP Gaylord Perry Jsy	10.00	25.00
HA Roy Halladay Jsy	12.50	30.00
JB Joe Blanton Jsy	6.00	15.00
JF Jeff Francis Jsy	6.00	15.00
JP Jake Peavy Jsy	10.00	25.00
JW Jake Westbrook Jsy	6.00	15.00
KW Kerry Wood Jsy	15.00	40.00
LH Livan Hernandez Jsy	10.00	25.00
MC Matt Clement Jsy	10.00	25.00
MM Mark Mulder Jsy	10.00	25.00
MP Mark Prior Jsy	12.50	30.00
MU Mike Mussina Jsy	20.00	50.00
NR1 Nolan Ryan Angels Jsy	60.00	120.00
NR2 Nolan Ryan Rgr Jsy	60.00	120.00
RO Roy Oswalt Jsy	10.00	25.00
SK Scott Kazmir Jsy	10.00	25.00
SM John Smoltz Jsy	30.00	60.00
TH Tim Hudson Jsy	15.00	40.00
TW Tim Wakefield Jsy	50.00	100.00

2005 Ultimate Collection Materials

OVERALL GAME-USED ODDS 1:4
STATED PRINT RUN 25 SERIAL #'d SETS
*PATCH p/r 25: .6X TO 1.5X BASIC
*PATCH p/r 15: .75X TO 2X BASIC
OVERALL PATCH ODDS 1:4
PATCH PRINT RUN B/WN 5-25 PER
NO PATCH PRICING ON QTY OF 10 OR LESS

AB Adrian Beltre Jsy	4.00	10.00
AD Adam Dunn Jsy	4.00	10.00
AH Aubrey Huff Jsy	4.00	10.00
AJ Andruw Jones Jsy	6.00	15.00
AP Albert Pujols Jsy	12.50	30.00
AR Aaron Rowand Jsy	4.00	10.00
BA Bobby Abreu Jsy	4.00	10.00
BC Bobby Crosby Jsy	4.00	10.00
BE Josh Beckett Jsy	4.00	10.00
BG Brian Giles Jsy	4.00	10.00
BJ B.J. Upton Jsy	4.00	10.00
BL Brad Lidge Jsy	4.00	10.00
BO Jeremy Bonderman Jsy	4.00	10.00
BR Brian Roberts Jsy	4.00	10.00
BS Ben Sheets Jsy	4.00	10.00
BU A.J. Burnett Jsy	4.00	10.00
CA Miguel Cabrera Jsy	6.00	15.00
CB Craig Biggio Jsy	6.00	15.00
CC C.C. Sabathia Jsy	4.00	10.00
CO Coco Crisp Jsy	4.00	10.00
CP Carl Pavano Jsy	4.00	10.00
CR Carl Crawford Jsy	4.00	10.00
CS Curt Schilling Jsy	6.00	15.00
CU Chase Utley Jsy	10.00	25.00
CW Rod Carew Jsy	6.00	15.00
CZ Carlos Zambrano Jsy	4.00	10.00
DJ Derek Jeter Jsy	15.00	40.00
DL Derek Lowe Jsy	4.00	10.00
DO David Ortiz Jsy	6.00	15.00
DW Dontrelle Willis Jsy	4.00	10.00
EC Eric Chavez Jsy	4.00	10.00
EG Eric Gagne Jsy	4.00	10.00
ER Edgar Renteria Jsy	4.00	10.00
ES Johnny Estrada Jsy	4.00	10.00
FH Felix Hernandez Jsy	12.50	30.00
FR Francisco Rodriguez Jsy	4.00	10.00
GF Gavin Floyd Jsy	4.00	10.00
GM Greg Maddux Jsy	12.50	30.00
GR Khalil Greene Jsy	6.00	15.00
GS Gary Sheffield Jsy	4.00	10.00
HA Roy Halladay Jsy	4.00	10.00
HB Hank Blalock Jsy	4.00	10.00
HO Trevor Hoffman Jsy	6.00	15.00
HU Torii Hunter Jsy	4.00	10.00
JA Jason Bay Jsy	4.00	10.00
JB Jeff Bagwell Jsy	8.00	20.00
JD J.D. Drew Jsy	4.00	10.00
JF Jeff Francis Jsy	4.00	10.00
JK Jeff Kent Jsy	4.00	10.00
JM Joe Mauer Jsy	8.00	20.00
JP Jake Peavy Jsy	4.00	10.00
JR Jeremy Reed Jsy	4.00	10.00
JV Jose Vidro Jsy	4.00	10.00
JW Jake Westbrook Jsy	4.00	10.00
KF Keith Foulke Jsy	4.00	10.00
KG Ken Griffey Jr. Jsy	12.50	30.00
LE Derrek Lee Jsy	6.00	15.00
MA Matt Cain Jsy	15.00	40.00
MC Matt Clement Jsy	4.00	10.00
MG Marcus Giles Jsy	4.00	10.00
ML Mark Loretta Jsy	4.00	10.00
MM Mark Mulder Jsy	4.00	10.00
MO Justin Morneau Jsy	4.00	10.00
MP Mark Prior Jsy	6.00	15.00
MS Mike Schmidt Jsy	15.00	40.00
MT Mark Teixeira Jsy	6.00	15.00
MY Michael Young Jsy	4.00	10.00
NR Nolan Ryan Jsy	15.00	40.00
OP Oliver Perez Jsy	4.00	10.00
OS Roy Oswalt Jsy	4.00	10.00
PA Corey Patterson Jsy	4.00	10.00
PF Prince Fielder Jsy	15.00	40.00
PM Pedro Martinez Jsy	6.00	15.00
RA Aramis Ramirez Jsy	4.00	10.00
RC Roger Clemens Jsy	12.50	30.00
RE Jose Reyes Jsy	4.00	10.00
RF Rafael Furcal Jsy	4.00	10.00
RH Rich Harden Jsy	4.00	10.00
RI Cal Ripken Jsy	30.00	60.00

RJ Randy Johnson Jsy 8.00 20.00
RP Rafael Palmeiro Jsy 6.00 15.00
RS Ryne Sandberg Jsy 15.00 40.00
RW Rickie Weeks Jsy 4.00 10.00
SA Johan Santana Jsy 8.00 20.00
SC Sean Casey Jsy 4.00 10.00
SK Scott Kazmir Jsy 4.00 10.00
SM John Smoltz Jsy 8.00 20.00
SP Scott Podsednik Jsy 6.00 15.00
SR Scott Rolen Jsy 6.00 15.00
TE Miguel Tejada Jsy 4.00 10.00
TH Tim Hudson Jsy 4.00 10.00
TI Tadahito Iguchi Jsy 12.50 30.00
TR Travis Hafner Jsy 4.00 10.00
TW Tim Wakefield Jsy 10.00 25.00
VG Vladimir Guerrero Jsy 8.00 20.00
VM Victor Martinez Jsy 4.00 10.00
WP Wily Mo Pena Jsy 4.00 10.00
WR David Wright Jsy 12.50 30.00
ZG Zack Greinke Jsy 4.00 10.00

2005 Ultimate Collection Materials Signature

STATED PRINT RUN 25 SERIAL #'d SETS
NO RC YR PRICING DUE TO SCARCITY
PATCH PRINT RUN 10 SERIAL #'d SETS
NO PATCH PRICING DUE TO SCARCITY
OVERALL AU-GU ODDS 1:4
EXCHANGE DEADLINE 01/10/09
AB Adrian Beltre Jsy 10.00 25.00
AD Adam Dunn Jsy 10.00 25.00
AH Aubrey Huff Jsy 6.00 15.00
AJ Andruw Jones Jsy 20.00 50.00
BC Bobby Crosby Jsy 10.00 25.00
BE Josh Beckett Jsy 15.00 40.00
BG Brian Giles Jsy 10.00 25.00
BJ B.J. Upton Jsy 12.50 30.00
BL Brad Lidge Jsy 15.00 40.00
BO Jeremy Bonderman Jsy 10.00 25.00
BR Brian Roberts Jsy 10.00 25.00
BS Ben Sheets Jsy 10.00 25.00
CA Miguel Cabrera Jsy 15.00 40.00
CA Rod Carew Jsy 15.00 40.00
CB Craig Biggio Jsy 20.00 50.00
CR Carl Crawford Jsy 10.00 25.00
CU Chase Utley Jsy 30.00 60.00
CZ Carlos Zambrano Jsy 10.00 25.00
DJ Derek Jeter Jsy 150.00 250.00
DO David Ortiz Jsy 30.00 60.00
DW Dontrelle Willis Jsy 15.00 40.00
EG Eric Gagne Jsy 10.00 25.00
ES Johnny Estrada Jsy 6.00 15.00
FH Felix Hernandez Jsy 60.00 120.00
FR Francisco Rodriguez Jsy 10.00 25.00
GF Gavin Floyd Jsy 6.00 15.00
GR Khalil Greene Jsy 15.00 40.00
GS Gary Sheffield Jsy 15.00 40.00
HA Roy Halladay Jsy 10.00 25.00
HB Hank Blalock Jsy 10.00 25.00
HU Torii Hunter Jsy 10.00 25.00
JA Jason Bay Jsy 10.00 25.00
JB Jeff Bagwell Jsy 40.00 80.00
JD J.D. Drew Jsy 10.00 25.00
JF Jeff Francis Jsy 6.00 15.00
JM Joe Mauer Jsy 30.00 60.00
JP Jake Peavy Jsy 10.00 25.00
JR Jeremy Reed Jsy 6.00 15.00
JV Jose Vidro Jsy 6.00 15.00
JW Jake Westbrook Jsy 6.00 15.00
KG Ken Griffey Jr. Jsy 75.00 150.00
LA Barry Larkin Jsy 20.00 50.00
LE Derrek Lee Jsy 15.00 40.00
MC Matt Clement Jsy 10.00 25.00
ML Mark Loretta Jsy 6.00 15.00
MM Mark Mulder Jsy 10.00 25.00
MO Justin Morneau Jsy 10.00 25.00
MP Mark Prior Jsy 12.50 30.00
MS Mike Schmidt Jsy 30.00 60.00
MT Mark Teixeira Jsy 12.50 30.00
MY Michael Young Jsy 10.00 25.00
NR Nolan Ryan Jsy 60.00 120.00
OS Roy Oswalt Jsy 10.00 25.00
RA Aramis Ramirez Jsy 10.00 25.00
RE Jose Reyes Jsy 10.00 25.00
RF Rafael Furcal Jsy 10.00 25.00
RP Rafael Palmeiro Jsy 20.00 50.00
RS Ryne Sandberg Jsy 40.00 80.00
RW Rickie Weeks Jsy 10.00 25.00
SK Scott Kazmir Jsy 10.00 25.00
SM John Smoltz Jsy 30.00 60.00
SP Scott Podsednik Jsy 15.00 40.00
TE Miguel Tejada Jsy 20.00 50.00
TH Tim Hudson Jsy 15.00 40.00
TI Tadahito Iguchi Jsy
TR Travis Hafner Jsy 10.00 25.00
TW Tim Wakefield Jsy 50.00 100.00
VG Vladimir Guerrero Jsy 30.00 60.00
VM Victor Martinez Jsy 10.00 25.00
WP Wily Mo Pena Jsy 10.00 25.00
WR David Wright Jsy 50.00 100.00
ZG Zack Greinke Jsy 8.00 20.00

2005 Ultimate Collection Signatures

PRINT RUNS B/WN 10-99 COPIES PER
NO PRICING ON QTY OF 10
PLATINUM PRINT RUN 5 SERIAL #'d SETS
NO PLATINUM PRICING DUE TO SCARCITY
OVERALL AUTO ODDS 1:4
EXCHANGE DEADLINE 01/10/09
AB Adrian Beltre/69 10.00 25.00
AD Adam Dunn/35 10.00 25.00
AP Albert Pujols/10
AR Aramis Ramirez/69 10.00 25.00
BA Jason Bay/69 10.00 25.00
BC Bobby Crosby/69 10.00 25.00
BE Josh Beckett/35 15.00 40.00
BJ Bo Jackson/35 30.00 60.00
BL Barry Larkin/69 20.00 50.00
BR Brian Roberts/35 10.00 25.00
BS Ben Sheets/69 10.00 25.00
BU B.J. Upton/69 12.50 30.00
CB Craig Biggio/69 15.00 40.00
CF Carlton Fisk/15 20.00 50.00
CJ Chipper Jones/10
CO Coco Crisp/69 20.00 50.00
CS Curt Schilling/10
CU Chase Utley/TBD
CW Rod Carew/35 15.00 40.00
CY Carl Yastrzemski/10
CZ Carlos Zambrano/69 10.00 25.00
DJ Derek Jeter/10
DL Derrek Lee/10
DO David Ortiz/35 20.00 50.00
DW Dontrelle Willis/69 15.00 40.00
EC Eric Chavez/52 10.00 25.00
EG Eric Gagne/35 10.00 25.00
FH Felix Hernandez/69 50.00 100.00
GC Gary Carter/35 10.00 25.00
GM Greg Maddux/10
GR Khalil Greene/69 15.00 40.00
GS Gary Sheffield/25 15.00 40.00
GW Tony Gwynn/25 30.00 60.00
HA Roy Halladay/35 10.00 25.00
HB Hank Blalock/69 10.00 25.00
HU Torii Hunter/69 10.00 25.00
JA Reggie Jackson/10
JB Johnny Bench/15 30.00 60.00
JD J.D. Drew/29 10.00 25.00
JE Jeff Bagwell/15 40.00 80.00
JK Jeff Kent/TBD
JM Joe Mauer/69 30.00 60.00
JN Jeff Niemann/69 6.00 15.00
JO Andruw Jones/35 20.00 50.00
JP Jake Peavy/69 10.00 25.00
JR Jose Reyes/69 10.00 25.00
JV Justin Verlander/69 50.00 100.00
KG Ken Griffey Jr./69 40.00 80.00
KM Kendry Morales/69 40.00 80.00
KW Kerry Wood/15 20.00 50.00
MA-Don Mattingly/25 50.00 100.00
MC Miguel Cabrera/69 15.00 40.00
MM Mark Mulder/69 10.00 25.00
MP Mark Prior/15 15.00 40.00
MS Mike Schmidt/25 30.00 60.00
MT Mark Teixeira/99 12.50 30.00
MU Mike Mussina/15 30.00 60.00
MY Michael Young/69 10.00 25.00
NG Nomar Garciaparra/10
NR Nolan Ryan/10
OS Ozzie Smith/35 20.00 50.00
PF Prince Fielder/35 75.00 150.00
PH Philip Humber/69 12.50 30.00
PI Mike Piazza/10
PM Paul Molitor/49 10.00 25.00
RC Roger Clemens/10
RH Rich Harden/69 10.00 25.00
RJ Randy Johnson/10
RO Roy Oswalt/69 10.00 25.00
RP Rafael Palmeiro/25 20.00 50.00
RS Ryne Sandberg/15 50.00 100.00
RW Rickie Weeks/30 10.00 25.00
RY Robin Yount/15 30.00 60.00
SD Stephen Drew/69
SK Scott Kazmir/69 10.00 25.00
SM John Smoltz/49 30.00 60.00
TE Miguel Tejada/10
TG Tom Glavine/10
TH Tim Hudson/69 15.00 40.00
TI Tadahito Iguchi/69 50.00 100.00
TR Travis Hafner/69 10.00 25.00
VG Vladimir Guerrero/10
VM Victor Martinez/69 10.00 25.00
WB Wade Boggs/15 20.00 50.00
WC Will Clark/69 15.00 40.00
WR David Wright/69 30.00 60.00
ZG Zack Greinke/69 20.00 50.00

2005 Ultimate Collection Sluggers Materials

OVERALL GAME-USED ODDS 1:4
STATED PRINT RUN 20 SERIAL #'d SETS
*PATCH p/r 25: .6X TO 1.5X BASIC
*PATCH p/r 19: .75X TO 2X BASIC
OVERALL PATCH ODDS 1:4
PATCH PRINT RUN B/WN 19-25 PER
AB Adrian Beltre Jsy 4.00 10.00
AD Adam Dunn Jsy 4.00 10.00
AH Aubrey Huff Jsy 4.00 10.00
AP Albert Pujols Jsy 12.50 30.00
AR Aramis Ramirez Jsy 4.00 10.00
BA Bobby Abreu Jsy 4.00 10.00
BC Bobby Crosby Jsy 4.00 10.00
BG Brian Giles Jsy 4.00 10.00
BR Brian Roberts Jsy 4.00 10.00
CA Rod Carew Jsy 6.00 15.00
CB Craig Biggio Jsy 6.00 15.00
CC Carl Crawford Jsy 4.00 10.00
CJ Chipper Jones Jsy 8.00 20.00
CO Coco Crisp Jsy 4.00 10.00
CP Corey Patterson Jsy 4.00 10.00
DJ Derek Jeter Jsy 15.00 40.00
DL Derrek Lee Jsy 6.00 15.00
DO David Ortiz Jsy 6.00 15.00
DW David Wright Jsy 12.50 30.00
EC Eric Chavez Jsy 4.00 10.00
ER Edgar Renteria Jsy 4.00 10.00
ES Johnny Estrada Jsy 4.00 10.00
GR Khalil Greene Jsy 6.00 15.00
GS Gary Sheffield Jsy 4.00 10.00
HA Travis Hafner Jsy 4.00 10.00
HB Hank Blalock Jsy 4.00 10.00
JA Jason Bay Jsy 4.00 10.00
JB Jeff Bagwell Jsy 8.00 20.00
JD J.D. Drew Jsy 4.00 10.00
JK Jeff Kent Jsy 4.00 10.00
JM Justin Morneau Jsy 4.00 10.00
JR Jose Reyes Jsy 4.00 10.00
JV Jose Vidro Jsy 4.00 10.00
KG Ken Griffey Jr. Jsy 12.50 30.00
MA Joe Mauer Jsy 8.00 20.00
MC Miguel Cabrera Jsy 6.00 15.00
MG Marcus Giles Jsy 4.00 10.00
ML Mark Loretta Jsy 4.00 10.00
MT Mark Teixeira Jsy 6.00 15.00
MY Michael Young Jsy 4.00 10.00
RF Rafael Furcal Jsy 4.00 10.00
RH Ryan Howard Jsy 15.00 40.00
RP Rafael Palmeiro Jsy 6.00 15.00
SC Sean Casey Jsy 4.00 10.00
SR Scott Rolen Jsy 6.00 15.00
TH Torii Hunter Jsy 4.00 10.00
VG Vladimir Guerrero Jsy 8.00 20.00
VM Victor Martinez Jsy 4.00 10.00
WP Wily Mo Pena Jsy 4.00 10.00

2005 Ultimate Collection Sluggers Signature Materials

STATED PRINT RUN 20 SERIAL #'d SETS
PATCH PRINT RUN B/WN 3-10 COPIES PER
NO PATCH PRICING DUE TO SCARCITY
OVERALL AU-GU ODDS 1:4
AB Adrian Beltre Jsy 10.00 25.00
AD Adam Dunn Jsy 10.00 25.00
AH Aubrey Huff Jsy 6.00 15.00
AR Aramis Ramirez Jsy 10.00 25.00
BC Bobby Crosby Jsy 10.00 25.00
BG Brian Giles Jsy 10.00 25.00
BR Brian Roberts Jsy 10.00 25.00
CA Rod Carew Jsy 15.00 40.00
CB Craig Biggio Jsy 20.00 50.00
CJ Chipper Jones Jsy 30.00 60.00
DJ Derek Jeter Jsy 150.00 250.00
DL Derrek Lee Jsy 15.00 40.00
DO David Ortiz Jsy 30.00 60.00
DW David Wright Jsy 50.00 100.00
EC Eric Chavez Jsy 10.00 25.00
ES Johnny Estrada Jsy 6.00 15.00
GR Khalil Greene Jsy 15.00 40.00
GS Gary Sheffield Jsy 15.00 40.00
HA Travis Hafner Jsy 10.00 25.00
HB Hank Blalock Jsy 10.00 25.00
JA Jason Bay Jsy 10.00 25.00
JB Jeff Bagwell Jsy 40.00 80.00
JD J.D. Drew Jsy 10.00 25.00
JM Justin Morneau Jsy 10.00 25.00
JR Jose Reyes Jsy 10.00 25.00
JV Jose Vidro Jsy 6.00 15.00
KG Ken Griffey Jr. Jsy 75.00 150.00
MA Joe Mauer Jsy 30.00 60.00
MC Miguel Cabrera Jsy 15.00 40.00
ML Mark Loretta Jsy 6.00 15.00
MT Mark Teixeira Jsy 20.00 50.00
MY Michael Young Jsy 10.00 25.00
RF Rafael Furcal Jsy 10.00 25.00
RH Ryan Howard Jsy 50.00 100.00
RP Rafael Palmeiro Jsy 20.00 50.00
TH Torii Hunter Jsy 10.00 25.00
VM Victor Martinez Jsy 10.00 25.00
WP Wily Mo Pena Jsy 10.00 25.00

2005 Ultimate Collection Veteran Materials

OVERALL GAME-USED ODDS 1:4
STATED PRINT RUN 20 SERIAL #'d SETS
*PATCH p/r 30: .6X TO 1.5X BASIC
*PATCH p/r 15-16: .75X TO 2X BASIC
OVERALL PATCH ODDS 1:4
PATCH PRINT RUN B/WN 7-30 PER
NO PATCH PRICING ON QTY OF 7
AB Adrian Beltre Jsy 4.00 10.00
AD Adam Dunn Jsy 4.00 10.00
AH Aubrey Huff Jsy 4.00 10.00
AJ Andruw Jones Jsy 6.00 15.00
AR Aramis Ramirez Jsy 4.00 10.00
AS Alfonso Soriano Jsy 4.00 10.00
BA Bobby Abreu Jsy 4.00 10.00
BE Josh Beckett Jsy 4.00 10.00
BG Brian Giles Jsy 4.00 10.00
BM Brett Myers Jsy 4.00 10.00
CA Rod Carew Jsy 6.00 15.00
CB Craig Biggio Jsy 6.00 15.00
CR Cal Ripken Jsy 30.00 60.00
CS C.C. Sabathia Jsy 4.00 10.00
DJ Derek Jeter Jsy 15.00 40.00
DL Derek Lowe Jsy 4.00 10.00
DO David Ortiz Jsy 6.00 15.00
DW Dontrelle Willis Jsy 4.00 10.00
EC Eric Chavez Jsy 4.00 10.00
EG Eric Gagne Jsy 4.00 10.00
ER Edgar Renteria Jsy 4.00 10.00
GM Greg Maddux Jsy 12.50 30.00
HB Hank Blalock Jsy 4.00 10.00
HO Trevor Hoffman Jsy 6.00 15.00
HU Torii Hunter Jsy 4.00 10.00
JB Jeff Bagwell Jsy 8.00 20.00
JD J.D. Drew Jsy 4.00 10.00
JK Jeff Kent Jsy 4.00 10.00
JV Jose Vidro Jsy 4.00 10.00
KF Keith Foulke Jsy 4.00 10.00
KG Ken Griffey Jr. Jsy 12.50 30.00
LE Derrek Lee Jsy 6.00 15.00
LH Livan Hernandez Jsy 4.00 10.00
MC Matt Clement Jsy 4.00 10.00
ML Mark Loretta Jsy 4.00 10.00
MM Mark Mulder Jsy 4.00 10.00
MP Mark Prior Jsy 6.00 15.00
MT Miguel Tejada Jsy 4.00 10.00
NR Nolan Ryan Jsy 15.00 40.00
OP Odalis Perez Jsy 4.00 10.00
RC Roger Clemens Jsy 12.50 30.00
RH Roy Halladay Jsy 4.00 10.00
RJ Randy Johnson Jsy 8.00 20.00
RO Roy Oswalt Jsy 4.00 10.00
SC Sean Casey Jsy 4.00 10.00
SM John Smoltz Jsy 8.00 20.00
SR Scott Rolen Jsy 6.00 15.00
TH Tim Hudson Jsy 4.00 10.00
TW Tim Wakefield Jsy 10.00 25.00
VG Vladimir Guerrero Jsy 8.00 20.00

2005 Ultimate Collection Veteran Materials Signature

STATED PRINT RUN 20 SERIAL #'d SETS
PATCH PRINT RUN 10 SERIAL #'d SETS
NO PATCH PRICING DUE TO SCARCITY
OVERALL AU-GU ODDS 1:4
EXCHANGE DEADLINE 01/10/09
AB Adrian Beltre Jsy 20.00 50.00
AD Adam Dunn Jsy 10.00 25.00
AH Aubrey Huff Jsy 6.00 15.00
AJ Andruw Jones Jsy 20.00 50.00
AR Aramis Ramirez Jsy 10.00 25.00
BE Josh Beckett Jsy 15.00 40.00
BG Brian Giles Jsy 10.00 25.00
BM Brett Myers Jsy 6.00 15.00
CA Rod Carew Jsy 15.00 40.00
CB Craig Biggio Jsy 20.00 50.00
DJ Derek Jeter Jsy 150.00 250.00
DO David Ortiz Jsy 30.00 60.00
DW Dontrelle Willis Jsy 15.00 40.00
EC Eric Chavez Jsy 10.00 25.00
EG Eric Gagne Jsy 10.00 25.00
HB Hank Blalock Jsy 10.00 25.00
HU Torii Hunter Jsy 10.00 25.00
JB Jeff Bagwell Jsy 40.00 80.00
JD J.D. Drew Jsy 10.00 25.00
JV Jose Vidro Jsy 6.00 15.00
KG Ken Griffey Jr. Jsy 75.00 150.00
LE Derrek Lee Jsy 15.00 40.00
LH Livan Hernandez Jsy 10.00 25.00
MC Matt Clement Jsy 10.00 25.00
ML Mark Loretta Jsy 6.00 15.00
MM Mark Mulder Jsy 10.00 25.00
MP Mark Prior Jsy 12.50 30.00
MT Miguel Tejada Jsy 20.00 50.00
NR Nolan Ryan Jsy 60.00 120.00
RH Roy Halladay Jsy 12.50 30.00
RO Roy Oswalt Jsy 10.00 25.00
SM John Smoltz Jsy 30.00 60.00
TH Tim Hudson Jsy 15.00 40.00
TW Tim Wakefield Jsy 50.00 100.00
VG Vladimir Guerrero Jsy 30.00 60.00

2005 Ultimate Collection Young Stars Materials

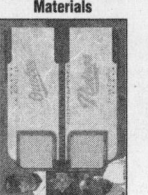

OVERALL GAME-USED ODDS 1:4
STATED PRINT RUN 20 SERIAL #'d SETS
*PATCH p/r 30: .6X TO 1.5X BASIC
*PATCH p/r 15: .75X TO 2X BASIC
OVERALL PATCH ODDS 1:4
PATCH PRINT RUN B/WN 6-30 PER
NO PATCH PRICING ON QTY OF 6
AB A.J. Burnett Jsy 4.00 10.00
AR Aaron Rowand Jsy 4.00 10.00
BA Jason Bay Jsy 4.00 10.00
BC Bobby Crosby Jsy 4.00 10.00
BL Brad Lidge Jsy 4.00 10.00
BO Jeremy Bonderman Jsy 4.00 10.00
BR Brian Roberts Jsy 4.00 10.00
BS Ben Sheets Jsy 4.00 10.00
BU B.J. Upton Jsy 4.00 10.00
CC Carl Crawford Jsy 4.00 10.00
CO Coco Crisp Jsy 4.00 10.00
CP Carl Pavano Jsy 4.00 10.00
CU Chase Utley Jsy 10.00 25.00
CZ Carlos Zambrano Jsy 4.00 10.00
DH Danny Haren Jsy 4.00 10.00
DW David Wright Jsy 12.50 30.00
FH Felix Hernandez Jsy 12.50 30.00
FR Francisco Rodriguez Jsy 4.00 10.00
GF Gavin Floyd Jsy 4.00 10.00
HO Ryan Howard Jsy 15.00 40.00
JB Joe Blanton Jsy 4.00 10.00
JE Johnny Estrada Jsy 4.00 10.00
JF Jeff Francis Jsy 4.00 10.00
JM Joe Mauer Jsy 6.00 15.00
JP Jake Peavy Jsy 4.00 10.00
JR Jeremy Reed Jsy 4.00 10.00
JS Johan Santana Jsy 6.00 15.00
JW Jake Westbrook Jsy 4.00 10.00
KG Khalil Greene Jsy 6.00 15.00
MA Matt Cain Jsy 15.00 40.00
MC Miguel Cabrera Jsy 6.00 15.00
MG Marcus Giles Jsy 4.00 10.00
MO Justin Morneau Jsy 4.00 10.00
MT Mark Teixeira Jsy 6.00 15.00
MY Michael Young Jsy 4.00 10.00
OP Oliver Perez Jsy 4.00 10.00
PA Corey Patterson Jsy 4.00 10.00
PF Prince Fielder Jsy 15.00 40.00
RE Jose Reyes Jsy 4.00 10.00
RF Rafael Furcal Jsy 4.00 10.00
RH Rich Harden Jsy 4.00 10.00
RW Rickie Weeks Jsy 4.00 10.00
SK Scott Kazmir Jsy 4.00 10.00
SP Scott Podsednik Jsy 6.00 15.00
TH Travis Hafner Jsy 4.00 10.00
TI Tadahito Iguchi Jsy 12.50 30.00
VM Victor Martinez Jsy 4.00 10.00
WP Wily Mo Pena Jsy 4.00 10.00
ZG Zack Greinke Jsy 4.00 10.00

2005 Ultimate Collection Young Stars Signature Materials

STATED PRINT RUN 20 SERIAL #'d SETS
NO RC YR PRICING DUE TO SCARCITY
PATCH PRINT RUN 10 SERIAL #'d SETS
NO PATCH PRICING DUE TO SCARCITY
OVERALL AU-GU ODDS 1:4
AR Aaron Rowand Jsy 10.00 25.00
BA Jason Bay Jsy 10.00 25.00
BC Bobby Crosby Jsy 10.00 25.00
BL Brad Lidge Jsy 15.00 40.00
BO Jeremy Bonderman Jsy 10.00 25.00
BR Brian Roberts Jsy 10.00 25.00
BS Ben Sheets Jsy 10.00 25.00
BU B.J. Upton Jsy 10.00 25.00
CC Carl Crawford Jsy 10.00 25.00
CZ Carlos Zambrano Jsy 10.00 25.00
DH Danny Haren Jsy 6.00 15.00
DW David Wright Jsy 30.00 60.00
FR Francisco Rodriguez Jsy 10.00 25.00
GF Gavin Floyd Jsy 6.00 15.00
JB Joe Blanton Jsy 6.00 15.00
JE Johnny Estrada Jsy 6.00 15.00
JF Jeff Francis Jsy 6.00 15.00
JM Joe Mauer Jsy 30.00 60.00
JP Jake Peavy Jsy 10.00 25.00
JR Jeremy Reed Jsy 6.00 15.00
JW Jake Westbrook Jsy 6.00 15.00
KG Khalil Greene Jsy 15.00 40.00
MA Matt Cain Jsy 75.00 150.00
MG Marcus Giles Jsy 10.00 25.00
MT Mark Teixeira Jsy 10.00 25.00
MY Michael Young Jsy 10.00 25.00
OP Oliver Perez Jsy 6.00 15.00
RE Jose Reyes Jsy 10.00 25.00
RF Rafael Furcal Jsy 10.00 25.00
RW Rickie Weeks Jsy 10.00 25.00
SK Scott Kazmir Jsy 10.00 25.00
SP Scott Podsednik Jsy 15.00 40.00
TH Travis Hafner Jsy 10.00 25.00
TI Tadahito Iguchi Jsy
VM Victor Martinez Jsy 10.00 25.00
WP Wily Mo Pena Jsy 10.00 25.00
ZG Zack Greinke Jsy 8.00 20.00

2005 Ultimate Collection Dual Materials

OVERALL GAME-USED ODDS 1:4
STATED PRINT RUN 15 SERIAL #'d SETS
NO RC YR PRICING DUE TO SCARCITY
OVERALL PATCH ODDS 1:4
PATCH PRINT RUN 10 SERIAL #'d SETS
NO PATCH PRICING DUE TO SCARCITY
AC Andruw Jones Jsy 12.50 30.00
Chipper Jones Jsy
AE Adrian Beltre Jsy 6.00 15.00
Eric Chavez Jsy
AH Adrian Beltre Jsy 6.00 15.00
Hank Blalock Jsy
AJ A.J. Burnett Jsy 6.00 15.00
Josh Beckett Jsy
AM Albert Pujols Jsy 20.00 50.00
Miguel Cabrera Jsy
AP Bobby Abreu Jsy 6.00 15.00
Corey Patterson Jsy
AU Bobby Abreu Jsy 15.00 40.00
Chase Utley Jsy
BC Josh Beckett Jsy 10.00 25.00
Miguel Cabrera Jsy
BG Jason Bay Jsy 12.50 30.00
Vladimir Guerrero Jsy
BH Adrian Beltre Jsy 15.00 40.00
Felix Hernandez Jsy
BJ Ben Sheets Jsy 6.00 15.00
Jake Peavy Jsy
BK Bobby Crosby Jsy 10.00 25.00
Khalil Greene Jsy
BM Jeremy Bonderman Jsy 30.00 60.00
Matt Cain Jsy
BS Ryne Sandberg Jsy 20.00 50.00
Wade Boggs Jsy
BT Hank Blalock Jsy 10.00 25.00
Mark Teixeira Jsy
BY Hank Blalock Jsy 6.00 15.00
Michael Young Jsy
CB Bobby Crosby Jsy 6.00 15.00
Jason Bay Jsy
CC Bobby Crosby Jsy 6.00 15.00
Eric Chavez Jsy
CG Miguel Cabrera Jsy 12.50 30.00
Vladimir Guerrero Jsy
CJ Craig Biggio Jsy 12.50 30.00
Jeff Bagwell Jsy
CO Roger Clemens Jsy 15.00 40.00
Roy Oswalt Jsy
CP Carl Crawford Jsy 10.00 25.00
Scott Podsednik Jsy
CR Eric Chavez Jsy 10.00 25.00
Scott Rolen Jsy
CT Cal Ripken Jsy 50.00 100.00
Tony Gwynn Jsy
CW Eric Chavez Jsy 15.00 40.00
David Wright Jsy
DG Adam Dunn Jsy 15.00 40.00
Ken Griffey Jr. Jsy
DJ David Wright Jsy 15.00 40.00
Jose Reyes Jsy
DP Adam Dunn Jsy 6.00 15.00
Wily Mo Pena Jsy
DR Derek Jeter Jsy 30.00 60.00
Randy Johnson Jsy
FW Prince Fielder Jsy
Rickie Weeks Jsy
GC Ken Griffey Jr. Jsy 15.00 40.00
Miguel Cabrera Jsy
GF Marcus Giles Jsy 6.00 15.00
Rafael Furcal Jsy
GG Brian Giles Jsy 6.00 15.00
Marcus Giles Jsy
GH Ken Griffey Jr. Jsy 15.00 40.00
Torii Hunter Jsy
GJ Derek Jeter Jsy 30.00 60.00
Ken Griffey Jr. Jsy
GL Khalil Greene Jsy 10.00 25.00
Mark Loretta Jsy
GP Ken Griffey Jr. Jsy 15.00 40.00
Wily Mo Pena Jsy
GR Eric Gagne Jsy 6.00 15.00
Francisco Rodriguez Jsy
HC Felix Hernandez Jsy 40.00 80.00
Matt Cain Jsy
HH Danny Haren Jsy 6.00 15.00
Rich Harden Jsy
HM Travis Hafner Jsy 6.00 15.00
Victor Martinez Jsy
HO Rich Harden Jsy 6.00 15.00
Roy Oswalt Jsy
HS Ben Sheets Jsy 6.00 15.00
Rich Harden Jsy
JC Randy Johnson Jsy 20.00 50.00
Roger Clemens Jsy
JF Johan Santana Jsy 15.00 40.00
Felix Hernandez Jsy
JG Andruw Jones Jsy 15.00 40.00
Ken Griffey Jr. Jsy
JH Andruw Jones Jsy 10.00 25.00
Torii Hunter Jsy
JJ Derek Jeter Jsy 30.00 60.00
Reggie Jackson Jsy
JL Derek Jeter Jsy 30.00 60.00
Barry Larkin Jsy
JO Johan Santana Jsy 10.00 25.00
Oliver Perez Jsy
JR Derek Jeter Jsy 30.00 60.00
Jose Reyes Jsy
JV Joe Mauer Jsy 10.00 25.00
Victor Martinez Jsy
LG Brad Lidge Jsy 6.00 15.00
Eric Gagne Jsy
LO Brad Lidge Jsy 6.00 15.00
Roy Oswalt Jsy
LR Brad Lidge Jsy 6.00 15.00
Francisco Rodriguez Jsy
ME Joe Mauer Jsy 10.00 25.00
Johnny Estrada Jsy
MG Greg Maddux Jsy 15.00 40.00
Mark Prior Jsy
MH Mark Mulder Jsy 6.00 15.00
Tim Hudson Jsy
MJ Pedro Martinez Jsy 12.50 30.00
Randy Johnson Jsy
MM Joe Mauer Jsy 10.00 25.00
Justin Morneau Jsy
MP Joe Mauer Jsy 10.00 25.00
Mark Prior Jsy
MR Mike Mussina Jsy 12.50 30.00
Randy Johnson Jsy
NR Nolan Ryan Jsy 30.00 60.00
Randy Johnson Jsy
OF David Ortiz Jsy
Prince Fielder Jsy
PC Mark Prior Jsy 15.00 40.00
Roger Clemens Jsy
PD Dwight Gooden Jsy 10.00 25.00
Pedro Martinez Jsy
PG Albert Pujols Jsy 30.00 60.00
Ken Griffey Jr. Jsy
PH Jake Peavy Jsy 6.00 15.00
Rich Harden Jsy
PJ Albert Pujols Jsy 30.00 60.00
Derek Jeter Jsy
PL Albert Pujols Jsy 20.00 50.00
Derrek Lee Jsy
PM Mike Piazza Jsy 12.50 30.00
Pedro Martinez Jsy
PS Ben Sheets Jsy 10.00 25.00
Mark Prior Jsy
RB Aramis Ramirez Jsy 6.00 15.00
Hank Blalock Jsy
RC Nolan Ryan Jsy 30.00 60.00
Roger Clemens Jsy
RE Aramis Ramirez Jsy 6.00 15.00
Eric Chavez Jsy
RF Jose Reyes Jsy 6.00 15.00
Rafael Furcal Jsy
RG Brian Roberts Jsy 6.00 15.00
Marcus Giles Jsy
RJ Cal Ripken Jsy 60.00 120.00
Derek Jeter Jsy
RL Aramis Ramirez Jsy 10.00 25.00
Derrek Lee Jsy
RP Aaron Rowand Jsy 10.00 25.00
Scott Podsednik Jsy
RR Aaron Rowand Jsy 6.00 15.00
Jeremy Reed Jsy
RS Mike Schmidt Jsy 50.00 100.00
Cal Ripken Jsy
RT Cal Ripken Jsy 40.00 80.00
Miguel Tejada Jsy
RU Jose Reyes Jsy 6.00 15.00
B.J. Upton Jsy
RW Aramis Ramirez Jsy 15.00 40.00
David Wright Jsy
SB Mike Schmidt Jsy 20.00 50.00
Wade Boggs Jsy
SC Johan Santana Jsy 15.00 40.00
Roger Clemens Jsy
SH John Smoltz Jsy 12.50 30.00
Tim Hudson Jsy
SJ Curt Schilling Jsy 12.50 30.00
Randy Johnson Jsy
SM Joe Mauer Jsy 10.00 25.00
Johan Santana Jsy
SO Curt Schilling Jsy 10.00 25.00
David Ortiz Jsy
SP Johan Santana Jsy 10.00 25.00
Mark Prior Jsy
SR Mike Schmidt Jsy 20.00 50.00
Scott Rolen Jsy
TC Mark Teixeira Jsy 10.00 25.00
Miguel Cabrera Jsy
UJ B.J. Upton Jsy 30.00 60.00
Derek Jeter Jsy
WR David Wright Jsy 15.00 40.00
Scott Rolen Jsy
ZH Carlos Zambrano Jsy 6.00 15.00
Rich Harden Jsy
ZO Carlos Zambrano Jsy 6.00 15.00
Roy Oswalt Jsy
ZP Carlos Zambrano Jsy 6.00 15.00
Oliver Perez Jsy

2005 Ultimate Collection Dual Signatures

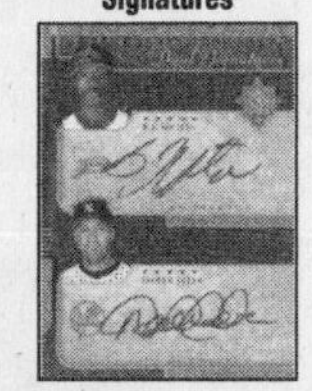

OVERALL AUTO ODDS 1:4
STATED PRINT RUN 25 SERIAL #'d SETS
NO RC YR PRICING DUE TO SCARCITY
EXCHANGE DEADLINE 01/10/09
BB Craig Biggio 60.00 120.00
Jeff Bagwell
BC Adrian Beltre 15.00 40.00
Eric Chavez
BH Adrian Beltre 75.00 150.00
Felix Hernandez
BJ Bobby Crosby 15.00 40.00
Jason Bay
BT Hank Blalock 30.00 60.00
Mark Teixeira
BV Jeremy Bonderman
Justin Verlander
BY Hank Blalock 15.00 40.00
Michael Young
CC Bobby Crosby 15.00 40.00
Eric Chavez
CG Bobby Crosby 30.00 60.00
Khalil Greene
CP Carl Crawford 30.00 60.00
Scott Podsednik
CY Carl Crawford 30.00 60.00
Delmon Young
DD J.D. Drew
Stephen Drew
DG Adam Dunn 60.00 120.00
Ken Griffey Jr.
DJ Derek Jeter 100.00 175.00
Jose Reyes
DK Derek Jeter 150.00 250.00
Ken Griffey Jr.
DM David Wright 60.00 120.00
Mike Schmidt
DP Andre Dawson 15.00 40.00
Corey Patterson
FF Gavin Floyd 10.00 25.00
Jeff Francis
FW Prince Fielder
Rickie Weeks
GC Ken Griffey Jr. 75.00 150.00
Miguel Cabrera
GH Ken Griffey Jr. 60.00 120.00
Torii Hunter
GJ Andruw Jones 75.00 150.00
Ken Griffey Jr.
GL Khalil Greene 30.00 60.00
Mark Loretta
GP Ken Griffey Jr. 60.00 120.00
Wily Mo Pena
GR Eric Gagne 30.00 60.00
Francisco Rodriguez
HH Danny Haren 15.00 40.00
Rich Harden
HM Travis Hafner 15.00 40.00
Victor Martinez
HO Rich Harden 15.00 40.00
Roy Oswalt
HS Ben Sheets 15.00 40.00
Rich Harden
JB Ben Sheets 15.00 40.00
Jake Peavy
JG Derek Jeter 125.00 200.00
Nomar Garciaparra
JH Andruw Jones 30.00 60.00
Torii Hunter
JJ Andruw Jones 75.00 150.00
Chipper Jones
JM Derek Jeter 200.00 300.00
Don Mattingly
JV Joe Mauer 50.00 100.00
Victor Martinez
KH Scott Kazmir 75.00 150.00
Felix Hernandez
LO Brad Lidge 30.00 60.00
Roy Oswalt
LR Brad Lidge 30.00 60.00
Francisco Rodriguez
MC Don Mattingly 50.00 100.00
Will Clark
MG Greg Maddux 125.00 200.00
Tom Glavine
MH Justin Morneau 15.00 40.00
Travis Hafner
MM Joe Mauer 50.00 100.00

Justin Morneau
MP Joe Mauer 50.00 100.00
Mark Prior
MT Mark Mulder 30.00 60.00
Tim Hudson
NH Jeff Niemann
Philip Humber
NK Jeff Niemann
Scott Kazmir
NV Jeff Niemann
Justin Verlander
PH Jake Peavy 15.00 40.00
Rich Harden
PJ Albert Pujols 500.00 700.00
Derek Jeter
PP Gaylord Perry 15.00 40.00
Jake Peavy
RB Aramis Ramirez 15.00 40.00
Hank Blalock
RC Nolan Ryan 150.00 250.00
Roger Clemens
RE Aramis Ramirez 15.00 40.00
Eric Chavez
RF Jose Reyes 15.00 40.00
Rafael Furcal
RJ Cal Ripken 250.00 400.00
Derek Jeter
RL Aramis Ramirez 30.00 60.00
Derrek Lee
RP Aaron Rowand 15.00 40.00
Corey Patterson
RP Aaron Rowand 30.00 60.00
Scott Podsednik
RR Aaron Rowand 15.00 40.00
Jeremy Reed
RW Ryne Sandberg 60.00 120.00
Wade Boggs
RW Aramis Ramirez 50.00 100.00
David Wright
SH John Smoltz 40.00 80.00
Tim Hudson
SP Ben Sheets 15.00 40.00
Mark Prior
SW Ben Sheets 15.00 40.00
Rickie Weeks
TC Mark Teixeira 40.00 80.00
Miguel Cabrera
UJ B.J. Upton 100.00 175.00
Derek Jeter
UW B.J. Upton 15.00 40.00
Rickie Weeks
WR David Wright 60.00 120.00
Jose Reyes
YU Delmon Young 30.00 60.00
B.J. Upton
YW Delmon Young 30.00 60.00
Rickie Weeks
ZH Carlos Zambrano 15.00 40.00
Rich Harden
ZO Carlos Zambrano 15.00 40.00
Roy Oswalt

2006 Ultimate Collection

This 274-card set was released in December, 2006. The base cards in this set were issued to a stated print run of 799 serial numbered sets while the signed Rookie Card subset (101-175) were issued to stated print runs between 150-180 serial numbered cards. The overall odds of recieving an autograph card from these packs were stated as one in two. Some players did not return their autographs in time for a pack out and those cards could be redeemed until December 20, 2009. No cards numbered 176-190 were issued as part of this product. Although a few retired greats were scattered throughout the set, there was also a subset which consisted of cards 191-219.

COMMON CARD (1-274) 1.00 2.50
VETERAN PRINT RUN 799 SER.#'d SETS
COMMON RC (1-274) 1.00 2.50
RC PRINT RUN 799 SERIAL #'d SETS
COMMON AU RC (101-175) 4.00 10.00
AU RC MINORS 4.00 10.00
OVERALL AU ODDS 1:2
AU RC PRINT RUNS B/WN 150-180
EXCHANGE DEADLINE 12/20/09
PLATE ODDS APPX. 7:10 BONUS PACKS
PLATE PRINT RUN 1 SET PER COLOR
BLACK-CYAN-MAGENTA-YELLOW ISSUED
NO PLATE PRICING DUE TO SCARCITY
1 Babe Ruth 6.00 15.00
2 Chad Tracy 1.00 2.50
3 Brandon Webb 1.50 4.00
4 Andruw Jones 1.00 2.50
5 Chipper Jones 2.50 6.00
6 John Smoltz 2.50 6.00
7 Eddie Mathews 2.50 6.00
8 Miguel Tejada 1.50 4.00
9 Brian Roberts 1.00 2.50
10 Mickey Cochrane 1.00 2.50
11 Curt Schilling 1.50 4.00
12 David Ortiz 1.50 4.00
13 Manny Ramirez 2.50 6.00
14 Johnny Bench 2.50 6.00
15 Cy Young 2.50 6.00
16 Greg Maddux 4.00 10.00
17 Derrek Lee 1.00 2.50
18 Yogi Berra 2.50 6.00
19 Walter Johnson 2.50 6.00
20 Jim Thome 1.50 4.00
21 Paul Konerko 1.50 4.00
22 Lou Gehrig 5.00 12.00
23 Jose Contreras 1.00 2.50
24 Ken Griffey Jr. 4.00 10.00
25 Adam Dunn 1.50 4.00
26 Reggie Jackson 1.50 4.00
27 Travis Hafner 1.00 2.50
28 Victor Martinez 1.50 4.00
29 Grady Sizemore 1.50 4.00
30 Casey Stengel 1.00 2.50
31 Todd Helton 1.50 4.00
32 Nolan Ryan 6.00 15.00
33 Clint Barmes 1.00 2.50
34 Ivan Rodriguez 1.50 4.00
35 Chris Shelton 1.00 2.50
36 Ty Cobb 4.00 10.00
37 Miguel Cabrera 2.50 6.00
38 Dontrelle Willis 1.00 2.50
39 Lance Berkman 1.50 4.00
40 Tom Seaver 1.50 4.00
41 Roy Oswalt 1.50 4.00
42 Christy Mathewson 2.50 6.00
43 Luis Aparicio 1.00 2.50
44 Vladimir Guerrero 2.50 6.00
45 Bartolo Colon 1.00 2.50
46 Roy Campanella 2.50 6.00
47 George Sisler 1.00 2.50
48 Jeff Kent 1.00 2.50
49 J.D. Drew 1.00 2.50
50 Carlos Lee 1.00 2.50
51 Willie Stargell 1.50 4.00
52 Rickie Weeks 1.50 4.00
53 Johan Santana 2.50 6.00
54 Torii Hunter 1.00 2.50
55 Joe Mauer 2.50 6.00
56 Pedro Martinez 1.50 4.00
57 David Wright 4.00 10.00
58 Carlos Beltran 1.00 2.50
59 Jimmie Foxx 2.50 6.00
60 Jose Reyes 1.50 4.00
61 Derek Jeter 6.00 15.00
62 Alex Rodriguez 4.00 10.00
63 Randy Johnson 2.50 6.00
64 Hideki Matsui 2.50 6.00
65 Thurman Munson 2.50 6.00
66 Rich Harden 1.00 2.50
67 Eric Chavez 1.00 2.50
68 Don Drysdale 1.50 4.00
69 Bobby Crosby 1.00 2.50
70 Pee Wee Reese 1.50 4.00
71 Ryan Howard 4.00 10.00
72 Chase Utley 2.50 6.00
73 Jackie Robinson 2.50 6.00
74 Jason Bay 1.00 2.50
75 Honus Wagner 2.50 6.00
76 Lefty Grove 1.00 2.50
77 Jake Peavy 1.00 2.50
78 Brian Giles 1.00 2.50
79 Eddie Murray 2.50 6.00
80 Omar Vizquel 1.50 4.00
81 Jason Schmidt 1.00 2.50
82 Ichiro Suzuki 4.00 10.00
83 Felix Hernandez 2.50 6.00
84 Kenji Johjima RC 2.50 6.00
85 Albert Pujols 6.00 15.00
86 Chris Carpenter 2.50 6.00
87 Brooks Robinson 1.50 4.00
88 Dizzy Dean 1.50 4.00
89 Carl Crawford 1.50 4.00
90 Rogers Hornsby 1.50 4.00
91 Scott Kazmir 1.50 4.00
92 Mark Teixeira 2.50 6.00
93 Michael Young 1.50 4.00
94 Johnny Mize 1.00 2.50
95 Vernon Wells 1.00 2.50
96 Roy Halladay 2.50 6.00
97 Mel Ott 1.00 2.50
98 Alfonso Soriano 1.50 4.00
99 Joe Morgan 1.00 2.50
100 Satchel Paige 2.50 6.00
101 Adam Wainwright AU/180 (RC) 20.00 50.00
102 Anderson Hernandez AU/180 (RC) 4.00 10.00
103 Andre Ethier AU/180 (RC) 20.00 50.00
104 Ben Johnson AU/180 (RC) 4.00 10.00
105 Boof Bonser AU/180 (RC) 6.00 15.00
106 Boone Logan AU/180 RC 4.00 10.00
107 Brian Anderson AU/180 (RC) 4.00 10.00
108 Brian Bannister AU/180 (RC) 20.00 50.00
109 Chris Demaria AU/180 RC 4.00 10.00
110 Chris Denorfia AU/180 (RC) 4.00 10.00
111 Cody Ross AU/180 (RC) 20.00 50.00
112 Cole Hamels AU/180 (RC) 20.00 50.00
113 Conor Jackson AU/180 (RC) 6.00 15.00
114 Dan Uggla AU/180 (RC) 12.50 30.00
115 Dave Gassner AU/180 (RC) 4.00 10.00
116 Eric Reed AU/180 (RC) 4.00 10.00
117 Fausto Carmona AU/180 (RC) 20.00 50.00
118 Fernando Nieve AU/180 (RC) 4.00 10.00
119 Francisco Liriano AU/180 (RC) 12.50 30.00
120 Freddie Bynum AU/180 (RC) 4.00 10.00
121 Hanley Ramirez AU/180 (RC) 15.00 40.00
123 Ian Kinsler AU/180 (RC) 30.00 60.00
124 Jason Hammel AU/180 (RC) 4.00 10.00
125 Jason Kubel AU/180 (RC) 4.00 10.00
126 Jeff Harris AU/180 RC 4.00 10.00
127 Jered Weaver AU/150 (RC) 10.00 25.00
128 Jeremy Accardo AU/180 (RC) 4.00 10.00
129 Jeremy Hermida AU/180 (RC) 6.00 15.00
130 Joel Zumaya AU/180 (RC) 15.00 40.00
131 Joey Devine AU/180 RC 4.00 10.00
132 John Koronka AU/180 (RC) 4.00 10.00
133 John Van Benschoten AU/180 (RC) 4.00 10.00
134 Jonathan Papelbon AU/180 (RC) 20.00 50.00
135 Jose Capellan AU/180 (RC) 4.00 10.00
136 Josh Johnson AU/180 (RC) 12.50 30.00
137 Josh Rupe AU/180 (RC) 4.00 10.00
138 Josh Willingham AU/180 (RC) 4.00 10.00
139 Josh Wilson AU/180 (RC) 4.00 10.00
140 Justin Verlander AU/180 (RC) 30.00 60.00
141 Kelly Shoppach AU/180 (RC) 4.00 10.00
142 Kendry Morales AU/180 (RC) 6.00 15.00
143 Macay McBride AU/180 (RC) 4.00 10.00
144 Martin Prado AU/180 (RC) 4.00 10.00
145 Matt Cain AU/180 (RC) 10.00 25.00
146 Mike Jacobs AU/180 (RC) 4.00 10.00
147 Mike Thompson AU/180 RC 4.00 10.00
148 Nate McLouth AU/180 (RC) 8.00 20.00
149 Paul Maholm AU/180 (RC) 4.00 10.00
150 Prince Fielder AU/180 (RC) 30.00 60.00
151 Reggie Abercrombie AU/180 (RC) 4.00 10.00
152 Rich Hill AU/180 (RC) 15.00 40.00
153 Ron Flores AU/180 RC 4.00 10.00
154 Ruddy Lugo AU/180 (RC) 4.00 10.00
155 Ryan Zimmerman AU/180 (RC) 30.00 60.00
156 Sean Marshall AU/180 (RC) 10.00 25.00
157 Takashi Saito AU/180 RC 10.00 25.00
158 Taylor Buchholz AU/180 (RC) 4.00 10.00
159 Tony Pena Jr. AU/180 (RC) 4.00 10.00
160 Wil Nieves AU/180 (RC) 4.00 10.00
161 Jamie Shields AU/180 RC 20.00 50.00
162 Jon Lester AU/180 RC 20.00 50.00
163 Craig Hansen AU/180 RC 15.00 40.00
164 Aaron Rakers AU/180 (RC) 4.00 10.00
166 Bobby Livingston AU/180 (RC) 4.00 10.00
167 Brendan Harris AU/180 (RC) 4.00 10.00
169 Carlos Ruiz AU/180 (RC) 8.00 20.00
170 Chris Britton AU/180 RC 4.00 10.00
171 Howie Kendrick AU/180 (RC) 15.00 40.00
172 Jermaine Van Buren AU/180 (RC) 4.00 10.00
173 Kevin Frandsen AU/180 (RC) 6.00 15.00
174 Matt Capps AU/180 (RC) 4.00 10.00
175 Peter Moylan AU/180 RC 4.00 10.00
191 Richie Ashburn 1.50 4.00
192 Lou Brock 1.50 4.00
193 Lou Boudreau 1.00 2.50
194 Orlando Cepeda 1.00 2.50
195 Bobby Doerr 1.00 2.50
196 Dennis Eckersley 1.00 2.50
197 Bob Feller 1.00 2.50
198 Rollie Fingers 1.00 2.50
199 Carlton Fisk 1.50 4.00
200 Bob Gibson 1.50 4.00
201 Catfish Hunter 1.00 2.50
202 Fergie Jenkins 1.00 2.50
203 Al Kaline 2.50 6.00
204 Harmon Killebrew 2.50 6.00
205 Ralph Kiner 1.50 4.00
206 Buck Leonard 1.00 2.50
207 Juan Marichal 1.00 2.50
208 Bill Mazeroski 1.50 4.00
209 Willie McCovey 1.50 4.00
210 Jim Palmer 1.00 2.50
211 Tony Perez 1.00 2.50
212 Gaylord Perry 1.00 2.50
213 Phil Rizzuto 1.50 4.00
214 Robin Roberts 1.00 2.50
215 Mike Schmidt 4.00 10.00
216 Enos Slaughter 1.00 2.50
217 Ozzie Smith 4.00 10.00
218 Billy Williams 1.00 2.50
219 Robin Yount 2.50 6.00
220 Carlos Quentin (RC) 1.50 4.00
221 Jeff Francoeur 2.50 6.00
222 Brian McCann 1.00 2.50
223 Nick Markakis (RC) 2.50 6.00
224 Josh Beckett 1.50 4.00
225 Jason Varitek 2.50 6.00
226 Mark Prior 1.50 4.00
227 Aramis Ramirez 1.00 2.50
228 Jermaine Dye 1.00 2.50
229 Tadahito Iguchi 1.00 2.50
230 Bobby Jenks 1.00 2.50
231 C.C. Sabathia 1.50 4.00
232 Jeff Francis 1.00 2.50
233 Matt Holliday 2.50 6.00
234 Magglio Ordonez 1.50 4.00
235 Kenny Rogers 1.00 2.50
236 Roger Clemens 3.00 8.00
237 Andy Pettitte 1.50 4.00
238 Craig Biggio 1.50 4.00
239 Chone Figgins 1.00 2.50
240 John Lackey 1.00 2.50
241 Nomar Garciaparra 2.50 6.00
242 Prince Fielder 4.00 10.00
243 Ben Sheets 1.00 2.50
244 Bill Hall 1.00 2.50
245 Justin Morneau 2.50 6.00
246 Joe Nathan 1.00 2.50
247 Carlos Delgado 1.00 2.50
248 Shawn Green 1.00 2.50
249 Billy Wagner 1.00 2.50
250 Jason Giambi 1.00 2.50
251 Mike Mussina 1.50 4.00
252 Mariano Rivera 2.50 6.00
253 Robinson Cano 2.50 6.00
254 Bobby Abreu 1.00 2.50
255 Huston Street 1.00 2.50
256 Frank Thomas 2.50 6.00
257 Danny Haren 1.00 2.50
258 Jason Kendall 1.00 2.50
259 Nick Swisher 2.50 6.00
260 Pat Burrell 1.00 2.50
261 Tom Gordon 1.00 2.50
262 Freddy Sanchez 1.00 2.50
263 Trevor Hoffman 1.50 4.00
264 Khalil Greene 1.00 2.50
265 Adrian Gonzalez 1.50 4.00
266 Moises Alou 1.00 2.50
267 Matt Morris 1.00 2.50
268 Pedro Feliz 1.00 2.50
269 Richie Sexson 1.00 2.50
270 Hoyt Wilhelm 1.00 2.50
271 Adrian Beltre 1.00 2.50
272 Jim Edmonds 1.50 4.00
273 Scott Rolen 1.50 4.00
274 Jason Isringhausen 1.00 2.50
275 Jorge Cantu 1.00 2.50
276 Hank Blalock 1.00 2.50
277 Kevin Millwood 1.00 2.50
278 Alex Rios 1.50 4.00
279 Troy Glaus 1.00 2.50
280 B.J. Ryan 1.00 2.50
281 Nick Johnson 1.00 2.50
282 Chad Cordero 1.00 2.50
283 Austin Kearns 1.00 2.50
284 Ricky Nolasco (RC) 1.00 2.50
285 Travis Ishikawa (RC) 1.00 2.50
286 Lastings Milledge (RC) 1.00 2.50
287 James Loney (RC) 1.50 4.00
288 Red Schoendienst 1.00 2.50
289 Warren Spahn 1.50 4.00
290 Early Wynn 1.00 2.50

2006 Ultimate Collection Ensemble Signatures Triple

OVERALL AU ODDS 1:2
STATED PRINT RUN 50 SER.#'d SETS
TRIPLE 15 PRINT RUN 15 SER.#'d SETS
NO TRI 15 PRICING DUE TO SCARCITY
TRIPLE 1 PRINT RUN 1 SER.#'d SET
NO TRI 1 PRICING DUE TO SCARCITY
EXCHANGE DEADLINE 12/20/09
AHW Josh Willingham 15.00 40.00
Reggie Abercrombie
Jeremy Hermida
BBW Taylor Buchholz 15.00 40.00
Adam Wainwright
Brian Bannister
BDD Andre Dawson 30.00 60.00
Eric Davis
George Bell
BKM Bill Mazeroski 50.00 100.00
Ralph Kiner
Jason Bay
BNO Roy Oswalt 15.00 40.00
Taylor Buchholz
Fernando Nieve
BSH Ben Sheets 20.00 50.00
Rich Harden
AJ Burnett
BUK Craig Biggio 40.00 80.00
Chase Utley
Ian Kinsler
BWC Adam Wainwright 15.00 40.00
Matt Cain
Brian Bannister
BWV Boof Bonser 20.00 50.00
Justin Verlander
Jered Weaver
CBP Sean Casey 15.00 40.00
Oliver Perez
Jason Bay
CBS Ron Cey 30.00 60.00
Don Sutton
Dusty Baker
CBZ Boof Bonser 20.00 50.00
Matt Cain
Joel Zumaya
CDV Andy Van Slyke 15.00 40.00
Eric Davis
Jack Clark
CHK Jason Kubel 20.00 50.00
Melky Cabrera
Jeremy Hermida
CHO Chris Carpenter 30.00 60.00
Roy Oswalt
Rich Harden
CKH Jason Kendall 15.00 40.00
Bobby Crosby
Rich Harden
CKS Carl Crawford 20.00 50.00
Scott Kazmir
Jamie Shields
CLH Francisco Liriano 30.00 60.00
Fausto Carmona
Cole Hamels
CMH Travis Hafner 10.00 25.00
Victor Martinez
Fausto Carmona
CNS Ron Santo 30.00 60.00
Graig Nettles
Ron Cey
CPC Carl Crawford 15.00 40.00
Coco Crisp
Scott Podsednik
CSS Roger Clemens 100.00 200.00
John Smoltz
Curt Schilling
CWW Miguel Cabrera 30.00 60.00
Josh Willingham
Dontrelle Willis
CZC Eric Chavez 20.00 50.00
Miguel Cabrera
Ryan Zimmerman
DJH Derek Jeter 150.00 250.00
Jose Reyes
Hanley Ramirez
DPA Jermaine Dye 20.00 50.00
Brian Anderson
Scott Podsednik
DPI Jermaine Dye 30.00 60.00
Scott Podsednik
Tadahito Iguchi
FGC David Cone 40.00 80.00
Dwight Gooden
Sid Fernandez
FJM Conor Jackson 30.00 60.00
Prince Fielder
Kendry Morales
FWL Carlos Lee 30.00 60.00
Rickie Weeks
Prince Fielder
GCN Goose Gossage 30.00 60.00
Graig Nettles
Chris Chambliss
GCS David Cone 15.00 40.00
Dwight Gooden
Bret Saberhagen
GJB Ken Griffey Jr. 250.00 500.00
Derek Jeter
Jason Bay
GJP Ken Griffey Jr. 600.00 800.00
Derek Jeter
Albert Pujols
GLK Francisco Liriano 20.00 50.00
Jason Kubel
Dave Gassner
GPN Eric Gagne 20.00 50.00
Joe Nathan
Jonathan Papelbon
GRS Vladimir Guerrero 30.00 60.00
Alfonso Soriano
Alex Rios
HBS Nick Swisher 20.00 50.00
Rich Harden
Joe Blanton
HKP John Kruk 20.00 50.00
Kent Hrbek
Boog Powell
HMK Mark Mulder 30.00 60.00
Scott Kazmir
Cole Hamels
HNP Trevor Hoffman 40.00 80.00
Joe Nathan
Jonathan Papelbon
HOT Travis Hafner 15.00 40.00
David Ortiz
Mark Teixeira
HWU Josh Willingham 15.00 40.00
Jeremy Hermida
Dan Uggla
IKU Tadahito Iguchi 30.00 60.00
Ian Kinsler
Dan Uggla
JCN Derek Jeter 150.00 200.00
Wil Nieves
Melky Cabrera
JGS Ken Griffey Jr. 60.00 120.00
Andruw Jones
Alfonso Soriano
JRR Derek Jeter 125.00 200.00
Jose Reyes
Hanley Ramirez
JWV Josh Johnson 50.00 100.00
Justin Verlander
Jered Weaver
KGJ Wally Joyner 50.00 100.00
Mark Grace
John Kruk
KLB Boof Bonser 20.00 50.00
Francisco Liriano
Jason Kubel
KUU Chase Utley 30.00 60.00
Ian Kinsler
Dan Uggla
KWM Jason Kendall 15.00 40.00
Victor Martinez
Josh Willingham
LGB Boof Bonser 20.00 50.00
Francisco Liriano
Dave Gassner
LHC Francisco Liriano 20.00 50.00
Fausto Carmona
Felix Hernandez
LPO Derrek Lee 150.00 250.00
David Ortiz
Albert Pujols
MCN Graig Nettles 20.00 50.00
Bill Madlock
Ron Cey
MMK Jason Kendall 40.00 80.00
Victor Martinez
Joe Mauer
MNL Joe Nathan 50.00 100.00
Joe Mauer
Francisco Liriano
MWC Mark Mulder 40.00 80.00
Chris Carpenter
Adam Wainwright
MWP Josh Willingham 15.00 40.00
Russell Martin
Ronny Paulino
NLP Joe Nathan 20.00 50.00
Brad Lidge
Jonathan Papelbon
OBL Roy Oswalt 15.00 40.00
Brad Lidge
Taylor Buchholz
PCL Oliver Perez 30.00 60.00
Francisco Liriano
Fausto Carmona
PHL Oliver Perez 40.00 80.00
Francisco Liriano
Cole Hamels
PSO Ben Sheets 20.00 50.00
Roy Oswalt
Jake Peavy
PVW Justin Verlander 75.00 150.00
Jonathan Papelbon
Jered Weaver
RHW Cody Ross 15.00 40.00
Josh Willingham
Jeremy Hermida
RMM Ivan Rodriguez 60.00 120.00
Victor Martinez
Joe Mauer
RRB Jose Reyes 30.00 60.00
Hanley Ramirez
Yuniesky Betancourt
SGM Greg Maddux 125.00 200.00
Tom Glavine
John Smoltz
SJF Prince Fielder 20.00 50.00
Chris Shelton
Mike Jacobs
SKM Hong-Chih Kuo 100.00 200.00
Russell Martin
Takashi Saito
SWB Taylor Buchholz 30.00 60.00
Jered Weaver
Jamie Shields
TGB Ken Griffey Jr. 150.00 250.00
Jeff Bagwell
Frank Thomas
TKY Michael Young 40.00 80.00
Mark Teixeira
Ian Kinsler
UHC Miguel Cabrera 30.00 60.00
Jeremy Hermida
Dan Uggla
URC Miguel Cabrera 20.00 50.00
Hanley Ramirez
Dan Uggla
URW Josh Willingham 20.00 50.00
Hanley Ramirez
Dan Uggla
VBZ Jeremy Bonderman 30.00 60.00
Justin Verlander
Joel Zumaya
VWL Francisco Liriano 30.00 60.00
Justin Verlander
Jered Weaver
WJC Josh Johnson 100.00 175.00
Matt Cain
Jered Weaver
WJO Josh Johnson 30.00 60.00
Dontrelle Willis
Scott Olsen
WSV Justin Verlander 75.00 150.00
Jered Weaver
Jamie Shields
ZBC Boof Bonser 15.00 40.00
Matt Cain
Joel Zumaya
ZHZ Carlos Zambrano 30.00 60.00
Felix Hernandez
Joel Zumaya

2006 Ultimate Collection Game Materials

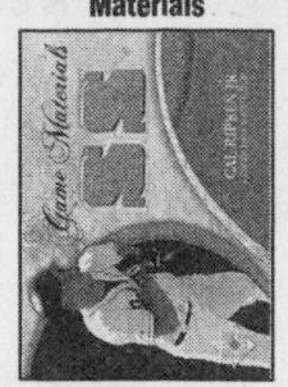

OVERALL GAME-USED ODDS 1:2
STATED PRINT RUN 50 SERIAL #'d SETS
PLATE ODDS APPX. 7:10 BONUS PACKS
PLATE PRINT RUN 1 SET PER COLOR
BLACK-CYAN-MAGENTA-YELLOW ISSUED
NO PLATE PRICING DUE TO SCARCITY
AB A.J. Burnett Jsy 4.00 10.00
AD Adam Dunn Jsy 4.00 10.00
AJ Andruw Jones Jsy 5.00 12.00
AP Albert Pujols Jsy 12.50 30.00
AR Alex Rios Jsy 4.00 10.00
AS Alfonso Soriano Jsy 4.00 10.00
BA Brian Bannister Jsy 4.00 10.00
BG Brian Giles Jsy 4.00 10.00
BM Bill Mazeroski Bat 5.00 12.00
BO Jeremy Bonderman Jsy 4.00 10.00
BR Brian Roberts Jsy 4.00 10.00
CA Melky Cabrera Jsy 6.00 15.00
CC Carl Crawford Jsy 4.00 10.00
CH Chris Carpenter Jsy 4.00 10.00
CJ Conor Jackson Jsy 5.00 12.00
CL Carlos Lee Jsy 4.00 10.00
CR Coco Crisp Jsy 4.00 10.00
CS Chris Shelton Jsy 4.00 10.00
CU Chase Utley Jsy 6.00 15.00
CZ Carlos Zambrano Jsy 4.00 10.00
DJ Derek Jeter Jsy 12.50 30.00
DJ2 Derek Jeter Jsy 12.50 30.00
DL Derrek Lee Jsy 4.00 10.00
DU Dan Uggla Jsy 6.00 15.00
DW Dontrelle Willis Jsy 4.00 10.00
FH Felix Hernandez Jsy 5.00 12.00
FL Francisco Liriano Jsy 4.00 10.00
GA Garrett Atkins Jsy 4.00 10.00
GP Gaylord Perry Jsy 5.00 12.00
HA Cole Hamels Jsy 6.00 15.00
HB Hank Blalock Jsy 4.00 10.00
HC Craig Hansen Jsy 6.00 15.00
HO Trevor Hoffman Jsy 4.00 10.00
HR Hanley Ramirez Jsy 6.00 15.00
HT Tim Hudson Jsy 4.00 10.00
HU Torii Hunter Jsy 4.00 10.00
HY Roy Halladay Jsy 4.00 10.00
IK Ian Kinsler Jsy 5.00 12.00
IR Ivan Rodriguez Jsy 5.00 12.00
JB Jason Bay Jsy 4.00 10.00
JD Jermaine Dye Jsy 4.00 10.00
JH Jeremy Hermida Jsy 4.00 10.00
JJ Josh Johnson Jsy 5.00 12.00
JK Jason Kendall Jsy 4.00 10.00
JM Joe Mauer Jsy 5.00 12.00
JN Joe Nathan Jsy 4.00 10.00
JP Jake Peavy Jsy 4.00 10.00
JR Jose Reyes Jsy 4.00 10.00
JS Johan Santana Jsy 5.00 12.00
JV Justin Verlander Jsy 6.00 15.00
JW Jered Weaver Jsy 6.00 15.00
JZ Joel Zumaya Jsy 6.00 15.00
KG Ken Griffey Jr. Jsy 10.00 25.00
KG2 Ken Griffey Jr. Jsy 10.00 25.00
KH Khalil Greene Jsy 5.00 12.00
KJ Kenji Johjima Jsy 8.00 20.00
KM Kendry Morales Jsy 5.00 12.00
KU Jason Kubel Jsy 4.00 10.00
KY Kevin Youkilis Jsy 4.00 10.00
LA Luis Aparicio Jsy 5.00 12.00
LM Lastings Milledge Jsy 5.00 12.00
LY Fred Lynn Jsy 5.00 12.00
MA Matt Cain Jsy 5.00 12.00
MC Miguel Cabrera Jsy 5.00 12.00
MG Marcus Giles Jsy 4.00 10.00
MH Matt Holliday Jsy 8.00 20.00
ML Mark Loretta Jsy 4.00 10.00
MM Melvin Mora Jsy 4.00 10.00
MO Justin Morneau Jsy 5.00 12.00
MS Mike Schmidt Jsy 8.00 20.00
MT Mark Teixeira Jsy 5.00 12.00
MU Mark Mulder Jsy 4.00 10.00
MY Michael Young Jsy 4.00 10.00
NS Nick Swisher Jsy 4.00 10.00
PA Jonathan Papelbon Jsy 8.00 20.00
PF Prince Fielder Jsy 6.00 15.00
PM Paul Molitor Jsy 5.00 12.00
RC Cal Ripken Jsy 20.00 50.00
RH Rich Harden Jsy 4.00 10.00
RI Jim Rice Jsy 5.00 12.00
RO Roy Oswalt Jsy 4.00 10.00
RW Rickie Weeks Jsy 4.00 10.00
RZ Ryan Zimmerman Jsy 8.00 20.00
SK Scott Kazmir Jsy 5.00 12.00
SP Scott Podsednik Jsy 4.00 10.00
TE Miguel Tejada Jsy 4.00 10.00
TG Tony Gwynn Jsy 6.00 15.00
TH Travis Hafner Jsy 4.00 10.00
TI Tadahito Iguchi Jsy 4.00 10.00
TP Tony Perez Jsy 5.00 12.00
VM Victor Martinez Jsy 4.00 10.00
WC Will Clark Pants 5.00 12.00
WI Josh Willingham Jsy 4.00 10.00
YB Yuniesky Betancourt Jsy 4.00 10.00

2006 Ultimate Collection Game Materials Signatures

STATED PRINT RUN 35 SERIAL #'d SETS
EXCHANGE DEADLINE 12/20/09
AB A.J. Burnett Jsy 10.00 25.00
AD Adam Dunn Jsy 10.00 25.00
AJ Andruw Jones Jsy 20.00 50.00
AP Albert Pujols Jsy
AR Alex Rios Jsy 10.00 25.00
AS Alfonso Soriano Jsy 30.00 60.00
BA Brian Bannister Jsy 10.00 25.00
BG Brian Giles Jsy 10.00 25.00
BM Bill Mazeroski Jsy 20.00 50.00
BO Jeremy Bonderman Jsy 15.00 40.00
BR Brian Roberts Jsy 10.00 25.00
CA Melky Cabrera Jsy 15.00 40.00
CC Carl Crawford Jsy 10.00 25.00
CH Chris Carpenter Jsy 10.00 25.00
CJ Conor Jackson Jsy 15.00 40.00
CL Carlos Lee Jsy 10.00 25.00
CR Coco Crisp Jsy 12.50 30.00
CS Chris Shelton Jsy 10.00 25.00
CU Chase Utley Jsy 30.00 60.00
CZ Carlos Zambrano Jsy 15.00 40.00
DJ Derek Jeter Jsy 200.00 300.00
DJ2 Derek Jeter Jsy 200.00 300.00
DL Derrek Lee Jsy 12.50 30.00
DU Dan Uggla Jsy 10.00 25.00
DW Dontrelle Willis Jsy 12.50 30.00
FH Felix Hernandez Jsy 15.00 40.00
FL Francisco Liriano Jsy 30.00 60.00
GA Garrett Atkins Jsy 10.00 25.00
GP Gaylord Perry Pants 10.00 25.00
HA Cole Hamels Jsy 30.00 60.00
HB Hank Blalock Jsy 10.00 25.00
HC Craig Hansen Jsy 15.00 40.00
HO Trevor Hoffman Jsy 15.00 40.00
HR Hanley Ramirez Jsy 30.00 60.00
HT Tim Hudson Jsy 10.00 25.00
HU Torii Hunter Jsy 10.00 25.00
HY Roy Halladay Jsy 30.00 60.00
IK Ian Kinsler Jsy 15.00 40.00
IR Ivan Rodriguez Jsy 15.00 40.00
JB Jason Bay Jsy 10.00 25.00
JD Jermaine Dye Jsy 10.00 25.00
JH Jeremy Hermida Jsy 10.00 25.00
JJ Josh Johnson Jsy 40.00 80.00
JK Jason Kendall Jsy 10.00 25.00
JM Joe Mauer Jsy 30.00 60.00
JN Joe Nathan Jsy 10.00 25.00
JP Jake Peavy Jsy 10.00 25.00
JR Jose Reyes Jsy 15.00 40.00
JS Johan Santana Jsy 15.00 40.00
JV Justin Verlander Jsy 40.00 80.00
JW Jered Weaver Jsy 15.00 40.00
JZ Joel Zumaya Jsy 30.00 60.00
KG Ken Griffey Jr. Jsy 60.00 120.00
KG2 Ken Griffey Jr. Jsy 60.00 120.00
KH Khalil Greene Jsy 12.50 30.00
KM Kendry Morales Jsy 15.00 40.00
KU Jason Kubel Jsy 10.00 25.00
KY Kevin Youkilis Jsy 10.00 25.00
LA Luis Aparicio Jsy 10.00 25.00
LY Fred Lynn Jsy 10.00 25.00
MA Matt Cain Jsy 15.00 40.00
MC Miguel Cabrera Jsy 30.00 60.00
MG Marcus Giles Jsy 10.00 25.00
MH Matt Holliday Jsy 15.00 40.00
ML Mark Loretta Jsy 10.00 25.00
MM Melvin Mora Jsy 10.00 25.00
MO Justin Morneau Jsy 15.00 40.00
MS Mike Schmidt Jsy 30.00 60.00
MU Mark Mulder Jsy 10.00 25.00
MY Michael Young Jsy 10.00 25.00
NS Nick Swisher Jsy 10.00 25.00
PA Jonathan Papelbon Jsy 30.00 60.00
PM Paul Molitor Jsy 12.50 30.00
RC Cal Ripken Jsy 50.00 100.00
RH Rich Harden Jsy 12.50 30.00
RI Jim Rice Jsy 12.50 30.00
RO Roy Oswalt Jsy 10.00 25.00
RW Rickie Weeks Jsy 10.00 25.00
RZ Ryan Zimmerman Jsy 40.00 80.00
SK Scott Kazmir Jsy 15.00 40.00
SP Scott Podsednik Jsy 10.00 25.00
TE Miguel Tejada Jsy 10.00 25.00
TG Tony Gwynn Jsy 30.00 60.00
TH Travis Hafner Jsy 10.00 25.00
TI Tadahito Iguchi Jsy 15.00 40.00
TP Tony Perez Jsy 10.00 25.00
VM Victor Martinez Jsy 10.00 25.00
WC Will Clark Pants 30.00 60.00
WI Josh Willingham Jsy 10.00 25.00
YB Yuniesky Betancourt Jsy 10.00 25.00

2006 Ultimate Collection Game Patches

*PATCH p/r 40-50: .6X TO 1.5X BASIC
*PATCH p/r 27-31: .6X TO 1.5X BASIC
OVERALL GAME-USED ODDS 1:2
PATCH PRINT RUN B/WN 3-50 PER
NO PRICING ON QTY 25 OR LESS
OVERALL AU-GU ODDS 1:4
PATCH SIG PRINT RUN 10 SER.#'d SETS
NO PATCH SIG PRICING
EXCHANGE DEADLINE 12/20/09
PLATE ODDS APPX. 7:10 BONUS PACKS
PLATE PRINT RUN 1 SET PER COLOR
BLACK-CYAN-MAGENTA-YELLOW ISSUED
NO PLATE PRICING DUE TO SCARCITY
AP Albert Pujols 30.00 60.00
AS Alfonso Soriano 12.50 30.00
BO Jeremy Bonderman 10.00 25.00
CU Chase Utley 15.00 40.00
JM Joe Mauer 15.00 40.00
JR Jose Reyes 12.50 30.00
JV Justin Verlander 20.00 50.00
KG Ken Griffey Jr. 20.00 50.00
KG2 Ken Griffey Jr. 20.00 50.00
KJ Kenji Johjima 20.00 50.00

MA Matt Cain 10.00 25.00
MC Miguel Cabrera 12.50 30.00
MO Justin Morneau 10.00 25.00
RZ Ryan Zimmerman 20.00 50.00
TI Tadahito Iguchi 10.00 25.00

2006 Ultimate Collection Ken Griffey Jr. 1989 Autograph Buyback

RANDOM INSERT IN BONUS PACKS
STATED PRINT RUN 15 CARDS
CARD IS NOT SERIAL-NUMBERED
PRINT RUN PROVIDED BY UPPER DECK
NO PRICING DUE TO SCARCITY
1 Ken Griffey Jr./15 *

2006 Ultimate Collection Legendary Materials

ODDS APPX. 3:10 BONUS PACKS
PRINT RUNS B/WN 5-55 PER
NO PRICING ON QTY 25 OR LESS
PLATE ODDS APPX. 7:10 BONUS PACKS
PLATE PRINT RUN 1 SET PER COLOR
BLACK-CYAN-MAGENTA-YELLOW ISSUED
NO PLATE PRICING DUE TO SCARCITY
AK Al Kaline Bat/15
AR Al Rosen Pants/55 6.00 15.00
BD Bill Dickey Jsy/55 12.50 30.00
BD2 Bill Dickey Jsy/55 12.50 30.00
BF Bob Feller Jsy/15
BG Bob Gibson Jsy/25
BM Bill Mazeroski Bat/25
BO Bo Jackson Bat/55 8.00 20.00
BO2 Bo Jackson Bat/55 8.00 20.00
BR Babe Ruth Pants/25
BR2 Babe Ruth Pants/25
BS Bruce Sutter Pants/25
BW Billy Williams Bat/25
CF Carlton Fisk Pants/55 4.00 10.00
CF2 Carlton Fisk Pants/55 4.00 10.00
CR Cal Ripken Pants/15
CR2 Cal Ripken Pants/15
CW Rod Carew Jsy/55 4.00 10.00
CW2 Rod Carew Jsy/55 4.00 10.00
CY Carl Yastrzemski Bat/25
CY2 Carl Yastrzemski Bat/25
DE Dennis Eckersley Jsy/25
DE2 Dennis Eckersley Jsy/25
DL Don Larsen Pants/15
DL2 Don Larsen Pants/15
DW Dave Winfield Bat/10
EB Ernie Banks Jsy/10
EM Eddie Murray Jsy/25
EM2 Eddie Murray Jsy/25
FJ Fergie Jenkins Jsy/10
FJ2 Fergie Jenkins Jsy/10
FR Frank Robinson Jsy/5
FR2 Frank Robinson Bat/25
GP Gaylord Perry Jsy/55 4.00 10.00
GP2 Gaylord Perry Jsy/55 4.00 10.00
JB Johnny Bench Jsy/55 8.00 20.00
JD Joe DiMaggio Jsy/15
JD2 Joe DiMaggio Jsy/15
JO Joe Morgan Jsy/55 4.00 10.00
JO2 Joe Morgan Jsy/55 4.00 10.00
JP Jim Palmer Jsy/25
JP2 Jim Palmer Jsy/25
JU Juan Marichal Jsy/55 4.00 10.00
KI Kirk Gibson Jsy/55 4.00 10.00
KP Kirby Puckett Jsy/55 8.00 20.00
KP2 Kirby Puckett Jsy/55 8.00 20.00
LB Lou Brock Jsy/25
LB2 Lou Brock Pants/25
MA Don Mattingly Pants/55 10.00 25.00
MA2 Don Mattingly Jsy/55 10.00 25.00
MS Mike Schmidt Jsy/25
MS2 Mike Schmidt Jsy/25
MW Maury Wills Bat/41 4.00 10.00
NR Nolan Ryan Jkt/55 15.00 40.00
NR2 Nolan Ryan Jsy/25
NR3 Nolan Ryan Jsy/25
OS Ozzie Smith Jsy/55 10.00 25.00
OS2 Ozzie Smith Jsy/55 10.00 25.00
PM Paul Molitor Bat/55 4.00 10.00
PM2 Paul Molitor Bat/55 4.00 10.00
PN Phil Niekro Jsy/55 4.00 10.00
PN2 Phil Niekro Jsy/55 4.00 10.00
PR Phil Rizzuto Pants/15
PR2 Phil Rizzuto Pants/15
RC Rocky Colavito Bat/15
RC2 Rocky Colavito Bat/15
RE Red Schoendienst Jsy/15
RF Rollie Fingers Jsy/25
RJ Reggie Jackson Bat/25
RJ2 Reggie Jackson Jsy/35 6.00 15.00
RK Ralph Kiner Bat/25
RO Brooks Robinson Pants/35 6.00 15.00
RO2 Brooks Robinson Jsy/35 6.00 15.00
RR Robin Roberts Pants/15
RS Ryne Sandberg Bat/35 10.00 25.00
RY Robin Yount Bat/25
RY2 Robin Yount Bat/25
SC Steve Carlton Bat/55 4.00 10.00
SC2 Steve Carlton Bat/47 4.00 10.00
SM Stan Musial Bat/25
SM2 Stan Musial Bat/25
SU Don Sutton Jsy/55 4.00 10.00
SU2 Don Sutton Jsy/55 4.00 10.00
TC Ty Cobb Pants/5
TG Tony Gwynn Jsy/55 10.00 25.00
TG2 Tony Gwynn Jsy/55 10.00 25.00
TL Tony Lazzeri Bat/15
TM Thurman Munson Pants/15
TP Tony Perez Pants/55 4.00 10.00
TP2 Tony Perez Jsy/55 4.00 10.00
TS Tom Seaver Pants/15
WB Wade Boggs Jsy/55 4.00 10.00
WB2 Wade Boggs Pants/55 4.00 10.00
WC Will Clark Pants/45 6.00 15.00
WC2 Will Clark Pants/45 6.00 15.00
WM Willie McCovey Pants/25
WM2 Willie McCovey Pants/25
YB Yogi Berra Pants/15
YB2 Yogi Berra Pants/15

2006 Ultimate Collection Maximum Materials

OVERALL GAME-USED ODDS 1:2
STATED PRINT RUN 25 SER.#'d SETS
NO PRICING DUE TO SCARCITY
PATCH PRINT RUN 15 SER.#'d SETS
AP Albert Pujols Jsy
AR Alex Rios Jsy
AS Alfonso Soriano Jsy
CA Melky Cabrera Jsy
CC Carl Crawford Jsy
CH Craig Hansen Jsy
CR Cal Ripken Jsy
CU Chase Utley Jsy
DJ Derek Jeter Jsy
DO David Ortiz Jsy
FL Francisco Liriano Jsy
GS Grady Sizemore Jsy
HR Hanley Ramirez Jsy
IK Ian Kinsler Jsy
JH Jeremy Hermida Jsy
JM Joe Mauer Jsy
JP Jonathan Papelbon Jsy
JV Justin Verlander Jsy
JW Jered Weaver Jsy
KG Ken Griffey Jr. Jsy
KJ Kenji Johjima Jsy
KM Kendry Morales Jsy
LM Lastings Milledge Jsy
MC Miguel Cabrera Jsy
MT Mark Teixeira Jsy
PF Prince Fielder Jsy
RC Roger Clemens Jsy
RH Ryan Howard Jsy
RZ Ryan Zimmerman Jsy
TG Tony Gwynn Jsy
TH Travis Hafner Jsy
VG Vladimir Guerrero Jsy
VM Victor Martinez Jsy
WC Will Clark Jsy
WI Josh Willingham Jsy

2006 Ultimate Collection Ultimate Numbers Materials

OVERALL GAME-USED ODDS 1:2
STATED PRINT RUN 35 SER.#'d SETS
PLATE ODDS APPX. 7:10 BONUS PACKS
PLATE PRINT RUN 1 SET PER COLOR
BLACK-CYAN-MAGENTA-YELLOW ISSUED
NO PLATE PRICING DUE TO SCARCITY
AB A.J. Burnett Jsy 5.00 12.00
AD Adam Dunn Jsy 5.00 12.00
AJ Andruw Jones Jsy 6.00 15.00
AP Albert Pujols Jsy 20.00 50.00
AR Alex Rios Jsy 5.00 12.00
AS Alfonso Soriano Jsy 5.00 12.00
BA Brian Bannister Jsy 6.00 15.00
BG Brian Giles Jsy 5.00 12.00
BM Bill Mazeroski Bat 6.00 15.00
BO Jeremy Bonderman Jsy 5.00 12.00
BR Brian Roberts Jsy 5.00 12.00
CA Melky Cabrera Jsy 8.00 20.00
CC Carl Crawford Jsy 5.00 12.00
CH Chris Carpenter Jsy 5.00 12.00
CJ Conor Jackson Jsy 6.00 15.00
CL Carlos Lee Jsy 5.00 12.00
CR Coco Crisp Jsy 5.00 12.00
CS Chris Shelton Jsy 5.00 12.00
CU Chase Utley Jsy 8.00 20.00
CZ Carlos Zambrano Jsy 5.00 12.00
DJ Derek Jeter Jsy 20.00 50.00
DJ2 Derek Jeter Jsy 20.00 50.00
DL Derrek Lee Jsy 5.00 12.00
DU Dan Uggla Jsy 8.00 20.00
DW Dontrelle Willis Jsy 5.00 12.00
FH Felix Hernandez Jsy 6.00 15.00
FL Francisco Liriano Jsy 8.00 20.00
GA Garrett Atkins Jsy 5.00 12.00
GP Gaylord Perry Pants 6.00 15.00
HA Cole Hamels Jsy 8.00 20.00
HB Hank Blalock Jsy 5.00 12.00
HC Craig Hansen Jsy 8.00 20.00
HO Trevor Hoffman Jsy 5.00 12.00
HR Hanley Ramirez Jsy 8.00 20.00
HT Tim Hudson Jsy 5.00 12.00
HU Torii Hunter Jsy 5.00 12.00
HY Roy Halladay Jsy 5.00 12.00
IK Ian Kinsler Jsy 5.00 12.00
IR Ivan Rodriguez Jsy 6.00 15.00
JB Jason Bay Jsy 5.00 12.00
JD Jermaine Dye Jsy 5.00 12.00
JH Jeremy Hermida Jsy 5.00 12.00
JJ Josh Johnson Jsy 6.00 15.00
JK Jason Kendall Jsy 5.00 12.00
JM Joe Mauer Jsy 6.00 15.00
JN Joe Nathan Jsy 5.00 12.00
JP Jake Peavy Jsy 5.00 12.00
JR Jose Reyes Jsy 5.00 12.00
JS Johan Santana Jsy 6.00 15.00
JV Justin Verlander Jsy 8.00 20.00
JW Jered Weaver Jsy 8.00 20.00
JZ Joel Zumaya Jsy 8.00 20.00
KG Ken Griffey Jr. Jsy 15.00 40.00
KG2 Ken Griffey Jr. Jsy 15.00 40.00
KH Khalil Greene Jsy 6.00 15.00
KJ Kenji Johjima Jsy 12.50 30.00
KM Kendry Morales Jsy 6.00 15.00
KU Jason Kubel Jsy 5.00 12.00
KY Kevin Youkilis Jsy 5.00 12.00
LA Luis Aparicio Jsy 6.00 15.00
LM Lastings Milledge Jsy 6.00 15.00
LY Fred Lynn Jsy 6.00 15.00
MA Matt Cain Jsy 6.00 15.00
MC Miguel Cabrera Jsy 6.00 15.00
MG Marcus Giles Jsy 5.00 12.00
MH Matt Holliday Jsy 6.00 15.00
ML Mark Loretta Jsy 5.00 12.00
MM Melvin Mora Jsy 5.00 12.00
MO Justin Morneau Jsy 6.00 15.00
MS Mike Schmidt Jsy 12.50 30.00
MT Mark Teixeira Jsy 6.00 15.00
MU Mark Mulder Jsy 5.00 12.00
MY Michael Young Jsy 5.00 12.00
NS Nick Swisher Jsy 5.00 12.00
PA Jonathan Papelbon Jsy 12.50 30.00
PF Prince Fielder Jsy 8.00 20.00
PM Paul Molitor Jsy 6.00 15.00
RC Cal Ripken Jsy 50.00 100.00
RH Rich Harden Jsy 5.00 12.00
RI Jim Rice Jsy 6.00 15.00
RO Roy Oswalt Jsy 5.00 12.00
RW Rickie Weeks Jsy 5.00 12.00
RZ Ryan Zimmerman Jsy 12.50 30.00
SK Scott Kazmir Jsy 6.00 15.00
SP Scott Podsednik Jsy 5.00 12.00
TE Miguel Tejada Jsy 5.00 12.00
TG Tony Gwynn Jsy 8.00 20.00
TH Travis Hafner Jsy 5.00 12.00
TI Tadahito Iguchi Jsy 5.00 12.00
TP Tony Perez Jsy 6.00 15.00
VM Victor Martinez Jsy 5.00 12.00
WC Will Clark Jsy 6.00 15.00
WI Josh Willingham Jsy 5.00 12.00
YB Yuniesky Betancourt Jsy 5.00 12.00

2006 Ultimate Collection Ultimate Numbers Patches

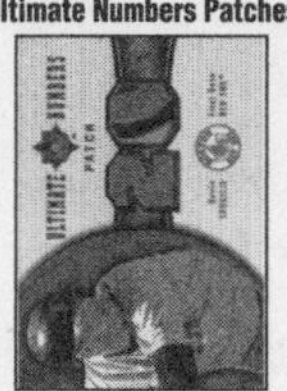

*PATCH p/r 35: .6X TO 1.5X BASIC
OVERALL GAME-USED ODDS 1:2
PATCH PRINT RUN B/WN 5-35 PER
NO PRICING ON QTY 25 OR LESS
AP Albert Pujols/35 50.00 100.00
AS Alfonso Soriano/35 10.00 25.00
BO Jeremy Bonderman/35 10.00 25.00
CU Chase Utley/35 15.00 40.00
DJ Derek Jeter/35 30.00 60.00
DJ2 Derek Jeter/35 30.00 60.00
IK Ian Kinsler/35 8.00 20.00
JV Justin Verlander/35 15.00 40.00
KG Ken Griffey Jr./35 20.00 50.00
KG2 Ken Griffey Jr./35 20.00 50.00
KJ Kenji Johjima/35 20.00 50.00
KY Kevin Youkilis/35 8.00 20.00
RC Cal Ripken/35 60.00 120.00
RZ Ryan Zimmerman/35 15.00 40.00
TI Tadahito Iguchi/35 10.00 25.00

2006 Ultimate Collection Tandem Materials

OVERALL GAME-USED ODDS 1:2
STATED PRINT RUN 25 SER.#'d SETS
NO PRICING DUE TO SCARCITY
OVERALL AU-GU ODDS 1:4
MAT.SIG. PRINT RUN 15 SER.#'d SETS
NO MAT.SIG.PRICING
SIG.PATCH PRINT RUN 5 SER.#'d SETS
NO SIG.PATCH PRICING
SIG.LOGO PRINT RUN 1 SER.#'d SET
NO SIG.LOGO PRICING
EXCHANGE DEADLINE 12/20/09

2006 Ultimate Collection Tandem Materials Patch

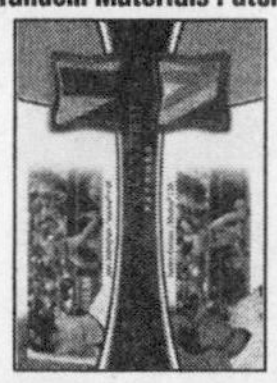

OVERALL GAME-USED ODDS 1:2
STATED PRINT RUN 35 SERIAL #'d SETS
AA Alfonso Soriano / Alex Rios 6.00 15.00
AH Garrett Atkins / Matt Holliday 8.00 20.00
AJ Derek Jeter / Luis Aparicio 15.00 40.00
BH Felix Hernandez / Yuniesky Betancourt 8.00 20.00
BM Lastings Milledge / Brian Bannister 8.00 20.00
BR Hanley Ramirez / Yuniesky Betancourt 6.00 15.00
BV Jeremy Bonderman / Justin Verlander 10.00 25.00
CH Melky Cabrera / Jeremy Hermida 8.00 20.00
CL Mark Loretta / Coco Crisp 6.00 15.00
CM Lastings Milledge / Melky Cabrera 10.00 25.00
CO Roger Clemens / Roy Oswalt 20.00 50.00
CP Carl Crawford / Scott Podsednik 6.00 15.00
CR Miguel Cabrera / Hanley Ramirez 8.00 20.00
CS Scott Kazmir / Cole Hamels 20.00 50.00
CV Justin Verlander / Matt Cain 10.00 25.00
CW Chris Carpenter / Dontrelle Willis 15.00 40.00
CZ Miguel Cabrera / Ryan Zimmerman 15.00 40.00
DH Derek Jeter / Hanley Ramirez 20.00 50.00
FW Rickie Weeks / Prince Fielder 12.50 30.00
GD Ken Griffey Jr. / Adam Dunn 15.00 40.00
GG Tony Gwynn / Brian Giles 15.00 40.00
GP Ken Griffey Jr. / Albert Pujols 40.00 80.00
GR Ken Griffey Jr. / Alex Rios 15.00 40.00
GT Ken Griffey Jr. / Frank Thomas 20.00 50.00
HB Matt Holliday / Jason Bay 10.00 25.00
HF Travis Hafner / Prince Fielder 12.50 30.00
HG Brian Giles / Trevor Hoffman 6.00 15.00
HJ Andruw Jones / Torii Hunter 12.50 30.00
HK Jason Kubel / Jeremy Hermida 6.00 15.00
HM Travis Hafner / Victor Martinez 8.00 20.00
HN Trevor Hoffman / Joe Nathan 6.00 15.00
HO Roy Oswalt / Rich Harden 6.00 15.00
HP Trevor Hoffman / Jonathan Papelbon 12.50 30.00
HR Hanley Ramirez / Jeremy Hermida 10.00 25.00
HW Josh Willingham / Jeremy Hermida 6.00 15.00
ID Jermaine Dye / Tadahito Iguchi 12.50 30.00
JC Derek Jeter / Melky Cabrera 30.00 60.00
JG Ken Griffey Jr. / Derek Jeter 40.00 80.00
JJ Derek Jeter / Reggie Jackson 30.00 60.00
JK Kendry Morales / Jered Weaver 10.00 25.00
JM Victor Martinez / Kenji Johjima 12.50 30.00
JR Cal Ripken / Derek Jeter 50.00 100.00
KB Brian Giles / Khalil Greene 12.50 30.00
KC Carl Crawford / Scott Kazmir 6.00 15.00
KM Jason Kendall / Joe Mauer 10.00 25.00
KU Ian Kinsler / Dan Uggla 10.00 25.00
KY Michael Young / Ian Kinsler 8.00 20.00
LC Fred Lynn / Coco Crisp 6.00 15.00
LF Carlos Lee / Prince Fielder 8.00 20.00
LH Francisco Liriano / Cole Hamels 12.50 30.00
MF Prince Fielder / Kendry Morales 10.00 25.00
MH Livan Hernandez / Kendry Morales 8.00 20.00
ML Joe Mauer / Francisco Liriano 15.00 40.00
MM Victor Martinez / Joe Mauer 10.00 25.00
MR Melvin Mora / Brian Roberts 6.00 15.00
MW Paul Molitor / Rickie Weeks 8.00 20.00
NJ Joe Nathan / Joe Mauer 8.00 20.00
NL Joe Nathan / Francisco Liriano 12.50 30.00
NM Joe Nathan / Joe Mauer 12.50 30.00
NP Joe Nathan / Jonathan Papelbon 12.50 30.00
PC Gaylord Perry / Matt Cain 12.50 30.00
PH Jonathan Papelbon / Craig Hansen 20.00 50.00
PO Roy Oswalt / Jake Peavy 6.00 15.00
PP Gaylord Perry / Jake Peavy 10.00 25.00
RC Coco Crisp / Alex Rios 6.00 15.00
RM Jose Reyes / Lastings Milledge 10.00 25.00
RR Jose Reyes / Hanley Ramirez 12.50 30.00
RS Cal Ripken / Mike Schmidt 40.00 80.00
RU Hanley Ramirez / Dan Uggla 15.00 40.00
RV Ivan Rodriguez / Justin Verlander 10.00 25.00
SH Nick Swisher / Rich Harden 6.00 15.00
SJ Conor Jackson / Chris Shelton 12.50 30.00
SZ Mike Schmidt / Ryan Zimmerman 20.00 50.00
TY Michael Young / Mark Teixeira 8.00 20.00
UK Chase Utley / Ian Kinsler 20.00 50.00
UM Joe Morgan / Chase Utley 20.00 50.00
UR Brian Roberts / Dan Uggla 6.00 15.00
VM Jack Morris / Justin Verlander 30.00 60.00
VZ Justin Verlander / Joel Zumaya 10.00 25.00
WM Joe Mauer / Josh Willingham 12.50 30.00
WR Josh Willingham / Hanley Ramirez 6.00 15.00
WV Justin Verlander / Jered Weaver 10.00 25.00
YL Mark Loretta / Kevin Youkilis 6.00 15.00
ZA Garrett Atkins / Ryan Zimmerman 15.00 40.00
ZC Miguel Cabrera / Ryan Zimmerman 15.00 40.00
ZJ Josh Johnson / Joel Zumaya 8.00 20.00
ZZ Carlos Zambrano / Joel Zumaya 10.00 25.00

2006 Ultimate Collection Tri-Marks Signatures

OVERALL AU ODDS 1:2
STATED PRINT RUN 15 SER.#'d SETS
NO PRICING DUE TO SCARCITY
EXCHANGE DEADLINE 12/20/09

2007 Ultimate Collection

This 141-card set was released in October, 2007. The set was issued in four-card packs, which came four packs to a box and four boxes to a case. Cards numbered 1-100 feature veteran players in team alphabetical order which is broken into National League (1-52) and American League (53-100). Those first 100 cards were issued to a stated print run of 450 serial numbered sets. Cards numbered 101-141 feature signed 2007 rookies and those cards were issued to stated print runs of between 289 and 299 serial numbered sets. A few players did not return their signatures in time for pack out and those cards could be redeemed until September 24, 2009.

COMMON CARD (1-100) .75 2.00
1-100 PRINT RUN 450 SER.#'d SETS
COMMON AU RC (101-141) 4.00 10.00
OVERALL AU ODDS ONE PER PACK
AU RC PRINT RUNS B/WN 289-299 COPIES PER
EXCHANGE DEADLINE 9/24/2009
1 Chipper Jones 2.00 5.00
2 Andruw Jones .75 2.00
3 Tim Hudson 1.25 3.00
4 Stephen Drew .75 2.00
5 Randy Johnson 2.00 5.00
6 Brandon Webb 1.25 3.00
7 Alfonso Soriano 1.25 3.00
8 Derrek Lee .75 2.00
9 Aramis Ramirez .75 2.00
10 Carlos Zambrano 1.25 3.00
11 Ken Griffey Jr. 3.00 8.00
12 Adam Dunn 1.25 3.00
13 Ryan Freel .75 2.00
14 Todd Helton 1.25 3.00
15 Garrett Atkins .75 2.00
16 Matt Holliday 2.00 5.00
17 Hanley Ramirez 2.00 5.00
18 Dontrelle Willis .75 2.00
19 Miguel Cabrera 2.00 5.00
20 Lance Berkman 1.25 3.00
21 Roy Oswalt 1.25 3.00
22 Carlos Lee .75 2.00
23 Nomar Garciaparra 2.00 5.00
24 Jason Schmidt .75 2.00
25 Juan Pierre .75 2.00
26 Russell Martin .75 2.00
27 Rickie Weeks 1.25 3.00
28 Prince Fielder 1.25 3.00
29 Ben Sheets .75 2.00
30 David Wright 3.00 8.00
31 Jose Reyes 1.25 3.00
32 Pedro Martinez 1.25 3.00
33 Carlos Beltran .75 2.00
34 Brett Myers .75 2.00
35 Jimmy Rollins 1.25 3.00
36 Ryan Howard 3.00 8.00
37 Jason Bay 1.25 3.00
38 Freddy Sanchez .75 2.00
39 Ian Snell .75 2.00
40 Jake Peavy .75 2.00
41 Greg Maddux 3.00 8.00
42 Brian Giles .75 2.00
43 Matt Cain 1.25 3.00
44 Barry Zito .75 2.00
45 Ray Durham .75 2.00
46 Albert Pujols 5.00 12.00
47 Chris Carpenter 2.00 5.00
48 Chris Duncan .75 2.00
49 Scott Rolen 1.25 3.00
50 Ryan Zimmerman 1.25 3.00
51 Chad Cordero .75 2.00
52 Ryan Church .75 2.00
53 Miguel Tejada 1.25 3.00
54 Erik Bedard .75 2.00
55 Brian Roberts .75 2.00
56 David Ortiz 1.25 3.00
57 Josh Beckett 1.25 3.00
58 Manny Ramirez 2.00 5.00
59 Daisuke Matsuzaka RC 12.50 30.00
60 Jim Thome 1.25 3.00
61 Paul Konerko 1.25 3.00
62 Jermaine Dye .75 2.00
63 Grady Sizemore 1.25 3.00
64 Victor Martinez 1.25 3.00
65 C.C. Sabathia 1.25 3.00
66 Ivan Rodriguez 1.25 3.00
67 Justin Verlander 2.50 6.00
68 Gary Sheffield .75 2.00
69 Jeremy Bonderman .75 2.00
70 Gil Meche .75 2.00
71 Mike Sweeney .75 2.00
72 Mark Teahen .75 2.00
73 Vladimir Guerrero 2.00 5.00
74 Howie Kendrick .75 2.00
75 Francisco Rodriguez 1.25 3.00
76 Johan Santana 2.00 5.00
77 Justin Morneau 2.00 5.00
78 Joe Mauer 2.00 5.00
79 Michael Cuddyer .75 2.00
80 Alex Rodriguez 3.00 8.00
81 Derek Jeter 5.00 12.00
82 Johnny Damon 1.25 3.00
83 Roger Clemens 2.50 6.00
84 Rich Harden .75 2.00
85 Mike Piazza 2.00 5.00
86 Huston Street .75 2.00
87 Ichiro Suzuki 3.00 8.00
88 Felix Hernandez 2.00 5.00
89 Kenji Johjima 2.00 5.00
90 Adrian Beltre .75 2.00
91 Carl Crawford 1.25 3.00
92 Scott Kazmir 1.25 3.00
93 B.J. Upton .75 2.00
94 Michael Young 1.25 3.00
95 Mark Teixeira 2.00 5.00
96 Sammy Sosa 2.00 5.00
97 Hank Blalock .75 2.00
98 Vernon Wells .75 2.00
99 Roy Halladay 2.00 5.00
100 Frank Thomas 2.00 5.00
101 Adam Lind AU (RC) 10.00 25.00
102 Akinori Iwamura AU RC 12.50 30.00
103 Andrew Miller AU RC 12.50 30.00
104 Michael Bourn AU (RC) 4.00 10.00
105 Kory Casto AU (RC) 4.00 10.00
106 Ryan Braun AU (RC) 30.00 60.00
107 Sean Gallagher AU (RC) 4.00 10.00
108 Billy Butler AU (RC) 15.00 40.00
109 Alexi Casilla AU RC 4.00 10.00
110 Chris Stewart AU RC 4.00 10.00
111 Matt DeSalvo AU (RC) 6.00 15.00
112 Chase Headley AU (RC) 6.00 15.00
113 Delmon Young AU/292 (RC) 12.50 30.00
114 Homer Bailey AU (RC) 6.00 15.00
115 Kurt Suzuki AU (RC) 6.00 15.00
116 Alex Gordon AU/297 RC 15.00 40.00
117 Josh Hamilton AU (RC) 10.00 25.00
118 Fred Lewis AU (RC) 4.00 10.00
119 Glen Perkins AU (RC) 4.00 10.00
120 Hector Gimenez AU (RC) 4.00 10.00
121 Phil Hughes AU (RC) 10.00 25.00
122 Jeff Baker AU (RC) 4.00 10.00
123 Andy LaRoche AU (RC) 4.00 10.00
124 Tim Lincecum AU RC 100.00 175.00
125 Joaquin Arias AU (RC) 4.00 10.00
126 Daisuke Matsuzaka AU 75.00 150.00
127 Micah Owings AU (RC) 6.00 15.00
128 Hunter Pence AU/297 (RC) 10.00 25.00
129 Matt Chico AU (RC) 4.00 10.00
130 Kei Igawa AU RC 12.50 30.00
131 Kevin Kouzmanoff AU (RC) 4.00 10.00
132 Miguel Montero AU/289 (RC) 4.00 10.00
133 Mike Rabelo AU RC 6.00 15.00
134 Felix Pie AU (RC) 4.00 10.00
135 Curtis Thigpen AU (RC) 4.00 10.00
136 Ryan Z. Braun AU RC 6.00 15.00
137 Ryan Sweeney AU (RC) 4.00 10.00
138 Brandon Wood AU (RC) 6.00 15.00
139 Troy Tulowitzki AU (RC) 15.00 40.00
140 Justin Upton AU RC 30.00 60.00

2007 Ultimate Collection Jerseys

OVERALL GU ODDS TWO PER PACK
STATED PRINT RUN 50 SER.#'d SETS
1 Chipper Jones/50 4.00 10.00
2 Andruw Jones/50 4.00 10.00
3 Tim Hudson/50 3.00 8.00
4 Stephen Drew/50 4.00 10.00
5 Randy Johnson/50 4.00 10.00
6 Brandon Webb/50 4.00 10.00
7 Alfonso Soriano/50 3.00 8.00
8 Derrek Lee/50 3.00 8.00
9 Aramis Ramirez/50 3.00 8.00
10 Carlos Zambrano/50 3.00 8.00
11 Ken Griffey Jr./50 6.00 15.00
12 Adam Dunn/50 3.00 8.00
13 Ryan Freel/50 3.00 8.00
14 Todd Helton/50 4.00 10.00
15 Garrett Atkins/50 3.00 8.00
16 Matt Holliday/50 4.00 10.00
17 Hanley Ramirez/50 4.00 10.00
18 Dontrelle Willis/50 3.00 8.00
19 Miguel Cabrera/50 4.00 10.00
20 Lance Berkman/50 3.00 8.00
21 Roy Oswalt/50 3.00 8.00
22 Carlos Lee/50 3.00 8.00
24 Jason Schmidt/50 3.00 8.00
25 Juan Pierre/50 3.00 8.00
26 Russell Martin/50 3.00 8.00
27 Rickie Weeks/50 3.00 8.00
28 Prince Fielder/50 4.00 10.00
29 Ben Sheets/50 3.00 8.00
31 Jose Reyes/50 4.00 10.00
32 Pedro Martinez/50 4.00 10.00
33 Carlos Beltran/50 3.00 8.00
34 Brett Myers/50 3.00 8.00
35 Jimmy Rollins/50 6.00 15.00
37 Jason Bay/50 3.00 8.00
38 Freddy Sanchez/50 3.00 8.00
39 Ian Snell/50 3.00 8.00
40 Jake Peavy/50 3.00 8.00
41 Greg Maddux/50 6.00 15.00
42 Brian Giles/50 3.00 8.00
43 Matt Cain/50 4.00 10.00
44 Barry Zito/50 3.00 8.00
45 Ray Durham/50 3.00 8.00
46 Albert Pujols/50 8.00 20.00
47 Chris Carpenter/50 3.00 8.00
48 Chris Duncan/50 4.00 10.00
49 Scott Rolen/50 4.00 10.00
50 Ryan Zimmerman/50 4.00 10.00
51 Chad Cordero/50 3.00 8.00
52 Ryan Church/50 3.00 8.00
53 Miguel Tejada/50 3.00 8.00
54 Erik Bedard/50 3.00 8.00
55 Brian Roberts/50 3.00 8.00
56 David Ortiz/50 4.00 10.00
57 Josh Beckett/50 4.00 10.00
58 Manny Ramirez/50 4.00 10.00
59 Daisuke Matsuzaka/50 20.00 50.00
60 Jim Thome/50 4.00 10.00
61 Paul Konerko/50 3.00 8.00
62 Jermaine Dye/50 3.00 8.00
63 Grady Sizemore/50 4.00 10.00
64 Victor Martinez/50 3.00 8.00
65 C.C. Sabathia/50 3.00 8.00
66 Ivan Rodriguez/50 4.00 10.00
67 Justin Verlander/50 4.00 10.00
68 Gary Sheffield/50 3.00 8.00
69 Jeremy Bonderman/50 3.00 8.00
70 Gil Meche/50 3.00 8.00
71 Mike Sweeney/50 3.00 8.00
72 Mark Teahen/50 3.00 8.00
73 Vladimir Guerrero/50 4.00 10.00
74 Howie Kendrick/50 3.00 8.00
75 Francisco Rodriguez/50 3.00 8.00
76 Johan Santana/50 4.00 10.00
77 Justin Morneau/50 3.00 8.00
78 Joe Mauer/50 4.00 10.00
79 Michael Cuddyer/50 3.00 8.00
81 Derek Jeter/50 10.00 25.00
83 Roger Clemens/50 6.00 15.00
84 Rich Harden/50 3.00 8.00
85 Mike Piazza/50 6.00 15.00
86 Huston Street/50 3.00 8.00
88 Felix Hernandez/50 4.00 10.00
89 Kenji Johjima/50 4.00 10.00
90 Adrian Beltre/50 3.00 8.00
91 Carl Crawford/50 3.00 8.00
92 Scott Kazmir/50 4.00 10.00
93 B.J. Upton/50 3.00 8.00
94 Michael Young/50 3.00 8.00
95 Mark Teixeira/50 4.00 10.00
97 Hank Blalock/50 3.00 8.00
98 Vernon Wells/50 3.00 8.00
99 Roy Halladay/50 3.00 8.00
100 Frank Thomas/50 6.00 15.00

2007 Ultimate Collection Patches

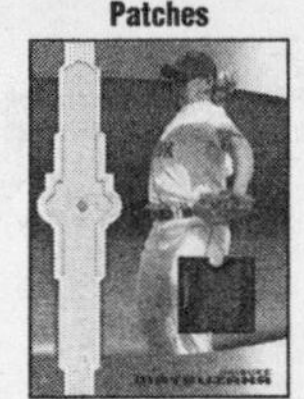

OVERALL GU ODDS TWO PER PACK
STATED PRINT RUN 25 SER.#'d SETS
NO PRICING DUE TO SCARCITY

2007 Ultimate Collection America's Pastime Memorabilia

OVERALL GU ODDS TWO PER PACK
PRINT RUNS B/WN 25-75 COPIES PER
NO PRICING ON QTY 25 OR LESS
AB Adrian Beltre/75 3.00 8.00
AJ Andruw Jones/75 4.00 10.00
AP Andy Pettitte/75 4.00 10.00
AS Alfonso Soriano/75 3.00 8.00
BA Bobby Abreu/75 3.00 8.00
BE Josh Beckett/75 4.00 10.00
BG Brian Giles/75 3.00 8.00
BJ Jeff Bagwell/75 4.00 10.00
BR Brian Roberts/75 3.00 8.00
BS Ben Sheets/75 3.00 8.00
BW Brandon Webb/75 4.00 10.00
CA Chris Carpenter/75 3.00 8.00
CB Carlos Beltran/75 3.00 8.00
CC Carl Crawford/75 3.00 8.00
CF Carlton Fisk/75 4.00 10.00

CF2 Carlton Fisk/75 4.00 10.00
CJ Chipper Jones/75 4.00 10.00
CL Carlos Lee/75 3.00 8.00
CR Cal Ripken Jr./75 15.00 40.00
CS Curt Schilling/75 4.00 10.00
CU Chase Utley/75 4.00 10.00
DJ Derek Jeter/75 10.00 25.00
DL Derrek Lee/75 3.00 8.00
DO David Ortiz/75 4.00 10.00
DW Dontrelle Willis/75 3.00 8.00
FH Felix Hernandez/75 4.00 10.00
FL Francisco Liriano/75 4.00 10.00
FR Francisco Rodriguez/64 3.00 8.00
GA Garrett Atkins/75 3.00 8.00
GM Greg Maddux/75 6.00 15.00
GS Gary Sheffield/75 3.00 8.00
GW Tony Gwynn/75 4.00 10.00
GW2 Tony Gwynn/75 4.00 10.00
HA Rich Harden/75 3.00 8.00
HB Hank Blalock/75 3.00 8.00
HR Hanley Ramirez/75 4.00 10.00
JA Jason Bay/75 3.00 8.00
JB Jeremy Bonderman/75 3.00 8.00
JE Jim Edmonds/75 4.00 10.00
JG Jason Giambi/75 3.00 8.00
JM Justin Morneau/75 3.00 8.00
JN Joe Nathan/75 3.00 8.00
JO Randy Johnson/75 4.00 10.00
JP Jonathan Papelbon/75 4.00 10.00
JR Jim Rice/75 3.00 8.00
JS Johan Santana/75 4.00 10.00
JT Jim Thome/75 4.00 10.00
JV Justin Verlander/75 4.00 10.00
JW Josh Willingham/75 3.00 8.00
KG Ken Griffey Jr./75 6.00 15.00
KP Kirby Puckett/75 15.00 40.00
KY Kevin Youkilis/75 4.00 10.00
LB Lance Berkman/75 3.00 8.00
LO Lou Brock/25
MA Joe Mauer/75 4.00 10.00
MC Matt Cain/75 4.00 10.00
MH Matt Holliday/75 4.00 10.00
MI Miguel Cabrera/75 4.00 10.00
MM Mike Mussina/75 4.00 10.00
MR Manny Ramirez/75 4.00 10.00
MR2 Manny Ramirez/75 4.00 10.00
MS Mike Schmidt/75 6.00 15.00
MT Miguel Tejada/75 3.00 8.00
MY Michael Young/75 3.00 8.00
MZ Pedro Martinez/75 4.00 10.00
NR Nolan Ryan/75 12.50 30.00
OR Magglio Ordonez/75 3.00 8.00
OS Ozzie Smith/75 10.00 25.00
PE Jake Peavy/75 3.00 8.00
PF Prince Fielder/75 4.00 10.00
PM Paul Molitor/75 3.00 8.00
PU Albert Pujols/75 8.00 20.00
RB Rocco Baldelli/75 3.00 8.00
RC Roger Clemens/75 6.00 15.00
RE Jose Reyes/75 4.00 10.00
RE2 Jose Reyes/75 4.00 10.00
RH Roy Halladay/75 3.00 8.00
RJ Reggie Jackson/75 6.00 15.00
RO Roy Oswalt/75 3.00 8.00
RS Ryne Sandberg/75 6.00 15.00
RW Rickie Weeks/75 3.00 8.00
RZ Ryan Zimmerman/75 4.00 10.00
SC Steve Carlton/75 3.00 8.00
SE Richie Sexson/75 3.00 8.00
SI Grady Sizemore/75 4.00 10.00
SI2 Grady Sizemore/75 4.00 10.00
SK Scott Kazmir/75 4.00 10.00
SM John Smoltz/75 4.00 10.00
TE Mark Teixeira/75 4.00 10.00
TG Troy Glaus/75 3.00 8.00
TH Todd Helton/75 4.00 10.00
TR Travis Hafner/75 3.00 8.00
TR2 Travis Hafner/75 3.00 8.00
VA Jason Varitek/75 4.00 10.00
VG Vladimir Guerrero/75 4.00 10.00
VG2 Vladimir Guerrero/75 4.00 10.00
VM Victor Martinez/75 3.00 8.00
WC Will Clark/75 4.00 10.00

2007 Ultimate Collection America's Pastime Memorabilia Gold

OVERALL GU ODDS TWO PER PACK
STATED PRINT RUN 25 SER.#'d SETS
NO PRICING DUE TO SCARCITY

2007 Ultimate Collection America's Pastime Memorabilia Patches

OVERALL GU ODDS TWO PER PACK
PRINT RUNS B/WN 5-50 COPIES PER
NO PRICING ON QTY 25 OR LESS
AB Adrian Beltre/50 5.00 12.00
AJ Andruw Jones/50 6.00 15.00
AP Andy Pettitte/50 6.00 15.00
AS Alfonso Soriano/50 6.00 15.00
BA Bobby Abreu/50 5.00 12.00
BE Josh Beckett/50 10.00 25.00
BG Brian Giles/50 5.00 12.00
BJ Jeff Bagwell/50 10.00 25.00
BR Brian Roberts/50 6.00 15.00
BS Ben Sheets/50 5.00 12.00
BW Brandon Webb/50 6.00 15.00
CA Chris Carpenter/50 5.00 12.00
CB Carlos Beltran/50 6.00 15.00
CC Carl Crawford/50 6.00 15.00
CF Carlton Fisk/50 5.00 12.00
CF2 Carlton Fisk/50 5.00 12.00
CJ Chipper Jones/50 12.50 30.00
CL Carlos Lee/50 5.00 12.00
CR Cal Ripken Jr./32 30.00 60.00
CS Curt Schilling/50 6.00 15.00
CU Chase Utley/50 6.00 15.00
DL Derrek Lee/50 5.00 12.00
DO David Ortiz/50 10.00 25.00
DW Dontrelle Willis/50 5.00 12.00
FH Felix Hernandez/50 6.00 15.00
FL Francisco Liriano/50 6.00 15.00
FR Francisco Rodriguez/50 5.00 12.00
GA Garrett Atkins/50 5.00 12.00
GM Greg Maddux/20
GS Gary Sheffield/50 5.00 12.00
GW Tony Gwynn/50 10.00 25.00
GW2 Tony Gwynn/50 10.00 25.00
HA Rich Harden/50 5.00 12.00
HB Hank Blalock/50 5.00 12.00
HR Hanley Ramirez/50 6.00 15.00
JA Jason Bay/50 5.00 12.00
JB Jeremy Bonderman/50 5.00 12.00
JE Jim Edmonds/50 6.00 15.00
JG Jason Giambi/50 5.00 12.00
JM Justin Morneau/50 6.00 15.00
JN Joe Nathan/50 5.00 12.00
JO Randy Johnson/50 6.00 15.00
JP Jonathan Papelbon/50 10.00 25.00
JS Johan Santana/50 6.00 15.00
JT Jim Thome/50 5.00 12.00
JW Josh Willingham/50 5.00 12.00
KG Ken Griffey Jr./50 15.00 40.00
KP Kirby Puckett/50 30.00 60.00
KY Kevin Youkilis/50 10.00 25.00
LB Lance Berkman/50 6.00 15.00
LO Lou Brock/50 10.00 25.00
MA Joe Mauer/40 6.00 15.00
MC Matt Cain/50 5.00 12.00
MH Matt Holliday/50 10.00 25.00
MI Miguel Cabrera/50 5.00 12.00
MM Mike Mussina/50 10.00 25.00
MP Mike Piazza/50 15.00 40.00
MR Manny Ramirez/30 6.00 15.00
MR2 Manny Ramirez/28 6.00 15.00
MS Mike Schmidt/50 15.00 40.00
MT Miguel Tejada/50 5.00 12.00
MY Michael Young/50 5.00 12.00
MZ Pedro Martinez/50 6.00 15.00
NR Nolan Ryan/50 20.00 50.00
OR Magglio Ordonez/50 6.00 15.00
PE Jake Peavy/50 5.00 12.00
PF Prince Fielder/50 10.00 25.00
PM Paul Molitor/50 10.00 25.00
PU Albert Pujols/25
RB Rocco Baldelli/50 5.00 12.00
RC Roger Clemens/50 10.00 25.00
RE Jose Reyes/50 10.00 25.00
RE2 Jose Reyes/50 10.00 25.00
RH Roy Halladay/50 5.00 12.00
RJ Reggie Jackson/50 10.00 25.00
RO Roy Oswalt/50 5.00 12.00
RS Ryne Sandberg/50 15.00 40.00
RW Rickie Weeks/9
RY Robin Yount/50 15.00 40.00
RZ Ryan Zimmerman/50 10.00 25.00
SC Steve Carlton/50 5.00 12.00
SE Richie Sexson/50 5.00 12.00
SI Grady Sizemore/50 10.00 25.00
SI2 Grady Sizemore/50 10.00 25.00
SK Scott Kazmir/50 6.00 15.00
SM John Smoltz/50 6.00 15.00
TE Mark Teixeira/50 6.00 15.00
TG Troy Glaus/50 6.00 15.00
TH Todd Helton/50 6.00 15.00
TR Travis Hafner/50 5.00 12.00
TR2 Travis Hafner/50 5.00 12.00
VA Jason Varitek/50 10.00 25.00
VG Vladimir Guerrero/5
VG2 Vladimir Guerrero/5
VM Victor Martinez/50 5.00 12.00
WC Will Clark/50 6.00 15.00

2007 Ultimate Collection America's Pastime Signatures

OVERALL AU ODDS ONE PER PACK
EXCHANGE DEADLINE 9/24/2009
AD Adam Dunn 4.00 10.00
AE Andre Ethier 12.50 30.00
AG Adrian Gonzalez 10.00 25.00
AJ A.J. Burnett 4.00 10.00
AL Adam LaRoche 4.00 10.00
AP Albert Pujols 100.00 150.00
AV Andy Van Slyke 4.00 10.00
BB Boof Bonser 4.00 10.00
BE Johnny Bench 10.00 25.00
BJ B.J. Upton 6.00 15.00
BM Bill Mazeroski 10.00 25.00
CB Chad Billingsley 10.00 25.00
CC Chad Cordero 4.00 10.00
CH Cole Hamels 10.00 25.00
CK Casey Kotchman 4.00 10.00
CQ Carlos Quentin 6.00 15.00
CR Craig Biggio 20.00 50.00
CT Curtis Thigpen 4.00 10.00
CW Chien-Ming Wang 50.00 100.00
CY Chris Young 4.00 10.00
DH Dan Haren 4.00 10.00
DJ Derek Jeter 75.00 150.00
DM Don Mattingly 30.00 60.00
DS Don Sutton 6.00 15.00
DU Dan Uggla 6.00 15.00
DY Delmon Young 6.00 15.00
FH Felix Hernandez 10.00 25.00
FR Frank Robinson 10.00 25.00
GA Garrett Atkins 4.00 10.00
GP Gaylord Perry 4.00 10.00
GR Khalil Greene 6.00 15.00
GW Tony Gwynn 30.00 60.00
HA Travis Hafner 4.00 10.00
HB Homer Bailey 6.00 15.00
HE Chase Headley 4.00 10.00
HO Howie Kendrick 4.00 10.00
HR Hanley Ramirez 6.00 15.00
HS Huston Street 4.00 10.00
HU Torii Hunter 6.00 15.00
IK Ian Kinsler 6.00 15.00
JB Jason Bay 4.00 10.00
JE Jeremy Bonderman 4.00 10.00
JI Jim Rice 6.00 15.00
JL James Loney 6.00 15.00
JM Jack Morris 4.00 10.00
JN Joe Nathan 4.00 10.00
JO Joe Blanton 4.00 10.00
JT Jim Thome 12.50 30.00
JV Justin Verlander 30.00 60.00
JZ Joel Zumaya 6.00 15.00
KI Kei Igawa 10.00 25.00
KJ Kelly Johnson 4.00 10.00
KM Kendry Morales 4.00 10.00
LA Andy LaRoche 4.00 10.00
LE Jon Lester 12.50 30.00
LY John Lackey 4.00 10.00
MA Daisuke Matsuzaka 60.00 120.00
MB Matt Brown 4.00 10.00
MC Matt Cain 8.00 20.00
MH Matt Holliday 8.00 20.00
MM Melvin Mora 4.00 10.00
MS Mike Schmidt 20.00 50.00
MT Mark Teixeira 6.00 15.00
NM Nick Markakis 8.00 20.00
NW Nick Swisher 4.00 10.00
OS Ozzie Smith 20.00 50.00
PA Jim Palmer 6.00 15.00
PB Jonathan Papelbon 8.00 20.00
PK Paul Konerko 10.00 25.00
RA Aramis Ramirez 6.00 15.00
RB Ryan Braun 20.00 50.00
RF Rafael Furcal 4.00 10.00
RG Ryan Garko 4.00 10.00
RH Rich Harden 4.00 10.00
RI Rich Hill 4.00 10.00
RT Ryan Theriot 6.00 15.00
RW Rickie Weeks 4.00 10.00
RZ Ryan Zimmerman 10.00 25.00
SD Stephen Drew 10.00 25.00
SG Sean Gallagher 4.00 10.00
SK Scott Kazmir 8.00 20.00
SM Stan Musial 30.00 60.00
SO Joakim Soria 10.00 25.00
TG Tom Glavine 20.00 50.00
TP Tony Perez 10.00 25.00
TR Tim Raines 4.00 10.00
TT Troy Tulowitzki 20.00 50.00
VM Victor Martinez 4.00 10.00
VW Vernon Wells 4.00 10.00
WC Will Clark 6.00 15.00
WI Josh Willingham 4.00 10.00
WM Willie McCovey
XN Xavier Nady 4.00 10.00

2007 Ultimate Collection The Ultimate Card

OVERALL AU ODDS ONE PER PACK
STATED PRINT RUN 1 SER.#'d SET
NO PRICING DUE TO SCARCITY

2007 Ultimate Collection The Ultimate Logo

OVERALL AU ODDS ONE PER PACK
STATED PRINT RUN 1 SER.#'D SET
NO PRICING DUE TO SCARCITY

2007 Ultimate Collection The Ultimate Patch

OVERALL AU ODDS ONE PER PACK
PRINT RUNS B/WN 5-25 COPIES PER
NO PRICING DUE TO SCARCITY

2007 Ultimate Collection The Ultimate Six Signatures

OVERALL AU ODDS ONE PER PACK
STATED PRINT RUN 10 SER.#'d SETS
NO PRICING DUE TO SCARCITY

2007 Ultimate Collection Ultimate Champions Signatures

OVERALL AU ODDS ONE PER PACK
PRINT RUNS B/WN 4-10 COPIES PER
NO PRICING DUE TO SCARCITY
EXCHANGE DEADLINE 9/24/2009

2007 Ultimate Collection Ultimate Ensemble Dual Swatches

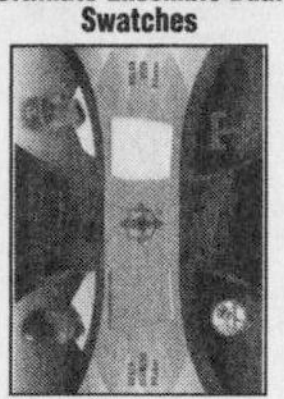

OVERALL GU ODDS TWO PER PACK
PRINT RUNS B/WN 52-75 COPIES PER
BD Jason Bay 4.00 10.00
J.D. Drew/75
BH Jeremy Bonderman 4.00 10.00
Rich Harden/75
BZ Wade Boggs 5.00 12.00
Ryan Zimmerman/75
CG Miguel Cabrera 5.00 12.00
Vladimir Guerrero/75
CJ Curt Schilling 6.00 15.00
Josh Beckett/75
CR Roger Clemens 12.50 30.00
Nolan Ryan/75
CW Matt Cain 4.00 10.00
Jered Weaver/75
FT Prince Fielder 5.00 12.00
Mark Teixeira/75
GD Ken Griffey Jr. 8.00 20.00
Adam Dunn/75
GM Tom Glavine 4.00 10.00
Pedro Martinez/75
GP Tony Gwynn 10.00 25.00
Jake Peavy/75
GR Tony Gwynn 15.00 40.00
Cal Ripken Jr./75
HH Todd Helton 5.00 12.00
Matt Holliday/75
HJ Felix Hernandez 5.00 12.00
Kenji Johjima/75
HR J.J. Hardy 5.00 12.00
Jose Reyes/75
HW Roy Halladay 4.00 10.00
Vernon Wells/75
IK Tadahito Iguchi 4.00 10.00
Paul Konerko/75
JJ Chipper Jones 5.00 12.00
Andruw Jones/75
JR Derek Jeter 20.00 50.00
Mariano Rivera/75
JV Joe Mauer 4.00 10.00
Victor Martinez/75
KY Scott Kazmir 4.00 10.00
Delmon Young/75
LS Derrek Lee 4.00 10.00
Alfonso Soriano/75
MB Mike Schmidt 12.50 30.00
Brooks Robinson/75
MC Justin Morneau 4.00 10.00
Michael Cuddyer/75
MM Justin Morneau 5.00 12.00
Joe Mauer/75
NR Joe Nathan 5.00 12.00
Mariano Rivera/75
OB Roy Oswalt 5.00 12.00
Lance Berkman/75
PC Albert Pujols 8.00 20.00
Chris Carpenter/75
PO Albert Pujols 8.00 20.00
David Ortiz/75
RB Ivan Rodriguez 5.00 12.00
Johnny Bench/75
SB Grady Sizemore 5.00 12.00
Carlos Beltran/75
SC Alfonso Soriano 5.00 12.00
Carl Crawford/52
SL Johan Santana 6.00 15.00
Francisco Liriano/75
SP John Smoltz 5.00 12.00
Jake Peavy/75
SR Ryne Sandberg 30.00 60.00
Cal Ripken Jr./63
SW Johan Santana 5.00 12.00
Brandon Webb/75
TR Miguel Tejada 6.00 15.00
Cal Ripken Jr./75
WU Rickie Weeks 5.00 12.00
Chase Utley/75
YR Michael Young 5.00 12.00
Jose Reyes/75

2007 Ultimate Collection Ultimate Ensemble Triple Swatches

OVERALL GU ODDS TWO PER PACK
STATED PRINT RUN 50 SER.#'d SETS
BCG Hank Blalock 6.00 15.00
Eric Chavez
Troy Glaus/50
CBG Will Clark 10.00 25.00
Wade Boggs
Tony Gwynn/50
CRS Steve Carlton 10.00 25.00
Nolan Ryan
Don Sutton/50
CSK Steve Carlton 6.00 15.00
Johan Santana
Scott Kazmir/50
FHS Prince Fielder 6.00 15.00
J.J. Hardy
Ben Sheets/50
GRR Khalil Greene 10.00 25.00
Jose Reyes
Hanley Ramirez/50
HTP Travis Hafner 6.00 15.00
Frank Thomas
Mike Piazza/50
LPD Barry Larkin 6.00 15.00
Tony Perez
Adam Dunn/50
LRS Barry Larkin 12.50 30.00
Cal Ripken
Jr.
Ozzie Smith/50
MCS Pedro Martinez 10.00 25.00
Roger Clemens
Don Sutton/50
MJG Joe Mauer 12.50 30.00
Chipper Jones
Ken Griffey Jr./50
MMP Joe Mauer 6.00 15.00
Victor Martinez
Jorge Posada/50
MSB Daisuke Matsuzaka 40.00 80.00
Curt Schilling
Josh Beckett/50
MSU Bill Mazeroski 10.00 25.00
Ryne Sandberg
Chase Utley/50
OCZ Roy Oswalt 6.00 15.00
Chris Carpenter
Carlos Zambrano/50
ODH David Ortiz 6.00 15.00
Jermaine Dye
Travis Hafner/50
OMT David Ortiz 6.00 15.00
Justin Morneau
Mark Teixeira/50
OPR David Ortiz 10.00 25.00
Albert Pujols
Jose Reyes/50
PJL Albert Pujols 10.00 25.00
Andruw Jones
Derrek Lee/50
RDB Ivan Rodriguez 6.00 15.00
Carlos Delgado
Carlos Beltran/50
RJG Cal Ripken 20.00 50.00
Jr.
Derek Jeter
Ken Griffey Jr./50
RPJ Jim Rice 40.00 80.00
Kirby Puckett
Reggie Jackson/50
RPS Manny Ramirez 10.00 25.00
Albert Pujols
Alfonso Soriano/50
RSB Brooks Robinson 15.00 40.00
Mike Schmidt
Wade Boggs/50
SHS Johan Santana 6.00 15.00
Roy Halladay
Josh Beckett/50
UWG Chase Utley 10.00 25.00
Rickie Weeks
Marcus Giles/50
YBO Carl Yastrzemski 10.00 25.00
Wade Boggs
David Ortiz/50
YJT Michael Young 10.00 25.00
Derek Jeter
Miguel Tejada/50
YTS Michael Young 10.00 25.00
Mark Teixeira
Sammy Sosa/50
ZAJ Ryan Zimmerman 6.00 15.00
Garrett Atkins
Chipper Jones/50

2007 Ultimate Collection Ultimate Ensemble Triple Patches

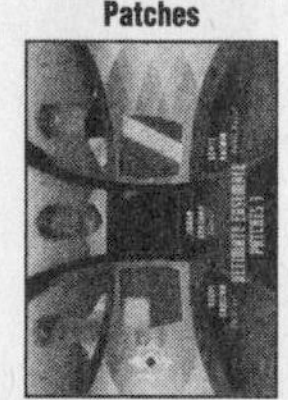

OVERALL GU ODDS TWO PER PACK
PRINT RUNS B/WN 7-15 COPIES PER
NO PRICING DUE TO SCARCITY

2007 Ultimate Collection Ultimate Ensemble Quad Swatches

OVERALL GU ODDS TWO PER PACK
PRINT RUNS B/WN 5-25 COPIES PER
NO PRICING DUE TO SCARCITY

2007 Ultimate Collection Ultimate Ensemble Quad Patches

OVERALL GU ODDS TWO PER PACK
STATED PRINT RUN 10 SER.#'d SETS
NO PRICING DUE TO SCARCITY

2007 Ultimate Collection Ultimate Futures Signatures

OVERALL AU ODDS ONE PER PACK
PRINT RUNS B/WN 8-25 COPIES PER
NO PRICING DUE TO SCARCITY
EXCHANGE DEADLINE 9/24/2009

2007 Ultimate Collection Ultimate Iron Man Signatures

COMMON CARD 125.00 250.00
OVERALL AU ODDS ONE PER PACK
STATED PRINT RUN 8 SER.#'d SETS

2007 Ultimate Collection Ultimate Legendary Signatures

OVERALL AU ODDS ONE PER PACK
PRINT RUNS B/WN 15-25 COPIES PER
NO PRICING DUE TO SCARCITY
EXCHANGE DEADLINE 9/24/2009

2007 Ultimate Collection Ultimate Numbers Match Signatures

OVERALL AU ODDS ONE PER PACK
PRINT RUNS B/WN 2-48 COPIES PER
NO PRICING ON QTY 25 OR LESS
EXCHANGE DEADLINE 9/24/2009
AR Garrett Atkins 6.00 15.00
Mark Reynolds/27
BG Craig Biggio
Alex Gordon/7
BP Johnny Bench
Albert Pujols/5
BR Yogi Berra
Cal Ripken Jr./8
BW Jeremy Bonderman 6.00 15.00
Chase Wright/38
BZ Jason Bay 10.00 25.00
Carlos Zambrano/38
CP Roger Clemens
Jim Palmer/22
FG Carlton Fisk 40.00 80.00
Vladimir Guerrero/27
GF Tony Gwynn
Bob Feller/19
HH Travis Hafner 12.50 30.00
Torii Hunter/48
HR Felix Hernandez 100.00 200.00
Nolan Ryan/34
HV Cole Hamels 30.00 60.00
Justin Verlander/35
HW Rich Harden 150.00 200.00
Chien-Ming Wang/40
JD Reggie Jackson 30.00 60.00
Adam Dunn/44
JT Derek Jeter
Troy Tulowitzki/2
KC Scott Kazmir
Tyler Clippard/19
KM Al Kaline
Stan Musial/6
LL Derrek Lee
Adam LaRoche/25
MB Nick Markakis
Billy Butler/21
MS Don Mattingly
Ryne Sandberg/23
PB Hunter Pence
Michael Bourn/9
RB Brooks Robinson
Johnny Bench/5
RU Hanley Ramirez
B.J. Upton/2
SH Ben Sheets
Tim Hudson/15
TW Mark Teixeira
Rickie Weeks/23
UD Dan Uggla
Stephen Drew/6
WH Dontrelle Willis 12.50 30.00
Cole Hamels/35
YR Carl Yastrzemski
Cal Ripken Jr./8

2007 Ultimate Collection Ultimate Numbers Materials

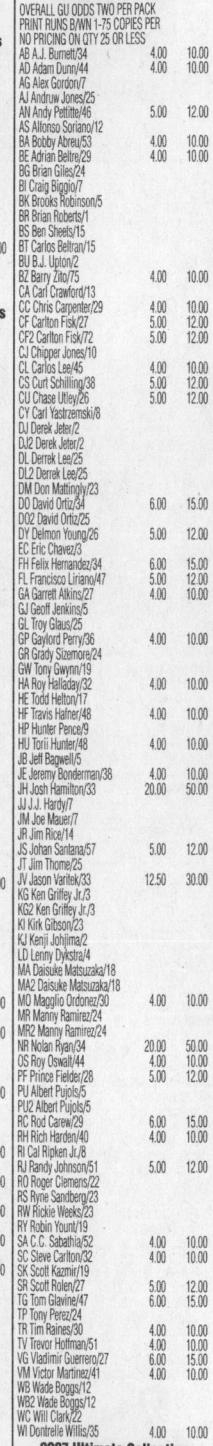

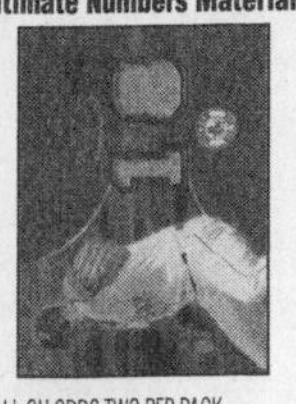

OVERALL GU ODDS TWO PER PACK
PRINT RUNS B/WN 1-75 COPIES PER
NO PRICING ON QTY 25 OR LESS
AB A.J. Burnett/34 4.00 10.00
AD Adam Dunn/44 4.00 10.00
AG Alex Gordon/7
AJ Andruw Jones/25
AN Andy Pettitte/46 5.00 12.00
AS Alfonso Soriano/12
BA Bobby Abreu/53 4.00 10.00
BE Adrian Beltre/29 4.00 10.00
BG Brian Giles/24
BI Craig Biggio/7
BK Brooks Robinson/5
BR Brian Roberts/1
BS Ben Sheets/15
BT Carlos Beltran/15
BU B.J. Upton/2
BZ Barry Zito/75 4.00 10.00
CA Carl Crawford/13
CC Chris Carpenter/29 4.00 10.00
CF Carlton Fisk/27 5.00 12.00
CF2 Carlton Fisk/72 5.00 12.00
CJ Chipper Jones/10
CL Carlos Lee/45 4.00 10.00
CS Curt Schilling/38 5.00 12.00
CU Chase Utley/26 5.00 12.00
CY Carl Yastrzemski/8
DJ Derek Jeter/2
DJ2 Derek Jeter/2
DL Derrek Lee/25
DL2 Derrek Lee/25
DM Don Mattingly/23
DO David Ortiz/34 6.00 15.00
DO2 David Ortiz/25
DY Delmon Young/26 5.00 12.00
EC Eric Chavez/3
FH Felix Hernandez/34 6.00 15.00
FL Francisco Liriano/47 5.00 12.00
GA Garrett Atkins/27 4.00 10.00
GJ Geoff Jenkins/5
GL Troy Glaus/25
GP Gaylord Perry/36 4.00 10.00
GR Grady Sizemore/24
GW Tony Gwynn/19
HA Roy Halladay/32 4.00 10.00
HE Todd Helton/17
HF Travis Hafner/48 4.00 10.00
HP Hunter Pence/9
HU Torii Hunter/48 4.00 10.00
JB Jeff Bagwell/5
JE Jeremy Bonderman/38 4.00 10.00
JH Josh Hamilton/33 20.00 50.00
JJ J.J. Hardy/7
JM Joe Mauer/7
JR Jim Rice/14
JS Johan Santana/57 5.00 12.00
JT Jim Thome/25
JV Jason Varitek/33 12.50 30.00
KG Ken Griffey Jr./3
KG2 Ken Griffey Jr./3
KI Kirk Gibson/23
KJ Kenji Johjima/2
LD Lenny Dykstra/4
MA Daisuke Matsuzaka/18
MA2 Daisuke Matsuzaka/18
MO Magglio Ordonez/30 4.00 10.00
MR Manny Ramirez/24
MR2 Manny Ramirez/24
NR Nolan Ryan/34 20.00 50.00
OS Roy Oswalt/44 4.00 10.00
PF Prince Fielder/28 5.00 12.00
PU Albert Pujols/5
PU2 Albert Pujols/5
RC Rod Carew/29 6.00 15.00
RH Rich Harden/40 4.00 10.00
RI Cal Ripken Jr./8
RJ Randy Johnson/51 5.00 12.00
RO Roger Clemens/22
RS Ryne Sandberg/23
RW Rickie Weeks/23
RY Robin Yount/19
SA C.C. Sabathia/52 4.00 10.00
SC Steve Carlton/32 4.00 10.00
SK Scott Kazmir/19
SR Scott Rolen/27 5.00 12.00
TG Tom Glavine/47 6.00 15.00
TP Tony Perez/24
TR Tim Raines/30 4.00 10.00
TV Trevor Hoffman/51 4.00 10.00
VG Vladimir Guerrero/27 6.00 15.00
VM Victor Martinez/41 4.00 10.00
WB Wade Boggs/12
WB2 Wade Boggs/12
WC Will Clark/22
WI Dontrelle Willis/35 4.00 10.00

2007 Ultimate Collection Ultimate Star Materials

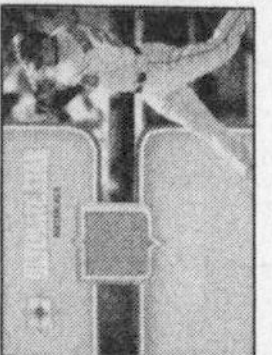

OVERALL GU ODDS TWO PER PACK
AD Adam Dunn 3.00 8.00
AG Alex Gordon 6.00 15.00
AG2 Alex Gordon 6.00 15.00
AK Austin Kearns 3.00 8.00
AK2 Austin Kearns 3.00 8.00
AP Albert Pujols 6.00 15.00
BG Brian Giles 3.00 8.00
BI Craig Biggio 4.00 10.00
BO Jeremy Bonderman 3.00 8.00
DC Don Chooto 3.00 0.00
BU B.J. Upton 3.00 8.00
CA Chris Carpenter 3.00 8.00
CF Carlton Fisk 4.00 10.00
CL Carlos Lee 3.00 8.00
CL2 Carlos Lee 3.00 8.00
CR Cal Ripken Jr. 8.00 20.00
CR2 Cal Ripken Jr. 8.00 20.00
CY Carl Yastrzemski 4.00 10.00
CZ Carlos Zambrano 3.00 8.00
DH Dan Haren 3.00 8.00
DJ Derek Jeter 8.00 20.00
DJ2 Derek Jeter 8.00 20.00
DL Derrek Lee 3.00 8.00
DM Don Mattingly 5.00 12.00
DO David Ortiz 4.00 10.00
DW Dontrelle Willis 3.00 8.00
DW2 Dontrelle Willis 3.00 8.00
EC Eric Chavez 3.00 8.00
FH Felix Hernandez 4.00 10.00
FH2 Felix Hernandez 4.00 10.00
FL Francisco Liriano 4.00 10.00
FR Francisco Rodriguez 3.00 8.00
FT Frank Thomas 5.00 12.00
GA Garrett Atkins 3.00 8.00
GA2 Garrett Atkins 3.00 8.00
GR Khalil Greene 4.00 10.00
GW Tony Gwynn 4.00 10.00
HA Roy Halladay 3.00 8.00
HP Hunter Pence 5.00 12.00
HR Hanley Ramirez 4.00 10.00
HS Huston Street 3.00 8.00
HU Torii Hunter 3.00 8.00
JA Jason Bay 3.00 8.00
JB Josh Beckett 5.00 12.00
JH Jeremy Hermida 3.00 8.00
JL John Lackey 3.00 8.00
JM Joe Mauer 4.00 10.00
JN Joe Nathan 3.00 8.00
JP Jonathan Papelbon 4.00 10.00
JR Jim Rice 3.00 8.00
JS John Smoltz 4.00 10.00
JT Jim Thome 4.00 10.00
JT2 Jim Thome 4.00 10.00
JU Justin Morneau 3.00 8.00
JU2 Justin Morneau 3.00 8.00
KG Ken Griffey Jr. 6.00 15.00
MA Matt Cain 3.00 8.00
MA2 Matt Cain 3.00 8.00
MC Miguel Cabrera 4.00 10.00
MH Matt Holliday 4.00 10.00
MH2 Matt Holliday 4.00 10.00
MS Mike Schmidt 5.00 12.00
MT Mark Teixeira 4.00 10.00
MT2 Mark Teixeira 4.00 10.00
MY Michael Young 3.00 8.00
MY2 Michael Young 3.00 8.00
NM Nick Markakis 4.00 10.00
NR Nolan Ryan 6.00 15.00
NS Nick Swisher 3.00 8.00
OR Roy Oswalt 3.00 8.00
OS Ozzie Smith 5.00 12.00
PA Jim Palmer 3.00 8.00
PE Jake Peavy 3.00 8.00
PE2 Jake Peavy 3.00 8.00
PF Prince Fielder 4.00 10.00
PK Paul Konerko 3.00 8.00
PM Paul Molitor 3.00 8.00
PM2 Paul Molitor 3.00 8.00
RA Roberto Alomar 4.00 10.00
RC Roger Clemens 5.00 12.00
RF Rollie Fingers 3.00 8.00
RH Rich Harden 3.00 8.00
RJ Randy Johnson 4.00 10.00
RO Rod Carew 4.00 10.00
RW Rickie Weeks 3.00 8.00
RY Robin Yount 4.00 10.00
RZ Ryan Zimmerman 4.00 10.00
RZ2 Ryan Zimmerman 4.00 10.00
SK Scott Kazmir 4.00 10.00
TG Tom Glavine 4.00 10.00
TH Travis Hafner 3.00 8.00
TH2 Travis Hafner 3.00 8.00
TI Tim Hudson 3.00 8.00
TT Troy Tulowitzki 4.00 10.00
VM Victor Martinez 3.00 8.00
VW Vernon Wells 3.00 8.00
WB Wade Boggs 4.00 10.00
WI Josh Willingham 3.00 8.00

2007 Ultimate Collection Ultimate Star Materials Autograph

OVERALL AU ODDS ONE PER PACK
PRINT RUNS B/WN 3-15 COPIES PER
NO PRICING DUE TO SCARCITY
EXCHANGE DEADLINE 9/24/2009

2007 Ultimate Collection Ultimate Star Materials Autograph Patch

OVERALL AU ODDS ONE PER PACK
STATED PRINT RUN 5 SER.#'d SETS
NO PRICING DUE TO SCARCITY
EXCHANGE DEADLINE 9/24/2009

2007 Ultimate Collection Ultimate Team Marks

OVERALL AU ODDS ONE PER PACK
PRINT RUNS B/WN 56-60 COPIES PER
EXCHANGE DEADLINE 9/24/2009
AP Albert Pujols/60
BG Bob Gibson/60 15.00 40.00
CC Carl Crawford/60 6.00 15.00
CL Carlos Lee/57 10.00 25.00
CY Carl Yastrzemski/58 30.00 60.00
DJ Derek Jeter/60 100.00 150.00
DL Derrek Lee/58 10.00 25.00
DO David Ortiz/60 40.00 80.00
DW Dontrelle Willis/56 4.00 10.00
FH Felix Hernandez/60 12.50 30.00
JM Joe Mauer/60 15.00 40.00
MO Justin Morneau/60 10.00 25.00
MT Mark Teixeira/60 6.00 15.00
PF Prince Fielder/60 30.00 60.00
VM Victor Martinez/60 10.00 25.00
VW Vernon Wells/60 4.00 10.00

2007 Ultimate Collection Ultimate Team Materials

OVERALL GU ODDS TWO PER PACK
PRINT RUNS B/WN 25-50 COPIES PER
NO PRICING ON QTY 25 OR LESS
AD Adam Dunn/50 3.00 8.00
AK Austin Kearns/50 3.00 8.00
AN Garret Anderson/50 3.00 8.00
AP Albert Pujols/50 8.00 20.00
BE Josh Beckett/50 4.00 10.00
BG Brian Giles/50 3.00 8.00
BS Ben Sheets/50 3.00 8.00
BU B.J. Upton/50 3.00 8.00
CA Rod Carew/50 4.00 10.00
CF Carlton Fisk/50 4.00 10.00
CH Chris Carpenter/50 3.00 8.00
CL Carlos Lee/50 3.00 8.00
CR Bobby Crosby/50 3.00 8.00
CY Carl Yastrzemski/50 6.00 15.00
DH Dan Haren/50 3.00 8.00
DJ Derek Jeter/50 10.00 25.00
DL Derrek Lee/50 3.00 8.00
DM Don Mattingly/50 6.00 15.00
DO David Ortiz/50 4.00 10.00
DW Dontrelle Willis/50 3.00 8.00
DW2 Dontrelle Willis/50 3.00 8.00
EC Eric Chavez/50 3.00 8.00
EC2 Eric Chavez/50 3.00 8.00
FH Felix Hernandez/50 4.00 10.00
FJ Fergie Jenkins/50 3.00 8.00
FL Francisco Liriano/50 4.00 10.00
FR Francisco Rodriguez/50 3.00 8.00
FT Frank Thomas/50 6.00 15.00
GA Garrett Atkins/50 3.00 8.00
GA2 Garrett Atkins/50 3.00 8.00
GR Khalil Greene/50 4.00 10.00
GW Tony Gwynn/50 4.00 10.00
HA Rich Harden/50 3.00 8.00
HP Hunter Pence/50 6.00 15.00
HR Hanley Ramirez/50 4.00 10.00
HS Huston Street/50 3.00 8.00
HS2 Huston Street/50 3.00 8.00
HU Tim Hudson/50 3.00 8.00
JA Jason Bay/50 3.00 8.00
JE Jeremy Bonderman/50 3.00 8.00
JG Jonny Gomes/50 3.00 8.00
JH Jeremy Hermida/50 3.00 8.00
JI Jim Palmer/50 4.00 10.00
JL John Lackey/50 3.00 8.00
JM Joe Mauer/50 4.00 10.00
JN Joe Nathan/50 3.00 8.00
JP Jake Peavy/50 3.00 8.00
JR Jim Rice/50 3.00 8.00
JS John Smoltz/50 4.00 10.00
JT Jim Thome/50 4.00 10.00
KG Ken Griffey Jr./50 6.00 15.00
KG2 Ken Griffey Jr./50 6.00 15.00
KM Kendry Morales/50 4.00 10.00
MA Daisuke Matsuzaka/50 30.00 60.00
MC Matt Cain/50 4.00 10.00
MH Matt Holliday/50 4.00 10.00
MH2 Matt Holliday/50 4.00 10.00
MI Miguel Cabrera/50 4.00 10.00
MI2 Miguel Cabrera/50 4.00 10.00
MO Justin Morneau/50 3.00 8.00
MO2 Justin Morneau/50 3.00 8.00
MS Mike Schmidt/50 6.00 15.00
MT Mark Teixeira/50 4.00 10.00
MY Michael Young/50 3.00 8.00
NM Nick Markakis/50 4.00 10.00
NR Nolan Ryan/50 12.50 30.00
OS Ozzie Smith/50 10.00 25.00
OS2 Ozzie Smith/50 10.00 25.00
PA Jonathan Papelbon/50 4.00 10.00
PF Prince Fielder/50 4.00 10.00
PK Paul Konerko/50 3.00 8.00
PM Paul Molitor/50 3.00 8.00
PN Phil Niekro/50 3.00 8.00
RA Roberto Alomar/50 6.00 15.00
RC Roger Clemens/50 6.00 15.00
RF Rollie Fingers/50 3.00 8.00
RH Roy Halladay/50 3.00 8.00
RI Cal Ripken Jr./50 15.00 40.00
RI2 Cal Ripken Jr./50 15.00 40.00
RJ Randy Johnson/50 4.00 10.00
RO Roy Oswalt/50 3.00 8.00
RS Ryne Sandberg/50 6.00 15.00
RW Rickie Weeks/50 3.00 8.00
RY Robin Yount/25
RZ Ryan Zimmerman/50 4.00 10.00
RZ2 Ryan Zimmerman/50 4.00 10.00
SK Scott Kazmir/50 4.00 10.00
SK2 Scott Kazmir/50 4.00 10.00
TG Tom Glavine/50 4.00 10.00
TH Torii Hunter/50 3.00 8.00
TR Travis Hafner/50 3.00 8.00
TR2 Travis Hafner/50 3.00 8.00
TT Troy Tulowitzki/50 4.00 10.00
VM Victor Martinez/50 3.00 8.00
WI Josh Willingham/50 3.00 8.00
WI2 Josh Willingham/50 3.00 8.00

2007 Ultimate Collection Ultimate Write of Passage

OVERALL AU ODDS ONE PER PACK
STATED PRINT RUN 60 SER.#'d SETS
NO PRICING DUE TO SCARCITY
EXCHANGE DEADLINE 9/24/2009
BH Jeff Baker AU 4.00 10.00
Matt Holliday/60
BR Ryan Braun AU 20.00 50.00
Scott Rolen/60
GR Alex Gordon AU 20.00 50.00
Alex Rodriguez/60
HS Cole Hamels AU 15.00 40.00
Johan Santana/60
IC Kei Igawa AU/60 15.00 40.00
IR Akinori Iwamura AU 15.00 40.00
Aramis Ramirez/60
KB Howie Kendrick AU 4.00 10.00
Craig Biggio/60
KJ Kevin Kouzmanoff AU 4.00 10.00
Chipper Jones/60
LZ Tim Lincecum AU 60.00 120.00
Barry Zito/60
MS Andrew Miller AU 12.50 30.00
C.C. Sabathia/60
PG Hunter Pence AU 30.00 60.00
Ken Griffey Jr./60
PK Glen Perkins AU 4.00 10.00
Scott Kazmir/60
QC Carlos Quentin AU 4.00 10.00
Carl Crawford/60
RF Hanley Ramirez AU 10.00 25.00
Rafael Furcal/60
SD Ryan Sweeney AU 4.00 10.00
Jermaine Dye/60
SS Jeremy Sowers AU 4.00 10.00
C.C. Sabathia/60
TD Curtis Thigpen AU 4.00 10.00
Carlos Delgado/60
TJ Troy Tulowitzki AU 30.00 60.00
Derek Jeter/60
UU B.J. Upton AU 4.00 10.00
Chase Utley/60
YG Delmon Young AU 6.00 15.00
Vladimir Guerrero/60

2008 Ultimate Collection

This set was released on January 6, 2009. The base set consists of 108 cards.

COMMON CARD (1-100) 1.00 2.50
1-100 PRINT RUN 350 SER.#'d SETS
OVERALL AUTO/MEM ODDS 1 PER PACK
101-108 PRINT RUN 99 SER.#'d SETS
EXCHANGE DEADLINE 12/12/2010
1 Jose Reyes 1.50 4.00
2 David Wright 3.00 8.00
3 Carlos Beltran 1.00 2.50
4 Johan Santana 2.50 6.00
5 Pedro Martinez 1.50 4.00
6 Jeff Francoeur 1.50 4.00
7 John Smoltz 2.50 6.00
8 Brian McCann 1.50 4.00
9 Chipper Jones 2.50 6.00
10 Cole Hamels 2.50 6.00
11 Ryan Howard 3.00 8.00
12 Jimmy Rollins 1.50 4.00
13 Chase Utley 2.50 6.00
14 Hanley Ramirez 2.50 6.00
15 Dan Uggla 1.50 4.00
16 Lastings Milledge 1.00 2.50
17 Ryan Zimmerman 1.50 4.00
18 Ryan Ludwick 1.00 2.50
19 Troy Glaus 1.50 4.00
20 Albert Pujols 6.00 15.00
21 Rick Ankiel 1.00 2.50
22 Ryan Doumit 1.00 2.50
23 Nate McLouth 1.00 2.50
24 Lance Berkman 1.50 4.00
25 Carlos Lee 1.00 2.50
26 Miguel Tejada 1.50 4.00
27 CC Sabathia 1.50 4.00
28 Ryan Braun 3.00 8.00
29 Prince Fielder 1.50 4.00
30 Alfonso Soriano 1.50 4.00
31 Derrek Lee 1.00 2.50
32 Carlos Zambrano 1.50 4.00
33 Aramis Ramirez 1.00 2.50
34 Rich Harden 1.00 2.50
35 Edinson Volquez 1.00 2.50
36 Brandon Phillips 1.00 2.50
37 Brandon Webb 1.50 4.00
38 Dan Haren 1.00 2.50
39 Chris B. Young 1.00 2.50
40 Randy Johnson 2.50 6.00
41 Adam Dunn 1.50 4.00
42 Matt Holliday 2.50 6.00
43 Troy Tulowitzki 2.50 6.00
44 Garrett Atkins 1.00 2.50
45 Manny Ramirez 2.50 6.00
46 Greg Maddux 3.00 8.00
47 Matt Kemp 1.50 4.00
48 Russell Martin 1.00 2.50
49 Aaron Rowand 1.00 2.50
50 Tim Lincecum 4.00 10.00
51 Adrian Gonzalez 1.50 4.00
52 Jake Peavy 1.00 2.50
53 Trevor Hoffman 1.50 4.00
54 Ivan Rodriguez 1.50 4.00
55 Alex Rodriguez 4.00 10.00
56 Derek Jeter 6.00 15.00
57 Hideki Matsui 2.50 6.00
58 Robinson Cano 2.50 6.00
59 Joba Chamberlain 1.50 4.00
60 Chien-Ming Wang 1.50 4.00
61 Mariano Rivera 2.50 6.00
62 Xavier Nady 1.00 2.50
63 Josh Beckett 1.50 4.00
64 David Ortiz 1.50 4.00
65 Dustin Pedroia 3.00 8.00
66 Jonathan Papelbon 1.50 4.00
67 Daisuke Matsuzaka 2.50 6.00
68 Kevin Youkilis 1.50 4.00
69 Jason Bay 1.50 4.00
70 Nick Markakis 2.50 6.00
71 Brian Roberts 1.00 2.50
72 Scott Kazmir 1.50 4.00
73 Carl Crawford 1.50 4.00
74 B.J. Upton 1.50 4.00
75 Vernon Wells 1.00 2.50
76 Roy Halladay 2.50 6.00
77 Jermaine Dye 1.00 2.50
78 Jim Thome 1.50 4.00
79 Ken Griffey Jr. 4.00 10.00
80 Carlos Quentin 1.00 2.50
81 Magglio Ordonez 1.50 4.00
82 Justin Verlander 3.00 8.00
83 Miguel Cabrera 2.50 6.00
84 Alex Gordon 1.50 4.00
85 Billy Butler 1.00 2.50
86 Grady Sizemore 1.50 4.00
87 Victor Martinez 1.50 4.00
88 Travis Hafner 1.00 2.50
89 Joe Mauer 2.50 6.00
90 Justin Morneau 2.50 6.00
91 Erik Bedard 1.00 2.50
92 Felix Hernandez 2.50 6.00
93 Ichiro Suzuki 4.00 10.00
94 Ian Kinsler 1.50 4.00
95 Josh Hamilton 2.50 6.00
96 Frank Thomas 2.50 6.00
97 Jack Cust 1.00 2.50
98 Torii Hunter 1.00 2.50
99 Vladimir Guerrero 2.50 6.00
100 Mark Teixeira 2.50 6.00
101 Evan Longoria Jsy AU/99 RC 150.00 250.00
102 Max Scherzer Jsy AU/99 RC 15.00 40.00
103 Kosuke Fukudome Jsy/99 RC 20.00 50.00
104 Ian Kennedy Jsy AU/99 RC 30.00 60.00
105 Clay Buchholz Jsy AU/99 (RC) 10.00 25.00
106 Jay Bruce Jsy AU/99 (RC) 12.50 30.00
107 Clayton Kershaw Jsy AU/99 RC 30.00 60.00
108 Chin-Lung Hu Jsy AU/99 (RC) 20.00 50.00

2008 Ultimate Collection Autographs Dual

OVERALL AUTO/MEM ODDS 1 PER PACK
PRINT RUNS B/WN 10-50 COPIES PER
NO PRICING ON QTY 25 OR LESS
EXCHANGE DEADLINE 12/12/2010
DR Tim Raines
Andre Dawson/25
FE Chone Figgins
Edwin Encarnacion/50
GC Kirk Gibson
Joe Carter/15
GG Ken Griffey Jr. 60.00 120.00
Ken Griffey Sr./50
IN Monte Irvin 15.00 40.00
Don Newcombe/35
JR Derek Jeter 100.00 175.00
Hanley Ramirez/50
JW Bo Jackson
Dave Winfield/10
KG Al Kaline 30.00 60.00
Curtis Granderson/35
MB Jack Morris
Josh Beckett/10
RB J.R. Richard 15.00 40.00
Dennis Boyd/50
SG Don Sutton
Steve Garvey/15
TK J.R. Towles 6.00 15.00
Ian Kennedy/50
YY Carl Yastrzemski
Kevin Youkilis/10

2008 Ultimate Collection Autographs Triple

OVERALL AUTO/MEM ODDS 1 PER PACK
PRINT RUNS B/WN 10-50 COPIES PER
NO PRICING ON QTY 25 OR LESS
EXCHANGE DEADLINE 12/12/2010
AJK Dick Allen 20.00 50.00
Geoff Jenkins
John Kruk/35
BCP Johnny Bench
Dave Concepcion
Tony Perez/15
CAH Joe Carter
Roberto Alomar
Roy Halladay/15
GSE Goose Gossage
Bruce Sutter
Dennis Eckersley/20
GWS Tony Gwynn
Dave Winfield
Ozzie Smith/5
LHJ Cliff Lee
Cole Hamels
Randy Johnson/5
MWB Don Mattingly
Dave Winfield
Wade Boggs/5
PNW Jonathan Papelbon 30.00 60.00
Joe Nathan
Billy Wagner/50
RHT Hanley Ramirez 40.00 80.00
Chin-Lung Hu
Troy Tulowitzki/50
SRJ Ozzie Smith
Cal Ripken Jr.
Derek Jeter/5
SRL Alfonso Soriano
Aramis Ramirez
Derrek Lee/15

2008 Ultimate Collection Barrel Autographs

OVERALL AUTO/MEM ODDS 1 PER PACK
PRINT RUNS B/WN 10-140 COPIES PER
NO PRICING ON QTY 25 OR LESS
EXCHANGE DEADLINE 12/12/2010
AR Aramis Ramirez/35 12.50 30.00
BE Johnny Bench/10
BW Billy Williams/25
CF Carlton Fisk/15
CH Chin-Lung Hu/68 40.00 80.00
CJ Chipper Jones/15
CR Cal Ripken Jr./10
CY Carl Yastrzemski/10
DJ Derek Jeter/99 100.00 175.00
DL Derrek Lee/50 15.00 40.00
DM Don Mattingly/15
FR Frank Robinson/10
JR Jim Rice/140 12.50 30.00
JV Jason Varitek/15
KG Ken Griffey Jr./75 75.00 150.00
KY Kevin Youkilis/50 20.00 50.00
MS Mike Schmidt/15
OS Ozzie Smith/15
PF Prince Fielder/25
RJ Reggie Jackson/10
SA Ryne Sandberg/15
SM Stan Musial/10
YO Chris B. Young/15

2008 Ultimate Collection Dual Memorabilia Autographs

OVERALL AUTO/MEM ODDS 1 PER PACK
PRINT RUNS B/WN 5-99 COPIES PER
NO PRICING ON QTY 25 OR LESS
EXCHANGE DEADLINE 12/12/2010
BE Johnny Bench/5
BO Bo Jackson/5
BP Brandon Phillips/75 8.00 20.00
BR Brian McCann/25
BU Clay Buchholz/25
CH Chin-Lung Hu/75 15.00 40.00
CJ Chipper Jones/5
CR Cal Ripken Jr./10
DJ Derek Jeter/50 150.00 300.00
DL Derrek Lee/10
DM Daisuke Matsuzaka/10
DO Don Mattingly/99 30.00 60.00
DW Dave Winfield/5
FL Fred Lynn/15
HA Cole Hamels/10
HR Hanley Ramirez/15
IK Ian Kennedy/25
JR Jim Rice/15
JV Jason Varitek/5
KG Ken Griffey Jr./50 90.00 150.00
KJ Kelly Johnson/75 4.00 10.00
MS Mike Schmidt/5
NM Nick Markakis/75 12.50 30.00
NR Nolan Ryan/5
OS Ozzie Smith/10
PA Jonathan Papelbon/15
PF Prince Fielder/10
PH Phil Hughes/15
RJ Reggie Jackson/5
RS Ryne Sandberg/5
TT Troy Tulowitzki/50 8.00 20.00
WB Wade Boggs/5

2008 Ultimate Collection Home Jersey Autographs

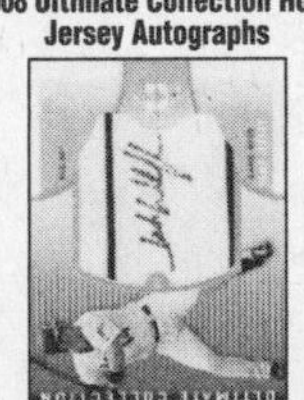

OVERALL AUTO/MEM ODDS 1 PER PACK
PRINT RUNS B/WN 5-99 COPIES PER
NO PRICING ON QTY 25 OR LESS
EXCHANGE DEADLINE 12/12/2010
BE Johnny Bench/25
BJ Bo Jackson/15
BW Billy Williams/25
CF Carlton Fisk/10
CH Cole Hamels/25
CJ Chipper Jones/10
CR Cal Ripken Jr./15
DA Daisuke Matsuzaka/10
DJ Derek Jeter/99 125.00 250.00
DL Derrek Lee/15
DM Daisuke Matsuzaka/10
FL Fred Lynn/25
GN Graig Nettles/25
JF Jeff Francoeur/99 10.00 25.00
JI Jim Rice/50 15.00 40.00
JM Jack Morris/50 8.00 20.00
JO John Maine/50 8.00 20.00
JP Jim Palmer/5
JR Cal Ripken Jr./25
JV Jason Varitek/10
JW Josh Willingham/99 5.00 12.00
KG Ken Griffey Jr./99 40.00 80.00
KY Kevin Youkilis/50 12.50 30.00
MA Don Mattingly/15
MS Mike Schmidt/15
NR Nolan Ryan/15
OS Ozzie Smith/25
PA Jonathan Papelbon/50 12.50 30.00
PF Prince Fielder/25
PH Phil Hughes/25
PM Paul Molitor/25
RC Roger Clemens/10
RJ Reggie Jackson/10
RS Ron Santo/35 30.00 60.00
TM Tino Martinez/25
TT Troy Tulowitzki/99 10.00 25.00
WB Wade Boggs/10
WI Josh Willingham/99 5.00 12.00

2008 Ultimate Collection Pants Autographs

OVERALL AUTO/MEM ODDS 1 PER PACK
PRINT RUNS B/WN 10-99 COPIES PER
NO PRICING ON QTY 25 OR LESS
EXCHANGE DEADLINE 12/12/2010
BE Johnny Bench/10
BJ Bo Jackson/10
BP Brandon Phillips/99 6.00 15.00
BW Billy Williams/25
CR Cal Ripken Jr./25
DA Daisuke Matsuzaka/10
DJ Derek Jeter/99 125.00 250.00
DL Derrek Lee/25
DM Daisuke Matsuzaka/10
HA Hanley Ramirez/25
HR Hanley Ramirez/25
JC Joe Carter/25
JF Jeff Francoeur/99 10.00 25.00
JI Jim Rice/50 15.00 40.00
JM Jack Morris/50 8.00 20.00
JO John Maine/50 8.00 20.00
JR Cal Ripken Jr./25
JV Jason Varitek/10
KG Ken Griffey Jr./99 90.00 150.00
KY Kevin Youkilis/50 12.50 30.00
NR Nolan Ryan/25
OS Ozzie Smith/25
PA Jonathan Papelbon/50 12.50 30.00
PH Phil Hughes/25
PM Paul Molitor/25
RJ Reggie Jackson/10
RS Ron Santo/50 30.00 60.00
SA Ryne Sandberg/25
SC Steve Carlton/25
TM Tino Martinez/50
TT Troy Tulowitzki/99 10.00 25.00
WB Wade Boggs/15

2008 Ultimate Collection Quad Memorabilia Autographs

OVERALL AUTO/MEM ODDS 1 PER PACK
PRINT RUNS B/WN 5-75 COPIES PER
NO PRICING ON QTY 25 OR LESS
EXCHANGE DEADLINE 12/12/2010
BE Johnny Bench/5
BO Bo Jackson/10
BP Brandon Phillips/75 6.00 15.00
BR Brian McCann/25
BU Clay Buchholz/25
CF Carlton Fisk/10
CH Chin-Lung Hu/75 20.00 50.00
CJ Chipper Jones/10
CR Cal Ripken Jr./10
CY Carl Yastrzemski/5
DJ Derek Jeter/50 150.00 300.00
DL Derrek Lee/10
DM Daisuke Matsuzaka/10
FL Fred Lynn/15
HA Cole Hamels/10
HR Hanley Ramirez/15
IK Ian Kennedy/25
JO John Maine/75 8.00 20.00
JR Jim Rice/15
JV Jason Varitek/10
KG Ken Griffey Jr./50 75.00 150.00
MS Mike Schmidt/5
NR Nolan Ryan/5
OS Ozzie Smith/15
PA Jonathan Papelbon/15
PF Prince Fielder/15
PH Phil Hughes/20
RJ Reggie Jackson/5
TT Troy Tulowitzki/50 10.00 25.00
WB Wade Boggs/10

2008 Ultimate Collection Quad Memorabilia Autographs Prime

OVERALL AUTO/MEM ODDS 1 PER PACK
STATED PRINT RUN 5 SER.#'d SETS
NO PRICING DUE TO SCARCITY
EXCHANGE DEADLINE 12/12/2010

2008 Ultimate Collection Road Jersey Autographs

OVERALL AUTO/MEM ODDS 1 PER PACK
PRINT RUNS B/WN 10-99 COPIES PER
NO PRICING ON QTY 25 OR LESS
EXCHANGE DEADLINE 12/12/2010
AR Aramis Ramirez/50 12.50 30.00
BP Brandon Phillips/99 6.00 15.00
BW Billy Williams/25
CH Cole Hamels/25
CJ Chipper Jones/10
CR Cal Ripken Jr./25
DA Daisuke Matsuzaka/10
DJ Derek Jeter/99 125.00 250.00
DL Derrek Lee/15
DM Daisuke Matsuzaka/10
FL Fred Lynn/25
GN Graig Nettles/25
HA Hanley Ramirez/25
JC Joe Carter/25
JF Jeff Francoeur/99 10.00 25.00
JI Jim Rice/50 15.00 40.00
JM Jack Morris/50 8.00 20.00
JO John Maine/75 6.00 15.00
JR Cal Ripken Jr./25
JV Jason Varitek/10
KG Ken Griffey Jr./99 40.00 80.00
KY Kevin Youkilis/50 12.50 30.00
OS Ozzie Smith/25
PA Jonathan Papelbon/25
PF Prince Fielder/25
PH Phil Hughes/35
PM Paul Molitor/25
RJ Reggie Jackson/10
RS Ron Santo/50 30.00 60.00
SM Stan Musial/25
TM Tino Martinez/25
WB Wade Boggs/15

2008 Ultimate Collection Triple Memorabilia Autographs

OVERALL AUTO/MEM ODDS 1 PER PACK
PRINT RUNS B/WN 5-99 COPIES PER
NO PRICING ON QTY 25 OR LESS
EXCHANGE DEADLINE 12/12/2010
BE Johnny Bench/5
BP Brandon Phillips/99 6.00 15.00
BR Brian McCann/25
BU Clay Buchholz/25
CH Chin-Lung Hu/99 20.00 50.00
CJ Chipper Jones/5
CR Cal Ripken Jr./10
DJ Derek Jeter/50 150.00 300.00
DL Derrek Lee/10
DM Daisuke Matsuzaka/5
DO Don Mattingly/5
FL Fred Lynn/15
HA Cole Hamels/15
HR Hanley Ramirez/25
IK Ian Kennedy/25
JO John Maine/99 8.00 20.00
JR Jim Rice/20
JV Jason Varitek/5
KG Ken Griffey Jr./50 75.00 150.00
MS Mike Schmidt/5
NR Nolan Ryan/5
OS Ozzie Smith/15
PA Jonathan Papelbon/20
PF Prince Fielder/10
PH Phil Hughes/25
RJ Reggie Jackson/5
RS Ryne Sandberg/5
TT Troy Tulowitzki/50 10.00 25.00
WB Wade Boggs/5

2009 Ultimate Collection

COMMON CARD (1-55) .75 2.00
1-55 PRINT RUN 599 SER.#'d SETS
COMMON CARD (56-100) 1.25 3.00
56-100 PRINT RUN 599 SER.#'d SETS
APPX. ROOKIE AU ODDS 1:8 HOBBY PACKS
101-109 PRINT RUNS B/WN 15-175 COPIES PER
NO D.PRICE PRICING AVAILABLE
1 Stephen Drew .75 2.00
2 Chipper Jones 2.00 5.00
3 Brian McCann 1.25 3.00
4 Nick Markakis 2.00 5.00
5 Adam Jones 1.25 3.00
6 Dustin Pedroia 2.50 6.00
7 Josh Beckett 1.25 3.00
8 Kevin Youkilis 1.25 3.00
9 Victor Martinez 1.25 3.00
10 Daisuke Matsuzaka 2.00 5.00
11 Kosuke Fukudome 2.00 5.00
12 Carlos Zambrano 1.25 3.00
13 Alfonso Soriano 1.25 3.00
14 Jim Thome 1.25 3.00
15 Joey Votto 2.00 5.00
16 Grady Sizemore 1.25 3.00
17 Todd Helton 1.25 3.00
18 Miguel Cabrera 2.00 5.00
19 Curtis Granderson 1.25 3.00
20 Hanley Ramirez 2.00 5.00
21 Josh Johnson 1.25 3.00
22 Lance Berkman 1.25 3.00
23 Roy Oswalt 1.25 3.00
24 Zack Greinke 1.25 3.00
25 Vladimir Guerrero 2.00 5.00
26 Clayton Kershaw 2.00 5.00
27 Manny Ramirez 2.00 5.00
28 Russell Martin .75 2.00
29 Prince Fielder 1.25 3.00
30 Ryan Braun 2.50 6.00
31 Joe Mauer 2.00 5.00
32 Justin Morneau 2.00 5.00
33 Francisco Liriano .75 2.00
34 Johan Santana 2.00 5.00
35 David Wright 2.50 6.00
36 Jose Reyes 1.25 3.00
37 Derek Jeter 5.00 12.00
38 CC Sabathia 1.25 3.00
39 Hideki Matsui 2.00 5.00
40 Alex Rodriguez 3.00 8.00
41 Chase Utley 2.00 5.00
42 Cole Hamels 2.00 5.00
43 Ryan Howard 2.50 6.00
44 Jimmy Rollins 1.25 3.00
45 Cliff Lee 1.25 3.00
46 Adrian Gonzalez 1.25 3.00
47 Randy Johnson 1.25 3.00
48 Ken Griffey Jr. 3.00 8.00
49 Ichiro Suzuki 3.00 8.00
50 Albert Pujols 5.00 12.00
51 Evan Longoria 2.50 6.00
52 B.J. Upton 1.25 3.00
53 Josh Hamilton 2.00 5.00
54 Roy Halladay 2.00 5.00
55 Adam Dunn 1.25 3.00
56 Brett Anderson RC 2.00 5.00
57 Elvis Andrus RC 2.00 5.00
58 Alex Avila RC 2.00 5.00
59 Andrew Bailey RC 3.00 8.00
60 Daniel Bard RC 1.25 3.00
61 Brad Bergesen (RC) 1.25 3.00
62 Kyle Blanks RC 2.00 5.00
63 Michael Bowden (RC) 1.25 3.00
64 Everth Cabrera RC 2.00 5.00
65 Trevor Cahill RC 3.00 8.00
66 Brett Cecil RC 1.25 3.00
67 Jhoulys Chacin RC 2.00 5.00
68 Aaron Cunningham RC 1.25 3.00
69 Travis Snider RC 2.00 5.00
70 Dexter Fowler (RC) 2.00 5.00
71 Lucas French (RC) 1.25 3.00
72 Mat Gamel RC 3.00 8.00

73 David Hernandez RC 1.25 3.00
74 Derek Holland RC 2.00 5.00
75 Tommy Hunter RC 2.00 5.00
76 Mat Latos RC 4.00 10.00
77 Fernando Martinez RC 3.00 8.00
78 Vin Mazzaro RC 1.25 3.00
79 Andrew McCutchen (RC) 5.00 12.00
80 Kris Medlen RC 2.00 5.00
81 Fu-Te Ni RC 2.00 5.00
82 Bud Norris RC 1.25 3.00
83 Gerardo Parra RC 2.00 5.00
84 Ryan Perry RC 3.00 8.00
85 Aaron Poreda RC 1.25 3.00
86 Sean O'Sullivan RC 1.25 3.00
87 Wilkin Ramirez RC 1.25 3.00
88 Josh Reddick RC 2.00 5.00
89 Nolan Reimold (RC) 1.25 3.00
90 Ricky Romero (RC) 3.00 8.00
91 Marc Rzepczynski RC 2.00 5.00
92 Pablo Sandoval 4.00 10.00
93 Michael Saunders RC 2.00 5.00
94 Jordan Schafer (RC) 2.00 5.00
95 Daniel Schlereth RC 1.25 3.00
96 Anthony Swarzak (RC) 1.25 3.00
97 Junichi Tazawa RC 4.00 10.00
98 Chris Tillman RC 2.00 5.00
99 Sean West (RC) 2.00 5.00
100 Trevor Bell (RC) 1.25 3.00
101 Koji Uehara AU/175 RC 12.50 30.00
102 Colby Rasmus AU/135 (RC) 15.00 40.00
103 Matt Wieters AU/135 RC 30.00 60.00
104 Kenshin Kawakami AU/135 8.00 20.00
105 David Price AU/15 RC
106 Tommy Hanson AU/135 RC 15.00 40.00
107 Matt LaPorta AU/160 RC 12.50 30.00
108 Neftali Feliz AU/135 RC 20.00 50.00
109 Gordon Beckham AU/135 RC 20.00 50.00
110 Rick Porcello AU/135 RC 20.00 50.00

2009 Ultimate Collection Blue Rookie Signatures

APPX. RC AU ODDS 1:8 HOBBY PACKS
STATED PRINT RUN 15 SER.#'d SETS
NO PRICING DUE TO SCARCITY

2009 Ultimate Collection Gold Rookie Signatures

ONE AU,MEM, OR AU MEM PER PACK
PRINT RUNS B/WN 5-75 COPIES PER
NO D.PRICE PRICING AVAILABLE
ALL VARIATIONS PRICED EQUALLY
101a Koji Uehara/75 12.50 30.00
101b Koji Uehara/75 12.50 30.00
102a Colby Rasmus/45 20.00 50.00
102b Colby Rasmus/45 20.00 50.00
103a Matt Wieters/45 50.00 100.00
103b Matt Wieters/45 50.00 100.00
105a David Price/5
105b David Price/5
106a Tommy Hanson/45 40.00 80.00
106b Tommy Hanson/45 40.00 80.00
107a Matt LaPorta/45 12.50 30.00
107b Matt LaPorta/45 12.50 30.00
108a Neftali Feliz/45 30.00 60.00
108b Neftali Feliz/45 30.00 60.00
109a Gordon Beckham/45 30.00 60.00
109b Gordon Beckham/45 30.00 60.00
110a Rick Porcello/45 30.00 60.00
110b Rick Porcello/45 30.00 60.00

2009 Ultimate Collection Career Highlight Signatures

ONE AU,MEM, OR AU MEM PER PACK
PRINT RUNS B/WN 1-40 COPIES PER
NO PRICING ON QTY 25 OR LESS
BD Bucky Dent/20
BF Bob Feller/19
BJ Bo Jackson/16
DE Dennis Eckersley/7
GP Gaylord Perry/6
JC Joba Chamberlain/20
JP Jim Palmer/22
NM Nick Markakis/21
TR Tim Raines/3
CH2 Cole Hamels/8
CR1 Cal Ripken Jr./8
CR2 Cal Ripken Jr./8
CR3 Cal Ripken Jr./8
DJ1 Derek Jeter/20
DJ2 Derek Jeter/21
DJ3 Derek Jeter/22
DJ4 Derek Jeter/30 100.00 200.00
DJ5 Derek Jeter/40 100.00 200.00
DJ6 Derek Jeter/28
DJ7 Derek Jeter/20
HR1 Hanley Ramirez/26 30.00 60.00
HR2 Hanley Ramirez/22
JL1 Jon Lester/23
JL2 Jon Lester/31 15.00 40.00
JR1 Ken Griffey Jr./19
JR2 Ken Griffey Jr./20
JR3 Ken Griffey Jr./25
JR4 Ken Griffey Jr./25
JR7 Ken Griffey Jr./40 40.00 80.00
JR8 Ken Griffey Jr./40 40.00 80.00
KG1 Ken Griffey Sr./25
KG2 Ken Griffey Sr./25
KG3 Ken Griffey Sr./26
KG4 Ken Griffey Sr./30 6.00 15.00
KG5 Ken Griffey Sr./40 12.50 30.00
NR1 Nolan Ryan/4
NR2 Nolan Ryan/1
NR3 Nolan Ryan/2
RJ1 Randy Johnson/5
RJ2 Randy Johnson/1
RJ3 Randy Johnson/1

2009 Ultimate Collection Generations Eight Memorabilia

ONE AU,MEM, OR AU MEM PER PACK
STATED PRINT RUN 35 SER.#'d SETS
G8M1 Bruce Sutter
Alfonso Soriano
Albert Pujols
Lou Brock
Ryne Sandberg
Lou Boudreau
Billy Williams
Red Schoendienst/35
G8M2 Justin Morneau
Prince Fielder
Harmon Killebrew
Eddie Murray
Albert Pujols
Willie McCovey
Tony Perez
Todd Helton/35
G8M3 Yogi Berra 50.00 100.00
Joe DiMaggio
Jorge Posada
Eddie Murray
Carlos Beltran
Carlos Delgado
Derek Jeter
Reggie Jackson/35
G8M4 Reggie Jackson 60.00 120.00
Bob Lemon
Catfish Hunter
Phil Rizzuto
Derek Jeter
Joe DiMaggio
Yogi Berra
Whitey Ford/35
G8M5 Yogi Berra 60.00 120.00
Joe DiMaggio
Jorge Posada
Derek Jeter
Phil Rizzuto
Chien-Ming Wang
Reggie Jackson
Robinson Cano/35
G8M6 Joey Votto
Jay Bruce
Aaron Harang
Johnny Bench
Joe Morgan
Brandon Phillips
Ken Griffey Jr.
Tony Perez/35
G8M7 Jorge Posada
Ivan Rodriguez
Yogi Berra
Carlton Fisk
Victor Martinez
Johnny Bench
Brian McCann
Russell Martin/35
G8M8 Satchel Paige 50.00 100.00
Jim Palmer
Fergie Jenkins
Nolan Ryan
Robin Roberts
Tom Seaver
Phil Niekro
Juan Marichal/35
G8M9 Edgar Martinez 12.50 30.00
Eddie Murray
Ken Griffey Jr.
Randy Johnson
Grady Sizemore
Victor Martinez
Kenji Johjima
Satchel Paige/35
G8M10 Harmon Killebrew
Denard Span
Justin Morneau
Rod Carew
Francisco Liriano
Johan Santana
Joe Mauer
Torii Hunter/35
G8M11 Mike Schmidt
Eddie Murray
Carlos Beltran
Carlos Delgado
Chase Utley
Jimmy Rollins
Cole Hamels
John Maine/35
G8M12 Ryan Zimmerman
Eddie Mathews
Evan Longoria
Kevin Youkilis
Mike Schmidt
Chipper Jones
Brooks Robinson
Aramis Ramirez/35
G8M13 Ozzie Smith 20.00 50.00
Cal Ripken Jr.
Derek Jeter
Jimmy Rollins
Brian Roberts
Troy Tulowitzki
Stephen Drew
Hanley Ramirez/35
G8M14 Hoyt Wilhelm 30.00 60.00
Reggie Jackson
Billy Williams
Tim Lincecum
Rollie Fingers
Willie McCovey
Gaylord Perry
Joe DiMaggio/35
G8M15 Jason Varitek 30.00 60.00
Carlton Fisk
Pedro Martinez
Manny Ramirez
Ted Williams
Daisuke Matsuzaka
Orlando Cepeda
Fergie Jenkins/35

2009 Ultimate Collection Generations Eight Memorabilia Gold

ONE AU,MEM, OR AU MEM PER PACK
PRINT RUNS B/WN 5-20 COPIES PER
NO PRICING DUE TO SCARCITY

2009 Ultimate Collection Generations Six Memorabilia

ONE AU,MEM, OR AU MEM PER PACK
PRINT RUNS B/WN 25-50 COPIES PER
NO PRICING ON QTY 25 OR LESS
G6M1 Tom Seaver
Jay Bruce
Joey Votto
Joe Morgan
Johnny Bench
Brandon Phillips/50
G6M2 Fergie Jenkins 20.00 50.00
Ted Williams
Jason Varitek
Carlton Fisk
Tony Perez
David Ortiz/50
G6M3 Jorge Posada 30.00 60.00
Yogi Berra
Joe DiMaggio
Derek Jeter
Chien-Ming Wang
Reggie Jackson/40
G6M4 Cole Hamels
Jim Bunning
Chase Utley
Jimmy Rollins
Mike Schmidt
Robin Roberts/25
G6M5 Willie Stargell
Ralph Kiner
Bill Mazeroski
Roberto Clemente
Jim Bunning
Zach Duke/25
G6M6 Tim Lincecum
Willie McCovey
Gaylord Perry
Juan Marichal
Barry Zito
Omar Vizquel/25
G6M7 Eric Chavez 20.00 50.00
Joe DiMaggio
Bobby Crosby
Billy Williams
Reggie Jackson
Harmon Killebrew/50
G6M8 Eddie Mathews
Orlando Cepeda
Brian McCann
Tim Hudson
Phil Niekro
Chipper Jones/50
G6M9 Derek Jeter 15.00 40.00
Johnny Damon
Jorge Posada
Whitey Ford
Reggie Jackson
Robinson Cano/50
G6M10 Daisuke Matsuzaka 30.00 60.00
Jacoby Ellsbury
Jon Lester
Pedro Martinez
Ted Williams
Manny Ramirez/50
G6M11 Ryne Sandberg
Derrek Lee
Lou Boudreau
Bruce Sutter
Carlos Zambrano
Billy Williams/50
G6M12 Red Schoendienst 30.00 60.00
Bruce Sutter
Enos Slaughter
Albert Pujols
Lou Brock
Ozzie Smith/50
G6M13 Cal Ripken Jr.
Jim Palmer
Earl Weaver
Brian Roberts
Nick Markakis
Adam Jones/40
G6M14 Ian Kinsler
Fergie Jenkins
Hank Blalock
Gaylord Perry
Josh Hamilton
Nolan Ryan/50
G6M15 Nolan Ryan
Lance Berkman
Carlos Lee
Roy Oswalt
Hunter Pence
Felipe Paulino/50
G6M16 Ryan Braun
Yovani Gallardo
Robin Yount
Don Sutton
Rickie Weeks
Prince Fielder/50
G6M17 Grady Sizemore 20.00 50.00
Victor Martinez
Satchel Paige
Travis Hafner
Dennis Eckersley
Bob Feller/50
G6M18 Lou Boudreau
Ryne Sandberg
Jim Thome
Jermaine Dye
Carlton Fisk
Billy Williams/50
G6M19 Reggie Jackson 30.00 60.00
Joe DiMaggio
Yogi Berra
Carlos Beltran
Eddie Murray
Derek Jeter/50
G6M20 Derek Jeter
Joe DiMaggio
Earl Weaver
Jim Palmer
Nick Markakis
Chien-Ming Wang/50

2009 Ultimate Collection Jumbo Bat Signatures

ONE AU,MEM, OR AU MEM PER PACK
PRINT RUNS B/WN 5-50 COPIES PER
NO PRICING ON QTY 25 OR LESS
CF Carlton Fisk/8
CJ Chipper Jones/10
CR Cal Ripken Jr./8
DJ Derek Jeter/50 100.00 175.00
JB Johnny Bench/5
KY Kevin Youkilis/50
LB Lou Brock/20
MS Mike Schmidt/20
OS Ozzie Smith/25
RC Rod Carew/29 20.00 50.00

2009 Ultimate Collection Jumbo Jersey

ONE AU,MEM, OR AU MEM PER PACK
PRINT RUNS B/WN 5-35 COPIES PER
NO PRICING ON QTY 25 OR LESS
JA Reggie Jackson/44 10.00 25.00
SP Satchel Paige/29 100.00 200.00

2009 Ultimate Collection Jumbo Jersey Signatures

ONE AU,MEM, OR AU MEM PER PACK
PRINT RUNS B/WN 8-50 COPIES PER
NO PRICING ON QTY 25 OR LESS
BF Bob Feller/28 15.00 40.00
BJ Bo Jackson/16
BM Brian McCann/35 20.00 50.00
BU B.J. Upton/40 12.50 30.00
CF Carlton Fisk/27 30.00 60.00
CJ Chipper Jones/40
CR Cal Ripken Jr./8
DJ Derek Jeter/50 100.00 175.00
GP Gaylord Perry/36 12.50 30.00
HR Hanley Ramirez/50 15.00 40.00
JB Johnny Bench/10
JL Jon Lester/31 20.00 50.00
JP Jim Palmer/50 15.00 40.00
JS James Shields/50 5.00 12.00
KG Ken Griffey Jr./50 50.00 100.00
LB Lou Brock/20
MK Matt Kemp/50 15.00 40.00
MS Mike Schmidt/20
NM Nick Markakis/49 15.00 40.00
OS Ozzie Smith/25
PA Jonathan Papelbon/50 10.00 25.00
WF Whitey Ford/40 30.00 60.00
ZG Zack Greinke/35 15.00 40.00

2009 Ultimate Collection Legendary Dual Patch Signature

OVERALL AU-MEM CARDS 1:5 HOBBY PACKS
PRINT RUNS B/WN 5-30 COPIES PER
NO PRICING ON QTY 25 OR LESS
BD Bucky Dent/10
CF Carlton Fisk/8
CR Cal Ripken Jr./8
JB Johnny Bench/5
LB Lou Brock/20
MS Mike Schmidt/20
NR Nolan Ryan/6
OS Ozzie Smith/11
PA Jim Palmer/22
RC Rod Carew/19
RF Rollie Fingers/12
RY Robin Yount/19
TR Tim Raines/30 30.00 60.00

2009 Ultimate Collection Legendary Eight Memorabilia

ONE AU,MEM, OR AU MEM PER PACK
PRINT RUNS B/WN 25-35 COPIES PER
L8M1 Phil Rizzuto 40.00 80.00
Catfish Hunter
Bob Lemon
Reggie Jackson
Bucky Dent
Whitey Ford
Yogi Berra
Joe DiMaggio/35
L8M2 Bill Mazeroski
Roberto Clemente
Tony Perez
Harmon Killebrew
Jim Palmer
Earl Weaver
Johnny Bench
Rod Carew/35
L8M3 Eddie Mathews
Orlando Cepeda
Ralph Kiner
Roberto Clemente
Whitey Ford
Yogi Berra
Ted Williams
Early Wynn/25
L8M4 Mike Schmidt 40.00 80.00
Eddie Murray
Phil Niekro
Ryne Sandberg
Ozzie Smith
Carlton Fisk
Robin Yount
Reggie Jackson/35
L8M5 Satchel Paige 60.00 120.00
Phil Rizzuto
Red Schoendienst
Joe DiMaggio
Yogi Berra
Ted Williams
Lou Boudreau
Bob Feller/35
L8M6 Roberto Clemente 40.00 80.00
Willie McCovey
Brooks Robinson
Lou Brock
Jim Palmer
Johnny Bench
Harmon Killebrew
Reggie Jackson/35
L8M7 Billy Williams 50.00 100.00
Fergie Jenkins
Lou Brock
Yogi Berra
Joe DiMaggio
Lou Boudreau
Ted Williams
Ozzie Smith/35
L8M8 Ryne Sandberg 40.00 80.00
Roberto Clemente
Lou Brock
Tony Perez
Jim Bunning
Johnny Bench
Red Schoendienst
Billy Williams/35

2009 Ultimate Collection Legendary Signatures

ONE AU,MEM, OR AU MEM PER PACK
PRINT RUNS B/WN 2-35 COPIES PER
NO PRICING ON QTY 25 OR LESS
EM Edgar Martinez/11
YB Yogi Berra/8
BD1 Bucky Dent/25
BD2 Bucky Dent/14
BD3 Bucky Dent/9
BF1 Bob Feller/35 12.50 30.00
BF2 Bob Feller/25
BJ1 Bo Jackson/16
BJ2 Bo Jackson/16
BJ3 Bo Jackson/14
CF1 Carlton Fisk/12
CF2 Carlton Fisk/9
CR1 Cal Ripken Jr./25
CR2 Cal Ripken Jr./8
DE1 Dennis Eckersley/35 10.00 25.00
DE2 Dennis Eckersley/6
DE3 Dennis Eckersley/8
DE4 Dennis Eckersley/35 10.00 25.00
DE5 Dennis Eckersley/25
GP1 Gaylord Perry/9
GP2 Gaylord Perry/6
GP3 Gaylord Perry/7
GP4 Gaylord Perry/5
GP5 Gaylord Perry/4
GP6 Gaylord Perry/5
GP7 Gaylord Perry/8
GP8 Gaylord Perry/2
JP1 Jim Palmer/22
JP2 Jim Palmer/14
KG1 Ken Griffey Sr./16
KG2 Ken Griffey Sr./9
KG3 Ken Griffey Sr./6
KG4 Ken Griffey Sr./25
NR1 Nolan Ryan/8
NR2 Nolan Ryan/35 75.00 150.00
NR3 Nolan Ryan/22
NR4 Nolan Ryan/8
TR1 Tim Raines/16
TR2 Tim Raines/6
TR3 Tim Raines/11
TR4 Tim Raines/7
TR5 Tim Raines/8
TR6 Tim Raines/6

2009 Ultimate Collection Legendary Six Memorabilia

ONE AU,MEM, OR AU MEM PER PACK
PRINT RUNS B/WN 25-50 COPIES PER
NO PRICING ON QTY 25 OR LESS
L6M1 Reggie Jackson 30.00 60.00
Catfish Hunter
Bob Lemon
Joe DiMaggio
Yogi Berra
Phil Niekro/50
L6M2 Phil Niekro 20.00 50.00
Ted Williams
Carlton Fisk
Catfish Hunter
Reggie Jackson
Orlando Cepeda/50
L6M3 Billy Williams 20.00 50.00
Joe Morgan
Johnny Bench
Ryne Sandberg
Lou Boudreau
Tom Seaver/50
L6M4 Ozzie Smith 20.00 50.00
Cal Ripken Jr.
Ryne Sandberg
Carlton Fisk
Nolan Ryan
Sparky Anderson/50
L6M5 Earl Weaver
Johnny Bench
Reggie Jackson
Robin Yount
Carlton Fisk
Mike Schmidt/50
L6M6 Phil Niekro 15.00 40.00
Lou Brock
Johnny Bench
Joe Morgan
Red Schoendienst
Don Sutton/50
L6M7 Bo Jackson 30.00 60.00
Nolan Ryan
Ryne Sandberg
Mike Schmidt
Cal Ripken Jr.
Ozzie Smith/50
L6M8 Lou Boudreau 50.00 100.00
Ted Williams
Joe DiMaggio
Yogi Berra
Phil Rizzuto
Eddie Mathews/50
L6M9 Billy Williams 60.00 120.00
Reggie Jackson
Joe DiMaggio
Roberto Clemente
Bo Jackson
Ted Williams/50
L6M10 Juan Marichal
Gaylord Perry
Bruce Sutter
Nolan Ryan
Don Sutton
Jim Bunning/25

2009 Ultimate Collection Signature Moments

ONE AU,MEM, OR AU MEM PER PACK
PRINT RUNS B/WN 3-40 COPIES PER
NO PRICING ON QTY 25 OR LESS
CJ Chipper Jones/10
CW Chien-Ming Wang/4
DJ Derek Jeter/40 100.00 175.00
EL Evan Longoria/3
HR Hanley Ramirez/25
JC Joba Chamberlain/30 20.00 50.00
JL Jon Lester/31 12.50 30.00
KG Ken Griffey Jr./40 60.00 120.00
NM Nick Markakis/21
RJ Randy Johnson/6

2009 Ultimate Collection Ultimate Dual Patch Signature

OVERALL AU-MEM CARDS 1:5 HOBBY PACKS
PRINT RUNS B/WN 4-34 COPIES PER
NO PRICING ON QTY 25 OR LESS
AG Adrian Gonzalez/23
BM Brian McCann/20
CH Cole Hamels/12
CJ Chipper Jones/34 100.00 175.00
DJ Derek Jeter/34 250.00 350.00
HP Hunter Pence/11
JL Jon Lester/19
JP Jonathan Papelbon/31 20.00 50.00
KG Ken Griffey Jr./24
MK Matt Kemp/29 20.00 50.00
NM Nick Markakis/33 30.00 60.00
RB Ryan Braun/16
RJ Randy Johnson/4
ZG Zack Greinke/24

2009 Ultimate Collection Ultimate Dual Signatures

ONE AU,MEM, OR AU MEM PER PACK
PRINT RUNS B/WN 19-75 COPIES PER
UDS1 Cal Ripken Jr. 100.00 175.00
Brooks Robinson/39
UDS2 Brooks Robinson 40.00 80.00
Nick Markakis/37
UDS3 Joba Chamberlain 100.00 175.00
Derek Jeter/38
UDS4 Bo Jackson 40.00 80.00
Zack Greinke/33
UDS8 Kevin Youkilis 20.00 50.00
Dennis Eckersley/39
UDS11 Dennis Eckersley 30.00 60.00
Ozzie Smith/42
UDS12 Derek Jeter 100.00 175.00
Bucky Dent/50
UDS13 Ken Griffey Jr.
Dick Allen/22
UDS14 Ken Griffey Jr. 50.00 100.00
Ken Griffey Sr./75
UDS15 Ken Griffey Sr. 50.00 100.00
Ken Griffey Jr./70
UDS16 Jon Lester 20.00 50.00
Kevin Youkilis/46
UDS17 Ryan Braun
Robin Yount/19
UDS18 Jonathan Papelbon 40.00 80.00
Joba Chamberlain/35
UDS23 Gaylord Perry
Zack Greinke/19
UDS24 Bo Jackson 60.00 120.00
Ken Griffey Jr./72
UDS25 Derek Jeter 75.00 150.00
Hanley Ramirez/72

2009 Ultimate Collection Ultimate Eight Memorabilia

ONE AU,MEM, OR AU MEM PER PACK
PRINT RUNS B/WN 25-35 COPIES PER
U8M1 Reggie Jackson
Jacoby Ellsbury
Jorge Posada
Carlton Fisk
Yogi Berra
Jason Varitek
Ted Williams
Johnny Damon/35
U8M2 Yogi Berra 30.00 60.00
Ivan Rodriguez
Carlton Fisk
Nolan Ryan
Whitey Ford
Fergie Jenkins
Joe Mauer
Johan Santana/35
U8M3 Roy Oswalt
Cole Hamels
Whitey Ford
Pedro Martinez
Nolan Ryan
Robin Roberts
Phil Niekro
Andy Pettitte/35
U8M4 Eddie Murray
Joe DiMaggio
Reggie Jackson
Robin Yount
Harmon Killebrew
Red Schoendienst
Earl Weaver
Rod Carew/35
U8M5 Grady Sizemore
Reggie Jackson
Joe DiMaggio
Josh Hamilton
Ralph Kiner
Manny Ramirez
Ted Williams
Ken Griffey Jr./35
U8M6 Ryne Sandberg
Derrek Lee
Lou Boudreau
Alfonso Soriano
Aramis Ramirez
Billy Williams
Kosuke Fukudome
Carlos Zambrano/35
U8M7 Zack Greinke 20.00 50.00
Billy Butler
Alex Gordon
Bruce Sutter
Albert Pujols
Bo Jackson
Lou Brock
Ozzie Smith/35
U8M8 Cal Ripken Jr.
Brooks Robinson
Melvin Mora
Adam Jones
Earl Weaver
Nick Markakis
Jim Palmer
Brian Roberts/35
U8M9 Reggie Jackson 40.00 80.00
Gary Sheffield
Willie McCovey
Ken Griffey Jr.
Eddie Murray
Manny Ramirez
Ted Williams
Jim Thome/35
U8M10 Eddie Murray
Carlos Beltran
Derek Jeter
Jorge Posada
Joe DiMaggio
Yogi Berra
Phil Rizzuto
Jose Reyes/25
U8M11 Rickie Weeks
Prince Fielder
Don Sutton
Robin Yount
Eddie Mathews
Yovani Gallardo
Ryan Braun
Phil Niekro/35
U8M12 Edgar Martinez 30.00 60.00
Randy Johnson
Ken Griffey Jr.
Gaylord Perry
Brandon Morrow
Felix Hernandez
Kenji Johjima
Erik Bedard/35
U8M13 Harmon Killebrew
Reggie Jackson
Gary Sheffield
Ken Griffey Jr.
Mike Schmidt
Manny Ramirez
Jim Thome
Ted Williams/35
U8M14 Ozzie Smith 30.00 60.00
Troy Glaus
Lou Brock
Chris Carpenter
Albert Pujols
Enos Slaughter
Bruce Sutter
Red Schoendienst/35
U8M15 Phil Rizzuto
Catfish Hunter
Reggie Jackson
Phil Hughes
Whitey Ford
Yogi Berra
Joe DiMaggio
Derek Jeter/25

2009 Ultimate Collection Ultimate Inscriptions

ONE AU,MEM, OR AU MEM PER PACK
PRINT RUNS B/WN 3-35 COPIES PER
NO PRICING ON QTY 25 OR LESS
AK Al Kaline/15
BF Bob Feller/19
BM Brian McCann/16
BU B.J. Upton/27 10.00 25.00
CF Carlton Fisk/8
CR Cal Ripken Jr./8
DE Dennis Eckersley/18
EL Evan Longoria/3
HR Hanley Ramirez/24
JP Jim Palmer/22
KG Ken Griffey Sr./21
LB Lou Brock/20
NM Nick Markakis/28 20.00 50.00
OS Ozzie Smith/18
RJ Randy Johnson/5
TR Tim Raines/30 10.00 25.00
BJ1 Bo Jackson/5
BJ2 Bo Jackson/5
JR1 Ken Griffey Jr./3
JR2 Ken Griffey Jr./17
JR3 Ken Griffey Jr./24
JR4 Ken Griffey Jr./24
JR5 Ken Griffey Jr./24
MK1 Matt Kemp/12
MK2 Matt Kemp/35 20.00 50.00
NR1 Nolan Ryan/6
NR2 Nolan Ryan/5

2009 Ultimate Collection Ultimate Patch

ONE AU,MEM, OR AU MEM PER PACK
PRINT RUNS B/WN 5-35 COPIES PER
NO PRICING ON QTY 25 OR LESS
PRICING FOR NON-PREMIUM PATCHES
AB Adrian Beltre/29
AD Adam Dunn/22
AJ Adam Jones/10
AK Al Kaline/6
AN Rick Ankiel/35 30.00 60.00
AP Albert Pujols/5
AR Alex Rios/35
AS Alfonso Soriano/12
BC Clay Buchholz/35
BE Josh Beckett/35 20.00 50.00
BH Johnny Bench/35 75.00 150.00
BI Chad Billingsley/35 30.00 60.00
BJ Bo Jackson/16
BM Brian McCann/20
BP Brandon Phillips/35 30.00 60.00
BU B.J. Upton/21
BW Brandon Webb/17
BZ Barry Zito/15
CB Carlos Beltran/15
CC Chris Carpenter/35 50.00 100.00
CD Carlos Delgado/35 40.00 80.00
CF Carl Crawford/35 40.00 80.00
CG Curtis Granderson/35 15.00 40.00
CH Cole Hamels/35 40.00 80.00
CJ Chipper Jones/35 75.00 150.00
CK Clayton Kershaw/35 50.00 100.00
CL Carlos Lee/35
CR Cal Ripken Jr./24
CU Chase Utley/35 50.00 100.00
CW Chien-Ming Wang/35 75.00 150.00
CY Chris B. Young/35 30.00 60.00
DE Dennis Eckersley/35
DJ Derek Jeter/5
DL Derrek Lee/35 60.00 120.00
DM Daisuke Matsuzaka/5
DO David Ortiz/35 40.00 80.00
DS Don Sutton/35 40.00 80.00
DU Dan Uggla/35
EC Eric Chavez/35 15.00 30.00
EL Evan Longoria/35 75.00 150.00
EM Edgar Martinez/35 100.00 175.00
FC Carlton Fisk/35 40.00 80.00
FH Felix Hernandez/35 60.00 120.00
FI Carlton Fisk/35 40.00 80.00
FJ Fergie Jenkins/10
FL Francisco Liriano/35
FR Rollie Fingers/35
GA Garrett Atkins/35
GP Gaylord Perry/35
GR Ken Griffey Sr./35 30.00 60.00
GS Grady Sizemore/35 40.00 80.00
GU Jeremy Guthrie/35
HA Travis Hafner/35
HB Hank Blalock/35
HK Howie Kendrick/35
HO Trevor Hoffman/35
HR Hanley Ramirez/35 50.00 100.00

IK Ian Kinsler/35 30.00 60.00
IR Ivan Rodriguez/35
IV Ivan Rodriguez/35
JG Jason Giambi/35
JH Josh Hamilton/35 40.00 80.00
JL James Loney/35 30.00 60.00
JM Joe Mauer/35 60.00 120.00
JO Randy Johnson/35
JP Jorge Posada/35 100.00 175.00
JR Ken Griffey Jr./35 150.00 250.00
JS John Smoltz/35
JT Jim Thome/35 40.00 80.00
JU Justin Upton/35 20.00 50.00
JV Jason Varitek/35 30.00 60.00
JW Jered Weaver/35 30.00 60.00
KG Ken Griffey Jr./35 150.00 250.00
KW Kerry Wood/35
KY Kevin Youkilis/35 30.00 60.00
LA Lance Berkman/35 40.00 80.00
LB Lou Brock/35 100.00 175.00
MB Mark Buehrle/35 40.00 80.00
MC Miguel Cabrera/35
MJ Joe Morgan/35 30.00 60.00
MK Matt Kemp/35
MO Justin Morneau/35 60.00 120.00
MP Pedro Martinez/35 60.00 120.00
MR Mariano Rivera/35 125.00 250.00
MS Max Scherzer/35
MT Miguel Tejada/35
MU Eddie Murray/35 60.00 120.00
MY Michael Young/35 30.00 60.00
NI Nick Markakis/35 30.00 60.00
NK Phil Niekro/35 40.00 80.00
NP Phil Niekro/35 40.00 80.00
NR Nolan Ryan/35 125.00 250.00
OM Magglio Ordonez/35 20.00 50.00
OS Ozzie Smith/35 100.00 200.00
OZ Ozzie Smith/35 100.00 200.00
PA Jonathan Papelbon/35 20.00 50.00
PE Jhonny Peralta/35 30.00 60.00
PF Prince Fielder/35 60.00 120.00
PJ Jake Peavy/35
PK Paul Konerko/35 40.00 80.00
PN Phil Niekro/35 40.00 80.00
PR Pedro Martinez/35 15.00 40.00
RA Aramis Ramirez/35 40.00 80.00
RB Ryan Braun/35 60.00 120.00
RC Roberto Clemente/35 800.00 1000.00
RD Rod Carew/35 60.00 120.00
RE Jose Reyes/35 30.00 60.00
RF Rafael Furcal/35 30.00 60.00
RH Roy Halladay/35
RJ Reggie Jackson/35 75.00 150.00
RM Manny Ramirez/35
RO Roy Oswalt/35 30.00 60.00
RS Red Schoendienst/35
RW Rickie Weeks/35
RY Robin Yount/35 50.00 100.00
RZ Ryan Zimmerman/35 50.00 100.00
SA Ryne Sandberg/35 100.00 175.00
SK Scott Kazmir/35
SM Mike Schmidt/35 75.00 150.00
SP Sparky Anderson/35 50.00 100.00
ST Tom Seaver/35 60.00 120.00
SU Bruce Sutter/20
TH Todd Helton/35 30.00 60.00
TL Tim Lincecum/35 150.00 300.00
TR Tim Raines/35 30.00 60.00
TS Tom Seaver/35 60.00 120.00
TT Troy Tulowitzki/35 40.00 80.00
TW Ted Williams/22
VG Vladimir Guerrero/35 30.00 60.00
VM Victor Martinez/35
VO Joey Votto/35 30.00 60.00
VW Vernon Wells/10
YM Yadier Molina/35 50.00 100.00

2009 Ultimate Collection Ultimate Signatures

ONE AU,MEM, OR AU MEM PER PACK
PRINT RUNS B/WN 2-50 COPIES PER
NO PRICING ON QTY 25 OR LESS
BM Brian McCann/46 10.00 25.00
BU B.J. Upton/35 6.00 15.00
EL Evan Longoria/3
JC Joba Chamberlain/27 20.00 50.00
JP Jonathan Papelbon/20
KU Koji Uehara/50 20.00 50.00
ZG Zack Greinke/21
DJ1 Derek Jeter/50 100.00 175.00
DJ2 Derek Jeter/50 100.00 175.00
DJ3 Derek Jeter/50 100.00 175.00
DJ4 Derek Jeter/50 100.00 175.00
HR1 Hanley Ramirez/26 15.00 40.00
HR2 Hanley Ramirez/50 12.50 30.00
JL1 Jon Lester/16
JL2 Jon Lester/12
KG1 Ken Griffey Jr./50 40.00 80.00
KG2 Ken Griffey Jr./24
KG3 Ken Griffey Jr./24
KG4 Ken Griffey Jr./24
KG5 Ken Griffey Jr./30 60.00 120.00
KG6 Ken Griffey Jr./30 60.00 120.00
KG7 Ken Griffey Jr./50 40.00 80.00
KG8 Ken Griffey Jr./17
KG9 Ken Griffey Jr./50 40.00 80.00
KG10 Ken Griffey Jr./50 40.00 80.00
NM1 Nick Markakis/39 12.50 30.00
NM2 Nick Markakis/21
RJ1 Randy Johnson/5
RJ2 Randy Johnson/2
RJ3 Randy Johnson/5
RJ4 Randy Johnson/2
RJ5 Randy Johnson/2
RJ6 Randy Johnson/2

2009 Ultimate Collection Ultimate Six Memorabilia

ONE AU,MEM, OR AU MEM PER PACK
PRINT RUNS B/WN 20-50 COPIES PER
NO PRICING ON QTY 25 OR LESS
U6M1 Roberto Clemente
Joe DiMaggio
Josh Hamilton
Carlos Beltran
Ted Williams
Ken Griffey Jr./25
U6M2 Jim Thome
Albert Pujols
Tony Perez
Willie McCovey
Rod Carew
Harmon Killebrew/50
U6M3 Ian Kinsler
Joe Morgan
Brian Roberts
Red Schoendienst
Chase Utley
Ryne Sandberg/50
U6M4 Lou Boudreau 30.00 60.00
Ozzie Smith
Cal Ripken Jr.
Derek Jeter
Phil Rizzuto
Robin Yount/50
U6M5 Eddie Mathews
Evan Longoria
Chipper Jones
Mike Schmidt
Brooks Robinson
Scott Rolen/50
U6M6 Gaylord Perry
Nolan Ryan
Phil Niekro
Tom Seaver
Randy Johnson
Don Sutton/50
U6M7 Johnny Bench
Brian McCann
Joe Mauer
Carlton Fisk
Yogi Berra
Jason Varitek/50
U6M8 Dennis Eckersley
Billy Wagner
Trevor Hoffman
Bruce Sutter
Joe Nathan
Jonathan Papelbon/20
U6M9 Billy Williams
Willie McCovey
Eric Chavez
Joe DiMaggio
Barry Zito
Juan Marichal/20
U6M10 Juan Marichal
Barry Zito
Phil Niekro
Andy Pettitte
Tim Hudson
Catfish Hunter/25
U6M11 Reggie Jackson 20.00 50.00
Albert Pujols
Ozzie Smith
Derek Jeter
Ryne Sandberg
Derrek Lee/50
U6M12 Magglio Ordonez
Chris Carpenter
Brian Roberts
Sparky Anderson
Red Schoendienst
Earl Weaver/50
U6M13 Roy Oswalt
Joe Morgan
Johnny Bench
Jay Bruce
Lance Berkman
Nolan Ryan/50
U6M14 Tony Perez 15.00 40.00
Ted Williams
Cal Ripken Jr.
Brian Roberts
Nick Markakis
Kevin Youkilis/50
U6M15 Hank Blalock 15.00 40.00
Ian Kinsler
Randy Johnson
Ken Griffey Jr.
Gaylord Perry
Nolan Ryan/50
U6M16 Lou Brock
Ozzie Smith
Ryne Sandberg
Carl Crawford
Jimmy Rollins
Joe Morgan/50
U6M17 Chase Utley
Jose Reyes
Cole Hamels
Carlos Delgado
Mike Schmidt
Yogi Berra/25
U6M18 Nolan Ryan
Gaylord Perry
Bob Feller
Satchel Paige
Jim Bunning
Don Sutton/25
U6M19 Carlos Zambrano
Jon Lester
Phil Niekro
Tom Seaver
Randy Johnson
Nolan Ryan/50
U6M20 Yogi Berra
Carlton Fisk
Tom Seaver
Andy Pettitte
Jon Lester
Johnny Bench/50
U6M21 Brian Roberts 12.50 30.00
Phil Rizzuto
Rickie Weeks
Robin Yount
Robinson Cano
Cal Ripken Jr./50
U6M22 Cal Ripken Jr. 15.00 40.00
Lou Boudreau
Robin Yount
Phil Rizzuto
Joe Morgan
Rod Carew/50
U6M23 Jim Bunning 50.00 100.00
Daisuke Matsuzaka
Ted Williams
Derek Jeter
Joe DiMaggio
Roberto Clemente/50
U6M24 Bo Jackson
Andy Pettitte
Ted Williams
Reggie Jackson
Jon Lester
Zack Greinke/50
U6M25 Grady Sizemore 30.00 60.00
Fergie Jenkins
Satchel Paige
Jacoby Ellsbury
Bob Feller
Jason Varitek/50

2009 Ultimate Collection Ultimate Triple Patch Signature

OVERALL AU MEM ODDS 1:6 HOBBY PACKS
PRINT RUNS B/WN 2-29 COPIES PER
NO PRICING ON QTY 25 OR LESS
AG Adrian Gonzalez/23
BM Brian McCann/20
CH Cole Hamels/12
CJ Chipper Jones/21
DJ Derek Jeter/2
HP Hunter Pence/26 30.00 60.00
HR Hanley Ramirez/28 20.00 50.00
JL Jon Lester/19
JP Jonathan Papelbon/22
KG Ken Griffey Jr./24
MK Matt Kemp/29 40.00 80.00
NM Nick Markakis/27 30.00 60.00
RB Ryan Braun/8
RJ Randy Johnson/4

2009 Ultimate Collection Ultimate Triple Signatures

OVERALL AU ODDS 1:15 HOBBY PACKS
PRINT RUNS B/WN 5-30 COPIES PER
NO PRICING ON QTY 25 OR LESS
UTS2 Brooks Robinson
Nick Markakis
Jim Palmer/17
UTS3 Joba Chamberlain 150.00 250.00
Derek Jeter
Bucky Dent/30
UTS4 Ken Griffey Jr. 75.00 150.00
Ryan Braun
Nick Markakis/26
UTS7 Jim Palmer
Bob Feller
Nolan Ryan/9
UTS10 Hanley Ramirez
Ozzie Smith
Derek Jeter/25
UTS11 Ken Griffey Jr. 100.00 175.00
Bo Jackson
B.J. Upton/26
UTS12 Jonathan Papelbon
Rollie Fingers
Dennis Eckersley/21
UTS13 Ken Griffey Jr.
Derek Jeter
Randy Johnson/6
UTS15 Chipper Jones
Mike Schmidt
Brooks Robinson/5

2005 Ultimate Signature

This 110-card set is composed of retired stars (1-50), active stars (51-100) and prospect autographs (101-110). Cards 1-100 are serial numbered to 825 copies and 101-110 are numbered to a mere 225 copies. The product was issued in three-card tin boxes of which carried a suggested retail price of $99.99. Each sealed hobby case contained 20 tins. The product went live at hobby shops nationwide on June 1st, 2005. Cards 101-193 were issued in February, 2006 within Upper Deck Update packs. Each of these Update cards is signed by the featured athlete and serial-numbered to 125 copies. Of note, the following cards do not exist: 113, 123, 126-127, 150, 163, 170 and 189.

COMMON CARD (1-50) .75 2.00
COMMON CARD (51-100) .75 2.00
1-100 PRINT RUN 825 SERIAL #'d SETS
COMMON AUTO (101-110) 4.00 10.00
COMMON AU RC (101-110) 4.00 10.00
101-110 STATED ODDS 1:20
101-110 PRINT RUN 225 SERIAL #'d SETS
COMMON AUTO (111-193) 4.00 10.00
111-193 ODDS APPX 1:8 '05 UD UPDATE
111-193 PRINT RUN 125 SERIAL #'d SETS
113, 123, 126-127, 150, 163 DO NOT EXIST
170, 189 DO NOT EXIST
1 Al Kaline 2.00 5.00
2 Babe Ruth 5.00 12.00
3 Billy Williams .75 2.00
4 Bob Feller .75 2.00
5 Bob Gibson 1.25 3.00
6 Brooks Robinson 1.25 3.00
7 Carlton Fisk 1.25 3.00
8 Cy Young 1.25 3.00
9 Dizzy Dean 1.25 3.00
10 Don Drysdale 1.25 3.00
11 Eddie Mathews 1.25 3.00
12 Enos Slaughter .75 2.00
13 Ernie Banks 2.00 5.00
14 Fergie Jenkins .75 2.00
15 Eddie Murray 2.00 5.00
16 Harmon Killebrew 2.00 5.00
17 Honus Wagner 1.25 3.00
18 Jackie Robinson 1.25 3.00
19 Jimmie Foxx 1.25 3.00
20 Joe DiMaggio 5.00 12.00
21 Joe Morgan .75 2.00
22 Juan Marichal .75 2.00
23 Larry Doby .75 2.00
24 Jim Palmer .75 2.00
25 Johnny Bench 2.00 5.00
26 Lou Brock 1.25 3.00
27 Lou Gehrig 4.00 10.00
28 Mel Ott 2.00 5.00
29 Mickey Cochrane .75 2.00
30 Mickey Mantle 6.00 15.00
31 Mike Schmidt 4.00 10.00
32 Nolan Ryan 5.00 12.00
33 Pee Wee Reese 1.25 3.00
34 Phil Rizzuto 1.25 3.00
35 Ralph Kiner .75 2.00
36 Robin Yount 2.00 5.00
37 Ozzie Smith 3.00 8.00
38 Roy Campanella 1.25 3.00
39 Satchel Paige 2.00 5.00
40 Stan Musial 3.00 8.00
41 Ted Williams 4.00 10.00
42 Thurman Munson 1.25 3.00
43 Tom Seaver 1.25 3.00
44 Ty Cobb 3.00 8.00
45 Walter Johnson 1.25 3.00
46 Warren Spahn 1.25 3.00
47 Whitey Ford 1.25 3.00
48 Willie McCovey 1.25 3.00
49 Willie Stargell 1.25 3.00
50 Yogi Berra 2.00 5.00
51 Adrian Beltre .75 2.00
52 Albert Pujols 5.00 12.00
53 Alex Rodriguez 3.00 8.00
54 Alfonso Soriano 1.25 3.00
55 Andruw Jones .75 2.00
56 B.J. Upton 1.25 3.00
57 Ben Sheets .75 2.00
58 Bret Boone .75 2.00
59 Brian Giles .75 2.00
60 Carlos Beltran .75 2.00
61 Carlos Delgado .75 2.00
62 Chipper Jones 2.00 5.00
63 Curt Schilling 1.25 3.00
64 David Ortiz 2.00 5.00
65 Derek Jeter 5.00 12.00
66 Eric Chavez .75 2.00
67 Frank Thomas 2.00 5.00
68 Gary Sheffield .75 2.00
69 Greg Maddux 3.00 8.00
70 Hank Blalock .75 2.00
71 Hideki Matsui 3.00 8.00
72 Ichiro Suzuki 3.00 8.00
73 Ivan Rodriguez 1.25 3.00
74 Jason Schmidt .75 2.00
75 Jeff Bagwell 1.25 3.00
76 Jim Thome 1.25 3.00
77 Johnny Damon 1.25 3.00
78 Jose Vidro .75 2.00
79 Ken Griffey Jr. 3.00 8.00
80 Kerry Wood .75 2.00
81 Manny Ramirez 2.00 5.00
82 Mark Prior 1.25 3.00
83 Mark Teixeira 2.00 5.00
84 Miguel Cabrera 2.00 5.00
85 Miguel Tejada 1.25 3.00
86 Mike Mussina 1.25 3.00
87 Mike Piazza 2.00 5.00
88 Mike Sweeney .75 2.00
89 Oliver Perez .75 2.00
90 Pedro Martinez 1.25 3.00
91 Rafael Palmeiro 1.25 3.00
92 Randy Johnson 2.00 5.00
93 Roger Clemens 2.50 6.00
94 Sammy Sosa 2.00 5.00
95 Scott Rolen 1.25 3.00
96 Tim Hudson 1.25 3.00
97 Todd Helton 1.25 3.00
98 Torii Hunter .75 2.00
99 Victor Martinez 1.25 3.00
100 Vladimir Guerrero 2.00 5.00
101 Adrian Gonzalez AU 4.00 10.00
102 Ambiorix Burgos AU RC 4.00 10.00
103 Ambiorix Concepcion AU RC 4.00 10.00
104 Dan Meyer AU 4.00 10.00
105 Ervin Santana AU 6.00 15.00
106 Gavin Floyd AU 4.00 10.00
107 Joe Blanton AU 4.00 10.00
108 Eric Crozier AU 4.00 10.00
109 Mark Teahen AU 4.00 10.00
110 Ryan Howard AU 30.00 60.00
111 Adam Shabala AU RC 4.00 10.00
112 Anibal Sanchez AU RC 30.00 60.00
114 Brandon McCarthy AU RC 12.50 30.00
115 Brian Burres AU RC 4.00 10.00
116 Carlos Ruiz AU RC 6.00 15.00
117 Casey Rogowski AU RC 6.00 15.00
118 Chad Orvella AU RC 4.00 10.00
119 Chris Resop AU RC 6.00 15.00
120 Chris Roberson AU RC 4.00 10.00
121 Chris Seddon AU RC 4.00 10.00
122 Colter Bean AU RC 6.00 15.00
124 Dave Gassner AU RC 4.00 10.00
125 Brian Anderson AU RC 15.00 40.00
128 Devon Lowery AU RC 4.00 10.00
129 Enrique Gonzalez AU RC 6.00 15.00
130 Eude Brito AU RC 4.00 10.00
131 Francisco Butto AU RC 4.00 10.00
132 Franquelis Osoria AU RC 4.00 10.00
133 Garrett Jones AU RC 20.00 50.00
134 Geovany Soto AU RC 100.00 175.00
135 Hayden Penn AU RC 8.00 20.00
136 Ismael Ramirez AU RC 4.00 10.00
137 Jared Gothreaux AU RC 4.00 10.00
138 Jason Hammel AU RC 4.00 10.00
139 Jeff Miller AU RC 4.00 10.00
140 Jeff Niemann AU RC 8.00 20.00
141 Joel Peralta AU RC 4.00 10.00
142 John Hattig AU RC 4.00 10.00
143 Jorge Campillo AU RC 4.00 10.00
144 Juan Morillo AU RC 4.00 10.00
145 Justin Verlander AU RC 75.00 150.00
146 Ryan Garko AU RC 12.50 30.00
147 Keiichi Yabu AU RC 6.00 15.00
148 Kendry Morales AU RC 50.00 100.00
149 Luis Hernandez AU RC 4.00 10.00
151 Luis O.Rodriguez AU RC 4.00 10.00
152 Luke Scott AU RC 12.50 30.00
153 Marcos Carvajal AU RC 4.00 10.00
154 Mark Woodyard AU RC 4.00 10.00
155 Matt A.Smith AU RC 4.00 10.00
156 Matthew Lindstrom AU RC 4.00 10.00
157 Miguel Negron AU RC 6.00 15.00
158 Mike Morse AU RC 6.00 15.00
159 Nate McLouth AU RC 20.00 50.00
160 Nelson Cruz AU RC 40.00 80.00
161 Nick Masset AU RC 4.00 10.00
162 Mark McLemore AU RC 4.00 10.00
164 Paulino Reynoso AU RC 4.00 10.00
165 Pedro Lopez AU RC 4.00 10.00
166 Pete Orr AU RC 4.00 10.00
167 Philip Humber AU RC 12.50 30.00
168 Prince Fielder AU RC 50.00 100.00
169 Randy Messenger AU RC 4.00 10.00
171 Raul Tablado AU RC 4.00 10.00
172 Ronny Paulino AU RC 6.00 15.00
173 Russ Rohlicek AU RC 4.00 10.00
174 Russell Martin AU RC 10.00 25.00
175 Scott Baker AU RC 6.00 15.00
176 Scott Munter AU RC 4.00 10.00
177 Sean Thompson AU RC 4.00 10.00
178 Sean Tracey AU RC 4.00 10.00
179 Shane Costa AU RC 4.00 10.00
180 Stephen Drew AU RC 40.00 80.00
181 Steve Schmoll AU RC 4.00 10.00
182 Tadahito Iguchi AU RC 30.00 60.00
183 Tony Giarratano AU RC 4.00 10.00
184 Tony Pena AU RC 4.00 10.00
185 Travis Bowyer AU RC 4.00 10.00
186 Ubaldo Jimenez AU RC 60.00 120.00
187 Wladimir Balentien AU RC 8.00 20.00
188 Yorman Bazardo AU RC 4.00 10.00
190 Ryan Zimmerman AU RC 50.00 100.00
191 Chris Denorfia AU RC 6.00 15.00
192 Ryan Speier AU RC 4.00 10.00
193 Jermaine Van Buren AU 4.00 10.00

2005 Ultimate Signature Platinum

101-110 OVERALL AU ODDS 1:20
111-APPX AU ODDS 1:8 '05 UD UPDATE
STATED PRINT RUN 1 SERIAL #'d SET
NO PRICING DUE TO SCARCITY

2005 Ultimate Signature Cuts

OVERALL RARE CUT AU ODDS 1:644
STATED PRINT RUN 1 SERIAL #'d SET
NO PRICING DUE TO SCARCITY
BR Babe Ruth
SP Satchel Paige
TC Ty Cobb
WJ Walter Johnson

2005 Ultimate Signature Cy Young Dual Autograph

OVERALL DUAL AU ODDS 1:4
PRINT RUNS B/WN 15-250 COPIES PER
NO PRICING ON QTY OF 25 OR LESS
EXCHANGE DEADLINE 06/07/08
CG Roger Clemens
Tom Glavine/15
EG Dennis Eckersley 15.00 40.00
Eric Gagne/200
GF Ron Guidry 30.00 60.00
Whitey Ford/250
GM Bob Gibson 15.00 40.00
Denny McLain/175
JC Randy Johnson
Roger Clemens/15
JM Fergie Jenkins
Greg Maddux/25
LC Sparky Lyle 12.50 30.00
Steve Carlton/250
MS Denny McLain 30.00 60.00
Tom Seaver/100
NF Don Newcombe 30.00 60.00
Whitey Ford/125
PC Gaylord Perry 12.50 30.00
Steve Carlton/250
PS Jim Palmer 40.00 80.00
Tom Seaver/100
SM Greg Maddux
John Smoltz/25

2005 Ultimate Signature Cy Young Dual Autograph-Cut

OVERALL RARE CUT AU ODDS 1:644
PRINT RUNS B/WN 1-3 COPIES PER
NO PRICING DUE TO SCARCITY
CY Roger Clemens
Cy Young Cut/1
JD Randy Johnson
Don Drysdale Cut/3

2005 Ultimate Signature Cy Young Quad Autograph-Cut

OVERALL RARE CUT AU ODDS 1:644
STATED PRINT RUN 1 SERIAL #'d SET
NO PRICING DUE TO SCARCITY
CSSD Steve Carlton
Tom Seaver
Warren Spahn Cut
Don Drysdale Cut

2005 Ultimate Signature Cy Young Triple Autograph-Cut

OVERALL RARE CUT AU ODDS 1:644
STATED PRINT RUN 1 SERIAL #'d SET
NO PRICING DUE TO SCARCITY
JCY Randy Johnson
Roger Clemens
Cy Young Cut/1

2005 Ultimate Signature Decades

TIER 3 PRINT RUNS 350+ PER
TIER 2 PRINT RUNS B/WN 225-275 PER
TIER 1 PRINT RUNS B/WN 100-175 PER
SERIAL #'d PRINT RUNS B/WN 10-99 PER
NO PRICING ON #'d QTY OF 25 OR LESS

TIER 1-3 PRINT RUN INFO PROVIDED BY UD
TIER 1-3 ARE NOT SERIAL-NUMBERED
STATED ODDS 3:5 TINS
PLATINUM OVERALL PREMIUM AU ODDS 1:5
PLATINUM PRINT RUN 1 SERIAL #'d SET
NO PLATINUM PRICING DUE TO SCARCITY
EXCHANGE DEADLINE 06/07/08
AD Andre Dawson T2 6.00 15.00
AK Al Kaline/99 20.00 50.00
AR Al Rosen T3 6.00 15.00
BD Bobby Doerr T3 6.00 15.00
BE Johnny Bench/15
BF Bob Feller T1 10.00 25.00
BG Bob Gibson/15
BJ Bo Jackson/50 40.00 80.00
BM Bill Mazeroski/99 15.00 40.00
BR Brooks Robinson T2 10.00 25.00
BS Ben Sheets T3 6.00 15.00
BU B.J. Upton T3 10.00 25.00
BW Billy Williams T2 6.00 15.00
CA Rod Carew/15
CF Carlton Fisk/15
CJ Chipper Jones/10
CL Roger Clemens/10
CY Carl Yastrzemski/10
DE Dennis Eckersley T1 6.00 15.00
DJ Derek Jeter/99 100.00 175.00
DM Don Mattingly/25
DN Don Newcombe/99 10.00 25.00
DO David Ortiz T1 20.00 50.00
DS Duke Snider/10
EB Ernie Banks/10
FJ Fergie Jenkins/50 12.50 30.00
FL Fred Lynn T2 6.00 15.00
FR Frank Robinson/25
GB George Brett/10
GC Gary Carter/50 12.50 30.00
GK George Kell T3 10.00 25.00
GM Greg Maddux/10
GP Gaylord Perry Giants T3 10.00 25.00
GP1 Gaylord Perry Rgr T3 10.00 25.00
HK Harmon Killebrew/99 30.00 60.00
JB Jim Bunning T2 6.00 15.00
JC Jose Canseco/99 20.00 50.00
JM Juan Marichal/99 10.00 25.00
JP Jim Palmer T2 6.00 15.00
JR Jim Rice T2 6.00 15.00
JS Johan Santana T1 10.00 25.00
KG Ken Griffey Jr. T3 30.00 60.00
KH Keith Hernandez Cards T3 6.00 15.00
KH1 Keith Hernandez Mets T3 6.00 15.00
LA Luis Aparicio W.Sox T1 6.00 15.00
LA1 Luis Aparicio R.Sox T1 6.00 15.00
LB Lou Brock/50 20.00 50.00
LT Luis Tiant Twins T3 6.00 15.00
LT1 Luis Tiant Sox T3 6.00 15.00
MC Miguel Cabrera T2 10.00 25.00
MI Monte Irvin T3 6.00 15.00
MO Joe Morgan/50 12.50 30.00
MP Mike Piazza/10
MS Mike Schmidt/15
MT Mark Teixeira T3 10.00 25.00
MU Dale Murphy T3 10.00 25.00
MW Maury Wills T2 6.00 15.00
NG Nomar Garciaparra/10
NR Nolan Ryan Angels/10
NR1 Nolan Ryan Astros/10
OC Orlando Cepeda T2 6.00 15.00
PM Paul Molitor/99 10.00 25.00
PN Phil Niekro T2 6.00 15.00
RC Rocky Colavito Indians T1 30.00 60.00
RC1 Rocky Colavito Tigers T1 30.00 60.00
RF Rollie Fingers T2 6.00 15.00
RG Ron Guidry T3 10.00 25.00
RJ Randy Johnson/10
RK Ralph Kiner/99 15.00 40.00
RO Roy Oswalt T3 6.00 15.00
RS Ron Santo T2 15.00 40.00
RW Rickie Weeks T3 6.00 15.00
RY Robin Yount/25
SA Ryne Sandberg/15
SC Steve Carlton Cards T1 6.00 15.00
SC1 Steve Carlton Phils T1 6.00 15.00
SM Stan Musial/10
SU Don Sutton T1 6.00 15.00
TG Tony Gwynn/15
TP Tony Perez T2 6.00 15.00
TS Tom Seaver/10
WB Wade Boggs Sox/25
WB1 Wade Boggs Yanks/25
WC Will Clark/99 15.00 40.00
WF Whitey Ford/15
WM Willie McCovey/10
YB Yogi Berra/25

2005 Ultimate Signature Hits Dual Autograph

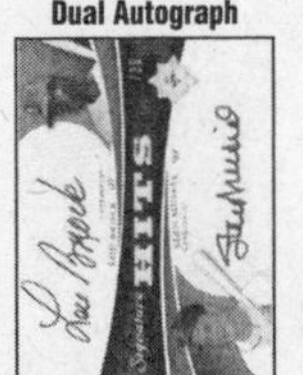

OVERALL DUAL AU ODDS 1:4
PRINT RUNS B/WN 15-125 COPIES PER
NO PRICING ON QTY OF 15
EXCHANGE DEADLINE 06/07/08
BM Lou Brock 60.00 120.00
Stan Musial/35
MY Paul Molitor 40.00 80.00
Robin Yount/125
WG Dave Winfield 50.00 100.00
Tony Gwynn/35
YB Carl Yastrzemski 75.00 150.00
Wade Boggs/35

2005 Ultimate Signature Hits Dual Autograph-Cut

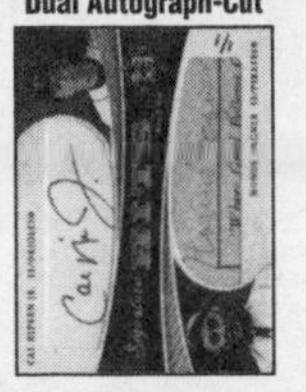

OVERALL RARE CUT AU ODDS 1:644
STATED PRINT RUN 1 SERIAL #'d SET
NO PRICING DUE TO SCARCITY
KC Al Kaline
Ty Cobb Cut/1
RW Cal Ripken
Honus Wagner Cut/1

2005 Ultimate Signature Hits Quad Autograph-Cut

OVERALL RARE CUT AU ODDS 1:644
STATED PRINT RUN 1 SERIAL #'d SET
NO PRICING DUE TO SCARCITY
RBCC Cal Ripken
George Brett
Roberto Clemente Cut
Ty Cobb Cut

2005 Ultimate Signature Hits Triple Autograph-Cut

OVERALL RARE CUT AU ODDS 1:644
STATED PRINT RUN 1 SERIAL #'d SET
NO PRICING DUE TO SCARCITY
GMW Tony Gwynn
Stan Musial
Honus Wagner Cut/1
YYC Robin Yount
Carl Yastrzemski
Roberto Clemente Cut/1

2005 Ultimate Signature Home Runs Dual Autograph

OVERALL DUAL AU ODDS 1:4
PRINT RUNS B/WN 15-250 COPIES PER
NO PRICING ON QTY OF 25 OR LESS
EXCHANGE DEADLINE 06/07/08
BS Ernie Banks
Mike Schmidt/25
GM Ken Griffey Jr. 50.00 100.00
Willie McCovey/250
KM Harmon Killebrew
Willie McCovey/35
MR Eddie Murray
Frank Robinson/15

2005 Ultimate Signature Home Runs Dual Autograph-Cut

OVERALL RARE CUT AU ODDS 1:644
STATED PRINT RUN 1 SERIAL #'d SET
NO PRICING DUE TO SCARCITY
GM Ken Griffey Jr.
Mickey Mantle Cut/1
MO Willie McCovey
Mel Ott Cut/1

2005 Ultimate Signature Home Runs Quad Autograph-Cut

OVERALL RARE CUT AU ODDS 1:644
STATED PRINT RUN 1 SERIAL #'d SET
NO PRICING DUE TO SCARCITY
GSWR Ken Griffey Jr.
Mike Schmidt
Ted Williams Cut
Babe Ruth Cut

2005 Ultimate Signature Home Runs Triple Autograph-Cut

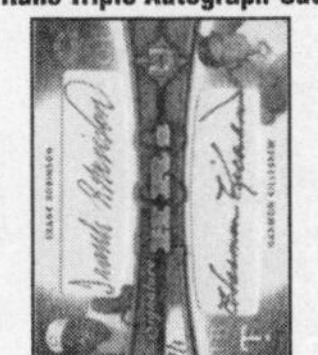

OVERALL RARE CUT AU ODDS 1:644
PRINT RUNS B/WN 1-5 COPIES PER
NO PRICING DUE TO SCARCITY
KMM Ken Griffey Jr.
Willie McCovey
Eddie Mathews Cut/5
RKF Frank Robinson
Harmon Killebrew
Jimmie Foxx Cut/1

2005 Ultimate Signature Immortal Inscriptions

OVERALL PREMIUM SINGLE AU 1:5
PRINT RUNS B/WN 10-99 COPIES PER
NO PRICING ON QTY OF 25 OR LESS
PLATINUM OVERALL PREMIUM AU ODDS 1:5
PLATINUM PRINT RUN 1 SERIAL #'d SET
NO PLATINUM PRICING DUE TO SCARCITY
BR Brooks Robinson/99 40.00 80.00
Hoover
CR Cal Ripken/10
2632

Card	Low	High
DM D.Mattingly/75 Donnie Baseball	150.00	250.00
EG Eric Gagne/99 Game Over	60.00	120.00
FT Frank Thomas/50 Big Hurt	100.00	200.00
GC Gary Carter/15 The Kid		
GM Greg Maddux/10 Mad Dog		
JB Jim Bunning/99 Senator	40.00	80.00
KG Ken Griffey Jr./99 Junior	400.00	500.00
NR Nolan Ryan/10 The Ryan Express		
OS Ozzie Smith/75 The Wizard	40.00	80.00
RC Roger Clemens/15 The Rocket		
RJ Randy Johnson/10 Big Unit		
SC Steve Carlton/99 Lefty	20.00	50.00
SM Stan Musial/25 HOF '69		
TG Tony Gwynn/50 The Tiger	60.00	120.00
TS Tom Seaver/25 HOF 92		
WB Wade Boggs/75 Chicken Man	40.00	80.00
WC Will Clark/99 The Thrill	40.00	80.00
WM Willie McCovey/15 HOF '86		

2005 Ultimate Signature MVP's Dual Autograph

OVERALL DUAL AU ODDS 1:4
PRINT RUNS B/WN 15-250 COPIES PER
NO PRICING ON QTY OF 25 OR LESS
EXCHANGE DEADLINE 06/07/08

Card	Low	High
BM Don Mattingly Yogi Berra/175	60.00	120.00
BS Ernie Banks Ryne Sandberg/25		
CM Orlando Cepeda Stan Musial/100	40.00	80.00
DS Andre Dawson Ryne Sandberg/175	60.00	120.00
EF Dennis Eckersley Rollie Fingers/250	12.50	30.00
HY Keith Hernandez Robin Yount/200	20.00	50.00
JR Chipper Jones Ivan Rodriguez/35	100.00	175.00
KC Harmon Killebrew Rod Carew/100	50.00	100.00
KM Harmon Killebrew Willie McCovey/35		
LM Fred Lynn Joe Morgan/200	12.50	30.00
LW Barry Larkin Maury Wills/250	15.00	40.00
MB Joe Morgan Johnny Bench/100		
MG Bob Gibson Denny McLain/175	15.00	40.00
PR Dave Parker Jim Rice/250	15.00	40.00
RM Cal Ripken Dale Murphy/25		
SB George Brett Mike Schmidt/15		
SF Mike Schmidt Rollie Fingers/175	30.00	60.00
SS Mike Schmidt Ryne Sandberg/75	100.00	175.00
TB Frank Thomas Jeff Bagwell/50	60.00	120.00
YC Carl Yastrzemski Orlando Cepeda/100	40.00	80.00
YS Carl Yastrzemski Jim Rice/100	40.00	80.00

2005 Ultimate Signature MVP's Dual Autograph-Cut

OVERALL RARE CUT AU ODDS 1:644
PRINT RUNS B/WN 1-2 COPIES PER
NO PRICING DUE TO SCARCITY
MM Joe Morgan
Thurman Munson Cut/2
RG Cal Ripken
Lou Gehrig Cut/1

2005 Ultimate Signature MVPs Quad Autograph-Cut

OVERALL RARE CUT AU ODDS 1:644
STATED PRINT RUN 1 SERIAL #'d SET
NO PRICING DUE TO SCARCITY
JMMD Derek Jeter
Don Mattingly
Mickey Mantle Cut
Joe DiMaggio Cut

2005 Ultimate Signature MVPs Triple Autograph-Cut

OVERALL RARE CUT AU ODDS 1:644
STATED PRINT RUN 1 SERIAL #'d SET
NO PRICING DUE TO SCARCITY
RBC Ivan Rodriguez
Johnny Bench
Mickey Cochrane Cut/1
SMC Mike Schmidt
Stan Musial
Roy Campanella Cut/1

2005 Ultimate Signature No-Hitters Dual Autograph

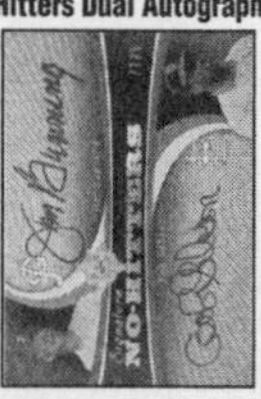

OVERALL DUAL AU ODDS 1:4
PRINT RUNS B/WN 15-250 COPIES PER
NO PRICING ON QTY OF 25 OR LESS
EXCHANGE DEADLINE 06/07/08

Card	Low	High
BG Jim Bunning Bob Gibson/125	20.00	50.00
FR Bob Feller Nolan Ryan/25		
GP Bob Gibson Jim Palmer/125	20.00	50.00
RJ Nolan Ryan Randy Johnson/15		

2005 Ultimate Signature No-Hitters Dual Autograph-Cut

OVERALL RARE CUT AU ODDS 1:644
PRINT RUNS B/WN 1-5 COPIES PER
NO PRICING DUE TO SCARCITY
FL Bob Feller
Bob Lemon Cut/5
RY Nolan Ryan
Cy Young Cut/1

2005 Ultimate Signature No-Hitters Quad Autograph-Cut

OVERALL RARE CUT AU ODDS 1:644
STATED PRINT RUN 1 SERIAL #'d SET
NO PRICING DUE TO SCARCITY
RJSJ Nolan Ryan
Randy Johnson
Warren Spahn Cut
Walter Johnson Cut

2005 Ultimate Signature No-Hitters Triple Autograph-Cut

OVERALL RARE CUT AU ODDS 1:644
STATED PRINT RUN 1 SERIAL #'d SET
NO PRICING DUE TO SCARCITY
PMH Gaylord Perry
Juan Marichal
Carl Hubbell Cut/1

2005 Ultimate Signature Numbers

OVERALL PREMIUM SINGLE AU 1:5
PRINT RUNS B/WN 1-49 COPIES PER
NO PRICING ON QTY OF 24 OR LESS
PLATINUM OVERALL PREMIUM AU ODDS 1:5
PLATINUM PRINT RUN 1 SERIAL #'d SET
NO PLATINUM PRICING DUE TO SCARCITY
EXCHANGE DEADLINE 06/07/08

Card	Low	High
AK Al Kaline/6		
BE Johnny Bench/5		
BF Bob Feller/19		
BG Bob Gibson/45	20.00	50.00
BM Bill Mazeroski/9		
BR Brooks Robinson/5		
BS Ben Sheets/15		
BW Billy Williams/26	12.50	30.00
CA Rod Carew/29	20.00	50.00
CB Carlos Beltran/15		
CF Carlton Fisk/27	20.00	50.00
CJ Chipper Jones/10		
CL Roger Clemens/22		
CR Cal Ripken/8		
CY Carl Yastrzemski/8		
DJ Derek Jeter/2		
DM Don Mattingly/23		
DO David Ortiz/34	30.00	60.00
DS Duke Snider/4		
DW Dave Winfield/31	20.00	50.00
EB Ernie Banks/14		
EC Eric Chavez/3		
EM Eddie Murray/33	75.00	150.00
FJ Fergie Jenkins/31	12.50	30.00
FR Frank Robinson/20		
FT Frank Thomas/35	40.00	80.00
GB George Brett/5		
GC Gary Carter/8		
GL Tom Glavine/47	20.00	50.00
GM Greg Maddux/31		
HB Hank Blalock/9		
HK Harmon Killebrew/3		
IR Ivan Rodriguez/7		
JB Jeff Bagwell/5		
JC Jose Canseco/33	30.00	60.00
JM Joe Morgan/8		
JP Jim Palmer/22		
JR Jim Rice/14		
JS John Smoltz/29	20.00	50.00
KG Ken Griffey Jr./30	75.00	150.00
KP Kirby Puckett/34	50.00	100.00
KW Kerry Wood/34	20.00	50.00
LA Luis Aparicio/11		
LB Lou Brock/20		
MA Juan Marichal/27	12.50	30.00
MC Miguel Cabrera/24		
MI Monte Irvin/20		
MM Mark Mulder/20		
MP Mark Prior/22		
MS Mike Schmidt/20		
MT Mark Teixeira/23		
NG Nomar Garciaparra/5		
NR Nolan Ryan/34	100.00	200.00
OC Orlando Cepeda/30	12.50	30.00
OS Ozzie Smith/1		
PM Paul Molitor/4		
RC Rocky Colavito/7		
RF Rollie Fingers/34	12.50	30.00
RG Ron Guidry/49	20.00	50.00
RJ Randy Johnson/41	50.00	100.00
RK Ralph Kiner/4		
RO Roy Oswalt/44	12.50	30.00
RS Ryne Sandberg/23		
RY Robin Yount/19		
SC Steve Carlton/32	12.50	30.00
SM Stan Musial/6		
SR Scott Rolen/27	20.00	50.00
TE Miguel Tejada/10		
TG Tony Gwynn/19		
TH Tim Hudson/15		
TP Tony Perez/24		
TS Tom Seaver/41	30.00	60.00
VG Vladimir Guerrero/27	30.00	60.00
WB Wade Boggs/26	20.00	50.00
WC Will Clark/22		
WF Whitey Ford/16		
WM Willie McCovey/44	20.00	50.00
YB Yogi Berra/8		

2005 Ultimate Signature ROY Dual Autograph

OVERALL DUAL AU ODDS 1:4
PRINT RUNS B/WN 15-250 COPIES PER
NO PRICING ON QTY OF 25 OR LESS
EXCHANGE DEADLINE 06/07/08

Card	Low	High
BP Johnny Bench Mike Piazza/15		
BR Jeff Bagwell Scott Rolen/15		
CM Orlando Cepeda Willie McCovey/75	30.00	60.00
CS Rod Carew Tom Seaver/25		
DM Andre Dawson Eddie Murray/25		
FB Carlton Fisk Johnny Bench/35	50.00	100.00
FL Carlton Fisk Fred Lynn/125	20.00	50.00
JG Derek Jeter Nomar Garciaparra/75	200.00	300.00
RA Frank Robinson Luis Aparicio/125	20.00	50.00
RJ Cal Ripken Derek Jeter/75	300.00	450.00
SG Darryl Strawberry Dwight Gooden/250	15.00	40.00
WD Billy Williams Andre Dawson/250	15.00	40.00

2005 Ultimate Signature ROY Dual Autograph-Cut

OVERALL RARE CUT AU ODDS 1:644
STATED PRINT RUN 3 SERIAL #'d SETS
NO PRICING DUE TO SCARCITY
JM Derek Jeter
Thurman Munson Cut/3
RR Frank Robinson
Jackie Robinson Cut/3

2005 Ultimate Signature ROY Quad Autograph-Cut

OVERALL RARE CUT AU ODDS 1:644
STATED PRINT RUN 1 SERIAL #'d SET
NO PRICING DUE TO SCARCITY
JPMR Derek Jeter
Mike Piazza
Thurman Munson Cut
Jackie Robinson Cut

2005 Ultimate Signature ROY Triple Autograph-Cut

OVERALL RARE CUT AU ODDS 1:644
STATED PRINT RUN 3 SERIAL #'d SETS
NO PRICING DUE TO SCARCITY
PNR Mike Piazza
Don Newcombe
Jackie Robinson Cut/3

2005 Ultimate Signature Signs of October Dual Autograph

OVERALL DUAL AU ODDS 1:4
PRINT RUNS B/WN 15-250 COPIES PER
NO PRICING ON QTY OF 25 OR LESS
EXCHANGE DEADLINE 06/07/08

Card	Low	High
BS George Brett Mike Schmidt/15		
EG Dennis Eckersley Kirk Gibson/200	30.00	60.00
FM Carlton Fisk Joe Morgan/100	20.00	50.00
GB Bob Gibson Lou Brock/100	30.00	60.00
GG Steve Garvey Ron Guidry/250	15.00	40.00
GL Bob Gibson Mickey Lolich/100	40.00	80.00
JC Randy Johnson Roger Clemens/15		
JG Derek Jeter Tony Gwynn/250	125.00	200.00
LB Don Larsen Yogi Berra/250	50.00	100.00
MP Jack Morris Kirby Puckett/100	150.00	250.00
PC Mike Piazza Roger Clemens/15		
PS Kirby Puckett Ozzie Smith/35	125.00	200.00
RM Cal Ripken Eddie Murray/15		
RR Brooks Robinson Frank Robinson/250	30.00	60.00
SB Ozzie Smith George Brett/25		
SY Ozzie Smith Robin Yount/100	40.00	80.00
TG Alan Trammell Kirk Gibson/250	12.50	30.00

2005 Ultimate Signature Signs of October Dual Autograph-Cut

OVERALL RARE CUT AU ODDS 1:644
PRINT RUNS B/WN 4-5 COPIES PER
NO PRICING DUE TO SCARCITY
DJ Derek Jeter
Joe DiMaggio Cut/5
SM Duke Snider
Mickey Mantle Cut/6

2005 Ultimate Signature Signs of October Quad Autograph-Cut

OVERALL RARE CUT AU ODDS 1:644
STATED PRINT RUN 1 SERIAL #'d SET
NO PRICING DUE TO SCARCITY
JMMR Derek Jeter
Don Mattingly
Mickey Mantle Cut
Babe Ruth Cut

2005 Ultimate Signature Signs of October Triple Autograph-Cut

OVERALL RARE CUT AU ODDS 1:644
STATED PRINT RUN 1 SERIAL #'d SET
NO PRICING DUE TO SCARCITY
GMD Bob Gibson
Stan Musial
Dizzy Dean Cut/1
MKC Bill Mazeroski
Ralph Kiner
Roberto Clemente Cut/1

2005 Ultimate Signature Supremacy

OVERALL PREMIUM SINGLE AU 1:5
PRINT RUNS B/WN 15-99 COPIES PER
NO PRICING ON QTY OF 25 OR LESS
EXCHANGE DEADLINE 06/07/08

Card	Low	High
AD Andre Dawson/99	10.00	25.00
AK Al Kaline/50	30.00	60.00
AR Al Rosen/99	10.00	25.00
AS Alfonso Soriano/25		
BD Bobby Doerr/99	10.00	25.00
BE Johnny Bench/25		
BF Bob Feller/99	15.00	40.00
BG Bob Gibson/25		
BM Bill Mazeroski/50	20.00	50.00
BR Brooks Robinson/99	15.00	40.00
BS Ben Sheets/99	10.00	25.00
BU Jim Bunning/99	10.00	25.00
BW Billy Williams/99	10.00	25.00
CA Rod Carew/25		
CF Carlton Fisk/25		
CJ Chipper Jones/25		
CL Roger Clemens/15		
CY Carl Yastrzemski/25		
DJ Derek Jeter/50	150.00	250.00
DM Dale Murphy/99	15.00	40.00
DN Don Newcombe/99	10.00	25.00
DO David Ortiz/99	20.00	50.00
DS Duke Snider/20		
DW Dave Winfield/25		
EB Ernie Banks/20		
EC Eric Chavez/99	10.00	25.00
EG Eric Gagne/50	20.00	50.00
EM Eddie Murray/15		
FJ Fergie Jenkins/25		
FR Frank Robinson/25		
FT Frank Thomas/25		
GB George Brett/15		
GC Gary Carter/25		
GK George Kell/99	15.00	40.00
GM Greg Maddux/15		
HB Hank Blalock/50	12.50	30.00
HK Harmon Killebrew/50	40.00	80.00
IR Ivan Rodriguez/25		
JB Jeff Bagwell/25		
JC Jose Canseco/25		
JM Joe Morgan/25		
JP Jim Palmer/99	10.00	25.00
JR Jim Rice/99	10.00	25.00
JS Johan Santana/99	15.00	40.00
JU Juan Marichal/25		
KG Ken Griffey Jr./99	50.00	100.00
KP Kirby Puckett/20		
KW Kerry Wood/25		
LA Luis Aparicio/50	12.50	30.00
LB Lou Brock/25		
MA Don Mattingly/25		
MC Miguel Cabrera/99	15.00	40.00
MI Monte Irvin/99	10.00	25.00
MM Mark Mulder/99	10.00	25.00
MP Mark Prior/25		
MS Mike Schmidt/25		
MT Mark Teixeira/99	15.00	40.00
MU Stan Musial/25		
NG Nomar Garciaparra/15		
NR Nolan Ryan/15		
OC Orlando Cepeda/99	10.00	25.00
OS Ozzie Smith/25		
PI Mike Piazza/15		
PM Paul Molitor/50	12.50	30.00
RC Rocky Colavito/25		
RF Rollie Fingers/99	10.00	25.00
RG Ron Guidry/99	15.00	40.00
RJ Randy Johnson/15		
RK Ralph Kiner/25		
RO Roy Oswalt/99	10.00	25.00
RR Robin Roberts/99	10.00	25.00
RS Ron Santo/99	15.00	40.00
SA Ryne Sandberg/25		
SC Steve Carlton/99	10.00	25.00
SM John Smoltz/50	20.00	50.00
SR Scott Rolen/25		
TE Miguel Tejada/25		
TG Tony Gwynn/25		
TH Tim Hudson/50	20.00	50.00
TP Tony Perez/99	10.00	25.00
TS Tom Seaver/25		
WB Wade Boggs/25		
WC Will Clark/50	20.00	50.00
WF Whitey Ford/25		
WM Willie McCovey/20		
YB Yogi Berra/25		

1999 Ultimate Victory

The 1999 Upper Deck Ultimate Victory Product was issued late in 1999. The cards were distributed in five card packs with a SRP of $2.99 per pack and each box had 24 packs in it. The set, consisting of 180 cards has 120 cards printed in normal quantites and 60 short prints. The cards from 121 through 150 feature players in their rookie campaign and cards numbered 151 through 180 all feature Mark McGwire in a set entitled "McGwire's Magic". Cards 121-180 were all released at a rate of one in four. Rookie Cards of Rick Ankiel, Josh Beckett, Pat Burrell, Freddy Garcia, Tim Hudson, Eric Munson, and Alfonso Soriano are all included in this set.

Card	Low	High
COMPLETE SET (180)	90.00	150.00
COMP.SET w/o SP's (120)	10.00	25.00
COMMON CARD (1-120)	.10	.30
COMMON SP (121-150)	.75	2.00
COMMON (151-180)	.75	2.00
1 Troy Glaus	.20	.50
2 Tim Salmon	.20	.50
3 Mo Vaughn	.10	.30
4 Garret Anderson	.10	.30
5 Darin Erstad	.10	.30
6 Randy Johnson	.30	.75
7 Matt Williams	.10	.30
8 Travis Lee	.10	.30
9 Jay Bell	.10	.30
10 Steve Finley	.10	.30
11 Luis Gonzalez	.10	.30
12 Greg Maddux	.50	1.25
13 Chipper Jones	.30	.75
14 Javy Lopez	.10	.30
15 Tom Glavine	.20	.50
16 John Smoltz	.20	.50
17 Cal Ripken	1.00	2.50
18 Charles Johnson	.10	.30
19 Albert Belle	.10	.30
20 Mike Mussina	.20	.50
21 Pedro Martinez	.20	.50
22 Nomar Garciaparra	.50	1.25
23 Jose Offerman	.10	.30
24 Sammy Sosa	.30	.75
25 Mark Grace	.20	.50
26 Kerry Wood	.10	.30
27 Frank Thomas	.30	.75
28 Ray Durham	.10	.30
29 Paul Konerko	.10	.30
30 Pete Harnisch	.10	.30
31 Greg Vaughn	.10	.30
32 Sean Casey	.10	.30
33 Manny Ramirez	.20	.50
34 Jim Thome	.20	.50
35 Sandy Alomar Jr.	.10	.30
36 Roberto Alomar	.20	.50
37 Travis Fryman	.10	.30
38 Kenny Lofton	.10	.30
39 Omar Vizquel	.20	.50
40 Larry Walker	.10	.30
41 Todd Helton	.20	.50
42 Vinny Castilla	.10	.30
43 Tony Clark	.10	.30
44 Juan Encarnacion	.10	.30
45 Dean Palmer	.10	.30
46 Damion Easley	.10	.30
47 Mark Kotsay	.10	.30
48 Cliff Floyd	.10	.30
49 Jeff Bagwell	.20	.50
50 Ken Caminiti	.10	.30
51 Craig Biggio	.20	.50
52 Moises Alou	.10	.30
53 Johnny Damon	.20	.50
54 Larry Sutton	.10	.30
55 Kevin Brown	.20	.50
56 Adrian Beltre	.10	.30
57 Raul Mondesi	.10	.30
58 Gary Sheffield	.10	.30
59 Jeromy Burnitz	.10	.30
60 Sean Berry	.10	.30
61 Jeff Cirillo	.10	.30
62 Brad Radke	.10	.30
63 Todd Walker	.10	.30
64 Matt Lawton	.10	.30
65 Vladimir Guerrero	.30	.75
66 Rondell White	.10	.30
67 Dustin Hermanson	.10	.30
68 Mike Piazza	.50	1.25
69 Rickey Henderson	.30	.75
70 Robin Ventura	.10	.30
71 John Olerud	.10	.30
72 Derek Jeter	.75	2.00
73 Roger Clemens	.60	1.50
74 Orlando Hernandez	.10	.30
75 Paul O'Neill	.20	.50
76 Bernie Williams	.20	.50
77 Chuck Knoblauch	.10	.30
78 Tino Martinez	.20	.50
79 Jason Giambi	.10	.30
80 Ben Grieve	.10	.30
81 Matt Stairs	.10	.30
82 Scott Rolen	.20	.50
83 Ron Gant	.10	.30
84 Bobby Abreu	.10	.30
85 Curt Schilling	.10	.30
86 Brian Giles	.10	.30
87 Jason Kendall	.10	.30
88 Kevin Young	.10	.30
89 Mark McGwire	.75	2.00
90 Fernando Tatis	.10	.30
91 Ray Lankford	.10	.30
92 Eric Davis	.10	.30
93 Tony Gwynn	.40	1.00
94 Reggie Sanders	.10	.30
95 Wally Joyner	.10	.30
96 Trevor Hoffman	.10	.30
97 Robb Nen	.10	.30
98 Barry Bonds	.75	2.00
99 Jeff Kent	.10	.30
100 J.T. Snow	.10	.30
101 Ellis Burks	.10	.30
102 Ken Griffey Jr.	.50	1.25
103 Alex Rodriguez	.50	1.25
104 Jay Buhner	.10	.30
105 Edgar Martinez	.20	.50
106 David Bell	.10	.30
107 Bobby Smith	.10	.30
108 Wade Boggs	.20	.50
109 Fred McGriff	.20	.50
110 Rolando Arrojo	.10	.30
111 Jose Canseco	.20	.50
112 Ivan Rodriguez	.20	.50
113 Juan Gonzalez	.10	.30
114 Rafael Palmeiro	.20	.50
115 Rusty Greer	.10	.30
116 Todd Zeile	.10	.30
117 Jose Cruz Jr.	.10	.30
118 Carlos Delgado	.10	.30
119 Shawn Green	.10	.30
120 David Wells	.10	.30
121 Eric Munson SP RC	1.25	3.00
122 Lance Berkman SP	1.25	3.00
123 Ed Yarnall SP	.75	2.00
124 Jacque Jones SP	1.25	3.00
125 K.Farnsworth SP RC	1.25	3.00
126 Ryan Rupe SP RC	.75	2.00
127 Jeff Weaver SP RC	2.00	5.00
128 Gabe Kapler SP	1.25	3.00
129 Alex Gonzalez SP	.75	2.00
130 Randy Wolf SP	.75	2.00
131 Ben Davis SP	.75	2.00
132 Carlos Beltran SP	2.00	5.00
133 Jim Morris SP RC	2.00	5.00
134 J.Zimmerman SP RC	1.25	3.00
135 Bruce Aven SP	.75	2.00
136 A.Soriano SP RC	8.00	20.00
137 Tim Hudson SP RC	5.00	12.00
138 Josh Beckett SP RC	10.00	25.00
139 Michael Barrett SP	.75	2.00
140 Eric Chavez SP	1.25	3.00
141 Pat Burrell SP RC	6.00	15.00
142 Kris Benson SP	.75	2.00
143 J.D. Drew SP	1.25	3.00
144 Matt Clement SP	1.25	3.00
145 Rick Ankiel SP RC	12.50	30.00
146 Vernon Wells SP	1.25	3.00
147 Ruben Mateo SP UER Card is misnumbered	.75	2.00
148 Roy Halladay SP	3.00	8.00
149 Joe McEwing SP RC	1.25	3.00
150 Freddy Garcia SP RC	3.00	8.00
151 Mark McGwire MM	.75	2.00
152 Mark McGwire MM	.75	2.00
153 Mark McGwire MM	.75	2.00
154 Mark McGwire MM	.75	2.00
155 Mark McGwire MM	.75	2.00
156 Mark McGwire MM	.75	2.00
157 Mark McGwire MM	.75	2.00
158 Mark McGwire MM	.75	2.00
159 Mark McGwire MM	.75	2.00
160 Mark McGwire MM	.75	2.00
161 Mark McGwire MM	.75	2.00
162 Mark McGwire MM	.75	2.00
163 Mark McGwire MM	.75	2.00
164 Mark McGwire MM	.75	2.00
165 Mark McGwire MM	.75	2.00
166 Mark McGwire MM	.75	2.00
167 Mark McGwire MM	.75	2.00
168 Mark McGwire MM	.75	2.00
169 Mark McGwire MM	.75	2.00
170 Mark McGwire MM	.75	2.00
171 Mark McGwire MM	.75	2.00
172 Mark McGwire MM	.75	2.00
173 Mark McGwire MM	.75	2.00
174 Mark McGwire MM	.75	2.00
175 Mark McGwire MM	.75	2.00
176 Mark McGwire MM	.75	2.00
177 Mark McGwire MM	.75	2.00
178 Mark McGwire MM	.75	2.00
179 Mark McGwire MM	.75	2.00
180 Mark McGwire MM	.75	2.00

1999 Ultimate Victory Parallel

Inserted at a rate of one in 12, these card parallel the regular set. They can be differentiated from the regular cards with the addition of linear holographic foil on each card.

*STARS 1-120: 2X TO 5X BASIC CARDS
*PARALLEL 121-150: .6X TO 1.5X BASIC
*PARALLEL 121-150: .6X TO 1.5X BASIC RC
STATED ODDS 1:12

Card	Low	High
136 Alfonso Soriano	40.00	80.00
138 Josh Beckett	10.00	25.00
145 Rick Ankiel	100.00	200.00

1999 Ultimate Victory Parallel 100

Randomly inserted into packs, these cards parallel the regular Ultimate Victory set. They feature silver holographic foil in trippy circular patterns and are sequentially numbered to 100 on the front.

*PAR.100 1-120: 5X TO 12X BASIC
*PAR.100 121-150: 1.5X TO 4X BASIC
*PAR.100 121-150: 2X TO 4X BASIC RC
*MCGWIRE 151-180: 3X TO 8X BASIC
RANDOM INSERTS IN PACKS

Card	Low	High
136 Alfonso Soriano	100.00	200.00
138 Josh Beckett	30.00	60.00
145 Rick Ankiel	200.00	300.00

1999 Ultimate Victory Bleacher Reachers

Inserted one every 23 packs, these horizontal cards feature 11 players who are among baseball's leading sluggers.

Card	Low	High
COMPLETE SET (11)	25.00	50.00
STATED ODDS 1:23		
BR1 Ken Griffey Jr.	1.50	4.00
BR2 Mark McGwire	2.50	6.00
BR3 Sammy Sosa	1.00	2.50
BR4 Barry Bonds	2.50	6.00
BR5 Nomar Garciaparra	1.50	4.00
BR6 Juan Gonzalez	.40	1.00
BR7 Jose Canseco	.60	1.50
BR8 Manny Ramirez	.60	1.50
BR9 Mike Piazza	1.50	4.00
BR10 Jeff Bagwell	.60	1.50
BR11 Alex Rodriguez	1.50	4.00

1999 Ultimate Victory Fame-Used Memorabilia

Randomly inserted into packs, these cards feature pieces of bats used by the four inductees into the Hall of Fame in 1999. Similar to the other bat cards Upper Deck has produced, approximately 350 of each card were made. There was also a special card made with bat pieces of all four of these players. Ninety-nine copies of that combo card were produced.

RANDOM INSERTS IN PACKS

Card	Low	High
GB George Brett	10.00	25.00
NR Nolan Ryan	15.00	40.00
OC Orlando Cepeda	4.00	10.00
RY Robin Yount	6.00	15.00
HOF Nolan Ryan George Brett Robin Yount Orlando Cepeda	60.00	120.00

1999 Ultimate Victory Frozen Ropes

Inserted one every 23 packs, these 10 cards feature players who consistently are among the best in the majors.

COMPLETE SET (10) 25.00 50.00
STATED ODDS 1:23
F1 Ken Griffey Jr. 1.50 4.00
F2 Mark McGwire 2.50 6.00
F3 Sammy Sosa 1.00 2.50
F4 Derek Jeter 2.50 6.00
F5 Tony Gwynn 1.25 3.00
F6 Nomar Garciaparra 1.50 4.00
F7 Alex Rodriguez 1.50 4.00
F8 Mike Piazza 1.50 4.00
F9 Mo Vaughn .40 1.00
F10 Craig Biggio .60 1.50

1999 Ultimate Victory STATure

Inserted one every six packs, these fifteen cards featured players who are among the statistical leaders.

COMPLETE SET (15) 12.50 25.00
STATED ODDS 1:6
S1 Ken Griffey Jr. .50 1.25
S2 Mark McGwire .75 2.00
S3 Sammy Sosa .30 .75
S4 Nomar Garciaparra .50 1.25
S5 Roger Clemens .60 1.50
S6 Greg Maddux .50 1.25
S7 Alex Rodriguez .50 1.25
S8 Derek Jeter .75 2.00
S9 Juan Gonzalez .10 .30
S10 Manny Ramirez .20 .50
S11 Mike Piazza .50 1.25
S12 Tony Gwynn .40 1.00
S13 Chipper Jones .30 .75
S14 Pedro Martinez .20 .50
S15 Frank Thomas .30 .75

1999 Ultimate Victory Tribute 1999

Inserted one every 11 packs, this set honors the four inductees into the Hall of Fame in 1999. Card backs carry a "T" prefix.

COMPLETE SET (4) 7.50 15.00
STATED ODDS 1:11
T1 Nolan Ryan 2.50 6.00
T2 Robin Yount 1.50 4.00
T3 George Brett 2.50 6.00
T4 Orlando Cepeda .60 1.50

1999 Ultimate Victory Ultimate Competitors

Inserted one every 23 packs, this 12 card set highlights the players who bring an winning attitude to the ballpark every day.

COMPLETE SET (12) 30.00 60.00
STATED ODDS 1:23
U1 Ken Griffey Jr. 2.00 5.00
U2 Roger Clemens 2.50 6.00
U3 Scott Rolen .75 2.00
U4 Greg Maddux 2.00 5.00
U5 Mark McGwire 3.00 8.00
U6 Derek Jeter 3.00 8.00
U7 Randy Johnson 1.25 3.00
U8 Cal Ripken 4.00 10.00
U9 Craig Biggio .75 2.00
U10 Kevin Brown .75 2.00
U11 Chipper Jones 1.25 3.00
U12 Vladimir Guerrero 1.25 3.00

1999 Ultimate Victory Ultimate Hit Men

Inserted one every 23 packs, this eight card set features players who were among the leading contenders for the 1999 batting titles in their respective leagues.

COMPLETE SET (8) 15.00 30.00
STATED ODDS 1:23
H1 Tony Gwynn 1.00 2.50
H2 Cal Ripken 2.50 6.00
H3 Wade Boggs .50 1.25
H4 Larry Walker .30 .75
H5 Alex Rodriguez 1.25 3.00
H6 Derek Jeter 2.00 5.00
H7 Ivan Rodriguez .50 1.25
H8 Ken Griffey Jr. 1.25 3.00

2000 Ultimate Victory

The 2000 Upper Deck Ultimate Victory product was released in October, 2000. The set features 120 cards broken into tiers as follows: 90 veterans (1-90), 10 Rookies serial numbered to 3500, 10 Rookies serial numbered to 2500, and 10 Rookies serial numbered to 1000. Each pack contained five cards and carried a suggested retail price of $3.99.

COMP.SET w/o SP's (90) 10.00 25.00
COMMON CARD (1-90) .10 .30
1 Mo Vaughn .10 .30
2 Darin Erstad .10 .30
3 Troy Glaus .10 .30
4 Adam Kennedy .10 .30
5 Jason Giambi .10 .30
6 Ben Grieve .10 .30
7 Terrence Long .10 .30
8 Tim Hudson .10 .30
9 David Wells .10 .30
10 Carlos Delgado .10 .30
11 Shannon Stewart .10 .30
12 Greg Vaughn .10 .30
13 Gerald Williams .10 .30
14 Manny Ramirez .20 .50
15 Roberto Alomar .20 .50
16 Jim Thome .20 .50
17 Edgar Martinez .20 .50
18 Alex Rodriguez .50 1.25
19 Matt Riley .10 .30
20 Cal Ripken 1.00 2.50
21 Mike Mussina .20 .50
22 Albert Belle .10 .30
23 Ivan Rodriguez .20 .50
24 Rafael Palmeiro .20 .50
25 Nomar Garciaparra .50 1.25
26 Pedro Martinez .20 .50
27 Carl Everett .10 .30
28 Tomokazu Ohka RC .10 .30
29 Jermaine Dye .10 .30
30 Johnny Damon .20 .50
31 Dean Palmer .10 .30
32 Juan Gonzalez .10 .30
33 Eric Milton .10 .30
34 Matt Lawton .10 .30
35 Frank Thomas .30 .75
36 Paul Konerko .10 .30
37 Magglio Ordonez .10 .30
38 Jon Garland .10 .30
39 Derek Jeter .75 2.00
40 Roger Clemens .60 1.50
41 Bernie Williams .20 .50
42 Nick Johnson .10 .30
43 Julio Lugo .10 .30
44 Jeff Bagwell .20 .50
45 Richard Hidalgo .10 .30
46 Chipper Jones .30 .75
47 Greg Maddux .50 1.25
48 Andruw Jones .20 .50
49 Andres Galarraga .10 .30
50 Rafael Furcal .10 .30
51 Jeromy Burnitz .10 .30
52 Geoff Jenkins .10 .30
53 Mark McGwire .75 2.00
54 Jim Edmonds .10 .30
55 Rick Ankiel .10 .30
56 Sammy Sosa .30 .75
57 Julio Zuleta RC .10 .30
58 Kerry Wood .10 .30
59 Randy Johnson .30 .75
60 Matt Williams .10 .30
61 Steve Finley .10 .30
62 Gary Sheffield .10 .30
63 Kevin Brown .10 .30
64 Shawn Green .10 .30
65 Milton Bradley .10 .30
66 Vladimir Guerrero .30 .75
67 Jose Vidro .10 .30
68 Barry Bonds .75 2.00
69 Jeff Kent .10 .30
70 Preston Wilson .10 .30
71 Mike Lowell .10 .30
72 Mike Piazza .50 1.25
73 Robin Ventura .10 .30
74 Edgardo Alfonzo .10 .30
75 Jay Payton .10 .30
76 Tony Gwynn .40 1.00
77 Adam Eaton .10 .30
78 Phil Nevin .10 .30
79 Scott Rolen .20 .50
80 Bob Abreu .10 .30
81 Pat Burrell .10 .30
82 Brian Giles .10 .30
83 Jason Kendall .10 .30
84 Kris Benson .10 .30
85 Gookie Dawkins .10 .30
86 Ken Griffey Jr. .50 1.25
87 Barry Larkin .20 .50
88 Larry Walker .10 .30
89 Todd Helton .20 .50
90 Ben Petrick .10 .30
91 Alex Cabrera/3500 RC 1.50 4.00
92 M.Wheatland/1000 RC 4.00 10.00
93 Joe Torres/1000 RC 4.00 10.00
94 Xavier Nady/1000 RC 5.00 12.00
95 Kenny Kelly/3500 RC 1.50 4.00
96 Matt Ginter/3500 RC 1.50 4.00
97 Ben Diggins/1000 RC 4.00 10.00
98 Dannys Baez/3500 RC 1.50 4.00
99 Daylan Holt/2500 RC 2.00 5.00
100 K.Sasaki/3500 RC 2.00 5.00
101 D.Artman/2500 RC 2.00 5.00
102 Mike Tonis/1000 RC 4.00 10.00
103 Timo Perez/2500 RC 2.00 5.00
104 Barry Zito/2500 RC 5.00 12.00
105 Koyie Hill/2500 RC 2.00 5.00
106 B.Wilkerson/2500 RC 3.00 8.00
107 Juan Pierre/3500 RC 2.00 5.00
108 A.McNeal/3500 RC 1.50 4.00
109 J.Spurgeon/3500 RC 1.50 4.00
110 Sean Burnett/1000 RC 4.00 10.00
111 Luis Matos/3500 RC 1.50 4.00
112 Dave Krynzel/1000 RC 4.00 10.00
113 Scott Heard/1000 RC 4.00 10.00
114 Ben Sheets/2500 RC 3.00 8.00
115 D.Sardinha/1000 RC 4.00 10.00
116 D.Espinosa/1000 RC 4.00 10.00
117 Leo Estrella/3500 RC 1.50 4.00
118 K.Ainsworth/2500 RC 2.00 5.00
119 Jon Rauch/2500 RC 2.00 5.00
120 R.Franklin/2500 RC 2.00 5.00

2000 Ultimate Victory Parallel 25

Randomly inserted into packs, this 120-card insert is a complete parallel of the base set. They can be differentiated from the regular cards with the addition of gold foil on each card. Each card is serial numbered to 25. Pricing for the rookie subset cards 91-120 is not provided due to volatility.

*STARS 1-90: 15X TO 40X BASIC 1-90

2000 Ultimate Victory Parallel 100

Randomly inserted into packs, this 120-card insert is a complete parallel of the base set. They can be differentiated from the regular cards with the addition of red foil on each card. Each card is serial numbered to 100.

*STARS 1-90: 8X TO 20X BASIC 1-90
*ROOKIES 1-90: 10X TO 25X BASIC 1-90
*TIER 1 91-120: .4X TO 1X BASIC RC 1000

*TIER 2 91-120: .75X TO 2X BASIC 2500
*TIER 3 91-120: 1X TO 2.5X BASIC 3500

2000 Ultimate Victory Parallel 250

Randomly inserted into packs, this 120-card insert is a complete parallel of the base set. They can be differentiated from the regular cards with the addition of silver foil on each card. Each card is serial numbered to 250.

*STARS 1-90: 3X TO 8X BASIC 1-90
*ROOKIES 1-90: 6X TO 15X BASIC 1-90
*TIER 1 91-120: .2X TO .5X BASIC 1000
*TIER 2 91-120: .4X TO 1X BASIC 2500
*TIER 3 91-120: .6X TO 1.5X BASIC 3500

2000 Ultimate Victory Diamond Dignitaries

Randomly inserted into packs at one in 23, this 10-card insert set features players that are leaders on the playing field. Card backs carry a "D" prefix.

COMPLETE SET (10) 25.00 60.00
D1 Ken Griffey Jr. 2.50 6.00
D2 Nomar Garciaparra 2.50 6.00
D3 Chipper Jones 1.50 4.00
D4 Ivan Rodriguez 1.00 2.50
D5 Mark McGwire 4.00 10.00
D6 Cal Ripken 5.00 12.00
D7 Vladimir Guerrero 1.50 4.00
D8 Alex Rodriguez 2.50 6.00
D9 Sammy Sosa 1.50 4.00
D10 Derek Jeter 4.00 10.00

2000 Ultimate Victory Hall of Fame Game Jersey

Randomly inserted into packs, this four-card insert set features jersey cards of players that were inducted into the Hall of Fame in 2000. Each "single-player" card has an announced print run of 500 copies, and the card backs carry the player's initials as numbering. Please note that the combo card of Fisk/Anderson/Perez was serial numbered to 100.

CF Carlton Fisk 6.00 15.00
SA Sparky Anderson 6.00 15.00
TP Tony Perez 6.00 15.00
HOF Carlton Fisk 30.00 60.00
Sparky Anderson
Tony Perez/100

2000 Ultimate Victory Lasting Impressions

Randomly inserted into packs at one in 11, this 10-card insert set features players that leave a lasting impression on those who watch them perform. Card backs carry a "L" prefix.

COMPLETE SET (10) 12.50 30.00
L1 Barry Bonds 2.00 5.00
L2 Mike Piazza 1.25 3.00
L3 Manny Ramirez .50 1.25
L4 Pedro Martinez .50 1.25
L5 Mark McGwire 2.00 5.00
L6 Ken Griffey Jr. 1.25 3.00
L7 Ivan Rodriguez .50 1.25
L8 Jeff Bagwell .50 1.25
L9 Randy Johnson .75 2.00
L10 Alex Rodriguez 1.25 3.00

2000 Ultimate Victory Starstruck

Randomly inserted into packs at one in 11, this 10-card insert set features players that have been starstruck. Card backs carry a "S" prefix.

COMPLETE SET (10) 12.50 30.00
S1 Alex Rodriguez 1.25 3.00
S2 Frank Thomas .75 2.00
S3 Derek Jeter 2.00 5.00
S4 Mark McGwire 2.00 5.00
S5 Nomar Garciaparra 1.25 3.00
S6 Chipper Jones .75 2.00
S7 Cal Ripken 2.50 6.00
S8 Sammy Sosa .75 2.00
S9 Vladimir Guerrero .75 2.00
S10 Ken Griffey Jr. 1.25 3.00

1991 Ultra

This 400-card standard-size set marked Fleer's first entry into the premium card market. The cards were distributed exclusively in foil-wrapped packs. Fleer claimed in their original press release that there would only be 15 percent the amount of Ultra issued as there was of the regular 1991 Fleer issue. The cards feature full color action photography on the fronts and three full-color photos on the backs. Fleer also issued the sets in their now traditional alphabetical order as well as the teams in alphabetical order. Subsets include Major League Prospects (373-390), Elite Performance (391-396), and Checklists (397-400). Rookie Cards include Eric Karros and Denny Neagle.

COMPLETE SET (400) 8.00 20.00
1 Steve Avery .02 .10
2 Jeff Blauser .02 .10
3 Francisco Cabrera .02 .10
4 Ron Gant .07 .20
5 Tom Glavine .10 .30
6 Tommy Gregg .02 .10
7 Dave Justice .07 .20
8 Oddibe McDowell .02 .10
9 Greg Olson .02 .10
10 Terry Pendleton .07 .20
11 Lonnie Smith .02 .10
12 John Smoltz .10 .30
13 Jeff Treadway .02 .10
14 Glenn Davis .02 .10
15 Mike Devereaux .02 .10
16 Leo Gomez .02 .10
17 Chris Hoiles .02 .10
18 Dave Johnson .02 .10
19 Ben McDonald .02 .10
20 Randy Milligan .02 .10
21 Gregg Olson .02 .10
22 Joe Orsulak .02 .10
23 Bill Ripken .02 .10
24 Cal Ripken .60 1.50
25 David Segui .02 .10
26 Craig Worthington .02 .10
27 Wade Boggs .10 .30
28 Tom Bolton .02 .10
29 Tom Brunansky .02 .10
30 Ellis Burks .07 .20
31 Roger Clemens .60 1.50
32 Mike Greenwell .02 .10
33 Greg A. Harris .02 .10
34 Daryl Irvine RC .02 .10
35 Mike Marshall UER .02 .10
(1990 in stats is shown as 990)
36 Tim Naehring .02 .10
37 Tony Pena .02 .10
38 Phil Plantier RC .05 .15
39 Carlos Quintana .02 .10
40 Jeff Reardon .07 .20
41 Jody Reed .02 .10
42 Luis Rivera .02 .10
43 Jim Abbott .10 .30
44 Chuck Finley .07 .20
45 Bryan Harvey .02 .10
46 Donnie Hill .02 .10
47 Jack Howell .02 .10
48 Wally Joyner .07 .20
49 Mark Langston .02 .10
50 Kirk McCaskill .02 .10
51 Lance Parrish .07 .20
52 Dick Schofield .02 .10
53 Lee Stevens .02 .10
54 Dave Winfield .07 .20
55 George Bell .02 .10
56 Damon Berryhill .02 .10
57 Mike Bielecki .02 .10
58 Andre Dawson .07 .20
59 Shawon Dunston .02 .10
60 Joe Girardi UER .02 .10
(Bats right, LH hitter shown is Doug Dascenzo)
61 Mark Grace .10 .30
62 Mike Harkey .02 .10
63 Les Lancaster .02 .10
64 Greg Maddux .30 .75
65 Derrick May .02 .10
66 Ryne Sandberg .30 .75
67 Luis Salazar .02 .10
68 Dwight Smith .02 .10
69 Hector Villanueva .02 .10
70 Jerome Walton .02 .10
71 Mitch Williams .02 .10
72 Carlton Fisk .10 .30
73 Scott Fletcher .02 .10
74 Ozzie Guillen .07 .20
75 Greg Hibbard .02 .10
76 Lance Johnson .02 .10
77 Steve Lyons .02 .10
78 Jack McDowell .02 .10
79 Dan Pasqua .02 .10
80 Melido Perez .02 .10
81 Tim Raines .07 .20
82 Sammy Sosa .20 .50
83 Cory Snyder .02 .10
84 Bobby Thigpen .02 .10
85 Frank Thomas .20 .50
(Card says he is an outfielder)
86 Robin Ventura .07 .20
87 Todd Benzinger .02 .10
88 Glenn Braggs .02 .10
89 Tom Browning UER .02 .10
(Front photo actually Norm Charlton)
90 Norm Charlton .02 .10
91 Eric Davis .07 .20
92 Rob Dibble .07 .20
93 Bill Doran .02 .10
94 Mariano Duncan UER .02 .10
(Right back photo is Billy Hatcher)
95 Billy Hatcher .02 .10
96 Barry Larkin .10 .30
97 Randy Myers .02 .10
98 Hal Morris .02 .10
99 Joe Oliver .02 .10
100 Paul O'Neill .10 .30
101 Jeff Reed .02 .10
(See also 104)
102 Jose Rijo .02 .10
103 Chris Sabo .02 .10
(See also 106)
104 Beau Allred UER .02 .10
(Card number is 101)
105 Sandy Alomar Jr. .02 .10
106 Carlos Baerga UER .02 .10
(Card number is 103)
107 Albert Belle .07 .20
108 Jerry Browne .02 .10
109 Tom Candiotti .02 .10
110 Alex Cole .02 .10
111 John Farrell .02 .10
(See also 114)
112 Felix Fermin .02 .10
113 Brook Jacoby .02 .10
114 Chris James UER .02 .10
(Card number is 111)
115 Doug Jones .02 .10
116 Steve Olin .02 .10
(See also 119)
117 Greg Swindell .02 .10
118 Turner Ward RC .05 .15
119 Mitch Webster UER .02 .10
(Card number is 116)
120 Dave Bergman .02 .10
121 Cecil Fielder .07 .20
122 Travis Fryman .07 .20
123 Mike Henneman .02 .10
124 Lloyd Moseby .02 .10
125 Dan Petry .02 .10
126 Tony Phillips .02 .10
127 Mark Salas .02 .10
128 Frank Tanana .02 .10
129 Alan Trammell .07 .20
130 Lou Whitaker .07 .20
131 Eric Anthony .02 .10
132 Craig Biggio .10 .30
133 Ken Caminiti .07 .20
134 Casey Candaele .02 .10
135 Andujar Cedeno .02 .10
136 Mark Davidson .02 .10
137 Jim Deshaies .02 .10
138 Mark Portugal .02 .10
139 Rafael Ramirez .02 .10
140 Mike Scott .02 .10
141 Eric Yelding .02 .10
142 Gerald Young .02 .10
143 Kevin Appier .07 .20
144 George Brett .50 1.25
145 Jeff Conine RC .20 .50
146 Jim Eisenreich .02 .10
147 Tom Gordon .02 .10
148 Mark Gubicza .02 .10
149 Bo Jackson .20 .50
150 Brent Mayne .02 .10
151 Mike Macfarlane .02 .10
152 Brian McRae RC .15 .40
153 Jeff Montgomery .02 .10
154 Bret Saberhagen .07 .20
155 Kevin Seitzer .02 .10
156 Terry Shumpert .02 .10
157 Kurt Stillwell .02 .10
158 Danny Tartabull .02 .10
159 Tim Belcher .02 .10
160 Kal Daniels .02 .10
161 Alfredo Griffin .02 .10
162 Lenny Harris .02 .10
163 Jay Howell .02 .10
164 Ramon Martinez .02 .10
165 Mike Morgan .02 .10
166 Eddie Murray .20 .50
167 Jose Offerman .02 .10
168 Juan Samuel .02 .10
169 Mike Scioscia .02 .10
170 Mike Sharperson .02 .10
171 Darryl Strawberry .07 .20
172 Greg Brock .02 .10
173 Chuck Crim .02 .10
174 Jim Gantner .02 .10
175 Ted Higuera .02 .10
176 Mark Knudson .02 .10
177 Tim McIntosh .02 .10
178 Paul Molitor .07 .20
179 Dan Plesac .02 .10
180 Gary Sheffield .07 .20
181 Bill Spiers .02 .10
182 B.J. Surhoff .07 .20
183 Greg Vaughn .02 .10
184 Robin Yount .30 .75
185 Rick Aguilera .07 .20
186 Greg Gagne .02 .10
187 Dan Gladden .02 .10
188 Brian Harper .02 .10
189 Kent Hrbek .07 .20
190 Gene Larkin .02 .10
191 Shane Mack .02 .10
192 Pedro Munoz RC .05 .15
193 Al Newman .02 .10
194 Junior Ortiz .02 .10
195 Kirby Puckett .20 .50
196 Kevin Tapani .02 .10
197 Dennis Boyd .02 .10
198 Tim Burke .02 .10
199 Ivan Calderon .02 .10
200 Delino DeShields .07 .20
201 Mike Fitzgerald .02 .10
202 Steve Frey .02 .10
203 Andres Galarraga .07 .20
204 Marquis Grissom .07 .20
205 Dave Martinez .02 .10
206 Dennis Martinez .07 .20
207 Junior Noboa .02 .10
208 Spike Owen .02 .10
209 Scott Ruskin .02 .10
210 Tim Wallach .02 .10
211 Daryl Boston .02 .10
212 Vince Coleman .02 .10
213 David Cone .07 .20
214 Ron Darling .02 .10
215 Kevin Elster .02 .10
216 Sid Fernandez .02 .10
217 John Franco .07 .20
218 Dwight Gooden .07 .20
219 Tom Herr .02 .10
220 Todd Hundley .02 .10
221 Gregg Jefferies .02 .10
222 Howard Johnson .02 .10
223 Dave Magadan .02 .10
224 Kevin McReynolds .02 .10
225 Keith Miller .02 .10
226 Mackey Sasser .02 .10
227 Frank Viola .07 .20
228 Jesse Barfield .02 .10
229 Greg Cadaret .02 .10
230 Alvaro Espinoza .02 .10
231 Bob Geren .02 .10
232 Lee Guetterman .02 .10
233 Mel Hall .02 .10
234 Andy Hawkins UER .02 .10
(Back center photo is not him)
235 Roberto Kelly .02 .10
236 Tim Leary .02 .10
237 Jim Leyritz .02 .10
238 Kevin Maas .02 .10
239 Don Mattingly .50 1.25
240 Hensley Meulens .02 .10
241 Eric Plunk .02 .10
242 Steve Sax .02 .10
243 Todd Burns .02 .10
244 Jose Canseco .10 .30
245 Dennis Eckersley .07 .20
246 Mike Gallego .02 .10
247 Dave Henderson .02 .10
248 Rickey Henderson .20 .50
249 Rick Honeycutt .02 .10
250 Carney Lansford .07 .20
251 Mark McGwire .60 1.50
252 Mike Moore .02 .10
253 Terry Steinbach .02 .10
254 Dave Stewart .07 .20
255 Walt Weiss .02 .10
256 Bob Welch .02 .10
257 Curt Young .02 .10
258 Wes Chamberlain RC .15 .40
259 Pat Combs .02 .10
260 Darren Daulton .07 .20
261 Jose DeJesus .02 .10
262 Len Dykstra .07 .20
263 Charlie Hayes .02 .10
264 Von Hayes .02 .10
265 Ken Howell .02 .10
266 John Kruk .07 .20
267 Roger McDowell .02 .10
268 Mickey Morandini .02 .10
269 Terry Mulholland .02 .10
270 Dale Murphy .10 .30
271 Randy Ready .02 .10
272 Dickie Thon .02 .10
273 Stan Belinda .02 .10
274 Jay Bell .07 .20
275 Barry Bonds .60 1.50
276 Bobby Bonilla .07 .20
277 Doug Drabek .02 .10
278 Carlos Garcia RC .05 .15
279 Neal Heaton .02 .10
280 Jeff King .02 .10
281 Bill Landrum .02 .10
282 Mike LaValliere .02 .10
283 Jose Lind .02 .10
284 Orlando Merced RC .05 .15
285 Gary Redus .02 .10
286 Don Slaught .02 .10
287 Andy Van Slyke .10 .30
288 Jose DeLeon .02 .10
289 Pedro Guerrero .07 .20
290 Ray Lankford .07 .20
291 Joe Magrane .02 .10
292 Jose Oquendo .02 .10
293 Tom Pagnozzi .02 .10
294 Bryn Smith .02 .10
295 Lee Smith .07 .20
296 Ozzie Smith UER .30 .75
(Born 12-26, 54, should have hyphen)
297 Milt Thompson .02 .10
298 Craig Wilson RC .02 .10
299 Todd Zeile .02 .10
300 Shawn Abner .02 .10
301 Andy Benes .02 .10
302 Paul Faries RC .02 .10
303 Tony Gwynn .25 .60
304 Greg W. Harris .02 .10
305 Thomas Howard .02 .10
306 Bruce Hurst .02 .10
307 Craig Lefferts .02 .10
308 Fred McGriff .10 .30
309 Dennis Rasmussen .02 .10
310 Bip Roberts .02 .10
311 Benito Santiago .07 .20
312 Garry Templeton .02 .10
313 Ed Whitson .02 .10
314 Dave Anderson .02 .10
315 Kevin Bass .02 .10
316 Jeff Brantley .02 .10
317 John Burkett .02 .10
318 Will Clark .10 .30
319 Steve Decker RC .02 .10
320 Scott Garrelts .02 .10
321 Terry Kennedy .02 .10
322 Mark Leonard RC .02 .10
323 Darren Lewis .02 .10
324 Greg Litton .02 .10
325 Willie McGee .07 .20
326 Kevin Mitchell .02 .10
327 Don Robinson .02 .10
328 Andres Santana .02 .10
329 Robby Thompson .02 .10
330 Jose Uribe .02 .10
331 Matt Williams .07 .20
332 Scott Bradley .02 .10
333 Henry Cotto .02 .10
334 Alvin Davis .02 .10
335 Ken Griffey Sr. .07 .20
336 Ken Griffey Jr. .40 1.00
337 Erik Hanson .02 .10
338 Brian Holman .02 .10
339 Randy Johnson .25 .60
340 Edgar Martinez UER .10 .30
(Listed as playing SS)
341 Tino Martinez .20 .50
342 Pete O'Brien .02 .10
343 Harold Reynolds .07 .20
344 Dave Valle .02 .10
345 Omar Vizquel .10 .30
346 Brad Arnsberg .02 .10
347 Kevin Brown .07 .20
348 Julio Franco .07 .20
349 Jeff Huson .02 .10
350 Rafael Palmeiro .10 .30
351 Geno Petralli .02 .10
352 Gary Pettis .02 .10
353 Kenny Rogers .07 .20
354 Jeff Russell .02 .10
355 Nolan Ryan .75 2.00
356 Ruben Sierra .07 .20
357 Bobby Witt .02 .10
358 Roberto Alomar .10 .30
359 Pat Borders .02 .10
360 Joe Carter UER .07 .20
(Reverse negative on back photo)
361 Kelly Gruber .02 .10
362 Tom Henke .02 .10
363 Glenallen Hill .02 .10
364 Jimmy Key .07 .20
365 Manny Lee .02 .10
366 Rance Mulliniks .02 .10
367 John Olerud UER .07 .20
(Throwing left on card; back has throws right; he does throw lefty)
368 Dave Stieb .02 .10
369 Duane Ward .02 .10
370 David Wells .07 .20
371 Mark Whiten .02 .10
372 Mookie Wilson .07 .20
373 Willie Banks MLP .02 .10
374 Steve Carter MLP .02 .10
375 S.Chiamparino MLP .02 .10
376 Steve Chitren MLP RC .02 .10
377 Darrin Fletcher MLP .02 .10
378 Rich Garces MLP RC .05 .15
379 Reggie Jefferson MLP .02 .10
380 Eric Karros MLP RC .30 .75
381 Pat Kelly MLP RC .05 .15
382 C.Knoblauch MLP .07 .20
383 Denny Neagle MLP RC .15 .40
384 Dan Opperman MLP RC .02 .10
385 John Ramos MLP RC .02 .10
386 Henry Rodriguez MLP RC .15 .40
387 Mo Vaughn MLP .07 .20
388 Gerald Williams MLP RC .15 .40
389 Mike York MLP RC .02 .10
390 Eddie Zosky MLP .02 .10
391 Barry Bonds EP .30 .75
392 Cecil Fielder EP .02 .10
393 Rickey Henderson EP .10 .30
394 Dave Justice EP .02 .10
395 Nolan Ryan EP .40 1.00
396 Bobby Thigpen EP .02 .10
397 Gregg Jefferies CL .02 .10
398 Von Hayes CL .02 .10
399 Terry Kennedy CL .02 .10
400 Nolan Ryan CL .20 .50

1991 Ultra Gold

This ten-card standard-size set presents Fleer's 1991 Ultra Team. These cards were randomly inserted into Ultra packs. The set is sequenced in alphabetical order.

COMPLETE SET (10) 5.00 10.00
RANDOM INSERTS IN FOIL PACKS
1 Barry Bonds 1.25 3.00
2 Will Clark .25 .60
3 Doug Drabek .07 .20
4 Ken Griffey Jr. .75 2.00
5 Rickey Henderson .40 1.00
6 Bo Jackson .40 1.00
7 Ramon Martinez .07 .20
8 Kirby Puckett UER .40 1.00
(Boggs won 1988 batting title, so Puckett didn't win consecutive titles)
9 Chris Sabo .07 .20

10 Ryne Sandberg UER (Johnson and Hornsby didn't hit 40 homers in 1990, Fielder did hit 51 in '90)	.60	1.50

1991 Ultra Update

The 120-card set was distributed exclusively in factory set form along with 20 team logo stickers through hobby dealers. The set includes the year's hottest rookies and important veteran players traded after the original Ultra series was produced. Card design is identical to regular issue 1991 cards except for the U-prefixed numbering on back. Cards are ordered alphabetically within and according to teams for each league. Rookie Cards in this set include Jeff Bagwell, Mike Mussina, and Ivan Rodriguez.

COMP.FACT.SET (120)	10.00	25.00
1 Dwight Evans	.30	.75
2 Chito Martinez RC	.08	.25
3 Bob Melvin	.08	.25
4 Mike Mussina RC	2.00	5.00
5 Jack Clark	.20	.50
6 Dana Kiecker	.08	.25
7 Steve Lyons	.08	.25
8 Gary Gaetti	.20	.50
9 Dave Gallagher	.08	.25
10 Dave Parker	.20	.50
11 Luis Polonia	.08	.25
12 Luis Sojo	.08	.25
13 Wilson Alvarez	.08	.25
14 Alex Fernandez	.08	.25
15 Craig Grebeck	.08	.25
16 Ron Karkovice	.08	.25
17 Warren Newson RC	.08	.25
18 Scott Radinsky	.08	.25
19 Glenallen Hill	.08	.25
20 Charles Nagy	.08	.25
21 Mark Whiten	.08	.25
22 Milt Cuyler	.08	.25
23 Paul Gibson	.08	.25
24 Mickey Tettleton	.08	.25
25 Todd Benzinger	.08	.25
26 Storm Davis	.08	.25
27 Kirk Gibson	.20	.50
28 Bill Pecota	.08	.25
29 Gary Thurman	.08	.25
30 Darryl Hamilton	.08	.25
31 Jaime Navarro	.08	.25
32 Willie Randolph	.20	.50
33 Bill Wegman	.08	.25
34 Randy Bush	.08	.25
35 Chili Davis	.20	.50
36 Scott Erickson	.08	.25
37 Chuck Knoblauch	.20	.50
38 Scott Leius	.08	.25
39 Jack Morris	.20	.50
40 John Habyan	.08	.25
41 Pat Kelly	.08	.25
42 Matt Nokes	.08	.25
43 Scott Sanderson	.08	.25
44 Bernie Williams	.75	2.00
45 Harold Baines	.20	.50
46 Brook Jacoby	.08	.25
47 Earnest Riles	.08	.25
48 Willie Wilson	.08	.25
49 Jay Buhner	.20	.50
50 Rich DeLucia RC	.08	.25
51 Mike Jackson	.08	.25
52 Bill Krueger	.08	.25
53 Bill Swift	.08	.25
54 Brian Downing	.08	.25
55 Juan Gonzalez	.60	1.50
56 Dean Palmer	.20	.50
57 Kevin Reimer	.08	.25
58 Ivan Rodriguez RC	3.00	8.00
59 Tom Candiotti	.08	.25
60 Juan Guzman RC	.20	.50
61 Bob MacDonald RC	.08	.25
62 Greg Myers	.08	.25
63 Ed Sprague	.08	.25
64 Devon White	.20	.50
65 Rafael Belliard	.08	.25
66 Juan Berenguer	.08	.25
67 Brian R. Hunter RC	.20	.50
68 Kent Mercker	.08	.25
69 Otis Nixon	.08	.25
70 Danny Jackson	.08	.25
71 Chuck McElroy	.08	.25
72 Gary Scott RC	.08	.25
73 Heathcliff Slocumb RC	.08	.25
74 Chico Walker	.08	.25
75 Rick Wilkins RC	.08	.25
76 Chris Hammond	.08	.25
77 Luis Quinones	.08	.25
78 Herm Winningham	.08	.25
79 Jeff Bagwell RC	2.50	6.00
80 Jim Corsi	.08	.25
81 Steve Finley	.20	.50
82 Luis Gonzalez RC	.60	1.50
83 Pete Harnisch	.08	.25
84 Darryl Kile	.20	.50
85 Brett Butler	.20	.50
86 Gary Carter	.20	.50
87 Tim Crews	.08	.25
88 Orel Hershiser	.20	.50
89 Bob Ojeda	.08	.25
90 Bret Barberie RC	.08	.25
91 Barry Jones	.08	.25
92 Gilberto Reyes	.08	.25
93 Larry Walker	.60	1.50
94 Hubie Brooks	.08	.25
95 Tim Burke	.08	.25
96 Rick Cerone	.08	.25
97 Jeff Innis	.08	.25
98 Wally Backman	.08	.25
99 Tommy Greene	.08	.25
100 Ricky Jordan	.08	.25
101 Mitch Williams	.08	.25
102 John Smiley	.08	.25
103 Randy Tomlin RC	.08	.25
104 Gary Varsho	.08	.25
105 Cris Carpenter	.08	.25
106 Ken Hill	.08	.25
107 Felix Jose	.08	.25
108 Omar Olivares RC	.08	.25
109 Gerald Perry	.08	.25
110 Jerald Clark	.08	.25
111 Tony Fernandez	.08	.25
112 Darrin Jackson	.08	.25
113 Mike Maddux	.08	.25
114 Tim Teufel	.08	.25
115 Bud Black	.08	.25
116 Kelly Downs	.08	.25
117 Mike Felder	.08	.25
118 Willie McGee	.20	.50
119 Trevor Wilson	.08	.25
120 Checklist 1-120	.08	.25

1992 Ultra

Consisting of 600 standard-size cards, the 1992 Ultra set was issued in two series of 300 cards each. Cards were distributed exclusively in foil packs. The cards are numbered on the back and ordered below alphabetically within and according to teams for each league with AL preceding NL. Some cards have been found without the word Fleer on the front.

COMPLETE SET (600)	12.00	30.00
COMP. SERIES 1 (300)	8.00	20.00
COMP. SERIES 2 (300)	4.00	10.00
1 Glenn Davis	.02	.10
2 Mike Devereaux	.02	.10
3 Dwight Evans	.10	.30
4 Leo Gomez	.02	.10
5 Chris Hoiles	.02	.10
6 Sam Horn	.02	.10
7 Chito Martinez	.02	.10
8 Randy Milligan	.02	.10
9 Mike Mussina	.20	.50
10 Billy Ripken	.02	.10
11 Cal Ripken	.60	1.50
12 Tom Brunansky	.02	.10
13 Ellis Burks	.07	.20
14 Jack Clark	.07	.20
15 Roger Clemens	.40	1.00
16 Mike Greenwell	.02	.10
17 Joe Hesketh	.02	.10
18 Tony Pena	.02	.10
19 Carlos Quintana	.02	.10
20 Jeff Reardon	.07	.20
21 Jody Reed	.02	.10
22 Luis Rivera	.02	.10
23 Mo Vaughn	.07	.20
24 Gary DiSarcina	.02	.10
25 Chuck Finley	.07	.20
26 Gary Gaetti	.07	.20
27 Bryan Harvey	.02	.10
28 Lance Parrish	.07	.20
29 Luis Polonia	.02	.10
30 Dick Schofield	.02	.10
31 Luis Sojo	.02	.10
32 Wilson Alvarez	.02	.10
33 Carlton Fisk	.10	.30
34 Craig Grebeck	.02	.10
35 Ozzie Guillen	.07	.20
36 Greg Hibbard	.02	.10
37 Charlie Hough	.07	.20
38 Lance Johnson	.02	.10
39 Ron Karkovice	.02	.10
40 Jack McDowell	.02	.10
41 Donn Pall	.02	.10
42 Melido Perez	.02	.10
43 Tim Raines	.07	.20
44 Frank Thomas	.20	.50
45 Sandy Alomar Jr.	.02	.10
46 Carlos Baerga	.02	.10
47 Albert Belle	.07	.20
48 Jerry Browne UER (Reversed negative on card back)	.02	.10
49 Felix Fermin	.02	.10
50 Reggie Jefferson UER (Born 1968, not 1966)	.02	.10
51 Mark Lewis	.02	.10
52 Carlos Martinez	.02	.10
53 Steve Olin	.02	.10
54 Jim Thome	.20	.50
55 Mark Whiten	.02	.10
56 Dave Bergman	.02	.10
57 Milt Cuyler	.02	.10
58 Rob Deer	.02	.10
59 Cecil Fielder	.07	.20
60 Travis Fryman	.07	.20
61 Scott Livingstone	.02	.10
62 Tony Phillips	.02	.10
63 Mickey Tettleton	.02	.10
64 Alan Trammell	.07	.20
65 Lou Whitaker	.07	.20
66 Kevin Appier	.07	.20
67 Mike Boddicker	.02	.10
68 George Brett	.50	1.25
69 Jim Eisenreich	.02	.10
70 Mark Gubicza	.02	.10
71 David Howard	.02	.10
72 Joel Johnson	.02	.10
73 Mike Macfarlane	.02	.10
74 Brent Mayne	.02	.10
75 Brian McRae	.02	.10
76 Jeff Montgomery	.02	.10
77 Terry Shumpert	.02	.10
78 Don August	.02	.10
79 Dante Bichette	.07	.20
80 Ted Higuera	.02	.10
81 Paul Molitor	.07	.20
82 Jaime Navarro	.02	.10
83 Gary Sheffield	.07	.20
84 Bill Spiers	.02	.10
85 B.J. Surhoff	.07	.20
86 Greg Vaughn	.02	.10
87 Robin Yount	.30	.75
88 Rick Aguilera	.07	.20
89 Chili Davis	.07	.20
90 Scott Erickson	.02	.10
91 Brian Harper	.02	.10
92 Kent Hrbek	.07	.20
93 Chuck Knoblauch	.07	.20
94 Scott Leius	.02	.10
95 Shane Mack	.02	.10
96 Mike Pagliarulo	.02	.10
97 Kirby Puckett	.20	.50
98 Kevin Tapani	.02	.10
99 Jesse Barfield	.02	.10
100 Alvaro Espinoza	.02	.10
101 Mel Hall	.02	.10
102 Pat Kelly	.02	.10
103 Roberto Kelly	.02	.10
104 Kevin Maas	.02	.10
105 Don Mattingly	.50	1.25
106 Hensley Meulens	.02	.10
107 Matt Nokes	.02	.10
108 Steve Sax	.02	.10
109 Harold Baines	.07	.20
110 Jose Canseco	.10	.30
111 Ron Darling	.02	.10
112 Mike Gallego	.02	.10
113 Dave Henderson	.02	.10
114 Rickey Henderson	.20	.50
115 Mark McGwire	.50	1.25
116 Terry Steinbach	.02	.10
117 Dave Stewart	.07	.20
118 Todd Van Poppel	.02	.10
119 Bob Welch	.02	.10
120 Greg Briley	.02	.10
121 Jay Buhner	.07	.20
122 Rick DeLucia	.02	.10
123 Ken Griffey Jr.	.30	.75
124 Erik Hanson	.02	.10
125 Randy Johnson	.20	.50
126 Edgar Martinez	.10	.30
127 Tino Martinez	.10	.30
128 Pete O'Brien	.02	.10
129 Harold Reynolds	.07	.20
130 Dave Valle	.02	.10
131 Julio Franco	.07	.20
132 Juan Gonzalez	.10	.30
133 Jeff Huson	.07	.20
134 Mike Jeffcoat	.02	.10
135 Terry Mathews	.02	.10
136 Rafael Palmeiro	.10	.30
137 Dean Palmer	.07	.20
138 Geno Petralli	.02	.10
139 Ivan Rodriguez	.20	.50
140 Jeff Russell	.02	.10
141 Nolan Ryan	.75	2.00
142 Ruben Sierra	.07	.20
143 Roberto Alomar	.10	.30
144 Pat Borders	.02	.10
145 Joe Carter	.07	.20
146 Kelly Gruber	.02	.10
147 Jimmy Key	.07	.20
148 Manny Lee	.02	.10
149 Rance Mulliniks	.02	.10
150 Greg Myers	.02	.10
151 John Olerud	.07	.20
152 Dave Stieb	.02	.10
153 Todd Stottlemyre	.02	.10
154 Duane Ward	.02	.10
155 Devon White	.07	.20
156 Eddie Zosky	.02	.10
157 Steve Avery	.02	.10
158 Rafael Belliard	.02	.10
159 Jeff Blauser	.02	.10
160 Sid Bream	.02	.10
161 Ron Gant	.07	.20
162 Tom Glavine	.10	.30
163 Brian Hunter	.02	.10
164 Dave Justice	.07	.20
165 Mark Lemke	.02	.10
166 Greg Olson	.02	.10
167 Terry Pendleton	.07	.20
168 Lonnie Smith	.02	.10
169 John Smoltz	.10	.30
170 Mike Stanton	.02	.10
171 Jeff Treadway	.02	.10
172 Paul Assenmacher	.02	.10
173 George Bell	.02	.10
174 Shawon Dunston	.02	.10
175 Mark Grace	.10	.30
176 Danny Jackson	.02	.10
177 Les Lancaster	.02	.10
178 Greg Maddux	.30	.75
179 Luis Salazar	.02	.10
180 Rey Sanchez RC	.08	.25
181 Ryne Sandberg	.30	.75
182 Jose Vizcaino	.02	.10
183 Chico Walker	.02	.10
184 Jerome Walton	.02	.10
185 Glenn Braggs	.02	.10
186 Tom Browning	.02	.10
187 Rob Dibble	.07	.20
188 Bill Doran	.02	.10
189 Chris Hammond	.02	.10
190 Billy Hatcher	.02	.10
191 Barry Larkin	.10	.30
192 Hal Morris	.02	.10
193 Joe Oliver	.02	.10
194 Paul O'Neill	.10	.30
195 Jeff Reed	.02	.10
196 Jose Rijo	.02	.10
197 Chris Sabo	.02	.10
198 Jeff Bagwell	.20	.50
199 Craig Biggio	.10	.30
200 Ken Caminiti	.07	.20
201 Andujar Cedeno	.02	.10
202 Steve Finley	.07	.20
203 Luis Gonzalez	.07	.20
204 Pete Harnisch	.02	.10
205 Xavier Hernandez	.02	.10
206 Darryl Kile	.07	.20
207 Al Osuna	.02	.10
208 Curt Schilling	.10	.30
209 Brett Butler	.07	.20
210 Kal Daniels	.02	.10
211 Lenny Harris	.02	.10
212 Stan Javier	.02	.10
213 Ramon Martinez	.02	.10
214 Roger McDowell	.02	.10
215 Jose Offerman	.02	.10
216 Juan Samuel	.02	.10
217 Mike Scioscia	.02	.10
218 Mike Sharperson	.02	.10
219 Darryl Strawberry	.07	.20
220 Delino DeShields	.02	.10
221 Tom Foley	.02	.10
222 Steve Frey	.02	.10
223 Dennis Martinez	.07	.20
224 Spike Owen	.02	.10
225 Gilberto Reyes	.02	.10
226 Tim Wallach	.02	.10
227 Daryl Boston	.02	.10
228 Tim Burke	.02	.10
229 Vince Coleman	.02	.10
230 David Cone	.07	.20
231 Kevin Elster	.02	.10
232 Dwight Gooden	.07	.20
233 Todd Hundley	.02	.10
234 Jeff Innis	.02	.10
235 Howard Johnson	.02	.10
236 Dave Magadan	.02	.10
237 Mackey Sasser	.02	.10
238 Anthony Young	.02	.10
239 Wes Chamberlain	.02	.10
240 Darren Daulton	.07	.20
241 Len Dykstra	.07	.20
242 Tommy Greene	.02	.10
243 Charlie Hayes	.02	.10
244 Dave Hollins	.02	.10
245 Ricky Jordan	.02	.10
246 John Kruk	.07	.20
247 Mickey Morandini	.02	.10
248 Terry Mulholland	.02	.10
249 Dale Murphy	.10	.30
250 Jay Bell	.07	.20
251 Barry Bonds	.60	1.50
252 Steve Buechele	.02	.10
253 Doug Drabek	.02	.10
254 Mike LaValliere	.02	.10
255 Jose Lind	.02	.10
256 Lloyd McClendon	.02	.10
257 Orlando Merced	.02	.10
258 Don Slaught	.02	.10
259 John Smiley	.02	.10
260 Zane Smith	.02	.10
261 Randy Tomlin	.02	.10
262 Andy Van Slyke	.10	.30
263 Pedro Guerrero	.07	.20
264 Felix Jose	.02	.10
265 Ray Lankford	.07	.20
266 Omar Olivares	.02	.10
267 Jose Oquendo	.02	.10
268 Tom Pagnozzi	.02	.10
269 Bryn Smith	.02	.10
270 Lee Smith UER (1991 record listed as 61-61)	.07	.20
271 Ozzie Smith UER (Comma before year of birth on card back)	.30	.75
272 Milt Thompson	.02	.10
273 Todd Zeile	.02	.10
274 Andy Benes	.02	.10
275 Jerald Clark	.02	.10
276 Tony Fernandez	.02	.10
277 Tony Gwynn	.25	.60
278 Greg W. Harris	.02	.10
279 Thomas Howard	.02	.10
280 Bruce Hurst	.02	.10
281 Mike Maddux	.02	.10
282 Fred McGriff	.10	.30
283 Benito Santiago	.07	.20
284 Kevin Bass	.02	.10
285 Jeff Brantley	.02	.10
286 John Burkett	.02	.10
287 Will Clark	.10	.30
288 Royce Clayton	.02	.10
289 Steve Decker	.02	.10
290 Kelly Downs	.02	.10
291 Mike Felder	.02	.10
292 Darren Lewis	.02	.10
293 Kirt Manwaring	.02	.10
294 Willie McGee	.07	.20
295 Robby Thompson	.02	.10
296 Matt Williams	.07	.20
297 Trevor Wilson	.02	.10
298 Checklist 1-100	.02	.10
299 Checklist 101-200	.02	.10
300 Nolan Ryan CL	.02	.10
301 Brady Anderson	.07	.20
302 Todd Frohwirth	.02	.10
303 Ben McDonald	.02	.10
304 Mark McLemore	.02	.10
305 Jose Mesa	.02	.10
306 Bob Milacki	.02	.10
307 Gregg Olson	.02	.10
308 David Segui	.02	.10
309 Rick Sutcliffe	.07	.20
310 Jeff Tackett	.02	.10
311 Wade Boggs	.10	.30
312 Scott Cooper	.02	.10
313 John Flaherty	.02	.10
314 Wayne Housie	.02	.10
315 Peter Hoy	.02	.10
316 John Marzano	.02	.10
317 Tim Naehring	.02	.10
318 Phil Plantier	.02	.10
319 Frank Viola	.07	.20
320 Matt Young	.02	.10
321 Jim Abbott	.10	.30
322 Hubie Brooks	.02	.10
323 Chad Curtis RC	.08	.25
324 Alvin Davis	.02	.10
325 Junior Felix	.02	.10
326 Von Hayes	.02	.10
327 Mark Langston	.02	.10
328 Scott Lewis	.02	.10
329 Don Robinson	.02	.10
330 Bobby Rose	.02	.10
331 Lee Stevens	.02	.10
332 George Bell	.02	.10
333 Esteban Beltre	.02	.10
334 Joey Cora	.02	.10
335 Alex Fernandez	.02	.10
336 Roberto Hernandez	.02	.10
337 Mike Huff	.02	.10
338 Kirk McCaskill	.02	.10
339 Dan Pasqua	.02	.10
340 Scott Radinsky	.02	.10
341 Steve Sax	.02	.10
342 Bobby Thigpen	.02	.10
343 Robin Ventura	.07	.20
344 Jack Armstrong	.02	.10
345 Alex Cole	.02	.10
346 Dennis Cook	.02	.10
347 Glenallen Hill	.02	.10
348 Thomas Howard	.02	.10
349 Brook Jacoby	.02	.10
350 Kenny Lofton	.10	.30
351 Charles Nagy	.02	.10
352 Rod Nichols	.02	.10
353 Junior Ortiz	.02	.10
354 Dave Otto	.02	.10
355 Tony Perezchica	.02	.10
356 Scott Scudder	.02	.10
357 Paul Sorrento	.02	.10
358 Skeeter Barnes	.02	.10
359 Mark Carreon	.02	.10
360 John Doherty RC	.02	.10
361 Dan Gladden	.02	.10
362 Bill Gullickson	.02	.10
363 Shawn Hare RC	.02	.10
364 Mike Henneman	.02	.10
365 Chad Kreuter	.02	.10
366 Mark Leiter	.02	.10
367 Mike Munoz	.02	.10
368 Kevin Ritz	.02	.10
369 Mark Davis	.02	.10
370 Tom Gordon	.02	.10
371 Chris Gwynn	.02	.10
372 Gregg Jefferies	.02	.10
373 Wally Joyner	.07	.20
374 Kevin McReynolds	.02	.10
375 Keith Miller	.02	.10
376 Rico Rossy	.02	.10
377 Curtis Wilkerson	.02	.10
378 Ricky Bones	.02	.10
379 Chris Bosio	.02	.10
380 Cal Eldred	.02	.10
381 Scott Fletcher	.02	.10
382 Jim Gantner	.02	.10
383 Darryl Hamilton	.02	.10
384 Doug Henry RC	.08	.25
385 Pat Listach RC	.08	.25
386 Tim McIntosh	.02	.10
387 Edwin Nunez	.02	.10
388 Dan Plesac	.02	.10
389 Kevin Seitzer	.02	.10
390 Franklin Stubbs	.02	.10
391 William Suero	.02	.10
392 Bill Wegman	.02	.10
393 Willie Banks	.02	.10
394 Jarvis Brown	.02	.10
395 Greg Gagne	.02	.10
396 Mark Guthrie	.02	.10
397 Bill Krueger	.02	.10
398 Pat Mahomes RC	.08	.25
399 Pedro Munoz	.02	.10
400 John Smiley	.02	.10
401 Gary Wayne	.02	.10
402 Lenny Webster	.02	.10
403 Carl Willis	.02	.10
404 Greg Cadaret	.02	.10
405 Steve Farr	.02	.10
406 Mike Gallego	.02	.10
407 Charlie Hayes	.02	.10
408 Steve Howe	.02	.10
409 Dion James	.02	.10
410 Jeff Johnson	.02	.10
411 Tim Leary	.02	.10
412 Jim Leyritz	.02	.10
413 Melido Perez	.02	.10
414 Scott Sanderson	.02	.10
415 Andy Stankiewicz	.02	.10
416 Mike Stanley	.02	.10
417 Danny Tartabull	.02	.10
418 Lance Blankenship	.02	.10
419 Mike Bordick	.02	.10
420 Scott Brosius RC	.15	.40
421 Dennis Eckersley	.07	.20
422 Scott Hemond	.02	.10
423 Carney Lansford	.07	.20
424 Henry Mercedes	.02	.10
425 Mike Moore	.02	.10
426 Gene Nelson	.02	.10
427 Randy Ready	.02	.10
428 Bruce Walton	.02	.10
429 Willie Wilson	.02	.10
430 Rich Amaral	.02	.10
431 Dave Cochrane	.02	.10
432 Henry Cotto	.02	.10
433 Calvin Jones	.02	.10
434 Kevin Mitchell	.02	.10
435 Clay Parker	.02	.10
436 Omar Vizquel	.10	.30
437 Floyd Bannister	.02	.10
438 Kevin Brown	.07	.20
439 John Cangelosi	.02	.10
440 Brian Downing	.02	.10
441 Monty Fariss	.02	.10
442 Jose Guzman	.02	.10
443 Donald Harris	.02	.10
444 Kevin Reimer	.02	.10
445 Kenny Rogers	.07	.20
446 Wayne Rosenthal	.02	.10
447 Dickie Thon	.02	.10
448 Derek Bell	.07	.20
449 Juan Guzman	.02	.10
450 Tom Henke	.02	.10
451 Candy Maldonado	.02	.10
452 Jack Morris	.07	.20
453 David Wells	.07	.20
454 Dave Winfield	.07	.20
455 Juan Berenguer	.02	.10
456 Damon Berryhill	.02	.10
457 Mike Bielecki	.02	.10
458 Marvin Freeman	.02	.10
459 Charlie Leibrandt	.02	.10
460 Kent Mercker	.02	.10
461 Otis Nixon	.02	.10
462 Alejandro Pena	.02	.10
463 Ben Rivera	.02	.10
464 Deion Sanders	.10	.30
465 Mark Wohlers	.02	.10
466 Shawn Boskie	.02	.10
467 Frank Castillo	.02	.10
468 Andre Dawson	.07	.20
469 Joe Girardi	.02	.10
470 Chuck McElroy	.02	.10
471 Mike Morgan	.02	.10
472 Ken Patterson	.02	.10
473 Bob Scanlan	.02	.10
474 Gary Scott	.02	.10
475 Dave Smith	.02	.10
476 Sammy Sosa	.20	.50
477 Hector Villanueva	.02	.10
478 Scott Bankhead	.02	.10
479 Tim Belcher	.02	.10
480 Freddie Benavides	.02	.10
481 Jacob Brumfield	.02	.10
482 Norm Charlton	.02	.10
483 Dwayne Henry	.02	.10
484 Dave Martinez	.02	.10
485 Bip Roberts	.02	.10
486 Reggie Sanders	.07	.20
487 Greg Swindell	.02	.10
488 Ryan Bowen	.02	.10
489 Casey Candaele	.02	.10
490 Juan Guerrero UER (photo on front is Andujar Cedeno	.02	.10
491 Pete Incaviglia	.02	.10
492 Jeff Juden	.02	.10
493 Rob Murphy	.02	.10
494 Mark Portugal	.02	.10
495 Rafael Ramirez	.02	.10
496 Scott Servais	.02	.10
497 Ed Taubensee RC	.08	.25
498 Brian Williams RC	.02	.10
499 Todd Benzinger	.02	.10
500 John Candelaria	.02	.10
501 Tom Candiotti	.02	.10
502 Tim Crews	.02	.10
503 Eric Davis	.07	.20
504 Jim Gott	.02	.10
505 Dave Hansen	.02	.10
506 Carlos Hernandez	.02	.10
507 Orel Hershiser	.07	.20
508 Eric Karros	.07	.20
509 Bob Ojeda	.02	.10
510 Steve Wilson	.02	.10
511 Moises Alou	.07	.20
512 Bret Barberie	.02	.10
513 Ivan Calderon	.02	.10
514 Gary Carter	.07	.20
515 Archi Cianfrocco RC	.02	.10
516 Jeff Fassero	.02	.10
517 Darrin Fletcher	.02	.10
518 Marquis Grissom	.07	.20
519 Chris Haney	.02	.10
520 Ken Hill	.02	.10
521 Chris Nabholz	.02	.10
522 Bill Sampen	.02	.10
523 John Vander Wal	.02	.10
524 Dave Wainhouse	.02	.10
525 Larry Walker	.10	.30
526 John Wetteland	.07	.20
527 Bobby Bonilla	.07	.20
528 Sid Fernandez	.02	.10
529 John Franco	.07	.20
530 Dave Gallagher	.02	.10
531 Paul Gibson	.02	.10
532 Eddie Murray	.20	.50
533 Junior Noboa	.02	.10
534 Charlie O'Brien	.02	.10
535 Bill Pecota	.02	.10
536 Willie Randolph	.07	.20
537 Bret Saberhagen	.07	.20
538 Dick Schofield	.02	.10
539 Pete Schourek	.02	.10
540 Ruben Amaro	.02	.10
541 Andy Ashby	.02	.10
542 Kim Batiste	.02	.10
543 Cliff Brantley	.02	.10
544 Mariano Duncan	.02	.10
545 Jeff Grotewold	.02	.10
546 Barry Jones	.02	.10
547 Julio Peguero	.02	.10
548 Curt Schilling	.10	.30
549 Mitch Williams	.02	.10
550 Stan Belinda	.02	.10
551 Scott Bullett RC	.02	.10
552 Cecil Espy	.02	.10
553 Jeff King	.02	.10
554 Roger Mason	.02	.10
555 Paul Miller	.02	.10
556 Denny Neagle	.07	.20
557 Vicente Palacios	.02	.10
558 Bob Patterson	.02	.10
559 Tom Prince	.02	.10
560 Gary Redus	.02	.10
561 Gary Varsho	.02	.10
562 Juan Agosto	.02	.10
563 Cris Carpenter	.02	.10
564 Mark Clark RC	.08	.25
565 Jose DeLeon	.02	.10
566 Rich Gedman	.02	.10
567 Bernard Gilkey	.02	.10
568 Rex Hudler	.02	.10
569 Tim Jones	.02	.10
570 Donovan Osborne	.02	.10
571 Mike Perez	.02	.10
572 Gerald Perry	.02	.10
573 Bob Tewksbury	.02	.10
574 Todd Worrell	.02	.10
575 Dave Eiland	.02	.10
576 Jeremy Hernandez RC	.02	.10
577 Craig Lefferts	.02	.10
578 Jose Melendez	.02	.10
579 Randy Myers	.02	.10
580 Gary Pettis	.02	.10
581 Rich Rodriguez	.02	.10
582 Gary Sheffield	.07	.20
583 Craig Shipley	.02	.10
584 Kurt Stillwell	.02	.10
585 Tim Teufel	.02	.10
586 Rod Beck RC	.15	.40
587 Dave Burba	.02	.10
588 Craig Colbert	.02	.10
589 Bryan Hickerson RC	.02	.10
590 Mike Jackson	.02	.10
591 Mark Leonard	.02	.10
592 Jim McNamara	.02	.10
593 John Patterson RC	.02	.10
594 Dave Righetti	.07	.20
595 Cory Snyder	.02	.10
596 Bill Swift	.02	.10
597 Ted Wood	.02	.10
598 Checklist 301-400	.02	.10
599 Checklist 401-500	.02	.10
600 Checklist 501-600	.02	.10

1992 Ultra All-Rookies

Cards from this ten-card standard-size set highlighting a selection of top rookies were randomly inserted in 1992 Ultra II foil packs.

COMPLETE SET (10)	2.50	6.00
COMMON CARD (1-10)	.20	.50
SER.2 STATED ODDS 1:13		
1 Eric Karros	.40	1.00
2 Andy Stankiewicz	.20	.50
3 Gary DiSarcina	.20	.50
4 Archi Cianfrocco	.20	.50
5 Jim McNamara	.20	.50
6 Chad Curtis	.50	1.25
7 Kenny Lofton	.60	1.50
8 Reggie Sanders	.40	1.00
9 Pat Mahomes	.50	1.25
10 Donovan Osborne	.20	.50

1992 Ultra All-Stars

Featuring many of the 1992 season's stars, cards from this 20-card standard-size set were randomly inserted in 1992 Ultra II foil packs.

COMPLETE SET (20)	10.00	25.00
COMMON CARD (1-20)	.15	.30
SER.2 STATED ODDS 1:6.5		
1 Mark McGwire	1.50	4.00
2 Roberto Alomar	.40	1.00
3 Cal Ripken Jr.	2.00	5.00
4 Wade Boggs	.40	1.00
5 Mickey Tettleton	.10	.30
6 Ken Griffey Jr.	1.00	2.50
7 Roberto Kelly	.10	.30
8 Kirby Puckett	.60	1.50
9 Frank Thomas	.60	1.50
10 Jack McDowell	.10	.30
11 Will Clark	.40	1.00
12 Ryne Sandberg	1.00	2.50
13 Barry Larkin	.40	1.00
14 Gary Sheffield	.25	.60
15 Tom Pagnozzi	.10	.30
16 Barry Bonds	2.00	5.00
17 Deion Sanders	.40	1.00
18 Darryl Strawberry	.25	.60
19 David Cone	.25	.60
20 Tom Glavine	.40	1.00

1992 Ultra Award Winners

This 25-card standard-size set features 18 Gold Glove winners, both Cy Young Award winners, both Rookies of the Year, both league MVP's, and the World Series MVP. The cards were randomly inserted in 1992 Fleer Ultra I packs.

COMPLETE SET (25)	15.00	40.00
COMMON CARD (1-25)	.20	.50
RANDOM INSERTS IN SER.1 PACKS		
1 Jack Morris	.40	1.00
2 Chuck Knoblauch	.40	1.00
3 Jeff Bagwell	1.00	2.50
4 Terry Pendleton	.40	1.00
5 Cal Ripken	3.00	8.00
6 Roger Clemens	2.00	5.00
7 Tom Glavine	.60	1.50
8 Tom Pagnozzi	.20	.50
9 Ozzie Smith	1.50	4.00
10 Andy Van Slyke	.60	1.50
11 Barry Bonds	3.00	8.00
12 Tony Gwynn	1.25	3.00
13 Matt Williams	.40	1.00
14 Will Clark	.60	1.50
15 Robin Ventura	.40	1.00
16 Mark Langston	.20	.50
17 Tony Pena	.20	.50
18 Devon White	.40	1.00
19 Don Mattingly	2.50	6.00
20 Roberto Alomar	.60	1.50
21A Cal Ripken ERR (Reversed negative on card back)	3.00	8.00
21B Cal Ripken COR	3.00	8.00
22 Ken Griffey Jr.	1.50	4.00
23 Kirby Puckett	1.00	2.50
24 Greg Maddux	1.50	4.00
25 Ryne Sandberg	1.50	4.00

1992 Ultra Gwynn

Tony Gwynn served as a spokesperson for Ultra during 1992 and was the exclusive subject of this 12-card standard-size set. The first ten cards of this set were randomly inserted in 1992 Ultra one packs. More than 2,000 of these cards were personally autographed by Gwynn. These cards are numbered on the back as " X of 10." An additional special two-card subset was available through a mail-in offer for ten 1992 Ultra baseball wrappers plus 1.00 for shipping and handling. This offer was good through October 31st and, according to Fleer, over 100,000 sets were produced. The standard-size cards display action shots of Gwynn framed by green marbled borders. The player's name and the words "Commemorative Series" appear in gold-foil lettering in the bottom border. On a green marbled background, the backs features a color head shot and either a player profile (Special No. 1 on the card back) or Gwynn's comments about other players or the game itself (Special No. 2 on the card back).

COMPLETE SET (10)	4.00	10.00
COMMON GWYNN (1-10)	.40	1.00
RANDOM INSERTS IN SER.1 PACKS		
COMMON MAIL(S1-S2)	.40	1.00
1AU Tony Gwynn AU	20.00	50.00

1993 Ultra

The 1993 Ultra baseball set was issued in two series and totaled 650 standard-size cards. The cards are numbered on the back, grouped alphabetically within teams, with NL teams preceding AL. The first series closes with checklist cards (298-300). The second series features 83 Ultra Rookies, 51 Rockies and Marlins, traded veteran players, and other major league veterans not included in the first series. The Rookie cards show a gold foil stamped Rookie "flag" as part of the card design. The key Rookie Card in this set is Jim Edmonds.

COMPLETE SET (650)	12.00	30.00
COMP. SERIES 1 (300)	6.00	15.00
COMP. SERIES 2 (350)	6.00	15.00
1 Steve Avery	.05	.15
2 Rafael Belliard	.05	.15
3 Damon Berryhill	.05	.15
4 Sid Bream	.05	.15
5 Ron Gant	.10	.30
6 Tom Glavine	.20	.50
7 Ryan Klesko	.10	.30
8 Mark Lemke	.05	.15
9 Javier Lopez	.20	.50
10 Greg Olson	.05	.15
11 Terry Pendleton	.10	.30
12 Deion Sanders	.20	.50
13 Mike Stanton	.05	.15
14 Paul Assenmacher	.05	.15
15 Steve Buechele	.05	.15
16 Frank Castillo	.05	.15
17 Shawon Dunston	.05	.15
18 Mark Grace	.20	.50
19 Derrick May	.05	.15
20 Chuck McElroy	.05	.15
21 Mike Morgan	.05	.15
22 Bob Scanlan	.05	.15
23 Dwight Smith	.05	.15
24 Sammy Sosa	.30	.75
25 Rick Wilkins	.05	.15
26 Tim Belcher	.05	.15
27 Jeff Branson	.05	.15
28 Bill Doran	.05	.15
29 Chris Hammond	.05	.15
30 Barry Larkin	.20	.50
31 Hal Morris	.05	.15
32 Joe Oliver	.05	.15
33 Jose Rijo	.05	.15
34 Bip Roberts	.05	.15
35 Chris Sabo	.05	.15
36 Reggie Sanders	.10	.30
37 Craig Biggio	.20	.50
38 Ken Caminiti	.10	.30
39 Steve Finley	.10	.30
40 Luis Gonzalez	.10	.30
41 Juan Guerrero	.05	.15
42 Pete Harnisch	.05	.15
43 Xavier Hernandez	.05	.15
44 Doug Jones	.05	.15
45 Al Osuna	.05	.15
46 Eddie Taubensee	.05	.15
47 Scooter Tucker	.05	.15
48 Brian Williams	.05	.15
49 Pedro Astacio	.05	.15
50 Rafael Bournigal	.05	.15
51 Brett Butler	.10	.30
52 Tom Candiotti	.05	.15
53 Eric Davis	.10	.30
54 Lenny Harris	.05	.15
55 Orel Hershiser	.10	.30
56 Eric Karros	.10	.30
57 Pedro Martinez	.60	1.50
58 Roger McDowell	.05	.15
59 Jose Offerman	.05	.15
60 Mike Piazza	1.25	3.00
61 Moises Alou	.10	.30
62 Kent Bottenfield	.05	.15
63 Archi Cianfrocco	.05	.15
64 Greg Colbrunn	.05	.15
65 Wil Cordero	.05	.15
66 Delino DeShields	.05	.15
67 Darrin Fletcher	.05	.15
68 Ken Hill	.05	.15
69 Chris Nabholz	.05	.15
70 Mel Rojas	.05	.15
71 Larry Walker	.10	.30
72 Sid Fernandez	.05	.15
73 John Franco	.10	.30
74 Dave Gallagher	.05	.15
75 Todd Hundley	.05	.15
76 Howard Johnson	.05	.15
77 Jeff Kent	.30	.75
78 Eddie Murray	.30	.75
79 Bret Saberhagen	.10	.30
80 Chico Walker	.05	.15
81 Anthony Young	.05	.15
82 Kyle Abbott	.05	.15
83 Ruben Amaro	.05	.15
84 Juan Bell	.05	.15
85 Wes Chamberlain	.05	.15
86 Darren Daulton	.10	.30
87 Mariano Duncan	.05	.15
88 Dave Hollins	.05	.15
89 Ricky Jordan	.05	.15
90 John Kruk	.10	.30
91 Mickey Morandini	.05	.15
92 Terry Mulholland	.05	.15
93 Ben Rivera	.05	.15
94 Mike Williams	.05	.15
95 Stan Belinda	.05	.15
96 Jay Bell	.10	.30
97 Jeff King	.05	.15
98 Mike LaValliere	.05	.15
99 Lloyd McClendon	.05	.15
100 Orlando Merced	.05	.15
101 Zane Smith	.05	.15
102 Randy Tomlin	.05	.15
103 Andy Van Slyke	.20	.50
104 Tim Wakefield	.30	.75
105 John Wehner	.05	.15
106 Bernard Gilkey	.05	.15
107 Brian Jordan	.10	.30
108 Ray Lankford	.10	.30
109 Donovan Osborne	.05	.15
110 Tom Pagnozzi	.05	.15
111 Mike Perez	.05	.15
112 Lee Smith	.10	.30
113 Ozzie Smith	.50	1.25
114 Bob Tewksbury	.05	.15
115 Todd Zeile	.05	.15
116 Andy Benes	.05	.15
117 Greg W. Harris	.05	.15
118 Darrin Jackson	.05	.15
119 Fred McGriff	.20	.50
120 Rich Rodriguez	.05	.15
121 Frank Seminara	.05	.15
122 Gary Sheffield	.10	.30
123 Craig Shipley	.05	.15
124 Kurt Stillwell	.05	.15
125 Dan Walters	.05	.15
126 Rod Beck	.05	.15
127 Mike Benjamin	.05	.15
128 Jeff Brantley	.05	.15
129 John Burkett	.05	.15
130 Will Clark	.20	.50
131 Royce Clayton	.05	.15
132 Steve Hosey	.05	.15
133 Mike Jackson	.05	.15
134 Darren Lewis	.05	.15
135 Kirt Manwaring	.05	.15
136 Bill Swift	.05	.15
137 Robby Thompson	.05	.15
138 Brady Anderson	.10	.30
139 Glenn Davis	.05	.15
140 Leo Gomez	.05	.15
141 Chito Martinez	.05	.15
142 Ben McDonald	.05	.15
143 Alan Mills	.05	.15
144 Mike Mussina	.20	.50
145 Gregg Olson	.05	.15
146 David Segui	.05	.15
147 Jeff Tackett	.05	.15
148 Jack Clark	.10	.30
149 Scott Cooper	.05	.15
150 Danny Darwin	.05	.15
151 John Dopson	.05	.15
152 Mike Greenwell	.05	.15
153 Tim Naehring	.05	.15
154 Tony Pena	.05	.15
155 Paul Quantrill	.05	.15
156 Mo Vaughn	.10	.30
157 Frank Viola	.10	.30
158 Bob Zupcic	.05	.15
159 Chad Curtis	.05	.15
160 Gary DiSarcina	.05	.15
161 Damion Easley	.05	.15
162 Chuck Finley	.10	.30
163 Tim Fortugno	.05	.15
164 Rene Gonzales	.05	.15
165 Joe Grahe	.05	.15
166 Mark Langston	.05	.15
167 John Orton	.05	.15
168 Luis Polonia	.05	.15
169 Julio Valera	.05	.15
170 Wilson Alvarez	.05	.15
171 George Bell	.05	.15
172 Joey Cora	.05	.15
173 Alex Fernandez	.05	.15
174 Lance Johnson	.05	.15
175 Ron Karkovice	.05	.15
176 Jack McDowell	.05	.15
177 Scott Radinsky	.05	.15
178 Tim Raines	.10	.30
179 Steve Sax	.05	.15
180 Bobby Thigpen	.05	.15
181 Frank Thomas	.30	.75
182 Sandy Alomar Jr.	.05	.15
183 Carlos Baerga	.05	.15
184 Felix Fermin	.05	.15
185 Thomas Howard	.05	.15
186 Mark Lewis	.05	.15
187 Derek Lilliquist	.05	.15
188 Carlos Martinez	.05	.15
189 Charles Nagy	.05	.15
190 Scott Scudder	.05	.15
191 Paul Sorrento	.05	.15
192 Jim Thome	.20	.50
193 Mark Whiten	.05	.15
194 Milt Cuyler UER (Reversed negative on card front)	.05	.15
195 Rob Deer	.05	.15
196 John Doherty	.05	.15
197 Travis Fryman	.10	.30
198 Dan Gladden	.05	.15
199 Mike Henneman	.05	.15
200 John Kiely	.05	.15
201 Chad Kreuter	.05	.15
202 Scott Livingstone	.05	.15
203 Tony Phillips	.05	.15
204 Alan Trammell	.10	.30
205 Mike Boddicker	.05	.15
206 George Brett	.75	2.00
207 Tom Gordon	.05	.15
208 Mark Gubicza	.05	.15
209 Gregg Jefferies	.05	.15
210 Wally Joyner	.10	.30
211 Kevin Koslofski	.05	.15
212 Brent Mayne	.05	.15
213 Brian McRae	.05	.15
214 Kevin McReynolds	.05	.15
215 Rusty Meacham	.05	.15
216 Steve Shifflett	.05	.15
217 Jim Austin	.05	.15
218 Cal Eldred	.05	.15
219 Darryl Hamilton	.05	.15
220 Doug Henry	.05	.15
221 John Jaha	.05	.15
222 Dave Nilsson	.05	.15
223 Jesse Orosco	.05	.15
224 B.J. Surhoff	.10	.30
225 Greg Vaughn	.05	.15
226 Bill Wegman	.05	.15
227 Robin Yount UER Born in Illinois, not in Virginia	.50	1.25
228 Rick Aguilera	.05	.15
229 J.T. Bruett	.05	.15
230 Scott Erickson	.05	.15
231 Kent Hrbek	.10	.30
232 Terry Jorgensen	.05	.15
233 Scott Leius	.05	.15
234 Pat Mahomes	.05	.15
235 Pedro Munoz	.05	.15
236 Kirby Puckett	.30	.75
237 Kevin Tapani	.05	.15
238 Lenny Webster	.05	.15
239 Carl Willis	.05	.15
240 Mike Gallego	.05	.15
241 John Habyan	.05	.15
242 Pat Kelly	.05	.15
243 Kevin Maas	.05	.15
244 Don Mattingly	.75	2.00
245 Hensley Meulens	.05	.15
246 Sam Militello	.05	.15
247 Matt Nokes	.05	.15
248 Melido Perez	.05	.15
249 Andy Stankiewicz	.05	.15
250 Randy Velarde	.05	.15
251 Bob Wickman	.05	.15
252 Bernie Williams	.20	.50
253 Lance Blankenship	.05	.15
254 Mike Bordick	.05	.15
255 Jerry Browne	.05	.15
256 Ron Darling	.05	.15
257 Dennis Eckersley	.10	.30
258 Rickey Henderson	.30	.75
259 Vince Horsman	.05	.15
260 Troy Neel	.05	.15
261 Jeff Parrett	.05	.15
262 Terry Steinbach	.05	.15
263 Bob Welch	.05	.15
264 Bobby Witt	.05	.15
265 Rich Amaral	.05	.15
266 Bret Boone	.10	.30
267 Jay Buhner	.10	.30
268 Dave Fleming	.05	.15
269 Randy Johnson	.30	.75
270 Edgar Martinez	.20	.50
271 Mike Schooler	.05	.15
272 Russ Swan	.05	.15
273 Dave Valle	.05	.15
274 Omar Vizquel	.20	.50
275 Kerry Woodson	.05	.15
276 Kevin Brown	.10	.30
277 Julio Franco	.10	.30
278 Jeff Frye	.05	.15
279 Juan Gonzalez	.10	.30
280 Jeff Huson	.05	.15
281 Rafael Palmeiro	.20	.50
282 Dean Palmer	.10	.30
283 Roger Pavlik	.05	.15
284 Ivan Rodriguez	.20	.50
285 Kenny Rogers	.10	.30
286 Derek Bell	.05	.15
287 Pat Borders	.05	.15
288 Joe Carter	.10	.30
289 Bob MacDonald	.05	.15
290 Jack Morris	.10	.30
291 John Olerud	.10	.30
292 Ed Sprague	.05	.15
293 Todd Stottlemyre	.05	.15
294 Mike Timlin	.05	.15
295 Duane Ward	.05	.15
296 David Wells	.10	.30
297 Devon White	.10	.30
298 Ray Lankford CL	.05	.15
299 Bobby Witt CL	.05	.15
300 Mike Piazza CL	.30	.75
301 Steve Bedrosian	.05	.15
302 Jeff Blauser	.05	.15
303 Francisco Cabrera	.05	.15
304 Marvin Freeman	.05	.15
305 Brian Hunter	.05	.15
306 David Justice	.10	.30
307 Greg Maddux	.50	1.25
308 Greg McMichael RC	.10	.30
309 Kent Mercker	.05	.15
310 Otis Nixon	.05	.15
311 Pete Smith	.05	.15
312 John Smoltz	.20	.50
313 Jose Guzman	.05	.15
314 Mike Harkey	.05	.15
315 Greg Hibbard	.05	.15
316 Candy Maldonado	.05	.15
317 Randy Myers	.05	.15
318 Dan Plesac	.05	.15
319 Rey Sanchez	.05	.15
320 Ryne Sandberg	.50	1.25
321 Tommy Shields	.05	.15
322 Jose Vizcaino	.05	.15
323 Matt Walbeck RC	.10	.30
324 Willie Wilson	.05	.15
325 Tom Browning	.05	.15
326 Tim Costo	.05	.15
327 Rob Dibble	.10	.30
328 Steve Foster	.05	.15
329 Roberto Kelly	.05	.15
330 Randy Milligan	.05	.15
331 Kevin Mitchell	.05	.15
332 Tim Pugh RC	.10	.30
333 Jeff Reardon	.10	.30
334 John Roper	.05	.15
335 Juan Samuel	.05	.15
336 John Smiley	.05	.15
337 Dan Wilson	.10	.30
338 Scott Aldred	.05	.15
339 Andy Ashby	.05	.15
340 Freddie Benavides	.05	.15
341 Dante Bichette	.10	.30
342 Willie Blair	.05	.15
343 Daryl Boston	.05	.15
344 Vinny Castilla	.30	.75
345 Jerald Clark	.05	.15
346 Alex Cole	.05	.15
347 Andres Galarraga	.10	.30
348 Joe Girardi	.05	.15
349 Ryan Hawblitzel	.05	.15
350 Charlie Hayes	.05	.15
351 Butch Henry	.05	.15
352 Darren Holmes	.05	.15
353 Dale Murphy	.20	.50
354 David Nied	.05	.15
355 Jeff Parrett	.05	.15
356 Steve Reed RC	.10	.30
357 Bruce Ruffin	.05	.15
358 Danny Sheaffer RC	.10	.30
359 Bryn Smith	.05	.15
360 Jim Tatum RC	.10	.30
361 Eric Young	.05	.15
362 Gerald Young	.05	.15
363 Luis Aquino	.05	.15
364 Alex Arias	.05	.15
365 Jack Armstrong	.05	.15
366 Bret Barberie	.05	.15
367 Ryan Bowen	.05	.15
368 Greg Briley	.05	.15
369 Cris Carpenter	.05	.15
370 Chuck Carr	.05	.15
371 Jeff Conine	.10	.30
372 Steve Decker	.05	.15
373 Orestes Destrade	.05	.15
374 Monty Fariss	.05	.15
375 Junior Felix	.05	.15
376 Chris Hammond	.05	.15
377 Bryan Harvey	.05	.15
378 Trevor Hoffman	.30	.75
379 Charlie Hough	.10	.30
380 Joe Klink	.05	.15
381 Richie Lewis RC	.10	.30
382 Dave Magadan	.05	.15
383 Bob McClure	.05	.15
384 Scott Pose RC	.10	.30
385 Rich Renteria	.05	.15
386 Benito Santiago	.10	.30
387 Walt Weiss	.05	.15
388 Nigel Wilson	.05	.15
389 Eric Anthony	.05	.15
390 Jeff Bagwell	.20	.50
391 Andujar Cedeno	.05	.15
392 Doug Drabek	.05	.15
393 Darryl Kile	.10	.30
394 Mark Portugal	.05	.15
395 Karl Rhodes	.05	.15
396 Scott Servais	.05	.15
397 Greg Swindell	.05	.15
398 Tom Goodwin	.05	.15
399 Kevin Gross	.05	.15
400 Carlos Hernandez	.05	.15
401 Ramon Martinez	.05	.15
402 Raul Mondesi	.10	.30
403 Jody Reed	.05	.15
404 Mike Sharperson	.05	.15
405 Cory Snyder	.05	.15
406 Darryl Strawberry	.10	.30
407 Rick Trlicek	.05	.15
408 Tim Wallach	.05	.15
409 Todd Worrell	.05	.15
410 Tavo Alvarez	.05	.15
411 Sean Berry	.05	.15
412 Frank Bolick	.05	.15
413 Cliff Floyd	.10	.30
414 Mike Gardiner	.05	.15
415 Marquis Grissom	.10	.30
416 Tim Laker RC	.10	.30
417 Mike Lansing RC	.20	.50
418 Dennis Martinez	.10	.30
419 John Vander Wal	.05	.15
420 John Wetteland	.10	.30
421 Rondell White	.10	.30
422 Bobby Bonilla	.10	.30
423 Jeromy Burnitz	.10	.30
424 Vince Coleman	.05	.15
425 Mike Draper	.05	.15
426 Tony Fernandez	.05	.15
427 Dwight Gooden	.10	.30
428 Jeff Innis	.05	.15
429 Bobby Jones	.10	.30
430 Mike Maddux	.05	.15
431 Charlie O'Brien	.05	.15
432 Joe Orsulak	.05	.15
433 Pete Schourek	.05	.15
434 Frank Tanana	.05	.15
435 Ryan Thompson	.05	.15
436 Kim Batiste	.05	.15
437 Mark Davis	.05	.15
438 Jose DeLeon	.05	.15
439 Len Dykstra	.10	.30
440 Jim Eisenreich	.05	.15
441 Tommy Greene	.05	.15
442 Pete Incaviglia	.05	.15
443 Danny Jackson	.05	.15
444 Todd Pratt RC	.20	.50
445 Curt Schilling	.10	.30
446 Milt Thompson	.05	.15
447 David West	.05	.15
448 Mitch Williams	.05	.15
449 Steve Cooke	.05	.15
450 Carlos Garcia	.05	.15
451 Al Martin	.05	.15
452 Blas Minor	.05	.15
453 Dennis Moeller	.05	.15
454 Denny Neagle	.10	.30
455 Don Slaught	.05	.15
456 Lonnie Smith	.05	.15
457 Paul Wagner	.05	.15
458 Bob Walk	.05	.15
459 Kevin Young	.10	.30
460 Rene Arocha RC	.20	.50
461 Brian Barber	.05	.15
462 Rheal Cormier	.05	.15
463 Gregg Jefferies	.05	.15
464 Joe Magrane	.05	.15
465 Omar Olivares	.05	.15
466 Geronimo Pena	.05	.15
467 Allen Watson	.05	.15
468 Mark Whiten	.05	.15
469 Derek Bell	.05	.15
470 Phil Clark	.05	.15
471 Pat Gomez RC	.10	.30
472 Tony Gwynn	.40	1.00
473 Jeremy Hernandez	.05	.15
474 Bruce Hurst	.05	.15
475 Phil Plantier	.05	.15
476 Scott Sanders RC	.10	.30
477 Tim Scott	.05	.15
478 Darrell Sherman RC	.10	.30
479 Guillermo Velasquez	.05	.15
480 Tim Worrell RC	.10	.30
481 Todd Benzinger	.05	.15
482 Bud Black	.05	.15
483 Barry Bonds	.75	2.00
484 Dave Burba	.05	.15
485 Bryan Hickerson	.05	.15
486 Dave Martinez	.05	.15
487 Willie McGee	.10	.30
488 Jeff Reed	.05	.15
489 Kevin Rogers	.05	.15
490 Matt Williams	.10	.30
491 Trevor Wilson	.05	.15
492 Harold Baines	.10	.30
493 Mike Devereaux	.05	.15
494 Todd Frohwirth	.05	.15
495 Chris Hoiles	.05	.15
496 Luis Mercedes	.05	.15
497 Sherman Obando RC	.10	.30
498 Brad Pennington	.05	.15
499 Harold Reynolds	.10	.30
500 Arthur Rhodes	.05	.15
501 Cal Ripken	1.00	2.50
502 Rick Sutcliffe	.10	.30
503 Fernando Valenzuela	.10	.30
504 Mark Williamson	.05	.15
505 Scott Bankhead	.05	.15
506 Greg Blosser	.05	.15
507 Ivan Calderon	.05	.15
508 Roger Clemens	.60	1.50
509 Andre Dawson	.10	.30
510 Scott Fletcher	.05	.15
511 Greg A. Harris	.05	.15
512 Billy Hatcher	.05	.15
513 Bob Melvin	.05	.15
514 Carlos Quintana	.05	.15
515 Luis Rivera	.05	.15
516 Jeff Russell	.05	.15
517 Ken Ryan RC	.10	.30
518 Chili Davis	.10	.30
519 Jim Edmonds RC	2.00	5.00
520 Gary Gaetti	.10	.30
521 Torey Lovullo	.05	.15
522 Troy Percival	.20	.50
523 Tim Salmon	.20	.50
524 Scott Sanderson	.05	.15
525 J.T. Snow RC	.30	.75
526 Jerome Walton	.05	.15
527 Jason Bere	.05	.15
528 Rod Bolton	.05	.15
529 Ellis Burks	.10	.30
530 Carlton Fisk	.20	.50
531 Craig Grebeck	.05	.15
532 Ozzie Guillen	.10	.30
533 Roberto Hernandez	.05	.15
534 Bo Jackson	.30	.75
535 Kirk McCaskill	.05	.15
536 Dave Stieb	.05	.15
537 Robin Ventura	.10	.30
538 Albert Belle	.10	.30
539 Mike Bielecki	.05	.15
540 Glenallen Hill	.05	.15
541 Reggie Jefferson	.05	.15
542 Kenny Lofton	.10	.30
543 Jeff Mutis	.05	.15
544 Junior Ortiz	.05	.15
545 Manny Ramirez	.50	1.25
546 Jeff Treadway	.05	.15
547 Kevin Wickander	.05	.15
548 Cecil Fielder	.10	.30
549 Kirk Gibson	.10	.30
550 Greg Gohr	.05	.15
551 David Haas	.05	.15
552 Bill Krueger	.05	.15
553 Mike Moore	.05	.15
554 Mickey Tettleton	.05	.15
555 Lou Whitaker	.10	.30
556 Kevin Appier	.10	.30
557 Billy Brewer	.05	.15
558 David Cone	.10	.30
559 Greg Gagne	.05	.15
560 Mark Gardner	.05	.15
561 Phil Hiatt	.05	.15
562 Felix Jose	.05	.15
563 Jose Lind	.05	.15
564 Mike Macfarlane	.05	.15
565 Keith Miller	.05	.15
566 Jeff Montgomery	.05	.15
567 Hipolito Pichardo	.05	.15
568 Ricky Bones	.05	.15
569 Tom Brunansky	.05	.15
570 Joe Kmak	.05	.15
571 Pat Listach	.05	.15
572 Graeme Lloyd RC	.20	.50
573 Carlos Maldonado	.05	.15
574 Josias Manzanillo	.05	.15
575 Matt Mieske	.05	.15
576 Kevin Reimer	.05	.15
577 Bill Spiers	.05	.15
578 Dickie Thon	.05	.15
579 Willie Banks	.05	.15
580 Jim Deshaies	.05	.15
581 Mark Guthrie	.05	.15
582 Brian Harper	.05	.15
583 Chuck Knoblauch	.10	.30
584 Gene Larkin	.05	.15
585 Shane Mack	.05	.15
586 David McCarty	.05	.15
587 Mike Pagliarulo	.05	.15
588 Mike Trombley	.05	.15
589 Dave Winfield	.10	.30
590 Jim Abbott	.20	.50
591 Wade Boggs	.20	.50
592 Russ Davis RC	.10	.30
593 Steve Farr	.05	.15
594 Steve Howe	.05	.15
595 Mike Humphreys	.05	.15
596 Jimmy Key	.10	.30
597 Jim Leyritz	.05	.15
598 Bobby Munoz	.05	.15
599 Paul O'Neill	.20	.50
600 Spike Owen	.05	.15
601 Mike Stanley	.05	.15
602 Danny Tartabull	.05	.15
603 Scott Brosius	.10	.30
604 Storm Davis	.05	.15
605 Eric Fox	.05	.15
606 Rich Gossage	.10	.30
607 Scott Hemond	.05	.15
608 Dave Henderson	.05	.15
609 Mark McGwire	.75	2.00
610 Mike Mohler RC	.10	.30
611 Edwin Nunez	.05	.15
612 Kevin Seitzer	.05	.15
613 Ruben Sierra	.10	.30
614 Chris Bosio	.05	.15
615 Norm Charlton	.05	.15
616 Jim Converse RC	.10	.30
617 John Cummings RC	.10	.30
618 Mike Felder	.05	.15
619 Ken Griffey Jr.	.50	1.25
620 Mike Hampton	.10	.30
621 Erik Hanson	.05	.15
622 Bill Haselman	.05	.15
623 Tino Martinez	.20	.50
624 Lee Tinsley	.05	.15
625 Fernando Vina RC	.20	.50
626 David Wainhouse	.05	.15
627 Jose Canseco	.20	.50
628 Benji Gil	.05	.15
629 Tom Henke	.05	.15
630 David Hulse RC	.10	.30
631 Manuel Lee	.05	.15
632 Craig Lefferts	.05	.15
633 Robb Nen	.10	.30
634 Gary Redus	.05	.15
635 Bill Ripken	.05	.15
636 Nolan Ryan	1.25	3.00
637 Dan Smith	.05	.15
638 Matt Whiteside RC	.10	.30
639 Roberto Alomar	.20	.50
640 Juan Guzman	.05	.15
641 Pat Hentgen	.05	.15
642 Darrin Jackson	.05	.15
643 Randy Knorr	.05	.15
644 Domingo Martinez RC	.10	.30
645 Paul Molitor	.10	.30
646 Dick Schofield	.05	.15
647 Dave Stewart	.10	.30
648 Rey Sanchez CL	.05	.15
649 Jeremy Hernandez CL	.05	.15
650 Junior Ortiz CL	.05	.15

1993 Ultra All-Rookies

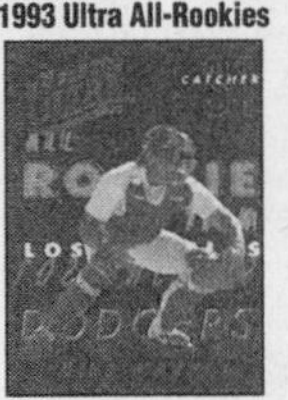

Inserted into series II packs at a rate of one in 18, this ten-card standard-size set features cutout color player action shots that are superposed upon a black background, which carries the player's uniform number, position, team name, and the set's title in multicolored lettering. The set is sequenced in alphabetical order. The key cards in this set are Mike Piazza and Tim Salmon.

COMPLETE SET (10)	6.00	15.00
SER.2 STATED ODDS 1:18		
1 Rene Arocha	.75	2.00
2 Jeff Conine	.50	1.25
3 Phil Hiatt	.25	.60
4 Mike Lansing	.75	2.00
5 Al Martin	.25	.60
6 David Nied	.25	.60
7 Mike Piazza	5.00	12.00
8 Tim Salmon	.75	2.00
9 J.T. Snow	1.25	3.00
10 Kevin Young	.50	1.25

1993 Ultra All-Stars

Inserted into series II packs at a rate of one in nine, this 20-card standard-size set features National League (1-10) and American League (11-20) All-Stars.

COMPLETE SET (20)	15.00	40.00
SER.2 STATED ODDS 1:9		
1 Darren Daulton	.50	1.25
2 Will Clark	.75	2.00
3 Ryne Sandberg	2.00	5.00
4 Barry Larkin	.75	2.00
5 Gary Sheffield	.50	1.25
6 Barry Bonds	3.00	8.00
7 Ray Lankford	.50	1.25
8 Larry Walker	.50	1.25
9 Greg Maddux	2.00	5.00
10 Lee Smith	.50	1.25
11 Ivan Rodriguez	.75	2.00
12 Mark McGwire	3.00	8.00
13 Carlos Baerga	.25	.60
14 Cal Ripken	4.00	10.00
15 Edgar Martinez	.75	2.00
16 Juan Gonzalez	.50	1.25
17 Ken Griffey Jr.	2.00	5.00
18 Kirby Puckett	1.25	3.00
19 Frank Thomas	1.25	3.00
20 Mike Mussina	.75	2.00

1993 Ultra Award Winners

Randomly inserted in first series packs, this 25-card standard-size insert set of 1993 Ultra Award Winners honors the Top Glove for the National (1-9) and American (10-18) Leagues and other major award winners (19-25).

COMPLETE SET (25)	15.00	40.00
RANDOM INSERTS IN SER.1 PACKS		
1 Greg Maddux	2.00	5.00
2 Tom Pagnozzi	.25	.60
3 Mark Grace	.75	2.00
4 Jose Lind	.25	.60
5 Terry Pendleton	.50	1.25
6 Ozzie Smith	2.00	5.00
7 Barry Bonds	3.00	8.00
8 Andy Van Slyke	.75	2.00
9 Larry Walker	.50	1.25
10 Mark Langston	.25	.60
11 Ivan Rodriguez	.75	2.00
12 Don Mattingly	3.00	8.00
13 Roberto Alomar	.75	2.00
14 Robin Ventura	.50	1.25
15 Cal Ripken	4.00	10.00
16 Ken Griffey	2.00	5.00
17 Kirby Puckett	1.25	3.00
18 Devon White	.50	1.25
19 Pat Listach	.25	.60
20 Eric Karros	.50	1.25
21 Pat Borders	.25	.60
22 Greg Maddux	2.00	5.00
23 Dennis Eckersley	.50	1.25
24 Barry Bonds	3.00	8.00
25 Gary Sheffield	.50	1.25

1993 Ultra Eckersley

Randomly inserted in first series foil packs, this 10-card (cards 11 and 12 were mail-aways) standard-size set salutes one of baseball's greatest relief pitchers, Dennis Eckersley. Two additional cards (11 and 12) were available through a mail-in offer for ten 1993 Fleer Ultra baseball wrappers plus 1.00 for postage and handling. The expiration for this offer was September 30, 1993. Eckersley personally autographed more than 2,000 of these cards. The cards feature silver foil stamping on both sides.

COMPLETE SET (10)	1.50	4.00
COMMON CARD (1-10)	.20	.50
RANDOM INSERTS IN SER.1 PACKS		
COMMON MAIL (11-12)	.40	1.00
P1 Dennis Eckersley Paul Mullan Promo	1.50	4.00
AU Dennis Eckersley AU	20.00	50.00

1993 Ultra Home Run Kings

Randomly inserted into all 1993 Ultra packs, this ten-card standard-size set features the best long ball hitters in baseball.

COMPLETE SET (10)	8.00	20.00
RANDOM INSERTS IN PACKS		
1 Juan Gonzalez	.60	1.50
2 Mark McGwire	4.00	10.00
3 Cecil Fielder	.60	1.50
4 Fred McGriff	1.00	2.50
5 Albert Belle	.60	1.50
6 Barry Bonds	4.00	10.00
7 Joe Carter	.60	1.50
8 Gary Sheffield	.60	1.50
9 Darren Daulton	.60	1.50
10 Dave Hollins	.30	.75

1993 Ultra Performers

This ten-card standard-size set could only be ordered directly from Fleer by sending in 9.95, five Fleer/Ultra baseball wrappers, and an order blank found in hobby and sports periodicals.

COMPLETE SET (10)	8.00	20.00
SETS DISTRIBUTED VIA MAIL-IN OFFER		
1 Barry Bonds	2.00	5.00
2 Juan Gonzalez	.30	.75
3 Ken Griffey Jr.	1.25	3.00
4 Eric Karros	.30	.75
5 Pat Listach	.15	.40
6 Greg Maddux	1.25	3.00
7 David Nied	.15	.40
8 Gary Sheffield	.30	.75
9 J.T. Snow	.75	2.00
10 Frank Thomas	.75	2.00

1993 Ultra Strikeout Kings

Inserted into series II packs at a rate of one in 37, this five-card standard-size showcases outstanding pitchers from both leagues.

COMPLETE SET (5)	12.50	25.00
SER.2 STATED ODDS 1:37		
1 Roger Clemens	4.00	10.00
2 Juan Guzman	.40	1.00
3 Randy Johnson	2.00	5.00

4 Nolan Ryan 8.00 20.00
5 John Smoltz 1.25 3.00

1994 Ultra

The 1994 Ultra baseball set consists of 600 standard-size cards that were issued in two series of 300. Each pack contains at least one insert card, while "Hot Packs" have nothing but insert cards in them. The cards are numbered on the back, grouped alphabetically within teams, and checklisted below alphabetically according to teams for each league with AL preceding NL. Rookie Cards include Ray Durham and Chan Ho Park.

COMPLETE SET (600) 12.00 30.00
COMP. SERIES 1 (300) 6.00 15.00
COMP. SERIES 2 (300) 6.00 15.00
1 Jeffrey Hammonds .05 .15
2 Chris Hoiles .05 .15
3 Ben McDonald .05 .15
4 Mark McLemore .05 .15
5 Alan Mills .05 .15
6 Jamie Moyer .10 .30
7 Brad Pennington .05 .15
8 Jim Poole .05 .15
9 Cal Ripken Jr. 1.00 2.50
10 Jack Voigt .05 .15
11 Roger Clemens .60 1.50
12 Danny Darwin .05 .15
13 Andre Dawson .10 .30
14 Scott Fletcher .05 .15
15 Greg A. Harris .05 .15
16 Billy Hatcher .05 .15
17 Jeff Russell .05 .15
18 Aaron Sele .05 .15
19 Mo Vaughn .10 .30
20 Mike Butcher .05 .15
21 Rod Correia .05 .15
22 Steve Frey .05 .15
23 Phil Leftwich RC .05 .15
24 Torey Lovullo .05 .15
25 Ken Patterson .05 .15
26 Eduardo Perez UER .05 .15
(listed as a Twin instead of Angel)
27 Tim Salmon .20 .50
28 J.T. Snow .10 .30
29 Chris Turner .05 .15
30 Wilson Alvarez .05 .15
31 Jason Bere .05 .15
32 Joey Cora .05 .15
33 Alex Fernandez .05 .15
34 Roberto Hernandez .05 .15
35 Lance Johnson .05 .15
36 Ron Karkovice .05 .15
37 Kirk McCaskill .05 .15
38 Jeff Schwarz .05 .15
39 Frank Thomas .30 .75
40 Sandy Alomar Jr. .05 .15
41 Albert Belle .10 .30
42 Felix Fermin .05 .15
43 Wayne Kirby .05 .15
44 Tom Kramer .05 .15
45 Kenny Lofton .10 .30
46 Jose Mesa .05 .15
47 Eric Plunk .05 .15
48 Paul Sorrento .05 .15
49 Jim Thome .20 .50
50 Bill Wertz .05 .15
51 John Doherty .05 .15
52 Cecil Fielder .10 .30
53 Travis Fryman .10 .30
54 Chris Gomez .05 .15
55 Mike Henneman .05 .15
56 Chad Kreuter .05 .15
57 Bob MacDonald .05 .15
58 Mike Moore .05 .15
59 Tony Phillips .05 .15
60 Lou Whitaker .10 .30
61 Kevin Appier .10 .30
62 Greg Gagne .05 .15
63 Chris Gwynn .05 .15
64 Bob Hamelin .05 .15
65 Chris Haney .05 .15
66 Phil Hiatt .05 .15
67 Felix Jose .05 .15
68 Jose Lind .05 .15
69 Mike Macfarlane .05 .15
70 Jeff Montgomery .05 .15
71 Hipolito Pichardo .05 .15
72 Juan Bell .05 .15
73 Cal Eldred .05 .15
74 Darryl Hamilton .05 .15
75 Doug Henry .05 .15
76 Mike Ignasiak .05 .15
77 John Jaha .05 .15
78 Graeme Lloyd .05 .15
79 Angel Miranda .05 .15
80 Dave Nilsson .05 .15
81 Troy O'Leary .05 .15
82 Kevin Reimer .05 .15
83 Willie Banks .05 .15
84 Larry Casian .05 .15
85 Scott Erickson .05 .15
86 Eddie Guardado .10 .30
87 Kent Hrbek .10 .30
88 Terry Jorgensen .05 .15
89 Chuck Knoblauch .10 .30
90 Pat Meares .05 .15
91 Mike Trombley .05 .15
92 Dave Winfield .10 .30
93 Wade Boggs .20 .50
94 Scott Kamieniecki .05 .15
95 Pat Kelly .05 .15
96 Jimmy Key .10 .30
97 Jim Leyritz .05 .15
98 Bobby Munoz .05 .15
99 Paul O'Neill .20 .50
100 Melido Perez .05 .15
101 Mike Stanley .05 .15
102 Danny Tartabull .05 .15
103 Bernie Williams .20 .50
104 Kurt Abbott RC .05 .15
105 Mike Bordick .05 .15
106 Ron Darling .05 .15
107 Brent Gates .05 .15
108 Miguel Jimenez .05 .15
109 Steve Karsay .05 .15
110 Scott Lydy .05 .15
111 Mark McGwire .75 2.00
112 Troy Neel .05 .15
113 Craig Paquette .05 .15
114 Bob Welch .05 .15
115 Bobby Witt .05 .15
116 Rich Amaral .05 .15
117 Mike Blowers .05 .15
118 Jay Buhner .10 .30
119 Dave Fleming .05 .15
120 Ken Griffey Jr. .50 1.25
121 Tino Martinez .20 .50
122 Marc Newfield .05 .15
123 Ted Power .05 .15
124 Mackey Sasser .05 .15
125 Omar Vizquel .20 .50
126 Kevin Brown .10 .30
127 Juan Gonzalez .10 .30
128 Tom Henke .05 .15
129 David Hulse .05 .15
130 Dean Palmer .10 .30
131 Roger Pavlik .05 .15
132 Ivan Rodriguez .20 .50
133 Kenny Rogers .10 .30
134 Doug Strange .05 .15
135 Pat Borders .05 .15
136 Joe Carter .10 .30
137 Darnell Coles .05 .15
138 Pat Hentgen .05 .15
139 Al Leiter .10 .30
140 Paul Molitor .10 .30
141 John Olerud .10 .30
142 Ed Sprague .05 .15
143 Dave Stewart .10 .30
144 Mike Timlin .05 .15
145 Duane Ward .05 .15
146 Devon White .10 .30
147 Steve Avery .05 .15
148 Steve Bedrosian .05 .15
149 Damon Berryhill .05 .15
150 Jeff Blauser .05 .15
151 Tom Glavine .20 .50
152 Chipper Jones .30 .75
153 Mark Lemke .05 .15
154 Fred McGriff .20 .50
155 Greg McMichael .05 .15
156 Deion Sanders .20 .50
157 John Smoltz .20 .50
158 Mark Wohlers .05 .15
159 Jose Bautista .05 .15
160 Steve Buechele .05 .15
161 Mike Harkey .05 .15
162 Greg Hibbard .05 .15
163 Chuck McElroy .05 .15
164 Mike Morgan .05 .15
165 Kevin Roberson .05 .15
166 Ryne Sandberg .50 1.25
167 Jose Vizcaino .05 .15
168 Rick Wilkins .05 .15
169 Willie Wilson .05 .15
170 Willie Greene .05 .15
171 Roberto Kelly .05 .15
172 Larry Luebbers RC .05 .15
173 Kevin Mitchell .05 .15
174 Joe Oliver .05 .15
175 John Roper .05 .15
176 Johnny Ruffin .05 .15
177 Reggie Sanders .10 .30
178 John Smiley .05 .15
179 Jerry Spradlin RC .05 .15
180 Freddie Benavides .05 .15
181 Dante Bichette .10 .30
182 Willie Blair .05 .15
183 Kent Bottenfield .05 .15
184 Jerald Clark .05 .15
185 Joe Girardi .05 .15
186 Roberto Mejia .05 .15
187 Steve Reed .05 .15
188 Armando Reynoso .05 .15
189 Bruce Ruffin .05 .15
190 Eric Young .05 .15
191 Luis Aquino .05 .15
192 Bret Barberie .05 .15
193 Ryan Bowen .05 .15
194 Chuck Carr .05 .15
195 Orestes Destrade .05 .15
196 Richie Lewis .05 .15
197 Dave Magadan .05 .15
198 Bob Natal .05 .15
199 Gary Sheffield .10 .30
200 Matt Turner .05 .15
201 Darrell Whitmore .05 .15
202 Eric Anthony .05 .15
203 Jeff Bagwell .20 .50
204 Andujar Cedeno .05 .15
205 Luis Gonzalez .10 .30
206 Xavier Hernandez .05 .15
207 Doug Jones .05 .15
208 Darryl Kile .10 .30
209 Scott Servais .05 .15
210 Greg Swindell .05 .15
211 Brian Williams .05 .15
212 Pedro Astacio .05 .15
213 Brett Butler .10 .30
214 Omar Daal .05 .15
215 Jim Gott .05 .15
216 Raul Mondesi .10 .30
217 Jose Offerman .05 .15
218 Mike Piazza .60 1.50
219 Cory Snyder .05 .15
220 Tim Wallach .05 .15
221 Todd Worrell .05 .15
222 Moises Alou .10 .30
223 Sean Berry .05 .15
224 Wil Cordero .05 .15
225 Jeff Fassero .05 .15
226 Darrin Fletcher .05 .15
227 Cliff Floyd .10 .30
228 Marquis Grissom .10 .30
229 Ken Hill .05 .15
230 Mike Lansing .05 .15
231 Kirk Rueter .05 .15
232 John Wetteland .10 .30
233 Rondell White .10 .30
234 Tim Bogar .05 .15
235 Jeromy Burnitz .10 .30
236 Dwight Gooden .10 .30
237 Todd Hundley .05 .15
238 Jeff Kent .20 .50
239 Josias Manzanillo .05 .15
240 Joe Orsulak .05 .15
241 Ryan Thompson .05 .15
242 Kim Batiste .05 .15
243 Darren Daulton .10 .30
244 Tommy Greene .05 .15
245 Dave Hollins .05 .15
246 Pete Incaviglia .05 .15
247 Danny Jackson .05 .15
248 Ricky Jordan .05 .15
249 John Kruk .10 .30
250 Mickey Morandini .05 .15
251 Terry Mulholland .05 .15
252 Ben Rivera .05 .15
253 Kevin Stocker .05 .15
254 Jay Bell .10 .30
255 Steve Cooke .05 .15
256 Jeff King .05 .15
257 Al Martin .05 .15
258 Danny Miceli .05 .15
259 Blas Minor .05 .15
260 Don Slaught .05 .15
261 Paul Wagner .05 .15
262 Tim Wakefield .20 .50
263 Kevin Young .05 .15
264 Rene Arocha .05 .15
265 Richard Batchelor RC .05 .15
266 Gregg Jefferies .05 .15
267 Brian Jordan .10 .30
268 Jose Oquendo .05 .15
269 Donovan Osborne .05 .15
270 Erik Pappas .05 .15
271 Mike Perez .05 .15
272 Bob Tewksbury .05 .15
273 Mark Whiten .05 .15
274 Todd Zeile .05 .15
275 Andy Ashby .05 .15
276 Brad Ausmus .20 .50
277 Phil Clark .05 .15
278 Jeff Gardner .05 .15
279 Ricky Gutierrez .05 .15
280 Tony Gwynn .40 1.00
281 Tim Mauser .05 .15
282 Scott Sanders .05 .15
283 Frank Seminara .05 .15
284 Wally Whitehurst .05 .15
285 Rod Beck .05 .15
286 Barry Bonds .75 2.00
287 Dave Burba .05 .15
288 Mark Carreon .05 .15
289 Royce Clayton .05 .15
290 Mike Jackson .05 .15
291 Darren Lewis .05 .15
292 Kirt Manwaring .05 .15
293 Dave Martinez .05 .15
294 Billy Swift .05 .15
295 Salomon Torres .05 .15
296 Matt Williams .10 .30
297 Checklist 1-75 .05 .15
298 Checklist 76-150 .05 .15
299 Checklist 151-225 .05 .15
300 Checklist 226-300 .05 .15
301 Brady Anderson .10 .30
302 Harold Baines .10 .30
303 Damon Buford .05 .15
304 Mike Devereaux .05 .15
305 Sid Fernandez .05 .15
306 Rick Krivda RC .05 .15
307 Mike Mussina .20 .50
308 Rafael Palmeiro .20 .50
309 Arthur Rhodes .05 .15
310 Chris Sabo .05 .15
311 Lee Smith .10 .30
312 Gregg Zaun RC .08 .25
313 Scott Cooper .05 .15
314 Mike Greenwell .05 .15
315 Tim Naehring .05 .15
316 Otis Nixon .05 .15
317 Paul Quantrill .05 .15
318 John Valentin .05 .15
319 Dave Valle .05 .15
320 Frank Viola .10 .30
321 Brian Anderson RC .15 .40
322 Garret Anderson .30 .75
323 Chad Curtis .05 .15
324 Chili Davis .10 .30
325 Gary DiSarcina .05 .15
326 Damion Easley .05 .15
327 Jim Edmonds .30 .75
328 Chuck Finley .10 .30
329 Joe Grahe .05 .15
330 Bo Jackson .30 .75
331 Mark Langston .05 .15
332 Harold Reynolds .10 .30
333 James Baldwin .05 .15
334 Ray Durham RC .40 1.00
335 Julio Franco .10 .30
336 Craig Grebeck .05 .15
337 Ozzie Guillen .10 .30
338 Joe Hall RC .05 .15
339 Darrin Jackson .05 .15
340 Jack McDowell .05 .15
341 Tim Raines .10 .30
342 Robin Ventura .10 .30
343 Carlos Baerga .05 .15
344 Derek Lilliquist .05 .15
345 Dennis Martinez .10 .30
346 Jack Morris .10 .30
347 Eddie Murray .30 .75
348 Chris Nabholz .05 .15
349 Charles Nagy .05 .15
350 Chad Ogea .05 .15
351 Manny Ramirez .30 .75
352 Omar Vizquel .20 .50
353 Tim Belcher .05 .15
354 Eric Davis .10 .30
355 Kirk Gibson .10 .30
356 Rick Greene .05 .15
357 Mickey Tettleton .05 .15
358 Alan Trammell .10 .30
359 David Wells .10 .30
360 Stan Belinda .05 .15
361 Vince Coleman .05 .15
362 David Cone .10 .30
363 Gary Gaetti .10 .30
364 Tom Gordon .05 .15
365 Dave Henderson .05 .15
366 Wally Joyner .10 .30
367 Brent Mayne .05 .15
368 Brian McRae .05 .15
369 Michael Tucker .05 .15
370 Ricky Bones .05 .15
371 Brian Harper .05 .15
372 Tyrone Hill .05 .15
373 Mark Kiefer .05 .15
374 Pat Listach .05 .15
375 Mike Matheny RC .30 .75
376 Jose Mercedes RC .05 .15
377 Jody Reed .05 .15
378 Kevin Seitzer .05 .15
379 B.J. Surhoff .10 .30
380 Greg Vaughn .05 .15
381 Turner Ward .05 .15
382 Wes Weger RC .05 .15
383 Bill Wegman .05 .15
384 Rick Aguilera .05 .15
385 Rich Becker .05 .15
386 Alex Cole .05 .15
387 Steve Dunn .05 .15
388 Keith Garagozzo RC .05 .15
389 LaTroy Hawkins RC .15 .40
390 Shane Mack .05 .15
391 David McCarty .05 .15
392 Pedro Munoz .05 .15
393 Derek Parks .05 .15
394 Kirby Puckett .30 .75
395 Kevin Tapani .05 .15
396 Matt Walbeck .05 .15
397 Jim Abbott .20 .50
398 Mike Gallego .05 .15
399 Xavier Hernandez .05 .15
400 Don Mattingly .75 2.00
401 Terry Mulholland .05 .15
402 Matt Nokes .05 .15
403 Luis Polonia .05 .15
404 Bob Wickman .05 .15
405 Mark Acre RC .05 .15
406 Fausto Cruz RC .05 .15
407 Dennis Eckersley .10 .30
408 Rickey Henderson .30 .75
409 Stan Javier .05 .15
410 Carlos Reyes RC .05 .15
411 Ruben Sierra .10 .30
412 Terry Steinbach .05 .15
413 Bill Taylor RC .05 .15
414 Todd Van Poppel .05 .15
415 Eric Anthony .05 .15
416 Bobby Ayala .05 .15
417 Chris Bosio .05 .15
418 Tim Davis .05 .15
419 Randy Johnson .30 .75
420 Kevin King RC .05 .15
421 Anthony Manahan RC .05 .15
422 Edgar Martinez .20 .50
423 Keith Mitchell .05 .15
424 Roger Salkeld .05 .15
425 Mac Suzuki RC .15 .40
426 Dan Wilson .05 .15
427 Duff Brumley RC .05 .15
428 Jose Canseco .20 .50
429 Will Clark .20 .50
430 Steve Dreyer RC .05 .15
431 Rick Helling .05 .15
432 Chris James .05 .15
433 Matt Whiteside .05 .15
434 Roberto Alomar .20 .50
435 Scott Brow .05 .15
436 Domingo Cedeno .05 .15
437 Carlos Delgado .20 .50
438 Juan Guzman .05 .15
439 Paul Spoljaric .05 .15
440 Todd Stottlemyre .05 .15
441 Woody Williams .05 .15
442 David Justice .10 .30
443 Mike Kelly .05 .15
444 Ryan Klesko .10 .30
445 Javier Lopez .10 .30
446 Greg Maddux .50 1.25
447 Kent Mercker .05 .15
448 Charlie O'Brien .05 .15
449 Terry Pendleton .10 .30
450 Mike Stanton .05 .15
451 Tony Tarasco .05 .15
452 Terrell Wade RC .05 .15
453 Willie Banks .05 .15
454 Shawon Dunston .05 .15
455 Mark Grace .20 .50
456 Jose Guzman .05 .15
457 Jose Hernandez .05 .15
458 Glenallen Hill .05 .15
459 Blaise Ilsley RC .05 .15
460 Brooks Kieschnick RC .05 .15
461 Derrick May .05 .15
462 Randy Myers .05 .15
463 Karl Rhodes .05 .15
464 Sammy Sosa .30 .75
465 Steve Trachsel .05 .15
466 Anthony Young .05 .15
467 Eddie Zambrano RC .05 .15
468 Bret Boone .10 .30
469 Tom Browning .05 .15
470 Hector Carrasco .05 .15
471 Rob Dibble .10 .30
472 Erik Hanson .05 .15
473 Thomas Howard .05 .15
474 Barry Larkin .20 .50
475 Hal Morris .05 .15
476 Jose Rijo .05 .15
477 John Burke .05 .15
478 Ellis Burks .10 .30
479 Marvin Freeman .05 .15
480 Andres Galarraga .10 .30
481 Greg W. Harris .05 .15
482 Charlie Hayes .05 .15
483 Darren Holmes .05 .15
484 Howard Johnson .05 .15
485 Marcus Moore .05 .15
486 David Nied .05 .15
487 Mark Thompson .05 .15
488 Walt Weiss .05 .15
489 Kurt Abbott .05 .15
490 Matias Carrillo RC .05 .15
491 Jeff Conine .10 .30
492 Chris Hammond .05 .15
493 Bryan Harvey .05 .15
494 Charlie Hough .10 .30
495 Yorkis Perez .05 .15
496 Pat Rapp .05 .15
497 Benito Santiago .10 .30
498 David Weathers .05 .15
499 Craig Biggio .20 .50
500 Ken Caminiti .10 .30
501 Doug Drabek .05 .15
502 Tony Eusebio .05 .15
503 Steve Finley .10 .30
504 Pete Harnisch .05 .15
505 Brian L. Hunter .05 .15
506 Domingo Jean .05 .15
507 Todd Jones .05 .15
508 Orlando Miller .05 .15
509 James Mouton .05 .15
510 Roberto Petagine .05 .15
511 Shane Reynolds .05 .15
512 Mitch Williams .05 .15
513 Billy Ashley .05 .15
514 Tom Candiotti .05 .15
515 Delino DeShields .05 .15
516 Kevin Gross .05 .15
517 Orel Hershiser .10 .30
518 Eric Karros .10 .30
519 Ramon Martinez .05 .15
520 Chan Ho Park RC .30 .75
521 Henry Rodriguez .05 .15
522 Joey Eischen .05 .15
523 Rod Henderson .05 .15
524 Pedro Martinez .30 .75
525 Mel Rojas .05 .15
526 Larry Walker .10 .30
527 Gabe White .05 .15
528 Bobby Bonilla .10 .30
529 Jonathan Hurst .05 .15
530 Bobby Jones .05 .15
531 Kevin McReynolds .05 .15
532 Bill Pulsipher .10 .30
533 Bret Saberhagen .10 .30
534 David Segui .05 .15
535 Pete Smith .05 .15
536 Kelly Stinnett RC .15 .40
537 Dave Telgheder .05 .15
538 Quilvio Veras .05 .15
539 Jose Vizcaino .05 .15
540 Pete Walker RC .05 .15
541 Ricky Bottalico RC .05 .15
542 Wes Chamberlain .05 .15
543 Mariano Duncan .05 .15
544 Lenny Dykstra .10 .30
545 Jim Eisenreich .05 .15
546 Phil Geisler RC .05 .15
547 Wayne Gomes RC .15 .40
548 Doug Jones .05 .15
549 Jeff Juden .05 .15
550 Mike Lieberthal .10 .30
551 Tony Longmire .05 .15
552 Tom Marsh .05 .15
553 Bobby Munoz .05 .15
554 Curt Schilling .10 .30
555 Carlos Garcia .05 .15
556 Ravelo Manzanillo RC .05 .15
557 Orlando Merced .05 .15
558 Will Pennyfeather .05 .15
559 Zane Smith .05 .15
560 Andy Van Slyke .20 .50
561 Rick White .05 .15
562 Luis Alicea .05 .15
563 Brian Barber .05 .15
564 Clint Davis RC .05 .15
565 Bernard Gilkey .05 .15
566 Ray Lankford .10 .30
567 Tom Pagnozzi .05 .15
568 Ozzie Smith .50 1.25
569 Rick Sutcliffe .10 .30
570 Allen Watson .05 .15
571 Dmitri Young .10 .30
572 Derek Bell .05 .15
573 Andy Benes .05 .15
574 Archi Cianfrocco .05 .15
575 Joey Hamilton .05 .15
576 Gene Harris .05 .15
577 Trevor Hoffman .20 .50
578 Tim Hyers RC .05 .15
579 Brian Johnson RC .05 .15
580 Keith Lockhart RC .15 .40
581 Pedro A. Martinez RC .05 .15
582 Ray McDavid .05 .15
583 Phil Plantier .05 .15
584 Bip Roberts .05 .15
585 Dave Staton .05 .15
586 Todd Benzinger .05 .15
587 John Burkett .05 .15
588 Bryan Hickerson .05 .15
589 Willie McGee .10 .30
590 John Patterson .05 .15
591 Mark Portugal .05 .15
592 Kevin Rogers .05 .15
593 Joe Rosselli .05 .15
594 Steve Soderstrom RC .05 .15
595 Robby Thompson .05 .15
596 125th Anniversary .05 .15
597 Jaime Navarro CL .05 .15
598 Andy Van Slyke CL .10 .30
599 Checklist .05 .15
600 Bryan Harvey CL .05 .15
P243 D.Daulton Promo .75 2.00
P249 John Kruk Promo .75 2.00

1994 Ultra All-Rookies

This 10-card standard-size set features top rookies of 1994 and were randomly inserted in second series jumbo and foil packs at a rate of one in 10.

COMPLETE SET (10) 3.00 8.00
SER.2 STATED ODDS 1:10
*JUMBOS: .75X TO 2X BASIC CARDS
ONE JUMBO SET PER 2ND SERIES HOBBY CASE
1 Kurt Abbott .20 .50
2 Carlos Delgado .40 1.00
3 Cliff Floyd .40 1.00
4 Jeffrey Hammonds .20 .50
5 Ryan Klesko .40 1.00
6 Javier Lopez .40 1.00
7 Raul Mondesi .40 1.00
8 James Mouton .20 .50
9 Chan Ho Park .40 1.00
10 Dave Staton .20 .50

1994 Ultra All-Stars

Randomly inserted in second series foil and jumbo packs at a rate of one in three, this 20-card standard-size set contains top major league stars.

COMPLETE SET (20) 6.00 15.00
SER.2 STATED ODDS 1:3
1 Chris Hoiles .08 .25
2 Frank Thomas .50 1.25
3 Roberto Alomar .30 .75
4 Cal Ripken Jr. 1.50 4.00
5 Robin Ventura .20 .50
6 Albert Belle .20 .50
7 Juan Gonzalez .20 .50
8 Ken Griffey Jr. .75 2.00
9 John Olerud .20 .50
10 Jack McDowell .08 .25
11 Mike Piazza 1.00 2.50
12 Fred McGriff .30 .75
13 Ryne Sandberg .75 2.00
14 Jay Bell .20 .50
15 Matt Williams .20 .50
16 Barry Bonds 1.25 3.00
17 Lenny Dykstra .20 .50
18 David Justice .20 .50
19 Tom Glavine .30 .75
20 Greg Maddux .75 2.00

1994 Ultra Award Winners

Randomly inserted in all first series packs at a rate of one in three, this 25-card standard-size set features three MVP's, two Rookies of the Year, and 18 Top Glove defensive standouts. The set is divided into American League Top Gloves (1-9), National League Top Gloves (10-18), and Award Winners (19-25).

COMPLETE SET (25) 6.00 15.00
SER.1 STATED ODDS 1:3
1 Ivan Rodriguez .30 .75
2 Don Mattingly 1.25 3.00
3 Roberto Alomar .30 .75
4 Robin Ventura .20 .50
5 Omar Vizquel .30 .75
6 Ken Griffey Jr. .75 2.00
7 Kenny Lofton .20 .50
8 Devon White .20 .50
9 Mark Langston .08 .25
10 Kirt Manwaring .08 .25
11 Mark Grace .30 .75
12 Robby Thompson .08 .25
13 Matt Williams .20 .50
14 Jay Bell .20 .50
15 Barry Bonds 1.25 3.00
16 Marquis Grissom .20 .50
17 Larry Walker .20 .50
18 Greg Maddux .75 2.00
19 Frank Thomas .50 1.25
20 Barry Bonds 1.25 3.00
21 Paul Molitor .20 .50
22 Jack McDowell .08 .25
23 Greg Maddux .75 2.00
24 Tim Salmon .30 .75
25 Mike Piazza 1.00 2.50

1994 Ultra Career Achievement

Randomly inserted in all second series packs at a rate of one in 21, this five card standard-size set highlights veteran stars and milestones they have reached during their brilliant careers.

COMPLETE SET (5) 4.00 10.00
SER.2 STATED ODDS 1:21
1 Joe Carter .40 1.00
2 Paul Molitor .40 1.00
3 Cal Ripken Jr. 3.00 8.00
4 Ryne Sandberg 1.50 4.00
5 Dave Winfield .40 1.00

1994 Ultra Firemen

Randomly inserted in all first series packs at a rate of one in 11, this ten-card standard-size set features ten of baseball's top relief pitchers. The set is arranged according to American League (1-5) and National League (6-10) players.

COMPLETE SET (10) 2.00 5.00
SER.1 STATED ODDS 1:11
1 Jeff Montgomery .20 .50
2 Duane Ward .20 .50
3 Tom Henke .20 .50
4 Roberto Hernandez .20 .50
5 Dennis Eckersley .40 1.00
6 Randy Myers .20 .50
7 Rod Beck .20 .50
8 Bryan Harvey .20 .50
9 John Wetteland .40 1.00
10 Mitch Williams .20 .50

1994 Ultra Hitting Machines

Randomly inserted in all second series packs at a rate of one in five, this 10-card horizontally designed standard-size set features top hitters from 1993.

COMPLETE SET (10) 4.00 10.00
SER.2 STATED ODDS 1:5
1 Roberto Alomar .30 .75
2 Carlos Baerga .08 .25
3 Barry Bonds 1.25 3.00
4 Andres Galarraga .20 .50
5 Juan Gonzalez .20 .50
6 Tony Gwynn .60 1.50
7 Paul Molitor .20 .50
8 John Olerud .20 .50
9 Mike Piazza 1.00 2.50
10 Frank Thomas .50 1.25

1994 Ultra Home Run Kings

Randomly inserted exclusively in first series foil packs at a rate of one in 36, these 12 standard-size cards highlight home run hitters by an etched metalized look. Cards 1-6 feature American League Home Run Kings while cards 7-12 present National League Home Run Kings.

COMPLETE SET (12) 25.00 60.00
SER.1 FOIL STATED ODDS 1:36
1 Juan Gonzalez 1.00 2.50
2 Ken Griffey Jr. 4.00 10.00
3 Frank Thomas 2.50 6.00
4 Albert Belle 1.00 2.50
5 Rafael Palmeiro 1.50 4.00
6 Joe Carter 1.00 2.50
7 Barry Bonds 6.00 15.00
8 David Justice 1.00 2.50
9 Matt Williams 1.00 2.50
10 Fred McGriff 1.50 4.00
11 Ron Gant .50 1.25
12 Mike Piazza 5.00 12.00

1994 Ultra League Leaders

Randomly inserted in all first series packs at a rate of one in 11, this ten-card standard-size set features ten of 1993's leading players. The set is arranged according to American League (1-5) and National League (6-10) players.

COMPLETE SET (10) 2.00 5.00
SER.1 STATED ODDS 1:11
1 John Olerud .30 .75
2 Rafael Palmeiro .50 1.25
3 Kenny Lofton .30 .75
4 Jack McDowell .15 .40
5 Randy Johnson .75 2.00
6 Andres Galarraga .30 .75
7 Lenny Dykstra .30 .75
8 Chuck Carr .15 .40
9 Tom Glavine .50 1.25
10 Jose Rijo .15 .40

1994 Ultra On-Base Leaders

Randomly inserted in second series jumbo packs at a rate of one in 36, this 12-card standard-size set features those that were among the Major League leaders in on-base percentage.

COMPLETE SET (12) 40.00 100.00
RANDOM INSERTS IN SER.2 17-CARD JUMBOS
1 Roberto Alomar 3.00 8.00
2 Barry Bonds 12.50 30.00
3 Lenny Dykstra 2.00 5.00
4 Andres Galarraga 2.00 5.00
5 Mark Grace 3.00 8.00
6 Ken Griffey Jr. 8.00 20.00
7 Gregg Jefferies 1.00 2.50
8 Orlando Merced 1.00 2.50
9 Paul Molitor 2.00 5.00
10 John Olerud 2.00 5.00
11 Tony Phillips 1.00 2.50
12 Frank Thomas 5.00 12.00

1994 Ultra Phillies Finest

As the "Highlight Series" insert set, this 20-card standard-size set features Darren Daulton and John Kruk of the 1993 National League champion Philadelphia Phillies. The cards were inserted at a rate of one in six first series and one in 10 second series packs. Ten cards spotlight each player's career. Daulton and Kruk each signed more than 1,000 of their cards for random insertion. Moreover, the collector could receive four more cards (two of each player) through a mail-in offer by sending in ten 1994 series I wrappers plus 1.50 for postage and handling. The expiration for this redemption was September 30, 1994.

COMPLETE SET (20) 4.00 10.00
COMPLETE SERIES 1 (10) 2.00 5.00
COMPLETE SERIES 2 (10) 2.00 5.00
COMMON (1-5/11-15) .20 .50
COMMON (6-10/16-20) .20 .50
SER.1 STATED ODDS 1:6
SER.2 STATED ODDS 1:10
COMMON MAIL-IN (M1-M4) .40 1.00
AU1 Darren Daulton Certified Autograph 30.00 60.00
AU2 John Kruk Certified Autograph 30.00 60.00

1994 Ultra RBI Kings

Randomly inserted in first series jumbo packs at a rate of one in 36, this 12-card standard-size set features RBI leaders. These horizontal, metallized cards have a color player photo on front that superimposes a player image.The backs have a write-up and a small color player photo. Cards 1-6 feature American League RBI Kings while cards 7-12 present National League RBI Kings.

COMPLETE SET (12) 25.00 60.00
RANDOM INSERTS IN SER.1 17-CARD JUMBOS
1 Albert Belle 1.25 3.00
2 Frank Thomas 3.00 8.00
3 Joe Carter 1.25 3.00
4 Juan Gonzalez 1.25 3.00
5 Cecil Fielder 1.25 3.00
6 Carlos Baerga .60 1.50
7 Barry Bonds 8.00 20.00
8 David Justice 1.25 3.00
9 Ron Gant .60 1.50
10 Mike Piazza 6.00 15.00
11 Matt Williams 1.25 3.00
12 Darren Daulton 1.25 3.00

1994 Ultra Rising Stars

Randomly inserted in second series foil packs and jumbo packs at a rate of one in 36, this 12-card set spotlights top young major league stars.

COMPLETE SET (12) 25.00 60.00
RANDOM INS.IN SER.2 FOIL/20-CARD JUMBOS
1 Carlos Baerga .75 2.00
2 Jeff Bagwell 2.50 6.00
3 Albert Belle 1.50 4.00
4 Cliff Floyd 1.50 4.00
5 Travis Fryman 1.50 4.00
6 Marquis Grissom 1.50 4.00
7 Kenny Lofton 1.50 4.00
8 John Olerud 1.50 4.00
9 Mike Piazza 8.00 20.00
10 Kirk Rueter .75 2.00
11 Tim Salmon 2.50 6.00
12 Aaron Sele .75 2.00

1994 Ultra Second Year Standouts

Randomly inserted in all first series packs at a rate of one in 11, this 10-card standard-size set included 10 1993 outstanding rookies who are destined to become future stars. The set is arranged in alphabetical order according to American League (1-5) and National League (6-10) players.

COMPLETE SET (10) 4.00 10.00
SER.1 STATED ODDS 1:11
1 Jason Bere .25 .60
2 Brent Gates .25 .60
3 Jeffrey Hammonds .25 .60
4 Tim Salmon .75 2.00
5 Aaron Sele .25 .60
6 Chuck Carr .25 .60
7 Jeff Conine .50 1.25
8 Greg McMichael .25 .60
9 Mike Piazza 2.50 6.00
10 Kevin Stocker .25 .60

1994 Ultra Strikeout Kings

Randomly inserted in all second series packs at a rate of one in seven, this five-card standard-size set features top strikeout artists.

COMPLETE SET (5) 1.50 4.00
SER.2 STATED ODDS 1:7
1 Randy Johnson .50 1.25
2 Mark Langston .08 .25
3 Greg Maddux .75 2.00
4 Jose Rijo .08 .25
5 John Smoltz .30 .75

1995 Ultra

This 450-card standard-size set was issued in two series. The first series contained 250 cards while the second series consisted of 200 cards. They were issued in 12-card packs (either hobby or retail) with a suggested retail price of $1.99. Also, 15-card pre-priced packs with a suggested retail of $2.69. Each pack contained two inserts: one is a Gold Medallion parallel while the other is from one of Ultra's many insert sets. "Hot Packs" contained nothing but insert cards. The full-bleed fronts feature the player's photo with the team name and player's name at the bottom. The "95 Fleer Ultra" logo is in the upper right corner. The backs have a two-photo design; one of which is a full-size duotone shot with the other being a full-color action shot. In each series the cards were grouped alphabetically within teams and checklisted alphabetically according to teams for each league with AL preceding NL.

COMPLETE SET (450) 12.00 30.00
COMP. SERIES 1 (250) 7.00 18.00
COMP.SERIES 2 (200) 5.00 12.00
1 Brady Anderson .10 .30
2 Sid Fernandez .05 .15
3 Jeffrey Hammonds .05 .15
4 Chris Hoiles .05 .15
5 Ben McDonald .05 .15
6 Mike Mussina .20 .50
7 Rafael Palmeiro .20 .50
8 Jack Voigt .05 .15
9 Wes Chamberlain .05 .15
10 Roger Clemens .60 1.50
11 Chris Howard .05 .15
12 Tim Naehring .05 .15
13 Otis Nixon .05 .15
14 Rich Rowland .05 .15
15 Ken Ryan .05 .15
16 John Valentin .05 .15
17 Mo Vaughn .10 .30
18 Brian Anderson .05 .15
19 Chili Davis .10 .30
20 Damion Easley .05 .15
21 Jim Edmonds .20 .50
22 Mark Langston .05 .15
23 Tim Salmon .20 .50
24 J.T. Snow .10 .30
25 Chris Turner .05 .15
26 Wilson Alvarez .05 .15
27 Joey Cora .05 .15
28 Alex Fernandez .05 .15
29 Roberto Hernandez .05 .15
30 Lance Johnson .05 .15
31 Ron Karkovice .05 .15
32 Kirk McCaskill .05 .15
33 Tim Raines .10 .30
34 Frank Thomas .30 .75
35 Sandy Alomar Jr. .05 .15
36 Albert Belle .10 .30
37 Mark Clark .05 .15
38 Kenny Lofton .10 .30
39 Eddie Murray .30 .75
40 Eric Plunk .05 .15
41 Manny Ramirez .20 .50
42 Jim Thome .20 .50
43 Omar Vizquel .20 .50
44 Danny Bautista .05 .15
45 Junior Felix .05 .15
46 Cecil Fielder .10 .30
47 Chris Gomez .05 .15
48 Chad Kreuter .05 .15
49 Mike Moore .05 .15
50 Tony Phillips .05 .15
51 Alan Trammell .10 .30
52 David Wells .10 .30
53 Kevin Appier .10 .30
54 Billy Brewer .05 .15
55 David Cone .10 .30
56 Greg Gagne .05 .15
57 Bob Hamelin .05 .15
58 Jose Lind .05 .15
59 Brent Mayne .05 .15
60 Brian McRae .05 .15
61 Terry Shumpert .05 .15
62 Ricky Bones .05 .15
63 Mike Fetters .05 .15
64 Darryl Hamilton .05 .15
65 John Jaha .05 .15
66 Graeme Lloyd .05 .15
67 Matt Mieske .05 .15
68 Kevin Seitzer .05 .15
69 Jose Valentin .05 .15
70 Turner Ward .05 .15
71 Rick Aguilera .05 .15
72 Rich Becker .05 .15
73 Alex Cole .05 .15
74 Scott Leius .05 .15
75 Pat Meares .05 .15
76 Kirby Puckett .30 .75
77 Dave Stevens .05 .15
78 Kevin Tapani .05 .15
79 Matt Walbeck .05 .15
80 Wade Boggs .20 .50
81 Scott Kamieniecki .05 .15
82 Pat Kelly .05 .15
83 Jimmy Key .10 .30
84 Paul O'Neill .20 .50
85 Luis Polonia .05 .15
86 Mike Stanley .05 .15
87 Danny Tartabull .05 .15
88 Bob Wickman .05 .15
89 Mark Acre .05 .15
90 Geronimo Berroa .05 .15
91 Mike Bordick .05 .15
92 Ron Darling .05 .15
93 Stan Javier .05 .15
94 Mark McGwire .75 2.00
95 Troy Neel .05 .15
96 Ruben Sierra .10 .30
97 Terry Steinbach .05 .15
98 Eric Anthony .05 .15
99 Chris Bosio .05 .15
100 Dave Fleming .05 .15
101 Ken Griffey Jr. .50 1.25
102 Reggie Jefferson .05 .15
103 Randy Johnson .30 .75
104 Edgar Martinez .20 .50
105 Bill Risley .05 .15
106 Dan Wilson .05 .15
107 Cris Carpenter .05 .15
108 Will Clark .20 .50
109 Juan Gonzalez .10 .30
110 Rusty Greer .10 .30
111 David Hulse .05 .15
112 Roger Pavlik .05 .15
113 Ivan Rodriguez .20 .50
114 Doug Strange .05 .15
115 Matt Whiteside .05 .15
116 Roberto Alomar .20 .50
117 Brad Cornett .05 .15
118 Carlos Delgado .10 .30
119 Alex Gonzalez .05 .15
120 Darren Hall .05 .15
121 Pat Hentgen .05 .15
122 Paul Molitor .10 .30
123 Ed Sprague .05 .15
124 Devon White .10 .30
125 Tom Glavine .20 .50
126 David Justice .10 .30
127 Roberto Kelly .05 .15
128 Mark Lemke .05 .15
129 Greg Maddux .50 1.25
130 Greg McMichael .05 .15
131 Kent Mercker .05 .15
132 Charlie O'Brien .05 .15
133 John Smoltz .20 .50
134 Willie Banks .05 .15
135 Steve Buechele .05 .15
136 Kevin Foster .05 .15
137 Glenallen Hill .05 .15
138 Rey Sanchez .05 .15
139 Sammy Sosa .30 .75
140 Steve Trachsel .05 .15
141 Rick Wilkins .05 .15
142 Jeff Brantley .05 .15
143 Hector Carrasco .05 .15
144 Kevin Jarvis .05 .15
145 Barry Larkin .20 .50
146 Chuck McElroy .05 .15
147 Jose Rijo .05 .15
148 Johnny Ruffin .05 .15
149 Deion Sanders .20 .50
150 Eddie Taubensee .05 .15
151 Dante Bichette .10 .30
152 Ellis Burks .10 .30
153 Joe Girardi .05 .15
154 Charlie Hayes .05 .15
155 Mike Kingery .05 .15
156 Steve Reed .05 .15
157 Kevin Ritz .05 .15
158 Bruce Ruffin .05 .15
159 Eric Young .05 .15
160 Kurt Abbott .05 .15
161 Chuck Carr .05 .15
162 Chris Hammond .05 .15
163 Bryan Harvey .05 .15
164 Terry Mathews .05 .15
165 Yorkis Perez .05 .15
166 Pat Rapp .05 .15
167 Gary Sheffield .10 .30
168 Dave Weathers .05 .15
169 Jeff Bagwell .20 .50
170 Ken Caminiti .10 .30
171 Doug Drabek .05 .15
172 Steve Finley .10 .30
173 John Hudek .05 .15
174 Todd Jones .05 .15
175 James Mouton .05 .15
176 Shane Reynolds .05 .15
177 Scott Servais .05 .15
178 Tom Candiotti .05 .15
179 Omar Daal .05 .15
180 Darren Dreifort .05 .15
181 Eric Karros .10 .30
182 Ramon J.Martinez .05 .15
183 Raul Mondesi .10 .30
184 Henry Rodriguez .05 .15
185 Todd Worrell .05 .15
186 Moises Alou .10 .30
187 Sean Berry .05 .15
188 Wil Cordero .05 .15
189 Jeff Fassero .05 .15
190 Darrin Fletcher .05 .15
191 Butch Henry .05 .15
192 Ken Hill .05 .15
193 Mel Rojas .05 .15
194 John Wetteland .10 .30
195 Bobby Bonilla .10 .30
196 Rico Brogna .05 .15
197 Bobby Jones .05 .15
198 Jeff Kent .10 .30
199 Josias Manzanillo .05 .15
200 Kelly Stinnett .05 .15
201 Ryan Thompson .05 .15
202 Jose Vizcaino .05 .15
203 Lenny Dykstra .10 .30
204 Jim Eisenreich .05 .15
205 Dave Hollins .05 .15
206 Mike Lieberthal .10 .30
207 Mickey Morandini .05 .15
208 Bobby Munoz .05 .15
209 Curt Schilling .10 .30
210 Heathcliff Slocumb .05 .15
211 David West .05 .15
212 Dave Clark .05 .15
213 Steve Cooke .05 .15
214 Midre Cummings .05 .15
215 Carlos Garcia .05 .15
216 Jeff King .05 .15
217 Jon Lieber .05 .15
218 Orlando Merced .05 .15
219 Don Slaught .05 .15
220 Rick White .05 .15
221 Rene Arocha .05 .15
222 Bernard Gilkey .05 .15
223 Brian Jordan .10 .30
224 Tom Pagnozzi .05 .15
225 Vicente Palacios .05 .15
226 Geronimo Pena .05 .15
227 Ozzie Smith .50 1.25
228 Allen Watson .05 .15
229 Mark Whiten .05 .15
230 Brad Ausmus .10 .30
231 Derek Bell .05 .15
232 Andy Benes .05 .15
233 Tony Gwynn .40 1.00
234 Joey Hamilton .05 .15
235 Luis Lopez .05 .15
236 Pedro A.Martinez .05 .15
237 Scott Sanders .05 .15
238 Eddie Williams .05 .15
239 Rod Beck .05 .15
240 Dave Burba .05 .15
241 Darren Lewis .05 .15
242 Kirt Manwaring .05 .15
243 Mark Portugal .05 .15
244 Darryl Strawberry .10 .30
245 Robby Thompson .05 .15
246 Wm.VanLandingham .05 .15
247 Matt Williams .10 .30
248 Checklist .05 .15
249 Checklist .05 .15
250 Checklist .05 .15
251 Harold Baines .10 .30
252 Bret Barberie .05 .15
253 Armando Benitez .05 .15
254 Mike Devereaux .05 .15
255 Leo Gomez .05 .15
256 Jamie Moyer .10 .30
257 Arthur Rhodes .05 .15
258 Cal Ripken 1.00 2.50
259 Luis Alicea .05 .15
260 Jose Canseco .20 .50
261 Scott Cooper .05 .15
262 Andre Dawson .10 .30
263 Mike Greenwell .05 .15
264 Aaron Sele .05 .15
265 Garret Anderson .10 .30
266 Chad Curtis .05 .15
267 Gary DiSarcina .05 .15
268 Chuck Finley .10 .30
269 Rex Hudler .05 .15
270 Andrew Lorraine .05 .15
271 Spike Owen .05 .15
272 Lee Smith .10 .30
273 Jason Bere .05 .15
274 Ozzie Guillen .10 .30
275 Norberto Martin .05 .15
276 Scott Ruffcorn .05 .15
277 Robin Ventura .10 .30
278 Carlos Baerga .05 .15
279 Jason Grimsley .05 .15
280 Dennis Martinez .10 .30
281 Charles Nagy .05 .15
282 Paul Sorrento .05 .15
283 Dave Winfield .10 .30
284 John Doherty .05 .15
285 Travis Fryman .10 .30
286 Kirk Gibson .10 .30
287 Lou Whitaker .10 .30
288 Gary Gaetti .10 .30
289 Tom Gordon .05 .15
290 Mark Gubicza .05 .15
291 Wally Joyner .10 .30
292 Mike Macfarlane .05 .15
293 Jeff Montgomery .05 .15
294 Jeff Cirillo .05 .15
295 Cal Eldred .05 .15
296 Pat Listach .05 .15
297 Jose Mercedes .05 .15
298 Dave Nilsson .05 .15
299 Duane Singleton .05 .15
300 Greg Vaughn .05 .15
301 Scott Erickson .05 .15
302 Denny Hocking .05 .15
303 Chuck Knoblauch .10 .30
304 Pat Mahomes .05 .15
305 Pedro Munoz .05 .15
306 Erik Schullstrom .05 .15
307 Jim Abbott .20 .50
308 Tony Fernandez .05 .15
309 Sterling Hitchcock .05 .15
310 Jim Leyritz .05 .15
311 Don Mattingly .75 2.00
312 Jack McDowell .05 .15
313 Melido Perez .05 .15
314 Bernie Williams .20 .50
315 Scott Brosius .10 .30
316 Dennis Eckersley .10 .30
317 Brent Gates .05 .15
318 Rickey Henderson .30 .75
319 Steve Karsay .05 .15
320 Steve Ontiveros .05 .15
321 Bill Taylor .05 .15
322 Todd Van Poppel .05 .15
323 Bob Welch .05 .15
324 Bobby Ayala .05 .15
325 Mike Blowers .05 .15
326 Jay Buhner .10 .30
327 Felix Fermin .05 .15
328 Tino Martinez .20 .50
329 Marc Newfield .05 .15
330 Greg Pirkl .05 .15
331 Alex Rodriguez .75 2.00
332 Kevin Brown .10 .30
333 John Burkett .05 .15
334 Jeff Frye .05 .15
335 Kevin Gross .05 .15
336 Dean Palmer .10 .30
337 Joe Carter .10 .30
338 Shawn Green .10 .30
339 Juan Guzman .05 .15
340 Mike Huff .05 .15
341 Al Leiter .10 .30
342 John Olerud .10 .30
343 Dave Stewart .10 .30
344 Todd Stottlemyre .05 .15
345 Steve Avery .05 .15
346 Jeff Blauser .05 .15
347 Chipper Jones .30 .75
348 Mike Kelly .05 .15
349 Ryan Klesko .10 .30
350 Javier Lopez .10 .30
351 Fred McGriff .20 .50
352 Jose Oliva .05 .15
353 Terry Pendleton .10 .30
354 Mike Stanton .05 .15
355 Tony Tarasco .05 .15
356 Mark Wohlers .05 .15
357 Jim Bullinger .05 .15
358 Shawon Dunston .05 .15
359 Mark Grace .20 .50
360 Derrick May .05 .15
361 Randy Myers .05 .15
362 Karl Rhodes .05 .15
363 Bret Boone .10 .30
364 Brian Dorsett .05 .15
365 Ron Gant .10 .30
366 Brian R.Hunter .05 .15
367 Hal Morris .05 .15
368 Jack Morris .10 .30
369 John Roper .05 .15
370 Reggie Sanders .10 .30
371 Pete Schourek .05 .15
372 John Smiley .05 .15
373 Marvin Freeman .05 .15
374 Andres Galarraga .10 .30
375 Mike Munoz .05 .15
376 David Nied .05 .15
377 Walt Weiss .05 .15
378 Greg Colbrunn .05 .15
379 Jeff Conine .10 .30
380 Charles Johnson .10 .30
381 Kurt Miller .05 .15
382 Robb Nen .10 .30
383 Benito Santiago .10 .30
384 Craig Biggio .20 .50
385 Tony Eusebio .05 .15
386 Luis Gonzalez .10 .30
387 Brian L.Hunter .05 .15
388 Darryl Kile .10 .30
389 Orlando Miller .05 .15
390 Phil Plantier .05 .15
391 Greg Swindell .05 .15
392 Billy Ashley .05 .15
393 Pedro Astacio .05 .15
394 Brett Butler .10 .30
395 Delino DeShields .05 .15
396 Orel Hershiser .10 .30
397 Garey Ingram .05 .15
398 Chan Ho Park .10 .30
399 Mike Piazza .50 1.25
400 Ismael Valdes .05 .15
401 Tim Wallach .05 .15
402 Cliff Floyd .10 .30
403 Marquis Grissom .10 .30
404 Mike Lansing .05 .15
405 Pedro Martinez .20 .50
406 Kirk Rueter .05 .15
407 Tim Scott .05 .15
408 Jeff Shaw .05 .15
409 Larry Walker .10 .30
410 Rondell White .10 .30
411 John Franco .10 .30
412 Todd Hundley .05 .15
413 Jason Jacome .05 .15
414 Joe Orsulak .05 .15
415 Bret Saberhagen .10 .30
416 David Segui .05 .15
417 Darren Daulton .10 .30
418 Mariano Duncan .05 .15
419 Tommy Greene .05 .15
420 Gregg Jefferies .05 .15
421 John Kruk .10 .30
422 Kevin Stocker .05 .15
423 Jay Bell .10 .30
424 Al Martin .05 .15
425 Denny Neagle .10 .30
426 Zane Smith .05 .15
427 Andy Van Slyke .20 .50
428 Paul Wagner .05 .15
429 Tom Henke .05 .15
430 Danny Jackson .05 .15
431 Ray Lankford .10 .30
432 John Mabry .05 .15
433 Bob Tewksbury .05 .15
434 Todd Zeile .05 .15
435 Andy Ashby .05 .15
436 Andujar Cedeno .05 .15
437 Donnie Elliott .05 .15
438 Bryce Florie .05 .15
439 Trevor Hoffman .10 .30
440 Melvin Nieves .05 .15
441 Bip Roberts .05 .15
442 Barry Bonds .75 2.00
443 Royce Clayton .05 .15
444 Mike Jackson .05 .15
445 John Patterson .05 .15
446 J.R. Phillips .05 .15
447 Bill Swift .05 .15
448 Checklist .05 .15
449 Checklist .05 .15
450 Checklist .05 .15

1995 Ultra Gold Medallion

This 450-card parallels the regular Ultra issue. These cards were issued one per pack and are differentiated from the regular cards by the Ultra logo being replaced by the "Ultra Gold Medallion Edition logo."

COMPLETE SET (450) 55.00 110.00
COMP. SERIES 1 (250) 30.00 60.00
COMP. SERIES 2 (200) 25.00 50.00
*STARS: 1.25X TO 3X BASIC CARDS

1995 Ultra All-Rookies

This 10-card standard-size set features rookies who emerged with an impact in 1994. These cards were inserted one in every five second series packs. The cards are numbered in the lower left as "X" of 10 and are sequenced in alphabetical order.

COMPLETE SET (10) 2.00 5.00
SER.2 STATED ODDS 1:5
*GOLD MEDAL: .75X TO 2X BASIC AR
GM SER.2 STATED ODDS 1:50
1 Cliff Floyd .30 .75
2 Chris Gomez .15 .40
3 Rusty Greer .30 .75
4 Bob Hamelin .15 .40
5 Joey Hamilton .15 .40
6 John Hudek .15 .40
7 Ryan Klesko .30 .75
8 Raul Mondesi .30 .75
9 Manny Ramirez .50 1.25
10 Steve Trachsel .15 .40

1995 Ultra All-Stars

This 20-card standard-size set feature players who are considered to be the top players in the game. Cards were inserted one in every four second series packs. The fronts feature two photos. The cards are numbered in the bottom left as "X" of 20 and are sequenced in alphabetical order.

COMPLETE SET (20) 6.00 15.00
SER.2 STATED ODDS 1:4
*GOLD MEDAL: .75X TO 2X BASIC ALL-STARS
GM SER.2 STATED ODDS 1:40
1 Moises Alou .20 .50
2 Albert Belle .20 .50
3 Craig Biggio .30 .75
4 Wade Boggs .30 .75
5 Barry Bonds 1.25 3.00
6 David Cone .20 .50
7 Ken Griffey Jr. .75 2.00
8 Tony Gwynn .60 1.50
9 Chuck Knoblauch .20 .50
10 Barry Larkin .30 .75
11 Kenny Lofton .20 .50
12 Greg Maddux .75 2.00
13 Fred McGriff .30 .75
14 Paul O'Neill .30 .75
15 Mike Piazza .75 2.00
16 Kirby Puckett .50 1.25
17 Cal Ripken 1.50 4.00
18 Ivan Rodriguez .30 .75
19 Frank Thomas .50 1.25
20 Matt Williams .20 .50

1995 Ultra Award Winners

Featuring players who won major awards in 1994, this 25-card standard-size set was inserted one in every four first series packs. The cards are numbered as "X" of 25.

COMPLETE SET (25) 8.00 20.00
SER.1 STATED ODDS 1:4
*GOLD MEDAL: .75X TO 2X BASIC BASIC AW
GM SER.1 STATED ODDS 1:40
1 Ivan Rodriguez .30 .75
2 Don Mattingly 1.25 3.00
3 Roberto Alomar .30 .75
4 Wade Boggs .30 .75
5 Omar Vizquel .30 .75
6 Ken Griffey Jr. .75 2.00
7 Kenny Lofton .20 .50
8 Devon White .20 .50
9 Mark Langston .08 .25
10 Tom Pagnozzi .08 .25
11 Jeff Bagwell .30 .75
12 Craig Biggio .30 .75
13 Matt Williams .20 .50
14 Barry Larkin .30 .75
15 Barry Bonds 1.25 3.00
16 Marquis Grissom .20 .50
17 Darren Lewis .08 .25
18 Greg Maddux .75 2.00
19 Frank Thomas .50 1.25
20 Jeff Bagwell .30 .75
21 David Cone .20 .50
22 Greg Maddux .75 2.00
23 Bob Hamelin .08 .25
24 Raul Mondesi .20 .50
25 Moises Alou .20 .50

1995 Ultra Gold Medallion Rookies

This 20-card standard-size set was available through a mail-in wrapper offer that expired 9/30/95. These players featured were all rookies in 1995 and were not included in the regular Ultra set. The design is essentially the same as the corresponding basic cards save for the medallion in the upper left-hand corner. The cards are numbered with an "M" prefix. The set is sequenced in alphabetical order.

COMPLETE SET (20) 3.00 8.00
M1 Manny Alexander .08 .25
M2 Edgardo Alfonzo .08 .25
M3 Jason Bates .08 .25
M4 Andres Berumen .08 .25
M5 Darren Bragg .08 .25
M6 Jamie Brewington .08 .25
M7 Jason Christiansen .08 .25
M8 Brad Clontz .08 .25
M9 Marty Cordova .08 .25
M10 Johnny Damon .30 .75
M11 Vaughn Eshelman .08 .25
M12 Chad Fonville .08 .25
M13 Curtis Goodwin .08 .25
M14 Tyler Green .08 .25
M15 Bobby Higginson .30 .75
M16 Jason Isringhausen .20 .50
M17 Hideo Nomo 1.00 2.50
M18 Jon Nunnally .08 .25
M19 Carlos Perez .20 .50
M20 Julian Tavarez .08 .25

1995 Ultra Golden Prospects

Inserted one every eight first series hobby packs, this 10-card standard-size set features potential impact players. The cards are numbered as "X" of 10 and are sequenced alphabetically.

COMPLETE SET (10) 5.00 10.00
SER.1 STATED ODDS 1:8 HOBBY
*GOLD MEDAL: .75X TO 2X BASIC PROSPECTS
GM SER.1 STATED ODDS 1:80
1 James Baldwin .20 .50
2 Alan Benes .20 .50
3 Armando Benitez .20 .50
4 Ray Durham .40 1.00
5 LaTroy Hawkins .20 .50
6 Brian L.Hunter .20 .50
7 Derek Jeter 1.50 4.00
8 Charles Johnson .40 1.00
9 Alex Rodriguez 1.50 4.00
10 Michael Tucker .20 .50

1995 Ultra Hitting Machines

This 10-card standard-size set features some of baseball's leading batters. Inserted one in every eight second-series retail packs, these horizontal cards have the player's photo against a background of the words "Hitting Machine." The cards are numbered as "X" of 10 in the upper right and are sequenced in alphabetical order.

COMPLETE SET (10) 5.00 12.00
SER.2 STATED ODDS 1:8 RETAIL
*GOLD MEDAL: .75X TO 2X BASIC HIT.MACH.
GM SER.2 STATED ODDS 1:80 RETAIL
1 Jeff Bagwell .30 .75
2 Albert Belle .20 .50
3 Dante Bichette .20 .50
4 Barry Bonds 1.25 3.00
5 Jose Canseco .30 .75
6 Ken Griffey Jr. .75 2.00
7 Tony Gwynn .60 1.50
8 Fred McGriff .30 .75
9 Mike Piazza .75 2.00
10 Frank Thomas .50 1.25

1995 Ultra Home Run Kings

This 10-card standard-size set featured the five leading home run hitters in each league. These cards were issued one every eight first series retail packs. The cards are numbered as "X" of 10 and are sequenced by league according to 1994's home run standings. A Barry Bonds sample card was issued to dealers to prior to the release of 1995 Ultra.

COMPLETE SET (10) 12.50 30.00
SER.1 STATED ODDS 1:8 RETAIL
*GOLD MEDAL: .75X TO 2X BASIC HR KINGS
GM SER.1 STATED ODDS 1:80 RETAIL
1 Ken Griffey Jr. 2.00 5.00
2 Frank Thomas 1.25 3.00
3 Albert Belle .50 1.25
4 Jose Canseco .75 2.00
5 Cecil Fielder .50 1.25
6 Matt Williams .50 1.25
7 Jeff Bagwell .75 2.00
8 Barry Bonds 3.00 8.00
9 Fred McGriff .75 2.00
10 Andres Galarraga .50 1.25
S8 Barry Bonds Sample .75 2.00

1995 Ultra League Leaders

This 10-card standard-size set was inserted one every three first series packs.

COMPLETE SET (10) 2.50 6.00
SER.1 STATED ODDS 1:3
*GOLD MEDAL: .75X TO 2X BASIC LL
GM SER.1 STATED ODDS 1:30
1 Paul O'Neill .30 .75
2 Kenny Lofton .20 .50
3 Jimmy Key .20 .50
4 Randy Johnson .50 1.25
5 Lee Smith .20 .50
6 Tony Gwynn .60 1.50
7 Craig Biggio .30 .75
8 Greg Maddux .75 2.00
9 Andy Benes .08 .25
10 John Franco .20 .50

1995 Ultra On-Base Leaders

This 10-card standard-size set features ten players who are constantly reaching base safely. These cards were inserted one in every eight pre-priced second series jumbo packs. The cards are numbered in the upper right corner as "X" of 10 and are sequenced in alphabetical order.

COMPLETE SET (10) 15.00 40.00
SER.2 STATED ODDS 1:8 JUMBO
*GOLD MEDAL: .75X TO 2X BASIC OBL
GM SER.2 STATED ODDS 1:80 JUMBO
1 Jeff Bagwell 1.25 3.00
2 Albert Belle .75 2.00
3 Craig Biggio 1.25 3.00
4 Wade Boggs 1.25 3.00
5 Barry Bonds 5.00 12.00
6 Will Clark 1.25 3.00
7 Tony Gwynn 2.50 6.00
8 David Justice .75 2.00
9 Paul O'Neill 1.25 3.00
10 Frank Thomas 2.00 5.00

1995 Ultra Power Plus

This six-card standard-size set was inserted one in every 37 first series packs. The six players portrayed are not only sluggers, but also excel at another part of the game. Unlike the 1995 Ultra cards and the other insert sets, these cards are 100 percent foil. The cards are numbered on the bottom right as "X" of 6 and are sequenced in alphabetical order by league.

COMPLETE SET (6) 10.00 25.00
SER.1 STATED ODDS 1:37
*GOLD MEDAL: .75X TO 2X BASIC PLUS
GM SER.1 STATED ODDS 1:370
1 Albert Belle .60 1.50
2 Ken Griffey Jr. 2.50 6.00
3 Frank Thomas 1.50 4.00
4 Jeff Bagwell 1.00 2.50
5 Barry Bonds 4.00 10.00
6 Matt Williams .60 1.50

1995 Ultra RBI Kings

This 10-card standard-size set was inserted into series one jumbo packs at a rate of one every 11. The cards are numbered in the upper left as "X" of 10 and are sequenced in order by league.

COMPLETE SET (10) 12.50 30.00
SER.1 STATED ODDS 1:11 JUMBO
*GOLD MEDAL: .75X TO 2X BASIC RBI KINGS
GM SER.1 STATED ODDS 1:110 JUMBO
1 Kirby Puckett 2.00 5.00
2 Joe Carter .75 2.00
3 Albert Belle .75 2.00
4 Frank Thomas 2.00 5.00
5 Julio Franco .40 1.00
6 Jeff Bagwell 1.25 3.00
7 Matt Williams .75 2.00
8 Dante Bichette .75 2.00
9 Fred McGriff 1.25 3.00
10 Mike Piazza 3.00 8.00

1995 Ultra Rising Stars

This nine-card standard-size set was inserted one every 37 second series packs. The cards are numbered "X" of 9 and are sequenced in alphabetical order.

COMPLETE SET (9) 15.00 40.00
SER.2 STATED ODDS 1:37
*GOLD MEDAL: .75X TO 2X BASIC RISING
GM SER.2 STATED ODDS 1:370
1 Moises Alou 1.25 3.00
2 Jeff Bagwell 2.00 5.00
3 Albert Belle 1.25 3.00
4 Juan Gonzalez 1.25 3.00
5 Chuck Knoblauch 1.25 3.00
6 Kenny Lofton 1.25 3.00
7 Raul Mondesi 1.25 3.00
8 Mike Piazza 5.00 12.00
9 Frank Thomas 3.00 8.00

1995 Ultra Second Year Standouts

This 15-card standard-size set was inserted into first series packs at a rate of not greater than one in six packs. The players in this set were all rookies in 1994 whom big things were expected from in 1995. The cards are numbered in the lower right as "X" of 15 and are sequenced in alphabetical order.

COMPLETE SET (15) 3.00 8.00
SER.1 STATED ODDS 1:6
*GOLD MEDAL: .75X TO 2X BASIC 2YS
GM SER.1 STATED ODDS 1:60
1 Cliff Floyd .50 1.25
2 Chris Gomez .25 .60
3 Rusty Greer .50 1.25
4 Darren Hall .25 .60
5 Bob Hamelin .25 .60
6 Joey Hamilton .25 .60
7 Jeffrey Hammonds .25 .60
8 John Hudek .25 .60
9 Ryan Klesko .50 1.25
10 Raul Mondesi .50 1.25
11 Manny Ramirez .75 2.00
12 Bill Risley .25 .60
13 Steve Trachsel .25 .60
14 W.VanLandingham .25 .60
15 Rondell White .50 1.25

1995 Ultra Strikeout Kings

This six-card standard-size set was inserted one every five second series packs. The cards are numbered as "X" of 6 and are sequenced in alphabetical order.

COMPLETE SET (6) 2.00 5.00
SER.2 STATED ODDS 1:5
*GOLD MEDAL: .75X TO 2X BASIC K KINGS
GM SER.2 STATED ODDS 1:50
1 Andy Benes .08 .25
2 Roger Clemens 1.00 2.50
3 Randy Johnson .50 1.25
4 Greg Maddux .75 2.00
5 Pedro Martinez .30 .75
6 Jose Rijo .08 .25

1996 Ultra Promos

This six card standard-size set previews the 1996 Ultra series. The Griffey card represents the basic set and has the same front and back as its regular issue counterpart. The Bonds and Ripken cards are from insert series and carry advertisements on their backs. The Gwynn and Lofton cards hail from the Season Crowns insert. Each card has the disclaimer "PROMOTIONAL SAMPLE" stamped diagonally across it.

COMPLETE SET (6) 3.20 8.00
SC2 Tony Gwynn Season Crown .60 1.50
SC4 Kenny Lofton Season Crown .30 .75
NNO Roberto Alomar Prime Leather .30 .75
NNO Ken Griffey Jr. .60 1.50
NNO Cal Ripken Prime Leather 1.25 3.00
NNO Barry Bonds HR King .50 1.25

1996 Ultra

The 1996 Ultra set, produced by Fleer, contains 600 standard-size cards. The cards were distributed in packs that included two inserts. One insert is a Gold Medallion parallel while the other insert comes from one of the many Ultra insert sets. The cards are thicker than their 1995 counterparts and the fronts feature the player in an action shot in full-bleed color. The cards are sequenced in alphabetical order within league and team order.

COMPLETE SET (600) 20.00 50.00
COMP.SERIES 1 (300) 10.00 25.00
COMP.SERIES 2 (300) 10.00 25.00
RIPKEN DUST AVAIL.VIA MAIL EXCHANGE
1 Manny Alexander .10 .30
2 Brady Anderson .10 .30
3 Bobby Bonilla .10 .30
4 Scott Erickson .10 .30
5 Curtis Goodwin .10 .30
6 Chris Hoiles .10 .30
7 Doug Jones .10 .30
8 Jeff Manto .10 .30
9 Mike Mussina .20 .50
10 Rafael Palmeiro .20 .50
11 Cal Ripken 1.00 2.50
12 Rick Aguilera .10 .30
13 Luis Alicea .10 .30
14 Stan Belinda .10 .30
15 Jose Canseco .20 .50
16 Roger Clemens .60 1.50
17 Mike Greenwell .10 .30
18 Mike Macfarlane .10 .30
19 Tim Naehring .10 .30
20 Troy O'Leary .10 .30
21 John Valentin .10 .30
22 Mo Vaughn .10 .30
23 Tim Wakefield .10 .30
24 Brian Anderson .10 .30
25 Garret Anderson .10 .30
26 Chili Davis .10 .30
27 Gary DiSarcina .10 .30
28 Jim Edmonds .10 .30
29 Jorge Fabregas .10 .30
30 Chuck Finley .10 .30
31 Mark Langston .10 .30
32 Troy Percival .10 .30
33 Tim Salmon .20 .50
34 Lee Smith .10 .30
35 Wilson Alvarez .10 .30
36 Ray Durham .10 .30
37 Alex Fernandez .10 .30
38 Ozzie Guillen .10 .30
39 Roberto Hernandez .10 .30
40 Lance Johnson .10 .30
41 Ron Karkovice .10 .30
42 Lyle Mouton .10 .30
43 Tim Raines .10 .30
44 Frank Thomas .30 .75
45 Carlos Baerga .10 .30
46 Albert Belle .10 .30
47 Orel Hershiser .10 .30
48 Kenny Lofton .10 .30
49 Dennis Martinez .10 .30
50 Jose Mesa .10 .30
51 Eddie Murray .30 .75
52 Chad Ogea .10 .30
53 Manny Ramirez .20 .50
54 Jim Thome .20 .50
55 Omar Vizquel .20 .50
56 Dave Winfield .10 .30
57 Chad Curtis .10 .30
58 Cecil Fielder .10 .30
59 John Flaherty .10 .30
60 Travis Fryman .10 .30
61 Chris Gomez .10 .30
62 Bob Higginson .10 .30
63 Felipe Lira .10 .30
64 Brian Maxcy .10 .30
65 Alan Trammell .10 .30
66 Lou Whitaker .10 .30
67 Kevin Appier .10 .30
68 Gary Gaetti .10 .30
69 Tom Goodwin .10 .30
70 Tom Gordon .10 .30
71 Jason Jacome .10 .30
72 Wally Joyner .10 .30
73 Brent Mayne .10 .30
74 Jeff Montgomery .10 .30
75 Jon Nunnally .10 .30
76 Joe Vitiello .10 .30
77 Ricky Bones .10 .30
78 Jeff Cirillo .10 .30
79 Mike Fetters .10 .30
80 Darryl Hamilton .10 .30
81 David Hulse .10 .30
82 Dave Nilsson .10 .30
83 Kevin Seitzer .10 .30
84 Steve Sparks .10 .30
85 B.J. Surhoff .10 .30
86 Jose Valentin .10 .30
87 Greg Vaughn .10 .30
88 Marty Cordova .10 .30
89 Chuck Knoblauch .10 .30
90 Pat Meares .10 .30
91 Pedro Munoz .10 .30
92 Kirby Puckett .30 .75
93 Brad Radke .10 .30
94 Scott Stahoviak .10 .30
95 Dave Stevens .10 .30
96 Mike Trombley .10 .30
97 Matt Walbeck .10 .30
98 Wade Boggs .20 .50
99 Russ Davis .10 .30
100 Jim Leyritz .10 .30
101 Don Mattingly .75 2.00
102 Jack McDowell .10 .30
103 Paul O'Neill .20 .50
104 Andy Pettitte .20 .50
105 Mariano Rivera .75 2.00
106 Ruben Sierra .10 .30
107 Darryl Strawberry .10 .30
108 John Wetteland .10 .30
109 Bernie Williams .20 .50
110 Geronimo Berroa .10 .30
111 Scott Brosius .10 .30
112 Dennis Eckersley .10 .30
113 Brent Gates .10 .30
114 Rickey Henderson .30 .75
115 Mark McGwire .75 2.00
116 Ariel Prieto .10 .30
117 Terry Steinbach .10 .30
118 Todd Stottlemyre .10 .30
119 Todd Van Poppel .10 .30
120 Steve Wojciechowski .10 .30
121 Rich Amaral .10 .30
122 Bobby Ayala .10 .30
123 Mike Blowers .10 .30
124 Chris Bosio .10 .30
125 Joey Cora .10 .30
126 Ken Griffey Jr. .50 1.25
127 Randy Johnson .30 .75
128 Edgar Martinez .20 .50
129 Tino Martinez .20 .50
130 Alex Rodriguez .60 1.50
131 Dan Wilson .10 .30
132 Will Clark .20 .50
133 Jeff Frye .10 .30
134 Benji Gil .10 .30
135 Juan Gonzalez .10 .30
136 Rusty Greer .10 .30
137 Mark McLemore .10 .30
138 Roger Pavlik .10 .30
139 Ivan Rodriguez .20 .50
140 Kenny Rogers .10 .30
141 Mickey Tettleton .10 .30
142 Roberto Alomar .20 .50
143 Joe Carter .10 .30
144 Tony Castillo .10 .30
145 Alex Gonzalez .10 .30
146 Shawn Green .10 .30
147 Pat Hentgen .10 .30
148 Sandy Martinez .10 .30
149 Paul Molitor .10 .30
150 John Olerud .10 .30
151 Ed Sprague .10 .30
152 Jeff Blauser .10 .30
153 Brad Clontz .10 .30
154 Tom Glavine .20 .50
155 Marquis Grissom .10 .30
156 Chipper Jones .30 .75
157 David Justice .10 .30
158 Ryan Klesko .10 .30
159 Javier Lopez .10 .30
160 Greg Maddux .50 1.25
161 John Smoltz .20 .50
162 Mark Wohlers .10 .30
163 Jim Bullinger .10 .30
164 Frank Castillo .10 .30
165 Shawon Dunston .10 .30
166 Kevin Foster .10 .30
167 Luis Gonzalez .10 .30
168 Mark Grace .20 .50
169 Rey Sanchez .10 .30
170 Scott Servais .10 .30
171 Sammy Sosa .30 .75
172 Ozzie Timmons .10 .30
173 Steve Trachsel .10 .30
174 Bret Boone .10 .30
175 Jeff Branson .10 .30
176 Jeff Brantley .10 .30
177 Dave Burba .10 .30
178 Ron Gant .10 .30
179 Barry Larkin .20 .50
180 Darren Lewis .10 .30
181 Mark Portugal .10 .30
182 Reggie Sanders .10 .30
183 Pete Schourek .10 .30
184 John Smiley .10 .30
185 Jason Bates .10 .30
186 Dante Bichette .10 .30
187 Ellis Burks .10 .30
188 Vinny Castilla .10 .30
189 Andres Galarraga .10 .30
190 Darren Holmes .10 .30
191 Armando Reynoso .10 .30
192 Kevin Ritz .10 .30
193 Bill Swift .10 .30
194 Larry Walker .10 .30
195 Kurt Abbott .10 .30
196 John Burkett .10 .30
197 Greg Colbrunn .10 .30
198 Jeff Conine .10 .30
199 Andre Dawson .10 .30
200 Chris Hammond .10 .30
201 Charles Johnson .10 .30
202 Robb Nen .10 .30
203 Terry Pendleton .10 .30
204 Quilvio Veras .10 .30
205 Jeff Bagwell .20 .50
206 Derek Bell .10 .30
207 Doug Drabek .10 .30
208 Tony Eusebio .10 .30
209 Mike Hampton .10 .30
210 Brian L. Hunter .10 .30
211 Todd Jones .10 .30
212 Orlando Miller .10 .30
213 James Mouton .10 .30
214 Shane Reynolds .10 .30
215 Dave Veres .10 .30
216 Billy Ashley .10 .30
217 Brett Butler .10 .30
218 Chad Fonville .10 .30
219 Todd Hollandsworth .10 .30
220 Eric Karros .10 .30
221 Ramon Martinez .10 .30
222 Raul Mondesi .10 .30
223 Hideo Nomo .30 .75
224 Mike Piazza .50 1.25
225 Kevin Tapani .10 .30
226 Ismael Valdes .10 .30
227 Todd Worrell .10 .30
228 Moises Alou .10 .30
229 Wil Cordero .10 .30
230 Jeff Fassero .10 .30
231 Darrin Fletcher .10 .30
232 Mike Lansing .10 .30
233 Pedro Martinez .20 .50
234 Carlos Perez .10 .30
235 Mel Rojas .10 .30
236 David Segui .10 .30
237 Tony Tarasco .10 .30
238 Rondell White .10 .30
239 Edgardo Alfonzo .10 .30
240 Rico Brogna .10 .30
241 Carl Everett .10 .30
242 Todd Hundley .10 .30
243 Butch Huskey .10 .30
244 Jason Isringhausen .10 .30
245 Bobby Jones .10 .30
246 Jeff Kent .10 .30
247 Bill Pulsipher .10 .30
248 Jose Vizcaino .10 .30
249 Ricky Bottalico .10 .30
250 Darren Daulton .10 .30
251 Jim Eisenreich .10 .30
252 Tyler Green .10 .30
253 Charlie Hayes .10 .30
254 Gregg Jefferies .10 .30
255 Tony Longmire .10 .30
256 Michael Mimbs .10 .30
257 Mickey Morandini .10 .30
258 Paul Quantrill .10 .30
259 Heathcliff Slocumb .10 .30
260 Jay Bell .10 .30
261 Jacob Brumfield .10 .30
262 A.Encarnacion RC .10 .30
263 John Ericks .10 .30
264 Mark Johnson .10 .30
265 Esteban Loaiza .10 .30
266 Al Martin .10 .30
267 Orlando Merced .10 .30
268 Dan Miceli .10 .30
269 Denny Neagle .10 .30
270 Brian Barber .10 .30
271 Scott Cooper .10 .30
272 Tripp Cromer .10 .30
273 Bernard Gilkey .10 .30
274 Tom Henke .10 .30
275 Brian Jordan .10 .30
276 John Mabry .10 .30
277 Tom Pagnozzi .10 .30
278 Mark Petkovsek .10 .30
279 Ozzie Smith .50 1.25
280 Andy Ashby .10 .30
281 Brad Ausmus .10 .30
282 Ken Caminiti .10 .30
283 Glenn Dishman .10 .30
284 Tony Gwynn .40 1.00
285 Joey Hamilton .10 .30
286 Trevor Hoffman .10 .30
287 Phil Plantier .10 .30
288 Jody Reed .10 .30
289 Eddie Williams .10 .30
290 Barry Bonds .75 2.00
291 Jamie Brewington RC .10 .30
292 Mark Carreon .10 .30
293 Royce Clayton .10 .30
294 Glenallen Hill .10 .30
295 Mark Leiter .10 .30
296 Kirt Manwaring .10 .30
297 J.R. Phillips .10 .30
298 Deion Sanders .20 .50
299 Wm. VanLandingham .10 .30
300 Matt Williams .10 .30
301 Roberto Alomar .20 .50
302 Armando Benitez .10 .30
303 Mike Devereaux .10 .30
304 Jeffrey Hammonds .10 .30
305 Jimmy Haynes .10 .30
306 Scott McClain .10 .30
307 Kent Mercker .10 .30
308 Randy Myers .10 .30
309 B.J. Surhoff .10 .30
310 Tony Tarasco .10 .30
311 David Wells .10 .30
312 Wil Cordero .10 .30
313 Alex Delgado .10 .30
314 Tom Gordon .10 .30
315 Dwayne Hosey .10 .30
316 Jose Malave .10 .30
317 Kevin Mitchell .10 .30
318 Jamie Moyer .10 .30
319 Aaron Sele .10 .30
320 Heathcliff Slocumb .10 .30
321 Mike Stanley .10 .30
322 Jeff Suppan .10 .30
323 Jim Abbott .20 .50
324 George Arias .10 .30
325 Todd Greene .10 .30
326 Bryan Harvey .10 .30
327 J.T. Snow .10 .30
328 Randy Velarde .10 .30
329 Tim Wallach .10 .30
330 Harold Baines .10 .30
331 Jason Bere .10 .30
332 Darren Lewis .10 .30
333 Norberto Martin .10 .30
334 Tony Phillips .10 .30
335 Bill Simas .10 .30
336 Chris Snopek .10 .30
337 Kevin Tapani .10 .30
338 Danny Tartabull .10 .30
339 Robin Ventura .10 .30
340 Sandy Alomar Jr. .10 .30
341 Julio Franco .10 .30
342 Jack McDowell .10 .30
343 Charles Nagy .10 .30
344 Julian Tavarez .10 .30
345 Kimera Bartee .10 .30
346 Greg Keagle .10 .30
347 Mark Lewis .10 .30
348 Jose Lima .10 .30
349 Melvin Nieves .10 .30
350 Mark Parent .10 .30
351 Eddie Williams .10 .30
352 Johnny Damon .20 .50
353 Sal Fasano .10 .30
354 Mark Gubicza .10 .30
355 Bob Hamelin .10 .30
356 Chris Haney .10 .30
357 Keith Lockhart .10 .30
358 Mike Macfarlane .10 .30
359 Jose Offerman .10 .30
360 Bip Roberts .10 .30
361 Michael Tucker .10 .30
362 Chuck Carr .10 .30
363 Bobby Hughes .10 .30
364 John Jaha .10 .30
365 Mark Loretta .10 .30
366 Mike Matheny .10 .30
367 Ben McDonald .10 .30
368 Matt Mieske .10 .30
369 Angel Miranda .10 .30
370 Fernando Vina .10 .30
371 Rick Aguilera .10 .30
372 Rich Becker .10 .30
373 LaTroy Hawkins .10 .30
374 Dave Hollins .10 .30
375 Roberto Kelly .10 .30
376 Matt Lawton RC .15 .40
377 Paul Molitor .10 .30
378 Dan Naulty .10 .30
379 Rich Robertson .10 .30
380 Frank Rodriguez .10 .30
381 David Cone .10 .30
382 Mariano Duncan .10 .30
383 Andy Fox .10 .30
384 Joe Girardi .10 .30
385 Dwight Gooden .10 .30
386 Derek Jeter 1.00 2.50
387 Pat Kelly .10 .30
388 Jimmy Key .10 .30
389 Matt Luke .10 .30
390 Tino Martinez .20 .50
391 Jeff Nelson .10 .30
392 Melido Perez .10 .30
393 Tim Raines .10 .30
394 Ruben Rivera .10 .30
395 Kenny Rogers .10 .30
396 Tony Batista RC .25 .60
397 Allen Battle .10 .30
398 Mike Bordick .10 .30
399 Steve Cox .10 .30
400 Jason Giambi .10 .30
401 Doug Johns .10 .30
402 Pedro Munoz .10 .30
403 Phil Plantier .10 .30
404 Scott Spiezio .10 .30
405 George Williams .10 .30
406 Ernie Young .10 .30
407 Darren Bragg .10 .30
408 Jay Buhner .10 .30
409 Norm Charlton .10 .30
410 Russ Davis .10 .30
411 Sterling Hitchcock .10 .30
412 Edwin Hurtado .10 .30
413 Raul Ibanez RC .75 2.00
414 Mike Jackson .10 .30
415 Luis Sojo .10 .30
416 Paul Sorrento .10 .30
417 Bob Wolcott .10 .30
418 Damon Buford .10 .30
419 Kevin Gross .10 .30
420 Darryl Hamilton UER .10 .30
421 Mike Henneman .10 .30
422 Ken Hill .10 .30
423 Dean Palmer .10 .30
424 Bobby Witt .10 .30
425 Tilson Brito RC .10 .30
426 Giovanni Carrara RC .10 .30
427 Domingo Cedeno .10 .30
428 Felipe Crespo .10 .30
429 Carlos Delgado .10 .30
430 Juan Guzman .10 .30
431 Erik Hanson .10 .30
432 Marty Janzen .10 .30
433 Otis Nixon .10 .30
434 Robert Perez .10 .30
435 Paul Quantrill .10 .30
436 Bill Risley .10 .30
437 Steve Avery .10 .30
438 Jermaine Dye .10 .30
439 Mark Lemke .10 .30
440 Marty Malloy RC .10 .30
441 Fred McGriff .20 .50
442 Greg McMichael .10 .30
443 Wonderful Monds RC .10 .30
444 Eddie Perez .10 .30
445 Jason Schmidt .20 .50
446 Terrell Wade .10 .30
447 Terry Adams .10 .30
448 Scott Bullett .10 .30
449 Robin Jennings .10 .30
450 Doug Jones .10 .30
451 Brooks Kieschnick .10 .30
452 Dave Magadan .10 .30
453 Jason Maxwell RC .10 .30
454 Brian McRae .10 .30
455 Rodney Myers RC .10 .30
456 Jaime Navarro .10 .30
457 Ryne Sandberg .50 1.25
458 Vince Coleman .10 .30
459 Eric Davis .10 .30
460 Steve Gibralter .10 .30
461 Thomas Howard .10 .30
462 Mike Kelly .10 .30
463 Hal Morris .10 .30
464 Eric Owens .10 .30
465 Jose Rijo .10 .30
466 Chris Sabo .10 .30
467 Eddie Taubensee .10 .30
468 Trenidad Hubbard .10 .30
469 Curt Leskanic .10 .30
470 Quinton McCracken .10 .30
471 Jayhawk Owens .10 .30
472 Steve Reed .10 .30
473 Bryan Rekar .10 .30
474 Bruce Ruffin .10 .30
475 Bret Saberhagen .10 .30
476 Walt Weiss .10 .30
477 Eric Young .10 .30
478 Kevin Brown .10 .30
479 Al Leiter .10 .30
480 Pat Rapp .10 .30
481 Gary Sheffield .10 .30
482 Devon White .10 .30
483 Bob Abreu .30 .75
484 Sean Berry .10 .30
485 Craig Biggio .20 .50
486 Jim Dougherty .10 .30
487 Richard Hidalgo .10 .30
488 Darryl Kile .10 .30
489 Derrick May .10 .30
490 Greg Swindell .10 .30
491 Rick Wilkins .10 .30
492 Mike Blowers .10 .30
493 Tom Candiotti .10 .30
494 Roger Cedeno .10 .30
495 Delino DeShields .10 .30
496 Greg Gagne .10 .30
497 Karim Garcia .10 .30
498 Wilton Guerrero RC .10 .30
499 Chan Ho Park .10 .30
500 Israel Alcantara .10 .30
501 Shane Andrews .10 .30
502 Yamil Benitez .10 .30
503 Cliff Floyd .10 .30
504 Mark Grudzielanek .10 .30
505 Ryan McGuire .10 .30
506 Sherman Obando .10 .30
507 Jose Paniagua .10 .30
508 Henry Rodriguez .10 .30
509 Kirk Rueter .10 .30
510 Juan Acevedo .10 .30
511 John Franco .10 .30
512 Bernard Gilkey .10 .30
513 Lance Johnson .10 .30
514 Rey Ordonez .10 .30
515 Robert Person .10 .30
516 Paul Wilson .10 .30
517 Toby Borland .10 .30
518 David Doster RC .10 .30
519 Lenny Dykstra .10 .30
520 Sid Fernandez .10 .30
521 Mike Grace RC .10 .30
522 Rich Hunter .10 .30
523 Benito Santiago .10 .30
524 Gene Schall .10 .30
525 Curt Schilling .10 .30
526 Kevin Sefcik RC .10 .30
527 Lee Tinsley .10 .30
528 David West .10 .30
529 Mark Whiten .10 .30
530 Todd Zeile .10 .30
531 Carlos Garcia .10 .30
532 Charlie Hayes .10 .30
533 Jason Kendall .10 .30
534 Jeff King .10 .30
535 Mike Kingery .10 .30
536 Nelson Liriano .10 .30
537 Dan Plesac .10 .30
538 Paul Wagner .10 .30
539 Luis Alicea .10 .30
540 David Bell .10 .30
541 Alan Benes .10 .30
542 Andy Benes .10 .30
543 Mike Busby RC .10 .30
544 Royce Clayton .10 .30
545 Dennis Eckersley .10 .30
546 Gary Gaetti .10 .30
547 Ron Gant .10 .30
548 Aaron Holbert .10 .30
549 Ray Lankford .10 .30
550 T.J. Mathews .10 .30
551 Willie McGee .10 .30
552 Miguel Mejia .10 .30
553 Todd Stottlemyre .10 .30
554 Sean Bergman .10 .30
555 Willie Blair .10 .30
556 Andujar Cedeno .10 .30
557 Steve Finley .10 .30
558 Rickey Henderson .30 .75
559 Wally Joyner .10 .30
560 Scott Livingstone .10 .30
561 Marc Newfield .10 .30
562 Bob Tewksbury .10 .30
563 Fernando Valenzuela .10 .30
564 Rod Beck .10 .30
565 Doug Creek .10 .30
566 Shawon Dunston .10 .30
567 O.Fernandez RC .10 .30
568 Stan Javier .10 .30
569 Marcus Jensen .10 .30
570 Steve Scarsone .10 .30
571 Robby Thompson .10 .30
572 Allen Watson .10 .30
573 Roberto Alomar STA .10 .30
574 Jeff Bagwell STA .10 .30
575 Albert Belle STA .10 .30
576 Wade Boggs STA .10 .30
577 Barry Bonds STA .40 1.00
578 Juan Gonzalez STA .10 .30
579 Ken Griffey Jr. STA .30 .75
580 Tony Gwynn STA .20 .50
581 Randy Johnson STA .20 .50
582 Chipper Jones STA .20 .50
583 Barry Larkin STA .10 .30
584 Kenny Lofton STA .10 .30
585 Greg Maddux STA .30 .75
586 Raul Mondesi STA .10 .30
587 Mike Piazza STA .30 .75
588 Cal Ripken STA .50 1.25
589 Tim Salmon STA .10 .30
590 Frank Thomas STA .20 .50
591 Mo Vaughn STA .10 .30
592 Matt Williams STA .10 .30
593 Marty Cordova RAW .10 .30
594 Jim Edmonds RAW .10 .30
595 Cliff Floyd RAW .10 .30
596 Chipper Jones RAW .20 .50
597 Ryan Klesko RAW .10 .30
598 Raul Mondesi RAW .10 .30
599 Manny Ramirez RAW .10 .30
600 Ruben Rivera RAW .10 .30
DD1 C. Ripken DD 20.00 50.00
Issued through dealers
Serial numbered to 2131
DD2 Cal Ripken DD 10.00 25.00
Issued through a wrapper redemption

1996 Ultra Gold Medallion

The 1996 Ultra Gold Medallion is a parallel to the regular Ultra issue. The cards were inserted one per pack in both first and second series. The card consists of a full gold foil paper with a full-color player cut out on top. Backs are identical to the regular cards.

COMPLETE SET (600)	80.00	200.00
COMP.SERIES 1 (300)	40.00	100.00
COMP.SERIES 2 (300)	40.00	100.00
*STARS: 1.25X TO 3X BASIC CARDS		
*ROOKIES: 1.25X TO 3X BASIC CARDS		

1996 Ultra Call to the Hall

Randomly inserted in second series packs at a rate of one in 24, this ten-card set features original illustrations of possible future Hall of Famers. The backs state why the player is a possible HOF.

COMPLETE SET (10)	25.00	60.00
SER.2 STATED ODDS 1:24		
*GOLD MEDAL: .75X TO 2X BASIC CALL		
GM SER.2 STATED ODDS 1:240		
1 Barry Bonds	5.00	12.00
2 Ken Griffey Jr.	3.00	8.00
3 Tony Gwynn	2.50	6.00
4 Rickey Henderson	2.00	5.00
5 Greg Maddux	3.00	8.00
6 Eddie Murray	2.00	5.00
7 Cal Ripken	6.00	15.00
8 Ryne Sandberg	3.00	8.00
9 Ozzie Smith	3.00	8.00
10 Frank Thomas	2.00	5.00

1996 Ultra Checklists

Randomly inserted in packs at a rate of one every four packs, this set of 20 standard-size cards features superstars of the game. Fronts are full-bleed color action photos of players with "Checklist" written in gold foil across the card. The horizontal backs are numbered and show the different card sets that are included in the Ultra line. The cards are sequenced in alphabetical order. A gold medallion parallel version of each card was issued.

COMPLETE SERIES 1 (10)	4.00	10.00
COMPLETE SERIES 2 (10)	3.00	8.00
STATED ODDS 1:4		
*GOLD MEDAL: .75X TO 2X BASIC CL		
GM STATED ODDS 1:40		
A1 Jeff Bagwell	.25	.60
A2 Barry Bonds	1.00	2.50
A3 Juan Gonzalez	.15	.40
A4 Ken Griffey Jr.	.60	1.50
A5 Chipper Jones	.40	1.00
A6 Mike Piazza	.60	1.50
A7 Manny Ramirez	.25	.60
A8 Cal Ripken	1.25	3.00
A9 Frank Thomas	.40	1.00
A10 Matt Williams	.15	.40
B1 Albert Belle	.15	.40
B2 Cecil Fielder	.15	.40
B3 Ken Griffey Jr.	.60	1.50
B4 Tony Gwynn	.50	1.25
B5 Derek Jeter	1.00	2.50
B6 Jason Kendall	.15	.40
B7 Ryan Klesko	.15	.40
B8 Greg Maddux	.60	1.50
B9 Cal Ripken	1.25	3.00
B10 Frank Thomas	.40	1.00

1996 Ultra Diamond Producers

This 12-card standard-size set highlights the achievements of Major League stars. The cards were randomly inserted at a rate of one in 20. The cards are sequenced in alphabetical order and there are also gold medallion versions of these cards.

COMPLETE SET (12)	25.00	60.00
SER.1 STATED ODDS 1:20		
*GOLD MEDAL: .75X TO 2X BASIC DIAMOND		
GM SER.1 STATED ODDS 1:200		
1 Albert Belle	.60	1.50
2 Barry Bonds	4.00	10.00
3 Ken Griffey Jr.	2.50	6.00
4 Tony Gwynn	2.00	5.00
5 Greg Maddux	2.50	6.00
6 Hideo Nomo	1.50	4.00
7 Mike Piazza	2.50	6.00
8 Kirby Puckett	1.50	4.00
9 Cal Ripken	5.00	12.00
10 Frank Thomas	1.50	4.00
11 Mo Vaughn	.60	1.50
12 Matt Williams	.60	1.50

1996 Ultra Fresh Foundations

Randomly inserted one every three packs, this 10-card standard-size set highlights the play of hot young players. The cards are sequenced in alphabetical order and there are also gold medallion versions of these cards.

COMPLETE SET (10)	1.25	3.00
SER.1 STATED ODDS 1:3		
*GOLD MEDAL: .75X TO 1.5X BASIC FRESH		
GM SER.1 STATED ODDS 1:30		
1 Garret Anderson	.10	.30
2 Marty Cordova	.10	.30
3 Jim Edmonds	.10	.30
4 Brian L.Hunter	.10	.30
5 Chipper Jones	.30	.75
6 Ryan Klesko	.10	.30
7 Raul Mondesi	.10	.30
8 Hideo Nomo	.30	.75
9 Manny Ramirez	.20	.50
10 Rondell White	.10	.30

1996 Ultra Golden Prospects

Randomly inserted at a rate of one in five hobby packs, this 10-card standard-size set features players who are likely to make it as major leaguers. The cards are sequenced in alphabetical order and there are also gold medallion versions of these cards.

COMPLETE SET (10)	2.00	5.00
SER.1 STATED ODDS 1:5 HOBBY		
*GOLD MEDAL: .75X TO 2X BASIC GOLDEN		
GM SER.1 STATED ODDS 1:50 HOBBY		
1 Yamil Benitez	.25	.60
2 Alberto Castillo	.25	.60
3 Roger Cedeno	.25	.60
4 Johnny Damon	.40	1.00
5 Micah Franklin	.25	.60
6 Jason Giambi	.25	.60
7 Jose Herrera	.25	.60
8 Derek Jeter	1.50	4.00
9 Kevin Jordan	.25	.60
10 Ruben Rivera	.25	.60

1996 Ultra Golden Prospects Hobby

Randomly inserted in hobby packs only at a rate of one in 72, this 15-card set is printed on crystal card stock and showcases players awaiting their Major League debut. The backs carry some information about their accomplishments in the Minor Leagues. A first year card of Tony Batista is featured within this set.

COMPLETE SET (15)	50.00	100.00
SER.2 STATED ODDS 1:72 HOBBY		
*GOLD MED: .75X TO 2X BASIC GOLD.HOB		
GM SER.2 STATED ODDS 1:720 HOBBY		
1 Bob Abreu	3.00	8.00
2 Israel Alcantara	1.50	4.00
3 Tony Batista	2.00	5.00
4 Mike Cameron	2.00	5.00
5 Steve Cox	1.50	4.00
6 Jermaine Dye	1.50	4.00
7 Wilton Guerrero	1.50	4.00
8 Richard Hidalgo	1.50	4.00
9 Raul Ibanez	2.50	6.00
10 Marty Janzen	1.50	4.00
11 Robin Jennings	1.50	4.00
12 Jason Maxwell	1.50	4.00
13 Scott McClain	1.50	4.00
14 Wonderful Monds	1.50	4.00
15 Chris Singleton	1.50	4.00

1996 Ultra Hitting Machines

Randomly inserted in second series packs at a rate of one in 288, this 10-card set features players who hit the ball hard and often.

COMPLETE SET (10)	40.00	100.00
SER.2 STATED ODDS 1:288		
*GOLD MEDAL: 1.25 TO 3X BASIC HIT.MACH.		
GM SER.2 STATED ODDS 1:2880		
1 Albert Belle	2.50	6.00
2 Barry Bonds	15.00	40.00
3 Juan Gonzalez	2.50	6.00
4 Ken Griffey Jr.	10.00	25.00
5 Edgar Martinez	4.00	10.00
6 Rafael Palmeiro	4.00	10.00
7 Mike Piazza	10.00	25.00
8 Tim Salmon	4.00	10.00
9 Frank Thomas	6.00	15.00
10 Matt Williams	2.50	6.00

1996 Ultra Home Run Kings

This 12-card standard-size set features leading power hitters. These cards were randomly inserted at a rate of one in 75 packs. The card fronts are thin wood with a color cut out of the player and HR KING printed diagonally in copper foil down the left side. The Fleer company was not happy with the final look of the card because of the transfer of the copper foil. Therefore all cards were made redemption cards. Backs of the cards have information about how to redeem the cards for replacement. The exchange offer expired on December 1, 1996. The cards are sequenced in alphabetical order.

COMPLETE SET (12)	20.00	50.00
SER.1 STATED ODDS 1:75		
*GOLD MEDAL: 4X TO 10X BASIC HR KINGS		
GM SER.1 STATED ODDS 1:750		
*REDEMPTION: .6X TO 1.5X BASIC HR KINGS		
ONE RDMP.CARD VIA MAIL PER HR CARD		
1 Albert Belle	.75	2.00
2 Dante Bichette	.75	2.00
3 Barry Bonds	5.00	12.00
4 Jose Canseco	1.25	3.00
5 Juan Gonzalez	.75	2.00
6 Ken Griffey Jr.	3.00	8.00
7 Mark McGwire	5.00	12.00
8 Manny Ramirez	1.25	3.00
9 Tim Salmon	1.25	3.00
10 Frank Thomas	2.00	5.00
11 Mo Vaughn	.75	2.00
12 Matt Williams	.75	2.00

1996 Ultra Home Run Kings Redemption Gold Medallion

These cards are parallel to the regular Home Run Kings Redemption cards. They are differentiated from the regular Home Run Kings Redemption cards by the Gold Medallion logo on the front of the cards.

*GM REDEMPTION CARDS: 4X TO 10X BASIC HOME RUN KINGS

1996 Ultra On-Base Leaders

Randomly inserted in second series packs at a rate of one in four, this 10-card set features players with consistently high on-base percentage.

COMPLETE SET (10)	2.00	5.00
SER.2 STATED ODDS 1:4		
*GOLD MEDAL: .75X TO 2X BASIC OBL		
GM SER.2 STATED ODDS 1:40		
1 Wade Boggs	.25	.60
2 Barry Bonds	1.00	2.50
3 Tony Gwynn	.50	1.25
4 Rickey Henderson	.40	1.00
5 Chuck Knoblauch	.15	.40
6 Edgar Martinez	.25	.60
7 Mike Piazza	.60	1.50
8 Tim Salmon	.25	.60
9 Frank Thomas	.40	1.00
10 Jim Thome	.25	.60

1996 Ultra Power Plus

Randomly inserted at a rate of one in ten packs, this 12-card standard-size set features top all-around players. The cards are sequenced in alphabetical order and gold medallion versions of these cards were also issued.

COMPLETE SET (12)	10.00	25.00
SER.1 STATED ODDS 1:10		
*GOLD MEDAL: .75X TO 2X BASIC PLUS		
GM SER.1 STATED ODDS 1:100		
1 Jeff Bagwell	.60	1.50
2 Barry Bonds	2.50	6.00
3 Ken Griffey Jr.	1.50	4.00
4 Raul Mondesi	.40	1.00
5 Rafael Palmeiro	.60	1.50
6 Mike Piazza	1.50	4.00
7 Manny Ramirez	.60	1.50
8 Tim Salmon	.60	1.50
9 Reggie Sanders	.40	1.00
10 Frank Thomas	1.00	2.50
11 Larry Walker	.40	1.00
12 Matt Williams	.40	1.00

1996 Ultra Prime Leather

Eighteen outstanding defensive players are featured in this standard-size set which is inserted approximately one in every eight packs. The cards are sequenced in alphabetical order and gold medallion versions of these cards were also issued.

COMPLETE SET (18)	10.00	25.00
SER.1 STATED ODDS 1:8		
*GOLD MEDAL: .75X TO 2X BASIC LEATHER		
GM SER.1 STATED ODDS 1:80		
1 Ivan Rodriguez	.60	1.50
2 Will Clark	.60	1.50
3 Roberto Alomar	.60	1.50
4 Cal Ripken	3.00	8.00
5 Wade Boggs	.60	1.50
6 Ken Griffey Jr.	1.50	4.00
7 Kenny Lofton	.40	1.00
8 Kirby Puckett	1.00	2.50
9 Tim Salmon	.60	1.50
10 Mike Piazza	1.50	4.00
11 Mark Grace	.60	1.50
12 Craig Biggio	.60	1.50
13 Barry Larkin	.60	1.50
14 Matt Williams	.40	1.00
15 Barry Bonds	2.50	6.00
16 Tony Gwynn	1.25	3.00
17 Brian McRae	.40	1.00
18 Raul Mondesi	.40	1.00
S4 Cal Ripken Jr Promo	3.00	8.00

1996 Ultra Rawhide

Randomly inserted in second series packs at a rate of one in eight, this 10-card set features leading defensive players.

COMPLETE SET (10)	6.00	15.00
SER.2 STATED ODDS 1:8		
*GOLD MEDAL: .75X TO 2X BASIC RAWHIDE		
GM SER.2 STATED ODDS 1:80		
1 Roberto Alomar	.40	1.00
2 Barry Bonds	1.50	4.00
3 Mark Grace	.40	1.00
4 Ken Griffey Jr.	1.00	2.50
5 Kenny Lofton	.25	.60
6 Greg Maddux	1.00	2.50
7 Raul Mondesi	.25	.60
8 Mike Piazza	1.00	2.50
9 Cal Ripken	2.00	5.00
10 Matt Williams	.25	.60

1996 Ultra RBI Kings

This 10-card standard-size set was randomly inserted at a rate of one in five retail packs. The cards are sequenced in alphabetical order and gold medallion versions of these cards were also issued.

COMPLETE SET (10)	12.50	30.00
SER.1 STATED ODDS 1:5 RETAIL		
*GOLD MEDAL: .75X TO 2X BASIC RBI KINGS		
GM SER.1 STATED ODDS 1:50 RETAIL		
1 Derek Bell	.75	2.00
2 Albert Belle	.75	2.00
3 Dante Bichette	.75	2.00
4 Barry Bonds	5.00	12.00
5 Jim Edmonds	.75	2.00
6 Manny Ramirez	1.25	3.00
7 Reggie Sanders	.75	2.00
8 Sammy Sosa	2.00	5.00
9 Frank Thomas	2.00	5.00
10 Mo Vaughn	.75	2.00

1996 Ultra Respect

Randomly inserted in second series packs at a rate of one in 18, this 10-card set features players who are well regarded by their peers for both on and off field activities.

COMPLETE SET (10)	20.00	50.00
SER.2 STATED ODDS 1:18		
*GOLD MEDAL: .75X TO 2X BASIC RESPECT		
GM SER.2 STATED ODDS 1:180		
1 Joe Carter	.60	1.50
2 Ken Griffey Jr.	2.50	6.00
3 Tony Gwynn	2.00	5.00
4 Greg Maddux	2.50	6.00
5 Eddie Murray	1.50	4.00
6 Kirby Puckett	1.50	4.00
7 Cal Ripken	5.00	12.00
8 Ryne Sandberg	2.50	6.00
9 Frank Thomas	1.50	4.00
10 Mo Vaughn	.60	1.50

1996 Ultra Rising Stars

Randomly inserted in second series packs at a rate of one in four, this 10-card set features leading players of tomorrow.

COMPLETE SET (10)	1.50	4.00
SER.2 STATED ODDS 1:4		
*GOLD MEDAL: .75X TO 2X BASIC RISING		
GM SER.2 STATED ODDS 1:40		
1 Garret Anderson	.10	.30
2 Marty Cordova	.10	.30
3 Jim Edmonds	.10	.30
4 Cliff Floyd	.10	.30
5 Brian L.Hunter	.10	.30
6 Chipper Jones	.30	.75
7 Ryan Klesko	.10	.30
8 Hideo Nomo	.30	.75
9 Manny Ramirez	.20	.50
10 Rondell White	.10	.30

1996 Ultra Season Crowns

This set features ten award winners and stat leaders. The cards were randomly inserted at a rate of one in ten. The clear acetate cards feature a full-color player cutout against a background of colored foliage and laurels.

COMPLETE SET (10)	12.50	30.00
SER.1 STATED ODDS 1:10		
*GOLD MEDAL: .75X TO 2X BASIC CROWNS		
GM SER.1 STATED ODDS 1:100		
1 Barry Bonds	2.50	6.00
2 Tony Gwynn	1.25	3.00
3 Randy Johnson	1.00	2.50
4 Kenny Lofton	.40	1.00
5 Greg Maddux	1.50	4.00
6 Edgar Martinez	.60	1.50
7 Hideo Nomo	1.00	2.50
8 Cal Ripken	3.00	8.00
9 Frank Thomas	1.00	2.50
10 Tim Wakefield	.40	1.00

1996 Ultra Thunderclap

Randomly inserted one in 72 retail packs, these cards feature the leading power hitters.

COMPLETE SET (20)	40.00	100.00
SER.2 STATED ODDS 1:72 RETAIL		
*GOLD MEDAL: 1.25X TO 3X BASIC THUNDER		
GM SER.2 STATED ODDS 1:720 RETAIL		
1 Albert Belle	2.00	5.00
2 Barry Bonds	12.50	30.00
3 Bobby Bonilla	2.00	5.00
4 Jose Canseco	3.00	8.00
5 Joe Carter	2.00	5.00
6 Will Clark	3.00	8.00
7 Andre Dawson	2.00	5.00
8 Cecil Fielder	2.00	5.00
9 Andres Galarraga	2.00	5.00
10 Juan Gonzalez	2.00	5.00
11 Ken Griffey Jr.	8.00	20.00
12 Fred McGriff	3.00	8.00
13 Mark McGwire	12.50	30.00
14 Eddie Murray	5.00	12.00
15 Rafael Palmeiro	3.00	8.00
16 Kirby Puckett	5.00	12.00
17 Cal Ripken	15.00	40.00
18 Ryne Sandberg	10.00	25.00
19 Frank Thomas	5.00	12.00
20 Matt Williams	2.00	5.00

1997 Ultra

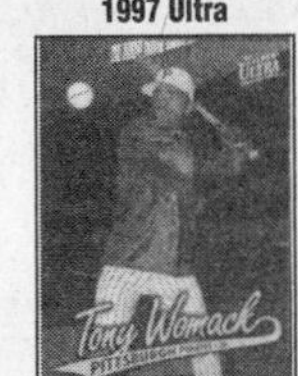

The 1997 Ultra was issued in two series totalling 553 cards. The first series consisted of 300 cards with the second containing 253. The 10-card packs had a suggested retail price of 2.49 each. Each pack had two insert cards, with one insert being a gold medallion parallel and the other insert being from one of serveral other insert sets. The fronts features borderless color action player photos with career statistics on the backs. As in most Fleer produced sets, the cards are arranged in alphabetical order by league, player and team. Second series retail packs contained only cards 301-450 while second series hobby packs contained all cards from 301-553. Rookie Cards include Jose Cruz Jr., Brian Giles and Fernando Tatis.

COMPLETE SET (553)	55.00	110.00
COMP.SERIES 1 (300)	15.00	30.00
COMP.SERIES 2 (253)	40.00	80.00
COMMON CARD (1-553)	.10	.30
COMMON RC	.15	.40
1 Roberto Alomar	.20	.50
2 Brady Anderson	.10	.30
3 Rocky Coppinger	.10	.30
4 Jeffrey Hammonds	.10	.30
5 Chris Hoiles	.10	.30
6 Eddie Murray	.30	.75
7 Mike Mussina	.20	.50
8 Jimmy Myers	.10	.30
9 Randy Myers	.10	.30
10 Arthur Rhodes	.10	.30
11 Cal Ripken	1.00	2.50
12 Jose Canseco	.20	.50
13 Roger Clemens	.60	1.50
14 Tom Gordon	.10	.30
15 Jose Malave	.10	.30
16 Tim Naehring	.10	.30
17 Troy O'Leary	.10	.30
18 Bill Selby	.10	.30
19 Heathcliff Slocumb	.10	.30
20 Mike Stanley	.10	.30
21 Mo Vaughn	.10	.30
22 Garret Anderson	.10	.30
23 George Arias	.10	.30
24 Chili Davis	.10	.30
25 Jim Edmonds	.10	.30
26 Darin Erstad	.10	.30
27 Chuck Finley	.10	.30
28 Todd Greene	.10	.30
29 Troy Percival	.10	.30
30 Tim Salmon	.20	.50
31 Jeff Schmidt	.10	.30
32 Randy Velarde	.10	.30
33 Shad Williams	.10	.30
34 Wilson Alvarez	.10	.30
35 Harold Baines	.10	.30
36 James Baldwin	.10	.30
37 Mike Cameron	.10	.30
38 Ray Durham	.10	.30
39 Ozzie Guillen	.10	.30
40 Roberto Hernandez	.10	.30
41 Darren Lewis	.10	.30
42 Jose Munoz	.10	.30
43 Tony Phillips	.10	.30
44 Frank Thomas	.30	.75
45 Sandy Alomar Jr.	.10	.30
46 Albert Belle	.10	.30
47 Mark Carreon	.10	.30
48 Julio Franco	.10	.30
49 Orel Hershiser	.10	.30
50 Kenny Lofton	.10	.30
51 Jack McDowell	.10	.30
52 Jose Mesa	.10	.30
53 Charles Nagy	.10	.30
54 Manny Ramirez	.20	.50
55 Julian Tavarez	.10	.30
56 Omar Vizquel	.20	.50
57 Raul Casanova	.10	.30
58 Tony Clark	.10	.30
59 Travis Fryman	.10	.30
60 Bob Higginson	.10	.30
61 Melvin Nieves	.10	.30
62 Curtis Pride	.10	.30
63 Justin Thompson	.10	.30
64 Alan Trammell	.10	.30
65 Kevin Appier	.10	.30
66 Johnny Damon	.20	.50
67 Keith Lockhart	.10	.30
68 Jeff Montgomery	.10	.30
69 Jose Offerman	.10	.30
70 Bip Roberts	.10	.30
71 Jose Rosado	.10	.30
72 Chris Stynes	.10	.30
73 Mike Sweeney	.10	.30
74 Jeff Cirillo	.10	.30
75 Jeff D'Amico	.10	.30
76 John Jaha	.10	.30
77 Scott Karl	.10	.30
78 Mike Matheny	.10	.30
79 Ben McDonald	.10	.30
80 Matt Mieske	.10	.30
81 Marc Newfield	.10	.30
82 Dave Nilsson	.10	.30
83 Jose Valentin	.10	.30
84 Fernando Vina	.10	.30
85 Rick Aguilera	.10	.30
86 Marty Cordova	.10	.30
87 Chuck Knoblauch	.10	.30
88 Matt Lawton	.10	.30
89 Pat Meares	.10	.30
90 Paul Molitor	.10	.30
91 Greg Myers	.10	.30
92 Dan Naulty	.10	.30
93 Kirby Puckett	.30	.75
94 Frank Rodriguez	.10	.30
95 Wade Boggs	.20	.50
96 Cecil Fielder	.10	.30
97 Joe Girardi	.10	.30
98 Dwight Gooden	.10	.30
99 Derek Jeter	.75	2.00
100 Tino Martinez	.20	.50
101 Ramiro Mendoza RC	.10	.30
102 Andy Pettitte	.20	.50
103 Mariano Rivera	.30	.75
104 Ruben Rivera	.10	.30
105 Kenny Rogers	.10	.30
106 Darryl Strawberry	.10	.30
107 Bernie Williams	.20	.50
108 Tony Batista	.10	.30
109 Geronimo Berroa	.10	.30
110 Bobby Chouinard	.10	.30
111 Brent Gates	.10	.30
112 Jason Giambi	.10	.30
113 Damon Mashore	.10	.30
114 Mark McGwire	.75	2.00
115 Scott Spiezio	.10	.30
116 John Wasdin	.10	.30
117 Steve Wojciechowski	.10	.30
118 Ernie Young	.10	.30
119 Norm Charlton	.10	.30
120 Joey Cora	.10	.30
121 Ken Griffey Jr.	.50	1.25
122 Sterling Hitchcock	.10	.30
123 Raul Ibanez	.10	.30
124 Randy Johnson	.30	.75
125 Edgar Martinez	.20	.50
126 Alex Rodriguez	.50	1.25
127 Matt Wagner	.10	.30
128 Bob Wells	.10	.30
129 Dan Wilson	.10	.30
130 Will Clark	.20	.50
131 Kevin Elster	.10	.30
132 Juan Gonzalez	.10	.30
133 Rusty Greer	.10	.30
134 Darryl Hamilton	.10	.30
135 Mike Henneman	.10	.30
136 Ken Hill	.10	.30
137 Mark McLemore	.10	.30
138 Dean Palmer	.10	.30
139 Roger Pavlik	.10	.30
140 Ivan Rodriguez	.20	.50
141 Joe Carter	.10	.30
142 Carlos Delgado	.10	.30
143 Alex Gonzalez	.10	.30
144 Juan Guzman	.10	.30
145 Pat Hentgen	.10	.30
146 Marty Janzen	.10	.30
147 Otis Nixon	.10	.30
148 Charlie O'Brien	.10	.30
149 John Olerud	.10	.30
150 Robert Perez	.10	.30
151 Jermaine Dye	.10	.30
152 Tom Glavine	.20	.50
153 Andruw Jones	.20	.50
154 Chipper Jones	.30	.75
155 Ryan Klesko	.10	.30
156 Javier Lopez	.10	.30
157 Greg Maddux	.50	1.25
158 Fred McGriff	.20	.50
159 Wonderful Monds	.10	.30
160 John Smoltz	.20	.50
161 Terrell Wade	.10	.30
162 Mark Wohlers	.10	.30
163 Brant Brown	.10	.30
164 Mark Grace	.20	.50
165 Tyler Houston	.10	.30
166 Robin Jennings	.10	.30
167 Jason Maxwell	.10	.30
168 Ryne Sandberg	.50	1.25
169 Sammy Sosa	.30	.75
170 Amaury Telemaco	.10	.30
171 Steve Trachsel	.10	.30
172 Pedro Valdes RC	.10	.30
173 Tim Belk	.10	.30
174 Bret Boone	.10	.30
175 Jeff Brantley	.10	.30
176 Eric Davis	.10	.30
177 Barry Larkin	.20	.50
178 Chad Mottola	.10	.30
179 Mark Portugal	.10	.30
180 Reggie Sanders	.10	.30
181 John Smiley	.10	.30
182 Eddie Taubensee	.10	.30
183 Dante Bichette	.10	.30
184 Ellis Burks	.10	.30
185 Andres Galarraga	.10	.30
186 Curt Leskanic	.10	.30
187 Quinton McCracken	.10	.30
188 Jeff Reed	.10	.30
189 Kevin Ritz	.10	.30
190 Walt Weiss	.10	.30
191 Jamey Wright	.10	.30
192 Eric Young	.10	.30
193 Kevin Brown	.10	.30
194 Luis Castillo	.10	.30
195 Jeff Conine	.10	.30
196 Andre Dawson	.10	.30
197 Charles Johnson	.10	.30
198 Al Leiter	.10	.30
199 Ralph Milliard	.10	.30
200 Robb Nen	.10	.30
201 Edgar Renteria	.10	.30
202 Gary Sheffield	.10	.30
203 Bob Abreu	.20	.50
204 Jeff Bagwell	.20	.50
205 Derek Bell	.10	.30
206 Sean Berry	.10	.30
207 Richard Hidalgo	.10	.30
208 Todd Jones	.10	.30
209 Darryl Kile	.10	.30
210 Orlando Miller	.10	.30
211 Shane Reynolds	.10	.30
212 Billy Wagner	.10	.30
213 Donne Wall	.10	.30
214 Roger Cedeno	.10	.30
215 Greg Gagne	.10	.30
216 Karim Garcia	.10	.30
217 Wilton Guerrero	.10	.30
218 Todd Hollandsworth	.10	.30
219 Ramon Martinez	.10	.30
220 Raul Mondesi	.10	.30
221 Hideo Nomo	.30	.75
222 Chan Ho Park	.10	.30
223 Mike Piazza	.50	1.25
224 Ismael Valdes	.10	.30
225 Moises Alou	.10	.30
226 Derek Aucoin	.10	.30
227 Yamil Benitez	.10	.30
228 Jeff Fassero	.10	.30
229 Darrin Fletcher	.10	.30
230 Mark Grudzielanek	.10	.30
231 Barry Manuel	.10	.30
232 Pedro Martinez	.20	.50
233 Henry Rodriguez	.10	.30
234 Ugueth Urbina	.10	.30
235 Rondell White	.10	.30
236 Carlos Baerga	.10	.30
237 John Franco	.10	.30
238 Bernard Gilkey	.10	.30
239 Todd Hundley	.10	.30
240 Butch Huskey	.10	.30
241 Jason Isringhausen	.10	.30
242 Lance Johnson	.10	.30
243 Bobby Jones	.10	.30
244 Alex Ochoa	.10	.30
245 Rey Ordonez	.10	.30
246 Paul Wilson	.10	.30
247 Ron Blazier	.10	.30
248 David Doster	.10	.30
249 Jim Eisenreich	.10	.30
250 Mike Grace	.10	.30
251 Mike Lieberthal	.10	.30
252 Wendell Magee	.10	.30
253 Mickey Morandini	.10	.30
254 Ricky Otero	.10	.30
255 Scott Rolen	.20	.50
256 Curt Schilling	.10	.30
257 Todd Zeile	.10	.30
258 Jermaine Allensworth	.10	.30
259 Trey Beamon	.10	.30
260 Carlos Garcia	.10	.30
261 Mark Johnson	.10	.30
262 Jason Kendall	.10	.30
263 Jeff King	.10	.30
264 Al Martin	.10	.30
265 Denny Neagle	.10	.30
266 Matt Ruebel	.10	.30
267 Marc Wilkins	.10	.30
268 Alan Benes	.10	.30
269 Dennis Eckersley	.10	.30
270 Ron Gant	.10	.30
271 Aaron Holbert	.10	.30
272 Brian Jordan	.10	.30
273 Ray Lankford	.10	.30
274 John Mabry	.10	.30
275 T.J. Mathews	.10	.30
276 Ozzie Smith	.50	1.25
277 Todd Stottlemyre	.10	.30

278 Mark Sweeney .10 .30
279 Andy Ashby .10 .30
280 Steve Finley .10 .30
281 John Flaherty .10 .30
282 Chris Gomez .10 .30
283 Tony Gwynn .40 1.00
284 Joey Hamilton .10 .30
285 Rickey Henderson .30 .75
286 Trevor Hoffman .10 .30
287 Jason Thompson .10 .30
288 Fernando Valenzuela .10 .30
289 Greg Vaughn .10 .30
290 Barry Bonds .75 2.00
291 Jay Canizaro .10 .30
292 Jacob Cruz .10 .30
293 Shawon Dunston .10 .30
294 Shawn Estes .10 .30
295 Mark Gardner .10 .30
296 Marcus Jensen .10 .30
297 Bill Mueller RC .50 1.25
298 Chris Singleton .10 .30
299 Allen Watson .10 .30
300 Matt Williams .10 .30
301 Rod Beck .10 .30
302 Jay Bell .10 .30
303 Shawon Dunston .10 .30
304 Reggie Jefferson .10 .30
305 Darren Oliver .10 .30
306 Benito Santiago .10 .30
307 Gerald Williams .10 .30
308 Damon Buford .10 .30
309 Jeromy Burnitz .10 .30
310 Sterling Hitchcock .10 .30
311 Dave Hollins .10 .30
312 Mel Rojas .10 .30
313 Robin Ventura .10 .30
314 David Wells .10 .30
315 Cal Eldred .10 .30
316 Gary Gaetti .10 .30
317 John Hudek .10 .30
318 Brian Johnson .10 .30
319 Denny Neagle .10 .30
320 Larry Walker .10 .30
321 Russ Davis .10 .30
322 Delino DeShields .10 .30
323 Charlie Hayes .10 .30
324 Jermaine Dye .10 .30
325 John Ericks .10 .30
326 Jeff Fassero .10 .30
327 Nomar Garciaparra .50 1.25
328 Willie Greene .10 .30
329 Greg McMichael .10 .30
330 Damion Easley .10 .30
331 Ricky Bones .10 .30
332 John Burkett .10 .30
333 Royce Clayton .10 .30
334 Greg Colbrunn .10 .30
335 Tony Eusebio .10 .30
336 Gregg Jefferies .10 .30
337 Wally Joyner .10 .30
338 Jim Leyritz .10 .30
339 Paul O'Neill .20 .50
340 Bruce Ruffin .10 .30
341 Michael Tucker .10 .30
342 Andy Benes .10 .30
343 Craig Biggio .20 .50
344 Rex Hudler .10 .30
345 Brad Radke .10 .30
346 Deion Sanders .20 .50
347 Moises Alou .10 .30
348 Brad Ausmus .10 .30
349 Armando Benitez .10 .30
350 Mark Gubicza .10 .30
351 Terry Steinbach .10 .30
352 Mark Whiten .10 .30
353 Ricky Bottalico .10 .30
354 Brian Giles RC .60 1.50
355 Eric Karros .10 .30
356 Jimmy Key .10 .30
357 Carlos Perez .10 .30
358 Alex Fernandez .10 .30
359 J.T. Snow .10 .30
360 Bobby Bonilla .10 .30
361 Scott Brosius .10 .30
362 Greg Swindell .10 .30
363 Jose Vizcaino .10 .30
364 Matt Williams .10 .30
365 Darren Daulton .10 .30
366 Shane Andrews .10 .30
367 Jim Eisenreich .10 .30
368 Ariel Prieto .10 .30
369 Bob Tewksbury .10 .30
370 Mike Bordick .10 .30
371 Rheal Cormier .10 .30
372 Cliff Floyd .10 .30
373 David Justice .10 .30
374 John Wetteland .10 .30
375 Mike Blowers .10 .30
376 Jose Canseco .20 .50
377 Roger Clemens .60 1.50
378 Kevin Mitchell .10 .30
379 Todd Zeile .10 .30
380 Jim Thome .20 .50
381 Turk Wendell .10 .30
382 Rico Brogna .10 .30
383 Eric Davis .10 .30
384 Mike Lansing .10 .30
385 Devon White .10 .30
386 Marquis Grissom .10 .30
387 Todd Worrell .10 .30
388 Jeff Kent .10 .30
389 Mickey Tettleton .10 .30
390 Steve Avery .10 .30
391 David Cone .10 .30
392 Scott Cooper .10 .30
393 Lee Stevens .10 .30
394 Kevin Elster .10 .30
395 Tom Goodwin .10 .30
396 Shawn Green .10 .30
397 Pete Harnisch .10 .30
398 Eddie Murray .30 .75
399 Joe Randa .10 .30
400 Scott Sanders .10 .30
401 John Valentin .10 .30
402 Todd Jones .10 .30
403 Terry Adams .10 .30
404 Brian Hunter .10 .30
405 Pat Listach .10 .30
406 Kenny Lofton .10 .30
407 Hal Morris .10 .30
408 Ed Sprague .10 .30
409 Rich Becker .10 .30
410 Edgardo Alfonzo .10 .30
411 Albert Belle .10 .30
412 Jeff King .10 .30
413 Kirt Manwaring .10 .30
414 Jason Schmidt .10 .30
415 Allen Watson .10 .30
416 Lee Tinsley .10 .30
417 Brett Butler .10 .30
418 Carlos Garcia .10 .30
419 Mark Lemke .10 .30
420 Jaime Navarro .10 .30
421 David Segui .10 .30
422 Ruben Sierra .10 .30
423 B.J. Surhoff .10 .30
424 Julian Tavarez .10 .30
425 Billy Taylor .10 .30
426 Ken Caminiti .10 .30
427 Chuck Carr .10 .30
428 Benji Gil .10 .30
429 Terry Mulholland .10 .30
430 Mike Stanton .10 .30
431 Wil Cordero .10 .30
432 Chili Davis .10 .30
433 Mariano Duncan .10 .30
434 Orlando Merced .10 .30
435 Kent Mercker .10 .30
436 John Olerud .10 .30
437 Quilvio Veras .10 .30
438 Mike Fetters .10 .30
439 Glenallen Hill .10 .30
440 Bill Swift .10 .30
441 Tim Wakefield .10 .30
442 Pedro Astacio .10 .30
443 Vinny Castilla .10 .30
444 Doug Drabek .10 .30
445 Alan Embree .10 .30
446 Lee Smith .10 .30
447 Darryl Hamilton .10 .30
448 Brian McRae .10 .30
449 Mike Timlin .10 .30
450 Bob Wickman .10 .30
451 Jason Dickson .10 .30
452 Chad Curtis .10 .30
453 Mark Leiter .10 .30
454 Damon Berryhill .10 .30
455 Kevin Orie .10 .30
456 Dave Burba .10 .30
457 Chris Holt .10 .30
458 Ricky Ledee RC .15 .40
459 Mike Devereaux .10 .30
460 Pokey Reese .10 .30
461 Tim Raines .10 .30
462 Ryan Jones .10 .30
463 Shane Mack .10 .30
464 Darren Dreifort .10 .30
465 Mark Parent .10 .30
466 Mark Portugal .10 .30
467 Dante Powell .10 .30
468 Craig Grebeck .10 .30
469 Ron Villone .10 .30
470 Dmitri Young .10 .30
471 Shannon Stewart .10 .30
472 Rick Helling .10 .30
473 Bill Haselman .10 .30
474 Albie Lopez .10 .30
475 Glendon Rusch .10 .30
476 Derrick May .10 .30
477 Chad Ogea .10 .30
478 Kirk Rueter .10 .30
479 Chris Hammond .10 .30
480 Russ Johnson .10 .30
481 James Mouton .10 .30
482 Mike Macfarlane .10 .30
483 Scott Ruffcorn .10 .30
484 Jeff Frye .10 .30
485 Richie Sexson .10 .30
486 Emil Brown RC .15 .40
487 Desi Wilson .10 .30
488 Brent Gates .10 .30
489 Tony Graffanino .10 .30
490 Dan Miceli .10 .30
491 Orlando Cabrera RC .40 1.00
492 Tony Womack RC .15 .40
493 Jerome Walton .10 .30
494 Mark Thompson .10 .30
495 Jose Guillen .10 .30
496 Willie Blair .10 .30
497 T.J. Staton RC .15 .40
498 Scott Kamieniecki .10 .30
499 Vince Coleman .10 .30
500 Jeff Abbott .10 .30
501 Chris Widger .10 .30
502 Kevin Tapani .10 .30
503 Carlos Castillo RC .15 .40
504 Luis Gonzalez .10 .30
505 Tim Belcher .10 .30
506 Armando Reynoso .10 .30
507 Jamie Moyer .10 .30
508 Randall Simon RC .15 .40
509 Vladimir Guerrero .30 .75
510 Wady Almonte RC .15 .40
511 Dustin Hermanson .10 .30
512 Deivi Cruz RC .15 .40
513 Luis Alicea .10 .30
514 Felix Heredia RC .15 .40
515 Don Slaught .10 .30
516 S.Hasegawa RC .25 .60
517 Matt Walbeck .10 .30
518 David Arias-Ortiz RC 20.00 50.00
519 Brady Raggio RC .15 .40
520 Rudy Pemberton .10 .30
521 Wayne Kirby .10 .30
522 Calvin Maduro .10 .30
523 Mark Lewis .10 .30
524 Mike Jackson .10 .30
525 Sid Fernandez .10 .30
526 Mike Bielecki .10 .30
527 Bubba Trammell RC .15 .40
528 Brent Brede RC .15 .40
529 Matt Morris .10 .30
530 Joe Borowski RC .15 .40
531 Orlando Miller .10 .30
532 Jim Bullinger .10 .30
533 Robert Person .10 .30
534 Doug Glanville .10 .30
535 Terry Pendleton .10 .30
536 Jorge Posada .20 .50
537 Marc Sagmoen RC .15 .40
538 Fernando Tatis RC .15 .40
539 Aaron Sele .10 .30
540 Brian Banks .10 .30
541 Derrek Lee .20 .50
542 John Wasdin .10 .30
543 Justin Towle RC .15 .40
544 Pat Cline .10 .30
545 Dave Magadan .10 .30
546 Jeff Blauser .10 .30
547 Phil Nevin .10 .30
548 Todd Walker .10 .30
549 Eli Marrero .10 .30
550 Bartolo Colon .10 .30
551 Jose Cruz Jr. RC .15 .40
552 Todd Dunwoody .10 .30
553 Hideki Irabu RC .15 .40
P11 Cal Ripken Promo .75 2.00
Three Card Strip

1997 Ultra Gold Medallion

This 553-card set is a gold-holofoil-stamped parallel version of the regular Ultra set and was inserted one per pack of both series one and series two cards. Unlike previous Gold Medallion sets, the 1997 edition features different photos than the corresponding regular cards.

COMPLETE SET (553) 110.00 270.00
COMP. SERIES 1 (300) 60.00 150.00
COMP. SERIES 2 (253) 50.00 120.00
*STARS: 1.25X TO 3X BASIC CARDS
*ROOKIES: .75X TO 2X BASIC
518 David Arias-Ortiz 20.00 50.00

1997 Ultra Platinum Medallion

This 553-card set is a parallel to the regular Ultra and was inserted one per 100 packs of both series 1 and series 2 cards. Sparkling platinum lettering on front differentiates these cards from their far more common regular issue brethren. No set price is provided due to scarcity. As with the 1997 Gold Medallion set, the Platinum Medallion set features different photos than the corresponding regular cards.

*STARS 1-450: 12.5X TO 30X BASIC CARDS
*STARS 451-553: 10X TO 25X BASIC CARDS
*ROOKIES 1-450: 6X TO 15X BASIC
*ROOKIES: 451-553: 5X TO 12X BASIC
STATED ODDS 1:100
518 David Arias-Ortiz 175.00 300.00

1997 Ultra Autographstix Emeralds

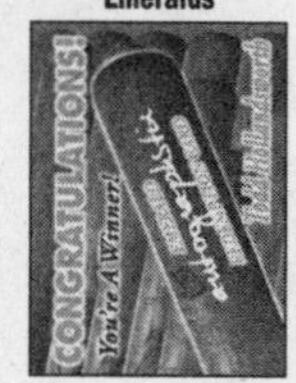

This six-card hobby exclusive Series two insert set consists of individually numbered Redemption cards for autographed bats from the players checklisted below. Only 25 of each card was produced. The deadline to exchange cards was July 1st, 1998. The bat a collector received for these cards was not easily identifiable as a special bat. Prices listed refer to the exchange cards.

EXCHANGE DEADLINE: 07/01/98
1 Alex Ochoa
2 Todd Walker
3 Scott Rolen
4 Darin Erstad
5 Alex Rodriguez
6 Todd Hollandsworth

1997 Ultra Baseball Rules

Randomly inserted into first series retail packs of 1997 Ultra at a rate of 1:36, cards from this 10-card set feature a selection of baseball's top performers from the 1996 season. The die cut cards feature a player photo surrounded by a group of baseballs. The back explains some of the rules involved in making various awards.

COMPLETE SET (10) 50.00 120.00
SER.1 STATED ODDS 1:36 RETAIL
1 Barry Bonds 6.00 15.00
2 Ken Griffey Jr. 4.00 10.00
3 Derek Jeter 6.00 15.00
4 Chipper Jones 2.50 6.00
5 Greg Maddux 4.00 10.00
6 Mark McGwire 6.00 15.00
7 Troy Percival 1.00 2.50
8 Mike Piazza 4.00 10.00
9 Cal Ripken 8.00 20.00
10 Frank Thomas 2.50 6.00

1997 Ultra Checklists

Randomly inserted in all first and second series packs at a rate of one in four, this 20-card set features borderless player photos on the front along with the word "Checklist", the player's name as well as the "ultra" logo at the bottom. The backs are checklists. The checklists for Series 1 are listed below with an "A" prefix and for Series 2 with a "B" prefix.

COMPLETE SERIES 1 (10) 3.00 8.00
COMPLETE SERIES 2 (10) 5.00 12.00
SER.1/2 STATED ODDS 1:4 HOBBY
A1 Dante Bichette .10 .30
A2 Barry Bonds .75 2.00
A3 Ken Griffey Jr. .50 1.25
A4 Greg Maddux .50 1.25
A5 Mark McGwire .75 2.00
A6 Mike Piazza .50 1.25
A7 Cal Ripken 1.00 2.50
A8 John Smoltz .20 .50
A9 Sammy Sosa .30 .75
A10 Frank Thomas .30 .75
B1 Andruw Jones .20 .50
B2 Ken Griffey Jr. .50 1.25
B3 Frank Thomas .30 .75
B4 Alex Rodriguez .50 1.25
B5 Cal Ripken 1.00 2.50
B6 Mike Piazza .50 1.25
B7 Greg Maddux .50 1.25
B8 Chipper Jones .30 .75
B9 Derek Jeter .75 2.00
B10 Juan Gonzalez .10 .30

1997 Ultra Diamond Producers

Randomly inserted in all first series packs at a rate of one in 288, this 12-card set features "flannel" material mounted on card stock and attempt to look and feel like actual uniforms.

COMPLETE SET (12) 100.00 250.00
SER.1 STATED ODDS 1:288
1 Jeff Bagwell 4.00 10.00
2 Barry Bonds 15.00 40.00
3 Ken Griffey Jr. 10.00 25.00
4 Chipper Jones 6.00 15.00
5 Kenny Lofton 2.50 6.00
6 Greg Maddux 10.00 25.00
7 Mark McGwire 15.00 40.00
8 Mike Piazza 10.00 25.00
9 Cal Ripken 20.00 50.00
10 Alex Rodriguez 10.00 25.00
11 Frank Thomas 6.00 15.00
12 Matt Williams 2.50 6.00

1997 Ultra Double Trouble

Randomly inserted in series one packs at a rate of one in four, this 20-card set features two players from each team. The horizontal cards feature players photos with their names in silver foil on the bottom and the words "double trouble" on the top. The backs feature information on what the players contributed to their team in 1996

COMPLETE SET (20) 4.00 10.00
SER.1 STATED ODDS 1:4
1 Roberto Alomar 1.00 2.50
Cal Ripken
2 Mo Vaughn .10 .30
Jose Canseco
3 Jim Edmonds .10 .30
Tim Salmon
4 Harold Baines .30 .75
Frank Thomas
5 Albert Belle .10 .30
Kenny Lofton
6 Marty Cordova .10 .30
Chuck Knoblauch
7 Derek Jeter .75 2.00
Andy Pettitte
8 Jason Giambi .75 2.00
Mark McGwire
9 Ken Griffey Jr. .50 1.25
Alex Rodriguez
10 Juan Gonzalez .10 .30
Will Clark
11 Greg Maddux .50 1.25
Chipper Jones
12 Mark Grace .30 .75
Sammy Sosa
13 Dante Bichette .10 .30
Andres Galarraga
14 Jeff Bagwell .20 .50
Derek Bell
15 Hideo Nomo .50 1.25
Mike Piazza
16 Henry Rodriguez .10 .30
Moises Alou
17 Rey Ordonez .10 .30
Alex Ochoa
18 Ray Lankford .10 .30
Ron Gant
19 Tony Gwynn .40 1.00
Rickey Henderson
20 Barry Bonds .75 2.00
Matt Williams

1997 Ultra Fame Game

Randomly inserted in series two hobby packs only at a rate of one in eight, this 18-card set features color photos of players who have displayed Hall of Fame potential on an elegant card design.

COMPLETE SET (18) 25.00 60.00
SER.2 STATED ODDS 1:8 HOBBY
1 Ken Griffey Jr. 2.00 5.00
2 Frank Thomas 1.25 3.00
3 Alex Rodriguez 2.00 5.00
4 Cal Ripken 4.00 10.00
5 Mike Piazza 2.00 5.00
6 Greg Maddux 2.00 5.00
7 Derek Jeter 3.00 8.00
8 Jeff Bagwell .75 2.00
9 Juan Gonzalez .50 1.25
10 Albert Belle .50 1.25
11 Tony Gwynn 1.50 4.00
12 Mark McGwire 3.00 8.00
13 Andy Pettitte .75 2.00
14 Kenny Lofton .50 1.25
15 Roberto Alomar .75 2.00
16 Ryne Sandberg 2.00 5.00
17 Barry Bonds 3.00 8.00
18 Eddie Murray 1.25 3.00

1997 Ultra Fielder's Choice

Randomly inserted in series one packs at a rate of one in 144, this 18-card set uses leather and gold foil to honor leading defensive players. The horizontal cards also include a player photo on the front as well as the big bold words "97 Fleer Ultra", "Fielder's Choice" and the player's name. The horizontal backs have another player photo as well as information about their defensive prowess.

COMPLETE SET (18) 80.00 200.00
SER.1 STATED ODDS 1:144
1 Roberto Alomar 3.00 8.00
2 Jeff Bagwell 3.00 8.00
3 Wade Boggs 3.00 8.00
4 Barry Bonds 12.50 30.00
5 Mark Grace 3.00 8.00
6 Ken Griffey Jr. 8.00 20.00
7 Marquis Grissom 2.00 5.00
8 Charles Johnson 2.00 5.00
9 Chuck Knoblauch 2.00 5.00
10 Barry Larkin 3.00 8.00
11 Kenny Lofton 2.00 5.00
12 Greg Maddux 8.00 20.00
13 Raul Mondesi 2.00 5.00
14 Rey Ordonez 2.00 5.00
15 Cal Ripken 15.00 40.00
16 Alex Rodriguez 8.00 20.00
17 Ivan Rodriguez 3.00 8.00
18 Matt Williams 2.00 5.00

1997 Ultra Golden Prospects

Randomly inserted in series two hobby packs only at a rate of one in four, this 10-card set features color action player images on a gold baseball background with commentary on what makes these players so promising..

COMPLETE SET (10) 2.00 5.00
SER.2 STATED ODDS 1:4 HOBBY
1 Andruw Jones .20 .50
2 Vladimir Guerrero .30 .75
3 Todd Walker .10 .30
4 Karim Garcia .10 .30
5 Kevin Orie .10 .30
6 Brian Giles .60 1.50
7 Jason Dickson .10 .30
8 Jose Guillen .10 .30
9 Ruben Rivera .10 .30
10 Derrek Lee .20 .50

1997 Ultra Hitting Machines

Randomly inserted in series two hobby packs only at a rate of one in 36, this 18-card set features color action player images of the MLB's most productive hitters in "machine-style" die-cut settings.

COMPLETE SET (18) 50.00 120.00
SER.2 STATED ODDS 1:36 HOBBY
1 Andruw Jones 1.50 4.00
2 Ken Griffey Jr. 4.00 10.00
3 Frank Thomas 2.50 6.00
4 Alex Rodriguez 4.00 10.00
5 Cal Ripken 8.00 20.00
6 Mike Piazza 4.00 10.00
7 Derek Jeter 6.00 15.00
8 Albert Belle 1.00 2.50
9 Tony Gwynn 3.00 8.00
10 Jeff Bagwell 1.50 4.00
11 Mark McGwire 6.00 15.00
12 Kenny Lofton 1.00 2.50
13 Manny Ramirez 1.50 4.00
14 Roberto Alomar 1.50 4.00
15 Ryne Sandberg 4.00 10.00
16 Eddie Murray 2.50 6.00
17 Sammy Sosa 2.50 6.00
18 Ken Caminiti 1.00 2.50

1997 Ultra Home Run Kings

Randomly inserted in series one hobby packs only at a rate of one in 36, this 12-card set feaures ultra crystal cards with transparent refractive holo-foil technology. The players pictured are all leading power hitters.

COMPLETE SET (12) 30.00 80.00
SER.1 STATED ODDS 1:36 HOBBY
1 Albert Belle 1.00 2.50
2 Barry Bonds 6.00 15.00
3 Juan Gonzalez 1.00 2.50
4 Ken Griffey Jr. 4.00 10.00
5 Todd Hundley 1.00 2.50
6 Ryan Klesko 1.00 2.50
7 Mark McGwire 6.00 15.00
8 Mike Piazza 4.00 10.00
9 Sammy Sosa 2.50 6.00
10 Frank Thomas 2.50 6.00
11 Mo Vaughn 1.00 2.50
12 Matt Williams 1.00 2.50

1997 Ultra Irabu Commemorative

These seven Irabu cards were distributed exclusively in 1997 Ultra series two International hobby boxes. Three of the seven cards are over-sized 5 x 7 issues, placed in each box as a chiptopper (within the sealed box, but laying on top of the packs). These three cards are serial numbered "of 2750" in silver foil on back. Due to poor sales overseas a number of these boxes made their way back to America but are still considered quite tricky to find.

COMPLETE SET (7) 6.00 15.00
COMMON 5 x 7 (C1-C3) .80 2.00
COMMON CARD (C4-C7) 1.20 3.00

1997 Ultra Leather Shop

Randomly inserted in series two hobby packs only at a rate of one in six, this 12-card set features color player images of some of the best fielders in the game highlighted by simulated leather backgrounds.

COMPLETE SET (12) 6.00 15.00
SER.2 STATED ODDS 1:6 HOBBY
1 Ken Griffey Jr. .60 1.50
2 Alex Rodriguez .60 1.50
3 Cal Ripken 1.25 3.00
4 Derek Jeter 1.00 2.50
5 Juan Gonzalez .15 .40
6 Tony Gwynn .50 1.25
7 Jeff Bagwell .25 .60
8 Roberto Alomar .25 .60
9 Ryne Sandberg .60 1.50
10 Ken Caminiti .15 .40
11 Kenny Lofton .15 .40
12 John Smoltz .25 .60

1997 Ultra Power Plus

Randomly inserted in series one packs at a rate of one in 24 and Series two hobby only packs at the rate of one in eight, this 12-card set utilizes silver rainbow holo-foil and features players who not only hit with power but also excel at other parts of the game. The cards in the Series one insert set have an "A" prefix while the cards in the Series two insert set carry a "B" prefix in the checklist below.

COMPLETE SERIES 1 (12) 30.00 80.00
SER.1 STATED ODDS 1:24
COMPLETE SERIES 2 (12) 1.50 4.00
SER.2 STATED ODDS 1:8 HOBBY
A1 Jeff Bagwell 1.00 2.50
A2 Barry Bonds 4.00 10.00
A3 Juan Gonzalez .60 1.50
A4 Ken Griffey Jr. 2.50 6.00
A5 Chipper Jones 1.50 4.00
A6 Mark McGwire 4.00 10.00
A7 Mike Piazza 2.50 6.00
A8 Cal Ripken 5.00 12.00
A9 Alex Rodriguez 2.50 6.00
A10 Sammy Sosa 1.50 4.00
A11 Frank Thomas 1.50 4.00
A12 Matt Williams .60 1.50
B1 Ken Griffey Jr. 1.00 2.50
B2 Frank Thomas .60 1.50
B3 Alex Rodriguez 1.00 2.50
B4 Cal Ripken 2.00 5.00
B5 Mike Piazza 1.00 2.50
B6 Chipper Jones .60 1.50
B7 Albert Belle .25 .60
B8 Juan Gonzalez .25 .60
B9 Jeff Bagwell .40 1.00
B10 Mark McGwire 1.50 4.00
B11 Mo Vaughn .25 .60
B12 Barry Bonds 1.50 4.00

1997 Ultra RBI Kings

Randomly inserted in series one packs at a rate of one in 18, this 10-card set features 100 percent etched-foil cards. The cards feature players who drive in many runs. The horizontal backs contain player information and another player photo.

COMPLETE SET (10) 12.50 30.00
SER.1 STATED ODDS 1:18
1 Jeff Bagwell 1.00 2.50
2 Albert Belle .60 1.50
3 Dante Bichette .60 1.50
4 Barry Bonds 4.00 10.00
5 Jay Buhner .60 1.50
6 Juan Gonzalez .60 1.50
7 Ken Griffey Jr. 2.50 6.00
8 Sammy Sosa 1.50 4.00
9 Frank Thomas 1.50 4.00
10 Mo Vaughn .60 1.50

1997 Ultra Rookie Reflections

Randomly inserted in series one packs at a rate of one in four, this 10-card set uses a silver foil design to feature young players. The horizontal backs contain player information as well as another player photo.

COMPLETE SET (10) 1.50 4.00
SER.1 STATED ODDS 1:4
1 James Baldwin .15 .40
2 Jermaine Dye .15 .40
3 Darin Erstad .15 .40
4 Todd Hollandsworth .15 .40
5 Derek Jeter 1.00 2.50
6 Jason Kendall .15 .40
7 Alex Ochoa .15 .40
8 Rey Ordonez .15 .40
9 Edgar Renteria .15 .40
10 Scott Rolen .25 .60

1997 Ultra Season Crowns

Randomly inserted in series one packs at a rate of one in eight, this 12-card set features color photos of baseball's top stars with etched foil backgrounds.

COMPLETE SET (12) 4.00 10.00
SER.1 STATED ODDS 1:8
1 Albert Belle .15 .40
2 Dante Bichette .15 .40
3 Barry Bonds 1.00 2.50
4 Kenny Lofton .15 .40
5 Edgar Martinez .25 .60
6 Mark McGwire 1.00 2.50
7 Andy Pettitte .25 .60
8 Mike Piazza .60 1.50
9 Alex Rodriguez .60 1.50
10 John Smoltz .25 .60
11 Sammy Sosa .40 1.00
12 Frank Thomas .40 1.00

1997 Ultra Starring Role

Randomly inserted in series two hobby packs only at a rate of one in 288, this 12-card set featues color photos of tried-and-true clutch performers on die-cut plastic cards with foil stamping.

COMPLETE SET (12) 100.00 250.00
SER.2 STATED ODDS 1:288 HOBBY
1 Andruw Jones 4.00 10.00
2 Ken Griffey Jr. 10.00 25.00
3 Frank Thomas 6.00 15.00
4 Alex Rodriguez 10.00 25.00
5 Cal Ripken 20.00 50.00
6 Mike Piazza 10.00 25.00
7 Greg Maddux 10.00 25.00
8 Chipper Jones 6.00 15.00
9 Derek Jeter 15.00 40.00
10 Juan Gonzalez 2.50 6.00
11 Albert Belle 2.50 6.00
12 Tony Gwynn 8.00 20.00

1997 Ultra Thunderclap

Randomly inserted in series two hobby packs only at a rate of one in 18, this 10-card set features color images of superstars who are feared by opponents for their ability to totally dominate a game on a background displaying lightning from a thunderstorm.

COMPLETE SET (10) 25.00 60.00
SER.2 STATED ODDS 1:18 HOBBY
1 Barry Bonds 4.00 10.00
2 Mo Vaughn .60 1.50
3 Mark McGwire 4.00 10.00
4 Jeff Bagwell 1.00 2.50
5 Juan Gonzalez .60 1.50
6 Alex Rodriguez 2.50 6.00
7 Chipper Jones 1.50 4.00
8 Ken Griffey Jr. 2.50 6.00
9 Mike Piazza 2.50 6.00
10 Frank Thomas 1.50 4.00

1997 Ultra Top 30

Randomly inserted one in every Ultra series two retail packs only, this 30-card set features color action player images of top stars with a "Top 30" circle in the team-colored background. The backs carry another player image with his team logo the backsground circle.

COMPLETE SET (30)	15.00	40.00
SER.2 STATED ODDS 1:1 RETAIL		
*GOLD MED: 2.5X TO 6X BASIC TOP 30		
G.MED SER.2 STATED ODDS 1:18 RETAIL		
1 Andruw Jones	.30	.75
2 Ken Griffey	.75	2.00
3 Frank Thomas	.50	1.25
4 Alex Rodriguez	.75	2.00
5 Cal Ripken	1.50	4.00
6 Mike Piazza	.75	2.00
7 Greg Maddux	.75	2.00
8 Chipper Jones	.50	1.25
9 Derek Jeter	1.25	3.00
10 Juan Gonzalez	.20	.50
11 Albert Belle	.20	.50
12 Tony Gwynn	.60	1.50
13 Jeff Bagwell	.30	.75
14 Mark McGwire	1.25	3.00
15 Andy Pettitte	.30	.75
16 Mo Vaughn	.20	.50
17 Kenny Lofton	.20	.50
18 Manny Ramirez	.30	.75
19 Roberto Alomar	.30	.75
20 Ryne Sandberg	.75	2.00
21 Hideo Nomo	.50	1.25
22 Barry Bonds	1.25	3.00
23 Eddie Murray	.50	1.25
24 Ken Caminiti	.20	.50
25 John Smoltz	.30	.75
26 Pat Hentgen	.20	.50
27 Todd Hollandsworth	.20	.50
28 Matt Williams	.20	.50
29 Bernie Williams	.30	.75
30 Brady Anderson	.20	.50

1998 Ultra

The complete 1998 Ultra set features 501 cards and was distributed in 10-card first and second series packs with a suggested retail price of $2.59. The fronts carry UV coated color action player photos printed on 20 pt. card stock. The backs display another player photo with player information and career statistics. The set contains the following subsets: Season's Crown (211-220) seeded 1:12 packs, Prospects (221-245) seeded 1:4 packs, Checklists (246-250), and Checklists (473-475) seeded 1:4 packs and Pizzazz (476-500) seeded 1:4 packs. Rookie Cards include Kevin Millwood and Magglio Ordonez. Though not confirmed by the manufacturer, it's believed that several cards within the Prospects subset are in shorter supply than others - most notably number 238 Ricky Ledee and number 243 Jorge Velandia. Also, seeded one in every pack, was one of 50 Million Dollar Moment cards which pictured some of the greatest moments in baseball histroy and gave the collector a chance to win a million dollars. As a special last minute promotion, Fleer/SkyBox got Alex Rodriguez to autograph 750 of his 1998 Fleer Promo cards. Each card is serial-numbered by hand on the card front. The signed cards were randomly seeded into Ultra Series two hobby packs.

COMPLETE SET (501)	65.00	160.00
COMP.SERIES 1 (250)	40.00	100.00
COMP.SERIES 2 (251)	25.00	60.00
COMP.SER.1 w/o SP's (210)	6.00	15.00
COMP.SER.2 w/o SP's (226)	6.00	15.00
COMMON (1-220/246-250)	.10	.30
COMMON (251-475/501)	.10	.30
COMMON SC (211-220)	.75	2.00
COMMON (221-245)	1.25	3.00
COMMON PZ (476-500)	.40	1.00
1 Ken Griffey Jr.	.50	1.25
2 Matt Morris	.10	.30
3 Roger Clemens	.60	1.50
4 Matt Williams	.10	.30
5 Roberto Hernandez	.10	.30
6 Rondell White	.10	.30
7 Tim Salmon	.20	.50
8 Brad Radke	.10	.30
9 Brett Butler	.10	.30
10 Carl Everett	.10	.30
11 Chili Davis	.10	.30
12 Chuck Finley	.10	.30
13 Darryl Kile	.10	.30
14 Deivi Cruz	.10	.30
15 Gary Gaetti	.10	.30
16 Matt Stairs	.10	.30
17 Pat Meares	.10	.30
18 Will Cunnane	.10	.30
19 Steve Woodard	.10	.30
20 Andy Ashby	.10	.30
21 Bobby Higginson	.10	.30
22 Brian Jordan	.10	.30
23 Craig Biggio	.20	.50
24 Jim Edmonds	.10	.30
25 Ryan McGuire	.10	.30
26 Scott Hatteberg	.10	.30
27 Willie Greene	.10	.30
28 Albert Belle	.10	.30
29 Ellis Burks	.10	.30
30 Hideo Nomo	.30	.75
31 Jeff Bagwell	.20	.50
32 Kevin Brown	.20	.50
33 Nomar Garciaparra	.50	1.25
34 Pedro Martinez	.20	.50
35 Raul Mondesi	.10	.30
36 Ricky Bottalico	.10	.30
37 Shawn Estes	.10	.30
38 Otis Nixon	.10	.30
39 Terry Steinbach	.10	.30
40 Tom Glavine	.20	.50
41 Todd Dunwoody	.10	.30
42 Deion Sanders	.20	.50
43 Gary Sheffield	.10	.30
44 Mike Lansing	.10	.30
45 Mike Lieberthal	.10	.30
46 Paul Sorrento	.10	.30
47 Paul O'Neill	.20	.50
48 Tom Goodwin	.10	.30
49 Andruw Jones	.20	.50
50 Barry Bonds	.75	2.00
51 Bernie Williams	.20	.50
52 Jeremi Gonzalez	.10	.30
53 Mike Piazza	.50	1.25
54 Russ Davis	.10	.30
55 Vinny Castilla	.10	.30
56 Rod Beck	.10	.30
57 Andres Galarraga	.10	.30
58 Ben McDonald	.10	.30
59 Billy Wagner	.10	.30
60 Charles Johnson	.10	.30
61 Fred McGriff	.20	.50
62 Dean Palmer	.10	.30
63 Frank Thomas	.30	.75
64 Ismael Valdes	.10	.30
65 Mark Bellhorn	.10	.30
66 Jeff King	.10	.30
67 John Wetteland	.10	.30
68 Mark Grace	.20	.50
69 Mark Kotsay	.10	.30
70 Scott Rolen	.20	.50
71 Todd Hundley	.10	.30
72 Todd Worrell	.10	.30
73 Wilson Alvarez	.10	.30
74 Bobby Jones	.10	.30
75 Jose Canseco	.20	.50
76 Kevin Appier	.10	.30
77 Neifi Perez	.10	.30
78 Paul Molitor	.10	.30
79 Quilvio Veras	.10	.30
80 Randy Johnson	.30	.75
81 Glendon Rusch	.10	.30
82 Curt Schilling	.10	.30
83 Alex Rodriguez	.50	1.25
84 Rey Ordonez	.10	.30
85 Jeff Juden	.10	.30
86 Mike Cameron	.10	.30
87 Ryan Klesko	.10	.30
88 Trevor Hoffman	.10	.30
89 Chuck Knoblauch	.10	.30
90 Larry Walker	.10	.30
91 Mark McLemore	.10	.30
92 B.J. Surhoff	.10	.30
93 Darren Daulton	.10	.30
94 Ray Durham	.10	.30
95 Sammy Sosa	.30	.75
96 Eric Young	.10	.30
97 Gerald Williams	.10	.30
98 Javy Lopez	.10	.30
99 John Smiley	.10	.30
100 Juan Gonzalez	.10	.30
101 Shawn Green	.10	.30
102 Charles Nagy	.10	.30
103 David Justice	.10	.30
104 Joey Hamilton	.10	.30
105 Pat Hentgen	.10	.30
106 Raul Casanova	.10	.30
107 Tony Phillips	.10	.30
108 Tony Gwynn	.40	1.00
109 Will Clark	.20	.50
110 Jason Giambi	.10	.30
111 Jay Bell	.10	.30
112 Johnny Damon	.20	.50
113 Alan Benes	.10	.30
114 Jeff Suppan	.10	.30
115 Kevin Polcovich	.10	.30
116 Shigetoshi Hasegawa	.10	.30
117 Steve Finley	.10	.30
118 Tony Clark	.10	.30
119 David Cone	.10	.30
120 Jose Guillen	.10	.30
121 Kevin Millwood RC	.40	1.00
122 Greg Maddux	.50	1.25
123 Dave Nilsson	.10	.30
124 Hideki Irabu	.10	.30
125 Jason Kendall	.10	.30
126 Jim Thome	.20	.50
127 Delino DeShields	.10	.30
128 Edgar Renteria	.10	.30
129 Edgardo Alfonzo	.10	.30
130 J.T. Snow	.10	.30
131 Jeff Abbott	.10	.30
132 Jeffrey Hammonds	.10	.30
133 Todd Greene	.10	.30
134 Vladimir Guerrero	.30	.75
135 Jay Buhner	.10	.30
136 Jeff Cirillo	.10	.30
137 Jeromy Burnitz	.10	.30
138 Mickey Morandini	.10	.30
139 Tino Martinez	.20	.50
140 Jeff Shaw	.10	.30
141 Rafael Palmeiro	.20	.50
142 Bobby Bonilla	.10	.30
143 Cal Ripken	1.00	2.50
144 Chad Fox RC	.10	.30
145 Dante Bichette	.10	.30
146 Dennis Eckersley	.10	.30
147 Mariano Rivera	.30	.75
148 Mo Vaughn	.10	.30
149 Reggie Sanders	.10	.30
150 Derek Jeter	.75	2.00
151 Rusty Greer	.10	.30
152 Brady Anderson	.10	.30
153 Brett Tomko	.10	.30
154 Jaime Navarro	.10	.30
155 Kevin Orie	.10	.30
156 Roberto Alomar	.20	.50
157 Edgar Martinez	.20	.50
158 John Olerud	.10	.30
159 John Smoltz	.20	.50
160 Ryne Sandberg	.50	1.25
161 Billy Taylor	.10	.30
162 Chris Holt	.10	.30
163 Damion Easley	.10	.30
164 Darin Erstad	.10	.30
165 Joe Carter	.10	.30
166 Kelvim Escobar	.10	.30
167 Ken Caminiti	.10	.30
168 Pokey Reese	.10	.30
169 Ray Lankford	.10	.30
170 Livan Hernandez	.10	.30
171 Steve Kline	.10	.30
172 Tom Gordon	.10	.30
173 Travis Fryman	.10	.30
174 Al Martin	.10	.30
175 Andy Pettitte	.20	.50
176 Jeff Kent	.10	.30
177 Jimmy Key	.10	.30
178 Mark Grudzielanek	.10	.30
179 Tony Saunders	.10	.30
180 Barry Larkin	.20	.50
181 Bubba Trammell	.10	.30
182 Carlos Delgado	.10	.30
183 Carlos Baerga	.10	.30
184 Derek Bell	.10	.30
185 Henry Rodriguez	.10	.30
186 Jason Dickson	.10	.30
187 Ron Gant	.10	.30
188 Tony Womack	.10	.30
189 Justin Thompson	.10	.30
190 Fernando Tatis	.10	.30
191 Mark Wohlers	.10	.30
192 Takashi Kashiwada	.10	.30
193 Garret Anderson	.10	.30
194 Jose Cruz Jr.	.10	.30
195 Ricardo Rincon	.10	.30
196 Tim Naehring	.10	.30
197 Moises Alou	.10	.30
198 Eric Karros	.10	.30
199 John Jaha	.10	.30
200 Marty Cordova	.10	.30
201 Ken Hill	.10	.30
202 Chipper Jones	.30	.75
203 Kenny Lofton	.10	.30
204 Mike Mussina	.20	.50
205 Manny Ramirez	.20	.50
206 Todd Hollandsworth	.10	.30
207 Cecil Fielder	.10	.30
208 Mark McGwire	.75	2.00
209 Jim Leyritz	.10	.30
210 Ivan Rodriguez	.20	.50
211 Jeff Bagwell SC	.75	2.00
212 Barry Bonds SC	3.00	8.00
213 Roger Clemens SC	2.50	6.00
214 N.Garciaparra SC	2.00	5.00
215 Ken Griffey Jr. SC	2.00	5.00
216 Tony Gwynn SC	1.50	4.00
217 Randy Johnson SC	1.25	3.00
218 Mark McGwire SC	3.00	8.00
219 Scott Rolen SC	.75	2.00
220 Frank Thomas SC	1.25	3.00
221 Matt Perisho PROS	1.25	3.00
222 Wes Helms PROS	1.25	3.00
223 D.Dellucci PROS RC	1.25	3.00
224 Todd Helton PROS	1.25	3.00
225 Brian Rose PROS	1.25	3.00
226 Aaron Boone PROS	1.25	3.00
227 Keith Foulke PROS	1.25	3.00
228 Homer Bush PROS	1.25	3.00
229 S.Stewart PROS	1.25	3.00
230 R.Hidalgo PROS	1.25	3.00
231 Russ Johnson PROS	1.25	3.00
232 H.Blanco PROS RC	1.25	3.00
233 Paul Konerko PROS	1.25	3.00
234 A.Williamson PROS	1.25	3.00
235 S.Bowers PROS RC	1.25	3.00
236 Jose Vidro PROS	1.25	3.00
237 Derek Wallace PROS	1.25	3.00
238 Ricky Ledee PROS SP	2.00	5.00
239 Ben Grieve PROS	1.25	3.00
240 Lou Collier PROS	1.25	3.00
241 Derrek Lee PROS	1.25	3.00
242 Ruben Rivera PROS	1.25	3.00
243 J.Velandia PROS SP	2.00	5.00
244 Andrew Vessel PROS	1.25	3.00
245 Chris Carpenter PROS	1.25	3.00
246 Ken Griffey Jr. CL	.30	.75
247 Alex Rodriguez CL	.30	.75
248 Diamond Ink CL	.10	.30
249 Frank Thomas CL	.20	.50
250 Cal Ripken CL	.50	1.25
251 Carlos Perez	.10	.30
252 Larry Sutton	.10	.30
253 Gary Sheffield	.10	.30
254 Wally Joyner	.10	.30
255 Todd Stottlemyre	.10	.30
256 Nerio Rodriguez	.10	.30
257 Charles Johnson	.10	.30
258 Pedro Astacio	.10	.30
259 Cal Eldred	.10	.30
260 Chili Davis	.10	.30
261 Freddy Garcia	.10	.30
262 Bobby Witt	.10	.30
263 Michael Coleman	.10	.30
264 Mike Caruso	.10	.30
265 Mike Lansing	.10	.30
266 Dennis Reyes	.10	.30
267 F.P. Santangelo	.10	.30
268 Darryl Hamilton	.10	.30
269 Mike Fetters	.10	.30
270 Charlie Hayes	.10	.30
271 Royce Clayton	.10	.30
272 Doug Drabek	.10	.30
273 James Baldwin	.10	.30
274 Brian Hunter	.10	.30
275 Chan Ho Park	.10	.30
276 John Franco	.10	.30
277 David Wells	.10	.30
278 Eli Marrero	.10	.30
279 Kerry Wood	.15	.40
280 Donnie Sadler	.10	.30
281 Scott Winchester RC	.10	.30
282 Hal Morris	.10	.30
283 Brad Fullmer	.10	.30
284 Bernard Gilkey	.10	.30
285 Ramiro Mendoza	.10	.30
286 Kevin Brown	.20	.50
287 David Segui	.10	.30
288 Willie McGee	.10	.30
289 Darren Oliver	.10	.30
290 Antonio Alfonseca	.10	.30
291 Eric Davis	.10	.30
292 Mickey Morandini	.10	.30
293 Frank Catalanotto RC	.25	.60
294 Derrek Lee	.20	.50
295 Todd Zeile	.10	.30
296 Chuck Knoblauch	.10	.30
297 Wilson Delgado	.10	.30
298 Bobby Bonilla	.10	.30
299 Orel Hershiser	.10	.30
300 Ozzie Guillen	.10	.30
301 Aaron Sele	.10	.30
302 Joe Carter	.10	.30
303 Darryl Kile	.10	.30
304 Shane Reynolds	.10	.30
305 Todd Dunn	.10	.30
306 Bob Abreu	.10	.30
307 Doug Strange	.10	.30
308 Jose Canseco	.20	.50
309 Lance Johnson	.10	.30
310 Harold Baines	.10	.30
311 Todd Pratt	.10	.30
312 Greg Colbrunn	.10	.30
313 Masato Yoshii RC	.15	.40
314 Felix Heredia	.10	.30
315 Dennis Martinez	.10	.30
316 Geronimo Berroa	.10	.30
317 Darren Lewis	.10	.30
318 Bill Ripken	.10	.30
319 Enrique Wilson	.10	.30
320 Alex Ochoa	.10	.30
321 Doug Glanville	.10	.30
322 Mike Stanley	.10	.30
323 Gerald Williams	.10	.30
324 Pedro Martinez	.20	.50
325 Jaret Wright	.10	.30
326 Terry Pendleton	.10	.30
327 LaTroy Hawkins	.10	.30
328 Emil Brown	.10	.30
329 Walt Weiss	.10	.30
330 Omar Vizquel	.20	.50
331 Carl Everett	.10	.30
332 Fernando Vina	.10	.30
333 Mike Blowers	.10	.30
334 Dwight Gooden	.10	.30
335 Mark Lewis	.10	.30
336 Jim Leyritz	.10	.30
337 Kenny Lofton	.10	.30
338 John Halama RC	.15	.40
339 Jose Valentin	.10	.30
340 Desi Relaford	.10	.30
341 Dante Powell	.10	.30
342 Ed Sprague	.10	.30
343 Reggie Jefferson	.10	.30
344 Mike Hampton	.10	.30
345 Marquis Grissom	.10	.30
346 Heathcliff Slocumb	.10	.30
347 Francisco Cordova	.10	.30
348 Ken Cloude	.10	.30
349 Benito Santiago	.10	.30
350 Denny Neagle	.10	.30
351 Sean Casey	.10	.30
352 Robb Nen	.10	.30
353 Orlando Merced	.10	.30
354 Adrian Brown	.10	.30
355 Gregg Jefferies	.10	.30
356 Otis Nixon	.10	.30
357 Michael Tucker	.10	.30
358 Eric Milton	.10	.30
359 Travis Fryman	.10	.30
360 Gary DiSarcina	.10	.30
361 Mario Valdez	.10	.30
362 Craig Counsell	.10	.30
363 Jose Offerman	.10	.30
364 Tony Fernandez	.10	.30
365 Jason McDonald	.10	.30
366 Sterling Hitchcock	.10	.30
367 Donovan Osborne	.10	.30
368 Troy Percival	.10	.30
369 Henry Rodriguez	.10	.30
370 Dmitri Young	.10	.30
371 Jay Powell	.10	.30
372 Jeff Conine	.10	.30
373 Orlando Cabrera	.10	.30
374 Butch Huskey	.10	.30
375 Mike Lowell RC	.60	1.50
376 Kevin Young	.10	.30
377 Jamie Moyer	.10	.30
378 Jeff D'Amico	.10	.30
379 Scott Erickson	.10	.30
380 Magglio Ordonez RC	1.25	3.00
381 Melvin Nieves	.10	.30
382 Ramon Martinez	.10	.30
383 A.J. Hinch	.10	.30
384 Jeff Brantley	.10	.30
385 Kevin Elster	.10	.30
386 Allen Watson	.10	.30
387 Moises Alou	.10	.30
388 Jeff Blauser	.10	.30
389 Pete Harnisch	.10	.30
390 Shane Andrews	.10	.30
391 Rico Brogna	.10	.30
392 Stan Javier	.10	.30
393 David Howard	.10	.30
394 Darryl Strawberry	.10	.30
395 Kent Mercker	.10	.30
396 Juan Encarnacion	.10	.30
397 Sandy Alomar Jr.	.10	.30
398 Al Leiter	.10	.30
399 Tony Graffanino	.10	.30
400 Terry Adams	.10	.30
401 Bruce Aven	.10	.30
402 Derrick Gibson	.10	.30
403 Jose Cabrera RC	.10	.30
404 Rich Becker	.10	.30
405 David Ortiz	.40	1.00
406 Brian McRae	.10	.30
407 Bobby Estalella	.10	.30
408 Bill Mueller	.10	.30
409 Dennis Eckersley	.10	.30
410 Sandy Martinez	.10	.30
411 Jose Vizcaino	.10	.30
412 Jermaine Allensworth	.10	.30
413 Miguel Tejada	.30	.75
414 Turner Ward	.10	.30
415 Glenallen Hill	.10	.30
416 Lee Stevens	.10	.30
417 Cecil Fielder	.10	.30
418 Ruben Sierra	.10	.30
419 Jon Nunnally	.10	.30
420 Rod Myers	.10	.30
421 Dustin Hermanson	.10	.30
422 James Mouton	.10	.30
423 Dan Wilson	.10	.30
424 Roberto Kelly	.10	.30
425 Antonio Osuna	.10	.30
426 Jacob Cruz	.10	.30
427 Brent Mayne	.10	.30
428 Matt Karchner	.10	.30
429 Damian Jackson	.10	.30
430 Roger Cedeno	.10	.30
431 Rickey Henderson	.30	.75
432 Joe Randa	.10	.30
433 Greg Vaughn	.10	.30
434 Andres Galarraga	.10	.30
435 Rod Beck	.10	.30
436 Curtis Goodwin	.10	.30
437 Brad Ausmus	.10	.30
438 Bob Hamelin	.10	.30
439 Todd Walker	.10	.30
440 Scott Brosius	.10	.30
441 Len Dykstra	.10	.30
442 Abraham Nunez	.10	.30
443 Brian Johnson	.10	.30
444 Randy Myers	.10	.30
445 Bret Boone	.10	.30
446 Oscar Henriquez	.10	.30
447 Mike Sweeney	.10	.30
448 Kenny Rogers	.10	.30
449 Mark Langston	.10	.30
450 Luis Gonzalez	.10	.30
451 John Burkett	.10	.30
452 Bip Roberts	.10	.30
453 Travis Lee	.10	.30
454 Felix Rodriguez	.10	.30
455 Andy Benes	.10	.30
456 Willie Blair	.10	.30
457 Brian Anderson	.10	.30
458 Jay Bell	.10	.30
459 Matt Williams	.10	.30
460 Devon White	.10	.30
461 Karim Garcia	.10	.30
462 Jorge Fabregas	.10	.30
463 Wilson Alvarez	.10	.30
464 Roberto Hernandez	.10	.30
465 Tony Saunders	.10	.30
466 Rolando Arrojo RC	.15	.40
467 Wade Boggs	.30	.75
468 Fred McGriff	.20	.50
469 Paul Sorrento	.10	.30
470 Kevin Stocker	.10	.30
471 Bubba Trammell	.10	.30
472 Quinton McCracken	.10	.30
473 Ken Griffey Jr. CL	.30	.75
474 Cal Ripken CL	.50	1.25
475 Frank Thomas CL	.20	.50
476 Ken Griffey Jr. PZ	1.50	4.00
477 Cal Ripken PZ	3.00	8.00
478 Frank Thomas PZ	1.00	2.50
479 Alex Rodriguez PZ	1.50	4.00
480 Nomar Garciaparra PZ	1.50	4.00
481 Derek Jeter PZ	2.50	6.00
482 Andruw Jones PZ	.60	1.50
483 Chipper Jones PZ	1.00	2.50
484 Greg Maddux PZ	1.50	4.00
485 Mike Piazza PZ	1.50	4.00
486 Juan Gonzalez PZ	.40	1.00
487 Jose Cruz Jr. PZ	.40	1.00
488 Jaret Wright PZ	.40	1.00
489 Hideo Nomo PZ	1.00	2.50
490 Scott Rolen PZ	.60	1.50
491 Tony Gwynn PZ	1.25	3.00
492 Roger Clemens PZ	2.00	5.00
493 Darin Erstad PZ	.40	1.00
494 Mark McGwire PZ	2.50	6.00
495 Jeff Bagwell PZ	.60	1.50
496 Mo Vaughn PZ	.40	1.00
497 Albert Belle PZ	.40	1.00
498 Kenny Lofton PZ	.40	1.00
499 Ben Grieve PZ	.40	1.00
500 Barry Bonds PZ	2.50	6.00
501 Mike Piazza	.50	1.25
S100 A.Rodriguez AU/750	50.00	100.00

1998 Ultra Gold Medallion

Randomly inserted one in every first and second series hobby pack, this 501-card set is parallel to the base set and features a gold metallic foil background.

COMPLETE SET (501)	80.00	200.00
COMP.SERIES 1 (250)	40.00	100.00
COMP.SERIES 2 (251)	40.00	100.00

*STARS: 1.25X TO 3X BASIC CARDS
*ROOKIES: .75X TO 2X BASIC CARDS
*SEASON CROWNS: .3X TO .8X BASIC SC
*PROSPECTS: .25X TO .6X BASIC PROS.
*CHECKLISTS: 1.25X TO 3X BASIC CL'S
*PIZZAZZ: .4X TO 1.X BASIC PIZZAZZ

1998 Ultra Platinum Medallion

Randomly inserted in first and second series hobby packs, this 498-card set is parallel to the base set. Only 100 first series sets and 98 second series sets were produced and each card is serially numbered in gold foil on back. Ten Platinum exchange cards good for a complete Platinum series one set were inserted into first series hobby packs. Another ten Platinum exchange cards good for a complete series two set were inserted in second series hobby packs. The three basic-issue checklist cards (473,474 and 475) were never printed in platinum form.

*STARS: 10X TO 25X BASIC CARDS
*ROOKIES: 10X TO 25X BASIC CARDS
*SEASON CROWNS: 1.5X TO 4X BASIC SC
*PROSPECTS: 2.5X TO 6X BASIC PROSP.
*CHECKLISTS: 12.5X TO 30X BASIC CL'S
*PIZZAZZ: 2X TO 5X BASIC PIZZAZZ

1998 Ultra Artistic Talents

Randomly inserted in Series one packs at the rate of one in eight, this 18-card set features color pictures of top players on art enhanced cards.

COMPLETE SET (18)	20.00	50.00
SER.1 STATED ODDS 1:8		
1 Ken Griffey Jr.	1.50	4.00
2 Andruw Jones	.60	1.50
3 Alex Rodriguez	1.50	4.00
4 Frank Thomas	1.00	2.50
5 Cal Ripken	3.00	8.00
6 Derek Jeter	2.50	6.00
7 Chipper Jones	1.00	2.50
8 Greg Maddux	1.50	4.00
9 Mike Piazza	1.50	4.00
10 Albert Belle	.40	1.00
11 Darin Erstad	.40	1.00
12 Juan Gonzalez	.40	1.00
13 Jeff Bagwell	.60	1.50
14 Tony Gwynn	1.25	3.00
15 Mark McGwire	2.50	6.00
16 Scott Rolen	.60	1.50
17 Barry Bonds	2.50	6.00
18 Kenny Lofton	.40	1.00

1998 Ultra Back to the Future

Randomly inserted in Series one packs at the rate of one in six, this 15-card set features color photos of top Rookies. The backs carry player information.

COMPLETE SET (15)	5.00	12.00
SER.1 STATED ODDS 1:6		
1 Andruw Jones	.30	.75
2 Alex Rodriguez	.75	2.00
3 Derek Jeter	1.25	3.00
4 Darin Erstad	.20	.50
5 Mike Cameron	.20	.50
6 Scott Rolen	.30	.75
7 Nomar Garciaparra	.75	2.00
8 Hideki Irabu	.20	.50
9 Jose Cruz Jr.	.20	.50
10 Vladimir Guerrero	.50	1.25
11 Mark Kotsay	.20	.50
12 Tony Womack	.20	.50
13 Jason Dickson	.20	.50
14 Jose Guillen	.20	.50
15 Tony Clark	.20	.50

1998 Ultra Big Shots

Randomly inserted in Series one packs at the rate of one in four, this 15-card set features color photos of players who hit the longest home runs in the 1997 season.

COMPLETE SET (15)	4.00	10.00
SER.1 STATED ODDS 1:4		
1 Ken Griffey Jr.	.60	1.50
2 Frank Thomas	.40	1.00
3 Chipper Jones	.40	1.00
4 Albert Belle	.15	.40
5 Juan Gonzalez	.15	.40
6 Jeff Bagwell	.25	.60
7 Mark McGwire	1.00	2.50
8 Barry Bonds	1.00	2.50
9 Manny Ramirez	.25	.60
10 Mo Vaughn	.15	.40
11 Matt Williams	.15	.40
12 Jim Thome	.25	.60
13 Tino Martinez	.25	.60
14 Mike Piazza	.60	1.50
15 Tony Clark	.15	.40

1998 Ultra Diamond Immortals

Randomly inserted in packs at a rate of one in 288, this 15-card insert set highlights color action photos of future Hall of Famers on die-cut cards with full silver holofoil backgrounds.

COMPLETE SET (15)	150.00	400.00
SER.2 STATED ODDS 1:288		
1 Ken Griffey Jr.	15.00	40.00
2 Frank Thomas	10.00	25.00
3 Alex Rodriguez	15.00	40.00
4 Cal Ripken	30.00	80.00
5 Mike Piazza	15.00	40.00
6 Mark McGwire	25.00	60.00
7 Greg Maddux	15.00	40.00
8 Andruw Jones	6.00	15.00
9 Chipper Jones	10.00	25.00
10 Derek Jeter	25.00	60.00
11 Tony Gwynn	12.50	30.00
12 Juan Gonzalez	4.00	10.00
13 Jose Cruz Jr.	4.00	10.00
14 Roger Clemens	20.00	50.00
15 Barry Bonds	25.00	60.00

1998 Ultra Diamond Producers

Randomly inserted in Series one packs at the rate of one in 288, this 15-card set features color photos of Major League Baseball's top players.

COMPLETE SET (15)	150.00	400.00
SER.1 STATED ODDS 1:288		
1 Ken Griffey Jr.	12.50	30.00
2 Andruw Jones	5.00	12.00
3 Alex Rodriguez	12.50	30.00
4 Frank Thomas	8.00	20.00
5 Cal Ripken	25.00	60.00
6 Derek Jeter	20.00	50.00
7 Chipper Jones	8.00	20.00
8 Greg Maddux	12.50	30.00
9 Mike Piazza	12.50	30.00
10 Juan Gonzalez	3.00	8.00
11 Jeff Bagwell	5.00	12.00
12 Tony Gwynn	10.00	25.00
13 Mark McGwire	20.00	50.00
14 Barry Bonds	20.00	50.00
15 Jose Cruz Jr.	3.00	8.00

1998 Ultra Double Trouble

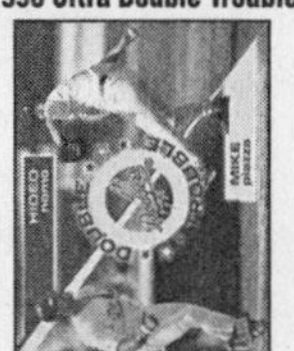

Randomly inserted in series one packs at the rate of one in four, this 20-card set features color photos of two star players per card.

COMPLETE SET (20)	6.00	15.00
SER.1 STATED ODDS 1:4		
1 Ken Griffey Jr.	.60	1.50
Alex Rodriguez		
2 Vladimir Guerrero	.40	1.00
Pedro Martinez		
3 Andruw Jones	.40	1.00
Kenny Lofton		
4 Chipper Jones	.60	1.50
Greg Maddux		
5 Derek Jeter	.75	2.00
Tino Martinez		
6 Frank Thomas	.40	1.00
Albert Belle		
7 Cal Ripken	1.25	3.00
Roberto Alomar		
8 Mike Piazza	.60	1.50
Hideo Nomo		
9 Darin Erstad	.30	.75
Jason Dickson		
10 Juan Gonzalez	.40	1.00
Ivan Rodriguez		
11 Jeff Bagwell	.40	1.00
Darryl Kile		
UER front Kyle		
12 Tony Gwynn	.50	1.25
Steve Finley		
13 Mark McGwire	1.00	2.50
Ray Lankford		
14 Barry Bonds	1.00	2.50
Jeff Kent		
15 Andy Pettitte	.40	1.00
Bernie Williams		
16 Mo Vaughn	.60	1.50
Nomar Garciaparra		
17 Matt Williams	.40	1.00
Jim Thome		
18 Hideki Irabu	.40	1.00
Mariano Rivera		
19 Roger Clemens	.75	2.00
Jose Cruz Jr.		
20 Manny Ramirez	.40	1.00
David Justice		

1998 Ultra Fall Classics

Randomly inserted in Series one packs at the rate of one in 18, this 15-card set features color photos of the top potential postseason heroes. The backs carry player information.

COMPLETE SET (15)	40.00	100.00
SER.1 STATED ODDS 1:18		
1 Ken Griffey Jr.	3.00	8.00
2 Andruw Jones	1.25	3.00
3 Alex Rodriguez	3.00	8.00
4 Frank Thomas	2.00	5.00
5 Cal Ripken	6.00	15.00
6 Derek Jeter	5.00	12.00
7 Chipper Jones	2.00	5.00
8 Greg Maddux	3.00	8.00
9 Mike Piazza	3.00	8.00
10 Albert Belle	.75	2.00
11 Juan Gonzalez	.75	2.00
12 Jeff Bagwell	1.25	3.00
13 Tony Gwynn	2.50	6.00
14 Mark McGwire	5.00	12.00
15 Barry Bonds	5.00	12.00

1998 Ultra Kid Gloves

Radomly inserted in Series one packs at the rate of one in eight, this 12-card set features color photos of top young defensive players. The backs carry player information.

COMPLETE SET (12)	6.00	15.00
SER.1 STATED ODDS 1:8		
1 Andruw Jones	.40	1.00
2 Alex Rodriguez	1.00	2.50
3 Derek Jeter	1.50	4.00
4 Chipper Jones	.60	1.50
5 Darin Erstad	.25	.60
6 Todd Walker	.25	.60
7 Scott Rolen	.40	1.00
8 Nomar Garciaparra	1.00	2.50
9 Jose Cruz Jr.	.25	.60
10 Charles Johnson	.25	.60
11 Rey Ordonez	.25	.60
12 Vladimir Guerrero	.60	1.50

1998 Ultra Millennium Men

Randomly inserted in hobby only packs at a rate of one in 35, this 15-card insert set features a player action photo on an irridescent silver foil underlay that opens to reveal a second photo with a personal profile. For an added touch, a foil stamp embossed in the center gives the feel of a wax seal.

COMPLETE SET (15)	50.00	120.00
SER.2 STATED ODDS 1:35 HOBBY		
1 Jose Cruz Jr.	1.00	2.50
2 Ken Griffey Jr.	4.00	10.00
3 Cal Ripken	8.00	20.00
4 Derek Jeter	6.00	15.00
5 Andruw Jones	1.50	4.00
6 Alex Rodriguez	4.00	10.00
7 Chipper Jones	2.50	6.00
8 Scott Rolen	1.50	4.00
9 Nomar Garciaparra	4.00	10.00
10 Frank Thomas	2.50	6.00
11 Mike Piazza	4.00	10.00
12 Greg Maddux	4.00	10.00
13 Juan Gonzalez	1.00	2.50
14 Ben Grieve	10.00	25.00
15 Jaret Wright	1.00	2.50

1998 Ultra Notables

Randomly inserted in packs at a rate of one in four, this 20-card insert set features a color action player photo on a borderless UV coated front with a design of the American Eagle in the background.

COMPLETE SET (20)	10.00	25.00
SER.2 STATED ODDS 1:4		
1 Frank Thomas	.50	1.25
2 Ken Griffey Jr.	.75	2.00
3 Edgar Renteria	.20	.50
4 Albert Belle	.20	.50
5 Juan Gonzalez	.20	.50
6 Jeff Bagwell	.30	.75
7 Mark McGwire	1.25	3.00
8 Barry Bonds	1.25	3.00
9 Scott Rolen	.30	.75
10 Mo Vaughn	.20	.50
11 Andruw Jones	.30	.75
12 Chipper Jones	.50	1.25
13 Tino Martinez	.30	.75
14 Mike Piazza	.75	2.00
15 Tony Clark	.20	.50
16 Jose Cruz Jr.	.20	.50
17 Nomar Garciaparra	.75	2.00
18 Cal Ripken	1.50	4.00
19 Alex Rodriguez	.75	2.00
20 Derek Jeter	1.25	3.00

1998 Ultra Power Plus

Randomly inserted in Series one packs at the rate of one in 36, this 10-card set features color action photos of top young and veteran players. The backs carry player information.

COMPLETE SET (10)	25.00	60.00
SER.1 STATED ODDS 1:36		
1 Ken Griffey Jr.	5.00	12.00
2 Andruw Jones	2.00	5.00
3 Alex Rodriguez	5.00	12.00
4 Frank Thomas	3.00	8.00
5 Mike Piazza	5.00	12.00
6 Albert Belle	1.25	3.00
7 Juan Gonzalez	1.25	3.00
8 Jeff Bagwell	2.00	5.00
9 Barry Bonds	8.00	20.00
10 Jose Cruz Jr.	1.25	3.00

1998 Ultra Prime Leather

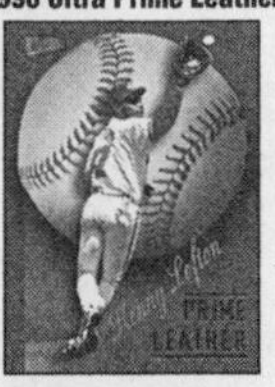

Randomly inserted in Series one packs at the rate of one in 144, this 18-card set features color photos of young and veteran players considered to be good glove men. The backs carry player information.

SER.1 STATED ODDS 1:144		
1 Ken Griffey Jr.	10.00	25.00
2 Andruw Jones	4.00	10.00
3 Alex Rodriguez	10.00	25.00
4 Frank Thomas	6.00	15.00
5 Cal Ripken	20.00	50.00
6 Derek Jeter	15.00	40.00
7 Chipper Jones	6.00	15.00
8 Greg Maddux	10.00	25.00
9 Mike Piazza	10.00	25.00
10 Albert Belle	2.50	6.00
11 Darin Erstad	2.50	6.00
12 Juan Gonzalez	2.50	6.00
13 Jeff Bagwell	4.00	10.00
14 Tony Gwynn	8.00	20.00
15 Roberto Alomar	4.00	10.00
16 Barry Bonds	15.00	40.00
17 Kenny Lofton	2.50	6.00
18 Jose Cruz Jr.	2.50	6.00

1998 Ultra Rocket to Stardom

Randomly inserted in packs at a rate of one in 20, this 15-card insert set showcases rookies on a sculpted embossed and die-cut card designed to resemble a cloud of smoke.

COMPLETE SET (15)	12.50	30.00
SER.2 STATED ODDS 1:20		
1 Ben Grieve	.75	2.00
2 Magglio Ordonez	2.50	6.00
3 Travis Lee	.75	2.00
4 Mike Caruso	.75	2.00
5 Brian Rose	.75	2.00
6 Brad Fullmer	.75	2.00
7 Michael Coleman	.75	2.00
8 Juan Encarnacion	.75	2.00
9 Karim Garcia	.75	2.00
10 Todd Helton	1.25	3.00
11 Richard Hidalgo	.75	2.00
12 Paul Konerko	.75	2.00
13 Rod Myers	.75	2.00
14 Jaret Wright	.75	2.00
15 Miguel Tejada	2.00	5.00

1998 Ultra Ticket Studs

Randomly inserted in packs at a rate of one in 144, this 15-card insert set features color action player photos on sculpture embossed ticket-like designed cards. The cards open up to give details on what makes fans so crazy about their favorite players.

COMPLETE SET (15)	100.00	250.00
SER.2 STATED ODDS 1:144		
1 Travis Lee	2.50	6.00
2 Tony Gwynn	10.00	20.00
3 Scott Rolen	4.00	10.00
4 Nomar Garciaparra	12.50	25.00
5 Mike Piazza	12.50	25.00
6 Mark McGwire	20.00	40.00
7 Ken Griffey Jr.	12.50	25.00
8 Juan Gonzalez	2.50	6.00
9 Jose Cruz Jr.	2.50	6.00
10 Frank Thomas	6.00	15.00
11 Derek Jeter	20.00	40.00
12 Chipper Jones	6.00	15.00
13 Cal Ripken	25.00	50.00
14 Andruw Jones	4.00	10.00
15 Alex Rodriguez	12.50	25.00

1998 Ultra Top 30

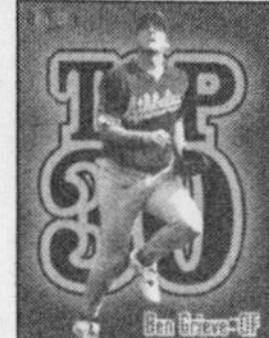

These cards which feature 30 of the leading baseball players were issued one per retail series two pack.

COMPLETE SET (30)	10.00	25.00
1 Barry Bonds	1.00	2.50
2 Ivan Rodriguez	.25	.60
3 Kenny Lofton	.15	.40
4 Albert Belle	.15	.40
5 Mo Vaughn	.15	.40
6 Jeff Bagwell	.25	.60
7 Mark McGwire	1.00	2.50
8 Darin Erstad	.15	.40
9 Roger Clemens	.75	2.00
10 Tony Gwynn	.50	1.25
11 Scott Rolen	.25	.60
12 Hideo Nomo	.40	1.00
13 Juan Gonzalez	.15	.40
14 Mike Piazza	.60	1.50
15 Greg Maddux	.60	1.50
16 Chipper Jones	.40	1.00
17 Andruw Jones	.25	.60
18 Derek Jeter	1.00	2.50
19 Nomar Garciaparra	.60	1.50
20 Alex Rodriguez	.60	1.50
21 Frank Thomas	.40	1.00
22 Cal Ripken	1.25	3.00
23 Ken Griffey Jr.	.60	1.50
24 Jose Cruz Jr.	.15	.40
25 Jaret Wright	.15	.40
26 Travis Lee	.15	.40
27 Wade Boggs	.40	1.00
28 Chuck Knoblauch	.15	.40
29 Joe Carter	.15	.40
30 Ben Grieve	.15	.40

1998 Ultra Win Now

Randomly inserted in packs at a rate of one in 72, this 20-card insert set features color action photos on plastic cards. A transparent section of the front allows you to see the player image in reverse from the back.

COMPLETE SET (20)	100.00	250.00
SER.2 STATED ODDS 1:72		
1 Alex Rodriguez	8.00	20.00
2 Andruw Jones	3.00	8.00
3 Cal Ripken	15.00	40.00
4 Chipper Jones	5.00	12.00
5 Darin Erstad	2.00	5.00
6 Derek Jeter	12.50	30.00
7 Frank Thomas	5.00	12.00
8 Greg Maddux	8.00	20.00
9 Hideo Nomo	5.00	12.00
10 Jeff Bagwell	3.00	8.00
11 Jose Cruz Jr.	2.00	5.00
12 Juan Gonzalez	2.00	5.00
13 Ken Griffey Jr.	8.00	20.00
14 Mark McGwire	12.50	30.00
15 Mike Piazza	8.00	20.00
16 Mo Vaughn	2.00	5.00
17 Nomar Garciaparra	8.00	20.00
18 Roger Clemens	10.00	25.00
19 Scott Rolen	3.00	8.00
20 Tony Gwynn	6.00	15.00

1999 Ultra Promo Sheet

This six card uncut sheet was distributed in dealer wholesale order forms and hobby media releases in late October, several weeks prior to the release of 1999 Ultra 1 baseball. The sheet is made up of six player cards, each of which parallel the player's regular issue Ultra card, except of course, for bold diagonal text stating "PROMOTIONAL SAMPLE" on the front and back of the cards.

NNO 99 Ultra 1 Sheet	2.00	5.00
Nomar Garciaparra		
Andruw Jones		
Kenny Lofton		
Mark McGwire		
Alex Rodriguez		
Kerry Wood		

1999 Ultra

This 250-card single-series set was distributed in 10-card packs with a suggested retail price of $2.69 and features color player photos on the fronts with stats by year in 15 categories and career highlights on the backs for 210 veterans. The set contains the following subsets: Prospects (25 rookie cards seeded 1:4 packs), Season Crowns (10 1998 statistical leaders seeded 1:8) and five checklist cards.

COMPLETE SET (250)	30.00	80.00
COMP.SET w/o SP's (215)	10.00	25.00
COMMON CARD (1-215)	.10	.30
COMMON SC (216-225)	.30	.75
COMMON (226-250)	.75	2.00
1 Greg Maddux	.50	1.25
2 Greg Vaughn	.10	.30
3 John Wetteland	.10	.30
4 Tino Martinez	.20	.50
5 Todd Walker	.10	.30
6 Troy O'Leary	.10	.30
7 Barry Larkin	.20	.50
8 Mike Lansing	.10	.30
9 Delino DeShields	.10	.30
10 Brett Tomko	.10	.30
11 Carlos Perez	.10	.30
12 Mark Langston	.10	.30
13 Jamie Moyer	.10	.30
14 Jose Guillen	.10	.30
15 Bartolo Colon	.10	.30
16 Brady Anderson	.10	.30
17 Walt Weiss	.10	.30
18 Shane Reynolds	.10	.30
19 David Segui	.10	.30
20 Vladimir Guerrero	.30	.75
21 Freddy Garcia	.10	.30
22 Carl Everett	.10	.30
23 Jose Cruz Jr.	.10	.30
24 David Ortiz	.30	.75
25 Andruw Jones	.20	.50
26 Darren Lewis	.10	.30
27 Ray Lankford	.10	.30
28 Wally Joyner	.10	.30
29 Charles Johnson	.10	.30
30 Derek Jeter	.75	2.00
31 Sean Casey	.10	.30
32 Bobby Bonilla	.10	.30
33 Todd Zeile	.10	.30
34 Todd Helton	.20	.50
35 David Wells	.10	.30
36 Darin Erstad	.10	.30
37 Ivan Rodriguez	.20	.50
38 Antonio Osuna	.10	.30
39 Mickey Morandini	.10	.30
40 Rusty Greer	.10	.30
41 Rod Beck	.10	.30
42 Larry Sutton	.10	.30
43 Edgar Renteria	.10	.30
44 Otis Nixon	.10	.30
45 Eli Marrero	.10	.30
46 Reggie Jefferson	.10	.30
47 Trevor Hoffman	.10	.30
48 Andres Galarraga	.10	.30
49 Scott Brosius	.10	.30
50 Vinny Castilla	.10	.30
51 Bret Boone	.10	.30
52 Masato Yoshii	.10	.30
53 Matt Williams	.10	.30
54 Robin Ventura	.10	.30
55 Jay Powell	.10	.30
56 Dean Palmer	.10	.30
57 Eric Milton	.10	.30
58 Willie McGee	.10	.30
59 Tony Gwynn	.40	1.00
60 Tom Gordon	.10	.30
61 Dante Bichette	.10	.30
62 Jaret Wright	.10	.30
63 Devon White	.10	.30
64 Frank Thomas	.30	.75
65 Mike Piazza	.50	1.25
66 Jose Offerman	.10	.30
67 Pat Meares	.10	.30
68 Brian Meadows	.10	.30
69 Nomar Garciaparra	.50	1.25
70 Mark McGwire	.75	2.00
71 Tony Graffanino	.10	.30
72 Ken Griffey Jr.	.50	1.25
73 Ken Caminiti	.10	.30
74 Todd Jones	.10	.30
75 A.J. Hinch	.10	.30
76 Marquis Grissom	.10	.30
77 Jay Buhner	.10	.30
78 Albert Belle	.10	.30
79 Brian Anderson	.10	.30
80 Quinton McCracken	.10	.30
81 Omar Vizquel	.20	.50
82 Todd Stottlemyre	.10	.30
83 Cal Ripken	1.00	2.50
84 Magglio Ordonez	.10	.30
85 John Olerud	.10	.30
86 Hal Morris	.10	.30
87 Derrek Lee	.20	.50
88 Doug Glanville	.10	.30
89 Marty Cordova	.10	.30
90 Kevin Brown	.10	.30
91 Kevin Young	.10	.30
92 Rico Brogna	.10	.30
93 Wilson Alvarez	.10	.30
94 Bob Wickman	.10	.30
95 Jim Thome	.20	.50
96 Mike Mussina	.20	.50
97 Al Leiter	.10	.30
98 Travis Lee	.10	.30
99 Jeff King	.10	.30
100 Kerry Wood	.10	.30
101 Cliff Floyd	.10	.30
102 Jose Valentin	.10	.30
103 Manny Ramirez	.20	.50
104 Butch Huskey	.10	.30
105 Scott Erickson	.10	.30
106 Ray Durham	.10	.30
107 Johnny Damon	.20	.50
108 Craig Counsell	.10	.30
109 Rolando Arrojo	.10	.30
110 Bob Abreu	.10	.30
111 Tony Womack	.10	.30
112 Mike Stanley	.10	.30
113 Kenny Lofton	.10	.30
114 Eric Davis	.10	.30
115 Jeff Conine	.10	.30
116 Carlos Baerga	.10	.30
117 Rondell White	.10	.30
118 Billy Wagner	.10	.30
119 Ed Sprague	.10	.30
120 Jason Schmidt	.10	.30
121 Edgar Martinez	.20	.50
122 Travis Fryman	.10	.30
123 Armando Benitez	.10	.30
124 Matt Stairs	.10	.30
125 Roberto Hernandez	.10	.30
126 Jay Bell	.10	.30
127 Justin Thompson	.10	.30
128 John Jaha	.10	.30
129 Mike Caruso	.10	.30
130 Miguel Tejada	.10	.30
131 Geoff Jenkins	.10	.30
132 Wade Boggs	.20	.50
133 Andy Benes	.10	.30
134 Aaron Sele	.10	.30
135 Bret Saberhagen	.10	.30
136 Mariano Rivera	.30	.75
137 Neifi Perez	.10	.30
138 Paul Konerko	.10	.30
139 Barry Bonds	.75	2.00
140 Garret Anderson	.10	.30
141 Bernie Williams	.20	.50
142 Gary Sheffield	.10	.30
143 Rafael Palmeiro	.20	.50
144 Orel Hershiser	.10	.30
145 Craig Biggio	.20	.50
146 Dmitri Young	.10	.30
147 Damion Easley	.10	.30
148 Henry Rodriguez	.10	.30
149 Brad Radke	.10	.30
150 Pedro Martinez	.20	.50
151 Mike Lieberthal	.10	.30
152 Jim Leyritz	.10	.30
153 Chuck Knoblauch	.10	.30
154 Darryl Kile	.10	.30
155 Brian Jordan	.10	.30
156 Chipper Jones	.30	.75
157 Pete Harnisch	.10	.30
158 Moises Alou	.10	.30
159 Ismael Valdes	.10	.30
160 Stan Javier	.10	.30
161 Mark Grace	.20	.50
162 Jason Giambi	.10	.30
163 Chuck Finley	.10	.30
164 Juan Encarnacion	.10	.30
165 Chan Ho Park	.10	.30
166 Randy Johnson	.30	.75
167 J.T. Snow	.10	.30
168 Tim Salmon	.20	.50
169 Brian L.Hunter	.10	.30
170 Rickey Henderson	.30	.75
171 Cal Eldred	.10	.30
172 Curt Schilling	.10	.30
173 Alex Rodriguez	.50	1.25
174 Dustin Hermanson	.10	.30
175 Mike Hampton	.10	.30
176 Shawn Green	.10	.30
177 Roberto Alomar	.20	.50
178 Sandy Alomar Jr.	.10	.30
179 Larry Walker	.10	.30
180 Mo Vaughn	.10	.30
181 Raul Mondesi	.10	.30
182 Hideki Irabu	.10	.30
183 Jim Edmonds	.10	.30
184 Shawn Estes	.10	.30
185 Tony Clark	.10	.30
186 Dan Wilson	.10	.30
187 Michael Tucker	.10	.30
188 Jeff Shaw	.10	.30
189 Mark Grudzielanek	.10	.30
190 Roger Clemens	.60	1.50
191 Juan Gonzalez	.10	.30
192 Sammy Sosa	.30	.75
193 Troy Percival	.10	.30
194 Robb Nen	.10	.30
195 Bill Mueller	.10	.30
196 Ben Grieve	.10	.30
197 Luis Gonzalez	.10	.30
198 Will Clark	.20	.50
199 Jeff Cirillo	.10	.30
200 Scott Rolen	.20	.50
201 Reggie Sanders	.10	.30
202 Fred McGriff	.20	.50
203 Denny Neagle	.10	.30
204 Brad Fullmer	.10	.30
205 Royce Clayton	.10	.30
206 Jose Canseco	.20	.50
207 Jeff Bagwell	.20	.50
208 Hideo Nomo	.30	.75
209 Karim Garcia	.10	.30
210 Kenny Rogers	.10	.30
211 Kerry Wood CL	.10	.30
212 Alex Rodriguez CL	.30	.75
213 Cal Ripken CL	.50	1.25
214 Frank Thomas CL	.20	.50
215 Ken Griffey Jr. CL	.30	.75
216 Alex Rodriguez SC	1.25	3.00
217 Greg Maddux SC	1.25	3.00
218 Juan Gonzalez SC	.30	.75
219 Ken Griffey Jr. SC	1.25	3.00
220 Kerry Wood SC	.30	.75
221 Mark McGwire SC	2.00	5.00
222 Mike Piazza SC	1.25	3.00
223 Rickey Henderson SC	.75	2.00
224 Sammy Sosa SC	.75	2.00
225 Travis Lee SC	.30	.75
226 Gabe Alvarez PROS	.75	2.00
227 Matt Anderson PROS	.75	2.00
228 Adrian Beltre PROS	.75	2.00
229 O.Cabrera PROS	.75	2.00
230 Orl. Hernandez PROS	.75	2.00
231 A.Ramirez PROS	.75	2.00
232 Troy Glaus PROS	1.25	3.00
233 Gabe Kapler PROS	.75	2.00
234 Jeremy Giambi PROS	.75	2.00
235 Derrick Gibson PROS	.75	2.00
236 Carlton Loewer PROS	.75	2.00
237 Mike Frank PROS	.75	2.00
238 Carlos Guillen PROS	.75	2.00
239 Alex Gonzalez PROS	.75	2.00
240 Enrique Wilson PROS	.75	2.00
241 J.D. Drew PROS	.75	2.00
242 Bruce Chen PROS	.75	2.00
243 Ryan Minor PROS	.75	2.00
244 Preston Wilson PROS	.75	2.00
245 Josh Booty PROS	.75	2.00
246 Luis Ordaz PROS	.75	2.00
247 G.Lombard PROS	.75	2.00
248 Matt Clement PROS	.75	2.00
249 Eric Chavez PROS	.75	2.00
250 Corey Koskie PROS	.75	2.00

1999 Ultra Gold Medallion

Randomly inserted one in every hobby only pack for regular cards, one in 40 for Prospects, and one in 80 for Season Crowns, this 250-card set is a gold parallel version of the base set.

*GOLD: 1.25X TO 3X BASIC CARDS
*GOLD SC: 2X TO 5X BASIC SC
SEASON CROWN ODDS 1:80 HOBBY
*GOLD PROS: 1X TO 2.5X BASIC PROS
PROSPECT ODDS 1:40 HOBBY

1999 Ultra Platinum Medallion

Randomly inserted in hobby packs only, this 250-card set is a parallel version of the base set. Only 99 of the 215 veteran cards were produced and numbered. Only 65 of the Prospects (cards numbered from 226 through 250) subset was produced and serially numbered. Only 50 of the Season Crowns (cards numbered from 216 through 225) subset was produced and serially numbered.

*PLAT: 15X TO 40X BASIC CARDS
*PLAT SC: 12.5X TO 30X BASIC SC
*PLAT PROS: 2.5X TO 6X BASIC PROS

1999 Ultra The Book On

Randomly inserted in packs at the rate of one in six, this 20-card set features action color photos of top players with a detailed analysis of why they are so good printed on the backs.

COMPLETE SET (20)	20.00	50.00
SER.1 STATED ODDS 1:6		
1 Kerry Wood	.30	.75
2 Ken Griffey Jr.	1.25	3.00
3 Frank Thomas	.75	2.00
4 Albert Belle	.30	.75
5 Juan Gonzalez	.30	.75
6 Jeff Bagwell	.50	1.25
7 Mark McGwire	2.00	5.00
8 Barry Bonds	2.00	5.00
9 Andruw Jones	.50	1.25
10 Mo Vaughn	.30	.75
11 Scott Rolen	.50	1.25
12 Travis Lee	.30	.75
13 Tony Gwynn	1.00	2.50
14 Greg Maddux	1.25	3.00
15 Mike Piazza	1.25	3.00
16 Chipper Jones	.75	2.00
17 Nomar Garciaparra	1.25	3.00
18 Cal Ripken	2.50	6.00
19 Derek Jeter	2.00	5.00
20 Alex Rodriguez	1.25	3.00

1999 Ultra Damage Inc.

Randomly inserted in packs at the rate of one in 72, this 15-card set features color images of top players printed on a business card design.

COMPLETE SET (15)	100.00	200.00
SER.1 STATED ODDS 1:72		
1 Alex Rodriguez	6.00	15.00
2 Greg Maddux	6.00	15.00
3 Cal Ripken	12.50	30.00
4 Chipper Jones	4.00	10.00
5 Derek Jeter	10.00	25.00
6 Frank Thomas	4.00	10.00
7 Juan Gonzalez	1.50	4.00
8 Ken Griffey Jr.	6.00	15.00
9 Kerry Wood	1.50	4.00
10 Mark McGwire	10.00	25.00
11 Mike Piazza	6.00	15.00
12 Nomar Garciaparra	6.00	15.00
13 Scott Rolen	2.50	6.00
14 Tony Gwynn	5.00	12.00
15 Travis Lee	1.50	4.00

1999 Ultra Diamond Producers

Randomly inserted in packs at the rate of one in 288, this 10-card set features action color player photos printed on full foil plastic die-cut cards with custom embossing.

COMPLETE SET (10)	125.00	300.00
SER.1 STATED ODDS 1:288		
1 Ken Griffey Jr.	8.00	20.00
2 Frank Thomas	5.00	12.00
3 Alex Rodriguez	8.00	20.00
4 Cal Ripken	15.00	40.00
5 Mike Piazza	8.00	20.00
6 Mark McGwire	12.50	30.00
7 Greg Maddux	8.00	20.00
8 Kerry Wood	2.00	5.00
9 Chipper Jones	5.00	12.00
10 Derek Jeter	12.50	30.00

1999 Ultra RBI Kings

Randomly inserted one in every retail pack only, this 30-card set features action color photos of top run producing players.

COMPLETE SET (30)	12.50	30.00
ONE PER RETAIL PACK		
1 Rafael Palmeiro	.25	.60
2 Mo Vaughn	.15	.40
3 Ivan Rodriguez	.25	.60
4 Barry Bonds	1.00	2.50
5 Albert Belle	.15	.40
6 Jeff Bagwell	.25	.60
7 Mark McGwire	1.00	2.50
8 Darin Erstad	.15	.40
9 Manny Ramirez	.25	.60
10 Chipper Jones	.40	1.00
11 Jim Thome	.25	.60
12 Scott Rolen	.25	.60
13 Tony Gwynn	.50	1.25
14 Juan Gonzalez	.15	.40
15 Mike Piazza	.60	1.50
16 Sammy Sosa	.40	1.00
17 Andruw Jones	.25	.60
18 Derek Jeter	1.00	2.50
19 Nomar Garciaparra	.60	1.50
20 Alex Rodriguez	.60	1.50
21 Frank Thomas	.40	1.00
22 Cal Ripken	1.25	3.00
23 Ken Griffey Jr.	.60	1.50
24 Travis Lee	.15	.40
25 Paul O'Neill	.15	.40
26 Greg Vaughn	.15	.40
27 Andres Galarraga	.15	.40
28 Tino Martinez	.25	.60
29 Jose Canseco	.25	.60
30 Ben Grieve	.15	.40

1999 Ultra Thunderclap

Randomly inserted in packs at the rate of one in 36, this 15-card set features color player photos printed on embossed cards with silver pattern holofoil.

COMPLETE SET (15)	40.00	100.00
SER.1 STATED ODDS 1:36		
1 Alex Rodriguez	3.00	8.00
2 Andruw Jones	1.25	3.00
3 Cal Ripken	6.00	15.00
4 Chipper Jones	2.00	5.00
5 Darin Erstad	.75	2.00
6 Derek Jeter	5.00	12.00
7 Frank Thomas	2.00	5.00
8 Jeff Bagwell	1.25	3.00
9 Juan Gonzalez	.75	2.00
10 Ken Griffey Jr.	3.00	8.00
11 Mark McGwire	5.00	12.00
12 Mike Piazza	3.00	8.00
13 Travis Lee	.75	2.00
14 Nomar Garciaparra	3.00	8.00
15 Scott Rolen	1.25	3.00

1999 Ultra World Premiere

Randomly inserted in packs at the rate of one in 18, this 15-card set features action color photos of top 1998 rookies printed on sculpture embossed silver holofoil cards.

COMPLETE SET (15)	8.00	20.00
SER.1 STATED ODDS 1:18		
1 Gabe Alvarez	.50	1.25
2 Kerry Wood	.75	2.00
3 Orlando Hernandez	.50	1.25
4 Mike Caruso	.75	2.00
5 Matt Anderson	.50	1.25
6 Randall Simon	.75	2.00
7 Adrian Beltre	.50	1.25
8 Scott Elarton	.75	2.00
9 Karim Garcia	.75	2.00
10 Mike Frank	.50	1.25
11 Richard Hidalgo	.75	2.00
12 Paul Konerko	.75	2.00
13 Travis Lee	.75	2.00
14 J.D. Drew	.75	2.00
15 Miguel Tejada	.75	2.00

2000 Ultra

This 300 card set was issued late in 1999. The cards were distributed in 10 card packs with an SRP of $2.69. The product was issued in either 8, 12 or 30 box cases. The prospect subset were numbered from 251 through 300 and were printed in shorter quantity than the regular cards and inserted one every four packs. Two separate Alex Rodriguez

Promo cards were distributed to dealers and hobby media several weeks prior to the product's release. The first card features identical glossy card front stock as the basic Ultra 2000 product and has the words "PROMOTIONAL SAMPLE" running diagonally across the back of the card. The second, more scarce, card features a lenticular ribbed plastic card front (creating a primitive 3-D effect). Both promos share the same photo of Rodriguez as is used on the basic issue A-Rod 2000 Ultra card.

COMPLETE SET (300)	40.00	100.00
COMP.SET w/o SP's (250)	10.00	25.00
COMMON CARD (1-250)	.10	.30
COMMON (251-300)	1.50	4.00
1 Alex Rodriguez	.50	1.25
2 Shawn Green	.10	.30
3 Magglio Ordonez	.10	.30
4 Tony Gwynn	.40	1.00
5 Joe McEwing	.10	.30
6 Jose Rosado	.10	.30
7 Sammy Sosa	.30	.75
8 Gary Sheffield	.10	.30
9 Mickey Morandini	.10	.30
10 Mo Vaughn	.10	.30
11 Todd Hollandsworth	.10	.30
12 Tom Gordon	.10	.30
13 Charles Johnson	.10	.30
14 Derek Bell	.10	.30
15 Kevin Young	.10	.30
16 Jay Buhner	.10	.30
17 J.T. Snow	.10	.30
18 Jay Bell	.10	.30
19 John Rocker	.10	.30
20 Ivan Rodriguez	.20	.50
21 Pokey Reese	.10	.30
22 Paul O'Neill	.20	.50
23 Ronnie Belliard	.10	.30
24 Ryan Rupe	.10	.30
25 Travis Fryman	.10	.30
26 Trot Nixon	.10	.30
27 Wally Joyner	.10	.30
28 Andy Pettitte	.20	.50
29 Dan Wilson	.10	.30
30 Orlando Hernandez	.10	.30
31 Dmitri Young	.10	.30
32 Edgar Renteria	.10	.30
33 Eric Karros	.10	.30
34 Fernando Seguignol	.10	.30
35 Jason Kendall	.10	.30
36 Jeff Shaw	.10	.30
37 Matt Lawton	.10	.30
38 Robin Ventura	.20	.50
39 Scott Williamson	.10	.30
40 Ben Grieve	.10	.30
41 Billy Wagner	.10	.30
42 Javy Lopez	.10	.30
43 Joe Randa	.10	.30
44 Neifi Perez	.10	.30
45 David Justice	.10	.30
46 Ray Durham	.10	.30
47 Dustin Hermanson	.10	.30
48 Andres Galarraga	.10	.30
49 Brad Fullmer	.10	.30
50 Nomar Garciaparra	.50	1.25
51 David Cone	.10	.30
52 David Nilsson	.10	.30
53 David Wells	.10	.30
54 Miguel Tejada	.10	.30
55 Ismael Valdes	.10	.30
56 Jose Lima	.10	.30
57 Juan Encarnacion	.10	.30
58 Fred McGriff	.20	.50
59 Kenny Rogers	.10	.30
60 Vladimir Guerrero	.30	.75
61 Benito Santiago	.10	.30
62 Chris Singleton	.10	.30
63 Carlos Lee	.10	.30
64 Sean Casey	.10	.30
65 Tom Goodwin	.10	.30
66 Todd Hundley	.10	.30
67 Ellis Burks	.10	.30
68 Tim Hudson	.10	.30
69 Matt Stairs	.10	.30
70 Chipper Jones UER	.30	.75
Dodgers logo on the back		
71 Craig Biggio	.20	.50
72 Brian Rose	.10	.30
73 Carlos Delgado	.10	.30
74 Eddie Taubensee	.10	.30
75 John Smoltz	.20	.50
76 Ken Caminiti	.10	.30
77 Rafael Palmeiro	.20	.50
78 Sidney Ponson	.10	.30
79 Todd Helton	.20	.50
80 Juan Gonzalez	.10	.30
81 Bruce Aven	.10	.30
82 Desi Relaford	.10	.30
83 Johnny Damon	.20	.50
84 Albert Belle	.10	.30
85 Mark McGwire	.75	2.00
86 Rico Brogna	.10	.30
87 Tom Glavine	.20	.50
88 Harold Baines	.10	.30
89 Chad Allen	.10	.30
90 Barry Bonds	.75	2.00
91 Mark Grace	.20	.50
92 Paul Byrd	.10	.30
93 Roberto Alomar	.20	.50
94 Roberto Hernandez	.10	.30
95 Steve Finley	.10	.30
96 Bret Boone	.10	.30
97 Charles Nagy	.10	.30
98 Eric Chavez	.10	.30
99 Jamie Moyer	.10	.30
100 Ken Griffey Jr.	.50	1.25
101 J.D. Drew	.10	.30
102 Todd Stottlemyre	.10	.30

103 Tony Fernandez .10 .30
104 Jeromy Burnitz .10 .30
105 Jeremy Giambi .10 .30
106 Livan Hernandez .10 .30
107 Marlon Anderson .10 .30
108 Troy Glaus .10 .30
109 Troy O'Leary .10 .30
110 Scott Rolen .20 .50
111 Bernard Gilkey .10 .30
112 Brady Anderson .10 .30
113 Chuck Knoblauch .10 .30
114 Jeff Weaver .10 .30
115 B.J. Surhoff .10 .30
116 Alex Gonzalez .10 .30
117 Vinny Castilla .10 .30
118 Tim Salmon .20 .50
119 Brian Jordan .10 .30
120 Corey Koskie .10 .30
121 Dean Palmer .10 .30
122 Gabe Kapler .10 .30
123 Jim Edmonds .10 .30
124 John Jaha .10 .30
125 Mark Grudzielanek .10 .30
126 Mike Bordick .10 .30
127 Mike Lieberthal .10 .30
128 Pete Harnisch .10 .30
129 Russ Ortiz .10 .30
130 Kevin Brown .20 .50
131 Troy Percival .10 .30
132 Alex Gonzalez .10 .30
133 Bartolo Colon .10 .30
134 John Valentin .10 .30
135 Jose Hernandez .10 .30
136 Marquis Grissom .10 .30
137 Wade Boggs .20 .50
138 Dante Bichette .10 .30
139 Bobby Higginson .10 .30
140 Frank Thomas .30 .75
141 Geoff Jenkins .10 .30
142 Jason Giambi .10 .30
143 Jeff Cirillo .10 .30
144 Sandy Alomar Jr. .10 .30
145 Luis Gonzalez .10 .30
146 Preston Wilson .10 .30
147 Carlos Beltran .10 .30
148 Greg Vaughn .10 .30
149 Carlos Febles .10 .30
150 Jose Canseco .20 .50
151 Kris Benson .10 .30
152 Chuck Finley .10 .30
153 Michael Barrett .10 .30
154 Rey Ordonez .10 .30
155 Adrian Beltre .10 .30
156 Andruw Jones .20 .50
157 Barry Larkin .20 .50
158 Brian Giles .10 .30
159 Carl Everett .10 .30
160 Manny Ramirez .20 .50
161 Darryl Kile .10 .30
162 Edgar Martinez .20 .50
163 Jeff Kent .10 .30
164 Matt Williams .10 .30
165 Mike Piazza .50 1.25
166 Pedro Martinez .20 .50
167 Ray Lankford .10 .30
168 Roger Cedeno .10 .30
169 Ron Coomer .10 .30
170 Cal Ripken 1.00 2.50
171 Jose Offerman .10 .30
172 Kenny Lofton .10 .30
173 Kent Bottenfield .10 .30
174 Kevin Millwood .10 .30
175 Omar Daal .10 .30
176 Orlando Cabrera .10 .30
177 Pat Hentgen .10 .30
178 Tino Martinez .20 .50
179 Tony Clark .10 .30
180 Roger Clemens .60 1.50
181 Brad Radke .10 .30
182 Darin Erstad .10 .30
183 Jose Jimenez .10 .30
184 Jim Thome .20 .50
185 John Wetteland .10 .30
186 Justin Thompson .10 .30
187 John Halama .10 .30
188 Lee Stevens .10 .30
189 Miguel Cairo .10 .30
190 Mike Mussina .20 .50
191 Raul Mondesi .10 .30
192 Armando Rios .10 .30
193 Trevor Hoffman .10 .30
194 Tony Batista .10 .30
195 Will Clark .20 .50
196 Brad Ausmus .10 .30
197 Chili Davis .10 .30
198 Cliff Floyd .10 .30
199 Curt Schilling .10 .30
200 Derek Jeter .75 2.00
201 Henry Rodriguez .10 .30
202 Jose Cruz Jr. .10 .30
203 Omar Vizquel .20 .50
204 Randy Johnson .30 .75
205 Reggie Sanders .10 .30
206 Al Leiter .10 .30
207 Damion Easley .10 .30
208 David Bell .10 .30
209 Fernando Tatis .10 .30
210 Kerry Wood .10 .30
211 Kevin Appier .10 .30
212 Mariano Rivera .30 .75
213 Mike Caruso .10 .30
214 Moises Alou .10 .30
215 Randy Winn .10 .30
216 Roy Halladay .10 .30
217 Shannon Stewart .10 .30
218 Todd Walker .10 .30
219 Jim Parque .10 .30
220 Travis Lee .10 .30
221 Andy Ashby .10 .30
222 Ed Sprague .10 .30
223 Larry Walker .10 .30
224 Rick Helling .10 .30
225 Rusty Greer .10 .30
226 Todd Zeile .10 .30
227 Freddy Garcia .10 .30
228 Hideo Nomo .30 .75
229 Marty Cordova .10 .30
230 Greg Maddux .50 1.25
231 Rondell White .10 .30
232 Paul Konerko .10 .30
233 Warren Morris .10 .30
234 Bernie Williams .20 .50
235 Bob Abreu .10 .30
236 John Olerud .10 .30
237 Doug Glanville .10 .30
238 Eric Young .10 .30
239 Robb Nen .10 .30
240 Jeff Bagwell .20 .50
241 Sterling Hitchcock .10 .30
242 Todd Greene .10 .30
243 Bill Mueller .10 .30
244 Rickey Henderson .30 .75
245 Chan Ho Park .10 .30
246 Jason Schmidt .10 .30
247 Jeff Zimmerman .10 .30
248 Jermaine Dye .10 .30
249 Randall Simon .10 .30
250 Richie Sexson .10 .30
251 Micah Bowie PROS 1.50 4.00
252 Joe Nathan PROS 1.50 4.00
253 C.Woodward PROS 1.50 4.00
254 Lance Berkman PROS 1.50 4.00
255 Ruben Mateo PROS 1.50 4.00
256 R.Branyan PROS 1.50 4.00
257 Randy Wolf PROS 1.50 4.00
258 A.J. Burnett PROS 1.50 4.00
259 Mark Quinn PROS 1.50 4.00
260 Buddy Carlyle PROS 1.50 4.00
261 Ben Davis PROS 1.50 4.00
262 Yamid Haad PROS 1.50 4.00
263 Mike Colangelo PROS 1.50 4.00
264 Rick Ankiel PROS 1.50 4.00
265 Jacque Jones PROS 1.50 4.00
266 Kelly Dransfeldt PROS 1.50 4.00
267 Matt Riley PROS 1.50 4.00
268 Adam Kennedy PROS 1.50 4.00
269 Octavio Dotel PROS 1.50 4.00
270 F.Cordero PROS 1.50 4.00
271 Wilton Veras PROS 1.50 4.00
272 C.Pickering PROS 1.50 4.00
273 Alex Sanchez PROS 1.50 4.00
274 Tony Armas Jr. PROS 1.50 4.00
275 Pat Burrell PROS 1.50 4.00
276 Chad Meyers PROS 1.50 4.00
277 Ben Petrick PROS 1.50 4.00
278 R.Hernandez PROS 1.50 4.00
279 Ed Yarnall PROS 1.50 4.00
280 Erubiel Durazo PROS 1.50 4.00
281 Vernon Wells PROS 1.50 4.00
282 G.Matthews Jr. PROS 1.50 4.00
283 Kip Wells PROS 1.50 4.00
284 Peter Bergeron PROS 1.50 4.00
285 Travis Dawkins PROS 1.50 4.00
286 Jorge Toca PROS 1.50 4.00
287 Cole Liniak PROS 1.50 4.00
288 C.Hermansen PROS 1.50 4.00
289 Eric Gagne PROS 2.00 5.00
290 C.Hutchinson PROS 1.50 4.00
291 Eric Munson PROS 1.50 4.00
292 Wiki Gonzalez PROS 1.50 4.00
293 A.Soriano PROS 2.00 5.00
294 T.Durrington PROS 1.50 4.00
295 Ben Molina PROS 1.50 4.00
296 Aaron Myette PROS 1.50 4.00
297 Wily Pena PROS 1.50 4.00
298 Kevin Barker PROS 1.50 4.00
299 Geoff Blum PROS 1.50 4.00
300 Josh Beckett PROS 2.00 5.00
P1 Alex Rodriguez Promo .60 1.50
P2 A.Rodriguez Promo 3-D 2.00 5.00

2000 Ultra Gold Medallion

This set is a parallel to the regular Ultra set. The regular cards from 1 through 250 were issued one per hobby pack and the prospect cards were issued one every 24 hobby packs. These cards have special die-cutting and have gold coating and gold foil stamping.

*GOLD 1-250: 1.25X TO 3X BASIC CARDS
*GOLD PROS: .75X TO 2X BASIC CARDS

2000 Ultra Platinum Medallion

Randomly inserted into hobby packs, these cards parallel the regular Ultra set. These cards are serial numbered to 50 for the veterans and 25 for the prospects (251-300). These die cut cards have silver coating and silver foil. Pricing is unavaiable due to scarcity on cards 251-300.

*PLAT 1-250: 15X TO 40X BASIC CARDS
*PROSPECTS: 4X TO 10X BASIC CARDS
251-300 NO PRICING DUE TO SCARCITY

2000 Ultra Crunch Time

Inserted one every 72 packs, these 15 cards feature players who are among those players known for their clutch performances. The horizontal cards are printed on suede stock and then are gold foil stamped.

COMPLETE SET (15) 100.00 200.00
1 Nomar Garciaparra 5.00 12.00
2 Ken Griffey Jr. 5.00 12.00
3 Mark McGwire 8.00 20.00
4 Alex Rodriguez 5.00 12.00
5 Derek Jeter 8.00 20.00
6 Sammy Sosa 3.00 8.00
7 Mike Piazza 5.00 12.00
8 Cal Ripken 10.00 25.00
9 Frank Thomas 3.00 8.00
10 Juan Gonzalez 1.25 3.00
11 J.D. Drew 1.25 3.00
12 Greg Maddux 5.00 12.00
13 Tony Gwynn 4.00 10.00
14 Vladimir Guerrero 3.00 8.00
15 Ben Grieve 1.25 3.00

2000 Ultra Diamond Mine

Inserted one every six packs, these 15 cards feature some of the brightest stars of the baseball diamond. The cards are printed on silver metallic ink and have silver foil stamping.

COMPLETE SET (15) 15.00 30.00
1 Greg Maddux .75 2.00
2 Mark McGwire 1.25 3.00
3 Ken Griffey Jr. .75 2.00
4 Cal Ripken 1.50 4.00
5 Nomar Garciaparra .75 2.00
6 Mike Piazza .75 2.00
7 Alex Rodriguez .75 2.00
8 Frank Thomas .50 1.25
9 Juan Gonzalez .20 .50
10 Derek Jeter 1.25 3.00
11 Tony Gwynn .60 1.50
12 Chipper Jones .50 1.25
13 Sammy Sosa .50 1.25
14 Roger Clemens 1.00 2.50
15 Vladimir Guerrero .50 1.25

2000 Ultra Feel the Game

Inserted at a rate of one in 168, these cards feature pieces of game used memorabilia of some of today's stars. There is a player photo to go with the swatch of material used (either jersey or batting gloves). It is widely believed that the Frank Thomas is the toughest card to find in the set.

1 Alex Rodriguez Jsy 10.00 25.00
2 Chipper Jones Jsy 6.00 15.00
3 Rob Alomar Btg Glv SP 20.00 50.00
4 Greg Maddux Jsy 6.00 15.00
5 Pedro Martinez Jsy 6.00 15.00
6 Cal Ripken Jsy 20.00 50.00
7 Robin Ventura Jsy 4.00 10.00
8 J.D. Drew Jsy 4.00 10.00
9 Randy Johnson Jsy 6.00 15.00
10 Scott Rolen Jsy 6.00 15.00
11 Kevin Millwood Jsy 4.00 10.00
12 Frank Thomas Btg Glv SP 40.00 80.00
13 Tony Gwynn Btg Glv SP 40.00 80.00
14 Curt Schilling Jsy 4.00 10.00
15 Edgar Martinez Btg Glv 6.00 15.00

2000 Ultra Fresh Ink

Randomly inserted into packs, these cards feature signed cards of either young players or veteran stars. One card in this set is a combo signature card of the three players used in the Club 3000 series. After each player name in our checklist is a number indicating how many cards they signed for this promotion.

1 Bob Abreu/200 10.00 25.00
2 Chad Allen/975 4.00 10.00
3 Marlon Anderson/975 4.00 10.00
4 Rick Ankiel/500 10.00 25.00
5 Glen Barker/975 4.00 10.00
6 Michael Barrett/975 4.00 10.00
7 Carlos Beltran/975 6.00 15.00
8 Adrian Beltre/900 8.00 20.00
9 Peter Bergeron/1000 4.00 10.00
10 Wade Boggs/250 15.00 40.00
11 Barry Bonds/250 100.00 175.00
12 Pat Burrell/600 6.00 15.00
13 Roger Cedeno/500 6.00 15.00
14 Eric Chavez/800 6.00 15.00
15 Bruce Chen/600 4.00 10.00
16 Johnny Damon/750 6.00 15.00
17 Ben Davis/1000 4.00 10.00
18 Carlos Delgado/275 10.00 25.00
19 Einar Diaz/975 4.00 10.00
20 Octavio Dotel/950 4.00 10.00
21 J.D. Drew/600 6.00 15.00
22 Scott Elarton/1000 4.00 10.00
23 Freddy Garcia/500 6.00 15.00
24 Jeremy Giambi/975 4.00 10.00
25 Troy Glaus/500 10.00 25.00
26 Shawn Green/350 15.00 40.00
27 Tony Gwynn/250 30.00 60.00
28 Richard Hidalgo/500 4.00 10.00
29 Bobby Higginson/975 4.00 10.00
30 Tim Hudson/975 10.00 25.00
31 Norm Hutchins/1000 4.00 10.00
32 Derek Jeter/95 200.00 300.00
33 Randy Johnson/240 40.00 80.00
34 Gabe Kapler/725 6.00 15.00
35 Jason Kendall/375 10.00 25.00
36 Paul Konerko/500 10.00 25.00
37 Matt Lawton/1000 4.00 10.00
38 Carlos Lee/900 6.00 15.00
39 Jose Macias/1000 4.00 10.00
40 Greg Maddux/225 60.00 120.00
41 Kevin Millwood/500 6.00 15.00
42 Warren Morris/1000 4.00 10.00
43 Eric Munson/900 4.00 10.00
44 Heath Murray/925 4.00 10.00
45 Joe Nathan/1000 10.00 25.00
46 Magglio Ordonez/335 10.00 25.00
47 Angel Pena/1000 4.00 10.00
48 Cal Ripken/350 60.00 120.00
49 Alex Rodriguez/350 50.00 100.00
50 Scott Rolen/250 15.00 40.00
51 Ryan Rupe/1000 4.00 10.00
52 Curt Schilling/375 20.00 50.00
53 Randall Simon/1000 4.00 10.00
54 Alfonso Soriano/975 6.00 15.00
55 Shannon Stewart/275 10.00 25.00
56 Miguel Tejada/1000 10.00 25.00
57 Frank Thomas/150 50.00 100.00
58 Jeff Weaver/1000 6.00 15.00
59 Randy Wolf/1000 6.00 15.00
60 Ed Yarnall/1000 4.00 10.00
61 Kevin Young/1000 4.00 10.00
62 Wade Boggs 250.00 450.00
Tony Gwynn
Nolan Ryan 100

2000 Ultra Fresh Ink Gold

These cards were actually distributed in 2001 Fleer Platinum Rack Packs, but are catalogued here for easier reference. According to representatives at Fleer, twenty-five different cards were featured in this set. All of the cards are hand-numbered "1 of 1's" and feature a gold (rather than silver) foil signed sticker on front. Our checklist is incomplete at this time due to lack of information.

1 Lance Berkman
2 Roger Cedeno
3 Troy Glaus
4 Richard Hidalgo
5 Derek Jeter
6 Jose Macias
7 Cal Ripken
8 Alfonso Soriano
9 Miguel Tejada

2000 Ultra Swing Kings

Inserted one every 24 packs, these 10 cards feature some of the leading power hitters in baseball. These cards are made of contemporary plastice with glittering silver foil highlights.

COMPLETE SET (10) 20.00 50.00
1 Cal Ripken 3.00 8.00
2 Nomar Garciaparra 1.50 4.00
3 Frank Thomas 1.00 2.50
4 Tony Gwynn 1.25 3.00
5 Ken Griffey Jr. 1.50 4.00
6 Chipper Jones 1.00 2.50
7 Mark McGwire 2.50 6.00
8 Sammy Sosa 1.00 2.50
9 Derek Jeter 2.50 6.00
10 Alex Rodriguez 1.50 4.00

2000 Ultra Talented

Randomly inserted into hobby packs, these 10 cards feature multi-talented players. These cards feature metallic ink on holofoil background with gold foil stamped accents. 100 serial-numbered sets were produced.

1 Sammy Sosa 12.50 30.00
2 Derek Jeter 30.00 80.00
3 Alex Rodriguez 20.00 50.00
4 Mike Piazza 20.00 50.00
5 Ken Griffey Jr. 20.00 50.00
6 Nomar Garciaparra 20.00 50.00
7 Mark McGwire 30.00 80.00
8 Cal Ripken 40.00 100.00
9 Frank Thomas 12.50 30.00
10 J.D. Drew 5.00 12.00

2000 Ultra World Premiere

Inserted one every 12 packs, these 10 cards feature 12 of the leading prospects in baseball. The die cut cards are printed with etched foil.

COMPLETE SET (10) 5.00 12.00
1 Ruben Mateo .40 1.00
2 Lance Berkman .50 1.25
3 Octavio Dotel .40 1.00
4 Ben Davis .40 1.00
5 Warren Morris .40 1.00
6 Carlos Beltran .50 1.25
7 Rick Ankiel .40 1.00
8 Adam Kennedy .40 1.00
9 Tim Hudson .50 1.25
10 Jorge Toca .40 1.00

2001 Ultra

The 2001 Ultra product was released in December, 2000 and features a 275-card base set. The base set is broken into tiers as follows: 250 Base Veterans, and 25 Prospects (1:4). Each pack contained 10-cards, and carried a suggested retail price of $2.99.

COMPLETE SET (275) 60.00 120.00
COMP.SET w/o SP's (250) 10.00 25.00
COMMON CARD (1-250) .10 .30
COMMON (251-275) 1.25 3.00
COMMON (276-280) 2.00 5.00
1 Pedro Martinez .20 .50
2 Derek Jeter .75 2.00
3 Cal Ripken 1.00 2.50
4 Alex Rodriguez .50 1.25
5 Vladimir Guerrero .30 .75
6 Troy Glaus .10 .30
7 Sammy Sosa .30 .75
8 Mike Piazza .50 1.25
9 Tony Gwynn .40 1.00
10 Tim Hudson .10 .30
11 John Flaherty .10 .30
12 Jeff Cirillo .10 .30
13 Ellis Burks .10 .30
14 Carlos Lee .10 .30
15 Carlos Beltran .10 .30
16 Ruben Rivera .10 .30
17 Richard Hidalgo .10 .30
18 Omar Vizquel .20 .50
19 Michael Barrett .10 .30
20 Jose Canseco .20 .50
21 Jason Giambi .10 .30
22 Greg Maddux .50 1.25
23 Charles Johnson .10 .30
24 Sandy Alomar Jr. .10 .30
25 Rick Ankiel .10 .30
26 Richie Sexson .10 .30
27 Matt Williams .10 .30
28 Joe Girardi .10 .30
29 Jason Kendall .10 .30
30 Brad Fullmer .10 .30
31 Alex Gonzalez .10 .30
32 Rick Helling .10 .30
33 Mike Mussina .20 .50
34 Joe Randa .10 .30
35 J.T. Snow .10 .30
36 Edgardo Alfonzo .10 .30
37 Dante Bichette .10 .30
38 Brad Ausmus .10 .30
39 Bobby Abreu .10 .30
40 Warren Morris .10 .30
41 Tony Womack .10 .30
42 Russell Branyan .10 .30
43 Mike Lowell .10 .30
44 Mark Grace .20 .50
45 Jeromy Burnitz .10 .30
46 J.D. Drew .10 .30
47 David Justice .10 .30
48 Alex Gonzalez .10 .30
49 Tino Martinez .20 .50
50 Raul Mondesi .10 .30
51 Rafael Furcal .10 .30
52 Marquis Grissom .10 .30
53 Kevin Young .10 .30
54 Jon Lieber .10 .30
55 Henry Rodriguez .10 .30
56 Dave Burba .10 .30
57 Shannon Stewart .10 .30
58 Preston Wilson .10 .30
59 Paul O'Neill .20 .50
60 Jimmy Haynes .10 .30
61 Darryl Kile .10 .30
62 Bret Boone .10 .30
63 Bartolo Colon .10 .30
64 Andres Galarraga .10 .30
65 Trot Nixon .10 .30
66 Steve Finley .10 .30
67 Shawn Green .10 .30
68 Robert Person .10 .30
69 Kenny Rogers .10 .30
70 Bobby Higginson .10 .30
71 Barry Larkin .20 .50
72 Al Martin .10 .30
73 Tom Glavine .20 .50
74 Rondell White .10 .30
75 Ray Lankford .10 .30
76 Moises Alou .10 .30
77 Matt Clement .10 .30
78 Geoff Jenkins .10 .30
79 David Wells .10 .30
80 Chuck Finley .10 .30
81 Andy Pettitte .20 .50
82 Travis Fryman .10 .30
83 Ron Coomer .10 .30
84 Mark McGwire .75 2.00
85 Kerry Wood .10 .30
86 Jorge Posada .20 .50
87 Jeff Bagwell .20 .50
88 Andruw Jones .20 .50
89 Ryan Klesko .10 .30
90 Mariano Rivera .30 .75
91 Lance Berkman .10 .30
92 Kenny Lofton .10 .30
93 Jacque Jones .10 .30
94 Eric Young .10 .30
95 Edgar Renteria .10 .30
96 Chipper Jones .30 .75
97 Todd Helton .20 .50
98 Shawn Estes .10 .30
99 Mark Mulder .10 .30
100 Lee Stevens .10 .30
101 Jermaine Dye .10 .30
102 Greg Vaughn .10 .30
103 Chris Singleton .10 .30
104 Brady Anderson .10 .30
105 Terrence Long .10 .30
106 Quilvio Veras .10 .30
107 Magglio Ordonez .10 .30
108 Johnny Damon .20 .50
109 Jeffrey Hammonds .10 .30
110 Fred McGriff .20 .50
111 Carl Pavano .10 .30
112 Bobby Estalella .10 .30
113 Todd Hundley .10 .30
114 Scott Rolen .20 .50
115 Robin Ventura .10 .30
116 Pokey Reese .10 .30
117 Luis Gonzalez .10 .30
118 Jose Offerman .10 .30
119 Edgar Martinez .20 .50
120 Dean Palmer .10 .30
121 David Segui .10 .30
122 Troy O'Leary .10 .30
123 Tony Batista .10 .30
124 Todd Zeile .10 .30
125 Randy Johnson .30 .75
126 Luis Castillo .10 .30
127 Kris Benson .10 .30
128 John Olerud .10 .30
129 Eric Karros .10 .30
130 Eddie Taubensee .10 .30
131 Neifi Perez .10 .30
132 Matt Stairs .10 .30
133 Luis Alicea .10 .30
134 Jeff Kent .10 .30
135 Javier Vazquez .10 .30
136 Garret Anderson .10 .30
137 Frank Thomas .30 .75
138 Carlos Febles .10 .30
139 Albert Belle .10 .30
140 Tony Clark .10 .30
141 Pat Burrell .10 .30
142 Mike Sweeney .10 .30
143 Jay Buhner .10 .30
144 Gabe Kapler .10 .30
145 Derek Bell .10 .30
146 B.J. Surhoff .10 .30
147 Adam Kennedy .10 .30
148 Aaron Boone .10 .30
149 Todd Stottlemyre .10 .30
150 Roberto Alomar .20 .50
151 Orlando Hernandez .10 .30
152 Jason Varitek .10 .30
153 Gary Sheffield .10 .30
154 Cliff Floyd .10 .30
155 Chad Hermansen .10 .30
156 Carlos Delgado .10 .30
157 Aaron Sele .10 .30
158 Sean Casey .10 .30
159 Ruben Mateo .10 .30
160 Mike Bordick .10 .30
161 Mike Cameron .10 .30
162 Doug Glanville .10 .30
163 Damion Easley .10 .30
164 Carl Everett .10 .30
165 Bengie Molina .10 .30
166 Adrian Beltre .10 .30
167 Tom Goodwin .10 .30
168 Rickey Henderson .30 .75
169 Mo Vaughn .10 .30
170 Mike Lieberthal .10 .30
171 Ken Griffey Jr. .50 1.25
172 Juan Gonzalez .10 .30
173 Ivan Rodriguez .20 .50
174 Al Leiter .10 .30
175 Vinny Castilla .10 .30
176 Peter Bergeron .10 .30
177 Pedro Astacio .10 .30
178 Paul Konerko .10 .30
179 Mitch Meluskey .10 .30
180 Kevin Millwood .10 .30
181 Ben Grieve .10 .30
182 Barry Bonds .75 2.00
183 Rusty Greer .10 .30
184 Miguel Tejada .10 .30
185 Mark Quinn .10 .30
186 Larry Walker .10 .30
187 Jose Valentin .10 .30
188 Jose Vidro .10 .30
189 Delino DeShields .10 .30
190 Darin Erstad .10 .30
191 Bill Mueller .10 .30
192 Ray Durham .10 .30
193 Ken Caminiti .10 .30
194 Jim Thome .20 .50
195 Javy Lopez .10 .30
196 Fernando Vina .10 .30
197 Eric Chavez .10 .30
198 Eric Owens .10 .30
199 Brad Radke .10 .30
200 Travis Lee .10 .30
201 Tim Salmon .20 .50
202 Rafael Palmeiro .20 .50
203 Nomar Garciaparra .50 1.25
204 Mike Hampton .10 .30
205 Kevin Brown .10 .30
206 Juan Encarnacion .10 .30
207 Danny Graves .10 .30
208 Carlos Guillen .10 .30
209 Phil Nevin .10 .30
210 Matt Lawton .10 .30
211 Manny Ramirez .20 .50
212 James Baldwin .10 .30
213 Fernando Tatis .10 .30
214 Craig Biggio .20 .50
215 Brian Jordan .10 .30
216 Bernie Williams .20 .50
217 Ryan Dempster .10 .30
218 Roger Clemens .60 1.50
219 Jose Cruz Jr. .10 .30
220 John Valentin .10 .30
221 Dmitri Young .10 .30
222 Curt Schilling .10 .30
223 Jim Edmonds .10 .30
224 Chan Ho Park .10 .30
225 Brian Giles .10 .30
226 Jimmy Anderson .10 .30
Tike Redman
227 Adam Piatt .10 .30
Jose Ortiz
228 Kenny Kelly .10 .30
Aubrey Huff
229 Randy Choate .10 .30
Craig Dingman
230 Eric Cammack .10 .30
Grant Roberts
231 Yovanny Lara .10 .30
Andy Tracy
232 Wayne Franklin .10 .30
Scott Linebrink
233 Cameron Cairncross .10 .30
Chan Perry
234 J.C. Romero .10 .30
Matt LeCroy
235 Geraldo Guzman .10 .30
Jason Conti
236 Morgan Burkhart .10 .30
Paxton Crawford
237 Pasqual Coco .10 .30
Leo Estrella
238 John Parrish .10 .30
Fernando Lunar
239 Keith McDonald .10 .30
Justin Brunette
240 Carlos Casimiro .10 .30
Ivanon Coffie
241 Daniel Garibay .10 .30
Ruben Quevedo
242 Sang-Hoon Lee .10 .30
Tomo Ohka
243 Hector Ortiz .10 .30
Jeff D'Amico
244 Jeff Sparks .10 .30
Travis Harper
245 Jason Boyd .10 .30
David Coggin
246 Mark Buehrle .20 .50
Lorenzo Barcelo
247 Adam Melhuse .10 .30
Ben Petrick
248 Kane Davis .10 .30
Paul Rigdon
249 Mike Darr .10 .30
Kory DeHaan
250 Vicente Padilla 1.25 3.00
Mark Brownson
251 Barry Zito PROS 2.00 5.00
252 Tim Drew PROS 1.25 3.00
253 Luis Matos PROS 1.25 3.00
254 Alex Cabrera PROS 1.25 3.00
255 Jon Garland PROS 1.25 3.00
256 Milton Bradley PROS 1.25 3.00
257 Juan Pierre PROS 1.25 3.00
258 Ismael Villegas PROS 1.25 3.00
259 Eric Munson PROS 1.25 3.00
260 T.De la Rosa PROS 1.25 3.00
261 Chris Richard PROS 1.25 3.00
262 Jason Tyner PROS 1.25 3.00
263 B.J. Waszgis PROS 1.25 3.00
264 Jason Marquis PROS 1.25 3.00
265 Dusty Allen PROS 1.25 3.00
266 C.Patterson PROS 1.25 3.00
267 Eric Byrnes PROS 1.25 3.00
268 Xavier Nady PROS 1.25 3.00
269 G.Lombard PROS 1.25 3.00
270 Timo Perez PROS 1.25 3.00
271 G.Matthews Jr. PROS 1.25 3.00
272 Chad Durbin PROS 1.25 3.00
273 Tony Armas Jr. PROS 1.25 3.00
274 F.Cordero PROS 1.25 3.00
275 A.Soriano PROS 2.00 5.00
276 Junior Spivey RC 3.00 8.00
Juan Uribe RC
277 Albert Pujols RC 30.00 60.00
Bud Smith RC
278 Ichiro Suzuki RC 12.50 30.00
Tsuyoshi Shinjo RC
279 Drew Henson RC 3.00 8.00
Jackson Melian RC
280 Matt White RC 2.00 5.00
Adrian Hernandez RC

2001 Ultra Gold Medallion

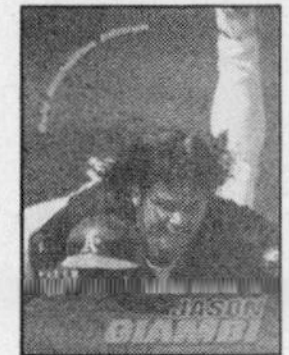

Inserted into packs at a rate of one per pack (251-275 were inserted at 1:24), this 275-card set is a complete parallel of the Ultra base set. Please note that these cards were produced with gold coating and gold foil stamping.

*STARS 1-225: 1.25X TO 3X BASIC CARDS
*PROSPECTS 226-250: 1.25X TO 3X BASIC
*PROSPECTS 251-275: .75X TO 2X BASIC

2001 Ultra Platinum Medallion

Randomly inserted into packs, this 275-card set is a complete parallel of the Ultra base set. Cards 1-250 were individually serial numbered to 50, and cards 251-275 were individually serial numbered to 25. Please note that these cards were produced with a silver coating and silver foil stamping.

*PLATINUM 1-225: 15X TO 40X BASIC
*PLATINUM 251-275: 3X TO 8X BASIC

2001 Ultra Decade of Dominance

Randomly inserted into packs at one in eight, this 15-card insert set features players that dominated Major League Baseball in the 1990's. Card backs carry a "DD" prefix.

COMPLETE SET (15) 12.50 30.00
PLATINUM PRINT RUN 10 SERIAL #'d SETS
PLATINUM NO PRICING DUE TO SCARCITY
DD1 Barry Bonds 1.50 4.00
DD2 Mark McGwire 1.50 4.00
DD3 Sammy Sosa .60 1.50
DD4 Ken Griffey Jr. 1.00 2.50
DD5 Cal Ripken 2.00 5.00
DD6 Tony Gwynn .75 2.00
DD7 Albert Belle .30 .75
DD8 Frank Thomas .60 1.50
DD9 Randy Johnson .60 1.50
DD10 Juan Gonzalez .30 .75
DD11 Greg Maddux 1.00 2.50
DD12 Craig Biggio .40 1.00
DD13 Edgar Martinez .40 1.00
DD14 Roger Clemens 1.25 3.00
DD15 Andres Galarraga .30 .75

2001 Ultra Fall Classics

Inserted into packs at one in 20, this 37-card insert set features some of the most legendary players of all time. Card backs carry a "FC" prefix.

FC1 Jackie Robinson 2.00 5.00
FC2 Enos Slaughter 1.25 3.00
FC3 Mariano Rivera 2.00 5.00
FC4 Hank Bauer 1.25 3.00
FC5 Cal Ripken 6.00 15.00
FC6 Babe Ruth 6.00 15.00
FC7 Thurman Munson 2.00 5.00
FC8 Tom Glavine 1.25 3.00
FC9 Fred Lynn 1.25 3.00
FC10 Johnny Bench 2.00 5.00
FC11 Tony Lazzeri 1.25 3.00
FC12 Al Kaline 2.00 5.00
FC13 Reggie Jackson 1.25 3.00
FC14 Derek Jeter 5.00 12.00
FC15 Willie Stargell 1.25 3.00
FC16 Roy Campanella 2.00 5.00
FC17 Phil Rizzuto 2.00 5.00
FC18 Roberto Clemente 6.00 15.00
FC19 Carlton Fisk 1.25 3.00
FC20 Duke Snider 1.25 3.00
FC21 Ted Williams 5.00 12.00
FC22 Bill Skowron 1.25 3.00
FC23 Bucky Dent 1.25 3.00
FC24 Mike Schmidt 4.00 10.00
FC25 Lou Brock 1.25 3.00
FC26 Whitey Ford 1.25 3.00
FC27 Brooks Robinson 1.25 3.00
FC28 Roberto Alomar 1.25 3.00
FC29 Yogi Berra 2.00 5.00

FC30 Joe Carter 1.25 3.00
FC31 Bill Mazeroski 1.25 3.00
FC32 Bob Gibson 1.25 3.00
FC33 Hank Greenberg 2.50 6.00
FC34 Andruw Jones 1.25 3.00
FC35 Bernie Williams 1.25 3.00
FC36 Don Larsen 1.25 3.00
FC37 Billy Martin 1.25 3.00

2001 Ultra Fall Classics Memorabilia

Randomly inserted into packs, this 26-card insert features game-used memorabilia from players like Derek Jeter, Al Kaline, and Cal Ripken. Please note that the cards a checklisted below in alphabetical order for convience.

1 Hank Bauer Bat 6.00 15.00
2 Johnny Bench Jsy 10.00 25.00
3 Lou Brock Jsy 10.00 25.00
4 Roy Campanella Bat 20.00 50.00
5 Roberto Clemente Bat 50.00 100.00
6 Bucky Dent Bat 6.00 15.00
7 Carlton Fisk Jsy 10.00 25.00
8 Tom Glavine Jsy 10.00 25.00
9 Reggie Jackson Jsy 10.00 25.00
10 Derek Jeter Jsy 15.00 40.00
11 Al Kaline Jsy 10.00 25.00
12 Tony Lazzeri Bat 6.00 15.00
13 Fred Lynn Bat 6.00 15.00
14 Thurman Munson Bat 15.00 40.00
15 Cal Ripken Jsy 15.00 40.00
16 Mariano Rivera Jsy 10.00 25.00
17 Phil Rizzuto Bat 10.00 25.00
18 Brooks Robinson Bat 10.00 25.00
19 Jackie Robinson Pants 30.00 60.00
20 Babe Ruth Bat 125.00 200.00
21 Mike Schmidt Jsy 10.00 25.00
22 Bill Skowron Bat 6.00 15.00
23 Enos Slaughter Bat 6.00 15.00
24 Duke Snider Bat 10.00 25.00
25 Willie Stargell Bat 10.00 25.00
26 Ted Williams Bat 50.00 100.00

2001 Ultra Fall Classics Memorabilia Autograph

Randomly inserted into packs, this nine-card insert features game-used memorabilia and autographs of legendary players. Due to market scarcity, not all cards are priced. All are listed for checklisting purposes. Please note that the Al Kaline jersey/autograph card contained an error, Kaline actually wore jersey number 6. However, Fleer produced seven of these cards. Reggie Jackson's card was distributed as an exchange card in packs. The exchange deadline was January 2nd, 2002.

1 Lou Brock Jsy AU/20
2 Carlton Fisk Jsy AU/27
3 Reggie Jackson Bat-Jsy/44 60.00 120.00
4 Derek Jeter Jsy AU/2
5 Al Kaline Jsy AU/7 UER
Kaline wore Jersey number 6
6 Cal Ripken Jsy AU/8
7 Mike Schmidt Jsy AU/20
8 Enos Slaughter Jsy AU/9
9 Willie Stargell Jsy AU/8

2001 Ultra Greatest Hits

Randomly inserted into packs at one in 12, this 10-card insert set features players that dominante the Major Leagues. Card backs carry a "GH" prefix.

COMPLETE SET (10) 10.00 25.00
PLATINUM PRINT RUN 10 SERIAL #'d SETS
PLATINUM NO PRICING DUE TO SCARCITY
GH1 Mark McGwire 1.50 4.00
GH2 Alex Rodriguez 1.00 2.50
GH3 Ken Griffey Jr. 1.00 2.50
GH4 Ivan Rodriguez .40 1.00
GH5 Cal Ripken 2.00 5.00
GH6 Todd Helton .40 1.00
GH7 Derek Jeter 1.50 4.00
GH8 Pedro Martinez .40 1.00
GH9 Tony Gwynn .75 2.00
GH10 Jim Edmonds .40 1.00

2001 Ultra Power Plus

Randomly inserted into packs at one in 24, this 10-card insert set features players that are among the league leaders in homeruns every year. Card backs carry a "PP" prefix.

COMPLETE SET (10) 15.00 40.00
PLATINUM PRINT RUN 10 SERIAL #'d SETS
PLATINUM NO PRICING DUE TO SCARCITY
PP1 Vladimir Guerrero 1.00 2.50
PP2 Mark McGwire 2.50 6.00
PP3 Mike Piazza 1.50 4.00
PP4 Derek Jeter 2.50 6.00
PP5 Chipper Jones 1.00 2.50
PP6 Carlos Delgado .60 1.50
PP7 Sammy Sosa 1.00 2.50
PP8 Ken Griffey Jr. 1.50 4.00
PP9 Nomar Garciaparra 1.50 4.00
PP10 Alex Rodriguez 1.50 4.00

2001 Ultra Tomorrow's Legends

Randomly inserted into packs at one in 4, this 15-card insert set features players that will most likely make the Hall of Fame when their careers are through. Card backs carry a "TL" prefix.

COMPLETE SET (15) 6.00 15.00
PLATINUM PRINT RUN 10 SERIAL #'d SETS
PLATINUM NO PRICING DUE TO SCARCITY
TL1 Rick Ankiel .20 .50
TL2 J.D. Drew .20 .50
TL3 Carlos Delgado .20 .50
TL4 Todd Helton .30 .75
TL5 Andruw Jones .30 .75
TL6 Troy Glaus .20 .50
TL7 Jermaine Dye .20 .50
TL8 Vladimir Guerrero .50 1.25
TL9 Brian Giles .20 .50
TL10 Scott Rolen .30 .75
TL11 Darin Erstad .20 .50
TL12 Derek Jeter 1.25 3.00
TL13 Alex Rodriguez .75 2.00
TL14 Pat Burrell .20 .50
TL15 Nomar Garciaparra .75 2.00

2002 Ultra

This 285 card set was issued in November, 2001. The following subsets were issued for this set: All-Stars (cards numbered 201-220), Teammates (a veteran and prospect from each team, numbered 221-250), and Prospects (cards numbered 251-285). All three of these subsets were issued at a rate of one in four packs.

COMPLETE SET (285) 80.00 200.00
COMP.SET w/o SP's (200) 10.00 25.00
COMMON CARD (1-200) .10 .30
COMMON (201-220) .40 1.00
COMMON (221-250) .40 1.00
COMMON (251-285) 1.25 3.00
1 Jeff Bagwell .20 .50
2 Derek Jeter .75 2.00
3 Alex Rodriguez .50 1.25
4 Eric Chavez .10 .30
5 Tsuyoshi Shinjo .10 .30
6 Chris Stynes .10 .30
7 Ivan Rodriguez .20 .50
8 Cal Ripken 1.00 2.50
9 Freddy Garcia .10 .30
10 Chipper Jones .30 .75
11 Hideo Nomo .30 .75
12 Rafael Furcal .10 .30
13 Preston Wilson .10 .30
14 Jimmy Rollins .10 .30
15 Cristian Guzman .10 .30
16 Garret Anderson .10 .30
17 Todd Helton .20 .50
18 Moises Alou .10 .30
19 Tony Gwynn .40 1.00
20 Jorge Posada .20 .50
21 Sean Casey .10 .30
22 Kazuhiro Sasaki .10 .30
23 Ray Lankford .10 .30
24 Manny Ramirez .20 .50
25 Barry Bonds .75 2.00
26 Fred McGriff .20 .50
27 Vladimir Guerrero .30 .75
28 Jermaine Dye .10 .30
29 Adrian Beltre .10 .30
30 Ken Griffey Jr. .50 1.25
31 Ramon Hernandez .10 .30
32 Kerry Wood .10 .30
33 Greg Maddux .50 1.25
34 Rondell White .10 .30
35 Mike Mussina .20 .50
36 Jim Edmonds .10 .30
37 Scott Rolen .20 .50
38 Mike Lowell .10 .30
39 Al Leiter .10 .30
40 Tony Clark .10 .30
41 Joe Mays .10 .30
42 Mo Vaughn .10 .30
43 Geoff Jenkins .10 .30
44 Curt Schilling .10 .30
45 Pedro Martinez .20 .50
46 Andy Pettitte .20 .50
47 Tim Salmon .20 .50
48 Carl Everett .10 .30
49 Lance Berkman .10 .30
50 Troy Glaus .10 .30
51 Ichiro Suzuki .60 1.50
52 Alfonso Soriano .10 .30
53 Tomo Ohka .10 .30
54 Dean Palmer .10 .30
55 Kevin Brown .10 .30
56 Albert Pujols .60 1.50
57 Homer Bush .10 .30
58 Tim Hudson .10 .30
59 Frank Thomas .30 .75
60 Joe Randa .10 .30
61 Chan Ho Park .10 .30
62 Bobby Higginson .10 .30
63 Bartolo Colon .10 .30
64 Aramis Ramirez .10 .30
65 Jeff Cirillo .10 .30
66 Roberto Alomar .20 .50
67 Mark Kotsay .10 .30
68 Mike Cameron .10 .30
69 Mike Hampton .10 .30
70 Trot Nixon .10 .30
71 Juan Gonzalez .10 .30
72 Damian Rolls .10 .30
73 Brad Fullmer .10 .30
74 David Ortiz .30 .75
75 Brandon Inge .10 .30
76 Orlando Hernandez .10 .30
77 Matt Stairs .10 .30
78 Jay Gibbons .10 .30
79 Greg Vaughn .10 .30
80 Brady Anderson .10 .30
81 Jim Thome .20 .50
82 Ben Sheets .10 .30
83 Rafael Palmeiro .20 .50
84 Edgar Renteria .10 .30
85 Doug Mientkiewicz .10 .30
86 Raul Mondesi .10 .30
87 Shane Reynolds .10 .30
88 Steve Finley .10 .30
89 Jose Cruz Jr. .10 .30
90 Edgardo Alfonzo .10 .30
91 Jose Valentin .10 .30
92 Mark McGwire .75 2.00
93 Mark Grace .20 .50
94 Mike Lieberthal .10 .30
95 Barry Larkin .20 .50
96 Chuck Knoblauch .10 .30
97 Deivi Cruz .10 .30
98 Jeromy Burnitz .10 .30
99 Shannon Stewart .10 .30
100 David Wells .10 .30
101 Brook Fordyce .10 .30
102 Rusty Greer .10 .30
103 Andruw Jones .20 .50
104 Jason Kendall .10 .30
105 Nomar Garciaparra .50 1.25
106 Shawn Green .10 .30
107 Craig Biggio .20 .50
108 Masato Yoshii .10 .30
109 Ben Petrick .10 .30
110 Gary Sheffield .10 .30
111 Travis Lee .10 .30
112 Matt Williams .10 .30
113 Billy Wagner .10 .30
114 Robin Ventura .10 .30
115 Jerry Hairston .10 .30
116 Paul LoDuca .10 .30
117 Darin Erstad .10 .30
118 Ruben Sierra .10 .30
119 Ricky Gutierrez .10 .30
120 Bret Boone .10 .30
121 John Rocker .10 .30
122 Roger Clemens .60 1.50
123 Eric Karros .10 .30
124 J.D. Drew .10 .30
125 Carlos Delgado .10 .30
126 Jeffrey Hammonds .10 .30
127 Jeff Kent .10 .30
128 David Justice .10 .30
129 Cliff Floyd .10 .30
130 Omar Vizquel .20 .50
131 Matt Morris .10 .30
132 Rich Aurilia .10 .30
133 Larry Walker .10 .30
134 Miguel Tejada .10 .30
135 Eric Young .10 .30
136 Aaron Sele .10 .30
137 Eric Milton .10 .30
138 Travis Fryman .10 .30
139 Magglio Ordonez .10 .30
140 Sammy Sosa .30 .75
141 Pokey Reese .10 .30
142 Adam Eaton .10 .30
143 Adam Kennedy .10 .30
144 Mike Piazza .50 1.25
145 Larry Barnes .10 .30
146 Darryl Kile .10 .30
147 Tom Glavine .20 .50
148 Ryan Klesko .10 .30
149 Jose Vidro .10 .30
150 Joe Kennedy .10 .30
151 Bernie Williams .20 .50
152 C.C. Sabathia .10 .30
153 Alex Ochoa .10 .30
154 A.J. Pierzynski .10 .30
155 Johnny Damon .20 .50
156 Omar Daal .10 .30
157 A.J. Burnett .10 .30
158 Eric Munson .10 .30
159 Fernando Vina .10 .30
160 Chris Singleton .10 .30
161 Juan Pierre .10 .30
162 John Olerud .10 .30
163 Randy Johnson .30 .75
164 Paul Konerko .10 .30
165 Tino Martinez .20 .50
166 Richard Hidalgo .10 .30
167 Luis Gonzalez .10 .30
168 Ben Grieve .10 .30
169 Matt Lawton .10 .30
170 Gabe Kapler .10 .30
171 Mariano Rivera .30 .75
172 Kenny Lofton .10 .30
173 Brian Jordan .10 .30
174 Brian Giles .10 .30
175 Mark Quinn .10 .30
176 Neifi Perez .10 .30
177 Ellis Burks .10 .30
178 Bobby Abreu .10 .30
179 Jeff Weaver .10 .30
180 Andres Galarraga .10 .30
181 Javy Lopez .10 .30
182 Todd Walker .10 .30
183 Fernando Tatis .10 .30
184 Charles Johnson .10 .30
185 Pat Burrell .10 .30
186 Jay Bell .10 .30
187 Aaron Boone .10 .30
188 Jason Giambi .10 .30
189 Jay Payton .10 .30
190 Carlos Lee .10 .30
191 Phil Nevin .10 .30
192 Mike Sweeney .10 .30
193 J.T. Snow .10 .30
194 Dmitri Young .10 .30
195 Richie Sexson .10 .30
196 Derrek Lee .20 .50
197 Corey Koskie .10 .30
198 Edgar Martinez .20 .50
199 Wade Miller .10 .30
200 Tony Batista .10 .30
201 John Olerud AS .40 1.00
202 Bret Boone AS .40 1.00
203 Cal Ripken AS 2.00 5.00
204 Alex Rodriguez AS 1.00 2.50
205 Ichiro Suzuki AS 1.25 3.00
206 Manny Ramirez AS .20 .50
207 Juan Gonzalez AS .40 1.00
208 Ivan Rodriguez AS .60 1.50
209 Roger Clemens AS 1.25 3.00
210 Edgar Martinez AS .60 1.50
211 Todd Helton AS .60 1.50
212 Jeff Kent AS .40 1.00
213 Chipper Jones AS .60 1.50
214 Rich Aurilia AS .40 1.00
215 Barry Bonds AS 1.50 4.00
216 Sammy Sosa AS .60 1.50
217 Luis Gonzalez AS .40 1.00
218 Mike Piazza AS 1.00 2.50
219 Randy Johnson AS .60 1.50
220 Larry Walker AS .40 1.00
221 Todd Helton .40 1.00
Juan Uribe
All team players subset cards are noted to be 2001
222 Pat Burrell .40 1.00
Eric Valent
223 Edgar Martinez 1.25 3.00
Ichiro Suzuki
224 Ben Grieve .40 1.00
Jason Tyner
225 Mark Quinn .40 1.00
Dee Brown
226 Cal Ripken 2.00 5.00
Brian Roberts
227 Cliff Floyd .40 1.00
Abraham Nunez
228 Jeff Bagwell .40 1.00
Adam Everett
229 Mark McGwire 1.50 4.00
Albert Pujols
230 Doug Mientkewicz .40 1.00
Luis Rivas
231 Juan Gonzalez .40 1.00
Danny Peoples
232 Kevin Brown .40 1.00
Luke Prokopec
233 Richie Sexson .40 1.00
Ben Sheets
234 Jason Giambi .40 1.00
Jason Hart
235 Barry Bonds 1.50 4.00
Carlos Valderrama
236 Tony Gwynn .75 2.00
Cesar Crespo
237 Ken Griffey Jr. 1.00 2.50
Adam Dunn
238 Frank Thomas .60 1.50
Joe Crede
239 Derek Jeter 1.50 4.00
Drew Henson
240 Chipper Jones .60 1.50
Wilson Betemit
241 Luis Gonzalez .40 1.00
Junior Spivey
242 Bobby Higginson .40 1.00
Andres Torres
243 Carlos Delgado .40 1.00
Vernon Wells
244 Sammy Sosa .60 1.50
Corey Patterson
245 Nomar Garciaparra 1.00 2.50
Shea Hillenbrand
246 Alex Rodriguez 1.00 2.50
Jason Romano
247 Troy Glaus .40 1.00
David Eckstein
248 Mike Piazza 1.00 2.50
Alex Escobar
249 Brian Giles .40 1.00
Jack Wilson
250 Vladimir Guerrero .60 1.50
Scott Hodges
251 Bud Smith PROS 1.25 3.00
252 Juan Diaz PROS 1.25 3.00
253 Wilkin Ruan PROS 1.25 3.00
254 C. Spurling PROS RC 1.25 3.00
255 Toby Hall PROS 1.25 3.00
256 Jason Jennings PROS 1.25 3.00
257 George Perez PROS 1.25 3.00
258 D. Jimenez PROS 1.25 3.00
259 Jose Acevedo PROS 1.25 3.00
260 Josue Perez PROS 1.25 3.00
261 Brian Rogers PROS 1.25 3.00
262 C. Maldonado PROS RC 1.25 3.00
263 Travis Phelps PROS 1.25 3.00
264 R. Mackowiak PROS 1.25 3.00
265 Ryan Drese PROS 1.25 3.00
266 Carlos Garcia PROS 1.25 3.00
267 Alexis Gomez PROS 1.25 3.00
268 Jeremy Affeldt PROS 1.25 3.00
269 S. Podsednik PROS 1.50 4.00
270 Adam Johnson PROS 1.25 3.00
271 Pedro Santana PROS 1.25 3.00
272 Les Walrond PROS 1.25 3.00
273 Jackson Melian PROS 1.25 3.00
274 C. Hernandez PROS 1.25 3.00
275 M. Nussbeck PROS RC 1.25 3.00
276 Cory Aldridge PROS 1.25 3.00
277 Troy Mattes PROS 1.25 3.00
278 B. Abernathy PROS 1.25 3.00
279 J.J. Davis PROS 1.25 3.00
280 B. Duckworth PROS 1.25 3.00
281 Kyle Lohse PROS 1.25 3.00
282 Justin Kaye PROS 1.25 3.00
283 Cody Ransom PROS 1.25 3.00
284 Dave Williams PROS 1.25 3.00
285 Luis Lopez PROS 1.25 3.00

2002 Ultra Gold Medallion

Issued at packs at different rates, this is a parallel to the Ultra set. Cards numbered 1-200 were issued at a rate of one per pack, cards numbered 201-250 were issued at a rate of one in 24 packs and cards numbered 251-285 were randomly inserted in packs. Cards numbered 251-285 were issued to 100 serial numbered sets.

COMP.SET w/o SP's (200) 60.00 150.00
*GOLD 1-200: 1.25X TO 3X BASIC
*GOLD 201-220: .75X TO 2X BASIC
*GOLD 221-250: 1X TO 2.5X BASIC
*GOLD 251-285: 3X TO 8X BASIC

2002 Ultra Fall Classic

Issued at a rate of one in 20 hobby packs, these 36 cards feature players who participated in the World Series.

COMPLETE SET (36) 100.00 200.00
1 Ty Cobb 4.00 10.00
2 Lou Gehrig 4.00 10.00
3 Babe Ruth 8.00 20.00
4 Stan Musial 4.00 10.00
5 Ted Williams 5.00 12.00
6 Dizzy Dean 3.00 8.00
7 Mickey Cochrane 2.00 5.00
8 Jimmie Foxx 3.00 8.00
9 Mel Ott 3.00 8.00
10 Rogers Hornsby 3.00 8.00
12 Clete Boyer 2.00 5.00
13 George Brett 6.00 15.00
14 Bob Gibson 3.00 8.00
15 Carlton Fisk 3.00 8.00
16 Johnny Bench 3.00 8.00
18 Willie McCovey 2.00 5.00
19 Paul Molitor 2.00 5.00
20 Jim Palmer 2.00 5.00
21 Frank Robinson 3.00 8.00
22 Derek Jeter 5.00 12.00
23 Earl Weaver 2.00 5.00
24 Lefty Grove 2.00 5.00
25 Tony Perez 2.00 5.00
26 Reggie Jackson 3.00 8.00
27 Sparky Anderson 2.00 5.00
28 Casey Stengel 2.00 5.00
29 Roy Campanella 3.00 8.00
31 Don Drysdale 3.00 8.00
32 Joe Morgan 2.00 5.00
33 Eddie Murray 3.00 8.00
34 Nolan Ryan 6.00 15.00
35 Tom Seaver 3.00 8.00
36 Bill Mazeroski 2.00 5.00
37 Jackie Robinson 3.00 8.00
38 Kirk Gibson 2.00 5.00
39 Robin Yount 3.00 8.00

2002 Ultra Fall Classic Autographs

This partial parallel to the Fall Classic set features authentic autographs from the featured players. All of the players except for Sparky Anderson and Earl Weaver were exchange cards. A few players were produced in lower quantities and those have been notated with SP's in our checklist.

1 Sparky Anderson 6.00 15.00
2 Johnny Bench SP 20.00 50.00
3 George Brett SP 50.00 100.00
4 Carlton Fisk 10.00 25.00
5 Bob Gibson 10.00 25.00
6 Kirk Gibson 6.00 15.00
7 Reggie Jackson SP 20.00 50.00
8 Derek Jeter SP
9 Bill Mazeroski 10.00 25.00
10 Willie McCovey SP 15.00 40.00
11 Joe Morgan 6.00 15.00
12 Eddie Murray SP 20.00 50.00
13 Stan Musial SP
14 Jim Palmer 6.00 15.00
15 Tony Perez 6.00 15.00
16 Frank Robinson 10.00 25.00
17 Nolan Ryan SP 125.00 250.00
18 Tom Seaver SP 15.00 40.00
19 Earl Weaver 6.00 15.00
20 Robin Yount SP 30.00 60.00

2002 Ultra Fall Classic Memorabilia

Inserted at a rate of one in 113, these 37 cards feature memorabila from players who participated in World Series. A few cards were printed in lesser quantities and those have been notated with print runs as provided by Fleer.

1 Sparky Anderson Pants 4.00 10.00
2 Johnny Bench Pants 6.00 15.00
3 Johnny Bench Jsy 6.00 15.00
4 George Brett White Jsy 10.00 25.00
5 George Brett Bat 10.00 25.00
6 George Brett Blue Jsy/65 *
7 Roy Campanella Bat/21 *
8 Carlton Fisk Jsy 6.00 15.00
9 Carlton Fisk Bat/42 * 20.00 50.00
10 Jimmie Foxx Bat 20.00 50.00
11 Bob Gibson Jsy 6.00 15.00
12 Kirk Gibson Bat 4.00 10.00
13 Reggie Jackson Bat 6.00 15.00
14 Reggie Jackson Bat
15 Reggie Jackson Jsy/73 *
16 Derek Jeter Pants 15.00 40.00
17 Willie McCovey Jsy 4.00 10.00
18 Paul Molitor Bat 4.00 10.00
19 Paul Molitor Jsy
20 Joe Morgan Bat 4.00 10.00
21 Joe Morgan Jsy
22 Eddie Murray Bat 6.00 15.00
23 Eddie Murray Jsy/91 * 20.00 50.00
24 Jim Palmer White Jsy 4.00 10.00
25 J.Palmer Gray Jsy/85 * 15.00 40.00
26 Tony Perez Bat 4.00 10.00
27 Frank Robinson Bat/40 * 15.00 40.00
28 Jackie Robinson Pants 30.00 60.00
29 Babe Ruth Bat/44 * 100.00 200.00
30 Nolan Ryan Pants 20.00 50.00
31 Tom Seaver Jsy 6.00 15.00
32 Earl Weaver Jsy 4.00 10.00
33 Ted Williams Jsy 50.00 100.00
34 Ted Williams Bat/30 *
35 Robin Yount Gray Jsy
36 Robin Yount White Jsy/30 *
37 Robin Yount Bat 6.00 15.00

2002 Ultra Glove Works

Inserted at a rate of one in 20, these 15 cards feature some of the leading fielders in the game.

COMPLETE SET (15) 20.00 50.00
1 Andruw Jones 1.25 3.00
2 Derek Jeter 3.00 8.00
3 Cal Ripken 4.00 10.00
4 Larry Walker 1.25 3.00
5 Chipper Jones 1.50 4.00
6 Barry Bonds 3.00 8.00
7 Scott Rolen 1.25 3.00
8 Jim Edmonds 1.25 3.00
9 Robin Ventura 1.25 3.00
10 Darin Erstad 1.25 3.00
11 Barry Larkin 1.25 3.00
12 Raul Mondesi 1.25 3.00
13 Mark Grace 1.25 3.00
14 Bernie Williams 1.25 3.00
15 Ivan Rodriguez 1.25 3.00

2002 Ultra Glove Works Memorabilia

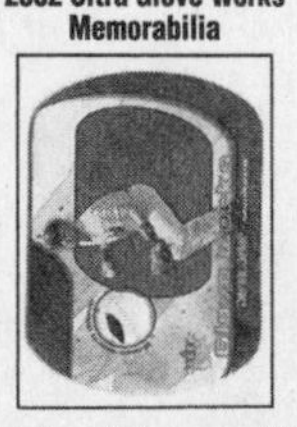

This 11-card insert set features game-used fielding mitts and batting gloves incorporated into the actual card. Each card is serial numbered to 450 copies - except for Barry Larkin (375 cards), Andruw Jones (100 cards) and Chipper Jones (100 cards). The first 75 serial numbered copies of the Cal Ripken, Barry Bonds and Ivan Rodriguez cards feature batting glove patches and cards serial numbered 76-450 for these players feature fielding mitt patches. The short-printed Andruw and Chipper Jones cards feature batting glove patches.

PLATINUM PRINT RUN 25 SERIAL #'d SETS
PLATINUM NO PRICING DUE TO SCARCITY
1 Derek Jeter/450 15.00 40.00
2 Andruw Jones/100
3 Cal Ripken/450 25.00 60.00
5 Chipper Jones/100
6 Barry Bonds/450 15.00 40.00
8 Robin Ventura/450 6.00 15.00
9 Barry Larkin/375 6.00 15.00
10 Raul Mondesi/450 6.00 15.00
11 Ivan Rodriguez/450 6.00 15.00

2002 Ultra Hitting Machines

Inserted at a rate of one in 20 retail packs, these 25 cards feature some of baseball's leading hitters.

COMPLETE SET (25) 60.00 120.00
1 Frank Thomas 2.00 5.00
2 Derek Jeter 5.00 12.00
3 Vladimir Guerrero 2.00 5.00
4 Jim Edmonds 1.00 2.50
5 Mike Piazza 3.00 8.00
6 Ivan Rodriguez 1.25 3.00
7 Chipper Jones 2.00 5.00
8 Tony Gwynn 2.50 6.00
9 Manny Ramirez 1.25 3.00
10 Andruw Jones 1.25 3.00
11 Carlos Delgado 1.00 2.50
12 Bernie Williams 1.25 3.00
13 Larry Walker 1.00 2.50
14 Juan Gonzalez 1.00 2.50
15 Ichiro Suzuki 4.00 10.00
16 Albert Pujols 4.00 10.00
17 Barry Bonds 5.00 12.00
18 Cal Ripken 6.00 15.00
19 Edgar Martinez 1.25 3.00
20 Luis Gonzalez 1.00 2.50
21 Moises Alou 1.00 2.50
22 Roberto Alomar 1.25 3.00
23 Todd Helton 1.25 3.00
24 Rafael Palmeiro 1.25 3.00
25 Bobby Abreu 1.00 2.50

2002 Ultra Hitting Machines Game Bat

Issued at a rate of one in 81 packs, these cards feature not only some of the leading hitters but also a slice of a game-used bat.

PLATINUM PRINT RUN 25 SERIAL #'d SETS
PLATINUM: NO PRICING DUE TO SCARCITY
1 Bobby Abreu 4.00 10.00
2 Roberto Alomar 6.00 15.00
3 Moises Alou 4.00 10.00
4 Barry Bonds 12.50 30.00
5 Carlos Delgado 4.00 10.00
6 Jim Edmonds 4.00 10.00
7 Juan Gonzalez 4.00 10.00
8 Luis Gonzalez 4.00 10.00
9 Tony Gwynn 6.00 15.00
10 Todd Helton 6.00 15.00
11 Derek Jeter 12.50 30.00
12 Andruw Jones 6.00 15.00
13 Chipper Jones 6.00 15.00
14 Edgar Martinez 6.00 15.00
15 Rafael Palmeiro 6.00 15.00
16 Mike Piazza 6.00 15.00
17 Albert Pujols 15.00 40.00
18 Manny Ramirez 6.00 15.00
19 Cal Ripken 20.00 50.00
20 Ivan Rodriguez 6.00 15.00
21 Frank Thomas 6.00 15.00
22 Larry Walker 4.00 10.00
23 Bernie Williams 6.00 15.00

2002 Ultra On the Road Game Jersey

Inserted at a rate of one in 93, these 14 cards feature swatches of away uniforms used by the featured players.

PLATINUM PRINT RUN 25 SERIAL #'d SETS
PLATINUM: NO PRICING DUE TO SCARCITY
1 Derek Jeter 15.00 40.00
2 Ivan Rodriguez 8.00 20.00
3 Carlos Delgado 6.00 15.00
4 Larry Walker 6.00 15.00
5 Roberto Alomar 8.00 20.00
6 Tony Gwynn 8.00 20.00
7 Greg Maddux 8.00 20.00
8 Barry Bonds 15.00 40.00
9 Todd Helton 8.00 20.00
10 Kazuhiro Sasaki 6.00 15.00
11 Jeff Bagwell 8.00 20.00
12 Omar Vizquel 8.00 20.00
13 Chan Ho Park 6.00 15.00
14 Tom Glavine 8.00 20.00

2002 Ultra Rising Stars

Issued at a rate of one in 12 packs, these 15 cards feature some of the leading young players in baseball.

COMPLETE SET (15) 12.50 30.00
1 Ichiro Suzuki 2.00 5.00
2 Derek Jeter 2.50 6.00
3 Albert Pujols 2.00 5.00

4 Jimmy Rollins .75 2.00
5 Adam Dunn .75 2.00
6 Sean Casey .75 2.00
7 Kerry Wood .75 2.00
8 Tsuyoshi Shinjo .75 2.00
9 Shea Hillenbrand .75 2.00
10 Pat Burrell .75 2.00
11 Ben Sheets .75 2.00
12 Alfonso Soriano .75 2.00
13 J.D. Drew .75 2.00
14 Kazuhiro Sasaki .75 2.00
15 Corey Patterson .75 2.00

2002 Ultra Rising Stars Game Hat

Randomly inserted in packs, these six cards feature not only some of the best young players in baseball but also a sliver of a cap they wore while playing.

PLATINUM PRINT RUN 25 SERIAL #'d SETS
PLATINUM NO PRICING DUE TO SCARCITY
1 Derek Jeter 40.00 80.00
2 Albert Pujols 20.00 50.00
3 Tsuyoshi Shinjo 15.00 40.00
4 Alfonso Soriano 15.00 40.00
5 J.D. Drew 15.00 40.00
6 Kazuhiro Sasaki 15.00 40.00

2003 Ultra

This 265-card set was issued in two separate series. The primary Ultra product - containing the first 250 cards from the basic set - was released in November, 2002. It was issued in 10 card packs which were packed 24 packs to a box and 16 boxes to a case. Cards numbered 1 through 200 featured veterans while cards numbered 201 through 220 featured All-Stars, cards numbered 221 through 240 featured rookies of 2002 and cards numbered 241 through 250 featured rookies of 2003. Cards numbered 201 through 220 were inserted at a stated rate of one in four while cards numbered 221 through 250 were inserted at a stated rate of one in two. Cards 251-265 were randomly seeded within Fleer Rookies and Greats packs of which was distributed in December, 2003. Each of these 15 update cards feature a top prospect and is serial numbered to 1,500 copies.

COMP.LO SET (250) 40.00 100.00
COMP.LO SET w/o SP's (200) 10.00 25.00
COMMON CARD (201-220) .60 1.50
COMMON CARD (221-250) .75 2.00
COMMON CARD (251-265) 1.25 3.00
1 Barry Bonds .75 2.00
2 Derek Jeter .75 2.00
3 Ichiro Suzuki .60 1.50
4 Mike Lowell .10 .30
5 Hideo Nomo .30 .75
6 Javier Vazquez .10 .30
7 Jeremy Giambi .10 .30
8 Jamie Moyer .10 .30
9 Rafael Palmeiro .20 .50
10 Magglio Ordonez .10 .30
11 Trot Nixon .10 .30
12 Luis Castillo .10 .30
13 Paul Byrd .10 .30
14 Adam Kennedy .10 .30
15 Trevor Hoffman .10 .30
16 Matt Morris .10 .30
17 Nomar Garciaparra .50 1.25
18 Matt Lawton .10 .30
19 Carlos Beltran .10 .30
20 Jason Giambi .10 .30
21 Brian Giles .10 .30
22 Jim Edmonds .10 .30
23 Garret Anderson .10 .30
24 Tony Batista .10 .30
25 Aaron Boone .10 .30
26 Mike Hampton .10 .30
27 Billy Wagner .10 .30
28 Kazuhisa Ishii .10 .30
29 Al Leiter .10 .30
30 Pat Burrell .10 .30
31 Jeff Kent .10 .30
32 Randy Johnson .30 .75
33 Ray Durham .10 .30
34 Josh Beckett .10 .30
35 Cristian Guzman .10 .30
36 Roger Clemens .60 1.50
37 Freddy Garcia .10 .30
38 Roy Halladay .10 .30
39 David Eckstein .10 .30
40 Jerry Hairston .10 .30
41 Barry Larkin .20 .50
42 Larry Walker .10 .30
43 Craig Biggio .20 .50
44 Edgardo Alfonzo .10 .30
45 Marlon Byrd .10 .30
46 J.T. Snow .10 .30
47 Juan Gonzalez .10 .30
48 Ramon Ortiz .10 .30
49 Jay Gibbons .10 .30
50 Adam Dunn .10 .30
51 Juan Pierre .10 .30
52 Jeff Bagwell .20 .50
53 Kevin Brown .10 .30
54 Pedro Astacio .10 .30
55 Mike Lieberthal .10 .30
56 Johnny Damon .20 .50
57 Tim Salmon .20 .50
58 Mike Bordick .10 .30
59 Ken Griffey Jr. .50 1.25
60 Jason Jennings .10 .30
61 Lance Berkman .10 .30
62 Jeromy Burnitz .10 .30
63 Jimmy Rollins .10 .30
64 Tsuyoshi Shinjo .10 .30
65 Alex Rodriguez .50 1.25
66 Greg Maddux .50 1.25
67 Mark Prior .20 .50
68 Mike Maroth .10 .30
69 Geoff Jenkins .10 .30
70 Tony Armas Jr. .10 .30
71 Jermaine Dye .10 .30
72 Albert Pujols .60 1.50
73 Shannon Stewart .10 .30
74 Troy Glaus .10 .30
75 Brook Fordyce .10 .30
76 Juan Encarnacion .10 .30
77 Todd Hollandsworth .10 .30
78 Roy Oswalt .10 .30
79 Paul Lo Duca .10 .30
80 Mike Piazza .50 1.25
81 Bobby Abreu .10 .30
82 Sean Burroughs .10 .30
83 Randy Winn .10 .30
84 Curt Schilling .10 .30
85 Chris Singleton .10 .30
86 Sean Casey .10 .30
87 Todd Zeile .10 .30
88 Richard Hidalgo .10 .30
89 Roberto Alomar .20 .50
90 Tim Hudson .10 .30
91 Ryan Klesko .10 .30
92 Greg Vaughn .10 .30
93 Tony Womack .10 .30
94 Fred McGriff .20 .50
95 Tom Glavine .20 .50
96 Todd Walker .10 .30
97 Travis Fryman .10 .30
98 Shane Reynolds .10 .30
99 Shawn Green .10 .30
100 Mo Vaughn .10 .30
101 Adam Piatt .10 .30
102 Deivi Cruz .10 .30
103 Steve Cox .10 .30
104 Luis Gonzalez .10 .30
105 Russell Branyan .10 .30
106 Daryle Ward .10 .30
107 Mariano Rivera .30 .75
108 Phil Nevin .10 .30
109 Ben Grieve .10 .30
110 Moises Alou .10 .30
111 Omar Vizquel .20 .50
112 Joe Randa .10 .30
113 Jorge Posada .20 .50
114 Mark Kotsay .10 .30
115 Ryan Rupe .10 .30
116 Javy Lopez .10 .30
117 Corey Patterson .10 .30
118 Bobby Higginson .10 .30
119 Jose Vidro .10 .30
120 Barry Zito .10 .30
121 Scott Rolen .20 .50
122 Gary Sheffield .10 .30
123 Kerry Wood .10 .30
124 Brandon Inge .10 .30
125 Jose Hernandez .10 .30
126 Michael Barrett .10 .30
127 Miguel Tejada .10 .30
128 Edgar Renteria .10 .30
129 Junior Spivey .10 .30
130 Jose Valentin .10 .30
131 Derrek Lee .20 .50
132 A.J. Pierzynski .10 .30
133 Mike Mussina .20 .50
134 Bret Boone .10 .30
135 Chan Ho Park .10 .30
136 Steve Finley .10 .30
137 Mark Buehrle .10 .30
138 A.J. Burnett .10 .30
139 Ben Sheets .10 .30
140 David Ortiz .30 .75
141 Nick Johnson .10 .30
142 Randall Simon .10 .30
143 Carlos Delgado .10 .30
144 Darin Erstad .10 .30
145 Shea Hillenbrand .10 .30
146 Todd Helton .20 .50
147 Preston Wilson .10 .30
148 Eric Gagne .10 .30
149 Vladimir Guerrero .30 .75
150 Brandon Duckworth .10 .30
151 Rich Aurilia .10 .30
152 Ivan Rodriguez .20 .50
153 Andruw Jones .20 .50
154 Carlos Lee .10 .30
155 Robert Fick .10 .30
156 Jacque Jones .10 .30
157 Bernie Williams .20 .50
158 John Olerud .10 .30
159 Eric Hinske .10 .30
160 Matt Clement .10 .30
161 Dmitri Young .10 .30
162 Torii Hunter .10 .30
163 Carlos Pena .10 .30
164 Mike Cameron .10 .30
165 Raul Mondesi .10 .30
166 Pedro Martinez .20 .50
167 Bob Wickman .10 .30
168 Mike Sweeney .10 .30
169 David Wells .10 .30
170 Jason Kendall .10 .30
171 Tino Martinez .20 .50
172 Matt Williams .10 .30
173 Frank Thomas .30 .75
174 Cliff Floyd .10 .30
175 Corey Koskie .10 .30
176 Orlando Hernandez .10 .30
177 Edgar Martinez .20 .50
178 Richie Sexson .10 .30
179 Manny Ramirez .20 .50
180 Jim Thome .20 .50
181 Andy Pettitte .20 .50
182 Aramis Ramirez .10 .30
183 J.D. Drew .10 .30
184 Brian Jordan .10 .30
185 Sammy Sosa .30 .75
186 Jeff Weaver .10 .30
187 Jeffrey Hammonds .10 .30
188 Eric Milton .10 .30
189 Eric Chavez .10 .30
190 Kazuhiro Sasaki .10 .30
191 Jose Cruz Jr. .10 .30
192 Derek Lowe .10 .30
193 C.C. Sabathia .10 .30
194 Adrian Beltre .10 .30
195 Alfonso Soriano .10 .30
196 Jack Wilson .10 .30
197 Fernando Vina .10 .30
198 Chipper Jones .30 .75
199 Paul Konerko .10 .30
200 Rusty Greer .10 .30
201 Jason Giambi AS .60 1.50
202 Alfonso Soriano AS .60 1.50
203 Shea Hillenbrand AS .60 1.50
204 Alex Rodriguez AS 1.00 2.50
205 Jorge Posada AS .60 1.50
206 Ichiro Suzuki AS 1.25 3.00
207 Manny Ramirez AS .60 1.50
208 Torii Hunter AS .60 1.50
209 Todd Helton AS .60 1.50
210 Jose Vidro AS .60 1.50
211 Scott Rolen AS .60 1.50
212 Jimmy Rollins AS .60 1.50
213 Mike Piazza AS 1.00 2.50
214 Barry Bonds AS 1.50 4.00
215 Sammy Sosa AS .60 1.50
216 Vladimir Guerrero AS .60 1.50
217 Lance Berkman AS .60 1.50
218 Derek Jeter AS 1.50 4.00
219 Nomar Garciaparra AS 1.00 2.50
220 Luis Gonzalez AS .60 1.50
221 Kazuhisa Ishii 02R .75 2.00
222 Satoru Komiyama 02R .75 2.00
223 So Taguchi 02R .75 2.00
224 Jorge Padilla 02R .75 2.00
225 Ben Howard 02R .75 2.00
226 Jason Simontacchi 02R .75 2.00
227 Barry Wesson 02R .75 2.00
228 Howie Clark 02R .75 2.00
229 Aaron Guiel 02R .75 2.00
230 Oliver Perez 02R .75 2.00
231 David Ross 02R .75 2.00
232 Julius Matos 02R .75 2.00
233 Chris Snelling 02R .75 2.00
234 Rodrigo Lopez 02R .75 2.00
235 Will Nieves 02R .75 2.00
236 Joe Borchard 02R .75 2.00
237 Aaron Cook 02R .75 2.00
238 Anderson Machado 02R .75 2.00
239 Corey Thurman 02R .75 2.00
240 Tyler Yates 02R .75 2.00
241 Coco Crisp 03R 1.25 3.00
242 Andy Van Hekken 03R .75 2.00
243 Jim Rushford 03R .75 2.00
244 Jeremy Robertson 03R .75 2.00
245 Shane Nance 03R .75 2.00
246 Kevin Cash 03R .75 2.00
247 Kirk Saarloos 03R .75 2.00
248 Josh Bard 03R .75 2.00
249 Dave Pember 03R RC .75 2.00
250 Freddy Sanchez 03R .75 2.00
251 Chien-Ming Wang PROS RC 4.00 10.00
252 Rickie Weeks PROS RC 2.50 6.00
253 Brandon Webb PROS RC 3.00 8.00
254 Hideki Matsui PROS RC 4.00 10.00
255 Michael Hessman PROS RC 1.25 3.00
256 Ryan Wagner PROS RC 1.25 3.00
257 Matt Kata PROS RC 1.25 3.00
258 Edwin Jackson PROS RC 1.50 4.00
259 Jose Contreras PROS RC 1.50 4.00
260 Delmon Young PROS RC 4.00 10.00
261 Bo Hart PROS RC 1.25 3.00
262 Jeff Duncan PROS RC 1.25 3.00
263 Robby Hammock PROS RC 1.25 3.00
264 Jeremy Bonderman PROS RC 4.00 10.00
265 Clint Barmes PROS RC 1.00 2.50

2003 Ultra Gold Medallion

This 250 card set is a parallel to the 2003 Ultra set. The first 200 cards were inserted at a stated rate of one per pack while cards numbered 221 through 250 were issued at a stated rate of one per 24 packs.

*GOLD MED 1-200: 1.25X TO 3X BASIC
*GOLD MED 201-220: 1X TO 2.5X BASIC
*GOLD MED 221-250: 1X TO 2.5X BASIC

2003 Ultra Back 2 Back

Randomly inserted into packs, these 17 cards feature some of the leading players in baseball. Each of these cards were printed to a stated print run of 1000 serial numbered sets.

1 Derek Jeter 6.00 15.00
2 Barry Bonds 6.00 15.00
3 Mike Piazza 4.00 10.00
4 Alex Rodriguez 4.00 10.00
5 Todd Helton 2.50 6.00
6 Edgar Martinez 2.50 6.00
7 Chipper Jones [illegible] [illegible]
8 Shawn Green 2.50 6.00
9 Chan Ho Park 2.50 6.00
10 Preston Wilson 2.50 6.00
11 Manny Ramirez 2.50 6.00
12 Aramis Ramirez 2.50 6.00
13 Pedro Martinez 2.50 6.00
14 Ivan Rodriguez 2.50 6.00
15 Ichiro Suzuki 5.00 12.00
16 Sammy Sosa 2.50 6.00
17 Jason Giambi 2.50 6.00

2003 Ultra Back 2 Back Memorabilia

Randomly inserted into packs, this is a parallel of the Ultra Back 2 Back insert set. Each of these cards feature a game-used memorabilia piece of the featured player and is issued to a stated print run of 500 serial numbered sets.

*GOLD: 1.25X TO 3X BASIC B2B MEMORABILIA
GOLD PRINT RUN 50 SERIAL #'d SETS
AR Aramis Ramirez Pants 4.00 10.00
AR1 Alex Rodriguez Jsy 8.00 20.00
BB Barry Bonds Bat 10.00 25.00
CJ Chipper Jones Jsy 6.00 15.00
CP Chan Ho Park Bat 4.00 10.00
DJ Derek Jeter Jsy 10.00 25.00
EM Edgar Martinez Jsy 6.00 15.00
IR Ivan Rodriguez Jsy 6.00 15.00
IS Ichiro Suzuki Base 8.00 20.00
JG Jason Giambi Base 4.00 10.00
MP Mike Piazza Jsy 6.00 15.00
MR Manny Ramirez Jsy 6.00 15.00
PM Pedro Martinez Jsy 6.00 15.00
PW Preston Wilson Jsy 4.00 10.00
SG Shawn Green Jsy 4.00 10.00
SS Sammy Sosa Base 6.00 15.00
TH Todd Helton Jsy 6.00 15.00

2003 Ultra Double Up

Inserted into packs at a stated rate of one in eight, each of these 16 cards feature two players with something in common. Among the common threads are teammates, nationality and position played.

COMPLETE SET (16) 15.00 40.00
1 Derek Jeter 2.50 6.00
Mike Piazza
2 Alex Rodriguez 1.50 4.00
Rafael Palmeiro
3 Chipper Jones 1.00 2.50
Andruw Jones
4 Derek Jeter 2.50 6.00
Alex Rodriguez
5 Nomar Garciaparra 2.50 6.00
Derek Jeter
6 Barry Bonds 2.50 6.00
Jason Giambi
7 Ichiro Suzuki 2.00 5.00
Hideo Nomo
8 Randy Johnson 1.00 2.50
Curt Schilling
9 Pedro Martinez 1.50 4.00
Nomar Garciaparra
10 Roger Clemens 2.00 5.00
Kevin Brown
11 Nomar Garciaparra 1.50 4.00
Manny Ramirez
12 Kazuhiro Sasaki 1.00 2.50
Hideo Nomo
13 Mike Piazza 1.50 4.00
Ivan Rodriguez
14 Ichiro Suzuki 2.00 5.00
Ken Griffey Jr.
15 Barry Bonds 2.50 6.00
Sammy Sosa
16 Alfonso Soriano 1.00 2.50
Roberto Alomar

2003 Ultra Double Up Memorabilia

Randomly inserted into packs, this is a parallel to the Double Up insert set. Each of these cards feature a piece of memorabilia from each of the players featured.

1 Derek Jeter Jsy 25.00 60.00
Mike Piazza Jsy
2 Alex Rodriguez Jsy 15.00 40.00
(Rafael Palmeiro Jsy
3 Chipper Jones Bat 10.00 25.00
Andruw Jones Jsy
4 Derek Jeter Jsy 25.00 60.00
Alex Rodriguez Jsy
5 Nomar Garciaparra Jsy [illegible] [illegible]
Derek Jeter Jsy
6 Barry Bonds Bat 15.00 40.00
Jason Giambi Base
7 Ichiro Suzuki Base 50.00 120.00
Hideo Nomo Jsy
8 Randy Johnson Jsy 10.00 25.00
Curt Schilling Jsy
9 Pedro Martinez Jsy 15.00 40.00
Nomar Garciaparra Jsy
10 Roger Clemens Jsy 15.00 40.00
Kevin Brown Jsy
11 Nomar Garciaparra Jsy 15.00 40.00
Manny Ramirez Jsy
12 Kazuhiro Sasaki Jsy 25.00 60.00
Hideo Nomo Jsy
13 Mike Piazza Jsy 15.00 40.00
Ivan Rodriguez Jsy
14 Ichiro Suzuki Base 30.00 80.00
Ken Griffey Jr. Base
15 Barry Bonds Bat 25.00 60.00
Sammy Sosa Base
16 Alfonso Soriano Pants 10.00 25.00
Roberto Alomar Jsy

2003 Ultra Moonshots

Inserted into packs at a stated rate of one in 12, these 20 cards feature some of the leading power hitters in baseball.

1 Mike Piazza 1.50 4.00
2 Alex Rodriguez 1.50 4.00
3 Manny Ramirez .75 2.00
4 Ivan Rodriguez .75 2.00
5 Luis Gonzalez .75 2.00
6 Shawn Green .75 2.00
7 Barry Bonds 2.50 6.00
8 Jason Giambi .75 2.00
9 Nomar Garciaparra 1.50 4.00
10 Edgar Martinez .75 2.00
11 Mo Vaughn .75 2.00
12 Chipper Jones 1.00 2.50
13 Todd Helton .75 2.00
14 Raul Mondesi .75 2.00
15 Preston Wilson .75 2.00
16 Rafael Palmeiro .75 2.00
17 Jim Edmonds .75 2.00
18 Bernie Williams .75 2.00
19 Vladimir Guerrero 1.00 2.50
20 Alfonso Soriano .75 2.00

2003 Ultra Moonshots Memorabilia

Inserted into packs at a stated rate of one in 20, this set parallels the Moonshot insert set except a game-used memorabilia piece is used on each of these cards.

AR Alex Rodriguez Jsy 6.00 15.00
AS Alfonso Soriano Pants 3.00 8.00
BB Barry Bonds Jsy 6.00 15.00
BW Bernie Williams Jsy 4.00 10.00
CG Vladimir Guerrero Base 4.00 10.00
CJ Chipper Jones Jsy 4.00 10.00
EM Edgar Martinez Jsy 4.00 10.00
IR Ivan Rodriguez Jsy 4.00 10.00
JE Jim Edmonds Jsy 3.00 8.00
JG Jason Giambi Base 3.00 8.00
LG Luis Gonzalez Jsy 3.00 8.00
MP Mike Piazza Jsy 6.00 15.00
MR Manny Ramirez Jsy 4.00 10.00
MV Mo Vaughn Jsy 3.00 8.00
NG Nomar Garciaparra Jsy 6.00 15.00
PW Preston Wilson Jsy 3.00 8.00
RM Raul Mondesi Jsy 3.00 8.00
RP Rafael Palmeiro Jsy 4.00 10.00
SG Shawn Green Jsy 3.00 8.00
TH Todd Helton Jsy 4.00 10.00

2003 Ultra Photo Effex

Inserted into packs at a stated rate of one in 12, these 20 cards feature intriguing photos of some of the leading players in the game.

GOLD PRINT RUN 25 SERIAL #'d SETS
GOLD NO PRICING DUE TO SCARCITY
1 Derek Jeter 2.50 6.00
2 Barry Bonds 2.50 6.00
3 Sammy Sosa 1.00 2.50
4 Troy Glaus .75 2.00
5 Albert Pujols 2.00 5.00
6 Alex Rodriguez 1.50 4.00
7 Ichiro Suzuki 2.00 5.00
8 Greg Maddux 1.50 4.00
9 Nomar Garciaparra 1.50 4.00
10 Jeff Bagwell .75 2.00
11 Chipper Jones 1.00 2.50
12 Mike Piazza 1.50 4.00
13 Randy Johnson 1.00 2.50
14 Vladimir Guerrero 1.00 2.50
15 Alfonso Soriano .75 2.00
16 Lance Berkman .75 2.00
17 Todd Helton .75 2.00
18 Mike Lowell .75 2.00
19 Carlos Delgado .75 2.00
20 Jason Giambi .75 2.00

2003 Ultra When It Was A Game

Inserted into packs at a stated rate of one in 20, these 40 cards basically feature retired stars from baseball's past. Other than Derek Jeter and Barry Bonds, all the players in this set were retired at the time of issue.

1 Derek Jeter 5.00 12.00
2 Barry Bonds 5.00 12.00
3 Luis Aparicio 2.00 5.00
4 Richie Ashburn 3.00 8.00
5 Ernie Banks 3.00 8.00
6 Enos Slaughter 2.00 5.00
7 Yogi Berra 3.00 8.00
8 Lou Boudreau 2.00 5.00
9 Lou Brock 3.00 8.00
10 Jim Bunning 2.00 5.00
11 Rod Carew 3.00 8.00
12 Orlando Cepeda 2.00 5.00
13 Larry Doby 2.00 5.00
14 Bobby Doerr 2.00 5.00
15 Bob Feller 2.00 5.00
16 Brooks Robinson 3.00 8.00
17 Rollie Fingers 2.00 5.00
18 Whitey Ford 3.00 8.00
19 Bob Gibson 3.00 8.00
20 Catfish Hunter 3.00 8.00
21 Nolan Ryan 6.00 15.00
22 Reggie Jackson 3.00 8.00
23 Fergie Jenkins 2.00 5.00
24 Al Kaline 3.00 8.00
25 Mike Schmidt 6.00 15.00
26 Harmon Killebrew 3.00 8.00
27 Ralph Kiner 2.00 5.00
28 Willie Stargell 3.00 8.00
29 Billy Williams 2.00 5.00
30 Tom Seaver 3.00 8.00
31 Juan Marichal 2.00 5.00
32 Eddie Mathews 3.00 8.00
33 Willie McCovey 2.00 5.00
34 Joe Morgan 2.00 5.00
35 Stan Musial 4.00 10.00
36 Robin Roberts 2.00 5.00
37 Robin Yount 3.00 8.00
38 Jim Palmer 2.00 5.00
39 Phil Rizzuto 3.00 8.00
40 Pee Wee Reese 3.00 8.00

2003 Ultra When It Was A Game Used

Randomly inserted into packs, these 12 cards form a partial parallel to the When it was a Game Insert set. Since several different print runs were used, we have notated that print run information next to the player's name in our checklist.

1 Yogi Berra Pants/100 20.00 50.00
2 Barry Bonds Bat/200 15.00 40.00
3 Larry Doby Bat/150 8.00 20.00
4 Catfish Hunter Jsy/200 8.00 20.00
5 Reggie Jackson Bat/300 8.00 20.00
6 Derek Jeter Jsy/200 15.00 40.00
7 Juan Marichal Jsy/300 6.00 15.00
8 Eddie Mathews Bat/300 10.00 25.00
9 Willie McCovey Jsy/150 8.00 20.00
10 Joe Morgan Pants/200 6.00 15.00
11 Jim Palmer Pants/300 6.00 15.00
12 Tom Seaver Pants/100 10.00 25.00

2004 Ultra

This 220-card set was released in November, 2003. This set was issued in eight-card packs with an $2.99 SRP which came 24 packs to a box and 16 boxes to a case. Please note that cards 201-220 feature leading prospects and were randomly inserted into packs. An 170-card update set was released in October, 2004. The set was issued in five card hobby packs with an $6 SRP which came 12 packs to a box and 16 boxes to a case and in eight-card retail packs with an $3 SRP which came 24 packs to a box and 20 boxes to a case. Cards numbered 221 through 295 feature players who switched teams in the off-season while cards numbered 296 through 382 featured Rookie Cards. Cards numbered 383 through 395 feature 13 of the Leading rookies and the reason they are the lucky 13 is that they are the final 13 cards in the set and the platinum parallel of these cards were printed to a stated print run of 13 serial numbered sets.

COMPLETE SERIES 1 (220) 30.00 60.00
COMP.SERIES 1 w/o SP's (200) 10.00 25.00
COMP.SERIES 2 w/o SP's (75) 10.00 25.00
COMP.SERIES 2 w/o L13 (162) 50.00 100.00
COMMON CARD (1-200) .10 .30
COMMON CARD (201-220) .40 1.00
201-220 APPROXIMATE ODDS 1:2 HOBBY
201-220 RANDOM IN RETAIL PACKS
COMMON CARD (221-295) .20 .50
COMMON CARD (296-382) .40 1.00
296-382 ODDS TWO PER HOBBY/RETAIL
COMMON CARD (383-395) 2.50 6.00
COMMON RC (383-395) 2.50 6.00
383-395 ODDS 1:28 HOBBY, 1:2000 RETAIL
383-395 PRINT RUN 500 SERIAL #'d SETS
1 Magglio Ordonez .20 .50
2 Bobby Abreu .12 .30
3 Eric Munson .12 .30
4 Eric Byrnes .12 .30
5 Bartolo Colon .12 .30
6 Juan Encarnacion .12 .30
7 Jody Gerut .12 .30
8 Eddie Guardado .12 .30
9 Shea Hillenbrand .12 .30
10 Andruw Jones .12 .30
11 Carlos Lee .12 .30
12 Pedro Martinez .20 .50
13 Barry Larkin .20 .50
14 Angel Berroa .12 .30
15 Edgar Martinez .20 .50
16 Sidney Ponson .12 .30
17 Mariano Rivera .30 .75
18 Richie Sexson .12 .30
19 Frank Thomas .30 .75
20 Jerome Williams .12 .30
21 Barry Zito .12 .30
22 Roberto Alomar .20 .50
23 Rocky Biddle .12 .30
24 Orlando Cabrera .12 .30
25 Placido Polanco .12 .30
26 Morgan Ensberg .12 .30
27 Jason Giambi .12 .30
28 Jim Thome .20 .50
29 Vladimir Guerrero .30 .75
30 Tim Hudson .20 .50
31 Jacque Jones .12 .30
32 Derrek Lee .12 .30
33 Rafael Palmeiro .20 .50
34 Mike Mussina .20 .50
35 Corey Patterson .12 .30
36 Mike Cameron .12 .30
37 Ivan Rodriguez .20 .50
38 Ben Sheets .12 .30
39 Woody Williams .12 .30
40 Ichiro Suzuki .50 1.25
41 Moises Alou .12 .30
42 Craig Biggio .20 .50
43 Jorge Posada .20 .50
44 Craig Monroe .12 .30
45 Darin Erstad .12 .30
46 Jay Gibbons .12 .30
47 Aaron Guiel .12 .30
48 Travis Lee .12 .30
49 Jorge Julio .12 .30
50 Torii Hunter .12 .30
51 Luis Matos .12 .30
52 Brett Myers .12 .30
53 Sean Casey .12 .30
54 Mark Prior .20 .50
55 Alex Rodriguez .50 1.25
56 Gary Sheffield .12 .30
57 Jason Varitek .30 .75
58 Dontrelle Willis .12 .30
59 Garret Anderson .12 .30
60 Casey Blake .12 .30
61 Jay Payton .12 .30
62 Carl Crawford .20 .50
63 Carl Everett .12 .30
64 Marcus Giles .12 .30
65 Jose Guillen .12 .30
66 Eric Karros .12 .30
67 Mike Lieberthal .12 .30
68 Hideki Matsui .50 1.25
69 Xavier Nady .12 .30
70 Hank Blalock .12 .30
71 Albert Pujols .75 2.00
72 Jose Cruz Jr. .12 .30
73 Randall Simon .12 .30
74 Javier Vazquez .12 .30
75 Preston Wilson .12 .30
76 Danys Baez .12 .30
77 Alex Cintron .12 .30
78 Jake Peavy .12 .30
79 Scott Rolen .20 .50
80 Robert Fick .12 .30
81 Brian Giles .12 .30
82 Roy Halladay .30 .75
83 Kazuhisa Ishii .12 .30
84 Austin Kearns .12 .30
85 Paul Lo Duca .12 .30
86 Darrell May .12 .30
87 Phil Nevin .12 .30
88 Carlos Pena .20 .50
89 Manny Ramirez .30 .75
90 C.C. Sabathia .20 .50
91 John Smoltz .30 .75
92 Jose Vidro .12 .30
93 Randy Wolf .12 .30
94 Jeff Bagwell .20 .50
95 Barry Bonds .60 1.50
96 Frank Catalanotto .12 .30

97 Zach Day .12 .30
98 David Ortiz .30 .75
99 Troy Glaus .12 .30
100 Bo Hart .12 .30
101 Geoff Jenkins .12 .30
102 Jason Kendall .12 .30
103 Esteban Loaiza .12 .30
104 Doug Mientkiewicz .12 .30
105 Trot Nixon .12 .30
106 Troy Percival .12 .30
107 Aramis Ramirez .12 .30
108 Alex Sanchez .12 .30
109 Alfonso Soriano .12 .30
110 Omar Vizquel .20 .50
111 Kerry Wood .12 .30
112 Rocco Baldelli .12 .30
113 Bret Boone .12 .30
114 Shawn Chacon .12 .30
115 Carlos Delgado .12 .30
116 Shawn Green .12 .30
117 Tim Worrell .12 .30
118 Tom Glavine .20 .50
119 Shigetoshi Hasegawa .12 .30
120 Derek Jeter .75 2.00
121 Jeff Kent .12 .30
122 Braden Looper .12 .30
123 Kevin Millwood .12 .30
124 Hideo Nomo .30 .75
125 Jason Phillips .12 .30
126 Tim Redding .12 .30
127 Reggie Sanders .12 .30
128 Sammy Sosa .30 .75
129 Billy Wagner .12 .30
130 Miguel Batista .12 .30
131 Milton Bradley .12 .30
132 Eric Chavez .12 .30
133 J.D. Drew .12 .30
134 Keith Foulke .12 .30
135 Luis Gonzalez .12 .30
136 LaTroy Hawkins .12 .30
137 Randy Johnson .30 .75
138 Byung-Hyun Kim .12 .30
139 Javy Lopez .12 .30
140 Melvin Mora .12 .30
141 Aubrey Huff .12 .30
142 Mike Piazza .30 .75
143 Mark Redman .12 .30
144 Kazuhiro Sasaki .12 .30
145 Shannon Stewart .12 .30
146 Larry Walker .20 .50
147 Dmitri Young .12 .30
148 Josh Beckett .20 .50
149 Jae Weong Seo .12 .30
150 Hee Seop Choi .12 .30
151 Adam Dunn .20 .50
152 Rafael Furcal .12 .30
153 Juan Gonzalez .12 .30
154 Todd Helton .20 .50
155 Carlos Zambrano .20 .50
156 Ryan Klesko .12 .30
157 Mike Lowell .12 .30
158 Jamie Moyer .12 .30
159 Russ Ortiz .12 .30
160 Juan Pierre .12 .30
161 Edgar Renteria .12 .30
162 Curt Schilling .20 .50
163 Mike Sweeney .12 .30
164 Brandon Webb .12 .30
165 Michael Young .12 .30
166 Carlos Beltran .12 .30
167 Sean Burroughs .12 .30
168 Luis Castillo .12 .30
169 David Eckstein .12 .30
170 Eric Gagne .12 .30
171 Chipper Jones .30 .75
172 Livan Hernandez .12 .30
173 Nick Johnson .12 .30
174 Corey Koskie .12 .30
175 Jason Schmidt .12 .30
176 Bill Mueller .12 .30
177 Steve Finley .12 .30
178 A.J. Pierzynski .12 .30
179 Rene Reyes .12 .30
180 Jason Johnson .12 .30
181 Mark Teixeira .30 .75
182 Kip Wells .12 .30
183 Mike MacDougal .12 .30
184 Lance Berkman .20 .50
185 Victor Zambrano .12 .30
186 Roger Clemens .40 1.00
187 Jim Edmonds .20 .50
188 Nomar Garciaparra .30 .75
189 Ken Griffey Jr. .50 1.25
190 Richard Hidalgo .12 .30
191 Cliff Floyd .12 .30
192 Greg Maddux .50 1.25
193 Mark Mulder .12 .30
194 Roy Oswalt .20 .50
195 Marlon Byrd .12 .30
196 Jose Reyes .20 .50
197 Kevin Brown .12 .30
198 Miguel Tejada .20 .50
199 Vernon Wells .12 .30
200 Joel Pineiro .12 .30
201 Rickie Weeks AR .40 1.00
202 Chad Gaudin AR .40 1.00
203 Ryan Wagner AR .40 1.00
204 Chris Bootcheck AR .40 1.00
205 Koyie Hill AR .40 1.00
206 Jeff Duncan AR .40 1.00
207 Rich Harden AR .40 1.00
208 Edwin Jackson AR .40 1.00
209 Robby Hammock AR .40 1.00
210 Khalil Greene AR .60 1.50
211 Chien-Ming Wang AR 2.00 5.00
212 Prentice Redman AR .40 1.00
213 Todd Wellemeyer AR .40 1.00
214 Clint Barmes AR .60 1.50
215 Matt Kata AR .40 1.00
216 Jon Leicester AR .40 1.00
217 Jeremy Guthrie AR .40 1.00
218 Chin-Hui Tsao AR .40 1.00
219 Dan Haren AR .40 1.00
220 Delmon Young AR .60 1.50
221 Vladimir Guerrero .20 .50
222 Andy Pettitte .30 .75
223 Gary Sheffield .20 .50
224 Javier Vazquez .20 .50
225 Alex Rodriguez .75 2.00
226 Billy Wagner .20 .50
227 Miguel Tejada .30 .75
228 Greg Maddux .75 2.00
229 Ivan Rodriguez .30 .75
230 Roger Clemens .60 1.50
231 Alfonso Soriano .20 .50
232 Miguel Cabrera .50 1.25
233 Javy Lopez .20 .50
234 David Wells .20 .50
235 Eric Milton .20 .50
236 Armando Benitez .20 .50
237 Mike Cameron .20 .50
238 J.D. Drew .20 .50
239 Carlos Beltran .20 .50
240 Bartolo Colon .20 .50
241 Jose Guillen .20 .50
242 Kevin Brown .20 .50
243 Carlos Guillen .20 .50
244 Kenny Lofton .20 .50
245 Pokey Reese .20 .50
246 Rafael Palmeiro .30 .75
247 Nomar Garciaparra .50 1.25
248 Hee Seop Choi .20 .50
249 Juan Uribe .20 .50
250 Nick Johnson .20 .50
251 Scott Podsednik .20 .50
252 Richie Sexson .20 .50
253 Keith Foulke Sox .20 .50
254 Jaret Wright .20 .50
255 Johnny Estrada .20 .50
256 Michael Barrett .20 .50
257 Bernie Williams .30 .75
258 Octavio Dotel .20 .50
259 Jeromy Burnitz .20 .50
260 Kevin Youkilis .30 .75
261 Derrek Lee .20 .50
262 Jack Wilson .20 .50
263 Craig Wilson .20 .50
264 Richard Hidalgo .20 .50
265 Royce Clayton .20 .50
266 Curt Schilling .30 .75
267 Joe Mauer .50 1.25
268 Bobby Crosby .30 .75
269 Zack Greinke .30 .75
270 Victor Martinez .30 .75
271 Pedro Feliz .20 .50
272 Tony Batista .20 .50
273 Casey Kotchman .20 .50
274 Freddy Garcia .20 .50
275 Adam Everett .20 .50
276 Alexis Rios .30 .75
277 Lew Ford .20 .50
278 Adam LaRoche .20 .50
279 Lyle Overbay .20 .50
280 Juan Gonzalez .20 .50
281 A.J. Pierzynski .20 .50
282 Scott Hairston .20 .50
283 Danny Bautista .20 .50
284 Brad Penny .20 .50
285 Paul Konerko .30 .75
286 Matt Lawton .20 .50
287 Carl Pavano .20 .50
288 Pat Burrell .20 .50
289 Kenny Rogers .20 .50
290 Laynce Nix .20 .50
291 Johnny Damon .30 .75
292 Paul Wilson .20 .50
293 Vinny Castilla .20 .50
294 Aaron Miles .20 .50
295 Ken Harvey .20 .50
296 Onil Joseph RC .40 1.00
297 Kazuhito Tadano RC .40 1.00
298 Jeff Bennett RC .40 1.00
299 Chad Bentz RC .40 1.00
300 Akinori Otsuka RC .40 1.00
301 Jon Knott RC .40 1.00
302 Ian Snell RC .40 1.00
303 Fernando Nieve RC .40 1.00
304 Mike Rouse RC .40 1.00
305 Dennis Sarfate RC .40 1.00
306 Josh Labandeira RC .40 1.00
307 Chris Oxspring RC .40 1.00
308 Alfredo Simon RC .40 1.00
309 Rusty Tucker RC .40 1.00
310 Lincoln Holdzkom RC .40 1.00
311 Justin Leone RC .40 1.00
312 Jorge Sequea RC .40 1.00
313 Brian Dallimore RC .40 1.00
314 Tim Bittner RC .40 1.00
315 Ronny Cedeno RC .40 1.00
316 Justin Hampson RC .40 1.00
317 Ryan Wing RC .40 1.00
318 Mariano Gomez RC .40 1.00
319 Carlos Vasquez RC .40 1.00
320 Casey Daigle RC .40 1.00
321 Renyel Pinto RC .40 1.00
322 Chris Shelton RC .40 1.00
323 Mike Gosling RC .40 1.00
324 Aarom Baldiris RC .40 1.00
325 Ramon Ramirez RC .40 1.00
326 Roberto Novoa RC .40 1.00
327 Sean Henn RC .40 1.00
328 Nick Regilio RC .40 1.00
329 Dave Crouthers RC .40 1.00
330 Greg Dobbs RC .40 1.00
331 Angel Chavez RC .40 1.00
332 Luis A. Gonzalez RC .40 1.00
333 Justin Knoedler RC .40 1.00
334 Jason Frasor RC .40 1.00
335 Jerry Gil RC .40 1.00
336 Carlos Hines RC .40 1.00
337 Ivan Ochoa RC .40 1.00
338 Jose Capellan RC .40 1.00
339 Hector Gimenez RC .40 1.00
340 Shawn Hill RC .40 1.00
341 Freddy Guzman RC .40 1.00
342 Scott Proctor RC .40 1.00
343 Frank Francisco RC .40 1.00
344 Brandon Medders RC .40 1.00
345 Andy Green RC .40 1.00
346 Eddy Rodriguez RC .40 1.00
347 Tim Hamulack RC .40 1.00
348 Michael Wuertz RC .40 1.00
349 Arnie Munoz .40 1.00
350 Enemencio Pacheco RC .40 1.00
351 Dusty Bergman RC .40 1.00
352 Charles Thomas RC .40 1.00
353 William Bergolla RC .40 1.00
354 Ramon Castro RC .40 1.00
355 Justin Lehr RC .40 1.00
356 Lino Urdaneta RC .40 1.00
357 Donnie Kelly RC .60 1.50
358 Kevin Cave RC .40 1.00
359 Franklyn Gracesqui RC .40 1.00
360 Chris Aguila RC .40 1.00
361 Jorge Vasquez RC .40 1.00
362 Andres Blanco RC .40 1.00
363 Orlando Rodriguez RC .40 1.00
364 Colby Miller RC .40 1.00
365 Shawn Camp RC .40 1.00
366 Jake Woods RC .40 1.00
367 George Sherrill RC .40 1.00
368 Justin Huisman RC .40 1.00
369 Jimmy Serrano RC .40 1.00
370 Mike Johnston RC .40 1.00
371 Ryan Meaux RC .40 1.00
372 Scott Dohmann RC .40 1.00
373 Brad Halsey RC .40 1.00
374 Joey Gathright RC .40 1.00
375 Yadier Molina RC 2.50 6.00
376 Travis Blackley RC .40 1.00
377 Steve Andrade RC .40 1.00
378 Phil Stockman RC .40 1.00
379 Roman Colon RC .40 1.00
380 Jesse Crain RC .40 1.00
381 Edwardo Sierra RC .40 1.00
382 Justin Germano RC .40 1.00
383 Kaz Matsui L13 RC 4.00 10.00
384 Shingo Takatsu L13 RC 2.50 6.00
385 John Gall L13 RC 2.50 6.00
386 Chris Saenz L13 RC 2.50 6.00
387 Merkin Valdez L13 RC 2.50 6.00
388 Jamie Brown L13 RC 2.50 6.00
389 Jason Bartlett L13 RC 8.00 20.00
390 David Aardsma L13 RC 2.50 6.00
391 Scott Kazmir L13 RC 12.00 30.00
392 David Wright L13 10.00 25.00
393 Dioner Navarro L13 RC 4.00 10.00
394 B.J. Upton L13 4.00 10.00
395 Gavin Floyd L13 2.50 6.00

2004 Ultra Gold Medallion

*GOLD 1-200: 1.25X TO 3X BASIC
1-200 SERIES 1 ODDS 1:1
*GOLD 201-220: 1X TO 2.5X BASIC
201-220 SERIES 1 ODDS 1:8
*GOLD 221-295: .75X TO 2X BASIC
221-295 SERIES 2 ODDS 1:1 H, 1:3 R
*GOLD 296-382: 1X TO 2.5X BASIC
*GOLD 383-395: .15X TO .4X BASIC
296-395 SERIES 2 ODDS 1:4 H, 1:12 R

2004 Ultra Platinum Medallion

*PLATINUM 1-200: 8X TO 20X BASIC
*PLATINUM 201-220: 2.5X TO 6X BASIC
1-220 SERIES 1 ODDS 1:36
1-220 PRINT RUN 66 SERIAL #'d SETS
*PLATINUM 221-295: 5X TO 12X BASIC
*PLATINUM 296-382: 2.5X TO 6X BASIC
221-382 PRINT RUN 100 SERIAL #'d SETS
383-395 PRINT RUN 13 SERIAL #'d SETS
383-395 NO PRICING DUE TO SCARCITY
221-395 SER.2 ODDS 1:12 HOB, 1:145 RET
CARDS HAVE BEEN KNOWN TO EXIST W/O SER.#

2004 Ultra Season Crowns Autograph

Rickie Weeks did not return his autographs in time for pack-out, thus those cards were issued as exchange cards. There is no expiration date for those redemptions.

STATED PRINT RUN 150 SERIAL #'d SETS
GOLD PRINT RUN 25 SERIAL #'d SETS
NO GOLD PRICING DUE TO SCARCITY
SERIES 1 AUTO PARALLEL ODDS 1:192
EXCHANGE DEADLINE INDEFINITE
35 Corey Patterson 5.00 12.00
58 Dontrelle Willis 12.50 30.00
70 Hank Blalock 8.00 20.00
79 Scott Rolen 12.50 30.00
84 Austin Kearns 5.00 12.00
88 Carlos Pena 5.00 12.00
100 Bo Hart 5.00 12.00
112 Rocco Baldelli 8.00 20.00
141 Aubrey Huff 8.00 20.00
151 Mike Lowell 8.00 20.00
164 Brandon Webb 5.00 12.00
171 Chipper Jones 30.00 60.00
196 Jose Reyes 8.00 20.00
198 Miguel Tejada 12.50 30.00

2004 Ultra Season Crowns Game Used

STATED PRINT RUN 399 SERIAL #'d SETS
*GOLD: .5X TO 1.2X BASIC
GOLD PRINT RUN 99 SERIAL #'d SETS
*PLATINUM: .75X TO 2X BASIC
PLATINUM PRINT RUN 25 SERIAL #'d SETS
SERIES 1 GU PARALLEL ODDS 1:24
10 Andruw Jones Bat 4.00 10.00
12 Pedro Martinez Jsy 4.00 10.00
14 Angel Berroa Jsy 3.00 8.00
19 Frank Thomas Jsy 4.00 10.00
22 Roberto Alomar Bat 4.00 10.00
27 Jason Giambi Jsy 3.00 8.00
28 Jim Thome Jsy 4.00 10.00
29 Vladimir Guerrero Jsy 4.00 10.00
30 Tim Hudson Jsy 3.00 8.00
40 Ichiro Suzuki Base 10.00 25.00
50 Torii Hunter Bat 3.00 8.00
53 Sean Casey Bat 3.00 8.00
55 Alex Rodriguez Jsy 6.00 15.00
56 Gary Sheffield Bat 3.00 8.00
58 Dontrelle Willis Jsy 4.00 10.00
68 Hideki Matsui Base 10.00 25.00
70 Hank Blalock Bat 3.00 8.00
71 Albert Pujols Jsy 8.00 20.00
79 Scott Rolen Bat 4.00 10.00
84 Austin Kearns Bat 3.00 8.00
88 Carlos Pena Bat 3.00 8.00
89 Manny Ramirez Jsy 4.00 10.00
94 Jeff Bagwell Pants 4.00 10.00
95 Barry Bonds Base 8.00 20.00
99 Troy Glaus Jsy 3.00 8.00
102 Jason Kendall Jsy 3.00 8.00
109 Alfonso Soriano Bat 3.00 8.00
110 Omar Vizquel Jsy 4.00 10.00
112 Rocco Baldelli Jsy 3.00 8.00
115 Carlos Delgado Jsy 3.00 8.00
116 Shawn Green Jsy 3.00 8.00
118 Tom Glavine Bat 4.00 10.00
120 Derek Jeter Jsy 10.00 25.00
124 Hideo Nomo Jsy 4.00 10.00
128 Sammy Sosa Jsy 4.00 10.00
137 Randy Johnson Jsy 4.00 10.00
142 Mike Piazza Bat 6.00 15.00
144 Kazuhiro Sasaki Jsy 3.00 8.00
146 Larry Walker Jsy 3.00 8.00
151 Adam Dunn Bat 3.00 8.00
154 Todd Helton Jsy 4.00 10.00
164 Brandon Webb Jsy 3.00 8.00
166 Carlos Beltran Jsy 3.00 8.00
167 Sean Burroughs Jsy 3.00 8.00
171 Chipper Jones Jsy 4.00 10.00
184 Lance Berkman Bat 3.00 8.00
186 Roger Clemens Jsy 6.00 15.00
192 Greg Maddux Jsy 6.00 15.00
193 Mark Mulder Jsy 3.00 8.00
196 Jose Reyes Jsy 3.00 8.00

2004 Ultra Diamond Producers

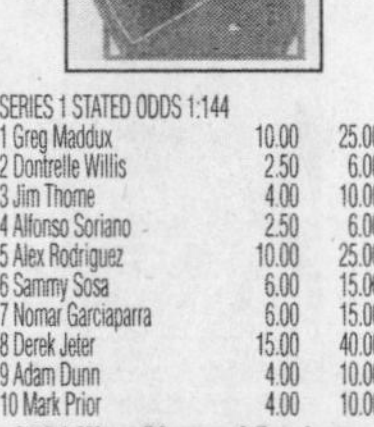

SERIES 1 STATED ODDS 1:144
1 Greg Maddux 10.00 25.00
2 Dontrelle Willis 2.50 6.00
3 Jim Thome 4.00 10.00
4 Alfonso Soriano 2.50 6.00
5 Alex Rodriguez 10.00 25.00
6 Sammy Sosa 6.00 15.00
7 Nomar Garciaparra 6.00 15.00
8 Derek Jeter 15.00 40.00
9 Adam Dunn 4.00 10.00
10 Mark Prior 4.00 10.00

2004 Ultra Diamond Producers Game Used

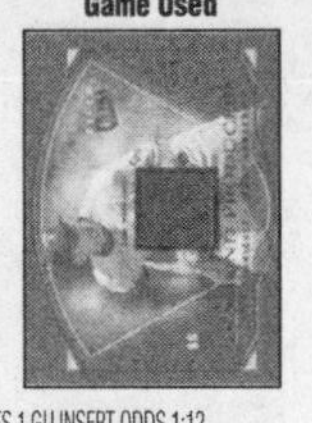

SERIES 1 GU INSERT ODDS 1:12
STATED PRINT RUN 1000 SERIAL #'d SETS
1 Greg Maddux Jsy 4.00 10.00
2 Dontrelle Willis Jsy 4.00 10.00
3 Jim Thome Jsy 4.00 10.00
4 Alfonso Soriano Bat 3.00 8.00
5 Alex Rodriguez Jsy 6.00 15.00
6 Sammy Sosa Jsy 4.00 10.00
7 Nomar Garciaparra Jsy 6.00 15.00
8 Derek Jeter Jsy 10.00 25.00
9 Adam Dunn Bat 3.00 8.00
10 Mark Prior Jsy 4.00 10.00

2004 Ultra Diamond Producers Game Used UltraSwatch

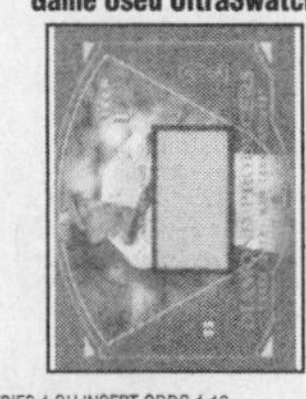

SERIES 1 GU INSERT ODDS 1:12
PRINT RUNS B/WN 2-44 COPIES PER
NO PRICING DUE TO SCARCITY
1 Greg Maddux Jsy/31
2 Dontrelle Willis Jsy/35
3 Jim Thome Jsy/25
4 Alfonso Soriano Bat/12
5 Alex Rodriguez Jsy/3
6 Sammy Sosa Jsy/21
7 Nomar Garciaparra Jsy/5
8 Derek Jeter Jsy/2
9 Adam Dunn Bat/44
10 Mark Prior Jsy/22

2004 Ultra Hitting Machines

SERIES 2 ODDS 1:12 HOBBY, 1:24 RETAIL
*DIE CUT: .75X TO 2X BASIC
DC RANDOM IN SER.2 VINTAGE/MVP RETAIL
1 Albert Pujols 2.50 6.00
2 Ken Griffey Jr. 1.50 4.00
3 Vladimir Guerrero 1.00 2.50
4 Mike Piazza 1.00 2.50
5 Ichiro Suzuki 1.50 4.00
6 Miguel Cabrera 1.00 2.50
7 Hideki Matsui 1.50 4.00
8 Nomar Garciaparra 1.00 2.50
9 Derek Jeter 2.50 6.00
10 Chipper Jones 1.00 2.50

2004 Ultra Hitting Machines Jersey Silver

*GOLD: 1.25X TO 3X SILVER
GOLD PRINT RUN 50 SERIAL #'d SETS
PLATINUM PRINT RUN 10 SERIAL #'d SETS
NO PLATINUM PRICING DUE TO SCARCITY
SER.2 OVERALL GU ODDS 1:6 H, 1:48 R
AD Adam Dunn 2.00 5.00
AP Albert Pujols 6.00 15.00
CJ Chipper Jones 3.00 8.00
FT Frank Thomas 3.00 8.00
HM Hideki Matsui 8.00 20.00
JB Jeff Bagwell 3.00 8.00
MC Miguel Cabrera 3.00 8.00
MP Mike Piazza 4.00 10.00
TH Todd Helton 3.00 8.00
VG Vladimir Guerrero 3.00 8.00

2004 Ultra HR Kings

SERIES 1 HR/K/RBI KING ODDS 1:12
*GOLD: 2X TO 5X BASIC
GOLD SER.1 HR/K/RBI KING ODDS 1:350
GOLD PRINT RUN 50 SERIAL #'d SETS
1 Barry Bonds 2.00 5.00
2 Albert Pujols 2.50 6.00
3 Jason Giambi .40 1.00
4 Jeff Bagwell .60 1.50
5 Ken Griffey Jr. 1.50 4.00
6 Alex Rodriguez 1.50 4.00
7 Sammy Sosa 1.00 2.50
8 Alfonso Soriano .40 1.00
9 Chipper Jones 1.00 2.50
10 Mike Piazza 1.00 2.50

2004 Ultra K Kings

SERIES 1 HR/K/RBI KING ODDS 1:12
*GOLD: 2X TO 5X BASIC
GOLD SER.1 HR/K/RBI KING ODDS 1:350
GOLD PRINT RUN 50 SERIAL #'d SETS
1 Randy Johnson 1.00 2.50
2 Pedro Martinez .60 1.50
3 Curt Schilling .60 1.50
4 Roger Clemens 1.25 3.00
5 Mike Mussina .60 1.50
6 Roy Halladay 1.00 2.50
7 Kerry Wood .40 1.00
8 Dontrelle Willis .40 1.00
9 Greg Maddux 1.50 4.00
10 Mark Prior .60 1.50

2004 Ultra Kings Triple Swatch

SERIES 1 GU INSERT ODDS 1:12
STATED PRINT RUN 33 SERIAL #'d SETS
NO PRICING DUE TO SCARCITY
1 Mike Piazza Bat
Roger Clemens Jsy
Alex Rodriguez Jsy
2 Albert Pujols Jsy
Mark Prior Jsy
Todd Helton Jsy
3 Alfonso Soriano Bat
Dontrelle Willis Jsy
Albert Pujols Jsy
4 Pedro Martinez Jsy
Sammy Sosa Jsy
Albert Pujols Jsy
5 Greg Maddux Jsy
Chipper Jones Jsy
Vladimir Guerrero Jsy
6 Randy Johnson Jsy
Albert Pujols Jsy
Todd Helton Jsy
7 Dontrelle Willis Jsy
Chipper Jones Jsy
Albert Pujols Jsy
8 Kerry Wood Jsy
Sammy Sosa Jsy
Nomar Garciaparra Jsy
9 Dontrelle Willis Jsy
Jeff Bagwell Pants
Jim Thome Jsy
10 Greg Maddux Jsy
Jason Giambi Jsy
Manny Ramirez Jsy

2004 Ultra Legendary 13 Collection Game Used

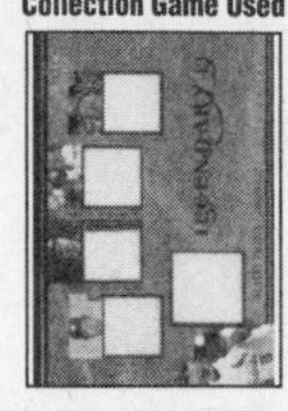

STATED PRINT RUN 13 SERIAL #'d SETS
KEY PLAYER HAS OVERSIZED SWATCH
AUTO MASTERPIECE PRINT RUN 1 #'d SET
AUTO MP KEY PLAYER HAS AUTOGRAPH
SER.2 OVERALL LGD 13 ODDS 1:192 HOBBY
EACH CARD FEATURES 13 JSY SWATCHES
NO PRICING DUE TO SCARCITY
AP A.Pujols Oversized Jsy
CF C.Fisk Oversized Jsy
CR C.Ripken Oversized Jsy
CY C.Yastrzemski Oversized Jsy
DM D.Mattingly Oversized Jsy
JB J.Bench Oversized Jsy
MP M.Prior Oversized Jsy
MS M.Schmidt Oversized Jsy
NR N.Ryan Oversized Jsy
RC R.Clemens Oversized Jsy
SM S.Musial Oversized Jsy
TW T.Williams Oversized Jsy
YB Y.Berra Oversized Jsy

2004 Ultra Legendary 13 Dual Game Used Gold

STATED PRINT RUN 22 SERIAL #'d SETS
MASTERPIECE PRINT RUN 1 #'d SET
NO M'PIECE PRICING DUE TO SCARCITY
PLATINUM PRINT RUN 10 #'d SETS
NO PLATINUM PRICING DUE TO SCARCITY
SER.2 OVERALL LGD 13 ODDS 1:192 HOBBY
APCF Albert Pujols Patch
Carlton Fisk Patch
APCY Albert Pujols Patch
Carl Yastrzemski Patch
CFMP Carlton Fisk Patch
Mark Prior Patch
CRMS Cal Ripken Patch
Mike Schmidt Patch
CYTW Carl Yastrzemski Jsy
Ted Williams Bat
DMAP Don Mattingly Patch
Albert Pujols Patch
DMCR Don Mattingly Patch
Cal Ripken Patch
MSSM Mike Schmidt Patch
Stan Musial Jsy
NRMP Nolan Ryan Patch
Mark Prior Patch
NRRC Nolan Ryan Jsy
Roger Clemens Patch
RCMP Roger Clemens Patch
Mark Prior Patch
YBDM Yogi Berra Bat
Don Mattingly Patch
YBJB Yogi Berra Bat
Johnny Bench Patch

2004 Ultra Legendary 13 Dual Game Used Autograph Platinum

STATED PRINT RUN 3 SERIAL #'d SETS
MASTERPIECE PRINT RUN 1 #'d SET
SER.2 OVERALL LGD 13 ODDS 1:192 HOBBY
NO PRICING DUE TO SCARCITY

2004 Ultra Legendary 13 Single Game Used Gold

PRINT RUNS B/WN 5-72 COPIES PER
NO PRICING ON QTY OF 9 OR LESS
MASTERPIECE PRINT RUN 1 #'d SET
NO M'PIECE PRICING DUE TO SCARCITY
SER.2 OVERALL LGD 13 ODDS 1:192 HOBBY
AP Albert Pujols Patch/5
CF Carlton Fisk Jsy/72 6.00 15.00
CR Cal Ripken Patch/8
CY Carl Yastrzemski Jsy/8
DM Don Mattingly Patch/23 40.00 80.00
JB Johnny Bench Patch/5
MP Mark Prior Patch/22 10.00 25.00
MS Mike Schmidt Patch/20 50.00 100.00
NR Nolan Ryan Jsy/34 15.00 40.00
RC Roger Clemens Patch/22 20.00 50.00
SM Stan Musial Jsy/6
TW Ted Williams Bat/9
YB Yogi Berra Bat/8

2004 Ultra Legendary 13 Single Game Used Autograph Platinum

STATED PRINT RUN 5 SERIAL #'d SETS
MASTERPIECE PRINT RUN 1 #'d SET
SER.2 OVERALL LGD 13 ODDS 1:192 HOBBY
NO PRICING DUE TO SCARCITY

2004 Ultra Performers

COMPLETE SET (15) 10.00 25.00
SERIES 1 STATED ODDS 1:6
1 Ichiro Suzuki 1.50 4.00
2 Albert Pujols 2.50 6.00
3 Barry Bonds 2.00 5.00
4 Hideki Matsui 1.50 4.00
5 Randy Johnson 1.00 2.50
6 Jason Giambi .40 1.00
7 Pedro Martinez .60 1.50
8 Hank Blalock .40 1.00
9 Chipper Jones 1.00 2.50
10 Mike Piazza 1.00 2.50
11 Derek Jeter 2.50 6.00
12 Vladimir Guerrero 1.00 2.50
13 Barry Zito .40 1.00
14 Rocco Baldelli .40 1.00
15 Hideo Nomo 1.00 2.50

2004 Ultra Performers Game Used

SERIES 1 GU INSERT ODDS 1:12
STATED PRINT RUN 500 SERIAL #'d SETS
1 Albert Pujols Jsy 8.00 20.00
2 Barry Bonds Base 8.00 20.00
3 Randy Johnson Jsy 4.00 10.00
4 Jason Giambi Jsy 3.00 8.00
5 Pedro Martinez Jsy 4.00 10.00
6 Hank Blalock Bat 3.00 8.00
7 Chipper Jones Jsy 4.00 10.00
8 Mike Piazza Bat 4.00 10.00
9 Derek Jeter Jsy 10.00 25.00
10 Vladimir Guerrero Jsy 4.00 10.00
11 Rocco Baldelli Jsy 3.00 8.00
12 Hideo Nomo Jsy 4.00 10.00

2004 Ultra Performers Game Used UltraSwatch

SERIES 1 GU INSERT ODDS 1:12
PRINT RUNS B/WN 2-51 COPIES PER
NO PRICING DUE TO SCARCITY
1 Albert Pujols Jsy/5
2 Barry Bonds Base/25
3 Randy Johnson Jsy/51
4 Jason Giambi Jsy/25
5 Pedro Martinez Jsy/45
6 Hank Blalock Bat/9
7 Chipper Jones Jsy/10
8 Mike Piazza Bat/31
9 Derek Jeter Jsy/2
10 Vladimir Guerrero Jsy/27
11 Rocco Baldelli Jsy/5
12 Hideo Nomo Jsy/10

2004 Ultra RBI Kings

OVERALL HR/K/RBI KING ODDS 1:12
*GOLD: 2X TO 5X BASIC
GOLD SER.1 HR/K/RBI KING ODDS 1:350
GOLD PRINT RUN 50 SERIAL #'d SETS
1 Hideki Matsui 1.50 4.00
2 Albert Pujols 2.50 6.00
3 Todd Helton .60 1.50
4 Jim Thome .60 1.50
5 Carlos Delgado .40 1.00
6 Alex Rodriguez 1.50 4.00
7 Barry Bonds 2.00 5.00
8 Manny Ramirez 1.00 2.50
9 Vladimir Guerrero 1.00 2.50
10 Nomar Garciaparra 1.00 2.50

2004 Ultra Turn Back the Clock

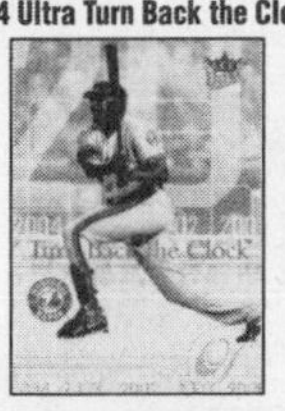

SERIES 2 ODDS 1:6 HOBBY, 1:12 RETAIL
1 Roger Clemens Sox 1.25 3.00
2 Alex Rodriguez Rgr 1.50 4.00
3 Randy Johnson M's 1.00 2.50
4 Pedro Martinez Expos .60 1.50
5 Alfonso Soriano Yanks .40 1.00
6 Curt Schilling Phils .60 1.50
7 Miguel Tejada A's .60 1.50
8 Scott Rolen Phils .60 1.50
9 Jim Thome Indians .60 1.50
10 Manny Ramirez Indians 1.00 2.50
11 Vladimir Guerrero Expos 1.00 2.50
12 Tom Glavine Braves .60 1.50
13 Andy Pettitte Yanks .60 1.50
14 Ivan Rodriguez Marlins .60 1.50
15 Jason Giambi A's .40 1.00
16 Rafael Palmeiro Rgr .60 1.50
17 Greg Maddux Braves 1.50 4.00
18 Hideo Nomo Sox 1.00 2.50
19 Mike Mussina O's .60 1.50
20 Sammy Sosa Sox 1.00 2.50

2004 Ultra Turn Back the Clock Jersey Copper

STATED PRINT RUN 399 SERIAL #'d SETS
*GOLD: .6X TO 1.5X COPPER
GOLD PRINT RUN 99 SERIAL #'d SETS
*SILVER: .5X TO 1.2X COPPER
SILVER PRINT RUN 199 SERIAL #'d SETS
*PATCH PLAT: 1.5X TO 4X COPPER
PATCH PLATINUM PRINT RUN 29 #'d SETS
SER.2 OVERALL GU ODDS 1:6 H, 1:48 R
AP Andy Pettitte Yanks 4.00 10.00
AR Alex Rodriguez Rgr 5.00 12.00
AS Alfonso Soriano Yanks 3.00 8.00
CS Curt Schilling Phils 3.00 8.00
GM Greg Maddux Braves 5.00 12.00
HM Hideo Nomo Sox 4.00 10.00
IR Ivan Rodriguez Marlins 4.00 10.00
JG Jason Giambi A's 3.00 8.00
JT Jim Thome Indians 4.00 10.00
MM Mike Mussina O's 4.00 10.00
MR Manny Ramirez Indians 4.00 10.00
MT Miguel Tejada A's 3.00 8.00
PR Pedro Martinez Expos 4.00 10.00
RC Roger Clemens Sox 5.00 12.00
RJ Randy Johnson M's 4.00 10.00
RP Rafael Palmeiro Rgr 4.00 10.00
SR Scott Rolen Phils 4.00 10.00
SS Sammy Sosa Sox 4.00 10.00
TG Tom Glavine Braves 4.00 10.00
VG Vladimir Guerrero Expos 4.00 10.00

2005 Ultra

This 220-card set, the first of the 2005 sets to hit the market, was released in November, 2004. Both the eight-card hobby and retail packs were issued with an $3 SRP although the insert ratios were far different between the two classes of packs. The hobby packs were issued 24 packs to a box and 16 boxes to a case while the hobby packs were issued 24 packs to a box and 20 boxes to a case. The first 200 cards of the set featured veterans while cards 201 through 220, which were issued at a stated rate of one in four hobby and one in five retail, feature leading prospects.

COMPLETE SET (220) 40.00 100.00
COMP.SET w/o SP's (200) 15.00 40.00
COMMON CARD (1-200) .10 .30
COMMON CARD (201-220) .75 2.00
201-220 ODDS 1:4 HOBBY, 1:5 RETAIL
1 Andy Pettitte .20 .50
2 Jose Cruz Jr. .12 .30
3 Cliff Floyd .12 .30
4 Paul Konerko .20 .50
5 Joe Mauer .30 .75
6 Scott Spiezio .12 .30
7 Ben Sheets .12 .30
8 Kerry Wood .12 .30
9 Carl Pavano .12 .30
10 Matt Morris .12 .30
11 Kaz Matsui .12 .30
12 Ivan Rodriguez .20 .50
13 Victor Martinez .20 .50
14 Justin Morneau .30 .75
15 Adam Everett .12 .30
16 Carl Crawford .20 .50
17 David Ortiz .30 .75
18 Jason Giambi .12 .30
19 Derrek Lee .12 .30
20 Magglio Ordonez .20 .50
21 Bobby Abreu .12 .30
22 Milton Bradley .12 .30
23 Jeff Bagwell .20 .50
24 Jim Edmonds .20 .50
25 Garret Anderson .12 .30
26 Jacque Jones .12 .30
27 Ted Lilly .12 .30
28 Greg Maddux .50 1.25
29 Jermaine Dye .12 .30
30 Bill Mueller .12 .30
31 Roy Oswalt .20 .50
32 Tony Womack .12 .30
33 Andruw Jones .12 .30
34 Tom Glavine .20 .50
35 Mariano Rivera .30 .75
36 Sean Casey .12 .30
37 Edgardo Alfonzo .12 .30
38 Brad Penny .12 .30
39 Johan Santana .30 .75
40 Mark Teixeira .30 .75
41 Manny Ramirez .30 .75
42 Gary Sheffield .12 .30
43 Matt Lawton .12 .30
44 Troy Percival .12 .30
45 Rocco Baldelli .12 .30
46 Doug Mientkiewicz .12 .30
47 Corey Patterson .12 .30
48 Austin Kearns .12 .30
49 Edgar Martinez .20 .50
50 Brad Radke .12 .30
51 Barry Larkin .20 .50
52 Chone Figgins .12 .30
53 Alexis Rios .20 .50
54 Alex Rodriguez .50 1.25
55 Vinny Castilla .12 .30
56 Javier Vazquez .12 .30
57 Javy Lopez .12 .30
58 Mike Cameron .12 .30
59 Brian Giles .12 .30
60 Dontrelle Willis .12 .30
61 Rafael Furcal .12 .30
62 Trot Nixon .12 .30
63 Mark Mulder .12 .30
64 Josh Beckett .20 .50
65 J.D. Drew .12 .30
66 Brandon Webb .20 .50
67 Wade Miller .12 .30
68 Lyle Overbay .12 .30
69 Pedro Martinez .20 .50
70 Rich Harden .12 .30
71 Al Leiter .12 .30
72 Adam Eaton .12 .30
73 Mike Sweeney .12 .30
74 Steve Finley .12 .30
75 Kris Benson .12 .30
76 Jim Thome .20 .50
77 Juan Pierre .12 .30
78 Bartolo Colon .12 .30
79 Carlos Delgado .12 .30
80 Jack Wilson .12 .30
81 Ken Harvey .12 .30
82 Nomar Garciaparra .30 .75
83 Paul Lo Duca .12 .30
84 Cesar Izturis .12 .30
85 Adrian Beltre .12 .30
86 Brian Roberts .12 .30
87 David Eckstein .12 .30
88 Jimmy Rollins .20 .50
89 Roger Clemens .40 1.00
90 Randy Johnson .30 .75
91 Orlando Hudson .12 .30
92 Tim Hudson .20 .50
93 Dmitri Young .12 .30
94 Chipper Jones .30 .75
95 John Smoltz .30 .75
96 Billy Wagner .12 .30
97 Hideo Nomo .30 .75
98 Sammy Sosa .30 .75
99 Darin Erstad .12 .30
100 Todd Helton .20 .50
101 Aubrey Huff .12 .30
102 Alfonso Soriano .20 .50
103 Jose Vidro .12 .30
104 Carlos Lee .12 .30
105 Corey Koskie .12 .30
106 Bret Boone .12 .30
107 Torii Hunter .12 .30
108 Aramis Ramirez .12 .30
109 Chase Utley .20 .50
110 Reggie Sanders .12 .30
111 Livan Hernandez .12 .30
112 Jeromy Burnitz .12 .30
113 Carlos Zambrano .20 .50
114 Hank Blalock .12 .30
115 Sidney Ponson .12 .30
116 Zack Greinke .20 .50
117 Trevor Hoffman .20 .50
118 Jeff Kent .12 .30
119 Richie Sexson .12 .30
120 Melvin Mora .12 .30
121 Eric Chavez .12 .30
122 Miguel Cabrera .30 .75
123 Ryan Freel .12 .30
124 Russ Ortiz .12 .30
125 Craig Wilson .12 .30
126 Craig Biggio .20 .50
127 Curt Schilling .20 .50
128 Kaz Ishii .12 .30
129 Marquis Grissom .12 .30
130 Bernie Williams .20 .50
131 Travis Hafner .12 .30
132 Hee Seop Choi .12 .30
133 Scott Rolen .20 .50
134 Tony Batista .12 .30
135 Frank Thomas .30 .75
136 Jason Varitek .30 .75
137 Ichiro Suzuki .50 1.25
138 Junior Spivey .12 .30
139 Adam Dunn .20 .50
140 Jorge Posada .20 .50
141 Edgar Renteria .12 .30
142 Hideki Matsui .50 1.25
143 Carlos Guillen .12 .30
144 Jody Gerut .12 .30
145 Wily Mo Pena .12 .30
146 Derek Jeter .75 2.00
147 C.C. Sabathia .20 .50
148 Geoff Jenkins .12 .30
149 Albert Pujols .75 2.00
150 Eric Munson .12 .30
151 Moises Alou .12 .30
152 Jerry Hairston .12 .30
153 Ray Durham .12 .30
154 Mike Piazza .30 .75
155 Omar Vizquel .20 .50
156 A.J. Pierzynski .12 .30
157 Michael Young .20 .50
158 Jason Bay .12 .30
159 Mark Loretta .12 .30
160 Shawn Green .12 .30
161 Luis Gonzalez .12 .30
162 Johnny Damon .20 .50
163 Eric Milton .12 .30
164 Mike Lowell .12 .30
165 Jose Guillen .12 .30
166 Eric Hinske .12 .30
167 Jason Kendall .12 .30
168 Carlos Beltran .12 .30
169 Johnny Estrada .12 .30
170 Scott Hatteberg .12 .30
171 Laynce Nix .12 .30
172 Eric Gagne .12 .30
173 Richard Hidalgo .12 .30
174 Bobby Crosby .12 .30
175 Woody Williams .12 .30
176 Justin Leone .12 .30
177 Orlando Cabrera .12 .30
178 Mark Prior .20 .50
179 Jorge Julio .12 .30
180 Jamie Moyer .12 .30
181 Jose Reyes .20 .50
182 Ken Griffey Jr. .50 1.25
183 Mike Lieberthal .12 .30
184 Kenny Rogers .12 .30
185 Mike Mussina .20 .50
186 Preston Wilson .12 .30
187 Khalil Greene .12 .30
188 Angel Berroa .12 .30
189 Miguel Tejada .20 .50
190 Freddy Garcia .12 .30
191 Pat Burrell .12 .30
192 Luis Castillo .12 .30
193 Vladimir Guerrero .30 .75
194 Roy Halladay .30 .75
195 Barry Zito .12 .30
196 Lance Berkman .20 .50
197 Rafael Palmeiro .20 .50
198 Nate Robertson .12 .30
199 Jason Schmidt .12 .30
200 Scott Podsednik .12 .30
201 Casey Kotchman AR .60 1.50
202 Scott Kazmir AR 1.50 4.00
203 Bucky Jacobsen AR .60 1.50
204 Jeff Keppinger AR .60 1.50
205 Dave Bush AR .60 1.50
206 Gavin Floyd AR .60 1.50
207 David Wright AR 2.50 6.00
208 B.J. Upton AR 1.00 2.50
209 David Aardsma AR .60 1.50
210 Jason Bartlett AR .60 1.50
211 Dioner Navarro AR .60 1.50
212 Jason Kubel AR .60 1.50
213 Ryan Howard AR 3.00 8.00
214 Charles Thomas AR .60 1.50
215 Freddy Guzman AR .60 1.50
216 Brad Halsey AR .60 1.50
217 Joey Gathright AR .60 1.50
218 Jeff Francis AR .60 1.50
219 Terry Tiffee AR .60 1.50
220 Nick Swisher AR 1.50 4.00

2005 Ultra Gold Medallion

*GOLD 1-200: 1.25X TO 3X BASIC
*GOLD 201-220: .6X TO 1.5X BASIC
STATED ODDS 1:1 HOBBY, 1:3 RETAIL

2005 Ultra Platinum Medallion

*PLATINUM 1-200: 8X TO 20X BASIC
*PLATINUM 201-220: 2X TO 5X BASIC
STATED PRINT RUN 50 SERIAL #'d SETS

2005 Ultra Season Crown Autographs Copper

OVERALL SC AU ODDS 1:192 HOBBY
STATED PRINT RUN 199 SERIAL #'d SETS
UER'S #'d OF 199 BUT 22-199 PER MADE
ACTUAL UER QTY PROVIDED BY FLEER
31 Roy Oswalt/50 UER 10.00 25.00
80 Jack Wilson/199 8.00 20.00
125 Craig Wilson/130 UER 5.00 12.00
157 Michael Young/150 UER 8.00 20.00
200 Scott Podsednik/22 UER 20.00 50.00

2005 Ultra Season Crown Autographs Gold

OVERALL SC AU ODDS 1:192 HOBBY
STATED PRINT RUN 99 SERIAL #'d SETS
UER'S ARE #'d OF 99 BUT 13-99 PER MADE
ACTUAL UER QTY PROVIDED BY FLEER
NO PRICING ON QTY OF 13 OR LESS
20 Magglio Ordonez/13 UER
31 Roy Oswalt/99 8.00 20.00
40 Mark Teixeira/25 UER 20.00 50.00
50 Brad Radke/89 UER 8.00 20.00
51 Barry Larkin/99 12.50 30.00
62 Trot Nixon/37 UER 10.00 25.00
70 Rich Harden/41 UER 10.00 25.00
80 Jack Wilson/99 8.00 20.00
88 Jimmy Rollins/45 UER 15.00 40.00
121 Eric Chavez/69 UER 8.00 20.00
125 Craig Wilson/99 5.00 12.00
157 Michael Young/99 8.00 20.00
200 Scott Podsednik/99 12.50 30.00
201 Casey Kotchman AR/21 UER 12.50 30.00

2005 Ultra Season Crown Autographs Masterpiece

OVERALL SC AU ODDS 1:192 HOBBY
STATED PRINT RUN 1 SERIAL #'d SET
NO PRICING DUE TO SCARCITY

2005 Ultra Season Crown Autographs Platinum

OVERALL SC AU ODDS 1:192 HOBBY
STATED PRINT RUN 50 SERIAL #'d SETS
UER'S ARE #'d OF 50 BUT 7-50 PER MADE
ACTUAL UER QTY PROVIDED BY FLEER
NO PRICING ON QTY OF 10 OR LESS
8 Kerry Wood/7 UER
12 Ivan Rodriguez/25 UER 30.00 60.00
20 Magglio Ordonez/50 10.00 25.00
25 Garret Anderson/50 10.00 25.00
31 Roy Oswalt/50 10.00 25.00
35 Mariano Rivera/25 UER 30.00 60.00
40 Mark Teixeira/50 15.00 40.00
41 Manny Ramirez/25 UER 30.00 60.00
50 Brad Radke/50 10.00 25.00
51 Barry Larkin/50 15.00 40.00
62 Trot Nixon/50 10.00 25.00
65 J.D. Drew/19 UER 15.00 40.00
70 Rich Harden/50 10.00 25.00
80 Jack Wilson/50 10.00 25.00
87 David Eckstein/45 UER 20.00 50.00
88 Jimmy Rollins/50 15.00 40.00
90 Randy Johnson/10 UER
94 Chipper Jones/19 UER 40.00 80.00
95 John Smoltz/23 UER 30.00 60.00
96 Billy Wagner/50 15.00 40.00
116 Zack Greinke/49 UER 12.50 30.00
121 Eric Chavez/50 10.00 25.00
125 Craig Wilson/50 6.00 15.00
130 Bernie Williams/15 UER 40.00 80.00
136 Jason Varitek/19 UER 40.00 80.00
149 Albett Pujols/10 UER
154 Mike Piazza/10 UER
157 Michael Young/50 10.00 25.00
161 Luis Gonzalez/50 10.00 25.00
185 Mike Mussina/50 15.00 40.00
195 Barry Zito/50 10.00 25.00
199 Jason Schmidt/50 10.00 25.00
200 Scott Podsednik/50 15.00 40.00
201 Casey Kotchman AR/50 10.00 25.00

2005 Ultra Season Crowns Game Used Copper

STATED PRINT RUN 399 SERIAL #'d SETS
*GOLD: .5X TO 1.2X COPPER
GOLD PRINT RUN 99 SERIAL #'d SETS
*PLATINUM: .75X TO 2X COPPER
*PLATINUM PATCH: ADD 100% PREMIUM
PLATINUM PRINT RUN 25 SERIAL #'d SETS
OVERALL SC GU 1:24 HOBBY
1 Andy Pettitte Jsy 4.00 10.00
3 Cliff Floyd Jsy 3.00 8.00
7 Ben Sheets Jsy 3.00 8.00
8 Kerry Wood Jsy 3.00 8.00
11 Kaz Matsui Bat 6.00 15.00
13 Victor Martinez Jsy 3.00 8.00
17 David Ortiz Jsy 4.00 10.00
20 Magglio Ordonez Bat 3.00 8.00
21 Bobby Abreu Bat 3.00 8.00
24 Jim Edmonds Jsy 3.00 8.00
31 Roy Oswalt Jsy 3.00 8.00
33 Andruw Jones Jsy 4.00 10.00
34 Tom Glavine Bat 4.00 10.00
36 Sean Casey Jsy 3.00 8.00
37 Edgardo Alfonzo Bat 3.00 8.00
41 Manny Ramirez Bat 4.00 10.00
42 Gary Sheffield Bat 3.00 8.00
45 Rocco Baldelli Jsy 3.00 8.00
48 Austin Kearns Jsy 3.00 8.00
49 Edgar Martinez Jsy 4.00 10.00
60 Dontrelle Willis Jsy 3.00 8.00
65 J.D. Drew Jsy 3.00 8.00
70 Rich Harden Jsy 3.00 8.00
71 Al Leiter Jsy 3.00 8.00
80 Jack Wilson Bat 3.00 8.00
93 Dmitri Young Bat 3.00 8.00
94 Chipper Jones Bat 4.00 10.00
97 Hideo Nomo Jsy 4.00 10.00
98 Sammy Sosa Bat 4.00 10.00
100 Todd Helton Bat 4.00 10.00
102 Alfonso Soriano Bat 3.00 8.00
107 Torii Hunter Jsy 3.00 8.00
114 Hank Blalock Bat 3.00 8.00
119 Richie Sexson Jsy 3.00 8.00
121 Eric Chavez Jsy 3.00 8.00
130 Bernie Williams Bat 4.00 10.00
135 Frank Thomas Bat 4.00 10.00
139 Adam Dunn Bat 3.00 8.00
142 Hideki Matsui Bat 10.00 25.00
144 Jody Gerut Bat 3.00 8.00
154 Mike Piazza Bat 4.00 10.00
158 Jason Bay Bat 3.00 8.00
162 Johnny Damon Jsy 4.00 10.00
168 Carlos Beltran Bat 3.00 8.00
173 Richard Hidalgo Jsy 3.00 8.00
181 Jose Reyes Bat 3.00 8.00
187 Khalil Greene Jsy 4.00 10.00
191 Pat Burrell Bat 3.00 8.00
193 Vladimir Guerrero Bat 4.00 10.00
197 Rafael Palmeiro Jsy 4.00 10.00

2005 Ultra 3 Kings Jersey Triple Swatch

BCB Jeff Bagwell 20.00 50.00
Roger Clemens
Lance Berkman
BCR Josh Beckett 15.00 40.00
Miguel Cabrera
Ivan Rodriguez
JMM Randy Johnson 15.00 40.00
Greg Maddux
Pedro Martinez
MPW Greg Maddux 20.00 50.00
Mark Prior
Kerry Wood
PDC Albert Pujols 20.00 50.00
Adam Dunn
Miguel Cabrera
RJB Scott Rolen 15.00 40.00
Chipper Jones
Adrian Beltre
SMP Gary Sheffield 20.00 50.00
Hideki Matsui
Mike Piazza
SMR Curt Schilling 30.00 60.00
Pedro Martinez
Manny Ramirez
TBS Mark Teixeira 15.00 40.00
Hank Blalock
Alfonso Soriano
TBW Jim Thome 15.00 40.00
Pat Burrell
Billy Wagner

2005 Ultra Follow the Leader

COMPLETE SET (15) 10.00 25.00
STATED ODDS 1:6 HOBBY, 1:8 RETAIL
*DIE CUT: .6X TO 1.5X BASIC
DIE CUT RANDOM IN EXCEL/MVP RETAIL
1 Roger Clemens 1.25 3.00
2 Albert Pujols 2.50 6.00
3 Sammy Sosa 1.00 2.50
4 Manny Ramirez 1.00 2.50
5 Vladimir Guerrero 1.00 2.50
6 Ivan Rodriguez .60 1.50
7 Mike Piazza 1.00 2.50
8 Scott Rolen .60 1.50
9 Ichiro Suzuki 1.50 4.00
10 Randy Johnson 1.00 2.50
11 Mark Prior .60 1.50
12 Jim Thome .60 1.50
13 Greg Maddux 1.50 4.00
14 Pedro Martinez .60 1.50
15 Miguel Cabrera 1.00 2.50

2005 Ultra Follow the Leader Jersey Copper

COPPER ISSUED ONLY IN HOBBY PACKS
*GOLD: .4X TO 1X COPPER
GOLD PRINT RUN 250 SERIAL #'d SETS
*PLATINUM: .5X TO 1.2X COPPER
*PLATINUM PATCH: ADD 100% PREMIUM
PLATINUM PRINT RUN 99 SERIAL #'d SETS
PLATINUM ISSUED ONLY IN HOBBY PACKS
*RED: .4X TO 1X COPPER
RED STATED ODDS 1:48 RETAIL
RED RANDOM IN HOBBY HOT PACKS
*ULTRA p/r 45-51: .75X TO 2X COPPER
*ULTRA p/r 21-31: 1X TO 2.5X COPPER
ULTRA PRINT RUNS B/WN 5-51 PER
NO ULTRA PRICING ON QTY OF 7 OR LESS
OVERALL GU ODDS 1:12 HOB, 1:48 RET
AP Albert Pujols 6.00 15.00
GM Greg Maddux 6.00 15.00
IR Ivan Rodriguez 4.00 10.00
JT Jim Thome 4.00 10.00
MC Miguel Cabrera 4.00 10.00
MPI Mike Piazza 4.00 10.00
MPR Mark Prior 4.00 10.00
MR Manny Ramirez 4.00 10.00
PM Pedro Martinez 4.00 10.00
RC Roger Clemens 6.00 15.00
RJ Randy Johnson 4.00 10.00
SR Scott Rolen 3.00 8.00
SS Sammy Sosa 4.00 10.00
VG Vladimir Guerrero 4.00 10.00

2005 Ultra Kings

OVERALL KINGS ODDS 1:12 HOB, 1:24 RET
K PERCEIVED 3X TOUGHER THAN HR-RBI
*GOLD: 2X TO 5X BASIC HR-RBI
*GOLD: 1.25X TO 3X BASIC K
GOLD RANDOM INSERTS IN HOBBY PACKS
GOLD PRINT RUN 50 SERIAL #'d SETS
H1 Jim Thome HR .60 1.50
H2 David Ortiz HR 1.00 2.50
H3 Adam Dunn HR .60 1.50
H4 Albert Pujols HR 2.50 6.00
H5 Manny Ramirez HR 1.00 2.50
H6 Vladimir Guerrero HR 1.00 2.50
H7 Miguel Tejada HR .60 1.50
H8 Rafael Palmeiro HR .60 1.50
H9 Mark Teixeira HR 1.00 2.50
H10 Sammy Sosa HR 1.00 2.50
H11 Frank Thomas HR 1.00 2.50
H12 Pat Burrell HR .40 1.00
H13 Adrian Beltre HR .40 1.00
H14 Miguel Cabrera HR 1.00 2.50
H15 Gary Sheffield HR .40 1.00
K1 Pedro Martinez K 1.00 2.50
K2 Randy Johnson K 1.50 4.00
K3 Mark Mulder K .60 1.50
K4 Barry Zito K .60 1.50
K5 Roger Clemens K 2.00 5.00
K6 Mark Prior K 1.00 2.50
K7 Ben Sheets K .60 1.50
K8 Curt Schilling K 1.00 2.50
K9 Billy Wagner K .60 1.50
K10 Eric Gagne K .60 1.50
K11 Josh Beckett K 1.00 2.50
K12 Kerry Wood K .60 1.50
K13 Jason Schmidt K .60 1.50
K14 Roy Halladay K 1.50 4.00
K15 Greg Maddux K 2.50 6.00
R1 Sean Casey RBI .40 1.00
R2 Ivan Rodriguez RBI .60 1.50
R3 Mike Piazza RBI 1.00 2.50
R4 Todd Helton RBI .60 1.50
R5 Scott Rolen RBI .60 1.50
R6 Hideki Matsui RBI 1.50 4.00
R7 Gary Sheffield RBI .40 1.00
R8 Alfonso Soriano RBI .60 1.50
R9 Bobby Abreu RBI .40 1.00
R10 Lance Berkman RBI .60 1.50
R11 Miguel Tejada RBI .60 1.50
R12 Travis Hafner RBI .40 1.00
R13 Hank Blalock RBI .40 1.00
R14 Jeff Bagwell RBI .60 1.50
R15 Chipper Jones RBI 1.00 2.50

2005 Ultra Kings Jersey Gold

STATED PRINT RUN 150 SERIAL #'d SETS
*ULTRA p/r 75: .5X TO 1.2X GOLD
*ULTRA p/r 38-55: .6X TO 1.5X GOLD
*ULTRA p/r 20-34: .75X TO 2X GOLD
*ULTRA p/r 15-17: 1X TO 2.5X GOLD
ULTRA PRINT RUN B/WN 5-75 #'d PER
NO ULTRA PRICING ON QTY 13 OR LESS
*PLATINUM: .6X TO 1.5X COPPER
*PLATINUM PATCH: ADD 100% PREMIUM
PLATINUM PRINT RUN 25 SERIAL #'d SETS
PLATINUM ISSUED ONLY IN HOBBY PACKS
OVERALL GU ODDS 1:12 HOB, 1:48 RET
AB Adrian Beltre HR 4.00 10.00
AD Adam Dunn HR 4.00 10.00
AP Albert Pujols HR 8.00 20.00
AS Alfonso Soriano RBI 4.00 10.00
BA Bobby Abreu RBI 4.00 10.00
BS Ben Sheets K 4.00 10.00
BW Billy Wagner K 4.00 10.00
BZ Barry Zito K 4.00 10.00
CJ Chipper Jones RBI 5.00 12.00
CS Curt Schilling K 5.00 12.00
DO David Ortiz HR 5.00 12.00
EG Eric Gagne K 4.00 10.00
FT Frank Thomas HR 5.00 12.00
GM Greg Maddux K 8.00 20.00
GSH Gary Sheffield HR 4.00 10.00
GSR Gary Sheffield RBI 4.00 10.00
HB Hank Blalock RBI 4.00 10.00
HM Hideki Matsui RBI 12.50 30.00
IR Ivan Rodriguez RBI 5.00 12.00
JBA Jeff Bagwell RBI 5.00 12.00
JBE Josh Beckett K 4.00 10.00
JS Jason Schmidt K 4.00 10.00
JT Jim Thome HR 5.00 12.00
KW Kerry Wood K 4.00 10.00
LB Lance Berkman RBI 4.00 10.00
MC Miguel Cabrera HR 5.00 12.00
MM Mark Mulder K 4.00 10.00
MPI Mike Piazza RBI 5.00 12.00
MPR Mark Prior K 5.00 12.00
MR Manny Ramirez HR 5.00 12.00
MTH Miguel Tejada HR 4.00 10.00
MTR Miguel Tejada RBI 4.00 10.00
MTX Mark Teixeira HR 5.00 12.00
PB Pat Burrell HR 4.00 10.00
PM Pedro Martinez K 5.00 12.00
RC Roger Clemens K 8.00 20.00
RH Roy Halladay K 4.00 10.00
RJ Randy Johnson K 5.00 12.00
RP Rafael Palmeiro HR 5.00 12.00
SC Sean Casey RBI 4.00 10.00
SR Scott Rolen RBI 5.00 12.00
SS Sammy Sosa HR 5.00 12.00
THA Travis Hafner RBI 4.00 10.00
THE Todd Helton RBI 5.00 12.00
VG Vladimir Guerrero HR 5.00 12.00

2006 Ultra

This 251-card set was released in June, 2006. The set was issued in eight-card hobby and retail packs, both of which had an $2.99 SRP and both came 24 packs to a box and 12 boxes to a case. Cards numbered 1-180 feature veterans while cards 181-200 feature 2006 rookies and cards 201-250 were a Retro Lucky 13 subset. Those Retro Lucky subset cards were inserted at a stated rate of one in four hobby or retail packs. Card number 251 was an exchange for Kenji Johjima, and that card was announced to have a print run of 5000 cards. The Johjima card was issued as an exchange and that card could be redeemed until May 25, 2008.

COMP.SET w/o RL13 (200) 15.00 40.00
COMMON CARD (1-180) .15 .40
RL13 201-250 ODDS 1:4 HOBBY, 1:4 RETAIL
251 PRINT RUN 5000 CARDS
251 JOHJIMA IS NOT SERIAL NUMBERED
251 PRINT RUN INFO PROVIDED BY UD
251 JOHJIMA EXCH. DEADLINE 05/25/08
1 Vladimir Guerrero .40 1.00
2 Bartolo Colon .15 .40
3 Francisco Rodriguez .25 .60
4 Darin Erstad .15 .40
5 Chone Figgins .15 .40
6 Bengie Molina .15 .40
7 Roger Clemens .50 1.25
8 Lance Berkman .25 .60
9 Morgan Ensberg .15 .40
10 Roy Oswalt .25 .60
11 Andy Pettitte .25 .60
12 Craig Biggio .25 .60
13 Eric Chavez .15 .40
14 Barry Zito .15 .40
15 Huston Street .15 .40
16 Bobby Crosby .15 .40
17 Nick Swisher .40 1.00
18 Rich Harden .15 .40
19 Vernon Wells .15 .40
20 Roy Halladay .40 1.00

21 Alex Rios .25 .60
22 Orlando Hudson .15 .40
23 Shea Hillenbrand .15 .40
24 Gustavo Chacin .15 .40
25 Chipper Jones .40 1.00
26 Andruw Jones .15 .40
27 Jeff Francoeur .40 1.00
28 John Smoltz .40 1.00
29 Tim Hudson .25 .60
30 Marcus Giles .15 .40
31 Carlos Lee .15 .40
32 Ben Sheets .15 .40
33 Rickie Weeks .25 .60
34 Chris Capuano .15 .40
35 Geoff Jenkins .15 .40
36 Brady Clark .15 .40
37 Albert Pujols 1.00 2.50
38 Jim Edmonds .25 .60
39 Chris Carpenter .40 1.00
40 Mark Mulder .15 .40
41 Yadier Molina .25 .60
42 Scott Rolen .25 .60
43 Derrek Lee .15 .40
44 Mark Prior .25 .60
45 Aramis Ramirez .15 .40
46 Carlos Zambrano .25 .60
47 Greg Maddux .60 1.50
48 Nomar Garciaparra .40 1.00
49 Jonny Gomes .15 .40
50 Carl Crawford .25 .60
51 Scott Kazmir .25 .60
52 Jorge Cantu .15 .40
53 Julio Lugo .15 .40
54 Aubrey Huff .15 .40
55 Luis Gonzalez .15 .40
56 Brandon Webb .25 .60
57 Troy Glaus .15 .40
58 Shawn Green .15 .40
59 Craig Counsell .15 .40
60 Conor Jackson (RC) .60 1.50
61 Jeff Kent .15 .40
62 Eric Gagne .15 .40
63 J.D. Drew .15 .40
64 Milton Bradley .15 .40
65 Jeff Weaver .15 .40
66 Cesar Izturis .15 .40
67 Jason Schmidt .15 .40
68 Moises Alou .15 .40
69 Pedro Feliz .15 .40
70 Randy Winn .15 .40
71 Omar Vizquel .25 .60
72 Noah Lowry .15 .40
73 Travis Hafner .15 .40
74 Victor Martinez .25 .60
75 C.C. Sabathia .25 .60
76 Grady Sizemore .25 .60
77 Coco Crisp .15 .40
78 Cliff Lee .25 .60
79 Raul Ibañez .25 .60
80 Ichiro Suzuki .60 1.50
81 Richie Sexson .15 .40
82 Felix Hernandez .40 1.00
83 Adrian Beltre .15 .40
84 Jamie Moyer .15 .40
85 Miguel Cabrera .40 1.00
86 A.J. Burnett .25 .60
87 Juan Pierre .15 .40
88 Carlos Delgado .15 .40
89 Dontrelle Willis .15 .40
90 Juan Encarnacion .15 .40
91 Carlos Beltran .15 .40
92 Jose Reyes .25 .60
93 David Wright .60 1.50
94 Tom Glavine .25 .60
95 Mike Piazza .40 1.00
96 Pedro Martinez .25 .60
97 Ryan Zimmerman (RC) 2.00 5.00
98 Nick Johnson .15 .40
99 Jose Vidro .15 .40
100 Jose Guillen .15 .40
101 Livan Hernandez .15 .40
102 John Patterson .15 .40
103 Miguel Tejada .25 .60
104 Melvin Mora .15 .40
105 Brian Roberts .15 .40
106 Erik Bedard .15 .40
107 Javy Lopez .15 .40
108 Rodrigo Lopez .15 .40
109 Jake Peavy .15 .40
110 Mike Cameron .15 .40
111 Mark Loretta .15 .40
112 Brian Giles .15 .40
113 Trevor Hoffman .25 .60
114 Ramon Hernandez .15 .40
115 Bobby Abreu .15 .40
116 Chase Utley .40 1.00
117 Pat Burrell .15 .40
118 Jimmy Rollins .25 .60
119 Ryan Howard .60 1.50
120 Billy Wagner .15 .40
121 Jason Bay .15 .40
122 Oliver Perez .15 .40
123 Jack Wilson .15 .40
124 Zach Duke .15 .40
125 Rob Mackowiak .15 .40
126 Freddy Sanchez .15 .40
127 Mark Teixeira .40 1.00
128 Michael Young .25 .60
129 Alfonso Soriano .25 .60
130 Hank Blalock .15 .40
131 Kenny Rogers .15 .40
132 Kevin Mench .15 .40
133 Manny Ramirez .40 1.00
134 Josh Beckett .25 .60
135 David Ortiz .25 .60
136 Johnny Damon .25 .60
137 Edgar Renteria .15 .40
138 Curt Schilling .25 .60
139 Ken Griffey Jr. .60 1.50
140 Adam Dunn .25 .60
141 Felipe Lopez .15 .40
142 Wily Mo Pena .15 .40
143 Aaron Harang .15 .40
144 Sean Casey .15 .40
145 Todd Helton .25 .60
146 Garrett Atkins .15 .40
147 Matt Holliday .40 1.00
148 Jeff Francis .15 .40
149 Clint Barmes .15 .40
150 Luis Gonzalez .15 .40
151 Mike Sweeney .15 .40
152 Zack Greinke .25 .60
153 Angel Berroa .15 .40
154 Emil Brown .15 .40
155 David DeJesus .15 .40
156 Ivan Rodriguez .25 .60
157 Jeremy Bonderman .15 .40
158 Brandon Inge .15 .40
159 Craig Monroe .15 .40
160 Chris Shelton .15 .40
161 Dmitri Young .15 .40
162 Johan Santana .40 1.00
163 Joe Mauer .40 1.00
164 Torii Hunter .15 .40
165 Shannon Stewart .15 .40
166 Scott Baker .15 .40
167 Brad Radke .15 .40
168 Jon Garland .15 .40
169 Tadahito Iguchi .15 .40
170 Paul Konerko .25 .60
171 Scott Podsednik .15 .40
172 Mark Buehrle .25 .60
173 Joe Crede .15 .40
174 Derek Jeter 1.00 2.50
175 Alex Rodriguez .60 1.50
176 Hideki Matsui .40 1.00
177 Randy Johnson .40 1.00
178 Gary Sheffield .15 .40
179 Mariano Rivera .40 1.00
180 Jason Giambi .15 .40
181 Joey Devine RC .40 1.00
182 Alejandro Freire RC .40 1.00
183 Craig Hansen RC .75 2.00
184 Robert Andino RC .40 1.00
185 Ryan Jorgensen RC .40 1.00
186 Chris Demaria RC .40 1.00
187 Jonah Bayliss RC .40 1.00
188 Ryan Theriot RC 1.00 2.50
189 Steve Stemle RC .40 1.00
190 Brian Myrow RC .40 1.00
191 Chris Heintz RC .40 1.00
192 Ron Flores RC .40 1.00
193 Danny Sandoval RC .40 1.00
194 Craig Breslow RC .40 1.00
195 Jeremy Accardo RC .40 1.00
196 Jeff Harris RC .40 1.00
197 Tim Corcoran RC .40 1.00
198 Scott Feldman RC .40 1.00
199 Robinson Cano .40 1.00
200 Jason Bergmann RC .40 1.00
201 Ken Griffey Jr. RL13 3.00 8.00
202 Frank Thomas RL13 2.00 5.00
203 Chipper Jones RL13 2.00 5.00
204 Tony Clark RL13 .75 2.00
205 Mike Lieberthal RL13 .75 2.00
206 Manny Ramirez RL13 2.00 5.00
207 Phil Nevin RL13 .75 2.00
208 Derek Jeter RL13 5.00 12.00
209 Preston Wilson RL13 .75 2.00
210 Billy Wagner RL13 .75 2.00
211 Alex Rodriguez RL13 3.00 8.00
212 Trot Nixon RL13 .75 2.00
213 Jaret Wright RL13 .75 2.00
214 Nomar Garciaparra RL13 2.00 5.00
215 Paul Konerko RL13 1.25 3.00
216 Paul Wilson RL13 .75 2.00
217 Dustin Hermanson RL13 .75 2.00
218 Todd Walker RL13 .75 2.00
219 Matt Morris RL13 .75 2.00
220 Darin Erstad RL13 .75 2.00
221 Todd Helton RL13 1.25 3.00
222 Geoff Jenkins RL13 .75 2.00
223 Eric Chavez RL13 .75 2.00
224 Kris Benson RL13 .75 2.00
225 Jon Garland RL13 .75 2.00
226 Troy Glaus RL13 .75 2.00
227 Vernon Wells RL13 .75 2.00
228 Michael Cuddyer RL13 .75 2.00
229 Justin Verlander RL13 6.00 15.00
230 Pat Burrell RL13 .75 2.00
231 Mark Mulder RL13 .75 2.00
232 Corey Patterson RL13 .75 2.00
233 J.D. Drew RL13 .75 2.00
234 Austin Kearns RL13 .60 1.50
235 Felipe Lopez RL13 .75 2.00
236 Sean Burroughs RL13 .75 2.00
237 Ben Sheets RL13 .75 2.00
238 Brett Myers RL13 .75 2.00
239 Josh Beckett RL13 1.25 3.00
240 Barry Zito RL13 .75 2.00
241 Adrian Gonzalez RL13 1.25 3.00
242 Rocco Baldelli RL13 .75 2.00
243 Chris Burke RL13 .75 2.00
244 Joe Mauer RL13 2.00 5.00
245 Mark Prior RL13 1.25 3.00
246 Mark Teixeira RL13 2.00 5.00
247 Khalil Greene RL13 .75 2.00
248 Zack Greinke RL13 1.25 3.00
249 Prince Fielder RL13 3.00 8.00
250 Rickie Weeks RL13 1.25 3.00
251 Kenji Johjima 4.00 10.00

2006 Ultra Gold Medallion

COMP.SET w/o RL13 (200) 60.00 120.00
*GOLD 1-180: 1X TO 2.5X BASIC
*GOLD 60/97/181-198/200: .6X TO 1.5X BASIC
GOLD 1-200 ODDS 1:1 HOBBY/RETAIL
*GOLD 201-250: .5X TO 1.2X BASIC
GOLD 201-250 ODDS 1:24 HOB, 1:72 RET

2006 Ultra Autographics

STATED ODDS 1:576 HOBBY, 1:1920 RETAIL
NO PRICING DUE TO SCARCITY
AF Alejandro Freire
AS Alfonso Soriano SP
BE Jason Bergmann
BR Brian Roberts
CA Chris Carpenter
CC Carl Crawford
CK Casey Kotchman

DL Derrek Lee
DS Danny Sandoval
DW Dontrelle Willis
FH Felix Hernandez
JA Jason Bay
JG Jonny Gomes
JH Jeff Harris
JM Joe Mauer
JO Joe Blanton
JR Jose Reyes
JV Justin Verlander
KG Ken Griffey Jr.
KW Kerry Wood SP
MC Matt Cain
MG Marcus Giles
MY Michael Young
NS Nick Swisher
PF Prince Fielder
PM Pedro Martinez
RC Roger Clemens
RO Roy Oswalt
RZ Ryan Zimmerman
SR Scott Rolen
SS Steve Stemle
TH Travis Hafner
TI Tadahito Iguchi
VG Vladimir Guerrero SP
VM Victor Martinez
YM Yadier Molina

2006 Ultra Diamond Producers

COMPLETE SET (25) 10.00 25.00
OVERALL INSERT ODDS 1:1 HOBBY/RETAIL
DP1 Derek Jeter 2.50 6.00
DP2 Chipper Jones .75 2.00
DP3 Jim Edmonds .60 1.50
DP4 Ken Griffey Jr. 1.50 4.00
DP5 David Ortiz .60 1.50
DP6 Manny Ramirez 1.00 2.50
DP7 Mark Teixeira 1.00 2.50
DP8 Alex Rodriguez 1.50 4.00
DP9 Jeff Kent .40 1.00
DP10 Albert Pujols 2.50 6.00
DP11 Todd Helton .60 1.50
DP12 Miguel Cabrera 1.00 2.50
DP13 Hideki Matsui 1.00 2.50
DP14 Derrek Lee .40 1.00
DP15 Vladimir Guerrero 1.00 2.50
DP16 Miguel Tejada .60 1.50
DP17 Jorge Cantu .40 1.00
DP18 Travis Hafner .40 1.00
DP19 Pat Burrell .40 1.00
DP20 Bobby Abreu .40 1.00
DP21 David Wright 1.50 4.00
DP22 Jason Bay .40 1.00
DP23 Adam Dunn .60 1.50
DP24 Eric Chavez .40 1.00
DP25 Paul Konerko .60 1.50

2006 Ultra Feel the Game

STATED ODDS 1:36 HOBBY, 1:72 RETAIL
AB Adrian Beltre Jsy 3.00 8.00
AJ Andruw Jones Jsy 4.00 10.00
AP Albert Pujols Jsy 8.00 20.00
AS Alfonso Soriano Jsy 3.00 8.00
BA Bobby Abreu Jsy 3.00 8.00
BG Brian Giles Jsy 3.00 8.00
CB Carlos Beltran Jsy 3.00 8.00
CD Carlos Delgado Jsy 3.00 8.00
CJ Chipper Jones Jsy 4.00 10.00
DJ Derek Jeter Jsy 10.00 25.00
DW David Wright Jsy 4.00 10.00
EC Eric Chavez Jsy 3.00 8.00
FH Felix Hernandez Jsy 4.00 10.00
FT Frank Thomas Jsy SP 4.00 10.00
GM Greg Maddux Jsy 4.00 10.00
IR Ivan Rodriguez Jsy 4.00 10.00
JB Josh Beckett Jsy 3.00 8.00
JR Jose Reyes Jsy SP 3.00 8.00
KG Ken Griffey Jr. Jsy 8.00 20.00
MC Matt Clement Jsy SP 3.00 8.00
MO Magglio Ordonez Jsy 3.00 8.00
MP Mike Piazza Jsy 4.00 10.00
MR Manny Ramirez Jsy 4.00 10.00
MT Miguel Tejada Jsy 3.00 8.00
PW Preston Wilson Jsy 3.00 8.00
RJ Randy Johnson Pants SP 4.00 10.00
RS Richie Sexson Jsy 3.00 8.00
SG Shawn Green Jsy 3.00 8.00
TG Troy Glaus Jsy 3.00 8.00
VG Vladimir Guerrero Jsy 4.00 10.00

2006 Ultra Fine Fabrics

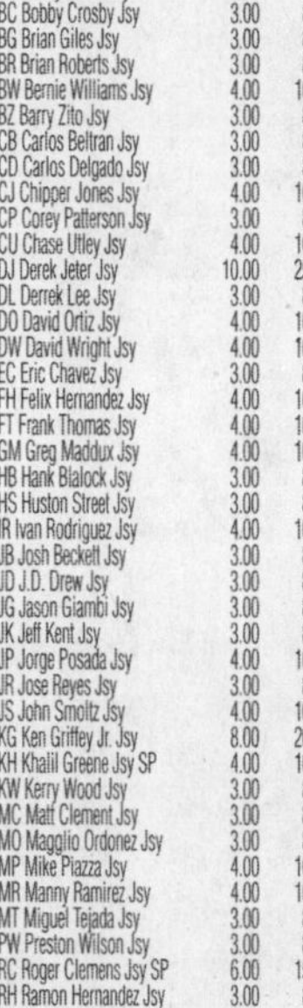

STATED ODDS 1:18 HOBBY, 1:36 RETAIL
AB Adrian Beltre Jsy 3.00 8.00
AD Adam Dunn Jsy 3.00 8.00
AJ Andruw Jones Jsy 4.00 10.00
AP Albert Pujols Jsy 8.00 20.00
AS Alfonso Soriano Jsy 3.00 8.00
BA Bobby Abreu Jsy 3.00 8.00
BC Bobby Crosby Jsy 3.00 8.00
BG Brian Giles Jsy 3.00 8.00
BR Brian Roberts Jsy 3.00 8.00
BW Bernie Williams Jsy 4.00 10.00
BZ Barry Zito Jsy 3.00 8.00
CB Carlos Beltran Jsy 3.00 8.00
CD Carlos Delgado Jsy 3.00 8.00
CJ Chipper Jones Jsy 4.00 10.00
CP Corey Patterson Jsy 3.00 8.00
CU Chase Utley Jsy 4.00 10.00
DJ Derek Jeter Jsy 10.00 25.00
DL Derrek Lee Jsy 3.00 8.00
DO David Ortiz Jsy 4.00 10.00
DW David Wright Jsy 4.00 10.00
EC Eric Chavez Jsy 3.00 8.00
FH Felix Hernandez Jsy 4.00 10.00
FT Frank Thomas Jsy 4.00 10.00
GM Greg Maddux Jsy 4.00 10.00
HB Hank Blalock Jsy 3.00 8.00
HS Huston Street Jsy 3.00 8.00
IR Ivan Rodriguez Jsy 4.00 10.00
JB Josh Beckett Jsy 3.00 8.00
JD J.D. Drew Jsy 3.00 8.00
JG Jason Giambi Jsy 3.00 8.00
JK Jeff Kent Jsy 3.00 8.00
JP Jorge Posada Jsy 4.00 10.00
JR Jose Reyes Jsy 3.00 8.00
JS John Smoltz Jsy 4.00 10.00
KG Ken Griffey Jr. Jsy 8.00 20.00
KH Khalil Greene Jsy SP 4.00 10.00
KW Kerry Wood Jsy 3.00 8.00
MC Matt Clement Jsy 3.00 8.00
MO Magglio Ordonez Jsy 3.00 8.00
MP Mike Piazza Jsy 4.00 10.00
MR Manny Ramirez Jsy 4.00 10.00
MT Miguel Tejada Jsy 3.00 8.00
PW Preston Wilson Jsy 3.00 8.00
RC Roger Clemens Jsy SP 6.00 15.00
RH Ramon Hernandez Jsy 3.00 8.00
RJ Randy Johnson Pants SP 4.00 10.00
RK Ryan Klesko Jsy 3.00 8.00
RS Richie Sexson Jsy 3.00 8.00
RY Ryan Howard Jsy 6.00 15.00
SB Sean Burroughs Jsy 3.00 8.00
SF Steve Finley Jsy 3.00 8.00
SG Shawn Green Jsy 3.00 8.00
SR Scott Rolen Jsy 4.00 10.00
SS Sammy Sosa Jsy 4.00 10.00
TG Troy Glaus Jsy 3.00 8.00
TH Travis Hafner Jsy 3.00 8.00
TX Mark Teixeira Jsy 4.00 10.00
VG Vladimir Guerrero Jsy 4.00 10.00
VW Vernon Wells Jsy 3.00 8.00
WI Dontrelle Willis Jsy 3.00 8.00

2006 Ultra Home Run Kings

COMPLETE SET (15) 8.00 20.00
OVERALL INSERT ODDS 1:1 HOBBY/RETAIL
HRK1 Albert Pujols 2.50 6.00
HRK2 Ken Griffey Jr. 1.50 4.00
HRK3 Andruw Jones .40 1.00
HRK4 Alex Rodriguez 1.50 4.00
HRK5 David Ortiz .60 1.50
HRK6 Manny Ramirez 1.00 2.50
HRK7 Derrek Lee .40 1.00
HRK8 Mark Teixeira 1.00 2.50
HRK9 Adam Dunn .60 1.50
HRK10 Paul Konerko .60 1.50
HRK11 Richie Sexson .40 1.00
HRK12 Alfonso Soriano .60 1.50
HRK13 Vladimir Guerrero 1.00 2.50
HRK14 Gary Sheffield .40 1.00
HRK15 Mike Piazza 1.00 2.50

2006 Ultra Midsummer Classic Kings

COMPLETE SET (10) 6.00 15.00
OVERALL INSERT ODDS 1:1 HOBBY/RETAIL
MCK1 Ken Griffey Jr. 1.50 4.00
MCK2 Mike Piazza 1.00 2.50
MCK3 Derek Jeter 2.50 6.00
MCK4 Roger Clemens 1.25 3.00
MCK5 Randy Johnson 1.00 2.50
MCK6 Miguel Tejada .60 1.50
MCK7 Alfonso Soriano .60 1.50
MCK8 Garret Anderson .40 1.00
MCK9 Pedro Martinez .60 1.50
MCK10 Ivan Rodriguez .60 1.50

2006 Ultra RBI Kings

COMPLETE SET (20) 8.00 20.00
OVERALL INSERT ODDS 1:1 HOBBY/RETAIL
RBI1 Ken Griffey Jr. 1.50 4.00
RBI2 David Ortiz .60 1.50
RBI3 Manny Ramirez 1.00 2.50
RBI4 Mark Teixeira 1.00 2.50
RBI5 Alex Rodriguez 1.50 4.00
RBI6 Andruw Jones .40 1.00
RBI7 Jeff Bagwell .60 1.50
RBI8 Gary Sheffield .40 1.00
RBI9 Richie Sexson .40 1.00
RBI10 Jeff Kent .40 1.00
RBI11 Albert Pujols 2.50 6.00
RBI12 Todd Helton .60 1.50
RBI13 Miguel Cabrera 1.00 2.50
RBI14 Hideki Matsui 1.00 2.50
RBI15 Carlos Delgado .40 1.00
RBI16 Carlos Lee .40 1.00
RBI17 Derrek Lee .40 1.00
RBI18 Vladimir Guerrero 1.00 2.50
RBI19 Luis Gonzalez .40 1.00
RBI20 Mike Piazza 1.00 2.50

2006 Ultra Rising Stars

COMPLETE SET (10) 6.00 15.00
OVERALL INSERT ODDS 1:1 HOBBY/RETAIL
URS1 Ryan Howard 1.50 4.00
URS2 Huston Street .40 1.00
URS3 Jeff Francoeur 1.00 2.50
URS4 Felix Hernandez 1.00 2.50
URS5 Chase Utley 1.00 2.50
URS6 Robinson Cano 1.00 2.50
URS7 Zach Duke .40 1.00
URS8 Scott Kazmir .60 1.50
URS9 Willy Taveras .40 1.00
URS10 Tadahito Iguchi .40 1.00

2006 Ultra Star

OVERALL ODDS 2:1 FAT PACKS
1 Ken Griffey Jr. 1.50 4.00
2 Derek Jeter 2.50 6.00
3 Albert Pujols 2.50 6.00
4 Alex Rodriguez 1.50 4.00
5 Vladimir Guerrero 1.00 2.50
6 Roger Clemens 1.25 3.00
7 Derrek Lee .40 1.00
8 David Ortiz .60 1.50
9 Miguel Cabrera 1.00 2.50
10 Bobby Abreu .40 1.00
11 Mark Teixeira 1.00 2.50
12 Johan Santana 1.00 2.50
13 Hideki Matsui 1.00 2.50
14 Ichiro Suzuki 1.50 4.00
15 Andruw Jones .40 1.00
16 Eric Chavez .40 1.00
17 Roy Oswalt .60 1.50
18 Curt Schilling .60 1.50
19 Randy Johnson 1.00 2.50
20 Ivan Rodriguez .60 1.50
21 Chipper Jones 1.00 2.50
22 Mark Prior .60 1.50
23 Jason Bay .40 1.00
24 Pedro Martinez .60 1.50
25 David Wright 1.50 4.00
26 Carlos Beltran .40 1.00
27 Jim Edmonds .60 1.50
28 Chris Carpenter 1.00 2.50
29 Roy Halladay 1.00 2.50
30 Jake Peavy .40 1.00
31 Paul Konerko .60 1.50
32 Travis Hafner .40 1.00
33 Barry Zito .60 1.50
34 Miguel Tejada .60 1.50
35 Josh Beckett .60 1.50
36 Todd Helton .60 1.50
37 Dontrelle Willis .40 1.00
38 Manny Ramirez 1.00 2.50
39 Mariano Rivera 1.00 2.50
40 Jeff Kent .40 1.00

2006 Ultra Strikeout Kings

COMPLETE SET (10) 6.00 15.00
OVERALL INSERT ODDS 1:1 HOBBY/RETAIL
SOK1 Roger Clemens 1.25 3.00
SOK2 Johan Santana 1.00 2.50
SOK3 Jake Peavy .40 1.00
SOK4 Randy Johnson 1.00 2.50
SOK5 Curt Schilling .60 1.50
SOK6 Chris Carpenter 1.00 2.50
SOK7 Pedro Martinez .60 1.50
SOK8 Mark Prior .60 1.50
SOK9 Carlos Zambrano .60 1.50
SOK10 John Smoltz 1.00 2.50

2007 Ultra

This 250-card set was released in July, 2007. This set was issued both in hobby and retail versions. The hobby version came five cards to a pack which came five packs to a box and 16 boxes to a case. Cards numbered 1-200 featured veterans sequenced in team alphabetical order while cards 201-250 featured rookies with the final 13 cards of the set being Lucky 13 rookies.

COMP.SET w/o RC's (200) 20.00 50.00
COMMON CARD .20 .50
COMMON ROOKIE .50 1.25
COMMON L13 .50 1.25
PRINTING PLATE ODDS 1:1252 HOB/RET
PLATE PRINT RUN 1 SET PER COLOR
BLACK-CYAN-MAGENTA-YELLOW ISSUED
NO PLATE PRICING DUE TO SCARCITY
1 Brandon Webb .30 .75
2 Randy Johnson .50 1.25
3 Conor Jackson .20 .50
4 Stephen Drew .20 .50
5 Eric Byrnes .20 .50
6 Carlos Quentin .20 .50
7 Andruw Jones .20 .50
8 Chipper Jones .50 1.25
9 Jeff Francoeur .50 1.25
10 Tim Hudson .30 .75
11 John Smoltz .50 1.25
12 Edgar Renteria .20 .50
13 Erik Bedard .20 .50
14 Kris Benson .20 .50
15 Miguel Tejada .30 .75
16 Nick Markakis .50 1.25
17 Brian Roberts .20 .50
18 Melvin Mora .20 .50
19 Aubrey Huff .20 .50
20 Curt Schilling .30 .75
21 Jonathan Papelbon .50 1.25
22 Josh Beckett .30 .75
23 Jason Varitek .50 1.25
24 David Ortiz .30 .75
25 Manny Ramirez .50 1.25
26 J.D. Drew .20 .50
27 Carlos Zambrano .30 .75
28 Derrek Lee .20 .50
29 Aramis Ramirez .20 .50
30 Alfonso Soriano .30 .75
31 Rich Hill .20 .50
32 Jacque Jones .20 .50
33 A.J. Pierzynski .20 .50
34 Jermaine Dye .20 .50
35 Paul Konerko .30 .75
36 Bobby Jenks .20 .50
37 Jon Garland .20 .50
38 Mark Buehrle .30 .75
39 Tadahito Iguchi .20 .50
40 Adam Dunn .30 .75
41 Ken Griffey Jr. .75 2.00
42 Aaron Harang .20 .50
43 Bronson Arroyo .20 .50
44 Ryan Freel .20 .50
45 Brandon Phillips .20 .50
46 Grady Sizemore .30 .75
47 Travis Hafner .20 .50
48 Victor Martinez .30 .75
49 Jhonny Peralta .20 .50
50 C.C. Sabathia .30 .75
51 Jeremy Sowers .20 .50
52 Ryan Garko .20 .50
53 Garrett Atkins .20 .50
54 Willy Taveras .20 .50
55 Todd Helton .30 .75
56 Jeff Francis .20 .50
57 Brad Hawpe .20 .50
58 Matt Holliday .50 1.25
59 Justin Verlander .60 1.50
60 Jeremy Bonderman .20 .50
61 Magglio Ordonez .30 .75
62 Ivan Rodriguez .30 .75
63 Gary Sheffield .20 .50
64 Kenny Rogers .20 .50
65 Brandon Inge .20 .50
66 Anibal Sanchez .20 .50
67 Scott Olsen .20 .50
68 Dontrelle Willis .20 .50
69 Dan Uggla .30 .75
70 Hanley Ramirez .50 1.25
71 Miguel Cabrera .50 1.25
72 Jeremy Hermida .20 .50
73 Roy Oswalt .30 .75
74 Brad Lidge .20 .50
75 Lance Berkman .30 .75
76 Carlos Lee .30 .75
77 Morgan Ensberg .20 .50
78 Craig Biggio .30 .75
79 Reggie Sanders .20 .50
80 Mike Sweeney .20 .50
81 Mark Teahen .20 .50
82 John Buck .20 .50
83 Mark Grudzielanek .20 .50
84 Gary Matthews .20 .50
85 Vladimir Guerrero .50 1.25
86 Garret Anderson .20 .50
87 Howie Kendrick .20 .50
88 Jered Weaver .30 .75
89 Chone Figgins .20 .50
90 Bartolo Colon .20 .50
91 Francisco Rodriguez .30 .75
92 Nomar Garciaparra .50 1.25
93 Andre Ethier .30 .75
94 Rafael Furcal .20 .50
95 Jeff Kent .20 .50
96 Derek Lowe .20 .50
97 Jason Schmidt .20 .50
98 Takashi Saito .20 .50
99 Ben Sheets .20 .50
100 Prince Fielder .30 .75
101 Bill Hall .20 .50
102 Rickie Weeks .30 .75
103 Francisco Cordero .20 .50
104 J.J. Hardy .20 .50
105 Johan Santana .50 1.25
106 Justin Morneau .50 1.25
107 Joe Mauer .50 1.25
108 Joe Nathan .20 .50
109 Torii Hunter .20 .50
110 Michael Cuddyer .20 .50
111 Boof Bonser .20 .50
112 Tom Glavine .30 .75
113 Pedro Martinez .30 .75
114 Billy Wagner .20 .50
115 Jose Reyes .30 .75
116 David Wright .75 2.00
117 Carlos Delgado .20 .50
118 Carlos Beltran .20 .50
119 Alex Rodriguez .75 2.00
120 Chien-Ming Wang .30 .75
121 Mariano Rivera .50 1.25
122 Bobby Abreu .20 .50
123 Hideki Matsui .50 1.25
124 Johnny Damon .30 .75
125 Robinson Cano .50 1.25
126 Derek Jeter 1.25 3.00
127 Nick Swisher .50 1.25
128 Eric Chavez .20 .50
129 Jason Kendall .20 .50
130 Bobby Crosby .20 .50
131 Huston Street .20 .50
132 Dan Haren .20 .50
133 Rich Harden .20 .50
134 Mike Piazza .50 1.25
135 Chase Utley .50 1.25
136 Jimmy Rollins .30 .75
137 Aaron Rowand .20 .50
138 Jamie Moyer .20 .50
139 Cole Hamels .50 1.25
140 Pat Burrell .20 .50
141 Ryan Howard .75 2.00
142 Freddy Sanchez .20 .50
143 Zach Duke .20 .50
144 Ian Snell .20 .50
145 Jack Wilson .20 .50
146 Jason Bay .30 .75
147 Albert Pujols 1.25 3.00
148 Scott Rolen .30 .75
149 Jim Edmonds .30 .75
150 Chris Carpenter .50 1.25
151 Yadier Molina .20 .50
152 Adam Wainwright .30 .75
153 David Eckstein .20 .50
154 Trevor Hoffman .30 .75
155 Brian Giles .20 .50
156 Adrian Gonzalez .30 .75
157 Jake Peavy .20 .50
158 Khalil Greene .20 .50
159 Chris Young .20 .50
160 Greg Maddux .75 2.00
161 Mike Cameron .20 .50
162 Matt Cain .30 .75
163 Matt Morris .20 .50
164 Pedro Feliz .20 .50
165 Omar Vizquel .30 .75
166 Randy Winn .20 .50
167 Barry Zito .30 .75
168 Adrian Beltre .20 .50
169 Yuniesky Betancourt .20 .50
170 Richie Sexson .20 .50
171 Raul Ibanez .30 .75
172 Kenji Johjima .50 1.25
173 Ichiro Suzuki .75 2.00
174 Felix Hernandez .50 1.25
175 Scott Kazmir .30 .75
176 Carl Crawford .30 .75
177 B.J. Upton .20 .50
178 James Shields .20 .50
179 Rocco Baldelli .20 .50
180 Jorge Cantu .20 .50
181 Ty Wigginton .20 .50
182 Mark Teixeira .50 1.25
183 Hank Blalock .20 .50
184 Ian Kinsler .30 .75
185 Michael Young .30 .75
186 Vicente Padilla .20 .50
187 Akinori Otsuka .20 .50
188 Kenny Lofton .20 .50
189 A.J. Burnett .30 .75
190 Roy Halladay .50 1.25
191 B.J. Ryan .20 .50
192 Vernon Wells .20 .50
193 Alex Rios .20 .50
194 Troy Glaus .20 .50
195 Frank Thomas .50 1.25
196 Ryan Zimmerman .30 .75
197 Michael O'Connor .20 .50
198 Chad Cordero .20 .50
199 Nick Johnson .20 .50
200 Felipe Lopez .20 .50
201 Miguel Montero (RC) .50 1.25
202 Doug Slaten RC .50 1.25
203 Joseph Bisenius RC .50 1.25
204 Jared Burton RC .50 1.25
205 Kevin Cameron RC .50 1.25
206 Matt Chico (RC) .50 1.25
207 Chris Stewart RC .50 1.25
208 Joe Smith RC .50 1.25
209 Zack Segovia (RC) .50 1.25
210 John Danks RC .75 2.00
211 Lee Gardner (RC) .50 1.25
212 Jeff Baker (RC) .50 1.25
213 Jamie Burke (RC) .50 1.25
214 Phil Hughes (RC) 2.50 6.00
215 Mike Rabelo RC .50 1.25
216 Jose Garcia RC .50 1.25
217 Hector Gimenez (RC) .50 1.25
218 Jesus Flores RC .50 1.25
219 Brandon Morrow RC 2.50 6.00
220 Hideki Okajima RC 2.50 6.00
221 Jay Marshall RC .50 1.25
222 Matt Lindstrom (RC) .50 1.25
223 Juan Salas (RC) .50 1.25
224 Juan Perez RC .50 1.25
225 Sean Henn (RC) .50 1.25
226 Travis Buck (RC) .50 1.25
227 Gustavo Molina RC .50 1.25

228 Hunter Pence (RC) 2.50 6.00
229 Michael Bourn (RC) .50 1.25
230 Brian Barden RC .50 1.25
231 Don Kelly (RC) .50 1.25
232 Joakim Soria RC .50 1.25
233 Cesar Jimenez RC .50 1.25
234 Levale Speigner RC .50 1.25
235 Micah Owings (RC) .50 1.25
236 Brian Stokes (RC) .50 1.25
237 Joaquin Arias (RC) .50 1.25
238 Josh Hamilton L13 (RC) 2.00 5.00
239 Daisuke Matsuzaka L13 RC 2.00 5.00
240 Alejandro De Aza L13 RC .75 2.00
241 Kory Casto L13 (RC) .50 1.25
242 Troy Tulowitzki L13 (RC) 3.00 8.00
243 Akinori Iwamura L13 RC 1.25 3.00
244 Angel Sanchez L13 RC .50 1.25
245 Ryan Braun L13 (RC) 2.50 6.00
246 Alex Gordon L13 RC 1.50 4.00
247 Elijah Dukes L13 RC .75 2.00
248 Kei Igawa L13 RC 1.25 3.00
249 Kevin Kouzmanoff L13 (RC) .50 1.25
250 Delmon Young L13 (RC) .75 2.00

2007 Ultra Gold

*GOLD 1-200: 1.5X TO 3X BASIC
*GOLD RC 201-237: .5X TO 1.2X BASIC RC
*GOLD L13 238-250: .5X TO 1.2X BASIC L13
STATED ODDS 1:10 HOBBY
239 Daisuke Matsuzaka L13 5.00 12.00
245 Ryan Braun L13 5.00 12.00

2007 Ultra Retail

*RETAIL 1-200: .25X TO .6X BASIC
*RETAIL RC 201-237: .3X TO .8X BASIC RC
*RETAIL L13 238-250: .3X TO .8X BASIC L13

2007 Ultra Retail Gold

*RETAIL GLD 1-200: 1.5X TO 4X BASIC
*RETAIL RC GLD 201-237: .6X TO 1.5X BASIC RC
*RETAIL L13 GLD 238-250: .6X TO 1.5X BASIC L13

STATED ODDS 2:1 FAT PACK
STATED PRINT RUN 999 SER.#'d SETS
239 Daisuke Matsuzaka L13 6.00 15.00
245 Ryan Braun L13 5.00 12.00

2007 Ultra Autographics

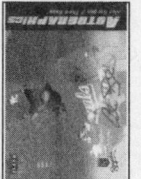

RANDOM INSERTS IN PACKS
PRINT RUNS B/WN 49-499 COPIES PER
AG Alex Gordon/499 10.00 25.00
AH Aaron Harang/499 4.00 10.00
BA Bronson Arroyo/49
BM Brandon McCarthy/499 3.00 8.00
CC Chad Cordero/499 3.00 8.00
CH Clay Hensley/499 3.00 8.00
CI Cesar Izturis/122 4.00 10.00
JA Jason Bay/499 4.00 10.00
JB Joe Blanton/299 3.00 8.00
JE Johnny Estrada/132 6.00 15.00
JS Johan Santana/173 15.00 40.00
KG Khalil Greene/299 6.00 15.00
KI Kei Igawa/199 15.00 40.00

2007 Ultra Autographics Retail

STATED ODDS 1:1440 RETAIL
NO PRICING DUE TO SCARCITY
AG Alex Gordon
AH Aaron Harang
BM Brandon McCarthy
CH Clay Hensley
JB Joe Blanton
JS Johan Santana
KG Khalil Greene
KI Kei Igawa

2007 Ultra Dual Materials

RANDOM INSERTS IN PACKS
PRINT RUNS B/WN 61-160 COPIES PER
GOLD p/r 39-75: .5X TO 1.2X BASIC
GOLD p/r 20-25: .6X TO 1.5X BASIC
GOLD RANDOMLY INSERTED
GOLD PRINT RUN B/WN 20-75 PER
PATCH: .75X TO 2X BASIC
PATCHES RANDOMLY INSERTED
PATCH PRINT RUN B/WN 1-25 PER
NO PATCH PRICING ON QTY 16 OR LESS
AB A.J. Burnett 3.00 8.00
AE Andre Ethier 3.00 8.00
AJ Andruw Jones 3.00 8.00
AK Austin Kearns 3.00 8.00
AL Adam LaRoche 3.00 8.00
AN Garret Anderson 3.00 8.00
AP Albert Pujols 6.00 15.00
AS Anibal Sanchez 3.00 8.00
BA Bobby Abreu 3.00 8.00
BC Bobby Crosby 3.00 8.00
BE Adrian Beltre 3.00 8.00
BG Brian Giles 3.00 8.00
BI Craig Biggio 3.00 8.00
BJ Bobby Jenks 3.00 8.00
BL Brad Lidge 3.00 8.00
BM Brandon McCarthy 3.00 8.00
BR Brian Roberts 3.00 8.00
BS Ben Sheets 3.00 8.00
BW Brandon Webb 3.00 8.00
CA Carlos Beltran 3.00 8.00
CB Chris Burke 3.00 8.00
CC Carl Crawford 3.00 8.00
CF Chone Figgins 3.00 8.00
CH Chris Carpenter/81 4.00 10.00
CJ Conor Jackson 3.00 8.00
CK Casey Kotchman 3.00 8.00
CL Carlos Lee 3.00 8.00
CP Corey Patterson 3.00 8.00
CR Coco Crisp 3.00 8.00
CS C.C. Sabathia/154 3.00 8.00
CU Curt Schilling 3.00 8.00
DJ Derek Jeter 8.00 20.00
DL Derek Lowe 3.00 8.00
DO David Ortiz 4.00 10.00
DR J.D. Drew 3.00 8.00
DU Dan Uggla 3.00 8.00
DW David Wells 3.00 8.00
ED Jim Edmonds 3.00 8.00
ES Ervin Santana 3.00 8.00
FG Freddy Garcia 3.00 8.00
FH Felix Hernandez 3.00 8.00
GA Garrett Atkins 3.00 8.00
GJ Geoff Jenkins 3.00 8.00
GM Greg Maddux 4.00 10.00
GS Gary Sheffield 3.00 8.00
HE Todd Helton 3.00 8.00
HO Trevor Hoffman 3.00 8.00
HR Hanley Ramirez 3.00 8.00
HU Torii Hunter 3.00 8.00
IS Ian Snell 3.00 8.00
JB Jeremy Bonderman 3.00 8.00
JC Chipper Jones 4.00 10.00
JD Jermaine Dye 3.00 8.00
JG Jonny Gomes 3.00 8.00
JH J.J. Hardy 4.00 10.00
JJ Josh Johnson 3.00 8.00
JK Jeff Kent 3.00 8.00
JM Justin Morneau 3.00 8.00
JN Joe Nathan 3.00 8.00
JO Josh Beckett 3.00 8.00
JP Jorge Posada 3.00 8.00
JS James Shields 3.00 8.00
JV Jason Varitek 4.00 10.00
JW Josh Willingham 3.00 8.00
KG Kahlil Greene 3.00 8.00
KW Kerry Wood 3.00 8.00
LB Lance Berkman 3.00 8.00
LE Derrek Lee 3.00 8.00
LG Luis Gonzalez 3.00 8.00
LM Lastings Milledge 3.00 8.00
LS Luke Scott 3.00 8.00
MC Matt Cain 3.00 8.00
ME Melky Cabrera 3.00 8.00
MH Matt Holliday 4.00 10.00
MI Mike Mussina 3.00 8.00
MM Melvin Mora 3.00 8.00
MO Magglio Ordonez 3.00 8.00
MR Manny Ramirez 3.00 8.00
MS Mike Sweeney 3.00 8.00
MT Miguel Tejada 3.00 8.00
MU Mark Mulder 3.00 8.00
PE Andy Pettitte 3.00 8.00
PF Prince Fielder 4.00 10.00
PJ Jhonny Peralta 3.00 8.00
RH Rich Harden 3.00 8.00
SC Jason Schmidt 3.00 8.00
SI Grady Sizemore 3.00 8.00
SO Scott Olsen 3.00 8.00
TE Mark Teixeira 3.00 8.00
TH Travis Hafner 3.00 8.00
TW Tim Wakefield 3.00 8.00
VG Vladimir Guerrero 3.00 8.00
VM Victor Martinez 3.00 8.00
VW Vernon Wells 3.00 8.00
WI Dontrelle Willis 3.00 8.00
ZD Zach Duke 3.00 8.00

2007 Ultra Faces of the Game

STATED ODDS 1:10 HOBBY/RETAIL
PRINTING PLATE ODDS 1:1252 HOB/RET
PLATE PRINT RUN 1 SET PER COLOR
BLACK-CYAN-MAGENTA-YELLOW ISSUED
NO PLATE PRICING DUE TO SCARCITY
AB Adrian Beltre .50 1.25
AJ Andruw Jones .50 1.25
BS Ben Sheets .50 1.25
CJ Chipper Jones 1.25 3.00
CS C.C. Sabathia .75 2.00
CU Chase Utley 1.25 3.00
DJ Derek Jeter 3.00 8.00
FR Francisco Rodriguez .75 2.00
GM Greg Maddux 2.00 5.00
HU Torii Hunter .50 1.25
JB Jason Bay .75 2.00
JG Jason Giambi .50 1.25
KG Ken Griffey Jr. 2.00 5.00
LG Luis Gonzalez .50 1.25
MC Miguel Cabrera 1.25 3.00
MP Mike Piazza 1.25 3.00
MR Mariano Rivera 1.25 3.00
OV Omar Vizquel .75 2.00
TG Tom Glavine .75 2.00
HO Trevor Hoffman .75 2.00

2007 Ultra Faces of the Game Materials

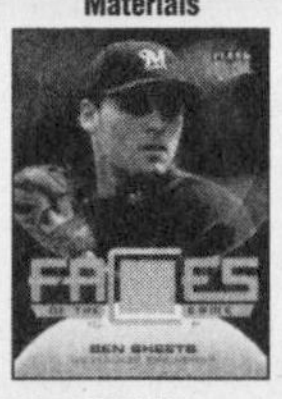

APPX.ODDS 1:8 HOBBY/RETAIL
AB Adrian Beltre 2.50 6.00
AJ Andruw Jones 3.00 8.00
BS Ben Sheets 2.50 6.00
CJ Chipper Jones 3.00 8.00
CS C.C. Sabathia 2.50 6.00
CU Chase Utley 4.00 10.00
DJ Derek Jeter 8.00 20.00
FR Francisco Rodriguez 2.50 6.00
GM Greg Maddux 4.00 10.00
HO Trevor Hoffman 2.50 6.00
JB Jason Bay 2.50 6.00
JG Jason Giambi 2.50 6.00
KG Ken Griffey Jr. 6.00 15.00
LG Luis Gonzalez 2.50 6.00
MC Miguel Cabrera 3.00 8.00
MP Mike Piazza 4.00 10.00
MR Mariano Rivera 4.00 10.00
OV Omar Vizquel 3.00 8.00
TG Tom Glavine 3.00 8.00
TH Torii Hunter 2.50 6.00

2007 Ultra Feel the Game

APPX.ODDS 1:7 HOBBY/RETAIL
PRINTING PLATE ODDS 1:1252 HOB/RET
PLATE PRINT RUN 1 SET PER COLOR
BLACK-CYAN-MAGENTA-YELLOW ISSUED
NO PLATE PRICING DUE TO SCARCITY
AP Albert Pujols 3.00 8.00
BA Bobby Abreu .50 1.25
BR Brian Roberts .50 1.25
BW Brandon Webb .75 2.00
CC Chris Carpenter 1.25 3.00
CJ Chipper Jones 1.25 3.00
CR Carl Crawford .75 2.00
CS Curt Schilling .75 2.00
CU Chase Utley 1.25 3.00
CZ Carlos Zambrano .75 2.00
DJ Derek Jeter 3.00 8.00
DW Dontrelle Willis .50 1.25
EC Eric Chavez .50 1.25
GS Grady Sizemore .75 2.00
HR Hanley Ramirez 1.25 3.00
IR Ivan Rodriguez .75 2.00
JM Justin Morneau 1.25 3.00
JP Jonathan Papelbon 1.25 3.00
JR Jose Reyes .75 2.00
JS John Smoltz 1.25 3.00
KG Ken Griffey Jr. 2.00 5.00
KJ Kenji Johjima 1.25 3.00
LB Lance Berkman .75 2.00
LG Luis Gonzalez .50 1.25
MC Miguel Cabrera 1.25 3.00
RC Robinson Cano 1.25 3.00
RJ Randy Johnson 1.25 3.00
SA Johan Santana 1.25 3.00
SC Jason Schmidt .50 1.25
VG Vladimir Guerrero 1.25 3.00

2007 Ultra Feel the Game Materials

APPX.ODDS 1:7 HOBBY/RETAIL
AP Albert Pujols 6.00 15.00
BA Bobby Abreu 2.50 6.00
BR Brian Roberts 3.00 8.00
BW Brandon Webb 2.50 6.00
CC Chris Carpenter 2.50 6.00
CJ Chipper Jones 3.00 8.00
CR Carl Crawford 2.50 6.00
CS Curt Schilling 3.00 8.00
CZ Carlos Zambrano 2.50 6.00
DJ Derek Jeter 8.00 20.00
DW Dontrelle Willis 2.50 6.00
EC Eric Chavez 2.50 6.00
GS Grady Sizemore 3.00 8.00
HR Hanley Ramirez 3.00 8.00
IR Ivan Rodriguez 3.00 8.00
JM Justin Morneau 2.50 6.00
JP Jonathan Papelbon 4.00 10.00
JR Jose Reyes 4.00 10.00
JS John Smoltz 3.00 8.00
KG Ken Griffey Jr. 6.00 15.00
KJ Kenji Johjima 4.00 10.00
LB Lance Berkman 2.50 6.00
LG Luis Gonzalez 2.50 6.00
MC Miguel Cabrera 3.00 8.00
RC Robinson Cano 4.00 10.00
RJ Randy Johnson 4.00 10.00
SA Johan Santana 3.00 8.00
SC Jason Schmidt 2.50 6.00
VG Vladimir Guerrero 3.00 8.00

2007 Ultra Hitting Machines

APPX.ODDS 1:13 HOBBY/RETAIL
PRINTING PLATE ODDS 1:1252 HOB/RET
PLATE PRINT RUN 1 SET PER COLOR
BLACK-CYAN-MAGENTA-YELLOW ISSUED
NO PLATE PRICING DUE TO SCARCITY
AR Aramis Ramirez .50 1.25
AS Alfonso Soriano .75 2.00
BI Craig Biggio .75 2.00
CB Carlos Beltran .50 1.25
DO David Ortiz .75 2.00
FS Freddy Sanchez .50 1.25
FT Frank Thomas 1.25 3.00
JK Jeff Kent .50 1.25
JM Joe Mauer 1.25 3.00
JT Jim Thome .75 2.00
MT Mark Teixeira 1.25 3.00
NS Nick Swisher 1.25 3.00
TE Miguel Tejada .75 2.00
TG Troy Glaus .50 1.25
TH Todd Helton .75 2.00

2007 Ultra Hitting Machines Materials

APPX.ODDS 1:12 HOBBY/RETAIL
AR Aramis Ramirez 2.50 6.00
AS Alfonso Soriano 2.50 6.00
BI Craig Biggio 3.00 8.00
CB Carlos Beltran 2.50 6.00
DO David Ortiz 4.00 10.00
FS Freddy Sanchez 2.50 6.00
FT Frank Thomas 4.00 10.00
JK Jeff Kent 2.50 6.00
JM Joe Mauer 3.00 8.00
JT Jim Thome 3.00 8.00
MT Mark Teixeira 3.00 8.00
NS Nick Swisher 2.50 6.00
TE Miguel Tejada 2.50 6.00
TG Troy Glaus 2.50 6.00
TH Todd Helton 3.00 8.00

2007 Ultra Iron Man

COMMON CARD 1.25 3.00
APPX.ODDS 1:3 HOBBY/RETAIL

2007 Ultra Iron Man Signatures

COMMON CARD 75.00 150.00
RANDOM INSERTS IN PACKS
STATED PRINT RUN 10 SER.#'d SETS

2007 Ultra Rookie Autographs

RANDOM INSERTS IN PACKS
PRINT RUNS B/WN 23-499 COPIES PER
NO PRICING ON QTY 38 OR LESS
201a Miguel Montero/299 3.00 8.00
201b Miguel Montero/149 4.00 10.00
202a Doug Slaten/299 3.00 8.00
202b Doug Slaten/349 3.00 8.00
203a Joseph Bisenius/299 3.00 8.00
203b Joseph Bisenius/349 3.00 8.00
204a Jared Burton/299 5.00 12.00
204b Jared Burton/349 5.00 12.00
205a Kevin Cameron/299 3.00 8.00
205b Kevin Cameron/349 3.00 8.00
206a Matt Chico/299 3.00 8.00
206b Matt Chico/349 3.00 8.00
207a Chris Stewart/299 3.00 8.00
207b Chris Stewart/349 3.00 8.00
209a Zack Segovia/299 4.00 10.00
209b Zack Segovia/149 5.00 12.00
210 John Danks/299 3.00 8.00
213a Jamie Burke/299 5.00 12.00
213b Jamie Burke/349 5.00 12.00
215a Mike Rabelo/299 3.00 8.00
215b Mike Rabelo/349 3.00 8.00
217a Hector Gimenez/299 3.00 8.00
217b Hector Gimenez/349 3.00 8.00
219a Brandon Morrow/299 10.00 25.00
219b Brandon Morrow/349 10.00 25.00
221a Jay Marshall/299 6.00 15.00
221b Jay Marshall/349 6.00 15.00
223 Juan Salas/23
225a Sean Henn/299 3.00 8.00
225b Sean Henn/349 3.00 8.00
226a Travis Buck/299 4.00 10.00
226b Travis Buck/99 6.00 15.00
227a Gustavo Molina/299 4.00 10.00
227b Gustavo Molina/349 4.00 10.00
229a Michael Bourn/299 4.00 10.00
229b Michael Bourn/349 4.00 10.00
232a Joakim Soria/299 4.00 10.00
232b Joakim Soria/349 4.00 10.00
233 Cesar Jimenez/38
234a Levale Speigner/299 3.00 8.00
234b Levale Speigner/349 3.00 8.00
236a Brian Stokes/299 3.00 8.00
236b Brian Stokes/349 3.00 8.00
237a Joaquin Arias/299 3.00 8.00
237b Joaquin Arias/349 3.00 8.00
238a Josh Hamilton L13/499 15.00 40.00
238b Josh Hamilton L13/99 20.00 50.00
241 Kory Casto L13/499 5.00 12.00
242 Troy Tulowitzki L13/499 12.50 30.00
243 Akinori Iwamura L13/99 30.00 60.00
245 Ryan Braun L13/499 40.00 80.00
246a Alex Gordon L13/499 6.00 15.00
246b Alex Gordon L13/99 10.00 25.00
248a Kei Igawa L13/299 12.50 30.00
248b Kei Igawa L13/99 20.00 50.00
249a Kevin Kouzmanoff L13/499 4.00 10.00
249b Kevin Kouzmanoff L13/199 5.00 12.00

2007 Ultra Strike Zone

STATED ODDS 1:20 HOBBY/RETAIL
PRINTING PLATE ODDS 1:1252 HOB/RET
PLATE PRINT RUN 1 SET PER COLOR
BLACK-CYAN-MAGENTA-YELLOW ISSUED
NO PLATE PRICING DUE TO SCARCITY
BZ Barry Zito .50 1.25
CC C.C. Sabathia .75 2.00
CZ Carlos Zambrano .75 2.00
DW Dontrelle Willis .50 1.25
JS Johan Santana 1.25 3.00
JV Justin Verlander 1.50 4.00
MM Mike Mussina .75 2.00
PM Pedro Martinez .75 2.00
RH Roy Halladay 1.25 3.00
RO Roy Oswalt .75 2.00

2007 Ultra Strike Zone Materials

APPX.ODDS 1:14 HOBBY/RETAIL
BZ Barry Zito 2.50 6.00
CC C.C. Sabathia 2.50 6.00
CZ Carlos Zambrano 2.50 6.00
DW Dontrelle Willis 2.50 6.00
JS Johan Santana 3.00 8.00
JV Justin Verlander 4.00 10.00
MM Mike Mussina 3.00 8.00
PM Pedro Martinez 3.00 8.00
RH Roy Halladay 2.50 6.00
RO Roy Oswalt 2.50 6.00

2007 Ultra Swing Kings

STATED ODDS 1:8 HOBBY/RETAIL
PRINTING PLATE ODDS 1:1252 HOB/RET
PLATE PRINT RUN 1 SET PER COLOR
BLACK-CYAN-MAGENTA-YELLOW ISSUED
NO PLATE PRICING DUE TO SCARCITY
AD Adam Dunn .75 2.00
AJ Andruw Jones .50 1.25
AP Albert Pujols 3.00 8.00
AR Aramis Ramirez .50 1.25
AS Alfonso Soriano .75 2.00
CB Carlos Beltran .50 1.25
CL Carlos Lee .50 1.25
DJ Derek Jeter 3.00 8.00
DO David Ortiz .75 2.00
FT Frank Thomas 1.25 3.00
GS Gary Sheffield .50 1.25
HE Todd Helton .75 2.00
JM Joe Mauer 1.25 3.00
JR Jose Reyes .75 2.00
JT Jim Thome .75 2.00
KG Ken Griffey Jr. 2.00 5.00
MC Miguel Cabrera 1.25 3.00
MR Manny Ramirez 1.25 3.00
MT Miguel Tejada .75 2.00
NG Nomar Garciaparra 1.25 3.00
PB Pat Burrell .50 1.25
TE Mark Teixeira 1.25 3.00
TH Travis Hafner .50 1.25
VG Vladimir Guerrero 1.25 3.00
VW Vernon Wells .50 1.25

2007 Ultra Swing Kings Materials

APPX ODDS 1:7 HOBBY/RETAIL
AD Adam Dunn 2.50 6.00
AJ Andruw Jones 3.00 8.00
AP Albert Pujols 6.00 15.00
AR Aramis Ramirez 2.50 6.00
AS Alfonso Soriano 2.50 6.00
CB Carlos Beltran 2.50 6.00
CL Carlos Lee 2.50 6.00
DJ Derek Jeter 8.00 20.00
DO David Ortiz 4.00 10.00
FT Frank Thomas 4.00 10.00
GS Gary Sheffield 2.50 6.00
HE Todd Helton 3.00 8.00
JM Joe Mauer 3.00 8.00
JR Jose Reyes 4.00 10.00
JT Jim Thome 3.00 8.00
KG Ken Griffey Jr. 6.00 15.00
MC Miguel Cabrera 3.00 8.00
MR Manny Ramirez 3.00 8.00
MT Miguel Tejada 2.50 6.00
NG Nomar Garciaparra 4.00 10.00
PB Pat Burrell 2.50 6.00
TE Mark Teixeira 3.00 8.00
TH Travis Hafner 2.50 6.00
VG Vladimir Guerrero 4.00 10.00
VW Vernon Wells 2.50 6.00

2007 Ultra Ultragraphs

RANDOM INSERTS IN PACKS
PRINT RUNS B/WN 49-499 COPIES PER
AI Akinori Iwamura/49
AK Austin Kearns/399 3.00 8.00
AL Adam LaRoche/499 3.00 8.00
AN Garret Anderson/499 3.00 8.00
BB Boof Bonser/499 3.00 8.00
GA Garrett Atkins/499 3.00 8.00
JJ Jorge Julio/499 3.00 8.00
JN Joe Nathan/299 4.00 10.00
JW Jered Weaver/150 6.00 15.00
MM Mark Mulder/319 3.00 8.00
RW Rickie Weeks/68 6.00 15.00
TH Travis Hafner/499 4.00 10.00
ZG Zack Greinke/199 10.00 25.00

2007 Ultra Ultragraphs Retail

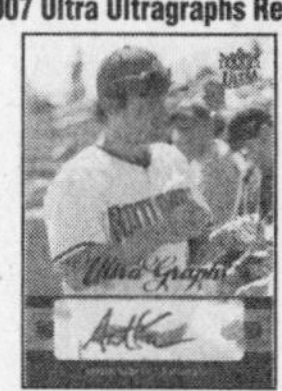

STATED ODDS 1:1440 RETAIL
NO PRICING DUE TO SCARCITY
AI Akinori Iwamura
AK Austin Kearns
AL Adam LaRoche
AN Garret Anderson
BB Boof Bonser
GA Garrett Atkins
JN Joe Nathan
MM Mark Mulder
TH Travis Hafner

1989 Upper Deck

This attractive 800-card standard-size set was introduced in 1989 as the premier issue by the then-fledgling Upper Deck company. Unlike other 1989 major releases, this set was issued in two separate series - a low series numbered 1-700 and a high series numbered 701-800. Cards were primarily issued in fin-wrapped low and high series foil packs, complete 800-card factory sets and 100-card high series factory sets. High series packs contained a mixture of both low and high series cards. Collectors should also note that many dealers

consider that Upper Deck's "planned" production of 1,000,000 of each player was increased (perhaps even doubled) later in the year due to the explosion in popularity of the product. The cards feature slick paper stock, full color on both the front and the back and carry a hologram on the reverse to protect against counterfeiting. Subsets include Rookie Stars (1-26) and Collector's Choice art cards (668-693). The more significant variations involving changed photos or changed type are listed below. According to the company, the Murphy and Sheridan cards were corrected very early, after only two percent of the cards had been produced. Similarly, the Sheffield was corrected after 15 percent had been printed; Varsho, Gallego, and Schroeder were corrected after 20 percent; and Holton, Manrique, and Winningham were corrected 30 percent of the way through. Rookie Cards in the set include Jim Abbott, Sandy Alomar Jr., Dante Bichette, Craig Biggio, Steve Finley, Ken Griffey Jr., Randy Johnson, Gary Sheffield, John Smoltz and Todd Zeile. Cards with missing or duplicate holograms appear to be relatively common and are generally considered to be flawed copies that sell for substantial discounts.

COMPLETE SET (800) 30.00 60.00
COMP.FACT.SET (800) 40.00 80.00
COMP.HI FACT.SET (100) 4.00 10.00
1 Ken Griffey Jr. RC 15.00 40.00
2 Luis Medina RC .08 .25
3 Tony Chance RC .08 .25
4 Dave Otto .08 .25
5 S.Alomar Jr. RC UER .40 1.00
Born 6/16/66,
should be 6/18/66
6 Rolando Roomes RC .08 .25
7 Dave West RC .08 .25
8 Cris Carpenter RC .08 .25
9 Gregg Jefferies .08 .25
10 Doug Dascenzo RC .08 .25
11 Ron Jones RC .08 .25
12 Luis DeLosSantos RC .08 .25
13 Gary Sheffield COR RC 2.00 5.00
13A G.Sheffield ERR 2.00 5.00
SS upside down
on card front
14 Mike Harkey RC .08 .25
15 Lance Blankenship RC .08 .25
16 William Brennan RC .08 .25
17 John Smoltz RC 2.00 5.00
18 Ramon Martinez RC .20 .50
19 Mark Lemke RC .40 1.00
20 Juan Bell RC .08 .25
21 Rey Palacios RC .08 .25
22 Felix Jose RC .08 .25
23 Van Snider RC .08 .25
24 Dante Bichette RC .40 1.00
25 Randy Johnson RC 3.00 8.00
26 Carlos Quintana RC .08 .25
27 Star Rookie CL .08 .25
28 Mike Schooler .08 .25
29 Randy St.Claire .08 .25
30 Jerald Clark RC .08 .25
31 Kevin Gross .08 .25
32 Dan Firova .08 .25
33 Jeff Calhoun .08 .25
34 Tommy Hinzo .08 .25
35 Ricky Jordan RC .20 .50
36 Larry Parrish .08 .25
37 Bret Saberhagen UER .15 .40
Hit total 931,
should be 1031
38 Mike Smithson .08 .25
39 Dave Dravecky .08 .25
40 Ed Romero .08 .25
41 Jeff Musselman .08 .25
42 Ed Hearn .08 .25
43 Rance Mulliniks .08 .25
44 Jim Eisenreich .08 .25
45 Sil Campusano .08 .25
46 Mike Krukow .08 .25
47 Paul Gibson .08 .25
48 Mike LaCoss .08 .25
49 Larry Herndon .08 .25
50 Scott Garrelts .08 .25
51 Dwayne Henry .08 .25
52 Jim Acker .08 .25
53 Steve Sax .08 .25
54 Pete O'Brien .08 .25
55 Paul Runge .08 .25
56 Rick Rhoden .08 .25
57 John Dopson .08 .25
58 Casey Candaele UER .08 .25
(No stats for Astros
for '88 season)
59 Dave Righetti .15 .40
60 Joe Hesketh .08 .25
61 Frank DiPino .08 .25
62 Tim Laudner .08 .25
63 Jamie Moyer .15 .40
64 Fred Toliver .08 .25
65 Mitch Webster .08 .25
66 John Tudor .15 .40
67 John Cangelosi .08 .25
68 Mike Devereaux .08 .25
69 Brian Fisher .08 .25
70 Mike Marshall .08 .25
71 Zane Smith .08 .25
72A Brian Holton ERR .40 1.00
(Photo actually
Shawn Hillegas)
72B Brian Holton COR .15 .40
73 Jose Guzman .08 .25
74 Rick Mahler .08 .25
75 John Shelby .08 .25
76 Jim Deshaies .08 .25
77 Bobby Meacham .08 .25
78 Bryn Smith .08 .25

79 Joaquin Andujar .15 .40
80 Richard Dotson .08 .25
81 Charlie Lea .08 .25
82 Calvin Schiraldi .08 .25
83 Les Straker .08 .25
84 Les Lancaster .08 .25
85 Allan Anderson .08 .25
86 Junior Ortiz .08 .25
87 Jesse Orosco .08 .25
88 Felix Fermin .08 .25
89 Dave Anderson .08 .25
90 Rafael Belliard UER .08 .25
(Born '61, not '51)
91 Franklin Stubbs .08 .25
92 Cecil Espy .08 .25
93 Albert Hall .08 .25
94 Tim Leary .08 .25
95 Mitch Williams .08 .25
96 Tracy Jones .08 .25
97 Danny Darwin .08 .25
98 Gary Ward .08 .25
99 Neal Heaton .08 .25
100 Jim Pankovits .08 .25
101 Bill Doran .08 .25
102 Tim Wallach .08 .25
103 Joe Magrane .08 .25
104 Ozzie Virgil .08 .25
105 Alvin Davis .08 .25
106 Tom Brookens .08 .25
107 Shawon Dunston .08 .25
108 Tracy Woodson .08 .25
109 Nelson Liriano .08 .25
110 Devon White UER .15 .40
(Doubles total 46,
should be 56)
111 Steve Balboni .08 .25
112 Buddy Bell .15 .40
113 German Jimenez .08 .25
114 Ken Dayley .08 .25
115 Andres Galarraga .15 .40
116 Mike Scioscia .15 .40
117 Gary Pettis .08 .25
118 Ernie Whitt .08 .25
119 Bob Boone .15 .40
120 Ryne Sandberg .60 1.50
121 Bruce Benedict .08 .25
122 Hubie Brooks .08 .25
123 Mike Moore .08 .25
124 Wallace Johnson .08 .25
125 Bob Horner .15 .40
126 Chili Davis .15 .40
127 Manny Trillo .08 .25
128 Chet Lemon .15 .40
129 John Cerutti .08 .25
130 Orel Hershiser .15 .40
131 Terry Pendleton .15 .40
132 Jeff Blauser .08 .25
133 Mike Fitzgerald .08 .25
134 Henry Cotto .08 .25
135 Gerald Young .08 .25
136 Luis Salazar .08 .25
137 Alejandro Pena .08 .25
138 Jack Howell .08 .25
139 Tony Fernandez .08 .25
140 Mark Grace .40 1.00
141 Ken Caminiti .25 .60
142 Mike Jackson .08 .25
143 Larry McWilliams .08 .25
144 Andres Thomas .08 .25
145 Nolan Ryan 3X 1.50 4.00
146 Mike Davis .08 .25
147 DeWayne Buice .08 .25
148 Jody Davis .08 .25
149 Jesse Barfield .15 .40
150 Matt Nokes .08 .25
151 Jerry Reuss .08 .25
152 Rick Cerone .08 .25
153 Storm Davis .08 .25
154 Marvell Wynne .08 .25
155 Will Clark .25 .60
156 Luis Aguayo .08 .25
157 Willie Upshaw .08 .25
158 Randy Bush .08 .25
159 Ron Darling .15 .40
160 Kal Daniels .08 .25
161 Spike Owen .08 .25
162 Luis Polonia .08 .25
163 Kevin Mitchell UER .15 .40
('88/total HR's 18/52,
should be 19/53)
164 Dave Gallagher .08 .25
165 Benito Santiago .15 .40
166 Greg Gagne .08 .25
167 Ken Phelps .08 .25
168 Sid Fernandez .08 .25
169 Bo Diaz .08 .25
170 Cory Snyder .08 .25
171 Eric Show .08 .25
172 Robby Thompson .08 .25
173 Marty Barrett .08 .25
174 Dave Henderson .08 .25
175 Ozzie Guillen .15 .40
176 Barry Lyons .08 .25
177 Kelvin Torve .08 .25
178 Don Slaught .08 .25
179 Steve Lombardozzi .08 .25
180 Chris Sabo RC .40 1.00
181 Jose Uribe .08 .25
182 Shane Mack .08 .25
183 Ron Karkovice .08 .25
184 Todd Benzinger .08 .25
185 Dave Stewart .15 .40
186 Julio Franco .15 .40
187 Ron Robinson .08 .25
188 Wally Backman .08 .25
189 Randy Velarde .08 .25
190 Joe Carter .15 .40
191 Bob Welch .15 .40
192 Kelly Paris .08 .25
193 Chris Brown .08 .25
194 Rick Reuschel .15 .40
195 Roger Clemens .75 2.00
196 Dave Concepcion .15 .40
197 Al Newman .08 .25
198 Brook Jacoby .08 .25
199 Mookie Wilson .15 .40
200 Don Mattingly 1.00 2.50
201 Dick Schofield .08 .25
202 Mark Gubicza .08 .25
203 Gary Gaetti .15 .40
204 Dan Pasqua .08 .25
205 Andre Dawson .15 .40
206 Chris Speier .08 .25
207 Kent Tekulve .08 .25
208 Rod Scurry .08 .25
209 Scott Bailes .08 .25
210 R.Henderson UER .40 1.00
Throws Right
211 Harold Baines .15 .40
212 Tony Armas .15 .40
213 Kent Hrbek .15 .40
214 Darrin Jackson .08 .25
215 George Brett 1.00 2.50
216 Rafael Santana .08 .25
217 Andy Allanson .08 .25
218 Brett Butler .15 .40
219 Steve Jeltz .08 .25
220 Jay Buhner .15 .40
221 Bo Jackson .40 1.00
222 Angel Salazar .08 .25
223 Kirk McCaskill .08 .25
224 Steve Lyons .08 .25
225 Bert Blyleven .15 .40
226 Scott Bradley .08 .25
227 Bob Melvin .08 .25
228 Ron Kittle .08 .25
229 Phil Bradley .08 .25
230 Tommy John .15 .40
231 Greg Walker .08 .25
232 Juan Berenguer .08 .25
233 Pat Tabler .08 .25
234 Terry Clark .08 .25
235 Rafael Palmeiro .40 1.00
236 Paul Zuvella .08 .25
237 Willie Randolph .15 .40
238 Bruce Fields .08 .25
239 Mike Aldrete .08 .25
240 Lance Parrish .15 .40
241 Greg Maddux 1.00 2.50
242 John Moses .08 .25
243 Melido Perez .08 .25
244 Willie Wilson .15 .40
245 Mark McLemore .08 .25
246 Von Hayes .08 .25
247 Matt Williams .40 1.00
248 John Candelaria UER .08 .25
Listed as Yankee for
part of '87,
should be Mets
249 Harold Reynolds .15 .40
250 Greg Swindell .08 .25
251 Juan Agosto .08 .25
252 Mike Felder .08 .25
253 Vince Coleman .08 .25
254 Larry Sheets .08 .25
255 George Bell .15 .40
256 Terry Steinbach .15 .40
257 Jack Armstrong RC .20 .50
258 Dickie Thon .08 .25
259 Ray Knight .15 .40
260 Darryl Strawberry .15 .40
261 Doug Sisk .08 .25
262 Alex Trevino .08 .25
263 Jeffrey Leonard .08 .25
264 Tom Henke .08 .25
265 Ozzie Smith .60 1.50
266 Dave Bergman .08 .25
267 Tony Phillips .08 .25
268 Mark Davis .08 .25
269 Kevin Elster .08 .25
270 Barry Larkin .25 .60
271 Manny Lee .08 .25
272 Tom Brunansky .08 .25
273 Craig Biggio RC 2.50 6.00
274 Jim Gantner .08 .25
275 Eddie Murray .40 1.00
276 Jeff Reed .08 .25
277 Tim Teufel .08 .25
278 Rick Honeycutt .08 .25
279 Guillermo Hernandez .08 .25
280 John Kruk .15 .40
281 Luis Alicea RC .20 .50
282 Jim Clancy .08 .25
283 Billy Ripken .08 .25
284 Craig Reynolds .08 .25
285 Robin Yount .60 1.50
286 Jimmy Jones .08 .25
287 Ron Oester .08 .25
288 Terry Leach .08 .25
289 Dennis Eckersley .25 .60
290 Alan Trammell .15 .40
291 Jimmy Key .15 .40
292 Chris Bosio .08 .25
293 Jose DeLeon .08 .25
294 Jim Traber .08 .25
295 Mike Scott .15 .40
296 Roger McDowell .08 .25
297 Garry Templeton .15 .40
298 Doyle Alexander .08 .25
299 Nick Esasky .08 .25
300 Mark McGwire UER 2.00 5.00
(Doubles total 52,
should be 51)
301 Darryl Hamilton RC .20 .50
302 Dave Smith .08 .25
303 Rick Sutcliffe .15 .40
304 Dave Stapleton .08 .25
305 Alan Ashby .08 .25
306 Pedro Guerrero .15 .40
307 Ron Guidry .15 .40
308 Steve Farr .08 .25
309 Curt Ford .08 .25
310 Claudell Washington .08 .25
311 Tom Prince .08 .25
312 Chad Kreuter RC .20 .50
313 Ken Oberkfell .08 .25
314 Jerry Browne .08 .25
315 R.J. Reynolds .08 .25
316 Scott Bankhead .08 .25
317 Milt Thompson .08 .25
318 Mario Diaz .08 .25
319 Bruce Ruffin .08 .25
320 Dave Valle .08 .25
321A Gary Varsho ERR .75 2.00
(Back photo actually
Mike Bielecki bunting)
321B Gary Varsho COR .08 .25
(In road uniform)
322 Paul Mirabella .08 .25
323 Chuck Jackson .08 .25
324 Drew Hall .08 .25
325 Don August .08 .25
326 Israel Sanchez .08 .25
327 Denny Walling .08 .25
328 Joel Skinner .08 .25
329 Danny Tartabull .08 .25
330 Tony Pena .08 .25
331 Jim Sundberg .15 .40
332 Jeff D. Robinson .08 .25
333 Oddibe McDowell .08 .25
334 Jose Lind .08 .25
335 Paul Kilgus .08 .25
336 Juan Samuel .08 .25
337 Mike Campbell .08 .25
338 Mike Maddux .08 .25
339 Darnell Coles .08 .25
340 Bob Dernier .08 .25
341 Rafael Ramirez .08 .25
342 Scott Sanderson .08 .25
343 B.J. Surhoff .15 .40
344 Billy Hatcher .08 .25
345 Pat Perry .08 .25
346 Jack Clark .15 .40
347 Gary Thurman .08 .25
348 Tim Jones .08 .25
349 Dave Winfield .15 .40
350 Frank White .15 .40
351 Dave Collins .08 .25
352 Jack Morris .15 .40
353 Eric Plunk .08 .25
354 Leon Durham .08 .25
355 Ivan DeJesus .08 .25
356 Brian Holman RC .08 .25
357A Dale Murphy ERR 15.00 40.00
(Front has
reverse negative)
357B Dale Murphy COR .25 .60
358 Mark Portugal .08 .25
359 Andy McGaffigan .08 .25
360 Tom Glavine .40 1.00
361 Keith Moreland .08 .25
362 Todd Stottlemyre .08 .25
363 Dave Leiper .08 .25
364 Cecil Fielder .15 .40
365 Carmelo Martinez .08 .25
366 Dwight Evans .25 .60
367 Kevin McReynolds .08 .25
368 Rich Gedman .08 .25
369 Len Dykstra .15 .40
370 Jody Reed .08 .25
371 Jose Canseco UER .40 1.00
(Strikeout total 391,
should be 491)
372 Rob Murphy .08 .25
373 Mike Henneman .08 .25
374 Walt Weiss .08 .25
375 Rob Dibble RC .40 1.00
376 Kirby Puckett .40 1.00
(Mark McGwire
in background)
377 Dennis Martinez .15 .40
378 Ron Gant .15 .40
379 Brian Harper .08 .25
380 Nelson Santovenia .08 .25
381 Lloyd Moseby .08 .25
382 Lance McCullers .08 .25
383 Dave Stieb .15 .40
384 Tony Gwynn .50 1.25
385 Mike Flanagan .08 .25
386 Bob Ojeda .08 .25
387 Bruce Hurst .08 .25
388 Dave Magadan .08 .25
389 Wade Boggs .25 .60
390 Gary Carter .15 .40
391 Frank Tanana .15 .40
392 Curt Young .08 .25
393 Jeff Treadway .08 .25
394 Darrell Evans .15 .40
395 Glenn Hubbard .08 .25
396 Chuck Cary .08 .25
397 Frank Viola .15 .40
398 Jeff Parrett .08 .25
399 Terry Blocker .08 .25
400 Dan Gladden .08 .25
401 Louie Meadows .08 .25
402 Tim Raines .15 .40
403 Joey Meyer .08 .25
404 Larry Andersen .08 .25
405 Rex Hudler .08 .25
406 Mike Schmidt .75 2.00
407 John Franco .15 .40
408 Brady Anderson RC .40 1.00
409 Don Carman .08 .25
410 Eric Davis .15 .40
411 Bob Stanley .08 .25
412 Pete Smith .08 .25
413 Jim Rice .15 .40
414 Bruce Sutter .15 .40
415 Oil Can Boyd .08 .25
416 Ruben Sierra .15 .40
417 Mike LaValliere .08 .25
418 Steve Buechele .08 .25
419 Gary Redus .08 .25
420 Scott Fletcher .08 .25
421 Dale Sveum .08 .25
422 Bob Knepper .08 .25
423 Luis Rivera .08 .25
424 Ted Higuera .08 .25
425 Kevin Bass .08 .25
426 Ken Gerhart .08 .25
427 Shane Rawley .08 .25
428 Paul O'Neill .25 .60
429 Joe Orsulak .08 .25
430 Jackie Gutierrez .08 .25
431 Gerald Perry .08 .25
432 Mike Greenwell .08 .25
433 Jerry Royster .08 .25
434 Ellis Burks .15 .40
435 Ed Olwine .08 .25
436 Dave Rucker .08 .25
437 Charlie Hough .15 .40
438 Bob Walk .08 .25
439 Bob Brower .08 .25
440 Barry Bonds 2.00 5.00
441 Tom Foley .08 .25
442 Rob Deer .08 .25
443 Glenn Davis .08 .25
444 Dave Martinez .08 .25
445 Bill Wegman .08 .25
446 Lloyd McClendon .08 .25
447 Dave Schmidt .08 .25
448 Darren Daulton .15 .40
449 Frank Williams .08 .25
450 Don Aase .08 .25
451 Lou Whitaker .15 .40
452 Rich Gossage .15 .40
453 Ed Whitson .08 .25
454 Jim Walewander .08 .25
455 Damon Berryhill .08 .25
456 Tim Burke .08 .25
457 Barry Jones .08 .25
458 Joel Youngblood .08 .25
459 Floyd Youmans .08 .25
460 Mark Salas .08 .25
461 Jeff Russell .08 .25
462 Darrell Miller .08 .25
463 Jeff Kunkel .08 .25
464 Sherman Corbett .08 .25
465 Curtis Wilkerson .08 .25
466 Bud Black .08 .25
467 Cal Ripken 1.25 3.00
468 John Farrell .08 .25
469 Terry Kennedy .08 .25
470 Tom Candiotti .08 .25
471 Roberto Alomar .40 1.00
472 Jeff M. Robinson .08 .25
473 Vance Law .08 .25
474 Randy Ready UER .08 .25
(Strikeout total 136,
should be 115)
475 Walt Terrell .08 .25
476 Kelly Downs .08 .25
477 Johnny Paredes .08 .25
478 Shawn Hillegas .08 .25
479 Bob Brenly .08 .25
480 Otis Nixon .08 .25
481 Johnny Ray .08 .25
482 Geno Petralli .08 .25
483 Stu Cliburn .08 .25
484 Pete Incaviglia .08 .25
485 Brian Downing .15 .40
486 Jeff Stone .08 .25
487 Carmen Castillo .08 .25
488 Tom Niedenfuer .08 .25
489 Jay Bell .15 .40
490 Rick Schu .08 .25
491 Jeff Pico .08 .25
492 Mark Parent .08 .25
493 Eric King .08 .25
494 Al Nipper .08 .25
495 Andy Hawkins .08 .25
496 Daryl Boston .08 .25
497 Ernie Riles .08 .25
498 Pascual Perez .08 .25
499 Bill Long UER .08 .25
(Games started total
70, should be 44)
500 Kirt Manwaring .08 .25
501 Chuck Crim .08 .25
502 Candy Maldonado .08 .25
503 Dennis Lamp .08 .25
504 Glenn Braggs .08 .25
505 Joe Price .08 .25
506 Ken Williams .08 .25
507 Bill Pecota .08 .25
508 Rey Quinones .08 .25
509 Jeff Bittiger .08 .25
510 Kevin Seitzer .08 .25
511 Steve Bedrosian .08 .25
512 Todd Worrell .08 .25
513 Chris James .08 .25
514 Jose Oquendo .08 .25
515 David Palmer .08 .25
516 John Smiley .08 .25
517 Dave Clark .08 .25
518 Mike Dunne .08 .25
519 Ron Washington .08 .25
520 Bob Kipper .08 .25
521 Lee Smith .15 .40
522 Juan Castillo .08 .25
523 Don Robinson .08 .25
524 Kevin Romine .08 .25
525 Paul Molitor .15 .40
526 Mark Langston .08 .25
527 Donnie Hill .08 .25
528 Larry Owen .08 .25
529 Jerry Reed .08 .25
530 Jack McDowell .15 .40
531 Greg Mathews .08 .25
532 John Russell .08 .25
533 Dan Quisenberry .08 .25
534 Greg Gross .08 .25
535 Danny Cox .08 .25
536 Terry Francona .15 .40
537 Andy Van Slyke .25 .60
538 Mel Hall .08 .25
539 Jim Gott .08 .25
540 Doug Jones .08 .25
541 Craig Lefferts .08 .25
542 Mike Boddicker .08 .25
543 Greg Brock .08 .25
544 Atlee Hammaker .08 .25
545 Tom Bolton .08 .25
546 Mike Macfarlane RC .20 .50
547 Rich Renteria .08 .25
548 John Davis .08 .25
549 Floyd Bannister .08 .25
550 Mickey Brantley .08 .25
551 Duane Ward .08 .25
552 Dan Petry .08 .25
553 Mickey Tettleton UER .08 .25
(Walks total 175,
should be 136)
554 Rick Leach .08 .25
555 Mike Witt .08 .25
556 Sid Bream .08 .25
557 Bobby Witt .08 .25
558 Tommy Herr .08 .25
559 Randy Milligan .08 .25
560 Jose Cecena .08 .25
561 Mackey Sasser .08 .25
562 Carney Lansford .15 .40
563 Rick Aguilera .08 .25
564 Ron Hassey .08 .25
565 Dwight Gooden .15 .40
566 Paul Assenmacher .08 .25
567 Neil Allen .08 .25
568 Jim Morrison .08 .25
569 Mike Pagliarulo .08 .25
570 Ted Simmons .15 .40
571 Mark Thurmond .08 .25
572 Fred McGriff .25 .60
573 Wally Joyner .15 .40
574 Jose Bautista RC .08 .25
575 Kelly Gruber .08 .25
576 Cecilio Guante .08 .25
577 Mark Davidson .08 .25
578 Bobby Bonilla UER .15 .40
(Total steals 2 in '87,
should be 3)
579 Mike Stanley .08 .25
580 Gene Larkin .08 .25
581 Stan Javier .08 .25
582 Howard Johnson .15 .40
583A Mike Gallego ERR .40 1.00
(Front reversed
negative)
583B Mike Gallego COR .40 1.00
584 David Cone .15 .40
585 Doug Jennings .08 .25
586 Charles Hudson .08 .25
587 Dion James .08 .25
588 Al Leiter .40 1.00
589 Charlie Puleo .08 .25
590 Roberto Kelly .08 .25
591 Thad Bosley .08 .25
592 Pete Stanicek .08 .25
593 Pat Borders RC .20 .50
594 Bryan Harvey RC .20 .50
595 Jeff Ballard .08 .25
596 Jeff Reardon .15 .40
597 Doug Drabek .08 .25
598 Edwin Correa .08 .25
599 Keith Atherton .08 .25
600 Dave LaPoint .08 .25
601 Don Baylor .15 .40
602 Tom Pagnozzi .08 .25
603 Tim Flannery .08 .25
604 Gene Walter .08 .25
605 Dave Parker .15 .40
606 Mike Diaz .08 .25
607 Chris Gwynn .08 .25
608 Odell Jones .08 .25
609 Carlton Fisk .25 .60
610 Jay Howell .08 .25
611 Tim Crews .08 .25
612 Keith Hernandez .15 .40
613 Willie Fraser .08 .25
614 Jim Eppard .08 .25
615 Jeff Hamilton .08 .25
616 Kurt Stillwell .08 .25
617 Tom Browning .08 .25
618 Jeff Montgomery .08 .25
619 Jose Rijo .15 .40
620 Jamie Quirk .08 .25
621 Willie McGee .15 .40
622 Mark Grant UER .08 .25
(Glove on wrong hand)
623 Bill Swift .08 .25
624 Orlando Mercado .08 .25
625 John Costello .08 .25
626 Jose Gonzalez .08 .25
627A Bill Schroeder ERR .25 .60
(Back photo actually
Ronn Reynolds buckling
shin guards)
627B Bill Schroeder COR .25 .60
628A Fred Manrique ERR .25 .60
(Back photo actually
Ozzie Guillen throwing)
628B Fred Manrique COR .08 .25
(Swinging bat on back)
629 Ricky Horton .08 .25
630 Dan Plesac .08 .25
631 Alfredo Griffin .08 .25
632 Chuck Finley .15 .40
633 Kirk Gibson .15 .40
634 Randy Myers .15 .40
635 Greg Minton .08 .25
636A Herm Winningham .40 1.00
ERR (W1nningham
on back)
636B H.Winningham COR .08 .25
637 Charlie Leibrandt .08 .25
638 Tim Birtsas .08 .25
639 Bill Buckner .15 .40
640 Danny Jackson .08 .25
641 Greg Booker .08 .25
642 Jim Presley .08 .25
643 Gene Nelson .08 .25
644 Rod Booker .08 .25
645 Dennis Rasmussen .08 .25
646 Juan Nieves .08 .25
647 Bobby Thigpen .08 .25
648 Tim Belcher .08 .25
649 Mike Young .08 .25
650 Ivan Calderon .08 .25
651 Oswald Peraza .08 .25
652A Pat Sheridan ERR 6.00 15.00
(No position on front)
652B Pat Sheridan COR .08 .25
653 Mike Morgan .08 .25
654 Mike Heath .08 .25
655 Jay Tibbs .08 .25
656 Fernando Valenzuela .15 .40
657 Lee Mazzilli .15 .40
658 Frank Viola AL CY .08 .25
659A J.Canseco AL MVP .25 .60
Eagle logo in black
659B J.Canseco AL MVP .25 .60
Eagle logo in blue
660 Walt Weiss AL ROY .08 .25
661 Orel Hershiser NL CY .08 .25
662 Kirk Gibson NL MVP .15 .40
663 Chris Sabo NL ROY .15 .40
664 Dennis Eckersley .15 .40
ALCS MVP
665 Orel Hershiser .15 .40
NLCS MVP
666 Kirk Gibson WS .40 1.00
667 O.Hershiser WS MVP .08 .25
668 Wally Joyner TC .08 .25
669 Nolan Ryan TC .50 1.25
670 Jose Canseco TC .25 .60
671 Fred McGriff TC .15 .40
672 Dale Murphy TC .15 .40
673 Paul Molitor TC .08 .25
674 Ozzie Smith TC .40 1.00
675 Ryne Sandberg TC .40 1.00
676 Kirk Gibson TC .15 .40
677 Andres Galarraga TC .08 .25
678 Will Clark TC .15 .40
679 Cory Snyder TC .08 .25
680 Alvin Davis TC .08 .25
681 Darryl Strawberry TC .08 .25
682 Cal Ripken TC .40 1.00
683 Tony Gwynn TC .25 .60
684 Mike Schmidt TC .40 1.00
685 A.Van Slyke TC UER .15 .40
96 Junior Ortiz
686 Ruben Sierra TC .08 .25
687 Wade Boggs TC .15 .40
688 Eric Davis TC .08 .25
689 George Brett TC .40 1.00
690 Alan Trammell TC .08 .25
691 Frank Viola TC .08 .25
692 Harold Baines TC .08 .25
693 Don Mattingly TC .40 1.00
694 Checklist 1-100 .08 .25
695 Checklist 101-200 .08 .25
696 Checklist 201-300 .08 .25
697 Checklist 301-400 .08 .25
698 CL 401-500 UER .08 .25
467 Cal Ripkin Jr.
699 CL 501-600 UER .08 .25
543 Greg Booker
700 Checklist 601-700 .08 .25
701 Checklist 701-800 .08 .25
702 Jesse Barfield .15 .40
703 Walt Terrell .08 .25
704 Dickie Thon .08 .25
705 Al Leiter .40 1.00
706 Dave LaPoint .08 .25
707 Charlie Hayes RC .20 .50
708 Andy Hawkins .08 .25
709 Mickey Hatcher .08 .25
710 Lance McCullers .08 .25
711 Ron Kittle .08 .25
712 Bert Blyleven .15 .40
713 Rick Dempsey .08 .25
714 Ken Williams .08 .25
715 Steve Rosenberg .08 .25
716 Joe Skalski .08 .25
717 Spike Owen .08 .25
718 Todd Burns .08 .25
719 Kevin Gross .08 .25
720 Tommy Herr .08 .25
721 Rob Ducey .08 .25
722 Gary Green .08 .25
723 Gregg Olson RC .20 .50
724 Greg W. Harris RC .08 .25
725 Craig Worthington .08 .25
726 Tom Howard RC .08 .25
727 Dale Mohorcic .08 .25
728 Rich Yett .08 .25
729 Mel Hall .08 .25
730 Floyd Youmans .08 .25
731 Lonnie Smith .08 .25
732 Wally Backman .08 .25
733 Trevor Wilson RC .08 .25
734 Jose Alvarez RC .08 .25
735 Bob Milacki .08 .25
736 Tom Gordon RC .60 1.50
737 Wally Whitehurst RC .08 .25
738 Mike Aldrete .08 .25
739 Keith Miller .08 .25
740 Randy Milligan .08 .25
741 Jeff Parrett .08 .25
742 Steve Finley RC .75 2.00
743 Junior Felix RC .08 .25
744 Pete Harnisch RC .20 .50
745 Bill Spiers RC .20 .50
746 Hensley Meulens RC .08 .25
747 Juan Bell RC .08 .25
748 Steve Sax .08 .25
749 Phil Bradley .08 .25
750 Rey Quinones .08 .25
751 Tommy Gregg .08 .25
752 Kevin Brown .40 1.00
753 Derek Lilliquist RC .08 .25
754 Todd Zeile RC .40 1.00
755 Jim Abbott RC .75 2.00
Triple exposure
756 Ozzie Canseco .08 .25
757 Nick Esasky .08 .25
758 Mike Moore .08 .25
759 Rob Murphy .08 .25
760 Rick Mahler .08 .25
761 Fred Lynn .15 .40
762 Kevin Blankenship .08 .25
763 Eddie Murray .40 1.00
764 Steve Searcy .08 .25
765 Jerome Walton RC .20 .50
766 Erik Hanson RC .20 .50
767 Bob Boone .15 .40
768 Edgar Martinez .40 1.00
769 Jose DeJesus .08 .25
770 Greg Briley .08 .25
771 Steve Peters .08 .25
772 Rafael Palmeiro .40 1.00
773 Jack Clark .15 .40
774 Nolan Ryan 1.50 4.00
(Throwing football)
775 Lance Parrish .15 .40
776 Joe Girardi RC .40 1.00
777 Willie Randolph .15 .40
778 Mitch Williams .08 .25
779 Dennis Cook RC .20 .50
780 Dwight Smith RC .20 .50
781 Lenny Harris RC .20 .50
782 Torey Lovullo RC .08 .25
783 Norm Charlton RC .20 .50
784 Chris Brown .08 .25
785 Todd Benzinger .08 .25
786 Shane Rawley .08 .25
787 Omar Vizquel RC 1.25 3.00
788 LaVel Freeman .08 .25
789 Jeffrey Leonard .08 .25
790 Eddie Williams .08 .25
791 Jamie Moyer .15 .40
792 Bruce Hurst UER .08 .25
(World Series)
793 Julio Franco .15 .40
794 Claudell Washington .08 .25
795 Jody Davis .08 .25
796 Oddibe McDowell .08 .25
797 Paul Kilgus .08 .25
798 Tracy Jones .08 .25
799 Steve Wilson .08 .25
800 Pete O'Brien .08 .25

1990 Upper Deck

The 1990 Upper Deck set contains 800 standard-size cards issued in two series, low numbers (1-700) and high numbers (701-800). Cards were distributed in fin-wrapped low and high series foil packs, complete 800-card factory sets and 100-card high series factory sets. High series foil packs contained a mixture of low and high series cards. The front and back borders are white, and both sides feature full-color photos. The horizontally oriented backs have recent stats and anti-counterfeiting holograms. Team checklist cards are mixed in with the first 100 cards of the set. Rookie Cards in the set include Juan Gonzalez, David Justice, Ray Lankford, Dean Palmer, Sammy Sosa and Larry Walker. The high series contains a Nolan Ryan variation; all cards produced before August 12th only discuss Ryan's sixth no-hitter while the later-issue cards include a stripe honoring Ryan's 300th victory. Card 702 (Rookie Threats) was originally scheduled to be Mike Witt. A few Witt cards with 702 on back and checklist cards showing Witt as 702 escaped into early packs; they are characterized by a black rectangle covering much of the card's back.

COMPLETE SET (800) 10.00 25.00
COMP.FACT.SET (800) 10.00 25.00
COMPLETE LO SET (700) 15.00 25.00
COMPLETE HI SET (100) 2.00 5.00
COMP.HI FACT.SET (100) 2.00 4.00
1 Star Rookie Checklist .02 .10
2 Randy Nosek RC .02 .10
3 Tom Drees UER RC .02 .10
(11th line, hulred,
should be hurled
4 Curt Young .02 .10
5 Devon White TC .02 .10
6 Luis Salazar .02 .10
7 Von Hayes TC .02 .10
8 Jose Bautista .02 .10
9 Marquis Grissom RC .20 .50
10 Orel Hershiser TC .02 .10
11 Rick Aguilera .07 .20
12 Benito Santiago TC .02 .10
13 Deion Sanders .20 .50
14 Marvell Wynne .02 .10
15 Dave West .02 .10
16 Bobby Bonilla TC .02 .10
17 Sammy Sosa RC 1.25 3.00
18 Steve Sax TC .02 .10
19 Jack Howell .02 .10
20 Mike Schmidt Special .40 1.00
UER (Suprising,
should be surprising)
21 Robin Ventura UER .20 .50
(Samta Maria)
22 Brian Meyer .02 .10
23 Blaine Beatty RC .02 .10
24 Ken Griffey Jr. TC .25 .60
25 Greg Vaughn UER .02 .10
(Association misspelled
as assication)
26 Xavier Hernandez RC .02 .10
27 Jason Grimsley RC .02 .10
28 Eric Anthony UER RC .02 .10
(Ashville, should
be Asheville)
29 Tim Raines TC UER .02 .10
(Wallach listed before Walker)
30 David Wells .07 .20
31 Hal Morris .02 .10
32 Bo Jackson TC .07 .20
33 Kelly Mann RC .02 .10
34 Nolan Ryan Special .40 1.00
35 Scott Service UER .02 .10
(Born Cincinatti on
7/27/67, should be
Cincinnati 2/27)
36 Mark McGwire TC .30 .75
37 Tino Martinez .40 1.00
38 Chili Davis .07 .20
39 Scott Sanderson .02 .10
40 Kevin Mitchell TC .02 .10
41 Lou Whitaker TC .02 .10
42 Scott Coolbaugh UER .02 .10
(Definately) RC
43 Jose Cano UER RC .02 .10
(Born 9/7/62, should
be 3/7/62)
44 Jose Vizcaino RC .08 .25
45 Bob Hamelin RC .08 .25
46 Jose Offerman UER RC .08 .25
(Posesses)
47 Kevin Blankenship .02 .10
48 Kirby Puckett TC .10 .30
49 Tommy Greene RC UER .02 .10
(Livest, should be
liveliest)
50 Will Clark Special .07 .20
UER (Perenial, should
be perennial)
51 Rob Nelson .02 .10
52 C.Hammond UER RC .02 .10
Chalanooga)
53 Joe Carter TC .02 .10
54A B.McDonald ERR 2.00 5.00
No Rookie designation
on card front
54B B.McDonald COR RC .08 .25
55 Andy Benes UER .07 .20
(Wichita)
56 John Olerud RC .30 .75
57 Roger Clemens TC .30 .75
58 Tony Armas .02 .10
59 George Canale RC .02 .10
60A Mickey Tettleton TC .75 2.00
ERR (683 Jamie Weston)

60B Mickey Tettleton TC .02 .10
COR (683 Mickey Weston)
61 Mike Stanton RC .08 .25
62 Dwight Gooden TC .02 .10
63 Kent Mercker RC UER .08 .25
(Albuquerque)
64 Francisco Cabrera .02 .10
65 Steve Avery UER .02 .10
(Born NJ, should be MI,
Merker should be Mercker
66 Jose Canseco .10 .30
67 Matt Merullo .02 .10
68 Vince Coleman TC UER .02 .10
(Guerrero)
69 Ron Karkovice .02 .10
70 Kevin Maas RC .08 .25
71 Dennis Cook UER .02 .10
(Shown with righty
glove on card back)
72 Juan Gonzalez UER RC .60 1.50
(135 games for Tulsa
in '89, should be 133)
73 Andre Dawson TC .02 .10
74 Dean Palmer UER RC .08 .25
(Permanent misspelled
as perminant)
75 Bo Jackson Special .07 .20
UER (Monsterous,
should be monstrous)
76 Rob Richie RC .02 .10
77 Bobby Rose UER .02 .10
(Pickin, should
be pick in)
78 Brian DuBois UER RC .02 .10
(Commiting)
79 Ozzie Guillen TC .02 .10
80 Gene Nelson .02 .10
81 Bob McClure .02 .10
82 Julio Franco TC .02 .10
83 Greg Minton .02 .10
84 John Smoltz TC UER .10 .30
(Oddibe not Odibbe)
85 Willie Fraser .02 .10
86 Neal Heaton .02 .10
87 Kevin Tapani UER RC .08 .25
(24th line has excpet,
should be except)
88 Mike Scott TC .02 .10
89A Jim Gott ERR .75 2.00
(Photo actually
Rick Reed)
89B Jim Gott COR .02 .10
90 Lance Johnson .02 .10
91 Robin Yount TC UER .20 .50
(Checklist on back has
178 Rob Deer and
176 Mike Felder)
92 Jeff Parrett .02 .10
93 Julio Machado UER RC .02 .10
(Valenzuelan, should
be Venezuelan)
94 Ron Jones .02 .10
95 George Bell TC .02 .10
96 Jerry Reuss .02 .10
97 Brian Fisher .02 .10
98 Kevin Ritz UER RC .02 .10
(Amercian)
99 Barry Larkin TC .07 .20
100 Checklist 1-100 .02 .10
101 Gerald Perry .02 .10
102 Kevin Appier .07 .20
103 Julio Franco .07 .20
104 Craig Biggio .20 .50
105 Bo Jackson UER .20 .50
('89 BA wrong,
should be .256)
106 Junior Felix .02 .10
107 Mike Harkey .02 .10
108 Fred McGriff .20 .50
109 Rick Sutcliffe .07 .20
110 Pete O'Brien .02 .10
111 Kelly Gruber .02 .10
112 Dwight Evans .10 .30
113 Pat Borders .02 .10
114 Dwight Gooden .07 .20
115 Kevin Batiste RC .02 .10
116 Eric Davis .07 .20
117 Kevin Mitchell UER .02 .10
(Career HR total 99,
should be 100)
118 Ron Oester .02 .10
119 Brett Butler .07 .20
120 Danny Jackson .02 .10
121 Tommy Gregg .02 .10
122 Ken Caminiti .07 .20
123 Kevin Brown .07 .20
124 George Brett UER .50 1.25
(133 runs, should
be 1300)
125 Mike Scott .02 .10
126 Cory Snyder .02 .10
127 George Bell .02 .10
128 Mark Grace .10 .30
129 Devon White .07 .20
130 Tony Fernandez .02 .10
131 Don Aase .02 .10
132 Rance Mulliniks .02 .10
133 Marty Barrett .02 .10
134 Nelson Liriano .02 .10
135 Mark Carreon .02 .10
136 Candy Maldonado .02 .10
137 Tim Birtsas .02 .10
138 Tom Brookens .02 .10
139 John Franco .07 .20
140 Mike LaCoss .02 .10
141 Jeff Treadway .02 .10
142 Pat Tabler .02 .10
143 Darrell Evans .07 .20
144 Rafael Ramirez .02 .10
145 O.McDowell UER .02 .10
Misspelled Odibbe
146 Brian Downing .02 .10
147 Curt Wilkerson .02 .10
148 Ernie Whitt .02 .10
149 Bill Schroeder .02 .10
150 Domingo Ramos UER .02 .10
(Says throws right,
but shows him
throwing lefty)
151 Rick Honeycutt .02 .10
152 Don Slaught .02 .10
153 Mitch Webster .02 .10
154 Tony Phillips .02 .10
155 Paul Kilgus .02 .10
156 Ken Griffey Jr. UER .60 1.50
(Simultaniously)
157 Gary Sheffield .20 .50
158 Wally Backman .02 .10
159 B.J. Surhoff .07 .20
160 Louie Meadows .02 .10
161 Paul O'Neill .10 .30
162 Jeff McKnight RC .02 .10
163 Alvaro Espinoza .02 .10
164 Scott Scudder .02 .10
165 Jeff Reed .02 .10
166 Gregg Jefferies .07 .20
167 Barry Larkin .10 .30
168 Gary Carter .07 .20
169 Robby Thompson .02 .10
170 Rolando Roomes .02 .10
171 Mark McGwire UER .60 1.50
(Total games 427 and
hits 479, should be
467 and 427)
172 Steve Sax .02 .10
173 Mark Williamson .02 .10
174 Mitch Williams .02 .10
175 Brian Holton .02 .10
176 Rob Deer .02 .10
177 Tim Raines .07 .20
178 Mike Felder .02 .10
179 Harold Reynolds .07 .20
180 Terry Francona .07 .20
181 Chris Sabo .02 .10
182 Darryl Strawberry .07 .20
183 Willie Randolph .07 .20
184 Bill Ripken .02 .10
185 Mackey Sasser .02 .10
186 Todd Benzinger .02 .10
187 Kevin Elster UER .02 .10
(16 homers in 1989,
should be 10)
188 Jose Uribe .02 .10
189 Tom Browning .02 .10
190 Keith Miller .02 .10
191 Don Mattingly .50 1.25
192 Dave Parker .07 .20
193 Roberto Kelly UER .02 .10
(96 RBI, should be 62)
194 Phil Bradley .02 .10
195 Ron Hassey .02 .10
196 Gerald Young .02 .10
197 Hubie Brooks .02 .10
198 Bill Doran .02 .10
199 Al Newman .02 .10
200 Checklist 101-200 .02 .10
201 Terry Puhl .02 .10
202 Frank DiPino .02 .10
203 Jim Clancy .02 .10
204 Bob Ojeda .02 .10
205 Alex Trevino .02 .10
206 Dave Henderson .02 .10
207 Henry Cotto .02 .10
208 Rafael Belliard UER .02 .10
(Born 1961, not 1951)
209 Stan Javier .02 .10
210 Jerry Reed .02 .10
211 Doug Dascenzo .02 .10
212 Andres Thomas .02 .10
213 Greg Maddux .30 .75
214 Mike Schooler .02 .10
215 Lonnie Smith .02 .10
216 Jose Rijo .02 .10
217 Greg Gagne .02 .10
218 Jim Gantner .02 .10
219 Allan Anderson .02 .10
220 Rick Mahler .02 .10
221 Jim Deshaies .02 .10
222 Keith Hernandez .07 .20
223 Vince Coleman .02 .10
224 David Cone .07 .20
225 Ozzie Smith .30 .75
226 Matt Nokes .02 .10
227 Barry Bonds .60 1.50
228 Felix Jose .02 .10
229 Dennis Powell .02 .10
230 Mike Gallego .02 .10
231 Shawon Dunston UER .02 .10
('89 stats are
Andre Dawson's)
232 Ron Gant .07 .20
233 Omar Vizquel .20 .50
234 Derek Lilliquist .02 .10
235 Erik Hanson .02 .10
236 Kirby Puckett UER .20 .50
(824 games, should
be 924)
237 Bill Spiers .02 .10
238 Dan Gladden .02 .10
239 Bryan Clutterbuck .02 .10
240 John Moses .02 .10
241 Ron Darling .02 .10
242 Joe Magrane .02 .10
243 Dave Magadan .02 .10
244 Pedro Guerrero UER .02 .10
(Misspelled Guerrero)
245 Glenn Davis .02 .10
246 Terry Steinbach .02 .10
247 Fred Lynn .02 .10
248 Gary Redus .02 .10
249 Ken Williams .02 .10
250 Sid Bream .02 .10
251 Bob Welch UER .02 .10
(2587 career strike-
outs, should be 1587)
252 Bill Buckner .02 .10
253 Carney Lansford .07 .20
254 Paul Molitor .07 .20
255 Jose DeJesus .02 .10
256 Orel Hershiser .07 .20
257 Tom Brunansky .02 .10
258 Mike Davis .02 .10
259 Jeff Ballard .02 .10
260 Scott Terry .02 .10
261 Sid Fernandez .02 .10
262 Mike Marshall .02 .10
263 Howard Johnson UER .02 .10
(192 SO, should be 592)
264 Kirk Gibson UER .07 .20
(659 runs, should
be 669)
265 Kevin McReynolds .02 .10
266 Cal Ripken .60 1.50
267 Ozzie Guillen UER .07 .20
(Career triples 27,
should be 29)
268 Jim Traber .02 .10
269 Bobby Thigpen UER .02 .10
(31 saves in 1989,
should be 34)
270 Joe Orsulak .02 .10
271 Bob Boone .07 .20
272 Dave Stewart UER .07 .20
(Totals wrong due to
omission of '86 stats)
273 Tim Wallach .02 .10
274 Luis Aquino UER .02 .10
(Says throws lefty,
but shows him
throwing righty)
275 Mike Moore .02 .10
276 Tony Pena .02 .10
277 Eddie Murray UER .20 .50
(Several typos in
career total stats)
278 Milt Thompson .02 .10
279 Alejandro Pena .02 .10
280 Ken Dayley .02 .10
281 Carmelo Castillo .02 .10
282 Tom Henke .02 .10
283 Mickey Hatcher .02 .10
284 Roy Smith .02 .10
285 Manny Lee .02 .10
286 Dan Pasqua .02 .10
287 Larry Sheets .02 .10
288 Garry Templeton .02 .10
289 Eddie Williams .02 .10
290 Brady Anderson UER .07 .20
(Home: Silver Springs,
not Siver Springs)
291 Spike Owen .02 .10
292 Storm Davis .02 .10
293 Chris Bosio .02 .10
294 Jim Eisenreich .02 .10
295 Don August .02 .10
296 Jeff Hamilton .02 .10
297 Mickey Tettleton .02 .10
298 Mike Scioscia .02 .10
299 Kevin Hickey .02 .10
300 Checklist 201-300 .02 .10
301 Shawn Abner .02 .10
302 Kevin Bass .02 .10
303 Bip Roberts .02 .10
304 Joe Girardi .10 .30
305 Danny Darwin .02 .10
306 Mike Heath .02 .10
307 Mike Macfarlane .02 .10
308 Ed Whitson .02 .10
309 Tracy Jones .02 .10
310 Scott Fletcher .02 .10
311 Darnell Coles .02 .10
312 Mike Brumley .02 .10
313 Bill Swift .02 .10
314 Charlie Hough .07 .20
315 Jim Presley .02 .10
316 Luis Polonia .02 .10
317 Mike Morgan .02 .10
318 Lee Guetterman .02 .10
319 Jose Oquendo .02 .10
320 Wayne Tolleson .02 .10
321 Jody Reed .02 .10
322 Damon Berryhill .02 .10
323 Roger Clemens .60 1.50
324 Ryne Sandberg .30 .75
325 Benito Santiago UER .07 .20
(Misspelled Santago
on card back)
326 Bret Saberhagen UER .07 .20
(1140 hits, should be
1240; 56 CG, should
be 52)
327 Lou Whitaker .07 .20
328 Dave Gallagher .02 .10
329 Mike Pagliarulo .02 .10
330 Doyle Alexander .02 .10
331 Jeffrey Leonard .02 .10
332 Torey Lovullo .02 .10
333 Pete Incaviglia .02 .10
334 Rickey Henderson .20 .50
335 Rafael Palmeiro .10 .30
336 Ken Hill .07 .20
337 Dave Winfield UER .07 .20
(1418 RBI, should
be 1438)
338 Alfredo Griffin .02 .10
339 Andy Hawkins .02 .10
340 Ted Power .02 .10
341 Steve Wilson .02 .10
342 Jack Clark UER .07 .20
(916 BB, should be
1006; 1142 SO,
should be 1130)
343 Ellis Burks .10 .30
344 Tony Gwynn UER .25 .60
(Doubles stats on
card back are wrong)
345 Jerome Walton UER .02 .10
(Total At Bats 476,
should be 475)
346 Roberto Alomar UER .10 .30
(61 doubles, should
be 51)
347 Carlos Martinez UER .02 .10
(Born 8/11/64, should
be 8/11/65)
348 Chet Lemon .02 .10
349 Willie Wilson .02 .10
350 Greg Walker .02 .10
351 Tom Bolton .02 .10
352 German Gonzalez .02 .10
353 Harold Baines .07 .20
354 Mike Greenwell .02 .10
355 Ruben Sierra .07 .20
356 Andres Galarraga .07 .20
357 Andre Dawson .07 .20
358 Jeff Brantley .02 .10
359 Mike Bielecki .02 .10
360 Ken Oberkfell .02 .10
361 Kurt Stillwell .02 .10
362 Brian Holman .02 .10
363 Kevin Seitzer UER .02 .10
(Career triples total
does not add up)
364 Alvin Davis .02 .10
365 Tom Gordon .07 .20
366 Bobby Bonilla UER .07 .20
(Two steals in 1987,
should be 3)
367 Carlton Fisk .10 .30
368 Steve Carter UER .02 .10
(Charlotesville)
369 Joel Skinner .02 .10
370 John Cangelosi .02 .10
371 Cecil Espy .02 .10
372 Gary Wayne .02 .10
373 Jim Rice .07 .20
374 Mike Dyer RC .02 .10
375 Joe Carter .07 .20
376 Dwight Smith .02 .10
377 John Wetteland .20 .50
378 Earnie Riles .02 .10
379 Otis Nixon .02 .10
380 Vance Law .02 .10
381 Dave Bergman .02 .10
382 Frank White .07 .20
383 Scott Bradley .02 .10
384 Israel Sanchez UER .02 .10
(Totals don't in-
clude '89 stats)
385 Gary Pettis .02 .10
386 Donn Pall .02 .10
387 John Smiley .02 .10
388 Tom Candiotti .02 .10
389 Junior Ortiz .02 .10
390 Steve Lyons .02 .10
391 Brian Harper .02 .10
392 Fred Manrique .02 .10
393 Lee Smith .07 .20
394 Jeff Kunkel .02 .10
395 Claudell Washington .02 .10
396 John Tudor .02 .10
397 Terry Kennedy UER .02 .10
(Career totals all
wrong)
398 Lloyd McClendon .02 .10
399 Craig Lefferts .02 .10
400 Checklist 301-400 .02 .10
401 Keith Moreland .02 .10
402 Rich Gedman .02 .10
403 Jeff D. Robinson .02 .10
404 Randy Ready .02 .10
405 Rick Cerone .02 .10
406 Jeff Blauser .02 .10
407 Larry Andersen .02 .10
408 Joe Boever .02 .10
409 Felix Fermin .02 .10
410 Glenn Wilson .02 .10
411 Rex Hudler .02 .10
412 Mark Grant .02 .10
413 Dennis Martinez .07 .20
414 Darrin Jackson .02 .10
415 Mike Aldrete .02 .10
416 Roger McDowell .02 .10
417 Jeff Reardon .07 .20
418 Darren Daulton .07 .20
419 Tim Laudner .02 .10
420 Don Carman .02 .10
421 Lloyd Moseby .02 .10
422 Doug Drabek .02 .10
423 Lenny Harris UER .02 .10
(Walks 2 in '89,
should be 20)
424 Jose Lind .02 .10
425 Dave Wayne Johnson RC .02 .10
426 Jerry Browne .02 .10
427 Eric Yelding RC .02 .10
428 Brad Komminsk .02 .10
429 Jody Davis .02 .10
430 Mariano Duncan .02 .10
431 Mark Davis .02 .10
432 Nelson Santovenia .02 .10
433 Bruce Hurst .02 .10
434 Jeff Huson RC .02 .10
435 Chris James .02 .10
436 Mark Guthrie RC .02 .10
437 Charlie Hayes .02 .10
438 Shane Rawley .02 .10
439 Dickie Thon .02 .10
440 Juan Berenguer .02 .10
441 Kevin Romine .02 .10
442 Bill Landrum .02 .10
443 Todd Frohwirth .02 .10
444 Craig Worthington .02 .10
445 Fernando Valenzuela .07 .20
446 Joey Belle .20 .50
447 Ed Whited UER RC .02 .10
(Ashville, should
be Asheville)
448 Dave Smith .02 .10
449 Dave Clark .02 .10
450 Juan Agosto .02 .10
451 Dave Valle .02 .10
452 Kent Hrbek .07 .20
453 Von Hayes .02 .10
454 Gary Gaetti .07 .20
455 Greg Briley .02 .10
456 Glenn Braggs .02 .10
457 Kirt Manwaring .02 .10
458 Mel Hall .02 .10
459 Brook Jacoby .02 .10
460 Pat Sheridan .02 .10
461 Rob Murphy .02 .10
462 Jimmy Key .07 .20
463 Nick Esasky .02 .10
464 Rob Ducey .02 .10
465 Carlos Quintana UER .02 .10
(Internatinoal)
466 Larry Walker RC .60 1.50
467 Todd Worrell .02 .10
468 Kevin Gross .02 .10
469 Terry Pendleton .07 .20
470 Dave Martinez .02 .10
471 Gene Larkin .02 .10
472 Len Dykstra UER .07 .20
('89 and total runs
understated by 10)
473 Barry Lyons .02 .10
474 Terry Mulholland .02 .10
475 Chip Hale RC .02 .10
476 Jesse Barfield .02 .10
477 Dan Plesac .02 .10
478A Scott Garrelts ERR .75 2.00
(Photo actually
Bill Bathe)
478B Scott Garrelts COR .02 .10
479 Dave Righetti .02 .10
480 Gus Polidor UER .02 .10
Wearing 14 on front,
but 10 on back
481 Mookie Wilson .07 .20
482 Luis Rivera .02 .10
483 Mike Flanagan .02 .10
484 Dennis Boyd .02 .10
485 John Cerutti .02 .10
486 John Costello .02 .10
487 Pascual Perez .02 .10
488 Tommy Herr .02 .10
489 Tom Foley .02 .10
490 Curt Ford .02 .10
491 Steve Lake .02 .10
492 Tim Teufel .02 .10
493 Randy Bush .02 .10
494 Mike Jackson .02 .10
495 Steve Jeltz .02 .10
496 Paul Gibson .02 .10
497 Steve Balboni .02 .10
498 Bud Black .02 .10
499 Dale Sveum .02 .10
500 Checklist 401-500 .02 .10
501 Tim Jones .02 .10
502 Mark Portugal .02 .10
503 Ivan Calderon .02 .10
504 Rick Rhoden .02 .10
505 Willie McGee .07 .20
506 Kirk McCaskill .02 .10
507 Dave LaPoint .02 .10
508 Jay Howell .02 .10
509 Johnny Ray .02 .10
510 Dave Anderson .02 .10
511 Chuck Crim .02 .10
512 Joe Hesketh .02 .10
513 Dennis Eckersley .07 .20
514 Greg Brock .02 .10
515 Tim Burke .02 .10
516 Frank Tanana .02 .10
517 Jay Bell .07 .20
518 Guillermo Hernandez .02 .10
519 Randy Kramer UER .02 .10
(Codiroli misspelled
as Codoroli)
520 Charles Hudson .02 .10
521 Jim Corsi .02 .10
Word 'originally' is
misspelled on back
522 Steve Rosenberg .02 .10
523 Cris Carpenter .02 .10
524 Matt Winters RC .02 .10
525 Melido Perez .02 .10
526 Chris Gwynn UER .02 .10
(Albeguerque)
527 Bert Blyleven UER .07 .20
(Games career total is
wrong, should be 644)
528 Chuck Cary .02 .10
529 Daryl Boston .02 .10
530 Dale Mohorcic .02 .10
531 Geronimo Berroa .02 .10
532 Edgar Martinez .10 .30
533 Dale Murphy .10 .30
534 Jay Buhner .07 .20
535 John Smoltz UER .20 .50
(HEA Stadium)
536 Andy Van Slyke .10 .30
537 Mike Henneman .02 .10
538 Miguel Garcia .02 .10
539 Frank Williams .02 .10
540 R.J. Reynolds .02 .10
541 Shawn Hillegas .02 .10
542 Walt Weiss .02 .10
543 Greg Hibbard RC .02 .10
544 Nolan Ryan .75 2.00
545 Todd Zeile .07 .20
546 Hensley Meulens .02 .10
547 Tim Belcher .02 .10
548 Mike Witt .02 .10
549 Greg Cadaret UER .02 .10
(Aquiring, should
be Acquiring)
550 Franklin Stubbs .02 .10
551 Tony Castillo .02 .10
552 Jeff M. Robinson .02 .10
553 Steve Olin RC .08 .25
554 Alan Trammell .07 .20
555 Wade Boggs 4X .10 .30
556 Will Clark .10 .30
557 Jeff King .02 .10
558 Mike Fitzgerald .02 .10
559 Ken Howell .02 .10
560 Bob Kipper .02 .10
561 Scott Bankhead .02 .10
562A Jeff Innis ERR .75 2.00
(Photo actually
David West)
562B Jeff Innis COR RC .02 .10
563 Randy Johnson .40 1.00
564 Wally Whitehurst .02 .10
565 Gene Harris .02 .10
566 Norm Charlton .02 .10
567 Robin Yount UER .30 .75
(7602 career hits,
should be 2606)
In addition, the career doubles are incorrect
568 Joe Oliver UER .02 .10
(Fl.orida)
569 Mark Parent .02 .10
570 John Farrell UER .02 .10
(Loss total added wrong)
571 Tom Glavine .10 .30
572 Rod Nichols .02 .10
573 Jack Morris .07 .20
574 Greg Swindell .02 .10
575 Steve Searcy .02 .10
576 Ricky Jordan .02 .10
577 Matt Williams .07 .20
578 Mike LaValliere .02 .10
579 Bryn Smith .02 .10
580 Bruce Ruffin .02 .10
581 Randy Myers .07 .20
582 Rick Wrona .02 .10
583 Juan Samuel .02 .10
584 Les Lancaster .02 .10
585 Jeff Musselman .02 .10
586 Rob Dibble .07 .20
587 Eric Show .02 .10
588 Jesse Orosco .02 .10
589 Herm Winningham .02 .10
590 Andy Allanson .02 .10
591 Dion James .02 .10
592 Carmelo Martinez .02 .10
593 Luis Quinones .02 .10
594 Dennis Rasmussen .02 .10
595 Rich Yett .02 .10
596 Bob Walk .02 .10
597A A.McGaffigan ERR .75 2.00
Photo actually
Rich Thompson
597B A.McGaffigan COR .02 .10
598 Billy Hatcher .02 .10
599 Bob Knepper .02 .10
600 CL 501-600 UER .02 .10
599 Bob Kneppers
601 Joey Cora .07 .20
602 Steve Finley .07 .20
603 Kal Daniels UER .02 .10
(12 hits in '87, should
be 123; 335 runs,
should be 235)
604 Gregg Olson .07 .20
605 Dave Stieb .07 .20
606 Kenny Rogers .07 .20
(Shown catching
football)
607 Zane Smith .02 .10
608 Bob Geren UER .02 .10
(Origionally)
609 Chad Kreuter .02 .10
610 Mike Smithson .02 .10
611 Jeff Wetherby RC .02 .10
612 Gary Mielke RC .02 .10
613 Pete Smith .02 .10
614 Jack Daugherty UER RC .02 .10
(Born 7/30/60, should
be 7/3/60)
615 Lance McCullers .02 .10
616 Don Robinson .02 .10
617 Jose Guzman .02 .10
618 Steve Bedrosian .02 .10
619 Jamie Moyer .07 .20
620 Atlee Hammaker .02 .10
621 Rick Luecken UER RC .02 .10
(Innings pitched wrong)
622 Greg W. Harris .02 .10
623 Pete Harnisch .02 .10
624 Jerald Clark .02 .10
625 Jack McDowell UER .02 .10
(Career totals for Games
and GS don't include
1987 season)
626 Frank Viola .02 .10
627 Teddy Higuera .02 .10
628 Marty Pevey RC .02 .10
629 Bill Wegman .02 .10
630 Eric Plunk .02 .10
631 Drew Hall .02 .10
632 Doug Jones .02 .10
633 Geno Petralli UER .02 .10
(Sacremento)
634 Jose Alvarez .02 .10
635 Bob Milacki .02 .10
636 Bobby Witt .02 .10
637 Trevor Wilson .02 .10
638 Jeff Russell UER .02 .10
(Shutout stats wrong)
639 Mike Krukow .02 .10
640 Rick Leach .02 .10
641 Dave Schmidt .02 .10
642 Terry Leach .02 .10
643 Calvin Schiraldi .02 .10
644 Bob Melvin .02 .10
645 Jim Abbott .10 .30
646 Jaime Navarro .02 .10
647 Mark Langston UER .02 .10
(Several errors in
stats totals)
648 Juan Nieves .02 .10
649 Damaso Garcia .02 .10
650 Charlie O'Brien .02 .10
651 Eric King .02 .10
652 Mike Boddicker .02 .10
653 Duane Ward .02 .10
654 Bob Stanley .02 .10
655 Sandy Alomar Jr. .07 .20
656 Danny Tartabull UER .02 .10
(395 BB, should be 295)
657 Randy McCament RC .02 .10
658 Charlie Leibrandt .02 .10
659 Dan Quisenberry .02 .10
660 Paul Assenmacher .02 .10
661 Walt Terrell .02 .10
662 Tim Leary .02 .10
663 Randy Milligan .02 .10
664 Bo Diaz .02 .10
665 Mark Lemke UER .02 .10
(Richmond misspelled
as Richomond)
666 Jose Gonzalez .02 .10
667 Chuck Finley UER .07 .20
(Born 11/16/62, should
be 11/26/62)
668 John Kruk .07 .20
669 Dick Schofield .02 .10
670 Tim Crews .02 .10
671 John Dopson .02 .10
672 John Orton RC .02 .10
673 Eric Hetzel .02 .10
674 Lance Parrish .02 .10
675 Ramon Martinez .02 .10
676 Mark Gubicza .02 .10
677 Greg Litton .02 .10
678 Greg Mathews .02 .10
679 Dave Dravecky .07 .20
680 Steve Farr .02 .10
681 Mike Devereaux .02 .10
682 Ken Griffey Sr. .07 .20
683A Mickey Weston ERR .75 2.00
(Listed as Jamie
on card)
683B Mickey Weston COR RC .02 .10
(Technically still an
error as birthdate is
listed as 3/26/81)
684 Jack Armstrong .02 .10
685 Steve Buechele .02 .10
686 Bryan Harvey .02 .10
687 Lance Blankenship .02 .10
688 Dante Bichette .07 .20
689 Todd Burns .02 .10
690 Dan Petry .02 .10
691 Kent Anderson .02 .10
692 Todd Stottlemyre .07 .20
693 Wally Joyner UER .07 .20
(Several stats errors)
694 Mike Rochford .02 .10
695 Floyd Bannister .02 .10
696 Rick Reuschel .02 .10
697 Jose DeLeon .02 .10
698 Jeff Montgomery .07 .20
699 Kelly Downs .02 .10
700A Checklist 601-700 .75 2.00
(683 Jamie Weston)
700B Checklist 601-700 .02 .10
(683 Mickey Weston)
701 Jim Gott .02 .10
702 Delino DeShields .20 .50
Marquis Grissom
Larry Walker
702A Mike Witt
Black rectangle covers much of back
703 Alejandro Pena .02 .10
704 Willie Randolph .07 .20
705 Tim Leary .02 .10
706 Chuck McElroy RC .02 .10
707 Gerald Perry .02 .10
708 Tom Brunansky .02 .10
709 John Franco .07 .20
710 Mark Davis .02 .10
711 David Justice RC .30 .75
712 Storm Davis .02 .10
713 Scott Ruskin RC .02 .10
714 Glenn Braggs .02 .10
715 Kevin Bearse RC .02 .10
716 Jose Nunez .02 .10
717 Tim Layana RC .02 .10
718 Greg Myers .02 .10
719 Pete O'Brien .02 .10
720 John Candelaria .02 .10
721 Craig Grebeck RC .02 .10
722 Shawn Boskie RC .02 .10
723 Jim Leyritz RC .08 .25
724 Bill Sampen RC .02 .10
725 Scott Radinsky RC .02 .10
726 Todd Hundley RC .08 .25
727 Scott Hemond RC .02 .10
728 Lenny Webster RC .02 .10
729 Jeff Reardon .07 .20
730 Mitch Webster .02 .10
731 Brian Bohanon RC .02 .10
732 Rick Parker RC .02 .10
733 Terry Shumpert RC .02 .10
734A Nolan Ryan 1.25 3.00
6th No-Hitter
(No stripe on front)
734B Nolan Ryan .40 1.00
6th No-Hitter
(stripe added on card
front for 300th win)
735 John Burkett .02 .10
736 Derrick May RC .02 .10
737 Carlos Baerga RC .08 .25
738 Greg Smith RC .02 .10
739 Scott Sanderson .02 .10
740 Joe Kraemer RC .02 .10
741 Hector Villanueva RC .02 .10
742 Mike Fetters RC .08 .25
743 Mark Gardner RC .02 .10
744 Matt Nokes .02 .10
745 Dave Winfield .07 .20
746 Delino DeShields RC .08 .25
747 Dann Howitt RC .02 .10
748 Tony Pena .02 .10
749 Oil Can Boyd .02 .10
750 Mike Benjamin RC .02 .10
751 Alex Cole RC .02 .10
752 Eric Gunderson RC .02 .10
753 Howard Farmer RC .02 .10
754 Joe Carter .07 .20
755 Ray Lankford RC .20 .50
756 Sandy Alomar Jr. .07 .20
757 Alex Sanchez .02 .10
758 Nick Esasky .02 .10
759 Stan Belinda RC .02 .10
760 Jim Presley .02 .10
761 Gary DiSarcina RC .08 .25
762 Wayne Edwards RC .02 .10
763 Pat Combs .02 .10
764 Mickey Pina RC .02 .10
765 Wilson Alvarez RC .08 .25
766 Dave Parker .07 .20
767 Mike Blowers RC .02 .10
768 Tony Phillips .02 .10
769 Pascual Perez .02 .10
770 Gary Pettis .02 .10
771 Fred Lynn .02 .10
772 Mel Rojas RC .02 .10
773 David Segui RC .20 .50
774 Gary Carter .07 .20
775 Rafael Valdez RC .02 .10
776 Glenallen Hill .02 .10
777 Keith Hernandez .07 .20
778 Billy Hatcher .02 .10
779 Marty Clary .02 .10
780 Candy Maldonado .02 .10
781 Mike Marshall .02 .10
782 Billy Joe Robidoux .02 .10
783 Mark Langston .02 .10
784 Paul Sorrento RC .08 .25
785 Dave Hollins RC .08 .25
786 Cecil Fielder .07 .20
787 Matt Young .02 .10
788 Jeff Huson .02 .10
789 Lloyd Moseby .02 .10
790 Ron Kittle .02 .10
791 Hubie Brooks .02 .10
792 Craig Lefferts .02 .10
793 Kevin Bass .02 .10
794 Bryn Smith .02 .10
795 Juan Samuel .02 .10
796 Sam Horn .02 .10
797 Randy Myers .07 .20
798 Chris James .02 .10
799 Bill Gullickson .02 .10
800 Checklist 701-800 .02 .10

1990 Upper Deck

1990 Upper Deck Jackson Heroes

This ten-card standard-size set was issued as an insert in 1990 Upper Deck High Number packs as part of the Upper Deck promotional giveaway of 2,500 officially signed and personally numbered Reggie Jackson cards. Signed cards ending with 00 have the words "Mr. October" added to the autograph. These cards cover Jackson's major league career. The complete set price refers only to the unautographed card set of ten. One-card packs of over-sized (3 1/2" by 5") versions of these cards were later inserted into retail blister repacks containing one foil pack each of 1993 Upper Deck Series I and II. These cards were later inserted into various forms of repackaging. The larger cards are also distinguishable by the Upper Deck Fifth Anniversary logo and "1993 Hall of Fame Inductee" logo on the front of the card. These over-sized cards were a limited edition of 10,000 numbered cards and have no extra value than the basic cards.

COMPLETE SET (10) 6.00 15.00
COMMON REGGIE (1-9) .60 1.50
RANDOM INSERTS IN HI SERIES
NNO Reggie Jackson 1.25 3.00
Header Card
AU1 Reggie Jackson AU 75.00 150.00
(Signed and Numbered out of 2500)

1991 Upper Deck

This set marked the third year Upper Deck issued a 800-card standard-size set in two separate series of 700 and 100 cards respectively. Cards were distributed in low and high series foil packs and factory sets. The 100-card extended or high-number series was issued by Upper Deck several months after the release of their first series. For the first time in Upper Deck's three-year history, they did not issue a factory Extended set. The basic cards are made on the typical Upper Deck slick, white card stock and features full-color photos on both the front and the back. Subsets include Star Rookies (1-26), Team Cards (28-34, 43-49, 77-82, 95-99) and Top Prospects (50-76). Several other special achievement cards are seeded throughout the set. The team checklist (TC) cards in the set feature an attractive Vernon Wells drawing of a featured player for that particular team. Rookie Cards in this set include Jeff Bagwell, Luis Gonzalez, Chipper Jones, Eric Karros, and Mike Mussina. A special Michael Jordan card (numbered SP1) was randomly included in packs on a somewhat limited basis. The Hank Aaron hologram card was randomly inserted in the 1991 Upper Deck high number foil packs. Neither card is included in the price of the regular issue set though both are listed at the end of our checklist.

COMPLETE SET (800) 6.00 15.00
COMP.FACT.SET (800) 8.00 20.00
COMPLETE LO SET (700) 6.00 15.00
COMPLETE HI SET (100) 2.00 5.00
1 Star Rookie Checklist .01 .05
2 Phil Plantier RC .02 .10
3 D.J. Dozier .01 .05
4 Dave Hansen .01 .05
5 Maurice Vaughn .02 .10
6 Leo Gomez .01 .05
7 Scott Aldred .01 .05
8 Scott Chiamparino .01 .05
9 Lance Dickson RC .02 .10
10 Sean Berry RC .02 .10
11 Bernie Williams .08 .25
12 Brian Barnes UER .02 .10
(Photo either not him or in wrong jersey)
13 Narciso Elvira RC .01 .05
14 Mike Gardiner RC .01 .05
15 Greg Colbrunn RC .08 .25
16 Bernard Gilkey .01 .05
17 Mark Lewis .01 .05
18 Mickey Morandini .01 .05
19 Charles Nagy .01 .05
20 Geronimo Pena .01 .05
21 Henry Rodriguez RC .08 .25
22 Scott Cooper .01 .05
23 Andujar Cedeno UER .01 .05
(Shown batting left, back says right)
24 Eric Karros RC .30 .75
25 Steve Decker UER RC .01 .05
Lewis-Clark State College, not Lewis and Clark)
26 Kevin Belcher RC .01 .05
27 Jeff Conine RC .20 .50
28 Dave Stewart TC .01 .05
29 Carlton Fisk TC .02 .10
30 Rafael Palmeiro TC .02 .10
31 Chuck Finley TC .01 .05
32 Harold Reynolds TC .01 .05
33 Bret Saberhagen TC .01 .05
34 Gary Gaetti TC .01 .05
35 Scott Leius .01 .05
36 Neal Heaton .01 .05
37 Terry Lee RC .01 .05
38 Gary Redus .01 .05
39 Barry Jones .01 .05
40 Chuck Knoblauch .02 .10
41 Larry Andersen .01 .05
42 Darryl Hamilton .01 .05
43 Mike Greenwell TC .01 .05
44 Kelly Gruber TC .01 .05
45 Jack Morris TC .01 .05
46 Sandy Alomar Jr. TC .01 .05
47 Gregg Olson TC .01 .05
48 Dave Parker TC .01 .05
49 Roberto Kelly TC .01 .05
50 Top Prospect Checklist .01 .05
51 Kyle Abbott .01 .05
52 Jeff Juden .01 .05
53 Todd Van Poppel UER RC .08 .25
Born Arlington and attended John Martin HS, should say Hinsdale and James Martin HS
54 Steve Karsay RC .08 .25
55 Chipper Jones RC 1.50 4.00
56 Chris Johnson UER RC .02 .10
(Called Tim on back)
57 John Ericks .01 .05
58 Gary Scott RC .01 .05
59 Kiki Jones .01 .05
60 Wil Cordero RC .02 .10
61 Royce Clayton .01 .05
62 Tim Costo RC .02 .10
63 Roger Salkeld .01 .05
64 Brook Fordyce RC .08 .25
65 Mike Mussina RC .75 2.00
66 Dave Staton RC .02 .10
67 Mike Lieberthal RC .20 .50
68 Kurt Miller RC .01 .05
69 Dan Peltier RC .02 .10
70 Greg Blosser .01 .05
71 Reggie Sanders RC .30 .75
72 Brent Mayne .01 .05
73 Rico Brogna .01 .05
74 Willie Banks .01 .05
75 Len Brutcher RC .01 .05
76 Pat Kelly RC .02 .10
77 Chris Sabo TC .01 .05
78 Ramon Martinez TC .01 .05
79 Matt Williams TC .01 .05
80 Roberto Alomar TC .02 .10
81 Glenn Davis TC .01 .05
82 Ron Gant TC .01 .05
83 Cecil Fielder FEAT .01 .05
84 Orlando Merced RC .02 .10
85 Domingo Ramos .01 .05
86 Tom Bolton .01 .05
87 Andres Santana .01 .05
88 John Dopson .01 .05
89 Kenny Williams .01 .05
90 Marty Barrett .01 .05
91 Tom Pagnozzi .01 .05
92 Carmelo Martinez .01 .05
93 Bobby Thigpen SAVE .01 .05
94 Barry Bonds TC .20 .50
95 Gregg Jefferies TC .01 .05
96 Tim Wallach TC .01 .05
97 Len Dykstra TC .01 .05
98 Pedro Guerrero TC .01 .05
99 Mark Grace TC .02 .10
100 Checklist 1-100 .01 .05
101 Kevin Elster .01 .05
102 Tom Brookens .01 .05
103 Mackey Sasser .01 .05
104 Felix Fermin .01 .05
105 Kevin McReynolds .01 .05
106 Dave Stieb .01 .05
107 Jeffrey Leonard .01 .05
108 Dave Henderson .01 .05
109 Sid Bream .01 .05
110 Henry Cotto .01 .05
111 Shawon Dunston .01 .05
112 Mariano Duncan .01 .05
113 Joe Girardi .01 .05
114 Billy Hatcher .01 .05
115 Greg Maddux .15 .40
116 Jerry Browne .01 .05
117 Juan Samuel .01 .05
118 Steve Olin .01 .05
119 Alfredo Griffin .01 .05
120 Mitch Webster .01 .05
121 Joel Skinner .01 .05
122 Frank Viola .02 .10
123 Cory Snyder .01 .05
124 Howard Johnson .01 .05
125 Carlos Baerga .01 .05
126 Tony Fernandez .01 .05
127 Dave Stewart .02 .10
128 Jay Buhner .02 .10
129 Mike LaValliere .01 .05
130 Scott Bradley .01 .05
131 Tony Phillips .01 .05
132 Ryne Sandberg .15 .40
133 Paul O'Neill .05 .15
134 Mark Grace .05 .15
135 Chris Sabo .01 .05
136 Ramon Martinez .01 .05
137 Brook Jacoby .01 .05
138 Candy Maldonado .01 .05
139 Mike Scioscia .01 .05
140 Chris James .01 .05
141 Craig Worthington .01 .05
142 Manny Lee .01 .05
143 Tim Raines .02 .10
144 Sandy Alomar Jr. .01 .05
145 John Olerud .02 .10
146 Ozzie Canseco .02 .10
(With Jose)
147 Pat Borders .01 .05
148 Harold Reynolds .02 .10
149 Tom Henke .01 .05
150 R.J. Reynolds .01 .05
151 Mike Gallego .01 .05
152 Bobby Bonilla .02 .10
153 Terry Steinbach .01 .05
154 Barry Bonds .40 1.00
155 Jose Canseco .05 .15
156 Gregg Jefferies .01 .05
157 Matt Williams .02 .10
158 Craig Biggio .05 .15
159 Daryl Boston .01 .05
160 Ricky Jordan .01 .05
161 Stan Belinda .01 .05
162 Ozzie Smith .15 .40
163 Tom Brunansky .01 .05
164 Todd Zeile .01 .05
165 Mike Greenwell .01 .05
166 Kal Daniels .01 .05
167 Kent Hrbek .02 .10
168 Franklin Stubbs .01 .05
169 Dick Schofield .01 .05
170 Junior Ortiz .01 .05
171 Hector Villanueva .01 .05
172 Dennis Eckersley .02 .10
173 Mitch Williams .01 .05
174 Mark McGwire .30 .75
175 F.Valenzuela 3X .02 .10
176 Gary Carter .02 .10
177 Dave Magadan .01 .05
178 Robby Thompson .01 .05
179 Bob Ojeda .01 .05
180 Ken Caminiti .02 .10
181 Don Slaught .01 .05
182 Luis Rivera .01 .05
183 Jay Bell .02 .10
184 Jody Reed .01 .05
185 Wally Backman .01 .05
186 Dave Martinez .01 .05
187 Luis Polonia .01 .05
188 Shane Mack .01 .05
189 Spike Owen .01 .05
190 Scott Bailes .01 .05
191 John Russell .01 .05
192 Walt Weiss .01 .05
193 Jose Oquendo .01 .05
194 Carney Lansford .02 .10
195 Jeff Huson .01 .05
196 Keith Miller .01 .05
197 Eric Yelding .01 .05
198 Ron Darling .01 .05
199 John Kruk .02 .10
200 Checklist 101-200 .01 .05
201 John Shelby .01 .05
202 Bob Geren .01 .05
203 Lance McCullers .01 .05
204 Alvaro Espinoza .01 .05
205 Mark Salas .01 .05
206 Mike Pagliarulo .01 .05
207 Jose Uribe .01 .05
208 Jim Deshaies .01 .05
209 Ron Karkovice .01 .05
210 Rafael Ramirez .01 .05
211 Donnie Hill .01 .05
212 Brian Harper .01 .05
213 Jack Howell .01 .05
214 Wes Gardner .01 .05
215 Tim Burke .01 .05
216 Doug Jones .01 .05
217 Hubie Brooks .01 .05
218 Tom Candiotti .01 .05
219 Gerald Perry .01 .05
220 Jose DeLeon .01 .05
221 Wally Whitehurst .01 .05
222 Alan Mills .01 .05
223 Alan Trammell .02 .10
224 Dwight Gooden .02 .10
225 Travis Fryman .02 .10
226 Joe Carter .02 .10
227 Julio Franco .02 .10
228 Craig Lefferts .01 .05
229 Gary Pettis .01 .05
230 Dennis Rasmussen .01 .05
231A Brian Downing ERR .01 .05
(No position on front)
231B Brian Downing COR .08 .25
(DH on front)
232 Carlos Quintana .01 .05
233 Gary Gaetti .02 .10
234 Mark Langston .01 .05
235 Tim Wallach .01 .05
236 Greg Swindell .01 .05
237 Eddie Murray .08 .25
238 Jeff Manto .01 .05
239 Lenny Harris .01 .05
240 Jesse Orosco .01 .05
241 Scott Lusader .01 .05
242 Sid Fernandez .01 .05
243 Jim Leyritz .01 .05
244 Cecil Fielder .02 .10
245 Darryl Strawberry .02 .10
246 Frank Thomas UER .08 .25
(Comiskey Park misspelled Comisky)
247 Kevin Mitchell .01 .05
248 Lance Johnson .01 .05
249 Rick Reuschel .01 .05
250 Mark Portugal .01 .05
251 Derek Lilliquist .01 .05
252 Brian Holman .01 .05
253 Rafael Valdez UER .01 .05
(Born 4/17/68, should be 12/17/67)
254 B.J. Surhoff .02 .10
255 Tony Gwynn .10 .30
256 Andy Van Slyke .05 .15
257 Todd Stottlemyre .01 .05
258 Jose Lind .01 .05
259 Greg Myers .01 .05
260 Jeff Ballard .01 .05
261 Bobby Thigpen .01 .05
262 Jimmy Kremers .01 .05
263 Robin Ventura .02 .10
264 John Smoltz .05 .15
265 Sammy Sosa .08 .25
266 Gary Sheffield .02 .10
267 Len Dykstra .02 .10
268 Bill Spiers .01 .05
269 Charlie Hayes .01 .05
270 Brett Butler .02 .10
271 Bip Roberts .01 .05
272 Rob Deer .01 .05
273 Fred Lynn .01 .05
274 Dave Parker .02 .10
275 Andy Benes .01 .05
276 Glenallen Hill .01 .05
277 Steve Howard .01 .05
278 Doug Drabek .01 .05
279 Joe Oliver .01 .05
280 Todd Benzinger .01 .05
281 Eric King .01 .05
282 Jim Presley .01 .05
283 Ken Patterson .01 .05
284 Jack Daugherty .01 .05
285 Ivan Calderon .01 .05
286 Edgar Diaz .01 .05
287 Kevin Bass .01 .05
288 Don Carman .01 .05
289 Greg Brock .01 .05
290 John Franco .02 .10
291 Joey Cora .01 .05
292 Bill Wegman .01 .05
293 Eric Show .01 .05
294 Scott Bankhead .01 .05
295 Garry Templeton .01 .05
296 Mickey Tettleton .01 .05
297 Luis Sojo .01 .05
298 Jose Rijo .01 .05
299 Dave Johnson .01 .05
300 Checklist 201-300 .01 .05
301 Mark Grant .01 .05
302 Pete Harnisch .01 .05
303 Greg Olson .01 .05
304 Anthony Telford RC .02 .10
305 Lonnie Smith .01 .05
306 Chris Hoiles .01 .05
307 Bryn Smith .01 .05
308 Mike Devereaux .01 .05
309A Milt Thompson ERR .08 .25
(Under yr information has print dot)
309B Milt Thompson COR .01 .05
(Under yr information says 86)
310 Bob Melvin .01 .05
311 Luis Salazar .01 .05
312 Ed Whitson .01 .05
313 Charlie Hough .02 .10
314 Dave Clark .01 .05
315 Eric Gunderson .01 .05
316 Dan Petry .01 .05
317 Dante Bichette UER .02 .10
(Assists misspelled as assissts)
318 Mike Heath .01 .05
319 Damon Berryhill .01 .05
320 Walt Terrell .01 .05
321 Scott Fletcher .01 .05
322 Dan Plesac .01 .05
323 Jack McDowell .01 .05
324 Paul Molitor .02 .10
325 Ozzie Guillen .02 .10
326 Gregg Olson .01 .05
327 Pedro Guerrero .02 .10
328 Bob Milacki .01 .05
329 John Tudor UER .01 .05
('90 Cardinals, should be '90 Dodgers)
330 Steve Finley UER .02 .10
(Born 3/12/65, should be 5/12)
331 Jack Clark .02 .10
332 Jerome Walton .01 .05
333 Andy Hawkins .01 .05
334 Derrick May .01 .05
335 Roberto Alomar .05 .15
336 Jack Morris .02 .10
337 Dave Winfield .02 .10
338 Steve Searcy .01 .05
339 Chili Davis .02 .10
340 Larry Sheets .01 .05
341 Ted Higuera .01 .05
342 David Segui .01 .05
343 Greg Cadaret .01 .05
344 Robin Yount .15 .40
345 Nolan Ryan .40 1.00
346 Ray Lankford .02 .10
347 Cal Ripken .30 .75
348 Lee Smith .02 .10
349 Brady Anderson .02 .10
350 Frank DiPino .01 .05
351 Hal Morris .01 .05
352 Deion Sanders .05 .15
353 Barry Larkin .05 .15
354 Don Mattingly .25 .60
355 Eric Davis .02 .10
356 Jose Offerman .01 .05
357 Mel Rojas .01 .05
358 Rudy Seanez .01 .05
359 Oil Can Boyd .01 .05
360 Nelson Liriano .01 .05
361 Ron Gant .02 .10
362 Howard Farmer .01 .05
363 David Justice .02 .10
364 Delino DeShields .02 .10
365 Steve Avery .01 .05
366 David Cone .02 .10
367 Lou Whitaker .02 .10
368 Von Hayes .01 .05
369 Frank Tanana .01 .05
370 Tim Teufel .01 .05
371 Randy Myers .01 .05
372 Roberto Kelly .01 .05
373 Jack Armstrong .01 .05
374 Kelly Gruber .01 .05
375 Kevin Maas .01 .05
376 Randy Johnson .10 .30
377 David West .01 .05
378 Brent Knackert .01 .05
379 Rick Honeycutt .01 .05
380 Kevin Gross .01 .05
381 Tom Foley .01 .05
382 Jeff Blauser .01 .05
383 Scott Ruskin .01 .05
384 Andres Thomas .01 .05
385 Dennis Martinez .02 .10
386 Mike Henneman .01 .05
387 Felix Jose .01 .05
388 Alejandro Pena .01 .05
389 Chet Lemon .01 .05
390 Craig Wilson RC .01 .05
391 Chuck Crim .01 .05
392 Mel Hall .01 .05
393 Mark Knudson .01 .05
394 Norm Charlton .01 .05
395 Mike Felder .01 .05
396 Tim Layana .01 .05
397 Steve Frey .01 .05
398 Bill Doran .01 .05
399 Dion James .01 .05
400 Checklist 301-400 .01 .05
401 Ron Hassey .01 .05
402 Don Robinson .01 .05
403 Gene Nelson .01 .05
404 Terry Kennedy .01 .05
405 Todd Burns .01 .05
406 Roger McDowell .01 .05
407 Bob Kipper .01 .05
408 Darren Daulton .02 .10
409 Chuck Cary .01 .05
410 Bruce Ruffin .01 .05
411 Juan Berenguer .01 .05
412 Gary Ward .01 .05
413 Al Newman .01 .05
414 Danny Jackson .01 .05
415 Greg Gagne .01 .05
416 Tom Herr .01 .05
417 Jeff Parrett .01 .05
418 Jeff Reardon .02 .10
419 Mark Lemke .01 .05
420 Charlie O'Brien .01 .05
421 Willie Randolph .02 .10
422 Steve Bedrosian .01 .05
423 Mike Moore .01 .05
424 Jeff Brantley .01 .05
425 Bob Welch .01 .05
426 Terry Mulholland .01 .05
427 Willie Blair .01 .05
428 Darrin Fletcher .01 .05
429 Mike Witt .01 .05
430 Joe Boever .01 .05
431 Tom Gordon .01 .05
432 Pedro Munoz RC .02 .10
433 Kevin Seitzer .01 .05
434 Kevin Tapani .01 .05
435 Bret Saberhagen .02 .10
436 Ellis Burks .02 .10
437 Chuck Finley .02 .10
438 Mike Boddicker .01 .05
439 Francisco Cabrera .01 .05
440 Todd Hundley .01 .05
441 Kelly Downs .01 .05
442 Dann Howitt .01 .05
443 Scott Garrelts .01 .05
444 Rickey Henderson 3X .08 .25
445 Will Clark .05 .15
446 Ben McDonald .01 .05
447 Dale Murphy .05 .15
448 Dave Righetti .02 .10
449 Dickie Thon .01 .05
450 Ted Power .01 .05
451 Scott Coolbaugh .01 .05
452 Dwight Smith .01 .05
453 Pete Incaviglia .01 .05
454 Andre Dawson .02 .10
455 Ruben Sierra .02 .10
456 Andres Galarraga .02 .10
457 Alvin Davis .01 .05
458 Tony Castillo .01 .05
459 Pete O'Brien .01 .05
460 Charlie Leibrandt .01 .05
461 Vince Coleman .01 .05
462 Steve Sax .01 .05
463 Omar Olivares RC .02 .10
464 Oscar Azocar .01 .05
465 Joe Magrane .01 .05
466 Karl Rhodes .01 .05
467 Benito Santiago .02 .10
468 Joe Klink .01 .05
469 Sil Campusano .01 .05
470 Mark Parent .01 .05
471 Shawn Boskie UER .01 .05
(Depleted misspelled as depleated)
472 Kevin Brown .02 .10
473 Rick Sutcliffe .02 .10
474 Rafael Palmeiro .05 .15
475 Mike Harkey .01 .05
476 Jaime Navarro .01 .05
477 Marquis Grissom UER .02 .10
(DeShields misspelled as DeSheilds)
478 Marty Clary .01 .05
479 Greg Briley .01 .05
480 Tom Glavine .05 .15
481 Lee Guetterman .01 .05
482 Rex Hudler .01 .05
483 Dave LaPoint .01 .05
484 Terry Pendleton .02 .10
485 Jesse Barfield .01 .05
486 Jose DeJesus .01 .05
487 Paul Abbott RC .02 .10
488 Ken Howell .01 .05
489 Greg W. Harris .01 .05
490 Roy Smith .01 .05
491 Paul Assenmacher .01 .05
492 Geno Petralli .01 .05
493 Steve Wilson .01 .05
494 Kevin Reimer .01 .05
495 Bill Long .01 .05
496 Mike Jackson .01 .05
497 Oddibe McDowell .01 .05
498 Bill Swift .01 .05
499 Jeff Treadway .01 .05
500 Checklist 401-500 .01 .05
501 Gene Larkin .01 .05
502 Bob Boone .02 .10
503 Allan Anderson .01 .05
504 Luis Aquino .01 .05
505 Mark Guthrie .01 .05
506 Joe Orsulak .01 .05
507 Dana Kiecker .01 .05
508 Dave Gallagher .01 .05
509 Greg A. Harris .01 .05
510 Mark Williamson .01 .05
511 Casey Candaele .01 .05
512 Mookie Wilson .02 .10
513 Dave Smith .01 .05
514 Chuck Carr .01 .05
515 Glenn Wilson .01 .05
516 Mike Fitzgerald .01 .05
517 Devon White .02 .10
518 Dave Hollins .01 .05
519 Mark Eichhorn .01 .05
520 Otis Nixon .01 .05
521 Terry Shumpert .01 .05
522 Scott Erickson .01 .05
523 Danny Tartabull .01 .05
524 Orel Hershiser .02 .10
525 George Brett .25 .60
526 Greg Vaughn .01 .05
527 Tim Naehring .01 .05
528 Curt Schilling .08 .25
529 Chris Bosio .01 .05
530 Sam Horn .01 .05
531 Mike Scott .01 .05
532 George Bell .01 .05
533 Eric Anthony .01 .05
534 Julio Valera .01 .05
535 Glenn Davis .01 .05
536 Larry Walker UER .08 .25
(Should have comma after Expos in text)
537 Pat Combs .01 .05
538 Chris Nabholz .01 .05
539 Kirk McCaskill .01 .05
540 Randy Ready .01 .05
541 Mark Gubicza .01 .05
542 Rick Aguilera .02 .10
543 Brian McRae RC .08 .25
544 Kirby Puckett .08 .25
545 Bo Jackson .08 .25
546 Wade Boggs .05 .15
547 Tim McIntosh .01 .05
548 Randy Milligan .01 .05
549 Dwight Evans .05 .15
550 Billy Ripken .01 .05
551 Erik Hanson .01 .05
552 Lance Parrish .02 .10
553 Tino Martinez .08 .25
554 Jim Abbott .05 .15
555 Ken Griffey Jr. UER .20 .50
(Second most votes for 1991 All-Star Game)
556 Milt Cuyler .01 .05
557 Mark Leonard RC .01 .05
558 Jay Howell .01 .05
559 Lloyd Moseby .01 .05
560 Chris Gwynn .01 .05
561 Mark Whiten .01 .05
562 Harold Baines .02 .10
563 Junior Felix .01 .05
564 Darren Lewis .01 .05
565 Fred McGriff .05 .15
566 Kevin Appier .02 .10
567 Luis Gonzalez RC .30 .75
568 Frank White .02 .10
569 Juan Agosto .01 .05
570 Mike Macfarlane .01 .05
571 Bert Blyleven .02 .10
572 Ken Griffey Sr. .08 .25
Ken Griffey Jr.
573 Lee Stevens .01 .05
574 Edgar Martinez .05 .15
575 Wally Joyner .02 .10
576 Tim Belcher .01 .05
577 John Burkett .01 .05
578 Mike Morgan .01 .05
579 Paul Gibson .01 .05
580 Jose Vizcaino .01 .05
581 Duane Ward .01 .05
582 Scott Sanderson .01 .05
583 David Wells .02 .10
584 Willie McGee .02 .10
585 John Cerutti .01 .05
586 Danny Darwin .01 .05
587 Kurt Stillwell .01 .05
588 Rich Gedman .01 .05
589 Mark Davis .01 .05
590 Bill Gullickson .01 .05
591 Matt Young .01 .05
592 Bryan Harvey .01 .05
593 Omar Vizquel .05 .15
594 Scott Lewis RC .02 .10
595 Dave Valle .01 .05
596 Tim Crews .01 .05
597 Mike Bielecki .01 .05
598 Mike Sharperson .01 .05
599 Dave Bergman .01 .05
600 Checklist 501-600 .01 .05
601 Steve Lyons .01 .05
602 Bruce Hurst .01 .05
603 Donn Pall .01 .05
604 Jim Vatcher RC .01 .05
605 Dan Pasqua .01 .05
606 Kenny Rogers .02 .10
607 Jeff Schulz RC .01 .05
608 Brad Arnsberg .01 .05
609 Willie Wilson .01 .05
610 Jamie Moyer .02 .10
611 Ron Oester .01 .05
612 Dennis Cook .01 .05
613 Rick Mahler .01 .05
614 Bill Landrum .01 .05
615 Scott Scudder .01 .05
616 Tom Edens RC .01 .05
617 1917 Revisited .02 .10
(White Sox vintage uniforms)
618 Jim Gantner .01 .05
619 Darrel Akerfelds .01 .05
620 Ron Robinson .01 .05
621 Scott Radinsky .01 .05
622 Pete Smith .01 .05
623 Melido Perez .01 .05
624 Jerald Clark .01 .05
625 Carlos Martinez .01 .05
626 Wes Chamberlain RC .08 .25
627 Bobby Witt .01 .05
628 Ken Dayley .01 .05
629 John Barfield .01 .05
630 Bob Tewksbury .01 .05
631 Glenn Braggs .01 .05
632 Jim Neidlinger RC .01 .05
633 Tom Browning .01 .05
634 Kirk Gibson .02 .10
635 Rob Dibble .02 .10
636 Rickey Henderson SB .08 .25
Lou Brock
May 1, 1991 on front
636A R.Henderson SB .08 .25
Lou Brock
no date on card
637 Jeff Montgomery .01 .05
638 Mike Schooler .01 .05
639 Storm Davis .01 .05
640 Rich Rodriguez RC .01 .05
641 Phil Bradley .01 .05
642 Kent Mercker .01 .05
643 Carlton Fisk .05 .15
644 Mike Bell RC .01 .05
645 Alex Fernandez .01 .05
646 Juan Gonzalez .08 .25
647 Ken Hill .01 .05
648 Jeff Russell .01 .05
649 Chuck Malone .01 .05
650 Steve Buechele .01 .05
651 Mike Benjamin .01 .05
652 Tony Pena .01 .05
653 Trevor Wilson .01 .05
654 Alex Cole .01 .05
655 Roger Clemens .30 .75
656 Mark McGwire BASH .15 .40
657 Joe Grahe RC .02 .10
658 Jim Eisenreich .01 .05
659 Dan Gladden .01 .05
660 Steve Farr .01 .05
661 Bill Sampen .01 .05
662 Dave Rohde .01 .05
663 Mark Gardner .01 .05
664 Mike Simms RC .01 .05
665 Moises Alou .02 .10
666 Mickey Hatcher .01 .05
667 Jimmy Key .02 .10
668 John Wetteland .02 .10
669 John Smiley .01 .05
670 Jim Acker .01 .05
671 Pascual Perez .01 .05
672 Reggie Harris UER .01 .05
(Opportunity misspelled as oppurtinity)
673 Matt Nokes .01 .05
674 Rafael Novoa RC .01 .05
675 Hensley Meulens .01 .05
676 Jeff M. Robinson .01 .05
677 Ground Breaking .02 .10
(New Comiskey Park; Carlton Fisk and Robin Ventura)
678 Johnny Ray .01 .05
679 Greg Hibbard .01 .05
680 Paul Sorrento .01 .05
681 Mike Marshall .01 .05
682 Jim Clancy .01 .05
683 Rob Murphy .01 .05
684 Dave Schmidt .01 .05
685 Jeff Gray RC .01 .05
686 Mike Hartley .01 .05
687 Jeff King .01 .05
688 Stan Javier .01 .05
689 Bob Walk .01 .05
690 Jim Gott .01 .05
691 Mike LaCoss .01 .05
692 John Farrell .01 .05
693 Tim Leary .01 .05
694 Mike Walker .01 .05
695 Eric Plunk .01 .05
696 Mike Fetters .01 .05
697 Wayne Edwards .01 .05
698 Tim Drummond .01 .05
699 Willie Fraser .01 .05
700 Checklist 601-700 .01 .05
701 Mike Heath .01 .05
702 Luis Gonzalez .40 1.00
Karl Rhodes
Jeff Bagwell
703 Jose Mesa .01 .05
704 Dave Smith .01 .05
705 Danny Darwin .01 .05
706 Rafael Belliard .01 .05
707 Rob Murphy .01 .05
708 Terry Pendleton .02 .10
709 Mike Pagliarulo .01 .05
710 Sid Bream .01 .05
711 Junior Felix .01 .05
712 Dante Bichette .02 .10
713 Kevin Gross .01 .05
714 Luis Sojo .01 .05
715 Bob Ojeda .01 .05
716 Julio Machado .01 .05
717 Steve Farr .01 .05
718 Franklin Stubbs .01 .05
719 Mike Boddicker .01 .05
720 Willie Randolph .02 .10
721 Willie McGee .02 .10
722 Chili Davis .02 .10
723 Danny Jackson .01 .05
724 Cory Snyder .01 .05
725 Andre Dawson .08 .25
George Bell
Ryne Sandberg
726 Rob Deer .01 .05
727 Rich DeLucia RC .01 .05
728 Mike Perez RC .02 .10
729 Mickey Tettleton .01 .05
730 Mike Blowers .01 .05
731 Gary Gaetti .02 .10
732 Brett Butler .02 .10
733 Dave Parker .02 .10
734 Eddie Zosky .01 .05
735 Jack Clark .02 .10
736 Jack Morris .02 .10
737 Kirk Gibson .02 .10
738 Steve Bedrosian .01 .05
739 Candy Maldonado .01 .05
740 Matt Young .01 .05
741 Rich Garces RC .02 .10
742 George Bell .01 .05
743 Deion Sanders .05 .15
744 Bo Jackson .08 .25
745 Luis Mercedes RC .02 .10
746 Reggie Jefferson UER .01 .05
(Throwing left on card; back has throws right)
747 Pete Incaviglia .01 .05
748 Chris Hammond .01 .05
749 Mike Stanton .01 .05
750 Scott Sanderson .01 .05
751 Paul Faries RC .01 .05
752 Al Osuna RC .01 .05
753 Steve Chitren RC .01 .05
754 Tony Fernandez .01 .05
755 Jeff Bagwell UER RC .60 1.50
(Strikeout and walk totals reversed)
756 Kirk Dressendorfer RC .02 .10
757 Glenn Davis .01 .05
758 Gary Carter .02 .10
759 Zane Smith .01 .05
760 Vance Law .01 .05
761 Denis Boucher RC .02 .10
762 Turner Ward RC .02 .10
763 Roberto Alomar .05 .15
764 Albert Belle .02 .10
765 Joe Carter .02 .10
766 Pete Schourek RC .02 .10
767 Heathcliff Slocumb RC .02 .10
768 Vince Coleman .01 .05
769 Mitch Williams .01 .05

Card	Low	High
770 Brian Downing	.01	.05
771 Dana Allison RC	.01	.05
772 Pete Harnisch	.01	.05
773 Tim Raines	.02	.10
774 Darryl Kile	.02	.10
775 Fred McGriff	.05	.15
776 Dwight Evans	.05	.15
777 Joe Slusarski RC	.01	.05
778 Dave Righetti	.02	.10
779 Jeff Hamilton	.01	.05
780 Ernest Riles	.01	.05
781 Ken Dayley	.01	.05
782 Eric King	.01	.05
783 Devon White	.02	.10
784 Beau Allred	.01	.05
785 Mike Timlin RC	.08	.25
786 Ivan Calderon	.01	.05
787 Hubie Brooks	.01	.05
788 Juan Agosto	.01	.05
789 Barry Jones	.01	.05
790 Wally Backman	.01	.05
791 Jim Presley	.01	.05
792 Charlie Hough	.02	.10
793 Larry Andersen	.01	.05
794 Steve Finley	.02	.10
795 Shawn Abner	.01	.05
796 Jeff M. Robinson	.01	.05
797 Joe Bitker RC	.01	.05
798 Eric Show	.01	.05
799 Bud Black	.01	.05
800 Checklist 701-800	.01	.05
HH1 H.Aaron Hologram	.60	1.50
SP1 Michael Jordan SP	3.00	8.00
(Shown batting in		
White Sox uniform)		
SP2 Rickey Henderson	.75	2.00
Nolan Ryan		
May 1, 1991 Records		

1991 Upper Deck Aaron Heroes

These standard-size cards were issued in honor of Hall of Famer Hank Aaron and inserted in Upper Deck high number wax packs. Aaron autographed 2,500 of card number 27, which featured his portrait by noted sports artist Vernon Wells. The cards are numbered on the back in continuation of the Baseball Heroes set.

Card	Low	High
COMPLETE SET (10)	2.00	5.00
COMMON AARON (19-27)	.20	.50
RANDOM INSERTS IN HI SERIES		
NNO Title/Header card SP	.40	1.00
AU3 Hank Aaron AU/2500	100.00	200.00

1991 Upper Deck Heroes of Baseball

These standard-size cards were randomly inserted in Upper Deck Baseball Heroes wax packs. The fourth card features a color portrait of the three players by noted sports artist Vernon Wells. Each of the features heroes also signed 3,000 of each card for inclusion in this product.

Card	Low	High
COMPLETE SET (4)	12.50	25.00
RANDOM INSERTS IN HEROES FOIL		
H1 Harmon Killebrew	3.00	8.00
H2 Gaylord Perry	2.00	5.00
H3 Ferguson Jenkins	2.00	5.00
H4 Harmon Killebrew ART	3.00	8.00
Ferguson Jenkins		
Gaylord Perry		
AU1 Harmon Killebrew AU/3000	20.00	50.00
AU2 Gaylord Perry AU/3000	6.00	15.00
AU3 Fergie Jenkins AU/3000	10.00	25.00

1991 Upper Deck Ryan Heroes

This nine-card standard-size set was included in first series 1991 Upper Deck packs. The set which honors Nolan Ryan and is numbered as a continuation of the Baseball Heroes set which began with Reggie Jackson in 1990. This set honors Ryan's long career and his place in Baseball History. Card number 18 features the artwork of Vernon Wells while the other cards are photos. The complete set price below does not include the signed Ryan card of which only 2500 were made. Signed cards ending with 00 have the expression "Strikeout King" added. These Ryan cards were apparently issued on 100-card sheets with the following configuration: ten each of the nine Ryan Baseball Heroes cards, five Michael Jordan cards and five Baseball Heroes header cards. The Baseball Heroes header card is a standard size card which explains the continuation of the Baseball Heroes series on the back while the front just says Baseball Heroes.

Card	Low	High
COMPLETE SET (10)	2.00	5.00
COMMON RYAN (10-18)	.20	.50
RANDOM INSERTS IN LO SERIES		
NNO Baseball Heroes SP	.40	1.00
(Header card)		
AU2 Nolan Ryan AU/2500	125.00	200.00

1991 Upper Deck Silver Sluggers

The Upper Deck Silver Slugger set features nine players from each league, representing the nine batting positions on the team. The cards were issued one per 1991 Upper Deck jumbo pack. The cards measure the standard size. The cards are numbered on the back with an "SS" prefix.

Card	Low	High
COMPLETE SET (18)	7.50	15.00
SS1 Julio Franco	.30	.75
SS2 Alan Trammell	.30	.75
SS3 Rickey Henderson	.75	2.00
SS4 Jose Canseco	.50	1.25
SS5 Barry Bonds	3.00	8.00
SS6 Eddie Murray	.75	2.00
SS7 Kelly Gruber	.15	.40
SS8 Ryne Sandberg	1.25	3.00
SS9 Darryl Strawberry	.30	.75
SS10 Ellis Burks	.30	.75
SS11 Lance Parrish	.30	.75
SS12 Cecil Fielder	.30	.75
SS13 Matt Williams	.30	.75
SS14 Dave Parker	.30	.75
SS15 Bobby Bonilla	.30	.75
SS16 Don Robinson	.15	.40
SS17 Benito Santiago	.30	.75
SS18 Barry Larkin	.50	1.25

1991 Upper Deck Final Edition

The 1991 Upper Deck Final Edition boxed set contains 100 standard-size cards and showcases players who made major contributions during their team's late-season pennant drive. In addition to the late season traded and impact rookie cards (22-78), the set includes two special subsets: Diamond Skills cards (1-21), depicting the best Minor League prospects, and All-Star cards (80-99). Six assorted team logo hologram cards were issued with each set. The cards are numbered on the back with an F suffix. Among the outstanding Rookie Cards in this set are Ryan Klesko, Kenny Lofton, Pedro Martinez, Ivan Rodriguez, Jim Thome, Rondell White, and Dmitri Young.

Card	Low	High
COMP.FACT.SET (100)	3.00	8.00
1F Ryan Klesko CL	.08	.25
Reggie Sanders		
2F Pedro Martinez RC	3.00	8.00
3F Lance Dickson	.01	.05
4F Royce Clayton	.01	.05
5F Scott Bryant	.01	.05
6F Dan Wilson RC	.08	.25
7F Dmitri Young RC	.30	.75
8F Ryan Klesko RC	.20	.50
9F Tom Goodwin	.01	.05
10F Rondell White RC	.20	.50
11F Reggie Sanders	.20	.50
12F Todd Van Poppel	.01	.05
13F Arthur Rhodes RC	.08	.25
14F Eddie Zosky	.01	.05
15F Gerald Williams RC	.08	.25
16F Robert Eenhoorn RC	.02	.10
17F Jim Thome RC	2.00	5.00
18F Marc Newfield RC	.02	.10
19F Kerwin Moore RC	.02	.10
20F Jeff McNeely RC	.02	.10
21F Frankie Rodriguez RC	.02	.10
22F Andy Mota RC	.01	.05
23F Chris Haney RC	.02	.10
24F Kenny Lofton RC	.30	.75
25F Dave Nilsson RC	.08	.25
26F Derek Bell	.02	.10
27F Frank Castillo RC	.08	.25
28F Candy Maldonado	.01	.05
29F Chuck McElroy	.01	.05
30F Chito Martinez RC	.01	.05
31F Steve Howe	.01	.05
32F Freddie Benavides RC	.01	.05
33F Scott Kamieniecki RC	.02	.10
34F Denny Neagle RC	.08	.25
35F Mike Humphreys RC	.02	.10
36F Mike Remlinger	.01	.05
37F Scott Coolbaugh	.01	.05
38F Darren Lewis	.01	.05
39F Thomas Howard	.01	.05
40F John Candelaria	.01	.05
41F Todd Benzinger	.01	.05
42F Wilson Alvarez	.01	.05
43F Patrick Lennon RC	.02	.10
44F Rusty Meacham RC	.02	.10
45F Ryan Bowen RC	.02	.10
46F Rick Wilkins RC	.02	.10
47F Ed Sprague	.01	.05
48F Bob Scanlan RC	.01	.05
49F Tom Candiotti	.01	.05
50F Dennis Martinez	.02	.10
(Perfecto)		
51F Oil Can Boyd	.01	.05
52F Glenallen Hill	.01	.05
53F Scott Livingstone RC	.02	.10
54F Brian R. Hunter RC	.08	.25
55F Ivan Rodriguez RC	.75	2.00
56F Keith Mitchell RC	.02	.10
57F Roger McDowell	.01	.05
58F Otis Nixon	.01	.05
59F Juan Bell	.01	.05
60F Bill Krueger	.01	.05
61F Chris Donnels RC	.01	.05
62F Tommy Greene	.01	.05
63F Doug Simons RC	.01	.05
64F Andy Ashby RC	.08	.25
65F Anthony Young RC	.02	.10
66F Kevin Morton RC	.01	.05
67F Bret Barberie RC	.02	.10
68F Scott Servais RC	.08	.25
69F Ron Darling	.01	.05
70F Tim Burke	.01	.05
71F Vicente Palacios	.01	.05
72F Gerald Alexander RC	.01	.05
73F Reggie Jefferson	.01	.05
74F Dean Palmer	.02	.10
75F Mark Whiten	.01	.05
76F Randy Tomlin RC	.02	.10
77F Mark Wohlers RC	.08	.25
78F Brook Jacoby	.01	.05
79F Ken Griffey Jr. CL	.15	.40
Ryne Sandberg		
80F Jack Morris AS	.01	.05
81F Sandy Alomar Jr. AS	.01	.05
82F Cecil Fielder AS	.01	.05
83F Roberto Alomar AS	.02	.10
84F Wade Boggs AS	.02	.10
85F Cal Ripken AS	.15	.40
86F Rickey Henderson AS	.05	.15
87F Ken Griffey Jr. AS	.08	.25
88F Dave Henderson AS	.01	.05
89F Danny Tartabull AS	.01	.05
90F Tom Glavine AS	.02	.10
91F Benito Santiago AS	.01	.05
92F Will Clark AS	.02	.10
93F Ryne Sandberg AS	.08	.25
94F Chris Sabo AS	.01	.05
95F Ozzie Smith AS	.08	.25
96F Ivan Calderon AS	.01	.05
97F Tony Gwynn AS	.05	.15
98F Andre Dawson AS	.01	.05
99F Bobby Bonilla AS	.01	.05
100F Checklist 1-100	.01	.05

1992 Upper Deck

The 1992 Upper Deck set contains 800 standard-size cards issued in two separate series of 700 and 100 cards respectively. The cards were distributed in low and high series foil packs in addition to factory sets. Factory sets feature a unique gold-foil hologram on the card backs (in contrast to the silver hologram on foil pack cards). Special subsets included in the set are Star Rookies (1-27), Team Checklists (29-40/86-99), with player portraits by Vernon Wells Sr.; Top Prospects (52-77); Bloodlines (79-85), Diamond Skills (640-650/711-721) and Diamond Debuts (771-780). Rookie Cards in the set include Shawn Green, Brian Jordan and Manny Ramirez. A special card picturing Tom Selleck and Frank Thomas, commemorating the forgettable movie "Mr. Baseball", was randomly inserted into high series packs. A standard-size Ted Williams hologram card was randomly inserted into low series packs. By mailing in 15 low series foil wrappers, a completed order form, and a handling fee, the collector could receive an 8 1/2" by 11" numbered, black and white lithograph picturing Ted Williams in his batting swing.

Card	Low	High
COMPLETE SET (800)	10.00	25.00
COMPLETE LO SET (700)	8.00	20.00
COMPLETE HI SET (100)	2.00	5.00
1 Ryan Klesko CL	.08	.25
Jim Thome		
2 Royce Clayton SR	.01	.05
3 Brian Jordan RC	.20	.50
4 Dave Fleming SR	.01	.05
5 Jim Thome SR	.08	.25
6 Jeff Juden SR	.01	.05
7 Roberto Hernandez SR	.01	.05
8 Kyle Abbott SR	.01	.05
9 Chris George SR	.01	.05
10 Rob Maurer SR	.01	.05
11 Donald Harris SR	.01	.05
12 Ted Wood SR	.01	.05
13 Patrick Lennon SR	.01	.05
14 Willie Banks SR	.01	.05
15 Roger Salkeld SR UER	.01	.05
(Bill was his grand-		
father, not his father)		
16 Wil Cordero SR	.01	.05
17 Arthur Rhodes SR	.01	.05
18 Pedro Martinez SR	.40	1.00
19 Andy Ashby SR	.01	.05
20 Tom Goodwin SR	.01	.05
21 Braulio Castillo SR	.01	.05
22 Todd Van Poppel SR	.01	.05
23 Brian Williams RC	.01	.05
24 Ryan Klesko SR	.02	.10
25 Kenny Lofton SR	.05	.15
26 Derek Bell SR	.02	.10
27 Reggie Sanders SR	.02	.10
28 Dave Winfield's 400th	.01	.05
29 David Justice TC	.01	.05
30 Rob Dibble TC	.01	.05
31 Craig Biggio TC	.02	.10
32 Eddie Murray TC	.05	.15
33 Fred McGriff TC	.02	.10
34 Willie McGee TC	.01	.05
35 Shawon Dunston TC	.01	.05
36 Delino DeShields TC	.01	.05
37 Howard Johnson TC	.01	.05
38 John Kruk TC	.01	.05
39 Doug Drabek TC	.01	.05
40 Todd Zeile TC	.01	.05
41 Steve Avery	.01	.05
Playoff Perfection		
42 Jeremy Hernandez RC	.01	.05
43 Doug Henry RC	.02	.10
44 Chris Donnels	.01	.05
45 Mo Sanford	.01	.05
46 Scott Kamieniecki	.01	.05
47 Mark Lemke	.01	.05
48 Steve Farr	.01	.05
49 Francisco Oliveras	.01	.05
50 Ced Landrum	.01	.05
51 Rondell White CL	.02	.10
Mark Newfield		
52 Eduardo Perez RC	.08	.25
53 Tom Nevers TP	.01	.05
54 David Zancanaro TP	.01	.05
55 Shawn Green RC	.40	1.00
56 Mark Wohlers TP	.01	.05
57 Dave Nilsson TP	.01	.05
58 Dmitri Young TP	.02	.10
59 Ryan Hawblitzel RC	.02	.10
60 Raul Mondesi TP	.02	.10
61 Rondell White TP	.02	.10
62 Steve Hosey TP	.01	.05
63 Manny Ramirez RC	1.50	4.00
64 Marc Newfield TP	.01	.05
65 Jeromy Burnitz TP	.02	.10
66 Mark Smith RC	.02	.10
67 Joey Hamilton RC	.02	.10
68 Tyler Green RC	.02	.10
69 Jon Farrell RC	.02	.10
70 Kurt Miller TP	.01	.05
71 Jeff Plympton TP	.01	.05
72 Dan Wilson TP	.01	.05
73 Joe Vitiello RC	.02	.10
74 Rico Brogna TP	.01	.05
75 David McCarty TP RC	.08	.25
76 Bob Wickman TP	.08	.25
77 Carlos Rodriguez TP	.01	.05
78 Jim Abbott	.02	.10
Stay In School		
79 Ramon Martinez	.08	.25
Pedro Martinez		
80 Kevin Mitchell	.01	.05
Keith Mitchell		
81 Sandy Alomar Jr.	.02	.10
Roberto Alomar		
82 Cal Ripken	.20	.50
Billy Ripken		
83 Tony Gwynn	.05	.15
Chris Gwynn		
84 Dwight Gooden	.02	.10
Gary Sheffield		
85 Ken Griffey Sr.	.08	.25
Ken Griffey Jr.		
Craig Griffey		
86 Jim Abbott TC	.02	.10
87 Frank Thomas TC	.05	.15
88 Danny Tartabull TC	.01	.05
89 Scott Erickson TC	.01	.05
90 Rickey Henderson TC	.05	.15
91 Edgar Martinez TC	.02	.10
92 Nolan Ryan TC	.20	.50
93 Ben McDonald TC	.01	.05
94 Ellis Burks TC	.01	.05
95 Greg Swindell TC	.01	.05
96 Cecil Fielder TC	.01	.05
97 Greg Vaughn TC	.01	.05
98 Kevin Maas TC	.01	.05
99 Dave Stieb TC	.01	.05
100 Checklist 1-100	.01	.05
101 Joe Oliver	.01	.05
102 Hector Villanueva	.01	.05
103 Ed Whitson	.01	.05
104 Danny Jackson	.01	.05
105 Chris Hammond	.01	.05
106 Ricky Jordan	.01	.05
107 Kevin Bass	.01	.05
108 Darrin Fletcher	.01	.05
109 Junior Ortiz	.01	.05
110 Tom Bolton	.01	.05
111 Jeff King	.01	.05
112 Dave Magadan	.01	.05
113 Mike LaValliere	.01	.05
114 Hubie Brooks	.01	.05
115 Jay Bell	.02	.10
116 David Wells	.02	.10
117 Jim Leyritz	.01	.05
118 Manuel Lee	.01	.05
119 Alvaro Espinoza	.01	.05
120 B.J. Surhoff	.02	.10
121 Hal Morris	.01	.05
122 Shawon Dawson	.01	.05
123 Chris Sabo	.01	.05
124 Andre Dawson	.02	.10
125 Eric Davis	.02	.10
126 Chili Davis	.02	.10
127 Dale Murphy	.05	.15
128 Kirk McCaskill	.01	.05
129 Terry Mulholland	.01	.05
130 Rick Aguilera	.02	.10
131 Vince Coleman	.01	.05
132 Andy Van Slyke	.05	.15
133 Gregg Jefferies	.01	.05
134 Barry Bonds	.40	1.00
135 Dwight Gooden	.02	.10
136 Dave Stieb	.01	.05
137 Albert Belle	.02	.10
138 Teddy Higuera	.01	.05
139 Jesse Barfield	.01	.05
140 Pat Borders	.01	.05
141 Bip Roberts	.01	.05
142 Rob Dibble	.02	.10
143 Mark Grace	.05	.15
144 Barry Larkin	.05	.15
145 Ryne Sandberg	.15	.40
146 Scott Erickson	.01	.05
147 Luis Polonia	.01	.05
148 John Burkett	.01	.05
149 Luis Sojo	.01	.05
150 Dickie Thon	.01	.05
151 Walt Weiss	.01	.05
152 Mike Scioscia	.01	.05
153 Mark McGwire	.25	.60
154 Matt Williams	.02	.10
155 Rickey Henderson	.08	.25
156 Sandy Alomar Jr.	.01	.05
157 Brian McRae	.01	.05
158 Harold Baines	.02	.10
159 Kevin Appier	.02	.10
160 Felix Fermin	.01	.05
161 Leo Gomez	.01	.05
162 Craig Biggio	.05	.15
163 Ben McDonald	.01	.05
164 Randy Johnson	.08	.25
165 Cal Ripken	.30	.75
166 Frank Thomas	.08	.25
167 Delino DeShields	.01	.05
168 Greg Gagne	.01	.05
169 Ron Karkovice	.01	.05
170 Charlie Leibrandt	.01	.05
171 Dave Righetti	.02	.10
172 Dave Henderson	.01	.05
173 Steve Decker	.01	.05
174 Darryl Strawberry	.02	.10
175 Will Clark	.05	.15
176 Ruben Sierra	.02	.10
177 Ozzie Smith	.15	.40
178 Charles Nagy	.01	.05
179 Gary Pettis	.01	.05
180 Kirk Gibson	.02	.10
181 Randy Milligan	.01	.05
182 Dave Valle	.01	.05
183 Chris Hoiles	.01	.05
184 Tony Phillips	.01	.05
185 Brady Anderson	.02	.10
186 Scott Fletcher	.01	.05
187 Gene Larkin	.01	.05
188 Lance Johnson	.01	.05
189 Greg Olson	.01	.05
190 Melido Perez	.01	.05
191 Lenny Harris	.01	.05
192 Terry Kennedy	.01	.05
193 Mike Gallego	.01	.05
194 Willie McGee	.02	.10
195 Juan Samuel	.01	.05
196 Jeff Huson	.02	.10
197 Alex Cole	.01	.05
198 Ron Robinson	.01	.05
199 Joel Skinner	.01	.05
200 Checklist 101-200	.01	.05
201 Kevin Reimer	.01	.05
202 Stan Belinda	.01	.05
203 Pat Tabler	.01	.05
204 Jose Guzman	.01	.05
205 Jose Lind	.01	.05
206 Spike Owen	.01	.05
207 Joe Orsulak	.01	.05
208 Charlie Hayes	.01	.05
209 Mike Devereaux	.01	.05
210 Mike Fitzgerald	.01	.05
211 Willie Randolph	.02	.10
212 Rod Nichols	.01	.05
213 Mike Boddicker	.01	.05
214 Bill Spiers	.01	.05
215 Steve Olin	.01	.05
216 David Howard	.01	.05
217 Gary Varsho	.01	.05
218 Mike Harkey	.01	.05
219 Luis Aquino	.01	.05
220 Chuck McElroy	.01	.05
221 Doug Drabek	.01	.05
222 Dave Winfield	.02	.10
223 Rafael Palmeiro	.05	.15
224 Joe Carter	.02	.10
225 Bobby Bonilla	.02	.10
226 Ivan Calderon	.01	.05
227 Gregg Olson	.01	.05
228 Tim Wallach	.01	.05
229 Terry Pendleton	.02	.10
230 Gilberto Reyes	.01	.05
231 Carlos Baerga	.01	.05
232 Greg Vaughn	.01	.05
233 Bret Saberhagen	.02	.10
234 Gary Sheffield	.02	.10
235 Mark Lewis	.01	.05
236 George Bell	.01	.05
237 Danny Tartabull	.01	.05
238 Willie Wilson	.01	.05
239 Doug Dascenzo	.01	.05
240 Bill Pecota	.01	.05
241 Julio Franco	.02	.10
242 Ed Sprague	.01	.05
243 Juan Gonzalez	.05	.15
244 Chuck Finley	.02	.10
245 Ivan Rodriguez	.08	.25
246 Len Dykstra	.02	.10
247 Deion Sanders	.05	.15
248 Dwight Evans	.05	.15
249 Larry Walker	.05	.15
250 Billy Ripken	.01	.05
251 Mickey Tettleton	.01	.05
252 Tony Pena	.01	.05
253 Benito Santiago	.02	.10
254 Kirby Puckett	.08	.25
255 Cecil Fielder	.02	.10
256 Howard Johnson	.01	.05
257 Andujar Cedeno	.01	.05
258 Jose Rijo	.01	.05
259 Al Osuna	.01	.05
260 Todd Hundley	.01	.05
261 Orel Hershiser	.02	.10
262 Ray Lankford	.02	.10
263 Robin Ventura	.02	.10
264 Felix Jose	.01	.05
265 Eddie Murray	.08	.25
266 Kevin Mitchell	.01	.05
267 Gary Carter	.02	.10
268 Mike Benjamin	.01	.05
269 Dick Schofield	.01	.05
270 Jose Uribe	.01	.05
271 Pete Incaviglia	.01	.05
272 Tony Fernandez	.01	.05
273 Alan Trammell	.02	.10
274 Tony Gwynn	.10	.30
275 Mike Greenwell	.01	.05
276 Jeff Bagwell	.08	.25
277 Frank Viola	.02	.10
278 Randy Myers	.01	.05
279 Ken Caminiti	.02	.10
280 Bill Doran	.01	.05
281 Dan Pasqua	.01	.05
282 Alfredo Griffin	.01	.05
283 Jose Oquendo	.01	.05
284 Kal Daniels	.01	.05
285 Bobby Thigpen	.01	.05
286 Robby Thompson	.01	.05
287 Mark Eichhorn	.01	.05
288 Mike Felder	.01	.05
289 Dave Gallagher	.01	.05
290 Dave Anderson	.01	.05
291 Mel Hall	.01	.05
292 Jerald Clark	.01	.05
293 Al Newman	.01	.05
294 Rob Deer	.01	.05
295 Matt Nokes	.01	.05
296 Jack Armstrong	.01	.05
297 Jim Deshaies	.01	.05
298 Jeff Innis	.01	.05
299 Jeff Reed	.01	.05
300 Checklist 201-300	.01	.05
301 Lonnie Smith	.01	.05
302 Jimmy Key	.02	.10
303 Junior Felix	.01	.05
304 Mike Heath	.01	.05
305 Mark Langston	.01	.05
306 Greg W. Harris	.01	.05
307 Brett Butler	.02	.10
308 Luis Rivera	.01	.05
309 Bruce Ruffin	.01	.05
310 Paul Faries	.01	.05
311 Terry Leach	.01	.05
312 Scott Brosius RC	.20	.50
313 Scott Leius	.01	.05
314 Harold Reynolds	.02	.10
315 Jack Morris	.02	.10
316 David Segui	.01	.05
317 Bill Gullickson	.01	.05
318 Todd Frohwirth	.01	.05
319 Mark Leiter	.01	.05
320 Jeff M. Robinson	.01	.05
321 Gary Gaetti	.02	.10
322 John Smoltz	.05	.15
323 Andy Benes	.01	.05
324 Kelly Gruber	.01	.05
325 Jim Abbott	.05	.15
326 John Kruk	.02	.10
327 Kevin Seitzer	.01	.05
328 Darrin Jackson	.01	.05
329 Kurt Stillwell	.01	.05
330 Mike Maddux	.01	.05
331 Dennis Eckersley	.02	.10
332 Dan Gladden	.01	.05
333 Jose Canseco	.05	.15
334 Kent Hrbek	.02	.10
335 Ken Griffey Sr.	.02	.10
336 Greg Swindell	.01	.05
337 Trevor Wilson	.01	.05
338 Sam Horn	.01	.05
339 Mike Henneman	.01	.05
340 Jerry Browne	.01	.05
341 Glenn Braggs	.01	.05
342 Tom Glavine	.05	.15
343 Wally Joyner	.02	.10
344 Fred McGriff	.05	.15
345 Ron Gant	.02	.10
346 Ramon Martinez	.01	.05
347 Wes Chamberlain	.01	.05
348 Terry Shumpert	.01	.05
349 Tim Teufel	.01	.05
350 Wally Backman	.01	.05
351 Joe Girardi	.01	.05
352 Devon White	.02	.10
353 Greg Maddux	.15	.40
354 Ryan Bowen	.01	.05
355 Roberto Alomar	.05	.15
356 Don Mattingly	.25	.60
357 Pedro Guerrero	.02	.10
358 Steve Sax	.01	.05
359 Joey Cora	.01	.05
360 Jim Gantner	.01	.05
361 Brian Barnes	.01	.05
362 Kevin McReynolds	.01	.05
363 Bret Barberie	.01	.05
364 David Cone	.02	.10
365 Dennis Martinez	.02	.10
366 Brian Hunter	.01	.05
367 Edgar Martinez	.05	.15
368 Steve Finley	.02	.10
369 Greg Briley	.01	.05
370 Jeff Blauser	.01	.05
371 Todd Stottlemyre	.01	.05
372 Luis Gonzalez	.02	.10
373 Rick Wilkins	.01	.05
374 Darryl Kile	.02	.10
375 John Olerud	.02	.10
376 Lee Smith	.02	.10
377 Kevin Maas	.01	.05
378 Dante Bichette	.02	.10
379 Tom Pagnozzi	.01	.05
380 Mike Flanagan	.01	.05
381 Charlie O'Brien	.01	.05
382 Dave Martinez	.01	.05
383 Keith Miller	.01	.05
384 Scott Ruskin	.01	.05
385 Kevin Elster	.01	.05
386 Alvin Davis	.01	.05
387 Casey Candaele	.01	.05
388 Pete O'Brien	.01	.05
389 Jeff Treadway	.01	.05
390 Scott Bradley	.01	.05
391 Mookie Wilson	.02	.10
392 Jimmy Jones	.01	.05
393 Candy Maldonado	.01	.05
394 Eric Yelding	.01	.05
395 Tom Henke	.01	.05
396 Franklin Stubbs	.01	.05
397 Milt Thompson	.01	.05
398 Mark Carreon	.01	.05
399 Randy Velarde	.01	.05
400 Checklist 301-400	.01	.05
401 Omar Vizquel	.05	.15
402 Joe Boever	.01	.05
403 Bill Krueger	.01	.05
404 Jody Reed	.01	.05
405 Mike Schooler	.01	.05
406 Jason Grimsley	.01	.05
407 Greg Myers	.01	.05
408 Randy Ready	.01	.05
409 Mike Timlin	.01	.05
410 Mitch Williams	.01	.05
411 Garry Templeton	.01	.05
412 Greg Cadaret	.01	.05
413 Donnie Hill	.01	.05
414 Wally Whitehurst	.01	.05
415 Scott Sanderson	.01	.05
416 Thomas Howard	.01	.05
417 Neal Heaton	.01	.05
418 Charlie Hough	.02	.10
419 Jack Howell	.01	.05
420 Greg Hibbard	.01	.05
421 Carlos Quintana	.01	.05
422 Kim Batiste	.01	.05
423 Paul Molitor	.02	.10
424 Ken Griffey Jr.	.15	.40
425 Phil Plantier	.01	.05
426 Denny Neagle	.02	.10
427 Von Hayes	.01	.05
428 Shane Mack	.01	.05
429 Darren Daulton	.02	.10
430 Dwayne Henry	.01	.05
431 Lance Parrish	.02	.10
432 Mike Humphreys	.01	.05
433 Tim Burke	.01	.05
434 Bryan Harvey	.01	.05
435 Pat Kelly	.01	.05
436 Ozzie Guillen	.02	.10
437 Bruce Hurst	.01	.05
438 Sammy Sosa	.08	.25
439 Dennis Rasmussen	.01	.05
440 Ken Patterson	.01	.05
441 Jay Buhner	.02	.10
442 Pat Combs	.01	.05
443 Wade Boggs	.05	.15
444 George Brett	.25	.60
445 Mo Vaughn	.02	.10
446 Chuck Knoblauch	.02	.10
447 Tom Candiotti	.01	.05
448 Mark Portugal	.01	.05
449 Mickey Morandini	.01	.05
450 Duane Ward	.01	.05
451 Otis Nixon	.01	.05
452 Bob Welch	.01	.05
453 Rusty Meacham	.01	.05
454 Keith Mitchell	.01	.05
455 Marquis Grissom	.02	.10
456 Robin Yount	.15	.40
457 Harvey Pulliam	.01	.05
458 Jose DeLeon	.01	.05
459 Mark Gubicza	.01	.05
460 Darryl Hamilton	.01	.05
461 Tom Browning	.01	.05
462 Monty Fariss	.01	.05
463 Jerome Walton	.01	.05
464 Paul O'Neill	.05	.15
465 Dean Palmer	.02	.10
466 Travis Fryman	.02	.10
467 John Smiley	.01	.05
468 Lloyd Moseby	.01	.05
469 John Wehner	.01	.05
470 Skeeter Barnes	.01	.05
471 Steve Chitren	.01	.05
472 Kent Mercker	.01	.05
473 Terry Steinbach	.01	.05
474 Andres Galarraga	.02	.10
475 Steve Avery	.01	.05
476 Tom Gordon	.01	.05
477 Cal Eldred	.01	.05
478 Omar Olivares	.01	.05
479 Julio Machado	.01	.05
480 Bob Milacki	.01	.05
481 Les Lancaster	.01	.05
482 John Candelaria	.01	.05
483 Brian Downing	.01	.05
484 Roger McDowell	.01	.05
485 Scott Scudder	.01	.05
486 Zane Smith	.01	.05
487 John Cerutti	.01	.05
488 Steve Buechele	.01	.05
489 Paul Gibson	.01	.05
490 Curtis Wilkerson	.01	.05
491 Marvin Freeman	.01	.05
492 Tom Foley	.01	.05
493 Juan Berenguer	.01	.05
494 Ernest Riles	.01	.05
495 Sid Bream	.01	.05
496 Chuck Crim	.01	.05
497 Mike Macfarlane	.01	.05
498 Dale Sveum	.01	.05
499 Storm Davis	.01	.05
500 Checklist 401-500	.01	.05
501 Jeff Reardon	.02	.10
502 Shawn Abner	.01	.05
503 Tony Fossas	.01	.05
504 Cory Snyder	.01	.05
505 Matt Young	.01	.05
506 Allan Anderson	.01	.05
507 Mark Lee	.01	.05
508 Gene Nelson	.01	.05
509 Mike Pagliarulo	.01	.05
510 Rafael Belliard	.01	.05
511 Jay Howell	.01	.05
512 Bob Tewksbury	.01	.05
513 Mike Morgan	.01	.05
514 John Franco	.02	.10
515 Kevin Gross	.01	.05
516 Lou Whitaker	.02	.10
517 Orlando Merced	.01	.05
518 Todd Benzinger	.01	.05
519 Gary Redus	.01	.05
520 Walt Terrell	.01	.05
521 Jack Clark	.02	.10
522 Dave Parker	.02	.10
523 Tim Naehring	.01	.05
524 Mark Whiten	.01	.05
525 Ellis Burks	.02	.10
526 Frank Castillo	.01	.05
527 Brian Harper	.01	.05
528 Brook Jacoby	.01	.05
529 Rick Sutcliffe	.02	.10
530 Joe Klink	.01	.05
531 Terry Bross	.01	.05
532 Jose Offerman	.01	.05
533 Todd Zeile	.01	.05
534 Eric Karros	.02	.10
535 Anthony Young	.01	.05
536 Milt Cuyler	.01	.05
537 Randy Tomlin	.01	.05
538 Scott Livingstone	.01	.05
539 Jim Eisenreich	.01	.05
540 Don Slaught	.01	.05
541 Scott Cooper	.01	.05
542 Joe Grahe	.01	.05
543 Tom Brunansky	.01	.05
544 Eddie Zosky	.01	.05
545 Roger Clemens	.20	.50
546 David Justice	.02	.10
547 Dave Stewart	.02	.10
548 David West	.01	.05
549 Dave Smith	.01	.05

550 Dan Plesac .01 .05
551 Alex Fernandez .01 .05
552 Bernard Gilkey .01 .05
553 Jack McDowell .01 .05
554 Tino Martinez .05 .15
555 Bo Jackson .08 .25
556 Bernie Williams .05 .15
557 Mark Gardner .01 .05
558 Glenallen Hill .01 .05
559 Oil Can Boyd .01 .05
560 Chris James .01 .05
561 Scott Servais .01 .05
562 Rey Sanchez RC .08 .25
563 Paul McClellan .01 .05
564 Andy Mota .01 .05
565 Darren Lewis .01 .05
566 Jose Melendez .01 .05
567 Tommy Greene .01 .05
568 Rich Rodriguez .01 .05
569 Heathcliff Slocumb .01 .05
570 Joe Hesketh .01 .05
571 Carlton Fisk .05 .15
572 Erik Hanson .01 .05
573 Wilson Alvarez .01 .05
574 Rheal Cormier .01 .05
575 Tim Raines .02 .10
576 Bobby Witt .01 .05
577 Roberto Kelly .01 .05
578 Kevin Brown .02 .10
579 Chris Nabholz .01 .05
580 Jesse Orosco .01 .05
581 Jeff Brantley .01 .05
582 Rafael Ramirez .01 .05
583 Kelly Downs .01 .05
584 Mike Simms .01 .05
585 Mike Remlinger .01 .05
586 Dave Hollins .01 .05
587 Larry Andersen .01 .05
588 Mike Gardiner .01 .05
589 Craig Lefferts .01 .05
590 Paul Assenmacher .01 .05
591 Bryn Smith .01 .05
592 Donn Pall .01 .05
593 Mike Jackson .01 .05
594 Scott Radinsky .01 .05
595 Brian Holman .01 .05
596 Geronimo Pena .01 .05
597 Mike Jeffcoat .01 .05
598 Carlos Martinez .01 .05
599 Geno Petralli .01 .05
600 Checklist 501-600 .01 .05
601 Jerry Don Gleaton .01 .05
602 Adam Peterson .01 .05
603 Craig Grebeck .01 .05
604 Mark Guthrie .01 .05
605 Frank Tanana .01 .05
606 Hensley Meulens .01 .05
607 Mark Davis .01 .05
608 Eric Plunk .01 .05
609 Mark Williamson .01 .05
610 Lee Guetterman .01 .05
611 Bobby Rose .01 .05
612 Bill Wegman .01 .05
613 Mike Hartley .01 .05
614 Chris Beasley .01 .05
615 Chris Bosio .01 .05
616 Henry Cotto .01 .05
617 Chico Walker .01 .05
618 Russ Swan .01 .05
619 Bob Walk .01 .05
620 Bill Swift .01 .05
621 Warren Newson .01 .05
622 Steve Bedrosian .01 .05
623 Ricky Bones .01 .05
624 Kevin Tapani .01 .05
625 Juan Guzman .01 .05
626 Jeff Johnson .01 .05
627 Jeff Montgomery .01 .05
628 Ken Hill .01 .05
629 Gary Thurman .01 .05
630 Steve Howe .01 .05
631 Jose DeJesus .01 .05
632 Kirk Dressendorfer .01 .05
633 Jaime Navarro .01 .05
634 Lee Stevens .01 .05
635 Pete Harnisch .01 .05
636 Bill Landrum .01 .05
637 Rich DeLucia .01 .05
638 Luis Salazar .01 .05
639 Rob Murphy .01 .05
640 Jose Canseco CL .05 .15
Rickey Henderson
641 Roger Clemens DS .08 .25
642 Jim Abbott DS .02 .10
643 Travis Fryman DS .01 .05
644 Jesse Barfield DS .01 .05
645 Cal Ripken DS .15 .40
646 Wade Boggs DS .02 .10
647 Cecil Fielder DS .01 .05
648 Rickey Henderson DS .05 .15
649 Jose Canseco DS .02 .10
650 Ken Griffey Jr. DS .08 .25
651 Kenny Rogers .02 .10
652 Luis Mercedes .01 .05
653 Mike Stanton .01 .05
654 Glenn Davis .01 .05
655 Nolan Ryan .40 1.00
656 Reggie Jefferson .01 .05
657 Javier Ortiz .01 .05
658 Greg A. Harris .01 .05
659 Mariano Duncan .01 .05
660 Jeff Shaw .01 .05
661 Mike Moore .01 .05
662 Chris Haney .01 .05
663 Joe Slusarski .01 .05
664 Wayne Housie .01 .05
665 Carlos Garcia .01 .05
666 Bob Ojeda .01 .05
667 Bryan Hickerson RC .02 .10
668 Tim Belcher .01 .05
669 Ron Darling .01 .05
670 Rex Hudler .01 .05
671 Sid Fernandez .01 .05
672 Chito Martinez .01 .05
673 Pete Schourek .01 .05
674 Armando Reynoso RC .08 .25
675 Mike Mussina .08 .25
676 Kevin Morton .01 .05
677 Norm Charlton .01 .05
678 Danny Darwin .01 .05
679 Eric King .01 .05
680 Ted Power .01 .05
681 Barry Jones .01 .05
682 Carney Lansford .02 .10
683 Mel Rojas .01 .05
684 Rick Honeycutt .01 .05
685 Jeff Fassero .01 .05
686 Cris Carpenter .01 .05
687 Tim Crews .01 .05
688 Scott Terry .01 .05
689 Chris Gwynn .01 .05
690 Gerald Perry .01 .05
691 John Barfield .01 .05
692 Bob Melvin .01 .05
693 Juan Agosto .01 .05
694 Alejandro Pena .01 .05
695 Jeff Russell .01 .05
696 Carmelo Martinez .01 .05
697 Bud Black .01 .05
698 Dave Otto .01 .05
699 Billy Hatcher .01 .05
700 Checklist 601-700 .01 .05
701 Clemente Nunez RC .01 .05
702 Mark Clark .01 .05
Donovan Osborne
Brian Jordan
703 Mike Morgan .01 .05
704 Keith Miller .01 .05
705 Kurt Stillwell .01 .05
706 Damon Berryhill .01 .05
707 Von Hayes .01 .05
708 Rick Sutcliffe .02 .10
709 Hubie Brooks .01 .05
710 Ryan Turner RC .02 .10
711 Barry Bonds CL .20 .50
Andy Van Slyke
712 Jose Rijo DS .01 .05
713 Tom Glavine DS .02 .10
714 Shawon Dunston DS .01 .05
715 Andy Van Slyke DS .02 .10
716 Ozzie Smith DS .08 .25
717 Tony Gwynn DS .05 .15
718 Will Clark DS .02 .10
719 Marquis Grissom DS .01 .05
720 Howard Johnson DS .01 .05
721 Barry Bonds DS .20 .50
722 Kirk McCaskill .01 .05
723 Sammy Sosa .30 .75
724 George Bell .01 .05
725 Gregg Jefferies .01 .05
726 Gary DiSarcina .01 .05
727 Mike Bordick .01 .05
728 Eddie Murray 400 HR .05 .15
729 Rene Gonzales .01 .05
730 Mike Bielecki .01 .05
731 Calvin Jones .01 .05
732 Jack Morris .02 .10
733 Frank Viola .02 .10
734 Dave Winfield .02 .10
735 Kevin Mitchell .01 .05
736 Bill Swift .01 .05
737 Dan Gladden .01 .05
738 Mike Jackson .01 .05
739 Mark Carreon .01 .05
740 Kirt Manwaring .01 .05
741 Randy Myers .01 .05
742 Kevin McReynolds .01 .05
743 Steve Sax .01 .05
744 Wally Joyner .02 .10
745 Gary Sheffield .02 .10
746 Danny Tartabull .01 .05
747 Julio Valera .01 .05
748 Denny Neagle .02 .10
749 Lance Blankenship .01 .05
750 Mike Gallego .01 .05
751 Bret Saberhagen .02 .10
752 Ruben Amaro .01 .05
753 Eddie Murray .08 .25
754 Kyle Abbott .01 .05
755 Bobby Bonilla .02 .10
756 Eric Davis .02 .10
757 Eddie Taubensee RC .08 .25
758 Andres Galarraga .02 .10
759 Pete Incaviglia .01 .05
760 Tom Candiotti .01 .05
761 Tim Belcher .01 .05
762 Ricky Bones .01 .05
763 Bip Roberts .01 .05
764 Pedro Munoz .01 .05
765 Greg Swindell .01 .05
766 Kenny Lofton .05 .15
767 Gary Carter .02 .10
768 Charlie Hayes .01 .05
769 Dickie Thon .01 .05
770 D. Osborne DD CL .01 .05
771 Bret Boone DD .05 .15
772 Archi Cianfrocco RC .02 .10
773 Mark Clark RC .02 .10
774 Chad Curtis RC .08 .25
775 Pat Listach RC .08 .25
776 Pat Mahomes RC .08 .25
777 Donovan Osborne DD .01 .05
778 John Patterson RC .02 .10
779 Andy Stankiewicz DD .01 .05
780 Turk Wendell RC .08 .25
781 Bill Krueger .01 .05
782 Rickey Henderson 1000 .05 .15
783 Kevin Seitzer .01 .05
784 Dave Martinez .01 .05
785 John Smiley .01 .05
786 Matt Stairs RC .08 .25
787 Scott Scudder .01 .05
788 John Wetteland .02 .10
789 Jack Armstrong .01 .05
790 Ken Hill .01 .05
791 Dick Schofield .01 .05
792 Mariano Duncan .01 .05
793 Bill Pecota .01 .05
794 Mike Kelly RC .02 .10
795 Willie Randolph .02 .10
796 Butch Henry .01 .05
797 Carlos Hernandez .01 .05
798 Doug Jones .01 .05
799 Melido Perez .01 .05
800 Checklist 701-800 .01 .05
HH2 T.Williams Hologram .75 2.00
Top left corner says
91 Upper Deck 92
SP3 Deion Sanders FB/BB .40 1.00
SP4 Tom Selleck .40 1.00
Frank Thomas SP
(Mr. Baseball)

1992 Upper Deck Gold Hologram

All cards issued in 1992 Upper Deck factory sets have a gold hologram on the back.

COMP.FACT.SET (800) 10.00 25.00
*STARS: .4X TO 1X BASIC CARDS
*ROOKIES: .4X TO 1X BASIC

1992 Upper Deck Bench/Morgan Heroes

This standard size 10-card set was randomly inserted in 1992 Upper Deck high number packs. Both Bench and Morgan autographed 2,500 of card number 45, which displays a portrait by sports artist Vernon Wells. The fronts feature color photos of Bench (37-39), Morgan (40-42), or both (43-44) at various stages of their baseball careers.

COMPLETE SET (10) 7.50 15.00
COMMON CARD (37-45) .60 1.50
RANDOM INSERTS IN HI SERIES PACKS
NNO Baseball Heroes SP 1.00 2.50
(Header card)
AU5 J.Bench/J.Morgan 100.00 175.00
AU/2500

1992 Upper Deck College POY Holograms

This three-card standard-size set was randomly inserted in 1992 Upper Deck high series foil packs. This set features College Player of the Year winners for 1989 through 1991. The cards are numbered on the back with the prefix "CP".

COMPLETE SET (3) .75 2.00
RANDOM INSERTS IN HI SERIES
CP1 David McCarty .40 1.00
CP2 Mike Kelly .40 1.00
CP3 Ben McDonald .40 1.00

1992 Upper Deck Heroes of Baseball

Continuing a popular insert set introduced the previous year, Upper Deck produced four new commemorative cards, including three player cards and one portrait card by sports artist Vernon Wells. These cards were randomly inserted in 1992 Upper Deck baseball low number foil packs. Three thousand of each card were personally numbered and autographed by each player.

RANDOM INSERTS IN HEROES FOIL
H5 Vida Blue .75 2.00
H6 Lou Brock .75 2.00
H7 Rollie Fingers .75 2.00
H8 Vida Blue ART .75 2.00
Lou Brock
Rollie Fingers
AU5 Vida Blue AU/3000 6.00 15.00
AU6 Lou Brock AU/3000 10.00 25.00
AU7 R.Fingers AU/3000 6.00 15.00

1992 Upper Deck Heroes Highlights

To dealers participating in Heroes of Baseball Collectors shows, Upper Deck made available this ten-card insert standard-size set, which commemorates one of the greatest moments in the careers of ten of baseball's all-time players. The cards were primarily randomly inserted in high number packs sold at these shows. However at the first Heroes show in Anaheim, the cards were inserted into low number packs. The fronts feature color player photos with a shadowed strip for a three-dimensional effect. The player's name and the date of the great moment in the hero's career appear with a "Heroes Highlights" logo in a bottom border of varying shades of brown and blue-green. The backs have white borders and display a blue-green and brown bordered monument design accented with baseballs. The major portion of the design is parchment-textured and contains text highlighting a special moment in the player's career. The cards are numbered on the back with an "HI" prefix. The card numbering follows alphabetical order by player's name.

COMPLETE SET (10) 6.00 15.00
HI1 Bobby Bonds .20 .50
HI2 Lou Brock 1.25 3.00
HI3 Rollie Fingers .75 2.00
HI4 Bob Gibson 1.25 3.00
HI5 Reggie Jackson 1.50 4.00
HI6 Gaylord Perry .75 2.00
HI7 Robin Roberts .75 2.00
HI8 Brooks Robinson 1.50 4.00
HI9 Billy Williams .75 2.00
HI10 Ted Williams 2.50 6.00

1992 Upper Deck Home Run Heroes

This 26-card standard-size set was inserted one per pack into 1992 Upper Deck low series jumbo packs. The set spotlights the 1991 home run leaders from each of the 26 Major League teams.

COMPLETE SET (26) 5.00 12.00
HR1 Jose Canseco .20 .50
HR2 Cecil Fielder .10 .30
HR3 Howard Johnson .05 .15
HR4 Cal Ripken 1.00 2.50
HR5 Matt Williams .10 .30
HR6 Joe Carter .10 .30
HR7 Ron Gant .10 .30
HR8 Frank Thomas .30 .75
HR9 Andre Dawson .10 .30
HR10 Fred McGriff .20 .50
HR11 Danny Tartabull .05 .15
HR12 Chili Davis .10 .30
HR13 Albert Belle .10 .30
HR14 Jack Clark .10 .30
HR15 Paul O'Neill .20 .50
HR16 Darryl Strawberry .10 .30
HR17 Dave Winfield .10 .30
HR18 Jay Buhner .10 .30
HR19 Juan Gonzalez .20 .50
HR20 Greg Vaughn .05 .15
HR21 Barry Bonds 1.25 3.00
HR22 Matt Nokes .05 .15
HR23 John Kruk .10 .30
HR24 Ivan Calderon .05 .15
HR25 Jeff Bagwell .30 .75
HR26 Todd Zeile .05 .15

1992 Upper Deck Scouting Report

Inserted one per high series jumbo pack, cards from this 25-card standard-size set feature outstanding prospects in baseball. Please note these cards are highly condition sensitive and are priced below in NmMt condition. Mint copies trade for premiums.

COMPLETE SET (25) 10.00 20.00
COMMON CARD (SR1-SR25) .40 1.00
SR1 Andy Ashby .40 1.00
SR2 Willie Banks .40 1.00
SR3 Kim Batiste .40 1.00
SR4 Derek Bell .40 1.00
SR5 Archi Cianfrocco .40 1.00
SR6 Royce Clayton .40 1.00
SR7 Gary DiSarcina .40 1.00
SR8 Dave Fleming .40 1.00
SR9 Butch Henry .40 1.00
SR10 Todd Hundley .40 1.00
SR11 Brian Jordan .40 1.00
SR12 Eric Karros .40 1.00
SR13 Pat Listach .40 1.00
SR14 Scott Livingstone .40 1.00
SR15 Kenny Lofton .40 1.00
SR16 Pat Mahomes .40 1.00
SR17 Denny Neagle .40 1.00
SR18 Dave Nilsson .40 1.00
SR19 Donovan Osborne .40 1.00
SR20 Reggie Sanders .40 1.00
SR21 Andy Stankiewicz .40 1.00
SR22 Jim Thome .75 2.00
SR23 Julio Valera .40 1.00
SR24 Mark Wohlers .40 1.00
SR25 Anthony Young .40 1.00

1992 Upper Deck Williams Best

This 20-card standard-size set contains Ted Williams' choices of best current and future hitters in the game. The cards were randomly inserted in Upper Deck high number foil packs. These cards are condition sensitive and priced below in NmMt condition. True mint condition copies do sell for more than these listed prices.

COMPLETE SET (20) 8.00 20.00
COMMON CARD (T1-T20) .10 .25
RANDOM INSERTS IN HI SERIES
T1 Wade Boggs .30 .75
T2 Barry Bonds 2.00 5.00
T3 Jose Canseco .30 .75
T4 Will Clark .30 .75
T5 Cecil Fielder .20 .50
T6 Tony Gwynn .60 1.50
T7 Rickey Henderson .50 1.25
T8 Fred McGriff .30 .75
T9 Kirby Puckett .50 1.25
T10 Ruben Sierra .20 .50
T11 Roberto Alomar .30 .75
T12 Jeff Bagwell .50 1.25
T13 Albert Belle .20 .50
T14 Juan Gonzalez .30 .75
T15 Ken Griffey Jr. .75 2.00
T16 Chris Hoiles .08 .25
T17 David Justice .20 .50
T18 Phil Plantier .08 .25
T19 Frank Thomas .50 1.25
T20 Robin Ventura .20 .50

1992 Upper Deck Williams Heroes

This standard-size ten-card set was randomly inserted in 1992 Upper Deck low number foil packs. Williams autographed 2,500 of card 36, which displays his portrait by sports artist Vernon Wells. The cards are numbered on the back in continuation of the Upper Deck heroes series.

COMPLETE SET (10) 3.00 6.00
COMMON (28-36) .20 .50
RANDOM INSERTS IN LO SERIES PACKS
NNO Baseball Heroes SP .75 2.00
(Header card)
AU4 Ted Williams AU/2500 300.00 500.00

1992 Upper Deck Williams Wax Boxes

These eight oversized blank-backed "cards," measuring approximately 5 1/4" by 7 1/4", were featured on the bottom panels of 1992 Upper Deck low series wax boxes. They are identical in design to the Williams Heroes insert cards, displaying color player photos in an oval frame. These boxes are unnumbered. We have checklisted them below according to the numbering of the Heroes cards.

COMMON CARD (28-35) .20 .50

1993 Upper Deck

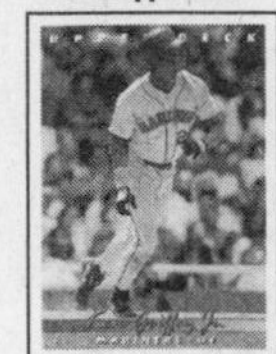

The 1993 Upper Deck set consists of two series of 420 standard-size cards. Special subsets featured include Star Rookies (1-29), Community Heroes (30-40), and American League Teammates (41-55), Top Prospects (421-449), Inside the Numbers (450-470), Team Stars (471-485), Award Winners (486-499), and Diamond Debuts (500-510). Derek Jeter is the only notable Rookie Card in this set. A special card (SP5) was randomly inserted in first series packs to commemorate the 3,000th hit of George Brett and Robin Yount. A special card (SP6) commemorating Nolan Ryan's last season was randomly inserted into second series packs. Both SP cards were inserted at a rate of one every 72 packs

COMPLETE SET (840) 15.00 40.00
COMP.FACT.SET (840) 20.00 50.00
COMP. SERIES 1 (420) 6.00 15.00
COMP. SERIES 2 (420) 10.00 25.00
1 Tim Salmon CL .07 .20
2 Mike Piazza SR 1.25 3.00
3 Rene Arocha SR RC .20 .50
4 Willie Greene SR .02 .10
5 Manny Alexander .02 .10
6 Dan Wilson .07 .20
7 Dan Smith .02 .10
8 Kevin Rogers .02 .10
9 Kurt Miller SR .02 .10
10 Joe Vitko .02 .10
11 Tim Costo .02 .10
12 Alan Embree SR .02 .10
13 Jim Tatum SR RC .05 .15
14 Cris Colon .02 .10
15 Steve Hosey .02 .10
16 S. Hitchcock SR RC .20 .50
17 Dave Mlicki .02 .10
18 Jessie Hollins .02 .10
19 Bobby Jones SR .07 .20
20 Kurt Miller .02 .10
21 Melvin Nieves SR .02 .10
22 Billy Ashley SR .02 .10
23 J.T. Snow SR RC .30 .75
24 Chipper Jones SR .20 .50
25 Tim Salmon SR .10 .30
26 Tim Pugh SR RC .05 .15
27 David Nied SR .02 .10
28 Mike Trombley .02 .10
29 Javier Lopez SR .10 .30
30 Jim Abbott CH CL .07 .20
31 Jim Abbott CH .02 .10
32 Dale Murphy CH .10 .30
33 Tony Pena CH .02 .10
34 Kirby Puckett CH .10 .30
35 Harold Reynolds CH .02 .10
36 Cal Ripken CH .30 .75
37 Nolan Ryan CH .40 1.00
38 Ryne Sandberg CH .20 .50
39 Dave Stewart CH .02 .10
40 Dave Winfield CH .02 .10
41 Joe Carter CL .20 .50
Mark McGwire
42 Joe Carter .07 .20
Roberto Alomar
43 Paul Molitor .20 .50
Pat Listach
Robin Yount
44 Cal Ripken .20 .50
Brady Anderson
45 Albert Belle .07 .20
Sandy Alomar Jr.
Jim Thome
Carlos Baerga
Kenny Lofton
46 Cecil Fielder .02 .10
Mickey Tettleton
47 Roberto Kelly .25 .60
Don Mattingly
48 Frank Viola .20 .50
Roger Clemens
49 Ruben Sierra .20 .50
Mark McGwire
50 Kent Hrbek .10 .30
Kirby Puckett
51 Robin Ventura .10 .30
Frank Thomas
52 Juan Gonzalez .10 .30
Jose Canseco
Ivan Rodriguez
Rafael Palmeiro
53 Mark Langston .07 .20
Jim Abbott
Chuck Finley
54 Wally Joyner .20 .50
Gregg Jefferies
George Brett
55 Kevin Mitchell .20 .50
Ken Griffey Jr.
Jay Buhner
56 George Brett .50 1.25
57 Scott Cooper .02 .10
58 Mike Maddux .02 .10
59 Rusty Meacham .02 .10
60 Wil Cordero .02 .10
61 Tim Teufel .02 .10
62 Jeff Montgomery .02 .10
63 Scott Livingstone .02 .10
64 Doug Dascenzo .02 .10
65 Bret Boone .07 .20
66 Tim Wakefield .20 .50
67 Curt Schilling .07 .20
68 Frank Tanana .02 .10
69 Len Dykstra .07 .20
70 Derek Lilliquist .02 .10
71 Anthony Young .02 .10
72 Hipolito Pichardo .02 .10
73 Rod Beck .02 .10
74 Kent Hrbek .07 .20
75 Tom Glavine .10 .30
76 Kevin Brown .07 .20
77 Chuck Finley .07 .20
78 Bob Walk .02 .10
79 Rheal Cormier UER .02 .10
(Born in New Brunswick,
not British Columbia)
80 Rick Sutcliffe .07 .20
81 Harold Baines .07 .20
82 Lee Smith .07 .20
83 Geno Petralli .02 .10
84 Jose Oquendo .02 .10
85 Mark Gubicza .02 .10
86 Mickey Tettleton .02 .10
87 Bobby Witt .02 .10
88 Mark Lewis .02 .10
89 Kevin Appier .07 .20
90 Mike Stanton .02 .10
91 Rafael Belliard .02 .10
92 Kenny Rogers .07 .20
93 Randy Velarde .02 .10
94 Luis Sojo .02 .10
95 Mark Leiter .02 .10
96 Jody Reed .02 .10
97 Pete Harnisch .02 .10
98 Tom Candiotti .02 .10
99 Mark Portugal .02 .10
100 Dave Valle .02 .10
101 Shawon Dunston .02 .10
102 B.J. Surhoff .07 .20
103 Jay Bell .07 .20
104 Sid Bream .02 .10
105 Frank Thomas CL .10 .30
106 Mike Morgan .02 .10
107 Bill Doran .02 .10
108 Lance Blankenship .02 .10
109 Mark Lemke .02 .10
110 Brian Harper .02 .10
111 Brady Anderson .07 .20
112 Bip Roberts .02 .10
113 Mitch Williams .02 .10
114 Craig Biggio .10 .30
115 Eddie Murray .20 .50
116 Matt Nokes .02 .10
117 Lance Parrish .07 .20
118 Bill Swift .02 .10
119 Jeff Innis .02 .10
120 Mike LaValliere .02 .10
121 Hal Morris .02 .10
122 Walt Weiss .02 .10
123 Ivan Rodriguez .10 .30
124 Andy Van Slyke .10 .30
125 Roberto Alomar .10 .30
126 Robby Thompson .02 .10
127 Sammy Sosa .20 .50
128 Mark Langston .02 .10
129 Jerry Browne .02 .10
130 Chuck McElroy .02 .10
131 Frank Viola .07 .20
132 Leo Gomez .02 .10
133 Ramon Martinez .02 .10
134 Don Mattingly .50 1.25
135 Roger Clemens .40 1.00
136 Rickey Henderson .20 .50
137 Darren Daulton .07 .20
138 Ken Hill .02 .10
139 Ozzie Guillen .07 .20
140 Jerald Clark .02 .10
141 Dave Fleming .02 .10
142 Delino DeShields .02 .10
143 Matt Williams .07 .20
144 Larry Walker .07 .20
145 Ruben Sierra .07 .20
146 Ozzie Smith .30 .75
147 Chris Sabo .02 .10
148 Carlos Hernandez .02 .10
149 Pat Borders .02 .10
150 Orlando Merced .02 .10
151 Royce Clayton .02 .10
152 Kurt Stillwell .02 .10
153 Dave Hollins .02 .10
154 Mike Greenwell .02 .10
155 Nolan Ryan .75 2.00
156 Felix Jose .02 .10
157 Junior Felix .02 .10
158 Derek Bell .02 .10
159 Steve Buechele .02 .10
160 John Burkett .02 .10
161 Pat Howell .02 .10
162 Milt Cuyler .02 .10
163 Terry Pendleton .07 .20
164 Jack Morris .07 .20
165 Tony Gwynn .25 .60
166 Deion Sanders .10 .30
167 Mike Devereaux .02 .10
168 Ron Darling .02 .10
169 Orel Hershiser .07 .20
170 Mike Jackson .02 .10
171 Doug Jones .02 .10
172 Dan Walters .02 .10
173 Darren Lewis .02 .10
174 Carlos Baerga .02 .10
175 Ryne Sandberg .30 .75
176 Gregg Jefferies .02 .10
177 John Jaha .02 .10
178 Luis Polonia .02 .10
179 Kirt Manwaring .02 .10
180 Mike Magnante .02 .10
181 Billy Ripken .02 .10

182 Mike Moore .02 .10
183 Eric Anthony .02 .10
184 Lenny Harris .02 .10
185 Tony Pena .02 .10
186 Mike Felder .02 .10
187 Greg Olson .02 .10
188 Rene Gonzales .02 .10
189 Mike Bordick .02 .10
190 Mel Rojas .02 .10
191 Todd Frohwirth .02 .10
192 Darryl Hamilton .02 .10
193 Mike Fetters .02 .10
194 Omar Olivares .02 .10
195 Tony Phillips .02 .10
196 Paul Sorrento .02 .10
197 Trevor Wilson .02 .10
198 Kevin Gross .02 .10
199 Ron Karkovice .02 .10
200 Brook Jacoby .02 .10
201 Mariano Duncan .02 .10
202 Dennis Cook .02 .10
203 Daryl Boston .02 .10
204 Mike Perez .02 .10
205 Manuel Lee .02 .10
206 Steve Olin .02 .10
207 Charlie Hough .07 .20
208 Scott Scudder .02 .10
209 Charlie O'Brien .02 .10
210 Barry Bonds CL .30 .75
211 Jose Vizcaino .02 .10
212 Scott Leius .02 .10
213 Kevin Mitchell .02 .10
214 Brian Barnes .02 .10
215 Pat Kelly .02 .10
216 Chris Hammond .02 .10
217 Rob Deer .02 .10
218 Cory Snyder .02 .10
219 Gary Carter .07 .20
220 Danny Darwin .02 .10
221 Tom Gordon .02 .10
222 Gary Sheffield .07 .20
223 Joe Carter .07 .20
224 Jay Buhner .07 .20
225 Jose Offerman .02 .10
226 Jose Rijo .02 .10
227 Mark Whiten .02 .10
228 Randy Milligan .02 .10
229 Bud Black .02 .10
230 Gary DiSarcina .02 .10
231 Steve Finley .07 .20
232 Dennis Martinez .07 .20
233 Mike Mussina .10 .30
234 Joe Oliver .02 .10
235 Chad Curtis .02 .10
236 Shane Mack .02 .10
237 Jaime Navarro .02 .10
238 Brian McRae .02 .10
239 Chili Davis .07 .20
240 Jeff King .02 .10
241 Dean Palmer .07 .20
242 Danny Tartabull .02 .10
243 Charles Nagy .02 .10
244 Ray Lankford .07 .20
245 Barry Larkin .10 .30
246 Steve Avery .02 .10
247 John Kruk .07 .20
248 Derrick May .02 .10
249 Stan Javier .02 .10
250 Roger McDowell .02 .10
251 Dan Gladden .02 .10
252 Wally Joyner .07 .20
253 Pat Listach .02 .10
254 Chuck Knoblauch .07 .20
255 Sandy Alomar Jr. .02 .10
256 Jeff Bagwell .10 .30
257 Andy Stankiewicz .02 .10
258 Darrin Jackson .02 .10
259 Brett Butler .07 .20
260 Joe Orsulak .02 .10
261 Andy Benes .02 .10
262 Kenny Lofton .07 .20
263 Robin Ventura .07 .20
264 Ron Gant .07 .20
265 Ellis Burks .07 .20
266 Juan Guzman .02 .10
267 Wes Chamberlain .02 .10
268 John Smiley .02 .10
269 Franklin Stubbs .02 .10
270 Tom Browning .02 .10
271 Dennis Eckersley .07 .20
272 Carlton Fisk .10 .30
273 Lou Whitaker .07 .20
274 Phil Plantier .02 .10
275 Bobby Bonilla .07 .20
276 Ben McDonald .02 .10
277 Bob Zupcic .02 .10
278 Terry Steinbach .02 .10
279 Terry Mulholland .02 .10
280 Lance Johnson .02 .10
281 Willie McGee .07 .20
282 Bret Saberhagen .07 .20
283 Randy Myers .02 .10
284 Randy Tomlin .02 .10
285 Mickey Morandini .02 .10
286 Brian Williams .02 .10
287 Tino Martinez .10 .30
288 Jose Melendez .02 .10
289 Jeff Huson .02 .10
290 Joe Grahe .02 .10
291 Mel Hall .02 .10
292 Otis Nixon .02 .10
293 Todd Hundley .02 .10
294 Casey Candaele .02 .10
295 Kevin Seitzer .02 .10
296 Eddie Taubensee .02 .10
297 Moises Alou .07 .20
298 Scott Radinsky .02 .10
299 Thomas Howard .02 .10
300 Kyle Abbott .02 .10
301 Omar Vizquel .10 .30
302 Keith Miller .02 .10
303 Rick Aguilera .02 .10
304 Bruce Hurst .02 .10
305 Ken Caminiti .07 .20
306 Mike Pagliarulo .02 .10
307 Frank Seminara .02 .10
308 Andre Dawson .07 .20
309 Jose Lind .02 .10
310 Joe Boever .02 .10
311 Jeff Parrett .02 .10
312 Alan Mills .02 .10
313 Kevin Tapani .02 .10
314 Darryl Kile .07 .20
315 Will Clark CL .07 .20
316 Mike Sharperson .02 .10
317 John Orton .02 .10
318 Bob Tewksbury .02 .10
319 Xavier Hernandez .02 .10
320 Paul Assenmacher .02 .10
321 John Franco .07 .20
322 Mike Timlin .02 .10
323 Jose Guzman .02 .10
324 Pedro Martinez .40 1.00
325 Bill Spiers .02 .10
326 Melido Perez .02 .10
327 Mike Macfarlane .02 .10
328 Ricky Bones .02 .10
329 Scott Bankhead .02 .10
330 Rich Rodriguez .02 .10
331 Geronimo Pena .02 .10
332 Bernie Williams .10 .30
333 Paul Molitor .07 .20
334 Carlos Garcia .02 .10
335 David Cone .07 .20
336 Randy Johnson .20 .50
337 Pat Mahomes .02 .10
338 Erik Hanson .02 .10
339 Duane Ward .02 .10
340 Al Martin .02 .10
341 Pedro Munoz .02 .10
342 Greg Colbrunn .02 .10
343 Julio Valera .02 .10
344 John Olerud .07 .20
345 George Bell .02 .10
346 Devon White .07 .20
347 Donovan Osborne .02 .10
348 Mark Gardner .02 .10
349 Zane Smith .02 .10
350 Wilson Alvarez .02 .10
351 Kevin Koslofski .02 .10
352 Roberto Hernandez .02 .10
353 Glenn Davis .02 .10
354 Reggie Sanders .07 .20
355 Ken Griffey Jr. .30 .75
356 Marquis Grissom .07 .20
357 Jack McDowell .02 .10
358 Jimmy Key .07 .20
359 Stan Belinda .02 .10
360 Gerald Williams .02 .10
361 Sid Fernandez .02 .10
362 Alex Fernandez .02 .10
363 John Smoltz .10 .30
364 Travis Fryman .07 .20
365 Jose Canseco .10 .30
366 David Justice .07 .20
367 Pedro Astacio .02 .10
368 Tim Belcher .02 .10
369 Steve Sax .02 .10
370 Gary Gaetti .07 .20
371 Jeff Frye .02 .10
372 Bob Wickman .02 .10
373 Ryan Thompson .02 .10
374 David Hulse RC .05 .15
375 Cal Eldred .02 .10
376 Ryan Klesko .07 .20
377 Damion Easley .02 .10
378 John Kiely .02 .10
379 Jim Bullinger .02 .10
380 Brian Bohanon .02 .10
381 Rod Brewer .02 .10
382 Fernando Ramsey RC .05 .15
383 Sam Militello .02 .10
384 Arthur Rhodes .02 .10
385 Eric Karros .07 .20
386 Rico Brogna .02 .10
387 John Valentin .02 .10
388 Kerry Woodson .02 .10
389 Ben Rivera .02 .10
390 Matt Whiteside RC .05 .15
391 Henry Rodriguez .02 .10
392 John Wetteland .07 .20
393 Kent Mercker .02 .10
394 Bernard Gilkey .02 .10
395 Doug Henry .02 .10
396 Mo Vaughn .07 .20
397 Scott Erickson .02 .10
398 Bill Gullickson .02 .10
399 Mark Guthrie .02 .10
400 Dave Martinez .02 .10
401 Jeff Kent .20 .50
402 Chris Hoiles .02 .10
403 Mike Henneman .02 .10
404 Chris Nabholz .02 .10
405 Tom Pagnozzi .02 .10
406 Kelly Gruber .02 .10
407 Bob Welch .02 .10
408 Frank Castillo .02 .10
409 John Dopson .02 .10
410 Steve Farr .02 .10
411 Henry Cotto .02 .10
412 Bob Patterson .02 .10
413 Todd Stottlemyre .02 .10
414 Greg A. Harris .02 .10
415 Denny Neagle .07 .20
416 Bill Wegman .02 .10
417 Willie Wilson .02 .10
418 Terry Leach .02 .10
419 Willie Randolph .07 .20
420 Mark McGwire CL .10 .30
421 Calvin Murray CL .02 .10
422 Pete Janicki TP RC .05 .15
423 Todd Jones TP .07 .20
424 Mike Neill TP .02 .10
425 Carlos Delgado TP .20 .50
426 Jose Oliva TP .02 .10
427 Tyrone Hill TP .02 .10
428 Dmitri Young TP .07 .20
429 Derek Wallace TP RC .05 .15
430 Michael Moore TP RC .05 .15
431 Cliff Floyd TP .07 .20
432 Calvin Murray TP .02 .10
433 Manny Ramirez TP .30 .75
434 Marc Newfield TP .02 .10
435 Charles Johnson TP .07 .20
436 Butch Huskey TP .02 .10
437 Brad Pennington TP .02 .10
438 Ray McDavid TP RC .05 .15
439 Chad McConnell TP .02 .10
440 M.Cummings TP RC .05 .15
441 Benji Gil TP .02 .10
442 Frankie Rodriguez TP .02 .10
443 Chad Mottola TP RC .05 .15
444 John Burke TP RC .05 .15
445 Michael Tucker TP .02 .10
446 Rick Greene TP .02 .10
447 Rich Becker TP .02 .10
448 Mike Robertson TP .02 .10
449 Derek Jeter TP RC 6.00 15.00
450 Ivan Rodriguez CL .10 .30
David McCarty
451 Jim Abbott IN .07 .20
452 Jeff Bagwell IN .07 .20
453 Jason Bere IN .02 .10
454 Delino DeShields IN .02 .10
455 Travis Fryman IN .02 .10
456 Alex Gonzalez IN .02 .10
457 Phil Hiatt IN .02 .10
458 Dave Hollins IN .02 .10
459 Chipper Jones IN .10 .30
460 David Justice IN .02 .10
461 Ray Lankford IN .02 .10
462 David McCarty IN .02 .10
463 Mike Mussina IN .07 .20
464 Jose Offerman IN .02 .10
465 Dean Palmer IN .02 .10
466 Geronimo Pena IN .02 .10
467 Eduardo Perez IN .02 .10
468 Ivan Rodriguez IN .07 .20
469 Reggie Sanders IN .02 .10
470 Bernie Williams IN .07 .20
471 Barry Bonds CL .30 .75
Matt Williams
Will Clark
472 Greg Maddux .20 .50
Steve Avery
John Smoltz
Tom Glavine
473 Jose Rijo .07 .20
Rob Dibble
Roberto Kelly
Reggie Sanders
Barry Larkin
474 Gary Sheffield .07 .20
Phil Plantier
Tony Gwynn
Fred McGriff
475 Doug Drabek .07 .20
Craig Biggio
Jeff Bagwell
476 Will Clark .30 .75
Barry Bonds
Matt Williams
477 Eric Davis .07 .20
Darryl Strawberry
478 Dante Bichette .07 .20
David Nied
Andres Galarraga
479 Dave Magadan .02 .10
Orestes Destrade
Bret Barberie
Jeff Conine
480 Tim Wakefield .07 .20
Andy Van Slyke
Jay Bell
481 Marquis Grissom .10 .30
Delino DeShields
Dennis Martinez
Larry Walker
482 Geronimo Pena .20 .50
Ray Lankford
Ozzie Smith
Bernard Gilkey
483 Randy Myers .20 .50
Ryne Sandberg
Mark Grace
484 Eddie Murray .10 .30
Howard Johnson
Bobby Bonilla
485 John Kruk .02 .10
Dave Hollins
Darren Daulton
Len Dykstra
486 Barry Bonds AW .30 .75
487 Dennis Eckersley AW .07 .20
488 Greg Maddux AW .20 .50
489 Dennis Eckersley AW .07 .20
490 Eric Karros AW .02 .10
491 Pat Listach AW .02 .10
492 Gary Sheffield AW .02 .10
493 Mark McGwire AW .25 .60
494 Gary Sheffield AW .02 .10
495 Edgar Martinez AW .07 .20
496 Fred McGriff AW .07 .20
497 Juan Gonzalez AW .07 .20
498 Darren Daulton AW .02 .10
499 Cecil Fielder AW .02 .10
500 Brent Gates CL .02 .10
501 Tavo Alvarez DD .02 .10
502 Rod Bolton .02 .10
503 J.Cummings DD RC .05 .15
504 Brent Gates DD .02 .10
505 Tyler Green .02 .10
506 Jose Martinez DD RC .05 .15
507 Troy Percival .10 .30
508 Kevin Stocker DD .02 .10
509 Matt Walbeck DD RC .05 .15
510 Rondell White DD .07 .20
511 Billy Ripken .02 .10
512 Mike Moore .02 .10
513 Jose Lind .02 .10
514 Chito Martinez .02 .10
515 Jose Guzman .02 .10
516 Kim Batiste .02 .10
517 Jeff Tackett .02 .10
518 Charlie Hough .07 .20
519 Marvin Freeman .02 .10
520 Carlos Martinez .02 .10
521 Eric Young .02 .10
522 Pete Incaviglia .02 .10
523 Scott Fletcher .02 .10
524 Orestes Destrade .02 .10
525 Ken Griffey Jr. CL .20 .50
526 Ellis Burks .07 .20
527 Juan Samuel .02 .10
528 Dave Magadan .02 .10
529 Jeff Parrett .02 .10
530 Bill Krueger .02 .10
531 Frank Bolick .02 .10
532 Alan Trammell .07 .20
533 Walt Weiss .02 .10
534 David Cone .07 .20
535 Greg Maddux .30 .75
536 Kevin Young .07 .20
537 Dave Hansen .02 .10
538 Alex Cole .02 .10
539 Greg Hibbard .02 .10
540 Gene Larkin .02 .10
541 Jeff Reardon .07 .20
542 Felix Jose .02 .10
543 Jimmy Key .07 .20
544 Reggie Jefferson .02 .10
545 Gregg Jefferies .02 .10
546 Dave Stewart .07 .20
547 Tim Wallach .02 .10
548 Spike Owen .02 .10
549 Tommy Greene .02 .10
550 Fernando Valenzuela .07 .20
551 Rich Amaral .02 .10
552 Bret Barberie .02 .10
553 Edgar Martinez .10 .30
554 Jim Abbott .10 .30
555 Frank Thomas .20 .50
556 Wade Boggs .10 .30
557 Tom Henke .02 .10
558 Milt Thompson .02 .10
559 Lloyd McClendon .02 .10
560 Vinny Castilla .20 .50
561 Ricky Jordan .02 .10
562 Andujar Cedeno .02 .10
563 Greg Vaughn .02 .10
564 Cecil Fielder .07 .20
565 Kirby Puckett .20 .50
566 Mark McGwire .50 1.25
567 Barry Bonds .60 1.50
568 Jody Reed .02 .10
569 Todd Zeile .02 .10
570 Mark Carreon .02 .10
571 Joe Girardi .02 .10
572 Luis Gonzalez .07 .20
573 Mark Grace .10 .30
574 Rafael Palmeiro .10 .30
575 Darryl Strawberry .07 .20
576 Will Clark .10 .30
577 Fred McGriff .10 .30
578 Kevin Reimer .02 .10
579 Dave Righetti .07 .20
580 Juan Bell .02 .10
581 Jeff Brantley .02 .10
582 Brian Hunter .02 .10
583 Tim Naehring .02 .10
584 Glenallen Hill .02 .10
585 Cal Ripken .60 1.50
586 Albert Belle .07 .20
587 Robin Yount .30 .75
588 Chris Bosio .02 .10
589 Pete Smith .02 .10
590 Chuck Carr .02 .10
591 Jeff Blauser .02 .10
592 Kevin McReynolds .02 .10
593 Andres Galarraga .07 .20
594 Kevin Maas .02 .10
595 Eric Davis .07 .20
596 Brian Jordan .07 .20
597 Tim Raines .07 .20
598 Rick Wilkins .02 .10
599 Steve Cooke .02 .10
600 Mike Gallego .02 .10
601 Mike Munoz .02 .10
602 Luis Rivera .02 .10
603 Junior Ortiz .02 .10
604 Brent Mayne .02 .10
605 Luis Alicea .02 .10
606 Damon Berryhill .02 .10
607 Dave Henderson .02 .10
608 Kirk McCaskill .02 .10
609 Jeff Fassero .02 .10
610 Mike Harkey .02 .10
611 Francisco Cabrera .02 .10
612 Rey Sanchez .02 .10
613 Scott Servais .02 .10
614 Darrin Fletcher .02 .10
615 Felix Fermin .02 .10
616 Kevin Seitzer .02 .10
617 Bob Scanlan .02 .10
618 Billy Hatcher .02 .10
619 John Vander Wal .02 .10
620 Joe Hesketh .02 .10
621 Hector Villanueva .02 .10
622 Randy Milligan .02 .10
623 Tony Tarasco RC .05 .15
624 Russ Swan .02 .10
625 Willie Wilson .02 .10
626 Frank Tanana .02 .10
627 Pete O'Brien .02 .10
628 Lenny Webster .02 .10
629 Mark Clark .02 .10
630 Roger Clemens CL .20 .50
631 Alex Arias .02 .10
632 Chris Gwynn .02 .10
633 Tom Bolton .02 .10
634 Greg Briley .02 .10
635 Kent Bottenfield .02 .10
636 Kelly Downs .02 .10
637 Manuel Lee .02 .10
638 Al Leiter .07 .20
639 Jeff Gardner .02 .10
640 Mike Gardiner .02 .10
641 Mark Gardner .02 .10
642 Jeff Branson .02 .10
643 Paul Wagner .02 .10
644 Sean Berry .02 .10
645 Phil Hiatt .02 .10
646 Kevin Mitchell .02 .10
647 Charlie Hayes .02 .10
648 Jim Deshaies .02 .10
649 Dan Pasqua .02 .10
650 Mike Maddux .02 .10
651 Domingo Martinez RC .05 .15
652 Greg McMichael RC .05 .15
653 Eric Wedge RC .20 .50
654 Mark Whiten .02 .10
655 Roberto Kelly .02 .10
656 Julio Franco .07 .20
657 Gene Harris .02 .10
658 Pete Schourek .02 .10
659 Mike Bielecki .02 .10
660 Ricky Gutierrez .02 .10
661 Chris Hammond .02 .10
662 Tim Scott .02 .10
663 Norm Charlton .02 .10
664 Doug Drabek .02 .10
665 Dwight Gooden .07 .20
666 Jim Gott .02 .10
667 Randy Myers .02 .10
668 Darren Holmes .02 .10
669 Tim Spehr .02 .10
670 Bruce Ruffin .02 .10
671 Bobby Thigpen .02 .10
672 Tony Fernandez .02 .10
673 Darrin Jackson .02 .10
674 Gregg Olson .02 .10
675 Rob Dibble .07 .20
676 Howard Johnson .02 .10
677 Mike Lansing RC .20 .50
678 Charlie Leibrandt .02 .10
679 Kevin Bass .02 .10
680 Hubie Brooks .02 .10
681 Scott Brosius .07 .20
682 Randy Knorr .02 .10
683 Dante Bichette .07 .20
684 Bryan Harvey .02 .10
685 Greg Gohr .02 .10
686 Willie Banks .02 .10
687 Robb Nen .07 .20
688 Mike Scioscia .02 .10
689 John Farrell .02 .10
690 John Candelaria .02 .10
691 Damon Buford .02 .10
692 Todd Worrell .02 .10
693 Pat Hentgen .02 .10
694 John Smiley .02 .10
695 Greg Swindell .02 .10
696 Derek Bell .02 .10
697 Terry Jorgensen .02 .10
698 Jimmy Jones .02 .10
699 David Wells .07 .20
700 Dave Martinez .02 .10
701 Steve Bedrosian .02 .10
702 Jeff Russell .02 .10
703 Joe Magrane .02 .10
704 Matt Mieske .02 .10
705 Paul Molitor .07 .20
706 Dale Murphy .10 .30
707 Steve Howe .02 .10
708 Greg Gagne .02 .10
709 Dave Eiland .02 .10
710 David West .02 .10
711 Luis Aquino .02 .10
712 Joe Orsulak .02 .10
713 Eric Plunk .02 .10
714 Mike Felder .02 .10
715 Joe Klink .02 .10
716 Lonnie Smith .02 .10
717 Monty Fariss .02 .10
718 Craig Lefferts .02 .10
719 John Habyan .02 .10
720 Willie Blair .02 .10
721 Darnell Coles .02 .10
722 Mark Williamson .02 .10
723 Bryn Smith .02 .10
724 Greg W. Harris .02 .10
725 Graeme Lloyd RC .20 .50
726 Cris Carpenter .02 .10
727 Chico Walker .02 .10
728 Tracy Woodson .02 .10
729 Jose Uribe .02 .10
730 Stan Javier .02 .10
731 Jay Howell .02 .10
732 Freddie Benavides .02 .10
733 Jeff Reboulet .02 .10
734 Scott Sanderson .02 .10
735 Ryne Sandberg CL .20 .50
736 Archi Cianfrocco .02 .10
737 Daryl Boston .02 .10
738 Craig Grebeck .02 .10
739 Doug Dascenzo .02 .10
740 Gerald Young .02 .10
741 Candy Maldonado .02 .10
742 Joey Cora .02 .10
743 Don Slaught .02 .10
744 Steve Decker .02 .10
745 Blas Minor .02 .10
746 Storm Davis .02 .10
747 Carlos Quintana .02 .10
748 Vince Coleman .02 .10
749 Todd Burns .02 .10
750 Steve Frey .02 .10
751 Ivan Calderon .02 .10
752 Steve Reed RC .05 .15
753 Danny Jackson .02 .10
754 Jeff Conine .07 .20
755 Juan Gonzalez .07 .20
756 Mike Kelly .02 .10
757 John Doherty .02 .10
758 Jack Armstrong .02 .10
759 John Wehner .02 .10
760 Scott Bankhead .02 .10
761 Jim Tatum .02 .10
762 Scott Pose RC .05 .15
763 Andy Ashby .02 .10
764 Ed Sprague .02 .10
765 Harold Baines .07 .20
766 Kirk Gibson .07 .20
767 Troy Neel .02 .10
768 Dick Schofield .02 .10
769 Dickie Thon .02 .10
770 Butch Henry .02 .10
771 Junior Felix .02 .10
772 Ken Ryan RC .05 .15
773 Trevor Hoffman .20 .50
774 Phil Plantier .02 .10
775 Bo Jackson .20 .50
776 Benito Santiago .07 .20
777 Andre Dawson .07 .20
778 Bryan Hickerson .02 .10
779 Dennis Moeller .02 .10
780 Ryan Bowen .02 .10
781 Eric Fox .02 .10
782 Joe Kmak .02 .10
783 Mike Hampton .07 .20
784 Darrell Sherman RC .05 .15
785 J.T. Snow .10 .30
786 Dave Winfield .07 .20
787 Jim Austin .02 .10
788 Craig Shipley .02 .10
789 Greg Myers .02 .10
790 Todd Benzinger .02 .10
791 Cory Snyder .02 .10
792 David Segui .02 .10
793 Armando Reynoso .02 .10
794 Chili Davis .07 .20
795 Dave Nilsson .02 .10
796 Paul O'Neill .10 .30
797 Jerald Clark .02 .10
798 Jose Mesa .02 .10
799 Brian Holman .02 .10
800 Jim Eisenreich .02 .10
801 Mark McLemore .02 .10
802 Luis Sojo .02 .10
803 Harold Reynolds .07 .20
804 Dan Plesac .02 .10
805 Dave Stieb .02 .10
806 Tom Brunansky .02 .10
807 Kelly Gruber .02 .10
808 Bob Ojeda .02 .10
809 Dave Burba .02 .10
810 Joe Boever .02 .10
811 Jeremy Hernandez .02 .10
812 Tim Salmon TC .07 .20
813 Jeff Bagwell TC .07 .20
814 Dennis Eckersley TC .07 .20
815 Roberto Alomar TC .07 .20
816 Steve Avery TC .02 .10
817 Pat Listach TC .02 .10
818 Gregg Jefferies TC .02 .10
819 Sammy Sosa TC .20 .50
820 Darryl Strawberry TC .07 .20
821 Dennis Martinez TC .02 .10
822 Robby Thompson TC .02 .10
823 Albert Belle TC .07 .20
824 Randy Johnson TC .10 .30
825 Nigel Wilson TC .02 .10
826 Bobby Bonilla TC .02 .10
827 Glenn Davis TC .02 .10
828 Gary Sheffield TC .02 .10
829 Darren Daulton TC .02 .10
830 Jay Bell TC .02 .10
831 Juan Gonzalez TC .02 .10
832 Andre Dawson TC .02 .10
833 Hal Morris TC .02 .10
834 David Nied TC .02 .10
835 Felix Jose TC .02 .10
836 Travis Fryman TC .02 .10
837 Shane Mack TC .02 .10
838 Robin Ventura TC .02 .10
839 Danny Tartabull TC .02 .10
840 Roberto Alomar CL .07 .20
SP5 George Brett .40 1.00
Robin Yount
SP6 Nolan Ryan .75 2.00

1993 Upper Deck Gold Hologram

These gold parallel cards were made available exclusively in factory set form. One set in every 15 ct. case of factory sets featured cards with gold foil holograms on the card backs, rather than the traditional silver foil holograms. The factory boxes for the basic sets and the much scarcer Gold Hologram sets are identical, thus all Gold Hologram sets offered for sale are for opened factory sets. Please refer to the multipliers provided below for values on single cards.

COMP.FACT.SET (840) 75.00 150.00
*STARS: 3X TO 8X BASIC CARDS
*ROOKIES: 3X TO 8X BASIC CARDS
449 Derek Jeter TP 75.00 150.00

1993 Upper Deck Clutch Performers

These 20 standard-size cards were inserted one every nine series II retail foil packs, as well as inserted one per series II retail jumbo packs. The cards are numbered on the back with an "R" prefix and appear in alphabetical order. These 20 cards represent Reggie Jackson's selection of players who have come through under pressure. Please note these cards are condition sensitive and trade for premium values if found in Mint.

COMPLETE SET (20) 8.00 20.00
R1 Roberto Alomar .30 .75
R2 Wade Boggs .30 .75
R3 Barry Bonds 1.50 4.00
R4 Jose Canseco .30 .75
R5 Joe Carter .20 .50
R6 Will Clark .30 .75
R7 Roger Clemens 1.00 2.50
R8 Dennis Eckersley .20 .50
R9 Cecil Fielder .20 .50
R10 Juan Gonzalez .20 .50
R11 Ken Griffey Jr. .75 2.00
R12 Rickey Henderson .50 1.25
R13 Barry Larkin .30 .75
R14 Don Mattingly 1.25 3.00
R15 Fred McGriff .30 .75
R16 Terry Pendleton .20 .50
R17 Kirby Puckett .50 1.25
R18 Ryne Sandberg .75 2.00
R19 John Smoltz .30 .75
R20 Frank Thomas .50 1.25

1993 Upper Deck Fifth Anniversary

This 15-card standard-size set celebrates Upper Deck's five years in the sports card business. The cards are essentially reprinted versions of some of Upper Deck's most popular cards in the last five years. These cards were inserted one every nine second series hobby packs. The black-bordered fronts feature player photos that previously appeared on an Upper Deck card. The cards are numbered on the back with an "A" prefix. These cards are condition sensitive and trade for premium values in Mint.

COMPLETE SET (15) 6.00 15.00
SER.2 STATED ODDS 1:9 HOBBY
A1 Ken Griffey Jr. .75 2.00
A2 Gary Sheffield .20 .50
A3 Roberto Alomar .30 .75
A4 Jim Abbott .30 .75
A5 Nolan Ryan 2.00 5.00
A6 Juan Gonzalez .20 .50
A7 David Justice .20 .50
A8 Carlos Baerga .08 .25
A9 Reggie Jackson .30 .75
A10 Eric Karros .20 .50
A11 Chipper Jones .50 1.25
A12 Ivan Rodriguez .30 .75
A13 Pat Listach .08 .25
A14 Frank Thomas .50 1.25
A15 Tim Salmon .30 .75

1993 Upper Deck Future Heroes

Inserted in second series foil packs at a rate of one every nine pack; this set continues the Heroes insert set begun in the 1990 Upper Deck high-number set, this ten-card standard-size set features eight different "Future Heroes" along with a checklist and header card.

COMPLETE SET (10) 5.00 12.00
SER.2 STATED ODDS 1:9
55 Roberto Alomar .30 .75
56 Barry Bonds 1.50 4.00

Card	Low	High
57 Roger Clemens	1.00	2.50
58 Juan Gonzalez	.20	.50
59 Ken Griffey Jr.	.75	2.00
60 Mark McGwire	1.25	3.00
61 Kirby Puckett	.50	1.25
62 Frank Thomas	.50	1.25
63 Checklist	.20	.50
NNO Header Card SP	.08	.25

1993 Upper Deck Home Run Heroes

This 28-card standard-size set features the home run leader from each Major League team. Each 1993 first series 27-card jumbo pack contained one of these cards. The cards are numbered on the back with an "HR" prefix and the set is arranged in descending order according to the number of home runs.

Card	Low	High
COMPLETE SET (28)	6.00	15.00
HR1 Juan Gonzalez	.20	.50
HR2 Mark McGwire	1.25	3.00
HR3 Cecil Fielder	.20	.50
HR4 Fred McGriff	.30	.75
HR5 Albert Belle	.20	.50
HR6 Barry Bonds	1.50	4.00
HR7 Joe Carter	.20	.50
HR8 Darren Daulton	.20	.50
HR9 Ken Griffey Jr.	.75	2.00
HR10 Dave Hollins	.08	.25
HR11 Ryne Sandberg	.75	2.00
HR12 George Bell	.08	.25
HR13 Danny Tartabull	.08	.25
HR14 Mike Devereaux	.08	.25
HR15 Greg Vaughn	.08	.25
HR16 Larry Walker	.20	.50
HR17 David Justice	.20	.50
HR18 Terry Pendleton	.20	.50
HR19 Eric Karros	.20	.50
HR20 Ray Lankford	.20	.50
HR21 Matt Williams	.20	.50
HR22 Eric Anthony	.08	.25
HR23 Bobby Bonilla	.20	.50
HR24 Kirby Puckett	.50	1.25
HR25 Mike Macfarlane	.08	.25
HR26 Tom Brunansky	.08	.25
HR27 Paul O'Neill	.30	.75
HR28 Gary Gaetti	.20	.50

1993 Upper Deck Iooss Collection

This 27-card standard-size set spotlights the work of famous sports photographer Walter Iooss Jr. by presenting 26 of the game's current greats in a candid photo set. The cards were inserted in series I retail foil packs at a rate of one every nine packs. They were also in retail jumbo packs at a rate of one in five packs. The cards are numbered on the back with a "WI" prefix. Please note these cards are condition sensitive and trade for premium values in Mint.

Card	Low	High
COMPLETE SET (27)	12.50	30.00
SER.1 STATED ODDS 1:9 RET, 1:5 JUM		
*JUMBO CARDS: 2X TO 5X BASIC IOOSS		
JUMBOS DISTRIBUTED IN RETAIL PACKS		
WI1 Tim Salmon	.40	1.00
WI2 Jeff Bagwell	.40	1.00
WI3 Mark McGwire	1.50	4.00
WI4 Roberto Alomar	.40	1.00
WI5 Steve Avery	.10	.30
WI6 Paul Molitor	.25	.60
WI7 Ozzie Smith	1.00	2.50
WI8 Mark Grace	.40	1.00
WI9 Eric Karros	.25	.60
WI10 Delino DeShields	.10	.30
WI11 Will Clark	.40	1.00
WI12 Albert Belle	.25	.60
WI13 Ken Griffey Jr.	1.00	2.50
WI14 Howard Johnson	.10	.30
WI15 Cal Ripken Jr.	2.00	5.00
WI16 Fred McGriff	.40	1.00
WI17 Darren Daulton	.25	.60
WI18 Andy Van Slyke	.40	1.00
WI19 Nolan Ryan	2.50	6.00
WI20 Wade Boggs	.40	1.00
WI21 Barry Larkin	.40	1.00
WI22 George Brett	1.50	4.00
WI23 Cecil Fielder	.25	.60
WI24 Kirby Puckett	.60	1.50
WI25 Frank Thomas	.60	1.50
WI26 Don Mattingly	1.50	4.00
NNO Title Card Iooss Header	.10	.30

1993 Upper Deck Mays Heroes

This standard-size ten-card set was randomly inserted in 1993 Upper Deck first series foil packs.

Mays Makes Historic Catch

The fronts feature color photos of Mays at various stages of his career that are partially contained within a black bordered circle. The cards are numbered in continuation of Upper Deck's Heroes series.

Card	Low	High
COMPLETE SET (10)	1.50	3.00
COMMON (46-54/HDR)	.20	.50
SER.1 STATED ODDS 1:9		

1993 Upper Deck On Deck

Inserted one per series II jumbo packs, these 25 standard-size cards profile baseball's top players. The cards are numbered on the back with a "D" prefix in alphabetical order by name.

Card	Low	High
COMPLETE SET (25)	8.00	20.00
SER.2 STAT.ODDS 1:1 RED/BLUE JUMBO		
D1 Jim Abbott	.30	.75
D2 Roberto Alomar	.30	.75
D3 Carlos Baerga	.08	.25
D4 Albert Belle	.20	.50
D5 Wade Boggs	.30	.75
D6 George Brett	1.25	3.00
D7 Jose Canseco	.30	.75
D8 Will Clark	.30	.75
D9 Roger Clemens	1.00	2.50
D10 Dennis Eckersley	.20	.50
D11 Cecil Fielder	.20	.50
D12 Juan Gonzalez	.20	.50
D13 Ken Griffey Jr.	.75	2.00
D14 Tony Gwynn	.60	1.50
D15 Bo Jackson	.50	1.25
D16 Chipper Jones	.50	1.25
D17 Eric Karros	.20	.50
D18 Mark McGwire	1.25	3.00
D19 Kirby Puckett	.50	1.25
D20 Nolan Ryan	2.00	5.00
D21 Tim Salmon	.30	.75
D22 Ryne Sandberg	.75	2.00
D23 Darryl Strawberry	.20	.50
D24 Frank Thomas	.50	1.25
D25 Andy Van Slyke	.30	.75

1993 Upper Deck Season Highlights

This 20-card standard-size insert set captures great moments of the 1992 Major League Baseball season. The cards were exclusively distributed in specially marked cases that were available only at Upper Deck Heroes of Baseball Card Shows and through the purchase of a specified quantity of second series cases. In these packs, the cards were inserted at a rate of one every nine. The cards are numbered on the back with an "HI" prefix in alphabetical order by player's name.

Card	Low	High
COMPLETE SET (20)	50.00	120.00
STATED ODDS 1:9 HOBBY SEASON HL		
HI1 Roberto Alomar	2.00	5.00
HI2 Steve Avery	.60	1.50
HI3 Harold Baines	1.25	3.00
HI4 Damon Berryhill	.60	1.50
HI5 Barry Bonds	10.00	25.00
HI6 Bret Boone	1.25	3.00
HI7 George Brett	8.00	20.00
HI8 Francisco Cabrera	.60	1.50
HI9 Ken Griffey Jr.	5.00	12.00
HI10 Rickey Henderson	3.00	8.00
HI11 Kenny Lofton	1.25	3.00
HI12 Mickey Morandini	.60	1.50
HI13 Eddie Murray	3.00	8.00
HI14 David Nied	.60	1.50
HI15 Jeff Reardon	1.25	3.00
HI16 Bip Roberts	.60	1.50
HI17 Nolan Ryan	12.50	30.00
HI18 Ed Sprague	.60	1.50
HI19 Dave Winfield	1.25	3.00
HI20 Robin Yount	5.00	12.00

1993 Upper Deck Then And Now

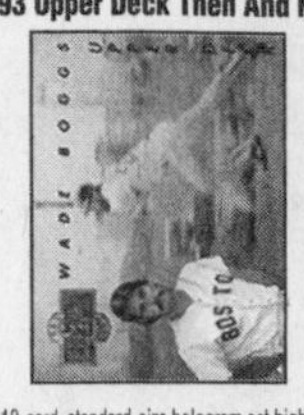

This 18-card, standard-size hologram set highlights veteran stars in their rookie year and today, reflecting on how they and the game have changed. Cards 1-9 were randomly inserted in series I foil packs; cards 10-18 were randomly inserted in series II foil packs. In either series, the cards were inserted one every 27 packs. The nine lithogram cards in the second series feature one card each of Hall of Famers Reggie Jackson, Mickey Mantle, and Willie Mays, as well as six active players. The cards are numbered on the back with a "TN" prefix and arranged alphabetically within subgroup according to player's last name.

Card	Low	High
COMPLETE SET (18)	15.00	40.00
COMPLETE SERIES 1 (9)	6.00	15.00
COMPLETE SERIES 2 (9)	10.00	25.00
STATED ODDS 1:27 HOBBY		
TN1 Wade Boggs	.50	1.25
TN2 George Brett	2.00	5.00
TN3 Rickey Henderson	.75	2.00
TN4 Cal Ripken	2.50	6.00
TN5 Nolan Ryan	3.00	8.00
TN6 Ryne Sandberg	1.25	3.00
TN7 Ozzie Smith	1.25	3.00
TN8 Darryl Strawberry	.30	.75
TN9 Dave Winfield	.30	.75
TN10 Dennis Eckersley	.30	.75
TN11 Tony Gwynn	1.00	2.50
TN12 Howard Johnson	.15	.40
TN13 Don Mattingly	2.00	5.00
TN14 Eddie Murray	.75	2.00
TN15 Robin Yount	1.25	3.00
TN16 Reggie Jackson	1.00	2.50
TN17 Mickey Mantle	5.00	12.00
TN18 Willie Mays	2.50	6.00

1993 Upper Deck Triple Crown

This ten-card, standard-size insert set highlights ten players who were selected by Upper Deck as having the best shot at winning Major League Baseball's Triple Crown. The cards were randomly inserted in series I hobby foil packs at a rate of one in 15. The cards are numbered on the back with a "TC" prefix and arranged alphabetically by player's last name.

Card	Low	High
COMPLETE SET (10)	5.00	12.00
STATED ODDS 1:15 HOBBY		
TC1 Barry Bonds	1.50	4.00
TC2 Jose Canseco	.30	.75
TC3 Will Clark	.30	.75
TC4 Ken Griffey Jr.	.75	2.00
TC5 Fred McGriff	.30	.75
TC6 Kirby Puckett	.50	1.25
TC7 Cal Ripken Jr.	1.50	4.00
TC8 Gary Sheffield	.20	.50
TC9 Frank Thomas	.50	1.25
TC10 Larry Walker	.20	.50

1993 Upper Deck Adventures in Toon World

Card	Low	High
NNO Joe Montana Wayne Gretzky Reggie Jackson Michael Jordan	1.00	2.50

1994 Upper Deck

The 1994 Upper Deck set was issued in two series of 280 and 270 standard-size cards for a total of 550. There are number of topical subsets including Star Rookies (1-30), Fantasy Team (31-40), The Future is Now (41-55), Home Field Advantage (267-294), Upper Deck Classic Alumni (295-299), Diamond Debuts (511-522) and Top Prospects (523-550). Three autograph cards were randomly inserted into first series retail packs. They are Ken Griffey Jr. (KG), Mickey Mantle (MM) and a combo card with Griffey and Mantle (GM). Though they lack serial-numbering, all three cards have an announced print run of 1,000 copies per. An Alex Rodriguez (298A) autograph card was randomly inserted into second series retail packs but production quantities were never divulged by the manufacturer. Rookie Cards include Michael Jordan (as an baseball player), Chan Ho Park, Alex Rodriguez and Billy Wagner. Many cards have been found with a significant variation on the back. The player's name, the horizontal bar containing the biographical information and the vertical bar containing the stats header are normally printed in copper-gold color. On the variation cards, these areas are printed in silver. It is not known exactly how many of the 550 cards have silver versions, nor has any premium been established for them. Also, all of the American League Home Field Advantage subset cards (numbers 281-294) are minor uncorrected errors because the Upper Deck logos on the front are missing the year "1994".

Card	Low	High
COMPLETE SET (550)	15.00	40.00
COMP. SERIES 1 (280)	12.50	25.00
COMP. SERIES 2 (270)	7.50	15.00
1 Brian Anderson RC	.15	.40
2 Shane Andrews	.05	.15
3 James Baldwin	.05	.15
4 Rich Becker	.05	.15
5 Greg Blosser	.05	.15
6 Ricky Bottalico RC	.05	.15
7 Midre Cummings	.05	.15
8 Carlos Delgado	.20	.50
9 Steve Dreyer RC	.05	.15
10 Joey Eischen	.05	.15
11 Carl Everett	.10	.30
12 Cliff Floyd UER (text indicates he throws left; should be right)	.10	.30
13 Alex Gonzalez	.05	.15
14 Jeff Granger	.05	.15
15 Shawn Green	.30	.75
16 Brian L. Hunter	.05	.15
17 Butch Huskey	.05	.15
18 Mark Hutton	.05	.15
19 Michael Jordan RC	3.00	8.00
20 Steve Karsay	.05	.15
21 Jeff McNeely	.05	.15
22 Marc Newfield	.05	.15
23 Manny Ramirez	.30	.75
24 Alex Rodriguez RC	6.00	15.00
25 Scott Ruffcorn UER (photo on back is Robert Ellis)	.05	.15
26 Paul Spoljaric UER (Expos logo on back)	.05	.15
27 Salomon Torres	.05	.15
28 Steve Trachsel	.05	.15
29 Chris Turner	.05	.15
30 Gabe White	.05	.15
31 Randy Johnson FT	.20	.50
32 John Wetteland FT	.05	.15
33 Mike Piazza FT	.30	.75
34 Rafael Palmeiro FT	.10	.30
35 Roberto Alomar FT	.10	.30
36 Matt Williams FT	.05	.15
37 Travis Fryman FT	.05	.15
38 Barry Bonds FT	.40	1.00
39 Marquis Grissom FT	.05	.15
40 Albert Belle FT	.10	.30
41 Steve Avery FUT	.05	.15
42 Jason Bere FUT	.05	.15
43 Alex Fernandez FUT	.05	.15
44 Mike Mussina FUT	.10	.30
45 Aaron Sele FUT	.05	.15
46 Rod Beck FUT	.05	.15
47 Mike Piazza FUT	.30	.75
48 John Olerud FUT	.05	.15
49 Carlos Baerga FUT	.05	.15
50 Gary Sheffield FUT	.05	.15
51 Travis Fryman FUT	.05	.15
52 Juan Gonzalez FUT	.05	.15
53 Ken Griffey Jr. FUT	.30	.75
54 Tim Salmon FUT	.10	.30
55 Frank Thomas FUT	.20	.50
56 Tony Phillips	.05	.15
57 Julio Franco	.10	.30
58 Kevin Mitchell	.05	.15
59 Raul Mondesi	.10	.30
60 Rickey Henderson	.30	.75
61 Jay Buhner	.10	.30
62 Bill Swift	.05	.15
63 Brady Anderson	.10	.30
64 Ryan Klesko	.10	.30
65 Darren Daulton	.10	.30
66 Damion Easley	.05	.15
67 Mark McGwire	.75	2.00
68 John Roper	.05	.15
69 Dave Telgheder	.05	.15
70 David Nied	.05	.15
71 Mo Vaughn	.10	.30
72 Tyler Green	.05	.15
73 Dave Magadan	.05	.15
74 Chili Davis	.10	.30
75 Archi Cianfrocco	.05	.15
76 Joe Girardi	.05	.15
77 Chris Hoiles	.05	.15
78 Ryan Bowen	.05	.15
79 Greg Gagne	.05	.15
80 Aaron Sele	.05	.15
81 Dave Winfield	.10	.30
82 Chad Curtis	.05	.15
83 Andy Van Slyke	.20	.50
84 Kevin Stocker	.05	.15
85 Deion Sanders	.20	.50
86 Bernie Williams	.20	.50
87 John Smoltz	.20	.50
88 Ruben Santana	.05	.15
89 Dave Stewart	.10	.30
90 Don Mattingly	.75	2.00
91 Joe Carter	.10	.30
92 Ryne Sandberg	.50	1.25
93 Chris Gomez	.05	.15
94 Tino Martinez	.20	.50
95 Terry Pendleton	.10	.30
96 Andre Dawson	.10	.30
97 Wil Cordero	.05	.15
98 Kent Hrbek	.10	.30
99 John Olerud	.10	.30
100 Kirt Manwaring	.05	.15
101 Tim Bogar	.05	.15
102 Mike Mussina	.20	.50
103 Nigel Wilson	.05	.15
104 Ricky Gutierrez	.05	.15
105 Roberto Mejia	.05	.15
106 Tom Pagnozzi	.05	.15
107 Mike Macfarlane	.05	.15
108 Jose Bautista	.05	.15
109 Luis Ortiz	.05	.15
110 Brent Gates	.05	.15
111 Tim Salmon	.20	.50
112 Wade Boggs	.20	.50
113 Tripp Cromer	.05	.15
114 Denny Hocking	.05	.15
115 Carlos Baerga	.05	.15
116 J.R. Phillips	.05	.15
117 Bo Jackson	.30	.75
118 Lance Johnson	.05	.15
119 Bobby Jones	.05	.15
120 Bobby Witt	.05	.15
121 Ron Karkovice	.05	.15
122 Jose Vizcaino	.05	.15
123 Danny Darwin	.05	.15
124 Eduardo Perez	.05	.15
125 Brian Looney RC	.05	.15
126 Pat Hentgen	.05	.15
127 Frank Viola	.10	.30
128 Darren Holmes	.05	.15
129 Wally Whitehurst	.05	.15
130 Matt Walbeck	.05	.15
131 Albert Belle	.10	.30
132 Steve Cooke	.05	.15
133 Kevin Appier	.10	.30
134 Joe Oliver	.05	.15
135 Benji Gil	.05	.15
136 Steve Buechele	.05	.15
137 Devon White	.10	.30
138 S.Hitchcock UER two losses for career; should be four	.05	.15
139 Phil Leftwich RC	.05	.15
140 Jose Canseco	.20	.50
141 Rick Aguilera	.05	.15
142 Rod Beck	.05	.15
143 Jose Rijo	.05	.15
144 Tom Glavine	.20	.50
145 Phil Plantier	.05	.15
146 Jason Bere	.05	.15
147 Jamie Moyer	.10	.30
148 Wes Chamberlain	.05	.15
149 Glenallen Hill	.05	.15
150 Mark Whiten	.05	.15
151 Bret Barberie	.05	.15
152 Chuck Knoblauch	.10	.30
153 Trevor Hoffman	.20	.50
154 Rick Wilkins	.05	.15
155 Juan Gonzalez	.10	.30
156 Ozzie Guillen	.10	.30
157 Jim Eisenreich	.05	.15
158 Pedro Astacio	.05	.15
159 Joe Magrane	.05	.15
160 Ryan Thompson	.05	.15
161 Jose Lind	.05	.15
162 Jeff Conine	.10	.30
163 Todd Benzinger	.05	.15
164 Roger Salkeld	.05	.15
165 Gary DiSarcina	.05	.15
166 Kevin Gross	.05	.15
167 Charlie Hayes	.05	.15
168 Tim Costo	.05	.15
169 Wally Joyner	.10	.30
170 Johnny Ruffin	.05	.15
171 Kirk Rueter	.05	.15
172 Lenny Dykstra	.10	.30
173 Ken Hill	.05	.15
174 Mike Bordick	.05	.15
175 Billy Hall	.05	.15
176 Rob Butler	.05	.15
177 Jay Bell	.10	.30
178 Jeff Kent	.20	.50
179 David Wells	.10	.30
180 Dean Palmer	.10	.30
181 Mariano Duncan	.05	.15
182 Orlando Merced	.05	.15
183 Brett Butler	.10	.30
184 Milt Thompson	.05	.15
185 Chipper Jones	.30	.75
186 Paul O'Neill	.20	.50
187 Mike Greenwell	.05	.15
188 Harold Baines	.10	.30
189 Todd Stottlemyre	.05	.15
190 Jeromy Burnitz	.10	.30
191 Rene Arocha	.05	.15
192 Jeff Fassero	.05	.15
193 Robby Thompson	.05	.15
194 Greg W. Harris	.05	.15
195 Todd Van Poppel	.05	.15
196 Jose Guzman	.05	.15
197 Shane Mack	.05	.15
198 Carlos Garcia	.05	.15
199 Kevin Roberson	.05	.15
200 David McCarty	.05	.15
201 Alan Trammell	.10	.30
202 Chuck Carr	.05	.15
203 Tommy Greene	.05	.15
204 Wilson Alvarez	.05	.15
205 Dwight Gooden	.10	.30
206 Tony Tarasco	.05	.15
207 Darren Lewis	.05	.15
208 Eric Karros	.10	.30
209 Chris Hammond	.05	.15
210 Jeffrey Hammonds	.05	.15
211 Rich Amaral	.05	.15
212 Danny Tartabull	.05	.15
213 Jeff Russell	.05	.15
214 Dave Staton	.05	.15
215 Kenny Lofton	.10	.30
216 Manuel Lee	.05	.15
217 Brian Koelling	.05	.15
218 Scott Lydy	.05	.15
219 Tony Gwynn	.40	1.00
220 Cecil Fielder	.10	.30
221 Royce Clayton	.05	.15
222 Reggie Sanders	.10	.30
223 Brian Jordan	.10	.30
224 Ken Griffey Jr.	.50	1.25
225 Fred McGriff	.20	.50
226 Felix Jose	.05	.15
227 Brad Pennington	.05	.15
228 Chris Bosio	.05	.15
229 Mike Stanley	.05	.15
230 Willie Greene	.05	.15
231 Alex Fernandez	.05	.15
232 Brad Ausmus	.20	.50
233 Darrell Whitmore	.05	.15
234 Marcus Moore	.05	.15
235 Allen Watson	.05	.15
236 Jose Offerman	.05	.15
237 Rondell White	.10	.30
238 Jeff King	.05	.15
239 Luis Alicea	.05	.15
240 Dan Wilson	.05	.15
241 Ed Sprague	.05	.15
242 Todd Hundley	.05	.15
243 Al Martin	.05	.15
244 Mike Lansing	.05	.15
245 Ivan Rodriguez	.20	.50
246 Dave Fleming	.05	.15
247 John Doherty	.05	.15
248 Mark McLemore	.05	.15
249 Bob Hamelin	.05	.15
250 Curtis Pride RC	.15	.40
251 Zane Smith	.05	.15
252 Eric Young	.05	.15
253 Brian McRae	.05	.15
254 Tim Raines	.10	.30
255 Javier Lopez	.10	.30
256 Melvin Nieves	.05	.15
257 Randy Myers	.05	.15
258 Willie McGee	.10	.30
259 Jimmy Key UER (birthdate missing on back)	.10	.30
260 Tom Candiotti	.05	.15
261 Eric Davis	.10	.30
262 Craig Paquette	.05	.15
263 Robin Ventura	.10	.30
264 Pat Kelly	.05	.15
265 Gregg Jefferies	.05	.15
266 Cory Snyder	.05	.15
267 David Justice HFA	.05	.15
268 Sammy Sosa HFA	.30	.75
269 Barry Larkin HFA	.10	.30
270 Andres Galarraga HFA	.05	.15
271 Gary Sheffield HFA	.05	.15
272 Jeff Bagwell HFA	.10	.30
273 Mike Piazza HFA	.30	.75
274 Larry Walker HFA	.05	.15
275 Bobby Bonilla HFA	.05	.15
276 John Kruk HFA	.05	.15
277 Jay Bell HFA	.05	.15
278 Ozzie Smith HFA	.30	.75
279 Tony Gwynn HFA	.20	.50
280 Barry Bonds HFA	.40	1.00
281 Cal Ripken Jr. HFA	.50	1.25
282 Mo Vaughn HFA	.05	.15
283 Tim Salmon HFA	.10	.30
284 Frank Thomas HFA	.20	.50
285 Albert Belle HFA	.10	.30
286 Cecil Fielder HFA	.05	.15
287 Wally Joyner HFA	.05	.15
288 Greg Vaughn HFA	.05	.15
289 Kirby Puckett HFA	.20	.50
290 Don Mattingly HFA	.40	1.00
291 Terry Steinbach HFA	.05	.15
292 Ken Griffey Jr. HFA	.30	.75
293 Juan Gonzalez HFA	.05	.15
294 Paul Molitor HFA	.05	.15
295 Tavo Alvarez UDC	.05	.15
296 Matt Brunson UDC	.05	.15
297 Shawn Green UDC	.10	.30
298 Alex Rodriguez UDC	2.00	5.00
299 S.Stewart UDC	.30	.75
300 Frank Thomas	.30	.75
301 Mickey Tettleton	.05	.15
302 Pedro Munoz	.05	.15
303 Jose Valentin	.05	.15
304 Orestes Destrade	.05	.15
305 Pat Listach	.05	.15
306 Scott Brosius	.10	.30
307 Kurt Miller	.05	.15
308 Rob Dibble	.10	.30
309 Mike Blowers	.05	.15
310 Jim Abbott	.20	.50
311 Mike Jackson	.05	.15
312 Craig Biggio	.20	.50
313 Kurt Abbott RC	.05	.15
314 Chuck Finley	.10	.30
315 Andres Galarraga	.10	.30
316 Mike Moore	.05	.15
317 Doug Strange	.05	.15
318 Pedro Martinez	.30	.75
319 Kevin McReynolds	.05	.15
320 Greg Maddux	.50	1.25
321 Mike Henneman	.05	.15
322 Scott Leius	.05	.15
323 John Franco	.10	.30
324 Jeff Blauser	.05	.15
325 Kirby Puckett	.30	.75
326 Darryl Hamilton	.05	.15
327 John Smiley	.05	.15
328 Derrick May	.05	.15
329 Jose Vizcaino	.05	.15
330 Randy Johnson	.30	.75
331 Jack Morris	.10	.30
332 Graeme Lloyd	.05	.15
333 Dave Valle	.05	.15
334 Greg Myers	.05	.15
335 John Wetteland	.10	.30
336 Jim Gott	.05	.15
337 Tim Naehring	.05	.15
338 Mike Kelly	.05	.15
339 Jeff Montgomery	.05	.15
340 Rafael Palmeiro	.20	.50
341 Eddie Murray	.30	.75
342 Xavier Hernandez	.05	.15
343 Bobby Munoz	.05	.15
344 Bobby Bonilla	.10	.30
345 Travis Fryman	.10	.30
346 Steve Finley	.10	.30
347 Chris Sabo	.05	.15
348 Armando Reynoso	.05	.15
349 Ramon Martinez	.05	.15
350 Will Clark	.20	.50
351 Moises Alou	.10	.30
352 Jim Thome	.20	.50
353 Bob Tewksbury	.05	.15
354 Andujar Cedeno	.05	.15
355 Orel Hershiser	.10	.30
356 Mike Devereaux	.05	.15
357 Mike Perez	.05	.15
358 Dennis Martinez	.10	.30
359 Dave Nilsson	.05	.15
360 Ozzie Smith	.50	1.25
361 Eric Anthony	.05	.15
362 Scott Sanders	.05	.15
363 Paul Sorrento	.05	.15
364 Tim Belcher	.05	.15
365 Dennis Eckersley	.10	.30
366 Mel Rojas	.05	.15
367 Tom Henke	.05	.15
368 Randy Tomlin	.05	.15
369 B.J. Surhoff	.10	.30
370 Larry Walker	.10	.30
371 Joey Cora	.05	.15
372 Mike Harkey	.05	.15
373 John Valentin	.05	.15
374 Doug Jones	.05	.15
375 David Justice	.10	.30
376 Vince Coleman	.05	.15
377 David Hulse	.05	.15
378 Kevin Seitzer	.05	.15
379 Pete Harnisch	.05	.15
380 Ruben Sierra	.10	.30
381 Mark Lewis	.05	.15
382 Bip Roberts	.05	.15
383 Paul Wagner	.05	.15
384 Stan Javier	.05	.15
385 Barry Larkin	.20	.50
386 Mark Portugal	.05	.15
387 Roberto Kelly	.05	.15
388 Andy Benes	.05	.15
389 Felix Fermin	.05	.15
390 Marquis Grissom	.10	.30
391 Troy Neel	.05	.15
392 Chad Kreuter	.05	.15
393 Gregg Olson	.05	.15
394 Charles Nagy	.05	.15
395 Jack McDowell	.05	.15
396 Luis Gonzalez	.10	.30
397 Benito Santiago	.10	.30
398 Chris James	.05	.15
399 Terry Mulholland	.05	.15
400 Barry Bonds	.75	2.00
401 Joe Grahe	.05	.15
402 Duane Ward	.05	.15
403 John Burkett	.05	.15
404 Scott Servais	.05	.15
405 Bryan Harvey	.05	.15
406 Bernard Gilkey	.05	.15
407 Greg McMichael	.05	.15
408 Tim Wallach	.05	.15
409 Ken Caminiti	.10	.30
410 John Kruk	.10	.30
411 Darrin Jackson	.05	.15
412 Mike Gallego	.05	.15
413 David Cone	.10	.30
414 Lou Whitaker	.10	.30
415 Sandy Alomar Jr.	.05	.15
416 Bill Wegman	.05	.15
417 Pat Borders	.05	.15
418 Roger Pavlik	.05	.15
419 Pete Smith	.05	.15
420 Steve Avery	.05	.15
421 David Segui	.05	.15
422 Rheal Cormier	.05	.15
423 Harold Reynolds	.10	.30
424 Edgar Martinez	.20	.50
425 Cal Ripken Jr.	1.00	2.50
426 Jaime Navarro	.05	.15
427 Sean Berry	.05	.15
428 Bret Saberhagen	.10	.30
429 Bob Welch	.05	.15
430 Juan Guzman	.05	.15
431 Cal Eldred	.05	.15
432 Dave Hollins	.05	.15
433 Sid Fernandez	.05	.15
434 Willie Banks	.05	.15
435 Darryl Kile	.10	.30
436 Henry Rodriguez	.05	.15
437 Tony Fernandez	.05	.15
438 Walt Weiss	.05	.15
439 Kevin Tapani	.05	.15
440 Mark Grace	.20	.50
441 Brian Harper	.05	.15
442 Kent Mercker	.05	.15
443 Anthony Young	.05	.15
444 Todd Zeile	.05	.15
445 Greg Vaughn	.05	.15
446 Ray Lankford	.10	.30
447 Dave Weathers	.05	.15
448 Bret Boone	.10	.30
449 Charlie Hough	.10	.30
450 Roger Clemens	.60	1.50
451 Mike Morgan	.05	.15
452 Doug Drabek	.05	.15
453 Danny Jackson	.05	.15
454 Dante Bichette	.10	.30
455 Roberto Alomar	.20	.50
456 Ben McDonald	.05	.15

457 Kenny Rogers .10 .30
458 Bill Gullickson .05 .15
459 Darrin Fletcher .05 .15
460 Curt Schilling .10 .30
461 Billy Hatcher .05 .15
462 Howard Johnson .05 .15
463 Mickey Morandini .05 .15
464 Frank Castillo .05 .15
465 Delino DeShields .05 .15
466 Gary Gaetti .10 .30
467 Steve Farr .05 .15
468 Roberto Hernandez .05 .15
469 Jack Armstrong .05 .15
470 Paul Molitor .10 .30
471 Melido Perez .05 .15
472 Greg Hibbard .05 .15
473 Jody Reed .05 .15
474 Tom Gordon .05 .15
475 Gary Sheffield .10 .30
476 John Jaha .05 .15
477 Shawon Dunston .05 .15
478 Reggie Jefferson .05 .15
479 Don Slaught .05 .15
480 Jeff Bagwell .20 .50
481 Tim Pugh .05 .15
482 Kevin Young .05 .15
483 Ellis Burks .10 .30
484 Greg Swindell .05 .15
485 Mark Langston .05 .15
486 Omar Vizquel .20 .50
487 Kevin Brown .10 .30
488 Terry Steinbach .05 .15
489 Mark Lemke .05 .15
490 Matt Williams .10 .30
491 Pete Incaviglia .05 .15
492 Karl Rhodes .05 .15
493 Shawn Green .30 .75
494 Hal Morris .05 .15
495 Derek Bell .05 .15
496 Luis Polonia .05 .15
497 Otis Nixon .05 .15
498 Ron Darling .05 .15
499 Mitch Williams .05 .15
500 Mike Piazza .60 1.50
501 Pat Meares .05 .15
502 Scott Cooper .05 .15
503 Scott Erickson .05 .15
504 Jeff Juden .05 .15
505 Lee Smith .10 .30
506 Bobby Ayala .05 .15
507 Dave Henderson .05 .15
508 Erik Hanson .05 .15
509 Bob Wickman .05 .15
510 Sammy Sosa .30 .75
511 Hector Carrasco .05 .15
512 Tim Davis .05 .15
513 Joey Hamilton .05 .15
514 Robert Eenhoorn .05 .15
515 Jorge Fabregas .05 .15
516 Tim Hyers RC .05 .15
517 John Hudek RC .05 .15
518 James Mouton .05 .15
519 Herbert Perry RC .05 .15
520 Chan Ho Park RC .30 .75
521 W.Va Landingham RC .05 .15
522 Paul Shuey .05 .15
523 Ryan Hancock RC .05 .15
524 Billy Wagner RC .75 2.00
525 Jason Giambi .30 .75
526 Jose Silva RC .05 .15
527 Terrell Wade RC .05 .15
528 Todd Dunn .05 .15
529 Alan Benes RC .15 .40
530 B.Kieschnick RC .05 .15
531 T.Hollandsworth .05 .15
532 Brad Fullmer RC .15 .40
533 S.Soderstrom RC .05 .15
534 Daron Kirkreit .05 .15
535 Arquimedez Pozo RC .05 .15
536 Charles Johnson .10 .30
537 Preston Wilson .10 .30
538 Alex Ochoa .05 .15
539 Derrek Lee RC 1.50 4.00
540 Wayne Gomes RC .05 .15
541 J.Allensworth RC .05 .15
542 Mike Bell RC .05 .15
543 Trot Nixon RC .75 2.00
544 Pokey Reese .05 .15
545 Neifi Perez RC .15 .40
546 Johnny Damon .30 .75
547 Matt Brunson RC .05 .15
548 L.Hawkins RC .15 .40
549 Eddie Pearson RC .05 .15
550 Derek Jeter 1.00 2.50
A298 Alex Rodriguez AU 200.00 400.00
P224 K.Griffey Jr. Promo .75 2.00
GM1 Ken Griffey Jr. AU 700.00 900.00
Mickey Mantle AU/1000
KG1 K.Griffey Jr. AU/1000 125.00 300.00
MM1 M.Mantle AU/1000 300.00 600.00

1994 Upper Deck Electric Diamond

This 550-card set is a parallel issue to the basic 1994 Upper Deck cards. The cards were issued one per foil pack and two per mini jumbo. The only differences between these and the basic cards is the "Electric Diamond" in silver foil toward the bottom and the player's name is also in silver foil.

COMPLETE SET (550) 40.00 100.00
COMP.SERIES 1 (280) 25.00 60.00
COMP.SERIES 2 (270) 15.00 40.00
*STARS: .75X TO 2X BASIC CARDS
*ROOKIES: .6X TO 1.5X BASIC CARDS

1994 Upper Deck Diamond Collection

This 30-card standard-size set was inserted regionally in first series hobby packs at a rate of one in 18. The three regions are Central (C1-C10), East (E1-E10) and West (W1-W10). While each card has the same horizontal format, the color scheme differs by region. The Central cards have a blue background, the East green and the West a deep shade of red. Color player photos are superimposed over the backgrounds. Each card has, "The Upper Deck Diamond Collection" as part of the background. The backs have a small photo and career highlights.

COMPLETE SET (30) 70.00 180.00
COMPLETE CENTRAL (10) 30.00 80.00
COMPLETE EAST (10) 15.00 40.00
COMPLETE WEST (10) 25.00 60.00
SER.1 STATED ODDS 1:18 HOBBY REGIONAL
C1 Jeff Bagwell 1.50 4.00
C2 Michael Jordan 6.00 15.00
C3 Barry Larkin 1.50 4.00
C4 Kirby Puckett 2.50 6.00
C5 Manny Ramirez 2.50 6.00
C6 Ryne Sandberg 4.00 10.00
C7 Ozzie Smith 4.00 10.00
C8 Frank Thomas 2.50 6.00
C9 Andy Van Slyke 1.50 4.00
C10 Robin Yount 2.50 6.00
E1 Roberto Alomar 1.50 4.00
E2 Roger Clemens 5.00 12.00
E3 Lenny Dykstra 1.00 2.50
E4 Cecil Fielder 1.00 2.50
E5 Cliff Floyd 1.00 2.50
E6 Dwight Gooden 1.00 2.50
E7 David Justice 1.00 2.50
E8 Don Mattingly 6.00 15.00
E9 Cal Ripken Jr. 8.00 20.00
E10 Gary Sheffield 1.00 2.50
W1 Barry Bonds 6.00 15.00
W2 Andres Galarraga 1.00 2.50
W3 Juan Gonzalez 1.00 2.50
W4 Ken Griffey Jr. 4.00 10.00
W5 Tony Gwynn 3.00 8.00
W6 Rickey Henderson 2.50 6.00
W7 Bo Jackson 2.50 6.00
W8 Mark McGwire 6.00 15.00
W9 Mike Piazza 5.00 12.00
W10 Tim Salmon 1.50 4.00

1994 Upper Deck Griffey Jumbos

Measuring 4 7/8" by 6 13/16", these four Griffey cards serve as checklists for first series Upper Deck issues. They were issued one per first series hobby foil box. Card fronts have a full color photo with a small Griffey hologram. The first three cards provide a numerical, alphabetical and team organized checklist for the basic set. The fourth card is a checklist of inserts. Each card was printed in different quantities with CL1 the most plentiful and CL4 the more scarce. The backs are numbered with a CL prefix.

COMPLETE SET (4) 4.00 10.00
COMMON GRIFFEY (CL1-CL4) 1.25 3.00

1994 Upper Deck Mantle Heroes

Randomly inserted in second series packs at a rate of one in 35, this 10-card standard-size set looks at various moments from The Mick's career. Metallic fronts feature a vintage photo with the card title at the bottom. The backs contain career highlights with a small scrapbook like photo. The numbering (64-72) is a continuation from previous Heroes sets.

COMPLETE SET (10) 30.00 60.00
COMMON (64-72/HDR) 4.00 10.00
SER.2 STATED ODDS 1:20

1994 Upper Deck Mantle's Long Shots

Randomly inserted in first series retail packs at a rate of one in 18, this 21-card silver foil standard-size set features top longball hitters as selected by Mickey Mantle. The cards are numbered on the back with a "MM" prefix and sequenced in alphabetical order. Two trade cards, were also random inserts and were redeemable (expiration: December 31, 1994) for either the basic silver foil set version (Silver Trade card) or the Electric Diamond version (blue Trade card).

COMPLETE SET (21) 15.00 40.00
SER.1 STATED ODDS 1:18 RETAIL
ONE SET VIA MAIL PER SILVER TRADE CARD
*ED: .5X TO 1.2X BASIC MANTLE LS
ONE ED SET VIA MAIL PER BLUE TRADE CARD
MANTLE TRADES: RANDOM IN SER.1 HOB
MM1 Jeff Bagwell .60 1.50
MM2 Albert Belle .40 1.00
MM3 Barry Bonds 2.50 6.00
MM4 Jose Canseco .60 1.50
MM5 Joe Carter .40 1.00
MM6 Carlos Delgado .60 1.50
MM7 Cecil Fielder .40 1.00
MM8 Cliff Floyd .40 1.00
MM9 Juan Gonzalez .40 1.00
MM10 Ken Griffey Jr. 1.50 4.00
MM11 David Justice .40 1.00
MM12 Fred McGriff .60 1.50
MM13 Mark McGwire 2.50 6.00
MM14 Dean Palmer .40 1.00
MM15 Mike Piazza 2.00 5.00
MM16 Manny Ramirez 1.00 2.50
MM17 Tim Salmon .60 1.50
MM18 Frank Thomas 1.00 2.50
MM19 Mo Vaughn .40 1.00
MM20 Matt Williams .40 1.00
MM21 Mickey Mantle 6.00 15.00
NNO Mickey Mantle 2.50 6.00
Silver Trade
NNO Mickey Mantle 6.00 15.00
Blue ED Trade

1994 Upper Deck Next Generation

Randomly inserted in second series retail packs at a rate of one in 20, this 18-card standard-size set spotlights young established stars and promising prospects. The set is sequenced in alphabetical order. A Next Generation Electric Diamond Trade Card and a Next Generation Trade Card were seeded randomly in second series hobby packs. Each card could be redeemed for that set. Expiration date for redemption was October 31, 1994.

COMPLETE SET (18) 40.00 100.00
SER.2 STATED ODDS 1:20 RETAIL
ONE SET VIA MAIL PER TRADE CARD
TRADES: RANDOM INSERTS IN SER.2 HOB
1 Roberto Alomar 1.25 3.00
2 Carlos Delgado 1.25 3.00
3 Cliff Floyd .75 2.00
4 Alex Gonzalez .40 1.00
5 Juan Gonzalez .75 2.00
6 Ken Griffey Jr. 3.00 8.00
7 Jeffrey Hammonds .40 1.00
8 Michael Jordan 6.00 15.00
9 David Justice .75 2.00
10 Ryan Klesko .75 2.00
11 Javier Lopez .75 2.00
12 Raul Mondesi .75 2.00
13 Mike Piazza 4.00 10.00
14 Kirby Puckett 2.00 5.00
15 Manny Ramirez 2.00 5.00
16 Alex Rodriguez 10.00 25.00
17 Tim Salmon 1.25 3.00
18 Gary Sheffield .75 2.00
NNO Exp. NG Trade Card .40 1.00

1994 Upper Deck Next Generation Electric Diamond

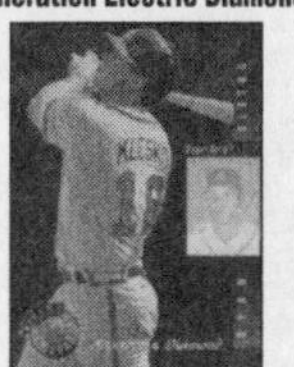

This 18 card set parallels the regular Next Generation insert set. The cards are differentiated by an "Electric Diamond" logo on the bottom. These cards were sent if a collector received a ED trade card in a pack.

*ELEC.DIAM: .5X TO 1.2X BASIC NEXT.GEN.
TRADES: RANDOM INSERTS IN SER.2 HOBBY
8 Michael Jordan 10.00 25.00
16 Alex Rodriguez 20.00 50.00

1995 Upper Deck

The 1995 Upper Deck baseball set was issued in two series of 225 cards for a total of 450. The cards were distributed in 12-card packs (36 per box) with a suggested retail price of $1.99. Subsets include Top Prospect (1-15, 251-265), 90's Midpoint (101-110), Star Rookie (211-240), and Diamond Debuts (241-250). Rookie Cards in this set include Hideo Nomo. Five randomly inserted Trade Cards were each redeemable for nine updated cards of new rookies or players who changed teams, comprising a 45-card Trade Redemption set. The Trade cards expired Feb

1, 1996. Autographed jumbo cards (Roger Clemens for series one, Alex Rodriguez for either series) were available through a wrapper redemption offer.

COMP.MASTER SET (495) 55.00 110.00
COMPLETE SET (450) 20.00 50.00
COMP. SERIES 1 (225) 10.00 25.00
COMP. SERIES 2 (225) 10.00 25.00
COMMON CARD (1-450) .05 .15
COMP.TRADE SET (45) 30.00 60.00
COMMON (451T-495T) .40 1.00
1 Ruben Rivera .05 .15
2 Bill Pulsipher .05 .15
3 Ben Grieve .05 .15
4 Curtis Goodwin .05 .15
5 Damon Hollins .05 .15
6 Todd Greene .05 .15
7 Glenn Williams .05 .15
8 Bret Wagner .05 .15
9 Karim Garcia RC .05 .15
10 Nomar Garciaparra .75 2.00
11 Raul Casanova RC .05 .15
12 Matt Smith .05 .15
13 Paul Wilson .05 .15
14 Jason Isringhausen .10 .30
15 Reid Ryan .10 .30
16 Lee Smith .10 .30
17 Chili Davis .10 .30
18 Brian Anderson .05 .15
19 Gary DiSarcina .05 .15
20 Bo Jackson .30 .75
21 Chuck Finley .10 .30
22 Darryl Kile .10 .30
23 Shane Reynolds .05 .15
24 Tony Eusebio .05 .15
25 Craig Biggio .20 .50
26 Doug Drabek .05 .15
27 Brian L. Hunter .05 .15
28 James Mouton .05 .15
29 Geronimo Berroa .05 .15
30 Rickey Henderson .30 .75
31 Steve Karsay .05 .15
32 Steve Ontiveros .05 .15
33 Ernie Young .05 .15
34 Dennis Eckersley .10 .30
35 Mark McGwire .75 2.00
36 Dave Stewart .10 .30
37 Pat Hentgen .05 .15
38 Carlos Delgado .10 .30
39 Joe Carter .10 .30
40 Roberto Alomar .20 .50
41 John Olerud .10 .30
42 Devon White .10 .30
43 Roberto Kelly .05 .15
44 Jeff Blauser .05 .15
45 Fred McGriff .20 .50
46 Tom Glavine .20 .50
47 Mike Kelly .05 .15
48 Javier Lopez .10 .30
49 Greg Maddux .50 1.25
50 Matt Mieske .05 .15
51 Troy O'Leary .05 .15
52 Jeff Cirillo .05 .15
53 Cal Eldred .05 .15
54 Pat Listach .05 .15
55 Jose Valentin .05 .15
56 John Mabry .05 .15
57 Bob Tewksbury .05 .15
58 Brian Jordan .10 .30
59 Gregg Jefferies .05 .15
60 Ozzie Smith .50 1.25
61 Geronimo Pena .05 .15
62 Mark Whiten .05 .15
63 Rey Sanchez .05 .15
64 Willie Banks .05 .15
65 Mark Grace .20 .50
66 Randy Myers .05 .15
67 Steve Trachsel .05 .15
68 Derrick May .05 .15
69 Brett Butler .10 .30
70 Eric Karros .10 .30
71 Tim Wallach .05 .15
72 Delino DeShields .05 .15
73 Darren Dreifort .05 .15
74 Orel Hershiser .10 .30
75 Billy Ashley .05 .15
76 Sean Berry .05 .15
77 Ken Hill .05 .15
78 John Wetteland .10 .30
79 Moises Alou .10 .30
80 Cliff Floyd .10 .30
81 Marquis Grissom .10 .30
82 Larry Walker .10 .30
83 Rondell White .10 .30
84 W.VanLandingham .05 .15
85 Matt Williams .10 .30
86 Rod Beck .05 .15
87 Darren Lewis .05 .15
88 Robby Thompson .05 .15
89 Darryl Strawberry .10 .30
90 Kenny Lofton .10 .30
91 Charles Nagy .05 .15
92 Sandy Alomar Jr. .05 .15
93 Mark Clark .05 .15
94 Dennis Martinez .10 .30
95 Dave Winfield .10 .30
96 Jim Thome .20 .50
97 Manny Ramirez .20 .50
98 Goose Gossage .10 .30
99 Tino Martinez .20 .50
100 Ken Griffey Jr. .50 1.25
101 Greg Maddux ANA .30 .75
102 Randy Johnson ANA .20 .50
103 Barry Bonds ANA .40 1.00
104 Juan Gonzalez ANA .05 .15
105 Frank Thomas ANA .20 .50
106 Matt Williams ANA .05 .15
107 Paul Molitor ANA .05 .15
108 Fred McGriff ANA .10 .30
109 Carlos Baerga ANA .05 .15
110 Ken Griffey Jr. ANA .30 .75
111 Reggie Jefferson .05 .15
112 Randy Johnson .30 .75
113 Marc Newfield .05 .15
114 Robb Nen .10 .30
115 Jeff Conine .10 .30
116 Kurt Abbott .05 .15
117 Charlie Hough .10 .30
118 Dave Weathers .05 .15
119 Juan Castillo .05 .15
120 Bret Saberhagen .10 .30
121 Rico Brogna .05 .15
122 John Franco .10 .30
123 Todd Hundley .05 .15
124 Jason Jacome .05 .15
125 Bobby Jones .05 .15
126 Bret Barberie .05 .15
127 Ben McDonald .05 .15
128 Harold Baines .10 .30
129 Jeffrey Hammonds .05 .15
130 Mike Mussina .20 .50
131 Chris Hoiles .05 .15
132 Brady Anderson .10 .30
133 Eddie Williams .05 .15
134 Andy Benes .05 .15
135 Tony Gwynn .40 1.00
136 Bip Roberts .05 .15
137 Joey Hamilton .05 .15
138 Luis Lopez .05 .15
139 Ray McDavid .05 .15
140 Lenny Dykstra .10 .30
141 Mariano Duncan .05 .15
142 Fernando Valenzuela .10 .30
143 Bobby Munoz .05 .15
144 Kevin Stocker .05 .15
145 John Kruk .10 .30
146 Jon Lieber .05 .15
147 Zane Smith .05 .15
148 Steve Cooke .05 .15
149 Andy Van Slyke .20 .50
150 Jay Bell .10 .30
151 Carlos Garcia .05 .15
152 John Dettmer .05 .15
153 Darren Oliver .05 .15
154 Dean Palmer .10 .30
155 Otis Nixon .05 .15
156 Rusty Greer .10 .30
157 Rick Helling .05 .15
158 Jose Canseco .20 .50
159 Roger Clemens .60 1.50
160 Andre Dawson .10 .30
161 Mo Vaughn .10 .30
162 Aaron Sele .05 .15
163 John Valentin .05 .15
164 Brian R. Hunter .05 .15
165 Bret Boone .10 .30
166 Hector Carrasco .05 .15
167 Pete Schourek .05 .15
168 Willie Greene .05 .15
169 Kevin Mitchell .05 .15
170 Deion Sanders .20 .50
171 John Roper .05 .15
172 Charlie Hayes .05 .15
173 David Nied .05 .15
174 Ellis Burks .10 .30
175 Dante Bichette .10 .30
176 Marvin Freeman .05 .15
177 Eric Young .05 .15
178 David Cone .10 .30
179 Greg Gagne .05 .15
180 Bob Hamelin .05 .15
181 Wally Joyner .10 .30
182 Jeff Montgomery .05 .15
183 Jose Lind .05 .15
184 Chris Gomez .05 .15
185 Travis Fryman .10 .30
186 Kirk Gibson .10 .30
187 Mike Moore .05 .15
188 Lou Whitaker .10 .30
189 Sean Bergman .05 .15
190 Shane Mack .05 .15
191 Rick Aguilera .05 .15
192 Denny Hocking .05 .15
193 Chuck Knoblauch .10 .30
194 Kevin Tapani .05 .15
195 Kent Hrbek .10 .30
196 Ozzie Guillen .10 .30
197 Wilson Alvarez .05 .15
198 Tim Raines .10 .30
199 Scott Ruffcorn .05 .15
200 Michael Jordan 1.00 2.50
Interviewed by famed annoucer Harry Caray
201 Robin Ventura .10 .30
202 Jason Bere .05 .15
203 Darrin Jackson .05 .15
204 Russ Davis .05 .15
205 Jimmy Key .10 .30
206 Jack McDowell .05 .15
207 Jim Abbott .20 .50
208 Paul O'Neill .20 .50
209 Bernie Williams .20 .50
210 Don Mattingly .75 2.00
211 Orlando Miller .05 .15
212 Alex Gonzalez .05 .15
213 Terrell Wade .05 .15
214 Jose Oliva .05 .15
215 Alex Rodriguez .75 2.00
216 Garret Anderson .20 .50
217 Alan Benes .05 .15
218 Armando Benitez .05 .15
219 Dustin Hermanson .05 .15
220 Charles Johnson .10 .30
221 Julian Tavarez .05 .15
222 Jason Giambi .20 .50
223 LaTroy Hawkins .05 .15
224 Todd Hollandsworth .05 .15
225 Derek Jeter .75 2.00
226 Hideo Nomo RC 1.00 2.50
227 Tony Clark .05 .15
228 Roger Cedeno .05 .15
229 Scott Stahoviak .05 .15
230 Michael Tucker .05 .15
231 Joe Rosselli .05 .15
232 Antonio Osuna .05 .15
233 Bobby Higginson RC .30 .75
234 Mark Grudzielanek RC .30 .75
235 Ray Durham .10 .30
236 Frank Rodriguez .05 .15
237 Quilvio Veras .05 .15
238 Darren Bragg .05 .15
239 Ugueth Urbina .05 .15
240 Jason Bates .05 .15
241 David Bell .05 .15
242 Ron Villone .05 .15
243 Joe Randa .10 .30
244 Carlos Perez RC .15 .40
245 Brad Clontz .05 .15
246 Steve Rodriguez .05 .15
247 Joe Vitiello .05 .15
248 Ozzie Timmons .05 .15
249 Rudy Pemberton .05 .15
250 Marty Cordova .05 .15
251 Tony Graffanino .05 .15
252 Mark Johnson RC .15 .40
253 Tomas Perez RC .05 .15
254 Jimmy Hurst .05 .15
255 Edgardo Alfonzo .05 .15
256 Jose Malave .05 .15
257 Brad Radke RC .30 .75
258 Jon Nunnally .05 .15
259 Dilson Torres RC .05 .15
260 Esteban Loaiza .05 .15
261 Freddy Adrian Garcia RC .05 .15
262 Don Wengert .05 .15
263 Robert Person RC .15 .40
264 Tim Unroe RC .05 .15
265 Juan Acevedo RC .05 .15
266 Eduardo Perez .05 .15
267 Tony Phillips .05 .15
268 Jim Edmonds .20 .50
269 Jorge Fabregas .05 .15
270 Tim Salmon .20 .50
271 Mark Langston .05 .15
272 J.T. Snow .10 .30
273 Phil Plantier .05 .15
274 Derek Bell .05 .15
275 Jeff Bagwell .20 .50
276 Luis Gonzalez .10 .30
277 John Hudek .05 .15
278 Todd Stottlemyre .05 .15
279 Mark Acre .05 .15
280 Ruben Sierra .10 .30
281 Mike Bordick .05 .15
282 Ron Darling .05 .15
283 Brent Gates .05 .15
284 Todd Van Poppel .05 .15
285 Paul Molitor .10 .30
286 Ed Sprague .05 .15
287 Juan Guzman .05 .15
288 David Cone .10 .30
289 Shawn Green .10 .30
290 Marquis Grissom .10 .30
291 Kent Mercker .05 .15
292 Steve Avery .05 .15
293 Chipper Jones .30 .75
294 John Smoltz .20 .50
295 David Justice .10 .30
296 Ryan Klesko .10 .30
297 Joe Oliver .05 .15
298 Ricky Bones .05 .15
299 John Jaha .05 .15
300 Greg Vaughn .05 .15
301 Dave Nilsson .05 .15
302 Kevin Seitzer .05 .15
303 Bernard Gilkey .05 .15
304 Allen Battle .05 .15
305 Ray Lankford .10 .30
306 Tom Pagnozzi .05 .15
307 Allen Watson .05 .15
308 Danny Jackson .05 .15
309 Ken Hill .05 .15
310 Todd Zeile .05 .15
311 Kevin Roberson .05 .15
312 Steve Buechele .05 .15
313 Rick Wilkins .05 .15
314 Kevin Foster .05 .15
315 Sammy Sosa .30 .75
316 Howard Johnson .05 .15
317 Greg Hansell .05 .15
318 Pedro Astacio .05 .15
319 Rafael Bournigal .05 .15
320 Mike Piazza .50 1.25
321 Ramon Martinez .05 .15
322 Raul Mondesi .10 .30
323 Ismael Valdes .05 .15
324 Wil Cordero .05 .15
325 Tony Tarasco .05 .15
326 Roberto Kelly .05 .15
327 Jeff Fassero .05 .15
328 Mike Lansing .05 .15
329 Pedro Martinez .20 .50
330 Kirk Rueter .05 .15
331 Glenallen Hill .05 .15
332 Kirt Manwaring .05 .15
333 Royce Clayton .05 .15
334 J.R. Phillips .05 .15
335 Barry Bonds .75 2.00
336 Mark Portugal .05 .15
337 Terry Mulholland .05 .15
338 Omar Vizquel .20 .50
339 Carlos Baerga .05 .15
340 Albert Belle .10 .30
341 Eddie Murray .30 .75
342 Wayne Kirby .05 .15
343 Chad Ogea .05 .15
344 Tim Davis .05 .15
345 Jay Buhner .10 .30
346 Bobby Ayala .05 .15
347 Mike Blowers .05 .15
348 Dave Fleming .05 .15
349 Edgar Martinez .20 .50
350 Andre Dawson .10 .30
351 Darrell Whitmore .05 .15
352 Chuck Carr .05 .15
353 John Burkett .05 .15
354 Chris Hammond .05 .15
355 Gary Sheffield .10 .30
356 Pat Rapp .05 .15
357 Greg Colbrunn .05 .15
358 David Segui .05 .15
359 Jeff Kent .10 .30
360 Bobby Bonilla .10 .30
361 Pete Harnisch .05 .15
362 Ryan Thompson .05 .15
363 Jose Vizcaino .05 .15
364 Brett Butler .10 .30
365 Cal Ripken Jr. 1.00 2.50
366 Rafael Palmeiro .20 .50
367 Leo Gomez .05 .15
368 Andy Van Slyke .20 .50
369 Arthur Rhodes .05 .15
370 Ken Caminiti .10 .30
371 Steve Finley .10 .30
372 Melvin Nieves .05 .15
373 Andujar Cedeno .05 .15
374 Trevor Hoffman .10 .30
375 Fernando Valenzuela .10 .30
376 Ricky Bottalico .05 .15
377 Dave Hollins .05 .15
378 Charlie Hayes .05 .15
379 Tommy Greene .05 .15
380 Darren Daulton .10 .30
381 Curt Schilling .10 .30
382 Midre Cummings .05 .15
383 Al Martin .05 .15
384 Jeff King .05 .15
385 Orlando Merced .05 .15
386 Denny Neagle .10 .30
387 Don Slaught .05 .15
388 Dave Clark .05 .15
389 Kevin Gross .05 .15
390 Will Clark .20 .50
391 Ivan Rodriguez .20 .50
392 Benji Gil .05 .15
393 Jeff Frye .05 .15
394 Kenny Rogers .10 .30
395 Juan Gonzalez .10 .30
396 Mike Macfarlane .05 .15
397 Lee Tinsley .05 .15
398 Tim Naehring .05 .15
399 Tim Vanegmond .05 .15
400 Mike Greenwell .05 .15
401 Ken Ryan .05 .15
402 John Smiley .05 .15
403 Tim Pugh .05 .15
404 Reggie Sanders .10 .30
405 Barry Larkin .20 .50
406 Hal Morris .05 .15
407 Jose Rijo .05 .15
408 Lance Painter .05 .15
409 Joe Girardi .05 .15
410 Andres Galarraga .10 .30
411 Mike Kingery .05 .15
412 Roberto Mejia .05 .15
413 Walt Weiss .05 .15
414 Bill Swift .05 .15
415 Larry Walker .10 .30
416 Billy Brewer .05 .15
417 Pat Borders .05 .15
418 Tom Gordon .05 .15
419 Kevin Appier .10 .30
420 Gary Gaetti .10 .30
421 Greg Gohr .05 .15
422 Felipe Lira .05 .15
423 John Doherty .05 .15
424 Chad Curtis .05 .15
425 Cecil Fielder .10 .30
426 Alan Trammell .10 .30
427 David McCarty .05 .15
428 Scott Erickson .05 .15
429 Pat Mahomes .05 .15
430 Kirby Puckett .30 .75
431 Dave Stevens .05 .15
432 Pedro Munoz .05 .15
433 Chris Sabo .05 .15
434 Alex Fernandez .05 .15
435 Frank Thomas .30 .75
436 Roberto Hernandez .05 .15
437 Lance Johnson .05 .15
438 Jim Abbott .20 .50
439 John Wetteland .10 .30
440 Melido Perez .05 .15
441 Tony Fernandez .05 .15
442 Pat Kelly .05 .15
443 Mike Stanley .05 .15
444 Danny Tartabull .05 .15
445 Wade Boggs .20 .50
446 Robin Yount .50 1.25
447 Ryne Sandberg .50 1.25
448 Nolan Ryan 1.25 3.00
449 George Brett .75 2.00
450 Mike Schmidt .50 1.25
451 Jim Abbott TRADE .75 2.00
452 D.Tartabull TRADE .40 1.00
453 Ariel Prieto TRADE .40 1.00
454 Scott Cooper TRADE .40 1.00
455 Tom Henke TRADE .40 1.00
456 Todd Zeile TRADE .40 1.00

457 Brian McRae TRADE .40 1.00
458 Luis Gonzalez TRADE .60 1.50
459 Jaime Navarro TRADE .40 1.00
460 Todd Worrell TRADE .40 1.00
461 Roberto Kelly TRADE .40 1.00
462 Chad Fonville TRADE .40 1.00
463 S.Andrews TRADE .40 1.00
464 David Segui TRADE .40 1.00
465 Deion Sanders TRADE .75 2.00
466 Orel Hershiser TRADE .60 1.50
467 Ken Hill TRADE .40 1.00
468 Andy Benes TRADE .40 1.00
469 T.Pendleton TRADE .60 1.50
470 Bobby Bonilla TRADE .60 1.50
471 Scott Erickson TRADE .40 1.00
472 Kevin Brown TRADE .60 1.50
473 G.Dishman TRADE .40 1.00
474 Phil Plantier TRADE .40 1.00
475 G.Jefferies TRADE .40 1.00
476 Tyler Green TRADE .40 1.00
477 H. Slocumb TRADE .40 1.00
478 Mark Whiten TRADE .40 1.00
479 M.Tettleton TRADE .40 1.00
480 Tim Wakefield TRADE .60 1.50
481 V. Eshelman TRADE .40 1.00
482 Rick Aguilera TRADE .40 1.00
483 Erik Hanson TRADE .40 1.00
484 Willie McGee TRADE .60 1.50
485 Troy O'Leary TRADE .40 1.00
486 B.Santiago TRADE .60 1.50
487 Darren Lewis TRADE .40 1.00
488 Dave Burba TRADE .40 1.00
489 Ron Gant TRADE .60 1.50
490 B.Saberhagen TRADE .60 1.50
491 Vinny Castilla TRADE .60 1.50
492 F.Rodriguez TRADE .40 1.00
493 Andy Pettitte TRADE .75 2.00
494 Ruben Sierra TRADE .60 1.50
495 David Cone TRADE .60 1.50
J159 R. Clemens Jumbo AU 40.00 80.00
J215 A. Rodriguez Jumbo AU 60.00 120.00
P100 K.Griffey Jr. Promo .75 2.00

1995 Upper Deck Electric Diamond

This 450-card parallel set was inserted one per retail pack or two per mini-jumbo pack. These cards are distinguished from their regular issue counterparts in that they are printed on a heavier cardstock and use a special foil treatment.

COMPLETE SET (450) 50.00 100.00
COMP. SERIES 1 (225) 25.00 50.00
COMP. SERIES 2 (225) 30.00 60.00
*STARS: 1.25X TO 3X BASIC CARDS
*ROOKIES: 1X TO 2.5X BASIC CARDS

1995 Upper Deck Autographs

Trade cards to redeem these autographed issues were randomly seeded into second series packs. The actual signed cards share the same front design as the basic issue 1995 Upper Deck cards. The cards were issued along with a card signed in fascimile by Brain Burr of Upper Deck along with instructions on how to register these cards.

SER.2 STATED ODDS 1:72 HOBBY
AC1 Reggie Jackson 15.00 40.00
AC2 Willie Mays 60.00 120.00
AC3 Frank Robinson 15.00 40.00
AC4 Roger Clemens 12.50 30.00
AC5 Raul Mondesi 10.00 25.00

1995 Upper Deck Checklists

Each of these 10 cards features a star player(s) on the front and a checklist on the back. The cards were randomly inserted in hobby and retail packs at a rate of one in 17. The horizontal fronts feature a player photo along with a sentence about the 1994 highlight. The cards are numbered as "X" of 5 in the upper left.

COMPLETE SET (5) 4.50 12.00
COMPLETE SERIES 1 (5) 1.50 4.00
COMPLETE SERIES 2 (5) 3.00 8.00
STATED ODDS 1:17 ALL PACKS
1A Montreal Expos .10 .30
2A Fred McGriff .40 1.00
3A John Valentin .10 .30
4A Kenny Rogers .25 .60
5A Greg Maddux 1.00 2.50
1B Cecil Fielder .25 .60
2B Tony Gwynn .75 2.00
3B Greg Maddux 1.00 2.50
4B Randy Johnson .60 1.50
5B Mike Schmidt 1.00 2.50

1995 Upper Deck Predictor Award Winners

Cards from this set were inserted in hobby packs at a rate of approximately one in 30. This 40-card standard-size set features nine players and a Long Shot in each league for each of two categories -- MVP and Rookie of the Year. If the player pictured on the card won his category, the card was redeemable for a special foil version of all 20 Hobby Predictor cards. Winning cards are marked with a "W" in the checklist below. Both MVP winners for the season (Barry Larkin in the NL and Mo Vaughn in the AL) were not featured on their own Predictor cards and thus the Longshot card became the winner. Fronts are full-color player action photos. Backs include the rules of the contest. These cards were redeemable until December 31, 1995.

COMPLETE SET (40) 30.00 80.00
COMPLETE SERIES 1 (20) 15.00 40.00
COMPLETE SERIES 2 (20) 15.00 40.00
STATED ODDS 1:30 HOBBY
*AW EXCH: .4X TO 1X BASIC PRED.AW
ONE EXCH.SET VIA MAIL PER PRED.WINNER
H1 Albert Belle MVP .50 1.25
H2 Juan Gonzalez MVP .50 1.25
H3 Ken Griffey Jr. MVP 2.00 5.00
H4 Kirby Puckett MVP 1.25 3.00
H5 Frank Thomas MVP 1.25 3.00
H6 Jeff Bagwell MVP .75 2.00
H7 Barry Bonds MVP 3.00 8.00
H8 Mike Piazza MVP 2.00 5.00
H9 Matt Williams MVP .50 1.25
H10 MVP Wild Card W .25 .60
Mo Vaughn, Barry Larkin
H11 A.Benitez ROY .25 .60
H12 Alex Gonzalez ROY .25 .60
H13 Shawn Green ROY .50 1.25
H14 Derek Jeter ROY 3.00 8.00
H15 Alex Rodriguez ROY 3.00 8.00
H16 Alan Benes ROY .25 .60
H17 Brian L.Hunter ROY .25 .60
H18 Charles Johnson ROY .50 1.25
H19 Jose Oliva ROY .25 .60
H20 ROY Wild Card .25 .60
H21 Cal Ripken MVP 4.00 10.00
H22 Don Mattingly MVP 3.00 8.00
H23 Roberto Alomar MVP .75 2.00
H24 Kenny Lofton MVP .50 1.25
H25 Will Clark MVP .75 2.00
H26 Mark McGwire MVP 3.00 8.00
H27 Greg Maddux MVP 2.00 5.00
H28 Fred McGriff MVP .75 2.00
H29 A.Galarraga MVP .50 1.25
H30 Jose Canseco MVP .75 2.00
H31 Ray Durham ROY .50 1.25
H32 M.Grudzielanek ROY 1.25 3.00
H33 Scott Ruffcorn ROY .25 .60
H34 Michael Tucker ROY .25 .60
H35 Garret Anderson ROY .50 1.25
H36 Darren Bragg ROY .25 .60
H37 Quilvio Veras ROY .25 .60
H38 Hideo Nomo ROY W 4.00 10.00
H39 Chipper Jones ROY 1.25 3.00
H40 M.Cordova ROY W .25 .60

1995 Upper Deck Predictor League Leaders

Cards from this 60-card standard size set were seeded exclusively in first and second series retail packs at a rate of 1:30 and ANCO packs at 1:17. Cards 1-30 were distributed in series one packs and cards 31-60 in series two packs. The set includes nine players and a Long Shot in each league for each of three categories -- Batting Average Leader, Home Run Leader and Runs Batted In Leader. If the player pictured on the card won his category, the card was redeemable for a special foil version of 30 Retail Predictor cards (based upon the first or second series that it was associated with). These cards were redeemable until December 31, 1995. Card fronts are full-color action photos of the player emerging from a marble diamond. Backs list the rules of the game. Winning cards are designated with a W in our listings and are in noticeably shorter supply than other cards from this set as the bulk of them were mailed in to Upper Deck (and destroyed) in exchange for the parallel card prizes.

COMPLETE SET (60) 40.00 100.00
COMPLETE SERIES 1 (30) 25.00 60.00
COMPLETE SERIES 2 (30) 15.00 40.00
STATED ODDS 1:30 RET, 1:17 ANCO
*EXCH: .5X TO 1.2X BASIC PREDICTOR LL
ONE EXCH.SET VIA MAIL PER PRED.WINNER
R1 Albert Belle HR W .50 1.25
R2 Jose Canseco HR .75 2.00
R3 Juan Gonzalez HR .50 1.25
R4 Ken Griffey Jr. HR 2.00 5.00
R5 Frank Thomas HR 1.25 3.00
R6 Jeff Bagwell HR .75 2.00
R7 Barry Bonds HR 3.00 8.00
R8 Fred McGriff HR .75 2.00
R9 Matt Williams HR .50 1.25
R10 HR Wild Card W .25 .60
Dante Bichette
R11 Albert Belle RBI W .50 1.25
R12 Joe Carter RBI .50 1.25
R13 Cecil Fielder RBI .50 1.25
R14 Kirby Puckett RBI 1.25 3.00
R15 Frank Thomas RBI 1.25 3.00
R16 Jeff Bagwell RBI .75 2.00
R17 Barry Bonds RBI 3.00 8.00
R18 Mike Piazza RBI 2.00 5.00
R19 Matt Williams RBI .50 1.25
R20 RBI Wild Card W .25 .60
Mo Vaughn
R21 Wade Boggs BAT .75 2.00
R22 Kenny Lofton BAT .50 1.25
R23 Paul Molitor BAT .50 1.25
R24 Paul O'Neill BAT .75 2.00
R25 Frank Thomas BAT 1.25 3.00
R26 Jeff Bagwell BAT .75 2.00
R27 Tony Gwynn BAT W 1.50 4.00
R28 Gregg Jefferies BAT .25 .60
R29 Hal Morris BAT .25 .60
R30 Batting WC W .25 .60
Edgar Martinez
R31 Joe Carter HR .50 1.25
R32 Cecil Fielder HR .50 1.25
R33 Rafael Palmeiro HR .75 2.00
R34 Larry Walker HR .50 1.25
R35 Manny Ramirez HR .75 2.00
R36 Tim Salmon HR .75 2.00
R37 Mike Piazza HR 2.00 5.00
R38 Andres Galarraga HR .50 1.25
R39 David Justice HR .50 1.25
R40 Gary Sheffield HR .50 1.25
R41 Juan Gonzalez RBI .50 1.25
R42 Jose Canseco RBI .75 2.00
R43 Will Clark RBI .75 2.00
R44 Rafael Palmeiro RBI .75 2.00
R45 Ken Griffey Jr. RBI 2.00 5.00
R46 Ruben Sierra RBI .50 1.25
R47 Larry Walker RBI .50 1.25
R48 Fred McGriff RBI .75 2.00
R49 Dante Bichette RBI W .50 1.25
R50 Darren Daulton RBI .50 1.25
R51 Will Clark BAT .75 2.00
R52 Ken Griffey Jr. BAT 2.00 5.00
R53 Don Mattingly BAT 3.00 8.00
R54 John Olerud BAT .50 1.25
R55 Kirby Puckett BAT 1.25 3.00
R56 Raul Mondesi BAT .50 1.25
R57 Moises Alou BAT .50 1.25
R58 Bret Boone BAT .50 1.25
R59 Albert Belle BAT .50 1.25
R60 Mike Piazza BAT 2.00 5.00

1995 Upper Deck Ruth Heroes

Randomly inserted in second series hobby and retail packs at a rate of 1:34, this set of 10 standard-size cards celebrates the achievements of one of baseball's all-time greats. The set was issued on the Centennial of Ruth's birth. The numbering (73-81) is a continuation from previous Heroes sets.

COMPLETE SET (10) 50.00 100.00
COMMON (73-81/HDR) 6.00 15.00
SER.2 STATED ODDS 1:34 HOBBY/RETAIL

1995 Upper Deck Special Edition

Inserted at a rate of one per pack, this 270 standard-size card set features full color action shots of players on a silver foil background. The back highlights the player's previous performance, including 1994 and career statistics. Another player photo is also featured on the back.

COMPLETE SET (270) 40.00 100.00
COMP. SERIES 1 (135) 20.00 50.00
COMP. SERIES 2 (135) 20.00 50.00
*SE GOLD: 2.5X TO 6X BASIC SE
*SE GOLD RC's: 2.5X TO 6X BASIC SE
SE GOLD ODDS 1:35 HOBBY
1 Cliff Floyd .30 .75
2 Wil Cordero .15 .40
3 Pedro Martinez .50 1.25
4 Larry Walker .30 .75
5 Derek Jeter 8.00 20.00
6 Mike Stanley .15 .40
7 Melido Perez .15 .40
8 Jim Leyritz .15 .40
9 Danny Tartabull .15 .40
10 Wade Boggs .50 1.25
11 Ryan Klesko .30 .75
12 Steve Avery .15 .40
13 Damon Hollins .15 .40
14 Chipper Jones .75 2.00
15 David Justice .30 .75
16 Glenn Williams .15 .40
17 Jose Oliva .15 .40
18 Terrell Wade .15 .40
19 Alex Fernandez .15 .40
20 Frank Thomas .75 2.00
21 Ozzie Guillen .30 .75
22 Roberto Hernandez .15 .40
23 Albie Lopez .15 .40
24 Eddie Murray .75 2.00
25 Albert Belle .30 .75
26 Omar Vizquel .50 1.25
27 Carlos Baerga .15 .40
28 Jose Rijo .15 .40
29 Hal Morris .15 .40
30 Reggie Sanders .30 .75
31 Jack Morris .30 .75
32 Raul Mondesi .30 .75
33 Karim Garcia .15 .40
34 Todd Hollandsworth .15 .40
35 Mike Piazza 1.25 3.00
36 Chan Ho Park .30 .75
37 Ramon Martinez .15 .40
38 Kenny Rogers .30 .75
39 Will Clark .50 1.25
40 Juan Gonzalez .30 .75
41 Ivan Rodriguez .50 1.25
42 Orlando Miller .15 .40
43 John Hudek .15 .40
44 Luis Gonzalez .30 .75
45 Jeff Bagwell .50 1.25
46 Cal Ripken 2.50 6.00
47 Mike Oquist .15 .40
48 Armando Benitez .15 .40
49 Ben McDonald .15 .40
50 Rafael Palmeiro .50 1.25
51 Curtis Goodwin .15 .40
52 Vince Coleman .15 .40
53 Tom Gordon .15 .40
54 Mike Macfarlane .15 .40
55 Brian McRae .15 .40
56 Matt Smith .15 .40
57 David Segui .15 .40
58 Paul Wilson .15 .40
59 Bill Pulsipher .15 .40
60 Bobby Bonilla .30 .75
61 Jeff Kent .30 .75
62 Ryan Thompson .15 .40
63 Jason Isringhausen .30 .75
64 Ed Sprague .15 .40
65 Paul Molitor .30 .75
66 Juan Guzman .15 .40
67 Alex Gonzalez .15 .40
68 Shawn Green .30 .75
69 Mark Portugal .15 .40
70 Barry Bonds 2.00 5.00
71 Robby Thompson .15 .40
72 Royce Clayton .15 .40
73 Ricky Bottalico .15 .40
74 Doug Jones .15 .40
75 Darren Daulton .30 .75
76 Gregg Jefferies .15 .40
77 Scott Cooper .15 .40
78 Nomar Garciaparra 1.25 3.00
79 Ken Ryan .15 .40
80 Mike Greenwell .15 .40
81 LaTroy Hawkins .15 .40
82 Rich Becker .15 .40
83 Scott Erickson .15 .40
84 Pedro Munoz .15 .40
85 Kirby Puckett .75 2.00
86 Orlando Merced .15 .40
87 Jeff King .15 .40
88 Midre Cummings .15 .40
89 Bernard Gilkey .15 .40
90 Ray Lankford .30 .75
91 Todd Zeile .15 .40
92 Alan Benes .15 .40
93 Bret Wagner .15 .40
94 Rene Arocha .15 .40
95 Cecil Fielder .30 .75
96 Alan Trammell .30 .75
97 Tony Phillips .15 .40
98 Junior Felix .15 .40
99 Brian Harper .15 .40
100 Greg Vaughn .15 .40
101 Ricky Bones .15 .40
102 Walt Weiss .15 .40
103 Lance Painter .15 .40
104 Roberto Mejia .15 .40
105 Andres Galarraga .30 .75
106 Todd Van Poppel .15 .40
107 Ben Grieve .15 .40
108 Brent Gates .15 .40
109 Jason Giambi .50 1.25
110 Ruben Sierra .30 .75
111 Terry Steinbach .15 .40
112 Chris Hammond .15 .40
113 Charles Johnson .30 .75
114 Jesus Tavarez .15 .40
115 Gary Sheffield .30 .75
116 Chuck Carr .15 .40
117 Bobby Ayala .15 .40
118 Randy Johnson .75 2.00
119 Edgar Martinez .50 1.25
120 Alex Rodriguez 2.00 5.00
121 Kevin Foster .15 .40
122 Kevin Roberson .15 .40
123 Sammy Sosa .75 2.00
124 Steve Trachsel .15 .40
125 Eduardo Perez .15 .40
126 Tim Salmon .50 1.25
127 Todd Greene .15 .40
128 Jorge Fabregas .15 .40
129 Mark Langston .15 .40
130 Mitch Williams .15 .40
131 Raul Casanova .15 .40
132 Mel Nieves .15 .40
133 Andy Benes .15 .40
134 Dustin Hermanson .15 .40
135 Trevor Hoffman .30 .75
136 Mark Grudzielanek .50 1.25
137 Ugueth Urbina .15 .40
138 Moises Alou .30 .75
139 Roberto Kelly .15 .40
140 Rondell White .30 .75
141 Paul O'Neill .50 1.25
142 Jimmy Key .30 .75
143 Jack McDowell .15 .40
144 Ruben Rivera .15 .40
145 Don Mattingly 2.00 5.00
146 John Wetteland .30 .75
147 Tom Glavine .50 1.25
148 Marquis Grissom .30 .75
149 Javier Lopez .30 .75
150 Fred McGriff .50 1.25
151 Greg Maddux 1.25 3.00
152 Chris Sabo .15 .40
153 Ray Durham .30 .75
154 Robin Ventura .30 .75
155 Jim Abbott .50 1.25
156 Jimmy Hurst .15 .40
157 Tim Raines .30 .75
158 Dennis Martinez .30 .75
159 Kenny Lofton .30 .75
160 Dave Winfield .30 .75
161 Manny Ramirez .50 1.25
162 Jim Thome .50 1.25
163 Barry Larkin .50 1.25
164 Bret Boone .30 .75
165 Deion Sanders .50 1.25
166 Ron Gant .30 .75
167 Benito Santiago .30 .75
168 Hideo Nomo 2.00 5.00
169 Billy Ashley .15 .40
170 Roger Cedeno .15 .40
171 Ismael Valdes .15 .40
172 Eric Karros .30 .75
173 Rusty Greer .30 .75
174 Rick Helling .15 .40
175 Nolan Ryan 3.00 8.00
176 Dean Palmer .30 .75
177 Phil Plantier .15 .40
178 Darryl Kile .30 .75
179 Derek Bell .15 .40
180 Doug Drabek .15 .40
181 Craig Biggio .50 1.25
182 Kevin Brown .30 .75
183 Harold Baines .30 .75
184 Jeffrey Hammonds .15 .40
185 Chris Hoiles .15 .40
186 Mike Mussina .50 1.25
187 Bob Hamelin .15 .40
188 Jeff Montgomery .15 .40
189 Michael Tucker .15 .40
190 George Brett 2.00 5.00
191 Edgardo Alfonzo .15 .40
192 Brett Butler .30 .75
193 Bobby Jones .15 .40
194 Todd Hundley .15 .40
195 Bret Saberhagen .30 .75
196 Pat Hentgen .15 .40
197 Roberto Alomar .50 1.25
198 David Cone .30 .75
199 Carlos Delgado .30 .75
200 Joe Carter .30 .75
201 Wm. VanLandingham .15 .40
202 Rod Beck .15 .40
203 J.R. Phillips .15 .40
204 Darren Lewis .15 .40
205 Matt Williams .30 .75
206 Lenny Dykstra .30 .75
207 Dave Hollins .15 .40
208 Mike Schmidt 1.25 3.00
209 Charlie Hayes .15 .40
210 Mo Vaughn .30 .75
211 Jose Malave .15 .40
212 Roger Clemens 1.50 4.00
213 Jose Canseco .50 1.25
214 Mark Whiten .15 .40
215 Marty Cordova .15 .40
216 Rick Aguilera .15 .40
217 Kevin Tapani .15 .40
218 Chuck Knoblauch .30 .75
219 Al Martin .15 .40
220 Jay Bell .30 .75
221 Carlos Garcia .15 .40
222 Freddy Adrian Garcia .15 .40
223 Jon Lieber .15 .40
224 Danny Jackson .15 .40
225 Ozzie Smith 1.25 3.00
226 Brian Jordan .30 .75
227 Ken Hill .15 .40
228 Scott Cooper .15 .40
229 Chad Curtis .15 .40
230 Lou Whitaker .30 .75
231 Kirk Gibson .30 .75
232 Travis Fryman .30 .75
233 Jose Valentin .15 .40
234 Dave Nilsson .15 .40
235 Cal Eldred .15 .40
236 Matt Mieske .15 .40
237 Bill Swift .15 .40
238 Marvin Freeman .15 .40
239 Jason Bates .15 .40
240 Larry Walker .30 .75
241 Dave Nied .15 .40
242 Dante Bichette .30 .75
243 Dennis Eckersley .30 .75
244 Todd Stottlemyre .15 .40
245 Rickey Henderson .75 2.00
246 Geronimo Berroa .15 .40
247 Mark McGwire 2.00 5.00
248 Quilvio Veras .15 .40
249 Terry Pendleton .30 .75
250 Andre Dawson .30 .75
251 Jeff Conine .30 .75
252 Kurt Abbott .15 .40
253 Jay Buhner .30 .75
254 Darren Bragg .15 .40
255 Ken Griffey Jr. 1.25 3.00
256 Tino Martinez .50 1.25
257 Mark Grace .50 1.25
258 Ryne Sandberg 1.25 3.00
259 Randy Myers .15 .40
260 Howard Johnson .15 .40
261 Lee Smith .30 .75
262 J.T. Snow .30 .75
263 Chili Davis .30 .75
264 Chuck Finley .30 .75
265 Eddie Williams .15 .40
266 Joey Hamilton .15 .40
267 Ken Caminiti .30 .75
268 Andujar Cedeno .15 .40
269 Steve Finley .30 .75
270 Tony Gwynn 1.00 2.50

1995 Upper Deck Steal of a Deal

This set was inserted in hobby and retail packs at a rate of approximately one in 34. This 15-card standard-size set focuses on players who were acquired through, according to Upper Deck, "astute trades" or low round draft picks. The cards are numbered in the upper left with an "SD" prefix.

COMPLETE SET (15) 30.00 80.00
SER.1 STATED ODDS 1:34 ALL PACKS
SD1 Mike Piazza 5.00 12.00
SD2 Fred McGriff 2.00 5.00
SD3 Kenny Lofton 1.25 3.00
SD4 Jose Oliva .60 1.50
SD5 Jeff Bagwell 2.00 5.00
SD6 Roberto Alomar 2.00 5.00
Joe Carter
SD7 Steve Karsay .60 1.50
SD8 Ozzie Smith 5.00 12.00
SD9 Dennis Eckersley 1.25 3.00
SD10 Jose Canseco 2.00 5.00
SD11 Carlos Baerga .60 1.50
SD12 Cecil Fielder 1.25 3.00
SD13 Don Mattingly 8.00 20.00
SD14 Bret Boone 1.25 3.00
SD15 Michael Jordan 10.00 25.00

1995 Upper Deck Trade Exchange

These five cards were randomly inserted into second series Upper Deck packs. A collector could send in these cards and receive nine cards from the trade set for the base 1995 Upper Deck set (numbers 451-495). These cards were redeemable until February 1, 1996.

COMPLETE SET (5) 2.50 5.00
TC1 Orel Hershiser .60 1.50
TC2 Terry Pendleton .40 1.00
TC3 Benito Santiago .60 1.50
TC4 Kevin Brown .75 2.00
TC5 Gregg Jefferies .40 1.00

1996 Upper Deck

The 1996 Upper Deck set was issued in two series of 240 cards, and a 30 card update set, for a total of 510 cards. The cards were distributed in 10-card packs with a suggested retail price of $1.99, and 28 packs were contained in each box. Upper Deck issued 15,000 factory sets (containing all 510 cards) at season's end. In addition to being included in factory sets, the 30-card Update sets (U481-U510) were also available via mail through a wrapper exchange program. The attractive fronts of each basic card feature a full-bleed photo above a bronze foil bar that includes the player's name, team and position in a white oval. Subsets include Young at Heart (100-117), Beat the Odds (145-153), Postseason Checklist (218-222), Best of a Generation (370-387), Strange But True (415-423) and Managerial Salute Checklists (476-480). The only Rookie Card of note is Livan Hernandez.

COMPLETE SET (480) 20.00 50.00
COMP.FACT.SET (510) 50.00 100.00
COMP. SERIES 1 (240) 10.00 25.00
COMP. SERIES 2 (240) 10.00 25.00
COMMON CARD (1-480) .10 .30
COMP.UPDATE SET (30) 10.00 20.00
COMMON (481U-510U) .20 .50
1 Cal Ripken 2131 1.50 4.00
2 Eddie Murray 3000 Hits .20 .50
3 Mark Wohlers .10 .30
4 David Justice .10 .30
5 Chipper Jones .30 .75
6 Javier Lopez .10 .30
7 Mark Lemke .10 .30
8 Marquis Grissom .10 .30
9 Tom Glavine .20 .50
10 Greg Maddux .50 1.25
11 Manny Alexander .10 .30
12 Curtis Goodwin .10 .30
13 Scott Erickson .10 .30
14 Chris Hoiles .10 .30
15 Rafael Palmeiro .20 .50
16 Rick Krivda .10 .30
17 Jeff Manto .10 .30
18 Mo Vaughn .10 .30
19 Tim Wakefield .10 .30
20 Roger Clemens .60 1.50
21 Tim Naehring .10 .30
22 Troy O'Leary .10 .30
23 Mike Greenwell .10 .30
24 Stan Belinda .10 .30
25 John Valentin .10 .30
26 J.T. Snow .10 .30
27 Gary DiSarcina .10 .30
28 Mark Langston .10 .30
29 Brian Anderson .10 .30
30 Jim Edmonds .10 .30
31 Garret Anderson .10 .30
32 Orlando Palmeiro .10 .30
33 Brian McRae .10 .30
34 Kevin Foster .10 .30
35 Sammy Sosa .30 .75
36 Todd Zeile .10 .30
37 Jim Bullinger .10 .30
38 Luis Gonzalez .10 .30
39 Lyle Mouton .10 .30
40 Ray Durham .10 .30
41 Ozzie Guillen .10 .30
42 Alex Fernandez .10 .30
43 Brian Keyser .10 .30
44 Robin Ventura .10 .30
45 Reggie Sanders .10 .30
46 Pete Schourek .10 .30
47 John Smiley .10 .30
48 Jeff Brantley .10 .30
49 Thomas Howard .10 .30
50 Bret Boone .10 .30
51 Kevin Jarvis .10 .30
52 Jeff Branson .10 .30
53 Carlos Baerga .10 .30
54 Jim Thome .20 .50
55 Manny Ramirez .20 .50
56 Omar Vizquel .20 .50
57 Jose Mesa .10 .30
58 Julian Tavarez UER .10 .30
59 Orel Hershiser .10 .30
60 Larry Walker .10 .30
61 Bret Saberhagen .10 .30
62 Vinny Castilla .10 .30
63 Eric Young .10 .30
64 Bryan Rekar .10 .30
65 Andres Galarraga .10 .30
66 Steve Reed .10 .30
67 Chad Curtis .10 .30
68 Bobby Higginson .10 .30
69 Phil Nevin .10 .30
70 Cecil Fielder .10 .30
71 Felipe Lira .10 .30
72 Chris Gomez .10 .30
73 Charles Johnson .10 .30
74 Quilvio Veras .10 .30
75 Jeff Conine .10 .30
76 John Burkett .10 .30
77 Greg Colbrunn .10 .30
78 Terry Pendleton .10 .30
79 Shane Reynolds .10 .30
80 Jeff Bagwell .20 .50
81 Orlando Miller .10 .30
82 Mike Hampton .10 .30
83 James Mouton .10 .30
84 Brian L. Hunter .10 .30
85 Derek Bell .10 .30
86 Kevin Appier .10 .30
87 Joe Vitiello .10 .30
88 Wally Joyner .10 .30
89 Michael Tucker .10 .30
90 Johnny Damon .20 .50
91 Jon Nunnally .10 .30
92 Jason Jacome .10 .30
93 Chad Fonville .10 .30
94 Chan Ho Park .10 .30
95 Hideo Nomo .30 .75
96 Ismael Valdes .10 .30
97 Greg Gagne .10 .30
98 Arizona Diamondbacks .30 .75
Tampa Bay Devil Rays
99 Raul Mondesi .10 .30
100 Dave Winfield YH .10 .30
101 Dennis Eckersley YH .10 .30
102 Andre Dawson YH .10 .30
103 Dennis Martinez YH .10 .30
104 Lance Parrish YH .10 .30
105 Eddie Murray YH .20 .50
106 Alan Trammell YH .10 .30
107 Lou Whitaker YH .10 .30
108 Ozzie Smith YH .30 .75
109 Paul Molitor YH .10 .30
110 Rickey Henderson YH .20 .50
111 Tim Raines YH .10 .30
112 Harold Baines YH .10 .30
113 Lee Smith YH .10 .30
114 F.Valenzuela YH .10 .30
115 Cal Ripken YH .50 1.25
116 Tony Gwynn YH .20 .50
117 Wade Boggs .20 .50
118 Todd Hollandsworth .10 .30
119 Dave Nilsson .10 .30
120 Jose Valentin .10 .30
121 Steve Sparks .10 .30
122 Chuck Carr .10 .30
123 John Jaha .10 .30
124 Scott Karl .10 .30
125 Chuck Knoblauch .10 .30
126 Brad Radke .10 .30
127 Pat Meares .10 .30
128 Ron Coomer .10 .30
129 Pedro Munoz .10 .30
130 Kirby Puckett .30 .75
131 David Segui .10 .30
132 Mark Grudzielanek .10 .30
133 Mike Lansing .10 .30
134 Sean Berry .10 .30
135 Rondell White .10 .30
136 Pedro Martinez .20 .50
137 Carl Everett .10 .30
138 Dave Mlicki .10 .30
139 Bill Pulsipher .10 .30
140 Jason Isringhausen .10 .30
141 Rico Brogna .10 .30
142 Edgardo Alfonzo .10 .30
143 Jeff Kent .10 .30
144 Andy Pettitte .20 .50
145 Mike Piazza BO .30 .75
146 Cliff Floyd BO .10 .30
147 J.Isringhausen BO .10 .30
148 Tim Wakefield BO .10 .30
149 Chipper Jones BO .20 .50
150 Hideo Nomo BO .20 .50
151 Mark McGwire BO .40 1.00
152 Ron Gant BO .10 .30
153 Gary Gaetti BO .10 .30
154 Don Mattingly .75 2.00
155 Paul O'Neill .20 .50
156 Derek Jeter .75 2.00
157 Joe Girardi .10 .30
158 Ruben Sierra .10 .30

Card	Low	High
159 Jorge Posada	.20	.50
160 Geronimo Berroa	.10	.30
161 Steve Ontiveros	.10	.30
162 George Williams	.10	.30
163 Doug Johns	.10	.30
164 Ariel Prieto	.10	.30
165 Scott Brosius	.10	.30
166 Mike Bordick	.10	.30
167 Tyler Green	.10	.30
168 Mickey Morandini	.10	.30
169 Darren Daulton	.10	.30
170 Gregg Jefferies	.10	.30
171 Jim Eisenreich	.10	.30
172 Heathcliff Slocumb	.10	.30
173 Kevin Stocker	.10	.30
174 Esteban Loaiza	.10	.30
175 Jeff King	.10	.30
176 Mark Johnson	.10	.30
177 Denny Neagle	.10	.30
178 Orlando Merced	.10	.30
179 Carlos Garcia	.10	.30
180 Brian Jordan	.10	.30
181 Mike Morgan	.10	.30
182 Mark Petkovsek	.10	.30
183 Bernard Gilkey	.10	.30
184 John Mabry	.10	.30
185 Tom Henke	.10	.30
186 Glenn Dishman	.10	.30
187 Andy Ashby	.10	.30
188 Bip Roberts	.10	.30
189 Melvin Nieves	.10	.30
190 Ken Caminiti	.10	.30
191 Brad Ausmus	.10	.30
192 Deion Sanders	.20	.50
193 Jamie Brewington RC	.10	.30
194 Glenallen Hill	.10	.30
195 Barry Bonds	.75	2.00
196 Wm. Van Landingham	.10	.30
197 Mark Carreon	.10	.30
198 Royce Clayton	.10	.30
199 Joey Cora	.10	.30
200 Ken Griffey Jr.	.50	1.25
201 Jay Buhner	.10	.30
202 Alex Rodriguez	.60	1.50
203 Norm Charlton	.10	.30
204 Andy Benes	.10	.30
205 Edgar Martinez	.20	.50
206 Juan Gonzalez	.10	.30
207 Will Clark	.20	.50
208 Kevin Gross	.10	.30
209 Roger Pavlik	.10	.30
210 Ivan Rodriguez	.20	.50
211 Rusty Greer	.10	.30
212 Angel Martinez	.10	.30
213 Tomas Perez	.10	.30
214 Alex Gonzalez	.10	.30
215 Joe Carter	.10	.30
216 Shawn Green	.10	.30
217 Edwin Hurtado	.10	.30
218 Edgar Martinez Tony Pena CL	.10	.30
219 Chipper Jones Barry Larkin CL	.20	.50
220 Orel Hershiser CL	.10	.30
221 Mike Devereaux CL	.10	.30
222 Tom Glavine CL	.10	.30
223 Karim Garcia	.10	.30
224 Arquimedez Pozo	.10	.30
225 Billy Wagner	.10	.30
226 John Wasdin	.10	.30
227 Jeff Suppan	.10	.30
228 Steve Gibralter	.10	.30
229 Jimmy Haynes	.10	.30
230 Ruben Rivera	.10	.30
231 Chris Snopek	.10	.30
232 Alex Ochoa	.10	.30
233 Shannon Stewart	.10	.30
234 Quinton McCracken	.10	.30
235 Trey Beamon	.10	.30
236 Billy McMillon	.10	.30
237 Steve Cox	.10	.30
238 George Arias	.10	.30
239 Yamil Benitez	.10	.30
240 Todd Greene	.10	.30
241 Jason Kendall	.10	.30
242 Brooks Kieschnick	.10	.30
243 O. Fernandez RC	.10	.30
244 Livan Hernandez RC	.40	1.00
245 Rey Ordonez	.10	.30
246 Mike Grace RC	.10	.30
247 Jay Canizaro	.10	.30
248 Bob Wolcott	.10	.30
249 Jermaine Dye	.10	.30
250 Jason Schmidt	.20	.50
251 Mike Sweeney RC	.40	1.00
252 Marcus Jensen	.10	.30
253 Mendy Lopez	.10	.30
254 Wilton Guerrero RC	.10	.30
255 Paul Wilson	.10	.30
256 Edgar Renteria	.10	.30
257 Richard Hidalgo	.10	.30
258 Bob Abreu	.30	.75
259 Robert Smith RC	.10	.30
260 Sal Fasano	.10	.30
261 Enrique Wilson	.10	.30
262 Rich Hunter RC	.10	.30
263 Sergio Nunez	.10	.30
264 Dan Serafini	.10	.30
265 David Doster	.10	.30
266 Ryan McGuire	.10	.30
267 Scott Spiezio	.10	.30
268 Rafael Orellano	.10	.30
269 Steve Avery	.10	.30
270 Fred McGriff	.20	.50
271 John Smoltz	.20	.50
272 Ryan Klesko	.10	.30
273 Jeff Blauser	.10	.30
274 Brad Clontz	.10	.30
275 Roberto Alomar	.20	.50
276 B.J. Surhoff	.10	.30
277 Jeffrey Hammonds	.10	.30
278 Brady Anderson	.10	.30
279 Bobby Bonilla	.10	.30
280 Cal Ripken	1.00	2.50
281 Mike Mussina	.20	.50
282 Wil Cordero	.10	.30
283 Mike Stanley	.10	.30
284 Aaron Sele	.10	.30
285 Jose Canseco	.20	.50
286 Tom Gordon	.10	.30
287 Heathcliff Slocumb	.10	.30
288 Lee Smith	.10	.30
289 Troy Percival	.10	.30
290 Tim Salmon	.20	.50
291 Chuck Finley	.10	.30
292 Jim Abbott	.20	.50
293 Chili Davis	.10	.30
294 Steve Trachsel	.10	.30
295 Mark Grace	.20	.50
296 Rey Sanchez	.10	.30
297 Scott Servais	.10	.30
298 Jaime Navarro	.10	.30
299 Frank Castillo	.10	.30
300 Frank Thomas	.30	.75
301 Jason Bere	.10	.30
302 Danny Tartabull	.10	.30
303 Darren Lewis	.10	.30
304 Roberto Hernandez	.10	.30
305 Tony Phillips	.10	.30
306 Wilson Alvarez	.10	.30
307 Jose Rijo	.10	.30
308 Hal Morris	.10	.30
309 Mark Portugal	.10	.30
310 Barry Larkin	.20	.50
311 Dave Burba	.10	.30
312 Eddie Taubensee	.10	.30
313 Sandy Alomar Jr.	.10	.30
314 Dennis Martinez	.10	.30
315 Albert Belle	.10	.30
316 Eddie Murray	.30	.75
317 Charles Nagy	.10	.30
318 Chad Ogea	.10	.30
319 Kenny Lofton	.10	.30
320 Dante Bichette	.10	.30
321 Armando Reynoso	.10	.30
322 Walt Weiss	.10	.30
323 Ellis Burks	.10	.30
324 Kevin Ritz	.10	.30
325 Bill Swift	.10	.30
326 Jason Bates	.10	.30
327 Tony Clark	.10	.30
328 Travis Fryman	.10	.30
329 Mark Parent	.10	.30
330 Alan Trammell	.10	.30
331 C.J. Nitkowski	.10	.30
332 Jose Lima	.10	.30
333 Phil Plantier	.10	.30
334 Kurt Abbott	.10	.30
335 Andre Dawson	.10	.30
336 Chris Hammond	.10	.30
337 Robb Nen	.10	.30
338 Pat Rapp	.10	.30
339 Al Leiter	.10	.30
340 Gary Sheffield UER (HR total says 17	.10	.30
341 Todd Jones	.10	.30
342 Doug Drabek	.10	.30
343 Greg Swindell	.10	.30
344 Tony Eusebio	.10	.30
345 Craig Biggio	.20	.50
346 Darryl Kile	.10	.30
347 Mike Macfarlane	.10	.30
348 Jeff Montgomery	.10	.30
349 Chris Haney	.10	.30
350 Bip Roberts	.10	.30
351 Tom Goodwin	.10	.30
352 Mark Gubicza	.10	.30
353 Joe Randa	.10	.30
354 Ramon Martinez	.10	.30
355 Eric Karros	.10	.30
356 Delino DeShields	.10	.30
357 Brett Butler	.10	.30
358 Todd Worrell	.10	.30
359 Mike Blowers	.10	.30
360 Mike Piazza	.50	1.25
361 Ben McDonald	.10	.30
362 Ricky Bones	.10	.30
363 Greg Vaughn	.10	.30
364 Matt Mieske	.10	.30
365 Kevin Seitzer	.10	.30
366 Jeff Cirillo	.10	.30
367 LaTroy Hawkins	.10	.30
368 Frank Rodriguez	.10	.30
369 Rick Aguilera	.10	.30
370 Roberto Alomar BG	.10	.30
371 Albert Belle BG	.10	.30
372 Wade Boggs BG	.10	.30
373 Barry Bonds BG	.40	1.00
374 Roger Clemens BG	.30	.75
375 Dennis Eckersley BG	.10	.30
376 Ken Griffey Jr. BG	.30	.75
377 Tony Gwynn BG	.20	.50
378 Rickey Henderson BG	.20	.50
379 Greg Maddux BG	.30	.75
380 Fred McGriff BG	.10	.30
381 Paul Molitor BG	.10	.30
382 Eddie Murray BG	.20	.50
383 Mike Piazza BG	.30	.75
384 Kirby Puckett BG	.20	.50
385 Cal Ripken BG	.50	1.25
386 Ozzie Smith BG	.30	.75
387 Frank Thomas BG	.20	.50
388 Matt Walbeck	.10	.30
389 Dave Stevens	.10	.30
390 Marty Cordova	.10	.30
391 Darrin Fletcher	.10	.30
392 Cliff Floyd	.10	.30
393 Mel Rojas	.10	.30
394 Shane Andrews	.10	.30
395 Moises Alou	.10	.30
396 Carlos Perez	.10	.30
397 Jeff Fassero	.10	.30
398 Bobby Jones	.10	.30
399 Todd Hundley	.10	.30
400 John Franco	.10	.30
401 Jose Vizcaino	.10	.30
402 Bernard Gilkey	.10	.30
403 Pete Harnisch	.10	.30
404 Pat Kelly	.10	.30
405 David Cone	.10	.30
406 Bernie Williams	.20	.50
407 John Wetteland	.10	.30
408 Scott Kamieniecki	.10	.30
409 Tim Raines	.10	.30
410 Wade Boggs	.20	.50
411 Terry Steinbach	.10	.30
412 Jason Giambi	.10	.30
413 Todd Van Poppel	.10	.30
414 Pedro Munoz	.10	.30
415 Eddie Murray SBT	.20	.50
416 Dennis Eckersley SBT	.10	.30
417 Bip Roberts SBT	.10	.30
418 Glenallen Hill SBT	.10	.30
419 John Hudek SBT	.10	.30
420 Derek Bell SBT	.10	.30
421 Larry Walker SBT	.10	.30
422 Greg Maddux SBT	.30	.75
423 Ken Caminiti SBT	.10	.30
424 Brent Gates	.10	.30
425 Mark McGwire	.75	2.00
426 Mark Whiten	.10	.30
427 Sid Fernandez	.10	.30
428 Ricky Bottalico	.10	.30
429 Mike Mimbs	.10	.30
430 Lenny Dykstra	.10	.30
431 Todd Zeile	.10	.30
432 Benito Santiago	.10	.30
433 Danny Miceli	.10	.30
434 Al Martin	.10	.30
435 Jay Bell	.10	.30
436 Charlie Hayes	.10	.30
437 Mike Kingery	.10	.30
438 Paul Wagner	.10	.30
439 Tom Pagnozzi	.10	.30
440 Ozzie Smith	.50	1.25
441 Ray Lankford	.10	.30
442 Dennis Eckersley	.10	.30
443 Ron Gant	.10	.30
444 Alan Benes	.10	.30
445 Rickey Henderson	.30	.75
446 Jody Reed	.10	.30
447 Trevor Hoffman	.10	.30
448 Andujar Cedeno	.10	.30
449 Steve Finley	.10	.30
450 Tony Gwynn	.40	1.00
451 Joey Hamilton	.10	.30
452 Mark Leiter	.10	.30
453 Rod Beck	.10	.30
454 Kirt Manwaring	.10	.30
455 Matt Williams	.10	.30
456 Robby Thompson	.10	.30
457 Shawon Dunston	.10	.30
458 Russ Davis	.10	.30
459 Paul Sorrento	.10	.30
460 Randy Johnson	.30	.75
461 Chris Bosio	.10	.30
462 Luis Sojo	.10	.30
463 Sterling Hitchcock	.10	.30
464 Benji Gil	.10	.30
465 Mickey Tettleton	.10	.30
466 Mark McLemore	.10	.30
467 Darryl Hamilton	.10	.30
468 Ken Hill	.10	.30
469 Dean Palmer	.10	.30
470 Carlos Delgado	.10	.30
471 Ed Sprague	.10	.30
472 Otis Nixon	.10	.30
473 Pat Hentgen	.10	.30
474 Juan Guzman	.10	.30
475 John Olerud	.10	.30
476 Buck Showalter CL	.10	.30
477 Bobby Cox CL	.10	.30
478 Tommy Lasorda CL	.10	.30
479 Buck Showalter CL	.10	.30
480 Sparky Anderson CL	.10	.30
481U Randy Myers	.20	.50
482U Kent Mercker	.20	.50
483U David Wells	.30	.75
484U Kevin Mitchell	.20	.50
485U Randy Velarde	.20	.50
486U Ryne Sandberg	1.50	4.00
487U Doug Jones	.20	.50
488U Terry Adams	.20	.50
489U Kevin Tapani	.20	.50
490U Harold Baines	.30	.75
491U Eric Davis	.30	.75
492U Julio Franco	.30	.75
493U Jack McDowell	.20	.50
494U Devon White	.30	.75
495U Kevin Brown	.30	.75
496U Rick Wilkins	.20	.50
497U Sean Berry	.20	.50
498U Keith Lockhart	.20	.50
499U Mark Loretta	.20	.50
500U Paul Molitor	.30	.75
501U Roberto Kelly	.20	.50
502U Lance Johnson	.20	.50
503U Tino Martinez	.50	1.25
504U Kenny Rogers	.30	.75
505U Todd Stottlemyre	.20	.50
506U Gary Gaetti	.30	.75
507U Royce Clayton	.20	.50
508U Andy Benes	.20	.50
509U Wally Joyner	.30	.75
510U Erik Hanson	.20	.50
P100 Ken Griffey Jr Promo	1.25	3.00

1996 Upper Deck Blue Chip Prospects

Randomly inserted in first series retail packs at a rate of one in 72, this 20-card set, diecut on the top and bottom, features some of the best young stars in the majors against a bluish background.

COMPLETE SET (20)	40.00	100.00
SER.1 STATED ODDS 1:72		
BC1 Hideo Nomo	4.00	10.00
BC2 Johnny Damon	2.50	6.00
BC3 Jason Isringhausen	1.50	4.00
BC4 Bill Pulsipher	1.50	4.00
BC5 Marty Cordova	1.50	4.00
BC6 Michael Tucker	1.50	4.00
BC7 John Wasdin	1.50	4.00
BC8 Karim Garcia	1.50	4.00
BC9 Ruben Rivera	1.50	4.00
BC10 Chipper Jones	4.00	10.00
BC11 Billy Wagner	1.50	4.00
BC12 Brooks Kieschnick	1.50	4.00
BC13 Alan Benes	1.50	4.00
BC14 Roger Cedeno	1.50	4.00
BC15 Alex Rodriguez	8.00	20.00
BC16 Jason Schmidt	2.50	6.00
BC17 Derek Jeter	10.00	25.00
BC18 Brian L.Hunter	1.50	4.00
BC19 Garret Anderson	1.50	4.00
BC20 Manny Ramirez	2.50	6.00

1996 Upper Deck Diamond Destiny

Issued one per Wal Mart pack, these 40 cards feature leading players of baseball. The cards have two photos on the front with the player's name listed on the bottom. The backs have another photo along with biographical information.

COMPLETE SET (40)	30.00	80.00
*GOLD: 5X TO 12 X BASIC DESTINY		
GOLD ODDS 1:143 UD TECH RETAIL PACKS		
*SILVER: 1.5X TO 4X BASIC DESTINY		
SILVER ODDS 1:35 UD TECH RETAIL PACKS		
DD1 Chipper Jones	1.00	2.50
DD2 Fred McGriff	.60	1.50
DD3 John Smoltz	.60	1.50
DD4 Ryan Klesko	.40	1.00
DD5 Greg Maddux	1.50	4.00
DD6 Cal Ripken	3.00	8.00
DD7 Roberto Alomar	.60	1.50
DD8 Eddie Murray	1.00	2.50
DD9 Brady Anderson	.40	1.00
DD10 Mo Vaughn	.40	1.00
DD11 Roger Clemens	2.00	5.00
DD12 Darin Erstad	.75	2.00
DD13 Sammy Sosa	1.00	2.50
DD14 Frank Thomas	1.00	2.50
DD15 Barry Larkin	.60	1.50
DD16 Albert Belle	.40	1.00
DD17 Manny Ramirez	.60	1.50
DD18 Kenny Lofton	.40	1.00
DD19 Dante Bichette	.40	1.00
DD20 Gary Sheffield	.40	1.00
DD21 Jeff Bagwell	.60	1.50
DD22 Hideo Nomo	1.00	2.50
DD23 Mike Piazza	1.50	4.00
DD24 Kirby Puckett	1.00	2.50
DD25 Paul Molitor	1.00	2.50
DD26 Chuck Knoblauch	.40	1.00
DD27 Wade Boggs	.60	1.50
DD28 Derek Jeter	2.50	6.00
DD29 Rey Ordonez	.40	1.00
DD30 Mark McGwire	2.50	6.00
DD31 Ozzie Smith	1.50	4.00
DD32 Tony Gwynn	1.25	3.00
DD33 Barry Bonds	2.50	6.00
DD34 Matt Williams	.40	1.00
DD35 Ken Griffey Jr.	1.50	4.00
DD36 Jay Buhner	.40	1.00
DD37 Randy Johnson	1.00	2.50
DD38 Alex Rodriguez	2.00	5.00
DD39 Juan Gonzalez	.40	1.00
DD40 Joe Carter	.40	1.00

1996 Upper Deck Future Stock Prospects

Randomly inserted in packs at a rate of one in 6, this 20-card set highlights the top prospects who made their major league debuts in 1995. The cards are diecut at the top and feature a purple border surrounding the player's picture.

COMPLETE SET (20)	3.00	8.00
SER.1 STATED ODDS 1:6 HOB/RET		
FS1 George Arias	.40	1.00
FS2 Brian Barber	.40	1.00
FS3 Trey Beamon	.40	1.00
FS4 Yamil Benitez	.40	1.00
FS5 Jamie Brewington	.40	1.00
FS6 Tony Clark	.40	1.00
FS7 Steve Cox	.40	1.00
FS8 Carlos Delgado	.40	1.00
FS9 Chad Fonville	.40	1.00
FS10 Alex Ochoa	.40	1.00
FS11 Curtis Goodwin	.40	1.00
FS12 Todd Greene	.40	1.00
FS13 Jimmy Haynes	.40	1.00
FS14 Quinton McCracken	.40	1.00
FS15 Billy McMillon	.40	1.00
FS16 Chan Ho Park	.40	1.00
FS17 Arquimedez Pozo	.40	1.00
FS18 Chris Snopek	.40	1.00
FS19 Shannon Stewart	.40	1.00
FS20 Jeff Suppan	.40	1.00

1996 Upper Deck Gameface

These Gameface cards were seeded at a rate of one per Upper Deck and Collector's Choice Wal Mart retail pack. The Upper Deck packs contained eight cards and the Collector's Choice packs contained sixteen cards. Both packs carried a suggested retail price of $1.50. The card fronts feature the player's photo surrounded by a "cloudy" white border along with a Gameface logo at the bottom.

COMPLETE SET (10)	5.00	12.00
GF1 Ken Griffey Jr.	.50	1.25
GF2 Frank Thomas	.30	.75
GF3 Barry Bonds	.75	2.00
GF4 Albert Belle	.10	.30
GF5 Cal Ripken	1.00	2.50
GF6 Mike Piazza	.50	1.25
GF7 Chipper Jones	.30	.75
GF8 Matt Williams	.10	.30
GF9 Hideo Nomo	.30	.75
GF10 Greg Maddux	.50	1.25

1996 Upper Deck Hot Commodities

Cards from this 20 card set double die-cut set were randomly inserted into series two Upper Deck packs at a rate of one in 37. The set features some of baseball's most popular players.

COMPLETE SET (20)	60.00	150.00
SER.2 STATED ODDS 1:36 HOB/RET/ANCO		
HC1 Ken Griffey Jr.	5.00	12.00
HC2 Hideo Nomo	3.00	8.00
HC3 Roberto Alomar	2.00	5.00
HC4 Paul Wilson	1.25	3.00
HC5 Albert Belle	1.25	3.00
HC6 Manny Ramirez	2.00	5.00
HC7 Kirby Puckett	3.00	8.00
HC8 Johnny Damon	2.00	5.00
HC9 Randy Johnson	3.00	8.00
HC10 Greg Maddux	5.00	12.00
HC11 Chipper Jones	3.00	8.00
HC12 Barry Bonds	8.00	20.00
HC13 Mo Vaughn	1.25	3.00
HC14 Mike Piazza	5.00	12.00
HC15 Cal Ripken	10.00	25.00
HC16 Tim Salmon	2.00	5.00
HC17 Sammy Sosa	3.00	8.00
HC18 Kenny Lofton	1.25	3.00
HC19 Tony Gwynn	4.00	10.00
HC20 Frank Thomas	3.00	8.00

1996 Upper Deck V.J. Lovero Showcase

Upper Deck utilized photos from the files of V.J. Lovero to produce this set. The cards feature the photos along with a story of how Lovero took the photos. The cards are numbered with a "VJ" prefix. These cards were inserted at a rate of one every six packs.

COMPLETE SET (19)	10.00	25.00
SER.2 STATED ODDS 1:6 HOB/RET,1:3 ANCO		
VJ1 Jim Abbott	.50	1.25
VJ2 Hideo Nomo	.75	2.00
VJ3 Derek Jeter	2.00	5.00
VJ4 Barry Bonds	2.00	5.00
VJ5 Greg Maddux	1.25	3.00
VJ6 Mark McGwire	2.00	5.00
VJ7 Jose Canseco	.50	1.25
VJ8 Ken Caminiti	.30	.75
VJ9 Raul Mondesi	.30	.75
VJ10 Ken Griffey Jr.	1.25	3.00
VJ11 Jay Buhner	.30	.75
VJ12 Randy Johnson	.75	2.00
VJ13 Roger Clemens	1.50	4.00
VJ14 Brady Anderson	.30	.75
VJ15 Frank Thomas	.75	2.00
VJ16 Garret Anderson Jim Edmonds Tim Salmon	.30	.75
VJ17 Mike Piazza	1.25	3.00
VJ18 Dante Bichette	.30	.75
VJ19 Tony Gwynn	1.00	2.50

1996 Upper Deck Nomo Highlights

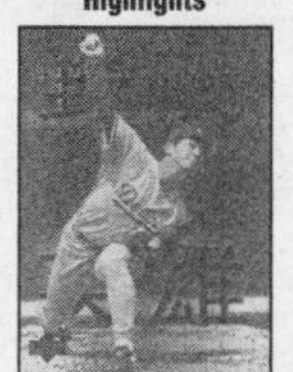

Los Angeles Dodgers star pitcher and Upper Deck spokesperson Hideo Nomo was featured in this special five card set. The cards were randomly seeded into second series packs at a rate of one in 24 and feature game action as well as descriptions of some of Nomo's key 1995 games.

COMPLETE SET (5)	8.00	20.00
COMMON CARD (1-5)	2.00	5.00
SER.2 STATED ODDS 1:24		

1996 Upper Deck Power Driven

Randomly inserted in first series packs at a rate of one in 36, this 20-card set consists of embossed rainbow foil inserts of baseball's top power hitters.

COMPLETE SET (20)	50.00	120.00
SER.1 STATED ODDS 1:36 HOB/RET		
PD1 Albert Belle	1.25	3.00
PD2 Barry Bonds	8.00	20.00
PD3 Jay Buhner	1.25	3.00
PD4 Jose Canseco	2.00	5.00
PD5 Cecil Fielder	1.25	3.00
PD6 Juan Gonzalez	1.25	3.00
PD7 Ken Griffey Jr.	5.00	12.00
PD8 Eric Karros	1.25	3.00
PD9 Fred McGriff	2.00	5.00
PD10 Mark McGwire	8.00	20.00
PD11 Rafael Palmeiro	2.00	5.00
PD12 Mike Piazza	5.00	12.00
PD13 Manny Ramirez	2.00	5.00
PD14 Tim Salmon	2.00	5.00
PD15 Reggie Sanders	1.25	3.00
PD16 Sammy Sosa	3.00	8.00
PD17 Frank Thomas	3.00	8.00
PD18 Mo Vaughn	1.25	3.00
PD19 Larry Walker	1.25	3.00
PD20 Matt Williams	1.25	3.00

1996 Upper Deck Predictor Hobby

Randomly inserted in both series hobby packs at a rate of one in 12, this 60-card predictor set offered six different 10-card parallel exchange sets for prizes as featured players competed for monthly milestones and awards. The fronts feature a cutout player photo against a pinstriped background surrounded by a gray marble border. Card backs feature game rules and guidelines. Winner cards are signified with a W in our listings and are in noticeably shorter supply since they had to be mailed in to Upper Deck (where they were destroyed) to claim your exchange cards. The deadline to mail in winning cards was November 18th, 1996.

COMPLETE SET (60)	25.00	60.00
COMPLETE SERIES 1 (30)	12.50	30.00
COMPLETE SERIES 2 (30)	12.50	30.00
STATED ODDS 1:12 HOBBY		
*EXCHANGE: .4X TO 1X BASIC PREDICTOR		
ONE EXCH.SET VIA MAIL PER PRED.WINNER		
H1 Albert Belle	.25	.60
H2 Kenny Lofton	.25	.60
H3 Rafael Palmeiro	.40	1.00
H4 Ken Griffey Jr.	1.00	2.50
H5 Tim Salmon	.40	1.00
H6 Cal Ripken	2.00	5.00
H7 Mark McGwire W	1.50	4.00
H8 Frank Thomas W	.60	1.50
H9 Mo Vaughn W	.25	.60
H10 Player of Month LS W	.25	.60
H11 Roger Clemens	1.25	3.00
H12 David Cone	.25	.60
H13 Joso Mosa	.25	.60
H14 Randy Johnson	.60	1.50
H15 Chuck Finley	.25	.60
H16 Mike Mussina	.40	1.00
H17 Kevin Appier	.25	.60
H18 Kenny Rogers	.60	1.50
H19 Lee Smith	.25	.60
H20 Pitcher of Month LS W	.25	.60
H21 George Arias	.25	.60
H22 Jose Herrera	.25	.60
H23 Tony Clark	.25	.60
H24 Todd Greene	.25	.60
H25 Derek Jeter W	1.50	4.00
H26 Arquimedez Pozo	.25	.60
H27 Matt Lawton	.25	.60
H28 Shannon Stewart	.25	.60
H29 Chris Snopek	.25	.60
H30 Most Rookie Hits LS	.25	.60
H31 Jeff Bagwell W	.40	1.00
H32 Dante Bichette	.25	.60
H33 Barry Bonds W	1.50	4.00
H34 Tony Gwynn	.75	2.00
H35 Chipper Jones	.60	1.50
H36 Eric Karros	.25	.60
H37 Barry Larkin	.40	1.00
H38 Mike Piazza	1.00	2.50
H39 Matt Williams	.25	.60
H40 Long Shot Card	.25	.60
H41 Osvaldo Fernandez	.25	.60
H42 Tom Glavine	.40	1.00
H43 Jason Isringhausen	.25	.60
H44 Greg Maddux	1.00	2.50
H45 Pedro Martinez	.40	1.00
H46 Hideo Nomo	.60	1.50
H47 Pete Schourek	.25	.60
H48 Paul Wilson	.25	.60
H49 Mark Wohlers	.25	.60
H50 Long Shot Card	.25	.60
H51 Bob Abreu	.60	1.50
H52 Trey Beamon	.25	.60
H53 Yamil Benitez	.25	.60
H54 Roger Cedeno	.25	.60
H55 Todd Hollandsworth	.25	.60
H56 Marvin Benard	.25	.60
H57 Jason Kendall	.25	.60
H58 Brooks Kieschnick	.25	.60
H59 Rey Ordonez W	.25	.60
H60 Long Shot Card	.25	.60

1996 Upper Deck Predictor Retail

Randomly inserted in both series retail packs at a rate of one in 12, this 60-card Predictor set offered six different 10-card parallel exchange sets as featured players competed for "monthly milestones and awards." The fronts feature a "cutout" player photo against a pinstriped background surrounded by a gray marble border. Card backs feature game rules and guidelines. Winner cards are signified with a W in our listings and are in noticeably shorter supply since they had to be mailed in to Upper Deck (where they were destroyed) to claim your exchange cards. The expiration date to send in cards was November 18th, 1996.

COMPLETE SET (60)	30.00	80.00
COMPLETE SERIES 1 (30)	15.00	40.00
COMPLETE SERIES 2 (30)	15.00	40.00
STATED ODDS 1:12 RETAIL		
*EXCHANGE: .4X TO 1X BASIC PREDICTOR		
ONE EXCH.SET VIA MAIL PER PRED.WINNER		
R1 Albert Belle W	.25	.60
R2 Jay Buhner W	.25	.60
R3 Juan Gonzalez	.25	.60
R4 Ken Griffey Jr.	1.00	2.50
R5 Mark McGwire W	1.50	4.00
R6 Rafael Palmeiro	.40	1.00
R7 Tim Salmon	.40	1.00
R8 Frank Thomas	.60	1.50
R9 Mo Vaughn W	.25	.60
R10 Monthly HR Ldr LS W	.25	.60
R11 Albert Belle W	.25	.60
R12 Jay Buhner	.25	.60
R13 Jim Edmonds	.25	.60
R14 Cecil Fielder	.25	.60
R15 Ken Griffey Jr.	1.00	2.50
R16 Edgar Martinez	.40	1.00
R17 Manny Ramirez	.40	1.00
R18 Frank Thomas	.60	1.50
R19 Mo Vaughn W	.25	.60
R20 Monthly RBI Ldr LS W	.25	.60
R21 Roberto Alomar W	.40	1.00
R22 Carlos Baerga	.25	.60
R23 Wade Boggs	.40	1.00
R24 Ken Griffey Jr.	1.00	2.50
R25 Chuck Knoblauch	.25	.60
R26 Kenny Lofton	.25	.60
R27 Edgar Martinez	.40	1.00
R28 Tim Salmon	.40	1.00
R29 Frank Thomas	.60	1.50
R30 Monthly Hits Ldr Longshot W	.25	.60
R31 Dante Bichette	.25	.60
R32 Barry Bonds W	1.50	4.00
R33 Ron Gant	.25	.60
R34 Chipper Jones	.60	1.50
R35 Fred McGriff	.40	1.00
R36 Mike Piazza	1.00	2.50
R37 Sammy Sosa	.60	1.50
R38 Larry Walker	.25	.60
R39 Matt Williams	.25	.60
R40 Long Shot Card	.25	.60
R41 Jeff Bagwell W	.40	1.00
R42 Dante Bichette	.25	.60
R43 Barry Bonds W	1.50	4.00
R44 Jeff Conine	.25	.60
R45 Andres Galarraga	.25	.60
R46 Mike Piazza	1.00	2.50
R47 Reggie Sanders	.25	.60
R48 Sammy Sosa	.60	1.50
R49 Matt Williams	.25	.60
R50 Long Shot Card	.25	.60
R51 Jeff Bagwell	.40	1.00
R52 Derek Bell	.25	.60
R53 Dante Bichette	.25	.60
R54 Craig Biggio	.40	1.00
R55 Barry Bonds	1.50	4.00
R56 Bret Boone	.25	.60
R57 Tony Gwynn	.75	2.00
R58 Barry Larkin	.40	1.00
R59 Mike Piazza W	1.00	2.50
R60 Long Shot Card	.25	.60

1996 Upper Deck Ripken Collection

This 23 card set was issued across all the various Upper Deck brands. The cards were issued to commemorate Cal Ripken's career, which had been capped the previous season by the breaking of the consecutive game streak long held by Lou Gehrig. The cards were inserted at the following ratios: Cards 1-4 were in Collector Choice first series packs at a rate of one in 12. Cards 5-8 were inserted into Upper Deck series one packs at a rate of one in 24. Cards 9-12 were placed into second series Collector Choice packs at a rate of one in 12. Cards 13-17 were in second series Upper Deck packs at a rate of one in 24. And Cards 18-22 were in SP Packs at a rate of one in 45. The header card (number 23) was also inserted into only Collector Choice packs.

COMPLETE SET (23)	60.00	120.00
COMP.COLC SER.1 (5)	6.00	12.00
COMP.COLC SER.2 (4)	5.00	10.00
COMP.UD SER.2 (5)	12.50	25.00
COMPLETE SP SET (5)	25.00	50.00

COMMON COLC (1-4/9-12) 1.25 3.00
COMMON UD (5-8/13-17) 2.50 6.00
COMMON SP (18-22) 6.00 15.00
CARDS 1-4 STATED ODDS 1:12 CC SER.1
CARDS 5-8 STATED ODDS 1:24 UD SER.1
CARDS 9-12 STATED ODDS 1:12 CC SER.2
CARDS 13-17 STATED ODDS 1:24 UD SER.2
CARDS 18-22 STATED ODDS 1:45 SP
NNO C.Ripken Header COLC 1.25 3.00

1996 Upper Deck Ripken Collection Jumbos

With a suggested retail price of $19.95, cards from this 22-card boxed set measures approximately 3 1/2" by 5" and features color borderless photos of Cal Ripken Jr. with a gold foil facsimile autograph. The cards parallel the standard Ripken Collection inserted into various 1996 Upper Deck Baseball products. The backs carry information about the player.

COMP.FACT SET 8.00 20.00
COMMON CARD .40 1.00
1 Cal Ripken COLC .75 2.00
after playing in 2131 consecutive games
2 Cal Ripken COLC 1.00 2.50
Barry Bonds
1995 All-Star Game
6 Cal Ripken UD. .60 1.50
Brian McRae sliding into second
1992
22 Cal Ripken SP 1.00 2.50
Eddie Murray
1981

1996 Upper Deck Run Producers

This 20 card set was randomly inserted into series two packs at a rate of one every 71 packs. The cards are thermographically printed, which gives the card a rubber surface texture. The cards are double die-cut and are foil stamped. These cards are highly condition sensitive, often found with noticable chipping on the edges.

COMPLETE SET (20) 60.00 150.00
SER.2 ODDS 1:72 HOB/RET, 1:36 ANCO
RP1 Albert Belle 1.50 4.00
RP2 Dante Bichette 1.50 4.00
RP3 Barry Bonds 10.00 25.00
RP4 Jay Buhner 1.50 4.00
RP5 Jose Canseco 2.50 6.00
RP6 Juan Gonzalez 1.50 4.00
RP7 Ken Griffey Jr. 6.00 15.00
RP8 Tony Gwynn 5.00 12.00
RP9 Kenny Lofton 1.50 4.00
RP10 Edgar Martinez 2.50 6.00
RP11 Fred McGriff 2.50 6.00
RP12 Mark McGwire 10.00 25.00
RP13 Rafael Palmeiro 2.50 6.00
RP14 Mike Piazza 6.00 15.00
RP15 Manny Ramirez 2.50 6.00
RP16 Tim Salmon 2.50 6.00
RP17 Sammy Sosa 4.00 10.00
RP18 Frank Thomas 4.00 10.00
RP19 Mo Vaughn 1.50 4.00
RP20 Matt Williams 1.50 4.00

1997 Upper Deck

The 1997 Upper Deck set was issued in two series (series one 1-240, series two 271-520). The 12-card packs retailed for $2.49 each. Many cards have dates on the front to identify when, and when possible, what significant event is pictured. The backs include a player photo, stats and a brief blurb to go with vital statistics. Subsets include Jackie Robinson Tribute (1-9), Strike Force (64-72), Defensive Gems (136-153), Global Impact (181-207), Season Highlight Checklists (214-222/316-324), Star Rookies (223-240/271-288), Capture the Flag (370-387), Griffey's Hot List (415-424) and Diamond Debuts (470-483). It's critical to note that the Griffey's Hot List subset cards (in an unannounced move by the manufacturer) were shortprinted (about 1:7 packs) in relation to other cards in the series two set. The comparatively low print run on these cards created a dramatic surge in demand amongst set collectors and the cards soared in value on the secondary market. A 30-card first series Update set (numbered 241-270) was available to collectors that mailed in 10 series one wrappers along with $3 for postage and handling. The Series One Update set is composed primarily of 1996 post-season highlights. An additional 30-card series two Trade set (numbered 521-550) was also released around the end of the season. It too was available to collectors that mailed in ten series two wrappers along with $3 for postage and handling. The Series Two Trade set is composed primarily of traded players pictured in their new uniforms and a selection of rookies and prospects highlighted by the inclusion of Jose Cruz Jr. and Hideki Irabu.

COMP.MASTER SET (550) 80.00 200.00
COMPLETE SET (490) 50.00 100.00
COMP. SERIES 1 (240) 20.00 40.00
COMP. SERIES 2 (250) 30.00 60.00
COMP.SER.2 w/o GHL (240) 10.00 25.00
COMMON (1-240/271-520) .10 .30
COMP.UPDATE SET (30) 40.00 80.00
COMMON (241-270) .40 1.00
ONE UPD.SET VIA MAIL PER 10 SER.1 WRAPPERS
COMMON GHL (415-424) .60 1.50
COMP.TRADE SET (30) 8.00 20.00
COMMON (521-550) .20 .50
1 Jackie Robinson .20 .50
The Beginnings
2 Jackie Robinson .20 .50
Breaking the Barrier
3 Jackie Robinson .20 .50
The MVP Season, 1949
4 Jackie Robinson .20 .50
1951 season
5 Jackie Robinson .20 .50
1952 and 1953 seasons
6 Jackie Robinson .20 .50
1954 season
7 Jackie Robinson .20 .50
1955 season
8 Jackie Robinson .20 .50
1956 season
9 Jackie Robinson HOF .20 .50
10 Chipper Jones .30 .75
11 Marquis Grissom .10 .30
12 Jermaine Dye .10 .30
13 Mark Lemke .10 .30
14 Terrell Wade .10 .30
15 Fred McGriff .20 .50
16 Tom Glavine .20 .50
17 Mark Wohlers .10 .30
18 Randy Myers .10 .30
19 Roberto Alomar .20 .50
20 Cal Ripken 1.00 2.50
21 Rafael Palmeiro .20 .50
22 Mike Mussina .20 .50
23 Brady Anderson .10 .30
24 Jose Canseco .20 .50
25 Mo Vaughn .10 .30
26 Roger Clemens .60 1.50
27 Tim Naehring .10 .30
28 Jeff Suppan .10 .30
29 Troy Percival .10 .30
30 Sammy Sosa .30 .75
31 Amaury Telemaco .10 .30
32 Rey Sanchez .10 .30
33 Scott Servais .10 .30
34 Steve Trachsel .10 .30
35 Mark Grace .20 .50
36 Wilson Alvarez .10 .30
37 Harold Baines .10 .30
38 Tony Phillips .10 .30
39 James Baldwin .10 .30
40 Frank Thomas UER .30 .75
Bio information is Ken Griffey Jr.'s
41 Lyle Mouton .10 .30
42 Chris Snopek .10 .30
43 Hal Morris .10 .30
44 Eric Davis .10 .30
45 Barry Larkin .20 .50
46 Reggie Sanders .10 .30
47 Pete Schourek .10 .30
48 Lee Smith .10 .30
49 Charles Nagy .10 .30
50 Albert Belle .10 .30
51 Julio Franco .10 .30
52 Kenny Lofton .10 .30
53 Orel Hershiser .10 .30
54 Omar Vizquel .20 .50
55 Eric Young .10 .30
56 Curtis Leskanic .10 .30
57 Quinton McCracken .10 .30
58 Kevin Ritz .10 .30
59 Walt Weiss .10 .30
60 Dante Bichette .10 .30
61 Mark Lewis .10 .30
62 Tony Clark .10 .30
63 Travis Fryman .10 .30
64 John Smoltz SF .10 .30
65 Greg Maddux SF .30 .75
66 Tom Glavine SF .10 .30
67 Mike Mussina SF .10 .30
68 Andy Pettitte SF .10 .30
69 Mariano Rivera SF .20 .50
70 Hideo Nomo SF .10 .30
71 Kevin Brown SF .10 .30
72 Randy Johnson SF .20 .50
73 Felipe Lira .10 .30
74 Kimera Bartee .10 .30
75 Alan Trammell .10 .30
76 Kevin Brown .10 .30
77 Edgar Renteria .10 .30
78 Al Leiter .10 .30
79 Charles Johnson .10 .30
80 Andre Dawson .10 .30
81 Billy Wagner .10 .30
82 Donne Wall .10 .30
83 Jeff Bagwell .20 .50
84 Keith Lockhart .10 .30
85 Jeff Montgomery .10 .30
86 Tom Goodwin .10 .30
87 Tim Belcher .10 .30
88 Mike Macfarlane .10 .30
89 Joe Randa .10 .30
90 Brett Butler .10 .30
91 Todd Worrell .10 .30
92 Todd Hollandsworth .10 .30
93 Ismael Valdes .10 .30
94 Hideo Nomo .30 .75
95 Mike Piazza .50 1.25
96 Jeff Cirillo .10 .30
97 Ricky Bones .10 .30
98 Fernando Vina .10 .30
99 Ben McDonald .10 .30
100 John Jaha .10 .30
101 Mark Loretta .10 .30
102 Paul Molitor .10 .30
103 Rick Aguilera .10 .30
104 Marty Cordova .10 .30
105 Kirby Puckett .30 .75
106 Dan Naulty .10 .30
107 Frank Rodriguez .10 .30
108 Shane Andrews .10 .30
109 Henry Rodriguez .10 .30
110 Mark Grudzielanek .10 .30
111 Pedro Martinez .20 .50
112 Ugueth Urbina .10 .30
113 David Segui .10 .30
114 Rey Ordonez .10 .30
115 Bernard Gilkey .10 .30
116 Butch Huskey .10 .30
117 Paul Wilson .10 .30
118 Alex Ochoa .10 .30
119 John Franco .10 .30
120 Dwight Gooden .10 .30
121 Ruben Rivera .10 .30
122 Andy Pettitte .20 .50
123 Tino Martinez .20 .50
124 Bernie Williams .20 .50
125 Wade Boggs .20 .50
126 Paul O'Neill .20 .50
127 Scott Brosius .10 .30
128 Ernie Young .10 .30
129 Doug Johns .10 .30
130 Geronimo Berroa .10 .30
131 Jason Giambi .10 .30
132 John Wasdin .10 .30
133 Jim Eisenreich .10 .30
134 Ricky Otero .10 .30
135 Ricky Bottalico .10 .30
136 Mark Langston DG .10 .30
137 Greg Maddux DG .30 .75
138 Ivan Rodriguez DG .10 .30
139 Charles Johnson DG .10 .30
140 J.T. Snow DG .10 .30
141 Mark Grace DG .10 .30
142 Roberto Alomar DG .10 .30
143 Craig Biggio DG .10 .30
144 Ken Caminiti DG .10 .30
145 Matt Williams DG .10 .30
146 Omar Vizquel DG .10 .30
147 Cal Ripken DG .50 1.25
148 Ozzie Smith DG .30 .75
149 Rey Ordonez DG .10 .30
150 Ken Griffey Jr. DG .30 .75
151 Devon White DG .10 .30
152 Barry Bonds DG .40 1.00
153 Kenny Lofton DG .10 .30
154 Mickey Morandini .10 .30
155 Gregg Jefferies .10 .30
156 Curt Schilling .10 .30
157 Jason Kendall .10 .30
158 Francisco Cordova .10 .30
159 Dennis Eckersley .10 .30
160 Ron Gant .10 .30
161 Ozzie Smith .50 1.25
162 Brian Jordan .10 .30
163 John Mabry .10 .30
164 Andy Ashby .10 .30
165 Steve Finley .10 .30
166 Fernando Valenzuela .10 .30
167 Archi Cianfrocco .10 .30
168 Wally Joyner .10 .30
169 Greg Vaughn .10 .30
170 Barry Bonds .75 2.00
171 W.VanLandingham .10 .30
172 Marvin Benard .10 .30
173 Rich Aurilia .10 .30
174 Jay Canizaro .10 .30
175 Ken Griffey Jr. .50 1.25
176 Bob Wells .10 .30
177 Jay Buhner .10 .30
178 Sterling Hitchcock .10 .30
179 Edgar Martinez .20 .50
180 Rusty Greer .10 .30
181 Dave Nilsson GI .10 .30
182 Larry Walker GI .10 .30
183 Edgar Renteria GI .10 .30
184 Rey Ordonez GI .10 .30
185 Rafael Palmeiro GI .10 .30
186 Osvaldo Fernandez GI .10 .30
187 Raul Mondesi GI .10 .30
188 Manny Ramirez GI .10 .30
189 Sammy Sosa GI UER .20 .50
The flag pictured is wrong
190 Robert Eenhoorn GI .10 .30
191 Devon White GI .10 .30
192 Hideo Nomo GI .10 .30
193 Mac Suzuki GI .10 .30
194 Chan Ho Park GI .10 .30
195 F.Valenzuela GI .10 .30
196 Andruw Jones GI .10 .30
197 Vinny Castilla GI .10 .30
198 Dennis Martinez GI .10 .30
199 Ruben Rivera GI .10 .30
200 Juan Gonzalez GI .10 .30
201 Roberto Alomar GI .10 .30
202 Edgar Martinez GI .10 .30
203 Ivan Rodriguez GI .10 .30
204 Carlos Delgado GI .10 .30
205 Andres Galarraga GI .10 .30
206 Ozzie Guillen GI .10 .30
207 Midre Cummings GI .10 .30
208 Roger Pavlik .10 .30
209 Darren Oliver .10 .30
210 Dean Palmer .10 .30
211 Ivan Rodriguez .20 .50
212 Otis Nixon .10 .30
213 Pat Hentgen .10 .30
214 Ozzie Smith .20 .50
Andre Dawson
Kirby Pucket HL CL
215 Barry Bonds .40 1.00
Gary Sheffield
Brady Anderson HL CL
216 Ken Caminiti SH CL .10 .30
217 John Smoltz SH CL .10 .30
218 Eric Young SH CL .10 .30
219 Juan Gonzalez SH CL .10 .30
220 Eddie Murray SH CL .20 .50
221 T. Lasorda SH CL .10 .30
222 Paul Molitor SH CL .10 .30
223 Luis Castillo .10 .30
224 Justin Thompson .10 .30
225 Rocky Coppinger .10 .30
226 Jermaine Allensworth .10 .30
227 Jeff D'Amico .10 .30
228 Jamey Wright .10 .30
229 Scott Rolen .20 .50
230 Darin Erstad .10 .30
231 Marty Janzen .10 .30
232 Jacob Cruz .10 .30
233 Raul Ibanez .10 .30
234 Nomar Garciaparra .50 1.25
235 Todd Walker .10 .30
236 Brian Giles RC .60 1.50
237 Matt Beech .10 .30
238 Mike Cameron .10 .30
239 Jose Paniagua .10 .30
240 Andruw Jones .20 .50
241 Brant Brown UPD .40 1.00
242 Robin Jennings UPD .40 1.00
243 Willie Adams UPD .40 1.00
244 Ken Caminiti UPD .60 1.50
245 Brian Jordan UPD .60 1.50
246 Chipper Jones UPD 1.50 4.00
247 Juan Gonzalez UPD .60 1.50
248 Bernie Williams UPD 1.00 2.50
249 Roberto Alomar UPD 1.00 2.50
250 Bernie Williams UPD 1.00 2.50
251 David Wells UPD .60 1.50
252 Cecil Fielder UPD .60 1.50
253 D.Strawberry UPD .60 1.50
254 Andy Pettitte UPD 1.00 2.50
255 Javier Lopez UPD .60 1.50
256 Gary Gaetti UPD .60 1.50
257 Ron Gant UPD .60 1.50
258 Brian Jordan UPD .60 1.50
259 John Smoltz UPD 1.00 2.50
260 Greg Maddux UPD 3.00 8.00
261 Tom Glavine UPD 1.00 2.50
262 Andruw Jones UPD 1.00 2.50
263 Greg Maddux UPD 3.00 8.00
264 David Cone UPD .60 1.50
265 Jim Leyritz UPD .40 1.00
266 Andy Pettitte UPD 1.00 2.50
267 John Wetteland UPD .60 1.50
268 Dario Veras UPD .40 1.00
269 Neifi Perez UPD .40 1.00
270 Bill Mueller UPD 1.50 4.00
271 Vladimir Guerrero .30 .75
272 Dmitri Young .10 .30
273 Nerio Rodriguez RC .10 .30
274 Kevin Orie .10 .30
275 Felipe Crespo .10 .30
276 Danny Graves .10 .30
277 Rod Myers .10 .30
278 Felix Heredia RC .10 .30
279 Ralph Milliard .10 .30
280 Greg Norton .10 .30
281 Derek Wallace .10 .30
282 Trot Nixon .10 .30
283 Bobby Chouinard .10 .30
284 Jay Witasick .10 .30
285 Travis Miller .10 .30
286 Brian Bevil .10 .30
287 Bobby Estalella .10 .30
288 Steve Soderstrom .10 .30
289 Mark Langston .10 .30
290 Tim Salmon .20 .50
291 Jim Edmonds .10 .30
292 Garret Anderson .10 .30
293 George Arias .10 .30
294 Gary DiSarcina .10 .30
295 Chuck Finley .10 .30
296 Todd Greene .10 .30
297 Randy Velarde .10 .30
298 David Justice .10 .30
299 Ryan Klesko .10 .30
300 John Smoltz .20 .50
301 Javier Lopez .10 .30
302 Greg Maddux .50 1.25
303 Denny Neagle .10 .30
304 B.J. Surhoff .10 .30
305 Chris Hoiles .10 .30
306 Eric Davis .10 .30
307 Scott Erickson .10 .30
308 Mike Bordick .10 .30
309 John Valentin .10 .30
310 Heathcliff Slocumb .10 .30
311 Tom Gordon .10 .30
312 Mike Stanley .10 .30
313 Reggie Jefferson .10 .30
314 Darren Bragg .10 .30
315 Troy O'Leary .10 .30
316 John Mabry SH CL .10 .30
317 Mark Whiten SH CL .10 .30
318 Edgar Martinez SH CL .10 .30
319 Alex Rodriguez SH CL .30 .75
320 Mark McGwire SH CL .40 1.00
321 Hideo Nomo SH CL .10 .30
322 Todd Hundley SH CL .10 .30
323 Barry Bonds SH CL .40 1.00
324 Andruw Jones SH CL .10 .30
325 Ryne Sandberg .50 1.25
326 Brian McRae .10 .30
327 Frank Castillo .10 .30
328 Shawon Dunston .10 .30
329 Ray Durham .10 .30
330 Robin Ventura .10 .30
331 Ozzie Guillen .10 .30
332 Roberto Hernandez .10 .30
333 Albert Belle .10 .30
334 Dave Martinez .10 .30
335 Willie Greene .10 .30
336 Jeff Brantley .10 .30
337 Kevin Jarvis .10 .30
338 John Smiley .10 .30
339 Eddie Taubensee .10 .30
340 Bret Boone .10 .30
341 Kevin Seitzer .10 .30
342 Jack McDowell .10 .30
343 Sandy Alomar Jr. .10 .30
344 Chad Curtis .10 .30
345 Manny Ramirez .20 .50
346 Chad Ogea .10 .30
347 Jim Thome .20 .50
348 Mark Thompson .10 .30
349 Ellis Burks .10 .30
350 Andres Galarraga .10 .30
351 Vinny Castilla .10 .30
352 Kirt Manwaring .10 .30
353 Larry Walker .10 .30
354 Omar Olivares .10 .30
355 Bobby Higginson .10 .30
356 Melvin Nieves .10 .30
357 Brian Johnson .10 .30
358 Devon White .10 .30
359 Jeff Conine .10 .30
360 Gary Sheffield .10 .30
361 Robb Nen .10 .30
362 Mike Hampton .10 .30
363 Bob Abreu .20 .50
364 Luis Gonzalez .10 .30
365 Derek Bell .10 .30
366 Sean Berry .10 .30
367 Craig Biggio .20 .50
368 Darryl Kile .10 .30
369 Shane Reynolds .10 .30
370 Jeff Bagwell CF .10 .30
371 Ron Gant CF .10 .30
372 Andy Benes CF .10 .30
373 Gary Gaetti CF .10 .30
374 Ramon Martinez CF .10 .30
375 Raul Mondesi CF .10 .30
376 Steve Finley CF .10 .30
377 Ken Caminiti CF .10 .30
378 Tony Gwynn CF .20 .50
379 Dario Veras RC .10 .30
380 Andy Pettitte CF .10 .30
381 Ruben Rivera CF .10 .30
382 David Cone CF .10 .30
383 Roberto Alomar CF .10 .30
384 Edgar Martinez CF .10 .30
385 Ken Griffey Jr. CF .30 .75
386 Mark McGwire CF .40 1.00
387 Rusty Greer CF .10 .30
388 Jose Rosado .10 .30
389 Kevin Appier .10 .30
390 Johnny Damon .20 .50
391 Jose Offerman .10 .30
392 Michael Tucker .10 .30
393 Craig Paquette .10 .30
394 Bip Roberts .10 .30
395 Ramon Martinez .10 .30
396 Greg Gagne .10 .30
397 Chan Ho Park .10 .30
398 Karim Garcia .10 .30
399 Wilton Guerrero .10 .30
400 Eric Karros .10 .30
401 Raul Mondesi .10 .30
402 Matt Mieske .10 .30
403 Mike Fetters .10 .30
404 Dave Nilsson .10 .30
405 Jose Valentin .10 .30
406 Scott Karl .10 .30
407 Marc Newfield .10 .30
408 Cal Eldred .10 .30
409 Rich Becker .10 .30
410 Terry Steinbach .10 .30
411 Chuck Knoblauch .10 .30
412 Pat Meares .10 .30
413 Brad Radke .10 .30
414 Kirby Puckett UER .30 .75
Card numbered 415
415 A.Jones GHL SP .60 1.50
416 C.Jones GHL SP 1.00 2.50
417 Mo Vaughn GHL SP .60 1.50
418 F.Thomas GHL SP 1.00 2.50
419 Albert Belle GHL SP .60 1.50
420 M.McGwire GHL SP 3.00 8.00
421 Derek Jeter GHL SP 3.00 8.00
422 A.Rodriguez GHL SP 2.00 5.00
423 J.Gonzalez GHL SP .60 1.50
424 K.Griffey Jr. GHL SP 2.00 5.00
425 Rondell White .10 .30
426 Darrin Fletcher .10 .30
427 Cliff Floyd .10 .30
428 Mike Lansing .10 .30
429 F.P. Santangelo .10 .30
430 Todd Hundley .10 .30
431 Mark Clark .10 .30
432 Pete Harnisch .10 .30
433 Jason Isringhausen .10 .30
434 Bobby Jones .10 .30
435 Lance Johnson .10 .30
436 Carlos Baerga .10 .30
437 Mariano Duncan .10 .30
438 David Cone .10 .30
439 Mariano Rivera .30 .75
440 Derek Jeter .75 2.00
441 Joe Girardi .10 .30
442 Charlie Hayes .10 .30
443 Tim Raines .10 .30
444 Darryl Strawberry .10 .30
445 Cecil Fielder .10 .30
446 Ariel Prieto .10 .30
447 Tony Batista .10 .30
448 Brent Gates .10 .30
449 Scott Spiezio .10 .30
450 Mark McGwire .75 2.00
451 Don Wengert .10 .30
452 Mike Lieberthal .10 .30
453 Lenny Dykstra .10 .30
454 Rex Hudler .10 .30
455 Darren Daulton .10 .30
456 Kevin Stocker .10 .30
457 Trey Beamon .10 .30
458 Midre Cummings .10 .30
459 Mark Johnson .10 .30
460 Al Martin .10 .30
461 Kevin Elster .10 .30
462 Jon Lieber .10 .30
463 Jason Schmidt .10 .30
464 Paul Wagner .10 .30
465 Andy Benes .10 .30
466 Alan Benes .10 .30
467 Royce Clayton .10 .30
468 Gary Gaetti .10 .30
469 Curt Lyons RC .10 .30
470 Eugene Kingsale DD .10 .30
471 Damian Jackson DD .10 .30
472 Wendell Magee DD .10 .30
473 Kevin L. Brown DD .10 .30
474 Raul Casanova DD .10 .30
475 R.Mendoza DD RC .10 .30
476 Todd Dunn DD .10 .30
477 Chad Mottola DD .10 .30
478 Andy Larkin DD .10 .30
479 Jaime Bluma DD .10 .30
480 Mac Suzuki DD .10 .30
481 Brian Banks DD .10 .30
482 Desi Wilson DD .10 .30
483 Einar Diaz DD .10 .30
484 Tom Pagnozzi .10 .30
485 Ray Lankford .10 .30
486 Todd Stottlemyre .10 .30
487 Donovan Osborne .10 .30
488 Trevor Hoffman .10 .30
489 Chris Gomez .10 .30
490 Ken Caminiti .10 .30
491 John Flaherty .10 .30
492 Tony Gwynn .40 1.00
493 Joey Hamilton .10 .30
494 Rickey Henderson .30 .75
495 Glenallen Hill .10 .30
496 Rod Beck .10 .30
497 Osvaldo Fernandez .10 .30
498 Rick Wilkins .10 .30
499 Joey Cora .10 .30
500 Alex Rodriguez .50 1.25
501 Randy Johnson .30 .75
502 Paul Sorrento .10 .30
503 Dan Wilson .10 .30
504 Jamie Moyer .10 .30
505 Will Clark .20 .50
506 Mickey Tettleton .10 .30
507 John Burkett .10 .30
508 Ken Hill .10 .30
509 Mark McLemore .10 .30
510 Juan Gonzalez .10 .30
511 Bobby Witt .10 .30
512 Carlos Delgado .10 .30
513 Alex Gonzalez .10 .30
514 Shawn Green .10 .30
515 Joe Carter .10 .30
516 Juan Guzman .10 .30
517 Charlie O'Brien .10 .30
518 Ed Sprague .10 .30
519 Mike Timlin .10 .30
520 Roger Clemens .60 1.50
521 Eddie Murray TRADE .75 2.00
522 Jason Dickson TRADE .20 .50
523 Jim Leyritz TRADE .20 .50
524 M.Tucker TRADE .20 .50
525 Kenny Lofton TRADE .30 .75
526 Jimmy Key TRADE .30 .75
527 Mel Rojas TRADE .20 .50
528 Deion Sanders TRADE .50 1.25
529 Bartolo Colon TRADE .30 .75
530 Matt Williams TRADE .30 .75
531 M.Grissom TRADE .30 .75
532 David Justice TRADE .30 .75
533 B.Trammell TRADE .30 .75
534 Moises Alou TRADE .30 .75
535 Bobby Bonilla TRADE .30 .75
536 A.Fernandez TRADE .20 .50
537 Jay Bell TRADE .30 .75
538 Chili Davis TRADE .30 .75
539 Jeff King TRADE .20 .50
540 Todd Zeile TRADE .20 .50
541 John Olerud TRADE .30 .75
542 Jose Guillen TRADE .30 .75
543 Derrek Lee TRADE .50 1.25
544 Dante Powell TRADE .20 .50
545 J.T. Snow TRADE .30 .75
546 Jeff Kent TRADE .30 .75
547 Jose Cruz Jr. TRADE .30 .75
548 J.Wetteland TRADE .30 .75
549 O.Merced TRADE .20 .50
550 Hideki Irabu TRADE .30 .75

1997 Upper Deck Amazing Greats

Randomly inserted in all first series packs at a rate of one in 69, this 20-card set features a horizontal design along with two player photos on the front. The cards feature translucent player images against a real wood grain stock.

SER.1 STATED ODDS 1:69
AG1 Ken Griffey Jr. 8.00 20.00
AG2 Roberto Alomar 3.00 8.00
AG3 Alex Rodriguez 8.00 20.00
AG4 Paul Molitor 2.00 5.00
AG5 Chipper Jones 5.00 12.00
AG6 Tony Gwynn 6.00 15.00
AG7 Kenny Lofton 2.00 5.00
AG8 Albert Belle 2.00 5.00
AG9 Matt Williams 2.00 5.00
AG10 Frank Thomas 5.00 12.00
AG11 Greg Maddux 8.00 20.00
AG12 Sammy Sosa 5.00 12.00
AG13 Kirby Puckett 5.00 12.00
AG14 Jeff Bagwell 3.00 8.00
AG15 Cal Ripken 15.00 40.00
AG16 Manny Ramirez 3.00 8.00
AG17 Barry Bonds 12.50 30.00
AG18 Mo Vaughn 2.00 5.00
AG19 Eddie Murray 5.00 12.00
AG20 Mike Piazza 8.00 20.00

1997 Upper Deck Blue Chip Prospects

This rare 20-card set, randomly inserted into series two packs, features color photos of high expectation prospects who are likely to have a big impact on Major League Baseball. Only 500 of this crash numbered, limited edition set was produced.

BC1 Andruw Jones 15.00 40.00
BC2 Derek Jeter 40.00 80.00
BC3 Scott Rolen 15.00 40.00
BC4 Manny Ramirez 15.00 40.00
BC5 Todd Walker 10.00 25.00
BC6 Rocky Coppinger 6.00 15.00
BC7 Nomar Garciaparra 20.00 50.00
BC8 Darin Erstad 10.00 25.00
BC9 Jermaine Dye 10.00 25.00
BC10 Vladimir Guerrero 20.00 50.00
BC11 Edgar Renteria 10.00 25.00
BC12 Bob Abreu 15.00 40.00
BC13 Karim Garcia 6.00 15.00
BC14 Jeff D'Amico 6.00 15.00
BC15 Chipper Jones 20.00 50.00
BC16 Todd Hollandsworth 6.00 15.00
BC17 Andy Pettitte 15.00 40.00
BC18 Ruben Rivera 6.00 15.00
BC19 Jason Kendall 10.00 25.00
BC20 Alex Rodriguez 30.00 60.00

1997 Upper Deck Game Jersey

Randomly inserted in all first series packs at a rate of one in 800, this three-card set feaures swatches of real game-worn jerseys cut up and placed on the cards. These cards represent the first memorabilia insert cards to hit the baseball card market and thus carry a significant impact in the development of the hobby in the late 1990's.

SER.1 STATED ODDS 1:800
GJ1 Ken Griffey Jr. 150.00 250.00
GJ2 Tony Gwynn 6.00 15.00
GJ3 Rey Ordonez 4.00 10.00

1997 Upper Deck Hot Commodities

Randomly inserted in series two packs at a rate of one in 13, this 20-card set features color player images on a flame background in a black border. The backs carry a player head photo, statistics, and a commentary by ESPN sportscaster Dan Patrick.

COMPLETE SET (20) 25.00 60.00
SER.2 STATED ODDS 1:13
HC1 Alex Rodriguez 1.50 4.00
HC2 Andruw Jones .60 1.50
HC3 Derek Jeter 2.50 6.00
HC4 Frank Thomas 1.00 2.50
HC5 Ken Griffey Jr. 1.50 4.00
HC6 Chipper Jones 1.00 2.50
HC7 Juan Gonzalez .40 1.00
HC8 Cal Ripken 3.00 8.00
HC9 John Smoltz .60 1.50
HC10 Mark McGwire 2.50 6.00
HC11 Barry Bonds 2.50 6.00
HC12 Albert Belle .40 1.00
HC13 Mike Piazza 1.50 4.00
HC14 Manny Ramirez .60 1.50
HC15 Mo Vaughn .40 1.00
HC16 Tony Gwynn 1.25 3.00
HC17 Vladimir Guerrero 1.00 2.50
HC18 Hideo Nomo 1.00 2.50
HC19 Greg Maddux 1.50 4.00
HC20 Kirby Puckett 1.00 2.50

1997 Upper Deck Long Distance Connection

Randomly inserted in series two packs at a rate of one in 35, this 20-card set features color player images of some of the League's top power hitters on backgrounds utilizing Light/FX technology. The backs carry the pictured player's statistics.

COMPLETE SET (20) 60.00 150.00
SER.2 STATED ODDS 1:35
LD1 Mark McGwire 6.00 15.00
LD2 Brady Anderson 1.00 2.50
LD3 Ken Griffey Jr. 4.00 10.00

LD4 Albert Belle 1.00 2.50
LD5 Juan Gonzalez 1.00 2.50
LD6 Andres Galarraga 1.00 2.50
LD7 Jay Buhner 1.00 2.50
LD8 Mo Vaughn 1.00 2.50
LD9 Barry Bonds 6.00 15.00
LD10 Gary Sheffield 1.00 2.50
LD11 Todd Hundley 1.00 2.50
LD12 Frank Thomas 2.50 6.00
LD13 Sammy Sosa 2.50 6.00
LD14 Rafael Palmeiro 1.50 4.00
LD15 Alex Rodriguez 4.00 10.00
LD16 Mike Piazza 4.00 10.00
LD17 Ken Caminiti 1.00 2.50
LD18 Chipper Jones 2.50 6.00
LD19 Manny Ramirez 1.50 4.00
LD20 Andruw Jones 1.50 4.00

1997 Upper Deck Memorable Moments

Cards from these sets were distributed exclusively in six-card retail Collector's Choice series one and two packs. Each pack contained one of ten different Memorable Moments inserts. Each set features a selection of top stars captured in highlights of season's gone by. Each card features wave-like die cut top and bottom borders with gold foil.

COMPLETE SERIES 1 (10) 5.00 12.00
COMPLETE SERIES 2 (10) 5.00 12.00
A1 Andruw Jones .20 .50
A2 Chipper Jones .30 .75
A3 Cal Ripken 1.00 2.50
A4 Frank Thomas .30 .75
A5 Manny Ramirez .20 .50
A6 Mike Piazza .50 1.25
A7 Mark McGwire .75 2.00
A8 Barry Bonds .75 2.00
A9 Ken Griffey Jr. .50 1.25
A10 Alex Rodriguez .50 1.25
B1 Ken Griffey Jr. .50 1.25
B2 Albert Belle .10 .30
B3 Derek Jeter .75 2.00
B4 Greg Maddux .50 1.25
B5 Tony Gwynn .40 1.00
B6 Ryne Sandberg .50 1.25
B7 Juan Gonzalez .10 .30
B8 Roger Clemens .60 1.50
B9 Jose Cruz Jr. .10 .30
B10 Mo Vaughn .10 .30

1997 Upper Deck Power Package

Randomly inserted in all first series packs at a rate of one in 24, this 20-card set features some of the best longball hitters. The die cut cards feature some of baseball's leading power hitters.

COMPLETE SET (20) 30.00 80.00
SER.1 STATED ODDS 1:24
*JUMBOS: 2X TO .5X BASIC PP
JUMBOS ONE PER RETAIL JUMBO PACK
PP1 Ken Griffey Jr. 3.00 8.00
PP2 Joe Carter .75 2.00
PP3 Rafael Palmeiro 1.25 3.00
PP4 Jay Buhner .75 2.00
PP5 Sammy Sosa 2.00 5.00
PP6 Fred McGriff 1.25 3.00
PP7 Jeff Bagwell 1.25 3.00
PP8 Albert Belle .75 2.00
PP9 Matt Williams .75 2.00
PP10 Mark McGwire 5.00 12.00
PP11 Gary Sheffield .75 2.00
PP12 Tim Salmon 1.25 3.00
PP13 Ryan Klesko .75 2.00
PP14 Manny Ramirez 1.25 3.00
PP15 Mike Piazza 3.00 8.00
PP16 Barry Bonds 5.00 12.00
PP17 Mo Vaughn .75 2.00
PP18 Jose Canseco 1.25 3.00
PP19 Juan Gonzalez .75 2.00
PP20 Frank Thomas 2.00 5.00

1997 Upper Deck Predictor

Randomly inserted in series two packs at a rate of one in five, this 30-card set features a color player photo alongside a series of bats. The collector could

activate the card by scratching off one of the bats to predict the performance of the pictured player during a single game. If the player matches or exceeds the predicted performance, the card could be mailed in with $2 to receive a Totally Virtual high-tech cel-card of the player pictured on the front. The backs carry the rules of the game. The deadline to redeem these cards was November 22nd, 1997. Winners and Losers are specified in our checklist with a "W" or a "L" after the player's name.

COMPLETE SET (30) 12.50 30.00
*SCRATCH LOSER: .25X TO .6X UNSCRATCH
*EXCH.WIN: 1X TO 2.5X BASIC PREDICTOR
SER.2 STATED ODDS 1:5
1 Andruw Jones L .25 .60
2 Chipper Jones L .40 1.00
3 Greg Maddux W .60 1.50
Complete Game Shutout
4 Fred McGriff W .25 .60
4 Hits/2HR/3B
5 John Smoltz W .25 .60
Complete Game Shutout
6 Brady Anderson W .15 .40
Leadoff HR
7 Cal Ripken W 1.25 3.00
Grand Slam
8 Mo Vaughn W .15 .40
3HR/6RBI
9 Sammy Sosa L .40 1.00
10 Albert Belle W .15 .40
Grand Slam/9th HR
11 Frank Thomas L .40 1.00
12 Kenny Lofton W .15 .40
5 Hits
13 Jim Thome L .25 .60
14 Dante Bichette W .15 .40
6RBI's
15 Andres Galarraga L .15 .40
16 Gary Sheffield L .15 .40
17 Hideo Nomo W .40 1.00
Base Hit
18 Mike Piazza W .60 1.50
Steal/9th HR
19 Derek Jeter W 1.00 2.50
2HR
20 Bernie Williams L .25 .60
21 Mark McGwire W 1.00 2.50
Grand Slam/4HR
22 Ken Caminiti W .15 .40
5RBI's
23 Tony Gwynn W .50 1.25
2 2B/3RBI
24 Barry Bonds W 1.00 2.50
5RBI's
25 Jay Buhner W .15 .40
5RBI's
26 Ken Griffey Jr. W .60 1.50
3HR's
27 Alex Rodriguez W .60 1.50
Cycle
28 Juan Gonzalez W .15 .40
5RBI's/4 Hits
29 Dean Palmer W .15 .40
2HR's/5RBI's
30 Roger Clemens W .75 2.00
Complete Game Shutout

1997 Upper Deck Rock Solid Foundation

Randomly inserted in all first series packs at a rate of one in seven, this 20-card set features players 25 and under who have made an impact in the majors. The fronts feature a player photo against a "silver" type background. The backs give player information as well as another player photo and are numbered with a "RS" prefix.

COMPLETE SET (20) 15.00 40.00
SER.1 STATED ODDS 1:7
RS1 Alex Rodriguez 2.50 6.00
RS2 Rey Ordonez .60 1.50
RS3 Derek Jeter 4.00 10.00
RS4 Darin Erstad .60 1.50
RS5 Chipper Jones 1.50 4.00
RS6 Johnny Damon 1.00 2.50
RS7 Ryan Klesko .60 1.50
RS8 Charles Johnson .60 1.50
RS9 Andy Pettitte 1.00 2.50
RS10 Manny Ramirez 1.00 2.50
RS11 Ivan Rodriguez 1.00 2.50
RS12 Jason Kendall .60 1.50
RS13 Rondell White .60 1.50
RS14 Alex Ochoa .60 1.50
RS15 Javier Lopez .60 1.50
RS16 Pedro Martinez 1.00 2.50
RS17 Carlos Delgado .60 1.50
RS18 Paul Wilson .60 1.50
RS19 Alan Benes .60 1.50
RS20 Raul Mondesi .60 1.50

1997 Upper Deck Run Producers

Randomly inserted in series two packs at a rate of one in 69, this 24-card set features color player images on die-cut cards that actually look and feel like home plate. The backs carry player information and career statistics.

COMPLETE SET (24) 60.00 150.00
SER.2 STATED ODDS 1:69
RP1 Ken Griffey Jr. 6.00 15.00
RP2 Barry Bonds 10.00 25.00
RP3 Albert Belle 1.50 4.00
RP4 Mark McGwire 10.00 25.00
RP5 Frank Thomas 4.00 10.00
RP6 Juan Gonzalez 1.50 4.00
RP7 Brady Anderson 1.50 4.00
RP8 Andres Galarraga 1.50 4.00
RP9 Rafael Palmeiro 2.50 6.00
RP10 Alex Rodriguez 6.00 15.00
RP11 Jay Buhner 1.50 4.00
RP12 Gary Sheffield 1.50 4.00
RP13 Sammy Sosa 4.00 10.00
RP14 Dante Bichette 1.50 4.00
RP15 Mike Piazza 6.00 15.00
RP16 Manny Ramirez 2.50 6.00
RP17 Kenny Lofton 1.50 4.00
RP18 Mo Vaughn 1.50 4.00
RP19 Tim Salmon 2.50 6.00
RP20 Chipper Jones 4.00 10.00
RP21 Jim Thome 2.50 6.00
RP22 Ken Caminiti 1.50 4.00
RP23 Jeff Bagwell 2.50 6.00
RP24 Paul Molitor 1.50 4.00

1997 Upper Deck Star Attractions

These 20 cards were issued one per pack in special Upper Deck Memorabilia Madness packs. The Memorabilia Madness packs included various redemptions for signed 8 by 10 photos with the grand prize being a grouping of Ken Griffey Jr. signed jersey, baseball and 8 by 10 photo. The die cut cards feature the words "Star Attraction" on the top with the player and team identification on the sides. The backs have a photo and a brief blurb on the player. Cards numbered 1-10 were inserted in Upper Deck packs while cards numbered 11-20 were in Collectors Choice packs.

COMPLETE SET (20) 10.00 25.00
11-20 ONE PER CC MADNESS RETAIL PACK
*GOLD: 2X TO 5X BASE STAR ATT.
GOLD INSERTS IN UD/CC MADNESS RETAIL
1 Ken Griffey Jr. .60 1.50
2 Barry Bonds 1.00 2.50
3 Jeff Bagwell .25 .60
4 Nomar Garciaparra .60 1.50
5 Tony Gwynn .50 1.25
6 Roger Clemens .75 2.00
7 Chipper Jones .40 1.00
8 Tino Martinez .25 .60
9 Albert Belle .15 .40
10 Kenny Lofton .15 .40
11 Alex Rodriguez .60 1.50
12 Mark McGwire 1.00 2.50
13 Cal Ripken 1.25 3.00
14 Larry Walker .15 .40
15 Mike Piazza .60 1.50
16 Frank Thomas .40 1.00
17 Juan Gonzalez .15 .40
18 Greg Maddux .60 1.50
19 Jose Cruz Jr. .40 1.00
20 Mo Vaughn .15 .40

1997 Upper Deck Ticket To Stardom

Randomly inserted in all first series packs at a rate of one in 34, this 20-card set is designed in the form of a ticket and are designed to be matched. The horizontal fronts feature two player photos as well as using "light f/x technology and embossed player images.

SER.1 STATED ODDS 1:34
TS1 Chipper Jones 2.50 6.00
TS2 Jermaine Dye 1.00 2.50
TS3 Rey Ordonez 1.00 2.50
TS4 Alex Ochoa 1.00 2.50
TS5 Derek Jeter 6.00 15.00
TS6 Ruben Rivera 1.00 2.50
TS7 Billy Wagner 1.00 2.50
TS8 Jason Kendall 1.00 2.50
TS9 Darin Erstad 1.00 2.50
TS10 Alex Rodriguez 4.00 10.00
TS11 Bob Abreu 1.50 4.00
TS12 Richard Hidalgo 2.50 6.00
TS13 Karim Garcia 1.00 2.50
TS14 Andruw Jones 1.50 4.00
TS15 Carlos Delgado 1.00 2.50
TS16 Rocky Coppinger 1.00 2.50
TS17 Jeff D'Amico 1.00 2.50
TS18 Johnny Damon 1.50 4.00
TS19 John Wasdin 1.00 2.50
TS20 Manny Ramirez 1.50 4.00

1998 Upper Deck

The 1998 Upper Deck set was issued in three series consisting of a 270-card first series, a 270-card second series and a 211-card third series. Each series was distributed in 12-card packs which carried a suggested retail price of $2.49. Card fronts feature game dated photographs of some of the season's most memorable moments. The following subsets are contained within the set: History in the Making (1-8/361-369), Griffey's Hot List (9-18), Define the Game (136-153), Season Highlights (244-252/532-540/748-750), Star Rookies (253-288/541-600), Postseason Headliners (415-432), Upper Echelon (451-459) and Eminent Prestige (601-630). The Eminent Prestige subset cards were slightly shortprinted (approximately 1:4 packs) and Upper Deck offered a free service to collectors trying to finish their Series three sets whereby Eminent Prestige cards were mailed to collectors who sent in proof of purchase of one-and-a-half boxes or more. The print run for Mike Piazza card number 681 was split exactly in half creating two shortprints: card number 681 (picturing Piazza as a New York Met) and card number 681A (picturing Piazza as a Florida Marlin). Both cards are exactly two times tougher to pull from packs than other regular issue Series three cards. The series three set is considered complete with both versions at 251 total cards. Notable Rookie Cards include Gabe Kapler and Magglio Ordonez.

COMPLETE SET (751) 80.00 200.00
COMP.SERIES 1 (270) 15.00 40.00
COMP.SERIES 2 (270) 15.00 40.00
COMP.SERIES 3 (211) 50.00 120.00
COMMON (1-600/631-750) .10 .30
COMMON EP (601-630) .75 2.00
EP SER.2 ODDS APPROXIMATELY 1:4
1 Tino Martinez HIST .10 .30
2 Jimmy Key HIST .10 .30
3 Jay Buhner HIST .10 .30
4 Mark Gardner HIST .10 .30
5 Greg Maddux HIST .30 .75
6 Pedro Martinez HIST .20 .50
7 Hideo Nomo HIST .20 .50
8 Sammy Sosa HIST .20 .50
9 Mark McGwire GHL .40 1.00
10 Ken Griffey Jr. GHL .30 .75
11 Larry Walker GHL .10 .30
12 Tino Martinez GHL .10 .30
13 Mike Piazza GHL .30 .75
14 Jose Cruz Jr. GHL .10 .30
15 Tony Gwynn GHL .20 .50
16 Greg Maddux GHL .30 .75
17 Roger Clemens GHL .30 .75
18 Alex Rodriguez GHL .30 .75
19 Shigetoshi Hasegawa .10 .30
20 Eddie Murray .30 .75
21 Jason Dickson .10 .30
22 Darin Erstad .10 .30
23 Chuck Finley .10 .30
24 Dave Hollins .10 .30
25 Garret Anderson .10 .30
26 Michael Tucker .10 .30
27 Kenny Lofton .10 .30
28 Javier Lopez .10 .30
29 Fred McGriff .20 .50
30 Greg Maddux .50 1.25
31 Jeff Blauser .10 .30
32 John Smoltz .20 .50
33 Mark Wohlers .10 .30
34 Scott Erickson .10 .30
35 Jimmy Key .10 .30
36 Harold Baines .10 .30
37 Randy Myers .10 .30
38 B.J. Surhoff .10 .30
39 Eric Davis .10 .30
40 Rafael Palmeiro .20 .50
41 Jeffrey Hammonds .10 .30
42 Mo Vaughn .10 .30
43 Tom Gordon .10 .30
44 Tim Naehring .10 .30
45 Darren Bragg .10 .30
46 Aaron Sele .10 .30
47 Troy O'Leary .10 .30
48 John Valentin .10 .30
49 Doug Glanville .10 .30
50 Ryne Sandberg .50 1.25
51 Steve Trachsel .10 .30
52 Mark Grace .20 .50
53 Kevin Foster .10 .30
54 Kevin Tapani .10 .30
55 Kevin Orie .10 .30
56 Lyle Mouton .10 .30
57 Ray Durham .10 .30
58 Jaime Navarro .10 .30
59 Mike Cameron .10 .30
60 Albert Belle .10 .30
61 Doug Drabek .10 .30
62 Chris Snopek .10 .30
63 Eddie Taubensee .10 .30
64 Terry Pendleton .10 .30
65 Barry Larkin .20 .50
66 Willie Greene .10 .30
67 Deion Sanders .20 .50
68 Pokey Reese .10 .30
69 Jeff Shaw .10 .30
70 Jim Thome .20 .50
71 Orel Hershiser .10 .30
72 Omar Vizquel .20 .50
73 Brian Giles .10 .30
74 David Justice .10 .30
75 Bartolo Colon .10 .30
76 Sandy Alomar Jr. .10 .30
77 Neifi Perez .10 .30
78 Dante Bichette .10 .30
79 Vinny Castilla .10 .30
80 Eric Young .10 .30
81 Quinton McCracken .10 .30
82 Jamey Wright .10 .30
83 John Thomson .10 .30
84 Damion Easley .10 .30
85 Justin Thompson .10 .30
86 Willie Blair .10 .30
87 Raul Casanova .10 .30
88 Bobby Higginson .10 .30
89 Bubba Trammell .10 .30
90 Tony Clark .10 .30
91 Livan Hernandez .10 .30
92 Charles Johnson .10 .30
93 Edgar Renteria .10 .30
94 Alex Fernandez .10 .30
95 Gary Sheffield .10 .30
96 Moises Alou .10 .30
97 Tony Saunders .10 .30
98 Robb Nen .10 .30
99 Darryl Kile .10 .30
100 Craig Biggio .20 .50
101 Chris Holt .10 .30
102 Bob Abreu .10 .30
103 Luis Gonzalez .10 .30
104 Billy Wagner .10 .30
105 Brad Ausmus .10 .30
106 Chili Davis .10 .30
107 Tim Belcher .10 .30
108 Dean Palmer .10 .30
109 Jeff King .10 .30
110 Jose Rosado .10 .30
111 Mike Macfarlane .10 .30
112 Jay Bell .10 .30
113 Todd Worrell .10 .30
114 Chan Ho Park .10 .30
115 Raul Mondesi .10 .30
116 Brett Butler .10 .30
117 Greg Gagne .10 .30
118 Hideo Nomo .30 .75
119 Todd Zeile .10 .30
120 Eric Karros .10 .30
121 Cal Eldred .10 .30
122 Jeff D'Amico .10 .30
123 Antone Williamson .10 .30
124 Doug Jones .10 .30
125 Dave Nilsson .10 .30
126 Gerald Williams .10 .30
127 Fernando Vina .10 .30
128 Ron Coomer .10 .30
129 Matt Lawton .10 .30
130 Paul Molitor .10 .30
131 Todd Walker .10 .30
132 Rick Aguilera .10 .30
133 Brad Radke .10 .30
134 Bob Tewksbury .10 .30
135 Vladimir Guerrero .30 .75
136 Tony Gwynn DG .20 .50
137 Roger Clemens DG .30 .75
138 Dennis Eckersley DG .10 .30
139 Brady Anderson DG .10 .30
140 Ken Griffey Jr. DG .30 .75
141 Derek Jeter DG .40 1.00
142 Ken Caminiti DG .10 .30
143 Frank Thomas DG .20 .50
144 Barry Bonds DG .40 1.00
145 Cal Ripken DG .50 1.25
146 Alex Rodriguez DG .30 .75
147 Greg Maddux DG .30 .75
148 Kenny Lofton DG .10 .30
149 Mike Piazza DG .30 .75
150 Mark McGwire DG .40 1.00
151 Andruw Jones DG .10 .30
152 Rusty Greer DG .10 .30
153 F.P. Santangelo DG .10 .30
154 Mike Lansing .10 .30
155 Lee Smith .10 .30
156 Carlos Perez .10 .30
157 Pedro Martinez .20 .50
158 Ryan McGuire .10 .30
159 F.P. Santangelo .10 .30
160 Rondell White .10 .30
161 T.Kashiwada RC .15 .40
162 Butch Huskey .10 .30
163 Edgardo Alfonzo .10 .30
164 John Franco .10 .30
165 Todd Hundley .10 .30
166 Rey Ordonez .10 .30
167 Armando Reynoso .10 .30
168 John Olerud .10 .30
169 Bernie Williams .20 .50
170 Andy Pettitte .20 .50
171 Wade Boggs .20 .50
172 Paul O'Neill .20 .50
173 Cecil Fielder .10 .30
174 Charlie Hayes .10 .30
175 David Cone .10 .30
176 Hideki Irabu .10 .30
177 Mark Bellhorn .10 .30
178 Steve Karsay .10 .30
179 Damon Mashore .10 .30
180 Jason McDonald .10 .30
181 Scott Spiezio .10 .30
182 Ariel Prieto .10 .30
183 Jason Giambi .10 .30
184 Wendell Magee .10 .30
185 Rico Brogna .10 .30
186 Garrett Stephenson .10 .30
187 Wayne Gomes .10 .30
188 Ricky Bottalico .10 .30
189 Mickey Morandini .10 .30
190 Mike Lieberthal .10 .30
191 Kevin Polcovich .10 .30
192 Francisco Cordova .10 .30
193 Kevin Young .10 .30
194 Jon Lieber .10 .30
195 Kevin Elster .10 .30
196 Tony Womack .10 .30
197 Lou Collier .10 .30
198 Mike Difelice RC .15 .40
199 Gary Gaetti .10 .30
200 Dennis Eckersley .10 .30
201 Alan Benes .10 .30
202 Willie McGee .10 .30
203 Ron Gant .10 .30
204 Fernando Valenzuela .10 .30
205 Mark McGwire .75 2.00
206 Archi Cianfrocco .10 .30
207 Andy Ashby .10 .30
208 Steve Finley .10 .30
209 Quilvio Veras .10 .30
210 Ken Caminiti .10 .30
211 Rickey Henderson .30 .75
212 Joey Hamilton .10 .30
213 Derrek Lee .20 .50
214 Bill Mueller .10 .30
215 Shawn Estes .10 .30
216 J.T. Snow .10 .30
217 Mark Gardner .10 .30
218 Terry Mulholland .10 .30
219 Dante Powell .10 .30
220 Jeff Kent .10 .30
221 Jamie Moyer .10 .30
222 Joey Cora .10 .30
223 Jeff Fassero .10 .30
224 Dennis Martinez .10 .30
225 Ken Griffey Jr. .50 1.25
226 Edgar Martinez .20 .50
227 Russ Davis .10 .30
228 Dan Wilson .10 .30
229 Will Clark .20 .50
230 Ivan Rodriguez .20 .50
231 Benji Gil .10 .30
232 Lee Stevens .10 .30
233 Mickey Tettleton .10 .30
234 Julio Santana .10 .30
235 Rusty Greer .10 .30
236 Bobby Witt .10 .30
237 Ed Sprague .10 .30
238 Pat Hentgen .10 .30
239 Kelvim Escobar .10 .30
240 Joe Carter .10 .30
241 Carlos Delgado .10 .30
242 Shannon Stewart .10 .30
243 Benito Santiago .10 .30
244 Tino Martinez SH .10 .30
245 Ken Griffey Jr. SH .30 .75
246 Kevin Brown SH .10 .30
247 Ryne Sandberg SH .20 .50
248 Mo Vaughn SH .10 .30
249 Darryl Hamilton SH .10 .30
250 Randy Johnson SH .20 .50
251 Steve Finley SH .10 .30
252 Bobby Higginson SH .10 .30
253 Brett Tomko .10 .30
254 Mark Kotsay .10 .30
255 Jose Guillen .10 .30
256 Eli Marrero .10 .30
257 Dennis Reyes .10 .30
258 Richie Sexson .10 .30
259 Pat Cline .10 .30
260 Todd Helton .20 .50
261 Juan Melo .10 .30
262 Matt Morris .10 .30
263 Jeremi Gonzalez .10 .30
264 Jeff Abbott .10 .30
265 Aaron Boone .10 .30
266 Todd Dunwoody .10 .30
267 Jaret Wright .10 .30
268 Derrick Gibson .10 .30
269 Mario Valdez .10 .30
270 Fernando Tatis .10 .30
271 Craig Counsell .10 .30
272 Brad Rigby .10 .30
273 Danny Clyburn .10 .30
274 Brian Rose .10 .30
275 Miguel Tejada .30 .75
276 Jason Varitek .30 .75
277 Dave Dellucci RC .25 .60
278 Michael Coleman .10 .30
279 Adam Riggs .10 .30
280 Ben Grieve .10 .30
281 Brad Fullmer .10 .30
282 Ken Cloude .10 .30
283 Tom Evans .10 .30
284 Kevin Millwood RC .40 1.00
285 Paul Konerko .10 .30
286 Juan Encarnacion .10 .30
287 Chris Carpenter .10 .30
288 Tom Fordham .10 .30
289 Gary DiSarcina .10 .30
290 Tim Salmon .20 .50
291 Troy Percival .10 .30
292 Todd Greene .10 .30
293 Ken Hill .10 .30
294 Dennis Springer .10 .30
295 Jim Edmonds .10 .30
296 Allen Watson .10 .30
297 Brian Anderson .10 .30
298 Keith Lockhart .10 .30
299 Tom Glavine .20 .50
300 Chipper Jones .30 .75
301 Randall Simon .10 .30
302 Mark Lemke .10 .30
303 Ryan Klesko .10 .30
304 Denny Neagle .10 .30
305 Andruw Jones .20 .50
306 Mike Mussina .20 .50
307 Brady Anderson .10 .30
308 Chris Hoiles .10 .30
309 Mike Bordick .10 .30
310 Cal Ripken 1.00 2.50
311 Geronimo Berroa .10 .30
312 Armando Benitez .10 .30
313 Roberto Alomar .20 .50
314 Tim Wakefield .10 .30
315 Reggie Jefferson .10 .30
316 Jeff Frye .10 .30
317 Scott Hatteberg .10 .30
318 Steve Avery .10 .30
319 Robinson Checo .10 .30
320 Nomar Garciaparra .50 1.25
321 Lance Johnson .10 .00
322 Tyler Houston .10 .30
323 Mark Clark .10 .30
324 Terry Adams .10 .30
325 Sammy Sosa .30 .75
326 Scott Servais .10 .30
327 Manny Alexander .10 .30
328 Norberto Martin .10 .30
329 Scott Eyre .10 .30
330 Frank Thomas .30 .75
331 Robin Ventura .10 .30
332 Matt Karchner .10 .30
333 Keith Foulke .10 .30
334 James Baldwin .10 .30
335 Chris Stynes .10 .30
336 Bret Boone .10 .30
337 Jon Nunnally .10 .30
338 Dave Burba .10 .30
339 Eduardo Perez .10 .30
340 Reggie Sanders .10 .30
341 Mike Remlinger .10 .30
342 Pat Watkins .10 .30
343 Chad Ogea .10 .30
344 John Smiley .10 .30
345 Kenny Lofton .10 .30
346 Jose Mesa .10 .30
347 Charles Nagy .10 .30
348 Enrique Wilson .10 .30
349 Bruce Aven .10 .30
350 Manny Ramirez .20 .50
351 Jerry DiPoto .10 .30
352 Ellis Burks .10 .30
353 Kirt Manwaring .10 .30
354 Vinny Castilla .10 .30
355 Larry Walker .10 .30
356 Kevin Ritz .10 .30
357 Pedro Astacio .10 .30
358 Scott Sanders .10 .30
359 Deivi Cruz .10 .30
360 Brian L. Hunter .10 .30
361 Pedro Martinez HM .20 .50
362 Tom Glavine HM .10 .30
363 Willie McGee HM .10 .30
364 J.T. Snow HM .10 .30
365 Rusty Greer HM .10 .30
366 Mike Grace HM .10 .30
367 Tony Clark HM .10 .30
368 Ben Grieve HM .10 .30
369 Gary Sheffield HM .10 .30
370 Joe Oliver .10 .30
371 Todd Jones .10 .30
372 Frank Catalanotto RC .25 .60
373 Brian Moehler .10 .30
374 Cliff Floyd .10 .30
375 Bobby Bonilla .10 .30
376 Al Leiter .10 .30
377 Josh Booty .10 .30
378 Darren Daulton .10 .30
379 Jay Powell .10 .30
380 Felix Heredia .10 .30
381 Jim Eisenreich .10 .30
382 Richard Hidalgo .10 .30
383 Mike Hampton .10 .30
384 Shane Reynolds .10 .30
385 Jeff Bagwell .20 .50
386 Derek Bell .10 .30
387 Ricky Gutierrez .10 .30
388 Bill Spiers .10 .30
389 Jose Offerman .10 .30
390 Johnny Damon .20 .50
391 Jermaine Dye .10 .30
392 Jeff Montgomery .10 .30
393 Glendon Rusch .10 .30
394 Mike Sweeney .10 .30
395 Kevin Appier .10 .30
396 Joe Vitiello .10 .30
397 Ramon Martinez .10 .30
398 Darren Dreifort .10 .30
399 Wilton Guerrero .10 .30
400 Mike Piazza .50 1.25
401 Eddie Murray .30 .75
402 Ismael Valdes .10 .30
403 Todd Hollandsworth .10 .30
404 Mark Loretta .10 .30
405 Jeromy Burnitz .10 .30
406 Jeff Cirillo .10 .30
407 Scott Karl .10 .30
408 Mike Matheny .10 .30
409 Jose Valentin .10 .30
410 John Jaha .10 .30
411 Terry Steinbach .10 .30
412 Torii Hunter .10 .30
413 Pat Meares .10 .30
414 Marty Cordova .10 .30
415 Jaret Wright PH .10 .30
416 Mike Mussina PH .10 .30
417 John Smoltz PH .10 .30
418 Devon White PH .10 .30
419 Denny Neagle PH .10 .30
420 Livan Hernandez PH .10 .30
421 Kevin Brown PH .10 .30
422 Marquis Grissom PH .10 .30
423 Mike Mussina PH .10 .30
424 Eric Davis PH .10 .30
425 Tony Fernandez PH .10 .30
426 Moises Alou PH .10 .30
427 Sandy Alomar Jr. PH .10 .30
428 Gary Sheffield PH .10 .30
429 Jaret Wright PH .10 .30
430 Livan Hernandez PH .10 .30

431 Chad Ogea PH .10 .30
432 Edgar Renteria PH .10 .30
433 LaTroy Hawkins .10 .30
434 Rich Robertson .10 .30
435 Chuck Knoblauch .10 .30
436 Jose Vidro .10 .30
437 Dustin Hermanson .10 .30
438 Jim Bullinger .10 .30
439 Orlando Cabrera .10 .30
440 Vladimir Guerrero .30 .75
441 Ugueth Urbina .10 .30
442 Brian McRae .10 .30
443 Matt Franco .10 .30
444 Bobby Jones .10 .30
445 Bernard Gilkey .10 .30
446 Dave Mlicki .10 .30
447 Brian Bohanon .10 .30
448 Mel Rojas .10 .30
449 Tim Raines .10 .30
450 Derek Jeter .75 2.00
451 Roger Clemens UE .30 .75
452 N.Garciaparra UE .30 .75
453 Mike Piazza UE .30 .75
454 Mark McGwire UE .40 1.00
455 Ken Griffey Jr. UE .30 .75
456 Larry Walker UE .10 .30
457 Alex Rodriguez UE .30 .75
458 Tony Gwynn UE .20 .50
459 Frank Thomas UE .20 .50
460 Tino Martinez .20 .50
461 Chad Curtis .10 .30
462 Ramiro Mendoza .10 .30
463 Joe Girardi .10 .30
464 David Wells .10 .30
465 Mariano Rivera .30 .75
466 Willie Adams .10 .30
467 George Williams .10 .30
468 Dave Telgheder .10 .30
469 Dave Magadan .10 .30
470 Matt Stairs .10 .30
471 Bill Taylor .10 .30
472 Jimmy Haynes .10 .30
473 Gregg Jefferies .10 .30
474 Midre Cummings .10 .30
475 Curt Schilling .10 .30
476 Mike Grace .10 .30
477 Mark Leiter .10 .30
478 Matt Beech .10 .30
479 Scott Rolen .20 .50
480 Jason Kendall .10 .30
481 Esteban Loaiza .10 .30
482 Jermaine Allensworth .10 .30
483 Mark Smith .10 .30
484 Jason Schmidt .10 .30
485 Jose Guillen .10 .30
486 Al Martin .10 .30
487 Delino DeShields .10 .30
488 Todd Stottlemyre .10 .30
489 Brian Jordan .10 .30
490 Ray Lankford .10 .30
491 Matt Morris .10 .30
492 Royce Clayton .10 .30
493 John Mabry .10 .30
494 Wally Joyner .10 .30
495 Trevor Hoffman .10 .30
496 Chris Gomez .10 .30
497 Sterling Hitchcock .10 .30
498 Pete Smith .10 .30
499 Greg Vaughn .10 .30
500 Tony Gwynn .40 1.00
501 Will Cunnane .10 .30
502 Darryl Hamilton .10 .30
503 Brian Johnson .10 .30
504 Kirk Rueter .10 .30
505 Barry Bonds .75 2.00
506 Osvaldo Fernandez .10 .30
507 Stan Javier .10 .30
508 Julian Tavarez .10 .30
509 Rich Aurilia .10 .30
510 Alex Rodriguez .50 1.25
511 David Segui .10 .30
512 Rich Amaral .10 .30
513 Raul Ibanez .10 .30
514 Jay Buhner .10 .30
515 Randy Johnson .30 .75
516 Heathcliff Slocumb .10 .30
517 Tony Saunders .10 .30
518 Kevin Elster .10 .30
519 John Burkett .10 .30
520 Juan Gonzalez .10 .30
521 John Wetteland .10 .30
522 Domingo Cedeno .10 .30
523 Darren Oliver .10 .30
524 Roger Pavlik .10 .30
525 Jose Cruz Jr. .10 .30
526 Woody Williams .10 .30
527 Alex Gonzalez .10 .30
528 Robert Person .10 .30
529 Juan Guzman .10 .30
530 Roger Clemens .60 1.50
531 Shawn Green .10 .30
532 Francisco Cordova SH .10 .30
Ricardo Rincon
Mark Smith
533 N.Garciaparra SH .30 .75
534 Roger Clemens SH .30 .75
535 Mark McGwire SH .40 1.00
536 Larry Walker SH .10 .30
537 Mike Piazza SH .30 .75
538 Curt Schilling SH .10 .30
539 Tony Gwynn SH .20 .50
540 Ken Griffey Jr. SH .30 .75
541 Carl Pavano .10 .30
542 Shane Monahan .10 .30
543 Gabe Kapler RC .25 .60
544 Eric Milton .10 .30
545 Gary Matthews Jr. RC .25 .60
546 Mike Kinkade RC .10 .30
547 Ryan Christenson RC .10 .30
548 Corey Koskie RC .25 .60
549 Norm Hutchins .10 .30
550 Russell Branyan .10 .30
551 Masato Yoshii RC .15 .40
552 Jesus Sanchez RC .10 .30
553 Anthony Sanders .10 .30
554 Edwin Diaz .10 .30
555 Gabe Alvarez .10 .30
556 Carlos Lee RC .75 2.00
557 Mike Darr .10 .30
558 Kerry Wood .15 .40
559 Carlos Guillen .10 .30
560 Sean Casey .10 .30
561 Manny Aybar RC .10 .30
562 Octavio Dotel .10 .30
563 Jarrod Washburn .10 .30
564 Mark L. Johnson .10 .30
565 Ramon Hernandez .10 .30
566 Rich Butler RC .10 .30
567 Mike Caruso .10 .30
568 Cliff Politte .10 .30
569 Scott Elarton .10 .30
570 Magglio Ordonez RC 1.25 3.00
571 Adam Butler RC .10 .30
572 Marlon Anderson .10 .30
573 Julio Ramirez RC .10 .30
574 Darron Ingram RC .10 .30
575 Bruce Chen .10 .30
576 Steve Woodard .10 .30
577 Hiram Bocachica .10 .30
578 Kevin Witt .10 .30
579 Javier Vazquez .10 .30
580 Alex Gonzalez .10 .30
581 Brian Powell .10 .30
582 Wes Helms .10 .30
583 Ron Wright .10 .30
584 Rafael Medina .10 .30
585 Daryle Ward .10 .30
586 Geoff Jenkins .10 .30
587 Preston Wilson .10 .30
588 Jim Chamblee RC .10 .30
589 Mike Lowell RC .60 1.50
590 A.J. Hinch .10 .30
591 Francisco Cordero RC .25 .60
592 Rolando Arrojo RC .15 .40
593 Braden Looper .10 .30
594 Sidney Ponson .10 .30
595 Matt Clement .10 .30
596 Carlton Loewer .10 .30
597 Brian Meadows .10 .30
598 Danny Klassen .10 .30
599 Larry Sutton .10 .30
600 Travis Lee .10 .30
601 Randy Johnson EP 1.00 2.50
602 Greg Maddux EP 1.50 4.00
603 Roger Clemens EP 2.00 5.00
604 Jaret Wright EP .75 2.00
605 Mike Piazza EP 1.50 4.00
606 Tino Martinez EP .75 2.00
607 Frank Thomas EP 1.00 2.50
608 Mo Vaughn EP .75 2.00
609 Todd Helton EP .75 2.00
610 Mark McGwire EP 2.50 6.00
611 Jeff Bagwell EP .75 2.00
612 Travis Lee EP .75 2.00
613 Scott Rolen EP .75 2.00
614 Cal Ripken EP 3.00 8.00
615 Chipper Jones EP 1.00 2.50
616 Nomar Garciaparra EP 1.50 4.00
617 Alex Rodriguez EP 1.50 4.00
618 Derek Jeter EP 2.50 6.00
619 Tony Gwynn EP 1.25 3.00
620 Ken Griffey Jr. EP 1.50 4.00
621 Kenny Lofton EP .75 2.00
622 Juan Gonzalez EP .75 2.00
623 Jose Cruz Jr. EP .75 2.00
624 Larry Walker EP .75 2.00
625 Barry Bonds EP 2.50 6.00
626 Ben Grieve EP .75 2.00
627 Andruw Jones EP .75 2.00
628 Vladimir Guerrero EP 1.00 2.50
629 Paul Konerko EP .75 2.00
630 Paul Molitor EP .75 2.00
631 Cecil Fielder .10 .30
632 Jack McDowell .10 .30
633 Mike James .10 .30
634 Brian Anderson .10 .30
635 Jay Bell .10 .30
636 Devon White .10 .30
637 Andy Stankiewicz .10 .30
638 Tony Batista .10 .30
639 Omar Daal .10 .30
640 Matt Williams .10 .30
641 Brent Brede .10 .30
642 Jorge Fabregas .10 .30
643 Karim Garcia .10 .30
644 Felix Rodriguez .10 .30
645 Andy Benes .10 .30
646 Willie Blair .10 .30
647 Jeff Suppan .10 .30
648 Yamil Benitez .10 .30
649 Walt Weiss .10 .30
650 Andres Galarraga .10 .30
651 Doug Drabek .10 .30
652 Ozzie Guillen .10 .30
653 Joe Carter .10 .30
654 Dennis Eckersley .10 .30
655 Pedro Martinez .20 .50
656 Jim Leyritz .10 .30
657 Henry Rodriguez .10 .30
658 Rod Beck .10 .30
659 Mickey Morandini .10 .30
660 Jeff Blauser .10 .30
661 Ruben Sierra .10 .30
662 Mike Sirotka .10 .30
663 Pete Harnisch .10 .30
664 Damian Jackson .10 .30
665 Dmitri Young .10 .30
666 Steve Cooke .10 .30
667 Geronimo Berroa .10 .30
668 Shawon Dunston .10 .30
669 Mike Jackson .10 .30
670 Travis Fryman .10 .30
671 Dwight Gooden .10 .30
672 Paul Assenmacher .10 .30
673 Eric Plunk .10 .30
674 Mike Lansing .10 .30
675 Darryl Kile .10 .30
676 Luis Gonzalez .10 .30
677 Frank Castillo .10 .30
678 Joe Randa .10 .30
679 Bip Roberts .10 .30
680 Derrek Lee .20 .50
681 Mike Piazza SP 1.25 3.00
New York Mets
681A Mike Piazza SP 1.25 3.00
Florida Marlins
682 Sean Berry .10 .30
683 Ramon Garcia .10 .30
684 Carl Everett .10 .30
685 Moises Alou .10 .30
686 Hal Morris .10 .30
687 Jeff Conine .10 .30
688 Gary Sheffield .10 .30
689 Jose Vizcaino .10 .30
690 Charles Johnson .10 .30
691 Bobby Bonilla .10 .30
692 Marquis Grissom .10 .30
693 Alex Ochoa .10 .30
694 Mike Morgan .10 .30
695 Orlando Merced .10 .30
696 David Ortiz .40 1.00
697 Brent Gates .10 .30
698 Otis Nixon .10 .30
699 Trey Moore .10 .30
700 Derrick May .10 .30
701 Rich Becker .10 .30
702 Al Leiter .10 .30
703 Chili Davis .10 .30
704 Scott Brosius .10 .30
705 Chuck Knoblauch .10 .30
706 Kenny Rogers .10 .30
707 Mike Blowers .10 .30
708 Mike Fetters .10 .30
709 Tom Candiotti .10 .30
710 Rickey Henderson .30 .75
711 Bob Abreu .10 .30
712 Mark Lewis .10 .30
713 Doug Glanville .10 .30
714 Desi Relaford .10 .30
715 Kent Mercker .10 .30
716 Kevin Brown .20 .50
717 James Mouton .10 .30
718 Mark Langston .10 .30
719 Greg Myers .10 .30
720 Orel Hershiser .10 .30
721 Charlie Hayes .10 .30
722 Robb Nen .10 .30
723 Glenallen Hill .10 .30
724 Tony Saunders .10 .30
725 Wade Boggs .20 .50
726 Kevin Stocker .10 .30
727 Wilson Alvarez .10 .30
728 Albie Lopez .10 .30
729 Dave Martinez .10 .30
730 Fred McGriff .20 .50
731 Quinton McCracken .10 .30
732 Bryan Rekar .10 .30
733 Paul Sorrento .10 .30
734 Roberto Hernandez .10 .30
735 Bubba Trammell .10 .30
736 Miguel Cairo .10 .30
737 John Flaherty .10 .30
738 Terrell Wade .10 .30
739 Roberto Kelly .10 .30
740 Mark McLemore .10 .30
741 Danny Patterson .10 .30
742 Aaron Sele .10 .30
743 Tony Fernandez .10 .30
744 Randy Myers .10 .30
745 Jose Canseco .20 .50
746 Darrin Fletcher .10 .30
747 Mike Stanley .10 .30
748 M.Grissom SH CL .10 .30
749 Fred McGriff SH CL .10 .30
750 Travis Lee SH CL .10 .30

1998 Upper Deck 5 x 7 Blow Ups

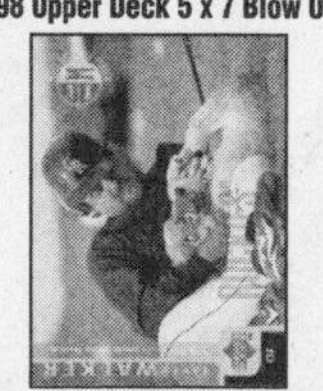

These jumbo parallel cards capture a selection of players taken from each of the three basic series of the 1998 Upper Deck set. Besides the obvious difference in size, these 5" by 7" cards also lack the silver foil coating on front that the standard 2 1/2" by 3 1/2" cards have. The first fifteen cards checklisted below (skip-numbered between 30 and 230) comprise the first series 5 x 7 Blow Up set. These first series jumbo cards were only available via redemption from Upper Deck. Collector's had to send in ten first series wrappers plus $3 to the UD redemption center. The next ten cards checklisted below (skip-numbered between 310 and 530) comprise the second series 5 x 7 Blow Up set. These second series jumbo cards were available only in specially marked mass market retail series 2 boxes (carrying an $11.99 SRP). Each box contained five basic series 2 retail packs and one 5 x 7 Blow Up. The third series 5 x 7 Blow Ups (numbered between 605 and 620 in the listings below) are comprised of selected stars from the Eminent Prestige subset within the basic issue Series 3 set.

27 Kenny Lofton .40 1.00
30 Greg Maddux 1.25 3.00
40 Rafael Palmeiro .50 1.25
50 Ryne Sandberg 1.25 3.00
60 Albert Belle .30 .75
65 Barry Larkin .50 1.25
68 Deion Sanders .30 .75
95 Gary Sheffield .60 1.50
130 Paul Molitor .60 1.50
135 Vladimir Guerrero .60 1.50
176 Hideki Irabu .20 .50
205 Mark McGwire 1.50 4.00
211 Rickey Henderson .75 2.00
225 Ken Griffey Jr. 1.25 3.00
230 Ivan Rodriguez .60 1.50
310 Cal Ripken 2.50 6.00
320 Nomar Garciaparra 1.25 3.00
330 Frank Thomas .60 1.50
355 Larry Walker .50 1.25
385 Jeff Bagwell .60 1.50
400 Mike Piazza 1.50 4.00
450 Derek Jeter 2.50 6.00
500 Tony Gwynn 1.25 3.00
510 Alex Rodriguez 1.50 4.00
530 Roger Clemens 1.25 3.00
605 Mike Piazza EP 1.50 4.00
607 Frank Thomas EP .60 1.50
610 Mark McGwire EP 1.25 3.00
611 Jeff Bagwell EP .60 1.50
612 Travis Lee EP .30 .75
614 Cal Ripken EP 2.50 6.00
616 Nomar Garciaparra EP 1.25 3.00
617 Alex Rodriguez EP 1.50 4.00
619 Tony Gwynn EP 1.25 3.00
620 Ken Griffey Jr. EP 1.25 3.00

1998 Upper Deck 10th Anniversary Preview

Randomly inserted in Series one packs at the rate of one in five, this 60-card set features color player photos in a design similar to the inaugural 1989 Upper Deck series. The backs carry a photo of that player's previous Upper Deck card. A 10th Anniversary Ballot Card was inserted one in four packs which allowed the collector to vote for the players they wanted to see in the 1999 Upper Deck tenth anniversary series.

COMPLETE SET (60) 50.00 120.00
SER.1 STATED ODDS 1:5
COMP.RETAIL SET (60) 8.00 20.00
*RETAIL: .08X TO .2X BASIC 10TH ANN
RETAIL DISTRIBUTED AS FACTORY SET
1 Greg Maddux 2.00 5.00
2 Mike Mussina .75 2.00
3 Roger Clemens 2.50 6.00
4 Hideo Nomo 1.25 3.00
5 David Cone .50 1.25
6 Tom Glavine .75 2.00
7 Andy Pettitte .75 2.00
8 Jimmy Key .50 1.25
9 Randy Johnson 1.25 3.00
10 Dennis Eckersley .50 1.25
11 Lee Smith .50 1.25
12 John Franco .50 1.25
13 Randy Myers .50 1.25
14 Mike Piazza 2.00 5.00
15 Ivan Rodriguez .75 2.00
16 Todd Hundley .50 1.25
17 Sandy Alomar Jr. .50 1.25
18 Frank Thomas 1.25 3.00
19 Rafael Palmeiro .75 2.00
20 Mark McGwire 3.00 8.00
21 Mo Vaughn .50 1.25
22 Fred McGriff .75 2.00
23 Andres Galarraga .50 1.25
24 Mark Grace .75 2.00
25 Jeff Bagwell .75 2.00
26 Roberto Alomar .75 2.00
27 Chuck Knoblauch .50 1.25
28 Ryne Sandberg 2.00 5.00
29 Eric Young .50 1.25
30 Craig Biggio .75 2.00
31 Carlos Baerga .50 1.25
32 Robin Ventura .50 1.25
33 Matt Williams .50 1.25
34 Wade Boggs .75 2.00
35 Dean Palmer .50 1.25
36 Chipper Jones 1.25 3.00
37 Vinny Castilla .50 1.25
38 Ken Caminiti .50 1.25
39 Omar Vizquel .75 2.00
40 Cal Ripken 4.00 10.00
41 Derek Jeter 3.00 8.00
42 Alex Rodriguez 2.00 5.00
43 Barry Larkin .75 2.00
44 Mark Grudzielanek .50 1.25
45 Albert Belle .50 1.25
46 Manny Ramirez .75 2.00
47 Jose Canseco .75 2.00
48 Ken Griffey Jr. 2.00 5.00
49 Juan Gonzalez .50 1.25
50 Kenny Lofton .50 1.25
51 Sammy Sosa 1.25 3.00
52 Larry Walker .50 1.25
53 Gary Sheffield .50 1.25
54 Rickey Henderson 1.25 3.00
55 Tony Gwynn 1.50 4.00
56 Barry Bonds 3.00 8.00
57 Paul Molitor .50 1.25
58 Edgar Martinez .75 2.00
59 Chili Davis .50 1.25
60 Eddie Murray 1.25 3.00

1998 Upper Deck 10th Anniversary Preview Retail

This 60 card set is a parallel to the 10th Anniversary Preview set inserted into 1998 Upper Deck Series 1. This set was only available as part of a retail package which also included 200 better 1997 Collectors Choice cards. The difference between these cards and the pack inserts are the gold foil printed on the card along with the words "Preview Edition" printed on the side. The box which contained all these cards had a SRP of $19.99.

COMPLETE SET (60) 8.00 20.00
*STARS: .4X TO 1X BASIC CARDS

1998 Upper Deck A Piece of the Action 1

Randomly inserted in first series packs at the rate of one in 2,500, cards from this set feature color photos of top players with pieces of actual game worn jerseys and/or game used bats embedded in the cards.

SER.1 STATED ODDS 1:2500
1 Jay Buhner Bat 10.00 25.00
2 Tony Gwynn Bat 15.00 40.00
3 Tony Gwynn Jersey 15.00 40.00
4 Todd Hollandsworth Bat 6.00 15.00
5 T.Hollandsworth Jersey 6.00 15.00
6 Greg Maddux Jersey 30.00 60.00
7 Alex Rodriguez Bat 30.00 60.00
8 Alex Rodriguez Jersey 30.00 60.00
9 Gary Sheffield Bat 10.00 25.00
10 Gary Sheffield Jersey 10.00 25.00

1998 Upper Deck A Piece of the Action 2

Randomly seeded into second series packs at a rate of 1:2500, each of these four different cards features pieces of both game-used bats and jerseys incorporated into the design of the card. According to information provided on the media release, only 225 of each card was produced. The cards are numbered by the player's initials.

SER.2 STATED ODDS 1:2500
AJ Andruw Jones 30.00 60.00
GS Gary Sheffield 15.00 40.00
JB Jay Buhner 15.00 40.00
RA Roberto Alomar 30.00 60.00

1998 Upper Deck A Piece of the Action 3

Randomly seeded into third series packs, each of these cards featured a jersey swatch embedded on the card. The portion of the bat which was in series two is now just a design element. Ken Griffey, Jr. signed 24 of these cards and they were inserted into the packs as well.

GRIFFEY AU PRINT RUN 24 #'d CARDS
NO GRIFFEY AU PRICE DUE TO SCARCITY
BG Ben Grieve/200 10.00 25.00
JC Jose Cruz Jr./200 10.00 25.00
KG Ken Griffey Jr./300 60.00 120.00
TL Travis Lee/200 10.00 25.00
KGS Ken Griffey Jr. AU/24

1998 Upper Deck All-Star Credentials

Randomly inserted in packs at a rate of one in nine, this 30-card insert set features players who have the best chance of appearing in future All-Star games.

COMPLETE SET (30) 40.00 100.00
SER.3 STATED ODDS 1:9
AS1 Ken Griffey Jr. 2.00 5.00
AS2 Travis Lee .50 1.25
AS3 Ben Grieve .50 1.25
AS4 Jose Cruz Jr. .50 1.25
AS5 Andruw Jones .75 2.00
AS6 Craig Biggio .75 2.00
AS7 Hideo Nomo 1.25 3.00
AS8 Cal Ripken 4.00 10.00
AS9 Jaret Wright .50 1.25
AS10 Mark McGwire 3.00 8.00
AS11 Derek Jeter 3.00 8.00
AS12 Scott Rolen .75 2.00
AS13 Jeff Bagwell .75 2.00
AS14 Manny Ramirez .75 2.00
AS15 Alex Rodriguez 2.00 5.00
AS16 Chipper Jones 1.25 3.00
AS17 Larry Walker .50 1.25
AS18 Barry Bonds 3.00 8.00
AS19 Tony Gwynn 1.50 4.00
AS20 Mike Piazza 2.00 5.00
AS21 Roger Clemens 2.50 6.00
AS22 Greg Maddux 2.00 5.00
AS23 Jim Thome .75 2.00
AS24 Tino Martinez .75 2.00
AS25 Nomar Garciaparra 2.00 5.00
AS26 Juan Gonzalez .50 1.25
AS27 Kenny Lofton .50 1.25
AS28 Randy Johnson 1.25 3.00
AS29 Todd Helton .75 2.00
AS30 Frank Thomas 1.25 3.00

1998 Upper Deck Amazing Greats

Randomly inserted in Series one packs, this 30-card set features color photos of amazing players printed on a hi-tech plastic card. Only 2000 of this set were produced and are sequentially numbered.

COMPLETE SET (30) 150.00 400.00
*DIE CUTS: 1X TO 2.5X BASIC AMAZING
DIE CUT PRINT RUN 250 SERIAL #'d SETS
RANDOM INSERTS IN SER.1 PACKS
AG1 Ken Griffey Jr. 5.00 12.00
AG2 Derek Jeter 8.00 20.00
AG3 Alex Rodriguez 5.00 12.00
AG4 Paul Molitor 1.25 3.00
AG5 Jeff Bagwell 2.00 5.00
AG6 Larry Walker 1.25 3.00
AG7 Kenny Lofton 1.25 3.00
AG8 Cal Ripken 10.00 25.00
AG9 Juan Gonzalez 1.25 3.00
AG10 Chipper Jones 3.00 8.00
AG11 Greg Maddux 5.00 12.00
AG12 Roberto Alomar 2.00 5.00
AG13 Mike Piazza 5.00 12.00
AG14 Andres Galarraga 1.25 3.00
AG15 Barry Bonds 8.00 20.00
AG16 Andy Pettitte 2.00 5.00
AG17 Nomar Garciaparra 5.00 12.00
AG18 Tino Martinez 2.00 5.00
AG19 Tony Gwynn 4.00 10.00
AG20 Frank Thomas 3.00 8.00
AG21 Roger Clemens 6.00 15.00
AG22 Sammy Sosa 3.00 8.00
AG23 Jose Cruz Jr. 1.25 3.00
AG24 Manny Ramirez 2.00 5.00
AG25 Mark McGwire 8.00 20.00
AG26 Randy Johnson 3.00 8.00
AG27 Mo Vaughn 1.25 3.00
AG28 Gary Sheffield 1.25 3.00
AG29 Andruw Jones 2.00 5.00
AG30 Albert Belle 1.25 3.00

1998 Upper Deck Blue Chip Prospects

Randomly inserted in Series two packs, this 30-card set features color photos of some of the league's most impressive prospects printed on die-cut acetate cards. Only 2,000 of each card were produced.

COMPLETE SET (30) 100.00 250.00
BC1 Nomar Garciaparra 10.00 25.00
BC2 Scott Rolen 4.00 10.00
BC3 Jason Dickson 1.50 4.00
BC4 Darin Erstad 2.50 6.00
BC5 Brad Fullmer 1.50 4.00
BC6 Jaret Wright 1.50 4.00
BC7 Justin Thompson 1.50 4.00
BC8 Matt Morris 2.50 6.00
BC9 Fernando Tatis 1.50 4.00
BC10 Alex Rodriguez 10.00 25.00
BC11 Todd Helton 4.00 10.00
BC12 Andy Pettitte 4.00 10.00
BC13 Jose Cruz Jr. 1.50 4.00
BC14 Mark Kotsay 2.50 6.00
BC15 Derek Jeter 15.00 40.00
BC16 Paul Konerko 2.50 6.00
BC17 Todd Dunwoody 1.50 4.00
BC18 Vladimir Guerrero 6.00 15.00
BC19 Miguel Tejada 6.00 15.00
BC20 Chipper Jones 6.00 15.00
BC21 Kevin Orie 1.50 4.00
BC22 Juan Encarnacion 1.50 4.00
BC23 Brian Rose 1.50 4.00
BC24 Livan Hernandez 2.50 6.00
BC25 Andruw Jones 4.00 10.00
BC26 Brian Giles 2.50 6.00
BC27 Brett Tomko 1.50 4.00
BC28 Jose Guillen 2.50 6.00
BC29 Aaron Boone 2.50 6.00
BC30 Ben Grieve 1.50 4.00

1998 Upper Deck Clearly Dominant

Randomly inserted in Series two packs, this 30-card set features color head photos of top players with a black-and-white action shot in the background printed on Light F/X plastic stock. Only 250 sequentially numbered sets were produced.

CD1 Mark McGwire 15.00 40.00
CD2 Derek Jeter 15.00 40.00
CD3 Alex Rodriguez 10.00 25.00
CD4 Paul Molitor 2.50 6.00
CD5 Jeff Bagwell 4.00 10.00
CD6 Ivan Rodriguez 4.00 10.00
CD7 Kenny Lofton 2.50 6.00
CD8 Cal Ripken 20.00 50.00
CD9 Albert Belle 2.50 6.00
CD10 Chipper Jones 6.00 15.00
CD11 Gary Sheffield 2.50 6.00
CD12 Roberto Alomar 4.00 10.00
CD13 Mo Vaughn 2.50 6.00
CD14 Andres Galarraga 2.50 6.00
CD15 Nomar Garciaparra 10.00 25.00
CD16 Randy Johnson 6.00 15.00
CD17 Mike Mussina 4.00 10.00
CD18 Greg Maddux 10.00 25.00
CD19 Tony Gwynn 8.00 20.00
CD20 Frank Thomas 6.00 15.00
CD21 Roger Clemens 12.50 30.00
CD22 Dennis Eckersley 2.50 6.00
CD23 Juan Gonzalez 2.50 6.00
CD24 Tino Martinez 4.00 10.00
CD25 Andruw Jones 4.00 10.00
CD26 Larry Walker 2.50 6.00
CD27 Ken Caminiti 2.50 6.00
CD28 Mike Piazza 10.00 25.00
CD29 Barry Bonds 15.00 40.00
CD30 Ken Griffey Jr. 10.00 25.00

1998 Upper Deck Destination Stardom

Randomly inserted in packs at a rate of one in five, this 60-card insert set features color action photos of today's star potential placed in a diamond-cut center with four colored corners. The cards are foil enhanced and die-cut.

COMPLETE SET (60) 40.00 100.00
SER.3 STATED ODDS 1:5
DS1 Travis Lee .40 1.00
DS2 Nomar Garciaparra 2.50 6.00
DS3 Alex Gonzalez .40 1.00
DS4 Richard Hidalgo .40 1.00
DS5 Jaret Wright .40 1.00
DS6 Mike Kinkade 1.25 3.00
DS7 Matt Morris .60 1.50
DS8 Gary Matthews Jr. 1.25 3.00
DS9 Brett Tomko .40 1.00
DS10 Todd Helton .75 2.00
DS11 Scott Elarton .40 1.00
DS12 Scott Rolen .75 2.00
DS13 Jose Cruz Jr. .40 1.00
DS14 Jarrod Washburn .40 1.00
DS15 Sean Casey .60 1.50
DS16 Magglio Ordonez 2.50 6.00
DS17 Gabe Alvarez .40 1.00
DS18 Todd Dunwoody .40 1.00
DS19 Kevin Witt .40 1.00
DS20 Ben Grieve .40 1.00
DS21 Daryle Ward .40 1.00
DS22 Matt Clement .60 1.50
DS23 Carlton Loewer .40 1.00
DS24 Javier Vazquez .60 1.50
DS25 Paul Konerko .60 1.50
DS26 Preston Wilson .60 1.50

DS27 Wes Helms .40 1.00
DS28 Derek Jeter 4.00 10.00
DS29 Corey Koskie 1.25 3.00
DS30 Russell Branyan .40 1.00
DS31 Vladimir Guerrero 1.25 3.00
DS32 Ryan Christenson .60 1.50
DS33 Carlos Lee 2.50 6.00
DS34 Dave Dellucci .75 2.00
DS35 Bruce Chen .40 1.00
DS36 Ricky Ledee .40 1.00
DS37 Ron Wright .40 1.00
DS38 Derrek Lee .75 2.00
DS39 Miguel Tejada 1.25 3.00
DS40 Brad Fullmer .40 1.00
DS41 Rich Butler .40 1.00
DS42 Chris Carpenter .60 1.50
DS43 Alex Rodriguez 2.50 6.00
DS44 Darron Ingram .60 1.50
DS45 Kerry Wood .60 1.50
DS46 Jason Varitek 1.25 3.00
DS47 Ramon Hernandez .40 1.00
DS48 Aaron Boone .60 1.50
DS49 Juan Encarnacion .40 1.00
DS50 A.J. Hinch .40 1.00
DS51 Mike Lowell 2.00 5.00
DS52 Fernando Tatis .40 1.00
DS53 Jose Guillen .60 1.50
DS54 Mike Caruso .40 1.00
DS55 Carl Pavano .60 1.50
DS56 Chris Clemons .40 1.00
DS57 Mark L. Johnson .40 1.00
DS58 Ken Cloude .40 1.00
DS59 Rolando Arrojo 1.25 3.00
DS60 Mark Kotsay .60 1.50

1998 Upper Deck Griffey Home Run Chronicles

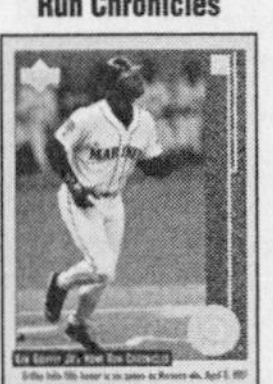

Randomly inserted in first and second series packs at the rate of one in nine, this 56-card set features color photos of Ken Griffey Jr.'s 56 home runs of the 1997 season. The fronts of the Series one inserts have photos and a brief headline of each homer. The backs all have the same photo and more details about each homer. The cards are notated on the back with what date each homer was hit. Series two inserts feature game-dated photos from the actual games in which the homers were hit.

COMPLETE SET (56) 40.00 100.00
COMPLETE SERIES 1 (30) 25.00 60.00
COMPLETE SERIES 2 (26) 15.00 40.00
COMMON GRIFFEY (1-56) .75 2.00
SER.1 AND 2 STATED ODDS 1:9

1998 Upper Deck National Pride

Randomly inserted in Series one packs at the rate of one in 23, this 42-card set features color photos of some of the league's great players from countries other than the United States printed on die-cut ranbow foil cards. The backs carry player information.

SER.1 STATED ODDS 1:23
NP1 Dave Nilsson 2.00 5.00
NP2 Larry Walker 2.00 5.00
NP3 Edgar Renteria 2.00 5.00
NP4 Jose Canseco 3.00 8.00
NP5 Rey Ordonez 2.00 5.00
NP6 Rafael Palmeiro 3.00 8.00
NP7 Livan Hernandez 2.00 5.00
NP8 Andruw Jones 3.00 8.00
NP9 Manny Ramirez 3.00 8.00
NP10 Sammy Sosa 5.00 12.00
NP11 Raul Mondesi 2.00 5.00
NP12 Moises Alou 2.00 5.00
NP13 Pedro Martinez 3.00 8.00
NP14 Vladimir Guerrero 5.00 12.00
NP15 Chili Davis 2.00 5.00
NP16 Hideo Nomo 5.00 12.00
NP17 Hideki Irabu 2.00 5.00
NP18 S.Hasegawa 2.00 5.00
NP19 Takashi Kashiwada 2.50 6.00
NP20 Chan Ho Park 2.00 5.00
NP21 Fernando Valenzuela 2.00 5.00
NP22 Vinny Castilla 2.00 5.00
NP23 Armando Reynoso 2.00 5.00
NP24 Karim Garcia 2.00 5.00
NP25 Marvin Benard 2.00 5.00
NP26 Mariano Rivera 5.00 12.00
NP27 Juan Gonzalez 2.00 5.00
NP28 Roberto Alomar 3.00 8.00
NP29 Ivan Rodriguez 3.00 8.00
NP30 Carlos Delgado 2.00 5.00
NP31 Bernie Williams 3.00 8.00
NP32 Edgar Martinez 3.00 8.00
NP33 Frank Thomas 5.00 12.00
NP34 Barry Bonds 12.50 30.00
NP35 Mike Piazza 8.00 20.00
NP36 Chipper Jones 5.00 12.00
NP37 Cal Ripken 15.00 40.00
NP38 Alex Rodriguez 8.00 20.00
NP39 Ken Griffey Jr. 8.00 20.00
NP40 Andres Galarraga 2.00 5.00
NP41 Omar Vizquel 3.00 8.00
NP42 Ozzie Guillen 2.00 5.00

1998 Upper Deck Power Deck Audio Griffey

In an effort to premier their new Power Deck Audio technology, Upper Deck created three special Ken Griffey Jr. cards (blue, green and silver backgrounds), each of which contained the same five minute interview with the Mariner's superstar. These cards were randomly seeded exclusively into test packs comprising only 10 percent of the total first series 1998 Upper Deck print run. The seeding ratios are as follows: blue 1:8, green 1:100 and silver 1:2400. Each test issue box contained a clear CD disc for which the card could be placed upon for playing on any common CD player. To play the card, the center hole had to be punched out. Prices below are for Mint unpunched cards. Punched out cards trade at twenty-five percent of the listed values.

GREY STATED ODDS 1:46
BLUE STATED ODDS 1:500
TEAL STATED ODDS 1:2400
1 Ken Griffey Jr. Blue .75 2.00
2 Ken Griffey Jr. Green 5.00 12.00
3 Ken Griffey Jr. Silver 15.00 40.00

1998 Upper Deck Prime Nine

Randomly inserted in Series two packs at the rate of one in five, this 60-card set features color photos of the current most popular players printed on premium silver card stock.

COMPLETE SET (60) 40.00 100.00
COMMON GRIFFEY (1-7) .75 2.00
COMMON PIAZZA (8-14) .75 2.00
COMMON THOMAS (15-21) .50 1.25
COMMON MCGWIRE (22-28) 1.25 3.00
COMMON RIPKEN (29-35) 1.50 4.00
COMMON GONZALEZ (36-42) .20 .50
COMMON GWYNN (43-49) .60 1.50
COMMON BONDS (50-55) 1.25 3.00
COMMON MADDUX (56-60) .75 2.00
SER.2 STATED ODDS 1:5

1998 Upper Deck Retrospectives

Randomly inserted in series three packs at a rate of one in 24, this 30-card insert set takes a look back at the unforgettable careers of some of baseball's most valuable contributors. The fronts feature a color action photo from each player's rookie season.

SER.3 STATED ODDS 1:24 3.00 8.00
1 Dennis Eckersley 1.25 3.00
2 Rickey Henderson 3.00 8.00
3 Harold Baines 1.25 3.00
4 Cal Ripken 10.00 25.00
5 Tony Gwynn 4.00 10.00
6 Wade Boggs 2.00 5.00
7 Orel Hershiser 1.25 3.00
8 Joe Carter 1.25 3.00
9 Roger Clemens 6.00 15.00
10 Barry Bonds 8.00 20.00
11 Mark McGwire 8.00 20.00
12 Greg Maddux 5.00 12.00
13 Fred McGriff 2.00 5.00
14 Rafael Palmeiro 2.00 5.00
15 Craig Biggio 2.00 5.00
16 Brady Anderson 1.25 3.00
17 Randy Johnson 3.00 8.00
18 Gary Sheffield 1.25 3.00
19 Albert Belle 1.25 3.00
20 Ken Griffey Jr. 5.00 12.00
21 Juan Gonzalez 1.25 3.00
22 Larry Walker 1.25 3.00
23 Tino Martinez 2.00 5.00
24 Frank Thomas 3.00 8.00
25 Jeff Bagwell 2.00 5.00
26 Kenny Lofton 1.25 3.00
27 Mo Vaughn 1.25 3.00
28 Mike Piazza 5.00 12.00
29 Alex Rodriguez 5.00 12.00
30 Chipper Jones 3.00 8.00

1998 Upper Deck Rookie Edition Preview

Randomly inserted in Upper Deck Series two packs at an approximate rate of one in six, this 10-card set features color photos of players who were top rookies. The backs carry player information.

COMPLETE SET (10) 2.50 6.00
1 Nomar Garciaparra .75 2.00
2 Scott Rolen .30 .75
3 Mark Kotsay .20 .50
4 Todd Helton .30 .75
5 Paul Konerko .20 .50
6 Juan Encarnacion .20 .50
7 Brad Fullmer .20 .50
8 Miguel Tejada .50 1.25
9 Richard Hidalgo .20 .50
10 Ben Grieve .20 .50

1998 Upper Deck Tape Measure Titans

Randomly inserted in Series two packs at the rate of one in 23, this 30-card set features color photos of the league's most productive long-ball hitters printed on unique retro cards.

COMPLETE SET (30) 60.00 150.00
SER.2 STATED ODDS 1:23
*GOLD: .4X TO 1X BASIC TITAN
GOLD: RANDOM IN RETAIL PACKS
GOLD PRINT RUN 2667 SERIAL #'d SETS
1 Mark McGwire 8.00 20.00
2 Andres Galarraga 1.25 3.00
3 Jeff Bagwell 2.00 5.00
4 Larry Walker 1.25 3.00
5 Frank Thomas 3.00 8.00
6 Rafael Palmeiro 2.00 5.00
7 Nomar Garciaparra 5.00 12.00
8 Mo Vaughn 1.25 3.00
9 Albert Belle 1.25 3.00
10 Ken Griffey Jr. 5.00 12.00
11 Manny Ramirez 2.00 5.00
12 Jim Thome 2.00 5.00
13 Tony Clark 1.25 3.00
14 Juan Gonzalez 1.25 3.00
15 Mike Piazza 5.00 12.00
16 Jose Canseco 2.00 5.00
17 Jay Buhner 1.25 3.00
18 Alex Rodriguez 5.00 12.00
19 Jose Cruz Jr. 1.25 3.00
20 Tino Martinez 2.00 5.00
21 Carlos Delgado 1.25 3.00
22 Andruw Jones 2.00 5.00
23 Chipper Jones 3.00 8.00
24 Fred McGriff 2.00 5.00
25 Matt Williams 1.25 3.00
26 Sammy Sosa 3.00 8.00
27 Vinny Castilla 1.25 3.00
28 Tim Salmon 2.00 5.00
29 Ken Caminiti 1.25 3.00
30 Barry Bonds 8.00 20.00

1998 Upper Deck Unparalleled

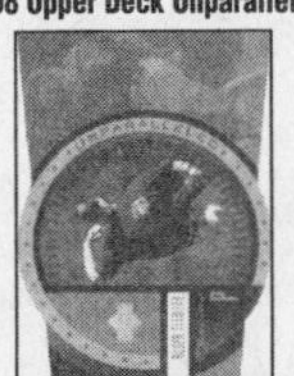

Randomly inserted in series three hobby packs only at a rate of one in 72, this 20-card insert set features color action photos on a high-tech designed card.

COMPLETE SET (20) 100.00 250.00
SER.3 STATED ODDS 1:72 HOBBY
1 Ken Griffey Jr. 6.00 15.00
2 Travis Lee 1.50 4.00
3 Ben Grieve 1.50 4.00
4 Jose Cruz Jr. 1.50 4.00
5 Nomar Garciaparra 6.00 15.00
6 Hideo Nomo 4.00 10.00
7 Kenny Lofton 1.50 4.00
8 Cal Ripken 12.50 30.00
9 Roger Clemens 8.00 20.00
10 Mike Piazza 6.00 15.00
11 Jeff Bagwell 2.50 6.00
12 Chipper Jones 4.00 10.00
13 Greg Maddux 6.00 15.00
14 Randy Johnson 4.00 10.00
15 Alex Rodriguez 6.00 15.00
16 Barry Bonds 10.00 25.00
17 Frank Thomas 4.00 10.00
18 Juan Gonzalez 1.50 4.00
19 Tony Gwynn 5.00 12.00
20 Mark McGwire 10.00 25.00

1998 Upper Deck Griffey Most Memorable Home Runs

This 10-card set features color action photos of Ken Griffey Jr. hitting the most memorable home runs of his career printed on cards measuring approximately 3 1/2" by 5" with gold foil highlights. The backs carry another photo of the home run along with the date and why the home run was important in his career. Limited Edition Ken Griffey Jr. Autograph cards were randomly inserted in the set boxes. Also inserted was a special redemption card to be redeemed for an exclusive Ken Griffey Jr. 300th HR Commemorative Card or a special oversized card of equal or geater value.

COMMON CARD (1-10) .50 1.25

1998 Upper Deck Griffey Most Memorable Home Runs Autographed

Randomly inserted into boxes of Griffey Most Memorable Home Runs sets were these autographed cards. Ken Griffey Jr. signed 10 each of the cards in the set and the cards are all serial numbered on the front "x"/10. No pricing is available due to scarcity.

1999 Upper Deck

This 525-card set was distributed in two separate series. Series one packs contained cards 1-255 and series two contained 266-535. Cards 256-265 were never created. Subsets are as follows: Star Rookies (1-18, 266-292), Foreign Focus (229-246), Season Highlights Checklists (247-255, 527-535), and Arms Race '99 (518-526). The product was distributed in 10-card packs with a suggested retail price of $2.99. Though not confirmed by Upper Deck, it's widely believed by dealers that broke a good deal of product that these subset cards were slightly short-printed in comparison to other cards in the set. Notable Rookie Cards include Pat Burrell. 100 signed 1989 Upper Deck Ken Griffey Jr. RC's were randomly seeded into series one packs. These signed cards are real 89 RC's and they contain an additional diamond shaped hologram on back signifying that UD has verified Griffey's signature. Approximately 350 Babe Ruth A Piece of History cards were randomly seeded into all series one packs at a rate of one in 15,000. 50 Babe Ruth A Piece of History 500 Club bat cards were randomly seeded into second series packs. Pricing for these bat cards can be referenced under 1999 Upper Deck A Piece of History 500 Club.

COMPLETE SET (525) 50.00 100.00
COMP. SERIES 1 (255) 30.00 60.00
COMP. SERIES 2 (270) 20.00 40.00
COMMON (19-255/293-535) .10 .30
COMMON SER.1 SR (1-18) .20 .50
COMMON (266-292) .20 .50
1 Troy Glaus SR .40 1.00
2 Adrian Beltre SR .25 .60
3 Matt Anderson SR .20 .50
4 Eric Chavez SR .25 .60
5 Jin Ho Cho SR .20 .50
6 Robert Smith SR .20 .50
7 George Lombard SR .20 .50
8 Mike Kinkade SR .20 .50
9 Seth Greisinger SR .20 .50
10 J.D. Drew SR .25 .60
11 Aramis Ramirez SR .25 .60
12 Carlos Guillen SR .25 .60
13 Justin Baughman SR .20 .50
14 Jim Parque SR .20 .50
15 Ryan Jackson SR .20 .50
16 Ramon E.Martinez SR RC .20 .50
17 Orlando Hernandez SR .25 .60
18 Jeremy Giambi SR .20 .50
19 Gary DiSarcina .10 .30
20 Darin Erstad .10 .30
21 Troy Glaus .20 .50
22 Chuck Finley .10 .30
23 Dave Hollins .10 .30
24 Troy Percival .10 .30
25 Tim Salmon .20 .50
26 Brian Anderson .10 .30
27 Jay Bell .10 .30
28 Andy Benes .10 .30
29 Brent Brede .10 .30
30 David Dellucci .10 .30
31 Karim Garcia .10 .30
32 Travis Lee .10 .30
33 Andres Galarraga .10 .30
34 Ryan Klesko .10 .30
35 Keith Lockhart .10 .30
36 Kevin Millwood .10 .30
37 Denny Neagle .10 .30
38 John Smoltz .20 .50
39 Michael Tucker .10 .30
40 Walt Weiss .10 .30
41 Dennis Martinez .10 .30
42 Javy Lopez .10 .30
43 Brady Anderson .10 .30
44 Harold Baines .10 .30
45 Mike Bordick .10 .30
46 Roberto Alomar .20 .50
47 Scott Erickson .10 .30
48 Mike Mussina .20 .50
49 Cal Ripken 1.00 2.50
50 Darren Bragg .10 .30
51 Dennis Eckersley .10 .30
52 Nomar Garciaparra .50 1.25
53 Scott Hatteberg .10 .30
54 Troy O'Leary .10 .30
55 Bret Saberhagen .10 .30
56 John Valentin .10 .30
57 Rod Beck .10 .30
58 Jeff Blauser .10 .30
59 Brant Brown .10 .30
60 Mark Clark .10 .30
61 Mark Grace .20 .50
62 Kevin Tapani .10 .30
63 Henry Rodriguez .10 .30
64 Mike Cameron .10 .30
65 Mike Caruso .10 .30
66 Ray Durham .10 .30
67 Jaime Navarro .10 .30
68 Magglio Ordonez .10 .30
69 Mike Sirotka .10 .30
70 Sean Casey .10 .30
71 Barry Larkin .20 .50
72 Jon Nunnally .10 .30
73 Paul Konerko .10 .30
74 Chris Stynes .10 .30
75 Brett Tomko .10 .30
76 Dmitri Young .10 .30
77 Sandy Alomar Jr. .10 .30
78 Bartolo Colon .10 .30
79 Travis Fryman .10 .30
80 Brian Giles .10 .30
81 David Justice .10 .30
82 Omar Vizquel .20 .50
83 Jaret Wright .10 .30
84 Jim Thome .20 .50
85 Charles Nagy .10 .30
86 Pedro Astacio .10 .30
87 Todd Helton .20 .50
88 Darryl Kile .10 .30
89 Mike Lansing .10 .30
90 Neifi Perez .10 .30
91 John Thomson .10 .30
92 Larry Walker .10 .30
93 Tony Clark .10 .30
94 Deivi Cruz .10 .30
95 Damion Easley .10 .30
96 Brian L.Hunter .10 .30
97 Todd Jones .10 .30
98 Brian Moehler .10 .30
99 Gabe Alvarez .10 .30
100 Craig Counsell .10 .30
101 Cliff Floyd .10 .30
102 Livan Hernandez .10 .30
103 Andy Larkin .10 .30
104 Derrek Lee .20 .50
105 Brian Meadows .10 .30
106 Moises Alou .10 .30
107 Sean Berry .10 .30
108 Craig Biggio .20 .50
109 Ricky Gutierrez .10 .30
110 Mike Hampton .10 .30
111 Jose Lima .10 .30
112 Billy Wagner .10 .30
113 Hal Morris .10 .30
114 Johnny Damon .20 .50
115 Jeff King .10 .30
116 Jeff Montgomery .10 .30
117 Glendon Rusch .10 .30
118 Larry Sutton .10 .30
119 Bobby Bonilla .10 .30
120 Jim Eisenreich .10 .30
121 Eric Karros .10 .30
122 Matt Luke .10 .30
123 Ramon Martinez .10 .30
124 Gary Sheffield .10 .30
125 Eric Young .10 .30
126 Charles Johnson .10 .30
127 Jeff Cirillo .10 .30
128 Marquis Grissom .10 .30
129 Jeromy Burnitz .10 .30
130 Bob Wickman .10 .30
131 Scott Karl .10 .30
132 Mark Loretta .10 .30
133 Fernando Vina .10 .30
134 Matt Lawton .10 .30
135 Pat Meares .10 .30
136 Eric Milton .10 .30
137 Paul Molitor .10 .30
138 David Ortiz .30 .75
139 Todd Walker .10 .30
140 Shane Andrews .10 .30
141 Brad Fullmer .10 .30
142 Vladimir Guerrero .30 .75
143 Dustin Hermanson .10 .30
144 Ryan McGuire .10 .30
145 Ugueth Urbina .10 .30
146 John Franco .10 .30
147 Butch Huskey .10 .30
148 Bobby Jones .10 .30
149 John Olerud .10 .30
150 Rey Ordonez .10 .30
151 Mike Piazza .50 1.25
152 Hideo Nomo .30 .75
153 Masato Yoshii .10 .30
154 Derek Jeter .75 2.00
155 Chuck Knoblauch .10 .30
156 Paul O'Neill .20 .50
157 Andy Pettitte .20 .50
158 Mariano Rivera .30 .75
159 Darryl Strawberry .10 .30
160 David Wells .10 .30
161 Jorge Posada .20 .50
162 Ramiro Mendoza .10 .30
163 Miguel Tejada .10 .30
164 Ryan Christenson .10 .30
165 Rickey Henderson .30 .75
166 A.J. Hinch .10 .30
167 Ben Grieve .10 .30
168 Kenny Rogers .10 .30
169 Matt Stairs .10 .30
170 Bob Abreu .10 .30
171 Rico Brogna .10 .30
172 Doug Glanville .10 .30
173 Mike Grace .10 .30
174 Desi Relaford .10 .30
175 Scott Rolen .20 .50
176 Jose Guillen .10 .30
177 Francisco Cordova .10 .30
178 Al Martin .10 .30
179 Jason Schmidt .10 .30
180 Turner Ward .10 .30
181 Kevin Young .10 .30
182 Mark McGwire .75 2.00
183 Delino DeShields .10 .30
184 Eli Marrero .10 .30
185 Tom Lampkin .10 .30
186 Ray Lankford .10 .30
187 Willie McGee .10 .30
188 Matt Morris UER .10 .30
Career strikeout totals are wrong
189 Andy Ashby .10 .30
190 Kevin Brown .20 .50
191 Ken Caminiti .10 .30
192 Trevor Hoffman .10 .30
193 Wally Joyner .10 .30
194 Greg Vaughn .10 .30
195 Danny Darwin .10 .30
196 Shawn Estes .10 .30
197 Orel Hershiser .10 .30
198 Jeff Kent .10 .30
199 Bill Mueller .10 .30
200 Robb Nen .10 .30
201 J.T. Snow .10 .30
202 Ken Cloude .10 .30
203 Russ Davis .10 .30
204 Jeff Fassero .10 .30
205 Ken Griffey Jr. .50 1.25
206 Shane Monahan .10 .30
207 David Segui .10 .30
208 Dan Wilson .10 .30
209 Wilson Alvarez .10 .30
210 Wade Boggs .20 .50
211 Miguel Cairo .10 .30
212 Bubba Trammell .10 .30
213 Quinton McCracken .10 .30
214 Paul Sorrento .10 .30
215 Kevin Stocker .10 .30
216 Will Clark .20 .50
217 Rusty Greer .10 .30
218 Rick Helling .10 .30
219 Mark McLemore .10 .30
220 Ivan Rodriguez .20 .50
221 John Wetteland .10 .30
222 Jose Canseco .20 .50
223 Roger Clemens .60 1.50
224 Carlos Delgado .10 .30
225 Darrin Fletcher .10 .30
226 Alex Gonzalez .10 .30
227 Jose Cruz Jr. .10 .30
228 Shannon Stewart .10 .30
229 Rolando Arrojo FF .10 .30
230 Livan Hernandez FF .10 .30
231 Orlando Hernandez FF .10 .30
232 Raul Mondesi FF .10 .30
233 Moises Alou FF .10 .30
234 Pedro Martinez FF .20 .50
235 Sammy Sosa FF .20 .50
236 Vladimir Guerrero FF .30 .75
237 Bartolo Colon FF .10 .30
238 Miguel Tejada FF .10 .30
239 Ismael Valdes FF .10 .30
240 Mariano Rivera FF .20 .50
241 Jose Cruz Jr. FF .10 .30
242 Juan Gonzalez FF .10 .30
243 Ivan Rodriguez FF .20 .50
244 Sandy Alomar Jr. FF .10 .30
245 Roberto Alomar FF .20 .50
246 Magglio Ordonez FF .10 .30
247 Kerry Wood SH CL .10 .30
248 Mark McGwire SH CL .75 2.00
249 David Wells SH CL .10 .30
250 Rolando Arrojo SH CL .10 .30
251 Ken Griffey Jr. SH CL .50 1.25
252 T.Hoffman SH CL .10 .30
253 Travis Lee SH CL .10 .30
254 R.Alomar SH CL .10 .30
255 Sammy Sosa SH CL .20 .50
266 Pat Burrell SR RC 1.25 3.00
267 S.Hillenbrand SR RC .60 1.50
268 Robert Fick SR .20 .50
269 Roy Halladay SR 2.00 5.00
270 Ruben Mateo SR .20 .50
271 Bruce Chen SR .20 .50
272 Angel Pena SR .20 .50
273 Michael Barrett SR .20 .50
274 Kevin Witt SR .20 .50
275 Damon Minor SR .20 .50
276 Ryan Minor SR .20 .50
277 A.J. Pierzynski SR .25 .60
278 A.J. Burnett SR RC .60 1.50
279 Dermal Brown SR .20 .50
280 Joe Lawrence SR .20 .50
281 Derrick Gibson SR .20 .50
282 Carlos Febles SR .20 .50
283 Chris Haas SR .20 .50
284 Cesar King SR .20 .50
285 Calvin Pickering SR .20 .50
286 Mitch Meluskey SR .20 .50
287 Carlos Beltran SR .40 1.00
288 Ron Belliard SR .20 .50
289 Jerry Hairston Jr. SR .20 .50
290 F.Seguignol SR .20 .50
291 Kris Benson SR .20 .50
292 C.Hutchinson SR RC .25 .60
293 Jarrod Washburn .10 .30
294 Jason Dickson .10 .30
295 Mo Vaughn .10 .30
296 Garret Anderson .10 .30
297 Jim Edmonds .10 .30
298 Ken Hill .10 .30
299 Shigetoshi Hasegawa .10 .30
300 Todd Stottlemyre .10 .30
301 Randy Johnson .30 .75
302 Omar Daal .10 .30
303 Steve Finley .10 .30
304 Matt Williams .10 .30
305 Danny Klassen .10 .30
306 Tony Batista .10 .30
307 Brian Jordan .10 .30
308 Greg Maddux .50 1.25
309 Chipper Jones .30 .75
310 Bret Boone .10 .30
311 Ozzie Guillen .10 .30
312 John Rocker .10 .30
313 Tom Glavine .20 .50
314 Andruw Jones .20 .50
315 Albert Belle .10 .30
316 Charles Johnson .10 .30
317 Will Clark .20 .50
318 B.J. Surhoff .10 .30
319 Delino DeShields .10 .30
320 Heathcliff Slocumb .10 .30
321 Sidney Ponson .10 .30
322 Juan Guzman .10 .30
323 Reggie Jefferson .10 .30
324 Mark Portugal .10 .30
325 Tim Wakefield .10 .30
326 Jason Varitek .30 .75
327 Jose Offerman .10 .30
328 Pedro Martinez .20 .50
329 Trot Nixon .10 .30
330 Kerry Wood .10 .30
331 Sammy Sosa .30 .75
332 Glenallen Hill .10 .30
333 Gary Gaetti .10 .30
334 Mickey Morandini .10 .30
335 Benito Santiago .10 .30
336 Jeff Blauser .10 .30
337 Frank Thomas .30 .75
338 Paul Konerko .10 .30
339 Jaime Navarro .10 .30
340 Carlos Lee .10 .30
341 Brian Simmons .10 .30
342 Mark Johnson .10 .30
343 Jeff Abbott .10 .30
344 Steve Avery .10 .30
345 Mike Cameron .10 .30
346 Michael Tucker .10 .30
347 Greg Vaughn .10 .30
348 Hal Morris .10 .30
349 Pete Harnisch .10 .30
350 Denny Neagle .10 .30
351 Manny Ramirez .20 .50
352 Roberto Alomar .20 .50
353 Dwight Gooden .10 .30
354 Kenny Lofton .10 .30
355 Mike Jackson .10 .30
356 Charles Nagy .10 .30
357 Enrique Wilson .10 .30
358 Russ Branyan .10 .30
359 Richie Sexson .10 .30
360 Vinny Castilla .10 .30
361 Dante Bichette .10 .30
362 Kirt Manwaring .10 .30
363 Darryl Hamilton .10 .30
364 Jamey Wright .10 .30
365 Curtis Leskanic .10 .30
366 Jeff Reed .10 .30
367 Bobby Higginson .10 .30
368 Justin Thompson .10 .30
369 Brad Ausmus .10 .30
370 Dean Palmer .10 .30
371 Gabe Kapler .10 .30
372 Juan Encarnacion .10 .30

373 Karim Garcia	.10	.30
374 Alex Gonzalez	.10	.30
375 Braden Looper	.10	.30
376 Preston Wilson	.10	.30
377 Todd Dunwoody	.10	.30
378 Alex Fernandez	.10	.30
379 Mark Kotsay	.10	.30
380 Matt Mantei	.10	.30
381 Ken Caminiti	.10	.30
382 Scott Elarton	.10	.30
383 Jeff Bagwell	.20	.50
384 Derek Bell	.10	.30
385 Ricky Gutierrez	.10	.30
386 Richard Hidalgo	.10	.30
387 Shane Reynolds	.10	.30
388 Carl Everett	.10	.30
389 Scott Service	.10	.30
390 Jeff Suppan	.10	.30
391 Joe Randa	.10	.30
392 Kevin Appier	.10	.30
393 Shane Halter	.10	.30
394 Chad Kreuter	.10	.30
395 Mike Sweeney	.10	.30
396 Kevin Brown	.20	.50
397 Devon White	.10	.30
398 Todd Hollandsworth	.10	.30
399 Todd Hundley	.10	.30
400 Chan Ho Park	.10	.30
401 Mark Grudzielanek	.10	.30
402 Raul Mondesi	.10	.30
403 Ismael Valdes	.10	.30
404 Rafael Roque RC	.10	.30
405 Sean Berry	.10	.30
406 Kevin Barker	.10	.30
407 Dave Nilsson	.10	.30
408 Geoff Jenkins	.10	.30
409 Jim Abbott	.20	.50
410 Bobby Hughes	.10	.30
411 Corey Koskie	.10	.30
412 Rick Aguilera	.10	.30
413 LaTroy Hawkins	.10	.30
414 Ron Coomer	.10	.30
415 Denny Hocking	.10	.30
416 Marty Cordova	.10	.30
417 Terry Steinbach	.10	.30
418 Rondell White	.10	.30
419 Wilton Guerrero	.10	.30
420 Shane Andrews	.10	.30
421 Orlando Cabrera	.10	.30
422 Carl Pavano	.10	.30
423 Javier Vazquez	.10	.30
424 Chris Widger	.10	.30
425 Robin Ventura	.10	.30
426 Rickey Henderson	.30	.75
427 Al Leiter	.10	.30
428 Bobby Jones	.10	.30
429 Brian McRae	.10	.30
430 Roger Cedeno	.10	.30
431 Bobby Bonilla	.10	.30
432 Edgardo Alfonzo	.10	.30
433 Bernie Williams	.20	.50
434 Ricky Ledee	.10	.30
435 Chili Davis	.10	.30
436 Tino Martinez	.20	.50
437 Scott Brosius	.10	.30
438 David Cone	.10	.30
439 Joe Girardi	.10	.30
440 Roger Clemens	.60	1.50
441 Chad Curtis	.10	.30
442 Hideki Irabu	.10	.30
443 Jason Giambi	.10	.30
444 Scott Spiezio	.10	.30
445 Tony Phillips	.10	.30
446 Ramon Hernandez	.10	.30
447 Mike Macfarlane	.10	.30
448 Tom Candiotti	.10	.30
449 Billy Taylor	.10	.30
450 Bobby Estalella	.10	.30
451 Curt Schilling	.10	.30
452 Carlton Loewer	.10	.30
453 Marlon Anderson	.10	.30
454 Kevin Jordan	.10	.30
455 Ron Gant	.10	.30
456 Chad Ogea	.10	.30
457 Abraham Nunez	.10	.30
458 Jason Kendall	.10	.30
459 Pat Meares	.10	.30
460 Brant Brown	.10	.30
461 Brian Giles	.10	.30
462 Chad Hermansen	.10	.30
463 Freddy Adrian Garcia	.10	.30
464 Edgar Renteria	.10	.30
465 Fernando Tatis	.10	.30
466 Eric Davis	.10	.30
467 Darren Bragg	.10	.30
468 Donovan Osborne	.10	.30
469 Manny Aybar	.10	.30
470 Jose Jimenez	.10	.30
471 Kent Mercker	.10	.30
472 Reggie Sanders	.10	.30
473 Ruben Rivera	.10	.30
474 Tony Gwynn	.40	1.00
475 Jim Leyritz	.10	.30
476 Chris Gomez	.10	.30
477 Matt Clement	.10	.30
478 Carlos Hernandez	.10	.30
479 Sterling Hitchcock	.10	.30
480 Ellis Burks	.10	.30
481 Barry Bonds	.75	2.00
482 Marvin Benard	.10	.30
483 Kirk Rueter	.10	.30
484 F.P. Santangelo	.10	.30
485 Stan Javier	.10	.30
486 Jeff Kent	.10	.30
487 Alex Rodriguez	.50	1.25
488 Tom Lampkin	.10	.30
489 Jose Mesa	.10	.30
490 Jay Buhner	.10	.30
491 Edgar Martinez	.20	.50
492 Butch Huskey	.10	.30
493 John Mabry	.10	.30
494 Jamie Moyer	.10	.30
495 Roberto Hernandez	.10	.30
496 Tony Saunders	.10	.30
497 Fred McGriff	.20	.50
498 Dave Martinez	.10	.30
499 Jose Canseco	.20	.50
500 Rolando Arrojo	.10	.30
501 Esteban Yan	.10	.30
502 Juan Gonzalez	.10	.30
503 Rafael Palmeiro	.20	.50
504 Aaron Sele	.10	.30
505 Royce Clayton	.10	.30
506 Todd Zeile	.10	.30
507 Tom Goodwin	.10	.30
508 Lee Stevens	.10	.30
509 Esteban Loaiza	.10	.30
510 Joey Hamilton	.10	.30
511 Homer Bush	.10	.30
512 Willie Greene	.10	.30
513 Shawn Green	.10	.30
514 David Wells	.10	.30
515 Kelvim Escobar	.10	.30
516 Tony Fernandez	.10	.30
517 Pat Hentgen	.10	.30
518 Mark McGwire AR	.40	1.00
519 Ken Griffey Jr. AR	.30	.75
520 Sammy Sosa AR	.20	.50
521 Juan Gonzalez AR	.10	.30
522 J.D. Drew AR	.10	.30
523 Chipper Jones AR	.20	.50
524 Alex Rodriguez AR	.30	.75
525 Mike Piazza AR	.30	.75
526 N.Garciaparra AR	.30	.75
527 Mark McGwire SH CL	.40	1.00
528 Sammy Sosa SH CL	.20	.50
529 Scott Brosius SH CL	.10	.30
530 Cal Ripken SH CL	.50	1.25
531 Barry Bonds SH CL	.40	1.00
532 Roger Clemens SH CL	.30	.75
533 Ken Griffey Jr. SH CL	.30	.75
534 Alex Rodriguez SH CL	.30	.75
535 Curt Schilling SH CL	.10	.30
NNO Ken Griffey Jr. 1989 AU/100	1000.00	1250.00

1999 Upper Deck Exclusives Level 1

This 525-card set is a hobby only parallel version of the base set. Each card is sequentially numbered to 100 on back. In addition, Bronze foil fronts make them easy to differentiate from their silver foiled basic issue brethren. As is the case with the basic set, cards 256-265 were never printed due to a numbering error at the manufacturer.

*STARS: 10X TO 25X BASIC CARDS
*SER.1 STAR ROOK: 4X TO 10X BASIC SR
*SER.2 STAR ROOK: 6X TO 15X BASIC SR

1999 Upper Deck 10th Anniversary Team

Randomly inserted in first series packs at the rate of one in four, this 30-card set features color photos of collectors' favorite players selected for this special All-Star team.

COMPLETE SET (30) 20.00 50.00
SER.1 STATED ODDS 1:4
*DOUBLES: 1.25X TO 3X BASIC 10TH ANN.
DOUBLES RANDOM INSERTS IN SER.1 PACKS
DOUBLES PRINT RUN 4000 SERIAL #'d SETS
*TRIPLES: 8X TO 20X BASIC 10TH ANN
TRIPLES RANDOM INSERTS IN SER.1 PACKS
TRIPLES PRINT RUN 100 SERIAL #'d SETS
HR'S RANDOM INSERTS IN SER.1 PACKS
HOME RUN PRINT RUN 1 SERIAL #'d SET
HR'S NOT PRICED DUE TO SCARCITY

X1 Mike Piazza	1.00	2.50
X2 Mark McGwire	1.50	4.00
X3 Roberto Alomar	.40	1.00
X4 Chipper Jones	.60	1.50
X5 Cal Ripken	2.00	5.00
X6 Ken Griffey Jr.	1.00	2.50
X7 Barry Bonds	1.50	4.00
X8 Tony Gwynn	.75	2.00
X9 Nolan Ryan	2.50	6.00
X10 Randy Johnson	.60	1.50
X11 Dennis Eckersley	.25	.60
X12 Ivan Rodriguez	.40	1.00
X13 Frank Thomas	.60	1.50
X14 Craig Biggio	.40	1.00
X15 Wade Boggs	.40	1.00
X16 Alex Rodriguez	1.00	2.50
X17 Albert Belle	.25	.60
X18 Juan Gonzalez	.25	.60
X19 Rickey Henderson	.60	1.50
X20 Greg Maddux	1.00	2.50
X21 Tom Glavine	.40	1.00
X22 Randy Myers	.25	.60
X23 Sandy Alomar Jr.	.25	.60
X24 Jeff Bagwell	.40	1.00
X25 Derek Jeter	1.50	4.00
X26 Matt Williams	.25	.60
X27 Kenny Lofton	.25	.60
X28 Sammy Sosa	.60	1.50
X29 Larry Walker	.25	.60
X30 Roger Clemens	1.25	3.00

1999 Upper Deck A Piece of History

This limited edition set features photos of Babe Ruth along with a bat chip from an actual game-used Louisville Slugger swung by him during the late 20's. Approximately 350 cards were made and seeded into packs at a rate of 1:15,000. Another insert card incorporates both a "cut" signature of Ruth along with a piece of his game-used bat. Only three of these cards were produced.

SER.1 STATED ODDS 1:15,000
B.RUTH AU RANDOM IN SER.1 PACKS
B.RUTH AU PRINT RUN 3 #'d CARDS
PHLC Babe Ruth AU/3
PH Babe Ruth 750.00 1000.00

1999 Upper Deck A Piece of History 500 Club

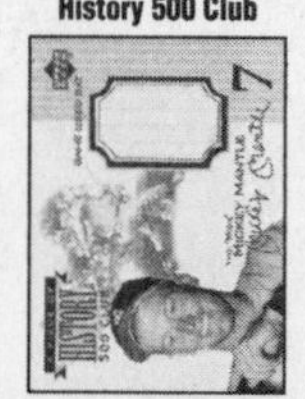

During the 1999 season, Upper Deck inserted into various products these cards which are cut up bats from all except one of the members of the 500 homer club. Mark McGwire asked that one of his bats not be included in this set, thus there was no Mark McGwire card in this grouping (until 2003 when McGwire signed a deal with Upper Deck). With the exception of Babe Ruth, approximately 350 of each card was produced. Only 50 Babe Ruth's were made. The cards were released in the following products: 1999 SP Authentic: Ernie Banks; 1999 SP Signature: Mel Ott; 1999 SPx: Willie Mays, 1999 UD Choice: Eddie Murray; 1999 UD Ionix: Frank Robinson; 1999 Upper Deck 2: Babe Ruth; 1999 Upper Deck Century Legends: Jimmie Foxx; 1999 Upper Deck Challengers for 70: Harmon Killebrew; 1999 Upper Deck HoloGrFx: Eddie Mathews and Willie McCovey; 1999 Upper Deck MVP: Mike Schmidt; 1999 Upper Deck Ovation: Mickey Mantle: 1999 Upper Deck Retro: Ted Williams; 2000 Black Diamond: Reggie Jackson; 2000 Upper Deck 1: Hank Aaron.

RANDOM INSERTS IN 1999-2000 UD BRANDS

BR Babe Ruth/50		
EB Ernie Banks	125.00	250.00
EM Eddie Mathews	150.00	300.00
EM Eddie Murray	100.00	200.00
FR Frank Robinson	100.00	200.00
HA Hank Aaron	150.00	300.00
HK Harmon Killebrew	100.00	200.00
JF Jimmie Foxx	100.00	200.00
MM Mickey Mantle	350.00	600.00
MO Mel Ott	100.00	200.00
MS Mike Schmidt	75.00	150.00
RJ Reggie Jackson	60.00	120.00
TW Ted Williams	150.00	300.00
WM Willie Mays	125.00	250.00
WM Willie McCovey	60.00	120.00
ARM Hank Aaron Babe Ruth Willie Mays SP		
XXX Instant Winner Card		

1999 Upper Deck A Piece of History 500 Club Autographs

As part of the Upper Deck A Piece of History 500 Club Autograph promotion, Upper Deck had most of the living members of the 500 homer club sign a number of cards which matched their uniform number (except for Mantle of which is a true 1/1, features a cut signature and altered card front design from the other cards in the set). On some of the players, the cards are not priced due to scarcity. Each card is serial numbered on the front except Mantle. Each of these cards was issued in a separate UD brand from 1999.

RANDOM INSERTS IN 1999-2000 UD BRANDS

536HR Mickey Mantle/1		
EBAU Ernie Banks/14		
EMAU Eddie Mathews/41	500.00	800.00
FRAU Frank Robinson/20		
HAAU Hank Aaron/44	700.00	1200.00
HKAU Harmon Killebrew/3		
MSAU Mike Schmidt/20		
RJAU Reggie Jackson/44	350.00	600.00
TWAU Ted Williams/9		
WMAU Willie Mays/24		
WMAU Willie McCovey/44	500.00	800.00

1999 Upper Deck Crowning Glory

Randomly inserted in first series packs at the rate of one in 23, this three-card set features color photos of players who reached major milestones during the '98 MLB season and printed on double sided cards.

COMPLETE SET (3) 25.00 60.00
*DOUBLES: .6X TO 1.5X BASIC CROWN
DOUBLES RANDOM INSERTS IN SER.1 PACKS
DOUBLES PRINT RUN 1000 SERIAL #'d SETS
*TRIPLES: 4X TO 10X BASIC CROWN
TRIPLES RANDOM INSERTS IN SER.1 PACKS
TRIPLES PRINT RUN 25 SERIAL #'d SETS
HR'S RANDOM INSERTS IN SER.1 PACKS
HOME RUNS PRINT RUN 1 SERIAL #'d SET
HOME RUNS NOT PRICED DUE TO SCARCITY

CG1 Roger Clemens Kerry Wood	6.00	15.00
CG2 Mark McGwire Barry Bonds	8.00	20.00
CG3 Ken Griffey Jr. Mark McGwire	6.00	15.00

1999 Upper Deck Forte

Randomly inserted in series two packs at the rate of one in 23, this 30-card set features color photos of the most collectible superstars captured on super premium cards with extensive rainbow foil coverage. Three limited parallel sets were also produced and randomly inserted into Series two packs. Forte Doubles was serially numbered to 2000; Forte Triples, to 100; and Forte Quadruples, to 10.

COMPLETE SET (30) 80.00 200.00
SER.2 STATED ODDS 1:23
*DOUBLES: .6X TO 1.5X BASIC FORTE
DOUBLES RANDOM INSERTS IN SER.2 PACKS
DOUBLES PRINT RUN 2000 SERIAL #'d SETS
*TRIPLES: 2X TO 5X BASIC FORTE
TRIPLES RANDOM INSERTS IN SER.2 PACKS
TRIPLES PRINT RUN 100 SERIAL #'d SETS
QUADS RANDOM INSERTS IN SER.2 PACKS
QUADRUPLES NOT PRICED DUE TO SCARCITY

F1 Darin Erstad	1.00	2.50
F2 Troy Glaus	1.50	4.00
F3 Mo Vaughn	1.00	2.50
F4 Greg Maddux	4.00	10.00
F5 Andres Galarraga	1.00	2.50
F6 Chipper Jones	2.50	6.00
F7 Cal Ripken	8.00	20.00
F8 Albert Belle	1.00	2.50
F9 Nomar Garciaparra	4.00	10.00
F10 Sammy Sosa	2.50	6.00
F11 Kerry Wood	1.00	2.50
F12 Frank Thomas	2.50	6.00
F13 Jim Thome	1.50	4.00
F14 Jeff Bagwell	1.50	4.00
F15 Vladimir Guerrero	2.50	6.00
F16 Mike Piazza	4.00	10.00
F17 Derek Jeter	6.00	15.00
F18 Ben Grieve	1.00	2.50
F19 Eric Chavez	.60	1.50
F20 Scott Rolen	1.50	4.00
F21 Mark McGwire	6.00	15.00
F22 J.D. Drew	.60	1.50
F23 Tony Gwynn	3.00	8.00
F24 Barry Bonds	6.00	15.00
F25 Alex Rodriguez	4.00	10.00
F26 Ken Griffey Jr.	4.00	10.00
F27 Ivan Rodriguez	1.50	4.00
F28 Juan Gonzalez	1.00	2.50
F29 Roger Clemens	5.00	12.00
F30 Andruw Jones	1.50	4.00

1999 Upper Deck Game Jersey

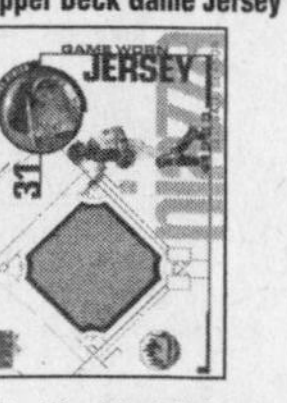

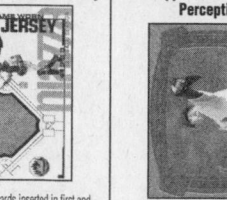

This set consists of 23 cards inserted in first and second series packs. Hobby packs contained Game Jersey hobby cards (signified in the listings with an H after the player's name) at a rate of 1:288. Hobby and retail packs contained much scarcer Game Jersey hobby/retail cards (signified with an H/R after the player's name in the listings below) at a rate of 1:2500. Each card features a piece of an actual game worn jersey. Five additional cards were signed by the athlete and serial numbered by hand to the player's respective jersey number. These rare signed Game Jersey cards are priced below but not considered part of the complete set.

H STATED ODDS 1:288 HOBBY
HR STATED ODDS 1:2500 HOBBY/RETAIL
H1 AND HR1 CARDS DIST.IN SER.1 PACKS
H2 AND HR2 CARDS DIST.IN SER.2 PACKS
AU'S RANDOM INSERTS IN PACKS

AB Adrian Beltre H1	4.00	10.00
AR Alex Rodriguez HR1	8.00	20.00
BF Brad Fullmer H2	4.00	10.00
BG Ben Grieve H1	4.00	10.00
BT Bubba Trammell H2	4.00	10.00
CJ Charles Johnson HR1	6.00	15.00
CJ Chipper Jones H2	6.00	15.00
DE Darin Erstad H1	6.00	15.00
EC Eric Chavez H2	6.00	15.00
FT Frank Thomas HR2	10.00	25.00
GM Greg Maddux HR2	12.50	30.00
IR Ivan Rodriguez H1	6.00	15.00
JD J.D. Drew H2	6.00	15.00
JG Juan Gonzalez HR1	6.00	15.00
JR K.Griffey Jr. HR2	15.00	40.00
KG K.Griffey Jr. H1	15.00	40.00
KW Kerry Wood HR1	6.00	15.00
MP Mike Piazza HR1	12.50	30.00
MR Manny Ramirez H2	6.00	15.00
NRA Nolan Ryan Astros H2	15.00	40.00
NRB Nolan Ryan Rangers HR2	15.00	40.00
SS Sammy Sosa H2	6.00	15.00
TH Todd Helton H2	6.00	15.00
TGW Tony Gwynn H2	6.00	15.00
TL Travis Lee H1	4.00	10.00
JDS J.Drew AU/8 H2		
JRS Ken Griffey Jr. AU/24 HR2		
KGAU Ken Griffey Jr. AU/24 H1		
KWAU Kerry Wood AU/34 HR1	150.00	250.00
NRAS Nolan Ryan Astros AU/34, H2	500.00	800.00

1999 Upper Deck Ken Griffey Jr. Box Blasters

These ten 5" by 7" cards were inserted one per Upper Deck special retail boxes. The cards feature oversize reprints of the regular issue Ken Griffey Jr. Upper Deck cards during both his 10 year career and the 10 seasons Upper Deck has made cards for. We have numbered the cards 1-10 based on the year of the card's original issue.

COMPLETE SET (1-10) 20.00 50.00
COMMON CARD (1-10) 2.00 5.00

1999 Upper Deck Ken Griffey Jr. Box Blasters Autographs

Randomly seeded into one in every 64 special retail boxes, each of these attractive cards was signed by Ken Griffey Jr. The cards are over-sized 5" by 7" replicas of each of Griffey's basic issue Upper Deck cards from 1989-1999. The backs of the cards provide a certificate of authenticity from UD Chairman and CEO Richard McWilliam.

COMMON CARD (90-99) 50.00 100.00
STATED ODDS 1:64 SPECIAL RETAIL BOXES
KG1989 Ken Griffey Jr. AU 89 150.00 250.00

1999 Upper Deck Immaculate Perception

Randomly inserted in Series one packs at the rate of one in 23, this 27-card set features top player photos printed on unique, foil-enhanced cards.

COMPLETE SET (27) 125.00 250.00
SER.1 STATED ODDS 1:23
*DOUBLES: .75X TO 2X BASIC IMM.PERC.
DOUBLES RANDOM INSERTS IN SER.1 PACKS
DOUBLES PRINT RUN 1000 SERIAL #'d SETS
*TRIPLES: 5X TO 12X BASIC IMM.PERC.
TRIPLES RANDOM INSERTS IN SER.1 PACKS
TRIPLES PRINT RUN 25 SERIAL #'d SETS
HR'S RANDOM INSERTS IN SER.1 PACKS
HOME RUNS PRINT RUN 1 SERIAL #'d SET
HOME RUNS NOT PRICED DUE TO SCARCITY

I1 Jeff Bagwell	2.00	5.00
I2 Craig Biggio	2.00	5.00
I3 Barry Bonds	8.00	20.00
I4 Roger Clemens	6.00	15.00
I5 Jose Cruz Jr.	1.25	3.00
I6 Nomar Garciaparra	5.00	12.00
I7 Tony Clark	1.25	3.00
I8 Ben Grieve	1.25	3.00
I9 Ken Griffey Jr.	5.00	12.00
I10 Tony Gwynn	4.00	10.00
I11 Randy Johnson	3.00	8.00
I12 Chipper Jones	3.00	8.00
I13 Travis Lee	1.25	3.00
I14 Kenny Lofton	1.25	3.00
I15 Greg Maddux	5.00	12.00
I16 Mark McGwire	8.00	20.00
I17 Hideo Nomo	3.00	8.00
I18 Mike Piazza	5.00	12.00
I19 Manny Ramirez	2.00	5.00
I20 Cal Ripken	10.00	25.00
I21 Alex Rodriguez	5.00	12.00
I22 Scott Rolen	2.00	5.00
I23 Frank Thomas	3.00	8.00
I24 Kerry Wood	1.25	3.00
I25 Larry Walker	1.25	3.00
I26 Vinny Castilla	1.25	3.00
I27 Derek Jeter	8.00	20.00

1999 Upper Deck Textbook Excellence

Inserted one every 23 second series packs, these cards offer information on the skills of some of the game's most fundamentally sound performers.

COMPLETE SET (30) 20.00 50.00
SER.2 STATED ODDS 1:4
*DOUBLES: 1.5X TO 4X BASIC TEXTBOOK
DOUBLES RANDOM INSERTS IN SER.2 PACKS
DOUBLES PRINT RUN 2000 SERIAL #'d SETS
*TRIPLES: 6X TO 15X BASIC TEXTBOOK
TRIPLES RANDOM INSERTS IN SER.2 PACKS
TRIPLES PRINT RUN 100 SERIAL #'d SETS
QUADS RANDOM INSERTS IN SER.2 PACKS
QUADRUPLES PRINT RUN 10 SERIAL #'d SETS
QUADRUPLES NOT PRICED DUE TO SCARCITY

T1 Mo Vaughn	.30	.75
T2 Greg Maddux	1.25	3.00
T3 Chipper Jones	.75	2.00
T4 Andruw Jones	.50	1.25
T5 Cal Ripken	2.50	6.00
T6 Albert Belle	.30	.75
T7 Roberto Alomar	.50	1.25
T8 Nomar Garciaparra	1.25	3.00
T9 Kerry Wood	.30	.75
T10 Sammy Sosa	.75	2.00
T11 Greg Vaughn	.30	.75
T12 Jeff Bagwell	.50	1.25
T13 Kevin Brown	.50	1.25
T14 Vladimir Guerrero	.75	2.00
T15 Mike Piazza	1.25	3.00
T16 Bernie Williams	.50	1.25
T17 Derek Jeter	2.00	5.00
T18 Ben Grieve	.30	.75
T19 Eric Chavez	.20	.50
T20 Scott Rolen	.50	1.25
T21 Mark McGwire	2.00	5.00
T22 David Wells	.30	.75
T23 J.D. Drew	.20	.50
T24 Tony Gwynn	1.00	2.50
T25 Barry Bonds	2.00	5.00
T26 Alex Rodriguez	1.25	3.00
T27 Ken Griffey Jr.	1.25	3.00
T28 Juan Gonzalez	.30	.75
T29 Ivan Rodriguez	.50	1.25
T30 Roger Clemens	1.50	4.00

1999 Upper Deck View to a Thrill

These cards, inserted one every seven second series packs feature special die-cuts and embossing and takes a new look at 30 of the best overall athletes in baseball.

COMPLETE SET (30) 40.00 100.00
SER.2 STATED ODDS 1:7
*DOUBLES: 1X TO 2.5X BASIC VIEW
DOUBLES RANDOM INSERTS IN SER.2 PACKS
DOUBLES PRINT RUN 2000 SERIAL #'d SETS
*TRIPLES: 4X TO 10X BASIC VIEW
TRIPLES RANDOM INSERTS IN SER.2 PACKS
TRIPLES PRINT RUN 100 SERIAL #'d SETS
QUADS RANDOM INSERTS IN SER.2 PACKS
QUADRUPLES PRINT RUN 10 SERIAL #'d SETS
QUADRUPLES NOT PRICED DUE TO SCARCITY

V1 Mo Vaughn	.50	1.25
V2 Darin Erstad	.50	1.25
V3 Travis Lee	.50	1.25
V4 Chipper Jones	1.25	3.00
V5 Greg Maddux	2.00	5.00
V6 Gabe Kapler	.50	1.25
V7 Cal Ripken	4.00	10.00
V8 Nomar Garciaparra	2.00	5.00
V9 Kerry Wood	.50	1.25
V10 Frank Thomas	1.25	3.00
V11 Manny Ramirez	.75	2.00
V12 Larry Walker	.50	1.25
V13 Tony Clark	.50	1.25
V14 Jeff Bagwell	.75	2.00
V15 Craig Biggio	.75	2.00
V16 Vladimir Guerrero	1.25	3.00
V17 Mike Piazza	2.00	5.00
V18 Bernie Williams	.75	2.00
V19 Derek Jeter	3.00	8.00
V20 Ben Grieve	.50	1.25
V21 Eric Chavez	.30	.75
V22 Scott Rolen	.75	2.00
V23 Mark McGwire	3.00	8.00
V24 Tony Gwynn	1.50	4.00
V25 Barry Bonds	3.00	8.00
V26 Ken Griffey Jr.	2.00	5.00
V27 Alex Rodriguez	2.00	5.00
V28 J.D. Drew	.30	.75
V29 Juan Gonzalez	.50	1.25
V30 Roger Clemens	2.50	6.00

1999 Upper Deck Wonder Years

Randomly inserted in Series one packs at the rate of one in seven, this 30-card set features color photos of top stars.

COMPLETE SET (30) 30.00 80.00
SER.1 STATED ODDS 1:7
*DOUBLES: 1X TO 2.5X BASIC WONDER
DOUBLES RANDOM INSERTS IN SER.1 PACKS
DOUBLES PRINT RUN 2000 SERIAL #'d SETS
*TRIPLES: 8X TO 20X BASIC WONDER
TRIPLES RANDOM INSERTS IN SER.1 PACKS
TRIPLES PRINT RUN 50 SERIAL #'d SETS
HR'S RANDOM INSERTS IN SER.1 PACKS
HOME RUNS PRINT RUN 1 SERIAL #'d SET
HOME RUNS NOT PRICED DUE TO SCARCITY

W1 Kerry Wood	.50	1.25
W2 Travis Lee	.50	1.25
W3 Jeff Bagwell	.75	2.00
W4 Barry Bonds	3.00	8.00
W5 Roger Clemens	2.50	6.00
W6 Jose Cruz Jr.	.50	1.25
W7 Andres Galarraga	.50	1.25
W8 Nomar Garciaparra	2.00	5.00
W9 Juan Gonzalez	.50	1.25
W10 Ken Griffey Jr.	2.00	5.00
W11 Tony Gwynn	1.50	4.00
W12 Derek Jeter	3.00	8.00
W13 Randy Johnson	1.25	3.00
W14 Andruw Jones	.75	2.00
W15 Chipper Jones	1.25	3.00
W16 Kenny Lofton	.50	1.25
W17 Greg Maddux	2.00	5.00
W18 Tino Martinez	.75	2.00
W19 Mark McGwire	3.00	8.00
W20 Paul Molitor	.50	1.25
W21 Mike Piazza	2.00	5.00
W22 Manny Ramirez	.75	2.00
W23 Cal Ripken	4.00	10.00
W24 Alex Rodriguez	2.00	5.00
W25 Sammy Sosa	1.25	3.00
W26 Frank Thomas	1.25	3.00
W27 Mo Vaughn	.50	1.25
W28 Larry Walker	.50	1.25
W29 Scott Rolen	.75	2.00
W30 Ben Grieve	.50	1.25

2000 Upper Deck

Upper Deck Series one was released in December, 1999 and offered 270 standard-size cards. The first series was distributed in 10 card packs with a SRP of $2.99 per pack. The second series was released in July, 2000 and offered 270 standard-size cards. The cards were issued in 24 pack boxes. Cards numbered 1-28 and 271-297 are Star Rookie subsets while cards numbered 262-270 and 532-540 feature 1999 season highlights and have checklists on back. Cards 523-531 feature the All-UD Team subset - a collection of top stars as selected by Upper Deck. Notable Rookie Cards include Kazuhiro Sasaki. Also, 350 1999 A Piece of History 500 Club Hank Aaron bat cards were randomly seeded into first series packs. In addition, Aaron signed and numbered 44 copies. Pricing for these bat cards can be referenced under 1999 Upper Deck A Piece of History 500 Club. Also, a selection of A Piece of History 3000 Club Hank Aaron memorabilia cards were randomly seeded into second series packs. 350 bat cards, 350 jersey cards, 100 hand-numbered, combination bat-jersey cards and forty-four hand-numbered, autographed, combination bat-jersey cards were produced. Pricing for these memorabilia cards can be referenced under 2000 Upper Deck A Piece of History 3000 Club.

COMPLETE SET (540)	40.00	100.00
COMP. SERIES 1 (270)	20.00	50.00
COMP. SERIES 2 (270)	20.00	50.00
COMMON (28-270/298-540)	.10	.30
COMMON (1-28/271-297)	.20	.50
1 Rick Ankiel SR	.20	.50
2 Vernon Wells SR	.30	.75
3 Ryan Anderson SR	.20	.50
4 Ed Yarnall SR	.20	.50
5 Brian McNichol SR	.20	.50
6 Ben Petrick SR	.20	.50
7 Kip Wells SR	.20	.50
8 Eric Munson SR	.20	.50
9 Matt Riley SR	.20	.50
10 Peter Bergeron SR	.20	.50
11 Eric Gagne SR	.75	2.00
12 Ramon Ortiz SR	.20	.50
13 Josh Beckett SR	.75	2.00
14 Alfonso Soriano SR	.75	2.00
15 Jorge Toca SR	.20	.50
16 Buddy Carlyle SR	.20	.50
17 Chad Hermansen SR	.20	.50
18 Matt Perisho SR	.20	.50
19 Tomokazu Ohka SR RC	.30	.75
20 Jacque Jones SR	.30	.75
21 Josh Paul SR	.20	.50
22 Dermal Brown SR	.20	.50
23 Adam Kennedy SR	.20	.50
24 Chad Harville SR	.20	.50
25 Calvin Murray SR	.20	.50
26 Chad Meyers SR	.20	.50
27 Brian Cooper SR	.20	.50
28 Troy Glaus	.10	.30
29 Ben Molina	.10	.30
30 Troy Percival	.10	.30
31 Ken Hill	.10	.30
32 Chuck Finley	.10	.30
33 Todd Greene	.10	.30
34 Tim Salmon	.20	.50
35 Gary DiSarcina	.10	.30
36 Luis Gonzalez	.10	.30
37 Tony Womack	.10	.30
38 Omar Daal	.10	.30
39 Randy Johnson	.30	.75
40 Erubiel Durazo	.10	.30
41 Jay Bell	.10	.30
42 Steve Finley	.10	.30
43 Travis Lee	.10	.30
44 Greg Maddux	.50	1.25
45 Bret Boone	.10	.30
46 Brian Jordan	.10	.30
47 Kevin Millwood	.10	.30
48 Odalis Perez	.10	.30
49 Javy Lopez	.10	.30
50 John Smoltz	.20	.50
51 Bruce Chen	.10	.30
52 Albert Belle	.10	.30
53 Jerry Hairston Jr.	.10	.30
54 Will Clark	.20	.50
55 Sidney Ponson	.10	.30
56 Charles Johnson	.10	.30
57 Cal Ripken	1.00	2.50
58 Ryan Minor	.10	.30
59 Mike Mussina	.20	.50
60 Tom Gordon	.10	.30
61 Jose Offerman	.10	.30
62 Trot Nixon	.10	.30
63 Pedro Martinez	.20	.50
64 John Valentin	.10	.30
65 Jason Varitek	.30	.75
66 Juan Pena	.10	.30
67 Troy O'Leary	.10	.30
68 Sammy Sosa	.30	.75
69 Henry Rodriguez	.10	.30
70 Kyle Farnsworth	.10	.30
71 Glenallen Hill	.10	.30
72 Lance Johnson	.10	.30
73 Mickey Morandini	.10	.30
74 Jon Lieber	.10	.30
75 Kevin Tapani	.10	.30
76 Carlos Lee	.10	.30
77 Ray Durham	.10	.30
78 Jim Parque	.10	.30
79 Bob Howry	.10	.30
80 Magglio Ordonez	.10	.30
81 Paul Konerko	.10	.30
82 Mike Caruso	.10	.30
83 Chris Singleton	.10	.30
84 Sean Casey	.10	.30
85 Barry Larkin	.20	.50
86 Pokey Reese	.10	.30
87 Eddie Taubensee	.10	.30
88 Scott Williamson	.10	.30
89 Jason LaRue	.10	.30
90 Aaron Boone	.10	.30
91 Jeffrey Hammonds	.10	.30
92 Omar Vizquel	.20	.50
93 Manny Ramirez	.20	.50
94 Kenny Lofton	.10	.30
95 Jaret Wright	.10	.30
96 Einar Diaz	.10	.30
97 Charles Nagy	.10	.30
98 David Justice	.10	.30
99 Richie Sexson	.10	.30
100 Steve Karsay	.10	.30
101 Todd Helton	.20	.50
102 Dante Bichette	.10	.30
103 Larry Walker	.10	.30
104 Pedro Astacio	.10	.30
105 Neifi Perez	.10	.30
106 Brian Bohanon	.10	.30
107 Edgard Clemente	.10	.30
108 Dave Veres	.10	.30
109 Gabe Kapler	.10	.30
110 Juan Encarnacion	.10	.30
111 Jeff Weaver	.10	.30
112 Damion Easley	.10	.30
113 Justin Thompson	.10	.30
114 Brad Ausmus	.10	.30
115 Frank Catalanotto	.10	.30
116 Todd Jones	.10	.30
117 Preston Wilson	.10	.30
118 Cliff Floyd	.10	.30
119 Mike Lowell	.10	.30
120 Antonio Alfonseca	.10	.30
121 Alex Gonzalez	.10	.30
122 Braden Looper	.10	.30
123 Bruce Aven	.10	.30
124 Richard Hidalgo	.10	.30
125 Mitch Meluskey	.10	.30
126 Jeff Bagwell	.20	.50
127 Jose Lima	.10	.30
128 Derek Bell	.10	.30
129 Billy Wagner	.10	.30
130 Shane Reynolds	.10	.30
131 Moises Alou	.10	.30
132 Carlos Beltran	.10	.30
133 Carlos Febles	.10	.30
134 Jermaine Dye	.10	.30
135 Jeremy Giambi	.10	.30
136 Joe Randa	.10	.30
137 Jose Rosado	.10	.30
138 Chad Kreuter	.10	.30
139 Jose Vizcaino	.10	.30
140 Adrian Beltre	.10	.30
141 Kevin Brown	.20	.50
142 Ismael Valdes	.10	.30
143 Angel Pena	.10	.30
144 Chan Ho Park	.10	.30
145 Mark Grudzielanek	.10	.30
146 Jeff Shaw	.10	.30
147 Geoff Jenkins	.10	.30
148 Jeromy Burnitz	.10	.30
149 Hideo Nomo	.30	.75
150 Ron Belliard	.10	.30
151 Sean Berry	.10	.30
152 Mark Loretta	.10	.30
153 Steve Woodard	.10	.30
154 Joe Mays	.10	.30
155 Eric Milton	.10	.30
156 Corey Koskie	.10	.30
157 Ron Coomer	.10	.30
158 Brad Radke	.10	.30
159 Terry Steinbach	.10	.30
160 Cristian Guzman	.10	.30
161 Vladimir Guerrero	.30	.75
162 Wilton Guerrero	.10	.30
163 Michael Barrett	.10	.30
164 Chris Widger	.10	.30
165 Fernando Seguignol	.10	.30
166 Ugueth Urbina	.10	.30
167 Dustin Hermanson	.10	.30
168 Kenny Rogers	.10	.30
169 Edgardo Alfonzo	.10	.30
170 Orel Hershiser	.10	.30
171 Robin Ventura	.10	.30
172 Octavio Dotel	.10	.30
173 Rickey Henderson	.30	.75
174 Roger Cedeno	.10	.30
175 John Olerud	.10	.30
176 Derek Jeter	.75	2.00
177 Tino Martinez	.20	.50
178 Orlando Hernandez	.10	.30
179 Chuck Knoblauch	.10	.30
180 Bernie Williams	.20	.50
181 Chili Davis	.10	.30
182 David Cone	.10	.30
183 Ricky Ledee	.10	.30
184 Paul O'Neill	.20	.50
185 Jason Giambi	.10	.30
186 Eric Chavez	.10	.30
187 Matt Stairs	.10	.30
188 Miguel Tejada	.10	.30
189 Olmedo Saenz	.10	.30
190 Tim Hudson	.10	.30
191 John Jaha	.10	.30
192 Randy Velarde	.10	.30
193 Rico Brogna	.10	.30
194 Mike Lieberthal	.10	.30
195 Marlon Anderson	.10	.30
196 Bob Abreu	.10	.30
197 Ron Gant	.10	.30
198 Randy Wolf	.10	.30
199 Desi Relaford	.10	.30
200 Doug Glanville	.10	.30
201 Warren Morris	.10	.30
202 Kris Benson	.10	.30
203 Kevin Young	.10	.30
204 Brian Giles	.10	.30
205 Jason Schmidt	.10	.30
206 Ed Sprague	.10	.30
207 Francisco Cordova	.10	.30
208 Mark McGwire	.75	2.00
209 Jose Jimenez	.10	.30
210 Fernando Tatis	.10	.30
211 Kent Bottenfield	.10	.30
212 Eli Marrero	.10	.30
213 Edgar Renteria	.10	.30
214 Joe McEwing	.10	.30
215 J.D. Drew	.10	.30
216 Tony Gwynn	.40	1.00
217 Gary Matthews Jr.	.10	.30
218 Eric Owens	.10	.30
219 Damian Jackson	.10	.30
220 Reggie Sanders	.10	.30
221 Trevor Hoffman	.10	.30
222 Ben Davis	.10	.30
223 Shawn Estes	.10	.30
224 F.P. Santangelo	.10	.30
225 Livan Hernandez	.10	.30
226 Ellis Burks	.10	.30
227 J.T. Snow	.10	.30
228 Jeff Kent	.10	.30
229 Robb Nen	.10	.30
230 Marvin Benard	.10	.30
231 Ken Griffey Jr.	.50	1.25
232 John Halama	.10	.30
233 Gil Meche	.10	.30
234 David Bell	.10	.30
235 Brian Hunter	.10	.30
236 Jay Buhner	.10	.30
237 Edgar Martinez	.20	.50
238 Jose Mesa	.10	.30
239 Wilson Alvarez	.10	.30
240 Wade Boggs	.20	.50
241 Fred McGriff	.20	.50
242 Jose Canseco	.20	.50
243 Kevin Stocker	.10	.30
244 Roberto Hernandez	.10	.30
245 Bubba Trammell	.10	.30
246 John Flaherty	.10	.30
247 Ivan Rodriguez	.20	.50
248 Rusty Greer	.10	.30
249 Rafael Palmeiro	.20	.50
250 Jeff Zimmerman	.10	.30
251 Royce Clayton	.10	.30
252 Todd Zeile	.10	.30
253 John Wetteland	.10	.30
254 Ruben Mateo	.10	.30
255 Kelvim Escobar	.10	.30
256 David Wells	.10	.30
257 Shawn Green	.10	.30
258 Homer Bush	.10	.30
259 Shannon Stewart	.10	.30
260 Carlos Delgado	.10	.30
261 Roy Halladay	.10	.30
262 Fernando Tatis SH CL	.10	.30
263 Jose Jimenez SH CL	.10	.30
264 Tony Gwynn SH CL	.20	.50
265 Wade Boggs SH CL	.10	.30
266 Cal Ripken SH CL	.50	1.25
267 David Cone SH CL	.10	.30
268 Mark McGwire SH CL	.50	1.25
269 Pedro Martinez SH CL	.20	.50
270 N. Garciaparra SH CL	.30	.75
271 Nick Johnson SR	.30	.75
272 Mark Quinn SR	.20	.50
273 Roosevelt Brown SR	.20	.50
274 Terrence Long SR	.20	.50
275 Jason Marquis SR	.20	.50
276 K.Sasaki SR RC	.50	1.25
277 Aaron Myette SR	.20	.50
278 Danys Baez SR RC	.30	.75
279 Travis Dawkins SR	.20	.50
280 Mark Mulder SR	.30	.75
281 Chris Haas SR	.20	.50
282 Milton Bradley SR	.30	.75
283 Brad Penny SR	.20	.50
284 Rafael Furcal SR	.30	.75
285 Luis Matos SR RC	.30	.75
286 Victor Santos SR RC	.30	.75
287 R.Washington SR RC	.20	.50
288 Rob Bell SR	.20	.50
289 Joe Crede SR	1.00	2.50
290 Pablo Ozuna SR	.20	.50
291 W.Serrano SR RC	.20	.50
292 S-H. Lee SR RC	.20	.50
293 C.Wakeland SR RC	.20	.50
294 Luis Rivera SR RC	.20	.50
295 Mike Lamb SR RC	.50	1.25
296 Wily Mo Pena SR	.30	.75
297 Mike Meyers SR RC	.30	.75
298 Mo Vaughn	.10	.30
299 Darin Erstad	.10	.30
300 Garret Anderson	.10	.30
301 Tim Belcher	.10	.30
302 Scott Spiezio	.10	.30
303 Kent Bottenfield	.10	.30
304 Orlando Palmeiro	.10	.30
305 Jason Dickson	.10	.30
306 Matt Williams	.10	.30
307 Brian Anderson	.10	.30
308 Hanley Frias	.10	.30
309 Todd Stottlemyre	.10	.30
310 Matt Mantei	.10	.30
311 David Dellucci	.10	.30
312 Armando Reynoso	.10	.30
313 Bernard Gilkey	.10	.30
314 Chipper Jones	.30	.75
315 Tom Glavine	.20	.50
316 Quilvio Veras	.10	.30
317 Andruw Jones	.20	.50
318 Bobby Bonilla	.10	.30
319 Reggie Sanders	.10	.30
320 Andres Galarraga	.10	.30
321 George Lombard	.10	.30
322 John Rocker	.10	.30
323 Wally Joyner	.10	.30
324 B.J. Surhoff	.10	.30
325 Scott Erickson	.10	.30
326 Delino DeShields	.10	.30
327 Jeff Conine	.10	.30
328 Mike Timlin	.10	.30
329 Brady Anderson	.10	.30
330 Mike Bordick	.10	.30
331 Harold Baines	.10	.30
332 Nomar Garciaparra	.50	1.25
333 Bret Saberhagen	.10	.30
334 Ramon Martinez	.10	.30
335 Donnie Sadler	.10	.30
336 Wilton Veras	.10	.30
337 Mike Stanley	.10	.30
338 Brian Rose	.10	.30
339 Carl Everett	.10	.30
340 Tim Wakefield	.10	.30
341 Mark Grace	.20	.50
342 Kerry Wood	.10	.30
343 Eric Young	.10	.30
344 Jose Nieves	.10	.30
345 Ismael Valdes	.10	.30
346 Joe Girardi	.10	.30
347 Damon Buford	.10	.30
348 Ricky Gutierrez	.10	.30
349 Frank Thomas	.30	.75
350 Brian Simmons	.10	.30
351 James Baldwin	.10	.30
352 Brook Fordyce	.10	.30
353 Jose Valentin	.10	.30
354 Mike Sirotka	.10	.30
355 Greg Norton	.10	.30
356 Dante Bichette	.10	.30
357 Deion Sanders	.20	.50
358 Ken Griffey Jr.	.50	1.25
359 Denny Neagle	.10	.30
360 Dmitri Young	.10	.30
361 Pete Harnisch	.10	.30
362 Michael Tucker	.10	.30
363 Roberto Alomar	.20	.50
364 Dave Roberts	.10	.30
365 Jim Thome	.20	.50
366 Bartolo Colon	.10	.30
367 Travis Fryman	.10	.30
368 Chuck Finley	.10	.30
369 Russell Branyan	.10	.30
370 Alex Ramirez	.10	.30
371 Jeff Cirillo	.10	.30
372 Jeffrey Hammonds	.10	.30
373 Scott Karl	.10	.30
374 Brent Mayne	.10	.30
375 Tom Goodwin	.10	.30
376 Jose Jimenez	.10	.30
377 Rolando Arrojo	.10	.30
378 Terry Shumpert	.10	.30
379 Juan Gonzalez	.10	.30
380 Bobby Higginson	.10	.30
381 Tony Clark	.10	.30
382 Dave Mlicki	.10	.30
383 Deivi Cruz	.10	.30
384 Brian Moehler	.10	.30
385 Dean Palmer	.10	.30
386 Luis Castillo	.10	.30
387 Mike Redmond	.10	.30
388 Alex Fernandez	.10	.30
389 Brant Brown	.10	.30
390 Dave Berg	.10	.30
391 A.J. Burnett	.10	.30
392 Mark Kotsay	.10	.30
393 Craig Biggio	.20	.50
394 Daryle Ward	.10	.30
395 Lance Berkman	.10	.30
396 Roger Cedeno	.10	.30
397 Scott Elarton	.10	.30
398 Octavio Dotel	.10	.30
399 Ken Caminiti	.10	.30
400 Johnny Damon	.20	.50
401 Mike Sweeney	.10	.30
402 Jeff Suppan	.10	.30
403 Rey Sanchez	.10	.30
404 Blake Stein	.10	.30
405 Ricky Bottalico	.10	.30
406 Jay Witasick	.10	.30
407 Shawn Green	.10	.30
408 Orel Hershiser	.10	.30
409 Gary Sheffield	.10	.30
410 Todd Hollandsworth	.10	.30
411 Terry Adams	.10	.30
412 Todd Hundley	.10	.30
413 Eric Karros	.10	.30
414 F.P. Santangelo	.10	.30
415 Alex Cora	.10	.30
416 Marquis Grissom	.10	.30
417 Henry Blanco	.10	.30
418 Jose Hernandez	.10	.30
419 Kyle Peterson	.10	.30
420 John Snyder RC	.10	.30
421 Bob Wickman	.10	.30
422 Jamey Wright	.10	.30
423 Chad Allen	.10	.30
424 Todd Walker	.10	.30
425 J.C. Romero RC	.10	.30
426 Butch Huskey	.10	.30
427 Jacque Jones	.10	.30
428 Matt Lawton	.10	.30
429 Rondell White	.10	.30
430 Jose Vidro	.10	.30
431 Hideki Irabu	.10	.30
432 Javier Vazquez	.10	.30
433 Lee Stevens	.10	.30
434 Mike Thurman	.10	.30
435 Geoff Blum	.10	.30
436 Mike Hampton	.10	.30
437 Mike Piazza	.50	1.25
438 Al Leiter	.10	.30
439 Derek Bell	.10	.30
440 Armando Benitez	.10	.30
441 Rey Ordonez	.10	.30
442 Todd Zeile	.10	.30
443 Roger Clemens	.60	1.50
444 Ramiro Mendoza	.10	.30
445 Andy Pettitte	.20	.50
446 Scott Brosius	.10	.30
447 Mariano Rivera	.30	.75
448 Jim Leyritz	.10	.30
449 Jorge Posada	.20	.50
450 Omar Olivares	.10	.30
451 Ben Grieve	.10	.30
452 A.J. Hinch	.10	.30
453 Gil Heredia	.10	.30
454 Kevin Appier	.10	.30
455 Ryan Christenson	.10	.30
456 Ramon Hernandez	.10	.30
457 Scott Rolen	.20	.50
458 Alex Arias	.10	.30
459 Andy Ashby	.10	.30
460 K.Jordan UER 474	.10	.30
461 Robert Person	.10	.30
462 Paul Byrd	.10	.30
463 Curt Schilling	.10	.30
464 Mike Jackson	.10	.30
465 Jason Kendall	.10	.30
466 Pat Meares	.10	.30
467 Bruce Aven	.10	.30
468 Todd Ritchie	.10	.30
469 Wil Cordero	.10	.30
470 Aramis Ramirez	.10	.30
471 Andy Benes	.10	.30
472 Ray Lankford	.10	.30
473 Fernando Vina	.10	.30
474 Jim Edmonds	.10	.30
475 Craig Paquette	.10	.30
476 Pat Hentgen	.10	.30
477 Darryl Kile	.10	.30
478 Sterling Hitchcock	.10	.30
479 Ruben Rivera	.10	.30
480 Ryan Klesko	.10	.30
481 Phil Nevin	.10	.30
482 Woody Williams	.10	.30
483 Carlos Hernandez	.10	.30
484 Brian Meadows	.10	.30
485 Bret Boone	.10	.30
486 Barry Bonds	.75	2.00
487 Russ Ortiz	.10	.30
488 Bobby Estalella	.10	.30
489 Rich Aurilia	.10	.30
490 Bill Mueller	.10	.30
491 Joe Nathan	.10	.30
492 Russ Davis	.10	.30
493 John Olerud	.10	.30
494 Alex Rodriguez	.50	1.25
495 Freddy Garcia	.10	.30
496 Carlos Guillen	.10	.30
497 Aaron Sele	.10	.30
498 Brett Tomko	.10	.30
499 Jamie Moyer	.10	.30
500 Mike Cameron	.10	.30
501 Vinny Castilla	.10	.30
502 Gerald Williams	.10	.30
503 Mike DiFelice	.10	.30
504 Ryan Rupe	.10	.30
505 Greg Vaughn	.10	.30
506 Miguel Cairo	.10	.30
507 Juan Guzman	.10	.30
508 Jose Guillen	.10	.30
509 Gabe Kapler	.10	.30
510 Rick Helling	.10	.30
511 David Segui	.10	.30
512 Doug Davis	.10	.30
513 Justin Thompson	.10	.30
514 Chad Curtis	.10	.30
515 Tony Batista	.10	.30
516 Billy Koch	.10	.30
517 Raul Mondesi	.10	.30
518 Joey Hamilton	.10	.30
519 Darrin Fletcher	.10	.30
520 Brad Fullmer	.10	.30
521 Jose Cruz Jr.	.10	.30
522 Kevin Witt	.10	.30
523 Mark McGwire AUT	.40	1.00
524 Roberto Alomar AUT	.10	.30
525 Chipper Jones AUT	.20	.50
526 Derek Jeter AUT	.40	1.00
527 Ken Griffey Jr. AUT	.30	.75
528 Sammy Sosa AUT	.20	.50
529 Manny Ramirez AUT	.20	.50
530 Ivan Rodriguez AUT	.10	.30
531 Pedro Martinez AUT	.20	.50
532 Mariano Rivera CL	.20	.50
533 Sammy Sosa CL	.20	.50
534 Cal Ripken CL	.50	1.25
535 Vladimir Guerrero CL	.20	.50
536 Tony Gwynn CL	.20	.50
537 Mark McGwire CL	.40	1.00
538 Bernie Williams CL	.10	.30
539 Pedro Martinez CL	.20	.50
540 Ken Griffey Jr. CL	.30	.75

2000 Upper Deck Exclusives Silver

This set parallels the regular Upper Deck set and cards were randomly seeded into packs. The cards feature coral and red borders and utilize silver foil stamping on front (instead of blue borders and bronze foil in the base set). In addition, each Exclusive Silver parallel is machine serial numbered to 100 on front.

*STARS: 8X TO 20X BASIC CARDS
*SR NON-RC'S: 2.5X TO 6X BASIC SR
*SR RC'S: 4X TO 10X BASIC SR

2000 Upper Deck 2K Plus

Inserted one every 23 first series packs, these 12 cards feature some players who are expected to be stars in the beginning of the 21st century.

COMPLETE SET (12)	25.00	60.00
*DIE CUTS: 2.5X TO 6X BASIC 2K PLUS		
DIE CUTS PRINT RUN 100 SERIAL #'d SETS		
GOLD DIE CUT PRINT RUN 1 SERIAL #'d SET		
GOLD DC NOT PRICED DUE TO SCARCITY		
2K1 Ken Griffey Jr.	2.50	6.00
2K2 J.D. Drew	.60	1.50
2K3 Derek Jeter	4.00	10.00
2K4 Nomar Garciaparra	2.50	6.00
2K5 Pat Burrell	4.00	10.00
2K6 Ruben Mateo	.60	1.50
2K7 Carlos Beltran	.60	1.50
2K8 Vladimir Guerrero	1.50	4.00
2K9 Scott Rolen	1.00	2.50
2K10 Chipper Jones	1.50	4.00
2K11 Alex Rodriguez	2.50	6.00
2K12 Magglio Ordonez	.60	1.50

2000 Upper Deck A Piece of History 3000 Club

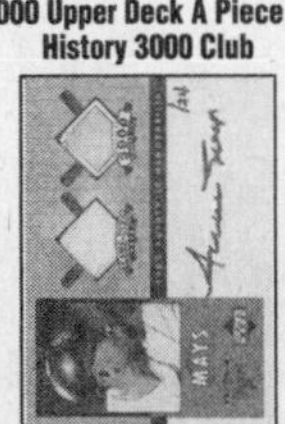

During the 2000 and early 2001 season, Upper Deck inserted a selection of memorabilia cards celebrating members of the 3000 hit club. Approximately 350 of each bat or jersey card was produced. In addition, a wide array of scarce, hand-numbered, autographed cards and combination memorabilia cards were made available. Complete print run information for these cards is provided in our checklist. The cards were released in the following products: 2000 SP Authentic: Tris Speaker and Paul Waner; 2000 SPx: Ty Cobb; 2000 UD Ionix: Roberto Clemente; 2000 Upper Deck 2: Hank Aaron; 2000 Upper Deck Gold Reserve: Al Kaline; 2000 Upper Deck Hitter's Club: Wade Boggs and Tony Gwynn; 2000 Upper Deck HoloGrFx: George Brett and Robin Yount; 2000 Upper Deck Legends: Paul Molitor and Carl Yastrzemski; 2000 Upper Deck MVP: Stan Musial; 2000 Upper Deck Ovation: Willie Mays; 2000 Upper Deck Pros and Prospects: Lou Brock and Rod Carew; 2000 Upper Deck Yankees Legends: Dave Winfield; 2001 Upper Deck: Eddie Murray and Cal Ripken. Exchange cards were seeded into packs for the following cards: Al Kaline Bat AU, Eddie Murray Bat AU, Cal Ripken Bat and Cal Ripken Bat-Jsy. The deadline to exchange the Kaline card was April 10th, 2001 and the Murray/Ripken cards was August 22nd, 2001.

AKB Al Kaline Bat/400	15.00	40.00
AKBS Al Kaline Bat AU/6		
BGB Wade Boggs Tony Gwynn Bat/99	75.00	150.00
BYB George Brett Robin Yount Bat/99	75.00	150.00
BYBS George Brett Robin Yount Bat AU/10		
BYJ George Brett Robin Yount Jersey/99	125.00	200.00
BYJS George Brett Robin Yount Jersey AU/10		
CRB Cal Ripken Bat/350	30.00	60.00
CRJ Cal Ripken Jersey/350	30.00	60.00
CRJB Cal Ripken Bat-Jsy/100	75.00	150.00
CRJBS Cal Ripken Bat-Jsy AU/8		
CYB Carl Yaz Bat/350	15.00	40.00
CYJ Carl Yaz Jersey/350	15.00	40.00
CYJB Carl Yaz Bat-Jsy/100	60.00	120.00
CYJBS Carl Yaz Bat-Jsy AU/8		
DWB Dave Winf. Bat/350	10.00	25.00
DWJ Dave Winf. Jersey/350	10.00	25.00
DWJB Dave Winf. Bat-Jsy/100	15.00	40.00
DWJBS Dave Winfield Bat-Jsy AU/31		
EMB Eddie Murray Bat/350	15.00	40.00
EMJ Eddie Murray Jersey/350	15.00	40.00
EMJB Eddie Murray Bat-Jsy/100	50.00	100.00
EMJBS Eddie Murray Bat-Jsy AU/33		
GBB George Brett Bat/350	20.00	50.00
GBJ George Brett Jersey/350	20.00	50.00
HAB Hank Aaron Bat/350	40.00	80.00
HABS Hank Aaron Bat-Jsy AU/44	700.00	1000.00
HAJ Hank Aaron Jersey/350	40.00	80.00
HAJB Hank Aaron Bat-Jsy/100	125.00	200.00
LBB Lou Brock Bat/350	15.00	40.00
LBJ Lou Brock Jsy/350	15.00	40.00
LBJB Lou Brock Bat-Jsy/100	30.00	60.00
LBJBS Lou Brock Bat-Jsy AU/20		
PMB Paul Molitor Bat/350	10.00	25.00
PWB Paul Waner Bat/350	40.00	80.00
PWBC Paul Waner Bat-Cut AU/5		
RCAB Rod Carew Bat/350	15.00	40.00
RCAJ Rod Carew Jsy/350	15.00	40.00
RCABJ Rod Carew Bat-Jsy/100	30.00	60.00
RCAJS Rod Carew Bat-Jsy AU/30		
RCLB Roberto Clemente Bat/350	75.00	150.00
RCLC Roberto Clemente Cut AU/4		
RCLBC Roberto Clemente Bat-Cut AU/5		
RYB Robin Yount Bat/350	10.00	25.00
RYJ Robin Yount Jersey/350	10.00	25.00
SMB Stan Musial Bat/350	20.00	50.00
SMJ Stan Musial Jersey/350	20.00	50.00
SMJB Stan Musial Bat-Jsy/100	75.00	150.00
SMJBS Stan Musial Bat-Jsy AU/6		
TCB Ty Cobb Bat/350	90.00	180.00
TCBC Ty Cobb Bat-Cut AU/1		
TCC Ty Cobb Cut AU/3		
TGB Tony Gwynn Bat/350	15.00	40.00
TGBC Tony Gwynn Bat-Cap/50	75.00	150.00
TGBS Tony Gwynn Bat AU/19		
TSB Tris Speaker Bat/350	90.00	180.00
TSBC Tris Speaker Bat-Cut AU/5		
WBB Wade Boggs Bat/350	15.00	40.00
WBBC Wade Boggs Bat-Cap/50	50.00	100.00
WBBS Wade Boggs Bat AU/12		
WMB Willie Mays Bat/300	30.00	60.00
WMJ Willie Mays Jersey/350	30.00	60.00
WMJB Willie Mays Bat-Jsy/50	150.00	250.00
WMJBS Willie Mays Bat-Jsy AU/24		

2000 Upper Deck Cooperstown Calling

Randomly inserted into Upper Deck Series two packs at one in 23, this 15-card insert features players that will be going to Cooperstown after they retire from baseball. Card backs carry a "CC" prefix.

COMPLETE SET (15)	40.00	100.00
CC1 Roger Clemens	3.00	8.00
CC2 Cal Ripken	5.00	12.00
CC3 Ken Griffey Jr.	2.50	6.00
CC4 Mike Piazza	2.50	6.00
CC5 Tony Gwynn	2.00	5.00
CC6 Sammy Sosa	1.50	4.00
CC7 Jose Canseco	1.00	2.50
CC8 Larry Walker	.60	1.50
CC9 Barry Bonds	4.00	10.00
CC10 Greg Maddux	2.50	6.00
CC11 Derek Jeter	4.00	10.00
CC12 Mark McGwire	4.00	10.00
CC13 Randy Johnson	1.50	4.00
CC14 Frank Thomas	1.50	4.00
CC15 Jeff Bagwell	1.00	2.50

2000 Upper Deck e-Card

Inserted as a two-pack box-topper in Upper Deck Series two, this six-card insert features cards that can be viewed over the Upper Deck website. Cards feature a serial number that is to be typed in a the Upper Deck website to reveal that card. Card backs carry an "E" prefix.

COMPLETE SET (6) 3.00 8.00
E1 Ken Griffey Jr. .60 1.50
E2 Alex Rodriguez .60 1.50
E3 Cal Ripken Jr. 1.25 3.00
E4 Jeff Bagwell .25 .60
E5 Barry Bonds 1.00 2.50
E6 Manny Ramirez .25 .60

2000 Upper Deck eVolve Autograph

Lucky participants in Upper Deck's E-Card program received special upgraded E-Cards available by checking the UD website (www.upperdeck.com) and entering their basic E-Card serial code (printed on the front of each basic E-Card). When viewed on the Upper Deck website, if an autographed card of the depicted player appeared, the bearer of the base card could then exchange their basic E-Card and receive the signed upgrade via mail. Only 200 serial numbered E-Card Autograph sets were produced. Signed E-Cards all have an ES prefix on the card numbers.

ES1 Ken Griffey Jr. 50.00 100.00
ES2 Alex Rodriguez 50.00 100.00
ES3 Cal Ripken 75.00 150.00
ES4 Jeff Bagwell 20.00 50.00
ES5 Barry Bonds 100.00 175.00
ES6 Manny Ramirez 20.00 50.00

2000 Upper Deck eVolve Game Jersey

Lucky participants in Upper Deck's E-Card program received special upgraded E-Cards available by checking the UD website (www.upperdeck.com) and entering their basic E-Card serial code (printed on the front of each basic E-Card). When viewed on the Upper Deck website, if a jersey card of the depicted player appeared, the bearer of the base card could then exchange their basic E-Card and receive the Game Jersey upgrade via mail. The cards closely parallel basic 2000 Game Jerseys that were distributed in first and second series packs except for the gold foil "e-volve" logo on front. Only 300 serial numbered E-Card Jersey sets were produced with each card being serial -numbered by hand in blue ink sharpie at the bottom right front corner. Unsigned E-Card Game Jerseys all have an EJ prefix on the card numbers.

EJ1 Ken Griffey Jr. 15.00 40.00
EJ2 Alex Rodriguez 15.00 40.00
EJ3 Cal Ripken 25.00 60.00
EJ4 Jeff Bagwell 10.00 25.00
EJ5 Barry Bonds 20.00 50.00
EJ6 Manny Ramirez 10.00 25.00

2000 Upper Deck eVolve Game Jersey Autograph

Lucky participants in Upper Deck's E-Card program received special upgraded E-Cards available by checking the UD website (www.upperdeck.com) and entering their basic E-Card serial code (printed on the front of each basic E-Card). When viewed on the Upper Deck website, if an autographed jersey card of the depicted player appeared, the bearer of the base card could then exchange their basic E-Card and receive the signed jersey upgrade via mail. A mere 50 serial numbered sets were produced. Signed jersey E-Cards all have an ESJ prefix on the card numbers.

ESJ1 Ken Griffey Jr. 75.00 150.00
ESJ2 Alex Rodriguez 90.00 150.00
ESJ3 Cal Ripken 75.00 150.00
ESJ4 Jeff Bagwell 50.00 100.00
ESJ5 Barry Bonds 125.00 200.00
ESJ6 Manny Ramirez 50.00 100.00

2000 Upper Deck Faces of the Game

Inserted one every 11 first series packs, these 20 cards feature leading players captured by exceptional photography.

COMPLETE SET (20) 30.00 80.00
*DIE CUTS: 3X TO 8X BASIC FACES
DIE CUTS PRINT RUN 100 SERIAL #'d SETS
GOLD DIE CUT PRINT RUN 1 SERIAL #'d SET
GOLD DC NOT PRICED DUE TO SCARCITY
F1 Ken Griffey Jr. 2.00 5.00
F2 Mark McGwire 3.00 8.00
F3 Sammy Sosa 1.25 3.00
F4 Alex Rodriguez 2.00 5.00
F5 Manny Ramirez .75 2.00
F6 Derek Jeter 3.00 8.00
F7 Jeff Bagwell .75 2.00
F8 Roger Clemens 2.50 6.00
F9 Scott Rolen .75 2.00
F10 Tony Gwynn 1.50 4.00
F11 Nomar Garciaparra 2.00 5.00
F12 Randy Johnson 1.25 3.00
F13 Greg Maddux 2.00 5.00
F14 Mike Piazza 2.00 5.00
F15 Frank Thomas 1.25 3.00
F16 Cal Ripken 4.00 10.00
F17 Ivan Rodriguez .75 2.00
F18 Mo Vaughn .50 1.25
F19 Chipper Jones 1.25 3.00
F20 Sean Casey .50 1.25

2000 Upper Deck Five-Tool Talents

Randomly inserted into packs at one in 11, this 15-card insert features players that possess all of the tools needed to succeed in the Major Leagues. Card backs carry a "FT" prefix.

COMPLETE SET (15) 12.50 30.00
FT1 Vladimir Guerrero .75 2.00
FT2 Barry Bonds 2.00 5.00
FT3 Jason Kendall .30 .75
FT4 Derek Jeter 2.00 5.00
FT5 Ken Griffey Jr. 1.25 3.00
FT6 Andruw Jones .50 1.25
FT7 Bernie Williams .50 1.25
FT8 Jose Canseco .50 1.25
FT9 Scott Rolen .50 1.25
FT10 Shawn Green .30 .75
FT11 Nomar Garciaparra 1.25 3.00
FT12 Jeff Bagwell .50 1.25
FT13 Larry Walker .30 .75
FT14 Chipper Jones .75 2.00
FT15 Alex Rodriguez 1.25 3.00

2000 Upper Deck Game Ball

Randomly inserted into packs at one in 287, this 10-card insert features game-used baseballs from the depicted players. Card backs carry a "B" prefix.

BAJ Andruw Jones 4.00 10.00
BAR Alex Rodriguez 6.00 15.00
BBW Bernie Williams 4.00 10.00
BDJ Derek Jeter 10.00 25.00
BJB Jeff Bagwell 4.00 10.00
BKG Ken Griffey Jr. 6.00 15.00
BMM Mark McGwire 20.00 50.00
BRC Roger Clemens 6.00 15.00
BTG Tony Gwynn 6.00 15.00
BVG Vladimir Guerrero 4.00 10.00

2000 Upper Deck Game Jersey

These cards feature swatches of jerseys of various major league stars. The cards with an "H" after the player names are available only in hobby packs at a rate of one every 288 first series and 1:287 second series. The cards which have an "HR" after the player names are available in either hobby or retail packs at a rate of one every 2500 packs.

AJ Andruw Jones HR2 10.00 25.00
AR Alex Rodriguez H1 20.00 50.00
AR Alex Rodriguez HR2 20.00 50.00
BG Ben Grieve HR2 6.00 15.00
CJ Chipper Jones HR1 15.00 40.00
CR Cal Ripken HR1 30.00 60.00
CY Tom Glavine H1 10.00 25.00
DC David Cone HR2 6.00 15.00
DJ Derek Jeter H1 30.00 60.00
EC Eric Chavez HR2 6.00 15.00
EM Edgar Martinez HR2 10.00 25.00
FT Frank Thomas H1 15.00 40.00
FT Frank Thomas HR2 15.00 40.00
GK Gabe Kapler HR1 6.00 15.00
GM Greg Maddux HR1 20.00 50.00
GM Greg Maddux HR2 20.00 50.00
GV Greg Vaughn HR1 6.00 15.00
JB Jeff Bagwell H1 10.00 25.00
JC Jose Canseco HR1 10.00 25.00
JR Ken Griffey Jr. H1 20.00 50.00
KG K.Griffey Jr. Reds HR2 20.00 50.00
KM Kevin Millwood HR2 6.00 15.00
MH Mike Hampton HR2 6.00 15.00
MP Mike Piazza H1 20.00 50.00
MR Manny Ramirez HR1 10.00 25.00
MV Mo Vaughn HR2 6.00 15.00
MW Matt Williams HR2 6.00 15.00
PM Pedro Martinez H1 10.00 25.00
RJ Randy Johnson HR2 15.00 40.00
RV Robin Ventura HR2 6.00 15.00
SA Sandy Alomar Jr. HR2 6.00 15.00
TG Tony Gwynn HR2 15.00 40.00
TH Todd Helton HR1 10.00 25.00
TH Todd Helton HR2 10.00 25.00
VG Vladimir Guerrero HR1 15.00 40.00
TGL Tom Glavine HR2 10.00 25.00
TRG Troy Glaus H1 6.00 15.00
TRG Troy Glaus HR2 6.00 15.00

2000 Upper Deck Game Jersey Autograph

Randomly inserted into Upper Deck Series two hobby packs, this insert set features autographed game-used jersey cards from some of the hottest players in major league baseball. Card backs carry an "H" prefix. A few autographs were not available in packs and had to be exchanged for signed cards. These cards had to be returned to Upper Deck by March 6th, 2001.

HAR A.Rodriguez 100.00 175.00
HBB Barry Bonds 60.00 120.00
HCR Cal Ripken 75.00 150.00
HDJ Derek Jeter 150.00 250.00
HIR I.Rodriguez AU H2 40.00 80.00
HJB Jeff Bagwell 40.00 80.00
HJC Jose Canseco 15.00 40.00
HJK Jason Kendall 15.00 40.00
HKG K.Griffey Jr. Reds 75.00 150.00
HMR Manny Ramirez 30.00 60.00
HPO Paul O'Neill 20.00 50.00
HSR Scott Rolen 20.00 50.00
HVG Vladimir Guerrero 20.00 50.00

2000 Upper Deck Game Jersey Autograph Numbered

Randomly inserted into Upper Deck hobby packs, this insert set features autographed game-used jersey cards of the hottest players in baseball. Please note that these cards are hand-numbered on front in blue ink sharpie pen to the depicted players jersey number. Due to scarcity, some of these cards are not priced. A few cards were available via exchange: Series one exchange cards had to be redeemed by July 15th, 2000 while series two exchange cards were to be redeemed by March 6th, 2001. Cards tagged with an H1 or H2 suffix in the description were distributed exclusively in first and second series hobby packs. Cards tagged with an HR1 or HR2 suffix were distributed in hobby and retail packs. The "hobby-only" cards carry an "HN" prefix for the numbering on the back of each card (i.e. Scott Rolen is HN-SR). In addition, each of these cards features a congratulations from UD President Richard McWilliams with the reference to the card being "crash numbered". These two differences make these scarce numbered inserts easy to legitimize against possible fakes whereby unscrupulous players may have numbered the cards themselves on front (not very tough to do given the cards were hand-numbered by UD). Unfortunately, the hobby-retail cards do not carry these key differences in design. It's believed that these Numbered inserts feature a gold hologram on back (lower left corner) rather than the silver hologram featured on the more common non-Numbered Game Jersey Autograph cards. Nonetheless, buyers are encouraged to exercise extreme caution for fakes when purchasing the hobby-retail versions of these cards.

AJ Andruw Jones/25 H2
AR Alex Rodriguez/3 HR1
BB Barry Bonds/25 H2
BG Ben Grieve /14 HR2
CR Cal Ripken/8 H2
DJ Derek Jeter/2 HR1
EM Edgar Martinez /11 HR2
FT Frank Thomas/35 HR2 75.00 150.00
GM Greg Maddux/31 HR2 175.00 300.00
IR Ivan Rodriguez/7 H2
JB Jeff Bagwell/5 H2
JC Jose Canseco/33 H2 50.00 100.00
JK Jason Kendall/18 H2
JR K.Griffey Jr./24 H1 EX
KG K.Griffey Jr. Reds/30 H2 250.00 500.00
MH Mike Hampton/10 HR2
MR Manny Ramirez/24 H1
MR M.Ramirez/24 H2 EX
MV Mo Vaughn/42 HR2 30.00 60.00
MW Matt Williams/9 HR2
PO Paul O'Neill/21 H2
RJ R.Johnson/51 HR2 125.00 200.00
SR Scott Rolen/17 H2
TG Tony Gwynn/19 HR2
VG V.Guerrero/27 HR2 150.00 250.00
TGl Tom Glavine/47 HR2 50.00 100.00
TRG Troy Glaus/14 HR2

2000 Upper Deck Game Jersey Patch

Randomly inserted into series one packs at one in 10,000 and series two packs at a rate of 1:7500, these cards feature game-worn uniform patches.

1 OF 1 PATCH PRINT RUN 1 SERIAL #'d SET
NO 1 OF 1 PATCH PRICING AVAILABLE
PAJ Andruw Jones 2 50.00 100.00
PAR Alex Rodriguez 1 75.00 150.00
PAR Alex Rodriguez 2 75.00 150.00
PBB Barry Bonds 2 100.00 200.00
PBG Ben Grieve 2 20.00 50.00
PCJ Chipper Jones 1 50.00 100.00
PCR Cal Ripken 1 75.00 150.00
PCR Cal Ripken 2 75.00 150.00
PCY Tom Glavine 1 50.00 100.00
PDC David Cone 30.00 60.00
PDJ Derek Jeter 1 75.00 150.00
PDJ Derek Jeter 2 75.00 150.00
PEC Eric Chavez 1 30.00 60.00
PFT Frank Thomas 1 50.00 100.00
PGK Gabe Kapler 1 30.00 60.00
PGM Greg Maddux 1 60.00 120.00
PGM Greg Maddux 2 60.00 120.00
PGV Greg Vaughn 1 20.00 50.00
PIR Ivan Rodriguez 2 50.00 100.00
PJB Jeff Bagwell 1 50.00 100.00
PJC Jose Canseco 1 50.00 100.00
PJR Ken Griffey Jr. 1 75.00 150.00
PKG K.Griffey Jr. Reds 2 75.00 150.00
PMP Mike Piazza 1 60.00 120.00
PMR Manny Ramirez 1 50.00 100.00
PMR Manny Ramirez 2 50.00 100.00
PMV Mo Vaughn 2 30.00 60.00
PMW Matt Williams 2 30.00 60.00
PPM Pedro Martinez 1 50.00 100.00
PRJ Randy Johnson 2 50.00 100.00
PSR Scott Rolen 2 50.00 100.00
PTG Tony Gwynn 2 50.00 100.00
PTH Todd Helton 1 50.00 100.00
PTRG Troy Glaus 1 30.00 60.00
PTRG Troy Glaus 2 30.00 60.00
PVG Vladimir Guerrero 1 60.00 120.00
PVG Vladimir Guerrero 2 60.00 120.00

2000 Upper Deck Hit Brigade

Inserted into first series packs at a rate of one in eight, these 15 cards feature some of the best hitters. These cards are printed in etched foil.

COMPLETE SET (15) 12.50 30.00
*DIE CUTS: 6X TO 15X BASIC HIT BRIGADE
DIE CUTS PRINT RUN 100 SERIAL #'d SETS
GOLD DIE CUT PRINT RUN 1 SERIAL #'d SET
GOLD DC NOT PRICED DUE TO SCARCITY
H1 Ken Griffey Jr. 1.00 2.50
H2 Tony Gwynn .75 2.00
H3 Alex Rodriguez 1.00 2.50
H4 Derek Jeter 1.50 4.00
H5 Mike Piazza 1.00 2.50
H6 Sammy Sosa .60 1.50
H7 Juan Gonzalez .25 .60
H8 Scott Rolen .40 1.00
H9 Nomar Garciaparra 1.00 2.50
H10 Barry Bonds 1.50 4.00
H11 Craig Biggio .40 1.00
H12 Chipper Jones .60 1.50
H13 Frank Thomas .60 1.50
H14 Larry Walker .25 .60
H15 Mark McGwire 1.50 4.00

2000 Upper Deck Hot Properties

Randomly inserted into Upper Deck series two packs at one in 11, this 15-card insert features the major league's top prospects. Card backs carry a "HP" prefix.

COMPLETE SET (15) 5.00 12.00
HP1 Carlos Beltran .30 .75
HP2 Rick Ankiel .30 .75
HP3 Sean Casey .30 .75
HP4 Preston Wilson .30 .75
HP5 Vernon Wells .50 1.25
HP6 Pat Burrell .30 .75
HP7 Eric Chavez .30 .75
HP8 J.D. Drew .30 .75
HP9 Alfonso Soriano 1.25 3.00
HP10 Gabe Kapler .30 .75
HP11 Rafael Furcal .50 1.25
HP12 Ruben Mateo .30 .75
HP13 Corey Koskie .20 .50
HP14 Kip Wells .30 .75
HP15 Ramon Ortiz .30 .75

2000 Upper Deck Legendary Cuts

Randomly inserted into Upper Deck series two packs, this eight-card insert features cut-signatures from some of the all-time great players of the 20th Century. Please note that only one set was produced of this insert.

1 Cap Anson
2 Roberto Clemente
3 Ty Cobb
4 Eddie Collins
5 Nap Lajoie
6 Tris Speaker
7 Honus Wagner
8 Paul Waner

2000 Upper Deck Pennant Driven

Randomly inserted into packs at one in four, this 10-card insert features players that are driven to win the pennant. Card backs carry a "PD" prefix.

COMPLETE SET (10) 4.00 10.00
PD1 Derek Jeter .75 2.00
PD2 Roberto Alomar .20 .50
PD3 Chipper Jones .30 .75
PD4 Jeff Bagwell .20 .50
PD5 Roger Clemens .60 1.50
PD6 Nomar Garciaparra .50 1.25
PD7 Manny Ramirez .20 .50
PD8 Mike Piazza .50 1.25
PD9 Ivan Rodriguez .20 .50
PD10 Randy Johnson .30 .75

2000 Upper Deck People's Choice

Randomly inserted into second series packs at one in 23, this 15-card set features players that people have voted as their favorites to watch. Card backs carry a "PC" prefix.

COMPLETE SET (15) 40.00 100.00
PC1 Mark McGwire 4.00 10.00
PC2 Nomar Garciaparra 2.50 6.00
PC3 Derek Jeter 4.00 10.00
PC4 Shawn Green .60 1.50
PC5 Manny Ramirez 1.00 2.50
PC6 Pedro Martinez 1.00 2.50
PC7 Ivan Rodriguez 1.00 2.50
PC8 Alex Rodriguez 2.50 6.00
PC9 Juan Gonzalez .60 1.50
PC10 Ken Griffey Jr. 2.50 6.00
PC11 Sammy Sosa 1.50 4.00
PC12 Jeff Bagwell 1.00 2.50
PC13 Chipper Jones 1.50 4.00
PC14 Cal Ripken 5.00 12.00
PC15 Mike Piazza 2.50 6.00

2000 Upper Deck Power MARK

Inserted one every 23 first series packs, these 10 cards all feature Mark McGwire.

COMPLETE SET (10) 25.00 50.00
COMMON (MC1-MC10) 2.50 6.00
*DIE CUTS: 3X TO 8X BASIC POWER MARK
DIE CUTS PRINT RUN 100 SERIAL #'d SETS
GOLD DIE CUT PRINT RUN 1 SERIAL #'d SET
GOLD DC NOT PRICED DUE TO SCARCITY

2000 Upper Deck Power Rally

Inserted one every 11 first series packs, these 15 cards feature baseball's leading power hitters.

COMPLETE SET (15) 15.00 40.00
*DIE CUTS: 5X TO 12X BASIC POWER RALLY
DIE CUTS PRINT RUN 100 SERIAL #'d SETS
GOLD DIE CUT PRINT RUN 1 SERIAL #'d SET
GOLD DC NOT PRICED DUE TO SCARCITY
P1 Ken Griffey Jr. 1.25 3.00
P2 Mark McGwire 2.00 5.00
P3 Sammy Sosa .75 2.00
P4 Jose Canseco .50 1.25
P5 Juan Gonzalez .30 .75
P6 Bernie Williams .50 1.25
P7 Jeff Bagwell .50 1.25
P8 Chipper Jones .75 2.00
P9 Vladimir Guerrero .75 2.00
P10 Mo Vaughn .30 .75
P11 Derek Jeter 2.00 5.00
P12 Mike Piazza 1.25 3.00
P13 Barry Bonds 2.00 5.00
P14 Alex Rodriguez 1.25 3.00
P15 Nomar Garciaparra 1.25 3.00

2000 Upper Deck PowerDeck Inserts

These CD's were inserted into packs at two different rates. PD1 through PD 8 were inserted at a rate of one every 23 packs while PD9 through PD 11 were inserted at a rate of one every 287 packs. Due to problems at the manufacturer, the Alex Rodriguez CD was not inserted into the first series packs so a collector could acquire one of those by sending in a UPC code on the bottom of the 2000 Upper Deck first series boxes. Also, some of the 1999 Upper Deck PowerDeck CD's were mistakenly inserted into this product. Those CD's are priced under the 1999 Upper Deck PowerDeck listings. Finally, Ken Griffey Jr., Reggie Jackson and Mark McGwire have all been confirmed as short prints by representatives at Upper Deck.

COMPLETE SET (11) 60.00 120.00
PD1 Ken Griffey Jr. 2.50 6.00
PD2 Cal Ripken 5.00 12.00
PD3 Mark McGwire 4.00 10.00
PD4 Tony Gwynn 2.00 5.00
PD5 Roger Clemens 3.00 8.00
PD6 Alex Rodriguez 3.00 8.00
PD7 Sammy Sosa 1.50 4.00
PD8 Derek Jeter 4.00 10.00
PD9 Ken Griffey Jr. SP 6.00 15.00
PD10 Mark McGwire SP 10.00 25.00
PD11 Reggie Jackson SP 6.00 15.00

2000 Upper Deck Prime Performers

Randomly inserted into series two packs at one in eight, this 10-card insert features players that are prime performers. Card backs carry a "PP" prefix.

COMPLETE SET (10) 5.00 12.00
PP1 Manny Ramirez .25 .60
PP2 Pedro Martinez .25 .60
PP3 Carlos Delgado .15 .40
PP4 Ken Griffey Jr. .60 1.50
PP5 Derek Jeter 1.00 2.50
PP6 Chipper Jones .40 1.00
PP7 Sean Casey .15 .40
PP8 Shawn Green .15 .40
PP9 Sammy Sosa .40 1.00
PP10 Alex Rodriguez .60 1.50

2000 Upper Deck Statitude

Inserted one every four packs, these 30 cards feature some of the most statistically dominant players in baseball.

COMPLETE SET (30) 15.00 40.00
*DIE CUTS: 6X TO 15X BASIC STATITUDE
DIE CUTS PRINT RUN 100 SERIAL #'d SETS
GOLD DIE CUT PRINT RUN 1 SERIAL #'d SET
GOLD DC NOT PRICED DUE TO SCARCITY
S1 Mo Vaughn .25 .60
S2 Matt Williams .25 .60
S3 Travis Lee .25 .60
S4 Chipper Jones .60 1.50
S5 Greg Maddux 1.00 2.50
S6 Gabe Kapler .25 .60
S7 Cal Ripken 2.00 5.00
S8 Nomar Garciaparra 1.00 2.50
S9 Sammy Sosa .60 1.50
S10 Frank Thomas .60 1.50
S11 Manny Ramirez .40 1.00
S12 Larry Walker .25 .60
S13 Ivan Rodriguez .40 1.00
S14 Jeff Bagwell .40 1.00
S15 Craig Biggio .40 1.00
S16 Vladimir Guerrero .60 1.50
S17 Mike Piazza 1.00 2.50
S18 Bernie Williams .40 1.00
S19 Derek Jeter 1.50 4.00
S20 Jose Canseco .40 1.00
S21 Eric Chavez .25 .60
S22 Scott Rolen .40 1.00
S23 Mark McGwire 1.50 4.00
S24 Tony Gwynn .75 2.00
S25 Barry Bonds 1.50 4.00
S26 Ken Griffey Jr. 1.00 2.50
S27 Alex Rodriguez 1.00 2.50
S28 J.D. Drew .25 .60
S29 Juan Gonzalez .25 .60
S30 Roger Clemens 1.25 3.00

2001 Upper Deck

The 2001 Upper Deck Series one product was released in November, 2000 and featured a 270-card base set. Series two (entitled Mid-Summer Classic) was released in June, 2001 and featured a 180-card base set. The complete set is broken into subsets as follows: Star Rookies (1-45/271-300), basic cards (46-261/301-444), and Season Highlight checklists (262-270/445-450). Each pack contained 8-cards and carried a suggested retail price of $2.99. Key Rookie Cards in the set include Albert Pujols and Ichiro Suzuki. Also, a selection of A Piece of History 3000 Club Eddie Murray and Cal Ripken memorabilia cards were randomly seeded into series one packs. 350 bat cards, 350 jersey cards and 100 hand-numbered, combination bat-jersey cards were produced for each player. In addition, thirty-three autographed, hand-numbered, combination bat-jersey Eddie Murray cards and eight autographed, hand-numbered, combination bat-jersey Cal Ripken cards were produced. The Ripken Bat, Ripken Bat-Jsy Combo and Murray Bat-Jsy Combo Autograph were all exchange cards. The deadline to send in the exchange cards was August 22nd, 2001. Pricing for these memorabilia cards can be referenced under 2000 Upper Deck A Piece of History 3000 Club.

COMPLETE SET (450) 90.00 150.00
COMP. SERIES 1 (270) 20.00 40.00
COMP. SERIES 2 (180) 60.00 100.00
COMMON (46-270/300-450) .10 .30
COMMON SR (1-45) .20 .50
1 Jeff DaVanon SR .20 .50
2 Aubrey Huff SR .20 .50
3 Pasqual Coco SR .20 .50
4 Barry Zito SR .25 .60
5 Augie Ojeda SR .20 .50
6 Chris Richard SR .20 .50
7 Josh Phelps SR .20 .50
8 Kevin Nicholson SR .20 .50
9 Juan Guzman SR .20 .50
10 Brandon Kolb SR .20 .50
11 Johan Santana SR 2.50 6.00
12 Josh Kalinowski SR .20 .50
13 Tike Redman SR .20 .50
14 Ivanon Coffie SR .20 .50
15 Chad Durbin SR .20 .50
16 Derrick Turnbow SR .20 .50
17 Scott Downs SR .20 .50
18 Jason Grilli SR .20 .50
19 Mark Buehrle SR .25 .60
20 Paxton Crawford SR .20 .50
21 Bronson Arroyo SR .40 1.00
22 Tomas De la Rosa SR .20 .50
23 Paul Rigdon SR .20 .50
24 Rob Ramsay SR .20 .50
25 Damian Rolls SR .20 .50
26 Jason Conti SR .20 .50
27 John Parrish SR .20 .50
28 Geraldo Guzman SR .20 .50
29 Tony Mota SR .20 .50
30 Luis Rivas SR .20 .50
31 Brian Tollberg SR .20 .50
32 Adam Bernero SR .20 .50
33 Michael Cuddyer SR .20 .50
34 Josue Espada SR .20 .50
35 Joe Lawrence SR .20 .50
36 Chad Moeller SR .20 .50
37 Nick Bierbrodt SR .20 .50
38 DeWayne Wise SR .20 .50
39 Javier Cardona SR .20 .50
40 Hiram Bocachica SR .20 .50
41 G.Chiaramonte SR .20 .50
42 Alex Cabrera SR .20 .50
43 Jimmy Rollins SR .20 .50
44 Pat Flury SR RC .20 .50
45 Leo Estrella SR .20 .50
46 Darin Erstad .10 .30
47 Seth Etherton .10 .30
48 Troy Glaus .10 .30
49 Brian Cooper .10 .30
50 Tim Salmon .20 .50
51 Adam Kennedy .10 .30
52 Bengie Molina .10 .30
53 Jason Giambi .10 .30
54 Miguel Tejada .10 .30
55 Tim Hudson .10 .30
56 Eric Chavez .10 .30
57 Terrence Long .10 .30
58 Jason Isringhausen .10 .30
59 Ramon Hernandez .10 .30
60 Raul Mondesi .10 .30
61 David Wells .10 .30
62 Shannon Stewart .10 .30
63 Tony Batista .10 .30
64 Brad Fullmer .10 .30
65 Chris Carpenter .10 .30
66 Homer Bush .10 .30
67 Gerald Williams .10 .30
68 Miguel Cairo .10 .30
69 Ryan Rupe .10 .30
70 Greg Vaughn .10 .30
71 John Flaherty .10 .30
72 Dan Wheeler .10 .30
73 Fred McGriff .20 .50
74 Roberto Alomar .20 .50
75 Bartolo Colon .10 .30
76 Kenny Lofton .10 .30
77 David Segui .10 .30
78 Omar Vizquel .20 .50
79 Russ Branyan .10 .30
80 Chuck Finley .10 .30
81 Manny Ramirez UER .20 .50
Back photo is of David Segui
82 Alex Rodriguez .50 1.25
83 John Halama .10 .30
84 Mike Cameron .10 .30
85 David Bell .10 .30
86 Jay Buhner .10 .30
87 Aaron Sele .10 .30
88 Rickey Henderson .30 .75
89 Brook Fordyce .10 .30
90 Cal Ripken 1.00 2.50
91 Mike Mussina .20 .50
92 Delino DeShields .10 .30
93 Melvin Mora .10 .30
94 Sidney Ponson .10 .30
95 Brady Anderson .10 .30
96 Ivan Rodriguez .20 .50
97 Ricky Ledee .10 .30
98 Rick Helling .10 .30
99 Ruben Mateo .10 .30
100 Luis Alicea .10 .30
101 John Wetteland .10 .30
102 Mike Lamb .10 .30
103 Carl Everett .10 .30
104 Troy O'Leary .10 .30
105 Wilton Veras .10 .30
106 Pedro Martinez UER .20 .50
Birthdate is incorrect
107 Rolando Arrojo .10 .30
108 Scott Hatteberg .10 .30
109 Jason Varitek .30 .75
110 Jose Offerman .10 .30
111 Carlos Beltran .10 .30
112 Johnny Damon .20 .50
113 Mark Quinn .10 .30
114 Rey Sanchez .10 .30
115 Mac Suzuki .10 .30
116 Jermaine Dye .10 .30
117 Chris Fussell .10 .30
118 Jeff Weaver .10 .30
119 Dean Palmer .10 .30
120 Robert Fick .10 .30
121 Brian Moehler .10 .30
122 Damion Easley .10 .30
123 Juan Encarnacion .10 .30
124 Tony Clark .10 .30
125 Cristian Guzman .10 .30
126 Matt LeCroy .10 .30
127 Eric Milton .10 .30
128 Jay Canizaro .10 .30
129 David Ortiz .30 .75

130 Brad Radke	.10	.30
131 Jacque Jones	.10	.30
132 Magglio Ordonez	.10	.30
133 Carlos Lee	.10	.30
134 Mike Sirotka	.10	.30
135 Ray Durham	.10	.30
136 Paul Konerko	.10	.30
137 Charles Johnson	.10	.30
138 James Baldwin	.10	.30
139 Jeff Abbott	.10	.30
140 Roger Clemens	.60	1.50
141 Derek Jeter	.75	2.00
142 David Justice	.10	.30
143 Ramiro Mendoza	.10	.30
144 Chuck Knoblauch	.10	.30
145 Orlando Hernandez	.10	.30
146 Alfonso Soriano	.20	.50
147 Jeff Bagwell	.20	.50
148 Julio Lugo	.10	.30
149 Mitch Meluskey	.10	.30
150 Jose Lima	.10	.30
151 Richard Hidalgo	.10	.30
152 Moises Alou	.10	.30
153 Scott Elarton	.10	.30
154 Andruw Jones	.20	.50
155 Quilvio Veras	.10	.30
156 Greg Maddux	.50	1.25
157 Brian Jordan	.10	.30
158 Andres Galarraga	.10	.30
159 Kevin Millwood	.10	.30
160 Rafael Furcal	.10	.30
161 Jeromy Burnitz	.10	.30
162 Jimmy Haynes	.10	.30
163 Mark Loretta	.10	.30
164 Ron Belliard	.10	.30
165 Richie Sexson	.10	.30
166 Kevin Barker	.10	.30
167 Jeff D'Amico	.10	.30
168 Rick Ankiel	.10	.30
169 Mark McGwire	.75	2.00
170 J.D. Drew	.10	.30
171 Eli Marrero	.10	.30
172 Darryl Kile	.10	.30
173 Edgar Renteria	.10	.30
174 Will Clark	.20	.50
175 Eric Young	.10	.30
176 Mark Grace	.20	.50
177 Jon Lieber	.10	.30
178 Damon Buford	.10	.30
179 Kerry Wood	.10	.30
180 Rondell White	.10	.30
181 Joe Girardi	.10	.30
182 Curt Schilling	.10	.30
183 Randy Johnson	.30	.75
184 Steve Finley	.10	.30
185 Kelly Stinnett	.10	.30
186 Jay Bell	.10	.30
187 Matt Mantei	.10	.30
188 Luis Gonzalez	.10	.30
189 Shawn Green	.10	.30
190 Todd Hundley	.10	.30
191 Chan Ho Park	.10	.30
192 Adrian Beltre	.10	.30
193 Mark Grudzielanek	.10	.30
194 Gary Sheffield	.10	.30
195 Tom Goodwin	.10	.30
196 Lee Stevens	.10	.30
197 Javier Vazquez	.10	.30
198 Milton Bradley	.10	.30
199 Vladimir Guerrero	.30	.75
200 Carl Pavano	.10	.30
201 Orlando Cabrera	.10	.30
202 Tony Armas Jr.	.10	.30
203 Jeff Kent	.10	.30
204 Calvin Murray	.10	.30
205 Ellis Burks	.10	.30
206 Barry Bonds	.75	2.00
207 Russ Ortiz	.10	.30
208 Marvin Benard	.10	.30
209 Joe Nathan	.10	.30
210 Preston Wilson	.10	.30
211 Cliff Floyd	.10	.30
212 Mike Lowell	.10	.30
213 Ryan Dempster	.10	.30
214 Brad Penny	.10	.30
215 Mike Redmond	.10	.30
216 Luis Castillo	.10	.30
217 Derek Bell	.10	.30
218 Mike Hampton	.10	.30
219 Todd Zeile	.10	.30
220 Robin Ventura	.10	.30
221 Mike Piazza	.50	1.25
222 Al Leiter	.10	.30
223 Edgardo Alfonzo	.10	.30
224 Mike Bordick	.10	.30
225 Phil Nevin	.10	.30
226 Ryan Klesko	.10	.30
227 Adam Eaton	.10	.30
228 Eric Owens	.10	.30
229 Tony Gwynn	.40	1.00
230 Matt Clement	.10	.30
231 Wiki Gonzalez	.10	.30
232 Robert Person	.10	.30
233 Doug Glanville	.10	.30
234 Scott Rolen	.20	.50
235 Mike Lieberthal	.10	.30
236 Randy Wolf	.10	.30
237 Bob Abreu	.10	.30
238 Pat Burrell	.10	.30
239 Bruce Chen	.10	.30
240 Kevin Young	.10	.30
241 Todd Ritchie	.10	.30
242 Adrian Brown	.10	.30
243 Chad Hermansen	.10	.30
244 Warren Morris	.10	.30
245 Kris Benson	.10	.30
246 Jason Kendall	.10	.30
247 Pokey Reese	.10	.30
248 Rob Bell	.10	.30
249 Ken Griffey Jr.	.50	1.25
250 Sean Casey	.10	.30
251 Aaron Boone	.10	.30
252 Pete Harnisch	.10	.30
253 Barry Larkin	.20	.50
254 Dmitri Young	.10	.30
255 Todd Hollandsworth	.10	.30
256 Pedro Astacio	.10	.30
257 Todd Helton	.20	.50
258 Terry Shumpert	.10	.30
259 Neifi Perez	.10	.30
260 Jeffrey Hammonds	.10	.30
261 Ben Petrick	.10	.30
262 Mark McGwire SH	.40	1.00
263 Derek Jeter SH	.40	1.00
264 Sammy Sosa SH	.20	.50
265 Cal Ripken SH	.50	1.25
266 Pedro Martinez SH	.20	.50
267 Barry Bonds SH	.40	1.00
268 Fred McGriff SH	.10	.30
269 Randy Johnson SH	.20	.50
270 Darin Erstad SH	.10	.30
271 Ichiro Suzuki SR RC	5.00	12.00
272 W. Betemit SR RC	.75	2.00
273 Corey Patterson SR	.20	.50
274 Sean Douglass SR RC	.20	.50
275 Mike Penney SR RC	.20	.50
276 Nate Teut SR RC	.20	.50
277 R. Rodriguez SR RC	.20	.50
278 B. Duckworth SR RC	.20	.50
279 Rafael Soriano SR RC	.20	.50
280 Juan Diaz SR RC	.20	.50
281 H. Ramirez SR RC	.25	.60
282 T. Shinjo SR RC	.25	.60
283 Keith Ginter SR	.20	.50
284 Esix Snead SR RC	.20	.50
285 Erick Almonte SR RC	.20	.50
286 Travis Hafner SR RC	2.00	5.00
287 Jason Smith SR RC	.20	.50
288 J. Melian SR RC	.20	.50
289 Tyler Walker SR RC	.20	.50
290 Jason Standridge SR	.20	.50
291 Juan Uribe SR RC	.25	.60
292 A. Hernandez SR RC	.20	.50
293 J. Michaels SR RC	.20	.50
294 Jason Hart SR	.20	.50
295 Albert Pujols SR RC	30.00	60.00
296 M. Ensberg SR RC	.75	2.00
297 Brandon Inge SR	.20	.50
298 Jesus Colome SR	.20	.50
299 K. Kessel SR RC UER	.20	.50
L Missing from MLB experience		
300 Timo Perez SR	.20	.50
301 Mo Vaughn	.10	.30
302 Ismael Valdes	.10	.30
303 Glenallen Hill	.10	.30
304 Garret Anderson	.10	.30
305 Johnny Damon	.20	.50
306 Jose Ortiz	.10	.30
307 Mark Mulder	.10	.30
308 Adam Piatt	.10	.30
309 Gil Heredia	.10	.30
310 Mike Sirotka	.10	.30
311 Carlos Delgado	.10	.30
312 Alex Gonzalez	.10	.30
313 Jose Cruz Jr.	.10	.30
314 Darrin Fletcher	.10	.30
315 Ben Grieve	.10	.30
316 Vinny Castilla	.10	.30
317 Wilson Alvarez	.10	.30
318 Brent Abernathy	.10	.30
319 Ellis Burks	.10	.30
320 Jim Thome	.20	.50
321 Juan Gonzalez	.10	.30
322 Ed Taubensee	.10	.30
323 Travis Fryman	.10	.30
324 John Olerud	.10	.30
325 Edgar Martinez	.20	.50
326 Freddy Garcia	.10	.30
327 Bret Boone	.20	.50
328 Kazuhiro Sasaki	.10	.30
329 Albert Belle	.10	.30
330 Mike Bordick	.10	.30
331 David Segui	.10	.30
332 Pat Hentgen	.10	.30
333 Alex Rodriguez	.50	1.25
334 Andres Galarraga	.10	.30
335 Gabe Kapler	.10	.30
336 Ken Caminiti	.10	.30
337 Rafael Palmeiro	.20	.50
338 Manny Ramirez Sox	.20	.50
339 David Cone	.10	.30
340 Nomar Garciaparra	.50	1.25
341 Trot Nixon	.10	.30
342 Derek Lowe	.10	.30
343 Roberto Hernandez	.10	.30
344 Mike Sweeney	.10	.30
345 Carlos Febles	.10	.30
346 Jeff Suppan	.10	.30
347 Roger Cedeno	.10	.30
348 Bobby Higginson	.10	.30
349 Deivi Cruz	.10	.30
350 Mitch Meluskey	.10	.30
351 Matt Lawton	.10	.30
352 Mark Redman	.10	.30
353 Jay Canizaro	.10	.30
354 Corey Koskie	.10	.30
355 Matt Kinney	.10	.30
356 Frank Thomas	.30	.75
357 Sandy Alomar Jr.	.10	.30
358 David Wells	.10	.30
359 Jim Parque	.10	.30
360 Chris Singleton	.10	.30
361 Tino Martinez	.20	.50
362 Paul O'Neill	.20	.50
363 Mike Mussina	.20	.50
364 Bernie Williams	.20	.50
365 Andy Pettitte	.20	.50
366 Mariano Rivera	.30	.75
367 Brad Ausmus	.10	.30
368 Craig Biggio	.20	.50
369 Lance Berkman	.10	.30
370 Shane Reynolds	.10	.30
371 Chipper Jones	.30	.75
372 Tom Glavine	.20	.50
373 B.J. Surhoff	.10	.30
374 John Smoltz	.20	.50
375 Rico Brogna	.10	.30
376 Geoff Jenkins	.10	.30
377 Jose Hernandez	.10	.30
378 Tyler Houston	.10	.30
379 Henry Blanco	.10	.30
380 Jeffrey Hammonds	.10	.30
381 Jim Edmonds	.10	.30
382 Fernando Vina	.10	.30
383 Andy Benes	.10	.30
384 Ray Lankford	.10	.30
385 Dustin Hermanson	.10	.30
386 Todd Hundley	.10	.30
387 Sammy Sosa	.30	.75
388 Tom Gordon	.10	.30
389 Bill Mueller	.10	.30
390 Ron Coomer	.10	.30
391 Matt Stairs	.10	.30
392 Mark Grace	.20	.50
393 Matt Williams	.10	.30
394 Todd Stottlemyre	.10	.30
395 Tony Womack	.10	.30
396 Erubiel Durazo	.10	.30
397 Reggie Sanders	.10	.30
398 Andy Ashby	.10	.30
399 Eric Karros	.10	.30
400 Kevin Brown	.10	.30
401 Darren Dreifort	.10	.30
402 Fernando Tatis	.10	.30
403 Jose Vidro	.10	.30
404 Peter Bergeron	.10	.30
405 Geoff Blum	.10	.30
406 J.T. Snow	.10	.30
407 Livan Hernandez	.10	.30
408 Robb Nen	.10	.30
409 Bobby Estalella	.10	.30
410 Rich Aurilia	.10	.30
411 Eric Davis	.10	.30
412 Charles Johnson	.10	.30
413 Alex Gonzalez	.10	.30
414 A.J. Burnett	.10	.30
415 Antonio Alfonseca	.10	.30
416 Derrek Lee	.20	.50
417 Jay Payton	.10	.30
418 Kevin Appier	.10	.30
419 Steve Trachsel	.10	.30
420 Rey Ordonez	.10	.30
421 Darryl Hamilton	.10	.30
422 Ben Davis	.10	.30
423 Damian Jackson	.10	.30
424 Mark Kotsay	.10	.30
425 Trevor Hoffman	.10	.30
426 Travis Lee	.10	.30
427 Omar Daal	.10	.30
428 Paul Byrd	.10	.30
429 Reggie Taylor	.10	.30
430 Brian Giles	.10	.30
431 Derek Bell	.10	.30
432 Francisco Cordova	.10	.30
433 Pat Meares	.10	.30
434 Scott Williamson	.10	.30
435 Jason LaRue	.10	.30
436 Michael Tucker	.10	.30
437 Wilton Guerrero	.10	.30
438 Mike Hampton	.10	.30
439 Ron Gant	.10	.30
440 Jeff Cirillo	.10	.30
441 Denny Neagle	.10	.30
442 Larry Walker	.10	.30
443 Juan Pierre	.10	.30
444 Todd Walker	.10	.30
445 Jason Giambi SH CL	.10	.30
446 Jeff Kent SH CL	.10	.30
447 Mariano Rivera SH CL	.20	.50
448 Edgar Martinez SH CL	.10	.30
449 Troy Glaus SH CL	.10	.30
450 Alex Rodriguez SH CL	.30	.75

2001 Upper Deck Exclusives Gold

Randomly inserted into series one packs, this 270-card set is a complete parallel of the 2001 Upper Deck series one base set. Please note that these cards were produced with gold lettering on the front and are individually serial numbered to 25. The words "Gold UD Exclusives" also run down the left side of each card front.

*STARS: 30X TO 80X BASIC CARDS
*SR STARS: 15X TO 40X BASIC SR
*SR ROOKIES: 15X TO 40X BASIC SR

11 Johan Santana SR	20.00	50.00

2001 Upper Deck Exclusives Silver

Randomly inserted into series one packs, this 270-card set is a complete parallel of the 2001 Upper Deck series one base set. Please note that these cards were produced with silver lettering on the front and are individually serial numbered to 100. The words "UD Exclusives" also run down the left side of each card front.

STARS: 12.5X TO 30X BASIC CARDS
*SR YNG.STARS: 6X TO 15X BASIC
*SR RC's: 6X TO 15X BASIC SR

11 Johan Santana SR	8.00	20.00

2001 Upper Deck 1971 All-Star Game Salute

Inserted in second series packs at a rate of one in 288, these 12 memorabilia cards feature players who participated in the 1971 All-Star Game which was highlighted by Reggie Jackson's home run off the light tower at Tiger Stadium.

ASBR B. Robinson Bat	8.00	20.00
ASFR Frank Robinson Jsy	6.00	15.00
ASHA Hank Aaron Bat	15.00	40.00
ASHA Hank Aaron Jsy	20.00	50.00
ASJB Johnny Bench Bat	8.00	20.00
ASJB Johnny Bench Jsy	8.00	20.00
ASLA Luis Aparicio Jsy	6.00	15.00
ASLB Lou Brock Bat	8.00	20.00
ASRC R. Clemente Jsy	50.00	100.00
ASRJ Reggie Jackson Jsy	8.00	20.00
ASTM T. Munson Jsy	15.00	40.00
ASTS Tom Seaver Jsy	8.00	20.00

2001 Upper Deck All-Star Heroes Memorabilia

Randomly inserted in second series packs, these 14 cards feature a mix of past and present players who have starred in All-Star Games. Since each player was issued to a different amount, we have notated that information in our checklist.

ASHAR Alex Rodriguez Bat/1998	6.00	15.00
ASHBR Babe Ruth Bat/1933	100.00	200.00
ASHCR Cal Ripken Bat/1991	15.00	40.00
ASHDJ Derek Jeter Base/2000	10.00	25.00
ASHJD Joe DiMaggio Jsy/36		
ASHKG Ken Griffey Jr. Bat/1992	6.00	15.00
ASHMM Mickey Mantle Jsy/54	175.00	300.00
ASHMP Mike Piazza Base/1996	6.00	15.00
ASHRC Roger Clemens Jsy/1986	6.00	15.00
ASHRJ Randy Johnson Jsy/1993	6.00	15.00
ASHSS Sammy Sosa Jsy/2000	6.00	15.00
ASHTG Tony Gwynn Jsy/1994	6.00	15.00
ASHTP Tony Perez Bat 1967	4.00	10.00
ASHROC R.Clemente Bat/1961	40.00	80.00

2001 Upper Deck Big League Beat

Randomly inserted into packs at one in three, this 20-card insert features some of the most prolific players in the Major Leagues. Card backs carry a "BB" prefix.

COMPLETE SET (20)	8.00	20.00
BB1 Barry Bonds	.75	2.00
BB2 Nomar Garciaparra	.50	1.25
BB3 Mark McGwire	.75	2.00
BB4 Roger Clemens	.60	1.50
BB5 Chipper Jones	.30	.75
BB6 Jeff Bagwell	.20	.50
BB7 Sammy Sosa	.30	.75
BB8 Cal Ripken	1.00	2.50
BB9 Randy Johnson	.30	.75
BB10 Carlos Delgado	.20	.50
BB11 Manny Ramirez	.20	.50
BB12 Derek Jeter	.75	2.00
BB13 Tony Gwynn	.40	1.00
BB14 Pedro Martinez	.20	.50
BB15 Jose Canseco	.20	.50
BB16 Frank Thomas	.30	.75
BB17 Alex Rodriguez	.50	1.25
BB18 Bernie Williams	.20	.50
BB19 Greg Maddux	.50	1.25
BB20 Rafael Palmeiro	.20	.50

2001 Upper Deck Big League Challenge Game Jerseys

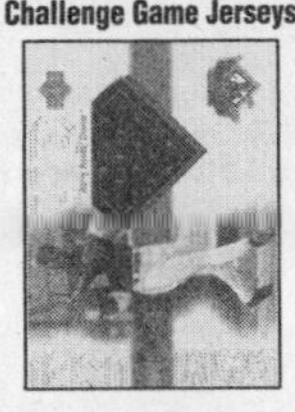

Issued at a rate of one in 288 second series packs, these 11 cards feature jersey pieces from participants in the 2001 Big League Challenge home run hitting contest.

BLCBB Barry Bonds	15.00	40.00
BLCFT Frank Thomas	8.00	20.00
BLCGS Gary Sheffield	6.00	15.00
BLCJC Jose Canseco	8.00	20.00
BLCJE Jim Edmonds	6.00	15.00
BLCMP Mike Piazza	10.00	25.00
BLCRH Richard Hidalgo	6.00	15.00
BLCRP Rafael Palmeiro	8.00	20.00
BLCSF Steve Finley	6.00	15.00
BLCTG Troy Glaus	6.00	15.00
BLCTH Todd Helton	8.00	20.00

2001 Upper Deck e-Card

Inserted as a two-pack box-topper, this six-card insert features cards that can be viewed over the Upper Deck website. Cards feature a serial number that is to be typed in a the Upper Deck website to reveal that card. Card backs carry an "E" prefix.

COMPLETE SET (12)	7.50	15.00
COMPLETE SERIES 1 (6)	3.00	6.00
COMPLETE SERIES 2 (6)	5.00	10.00
E1 Andruw Jones	.40	1.00
E2 Alex Rodriguez	.60	1.50
E3 Frank Thomas	.40	1.00
E4 Todd Helton	.40	1.00
E5 Troy Glaus	.40	1.00
E6 Barry Bonds	1.00	2.50
E7 Alex Rodriguez	.60	1.50
E8 Ken Griffey Jr.	.60	1.50
E9 Sammy Sosa	.40	1.00
E10 Gary Sheffield	.40	1.00
E11 Barry Bonds	1.00	2.50
E12 Andruw Jones	.40	1.00

2001 Upper Deck eVolve Autograph

Lucky participants in Upper Deck's E-Card program received special upgraded E-Cards available by checking the UD website (www.upperdeck.com) and entering their basic E-Card serial code (printed on the front of each basic E-Card). When viewed on the Upper Deck website, if an autographed card of the depicted player appeared, the bearer of the base card could then exchange their basic E-Card and receive the signed upgrade via mail. Only 200 serial numbered E-Card Autograph sets were produced. Signed E-Cards all have an ES prefix on the card numbers.

ESAJ Andruw Jones S1	10.00	25.00
ESAJ Andruw Jones S2	10.00	25.00
ESAR Alex Rodriguez S1	50.00	100.00
ESAR Alex Rodriguez S2	50.00	100.00
ESBB Barry Bonds S1	125.00	200.00
ESBB Barry Bonds S2	125.00	200.00
ESFT Frank Thomas S1	30.00	60.00
ESGS Gary Sheffield S2	20.00	50.00
ESKG Ken Griffey Jr. S2	50.00	100.00
ESSS Sammy Sosa S2	30.00	60.00
ESTG Troy Glaus S1	20.00	50.00
ESTH Todd Helton S1	20.00	50.00

2001 Upper Deck eVolve Game Jersey

Lucky participants in Upper Deck's E-Card program received special upgraded E-Cards available by checking the UD website (www.upperdeck.com) and entering their basic E-Card serial code (printed on the front of each basic E-Card). When viewed on the Upper Deck website, if a jersey card of the depicted player appeared, the bearer of the base card could then exchange their basic E-Card and receive the Game Jersey upgrade via mail. The cards closely parallel basic 2000 Game Jerseys that were distributed in first and second series packs except for the gold foil "e-volve" logo on front. Only 300 serial numbered E-Card Jersey sets were produced with each card being serial -numbered by hand in blue ink sharpie at the bottom right front corner. Unsigned E-Card Game Jerseys all have an EJ prefix on the card numbers.

EJAJ Andruw Jones S1	6.00	15.00
EJAJ Andruw Jones S2	6.00	15.00
EJAR Alex Rodriguez S1	8.00	20.00
EJAR Alex Rodriguez S2	8.00	20.00
EJBB Barry Bonds S1	12.50	30.00
EJBB Barry Bonds S2	12.50	30.00
EJFT Frank Thomas S1	6.00	15.00
EJGS Gary Sheffield S2	4.00	10.00
EJKG Ken Griffey Jr. S2	10.00	25.00
EJSS Sammy Sosa S2	6.00	15.00
EJTG Troy Glaus S1	4.00	10.00
EJTH Todd Helton S1	6.00	15.00

2001 Upper Deck eVolve Game Jersey Autograph

Lucky participants in Upper Deck's E-Card program received special upgraded E-Cards available by checking the UD website (www.upperdeck.com) and entering their basic E-Card serial code (printed on the front of each basic E-Card). When viewed on the Upper Deck website, if an autographed card of the depicted player appeared, the bearer of the base card could then exchange their basic E-Card and receive the signed jersey upgrade via mail. A mere 50 serial numbered sets were produced. Signed jersey E-Cards all have an ESJ prefix on the card numbers.

ESJAJ Andruw Jones S1	30.00	60.00
ESJAJ Andruw Jones S2	30.00	60.00
ESJAR Alex Rodriguez S1	60.00	120.00
ESJAR Alex Rodriguez S2	60.00	120.00
ESJBB Barry Bonds S1	125.00	250.00
ESJBB Barry Bonds S2	125.00	250.00
ESJFT Frank Thomas S1	40.00	80.00
ESJGS Gary Sheffield S2	30.00	60.00
ESJKG Ken Griffey Jr. S2	60.00	120.00
ESJSS Sammy Sosa S2	50.00	100.00
ESJTG Troy Glaus S1	30.00	60.00
ESJTH Todd Helton S1	30.00	60.00

2001 Upper Deck Franchise

Inserted at a rate of one in 36 second series packs, these 10 cards feature players who are considered the money players for their franchise.

COMPLETE SET (10)	25.00	60.00
F1 Frank Thomas	1.50	4.00
F2 Mark McGwire	4.00	10.00
F3 Ken Griffey Jr.	2.50	6.00
F4 Manny Ramirez Sox	1.50	4.00
F5 Alex Rodriguez	2.50	6.00
F6 Greg Maddux	2.50	6.00
F7 Sammy Sosa	1.50	4.00
F8 Derek Jeter	4.00	10.00
F9 Mike Piazza	2.50	6.00
F10 Vladimir Guerrero	1.50	4.00

2001 Upper Deck Game Ball 1

Randomly inserted into packs, this 18-card insert features game-used baseballs from the depicted players. Card backs carry a "B" prefix. Please note that only 100 serial numbered sets were produced.

BAJ Andruw Jones	15.00	40.00
BAR A.Rodriguez Mariners	30.00	60.00
BBB Barry Bonds	40.00	80.00
BDJ Derek Jeter	40.00	80.00
BIR Ivan Rodriguez	15.00	40.00
BJG Jason Giambi -	10.00	25.00
BJG Jeff Bagwell	15.00	40.00
BKG Ken Griffey Jr.	20.00	50.00
BMM Mark McGwire	75.00	150.00
BMP Mike Piazza	30.00	60.00
BRA Rick Ankiel	10.00	25.00
BRJ Randy Johnson	15.00	40.00
BSG Shawn Green	10.00	25.00
BSS Sammy Sosa	15.00	40.00
BTH Todd Helton	15.00	40.00
BTOG Tony Gwynn	15.00	40.00
BTRG Troy Glaus	10.00	25.00
BVG Vladimir Guerrero	15.00	40.00

2001 Upper Deck Game Ball 2

Inserted into second series packs at a rate of one in 288, this 18-card insert features game-used baseballs from the depicted players. Card backs carry a "B" prefix. The Nomar Garciaparra card was short printed and has been notated as such in our checklist.

BAJ Andruw Jones	6.00	15.00
BAR A.Rodriguez Rangers	10.00	25.00
BBB Barry Bonds	15.00	40.00
BBW Bernie Williams	6.00	15.00
BCJ Chipper Jones	6.00	15.00
BCR Cal Ripken	15.00	40.00
BDJ Derek Jeter	15.00	40.00
BGS Gary Sheffield	4.00	10.00
BJB Jeff Bagwell	6.00	15.00
BJK Jeff Kent	4.00	10.00
BKG Ken Griffey Jr.	10.00	25.00
BMM Mark McGwire	20.00	50.00
BMP Mike Piazza	10.00	25.00
BMR Mariano Rivera	6.00	15.00
BNG N.Garciaparra SP	15.00	40.00
BRC Roger Clemens	10.00	25.00
BSS Sammy Sosa	6.00	15.00
BVG Vladimir Guerrero	6.00	15.00

2001 Upper Deck Game Ball Gold Autograph

Randomly inserted into packs, this nine-card insert set features autographs and game-used baseball swatches from the depicted players below. Card backs carry a "SB" prefix. Please note that only 25 serial numbered sets were produced. The following cards packed out as exchange cards with a redemption deadline of August 7th, 2001: Alex Rodriguez, Jeff Bagwell, Ken Griffey Jr. and Rick Ankiel.

SBAR Alex Rodriguez
SBBB Barry Bonds
SBJB Jeff Bagwell
SBJG Jason Giambi
SBKG Ken Griffey Jr.
SBRA Rick Ankiel
SBRJ Randy Johnson
SBSG Shawn Green
SBTH Todd Helton

2001 Upper Deck Game Jersey

These cards feature swatches of jerseys of various major league stars. These cards were available in either series one hobby or retail packs at a rate of one every 288 packs. Card backs carry a "C" prefix.

CAJ A.Jones HR1	10.00	25.00
CAR Alex Rodriguez	10.00	25.00
CBW B.Williams HR1	10.00	25.00
CCR Cal Ripken	20.00	50.00
CDJ Derek Jeter	20.00	50.00
CFT Fernando Tatis	6.00	15.00
CIR Ivan Rodriguez	10.00	25.00
CKG Ken Griffey Jr.	15.00	40.00
CMR M.Ramirez HR1	10.00	25.00
CMW Matt Williams	6.00	15.00
CNRA Nolan Ryan Astros HR1	20.00	50.00
CNRR Nolan Ryan Rangers HR1	20.00	50.00
CPO Paul O'Neill	10.00	25.00
CRV Robin Ventura	6.00	15.00
CSK Sandy Koufax	40.00	80.00
CTG Tony Gwynn	10.00	25.00
CTH Todd Helton	10.00	25.00
CTIH Tim Hudson	6.00	15.00

2001 Upper Deck Game Jersey Autograph 1

These cards feature both autographs and swatches of jerseys from various major league stars. The cards which have an "H1" after the player names are available in series one hobby packs at a rate of one in every 288 packs. Card backs carry a "H" prefix. The following cards were distributed in packs as exchange cards: Alex Rodriguez, Jeff Bagwell, Ken Griffey Jr., Mike Hampton and Rick Ankiel. The deadline to exchange these cards was August 7th, 2001.

HAR A.Rodriguez H1 60.00 120.00
HBB Barry Bonds 125.00 200.00
HFT Frank Thomas 40.00 80.00
HGM Greg Maddux 75.00 150.00
HJB J.Bagwell H1 40.00 80.00
HJC Jose Canseco 20.00 50.00
HJD J.D. Drew 15.00 40.00
HJG Jason Giambi 15.00 40.00
HJL Javy Lopez 15.00 40.00
HKG K.Griffey Jr. H1 60.00 120.00
HMH M.Hampton H1 15.00 40.00
HNRA Nolan Ryan Angels 50.00 100.00
HNRM Nolan Ryan Mets 100.00 200.00
HRA R.Ankiel H1 12.50 30.00
HRJ Randy Johnson 50.00 100.00
HRP Rafael Palmeiro 40.00 80.00
HSC Sean Casey 15.00 40.00
HSG Shawn Green 20.00 50.00

2001 Upper Deck Game Jersey Autograph 2

These cards feature both autographs and swatches of jerseys from various major league stars. The cards which have an "H2" after the player names are available in series one hobby packs at a rate of one in every 288 packs. Card backs carry a "H" prefix. Please note a few of the players were issued in lesser quantites and we have notated those as SP's. The following players packed out as exchange cards: Alex Rodriguez and Ken Griffey Jr. The deadline for exchange was June 26th, 2006.

AJ Andruw Jones 12.50 30.00
AR Alex Rodriguez 60.00 120.00
BB Barry Bonds 125.00 200.00
CJ Chipper Jones 40.00 80.00
CR Cal Ripken SP 75.00 150.00
GS Gary Sheffield 20.00 50.00
IR Ivan Rodriguez SP 50.00 100.00
JB Johnny Bench 40.00 80.00
JC Jose Canseco 20.00 50.00
KG Ken Griffey Jr. 60,00 120.00
NR Nolan Ryan 75.00 150.00
RC Roger Clemens 75.00 150.00
SS Sammy Sosa SP 50.00 100.00
TG Troy Glaus 20.00 50.00

2001 Upper Deck Game Jersey Autograph Numbered

These cards feature both autographs and swatches of jerseys from various major league stars. The cards which have an "H" after the player names were only available in series one hobby packs, while the cards with a "C" can be found in either series one hobby or retail packs. Hobby cards feature gold backgrounds and say "Signed Game Jersey" on front. Hobby/Retail cards feature white backgrounds and simply say "Game Jersey" on front. These cards are individually serial numbered to the depicted player's jersey number. The following players packed out as exchange cards: Alex Rodriguez, Ken Griffey Jr., Jeff Bagwell, Mike Hampton and Rick Ankiel. The exchange deadline was August 7th, 2001.

CAJ Andruw Jones/25
CAR Alex Rodriguez/3
CFT Fernando Tatis/23
CIR Ivan Rodriguez/7
CJL Javy Lopez/8
CKG Ken Griffey Jr./30 HR1 125.00 250.00
CMW Matt Williams/9
CNRA Nolan Ryan Astros/34 HR1 175.00 300.00
CNRR Nolan Ryan Rangers 34 HR1 175.00 300.00
CPO Paul O'Neill/21
CRV Robin Ventura/4
CSK Sandy Koufax 32 HR1 600.00 1000.00
CTG Tony Gwynn/19
CTH Todd Helton/17
CTIH Tim Hudson/15
HAR Alex Rodriguez/3
HBB Barry Bonds/25
HFT Frank Thomas/35 75.00 150.00
HGM Greg Maddux/31 175.00 300.00
HJB Jeff Bagwell/5
HJC Jose Canseco/33 50.00 100.00
HJD J.D. Drew/7
HJG Jason Giambi/16
HKG Ken Griffey Jr. 30 H1 125.00 250.00
HMH Mike Hampton/32 30.00 60.00
HNRA Nolan Ryan 30/Angels H1 200.00 350.00
HNRM Nolan Ryan 30/Mets H1 250.00 400.00
HRA Rick Ankiel 66 H1 30.00 60.00
HRJ Randy Johnson 51 H1 125.00 200.00
HRP Rafael Palmeiro 25 H1
HSC Sean Casey/21
HSG Shawn Green/15

2001 Upper Deck Game Jersey Combo

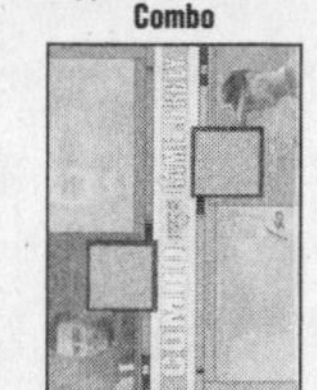

Randomly inserted into series one packs, these 13 cards feature dual player game-worn uniform patches. Card backs carry both players initials as numbering. Please note that there were only 50 serial numbered sets produced.

AJKG Andruw Jones Ken Griffey Jr. 40.00 80.00
BBJC Barry Bonds Jose Canseco 50.00 100.00
BBKG Barry Bonds Ken Griffey Jr. 50.00 100.00
DJAR Derek Jeter Alex Rodriguez 50.00 100.00
FTJB Frank Thomas Jeff Bagwell 20.00 50.00
IRRP Ivan Rodriguez Rafael Palmeiro 20.00 50.00
JDRA J.D. Drew Rick Ankiel 15.00 40.00
MMKG Mickey Mantle Ken Griffey Jr.
NRAR Nolan Rya Astros-Rangers 60.00 120.00
NRMA Nolan Ryan Mets-Angels 60.00 120.00
RATH Rick Ankiel Tim Hudson 15.00 40.00
RJGM Randy Johnson Greg Maddux 30.00 60.00
TGCR Tony Gwynn Cal Ripken 50.00 100.00
VGMR Vladimir Guerrero Manny Ramirez 20.00 50.00

2001 Upper Deck Game Jersey Combo Autograph

Randomly inserted into series one hobby packs, these seven cards feature autographed dual player game-worn uniform patches. Card backs carry both players initials as numbering with a "S" prefix. Please note that there were only 10 serial numbered sets produced. Cards SAJ-KG and SJD-RA both packed out as exchange cards with a redemption deadline of 8/07/01. Due to market scarcity, no pricing is provided.

SAJKG Andruw Jones Ken Griffey Jr. EXCH
SBBJC Barry Bonds Jose Canseco
SBBKG Barry Bonds Ken Griffey Jr.
SDJAR Derek Jeter Alex Rodriguez
SJDRA J.D. Drew Rick Ankiel
SNRAR Nolan Ryan Astros-Rangers
SNRMA Nolan Ryan Mets-Angels

2001 Upper Deck Game Jersey Patch

Randomly inserted into series one packs at one in 7500 and series 2 packs at 1:5000, these cards feature game-worn uniform patches. Card backs carry a "P" prefix.

PAR Alex Rodriguez S1 60.00 120.00
PAR Alex Rodriguez S2 60.00 120.00
PBB Barry Bonds S1 75.00 150.00
PBB Barry Bonds S2 75.00 150.00
PCJ Chipper Jones S2 50.00 100.00
PCR Cal Ripken S1 75.00 150.00
PCR Cal Ripken S2 75.00 150.00
PDJ Derek Jeter S1 75.00 150.00
PFT Frank Thomas S1 50.00 100.00
PIR Ivan Rodriguez S1 40.00 80.00
PIR Ivan Rodriguez S2 40.00 80.00
PJB Johnny Bench S2 50.00 100.00
PJB Jeff Bagwell S1 40.00 80.00
PJC Jose Canseco S1 40.00 80.00
PJG Jason Giambi S1 30.00 60.00
PKG Ken Griffey Jr. S1 60.00 120.00
PKG Ken Griffey Jr. S2 60.00 120.00
PNRA Nolan Ryan Astros 60.00 120.00
PNRR N.Ryan Rangers S1 60.00 120.00
PNRR N.Ryan Rangers S2 60.00 120.00
PRA Rick Ankiel S1 15.00 40.00
PRP Rafael Palmeiro S1 40.00 80.00
PSS Sammy Sosa S2 30.00 60.00
PTG Tony Gwynn S1 50.00 100.00

2001 Upper Deck Game Jersey Patch Autograph Numbered

Randomly inserted into series one hobby packs, these cards feature both autographs and game-worn uniform patches. Card backs carry a "SP" prefix. Please note that these cards are hand-numbered to the depicted players jersey number. All of these cards packed out as exchange cards with a redemption deadline of 8/07/01.

SPAR Alex Rodriguez/3
SPKG K.Griffey Jr./30 250.00 400.00
SPRA Rick Ankiel/66 40.00 80.00

2001 Upper Deck Home Run Derby Heroes

Inserted in second series packs at a rate of one in 36, these 10 cards features a look back at some of the most explosive performances from past Home Run Derby competitions.

COMPLETE SET (10) 20.00 50.00
HD1 Mark McGwire 99 4.00 10.00
HD2 Sammy Sosa 00 1.50 4.00
HD3 Frank Thomas 96 1.50 4.00
HD4 Cal Ripken 91 5.00 12.00
HD5 Tino Martinez 97 1.00 2.50
HD6 Ken Griffey Jr. 99 2.50 6.00
HD7 Barry Bonds 96 4.00 10.00
HD8 Albert Belle 95 .75 2.00
HD9 Mark McGwire 92 4.00 10.00
HD10 Juan Gonzalez 93 .75 2.00

2001 Upper Deck Home Run Explosion

Randomly inserted into series one packs at one in 12, this 15-card insert features players that are among the league leaders in homeruns every year. Card backs carry a "HR" prefix.

COMPLETE SET (15) 15.00 40.00
HR1 Mark McGwire 2.00 5.00
HR2 Chipper Jones .75 2.00
HR3 Jeff Bagwell .50 1.25
HR4 Carlos Delgado .40 1.00
HR5 Barry Bonds 2.00 5.00
HR6 Troy Glaus .40 1.00
HR7 Sammy Sosa .75 2.00
HR8 Alex Rodriguez 1.25 3.00
HR9 Mike Piazza 1.25 3.00
HR10 Vladimir Guerrero .75 2.00
HR11 Ken Griffey Jr. 1.25 3.00
HR12 Frank Thomas .75 2.00
HR13 Ivan Rodriguez .50 1.25
HR14 Jason Giambi .40 1.00
HR15 Carl Everett .40 1.00

2001 Upper Deck Midseason Superstar Summit

Inserted in series two packs at a rate of one in 24, these 15 cards feature some of the most dominant players of the 2000 season.

COMPLETE SET (15) 25.00 60.00
MS1 Derek Jeter 4.00 10.00
MS2 Sammy Sosa 1.50 4.00
MS3 Jeff Bagwell 1.00 2.50
MS4 Tony Gwynn 2.00 5.00
MS5 Alex Rodriguez 2.50 6.00
MS6 Greg Maddux 2.50 6.00
MS7 Jason Giambi .75 2.00
MS8 Mark McGwire 4.00 10.00
MS9 Barry Bonds 4.00 10.00
MS10 Ken Griffey Jr. 2.50 6.00
MS11 Carlos Delgado .75 2.00
MS12 Troy Glaus .75 2.00
MS13 Todd Helton 1.00 2.50
MS14 Manny Ramirez Sox 1.00 2.50
MS15 Jeff Kent .75 2.00

2001 Upper Deck Midsummer Classic Moments

Inserted in series two packs at a rate of one in 12, these 20 cards feature some of the most memorable moments from All Star Game history.

COMPLETE SET (20) 15.00 40.00
CM1 Joe DiMaggio 36 1.25 3.00
CM2 Joe DiMaggio 51 1.25 3.00
CM3 Mickey Mantle 52 2.50 6.00
CM4 Mickey Mantle 68 2.50 6.00
CM5 Roger Clemens 86 1.50 4.00
CM6 Mark McGwire 87 2.00 5.00
CM7 Cal Ripken 91 2.50 6.00
CM8 Ken Griffey Jr. 92 1.25 3.00
CM9 Randy Johnson 93 .75 2.00
CM10 Tony Gwynn 94 1.00 2.50
CM11 Fred McGriff 94 .50 1.25
CM12 Hideo Nomo 95 .75 2.00
CM13 Jeff Conine 95 .40 1.00
CM14 Mike Piazza 96 1.25 3.00
CM15 Sandy Alomar Jr. .40 1.00
CM16 Alex Rodriguez 98 1.00 2.50
CM17 Roberto Alomar 98 .50 1.25
CM18 Pedro Martinez 99 .50 1.25
CM19 Andres Galarraga .40 1.00
CM20 Derek Jeter 00 1.50 4.00

2001 Upper Deck People's Choice

Inserted one per 24 series two packs, these 15 cards feature the players who fans want to see the most.

COMPLETE SET (15) 30.00 80.00
PC1 Alex Rodriguez 2.50 6.00
PC2 Ken Griffey Jr. 2.50 6.00
PC3 Mark McGwire 4.00 10.00
PC4 Todd Helton 1.00 2.50
PC5 Manny Ramirez 1.00 2.50
PC6 Mike Piazza 2.50 6.00
PC7 Vladimir Guerrero 1.50 4.00
PC8 Randy Johnson 1.50 4.00
PC9 Cal Ripken 5.00 12.00
PC10 Andruw Jones 1.00 2.50
PC11 Sammy Sosa 1.50 4.00
PC12 Derek Jeter 4.00 10.00
PC13 Pedro Martinez 1.00 2.50
PC14 Frank Thomas 1.50 4.00
PC15 Nomar Garciaparra 2.50 6.00

2001 Upper Deck Rookie Roundup

Randomly inserted into series one packs at one in six, this 10-card insert features some of the younger players in Major League baseball. Card backs carry a "RR" prefix.

COMPLETE SET (10) 2.00 5.00
RR1 Rick Ankiel .20 .50
RR2 Adam Kennedy .20 .50
RR3 Mike Lamb .20 .50
RR4 Adam Eaton .20 .50
RR5 Rafael Furcal .30 .75
RR6 Pat Burrell .30 .75
RR7 Adam Piatt .20 .50
RR8 Eric Munson .20 .50
RR9 Brad Penny .20 .50
RR10 Mark Mulder .30 .75

2001 Upper Deck Subway Series Game Jerseys

While the set name seemed to indicate that these cards were from jerseys worn during the 2000 World series, they were actually swatches from regular-season game jerseys.

SSAL Al Leiter 4.00 10.00
SSAP Andy Pettitte 10.00 25.00
SSBW Bernie Williams 10.00 25.00
SSEA Edgardo Alfonzo 3.00 8.00
SSJF John Franco 4.00 10.00
SSJP Jay Payton 3.00 8.00
SSOH Orlando Hernandez 8.00 20.00
SSPO Paul O'Neill 10.00 25.00
SSRC Roger Clemens 15.00 40.00
SSTP Timo Perez 3.00 8.00

2001 Upper Deck Superstar Summit

Randomly inserted into packs at one in 12, this 15-card insert features the Major League's top superstar caliber players. Card backs carry a "SS" prefix.

COMPLETE SET (15) 20.00 50.00
SS1 Derek Jeter 2.00 5.00
SS2 Randy Johnson .75 2.00
SS3 Barry Bonds 2.00 5.00
SS4 Frank Thomas .75 2.00
SS5 Cal Ripken 2.50 6.00
SS6 Pedro Martinez .75 2.00
SS7 Ivan Rodriguez .75 2.00
SS8 Mike Piazza 1.25 3.00
SS9 Mark McGwire 2.00 5.00
SS10 Manny Ramirez Sox .75 2.00
SS11 Ken Griffey Jr. 1.25 3.00
SS12 Sammy Sosa .75 2.00
SS13 Alex Rodriguez 1.25 3.00
SS14 Chipper Jones .75 2.00
SS15 Nomar Garciaparra 1.25 3.00

2001 Upper Deck UD's Most Wanted

Randomly inserted into packs at one in 14, this 15-card insert features players that are in high demand on the collectibles market. Card backs carry a "MW" prefix.

COMPLETE SET (15) 25.00 60.00
MW1 Mark McGwire 2.50 6.00
MW2 Cal Ripken 3.00 8.00
MW3 Ivan Rodriguez 1.00 2.50
MW4 Pedro Martinez 1.00 2.50
MW5 Sammy Sosa 1.00 2.50
MW6 Tony Gwynn 1.25 3.00
MW7 Vladimir Guerrero 1.00 2.50
MW8 Derek Jeter 2.50 6.00
MW9 Mike Piazza 1.50 4.00
MW10 Chipper Jones 1.00 2.50
MW11 Alex Rodriguez 1.50 4.00
MW12 Barry Bonds 2.50 6.00
MW13 Jeff Bagwell 1.00 2.50
MW14 Frank Thomas 1.00 2.50
MW15 Nomar Garciaparra 1.50 4.00

2001 Upper Deck Pinstripe Exclusives DiMaggio

This 56-card set features a wide selection of cards focusing on Yankees legend Joe DiMaggio. The cards were distributed in special three-card foil wrapped packs, exclusively seeded into 2001 SP Game Bat Milestone, SP Game-Used, SPx, Upper Deck Decade 1970's, Upper Deck Gold Glove, Upper Deck Legends, Upper Deck Ovation and Upper Deck Sweet Spot hobby boxes at a rate of one pack per sealed box.

COMPLETE SET (56) 30.00 60.00
COMMON (JD1-JD56) .60 1.50

2001 Upper Deck Pinstripe Exclusives DiMaggio Memorabilia

Randomly seeded into special three-card Pinstripe Exclusives DiMaggio foil packs (of which were distributed exclusively in 2001 SP Game Bat Milestone, SP Game-Used, SPx, Upper Deck Decade 1970's, Upper Deck Gold Glove, Upper Deck Legends, Upper Deck Ovation and Upper Deck Sweet Spot Sweet Spot hobby boxes) were a selection of scarce game-used memorabilia and autograph cut cards featuring Joe DiMaggio. Each card is serial-numbered and features either a game-used bat chip, jersey swatch or autograph cut.

COMMON BAT (B1-B9) 30.00 60.00
COMMON JERSEY (J1-J9) 50.00 100.00
SUFFIX 1 CARDS DIST.IN SWEET SPOT
SUFFIX 2 CARDS DIST.IN OVATION
SUFFIX 3 CARDS DIST.IN SPX
SUFFIX 4 CARDS DIST.IN SP GAME USED
SUFFIX 5 CARDS DIST.IN LEGENDS
SUFFIX 6 CARDS DIST. IN DECADE 1970
SUFFIX 7 CARDS DIST.IN SP BAT MILE
SUFFIX 8 CARDS DIST.IN UD GOLD GLOVE
BAT 1-9 PRINT RUN 100 SERIAL #'d SETS
BAT-CUT 1-7 PRINT RUN 5 SERIAL #'d SETS
COMBO 1-6 PRINT RUN 50 SERIAL #'D SETS
CUT 1-8 PRINT RUN 5 SERIAL #'d SETS
JERSEY 1-8 PRINT RUN 100 SERIAL #'d SETS
CJ1 Joe DiMaggio Jsy Lou Gehrig Pants/50 300.00 600.00
CJ2 Joe DiMaggio Jsy Mickey Mantle Jsy/50 175.00 300.00
CJ3 Joe DiMaggio Jsy Ken Griffey Jr. Jsy/50 100.00 200.00
CJ4 Joe DiMaggio Jsy Dom DiMaggio Jsy/50 150.00 250.00
CJ5 Joe DiMaggio Jsy Mickey Mantle Jsy/50 175.00 300.00
CJ6 Joe DiMaggio Jsy Mickey Mantle Jsy/50 175.00 300.00

2001 Upper Deck Pinstripe Exclusives Mantle

This 56-card set features a wide selection of cards focusing on Yankees legend Mickey Mantle. The cards were distributed in special three-card foil wrapped packs, seeded into 2001 Upper Deck Series 2, Upper Deck Hall of Famers, Upper Deck MVP and Upper Deck Vintage hobby boxes at a rate of one pack per 24 ct. box.

COMPLETE SET (56) 50.00 100.00
COMMON (MM1-MM56) 1.00 2.50

2001 Upper Deck Pinstripe Exclusives Mantle Memorabilia

Randomly seeded into special three-card Pinstripe Exclusives Mantle foil packs (of which were distributed in hobby boxes of 2001 SP Authentic, 2001 SP Game Bat Milestone, 2001 Upper Deck series 2, 2001 Upper Deck Hall of Famers, 2001 Upper Deck Legends of New York, 2001 Upper Deck MVP and 2001 Upper Deck Vintage) were a selection of scarce game-used memorabilia and autograph cut cards featuring Mickey Mantle. Each card is serial-numbered and features either a game-used bat chip, jersey swatch or autograph cut.

COMMON BAT (B1-B4) 75.00 150.00
COMMON JERSEY (J1-J7) 100.00 200.00
COMMON BAT CUT (BC1-BC4)
COMMON CUT (C1-C4)
SUFFIX 1 CARDS DIST.IN UD VINTAGE
SUFFIX 2 CARDS DIST.IN UD HOF'ers
SUFFIX 3 CARDS DIST.IN UD MVP
SUFFIX 4 CARDS DIST.IN UD SER.2
SUFFIX 5 CARDS DIST. IN SP AUTH
SUFFIX 6 CARDS DIST. IN SP GAME BAT MILE
SUFFIX 7 CARDS DIST. IN UD LEG OF NY
BAT 1-9 PRINT RUN 100 SERIAL #'d SETS
BAT-CUT 1-4 PRINT RUN 7 SERIAL #'d SETS
COMBO 1-6 PRINT RUN 50 SERIAL #'d SETS
CUT 1-4 PRINT RUN 7 SERIAL #'D SETS
JERSEY 1-7 PRINT RUN 100 SERIAL #'d SETS
CJ1 Mickey Mantle Roger Maris Jsy/50 175.00 300.00
CJ2 Mickey Mantle Joe DiMag Jsy/50 150.00 250.00
CJ3 Mickey Mantle Ken Griffey Jsy/50 75.00 150.00
CJ4 Mickey Mantle Roger Maris Jsy/50 175.00 300.00
CJ5 Mickey Mantle Joe DiMaggio Jsy/50 150.00 250.00
CJ6 Mickey Mantle Joe DiMaggio Jsy/50 150.00 250.00
CJ7 Mickey Mantle Joe DiMaggio Jsy 50 150.00 250.00

2002 Upper Deck

The 500 card first series set was issued in November, 2001. The 245-card second series set was issued in May, 2002. The cards were issued in eight card packs with 24 packs to a box. Subsets include Star Rookies (cards numbered 1-50, 501-545), World Stage (cards numbered 461-480), Griffey Gallery (481-490) and Checklists (491-500, 736-745) and Year of the Record (726-735). Star Rookies were inserted at a rate of one per pack into second series packs, making them 1.75X times tougher to pull than veteran second series cards.

COMPLETE SET (745) 85.00 160.00
COMPLETE SERIES 1 (500) 60.00 110.00
COMPLETE SERIES 2 (245) 25.00 50.00
COMMON (51-500/546-745) .10 .30
COMMON SR (1-50/501-545) .40 1.00
1 Mark Prior SR .75 2.00
2 Mark Teixeira SR 3.00 8.00
3 Brian Roberts SR .75 2.00
4 Jason Romano SR .40 1.00
5 Dennis Stark SR .40 1.00
6 Oscar Salazar SR .40 1.00
7 John Patterson SR .40 1.00
8 Shane Loux SR .40 1.00
9 Marcus Giles SR .40 1.00
10 Juan Cruz SR .40 1.00
11 Jorge Julio SR .40 1.00
12 Adam Dunn SR .40 1.00
13 Delvin James SR .40 1.00
14 Jeremy Affeldt SR .40 1.00
15 Tim Raines Jr. SR .40 1.00
16 Luke Hudson SR .40 1.00
17 Todd Sears SR .40 1.00
18 George Perez SR .40 1.00
19 Wilmy Caceres SR .40 1.00
20 Abraham Nunez SR .40 1.00
21 Mike Amrhein SR RC .40 1.00
22 Carlos Hernandez SR .40 1.00
23 Scott Hodges SR .40 1.00
24 Brandon Knight SR .40 1.00
25 Geoff Goetz SR .40 1.00
26 Carlos Garcia SR .40 1.00
27 Luis Pineda SR .40 1.00
28 Chris Gissell SR .40 1.00
29 Jae Weong Seo SR .40 1.00
30 Paul Phillips SR .40 1.00
31 Cory Aldridge SR .40 1.00
32 Aaron Cook SR RC .40 1.00
33 Rendy Espina SR RC .40 1.00
34 Jason Phillips SR .40 1.00
35 Carlos Silva SR .40 1.00
36 Ryan Mills SR .40 1.00
37 Pedro Santana SR .40 1.00
38 John Grabow SR .40 1.00
39 Cody Ransom SR .40 1.00
40 Orlando Woodards SR .40 1.00
41 Bud Smith SR .40 1.00
42 Junior Guerrero SR .40 1.00
43 David Brous SR .40 1.00
44 Steve Green SR .40 1.00
45 Brian Rogers SR .40 1.00
46 Juan Figueroa SR RC .40 1.00
47 Nick Punto SR .40 1.00
48 Junior Herndon SR .40 1.00
49 Justin Kaye SR .40 1.00
50 Jason Karnuth SR .40 1.00
51 Troy Glaus .10 .30
52 Bengie Molina .10 .30
53 Ramon Ortiz .10 .30
54 Adam Kennedy .10 .30
55 Jarrod Washburn .10 .30
56 Troy Percival .10 .30
57 David Eckstein .10 .30
58 Ben Weber .10 .30
59 Larry Barnes .10 .30
60 Ismael Valdes .10 .30
61 Benji Gil .10 .30
62 Scott Schoeneweis .10 .30
63 Pat Rapp .10 .30
64 Jason Giambi .10 .30
65 Mark Mulder .10 .30
66 Ron Gant .10 .30
67 Johnny Damon .20 .50
68 Adam Piatt .10 .30
69 Jermaine Dye .10 .30
70 Jason Hart .10 .30
71 Eric Chavez .10 .30
72 Jim Mecir .10 .30
73 Barry Zito .10 .30
74 Jason Isringhausen .10 .30
75 Jeremy Giambi .10 .30
76 Olmedo Saenz .10 .30
77 Terrence Long .10 .30
78 Ramon Hernandez .10 .30
79 Chris Carpenter .10 .30
80 Raul Mondesi .10 .30
81 Carlos Delgado .10 .30
82 Billy Koch .10 .30
83 Vernon Wells .10 .30
84 Darrin Fletcher .10 .30
85 Homer Bush .10 .30
86 Pasqual Coco .10 .30
87 Shannon Stewart .10 .30
88 Chris Woodward .10 .30

89 Joe Lawrence .10 .30
90 Esteban Loaiza .10 .30
91 Cesar Izturis .10 .30
92 Kelvim Escobar .10 .30
93 Greg Vaughn .10 .30
94 Brent Abernathy .10 .30
95 Tanyon Sturtze .10 .30
96 Steve Cox .10 .30
97 Aubrey Huff .10 .30
98 Jesus Colome .10 .30
99 Ben Grieve .10 .30
100 Esteban Yan .10 .30
101 Joe Kennedy .10 .30
102 Felix Martinez .10 .30
103 Nick Bierbrodt .10 .30
104 Damian Rolls .10 .30
105 Russ Johnson .10 .30
106 Toby Hall .10 .30
107 Roberto Alomar .20 .50
108 Bartolo Colon .10 .30
109 John Rocker .10 .30
110 Juan Gonzalez .10 .30
111 Einar Diaz .10 .30
112 Chuck Finley .10 .30
113 Kenny Lofton .10 .30
114 Danys Baez .10 .30
115 Travis Fryman .10 .30
116 C.C. Sabathia .10 .30
117 Paul Shuey .10 .30
118 Marty Cordova .10 .30
119 Ellis Burks .10 .30
120 Bob Wickman .10 .30
121 Edgar Martinez .20 .50
122 Freddy Garcia .10 .30
123 Ichiro Suzuki .60 1.50
124 John Olerud .10 .30
125 Gil Meche .10 .30
126 Dan Wilson .10 .30
127 Aaron Sele .10 .30
128 Kazuhiro Sasaki .10 .30
129 Mark McLemore .10 .30
130 Carlos Guillen .10 .30
131 Al Martin .10 .30
132 David Bell .10 .30
133 Jay Buhner .10 .30
134 Stan Javier .10 .30
135 Tony Batista .10 .30
136 Jason Johnson .10 .30
137 Brook Fordyce .10 .30
138 Mike Kinkade .10 .30
139 Willis Roberts .10 .30
140 David Segui .10 .30
141 Josh Towers .10 .30
142 Jeff Conine .10 .30
143 Chris Richard .10 .30
144 Pat Hentgen .10 .30
145 Melvin Mora .10 .30
146 Jerry Hairston Jr. .10 .30
147 Calvin Maduro .10 .30
148 Brady Anderson .10 .30
149 Alex Rodriguez .50 1.25
150 Kenny Rogers .10 .30
151 Chad Curtis .10 .30
152 Ricky Ledee .10 .30
153 Rafael Palmeiro .20 .50
154 Rob Bell .10 .30
155 Rick Helling .10 .30
156 Doug Davis .10 .30
157 Mike Lamb .10 .30
158 Gabe Kapler .10 .30
159 Jeff Zimmerman .10 .30
160 Bill Haselman .10 .30
161 Tim Crabtree .10 .30
162 Carlos Pena .10 .30
163 Nomar Garciaparra .50 1.25
164 Shea Hillenbrand .10 .30
165 Hideo Nomo .30 .75
166 Manny Ramirez .20 .50
167 Jose Offerman .10 .30
168 Scott Hatteberg .10 .30
169 Trot Nixon .10 .30
170 Darren Lewis .10 .30
171 Derek Lowe .10 .30
172 Troy O'Leary .10 .30
173 Tim Wakefield .10 .30
174 Chris Stynes .10 .30
175 John Valentin .10 .30
176 David Cone .10 .30
177 Neifi Perez .10 .30
178 Brent Mayne .10 .30
179 Dan Reichert .10 .30
180 A.J. Hinch .10 .30
181 Chris George .10 .30
182 Mike Sweeney .10 .30
183 Jeff Suppan .10 .30
184 Roberto Hernandez .10 .30
185 Joe Randa .10 .30
186 Paul Byrd .10 .30
187 Luis Ordaz .10 .30
188 Kris Wilson .10 .30
189 Dee Brown .10 .30
190 Tony Clark .10 .30
191 Matt Anderson .10 .30
192 Robert Fick .10 .30
193 Juan Encarnacion .10 .30
194 Dean Palmer .10 .30
195 Victor Santos .10 .30
196 Damion Easley .10 .30
197 Jose Lima .10 .30
198 Deivi Cruz .10 .30
199 Roger Cedeno .10 .30
200 Jose Macias .10 .30
201 Jeff Weaver .10 .30
202 Brandon Inge .10 .30
203 Brian Moehler .10 .30
204 Brad Radke .10 .30
205 Doug Mientkiewicz .10 .30
206 Cristian Guzman .10 .30
207 Corey Koskie .10 .30
208 LaTroy Hawkins .10 .30
209 J.C. Romero .10 .30
210 Chad Allen .10 .30
211 Torii Hunter .10 .30
212 Travis Miller .10 .30
213 Joe Mays .10 .30
214 Todd Jones .10 .30
215 David Ortiz .30 .75
216 Brian Buchanan .10 .30
217 A.J. Pierzynski .10 .30
218 Carlos Lee .10 .30
219 Gary Glover .10 .30
220 Jose Valentin .10 .30
221 Aaron Rowand .10 .30
222 Sandy Alomar Jr. .10 .30
223 Herbert Perry .10 .30
224 Jon Garland .10 .30
225 Mark Buehrle .10 .30
226 Chris Singleton .10 .30
227 Kip Wells .10 .30
228 Ray Durham .10 .30
229 Joe Crede .10 .30
230 Keith Foulke .10 .30
231 Royce Clayton .10 .30
232 Andy Pettitte .20 .50
233 Derek Jeter .75 2.00
234 Jorge Posada .20 .50
235 Roger Clemens .60 1.50
236 Paul O'Neill .20 .50
237 Nick Johnson .10 .30
238 Gerald Williams .10 .30
239 Mariano Rivera .30 .75
240 Alfonso Soriano .10 .30
241 Ramiro Mendoza .10 .30
242 Mike Mussina .20 .50
243 Luis Sojo .10 .30
244 Scott Brosius .10 .30
245 David Justice .10 .30
246 Wade Miller .10 .30
247 Brad Ausmus .10 .30
248 Jeff Bagwell .20 .50
249 Daryle Ward .10 .30
250 Shane Reynolds .10 .30
251 Chris Truby .10 .30
252 Billy Wagner .10 .30
253 Craig Biggio .20 .50
254 Moises Alou .10 .30
255 Vinny Castilla .10 .30
256 Tim Redding .10 .30
257 Roy Oswalt .10 .30
258 Julio Lugo .10 .30
259 Chipper Jones .30 .75
260 Greg Maddux .50 1.25
261 Ken Caminiti .10 .30
262 Kevin Millwood .10 .30
263 Keith Lockhart .10 .30
264 Rey Sanchez .10 .30
265 Jason Marquis .10 .30
266 Brian Jordan .10 .30
267 Steve Karsay .10 .30
268 Wes Helms .10 .30
269 B.J. Surhoff .10 .30
270 Wilson Betemit .10 .30
271 John Smoltz .20 .50
272 Rafael Furcal .10 .30
273 Jeromy Burnitz .10 .30
274 Jimmy Haynes .10 .30
275 Mark Loretta .10 .30
276 Jose Hernandez .10 .30
277 Paul Rigdon .10 .30
278 Alex Sanchez .10 .30
279 Chad Fox .10 .30
280 Devon White .10 .30
281 Tyler Houston .10 .30
282 Ronnie Belliard .10 .30
283 Luis Lopez .10 .30
284 Ben Sheets .10 .30
285 Curtis Leskanic .10 .30
286 Henry Blanco .10 .30
287 Mark McGwire .75 2.00
288 Edgar Renteria .10 .30
289 Matt Morris .10 .30
290 Gene Stechschulte .10 .30
291 Dustin Hermanson .10 .30
292 Eli Marrero .10 .30
293 Albert Pujols .60 1.50
294 Luis Saturria .10 .30
295 Bobby Bonilla .10 .30
296 Garrett Stephenson .10 .30
297 Jim Edmonds .10 .30
298 Rick Ankiel .10 .30
299 Placido Polanco .10 .30
300 Dave Veres .10 .30
301 Sammy Sosa .30 .75
302 Eric Young .10 .30
303 Kerry Wood .10 .30
304 Jon Lieber .10 .30
305 Joe Girardi .10 .30
306 Fred McGriff .20 .50
307 Jeff Fassero .10 .30
308 Julio Zuleta .10 .30
309 Kevin Tapani .10 .30
310 Rondell White .10 .30
311 Julian Tavarez .10 .30
312 Tom Gordon .10 .30
313 Corey Patterson .10 .30
314 Bill Mueller .10 .30
315 Randy Johnson .30 .75
316 Chad Moeller .10 .30
317 Tony Womack .10 .30
318 Erubiel Durazo .10 .30
319 Luis Gonzalez .10 .30
320 Brian Anderson .10 .30
321 Reggie Sanders .10 .30
322 Greg Colbrunn .10 .30
323 Robert Ellis .10 .30
324 Jack Cust .10 .30
325 Bret Prinz .10 .30
326 Steve Finley .10 .30
327 Byung-Hyun Kim .10 .30
328 Albie Lopez .10 .30
329 Gary Sheffield .10 .30
330 Mark Grudzielanek .10 .30
331 Paul LoDuca .10 .30
332 Tom Goodwin .10 .30
333 Andy Ashby .10 .30
334 Hiram Bocachica .10 .30
335 Dave Hansen .10 .30
336 Kevin Brown .10 .30
337 Marquis Grissom .10 .30
338 Terry Adams .10 .30
339 Chan Ho Park .10 .30
340 Adrian Beltre .10 .30
341 Luke Prokopec .10 .30
342 Jeff Shaw .10 .30
343 Vladimir Guerrero .30 .75
344 Orlando Cabrera .10 .30
345 Tony Armas Jr. .10 .30
346 Michael Barrett .10 .30
347 Geoff Blum .10 .30
348 Ryan Minor .10 .30
349 Peter Bergeron .10 .30
350 Graeme Lloyd .10 .30
351 Jose Vidro .10 .30
352 Javier Vazquez .10 .30
353 Matt Blank .10 .30
354 Masato Yoshii .10 .30
355 Carl Pavano .10 .30
356 Barry Bonds .75 2.00
357 Shawon Dunston .10 .30
358 Livan Hernandez .10 .30
359 Felix Rodriguez .10 .30
360 Pedro Feliz .10 .30
361 Calvin Murray .10 .30
362 Robb Nen .10 .30
363 Marvin Benard .10 .30
364 Russ Ortiz .10 .30
365 Jason Schmidt .10 .30
366 Rich Aurilia .10 .30
367 John Vander Wal .10 .30
368 Benito Santiago .10 .30
369 Ryan Dempster .10 .30
370 Charles Johnson .10 .30
371 Alex Gonzalez .10 .30
372 Luis Castillo .10 .30
373 Mike Lowell .10 .30
374 Antonio Alfonseca .10 .30
375 A.J. Burnett .10 .30
376 Brad Penny .10 .30
377 Jason Grilli .10 .30
378 Derrek Lee .10 .30
379 Matt Clement .10 .30
380 Eric Owens .10 .30
381 Vladimir Nunez .10 .30
382 Cliff Floyd .10 .30
383 Mike Piazza .50 1.25
384 Lenny Harris .10 .30
385 Glendon Rusch .10 .30
386 Todd Zeile .10 .30
387 Al Leiter .10 .30
388 Armando Benitez .10 .30
389 Alex Escobar .10 .30
390 Kevin Appier .10 .30
391 Matt Lawton .10 .30
392 Bruce Chen .10 .30
393 John Franco .10 .30
394 Tsuyoshi Shinjo .10 .30
395 Rey Ordonez .10 .30
396 Joe McEwing .10 .30
397 Ryan Klesko .10 .30
398 Brian Lawrence .10 .30
399 Kevin Walker .10 .30
400 Phil Nevin .10 .30
401 Bubba Trammell .10 .30
402 Wiki Gonzalez .10 .30
403 D'Angelo Jimenez .10 .30
404 Rickey Henderson .30 .75
405 Mike Darr .10 .30
406 Trevor Hoffman .10 .30
407 Damian Jackson .10 .30
408 Santiago Perez .10 .30
409 Cesar Crespo .10 .30
410 Robert Person .10 .30
411 Travis Lee .10 .30
412 Scott Rolen .20 .50
413 Turk Wendell .10 .30
414 Randy Wolf .10 .30
415 Kevin Jordan .10 .30
416 Jose Mesa .10 .30
417 Mike Lieberthal .10 .30
418 Bobby Abreu .10 .30
419 Tomas Perez .10 .30
420 Doug Glanville .10 .30
421 Reggie Taylor .10 .30
422 Jimmy Rollins .10 .30
423 Brian Giles .10 .30
424 Rob Mackowiak .10 .30
425 Bronson Arroyo .10 .30
426 Kevin Young .10 .30
427 Jack Wilson .10 .30
428 Adrian Brown .10 .30
429 Chad Hermansen .10 .30
430 Jimmy Anderson .10 .30
431 Aramis Ramirez .10 .30
432 Todd Ritchie .10 .30
433 Pat Meares .10 .30
434 Warren Morris .10 .30
435 Derek Bell .10 .30
436 Ken Griffey Jr. .50 1.25
437 Elmer Dessens .10 .30
438 Ruben Rivera .10 .30
439 Jason LaRue .10 .30
440 Sean Casey .10 .30
441 Pete Harnisch .10 .30
442 Danny Graves .10 .30
443 Aaron Boone .10 .30
444 Dmitri Young .10 .30
445 Brandon Larson .10 .30
446 Pokey Reese .10 .30
447 Todd Walker .10 .30
448 Juan Castro .10 .30
449 Todd Helton .20 .50
450 Ben Petrick .10 .30
451 Juan Pierre .10 .30
452 Jeff Cirillo .10 .30
453 Juan Uribe .10 .30
454 Brian Bohanon .10 .30
455 Terry Shumpert .10 .30
456 Mike Hampton .10 .30
457 Shawn Chacon .10 .30
458 Adam Melhuse .10 .30
459 Greg Norton .10 .30
460 Gabe White .10 .30
461 Ichiro Suzuki WS .30 .75
462 Carlos Delgado WS .10 .30
463 Manny Ramirez WS .20 .50
464 Miguel Tejada WS .10 .30
465 Tsuyoshi Shinjo WS .10 .30
466 Bernie Williams WS .10 .30
467 Juan Gonzalez WS .10 .30
468 Andruw Jones WS .10 .30
469 Ivan Rodriguez WS .10 .30
470 Larry Walker WS .10 .30
471 Hideo Nomo WS .10 .30
472 Albert Pujols WS .30 .75
473 Pedro Martinez WS .20 .50
474 Vladimir Guerrero WS .20 .50
475 Tony Batista WS .10 .30
476 Kazuhiro Sasaki WS .10 .30
477 Richard Hidalgo WS .10 .30
478 Carlos Lee WS .10 .30
479 Roberto Alomar WS .10 .30
480 Rafael Palmeiro WS .10 .30
481 Ken Griffey Jr. GG .30 .75
482 Ken Griffey Jr. GG .30 .75
483 Ken Griffey Jr. GG .30 .75
484 Ken Griffey Jr. GG .30 .75
485 Ken Griffey Jr. GG .30 .75
486 Ken Griffey Jr. GG .30 .75
487 Ken Griffey Jr. GG .30 .75
488 Ken Griffey Jr. GG .30 .75
489 Ken Griffey Jr. GG .30 .75
490 Ken Griffey Jr. GG .30 .75
491 Barry Bonds CL .40 1.00
492 Hideo Nomo CL .10 .30
493 Ichiro Suzuki CL .30 .75
494 Cal Ripken CL .50 1.25
495 Tony Gwynn CL .20 .50
496 Randy Johnson CL .20 .50
497 A.J. Burnett CL .10 .30
498 Rickey Henderson CL .20 .50
499 Albert Pujols CL .30 .75
500 Luis Gonzalez CL .10 .30
501 Brandon Puffer SR RC .40 1.00
502 Rodrigo Rosario SR RC .40 1.00
503 Tom Shearn SR RC .40 1.00
504 Reed Johnson SR RC .60 1.50
505 Chris Baker SR RC .40 1.00
506 John Ennis SR RC .40 1.00
507 Luis Martinez SR RC .40 1.00
508 So Taguchi SR RC .60 1.50
509 Scotty Layfield SR RC .40 1.00
510 Francis Beltran SR RC .40 1.00
511 Brandon Backe SR RC .60 1.50
512 Doug Devore SR RC .40 1.00
513 Jeremy Ward SR RC .40 1.00
514 Jose Valverde SR RC 1.25 3.00
515 P.J. Bevis SR RC .40 1.00
516 Victor Alvarez SR RC .40 1.00
517 Kazuhisa Ishii SR RC .60 1.50
518 Jorge Nunez SR RC .40 1.00
519 Eric Good SR RC .40 1.00
520 Ron Calloway SR RC .40 1.00
521 Val Pascucci SR .40 1.00
522 Nelson Castro SR RC .40 1.00
523 Deivis Santos SR .40 1.00
524 Luis Ugueto SR RC .40 1.00
525 Matt Thornton SR RC .40 1.00
526 Hansel Izquierdo SR RC .40 1.00
527 Tyler Yates SR RC .40 1.00
528 Mark Corey SR RC .40 1.00
529 Jaime Cerda SR RC .40 1.00
530 Satoru Komiyama SR RC .40 1.00
531 Steve Bechler SR RC .40 1.00
532 Ben Howard SR RC .40 1.00
533 An. Machado SR RC .40 1.00
534 Jorge Padilla SR RC .40 1.00
535 Eric Junge SR RC .40 1.00
536 Adrian Burnside SR RC .40 1.00
537 Mike Gonzalez SR RC .40 1.00
538 Josh Hancock SR RC .50 1.25
539 Colin Young SR RC .40 1.00
540 Rene Reyes SR RC .40 1.00
541 Cam Esslinger SR RC .40 1.00
542 Tim Kalita SR RC .40 1.00
543 Kevin Frederick SR RC .40 1.00
544 Kyle Kane SR RC .40 1.00
545 Edwin Almonte SR RC .40 1.00
546 Aaron Sele .10 .30
547 Garret Anderson .10 .30
548 Darin Erstad .10 .30
549 Brad Fullmer .10 .30
550 Kevin Appier .10 .30
551 Tim Salmon .20 .50
552 David Justice .10 .30
553 Billy Koch .10 .30
554 Scott Hatteberg .10 .30
555 Tim Hudson .10 .30
556 Miguel Tejada .10 .30
557 Carlos Pena .10 .30
558 Mike Sirotka .10 .30
559 Jose Cruz Jr. .10 .30
560 Josh Phelps .10 .30
561 Brandon Lyon .10 .30
562 Luke Prokopec .10 .30
563 Felipe Lopez .10 .30
564 Jason Standridge .10 .30
565 Chris Gomez .10 .30
566 John Flaherty .10 .30
567 Jason Tyner .10 .30
568 Bobby Smith .10 .30
569 Wilson Alvarez .10 .30
570 Matt Lawton .10 .30
571 Omar Vizquel .20 .50
572 Jim Thome .20 .50
573 Brady Anderson .10 .30
574 Alex Escobar .10 .30
575 Russell Branyan .10 .30
576 Bret Boone .10 .30
577 Ben Davis .10 .30
578 Mike Cameron .10 .30
579 Jamie Moyer .10 .30
580 Ruben Sierra .10 .30
581 Jeff Cirillo .10 .30
582 Marty Cordova .10 .30
583 Mike Bordick .10 .30
584 Brian Roberts .10 .30
585 Luis Matos .10 .30
586 Geronimo Gil .10 .30
587 Jay Gibbons .10 .30
588 Carl Everett .10 .30
589 Ivan Rodriguez .20 .50
590 Chan Ho Park .10 .30
591 Juan Gonzalez .10 .30
592 Hank Blalock .20 .50
593 Todd Van Poppel .10 .30
594 Pedro Martinez .20 .50
595 Jason Varitek .30 .75
596 Tony Clark .10 .30
597 Johnny Damon Sox .20 .50
598 Dustin Hermanson .10 .30
599 John Burkett .10 .30
600 Carlos Beltran .10 .30
601 Mark Quinn .10 .30
602 Chuck Knoblauch .10 .30
603 Michael Tucker .10 .30
604 Carlos Febles .10 .30
605 Jose Rosado .10 .30
606 Dmitri Young .10 .30
607 Bobby Higginson .10 .30
608 Craig Paquette .10 .30
609 Mitch Meluskey .10 .30
610 Wendell Magee .10 .30
611 Mike Rivera .10 .30
612 Jacque Jones .10 .30
613 Luis Rivas .10 .30
614 Eric Milton .10 .30
615 Eddie Guardado .10 .30
616 Matt LeCroy .10 .30
617 Mike Jackson .10 .30
618 Magglio Ordonez .10 .30
619 Frank Thomas .30 .75
620 Rocky Biddle .10 .30
621 Paul Konerko .10 .30
622 Todd Ritchie .10 .30
623 Jon Rauch .10 .30
624 John Vander Wal .10 .30
625 Rondell White .10 .30
626 Jason Giambi .10 .30
627 Robin Ventura .10 .30
628 David Wells .10 .30
629 Bernie Williams .20 .50
630 Lance Berkman .10 .30
631 Richard Hidalgo .10 .30
632 Greg Zaun .10 .30
633 Jose Vizcaino .10 .30
634 Octavio Dotel .10 .30
635 Morgan Ensberg .10 .30
636 Andruw Jones .20 .50
637 Tom Glavine .20 .50
638 Gary Sheffield .10 .30
639 Vinny Castilla .10 .30
640 Javy Lopez .10 .30
641 Albie Lopez .10 .30
642 Geoff Jenkins .10 .30
643 Jeffrey Hammonds .10 .30
644 Alex Ochoa .10 .30
645 Richie Sexson .10 .30
646 Eric Young .10 .30
647 Glendon Rusch .10 .30
648 Tino Martinez .20 .50
649 Fernando Vina .10 .30
650 J.D. Drew .10 .30
651 Woody Williams .10 .30
652 Darryl Kile .10 .30
653 Jason Isringhausen .10 .30
654 Moises Alou .10 .30
655 Alex Gonzalez .10 .30
656 Delino DeShields .10 .30
657 Todd Hundley .10 .30
658 Chris Stynes .10 .30
659 Jason Bere .10 .30
660 Curt Schilling .10 .30
661 Craig Counsell .10 .30
662 Mark Grace .20 .50
663 Matt Williams .10 .30
664 Jay Bell .10 .30
665 Rick Helling .10 .30
666 Shawn Green .10 .30
667 Eric Karros .10 .30
668 Hideo Nomo .30 .75
669 Omar Daal .10 .30
670 Brian Jordan .10 .30
671 Cesar Izturis .10 .30
672 Fernando Tatis .10 .30
673 Lee Stevens .10 .30
674 Tomo Ohka .10 .30
675 Brian Schneider .10 .30
676 Brad Wilkerson .10 .30
677 Bruce Chen .10 .30
678 Tsuyoshi Shinjo .10 .30
679 Jeff Kent .10 .30
680 Kirk Rueter .10 .30
681 J.T. Snow .10 .30
682 David Bell .10 .30
683 Reggie Sanders .10 .30
684 Preston Wilson .10 .30
685 Vic Darensbourg .10 .30
686 Josh Beckett .10 .30
687 Pablo Ozuna .10 .30
688 Mike Redmond .10 .30
689 Scott Strickland .10 .30
690 Mo Vaughn .10 .30
691 Roberto Alomar .20 .50
692 Edgardo Alfonzo .10 .30
693 Shawn Estes .10 .30
694 Roger Cedeno .10 .30
695 Jeromy Burnitz .10 .30
696 Ray Lankford .10 .30
697 Mark Kotsay .10 .30
698 Kevin Jarvis .10 .30
699 Bobby Jones .10 .30
700 Sean Burroughs .10 .30
701 Ramon Vazquez .10 .30
702 Pat Burrell .10 .30
703 Marlon Byrd .10 .30
704 Brandon Duckworth .10 .30
705 Marlon Anderson .10 .30
706 Vicente Padilla .10 .30
707 Kip Wells .10 .30
708 Jason Kendall .10 .30
709 Pokey Reese .10 .30
710 Pat Meares .10 .30
711 Kris Benson .10 .30
712 Armando Rios .10 .30
713 Mike Williams .10 .30
714 Barry Larkin .20 .50
715 Adam Dunn .10 .30
716 Juan Encarnacion .10 .30
717 Scott Williamson .10 .30
718 Wilton Guerrero .10 .30
719 Chris Reitsma .10 .30
720 Larry Walker .10 .30
721 Denny Neagle .10 .30
722 Todd Zeile .10 .30
723 Jose Ortiz .10 .30
724 Jason Jennings .10 .30
725 Tony Eusebio .10 .30
726 Ichiro Suzuki YR .30 .75
727 Barry Bonds YR .40 1.00
728 Randy Johnson YR .20 .50
729 Albert Pujols YR .30 .75
730 Roger Clemens YR .30 .75
731 Sammy Sosa YR .20 .50
732 Alex Rodriguez YR .30 .75
733 Chipper Jones YR .20 .50
734 Rickey Henderson YR .20 .50
735 Ichiro Suzuki YR .30 .75
736 Luis Gonzalez SH CL .10 .30
737 Derek Jeter SH CL .40 1.00
738 Ichiro Suzuki SH CL .30 .75
739 Barry Bonds SH CL .40 1.00
740 Curt Schilling SH CL .10 .30
741 Shawn Green SH CL .10 .30
742 Jason Giambi SH CL .10 .30
743 Roberto Alomar SH CL .10 .30
744 Larry Walker SH CL .10 .30
745 Mark McGwire SH CL .40 1.00

2002 Upper Deck 2001 Greatest Hits

Issued into first series packs at a rate of one in 14, these 10 cards feature some of the leading hitters during the 2001 season.

COMPLETE SET (10) 15.00 40.00
GH1 Barry Bonds 2.50 6.00
GH2 Ichiro Suzuki 2.00 5.00
GH3 Albert Pujols 2.00 5.00
GH4 Mike Piazza 1.50 4.00
GH5 Alex Rodriguez 1.50 4.00
GH6 Mark McGwire 2.50 6.00
GH7 Manny Ramirez 1.00 2.50
GH8 Ken Griffey Jr. 1.50 4.00
GH9 Sammy Sosa 1.00 2.50
GH10 Derek Jeter 2.50 6.00

2002 Upper Deck A Piece of History 500 Club

Randomly inserted in 2002 Upper Deck second series packs, this card features a bat slice from Mark McGwire and continues the Upper Deck A Piece of History set begun in 1999. Though lacking actual serial-numbering, according to Upper Deck this card was printed to a stated print run of 350 copies.

MMC Mark McGwire 250.00 400.00

2002 Upper Deck A Piece of History 500 Club Autograph

Randomly inserted in 2002 Upper Deck second series packs, this card features a bat slice from Mark McGwire and an authentic autograph and continues the Upper Deck A Piece of History set begun in 1999. This card was printed to a stated print run of 25 serial numbered sets.

SMMC Mark McGwire/25

2002 Upper Deck AL Centennial Memorabilia

Inserted into first series packs at a rate of one in 144, these 10 cards feature memorabilia from some of the leading players in American League history. The bat jersey cards were produced in smaller quantities than the jersey cards and we have notated those cards with SP's in our checklist.

ALBBR Babe Ruth Bat SP 75.00 150.00
ALBJD Joe DiMaggio Bat SP 50.00 100.00
ALBMM M. Mantle Bat SP 75.00 150.00
ALJAR A. Rodriguez Jsy 6.00 15.00
ALJCR Cal Ripken Jsy 15.00 40.00
ALJFT Frank Thomas Jsy 6.00 15.00
ALJIR Ivan Rodriguez Jsy 6.00 15.00
ALJNR Nolan Ryan Jsy 15.00 40.00
ALJPM P. Martinez Jsy 6.00 15.00
ALJRA R. Alomar Jsy 6.00 15.00

2002 Upper Deck AL Centennial Memorabilia Autograph

Randomly inserted into first series packs, these four cards featured autographs of players whose memorabilia is featured in the Centennial Memorabilia set. These cards are serial numbered to 25. Due to market scarcity, no pricing is provided.

SALCR Cal Ripken Jsy
SALIR Ivan Rodriguez Jsy
SALNR Nolan Ryan Jsy
SALPM Pedro Martinez Jsy

2002 Upper Deck All-Star Home Run Derby Game Jersey

Inserted into first series packs at a rate of one in 288, these seven cards feature jersey swatches from these players who participated in the Home Run Derby. A couple of the jerseys were from regular use and we have notated that information in our checklist.

GOLD PRINT RUN 25 SERIAL #'d SETS
NO GOLD PRICING DUE TO SCARCITY
ASAR Alex Rodriguez 10.00 25.00
ASBRB Bret Boone 6.00 15.00
ASJG1 Jason Giambi 6.00 15.00
ASJG2 Jason Giambi A's 6.00 15.00
ASSS1 Sammy Sosa 8.00 20.00
ASSS2 S. Sosa Cubs 8.00 20.00
ASTH Todd Helton 6.00 15.00

2002 Upper Deck All-Star Salute Game Jersey

Inserted into first series packs at a rate of one in 288, these nine cards feature game jersey swatches of some of the most exciting All-Star performers.

GOLD PRINT RUN 25 SERIAL #'d SETS
NO GOLD PRICING DUE TO SCARCITY
SJAR1 A.Rodriguez Mariners 10.00 25.00
SJAR2 A.Rodriguez Rangers 10.00 25.00
SJDE Dennis Eckersley 6.00 15.00
SJDS Don Sutton 6.00 15.00
SJIS Ichiro Suzuki 20.00 50.00

SJKG Ken Griffey Jr.	12.50	30.00
SJLB Lou Boudreau	6.00	15.00
SJNF Nellie Fox	6.00	15.00
SJSA Sparky Anderson	6.00	15.00

2002 Upper Deck Authentic McGwire

Randomly inserted in second series packs, these two cards feature authentic memorabilia from Mark McGwire's career. These cards have a stated print run of 70 serial numbered sets.

AMB Mark McGwire Bat	50.00	100.00
AMJ Mark McGwire Jsy	50.00	100.00

2002 Upper Deck Big Fly Zone

Issued into first series packs at a rate of one in 14, these 10 cards feature some of the leading power hitters in the game.

COMPLETE SET (10)	12.50	30.00
Z1 Mark McGwire	2.50	6.00
Z2 Ken Griffey Jr.	1.50	4.00
Z3 Manny Ramirez	.60	1.50
Z4 Sammy Sosa	1.00	2.50
Z5 Todd Helton	.60	1.50
Z6 Barry Bonds	2.50	6.00
Z7 Luis Gonzalez	.60	1.50
Z8 Alex Rodriguez	1.50	4.00
Z9 Carlos Delgado	.60	1.50
Z10 Chipper Jones	1.00	2.50

2002 Upper Deck Breakout Performers

Issued into first series packs at a rate of one in 14, these 10 cards feature players who had breakout seasons in 2001.

COMPLETE SET (10)	10.00	25.00
BP1 Ichiro Suzuki	2.00	5.00
BP2 Albert Pujols	2.00	5.00
BP3 Doug Mientkiewicz	.60	1.50
BP4 Lance Berkman	.60	1.50
BP5 Tsuyoshi Shinjo	.60	1.50
BP6 Ben Sheets	.60	1.50
BP7 Jimmy Rollins	.60	1.50
BP8 J.D. Drew	.60	1.50
BP9 Bret Boone	.60	1.50
BP10 Alfonso Soriano	.60	1.50

2002 Upper Deck Championship Caliber

Inserted into first series packs at a rate of one in 23, these six cards feature players who have all earned World Series rings.

COMPLETE SET (6)	8.00	20.00
CC1 Derek Jeter	2.50	6.00
CC2 Roberto Alomar	.60	1.50
CC3 Chipper Jones	1.00	2.50
CC4 Gary Sheffield	.60	1.50
CC5 Roger Clemens	2.00	5.00
CC6 Greg Maddux	1.50	4.00

2002 Upper Deck Championship Caliber Swatch

Inserted in second series packs at a stated rate of one in 288, these 14 cards feature not only players who have been on World Champions but also a game-worn swatch. A few players were issued in shorter supply and we have notated that information in our checklist.

AP Andy Pettitte	6.00	15.00
BL Barry Larkin	6.00	15.00
BW Bernie Williams	6.00	15.00
CF Cliff Floyd	4.00	10.00
CHJ Charles Johnson	4.00	10.00
CJO Chipper Jones SP		
CS Curt Schilling	4.00	10.00
GM Greg Maddux SP		
JO John Olerud	4.00	10.00
JP Jorge Posada	6.00	15.00
KB Kevin Brown SP	6.00	15.00
RA Roberto Alomar SP		
RJ Randy Johnson	6.00	15.00
TM Tino Martinez	6.00	15.00

2002 Upper Deck Chasing History

Inserted at stated odds of one in 11, these 15 cards feature players who are moving up in the record books.

COMPLETE SET (15)	15.00	40.00
CH1 Sammy Sosa	1.25	3.00
CH2 Ken Griffey Jr.	2.00	5.00
CH3 Roger Clemens	2.50	6.00
CH4 Barry Bonds	3.00	8.00
CH5 Rafael Palmeiro	.75	2.00
CH6 Andres Galarraga	.75	2.00
CH7 Juan Gonzalez	.75	2.00
CH8 Roberto Alomar	.75	2.00
CH9 Randy Johnson	1.25	3.00
CH10 Jeff Bagwell	.75	2.00
CH11 Fred McGriff	.75	2.00
CH12 Matt Williams	.75	2.00
CH13 Greg Maddux	2.00	5.00
CH14 Robb Nen	.75	2.00
CH15 Kenny Lofton	.75	2.00

2002 Upper Deck Combo Memorabilia

Issued into first series packs at a rate of one in 288, these seven cards feature two pieces of game-used memorabilia from players who have something in common.

GOLD PRINT RUN 25 SERIAL #'d SETS
NO GOLD PRICING DUE TO SCARCITY

BDM Joe DiMaggio Bat / Mickey Mantle Bat	60.00	120.00
BRG Alex Rodriguez Bat / Ken Griffey Jr. Bat	15.00	40.00
JBS Barry Bonds Jsy / Sammy Sosa Jsy	20.00	50.00
JHK S. Hasegawa Jsy / Byung-Hyun Kim Jsy	6.00	15.00
JRC Nolan Ryan Jsy / Roger Clemens Jsy	30.00	60.00
JRM Nolan Ryan Jsy / Pedro Martinez Jsy	25.00	50.00
JRS Alex Rodriguez Jsy / Sammy Sosa Jsy	15.00	40.00

2002 Upper Deck Double Game Worn Gems

Randomly inserted in second series retail packs, these 12 cards feature two teammates along with pieces of game used memorabilia. These cards have a stated print run of 450 serial numbered sets, except for the Martinez/Ichiro card of which only 150 #'d copies were issued.

DGAP Roberto Alomar / Mike Piazza	10.00	25.00
DGDF Carlos Delgado / Shannon Stewart	6.00	15.00
DGDH Jermaine Dye / Tim Hudson	6.00	15.00
DGGS Luis Gonzalez / Curt Schilling	6.00	15.00
DGKG Jason Kendall / Brian Giles	6.00	15.00
DGMI Edgar Martinez / Ichiro Suzuki SP/150		
DGMM Kevin Millwood / Greg Maddux	10.00	25.00
DGNK Phil Nevin / Ryan Klesko	6.00	15.00
DGPL Robert Person / Mike Lieberthal	6.00	15.00
DGPN Chan Ho Park / Hideo Nomo	20.00	50.00
DGTO Frank Thomas / Magglio Ordonez	8.00	20.00
DGVB Omar Vizquel / Russell Branyan	6.00	15.00

2002 Upper Deck Double Game Worn Gems Gold

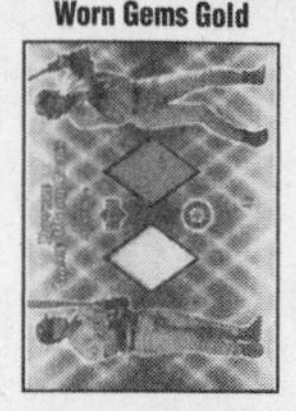

Randomly inserted in second series retail packs, these cards parallel the Double Game Worn Gem insert set. These cards have a stated print run of 100 serial numbered sets except for the Martinez/Ichiro card of which only 40 #'d copies were issued.

DGAP Roberto Alomar / Mike Piazza	20.00	50.00
DGDF Carlos Delgado / Shannon Stewart	12.50	30.00
DGDH Jermaine Dye / Tim Hudson	12.50	30.00
DGGS Luis Gonzalez / Curt Schilling	12.50	30.00
DGKG Jason Kendall / Brian Giles	12.50	30.00
DGMI Edgar Martinez / Ichiro Suzuki/40	50.00	100.00
DGMM Kevin Millwood / Greg Maddux	20.00	50.00
DGNK Phil Nevin / Ryan Klesko	12.50	30.00
DGPL Robert Person / Mike Lieberthal	12.50	30.00
DGPN Chan Ho Park / Hideo Nomo	40.00	100.00
DGTO Frank Thomas / Magglio Ordonez	15.00	40.00
DGVB Omar Vizquel / Russell Branyan	12.50	30.00

2002 Upper Deck First Timers Game Jersey

Inserted into first series hobby packs at a rate of one in 288 hobby packs, these nine cards feature players who have never been featured on a Upper Deck game jersey card before.

FTAP Albert Pujols	20.00	50.00
FTCP Corey Patterson	4.00	10.00
FTEM Eric Milton	4.00	10.00
FTFG Freddy Garcia	4.00	10.00
FTJM Joe Mays	4.00	10.00
FTML Matt Lawton	4.00	10.00
FTOD Omar Daal	4.00	10.00
FTRB Russell Branyan	4.00	10.00
FTSS Shannon Stewart	4.00	10.00

2002 Upper Deck First Timers Game Jersey Autograph

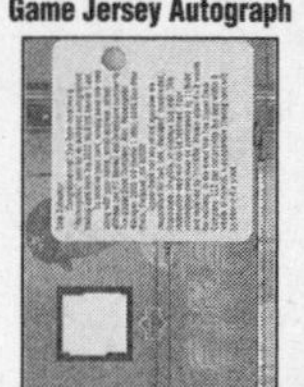

This parallel to the First Timers Game Jersey set features the players signing 25 copies of these cards. These cards were distributed exclusively in first series hobby packs. Freddy Garcia did not return his cards in time for packout and thus was available only in exchange format with a redemption deadline of 11/19/04. Due to market scarcity, no pricing is provided.

SFTAP Albert Pujols
SFTCP Corey Patterson
SFTFG Freddy Garcia
SFTJM Joe Mays
SFTSS Shannon Stewart

2002 Upper Deck Game Base

Inserted into first series packs at a rate of one in 288, these 22 cards feature authentic pieces of bases used in official Major League games.

BAJ Andruw Jones	6.00	15.00
BAR Alex Rodriguez	8.00	20.00
BBB Barry Bonds	12.50	30.00
BCD Carlos Delgado	4.00	10.00
BCJ Chipper Jones	6.00	15.00
BCR Cal Ripken	15.00	40.00
BDJ Derek Jeter	12.50	30.00
BIR Ivan Rodriguez	6.00	15.00
BIS Ichiro Suzuki	20.00	50.00
BJG Jason Giambi	4.00	10.00
BJG Juan Gonzalez	4.00	10.00
BKG Ken Griffey Jr.	8.00	20.00
BKS Kazuhiro Sasaki	4.00	10.00
BLG Luis Gonzalez	4.00	10.00
BMM Mark McGwire	20.00	50.00
BMP Mike Piazza	6.00	15.00
BRC Roger Clemens	10.00	25.00
BSG Shawn Green	4.00	10.00
BSS Sammy Sosa	6.00	15.00
BTG Troy Glaus	4.00	10.00
CBMJ Mark McGwire / Derek Jeter	30.00	60.00
CBRG Alex Rodriguez / Ken Griffey Jr.	15.00	40.00

2002 Upper Deck Game Base Autograph

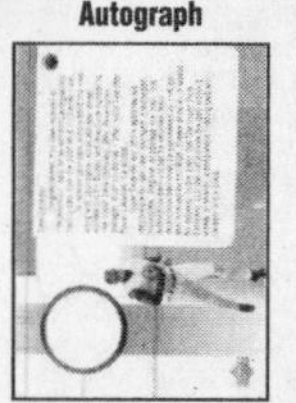

Randomly inserted into first series packs, Ken Griffey Jr. signed 25 cards for inclusion in this set. However, Griffey did not return his cards in time for inclusion in the packs and therefore these cards could be redeemed until November 5, 2004. Due to market scarcity, no pricing is provided.

SBKG Ken Griffey Jr.

2002 Upper Deck Game Jersey

Randomly inserted in packs, these 11 cards feature some of today's star players along with a game-worn swatch of the featured player.

AB Adrian Beltre	4.00	10.00
CS Curt Schilling	4.00	10.00
FT Frank Thomas	6.00	15.00
JC Jeff Cirillo Pants	4.00	10.00
KG Ken Griffey Jr.	10.00	25.00
MP Mike Piazza Pants	6.00	15.00
PW Preston Wilson	4.00	10.00
SR Scott Rolen	6.00	15.00
SS Sammy Sosa	6.00	15.00
TB Tony Batista	4.00	10.00
TH Tim Hudson	4.00	10.00

2002 Upper Deck Game Jersey Autograph

Randomly inserted into first series hobby packs, these 12 cards feature not only a game jersey swatch but also an authentic autograph of the player featured. These cards are serial numbered to 200. The following players did not return their signed cards in time for release in the packs and those cards had an exchange deadline of November 19, 2004: Andruw Jones, Albert Pujols and Ken Griffey Jr.

JAJ Andruw Jones	20.00	50.00
JAP Albert Pujols	150.00	250.00
JBB Barry Bonds	100.00	175.00
JCD Carlos Delgado	15.00	40.00
JCR Cal Ripken	75.00	150.00
JGS Gary Sheffield	20.00	50.00
JIS Ichiro Suzuki UER Word Close repeated in ninth line of text	250.00	400.00
JJG Jason Giambi	15.00	40.00
JKG Ken Griffey Jr.	60.00	120.00
JNR Nolan Ryan	75.00	150.00
JPW Preston Wilson	15.00	40.00
JRF Rafael Furcal	15.00	40.00

2002 Upper Deck Game Jersey Patch

Inserted at a rate of one in 2,500 first series packs, these cards feature a jersey patch from the star players featured.

PLAR Alex Rodriguez L	75.00	150.00
PLBB Barry Bonds L	75.00	150.00
PLCR Cal Ripken L	60.00	120.00
PLJG Jason Giambi L	20.00	50.00
PLKG Ken Griffey Jr. L	50.00	100.00
PLPM Pedro Martinez L	40.00	80.00
PLSS Sammy Sosa L	40.00	80.00
PNAR Alex Rodriguez N	50.00	100.00
PNBB Barry Bonds N	75.00	150.00
PNCR Cal Ripken N	60.00	120.00
PNJG Jason Giambi N	20.00	50.00
PNKG Ken Griffey Jr. N	50.00	100.00
PNPM Pedro Martinez N	40.00	80.00
PNSS Sammy Sosa N	40.00	80.00
PSAR Alex Rodriguez S	50.00	100.00
PSBB Barry Bonds S	75.00	150.00
PSCR Cal Ripken S	60.00	120.00
PSJG Jason Giambi S	20.00	50.00
PSKG Ken Griffey Jr. S	60.00	120.00
PSPM Pedro Martinez S	40.00	80.00
PSSS Sammy Sosa S	40.00	80.00

2002 Upper Deck Game Jersey Patch Autograph

Randomly inserted into first series packs, these six cards feature not only a game jersey patch swatch but also an authentic autograph of the player featured. These cards are serial numbered to 25. Ken Griffey Jr. did not return his cards in time for pack out and those cards were issued as exchange cards with a redemption deadline of 11/5/04. Due to market scarcity, no pricing is provided.

SPNBB Barry Bonds N
SPNCR Cal Ripken N
SPNKG Ken Griffey Jr. N
SPNSS Sammy Sosa N
SPSBB Barry Bonds S
SPSCR Cal Ripken S

2002 Upper Deck Game Worn Gems

Inserted in second series retail packs at a stated rate of one in 48 retail packs, these 31 cards feature leading stars along a game-used memorabilia piece. A few cards were issued in shorter supply and those cards are notated in our checklist with an SP. Cards notated with an SP are not priced due to market scarcity.

GAS Aaron Sele	4.00	10.00
GCD Carlos Delgado	4.00	10.00
GCJ Chipper Jones	6.00	15.00
GCR Cal Ripken	20.00	50.00
GCS Curt Schilling	4.00	10.00
GDE Darin Erstad SP		
GEC Eric Chavez	4.00	10.00
GEM Edgar Martinez	6.00	15.00
GEM Eric Milton	4.00	10.00
GFG Freddy Garcia SP		
GFT Frank Thomas	6.00	15.00
GGM Greg Maddux	6.00	15.00
GGS Gary Sheffield SP		
GHN Hideo Nomo SP		
GIR Ivan Rodriguez	6.00	15.00
GJG Juan Gonzalez	4.00	10.00
GJK Jason Kendall	4.00	10.00
GJM Joe Mays	4.00	10.00
GJO John Olerud SP		
GLG Luis Gonzalez SP		
GMH Mike Hampton SP		
GOV Omar Vizquel SP		
GPM Pedro Martinez SP		
GPN Phil Nevin	4.00	10.00
GRA Roberto Alomar	6.00	15.00
GRK Ryan Klesko SP		
GRP Robert Person	4.00	10.00
GRY Robin Yount	6.00	15.00
GSR Scott Rolen	6.00	15.00
GTG Tom Glavine	6.00	15.00
GTM Tino Martinez	6.00	15.00

2002 Upper Deck Global Swatch Game Jersey

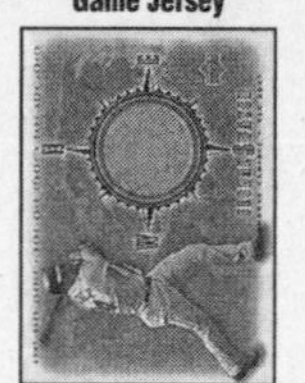

Issued at a rate of one in 144 first series packs, these 10 cards feature swatches of game jerseys worn by players who were born outside the continental United States.

GSBK Byung-Hyun Kim	4.00	10.00
GSCD Carlos Delgado	4.00	10.00
GSCP Chan Ho Park	4.00	10.00
GSHN Hideo Nomo	15.00	40.00
GSIS Ichiro Suzuki	20.00	50.00
GSKS Kazuhiro Sasaki	4.00	10.00
GSMR Manny Ramirez	6.00	15.00
GSMY Masato Yoshii	4.00	10.00
GSSH Shig Hasegawa	4.00	10.00
GSTS Tsuyoshi Shinjo	4.00	10.00

2002 Upper Deck Global Swatch Game Jersey Autograph

Randomly inserted into first series packs, these five cards feature not only a game-jersey swatch but also authentic autographs from the players. These cards are serial numbered to 25. Due to market scarcity, no pricing is provided.

SGSBK Byung-Hyun Kim
SGSCD Carlos Delgado
SGSCP Chan Ho Park
SGSHN Hideo Nomo
SGSTS Tsuyoshi Shinjo

2002 Upper Deck McGwire Combo Jersey

Randomly inserted in second series packs, these three cards feature swatches of Mark McGwire pictured alongside another active slugger. These cards were printed to a stated print run of 25 serial numbered sets and no pricing is available due to market scarcity.

MMJG Mark McGwire / Jason Giambi
MMKG Mark McGwire / Ken Griffey Jr.
MMSS Mark McGwire / Sammy Sosa

2002 Upper Deck Peoples Choice Game Jersey

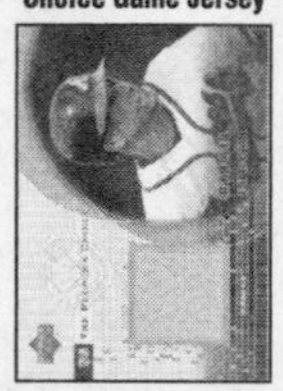

Inserted in second series hobby packs at a stated rate of one in 24, these 39 cards feature some of the most popular player in baseball along with a game-worn memorabilia swatch. A few cards were issued in lesser quantity and we have notated those cards with an SP in our checklist.

PJAG Andres Galarraga SP	6.00	15.00
PJAP Andy Pettitte	6.00	15.00
PJAR Alex Rodriguez	6.00	15.00
PJBG Brian Giles	4.00	10.00
PJBW Bernie Williams	6.00	15.00
PJCD Carlos Delgado	4.00	10.00
PJCJ Charles Johnson	4.00	10.00
PJCS Curt Schilling	4.00	10.00
PJDL Derek Lowe	4.00	10.00
PJDW David Wells	4.00	10.00
PJEB Ellis Burks SP	6.00	15.00
PJFT Frank Thomas	6.00	15.00
PJGM Greg Maddux	6.00	15.00
PJHI Hideki Irabu	4.00	10.00
PJJG Juan Gonzalez	4.00	10.00
PJJN Jeff Nelson	4.00	10.00
PJJS J.T. Snow	4.00	10.00
PJBA Jeff Bagwell	6.00	15.00
PJJBU Jeromy Burnitz	4.00	10.00
PJKG Ken Griffey Jr.	8.00	20.00
PJMP Mike Piazza	6.00	15.00
PJMS Mike Stanton	4.00	10.00
PJMW Matt Williams SP	6.00	15.00
PJMRA Manny Ramirez	6.00	15.00
PJMRI Mariano Rivera	6.00	15.00
PJOD Omar Daal	4.00	10.00
PJOV Omar Vizquel	6.00	15.00
PJRF Rafael Furcal	4.00	10.00
PJRO Rey Ordonez	4.00	10.00
PJRP Rafael Palmeiro SP	10.00	25.00
PJRP Robert Person SP	6.00	15.00
PJRV Robin Ventura	4.00	10.00
PJSH Sterling Hitchcock	4.00	10.00
PJSS Sammy Sosa	6.00	15.00
PJTG Tony Gwynn	6.00	15.00
PJTM Tino Martinez	6.00	15.00
PJTR Tim Raines Sr.	4.00	10.00
PJTS Tim Salmon	6.00	15.00
PJTSh Tsuyoshi Shinjo	4.00	10.00

2002 Upper Deck Return of the Ace

Inserted into second series packs at a stated rate of one in 11 packs, these 15 cards feature some of today's leading pitchers.

COMPLETE SET (15)	12.50	30.00
RA1 Randy Johnson	1.25	3.00
RA2 Greg Maddux	2.00	5.00
RA3 Pedro Martinez	.75	2.00
RA4 Freddy Garcia	.75	2.00
RA5 Matt Morris	.75	2.00
RA6 Mark Mulder	.75	2.00
RA7 Wade Miller	.75	2.00
RA8 Kevin Brown	.75	2.00
RA9 Roger Clemens	2.50	6.00
RA10 Jon Lieber	.75	2.00
RA11 C.C. Sabathia	.75	2.00
RA12 Tim Hudson	.75	2.00
RA13 Curt Schilling	.75	2.00
RA14 Al Leiter	.75	2.00
RA15 Mike Mussina	.75	2.00

2002 Upper Deck Sons of Summer Game Jersey

Inserted at a stated rate of one in 288 second series packs, these eight cards feature some of the best players in the game along with a game jersey swatch. According to Upper Deck, the Pedro Martinez card was issued in shorter supply.

SSAR Alex Rodriguez	8.00	20.00
SSGM Greg Maddux	8.00	20.00
SSJB Jeff Bagwell	8.00	20.00
SSJG Juan Gonzalez	6.00	15.00
SSMP Mike Piazza	8.00	20.00
SSPM Pedro Martinez SP	10.00	25.00
SSRA Roberto Alomar	8.00	20.00
SSRC Roger Clemens	12.50	30.00

2002 Upper Deck Superstar Summit I

Inserted into first series packs at a rate of one in 23, these six cards feature the most popular players in the game.

COMPLETE SET (6)	10.00	25.00
SS1 Sammy Sosa	1.50	4.00
SS2 Alex Rodriguez	1.50	4.00
SS3 Mark McGwire	2.50	6.00
SS4 Barry Bonds	2.50	6.00
SS5 Mike Piazza	1.50	4.00
SS6 Ken Griffey Jr.	1.50	4.00

2002 Upper Deck Superstar Summit II

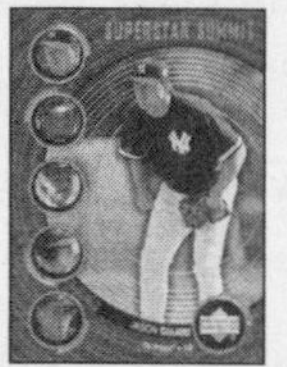

Inserted into second series packs at a rate of one in 11, these fifteen cards feature the most popular players in the game.

COMPLETE SET (15)	25.00	60.00
SS1 Alex Rodriguez	2.00	5.00
SS2 Jason Giambi	1.25	3.00
SS3 Vladimir Guerrero	1.25	3.00
SS4 Randy Johnson	1.25	3.00
SS5 Chipper Jones	1.25	3.00
SS6 Ichiro Suzuki	2.50	6.00
SS7 Sammy Sosa	1.25	3.00
SS8 Greg Maddux	2.00	5.00
SS9 Ken Griffey Jr.	2.00	5.00
SS10 Todd Helton	1.25	3.00
SS11 Barry Bonds	3.00	8.00
SS12 Derek Jeter	3.00	8.00
SS13 Mike Piazza	2.00	5.00
SS14 Ivan Rodriguez	1.25	3.00
SS15 Frank Thomas	1.25	3.00

2002 Upper Deck UD Plus Hobby

Issued as a two-card box topper in second series Upper Deck packs, these 100 cards could be exchanged for Joe DiMaggio or Mickey Mantle jersey cards if a collector finished the entire set. These cards were numbered to a stated print run of 1125 serial numbered sets. Hobby cards feature silver foil accents on front (unlike the Retail UD Plus cards - of which feature bronze fronts and backs). These cards could be exchanged until May 16, 2003.

UD1 Darin Erstad	2.00	5.00
UD2 Troy Glaus	2.00	5.00
UD3 Tim Hudson	2.00	5.00
UD4 Jermaine Dye	2.00	5.00

UD5 Barry Zito 2.00 5.00
UD6 Carlos Delgado 2.00 5.00
UD7 Shannon Stewart 2.00 5.00
UD8 Greg Vaughn 2.00 5.00
UD9 Jim Thome 2.00 5.00
UD10 C.C. Sabathia 2.00 5.00
UD11 Ichiro Suzuki 5.00 12.00
UD12 Edgar Martinez 2.00 5.00
UD13 Bret Boone 2.00 5.00
UD14 Freddy Garcia 2.00 5.00
UD15 Matt Thornton 2.00 5.00
UD16 Jeff Conine 2.00 5.00
UD17 Steve Bechler 2.00 5.00
UD18 Rafael Palmeiro 2.00 5.00
UD19 Juan Gonzalez 2.00 5.00
UD20 Alex Rodriguez 4.00 10.00
UD21 Ivan Rodriguez 2.00 5.00
UD22 Carl Everett 2.00 5.00
UD23 Manny Ramirez 2.00 5.00
UD24 Nomar Garciaparra 4.00 10.00
UD25 Pedro Martinez 2.00 5.00
UD26 Mike Sweeney 2.00 5.00
UD27 Chuck Knoblauch 2.00 5.00
UD28 Dmitri Young 2.00 5.00
UD29 Bobby Higginson 2.00 5.00
UD30 Dean Palmer 2.00 5.00
UD31 Doug Mientkiewicz 2.00 5.00
UD32 Corey Koskie 2.00 5.00
UD33 Brad Radke 2.00 5.00
UD34 Cristian Guzman 2.00 5.00
UD35 Frank Thomas 2.50 6.00
UD36 Magglio Ordonez 2.00 5.00
UD37 Carlos Lee 2.00 5.00
UD38 Roger Clemens 5.00 12.00
UD39 Bernie Williams 2.00 5.00
UD40 Derek Jeter 6.00 15.00
UD41 Jason Giambi 2.00 5.00
UD42 Mike Mussina 2.00 5.00
UD43 Jeff Bagwell 2.00 5.00
UD44 Lance Berkman 2.00 5.00
UD45 Wade Miller 2.00 5.00
UD46 Greg Maddux 4.00 10.00
UD47 Chipper Jones 2.50 6.00
UD48 Andruw Jones 2.00 5.00
UD49 Gary Sheffield 2.00 5.00
UD50 Richie Sexson 2.00 5.00
UD51 Albert Pujols 5.00 12.00
UD52 J.D. Drew 2.00 5.00
UD53 Matt Morris 2.00 5.00
UD54 Jim Edmonds 2.00 5.00
UD55 So Taguchi 2.00 5.00
UD56 Sammy Sosa 2.50 6.00
UD57 Fred McGriff 2.00 5.00
UD58 Kerry Wood 2.00 5.00
UD59 Moises Alou 2.00 5.00
UD60 Randy Johnson 2.50 6.00
UD61 Luis Gonzalez 2.00 5.00
UD62 Mark Grace 2.00 5.00
UD63 Curt Schilling 2.00 5.00
UD64 Matt Williams 2.00 5.00
UD65 Kevin Brown 2.00 5.00
UD66 Brian Jordan 2.00 5.00
UD67 Shawn Green 2.00 5.00
UD68 Hideo Nomo 5.00 12.00
UD69 Kazuhisa Ishii 2.00 5.00
UD70 Vladimir Guerrero 2.50 6.00
UD71 Jose Vidro 2.00 5.00
UD72 Eric Good 2.00 5.00
UD73 Barry Bonds 6.00 15.00
UD74 Jeff Kent 2.00 5.00
UD75 Rich Aurilia 2.00 5.00
UD76 Deivis Santos 2.00 5.00
UD77 Preston Wilson 2.00 5.00
UD78 Cliff Floyd 2.00 5.00
UD79 Josh Beckett 2.00 5.00
UD80 Hansel Izquierdo 2.00 5.00
UD81 Mike Piazza 4.00 10.00
UD82 Roberto Alomar 2.00 5.00
UD83 Mo Vaughn 2.00 5.00
UD84 Jeromy Burnitz 2.00 5.00
UD85 Phil Nevin 2.00 5.00
UD86 Ryan Klesko 2.00 5.00
UD87 Bobby Abreu 2.00 5.00
UD88 Scott Rolen 2.00 5.00
UD89 Jimmy Rollins 2.00 5.00
UD90 Jason Kendall 2.00 5.00
UD91 Brian Giles 2.00 5.00
UD92 Aramis Ramirez 2.00 5.00
UD93 Ken Griffey Jr. 4.00 10.00
UD94 Sean Casey 2.00 5.00
UD95 Barry Larkin 2.00 5.00
UD96 Adam Dunn 2.00 5.00
UD97 Todd Helton 2.00 5.00
UD98 Larry Walker 2.00 5.00
UD99 Mike Hampton 2.00 5.00
UD100 Rene Reyes 2.00 5.00

2002 Upper Deck UD Plus Memorabilia Moments Game Uniform

These cards were available only through a mail exchange. Collectors who finished the UD Plus set earliest had an opportunity to receive cards with game-used jersey swatches of either Mickey Mantle or Joe DiMaggio. These cards were issued to a stated print run of 25 serial numbred sets. The deadline to redeem these cards was 5/16/03. Due to market scarcity, no pricing will be provided for these cards.

COMMON DIMAGGIO (1-5) 60.00 120.00
COMMON MANTLE (1-5) 150.00 250.00
AVAILABLE VIA MAIL EXCHANGE
STATED PRINT RUN 25 SERIAL #'d SETS

2002 Upper Deck World Series Heroes Memorabilia

Issued into first series packs at a rate of one in 288 hobby packs, these eight cards feature memorabilia from players who had star moments in the World Series.

BDJ Derek Jeter Base SP 15.00 40.00
BES E.Slaughter Bat 6.00 15.00
BJD Joe DiMaggio Bat SP 50.00 100.00
BKP Kirby Puckett Bat 10.00 25.00
BMM M.Mantle Bat 75.00 150.00
SBM B.Mazeroski Jsy 8.00 20.00
SCF Carlton Fisk Jsy 8.00 20.00
SDL Don Larsen Jsy 8.00 20.00
SJC Joe Carter Jsy 6.00 15.00

2002 Upper Deck World Series Heroes Memorabilia Autograph

Randomly inserted in first series hobby packs, these four cards feature not only a piece of memorabilia from a World Series hero but also were signed by the featured player. A stated print run of twenty-five serial numbered cards were produced. Due to market scarcity, no pricing is provided for these cards.

SBM Bill Mazeroski Jsy
SCF Carlton Fisk Jsy
SDL Don Larsen Jsy
SJC Joe Carter Jsy

2002 Upper Deck Yankee Dynasty Memorabilia

Issued into first series packs at a rate of one in 144, these 13 cards feature two pieces of game-worn memorabilia from various members of the Yankees Dynasty.

YBCJ Roger Clemens Base 75.00 150.00
Derek Jeter Base SP
YBJW Derek Jeter Base 50.00 100.00
Bernie Williams Base
YJBJ Scott Brosius Jsy 10.00 25.00
David Justice Jsy
YJBT Wade Bogg Jsys 10.00 25.00
Joe Torre Jsy
YJCP Roger Clemens Jsy 20.00 50.00
Jorge Posada Jsy
YJDM Joe DiMaggio Jsy 150.00 250.00
Mickey Mantle Jsy
YJGC Joe Girardi Jsy 10.00 25.00
David Cone Jsy
YJKR Chuck Knoblauch Jsy 10.00 25.00
Tim Raines Jsy
YJOM Paul O'Neill Jsy 10.00 25.00
Tino Martinez Jsy
YJPR Andy Pettitte Jsy 15.00 40.00
Mariano Rivera Jsy
YJRK Willie Randolph Jsy 10.00 25.00
Chuck Knoblauch Jsy
YJWG David Wells Jsy 10.00 25.00
Dwight Gooden Jsy
YJWO Bernie Williams Jsy 10.00 25.00
Paul O'Neill Jsy

2003 Upper Deck

The 270 card first series was released in November, 2002. The 270 card second series was released in June, 2003. The final 60 cards were released as part of an special boxed insert in the 2004 Upper Deck Series one product. The first tw series cards were issued in eight card packs which came 24 packs to a box and 12 boxes to a case with an SRP of $3 per pack. Cards numbered from 1 through 30 featured leading rookie prospects while cards numbered from 261 through 270 featured checklist cards honoring the leading events of the 2002 season. In the second series the following subsets were issued: Cards numbered 501 through 530 feature Star Rookies while cards numbered 531 through 540 feature Season Highlight fronts and checklist backs. Due to an error in printing, card 19 was originally intended to feature Marcos Scutaro but the card was erroneously numbered as card 96. Thus, the set features two card 96's (Scutaro and Nomar Garciaparra) and no card number 19.

COMPLETE SERIES 1 (270) 20.00 50.00
COMPLETE SERIES 2 (270) 20.00 50.00
COMP.UPDATE SET (60) 10.00 20.00
COMMON (31-500/531-600) .10 .30
COMMON (1-30/501-530) .40 1.00
COMMON RC (541-600) .20 .50
SR 1-30/501-530 ARE NOT SHORT PRINTS
CARD 19 DOES NOT EXIST
SCUTARO/NOMAR ARE BOTH CARD 96
541-600 ISSUED IN 04 UD1 HOBBY BOXES
UPDATE SET EXCH 1:240 '04 UD1 RETAIL
UPDATE SET EXCH.DEADLINE 11/10/06

1 John Lackey SR .40 1.00
2 Alex Cintron SR .40 1.00
3 Jose Leon SR .40 1.00
4 Bobby Hill SR .40 1.00
5 Brandon Larson SR .40 1.00
6 Raul Gonzalez SR .40 1.00
7 Ben Broussard SR .40 1.00
8 Earl Snyder SR .40 1.00
9 Ramon Santiago SR .40 1.00
10 Jason Lane SR .40 1.00
11 Keith Ginter SR .40 1.00
12 Kirk Saarloos SR .40 1.00
13 Juan Brito SR .40 1.00
14 Runelvys Hernandez SR .40 1.00
15 Shawn Sedlacek SR .40 1.00
16 Jayson Durocher SR .40 1.00
17 Kevin Frederick SR .40 1.00
18 Zach Day SR .40 1.00
19 Marcos Scutaro SR UER .40 1.00
Card number 96 on back
20 Marcus Thames SR .40 1.00
21 Esteban German SR .40 1.00
22 Brett Myers SR .40 1.00
23 Oliver Perez SR .40 1.00
24 Dennis Tankersley SR .40 1.00
25 Julius Matos SR .40 1.00
26 Jake Peavy SR .40 1.00
27 Eric Cyr SR .40 1.00
28 Mike Crudale SR .40 1.00
29 Josh Pearce SR .40 1.00
30 Carl Crawford SR .40 1.00
31 Tim Salmon .20 .50
32 Troy Glaus .10 .30
33 Adam Kennedy .10 .30
34 David Eckstein .10 .30
35 Ben Molina .10 .30
36 Jarrod Washburn .10 .30
37 Ramon Ortiz .10 .30
38 Eric Chavez .10 .30
39 Miguel Tejada .10 .30
40 Adam Piatt .10 .30
41 Jermaine Dye .10 .30
42 Olmedo Saenz .10 .30
43 Tim Hudson .10 .30
44 Barry Zito .10 .30
45 Billy Koch .10 .30
46 Shannon Stewart .10 .30
47 Kelvim Escobar .10 .30
48 Jose Cruz Jr. .10 .30
49 Vernon Wells .10 .30
50 Roy Halladay .10 .30
51 Esteban Loaiza .10 .30
52 Eric Hinske .10 .30
53 Steve Cox .10 .30
54 Brent Abernathy .10 .30
55 Ben Grieve .10 .30
56 Aubrey Huff .10 .30
57 Jared Sandberg .10 .30
58 Paul Wilson .10 .30
59 Tanyon Sturtze .10 .30
60 Jim Thome .20 .50
61 Omar Vizquel .20 .50
62 C.C. Sabathia .10 .30
63 Chris Magruder .10 .30
64 Ricky Gutierrez .10 .30
65 Einar Diaz .10 .30
66 Danys Baez .10 .30
67 Ichiro Suzuki .60 1.50
68 Ruben Sierra .10 .30
69 Carlos Guillen .10 .30
70 Mark McLemore .10 .30
71 Dan Wilson .10 .30
72 Jamie Moyer .10 .30
73 Joel Pineiro .10 .30
74 Edgar Martinez .20 .50
75 Tony Batista .10 .30
76 Jay Gibbons .10 .30
77 Chris Singleton .10 .30
78 Melvin Mora .10 .30
79 Geronimo Gil .10 .30
80 Rodrigo Lopez .10 .30
81 Jorge Julio .10 .30
82 Rafael Palmeiro .20 .50
83 Juan Gonzalez .10 .30
84 Mike Young .20 .50
85 Hideki Irabu .10 .30
86 Chan Ho Park .10 .30
87 Kevin Mench .10 .30
88 Doug Davis .10 .30
89 Pedro Martinez .20 .50
90 Shea Hillenbrand .10 .30
91 Derek Lowe .10 .30
92 Jason Varitek .30 .75
93 Tony Clark .10 .30
94 John Burkett .10 .30
95 Frank Castillo .10 .30
96 Nomar Garciaparra .50 1.25
97 Rickey Henderson .30 .75
98 Mike Sweeney .10 .30
99 Carlos Febles .10 .30
100 Mark Quinn .10 .30
101 Raul Ibanez .10 .30
102 A.J. Hinch .10 .30
103 Paul Byrd .10 .30
104 Chuck Knoblauch .10 .30
105 Dmitri Young .10 .30
106 Randall Simon .10 .30
107 Brandon Inge .10 .30
108 Damion Easley .10 .30
109 Carlos Pena .10 .30
110 George Lombard .10 .30
111 Juan Acevedo .10 .30
112 Torii Hunter .10 .30
113 Doug Mientkiewicz .10 .30
114 David Ortiz .20 .50
115 Eric Milton .10 .30
116 Eddie Guardado .10 .30
117 Cristian Guzman .10 .30
118 Corey Koskie .10 .30
119 Magglio Ordonez .10 .30
120 Mark Buehrle .10 .30
121 Todd Ritchie .10 .30
122 Jose Valentin .10 .30
123 Paul Konerko .10 .30
124 Carlos Lee .10 .30
125 Jon Garland .10 .30
126 Jason Giambi .10 .30
127 Derek Jeter .75 2.00
128 Roger Clemens .60 1.50
129 Raul Mondesi .10 .30
130 Jorge Posada .20 .50
131 Rondell White .10 .30
132 Robin Ventura .10 .30
133 Mike Mussina .20 .50
134 Jeff Bagwell .20 .50
135 Craig Biggio .20 .50
136 Morgan Ensberg .10 .30
137 Richard Hidalgo .10 .30
138 Brad Ausmus .10 .30
139 Roy Oswalt .10 .30
140 Carlos Hernandez .10 .30
141 Shane Reynolds .10 .30
142 Gary Sheffield .10 .30
143 Andruw Jones .20 .50
144 Tom Glavine .20 .50
145 Rafael Furcal .10 .30
146 Javy Lopez .10 .30
147 Vinny Castilla .10 .30
148 Marcus Giles .10 .30
149 Kevin Millwood .10 .30
150 Jason Marquis .10 .30
151 Ruben Quevedo .10 .30
152 Ben Sheets .10 .30
153 Geoff Jenkins .10 .30
154 Jose Hernandez .10 .30
155 Glendon Rusch .10 .30
156 Jeffrey Hammonds .10 .30
157 Alex Sanchez .10 .30
158 Jim Edmonds .10 .30
159 Tino Martinez .20 .50
160 Albert Pujols .60 1.50
161 Eli Marrero .10 .30
162 Woody Williams .10 .30
163 Fernando Vina .10 .30
164 Jason Isringhausen .10 .30
165 Jason Simontacchi .10 .30
166 Kerry Robinson .10 .30
167 Sammy Sosa .30 .75
168 Juan Cruz .10 .30
169 Fred McGriff .20 .50
170 Antonio Alfonseca .10 .30
171 Jon Lieber .10 .30
172 Mark Prior .20 .50
173 Moises Alou .10 .30
174 Matt Clement .10 .30
175 Mark Bellhorn .10 .30
176 Randy Johnson .30 .75
177 Luis Gonzalez .10 .30
178 Tony Womack .10 .30
179 Mark Grace .20 .50
180 Junior Spivey .10 .30
181 Byung Hyun Kim .10 .30
182 Danny Bautista .10 .30
183 Brian Anderson .10 .30
184 Shawn Green .10 .30
185 Brian Jordan .10 .30
186 Eric Karros .10 .30
187 Andy Ashby .10 .30
188 Cesar Izturis .10 .30
189 Dave Roberts .10 .30
190 Eric Gagne .10 .30
191 Kazuhisa Ishii .10 .30
192 Adrian Beltre .10 .30
193 Vladimir Guerrero .30 .75
194 Tony Armas Jr. .10 .30
195 Bartolo Colon .10 .30
196 Troy O'Leary .10 .30
197 Tomo Ohka .10 .30
198 Brad Wilkerson .10 .30
199 Orlando Cabrera .10 .30
200 Barry Bonds .75 2.00
201 David Bell .10 .30
202 Tsuyoshi Shinjo .10 .30
203 Benito Santiago .10 .30
204 Livan Hernandez .10 .30
205 Jason Schmidt .10 .30
206 Kirk Rueter .10 .30
207 Ramon E. Martinez .10 .30
208 Mike Lowell .10 .30
209 Luis Castillo .10 .30
210 Derrek Lee .20 .50
211 Andy Fox .10 .30
212 Eric Owens .10 .30
213 Charles Johnson .10 .30
214 Brad Penny .10 .30
215 A.J. Burnett .10 .30
216 Edgardo Alfonzo .10 .30
217 Roberto Alomar .20 .50
218 Rey Ordonez .10 .30
219 Al Leiter .10 .30
220 Roger Cedeno .10 .30
221 Timo Perez .10 .30
222 Jeromy Burnitz .10 .30
223 Pedro Astacio .10 .30
224 Joe McEwing .10 .30
225 Ryan Klesko .10 .30
226 Ramon Vazquez .10 .30
227 Mark Kotsay .10 .30
228 Bubba Trammell .10 .30
229 Wiki Gonzalez .10 .30
230 Trevor Hoffman .10 .30
231 Ron Gant .10 .30
232 Bob Abreu .10 .30
233 Marlon Anderson .10 .30
234 Jeremy Giambi .10 .30
235 Jimmy Rollins .10 .30
236 Mike Lieberthal .10 .30
237 Vicente Padilla .10 .30
238 Randy Wolf .10 .30
239 Pokey Reese .10 .30
240 Brian Giles .10 .30
241 Jack Wilson .10 .30
242 Mike Williams .10 .30
243 Kip Wells .10 .30
244 Rob Mackowiak .10 .30
245 Craig Wilson .10 .30
246 Adam Dunn .10 .30
247 Sean Casey .10 .30
248 Todd Walker .10 .30
249 Corky Miller .10 .30
250 Ryan Dempster .10 .30
251 Reggie Taylor .10 .30
252 Aaron Boone .10 .30
253 Larry Walker .10 .30
254 Jose Ortiz .10 .30
255 Todd Zeile .10 .30
256 Bobby Estalella .10 .30
257 Juan Pierre .10 .30
258 Terry Shumpert .10 .30
259 Mike Hampton .10 .30
260 Denny Stark .10 .30
261 Shawn Green SH CL .10 .30
262 Derek Lowe SH CL .10 .30
263 Barry Bonds SH CL .40 1.00
264 Mike Cameron SH CL .10 .30
265 Luis Castillo SH CL .10 .30
266 Vladimir Guerrero SH CL .20 .50
267 Jason Giambi SH CL .10 .30
268 Eric Gagne SH CL .10 .30
269 Magglio Ordonez SH CL .10 .30
270 Jim Thome SH CL .10 .30
271 Garret Anderson .10 .30
272 Troy Percival .10 .30
273 Brad Fullmer .10 .30
274 Scott Spiezio .10 .30
275 Darin Erstad .10 .30
276 Francisco Rodriguez .10 .30
277 Kevin Appier .10 .30
278 Shawn Wooten .10 .30
279 Eric Owens .10 .30
280 Scott Hatteberg .10 .30
281 Terrence Long .10 .30
282 Mark Mulder .10 .30
283 Ramon Hernandez .10 .30
284 Ted Lilly .10 .30
285 Erubiel Durazo .10 .30
286 Mark Ellis .10 .30
287 Carlos Delgado .10 .30
288 Orlando Hudson .10 .30
289 Chris Woodward .10 .30
290 Mark Hendrickson .10 .30
291 Josh Phelps .10 .30
292 Ken Huckaby .10 .30
293 Justin Miller .10 .30
294 Travis Lee .10 .30
295 Jorge Sosa .10 .30
296 Joe Kennedy .10 .30
297 Carl Crawford .10 .30
298 Toby Hall .10 .30
299 Rey Ordonez .10 .30
300 Brandon Phillips .10 .30
301 Matt Lawton .10 .30
302 Ellis Burks .10 .30
303 Bill Selby .10 .30
304 Travis Hafner .10 .30
305 Milton Bradley .10 .30
306 Karim Garcia .10 .30
307 Cliff Lee 1.25 3.00
308 Jeff Cirillo .10 .30
309 John Olerud .10 .30
310 Kazuhiro Sasaki .10 .30
311 Freddy Garcia .10 .30
312 Bret Boone .10 .30
313 Mike Cameron .10 .30
314 Ben Davis .10 .30
315 Randy Winn .10 .30
316 Gary Matthews Jr. .10 .30
317 Jeff Conine .10 .30
318 Sidney Ponson .10 .30
319 Jerry Hairston .10 .30
320 David Segui .10 .30
321 Scott Erickson .10 .30
322 Marty Cordova .10 .30
323 Hank Blalock .10 .30
324 Herbert Perry .10 .30
325 Alex Rodriguez .50 1.25
326 Carl Everett .10 .30
327 Einar Diaz .10 .30
328 Ugueth Urbina .10 .30
329 Mark Teixeira .20 .50
330 Manny Ramirez .20 .50
331 Johnny Damon .20 .50
332 Trot Nixon .10 .30
333 Tim Wakefield .10 .30
334 Casey Fossum .10 .30
335 Todd Walker .10 .30
336 Jeremy Giambi .10 .30
337 Bill Mueller .10 .30
338 Ramiro Mendoza .10 .30
339 Carlos Beltran .10 .30
340 Jason Grimsley .10 .30
341 Brent Mayne .10 .30
342 Angel Berroa .10 .30
343 Albie Lopez .10 .30
344 Michael Tucker .10 .30
345 Bobby Higginson .10 .30
346 Shane Halter .10 .30
347 Jeremy Bonderman RC 1.50 4.00
348 Eric Munson .10 .30
349 Andy Van Hekken .10 .30
350 Matt Anderson .10 .30
351 Jacque Jones .10 .30
352 A.J. Pierzynski .10 .30
353 Joe Mays .10 .30
354 Brad Radke .10 .30
355 Dustan Mohr .10 .30
356 Bobby Kielty .10 .30
357 Michael Cuddyer .10 .30
358 Luis Rivas .10 .30
359 Frank Thomas .30 .75
360 Joe Borchard .10 .30
361 D'Angelo Jimenez .10 .30
362 Bartolo Colon .10 .30
363 Joe Crede .10 .30
364 Miguel Olivo .10 .30
365 Billy Koch .10 .30
366 Bernie Williams .20 .50
367 Nick Johnson .10 .30
368 Andy Pettitte .20 .50
369 Mariano Rivera .30 .75
370 Alfonso Soriano .10 .30
371 David Wells .10 .30
372 Drew Henson .10 .30
373 Juan Rivera .10 .30
374 Steve Karsay .10 .30
375 Jeff Kent .10 .30
376 Lance Berkman .10 .30
377 Octavio Dotel .10 .30
378 Julio Lugo .10 .30
379 Jason Lane .10 .30
380 Wade Miller .10 .30
381 Billy Wagner .10 .30
382 Brad Ausmus .10 .30
383 Mike Hampton .10 .30
384 Chipper Jones .30 .75
385 John Smoltz .20 .50
386 Greg Maddux .50 1.25
387 Javy Lopez .10 .30
388 Robert Fick .10 .30
389 Mark DeRosa .10 .30
390 Russ Ortiz .10 .30
391 Julio Franco .10 .30
392 Richie Sexson .10 .30
393 Eric Young .10 .30
394 Robert Machado .10 .30
395 Mike DeJean .10 .30
396 Todd Ritchie .10 .30
397 Royce Clayton .10 .30
398 Nick Neugebauer .10 .30
399 J.D. Drew .10 .30
400 Edgar Renteria .10 .30
401 Scott Rolen .20 .50
402 Matt Morris .10 .30
403 Garrett Stephenson .10 .30
404 Eduardo Perez .10 .30
405 Mike Matheny .10 .30
406 Miguel Cairo .10 .30
407 Brett Tomko .10 .30
408 Bobby Hill .10 .30
409 Troy O'Leary .10 .30
410 Corey Patterson .10 .30
411 Kerry Wood .10 .30
412 Eric Karros .10 .30
413 Hee Seop Choi .10 .30
414 Alex Gonzalez .10 .30
415 Matt Clement .10 .30
416 Mark Grudzielanek .10 .30
417 Curt Schilling .10 .30
418 Steve Finley .10 .30
419 Craig Counsell .10 .30
420 Matt Williams .10 .30
421 Quinton McCracken .10 .30
422 Chad Moeller .10 .30
423 Lyle Overbay .10 .30
424 Miguel Batista .10 .30
425 Paul Lo Duca .10 .30
426 Kevin Brown .10 .30
427 Hideo Nomo .30 .75
428 Fred McGriff .20 .50
429 Joe Thurston .10 .30
430 Odalis Perez .10 .30
431 Darren Dreifort .10 .30
432 Todd Hundley .10 .30
433 Dave Roberts .10 .30
434 Jose Vidro .10 .30
435 Javier Vazquez .10 .30
436 Michael Barrett .10 .30
437 Fernando Tatis .10 .30
438 Peter Bergeron .10 .30
439 Endy Chavez .10 .30
440 Orlando Hernandez .10 .30
441 Marvin Benard .10 .30
442 Rich Aurilia .10 .30
443 Pedro Feliz .10 .30
444 Robb Nen .10 .30
445 Ray Durham .10 .30
446 Marquis Grissom .10 .30
447 Damian Moss .10 .30
448 Edgardo Alfonzo .10 .30
449 Juan Pierre .10 .30
450 Braden Looper .10 .30
451 Alex Gonzalez .10 .30
452 Justin Wayne .10 .30
453 Josh Beckett .10 .30
454 Juan Encarnacion .10 .30
455 Ivan Rodriguez .20 .50
456 Todd Hollandsworth .10 .30
457 Cliff Floyd .10 .30
458 Rey Sanchez .10 .30
459 Mike Piazza .50 1.25
460 Mo Vaughn .10 .30
461 Armando Benitez .10 .30
462 Tsuyoshi Shinjo .10 .30
463 Tom Glavine .20 .50
464 David Cone .10 .30
465 Phil Nevin .10 .30
466 Sean Burroughs .10 .30
467 Jake Peavy .10 .30
468 Brian Lawrence .10 .30
469 Mark Loretta .10 .30
470 Dennis Tankersley .10 .30
471 Jesse Orosco .10 .30
472 Jim Thome .20 .50
473 Kevin Millwood .10 .30
474 David Bell .10 .30
475 Pat Burrell .10 .30
476 Brandon Duckworth .10 .30
477 Jose Mesa .10 .30
478 Marlon Byrd .10 .30
479 Reggie Sanders .10 .30
480 Jason Kendall .10 .30
481 Aramis Ramirez .10 .30
482 Kris Benson .10 .30
483 Matt Stairs .10 .30
484 Kevin Young .10 .30
485 Kenny Lofton .10 .30
486 Austin Kearns .10 .30
487 Barry Larkin .20 .50
488 Jason LaRue .10 .30
489 Ken Griffey Jr. .50 1.25
490 Danny Graves .10 .30
491 Russell Branyan .10 .30
492 Reggie Taylor .10 .30
493 Jimmy Haynes .10 .30
494 Charles Johnson .10 .30
495 Todd Helton .20 .50
496 Juan Uribe .10 .30
497 Preston Wilson .10 .30
498 Chris Stynes .10 .30
499 Jason Jennings .10 .30
500 Jay Payton .10 .30
501 Hideki Matsui SR RC 2.00 5.00
502 Jose Contreras SR RC .60 1.50
503 Brandon Webb SR RC 1.25 3.00
504 Robby Hammock SR RC .40 1.00
505 Matt Kata SR RC .40 1.00
506 Tim Olson SR RC .40 1.00
507 Michael Hessman SR RC .40 1.00
508 Jon Leicester SR RC .40 1.00
509 Todd Wellemeyer SR RC .40 1.00
510 David Sanders SR RC .40 1.00
511 Josh Stewart SR RC .40 1.00
512 Luis Ayala SR RC .40 1.00
513 Clint Barmes SR RC .50 1.25
514 Josh Willingham SR RC .75 2.00
515 Al. Machado SR RC .40 1.00
516 Felix Sanchez SR RC .40 1.00
517 Willie Eyre SR RC .40 1.00
518 Brent Hoard SR RC .40 1.00
519 Lew Ford SR RC .60 1.50
520 Termel Sledge SR RC .40 1.00
521 Jeremy Griffiths SR RC .40 1.00
522 Phil Seibel SR RC .40 1.00
523 Craig Brazell SR RC .40 1.00
524 Prentice Redman SR RC .40 1.00
525 Jeff Duncan SR RC .40 1.00
526 Shane Bazzell SR RC .40 1.00
527 Bernie Castro SR RC .40 1.00
528 Rett Johnson SR RC .40 1.00
529 Bobby Madritsch SR RC .40 1.00
530 Rocco Baldelli SR .40 1.00
531 Alex Rodriguez SH CL .30 .75
532 Eric Chavez SH CL .10 .30
533 Miguel Tejada SH CL .10 .30
534 Ichiro Suzuki SH CL .30 .75
535 Sammy Sosa SH CL .20 .50
536 Barry Zito SH CL .10 .30
537 Darin Erstad SH CL .10 .30
538 Alfonso Soriano SH CL .10 .30
539 Troy Glaus SH CL .10 .30
540 N.Garciaparra SH CL .30 .75
541 Bo Hart RC .20 .50
542 Dan Haren RC .30 .75
543 Ryan Wagner RC .20 .50
544 Rich Harden .20 .50
545 Dontrelle Willis .30 .75
546 Jerome Williams .10 .30
547 Bobby Crosby .20 .50
548 Greg Jones RC .20 .50
549 Todd Linden .10 .30
550 Byung-Hyun Kim .10 .30
551 Rickie Weeks RC 1.25 3.00
552 Jason Roach RC .20 .50
553 Oscar Villarreal RC .20 .50
554 Justin Duchscherer .10 .30
555 Chris Capuano RC .60 1.50
556 Josh Hall RC .20 .50
557 Luis Matos .10 .30
558 Miguel Ojeda RC .20 .50
559 Kevin Ohme RC .20 .50
560 Julio Manon RC .20 .50
561 Kevin Correia RC .20 .50
562 Delmon Young RC 2.00 5.00
563 Aaron Boone .10 .30
564 Aaron Looper RC .20 .50
565 Mike Neu RC .20 .50
566 Aquilino Lopez RC .20 .50

567 Jhonny Peralta .30 .75
568 Duaner Sanchez .10 .30
569 Stephen Randolph RC .20 .50
570 Nate Bland RC .20 .50
571 Chin-Hui Tsao .10 .30
572 Michel Hernandez RC .20 .50
573 Rocco Baldelli .10 .30
574 Robb Quinlan .10 .30
575 Aaron Heilman .10 .30
576 Jae Weong Seo .10 .30
577 Joe Borowski .10 .30
578 Chris Bootcheck .10 .30
579 Michael Ryan RC .20 .50
580 Mark Malaska RC .20 .50
581 Jose Guillen .10 .30
582 Josh Towers .10 .30
583 Tom Gregorio RC .20 .50
584 Edwin Jackson RC .20 .50
585 Jason Anderson .10 .30
586 Jose Reyes .10 .30
587 Miguel Cabrera .30 .75
588 Nate Bump .10 .30
589 Jeromy Burnitz .10 .30
590 David Ross .10 .30
591 Chase Utley .30 .75
592 Brandon Webb .60 1.50
593 Masao Kida .10 .30
594 Jimmy Journell .10 .30
595 Eric Young .10 .30
596 Tony Womack .10 .30
597 Amaury Telemaco .10 .30
598 Rickey Henderson .30 .75
599 Esteban Loaiza .10 .30
600 Sidney Ponson .10 .30

2003 Upper Deck Gold

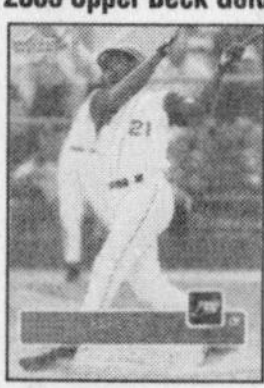

COMP.FACT.SET (60) 15.00 40.00
*GOLD: 2X TO 5X BASIC
*GOLD: 1.25X TO 3X BASIC RC'S
ONE GOLD SET PER 12 CT HOBBY CASE

2003 Upper Deck A Piece of History 500 Club

This card, which continues the Upper Deck A Piece of History 500 club set which began in 1999, was randomly inserted into second series packs. These cards were issued to a stated print run of 350 cards.

SS Sammy Sosa 75.00 150.00

2003 Upper Deck A Piece of History 500 Club Autograph

Randomly inserted into packs, this is a parallel to the Piece of History insert card of Sammy Sosa. Sosa signed 21 copies of this card but did not return them in time for pack-out. Please note that the exchange date for these cards are June 9th, 2006 and since only 21 cards were created there is no pricing due to market scarcity.

STATED PRINT RUN 21 SERIAL #'d CARDS
NO PRICING DUE TO SCARCITY
EXCHANGE DEADLINE 06/09/06
SSAU Sammy Sosa AU/21

2003 Upper Deck AL All-Star Swatches

Inserted into first series retail packs at a stated rate of one in 144, these 13 cards feature game-used uniform swatches of players who had made the AL All-Star game during their career.

AP Andy Pettitte 6.00 15.00
AS Aaron Sele 4.00 10.00
CE Carl Everett 4.00 10.00
CF Chuck Finley 4.00 10.00
JG Juan Gonzalez 4.00 10.00
JM Joe Mays 4.00 10.00
JP Jorge Posada 6.00 15.00
MC Mike Cameron 4.00 10.00
MO Magglio Ordonez 4.00 10.00
MR Mariano Rivera 6.00 15.00
MS Mike Sweeney 4.00 10.00
RD Ray Durham 4.00 10.00
TF Travis Fryman 4.00 10.00

2003 Upper Deck Big League Breakdowns

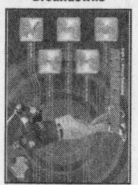

Inserted into series one packs at a stated rate of one in eight, these 15 cards feature some of the leading hitters in the game.

COMPLETE SET (15) 15.00 40.00
BL1 Troy Glaus .75 2.00
BL2 Miguel Tejada .75 2.00
BL3 Chipper Jones 1.00 2.50
BL4 Torii Hunter .75 2.00
BL5 Nomar Garciaparra 1.50 4.00
BL6 Sammy Sosa 1.00 2.50
BL7 Todd Helton .75 2.00
BL8 Lance Berkman .75 2.00
BL9 Shawn Green .75 2.00
BL10 Vladimir Guerrero 1.00 2.50
BL11 Jason Giambi .75 2.00
BL12 Derek Jeter 2.50 6.00
BL13 Barry Bonds 2.50 6.00
BL14 Ichiro Suzuki 2.00 5.00
BL15 Alex Rodriguez 1.50 4.00

2003 Upper Deck Chase for 755

Inserted into first series packs at a stated rate of one in eight, these 15 cards feature players who are considered to have some chance of surpassing Hank Aaron's career home run total.

COMPLETE SET (15) 12.50 30.00
C1 Troy Glaus .75 2.00
C2 Andruw Jones .75 2.00
C3 Manny Ramirez .75 2.00
C4 Sammy Sosa 1.00 2.50
C5 Ken Griffey Jr. 1.50 4.00
C6 Adam Dunn .75 2.00
C7 Todd Helton .75 2.00
C8 Lance Berkman .75 2.00
C9 Jeff Bagwell .75 2.00
C10 Shawn Green .75 2.00
C11 Vladimir Guerrero 1.00 2.50
C12 Barry Bonds 2.50 6.00
C13 Alex Rodriguez 1.50 4.00
C14 Juan Gonzalez .75 2.00
C15 Carlos Delgado .75 2.00

2003 Upper Deck Game Swatches

Inserted into first series packs at a stated rate of one in 72, these 25 cards feature game-used memorabilia swatches. A few cards were printed to a lesser quantity and we have notated those cards in our checklist.

HJAR Alex Rodriguez 6.00 15.00
HJBW Bernie Williams 4.00 10.00
HJCC C.C. Sabathia 3.00 8.00
HJCD Carlos Delgado SP 6.00 15.00
HJCP Carlos Pena 3.00 8.00
HJCS Curt Schilling SP/100 6.00 15.00
HJGM Greg Maddux 4.00 10.00
HJMM Mike Mussina 4.00 10.00
HJMO Magglio Ordonez 3.00 8.00
HJMP Mike Piazza SP 10.00 25.00
HJSB Sean Burroughs SP 6.00 15.00
HJSS Sammy Sosa 4.00 10.00
RJAD Adam Dunn 3.00 8.00
RJDE Darin Erstad 3.00 8.00
RJEM Edgar Martinez 4.00 10.00
RJFT Frank Thomas 4.00 10.00
RJIR Ivan Rodriguez 4.00 10.00
RJJD J.D. Drew 3.00 8.00
RJJE Jim Edmonds 3.00 8.00
RJJG Jason Giambi 3.00 8.00
RJJK Jeff Kent 3.00 8.00
RJKG Ken Griffey Jr. 6.00 15.00
RJRC Roger Clemens 8.00 20.00
RJRJ Randy Johnson 4.00 10.00
RJTH Tim Hudson 3.00 8.00

2003 Upper Deck Leading Swatches

SERIES 2 STATED ODDS 1:24 HOB/1:48 RET
SP INFO PROVIDED BY UPPER DECK
SP'S ARE NOT SERIAL-NUMBERED
*GOLD: .75X TO 2X BASIC SWATCHES
*GOLD: .6X TO 1.5X BASIC SP SWATCHES
*GOLD MATSUI HR: .75X TO 1.5X BASIC HR
*GOLD MATSUI RBI: .6X TO 1.2X BASIC RBI
GOLD PRINT RUN 100 SERIAL #'d SETS
AB Adrian Beltre GM 3.00 8.00
AD Adam Dunn RUN 3.00 8.00
AD1 Adam Dunn BB SP 4.00 10.00
AJ Andruw Jones HR 4.00 10.00
AJ1 Andruw Jones AB SP 6.00 15.00
AP Andy Pettitte WIN SP 6.00 15.00
AR Alex Rodriguez HR 6.00 15.00
AR1 Alex Rodriguez RBI 6.00 15.00
AS Alfonso Soriano SB 3.00 8.00
AS1 Alfonso Soriano RUN 3.00 8.00
AS2 Aaron Sele WIN 3.00 8.00
BA Bobby Abreu 2B 3.00 8.00
BG Brian Giles HR 3.00 8.00
BG1 Brian Giles OBP 3.00 8.00
BW Bernie Williams 333 AVG 4.00 10.00
BW1 Bernie Williams 339 AVG 4.00 10.00
BZ Barry Zito WIN 3.00 8.00
CD Carlos Delgado RBI 3.00 8.00
CJ Chipper Jones AVG-RBI 4.00 10.00
CP Corey Patterson HR 3.00 8.00
CS Curt Schilling WIN 3.00 8.00
EC Eric Chavez HR 3.00 8.00
GA Garret Anderson RBI 3.00 8.00
GM Greg Maddux 2.62 ERA 4.00 10.00
GM1 Greg Maddux 1.56 ERA SP 6.00 15.00
GO Juan Gonzalez RBI 3.00 8.00
HM Hideki Matsui HR 15.00 40.00
HM1 Hideki Matsui RBI SP 20.00 50.00
HN Hideo Nomo WIN 6.00 15.00
IR Ivan Rodriguez AVG 4.00 10.00
IS Ichiro Suzuki HIT 12.50 30.00
IS1 Ichiro Suzuki SB SP 15.00 40.00
JB Jeff Bagwell RBI 4.00 10.00
JB1 Jeff Bagwell SLG SP 6.00 15.00
JD J.D. Drew RBI 3.00 8.00
JE Jim Edmonds RUN 3.00 8.00
JG Jason Giambi HR 3.00 8.00
JG1 Jason Giambi SLG 3.00 8.00
JL Javy Lopez NLCS 3.00 8.00
JP Jay Payton 3B 3.00 8.00
JS J.T. Snow GLV 3.00 8.00
JT Jim Thome HR 4.00 10.00
JT1 Jim Thome SLG 4.00 10.00
KE Jason Kendall RUN 3.00 8.00
KG Ken Griffey Jr. 40 HR 6.00 15.00
KG1 Ken Griffey Jr. 56 HR SP 8.00 20.00
KI Kazuhisa Ishii K 3.00 8.00
KS Kazuhiro Sasaki SV 3.00 8.00
KW Kerry Wood K 3.00 8.00
LB Lance Berkman HR 3.00 8.00
LG Luis Gonzalez RUN 3.00 8.00
LW Larry Walker AVG 3.00 8.00
MP Mike Piazza HR 6.00 15.00
MP1 Mike Piazza SLG 6.00 15.00
MR Manny Ramirez AVG 4.00 10.00
MSL Mike Sweeney AVG 3.00 8.00
MSW Mike Stanton Pants GM 3.00 8.00
MT Miguel Tejada RBI 3.00 8.00
MT1 Miguel Tejada GM SP 4.00 10.00
OV Omar Vizquel SAC 4.00 10.00
PB Pat Burrell HR 3.00 8.00
PB1 Pat Burrell RBI 3.00 8.00
PM Pedro Martinez K 4.00 10.00
RC Roger Clemens K 6.00 15.00
RC1 Roger Clemens ERA 6.00 15.00
RJ Randy Johnson K 4.00 10.00
RJ1 Randy Johnson ERA 4.00 10.00
RO Roy Oswalt WIN 3.00 8.00
RO1 Roy Oswalt PCT SP 4.00 10.00
RP Rafael Palmeiro RBI 4.00 10.00
RP1 Rafael Palmeiro 2B 4.00 10.00
SG Shawn Green HR 3.00 8.00
SG1 Shawn Green TB 3.00 8.00
SR Scott Rolen HR 4.00 10.00
SS Sammy Sosa 49 HR 4.00 10.00
SS1 Sammy Sosa 50 HR SP/170 6.00 15.00
TB Tony Batista HR 3.00 8.00
TG Troy Glaus HR 3.00 8.00
THE Todd Helton RBI 4.00 10.00
THU Tim Hudson IP 3.00 8.00
THU1 Tim Hudson GM SP 4.00 10.00
TP Troy Percival SV 3.00 8.00
VG Vladimir Guerrero HIT 4.00 10.00

2003 Upper Deck Lineup Time Jerseys

Inserted into first series hobby packs at a stated rate of one in 96, these 10 cards feature game-used uniform swatches from some of the leading players in the game. A couple of cards were printed to a smaller quantity and we have notated those cards with an SP in our checklist.

BW Bernie Williams 4.00 10.00
CD Carlos Delgado 3.00 8.00
GM Greg Maddux 4.00 10.00
IS Ichiro Suzuki 15.00 40.00
JD J.D. Drew 3.00 8.00
JT Jim Thome 4.00 10.00
RC Roger Clemens SP 10.00 25.00
RJ Randy Johnson SP 8.00 20.00
SG Shawn Green 3.00 8.00
TH Todd Helton 4.00 10.00

2003 Upper Deck Magical Performances

*GOLD: 1X TO 2.5X BASIC MAGIC
GOLD PRINT RUN 50 SERIAL #'d SETS
DUPE STARS EQUALLY VALUED
MP1 Hideki Matsui 8.00 20.00
MP2 Ken Griffey Jr. 8.00 20.00
MP3 Ichiro Suzuki 8.00 20.00
MP4 Ken Griffey Jr. 8.00 20.00
MP5 Hideo Nomo 6.00 15.00
MP6 Mickey Mantle 20.00 50.00
MP7 Ken Griffey Jr. 8.00 20.00
MP8 Barry Bonds 10.00 25.00
MP9 Mickey Mantle 20.00 50.00
MP10 Tom Seaver 6.00 15.00
MP11 Mike Piazza 8.00 20.00
MP12 Roger Clemens 8.00 20.00
MP13 Nolan Ryan 15.00 40.00
MP14 Nomar Garciaparra 8.00 20.00
MP15 Ernie Banks 6.00 15.00
MP16 Stan Musial 10.00 25.00
MP17 Mickey Mantle 20.00 50.00
MP18 Nolan Ryan 15.00 40.00
MP19 Nolan Ryan 15.00 40.00
MP20 Mickey Mantle 20.00 50.00
MP21 Ichiro Suzuki 8.00 20.00
MP22 Nolan Ryan 15.00 40.00
MP23 Tom Seaver 6.00 15.00
MP24 Ken Griffey Jr. 8.00 20.00
MP25 Hideo Nomo 6.00 15.00
MP26 Ken Griffey Jr. 8.00 20.00
MP27 Mark McGwire 10.00 25.00
MP28 Barry Bonds 10.00 25.00
MP29 Alex Rodriguez 8.00 20.00
MP30 Nolan Ryan 15.00 40.00
MP31 Mark McGwire 10.00 25.00
MP32 Nolan Ryan 15.00 40.00
MP33 Sammy Sosa 6.00 15.00
MP34 Ichiro Suzuki 8.00 20.00
MP35 Barry Bonds 10.00 25.00
MP36 Derek Jeter 10.00 25.00
MP37 Roger Clemens 8.00 20.00
MP38 Jason Giambi 6.00 15.00
MP39 Mickey Mantle 20.00 50.00
MP40 Ted Williams 12.50 30.00
MP41 Ted Williams 12.50 30.00
MP42 Ted Williams 12.50 30.00

2003 Upper Deck Mark of Greatness Autograph Jerseys

Randomly inserted into first series packs, these three cards feature authentically signed Mark McGwire cards. There are three different versions of this card, which were all signed to a different print run, and we have notated that information in our checklist.

MOG M.McGwire/400 * 175.00 300.00
MOGG M.McGwire Gold/25
MOGS M.McGwire Silver/70 250.00 400.00

2003 Upper Deck Masters with the Leather

COMPLETE SET (12) 10.00 25.00
L1 Darin Erstad .75 2.00
L2 Andruw Jones .75 2.00
L3 Greg Maddux 1.50 4.00
L4 Nomar Garciaparra 1.50 4.00
L5 Torii Hunter .75 2.00
L6 Roberto Alomar .75 2.00
L7 Derek Jeter 2.50 6.00
L8 Eric Chavez .75 2.00
L9 Ichiro Suzuki 2.00 5.00
L10 Jim Edmonds .75 2.00
L11 Scott Rolen .75 2.00
L12 Alex Rodriguez 1.50 4.00

2003 Upper Deck Mid-Summer Stars Swatches

Inserted into first series packs at a stated rate of one in 72, these 23 cards feature a mix of players who shine all during the season. A few cards do not feature jersey swatches and we have notated that information in our checklist. In addition, a few cards were issued to a smaller quantity and we have notated those cards with an SP in our checklist.

AJ Andruw Jones 4.00 10.00
AR Alex Rodriguez 6.00 15.00
BZ Barry Zito 3.00 8.00
CD Carlos Delgado 3.00 8.00
CS Curt Schilling 3.00 8.00
DE Darin Erstad 3.00 8.00
DW David Wells 3.00 8.00
EM Edgar Martinez 4.00 10.00
FG Freddy Garcia 3.00 8.00
FT Frank Thomas 4.00 10.00
HN Hideo Nomo 8.00 20.00
IS Ichiro Suzuki Turtleneck SP 20.00 50.00
JE Jim Edmonds SP * 4.00 10.00
JG Juan Gonzalez Pants 3.00 8.00
KS Kazuhiro Sasaki 3.00 8.00
MP Mike Piazza 6.00 15.00
MR Manny Ramirez 4.00 10.00
RC Roger Clemens 6.00 15.00
RJ Randy Johnson Shirt 4.00 10.00
RV Robin Ventura 4.00 10.00
SG Shawn Green SP 4.00 10.00
SS Sammy Sosa 4.00 10.00
TG Tom Glavine 4.00 10.00

2003 Upper Deck NL All-Star Swatches

Inserted into first series hobby packs at a stated rate of one in 72, these 12 cards feature game-used memorabilia swatch of players who had participated in the All-Star game for the National League.

AL Al Leiter 3.00 8.00
CF Cliff Floyd 3.00 8.00
CS Curt Schilling 3.00 8.00
FM Fred McGriff 4.00 10.00
JV Jose Vidro 3.00 8.00
MH Mike Hampton 3.00 8.00
MM Matt Morris 3.00 8.00
RK Ryan Klesko 3.00 8.00
SC Sean Casey 3.00 8.00
TG Tom Glavine 4.00 10.00
TG Tony Gwynn 6.00 15.00
TH Trevor Hoffman 3.00 8.00

2003 Upper Deck National Pride Memorabilia

SERIES 2 ODDS 1:24 HOBBY/1:48 RETAIL
SP PRINT RUNS PROVIDED BY UPPER DECK
SP'S ARE NOT SERIAL-NUMBERED
ALL FEATURE PANTS UNLESS NOTED
AA Abe Alvarez 3.00 8.00
AH Aaron Hill 3.00 8.00
AJ A.J. Hinch Jsy 3.00 8.00
AK A.Kearns Right Jsy 3.00 8.00
AK1 A.Kearns Left Jsy SP/250 6.00 15.00
BH Bobby Hill Field Jsy 3.00 8.00
BH1 Bobby Hill Run Jsy SP/100 8.00 20.00
BS Brad Sullivan Wind Up 3.00 8.00
BS1 Brad Sullivan Throw SP/250 6.00 15.00
BZ Bob Zimmermann 2.00 5.00
CC Chad Cordero 3.00 8.00
CJ Conor Jackson 4.00 10.00
CQ Carlos Quentin 4.00 10.00
CS Clint Sammons 3.00 8.00
DP Dustin Pedroia 4.00 10.00
EM Eric Milton White Jsy 3.00 8.00
EM1 Eric Milton Blue Jsy SP/50 8.00 20.00
EP Eric Patterson 3.00 8.00
GJ Grant Johnson 3.00 8.00
HS Huston Street 3.00 8.00
JJO J.Jones White Jsy 3.00 8.00
JJ1 J.Jones Blue Jsy SP/250 6.00 15.00
JJE Jason Jennings Jsy 3.00 8.00
KB Kyle Bakker 2.00 5.00
KSA K.Saarloos Red Jsy 3.00 8.00
KSL Kyle Sleeth 3.00 8.00
KSA1 K.Saarloos Grey Jsy SP/250 6.00 15.00
LP Landon Powell 3.00 8.00
MA Michael Aubrey 3.00 8.00
MJ Mark Jurich 2.00 5.00
MP Mark Prior Pinstripes Jsy 4.00 10.00
MP1 Mark Prior Grey Jsy SP/100 10.00 25.00
PH Philip Humber 3.00 8.00
RF Robert Fick Jsy 3.00 8.00
RO R.Oswalt Behind Jsy 3.00 8.00
RO1 R.Oswalt Beside Jsy SP/100 8.00 20.00
RW R.Weeks Glove-Chest 5.00 12.00
RW1 R.Weeks Glove-Head SP/250
SB Sean Burroughs 3.00 8.00
SC Shane Costa 2.00 5.00
SF Sam Fuld 4.00 10.00
WL Wes Littleton 3.00 8.00

2003 Upper Deck Piece of the Action Game Ball

SERIES 2 ODDS 1:288 HOBBY/1:576 RETAIL
PRINT RUNS B/WN 10-175 COPIES PER
PRINT RUNS PROVIDED BY UPPER DECK
CARDS ARE NOT SERIAL-NUMBERED
NO PRICING ON QTY OF 25 OR LESS
AB Adrian Beltre/100 4.00 10.00
ARA Aramis Ramirez/100 4.00 10.00
ARO Alex Rodriguez/100 10.00 25.00
BA Bobby Abreu/125 4.00 10.00
BB Barry Bonds/125 15.00 40.00
BG Brian Giles/100 4.00 10.00
BW Bernie Williams/125 6.00 15.00
CJ Chipper Jones/62 10.00 25.00
CS Curt Schilling/100 4.00 10.00
DE Darin Erstad/125 4.00 10.00
DJ Derek Jeter/65 15.00 40.00
EM Edgar Martinez/125 6.00 15.00
FG Freddy Garcia/100 4.00 10.00
FT Frank Thomas/150 6.00 15.00
GA Garret Anderson/150 4.00 10.00
GS Gary Sheffield/100 4.00 10.00
HN Hideo Nomo/100 15.00 40.00
IR Ivan Rodriguez/10
IS Ichiro Suzuki/25
JG Juan Gonzalez/100 4.00 10.00
JK Jason Kendall/100 4.00 10.00
JT Jim Thome/125 6.00 15.00
JV Jose Vidro/100 4.00 10.00
KB Kevin Brown/100 4.00 10.00
KE Jeff Kent/150 4.00 10.00
KS Kazuhiro Sasaki/100 4.00 10.00
LG Luis Gonzalez/100 4.00 10.00
LW Larry Walker/150 4.00 10.00
MP Mike Piazza/150 10.00 25.00
PB Pat Burrell/150 4.00 10.00
PM Pedro Martinez/150 6.00 15.00
PN Phil Nevin/75 6.00 15.00
RJ Randy Johnson/100 6.00 15.00
RK Ryan Klesko/75 6.00 15.00
RP Rafael Palmeiro/150 6.00 15.00
RS Richie Sexson/160 4.00 10.00
SG Shawn Green/175 4.00 10.00
SS Sammy Sosa/85 10.00 25.00
TG Troy Glaus/150 4.00 10.00
THE Todd Helton/100 6.00 15.00
THO Trevor Hoffman/150 4.00 10.00
VG Vladimir Guerrero/50 10.00 25.00

2003 Upper Deck Piece of the Action Game Ball Gold

*GOLD: 1X TO 2.5X GAME BALL p/r 150-175
*GOLD: 1X TO 2.5X GAME BALL p/r 100-125
*GOLD: .6X TO 1.5X GAME BALL p/r 50-85
STATED PRINT RUN 50 SERIAL #'d SETS
IR Ivan Rodriguez 15.00 40.00
IS Ichiro Suzuki

2003 Upper Deck Signed Game Jerseys

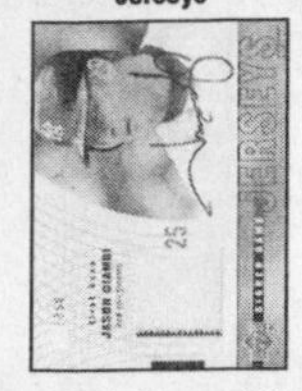

Randomly inserted into first series packs, these seven cards feature not only game-used memorabilia swatches but also an authentic autograph of the player. We have notated the print run for each card next to the player's name. In addition, Ken Griffey Jr. did not sign cards in time for inclusion into packs and those cards could be redeemed until February 11th, 2006.

PRINT RUNS B/WN 150-350 COPIES PER
AR Alex Rodriguez/350 60.00 120.00
CR Cal Ripken/350 75.00 150.00
JG Jason Giambi/350 20.00 50.00
KG Ken Griffey Jr./350 60.00 120.00
MM Mark McGwire/150 250.00 400.00
RC Roger Clemens/350 60.00 120.00
SS Sammy Sosa/150 50.00 100.00

2003 Upper Deck Signed Game Jerseys Gold

Randomly inserted into first series packs, this is a partial parallel to the Signed Game Jersey insert set. These three cards were issued to a stated print run of 25 serial numbered sets and no pricing is provided due to market scarcity. Please note that Ken Griffey Jr. did not return his cards in time for inclusion in packs and those cards could be redeemed until February 11th, 2006.

KG Ken Griffey Jr.
MM Mark McGwire
SS Sammy Sosa

2003 Upper Deck Signed Game Jerseys Silver

Randomly inserted into first series packs, this is a partial parallel to the Signed Game Jersey insert set. These five cards were issued to a stated print run of 75 serial numbered sets. Please note that Ken Griffey Jr. did not return his cards in time for inclusion in packs and those cards could be redeemed until February 11, 2006.

STATED PRINT RUN 75 SERIAL #'d SETS
AR Alex Rodriguez
JG Jason Giambi 30.00 60.00
KG Ken Griffey Jr.
MM Mark McGwire
SS Sammy Sosa

2003 Upper Deck Slammin Sammy Autograph Jerseys

Randomly inserted into first series packs, these three cards feature authentically signed Sammy Sosa cards. Each of these cards also have a game-worn uniform swatch on them. There are three different versions of this card, which were all signed to a different print run, and we have notated that information in our checklist.

PRINT RUNS B/WN 25-384 COPIES PER
NO PRICING ON QTY OF 25 OR LESS
SST Sammy Sosa/384 75.00 150.00
SSTG Sammy Sosa Gold/25
SSTS Sammy Sosa Silver/66 125.00 200.00

2003 Upper Deck Star-Spangled Swatches

Inserted into first series packs at a stated rate of one in 72, these 16 cards feature game-worn uniform swatches of players who were on the USA National Team.

AH Aaron Hill H 3.00 8.00
BS Brad Sullivan H 3.00 8.00
CC Chad Cordero H 3.00 8.00
CJ Conor Jackson Pants R 4.00 10.00
CQ Carlos Quentin H 4.00 10.00
DP Dustin Pedroia R 8.00 20.00
EP Eric Patterson H 3.00 8.00
GJ Grant Johnson H 3.00 8.00
HS Huston Street R 3.00 8.00
KB Kyle Bakker R 2.00 5.00
KS Kyle Sleeth R 3.00 8.00
LP Landon Powell R 3.00 8.00
MA Michael Aubrey H 3.00 8.00
PH Philip Humber R 3.00 8.00
RW Rickie Weeks H 6.00 15.00
SC Shane Costa R 2.00 5.00

2003 Upper Deck Superior Sluggers

Inserted into second series packs at a stated rate of one in eight, these cards feature a mix of active and retired players known for their extra base power while batting.

COMPLETE SET (18) 15.00 40.00
S1 Troy Glaus .75 2.00
S2 Chipper Jones 1.00 2.50
S3 Manny Ramirez .75 2.00
S4 Ken Griffey Jr. 1.50 4.00
S5 Jim Thome .75 2.00
S6 Todd Helton .75 2.00
S7 Lance Berkman .75 2.00
S8 Derek Jeter 2.50 6.00
S9 Vladimir Guerrero 1.00 2.50
S10 Mike Piazza 1.50 4.00
S11 Hideki Matsui 2.00 5.00
S12 Barry Bonds 2.50 6.00
S13 Mickey Mantle 4.00 10.00
S14 Alex Rodriguez 1.50 4.00
S15 Ted Williams 2.50 6.00
S16 Carlos Delgado .75 2.00
S17 Frank Thomas 1.00 2.50
S18 Adam Dunn .75 2.00

2003 Upper Deck Superstar Scrapbooks

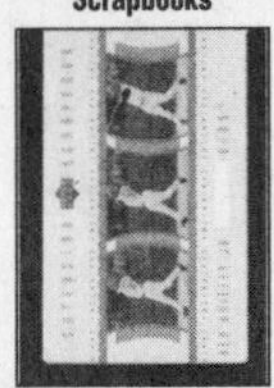

Randomly inserted into series one packs, these seven cards feature game-worn jersey swatches of some of baseball's major superstars. Each of these cards was issued to a stated print run of 24 serial numbered sets and there is no pricing due to market scarcity.

AR Alex Rodriguez
IS Ichiro Suzuki
JG Jason Giambi
KG Ken Griffey Jr.
MP Mike Piazza
RC Roger Clemens
SS Sammy Sosa

2003 Upper Deck Superstar Scrapbooks Gold

Randomly inserted into series one packs, these seven cards are a parallel of the Superstar Scrapbook set. Each of these cards feature game-worn jersey swatches of some of baseball's major superstars. Each of these cards was issued to a stated print run of one serial numbered set and there is no pricing due to market scarcity.

STATED PRINT RUN 1 SERIAL #'d SET
NO PRICING DUE TO SCARCITY
IS Ichiro Suzuki
KG Ken Griffey Jr.
SS Sammy Sosa

2003 Upper Deck Superstar Scrapbooks Silver

Randomly inserted into series one packs, these seven cards are a parallel of the Superstar Scrapbook set. Each of these cards feature game-worn jersey swatches of some of baseball's major superstars. Each of these cards was issued to a stated print run of six serial numbered set and there is no pricing due to market scarcity.

STATED PRINT RUN 6 SERIALS #'d SETS
NO PRICING DUE TO SCARCITY
AR Alex Rodriguez
IS Ichiro Suzuki
JG Jason Giambi
KG Ken Griffey Jr.
SS Sammy Sosa

2003 Upper Deck Triple Game Jersey

Randomly inserted into first series packs, these nine cards feature three game-worn uniform swatches of teammates. These cards were issued to a stated print run of anywhere from 25 to 150 serial numbered sets depending on which group the card belongs to. Please note the cards from group C are not priced due to market scarcity.

GROUP A 150 SERIAL #'d SETS
GROUP B 75 SERIAL #'d SETS
GROUP C 25 SERIAL #'d SETS
ARZ Randy Johnson 20.00 50.00
Curt Schilling
Luis Gonzalez A
ATL Chipper Jones 40.00 80.00
Greg Maddux
Gary Sheffield B
CHC Sammy Sosa 20.00 50.00
Moises Alou
Kerry Wood B
CIN Ken Griffey Jr. 15.00 40.00
Sean Casey
Adam Dunn A
HOU Jeff Bagwell 20.00 50.00
Lance Berkman
Craig Biggio A
NYM Mike Piazza Pants 20.00 50.00
Roberto Alomar
Mo Vaughn B
NYY Roger Clemens
Jason Giambi
Bernie Williams C
SEA Ichiro Suzuki 60.00 120.00
Freddy Garcia
Bret Boone B
TEX Rafael Palmeiro 20.00 50.00
Alex Rodriguez
Juan Gonzalez A

2003 Upper Deck Triple Game Jersey Gold

Randomly inserted in packs, this is a parallel to the Triple Game Jersey insert set. Depending on the group, each card is printed to a stated print run of between 10 and 50 serial numbered sets. Those cards in group B and C are not priced due to market scarcity.

GROUP A 50 SERIAL #'d SETS
GROUP B 25 SERIAL #'d SETS
GROUP C 10 SERIAL #'d SETS

2003 Upper Deck UD Bonus

Inserted into second series packs at a stated rate of one in 288, these are copies of various recent year Upper Deck cards which were repurchased for insertion in 2003 Upper Deck 2nd series. Please note that these cards were all stamped with a "UD Bonus" logo. Each of these cards was issued to differening print runs and we have notated the print runs next to the player's name in our checklist.

1 Jeff Bagwell 01 GG Glv/6
2 Josh Beckett 01 TP AU/55 12.50 30.00
3 C.Beltran 00 SPA AU/118 6.00 15.00
4 Barry Bonds 01 UD Ball/34
5 Barry Bonds 01 GG Glv/5
6 Barry Bonds 01 P/P Jsy/117 10.00 25.00
7 Lou Brock 00 LGD AU/198 10.00 25.00
8 Gary Carter 00 LGD AU/63 8.00 20.00
9 Sean Casey 00 SPA AU/11
10 Roger Clemens 00 HFX Base/12
11 Roger Clemens 00 LGD Jsy/12
12 Roger Clemens 01 P/P Jsy/117 6.00 15.00
13 A.Dawson 00 LGD AU/140 6.00 15.00
14 J.D. Drew 00 SPA AU/55 8.00 20.00
15 Rollie Fingers 00 LGD AU/116 6.00 15.00
16 Rafael Furcal 00 SPA AU/87 6.00 15.00
17 Rafael Furcal 00 SPA AU/39
18 Jason Giambi 00 SPA AU/106 6.00 15.00
19 Jason Giambi 01 UD Ball/35
20 Jason Giambi 01 P/P Jsy/97 4.00 10.00
21 Troy Glaus 00 SPA AU/110 10.00 25.00
22 Shawn Green 01 UD Ball/10
23 Ken Griffey Jr. 01 UD Ball/28
24 Ken Griffey Jr. 01 GG Glv/2
25 Vladimir Guerrero 00 SPA AU/8
26 Vladimir Guerrero 00 LGD AU/26
27 Vladimir Guerrero 00 OV Bat/16
28 Brandon Inge 01 TP AU/113 4.00 10.00
29 Derek Jeter 01 UD Ball/17
30 Randy Johnson 01 UD Ball/37
31 Andruw Jones 01 UD Ball/38
32 Chipper Jones 00 HFX AU/5
33 Chipper Jones 00 OV Bat/19
34 Harmon Killebrew 00 LGD AU/31
35 Roger Maris 00 YL Jsy/11
36 Eddie Mathews 00 LGD Jsy/12
37 Hideki Matsui 03 PB AU/31
38 Hideki Matsui 03 PB Red AU/20
39 Don Mattingly 00 YL Jsy/26
40 Don Mattingly 01 LGD NY Bat/20
41 Joe Mays 00 SPA AU/30
42 Mark McGwire 01 UD Ball/19
43 D.Mientkiewicz 00 BD Jsy/57 4.00 10.00
44 Dale Murphy 00 LGD AU/91 10.00 25.00
45 Stan Musial 00 LGD AU/5
46 Jim Palmer 00 LGD AU/121 6.00 15.00
47 P.Reese 01 HOF Jsy/46 6.00 15.00
48 Phil Rizzuto 00 YL Jsy/19
49 Ivan Rodriguez 00 SPA AU/27
50 Ivan Rodriguez 01 GG Glv/4
51 Nolan Ryan 01 HOF Bat/37
52 Nolan Ryan 01 HOF Jsy/76
53 C.C. Sabathia 01 TP AU/64 8.00 20.00
54 Tim Salmon 01 GG Glv/12
55 Tom Seaver 00 LGD Jsy/18
56 Ben Sheets 01 TP AU/60 8.00 20.00
57 Ozzie Smith 00 LGD Jsy/14
58 Alf Soriano 00 SPA AU/80 10.00 25.00
59 Sammy Sosa 01 P/P Jsy/77 6.00 15.00
60 Larry Walker 01 GG Glv/10
61 Bernie Williams 01 GG Glv/10
62 Maury Wills 00 LGD Jsy/22
63 Dave Winfield 00 YL Bat/53 4.00 10.00
64 Bernie Williams 20.00 50.00
Ichiro Suzuki 01 P/P Bat/87
65 Sammy Sosa 6.00 15.00
Luis Gonzalez 01 P/P Bat/61

2003 Upper Deck UD Patch Logos

Inserted into first series packs at a stated rate of one in 7500, these eight cards feature game-used patch pieces. Each card has a print run between 41 and 54 and we have notated that print run information next to the player's name in our checklist.

BW Bernie Williams/42
CJ Chipper Jones/52 60.00 120.00
FT Frank Thomas/52 60.00 120.00
GM Greg Maddux/50 75.00 150.00
JB Jeff Bagwell/41
KI Kazuhisa Ishii/54 50.00 100.00
RJ Randy Johnson/50 60.00 120.00
TH Todd Helton/41

2003 Upper Deck UD Patch Logos Exclusives

Inserted into first series packs at a stated rate of one in 7500, these ten cards feature game-used patch pieces. Each card has a print run between nine and 61 and we have notated that print run information next to the player's name in our checklist. The cards with a print run of 25 or fewer are not priced due to market scarcity.

AR Alex Rodriguez/34
IS Ichiro Suzuki/46
JD Joe DiMaggio/9
JG Jason Giambi/34
KG Ken Griffey Jr./50 75.00 150.00
MG Mark McGwire/43
MM Mickey Mantle/10
MP Mike Piazza/61 60.00 120.00
RC Roger Clemens/34
SS Sammy Sosa/60 40.00 80.00

2003 Upper Deck UD Patch Numbers

Inserted into first series packs at a stated rate of one in 7500, these six cards feature game-used patch number pieces. Each card has a print run between 27 and 90 and we have notated that print run information next to the player's name in our checklist.

BW Bernie Williams/66 40.00 80.00
CJ Chipper Jones/44
FT Frank Thomas/91 40.00 80.00
KI Kazuhisa Ishii/63 30.00 60.00
RJ Randy Johnson/90 40.00 80.00
TH Todd Helton/27

2003 Upper Deck UD Patch Numbers Exclusives

Inserted into first series packs at a stated rate of one in 7500, these six cards feature game-used patch number pieces. Each card has a print run between 56 and 100 and we have notated that print run information next to the player's name in our checklist.

AR Alex Rodriguez/56 75.00 150.00
JG Jason Giambi/68 30.00 60.00
KG Ken Griffey Jr./97 50.00 100.00
MG Mark McGwire/60 150.00 250.00
SS Sammy Sosa/100 40.00 80.00

2003 Upper Deck UD Patch Stripes

Inserted into first series packs at a stated rate of one in 7500, these seven cards feature game-used patch striped pieces. Each card has a print run between 43 and 73 and we have notated that print run information next to the player's name in our checklist.

BW Bernie Williams/58 40.00 80.00
CJ Chipper Jones/58 40.00 80.00
FT Frank Thomas/58 40.00 80.00
JB Jeff Bagwell/73 40.00 80.00
KI Kazuhisa Ishii/58 30.00 60.00
RJ Randy Johnson/58 40.00 80.00
TH Todd Helton/43

2003 Upper Deck UD Patch Stripes Exclusives

Inserted into first series packs at a stated rate of one in 7500, these seven cards feature game-used patch striped pieces. Each card has a print run between 63 and 66 and we have notated that print run information next to the player's name in our checklist.

AR Alex Rodriguez/63 60.00 120.00
IS Ichiro Suzuki/63 150.00 250.00
JG Jason Giambi/66 30.00 60.00
KG Ken Griffey Jr./63 60.00 120.00
MG Mark McGwire/63 150.00 250.00
SS Sammy Sosa/63 60.00 120.00

2003 Upper Deck UD Super Patch Logos

NO PRICING DUE TO VOLATILITY
AJ Andruw Jones/92
AR Alex Rodriguez/45
AS Alfonso Soriano/15
GM Greg Maddux/95
HM Hideki Matsui/8
IS Ichiro Suzuki/20
KG Ken Griffey Jr./22
MP Mike Piazza/30
MR Manny Ramirez/22
SS Sammy Sosa/21

2003 Upper Deck UD Super Patch Numbers

AP Albert Pujols/8
AR Alex Rodriguez/13
CJ Chipper Jones/11
CS Curt Schilling/18
IR Ivan Rodriguez/10
IS Ichiro Suzuki/14
JB Jeff Bagwell/8
JG Jason Giambi/40
RC Roger Clemens/12

2003 Upper Deck UD Super Patch Stripes

AD Adam Dunn/70
AS Alfonso Soriano/16
JG Jason Giambi/50
KG Ken Griffey Jr./12
LB Lance Berkman/30
MP Mike Piazza/10
RJ Randy Johnson/73
SS Sammy Sosa/70
TH Todd Helton/50
VG Vladimir Guerrero/75

2003 Upper Deck UD Superstar Slam Jerseys

Inserted into first series hobby packs at a stated rate of one in 48, these 10 cards feature game-used jersey pieces of the featured players.

AR Alex Rodriguez 6.00 15.00
CJ Chipper Jones 4.00 10.00
FT Frank Thomas 4.00 10.00
JB Jeff Bagwell 4.00 10.00
JG Jason Giambi 3.00 8.00
KG Ken Griffey Jr. 6.00 15.00
LG Luis Gonzalez 3.00 8.00
MP Mike Piazza 6.00 15.00
SS Sammy Sosa 4.00 10.00
JGO Juan Gonzalez 3.00 8.00

2003 Upper Deck Star Rookie Sportsfest

This six-card set was distributed at the Chicago Sportsfest show in June, 2003. These cards were available if a collector opened a 2003 Upper Deck full box at the Upper Deck booth during the show. The collectors received not just this set but the first liscenced LeBron James card as well as a six-card football set. Since these cards are unnumbered, we have sequenced them in alphabetical order by first name.

COMPLETE SET 3.00 8.00
AM Alejandro Machado .40 1.00
HB Hank Blalock .40 1.00
HC Hee Seop Choi .60 1.50
HM Hideki Matsui .75 2.00
RB Rocco Baldelli .50 1.25
RH Runelvys Hernandez .40 1.00

2003 Upper Deck Collectibles UD Classics

IS Ichiro Suzuki/800

2004 Upper Deck

The 270-card first series was released in November, 2003. The cards were issued in eight-card hobby packs with an $3 SRP which came 24 packs to a box and 12 boxes to a case. These cards were also issued in nine-card retail packs also with a $3 SRP which came 24 packs to a box and 12 boxes to a case. Please note that insert cards were much more prevalent in the hobby packs. The following subsets were included in the first series: Super Rookies (1-30); Season Highlights Checklists (261-270). In addition, please note that the Super Rookie cards were not short printed. The second series, also of 270 cards, was released in June 2004. That series was highlighted by the following subsets: Season Highlights Checklists (471-480), Super Rookies (481-540). In addition, an update set was issued as a complete set with the 2005 Upper Deck I product. Those cards feature a mix of players who changed teams and Rookie Cards.

COMPLETE SERIES 1 (270) 20.00 50.00
COMPLETE SERIES 2 (270) 20.00 50.00
COMP.UPDATE SET (50) 7.50 15.00
COMMON (31-480/541-565) .10 .30
COMMON (1-30/481-540) .40 1.00
1-30/481-540 ARE NOT SHORT PRINTS
COMMON CARD (566-590) .20 .50
541-590 ONE SET PER '05 UD1 HOBBY BOX
UPDATE SET EXCH 1:480 '05 UD1 RETAIL
UPDATE SET EXCH.DEADLINE TBD
1 Dontrelle Willis SR .40 1.00
2 Edgar Gonzalez SR .40 1.00
3 Jose Reyes SR .60 1.50
4 Jae Weong Seo SR .40 1.00
5 Miguel Cabrera SR 1.00 2.50
6 Jesse Foppert SR .40 1.00
7 Mike Neu SR .40 1.00
8 Michael Nakamura SR .40 1.00
9 Luis Ayala SR .40 1.00
10 Jared Sandberg SR .40 1.00
11 Jhonny Peralta SR .40 1.00
12 Wil Ledezma SR .40 1.00
13 Jason Roach SR .40 1.00
14 Kirk Saarloos SR .40 1.00
15 Cliff Lee SR .60 1.50
16 Bobby Hill SR .40 1.00
17 Lyle Overbay SR .40 1.00
18 Josh Hall SR .40 1.00
19 Joe Thurston SR .40 1.00
20 Matt Kata SR .40 1.00
21 Jeremy Bonderman SR .40 1.00
22 Julio Manon SR .40 1.00
23 Rodrigo Rosario SR .40 1.00
24 Robby Hammock SR .40 1.00
25 David Sanders SR .40 1.00
26 Miguel Ojeda SR .40 1.00
27 Mark Teixeira SR 1.00 2.50
28 Franklyn German SR .40 1.00
29 Ken Harvey SR .40 1.00
30 Xavier Nady SR .40 1.00
31 Tim Salmon .12 .30
32 Troy Glaus .12 .30
33 Adam Kennedy .12 .30
34 David Eckstein .12 .30
35 Ben Molina .12 .30
36 Jarrod Washburn .12 .30
37 Ramon Ortiz .12 .30
38 Eric Chavez .12 .30
39 Miguel Tejada .20 .50
40 Chris Singleton .12 .30
41 Jermaine Dye .12 .30
42 John Halama .12 .30
43 Tim Hudson .20 .50
44 Barry Zito .12 .30
45 Ted Lilly .12 .30
46 Bobby Kielty .12 .30
47 Kelvim Escobar .12 .30
48 Josh Phelps .12 .30
49 Vernon Wells .12 .30
50 Roy Halladay .30 .75
51 Orlando Hudson .12 .30
52 Eric Hinske .12 .30
53 Brandon Backe .12 .30
54 Dewon Brazelton .12 .30
55 Ben Grieve .12 .30
56 Aubrey Huff .12 .30
57 Toby Hall .12 .30
58 Rocco Baldelli .12 .30
59 Al Martin .12 .30
60 Brandon Phillips .12 .30
61 Omar Vizquel .20 .50
62 C.C. Sabathia .20 .50
63 Milton Bradley .12 .30
64 Ricky Gutierrez .12 .30
65 Matt Lawton .12 .30
66 Danys Baez .12 .30
67 Ichiro Suzuki .50 1.25
68 Randy Winn .12 .30
69 Carlos Guillen .12 .30
70 Mark McLemore .12 .30
71 Dan Wilson .12 .30
72 Jamie Moyer .12 .30
73 Joel Pineiro .12 .30
74 Edgar Martinez .20 .50
75 Tony Batista .12 .30
76 Jay Gibbons .12 .30
77 Jeff Conine .12 .30
78 Melvin Mora .12 .30
79 Geronimo Gil .12 .30
80 Rodrigo Lopez .12 .30
81 Jorge Julio .12 .30
82 Rafael Palmeiro .20 .50
83 Juan Gonzalez .12 .30
84 Mike Young .12 .30
85 Alex Rodriguez .50 1.25
86 Einar Diaz .12 .30
87 Kevin Mench .12 .30
88 Hank Blalock .12 .30
89 Pedro Martinez .20 .50
90 Byung-Hyun Kim .12 .30
91 Derek Lowe .12 .30
92 Jason Varitek .30 .75
93 Manny Ramirez .30 .75
94 John Burkett .12 .30
95 Todd Walker .12 .30
96 Nomar Garciaparra .30 .75
97 Trot Nixon .12 .30
98 Mike Sweeney .12 .30
99 Carlos Febles .12 .30
100 Mike MacDougal .12 .30
101 Raul Ibanez .12 .30
102 Jason Grimsley .12 .30
103 Chris George .12 .30
104 Brent Mayne .12 .30
105 Dmitri Young .12 .30
106 Eric Munson .12 .30
107 A.J. Hinch .12 .30
108 Andres Torres .12 .30
109 Bobby Higginson .12 .30
110 Shane Halter .12 .30
111 Matt Walbeck .12 .30
112 Torii Hunter .12 .30
113 Doug Mientkiewicz .12 .30
114 Lew Ford .12 .30
115 Eric Milton .12 .30
116 Eddie Guardado .12 .30
117 Cristian Guzman .12 .30
118 Corey Koskie .12 .30
119 Magglio Ordonez .20 .50
120 Mark Buehrle .20 .50
121 Billy Koch .12 .30
122 Jose Valentin .12 .30
123 Paul Konerko .20 .50
124 Carlos Lee .12 .30
125 Jon Garland .12 .30
126 Jason Giambi .12 .30
127 Derek Jeter .75 2.00
128 Roger Clemens .40 1.00
129 Andy Pettitte .20 .50
130 Jorge Posada .20 .50
131 David Wells .12 .30
132 Hideki Matsui .50 1.25
133 Mike Mussina .20 .50
134 Jeff Bagwell .20 .50
135 Craig Biggio .20 .50
136 Morgan Ensberg .12 .30
137 Richard Hidalgo .12 .30
138 Brad Ausmus .12 .30
139 Roy Oswalt .20 .50
140 Billy Wagner .12 .30
141 Octavio Dotel .12 .30
142 Gary Sheffield .12 .30
143 Andruw Jones .12 .30
144 John Smoltz .30 .75
145 Rafael Furcal .12 .30
146 Javy Lopez .12 .30
147 Shane Reynolds .12 .30
148 Horacio Ramirez .12 .30
149 Mike Hampton .12 .30
150 Jung Bong .12 .30
151 Ruben Quevedo .12 .30
152 Ben Sheets .12 .30
153 Geoff Jenkins .12 .30
154 Royce Clayton .12 .30
155 Glendon Rusch .12 .30
156 John Vander Wal .12 .30
157 Scott Podsednik .12 .30
158 Jim Edmonds .20 .50
159 Tino Martinez .20 .50
160 Albert Pujols .75 2.00
161 Matt Morris .12 .30
162 Woody Williams .12 .30
163 Edgar Renteria .12 .30
164 Jason Isringhausen .12 .30
165 Jason Simontacchi .12 .30
166 Kerry Robinson .12 .30
167 Sammy Sosa .30 .75
168 Joe Borowski .12 .30
169 Tony Womack .12 .30
170 Antonio Alfonseca .12 .30
171 Corey Patterson .12 .30
172 Mark Prior .20 .50
173 Moises Alou .12 .30
174 Matt Clement .12 .30
175 Randall Simon .12 .30
176 Randy Johnson .30 .75
177 Luis Gonzalez .12 .30
178 Craig Counsell .12 .30
179 Miguel Batista .12 .30
180 Steve Finley .12 .30
181 Brandon Webb .12 .30
182 Danny Bautista .12 .30
183 Oscar Villarreal .12 .30
184 Shawn Green .12 .30
185 Brian Jordan .12 .30
186 Fred McGriff .12 .30
187 Andy Ashby .12 .30
188 Rickey Henderson .30 .75
189 Dave Roberts .12 .30
190 Eric Gagne .12 .30
191 Kazuhisa Ishii .12 .30

2004 Upper Deck

192 Adrian Beltre .12 .30
193 Vladimir Guerrero .30 .75
194 Livan Hernandez .12 .30
195 Ron Calloway .12 .30
196 Sun Woo Kim .12 .30
197 Wil Cordero .12 .30
198 Brad Wilkerson .12 .30
199 Orlando Cabrera .12 .30
200 Barry Bonds .60 1.50
201 Ray Durham .12 .30
202 Andres Galarraga .12 .30
203 Benito Santiago .12 .30
204 Jose Cruz Jr. .12 .30
205 Jason Schmidt .12 .30
206 Kirk Rueter .12 .30
207 Felix Rodriguez .12 .30
208 Mike Lowell .12 .30
209 Luis Castillo .12 .30
210 Derrek Lee .12 .30
211 Andy Fox .12 .30
212 Tommy Phelps .12 .30
213 Todd Hollandsworth .12 .30
214 Brad Penny .12 .30
215 Juan Pierre .12 .30
216 Mike Piazza .30 .75
217 Jae Weong Seo .12 .30
218 Ty Wigginton .12 .30
219 Al Leiter .12 .30
220 Roger Cedeno .12 .30
221 Timo Perez .12 .30
222 Aaron Heilman .12 .30
223 Pedro Astacio .12 .30
224 Joe McEwing .12 .30
225 Ryan Klesko .12 .30
226 Brian Giles .12 .30
227 Mark Kotsay .12 .30
228 Brian Lawrence .12 .30
229 Rod Beck .12 .30
230 Trevor Hoffman .20 .50
231 Sean Burroughs .12 .30
232 Bob Abreu .12 .30
233 Jim Thome .20 .50
234 David Bell .12 .30
235 Jimmy Rollins .20 .50
236 Mike Lieberthal .12 .30
237 Vicente Padilla .12 .30
238 Randy Wolf .12 .30
239 Reggie Sanders .12 .30
240 Jason Kendall .12 .30
241 Jack Wilson .12 .30
242 Jose Hernandez .12 .30
243 Kip Wells .12 .30
244 Carlos Rivera .12 .30
245 Craig Wilson .12 .30
246 Adam Dunn .20 .50
247 Sean Casey .12 .30
248 Danny Graves .12 .30
249 Ryan Dempster .12 .30
250 Barry Larkin .20 .50
251 Reggie Taylor .12 .30
252 Wily Mo Pena .12 .30
253 Larry Walker .20 .50
254 Mark Sweeney .12 .30
255 Preston Wilson .12 .30
256 Jason Jennings .12 .30
257 Charles Johnson .12 .30
258 Jay Payton .12 .30
259 Chris Stynes .12 .30
260 Juan Uribe .12 .30
261 Hideki Matsui SH CL .50 1.25
262 Barry Bonds SH CL .60 1.50
263 Dontrelle Willis SH CL .12 .30
264 Kevin Millwood SH CL .12 .30
265 Billy Wagner SH CL .12 .30
266 Rocco Baldelli SH CL .12 .30
267 Roger Clemens SH CL .40 1.00
268 Rafael Palmeiro SH CL .20 .50
269 Miguel Cabrera SH CL .30 .75
270 Jose Contreras SH CL .12 .30
271 Aaron Sele .12 .30
272 Bartolo Colon .12 .30
273 Darin Erstad .12 .30
274 Francisco Rodriguez .20 .50
275 Garret Anderson .12 .30
276 Jose Guillen .12 .30
277 Troy Percival .12 .30
278 Alex Cintron .12 .30
279 Casey Fossum .12 .30
280 Elmer Dessens .12 .30
281 Jose Valverde .12 .30
282 Matt Mantei .12 .30
283 Richie Sexson .12 .30
284 Roberto Alomar .20 .50
285 Shea Hillenbrand .12 .30
286 Chipper Jones .30 .75
287 Greg Maddux .50 1.25
288 J.D. Drew .12 .30
289 Marcus Giles .12 .30
290 Mike Hessman .12 .30
291 John Thomson .12 .30
292 Russ Ortiz .12 .30
293 Adam Loewen .12 .30
294 Jack Cust .12 .30
295 Jerry Hairston Jr. .12 .30
296 Kurt Ainsworth .12 .30
297 Luis Matos .12 .30
298 Marty Cordova .12 .30
299 Sidney Ponson .12 .30
300 Bill Mueller .12 .30
301 Curt Schilling .20 .50
302 David Ortiz .30 .75
303 Johnny Damon .20 .50
304 Keith Foulke Sox .12 .30
305 Pokey Reese .12 .30
306 Scott Williamson .12 .30
307 Tim Wakefield .12 .30
308 Alex S. Gonzalez .12 .30
309 Aramis Ramirez .12 .30
310 Carlos Zambrano .20 .50
311 Juan Cruz .12 .30
312 Kerry Wood .12 .30
313 Kyle Farnsworth .12 .30
314 Aaron Rowand .12 .30
315 Esteban Loaiza .12 .30
316 Frank Thomas .30 .75
317 Joe Borchard .12 .30
318 Joe Crede .12 .30
319 Miguel Olivo .12 .30
320 Willie Harris .12 .30
321 Aaron Harang .12 .30
322 Austin Kearns .12 .30
323 Brandon Claussen .12 .30
324 Brandon Larson .12 .30
325 Ryan Freel .12 .30
326 Ken Griffey Jr. .50 1.25
327 Ryan Wagner .12 .30
328 Alex Escobar .12 .30
329 Coco Crisp .12 .30
330 David Riske .12 .30
331 Jody Gerut .12 .30
332 Josh Bard .12 .30
333 Travis Hafner .12 .30
334 Chin-Hui Tsao .12 .30
335 Denny Stark .12 .30
336 Jeromy Burnitz .12 .30
337 Shawn Chacon .12 .30
338 Todd Helton .20 .50
339 Vinny Castilla .12 .30
340 Alex Sanchez .12 .30
341 Carlos Pena .20 .50
342 Fernando Vina .12 .30
343 Jason Johnson .12 .30
344 Matt Anderson .12 .30
345 Mike Maroth .12 .30
346 Rondell White .12 .30
347 A.J. Burnett .20 .50
348 Alex Gonzalez .12 .30
349 Armando Benitez .12 .30
350 Carl Pavano .12 .30
351 Hee Seop Choi .12 .30
352 Ivan Rodriguez .20 .50
353 Josh Beckett .20 .50
354 Josh Willingham .12 .30
355 Adam Everett .12 .30
356 Brandon Duckworth .12 .30
357 Jason Lane .12 .30
358 Jeff Kent .12 .30
359 Jeriome Robertson .12 .30
360 Lance Berkman .20 .50
361 Wade Miller .12 .30
362 Aaron Guiel .12 .30
363 Angel Berroa .12 .30
364 Carlos Beltran .12 .30
365 David DeJesus .12 .30
366 Desi Relaford .12 .30
367 Joe Randa .12 .30
368 Runelvys Hernandez .12 .30
369 Edwin Jackson .12 .30
370 Hideo Nomo .30 .75
371 Jeff Weaver .12 .30
372 Juan Encarnacion .12 .30
373 Odalis Perez .12 .30
374 Paul Lo Duca .12 .30
375 Robin Ventura .12 .30
376 Bill Hall .12 .30
377 Chad Moeller .12 .30
378 Chris Capuano .12 .30
379 Junior Spivey .12 .30
380 Rickie Weeks .12 .30
381 Wes Helms .12 .30
382 Brad Radke .12 .30
383 Jacque Jones .12 .30
384 Joe Mays .12 .30
385 Joe Nathan .12 .30
386 Johan Santana .30 .75
387 Nick Punto .12 .30
388 Shannon Stewart .12 .30
389 Carl Everett .12 .30
390 Claudio Vargas .12 .30
391 Jose Vidro .12 .30
392 Nick Johnson .12 .30
393 Rocky Biddle .12 .30
394 Tony Armas Jr. .12 .30
395 Braden Looper .12 .30
396 Cliff Floyd .12 .30
397 Jason Phillips .12 .30
398 Mike Cameron .12 .30
399 Tom Glavine .20 .50
400 Kenny Lofton .12 .30
401 Alfonso Soriano .12 .30
402 Bernie Williams .20 .50
403 Javier Vazquez .12 .30
404 Jon Lieber .12 .30
405 Jose Contreras .12 .30
406 Kevin Brown .12 .30
407 Mariano Rivera .30 .75
408 Arthur Rhodes .12 .30
409 Eric Byrnes .12 .30
410 Erubiel Durazo .12 .30
411 Graham Koonce .12 .30
412 Marco Scutaro .12 .30
413 Mark Mulder .12 .30
414 Mark Redman .12 .30
415 Rich Harden .12 .30
416 Brett Myers .12 .30
417 Chase Utley .30 .75
418 Kevin Millwood .12 .30
419 Marlon Byrd .12 .30
420 Pat Burrell .12 .30
421 Placido Polanco .12 .30
422 Tim Worrell .12 .30
423 Jason Bay .20 .50
424 Josh Fogg .12 .30
425 Kris Benson .12 .30
426 Mike Gonzalez .12 .30
427 Oliver Perez .12 .30
428 Tike Redman .12 .30
429 Adam Eaton .12 .30
430 Ismael Valdes .12 .30
431 Jake Peavy .12 .30
432 Khalil Greene .20 .50
433 Mark Loretta .12 .30
434 Phil Nevin .12 .30
435 Ramon Hernandez .12 .30
436 A.J. Pierzynski .12 .30
437 Edgardo Alfonzo .12 .30
438 J.T. Snow .12 .30
439 Jerome Williams .12 .30
440 Marquis Grissom .12 .30
441 Robb Nen .12 .30
442 Bret Boone .12 .30
443 Freddy Garcia .12 .30
444 Gil Meche .12 .30
445 John Olerud .12 .30
446 Rich Aurilia .12 .30
447 Shigetoshi Hasegawa .12 .30
448 Bo Hart .12 .30
449 Danny Haren .12 .30
450 Jason Marquis .12 .30
451 Marlon Anderson .12 .30
452 Scott Rolen .20 .50
453 So Taguchi .12 .30
454 Carl Crawford .20 .50
455 Delmon Young .20 .50
456 Geoff Blum .12 .30
457 Jesus Colome .12 .30
458 Jonny Gomes .12 .30
459 Lance Carter .12 .30
460 Robert Fick .12 .30
461 Chan Ho Park .20 .50
462 Francisco Cordero .12 .30
463 Jeff Nelson .12 .30
464 Jeff Zimmerman .12 .30
465 Kenny Rogers .12 .30
466 Aquilino Lopez .12 .30
467 Carlos Delgado .12 .30
468 Frank Catalanotto .12 .30
469 Reed Johnson .12 .30
470 Pat Hentgen .12 .30
471 Curt Schilling SH CL .20 .50
472 Gary Sheffield SH CL .12 .30
473 Javier Vazquez SH CL .12 .30
474 Kazuo Matsui SH CL .20 .50
475 Kevin Brown SH CL .12 .30
476 Rafael Palmeiro SH CL .20 .50
477 Richie Sexson SH CL .12 .30
478 Roger Clemens SH CL .40 1.00
479 Vladimir Guerrero SH CL .30 .75
480 Alex Rodriguez SH CL .50 1.25
481 Jake Woods SR RC .40 1.00
482 Tim Bittner SR RC .40 1.00
483 Brandon Medders SR RC .40 1.00
484 Casey Daigle SR RC .40 1.00
485 Jerry Gil SR RC .40 1.00
486 Mike Gosling SR RC .40 1.00
487 Jose Capellan SR RC .40 1.00
488 Onil Joseph SR RC .40 1.00
489 Roman Colon SR RC .40 1.00
490 Dave Crouthers SR RC .40 1.00
491 Eddy Rodriguez SR RC .40 1.00
492 Franklyn Gracesqui SR RC .40 1.00
493 Jamie Brown SR RC .40 1.00
494 Jerome Gamble SR RC .40 1.00
495 Tim Hamulack SR RC .40 1.00
496 Carlos Vasquez SR RC .40 1.00
497 Renyel Pinto SR RC .40 1.00
498 Ronny Cedeno SR RC .40 1.00
499 Enemencio Pacheco SR RC .40 1.00
500 Ryan Meaux SR RC .40 1.00
501 Ryan Wing SR RC .40 1.00
502 Shingo Takatsu SR RC .40 1.00
503 William Bergolla SR RC .40 1.00
504 Ivan Ochoa SR RC .40 1.00
505 Mariano Gomez SR RC .40 1.00
506 Justin Hampson SR RC .40 1.00
507 Justin Huisman SR RC .40 1.00
508 Scott Dohmann SR RC .40 1.00
509 Donnie Kelly SR RC .60 1.50
510 Chris Aguila SR RC .40 1.00
511 Lincoln Holdzkom SR RC .40 1.00
512 Freddy Guzman SR RC .40 1.00
513 Hector Gimenez SR RC .40 1.00
514 Jorge Vasquez SR RC .40 1.00
515 Jason Frasor SR RC .40 1.00
516 Chris Saenz SR RC .40 1.00
517 Dennis Sarfate SR RC .40 1.00
518 Colby Miller SR RC .40 1.00
519 Jason Bartlett SR RC 1.25 3.00
520 Chad Bentz SR RC .40 1.00
521 Josh Labandeira SR RC .40 1.00
522 Shawn Hill SR RC .40 1.00
523 Kazuo Matsui SR RC .60 1.50
524 Carlos Hines SR RC .40 1.00
525 Mike Vento SR RC .40 1.00
526 Scott Proctor SR RC .40 1.00
527 Sean Henn SR RC .40 1.00
528 David Aardsma SR RC .40 1.00
529 Ian Snell SR RC .40 1.00
530 Mike Johnston SR RC .40 1.00
531 Akinori Otsuka SR RC .40 1.00
532 Rusty Tucker SR RC .40 1.00
533 Justin Knoedler SR RC .40 1.00
534 Merkin Valdez SR RC .40 1.00
535 Greg Dobbs SR RC .40 1.00
536 Justin Leone SR RC .40 1.00
537 Shawn Camp SR RC .40 1.00
538 Edwin Moreno SR RC .40 1.00
539 Angel Chavez SR RC .40 1.00
540 Jesse Harper SR RC .40 1.00
541 Alex Rodriguez .50 1.25
542 Roger Clemens .40 1.00
543 Andy Pettitte .20 .50
544 Vladimir Guerrero .30 .75
545 David Wells .12 .30
546 Derrek Lee .12 .30
547 Carlos Beltran .12 .30
548 Orlando Cabrera Sox .12 .30
549 Paul Lo Duca .12 .30
550 Dave Roberts .12 .30
551 Guillermo Mota .12 .30
552 Steve Finley .12 .30
553 Juan Encarnacion .12 .30
554 Larry Walker .20 .50
555 Ty Wigginton .12 .30
556 Doug Mientkiewicz .12 .30
557 Roberto Alomar .20 .50
558 B.J. Upton .20 .50
559 Brad Penny .12 .30
560 Hee Seop Choi .12 .30
561 David Wright .50 1.25
562 Nomar Garciaparra .30 .75
563 Felix Rodriguez .12 .30
564 Victor Zambrano .12 .30
565 Kris Benson .12 .30
566 Aarom Baldiris SR RC .20 .50
567 Joey Gathright SR RC .20 .50
568 Charles Thomas SR RC .20 .50
569 Brian Dallimore SR RC .20 .50
570 Chris Oxspring SR RC .20 .50
571 Chris Shelton SR RC .20 .50
572 Dioner Navarro SR RC .30 .75
573 Edwardo Sierra SR RC .20 .50
574 Fernando Nieve SR RC .20 .50
575 Frank Francisco SR RC .20 .50
576 Jeff Bennett SR RC .20 .50
577 Justin Lehr SR RC .20 .50
578 John Gall SR RC .20 .50
579 Jorge Sequea SR RC .20 .50
580 Justin Germano SR RC .20 .50
581 Kazuhito Tadano SR RC .20 .50
582 Kevin Cave SR RC .20 .50
583 Jesse Crain SR RC .20 .50
584 Luis A. Gonzalez SR RC .20 .50
585 Michael Wuertz SR RC .20 .50
586 Orlando Rodriguez SR RC .20 .50
587 Phil Stockman SR RC .20 .50
588 Ramon Ramirez SR RC .20 .50
589 Roberto Novoa SR RC .20 .50
590 Scott Kazmir SR RC 1.00 2.50

2004 Upper Deck Glossy

COMP.FACT.SET (590) 70.00 100.00
*GLOSSY: .75X TO 2X BASIC
ISSUED ONLY IN FACTORY SET FORM

2004 Upper Deck A Piece of History 500 Club

SERIES 1 STATED ODDS 1:8700
STATED PRINT RUN 350 SERIAL #'D CARDS
504HR Rafael Palmeiro 100.00 200.00

2004 Upper Deck A Piece of History 500 Club Autograph

STATED PRINT RUN 25 SERIAL #'d CARDS
NO PRICING DUE TO SCARCITY
RPAU0 Rafael Palmeiro AU/25

2004 Upper Deck Authentic Stars Jersey

SERIES 1 ODDS 1:48 HOBBY, 1:96 RETAIL
*GOLD: .75X TO 2X BASIC AS JSY
GOLD RANDOM INSERTS IN SERIES 1 PACKS
GOLD PRINT RUN 100 SERIAL #'d SETS
AJ Andruw Jones 4.00 10.00
AP Albert Pujols 6.00 15.00
AR Alex Rodriguez 4.00 10.00
AS Alfonso Soriano 3.00 8.00
BA Bob Abreu 3.00 8.00
BW Bernie Williams 4.00 10.00
BZ Barry Zito 3.00 8.00
CD Carlos Delgado 3.00 8.00
CJ Chipper Jones 4.00 10.00
CS Curt Schilling 3.00 8.00
DE Darin Erstad 3.00 8.00
EC Eric Chavez 3.00 8.00
FT Frank Thomas 4.00 10.00
GM Greg Maddux 4.00 10.00
HB Hank Blalock 3.00 8.00
HM Hideki Matsui 15.00 40.00
IR Ivan Rodriguez 4.00 10.00
IS Ichiro Suzuki 10.00 25.00
JB Jeff Bagwell 4.00 10.00
JD J.D. Drew 3.00 8.00
JG Jason Giambi 3.00 8.00
JH Josh Beckett 3.00 8.00
JK Jeff Kent 3.00 8.00
KG Ken Griffey Jr. 6.00 15.00
LW Larry Walker 3.00 8.00
MI Mike Piazza 4.00 10.00
MP Mark Prior 4.00 10.00
MT Mark Teixeira 4.00 10.00
PM Pedro Martinez 4.00 10.00
PN Phil Nevin 3.00 8.00
RB Rocco Baldelli 3.00 8.00
RC Roger Clemens 6.00 15.00
RJ Randy Johnson 4.00 10.00
RO Roberto Alomar 4.00 10.00
SG Shawn Green 3.00 8.00
SS Sammy Sosa 4.00 10.00
TG Troy Glaus 3.00 8.00
TH Todd Helton 4.00 10.00
TL Tom Glavine 4.00 10.00
TM Tino Martinez 4.00 10.00
TO Torii Hunter 3.00 8.00
VG Vladimir Guerrero 4.00 10.00

2004 Upper Deck Authentic Stars Jersey Update

UPDATE GU ODDS 1:12 '04 UPDATE SETS
STATED PRINT RUN 75 SERIAL #'d SETS
AK Austin Kearns 4.00 10.00
CB Carlos Beltran 4.00 10.00
DJ Derek Jeter 15.00 40.00
HA Roy Halladay 4.00 10.00
HN Hideo Nomo 10.00 25.00
HU Tim Hudson 4.00 10.00
JE Jim Edmonds 4.00 10.00
JR Jose Reyes 4.00 10.00
JT Jim Thome 6.00 15.00
KW Kerry Wood 4.00 10.00
LB Lance Berkman 4.00 10.00
MO Magglio Ordonez 4.00 10.00
MR Manny Ramirez 6.00 15.00
OS Roy Oswalt 4.00 10.00
PW Preston Wilson 4.00 10.00
RF Rafael Furcal 4.00 10.00
RH Rich Harden 4.00 10.00
RP Rafael Palmeiro 6.00 15.00
SR Scott Rolen 6.00 15.00
TE Miguel Tejada 4.00 10.00
VW Vernon Wells 4.00 10.00
WE Brandon Webb 4.00 10.00

2004 Upper Deck Awesome Honors

COMPLETE SET (10) 8.00 20.00
SERIES 2 STATED ODDS 1:12 H/R
1 Albert Pujols 2.50 6.00
2 Alex Rodriguez 1.50 4.00
3 Angel Berroa .40 1.00
4 Dontrelle Willis .40 1.00
5 Eric Gagne .40 1.00
6 Garret Anderson .40 1.00
7 Ivan Rodriguez .60 1.50
8 Josh Beckett .60 1.50
9 Mariano Rivera 1.00 2.50
10 Roy Halladay 1.00 2.50

2004 Upper Deck Awesome Honors Jersey

*GOLD: .6X TO 1.5X BASIC
GOLD PRINT RUN 165 SERIAL #'d SETS
OVERALL SER.2 GU ODDS 1:12 H, 1:24 R
AJ Andruw Jones GG 3.00 8.00
AP Albert Pujols PC 6.00 15.00
AP1 Albert Pujols HA 6.00 15.00
AP2 Albert Pujols POM 6.00 15.00
AR Alex Rodriguez MVP 5.00 12.00
AR1 Alex Rodriguez GG 5.00 12.00
AR2 Alex Rodriguez HA 5.00 12.00
AR3 Alex Rodriguez POM 5.00 12.00
AS Alfonso Soriano POM 2.00 5.00
BB Bret Boone GG 2.00 5.00
BM Ben Molina GG 2.00 5.00
DL Derrek Lee GG 3.00 8.00
DW Dontrelle Willis ROY 3.00 8.00
EC Eric Chavez GG 2.00 5.00
EG Eric Gagne CY 2.00 5.00
EG1 Eric Gagne RA 2.00 5.00
EM Edgar Martinez POM 3.00 8.00
GA Garret Anderson AS MVP 2.00 5.00
HU Torii Hunter GG 2.00 5.00
IR Ivan Rodriguez NLCS MVP 3.00 8.00
IS Ichiro Suzuki GG 10.00 25.00
JB Josh Beckett WS MVP 2.00 5.00
JE Jim Edmonds GG 2.00 5.00
JG Jason Giambi POM 2.00 5.00
JM Jamie Moyer MAN 2.00 5.00
JO John Olerud GG 2.00 5.00
JS John Smoltz MAN 3.00 8.00
JT Jim Thome POM 3.00 8.00
LC Luis Castillo GG 2.00 5.00
MC Mike Cameron GG 2.00 5.00
MH Mike Hampton GG 2.00 5.00
MO Magglio Ordonez POM 2.00 5.00
MR Mariano Rivera ALCS MVP 3.00 8.00
MU Mike Mussina GG 3.00 8.00
RH Roy Halladay CY 2.00 5.00
SR Scott Rolen GG 3.00 8.00
TH Todd Helton POM 3.00 8.00
VG Vladimir Guerrero POM 3.00 8.00

2004 Upper Deck Awesome Honors Jersey Update

UPDATE GU ODDS 1:12 '04 UPDATE SETS
AB Angel Berroa 4.00 10.00
AP Albert Pujols 10.00 25.00
AS Alfonso Soriano 4.00 10.00
BE Adrian Beltre 4.00 10.00
BG Brian Giles 4.00 10.00
DL Derrek Lee 6.00 15.00
EG Eric Gagne 4.00 10.00
GS Gary Sheffield 4.00 10.00
IR Ivan Rodriguez 6.00 15.00
JM Joe Mauer 4.00 10.00
KB Kevin Brown 4.00 10.00
KM Kazuo Matsui 4.00 10.00
MC Miguel Cabrera 6.00 15.00
PE Andy Pettitte 6.00 15.00
RC Roger Clemens 10.00 25.00
RS Richie Sexson 4.00 10.00
SC Curt Schilling 6.00 15.00
SP Scott Podsednik 4.00 10.00
VA Javier Vazquez 4.00 10.00

2004 Upper Deck First Pitch Inserts

SERIES 1 STATED ODDS 1:72
CARD SP9 DOES NOT EXIST
SP7 LeBron James 6.00 15.00
SP8 Gordie Howe 4.00 10.00
SP10 Ernie Banks 4.00 10.00
SP11 General Tommy Franks 2.00 5.00
SP12 Ben Affleck 4.00 10.00
SP13 Halle Berry UER 4.00 10.00
Last name misspelled Barry
SP14 George H.W. Bush 2.00 5.00
SP15 George W. Bush 4.00 10.00

2004 Upper Deck Game Winners Bat

*GOLD: .6X TO 1.5X BASIC
GOLD PRINT RUN 50 SERIAL #'d SETS
OVERALL SER.2 GU ODDS 1:12 H, 1:24 R
AG Alex Gonzalez 3.00 8.00
AJ Andruw Jones 4.00 10.00
AP Albert Pujols 8.00 20.00
AS Alfonso Soriano 3.00 8.00
BA Bobby Abreu 3.00 8.00
BW Bernie Williams 4.00 10.00
CJ Chipper Jones 4.00 10.00
CP Corey Patterson 3.00 8.00
DE Darin Erstad 3.00 8.00
DJ Derek Jeter 10.00 25.00
GA Garret Anderson
GS Gary Sheffield 3.00 8.00
HB Hank Blalock 3.00 8.00
HM Hideki Matsui 12.50 30.00
HU Torii Hunter 3.00 8.00
IR Ivan Rodriguez 4.00 10.00
JB Jeff Bagwell 4.00 10.00
JE Jim Edmonds 3.00 8.00
JG Jason Giambi 3.00 8.00
JL Javy Lopez
JP Jorge Posada 4.00 10.00
JT Jim Thome 4.00 10.00
KG Ken Griffey Jr.
MC Miguel Cabrera 4.00 10.00
ML Mike Lowell 3.00 8.00
MO Magglio Ordonez 3.00 8.00
MP Mike Piazza 6.00 15.00
MT Mark Teixeira 4.00 10.00
RF Rafael Furcal 3.00 8.00
RH Ramon Hernandez 3.00 8.00
RK Ryan Klesko 3.00 8.00
SG Shawn Green 3.00 8.00
SR Scott Rolen 4.00 10.00
TE Miguel Tejada 3.00 8.00
TG Troy Glaus 3.00 8.00
TH Todd Helton 4.00 10.00
TN Trot Nixon 3.00 8.00
VG Vladimir Guerrero 4.00 10.00

2004 Upper Deck Going Deep Bat

SERIES 1 ODDS 1:288 HOB, 1:576 RET
SP PRINT RUNS B/WN 12-123 COPIES PER
SP PRINT RUNS PROVIDED BY UPPER DECK
NO PRICING ON QTY OF 41 OR LESS
GOLD PRINT RUN 50 SERIAL #'d SETS
NO GOLD PRICING DUE TO SCARCITY
AJ Andruw Jones SP/12
AP Albert Pujols 10.00 25.00
AS Alfonso Soriano SP/53 4.00 10.00
BA Bob Abreu SP/110 4.00 10.00
BW Bernie Williams SP/56 6.00 15.00
CB Craig Biggio SP/89 6.00 15.00
CJ Chipper Jones SP/69 6.00 15.00
CP Corey Patterson SP/41
CS Curt Schilling SP/57 4.00 10.00
DE Darin Erstad 4.00 10.00
DM Doug Mientkiewicz SP/123 4.00 10.00
GA Garret Anderson 4.00 10.00
HM Hideki Matsui SP/70 15.00 40.00
HN Hideo Nomo 6.00 15.00
JB Jeff Bagwell SP/92 6.00 15.00
JE Jim Edmonds SP 4.00 10.00
JL Javy Lopez SP/77 4.00 10.00
JPA Jorge Posada 6.00 15.00
JPO Jay Payton SP/100 4.00 10.00
JT Jim Thome 6.00 15.00
KG Ken Griffey Jr. SP 15.00 40.00
KW Kerry Wood SP/108 4.00 10.00
MO Magglio Ordonez 4.00 10.00
MP Mike Piazza 6.00 15.00
MT Miguel Tejada SP/23
OV Omar Vizquel SP/115 6.00 15.00
RA Rich Aurilia SP/102 4.00 10.00
RB Rocco Baldelli SP 4.00 10.00
RF Rafael Furcal SP 4.00 10.00
RH Rickey Henderson SP/77 6.00 15.00
RO Roberto Alomar 6.00 15.00
SC Sandy Alomar Jr. SP/95 4.00 10.00
SG Shawn Green SP/100 4.00 10.00
SR Scott Rolen SP/77 6.00 15.00
TG Troy Glaus SP/113 4.00 10.00
TH Torii Hunter SP/115 4.00 10.00

2004 Upper Deck Headliners Jersey

SERIES 1 ODDS 1:48 HOBBY, 1:96 RETAIL
SP PRINT RUNS B/WN 97-153 COPIES PER
SP PRINT RUNS PROVIDED BY UPPER DECK
*GOLD: .75X TO 2X BASIC
GOLD RANDOM INSERTS IN SERIES 1 PACKS
GOLD PRINT RUN 100 SERIAL #'d SETS
AD Adam Dunn 3.00 8.00
BK Byung-Hyun Kim AS 3.00 8.00
BS Benito Santiago AS 3.00 8.00
CS Curt Schilling 3.00 8.00
GM Greg Maddux 4.00 10.00
HM Hideki Matsui 15.00 40.00
IS Ichiro Suzuki SP/153 15.00 40.00
JB Josh Beckett 3.00 8.00
JD Joe DiMaggio SP/153 50.00 100.00
JE Jim Edmonds 3.00 8.00
JH Jose Hernandez AS 3.00 8.00
JR Jimmy Rollins AS 3.00 8.00
JS Junior Spivey AS 3.00 8.00
JT Jim Thome 4.00 10.00
JV Jose Vidro AS 3.00 8.00
KG Ken Griffey Jr. 6.00 15.00
LB Lance Berkman 3.00 8.00
LC Luis Castillo AS 3.00 8.00
LG Luis Gonzalez 3.00 8.00
MA Mariano Rivera 4.00 10.00
MB Mark Buehrle AS 3.00 8.00
ML Mike Lowell AS 3.00 8.00
MM Mickey Mantle SP/97 75.00 150.00
MO Magglio Ordonez 3.00 8.00
MR Manny Ramirez 4.00 10.00
MS Matt Morris AS 3.00 8.00
MT Miguel Tejada 3.00 8.00
MU Mike Mussina 4.00 10.00
MY Mike Sweeney AS 3.00 8.00

PK Paul Konerko AS 3.00 8.00
PM Pedro Martinez 4.00 10.00
RF Robert Fick AS 3.00 8.00
RH Roy Halladay AS 3.00 8.00
RK Ryan Klesko 3.00 8.00
RO Roy Oswalt 3.00 8.00
SG Shawn Green 3.00 8.00
TB Tony Batista AS 3.00 8.00
TG Tom Glavine 4.00 10.00
TH Trevor Hoffman AO 0.00 0.00
TW Ted Williams SP/153 40.00 80.00
VG Vladimir Guerrero SP/153 6.00 15.00

2004 Upper Deck Derek Jeter Bonus

COMMON CARD (1-25) 2.00 5.00
1-25 THREE PER JETER BONUS PACK
COMMON JSY (26-32) 15.00 40.00
26-32 JSY PRINT RUN 99 #'d SETS
COMMON AU (33-37) 100.00 175.00
33-37 AU PRINT RUN 50 #'d SETS
38-42 AU JSY PRINT RUN 10 #'d SETS
AU JSY NO PRICING DUE TO SCARCITY
26-42 RANDOM IN JETER BONUS PACKS
ONE JETER BONUS PACK PER FACT.SET

2004 Upper Deck Magical Performances

SERIES 1 STATED ODDS 1:96 HOBBY
GOLD RANDOM INSERTS IN SER.1 HOBBY
GOLD STATED ODDS 1:1300 RETAIL
GOLD PRINT RUN 50 SERIAL #'d SETS
NO GOLD PRICING DUE TO SCARCITY
1 Mickey Mantle USC HR 12.00 30.00
2 Mickey Mantle 56 Triple Crown 12.00 30.00
3 Joe DiMaggio 56th Game 10.00 25.00
4 Joe DiMaggio Slides Home 10.00 25.00
5 Derek Jeter The Flip 10.00 25.00
6 Derek Jeter 00 AS/MVP 10.00 25.00
7 R.Clemens 300 Win/4000 K 5.00 12.00
8 Roger Clemens 20-1 5.00 12.00
9 Alfonso Soriano Walkoff 1.50 4.00
10 Andy Pettitte 96 2.50 6.00
11 Hideki Matsui Grand Slam 6.00 15.00
12 Mike Mussina 1-Hitter 2.50 6.00
13 Jorge Posada ALDS HR 2.50 6.00
14 Jason Giambi Grand Slam 1.50 4.00
15 David Wells Perfect 1.50 4.00
16 Mariano Rivera 99 WS MVP 4.00 10.00
17 Yogi Berra 12 K's 4.00 10.00
18 Phil Rizzuto 50 MVP 2.50 6.00
19 Whitey Ford 61 CY 2.50 6.00
20 Jose Contreras 1st Win 1.50 4.00
21 Catfish Hunter Free Agent 1.50 4.00
22 Mickey Mantle Cycle 12.00 30.00
23 M.Mantle HR's Both Sides 12.00 30.00
24 Joe DiMaggio 3-Time MVP 10.00 25.00
25 Joe DiMaggio Cycle 10.00 25.00
26 Derek Jeter 7 Seasons 10.00 25.00
27 Derek Jeter Mr. November 10.00 25.00
28 Roger Clemens 1-Hitter 5.00 12.00
29 Roger Clemens 01 CY 5.00 12.00
30 Alfonso Soriano HR Record 1.50 4.00
31 Andy Pettitte ALCS 2.50 6.00
32 Hideki Matsui 4 Hits 6.00 15.00
33 Mike Mussina 1st Postseason 2.50 6.00
34 Jorge Posada 40 Doubles 2.50 6.00
35 Jason Giambi 200th HR 1.50 4.00
36 David Wells 3-Hitter 1.50 4.00
37 Mariano Rivera Saves 3 4.00 10.00
38 Yogi Berra 3-Time MVP 4.00 10.00
39 Phil Rizzuto Broadcasting 2.50 6.00
40 Whitey Ford 10 WS Wins 2.50 6.00
41 Jose Contreras 2 Hits 1.50 4.00
42 Catfish Hunter 200th Win 1.50 4.00

2004 Upper Deck Matsui Chronicles

COMPLETE SET (60) 30.00 60.00
COMMON CARD (HM1-HM60) .75 2.00
ONE PER SERIES 1 RETAIL PACK

2004 Upper Deck National Pride

SERIES 1 STATED ODDS 1:6
1 Justin Orenduff .40 1.00
2 Micah Owings .25 .60
3 Steven Register .25 .60
4 Huston Street .60 1.50
5 Justin Verlander 1.50 4.00
6 Jered Weaver 1.00 2.50
7 Matt Campbell .25 .60
8 Stephen Head .25 .60
9 Mark Romanczuk .25 .60
10 Jeff Clement .75 2.00
11 Mike Nickeas .25 .60
12 Tyler Greene .25 .60
13 Paul Janish .40 1.00
14 Jeff Larish .25 .60
15 Eric Patterson .25 .60
16 Dustin Pedroia 1.25 3.00
17 Michael Griffin .25 .60
18 Brent Lillibridge .25 .60
19 Danny Putnam .25 .60
20 Seth Smith .60 1.50

2004 Upper Deck National Pride Jersey 1

SERIES 1 ODDS 1:24 HOBBY, 1:48 RETAIL
1 Justin Orenduff 2.00 5.00
2 Micah Owings 2.00 5.00
3 Steven Register 2.00 5.00
4 Huston Street 2.50 6.00
5 Justin Verlander 10.00 25.00
6 Jered Weaver 5.00 12.00
7 Matt Campbell 2.00 5.00
8 Stephen Head 2.00 5.00
9 Mark Romanczuk 2.00 5.00
10 Jeff Clement 4.00 10.00
11 Mike Nickeas 2.00 5.00
12 Tyler Greene 2.00 5.00
13 Paul Janish 2.00 5.00
14 Jeff Larish 2.00 5.00
15 Eric Patterson 2.00 5.00
16 Dustin Pedroia 2.00 5.00
17 Michael Griffin 2.00 5.00
18 Brent Lillibridge 2.00 5.00
19 Danny Putnam 2.00 5.00
20 Seth Smith 3.00 8.00
21 Justin Orenduff SP 3.00 8.00
22 Micah Owings SP 3.00 8.00
23 Steven Register SP 3.00 8.00
24 Huston Street SP 3.00 8.00
25 Justin Verlander SP 10.00 25.00
26 Jered Weaver SP 6.00 15.00
27 Matt Campbell SP 3.00 8.00
28 Stephen Head SP 3.00 8.00
29 Mark Romanczuk SP 3.00 8.00
30 Jeff Clement SP 5.00 12.00
31 Mike Nickeas SP 3.00 8.00
32 Tyler Greene SP 3.00 8.00
33 Paul Janish SP 3.00 8.00
34 Jeff Larish SP 3.00 8.00
35 Eric Patterson SP 3.00 8.00
36 Dustin Pedroia SP 3.00 8.00
37 Michael Griffin SP 3.00 8.00
38 Brent Lillibridge SP 3.00 8.00
39 Danny Putnam SP 3.00 8.00
40 Seth Smith SP 4.00 10.00
41 Delmon Young SP 6.00 15.00
42 Rickie Weeks SP 4.00 10.00

2004 Upper Deck National Pride Memorabilia 2

OVERALL SER.2 GU ODDS 1:12 H, 1:24 R
BBJ Brian Bruney Jsy 2.00 5.00
CBJ Chris Burke Jsy 2.00 5.00
CBP Chris Burke Pants 2.00 5.00
DUJ Justin Duchscherer Jsy 2.00 5.00
DUP Justin Duchscherer Pants 2.00 5.00
ERJ Eddie Rodriguez CO Jsy 2.00 5.00
ERP Eddie Rodriguez CO Pants 2.00 5.00
EYJ Ernie Young Jsy 2.00 5.00
GGJ Gabe Gross Jsy 2.00 5.00
GKJ Graham Koonce Jsy 2.00 5.00
GKP Graham Koonce Pants 2.00 5.00
GLJ Gerald Laird Jsy 2.00 5.00
GSJ Grady Sizemore Jsy 3.00 8.00
GSP Grady Sizemore Pants 3.00 8.00
HRJ Horacio Ramirez Jsy 2.00 5.00
HRP Horacio Ramirez Pants 2.00 5.00
JBJ John Van Benschoten Jsy 2.00 5.00
JBP John Van Benschoten Pants 2.00 5.00
JCJ Jesse Crain Jsy 3.00 8.00
JCP Jesse Crain Pants 3.00 8.00
JDJ J.D. Durbin Jsy 2.00 5.00
JGJ John Grabow Jsy 2.00 5.00
JHJ J.J. Hardy Jsy 2.00 5.00
JLJ Justin Leone Jsy 3.00 8.00
JLP Justin Leone Pants 3.00 8.00
JMJ Joe Mauer Jsy 6.00 15.00
JMP Joe Mauer Pants 6.00 15.00
JRJ Jeremy Reed Jsy 4.00 10.00
JSJ Jason Stanford Jsy 2.00 5.00
JSP Jason Stanford Pants 2.00 5.00
MLJ Mike Lamb Jsy 2.00 5.00
MRJ Mike Rouse Jsy 2.00 5.00
MRP Mike Rouse Pants 2.00 5.00
RMP Ryan Madson Pants 2.00 5.00
RRJ Royce Ring Jsy 2.00 5.00
RRP Royce Ring Pants 2.00 5.00
TBJ Thad Bosley CO Jsy 2.00 5.00
TWJ Todd Williams Jsy 2.00 5.00

2004 Upper Deck Peak Performers Jersey

*GOLD: .6X TO 1.5X BASIC
GOLD PRINT RUN 165 SERIAL #'d SETS
OVERALL SER.2 GU ODDS 1:12 H, 1:24 R
AP Albert Pujols 6.00 15.00
AS Alfonso Soriano 2.00 5.00
BE Josh Beckett 2.00 5.00
BP Brandon Phillips 2.00 5.00
CB Craig Biggio 3.00 8.00
CD Carlos Delgado 2.00 5.00
CS Curt Schilling 3.00 8.00
EG Eric Gagne 2.00 5.00
FT Frank Thomas 3.00 8.00
HB Hank Blalock 2.00 5.00
HM Hideki Matsui 10.00 25.00
HN Hideo Nomo 3.00 8.00
IR Ivan Rodriguez 3.00 8.00
IS Ichiro Suzuki 10.00 25.00
JB Jeff Bagwell 3.00 8.00
JR Jose Reyes 2.00 5.00
JT Jim Thome 3.00 8.00
KG Ken Griffey Jr. 6.00 15.00
KW Kerry Wood 2.00 5.00
LB Lance Berkman 2.00 5.00
LC Luis Castillo 2.00 5.00
MM Mike Mussina 3.00 8.00
MO Magglio Ordonez 2.00 5.00
MP Mark Prior 3.00 8.00
MT Miguel Tejada 2.00 5.00
OV Omar Vizquel 3.00 8.00
PB Pat Burrell 2.00 5.00
PE Andy Pettitte 3.00 8.00
PL Paul Lo Duca 2.00 5.00
PM Pedro Martinez 3.00 8.00
RF Rafael Furcal 2.00 5.00
RP Rafael Palmeiro 3.00 8.00
SA C.C. Sabathia 2.00 5.00
SG Shawn Green 2.00 5.00
SR Scott Rolen 3.00 8.00
TH Todd Helton 3.00 8.00
VG Vladimir Guerrero 3.00 8.00
VW Vernon Wells 2.00 5.00

2004 Upper Deck Famous Quotes

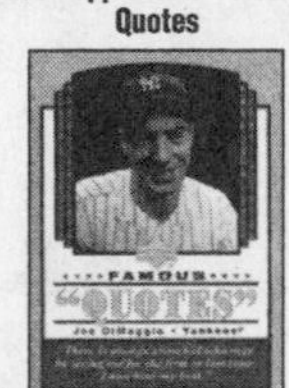

COMPLETE SET (20) 15.00 40.00
SERIES 2 STATED ODDS 1:6 H/R
1 Al Lopez .40 1.00
2 Bob Feller .40 1.00
3 Bob Gibson .60 1.50
4 Brooks Robinson .60 1.50
5 Cal Ripken 4.00 10.00
6 Carl Yastrzemski 1.00 2.50
7 Earl Weaver .40 1.00
8 Eddie Mathews 1.00 2.50
9 Ernie Banks 1.00 2.50
10 Greg Maddux 1.50 4.00
11 Joe DiMaggio 2.50 6.00
12 Mickey Mantle 3.00 8.00
13 Nolan Ryan 3.00 8.00
14 Stan Musial 1.50 4.00
15 Ted Williams 2.50 6.00
16 Tom Seaver .60 1.50
17 Tommy Lasorda .40 1.00
18 Warren Spahn .60 1.50
19 Whitey Ford .60 1.50
20 Yogi Berra 1.00 2.50

2004 Upper Deck Signature Stars Black Ink 1

Please note that Roger Clemens did not return his cards in time for pack-out and those cards could be redeemed until November 10, 2006.

SER.1 ODDS 1:288 H,1:24 UPD BOX, 1:1800 R
PRINT RUNS B/WN 18-479 COPIES PER
NO PRICING ON QTY OF 25 OR LESS
EXCHANGE DEADLINE 11/10/06
AG Andres Galarraga/248 6.00 15.00
AH Aaron Heilman/49 10.00 25.00
BG Bob Gibson/19
BK Billy Koch/429 4.00 10.00
CR Cal Ripken/69 125.00 200.00
DR1 Dave Roberts/278 4.00 10.00
HM Hideki Matsui/25
IS1 Ichiro Suzuki/19
JRA Joe Randa/271 6.00 15.00
KI Kazuhisa Ishii/58 10.00 25.00
MO Magglio Ordonez/377 6.00 15.00
MU Mike Mussina/68 15.00 40.00
NG Nomar Garciaparra/69 60.00 120.00
NR1 Nolan Ryan/69 75.00 150.00
RA Rich Aurilia/479 4.00 10.00
RH1 Rich Harden/163 6.00 15.00
RP Rafael Palmeiro/18
TH Torii Hunter/374 6.00 15.00
VG Vladimir Guerrero/68 30.00 60.00

2004 Upper Deck Signature Stars Black Ink 2

OVERALL SER.2 SIG ODDS 1:288 H, 1:1500 R
PRINT RUNS B/WN 43-450 COPIES PER
BB Bret Boone/43 15.00 40.00
BW Brandon Webb/60 6.00 15.00
DB Dewon Brazelton/96 4.00 10.00
DR2 Dave Roberts/450 4.00 10.00
DS Darryl Strawberry/160 10.00 25.00
DW Dontrelle Willis/160 10.00 25.00
EC Eric Chavez/60 10.00 25.00
EG Eric Gagne/160 10.00 25.00
JC Jose Canseco/160 10.00 25.00
JV Javier Vazquez/60 10.00 25.00
KG Ken Griffey Jr./450 50.00 100.00
MT Mark Teixeira/200 10.00 25.00
RH2 Rich Harden/65 10.00 25.00
RW Rickie Weeks/65 10.00 25.00

2004 Upper Deck Signature Stars Blue Ink 1

SER.1 ODDS 1:288 H,1:24 UPD BOX, 1:1800 R
STATED PRINT RUN 25 SERIAL #'d SETS
MATSUI PRINT RUN 324 SERIAL #'d CARDS
NO PRICING ON QTY OF 25 OR LESS
EXCHANGE DEADLINE 11/10/06
HM Hideki Matsui/324 175.00 300.00

2004 Upper Deck Signature Stars Blue Ink 2

OVERALL SER.2 SIG ODDS 1:288 H, 1:1500 R
PRINT RUNS B/WN 20-95 COPIES PER
NO PRICING ON QTY OF 25 OR LESS
NR2 Nolan Ryan/95 75.00 150.00

2004 Upper Deck Super Sluggers

COMPLETE SET (30) 10.00 25.00
ONE PER SERIES 2 RETAIL PACK
1 Albert Pujols 2.00 5.00
2 Alex Rodriguez 1.25 3.00
3 Alfonso Soriano .30 .75
4 Andruw Jones .30 .75
5 Bret Boone .30 .75
6 Carlos Delgado .30 .75
7 Edgar Renteria .30 .75
8 Eric Chavez .30 .75
9 Frank Thomas .75 2.00
10 Garret Anderson .30 .75
11 Gary Sheffield .30 .75
12 Jason Giambi .30 .75
13 Javy Lopez .30 .75
14 Jeff Bagwell .50 1.25
15 Jim Edmonds .50 1.25
16 Jim Thome .50 1.25
17 Jorge Posada .50 1.25
18 Lance Berkman .50 1.25
19 Magglio Ordonez .50 1.25
20 Manny Ramirez .75 2.00
21 Mike Lowell .30 .75
22 Nomar Garciaparra .75 2.00
23 Preston Wilson .30 .75
24 Rafael Palmeiro .50 1.25
25 Richie Sexson .30 .75
26 Sammy Sosa .75 2.00
27 Shawn Green .30 .75
28 Todd Helton .50 1.25
29 Vernon Wells .30 .75
30 Vladimir Guerrero .75 2.00

2004 Upper Deck Twenty-Five Salute

COMPLETE SET (10) 4.00 10.00
SERIES 1 STATED ODDS 1:12
1 Barry Bonds 2.00 5.00
2 Troy Glaus .40 1.00
3 Andruw Jones .40 1.00
4 Jay Gibbons .40 1.00
5 Jeremy Giambi .40 1.00
6 Jason Giambi .40 1.00
7 Jim Thome .60 1.50
8 Rafael Palmeiro .60 1.50
9 Carlos Delgado .40 1.00
10 Dmitri Young .40 1.00

2005 Upper Deck

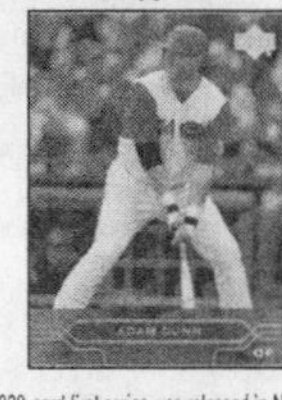

This 300-card first series was released in November, 2004.The set was issued in 10-card hobby packs with an $3 SRP which came 24 packs to a box and 12 boxes to a case. The set was also issued in 10-card retail packs which also had a $3 SRP and came 24 packs to a box and 12 boxes to a case. The hobby and retail packs are differentiated as there is different insert odds depending on which class of pack it is. Subsets include: Super Rookies (211-260); Team Leaders (261-290) and Pennant Race (291-300). The 200-card second series was released in June, 2004 and had the following subsets: Super Rookies (431-450); Bound for Glory (451-470) and Team Checklists (471-500).

COMPLETE SET (500) 60.00 100.00
COMPLETE SERIES 1 (300) 30.00 50.00
COMPLETE SERIES 2 (200) 30.00 50.00
COMMON (1-210) .10 .30
COMMON (211-250) .25 .60
OVERALL PLATES SER.1 ODDS 1:1080 H
PLATES PRINT RUN 1 #'d SET PER COLOR
BLACK-CYAN-MAGENTA-YELLOW ISSUED
NO PLATES PRICING DUE TO SCARCITY
1 Casey Kotchman .12 .30
2 Chone Figgins .12 .30
3 David Eckstein .12 .30
4 Jarrod Washburn .12 .30
5 Robb Quinlan .12 .30
6 Troy Glaus .12 .30
7 Vladimir Guerrero .30 .75
8 Brandon Webb .20 .50
9 Danny Bautista .12 .30
10 Luis Gonzalez .12 .30
11 Matt Kata .12 .30
12 Randy Johnson .30 .75
13 Robby Hammock .12 .30
14 Shea Hillenbrand .12 .30
15 Adam LaRoche .12 .30
16 Andruw Jones .12 .30
17 Horacio Ramirez .12 .30
18 John Smoltz .30 .75
19 Johnny Estrada .12 .30
20 Mike Hampton .12 .30
21 Rafael Furcal .12 .30
22 Brian Roberts .12 .30
23 Javy Lopez .12 .30
24 Jay Gibbons .12 .30
25 Jorge Julio .12 .30
26 Melvin Mora .12 .30
27 Miguel Tejada .20 .50
28 Rafael Palmeiro .20 .50
29 Derek Lowe .12 .30
30 Jason Varitek .30 .75
31 Kevin Youkilis .12 .30
32 Manny Ramirez .30 .75
33 Curt Schilling .20 .50
34 Pedro Martinez .20 .50
35 Trot Nixon .12 .30
36 Corey Patterson .12 .30
37 Derrek Lee .12 .30
38 LaTroy Hawkins .12 .30
39 Mark Prior .20 .50
40 Matt Clement .12 .30
41 Moises Alou .12 .30
42 Sammy Sosa .30 .75
43 Aaron Rowand .12 .30
44 Carlos Lee .12 .30
45 Jose Valentin .12 .30
46 Juan Uribe .12 .30
47 Magglio Ordonez .20 .50
48 Mark Buehrle .20 .50
49 Paul Konerko .20 .50
50 Adam Dunn .20 .50
51 Barry Larkin .20 .50
52 D'Angelo Jimenez .12 .30
53 Danny Graves .12 .30
54 Paul Wilson .12 .30
55 Sean Casey .12 .30
56 Wily Mo Pena .12 .30
57 Ben Broussard .12 .30
58 C.C. Sabathia .20 .50
59 Casey Blake .12 .30
60 Cliff Lee .20 .50
61 Matt Lawton .12 .30
62 Omar Vizquel .20 .50
63 Victor Martinez .20 .50
64 Charles Johnson .12 .30
65 Joe Kennedy .12 .30
66 Jeromy Burnitz .12 .30
67 Matt Holliday .30 .75
68 Preston Wilson .12 .30
69 Royce Clayton .12 .30
70 Shawn Estes .12 .30
71 Bobby Higginson .12 .30
72 Brandon Inge .12 .30
73 Carlos Guillen .12 .30
74 Dmitri Young .12 .30
75 Eric Munson .12 .30
76 Jeremy Bonderman .12 .30
77 Ugueth Urbina .12 .30
78 Josh Beckett .20 .50
79 Dontrelle Willis .12 .30
80 Jeff Conine .12 .30
81 Juan Pierre .12 .30
82 Luis Castillo .12 .30
83 Miguel Cabrera .30 .75
84 Mike Lowell .12 .30
85 Andy Pettitte .20 .50
86 Brad Lidge .12 .30
87 Carlos Beltran .12 .30
88 Craig Biggio .20 .50
89 Jeff Bagwell .20 .50
90 Roger Clemens .40 1.00
91 Roy Oswalt .20 .50
92 Benito Santiago .12 .30
93 Jeremy Affeldt .12 .30
94 Juan Gonzalez .12 .30
95 Ken Harvey .12 .30
96 Mike MacDougal .12 .30
97 Mike Sweeney .12 .30
98 Zack Greinke .20 .50
99 Adrian Beltre .12 .30
100 Alex Cora .12 .30
101 Cesar Izturis .12 .30
102 Eric Gagne .12 .30
103 Kazuhisa Ishii .12 .30
104 Milton Bradley .12 .30
105 Shawn Green .12 .30
106 Danny Kolb .12 .30
107 Ben Sheets .12 .30
108 Brooks Kieschnick .12 .30
109 Craig Counsell .12 .30
110 Geoff Jenkins .12 .30
111 Lyle Overbay .12 .30
112 Scott Podsednik .12 .30
113 Corey Koskie .12 .30
114 Johan Santana .30 .75
115 Joe Mauer .30 .75
116 Justin Morneau .30 .75
117 Lew Ford .12 .30
118 Matt LeCroy .12 .30
119 Torii Hunter .12 .30
120 Brad Wilkerson .12 .30
121 Chad Cordero .12 .30
122 Livan Hernandez .12 .30
123 Jose Vidro .12 .30
124 Termel Sledge .12 .30
125 Tony Batista .12 .30
126 Zach Day .12 .30
127 Al Leiter .12 .30
128 Jae Weong Seo .12 .30
129 Jose Reyes .20 .50
130 Kazuo Matsui .12 .30
131 Mike Piazza .30 .75
132 Todd Zeile .12 .30
133 Cliff Floyd .12 .30
134 Alex Rodriguez .50 1.25
135 Derek Jeter .75 2.00
136 Gary Sheffield .12 .30
137 Hideki Matsui .50 1.25
138 Jason Giambi .12 .30
139 Jorge Posada .20 .50
140 Mike Mussina .20 .50
141 Barry Zito .12 .30
142 Bobby Crosby .12 .30
143 Octavio Dotel .12 .30
144 Eric Chavez .12 .30
145 Jermaine Dye .12 .30
146 Mark Kotsay .12 .30
147 Tim Hudson .20 .50
148 Billy Wagner .12 .30
149 Bobby Abreu .12 .30
150 David Bell .12 .30
151 Jim Thome .20 .50
152 Jimmy Rollins .20 .50
153 Mike Lieberthal .12 .30
154 Randy Wolf .12 .30
155 Craig Wilson .12 .30
156 Daryle Ward .12 .30
157 Jack Wilson .12 .30
158 Jason Kendall .12 .30
159 Kip Wells .12 .30
160 Oliver Perez .12 .30
161 Rob Mackowiak .12 .30
162 Brian Giles .12 .30
163 Brian Lawrence .12 .30
164 David Wells .12 .30
165 Jay Payton .12 .30
166 Ryan Klesko .12 .30
167 Sean Burroughs .12 .30
168 Trevor Hoffman .20 .50
169 Brett Tomko .12 .30
170 J.T. Snow .12 .30
171 Jason Schmidt .12 .30
172 Kirk Rueter .12 .30
173 A.J. Pierzynski .12 .30
174 Pedro Feliz .12 .30
175 Ray Durham .12 .30
176 Eddie Guardado .12 .30
177 Edgar Martinez .20 .50
178 Ichiro Suzuki .50 1.25
179 Jamie Moyer .12 .30
180 Joel Pineiro .12 .30
181 Randy Winn .12 .30
182 Raul Ibanez .12 .30
183 Albert Pujols .75 2.00
184 Edgar Renteria .12 .30
185 Jason Isringhausen .12 .30
186 Jim Edmonds .20 .50
187 Matt Morris .12 .30
188 Reggie Sanders .12 .30
189 Tony Womack .12 .30
190 Aubrey Huff .12 .30
191 Danys Baez .12 .30
192 Carl Crawford .20 .50
193 Jose Cruz Jr. .12 .30
194 Rocco Baldelli .12 .30
195 Tino Martinez .20 .50
196 Dewon Brazelton .12 .30
197 Alfonso Soriano .20 .50
198 Brad Fullmer .12 .30
199 Gerald Laird .12 .30
200 Hank Blalock .12 .30
201 Laynce Nix .12 .30
202 Mark Teixeira .30 .75
203 Michael Young .20 .50
204 Alexis Rios .20 .50
205 Eric Hinske .12 .30
206 Miguel Batista .12 .30
207 Orlando Hudson .12 .30
208 Roy Halladay .30 .75
209 Ted Lilly .12 .30
210 Vernon Wells .12 .30
211 Aarom Baldiris SR .25 .60
212 B.J. Upton SR .40 1.00
213 Dallas McPherson SR .25 .60
214 Brian Dallimore SR .25 .60
215 Chris Oxspring SR .25 .60
216 Chris Shelton SR .25 .60
217 David Wright SR 1.00 2.50
218 Edwardo Sierra SR .25 .60
219 Fernando Nieve SR .25 .60
220 Frank Francisco SR .25 .60
221 Jeff Bennett SR .25 .60
222 Justin Lehr SR .25 .60
223 John Gall SR .25 .60
224 Jorge Sequea SR .25 .60
225 Justin Germano SR .25 .60
226 Kazuhito Tadano SR .25 .60
227 Kevin Cave SR .25 .60
228 Joe Blanton SR .25 .60
229 Luis A. Gonzalez SR .25 .60
230 Michael Wuertz SR .25 .60
231 Mike Rouse SR .25 .60
232 Nick Regilio SR .25 .60
233 Orlando Rodriguez SR .25 .60
234 Phil Stockman SR .25 .60
235 Ramon Ramirez SR .25 .60
236 Roberto Novoa SR .25 .60
237 Dioner Navarro SR .25 .60
238 Tim Bausher SR .25 .60
239 Logan Kensing SR .25 .60
240 Andy Green SR .25 .60
241 Brad Halsey SR .25 .60
242 Charles Thomas SR .25 .60
243 George Sherrill SR .25 .60
244 Jesse Crain SR .25 .60
245 Jimmy Serrano SR .25 .60
246 Joe Horgan SR .25 .60
247 Chris Young SR .40 1.00
248 Joey Gathright SR .25 .60
249 Gavin Floyd SR .25 .60
250 Ryan Howard SR 1.25 3.00
251 Lance Cormier SR .25 .60

252 Matt Treanor SR .25 .60
253 Jeff Francis SR .25 .60
254 Nick Swisher SR .60 1.50
255 Scott Atchison SR .25 .60
256 Travis Blackley SR .25 .60
257 Travis Smith SR .25 .60
258 Yadier Molina SR .40 1.00
259 Jeff Keppinger SR .25 .60
260 Scott Kazmir SR .60 1.50
261 Garret Anderson .30 .75
Vladimir Guerrero TL
262 Luis Gonzalez .30 .75
Randy Johnson TL
263 Andruw Jones .30 .75
Chipper Jones TL
264 Miguel Tejada .20 .50
Rafael Palmeiro TL
265 Curt Schilling .30 .75
Manny Ramirez TL
266 Mark Prior .30 .75
Sammy Sosa TL
267 Frank Thomas .30 .75
Maggio Ordonez TL
268 Barry Larkin .50 1.25
Ken Griffey Jr. TL
269 C.C. Sabathia .20 .50
Victor Martinez TL
270 Jeromy Burnitz .20 .50
Todd Helton TL
271 Dmitri Young .20 .50
Ivan Rodriguez TL
272 Josh Beckett .30 .75
Miguel Cabrera TL
273 Jeff Bagwell .40 1.00
Roger Clemens TL
274 Ken Harvey .12 .30
Mike Sweeney TL
275 Adrian Beltre .12 .30
Eric Gagne TL
276 Ben Sheets .12 .30
Geoff Jenkins TL
277 Joe Mauer .30 .75
Torii Hunter TL
278 Jose Vidro .12 .30
Livan Hernandez TL
279 Kazuo Matsui .30 .75
Mike Piazza TL
280 Alex Rodriguez .75 2.00
Derek Jeter TL
281 Eric Chavez .20 .50
Tim Hudson TL
282 Bobby Abreu .20 .50
Jim Thome TL
283 Craig Wilson .12 .30
Jason Kendall TL
284 Brian Giles .12 .30
Phil Nevin TL
285 A.J. Pierzynski .12 .30
Jason Schmidt TL
286 Bret Boone .50 1.25
Ichiro Suzuki TL
287 Albert Pujols .75 2.00
Scott Rolen TL
288 Aubrey Huff .20 .50
Tino Martinez TL
289 Hank Blalock .30 .75
Mark Teixeira TL
290 Carlos Delgado .30 .75
Roy Halladay TL
291 Vladimir Guerrero PR .30 .75
292 Curt Schilling PR .20 .50
293 Mark Prior PR .20 .50
294 Josh Beckett PR .20 .50
295 Roger Clemens PR .40 1.00
296 Derek Jeter PR .75 2.00
297 Eric Chavez PR .12 .30
298 Jim Thome PR .20 .50
299 Albert Pujols PR .75 2.00
300 Hank Blalock PR .12 .30
301 Bartolo Colon .12 .30
302 Darin Erstad .12 .30
303 Garret Anderson .12 .30
304 Orlando Cabrera .12 .30
305 Steve Finley .12 .30
306 Javier Vazquez .12 .30
307 Russ Ortiz .12 .30
308 Chipper Jones .30 .75
309 Marcus Giles .12 .30
310 Raul Mondesi .12 .30
311 B.J. Ryan .12 .30
312 Luis Matos .12 .30
313 Sidney Ponson .12 .30
314 Bill Mueller .12 .30
315 David Ortiz .30 .75
316 Johnny Damon .20 .50
317 Keith Foulke .12 .30
318 Mark Bellhorn .12 .30
319 Wade Miller .12 .30
320 Aramis Ramirez .12 .30
321 Carlos Zambrano .20 .50
322 Greg Maddux .50 1.25
323 Kerry Wood .12 .30
324 Nomar Garciaparra .30 .75
325 Todd Walker .12 .30
326 Frank Thomas .30 .75
327 Freddy Garcia .12 .30
328 Joe Crede .12 .30
329 Jose Contreras .12 .30
330 Orlando Hernandez .12 .30
331 Shingo Takatsu .12 .30
332 Austin Kearns .12 .30
333 Eric Milton .12 .30
334 Ken Griffey Jr. .50 1.25
335 Aaron Boone .12 .30
336 David Riske .12 .30
337 Jake Westbrook .12 .30
338 Kevin Millwood .12 .30
339 Travis Hafner .12 .30
340 Aaron Miles .12 .30
341 Jeff Baker .12 .30
342 Todd Helton .20 .50
343 Garrett Atkins .12 .30
344 Carlos Pena .20 .50
345 Ivan Rodriguez .20 .50
346 Rondell White .12 .30
347 Troy Percival .12 .30
348 A.J. Burnett .20 .50
349 Carlos Delgado .12 .30
350 Guillermo Mota .12 .30
351 Paul Lo Duca .12 .30
352 Jason Lane .12 .30
353 Lance Berkman .20 .50
354 Angel Berroa .12 .30
355 David DeJesus .12 .30
356 Ruben Gotay .12 .30
357 Jose Lima .12 .30
358 Brad Penny .12 .30
359 J.D. Drew .12 .30
360 Jayson Werth .20 .50
361 Jeff Kent .12 .30
362 Odalis Perez .12 .30
363 Brady Clark .12 .30
364 Junior Spivey .12 .30
365 Rickie Weeks .20 .50
366 Jacque Jones .12 .30
367 Joe Nathan .12 .30
368 Nick Punto .12 .30
369 Shannon Stewart .12 .30
370 Doug Mientkiewicz .12 .30
371 Kris Benson .12 .30
372 Tom Glavine .20 .50
373 Victor Zambrano .12 .30
374 Bernie Williams .20 .50
375 Carl Pavano .12 .30
376 Jaret Wright .12 .30
377 Kevin Brown .12 .30
378 Mariano Rivera .30 .75
379 Danny Haren .12 .30
380 Eric Byrnes .12 .30
381 Erubiel Durazo .12 .30
382 Rich Harden .12 .30
383 Brett Myers .12 .30
384 Chase Utley .20 .50
385 Marlon Byrd .12 .30
386 Pat Burrell .12 .30
387 Placido Polanco .12 .30
388 Freddy Sanchez .12 .30
389 Jason Bay .12 .30
390 Josh Fogg .12 .30
391 Adam Eaton .12 .30
392 Jake Peavy .12 .30
393 Khalil Greene .12 .30
394 Mark Loretta .12 .30
395 Phil Nevin .12 .30
396 Ramon Hernandez .12 .30
397 Woody Williams .12 .30
398 Armando Benitez .12 .30
399 Edgardo Alfonzo .12 .30
400 Marquis Grissom .12 .30
401 Mike Matheny .12 .30
402 Richie Sexson .12 .30
403 Bret Boone .12 .30
404 Gil Meche .12 .30
405 Chris Carpenter .30 .75
406 Jeff Suppan .12 .30
407 Larry Walker .20 .50
408 Mark Grudzielanek .12 .30
409 Mark Mulder .12 .30
410 Scott Rolen .20 .50
411 Josh Phelps .12 .30
412 Jonny Gomes .12 .30
413 Francisco Cordero .12 .30
414 Kenny Rogers .12 .30
415 Richard Hidalgo .12 .30
416 Dave Bush .12 .30
417 Frank Catalanotto .12 .30
418 Gabe Gross .12 .30
419 Guillermo Quiroz .12 .30
420 Reed Johnson .12 .30
421 Cristian Guzman .12 .30
422 Esteban Loaiza .12 .30
423 Jose Guillen .12 .30
424 Nick Johnson .12 .30
425 Vinny Castilla .12 .30
426 Pete Orr SR RC .40 1.00
427 Tadahito Iguchi SR RC .40 1.00
428 Jeff Baker SR .25 .60
429 Marcos Carvajal SR RC .25 .60
430 Justin Verlander SR RC 5.00 12.00
431 Luke Scott SR RC .60 1.50
432 Willy Taveras SR .25 .60
433 Ambiorix Burgos SR RC .25 .60
434 Andy Sisco SR .25 .60
435 Denny Bautista SR .25 .60
436 Mark Teahen SR .25 .60
437 Ervin Santana SR .25 .60
438 Dennis Houlton SR RC .25 .60
439 Philip Humber SR RC .60 1.50
440 Steve Schmoll SR RC .25 .60
441 J.J. Hardy SR .25 .60
442 Ambiorix Concepcion SR RC .25 .60
443 Dae-Sung Koo SR RC .25 .60
444 Andy Phillips SR .25 .60
445 Dan Meyer SR .25 .60
446 Huston Street SR .25 .60
447 Keiichi Yabu SR RC .25 .60
448 Jeff Niemann SR RC .60 1.50
449 Jeremy Reed SR .25 .60
450 Tony Blanco SR .25 .60
451 Albert Pujols BG .75 2.00
452 Alex Rodriguez BG .50 1.25
453 Curt Schilling BG .20 .50
454 Derek Jeter BG .75 2.00
455 Greg Maddux BG .50 1.25
456 Ichiro Suzuki BG .50 1.25
457 Ivan Rodriguez BG .20 .50
458 Jeff Bagwell BG .20 .50
459 Jim Thome BG .20 .50
460 Ken Griffey Jr. BG .50 1.25
461 Manny Ramirez BG .30 .75
462 Mike Mussina BG .20 .50
463 Mike Piazza BG .30 .75
464 Pedro Martinez BG .20 .50
465 Rafael Palmeiro BG .20 .50
466 Randy Johnson BG .30 .75
467 Roger Clemens BG .40 1.00
468 Sammy Sosa BG .30 .75
469 Todd Helton BG .20 .50
470 Vladimir Guerrero BG .30 .75
471 Vladimir Guerrero TC .30 .75
472 Shawn Green TC .12 .30
473 John Smoltz TC .20 .50
474 Miguel Tejada TC .20 .50
475 Curt Schilling TC .20 .50
476 Mark Prior TC .20 .50
477 Frank Thomas TC .30 .75
478 Ken Griffey Jr. TC .50 1.25
479 C.C. Sabathia TC .20 .50
480 Todd Helton TC .20 .50
481 Ivan Rodriguez TC .20 .50
482 Miguel Cabrera TC .30 .75
483 Roger Clemens TC .40 1.00
484 Mike Sweeney TC .12 .30
485 Eric Gagne TC .12 .30
486 Ben Sheets TC .12 .30
487 Johan Santana TC .30 .75
488 Mike Piazza TC .30 .75
489 Derek Jeter TC .75 2.00
490 Eric Chavez TC .12 .30
491 Jim Thome TC .20 .50
492 Craig Wilson TC .12 .30
493 Jake Peavy TC .12 .30
494 Jason Schmidt TC .12 .30
495 Ichiro Suzuki TC .50 1.25
496 Albert Pujols TC .75 2.00
497 Carl Crawford TC .20 .50
498 Mark Teixeira TC .30 .75
499 Vernon Wells TC .12 .30
500 Jose Vidro TC .12 .30

2005 Upper Deck Blue

*BLUE 300-425/451-500: 4X TO 10X BASIC
*BLUE 426-450: 2.5X TO 6X BASIC
OVERALL SER.2 PARALLEL ODDS 1:12 H
STATED PRINT RUN 150 SERIAL #'d SETS

2005 Upper Deck Emerald

*EMER 300-425/451-500: 12.5X TO 30X BASIC
OVERALL SER.2 PARALLEL ODDS 1:12 H
STATED PRINT RUN 25 SERIAL #'d SETS
NO PRICING AVAILABLE ON 426-450

2005 Upper Deck Gold

*GOLD 300-425/451-500: 5X TO 12X BASIC
*GOLD 426-450: 3X TO 8X BASIC
OVERALL SER.2 PARALLEL ODDS 1:12 H
STATED PRINT RUN 99 SERIAL #'d SETS

2005 Upper Deck Platinum

OVERALL SER.2 PARALLEL ODDS 1:12 H
STATED PRINT RUN 5 SERIAL #'d SETS
NO PRICING DUE TO SCARCITY

2005 Upper Deck Retro

*RETRO: 1.25X TO 3X BASIC
ONE RETRO BOX PER SER.1 HOBBY CASE
SER.1 HOBBY CASES CONTAIN 12 BOXES
OVERALL PLATES SER.1 ODDS 1:1080 H
PLATES PRINT RUN 1 #'d SET PER COLOR
BLACK-CYAN-MAGENTA-YELLOW ISSUED
NO PLATES PRICING DUE TO SCARCITY

2005 Upper Deck 4000 Strikeout

RANDOM INSERTS IN SERIES 1 PACKS
STATED PRINT RUN 4000 SERIAL #'d SETS
CRCJ Steve Carlton 6.00 15.00
Nolan Ryan
Roger Clemens
Randy Johnson/4000

2005 Upper Deck 4000 Strikeout Autographs

RANDOM INSERTS IN SERIES 1 PACKS
STATED PRINT RUN 50 SERIAL #'d SETS
QUAD PRINT RUN 10 SERIAL #'d CARDS
NO PRICING DUE TO SCARCITY
ALL ARE EXCHANGE CARDS
EXCHANGE DEADLINE 11/16/07
NR Nolan Ryan AU/50
Steve Carlton
Roger Clemens
Randy Johnson
RC Roger Clemens AU/50
Steve Carlton
Nolan Ryan
Randy Johnson
RJ Randy Johnson AU/50
Steve Carlton
Nolan Ryan
Roger Clemens
SC Steve Carlton AU/50
Nolan Ryan
Roger Clemens
Randy Johnson
CRCJ Steve Carlton AU
Nolan Ryan AU
Roger Clemens AU
Randy Johnson AU/10

2005 Upper Deck Baseball Heroes Jeter

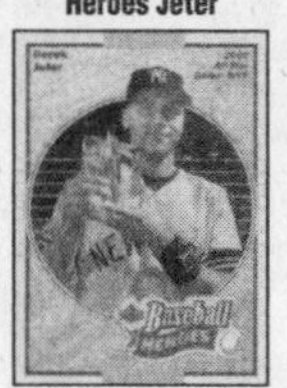

COMPLETE SET (10) 12.50 30.00
COMMON CARD (91-99) 1.50 4.00
SERIES 1 STATED ODDS 1:6 H/R

2005 Upper Deck Baseball Heroes Jeter Jersey

COMMON CARD (1-9)
SERIES 1 STATED ODDS 1:3500 H/R
STATED PRINT RUN 75 SERIAL #'d SETS
NO PRICING DUE TO LACK OF INFO

2005 Upper Deck Baseball Heroes Jeter Signature

SERIES 1 STATED ODDS 1:1,200,000 H/R
STATED PRINT RUN 2 SERIAL #'d SETS
NO PRICING DUE TO SCARCITY

2005 Upper Deck Flyball

ONE PER '05 PRO SIGS PACK
1 Johan Santana .25 .60
2 Randy Johnson .25 .60
3 Pedro Martinez .15 .40
4 Jason Schmidt .10 .25
5 Curt Schilling .15 .40
6 Roger Clemens .30 .75
7 Eric Gagne .10 .25
8 Mariano Rivera .25 .60
9 Mike Piazza .25 .60
11 Ivan Rodriguez .15 .40
13 Albert Pujols .60 1.50
14 Todd Helton .15 .40
15 Jim Thome .15 .40
16 Alfonso Soriano .15 .40
17 Jeff Kent .10 .25
18 Bret Boone .10 .25
19 Scott Rolen .15 .40
20 Alex Rodriguez .40 1.00
21 Adrian Beltre .10 .25
22 Nomar Garciaparra .25 .60
23 Derek Jeter .60 1.50
24 Miguel Tejada .15 .40
25 Manny Ramirez .25 .60
26 Adam Dunn .15 .40
27 Miguel Cabrera .25 .60
29 Jim Edmonds .15 .40
30 Ken Griffey Jr. .40 1.00
31 Vladimir Guerrero .25 .60
32 Ichiro Suzuki .40 1.00
34 Sammy Sosa .25 .60
35 Gary Sheffield .10 .25
37 Roy Oswalt .15 .40
38 Carlos Zambrano .15 .40
40 Mark Prior .15 .40
42 Tim Hudson .15 .40
43 Kerry Wood .10 .25
44 Joe Nathan .10 .25
45 Brad Lidge .10 .25
46 Jason Isringhausen .10 .25
47 Armando Benitez .10 .25
48 Keith Foulke .10 .25
49 Octavio Dotel .10 .25
50 Trevor Hoffman .15 .40
51 Johnny Estrada .10 .25
52 Victor Martinez .15 .40
53 Jason Varitek .25 .60
54 Paul Lo Duca .10 .25
55 Jason Kendall .10 .25
56 Michael Barrett .10 .25
57 Mike Lieberthal .10 .25
58 Carlos Delgado .10 .25
59 Derrek Lee .10 .25
60 Jason Giambi .10 .25
61 Rafael Palmeiro .15 .40
62 David Ortiz .25 .60
63 Jeff Bagwell .15 .40
64 Paul Konerko .15 .40
65 Mark Loretta .10 .25
66 Ray Durham .10 .25
67 Luis Castillo .10 .25
68 Marcus Giles .10 .25
69 Adam Kennedy .10 .25
70 Jose Vidro .10 .25
72 Eric Chavez .10 .25
74 Vinny Castilla .10 .25
75 Hank Blalock .10 .25
77 Michael Young .15 .40
78 Carlos Guillen .10 .25
79 Jimmy Rollins .15 .40
80 Rafael Furcal .10 .25
81 Edgar Renteria .10 .25
82 Alex Gonzalez .10 .25
83 Carlos Lee .10 .25
84 Hideki Matsui .40 1.00
86 Craig Biggio .15 .40
87 Moises Alou .10 .25
88 Chipper Jones .25 .60
89 Andruw Jones .10 .25
90 Corey Patterson .10 .25
91 Torii Hunter .10 .25
92 Carl Crawford .15 .40
93 Steve Finley .10 .25
95 J.D. Drew .10 .25
96 Brian Giles .10 .25
97 Lance Berkman .15 .40
98 Shawn Green .10 .25
99 Larry Walker .15 .40
100 Magglio Ordonez .15 .40
101 Mark Mulder .10 .25
103 Oliver Perez .10 .25
104 Carl Pavano .10 .25
105 Matt Clement .10 .25
106 Bartolo Colon .10 .25
107 Roy Halladay .25 .60
109 Javier Vazquez .10 .25
110 Josh Beckett .15 .40
111 Tom Gordon .10 .25
112 Francisco Rodriguez .15 .40
113 Guillermo Mota .10 .25
114 Juan Rincon .10 .25
115 Steve Kline .10 .25
116 Ray King .10 .25
117 Giovanni Carrara .10 .25
118 Akinori Otsuka .10 .25
119 Kyle Farnsworth .10 .25
121 Brandon Inge .10 .25
123 Yadier Molina .15 .40
124 Miguel Olivo .10 .25
125 Joe Mauer .25 .60
126 Rod Barajas .10 .25
127 Aubrey Huff .10 .25
128 Travis Hafner .10 .25
129 Phil Nevin .10 .25
130 Pedro Feliz .10 .25
131 Lyle Overbay .10 .25
132 Carlos Pena .15 .40
133 Craig Wilson .10 .25
134 Brad Wilkerson .10 .25
135 Mike Sweeney .10 .25
138 Todd Walker .10 .25
139 D'Angelo Jimenez .10 .25
140 Jose Reyes .15 .40
141 Juan Uribe .10 .25
142 Mark Bellhorn .10 .25
143 Orlando Hudson .10 .25
144 Tony Womack .10 .25
146 Aaron Miles .10 .25
147 Miguel Cairo .10 .25
148 Ken Griffey Jr. .40 1.00
149 Casey Blake .10 .25
150 Chone Figgins .10 .25
151 Mike Lowell .10 .25
152 Shea Hillenbrand .10 .25
153 Corey Koskie .10 .25
154 David Bell .10 .25
155 Eric Hinske .10 .25
157 Morgan Ensberg .10 .25
158 Cesar Izturis .10 .25
159 Julio Lugo .10 .25
160 Jose Valentin .10 .25
161 Omar Vizquel .15 .40
162 Bobby Crosby .10 .25
163 Khalil Greene .10 .25
164 Angel Berroa .10 .25
165 David Eckstein .10 .25
166 Cristian Guzman .10 .25
167 Kaz Matsui .10 .25
168 Lew Ford .10 .25
169 Geoff Jenkins .10 .25
171 Jason Bay .10 .25
173 Reggie Sanders .10 .25
174 Pat Burrell .10 .25
176 Cliff Floyd .10 .25
177 Ryan Klesko .10 .25
179 Jose Guillen .10 .25
180 Mike Cameron .10 .25
181 Vernon Wells .10 .25
182 Aaron Rowand .10 .25
183 Scott Podsednik .10 .25
186 Bernie Williams .15 .40
187 Mark Kotsay .10 .25
188 Milton Bradley .10 .25
189 Garret Anderson .10 .25
191 Wily Mo Pena .10 .25
192 Jeromy Burnitz .10 .25
193 Jermaine Dye .10 .25
194 Jose Cruz Jr. .10 .25
195 Richard Hidalgo .10 .25
196 Derek Jeter .60 1.50
197 Juan Encarnacion .10 .25
198 Bobby Higginson .10 .25
199 Alex Rios .15 .40
200 Austin Kearns .10 .25
201 Yogi Berra .25 .60
202 Harmon Killebrew .25 .60
203 Joe Morgan .10 .25
204 Ernie Banks .25 .60
205 Mike Schmidt .50 1.25
206 Mickey Mantle .75 2.00
207 Ted Williams .50 1.25
208 Babe Ruth .60 1.50
209 Nolan Ryan .60 1.50
210 Bob Gibson .15 .40

2005 Upper Deck Game Jersey

SERIES 2 OVERALL GU ODDS 1:8
SP INFO PROVIDED BY UPPER DECK
AB Adrian Beltre 3.00 8.00
AP Albert Pujols 6.00 15.00
AS Alfonso Soriano 3.00 8.00
CB Carlos Beltran SP 3.00 8.00
CJ Chipper Jones 4.00 10.00
CS Curt Schilling 4.00 10.00
DJ Derek Jeter 8.00 20.00
DO David Ortiz SP 4.00 10.00
DW David Wright 6.00 15.00
EC Eric Chavez 3.00 8.00
EG Eric Gagne 3.00 8.00
FT Frank Thomas 4.00 10.00
GM Greg Maddux SP 4.00 10.00
HB Hank Blalock 3.00 8.00
HE Todd Helton 4.00 10.00
HU Torii Hunter 3.00 8.00
IR Ivan Rodriguez 4.00 10.00
JB Jeff Bagwell SP 4.00 10.00
JK Jeff Kent 3.00 8.00
JS Johan Santana SP 4.00 10.00
JT Jim Thome SP 4.00 10.00
KG Ken Griffey Jr. SP 6.00 15.00
KW Kerry Wood 3.00 8.00
LB Lance Berkman 3.00 8.00
MC Miguel Cabrera 4.00 10.00
MM Mark Mulder 3.00 8.00
MP Mark Prior 4.00 10.00
MR Manny Ramirez SP 4.00 10.00
MT Mark Teixeira SP 4.00 10.00
PI Mike Piazza 4.00 10.00
PM Pedro Martinez 4.00 10.00
RJ Randy Johnson SP 4.00 10.00
SM John Smoltz 4.00 10.00
SR Scott Rolen 4.00 10.00
SS Sammy Sosa 4.00 10.00
TE Miguel Tejada 3.00 8.00
TG Troy Glaus 3.00 8.00
TH Tim Hudson 3.00 8.00
VG Vladimir Guerrero 4.00 10.00

2005 Upper Deck Game Patch

SERIES 2 STATED ODDS 1:288 H
STATED PRINT RUN 45 SETS
CARDS ARE NOT SERIAL-NUMBERED
PRINT RUN INFO PROVIDED BY UD
NO PRICING DUE TO SCARCITY

2005 Upper Deck Hall of Fame Plaques

SERIES 1 STATED ODDS 1:36 H/R
16 Ernie Banks 2.50 6.00
17 Yogi Berra 2.50 6.00
18 Whitey Ford 1.50 4.00
19 Bob Gibson 1.50 4.00
20 Willie McCovey 1.50 4.00
21 Stan Musial 4.00 10.00
22 Nolan Ryan 6.00 15.00
23 Mike Schmidt 5.00 12.00
24 Tom Seaver 1.50 4.00
25 Robin Yount 2.50 6.00

2005 Upper Deck Marquee Attractions Jersey

SER.1 OVERALL GU ODDS 1:12 H
AD Adam Dunn 3.00 8.00
AJ Andruw Jones 4.00 10.00
AP Albert Pujols 6.00 15.00
BE Josh Beckett 3.00 8.00
BG Brian Giles 3.00 8.00
BW Billy Wagner 3.00 8.00
CD Carlos Delgado 3.00 8.00
CJ Chipper Jones 4.00 10.00
CS Curt Schilling 4.00 10.00
DJ Derek Jeter 8.00 20.00
DW Dontrelle Willis 3.00 8.00
EG Eric Gagne 3.00 8.00
GM Greg Maddux 5.00 12.00
HM Hideki Matsui 10.00 25.00
HN Hideo Nomo 4.00 10.00
HO Trevor Hoffman 3.00 8.00
IR Ivan Rodriguez 4.00 10.00
IS Ichiro Suzuki 10.00 25.00
JB Jeff Bagwell 4.00 10.00
JG Jason Giambi 3.00 8.00
JM Joe Mauer 4.00 10.00
JS Jason Schmidt 3.00 8.00
JT Jim Thome 4.00 10.00
KB Kevin Brown 3.00 8.00
KM Kazuo Matsui 3.00 8.00
KW Kerry Wood 3.00 8.00
MC Miguel Cabrera 4.00 10.00
MP Mark Prior 4.00 10.00
MT Miguel Tejada 3.00 8.00
PE Andy Pettitte 4.00 10.00
PI Mike Piazza 4.00 10.00
PM Pedro Martinez 4.00 10.00
PW Preston Wilson 3.00 8.00
RC Roger Clemens 5.00 12.00
RJ Randy Johnson 4.00 10.00
SG Shawn Green 3.00 8.00
SS Sammy Sosa 4.00 10.00
TH Todd Helton 4.00 10.00
VG Vladimir Guerrero 4.00 10.00

2005 Upper Deck Marquee Attractions Jersey Gold

*GOLD: .6X TO 1.5X BASIC
SER.1 OVERALL GU ODDS 1:12 H
GA Garret Anderson 5.00 12.00
KG Ken Griffey Jr.
RO Roy Oswalt 5.00 12.00

2005 Upper Deck Matinee Idols Jersey

SER.1 OVERALL GU ODDS 1:12 H, 1:24 R
SP INFO PROVIDED BY UPPER DECK
BB Bret Boone SP 4.00 10.00
BE Josh Beckett 3.00 8.00
BW Billy Wagner 3.00 8.00
BZ Barry Zito 3.00 8.00
CD Carlos Delgado 3.00 8.00
CJ Chipper Jones 4.00 10.00
CR Cal Ripken 15.00 40.00
CS Curt Schilling 4.00 10.00
DJ Derek Jeter 8.00 20.00
DW Dontrelle Willis 3.00 8.00
EC Eric Chavez 3.00 8.00
GS Gary Sheffield 3.00 8.00
HB Hank Blalock 3.00 8.00
HU Torii Hunter 3.00 8.00
JB Jeff Bagwell 4.00 10.00
JE Jim Edmonds 3.00 8.00
JG Jason Giambi 3.00 8.00
JT Jim Thome 4.00 10.00
KG Ken Griffey Jr. 6.00 15.00
KW Kerry Wood 3.00 8.00
ML Mike Lowell 4.00 10.00
MM Mike Mussina 4.00 10.00
MP Mark Prior 4.00 10.00
MT Mark Teixeira 4.00 10.00
NR Nolan Ryan 15.00 40.00
PB Pat Burrell 3.00 8.00
PI Mike Piazza 4.00 10.00
RB Rocco Baldelli 3.00 8.00
RC Roger Clemens 5.00 12.00
RH Roy Halladay 3.00 8.00
RJ Randy Johnson 4.00 10.00
RW Rickie Weeks 3.00 8.00
SG Shawn Green 3.00 8.00
SR Scott Rolen 4.00 10.00
SS Sammy Sosa 4.00 10.00
TG Troy Glaus 3.00 8.00
TH Todd Helton 4.00 10.00
TS Tom Seaver 6.00 15.00
VG Vladimir Guerrero 4.00 10.00
VW Vernon Wells 3.00 8.00

2005 Upper Deck Milestone Materials

SERIES 2 OVERALL GU ODDS 1:8
AP Albert Pujols 6.00 15.00
BA Jeff Bagwell 4.00 10.00
BC Bobby Crosby 3.00 8.00
CB Carlos Beltran 3.00 8.00
CS Curt Schilling 4.00 10.00
DO David Ortiz 4.00 10.00
EG Eric Gagne 3.00 8.00
GM Greg Maddux 4.00 10.00
JB Jason Bay 3.00 8.00
JP Jake Peavy 3.00 8.00
JS Johan Santana 4.00 10.00
JT Jim Thome 4.00 10.00
KG Ken Griffey Jr. 6.00 15.00
MR Manny Ramirez 4.00 10.00
MT Mark Teixeira 4.00 10.00
RJ Randy Johnson 4.00 10.00
RP Rafael Palmeiro 4.00 10.00
TE Miguel Tejada 3.00 8.00
VG Vladimir Guerrero 4.00 10.00

2005 Upper Deck Origins Jersey

SER.1 OVERALL GU ODDS 1:12 H, 1:24 R
AB Adrian Beltre 3.00 8.00
AJ Andruw Jones 4.00 10.00
AP Albert Pujols 6.00 15.00
AS Alfonso Soriano 3.00 8.00
BG Brian Giles 3.00 8.00
BU B.J. Upton 4.00 10.00
CB Carlos Beltran 3.00 8.00
EG Eric Gagne 3.00 8.00
GA Garret Anderson 3.00 8.00
GM Greg Maddux 5.00 12.00
HM Hideki Matsui 10.00 25.00
HN Hideo Nomo 4.00 10.00
IR Ivan Rodriguez 4.00 10.00
IS Ichiro Suzuki 10.00 25.00
JG Juan Gonzalez 3.00 8.00
JK Jeff Kent 3.00 8.00
JL Javy Lopez 3.00 8.00
JP Jorge Posada 4.00 10.00
JR Jose Reyes 3.00 8.00
JS Jason Schmidt 3.00 8.00
JV Javier Vazquez 3.00 8.00
KM Kazuo Matsui 3.00 8.00
LB Lance Berkman 3.00 8.00
LG Luis Gonzalez 3.00 8.00
MC Miguel Cabrera 4.00 10.00
MM Mark Mulder 3.00 8.00
MO Magglio Ordonez 3.00 8.00
MR Manny Ramirez 4.00 10.00
MT Miguel Tejada 3.00 8.00
PE Jake Peavy 3.00 8.00
PM Pedro Martinez 4.00 10.00
PW Preston Wilson 3.00 8.00
RF Rafael Furcal 3.00 8.00
RP Rafael Palmeiro 4.00 10.00
RS Richie Sexson 3.00 8.00
SS Sammy Sosa 4.00 10.00
TH Tim Hudson 3.00 8.00
VG Vladimir Guerrero 4.00 10.00

2005 Upper Deck Rewind to 1997 Jersey

SER.2 STATED ODDS 1:288 H, 1:480 R
PRINT RUNS B/WN 100-150 COPIES PER
CARDS ARE NOT SERIAL-NUMBERED
PRINT RUN INFO PROVIDED BY UD
AJ Andruw Jones 15.00 40.00
CJ Chipper Jones 15.00 40.00
CR Cal Ripken 20.00 50.00
CS Curt Schilling Phils 10.00 25.00
DJ Derek Jeter 20.00 50.00
FT Frank Thomas 15.00 40.00
GM Greg Maddux Braves 15.00 40.00
IR Ivan Rodriguez Rgr 15.00 40.00
JB Jeff Bagwell 15.00 40.00
JS John Smoltz 15.00 40.00
JT Jim Thome Indians 15.00 40.00
KG Ken Griffey Jr. M's 30.00 60.00
MP Mike Piazza Dgr 15.00 40.00
MR Manny Ramirez Indians 15.00 40.00
PM Pedro Martinez Expos 15.00 40.00
RJ Randy Johnson M's 15.00 40.00
SR Scott Rolen Phils Pants 15.00 40.00
TG Tony Gwynn 15.00 40.00
VG Vladimir Guerrero Expos 15.00 40.00
WC Will Clark Rgr 15.00 40.00

2005 Upper Deck Season Opener MLB Game-Worn Jersey Collection

STATED ODDS 1:8
AB Angel Berroa 2.00 5.00
AD Adam Dunn 2.00 5.00
AJ Andruw Jones 3.00 8.00
CD Carlos Delgado 2.00 5.00
CP Corey Patterson 2.00 5.00
DJ Derek Jeter 10.00 25.00
EB Eric Byrnes 2.00 5.00
EH Eric Hinske 2.00 5.00
JB Josh Beckett 2.00 5.00
JG Jody Gerut 2.00 5.00
JT Jim Thome 3.00 8.00
MO Magglio Ordonez 2.00 5.00
MT Michael Tucker 2.00 5.00
PM Pedro Martinez 3.00 8.00
RB Rocco Baldelli 2.00 5.00
RK Ryan Klesko 2.00 5.00
SG Shawn Green 2.00 5.00
SR Scott Rolen 3.00 8.00

2005 Upper Deck Signature Sensations

STATED PRINT RUN 15 SERIAL #'d SETS
DIE CUT PRINT RUN 10 SERIAL #'d SETS
SERIES 2 OVERALL AU ODDS 1:288 H
NO PRICING DUE TO SCARCITY

2005 Upper Deck Signature Stars Hobby

SERIES 1 STATED ODDS 1:288 HOBBY
SP INFO PROVIDED BY UPPER DECK
BB Bret Boone
BC Bobby Crosby 6.00 15.00
BS Ben Sheets 6.00 15.00
BZ Barry Zito
CB Carlos Beltran SP
CR Cal Ripken SP 125.00 200.00
DW Dontrelle Willis 6.00 15.00
DY Delmon Young 10.00 25.00
HB Hank Blalock 6.00 15.00
JB Josh Beckett SP
JL Javy Lopez 6.00 15.00
JM Joe Mauer 20.00 50.00
KG Ken Griffey Jr. 50.00 100.00
KW Kerry Wood 10.00 25.00
LB Lance Berkman SP
LF Lew Ford 4.00 10.00
MC Miguel Cabrera 10.00 25.00
MO Magglio Ordonez SP
MP Mark Prior
MT Mark Teixeira SP
NG Nomar Garciaparra SP
OP Odalis Perez
RO Roy Oswalt SP
RW Rickie Weeks SP

2005 Upper Deck Wingfield Collection

COMPLETE SET (20) 15.00 40.00
SERIES 1 STATED ODDS 1:9 H/R
1 Eddie Mathews .75 2.00
2 Ernie Banks 1.25 3.00
3 Joe DiMaggio 3.00 8.00
4 Mickey Mantle 4.00 10.00
5 Pee Wee Reese .75 2.00
6 Phil Rizzuto .75 2.00
7 Stan Musial 2.00 5.00
8 Ted Williams 2.50 6.00
9 Bob Feller .50 1.25
10 Whitey Ford .75 2.00
11 Willie Stargell .75 2.00
12 Yogi Berra 1.25 3.00
13 Roy Campanella .75 2.00
14 Franklin D. Roosevelt .50 1.25
15 Harry Truman .50 1.25
16 Dwight D. Eisenhower .50 1.25
17 John F. Kennedy 1.25 3.00
18 Lyndon Johnson .50 1.25
19 Richard Nixon .50 1.25
20 Thurman Munson .75 2.00

2005 Upper Deck World Series Heroes

COMPLETE SET (45) 10.00 25.00
SERIES 1 STATED ODDS 1:1 RETAIL
1 Garret Anderson .20 .50
2 Troy Glaus .20 .50
3 Vladimir Guerrero .50 1.25
4 Andruw Jones .20 .50
5 Chipper Jones .50 1.25
6 Curt Schilling .30 .75
7 Keith Foulke .20 .50
8 Manny Ramirez .50 1.25
9 Nomar Garciaparra .50 1.25
10 Pedro Martinez .30 .75
11 Kerry Wood .20 .50
12 Mark Prior .30 .75
13 Sammy Sosa .50 1.25
14 Frank Thomas .50 1.25
15 Magglio Ordonez .20 .50
16 Dontrelle Willis .20 .50
17 Josh Beckett .30 .75
18 Miguel Cabrera .50 1.25
19 Jeff Bagwell .30 .75
20 Lance Berkman .30 .75
21 Roger Clemens .60 1.50
22 Eric Gagne .20 .50
23 Torii Hunter .20 .50
24 Mike Piazza .50 1.25
25 Alex Rodriguez .75 2.00
26 Derek Jeter 1.25 3.00
27 Gary Sheffield .20 .50
28 Hideki Matsui .75 2.00
29 Jason Giambi .20 .50
30 Jorge Posada .30 .75
31 Kevin Brown .20 .50
32 Mariano Rivera .50 1.25
33 Mike Mussina .30 .75
34 Eric Chavez .20 .50
35 Mark Mulder .20 .50
36 Tim Hudson .30 .75
37 Billy Wagner .20 .50
38 Jim Thome .30 .75
39 Brian Giles .20 .50
40 Jason Schmidt .20 .50
41 Albert Pujols 1.25 3.00
42 Scott Rolen .30 .75
43 Alfonso Soriano .30 .75
44 Hank Blalock .20 .50
45 Mark Teixeira .50 1.25

2006 Upper Deck

This 1,252-card set was issued over three series in 2006. The first series was released in April, the second series in August, and the Update set in December. All three series were issued in eight-card packs with an $2.99 SRP. These cards came 24 packs to a box and 12 boxes to a case. The first two series were sequenced in alphabetical team order, with the players in first name alphabetical order in the first series as well. However, if the player was traded, he was still sequenced as if he were with his 2005 team. The second series was just sequenced in alphabetical team order. Cards 871-900 were checklists while cards 901-999 featured 2006 rookies. The final cards in this set feature a mix of players with new teams and more 2006 rookies. Cards numbered 1221-1250 were also checklist cards sequenced in alphabetical team order and were printed to stated odds of one in two update packs. Jason Repko card number 245 was not issued in packs; however, when the Upper Deck Fat Packs, which included series one and two cards that situation was rectified. However, the Repko card was issued as card number 283.

COMPLETE SET (1250) 375.00 600.00
COMPLETE SERIES 1 (500) 125.00 200.00
COMPLETE SERIES 2 (500) 125.00 200.00
COMPLETE UPDATE (250) 125.00 200.00
COMP.UPDATE w/o SP's (200) 30.00 50.00
COMMON CARD (1-1250) .15 .40
1-500 ISSUED IN SERIES 1 PACKS
501-1000 ISSUED IN SERIES 2 PACKS
1001-1250 ISSUED IN UPDATE PACKS
BAKER & REPKO BOTH CARD 283
1001-1250 SP STATED ODDS 1:2
SP: 1005/1013/1021/1037/1045/1061/1069
SP: 1077/1093/1101/1117/1125/1133/1149
SP: 1157/1173/1181/1189/1205/1213
SP: 1221-1250
4 MATCHED PLATES 1:2 SER.2 HOBBY CASES
PLATE PRINT RUN 1 SET PER COLOR
BLACK-CYAN-MAGENTA-YELLOW ISSUED
NO PLATE PRICING DUE TO SCARCITY
EXQUISITE EXCH 1 PER SER.2 HOBBY CASE
EXQUISITE EXCH RANDOM IN UPD.CASES
EXQUISITE EXCH DEADLINE 07/27/07

1 Adam Kennedy .15 .40
2 Bartolo Colon .15 .40
3 Bengie Molina .15 .40
4 Casey Kotchman .15 .40
5 Chone Figgins .15 .40
6 Dallas McPherson .15 .40
7 Darin Erstad .15 .40
8 Ervin Santana .15 .40
9 Francisco Rodriguez .25 .60
10 Garret Anderson .15 .40
11 Jarrod Washburn .15 .40
12 John Lackey .15 .40
13 Juan Rivera .15 .40
14 Orlando Cabrera .15 .40
15 Paul Byrd .15 .40
16 Steve Finley .15 .40
17 Vladimir Guerrero .40 1.00
18 Alex Cintron .15 .40
19 Brandon Lyon .15 .40
20 Brandon Webb .25 .60
21 Chad Tracy .15 .40
22 Chris Snyder .15 .40
23 Claudio Vargas .15 .40
24 Conor Jackson .25 .60
25 Craig Counsell .15 .40
26 Javier Vazquez .15 .40
27 Jose Valverde .15 .40
28 Luis Gonzalez .15 .40
29 Royce Clayton .15 .40
30 Russ Ortiz .15 .40
31 Shawn Green .15 .40
32 Dustin Nippert (RC) .30 .75
33 Tony Clark .15 .40
34 Troy Glaus .15 .40
35 Adam LaRoche .15 .40
36 Andruw Jones .15 .40
37 Craig Hansen RC .75 2.00
38 Chipper Jones .40 1.00
39 Horacio Ramirez .15 .40
40 Jeff Francoeur .40 1.00
41 John Smoltz .40 1.00
42 Joey Devine RC .30 .75
43 Johnny Estrada .15 .40
44 Anthony Lerew (RC) .30 .75
45 Julio Franco .15 .40
46 Kyle Farnsworth .15 .40
47 Marcus Giles .15 .40
48 Mike Hampton .15 .40
49 Rafael Furcal .15 .40
50 Chuck James (RC) .30 .75
51 Tim Hudson .25 .60
52 B.J. Ryan .15 .40
53 Bernie Castro (RC) .30 .75
54 Brian Roberts .15 .40
55 Walter Young (RC) .30 .75
56 Daniel Cabrera .15 .40
57 Eric Byrnes .15 .40
58 Alejandro Freire RC .30 .75
59 Erik Bedard .15 .40
60 Javy Lopez .15 .40
61 Jay Gibbons .15 .40
62 Jorge Julio .15 .40
63 Luis Matos .15 .40
64 Melvin Mora .15 .40
65 Miguel Tejada .25 .60
66 Rafael Palmeiro .25 .60
67 Rodrigo Lopez .15 .40
68 Sammy Sosa .40 1.00
69 Alejandro Machado (RC) .30 .75
70 Bill Mueller .15 .40
71 Bronson Arroyo .15 .40
72 Curt Schilling .25 .60
73 David Ortiz .25 .60
74 David Wells .15 .40
75 Edgar Renteria .15 .40
76 Ryan Jorgensen RC .30 .75
77 Jason Varitek .40 1.00
78 Johnny Damon .25 .60
79 Keith Foulke .15 .40
80 Kevin Youkilis .15 .40
81 Manny Ramirez .40 1.00
82 Matt Clement .15 .40
83 Hanley Ramirez (RC) .75 2.00
84 Tim Wakefield .15 .40
85 Trot Nixon .15 .40
86 Wade Miller .15 .40
87 Aramis Ramirez .15 .40
88 Carlos Zambrano .25 .60
89 Corey Patterson .15 .40
90 Derrek Lee .15 .40
91 Geovany Soto (RC) .75 2.00
92 Greg Maddux .60 1.50
93 Jeromy Burnitz .15 .40
94 Jerry Hairston .15 .40
95 Kerry Wood .15 .40
96 Mark Prior .25 .60
97 Matt Murton .15 .40
98 Michael Barrett .15 .40
99 Neifi Perez .15 .40
100 Nomar Garciaparra .40 1.00
101 Rich Hill .15 .40
102 Ryan Dempster .15 .40
103 Todd Walker .15 .40
104 A.J. Pierzynski .15 .40
105 Aaron Rowand .15 .40
106 Bobby Jenks .15 .40
107 Carl Everett .15 .40
108 Dustin Hermanson .15 .40
109 Frank Thomas UER .40 1.00
Card has wrong birthdate
110 Freddy Garcia .15 .40
111 Jermaine Dye .15 .40
112 Joe Crede .15 .40
113 Jon Garland .15 .40
114 Jose Contreras .15 .40
115 Juan Uribe .15 .40
116 Mark Buehrle .25 .60
117 Orlando Hernandez .15 .40
118 Paul Konerko .25 .60
119 Scott Podsednik .15 .40
120 Tadahito Iguchi .15 .40
121 Aaron Harang .15 .40
122 Adam Dunn .25 .60
123 Austin Kearns .15 .40
124 Brandon Claussen .15 .40
125 Chris Denorfia (RC) .30 .75
126 Edwin Encarnacion .15 .40
127 Miguel Perez (RC) .30 .75
128 Felipe Lopez .15 .40
129 Jason LaRue .15 .40
130 Ken Griffey Jr. .60 1.50
131 Chris Booker (RC) .30 .75
132 Luke Hudson .15 .40
133 Jason Bergmann RC .30 .75
134 Ryan Freel .15 .40
135 Sean Casey .15 .40
136 Wily Mo Pena .15 .40
137 Aaron Boone .15 .40
138 Ben Broussard .15 .40
139 Ryan Garko (RC) .30 .75
140 C.C. Sabathia .25 .60
141 Casey Blake .15 .40
142 Cliff Lee .25 .60
143 Coco Crisp .15 .40
144 David Riske .15 .40
145 Grady Sizemore .25 .60
146 Jake Westbrook .15 .40
147 Jhonny Peralta .15 .40
148 Josh Bard .15 .40
149 Kevin Millwood .15 .40
150 Ronnie Belliard .15 .40
151 Scott Elarton .15 .40
152 Travis Hafner .15 .40
153 Victor Martinez .25 .60
154 Aaron Cook .15 .40
155 Aaron Miles .15 .40
156 Brad Hawpe .15 .40
157 Mike Esposito (RC) .30 .75
158 Chin-Hui Tsao .15 .40
159 Clint Barmes .15 .40
160 Cory Sullivan .15 .40
161 Garrett Atkins .15 .40
162 J.D. Closser .15 .40
163 Jason Jennings .15 .40
164 Jeff Baker .15 .40
165 Jeff Francis .15 .40
166 Luis A. Gonzalez .15 .40
167 Matt Holliday .40 1.00
168 Todd Helton .25 .60
169 Bradon Inge .15 .40
170 Carlos Guillen .25 .60
171 Carlos Pena .25 .60
172 Chris Shelton .15 .40
173 Craig Monroe .15 .40
174 Curtis Granderson .25 .60
175 Dmitri Young .15 .40
176 Ivan Rodriguez .25 .60
177 Jason Johnson .15 .40
178 Jeremy Bonderman .15 .40
179 Magglio Ordonez .25 .60
180 Mark Woodyard (RC) .30 .75
181 Nook Logan .15 .40
182 Omar Infante .15 .40
183 Placido Polanco .15 .40
184 Chris Heintz RC .30 .75
185 A.J. Burnett .25 .60
186 Alex Gonzalez .15 .40
187 Josh Johnson (RC) .75 2.00
188 Carlos Delgado .15 .40
189 Dontrelle Willis .15 .40
190 Josh Wilson (RC) .30 .75
191 Jason Vargas .15 .40
192 Jeff Conine .15 .40
193 Jeremy Hermida .15 .40
194 Josh Beckett .25 .60
195 Juan Encarnacion .15 .40
196 Juan Pierre .15 .40
197 Luis Castillo .15 .40
198 Miguel Cabrera .40 1.00
199 Mike Lowell .15 .40
200 Paul Lo Duca .15 .40
201 Todd Jones .15 .40
202 Adam Everett .15 .40
203 Andy Pettitte .25 .60
204 Brad Ausmus .15 .40
205 Brad Lidge .15 .40
206 Brandon Backe .15 .40
207 Charlton Jimerson (RC) .30 .75
208 Chris Burke .15 .40
209 Craig Biggio .25 .60
210 Dan Wheeler .15 .40
211 Jason Lane .15 .40
212 Jeff Bagwell .25 .60
213 Lance Berkman .25 .60
214 Luke Scott .15 .40
215 Morgan Ensberg .15 .40
216 Roger Clemens .50 1.25
217 Roy Oswalt .25 .60
218 Willy Taveras .15 .40
219 Andres Blanco .15 .40
220 Angel Berroa .15 .40
221 Ruben Gotay .15 .40
222 David DeJesus .15 .40
223 Emil Brown .15 .40
224 J.P. Howell .15 .40
225 Jeremy Affeldt .15 .40
226 Jimmy Gobble .15 .40
227 John Buck .15 .40
228 Jose Lima .15 .40
229 Mark Teahen .15 .40
230 Matt Stairs .15 .40
231 Mike MacDougal .15 .40
232 Mike Sweeney .15 .40
233 Runelvys Hernandez .15 .40
234 Terrence Long .15 .40
235 Zack Greinke .25 .60
236 Ron Flores RC .30 .75
237 Brad Penny .15 .40
238 Cesar Izturis .15 .40
239 J.D. Houlton .15 .40
240 Derek Lowe .15 .40
241 Eric Gagne .15 .40
242 Hee Seop Choi .15 .40
243 J.D. Drew .15 .40
244 Jason Phillips .15 .40
245 Jason Repko .15 .40
246 Jayson Werth .25 .60
247 Jeff Kent .15 .40
248 Jeff Weaver .15 .40
249 Milton Bradley .15 .40
250 Odalis Perez .15 .40
251 Hong-Chih Kuo (RC) .75 2.00
252 Oscar Robles .15 .40
253 Ben Sheets .15 .40
254 Bill Hall .15 .40
255 Brady Clark .15 .40
256 Carlos Lee .15 .40
257 Chris Capuano .15 .40
258 Nelson Cruz (RC) .50 1.25
259 Derrick Turnbow .15 .40
260 Doug Davis .15 .40
261 Geoff Jenkins .15 .40
262 J.J. Hardy .15 .40
263 Lyle Overbay .15 .40
264 Prince Fielder .60 1.50
265 Rickie Weeks .25 .60
266 Russell Branyan .15 .40
267 Tomo Ohka .15 .40
268 Jonah Bayliss RC .30 .75
269 Brad Radke .15 .40
270 Carlos Silva .15 .40
271 Francisco Liriano (RC) .75 2.00
272 Jacque Jones .15 .40
273 Joe Mauer .40 1.00
274 Travis Bowyer (RC) .30 .75
275 Joe Nathan .15 .40
276 Johan Santana .40 1.00
277 Justin Morneau .40 1.00
278 Kyle Lohse .15 .40
279 Lew Ford .15 .40
280 Matt LeCroy .15 .40
281 Michael Cuddyer .15 .40
282 Nick Punto .15 .40
283a Scott Baker .15 .40
283b Jason Repko UER .15 .40
Intended as card 245
284 Shannon Stewart .15 .40
285 Torii Hunter .15 .40
286 Braden Looper .15 .40
287 Carlos Beltran .15 .40
288 Cliff Floyd .15 .40
289 David Wright .60 1.50
290 Doug Mientkiewicz .15 .40
291 Anderson Hernandez (RC) .30 .75
292 Jose Reyes .25 .60
293 Kazuo Matsui .15 .40
294 Kris Benson .15 .40
295 Miguel Cairo .15 .40
296 Mike Cameron .15 .40
297 Robert Andino RC .30 .75
298 Mike Piazza .40 1.00
299 Pedro Martinez .25 .60
300 Tom Glavine .25 .60
301 Victor Diaz .15 .40
302 Tim Hamulack (RC) .30 .75
303 Alex Rodriguez .60 1.50
304 Bernie Williams .25 .60
305 Carl Pavano .15 .40
306 Chien-Ming Wang .25 .60
307 Derek Jeter 1.00 2.50
308 Gary Sheffield .15 .40
309 Hideki Matsui .40 1.00
310 Jason Giambi .15 .40
311 Jorge Posada .25 .60
312 Kevin Brown .15 .40
313 Mariano Rivera .40 1.00
314 Matt Lawton .15 .40
315 Mike Mussina .25 .60
316 Randy Johnson .40 1.00
317 Robinson Cano .40 1.00
318 Mike Vento (RC) .30 .75
319 Tino Martinez .15 .40
320 Tony Womack .15 .40
321 Barry Zito .15 .40
322 Bobby Crosby .15 .40
323 Bobby Kielty .15 .40
324 Dan Johnson .15 .40
325 Danny Haren .15 .40
326 Eric Chavez .15 .40
327 Erubiel Durazo .15 .40
328 Huston Street .15 .40
329 Jason Kendall .15 .40
330 Jay Payton .15 .40
331 Joe Blanton .15 .40
332 Joe Kennedy .15 .40
333 Kirk Saarloos .15 .40
334 Mark Kotsay .15 .40
335 Nick Swisher .40 1.00
336 Rich Harden .15 .40
337 Scott Hatteberg .15 .40
338 Billy Wagner .15 .40
339 Bobby Abreu .15 .40
340 Brett Myers .15 .40
341 Chase Utley .40 1.00
342 Danny Sandoval RC .30 .75
343 David Bell .15 .40
344 Gavin Floyd .15 .40
345 Jim Thome .25 .60
346 Jimmy Rollins .25 .60
347 Jon Lieber .15 .40
348 Kenny Lofton .15 .40
349 Mike Lieberthal .15 .40
350 Pat Burrell .15 .40
351 Randy Wolf .15 .40
352 Ryan Howard .60 1.50
353 Vicente Padilla .15 .40
354 Bryan Bullington (RC) .30 .75
355 J.J. Furmaniak (RC) .30 .75
356 Craig Wilson .15 .40
357 Matt Capps (RC) .30 .75
358 Tom Gorzelanny (RC) .30 .75
359 Jack Wilson .15 .40
360 Jason Bay .15 .40
361 Jose Mesa .15 .40
362 Josh Fogg .15 .40
363 Kip Wells .15 .40
364 Steve Stemle RC .30 .75
365 Oliver Perez .15 .40
366 Rob Mackowiak .15 .40
367 Ronny Paulino (RC) .30 .75
368 Tike Redman .15 .40
369 Zach Duke .15 .40
370 Adam Eaton .15 .40
371 Scott Feldman RC .30 .75
372 Brian Giles .15 .40
373 Brian Lawrence .15 .40
374 Damian Jackson .15 .40
375 Dave Roberts .15 .40
376 Jake Peavy .15 .40
377 Joe Randa .15 .40
378 Khalil Greene .15 .40
379 Mark Loretta .15 .40
380 Ramon Hernandez .15 .40
381 Robert Fick .15 .40
382 Ryan Klesko .15 .40
383 Trevor Hoffman .25 .60
384 Woody Williams .15 .40
385 Xavier Nady .15 .40
386 Armando Benitez .15 .40
387 Brad Hennessey .15 .40
388 Brian Myrow RC .30 .75
389 Edgardo Alfonzo .15 .40
390 J.T. Snow .15 .40
391 Jeremy Accardo RC .30 .75
392 Jason Schmidt .15 .40
393 Lance Niekro .15 .40
394 Matt Cain .40 1.00
395 Dan Ortmeier (RC) .30 .75
396 Moises Alou .15 .40
397 Doug Clark (RC) .30 .75
398 Omar Vizquel .25 .60
399 Pedro Feliz .15 .40
400 Randy Winn .15 .40
401 Ray Durham .15 .40
402 Adrian Beltre .15 .40
403 Eddie Guardado .15 .40
404 Felix Hernandez .40 1.00
405 Gil Meche .15 .40
406 Ichiro Suzuki .60 1.50
407 Jamie Moyer .15 .40
408 Jeff Nelson .15 .40
409 Jeremy Reed .15 .40
410 Joel Pineiro .15 .40
411 Jaime Bubela (RC) .30 .75
412 Raul Ibanez .25 .60
413 Richie Sexson .15 .40
414 Ryan Franklin .15 .40
415 Willie Bloomquist .15 .40
416 Yorvit Torrealba .15 .40
417 Yuniesky Betancourt .15 .40
418 Jeff Harris RC .30 .75
419 Albert Pujols 1.00 2.50
420 Chris Carpenter .40 1.00
421 David Eckstein .15 .40
422 Jason Isringhausen .15 .40
423 Jason Marquis .15 .40
424 Adam Wainwright (RC) .75 2.00
425 Jim Edmonds .25 .60
426 Ryan Theriot RC 1.00 2.50
427 Chris Duncan (RC) .50 1.25
428 Mark Grudzielanek .15 .40
429 Mark Mulder .15 .40
430 Matt Morris .15 .40
431 Reggie Sanders .15 .40
432 Scott Rolen .25 .60
433 Tyler Johnson (RC) .30 .75
434 Yadier Molina .25 .60
435 Alex S. Gonzalez .15 .40
436 Aubrey Huff .15 .40
437 Tim Corcoran RC .30 .75
438 Carl Crawford .25 .60
439 Casey Fossum .15 .40
440 Danys Baez .15 .40
441 Edwin Jackson .15 .40
442 Joey Gathright .15 .40
443 Jonny Gomes .15 .40
444 Jorge Cantu .15 .40
445 Julio Lugo .15 .40
446 Nick Green .15 .40
447 Rocco Baldelli .15 .40
448 Scott Kazmir .25 .60
449 Seth McClung .15 .40
450 Toby Hall .15 .40
451 Travis Lee .15 .40
452 Craig Breslow RC .30 .75
453 Alfonso Soriano .25 .60
454 Chris R. Young .15 .40
455 David Dellucci .15 .40
456 Francisco Cordero .15 .40
457 Gary Matthews .15 .40
458 Hank Blalock .15 .40
459 Juan Dominguez .15 .40
460 Josh Rupe (RC) .30 .75
461 Kenny Rogers .15 .40
462 Kevin Mench .15 .40
463 Laynce Nix .15 .40
464 Mark Teixeira .40 1.00
465 Michael Young .25 .60
466 Richard Hidalgo .15 .40
467 Jason Botts (RC) .30 .75
468 Aaron Hill .15 .40
469 Alex Rios .25 .60
470 Corey Koskie .15 .40
471 Chris Demaria RC .30 .75
472 Eric Hinske .15 .40
473 Frank Catalanotto .15 .40
474 John-Ford Griffin (RC) .30 .75
475 Gustavo Chacin .15 .40
476 Josh Towers .15 .40
477 Miguel Batista .15 .40

478 Orlando Hudson .15 .40
479 Reed Johnson .15 .40
480 Roy Halladay .40 1.00
481 Shaun Marcum (RC) .30 .75
482 Shea Hillenbrand .15 .40
483 Ted Lilly .15 .40
484 Vernon Wells .15 .40
485 Brad Wilkerson .15 .40
486 Darrell Rasner (RC) .30 .75
487 Chad Cordero .15 .40
488 Cristian Guzman .15 .40
489 Esteban Loaiza .15 .40
490 John Patterson .15 .40
491 Jose Guillen .15 .40
492 Jose Vidro .15 .40
493 Livan Hernandez .15 .40
494 Marlon Byrd .15 .40
495 Nick Johnson .15 .40
496 Preston Wilson .15 .40
497 Ryan Church .15 .40
498 Ryan Zimmerman (RC) 1.50 4.00
499 Tony Armas Jr. .15 .40
500 Vinny Castilla .15 .40
501 Andy Green .15 .40
502 Damion Easley .15 .40
503 Eric Byrnes .15 .40
504 Jason Grimsley .15 .40
505 Jeff DaVanon .15 .40
506 Johnny Estrada .15 .40
507 Luis Vizcaino .15 .40
508 Miguel Batista .15 .40
509 Orlando Hernandez .15 .40
510 Orlando Hudson .15 .40
511 Terry Mulholland .15 .40
512 Chris Reitsma .15 .40
513 Edgar Renteria .15 .40
514 John Thomson .15 .40
515 Jorge Sosa .15 .40
516 Oscar Villarreal .15 .40
517 Pete Orr .15 .40
518 Ryan Langerhans .15 .40
519 Todd Pratt .15 .40
520 Wilson Betemit .15 .40
521 Brian Jordan .15 .40
522 Lance Cormier .15 .40
523 Matt Diaz .15 .40
524 Mike Remlinger .15 .40
525 Bruce Chen .15 .40
526 Chris Gomez .15 .40
527 Chris Ray .15 .40
528 Corey Patterson .15 .40
529 David Newhan .15 .40
530 Ed Rogers (RC) .30 .75
531 John Halama .15 .40
532 Kris Benson .15 .40
533 LaTroy Hawkins .15 .40
534 Raul Chavez .15 .40
535 Alex Cora .15 .40
536 Alex Gonzalez .15 .40
537 Coco Crisp .15 .40
538 David Riske .15 .40
539 Doug Mirabelli .15 .40
540 Josh Beckett .25 .60
541 J.T. Snow .15 .40
542 Mike Timlin .15 .40
543 Julian Tavarez .15 .40
544 Rudy Seanez .15 .40
545 Wily Mo Pena .15 .40
546 Bob Howry .15 .40
547 Glendon Rusch .15 .40
548 Henry Blanco .15 .40
549 Jacque Jones .15 .40
550 Jerome Williams .15 .40
551 John Mabry .15 .40
552 Juan Pierre .15 .40
553 Scott Eyre .15 .40
554 Scott Williamson .15 .40
555 Wade Miller .15 .40
556 Will Ohman .15 .40
557 Alex Cintron .15 .40
558 Rob Mackowiak .15 .40
559 Brandon McCarthy .15 .40
560 Chris Widger .15 .40
561 Cliff Politte .15 .40
562 Javier Vazquez .15 .40
563 Jim Thome .25 .60
564 Matt Thornton .15 .40
565 Neal Cotts .15 .40
566 Pablo Ozuna .15 .40
567 Ross Gload .15 .40
568 Brandon Phillips .15 .40
569 Bronson Arroyo .15 .40
570 Dave Williams .15 .40
571 David Ross .15 .40
572 David Weathers .15 .40
573 Eric Milton .15 .40
574 Javier Valentin .15 .40
575 Kent Mercker .15 .40
576 Matt Belisle .15 .40
577 Paul Wilson .15 .40
578 Rich Aurilia .15 .40
579 Rick White .15 .40
580 Scott Hatteberg .15 .40
581 Todd Coffey .15 .40
582 Bob Wickman .15 .40
583 Danny Graves .15 .40
584 Eduardo Perez .15 .40
585 Guillermo Mota .15 .40
586 Jason Davis .15 .40
587 Jason Johnson .15 .40
588 Jason Michaels .15 .40
589 Rafael Betancourt .15 .40
590 Ramon Vazquez .15 .40
591 Scott Sauerbeck .15 .40
592 Todd Hollandsworth .15 .40
593 Brian Fuentes .15 .40
594 Danny Ardoin .15 .40
595 David Cortes .15 .40
596 Eli Marrero .15 .40
597 Jamey Carroll .15 .40
598 Jason Smith .15 .40
599 Josh Fogg .15 .40
600 Miguel Ojeda .15 .40
601 Mike DeJean .15 .40
602 Ray King .15 .40
603 Omar Quintanilla (RC) .30 .75
604 Zach Day .15 .40
605 Fernando Rodney .15 .40
606 Kenny Rogers .15 .40
607 Mike Maroth .15 .40
608 Nate Robertson .15 .40
609 Todd Jones .15 .40
610 Vance Wilson .15 .40
611 Bobby Seay .15 .40
612 Chris Spurling .15 .40
613 Roman Colon .15 .40
614 Jason Grilli .15 .40
615 Marcus Thames .15 .40
616 Ramon Santiago .15 .40
617 Alfredo Amezaga .15 .40
618 Brian Moehler .15 .40
619 Chris Aguila .15 .40
620 Franklyn German .15 .40
621 Joe Borowski .15 .40
622 Logan Kensing (RC) .30 .75
623 Matt Treanor .15 .40
624 Miguel Olivo .15 .40
625 Sergio Mitre .15 .40
626 Todd Wellemeyer .15 .40
627 Wes Helms .15 .40
628 Chad Qualls .15 .40
629 Eric Bruntlett .15 .40
630 Mike Gallo .15 .40
631 Mike Lamb .15 .40
632 Orlando Palmeiro .15 .40
633 Russ Springer .15 .40
634 Dan Wheeler .15 .40
635 Eric Munson .15 .40
636 Preston Wilson .15 .40
637 Trever Miller .15 .40
638 Ambiorix Burgos .15 .40
639 Andy Sisco .15 .40
640 Denny Bautista .15 .40
641 Doug Mientkiewicz .15 .40
642 Elmer Dessens .15 .40
643 Esteban German .15 .40
644 Joe Nelson (RC) .30 .75
645 Mark Grudzielanek .15 .40
646 Mark Redman .15 .40
647 Mike Wood .15 .40
648 Paul Bako .15 .40
649 Reggie Sanders .15 .40
650 Scott Elarton .30 .75
651 Shane Costa .15 .40
652 Tony Graffanino .15 .40
653 Jason Bulger (RC) .30 .75
654 Chris Bootcheck (RC) .30 .75
655 Esteban Yan .15 .40
656 Hector Carrasco .15 .40
657 J.C. Romero .15 .40
658 Jeff Weaver .15 .40
659 Jose Molina .15 .40
660 Kelvim Escobar .15 .40
661 Maicer Izturis .15 .40
662 Robb Quinlan .15 .40
663 Scot Shields .15 .40
664 Tim Salmon .15 .40
665 Bill Mueller .15 .40
666 Brett Tomko .15 .40
667 Dioner Navarro .15 .40
668 Jae Seo .15 .40
669 Jose Cruz Jr. .15 .40
670 Kenny Lofton .15 .40
671 Lance Carter .15 .40
672 Nomar Garciaparra .40 1.00
673 Olmedo Saenz .15 .40
674 Rafael Furcal .15 .40
675 Ramon Martinez .15 .40
676 Ricky Ledee .15 .40
677 Sandy Alomar Jr. .15 .40
678 Yhency Brazoban .15 .40
679 Corey Koskie .15 .40
680 Dan Kolb .15 .40
681 Gabe Gross .15 .40
682 Jeff Cirillo .15 .40
683 Matt Wise .15 .40
684 Rick Helling .15 .40
685 Chad Moeller .15 .40
686 Dave Bush .15 .40
687 Jorge De La Rosa .15 .40
688 Justin Lehr .15 .40
689 Jason Bartlett .15 .40
690 Jesse Crain .15 .40
691 Juan Rincon .15 .40
692 Luis Castillo .15 .40
693 Mike Redmond .15 .40
694 Rondell White .15 .40
695 Tony Batista .15 .40
696 Juan Castro .15 .40
697 Luis Rodriguez .15 .40
698 Matt Guerrier .15 .40
699 Willie Eyre (RC) .30 .75
700 Aaron Heilman .15 .40
701 Billy Wagner .15 .40
702 Carlos Delgado .15 .40
703 Chad Bradford .15 .40
704 Chris Woodward .15 .40
705 Darren Oliver .15 .40
706 Duaner Sanchez .15 .40
707 Endy Chavez .15 .40
708 Jorge Julio .15 .40
709 Jose Valentin .15 .40
710 Julio Franco .15 .40
711 Paul Lo Duca .15 .40
712 Ramon Castro .15 .40
713 Steve Trachsel .15 .40
714 Victor Zambrano .15 .40
715 Xavier Nady .15 .40
716 Andy Phillips .15 .40
717 Bubba Crosby .15 .40
718 Jaret Wright .15 .40
719 Kelly Stinnett .15 .40
720 Kyle Farnsworth .15 .40
721 Mike Myers .15 .40
722 Octavio Dotel .15 .40
723 Ron Villone .15 .40
724 Scott Proctor .15 .40
725 Shawn Chacon .15 .40
726 Tanyon Sturtze .15 .40
727 Adam Melhuse .15 .40
728 Brad Halsey .15 .40
729 Esteban Loaiza .15 .40
730 Frank Thomas .40 1.00
731 Jay Witasick .15 .40
732 Justin Duchscherer .15 .40
733 Kiko Calero .15 .40
734 Marco Scutaro .15 .40
735 Mark Ellis .15 .40
736 Milton Bradley .15 .40
737 Aaron Fultz .15 .40
738 Aaron Rowand .15 .40
739 Geoff Geary .15 .40
740 Arthur Rhodes .15 .40
741 Chris Coste RC .75 2.00
742 Rheal Cormier .15 .40
743 Ryan Franklin .15 .40
744 Ryan Madson .15 .40
745 Sal Fasano .15 .40
746 Tom Gordon .15 .40
747 Abraham Nunez .15 .40
748 David Dellucci .15 .40
749 Julio Santana .15 .40
750 Shane Victorino .15 .40
751 Damaso Marte .15 .40
752 Freddy Sanchez .15 .40
753 Humberto Cota .15 .40
754 Jeromy Burnitz .15 .40
755 Joe Randa .15 .40
756 Jose Castillo .15 .40
757 Mike Gonzalez .15 .40
758 Ryan Doumit .15 .40
759 Sean Burnett .15 .40
760 Sean Casey .15 .40
761 Ian Snell .15 .40
762 John Grabow .15 .40
763 Jose Hernandez .15 .40
764 Roberto Hernandez .15 .40
765 Ryan Vogelsong .15 .40
766 Victor Santos .15 .40
767 Adrian Gonzalez .25 .60
768 Alan Embree .15 .40
769 Brian Sweeney (RC) .30 .75
770 Chan Ho Park .25 .60
771 Clay Hensley .15 .40
772 Dewon Brazelton .15 .40
773 Doug Brocail .15 .40
774 Eric Young .15 .40
775 Geoff Blum .15 .40
776 Josh Bard .15 .40
777 Mark Bellhorn .15 .40
778 Mike Cameron .15 .40
779 Mike Piazza .40 1.00
780 Rob Bowen .15 .40
781 Scott Cassidy .15 .40
782 Scott Linebrink .15 .40
783 Shawn Estes .15 .40
784 Terrmel Sledge .15 .40
785 Vinny Castilla .15 .40
786 Jeff Fassero .15 .40
787 Jose Vizcaino .15 .40
788 Mark Sweeney .15 .40
789 Matt Morris .15 .40
790 Steve Finley .15 .40
791 Tim Worrell .15 .40
792 Jamey Wright .15 .40
793 Jason Ellison .15 .40
794 Noah Lowry .15 .40
795 Steve Kline .15 .40
796 Todd Greene .15 .40
797 Carl Everett .15 .40
798 George Sherrill .15 .40
799 J.J. Putz .15 .40
800 Jake Woods .15 .40
801 Jose Lopez .15 .40
802 Julio Mateo .15 .40
803 Mike Morse .15 .40
804 Rafael Soriano .15 .40
805 Roberto Petagine .15 .40
806 Aaron Miles .15 .40
807 Braden Looper .15 .40
808 Gary Bennett .15 .40
809 Hector Luna .15 .40
810 Jeff Suppan .15 .40
811 John Rodriguez .15 .40
812 Josh Hancock .15 .40
813 Juan Encarnacion .15 .40
814 Larry Bigbie .15 .40
815 Scott Spiezio .15 .40
816 Sidney Ponson .15 .40
817 So Taguchi .15 .40
818 Brian Meadows .15 .40
819 Damon Hollins .15 .40
820 Dan Miceli .15 .40
821 Doug Waechter .15 .40
822 Jason Childers RC .30 .75
823 Josh Paul .15 .40
824 Julio Lugo .15 .40
825 Mark Hendrickson .15 .40
826 Sean Burroughs .15 .40
827 Shawn Camp .15 .40
828 Travis Harper .15 .40
829 Ty Wigginton .15 .40
830 Adam Eaton .15 .40
831 Adrian Brown .15 .40
832 Akinori Otsuka .15 .40
833 Antonio Alfonseca .15 .40
834 Brad Wilkerson .15 .40
835 D'Angelo Jimenez .15 .40
836 Gerald Laird .15 .40
837 Joaquin Benoit .15 .40
838 Kameron Loe .15 .40
839 Kevin Millwood .15 .40
840 Mark DeRosa .15 .40
841 Phil Nevin .15 .40
842 Rod Barajas .15 .40
843 Vicente Padilla .15 .40
844 A.J. Burnett .25 .60
845 Bengie Molina .15 .40
846 Gregg Zaun .15 .40
847 John McDonald .15 .40
848 Lyle Overbay .15 .40
849 Russ Adams .15 .40
850 Troy Glaus .15 .40
851 Vinny Chulk .15 .40
852 B.J. Ryan .15 .40
853 Justin Speier .15 .40
854 Pete Walker .15 .40
855 Scott Downs .15 .40
856 Scott Schoeneweis .15 .40
857 Alfonso Soriano .25 .60
858 Brian Schneider .15 .40
859 Daryle Ward .15 .40
860 Felix Rodriguez .15 .40
861 Gary Majewski .15 .40
862 Joey Eischen .15 .40
863 Jon Rauch .15 .40
864 Marlon Anderson .15 .40
865 Matt LeCroy .15 .40
866 Mike Stanton .15 .40
867 Ramon Ortiz .15 .40
868 Robert Fick .15 .40
869 Royce Clayton .15 .40
870 Ryan Drese .15 .40
871 Vladimir Guerrero CL .40 1.00
872 Craig Biggio CL .25 .60
873 Barry Zito CL .25 .60
874 Vernon Wells CL .15 .40
875 Chipper Jones CL .40 1.00
876 Prince Fielder CL .60 1.50
877 Albert Pujols CL 1.00 2.50
878 Greg Maddux CL .60 1.50
879 Carl Crawford CL .25 .60
880 Brandon Webb CL .25 .60
881 J.D. Drew CL .15 .40
882 Jason Schmidt CL .15 .40
883 Victor Martinez CL .25 .60
884 Ichiro Suzuki CL .60 1.50
885 Miguel Cabrera CL .40 1.00
886 David Wright CL .60 1.50
887 Alfonso Soriano CL .25 .60
888 Miguel Tejada CL .25 .60
889 Khalil Greene CL .15 .40
890 Ryan Howard CL .60 1.50
891 Jason Bay CL .15 .40
892 Mark Teixeira CL .25 .60
893 Manny Ramirez CL .40 1.00
894 Ken Griffey Jr. CL .60 1.50
895 Todd Helton CL .25 .60
896 Angel Berroa CL .15 .40
897 Ivan Rodriguez CL .25 .60
898 Johan Santana CL .40 1.00
899 Paul Konerko CL .25 .60
900 Derek Jeter CL 1.00 2.50
901 Macay McBride (RC) .30 .75
902 Tony Pena (RC) .30 .75
903 Peter Moylan RC .30 .75
904 Aaron Rakers (RC) .30 .75
905 Chris Britton RC .30 .75
906 Nick Markakis (RC) .75 2.00
907 Sendy Rleal RC .30 .75
908 Val Majewski (RC) .30 .75
909 Jermaine Van Buren (RC) .30 .75
910 Jonathan Papelbon (RC) 1.50 4.00
911 Angel Pagan (RC) .30 .75
912 David Aardsma (RC) .30 .75
913 Sean Marshall (RC) .50 1.25
914 Brian Anderson (RC) .30 .75
915 Freddie Bynum (RC) .30 .75
916 Fausto Carmona (RC) .30 .75
917 Kelly Shoppach (RC) .30 .75
918 Choo Freeman (RC) .30 .75
919 Ryan Shealy (RC) .30 .75
920 Joel Zumaya (RC) .75 2.00
921 Jordan Tata RC .30 .75
922 Justin Verlander (RC) 2.50 6.00
923 Carlos Martinez RC .30 .75
924 Chris Resop (RC) .30 .75
925 Dan Uggla (RC) .75 2.00
926 Eric Reed (RC) .30 .75
927 Hanley Ramirez .75 2.00
928 Yusmeiro Petit (RC) .30 .75
929 Josh Willingham (RC) .30 .75
930 Mike Jacobs (RC) .30 .75
931 Reggie Abercrombie (RC) .30 .75
932 Ricky Nolasco (RC) .30 .75
933 Scott Olsen (RC) .30 .75
934 Fernando Nieve (RC) .30 .75
935 Taylor Buchholz (RC) .30 .75
936 Cody Ross (RC) .75 2.00
937 James Loney (RC) .50 1.25
938 Takashi Saito RC .50 1.25
939 Tim Hamulack .30 .75
940 Chris Demaria .30 .75
941 Jose Capellan (RC) .30 .75
942 David Gassner (RC) .30 .75
943 Jason Kubel (RC) .30 .75
944 Brian Bannister (RC) .30 .75
945 Mike Thompson RC .30 .75
946 Cole Hamels (RC) 1.25 3.00
947 Paul Maholm (RC) .30 .75
948 John Van Benschoten (RC) .30 .75
949 Nate McLouth (RC) .30 .75
950 Ben Johnson (RC) .30 .75
951 Josh Barfield (RC) .30 .75
952 Travis Ishikawa (RC) .30 .75
953 Jack Taschner (RC) .30 .75
954 Kenji Johjima RC .75 2.00
955 Skip Schumaker (RC) .30 .75
956 Ruddy Lugo (RC) .30 .75
957 Jason Hammel (RC) .30 .75
958 Chris Roberson (RC) .30 .75
959 Fabio Castro RC .30 .75
960 Ian Kinsler (RC) 1.00 2.50
961 John Koronka (RC) .30 .75
962 Brandon Watson (RC) .30 .75
963 Jon Lester RC 1.25 3.00
964 Ben Hendrickson (RC) .30 .75
965 Martin Prado (RC) .50 1.25
966 Erick Aybar (RC) .30 .75
967 Bobby Livingston (RC) .30 .75
968 Ryan Spilborghs (RC) .30 .75
969 Tommy Murphy (RC) .30 .75
970 Howie Kendrick (RC) .75 2.00
971 Casey Janssen RC .30 .75
972 Michael O'Connor RC .30 .75
973 Conor Jackson (RC) .50 1.25
974 Jeremy Hermida (RC) .30 .75
975 Renyel Pinto (RC) .30 .75
976 Prince Fielder (RC) 1.25 3.00
977 Kevin Frandsen (RC) .30 .75
978 Ty Taubenheim RC .50 1.25
979 Rich Hill (RC) .30 .75
980 Jonathan Broxton (RC) .30 .75
981 Jamie Shields RC 1.00 2.50
982 Carlos Villanueva RC .30 .75
983 Boone Logan RC .30 .75
984 Brian Wilson RC 5.00 12.00
985 Andre Ethier (RC) 1.25 3.00
986 Mike Napoli RC 1.00 2.50
987 Agustin Montero (RC) .30 .75
988 Jack Hannahan RC .30 .75
989 Boof Bonser (RC) .50 1.25
990 Carlos Ruiz (RC) .30 .75
991 Jason Botts .30 .75
992 Kendry Morales (RC) .75 2.00
993 Alay Soler RC .30 .75
994 Santiago Ramirez (RC) .30 .75
995 Saul Rivera (RC) .30 .75
996 Anthony Reyes (RC) .30 .75
997 Matt Kemp (RC) 1.50 4.00
998 Jae Kuk Ryu RC .30 .75
999 Lastings Milledge (RC) .30 .75
NNO Exquisite Redemption
1000 Jered Weaver (RC) .75 2.00
1001 Stephen Drew (RC) .75 2.00
1002 Carlos Quentin (RC) .75 2.00
1003 Livan Hernandez .15 .40
1004 Chris B. Young (RC) .75 2.00
1005 Alberto Callaspo SP (RC) 2.50 6.00
1006 Enrique Gonzalez (RC) .30 .75
1007 Tony Pena (RC) .30 .75
1008 Bob Melvin MG .15 .40
1009 Fernando Tatis .15 .40
1010 Willy Aybar (RC) .30 .75
1011 Ken Ray (RC) .30 .75
1012 Scott Thorman (RC) .30 .75
1013 Eric Hinske SP 2.50 6.00
1014 Kevin Barry (RC) .30 .75
1015 Bobby Cox MG .15 .40
1016 Phil Stockman (RC) .30 .75
1017 Brayan Pena (RC) .30 .75
1018 Adam Loewen (RC) .30 .75
1019 Brandon Fahey RC .30 .75
1020 Jim Hoey RC .30 .75
1021 Kurt Birkins SP RC 2.50 6.00
1022 Jim Johnson RC .30 .75
1023 Sam Perlozzo MG .15 .40
1024 Cory Morris RC .30 .75
1025 Hayden Penn (RC) .30 .75
1026 Javy Lopez .15 .40
1027 Dustin Pedroia (RC) 5.00 12.00
1028 Kason Gabbard (RC) .30 .75
1029 David Pauley (RC) .30 .75
1030 Kyle Snyder .15 .40
1031 Terry Francona MG .15 .40
1032 Craig Breslow .30 .75
1033 Bryan Corey (RC) .30 .75
1034 Manny Delcarmen (RC) .30 .75
1035 Carlos Marmol RC 1.00 2.50
1036 Buck Coats (RC) .30 .75
1037 Ryan O'Malley SP RC 2.50 6.00
1038 Angel Guzman (RC) .30 .75
1039 Ronny Cedeno .15 .40
1040 Juan Mateo RC .30 .75
1041 Cesar Izturis .15 .40
1042 Les Walrond (RC) .30 .75
1043 Geovany Soto .75 2.00
1044 Sean Tracey (RC) .30 .75
1045 Ozzie Guillen MG SP 2.50 6.00
1046 Royce Clayton .15 .40
1047 Norris Hopper RC .30 .75
1048 Bill Bray (RC) .30 .75
1049 Jerry Narron MG .15 .40
1050 Brendan Harris (RC) .30 .75
1051 Brian Shackelford .15 .40
1052 Jeremy Sowers (RC) .30 .75
1053 Joe Inglett RC .30 .75
1054 Brian Slocum (RC) .30 .75
1055 Andrew Brown (RC) .75 2.00
1056 Rafael Perez RC .50 1.25
1057 Edward Mujica RC .30 .75
1058 Andy Marte (RC) .30 .75
1059 Shin-Soo Choo (RC) .50 1.25
1060 Jeremy Guthrie (RC) .30 .75
1061 Franklin Gutierrez SP (RC) 2.50 6.00
1062 Kazuo Matsui .15 .40
1063 Chris Iannetta RC .30 .75
1064 Manny Corpas RC .30 .75
1065 Clint Hurdle MG .15 .40
1066 Ramon Ramirez (RC) .30 .75
1067 Sean Casey .15 .40
1068 Zach Miner (RC) .30 .75
1069 Brent Clevlen SP (RC) 4.00 10.00
1070 Bob Wickman .15 .40
1071 Jim Leyland MG .15 .40
1072 Alexis Gomez (RC) .30 .75
1073 Anibal Sanchez (RC) .75 2.00
1074 Taylor Tankersley (RC) .30 .75
1075 Eric Wedge MG .15 .40
1076 Jonah Bayliss .30 .75
1077 Paul Hoover SP (RC) 2.50 6.00
1078 Eddie Guardado .15 .40
1079 Cody Ross .75 2.00
1080 Aubrey Huff .15 .40
1081 Jason Hirsh (RC) .30 .75
1082 Brandon League .15 .40
1083 Matt Albers (RC) .30 .75
1084 Chris Sampson RC .30 .75
1085 Phil Garner MG .15 .40
1086 J.R. House (RC) .30 .75
1087 Ryan Shealy .30 .75
1088 Stephen Andrade (RC) .30 .75
1089 Bob Keppel (RC) .30 .75
1090 Buddy Bell MG .15 .40
1091 Justin Huber (RC) .30 .75
1092 Paul Phillips (RC) .30 .75
1093 Greg Jones SP (RC) 2.50 6.00
1094 Jeff Mathis (RC) .30 .75
1095 Dustin Moseley (RC) .30 .75
1096 Joe Saunders (RC) .30 .75
1097 Reggie Willits RC .75 2.00
1098 Mike Scioscia MG .15 .40
1099 Greg Maddux .60 1.50
1100 Wilson Betemit .15 .40
1101 Chad Billingsley SP (RC) 4.00 10.00
1102 Russell Martin (RC) .50 1.25
1103 Grady Little MG .15 .40
1104 David Bell .15 .40
1105 Kevin Mench .15 .40
1106 Laynce Nix .15 .40
1107 Chris Barnwell RC .30 .75
1108 Tony Gwynn Jr. (RC) .30 .75
1109 Corey Hart (RC) .30 .75
1110 Zach Jackson (RC) .30 .75
1111 Francisco Cordero .15 .40
1112 Joe Winkelsas (RC) .30 .75
1113 Ned Yost MG .15 .40
1114 Matt Garza (RC) .30 .75
1115 Chris Heintz .15 .40
1116 Pat Neshek RC 3.00 8.00
1117 Josh Rabe SP RC 2.50 6.00
1118 Mike Rivera .15 .40
1119 Ron Gardenhire MG .15 .40
1120 Shawn Green .15 .40
1121 Oliver Perez .15 .40
1122 Heath Bell .25 .60
1123 Bartolome Fortunato (RC) .30 .75
1124 Anderson Garcia RC .30 .75
1125 John Maine SP (RC) 4.00 10.00
1126 Henry Owens RC .30 .75
1127 Mike Pelfrey RC .75 2.00
1128 Royce Ring (RC) .30 .75
1129 Willie Randolph MG .15 .40
1130 Bobby Abreu .15 .40
1131 Craig Wilson .15 .40
1132 T.J. Beam (RC) .30 .75
1133 Colter Bean SP (RC) 2.50 6.00
1134 Melky Cabrera (RC) .50 1.25
1135 Mitch Jones (RC) .30 .75
1136 Jeffrey Karstens RC .30 .75
1137 Wil Nieves (RC) .30 .75
1138 Kevin Reese (RC) .30 .75
1139 Kevin Thompson (RC) .30 .75
1140 Jose Veras RC .30 .75
1141 Joe Torre MG .25 .60
1142 Jeremy Brown (RC) .30 .75
1143 Santiago Casilla (RC) .30 .75
1144 Shane Komine RC .50 1.25
1145 Mike Rouse (RC) .30 .75
1146 Jason Windsor (RC) .30 .75
1147 Ken Macha MG .15 .40
1148 Jamie Moyer .15 .40
1149 Phil Nevin SP 2.50 6.00
1150 Eude Brito (RC) .30 .75
1151 Fabio Castro .15 .40
1152 Jeff Conine .15 .40
1153 Scott Mathieson (RC) .30 .75
1154 Brian Sanches (RC) .30 .75
1155 Matt Smith RC .30 .75
1156 Joe Thurston (RC) .30 .75
1157 Marlon Anderson SP 2.50 6.00
1158 Xavier Nady .15 .40
1159 Shawn Chacon .15 .40
1160 Rajai Davis (RC) .30 .75
1161 Yurendell DeCaster (RC) .30 .75
1162 Marty McLeary (RC) .30 .75
1163 Chris Duffy .15 .40
1164 Josh Sharpless RC .30 .75
1165 Jim Tracy MG .15 .40
1166 David Wells .15 .40
1167 Russell Branyan .15 .40
1168 Todd Walker .15 .40
1169 Paul McAnulty (RC) .30 .75
1170 Bruce Bochy MG .15 .40
1171 Shea Hillenbrand .15 .40
1172 Eliezer Alfonzo RC .30 .75
1173 Justin Knoedler SP (RC) 2.50 6.00
1174 Jonathan Sanchez (RC) .75 2.00
1175 Travis Smith (RC) .30 .75
1176 Cha-Seung Baek .15 .40
1177 T.J. Bohn (RC) .30 .75
1178 Emiliano Fruto RC .30 .75
1179 Sean Green RC .30 .75
1180 Jon Huber RC .30 .75
1181 Adam Jones SP RC 10.00 25.00
1182 Mark Lowe (RC) .30 .75
1183 Eric O'Flaherty RC .30 .75
1184 Preston Wilson .15 .40
1185 Mike Hargrove MG .15 .40
1186 Jeff Weaver .15 .40
1187 Ronnie Belliard .15 .40
1188 John Gall (RC) .30 .75
1189 Josh Kinney SP RC 2.50 6.00
1190 Tony LaRussa MG .25 .60
1191 Scott Dunn (RC) .30 .75
1192 B.J. Upton .15 .40
1193 Jon Switzer (RC) .30 .75
1194 Ben Zobrist (RC) .75 2.00
1195 Joe Maddon .15 .40
1196 Carlos Lee .15 .40
1197 Matt Stairs .15 .40
1198 Nick Masset (RC) .30 .75
1199 Nelson Cruz .50 1.25
1200 Francisco Rosario (RC) .30 .75
1201 Wes Littleton (RC) .30 .75
1202 Drew Meyer (RC) .30 .75
1203 John Rheinecker (RC) .30 .75
1204 Robinson Tejeda .15 .40
1205 Jeremy Accardo SP 2.50 6.00
1206 Luis Figueroa RC .30 .75
1207 John Hattig (RC) .30 .75
1208 Dustin McGowan (RC) .30 .75
1209 Ryan Roberts RC .30 .75
1210 Davis Romero (RC) .30 .75
1211 Ty Taubenheim .50 1.25
1212 John Gibbons MG .15 .40
1213 Shawn Hill SP (RC) 2.50 6.00
1214 Brandon Harper RC .30 .75
1215 Travis Hughes (RC) .30 .75
1216 Chris Schroder RC .30 .75
1217 Austin Kearns .15 .40
1218 Felipe Lopez .15 .40
1219 Roy Corcoran RC .30 .75
1220 Melvin Dorta RC .30 .75
1221 Brandon Webb CL SP 1.25 3.00
1222 Andruw Jones CL SP .75 2.00
1223 Miguel Tejada CL SP 1.25 3.00
1224 David Ortiz CL SP 1.25 3.00
1225 Derrek Lee CL SP .75 2.00
1226 Jim Thome CL SP 1.25 3.00
1227 Ken Griffey Jr. CL SP UER 3.00 8.00
Royce Clayton card #1046 not listed on back
1228 Travis Hafner CL SP .75 2.00
1229 Todd Helton CL SP 1.25 3.00
1230 Magglio Ordonez CL SP 1.25 3.00
1231 Miguel Cabrera CL SP 2.00 5.00
1232 Lance Berkman CL SP 1.25 3.00
1233 Mike Sweeney CL SP .75 2.00
1234 Vladimir Guerrero CL SP 2.00 5.00
1235 Nomar Garciaparra CL SP 2.00 5.00
1236 Prince Fielder CL SP 3.00 8.00
1237 Johan Santana CL SP 2.00 5.00
1238 Pedro Martinez CL SP 1.25 3.00
1239 Derek Jeter CL SP 5.00 12.00
1240 Barry Zito CL SP .75 2.00
1241 Ryan Howard CL SP UER 3.00 8.00
Chris Coste is listed as card 1046
1242 Jason Bay CL SP .75 2.00
1243 Trevor Hoffman CL SP 1.25 3.00
1244 Jason Schmidt CL SP .75 2.00
1245 Ichiro Suzuki CL SP 3.00 8.00
1246 Albert Pujols CL SP 5.00 12.00
1247 Carl Crawford CL SP 1.25 3.00
1248 Mark Teixeira CL SP 2.00 5.00
1249 Vernon Wells CL SP .75 2.00
1250 Alfonso Soriano CL SP 1.25 3.00

2006 Upper Deck Gold

*GOLD 1-1000: 2X TO 5X BASIC
*GOLD 1-1000: 1X TO 2.5X BASIC RC's
*GOLD 1001-1250: 3X TO 8X BASIC
*GOLD 1001-1250: 1.5X TO 4X BASIC RC'S
*GOLD 1001-1220: .15X TO .4X BASIC SP
COMMON (1221-1250) 1.25 3.00
SEMIS 1221-1250 2.00 5.00
UNLISTED 1221-1250 3.00 8.00
1-500 FIVE #'d INSERTS PER SER.1 HOB.BOX
501-1000 SER.2 ODDS 1:8 H, RANDOM IN RET
1001-1250 UPDATE ODDS 1:24 RET
1-1000 PRINT RUN 299 SERIAL #'d SETS
1001-1250 PRINT RUN 99 SERIAL #'d SETS
984 Brian Wilson 20.00 50.00

2006 Upper Deck Silver Spectrum

*501-1000: 3X TO 8X BASIC
*501-1000: 1.5X TO 4X BASIC RC's
1-500 FIVE #'d INSERTS PER SER.1 HOB.BOX
501-1000 SER.2 ODDS1:24 H,RANDOM IN RET
1-500 PRINT RUN 25 SERIAL #'d SETS
501-1000 PRINT RUN 99 SERIAL #'d SETS
1-500 NO PRICING DUE TO SCARCITY

2006 Upper Deck Ozzie Smith SABR San Diego

1 Ozzie Smith 1.50 4.00

2006 Upper Deck Rookie Foil Silver

*SILVER: 1X TO 2.5X BASIC
2-3 PER SER.2 RC PACK
ONE RC PACK PER SER.2 HOBBY BOX
3-CARDS PER SEALED RC PACK
STATED PRINT RUN 399 SERIAL #'d SETS
*GOLD: 1.5X TO 4X BASIC
GOLD RANDOM IN SER.2 RC PACKS
GOLD PRINT RUN 99 SERIAL #'d SETS
PLAT.RANDOM IN SER.2 RC PACKS
PLATINUM PRINT RUN 15 #'d SETS
NO PLATINUM PRICING DUE TO SCARCITY
AU PLATES RANDOM IN RC PACKS
AU PLATE PRINT RUN 1 SET PER COLOR
BLACK-CYAN-MAGENTA-YELLOW ISSUED
NO AU PLATE PRICING DUE TO SCARCITY
AU PLATES ISSUED FOR 28 OF 100 FOILS
SEE BECKETT.COM FOR AU PLATE CL

2006 Upper Deck All-Time Legends

TWO PER SERIES 2 FAT PACK
AT1 Ty Cobb 1.50 4.00
AT2 Lou Gehrig 2.00 5.00
AT3 Babe Ruth 2.50 6.00
AT4 Jimmie Foxx 1.00 2.50
AT5 Honus Wagner 1.00 2.50
AT6 Lou Brock .60 1.50
AT7 Joe Morgan .40 1.00
AT8 Christy Mathewson 1.00 2.50
AT9 Walter Johnson 1.00 2.50
AT10 Mike Schmidt 1.50 4.00
AT11 Al Kaline 1.00 2.50
AT12 Robin Yount 1.00 2.50
AT13 Johnny Bench 1.00 2.50
AT14 Yogi Berra 1.00 2.50
AT15 Rod Carew .60 1.50
AT16 Bob Feller .40 1.00
AT17 Carlton Fisk .60 1.50
AT18 Bob Gibson .60 1.50
AT19 Cy Young 1.00 2.50
AT20 Reggie Jackson .60 1.50
AT21 Jackie Robinson 1.00 2.50
AT22 Harmon Killebrew 1.00 2.50
AT23 Mickey Cochrane .40 1.00
AT24 Eddie Mathews 1.00 2.50
AT25 Bill Mazeroski .60 1.50
AT26 Willie McCovey .60 1.50
AT27 Eddie Murray 1.00 2.50
AT28 Lefty Grove .40 1.00
AT29 Jim Palmer .40 1.00
AT30 Pee Wee Reese .60 1.50
AT31 Phil Rizzuto .60 1.50
AT32 Brooks Robinson .60 1.50
AT33 Nolan Ryan 2.50 6.00
AT34 Tom Seaver .60 1.50
AT35 Ozzie Smith 1.50 4.00
AT36 Roy Campanella 1.00 2.50
AT37 Thurman Munson 1.00 2.50
AT38 Mel Ott .40 1.00
AT39 Satchel Paige 1.00 2.50
AT40 Rogers Hornsby .60 1.50

2006 Upper Deck All-Upper Deck Team

TWO PER SERIES 1 FAT PACK
UD1 Ken Griffey Jr. 1.50 4.00
UD2 Derek Jeter 2.50 6.00
UD3 Albert Pujols 2.50 6.00
UD4 Alex Rodriguez 1.50 4.00
UD5 Vladimir Guerrero 1.00 2.50
UD6 Roger Clemens 1.25 3.00
UD7 Derrek Lee .40 1.00
UD8 David Ortiz .60 1.50
UD9 Miguel Cabrera 1.00 2.50
UD10 Bobby Abreu .40 1.00
UD11 Mark Teixeira 1.00 2.50
UD12 Johan Santana 1.00 2.50
UD13 Hideki Matsui 1.00 2.50
UD14 Ichiro Suzuki 1.50 4.00
UD15 Andruw Jones .40 1.00
UD16 Eric Chavez .40 1.00
UD17 Roy Oswalt .60 1.50
UD18 Curt Schilling .60 1.50
UD19 Randy Johnson 1.00 2.50
UD20 Ivan Rodriguez .60 1.50
UD21 Chipper Jones 1.00 2.50
UD22 Mark Prior .60 1.50
UD23 Jason Bay .40 1.00
UD24 Pedro Martinez .60 1.50
UD25 David Wright 1.50 4.00
UD26 Carlos Beltran .40 1.00
UD27 Jim Edmonds .60 1.50
UD28 Chris Carpenter 1.00 2.50
UD29 Roy Halladay 1.00 2.50
UD30 Jake Peavy .40 1.00
UD31 Paul Konerko .60 1.50
UD32 Travis Hafner .40 1.00
UD33 Barry Zito .40 1.00
UD34 Miguel Tejada .60 1.50
UD35 Josh Beckett .60 1.50
UD36 Todd Helton .60 1.50
UD37 Dontrelle Willis .40 1.00
UD38 Manny Ramirez 1.00 2.50
UD39 Mariano Rivera 1.00 2.50
UD40 Jeff Kent .40 1.00

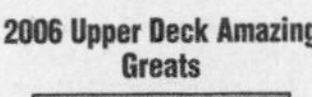

2006 Upper Deck Amazing Greats

SER.1 ODDS 1:6 HOBBY, 1:12 RETAIL
*GOLD: .6X TO 1.5X BASIC
FIVE #'d INSERTS PER SER.1 HOBBY BOX
GOLD STATED PRINT RUN 699 SERIAL #'d SETS
AB Adrian Beltre .50 1.25
AJ Andruw Jones .50 1.25
AP Albert Pujols 3.00 8.00
AS Alfonso Soriano .75 2.00
BA Bobby Abreu .50 1.25
CB Carlos Beltran .50 1.25
CC Carl Crawford .75 2.00
CJ Chipper Jones 1.25 3.00
CL Carlos Lee .50 1.25
CP Corey Patterson .50 1.25
CS Curt Schilling .75 2.00
DJ Derek Jeter 3.00 8.00
DO David Ortiz .75 2.00
DW Dontrelle Willis .50 1.25
EG Eric Gagne .50 1.25
FT Frank Thomas 1.25 3.00
GM Greg Maddux 2.00 5.00
GS Gary Sheffield .50 1.25
HE Todd Helton .75 2.00
IR Ivan Rodriguez .75 2.00
JB Jeff Bagwell .75 2.00
JD Johnny Damon .75 2.00
JE Jim Edmonds .75 2.00
JG Jason Giambi .75 2.00
JJ Jacque Jones .50 1.25
JL Javy Lopez .50 1.25
JR Jose Reyes .75 2.00
JS Johan Santana 1.25 3.00
JT Jim Thome .75 2.00
KG Ken Griffey Jr. 2.00 5.00
KW Kerry Wood .50 1.25
MC Miguel Cabrera 1.25 3.00
MP Mike Piazza 1.25 3.00
MR Manny Ramirez 1.25 3.00
MT Mark Teixeira 1.25 3.00
PK Paul Konerko .75 2.00
PM Pedro Martinez .75 2.00
PR Mark Prior .75 2.00
RC Roger Clemens 1.50 4.00
RF Rafael Furcal .50 1.25
RJ Randy Johnson 1.25 3.00
RO Roy Oswalt .75 2.00
RP Rafael Palmeiro .75 2.00
SM John Smoltz 1.25 3.00
SR Scott Rolen .75 2.00
SS Sammy Sosa 1.25 3.00
TE Miguel Tejada .75 2.00
TG Tom Glavine .75 2.00
TH Tim Hudson .75 2.00
WR David Wright 2.00 5.00

2006 Upper Deck Amazing Greats Materials

SER.1 ODDS 1:48 HOBBY, 1:288 RETAIL
AB Adrian Beltre Jsy 3.00 8.00
AJ Andruw Jones Jsy 4.00 10.00
AP Albert Pujols Jsy 6.00 15.00
AS Alfonso Soriano Jsy 3.00 8.00
BA Bobby Abreu Jsy 3.00 8.00
CB Carlos Beltran Jsy 3.00 8.00
CC Carl Crawford Jsy 3.00 8.00
CJ Chipper Jones Jsy 4.00 10.00
CL Carlos Lee Jsy 3.00 8.00
CP Corey Patterson Jsy 3.00 8.00
CS Curt Schilling Jsy 4.00 10.00
DJ Derek Jeter Jsy 10.00 25.00
DO David Ortiz Jsy 4.00 10.00
DW Dontrelle Willis Jsy 3.00 8.00
EG Eric Gagne Jsy 3.00 8.00
FT Frank Thomas Jsy 4.00 10.00
GM Greg Maddux Jsy 4.00 10.00
GS Gary Sheffield Jsy 3.00 8.00
HE Todd Helton Jsy 4.00 10.00
IR Ivan Rodriguez Jsy 4.00 10.00
JB Jeff Bagwell Jsy 4.00 10.00
JD Johnny Damon Jsy 4.00 10.00
JE Jim Edmonds Jsy 3.00 8.00
JG Jason Giambi Jsy 4.00 10.00
JJ Jacque Jones Jsy 3.00 8.00
JL Javy Lopez Jsy 3.00 8.00
JR Jose Reyes Jsy 3.00 8.00
JS Johan Santana Jsy 4.00 10.00
JT Jim Thome Jsy 4.00 10.00
KG Ken Griffey Jr. Jsy 6.00 15.00
KW Kerry Wood Jsy 3.00 8.00
MC Miguel Cabrera Jsy 4.00 10.00
MP Mike Piazza Jsy 4.00 10.00
MR Manny Ramirez Jsy 4.00 10.00
MT Mark Teixeira Jsy 4.00 10.00
PK Paul Konerko Jsy 3.00 8.00
PM Pedro Martinez Jsy 4.00 10.00
PR Mark Prior Jsy 3.00 8.00
RC Roger Clemens Jsy 6.00 15.00
RF Rafael Furcal Jsy 3.00 8.00
RJ Randy Johnson Pants 4.00 10.00
RO Roy Oswalt Jsy 3.00 8.00
RP Rafael Palmeiro Jsy 4.00 10.00
SM John Smoltz Jsy 4.00 10.00
SR Scott Rolen Jsy 4.00 10.00
SS Sammy Sosa Jsy 4.00 10.00
TE Miguel Tejada Jsy 3.00 8.00
TG Tom Glavine Jsy 4.00 10.00
TH Tim Hudson Jsy 3.00 8.00
WR David Wright Jsy 4.00 10.00

2006 Upper Deck Diamond Collection

SER.1 ODDS 1:6 HOBBY, 1:12 RETAIL
*GOLD: .6X TO 1.5X BASIC
FIVE #'d INSERTS PER SER.1 HOBBY BOX
GOLD PRINT RUN 699 SERIAL #'d SETS
AE Adam Eaton .50 1.25
AH Aubrey Huff .50 1.25
AK Adam Kennedy .50 1.25
AL Moises Alou .50 1.25
AO Akinori Otsuka .50 1.25
BC Bobby Crosby .50 1.25
BR Brad Radke .50 1.25
CC C.C. Sabathia .75 2.00
CK Casey Kotchman .50 1.25
CO Jose Contreras .50 1.25
CP Carl Pavano .50 1.25
CS Chris Shelton .50 1.25
DJ Derek Jeter 3.00 8.00
DO David Ortiz .75 2.00
EC Eric Chavez .50 1.25
EJ Edwin Jackson .50 1.25
FG Freddy Garcia .50 1.25
GM Greg Maddux 2.00 5.00
GO Juan Gonzalez .50 1.25
IR Ivan Rodriguez .75 2.00
JB Jeff Bagwell .75 2.00
JC Jesse Crain .50 1.25
JD Johnny Damon .75 2.00
JE Jim Edmonds .75 2.00
JG Jose Guillen .50 1.25
JJ Jacque Jones .50 1.25
JK Jason Kendall .50 1.25
JP Jorge Posada .75 2.00
JS John Smoltz 1.25 3.00
JT Jim Thome .75 2.00
JW Jayson Werth .75 2.00
KE Austin Kearns .50 1.25
KG Ken Griffey Jr. 2.00 5.00
KL Kenny Lofton .50 1.25
KM Kevin Millwood .50 1.25
LA Matt Lawton .50 1.25
LO Mike Lowell .50 1.25
MA Kazuo Matsui .50 1.25
MC Mike Cameron .50 1.25
MH Mike Hampton .50 1.25
ML Mike Lieberthal .50 1.25
NJ Nick Johnson .50 1.25
OC Orlando Cabrera .50 1.25
PL Paul Lo Duca .50 1.25
PW Preston Wilson .50 1.25
RB Rocco Baldelli .50 1.25
RJ Randy Johnson 1.25 3.00
SF Steve Finley .50 1.25
SK Scott Kazmir .75 2.00
SS Shannon Stewart .50 1.25

2006 Upper Deck Diamond Collection Materials

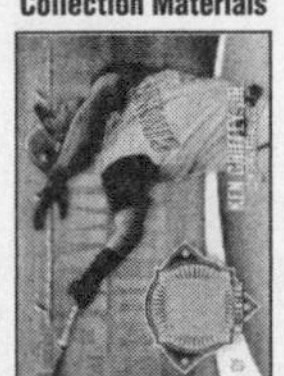

SER.1 ODDS 1:48 HOBBY, 1:288 RETAIL
AE Adam Eaton Jsy 3.00 8.00
AH Aubrey Huff Jsy 3.00 8.00
AK Adam Kennedy Jsy 3.00 8.00
AL Moises Alou Jsy 3.00 8.00
AO Akinori Otsuka Jsy 3.00 8.00
BC Bobby Crosby Jsy 3.00 8.00
BR Brad Radke Jsy 3.00 8.00
CC C.C. Sabathia Jsy 3.00 8.00
CK Casey Kotchman Jsy 3.00 8.00
CO Jose Contreras Jsy 3.00 8.00
CP Carl Pavano Jsy 3.00 8.00
CS Chris Shelton Jsy 4.00 10.00
DJ Derek Jeter Jsy 10.00 25.00
DO David Ortiz Jsy 4.00 10.00
EC Eric Chavez Jsy 3.00 8.00
EJ Edwin Jackson Jsy 3.00 8.00
FG Freddy Garcia Jsy 3.00 8.00
GM Greg Maddux Jsy 4.00 10.00
GO Juan Gonzalez Jsy 3.00 8.00
IR Ivan Rodriguez Jsy 4.00 10.00
JB Jeff Bagwell Jsy 4.00 10.00
JC Jesse Crain Jsy 3.00 8.00
JD Johnny Damon Jsy 4.00 10.00
JE Jim Edmonds Jsy 3.00 8.00
JG Jose Guillen Jsy 3.00 8.00
JJ Jacque Jones Jsy 3.00 8.00
JK Jason Kendall Jsy 3.00 8.00
JP Jorge Posada Jsy 4.00 10.00
JS John Smoltz Jsy 4.00 10.00
JT Jim Thome Jsy 4.00 10.00
JW Jayson Werth Jsy 3.00 8.00
KE Austin Kearns Jsy 3.00 8.00
KG Ken Griffey Jr. Jsy 6.00 15.00
KL Kenny Lofton Jsy 3.00 8.00
KM Kevin Millwood Jsy 3.00 8.00
LA Matt Lawton Jsy 3.00 8.00
LO Mike Lowell Jsy 3.00 8.00
MA Kazuo Matsui Jsy 3.00 8.00
MC Mike Cameron Jsy 3.00 8.00
MH Mike Hampton Jsy 3.00 8.00
ML Mike Lieberthal Jsy 3.00 8.00
NJ Nick Johnson Jsy 3.00 8.00
OC Orlando Cabrera Jsy 3.00 8.00
PL Paul Lo Duca Jsy 3.00 8.00
PW Preston Wilson Jsy 3.00 8.00
RB Rocco Baldelli Jsy 3.00 8.00
RJ Randy Johnson Pants 4.00 10.00
SF Steve Finley Jsy 3.00 8.00
SK Scott Kazmir Jsy 3.00 8.00
SS Shannon Stewart Jsy 3.00 8.00

2006 Upper Deck Diamond Debut

STATED ODDS 1:4 WAL MART PACKS
1-40 ISSUED IN SERIES 1 PACKS
41-82 ISSUED IN SERIES 2 PACKS
DD1 Tadahito Iguchi .60 1.50
DD2 Huston Street .60 1.50
DD3 Norihiro Nakamura .60 1.50
DD4 Chien-Ming Wang 1.00 2.50
DD5 Pedro Lopez
DD6 Robinson Cano 1.50 4.00
DD7 Tim Stauffer .60 1.50
DD8 Ervin Santana .60 1.50
DD9 Brandon McCarthy .60 1.50
DD10 Hayden Penn .60 1.50
DD11 Derek Jeter 4.00 10.00
DD12 Ken Griffey Jr. 2.50 6.00
DD13 Prince Fielder 2.50 6.00
DD14 Edwin Encarnacion .60 1.50
DD15 Scott Olsen .60 1.50
DD16 Chris Resop .60 1.50
DD17 Justin Verlander 5.00 12.00
DD18 Melky Cabrera 1.00 2.50
DD19 Jeff Francoeur 1.50 4.00
DD20 Yuniesky Betancourt .60 1.50
DD21 Conor Jackson 1.00 2.50
DD22 Felix Hernandez 1.50 4.00
DD23 Anthony Reyes .60 1.50
DD24 John-Ford Griffin .60 1.50
DD25 Adam Wainwright 1.50 4.00
DD26 Ryan Garko .60 1.50
DD27 Ryan Zimmerman 3.00 8.00
DD28 Tom Seaver 1.00 2.50
DD29 Johnny Bench 1.50 4.00
DD30 Reggie Jackson 1.00 2.50
DD31 Rod Carew 1.00 2.50
DD32 Nolan Ryan 4.00 10.00
DD33 Richie Ashburn 1.00 2.50
DD34 Yogi Berra 1.50 4.00
DD35 Lou Brock 1.00 2.50
DD36 Carlton Fisk 1.00 2.50
DD37 Joe Morgan .60 1.50
DD38 Bob Gibson 1.00 2.50
DD39 Willie McCovey 1.00 2.50
DD40 Harmon Killebrew 1.50 4.00
DD41 Takashi Saito 1.00 2.50
DD42 Kenji Johjima 1.50 4.00
DD43 Joel Zumaya 1.50 4.00
DD44 Dan Uggla 1.50 4.00
DD45 Taylor Buchholz .60 1.50
DD46 Josh Barfield .60 1.50
DD47 Brian Bannister .60 1.50
DD48 Nick Markakis 1.50 4.00
DD49 Carlos Martinez .60 1.50
DD50 Macay McBride .60 1.50
DD51 Brian Anderson .60 1.50
DD52 Freddie Bynum .60 1.50
DD53 Kelly Shoppach .60 1.50
DD54 Choo Freeman .60 1.50
DD55 Ryan Shealy .60 1.50
DD56 Chris Resop .60 1.50
DD57 Hanley Ramirez 1.50 4.00
DD58 Mike Jacobs .60 1.50
DD59 Cody Ross 1.50 4.00
DD60 Jose Capellan .60 1.50
DD61 David Gassner .60 1.50
DD62 Jason Kubel .60 1.50
DD63 Jered Weaver 1.50 4.00
DD64 Paul Maholm .60 1.50
DD65 Nate McLouth .60 1.50
DD66 Ben Johnson .60 1.50
DD67 Jack Taschner .60 1.50
DD68 Skip Schumaker .60 1.50
DD69 Brandon Watson .60 1.50
DD70 David Wright 2.50 6.00
DD71 David Ortiz 1.00 2.50
DD72 Alex Rodriguez 2.50 6.00
DD73 Johan Santana 1.50 4.00
DD74 Greg Maddux 2.50 6.00
DD75 Ichiro Suzuki 2.50 6.00
DD76 Albert Pujols 4.00 10.00
DD77 Hideki Matsui 1.50 4.00
DD78 Vladimir Guerrero 1.50 4.00
DD79 Pedro Martinez 1.00 2.50
DD80 Mike Schmidt 2.50 6.00
DD81 Al Kaline 1.50 4.00
DD82 Robin Yount 1.50 4.00

2006 Upper Deck First Class Cuts

RANDOM INSERTS IN SERIES 1 PACKS
STATED PRINT RUN 1 SERIAL #'d SET
NO PRICING DUE TO SCARCITY
BR Babe Ruth
HW Honus Wagner
TC Ty Cobb
WJ Walter Johnson

2006 Upper Deck First Class Legends

COMMON RUTH (1-20) 1.25 3.00
COMMON COBB (21-40) .75 2.00
COMMON WAGNER (41-60 .40 1.00
COMMON MATHEWSON (61-80) .40 1.00
COMMON W.JOHNSON (81-100) .40 1.00
SER.1 STATED ODDS: 1:6 HOBBY
SER.2 ODDS APPROX. 1:12 HOBBY
*GOLD: .75X TO 2X BASIC
GOLD PRINT RUN 699 SERIAL #'d SETS
*SILVER SPECTRUM: 1.25X TO 3X BASIC
SILVER SPEC. PRINT RUN 99 SERIAL #'d SETS
FIVE #'d INSERTS PER SER.1 HOBBY BOX
GOLD-SILVER AVAIL ONLY IN SER.1 PACKS

2006 Upper Deck Collect the Mascots

COMPLETE SET (3) .40 1.00
ISSUED IN 06 UD 1 AND 2 FAT PACKS
MLB1 Wally the Green Monster .20 .50
MLB2 Phillie Phanatic .20 .50
MLB3 Mr. Met .20 .50

2006 Upper Deck Inaugural Images

SER.2 ODDS 1:8 H, RANDOM IN RETAIL
II1 Sung-Heon Hong .75 2.00
II2 Yulieski Gourriel 1.25 3.00
II3 Tsuyoshi Nishioka 3.00 8.00
II4 Miguel Cabrera 1.25 3.00
II5 Yung Chi Chen .75 2.00
II6 Ormari Romero .50 1.25
II7 Ken Griffey Jr. 2.00 5.00
II8 Bernie Williams .75 2.00
II9 Daniel Cabrera .50 1.25
II10 David Ortiz .75 2.00
II11 Alex Rodriguez 2.00 5.00
II12 Frederich Cepeda .50 1.25
II13 Derek Jeter 3.00 8.00
II14 Jorge Cantu .50 1.25
II15 Alexi Ramirez 6.00 15.00
II16 Yoandy Garlobo .50 1.25
II17 Koji Uehara 1.25 3.00
II18 Nobuhiko Matsunaka .75 2.00
II19 Tomoya Satozaki .75 2.00
II20 Seung Yeop Lee .75 2.00
II21 Yulieski Gourriel 1.25 3.00
II22 Adrian Beltre .50 1.25
II23 Ken Griffey Jr. 2.00 5.00
II24 Jong Beom Lee .50 1.25
II25 Ichiro Suzuki 2.00 5.00
II26 Yoandy Garlobo .50 1.25
II27 Daisuke Matsuzaka 1.50 4.00
II28 Yadel Marti .50 1.25
II29 Chan Ho Park .75 2.00
II30 Daisuke Matsuzaka 1.50 4.00

2006 Upper Deck INKredible

SER.2 ODDS 1:288 H, RANDOM IN RETAIL
UPDATE ODDS 1:24 RETAIL
SP INFO/PRINT RUNS PROVIDED BY UD
SP * INFO PROVIDED BY BECKETT
SP's ARE NOT SERIAL-NUMBERED
NO PRICING ON QTY OF 36 OR LESS
AB Ambiorix Burgos UPD SP * 6.00 15.00
AH Aaron Harang UPD 4.00 10.00
AJ Adam Jones UPD 20.00 50.00
AL Eliezer Alfonzo UPD SP *
AM Aaron Miles UPD SP
AP Angel Pagan UPD 6.00 15.00
AR2 Alex Rios UPD SP 15.00 40.00
AR Alexis Rios 6.00 15.00
BA Brandon Backe UPD 4.00 10.00
BB Ben Broussard UPD 6.00 15.00
BC Brandon Claussen UPD 4.00 10.00
BM Brandon McCarthy UPD SP 10.00 25.00
BM Brett Myers SP/72 * 6.00 15.00
BR Brian Roberts 6.00 15.00
BR2 Brian Roberts UPD 6.00 15.00
BW Brian Wilson UPD 15.00 40.00
CA Miguel Cabrera 15.00 40.00
CB Colter Bean UPD 4.00 10.00
CC Coco Crisp UPD 10.00 25.00
CC Carl Crawford 6.00 15.00
CC2 Carl Crawford UPD 6.00 15.00
CD Chris Duffy UPD 4.00 10.00
CI Cesar Izturis UPD SP * 6.00 15.00
CK Casey Kotchman 4.00 10.00
CK2 Casey Kotchman UPD 4.00 10.00
CL Cliff Lee UPD 10.00 25.00
CO Chad Cordero 6.00 15.00
CO2 Chad Cordero UPD SP 6.00 15.00
CW C.J. Wilson UPD 4.00 10.00
DJ Derek Jeter 60.00 120.00
DJ2 Derek Jeter UPD SP 125.00 200.00
DR Darrell Rasner UPD 4.00 10.00
DW David Wright SP/91 * 10.00 25.00
EA Erick Aybar UPD 4.00 10.00
EB Eude Brito UPD 6.00 15.00
EF Emiliano Fruto UPD SP *
EG Eric Gagne UPD SP 30.00 60.00
GC Gustavo Chacin UPD 4.00 10.00
GF Gavin Floyd UPD 4.00 10.00
JB Joe Blanton 6.00 15.00
JC Jesse Crain 4.00 10.00
JD Jermaine Dye UPD 6.00 15.00
JE Johnny Estrada UPD SP
JH John Hattig UPD 4.00 10.00
JH J.J. Hardy 4.00 10.00
JJ Jorge Julio UPD SP 6.00 15.00
JM Joe Mauer SP/91 * 30.00 60.00
JO Jacque Jones UPD 6.00 15.00
JP Jhonny Peralta UPD 4.00 10.00
JR Juan Rivera UPD SP 10.00 25.00
JR Jeremy Reed 4.00 10.00
JV Justin Verlander SP/91 * 12.50 30.00
KG Ken Griffey Jr. 40.00 80.00
KG2 Ken Griffey Jr. UPD SP 40.00 80.00
KR Ken Ray UPD 4.00 10.00
KY Kevin Youkilis 6.00 15.00
KY2 Kevin Youkilis UPD 6.00 15.00
LN Leo Nunez UPD 4.00 10.00
LO Lyle Overbay SP/91 * 6.00 15.00
MC Matt Clement SP/36 *
MH Matt Holliday UPD 8.00 20.00
MM Matt Murton UPD 10.00 25.00
MO Justin Morneau 10.00 25.00
MR Mike Rouse UPD 4.00 10.00
MT Matt Teahen UPD 6.00 15.00
MT Mark Teixeira 10.00 25.00
MV Mike Vento UPD 4.00 10.00
NG Nomar Garciaparra 30.00 60.00
NL Noah Lowry UPD 6.00 15.00
NS Nick Swisher UPD 6.00 15.00
PA John Patterson UPD 4.00 10.00
PE Joel Peralta UPD 4.00 10.00
PF Prince Fielder SP/10 *
PI Joel Pineiro UPD 6.00 15.00
RE Jose Reyes SP/91 * 15.00 40.00
RF Ryan Freel UPD 6.00 15.00
RG Ryan Garko UPD 4.00 10.00
RP Ronny Paulino UPD 10.00 25.00
RS Ryan Shealy UPD 6.00 15.00
RZ Ryan Zimmerman SP/91 * 20.00 50.00
SK Scott Kazmir 8.00 20.00
TH Travis Hafner 10.00 25.00
TI Tadahito Iguchi SP/91 * 20.00 50.00
TI2 Tadahito Iguchi UPD SP 30.00 60.00
VM Victor Martinez 6.00 15.00
WI Dontrelle Willis 10.00 25.00
YB Yuniesky Betancourt UPD 6.00 15.00
YM Yadier Molina UPD 6.00 15.00
ZM Zach Miner UPD 6.00 15.00

2006 Upper Deck Derek Jeter Spell and Win

COMPLETE SET (5) 6.00 15.00
COMMON CARD (1-5) 1.25 3.00
RANDOM IN SER.2 WAL-MART PACKS

2006 Upper Deck Player Highlights

SER.2 ODDS 1:6 H, RANDOM IN RETAIL
PH1 Andruw Jones .40 1.00
PH2 Manny Ramirez 1.00 2.50
PH3 Travis Hafner .40 1.00
PH4 Johnny Damon .60 1.50
PH5 Miguel Cabrera 1.00 2.50
PH6 Chris Carpenter 1.00 2.50
PH7 Derrek Lee .40 1.00
PH8 Jason Bay .40 1.00
PH9 Jason Varitek 1.00 2.50
PH10 Ryan Howard 1.50 4.00
PH11 Mark Teixeira 1.00 2.50
PH12 Carlos Delgado .40 1.00
PH13 Bartolo Colon .40 1.00
PH14 David Wright 1.50 4.00
PH15 Miguel Tejada .60 1.50
PH16 Mike Piazza 1.00 2.50
PH17 Paul Konerko .60 1.50
PH18 Jermaine Dye .40 1.00
PH19 Ichiro Suzuki 1.50 4.00
PH20 Brad Wilkerson .40 1.00
PH21 Hideki Matsui 1.00 2.50
PH22 Albert Pujols 2.50 6.00
PH23 Chris Burke .40 1.00
PH24 Derek Jeter 2.50 6.00
PH25 Brian Roberts .40 1.00
PH26 David Ortiz .60 1.50
PH27 Alex Rodriguez 1.50 4.00
PH28 Ken Griffey Jr. 1.50 4.00
PH29 Prince Fielder 1.50 4.00
PH30 Bobby Abreu .40 1.00
PH31 Vladimir Guerrero 1.00 2.50
PH32 Tadahito Iguchi .40 1.00
PH33 Jose Reyes .60 1.50
PH34 Scott Podsednik .40 1.00
PH35 Gary Sheffield .40 1.00

2006 Upper Deck Run Producers

SER.2 ODDS 1:8 H, RANDOM IN RETAIL
RP1 Ty Cobb 1.50 4.00
RP2 Derrek Lee .40 1.00
RP3 Andruw Jones .40 1.00
RP4 David Ortiz .60 1.50
RP5 Lou Gehrig 2.00 5.00
RP6 Ken Griffey Jr. 1.50 4.00
RP7 Albert Pujols 2.50 6.00
RP8 Derek Jeter 2.50 6.00
RP9 Manny Ramirez 1.00 2.50
RP10 Alex Rodriguez 1.50 4.00
RP11 Gary Sheffield .40 1.00
RP12 Miguel Cabrera 1.00 2.50
RP13 Hideki Matsui 1.00 2.50
RP14 Vladimir Guerrero 1.00 2.50
RP15 David Wright 1.50 4.00
RP16 Mike Schmidt 1.50 4.00
RP17 Mark Teixeira 1.00 2.50
RP18 Babe Ruth 2.50 6.00
RP19 Jimmie Foxx 1.00 2.50
RP20 Honus Wagner 1.00 2.50

2006 Upper Deck Season Highlights

ISSUED IN 06 UD 1 AND 2 FAT PACKS
SH1 Albert Pujols 2.50 6.00
SH2 Ken Griffey Jr. 1.50 4.00
SH3 Travis Hafner .40 1.00
SH4 David Ortiz .60 1.50
SH5 David Ortiz .60 1.50
SH6 Ryan Howard 1.50 4.00
SH7 Chase Utley 1.00 2.50
SH8 Manny Ramirez 1.00 2.50
SH9 Barry Zito .40 1.00
SH10 Roger Clemens 1.25 3.00
SH11 Francisco Liriano 1.00 2.50
SH12 Jered Weaver 1.00 2.50
SH13 Roy Halladay 1.00 2.50
SH14 Johan Santana 1.00 2.50
SH15 Tom Glavine .60 1.50
SH16 Pedro Martinez .60 1.50
SH17 Mike Piazza 1.00 2.50
SH18 Alfonso Soriano .60 1.50
SH19 Miguel Cabrera 1.00 2.50
SH20 Vladimir Guerrero 1.00 2.50
SH21 Joe Mauer 1.00 2.50
SH22 Ryan Zimmerman 2.00 5.00
SH23 Carlos Delgado .40 1.00
SH24 Jim Thome .60 1.50
SH25 Jermaine Dye .40 1.00
SH26 Derek Jeter 2.50 6.00
SH27 Ivan Rodriguez .60 1.50
SH28 Bobby Abreu .40 1.00
SH29 Greg Maddux 1.50 4.00
SH30 Alex Rodriguez 1.50 4.00

2006 Upper Deck Signature Sensations

SER.1 ODDS 1:288 HOBBY, 1:1920 RETAIL
SP INFO PROVIDED BY UPPER DECK
AL Al Leiter 6.00 15.00
AM Aaron Miles 4.00 10.00
AO Akinori Otsuka SP
AR Aaron Rowand 6.00 15.00
BA Bronson Arroyo 6.00 15.00
BH Bobby Hill SP
CD Carlos Delgado SP
CS Cory Sullivan 4.00 10.00
DY Delmon Young SP
EG Eric Gagne SP
GA Garrett Atkins 4.00 10.00
HS Huston Street SP
JA Javier Vazquez SP
JE Johnny Estrada 4.00 10.00

JJ Josh Johnson 4.00 10.00
JK Jason Kendall SP
JS Jeff Suppan 4.00 10.00
JV Joe Valentine 4.00 10.00
KC Kiko Calero 4.00 10.00
KG Ken Griffey Jr. SP
MH Mike Hampton SP
MP Mark Prior SP
NP Nick Punto 4.00 10.00
SB Scott Baker 6.00 15.00
TH Trevor Hoffman SP
TR Travis Hafner 6.00 15.00
YM Yadier Molina 12.50 30.00

2006 Upper Deck Speed To Burn

SER.2 ODDS 1:12 H, RANDOM IN RETAIL
CARDS 2/10/13 DO NOT EXIST
SB1 Lou Brock .60 1.50
SB3 Alfonso Soriano .60 1.50
SB4 Carl Crawford .60 1.50
SB5 Chone Figgins .40 1.00
SB6 Ichiro Suzuki 1.50 4.00
SB7 Jose Reyes .60 1.50
SB8 Juan Pierre .40 1.00
SB9 Scott Podsednik .40 1.00
SB11 Alex Rodriguez 1.50 4.00
SB12 David Wright 1.50 4.00
SB14 Bobby Abreu .40 1.00
SB15 Brian Roberts .40 1.00

2006 Upper Deck Star Attractions

COMPLETE UPDATE (50) 20.00 50.00
SER.1 ODDS 1:6 HOBBY, 1:12 RETAIL
UPDATE ODDS 1:2 RETAIL
*GOLD: .6X TO 1.5X BASIC
FIVE #'d INSERTS PER SER.1 HOBBY BOX
GOLD PRINT RUN 699 SERIAL #'d SETS
*SILVER: 1.25X TO 3X BASIC
ONE #'d INSERT PER UPDATE BOX
SILVER PRINT RUN 99 SERIAL #'d SETS
AB Adrian Beltre .40 1.00
AE Andre Ethier UPD 1.50 4.00
AH Aubrey Huff .40 1.00
AJ Andruw Jones .40 1.00
AJ Adam Jones UPD 1.50 4.00
AL Adam Loewen UPD .40 1.00
AM Andy Marte UPD .40 1.00
AN Anibal Sanchez UPD .40 1.00
AP Andy Pettitte .60 1.50
AR Anthony Reyes UPD .40 1.00
AS Alfonso Soriano .60 1.50
AW Adam Wainwright UPD 1.00 2.50
BA Bobby Abreu .40 1.00
BI Chad Billingsley UPD .60 1.50
BR Brian Anderson UPD .40 1.00
BZ Barry Zito .40 1.00
CB Carlos Beltran .40 1.00
CD Carlos Delgado .40 1.00
CH Cole Hamels UPD 1.50 4.00
CJ Chipper Jones 1.00 2.50
CL Carlos Lee .40 1.00
CO Conor Jackson UPD .60 1.50
CQ Carlos Quentin UPD .60 1.50
CS Curt Schilling .60 1.50
CY Chris Young UPD .40 1.00
DJ Derek Jeter 2.50 6.00
DL Derrek Lee .40 1.00
DM Dustin McGowan UPD .40 1.00
DO David Ortiz .60 1.50
DP Dustin Pedroia UPD 8.00 20.00
DU Dan Uggla UPD 1.00 2.50
DW Dontrelle Willis .40 1.00
EA Erick Aybar UPD .40 1.00
EG Eric Gagne .40 1.00
FL Francisco Liriano UPD 1.00 2.50
FT Frank Thomas 1.00 2.50
GA Garret Anderson .40 1.00
GM Greg Maddux 1.50 4.00
GR Khalil Greene .40 1.00
GS Gary Sheffield .40 1.00
GU Jose Guillen .40 1.00
HI Jason Hirsh UPD .40 1.00
HK Howie Kendrick UPD 1.00 2.50
HP Hayden Penn UPD .40 1.00
HR Hanley Ramirez UPD 1.00 2.50
HU Justin Huber UPD .40 1.00
JA Chuck James UPD .40 1.00
JB Josh Beckett .60 1.50
JC Jose Contreras .40 1.00
JD Johnny Damon .60 1.50
JE Jim Edmonds .60 1.50
JG Jason Giambi .40 1.00
JH Jeremy Hermida UPD .40 1.00
JJ Jacque Jones .40 1.00
JJ Josh Johnson UPD 1.00 2.50
JK Jason Kubel UPD .40 1.00
JL Javy Lopez .40 1.00
JM Joe Mauer 1.00 2.50
JO Josh Barfield UPD .40 1.00
JP Jorge Posada .60 1.50
JR Jose Reyes .60 1.50
JS Jason Schmidt .40 1.00
JV Justin Verlander UPD 3.00 8.00
JW Jered Weaver UPD 1.00 2.50
JZ Joel Zumaya UPD 1.00 2.50
KG Ken Griffey Jr. 1.50 4.00
KJ Kenji Johjima UPD 1.00 2.50
KM Kendry Morales UPD 1.00 2.50
KW Kerry Wood .40 1.00
LB Lance Berkman .60 1.50
LE Jon Lester UPD 1.50 4.00
LM Lastings Milledge UPD .40 1.00
MA Jeff Mathis UPD .40 1.00
MC Matt Cain UPD 1.00 2.50
MK Matt Kemp UPD 2.00 5.00
MM Mark Mulder .40 1.00
MO Magglio Ordonez .60 1.50
MP Mark Prior .60 1.50
MR Manny Ramirez 1.00 2.50
MT Mark Teixeira 1.00 2.50
NM Nick Markakis UPD 1.00 2.50
PA Jonathan Papelbon UPD 2.00 5.00
PE Mike Pelfrey UPD 1.00 2.50
PF Prince Fielder UPD 1.50 4.00
PM Pedro Martinez .60 1.50
PU Albert Pujols 2.50 6.00
RC Ronny Cedeno UPD .40 1.00
RH Rich Harden .40 1.00
RM Russell Martin UPD .60 1.50
RZ Ryan Zimmerman UPD 2.00 5.00
SD Stephen Drew UPD 1.00 2.50
SG Shawn Green .40 1.00
SM John Smoltz 1.00 2.50
SO Scott Olsen UPD .40 1.00
SW Jeremy Sowers UPD .40 1.00
TG Tony Gwynn Jr. UPD .40 1.00
TH Torii Hunter .40 1.00
TI Tadahito Iguchi .40 1.00
WA Willy Aybar UPD .40 1.00
WR David Wright 1.50 4.00

2006 Upper Deck Star Attractions Swatches

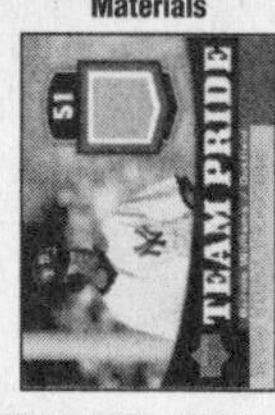

SER.1 ODDS 1:48 HOBBY, 1:288 RETAIL
AB Adrian Beltre Jsy 3.00 8.00
AH Aubrey Huff Jsy 3.00 8.00
AJ Andruw Jones Jsy 4.00 10.00
AP Andy Pettitte Jsy 3.00 8.00
AS Alfonso Soriano Jsy 3.00 8.00
BA Bobby Abreu Jsy 3.00 8.00
BZ Barry Zito Jsy 3.00 8.00
CB Carlos Beltran Jsy 3.00 8.00
CD Carlos Delgado Jsy 3.00 8.00
CJ Chipper Jones Jsy 4.00 10.00
CL Carlos Lee Jsy 3.00 8.00
CS Curt Schilling Jsy 4.00 10.00
DJ Derek Jeter Jsy 10.00 25.00
DL Derrek Lee Jsy 3.00 8.00
DO David Ortiz Jsy 4.00 10.00
DW Dontrelle Willis Jsy 3.00 8.00
EG Eric Gagne Jsy 3.00 8.00
FT Frank Thomas Jsy 4.00 10.00
GA Garret Anderson Jsy 3.00 8.00
GM Greg Maddux Jsy 4.00 10.00
GR Khalil Greene Jsy 4.00 10.00
GS Gary Sheffield Jsy 3.00 8.00
GU Jose Guillen Jsy 3.00 8.00
JB Josh Beckett Jsy 3.00 8.00
JC Jose Contreras Jsy 3.00 8.00
JD Johnny Damon Jsy 4.00 10.00
JE Jim Edmonds Jsy 3.00 8.00
JG Jason Giambi Jsy 3.00 8.00
JJ Jacque Jones Jsy 3.00 8.00
JL Javy Lopez Jsy 3.00 8.00
JM Joe Mauer Jsy 4.00 10.00
JP Jorge Posada Jsy 4.00 10.00
JR Jose Reyes Jsy 3.00 8.00
JS Jason Schmidt Jsy 3.00 8.00
KG Ken Griffey Jr. Jsy 6.00 15.00
KW Kerry Wood Jsy 3.00 8.00
LB Lance Berkman Jsy 3.00 8.00
MM Mark Mulder Jsy 3.00 8.00
MO Magglio Ordonez Jsy 3.00 8.00
MP Mark Prior Jsy 3.00 8.00
MR Manny Ramirez Jsy 4.00 10.00
MT Mark Teixeira Jsy 4.00 10.00
PM Pedro Martinez Jsy 4.00 10.00
PU Albert Pujols Jsy 6.00 15.00
RH Rich Harden Jsy 3.00 8.00
SG Shawn Green Jsy 3.00 8.00
SM John Smoltz Jsy 4.00 10.00
TH Torii Hunter Jsy 3.00 8.00
TI Tadahito Iguchi Jsy 4.00 10.00
WR David Wright Jsy 4.00 10.00

2006 Upper Deck Team Pride

SER.1 ODDS 1:6 HOBBY, 1:12 RETAIL
*GOLD: .6X TO 1.5X BASIC
FIVE #'d INSERTS PER SER.1 HOBBY BOX
GOLD PRINT RUN 699 SERIAL #'d SETS
AH Aubrey Huff .50 1.25
AJ Andruw Jones .50 1.25
AP Albert Pujols 3.00 8.00
BA Bobby Abreu .50 1.25
BW Bernie Williams .75 2.00
BZ Barry Zito .50 1.25
CC C.C. Sabathia .75 2.00
CD Carlos Delgado .50 1.25
CJ Chipper Jones 1.25 3.00
CK Casey Kotchman .50 1.25
CS Curt Schilling .75 2.00
DJ Derek Jeter 3.00 8.00
DO David Ortiz .75 2.00
DW Dontrelle Willis .50 1.25
EC Eric Chavez .50 1.25
EG Eric Gagne .50 1.25
FT Frank Thomas 1.25 3.00
GA Garret Anderson .50 1.25
GM Greg Maddux 2.00 5.00
GR Khalil Greene .50 1.25
IR Ivan Rodriguez .75 2.00
JB Jeff Bagwell .75 2.00
JD Johnny Damon .75 2.00
JE Jim Edmonds .75 2.00
JM Jamie Moyer .50 1.25
JP Jorge Posada .75 2.00
JR Jose Reyes .75 2.00
JS John Smoltz 1.25 3.00
JT Jim Thome .75 2.00
JV Jose Vidro .50 1.25
KF Keith Foulke .50 1.25
KG Ken Griffey Jr. 2.00 5.00
KW Kerry Wood .50 1.25
LC Luis Castillo .50 1.25
LG Luis Gonzalez .50 1.25
LO Mike Lowell .50 1.25
MA Joe Mauer 1.25 3.00
ME Morgan Ensberg .50 1.25
ML Mike Lieberthal .50 1.25
MP Mark Prior .75 2.00
MS Mike Sweeney .50 1.25
MY Michael Young .75 2.00
NJ Nick Johnson .50 1.25
PE Andy Pettitte .75 2.00
RB Rocco Baldelli .50 1.25
RH Rich Harden .50 1.25
RK Ryan Klesko .50 1.25
SC Sean Casey .50 1.25
TH Trevor Hoffman .75 2.00
VA Jason Varitek 1.25 3.00

2006 Upper Deck Team Pride Materials

SER.1 ODDS 1:48 HOBBY, 1:288 RETAIL
AH Aubrey Huff Jsy 3.00 8.00
AJ Andruw Jones Jsy 4.00 10.00
AP Albert Pujols Jsy 6.00 15.00
BA Bobby Abreu Jsy 3.00 8.00
BW Bernie Williams Jsy 4.00 10.00
BZ Barry Zito Jsy 3.00 8.00
CC C.C. Sabathia Jsy 3.00 8.00
CD Carlos Delgado Jsy 3.00 8.00
CJ Chipper Jones Jsy 4.00 10.00
CK Casey Kotchman Jsy 3.00 8.00
CS Curt Schilling Jsy 4.00 10.00
DJ Derek Jeter Jsy 10.00 25.00
DO David Ortiz Jsy 4.00 10.00
DW Dontrelle Willis Jsy 3.00 8.00
EC Eric Chavez Jsy 3.00 8.00
EG Eric Gagne Jsy 3.00 8.00
FT Frank Thomas Jsy 4.00 10.00
GA Garret Anderson Jsy 3.00 8.00
GM Greg Maddux Jsy 4.00 10.00
GR Khalil Greene Jsy 4.00 10.00
IR Ivan Rodriguez Jsy 4.00 10.00
JB Jeff Bagwell Jsy 4.00 10.00
JD Johnny Damon Jsy 4.00 10.00
JE Jim Edmonds Jsy 3.00 8.00
JM Jamie Moyer Jsy 3.00 8.00
JP Jorge Posada Jsy 4.00 10.00
JR Jose Reyes Jsy 3.00 8.00
JS John Smoltz Jsy 4.00 10.00
JT Jim Thome Jsy 4.00 10.00
JV Jose Vidro Jsy 3.00 8.00
KF Keith Foulke Jsy 3.00 8.00
KG Ken Griffey Jr. Jsy 6.00 15.00
KW Kerry Wood Jsy 3.00 8.00
LC Luis Castillo Jsy 3.00 8.00
LG Luis Gonzalez Jsy 3.00 8.00
LO Mike Lowell Jsy 3.00 8.00
MA Joe Mauer Jsy 4.00 10.00
ME Morgan Ensberg Jsy 3.00 8.00
ML Mike Lieberthal Jsy 3.00 8.00
MP Mark Prior Jsy 3.00 8.00
MS Mike Sweeney Jsy 3.00 8.00
MY Michael Young Jsy 3.00 8.00
NJ Nick Johnson Jsy 3.00 8.00
PE Andy Pettitte Jsy 4.00 10.00
RB Rocco Baldelli Jsy 3.00 8.00
RH Rich Harden Jsy 3.00 8.00
RK Ryan Klesko Jsy 3.00 8.00
SC Sean Casey Jsy 3.00 8.00
TH Trevor Hoffman Jsy 3.00 8.00
VA Jason Varitek Jsy 4.00 10.00

2006 Upper Deck UD Game Materials

SER.1 ODDS 1:24 HOBBY, 1:24 RETAIL
SER.2 GU ODDS 1:24 H, RANDOM IN RETAIL
SP INFO PROVIDED BY UPPER DECK
SER.1 PATCH ODDS 1:288 H, 1:1500 R
SER.2 PATCH RANDOM IN HOBBY/RETAIL
SER.2 PATCH PRINT RUN 11 SETS
SER.2 PATCH PRINT RUN PROVIDED BY UD
NO PATCH PRICING DUE TO SCARCITY
AB Adrian Beltre Bat S2 3.00 8.00
AD Adam Dunn Jsy S2 3.00 8.00
AJ Andruw Jones Pants S1 4.00 10.00
AP1 Andy Pettitte Jsy S1 4.00 10.00
AP2 Albert Pujols Pants S1 6.00 15.00
AS Alfonso Soriano Jsy S1 3.00 8.00
BA Bobby Abreu Jsy S2 3.00 8.00
BI Craig Biggio Jsy S2 4.00 10.00
BR Brian Roberts Jsy S1 3.00 8.00
BZ Barry Zito Jsy S2 3.00 8.00
CB Carlos Beltran Jsy S2 3.00 8.00
CD Carlos Delgado Jsy S2 3.00 8.00
CJ Chipper Jones Pants S1 4.00 10.00
CL Carlos Lee Jsy S2 3.00 8.00
CP Corey Patterson Jsy S1 3.00 8.00
CS Curt Schilling Jsy S1 4.00 10.00
DJ1 Derek Jeter Jsy S1 8.00 20.00
DJ2 Derek Jeter Jsy S2 8.00 20.00
DL Derrek Lee Pants S1 4.00 10.00
DO David Ortiz Jsy S2 4.00 10.00
DW Dontrelle Willis Jsy S1 3.00 8.00
EC Eric Chavez Jsy S1 3.00 8.00
EG Eric Gagne Jsy S1 3.00 8.00
FT Frank Thomas Jsy S1 4.00 10.00
GA Garrett Atkins Jsy S2 3.00 8.00
GM Greg Maddux Jsy S1 4.00 10.00
GR Khalil Greene Jsy S2 3.00 8.00
GS Gary Sheffield Jsy S2 3.00 8.00
HA Travis Hafner Jsy S2 3.00 8.00
HB Hank Blalock Jsy S2 3.00 8.00
IR Ivan Rodriguez Jsy S1 4.00 10.00
JB1 Jeff Bagwell Pants S1 4.00 10.00
JB2 Josh Beckett Jsy S2 3.00 8.00
JD1 Johnny Damon Jsy S1 4.00 10.00
JD2 Johnny Damon Jsy S2 4.00 10.00
JE Jim Edmonds Jsy S1 3.00 8.00
JG Jason Giambi Jsy S1 3.00 8.00
JJ Jacque Jones Jsy S1 3.00 8.00
JL Javy Lopez Jsy S2 3.00 8.00
JM Joe Mauer Jsy S2 4.00 10.00
JP Jake Peavy Jsy S1 3.00 8.00
JR Jose Reyes Jsy S2 3.00 8.00
JS Johan Santana Pants S1 4.00 10.00
JT Jim Thome Jsy S1 4.00 10.00
JV Jason Varitek Jsy S2 4.00 10.00
KG1 Ken Griffey Jr. Jsy S1 6.00 15.00
KG2 Ken Griffey Jr. Jsy S2 6.00 15.00
KW Kerry Wood Jsy S2 3.00 8.00
MC Miguel Cabrera Pants S1 4.00 10.00
MM Mike Mussina Pants S2 4.00 10.00
MO Magglio Ordonez Jsy S2 3.00 8.00
MP1 Mike Piazza Jsy S1 4.00 10.00
MP2 Mike Piazza Bat S2 4.00 10.00
MR Manny Ramirez Jsy S1 4.00 10.00
MT Mark Teixeira Jsy S1 4.00 10.00
MY Michael Young Jsy S2 3.00 8.00
PF Prince Fielder Jsy S2 4.00 10.00
PK Paul Konerko Jsy S2 3.00 8.00
PM Pedro Martinez Pants S1 4.00 10.00
PO Jorge Posada Jsy S1 4.00 10.00
PR Mark Prior Jsy S1 3.00 8.00
RC Roger Clemens Jsy S1 6.00 15.00
RF Rafael Furcal Jsy S1 3.00 8.00
RH1 Roy Halladay Jsy S1 3.00 8.00
RH2 Ryan Howard Jsy S2 10.00 25.00
RJ R.Johnson Jsy SP S1
RO Roy Oswalt Jsy S2 3.00 8.00
RP Rafael Palmeiro Jsy S1 4.00 10.00
RW Rickie Weeks Jsy S2 3.00 8.00
RZ Ryan Zimmerman Jsy S2 6.00 15.00
SC Sean Casey Jsy S2 3.00 8.00
SI Grady Sizemore Jsy S2 4.00 10.00
SM John Smoltz Jsy S1 4.00 10.00
SR Scott Rolen Jsy S1 4.00 10.00
TE Miguel Tejada Pants S1 3.00 8.00
TG Tom Glavine Jsy S2 4.00 10.00
TH Todd Helton Jsy S2 4.00 10.00
TI Tadahito Iguchi Jsy S2 3.00 8.00
VG Vladimir Guerrero Jsy S1 4.00 10.00
VM Victor Martinez Jsy S2 3.00 8.00
WR David Wright Pants S1 4.00 10.00

2006 Upper Deck WBC Collection Jersey

SER.2 GU ODDS 1:24 H, RANDOM IN RETAIL
SER.2 PATCH RANDOM IN HOBBY/RETAIL
PATCH PRINT RUN 8 SETS
PATCH PRINT RUN PROVIDED BY UD
NO PATCH PRICING DUE TO SCARCITY
AI Akinori Iwamura 20.00 50.00
AJ Andruw Jones 8.00 20.00
AP Albert Pujols 15.00 40.00
AR Alex Rodriguez 20.00 50.00
AS Alfonso Soriano 6.00 15.00
CB Carlos Beltran 6.00 15.00
CD Carlos Delgado 6.00 15.00
CH Chin-Lung Hu 50.00 100.00
CL Carlos Lee 4.00 10.00
DL Derrek Lee 6.00 15.00
DM Daisuke Matsuzaka 100.00 200.00
DO David Ortiz 10.00 25.00
EB Erik Bedard 6.00 15.00
EP Eduardo Paret 10.00 25.00
FC Frederich Cepeda 10.00 25.00
FG Freddy Garcia 6.00 15.00
FR Jeff Francoeur 15.00 40.00
GL Guangbiao Liu 6.00 15.00
GY Guogan Yang 6.00 15.00
HS Chia-Hsien Hseih 40.00 80.00
HT Hitoshi Tamura 30.00 60.00
IR Ivan Rodriguez 8.00 20.00
IS Ichiro Suzuki 125.00 250.00
JB Jason Bay 6.00 15.00
JD Johnny Damon 6.00 15.00
JF Jeff Francis 6.00 15.00
JG Jason Grilli 4.00 10.00
JH Justin Huber 6.00 15.00
JL Jong Beom Lee 6.00 15.00
JM Justin Morneau 8.00 20.00
JP Jin Man Park 6.00 15.00
JS Johan Santana 10.00 25.00
JV Jason Varitek 10.00 25.00
KG Ken Griffey Jr. 20.00 50.00
KU Koji Uehara 30.00 60.00
MC Miguel Cabrera 6.00 15.00
ME Michel Enriquez 10.00 25.00
MF Maikel Folch 10.00 25.00
MK Munenori Kawasaki 20.00 50.00
MO Michihiro Ogasawara 20.00 50.00
MP Mike Piazza 20.00 50.00
MS Min Han Son 6.00 15.00
MT Mark Teixeira 6.00 15.00
NM Nobuhiko Matasunaka 30.00 60.00
OP Oliver Perez 4.00 10.00
PE Ariel Pestano 10.00 25.00
PL Pedro Lazo 10.00 25.00
RC Roger Clemens 12.50 30.00
SW Shunsuke Watanabe 30.00 60.00
TC Tai-San Chang 10.00 25.00
TE Miguel Tejada 6.00 15.00
TN Tsuyoshi Nishioka 30.00 60.00
TW Tsuyoshi Wada 30.00 60.00
VC Vinny Castilla 6.00 15.00
VM Victor Martinez 6.00 15.00
WL Wei-Chu Lin 75.00 150.00
WP Wei-Lun Pan 10.00 25.00
WW Wei Wang 6.00 15.00
YG Yuliesky Gourriel 15.00 40.00
YM Yunieski Maya 10.00 25.00

2007 Upper Deck

This 1024-card set was issued over two series. In addition, a 20-card Rookie Exchange set was also produced and numbered sequentially at the beginning of the second series. The first series was released in March, 2007 and the second series was released in June, 2007. The cards were released in both hobby and retail packs. The hobby packs contained 15 cards per pack which came 16 packs to a box and 12 boxes to a case. Cards numbered 1-50 and 501-520 are rookie subsets while cards numbered 471-500 are checklist cards. There was a Rookie Exchange card for cards 501-520 which was redeemable until February 27, 2010. The rest of the set is sequenced alphabetically by what team the player featured was playing for when the individual series went to press.

COMPLETE SET (1020) 200.00 300.00
COMP.SET w/o RC EXCH (1000) 120.00 200.00
COMP.SER.1 w/o RC EXCH (500) 40.00 80.00
COMP.SER.2 w/o RC EXCH (500) 80.00 120.00
COMMON CARD (1-1020) .15 .40
COMMON ROOKIE .30 .75
COMMON ROOKIE (501-520) 1.00 2.50
1-500 ISSUED IN SERIES 1 PACKS
501-1020 ISSUED IN SERIES 2 PACKS
MATSUZAKA JSY RANDOMLY INSERTED
NO MATSUZAKA JSY PRICING AVAILABLE
OVERALL PLATE SER.1 ODDS 1:192 H
OVERALL PLATE SER.2 ODDS 1:96 H
PLATE PRINT RUN 1 SET PER COLOR
BLACK-CYAN-MAGENTA-YELLOW ISSUED
NO PLATE PRICING DUE TO SCARCITY
ROOKIE EXCH APPX. 1-2 PER CASE
ROOKIE EXCH DEADLINE 02/27/2010
1 Doug Slaten RC .30 .75
2 Miguel Montero (RC) .30 .75
3 Brian Burres (RC) .30 .75
4 Devern Hansack RC .30 .75
5 David Murphy (RC) .30 .75
6 Jose Reyes RC .30 .75
7 Scott Moore (RC) .30 .75
8 Josh Fields (RC) .30 .75
9 Chris Stewart RC .30 .75
10 Jerry Owens (RC) .30 .75
11 Ryan Sweeney (RC) .30 .75
12 Kevin Kouzmanoff (RC) .30 .75
13 Jeff Baker (RC) .30 .75
14 Justin Hampson (RC) .30 .75
15 Jeff Salazar (RC) .30 .75
16 Alvin Colina RC .75 2.00
17 Troy Tulowitzki (RC) 2.00 5.00
18 Andrew Miller RC .75 2.00
19 Mike Rabelo RC .30 .75
20 Jose Diaz (RC) .30 .75
21 Angel Sanchez RC .30 .75
22 Ryan Braun RC .30 .75
23 Delwyn Young (RC) .30 .75
24 Drew Anderson RC .30 .75
25 Dennis Sarfate (RC) .30 .75
26 Vinny Rottino (RC) .30 .75
27 Glen Perkins (RC) .30 .75
28 Alexi Casilla RC .50 1.25
29 Philip Humber (RC) .30 .75
30 Andy Cannizaro RC .30 .75
31 Jeremy Brown .15 .40
32 Sean Henn (RC) .30 .75
33 Brian Rogers .15 .40
34 Carlos Maldonado (RC) .30 .75
35 Juan Morillo (RC) .30 .75
36 Fred Lewis (RC) .50 1.25
37 Patrick Misch (RC) .30 .75
38 Billy Sadler (RC) .30 .75
39 Ryan Feierabend (RC) .30 .75
40 Cesar Jimenez RC .30 .75
41 Oswaldo Navarro RC .30 .75
42 Travis Chick (RC) .30 .75
43 Delmon Young (RC) .75 2.00
44 Shawn Riggans (RC) .30 .75
45 Brian Stokes (RC) .30 .75
46 Juan Salas (RC) .30 .75
47 Joaquin Arias (RC) .30 .75
48 Adam Lind (RC) .30 .75
49 Beltran Perez (RC) .30 .75
50 Brett Campbell RC .30 .75
51 Brian Roberts .15 .40
52 Miguel Tejada .25 .60
53 Brandon Fahey .15 .40
54 Jay Gibbons .15 .40
55 Corey Patterson .15 .40
56 Nick Markakis .40 1.00
57 Ramon Hernandez .15 .40
58 Kris Benson .15 .40
59 Adam Loewen .15 .40
60 Erik Bedard .15 .40
61 Chris Ray .15 .40
62 Chris Britton .15 .40
63 Daniel Cabrera .15 .40
64 Sendy Rleal .15 .40
65 Manny Ramirez .40 1.00
66 David Ortiz .25 .60
67 Gabe Kapler .15 .40
68 Alex Cora .15 .40
69 Dustin Pedroia .50 1.25
70 Trot Nixon .15 .40
71 Doug Mirabelli .15 .40
72 Mark Loretta .15 .40
73 Curt Schilling .25 .60
74 Jonathan Papelbon .40 1.00
75 Tim Wakefield .15 .40
76 Jon Lester .40 1.00
77 Craig Hansen .15 .40
78 Keith Foulke .15 .40
79 Jermaine Dye .15 .40
80 Jim Thome .25 .60
81 Tadahito Iguchi .15 .40
82 Rob Mackowiak .15 .40
83 Brian Anderson .15 .40
84 Juan Uribe .15 .40
85 A.J. Pierzynski .15 .40
86 Alex Cintron .15 .40
87 Jon Garland .15 .40
88 Jose Contreras .15 .40
89 Neal Cotts .15 .40
90 Bobby Jenks .15 .40
91 Mike MacDougal .15 .40
92 Javier Vazquez .15 .40
93 Travis Hafner .15 .40
94 Jhonny Peralta .15 .40
95 Ryan Garko .15 .40
96 Victor Martinez .25 .60
97 Hector Luna .15 .40
98 Casey Blake .15 .40
99 Jason Michaels .15 .40
100 Shin-Soo Choo .25 .60
101 C.C. Sabathia .25 .60
102 Paul Byrd .15 .40
103 Jeremy Sowers .15 .40
104 Cliff Lee .25 .60
105 Rafael Betancourt .15 .40
106 Francisco Cruceta .15 .40
107 Sean Casey .15 .40
108 Brandon Inge .15 .40
109 Placido Polanco .15 .40
110 Omar Infante .15 .40
111 Ivan Rodriguez .25 .60
112 Magglio Ordonez .25 .60
113 Craig Monroe .15 .40
114 Marcus Thames .15 .40
115 Justin Verlander .50 1.25
116 Todd Jones .15 .40
117 Kenny Rogers .15 .40
118 Joel Zumaya .25 .60
119 Jeremy Bonderman .15 .40
120 Nate Robertson .15 .40
121 Mark Teahen .15 .40
122 Ryan Shealy .15 .40
123 Mitch Maier RC .30 .75
124 Doug Mientkiewicz .15 .40
125 Mark Grudzielanek .15 .40
126 Shane Costa .15 .40
127 John Buck .15 .40
128 Reggie Sanders .15 .40
129 Mike Sweeney .15 .40
130 Mark Redman .15 .40
131 Todd Wellemeyer .15 .40
132 Scott Elarton .15 .40
133 Ambiorix Burgos .15 .40
134 Joe Nelson .15 .40
135 Howie Kendrick .15 .40
136 Chone Figgins .15 .40
137 Orlando Cabrera .15 .40
138 Maicer Izturis .15 .40
139 Jose Molina .15 .40
140 Vladimir Guerrero .40 1.00
141 Darin Erstad .15 .40
142 Juan Rivera .15 .40
143 Jered Weaver .25 .60
144 John Lackey .15 .40
145 Joe Saunders .15 .40
146 Bartolo Colon .15 .40
147 Scot Shields .15 .40
148 Francisco Rodriguez .25 .60
149 Justin Morneau .40 1.00
150 Jason Bartlett .15 .40
151 Luis Castillo .15 .40
152 Nick Punto .15 .40
153 Shannon Stewart .15 .40
154 Michael Cuddyer .15 .40
155 Jason Kubel .15 .40
156 Joe Mauer .40 1.00
157 Francisco Liriano .40 1.00
158 Joe Nathan .15 .40
159 Dennys Reyes .15 .40
160 Brad Radke .15 .40
161 Boof Bonser .15 .40
162 Juan Rincon .15 .40
163 Derek Jeter 1.00 2.50
164 Jason Giambi .15 .40
165 Robinson Cano .40 1.00
166 Andy Phillips .15 .40
167 Bobby Abreu .15 .40
168 Gary Sheffield .15 .40
169 Bernie Williams .25 .60
170 Melky Cabrera .15 .40
171 Mike Mussina .25 .60
172 Chien-Ming Wang .25 .60
173 Mariano Rivera .40 1.00
174 Scott Proctor .15 .40
175 Jaret Wright .15 .40
176 Kyle Farnsworth .15 .40
177 Eric Chavez .15 .40
178 Bobby Crosby .15 .40
179 Frank Thomas .40 1.00
180 Dan Johnson .15 .40
181 Marco Scutaro .15 .40
182 Nick Swisher .40 1.00
183 Milton Bradley .15 .40
184 Jay Payton .15 .40
185 Joe Blanton .15 .40
186 Barry Zito .15 .40
187 Rich Harden .15 .40
188 Esteban Loaiza .15 .40
189 Huston Street .15 .40
190 Chad Gaudin .15 .40
191 Richie Sexson .15 .40
192 Yuniesky Betancourt .15 .40
193 Willie Bloomquist .15 .40
194 Ben Broussard .15 .40
195 Kenji Johjima .40 1.00
196 Ichiro Suzuki .60 1.50
197 Raul Ibanez .25 .60
198 Chris Snelling .15 .40
199 Felix Hernandez .40 1.00
200 Cha-Seung Baek .15 .40
201 Joel Pineiro .15 .40
202 Julio Mateo .15 .40
203 J.J. Putz .15 .40
204 Rafael Soriano .15 .40
205 Jorge Cantu .15 .40
206 B.J. Upton .15 .40
207 Ty Wigginton .15 .40
208 Greg Norton .15 .40
209 Dioner Navarro .15 .40
210 Carl Crawford .25 .60
211 Jonny Gomes .15 .40
212 Damon Hollins .15 .40
213 Scott Kazmir .25 .60
214 Casey Fossum .15 .40
215 Ruddy Lugo .15 .40
216 James Shields .15 .40
217 Tyler Walker .15 .40
218 Shawn Camp .15 .40
219 Mark Teixeira .40 1.00
220 Hank Blalock .15 .40
221 Ian Kinsler .25 .60
222 Jerry Hairston Jr. .15 .40
223 Gerald Laird .15 .40
224 Carlos Lee .15 .40
225 Gary Matthews .15 .40
226 Mark DeRosa .15 .40
227 Kip Wells .15 .40
228 Akinori Otsuka .15 .40
229 Vicente Padilla .15 .40
230 John Koronka .15 .40
231 Kevin Millwood .15 .40
232 Wes Littleton .15 .40
233 Troy Glaus .15 .40

234 Lyle Overbay .15 .40
235 Aaron Hill .15 .40
236 John McDonald .15 .40
237 Bengie Molina .15 .40
238 Vernon Wells .15 .40
239 Reed Johnson .15 .40
240 Frank Catalanotto .15 .40
241 Roy Halladay .40 1.00
242 B.J. Ryan .15 .40
243 Gustavo Chacin .15 .40
244 Scott Downs .15 .40
245 Casey Janssen .15 .40
246 Justin Speier .15 .40
247 Stephen Drew .15 .40
248 Conor Jackson .15 .40
249 Orlando Hudson .15 .40
250 Chad Tracy .15 .40
251 Johnny Estrada .15 .40
252 Luis Gonzalez .15 .40
253 Eric Byrnes .15 .40
254 Carlos Quentin .15 .40
255 Brandon Webb .25 .60
256 Claudio Vargas .15 .40
257 Juan Cruz .15 .40
258 Jorge Julio .15 .40
259 Luis Vizcaino .15 .40
260 Livan Hernandez .15 .40
261 Chipper Jones .40 1.00
262 Edgar Renteria .15 .40
263 Adam LaRoche .15 .40
264 Willy Aybar .15 .40
265 Brian McCann .15 .40
266 Ryan Langerhans .15 .40
267 Jeff Francoeur .40 1.00
268 Matt Diaz .15 .40
269 Tim Hudson .25 .60
270 John Smoltz .40 1.00
271 Oscar Villarreal .15 .40
272 Horacio Ramirez .15 .40
273 Bob Wickman .15 .40
274 Chad Paronto .15 .40
275 Derrek Lee .15 .40
276 Ryan Theriot .15 .40
277 Cesar Izturis .15 .40
278 Ronny Cedeno .15 .40
279 Michael Barrett .15 .40
280 Juan Pierre .15 .40
281 Jacque Jones .15 .40
282 Matt Murton .15 .40
283 Carlos Zambrano .25 .60
284 Mark Prior .25 .60
285 Rich Hill .15 .40
286 Sean Marshall .15 .40
287 Ryan Dempster .15 .40
288 Ryan O'Malley .15 .40
289 Scott Hatteberg .15 .40
290 Brandon Phillips .15 .40
291 Edwin Encarnacion .15 .40
292 Rich Aurilia .15 .40
293 David Ross .15 .40
294 Ken Griffey Jr. .60 1.50
295 Ryan Freel .15 .40
296 Chris Denorfia .15 .40
297 Bronson Arroyo .15 .40
298 Aaron Harang .15 .40
299 Brandon Claussen .15 .40
300 Todd Coffey .15 .40
301 David Weathers .15 .40
302 Eric Milton .15 .40
303 Todd Helton .25 .60
304 Clint Barmes .15 .40
305 Kazuo Matsui .15 .40
306 Jamey Carroll .15 .40
307 Yorvit Torrealba .15 .40
308 Matt Holliday .40 1.00
309 Choo Freeman .15 .40
310 Brad Hawpe .15 .40
311 Jason Jennings .15 .40
312 Jeff Francis .15 .40
313 Josh Fogg .15 .40
314 Aaron Cook .15 .40
315 Ubaldo Jimenez (RC) 2.00 5.00
316 Manny Corpas .15 .40
317 Miguel Cabrera .40 1.00
318 Dan Uggla .25 .60
319 Hanley Ramirez .40 1.00
320 Wes Helms .15 .40
321 Miguel Olivo .15 .40
322 Jeremy Hermida .15 .40
323 Cody Ross .15 .40
324 Josh Willingham .15 .40
325 Dontrelle Willis .15 .40
326 Anibal Sanchez .15 .40
327 Josh Johnson .40 1.00
328 Jose Garcia RC .30 .75
329 Joe Borowski .15 .40
330 Taylor Tankersley .15 .40
331 Lance Berkman .25 .60
332 Craig Biggio .25 .60
333 Aubrey Huff .15 .40
334 Adam Everett .15 .40
335 Brad Ausmus .15 .40
336 Willy Taveras .15 .40
337 Luke Scott .15 .40
338 Chris Burke .15 .40
339 Roger Clemens .50 1.25
340 Andy Pettitte .25 .60
341 Brandon Backe .15 .40
342 Hector Gimenez (RC) .30 .75
343 Brad Lidge .15 .40
344 Dan Wheeler .15 .40
345 Nomar Garciaparra .40 1.00
346 Rafael Furcal .15 .40
347 Wilson Betemit .15 .40
348 Julio Lugo .15 .40
349 Russell Martin .15 .40
350 Andre Ethier .25 .60
351 Matt Kemp .25 .60
352 Kenny Lofton .15 .40
353 Brad Penny .15 .40
354 Derek Lowe .15 .40
355 Chad Billingsley .15 .40
356 Greg Maddux .60 1.50
357 Takashi Saito .15 .40
358 Jonathan Broxton .15 .40
359 Prince Fielder .25 .60
360 Rickie Weeks .25 .60
361 Bill Hall .15 .40
362 J.J. Hardy .15 .40
363 Jeff Cirillo .15 .40
364 Tony Gwynn Jr. .15 .40
365 Corey Hart .15 .40
366 Laynce Nix .15 .40
367 Doug Davis .15 .40
368 Ben Sheets .15 .40
369 Chris Capuano .15 .40
370 Dave Bush .15 .40
371 Derrick Turnbow .15 .40
372 Francisco Cordero .15 .40
373 Jose Reyes .25 .60
374 Carlos Delgado .15 .40
375 Julio Franco .15 .40
376 Jose Valentin .15 .40
377 Paul LoDuca .15 .40
378 Carlos Beltran .15 .40
379 Shawn Green .15 .40
380 Lastings Milledge .25 .60
381 Endy Chavez .15 .40
382 Pedro Martinez .25 .60
383 John Maine .15 .40
384 Orlando Hernandez .15 .40
385 Steve Trachsel .15 .40
386 Billy Wagner .15 .40
387 Ryan Howard .60 1.50
388 Chase Utley .40 1.00
389 Jimmy Rollins .25 .60
390 Chris Coste .15 .40
391 Jeff Conine .15 .40
392 Aaron Rowand .15 .40
393 Shane Victorino .15 .40
394 David Dellucci .15 .40
395 Cole Hamels .40 1.00
396 Jamie Moyer .15 .40
397 Ryan Madson .15 .40
398 Brett Myers .15 .40
399 Tom Gordon .15 .40
400 Geoff Geary .15 .40
401 Freddy Sanchez .15 .40
402 Xavier Nady .15 .40
403 Jose Castillo .15 .40
404 Joe Randa .15 .40
405 Jason Bay .25 .60
406 Chris Duffy .15 .40
407 Jose Bautista .25 .60
408 Ronny Paulino .15 .40
409 Ian Snell .15 .40
410 Zach Duke .15 .40
411 Tom Gorzelanny .15 .40
412 Shane Youman RC .30 .75
413 Mike Gonzalez .15 .40
414 Matt Capps .15 .40
415 Adrian Gonzalez .25 .60
416 Josh Barfield .15 .40
417 Todd Walker .15 .40
418 Khalil Greene .15 .40
419 Mike Piazza .40 1.00
420 Dave Roberts .15 .40
421 Mike Cameron .15 .40
422 Geoff Blum .15 .40
423 Jake Peavy .25 .60
424 Chris R. Young .15 .40
425 Woody Williams .15 .40
426 Clay Hensley .15 .40
427 Cla Meredith .15 .40
428 Trevor Hoffman .25 .60
429 Shea Hillenbrand .15 .40
430 Pedro Feliz .15 .40
431 Ray Durham .15 .40
432 Mark Sweeney .15 .40
433 Eliezer Alfonzo .15 .40
434 Moises Alou .15 .40
435 Steve Finley .15 .40
436 Todd Linden .15 .40
437 Jason Schmidt .15 .40
438 Matt Cain .25 .60
439 Noah Lowry .15 .40
440 Brad Hennessey .15 .40
441 Armando Benitez .15 .40
442 Jonathan Sanchez .15 .40
443 Albert Pujols 1.00 2.50
444 Ronnie Belliard .15 .40
445 David Eckstein .15 .40
446 Aaron Miles .15 .40
447 Yadier Molina .25 .60
448 Jim Edmonds .25 .60
449 Chris Duncan .15 .40
450 Juan Encarnacion .15 .40
451 Chris Carpenter .40 1.00
452 Jeff Suppan .15 .40
453 Jason Marquis .15 .40
454 Jeff Weaver .15 .40
455 Jason Isringhausen .15 .40
456 Braden Looper .15 .40
457 Ryan Zimmerman .25 .60
458 Nick Johnson .15 .40
459 Felipe Lopez .15 .40
460 Brian Schneider .15 .40
461 Alfonso Soriano .25 .60
462 Austin Kearns .15 .40
463 Ryan Church .15 .40
464 Alex Escobar .15 .40
465 Ramon Ortiz .15 .40
466 Tony Armas .15 .40
467 Michael O'Connor .15 .40
468 Chad Cordero .15 .40
469 Jon Rauch .15 .40
470 Pedro Astacio .15 .40
471 Miguel Tejada CL .25 .60
472 David Ortiz CL .25 .60
473 Jermaine Dye CL .15 .40
474 Travis Hafner CL .15 .40
475 Magglio Ordonez CL .25 .60
476 Mark Teahen CL .15 .40
477 Vladimir Guerrero CL .40 1.00
478 Justin Morneau CL .40 1.00
479 Derek Jeter CL 1.00 2.50
480 Nick Swisher CL .40 1.00
481 Ichiro Suzuki CL .60 1.50
482 Scott Kazmir CL .25 .60
483 Mark Teixeira CL .40 1.00
484 Vernon Wells CL .15 .40
485 Brandon Webb CL .25 .60
486 Andruw Jones CL .15 .40
487 Carlos Zambrano CL .25 .60
488 Adam Dunn CL .25 .60
489 Matt Holliday CL .40 1.00
490 Miguel Cabrera CL .40 1.00
491 Lance Berkman CL .25 .60
492 Nomar Garciaparra CL .40 1.00
493 Prince Fielder CL .25 .60
494 Carlos Beltran CL .15 .40
495 Ryan Howard CL .60 1.50
496 Jason Bay CL .25 .60
497 Adrian Gonzalez CL .25 .60
498 Matt Cain CL .25 .60
499 Albert Pujols CL 1.00 2.50
500 Ryan Zimmerman CL .25 .60
501a Daisuke Matsuzaka Suit RC 20.00 50.00
501b Daisuke Matsuzaka Throwing RC 6.00 15.00
501c Daisuke Matsuzaka Jsy/100
501d Daisuke Matsuzaka Ball/150
502 Kei Igawa RC 1.50 4.00
503 Akinori Iwamura RC 2.50 6.00
504 Alex Gordon RC 6.00 15.00
505 Matt Chico (RC) 1.00 2.50
506 John Danks RC 1.00 2.50
507 Elijah Dukes RC 1.00 2.50
508 Gustavo Molina RC 1.00 2.50
509 Joakim Soria RC 2.50 6.00
510 Jay Marshall RC 2.50 6.00
511 Travis Buck (RC) 1.00 2.50
512 Brandon Wood (RC) 1.00 2.50
513 Kevin Cameron RC 1.00 2.50
514 Jared Burton RC 2.50 6.00
515 Kory Casto (RC) 1.00 2.50
516 Joe Smith RC 1.00 2.50
517 Jose Garcia 1.00 2.50
518 Hunter Pence (RC) 6.00 15.00
519 Felix Pie (RC) 1.00 2.50
520 Zach Segovia (RC) 1.00 2.50
521 Randy Johnson .40 1.00
522 Brandon Lyon .15 .40
523 Robby Hammock .15 .40
524 Micah Owings (RC) .30 .75
525 Doug Davis .15 .40
526 Brian Barden RC .30 .75
527 Alberto Callaspo .15 .40
528 Stephen Drew .15 .40
529 Chris Young .15 .40
530 Edgar Gonzalez .15 .40
531 Brandon Medders .15 .40
532 Tony Pena .15 .40
533 Jose Valverde .15 .40
534 Chris Snyder .15 .40
535 Tony Clark .15 .40
536 Scott Hairston .15 .40
537 Jeff DaVanon .15 .40
538 Randy Johnson CL .40 1.00
539 Mark Redman .15 .40
540 Andruw Jones .15 .40
541 Rafael Soriano .15 .40
542 Scott Thorman .15 .40
543 Chipper Jones .40 1.00
544 Mike Gonzalez .15 .40
545 Lance Cormier .15 .40
546 Kyle Davies .15 .40
547 Mike Hampton .15 .40
548 Chuck James .15 .40
549 Macay McBride .15 .40
550 Tanyon Sturtze .15 .40
551 Tyler Yates .15 .40
552 Pete Orr .15 .40
553 Craig Wilson .15 .40
554 Chris Woodward .15 .40
555 Kelly Johnson .15 .40
556 Chipper Jones CL .40 1.00
557 Chad Bradford .15 .40
558 John Parrish .15 .40
559 Jeremy Guthrie .15 .40
560 Steve Trachsel .15 .40
561 Scott Williamson .15 .40
562 Jaret Wright .15 .40
563 Paul Bako .15 .40
564 Chris Gomez .15 .40
565 Melvin Mora .15 .40
566 Freddie Bynum .15 .40
567 Aubrey Huff .15 .40
568 Jay Payton .15 .40
569 Miguel Tejada .25 .60
570 Kurt Birkins .15 .40
571 Danys Baez .15 .40
572 Brian Roberts CL .15 .40
573 Josh Beckett .25 .60
574 Matt Clement .15 .40
575 Hideki Okajima RC 2.00 5.00
576 Javier Lopez .15 .40
577 Joel Pineiro .15 .40
578 J.C. Romero .15 .40
579 Kyle Snyder .15 .40
580 Julian Tavarez .15 .40
581 Mike Timlin .15 .40
582 Jason Varitek .40 1.00
583 Mike Lowell .15 .40
584 Kevin Youkilis .15 .40
585 Coco Crisp .15 .40
586 J.D. Drew .15 .40
587 Eric Hinske .15 .40
588 Wily Mo Pena .15 .40
589 Julio Lugo .15 .40
590 David Ortiz .25 .60
591 Manny Ramirez .40 1.00
592 Daisuke Matsuzaka CL 1.50 4.00
593 Curt Schilling .15 .40
594 Angel Guzman .15 .40
595 Bob Howry .15 .40
596 Ted Lilly .15 .40
597 Juan Mateo .15 .40
598 Wade Miller .15 .40
599 Carlos Zambrano .25 .60
600 Will Ohman .15 .40
601 Michael Wuertz .15 .40
602 Henry Blanco .15 .40
603 Aramis Ramirez .15 .40
604 Cliff Floyd .15 .40
605 Kerry Wood .15 .40
606 Alfonso Soriano .25 .60
607 Daryle Ward .15 .40
608 Jason Marquis .15 .40
609 Mark DeRosa .15 .40
610 Neal Cotts .15 .40
611 Derrek Lee .15 .40
612 Aramis Ramirez CL .15 .40
613 David Aardsma .15 .40
614 Mark Buehrle .25 .60
615 Nick Masset .15 .40
616 Andrew Sisco .15 .40
617 Matt Thornton .15 .40
618 Toby Hall .15 .40
619 Joe Crede .15 .40
620 Paul Konerko .25 .60
621 Darin Erstad .15 .40
622 Pablo Ozuna .15 .40
623 Scott Podsednik .15 .40
624 Jim Thome .25 .60
625 Jermaine Dye .15 .40
626 Jim Thome CL .25 .60
627 Adam Dunn .25 .60
628 Bill Bray .15 .40
629 Alex Gonzalez .15 .40
630 Josh Hamilton (RC) 4.00 10.00
631 Matt Belisle .15 .40
632 Rheal Cormier .15 .40
633 Kyle Lohse .15 .40
634 Eric Milton .15 .40
635 Kirk Saarloos .15 .40
636 Mike Stanton .15 .40
637 Javier Valentin .15 .40
638 Juan Castro .15 .40
639 Jeff Conine .15 .40
640 Jon Coutlangus (RC) .30 .75
641 Ken Griffey Jr. .60 1.50
642 Ken Griffey Jr. CL .60 1.50
643 Fernando Cabrera .15 .40
644 Fausto Carmona .15 .40
645 Jason Davis .15 .40
646 Aaron Fultz .15 .40
647 Roberto Hernandez .15 .40
648 Jake Westbrook .15 .40
649 Kelly Shoppach .15 .40
650 Josh Barfield .15 .40
651 Andy Marte .15 .40
652 Joe Inglett .15 .40
653 David Dellucci .15 .40
654 Joe Borowski .15 .40
655 Franklin Gutierrez .15 .40
656 Trot Nixon .15 .40
657 Grady Sizemore .25 .60
658 Mike Rouse .15 .40
659 Travis Hafner .15 .40
660 Victor Martinez .25 .60
661 C.C. Sabathia .25 .60
662 Grady Sizemore CL .25 .60
663 Jeremy Affeldt .15 .40
664 Taylor Buchholz .15 .40
665 Brian Fuentes .15 .40
666 LaTroy Hawkins .15 .40
667 Byung-Hyun Kim .15 .40
668 Brian Lawrence .15 .40
669 Rodrigo Lopez .15 .40
670 Jeff Francis .15 .40
671 Chris Ianetta .15 .40
672 Garrett Atkins .15 .40
673 Todd Helton .25 .60
674 Steve Finley .15 .40
675 John Mabry .15 .40
676 Willy Taveras .15 .40
677 Jason Hirsh .15 .40
678 Ramon Ramirez .15 .40
679 Matt Holliday .40 1.00
680 Todd Helton CL .25 .60
681 Roman Colon .15 .40
682 Chad Durbin .15 .40
683 Jason Grilli .15 .40
684 Wilfredo Ledezma .15 .40
685 Mike Maroth .15 .40
686 Jose Mesa .15 .40
687 Justin Verlander .50 1.25
688 Fernando Rodney .15 .40
689 Vance Wilson .15 .40
690 Carlos Guillen .15 .40
691 Neifi Perez .15 .40
692 Curtis Granderson .25 .60
693 Gary Sheffield .15 .40
694 Justin Verlander CL .50 1.25
695 Kevin Gregg .15 .40
696 Logan Kensing .15 .40
697 Randy Messenger .15 .40
698 Sergio Mitre .15 .40
699 Ricky Nolasco .15 .40
700 Scott Olsen .15 .40
701 Renyel Pinto .15 .40
702 Matt Treanor .15 .40
703 Alfredo Amezaga .15 .40
704 Aaron Boone .15 .40
705 Mike Jacobs .15 .40
706 Miguel Cabrera .40 1.00
707 Joe Borchard .15 .40
708 Jorge Julio .15 .40
709 Rick Vanden Hurk RC .30 .75
710 Lee Gardner (RC) .30 .75
711 Matt Lindstrom (RC) .30 .75
712 Henry Owens .15 .40
713 Hanley Ramirez .40 1.00
714 Alejandro De Aza RC .50 1.25
715 Hanley Ramirez CL .40 1.00
716 Dave Borkowski .15 .40
717 Jason Jennings .15 .40
718 Trever Miller .15 .40
719 Roy Oswalt .25 .60
720 Wandy Rodriguez .15 .40
721 Humberto Quintero .15 .40
722 Morgan Ensberg .15 .40
723 Mike Lamb .15 .40
724 Mark Loretta .15 .40
725 Jason Lane .15 .40
726 Carlos Lee .15 .40
727 Orlando Palmeiro .15 .40
728 Woody Williams .15 .40
729 Chad Qualls .15 .40
730 Lance Berkman .25 .60
731 Rick White .15 .40
732 Chris Sampson .15 .40
733 Carlos Lee CL .15 .40
734 Jorge De La Rosa .15 .40
735 Octavio Dotel .15 .40
736 Jimmy Gobble .15 .40
737 Zack Greinke .25 .60
738 Luke Hudson .15 .40
739 Gil Meche .15 .40
740 Joel Peralta .15 .40
741 Odalis Perez .15 .40
742 David Riske .15 .40
743 Jason LaRue .15 .40
744 Tony Pena .15 .40
745 Esteban German .15 .40
746 Ross Gload .15 .40
747 Emil Brown .15 .40
748 David DeJesus .15 .40
749 Brandon Duckworth .15 .40
750 Alex Gordon CL .50 1.25
751 Jered Weaver .25 .60
752 Vladimir Guerrero .40 1.00
753 Hector Carrasco .15 .40
754 Kelvim Escobar .15 .40
755 Darren Oliver .15 .40
756 Dustin Moseley .15 .40
757 Ervin Santana .15 .40
758 Mike Napoli .25 .60
759 Shea Hillenbrand .15 .40
760 Casey Kotchman .15 .40
761 Reggie Willits .15 .40
762 Robb Quinlan .15 .40
763 Garret Anderson .15 .40
764 Gary Matthews .15 .40
765 Justin Speier .15 .40
766 Jered Weaver CL .25 .60
767 Joe Beimel .15 .40
768 Yhency Brazoban .15 .40
769 Elmer Dessens .15 .40
770 Mark Hendrickson .15 .40
771 Hong-Chih Kuo .15 .40
772 Jason Schmidt .15 .40
773 Brett Tomko .15 .40
774 Randy Wolf .15 .40
775 Mike Liberthal .15 .40
776 Marlon Anderson .15 .40
777 Jeff Kent .15 .40
778 Ramon Martinez .15 .40
779 Olmedo Saenz .15 .40
780 Luis Gonzalez .15 .40
781 Juan Pierre .15 .40
782 Jason Repko .15 .40
783 Nomar Garciaparra .40 1.00
784 Wilson Valdez .15 .40
785 Jason Schmidt CL .15 .40
786 Greg Aquino .15 .40
787 Brian Shouse .15 .40
788 Jeff Suppan .15 .40
789 Carlos Villanueva .15 .40
790 Matt Wise .15 .40
791 Johnny Estrada .15 .40
792 Craig Counsell .15 .40
793 Tony Graffanino .15 .40
794 Corey Koskie .15 .40
795 Claudio Vargas .15 .40
796 Brady Clark .15 .40
797 Gabe Gross .15 .40
798 Geoff Jenkins .15 .40
799 Kevin Mench .15 .40
800 Bill Hall CL .15 .40
801 Sidney Ponson .15 .40
802 Jesse Crain .15 .40
803 Matt Guerrier .15 .40
804 Pat Neshek .25 .60
805 Ramon Ortiz .15 .40
806 Johan Santana .40 1.00
807 Carlos Silva .15 .40
808 Mike Redmond .15 .40
809 Jeff Cirillo .15 .40
810 Luis Rodriguez .15 .40
811 Lew Ford .15 .40
812 Torii Hunter .15 .40
813 Jason Tyner .15 .40
814 Rondell White .15 .40
815 Justin Morneau .40 1.00
816 Joe Mauer .40 1.00
817 Johan Santana CL .40 1.00
818 David Newhan .15 .40
819 Aaron Sele .15 .40
820 Ambiorix Burgos .15 .40
821 Pedro Feliciano .15 .40
822 Tom Glavine .25 .60
823 Aaron Heilman .15 .40
824 Guillermo Mota .15 .40
825 Jose Reyes .25 .60
826 Oliver Perez .15 .40
827 Duaner Sanchez .15 .40
828 Scott Schoeneweis .15 .40
829 Ramon Castro .15 .40
830 Damion Easley .15 .40
831 David Wright .60 1.50
832 Moises Alou .15 .40
833 Carlos Beltran .15 .40
834 Dave Williams .15 .40
835 David Wright CL .60 1.50
836 Brian Bruney .15 .40
837 Mike Myers .15 .40
838 Carl Pavano .15 .40
839 Andy Pettitte .25 .60
840 Luis Vizcaino .15 .40
841 Jorge Posada .25 .60
842 Miguel Cairo .15 .40
843 Doug Mientkiewicz .15 .40
844 Derek Jeter 1.00 2.50
845 Alex Rodriguez .60 1.50
846 Johnny Damon .25 .60
847 Hideki Matsui .40 1.00
848 Josh Phelps .15 .40
849 Phil Hughes (RC) 1.50 4.00
850 Roger Clemens .50 1.25
851 Jason Giambi CL .15 .40
852 Kiko Calero .15 .40
853 Justin Duchscherer .15 .40
854 Alan Embree .15 .40
855 Todd Walker .15 .40
856 Rich Harden .15 .40
857 Dan Haren .15 .40
858 Joe Kennedy .15 .40
859 Jason Kendall .15 .40
860 Adam Melhuse .15 .40
861 Mark Ellis .15 .40
862 Bobby Kielty .15 .40
863 Mark Kotsay .15 .40
864 Shannon Stewart .15 .40
865 Mike Piazza .40 1.00
866 Mike Piazza CL .40 1.00
867 Antonio Alfonseca .15 .40
868 Carlos Ruiz .15 .40
869 Adam Eaton .15 .40
870 Freddy Garcia .15 .40
871 Jon Lieber .15 .40
872 Matt Smith .15 .40
873 Rod Barajas .15 .40
874 Wes Helms .15 .40
875 Abraham Nunez .15 .40
876 Pat Burrell .15 .40
877 Jayson Werth .25 .60
878 Greg Dobbs .15 .40
879 Joseph Bisenius RC .30 .75
880 Michael Bourn (RC) .30 .75
881 Chase Utley .40 1.00
882 Ryan Howard .60 1.50
883 Chase Utley CL .40 1.00
884 Tony Armas .15 .40
885 Shawn Chacon .15 .40
886 John Grabow .15 .40
887 Paul Maholm .15 .40
888 Damaso Marte .15 .40
889 Salomon Torres .15 .40
890 Humberto Cota .15 .40
891 Ryan Doumit .15 .40
892 Adam LaRoche .15 .40
893 Jack Wilson .15 .40
894 Nate McLouth .15 .40
895 Brad Eldred .15 .40
896 Jonah Bayliss .15 .40
897 Juan Perez RC .30 .75
898 Jason Bay .25 .60
899 Adam LaRoche CL .15 .40
900 Doug Brocail .15 .40
901 Scott Cassidy .15 .40
902 Scott Linebrink .15 .40
903 Greg Maddux .60 1.50
904 Jake Peavy .15 .40
905 Mike Thompson .15 .40
906 David Wells .15 .40
907 Josh Bard .15 .40
908 Rob Bowen .15 .40
909 Marcus Giles .15 .40
910 Russell Branyan .15 .40
911 Jose Cruz .15 .40
912 Termel Sledge .15 .40
913 Trevor Hoffman .25 .60
914 Brian Giles .15 .40
915 Trevor Hoffman CL .25 .60
916 Vinnie Chulk .15 .40
917 Kevin Correia .15 .40
918 Tim Lincecum RC 5.00 12.00
919 Matt Morris .15 .40
920 Russ Ortiz .15 .40
921 Barry Zito .15 .40
922 Bengie Molina .15 .40
923 Rich Aurilia .15 .40
924 Omar Vizquel .25 .60
925 Jason Ellison .15 .40
926 Ryan Klesko .15 .40
927 Dave Roberts .15 .40
928 Randy Winn .15 .40
929 Barry Zito CL .15 .40
930 Miguel Batista .15 .40
931 Horacio Ramirez .15 .40
932 Chris Reitsma .15 .40
933 George Sherrill .15 .40
934 Jarrod Washburn .15 .40
935 Jeff Weaver .15 .40
936 Jake Woods .15 .40
937 Adrian Beltre .15 .40
938 Jose Lopez .15 .40
939 Ichiro Suzuki .60 1.50
940 Jose Vidro .15 .40
941 Jose Guillen .15 .40
942 Sean White RC .30 .75
943 Brandon Morrow RC 1.50 4.00
944 Felix Hernandez .40 1.00
945 Felix Hernandez CL .40 1.00
946 Randy Flores .15 .40
947 Ryan Franklin .15 .40
948 Kelvin Jimenez RC .30 .75
949 Tyler Johnson .15 .40
950 Mark Mulder .15 .40
951 Anthony Reyes .15 .40
952 Russ Springer .15 .40
953 Brad Thompson .15 .40
954 Adam Wainwright .25 .60
955 Kip Wells .15 .40
956 Gary Bennett .15 .40
957 Adam Kennedy .15 .40
958 Scott Rolen .25 .60
959 Scott Spiezio .15 .40
960 So Taguchi .15 .40
961 Preston Wilson .15 .40
962 Skip Schumaker .15 .40
963 Albert Pujols 1.00 2.50
964 Chris Carpenter .40 1.00
965 Chris Carpenter CL .40 1.00
966 Edwin Jackson .15 .40
967 Jae Kuk Ryu .15 .40
968 Jae Seo .15 .40
969 Jon Switzer .15 .40
970 Josh Paul .15 .40
971 Ben Zobrist .15 .40
972 Rocco Baldelli .15 .40
973 Scott Kazmir .25 .60
974 Carl Crawford .25 .60
975 Delmon Young CL .25 .60
976 Bruce Chen .15 .40
977 Joaquin Benoit .15 .40
978 Scott Feldman .25 .60
979 Eric Gagne .15 .40
980 Kameron Loe .15 .40
981 Brandon McCarthy .15 .40
982 Robinson Tejeda .15 .40
983 C.J. Wilson .15 .40
984 Mark Teixeira .40 1.00
985 Michael Young .25 .60
986 Kenny Lofton .15 .40
987 Brad Wilkerson .15 .40
988 Nelson Cruz .25 .60
989 Sammy Sosa .40 1.00
990 Michael Young CL .25 .60
991 Vernon Wells .15 .40
992 Matt Stairs .15 .40
993 Jeremy Accardo .15 .40
994 A.J. Burnett .25 .60
995 Jason Frasor .15 .40
996 Roy Halladay .40 1.00
997 Shaun Marcum .15 .40
998 Tomo Ohka .15 .40
999 Josh Towers .15 .40
1000 Gregg Zaun .15 .40
1001 Royce Clayton .15 .40
1002 Jason Smith .15 .40
1003 Alex Rios .25 .60
1004 Frank Thomas .40 1.00
1005 Roy Halladay CL .40 1.00
1006 Jesus Flores RC .30 .75
1007 Dmitri Young .15 .40
1008 Ray King .15 .40
1009 Micah Bowie .15 .40
1010 Shawn Hill .15 .40
1011 John Patterson .15 .40
1012 Levale Speigner RC .30 .75
1013 Ryan Wagner .15 .40
1014 Jerome Williams .15 .40
1015 Ryan Zimmerman .25 .60
1016 Cristian Guzman .15 .40
1017 Nook Logan .15 .40
1018 Chris Snelling .15 .40
1019 Ronnie Belliard .15 .40
1020 Nick Johnson CL .15 .40

2007 Upper Deck Gold

*GOLD: 3X TO 8X BASIC
*GOLD RC: 2.5X TO 6X BASIC RC
STATED ODDS 1:16 HOBBY
RANDOM INSERTS IN RETAIL PACKS
STATED PRINT RUN 75 SER.#'d SETS
18 Andrew Miller 10.00 25.00
163 Derek Jeter 10.00 25.00
172 Chien-Ming Wang 10.00 25.00
196 Ichiro Suzuki 6.00 15.00
443 Albert Pujols 10.00 25.00
479 Derek Jeter CL 10.00 25.00
481 Ichiro Suzuki CL 6.00 15.00
499 Albert Pujols CL 10.00 25.00

2007 Upper Deck 1989 Reprints

COMPLETE SET (26) 20.00 50.00
STATED ODDS 1:4 HOBBY
AK Al Kaline 1.25 3.00
BF Bob Feller .75 2.00
BR Babe Ruth 3.00 8.00
CA Rod Carew .75 2.00
CF Carlton Fisk .75 2.00
CM Christy Mathewson 1.25 3.00

CS Casey Stengel	.75	2.00
CY Cy Young	1.25	3.00
DR Don Drysdale	.75	2.00
FR Frank Robinson	.75	2.00
GE Lou Gehrig	2.50	6.00
HW Honus Wagner	1.25	3.00
JB Johnny Bench	1.25	3.00
JF Jimmie Foxx	1.25	3.00
JR Jackie Robinson	1.25	3.00
LG Lefty Grove	.75	2.00
MO Mel Ott	.75	2.00
RC Roy Campanella	1.25	3.00
RH Rogers Hornsby	.75	2.00
RJ Reggie Jackson	.75	2.00
RO Brooks Robinson	.75	2.00
SM Stan Musial	2.00	5.00
SP Satchel Paige	1.25	3.00
TC Ty Cobb	2.00	5.00
TM Thurman Munson	1.25	3.00
WJ Walter Johnson	1.25	3.00

2007 Upper Deck 1989 Rookie Reprints

STATED ODDS 1:4 HOBBY
OVERALL PRINTING PLATE ODDS 1:96 H
PLATE PRINT RUN 1 SET PER COLOR
BLACK-CYAN-MAGENTA-YELLOW ISSUED
NO PLATE PRICING DUE TO SCARCITY

AD Alejandro De Aza	1.00	2.50
AG Alex Gordon	2.00	5.00
AI Akinori Iwamura	1.50	4.00
AS Angel Sanchez	.60	1.50
BB Brian Barden	.60	1.50
BI Joseph Bisenius	.60	1.50
BM Brandon Morrow	3.00	8.00
BN Jared Burton	.60	1.50
BU Jamie Burke	.60	1.50
CJ Cesar Jimenez	.60	1.50
CS Chris Stewart	.60	1.50
CW Chase Wright	1.50	4.00
DK Don Kelly	.60	1.50
DM Daisuke Matsuzaka	2.50	6.00
DY Delmon Young	1.00	2.50
ED Elijah Dukes	1.00	2.50
FP Felix Pie	.60	1.50
GM Gustavo Molina	.60	1.50
HG Hector Gimenez	.60	1.50
HO Hideki Okajima	3.00	8.00
JA Joaquin Arias	.60	1.50
JB Jeff Baker	.60	1.50
JD John Danks	1.00	2.50
JF Jesus Flores	.60	1.50
JG Jose Garcia	.60	1.50
JH Josh Hamilton	2.50	6.00
JM Jay Marshall	.60	1.50
JP Juan Perez	.60	1.50
JS Joe Smith	.60	1.50
KC Kevin Cameron	.60	1.50
KI Kei Igawa	1.50	4.00
KK Kevin Kouzmanoff	.60	1.50
KO Kory Casto	.60	1.50
LG Lee Gardner	.60	1.50
LS Levale Speigner	.60	1.50
MB Michael Bourn	.60	1.50
MC Matt Chico	.60	1.50
ML Matt Lindstrom	.60	1.50
MM Miguel Montero	.60	1.50
MO Micah Owings	.60	1.50
MR Mike Rabelo	.60	1.50
RB Ryan Z. Braun	.60	1.50
SA Juan Salas	.60	1.50
SH Sean Henn	.60	1.50
SL Doug Slaten	.60	1.50
SO Joakim Soria	.60	1.50
ST Brian Stokes	.60	1.50
TB Travis Buck	.60	1.50
TT Troy Tulowitzki	4.00	10.00
ZS Zack Segovia	.60	1.50

2007 Upper Deck Ken Griffey Jr. Chronicles

COMMON GRIFFEY	2.00	5.00

STATED ODDS 1:8 H, 1:72 R
PRINTING PLATE ODDS 1:192 H
PLATE PRINT RUN 1 SET PER COLOR
BLACK-CYAN-MAGENTA-YELLOW ISSUED
NO PLATE PRICING DUE TO SCARCITY

2007 Upper Deck MLB Rookie Card of the Month

COMPLETE SET (9)	8.00	20.00
ROM1 Daisuke Matsuzaka	1.00	2.50
ROM2 Fred Lewis	.40	1.00
ROM3 Hunter Pence	1.25	3.00
ROM4 Ryan Braun	1.25	3.00
ROM5 Tim Lincecum	4.00	10.00
ROM6 Joba Chamberlain	1.25	3.00
ROM7 Troy Tulowitzki	1.50	4.00
ROMAL Dustin Pedroia	.75	2.00
ROMNL Ryan Braun	1.25	3.00

2007 Upper Deck MVP Potential

STATED ODDS 2:1 FAT PACKS

MVP1 Stephen Drew	.40	1.00
MVP2 Brian McCann	.40	1.00
MVP3 Adam LaRoche	.40	1.00
MVP4 Brian Roberts	.40	1.00
MVP5 Manny Ramirez	1.00	2.50
MVP6 David Ortiz	.60	1.50
MVP7 J.D. Drew	.40	1.00
MVP8 Alfonso Soriano	.60	1.50
MVP9 Aramis Ramirez	.40	1.00
MVP10 Derrek Lee	.40	1.00
MVP11 Jermaine Dye	.40	1.00
MVP12 Paul Konerko	.60	1.50
MVP13 Jim Thome	.60	1.50
MVP14 Adam Dunn	.60	1.50
MVP15 Travis Hafner	.40	1.00
MVP16 Victor Martinez	.60	1.50
MVP17 Grady Sizemore	.60	1.50
MVP18 Garrett Atkins	.40	1.00
MVP19 Matt Holliday	1.00	2.50
MVP20 Magglio Ordonez	.60	1.50
MVP21 Miguel Cabrera	1.00	2.50
MVP22 Hanley Ramirez	1.00	2.50
MVP23 Dan Uggla	.60	1.50
MVP24 Lance Berkman	.60	1.50
MVP25 Carlos Lee	.40	1.00
MVP26 Jered Weaver	.60	1.50
MVP27 Nomar Garciaparra	1.00	2.50
MVP28 Rafael Furcal	.40	1.00
MVP29 Prince Fielder	.60	1.50
MVP30 Joe Mauer	1.00	2.50
MVP31 Johan Santana	1.00	2.50
MVP32 David Wright	1.50	4.00
MVP33 Jose Reyes	.60	1.50
MVP34 Carlos Beltran	.40	1.00
MVP35 Robinson Cano	1.00	2.50
MVP36 Derek Jeter	2.50	6.00
MVP37 Bobby Abreu	.40	1.00
MVP38 Johnny Damon	.60	1.50
MVP39 Nick Swisher	1.00	2.50
MVP40 Chase Utley	1.00	2.50
MVP41 Jason Bay	.60	1.50
MVP42 Adrian Gonzalez	.60	1.50
MVP43 Adrian Beltre	.40	1.00
MVP44 Scott Rolen	.60	1.50
MVP45 Carl Crawford	.60	1.50
MVP46 Mark Teixeira	1.00	2.50
MVP47 Michael Young	.60	1.50
MVP48 Vernon Wells	.40	1.00
MVP49 Roy Halladay	1.00	2.50
MVP50 Ryan Zimmerman	.60	1.50

2007 Upper Deck MVP Predictors

STATED ODDS 1:16 H, 1:240 R

MVP1 Miguel Tejada	2.00	5.00
MVP2 David Ortiz	4.00	10.00
MVP3 Manny Ramirez	2.00	5.00
MVP4 Jermaine Dye	2.00	5.00
MVP5 Jim Thome	2.00	5.00
MVP6 Paul Konerko	2.00	5.00
MVP7 Travis Hafner	2.00	5.00
MVP8 Grady Sizemore	2.00	5.00
MVP9 Victor Martinez	2.00	5.00
MVP10 Magglio Ordonez	2.00	5.00
MVP11 Justin Verlander	2.00	5.00
MVP12 Vladimir Guerrero	4.00	10.00
MVP13 Jered Weaver	2.00	5.00
MVP14 Justin Morneau	2.00	5.00
MVP15 Joe Mauer	2.00	5.00
MVP16 Johan Santana	2.00	5.00
MVP17 Alex Rodriguez	6.00	15.00
MVP18 Derek Jeter	12.50	30.00
MVP19 Jason Giambi	2.00	5.00
MVP20 Johnny Damon	3.00	8.00
MVP21 Bobby Abreu	2.00	5.00
MVP22 American League Field	6.00	15.00
MVP23 Frank Thomas	3.00	8.00
MVP24 Eric Chavez	2.00	5.00
MVP25 Ichiro Suzuki	2.00	5.00
MVP26 Adrian Beltre	2.00	5.00
MVP27 Carl Crawford	2.00	5.00
MVP28 Scott Kazmir	2.00	5.00
MVP29 Mark Teixeira	2.00	5.00
MVP30 Michael Young	2.00	5.00
MVP31 Carlos Lee	2.00	5.00
MVP32 Vernon Wells	2.00	5.00
MVP33 Roy Halladay	2.00	5.00
MVP34 Troy Glaus	2.00	5.00
MVP35 Stephen Drew	2.00	5.00
MVP36 Chipper Jones	2.00	5.00
MVP37 Andruw Jones	2.00	5.00
MVP38 Adam LaRoche	2.00	5.00
MVP39 Derrek Lee	3.00	8.00
MVP40 Aramis Ramirez	2.00	5.00
MVP41 Adam Dunn	2.00	5.00
MVP42 Ken Griffey Jr.	12.50	30.00
MVP43 Matt Holliday	2.50	6.00
MVP44 Garrett Atkins	2.00	5.00
MVP45 Miguel Cabrera	2.00	5.00
MVP46 Hanley Ramirez	2.00	5.00
MVP47 Dan Uggla	2.00	5.00
MVP48 Lance Berkman	2.00	5.00
MVP49 Roy Oswalt	2.00	5.00
MVP50 Nomar Garciaparra	2.00	5.00
MVP51 J.D. Drew	2.00	5.00
MVP52 Rafael Furcal	2.00	5.00
MVP53 Prince Fielder	15.00	40.00
MVP54 Bill Hall	3.00	8.00
MVP55 Jose Reyes	4.00	10.00
MVP56 Carlos Beltran	2.00	5.00
MVP57 Carlos Delgado	2.00	5.00
MVP58 David Wright	4.00	10.00
MVP59 National League Field	6.00	15.00
MVP60 Chase Utley	3.00	8.00
MVP61 Ryan Howard	6.00	15.00
MVP62 Jimmy Rollins	2.00	5.00
MVP63 Jason Bay	2.00	5.00
MVP64 Freddy Sanchez	2.00	5.00
MVP65 Adrian Gonzalez	2.00	5.00
MVP66 Albert Pujols	10.00	25.00
MVP67 Scott Rolen	2.00	5.00
MVP68 Chris Carpenter	2.00	5.00
MVP69 Alfonso Soriano	4.00	10.00
MVP70 Ryan Zimmerman	2.00	5.00

2007 Upper Deck Mystery Cuts Dual

ISSUED VIA RANDOM REDEMPTION
STATED PRINT RUN 1 SER.#'d SET
NO PRICING DUE TO SCARCITY

2007 Upper Deck Postseason Predictors

STATED ODDS 1:16 H, 1:240 R

PP1 Arizona Diamondbacks	2.00	5.00
PP2 Atlanta Braves	4.00	10.00
PP3 Baltimore Orioles	2.00	5.00
PP4 Boston Red Sox	10.00	25.00
PP5 Chicago Cubs	6.00	15.00
PP6 Chicago White Sox	4.00	10.00
PP7 Cincinnati Reds	2.00	5.00
PP8 Cleveland Indians	4.00	10.00
PP9 Colorado Rockies	2.00	5.00
PP10 Detroit Tigers	6.00	15.00
PP11 Florida Marlins	2.00	5.00
PP12 Houston Astros	2.00	5.00
PP13 Kansas City Royals	2.00	5.00
PP14 Los Angeles Angels	6.00	15.00
PP15 Los Angeles Dodgers	4.00	10.00
PP16 Milwaukee Brewers	2.00	5.00
PP17 Minnesota Twins	6.00	15.00
PP18 New York Mets	10.00	25.00
PP19 New York Yankees	12.50	30.00
PP20 Oakland Athletics	4.00	10.00
PP21 Philadelphia Phillies	4.00	10.00
PP22 Pittsburgh Pirates	2.00	5.00
PP23 San Diego Padres	4.00	10.00
PP24 San Francisco Giants	4.00	10.00
PP25 Seattle Mariners	2.00	5.00
PP26 St. Louis Cardinals	6.00	15.00
PP27 Tampa Bay Devil Rays	2.00	5.00
PP28 Texas Rangers	2.00	5.00
PP29 Toronto Blue Jays	2.00	5.00
PP30 Washington Nationals	2.00	5.00

2007 Upper Deck Rookie of the Year Predictor

STATED ODDS 1:16 HOBBY, 1:96 RETAIL
OVERALL PRINTING PLATE ODDS 1:96 H
PLATE PRINT RUN 1 SET PER COLOR
BLACK-CYAN-MAGENTA-YELLOW ISSUED
NO PLATE PRICING DUE TO SCARCITY

ROY1 Doug Slaten	1.25	3.00
ROY2 Miguel Montero	1.25	3.00
ROY3 Joseph Bisenius	1.25	3.00
ROY4 Kory Casto	1.25	3.00
ROY5 Jesus Flores	1.25	3.00
ROY6 John Danks	1.25	3.00
ROY7 Daisuke Matsuzaka	12.50	30.00
ROY8 Matt Lindstrom	1.25	3.00
ROY9 Chris Stewart	1.25	3.00
ROY10 Kevin Cameron	1.25	3.00
ROY11 Hideki Okajima	6.00	15.00
ROY12 Levale Speigner	1.25	3.00
ROY13 Kevin Kouzmanoff	1.25	3.00
ROY14 Jeff Baker	1.25	3.00
ROY15 Don Kelly	1.25	3.00
ROY16 Troy Tulowitzki	4.00	10.00
ROY17 Felix Pie	4.00	10.00
ROY18 Cesar Jimenez	1.25	3.00
ROY19 Alejandro De Aza	1.25	3.00
ROY20 Jose Garcia	1.25	3.00
ROY21 Micah Owings	1.25	3.00
ROY22 Josh Hamilton	30.00	60.00
ROY23 Brian Barden	1.25	3.00
ROY24 Jamie Burke	1.25	3.00
ROY25 Mike Rabelo	1.25	3.00
ROY26 Elijah Dukes	2.00	5.00
ROY27 Travis Buck	1.25	3.00
ROY28 Kei Igawa	2.00	5.00
ROY29 Sean Henn	1.25	3.00
ROY30 American League Field	10.00	25.00
ROY31 National League Field	10.00	25.00
ROY32 Michael Bourn	1.25	3.00
ROY33 Alex Gordon	10.00	25.00
ROY34 Chase Wright	2.00	5.00
ROY35 Matt Chico	1.25	3.00
ROY36 Joe Smith	1.25	3.00
ROY37 Lee Gardner	1.25	3.00
ROY38 Gustavo Molina	1.25	3.00
ROY39 Jared Burton	1.25	3.00
ROY40 Jay Marshall	1.25	3.00
ROY41 Brandon Morrow	2.00	5.00
ROY42 Akinori Iwamura	4.00	10.00
ROY43 Delmon Young	2.00	5.00
ROY44 Juan Salas	1.25	3.00
ROY45 Zack Segovia	1.25	3.00
ROY46 Brian Stokes	1.25	3.00
ROY47 Joaquin Arias	1.25	3.00
ROY48 Hector Gimenez	1.25	3.00
ROY49 Ryan Z. Braun	1.25	3.00
ROY50 Juan Perez	1.25	3.00

2007 Upper Deck Star Power

COMMON CARD	.40	1.00
SEMISTARS	.60	1.50
UNLISTED STARS	1.00	2.50

STATED ODDS 2:1 FAT PACKS

AJ Andruw Jones	.60	1.50
AP Albert Pujols	2.00	5.00
AR Alex Rodriguez	1.50	4.00
BR Brian Roberts	.40	1.00
BZ Barry Zito	.40	1.00
CA Chris Carpenter	.40	1.00
CB Carlos Beltran	.40	1.00
CC Carl Crawford	.40	1.00
CJ Chipper Jones	1.00	2.50
CS Curt Schilling	.60	1.50
CU Chase Utley	1.00	2.50
CZ Carlos Zambrano	.40	1.00
DA Johnny Damon	.60	1.50
DJ Derek Jeter	2.50	6.00
DO David Ortiz	1.00	2.50
DW Dontrelle Willis	.40	1.00
FS Freddy Sanchez	.40	1.00
FT Frank Thomas	1.00	2.50
HA Roy Halladay	.40	1.00
HO Trevor Hoffman	.40	1.00
IS Ichiro Suzuki	1.50	4.00
JB Jason Bay	.40	1.00
JD Jermaine Dye	.40	1.00
JM Joe Mauer	.60	1.50
JP Jake Peavy	.40	1.00
JR Jose Reyes	.40	1.00
JS Johan Santana	.60	1.50
JT Jim Thome	.60	1.50
JU Justin Morneau	.40	1.00
JV Justin Verlander	1.00	2.50
KG Ken Griffey Jr.	1.50	4.00
KR Kenny Rogers	.40	1.00
LB Lance Berkman	.40	1.00
MA Matt Cain	.60	1.50
MC Miguel Cabrera	.60	1.50
MH Matt Holliday	.50	1.25
MO Magglio Ordonez	.40	1.00
MR Manny Ramirez	.60	1.50
MT Mark Teixeira	.60	1.50
MY Michael Young	.40	1.00
NG Nomar Garciaparra	1.00	2.50
NS Nick Swisher	.40	1.00
PF Prince Fielder	1.00	2.50
RH Ryan Howard	1.50	4.00
RO Roy Oswalt	.40	1.00
RZ Ryan Zimmerman	1.00	2.50
SM John Smoltz	.60	1.50
TH Travis Hafner	.40	1.00
VG Vladimir Guerrero	1.00	2.50
WR David Wright	1.50	4.00

2007 Upper Deck Star Rookies

SR1 Adam Lind	.40	1.00
SR2 Akinori Iwamura	1.00	2.50
SR3 Alexi Casilla	.60	1.50
SR4 Alex Gordon	1.25	3.00
SR5 Matt Chico	.40	1.00
SR6 John Danks	.60	1.50
SR7 Angel Sanchez	.40	1.00
SR8 Elijah Dukes	.60	1.50
SR9 Brian Burres	.40	1.00
SR10 Gustavo Molina	.40	1.00
SR11 Chris Stewart	.40	1.00
SR12 Daisuke Matsuzaka	1.50	4.00
SR13 Joakim Soria	.40	1.00
SR14 Delmon Young	.60	1.50
SR15 Jay Marshall	.40	1.00
SR16 Travis Buck	.40	1.00
SR17 Doug Slaten	.40	1.00
SR18 Don Kelly	.40	1.00
SR19 Kevin Cameron	.40	1.00
SR20 Glen Perkins	.40	1.00
SR21 Hector Gimenez	.40	1.00
SR22 Jeff Baker	.40	1.00
SR23 Jared Burton	.40	1.00
SR24 Kory Casto	.40	1.00
SR25 Joe Smith	.40	1.00
SR26 Joaquin Arias	.40	1.00
SR27 Dallas Braden	2.50	6.00
SR28 Jon Knott	.40	1.00
SR29 Jose Garcia	.40	1.00
SR30 Jamie Burke	.40	1.00
SR31 Zach Segovia	.40	1.00
SR32 Felix Pie	.40	1.00
SR33 Juan Salas	.40	1.00
SR34 Kei Igawa	1.00	2.50
SR35 Philip Hughes	2.00	5.00
SR36 Kevin Kouzmanoff	.40	1.00
SR37 Michael Bourn	.40	1.00
SR38 Miguel Montero	.40	1.00
SR39 Mike Rabelo	.40	1.00
SR40 Josh Hamilton	1.50	4.00
SR41 Micah Owings	.40	1.00
SR42 Alejandro De Aza	.60	1.50
SR43 Brian Barden	.40	1.00
SR44 Andy Gonzalez	.40	1.00
SR45 Chase Wright	1.00	2.50
SR46 Sean Henn	.40	1.00
SR47 Rick Vanden Hurk	.40	1.00
SR48 Troy Tulowitzki	2.50	6.00
SR49 Rocky Cherry	1.00	2.50
SR50 Jesus Flores	.40	1.00

2007 Upper Deck Star Signings

SER.1 ODDS 1:16 HOBBY, 1:960 RETAIL
SER.2 ODDS 1:16 HOBBY, 1:960 RETAIL
SP INFO PROVIDED BY UPPER DECK
EXCH DEADLINE 02/27/2010

AB Adrian Beltre S2 SP	5.00	12.00
AB Ambiorix Burgos	3.00	8.00
AC Aaron Cook	3.00	8.00
AC Alberto Callaspo S2	3.00	8.00
AG Alex Gordon S2	10.00	25.00
AH Aubrey Huff SP	5.00	12.00
AP Albert Pujols SP		
AR Alex Rios	6.00	15.00
AS Angel Sanchez S2	3.00	8.00
BA Jeff Baker S2	3.00	8.00
BA Bobby Abreu	10.00	25.00
BB Brian Burres S2	3.00	8.00
BC Bobby Crosby S2 SP		
BE Josh Beckett S2 SP	20.00	50.00
BL Joe Blanton	3.00	8.00
BO Jeremy Bonderman	6.00	15.00
BO Ben Broussard S2	4.00	10.00
BR Brandon Backe	3.00	8.00
BU B.J. Upton S2 SP	20.00	50.00
CB Craig Biggio S2 SP	15.00	40.00
CC Carl Crawford S2 SP	8.00	20.00
CJ Conor Jackson	6.00	15.00
CO Chad Cordero	3.00	8.00
CP Corey Patterson	3.00	8.00
CR Coco Crisp SP	5.00	12.00
CR Cal Ripken Jr. S2 SP	75.00	125.00
CS Chris Shelton	3.00	8.00
CY Chris Young SP	6.00	15.00
DC Daniel Cabrera SP	5.00	12.00
DH Danny Haren	4.00	10.00
DJ Derek Jeter	75.00	150.00
DJ Derek Jeter S2	75.00	150.00
DL Derrek Lee SP	6.00	15.00
DU Chris Duffy	3.00	8.00
DY Delmon Young S2 SP	6.00	15.00
ED Elijah Dukes S2	6.00	15.00
FH Felix Hernandez S2	10.00	25.00
GA Garrett Atkins	3.00	8.00
GC Gustavo Chacin	3.00	8.00
HS Huston Street	3.00	8.00
HU Torii Hunter	6.00	15.00
IK Ian Kinsler S2 SP	6.00	15.00
IS Ian Snell S2	5.00	12.00
IS Ian Snell SP	5.00	12.00
JA Jeremy Accardo	3.00	8.00
JB Jason Bergmann SP	5.00	12.00
JD Joey Devine	3.00	8.00
JD J.D. Drew S2 SP	8.00	20.00
JG Jonny Gomes	3.00	8.00
JJ Jorge Julio	3.00	8.00
JK Jason Kubel	3.00	8.00
JM Justin Morneau	10.00	25.00
JN Joe Nathan	6.00	15.00
JS Jason Bay	6.00	15.00
JT Jim Thome S2 SP		
JW Jake Westbrook	3.00	8.00
KF Keith Foulke	4.00	10.00
KG Ken Griffey Jr.	40.00	80.00
KG Ken Griffey Jr. S2 SP		
KI Kei Igawa S2 SP	15.00	40.00
KJ Kelly Johnson S2	6.00	15.00
KM Kevin Mench	3.00	8.00
KS Kirk Saarloos	3.00	8.00
KY Kevin Youkilis	10.00	25.00
LN Laynce Nix SP	5.00	12.00
LO Lyle Overbay	3.00	8.00
MA Matt Cain SP	6.00	15.00
MH Matt Holliday	5.00	12.00
MK Mark Kotsay	4.00	10.00
MM Melvin Mora	4.00	10.00
MT Mark Teahen SP	5.00	12.00
NC Nelson Cruz S2	4.00	10.00
NM Nate McLouth SP	5.00	12.00
OP Oliver Perez S2 SP	15.00	40.00
RA Chris Ray S2	4.00	10.00
RC Roger Clemens S2 SP		
RC Ryan Church	3.00	8.00
RF Rafael Furcal SP	5.00	12.00
RG Ryan Garko	4.00	10.00
RI Juan Rivera SP	5.00	12.00
RJ Reed Johnson	3.00	8.00
RO Aaron Rowand SP	5.00	12.00
RU Carlos Ruiz	12.50	30.00
SA Juan Salas S2	3.00	8.00
SC Sean Casey SP	5.00	12.00
SD Stephen Drew	10.00	25.00
SH Sean Henn S2	3.00	8.00
SP Scott Podsednik SP	6.00	15.00
TI Tadahito Iguchi	8.00	20.00
VE Justin Verlander	12.50	30.00
WM Wily Mo Pena	6.00	15.00
XN Xavier Nady	4.00	10.00
YB Yuniesky Betancourt	4.00	10.00
YO Chris Young S2	10.00	25.00
ZS Zack Segovia S2	3.00	8.00

2007 Upper Deck Ticket to Stardom

STATED ODDS 1:4 TARGET PACKS
NO PRICING DUE TO LACK OF MARKET INFO
OVERALL PRINTING PLATE ODDS 1:96 HOBBY
PLATE PRINT RUN 1 SET PER COLOR
BLACK-CYAN-MAGENTA-YELLOW ISSUED
NO PLATE PRICING DUE TO SCARCITY

AD Alejandro De Aza	.60	1.50
AG Alex Gordon	1.25	3.00
AI Akinori Iwamura	1.00	2.50
AS Angel Sanchez	.40	1.00
BB Brian Barden	.40	1.00
BI Joseph Bisenius	.40	1.00
BM Brandon Morrow	2.00	5.00
BN Jared Burton	.40	1.00
BU Jamie Burke	.40	1.00
CH Matt Chico	.40	1.00
CJ Cesar Jimenez	.40	1.00
CS Chris Stewart	.40	1.00
CW Chase Wright	1.00	2.50
DA John Danks	.60	1.50
DK Don Kelly	.40	1.00
DM Daisuke Matsuzaka	1.50	4.00
DS Doug Slaten	.40	1.00
DY Delmon Young	.60	1.50
ED Elijah Dukes	.60	1.50
FP Felix Pie	.40	1.00
GM Gustavo Molina	.40	1.00
HG Hector Gimenez	.40	1.00
HO Hideki Okajima	2.00	5.00
JA Joaquin Arias	.40	1.00
JB Jeff Baker	.40	1.00
JF Jesus Flores	.40	1.00
JG Jose Garcia	.40	1.00
JH Josh Hamilton	1.50	4.00
JM Jay Marshall	.40	1.00
JO Joe Smith	.40	1.00
JP Juan Perez	.40	1.00
KC Kevin Cameron	.40	1.00
KI Kei Igawa	1.00	2.50
KK Kevin Kouzmanoff	.40	1.00
KO Kory Casto	.40	1.00
LG Lee Gardner	.40	1.00
LS Levale Speigner	.40	1.00
MB Michael Bourn	.40	1.00
ML Matt Lindstrom	.40	1.00
MM Miguel Montero	.40	1.00
MO Micah Owings	.40	1.00
MR Mike Rabelo	.40	1.00
RB Ryan Z. Braun	.40	1.00
SA Juan Salas	.40	1.00
SH Sean Henn	.40	1.00
SO Joakim Soria	.40	1.00
ST Brian Stokes	.40	1.00
TB Travis Buck	.40	1.00
TT Troy Tulowitzki	2.50	6.00
ZS Zack Segovia	.40	1.00

2007 Upper Deck Triple Play Performers

COMPLETE SET	12.50	30.00
TPAP Albert Pujols	2.50	6.00
TPAR Alex Rodriguez	1.50	4.00
TPAS Alfonso Soriano	.60	1.50
TPCC Carl Crawford	.60	1.50
TPCJ Chipper Jones	1.00	2.50
TPDJ Derek Jeter	2.50	6.00
TPDL Derrek Lee	.40	1.00
TPDM Daisuke Matsuzaka	1.50	4.00
TPDO David Ortiz	.60	1.50
TPDW David Wright	1.50	4.00
TPGS Grady Sizemore	.60	1.50
TPHE Todd Helton	.60	1.50
TPIS Ichiro Suzuki	1.50	4.00
TPJM Justin Morneau	1.00	2.50
TPJP Jake Peavy	.40	1.00
TPJR Jose Reyes	.60	1.50
TPJS Johan Santana	1.00	2.50
TPJT Jim Thome	.60	1.50
TPJV Justin Verlander	1.25	3.00
TPKG Ken Griffey	1.50	4.00
TPLB Lance Berkman	.60	1.50
TPMC Miguel Cabrera	1.00	2.50
TPMO Magglio Ordonez	.60	1.50
TPMT Mark Teixeira	1.00	2.50
TPMT Miguel Tejada	.60	1.50
TPPF Prince Fielder	.60	1.50
TPRH Ryan Howard	1.50	4.00
TPRJ Randy Johnson	1.00	2.50
TPTH Travis Hafner	.40	1.00
TPVG Vladimir Guerrero	1.00	2.50

2007 Upper Deck UD Game Materials

SER.1 STATED ODDS 1:8 H, 1:24 R
SER.2 STATED ODDS 1:8 H, 1:24 R

AB A.J. Burnett S2	3.00	8.00
AJ Andruw Jones Jsy S1	3.00	8.00
AP Albert Pujols Pants S1	6.00	15.00
AP Albert Pujols S2	6.00	15.00
AR Alex Rios S2	4.00	10.00
BA Bobby Abreu S2	3.00	8.00
BC Bartolo Colon S2	3.00	8.00
BE Josh Beckett Jsy S1	3.00	8.00
BJ Bobby Jenks S2	3.00	8.00
BR Brian Roberts Jsy S1	3.00	8.00
BS Ben Sheets Jsy S1	3.00	8.00
CA Chris Carpenter Jsy S1	3.00	8.00
CB Carlos Beltran Pants S1	4.00	10.00
CC Carl Crawford Pants S1	3.00	8.00
CC Carl Crawford S2	3.00	8.00
CD Carlos Delgado Jsy S1	3.00	8.00
CJ Chipper Jones S2	3.00	8.00
CL Carlos Lee Jsy S1	3.00	8.00
CP Corey Patterson Jsy S1	3.00	8.00
CS C.C. Sabathia Jsy S1	3.00	8.00
CS Curt Schilling S2	4.00	10.00
CU Chase Utley S2	4.00	10.00
DJ Derek Jeter Pants S1	12.50	30.00
DJ Derek Jeter S2	12.50	30.00
DO David Ortiz Jsy S1	4.00	10.00
DW Dontrelle Willis Jsy S1	3.00	8.00
EB Erik Bedard S2	4.00	10.00
EC Eric Chavez Jsy S1	3.00	8.00
EN Juan Encarnacion S2	3.00	8.00
FH Felix Hernandez Jsy S1	4.00	10.00
FR Jeff Francoeur S2	4.00	10.00
GS Gary Sheffield S2	3.00	8.00
HB Hank Blalock S2	3.00	8.00
HO Trevor Hoffman S2	3.00	8.00
HU Torii Hunter Jsy S1	3.00	8.00
IR Ivan Rodriguez Jsy S1	3.00	8.00
JB Jason Bay Jsy S1	3.00	8.00
JD Johnny Damon S2	3.00	8.00
JE Jim Edmonds S2	3.00	8.00
JF Jeff Francis S2	3.00	8.00
JG Jason Giambi Jsy S1	3.00	8.00
JM Joe Mauer Jsy S1	3.00	8.00
JR Jose Reyes Jsy S1	4.00	10.00
JS Johan Santana Jsy S1	3.00	8.00
JS John Smoltz S2	4.00	10.00
JT Jim Thome S2	3.00	8.00
JU Juan Uribe Jsy S1	3.00	8.00
JV Justin Verlander Jsy S1	4.00	10.00
JV Jose Vidro S2	3.00	8.00
KG Ken Griffey Jr. Pants S1	6.00	15.00
KG Ken Griffey Jr. S2	6.00	15.00
LB Lance Berkman S2	3.00	8.00
LG Luis Gonzalez S2	3.00	8.00
MC Miguel Cabrera Jsy S1	4.00	10.00
MH Matt Holliday Jsy S1	4.00	10.00
MM Melvin Mora Jsy S1	3.00	8.00
MO Justin Morneau Jsy S1	4.00	10.00
MR Manny Ramirez Jsy S1	4.00	10.00
MR Manny Ramirez S2	4.00	10.00
MS Mike Sweeney Jsy S1	3.00	8.00
MT Miguel Tejada Jsy S1	3.00	8.00
MT Mark Teixeira S2	3.00	8.00
MU Mike Mussina Jsy S1	4.00	10.00
OR Magglio Ordonez Jsy S1	3.00	8.00
PF Prince Fielder Jsy S1	4.00	10.00
RB Rocco Baldelli S2	3.00	8.00
RH Roy Halladay Jsy S1	3.00	8.00
RJ Randy Johnson S2	4.00	10.00
RN Ricky Nolasco S2	3.00	8.00
RO Roy Oswalt S2	3.00	8.00
RW Rickie Weeks S2	3.00	8.00
RZ Ryan Zimmerman Jsy S1	4.00	10.00
SD Stephen Drew S2	3.00	8.00
SK Scott Kazmir S2	3.00	8.00
SR Scott Rolen Jsy S1	4.00	10.00
SR Scott Rolen S2	3.00	8.00
TG Tom Glavine S2	4.00	10.00
TH Tim Hudson Jsy S1	3.00	8.00
TH Todd Helton S2	3.00	8.00
TN Trot Nixon S2	3.00	8.00
VG Vladimir Guerrero S2	4.00	10.00
VM Victor Martinez Jsy S1	3.00	8.00
ZD Zach Duke S2	3.00	8.00

2007 Upper Deck UD Game Patch

STATED ODDS 1:192 H, 1:2500 R

AJ Andruw Jones	15.00	40.00
AP Albert Pujols	40.00	80.00
BE Josh Beckett	10.00	25.00
BR Brian Roberts	10.00	25.00
BS Ben Sheets	10.00	25.00

Card	Low	High
CA Chris Carpenter	15.00	40.00
CB Carlos Beltran	15.00	40.00
CC Carl Crawford	10.00	25.00
CD Carlos Delgado	10.00	25.00
CL Carlos Lee	10.00	25.00
CP Corey Patterson	10.00	25.00
CS C.C. Sabathia	10.00	25.00
DJ Derek Jeter	40.00	80.00
DO David Ortiz	20.00	50.00
DW Dontrelle Willis	10.00	25.00
EC Eric Chavez	10.00	25.00
FH Felix Hernandez	15.00	40.00
HU Torii Hunter	15.00	40.00
IR Ivan Rodriguez	15.00	40.00
JB Jason Bay	15.00	40.00
JG Jason Giambi	15.00	40.00
JM Joe Mauer	15.00	40.00
JR Jose Reyes	20.00	50.00
JS Johan Santana	15.00	40.00
JU Juan Uribe	10.00	25.00
KG Ken Griffey Jr.	40.00	80.00
MC Miguel Cabrera	15.00	40.00
MH Matt Holliday	12.50	30.00
MM Melvin Mora	10.00	25.00
MO Justin Morneau	10.00	25.00
MR Manny Ramirez	20.00	50.00
MS Mike Sweeney	10.00	25.00
MT Miguel Tejada	10.00	25.00
MU Mike Mussina	10.00	25.00
OR Maggio Ordonez	10.00	25.00
PF Prince Fielder	15.00	40.00
RH Roy Halladay	10.00	25.00
RZ Ryan Zimmerman	20.00	50.00
SR Scott Rolen	20.00	50.00
TH Tim Hudson	10.00	25.00
VM Victor Martinez	15.00	40.00

2008 Upper Deck

This 400-card first series was released in February, 2008. The set was issued into the hobby in 20-card packs, with an $4.99 SRP, which came 16 packs to a box and 12 boxes to a case. Cards numbered 1-300 feature veterans in team nickname alphabetical order while cards numbered 301-350 feature 2007 rookies in alphabetical order. The first series concludes with team checklist cards (also in team nickname alphabetical order) from cards 351-380 and 20 highlight cards from 381-400.

Card	Low	High
COMPLETE SET (799)	50.00	100.00
COMP.SER.1 (1-400)	20.00	50.00
COMP.SER.2 (401-799)	20.00	50.00
COMMON CARD (1-799)	.15	.40
COMMON ROOKIE (1-799)	.40	1.00
1 Joe Saunders	.15	.40
2 Kelvim Escobar	.15	.40
3 Jered Weaver	.15	.40
4 Justin Speier	.15	.40
5 Scot Shields	.15	.40
6 Mike Napoli	.25	.60
7 Orlando Cabrera	.15	.40
8 Casey Kotchman	.15	.40
9 Vladimir Guerrero	.40	1.00
10 Garret Anderson	.15	.40
11 Roy Oswalt	.25	.60
12 Wandy Rodriguez	.15	.40
13 Woody Williams	.15	.40
14 Chad Qualls	.15	.40
15 Brian Moehler	.15	.40
16 Mark Loretta	.15	.40
17 Brad Ausmus	.15	.40
18 Ty Wigginton	.15	.40
19 Carlos Lee	.15	.40
20 Hunter Pence	.40	1.00
21 Dan Haren	.15	.40
22 Lenny DiNardo	.15	.40
23 Chad Gaudin	.15	.40
24 Huston Street	.15	.40
25 Andrew Brown	.15	.40
26 Mike Piazza	.40	1.00
27 Jack Cust	.15	.40
28 Mark Ellis	.15	.40
29 Shannon Stewart	.15	.40
30 Travis Buck	.15	.40
31 Shaun Marcum	.15	.40
32 A.J. Burnett	.25	.60
33 Jesse Litsch	.15	.40
34 Casey Janssen	.15	.40
35 Jeremy Accardo	.15	.40
36 Gregg Zaun	.15	.40
37 Aaron Hill	.15	.40
38 Frank Thomas	.40	1.00
39 Matt Stairs	.15	.40
40 Vernon Wells	.15	.40
41 Tim Hudson	.25	.60
42 Chuck James	.15	.40
43 Buddy Carlyle	.15	.40
44 Rafael Soriano	.15	.40
45 Peter Moylan	.15	.40
46 Brian McCann	.25	.60
47 Edgar Renteria	.15	.40
48 Mark Teixeira	.40	1.00
49 Willie Harris	.15	.40
50 Andruw Jones	.15	.40
51 Ben Sheets	.15	.40
52 Dave Bush	.15	.40
53 Yovani Gallardo	.15	.40
54 Francisco Cordero	.15	.40
55 Matt Wise	.15	.40
56 Johnny Estrada	.15	.40
57 Prince Fielder	.25	.60
58 J.J. Hardy	.15	.40
59 Corey Hart	.15	.40
60 Geoff Jenkins	.15	.40
61 Adam Wainwright	.25	.60
62 Joel Pineiro	.15	.40
63 Brad Thompson	.15	.40
64 Jason Isringhausen	.15	.40
65 Troy Percival	.15	.40
66 Yadier Molina	.25	.60
67 Albert Pujols	1.00	2.50
68 David Eckstein	.15	.40
69 Jim Edmonds	.25	.60
70 Rick Ankiel	.15	.40
71 Ted Lilly	.15	.40
72 Rich Hill	.15	.40
73 Jason Marquis	.15	.40
74 Carlos Marmol	.25	.60
75 Ryan Dempster	.15	.40
76 Jason Kendall	.15	.40
77 Aramis Ramirez	.15	.40
78 Ryan Theriot	.15	.40
79 Alfonso Soriano	.25	.60
80 Jacque Jones	.15	.40
81 James Shields	.15	.40
82 Andy Sonnanstine	.15	.40
83 Scott Dohmann	.15	.40
84 Al Reyes	.15	.40
85 Dioner Navarro	.15	.40
86 B.J. Upton	.25	.60
87 Carlos Pena	.25	.60
88 Brendan Harris	.15	.40
89 Josh Wilson	.15	.40
90 Jonny Gomes	.15	.40
91 Brandon Webb	.25	.60
92 Micah Owings	.15	.40
93 Livan Hernandez	.15	.40
94 Doug Slaten	.15	.40
95 Brandon Lyon	.15	.40
96 Miguel Montero	.15	.40
97 Stephen Drew	.15	.40
98 Mark Reynolds	.15	.40
99 Conor Jackson	.15	.40
100 Chris B. Young	.15	.40
101 Chad Billingsley	.15	.40
102 Derek Lowe	.15	.40
103 Mark Hendrickson	.15	.40
104 Takashi Saito	.15	.40
105 Rudy Seanez	.15	.40
106 Russell Martin	.15	.40
107 Jeff Kent	.15	.40
108 Nomar Garciaparra	.40	1.00
109 Matt Kemp	.25	.60
110 Juan Pierre	.15	.40
111 Matt Cain	.15	.40
112 Barry Zito	.15	.40
113 Kevin Correia	.15	.40
114 Brad Hennessey	.15	.40
115 Jack Taschner	.15	.40
116 Bengie Molina	.15	.40
117 Ryan Klesko	.15	.40
118 Omar Vizquel	.25	.60
119 Dave Roberts	.15	.40
120 Rajai Davis	.15	.40
121 Fausto Carmona	.15	.40
122 Jake Westbrook	.15	.40
123 Cliff Lee	.25	.60
124 Rafael Betancourt	.15	.40
125 Joe Borowski	.15	.40
126 Victor Martinez	.25	.60
127 Travis Hafner	.15	.40
128 Ryan Garko	.15	.40
129 Kenny Lofton	.15	.40
130 Franklin Gutierrez	.15	.40
131 Felix Hernandez	.40	1.00
132 Jeff Weaver	.15	.40
133 J.J. Putz	.15	.40
134 Brandon Morrow	.15	.40
135 Sean Green	.15	.40
136 Kenji Johjima	.15	.40
137 Jose Vidro	.15	.40
138 Richie Sexson	.15	.40
139 Ichiro Suzuki	.60	1.50
140 Ben Broussard	.15	.40
141 Sergio Mitre	.15	.40
142 Scott Olsen	.15	.40
143 Rick Vanden Hurk	.15	.40
144 Justin Miller	.15	.40
145 Lee Gardner	.15	.40
146 Miguel Olivo	.15	.40
147 Hanley Ramirez	.40	1.00
148 Mike Jacobs	.15	.40
149 Josh Willingham	.15	.40
150 Alfredo Amezaga	.15	.40
151 John Maine	.15	.40
152 Tom Glavine	.25	.60
153 Orlando Hernandez	.15	.40
154 Billy Wagner	.15	.40
155 Aaron Heilman	.15	.40
156 David Wright	.50	1.25
157 Luis Castillo	.15	.40
158 Shawn Green	.15	.40
159 Damion Easley	.15	.40
160 Carlos Delgado	.15	.40
161 Shawn Hill	.15	.40
162 Mike Bacsik	.15	.40
163 John Lannan	.15	.40
164 Chad Cordero	.15	.40
165 Jon Rauch	.15	.40
166 Jesus Flores	.15	.40
167 Dmitri Young	.15	.40
168 Cristian Guzman	.15	.40
169 Austin Kearns	.15	.40
170 Nook Logan	.15	.40
171 Erik Bedard	.15	.40
172 Daniel Cabrera	.15	.40
173 Chris Ray	.15	.40
174 Danys Baez	.15	.40
175 Chad Bradford	.15	.40
176 Ramon Hernandez	.15	.40
177 Miguel Tejada	.25	.60
178 Freddie Bynum	.15	.40
179 Corey Patterson	.15	.40
180 Aubrey Huff	.15	.40
181 Chris Young	.15	.40
182 Greg Maddux	.50	1.25
183 Clay Hensley	.15	.40
184 Kevin Cameron	.15	.40
185 Doug Brocail	.15	.40
186 Josh Bard	.15	.40
187 Kevin Kouzmanoff	.15	.40
188 Geoff Blum	.15	.40
189 Milton Bradley	.15	.40
190 Brian Giles	.15	.40
191 Jamie Moyer	.15	.40
192 Kyle Kendrick	.15	.40
193 Kyle Lohse	.15	.40
194 Antonio Alfonseca	.15	.40
195 Ryan Madson	.15	.40
196 Chris Coste	.15	.40
197 Chase Utley	.40	1.00
198 Tadahito Iguchi	.15	.40
199 Aaron Rowand	.15	.40
200 Shane Victorino	.15	.40
201 Paul Maholm	.15	.40
202 Ian Snell	.15	.40
203 Shane Youman	.15	.40
204 Damaso Marte	.15	.40
205 Shawn Chacon	.15	.40
206 Ronny Paulino	.15	.40
207 Jack Wilson	.15	.40
208 Adam LaRoche	.15	.40
209 Ryan Doumit	.15	.40
210 Xavier Nady	.15	.40
211 Kevin Millwood	.15	.40
212 Brandon McCarthy	.15	.40
213 Joaquin Benoit	.15	.40
214 Wes Littleton	.15	.40
215 Mike Wood	.15	.40
216 Gerald Laird	.15	.40
217 Hank Blalock	.15	.40
218 Ian Kinsler	.25	.60
219 Marlon Byrd	.15	.40
220 Brad Wilkerson	.15	.40
221 Tim Wakefield	.15	.40
222 Daisuke Matsuzaka	.40	1.00
223 Julian Tavarez	.15	.40
224 Hideki Okajima	.15	.40
225 Manny Delcarmen	.15	.40
226 Doug Mirabelli	.15	.40
227 Dustin Pedroia	.50	1.25
228 Mike Lowell	.15	.40
229 Manny Ramirez	.40	1.00
230 Coco Crisp	.15	.40
231 Bronson Arroyo	.15	.40
232 Matt Belisle	.15	.40
233 Jared Burton	.15	.40
234 David Weathers	.15	.40
235 Mike Gosling	.15	.40
236 David Ross	.15	.40
237 Jeff Keppinger	.15	.40
238 Edwin Encarnacion	.15	.40
239 Ken Griffey Jr.	.60	1.50
240 Adam Dunn	.25	.60
241 Jeff Francis	.15	.40
242 Jason Hirsh	.15	.40
243 Josh Fogg	.15	.40
244 Manny Corpas	.15	.40
245 Jeremy Affeldt	.15	.40
246 Yorvit Torrealba	.15	.40
247 Todd Helton	.25	.60
248 Kazuo Matsui	.15	.40
249 Brad Hawpe	.15	.40
250 Willy Taveras	.15	.40
251 Brian Bannister	.15	.40
252 Zack Greinke	.25	.60
253 Kyle Davies	.15	.40
254 David Riske	.15	.40
255 Joel Peralta	.15	.40
256 John Buck	.15	.40
257 Mark Grudzielanek	.15	.40
258 Ross Gload	.15	.40
259 Billy Butler	.15	.40
260 David DeJesus	.15	.40
261 Jeremy Bonderman	.15	.40
262 Chad Durbin	.15	.40
263 Andrew Miller	.15	.40
264 Bobby Seay	.15	.40
265 Todd Jones	.15	.40
266 Brandon Inge	.15	.40
267 Sean Casey	.15	.40
268 Placido Polanco	.15	.40
269 Gary Sheffield	.15	.40
270 Magglio Ordonez	.25	.60
271 Matt Garza	.15	.40
272 Boof Bonser	.15	.40
273 Scott Baker	.15	.40
274 Joe Nathan	.15	.40
275 Dennys Reyes	.15	.40
276 Joe Mauer	.40	1.00
277 Michael Cuddyer	.15	.40
278 Jason Bartlett	.15	.40
279 Torii Hunter	.15	.40
280 Jason Tyner	.15	.40
281 Mark Buehrle	.25	.60
282 Jon Garland	.15	.40
283 Jose Contreras	.15	.40
284 Matt Thornton	.15	.40
285 Ryan Bukvich	.15	.40
286 Juan Uribe	.15	.40
287 Jim Thome	.25	.60
288 Scott Podsednik	.15	.40
289 Jerry Owens	.15	.40
290 Jermaine Dye	.15	.40
291 Andy Pettitte	.25	.60
292 Phil Hughes	.40	1.00
293 Mike Mussina	.25	.60
294 Joba Chamberlain	.25	.60
295 Brian Bruney	.15	.40
296 Jorge Posada	.25	.60
297 Derek Jeter	1.00	2.50
298 Jason Giambi	.15	.40
299 Johnny Damon	.25	.60
300 Melky Cabrera	.15	.40
301 Jonathan Albaladejo RC	.60	1.50
302 Josh Anderson (RC)	.40	1.00
303 Wladimir Balentien (RC)	.40	1.00
304 Josh Banks (RC)	.40	1.00
305 Daric Barton (RC)	.40	1.00
306 Jerry Blevins RC	.60	1.50
307 Emilio Bonifacio RC	1.00	2.50
308 Lance Broadway (RC)	.40	1.00
309 Clay Buchholz (RC)	1.00	2.50
310 Billy Buckner (RC)	.40	1.00
311 Jeff Clement (RC)	.60	1.50
312 Willie Collazo RC	.60	1.50
313 Ross Detwiler RC	1.00	2.50
314 Sam Fuld RC	1.25	3.00
315 Harvey Garcia (RC)	.40	1.00
316 Alberto Gonzalez RC	.60	1.50
317 Ryan Hanigan RC	.60	1.50
318 Kevin Hart (RC)	.40	1.00
319 Luke Hochevar RC	.60	1.50
320 Chin-Lung Hu (RC)	.60	1.50
321 Rob Johnson (RC)	.40	1.00
322 Radhames Liz RC	.60	1.50
323 Ian Kennedy RC	1.00	2.50
324 Joe Koshansky (RC)	.40	1.00
325 Donny Lucy (RC)	.40	1.00
326 Justin Maxwell RC	.60	1.50
327 Jonathan Meloan RC	.60	1.50
328 Luis Mendoza (RC)	.40	1.00
329 Jose Morales (RC)	.40	1.00
330 Nyjer Morgan (RC)	.40	1.00
331 Carlos Muniz RC	.60	1.50
332 Bill Murphy (RC)	.40	1.00
333 Josh Newman RC	.60	1.50
334 Ross Ohlendorf RC	.60	1.50
335 Troy Patton (RC)	.40	1.00
336 Felipe Paulino RC	.60	1.50
337 Steve Pearce RC	.60	1.50
338 Heath Phillips RC	.60	1.50
339 Justin Ruggiano RC	.60	1.50
340 Clint Sammons (RC)	.40	1.00
341 Bronson Sardinha (RC)	.40	1.00
342 Chris Seddon (RC)	.40	1.00
343 Seth Smith (RC)	.40	1.00
344 Mitch Stetter RC	.60	1.50
345 Dave Davidson RC	.60	1.50
346 Rich Thompson RC	.60	1.50
347 J.R. Towles RC	.60	1.50
348 Eugenio Velez RC	.40	1.00
349 Joey Votto (RC)	1.50	4.00
350 Bill White RC	.40	1.00
351 Vladimir Guerrero CL	.40	1.00
352 Lance Berkman CL	.25	.60
353 Dan Haren CL	.15	.40
354 Frank Thomas CL	.40	1.00
355 Chipper Jones CL	.40	1.00
356 Prince Fielder CL	.25	.60
357 Albert Pujols CL	1.00	2.50
358 Alfonso Soriano CL	.25	.60
359 B.J. Upton CL	.25	.60
360 Eric Byrnes CL	.15	.40
361 Russell Martin CL	.15	.40
362 Tim Lincecum CL	.60	1.50
363 Grady Sizemore CL	.25	.60
364 Ichiro Suzuki CL	.60	1.50
365 Hanley Ramirez CL	.40	1.00
366 David Wright CL	.50	1.25
367 Ryan Zimmerman CL	.25	.60
368 Nick Markakis CL	.40	1.00
369 Jake Peavy CL	.15	.40
370 Ryan Howard CL	.50	1.25
371 Freddy Sanchez CL	.15	.40
372 Michael Young CL	.25	.60
373 David Ortiz CL	.25	.60
374 Ken Griffey Jr. CL	.60	1.50
375 Matt Holliday CL	.40	1.00
376 Brian Bannister CL	.15	.40
377 Magglio Ordonez CL	.25	.60
378 Johan Santana CL	.40	1.00
379 Jim Thome CL	.25	.60
380 Alex Rodriguez CL	.60	1.50
381 Alex Rodriguez HL	.60	1.50
382 Brandon Webb HL	.25	.60
383 Chone Figgins HL	.15	.40
384 Clay Buchholz HL	.40	1.00
385 Curtis Granderson HL	.25	.60
386 Frank Thomas HL	.40	1.00
387 Fred Lewis HL	.15	.40
388 Garret Anderson HL	.15	.40
389 J.R. Towles HL	.25	.60
390 Jake Peavy HL	.15	.40
391 Jim Thome HL	.25	.60
392 Jimmy Rollins HL	.25	.60
393 Johan Santana HL	.40	1.00
394 Justin Verlander HL	.50	1.25
395 Mark Buehrle HL	.25	.60
396 Matt Holliday HL	.40	1.00
397 Jarrod Saltalamacchia HL	.15	.40
398 Sammy Sosa HL	.40	1.00
399 Tom Glavine HL	.25	.60
400 Trevor Hoffman HL	.25	.60
401 Dan Haren	.15	.40
402 Randy Johnson	.40	1.00
403 Chris Burke	.15	.40
404 Orlando Hudson	.15	.40
405 Justin Upton	.25	.60
406 Eric Byrnes	.15	.40
407 Doug Davis	.15	.40
408 Chad Tracy	.15	.40
409 Tom Glavine	.25	.60
410 Kelly Johnson	.15	.40
411 Chipper Jones	.40	1.00
412 Matt Diaz	.15	.40
413 Jeff Francoeur	.25	.60
414 Mark Kotsay	.15	.40
415 John Smoltz	.40	1.00
416 Tyler Yates	.15	.40
417 Yunel Escobar	.15	.40
418 Mike Hampton	.15	.40
419 Luke Scott	.15	.40
420 Adam Jones	.25	.60
421 Jeremy Guthrie	.15	.40
422 Nick Markakis	.40	1.00
423 Jay Payton	.15	.40
424 Brian Roberts	.15	.40
425 Melvin Mora	.15	.40
426 Adam Loewen	.15	.40
427 Luis Hernandez	.15	.40
428 Steve Trachsel	.15	.40
429 Josh Beckett	.25	.60
430 Jon Lester	.40	1.00
431 Curt Schilling	.25	.60
432 Jonathan Papelbon	.25	.60
433 Jason Varitek	.40	1.00
434 David Ortiz	.25	.60
435 Jacoby Ellsbury	.60	1.50
436 Julio Lugo	.15	.40
437 Sean Casey	.15	.40
438 Kevin Youkilis	.25	.60
439 J.D. Drew	.15	.40
440 Alex Cora	.15	.40
441 Derrek Lee	.15	.40
442 Carlos Zambrano	.25	.60
443 Sean Marshall	.15	.40
444 Matt Murton	.15	.40
445 Kerry Wood	.15	.40
446 Felix Pie	.15	.40
447 Mark DeRosa	.15	.40
448 Ronny Cedeno	.15	.40
449 Jon Lieber	.15	.40
450 Geovany Soto	.40	1.00
451 Gavin Floyd	.15	.40
452 Bobby Jenks	.15	.40
453 Scott Linebrink	.15	.40
454 Javier Vazquez	.15	.40
455 A.J. Pierzynski	.15	.40
456 Orlando Cabrera	.15	.40
457 Joe Crede	.15	.40
458 Josh Fields	.15	.40
459 Paul Konerko	.25	.60
460 Brian Anderson	.15	.40
461 Nick Swisher	.40	1.00
462 Carlos Quentin	.15	.40
463 Homer Bailey	.25	.60
464 Francisco Cordero	.15	.40
465 Aaron Harang	.15	.40
466 Alex Gonzalez	.15	.40
467 Brandon Phillips	.15	.40
468 Ryan Freel	.15	.40
469 Scott Hatteberg	.15	.40
470 Juan Castro	.15	.40
471 Norris Hopper	.15	.40
472 Josh Barfield	.15	.40
473 Casey Blake	.15	.40
474 Paul Byrd	.15	.40
475 Grady Sizemore	.25	.60
476 Jason Michaels	.15	.40
477 Jhonny Peralta	.15	.40
478 Asdrubal Cabrera	.25	.60
479 David Dellucci	.15	.40
480 C.C. Sabathia	.25	.60
481 Andy Marte	.15	.40
482 Troy Tulowitzki	.40	1.00
483 Matt Holliday	.40	1.00
484 Garrett Atkins	.15	.40
485 Aaron Cook	.15	.40
486 Brian Fuentes	.15	.40
487 Ryan Spilborghs	.15	.40
488 Ubaldo Jimenez	.25	.60
489 Jayson Nix	.15	.40
490 Nate Robertson	.15	.40
491 Kenny Rogers	.15	.40
492 Justin Verlander	.50	1.25
493 Dontrelle Willis	.15	.40
494 Joel Zumaya	.15	.40
495 Ivan Rodriguez	.25	.60
496 Miguel Cabrera	.40	1.00
497 Carlos Guillen	.15	.40
498 Edgar Renteria	.15	.40
499 Curtis Granderson	.25	.60
500 Jacque Jones	.15	.40
501 Marcus Thames	.15	.40
502 Josh Johnson	.25	.60
503 Jeremy Hermida	.15	.40
504 Dan Uggla	.25	.60
505 Mark Hendrickson	.15	.40
506 Luis Gonzalez	.15	.40
507 Dallas McPherson	.15	.40
508 Cody Ross	.15	.40
509 Matt Treanor	.15	.40
510 Andrew Miller	.15	.40
511 Jorge Cantu	.15	.40
512 Kazuo Matsui	.15	.40
513 Lance Berkman	.25	.60
514 Darin Erstad	.15	.40
515 Miguel Tejada	.25	.60
516 Jose Valverde	.15	.40
517 Geoff Blum	.15	.40
518 Reggie Abercrombie	.15	.40
519 Brandon Backe	.15	.40
520 Michael Bourn	.15	.40
521 Gil Meche	.15	.40
522 Brett Tomko	.15	.40
523 Miguel Olivo	.15	.40
524 Shane Costa	.15	.40
525 Joey Gathright	.15	.40
526 Mark Teahen	.15	.40
527 Alex Gordon	.25	.60
528 Tony Pena	.15	.40
529 Jose Guillen	.15	.40
530 Torii Hunter	.15	.40
531 Ervin Santana	.15	.40
532 Francisco Rodriguez	.25	.60
533 Howie Kendrick	.15	.40
534 Reggie Willits	.15	.40
535 John Lackey	.15	.40
536 Gary Matthews	.15	.40
537 Jon Garland	.15	.40
538 Kendry Morales	.15	.40
539 Chone Figgins	.15	.40
540 Andruw Jones	.15	.40
541 Jason Schmidt	.15	.40
542 James Loney	.25	.60
543 Andre Ethier	.25	.60
544 Rafael Furcal	.15	.40
545 Brad Penny	.15	.40
546 Hong-Chih Kuo	.15	.40
547 Jonathan Broxton	.15	.40
548 Esteban Loaiza	.15	.40
549 Delwyn Young	.15	.40
550 Mike Cameron	.15	.40
551 Ryan Braun	.50	1.25
552 Rickie Weeks	.25	.60
553 Bill Hall	.15	.40
554 Tony Gwynn Jr.	.15	.40
555 Eric Gagne	.15	.40
556 Jeff Suppan	.15	.40
557 Chris Capuano	.15	.40
558 Derrick Turnbow	.15	.40
559 Jason Kendall	.15	.40
560 Livan Hernandez	.15	.40
561 Philip Humber	.15	.40
562 Francisco Liriano	.25	.60
563 Pat Neshek	.15	.40
564 Adam Everett	.15	.40
565 Brendan Harris	.15	.40
566 Justin Morneau	.40	1.00
567 Craig Monroe	.15	.40
568 Carlos Gomez	.15	.40
569 Delmon Young	.25	.60
570 Mike Lamb	.15	.40
571 Oliver Perez	.15	.40
572 Jose Reyes	.25	.60
573 Moises Alou	.15	.40
574 Carlos Beltran	.15	.40
575 Endy Chavez	.15	.40
576 Ryan Church	.15	.40
577 Pedro Martinez	.25	.60
578 Johan Santana	.40	1.00
579 Mike Pelfrey	.15	.40
580 Brian Schneider	.15	.40
581 Joe Smith	.15	.40
582 Matt Wise	.15	.40
583 Duaner Sanchez	.15	.40
584 Ramon Castro	.15	.40
585 Kei Igawa	.15	.40
586 Mariano Rivera	.40	1.00
587 Chien-Ming Wang	.25	.60
588 Wilson Betemit	.15	.40
589 Robinson Cano	.40	1.00
590 Alex Rodriguez	.60	1.50
591 Bobby Abreu	.15	.40
592 Shelley Duncan	.15	.40
593 Hideki Matsui	.40	1.00
594 Kyle Farnsworth	.15	.40
595 Joe Blanton	.15	.40
596 Bobby Crosby	.15	.40
597 Eric Chavez	.15	.40
598 Dan Johnson	.15	.40
599 Rich Harden	.15	.40
600 Justin Duchscherer	.15	.40
601 Kurt Suzuki	.15	.40
602 Chris Denorfia	.15	.40
603 Emil Brown	.15	.40
604 Ryan Howard	.50	1.25
605 Jimmy Rollins	.25	.60
606 Pedro Feliz	.15	.40
607 Adam Eaton	.15	.40
608 Brad Lidge	.15	.40
609 Brett Myers	.15	.40
610 Pat Burrell	.15	.40
611 So Taguchi	.15	.40
612 Geoff Jenkins	.15	.40
613 Tom Gordon	.15	.40
614 Zach Duke	.15	.40
615 Matt Morris	.15	.40
616 Tom Gorzelanny	.15	.40
617 Jason Bay	.25	.60
618 Chris Duffy	.15	.40
619 Freddy Sanchez	.15	.40
620 Jose Bautista	.25	.60
621 Nyjer Morgan	.15	.40
622 Matt Capps	.15	.40
623 Paul Maholm	.15	.40
624 Tadahito Iguchi	.15	.40
625 Adrian Gonzalez	.25	.60
626 Jim Edmonds	.25	.60
627 Jake Peavy	.15	.40
628 Khalil Greene	.15	.40
629 Trevor Hoffman	.25	.60
630 Mark Prior	.25	.60
631 Randy Wolf	.15	.40
632 Michael Barrett	.15	.40
633 Scott Hairston	.15	.40
634 Tim Lincecum	.60	1.50
635 Noah Lowry	.15	.40
636 Rich Aurilia	.15	.40
637 Aaron Rowand	.15	.40
638 Randy Winn	.15	.40
639 Daniel Ortmeier	.15	.40
640 Ray Durham	.15	.40
641 Brian Wilson	.40	1.00
642 Adrian Beltre	.15	.40
643 Jeremy Reed	.15	.40
644 Jarrod Washburn	.15	.40
645 Yuniesky Betancourt	.15	.40
646 Jose Lopez	.15	.40
647 Raul Ibanez	.25	.60
648 Mike Morse	.15	.40
649 Erik Bedard	.15	.40
650 Brad Wilkerson	.15	.40
651 Chris Carpenter	.40	1.00
652 Mark Mulder	.15	.40
653 Juan Encarnacion	.15	.40
654 Skip Schumaker	.15	.40
655 Troy Glaus	.25	.60
656 Anthony Reyes	.15	.40
657 Cesar Izturis	.15	.40
658 Adam Kennedy	.15	.40
659 Chris Duncan	.15	.40
660 Matt Clement	.15	.40
661 Scott Kazmir	.25	.60
662 Troy Percival	.15	.40
663 Akinori Iwamura	.15	.40
664 Carl Crawford	.25	.60
665 Cliff Floyd	.15	.40
666 Jason Bartlett	.15	.40
667 Rocco Baldelli	.15	.40
668 Matt Garza	.15	.40
669 Edwin Jackson	.15	.40
670 Vicente Padilla	.15	.40
671 Josh Hamilton	.40	1.00
672 Jason Botts	.15	.40
673 Milton Bradley	.15	.40
674 Michael Young	.25	.60
675 Eddie Guardado	.15	.40
676 David Murphy	.15	.40
677 Ramon Vazquez	.15	.40
678 Ben Broussard	.15	.40
679 C.J. Wilson	.15	.40
680 Jason Jennings	.15	.40
681 Gustavo Chacin	.15	.40
682 BJ Ryan	.15	.40
683 David Eckstein	.15	.40
684 Alex Rios	.25	.60
685 John McDonald	.15	.40
686 Rod Barajas	.15	.40
687 Lyle Overbay	.15	.40
688 Scott Rolen	.25	.60
689 Reed Johnson	.15	.40
690 Marco Scutaro	.15	.40
691 Lastings Milledge	.15	.40
692 Johnny Estrada	.15	.40
693 Paul Lo Duca	.15	.40
694 Ryan Zimmerman	.25	.60
695 Odalis Perez	.15	.40
696 Wily Mo Pena	.15	.40
697 Elijah Dukes	.15	.40
698 Aaron Boone	.15	.40
699 Ronnie Belliard	.15	.40
700 Nick Johnson	.15	.40
701 Randor Bierd RC	.40	1.00
702 Brian Barton RC	.60	1.50
703 Brian Bass (RC)	.40	1.00
704 Brian Bocock RC	.40	1.00
705 Gregor Blanco (RC)	.40	1.00
706 Callix Crabbe (RC)	.40	1.00
707 Johnny Cueto RC	.60	1.50
708 Kosuke Fukudome RC	4.00	10.00
708b Kosuke Fukudome Japanese	40.00	80.00
709 Scott Kazmir SH	.25	.60
710 Steve Holm RC	.40	1.00
711 Fernando Hernandez RC	.40	1.00
712 Elliot Johnson (RC)	.40	1.00
713 Masahide Kobayashi RC	.60	1.50
714 Hiroki Kuroda RC	.60	1.50
715 Blake DeWitt (RC)	1.00	2.50
716 Kyle McClellan RC	.40	1.00
717 Evan Meek RC	.40	1.00
718 Denard Span (RC)	.60	1.50
719 Darren O'Day RC	.40	1.00
720 Alexei Ramirez RC	1.50	4.00
721 Alex Romero (RC)	.60	1.50
722 Clete Thomas RC	.60	1.50
723 Matt Tolbert RC	.60	1.50
724 Ramon Troncoso RC	.40	1.00
725 Matt Tupman RC	.40	1.00
726 Rico Washington (RC)	.40	1.00
727 Randy Wells RC	.60	1.50
728 Wesley Wright RC	.40	1.00
729 Yasuhiko Yabuta RC	.40	1.00
730 Alex Rodriguez SH	.60	1.50
731 Andruw Jones SH	.15	.40
732 C.C. Sabathia SH	.25	.60
733 Carlos Beltran SH	.15	.40
734 David Wright SH	.50	1.25
735 Derrek Lee SH	.15	.40
736 Dustin Pedroia SH	.50	1.25
737 Grady Sizemore SH	.25	.60
738 Greg Maddux SH	.50	1.25
739 Ichiro Suzuki SH	.60	1.50
740 Ivan Rodriguez SH	.25	.60
741 Jake Peavy SH	.15	.40
742 Jimmy Rollins SH	.25	.60
743 Johan Santana SH	.40	1.00
744 Josh Beckett SH	.25	.60
745 Kevin Youkilis SH	.25	.60
746 Matt Holliday SH	.40	1.00
747 Mike Lowell SH	.15	.40
748 Ryan Braun SH	.50	1.25
749 Torii Hunter SH	.15	.40
750 Alex Rodriguez SH	.60	1.50
751 Torii Hunter CL	.15	.40
752 Miguel Tejada CL	.25	.60
753 Huston Street CL	.15	.40
754 Scott Rolen CL	.25	.60
755 Tom Glavine CL	.25	.60
756 Ryan Braun CL	.50	1.25
757 Troy Glaus CL	.25	.60
758 Carlos Zambrano CL	.25	.60
759 Carl Crawford CL	.25	.60
760 Dan Haren CL	.15	.40
761 Andruw Jones CL	.15	.40
762 Barry Zito CL	.15	.40
763 Victor Martinez CL	.25	.60
764 Erik Bedard CL	.15	.40
765 Josh Willingham CL	.15	.40
766 Johan Santana CL	.40	1.00
767 Dmitri Young CL	.15	.40
768 Brian Roberts CL	.15	.40
769 Jim Edmonds CL	.25	.60
770 Jimmy Rollins CL	.25	.60
771 Jason Bay CL	.25	.60
772 Josh Hamilton CL	.40	1.00
773 Josh Beckett CL	.25	.60
774 Aaron Harang CL	.25	.60

775 Troy Tulowitzki CL .40 1.00
776 Jose Guillen CL .15 .40
777 Miguel Cabrera CL .40 1.00
778 Joe Mauer CL .40 1.00
779 Nick Swisher CL .40 1.00
780 Derek Jeter CL 1.00 2.50
781 Brandon Webb SH .25 .60
782 Brian Roberts SH .15 .40
783 C.C. Sabathia SH .25 .60
784 Carl Crawford SH .25 .60
785 Curtis Granderson SH .25 .60
786 David Ortiz SH .25 .60
787 Ichiro Suzuki SH .60 1.50
788 Jake Peavy SH .15 .40
789 Jimmy Rollins SH .25 .60
790 Joe Borowski SH .15 .40
791 Johan Santana SH .40 1.00
792 John Lackey SH .15 .40
793 Jose Reyes SH .25 .60
794 Jose Valverde SH .15 .40
795 Josh Beckett SH .25 .60
796 Juan Pierre SH .15 .40
797 Magglio Ordonez SH .25 .60
798 Matt Holliday SH .40 1.00
799 Prince Fielder SH .25 .60

2008 Upper Deck Gold

*GOLD VET: 4X TO 10X BASIC
*GOLD RC: 3X TO 8X BASIC
RANDOM INSERTS IN PACKS
STATED PRINT RUN 99 SER.#'d SETS
708 Kosuke Fukudome 50.00 100.00

2008 Upper Deck A Piece of History 500 Club

STATED ODDS 1:192 HOBBY
EXCHANGE DEADLINE 1/14/2010
FT Frank Thomas 20.00 50.00
JT Jim Thome 15.00 40.00

2008 Upper Deck All Rookie Team Signatures

STATED ODDS 1:80 H, 1:7500 R
AI Akinori Iwamura 10.00 25.00
AL Adam Lind 3.00 8.00
AM Andrew Miller
BB Billy Butler 5.00 12.00
BU Brian Burres 3.00 8.00
DM Daisuke Matsuzaka EXCH
DY Delmon Young 6.00 15.00
HA Justin Hampson 3.00 8.00
HP Hunter Pence
JH Josh Hamilton 5.00 12.00
KC Kevin Cameron 3.00 8.00
KK Kyle Kendrick 6.00 15.00
MB Michael Bourn 3.00 8.00
MF Mike Fontenot 5.00 12.00
MO Micah Owings 5.00 12.00
RB Ryan Braun 20.00 50.00
SO Joakim Soria 3.00 8.00
TL Tim Lincecum
TT Troy Tulowitzki
YG Yovani Gallardo

2008 Upper Deck Derek Jeter Chronicles

STATED ODDS 1:6 TARGET
DJC1 Derek Jeter 1.50 4.00
DJC2 Derek Jeter 1.50 4.00
DJC3 Derek Jeter 1.50 4.00
DJC4 Derek Jeter 1.50 4.00
DJC5 Derek Jeter 1.50 4.00
DJC6 Derek Jeter 1.50 4.00
DJC7 Derek Jeter 1.50 4.00
DJC8 Derek Jeter 1.50 4.00
DJC9 Derek Jeter 1.50 4.00
DJC10 Derek Jeter 1.50 4.00
DJC11 Derek Jeter 1.50 4.00
DJC12 Derek Jeter 1.50 4.00
DJC13 Derek Jeter 1.50 4.00
DJC14 Derek Jeter 1.50 4.00
DJC15 Derek Jeter 1.50 4.00
DJC16 Derek Jeter 1.50 4.00
DJC17 Derek Jeter 1.50 4.00
DJC18 Derek Jeter 1.50 4.00
DJC19 Derek Jeter 1.50 4.00
DJC20 Derek Jeter 1.50 4.00

2008 Upper Deck Derek Jeter Chronicles Autographs

RANDOM INSERTS IN PACKS
STATED PRINT RUN 1 SER.#'d SET
NO PRICING DUE TO SCARCITY

2008 Upper Deck Derek Jeter O-Pee-Chee Reprints

STATED ODDS 1:6 TARGET
DJ1 Derek Jeter 1.50 4.00
DJ2 Derek Jeter 1.50 4.00
DJ3 Derek Jeter 1.50 4.00
DJ4 Derek Jeter 1.50 4.00
DJ5 Derek Jeter 1.50 4.00
DJ6 Derek Jeter 1.50 4.00
DJ7 Derek Jeter 1.50 4.00
DJ8 Derek Jeter 1.50 4.00
DJ9 Derek Jeter 1.50 4.00
DJ10 Derek Jeter 1.50 4.00
DJ11 Derek Jeter 1.50 4.00
DJ12 Derek Jeter 1.50 4.00
DJ13 Derek Jeter 1.50 4.00
DJ14 Derek Jeter 1.50 4.00
DJ15 Derek Jeter 1.50 4.00

2008 Upper Deck Diamond Collection

COMPLETE SET (20) 6.00 15.00
1 Adam LaRoche .40 1.00
2 Brian McCann .60 1.50
3 Bronson Arroyo .40 1.00
4 Chad Billingsley .40 1.00
5 Chin-Lung Hu .60 1.50
6 Felix Pie .40 1.00
7 Garrett Atkins .40 1.00
8 Homer Bailey .60 1.50
9 Ian Kennedy 1.00 2.50
10 James Shields .40 1.00
11 Jarrod Saltalamacchia .40 1.00
12 Manny Corpas .40 1.00
13 Mark Ellis .40 1.00
14 Micah Owings .40 1.00
15 Nick Swisher 1.00 2.50
16 Rich Hill .40 1.00
17 Russell Martin .40 1.00
18 Ryan Theriot .40 1.00
19 Steve Pearce .60 1.50
20 Victor Martinez .60 1.50

2008 Upper Deck Hit Brigade

HB1 Albert Pujols 2.50 6.00
HB2 Alex Rodriguez 1.50 4.00
HB3 David Ortiz .60 1.50
HB4 David Wright 1.25 3.00
HB5 Derek Jeter 2.50 6.00
HB6 Derrek Lee .40 1.00
HB7 Freddy Sanchez .40 1.00
HB8 Hanley Ramirez 1.00 2.50
HB9 Ichiro Suzuki 1.50 4.00
HB10 Joe Mauer 1.00 2.50
HB11 Magglio Ordonez .60 1.50
HB12 Matt Holliday 1.00 2.50
HB13 Miguel Cabrera 1.00 2.50
HB14 Todd Helton .60 1.50
HB15 Vladimir Guerrero 1.00 2.50

2008 Upper Deck Hit Brigade Autographs

STATED PRINT RUN 5 SER.#'d SETS
NO PRICING DUE TO SCARCITY
HB6 Derrek Lee
HB8 Hanley Ramirez
HB10 Joe Mauer
HB12 Matt Holliday
HB13 Miguel Cabrera

2008 Upper Deck Hot Commodities

COMPLETE SET (50) 30.00 60.00
STATED ODDS 2:1 WALMART/FAT PACKS
HC1 Miguel Tejada .60 1.50
HC2 Daisuke Matsuzaka 1.00 2.50
HC3 David Ortiz .60 1.50
HC4 Manny Ramirez 1.00 2.50
HC5 Alex Rodriguez 1.50 4.00
HC6 Derek Jeter 2.50 6.00
HC7 Carl Crawford .60 1.50
HC8 Alex Rios .60 1.50
HC9 Jim Thome .60 1.50
HC10 Grady Sizemore .60 1.50
HC11 Travis Hafner .40 1.00
HC12 Victor Martinez .60 1.50
HC13 Justin Verlander 1.25 3.00
HC14 Magglio Ordonez .60 1.50
HC15 Gary Sheffield .40 1.00
HC16 Alex Gordon .60 1.50
HC17 Justin Morneau 1.00 2.50
HC18 Johan Santana 1.00 2.50
HC19 Vladimir Guerrero 1.00 2.50
HC20 Dan Haren .40 1.00
HC21 Ichiro Suzuki 1.50 4.00
HC22 Mark Teixeira 1.00 2.50
HC23 Chipper Jones 1.00 2.50
HC24 John Smoltz 1.00 2.50
HC25 Miguel Cabrera 1.00 2.50
HC26 Hanley Ramirez 1.00 2.50
HC27 Jose Reyes .60 1.50
HC28 David Wright 1.25 3.00
HC29 Carlos Beltran .40 1.00
HC30 Ryan Howard 1.25 3.00
HC31 Chase Utley 1.00 2.50
HC32 Ryan Zimmerman .60 1.50
HC33 Aramis Ramirez .40 1.00
HC34 Derrek Lee .40 1.00
HC35 Alfonso Soriano .60 1.50
HC36 Ken Griffey Jr. 1.50 4.00
HC37 Adam Dunn .60 1.50
HC38 Carlos Lee .40 1.00
HC39 Lance Berkman .60 1.50
HC40 Prince Fielder .60 1.50
HC41 Ryan Braun 1.25 3.00
HC42 Jason Bay .60 1.50
HC43 Albert Pujols 2.50 6.00
HC44 Brandon Webb .60 1.50
HC45 Matt Holliday 1.00 2.50
HC46 Brad Penny .40 1.00
HC47 Russell Martin .40 1.00
HC48 Trevor Hoffman .60 1.50
HC49 Jake Peavy .40 1.00
HC50 Tim Lincecum 1.50 4.00

2008 Upper Deck Infield Power

RANDOM INSERTS IN RETAIL PACKS
AB Adrian Beltre .25 .60
AG Alex Gordon .40 1.00
AP Albert Pujols 1.50 4.00
AR Aramis Ramirez .25 .60
BP Brandon Phillips .25 .60
BR Brian Roberts .25 .60
CJ Chipper Jones .60 1.50
CP Carlos Pena .40 1.00
CU Chase Utley .60 1.50
DJ Derek Jeter 1.50 4.00
DW David Wright .75 2.00
GA Garrett Atkins .25 .60
GO Adrian Gonzalez .40 1.00
HK Howie Kendrick .25 .60
HR Hanley Ramirez .60 1.50
JI Jimmy Rollins .40 1.00
JK Jeff Kent .25 .60
JM Justin Morneau .60 1.50
JR Jose Reyes .40 1.00
LB Lance Berkman .40 1.00
MC Miguel Cabrera .60 1.50
ML Mike Lowell .25 .60
MT Mark Teixeira .60 1.50
PF Prince Fielder .40 1.00
PK Paul Konerko .40 1.00
RG Ryan Garko .25 .60
RH Ryan Howard .75 2.00
RO Alex Rodriguez 1.00 2.50
RZ Ryan Zimmerman .40 1.00
TT Troy Tulowitzki .60 1.50

2008 Upper Deck Inkredible

STATED ODDS 1:80 H, 1:7500 R
AL Adam Lind 3.00 8.00
CC Chris Carpenter
CP Corey Patterson 3.00 8.00
CR Cody Ross 6.00 15.00
DL Derrek Lee 6.00 15.00
EA Erick Aybar 3.00 8.00
IK Ian Kinsler 5.00 12.00
IR Ivan Rodriguez 20.00 50.00
JB Josh Barfield 5.00 12.00
JH Jason Hammel 3.00 8.00
JS James Shields 5.00 12.00
KE Ian Kennedy
LS Luke Scott 3.00 8.00
MJ Mike Jacobs 5.00 12.00
RC Ryan Church 3.00 8.00
RL Ruddy Lugo 3.00 8.00
RS Ryan Shealy 3.00 8.00
RT Ryan Theriot 6.00 15.00
SO Jorge Sosa 5.00 12.00
TB Taylor Buchholz 3.00 8.00

2008 Upper Deck Milestone Memorabilia

STATED ODDS 1:192 HOBBY
GS Gary Sheffield 4.00 10.00
KG Ken Griffey Jr. 12.50 30.00
SS Sammy Sosa
TG Tom Glavine 8.00 20.00
TH Trevor Hoffman 4.00 10.00

2008 Upper Deck Mr. November

STATED ODDS 1:6 TARGET
1 Derek Jeter 1.50 4.00
2 Derek Jeter 1.50 4.00
3 Derek Jeter 1.50 4.00
4 Derek Jeter 1.50 4.00
5 Derek Jeter 1.50 4.00
6 Derek Jeter 1.50 4.00
7 Derek Jeter 1.50 4.00
8 Derek Jeter 1.50 4.00
9 Derek Jeter 1.50 4.00
10 Derek Jeter 1.50 4.00
11 Derek Jeter 1.50 4.00
12 Derek Jeter 1.50 4.00
13 Derek Jeter 1.50 4.00
14 Derek Jeter 1.50 4.00
15 Derek Jeter 1.50 4.00

2008 Upper Deck O-Pee-Chee

COMPLETE SET (50) 30.00 60.00
STATED ODDS 1:2 HOBBY
AG Alex Gordon .60 1.50
AP Albert Pujols 2.50 6.00
AR Alex Rodriguez 1.50 4.00
BP Brad Penny .40 1.00
BR Babe Ruth 2.50 6.00
BU B.J. Upton .60 1.50
BW Brandon Webb .60 1.50
CD Chris Duncan .40 1.00
CJ Chipper Jones 1.00 2.50
CL Carlos Lee .40 1.00
CP Carlos Pena .60 1.50
CU Chase Utley 1.00 2.50
CY Chris Young .40 1.00
DH Dan Haren .40 1.00
DJ Derek Jeter 2.50 6.00
DL Derrek Lee .40 1.00
DM Daisuke Matsuzaka 1.00 2.50
DO David Ortiz .60 1.50
DW David Wright 1.25 3.00
EB Erik Bedard .40 1.00
ER Edgar Renteria .40 1.00
GS Gary Sheffield .40 1.00
HP Hunter Pence 1.00 2.50
HR Hanley Ramirez 1.00 2.50
IS Ichiro Suzuki 1.50 4.00
JB Jason Bay .60 1.50
JJ J.J. Putz .40 1.00
JM Justin Morneau 1.00 2.50
JP Jake Peavy .40 1.00
JR Jose Reyes .60 1.50
JS Johan Santana 1.00 2.50
JT Jim Thome .60 1.50
JW Jered Weaver .40 1.00
KG Ken Griffey Jr. 1.50 4.00
MC Miguel Cabrera 1.00 2.50
MH Matt Holliday 1.00 2.50
MO Magglio Ordonez .60 1.50
MR Manny Ramirez 1.00 2.50
MT Mark Teixeira 1.00 2.50
NL Noah Lowry .40 1.00
PF Prince Fielder .60 1.50
PH Brandon Phillips .40 1.00
RA Aramis Ramirez .40 1.00
RB Ryan Braun 1.25 3.00
RH Ryan Howard 1.25 3.00
RM Russell Martin .40 1.00
RZ Ryan Zimmerman .60 1.50
TH Todd Helton .60 1.50
VG Vladimir Guerrero 1.00 2.50
VW Vernon Wells .40 1.00

2008 Upper Deck Presidential Predictors

COMP.SET w/o HILLARY (8) 15.00 40.00
STATED ODDS 1:6 H,1:6 R,1:10 WAL MART
PP1 Rudy Giuliani 2.00 5.00
PP2 John Edwards 2.00 5.00
PP3 John McCain 2.00 5.00
PP4 Barack Obama 4.00 10.00
PP5 Mitt Romney 2.00 5.00
PP6 Fred Thompson 2.00 5.00
PP7 Hillary Clinton SP 75.00 150.00
PP8 Al Gore 2.00 5.00
George Bush
PP9 Wild Card 2.00 5.00
PV1 Barack Obama Victor 4.00 10.00
PP15 Sarah Palin 60.00 120.00
PP16 Joe Biden 125.00 250.00

2008 Upper Deck Presidential Running Mate Predictors

PP7B Hillary Clinton 10.00 25.00
Barack Obama
PP7H Hillary Clinton 75.00 150.00
Barack Obama
PP10 Barack Obama 4.00 10.00
John McCain
PP10A John McCain 4.00 10.00
Hillary Clinton
PP11 Barack Obama 4.00 10.00
John McCain
PP11A John McCain 2.00 5.00
Hillary Clinton
PP12 Barack Obama 4.00 10.00
John McCain
PP12A John McCain 2.00 5.00
Hillary Clinton
PP13 Barack Obama 4.00 10.00
John McCain
PP13A John McCain 2.00 5.00
Hillary Clinton
PP14 Barack Obama 4.00 10.00
John McCain
PP14A John McCain 2.00 5.00
Hillary Clinton
PP15 Barack Obama 150.00 300.00
John McCain

2008 Upper Deck Rookie Debut

COMPLETE SET (30) 12.50 30.00
1 Emilio Bonafacio 1.00 2.50
2 Billy Buckner .40 1.00
3 Brandon Jones 1.00 2.50
4 Clay Buchholz 1.00 2.50
5 Lance Broadway .40 1.00
6 Joey Votto 1.50 4.00
7 Ryan Hanigan .60 1.50
8 Seth Smith .40 1.00
9 Joe Koshansky .40 1.00
10 Chris Seddon .40 1.00
11 J.R. Towles .60 1.50
12 Luke Hochevar .60 1.50
13 Chin-Lung Hu .60 1.50
14 Sam Fuld 1.25 3.00
15 Jose Morales .40 1.00
16 Carlos Muniz .60 1.50
17 Ian Kennedy 1.00 2.50
18 Alberto Gonzalez .60 1.50
19 Jonathan Albaladejo .60 1.50
20 Daric Barton .40 1.00
21 Jerry Blevins .60 1.50
22 Steve Pearce .60 1.50
23 Dave Davidson .60 1.50
24 Eugenio Velez .40 1.00
25 Erick Threets .40 1.00
26 Bronson Sardinha .40 1.00
27 Wladimir Balentien .40 1.00
28 Justin Ruggiano .60 1.50
29 Luis Mendoza .40 1.00
30 Justin Maxwell .40 1.00

2008 Upper Deck Season Highlights Signatures

STATED ODDS 1:80 H, 1:7500 R
BB Brian Bannister 6.00 15.00
BF Ben Francisco 3.00 8.00
CG Curtis Granderson 12.50 30.00
CS Curt Schilling 20.00 50.00
FL Fred Lewis 3.00 8.00
FT Frank Thomas
GA Garret Anderson
JS Jarrod Saltalamacchia 5.00 12.00
JV Justin Verlander
JW Josh Willingham 3.00 8.00
KK Kevin Kouzmanoff 3.00 8.00
MO Micah Owings 5.00 12.00
MR Mark Reynolds 6.00 15.00
MT Miguel Tejada 12.50 30.00
PF Prince Fielder
PM Pedro Martinez
RB Ryan Braun 20.00 50.00
RM Russell Martin
RS Ryan Spilborghs 6.00 15.00
TG Tom Glavine

2008 Upper Deck Signature Sensations

STATED ODDS 1:80 H, 1:7500 R
AE Andre Ethier 3.00 8.00
AK Austin Kearns 5.00 12.00
AM Aaron Miles 5.00 12.00
BB Boof Bonser 3.00 8.00
BH Brendan Harris 3.00 8.00
BM Brandon McCarthy 3.00 8.00
CB Cha-Seung Baek 3.00 8.00
CC Chris Carpenter
DL Derrek Lee 6.00 15.00
IR Ivan Rodriguez 20.00 50.00
JP Joel Peralta 3.00 8.00
JS James Shields 3.00 8.00
JV John Van Benschoten 3.00 8.00
KG Ken Griffey Jr.
LS Luke Scott 3.00 8.00
MC Matt Cain 5.00 12.00
NS Nick Swisher 5.00 12.00
RA Reggie Abercrombie 3.00 8.00
SM Sean Marshall 3.00 8.00
YP Yusmeiro Petit 3.00 8.00

2008 Upper Deck Signs of History Cut Signatures

AJ Andrew Johnson/5
BC Bill Clinton/12
BH Benjamin Harrison/45 700.00 1000.00
CC Calvin Coolidge/18
FP Franklin Pierce/8
FR Franklin D. Roosevelt/5
GB George H.W. Bush/18
GC Grover Cleveland/30 600.00 850.00
GF Gerald Ford/75 100.00 200.00
GW George Washington/1
HH Herbert Hoover/34
HT Harry Truman/47 400.00 700.00
JC Jimmy Carter/49 250.00 350.00
JG James Garfield/8
JT John Tyler/8
NNO Exchange Card 700.00 1000.00
RH Rutherford B. Hayes/75 400.00 650.00
RN Richard Nixon/19
RR Ronald Reagan/16
TR Theodore Roosevelt/3
WH William Henry Harrison/1
WM William McKinley/6
WT William H. Taft/50 500.00 750.00
WW Woodrow Wilson/22
NNO EXCH Card

2008 Upper Deck Star Attractions

SA1 B.J. Upton .60 1.50
SA2 Carl Crawford .60 1.50
SA3 Chris B. Young .40 1.00
SA4 John Maine .40 1.00
SA5 Jonathan Papelbon .60 1.50
SA6 Nick Markakis 1.00 2.50
SA7 Prince Fielder .60 1.50
SA8 Takashi Saito .40 1.00
SA9 Tom Gorzelanny .40 1.00
SA10 Troy Tulowitzki 1.00 2.50

2008 Upper Deck Star Attractions Autographs

STATED PRINT RUN 5 SER.#'d SETS
NO PRICING DUE TO SCARCITY
SA1 B.J. Upton
SA2 Carl Crawford
SA3 Chris B. Young
SA4 John Maine
SA5 Jonathan Papelbon
SA6 Nick Markakis
SA7 Prince Fielder
SA8 Takashi Saito
SA9 Tom Gorzelanny
SA10 Troy Tulowitzki

2008 Upper Deck Star Quest

SER.1 ODDS 1:1 RETAIL/TARGET
SER.1 ODDS 1:1 WAL MART
*UNCOMMON: .4X TO 1X COMMON
SER.1 UNC ODDS 1:4 RETAIL/TARGET
SER.1 UNC ODDS 1:6 WAL MART
*RARE: .6X TO 1.5X COMMON
SER.1 RARE ODDS 1:8 RETAIL/TARGET
SER.1 RARE ODDS 1:12 WAL MART
*SUPER: 1X TO 2.5X COMMON
SER.1 SUPER ODDS 1:16 RETAIL/TARGET
SER.1 SUPER ODDS 1:24 WAL MART
*ULTRA: 1.5X TO 4X BASIC
SER.1 ULTRA ODDS 1:24 RETAIL/TARGET
SER.1 ULTRA ODDS 1:36 WAL MART
1 Ichiro Suzuki 1.50 4.00
2 Ryan Braun 1.25 3.00
3 Prince Fielder .60 1.50
4 Ken Griffey Jr. 1.50 4.00
5 Vladimir Guerrero 1.00 2.50
6 Travis Hafner .40 1.00
7 Matt Holliday 1.00 2.50
8 Ryan Howard 1.25 3.00
9 Derek Jeter 2.50 6.00
10 Chipper Jones 1.00 2.50
11 Carlos Lee .40 1.00
12 Justin Morneau 1.00 2.50
13 Magglio Ordonez .60 1.50
14 David Ortiz .60 1.50
15 Jake Peavy .40 1.00
16 Albert Pujols 2.50 6.00
17 Hanley Ramirez 1.00 2.50
18 Manny Ramirez 1.00 2.50
19 Jose Reyes .60 1.50
20 Alex Rodriguez 1.50 4.00
21 Johan Santana 1.00 2.50
22 Grady Sizemore .60 1.50
23 Alfonso Soriano .60 1.50
24 Mark Teixeira 1.00 2.50
25 Frank Thomas 1.00 2.50
26 Jim Thome .60 1.50
27 Chase Utley 1.00 2.50
28 Brandon Webb .60 1.50
29 David Wright 1.25 3.00
30 Michael Young .60 1.50
31 Adam Dunn .60 1.50
32 Albert Pujols 2.50 6.00
33 Alex Rodriguez 1.50 4.00
34 B.J. Upton .60 1.50
35 C.C. Sabathia .60 1.50
36 Carlos Beltran .40 1.00
37 Carlos Pena .60 1.50
38 Cole Hamels 1.00 2.50
39 Curtis Granderson .60 1.50
40 Daisuke Matsuzaka 1.00 2.50
41 David Ortiz .60 1.50
42 Derek Jeter 2.50 6.00
43 Derrek Lee .40 1.00
44 Eric Byrnes .40 1.00
45 Felix Hernandez 1.00 2.50
46 Ichiro Suzuki 1.50 4.00
47 Jeff Francoeur .60 1.50
48 Jimmy Rollins .60 1.50
49 Joe Mauer 1.00 2.50
50 John Smoltz 1.00 2.50
51 Ken Griffey Jr. 1.50 4.00
52 Lance Berkman .60 1.50
53 Miguel Cabrera 1.00 2.50
54 Paul Konerko .60 1.50
55 Pedro Martinez .60 1.50
56 Randy Johnson 1.00 2.50
57 Russell Martin .40 1.00
58 Troy Tulowitzki 1.00 2.50
59 Vernon Wells .40 1.00
60 Vladimir Guerrero 1.00 2.50

2008 Upper Deck Superstar Scrapbooks

SS1 Albert Pujols 2.50 6.00
SS2 Alex Rodriguez 1.50 4.00
SS3 Chase Utley 1.00 2.50
SS4 Chipper Jones 1.00 2.50
SS5 David Ortiz .60 1.50
SS6 Derek Jeter 2.50 6.00
SS7 Ichiro Suzuki 1.50 4.00
SS8 Johan Santana 1.00 2.50
SS9 Jose Reyes .60 1.50
SS10 Ken Griffey Jr. 1.50 4.00
SS11 Manny Ramirez 1.00 2.50
SS12 Prince Fielder .60 1.50
SS13 Randy Johnson 1.00 2.50
SS14 Ryan Howard 1.25 3.00
SS15 Vladimir Guerrero 1.00 2.50

2008 Upper Deck The House That Ruth Built

STATED ODDS 1:4 WAL MART BLISTER
STATED ODDS 1:6 WAL MART BLASTER
SILVER INSERTED IN WAL MART PACKS
SILVER PRINT RUN 1 SER.#'d SET
NO SILVER PRICING DUE TO SCARCITY
HRB1 Babe Ruth 1.50 4.00
HRB2 Babe Ruth 1.50 4.00
HRB3 Babe Ruth 1.50 4.00
HRB4 Babe Ruth 1.50 4.00
HRB5 Babe Ruth 1.50 4.00
HRB6 Babe Ruth 1.50 4.00
HRB7 Babe Ruth 1.50 4.00
HRB8 Babe Ruth 1.50 4.00
HRB9 Babe Ruth 1.50 4.00
HRB10 Babe Ruth 1.50 4.00
HRB11 Babe Ruth 1.50 4.00
HRB12 Babe Ruth 1.50 4.00
HRB13 Babe Ruth 1.50 4.00
HRB14 Babe Ruth 1.50 4.00
HRB15 Babe Ruth 1.50 4.00
HRB16 Babe Ruth 1.50 4.00
HRB17 Babe Ruth 1.50 4.00
HRB18 Babe Ruth 1.50 4.00
HRB19 Babe Ruth 1.50 4.00
HRB20 Babe Ruth 1.50 4.00
HRB21 Babe Ruth 1.50 4.00
HRB22 Babe Ruth 1.50 4.00
HRB23 Babe Ruth 1.50 4.00
HRB24 Babe Ruth 1.50 4.00
HRB25 Babe Ruth 1.50 4.00

2008 Upper Deck UD Autographs

STATED ODDS 1:80 H, 1:7500 R
CD Chris Duffy 3.00 8.00
CS Curt Schilling 20.00 50.00
JK Jeff Karstens 3.00 8.00
JP Joel Peralta 3.00 8.00
JS Jorge Sosa 5.00 12.00
JV John Van Benschoten 3.00 8.00
KI Kei Igawa 6.00 15.00
KS Kelly Shoppach 3.00 8.00
LS Luke Scott 3.00 8.00
MC Manny Corpas 6.00 15.00

MP Mike Pelfrey 5.00 12.00
MT Miguel Tejada 12.50 30.00
NM Nate McLouth 6.00 15.00
RH Ramon Hernandez 5.00 12.00
SA Kirk Saarloos 3.00 8.00
SF Scott Feldman 4.00 10.00
SH James Shields 3.00 8.00
SR Saul Rivera 3.00 8.00
SS Skip Schumaker 4.00 10.00
ZG Zack Greinke

2008 Upper Deck UD Game Materials

SER.1 ODDS 1:32 HOBBY,1:96 RETAIL
SER.1 ODDS 1:40 WAL MART BLASTER
SER.1 ODDS 1:96 TARGET/WM BLISTER
AJ Andruw Jones S2 3.00 8.00
AP Albert Pujols S2 6.00 15.00
BB Boof Bonser S2 3.00 8.00
BM Brandon McCarthy S2 3.00 8.00
BP Brandon Phillips S2 3.00 8.00
BR Brian Roberts 3.00 8.00
BU B.J. Upton S2 3.00 8.00
BZ Barry Zito S2 3.00 8.00
CA Matt Cain S2 3.00 8.00
CB Carlos Beltran 3.00 8.00
CB Chris Burke S2 3.00 8.00
CC Coco Crisp 3.00 8.00
CC Chris Carpenter S2 3.00 8.00
CD Chris Duncan S2 3.00 8.00
CG Carlos Guillen 3.00 8.00
CJ Conor Jackson S2 3.00 8.00
CL Cliff Lee S2 3.00 8.00
CQ Carlos Quentin S2 3.00 8.00
CU Michael Cuddyer S2 3.00 8.00
DC Daniel Cabrera 3.00 8.00
DJ Derek Jeter 8.00 20.00
DJ Derek Jeter S2 8.00 20.00
DL Derrek Lee S2 3.00 8.00
DO David Ortiz 4.00 10.00
DO David Ortiz S2 4.00 10.00
DW Dontrelle Willis 3.00 8.00
DW David Wells S2 3.00 8.00
EC Eric Chavez S2 3.00 8.00
EG Eric Gagne 3.00 8.00
ES Ervin Santana S2 3.00 8.00
FH Felix Hernandez S2 3.00 8.00
FL Francisco Liriano S2 3.00 8.00
FR Francisco Rodriguez S2 3.00 8.00
FS Freddy Sanchez S2 3.00 8.00
GA Garrett Atkins S2 3.00 8.00
GC Gustavo Chacin 1.50 4.00
GJ Geoff Jenkins 3.00 8.00
GL Troy Glaus S2 3.00 8.00
GM Gil Meche S2 3.00 8.00
GO Jonny Gomes S2 3.00 8.00
HR Hanley Ramirez S2 3.00 8.00
IR Ivan Rodriguez S2 6.00 15.00
JB Jason Bay 3.00 8.00
JB Jeremy Bonderman S2 3.00 8.00
JD Justin Duchscherer 3.00 8.00
JD Jermaine Dye S2 3.00 8.00
JG Jason Giambi S2 3.00 8.00
JH Jeremy Hermida S2 3.00 8.00
JJ Josh Johnson S2 3.00 8.00
JL James Loney S2 3.00 8.00
JP Jake Peavy 4.00 10.00
JP Jonathan Papelbon S2 4.00 10.00
JR Jeremy Reed S2 3.00 8.00
JS Jeremy Sowers 3.00 8.00
JS Jason Schmidt S2 3.00 8.00
JV Jason Varitek 4.00 10.00
JV Justin Verlander S2 3.00 8.00
JW Jered Weaver S2 3.00 8.00
KG Khalil Greene S2 3.00 8.00
KJ Kenji Johjima S2 3.00 8.00
KM Kazuo Matsui 3.00 8.00
KW Kerry Wood S2 3.00 8.00
MC Miguel Cabrera S2 4.00 10.00
ME Morgan Ensberg 3.00 8.00
ME Melky Cabrera S2 3.00 8.00
MG Marcus Giles S2 3.00 8.00
MJ Mike Jacobs S2 3.00 8.00
MK Masumi Kuwata 3.00 8.00
MM Melvin Mora 3.00 8.00
MN Mike Napoli S2 3.00 8.00
MP Mark Prior S2 3.00 8.00
MS Mike Sweeney 3.00 8.00
MY Michael Young 3.00 8.00
MY Brett Myers S2 3.00 8.00
OL Scott Olsen S2 3.00 8.00
PA Jonathan Papelbon 4.00 10.00
PE Mike Pelfrey S2 3.00 8.00
PF Prince Fielder S2 4.00 10.00
PK Paul Konerko S2 3.00 8.00
RC Ryan Church S2 3.00 8.00
RD Ray Durham S2 3.00 8.00
RF Ryan Freel S2 3.00 8.00
RH Roy Halladay 3.00 8.00
RJ Reed Johnson S2 3.00 8.00
RQ Robb Quinlan S2 3.00 8.00
RW Rickie Weeks S2 3.00 8.00
RZ Ryan Zimmerman S2 4.00 10.00
SK Scott Kazmir S2 3.00 8.00
SO Jeremy Sowers S2 3.00 8.00
TG Tom Glavine S2 3.00 8.00
TS Takashi Saito 3.00 8.00
VW Vernon Wells S2 3.00 8.00
WI Dontrelle Willis S2 3.00 8.00
YM Yadier Molina S2 3.00 8.00
ZD Zach Duke S2 3.00 8.00

2008 Upper Deck UD Game Patch

SER.1 ODDS 1:768 H,1:7500 R
AJ Andruw Jones S2 8.00 20.00
AP Albert Pujols S2 30.00 60.00
BB Boof Bonser S2 8.00 20.00
BM Brandon McCarthy S2 8.00 20.00
BP Brandon Phillips S2 8.00 20.00
BR Brian Roberts 8.00 20.00
BU B.J. Upton S2 8.00 20.00
BZ Barry Zito S2 8.00 20.00
CA Matt Cain S2 8.00 20.00
CB Carlos Beltran 8.00 20.00
CB Chris Burke S2 8.00 20.00
CC Coco Crisp 8.00 20.00
CC Chris Carpenter S2 8.00 20.00
CD Chris Duncan S2 8.00 20.00
CG Carlos Guillen 8.00 20.00
CJ Conor Jackson S2 8.00 20.00
CL Cliff Lee S2 8.00 20.00
CQ Carlos Quentin S2 8.00 20.00
CU Michael Cuddyer S2 8.00 20.00
DC Daniel Cabrera 8.00 20.00
DJ Derek Jeter 50.00 100.00
DJ Derek Jeter S2 50.00 100.00
DL Derrek Lee S2 8.00 20.00
DO David Ortiz 12.50 30.00
DO David Ortiz S2 12.50 30.00
DW Dontrelle Willis 8.00 20.00
DW David Wells S2 8.00 20.00
EC Eric Chavez S2 8.00 20.00
EG Eric Gagne 8.00 20.00
ES Ervin Santana S2 8.00 20.00
FH Felix Hernandez S2 8.00 20.00
FL Francisco Liriano S2 8.00 20.00
FR Francisco Rodriguez S2 8.00 20.00
FS Freddy Sanchez S2 8.00 20.00
GA Garrett Atkins S2 8.00 20.00
GC Gustavo Chacin 8.00 20.00
GJ Geoff Jenkins 8.00 20.00
GL Troy Glaus S2 8.00 20.00
GM Gil Meche S2 8.00 20.00
GO Jonny Gomes S2 8.00 20.00
HR Hanley Ramirez S2 8.00 20.00
IR Ivan Rodriguez S2 8.00 20.00
JB Jason Bay 8.00 20.00
JB Jeremy Bonderman S2 8.00 20.00
JD Justin Duchscherer 8.00 20.00
JD Jermaine Dye S2 8.00 20.00
JG Jason Giambi S2 8.00 20.00
JH Jeremy Hermida S2 8.00 20.00
JJ Josh Johnson S2 8.00 20.00
JL James Loney S2 8.00 20.00
JP Jake Peavy 12.50 30.00
JP Jonathan Papelbon S2 12.50 30.00
JR Jeremy Reed S2 8.00 20.00
JS Jeremy Sowers 8.00 20.00
JS Jason Schmidt S2 8.00 20.00
JV Jason Varitek 12.50 30.00
JV Justin Verlander S2 8.00 20.00
JW Jered Weaver S2 8.00 20.00
KG Khalil Greene S2 8.00 20.00
KJ Kenji Johjima S2 8.00 20.00
KM Kazuo Matsui 8.00 20.00
KW Kerry Wood S2 8.00 20.00
MC Miguel Cabrera S2 12.50 30.00
ME Morgan Ensberg 8.00 20.00
ME Melky Cabrera S2 8.00 20.00
MG Marcus Giles S2 8.00 20.00
MJ Mike Jacobs S2 8.00 20.00
MK Masumi Kuwata 8.00 20.00
MM Melvin Mora 8.00 20.00
MN Mike Napoli S2 8.00 20.00
MP Mark Prior S2 8.00 20.00
MS Mike Sweeney 8.00 20.00
MY Michael Young 8.00 20.00
MY Brett Myers S2 8.00 20.00
OL Scott Olsen S2 8.00 20.00
PA Jonathan Papelbon 12.50 30.00
PE Mike Pelfrey S2 8.00 20.00
PF Prince Fielder S2 12.50 30.00
PK Paul Konerko S2 8.00 20.00
RC Ryan Church S2 8.00 20.00
RD Ray Durham S2 8.00 20.00
RF Ryan Freel S2 8.00 20.00
RH Roy Halladay 8.00 20.00
RJ Reed Johnson S2 8.00 20.00
RQ Robb Quinlan S2 8.00 20.00
RW Rickie Weeks S2 8.00 20.00
RZ Ryan Zimmerman S2 12.50 30.00
SK Scott Kazmir S2 8.00 20.00
SO Jeremy Sowers S2 8.00 20.00
TG Tom Glavine S2 8.00 20.00
TS Takashi Saito 8.00 20.00
VW Vernon Wells S2 8.00 20.00
WI Dontrelle Willis S2 8.00 20.00
YM Yadier Molina S2 8.00 20.00
ZD Zach Duke S2 8.00 20.00

2008 Upper Deck UD Game Materials 1997

SER.1 ODDS 1:32 HOBBY,1:96 RETAIL
SER.1 ODDS 1:40 WAL MART BLASTER
SER.1 ODDS 1:96 TARGET/WM BLISTER
AP Albert Pujols 8.00 20.00
BC Bobby Crosby 3.00 8.00
BG Brian Giles 3.00 8.00
BR B.J. Ryan 3.00 8.00
BS Ben Sheets 3.00 8.00
CH Cole Hamels S2 3.00 8.00
CS Curt Schilling 4.00 10.00
DL Derek Lowe 3.00 8.00
DO David Ortiz 4.00 10.00
DO David Ortiz S2 4.00 10.00
DU Dan Uggla S2 3.00 8.00
GJ Geoff Jenkins 3.00 8.00
HK Hong-Chih Kuo 4.00 10.00
IR Ivan Rodriguez 4.00 10.00
JB Joe Blanton 3.00 8.00
JC Joe Crede 3.00 8.00
JJ Josh Johnson 3.00 8.00
JM Justin Morneau S2 3.00 8.00
JP Jonathan Papelbon S2 4.00 10.00
JS James Shields 3.00 8.00
JV Justin Verlander S2 3.00 8.00
JW Jake Westbrook 3.00 8.00
JZ Joel Zumaya S2 3.00 8.00
LM Lastings Milledge 3.00 8.00
MC Miguel Cabrera 4.00 10.00
MO Magglio Ordonez 4.00 10.00
NM Nick Markakis 4.00 10.00
PE Andy Pettitte 4.00 10.00
PF Prince Fielder S2 4.00 10.00
PO Jorge Posada S2 3.00 8.00
RB Rocco Baldelli 3.00 8.00
TH Todd Helton 4.00 10.00
VG Vladimir Guerrero S2 3.00 8.00
VM Victor Martinez 3.00 8.00
XN Xavier Nady 3.00 8.00

2008 Upper Deck UD Game Materials 1997 Patch

SER.1 ODDS 1:768 H,1:7500 R
AP Albert Pujols 15.00 40.00
BC Bobby Crosby 8.00 20.00
BG Brian Giles 8.00 20.00
BR BJ Ryan 8.00 20.00
BS Ben Sheets 8.00 20.00
CH Cole Hamels S2 8.00 20.00
CS Curt Schilling 12.50 30.00
DL Derek Lowe 8.00 20.00
DO David Ortiz 12.50 30.00
DO David Ortiz S2 12.50 30.00
DU Dan Uggla S2 8.00 20.00
GJ Geoff Jenkins 8.00 20.00
HK Hong-Chih Kuo 8.00 20.00
IR Ivan Rodriguez 12.50 30.00
JB Joe Blanton 8.00 20.00
JC Joe Crede 8.00 20.00
JJ Josh Johnson 8.00 20.00
JM Justin Morneau S2 8.00 20.00
JP Jonathan Papelbon S2 12.50 30.00
JS James Shields 8.00 20.00
JV Justin Verlander S2 8.00 20.00
JW Jake Westbrook 8.00 20.00
JZ Joel Zumaya S2 8.00 20.00
LM Lastings Milledge 8.00 20.00
MC Miguel Cabrera 12.50 30.00
MO Magglio Ordonez 12.50 30.00
NM Nick Markakis 12.50 30.00
PE Andy Pettitte 12.50 30.00
PF Prince Fielder S2 12.50 30.00
PO Jorge Posada S2 8.00 20.00
RB Rocco Baldelli 8.00 20.00
TH Todd Helton 12.50 30.00
VG Vladimir Guerrero S2 8.00 20.00
VM Victor Martinez 8.00 20.00
XN Xavier Nady 8.00 20.00

2008 Upper Deck UD Game Materials 1998

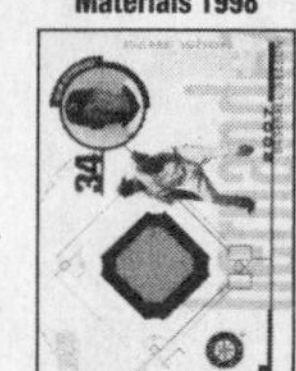

SER.1 ODDS 1:32 HOBBY,1:96 RETAIL
SER.1 ODDS 1:40 WAL MART BLASTER
SER.1 ODDS 1:96 TARGET/WM BLISTER
AJ Andruw Jones S2 3.00 8.00
BH Bill Hall 3.00 8.00
BS Ben Sheets 3.00 8.00
CD Chris Duncan S2 3.00 8.00
CF Chone Figgins 3.00 8.00
CZ Carlos Zambrano 3.00 8.00
DJ Derek Jeter S2 10.00 25.00
DL Derrek Lee S2 3.00 8.00
EG Eric Gagne 3.00 8.00
FC Fausto Carmona 3.00 8.00
FH Felix Hernandez 4.00 10.00
GM Greg Maddux S2 5.00 12.00
GS Grady Sizemore 4.00 10.00
HB Hank Blalock 3.00 8.00
IS Ian Snell 3.00 8.00
JE Johnny Estrada 3.00 8.00
JJ Jacque Jones 3.00 8.00
JK Jason Kendall 3.00 8.00
JS Johan Santana 4.00 10.00
KM Kevin Millwood 3.00 8.00
MB Mark Buehrle 3.00 8.00
MG Marcus Giles 3.00 8.00
NM Nick Markakis 4.00 10.00
PK Paul Konerko 3.00 8.00
RM Russell Martin S2 3.00 8.00
RO Roy Oswalt S2 3.00 8.00
TH Travis Hafner S2 3.00 8.00
VG Vladimir Guerrero S2 3.00 8.00
VM Victor Martinez 3.00 8.00
VM Victor Martinez S2 3.00 8.00

2008 Upper Deck UD Game Materials 1998 Patch

SER.1 ODDS 1:768 H,1:7500 R
AJ Andruw Jones S2 8.00 20.00
BH Bill Hall 8.00 20.00
BS Ben Sheets 8.00 20.00
CD Chris Duncan S2 8.00 20.00
CF Chone Figgins 8.00 20.00
CZ Carlos Zambrano 8.00 20.00
DJ Derek Jeter S2 20.00 50.00
DL Derrek Lee S2 8.00 20.00
EG Eric Gagne 8.00 20.00
FC Fausto Carmona 8.00 20.00
FH Felix Hernandez 12.50 30.00
GM Greg Maddux S2 12.50 30.00
GS Grady Sizemore 12.50 30.00
HB Hank Blalock 8.00 20.00
IS Ian Snell 8.00 20.00
JE Johnny Estrada 8.00 20.00
JJ Jacque Jones 8.00 20.00
JK Jason Kendall 8.00 20.00
JS Johan Santana 12.50 30.00
KM Kevin Millwood 8.00 20.00
MB Mark Buehrle 8.00 20.00
MG Marcus Giles 8.00 20.00
NM Nick Markakis 12.50 30.00
PK Paul Konerko 8.00 20.00
RM Russell Martin S2 8.00 20.00
RO Roy Oswalt S2 8.00 20.00
TH Travis Hafner S2 8.00 20.00
VG Vladimir Guerrero S2 8.00 20.00
VM Victor Martinez 8.00 20.00
VM Victor Martinez S2 8.00 20.00

2008 Upper Deck UD Game Materials 1999

SER.1 ODDS 1:32 HOBBY,1:96 RETAIL
SER.1 ODDS 1:40 WAL MART BLASTER
SER.1 ODDS 1:96 TARGET/WM BLISTER
BR Brian Roberts 3.00 8.00
BU B.J. Upton S2 3.00 8.00
BW Brandon Webb S2 3.00 8.00
CA Matt Cain S2 3.00 8.00
CD Chris Duffy 3.00 8.00
CJ Chipper Jones 4.00 10.00
CS C.C. Sabathia 3.00 8.00
DL Derrek Lee 3.00 8.00
DO David Ortiz S2 4.00 10.00
DW David Wells 3.00 8.00
EB Erik Bedard 3.00 8.00
FS Freddy Sanchez 3.00 8.00
HR Hanley Ramirez S2 3.00 8.00
JB Jason Bay 3.00 8.00
JD Johnny Damon 3.00 8.00
JG Jeremy Guthrie 3.00 8.00
JH J.J. Hardy 3.00 8.00
JK Jason Kubel 3.00 8.00
JM Joe Mauer S2 3.00 8.00
JP Jorge Posada 4.00 10.00
KG Khalil Greene S2 3.00 8.00
KJ Kenji Johjima 3.00 8.00
KM Kendry Morales 3.00 8.00
MC Miguel Cabrera S2 3.00 8.00
MT Mark Teixeira 4.00 10.00
NM Nick Markakis S2 3.00 8.00
RW Rickie Weeks 3.00 8.00
TE Miguel Tejada 3.00 8.00
TH Travis Hafner 3.00 8.00
TH Torii Hunter S2 3.00 8.00

2008 Upper Deck UD Game Materials 1999 Patch

SER.1 ODDS 1:768 H,1:7500 R
BR Brian Roberts 8.00 20.00
BU B.J. Upton S2 8.00 20.00
BW Brandon Webb S2 8.00 20.00
CA Matt Cain S2 8.00 20.00
CD Chris Duffy 8.00 20.00
CJ Chipper Jones 12.50 30.00
CS C.C. Sabathia 8.00 20.00
DL Derrek Lee 8.00 20.00
DO David Ortiz S2 12.50 30.00
DW David Wells 8.00 20.00
EB Erik Bedard 8.00 20.00
FS Freddy Sanchez 8.00 20.00
HR Hanley Ramirez S2 8.00 20.00
JB Jason Bay 8.00 20.00
JD Johnny Damon 8.00 20.00
JG Jeremy Guthrie 8.00 20.00
JH J.J. Hardy 8.00 20.00
JK Jason Kubel 8.00 20.00
JM Joe Mauer S2 8.00 20.00
JP Jorge Posada 12.50 30.00
KG Khalil Greene S2 8.00 20.00
KJ Kenji Johjima 8.00 20.00
KM Kendry Morales 8.00 20.00
MC Miguel Cabrera S2 8.00 20.00
MT Mark Teixeira 12.50 30.00
NM Nick Markakis S2 8.00 20.00
RW Rickie Weeks 8.00 20.00
TE Miguel Tejada 8.00 20.00
TH Travis Hafner 8.00 20.00
TH Torii Hunter S2 8.00 20.00

2008 Upper Deck Superstar

COMPLETE SET (10) 6.00 15.00
STATED ODDS 3:1 SUPER PACKS
9 Vladimir Guerrero .60 1.50
48 Mark Teixeira .60 1.50
57 Prince Fielder .40 1.00
67 Albert Pujols 1.50 4.00
139 Ichiro Suzuki 1.00 2.50
147 Hanley Ramirez .60 1.50
156 David Wright .75 2.00
239 Ken Griffey Jr. 1.00 2.50
270 Magglio Ordonez .40 1.00
297 Derek Jeter 1.50 4.00

2008 Upper Deck USA Junior National Team

USJR1 Eric Hosmer 10.00 25.00
USJR2 Garrison Lassiter 1.25 3.00
USJR3 Harold Martinez 1.25 3.00
USJR4 J.P. Ramirez 1.25 3.00
USJR5 Jeff Malm 2.00 5.00
USJR6 Jordan Swagerty 1.25 3.00
USJR7 Kyle Buchanan 1.25 3.00
USJR8 Kyle Skipworth 2.00 5.00
USJR9 L.J. Hoes 3.00 8.00
USJR10 Matthew Purke 1.25 3.00
USJR11 Mychal Givens 1.25 3.00
USJR12 Nick Maronde 1.25 3.00
USJR13 Riccio Torrez 1.25 3.00
USJR14 Robbie Grossman 2.00 5.00
USJR15 Ryan Weber 1.25 3.00
USJR16 T.J. House 1.25 3.00
USJR17 Tim Melville 1.25 3.00
USJR18 Tyler Hibbs 1.25 3.00
USJR19 Tyler Stovall 1.25 3.00
USJR20 Tyler Wilson 1.25 3.00

2008 Upper Deck USA Junior National Team Autographs

PRINT RUNS B/WN 133-500 COPIES PER
EH Eric Hosmer/238 30.00 60.00
GL Garrison Lassiter/375 4.00 10.00
HI Tyler Hibbs/375 4.00 10.00
HM Harold Martinez/237 4.00 10.00
JM Jeff Malm/375 4.00 10.00
JR J.P. Ramirez/239 4.00 10.00
JS Jordan Swagerty/350 4.00 10.00
KB Kyle Buchanan/375 4.00 10.00
KS Kyle Skipworth/177 4.00 10.00
LH L.J. Hoes/158 4.00 10.00
MG Mychal Givens/209 4.00 10.00
MP Matthew Purke/375 4.00 10.00
NM Nick Maronde/166 4.00 10.00
RG Robbie Grossman/155 4.00 10.00
RT Riccio Torrez/500 4.00 10.00
RW Ryan Weber/375 4.00 10.00
TH T.J. House/147 4.00 10.00
TM Tim Melville/133 4.00 10.00
TS Tyler Stovall/375 4.00 10.00
TW Tyler Wilson/375 4.00 10.00

2008 Upper Deck USA Junior National Team Autographs Blue

*BLUE AU: .4X TO 1X BASIC AU
PRINT RUNS B/WN 75-400 COPIES PER
EH Eric Hosmer/75 40.00 80.00
GL Garrison Lassiter/175 4.00 10.00
HI Tyler Hibbs/400 4.00 10.00
HM Harold Martinez/275 4.00 10.00
JM Jeff Malm/175 4.00 10.00
JR J.P. Ramirez/90 4.00 10.00
JS Jordan Swagerty/195 4.00 10.00
KB Kyle Buchanan/175 4.00 10.00
LH L.J. Hoes/300 4.00 10.00
MG Mychal Givens/309 4.00 10.00
MP Matthew Purke/390 4.00 10.00
NM Nick Maronde/100 4.00 10.00
RG Robbie Grossman/175 4.00 10.00
RT Riccio Torrez/400 4.00 10.00
RW Ryan Weber/392 4.00 10.00
TH T.J. House/75 4.00 10.00
TM Tim Melville/330 4.00 10.00
TS Tyler Stovall/186 4.00 10.00
TW Tyler Wilson/75 4.00 10.00

2008 Upper Deck USA Junior National Team Autographs Green

STATED PRINT RUN 10 SER.#'d SETS
NO PRICING DUE TO SCARCITY

2008 Upper Deck USA Junior National Team Autographs Red

*RED AU: .5X TO 1.2X BASIC AU
PRINT RUNS B/WN 50-150 COPIES PER
EH Eric Hosmer/50 50.00 100.00

2008 Upper Deck USA Junior National Team Jerseys

EH Eric Hosmer 5.00 12.00
GL Garrison Lassiter 3.00 8.00
HI Tyler Hibbs 3.00 8.00
HM Harold Martinez 3.00 8.00
JM Jeff Malm 3.00 8.00
JR J.P. Ramirez 3.00 8.00
JS Jordan Swagerty 3.00 8.00
KB Kyle Buchanan 3.00 8.00
KS Kyle Skipworth 4.00 10.00
LH L.J. Hoes 3.00 8.00
MG Mychal Givens 3.00 8.00
MP Matthew Purke 3.00 8.00
NM Nick Maronde 3.00 8.00
RG Robbie Grossman 3.00 8.00
RT Riccio Torrez 3.00 8.00
RW Ryan Weber 3.00 8.00
TH T.J. House 3.00 8.00
TM Tim Melville 3.00 8.00
TS Tyler Stovall 3.00 8.00
TW Tyler Wilson 3.00 8.00

2008 Upper Deck USA Junior National Team Jerseys Autographs Black

PRINT RUNS B/WN 99-400 COPIES PER
EH Eric Hosmer/100 50.00 100.00
GL Garrison Lassiter/226 4.00 10.00
HI Tyler Hibbs/222 4.00 10.00
HM Harold Martinez/99 4.00 10.00
JM Jeff Malm/258 4.00 10.00
JR J.P. Ramirez/99 4.00 10.00
JS Jordan Swagerty/199 4.00 10.00
KB Kyle Buchanan/205 4.00 10.00
KS Kyle Skipworth/99 4.00 10.00
LH L.J. Hoes/150 4.00 10.00
MG Mychal Givens/99 4.00 10.00
MP Matthew Purke/209 4.00 10.00
NM Nick Maronde/99 4.00 10.00
RG Robbie Grossman/150 4.00 10.00
RT Riccio Torrez/400 4.00 10.00
RW Ryan Weber/222 4.00 10.00
TH T.J. House/149 4.00 10.00
TM Tim Melville/175 4.00 10.00
TS Tyler Stovall/199 4.00 10.00
TW Tyler Wilson/199 4.00 10.00

2008 Upper Deck USA Junior National Team Jerseys Autographs Blue

*JSY BLUE: .4X TO 1X JSY BLACK
PRINT RUNS B/WN 50-400 COPIES PER
EH Eric Hosmer/121 50.00 100.00
GL Garrison Lassiter/172 4.00 10.00
HI Tyler Hibbs/392 4.00 10.00
HM Harold Martinez/375 4.00 10.00
JM Jeff Malm/107 4.00 10.00
JR J.P. Ramirez/200 4.00 10.00
JS Jordan Swagerty/173 4.00
KB Kyle Buchanan/131 4.00
LH L.J. Hoes/340 4.00
MG Mychal Givens/300 4.00
MP Matthew Purke/390 4.00
NM Nick Maronde/50 4.00
RG Robbie Grossman/100 4.00
RT Riccio Torrez/400 4.00
RW Ryan Weber/400 4.00 10.00
TH T.J. House/75 4.00
TM Tim Melville/350 4.00
TS Tyler Stovall/125 4.00
TW Tyler Wilson/235 4.00

2008 Upper Deck USA Junior National Team Jerseys Autographs Red

*JSY RED: .5X TO 1.2X JSY BLACK
PRINT RUNS B/WN 25-150 COPIES PER
NO PRICING ON QTY 25 OR LESS
EH Eric Hosmer/50 60.00 120.00
GL Garrison Lassiter/50 5.00 12.00
HI Tyler Hibbs/75 5.00 12.00
HM Harold Martinez/50 5.00 12.00
JM Jeff Malm/75 5.00 12.00
JR J.P. Ramirez/50 5.00 12.00
JS Jordan Swagerty/60 5.00 12.00
KB Kyle Buchanan/85 5.00 21.00
LH L.J. Hoes/60 5.00 12.00
MG Mychal Givens/60 5.00 12.00
MP Matthew Purke/74 5.00 12.00
NM Nick Maronde/25
RG Robbie Grossman/50 5.00 12.00
RT Riccio Torrez/150 5.00 12.00
RW Ryan Weber/50 5.00 12.00
TH T.J. House/50 5.00 12.00
TM Tim Melville/50 5.00 12.00
TS Tyler Stovall/85 5.00 12.00
TW Tyler Wilson/85 5.00 12.00

2008 Upper Deck USA Junior National Team Patch

*PATCH 99: .5X TO 1.2X BASIC JSY
STATED PRINT RUN 99 SER.#'d SETS
EH Eric Hosmer 8.00 20.00
KS Kyle Skipworth 6.00 15.00

2008 Upper Deck USA Junior National Team Patch Autographs

STATED PRINT RUN 99 SER.#'d SETS
EH Eric Hosmer 60.00 120.00
GL Garrison Lassiter 6.00 15.00
HI Tyler Hibbs 6.00 15.00
HM Harold Martinez 6.00 15.00
JM Jeff Malm 6.00 15.00
JR J.P. Ramirez 6.00 15.00
JS Jordan Swagerty 6.00 15.00
KB Kyle Buchanan 6.00 15.00
KS Kyle Skipworth 10.00 25.00
LH L.J. Hoes 6.00 15.00
MG Mychal Givens 6.00 15.00
MP Matthew Purke 6.00 15.00
NM Nick Maronde 6.00 15.00
RG Robbie Grossman 6.00 15.00
RT Riccio Torrez 6.00 15.00
RW Ryan Weber 6.00 15.00
TH T.J. House 6.00 15.00
TM Tim Melville 6.00 15.00
TS Tyler Stovall 6.00 15.00
TW Tyler Wilson 6.00 15.00

2008 Upper Deck USA National Team

USA1 Brett Hunter 1.25 3.00
USA2 Brian Matusz 1.25 3.00
USA3 Brett Wallace 1.25 3.00
USA4 Cody Satterwhite 1.25 3.00
USA5 Danny Espinosa 1.25 3.00
USA6 Eric Surkamp 1.25 3.00
USA7 Jordan Danks 1.25 3.00
USA8 Jeremy Hamilton 1.25 3.00
USA9 Joe Kelly 1.25 3.00
USA10 Jordy Mercer 1.25 3.00
USA11 Josh Romanski 1.25 3.00
USA12 Justin Smoak 1.25 3.00
USA13 Jacob Thompson 1.25 3.00
USA14 Logan Forsythe 1.25 3.00
USA15 Lance Lynn 1.25 3.00
USA16 Mike Minor 1.25 3.00
USA17 Pedro Alvarez 1.25 3.00
USA18 Petey Paramore 1.25 3.00
USA19 Ryan Berry 1.25 3.00
USA20 Ryan Flaherty 1.25 3.00
USA21 Roger Kieschnick 1.25 3.00
USA22 Seth Frankoff 1.25 3.00
USA23 Scott Gorgen 1.25 3.00
USA24 Tommy Medica 1.25 3.00
USA25 Tyson Ross 1.25 3.00

2008 Upper Deck USA National Team Autographs

PRINT RUNS B/WN 183-500 COPIES PER
BH Brett Hunter/297 4.00 10.00
BM Brian Matusz/264 10.00 25.00
BW Brett Wallace/183 6.00 15.00
CS Cody Satterwhite/375 4.00 10.00
DE Danny Espinosa/311 12.50 30.00
ES Eric Surkamp/
JD Jordan Danks/311 4.00 10.00
JH Jeremy Hamilton/375 4.00 10.00
JK Joe Kelly/457 4.00 10.00
JM Jordy Mercer/375 4.00 10.00
JR Josh Romanski/375 4.00 10.00
JS Justin Smoak/345 12.50 30.00
JT Jacob Thompson/267 4.00 10.00
LF Logan Forsythe/201 5.00 12.00
LL Lance Lynn/425 4.00 10.00
MM Mike Minor/375 4.00 10.00
PA Pedro Alvarez/205 15.00 40.00
PP Petey Paramore/237 4.00 10.00
RB Ryan Berry/375 4.00 10.00
RF Ryan Flaherty/244 4.00 10.00
RK Roger Kieschnick/272 4.00 10.00
SF Seth Frankoff/
SG Scott Gorgen/
TM Tommy Medica/487 4.00 10.00
TR Tyson Ross/500 4.00 10.00

2008 Upper Deck USA National Team Autographs Blue

*BLUE AU: .4X TO 1X BASIC AU
PRINT RUNS B/WN 50-204 COPIES PER
BH Brett Hunter/129 4.00 10.00
BM Brian Matusz/50 15.00 40.00
BW Brett Wallace/75 6.00 15.00
CS Cody Satterwhite/131 4.00 10.00
DE Danny Espinosa/75 12.50 30.00
ES Eric Surkamp/117 4.00 10.00
JD Jordan Danks/75 6.00 15.00
JH Jeremy Hamilton/204 4.00 10.00
JK Joe Kelly/125 4.00 10.00
JM Jordy Mercer/175 4.00 10.00
JR Josh Romanski/175 4.00 10.00
JS Justin Smoak/60 30.00 60.00
JT Jacob Thompson/105 4.00 10.00
LF Logan Forsythe/75 5.00 12.00
LL Lance Lynn/
MM Mike Minor/175 4.00 10.00
PA Pedro Alvarez/75 20.00 50.00
PP Petey Paramore/175 4.00 10.00
RB Ryan Berry/175 4.00 10.00
RF Ryan Flaherty/75 4.00 10.00
RK Roger Kieschnick/113 5.00 12.00
SF Seth Frankoff/175 4.00 10.00
SG Scott Gorgen/175 4.00 10.00

TM Tommy Medica/175 4.00 10.00
TR Tyson Ross/75 4.00 10.00

2008 Upper Deck USA National Team Autographs Green

STATED PRINT RUN 10 SER.#'d SETS
NO PRICING DUE TO SCARCITY

2008 Upper Deck USA National Team Autographs Red

*RED AU: .5X TO 1.2X BASIC AU
STATED PRINT RUN 50 SER.#'d SETS
BM Brian Matusz 15.00 40.00
BW Brett Wallace 6.00 15.00
JD Jordan Danks 6.00 15.00
JS Justin Smoak 30.00 60.00
LF Logan Forsythe 5.00 12.00
LL Lance Lynn 4.00 10.00
RF Ryan Flaherty 4.00 10.00
TR Tyson Ross 4.00 10.00

2008 Upper Deck USA National Team Highlights

H1 Game 1 1.00 2.50
H2 Game 2 1.00 2.50
H3 Game 3 1.00 2.50
H4 Game 4 1.00 2.50
H5 Game 5 1.00 2.50

2008 Upper Deck USA National Team Jerseys

BH Brett Hunter 3.00 8.00
BM Brian Matusz 3.00 8.00
BW Brett Wallace 3.00 8.00
CS Cody Satterwhite 3.00 8.00
DE Danny Espinosa 4.00 10.00
ES Eric Surkamp 3.00 8.00
JD Jordan Danks 3.00 8.00
JH Jeremy Hamilton 3.00 8.00
JK Joe Kelly 3.00 8.00
JM Jordy Mercer 3.00 8.00
JR Josh Romanski 3.00 8.00
JS Justin Smoak 5.00 12.00
JT Jacob Thompson 3.00 8.00
LF Logan Forsythe 3.00 8.00
LL Lance Lynn 3.00 8.00
MM Mike Minor 3.00 8.00
PA Pedro Alvarez 4.00 10.00
PP Petey Paramore 3.00 8.00
RB Ryan Berry 3.00 8.00
RF Ryan Flaherty 3.00 8.00
RK Roger Kieschnick 3.00 8.00
SF Seth Frankoff 3.00 8.00
SG Scott Gorgen 3.00 8.00
TM Tommy Medica 3.00 8.00
TR Tyson Ross 3.00 8.00

2008 Upper Deck USA National Team Jerseys Autographs Black

PRINT RUNS B/WN 99-400 COPIES PER
BH Brett Hunter/99 4.00 10.00
BM Brian Matusz/181 20.00 50.00
BW Brett Wallace/199 4.00 10.00
CS Cody Satterwhite/273 6.00 15.00
DE Danny Espinosa/130 10.00 25.00
ES Eric Surkamp/
JD Jordan Danks/99 6.00 15.00
JH Jeremy Hamilton/271 4.00 10.00
JK Joe Kelly/300 4.00 10.00
JM Jordy Mercer/287 4.00 10.00
JR Josh Romanski/311 4.00 10.00
JS Justin Smoak/199 12.50 30.00
JT Jacob Thompson/199 4.00 10.00
LF Logan Forsythe/199 4.00 10.00
LL Lance Lynn/149 4.00 10.00
MM Mike Minor/359 4.00 10.00
PA Pedro Alvarez/275 10.00 25.00
PP Petey Paramore/199 4.00 10.00
RB Ryan Berry/284 4.00 10.00
RF Ryan Flaherty/149 6.00 15.00
RK Roger Kieschnick/199 4.00 10.00
SF Seth Frankoff/
SG Scott Gorgen/
TM Tommy Medica/400 4.00 10.00
TR Tyson Ross/400 4.00 10.00

2008 Upper Deck USA National Team Jerseys Autographs Blue

*BLUE JSY AU: .4X TO 1X BLACK JSY AU
PRINT RUNS B/WN 69-292 COPIES PER
ES Eric Surkamp/200 4.00 10.00
LL Lance Lynn/
SF Seth Frankoff/69 4.00 10.00
SG Scott Gorgen/247 4.00 10.00

2008 Upper Deck USA National Team Jerseys Autographs Green

STATED PRINT RUN 10 SER.#'d SETS
NO PRICING DUE TO SCARCITY

2008 Upper Deck USA National Team Jerseys Autographs Red

*RED JSY AU: .5X TO 1.2X BASIC JSY AU
PRINT RUNS B/WN 50-182 COPIES PER
ES Eric Surkamp/50 5.00 12.00
PA Pedro Alvarez/50 15.00 40.00
SF Seth Frankoff/50 5.00 12.00
SG Scott Gorgen/50 5.00 12.00

2008 Upper Deck USA National Team Patch

*PATCH: .5X TO 1.2X BASIC JSY
STATED PRINT RUN 99 SER.#'d SETS
BM Brian Matusz 15.00 40.00
PA Pedro Alvarez 10.00 25.00

2008 Upper Deck USA National Team Patch Autographs

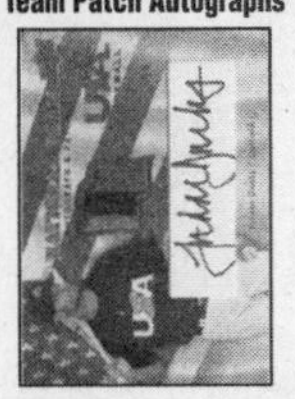

STATED PRINT RUN 99 SER.#'d SETS
BH Brett Hunter 6.00 15.00
BM Brian Matusz 30.00 60.00
BW Brett Wallace 12.50 30.00
CS Cody Satterwhite 15.00 40.00
DE Danny Espinosa 30.00 60.00
ES Eric Surkamp 6.00 15.00
JD Jordan Danks 15.00 40.00
JH Jeremy Hamilton 6.00 15.00
JK Joe Kelly 6.00 15.00
JM Jordy Mercer 6.00 15.00
JR Josh Romanski 6.00 15.00
JS Justin Smoak 20.00 50.00
JT Jacob Thompson 6.00 15.00
LF Logan Forsythe 6.00 15.00
LL Lance Lynn 6.00 15.00
MM Mike Minor 8.00 20.00
PA Pedro Alvarez 30.00 60.00
PP Petey Paramore 6.00 15.00
RB Ryan Berry 6.00 15.00
RF Ryan Flaherty 6.00 15.00
RK Roger Kieschnick 6.00 15.00
SF Seth Frankoff 6.00 15.00
SG Scott Gorgen 6.00 15.00
TM Tommy Medica 6.00 15.00
TR Tyson Ross 10.00 25.00

2008 Upper Deck Heroes Cut Signatures

UNPRICED CUT AUTOS PRINT RUN 1

2008 Upper Deck Sportsfest

COMPLETE SET (12) 15.00 40.00
SF1 Ken Griffey Jr. 1.00 2.50
SF5 Daisuke Matsuzaka 1.00 2.50
SF9 Derek Jeter 1.50 4.00

2008 Upper Deck Yankee Stadium Legacy Collection Memorabilia

AP Andy Pettitte 12.50 30.00
BD Bill Dickey 30.00 60.00
BM Billy Martin 12.50 30.00
BR Babe Ruth 250.00 500.00
CL Roger Clemens 12.50 30.00
CS Casey Stengel 15.00 40.00
CW Chien-Ming Wang 15.00 40.00
DE Bucky Dent 15.00 40.00
DJ Derek Jeter 15.00 40.00
DM Don Mattingly 20.00 50.00
DW Dave Winfield 10.00 25.00
EH Elston Howard 20.00 50.00
FC Frankie Crosetti 30.00 60.00
GG Goose Gossage 12.50 30.00
GM Gil McDougald 30.00 60.00
GN Graig Nettles 15.00 40.00
GS Gary Sheffield 6.00 15.00
JA Reggie Jackson 20.00 50.00
JC Joba Chamberlain 8.00 20.00
JD Joe DiMaggio 100.00 200.00
JG Jason Giambi 6.00 15.00
JP Joe Pepitone 50.00 100.00
LG Lou Gehrig 150.00 250.00
LP Lou Piniella 60.00 120.00
MC Melky Cabrera 15.00 40.00
MM Mike Mussina 15.00 40.00
MU Bobby Murcer 10.00 25.00
ON Paul O'Neill 15.00 40.00
PN Phil Niekro 20.00 50.00
PO Jorge Posada 10.00 25.00
RC Robinson Cano 12.50 30.00
RE Allie Reynolds 30.00 60.00
RG Ron Guidry 20.00 50.00
RJ Randy Johnson 6.00 15.00
RM Roger Maris 40.00 80.00
SL Sparky Lyle 12.50 30.00
TH Tommy Henrich 15.00 40.00
TM Thurman Munson 15.00 40.00
WB Wade Boggs 15.00 40.00
WF Whitey Ford 12.50 30.00
WR Willie Randolph 15.00 40.00
YB Yogi Berra 12.50 30.00

2009 Upper Deck

This set was released on February 3, 2009. The base set consists of 500 cards.

COMP.SER 1 SET w/o #0 (500) 40.00 80.00
COMP.SER 2 SET w/SP RC (506) 75.00 150.00
COMP.SER 2 SET w/o SP RC (500) 50.00 100.00
COMMON CARD (1-1000) .15 .40
COMMON RC (1-1000) .40 1.00
COMMON RC (1001-1006) 1.25 3.00
0 Joe DiMaggio SP 40.00 80.00
1 Randy Johnson .25 .60
2 Conor Jackson .15 .40
3 Brandon Webb .25 .60
4 Dan Haren .15 .40
5 Orlando Hudson .15 .40
6 Stephen Drew .15 .40
7 Mark Reynolds .15 .40
8 Eric Byrnes .15 .40
9 Justin Upton .25 .60
10 Chris B. Young .15 .40
11 Max Scherzer .25 .60
12 Alex Romero .15 .40
13 Chad Tracy .15 .40
14 Brandon Lyon .15 .40
15 Adam Dunn .25 .60
16 David Eckstein .15 .40
17 Jair Jurrjens .15 .40
18 Mike Hampton .15 .40
19 Brandon Jones .15 .40
20 Tom Glavine .25 .60
21 John Smoltz .40 1.00
22 Chipper Jones .40 1.00
23 Yunel Escobar .15 .40
24 Kelly Johnson .15 .40
25 Brian McCann .25 .60
26 Jeff Francoeur .25 .60
27 Tim Hudson .25 .60
28 Casey Kotchman .15 .40
29 Nick Markakis .40 1.00
30 Brian Roberts .15 .40
31 Jeremy Guthrie .15 .40
32 Ramon Hernandez .15 .40
33 Adam Jones .25 .60
34 Luke Scott .15 .40
35 Aubrey Huff .15 .40
36 Daniel Cabrera .15 .40
37 George Sherrill .15 .40
38 Melvin Mora .15 .40
39 Jay Payton .15 .40
40 Mark Kotsay .15 .40
41 David Ortiz .25 .60
42 Jacoby Ellsbury .40 1.00
43 Coco Crisp .15 .40
44 J.D. Drew .15 .40
45 Daisuke Matsuzaka .40 1.00
46 Josh Beckett .25 .60
47 Curt Schilling .25 .60
48 Clay Buchholz .25 .60
49 Dustin Pedroia .50 1.25
50 Julio Lugo .15 .40
51 Mike Lowell .15 .40
52 Jonathan Papelbon .25 .60
53 Jason Varitek .40 1.00
54 Hideki Okajima .15 .40
55 Jon Lester .40 1.00
56 Tim Wakefield .15 .40
57 Kevin Youkilis .25 .60
58 Jason Bay .25 .60
59 Justin Masterson .15 .40
60 Jeff Samardzija .25 .60
61 Alfonso Soriano .25 .60
62 Derrek Lee .15 .40
63 Aramis Ramirez .15 .40
64 Kerry Wood .15 .40
65 Jim Edmonds .25 .60
66 Kosuke Fukudome .40 1.00
67 Geovany Soto .25 .60
68 Ted Lilly .15 .40
69 Carlos Zambrano .25 .60
70 Ryan Theriot .15 .40
71 Mark DeRosa .25 .60
72 Ronny Cedeno .15 .40
73 Ryan Dempster .15 .40
74 Jon Lieber .15 .40
75 Rich Hill .15 .40
76 Rich Harden .15 .40
77 Alexei Ramirez .25 .60
78 Nick Swisher .40 1.00
79 Carlos Quentin .25 .60
80 Jermaine Dye .15 .40
81 Paul Konerko .25 .60
82 Orlando Cabrera .15 .40
83 Joe Crede .25 .60
84 Jim Thome .25 .60
85 Gavin Floyd .15 .40
86 Javier Vazquez .15 .40
87 Mark Buehrle .25 .60
88 Bobby Jenks .15 .40
89 Brian Anderson .15 .40
90 A.J. Pierzynski .15 .40
91 Jose Contreras .15 .40
92 Juan Uribe .15 .40
93a Ken Griffey Jr. .60 1.50
93b Ken Griffey Jr. 50.00 100.00
Seattle Mariners Press Conference
94 Chris Dickerson .15 .40
95 Brandon Phillips .15 .40
96 Aaron Harang .15 .40
97 Bronson Arroyo .15 .40
98 Edinson Volquez .15 .40
99 Johnny Cueto .15 .40
100 Edwin Encarnacion .15 .40
101 Jeff Keppinger .15 .40
102 Joey Votto .40 1.00
103 Jay Bruce .25 .60
104 Ryan Freel .15 .40
105 Travis Hafner .15 .40
106 Victor Martinez .25 .60
107 Grady Sizemore .25 .60
108 Cliff Lee .25 .60
109 Ryan Garko .15 .40
110 Jhonny Peralta .15 .40
111 Franklin Gutierrez .15 .40
112 Fausto Carmona .15 .40
113 Jeff Baker .15 .40
114 Troy Tulowitzki .40 1.00
115 Matt Holliday .40 1.00
116 Todd Helton .25 .60
117 Ubaldo Jimenez .25 .60
118 Brian Fuentes .15 .40
119 Willy Taveras .15 .40
120 Aaron Cook .15 .40
121 Jason Grilli .15 .40
122 Garrett Atkins .15 .40
123 Jeff Francis .15 .40
124 Ryan Spilborghs .15 .40
125 Armando Galarraga .15 .40
126 Miguel Cabrera .40 1.00
127 Placido Polanco .15 .40
128 Edgar Renteria .15 .40
129 Carlos Guillen .15 .40
130 Gary Sheffield .15 .40
131 Curtis Granderson .25 .60
132 Marcus Thames .15 .40
133 Magglio Ordonez .25 .60
134 Jeremy Bonderman .15 .40
135 Dontrelle Willis .15 .40
136 Kenny Rogers .15 .40
137 Justin Verlander .50 1.25
138 Nate Robertson .15 .40
139 Todd Jones .15 .40
140 Joel Zumaya .15 .40
141 Hanley Ramirez .40 1.00
142 Jeremy Hermida .15 .40
143 Mike Jacobs .15 .40
144 Andrew Miller .15 .40
145 Josh Willingham .15 .40
146 Luis Gonzalez .15 .40
147 Dan Uggla .25 .60
148 Scott Olsen .15 .40
149 Josh Johnson .25 .60
150 Darin Erstad .15 .40
151 Hunter Pence .25 .60
152 Roy Oswalt .25 .60
153 Lance Berkman .25 .60
154 Carlos Lee .15 .40
155 Michael Bourn .15 .40
156 Kazuo Matsui .15 .40
157 Miguel Tejada .25 .60
158 Ty Wigginton .25 .60
159 Jose Valverde .15 .40
160 J.R. Towles .15 .40
161 Brandon Backe .15 .40
162 Randy Wolf .15 .40
163 Mike Aviles .15 .40
164 Brian Bannister .15 .40
165 Zack Greinke .25 .60
166 Gil Meche .15 .40
167 Alex Gordon .25 .60
168 Tony Pena .15 .40
169 Luke Hochevar .15 .40
170 Mark Grudzielanek .15 .40
171 Jose Guillen .15 .40
172 Billy Butler .15 .40
173 David DeJesus .15 .40
174 Joey Gathright .15 .40
175 Mark Teahen .15 .40
176 Joakim Soria .15 .40
177 Mark Teixeira .40 1.00
178 Vladimir Guerrero .40 1.00
179 Torii Hunter .15 .40
180 Jered Weaver .15 .40
181 Chone Figgins .15 .40
182 Francisco Rodriguez .25 .60
183 Garret Anderson .15 .40
184 Howie Kendrick .15 .40
185 John Lackey .15 .40
186 Ervin Santana .15 .40
187 Joe Saunders .15 .40
188 Gary Matthews .15 .40
189 Jon Garland .15 .40
190 Nick Adenhart .15 .40
191 Manny Ramirez .40 1.00
192 Casey Blake .15 .40
193 Chad Billingsley .15 .40
194 Russell Martin .15 .40
195 Matt Kemp .25 .60
196 James Loney .25 .60
197 Jeff Kent .15 .40
198 Nomar Garciaparra .40 1.00
199 Rafael Furcal .15 .40
200 Andruw Jones .15 .40
201 Andre Ethier .25 .60
202 Takashi Saito .15 .40
203 Brad Penny .15 .40
204 Hiroki Kuroda .15 .40
205 Jonathan Broxton .15 .40
206 Chin-Lung Hu .15 .40
207 Juan Pierre .15 .40
208 Blake DeWitt .15 .40
209 Derek Lowe .15 .40
210 Clayton Kershaw .40 1.00
211 Greg Maddux .50 1.25
212 CC Sabathia .25 .60
213 Yovani Gallardo .15 .40
214 Ryan Braun .50 1.25
215 Prince Fielder .25 .60
216 Corey Hart .15 .40
217 Bill Hall .15 .40
218 Rickie Weeks .25 .60
219 Mike Cameron .15 .40
220 Ben Sheets .15 .40
221 Jason Kendall .15 .40
222 J.J. Hardy .15 .40
223 Jeff Suppan .15 .40
224 Ray Durham .15 .40
225 Denard Span .15 .40
226 Carlos Gomez .15 .40
227 Joe Mauer .40 1.00
228 Justin Morneau .40 1.00
229 Michael Cuddyer .15 .40
230 Joe Nathan .15 .40
231 Kevin Slowey .25 .60
232 Delmon Young .25 .60
233 Jason Kubel .15 .40
234 Craig Monroe .15 .40
235 Livan Hernandez .15 .40
236 Francisco Liriano .15 .40
237 Pat Neshek .25 .60
238 Boof Bonser .15 .40
239 Nick Blackburn .15 .40
240 Daniel Murphy RC 1.00 2.50
241 Nick Evans .15 .40
242 Jose Reyes .25 .60
243 David Wright .50 1.25
244 Carlos Delgado .15 .40
245 Luis Castillo .15 .40
246 Ryan Church .15 .40
247 Carlos Beltran .15 .40
248 Moises Alou .15 .40
249 Pedro Martinez .25 .60
250 Johan Santana .40 1.00
251 John Maine .15 .40
252 Endy Chavez .15 .40
253 Oliver Perez .15 .40
254 Brian Schneider .15 .40
255 Fernando Tatis .15 .40
256 Mike Pelfrey .15 .40
257 Billy Wagner .15 .40
258 Ramon Castro .15 .40
259 Ivan Rodriguez .25 .60
260 Alex Rodriguez .60 1.50
261 Derek Jeter 1.00 2.50
262 Robinson Cano .40 1.00
263 Jason Giambi .15 .40
264 Bobby Abreu .15 .40
265 Johnny Damon .25 .60
266 Melky Cabrera .15 .40
267 Hideki Matsui .40 1.00
268 Jorge Posada .25 .60
269 Joba Chamberlain .25 .60
270 Ian Kennedy .25 .60
271 Mike Mussina .25 .60
272 Andy Pettitte .25 .60
273 Mariano Rivera .40 1.00
274 Chien-Ming Wang .25 .60
275 Phil Hughes .25 .60
276 Xavier Nady .15 .40
277 Richie Sexson .15 .40
278 Brad Ziegler .15 .40
279 Justin Duchscherer .15 .40
280 Eric Chavez .15 .40
281 Bobby Crosby .15 .40
282 Mark Ellis .15 .40
283 Daric Barton .15 .40
284 Frank Thomas .40 1.00
285 Emil Brown .15 .40
286 Huston Street .15 .40
287 Jack Cust .15 .40
288 Kurt Suzuki .15 .40
289 Joe Blanton .15 .40
290 Ryan Howard .50 1.25
291 Chase Utley .40 1.00
292 Jimmy Rollins .25 .60
293 Pedro Feliz .15 .40
294 Pat Burrell .15 .40
295 Geoff Jenkins .15 .40
296 Shane Victorino .15 .40
297 Brett Myers .15 .40
298 Brad Lidge .15 .40
299 Cole Hamels .40 1.00
300 Jamie Moyer .15 .40
301 Adam Eaton .15 .40
302 Matt Stairs .15 .40
303 Nate McLouth .15 .40
304 Ian Snell .15 .40
305 Matt Capps .15 .40
306 Freddy Sanchez .15 .40
307 Ryan Doumit .15 .40
308 Adam LaRoche .15 .40
309 Jack Wilson .15 .40
310 Tom Gorzelanny .15 .40
311 Jody Gerut .15 .40
312 Jake Peavy .15 .40
313 Chris Young .15 .40
314 Trevor Hoffman .25 .60
315 Adrian Gonzalez .25 .60
316 Chase Headley .15 .40
317 Khalil Greene .15 .40
318 Kevin Kouzmanoff .15 .40
319 Brian Giles .15 .40
320 Josh Bard .15 .40
321 Scott Hairston .15 .40
322 Barry Zito .15 .40
323 Tim Lincecum .60 1.50
324 Matt Cain .15 .40
325 Brian Wilson .40 1.00
326 Aaron Rowand .15 .40
327 Randy Winn .15 .40
328 Omar Vizquel .25 .60
329 Bengie Molina .15 .40
330 Fred Lewis .15 .40
331 Erik Bedard .15 .40
332 Felix Hernandez .40 1.00
333 Ichiro Suzuki .60 1.50
334 J.J. Putz .15 .40
335 Raul Ibanez .25 .60
336 Adrian Beltre .15 .40
337 Jose Vidro .15 .40
338 Jeff Clement .15 .40
339 Kenji Johjima .25 .60
340 Wladimir Balentien .15 .40
341 Jose Lopez .15 .40
342 Kyle Lohse .15 .40
343 Albert Pujols 1.00 2.50
344 Troy Glaus .15 .40
345 Chris Carpenter .40 1.00
346 Adam Kennedy .15 .40
347 Rick Ankiel .15 .40
348 Adam Wainwright .25 .60
349 Jason Isringhausen .15 .40
350 Chris Duncan .15 .40
351 Skip Schumaker .15 .40
352 Mark Mulder .15 .40
353 Todd Wellemeyer .15 .40
354 Cesar Izturis .15 .40
355 Ryan Ludwick .25 .60
356 Yadier Molina .25 .60
357 Braden Looper .15 .40
358 B.J. Upton .25 .60
359 Carl Crawford .25 .60
360 Evan Longoria .50 1.25
361 James Shields .15 .40
362 Scott Kazmir .15 .40
363 Carlos Pena .25 .60
364 Akinori Iwamura .15 .40
365 Jonny Gomes .15 .40
366 Cliff Floyd .15 .40
367 Troy Percival .15 .40
368 Edwin Jackson .15 .40
369 Matt Garza .15 .40
370 Eric Hinske .15 .40
371 Rocco Baldelli .15 .40
372 Chris Davis .15 .40
373 Marlon Byrd .15 .40
374 Michael Young .25 .60
375 Ian Kinsler .25 .60
376 Josh Hamilton .40 1.00
377 Hank Blalock .15 .40
378 Milton Bradley .15 .40
379 Kevin Millwood .15 .40
380 Vicente Padilla .15 .40
381 Jarrod Saltalamacchia .15 .40
382 Jesse Litsch .15 .40
383 Roy Halladay .40 1.00
384 A.J. Burnett .25 .60
385 Dustin McGowan .15 .40
386 Scott Rolen .25 .60
387 Alex Rios .25 .60
388 Vernon Wells .15 .40
389 Shannon Stewart .15 .40
390 B.J. Ryan .15 .40
391 Lyle Overbay .15 .40
392 Elijah Dukes .15 .40
393 Lastings Milledge .15 .40
394 Chad Cordero .15 .40
395 Ryan Zimmerman .25 .60
396 Austin Kearns .15 .40
397 Wily Mo Pena .15 .40
398 Ronnie Belliard .15 .40
399 Cristian Guzman .15 .40
400 Jesus Flores .15 .40
401a David Price RC 1.00 2.50
401b David Price 50.00 100.00
Pictured in white uniform SP
402 Matt Antonelli RC .60 1.50
403 Jonathon Niese RC .60 1.50
404 Phil Coke RC .60 1.50
405 Jason Pridie (RC) .40 1.00
406 Mark Saccomanno RC .40 1.00
407 Freddy Sandoval (RC) .40 1.00
408 Travis Snider RC .60 1.50
409 Matt Tuiasosopo (RC) .40 1.00
410 Will Venable RC .40 1.00
411 Brad Nelson (RC) .40 1.00
412 Aaron Cunningham RC .40 1.00
413 Wilkin Castillo RC .40 1.00
414 Robert Parnell RC .60 1.50
415 Conor Gillaspie RC 1.00 2.50
416 Dexter Fowler (RC) .60 1.50
417 George Kottaras (RC) .40 1.00
418 Josh Roenicke RC .40 1.00
419 Luis Valbuena RC .60 1.50
420 Casey McGehee (RC) .40 1.00
421 Mat Gamel RC 1.00 2.50
422 Greg Golson (RC) .40 1.00
423 Alfredo Aceves RC .60 1.50
424 Michael Bowden (RC) .40 1.00
425 Kila Kaaihue (RC) .60 1.50
426 Josh Geer (RC) .40 1.00
427 James Parr (RC) .40 1.00
428 Chris Lambert (RC) .40 1.00
429 Fernando Perez (RC) .40 1.00
430 Josh Whitesell RC .60 1.50
431 Dustin Pedroia .40 1.00
Daisuke Matsuzaka
Josh Beckett TL
432 Ryan Howard .50 1.25
Cole Hamels
Jimmy Rollins TL
433 Jose Reyes .50 1.25
David Wright
Carlos Delgado TL
434 Alex Rodriguez 1.00 2.50
Derek Jeter
Mike Mussina TL
435 Carlos Quentin .25 .60
Gavin Floyd
Javier Vazquez TL
436 Ryan Ludwick 1.00 2.50
Albert Pujols
Todd Wellemeyer TL
437 Miguel Cabrera .50 1.25
Curtis Granderson
Justin Verlander TL
438 Adrian Gonzalez .15 .40
Jake Peavy
Brian Giles TL
439 Ryan Braun .25 .60
Prince Fielder
Ben Sheets TL
440 Cliff Lee .25 .60
Grady Sizemore
Jhonny Peralta TL
441 Josh Hamilton .40 1.00
Ian Kinsler
Vicente Padilla TL
442 Jorge Cantu .40 1.00
Hanley Ramirez
Ricky Nolasco TL
443 Carlos Pena .25 .60
Akinori Iwamura
B.J. Upton TL
444 Jack Cust .15 .40
Dana Eveland
Kurt Suzuki TL
445 Alfonso Soriano .25 .60
Ryan Dempster
Aramis Ramirez TL
446 Lance Berkman .25 .60
Roy Oswalt
Miguel Tejada TL
447 Matt Holliday .40 1.00
Aaron Cook
Willy Taveras TL
448 Nate McLouth .15 .40
Adam LaRoche
Paul Maholm TL
449 Brian Roberts .15 .40
Aubrey Huff
Jeremy Guthrie TL
450 Justin Morneau .40 1.00
Joe Mauer
Carlos Gomez TL
451 Raul Ibanez .40 1.00
Ichiro Suzuki
Felix Hernandez TL
452 Chipper Jones .15 .40
Jair Jurrjens
Brian McCann TL
453 Brandon Webb .15 .40
Dan Haren
Stephen Drew TL
454 Tim Lincecum .60 1.50
Randy Winn
Bengie Molina TL
455 Roy Halladay .40 1.00
A.J. Burnett
Alex Rios TL
456 Edinson Volquez .15 .40
Brandon Phillips
Edwin Encarnacion TL
457 Chad Billingsley .25 .60
Matt Kemp
James Loney TL
458 Ervin Santana .40 1.00
Vladimir Guerrero
Francisco Rodriguez TL
459 Zack Greinke .25 .60
Gil Meche
David DeJesus TL
460 Tim Redding .15 .40
Cristian Guzman
Lastings Milledge TL
461 Carlos Zambrano HL .25 .60
462 Jon Lester HL .40 1.00
463 Jim Thome HL .25 .60
464 Ken Griffey Jr. HL .60 1.50
465 Manny Ramirez HL .40 1.00
466 Derek Jeter HL 1.00 2.50
467 Josh Hamilton HL .40 1.00
468 Francisco Rodriguez HL .25 .60
469 Alex Rodriguez HL .60 1.50
470 J.D. Drew HL .15 .40
471 David Wright CL .50 1.25
472 Chase Utley CL .40 1.00
473 Chipper Jones CL .40 1.00
474 Cristian Guzman CL .15 .40
475 Hanley Ramirez CL .40 1.00
476 CC Sabathia CL .25 .60
477 Lance Berkman CL .25 .60
478 Alfonso Soriano CL .25 .60
479 Albert Pujols CL 1.00 2.50
480 Nate McLouth CL .15 .40
481 Brandon Phillips CL .15 .40
482 Adrian Gonzalez CL .25 .60
483 Brandon Webb CL .25 .60
484 Manny Ramirez CL .40 1.00
485 Tim Lincecum CL .60 1.50
486 Matt Holliday CL .40 1.00
487 Dustin Pedroia CL .50 1.25
488 Alex Rodriguez CL .60 1.50
489 Evan Longoria CL .50 1.25
490 Roy Halladay CL .40 1.00
491 Nick Markakis CL .40 1.00
492 Grady Sizemore CL .25 .60
493 Carlos Quentin CL .25 .60
494 Joakim Soria CL .15 .40
495 Miguel Cabrera CL .40 1.00
496 Joe Mauer CL .40 1.00
497 Francisco Rodriguez CL .25 .60
498 Jack Cust CL .15 .40
499 Ichiro Suzuki CL .60 1.50

500 Josh Hamilton CL .40 1.00
501 Brandon Webb .25 .60
502 Miguel Montero .15 .40
503 Tony Pena .15 .40
504 Jon Rauch .15 .40
505 Augie Ojeda .15 .40
506 Yusmeiro Petit .15 .40
507 Chris Snyder .15 .40
508 Chris B. Young .15 .40
509 Doug Slaten .15 .40
510 Tony Clark .15 .40
511 Justin Upton .25 .60
512 Chad Qualls .15 .40
513 Doug Davis .15 .40
514 Eric Byrnes .15 .40
515 Conor Jackson .15 .40
516 Mike Gonzalez .15 .40
517 Josh Anderson .15 .40
518 Tom Glavine .25 .60
519 Clint Sammons .15 .40
520 Martin Prado .15 .40
521 Jorge Campillo .15 .40
522 Omar Infante .15 .40
523 Javier Vazquez .15 .40
524 Jo Jo Reyes .15 .40
525 Gregor Blanco .15 .40
526 Rafael Soriano .15 .40
527 Manny Acosta .15 .40
528 Chipper Jones .40 1.00
529 Buddy Carlyle .15 .40
530 Radhames Liz .15 .40
531 Scott Moore .15 .40
532 Jim Johnson .15 .40
533 Oscar Salazar .15 .40
534 Nick Markakis .40 1.00
535 Brian Roberts .15 .40
536 Jeremy Guthrie .15 .40
537 Adam Jones .25 .60
538 Chris Ray .15 .40
539 Aubrey Huff .15 .40
540 Ty Wigginton .25 .60
541 Dennis Sarfate .15 .40
542 Melvin Mora .15 .40
543 Chris Waters .15 .40
544 John Smoltz .40 1.00
545 Brad Penny .15 .40
546 Josh Bard .15 .40
547 Takashi Saito .15 .40
548 Jacoby Ellsbury .40 1.00
549 Jeff Bailey .15 .40
550 Ramon Ramirez .15 .40
551 Daisuke Matsuzaka .40 1.00
552 Josh Beckett .25 .60
553 Jed Lowrie .25 .60
554 Dustin Pedroia .50 1.25
555 David Ortiz .25 .60
556 Jonathan Van Every .15 .40
557 Jonathan Papelbon .25 .60
558 Manny Delcarmen .15 .40
559 Hideki Okajima .15 .40
560 Jon Lester .40 1.00
561 Javier Lopez .15 .40
562 Kevin Youkilis .25 .60
563 Jason Varitek .40 1.00
564 Milton Bradley .15 .40
565 Mike Fontenot .15 .40
566 Micah Hoffpauir .15 .40
567 Sean Marshall .25 .60
568 Alfonso Soriano .25 .60
569 Neal Cotts .15 .40
570 Kosuke Fukudome .40 1.00
571 Reed Johnson .15 .40
572 Carlos Marmol .25 .60
573 Chad Gaudin .15 .40
574 Rich Harden .15 .40
575 Ted Lilly .15 .40
576 Carlos Zambrano .25 .60
577 Ryan Theriot .15 .40
578 Ryan Dempster .15 .40
579 Matt Thornton .15 .40
580 Jerry Owens .15 .40
581 Alexei Ramirez .25 .60
582 John Danks .15 .40
583 Carlos Quentin .25 .60
584 D.J. Carrasco .15 .40
585 Dewayne Wise .15 .40
586 Clayton Richard .15 .40
587 Brent Lillibridge .15 .40
588 Jim Thome .25 .60
589 Chris Getz .15 .40
590 Octavio Dotel .15 .40
591 Mark Buehrle .25 .60
592 Bobby Jenks .15 .40
593 Joey Votto .40 1.00
594 Jay Bruce .25 .60
595 David Weathers .15 .40
596 Bill Bray .15 .40
597 Mike Lincoln .15 .40
598 Norris Hopper .15 .40
599 Alex Gonzalez .15 .40
600 Jerry Hairston Jr. .15 .40
601 Brandon Phillips .15 .40
602 Aaron Harang .15 .40
603 Bronson Arroyo .15 .40
604 Edinson Volquez .15 .40
605 Ryan Hanigan .15 .40
606 Jared Burton .15 .40
607 Aaron Laffey .15 .40
608 Kerry Wood .15 .40
609 Shin-Soo Choo .25 .60
610 David Dellucci .15 .40
611 Mark DeRosa .25 .60
612 Masahide Kobayashi .15 .40
613 Rafael Perez .15 .40
614 Grady Sizemore .25 .60
615 Cliff Lee .25 .60
616 Ben Francisco .15 .40
617 Jensen Lewis .15 .40
618 Joe Smith .15 .40
619 Asdrubal Cabrera .25 .60
620 Brad Hawpe .15 .40
621 Chris Iannetta .15 .40
622 Clint Barmes .15 .40
623 Seth Smith .15 .40
624 Aaron Cook .15 .40
625 Troy Tulowitzki .40 1.00
626 Todd Helton .25 .60
627 Taylor Buchholz .15 .40
628 Jason Marquis .15 .40
629 Ian Stewart .15 .40
630 Ryan Speier .15 .40
631 Manny Corpas .15 .40
632 Yorvit Torrealba .15 .40
633 Fernando Rodney .15 .40
634 Justin Verlander .50 1.25
635 Bobby Seay .15 .40
636 Clete Thomas .15 .40
637 Placido Polanco .15 .40
638 Ramon Santiago .15 .40
639 Adam Everett .15 .40
640 Gary Sheffield .15 .40
641 Curtis Granderson .25 .60
642 Freddy Dolis .15 .40
643 Magglio Ordonez .25 .60
644 Zach Miner .15 .40
645 Brandon Inge .15 .40
646 Dallas McPherson .15 .40
647 Anibal Sanchez .15 .40
648 Jorge Cantu .15 .40
649 John Baker .15 .40
650 Wes Helms .15 .40
651 Ricky Nolasco .15 .40
652 Chris Volstad .15 .40
653 Renyel Pinto .15 .40
654 Alfredo Amezaga .15 .40
655 Cameron Maybin .15 .40
656 Matt Lindstrom .15 .40
657 Cody Ross .15 .40
658 Logan Kensing .15 .40
659 Tim Byrdak .15 .40
660 Reggie Abercrombie .15 .40
661 Geoff Blum .15 .40
662 Humberto Quintero .15 .40
663 Doug Brocail .15 .40
664 Roy Oswalt .25 .60
665 Lance Berkman .25 .60
666 Carlos Lee .15 .40
667 Latroy Hawkins .15 .40
668 Geoff Geary .15 .40
669 Brian Moehler .15 .40
670 Wandy Rodriguez .15 .40
671 Esteban German .15 .40
672 Ross Gload .15 .40
673 Joakim Soria .15 .40
674 Kyle Farnsworth .15 .40
675 Ryan Shealy .15 .40
676 Mike Aviles .15 .40
677 John Buck .15 .40
678 Zack Greinke .25 .60
679 John Bale .15 .40
680 Alex Gordon .25 .60
681 Coco Crisp .15 .40
682 Miguel Olivo .15 .40
683 Alberto Callaspo .15 .40
684 Kyle Davies .15 .40
685 Brandon Wood .15 .40
686 Erick Aybar .15 .40
687 Robb Quinlan .15 .40
688 Bobby Abreu .15 .40
689 Jose Arredondo .15 .40
690 Juan Rivera .15 .40
691 Kendry Morales .15 .40
692 Vladimir Guerrero .40 1.00
693 Darren Oliver .15 .40
694 Jeff Mathis .15 .40
695 Maicer Izturis .15 .40
696 Mike Napoli .25 .60
697 Reggie Willits .15 .40
698 Scot Shields .15 .40
699 John Lackey .15 .40
700 Manny Ramirez .40 1.00
701 Danny Ardoin .15 .40
702 Orlando Hudson .15 .40
703 Hong-Chih Kuo .15 .40
704 Mark Loretta .15 .40
705 Cory Wade .15 .40
706 Casey Blake .15 .40
707 Eric Stults .15 .40
708 Jason Schmidt .15 .40
709 Chad Billingsley .15 .40
710 Russell Martin .15 .40
711 Matt Kemp .25 .60
712 James Loney .25 .60
713 Rafael Furcal .15 .40
714 Ramon Troncoso .15 .40
715 Jonathan Broxton .15 .40
716 Hiroki Kuroda .15 .40
717 Andre Ethier .25 .60
718 Corey Hart .15 .40
719 Mitch Stetter .15 .40
720 Manny Parra .15 .40
721 Dave Bush .15 .40
722 Trevor Hoffman .25 .60
723 Tony Gwynn .15 .40
724 Chris Duffy .15 .40
725 Seth McClung .15 .40
726 J.J. Hardy .15 .40
727 David Riske .15 .40
728 Todd Coffey .15 .40
729 Rickie Weeks .25 .60
730 Mike Rivera .15 .40
731 Carlos Villanueva .15 .40
732 Ryan Braun .50 1.25
733 Nick Punto .15 .40
734 Francisco Liriano .15 .40
735 Craig Breslow .15 .40
736 Matt Macri .15 .40
737 Scott Baker .15 .40
738 Jesse Crain .15 .40
739 Brendan Harris .15 .40
740 Alexi Casilla .15 .40
741 Nick Blackburn .15 .40
742 Brian Buscher .15 .40
743 Denard Span .15 .40
744 Mike Redmond .15 .40
745 Joe Mauer .40 1.00
746 Carlos Gomez .15 .40
747 Matt Guerrier .15 .40
748 Joe Nathan .15 .40
749 Livan Hernandez .15 .40
750 Ryan Church .15 .40
751 Carlos Beltran .15 .40
752 Jeremy Reed .15 .40
753 Oliver Perez .15 .40
754 Duaner Sanchez .15 .40
755 J.J. Putz .15 .40
756 Mike Pelfrey .15 .40
757 Brian Schneider .15 .40
758 Francisco Rodriguez .25 .60
759 John Maine .15 .40
760 Daniel Murphy .40 1.00
761 Johan Santana .40 1.00
762 Jose Reyes .25 .60
763 David Wright .50 1.25
764 Carlos Delgado .15 .40
765 Pedro Feliciano .15 .40
766 Derek Jeter 1.00 2.50
767 Brian Bruney .15 .40
768 A.J. Burnett .25 .60
769 Andy Pettitte .25 .60
770 Nick Swisher .40 1.00
771 Damaso Marte .15 .40
772 Edwar Ramirez .15 .40
773 CC Sabathia .25 .60
774 Chien-Ming Wang .25 .60
775 Mariano Rivera .40 1.00
776 Mark Teixeira .40 1.00
777 Joba Chamberlain .25 .60
778 Jose Veras .15 .40
779 Hideki Matsui .40 1.00
780 Jose Molina .15 .40
781 Alex Rodriguez .60 1.50
782 Michael Wuertz .15 .40
783 Orlando Cabrera .15 .40
784 Sean Gallagher .15 .40
785 Dallas Braden .25 .60
786 Gio Gonzalez .15 .40
787 Rajai Davis .15 .40
788 Brad Ziegler .15 .40
789 Matt Holliday .40 1.00
790 Jack Cust .15 .40
791 Santiago Casilla .15 .40
792 Jason Giambi .15 .40
793 Joey Devine .15 .40
794 Travis Buck .15 .40
795 Justin Duchscherer .15 .40
796 Rob Bowen .15 .40
797 Andrew Brown .15 .40
798 Ryan Sweeney .15 .40
799 Jimmy Rollins .25 .60
800 Chad Durbin .15 .40
801 Clay Condrey .15 .40
802 Chris Coste .15 .40
803 Ryan Madson .15 .40
804 Chan Ho Park .25 .60
805 Carlos Ruiz .15 .40
806 Kyle Kendrick .15 .40
807 Jayson Werth .25 .60
808 Cole Hamels .40 1.00
809 Brad Lidge .15 .40
810 Greg Dobbs .15 .40
811 Scott Eyre .15 .40
812 Eric Bruntlett .15 .40
813 Ryan Howard .50 1.25
814 Chase Utley .40 1.00
815 Paul Maholm .15 .40
816 Andy LaRoche .15 .40
817 Brandon Moss .15 .40
818 Nyjer Morgan .15 .40
819 John Grabow .15 .40
820 Tom Gorzelanny .15 .40
821 Steve Pearce .15 .40
822 Sean Burnett .15 .40
823 Tyler Yates .15 .40
824 Zach Duke .15 .40
825 Matt Capps .15 .40
826 Ross Ohlendorf .15 .40
827 Nate McLouth .15 .40
828 Adrian Gonzalez .25 .60
829 Heath Bell .25 .60
830 Luis Rodriguez .15 .40
831 Kevin Kouzmanoff .15 .40
832 Edgar Gonzalez .15 .40
833 Cha-Seung Baek .15 .40
834 Cla Meredith .15 .40
835 Justin Hampson .15 .40
836 Nick Hundley .15 .40
837 Mike Adams .15 .40
838 Jake Peavy .15 .40
839 Chris Young .15 .40
840 Brian Giles .15 .40
841 Steve Holm .15 .40
842 Dave Roberts .15 .40
843 Travis Ishikawa .15 .40
844 Pablo Sandoval .50 1.25
845 Emmanuel Burriss .15 .40
846 Nate Schierholtz .15 .40
847 Randy Johnson .25 .60
848 Kevin Frandsen .15 .40
849 Edgar Renteria .15 .40
850 Jack Taschner .15 .40
851 Tim Lincecum .60 1.50
852 Alex Hinshaw .15 .40
853 Jonathan Sanchez .15 .40
854 Eugenio Velez .15 .40
855a Ken Griffey Jr. .60 1.50
2009 Seattle Mariners
855b Ken Griffey Jr. 15.00 40.00
1989 Seattle Mariners
855c Ken Griffey Jr. 15.00 40.00
1990 Seattle Mariners
855d Ken Griffey Jr. 15.00 40.00
1991 Seattle Mariners
855e Ken Griffey Jr. 15.00 40.00
1992 Seattle Mariners
855f Ken Griffey Jr. 15.00 40.00
1993 Seattle Mariners
855g Ken Griffey Jr. 15.00 40.00
1994 Seattle Mariners
855h Ken Griffey Jr. 15.00 40.00
1995 Seattle Mariners
855i Ken Griffey Jr. 15.00 40.00
1996 Seattle Mariners
855j Ken Griffey Jr. 15.00 40.00
1997 Seattle Mariners
855k Ken Griffey Jr. 15.00 40.00
1998 Seattle Mariners
855l Ken Griffey Jr. 15.00 40.00
1999 Seattle Mariners
855m Ken Griffey Jr. 15.00 40.00
2000 Cincinnati Reds
855n Ken Griffey Jr. 15.00 40.00
2001 Cincinnati Reds
855o Ken Griffey Jr. 15.00 40.00
2002 Cincinnati Reds
855p Ken Griffey Jr. 15.00 40.00
2003 Cincinnati Reds
855q Ken Griffey Jr. 15.00 40.00
2004 Cincinnati Reds
855r Ken Griffey Jr. 15.00 40.00
2005 Cincinnati Reds
855s Ken Griffey Jr. 15.00 40.00
2006 Cincinnati Reds
855t Ken Griffey Jr. 15.00 40.00
2007 Cincinnati Reds
855u Ken Griffey Jr. 15.00 40.00
2008 Chicago White Sox
856 Garrett Olson .15 .40
857 Cesar Jimenez .15 .40
858 Bryan LaHair .15 .40
859 Franklin Gutierrez .15 .40
860 Brandon Morrow .15 .40
861 Roy Corcoran .15 .40
862 Carlos Silva .15 .40
863 Kenji Johjima .25 .60
864 Jarrod Washburn .15 .40
865 Felix Hernandez .40 1.00
866 Ichiro Suzuki .60 1.50
867 Miguel Batista .15 .40
868 Yuniesky Betancourt .15 .40
869 Adrian Beltre .15 .40
870 Ryan Rowland-Smith .15 .40
871 Khalil Greene .15 .40
872 Kyle McClellan .15 .40
873 Ryan Franklin .25 .60
874 Brian Barton .15 .40
875 Josh Kinney .15 .40
876 Ryan Ludwick .25 .60
877 Brendan Ryan .15 .40
878 Albert Pujols 1.00 2.50
879 Troy Glaus .15 .40
880 Joel Pineiro .15 .40
881 Jason LaRue .15 .40
882 Yadier Molina .25 .60
883 Adam Wainwright .25 .60
884 Chris Perez .15 .40
885 Adam Kennedy .15 .40
886 Akinori Iwamura .15 .40
887 J.P. Howell .15 .40
888 Ben Zobrist .15 .40
889 Gabe Gross .15 .40
890 Matt Joyce .15 .40
891 Dan Wheeler .15 .40
892 Willie Aybar .15 .40
893 Jason Bartlett .15 .40
894 Dioner Navarro .15 .40
895 Andy Sonnanstine .15 .40
896 B.J. Upton .25 .60
897 Chad Bradford .15 .40
898 Evan Longoria .50 1.25
899 Shawn Riggans .15 .40
900 Scott Kazmir .15 .40
901 Grant Balfour .15 .40
902 Josh Hamilton .40 1.00
903 Frank Francisco .15 .40
904 Frank Catalanotto .15 .40
905 German Duran .15 .40
906 Brandon Boggs .15 .40
907 Matt Harrison .15 .40
908 David Murphy .15 .40
909 Nelson Cruz .25 .60
910 Joaquin Benoit .15 .40
911 Taylor Teagarden .25 .60
912 Joaquin Arias .15 .40
913 Kevin Millwood .15 .40
914 Ian Kinsler .25 .60
915 T.J. Beam .15 .40
916 Marco Scutaro .15 .40
917 Adam Lind .15 .40
918 John McDonald .15 .40
919 Scott Downs .15 .40
920 Rod Barajas .15 .40
921 Joe Inglett .15 .40
922 Alex Rios .25 .60
923 David Purcey .15 .40
924 Roy Halladay .40 1.00
925 Jason Frasor .15 .40
926 Shaun Marcum .15 .40
927 Aaron Hill .15 .40
928 Adam Dunn .25 .60
929 Shawn Hill .15 .40
930 Steven Shell .15 .40
931 Saul Rivera .15 .40
932 Josh Willingham .15 .40
933 John Lannan .15 .40
934 Joel Hanrahan .25 .60
935 Daniel Cabrera .15 .40
936 Willie Harris .15 .40
937 Wil Nieves .15 .40
938 Nick Johnson .15 .40
939 Garrett Mock .15 .40
940 Anderson Hernandez .15 .40
941 Koji Uehara RC .60 1.50
942 Kenshin Kawakami RC .60 1.50
943 Jason Motte (RC) .60 1.50
944 Elvis Andrus RC .60 1.50
945 Rick Porcello RC 1.25 3.00
946 Colby Rasmus (RC) 1.00 2.50
947 Shairon Martis RC .60 1.50
948 Ricky Romero (RC) 1.00 2.50
949 Kevin Jensen (RC) .40 1.00
950 James McDonald RC .60 1.50
951 Joe Mauer AW .40 1.00
952 Carlos Pena AW .25 .60
953 Dustin Pedroia AW .50 1.25
954 Adrian Beltre AW .15 .40
955 Michael Young AW .25 .60
956 Torii Hunter AW .15 .40
957 Grady Sizemore AW .25 .60
958 Ichiro Suzuki AW .60 1.50
959 Yadier Molina AW .25 .60
960 Adrian Gonzalez AW .25 .60
961 Brandon Phillips AW .15 .40
962 David Wright AW .50 1.25
963 Jimmy Rollins AW .25 .60
964 Nate McLouth AW .15 .40
965 Carlos Beltran AW .15 .40
966 Shane Victorino AW .15 .40
967 Cliff Lee AW .25 .60
968 Brad Lidge AW .15 .40
969 Evan Longoria AW .50 1.25
970 Geovany Soto AW .25 .60
971 Francisco Rodriguez CL .25 .60
972 Raul Ibanez CL .25 .60
973 Derek Lowe CL .15 .40
974 Scott Olsen CL .15 .40
975 Josh Johnson CL .25 .60
976 Prince Fielder CL .25 .60
977 Mike Hampton CL .15 .40
978 Kevin Gregg CL .15 .40
979 Rick Ankiel CL .15 .40
980 Nate McLouth CL .15 .40
981 Ramon Hernandez CL .15 .40
982 David Eckstein CL .15 .40
983 Felipe Lopez CL .15 .40
984 Clayton Kershaw CL .40 1.00
985 Randy Johnson CL .25 .60
986 Huston Street CL .15 .40
987 Rocco Baldelli CL .15 .40
988 Mark Teixeira CL .40 1.00
989 Pat Burrell CL .15 .40
990 Vernon Wells CL .15 .40
991 Cesar Izturis CL .15 .40
992 Kerry Wood CL .15 .40
993 Wilson Betemit CL .15 .40
994 Mike Jacobs CL .15 .40
995 Gerald Laird CL .15 .40
996 Justin Morneau CL .40 1.00
997 Brian Fuentes CL .15 .40
998 Jason Giambi CL .15 .40
999 Endy Chavez CL .15 .40
1000 Michael Young CL .25 .60
1001 Brett Anderson SP RC 2.00 5.00
1002 Trevor Cahill SP RC 3.00 8.00
1003 Jordan Schafer SP (RC) 2.00 5.00
1004 Trevor Crowe SP RC 1.25 3.00
1005 Everth Cabrera SP RC 2.00 5.00
1006 Ryan Perry SP RC 3.00 8.00
SP1 Mark Buehrle 5.00 12.00
Perfect Game SP
SP2 Barack Obama 8.00 20.00
Albert Pujols
All Star Game SP
SP3 Derek Jeter 20.00 50.00
All Time Hit King SP

2009 Upper Deck Gold

*GOLD VET: 12X TO 30X BASIC VET
*GOLD RC: 5X TO 12X BASIC RC
RANDOM INSERTS IN PACKS
STATED PRINT RUN 99 SER.#'d SETS
0 Joe DiMaggio

2009 Upper Deck 1989 Design

RANDOM INSERTS IN PACKS
801 Ken Griffey Jr. 30.00 60.00
802 Randy Johnson 6.00 15.00
803 Ronald Reagan 12.50 30.00
804 George H.W. Bush 30.00 60.00

2009 Upper Deck A Piece of History 500 Club

RANDOM INSERTS IN PACKS
MR Manny Ramirez 20.00 50.00

2009 Upper Deck A Piece of History 600 Club

RANDOM INSERTS IN PACKS
600KG Ken Griffey Jr. 20.00 50.00

2009 Upper Deck Derek Jeter 1993 Buyback Autograph

RANDOM INSERTS IN PACKS
STATED PRINT RUN 93 SER.#'d SETS
449 Derek Jeter/93 500.00 800.00

2009 Upper Deck Goodwin Champions Preview

RANDOM INSERTS IN PACKS
GCP1 Joe DiMaggio 5.00 12.00
GCP2 Tony Gwynn 3.00 8.00
GCP3 Cole Hamels 3.00 8.00
GCP4 Laird Hamilton 1.25 3.00
GCP5 Gordie Howe 6.00 15.00
GCP6 Ichiro Suzuki 3.00 8.00
GCP7 Derek Jeter 6.00 15.00
GCP8 Michael Jordan 6.00 15.00
GCP9 Barack Obama 6.00 15.00
GCP10 Albert Pujols 5.00 12.00
GCP11 Cal Ripken Jr. 10.00 25.00
GCP12 Bill Rodgers 1.25 3.00

2009 Upper Deck Griffey-Jordan

RANDOM INSERTS IN PACKS
KGMJ Ken Griffey Jr. 10.00 25.00
Michael Jordan

2009 Upper Deck Historic Firsts

ODDS 1:4 HOB,1:6 RET,1:10 BLAST
HF1 Barack Obama 4.00 10.00
HF2 First Athlete to Win Eight Medals .75 2.00
HF3 First World Series Game .75 2.00
HF4 First Woman to Run as VP 2.00 5.00
HF5 SpaceX Falcon 1 Successful Orbit .75 2.00
HF6 First Indian Players Signed .75 2.00
HF7 First Asian-American Manager .75 2.00
HF8 Largest Insert Set Produced (YSL) .75 2.00
HF9 NHL Winter Classic .75 2.00
HF10 Woman Becomes General .75 2.00
HF11 Bo The First Puppy 10.00 25.00

2009 Upper Deck Historic Predictors

ODDS 1:4 HOB,1:6 RET,1:10 BLAST
HP1 NL Wins All Star Game .75 2.00
HP2 Gas Reaches 99 Cents .75 2.00
HP3 Dow Reaches 15000 .75 2.00
HP4 African Amer.Woman Justice .75 2.00
HP5 Life Discovered on Another Planet .75 2.00
HP6 Bigfoot Discovered .75 2.00
HP7 College Football Playoff System .75 2.00
HP8 Cure for AIDS .75 2.00
HP9 Chicago 2016 Summer Games .75 2.00

2009 Upper Deck Inkredible

ODDS 1:17 HOB,1:1000 RET,1:1980 BLAST
EXCHANGE DEADLINE 1/12/2011
AC Aaron Cook 4.00 10.00
AD Adam Dunn
AE Andre Ethier 10.00 25.00
AG Adrian Gonzalez
AG Alberto Gonzalez S2 3.00 8.00
AI Akinori Iwamura 6.00 15.00
AK Austin Kearns 6.00 15.00
AL Aaron Laffey 3.00 8.00
AM Andrew Miller
AR Bronson Arroyo 6.00 15.00
AR Alexei Ramirez S2 12.50 30.00
AS Alfonso Soriano
BA Brian Bannister 3.00 8.00
BA Burke Badenhop S2 3.00 8.00
BB Billy Butler 10.00 25.00
BB Brian Barton S2 3.00 8.00
BE Josh Beckett
BI Brian Bixler S2 3.00 8.00
BJ Jay Bruce S2 10.00 25.00
BK Bobby Korecky S2 4.00 10.00
BL Joe Blanton 6.00 15.00
BO Boof Bonser 3.00 8.00
BP Brandon Phillips 5.00 12.00
BR Brian Bruney 3.00 8.00
BR Brandon Jones S2 4.00 10.00
BU B.J. Upton
BW Billy Wagner 15.00 40.00
CA Chris Capuano 20.00 50.00
CB Craig Breslow 3.00 8.00
CC Chad Cordero 3.00 8.00
CD Chris Duffy 3.00 8.00
CG Carlos Gomez 8.00 20.00
CH Cole Hamels 50.00 100.00
CH Corey Hart S2 4.00 10.00
CM Chien-Ming Wang S2
CR Chris Resop 3.00 8.00
CS Clint Sammons S2 3.00 8.00
CT Clete Thomas S2 10.00 25.00
CW Cory Wade S2
DE David Eckstein 4.00 10.00
DL Derek Lowe 8.00 20.00
DL Derek Lowe S2
DM David Murphy 3.00 8.00
DP Dustin Pedroia S2
DU Dan Uggla
EA Erick Aybar 3.00 8.00
ED Elijah Dukes 3.00 8.00
ED Elijah Dukes S2 3.00 8.00
ES Johnny Estrada
ET Eider Torres S2 5.00 12.00
EV Edinson Volquez 6.00 15.00
FC Fausto Carmona 4.00 10.00
FH Felix Hernandez 15.00 40.00
GA Garrett Atkins 4.00 10.00
GF Gavin Floyd 6.00 15.00
GP Glen Perkins 3.00 8.00
GP Gregorio Petit S2 3.00 8.00
GS Greg Smith S2 4.00 10.00
GW Tony Gwynn (Brewers) 5.00 12.00
HA Brendan Harris 3.00 8.00
HA Josh Hamilton S2
HF Jonathan Herrera S2 4.00 10.00
HI Hernan Iribarren S2 4.00 10.00
HU Chin-Lung Hu S2
IK Ian Kinsler 10.00 25.00
IK Ian Kennedy S2 6.00 15.00
JA Jeremy Accardo
JA Joaquin Arias S2 3.00 8.00
JB Jeff Baker 3.00 8.00
JB Jason Bay S2 10.00 25.00
JC Jack Cust 3.00 8.00
JE Jeff Francoeur 10.00 25.00
JE Jeremy Hermida S2 4.00 10.00
JF Jeff Francis 4.00 10.00
JG Jeremy Guthrie 15.00 40.00
JH Josh Hamilton 12.50 30.00
JH J.A. Happ S2 8.00 20.00
JK Jeff Keppinger 4.00 10.00
JL James Loney 8.00 20.00
JL Jed Lowrie S2
JM John Maine 30.00 60.00
JM John Maine S2 6.00 15.00
JN Joe Nathan 15.00 40.00
JO Joey Gathright 3.00 8.00
JO Jonathan Albaladejo S2 4.00 10.00
JP Jonathan Papelbon 10.00 25.00
JP Jonathan Papelbon S2
JS James Shields 4.00 10.00
JS Joe Smith S2 4.00 10.00
JT Jim Thome
JW Jered Weaver 5.00 12.00
KG Ken Griffey Jr. EXCH 75.00 150.00
KG Ken Griffey Jr. S2 75.00 150.00
KH Kevin Hart S2 4.00 10.00
KJ Kelly Johnson S2 3.00 8.00
KK Kevin Kouzmanoff 4.00 10.00
KM Kyle McClellan S2 4.00 10.00
KS Kevin Slowey S2 10.00 25.00
KY Kevin Youkilis
KY Kevin Youkilis S2
LA Adam LaRoche 6.00 15.00
LB Lance Berkman
LB Lance Broadway S2 3.00 8.00
LC Luke Carlin S2 5.00 12.00
LE Jon Lester
LJ John Lackey 5.00 12.00
LM Luis Mendoza S2
LS Luke Scott 3.00 8.00
MA Matt Chico 3.00 8.00
MA Michael Aubrey S2 5.00 12.00
MB Marlon Byrd 3.00 8.00
MB Mitchell Boggs S2 10.00 25.00
MC Matt Cain 10.00 25.00
ME Mark Ellis 3.00 8.00
ME Mark Ellis S2 3.00 8.00
MG Matt Garza
MI Michael Bourn 4.00 10.00
MI Michael Bourn S2
MK Matt Kemp
ML Matt Lindstrom S2 3.00 8.00
MO Dustin Moseley 3.00 8.00
MP Mike Pelfrey S2
MR Mike Rabelo S2 3.00 8.00
MT Mark Teahen 4.00 10.00
MU David Murphy S2 3.00 8.00
NB Nick Blackburn S2 6.00 15.00
NL Noah Lowry S2 4.00 10.00
NM Nick Markakis 10.00 25.00
NM Nyjer Morgan S2 4.00 10.00
NS Nick Swisher 5.00 12.00
OW Micah Owings 4.00 10.00
PA Mike Parisi S2 3.00 8.00
PE Glen Perkins S2
PF Prince Fielder 12.50 30.00
RB Ryan Braun 15.00 40.00
RG Ryan Garko 3.00 8.00
RH Ramon Hernandez 6.00 15.00
RH Ramon Hernandez S2 6.00 15.00
RM Russell Martin S2
RO Ross Ohlendorf S2 5.00 12.00
RT Ryan Theriot 6.00 15.00
RT Ramon Troncoso S2 5.00 12.00
SD Stephen Drew 4.00 10.00
SH Steve Holm S2 3.00 8.00
SJ James Shields S2
SM Sean Marshall 4.00 10.00
SO Andy Sonnanstine 3.00 8.00
TB Taylor Buchholz 4.00 10.00
TG Tom Gorzelanny 20.00 50.00
TG Tom Gorzelanny S2
TH Travis Hafner S2
TT Troy Tulowitzki
UJ Ubaldo Jimenez 5.00 12.00
VM Victor Martinez S2
VR Vinny Rottino S2 3.00 8.00
WI Josh Willingham 3.00 8.00
WW Wesley Wright S2 3.00 8.00
XN Xavier Nady 10.00 25.00
YE Yunel Escobar 6.00 15.00

2009 Upper Deck Ken Griffey Jr. 1989 Buyback Gold

RANDOM INSERTS IN PACKS
NNO Ken Griffey Jr. 12.50 30.00

2009 Upper Deck Ken Griffey Jr. 1989 Buyback Autograph

RANDOM INSERTS IN PACKS
ALL CARDS HAND NUMBERED TO 89
NO PRICING DUE TO SCARCITY
1a Ken Griffey Jr 89 UD Blue/76 *
1b Ken Griffey Jr 89 UD Black/13 *

2009 Upper Deck O-Pee-Chee

ODDS 1:6 HOB,1:30 RET,1:90 BLAST

*MINI: 1X TO 2.5X BASIC

MINI ODDS 1:48 HOB,1:240 RET,1:720 BLAST

Card	Low	High
OPC1 Albert Pujols	3.00	8.00
OPC2 Alex Rodriguez	2.00	5.00
OPC3 Alfonso Soriano	.75	2.00
OPC4 B.J. Upton	.75	2.00
OPC5 Brandon Webb	.75	2.00
OPC6 CC Sabathia	.75	2.00
OPC7 Carl Crawford	.75	2.00
OPC8 Carlos Beltran	.50	1.25
OPC9 Carlos Quentin	.75	2.00
OPC10 Chase Utley	1.25	3.00
OPC11 Chien-Ming Wang	.75	2.00
OPC12 Chipper Jones	1.25	3.00
OPC13 Daisuke Matsuzaka	1.25	3.00
OPC14 David Ortiz	.75	2.00
OPC15 David Wright	1.50	4.00
OPC16 Derek Jeter	3.00	8.00
OPC17 Derrek Lee	.50	1.25
OPC18 Evan Longoria	1.50	4.00
OPC19 Felix Hernandez	1.25	3.00
OPC20 Frank Thomas	1.25	3.00
OPC21 Grady Sizemore	.75	2.00
OPC22 Greg Maddux	1.50	4.00
OPC23 Hanley Ramirez	1.25	3.00
OPC24 Ichiro Suzuki	2.00	5.00
OPC25 Jake Peavy	.50	1.25
OPC26 Jimmy Rollins	.75	2.00
OPC27 Joba Chamberlain	.75	2.00
OPC28 Joe Mauer	1.25	3.00
OPC29 Johan Santana	1.25	3.00
OPC30 John Smoltz	1.25	3.00
OPC31 Jose Reyes	.75	2.00
OPC32 Josh Beckett	.75	2.00
OPC33 Josh Hamilton	1.25	3.00
OPC34 Ken Griffey Jr.	2.00	5.00
OPC35 Kosuke Fukudome	1.25	3.00
OPC36 Lance Berkman	.75	2.00
OPC37 Magglio Ordonez	.75	2.00
OPC38 Manny Ramirez	1.25	3.00
OPC39 Mark Teixeira	1.25	3.00
OPC40 Matt Holliday	1.25	3.00
OPC41 Matt Kemp	.75	2.00
OPC42 Miguel Cabrera	1.25	3.00
OPC43 Prince Fielder	.75	2.00
OPC44 Randy Johnson	.75	2.00
OPC45 Rick Ankiel	.50	1.25
OPC46 Russell Martin	.50	1.25
OPC47 Ryan Braun	1.50	4.00
OPC48 Ryan Howard	1.50	4.00
OPC49 Travis Hafner	.50	1.25
OPC50 Vladimir Guerrero	1.25	3.00

2009 Upper Deck O-Pee-Chee 1977 Preview

RANDOM INSERTS IN PACKS

Card	Low	High
OPC1 Prince Fielder	.75	2.00
OPC2 Russell Martin	.50	1.25
OPC3 Vladimir Guerrero	1.25	3.00
OPC4 Joe Mauer	1.25	3.00
OPC5 Justin Morneau	1.25	3.00
OPC6 Dustin Pedroia	1.50	4.00
OPC7 Mark Teixeira	1.25	3.00
OPC8 Tim Lincecum	2.00	5.00
OPC9 Jimmy Rollins	.75	2.00
OPC10 Carlos Lee	.50	1.25
OPC11 Hanley Ramirez	1.25	3.00
OPC12 Chipper Jones	1.25	3.00
OPC13 Matt Holliday	1.25	3.00
OPC14 Travis Hafner	.50	1.25
OPC15 Magglio Ordonez	.75	2.00
OPC16 Carlos Quentin	.75	2.00
OPC17 Derrek Lee	.50	1.25
OPC18 Aramis Ramirez	.50	1.25
OPC19 Randy Johnson	.75	2.00
OPC20 Brandon Webb	.75	2.00
OPC21 Josh Hamilton	1.25	3.00
OPC22 CC Sabathia	.75	2.00
OPC23 Carlos Beltran	.50	1.25
OPC24 Adrian Gonzalez	.75	2.00
OPC25 Jake Peavy	.50	1.25
OPC26 Matt Kemp	.75	2.00
OPC27 Joba Chamberlain	.75	2.00
OPC28 Jonathan Papelbon	.75	2.00
OPC29 Carlos Zambrano	.75	2.00
OPC30 Jay Bruce	.75	2.00
OPC31 Albert Pujols	3.00	8.00
OPC32 Alex Rodriguez	2.00	5.00
OPC33 Alfonso Soriano	.75	2.00
OPC34 Chase Utley	1.25	3.00
OPC35 Daisuke Matsuzaka	1.25	3.00
OPC36 David Ortiz	.75	2.00
OPC37 David Wright	1.50	4.00
OPC38 Derek Jeter	3.00	8.00
OPC39 Evan Longoria	1.50	4.00
OPC40 Grady Sizemore	.75	2.00
OPC41 Ichiro Suzuki	2.00	5.00
OPC42 Johan Santana	1.25	3.00
OPC43 Jose Reyes	.75	2.00
OPC44 Josh Beckett	.75	2.00
OPC45 Ken Griffey Jr.	2.00	5.00
OPC46 Lance Berkman	.75	2.00
OPC47 Manny Ramirez	1.25	3.00
OPC48 Miguel Cabrera	1.25	3.00
OPC49 Ryan Braun	1.50	4.00
OPC50 Ryan Howard	1.50	4.00

2009 Upper Deck Rivals

ODDS 1:12 HOB,1:50 RET,1:240 BLAST

Card	Low	High
R1 Jose Reyes	.75	2.00
Jimmy Rollins		
R2 David Ortiz	3.00	8.00
Derek Jeter		
R3 Albert Pujols	.50	1.25
Derrek Lee		
R4 Russell Martin	.50	1.25
Bengie Molina		
R5 Travis Hafner	.75	2.00
Jim Thome		
R6 Carlos Zambrano	.75	2.00
CC Sabathia		
R7 David Wright	2.00	5.00
Alex Rodriguez		
R8 Josh Beckett	.75	2.00
Scott Kazmir		
R9 Vladimir Guerrero	1.25	3.00
Manny Ramirez		
R10 Carlos Quentin	.75	2.00
Alfonso Soriano		
R11 Lance Berkman	3.00	8.00
Albert Pujols		
R12 Alex Rodriguez	1.50	4.00
Evan Longoria		
R13 Jake Peavy	.50	1.25
Chad Billingsley		
R14 Brandon Webb	.75	2.00
Matt Kemp		
R15 Johan Santana	1.25	3.00
Chipper Jones		
R16 Jim Thome	1.25	3.00
Justin Morneau		
R17 Miguel Cabrera	1.25	3.00
Joe Mauer		
R18 Hanley Ramirez	.75	2.00
Jose Reyes		
R19 Roy Halladay	1.25	3.00
Joba Chamberlain		
R20 Josh Hamilton	1.25	3.00
Roy Oswalt		
R21 Tim Lincecum	2.00	5.00
Jack Cust		
R22 Albert Pujols	.75	2.00
Prince Fielder		
R23 Francisco Rodriguez	2.00	5.00
Ichiro Suzuki		
R24 Daisuke Matsuzaka	1.25	3.00
Nick Markakis		
R25 Grady Sizemore	.75	2.00
Jay Bruce		

2009 Upper Deck Stars of the Game

ODDS 1:12 HOB,1:50 RET,1:240 BLAST

Card	Low	High
GGAP Albert Pujols	3.00	8.00
GGAR Alex Rodriguez	2.00	5.00
GGAS Alfonso Soriano	.75	2.00
GGBW Brandon Webb	.75	2.00
GGCJ Chipper Jones	1.25	3.00
GGCS CC Sabathia	.75	2.00
GGCU Chase Utley	1.25	3.00
GGDJ Derek Jeter	3.00	8.00
GGDO David Ortiz	.75	2.00
GGDP Dustin Pedroia	1.50	4.00
GGDW David Wright	1.50	4.00
GGEL Evan Longoria	1.50	4.00
GGGS Grady Sizemore	.75	2.00
GGHR Hanley Ramirez	1.25	3.00
GGIS Ichiro Suzuki	2.00	5.00
GGJH Josh Hamilton	1.25	3.00
GGJR Jose Reyes	.75	2.00
GGJS Johan Santana	1.25	3.00
GGLB Lance Berkman	.75	2.00
GGMC Miguel Cabrera	1.25	3.00
GGMR Manny Ramirez	1.25	3.00
GGRB Ryan Braun	1.50	4.00
GGRH Ryan Howard	1.50	4.00
GGTL Tim Lincecum	2.00	5.00
GGVG Vladimir Guerrero	1.25	3.00

2009 Upper Deck Starquest Common Purple

STATED ODDS 2:1 FAT PACK

*SILVER: .4X TO 1X PURPLE

SILVER ODDS 1:4 RETAIL,3:1 SUPER

*BLUE: .4X TO 1X PURPLE

BLUE ODDS 1:8 RET,1:32 BLAST,1:3 SUP

*GOLD: 5X TO 1.2X PURPLE

GLD ODDS 1:12 RET,1:48 BLAST,1:4 SUP

*EMERALD: .75X TO 2X PURPLE

EMLD ODDS 1:24 RET,1:96 BLAST,1:8 SUP

*BLACK: 1.2X TO 3X PURPLE

BLK ODDS 1:48 RET,1:192 BLAST,1:12 SUP

Card	Low	High
SQ1 Albert Pujols	3.00	8.00
SQ2 Alex Rodriguez	2.00	5.00
SQ3 Alfonso Soriano	.75	2.00
SQ4 Chipper Jones	1.25	3.00
SQ5 Chase Utley	1.25	3.00
SQ6 Derek Jeter	3.00	8.00
SQ7 Daisuke Matsuzaka	1.25	3.00
SQ8 David Ortiz	.75	2.00
SQ9 David Wright	1.50	4.00
SQ10 Grady Sizemore	.75	2.00
SQ11 Hanley Ramirez	1.25	3.00
SQ12 Ichiro Suzuki	2.00	5.00
SQ13 Josh Beckett	.75	2.00
SQ14 Jake Peavy	.50	1.25
SQ15 Jose Reyes	.75	2.00
SQ16 Johan Santana	1.25	3.00
SQ17 Ken Griffey Jr.	2.00	5.00
SQ18 Lance Berkman	.75	2.00
SQ19 Miguel Cabrera	1.25	3.00
SQ20 Matt Holliday	1.25	3.00
SQ21 Manny Ramirez	1.25	3.00
SQ22 Prince Fielder	.75	2.00
SQ23 Ryan Braun	1.50	4.00
SQ24 Ryan Howard	1.50	4.00
SQ25 Vladimir Guerrero	1.25	3.00
SQ26 B.J. Upton	.75	2.00
SQ27 Brandon Phillips	.50	1.25
SQ28 Brandon Webb	.75	2.00
SQ29 Brian McCann	.75	2.00
SQ30 Carl Crawford	.75	2.00
SQ31 Carlos Beltran	.50	1.25
SQ32 Carlos Quentin	.75	2.00
SQ33 Chien-Ming Wang	.75	2.00
SQ34 Cliff Lee	.75	2.00
SQ35 Cole Hamels	1.25	3.00
SQ36 Curtis Granderson	.75	2.00
SQ37 David Price	1.25	3.00
SQ38 Dustin Pedroia	1.50	4.00
SQ39 Evan Longoria	1.50	4.00
SQ40 Francisco Liriano	.50	1.25
SQ41 Geovany Soto	.75	2.00
SQ42 Ian Kinsler	.75	2.00
SQ43 Jay Bruce	.75	2.00
SQ44 Jimmy Rollins	.75	2.00
SQ45 Jonathan Papelbon	.75	2.00
SQ46 Josh Hamilton	1.25	3.00
SQ47 Justin Morneau	1.25	3.00
SQ48 Kevin Youkilis	.75	2.00
SQ49 Nick Markakis	1.25	3.00
SQ50 Tim Lincecum	2.00	5.00

2009 Upper Deck UD Game Jersey

STATED ODDS 1:19 HOB,1:24 RET,1:9 BLAST

Card	Low	High
GJAD Adam Dunn	3.00	8.00
GJAE Andre Ethier	3.00	8.00
GJAG Adrian Gonzalez	3.00	8.00
GJAH Aaron Harang	3.00	8.00
GJAI Akinori Iwamura	3.00	8.00
GJAN Rick Ankiel	4.00	10.00
GJAP Albert Pujols	8.00	20.00
GJAR Aaron Rowand	3.00	8.00
GJAS Alfonso Soriano		
GJBA Rocco Baldelli Pants	2.50	6.00
GJBE Josh Beckett	4.00	10.00
GJBH Bill Hall		
GJBM Brian McCann	3.00	8.00
GJBP Brandon Phillips		
GJBR Brian Bass	2.50	6.00
GJBU B.J. Upton	2.50	6.00
GJBW Billy Wagner	4.00	10.00
GJCB Chad Billingsley	3.00	8.00
GJCD Chris Duncan	3.00	8.00
GJCH Chin-Lung Hu	3.00	8.00
GJCJ Chipper Jones	4.00	10.00
GJCL Clay Buchholz	3.00	8.00
GJCO Corey Hart		
GJCS CC Sabathia	4.00	10.00
Card pictures him in an Indians Cap, Card has Brewers logo		
GJCT Clay Timpner		
GJCW Chien-Ming Wang	5.00	12.00
GJDA Johnny Damon		
GJDB Daric Barton	3.00	8.00
GJDH Dan Haren	2.50	6.00
GJDJ Derek Jeter	10.00	25.00
GJDL Derrek Lee	2.50	6.00
GJDM David Murphy		
GJDO David Ortiz	2.50	6.00
GJDU Dan Uggla	2.50	6.00
GJGA Garrett Atkins	2.50	6.00
GJGM Greg Maddux		
GJGO Alex Gordon	4.00	10.00
GJGR Curtis Granderson	3.00	8.00
GJGS Grady Sizemore		
GJHA Cole Hamels	5.00	12.00
GJHI Aaron Hill		
GJHJ Josh Hamilton	8.00	20.00
GJIK Ian Kennedy	2.50	6.00
GJJA Conor Jackson	2.50	6.00
GJJD J.D. Drew		
GJJF Jeff Francis	2.50	6.00
GJJG Jeremy Guthrie	2.50	6.00
GJJH Jeremy Hermida		
GJJJ Josh Johnson		
GJJL James Loney	3.00	8.00
GJJM John Maine	4.00	10.00
GJJN Joe Nathan	2.50	6.00
GJJO John Lackey	2.50	6.00
GJJP Jake Peavy	3.00	8.00
GJJT J.R. Towles	2.50	6.00
GJJU Justin Upton	4.00	10.00
GJJV Jason Varitek	4.00	10.00
GJJW Josh Willingham	2.50	6.00
GJKG Ken Griffey Jr.	10.00	25.00
GJKI Ian Kinsler		
GJKK Kevin Kouzmanoff	2.50	6.00
GJKY Kevin Youkilis	4.00	10.00
GJLA Adam LaRoche UER	4.00	10.00
Andy LaRoche pictured		
GJMC Matt Cain	3.00	8.00
GJMK Matt Kemp	3.00	8.00
GJMT Mark Teahen	2.50	6.00
GJNB Nick Blackburn	2.50	6.00
GJNM Nick Markakis	3.00	8.00
GJNS Nick Swisher	2.50	6.00
GJPA Jonathan Papelbon	3.00	8.00
GJPB Pat Burrell	6.00	15.00
GJPE Jhonny Peralta	2.50	6.00
GJPH Phil Hughes	3.00	8.00
GJPK Paul Konerko	3.00	8.00
GJRA Aramis Ramirez	2.50	6.00
GJRB Ryan Braun	5.00	12.00
GJRF Rafael Furcal	3.00	8.00
GJRH Rich Harden		
GJRM Russell Martin	4.00	10.00
GJRO Roy Halladay	5.00	12.00
GJRW Rickie Weeks	2.50	6.00
GJRZ Ryan Zimmerman		
GJSA Jarrod Saltalamacchia	3.00	8.00
GJSM Greg Smith	2.50	6.00
GJSO Joakim Soria		
GJSP Scott Podsednik	2.50	6.00
GJTG Tom Glavine		
GJTH Tim Hudson	4.00	10.00
GJTR Travis Hafner	3.00	8.00
GJTT Troy Tulowitzki	4.00	10.00
GJVM Victor Martinez	3.00	8.00
GJWE Jered Weaver	2.50	6.00

2009 Upper Deck UD Game Jersey Autographs

RANDOM INSERTS IN PACKS

PRINT RUNS B/WN 5-99 COPIES PER

NO PRICING ON QTY 25 OR LESS

Card	Low	High
GJAD Adam Dunn/25		
GJAE Andre Ethier/99		
GJAG Adrian Gonzalez/99	12.50	30.00
GJAH Aaron Harang/99	5.00	12.00
GJAI Akinori Iwamura/25		
GJAK Austin Kearns/99	5.00	12.00
GJBE Josh Beckett/5		
GJBM Brian McCann/99	10.00	25.00
GJBP Brandon Phillips/99	8.00	20.00
GJBR Brian Bass/99	5.00	12.00
GJBU B.J. Upton/20		
GJBW Billy Wagner/35	10.00	25.00
GJCB Chad Billingsley/99	10.00	25.00
GJCC Carl Crawford/15		
GJCD Chris Duncan/99	12.50	30.00
GJCH Chin-Lung Hu/99	12.50	30.00
GJCJ Chipper Jones/5		
GJCL Clay Buchholz/35		
GJCO Corey Hart/99	15.00	40.00
GJCT Clay Timpner/99		
GJCW Chien-Ming Wang/15		
GJDB Daric Barton/99	6.00	15.00
GJDL Derrek Lee/20		
GJDM David Murphy/99		
GJDU Dan Uggla/99		
GJDY Delmon Young/25		
GJGA Garrett Atkins/99	5.00	12.00
GJGO Alex Gordon/49	8.00	20.00
GJGS Grady Sizemore/15		
GJHA Cole Hamels/20		
GJHJ Josh Hamilton/99	10.00	25.00
GJIK Ian Kennedy/35	5.00	12.00
GJJA Conor Jackson/49	8.00	20.00
GJJF Jeff Francis/99		
GJJG Jeremy Guthrie/35		
GJJH Jeremy Hermida/99	6.00	15.00
GJJL James Loney/99	10.00	25.00
GJJN Joe Nathan/99	6.00	15.00
GJJO John Lackey/99	6.00	15.00
GJJT J.R. Towles/99	5.00	12.00
GJJW Josh Willingham/99	5.00	12.00
GJKG Ken Griffey Jr./99		
GJKI Ian Kinsler/99	8.00	20.00
GJKK Kevin Kouzmanoff/99	5.00	12.00
GJKY Kevin Youkilis/99	20.00	50.00
GJLA Adam LaRoche/99	6.00	15.00
GJMC Matt Cain/99	15.00	40.00
GJMK Matt Kemp/99	10.00	25.00
GJMM Melvin Mora/99	5.00	12.00
GJMT Mark Teahen/99	6.00	15.00
GJNB Nick Blackburn/99	10.00	25.00
GJNM Nick Markakis/99	12.50	30.00
GJNS Nick Swisher/99	6.00	15.00
GJPA Jonathan Papelbon/10		
GJPH Phil Hughes/25		
GJPK Paul Konerko/25		
GJRB Ryan Braun/25		
GJRH Rich Harden/25		
GJRM Russell Martin/35	10.00	25.00
GJRO Roy Halladay/15		
GJRW Rickie Weeks/35		
GJRZ Ryan Zimmerman/50	12.50	30.00
GJSA Jarrod Saltalamacchia/99	5.00	12.00
GJSM Greg Smith/99	6.00	15.00
GJTH Tim Hudson/5		
GJTR Travis Hafner/99	6.00	15.00
GJTT Troy Tulowitzki/99	6.00	15.00
GJVM Victor Martinez/35		
GJWE Jered Weaver/25		
GJYG Yovani Gallardo/99		

2009 Upper Deck UD Game Jersey Dual

RANDOM INSERTS IN PACKS

PRINT RUNS B/WN 37-149 COPIES PER

Card	Low	High
GJAD Adam Dunn/149	4.00	10.00
GJAE Andre Ethier/149	4.00	10.00
GJAG Adrian Gonzalez/149	4.00	10.00
GJAH Aaron Harang/149	4.00	10.00
GJAI Akinori Iwamura/88	4.00	10.00
GJAN Rick Ankiel/149	5.00	12.00
GJAP Albert Pujols/149	10.00	25.00
GJAR Aaron Rowand/149	4.00	10.00
GJAS Alfonso Soriano/149	4.00	10.00
GJBA Rocco Baldelli/50	3.00	8.00
GJBE Josh Beckett/149		
GJBH Bill Hall/129		
GJBM Brian McCann/149	4.00	10.00
GJBP Brandon Phillips/149	3.00	8.00
GJBR Brian Bass/149	3.00	8.00
GJBU B.J. Upton/149	3.00	8.00
GJBW Billy Wagner/149	5.00	12.00
GJCB Chad Billingsley/149	4.00	10.00
GJCC Carl Crawford/149	3.00	8.00
GJCD Chris Duncan/148	4.00	10.00
GJCH Chin-Lung Hu/149	4.00	10.00
GJCJ Chipper Jones/149	5.00	12.00
GJCL Clay Buchholz/149	4.00	10.00
GJCS CC Sabathia/149	5.00	12.00
GJCW Chien-Ming Wang/149	6.00	15.00
GJDA Johnny Damon/50		
GJDB Daric Barton/149	4.00	10.00
GJDH Dan Haren/149	3.00	8.00
GJDJ Derek Jeter/139	12.50	30.00
GJDL Derrek Lee/149	3.00	8.00
GJDO David Ortiz/149	3.00	8.00
GJDU Dan Uggla/149	3.00	8.00
GJDY Delmon Young/50		
GJGA Garrett Atkins/149		
GJGO Alex Gordon/149	5.00	12.00
GJGR Curtis Granderson/149	4.00	10.00
GJGS Grady Sizemore/149		
GJHA Cole Hamels/149	6.00	15.00
GJHI Aaron Hill/52		
GJHJ Josh Hamilton/149	10.00	25.00
GJIK Ian Kennedy/149	3.00	8.00
GJJA Conor Jackson/149	3.00	8.00
GJJD J.D. Drew/112	4.00	10.00
GJJF Jeff Francis/149	3.00	8.00
GJJG Jeremy Guthrie/149	3.00	8.00
GJJH Jeremy Hermida/149	3.00	8.00
GJJJ Josh Johnson/149	3.00	8.00
GJJL James Loney/149	5.00	12.00
GJJM John Maine/149	5.00	12.00
GJJN Joe Nathan/149	3.00	8.00
GJJO John Lackey/149	3.00	8.00
GJJP Jake Peavy/149		
GJJT J.R. Towles/149	3.00	8.00
GJJU Justin Upton/149	5.00	12.00
GJJV Jason Varitek/149	5.00	12.00
GJJW Josh Willingham/149	3.00	8.00
GJKG Ken Griffey Jr./50	12.50	30.00
GJKI Ian Kinsler/75	3.00	8.00
GJKK Kevin Kouzmanoff/149	3.00	8.00
GJKY Kevin Youkilis/149	5.00	12.00
GJLA Adam LaRoche/75	5.00	12.00
GJMC Matt Cain/149	4.00	10.00
GJMK Matt Kemp/149	4.00	10.00
GJMM Melvin Mora/149	3.00	8.00
GJMT Mark Teahen/149	3.00	8.00
GJNB Nick Blackburn/149	3.00	8.00
GJNM Nick Markakis/149	4.00	10.00
GJNS Nick Swisher/149		
GJPA Jonathan Papelbon/149	4.00	10.00
GJPB Pat Burrell/37	15.00	40.00
GJPE Jhonny Peralta/125	3.00	8.00
GJPH Phil Hughes/149	4.00	10.00
GJPK Paul Konerko/149	4.00	10.00
GJRA Aramis Ramirez/149	3.00	8.00
GJRB Ryan Braun/149	6.00	15.00
GJRF Rafael Furcal/149	4.00	10.00
GJRH Rich Harden/149	3.00	8.00
GJRM Russell Martin/149	5.00	12.00
GJRO Roy Halladay/50	6.00	15.00
GJRW Rickie Weeks/149	3.00	8.00
GJRZ Ryan Zimmerman/149	3.00	8.00
GJSM Greg Smith/149		
GJSO Joakim Soria/75	4.00	10.00
GJSP Scott Podsednik/149	3.00	8.00
GJTH Tim Hudson/149	5.00	12.00
GJTR Travis Hafner/149		
GJTT Troy Tulowitzki/149	5.00	12.00
GJVM Victor Martinez/149		
GJWE Jered Weaver/149	3.00	8.00

2009 Upper Deck UD Game Jersey Triple

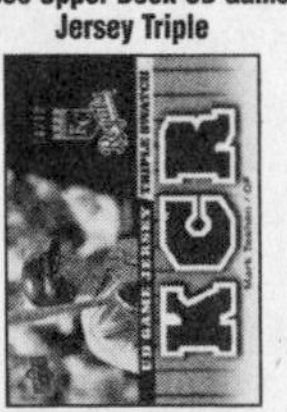

RANDOM INSERTS IN PACKS

PRINT RUNS B/WN 15-100 COPIES PER

NO PRICING ON QTY 25 OR LESS

Card	Low	High
GJAD Adam Dunn/99	5.00	12.00
GJAE Andre Ethier/99		
GJAG Adrian Gonzalez/99	5.00	12.00
GJAH Aaron Harang/99	5.00	12.00
GJAI Akinori Iwamura/25		
GJAN Rick Ankiel/99	6.00	15.00
GJAP Albert Pujols/99	12.50	30.00
GJAR Aaron Rowand/99		
GJAS Alfonso Soriano/79	5.00	12.00
GJBA Rocco Baldelli/15		
GJBE Josh Beckett/99		
GJBH Bill Hall/73	4.00	10.00
GJBM Brian McCann/99	5.00	12.00
GJBP Brandon Phillips/99		
GJBR Brian Bass/65	4.00	10.00
GJBU B.J. Upton/99	4.00	10.00
GJBW Billy Wagner/99		
GJCB Chad Billingsley/99	5.00	12.00
GJCC Carl Crawford/99	4.00	10.00
GJCD Chris Duncan/99	5.00	12.00
GJCH Chin-Lung Hu/99	5.00	12.00
GJCJ Chipper Jones/99	8.00	20.00
GJCL Clay Buchholz/99		
GJCO Corey Hart/63	5.00	12.00
GJCS CC Sabathia/99	6.00	15.00
GJCW Chien-Ming Wang/99	8.00	20.00
GJDA Johnny Damon/25		
GJDB Daric Barton/99	5.00	12.00
GJDH Dan Haren/99	4.00	10.00
GJDJ Derek Jeter/69	15.00	40.00
GJDL Derrek Lee/99		
GJDO David Ortiz/99	4.00	10.00
GJDU Dan Uggla/99		
GJDY Delmon Young/15		
GJGA Garrett Atkins/99	4.00	10.00
GJGO Alex Gordon/99	6.00	15.00
GJGR Curtis Granderson/99	5.00	12.00
GJGS Grady Sizemore/99	5.00	12.00
GJHA Cole Hamels/99		
GJHI Aaron Hill/44	5.00	12.00
GJHJ Josh Hamilton/83	12.50	30.00
GJIK Ian Kennedy/99	4.00	10.00
GJJA Conor Jackson/99	4.00	10.00
GJJD J.D. Drew/58	5.00	12.00
GJJF Jeff Francis/99	4.00	10.00
GJJG Jeremy Guthrie/99	4.00	10.00
GJJH Jeremy Hermida/99	4.00	10.00
GJJJ Josh Johnson/33		
GJJL James Loney/99	5.00	12.00
GJJM John Maine/99	6.00	15.00
GJJN Joe Nathan/99	4.00	10.00
GJJO John Lackey/99		
GJJP Jake Peavy/53		
GJJT J.R. Towles/99	4.00	10.00
GJJU Justin Upton/99	6.00	15.00
GJJV Jason Varitek/66	6.00	15.00
GJJW Josh Willingham/91		
GJKG Ken Griffey Jr./33		
GJKI Ian Kinsler/43	4.00	10.00
GJKK Kevin Kouzmanoff/99	4.00	10.00
GJKY Kevin Youkilis/99	6.00	15.00
GJLA Adam LaRoche/25		
GJMC Matt Cain/99	5.00	12.00
GJMK Matt Kemp/99	5.00	12.00
GJMM Melvin Mora/68		
GJMT Mark Teahen/99	4.00	10.00
GJNB Nick Blackburn/91	4.00	10.00
GJNM Nick Markakis/100	5.00	12.00
GJNS Nick Swisher/62		
GJPA Jonathan Papelbon/100	5.00	12.00
GJPB Pat Burrell/15		
GJPE Jhonny Peralta/53	4.00	10.00
GJPH Phil Hughes/66	5.00	12.00
GJPK Paul Konerko/83	5.00	12.00
GJRA Aramis Ramirez/99	4.00	10.00
GJRB Ryan Braun/99	8.00	20.00
GJRF Rafael Furcal/50		
GJRH Rich Harden/99	4.00	10.00
GJRM Russell Martin/99	6.00	15.00
GJRO Roy Halladay/15		
GJRW Rickie Weeks/99	4.00	10.00
GJRZ Ryan Zimmerman/99	4.00	10.00
GJSM Greg Smith/66	4.00	10.00
GJSO Joakim Soria/50	5.00	12.00
GJSP Scott Podsednik/65	4.00	10.00
GJTH Tim Hudson/50	6.00	15.00
GJTR Travis Hafner/99	5.00	12.00
GJTT Troy Tulowitzki/99	6.00	15.00
GJVM Victor Martinez/99		
GJWE Jered Weaver/66	4.00	10.00

2009 Upper Deck UD Game Materials

RANDOM INSERTS IN PACKS

Card	Low	High
GMAH Aaron Harang	3.00	8.00
GMAJ Andruw Jones	2.50	6.00
GMAP Albert Pujols	6.00	15.00
GMAR Alex Romero	2.50	6.00
GMBA Josh Barfield	2.50	6.00
GMBB Brian Bocock	2.50	6.00
GMBC Bartolo Colon	2.50	6.00
GMBH Bill Hall	2.50	6.00
GMBI Brandon Inge	2.50	6.00
GMBM Brian McCann	3.00	8.00
GMBP Brandon Phillips	3.00	8.00
GMCB Chris Burke	2.50	6.00
GMCD Carlos Delgado	3.00	8.00
GMCH Chin-Lung Hu	2.50	6.00
GMCL Carlos Lee	2.50	6.00
GMCM Colt Morton	2.50	6.00
GMCR Bobby Crosby	2.50	6.00
GMCY Chris Young	3.00	8.00
GMDB Daric Barton	2.50	6.00
GMDE Darin Erstad	2.50	6.00
GMDL Derrek Lee	2.50	6.00
GMDM Daisuke Matsuzaka	3.00	8.00
GMDU Chris Duncan	2.50	6.00
GMEC Eric Chavez	2.50	6.00
GMED Jim Edmonds	3.00	8.00
GMEG Eric Gagne	2.50	6.00
GMFH Felix Hernandez	4.00	10.00
GMFS Freddy Sanchez	2.50	6.00
GMHB Hank Blalock	2.50	6.00
GMHE Ramon Hernandez	2.50	6.00
GMHI Hernan Iribarren	2.50	6.00
GMHK Hong-Chih Kuo	2.50	6.00
GMIK Ian Kinsler	3.00	8.00
GMJB Jason Bay	4.00	10.00
GMJE Jeff Baker	2.50	6.00
GMJG Jason Giambi	3.00	8.00
GMJH Josh Hamilton	3.00	8.00
GMJK Jason Kubel	2.50	6.00
GMJP Jhonny Peralta	2.50	6.00
GMJW Jake Westbrook	2.50	6.00
GMKG Ken Griffey Jr.	6.00	15.00
GMKJ Kelly Johnson	2.50	6.00
GMKM Kendry Morales	2.50	6.00
GMLM Lastings Milledge	2.50	6.00
GMMK Matt Kemp	3.00	8.00
GMMM Melvin Mora	2.50	6.00
GMMP Mark Prior	2.50	6.00
GMNM Nyjer Morgan	2.50	6.00
GMPK Paul Konerko	2.50	6.00
GMRA Aramis Ramirez	3.00	8.00
GMRB Rocco Baldelli	2.50	6.00
GMRF Rafael Furcal	3.00	8.00
GMTG Troy Glaus	2.50	6.00
GMTT Troy Tulowitzki	2.50	6.00
GMTW Tim Wakefield	3.00	8.00
GMUG Dan Uggla	2.50	6.00
GMVM Victor Martinez	3.00	8.00
GMYG Yovani Gallardo	2.50	6.00
GMZG Zack Greinke	4.00	10.00

2009 Upper Deck UD Game Materials Autographs

RANDOM INSERTS IN PACKS

PRINT RUNS B/WN 5-99 COPIES PER

Card	Low	High
GMAH Aaron Harang/76	5.00	12.00
GMAJ Andruw Jones/20		
GMAP Albert Pujols/99		
GMAR Alex Romero/72	4.00	10.00
GMBA Josh Barfield/69		
GMBB Brian Bocock/61	4.00	10.00
GMBC Bartolo Colon/99		
GMBH Bill Hall/99	6.00	15.00
GMBI Brandon Inge/99		
GMBM Brian McCann/71	15.00	40.00
GMBP Brandon Phillips/99	8.00	20.00
GMCB Chris Burke/7		
GMCB Chad Billingsley/99	15.00	40.00
GMCH Chin-Lung Hu/99	5.00	12.00
GMCL Carlos Lee/25		
GMCM Colt Morton/99	4.00	10.00
GMDB Daric Barton/99	6.00	15.00
GMDL Derrek Lee/25		
GMDM Daisuke Matsuzaka/5		
GMDU Chris Duncan/99	6.00	15.00
GMEC Eric Chavez/25		
GMED Jim Edmonds/99		
GMFH Felix Hernandez/25		
GMHE Ramon Hernandez/25		
GMHI Hernan Iribarren/99		
GMHK Hong-Chih Kuo/99		
GMJB Jason Bay/25		
GMJE Jeff Baker/99	4.00	10.00
GMJS Jarrod Saltalamacchia/99	4.00	10.00
GMKG Ken Griffey Jr./10		
GMKJ Kelly Johnson/99	6.00	15.00
GMMK Matt Kemp/99	8.00	20.00
GMMM Melvin Mora/99	6.00	15.00
GMNM Nyjer Morgan/99	4.00	10.00
GMPK Paul Konerko/20		
GMVM Victor Martinez/25		
GMYG Yovani Gallardo/99	10.00	25.00

2009 Upper Deck USA 18U National Team

ODDS 1:3 HOB,1:6 RET,1:200 BLAST

Card	Low	High
18UAA Andrew Aplin	.75	2.00
18UAM Austin Maddox	1.25	3.00
18UCC Colton Cain	1.25	3.00
18UCG Cameron Garfield	.75	2.00
18UCT Cecil Tanner	.75	2.00
18UDN David Nick	1.25	3.00
18UDT Donavan Tate	2.00	5.00
18UFO Nolan Fontana	.75	2.00
18UHM Harold Martinez	1.25	3.00
18UJB Jake Barrett	.75	2.00
18UJM Jeff Malm	.75	2.00
18UJT Jacob Turner	2.50	6.00
18UME Jonathan Meyer	.75	2.00
18UMP Matthew Purke	.75	2.00
18UMS Max Stassi	1.25	3.00
18UNF Nick Franklin	2.00	5.00
18URW Ryan Weber	.75	2.00
18UWH Wes Hatton	.75	2.00

2009 Upper Deck USA 18U National Team Jersey

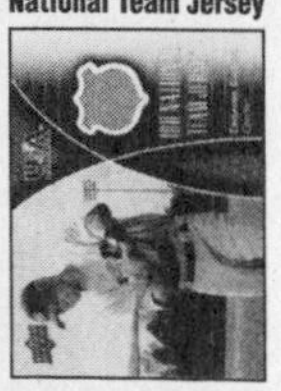

STATED ODDS 1:96 HOB,1:1715 RET,1:3163 BLAST

Card	Low	High
18UAA Andrew Aplin	4.00	10.00
18UAM Austin Maddox	4.00	10.00
18UCC Colton Cain	2.50	6.00
18UCG Cameron Garfield	4.00	10.00
18UCT Cecil Tanner	2.50	6.00
18UDN David Nick	2.50	6.00
18UDT Donavan Tate	4.00	10.00
18UFO Nolan Fontana	4.00	10.00
18UHM Harold Martinez	4.00	10.00
18UJB Jake Barrett	2.50	6.00
18UJM Jeff Malm	2.50	6.00

18UJT Jacob Turner 4.00 10.00
18UME Jonathan Meyer 2.50 6.00
18UMP Matthew Purke 4.00 10.00
18UMS Max Stassi 4.00 10.00
18UNF Nick Franklin 4.00 10.00
18URW Ryan Weber 2.50 6.00
18UWH Wes Hatton 4.00 10.00

2009 Upper Deck USA National Team

RANDOM INSERTS IN PACKS
AG A.J. Griffin 1.25 3.00
AO Andrew Oliver .75 2.00
BS Blake Smith .75 2.00
CC Christian Colon 1.25 3.00
CH Chris Hernandez .75 2.00
DD Derek Dietrich 2.50 6.00
HM Hunter Morris .75 2.00
JC Jared Clark .75 2.00
JF Josh Fellhauer .75 2.00
KD Kentrail Davis 1.25 3.00
KG Kyle Gibson 2.00 5.00
KV Kendal Volz 1.25 3.00
MD Matt den Dekker 1.25 3.00
MG Micah Gibbs .75 2.00
ML Mike Leake 2.50 6.00
MM Mike Minor 1.25 3.00
RJ Ryan Jackson .75 2.00
RL Ryan Lipkin .75 2.00
SS Stephen Strasburg 8.00 20.00
SW Scott Woodward .75 2.00
TL Tyler Lyons 1.25 3.00
TM Tommy Mendonca 1.25 3.00

2009 Upper Deck USA National Team Autographs

RANDOM INSERTS IN PACKS
AG A.J. Griffin 4.00 10.00
AO Andrew Oliver 3.00 8.00
BS Blake Smith 3.00 8.00
CC Christian Colon 4.00 10.00
CH Chris Hernandez 3.00 8.00
DD Derek Dietrich 5.00 12.00
HM Hunter Morris 3.00 8.00
JF Josh Fellhauer 3.00 8.00
KD Kentrail Davis 4.00 10.00
KV Kendal Volz 3.00 8.00
MD Matt den Dekker 4.00 10.00
MG Micah Gibbs 4.00 10.00
ML Mike Leake 6.00 15.00
MM Mike Minor 4.00 10.00
RJ Ryan Jackson 3.00 8.00
RL Ryan Lipkin 3.00 8.00
TL Tyler Lyons 3.00 8.00

2009 Upper Deck USA National Team Jerseys

AG A.J. Griffin 3.00 8.00
AO Andrew Oliver 3.00 8.00
BS Blake Smith 3.00 8.00
CC Christian Colon 3.00 8.00
CH Chris Hernandez 3.00 8.00
DD Derek Dietrich 3.00 8.00
HM Hunter Morris 3.00 8.00
JF Josh Fellhauer 3.00 8.00
KD Kentrail Davis 3.00 8.00
KG Kyle Gibson 3.00 8.00
KR Kevin Rhoderick 3.00 8.00
KV Kendal Volz 3.00 8.00
MD Matt den Dekker 3.00 8.00
MG Micah Gibbs 3.00 8.00
ML Mike Leake 4.00 10.00
MM Mike Minor 3.00 8.00
RJ Ryan Jackson 3.00 8.00
RL Ryan Lipkin 3.00 8.00
SS Stephen Strasburg 12.50 30.00
TL Tyler Lyons 3.00 8.00

2009 Upper Deck USA National Team Jersey Autographs

RANDOM INSERTS IN PACKS
STATED PRINT RUN 225 SER.#'d SETS
AG A.J. Griffin 4.00 10.00
AO Andrew Oliver 4.00 10.00
BS Blake Smith 6.00 15.00
CC Christian Colon 8.00 20.00
CH Chris Hernandez 5.00 12.00
DD Derek Dietrich 5.00 12.00
HM Hunter Morris 4.00 10.00
JF Josh Fellhauer 5.00 12.00
KD Kentrail Davis 4.00 10.00
KG Kyle Gibson 15.00 40.00
KR Kevin Rhoderick 4.00 10.00
KV Kendal Volz 4.00 10.00
MD Matt den Dekker 4.00 10.00
MG Micah Gibbs 4.00 10.00
ML Mike Leake 12.50 30.00
MM Mike Minor 6.00 12.00
RJ Ryan Jackson 4.00 10.00
RL Ryan Lipkin 4.00 10.00
SS Stephen Strasburg 150.00 300.00
TL Tyler Lyons 4.00 10.00

2009 Upper Deck USA National Team Retrospective

ODDS 1:8 HOB,1:36 RET,1:108 BLAST
USA1 Matt Brown .75 2.00
USA2 Stephen Strasburg 4.00 10.00
USA3 Jayson Nix .75 2.00
USA4 Brian Duensing 1.25 3.00
USA5 Jake Arrieta 1.25 3.00
USA6 Dexter Fowler 1.25 3.00
USA7 Casey Weathers .75 2.00
USA8 Mike Koplove .75 2.00
USA9 Jason Donald .75 2.00
USA10 Taylor Teagarden 1.25 3.00
USA11 Kevin Jepsen .75 2.00
USA12 Matt LaPorta 2.00 5.00
USA13 Team USA Wins Bronze Medal .75 2.00
USA14 Team USA Wins Third Olympic Medal .75 2.00

2010 Upper Deck

COMMON CARD (2-40) 1.00 2.50
COMMON CARD (1/41-600) .15 .40
C EQUALS COMMON VARIATION
R EQUALS RARE VARIATION
S EQUALS SUPER RARE VARIATION
U EQUALS ULTRA RARE VARIATION
1 Star Rookie CL .15 .40
2 Daniel McCutchen RC 1.50 4.00
3 Eric Young Jr. (RC) 1.00 2.50
4 Michael Brantley RC 1.00 2.50
5 Brian Matusz RC 2.50 6.00
6 Ian Desmond (RC) 1.50 4.00
7 Carlos Carrasco (RC) 2.50 6.00
8 Dustin Richardson RC 1.00 2.50
9 Tyler Flowers RC 1.50 4.00
10 Drew Stubbs RC 2.50 6.00
11 Reid Gorecki (RC) 1.50 4.00
12 Tommy Manzella (RC) 1.00 2.50
13 Wade Davis (RC) 1.00 2.50
14 Esmil Rogers RC 1.00 2.50
15 Michael Dunn RC 1.00 2.50
16 Luis Durango RC 1.00 2.50
17 Juan Francisco RC 1.50 4.00
18 Ernesto Frieri RC 1.00 2.50
19 Tyler Colvin RC 1.50 4.00
20 Armando Gabino RC 1.00 2.50
21 Adam Moore RC 1.00 2.50
22 Cesar Ramos (RC) 1.00 2.50
23 Chris Johnson RC 2.50 6.00
24 Chris Pettit RC 1.00 2.50
25 Brandon Allen (RC) 1.00 2.50
26 Brad Kilby RC 1.00 2.50
27 Dusty Hughes RC 1.00 2.50
28 Buster Posey RC 10.00 25.00
29 Kevin Richardson (RC) 1.00 2.50
30 Josh Thole RC 1.50 4.00
31 John Hester RC 1.00 2.50
32 Kyle Phillips RC 1.00 2.50
33 Neil Walker (RC) 1.50 4.00
34 Matt Carson (RC) 1.00 2.50
35 Pedro Strop RC 2.50 6.00
36 Pedro Viola RC 1.00 2.50
37 Daniel Runzler RC 1.50 4.00
38 Henry Rodriguez RC 1.00 2.50
39 Justin Turner RC 1.00 2.50
40 Madison Bumgarner RC 2.50 6.00
41 Chris B. Young .15 .40
42A Justin Upton .25 .60
42B Justin Upton C VAR SP
All black bat
43 Conor Jackson .15 .40
44 Augie Ojeda .15 .40
45 Mark Reynolds .15 .40
46 Miguel Montero .15 .40
47 Max Scherzer .15 .40
48 Doug Slaten .15 .40
49 Chad Qualls .15 .40
50 Dan Haren .15 .40
51 Juan Gutierrez .15 .40
52 Doug Davis .15 .40
53 Leo Rosales .15 .40
54 Chad Tracy .15 .40
55 Stephen Drew .15 .40
56 Jordan Schafer .15 .40
57 Rafael Soriano .15 .40
58 Javier Vazquez .15 .40
59 Brandon Jones .15 .40
60 Matt Diaz .15 .40
61 Jair Jurrjens .15 .40
62 Adam LaRoche .15 .40
63 Martin Prado .15 .40
64 Omar Infante .15 .40
65 Chipper Jones .40 1.00
66A Yunel Escobar .15 .40
67 David Ross .15 .40
68 Derek Lowe .15 .40
69 James Parr .15 .40
70 Kenshin Kawakami .25 .60
71 Kris Medlen .15 .40
72 Ryan Church .15 .40
73 Nate McLouth .15 .40
74 Adam Jones .25 .60
75 Luke Scott .15 .40
76 Nolan Reimold .25 .60
77 Felix Pie .15 .40
78 Lou Montanez .15 .40
79 Ty Wigginton .15 .40
80 Cesar Izturis .15 .40
81 Robert Andino .15 .40
82 Chad Moeller .15 .40
83A Koji Uehara .25 .60
84 Matt Wieters .40 1.00
85 Jim Johnson .15 .40
86 Chris Ray .15 .40
87 Danys Baez .15 .40
88 David Hernandez .15 .40
89 Jeremy Guthrie .15 .40
90 Rich Hill .15 .40
91 Dustin Pedroia .50 1.25
92 David Ortiz .25 .60
93 J.D. Drew .15 .40
94 Jeff Bailey .15 .40
95 Kevin Youkilis .25 .60
96 Clay Buchholz .25 .60
97 Jed Lowrie .25 .60
98 Mike Lowell .15 .40
99 George Kottaras .15 .40
100 Takashi Saito .15 .40
101 Hideki Okajima .15 .40
102 Jason Varitek .40 1.00
103 Jon Lester .40 1.00
104A Josh Beckett .25 .60
105 Daniel Bard .15 .40
106 Jonathan Papelbon .25 .60
107 Nick Green .15 .40
108 Kevin Gregg .15 .40
109A Ryan Theriot .15 .40
110A Kosuke Fukudome .40 1.00
111 Derrek Lee .15 .40
112 Bobby Scales .15 .40
113 Aramis Ramirez .15 .40
114 Aaron Miles .15 .40
115 Mike Fontenot .15 .40
116 Koyie Hill .15 .40
117 Carlos Zambrano .25 .60
118 Jeff Samardzija .15 .40
119 Randy Wells .15 .40
120 Sean Marshall .15 .40
121 Carlos Marmol .25 .60
122 Ryan Dempster .15 .40
123 Reed Johnson .15 .40
124 Jake Fox .15 .40
125 Tony Pena .15 .40
126 Carlos Quentin .25 .60
127 A.J. Pierzynski .15 .40
128 Scott Podsednik .15 .40
129A Alexei Ramirez .15 .40
129B Alexei Ramirez R VAR SP
No swoosh on armband
130 Paul Konerko .25 .60
131 Josh Fields .15 .40
132 Alex Rios .25 .60
133 Matt Thornton .15 .40
134 Mark Buehrle .25 .60
135 Scott Linebrink .15 .40
136 Freddy Garcia .15 .40
137 John Danks .15 .40
138 Bobby Jenks .15 .40
139 Gavin Floyd .15 .40
140 DJ Carrasco .15 .40
141 Jake Peavy .15 .40
142 Justin Lehr .15 .40
143 Wladimir Balentien .15 .40
144 Laynce Nix .15 .40
145 Chris Dickerson .15 .40
146A Joey Votto .40 1.00
147 Paul Janish .15 .40
148 Brandon Phillips .15 .40
149 Scott Rolen .25 .60
150 Ryan Hanigan .15 .40
151 Edinson Volquez .15 .40
152 Arthur Rhodes .15 .40
153 Micah Owings .15 .40
154 Ramon Hernandez .15 .40
155 Francisco Cordero .15 .40
156 Bronson Arroyo .15 .40
157 Jared Burton .15 .40
158 Homer Bailey .15 .40
159 Travis Hafner .15 .40
160 Grady Sizemore .25 .60
161 Matt LaPorta .40 1.00
162 Jeremy Sowers .15 .40
163 Trevor Crowe .15 .40
164 Asdrubal Cabrera .25 .60
165A Shin-Soo Choo .25 .60
166 Kelly Shoppach .15 .40
167 Kerry Wood .15 .40
168 Jake Westbrook .15 .40
169 Fausto Carmona .15 .40
170 Aaron Laffey .15 .40
171 Justin Masterson .15 .40
172 Jhonny Peralta .15 .40
173 Jensen Lewis .15 .40
174 Luis Valbuena .15 .40
175 Jason Giambi .15 .40
176 Ryan Spilborghs .15 .40
177 Seth Smith .15 .40
178 Matt Murton .15 .40
179 Dexter Fowler .15 .40
180A Troy Tulowitzki .40 1.00
181 Ian Stewart .15 .40
182 Omar Quintanilla .15 .40
183 Clint Barmes .15 .40
184 Garrett Atkins .15 .40
185 Chris Iannetta .15 .40
186 Huston Street .15 .40
187 Franklin Morales .15 .40
188 Todd Helton .25 .60
189 Carlos Gonzalez .25 .60
190 Aaron Cook .15 .40
191 Jason Hammel .15 .40
192 Edwin Jackson .15 .40
193 Clete Thomas .15 .40
194 Marcus Thames .15 .40
195 Ryan Raburn .15 .40
196 Fernando Rodney .15 .40
197 Adam Everett .15 .40
198A Brandon Inge .25 .60
199 Miguel Cabrera .40 1.00
200 Gerald Laird .15 .40
201 Joel Zumaya .15 .40
202 Curtis Granderson .25 .60
203 Justin Verlander .50 1.25
204 Bobby Seay .15 .40
205 Nate Robertson .15 .40
206 Rick Porcello .15 .40
207 Ryan Perry .15 .40
208 Fu-Te Ni .25 .60
209 Cody Ross .15 .40
210 Jeremy Hermida .15 .40
211 Alfredo Amezaga .15 .40
212A Chris Coghlan .15 .40
213 Wes Helms .15 .40
214 Emilio Bonifacio .15 .40
215 Ricky Nolasco .15 .40
216 Anibal Sanchez .15 .40
217 Josh Johnson .25 .60
218 Burke Badenhop .15 .40
219 Kiko Calero .15 .40
220 Renyel Pinto .15 .40
221 Andrew Miller .15 .40
222 Hanley Ramirez .40 1.00
223 Gaby Sanchez .15 .40
224 Hunter Pence .25 .60
225 Carlos Lee .15 .40
226A Michael Bourn .15 .40
227 Kazuo Matsui .15 .40
228 Darin Erstad .15 .40
229 Lance Berkman .25 .60
230 Humberto Quintero .15 .40
231 J.R. Towles .15 .40
232 Wesley Wright .15 .40
233 Jose Valverde .15 .40
234 Wandy Rodriguez .15 .40
235 Roy Oswalt .25 .60
236 Latroy Hawkins .15 .40
237 Bud Norris .15 .40
238 Alberto Arias .15 .40
239 Billy Butler .15 .40
240 Jose Guillen .15 .40
241 David DeJesus .15 .40
242 Willie Bloomquist .15 .40
243 Mike Aviles .15 .40
244 Alberto Callaspo .15 .40
245 John Buck .15 .40
246 Joakim Soria .15 .40
247 Zack Greinke .25 .60
248 Miguel Olivo .15 .40
249 Kyle Davies .15 .40
250 Juan Cruz .15 .40
251 Luke Hochevar .15 .40
252 Brian Bannister .15 .40
253 Robinson Tejeda .15 .40
254 Kyle Farnsworth .15 .40
255 John Lackey .15 .40
256 Torii Hunter .15 .40
257 Chone Figgins .15 .40
258 Kevin Jepsen .15 .40
259 Reggie Willits .15 .40
260 Kendry Morales .15 .40
261 Howie Kendrick .15 .40
262 Erick Aybar .15 .40
263 Brandon Wood .15 .40
264 Maicer Izturis .15 .40
265 Mike Napoli .25 .60
266 Jeff Mathis .15 .40
267A Jered Weaver .15 .40
268 Joe Saunders .15 .40
269 Ervin Santana .15 .40
270 Brian Fuentes .15 .40
271 Jose Arredondo .15 .40
272 Chad Billingsley .15 .40
273 Juan Pierre .15 .40
274 Matt Kemp .25 .60
275 Randy Wolf .15 .40
276 Doug Mientkiewicz .15 .40
277 James Loney .25 .60
278 Casey Blake .15 .40
279 Rafael Furcal .15 .40
280 Blake DeWitt .15 .40
281 Russell Martin .15 .40
282 Jeff Weaver .15 .40
283 Cory Wade .15 .40
284 Eric Stults .15 .40
285 George Sherrill .15 .40
286 Hiroki Kuroda .15 .40
287 Hong-Chih Kuo .15 .40
288A Clayton Kershaw .40 1.00
289 Corey Hart .15 .40
290 Jody Gerut .15 .40
291A Ryan Braun .50 1.25
291B Ryan Braun C VAR SP
Short bat barrel
292 Mike Cameron .15 .40
293 Casey McGehee .15 .40
294 Mat Gamel .15 .40
295 J.J. Hardy .15 .40
296 Braden Looper .15 .40
297 Yovani Gallardo .15 .40
298 Mike Rivera .15 .40
299 Carlos Villanueva .15 .40
300 Jeff Suppan .15 .40
301 Mitch Stetter .15 .40
302 David Riske .15 .40
303 Manny Parra .15 .40
304 Seth McClung .15 .40
305 Todd Coffey .15 .40
306 Joe Mauer .40 1.00
307 Delmon Young .25 .60
308 Michael Cuddyer .15 .40
309 Matt Tolbert .15 .40
310 Nick Punto .15 .40
311 Jason Kubel .15 .40
312 Brendan Harris .15 .40
313 Brian Buscher .15 .40
314 Kevin Slowey .15 .40
315 Glen Perkins .15 .40
316 Joe Nathan .15 .40
317 Nick Blackburn .15 .40
318 Jesse Crain .15 .40
319 Matt Guerrier .15 .40
320 Scott Baker .15 .40
321 Anthony Swarzak .15 .40
322 Jon Rauch .15 .40
323A David Wright .50 1.25
324 Jeremy Reed .15 .40
325 Angel Pagan .15 .40
326 Jose Reyes .25 .60
327 Jeff Francoeur .25 .60
328 Luis Castillo .15 .40
329 Daniel Murphy .15 .40
330 Omir Santos .15 .40
331 John Maine .15 .40
332 Brian Schneider .15 .40
333 Johan Santana .40 1.00
334 Francisco Rodriguez .25 .60
335 Tim Redding .15 .40
336 Mike Pelfrey .15 .40
337 Bobby Parnell .15 .40
338 Pat Misch .15 .40
339 Pedro Feliciano .15 .40
340 Nick Swisher .40 1.00
341 Melky Cabrera .15 .40
342 Mark Teixeira .40 1.00
343 CC Sabathia .25 .60
344 Ramiro Pena .15 .40
345 Derek Jeter 1.00 2.50
346 Andy Pettitte .25 .60
347A Jorge Posada .25 .60
347B Jorge Posada C VAR SP
Black shirts in crowd
348 Francisco Cervelli .15 .40
349 Chien-Ming Wang .25 .60
350A Mariano Rivera .40 1.00
351 Phil Hughes .15 .40
352 Phil Coke .15 .40
353 A.J. Burnett .25 .60
354 Jose Molina .15 .40
355 Jonathan Albaladejo .15 .40
356 Ryan Sweeney .15 .40
357 Jack Cust .15 .40
358 Rajai Davis .15 .40
359 Andrew Bailey .15 .40
360 Aaron Cunningham .15 .40
361 Adam Kennedy .15 .40
362 Mark Ellis .15 .40
363 Daric Barton .15 .40
364 Kurt Suzuki .15 .40
365 Brad Ziegler .15 .40
366 Michael Wuertz .15 .40
367 Josh Outman .15 .40
368 Edgar Gonzalez .15 .40
369 Joey Devine .15 .40
370 Craig Breslow .15 .40
371 Trevor Cahill .15 .40
372 Brett Anderson .25 .60
373 Scott Hairston .15 .40
374 Jayson Werth .25 .60
375 Raul Ibanez .25 .60
376A Chase Utley .40 1.00
376B Chase Utley C VAR SP
Striped grass
377 Greg Dobbs .15 .40
378 Eric Bruntlett .15 .40
379 Shane Victorino .25 .60
380 Jimmy Rollins .25 .60
381 Jack Taschner .15 .40
382 Ryan Madson .15 .40
383 Brad Lidge .15 .40
384 J.A. Happ .25 .60
385 Cole Hamels .40 1.00
386 Carlos Ruiz .15 .40
387 JC Romero .15 .40
388 Kyle Kendrick .15 .40
389 Chad Durbin .15 .40
390 Cliff Lee .25 .60
391 Delwyn Young .15 .40
392 Brandon Moss .15 .40
393 Ramon Vazquez .15 .40
394 Andy LaRoche .15 .40
395 Jason Jaramillo .15 .40
396 Ross Ohlendorf .15 .40
397 Paul Maholm .15 .40
398 Jeff Karstens .15 .40
399 Charlie Morton .15 .40
400 Zach Duke .15 .40
401 Jesse Chavez .15 .40
402 Lastings Milledge .15 .40
403 Matt Capps .15 .40
404 Evan Meek .15 .40
405 Ryan Doumit .15 .40
406 Drew Macias .15 .40
407 Chase Headley .15 .40
408A Tony Gwynn Jr. .15 .40
409 Kevin Kouzmanoff .15 .40
410 Edgar Gonzalez .15 .40
411 David Eckstein .15 .40
412 Everth Cabrera .15 .40
413 Nick Hundley .15 .40
414 Chris Young .15 .40
415 Luis Perdomo .15 .40
416 Edward Mujica .15 .40
417 Clayton Richard .15 .40
418A Luke Gregerson .15 .40
419 Heath Bell .25 .60
420 Kevin Correia .15 .40
421 Cha-Seung Baek .15 .40
422 Joe Thatcher .15 .40
423 Luis Rodriguez .15 .40
424 Bengie Molina .15 .40
425 Ryan Garko .15 .40
426 Nate Schierholtz .15 .40
427 Aaron Rowand .15 .40
428 Eugenio Velez .15 .40
429 Pablo Sandoval .25 .60
430 Edgar Renteria .15 .40
431 Kevin Frandsen .15 .40
432 Rich Aurilia .15 .40
433 Jonathan Sanchez .15 .40
434 Barry Zito .15 .40
435 Brian Wilson .40 1.00
436 Merkin Valdez .15 .40
437 Juan Uribe .15 .40
438 Brandon Medders .15 .40
439 Noah Lowry .15 .40
440 Tim Lincecum .60 1.50
441 Jeremy Affeldt .15 .40
442 Russell Branyan .15 .40
443 Ian Snell .15 .40
444 Franklin Gutierrez .15 .40
445 Ken Griffey Jr. .60 1.50
446 Matt Tuiasosopo .15 .40
447 Jose Lopez .15 .40
448 Michael Saunders .15 .40
449 Ryan Rowland-Smith .15 .40
450 Carlos Silva .15 .40
451A Ichiro Suzuki .60 1.50
452 Brandon Morrow .15 .40
453 Chris Jakubauskas .15 .40
454 Felix Hernandez .40 1.00
455 David Aardsma .15 .40
456 Mark Lowe .15 .40
457 Rob Johnson .15 .40
458 Garrett Olson .15 .40
459 Ryan Ludwick .15 .40
460 Colby Rasmus .40 1.00
461 Brendan Ryan .15 .40
462 Skip Schumaker .15 .40
463 Albert Pujols 1.00 2.50
464 Joe Thurston .15 .40
465 Julio Lugo .15 .40
466A Yadier Molina .25 .60
467 Adam Wainwright .25 .60
468 Brad Thompson .15 .40
469 Dennys Reyes .15 .40
470 Mitchell Boggs .15 .40
471 Jason Motte .15 .40
472 Kyle McClellan .15 .40
473 Kyle Lohse .15 .40
474 Chris Carpenter .40 1.00
475 Ryan Franklin .15 .40
476 Fernando Perez .15 .40
477 Ben Zobrist .15 .40
478 Evan Longoria .50 1.25
479 Gabe Gross .15 .40
480 Pat Burrell .15 .40
481 Carlos Pena .25 .60
482 Jason Bartlett .15 .40
483 Willie Aybar .15 .40
484 Dioner Navarro .15 .40
485 Dan Wheeler .15 .40
486 Andy Sonnanstine .15 .40
487 James Shields .15 .40
488 Jeff Niemann .15 .40
489 J.P. Howell .15 .40
490 Grant Balfour .15 .40
491 David Price .40 1.00
492 Matt Garza .15 .40
493 David Murphy .15 .40
494 Nelson Cruz .25 .60
495 Michael Young .25 .60
496 Ian Kinsler .25 .60
497 Chris Davis .15 .40
498A Elvis Andrus .25 .60
498B Elvis Andrus R VAR SP
All black glove
499 Taylor Teagarden .15 .40
500 Jarrod Saltalamacchia .15 .40
501 CJ Wilson .15 .40
502 Derek Holland .15 .40
503 Darren O'Day .15 .40
504 Brandon McCarthy .15 .40
505 Scott Feldman .15 .40
506 Jason Jennings .15 .40
507 Eddie Guardado .15 .40
508 Frank Francisco .15 .40
509 Marlon Byrd .15 .40
510 Scott Downs .15 .40
511 Adam Lind .25 .60
512 Brett Cecil .15 .40
513 Travis Snider .15 .40
514 Ricky Romero .15 .40
515 Lyle Overbay .15 .40
516 Aaron Hill .15 .40
517 Jose Bautista .25 .60
518 Michael Barrett .15 .40
519 Roy Halladay .40 1.00
520 Brian Tallet .15 .40
521 Marc Rzepczynski .15 .40
522 Robert Ray .15 .40
523 Dustin McGowan .15 .40
524 Shaun Marcum .15 .40
525 Jesse Litsch .15 .40
526 Josh Willingham .15 .40
527 Nyjer Morgan .15 .40
528 Adam Dunn .25 .60
529 Ryan Zimmerman .25 .60
530 Willie Harris .15 .40
531 Wil Nieves .15 .40
532 Ron Villone .15 .40
533 Livan Hernandez .15 .40
534 Austin Kearns .15 .40
535 Alberto Gonzalez .15 .40
536 Shairon Martis .15 .40
537 Ross Detwiler .15 .40
538 Garrett Mock .15 .40
539 Mike MacDougal .15 .40
540 Jason Bergmann .15 .40
541 Arizona Diamondbacks BP .15 .40
542 Atlanta Braves BP .15 .40
543 Baltimore Orioles BP .15 .40
544 Boston Red Sox BP .25 .60
545 Chicago Cubs BP .25 .60
546 Chicago White Sox BP .15 .40
547 Cincinnati Reds BP .15 .40
548 Cleveland Indians BP .15 .40
549 Colorado Rockies BP .15 .40
550 Detroit Tigers BP .15 .40
551 Florida Marlins BP .15 .40
552 Houston Astros BP .15 .40
553 Kansas City Royals BP .15 .40
554 Los Angeles Angels BP .15 .40
555 Los Angeles Dodgers BP .25 .60
556 Milwaukee Brewers BP .15 .40
557 Minnesota Twins BP .15 .40
558 New York Mets BP .25 .60
559 New York Yankees BP .40 1.00
560 Oakland Athletics BP .15 .40
561 Philadelphia Phillies .15 .40
562 Pittsburgh Pirates .15 .40
563 San Diego Padres .15 .40
564 San Francisco Giants .15 .40
565 St. Louis Cardinals .25 .60
566 Seattle Mariners .15 .40
567 Tampa Bay Rays .15 .40
568 Texas Rangers .15 .40
569 Toronto Blue Jays .15 .40
570 Washington Nationals .15 .40
571 Arizona Diamondbacks CL .15 .40
572 Atlanta Braves CL .15 .40
573 Baltimore Orioles CL .15 .40
574 Boston Red Sox CL .25 .60
575 Chicago Cubs CL .25 .60
576 Chicago White Sox CL .15 .40
577 Cincinnati Reds CL .15 .40
578 Cleveland Indians CL .15 .40
579 Colorado Rockies CL .15 .40
580 Detroit Tigers CL .15 .40
581 Florida Marlins CL .15 .40
582 Houston Astros CL .15 .40
583 Kansas City Royals CL .15 .40
584 Los Angeles Angels CL .15 .40
585 Los Angeles Dodgers CL .25 .60
586 Milwaukee Brewers CL .15 .40
587 Minnesota Twins CL .15 .40
588 New York Mets CL .25 .60
589 New York Yankees CL .40 1.00
590 Oakland Athletics CL .15 .40
591 Philadelphia Phillies CL .15 .40
592 Pittsburgh Pirates CL .15 .40
593 San Diego Padres CL .15 .40
594 San Francisco Giants CL .15 .40
595 St. Louis Cardinals CL .25 .60
596 Seattle Mariners CL .15 .40
597 Tampa Bay Rays CL .15 .40
598 Texas Rangers CL .15 .40
599 Toronto Blue Jays CL .15 .40
600 Washington Nationals CL .15 .40
R1 Pete Rose ATHK SP 50.00 100.00
R2 Jorge Posada 50.00 100.00
Derek Jeter
Mariano Rivera
Andy Pettitte SP
R3 Joe Jackson SP 75.00 150.00

2010 Upper Deck Gold

*GOLD 2-40: 3X TO 8X BASIC RC
*GOLD 1/41-600: 12X TO 30X BASIC VET
STATED PRINT RUN 99 SER.#'d SETS
28 Buster Posey 150.00 300.00

2010 Upper Deck 2000 Star Rookie Update

541 Mark Buehrle 3.00 8.00
542 Miguel Cabrera 5.00 12.00
543 Jorge Cantu 2.00 5.00
544 Carl Crawford 3.00 8.00
545 Adam Dunn 3.00 8.00
546 Adrian Gonzalez 3.00 8.00
547 Matt Holliday 5.00 12.00
548 Brandon Inge 3.00 8.00
549 Roy Oswalt 3.00 8.00
550 Carlos Pena 3.00 8.00
551 Brandon Phillips 2.00 5.00
552 Francisco Rodriguez 3.00 8.00
553 Jimmy Rollins 3.00 8.00
554 Aaron Rowand 2.00 5.00
555 CC Sabathia 3.00 8.00
556 Johan Santana 5.00 12.00
557 Grady Sizemore 3.00 8.00
558 Adam Wainwright 3.00 8.00
559 Michael Young 3.00 8.00
560 Carlos Zambrano 3.00 8.00

2010 Upper Deck A Piece of History 500 Club

GS Gary Sheffield 75.00 150.00

2010 Upper Deck All World

AW1 Albert Pujols 2.50 6.00
AW2 Carlos Beltran .40 1.00
AW3 Carlos Lee .40 1.00
AW4 Chien-Ming Wang .60 1.50
AW5 Daisuke Matsuzaka 1.00 2.50
AW6 Derek Jeter 2.50 6.00
AW7 Felix Hernandez 1.00 2.50
AW8 Hanley Ramirez 1.00 2.50
AW9 Ichiro Suzuki 1.50 4.00
AW10 Johan Santana 1.00 2.50
AW11 Justin Morneau 1.00 2.50
AW12 Kendry Morales .40 1.00
AW13 Magglio Ordonez .60 1.50
AW14 Russell Martin .40 1.00
AW15 Vladimir Guerrero 1.00 2.50

2010 Upper Deck Baseball Heroes

JD Joe DiMaggio 1.50 4.00
BH1 Joe DiMaggio 1.50 4.00
BH2 Joe DiMaggio 1.50 4.00
BH3 Joe DiMaggio 1.50 4.00
BH4 Joe DiMaggio 1.50 4.00
BH5 Joe DiMaggio 1.50 4.00
BH6 Joe DiMaggio 1.50 4.00
BH7 Joe DiMaggio 1.50 4.00
BH8 Joe DiMaggio 1.50 4.00
NNO Heroes Header

2010 Upper Deck Baseball Heroes 20th Anniversary Art

BHA1 Ken Griffey Jr. 1.50 4.00
BHA2 Derek Jeter 2.50 6.00
BHA3 Evan Longoria 1.25 3.00
BHA4 Hanley Ramirez 1.00 2.50
BHA5 David Price 1.00 2.50
BHA6 Jon Lester 1.00 2.50
BHA7 Nick Markakis 1.00 2.50
BHA8 Cole Hamels 1.00 2.50
BHA9 Jonathan Papelbon .60 1.50
BHA10 Chipper Jones 1.00 2.50

2010 Upper Deck Baseball Heroes 20th Anniversary Art Autographs

STATED PRINT RUN 90 SER.#'d SETS
BHA1 Ken Griffey Jr. 125.00 250.00
BHA2 Derek Jeter 100.00 200.00
BHA3 Evan Longoria 50.00 100.00
BHA4 Hanley Ramirez
BHA5 David Price 12.50 30.00
BHA6 Jon Lester
BHA7 Nick Markakis 30.00 60.00
BHA8 Cole Hamels 30.00 60.00

BHA9 Jonathan Papelbon 20.00 50.00
BHA10 Chipper Jones

2010 Upper Deck Baseball Heroes DiMaggio Cut Signature

STATED PRINT RUN 56 SER.#'d SETS
JD Joe DiMaggio 300.00 500.00

2010 Upper Deck Celebrity Predictors

CP1/CP2 Jennifer Aniston 1.50 4.00
John Mayer
CP3/CP4 Cameron Diaz 1.50 4.00
Justin Timberlake
CP5/CP6 Megan Fox 1.50 4.00
Shia LaBeouf
CP7/CP8 Katie Holmes 1.50 4.00
Tom Cruise
CP11/CP12 Anna Kournikova 1.50 4.00
Enrique Iglesias
CP13/CP14 Mariah Carey 1.50 4.00
Nick Cannon
CP15/CP16 Rob Pattinson 1.50 4.00
Kristen Stewart
CP17/CP18 Angelina Jolie 6.00 15.00
Brad Pitt
CP19/CP20 Cristiano Ronaldo 6.00 15.00
Paris Hilton
CP9/CP10 Chris Martin 1.50 4.00
Gwyneth Paltrow

2010 Upper Deck Portraits

*GOLD: 1.5X TO 4X BASIC
GOLD PRINT RUN 99 SER.#'d SETS
SE1 Justin Upton .60 1.50
SE2 Dan Haren .40 1.00
SE3 Chipper Jones 1.00 2.50
SE4 Yunel Escobar .40 1.00
SE5 Derek Lowe .40 1.00
SE6 Nick Markakis 1.00 2.50
SE7 Brian Roberts .40 1.00
SE8 Koji Uehara .60 1.50
SE9 Josh Beckett .60 1.50
SE10 Jon Lester 1.00 2.50
SE11 David Ortiz .60 1.50
SE12 Jason Varitek 1.00 2.50
SE13 Carlos Zambrano .60 1.50
SE14 Kosuke Fukudome 1.00 2.50
SE15 Aramis Ramirez .40 1.00
SE16 Mark Buehrle .60 1.50
SE17 Paul Konerko .60 1.50
SE18 Carlos Quentin .60 1.50
SE19 Joey Votto 1.00 2.50
SE20 Brandon Phillips .40 1.00
SE21 Edinson Volquez .40 1.00
SE22 Shin-Soo Choo .60 1.50
SE23 Kerry Wood .40 1.00
SE24 Grady Sizemore .60 1.50
SE25 Troy Tulowitzki 1.00 2.50
SE26 Aaron Cook .40 1.00
SE27 Todd Helton .60 1.50
SE28 Justin Verlander 1.25 3.00
SE29 Miguel Cabrera 1.00 2.50
SE30 Rick Porcello .40 1.00
SE31 Chris Coghlan .40 1.00
SE32 Josh Johnson .60 1.50
SE33 Carlos Lee .40 1.00
SE34 Lance Berkman .60 1.50
SE35 Roy Oswalt .60 1.50
SE36 Zack Greinke .60 1.50
SE37 Billy Butler .40 1.00
SE38 Joakim Soria .40 1.00
SE39 Jered Weaver .40 1.00
SE40 Torii Hunter .40 1.00
SE41 Kendry Morales .40 1.00
SE42 Chone Figgins .40 1.00
SE43 Russell Martin .40 1.00
SE44 Clayton Kershaw 1.00 2.50
SE45 Matt Kemp .60 1.50
SE46 Hiroki Kuroda .40 1.00
SE47 Alcides Escobar .60 1.50
SE48 Yovani Gallardo .40 1.00
SE49 Ryan Braun 1.25 3.00
SE50 Justin Morneau 1.00 2.50
SE51 Joe Nathan .40 1.00
SE52 Michael Cuddyer .40 1.00
SE53 Johan Santana 1.00 2.50
SE54 David Wright 1.25 3.00
SE55 Jose Reyes .60 1.50
SE56 Francisco Rodriguez .60 1.50
SE57 Mark Teixeira 1.00 2.50
SE58 Derek Jeter 2.50 6.00
SE59 Mariano Rivera 1.00 2.50
SE60 A.J. Burnett .60 1.50
SE61 Jorge Posada .60 1.50
SE62 Jack Cust .40 1.00
SE63 Mark Ellis .40 1.00
SE64 Andrew Bailey .40 1.00
SE65 Chase Utley 1.00 2.50
SE66 Cole Hamels 1.00 2.50
SE67 Raul Ibanez .60 1.50
SE68 Jimmy Rollins .60 1.50
SE69 Ryan Doumit .40 1.00
SE70 Zach Duke .40 1.00
SE71 Tony Gwynn Jr. .40 1.00
SE72 Chris Young .40 1.00
SE73 Heath Bell .60 1.50
SE74 Barry Zito .60 1.50
SE75 Pablo Sandoval .60 1.50
SE76 Aaron Rowand .40 1.00
SE77 Tim Lincecum 1.50 4.00
SE78 Felix Hernandez 1.00 2.50
SE79 Ichiro Suzuki 1.50 4.00
SE80 Franklin Gutierrez .40 1.00
SE81 Albert Pujols 2.50 6.00
SE82 Adam Wainwright .60 1.50
SE83 Chris Carpenter 1.00 2.50
SE84 Colby Rasmus 1.00 2.50
SE85 Yadier Molina .60 1.50
SE86 Evan Longoria 1.25 3.00
SE87 Jeff Niemann .40 1.00
SE88 James Shields .40 1.00
SE89 Carlos Pena .60 1.50
SE90 Scott Feldman .40 1.00
SE91 Michael Young .60 1.50
SE92 Ian Kinsler .60 1.50
SE93 Elvis Andrus .60 1.50
SE94 Ricky Romero .40 1.00
SE95 Roy Halladay 1.00 2.50
SE96 Adam Lind .60 1.50
SE97 Aaron Hill .40 1.00
SE98 Ryan Zimmerman .60 1.50
SE99 Adam Dunn .60 1.50
SE100 Nyjer Morgan .40 1.00

2010 Upper Deck Pure Heat

PH1 Adrian Gonzalez .60 1.50
PH2 Albert Pujols 2.50 6.00
PH3 Alex Rodriguez 1.50 4.00
PH4 Cole Hamels 1.00 2.50
PH5 CC Sabathia .60 1.50
PH6 Evan Longoria 1.25 3.00
PH7 Josh Beckett .60 1.50
PH8 Joe Mauer 1.00 2.50
PH9 Justin Verlander 1.25 3.00
PH10 Manny Ramirez 1.00 2.50
PH11 Mark Teixeira 1.00 2.50
PH12 Prince Fielder .60 1.50
PH13 Ryan Howard 1.25 3.00
PH14 Tim Lincecum 1.50 4.00
PH15 Troy Tulowitzki 1.00 2.50

2010 Upper Deck Season Biography

SB1 Derek Lowe .40 1.00
SB2 Johan Santana 1.00 2.50
SB3 Aaron Rowand .40 1.00
SB4 Koji Uehara .60 1.50
SB5 Everth Cabrera .40 1.00
SB6 Miguel Cabrera 1.00 2.50
SB7 Justin Verlander 1.25 3.00
SB8 Evan Longoria 1.25 3.00
SB9 Orlando Hudson .40 1.00
SB10 Zach Duke .40 1.00
SB11 Ken Griffey Jr. 1.50 4.00
SB12 Ian Kinsler .60 1.50
SB13 Tim Wakefield .40 1.00
SB14 Grady Sizemore .60 1.50
SB15 Gary Sheffield .40 1.00
SB16 Tim Lincecum 1.50 4.00
SB17 Randy Johnson .60 1.50
SB18 Dustin Pedroia 1.25 3.00
SB19 Ryan Braun 1.25 3.00
SB20 Dan Haren .40 1.00
SB21 Dave Bush .40 1.00
SB22 Carlos Pena .60 1.50
SB23 Albert Pujols 2.50 6.00
SB24 Jacoby Ellsbury 1.00 2.50
SB25 Dexter Fowler .40 1.00
SB26 Ryan Howard 1.25 3.00
SB27 Jorge Cantu .40 1.00
SB28 Yovani Gallardo .40 1.00
SB29 Evan Longoria 1.25 3.00
SB30 Matt Garza .40 1.00
SB31 Jake Peavy .40 1.00
SB32 Jason Marquis .40 1.00
SB33 Carl Crawford .60 1.50
SB34 Zack Greinke .60 1.50
SB35 Vicente Padilla .40 1.00
SB36 Manny Ramirez 1.00 2.50
SB37 Hanley Ramirez 1.00 2.50
SB38 Alex Rodriguez 1.50 4.00
SB39 Joe Saunders .40 1.00
SB40 Torii Hunter .40 1.00
SB41 Brett Cecil .40 1.00
SB42 Ryan Zimmerman .60 1.50
SB43 Derek Holland .40 1.00
SB44 Ryan Zimmerman .60 1.50
SB45 Torii Hunter .40 1.00
SB46 Jimmy Rollins .60 1.50
Barack Obama
SB47 Alex Rodriguez 1.50 4.00
SB48 Ivan Rodriguez .60 1.50
SB49 Clayton Kershaw 1.00 2.50
SB50 Jake Peavy .40 1.00
SB51 Jason Kendall .40 1.00
SB52 Mark Teixeira 1.00 2.50
SB53 David Ortiz .60 1.50
SB54 Joe Mauer 1.00 2.50
SB55 Raul Ibanez .60 1.50
SB56 Kenshin Kawakami .60 1.50
SB57 Nelson Cruz .60 1.50
SB58 Alex Gonzalez .40 1.00
SB59 Freddy Sanchez .40 1.00
SB60 Chris B. Young .40 1.00
SB61 Rick Porcello .40 1.00
SB62 Nolan Reimold .60 1.50
SB63 Scott Feldman .40 1.00
SB64 Ryan Howard 1.25 3.00
SB65 Ryan Dempster .40 1.00
SB66 Jamie Moyer .40 1.00
SB67 Jim Thome .60 1.50
SB68 Roy Halladay 1.00 2.50
SB69 Jeff Niemann .40 1.00
SB70 Randy Johnson .60 1.50
SB71 Jonathan Broxton .40 1.00
SB72 Carlos Zambrano .60 1.50
SB73 Jon Lester 1.00 2.50
SB74 Alfonso Soriano .60 1.50
SB75 Dan Haren .40 1.00
SB76 Vin Mazzaro .40 1.00
SB77 Sean West .40 1.00
SB78 Andre Ethier .60 1.50
SB79 Colby Rasmus 1.00 2.50
SB80 Jim Thome .60 1.50
SB81 Tim Lincecum 1.50 4.00
SB82 Miguel Tejada .60 1.50
SB83 Torii Hunter .40 1.00
SB84 Albert Pujols 2.50 6.00
SB85 Todd Helton .60 1.50
SB86 Jered Weaver .40 1.00
SB87 Prince Fielder .60 1.50
SB88 Robinson Cano 1.00 2.50
SB89 Ivan Rodriguez .60 1.50
SB90 Tommy Hanson .60 1.50
SB91 Kenshin Kawakami .60 1.50
SB92 Jeff Weaver .40 1.00
SB93 Albert Pujols 2.50 6.00
SB94 B.J. Upton .60 1.50
SB95 Trevor Cahill .40 1.00
SB96 Tim Lincecum 1.50 4.00
SB97 Troy Tulowitzki 1.00 2.50
SB98 Jermaine Dye .40 1.00
SB99 Lance Berkman .60 1.50
SB100 Hanley Ramirez 1.00 2.50
SB101 Alex Rodriguez 1.50 4.00
SB102 Albert Pujols 2.50 6.00
SB103 Tommy Hanson .60 1.50
SB104 Zack Greinke .60 1.50
SB105 Brandon Phillips .40 1.00
SB106 Dallas Braden .60 1.50
SB107 Joey Votto 1.00 2.50
SB108 Albert Pujols 2.50 6.00
SB109 Adam Dunn .60 1.50
SB110 Ricky Nolasco .40 1.00
SB111 Ted Lilly .40 1.00
SB112 Vladimir Guerrero 1.00 2.50
SB113 Ryan Spilborghs .40 1.00
SB114 Garrett Atkins .40 1.00
SB115 Jonathan Sanchez .40 1.00
SB116 Josh Beckett .60 1.50
SB117 Kurt Suzuki .40 1.00
SB118 Ichiro Suzuki 1.50 4.00
Barack Obama
SB119 Ryan Howard 1.25 3.00
SB120 Marc Rzepczynski .40 1.00
SB121 Clayton Kershaw 1.00 2.50
SB122 Roy Halladay 1.00 2.50
SB123 Jason Marquis .40 1.00
SB124 Manny Ramirez 1.00 2.50
SB125 Scott Hairston .40 1.00
SB126 A.J. Burnett .60 1.50
SB127 Mark Buehrle .60 1.50
SB128 Jeremy Sowers .40 1.00
SB129 Chone Figgins .40 1.00
SB130 Cliff Lee .60 1.50
SB131 Michael Young .60 1.50
SB132 Josh Willingham .40 1.00
SB133 Pablo Sandoval .60 1.50
SB134 Cliff Lee .60 1.50
SB135 Aaron Hill .40 1.00
SB136 Bud Norris .40 1.00
SB137 Neftali Feliz .40 1.00
SB138 Chase Utley 1.00 2.50
SB139 Fausto Carmona .40 1.00
SB140 Barry Zito .60 1.50
SB141 Jered Weaver .40 1.00
SB142 Roy Halladay 1.00 2.50
SB143 Wandy Rodriguez .40 1.00
SB144 Mark Teixeira 1.00 2.50
SB145 Vladimir Guerrero 1.00 2.50
SB146 Adrian Gonzalez .60 1.50
SB147 Tim Lincecum 1.50 4.00
SB148 Pedro Martinez .60 1.50
SB149 Felix Pie .40 1.00
SB150 Jim Thome .60 1.50
SB151 Derek Jeter 2.50 6.00
SB152 Gregg Zaun .40 1.00
SB153 Ian Kinsler .60 1.50
SB154 Brandon Inge .60 1.50
SB155 Hanley Ramirez 1.00 2.50
SB156 Russell Branyan .40 1.00
SB157 Pedro Martinez .60 1.50
SB158 Michael Cuddyer .40 1.00
SB159 Jake Fox .40 1.00
SB160 John Smoltz 1.00 2.50
SB161 Ryan Howard 1.25 3.00
SB162 Matt LaPorta .40 1.00
SB163 Joe Saunders .40 1.00
SB164 Tony Gwynn Jr. .40 1.00
SB165 Carlos Ruiz .40 1.00
SB166 Edgar Renteria .40 1.00
SB167 Josh Hamilton 1.00 2.50
SB168 Tim Hudson .60 1.50
SB169 Brandon Allen .40 1.00
SB170 Landon Powell .40 1.00
SB171 Casey McGehee .40 1.00
SB172 Ichiro Suzuki 1.50 4.00
SB173 Daniel Murphy .40 1.00
SB174 Jon Lester 1.00 2.50
SB175 Derrek Lee .40 1.00
SB176 Mark Buehrle .60 1.50
SB177 Mark Teixeira 1.00 2.50
SB178 Brad Penny .40 1.00
SB179 Wade LeBlanc .40 1.00
SB180 Micah Hoffpauir .40 1.00
SB181 Ian Desmond .60 1.50
SB182 Derek Jeter 2.50 6.00
SB183 Brian Matusz 1.00 2.50
SB184 Ichiro Suzuki 1.50 4.00
SB185 Josh Johnson .60 1.50
SB186 Luis Durango .40 1.00
SB187 Jody Gerut .40 1.00
SB188 Francisco Rodriguez .60 1.50
SB189 Jake Peavy .40 1.00
SB190 Mariano Rivera 1.00 2.50
SB191 Sonia Sotomayor .40 1.00
SB192 Willy Aybar .40 1.00
SB193 Wade Davis .40 1.00
SB194 Cesear Ramos .40 1.00
SB195 Kevin Millwood .40 1.00
SB196 Andres Torres .40 1.00
SB197 Willy Aybar .40 1.00
SB198 Clayton Kershaw 1.00 2.50
SB199 Justin Verlander 1.25 3.00
SB200 Alexi Casilla .40 1.00

2010 Upper Deck Signature Sensations

AA Aaron Rowand 8.00 20.00
AD Adam Dunn
AE Alcides Escobar 8.00 20.00
AG Adrian Gonzalez
AH Aaron Harang 8.00 20.00
AI Akinori Iwamura 8.00 20.00
AL Andy LaRoche 6.00 15.00
AM Andrew McCutchen
AP Albert Pujols
AR Alex Romero 3.00 8.00
AS Anibal Sanchez 4.00 10.00
AW Adam Wainwright
BA Burke Badenhop 3.00 8.00
BB Brian Bixler 5.00 12.00
BE Josh Beckett
BO Jeremy Bonderman
BU Billy Butler
BW Brandon Webb
CB Clay Buchholz 5.00 12.00
CC Chris Carpenter
CF Chone Figgins 4.00 10.00
CG Curtis Granderson
CH Chase Headley 3.00 8.00
CJ Chipper Jones
CK Clayton Kershaw
CL Carlos Lee 3.00 8.00
CP Carlos Pena
DE David Eckstein 5.00 12.00
DJ Derek Jeter 150.00 250.00
DO Darren O'Day 4.00 10.00
DP Dustin Pedroia 12.50 30.00
DS Denard Span 4.00 10.00
DU Dan Uggla
DV Donald Veal 5.00 12.00
EB Emilio Bonifacio 3.00 8.00
ED Elijah Dukes 3.00 8.00
EM Evan Meek 12.50 30.00
EV Eugenio Velez 4.00 10.00
FC Fausto Carmona
FP Felix Pie 8.00 20.00
GP Gerardo Parra
GS Grady Sizemore
HA Cole Hamels
HE Jeremy Hermida 3.00 8.00
HJ Josh Hamilton
HP Hunter Pence
JA Jonathan Albaladejo 3.00 8.00
JB Jason Bay
JC Johnny Cueto 4.00 10.00
JH J.A. Happ 8.00 20.00
JL Jesse Litsch 4.00 10.00
JM John Maine 4.00 10.00
JO Joaquin Arias 3.00 8.00
JP Jonathan Papelbon 8.00 20.00
JS James Shields
JW Josh Willingham 3.00 8.00
KG Khalil Greene 8.00 20.00
KH Kevin Hart 4.00 10.00
KJ Kelly Johnson 3.00 8.00
KK Kevin Kouzmanoff 3.00 8.00
KS Kevin Slowey 6.00 15.00
KU Koji Uehara
KY Kevin Youkilis 10.00 25.00
LA John Lackey
LB Lance Berkman
MA Joe Mauer
MB Marlon Byrd 3.00 8.00
MC Miguel Cabrera
MG Mat Gamel 4.00 10.00
MM Miguel Montero
MO Micah Owings 5.00 12.00
MP Mike Pelfrey 8.00 20.00
MR Mark Reynolds
MT Matt Tolbert
NM Nick Markakis
NY Nyjer Morgan 4.00 10.00
PA Felipe Paulino 3.00 8.00
PF Prince Fielder 15.00 40.00
RA Alexei Ramirez
RB Ryan Braun
RH Roy Halladay
RM Russell Martin 6.00 15.00
RO Ross Ohlendorf 5.00 12.00
RT Ryan Theriot 10.00 25.00
RV Rick Vanden Hurk
SA Alfonso Soriano
SK Scott Kazmir 15.00 40.00
SM Sean Marshall 3.00 8.00
SO Sean O'Sullivan
TC Trevor Crowe
TE Miguel Tejada 3.00 8.00
TH Travis Hafner
TP Troy Patton 3.00 8.00
TR Ramon Troncoso 3.00 8.00
TS Takashi Saito 10.00 25.00
VO Edinson Volquez 4.00 10.00
WW Wesley Wright 3.00 8.00
YE Yunel Escobar 5.00 12.00
YG Yovani Gallardo 6.00 15.00
ZD Zach Duke 5.00 12.00

2010 Upper Deck Supreme Green

STATED PRINT RUN 100 SER.#'d SETS

2010 Upper Deck Tape Measure Shots

TMS1 Mark Reynolds .40 1.00
TMS2 Raul Ibanez .60 1.50
TMS3 Joey Votto 1.00 2.50
TMS4 Adam Dunn .60 1.50
TMS5 Josh Hamilton 1.00 2.50
TMS6 Adrian Gonzalez .60 1.50
TMS7 Miguel Montero .40 1.00
TMS8 Seth Smith .40 1.00
TMS9 Nelson Cruz .60 1.50
TMS10 Carlos Pena .60 1.50
TMS11 Albert Pujols 2.50 6.00
TMS12 Pablo Sandoval .60 1.50
TMS13 Josh Willingham .40 1.00
TMS14 Manny Ramirez 1.00 2.50
TMS15 Prince Fielder .60 1.50
TMS16 Jermaine Dye .40 1.00
TMS17 Brandon Inge .60 1.50
TMS18 Lance Berkman .60 1.50
TMS19 Kelly Shoppach .40 1.00
TMS20 Ian Stewart .40 1.00
TMS21 Magglio Ordonez .60 1.50
TMS22 Michael Cuddyer .40 1.00
TMS23 Ryan Howard 1.25 3.00
TMS24 Troy Tulowitzki 1.00 2.50
TMS25 Colby Rasmus 1.00 2.50

2010 Upper Deck UD Game Jersey

AE Andre Ethier 3.00 8.00
AG Alex Gordon 5.00 12.00
AJ Adam Jones 4.00 10.00
AP Albert Pujols 6.00 15.00
AR Aramis Ramirez 3.00 8.00
BE Josh Beckett 3.00 8.00
BI Brandon Inge 4.00 10.00
BM Brandon Morrow 3.00 8.00
BO John Bowker 3.00 8.00
BR Ryan Braun 3.00 8.00
BU B.J. Upton 4.00 10.00
BZ Barry Zito 3.00 8.00
CA Matt Cain 3.00 8.00
CB Clay Buchholz 3.00 8.00
CC Chris Carpenter 3.00 8.00
CF Chone Figgins 3.00 8.00
CG Curtis Granderson 3.00 8.00
CH Cole Hamels 3.00 8.00
CJ Chipper Jones 4.00 10.00
CR Carl Crawford 3.00 8.00
CU Chase Utley 5.00 12.00
CY Chris Young 3.00 8.00
DA Johnny Damon 3.00 8.00
DE David Eckstein 3.00 8.00
DH Dan Haren 3.00 8.00
DJ Derek Jeter 8.00 20.00
DL Derrek Lee 3.00 8.00
DO David Ortiz 3.00 8.00
EJ Edwin Jackson 3.00 8.00
EL Evan Longoria 8.00 20.00
EM Evan Meek 4.00 10.00
EV Eugenio Velez 3.00 8.00
FC Fausto Carmona 3.00 8.00
FH Felix Hernandez 3.00 8.00
FL Francisco Liriano 3.00 8.00
FN Fu-Te Ni 4.00 10.00
FR Fernando Rodney 3.00 8.00
GA Armando Galarraga 4.00 10.00
GO Adrian Gonzalez 3.00 8.00
GS Grady Sizemore 3.00 8.00
HB Hank Blalock 3.00 8.00
HE Chase Headley 3.00 8.00
HK Howie Kendrick 3.00 8.00
HR Hanley Ramirez 3.00 8.00
IK Ian Kinsler 3.00 8.00
JB Jeremy Bonderman 3.00 8.00
JD Jermaine Dye 3.00 8.00
JE Jacoby Ellsbury 10.00 25.00
JH Josh Hamilton 3.00 8.00
JN Jayson Nix 3.00 8.00
JP Jonathan Papelbon 3.00 8.00
JR Jimmy Rollins 3.00 8.00
JS Johan Santana 3.00 8.00
JU Justin Morneau 4.00 10.00
JV Jason Varitek 3.00 8.00
KE Kendry Morales 3.00 8.00
KF Kosuke Fukudome 3.00 8.00
KG Ken Griffey Jr. 6.00 15.00
KH Kevin Hart 3.00 8.00
KK Kevin Kouzmanoff 3.00 8.00
KM Kevin Millwood 3.00 8.00
KY Kevin Youkilis 4.00 10.00
MA Max Scherzer 3.00 8.00
MB Mark Buehrle 3.00 8.00
MC Michael Cuddyer 3.00 8.00
MI Miguel Cabrera 3.00 8.00
MK Matt Kemp 3.00 8.00
ML Matt LaPorta 5.00 12.00
MM Melvin Mora 3.00 8.00
MO Magglio Ordonez 4.00 10.00
MR Mariano Rivera 4.00 10.00
MT Matt Tolbert 4.00 10.00
MY Michael Young 3.00 8.00
NM Nick Markakis 4.00 10.00
PF Prince Fielder 3.00 8.00
PH Phil Hughes 3.00 8.00
PM Pedro Martinez 3.00 8.00
PO Jorge Posada 3.00 8.00
RC Robinson Cano 4.00 10.00
RE Jose Reyes 3.00 8.00
RH Roy Halladay 3.00 8.00
RI Raul Ibanez 3.00 8.00
RM Russell Martin 3.00 8.00
RO Alex Rodriguez 8.00 20.00
RT Ramon Troncoso 3.00 8.00
RW Randy Wells 3.00 8.00
RZ Ryan Zimmerman 3.00 8.00
SC Shin-Soo Choo 4.00 10.00
SD Stephen Drew 3.00 8.00
SK Scott Kazmir 3.00 8.00
TH Travis Hafner 3.00 8.00
TL Tim Lincecum 5.00 12.00
TO Todd Helton 3.00 8.00
TT Troy Tulowitzki 3.00 8.00
UP Justin Upton 3.00 8.00
VE Justin Verlander 3.00 8.00
VG Vladimir Guerrero 4.00 10.00
WW Wesley Wright 3.00 8.00
YY Yasuhiko Yabuta 3.00 8.00
ZG Zack Greinke 4.00 10.00

2010 Upper Deck UD Game Patch

STATED PRINT RUN 25 SER.#'d SETS
NO PRICING DUE TO SCARCITY

2010 Upper Deck National Convention Million Pack March

MPM5 Hank Greenberg
MPM10 Ken Griffey Jr.

2011 Upper Deck National Convention

NSCC2 Ryne Sandberg 1.25 3.00
NSCC9 Greg Maddux 1.25 3.00
NSCC10 Bo Jackson .75 2.00
NSCC20 Matt Szczur 2.00 5.00

2011 Upper Deck National Convention Autographs

NSCCBJ Bo Jackson/8
NSCCRS Ryne Sandberg/10
NSCCSZ Matt Szczur/35 20.00 50.00

2008 Upper Deck 20th Anniversary

Upper Deck produced this 80-card set featuring past and present athletes from baseball, football, basketball and hockey and issued them through their Certified Diamond Dealers program. Eight cards were released every month from March through December 2008. By entering in all 80 unique codes from the back of the cards on the company's website by December 31, 2008, collectors had a chance to win a trip to four major sporting events.

UD46 Ken Griffey Jr. .75 2.00
UD47 Derek Jeter 1.25 3.00
UD48 Ichiro Suzuki .75 2.00
UD49 Albert Pujols 1.25 3.00
UD50 Daisuke Matsuzaka .75 2.00
UD51 Babe Ruth 1.25 3.00
UD52 Joe DiMaggio 1.25 3.00
UD53 Alex Rodriguez .75 2.00
UD54 Cal Ripken Jr. 2.00 5.00
UD55 Frank Thomas .30 .75
UD56 Nolan Ryan 1.50 4.00
UD57 Roger Clemens .30 .75
UD58 Randy Johnson .30 .75
UD59 Greg Maddux .25 .60
UD60 Ryne Sandberg 1.00 2.50
UD76 Kosuke Fukudome .30 .75
UD77 Evan Longoria .75 2.00
UD78 Josh Hamilton .30 .75
UD79 Jay Bruce .30 .75
UD80 Clayton Kershaw .30 .75

2009 Upper Deck 20th Anniversary

CARDS ISSUED IN FIVE CARD RUNS
EACH PRICED EQUALLY WITHIN RUNS
1 Ken Griffey Jr. .75 2.00
2 Ken Griffey Jr. .75 2.00
3 Ken Griffey Jr. .75 2.00
4 Ken Griffey Jr. .75 2.00
5 Ken Griffey Jr. .75 2.00
11 Johnny Bench .40 1.00
12 Johnny Bench .40 1.00
13 Johnny Bench .40 1.00
14 Johnny Bench .40 1.00
15 Johnny Bench .40 1.00
16 Carl Yastrzemski .75 2.00
17 Carl Yastrzemski .75 2.00
18 Carl Yastrzemski .75 2.00
19 Carl Yastrzemski .75 2.00
20 Carl Yastrzemski .75 2.00
51 Ken Griffey Jr. .75 2.00
52 Ken Griffey Jr. .75 2.00
53 Ken Griffey Jr. .75 2.00
54 Ken Griffey Jr. .75 2.00
55 Ken Griffey Jr. .75 2.00
61 Mike Schmidt .75 2.00
62 Mike Schmidt .75 2.00
63 Mike Schmidt .75 2.00
64 Mike Schmidt .75 2.00
65 Mike Schmidt .75 2.00
66 Oakland Athletics .20 .50
67 Oakland Athletics .20 .50
68 Oakland Athletics .20 .50
69 Oakland Athletics .20 .50
70 Oakland Athletics .20 .50
71 Gary Sheffield .20 .50
72 Gary Sheffield .20 .50
73 Gary Sheffield .20 .50
74 Gary Sheffield .20 .50
75 Gary Sheffield .20 .50
126 Randy Johnson .40 1.00
127 Randy Johnson .40 1.00
128 Randy Johnson .40 1.00
129 Randy Johnson .40 1.00
130 Randy Johnson .40 1.00
131 John Smoltz .40 1.00
132 John Smoltz .40 1.00
133 John Smoltz .40 1.00
134 John Smoltz .40 1.00
135 John Smoltz .40 1.00
146 Oriole Park At Camden Yards .20 .50
147 Oriole Park At Camden Yards .20 .50
148 Oriole Park At Camden Yards .20 .50
149 Oriole Park At Camden Yards .20 .50
150 Oriole Park At Camden Yards .20 .50
151 Frank Thomas .40 1.00
152 Frank Thomas .40 1.00
153 Frank Thomas .40 1.00
154 Frank Thomas .40 1.00
155 Frank Thomas .40 1.00
201 Randy Johnson .40 1.00
202 Randy Johnson .40 1.00
203 Randy Johnson .40 1.00
204 Randy Johnson .40 1.00
205 Randy Johnson .40 1.00
206 Nolan Ryan 1.50 4.00
207 Nolan Ryan 1.50 4.00
208 Nolan Ryan 1.50 4.00
209 Nolan Ryan 1.50 4.00
210 Nolan Ryan 1.50 4.00
226 Nolan Ryan 1.50 4.00
227 Nolan Ryan 1.50 4.00
228 Nolan Ryan 1.50 4.00
229 Nolan Ryan 1.50 4.00
230 Nolan Ryan 1.50 4.00
236 Ken Griffey Jr. .75 2.00
Ken Griffey Sr.
237 Ken Griffey Jr. .75 2.00
Ken Griffey Sr.
238 Ken Griffey Jr. .75 2.00
Ken Griffey Sr.
239 Ken Griffey Jr. .75 2.00
Ken Griffey Sr.
240 Ken Griffey Jr. .75 2.00
Ken Griffey Sr.
241 Comiskey Park .20 .50
242 Comiskey Park .20 .50
243 Comiskey Park .20 .50
244 Comiskey Park .20 .50
245 Comiskey Park .20 .50
246 Cincinnati Reds .20 .50
247 Cincinnati Reds .20 .50
248 Cincinnati Reds .20 .50
249 Cincinnati Reds .20 .50
250 Cincinnati Reds .20 .50
261 Gaylord Perry .20 .50
262 Gaylord Perry .20 .50
263 Gaylord Perry .20 .50
264 Gaylord Perry .20 .50
265 Gaylord Perry .20 .50
266 Jim Thome .25 .60
267 Jim Thome .25 .60
268 Jim Thome .25 .60
269 Jim Thome .25 .60
270 Jim Thome .25 .60
271 Don Mattingly 1.00 2.50
272 Don Mattingly 1.00 2.50
273 Don Mattingly 1.00 2.50
274 Don Mattingly 1.00 2.50
275 Don Mattingly 1.00 2.50
281 Nolan Ryan 1.50 4.00
282 Nolan Ryan 1.50 4.00
283 Nolan Ryan 1.50 4.00
284 Nolan Ryan 1.50 4.00
285 Nolan Ryan 1.50 4.00
286 Ivan Rodriguez .25 .60
287 Ivan Rodriguez .25 .60
288 Ivan Rodriguez .25 .60
289 Ivan Rodriguez .25 .60
290 Ivan Rodriguez .25 .60
321 Minnesota Twins .20 .50
322 Minnesota Twins .20 .50
323 Minnesota Twins .20 .50
324 Minnesota Twins .20 .50
325 Minnesota Twins .20 .50
391 Ken Griffey Jr. .75 2.00
392 Ken Griffey Jr. .75 2.00
393 Ken Griffey Jr. .75 2.00
394 Ken Griffey Jr. .75 2.00
395 Ken Griffey Jr. .75 2.00
396 Pedro Martinez .25 .60
397 Pedro Martinez .25 .60
398 Pedro Martinez .25 .60
399 Pedro Martinez .25 .60
400 Pedro Martinez .25 .60
416 Toronto Blue Jays .20 .50
417 Toronto Blue Jays .20 .50
418 Toronto Blue Jays .20 .50
419 Toronto Blue Jays .20 .50
420 Toronto Blue Jays .20 .50
431 Derek Jeter 1.25 3.00
432 Derek Jeter 1.25 3.00
433 Derek Jeter 1.25 3.00
434 Derek Jeter 1.25 3.00
435 Derek Jeter 1.25 3.00
461 Greg Maddux .50 1.25
462 Greg Maddux .50 1.25
463 Greg Maddux .50 1.25
464 Greg Maddux .50 1.25
465 Greg Maddux .50 1.25
466 Tim Wakefield .20 .50
467 Tim Wakefield .20 .50
468 Tim Wakefield .20 .50
469 Tim Wakefield .20 .50
470 Tim Wakefield .20 .50
481 Jeff Kent .20 .50
482 Jeff Kent .20 .50
483 Jeff Kent .20 .50
484 Jeff Kent .20 .50
485 Jeff Kent .20 .50
486 Dennis Eckersley .20 .50
487 Dennis Eckersley .20 .50
488 Dennis Eckersley .20 .50
489 Dennis Eckersley .20 .50
490 Dennis Eckersley .20 .50
491 Rollie Fingers .20 .50
492 Rollie Fingers .20 .50
493 Rollie Fingers .20 .50
494 Rollie Fingers .20 .50
495 Rollie Fingers .20 .50
506 Reggie Jackson .25 .60
507 Reggie Jackson .25 .60
508 Reggie Jackson .25 .60
509 Reggie Jackson .25 .60
510 Reggie Jackson .25 .60
511 Jim Edmonds .25 .60
512 Jim Edmonds .25 .60
513 Jim Edmonds .25 .60
514 Jim Edmonds .25 .60
515 Jim Edmonds .25 .60
516 Florida Marlins .20 .50
517 Florida Marlins .20 .50
518 Florida Marlins .20 .50
519 Florida Marlins .20 .50
520 Florida Marlins .20 .50
531 Ken Griffey Jr. .75 2.00
532 Ken Griffey Jr. .75 2.00
533 Ken Griffey Jr. .75 2.00
534 Ken Griffey Jr. .75 2.00
535 Ken Griffey Jr. .75 2.00
546 Derek Jeter 1.25 3.00
547 Derek Jeter 1.25 3.00
548 Derek Jeter 1.25 3.00
549 Derek Jeter 1.25 3.00
550 Derek Jeter 1.25 3.00
551 Ken Griffey Jr. .75 2.00

552 Ken Griffey Jr. .75 2.00
553 Ken Griffey Jr. .75 2.00
554 Ken Griffey Jr. .75 2.00
555 Ken Griffey Jr. .75 2.00
571 Nolan Ryan 1.50 4.00
572 Nolan Ryan 1.50 4.00
573 Nolan Ryan 1.50 4.00
574 Nolan Ryan 1.50 4.00
575 Nolan Ryan 1.50 4.00
586 Toronto Blue Jays .20 .50
Paul Molitor
587 Toronto Blue Jays .20 .50
588 Toronto Blue Jays .20 .50
589 Toronto Blue Jays .20 .50
590 Toronto Blue Jays .20 .50
591 Frank Thomas .40 1.00
592 Frank Thomas .40 1.00
593 Frank Thomas .40 1.00
594 Frank Thomas .40 1.00
595 Frank Thomas .40 1.00
621 Manny Ramirez .40 1.00
622 Manny Ramirez .40 1.00
623 Manny Ramirez .40 1.00
624 Manny Ramirez .40 1.00
625 Manny Ramirez .40 1.00
626 Michael Jordan 4.00 10.00
627 Michael Jordan 4.00 10.00
628 Michael Jordan 4.00 10.00
629 Michael Jordan 4.00 10.00
630 Michael Jordan 4.00 10.00
636 Steve Carlton .20 .50
637 Steve Carlton .20 .50
638 Steve Carlton .20 .50
639 Steve Carlton .20 .50
640 Steve Carlton .20 .50
641 Tony Gwynn .40 1.00
642 Tony Gwynn .40 1.00
643 Tony Gwynn .40 1.00
644 Tony Gwynn .40 1.00
645 Tony Gwynn .40 1.00
661 Kenny Rogers .20 .50
662 Kenny Rogers .20 .50
663 Kenny Rogers .20 .50
664 Kenny Rogers .20 .50
665 Kenny Rogers .20 .50
671 Don Mattingly 1.00 2.50
672 Don Mattingly 1.00 2.50
673 Don Mattingly 1.00 2.50
674 Don Mattingly 1.00 2.50
675 Don Mattingly 1.00 2.50
676 Ken Griffey Jr. .75 2.00
677 Ken Griffey Jr. .75 2.00
678 Ken Griffey Jr. .75 2.00
679 Ken Griffey Jr. .75 2.00
680 Ken Griffey Jr. .75 2.00
701 Alex Rodriguez .75 2.00
702 Alex Rodriguez .75 2.00
703 Alex Rodriguez .75 2.00
704 Alex Rodriguez .75 2.00
705 Alex Rodriguez .75 2.00
716 Frank Thomas .40 1.00
717 Frank Thomas .40 1.00
718 Frank Thomas .40 1.00
719 Frank Thomas .40 1.00
720 Frank Thomas .40 1.00
756 Derek Jeter 1.25 3.00
757 Derek Jeter 1.25 3.00
758 Derek Jeter 1.25 3.00
759 Derek Jeter 1.25 3.00
760 Derek Jeter 1.25 3.00
761 Mike Schmidt .75 2.00
762 Mike Schmidt .75 2.00
763 Mike Schmidt .75 2.00
764 Mike Schmidt .75 2.00
765 Mike Schmidt .75 2.00
766 Mariano Rivera .40 1.00
767 Mariano Rivera .40 1.00
768 Mariano Rivera .40 1.00
769 Mariano Rivera .40 1.00
770 Mariano Rivera .40 1.00
776 Andy Pettitte .25 .60
777 Andy Pettitte .25 .60
778 Andy Pettitte .25 .60
779 Andy Pettitte .25 .60
780 Andy Pettitte .25 .60
806 Cal Ripken Jr. 2.00 5.00
807 Cal Ripken Jr. 2.00 5.00
808 Cal Ripken Jr. 2.00 5.00
809 Cal Ripken Jr. 2.00 5.00
810 Cal Ripken Jr. 2.00 5.00
811 Cal Ripken Jr. 2.00 5.00
812 Cal Ripken Jr. 2.00 5.00
813 Cal Ripken Jr. 2.00 5.00
814 Cal Ripken Jr. 2.00 5.00
815 Cal Ripken Jr. 2.00 5.00
816 Ozzie Smith .75 2.00
817 Ozzie Smith .75 2.00
818 Ozzie Smith .75 2.00
819 Ozzie Smith .75 2.00
820 Ozzie Smith .75 2.00
821 New York Yankees .40 1.00
Don Mattingly
822 New York Yankees .40 1.00
Don Mattingly
823 New York Yankees .40 1.00
Don Mattingly
824 New York Yankees .40 1.00
Don Mattingly
825 New York Yankees .40 1.00
Don Mattingly
831 Jorge Posada .25 .60
832 Jorge Posada .25 .60
833 Jorge Posada .25 .60
834 Jorge Posada .25 .60
835 Jorge Posada .25 .60
836 John Smoltz .40 1.00
837 John Smoltz .40 1.00
838 John Smoltz .40 1.00
839 John Smoltz .40 1.00
840 John Smoltz .40 1.00
861 Joe Torre .25 .60
862 Joe Torre .25 .60
863 Joe Torre .25 .60
864 Joe Torre .25 .60
865 Joe Torre .25 .60
871 Greg Maddux .50 1.25
872 Greg Maddux .50 1.25
873 Greg Maddux .50 1.25
874 Greg Maddux .50 1.25
875 Greg Maddux .50 1.25
876 Alex Rodriguez .75 2.00
877 Alex Rodriguez .75 2.00
878 Alex Rodriguez .75 2.00
879 Alex Rodriguez .75 2.00
880 Alex Rodriguez .75 2.00
891 Derek Jeter 1.25 3.00
892 Derek Jeter 1.25 3.00
893 Derek Jeter 1.25 3.00
894 Derek Jeter 1.25 3.00
895 Derek Jeter 1.25 3.00
906 Vladimir Guerrero .40 1.00
907 Vladimir Guerrero .40 1.00
908 Vladimir Guerrero .40 1.00
909 Vladimir Guerrero .40 1.00
910 Vladimir Guerrero .40 1.00
921 Nomar Garciaparra .40 1.00
922 Nomar Garciaparra .40 1.00
923 Nomar Garciaparra .40 1.00
924 Nomar Garciaparra .40 1.00
925 Nomar Garciaparra .40 1.00
951 New York Yankees .40 1.00
952 New York Yankees .40 1.00
953 New York Yankees .40 1.00
954 New York Yankees .40 1.00
955 New York Yankees .40 1.00
1011 First Year of Interleague Baseball .20 .50
1012 First Year of Interleague Baseball .20 .50
1013 First Year of Interleague Baseball .20 .50
1014 First Year of Interleague Baseball .20 .50
1015 First Year of Interleague Baseball .20 .50
1046 Don Mattingly 1.00 2.50
1047 Don Mattingly 1.00 2.50
1048 Don Mattingly 1.00 2.50
1049 Don Mattingly 1.00 2.50
1050 Don Mattingly 1.00 2.50
1061 Florida Marlins .20 .50
1062 Florida Marlins .20 .50
1063 Florida Marlins .20 .50
1064 Florida Marlins .20 .50
1065 Florida Marlins .20 .50
1066 Ken Griffey Jr. .75 2.00
1067 Ken Griffey Jr. .75 2.00
1068 Ken Griffey Jr. .75 2.00
1069 Ken Griffey Jr. .75 2.00
1070 Ken Griffey Jr. .75 2.00
1076 Pedro Martinez .25 .60
1077 Pedro Martinez .25 .60
1078 Pedro Martinez .25 .60
1079 Pedro Martinez .25 .60
1080 Pedro Martinez .25 .60
1081 Jason Varitek .40 1.00
1082 Jason Varitek .40 1.00
1083 Jason Varitek .40 1.00
1084 Jason Varitek .40 1.00
1085 Jason Varitek .40 1.00
1101 Derrek Lee .20 .50
1102 Derrek Lee .20 .50
1103 Derrek Lee .20 .50
1104 Derrek Lee .20 .50
1105 Derrek Lee .20 .50
1111 Nomar Garciaparra .40 1.00
1112 Nomar Garciaparra .40 1.00
1113 Nomar Garciaparra .40 1.00
1114 Nomar Garciaparra .40 1.00
1115 Nomar Garciaparra .40 1.00
1141 Tampa Bay Rays .20 .50
1142 Tampa Bay Rays .20 .50
1143 Tampa Bay Rays .20 .50
1144 Tampa Bay Rays .20 .50
1145 Tampa Bay Rays .20 .50
1156 New York Yankees .40 1.00
1157 New York Yankees .40 1.00
1158 New York Yankees .40 1.00
1159 New York Yankees .40 1.00
1160 New York Yankees .40 1.00
1166 Cal Ripken Jr. 2.00 5.00
1167 Cal Ripken Jr. 2.00 5.00
1168 Cal Ripken Jr. 2.00 5.00
1169 Cal Ripken Jr. 2.00 5.00
1170 Cal Ripken Jr. 2.00 5.00
1191 Kerry Wood .20 .50
1192 Kerry Wood .20 .50
1193 Kerry Wood .20 .50
1194 Kerry Wood .20 .50
1195 Kerry Wood .20 .50
1241 Carlos Beltran .20 .50
1242 Carlos Beltran .20 .50
1243 Carlos Beltran .20 .50
1244 Carlos Beltran .20 .50
1245 Carlos Beltran .20 .50
1246 New York Yankees .40 1.00
1247 New York Yankees .40 1.00
1248 New York Yankees .40 1.00
1249 New York Yankees .40 1.00
1250 New York Yankees .40 1.00
1256 Orlando Cepeda .20 .50
1257 Orlando Cepeda .20 .50
1258 Orlando Cepeda .20 .50
1259 Orlando Cepeda .20 .50
1260 Orlando Cepeda .20 .50
1276 New York Yankees .40 1.00
1277 New York Yankees .40 1.00
1278 New York Yankees .40 1.00
1279 New York Yankees .40 1.00
1280 New York Yankees .40 1.00
1281 Chipper Jones .50 1.25
1282 Chipper Jones .50 1.25
1283 Chipper Jones .50 1.25
1284 Chipper Jones .50 1.25
1285 Chipper Jones .50 1.25
1286 Pedro Martinez .25 .60
1287 Pedro Martinez .25 .60
1288 Pedro Martinez .25 .60
1289 Pedro Martinez .25 .60
1290 Pedro Martinez .25 .60
1291 Nolan Ryan 1.50 4.00
1292 Nolan Ryan 1.50 4.00
1293 Nolan Ryan 1.50 4.00
1294 Nolan Ryan 1.50 4.00
1295 Nolan Ryan 1.50 4.00
1296 Robin Yount .40 1.00
1297 Robin Yount .40 1.00
1298 Robin Yount .40 1.00
1299 Robin Yount .40 1.00
1300 Robin Yount .40 1.00
1301 Tony Gwynn .40 1.00
1302 Tony Gwynn .40 1.00
1303 Tony Gwynn .40 1.00
1304 Tony Gwynn .40 1.00
1305 Tony Gwynn .40 1.00
1306 Bob Gibson .25 .60
1307 Bob Gibson .25 .60
1308 Bob Gibson .25 .60
1309 Bob Gibson .25 .60
1310 Bob Gibson .25 .60
1311 Johnny Bench .40 1.00
1312 Johnny Bench .40 1.00
1313 Johnny Bench .40 1.00
1314 Johnny Bench .40 1.00
1315 Johnny Bench .40 1.00
1316 Yogi Berra .40 1.00
1317 Yogi Berra .40 1.00
1318 Yogi Berra .40 1.00
1319 Yogi Berra .40 1.00
1320 Yogi Berra .40 1.00
1321 Mike Schmidt .75 2.00
1322 Mike Schmidt .75 2.00
1323 Mike Schmidt .75 2.00
1324 Mike Schmidt .75 2.00
1325 Mike Schmidt .75 2.00
1326 Brooks Robinson .25 .60
1327 Brooks Robinson .25 .60
1328 Brooks Robinson .25 .60
1329 Brooks Robinson .25 .60
1330 Brooks Robinson .25 .60
1331 Cal Ripken Jr. 2.00 5.00
1332 Cal Ripken Jr. 2.00 5.00
1333 Cal Ripken Jr. 2.00 5.00
1334 Cal Ripken Jr. 2.00 5.00
1335 Cal Ripken Jr. 2.00 5.00
1336 Ernie Banks .40 1.00
1337 Ernie Banks .40 1.00
1338 Ernie Banks .40 1.00
1339 Ernie Banks .40 1.00
1340 Ernie Banks .40 1.00
1341 Ted Williams 1.25 3.00
1342 Ted Williams 1.25 3.00
1343 Ted Williams 1.25 3.00
1344 Ted Williams 1.25 3.00
1345 Ted Williams 1.25 3.00
1346 Joe DiMaggio 1.25 3.00
1347 Joe DiMaggio 1.25 3.00
1348 Joe DiMaggio 1.25 3.00
1349 Joe DiMaggio 1.25 3.00
1350 Joe DiMaggio 1.25 3.00
1351 Ken Griffey Jr. .75 2.00
1352 Ken Griffey Jr. .75 2.00
1353 Ken Griffey Jr. .75 2.00
1354 Ken Griffey Jr. .75 2.00
1355 Ken Griffey Jr. .75 2.00
1356 Alfonso Soriano .20 .50
1357 Alfonso Soriano .20 .50
1358 Alfonso Soriano .20 .50
1359 Alfonso Soriano .20 .50
1360 Alfonso Soriano .20 .50
1361 Lance Berkman .25 .60
1362 Lance Berkman .25 .60
1363 Lance Berkman .25 .60
1364 Lance Berkman .25 .60
1365 Lance Berkman .25 .60
1366 Rick Ankiel .25 .60
1367 Rick Ankiel .25 .60
1368 Rick Ankiel .25 .60
1369 Rick Ankiel .25 .60
1370 Rick Ankiel .25 .60
1386 Derek Jeter 1.25 3.00
1387 Derek Jeter 1.25 3.00
1388 Derek Jeter 1.25 3.00
1389 Derek Jeter 1.25 3.00
1390 Derek Jeter 1.25 3.00
1416 New York Yankees .40 1.00
1417 New York Yankees .40 1.00
1418 New York Yankees .40 1.00
1419 New York Yankees .40 1.00
1420 New York Yankees .40 1.00
1426 Derek Jeter 1.25 3.00
1427 Derek Jeter 1.25 3.00
1428 Derek Jeter 1.25 3.00
1429 Derek Jeter 1.25 3.00
1430 Derek Jeter 1.25 3.00
1441 Jimmy Rollins .25 .60
1442 Jimmy Rollins .25 .60
1443 Jimmy Rollins .25 .60
1444 Jimmy Rollins .25 .60
1445 Jimmy Rollins .25 .60
1446 Carlton Fisk .25 .60
1447 Carlton Fisk .25 .60
1448 Carlton Fisk .25 .60
1449 Carlton Fisk .25 .60
1450 Carlton Fisk .25 .60
1451 Ken Griffey Jr. .75 2.00
1452 Ken Griffey Jr. .75 2.00
1453 Ken Griffey Jr. .75 2.00
1454 Ken Griffey Jr. .75 2.00
1455 Ken Griffey Jr. .75 2.00
1456 Baseball Season Opens in Japan .20 .50
1457 Baseball Season Opens in Japan .20 .50
1458 Baseball Season Opens in Japan .20 .50
1459 Baseball Season Opens in Japan .20 .50
1460 Baseball Season Opens in Japan .20 .50
1461 Cal Ripken Jr. 2.00 5.00
1462 Cal Ripken Jr. 2.00 5.00
1463 Cal Ripken Jr. 2.00 5.00
1464 Cal Ripken Jr. 2.00 5.00
1465 Cal Ripken Jr. 2.00 5.00
1471 Michael Young .25 .60
1472 Michael Young .25 .60
1473 Michael Young .25 .60
1474 Michael Young .25 .60
1475 Michael Young .25 .60
1476 Pedro Martinez .25 .60
1477 Pedro Martinez .25 .60
1478 Pedro Martinez .25 .60
1479 Pedro Martinez .25 .60
1480 Pedro Martinez .25 .60
1496 Tony Perez .20 .50
1497 Tony Perez .20 .50
1498 Tony Perez .20 .50
1499 Tony Perez .20 .50
1500 Tony Perez .20 .50
1506 Josh Beckett .25 .60
1507 Josh Beckett .25 .60
1508 Josh Beckett .25 .60
1509 Josh Beckett .25 .60
1510 Josh Beckett .25 .60
1531 Arizona Diamondbacks .20 .50
1532 Arizona Diamondbacks .20 .50
1533 Arizona Diamondbacks .20 .50
1534 Arizona Diamondbacks .20 .50
1535 Arizona Diamondbacks .20 .50
1536 Willie Stargell .25 .60
1537 Willie Stargell .25 .60
1538 Willie Stargell .25 .60
1539 Willie Stargell .25 .60
1540 Willie Stargell .25 .60
1546 Mets Win 9/11 Game .25 .60
1547 Mets Win 9/11 Game .25 .60
1548 Mets Win 9/11 Game .25 .60
1549 Mets Win 9/11 Game .25 .60
1550 Mets Win 9/11 Game .25 .60
1551 Ichiro Suzuki .75 2.00
1552 Ichiro Suzuki .75 2.00
1553 Ichiro Suzuki .75 2.00
1554 Ichiro Suzuki .75 2.00
1555 Ichiro Suzuki .75 2.00
1556 Albert Pujols 1.25 3.00
1557 Albert Pujols 1.25 3.00
1558 Albert Pujols 1.25 3.00
1559 Albert Pujols 1.25 3.00
1560 Albert Pujols 1.25 3.00
1566 Dave Winfield .20 .50
1567 Dave Winfield .20 .50
1568 Dave Winfield .20 .50
1569 Dave Winfield .20 .50
1570 Dave Winfield .20 .50
1571 Cal Ripken Jr. 2.00 5.00
1572 Cal Ripken Jr. 2.00 5.00
1573 Cal Ripken Jr. 2.00 5.00
1574 Cal Ripken Jr. 2.00 5.00
1575 Cal Ripken Jr. 2.00 5.00
1576 Tony Gwynn .40 1.00
1577 Tony Gwynn .40 1.00
1578 Tony Gwynn .40 1.00
1579 Tony Gwynn .40 1.00
1580 Tony Gwynn .40 1.00
1581 Bill Mazeroski .25 .60
1582 Bill Mazeroski .25 .60
1583 Bill Mazeroski .25 .60
1584 Bill Mazeroski .25 .60
1585 Bill Mazeroski .25 .60
1611 Ichiro Suzuki .75 2.00
1612 Ichiro Suzuki .75 2.00
1613 Ichiro Suzuki .75 2.00
1614 Ichiro Suzuki .75 2.00
1615 Ichiro Suzuki .75 2.00
1621 New York Yankees .40 1.00
1622 New York Yankees .40 1.00
1623 New York Yankees .40 1.00
1624 New York Yankees .40 1.00
1625 New York Yankees .40 1.00
1641 Anaheim Angels .20 .50
1642 Anaheim Angels .20 .50
1643 Anaheim Angels .20 .50
1644 Anaheim Angels .20 .50
1645 Anaheim Angels .20 .50
1646 Ted Williams 1.25 3.00
1647 Ted Williams 1.25 3.00
1648 Ted Williams 1.25 3.00
1649 Ted Williams 1.25 3.00
1650 Ted Williams 1.25 3.00
1661 Ozzie Smith .75 2.00
1662 Ozzie Smith .75 2.00
1663 Ozzie Smith .75 2.00
1664 Ozzie Smith .75 2.00
1665 Ozzie Smith .75 2.00
1696 Randy Johnson .40 1.00
1697 Randy Johnson .40 1.00
1698 Randy Johnson .40 1.00
1699 Randy Johnson .40 1.00
1700 Randy Johnson .40 1.00
1736 Francisco Rodriguez .20 .50
1737 Francisco Rodriguez .20 .50
1738 Francisco Rodriguez .20 .50
1739 Francisco Rodriguez .20 .50
1740 Francisco Rodriguez .20 .50
1756 Derek Jeter 1.25 3.00
1757 Derek Jeter 1.25 3.00
1758 Derek Jeter 1.25 3.00
1759 Derek Jeter 1.25 3.00
1760 Derek Jeter 1.25 3.00
1766 Chase Utley .40 1.00
1767 Chase Utley .40 1.00
1768 Chase Utley .40 1.00
1769 Chase Utley .40 1.00
1770 Chase Utley .40 1.00
1776 Hideki Matsui .40 1.00
1777 Hideki Matsui .40 1.00
1778 Hideki Matsui .40 1.00
1779 Hideki Matsui .40 1.00
1780 Hideki Matsui .40 1.00
1781 Florida Marlins .20 .50
1782 Florida Marlins .20 .50
1783 Florida Marlins .20 .50
1784 Florida Marlins .20 .50
1785 Florida Marlins .20 .50
1836 Eddie Murray .40 1.00
1837 Eddie Murray .40 1.00
1838 Eddie Murray .40 1.00
1839 Eddie Murray .40 1.00
1840 Eddie Murray .40 1.00
1881 Boston Red Sox .40 1.00
1882 Boston Red Sox .40 1.00
1883 Boston Red Sox .40 1.00
1884 Boston Red Sox .40 1.00
1885 Boston Red Sox .40 1.00
1931 Ryan Howard .50 1.25
1932 Ryan Howard .50 1.25
1933 Ryan Howard .50 1.25
1934 Ryan Howard .50 1.25
1935 Ryan Howard .50 1.25
1936 Boston Red Sox .40 1.00
1937 Boston Red Sox .40 1.00
1938 Boston Red Sox .40 1.00
1939 Boston Red Sox .40 1.00
1940 Boston Red Sox .40 1.00
1941 Ichiro Suzuki .75 2.00
1942 Ichiro Suzuki .75 2.00
1943 Ichiro Suzuki .75 2.00
1944 Ichiro Suzuki .75 2.00
1945 Ichiro Suzuki .75 2.00
1946 Montreal Expos .20 .50
1947 Montreal Expos .20 .50
1948 Montreal Expos .20 .50
1949 Montreal Expos .20 .50
1950 Montreal Expos .20 .50
1951 Alex Rodriguez .75 2.00
1952 Alex Rodriguez .75 2.00
1953 Alex Rodriguez .75 2.00
1954 Alex Rodriguez .75 2.00
1955 Alex Rodriguez .75 2.00
1956 David Wright .50 1.25
1957 David Wright .50 1.25
1958 David Wright .50 1.25
1959 David Wright .50 1.25
1960 David Wright .50 1.25
1961 Chipper Jones .50 1.25
1962 Chipper Jones .50 1.25
1963 Chipper Jones .50 1.25
1964 Chipper Jones .50 1.25
1965 Chipper Jones .50 1.25
1966 Ken Griffey Jr. .75 2.00
1967 Ken Griffey Jr. .75 2.00
1968 Ken Griffey Jr. .75 2.00
1969 Ken Griffey Jr. .75 2.00
1970 Ken Griffey Jr. .75 2.00
2016 Washington Nationals .20 .50
2017 Washington Nationals .20 .50
2018 Washington Nationals .20 .50
2019 Washington Nationals .20 .50
2020 Washington Nationals .20 .50
2066 Jonathan Papelbon .25 .60
2067 Jonathan Papelbon .25 .60
2068 Jonathan Papelbon .25 .60
2069 Jonathan Papelbon .25 .60
2070 Jonathan Papelbon .25 .60
2071 Chicago White Sox .20 .50
2072 Chicago White Sox .20 .50
2073 Chicago White Sox .20 .50
2074 Chicago White Sox .20 .50
2075 Chicago White Sox .20 .50
2076 Wade Boggs .25 .60
2077 Wade Boggs .25 .60
2078 Wade Boggs .25 .60
2079 Wade Boggs .25 .60
2080 Wade Boggs .25 .60
2081 Ryne Sandberg 1.00 2.50
2082 Ryne Sandberg 1.00 2.50
2083 Ryne Sandberg 1.00 2.50
2084 Ryne Sandberg 1.00 2.50
2085 Ryne Sandberg 1.00 2.50
2086 Albert Pujols 1.25 3.00
2087 Albert Pujols 1.25 3.00
2088 Albert Pujols 1.25 3.00
2089 Albert Pujols 1.25 3.00
2090 Albert Pujols 1.25 3.00
2116 Chien-Ming Wang .40 1.00
2117 Chien-Ming Wang .40 1.00
2118 Chien-Ming Wang .40 1.00
2119 Chien-Ming Wang .40 1.00
2120 Chien-Ming Wang .40 1.00
2151 St. Louis Cardinals .25 .60
2152 St. Louis Cardinals .25 .60
2153 St. Louis Cardinals .25 .60
2154 St. Louis Cardinals .25 .60
2155 St. Louis Cardinals .25 .60
2156 Daisuke Matsuzaka .75 2.00
2157 Daisuke Matsuzaka .75 2.00
2158 Daisuke Matsuzaka .75 2.00
2159 Daisuke Matsuzaka .75 2.00
2160 Daisuke Matsuzaka .75 2.00
2161 Dustin Pedroia .75 2.00
2162 Dustin Pedroia .75 2.00
2163 Dustin Pedroia .75 2.00
2164 Dustin Pedroia .75 2.00
2165 Dustin Pedroia .75 2.00
2176 Cole Hamels .40 1.00
2177 Cole Hamels .40 1.00
2178 Cole Hamels .40 1.00
2179 Cole Hamels .40 1.00
2180 Cole Hamels .40 1.00
2201 Ryan Howard .50 1.25
2202 Ryan Howard .50 1.25
2203 Ryan Howard .50 1.25
2204 Ryan Howard .50 1.25
2205 Ryan Howard .50 1.25
2206 Hanley Ramirez .40 1.00
2207 Hanley Ramirez .40 1.00
2208 Hanley Ramirez .40 1.00
2209 Hanley Ramirez .40 1.00
2210 Hanley Ramirez .40 1.00
2221 Joe Mauer .40 1.00
2222 Joe Mauer .40 1.00
2223 Joe Mauer .40 1.00
2224 Joe Mauer .40 1.00
2225 Joe Mauer .40 1.00
2226 Brandon Webb .25 .60
2227 Brandon Webb .25 .60
2228 Brandon Webb .25 .60
2229 Brandon Webb .25 .60
2230 Brandon Webb .25 .60
2256 Josh Hamilton .40 1.00
2257 Josh Hamilton .40 1.00
2258 Josh Hamilton .40 1.00
2259 Josh Hamilton .40 1.00
2260 Josh Hamilton .40 1.00
2261 Tom Glavine .25 .60
2262 Tom Glavine .25 .60
2263 Tom Glavine .25 .60
2264 Tom Glavine .25 .60
2265 Tom Glavine .25 .60
2266 Boston Red Sox .40 1.00
2267 Boston Red Sox .40 1.00
2268 Boston Red Sox .40 1.00
2269 Boston Red Sox .40 1.00
2270 Boston Red Sox .40 1.00
2291 Cal Ripken Jr. 2.00 5.00
2292 Cal Ripken Jr. 2.00 5.00
2293 Cal Ripken Jr. 2.00 5.00
2294 Cal Ripken Jr. 2.00 5.00
2295 Cal Ripken Jr. 2.00 5.00
2296 Tony Gwynn .40 1.00
2297 Tony Gwynn .40 1.00
2298 Tony Gwynn .40 1.00
2299 Tony Gwynn .40 1.00
2300 Tony Gwynn .40 1.00
2301 Ryan Braun .50 1.25
2302 Ryan Braun .50 1.25
2303 Ryan Braun .50 1.25
2304 Ryan Braun .50 1.25
2305 Ryan Braun .50 1.25
2306 Jimmy Rollins .25 .60
2307 Jimmy Rollins .25 .60
2308 Jimmy Rollins .25 .60
2309 Jimmy Rollins .25 .60
2310 Jimmy Rollins .25 .60
2311 Alex Rodriguez .75 2.00
2312 Alex Rodriguez .75 2.00
2313 Alex Rodriguez .75 2.00
2314 Alex Rodriguez .75 2.00
2315 Alex Rodriguez .75 2.00
2316 Ichiro Suzuki .75 2.00
2317 Ichiro Suzuki .75 2.00
2318 Ichiro Suzuki .75 2.00
2319 Ichiro Suzuki .75 2.00
2320 Ichiro Suzuki .75 2.00
2331 Joba Chamberlain .50 1.25
2332 Joba Chamberlain .50 1.25
2333 Joba Chamberlain .50 1.25
2334 Joba Chamberlain .50 1.25
2335 Joba Chamberlain .50 1.25
2366 Alex Rodriguez .75 2.00
2367 Alex Rodriguez .75 2.00
2368 Alex Rodriguez .75 2.00
2369 Alex Rodriguez .75 2.00
2370 Alex Rodriguez .75 2.00
2381 Manny Ramirez .40 1.00
2382 Manny Ramirez .40 1.00
2383 Manny Ramirez .40 1.00
2384 Manny Ramirez .40 1.00
2385 Manny Ramirez .40 1.00
2386 Ken Griffey Jr. .75 2.00
2387 Ken Griffey Jr. .75 2.00
2388 Ken Griffey Jr. .75 2.00
2389 Ken Griffey Jr. .75 2.00
2390 Ken Griffey Jr. .75 2.00
2401 Josh Hamilton .40 1.00
2402 Josh Hamilton .40 1.00
2403 Josh Hamilton .40 1.00
2404 Josh Hamilton .40 1.00
2405 Josh Hamilton .40 1.00
2451 Jay Bruce .40 1.00
2452 Jay Bruce .40 1.00
2453 Jay Bruce .40 1.00
2454 Jay Bruce .40 1.00
2455 Jay Bruce .40 1.00
2476 Philadelphia Phillies .20 .50
2477 Philadelphia Phillies .20 .50
2478 Philadelphia Phillies .20 .50
2479 Philadelphia Phillies .20 .50
2480 Philadelphia Phillies .20 .50
2481 Manny Ramirez .40 1.00
2482 Manny Ramirez .40 1.00
2483 Manny Ramirez .40 1.00
2484 Manny Ramirez .40 1.00
2485 Manny Ramirez .40 1.00
2486 Travis Snider .40 1.00
2487 Travis Snider .40 1.00
2488 Travis Snider .40 1.00
2489 Travis Snider .40 1.00
2490 Travis Snider .40 1.00
2491 Evan Longoria .75 2.00
2492 Evan Longoria .75 2.00
2493 Evan Longoria .75 2.00
2494 Evan Longoria .75 2.00
2495 Evan Longoria .75 2.00

2009 Upper Deck 20th Anniversary Memorabilia

MLBAP Andy Pettitte
MLBAR Aramis Ramirez 3.00 8.00
MLBBO Bo Jackson 8.00 20.00
MLBBS Ben Sheets 4.00 10.00
MLBBW Brandon Webb 10.00 25.00
MLBBZ Barry Zito 4.00 10.00
MLBCC Chris Carpenter 3.00 8.00
MLBCD Carlos Delgado 3.00 8.00
MLBCG Carlos Guillen 3.00 8.00
MLBCL Carlos Lee 3.00 8.00
MLBCR Cal Ripken Jr. 20.00 50.00
MLBCS Curt Schilling 3.00 8.00
MLBCY Chris B. Young 4.00 10.00
MLBDJ Derek Jeter 10.00 25.00
MLBDL Derrek Lee 4.00 10.00
MLBDO David Ortiz 10.00 25.00
MLBEG Eric Gagne 4.00 10.00
MLBFL Francisco Liriano 4.00 10.00
MLBFT Frank Thomas 30.00 60.00
MLBGL Tom Glavine 4.00 10.00
MLBGM Greg Maddux
MLBGS Gary Sheffield 3.00 8.00
MLBGT Garret Anderson 5.00 12.00
MLBHE Todd Helton 5.00 12.00
MLBIR Ivan Rodriguez 3.00 8.00
MLBJD Johnny Damon 5.00 12.00
MLBJE Jim Edmonds 3.00 8.00
MLBJG Jason Giambi 5.00 12.00
MLBJM Joe Mauer 6.00 15.00
MLBJO Jonathan Papelbon 5.00 12.00
MLBJP Jorge Posada 4.00 10.00
MLBJS Johan Santana 3.00 8.00
MLBJT Jim Thome 5.00 12.00
MLBJU Justin Verlander 3.00 8.00
MLBJV Jason Varitek 6.00 15.00
MLBKG Ken Griffey Jr. 5.00 12.00
MLBMH Matt Holliday 4.00 10.00
MLBMM Mike Mussina
MLBMO Magglio Ordonez 3.00 8.00
MLBMP Mark Prior 3.00 8.00
MLBMR Mariano Rivera
MLBMT Mark Teixeira 3.00 8.00
MLBPM Pedro Martinez 6.00 15.00
MLBRA Manny Ramirez 10.00 25.00
MLBRB Roy Halladay 4.00 10.00
MLBRC Roger Clemens 5.00 12.00
MLBRC2 Roger Clemens 5.00 12.00
MLBRC3 Roger Clemens 5.00 12.00
MLBRJ Randy Johnson 6.00 15.00
MLBRO Roy Oswalt 3.00 8.00
MLBSK Scott Kazmir 5.00 12.00
MLBTE Miguel Tejada 3.00 8.00
MLBTG Tony Gwynn 20.00 50.00
MLBTG2 Tony Gwynn 20.00 50.00
MLBTH Trevor Hoffman 3.00 8.00
MLBTI Tim Hudson 10.00 25.00
MLBTR Tim Raines 6.00 15.00
MLBVG Vladimir Guerrero 6.00 15.00
MLBWB Wade Boggs 8.00 20.00

2008 Upper Deck Ballpark Collection

This set was released on September 17, 2008. The base set consists of 340 cards.

COMMON CARD (1-100) .60 1.50
COMMON AU RC (101-150) 3.00 8.00
OVERALL AU ODDS 1:5 HOBBY
EXCHANGE DEADLINE 08/27/2010
COMMON 2X GU (151-200) 4.00 10.00
COMMON 4X GU (201-250) 4.00 10.00
COMMON 6X GU (251-295) 5.00 12.00
COMMON 8X GU (296-340) 6.00 15.00
OVERALL GU ODDS 2:1 HOBBY
1 Brandon Webb 1.00 2.50
2 Dan Haren .60 1.50
3 Chris B. Young .60 1.50
4 Randy Johnson 1.50 4.00
5 Mark Teixeira 1.50 4.00
6 John Smoltz 1.50 4.00
7 Tom Glavine 1.00 2.50
8 Brian McCann 1.00 2.50
9 Chipper Jones 1.50 4.00
10 Nick Markakis 1.50 4.00
11 Brian Roberts .60 1.50
12 Josh Beckett 1.00 2.50
13 David Ortiz 1.00 2.50
14 Manny Ramirez 1.50 4.00
15 Dustin Pedroia 2.00 5.00
16 Jonathan Papelbon 1.00 2.50
17 Daisuke Matsuzaka 1.50 4.00
18 Alfonso Soriano 1.00 2.50
19 Aramis Ramirez .60 1.50
20 Carlos Zambrano 1.00 2.50
21 Nick Swisher 1.50 4.00
22 Jim Thome 1.00 2.50
23 Ken Griffey Jr. 2.50 6.00
24 Adam Dunn 1.00 2.50
25 Grady Sizemore 1.00 2.50
26 Victor Martinez 1.00 2.50
27 Travis Hafner .60 1.50
28 C.C. Sabathia 1.00 2.50
29 Garrett Atkins .60 1.50
30 Matt Holliday 1.50 4.00
31 Troy Tulowitzki 1.50 4.00
32 Magglio Ordonez 1.00 2.50
33 Justin Verlander 2.00 5.00
34 Miguel Cabrera 1.50 4.00
35 Gary Sheffield .60 1.50
36 Ivan Rodriguez 1.00 2.50
37 Dontrelle Willis .60 1.50
38 Curtis Granderson 1.00 2.50
39 Hanley Ramirez 1.50 4.00
40 Dan Uggla 1.00 2.50
41 Lance Berkman 1.00 2.50
42 Roy Oswalt 1.00 2.50
43 Carlos Lee .60 1.50
44 Hunter Pence 1.50 4.00
45 Alex Gordon 1.00 2.50
46 Jose Guillen .60 1.50
47 Torii Hunter .60 1.50

48 Vladimir Guerrero 1.50 4.00
49 Andruw Jones .60 1.50
50 Matt Kemp 1.00 2.50
51 Russell Martin .60 1.50
52 Jeff Kent .60 1.50
53 Ryan Braun 2.00 5.00
54 Prince Fielder 1.00 2.50
55 Delmon Young 1.00 2.50
56 Joe Mauer 1.50 4.00
57 Justin Morneau 1.50 4.00
58 Jose Reyes 1.00 2.50
59 David Wright 2.00 5.00
60 Carlos Beltran .60 1.50
61 Johan Santana 1.50 4.00
62 Pedro Martinez 1.00 2.50
63 Alex Rodriguez 2.50 6.00
64 Derek Jeter 4.00 10.00
65 Hideki Matsui 1.50 4.00
66 Robinson Cano 1.50 4.00
67 Joba Chamberlain 1.00 2.50
68 Phil Hughes 1.50 4.00
69 Mariano Rivera 1.50 4.00
70 Eric Chavez .60 1.50
71 Bobby Crosby .60 1.50
72 Cole Hamels 1.50 4.00
73 Ryan Howard 2.00 5.00
74 Jimmy Rollins 1.00 2.50
75 Chase Utley 1.50 4.00
76 Jason Bay 1.00 2.50
77 Freddy Sanchez .60 1.50
78 Jake Peavy .60 1.50
79 Greg Maddux 2.00 5.00
80 Trevor Hoffman 1.00 2.50
81 Kosuke Fukudome RC 2.50 6.00
82 Barry Zito .60 1.50
83 Tim Lincecum 2.50 6.00
84 Erik Bedard .60 1.50
85 Felix Hernandez 1.50 4.00
86 Ichiro Suzuki 2.50 6.00
87 Troy Glaus 1.00 2.50
88 Albert Pujols 4.00 10.00
89 Chris Carpenter 1.50 4.00
90 Scott Kazmir 1.00 2.50
91 Carl Crawford 1.00 2.50
92 Michael Young 1.00 2.50
93 Hank Blalock .60 1.50
94 Roy Halladay 1.50 4.00
95 Vernon Wells .60 1.50
96 Alex Rios 1.00 2.50
97 Scott Rolen 1.00 2.50
98 Frank Thomas 1.50 4.00
99 Lastings Milledge .60 1.50
100 Ryan Zimmerman 1.00 2.50
101 Bobby Wilson AU RC 3.00 8.00
102 Alex Romero AU (RC) 4.00 10.00
104 Brandon Boggs AU (RC) 3.00 8.00
105 Brian Barton AU RC 4.00 10.00
106 Brian Bass AU (RC) 6.00 15.00
107 Brian Bixler AU (RC) 3.00 8.00
108 Brian Bocock AU RC 3.00 8.00
109 Burke Badenhop AU RC 3.00 8.00
110 Callix Crabbe AU (RC) 3.00 8.00
111 Clayton Kershaw AU RC 12.50 30.00
112 Chin-Lung Hu AU (RC) 12.50 30.00
113 Clay Buchholz AU (RC) 8.00 20.00
114 Eider Torres AU (RC) 5.00 12.00
115 Clete Thomas AU RC 3.00 8.00
116 Colt Morton AU RC 3.00 8.00
117 Daric Barton AU (RC) 3.00 8.00
118 Cory Wade AU (RC) 5.00 12.00
119 Elliot Johnson AU (RC) 3.00 8.00
121 Evan Longoria AU RC 40.00 80.00
122 Evan Meek AU RC 3.00 8.00
123 German Duran AU RC 3.00 8.00
124 Fernando Hernandez AU RC 3.00 8.00
125 Greg Smith AU RC 3.00 8.00
126 Jay Bruce AU (RC) EXCH 20.00 50.00
127 Wladimir Balentien AU (RC) 4.00 10.00
128 Hernan Iribarren AU (RC) 3.00 8.00
129 Jed Lowrie AU (RC) 20.00 50.00
130 Ian Kennedy AU RC 3.00 8.00
131 Jeff Clement AU (RC) 8.00 20.00
132 Jesse Carlson AU RC 6.00 15.00
133 Jonathan Herrera AU RC 3.00 8.00
134 Johnny Cueto AU RC 6.00 15.00
135 Jonathan Albaladejo AU RC 4.00 10.00
136 Josh Newman AU RC 3.00 8.00
137 Kevin Hart AU (RC) 4.00 10.00
138 Justin Masterson AU RC 15.00 40.00
139 Luke Hochevar AU (RC)
140 Luis Mendoza AU (RC) 3.00 8.00
141 Matt Tupman AU RC 8.00 20.00
142 Max Scherzer AU RC EXCH 10.00 25.00
143 Nick Blackburn AU RC 12.50 30.00
144 Nick Adenhart AU (RC) 12.50 30.00
145 Ramon Troncoso AU RC 5.00 12.00
146 Paul Janish AU (RC) 4.00 10.00
147 Randor Bierd AU RC 15.00 40.00
148 Robinzon Diaz AU (RC) 3.00 8.00
149 Steve Holm AU RC 4.00 10.00
150 Wesley Wright AU RC 6.00 15.00
151 Jason Giambi 4.00 10.00
David Ortiz
152 Jonathan Papelbon 5.00 12.00
Mariano Rivera
153 Nolan Ryan 6.00 15.00
Johan Santana
154 Mike Mussina 5.00 12.00
Jorge Posada
155 Jonathan Papelbon 5.00 12.00
Jason Varitek
156 Dan Uggla 4.00 10.00
Howie Kendrick
157 Kenji Johjima 4.00 10.00
Jason Varitek
158 Carlos Lee 4.00 10.00
Roy Oswalt
159 Albert Pujols 5.00 12.00
Derrek Lee
160 Albert Pujols 12.50 30.00
Ozzie Smith
161 Alfonso Soriano 6.00 15.00
Carlos Zambrano
162 Tony Gwynn 4.00 10.00
Trevor Hoffman
163 Cole Hamels 4.00 10.00
Johan Santana
164 David Ortiz 4.00 10.00
Kendry Morales
165 Curt Schilling 4.00 10.00
Randy Johnson
166 Curtis Granderson 4.00 10.00
B.J. Upton
167 Chase Utley 12.50 30.00
Ryne Sandberg
168 Nick Markakis 4.00 10.00
Melvin Mora
169 Conor Jackson 4.00 10.00
Prince Fielder
170 Roy Halladay 4.00 10.00
Ben Sheets
171 Kerry Wood 4.00 10.00
Mark Mulder
172 Andruw Jones 5.00 12.00
Ken Griffey Jr.
173 Troy Tulowitzki 4.00 10.00
J.J. Hardy
174 Matt Cain 10.00 25.00
Tim Lincecum
175 Derek Jeter 5.00 12.00
Orlando Cabrera
176 Albert Pujols 5.00 12.00
Prince Fielder
177 Frank Thomas 5.00 12.00
Roy Halladay
178 Josh Beckett 4.00 10.00
Jason Varitek
179 Miguel Cabrera 5.00 12.00
Mike Schmidt
180 Albert Pujols 5.00 12.00
Chris Duncan
181 C.C. Sabathia 4.00 10.00
Dontrelle Willis
182 Matt Holliday 4.00 10.00
Manny Ramirez
183 Roy Halladay 4.00 10.00
Zack Greinke
184 Nick Markakis 4.00 10.00
Vladimir Guerrero
185 Ben Sheets 4.00 10.00
Roy Halladay
186 Albert Pujols 5.00 12.00
Vladimir Guerrero
187 Johnny Damon 4.00 10.00
Manny Ramirez
188 Johan Santana 4.00 10.00
Chris Carpenter
191 Curt Schilling 5.00 12.00
Jonathan Papelbon
192 Derek Jeter 12.50 30.00
Cal Ripken Jr.
193 Jason Varitek 4.00 10.00
Wade Boggs
194 Derrek Lee 5.00 12.00
Alfonso Soriano
196 Hong-Chih Kuo 4.00 10.00
Kenji Johjima
197 Kerry Wood 4.00 10.00
Alfonso Soriano
198 Albert Pujols 5.00 12.00
Carlos Delgado
199 Don Mattingly 12.50 30.00
Derek Jeter
200 Derek Jeter 6.00 15.00
Johnny Damon
201 Prince Fielder 6.00 15.00
Ben Sheets
Matt Kemp
James Loney
202 David Ortiz 8.00 20.00
Kevin Youkilis
Jason Giambi
Derek Jeter
203 Cal Ripken Jr. 10.00 25.00
Derek Jeter
Khalil Greene
Troy Tulowitzki
204 Robin Yount 6.00 15.00
Prince Fielder
Rickie Weeks
J.J. Hardy
205 Vladimir Guerrero 4.00 10.00
Howie Kendrick
Casey Kotchman
Chone Figgins
206 Jason Varitek 4.00 10.00
Jorge Posada
Ivan Rodriguez
Kenji Johjima
207 Trevor Hoffman 4.00 10.00
Mariano Rivera
Eric Gagne
Joe Nathan
208 Carlos Guillen 4.00 10.00
Brandon Inge
Gary Sheffield
Ivan Rodriguez
209 Scott Kazmir 5.00 12.00
Randy Johnson
Francisco Liriano
Johan Santana
210 Johan Santana 5.00 12.00
Billy Wagner
John Maine
Pedro Martinez
211 Conor Jackson 6.00 15.00
Prince Fielder
Albert Pujols
Derrek Lee
212 Josh Beckett 4.00 10.00
Justin Verlander
Jered Weaver
Zack Greinke
213 Greg Maddux 5.00 12.00
Jake Peavy
Chris Young
Trevor Hoffman
215 Greg Maddux 6.00 15.00
Trevor Hoffman
Khalil Greene
Tony Gwynn
216 Ken Griffey Jr. 6.00 15.00
Aaron Harang
Alfonso Soriano
Carlos Zambrano
217 Greg Maddux 6.00 15.00
John Smoltz
Mike Mussina
Roy Halladay
218 Ken Griffey Jr. 6.00 15.00
Jim Thome
Frank Thomas
Manny Ramirez
220 Vladimir Guerrero 6.00 15.00
Manny Ramirez
Albert Pujols
Carlos Lee
221 Ken Griffey Jr. 6.00 15.00
Alfonso Soriano
Carlos Lee
Jason Bay
223 Derrek Lee 6.00 15.00
Alfonso Soriano
Derek Jeter
Jason Giambi
225 C.C. Sabathia 4.00 10.00
Randy Johnson
Scott Kazmir
Cole Hamels
226 Albert Pujols 10.00 25.00
Rick Ankiel
Chris Carpenter
Ozzie Smith
227 Mike Schmidt 10.00 25.00
Albert Pujols
Ken Griffey Jr.
David Ortiz
228 Curtis Granderson 5.00 12.00
Rafael Furcal
Derek Jeter
Rickie Weeks
229 David Ortiz 6.00 15.00
Manny Ramirez
Jason Varitek
Wade Boggs
230 Andy Pettitte 6.00 15.00
Derek Jeter
Jake Peavy
Khalil Greene
231 Don Mattingly 12.50 30.00
Derek Jeter
Manny Ramirez
David Ortiz
232 John Smoltz 5.00 12.00
Chipper Jones
Johan Santana
Carlos Delgado
233 Derek Jeter 6.00 15.00
Jason Giambi
Melvin Mora
Brian Roberts
234 Derrek Lee 6.00 15.00
Aramis Ramirez
Albert Pujols
Chris Duncan
235 Mark Mulder 6.00 15.00
Albert Pujols
Ben Sheets
Prince Fielder
237 Manny Ramirez 6.00 15.00
Vladimir Guerrero
Pat Burrell
Albert Pujols
238 Andy Pettitte 6.00 15.00
Derek Jeter
Ivan Rodriguez
Justin Verlander
239 Jason Varitek 5.00 12.00
Ivan Rodriguez
Jorge Posada
Kenji Johjima
240 Brian Roberts 4.00 10.00
Rickie Weeks
Chase Utley
Dan Uggla
241 Mark Mulder 6.00 15.00
Albert Pujols
Ivan Rodriguez
Magglio Ordonez
242 Ken Griffey Jr. 6.00 15.00
Prince Fielder
David Ortiz
Nick Markakis
243 Derek Jeter 6.00 15.00
Brian Roberts
Michael Young
Dan Uggla
244 Manny Ramirez 5.00 12.00
David Ortiz
Magglio Ordonez
Vladimir Guerrero
245 Randy Johnson 4.00 10.00
Conor Jackson
Chad Billingsley
James Loney
246 Manny Ramirez 4.00 10.00
Magglio Ordonez
Pat Burrell
Josh Willingham
247 Derek Jeter 12.50 30.00
Jason Giambi
Mariano Rivera
Chien-Ming Wang
248 Carl Crawford 4.00 10.00
B.J. Upton
Hanley Ramirez
Dan Uggla
249 Albert Pujols 6.00 15.00
Ken Griffey Jr.
Derrek Lee
Prince Fielder
251 Chris Carpenter 5.00 12.00
Ben Sheets
Dan Haren
Josh Johnson
Jake Peavy
Cole Hamels
252 Vladimir Guerrero 6.00 15.00
Manny Ramirez
Curtis Granderson
Mark Teahen
Rocco Baldelli
Nick Markakis
253 Randy Johnson 5.00 12.00
Barry Zito
Johan Santana
Francisco Liriano
Mark Mulder
Scott Kazmir
255 Travis Hafner 10.00 25.00
Victor Martinez
C.C. Sabathia
Vladimir Guerrero
John Lackey
Howie Kendrick
256 Albert Pujols 10.00 25.00
Derrek Lee
Carlos Delgado
Adrian Gonzalez
Prince Fielder
Adam LaRoche
257 Ken Griffey Jr. 12.50 30.00
Carlos Lee
Matt Holliday
Jason Bay
Josh Willingham
Tony Gwynn
260 Derek Jeter 12.50 30.00
Andy Pettitte
Jason Giambi
Carlos Delgado
Johan Santana
Moises Alou
262 Jered Weaver 5.00 12.00
Rickie Weeks
Zack Greinke
Khalil Greene
Scott Kazmir
Howie Kendrick
263 Mike Mussina 6.00 15.00
Andy Pettitte
John Smoltz
Randy Johnson
Roy Halladay
Tom Glavine
265 Derrek Lee 10.00 25.00
Kerry Wood
Aramis Ramirez
Albert Pujols
Mark Mulder
Chris Duncan
266 Andruw Jones 5.00 12.00
Rafael Furcal
Takashi Saito
Vladimir Guerrero
Howie Kendrick
Jered Weaver
267 Albert Pujols 8.00 20.00
Mark Mulder
Derrek Lee
Kerry Wood
Prince Fielder
Ben Sheets
268 Ken Griffey Jr. 15.00 40.00
Derek Jeter
Manny Ramirez
Vladimir Guerrero
David Ortiz
Albert Pujols
269 Mark Teixeira 8.00 20.00
Chipper Jones
Carlos Delgado
Moises Alou
Josh Willingham
Dan Uggla
270 Frank Thomas 10.00 25.00
Manny Ramirez
Vladimir Guerrero
Carlos Lee
Mike Schmidt
Albert Pujols
271 Ivan Rodriguez 6.00 15.00
Jason Varitek
Jorge Posada
Joe Mauer
Brian McCann
Kenji Johjima
272 Manny Ramirez 5.00 12.00
Magglio Ordonez
Pat Burrell
Josh Willingham
Delmon Young
Nick Markakis
273 Miguel Tejada 6.00 15.00
Mark Loretta
Roy Oswalt
Kevin Millwood
Michael Young
Josh Hamilton
274 Johan Santana 10.00 25.00
Carlos Delgado
Moises Alou
Cole Hamels
Pat Burrell
Chase Utley
275 Chase Utley 5.00 12.00
Aaron Hill
Rickie Weeks
Chris Burke
Dan Uggla
Akinori Iwamura
276 Kerry Wood 10.00 25.00
Derrek Lee
Aramis Ramirez
Randy Johnson
Dan Haren
Chad Tracy
277 Ivan Rodriguez 8.00 20.00
Magglio Ordonez
Brandon Inge
Albert Pujols
Mark Mulder
Chris Duncan
278 Ken Griffey Jr. 8.00 20.00
Prince Fielder
Geoff Jenkins
David Ortiz
Garret Anderson
Nick Markakis
280 Manny Ramirez 6.00 15.00
Vladimir Guerrero
Magglio Ordonez
David Ortiz
Aramis Ramirez
Kendry Morales
281 Jason Varitek 5.00 12.00
Jorge Posada
Kenji Johjima
Miguel Cabrera
Melvin Mora
Eric Chavez
282 Ken Griffey Jr. 6.00 15.00
Mike Cameron
Jason Bay
Grady Sizemore
Mark Teahen
Delmon Young
284 David Ortiz 6.00 15.00
Jonathan Papelbon
Josh Beckett
Magglio Ordonez
Dontrelle Willis
Joel Zumaya
285 Prince Fielder 6.00 15.00
Mike Cameron
Rickie Weeks
Justin Morneau
Delmon Young
Francisco Liriano
286 Carl Crawford 5.00 12.00
Scott Kazmir
Akinori Iwamura
Luis Gonzalez
Josh Johnson
Dan Uggla
287 Nick Markakis 8.00 20.00
Rick Ankiel
Josh Hamilton
Xavier Nady
J.D. Drew
Chris Duncan
288 Jake Peavy 5.00 12.00
Chris Young
Troy Tulowitzki
Jeff Francis
Matt Cain
Aaron Rowand
290 Derek Jeter 20.00 50.00
Jason Giambi
Mariano Rivera
Jorge Posada
Chien-Ming Wang
Don Mattingly
291 Manny Ramirez 10.00 25.00
Jason Varitek
Josh Beckett
J.D. Drew
Jonathan Papelbon
Wade Boggs
292 Dan Haren 5.00 12.00
Conor Jackson
Jeff Francis
Troy Tulowitzki
Rafael Furcal
Chad Billingsley
294 Gary Sheffield 10.00 25.00
Ivan Rodriguez
Carlos Guillen
Magglio Ordonez
Miguel Cabrera
Dontrelle Willis
295 Vladimir Guerrero 6.00 15.00
Garret Anderson
John Lackey
Chone Figgins
Jered Weaver
Casey Kotchman
296 Kerry Wood 5.00 12.00
Eric Gagne
Brad Lidge
Chad Cordero
Joe Nathan
Joel Zumaya
Jonathan Papelbon
Mariano Rivera
297 Manny Ramirez 20.00 50.00
David Ortiz
Jason Varitek
Jonathan Papelbon
Derek Jeter
Jason Giambi
Jorge Posada
Mariano Rivera
298 Vladimir Guerrero 8.00 20.00
John Lackey
Howie Kendrick
Kendry Morales
Travis Hafner
C.C. Sabathia
Victor Martinez
Grady Sizemore
299 Albert Pujols 12.50 30.00
Prince Fielder
Lance Berkman
Derrek Lee
Mark Teixeira
Carlos Delgado
Adrian Gonzalez
Adam LaRoche
300 Matt Holliday 8.00 20.00
Carlos Lee
Josh Willingham
Jason Bay
Ken Griffey Jr.
Carlos Beltran
Chris Duncan
Mike Cameron
301 Johan Santana 6.00 15.00
Carlos Delgado
Josh Johnson
Josh Willingham
John Smoltz
Chipper Jones
Cole Hamels
Pat Burrell
303 Johan Santana 15.00 40.00
Jose Reyes
Carlos Delgado
Moises Alou
Andy Pettitte
Derek Jeter
Jason Giambi
Johnny Damon
304 David Ortiz 15.00 40.00
Casey Kotchman
Jason Giambi
Frank Thomas
Richie Sexson
Aubrey Huff
Jim Thome
Justin Morneau
306 Ken Griffey Jr. 12.50 30.00
Albert Pujols
Carlos Lee
Derrek Lee
Prince Fielder
Chris Duncan
Lance Berkman
Alfonso Soriano
311 Albert Pujols 10.00 25.00
Mark Mulder
Derrek Lee
Kerry Wood
Prince Fielder
Ben Sheets
Tom Gorzelanny
Xavier Nady
312 Cal Ripken Jr. 20.00 50.00
Derek Jeter
Albert Pujols
David Ortiz
Ken Griffey Jr.
Manny Ramirez
Mark Teixeira
Vladimir Guerrero
314 Albert Pujols 12.50 30.00
Vladimir Guerrero
Pat Burrell
Jason Giambi
Frank Thomas
Carlos Lee
Aramis Ramirez
Manny Ramirez
317 Manny Ramirez 6.00 15.00
Magglio Ordonez
Nick Markakis
RoC.C.o Baldelli
Moises Alou
Pat Burrell
Josh Willingham
Delmon Young
318 Michael Young 8.00 20.00
Kevin Millwood
Hank Blalock
Josh Hamilton
Carlos Lee
Roy Oswalt
Miguel Tejada
Mark Loretta
319 Chase Utley 8.00 20.00
Cole Hamels
Pat Burrell
Brad Lidge
Carlos Delgado
Johan Santana
Moises Alou
Billy Wagner
320 Chase Utley 10.00 25.00
Robinson Cano
Rickie Weeks
Brian Roberts
Dan Uggla
Mark Loretta
Aaron Hill
Chris Burke
321 Randy Johnson 6.00 15.00
Chad Tracy
Chris Burke
Stephen Drew
Kerry Wood
Alfonso Soriano
Derrek Lee
Aramis Ramirez
322 Magglio Ordonez 12.50 30.00
Joel Zumaya
Brandon Inge
Ivan Rodriguez
Albert Pujols
Chris Carpenter
Chris Duncan
Mark Mulder
323 David Ortiz 8.00 20.00
Manny Ramirez
Jonathan Papelbon
Jason Varitek
Matt Holliday
Troy Tulowitzki
Jeff Francis
Garrett Atkins
324 Ken Griffey Jr. 15.00 40.00
Prince Fielder
Geoff Jenkins
Chad Tracy
David Ortiz
Nick Markakis
Garret Anderson
Eric Chavez
327 Johan Santana 6.00 15.00
Magglio Ordonez
Vladimir Guerrero
David Ortiz
Aramis Ramirez
Kendry Morales
Ivan Rodriguez
Manny Ramirez
329 Ken Griffey Jr. 15.00 40.00
Mike Cameron
Chris Duncan
Jason Bay
Magglio Ordonez
Grady Sizemore
Delmon Young
Mark Teahen
330 James Loney 6.00 15.00
Adam LaRoche
Mark Teixeira
Aaron Boone
Casey Kotchman
Kevin Youkilis
Jason Giambi
Aubrey Huff
331 Miguel Cabrera 6.00 15.00
Magglio Ordonez
Dontrelle Willis
Joel Zumaya
Manny Ramirez
David Ortiz
Jonathan Papelbon
Josh Beckett
333 Carl Crawford 6.00 15.00
Scott Kazmir
RoC.C.o Baldelli
B.J. Upton
Hanley Ramirez
Josh Johnson
Josh Willingham
Dan Uggla
334 Pat Burrell 8.00 20.00
Nick Markakis
Josh Willingham
Xavier Nady
J.D. Drew
Chris Duncan
Rick Ankiel
Josh Hamilton
335 Jake Peavy 8.00 20.00
Chris Young
Jeff Francis
Troy Tulowitzki
Randy Johnson
Chad Tracy
Tim Lincecum
Matt Cain
336 Derek Jeter 30.00 60.00
Mike Mussina
Mariano Rivera
Chien-Ming Wang
Andy Pettitte
Jason Giambi
Don Mattingly
Jorge Posada
337 David Ortiz 12.50 30.00
Manny Ramirez
Jonathan Papelbon
Josh Beckett
J.D. Drew
Jason Varitek
Kevin Youkilis
Wade Boggs
338 Ken Griffey Jr. 10.00 25.00
Aaron Harang
Derrek Lee
Carlos Zambrano
Prince Fielder
Ben Sheets
Albert Pujols
Mark Mulder
339 Aaron Harang 6.00 15.00
Dan Haren
Roy Oswalt
Chad Billingsley
Josh Johnson
Zack Greinke
A.J. Burnett
Jered Weaver

2008 Upper Deck Ballpark Collection Jersey Autographs

OVERALL AU ODDS 1:5 HOBBY
1 Aaron Harang 4.00 10.00

2 Takashi Saito	10.00	25.00
3 Troy Tulowitzki	10.00	25.00
4 Adam LaRoche	5.00	12.00
5 Adrian Gonzalez	10.00	25.00
6 Albert Pujols		
7 Andre Ethier	10.00	25.00
8 Joe Mauer	20.00	50.00
9 Justin Upton	12.50	30.00
10 Aramis Ramirez	6.00	15.00
11 Scott Baker	4.00	10.00
12 B.J. Upton	12.50	30.00
13 Bill Hall	5.00	12.00
14 Billy Wagner	30.00	60.00
15 Brandon Phillips	6.00	15.00
16 Brandon Webb	30.00	60.00
17 Sean Marshall		
18 Brian McCann	8.00	20.00
19 Brian Roberts	10.00	25.00
20 Bronson Arroyo	5.00	12.00
21 Tim Lincecum	40.00	80.00
22 Mark Reynolds	5.00	12.00
23 Chad Billingsley	12.50	30.00
24 Chad Cordero	4.00	10.00
25 Chone Figgins	5.00	12.00
26 Chris Duffy		
27 Chris B. Young	6.00	15.00
28 Tom Gorzelanny	4.00	10.00
29 Corey Hart	10.00	25.00
30 Dan Uggla	4.00	10.00
31 David Murphy		
32 Derek Jeter EXCH	75.00	150.00
33 Edinson Volquez	8.00	20.00
34 Elijah Dukes		
35 Edwin Encarnacion		
36 Fausto Carmona		
37 Ubaldo Jimenez		
38 Xavier Nady	4.00	10.00
39 Felix Pie	4.00	10.00
40 Yovani Gallardo		
41 Yunel Escobar		
42 Garrett Atkins	4.00	10.00
43 Ken Griffey Jr. EXCH	40.00	80.00
44 Derek Jeter EXCH	75.00	150.00
45 Hanley Ramirez	10.00	25.00
46 Hong-Chih Kuo	20.00	50.00
47 Ian Kinsler	6.00	15.00
48 Jack Cust		
49 Derek Lowe	6.00	15.00
50 Alfonso Soriano	20.00	50.00
51 Jeff Baker	4.00	10.00
52 Jeff Francis	4.00	10.00
53 Jeff Francoeur	10.00	25.00
54 Jered Weaver	6.00	15.00
55 Ben Sheets	10.00	25.00
56 Jeremy Guthrie	6.00	15.00
57 Jeremy Hermida	4.00	10.00
58 Jerry Owens		
59 Brian Giles		
60 Joakim Soria	6.00	15.00
61 Joe Blanton	4.00	10.00
62 Joe Nathan	6.00	15.00
63 Joe Smith		
64 Chien-Ming Wang	60.00	120.00
65 Chris Young	4.00	10.00
66 Jon Lester	15.00	40.00
67 Jonathan Papelbon		
68 Cole Hamels	8.00	20.00
69 Josh Johnson	5.00	12.00
70 Josh Willingham	4.00	10.00
71 Kelly Johnson	4.00	10.00
72 Ken Griffey Jr. EXCH	40.00	80.00
73 Kevin Kouzmanoff	4.00	10.00
74 Kevin Youkilis	12.50	30.00
75 Derrek Lee	12.50	30.00
76 James Shields	8.00	20.00
77 Jason Bay	8.00	20.00
78 Jason Varitek	20.00	50.00
79 Manny Corpas		
80 Mark Ellis		
81 Mark Teahen	4.00	10.00
82 Marlon Byrd		
83 Matt Cain	5.00	12.00
84 John Lackey	6.00	15.00
85 Matt Kemp	10.00	25.00
86 John Maine	5.00	12.00
87 Matt Lindstrom		
88 Melvin Mora	5.00	12.00
89 Micah Owings		
90 Michael Bourn		
91 Kerry Wood	8.00	20.00
92 Nick Markakis	12.50	30.00
93 Lance Berkman	8.00	20.00
94 Noah Lowry	4.00	10.00
95 Rickie Weeks	8.00	20.00
96 Prince Fielder	12.50	30.00
97 Roy Halladay	15.00	40.00
98 Tim Hudson	8.00	20.00
99 Grady Sizemore	20.00	50.00
100 Ryan Braun		

2009 Upper Deck Ballpark Collection

COMMON CARD (1-70)	.60	1.50
COMMON AU RC (71-100)	3.00	8.00
OVERALL AU ODDS .5:1 HOBBY		
AU PRINT RUN B/WN 75-500 COPIES PER		
COMMON 2X GU (101-200)	3.00	8.00
2X PRINT RUNS B/WN 25-500 COPIES PER		
NO 2X PRICING ON QTY 25 OR LESS		
COMMON 4X GU (201-300)	3.00	8.00
4X PRINT RUNS B/WN 25-500 COPIES PER		
NO 4X PRICING ON QTY 25 OR LESS		
COMMON 6X GU (301-350)	4.00	10.00
6X PRINT RUNS B/WN 20-300 COPIES PER		
NO 6X PRICING ON QTY 25 OR LESS		
COMMON 8X GU (351-400)	4.00	10.00
OVERALL GU ODDS 2.5:1 HOBBY		
8X PRINT RUNS B/WN 25-350 COPIES PER		
NO 8X PRICING ON QTY 25 OR LESS		
1 Adrian Beltre	.60	1.50
2 Adrian Gonzalez	1.00	2.50
3 Akinori Iwamura	.60	1.50
4 Albert Pujols	4.00	10.00
5 Alex Gordon	1.00	2.50
6 Alex Rodriguez	2.50	6.00
7 Alfonso Soriano	1.00	2.50
8 B.J. Upton	1.00	2.50
9 Brandon Webb	1.00	2.50
10 Brian McCann	1.00	2.50
11 Brian Roberts	.60	1.50
12 Carl Crawford	1.00	2.50
13 Carlos Beltran	.60	1.50
14 Carlos Zambrano	1.00	2.50
15 CC Sabathia	1.00	2.50
16 Chase Utley	1.50	4.00
17 Chien-Ming Wang	1.00	2.50
18 Chipper Jones	1.50	4.00
19 Cliff Lee	1.00	2.50
20 Cole Hamels	1.50	4.00
21 Daisuke Matsuzaka	1.50	4.00
22 David Ortiz	1.00	2.50
23 David Wright	2.00	5.00
24 Derek Jeter	4.00	10.00
25 Dustin Pedroia	2.00	5.00
26 Evan Longoria	2.00	5.00
27 Felix Hernandez	1.50	4.00
28 Francisco Liriano	.60	1.50
29 Freddy Sanchez	.60	1.50
30 Gary Sheffield	.60	1.50
31 Grady Sizemore	1.00	2.50
32 Hanley Ramirez	1.50	4.00
33 Hideki Matsui	1.50	4.00
34 Ichiro Suzuki	2.50	6.00
35 Ivan Rodriguez	1.00	2.50
36 Jason Giambi	.60	1.50
37 Jason Varitek	1.50	4.00
38 Jay Bruce	1.00	2.50
39 Jim Thome	1.00	2.50
40 Joba Chamberlain	1.00	2.50
41 Joe Mauer	1.50	4.00
42 Joe Nathan	.60	1.50
43 Johan Santana	1.50	4.00
44 John Lackey	.60	1.50
45 Jon Lester	1.50	4.00
46 Jorge Posada	1.00	2.50
47 Jose Reyes	1.00	2.50
48 Josh Beckett	1.00	2.50
49 Josh Hamilton	1.50	4.00
50 Justin Morneau	1.50	4.00
51 Ken Griffey Jr.	2.50	6.00
52 Kevin Youkilis	1.00	2.50
53 Lance Berkman	1.00	2.50
54 Manny Ramirez	1.50	4.00
55 Mariano Rivera	1.50	4.00
56 Mark Teixeira	1.50	4.00
57 Matt Kemp	1.00	2.50
58 Miguel Cabrera	1.50	4.00
59 Nick Markakis	1.50	4.00
60 Prince Fielder	1.00	2.50
61 Roy Halladay	1.50	4.00
62 Roy Oswalt	1.00	2.50
63 Ryan Braun	2.00	5.00
64 Ryan Howard	2.00	5.00
65 Ryan Zimmerman	1.00	2.50
66 Tim Hudson	1.00	2.50
67 Tim Lincecum	2.50	6.00
68 Todd Helton	1.00	2.50
69 Tom Glavine	1.00	2.50
70 Vladimir Guerrero	1.50	4.00
71 Bobby Parnell AU/500 RC	4.00	10.00
72 Brett Anderson AU/200 RC	4.00	10.00
73 Colby Rasmus AU/200 (RC)	20.00	50.00
74 David Freese AU/100 RC	40.00	80.00
75 David Patton AU/500 RC	3.00	8.00
76 David Price AU/150 RC	12.50	30.00
77 Dexter Fowler AU/500 (RC)	5.00	12.00
78 Elvis Andrus AU/200 RC	12.50	30.00
79 Fernando Martinez AU/375 RC	5.00	12.00
80 George Kottaras AU/100 (RC)	12.50	30.00
81 Gordon Beckham AU/200 RC	15.00	40.00
82 James McDonald AU/500 RC	3.00	8.00
83 James Parr AU/500 (RC)	3.00	8.00
84 Jason Motte AU/500 (RC)	6.00	15.00
85 Jordan Schafer AU/199 (RC)	4.00	10.00
86 Jordan Zimmermann AU/400 RC	5.00	12.00
87 Kenshin Kawakami AU/200 RC	30.00	60.00
88 Kevin Jepsen AU/400 (RC)	3.00	8.00
89 Koji Uehara AU/100 RC	50.00	100.00
90 Matt Wieters AU/150 RC	40.00	80.00
91 Nolan Reimold AU/500 (RC)	12.50	30.00
92 Pablo Sandoval AU/300 (RC)	30.00	60.00
93 Phil Coke AU/375 RC	5.00	12.00
94 Rick Porcello AU/100 RC	30.00	60.00
95 Ricky Romero AU/75 (RC)	8.00	20.00
96 Ryan Perry AU/300 RC	5.00	12.00
97 Shairon Martis AU/500 RC	3.00	8.00
98 Tommy Hanson AU/125 RC	15.00	40.00
99 Travis Snider AU/125 RC	15.00	40.00
100 Trevor Cahill AU/300 RC	4.00	10.00
101 David Murphy	3.00	8.00
Adam Jones/500		
102 Kerry Wood	3.00	8.00
Travis Hafner/500		
103 Hank Blalock	3.00	8.00
Prince Fielder/500		
104 Chone Figgins	3.00	8.00
Juan Pierre/400		
105 Randy Johnson	4.00	10.00
Carlos Delgado/400		
106 John Smoltz	3.00	8.00
Jake Peavy/400		
107 Joe DiMaggio		
Ted Williams/25		
108 Yunel Escobar	3.00	8.00
Miguel Tejada/400		
109 Carlos Lee		
Miguel Cabrera/25		
110 Prince Fielder		
Reggie Jackson/25		
111 Justin Verlander	3.00	8.00
Josh Johnson/400		
112 Hank Blalock	3.00	8.00
David Ortiz/500		
113 Jake Peavy	3.00	8.00
Barry Zito/400		
114 Jermaine Dye	3.00	8.00
Bobby Abreu/500		
115 Chad Billingsley	3.00	8.00
Kerry Wood/400		
116 Jorge Posada	3.00	8.00
Michael Young/400		
117 Ozzie Smith		
Ken Griffey Jr./25		
118 David Murphy	3.00	8.00
Delmon Young/400		
119 Jered Weaver	3.00	8.00
Aramis Ramirez/400		
120 Francisco Liriano	3.00	8.00
Barry Zito/400		
121 Francisco Liriano	4.00	10.00
Brandon Webb/400		
122 Chris Carpenter	5.00	12.00
Randy Johnson/400		
123 Travis Hafner	3.00	8.00
Derrek Lee/500		
124 Ozzie Smith		
Frank Robinson/25		
125 Randy Johnson	3.00	8.00
Brandon Webb/400		
126 Justin Verlander	3.00	8.00
Victor Martinez/400		
127 Yunel Escobar	3.00	8.00
Chone Figgins/325		
128 Prince Fielder	3.00	8.00
Jonathan Papelbon/300		
129 Juan Rivera	3.00	8.00
Matt Kemp/400		
130 B.J. Upton	3.00	8.00
Justin Upton/400		
131 Clayton Kershaw	3.00	8.00
Jake Peavy/240		
132 Chad Billingsley	3.00	8.00
Chris B. Young/500		
133 James Shields	3.00	8.00
Josh Beckett/400		
134 Ryan Zimmerman	3.00	8.00
Josh Fields/400		
135 Dan Uggla	4.00	10.00
Kevin Youkilis/230		
136 Robinson Cano	3.00	8.00
Yunel Escobar/335		
137 Max Scherzer	3.00	8.00
Jered Weaver/400		
138 Nolan Ryan		
Roy Oswalt/25		
139 Jonathan Papelbon	5.00	12.00
Daisuke Matsuzaka/200		
140 Grady Sizemore	3.00	8.00
Fausto Carmona/500		
141 John Maine	4.00	10.00
Jose Reyes/400		
142 Josh Beckett	3.00	8.00
A.J. Burnett/400		
143 Michael Young	4.00	10.00
Josh Hamilton/200		
144 Kosuke Fukudome		
Ryne Sandberg/25		
145 Jorge Posada	3.00	8.00
Robinson Cano/400		
146 Randy Johnson		
Ken Griffey Jr./25		
147 CC Sabathia	3.00	8.00
Fausto Carmona/500		
148 Ryan Braun	4.00	10.00
Prince Fielder/400		
149 Kevin Youkilis	4.00	10.00
Josh Beckett/275		
150 Francisco Liriano	4.00	10.00
Joe Mauer/400		
151 Ross Ohlendorf	3.00	8.00
Robinson Cano/400		
152 Curtis Granderson	4.00	10.00
Justin Verlander/350		
153 Kevin Youkilis	4.00	10.00
Jonathan Papelbon/300		
154 Jonathan Papelbon	4.00	10.00
Josh Beckett/400		
155 Jason Varitek	3.00	8.00
Jonathan Papelbon/400		
156 Jonathan Papelbon	3.00	8.00
Mike Lowell/375		
157 Stephen Drew	3.00	8.00
Chris B. Young/350		
158 Ozzie Smith		
Albert Pujols/25		
159 Jorge Posada	3.00	8.00
Chien-Ming Wang/400		
160 Prince Fielder	3.00	8.00
Bill Hall/500		
161 Chris B. Young	3.00	8.00
Brandon Webb/500		
162 Roy Halladay	5.00	12.00
Alex Rios/350		
163 Ian Kinsler	3.00	8.00
David Murphy/400		
164 Adam Lind	3.00	8.00
A.J. Burnett/340		
165 Chad Billingsley	5.00	12.00
Juan Pierre/400		
166 David Ortiz	3.00	8.00
Josh Beckett/400		
167 Nick Markakis	4.00	10.00
Jeremy Guthrie/400		
168 Jeff Francoeur	3.00	8.00
Kelly Johnson/500		
169 Rich Aurilia	3.00	8.00
Omar Vizquel/400		
170 Jonathan Papelbon	5.00	12.00
Jon Lester/400		
171 Cal Ripken Jr.		
Frank Robinson/25		
172 Nate McLouth	3.00	8.00
Freddy Sanchez/400		
173 Johnny Damon	4.00	10.00
Robinson Cano/400		
174 Kerry Wood	3.00	8.00
Derrek Lee/400		
175 Jesse Litsch	3.00	8.00
Roy Halladay/400		
176 Juan Rivera	3.00	8.00
Jered Weaver/400		
177 Derrek Lee	3.00	8.00
Kerry Wood/400		
178 Melvin Mora	4.00	10.00
Nick Markakis/400		
179 Carlos Delgado	3.00	8.00
Prince Fielder/350		
180 Johnny Bench	3.00	8.00
Brian McCann/125		
181 Michael Young	3.00	8.00
Miguel Cabrera/300		
182 Brandon Webb	4.00	10.00
Jake Peavy/300		
183 Kerry Wood	4.00	10.00
Justin Verlander/300		
184 Michael Young	3.00	8.00
Robinson Cano/350		
185 Kelly Johnson	3.00	8.00
Felipe Lopez/400		
186 Carlos Guillen	4.00	10.00
Melvin Mora/390		
187 Kerry Wood	3.00	8.00
Jonathan Papelbon/400		
188 Jermaine Dye	3.00	8.00
CC Sabathia/350		
189 Jon Lester	4.00	10.00
Manny Ramirez/250		
190 Justin Verlander	3.00	8.00
Josh Beckett/300		
191 Alfonso Soriano	3.00	8.00
Vladimir Guerrero/400		
192 Manny Ramirez	4.00	10.00
Johnny Damon/300		
193 Fausto Carmona	3.00	8.00
Brandon Webb/400		
194 Joe DiMaggio		
Ted Williams/25		
195 Chad Billingsley	3.00	8.00
Bronson Arroyo/400		
196 Magglio Ordonez	3.00	8.00
Aramis Ramirez/350		
197 Stephen Drew	3.00	8.00
J.D. Drew/400		
198 Billy Wagner	3.00	8.00
Trevor Hoffman/225		
199 Michael Young	3.00	8.00
Khalil Greene/350		
200 Jorge Posada	3.00	8.00
Victor Martinez/350		
201 Nick Markakis	6.00	15.00
Michael Young		
Joe Mauer		
Ryan Braun/400		
202 Justin Verlander	5.00	12.00
Kevin Slowey		
Chad Billingsley		
Jesse Litsch/400		
203 Matt Holliday	3.00	8.00
Grady Sizemore		
Andruw Jones		
Chris B. Young/400		
204 Ozzie Smith		
Joe DiMaggio		
Cal Ripken Jr.		
Carl Yastrzemski/25		
205 Jose Reyes	5.00	12.00
Yunel Escobar		
Ian Kinsler		
Hanley Ramirez/500		
206 Billy Wagner	3.00	8.00
Roy Halladay		
Josh Beckett		
Jonathan Papelbon/500		
207 Justin Verlander	4.00	10.00
Joe Mauer		
Chad Billingsley		
Manny Ramirez/400		
208 James Shields	3.00	8.00
Jonathan Papelbon		
Josh Beckett		
Brandon Morrow/400		
209 Rich Hill	5.00	12.00
Tim Lincecum		
Barry Zito		
Carlos Zambrano/400		
210 Carlos Lee	3.00	8.00
Travis Hafner		
Carlos Delgado		
Matt Holliday/500		
211 Alex Gordon		
Ozzie Smith		
Ryne Sandberg		
Mike Schmidt/25		
212 Hiroki Kuroda	5.00	12.00
Chien-Ming Wang		
Daisuke Matsuzaka		
Kenji Johjima/500		
213 Ian Kinsler	3.00	8.00
Joe Crede		
Bill Hall		
Hanley Ramirez/385		
214 Joe Mauer	3.00	8.00
Russell Martin		
Kenji Johjima		
Victor Martinez/500		
215 Chien-Ming Wang	3.00	8.00
Jonathan Papelbon		
Roy Halladay		
Joe Nathan/400		
216 Chad Billingsley	3.00	8.00
James Shields		
Jonathan Papelbon		
Chien-Ming Wang/400		
217 Travis Hafner	3.00	8.00
Carlos Delgado		
Alfonso Soriano		
Manny Ramirez/400		
218 Freddy Sanchez	3.00	8.00
Ian Kinsler		
Howie Kendrick		
Yunel Escobar/400		
219 Frank Robinson		
Cal Ripken Jr.		
Johnny Bench		
Ozzie Smith/25		
220 Troy Glaus	4.00	10.00
Ian Kinsler		
Howie Kendrick		
Melvin Mora/500		
221 Prince Fielder		
Josh Johnson		
Rick Ankiel		
Jon Lester/25		
222 Adrian Gonzalez		
Chipper Jones		
Albert Pujols		
Lance Berkman/25		
223 Francisco Liriano		
Reggie Jackson		
Johan Santana		
Ozzie Smith/25		
224 Fausto Carmona	3.00	8.00
Jonathan Albaladejo		
Kelly Johnson		
Ross Ohlendorf/400		
225 Michael Young	4.00	10.00
Matt Garza		
Nick Markakis		
Fausto Carmona/500		
226 Jonathan Papelbon	3.00	8.00
James Shields		
Chris B. Young		
Hunter Pence/400		
227 Joe Mauer	4.00	10.00
Russell Martin		
Victor Martinez		
Kenji Johjima/500		
228 Jose Reyes		
Jonathan Papelbon		
Lance Berkman		
Scott Kazmir/25		
229 Joe Mauer	3.00	8.00
Grady Sizemore		
Chien-Ming Wang		
Nick Markakis/400		
230 Chien-Ming Wang	3.00	8.00
Michael Young		
Chad Billingsley		
Prince Fielder/400		
231 Chris B. Young	4.00	10.00
Matt Kemp		
Adam Jones		
Jeff Francoeur/400		
232 Jesse Litsch	3.00	8.00
Yunel Escobar		
Jonathan Albaladejo		
Josh Willingham/400		
233 Juan Rivera	4.00	10.00
Matt Holliday		
Erik Bedard		
Rich Hill/400		
234 Jose Reyes		
Josh Beckett		
Josh Johnson		
Prince Fielder/25		
235 Prince Fielder	4.00	10.00
Michael Young		
Adam Jones		
Fausto Carmona/500		
236 Adam Jones	5.00	12.00
Nick Markakis		
Nate McLouth		
Ryan Braun/400		
237 Jeremy Hermida	4.00	10.00
Joe Mauer		
Adam Jones		
Nick Markakis/500		
238 Yunel Escobar	5.00	12.00
Felix Hernandez		
Tim Lincecum		
Prince Fielder/400		
239 Ryan Braun	4.00	10.00
Josh Hamilton		
Hiroki Kuroda		
Chien-Ming Wang/400		
240 Joba Chamberlain	6.00	15.00
Fausto Carmona		
Chad Billingsley		
Justin Verlander/400		
241 Carl Yastrzemski		
Ted Williams		
Reggie Jackson		
Joe DiMaggio/25		
242 Yunel Escobar	4.00	10.00
Kelly Johnson		
Tom Glavine		
Brian McCann/400		
243 Joe DiMaggio		
Yogi Berra		
Derek Jeter		
Reggie Jackson/25		
244 Daisuke Matsuzaka	4.00	10.00
Jon Lester		
David Ortiz		
Manny Ramirez/500		
245 Troy Glaus	5.00	12.00
Alex Rios		
Carlos Delgado		
Roy Halladay/500		
246 Ozzie Smith		
Omar Vizquel		
Albert Pujols		
Jim Thome/25		
247 Manny Ramirez	4.00	10.00
Jason Varitek		
Mike Lowell		
Josh Beckett/490		
248 Adam Jones	3.00	8.00
Nick Markakis		
Jon Lester		
Daisuke Matsuzaka/400		
249 Carlos Zambrano	4.00	10.00
Alfonso Soriano		
Aramis Ramirez		
Derrek Lee/400		
250 Nolan Ryan		
Josh Hamilton		
Daisuke Matsuzaka		
Ted Williams/25		
251 Josh Beckett	5.00	12.00
David Ortiz		
Jon Lester		
Manny Ramirez/400		
252 Nolan Ryan		
Roy Oswalt		
Yogi Berra		
Carlos Delgado/25		
253 Melvin Mora	5.00	12.00
Nick Markakis		
Justin Verlander		
Miguel Cabrera/400		
254 Bill Hall	5.00	12.00
Trevor Hoffman		
Ryan Braun		
Prince Fielder/400		
255 Manny Ramirez		
Ted Williams		
Carl Yastrzemski		
Kevin Youkilis/25		
256 Victor Martinez	3.00	8.00
Grady Sizemore		
Nick Markakis		
Adam Jones/400		
257 Ozzie Smith		
Trevor Hoffman		
Ryne Sandberg		
Carlos Zambrano/25		
258 Jonathan Papelbon	3.00	8.00
Nick Markakis		
Adam Jones		
Josh Beckett/400		
259 Andruw Jones	4.00	10.00
Matt Kemp		
Chad Billingsley		
Russell Martin/400		
260 Nolan Ryan		
Miguel Tejada		
Josh Hamilton		
Reggie Jackson/25		
261 Josh Beckett	4.00	10.00
Jason Varitek		
Jorge Posada		
Chien-Ming Wang/400		
262 Jonathan Papelbon	3.00	8.00
Josh Beckett		
Carlos Delgado		
John Maine/500		
263 Grady Sizemore	3.00	8.00
Victor Martinez		
Cliff Lee		
Travis Hafner/400		
264 Robinson Cano	20.00	50.00
Jorge Posada		
Yogi Berra		
Derek Jeter/400		
265 Takashi Saito	3.00	8.00
Jonathan Albaladejo		
Mike Lowell		
Ross Ohlendorf/400		
266 Josh Beckett	4.00	10.00
Nick Markakis		
Melvin Mora		
Jonathan Papelbon/400		
267 Cal Ripken Jr.	10.00	25.00
Melvin Mora		
Brian Roberts		
Nick Markakis/400		
268 Rich Hill	4.00	10.00
Kerry Wood		
Aramis Ramirez		
Derrek Lee/400		
269 Carlos Lee	3.00	8.00
Hunter Pence		
Roy Oswalt		
Ivan Rodriguez/500		
270 Chase Utley		
Ryne Sandberg		
Mike Schmidt		
Aramis Ramirez/25		
271 Torii Hunter	4.00	10.00
Matt Garza		
Manny Ramirez		
Johnny Damon/500		
272 Francisco Liriano	6.00	15.00
Joe Mauer		
Denard Span		
Justin Morneau/500		
273 Joe DiMaggio		
Derek Jeter		
Frank Robinson		
Cal Ripken Jr./25		
274 Chris Carpenter	8.00	20.00
Khalil Greene		
Albert Pujols		
Ryan Ludwick/400		
275 Manny Ramirez	4.00	10.00
Jonathan Papelbon		
Travis Hafner		
Victor Martinez/400		
276 Ivan Rodriguez	4.00	10.00
Carlos Guillen		
Magglio Ordonez		
Justin Verlander/400		
277 Josh Hamilton	3.00	8.00
Hank Blalock		
Victor Martinez		
Grady Sizemore/400		
278 Cole Hamels		
Reggie Jackson		
Mike Schmidt		
John Lackey/25		
279 John Lackey	3.00	8.00
Vladimir Guerrero		
Jered Weaver		
Troy Glaus/400		
280 Michael Cuddyer	5.00	12.00
Joe Nathan		
Kevin Slowey		
Torii Hunter/472		
281 Chien-Ming Wang		
Derek Jeter		
Joe DiMaggio		
Yogi Berra/25		
282 Derek Jeter	6.00	15.00
Daisuke Matsuzaka		
Chien-Ming Wang		
Josh Beckett/400		
283 Josh Beckett	3.00	8.00
Jonathan Papelbon		
Matt Garza		
James Shields/400		
284 Troy Tulowitzki	4.00	10.00
Hank Blalock		
Yunel Escobar		
Melvin Mora/500		
285 Roy Halladay	4.00	10.00
Randy Johnson		
Jake Peavy		
Carlos Zambrano/400		
286 James Shields	4.00	10.00
Barry Zito		
Daisuke Matsuzaka		
Roy Halladay/400		
287 Jonathan Papelbon	4.00	10.00
Andy Pettitte		
Jake Peavy		
Joe Nathan/500		
288 Matt Garza	4.00	10.00
Trevor Hoffman		
CC Sabathia		
Johan Santana/500		
289 Nick Markakis	5.00	12.00
David Ortiz		
Curtis Granderson		
Carl Crawford/400		
290 Torii Hunter	3.00	8.00
Andruw Jones		
Mark Teixeira		
Jason Bay/400		
291 Tim Lincecum	6.00	15.00
Josh Beckett		
Roy Halladay		
Justin Verlander/400		
292 Chris Carpenter	4.00	10.00
Josh Beckett		
Chris Young		
Randy Johnson/500		
293 Kerry Wood	3.00	8.00
Roy Halladay		
Hank Blalock		
Aramis Ramirez/400		
294 Derrek Lee	3.00	8.00
Miguel Cabrera		
Jeremy Hermida		
Ian Kinsler/500		
295 Chris B. Young	4.00	10.00
Ryan Braun		
Nate McLouth		
Matt Holliday/400		
296 Matt Holliday	3.00	8.00
Nick Markakis		
Chris B. Young		
Josh Hamilton/400		

297 Justin Verlander 4.00 10.00
Jered Weaver
Josh Beckett
Roy Halladay/400
298 Cal Ripken Jr.
Ryne Sandberg
Johnny Bench
Ozzie Smith/25
299 Troy Tulowitzki 4.00 10.00
Ian Kinsler
Prince Fielder
Melvin Mora/400
300 Ichiro 30.00 60.00
Chien-Ming Wang
Hideki Matsui
Daisuke Matsuzaka/100
301 Jon Lester 4.00 10.00
Prince Fielder
Chris B. Young
James Shields
Troy Tulowitzki
Chad Billingsley/200
302 Jim Thome 6.00 15.00
Todd Helton
Kevin Slowey
Justin Verlander
Kevin Youkilis
Tim Wakefield/300
303 Cal Ripken Jr. 50.00 100.00
Carlos Delgado
Derek Jeter
Adrian Gonzalez
Ozzie Smith
Jim Thome/30
304 Andrew Miller 10.00 25.00
Chien-Ming Wang
Jonathan Papelbon
John Maine
Roy Halladay
Tim Hudson/200
305 Johan Santana 4.00 10.00
Jorge Posada
Randy Johnson
Kerry Wood
Joe Mauer
Ivan Rodriguez/300
306 Randy Johnson
Tim Lincecum
Ozzie Smith
Josh Beckett
Reggie Jackson
Ken Griffey Jr./25
307 Ken Griffey Jr.
Frank Robinson
Johnny Bench
Jim Thome
Ozzie Smith
Albert Pujols/20
308 Andruw Jones 5.00 12.00
Pat Burrell
Torii Hunter
Gary Sheffield
Matt Holliday
J.D. Drew/300
309 Kevin Youkilis 12.50 30.00
Jermaine Dye
Nate McLouth
Miguel Cabrera
Curtis Granderson
Troy Tulowitzki/205
310 Matt Kemp
Josh Hamilton
Francisco Liriano
Carlos Zambrano
Josh Johnson
Carl Crawford/25
311 Miguel Tejada 4.00 10.00
Troy Glaus
Matt Holliday
Nick Markakis
Josh Beckett
Fausto Carmona/200
312 Brian McCann 5.00 12.00
Nate McLouth
Bronson Arroyo
Jered Weaver
Max Scherzer
Miguel Cabrera/230
313 Huston Street
Jim Thome
Scott Rolen
Ozzie Smith
CC Sabathia
Mark Teixeira/25
314 Brian McCann
Bobby Crosby
James Loney
Joey Votto
Stephen Drew
Ryan Zimmerman/160
315 John Lackey 8.00 20.00
Prince Fielder
Justin Morneau
Albert Pujols
Jeremy Guthrie
Fausto Carmona/200
316 Chien-Ming Wang 10.00 25.00
Reggie Jackson
Derek Jeter
Josh Beckett
Jason Varitek
David Ortiz/200
317 Derek Jeter 20.00 50.00
Andy Pettitte
Yogi Berra
Reggie Jackson
Chien-Ming Wang
Joba Chamberlain/200
318 Jacoby Ellsbury 8.00 20.00
Jon Lester
Daisuke Matsuzaka
Jason Varitek
David Ortiz
Carl Yastrzemski/200
319 Travis Hafner 4.00 10.00
Grady Sizemore
Victor Martinez
Francisco Liriano
Joe Mauer
Michael Cuddyer/200
320 Albert Pujols 8.00 20.00
Chris Carpenter
Ryan Ludwick
Carlos Zambrano
Derrek Lee
Kerry Wood/300
321 Daisuke Matsuzaka 5.00 12.00
Kevin Youkilis
Josh Beckett
Nick Markakis
Adam Jones
Brian Roberts/200
322 Reggie Jackson 15.00 40.00
Eric Chavez
Tim Hudson
Dan Haren
Joe Blanton
Miguel Tejada/150
323 Conor Jackson 12.50 30.00
Stephen Drew
Brandon Webb
Max Scherzer
Justin Upton
Randy Johnson/200
324 J.D. Drew 8.00 20.00
Mark Teixeira
Jeff Francoeur
Brian McCann
Chipper Jones
John Smoltz/170
325 John Smoltz 5.00 12.00
Mark Teixeira
A.J. Burnett
Xavier Nady
J.D. Drew
Rocco Baldelli/160
326 J.D. Drew 10.00 25.00
Kerry Wood
John Smoltz
Ryne Sandberg
Kosuke Fukudome
Andruw Jones/160
327 Mike Lowell 4.00 10.00
Josh Beckett
Rich Hill
Aubrey Huff
Luke Scott
Jason Bay/200
328 Josh Beckett 4.00 10.00
Ivan Rodriguez
Derrek Lee
Miguel Cabrera
Hanley Ramirez
Jeremy Hermida/200
329 Jason Varitek 15.00 40.00
Josh Beckett
David Ortiz
Nick Markakis
Cal Ripken Jr.
Brian Roberts/200
330 Tim Lincecum 10.00 25.00
Noah Lowry
Barry Zito
Josh Hamilton
Ian Kinsler
Hank Blalock/200
331 Brian Roberts 8.00 20.00
Yogi Berra
Adam Jones
Nick Markakis
Billy Wagner
Carlos Delgado/200
332 Joba Chamberlain 5.00 12.00
Robinson Cano
Chien-Ming Wang
Jon Lester
Daisuke Matsuzaka
Manny Ramirez/200
333 Ozzie Smith
Albert Pujols
Derek Jeter
Joba Chamberlain
Cal Ripken Jr.
Brian Roberts/25
334 Ted Williams
Carl Yastrzemski
Reggie Jackson
Joe DiMaggio
Yogi Berra
Daisuke Matsuzaka/25
335 Andy Pettitte 8.00 20.00
Derek Jeter
Chien-Ming Wang
Ian Kinsler
Josh Hamilton
Michael Young/200
336 Derrek Lee
Ryne Sandberg
Kosuke Fukudome
Carlos Zambrano
Aramis Ramirez
Kerry Wood/200
337 Jon Lester 6.00 15.00
David Ortiz
Josh Beckett
Jason Varitek
Mike Lowell
Manny Ramirez/300
338 Albert Pujols 40.00 80.00
Ozzie Smith
Ryan Ludwick
Manny Ramirez
Mike Lowell
Kevin Youkilis/200
339 Juan Pierre 4.00 10.00
Chad Billingsley
Hiroki Kuroda
Russell Martin
Matt Kemp
Andruw Jones/200
340 Hank Blalock 6.00 15.00
Josh Fields
Ryan Braun
Ryan Zimmerman
Kevin Youkilis
Melvin Mora/160
341 Ted Williams 30.00 60.00
Ken Griffey Jr.
Reggie Jackson
Jim Thome
Josh Hamilton
Justin Morneau/40
342 Francisco Liriano
Todd Helton
Reggie Jackson
Randy Johnson
Billy Wagner
Ted Williams/40
343 Josh Beckett 6.00 15.00
Roy Halladay
Chien-Ming Wang
Jon Lester
Chris Carpenter
James Shields/200
344 Carl Crawford 5.00 12.00
Curtis Granderson
Mike Cameron
Chris B. Young
Delmon Young
Nate McLouth/215
345 Jason Bay 4.00 10.00
Aaron Rowand
Delmon Young
Manny Ramirez
Andruw Jones
Mike Cameron/200
346 Hanley Ramirez 20.00 50.00
Omar Vizquel
Jimmy Rollins
Derek Jeter
Jose Reyes
Cal Ripken Jr./160
347 Yogi Berra 10.00 25.00
Jason Varitek
Brian McCann
Kenji Johjima
Jorge Posada
Russell Martin/160
348 Ryan Ludwick 8.00 20.00
Carlos Lee
Miguel Cabrera
Chris B. Young
Prince Fielder
Ryan Braun/200
349 Ryne Sandberg
Mike Schmidt
Johnny Bench
Joe DiMaggio
Ted Williams
Cal Ripken Jr./25
350 Matt Holliday 4.00 10.00
Nate McLouth
Hunter Pence
Alfonso Soriano
Curtis Granderson
Chris B. Young/300
351 Evan Longoria
Vladimir Guerrero
Josh Hamilton
Cole Hamels
Albert Pujols
Dustin Pedroia
Tim Lincecum
Chien-Ming Wang/25
352 Randy Johnson 40.00 80.00
Reggie Jackson
Gary Sheffield
Ted Williams
Carl Yastrzemski
Jason Varitek
Manny Ramirez
Alfonso Soriano/50
353 Jeremy Hermida 15.00 40.00
Hanley Ramirez
Cole Hamels
Brett Myers
Jose Reyes
John Maine
Jeff Francoeur
Brian McCann/200
354 Victor Martinez 6.00 15.00
Jermaine Dye
Grady Sizemore
Nick Swisher
Michael Cuddyer
Joe Mauer
Justin Verlander
Miguel Cabrera/300
355 Ryan Braun 8.00 20.00
Carl Crawford
Delmon Young
David Murphy
Carlos Lee
Juan Pierre
Johnny Damon
Jeff Francoeur/300
356 Troy Glaus 6.00 15.00
Albert Pujols
Carlos Lee
Roy Oswalt
Derrek Lee
Carlos Zambrano
Bill Hall
Prince Fielder/300
357 Bill Hall 4.00 10.00
Hanley Ramirez
Ian Kinsler
Yunel Escobar
Carlos Delgado
Melvin Mora
David Ortiz
Travis Hafner/300
358 Jonathan Albaladejo 4.00 10.00
Andy Pettitte
Josh Beckett
Mike Lowell
Nick Markakis
Adam Jones
Roy Halladay
Jesse Litsch/200
359 Reggie Jackson
Johan Santana
Yogi Berra
Josh Beckett
Mark Teixeira
Ozzie Smith
Josh Hamilton
Nolan Ryan/25
360 Nolan Ryan
Vladimir Guerrero
Ozzie Smith
Randy Johnson
Derek Jeter
Cal Ripken Jr.
Reggie Jackson
Roy Halladay/25
361 Kenji Johjima 40.00 80.00
Ichiro
Takashi Saito
Daisuke Matsuzaka
Hideki Matsui
Chien-Ming Wang
Akinori Iwamura
Hiroki Kuroda/75
362 Jim Thome
Albert Pujols
Vladimir Guerrero
Mark Teixeira
Miguel Cabrera
Derek Jeter
Ken Griffey Jr.
Chipper Jones/25
363 Rich Hill 4.00 10.00
Josh Beckett
J.D. Drew
Kerry Wood
Josh Willingham
Huston Street
Miguel Tejada
Andy LaRoche/300
364 Huston Street 4.00 10.00
B.J. Upton
Curtis Granderson
Kerry Wood
Joba Chamberlain
Jonathan Papelbon
Nick Swisher
Matt Holliday/300
365 Jeff Francoeur 4.00 10.00
Nick Markakis
Adam Jones
Curtis Granderson
Chris B. Young
Juan Rivera
Nyjer Morgan
David Murphy/250
366 Joe Mauer 12.50 30.00
Justin Morneau
James Shields
Josh Beckett
Kevin Youkilis
Kerry Wood
Zack Greinke
Tim Lincecum/175
367 Jonathan Papelbon
Jose Reyes
Brian McCann
Carl Crawford
Conor Jackson
Justin Morneau
Chase Utley
Michael Young/25
368 Troy Tulowitzki 12.50 30.00
Matt Kemp
Chad Billingsley
Scott Kazmir
Evan Longoria
Matt Holliday
Adam Jones
Nick Markakis/75
369 Jose Reyes 10.00 25.00
Carlos Beltran
Jacoby Ellsbury
Dustin Pedroia
B.J. Upton
Carl Crawford
Jimmy Rollins
Chase Utley/75
370 Josh Hamilton 4.00 10.00
David Murphy
Troy Tulowitzki
Prince Fielder
Jonathan Papelbon
Jhonny Peralta
Mike Pelfrey
Kelly Johnson/200
371 Yunel Escobar 4.00 10.00
Adam Jones
Nick Markakis
Fausto Carmona
Bill Hall
Troy Tulowitzki
Chad Billingsley
David Murphy/350
372 Freddy Sanchez 8.00 20.00
Prince Fielder
Jeremy Hermida
Justin Verlander
James Shields
Jered Weaver
Kevin Youkilis
Jon Lester/150
373 Mariano Rivera 20.00 50.00
Jorge Posada
Andy Pettitte
Derek Jeter
Joba Chamberlain
Chien-Ming Wang
Robinson Cano
Reggie Jackson/200
374 A.J. Burnett 4.00 10.00
Josh Beckett
Mike Lowell
Josh Willingham
Hanley Ramirez
Dan Uggla
Jeremy Hermida
Josh Johnson/350
375 John Lackey 5.00 12.00
Jered Weaver
Howie Kendrick
Juan Rivera
David Murphy
Ian Kinsler
Michael Young
Hank Blalock/250
376 Huston Street 5.00 12.00
Miguel Tejada
Dan Haren
Rich Harden
Tim Hudson
Travis Buck
Eric Chavez
Barry Zito/250
377 Billy Wagner 15.00 40.00
Pat Burrell
Cole Hamels
Chase Utley
Brett Myers
Mike Schmidt
Kevin Millwood
Jim Thome/100
378 Manny Ramirez 6.00 15.00
Mike Lowell
David Ortiz
Jason Varitek
Jon Lester
Josh Beckett
Kevin Youkilis
Jonathan Papelbon/300
379 Russell Martin 6.00 15.00
Matt Kemp
Chad Billingsley
Hiroki Kuroda
Juan Rivera
Howie Kendrick
Jered Weaver
John Lackey/200
380 Mariano Rivera
Yogi Berra
Andy Pettitte
Derek Jeter
Reggie Jackson
Robinson Cano
Joba Chamberlain
Jorge Posada/50
381 Kevin Youkilis
David Ortiz
Chase Utley
Cole Hamels
Justin Morneau
Joe Mauer
Lance Berkman
Roy Oswalt/50
382 Manny Ramirez 30.00 60.00
Jason Varitek
Josh Beckett
Carl Yastrzemski
Ted Williams
Kevin Youkilis
Jonathan Papelbon
Dustin Pedroia/50
383 J.D. Drew 8.00 20.00
Chipper Jones
Tom Glavine
Tim Hudson
Kelly Johnson
Brian McCann
Jeff Francoeur
Yunel Escobar/275
384 Ivan Rodriguez 10.00 25.00
Carlos Guillen
Justin Verlander
Miguel Cabrera
Curtis Granderson
Magglio Ordonez
Joel Zumaya
Jeremy Bonderman/125
385 Alfonso Soriano 30.00 60.00
Michael Young
Josh Hamilton
Ian Kinsler
David Murphy
Jarrod Saltalamacchia
Nolan Ryan
Chris Young/50
386 Joba Chamberlain
Chien-Ming Wang
Reggie Jackson
Derek Jeter
Yogi Berra
Joe DiMaggio
Mariano Rivera
Jorge Posada/25
387 Yunel Escobar 6.00 15.00
Chipper Jones
Nick Markakis
Adam Jones
Ryan Braun
Prince Fielder
Miguel Cabrera
Justin Verlander/300
388 Justin Verlander 6.00 15.00
Scott Kazmir
Chad Billingsley
Matt Kemp
Lance Berkman
Justin Morneau
Eric Chavez
Phil Hughes/300
389 Jake Peavy 5.00 12.00
Fausto Carmona
Tim Hudson
John Maine
Roy Halladay
Josh Beckett
Scott Kazmir
Justin Verlander/175
390 Conor Jackson 8.00 20.00
Prince Fielder
Aramis Ramirez
Vladimir Guerrero
Joe Mauer
Michael Young
Manny Ramirez
Nick Markakis/200
391 Cal Ripken Jr.
Frank Robinson
Ted Williams
Carl Yastrzemski
Ken Griffey Jr.
Joe DiMaggio
Derek Jeter
Johnny Bench/25
392 Bronson Arroyo 6.00 15.00
Chad Billingsley
Jered Weaver
Justin Verlander
Fausto Carmona
Tim Lincecum
Roy Halladay
Josh Beckett/300
393 Josh Beckett
Johan Santana
Cal Ripken Jr.
Ken Griffey Jr.
Reggie Jackson
Ozzie Smith
Mark Teixeira
Evan Longoria/75
394 Carl Crawford 4.00 10.00
Bobby Abreu
Miguel Cabrera
Magglio Ordonez
Curtis Granderson
Johnny Damon
Grady Sizemore
Nick Markakis/200
395 Jake Peavy 4.00 10.00
Mariano Rivera
Kevin Youkilis
Trevor Hoffman
Alfonso Soriano
Manny Ramirez
Todd Helton
Matt Holliday/300
396 Manny Ramirez
Lance Berkman
Miguel Tejada
Justin Morneau
Prince Fielder
Vladimir Guerrero
Tim Lincecum
Tim Hudson/100
397 Billy Wagner
Josh Beckett
Chien-Ming Wang
Jonathan Papelbon
Mariano Rivera
Brandon Webb
Joe Nathan
Chad Billingsley/100
398 Troy Tulowitzki 10.00 25.00

Freddy Sanchez
Hanley Ramirez
Prince Fielder
Bill Hall
Aramis Ramirez
Derrek Lee
Yunel Escobar/200
399 David Ortiz 6.00 15.00
Prince Fielder
Magglio Ordonez
Vladimir Guerrero
Lance Berkman
Manny Ramirez
Troy Glaus
Jim Thome/200
400 Jim Thome
Ozzie Smith
Albert Pujols
Cal Ripken Jr.
Chipper Jones
Ken Griffey Jr.
Derek Jeter
Hideki Matsui/25

2009 Upper Deck Ballpark Collection Jersey Autographs

OVERALL AUTO ODDS .5:1 HOBBY
AA Aaron Rowand 4.00 10.00
AE Andre Ethier 8.00 20.00
AL Andy LaRoche 3.00 8.00
AP Albert Pujols
AR Aramis Ramirez 5.00 12.00
BE Josh Beckett
BI Chad Billingsley 6.00 15.00
BM Brian McCann 8.00 20.00
BR Brian Roberts 12.50 30.00
BW Brandon Webb 15.00 40.00
CF Chone Figgins 5.00 12.00
CH Cole Hamels 20.00 50.00
CJ Chipper Jones 75.00 150.00
CL Carlos Lee 5.00 12.00
CR Cal Ripken Jr.
DJ Derek Jeter 90.00 150.00
DL Derrek Lee
DM David Murphy 3.00 8.00
DP Dustin Pedroia 20.00 50.00
DS Denard Span 8.00 20.00
DU Dan Uggla 4.00 10.00
EC Eric Chavez 8.00 20.00
FC Fausto Carmona 3.00 8.00
FH Felix Hernandez
GA Garrett Atkins 3.00 8.00
GR Khalil Greene
GS Grady Sizemore
HA Corey Hart 4.00 10.00
HR Hanley Ramirez 8.00 20.00
JA Jonathan Albaladejo 3.00 8.00
JB Jason Bay 10.00 25.00
JF Jeff Francoeur 10.00 25.00
JH Jeremy Hermida 3.00 8.00
JL Jon Lester 30.00 60.00
JM Joe Mauer 50.00 100.00
JN Joe Nathan 5.00 12.00
JO Josh Hamilton 12.50 30.00
JP Jonathan Papelbon 10.00 25.00
JS Jarrod Saltalamacchia 3.00 8.00
JW Josh Willingham 3.00 8.00
JZ Joel Zumaya 3.00 8.00
KG Ken Griffey Jr. 30.00 60.00
KJ Kelly Johnson 3.00 8.00
KY Kevin Youkilis 10.00 25.00
LB Lance Berkman
LE Cliff Lee 10.00 25.00
LI Adam Lind 5.00 12.00
MA John Maine 4.00 10.00
MD Daisuke Matsuzaka 60.00 120.00
MG Matt Garza 4.00 10.00
MH Matt Holliday 8.00 20.00
MK Matt Kemp 12.50 30.00
MO Justin Morneau
MS Mike Schmidt
MT Miguel Tejada 3.00 8.00
NM Nick Markakis 12.50 30.00
NS Nick Swisher 4.00 10.00
NY Nyjer Morgan 3.00 8.00
PF Prince Fielder 12.50 30.00
PK Paul Konerko 4.00 10.00
RB Ryan Braun 20.00 50.00
RH Roy Halladay
RM Russell Martin 8.00 20.00
RO Ross Ohlendorf 3.00 8.00
RS Ryne Sandberg 75.00 150.00
RW Rickie Weeks 5.00 12.00
RZ Ryan Zimmerman
SH James Shields 4.00 10.00
SK Scott Kazmir 6.00 15.00
TH Travis Hafner 4.00 10.00
TT Troy Tulowitzki 10.00 25.00
VM Victor Martinez 6.00 15.00
ZG Zack Greinke 10.00 25.00

1999 Upper Deck Century Legends

This set was released in June, 1999 and was distributed in five card packs with an SRP of $4.99 per pack. The packs came 24 to a box. The first 47 card of the set feature an assortment of players honored from the Sporting News of 100 Greatest Players. The next 50 cards feature Upper Deck's choices of the best active players. The final cards are utilized for the following subsets: 21 CP (Cards numbered 101 through 120) and Memorablue Shots (Cards numbered 122 through 135.) Cards 11, 25, 26 and 126 do not exist. Due to contractual problems, Upper Deck had to pull the player's originally intended to be featured on these cards. Thus, though the set is numbered 1-135, it is complete at only 131 cards. A game-used bat from legendary slugger Jimmie Foxx was cut into approximately 350 pieces, incorporated into special A Piece of History 500 Club cards and randomly seeded into packs. Pricing for these scarce Foxx bat cards can be referenced under 1999 Upper Deck A Piece of History 500 Club. A Babe Ruth sample card was distributed to dealers and media several weeks prior to the product's national release. The card parallels Ruth's regular issue card except for the word "SAMPLE" running in red text diagonally across the card back.

COMPLETE SET (131) 25.00 50.00
1 Babe Ruth 1.00 2.50
2 Willie Mays .60 1.50
3 Ty Cobb .50 1.25
4 Walter Johnson .30 .75
5 Hank Aaron .60 1.50
6 Lou Gehrig .60 1.50
7 Christy Mathewson .30 .75
8 Ted Williams .60 1.50
9 Rogers Hornsby .30 .75
10 Stan Musial .50 1.25
12 Grover Alexander .30 .75
13 Honus Wagner .30 .75
14 Cy Young .30 .75
15 Jimmie Foxx .30 .75
16 Johnny Bench .30 .75
17 Mickey Mantle 1.25 3.00
18 Josh Gibson .30 .75
19 Satchel Paige .30 .75
20 Roberto Clemente .60 1.50
21 Warren Spahn .20 .50
22 Frank Robinson .20 .50
23 Lefty Grove .30 .75
24 Eddie Collins .20 .50
27 Tris Speaker .30 .75
28 Mike Schmidt .60 1.50
29 Napoleon Lajoie .30 .75
30 Steve Carlton .15 .40
31 Bob Gibson .20 .50
32 Tom Seaver .20 .50
33 George Sisler .15 .40
34 Barry Bonds .75 2.00
35 Joe Jackson NNO UER .40 1.00
36 Bob Feller .15 .40
37 Hank Greenberg .30 .75
38 Ernie Banks .30 .75
39 Greg Maddux .50 1.25
40 Yogi Berra .30 .75
41 Nolan Ryan .75 2.00
42 Mel Ott .30 .75
43 Al Simmons .15 .40
44 Jackie Robinson .30 .75
45 Carl Hubbell .20 .50
46 Charley Gehringer .15 .40
47 Buck Leonard .15 .40
48 Reggie Jackson .20 .50
49 Tony Gwynn .40 1.00
50 Roy Campanella .30 .75
51 Ken Griffey Jr. .50 1.25
52 Barry Bonds .75 2.00
53 Roger Clemens .60 1.50
54 Tony Gwynn .40 1.00
55 Cal Ripken 1.00 2.50
56 Greg Maddux .50 1.25
57 Frank Thomas .30 .75
58 Mark McGwire .75 2.00
59 Mike Piazza .50 1.25
60 Wade Boggs .20 .50
61 Alex Rodriguez .50 1.25
62 Juan Gonzalez .15 .40
63 Mo Vaughn .15 .40
64 Albert Belle .15 .40
65 Sammy Sosa .30 .75
66 Nomar Garciaparra .50 1.25
67 Derek Jeter .75 2.00
68 Kevin Brown .20 .50
69 Jose Canseco .20 .50
70 Randy Johnson .30 .75
71 Tom Glavine .20 .50
72 Barry Larkin .20 .50
73 Curt Schilling .15 .40
74 Moises Alou .15 .40
75 Fred McGriff .20 .50
76 Pedro Martinez .20 .50
77 Andres Galarraga .15 .40
78 Will Clark .20 .50
79 Larry Walker .15 .40
80 Ivan Rodriguez .20 .50
81 Chipper Jones .30 .75
82 Jeff Bagwell .20 .50
83 Craig Biggio .20 .50
84 Kerry Wood .15 .40
85 Roberto Alomar .20 .50
86 Vinny Castilla .15 .40
87 Kenny Lofton .15 .40
88 Rafael Palmeiro .20 .50
89 Manny Ramirez .20 .50
90 David Wells .15 .40
91 Mark Grace .20 .50
92 Bernie Williams .20 .50
93 David Cone .15 .40
94 John Olerud .15 .40
95 John Smoltz .20 .50
96 Tino Martinez .20 .50
97 Raul Mondesi .15 .40
98 Gary Sheffield .15 .40
99 Orel Hershiser .15 .40
100 Rickey Henderson .30 .75
101 J.D. Drew 21CP .15 .40
102 Troy Glaus 21CP .20 .50
103 N.Garciaparra 21CP .50 1.25
104 Scott Rolen 21CP .15 .40
105 Ryan Minor 21CP .10 .30
106 Travis Lee 21CP .10 .30
107 Roy Halladay 21CP .40 1.00
108 Carlos Beltran 21CP .20 .50
109 Alex Rodriguez 21CP .50 1.25
110 Eric Chavez 21CP .15 .40
111 V.Guerrero 21CP .30 .75
112 Ben Grieve 21CP .10 .30
113 Kerry Wood 21CP .15 .40
114 Alex Gonzalez 21CP .10 .30
115 Darin Erstad 21CP .15 .40
116 Derek Jeter 21CP .75 2.00
117 Jaret Wright 21CP .10 .30
118 Jose Cruz Jr. 21CP .10 .30
119 Chipper Jones 21CP .30 .75
120 Gabe Kapler 21CP .15 .40
121 Satchel Paige MEM .30 .75
122 Willie Mays MEM .60 1.50
123 R.Clemente MEM .60 1.50
124 Lou Gehrig MEM .60 1.50
125 Mark McGwire MEM .75 2.00
127 Bob Gibson MEM .20 .50
128 J.VanderMeer MEM .10 .30
129 Walter Johnson MEM .30 .75
130 Ty Cobb MEM .50 1.25
131 Don Larsen MEM .15 .40
132 Jackie Robinson MEM .30 .75
133 Tom Seaver MEM .15 .40
134 Johnny Bench MEM .20 .50
135 Frank Robinson MEM .20 .50
S1 Babe Ruth Sample .75 2.00

1999 Upper Deck Century Legends Century Collection

Randomly inserted into hobby packs only, this 131-card set is a die-cut parallel version of the base set and is sequentially numbered to 100. Cards 11, 25, 26, and 126 do not exist.

*ACTIVE STARS: 8X TO 20X BASIC
*POST-WAR STARS: 12.5X TO 30X BASIC
*PRE-WAR STARS: 6X TO 15X BASIC
*21ST CENT: 8X TO 20X BASIC

1999 Upper Deck Century Legends All-Century Team

Randomly inserted in packs at the rate of one in 23, this 10-card set features photos of Upper Deck's All-Time All-Star Team.

COMPLETE SET (10) 30.00 60.00
STATED ODDS 1:23
AC1 Babe Ruth 5.00 12.00
AC2 Ty Cobb 2.50 6.00
AC3 Willie Mays 3.00 8.00
AC4 Lou Gehrig 3.00 8.00
AC5 Jackie Robinson 1.50 4.00
AC6 Mike Schmidt 3.00 8.00
AC7 Ernie Banks 1.50 4.00
AC8 Johnny Bench 1.50 4.00
AC9 Cy Young 1.50 4.00
AC10 Lineup Sheet .60 1.50

1999 Upper Deck Century Legends Artifacts

Randomly inserted in packs, this nine-card set features redemption cards for memorabilia from some of the top players of the century. Only one of each card was produced. No pricing is available due to the scarcity of these cards.

1900 Ty Cobb Framed Cut
1910 Babe Ruth Framed Cut
1920 Rogers Hornsby Framed Cut
1930 Satchel Paige Framed Cut
1950 Hank Aaron
Willie Mays
Mickey Mantle AU Balls
1960 Ernie Banks
Bob Gibson
Johnny Bench AU Balls
1970 Tom Seaver
Mike Schmidt
Steve Carlton AU Balls
1980 Nolan Ryan
Ken Griffey Jr. AU Balls
1990 Ken Griffey Jr. AU Jersey

1999 Upper Deck Century Legends Epic Milestones

Randomly inserted into packs at the rate of one in 12, this nine-card set features color photos of players with the most impressive milestones in MLB history. Card EM1 does not exist.

COMPLETE SET (9) 20.00 40.00
STATED ODDS 1:12
EM2 Jackie Robinson 1.00 2.50
EM3 Nolan Ryan 2.50 6.00
EM4 Mark McGwire 2.50 6.00
EM5 Roger Clemens 2.00 5.00
EM6 Sammy Sosa 1.00 2.50
EM7 Cal Ripken 3.00 8.00
EM8 Rickey Henderson 1.00 2.50
EM9 Hank Aaron 2.00 5.00
EM10 Barry Bonds 2.50 6.00

1999 Upper Deck Century Legends Epic Signatures

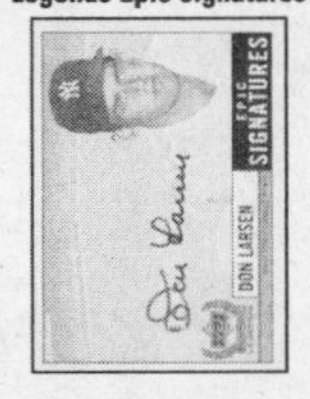

Randomly inserted into packs at the rate of one in 24, this 30-card set features autographed photos of retired stars and current players. Stickered exchange cards for Johnny Bench, Yogi Berra, Carlton Fisk and Willie McCovey were seeded into packs. The deadline to exchange those cards was December 31, 1999.

STATED ODDS 1:24
AR Alex Rodriguez 100.00 200.00
BB Barry Bonds 200.00 300.00
BD Bucky Dent 6.00 15.00
BF Bob Feller 10.00 25.00
BG Bob Gibson 12.50 30.00
BM Bill Mazeroski 20.00 50.00
BT Bobby Thomson 6.00 15.00
CF Carlton Fisk 10.00 25.00
CFX Carlton Fisk EXCH 2.00 5.00
DL Don Larsen 10.00 25.00
EB Ernie Banks 30.00 60.00
EMA Eddie Mathews 20.00 50.00
FR Frank Robinson 12.50 30.00
FT Frank Thomas 60.00 120.00
GM Greg Maddux 100.00 200.00
HK Harmon Killebrew 15.00 40.00
JB Johnny Bench 30.00 60.00
JBX Johnny Bench EXCH 4.00 10.00
JG Juan Gonzalez 20.00 50.00
JR Ken Griffey Jr. 75.00 150.00
MS Mike Schmidt 30.00 60.00
NR Nolan Ryan 175.00 350.00
RJ Reggie Jackson 50.00 100.00
SC Steve Carlton 10.00 25.00
SM Stan Musial 50.00 100.00
SR Ken Griffey Sr. 10.00 25.00
TG Tony Gwynn 30.00 60.00
TS Tom Seaver 50.00 100.00
VG Vladimir Guerrero 10.00 25.00
WMC Willie McCovey 15.00 40.00
WMCX W.McCovey EXCH 2.00 5.00
WS Warren Spahn 30.00 60.00
YB Yogi Berra 30.00 60.00
YBX Yogi Berra EXCH 4.00 10.00

1999 Upper Deck Century Legends Epic Signatures Century

Randomly inserted in packs, this 32-card set features autographed color photos of past and present players with gold-foil stamping. Each card is hand-numbered to 100.

RANDOM INSERTS IN PACKS
AR Alex Rodriguez 200.00 400.00
BB Barry Bonds 250.00 400.00
BD Bucky Dent 20.00 50.00
BF Bob Feller 20.00 50.00
BG Bob Gibson 30.00 60.00
BM Bill Mazeroski 40.00 80.00
BT Bobby Thomson 20.00 50.00
CF Carlton Fisk 20.00 50.00
CFX Carlton Fisk EXCH
DL Don Larsen 20.00 50.00
EB Ernie Banks 75.00 150.00
EMA Eddie Mathews 90.00 150.00
FR Frank Robinson 30.00 60.00
FT Frank Thomas 75.00 150.00
GM Greg Maddux 175.00 300.00
HK Harmon Killebrew 40.00 80.00
JB Johnny Bench 60.00 120.00
JBX Johnny Bench EXCH
JG Juan Gonzalez 20.00 50.00
JR Ken Griffey Jr. 150.00 250.00
MS Mike Schmidt 125.00 200.00
NR Nolan Ryan 300.00 500.00
RJ Reggie Jackson 100.00 200.00
SC Steve Carlton 20.00 50.00
SM Stan Musial 125.00 200.00
SR Ken Griffey Sr. 20.00 50.00
TG Tony Gwynn 60.00 120.00
TS Tom Seaver 75.00 150.00
TW Ted Williams 1200.00 1800.00
VG Vladimir Guerrero 20.00 50.00
WM Willie Mays 600.00 800.00
WMC Willie McCovey 40.00 80.00
WMCX W.McCovey EXCH
WS Warren Spahn 75.00 150.00
YB Yogi Berra 60.00 120.00
YBX Yogi Berra EXCH

1999 Upper Deck Century Legends Jerseys of the Century

Randomly inserted in packs at the rate of one in 418, this nine-card set features color photos of top current and retired players with pieces of their actual game-worn jerseys embedded in the cards.

STATED ODDS 1:418
DW Dave Winfield 6.00 15.00
EM Eddie Murray 6.00 15.00
GB George Brett 15.00 40.00
GM Greg Maddux 10.00 25.00
MS Mike Schmidt 15.00 40.00
NR Nolan Ryan 50.00 100.00
OZ Ozzie Smith 10.00 25.00
RC Roger Clemens 15.00 40.00
TG Tony Gwynn 12.50 30.00

1999 Upper Deck Century Legends Legendary Cuts

Randomly inserted into packs, this nine-card set features actual signature cuts from some of baseball's greatest players. Only one of each of these cards was produced.

RANDOM INSERTS IN PACKS
BR Babe Ruth
CY Cy Young
LG Lefty Grove
MO Mel Ott
RC Roy Campanella
SP Satchel Paige
TY Ty Cobb
WJ Walter Johnson
XX Jimmie Foxx

1999 Upper Deck Century Legends Memorable Shots

Randomly inserted into packs at the rate of one in 12, this 10-card set features photos of the most memorable home runs launched during this century.

COMPLETE SET (10) 15.00 30.00
STATED ODDS 1:12
HR1 Babe Ruth 4.00 10.00
HR2 Bobby Thomson .40 1.00
HR3 Kirk Gibson .40 1.00
HR4 Carlton Fisk .40 1.00
HR5 Bill Mazeroski .40 1.00
HR6 Bucky Dent .40 1.00
HR7 Mark McGwire 2.00 5.00
HR8 Mickey Mantle 4.00 10.00
HR9 Joe Carter .40 1.00
HR10 Mark McGwire 2.00 5.00

1999 Upper Deck Century Legends MVPs

Randomly inserted in packs, this 100-card set features color action photos of Upper Deck's 1999 MVP players printed with rainbow-foil. Only one of each card was produced. Pricing for stars is unavailable due to scarcity. A checklist has been provided for cataloging purposes.

RANDOM INSERTS IN PACKS

2008 Upper Deck Documentary

This set was released on December 16, 2008. The base set consists of 4,890 cards.

COMMON CARD (1-4954) .20 .50
SEMISTARS .30 .75
UNLISTED STARS .50 1.25
ALL PLAYER VARIATIONS PRICED SAME
4891-4954 ISSUED IN 2009 UD1
4891-4954 ODDS 1:4 H,1:10 R,1:72 BLAST
1 Vladimir Guerrero .50 1.25
2 Garret Anderson .20 .50
3 Torii Hunter .20 .50
4 Howie Kendrick .20 .50
5 Jered Weaver .20 .50
6 John Lackey .20 .50
7 Chone Figgins .20 .50
8 Jon Garland .20 .50
9 Francisco Rodriguez .30 .75
10 Casey Kotchman .20 .50
11 Justin Upton .30 .75
12 Brandon Webb .30 .75
13 Chris B. Young .20 .50
14 Stephen Drew .20 .50
15 Chris B. Young .20 .50
16 Mark Reynolds .20 .50
17 Orlando Hudson .20 .50
18 Brandon Webb .30 .75
19 Dan Haren .20 .50
20 Justin Upton .30 .75
21 Chipper Jones .50 1.25
22 Mark Teixeira .50 1.25
23 Tom Glavine .30 .75
24 Kelly Johnson .20 .50
25 John Smoltz .50 1.25
26 Brian McCann .30 .75
27 Chipper Jones .50 1.25
28 Tim Hudson .30 .75
29 Yunel Escobar .20 .50
30 Jeff Francoeur .30 .75
31 Adam Jones .30 .75
32 Nick Markakis .50 1.25
33 Melvin Mora .20 .50
34 Jeremy Guthrie .20 .50
35 Adam Loewen .20 .50
36 Luke Scott .20 .50
37 Adam Jones .30 .75
38 Nick Markakis .50 1.25
39 Ramon Hernandez .20 .50
40 Nick Markakis .50 1.25
41 Manny Ramirez .50 1.25
42 Kevin Youkilis .30 .75
43 Jacoby Ellsbury .75 2.00
44 Jonathan Papelbon .30 .75
45 Jason Varitek .50 1.25
46 Mike Lowell .20 .50
47 Daisuke Matsuzaka .50 1.25
48 Josh Beckett .30 .75
49 David Ortiz .30 .75
50 Tim Wakefield .20 .50
51 Alfonso Soriano .30 .75
52 Kosuke Fukudome RC .60 1.50
53 Carlos Zambrano .30 .75
54 Derrek Lee .20 .50
55 Rich Hill .20 .50
56 Ryan Theriot .20 .50
57 Aramis Ramirez .20 .50
58 Kosuke Fukudome RC .60 1.50
59 Kerry Wood .20 .50
60 Felix Pie .20 .50
61 Paul Konerko .30 .75
62 Jim Thome .30 .75
63 Nick Swisher .50 1.25
64 Mark Buehrle .30 .75
65 Orlando Cabrera .20 .50
66 Jermaine Dye .20 .50
67 Alexei Ramirez RC .75 2.00
68 Jim Thome .30 .75
69 Javier Vazquez .20 .50
70 Bobby Jenks .20 .50
71 Adam Dunn .30 .75
72 Aaron Harang .20 .50
73 Ken Griffey Jr. .75 2.00
74 Brandon Phillips .20 .50
75 Francisco Cordero .20 .50
76 Ken Griffey Jr. .75 2.00
77 Edwin Encarnacion .20 .50
78 Corey Patterson .20 .50
79 Ken Griffey Jr. .75 2.00
80 Joey Votto (RC) .75 2.00
81 C.C. Sabathia .30 .75
82 Grady Sizemore .30 .75
83 Victor Martinez .30 .75
84 Travis Hafner .20 .50
85 C.C. Sabathia .30 .75
86 Fausto Carmona .20 .50
87 Grady Sizemore .30 .75
88 Jhonny Peralta .20 .50
89 Travis Hafner .20 .50
90 Franklin Gutierrez .20 .50
91 Matt Holliday .50 1.25
92 Jeff Francis .20 .50
93 Todd Helton .30 .75
94 Garrett Atkins .20 .50
95 Manny Corpas .20 .50
96 Troy Tulowitzki .50 1.25
97 Aaron Cook .20 .50
98 Willy Taveras .20 .50
99 Matt Holliday .50 1.25
100 Brad Hawpe .20 .50
101 Ivan Rodriguez .30 .75
102 Miguel Cabrera .50 1.25
103 Curtis Granderson .30 .75
104 Magglio Ordonez .30 .75
105 Justin Verlander .60 1.50
106 Kenny Rogers .20 .50
107 Dontrelle Willis .20 .50
108 Edgar Renteria .20 .50
109 Gary Sheffield .20 .50
110 Miguel Cabrera .50 1.25
111 Josh Willingham .20 .50
112 Hanley Ramirez .50 1.25
113 Dan Uggla .30 .75
114 Andrew Miller .20 .50
115 Mike Jacobs .20 .50
116 Jorge Cantu .20 .50
117 Luis Gonzalez .20 .50
118 Mark Hendrickson .20 .50
119 Dan Uggla .30 .75
120 Hanley Ramirez .50 1.25
121 Carlos Lee .20 .50
122 Roy Oswalt .30 .75
123 Lance Berkman .30 .75
124 J.R. Towles RC .30 .75
125 Hunter Pence .50 1.25
126 Miguel Tejada .30 .75
127 Michael Bourn .20 .50
128 Mark Loretta .20 .50
129 Lance Berkman .30 .75
130 Brandon Backe .20 .50
131 Gil Meche .20 .50
132 Alex Gordon .30 .75
133 Mark Teahen .20 .50
134 David DeJesus .20 .50
135 Brian Bannister .20 .50
136 Alex Gordon .30 .75
137 Billy Butler .20 .50
138 Zack Greinke .30 .75
139 Alex Gordon .30 .75
140 Jose Guillen .20 .50
141 Russell Martin .20 .50
142 Matt Kemp .30 .75
143 Chad Billingsley .20 .50
144 Rafael Furcal .20 .50
145 Andre Ethier .30 .75
146 Andruw Jones .20 .50
147 James Loney .30 .75
148 Derek Lowe .20 .50
149 Jeff Kent .20 .50
150 Takashi Saito .20 .50
151 Ryan Braun .60 1.50
152 Prince Fielder .30 .75
153 Rickie Weeks .30 .75
154 J.J. Hardy .20 .50
155 Ben Sheets .20 .50
156 Eric Gagne .20 .50
157 Prince Fielder .30 .75
158 Bill Hall .20 .50
159 Jason Kendall .20 .50
160 Ryan Braun .60 1.50
161 Justin Morneau .50 1.25
162 Joe Mauer .50 1.25
163 Joe Nathan .20 .50
164 Carlos Gomez .20 .50
165 Pat Neshek .20 .50
166 Justin Morneau .50 1.25
167 Michael Cuddyer .20 .50
168 Jason Kubel .20 .50
169 Delmon Young .30 .75

170 Joe Mauer .50 1.25
171 Johan Santana .50 1.25
172 Jose Reyes .30 .75
173 David Wright .60 1.50
174 Carlos Delgado .20 .50
175 Pedro Martinez .30 .75
176 Carlos Beltran .20 .50
177 John Maine .20 .50
178 Jose Reyes .30 .75
179 Billy Wagner .20 .50
180 David Wright .60 1.50
181 Derek Jeter 1.25 3.00
182 Chien-Ming Wang .30 .75
183 Mariano Rivera .50 1.25
184 Jorge Posada .30 .75
185 Robinson Cano .50 1.25
186 Alex Rodriguez .75 2.00
187 Ian Kennedy RC .50 1.25
188 Alex Rodriguez .75 2.00
189 Phil Hughes .50 1.25
190 Derek Jeter 1.25 3.00
191 Daric Barton .20 .50
192 Joe Blanton .20 .50
193 Mark Ellis .20 .50
194 Ryan Sweeney .20 .50
195 Rich Harden .20 .50
196 Huston Street .20 .50
197 Jack Cust .20 .50
198 Bobby Crosby .20 .50
199 Travis Buck .20 .50
200 Joe Blanton .20 .50
201 Ryan Howard .60 1.50
202 Chase Utley .50 1.25
203 Jimmy Rollins .30 .75
204 Cole Hamels .50 1.25
205 Pat Burrell .20 .50
206 Chase Utley .50 1.25
207 Brett Myers .20 .50
208 Shane Victorino .20 .50
209 Ryan Howard .60 1.50
210 Jamie Moyer .20 .50
211 Ian Snell .20 .50
212 Adam LaRoche .20 .50
213 Jack Wilson .20 .50
214 Tom Gorzelanny .20 .50
215 Freddy Sanchez .20 .50
216 Jason Bay .30 .75
217 Nate McLouth .20 .50
218 Freddy Sanchez .20 .50
219 Xavier Nady .20 .50
220 Ian Snell .20 .50
221 Jake Peavy .20 .50
222 Khalil Greene .20 .50
223 Chris Young .20 .50
224 Greg Maddux .60 1.50
225 Brian Giles .20 .50
226 Trevor Hoffman .30 .75
227 Jake Peavy .20 .50
228 Adrian Gonzalez .30 .75
229 Kevin Kouzmanoff .20 .50
230 Greg Maddux .60 1.50
231 Barry Zito .20 .50
232 Bengie Molina .20 .50
233 Matt Cain .20 .50
234 Rich Aurilia .20 .50
235 Tim Lincecum .75 2.00
236 Aaron Rowand .20 .50
237 Ray Durham .20 .50
238 Randy Winn .20 .50
239 Barry Zito .20 .50
240 Dave Roberts .20 .50
241 Ichiro Suzuki .75 2.00
242 Erik Bedard .20 .50
243 Richie Sexson .20 .50
244 Adrian Beltre .20 .50
245 Ichiro Suzuki .75 2.00
246 Felix Hernandez .50 1.25
247 Kenji Johjima .20 .50
248 Felix Hernandez .50 1.25
249 J.J. Putz .20 .50
250 Ichiro Suzuki .75 2.00
251 Troy Glaus .30 .75
252 Chris Carpenter .50 1.25
253 Albert Pujols 1.25 3.00
254 Chris Duncan .20 .50
255 Rick Ankiel .20 .50
256 Adam Kennedy .20 .50
257 Albert Pujols 1.25 3.00
258 Adam Wainwright .30 .75
259 Jason Isringhausen .20 .50
260 Albert Pujols 1.25 3.00
261 B.J. Upton .30 .75
262 Carl Crawford .30 .75
263 Carlos Pena .30 .75
264 Matt Garza .20 .50
265 James Shields .20 .50
266 Akinori Iwamura .20 .50
267 Jonny Gomes .20 .50
268 B.J. Upton .30 .75
269 Carl Crawford .30 .75
270 Scott Kazmir .30 .75
271 Michael Young .30 .75
272 Hank Blalock .20 .50
273 Ian Kinsler .30 .75
274 Michael Young .30 .75
275 Ben Broussard .20 .50
276 Josh Hamilton .50 1.25
277 Marlon Byrd .20 .50
278 David Murphy .20 .50
279 Ian Kinsler .30 .75
280 Kevin Millwood .20 .50
281 Frank Thomas .50 1.25
282 Vernon Wells .20 .50
283 Roy Halladay .50 1.25
284 A.J. Burnett .30 .75
285 David Eckstein .20 .50
286 Lyle Overbay .20 .50
287 Frank Thomas .50 1.25
288 Alex Rios .30 .75
289 Roy Halladay .50 1.25
290 Frank Thomas .50 1.25
291 Lastings Milledge .20 .50
292 Austin Kearns .20 .50
293 Odalis Perez .20 .50
294 Nick Johnson .20 .50
295 Chad Cordero .20 .50
296 Ryan Zimmerman .30 .75
297 Paul Lo Duca .20 .50
298 Ronnie Belliard .20 .50
299 Ryan Zimmerman .30 .75
300 Matt Chico .20 .50
4891 Torii Hunter .20 .50
4892 Mark Teixeira .50 1.25
4893 Francisco Rodriguez .30 .75
4894 Vladimir Guerrero .50 1.25
4895 Alfonso Soriano .30 .75
4896 Derrek Lee .20 .50
4897 Aramis Ramirez .20 .50
4898 Paul Konerko .30 .75
4899 Jermaine Dye .20 .50
4900 Ken Griffey Jr. .75 2.00
4901 Jim Thome .30 .75
4902 Ryan Braun .60 1.50
4903 CC Sabathia .30 .75
4904 J.J. Hardy .20 .50
4905 Prince Fielder .30 .75
4906 Jason Bay .30 .75
4907 J.D. Drew .20 .50
4908 Jacoby Ellsbury .75 2.00
4909 Jon Lester .50 1.25
4910 Evan Longoria 1.00 2.50
4911 Carl Crawford .30 .75
4912 B.J. Upton .30 .75
4913 Carlos Pena .30 .75
4914 James Loney .30 .75
4915 Manny Ramirez .50 1.25
4916 Russell Martin .20 .50
4917 Chase Utley .50 1.25
4918 Shane Victorino .20 .50
4919 Ryan Howard .60 1.50
4920 Pat Burrell .20 .50
4921 Daisuke Matsuzaka .50 1.25
4922 Jason Bay .30 .75
4923 Dustin Pedroia .60 1.50
4924 Kevin Youkilis .30 .75
4925 J.D. Drew .20 .50
4926 Jason Varitek .50 1.25
4927 David Ortiz .30 .75
4928 Andre Ethier .30 .75
4929 Manny Ramirez .50 1.25
4930 Nomar Garciaparra .50 1.25
4931 Rafael Furcal .20 .50
4932 Matt Kemp .30 .75
4933 James Shields .20 .50
4934 David Price .50 1.25
4935 B.J. Upton .30 .75
4936 Willy Aybar .20 .50
4937 Evan Longoria 1.00 2.50
4938 Carl Crawford .30 .75
4939 Matt Garza .20 .50
4940 Chase Utley .50 1.25
4941 Brett Myers .20 .50
4942 Ryan Howard .60 1.50
4943 Matt Stairs .20 .50
4944 Jimmy Rollins .30 .75
4945 Akinori Iwamura .20 .50
4946 B.J. Upton .30 .75
4947 Carl Crawford .30 .75
4948 Evan Longoria 1.00 2.50
4949 Rocco Baldelli .20 .50
4950 Chase Utley .50 1.25
4951 Shane Victorino .20 .50
4952 Jimmy Rollins .30 .75
4953 Ryan Howard .60 1.50
4954 Cole Hamels .50 1.25

2008 Upper Deck Documentary Gold

*GOLD: .75X TO 2X BASIC
STATED ODDS 1:1

2008 Upper Deck Documentary All Star Game

STATED ODDS 1:4
AC Aaron Cook .40 1.00
AG Adrian Gonzalez .60 1.50
AP Albert Pujols 2.00 5.00
AR Alex Rodriguez 1.25 3.00
BM Brian McCann .60 1.50
BS Ben Sheets .40 1.00
BW Billy Wagner .40 1.00
CG Carlos Guillen .40 1.00
CJ Chipper Jones .75 2.00
CL Cliff Lee .60 1.50
CQ Carlos Quentin .40 1.00
CU Chase Utley 1.00 2.50
CZ Carlos Zambrano .60 1.50
DH Dan Haren .40 1.00
DJ Derek Jeter 2.00 5.00
DN Dioner Navarro .40 1.00
DP Dustin Pedroia 1.00 2.50
DU Dan Uggla .60 1.50
DW David Wright 1.00 2.50
EL Evan Longoria 1.50 4.00
EV Edinson Volquez .40 1.00
FR Francisco Rodriguez .60 1.50
GS Grady Sizemore .60 1.50
GU Cristian Guzman .40 1.00
HR Hanley Ramirez 1.00 2.50
IK Ian Kinsler .60 1.50
IS Ichiro Suzuki 1.25 3.00
JD J.D. Drew .40 1.00
JH Josh Hamilton .75 2.00
JM Justin Morneau 1.00 2.50
JN Joe Nathan .40 1.00
JO Joe Mauer 1.00 2.50
JP Jonathan Papelbon .60 1.50
JS Joakim Soria .40 1.00
JU Justin Duchscherer .40 1.00
KF Kosuke Fukudome 1.00 2.50
KY Kevin Youkilis .60 1.50
LB Lance Berkman .60 1.50
MB Milton Bradley .40 1.00
MH Matt Holliday 1.00 2.50
MR Manny Ramirez 1.00 2.50
MT Miguel Tejada .60 1.50
MY Michael Young .60 1.50
NM Nate McLouth .40 1.00
RB Ryan Braun 1.00 2.50
RD Ryan Dempster .40 1.00
RH Roy Halladay 1.00 2.50
RI Mariano Rivera 1.00 2.50
RL Ryan Ludwick .40 1.00
RM Russell Martin .40 1.00
SH George Sherrill .40 1.00
SK Scott Kazmir .60 1.50
SO Geovany Soto 1.00 2.50
WE Brandon Webb .60 1.50
WI Brian Wilson 1.00 2.50

2008 Upper Deck Documentary Home Run Derby

STATED ODDS 1:4
HRD1 Josh Hamilton .75 2.00
HRD2 Josh Hamilton .75 2.00
HRD3 Josh Hamilton .75 2.00
HRD4 Josh Hamilton .75 2.00
HRD5 Justin Morneau 1.00 2.50

2008 Upper Deck Documentary Seasonal Signatures

STATED ODDS 1:24
AC Alexi Casilla
AL Aaron Laffey 8.00 20.00
AR Alex Romero 3.00 8.00
BA Brian Bannister
BB Brandon Boggs 4.00 10.00
BL Brent Lillibridge 3.00 8.00
BO Brian Bocock 3.00 8.00
BR Brian Bass 5.00 12.00
BW Bobby Wilson 3.00 8.00
CC Callix Crabbe 3.00 8.00
CH Corey Hart
CK Clayton Kershaw
CP Chris Perez 8.00 20.00
CR Carlos Rosa
CS Chris Smith 3.00 8.00
CT Clay Timpner 4.00 10.00
CW Cory Wade
DB Daric Barton 3.00 8.00
DJ Derek Jeter
DM David Murphy 4.00 10.00
DP David Purcey 4.00 10.00
ED Elijah Dukes
EJ Elliot Johnson 3.00 8.00
FC Fausto Carmona 4.00 10.00
FP Felipe Paulino 3.00 8.00
GD German Duran 3.00 8.00
GS Greg Smith 3.00 8.00
HG Harvey Garcia 3.00 8.00
HI Hernan Iribarren 3.00 8.00
JB Jerry Blevins 3.00 8.00
JK Joe Koshansky 3.00 8.00
JN Jayson Nix
KG Ken Griffey Jr.
KK Kevin Kouzmanoff
KM Kyle McClellan 8.00 20.00
LB Lance Broadway 3.00 8.00
LC Luke Carlin 3.00 8.00
LI Adam Lind 4.00 10.00
LS Luke Scott
MH Micah Hoffpauir 10.00 25.00
MJ Matt Joyce 8.00 20.00
ML Matt Lindstrom
MO Micah Owings
MT Matt Tolbert 3.00 8.00
NB Nick Blackburn
NM Nyjer Morgan 4.00 10.00
NS Nick Swisher
OH Ross Ohlendorf 4.00 10.00
RB Randor Bierd 3.00 8.00
RC Ryan Church 8.00 20.00
RD Robinzon Diaz 3.00 8.00
RO Alex Romero 3.00 8.00
RT Ramon Troncoso 3.00 8.00
RW Rico Washington
SH Steve Holm 3.00 8.00
SP Steve Pearce 4.00 10.00
TS Takashi Saito
TU Matt Tupman 10.00 25.00
UJ Ubaldo Jimenez
WW Wesley Wright 3.00 8.00

2007 Upper Deck Elements

This 252-card set was released in August, 2007. The set was issued in three-card packs which came five packs per mini-box, three mini-boxes per full box and 16 full boxes in a case. The first 125 cards in this set featured veteran players who were only available in these packs: Cards 1-42 were available in packs featuring Ken Griffey Jr., cards 43-84 were in packs featuring Cal Ripken Jr., and cards 85-126 were in packs featuring Derek Jeter. Rookie Cards (Cards numbered 127-252) were also in specific packs. Cards numbered 127-168 were in Ken Griffey Jr packs while cards numbered 169-210 were in Cal Ripken Jr packs and cards numbered 211-252 were in Derek Jeter packs. These rookie cards were all issued to a stated print run of 550 serial numbered sets. A Gift Exchange card was seeded into packs at a stated rate of one per case.

COMMON CARD .30 .75
CARDS 1-42 FOUND IN GRIFFEY PACKS
CARDS 43-84 FOUND IN RIPKEN PACKS
CARDS 85-126 FOUND IN JETER PACKS
ALL VETERAN VERSIONS EQUAL VALUE
COMMON RC (127-168) .75 2.00
RC 127-168 FOUND IN GRIFFEY PACKS
RC 169-210 FOUND IN RIPKEN PACKS
COMMON RC (211-252) .75 2.00
RC 211-252 FOUND IN JETER PACKS
ROOKIE PRINT RUN 550 SER.#'d SETS
PRINTING PLATES RANDOMLY INSERTED
PLATE PRINT RUN 1 SET PER COLOR
BLACK-CYAN-MAGENTA-YELLOW ISSUED
NO PLATE PRICING DUE TO SCARCITY
GIFT EXCH ODDS 1 PER CASE
GIFT EXCH DEADLINE 9/30/2007
1 Stephen Drew .30 .75
2 Andruw Jones .30 .75
3 Chipper Jones .75 2.00
4 Miguel Tejada .50 1.25
5 David Ortiz .50 1.25
6 Manny Ramirez .75 2.00
7 Derrek Lee .30 .75
8 Alfonso Soriano .50 1.25
9 Jermaine Dye .30 .75
10 Jim Thome .50 1.25
11 Ken Griffey Jr. 1.25 3.00
12 Adam Dunn .50 1.25
13 Travis Hafner .30 .75
14 Grady Sizemore .50 1.25
15 Todd Helton .50 1.25
16 Gary Sheffield .30 .75
17 Miguel Cabrera .75 2.00
18 Lance Berkman .50 1.25
19 Mark Teahen .30 .75
20 Vladimir Guerrero .75 2.00
21 Jered Weaver .50 1.25
22 Rafael Furcal .30 .75
23 Prince Fielder .50 1.25
24 Justin Morneau .75 2.00
25 Johan Santana .75 2.00
26 David Wright 1.25 3.00
27 Jose Reyes .50 1.25
28 Derek Jeter 2.00 5.00
29 Alex Rodriguez 1.25 3.00
30 Nick Swisher .75 2.00
31 Ryan Howard 1.25 3.00
32 Jason Bay .50 1.25
33 Adrian Gonzalez .50 1.25
34 Ray Durham .30 .75
35 Ichiro Suzuki 1.25 3.00
36 Albert Pujols 2.00 5.00
37 Scott Rolen .50 1.25
38 Carl Crawford .50 1.25
39 Mark Teixeira .75 2.00
40 Michael Young .50 1.25
41 Vernon Wells .30 .75
42 Ryan Zimmerman .50 1.25
43 Stephen Drew .30 .75
44 Andruw Jones .30 .75
45 Chipper Jones .75 2.00
46 Miguel Tejada .50 1.25
47 David Ortiz .50 1.25
48 Manny Ramirez .75 2.00
49 Derrek Lee .30 .75
50 Alfonso Soriano .50 1.25
51 Jermaine Dye .30 .75
52 Jim Thome .50 1.25
53 Ken Griffey Jr. 1.25 3.00
54 Adam Dunn .50 1.25
55 Travis Hafner .30 .75
56 Grady Sizemore .50 1.25
57 Todd Helton .50 1.25
58 Gary Sheffield .30 .75
59 Miguel Cabrera .75 2.00
60 Lance Berkman .50 1.25
61 Mark Teahen .30 .75
62 Vladimir Guerrero .75 2.00
63 Jered Weaver .50 1.25
64 Rafael Furcal .30 .75
65 Prince Fielder .50 1.25
66 Justin Morneau .75 2.00
67 Johan Santana .75 2.00
68 David Wright 1.25 3.00
69 Jose Reyes .50 1.25
70 Derek Jeter 2.00 5.00
71 Alex Rodriguez 1.25 3.00
72 Nick Swisher .75 2.00
73 Ryan Howard 1.25 3.00
74 Jason Bay .50 1.25
75 Adrian Gonzalez .50 1.25
76 Ray Durham .30 .75
77 Ichiro Suzuki 1.25 3.00
78 Albert Pujols 2.00 5.00
79 Scott Rolen .50 1.25
80 Carl Crawford .50 1.25
81 Mark Teixeira .75 2.00
82 Michael Young .50 1.25
83 Vernon Wells .30 .75
84 Ryan Zimmerman .50 1.25
85 Stephen Drew .30 .75
86 Andruw Jones .30 .75
87 Chipper Jones .75 2.00
88 Miguel Tejada .50 1.25
89 David Ortiz .50 1.25
90 Manny Ramirez .75 2.00
91 Derrek Lee .30 .75
92 Alfonso Soriano .50 1.25
93 Jermaine Dye .30 .75
94 Jim Thome .50 1.25
95 Ken Griffey Jr. 1.25 3.00
96 Adam Dunn .50 1.25
97 Travis Hafner .30 .75
98 Grady Sizemore .50 1.25
99 Todd Helton .50 1.25
100 Gary Sheffield .30 .75
101 Miguel Cabrera .75 2.00
102 Lance Berkman .50 1.25
103 Mark Teahen .30 .75
104 Vladimir Guerrero .75 2.00
105 Jered Weaver .50 1.25
106 Rafael Furcal .30 .75
107 Prince Fielder .50 1.25
108 Justin Morneau .75 2.00
109 Johan Santana .75 2.00
110 David Wright 1.25 3.00
111 Jose Reyes .50 1.25
112 Derek Jeter 2.00 5.00
113 Alex Rodriguez 1.25 3.00
114 Nick Swisher .75 2.00
115 Ryan Howard 1.25 3.00
116 Jason Bay .50 1.25
117 Adrian Gonzalez .50 1.25
118 Ray Durham .30 .75
119 Ichiro Suzuki 1.25 3.00
120 Albert Pujols 2.00 5.00
121 Scott Rolen .50 1.25
122 Carl Crawford .50 1.25
123 Mark Teixeira .75 2.00
124 Michael Young .50 1.25
125 Vernon Wells .30 .75
126 Ryan Zimmerman .50 1.25
127 Miguel Montero (RC) .75 2.00
128 Doug Slaten RC .75 2.00
129 Hunter Pence (RC) 4.00 10.00
130 Brian Burres (RC) .75 2.00
131 Daisuke Matsuzaka RC 3.00 8.00
132 Hideki Okajima RC 4.00 10.00
133 Devern Hansack RC .75 2.00
134 Felix Pie (RC) .75 2.00
135 Ryan Sweeney (RC) .75 2.00
136 Chris Stewart RC .75 2.00
137 Jarrod Saltalamacchia (RC) 1.25 3.00
138 John Danks RC 1.25 3.00
139 Travis Buck (RC) .75 2.00
140 Troy Tulowitzki (RC) 5.00 12.00
141 Chase Wright RC 2.00 5.00
142 Matt DeSalvo (RC) .75 2.00
143 Micah Owings (RC) .75 2.00
144 Jeff Baker (RC) .75 2.00
145 Andy LaRoche (RC) .75 2.00
146 Billy Butler (RC) 1.25 3.00
147 Jose Garcia RC .75 2.00
148 Angel Sanchez RC .75 2.00
149 Alex Gordon RC 2.50 6.00
150 Glen Perkins (RC) .75 2.00
151 Alexi Casilla RC 1.25 3.00
152 Joe Smith RC .75 2.00
153 Kei Igawa RC 2.00 5.00
154 Sean Henn (RC) .75 2.00
155 Phil Hughes (RC) 4.00 10.00
156 Michael Bourn (RC) .75 2.00
157 Josh Hamilton (RC) 3.00 8.00
158 Kevin Kouzmanoff (RC) .75 2.00
159 Tim Lincecum RC 12.00 30.00
160 Brandon Morrow RC 4.00 10.00
161 Brandon Wood (RC) .75 2.00
162 Akinori Iwamura RC 2.00 5.00
163 Delmon Young (RC) 1.25 3.00
164 Juan Salas (RC) .75 2.00
165 Elijah Dukes RC 1.25 3.00
166 Joaquin Arias (RC) .75 2.00
167 Adam Lind (RC) .75 2.00
168 Matt Chico (RC) .75 2.00
169 Miguel Montero (RC) .75 2.00
170 Doug Slaten RC .75 2.00
171 Hunter Pence (RC) 4.00 10.00
172 Brian Burres (RC) .75 2.00
173 Daisuke Matsuzaka RC 3.00 8.00
174 Hideki Okajima RC 4.00 10.00
175 Devern Hansack RC .75 2.00
176 Felix Pie (RC) .75 2.00
177 Ryan Sweeney (RC) .75 2.00
178 Chris Stewart RC .75 2.00
179 Jarrod Saltalamacchia (RC) 1.25 3.00
180 John Danks RC 1.25 3.00
181 Travis Buck (RC) .75 2.00
182 Troy Tulowitzki (RC) 5.00 12.00
183 Chase Wright RC 2.00 5.00
184 Matt DeSalvo (RC) .75 2.00
185 Micah Owings (RC) .75 2.00
186 Jeff Baker (RC) .75 2.00
187 Andy LaRoche (RC) .75 2.00
188 Billy Butler (RC) 1.25 3.00
189 Jose Garcia RC .75 2.00
190 Angel Sanchez RC .75 2.00
191 Alex Gordon RC 2.50 6.00
192 Glen Perkins (RC) .75 2.00
193 Alexi Casilla RC 1.25 3.00
194 Joe Smith RC .75 2.00
195 Kei Igawa RC 2.00 5.00
196 Sean Henn (RC) .75 2.00
197 Phil Hughes (RC) 4.00 10.00
198 Michael Bourn (RC) .75 2.00
199 Josh Hamilton (RC) 3.00 8.00
200 Kevin Kouzmanoff (RC) .75 2.00
201 Tim Lincecum RC 12.00 30.00
202 Brandon Morrow RC 4.00 10.00
203 Brandon Wood (RC) .75 2.00
204 Akinori Iwamura RC 2.00 5.00
205 Delmon Young (RC) 1.25 3.00
206 Juan Salas (RC) .75 2.00
207 Elijah Dukes RC 1.25 3.00
208 Joaquin Arias (RC) .75 2.00
209 Adam Lind (RC) .75 2.00
210 Matt Chico (RC) .75 2.00
211 Miguel Montero (RC) .75 2.00
212 Doug Slaten RC .75 2.00
213 Hunter Pence (RC) 4.00 10.00
214 Brian Burres (RC) .75 2.00
215 Daisuke Matsuzaka RC 3.00 8.00
216 Hideki Okajima RC 4.00 10.00
217 Devern Hansack RC .75 2.00
218 Felix Pie (RC) .75 2.00
219 Ryan Sweeney (RC) .75 2.00
220 Chris Stewart RC .75 2.00
221 Jarrod Saltalamacchia (RC) 1.25 3.00
222 John Danks RC 1.25 3.00
223 Travis Buck (RC) .75 2.00
224 Troy Tulowitzki (RC) 5.00 12.00
225 Chase Wright RC 2.00 5.00
226 Matt DeSalvo (RC) .75 2.00
227 Micah Owings (RC) .75 2.00
228 Jeff Baker (RC) .75 2.00
229 Andy LaRoche (RC) .75 2.00
230 Billy Butler (RC) 1.25 3.00
231 Jose Garcia RC .75 2.00
232 Angel Sanchez RC .75 2.00
233 Alex Gordon RC 2.50 6.00
234 Glen Perkins (RC) .75 2.00
235 Alexi Casilla RC 1.25 3.00
236 Joe Smith RC .75 2.00
237 Kei Igawa RC 2.00 5.00
238 Sean Henn (RC) .75 2.00
239 Phil Hughes (RC) 4.00 10.00
240 Michael Bourn (RC) .75 2.00
241 Josh Hamilton (RC) 3.00 8.00
242 Kevin Kouzmanoff (RC) .75 2.00
243 Tim Lincecum RC 12.00 30.00
244 Brandon Morrow RC 4.00 10.00
245 Brandon Wood (RC) .75 2.00
246 Akinori Iwamura RC 2.00 5.00
247 Delmon Young (RC) 1.25 3.00
248 Juan Salas (RC) .75 2.00
249 Elijah Dukes RC 1.25 3.00
250 Joaquin Arias (RC) .75 2.00
251 Adam Lind (RC) .75 2.00
252 Matt Chico (RC) .75 2.00

2007 Upper Deck Elements Clear Cut Elements Bronze

RANDOM INSERTS IN PACKS
PRINT RUNS B/WN 149-350 COPIES PER
EXCH DEADLINE 7/14/2010
AH Aaron Harang 6.00 15.00
AK Austin Kearns/234 4.00 10.00
BB Brian Bannister 4.00 10.00
BR Brian Roberts 6.00 15.00
CA Matt Cain 10.00 25.00
CC Chris Carpenter 10.00 25.00
CP Corey Patterson 4.00 10.00
CR Cal Ripken Jr. 50.00 80.00
CR Carl Crawford 4.00 10.00
DJ Derek Jeter 100.00 150.00
DW Dontrelle Willis 6.00 15.00
HR Hanley Ramirez/314 8.00 20.00
JB Jason Bay 4.00 10.00
JG Jonny Gomes 4.00 10.00
JH Jeremy Hermida 4.00 10.00
JP Jake Peavy 6.00 15.00
JV Justin Verlander 20.00 50.00
JZ Joel Zumaya 6.00 15.00
KG Khalil Greene 4.00 10.00
KW Kerry Wood/199
MG Marcus Giles/290 4.00 10.00
MH Matt Holliday 8.00 20.00
ML Mark Loretta/199 4.00 10.00
MM Melvin Mora 4.00 10.00
MT Miguel Tejada/149 4.00 10.00
RH Rich Harden 4.00 10.00
RJ Reed Johnson 4.00 10.00
RZ Ryan Zimmerman 10.00 25.00
SA Johan Santana/299 12.50 30.00
SK Scott Kazmir 8.00 20.00
SR Scott Rolen/299 6.00 15.00
TH Travis Hafner 4.00 10.00
VM Victor Martinez 4.00 10.00

2007 Upper Deck Elements Clear Cut Elements Gold

RANDOM INSERTS IN PACKS
PRINT RUNS B/W 49-199 COPIES PER
EXCH DEADLINE 7/14/2010
AK Austin Kearns/99 5.00 12.00
BB Brian Bannister 5.00 12.00
BR Brian Roberts 8.00 20.00
CA Matt Cain 12.50 30.00
CC Chris Carpenter 12.50 30.00
CP Corey Patterson 5.00 12.00
CR Miguel Cabrera/149 EXCH 60.00 100.00
CR Carl Crawford 5.00 12.00
DJ Derek Jeter 125.00 175.00
DW Dontrelle Willis 8.00 20.00
GS Khalil Greene 5.00 12.00
HR Hanley Ramirez 10.00 25.00
JB Jason Bay 5.00 12.00
JG Jonny Gomes 5.00 12.00
JH Jeremy Hermida 5.00 12.00
JP Jake Peavy 8.00 20.00
JV Justin Verlander 25.00 60.00
JZ Joel Zumaya 8.00 20.00
KW Kerry Wood/99 12.50 30.00
MG Marcus Giles/99 5.00 12.00
MH Matt Holliday 10.00 25.00
ML Mark Loretta/99 5.00 12.00
MT Miguel Tejada/49
RC Johan Santana/99 15.00 40.00
RJ Reed Johnson 5.00 12.00
RO Melvin Mora 5.00 12.00
RZ Ryan Zimmerman 12.50 30.00
SK Scott Kazmir 10.00 25.00
SR Scott Rolen/99 8.00 20.00
TH Travis Hafner 5.00 12.00
VM Victor Martinez 5.00 12.00

2007 Upper Deck Elements Clear Cut Elements Silver

RANDOM INSERTS IN PACKS
PRINT RUNS B/WN 13-99 COPIES PER
NO PRICING ON QTY 13 OR LESS
EXCH DEADLINE 7/14/2010
AK Austin Kearns/49 6.00 15.00
BB Brian Bannister 6.00 15.00
BR Brian Roberts 10.00 25.00
CA Matt Cain/49 15.00 40.00
CC Chris Carpenter 15.00 40.00
CP Corey Patterson 6.00 15.00
CR Cal Ripken Jr. 60.00 120.00
CR Carl Crawford 6.00 15.00
DJ Derek Jeter 150.00 200.00
DW Dontrelle Willis 10.00 25.00
HR Hanley Ramirez 12.50 30.00
JB Jason Bay 6.00 15.00
JG Jonny Gomes 6.00 15.00
JH Jeremy Hermida 6.00 15.00
JP Jake Peavy 10.00 25.00
JV Justin Verlander 30.00 80.00
JZ Joel Zumaya 10.00 25.00
KW Kerry Wood/49
MG Marcus Giles/49 6.00 15.00
MH Matt Holliday 12.50 30.00
ML Mark Loretta/13
MT Miguel Tejada/9
RC Johan Santana/49 20.00 50.00
RJ Reed Johnson 6.00 15.00
RO Melvin Mora 6.00 15.00
RZ Ryan Zimmerman 15.00 40.00
SK Scott Kazmir 10.00 25.00
SR Scott Rolen/49 10.00 25.00
TH Travis Hafner 6.00 15.00
VM Victor Martinez 6.00 15.00

2007 Upper Deck Elements Dual Elements Dual Memorabilia

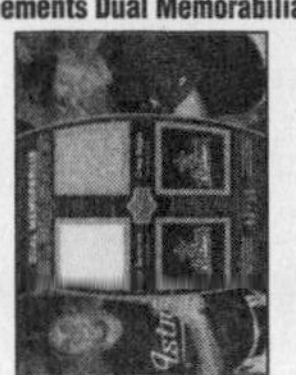

RANDOM INSERTS IN PACKS
STATED PRINT RUN 50 SER.#'d SETS
BB Lance Berkman 6.00 15.00
Craig Biggio
BM Josh Beckett 30.00 60.00
Daisuke Matsuzaka
BS Jason Bay 6.00 15.00
Freddy Sanchez
CA Carlos Beltran 6.00 15.00
Alfonso Soriano
CB Carl Crawford 4.00 10.00
Rocco Baldelli
CM Chris Carpenter 4.00 10.00
Mark Mulder
DB Carlos Delgado 4.00 10.00
Carlos Beltran
DG Adam Dunn 12.50 30.00
Ken Griffey Jr./29
DJ Johnny Damon 10.00 25.00
Derek Jeter
GG Brian Giles 4.00 10.00
Marcus Giles
GJ Ken Griffey Jr. 15.00 40.00
Derek Jeter
GM Tom Glavine 6.00 15.00
Pedro Martinez
GS Vladimir Guerrero 6.00 15.00
Alfonso Soriano
GT Ken Griffey Jr. 12.50 30.00
Frank Thomas
HB Roy Halladay 4.00 10.00
A.J. Burnett
HU Cole Hamels 6.00 15.00
Chase Utley
JJ Chipper Jones 6.00 15.00
Andruw Jones
JR Derek Jeter 25.00 50.00
Jose Reyes
JT Derek Jeter 10.00 25.00
Miguel Tejada
LP Jon Lester 10.00 25.00
Jonathan Papelbon
MM Victor Martinez 6.00 15.00
Joe Mauer
MS Greg Maddux 30.00 60.00
John Smoltz
MT Joe Mauer 6.00 15.00
Justin Morneau
OR David Ortiz 10.00 25.00
Manny Ramirez
PG Albert Pujols 15.00 40.00
Ken Griffey Jr.
PZ Jonathan Papelbon 10.00 25.00
Joel Zumaya
RH Mariano Rivera 6.00 15.00
Trevor Hoffman
RR Jose Reyes 10.00 25.00
Hanley Ramirez
RW Alex Rios 4.00 10.00
Vernon Wells
SB Curt Schilling 12.50 30.00
Josh Beckett
SH Grady Sizemore 6.00 15.00
Travis Hafner
SZ Johan Santana 6.00 15.00
Barry Zito
TH Jim Thome 6.00 15.00
Travis Hafner
TK Jim Thome 6.00 15.00
Paul Konerko
TM Mark Teixeira 4.00 10.00
Justin Morneau
TR Miguel Tejada 4.00 10.00
Brian Roberts
TY Mark Teixeira 4.00 10.00
Michael Young
UU Dan Uggla 6.00 15.00
Chase Utley
VB Justin Verlander 6.00 15.00
Jeremy Bonderman
WH Vernon Wells 6.00 15.00
Torii Hunter
WJ Brandon Webb 6.00 15.00
Randy Johnson
WS Brandon Webb 6.00 15.00
Johan Santana
ZR Ryan Zimmerman 6.00 15.00
Scott Rolen

2007 Upper Deck Elements Elemental Autographs

RANDOM INSERTS IN PACKS
AI Akinori Iwamura 12.50 30.00
AL Adam LaRoche
BA Bronson Arroyo 4.00 10.00
BH Bill Hall 4.00 10.00
BL Joe Blanton 3.00 8.00
BN Brendan Harris 3.00 8.00
BO Jeremy Bonderman 4.00 10.00
BR Jared Burton 12.50 30.00
BT Jason Bartlett 3.00 8.00
BU Brian Burres 3.00 8.00
BW Brandon Wood 4.00 10.00
CB Cha-Seung Baek 3.00 8.00
CO Jon Coutlangus 4.00 10.00
CR Cal Ripken Jr. 60.00 120.00
CU Chase Utley 15.00 40.00
CW Chase Wright 6.00 15.00
DB Denny Bautista 3.00 8.00
DC Daniel Cabrera 3.00 8.00
DJ Derek Jeter 60.00 120.00
DO David Ortiz
DU Dan Uggla 4.00 10.00
DW Dontrelle Willis
FP Felix Pie 4.00 10.00
GA Garrett Atkins 3.00 8.00
GC Gustavo Chacin
GO Alex Gordon 12.50 30.00
GP Glen Perkins 3.00 8.00
HA Rich Harden 3.00 8.00
HE Sean Henn 3.00 8.00
HR Hanley Ramirez 6.00 15.00
IK Ian Kinsler 8.00 20.00
JA Joaquin Arias 3.00 8.00
JB Jason Bay 6.00 15.00
JC Jesse Crain 3.00 8.00
JG Jonny Gomes 3.00 8.00
JH Josh Hamilton 8.00 20.00
JK Jon Knott 3.00 8.00
JO Josh Willingham 3.00 8.00
JP Jake Peavy 6.00 15.00
JV Justin Verlander 8.00 20.00
JW Jayson Werth 12.50 30.00
KE Howie Kendrick 4.00 10.00
KI Kei Igawa 10.00 25.00
KM Kendry Morales 4.00 10.00
KY Kevin Youkilis 6.00 15.00
LA Andy LaRoche 4.00 10.00
LI Bobby Livingston 3.00 8.00
LS Luke Scott 4.00 10.00
PA Jonathan Papelbon 12.50 30.00
PE Jhonny Peralta
RC Roger Clemens
RH Rich Hill 6.00 15.00
RL Ruddy Lugo 3.00 8.00
RO Scott Rolen 6.00 15.00
RT Ryan Theriot 4.00 10.00
SD Stephen Drew 10.00 25.00
SH James Shields
SK Scott Kazmir 5.00 12.00
SM John Smoltz 12.50 30.00
SO Jeremy Sowers
SS Skip Schumaker 10.00 25.00
ST Scott Thorman 3.00 8.00
TB Travis Buck 6.00 15.00
TH Travis Hafner 6.00 15.00
TI Tadahito Iguchi 6.00 15.00
VG Vladimir Guerrero 10.00 25.00
VM Victor Martinez 4.00 10.00
WO Jason Wood 3.00 8.00

2007 Upper Deck Elements Elemental Autographs Dual

RANDOM INSERTS IN PACKS
STATED PRINT RUN 15 SER.#'d SETS
NO PRICING DUE TO SCARCITY

2007 Upper Deck Elements Elemental Autographs Quad

RANDOM INSERTS IN PACKS
STATED PRINT RUN 1 SER.#'d SET
NO PRICING DUE TO SCARCITY

2007 Upper Deck Elements Elemental Autographs Triple

RANDOM INSERTS IN PACKS
STATED PRINT RUN 5 SER.#'d SETS
NO PRICING DUE TO SCARCITY

2007 Upper Deck Elements Essential Elements

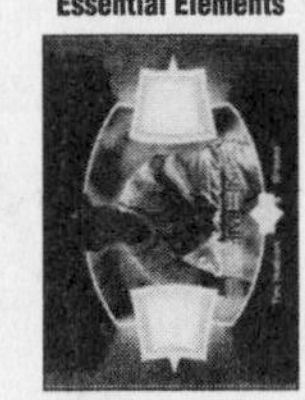

RANDOM INSERTS IN PACKS
AB Adrian Beltre 3.00 8.00
AD Adam Dunn 3.00 8.00
AJ Andruw Jones 3.00 8.00
AP Andy Pettitte 4.00 10.00
AR Aramis Ramirez 3.00 8.00
AS Alfonso Soriano 3.00 8.00
BA Bobby Abreu 3.00 8.00
BC Bobby Crosby 3.00 8.00
BE Carlos Beltran 3.00 8.00
BG Brian Giles 3.00 8.00
BO Jeremy Bonderman 3.00 8.00
BR Brian Roberts 3.00 8.00
BU B.J. Upton 3.00 8.00
BW Billy Wagner 4.00 10.00
BZ Barry Zito 3.00 8.00
CA Miguel Cabrera 3.00 8.00
CB Craig Biggio 4.00 10.00
CC Carl Crawford 3.00 8.00
CH Cole Hamels 4.00 10.00
CJ Chipper Jones 4.00 10.00
CS Curt Schilling 4.00 10.00
CU Chase Utley 4.00 10.00
DA Johnny Damon 4.00 10.00
DM Daisuke Matsuzaka 10.00 25.00
DO David Ortiz 6.00 15.00
DR JD Drew 3.00 8.00
DU Dan Uggla 4.00 10.00
DW Dontrelle Willis 3.00 8.00
EC Eric Chavez 3.00 8.00
ED Jim Edmonds 3.00 8.00
FG Freddy Garcia 3.00 8.00
FH Felix Hernandez 3.00 8.00
FL Francisco Liriano 4.00 10.00
FT Frank Thomas 4.00 10.00
GA Garret Anderson 3.00 8.00
GJ Geoff Jenkins 3.00 8.00
GM Greg Maddux 10.00 25.00
GS Grady Sizemore 6.00 15.00
HA Rich Harden 3.00 8.00
HB Hank Blalock 3.00 8.00
HO Trevor Hoffman 3.00 8.00
HS Huston Street 3.00 8.00
HU Torii Hunter 3.00 8.00
IR Ivan Rodriguez 4.00 10.00
JA Jason Bay 3.00 8.00
JB Josh Beckett 3.00 8.00
JC Jorge Cantu 3.00 8.00
JD Jermaine Dye 3.00 8.00
JE Johnny Estrada 3.00 8.00
JF Jeff Francoeur 6.00 15.00
JG Jason Giambi 3.00 8.00
JJ Josh Johnson 3.00 8.00
JK Jeff Kent 3.00 8.00
JM Joe Mauer 4.00 10.00
JP Jake Peavy 3.00 8.00
JR Jimmy Rollins 3.00 8.00
JS Johan Santana 4.00 10.00
JT Jim Thome 4.00 10.00
JV Justin Verlander 4.00 10.00
KG Khalil Greene 4.00 10.00
LB Lance Berkman 3.00 8.00
LG Luis Gonzalez 3.00 8.00
MM Mike Mussina 4.00 10.00
MO Justin Morneau 4.00 10.00
MP Mike Piazza 6.00 15.00
MR Manny Ramirez 4.00 10.00
MT Mark Teixeira 4.00 10.00
MY Michael Young 3.00 8.00
OR Magglio Ordonez 4.00 10.00
PA Jonathan Papelbon 6.00 15.00
PB Pat Burrell 3.00 8.00
PE Jhonny Peralta 3.00 8.00
PF Prince Fielder 4.00 10.00
PO Jorge Posada 4.00 10.00
PU Albert Pujols 10.00 25.00
RE Jose Reyes 4.00 10.00
RH Roy Halladay 3.00 8.00
RI Mariano Rivera 6.00 15.00
RJ Randy Johnson 4.00 10.00
RO Roy Oswalt 3.00 8.00
RW Rickie Weeks 3.00 8.00
RZ Ryan Zimmerman 4.00 10.00
SK Scott Kazmir 3.00 8.00
SM John Smoltz 4.00 10.00
SR Scott Rolen 4.00 10.00
TE Miguel Tejada 3.00 8.00
TH Todd Helton 4.00 10.00
TI Tim Hudson 3.00 8.00
TR Travis Hafner 3.00 8.00
VG Vladimir Guerrero 4.00 10.00
VM Victor Martinez 3.00 8.00

2007 Upper Deck Elements Quad Memorabilia

RANDOM INSERTS IN PACKS
STATED PRINT RUN 10 SER.#'d SETS
NO PRICING DUE TO SCARCITY

2007 Upper Deck Elements Rare Elements Patches

RANDOM INSERTS IN PACKS
PRINT RUNS B/WN 4-35 COPIES PER
NO PRICING ON QTY 19 OR LESS
AB Adrian Beltre/35 6.00 15.00
AJ Andruw Jones/35 10.00 25.00
AP Andy Pettitte/35 15.00 40.00
AR Aramis Ramirez/35 6.00 15.00
BA Bobby Abreu/35 6.00 15.00
BC Bobby Crosby/35 10.00 25.00
BE Carlos Beltran/35 10.00 25.00
BG Brian Giles/35 6.00 15.00
BO Jeremy Bonderman/35 10.00 25.00
BR Brian Roberts/30 10.00 25.00
BW Billy Wagner/35 10.00 25.00
BZ Barry Zito/35 6.00 15.00
CA Miguel Cabrera/35 6.00 15.00
CB Craig Biggio/35 15.00 40.00
CC Carl Crawford/35 10.00 25.00
CJ Chipper Jones/35 20.00 50.00
CL Carlos Lee/35 10.00 25.00
CS Curt Schilling/35 10.00 25.00
DA Johnny Damon/28 10.00 25.00
DM Daisuke Matsuzaka/35
DR JD Drew/35 6.00 15.00
DU Dan Uggla/35 10.00 25.00
DW Dontrelle Willis/35 6.00 15.00
EC Eric Chavez/35 6.00 15.00
ED Jim Edmonds/35 10.00 25.00
FG Freddy Garcia/35 6.00 15.00
FH Felix Hernandez/35 6.00 15.00
FL Francisco Liriano/35 15.00 40.00
FT Frank Thomas/35 15.00 40.00
GA Garret Anderson/35 6.00 15.00
GJ Geoff Jenkins/35 6.00 15.00
GM Greg Maddux/35 30.00 60.00
GR Ken Griffey Jr./35 40.00 80.00
GS Grady Sizemore/35 10.00 25.00
HA Rich Harden/35 6.00 15.00
HB Hank Blalock/35 6.00 15.00
HO Trevor Hoffman/35 6.00 15.00
HR Hanley Ramirez/35 10.00 25.00
HS Huston Street/35 6.00 15.00
HU Torii Hunter/35 6.00 15.00
IR Ivan Rodriguez/28 10.00 25.00
JA Jason Bay/35 10.00 25.00
JB Josh Beckett/35 15.00 40.00
JC Jorge Cantu/35 6.00 15.00
JD Jermaine Dye/35 6.00 15.00
JE Johnny Estrada/35 6.00 15.00
JF Jeff Francoeur/35 20.00 50.00
JG Jason Giambi/35 20.00 50.00
JJ Josh Johnson/29 6.00 15.00
JK Jeff Kent/35 10.00 25.00
JP Jake Peavy/35 6.00 15.00
JR Jimmy Rollins/35 10.00 25.00
JS Johan Santana/35 10.00 25.00
JT Jim Thome/35 10.00 25.00
KG Khalil Greene/35 10.00 25.00
LB Lance Berkman/35 6.00 15.00
LG Luis Gonzalez/35 6.00 15.00
MM Mike Mussina/19
MP Mike Piazza/35 30.00 60.00
MT Mark Teixeira/35 15.00 40.00
MY Michael Young/35 10.00 25.00
OR Magglio Ordonez/35 10.00 25.00
PB Pat Burrell/35 6.00 15.00
PE Jhonny Peralta/35 6.00 15.00
PM Pedro Martinez/15
PO Jorge Posada/35 10.00 25.00
RC Roger Clemens/35 30.00 60.00
RE Jose Reyes/35 15.00 40.00
RH Roy Halladay/35 10.00 25.00
RI Mariano Rivera/35 15.00 40.00
RJ Randy Johnson/35 10.00 25.00
RO Roy Oswalt/35 6.00 15.00
RZ Ryan Zimmerman/4
SK Scott Kazmir/35 10.00 25.00
SM John Smoltz/35 20.00 50.00
SR Scott Rolen/35 10.00 25.00
TE Miguel Tejada/18
TH Todd Helton/35 10.00 25.00
TI Tim Hudson/35 6.00 15.00
TR Travis Hafner/35 10.00 25.00
VA Jason Varitek/35 15.00 40.00
VG Vladimir Guerrero/35 15.00 40.00

2007 Upper Deck Elements Triple Memorabilia

RANDOM INSERTS IN PACKS
STATED PRINT RUN 25 SER.#'d SETS
NO PRICING DUE TO SCARCTIY

2007 Upper Deck First Edition

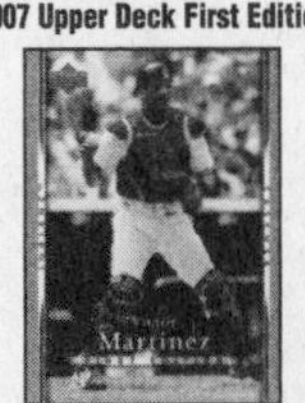

This 300-card set was released in March, 2007. The set was issued in 10-card packs which came 36 packs to a box and 20 boxes to a case. Just as in the first series of the regular Upper Deck product, cards numbered 1-50 feature players eligible for the 2007 Rookie Card logo.

COMPLETE SET (300) 20.00 50.00
COMMON CARD (1-300) .12 .30
COMMON ROOKIE (1-310) .15 .40
PRINTING PLATE ODDS 1 PER CASE
PLATE PRINT RUN 1 SET PER COLOR
BLACK-CYAN-MAGENTA-YELLOW ISSUED
NO PLATE PRICING DUE TO SCARCITY
1 Doug Slaten RC .15 .40
2 Miguel Montero (RC) .15 .40
3 Brian Burres (RC) .15 .40
4 Devern Hansack RC .15 .40
5 David Murphy (RC) .15 .40
6 Jose Reyes RC .15 .40
7 Scott Moore (RC) .15 .40
8 Josh Fields (RC) .15 .40
9 Chris Stewart RC .15 .40
10 Jerry Owens (RC) .15 .40
11 Ryan Sweeney (RC) .15 .40
12 Kevin Kouzmanoff (RC) .15 .40
13 Jeff Baker (RC) .15 .40
14 Justin Hampson (RC) .15 .40
15 Jeff Salazar (RC) .15 .40
16 Alvin Colina RC .40 1.00
17 Troy Tulowitzki (RC) 1.00 2.50
18 Andrew Miller RC .40 1.00
19 Mike Rabelo RC .15 .40
20 Jose Diaz (RC) .15 .40
21 Angel Sanchez RC .15 .40
22 Ryan Braun RC .15 .40
23 Delwyn Young (RC) .15 .40
24 Drew Anderson RC .15 .40
25 Dennis Sarfate (RC) .15 .40
26 Vinny Rottino (RC) .15 .40
27 Glen Perkins (RC) .15 .40
28 Alexi Casilla RC .25 .60
29 Philip Humber (RC) .25 .60
30 Andy Cannizaro RC .15 .40
31 Jeremy Brown .12 .30
32 Sean Henn (RC) .15 .40
33 Brian Rogers (RC) .15 .40
34 Carlos Maldonado (RC) .15 .40
35 Juan Morillo (RC) .15 .40
36 Fred Lewis (RC) .15 .40
37 Patrick Misch (RC) .15 .40
38 Billy Sadler (RC) .15 .40
39 Ryan Feierabend (RC) .15 .40
40 Cesar Jimenez RC .15 .40
41 Oswaldo Navarro RC .15 .40
42 Travis Chick (RC) .15 .40
43 Delmon Young (RC) .40 1.00
44 Shawn Riggans (RC) .15 .40
45 Brian Stokes (RC) .15 .40
46 Juan Salas (RC) .15 .40
47 Joaquin Arias (RC) .15 .40
48 Adam Lind (RC) .15 .40
49 Beltran Perez (RC) .15 .40
50 Brett Campbell RC .15 .40
51 Miguel Tejada .20 .50
52 Brandon Fahey .12 .30
53 Jay Gibbons .12 .30
54 Nick Markakis .30 .75
55 Kris Benson .12 .30
56 Erik Bedard .12 .30
57 Chris Ray .12 .30
58 Chris Britton .12 .30
59 Manny Ramirez .30 .75
60 David Ortiz .20 .50
61 Alex Cora .12 .30
62 Trot Nixon .12 .30
63 Doug Mirabelli .12 .30
64 Curt Schilling .20 .50
65 Jonathan Papelbon .30 .75
66 Craig Hansen .12 .30
67 Jermaine Dye .12 .30
68 Jim Thome .20 .50
69 Rob Mackowiak .12 .30
70 Brian Anderson .12 .30
71 A.J. Pierzynski .12 .30
72 Alex Cintron .12 .30
73 Jose Contreras .12 .30
74 Bobby Jenks .12 .30
75 Mike MacDougal .12 .30
76 Travis Hafner .12 .30
77 Ryan Garko .12 .30
78 Victor Martinez .20 .50
79 Casey Blake .12 .30
80 Shin-Soo Choo .20 .50
81 Paul Byrd .12 .30
82 Jeremy Sowers .12 .30
83 Cliff Lee .20 .50
84 Sean Casey .12 .30
85 Brandon Inge .12 .30
86 Omar Infante .12 .30
87 Magglio Ordonez .20 .50
88 Marcus Thames .12 .30
89 Justin Verlander .40 1.00
90 Todd Jones .12 .30
91 Joel Zumaya .20 .50
92 Nate Robertson .12 .30
93 Mark Teahen .12 .30
94 Ryan Shealy .12 .30
95 Mark Grudzielanek .12 .30
96 Shane Costa .12 .30
97 Reggie Sanders .12 .30
98 Mark Redman .12 .30
99 Todd Wellemeyer .12 .30
100 Ambiorix Burgos .12 .30
101 Joe Nelson .12 .30
102 Orlando Cabrera .12 .30
103 Maicer Izturis .12 .30
104 Vladimir Guerrero .30 .75
105 Juan Rivera .12 .30
106 Jered Weaver .20 .50
107 Joe Saunders .12 .30
108 Bartolo Colon .12 .30
109 Francisco Rodriguez .20 .50
110 Justin Morneau .30 .75
111 Luis Castillo .12 .30
112 Michael Cuddyer .12 .30
113 Joe Mauer .30 .75
114 Francisco Liriano .30 .75
115 Joe Nathan .12 .30
116 Brad Radke .12 .30
117 Juan Rincon .12 .30
118 Derek Jeter .75 2.00
119 Jason Giambi .12 .30
120 Bobby Abreu .12 .30
121 Gary Sheffield .12 .30
122 Melky Cabrera .12 .30
123 Chien-Ming Wang .20 .50
124 Mariano Rivera .30 .75
125 Jaret Wright .12 .30
126 Kyle Farnsworth .12 .30
127 Frank Thomas .30 .75
128 Dan Johnson .12 .30
129 Marco Scutaro .12 .30
130 Jay Payton .12 .30
131 Joe Blanton .12 .30
132 Rich Harden .12 .30
133 Esteban Loaiza .12 .30
134 Chad Gaudin .12 .30
135 Yuniesky Betancourt .12 .30
136 Willie Bloomquist .12 .30
137 Ichiro Suzuki .50 1.25
138 Raul Ibanez .20 .50
139 Chris Snelling .12 .30
140 Cha-Seung Baek .12 .30
141 Julio Mateo .12 .30
142 Rafael Soriano .12 .30
143 Jorge Cantu .12 .30
144 B.J. Upton .12 .30
145 Dioner Navarro .12 .30
146 Carl Crawford .20 .50
147 Damon Hollins .12 .30
148 Casey Fossum .12 .30
149 Ruddy Lugo .12 .30
150 Tyler Walker .12 .30
151 Shawn Camp .12 .30
152 Ian Kinsler .20 .50
153 Jerry Hairston Jr. .12 .30
154 Gerald Laird .12 .30
155 Mark DeRosa .12 .30
156 Kip Wells .12 .30
157 Vicente Padilla .12 .30
158 John Koronka .12 .30
159 Wes Littleton .12 .30
160 Lyle Overbay .12 .30
161 Aaron Hill .12 .30
162 John McDonald .12 .30
163 Vernon Wells .12 .30
164 Frank Catalanotto .12 .30
165 Roy Halladay .30 .75
166 B.J. Ryan .12 .30
167 Casey Janssen .12 .30
168 Stephen Drew .12 .30
169 Conor Jackson .12 .30
170 Chad Tracy .12 .30
171 Johnny Estrada .12 .30
172 Eric Byrnes .12 .30
173 Carlos Quentin .12 .30
174 Brandon Webb .20 .50
175 Jorge Julio .12 .30
176 Luis Vizcaino .12 .30
177 Chipper Jones .30 .75
178 Adam LaRoche .12 .30
179 Brian McCann .12 .30
180 Ryan Langerhans .12 .30
181 Matt Diaz .12 .30
182 John Smoltz .30 .75
183 Oscar Villarreal .12 .30
184 Chad Paronto .12 .30
185 Derrek Lee .12 .30
186 Ryan Theriot .12 .30
187 Ronny Cedeno .12 .30
188 Juan Pierre .12 .30
189 Matt Murton .12 .30
190 Carlos Zambrano .20 .50
191 Mark Prior .20 .50
192 Ryan Dempster .12 .30
193 Ryan O'Malley .12 .30

194 Brandon Phillips .12 .30
195 Rich Aurilia .12 .30
196 Ken Griffey Jr. .50 1.25
197 Ryan Freel .12 .30
198 Aaron Harang .12 .30
199 Brandon Claussen .12 .30
200 David Weathers .12 .30
201 Eric Milton .12 .30
202 Kazuo Matsui .12 .30
203 Jamey Carroll .12 .30
204 Matt Holliday .30 .75
205 Brad Hawpe .12 .30
206 Jason Jennings .12 .30
207 Josh Fogg .12 .30
208 Aaron Cook .12 .30
209 Miguel Cabrera .30 .75
210 Dan Uggla .20 .50
211 Hanley Ramirez .30 .75
212 Jeremy Hermida .12 .30
213 Cody Ross .12 .30
214 Josh Willingham .12 .30
215 Anibal Sanchez .12 .30
216 Jose Garcia RC .15 .40
217 Taylor Tankersley .12 .30
218 Lance Berkman .20 .50
219 Craig Biggio .20 .50
220 Brad Ausmus .12 .30
221 Willy Taveras .12 .30
222 Chris Burke .12 .30
223 Roger Clemens .40 1.00
224 Brandon Backe .12 .30
225 Brad Lidge .12 .30
226 Dan Wheeler .12 .30
227 Wilson Betemit .12 .30
228 Julio Lugo .12 .30
229 Russell Martin .12 .30
230 Kenny Lofton .12 .30
231 Brad Penny .12 .30
232 Chad Billingsley .12 .30
233 Greg Maddux .50 1.25
234 Jonathan Broxton .12 .30
235 Rickie Weeks .20 .50
236 Bill Hall .12 .30
237 Tony Gwynn Jr. .12 .30
238 Corey Hart .12 .30
239 Laynce Nix .12 .30
240 Ben Sheets .12 .30
241 Dave Bush .12 .30
242 Francisco Cordero .12 .30
243 Jose Reyes .20 .50
244 Carlos Delgado .12 .30
245 Paul Lo Duca .12 .30
246 Carlos Beltran .12 .30
247 Lastings Milledge .20 .50
248 Pedro Martinez .20 .50
249 John Maine .12 .30
250 Steve Trachsel .12 .30
251 Ryan Howard .50 1.25
252 Jimmy Rollins .20 .50
253 Chris Coste .12 .30
254 Jeff Conine .12 .30
255 David Dellucci .12 .30
256 Cole Hamels .30 .75
257 Ryan Madson .12 .30
258 Brett Myers .12 .30
259 Freddy Sanchez .12 .30
260 Xavier Nady .12 .30
261 Jose Castillo .12 .30
262 Jason Bay .20 .50
263 Jose Bautista .20 .50
264 Ronny Paulino .12 .30
265 Zach Duke .12 .30
266 Shane Youman RC .15 .40
267 Matt Capps .12 .30
268 Adrian Gonzalez .20 .50
269 Josh Barfield .12 .30
270 Mike Piazza .30 .75
271 Dave Roberts .12 .30
272 Geoff Blum .12 .30
273 Chris Young .12 .30
274 Woody Williams .12 .30
275 Cla Meredith .12 .30
276 Trevor Hoffman .20 .50
277 Ray Durham .12 .30
278 Mark Sweeney .12 .30
279 Eliezer Alfonzo .12 .30
280 Todd Linden .12 .30
281 Jason Schmidt .12 .30
282 Noah Lowry .12 .30
283 Brad Hennessey .12 .30
284 Jonathan Sanchez .12 .30
285 Albert Pujols .75 2.00
286 David Eckstein .12 .30
287 Jim Edmonds .20 .50
288 Chris Duncan .12 .30
289 Juan Encarnacion .12 .30
290 Jeff Suppan .12 .30
291 Jeff Weaver .12 .30
292 Braden Looper .12 .30
293 Ryan Zimmerman .20 .50
294 Nick Johnson .12 .30
295 Alfonso Soriano .20 .50
296 Austin Kearns .12 .30
297 Alex Escobar .12 .30
298 Tony Armas .12 .30
299 Chad Cordero .12 .30
300 Jon Rauch .12 .30
301 Daisuke Matsuzaka RC .60 1.50
302 Kei Igawa RC .40 1.00
303 Akinori Iwamura RC .40 1.00
304 Alex Gordon RC .50 1.25
305 Matt Chico (RC) .15 .40
306 John Danks RC .25 .60
307 Elijah Dukes RC .25 .60
308 Gustavo Molina RC .15 .40
309 Joakim Soria RC .15 .40
310 Jay Marshall RC .15 .40

2007 Upper Deck First Edition First Pitch Aces

COMPLETE SET (15) 6.00 15.00
STATED ODDS 1:6
BW Brandon Webb .40 1.00
CC Chris Carpenter .40 1.00
CS Curt Schilling .60 1.50
CZ Carlos Zambrano .40 1.00
DW Dontrelle Willis .40 1.00
FH Felix Hernandez .60 1.50
JS Johan Santana .60 1.50
JV Justin Verlander 1.00 2.50
PM Pedro Martinez .60 1.50
RC Roger Clemens 1.25 3.00
RH Roy Halladay .40 1.00
RJ Randy Johnson 1.00 2.50
SA C.C. Sabathia .40 1.00
SK Scott Kazmir .60 1.50
SM John Smoltz .60 1.50

2007 Upper Deck First Edition First Pitch Foundations

COMPLETE SET (20) 6.00 15.00
STATED ODDS 1:6
AL Adam Lind .40 1.00
AM Andrew Miller 1.50 4.00
DM David Murphy .40 1.00
DY Delmon Young 1.00 2.50
FL Fred Lewis .60 1.50
GP Glen Perkins .40 1.00
JA Joaquin Arias .40 1.00
JF Josh Fields .40 1.00
JO Jerry Owens .40 1.00
JS Jeff Salazar .40 1.00
MM Mitch Maier .40 1.00
MO Miguel Montero .40 1.00
PH Philip Humber .40 1.00
RB Ryan Braun .40 1.00
RS Ryan Sweeney .40 1.00
SM Scott Moore .40 1.00
SR Shawn Riggans .40 1.00
TC Travis Chick .40 1.00
TT Troy Tulowitzki 2.50 6.00
UJ Ubaldo Jimenez 2.50 6.00

2007 Upper Deck First Edition Leading Off

COMPLETE SET (15) 6.00 15.00
STATED ODDS 1:6
AS Alfonso Soriano .60 1.50
BR Brian Roberts .40 1.00
CF Chone Figgins .40 1.00
DR Dave Roberts .40 1.00
FR Ryan Freel .40 1.00
GS Grady Sizemore .60 1.50
HR Hanley Ramirez 1.00 2.50
IS Ichiro Suzuki 1.25 3.00
JD Johnny Damon .60 1.50
JP Juan Pierre .40 1.00
JR Jose Reyes .60 1.50
RF Rafael Furcal .40 1.00
RO Jimmy Rollins .60 1.50
SP Scott Podsednik .40 1.00
WT Willy Taveras .40 1.00

2007 Upper Deck First Edition Momentum Swing

COMPLETE SET (20) 6.00 15.00
STATED ODDS 1:6
AD Adam Dunn .60 1.50
AJ Andruw Jones .40 1.00
AP Albert Pujols 1.50 4.00
AR Alex Rodriguez 1.25 3.00
AS Alfonso Soriano .60 1.50
CB Carlos Beltran .40 1.00
CD Carlos Delgado .40 1.00
DL Derrek Lee .40 1.00
DO David Ortiz .60 1.50
JB Jason Bay .60 1.50
JD Jermaine Dye .40 1.00
JG Jason Giambi .40 1.00
JM Justin Morneau 1.00 2.50
JT Jim Thome .60 1.50
LB Lance Berkman .60 1.50
MC Miguel Cabrera 1.00 2.50
MT Mark Teixeira 1.00 2.50
RH Ryan Howard 1.25 3.00
TH Travis Hafner .40 1.00
VG Vladimir Guerrero 1.00 2.50

2007 Upper Deck First Edition Pennant Chasers

COMPLETE SET (30) 6.00 15.00
STATED ODDS 1:4
AR Aramis Ramirez .25 .60
CC Carl Crawford .25 .60
CG Carlos Guillen .25 .60
CJ Chipper Jones .60 1.50
CU Chase Utley .60 1.50
DA Johnny Damon .40 1.00
DU Dan Uggla .40 1.00
DW David Wright 1.00 2.50
FS Freddy Sanchez .25 .60
JM Joe Mauer .40 1.00
JR Juan Rivera .25 .60
KG Ken Griffey Jr. 1.00 2.50
MH Matt Holliday .30 .75
MR Manny Ramirez .40 1.00
MT Miguel Tejada .25 .60
MY Michael Young .25 .60
NG Nomar Garciaparra .60 1.50
NS Nick Swisher .25 .60
OH Orlando Hudson .25 .60
PF Prince Fielder .60 1.50
PK Paul Konerko .25 .60
RD Ray Durham .25 .60
RI Raul Ibanez .25 .60
RO Roy Oswalt .25 .60
RZ Ryan Zimmerman .60 1.50
SR Scott Rolen .40 1.00
TE Mark Teahen .25 .60
TH Trevor Hoffman .25 .60
VM Victor Martinez .25 .60
VW Vernon Wells .25 .60

2008 Upper Deck First Edition

COMPLETE SET (1-300) 10.00 25.00
COMP.UPD.SET (301-500) 10.00 25.00
COMMON CARD (1-250/301-500) .12 .30
COMMON RC (250-300/329/390) .20 .50
1 Joe Saunders .12 .30
2 Kelvim Escobar .12 .30
3 Jered Weaver .12 .30
4 Justin Speier .12 .30
5 Scot Shields .12 .30
6 Orlando Cabrera .12 .30
7 Casey Kotchman .12 .30
8 Vladimir Guerrero .30 .75
9 Garret Anderson .12 .30
10 Roy Oswalt .20 .50
11 Wandy Rodriguez .12 .30
12 Woody Williams .12 .30
13 Chad Qualls .12 .30
14 Mark Loretta .12 .30
15 Brad Ausmus .12 .30
16 Carlos Lee .12 .30
17 Hunter Pence .30 .75
18 Dan Haren .12 .30
19 Lenny DiNardo .12 .30
20 Chad Gaudin .12 .30
21 Huston Street .12 .30
22 Andrew Brown .12 .30
23 Mike Piazza .30 .75
24 Mark Ellis .12 .30
25 Shannon Stewart .12 .30
26 Shaun Marcum .12 .30
27 A.J. Burnett .20 .50
28 Casey Janssen .12 .30
29 Jeremy Accardo .12 .30
30 Aaron Hill .12 .30
31 Frank Thomas .30 .75
32 Matt Stairs .12 .30
33 Vernon Wells .12 .30
34 Tim Hudson .20 .50
35 Buddy Carlyle .12 .30
36 Rafael Soriano .12 .30
37 Brian McCann .20 .50
38 Edgar Renteria .12 .30
39 Mark Teixeira .30 .75
40 Willie Harris .12 .30
41 Andruw Jones .12 .30
42 Ben Sheets .12 .30
43 Dave Bush .12 .30
44 Yovani Gallardo .12 .30
45 Matt Wise .12 .30
46 Johnny Estrada .12 .30
47 Prince Fielder .20 .50
48 J.J. Hardy .12 .30
49 Corey Hart .12 .30
50 Adam Wainwright .20 .50
51 Joel Pineiro .12 .30
52 Jason Isringhausen .12 .30
53 Troy Percival .12 .30
54 Albert Pujols .75 2.00
55 David Eckstein .12 .30
56 Jim Edmonds .20 .50
57 Rick Ankiel .12 .30
58 Ted Lilly .12 .30
59 Rich Hill .12 .30
60 Jason Marquis .12 .30
61 Carlos Marmol .20 .50
62 Jason Kendall .12 .30
63 Aramis Ramirez .12 .30
64 Ryan Theriot .12 .30
65 Alfonso Soriano .20 .50
66 Jacque Jones .12 .30
67 James Shields .12 .30
68 Andy Sonnanstine .12 .30
69 Scott Dohmann .12 .30
70 Dioner Navarro .12 .30
71 B.J. Upton .20 .50
72 Carlos Pena .20 .50
73 Brendan Harris .12 .30
74 Josh Wilson .12 .30
75 Brandon Webb .20 .50
76 Micah Owings .12 .30
77 Doug Slaten .12 .30
78 Brandon Lyon .12 .30
79 Miguel Montero .12 .30
80 Stephen Drew .12 .30
81 Mark Reynolds .12 .30
82 Chris B. Young .12 .30
83 Chad Billingsley .12 .30
84 Derek Lowe .12 .30
85 Mark Hendrickson .12 .30
86 Takashi Saito .12 .30
87 Russell Martin .12 .30
88 Jeff Kent .12 .30
89 Matt Kemp .20 .50
90 Juan Pierre .12 .30
91 Matt Cain .12 .30
92 Barry Zito .12 .30
93 Kevin Correia .12 .30
94 Jack Taschner .12 .30
95 Bengie Molina .12 .30
96 Omar Vizquel .20 .50
97 Dave Roberts .12 .30
98 Rajai Davis .12 .30
99 Fausto Carmona .12 .30
100 Jake Westbrook .12 .30
101 Rafael Betancourt .12 .30
102 Joe Borowski .12 .30
103 Victor Martinez .20 .50
104 Travis Hafner .12 .30
105 Ryan Garko .12 .30
106 Kenny Lofton .12 .30
107 Franklin Gutierrez .12 .30
108 Felix Hernandez .30 .75
109 J.J. Putz .12 .30
110 Brandon Morrow .12 .30
111 Kenji Johjima .12 .30
112 Jose Vidro .12 .30
113 Richie Sexson .12 .30
114 Ichiro Suzuki .50 1.25
115 Ben Broussard .12 .30
116 Sergio Mitre .12 .30
117 Scott Olsen .12 .30
118 Rick Vanden Hurk .12 .30
119 Lee Gardner .12 .30
120 Miguel Olivo .12 .30
121 Hanley Ramirez .30 .75
122 Mike Jacobs .12 .30
123 Josh Willingham .12 .30
124 John Maine .12 .30
125 Tom Glavine .20 .50
126 Billy Wagner .12 .30
127 Aaron Heilman .12 .30
128 David Wright .40 1.00
129 Luis Castillo .12 .30
130 Shawn Green .12 .30
131 Damion Easley .12 .30
132 Carlos Delgado .12 .30
133 Shawn Hill .12 .30
134 John Lannan .12 .30
135 Chad Cordero .12 .30
136 Jon Rauch .12 .30
137 Jesus Flores .12 .30
138 Dmitri Young .12 .30
139 Cristian Guzman .12 .30
140 Austin Kearns .12 .30
141 Nook Logan .12 .30
142 Erik Bedard .12 .30
143 Daniel Cabrera .12 .30
144 Chris Ray .12 .30
145 Chad Bradford .12 .30
146 Ramon Hernandez .12 .30
147 Miguel Tejada .20 .50
148 Freddie Bynum .12 .30
149 Corey Patterson .12 .30
150 Chris Young .12 .30
151 Greg Maddux .40 1.00
152 Kevin Cameron .12 .30
153 Doug Brocail .12 .30
154 Kevin Kouzmanoff .12 .30
155 Geoff Blum .12 .30
156 Milton Bradley .12 .30
157 Brian Giles .12 .30
158 Jamie Moyer .12 .30
159 Kyle Kendrick .12 .30
160 Kyle Lohse .12 .30
161 Antonio Alfonseca .12 .30
162 Chris Coste .12 .30
163 Chase Utley .30 .75
164 Tadahito Iguchi .12 .30
165 Aaron Rowand .12 .30
166 Shane Victorino .12 .30
167 Ian Snell .12 .30
168 Shane Youman .12 .30
169 Shawn Chacon .12 .30
170 Ronny Paulino .12 .30
171 Jack Wilson .12 .30
172 Adam LaRoche .12 .30
173 Ryan Doumit .12 .30
174 Xavier Nady .12 .30
175 Kevin Millwood .12 .30
176 Brandon McCarthy .12 .30
177 Wes Littleton .12 .30
178 Mike Wood .12 .30
179 Hank Blalock .12 .30
180 Ian Kinsler .20 .50
181 Marlon Byrd .12 .30
182 Brad Wilkerson .12 .30
183 Tim Wakefield .20 .50
184 Daisuke Matsuzaka .30 .75
185 Julian Tavarez .12 .30
186 Hideki Okajima .12 .30
187 Doug Mirabelli .12 .30
188 Dustin Pedroia .40 1.00
189 Mike Lowell .12 .30
190 Manny Ramirez .30 .75
191 Coco Crisp .12 .30
192 Bronson Arroyo .12 .30
193 Matt Belisle .12 .30
194 Jared Burton .12 .30
195 Mike Gosling .12 .30
196 David Ross .12 .30
197 Edwin Encarnacion .12 .30
198 Ken Griffey Jr. .50 1.25
199 Adam Dunn .20 .50
200 Jeff Francis .12 .30
201 Jason Hirsh .12 .30
202 Manny Corpas .12 .30
203 Jeremy Affeldt .12 .30
204 Yorvit Torrealba .12 .30
205 Todd Helton .20 .50
206 Kazuo Matsui .12 .30
207 Brad Hawpe .12 .30
208 Willy Taveras .12 .30
209 Brian Bannister .12 .30
210 Zack Greinke .20 .50
211 Kyle Davies .12 .30
212 David Riske .12 .30
213 John Buck .12 .30
214 Mark Grudzielanek .12 .30
215 Billy Butler .12 .30
216 David DeJesus .12 .30
217 Jeremy Bonderman .12 .30
218 Chad Durbin .12 .30
219 Andrew Miller .12 .30
220 Todd Jones .12 .30
221 Brandon Inge .12 .30
222 Placido Polanco .12 .30
223 Gary Sheffield .12 .30
224 Magglio Ordonez .20 .50
225 Matt Garza .12 .30
226 Boof Bonser .12 .30
227 Joe Nathan .12 .30
228 Dennys Reyes .12 .30
229 Joe Mauer .30 .75
230 Michael Cuddyer .12 .30
231 Jason Bartlett .12 .30
232 Torii Hunter .12 .30
233 Jason Tyner .12 .30
234 Mark Buehrle .20 .50
235 Jon Garland .12 .30
236 Jose Contreras .12 .30
237 Matt Thornton .12 .30
238 Juan Uribe .12 .30
239 Jim Thome .20 .50
240 Jerry Owens .12 .30
241 Jermaine Dye .12 .30
242 Andy Pettitte .20 .50
243 Phil Hughes .30 .75
244 Mike Mussina .20 .50
245 Joba Chamberlain .20 .50
246 Brian Bruney .12 .30
247 Jorge Posada .20 .50
248 Derek Jeter .75 2.00
249 Jason Giambi .12 .30
250 Johnny Damon .20 .50
251 Jonathan Albaladejo RC .30 .75
252 Josh Anderson (RC) .20 .50
253 Wladimir Balentien (RC) .20 .50
254 Josh Banks (RC) .20 .50
255 Daric Barton (RC) .20 .50
256 Jerry Blevins RC .30 .75
257 Emilio Bonifacio RC .50 1.25
258 Lance Broadway (RC) .20 .50
259 Clay Buchholz (RC) .50 1.25
260 Billy Buckner (RC) .20 .50
261 Jeff Clement (RC) .30 .75
262 Willie Collazo RC .30 .75
263 Ross Detwiler RC .50 1.25
264 Sam Fuld RC .60 1.50
265 Harvey Garcia (RC) .20 .50
266 Alberto Gonzalez RC .30 .75
267 Ryan Hanigan RC .30 .75
268 Kevin Hart (RC) .20 .50
269 Luke Hochevar RC .30 .75
270 Chin-Lung Hu (RC) .30 .75
271 Rob Johnson (RC) .20 .50
272 Radhames Liz RC .30 .75
273 Ian Kennedy RC .50 1.25
274 Joe Koshansky (RC) .20 .50
275 Donny Lucy (RC) .20 .50
276 Justin Maxwell RC .30 .75
277 Jonathan Meloan RC .30 .75
278 Luis Mendoza (RC) .20 .50
279 Jose Morales (RC) .20 .50
280 Nyjer Morgan (RC) .20 .50
281 Carlos Muniz RC .30 .75
282 Bill Murphy (RC) .20 .50
283 Josh Newman RC .30 .75
284 Ross Ohlendorf RC .30 .75
285 Troy Patton (RC) .20 .50
286 Felipe Paulino RC .30 .75
287 Steve Pearce RC .30 .75
288 Heath Phillips RC .30 .75
289 Justin Ruggiano RC .30 .75
290 Clint Sammons (RC) .20 .50
291 Bronson Sardinha (RC) .20 .50
292 Chris Seddon (RC) .20 .50
293 Seth Smith (RC) .20 .50
294 Mitch Stetter RC .30 .75
295 Dave Davidson RC .30 .75
296 Rich Thompson RC .30 .75
297 J.R. Towles RC .30 .75
298 Eugenio Velez RC .20 .50
299 Joey Votto (RC) .75 2.00
300 Bill White RC .20 .50
301 Dan Haren .12 .30
302 Randy Johnson .30 .75
303 Justin Upton .20 .50
304 Tom Glavine .20 .50
305 Chipper Jones .30 .75
306 Jeff Francoeur .20 .50
307 John Smoltz .30 .75
308 Yunel Escobar .12 .30
309 Adam Jones .20 .50
310 Jeremy Guthrie .12 .30
311 Nick Markakis .30 .75
312 Brian Roberts .12 .30
313 Melvin Mora .12 .30
314 Josh Beckett .20 .50
315 Jon Lester .20 .50
316 Curt Schilling .20 .50
317 Jonathan Papelbon .20 .50
318 Jason Varitek .30 .75
319 David Ortiz .20 .50
320 Jacoby Ellsbury .50 1.25
321 Julio Lugo .12 .30
322 Sean Casey .12 .30
323 Kevin Youkilis .20 .50
324 J.D. Drew .12 .30
325 Derrek Lee .12 .30
326 Carlos Zambrano .20 .50
327 Kerry Wood .12 .30
328 Geovany Soto .30 .75
329 Kosuke Fukudome RC .60 1.50
330 Gavin Floyd .12 .30
331 Bobby Jenks .12 .30
332 Javier Vazquez .12 .30
333 A.J. Pierzynski .12 .30
334 Orlando Cabrera .12 .30
335 Joe Crede .12 .30
336 Paul Konerko .20 .50
337 Nick Swisher .30 .75
338 Carlos Quentin .12 .30
339 Alexei Ramirez .50 1.25
340 Johnny Cueto .20 .50
341 Aaron Harang .12 .30
342 Brandon Phillips .12 .30
343 Paul Byrd .12 .30
344 Grady Sizemore .20 .50
345 Jhonny Peralta .12 .30
346 Asdrubal Cabrera .20 .50
347 C.C. Sabathia .20 .50
348 Troy Tulowitzki .30 .75
349 Matt Holliday .30 .75
350 Garrett Atkins .12 .30
351 Ubaldo Jimenez .20 .50
352 Kenny Rogers .12 .30
353 Justin Verlander .40 1.00
354 Dontrelle Willis .12 .30
355 Joel Zumaya .12 .30
356 Ivan Rodriguez .20 .50
357 Miguel Cabrera .30 .75
358 Carlos Guillen .12 .30
359 Edgar Renteria .12 .30
360 Curtis Granderson .20 .50
361 Jeremy Hermida .12 .30
362 Dan Uggla .20 .50
363 Luis Gonzalez .12 .30
364 Andrew Miller .12 .30
365 Jorge Cantu .12 .30
366 Kazuo Matsui .12 .30
367 Lance Berkman .20 .50
368 Miguel Tejada .20 .50
369 Jose Valverde .12 .30
370 Michael Bourn .12 .30
371 Gil Meche .12 .30
372 Joey Gathright .12 .30
373 Mark Teahen .12 .30
374 Alex Gordon .20 .50
375 Tony Pena .12 .30
376 Jose Guillen .12 .30
377 Torii Hunter .12 .30
378 Ervin Santana .12 .30
379 Francisco Rodriguez .20 .50
380 Howie Kendrick .12 .30
381 John Lackey .12 .30
382 Gary Matthews .12 .30
383 Jon Garland .12 .30
384 Chone Figgins .12 .30
385 Andruw Jones .12 .30
386 James Loney .20 .50
387 Andre Ethier .20 .50
388 Rafael Furcal .12 .30
389 Brad Penny .12 .30
390 Hiroki Kuroda RC .30 .75
391 Blake DeWitt .30 .75
392 Mike Cameron .12 .30
393 Ryan Braun .40 1.00
394 Rickie Weeks .20 .50
395 Bill Hall .12 .30
396 Tony Gwynn .12 .30
397 Eric Gagne .12 .30
398 Jeff Suppan .12 .30
399 Jason Kendall .12 .30
400 Livan Hernandez .12 .30
401 Francisco Liriano .20 .50
402 Pat Neshek .12 .30
403 Adam Everett .12 .30
404 Justin Morneau .30 .75
405 Craig Monroe .12 .30
406 Carlos Gomez .12 .30
407 Delmon Young .20 .50
408 Oliver Perez .12 .30
409 Jose Reyes .20 .50
410 Moises Alou .12 .30
411 Carlos Beltran .12 .30
412 Endy Chavez .12 .30
413 Ryan Church .12 .30
414 Pedro Martinez .20 .50
415 Johan Santana .30 .75
416 Mike Pelfrey .12 .30
417 Brian Schneider .12 .30
418 Ramon Castro .12 .30
419 Kei Igawa .12 .30
420 Mariano Rivera .30 .75
421 Chien-Ming Wang .20 .50
422 Wilson Betemit .12 .30
423 Robinson Cano .30 .75
424 Alex Rodriguez .50 1.25
425 Bobby Abreu .12 .30
426 Shelley Duncan .12 .30
427 Hideki Matsui .30 .75
428 Joe Blanton .12 .30
429 Bobby Crosby .12 .30
430 Eric Chavez .12 .30
431 Dan Johnson .12 .30
432 Rich Harden .12 .30
433 Kurt Suzuki .12 .30
434 Ryan Howard .40 1.00
435 Jimmy Rollins .20 .50
436 Pedro Feliz .12 .30
437 Adam Eaton .12 .30
438 Brad Lidge .12 .30
439 Brett Myers .12 .30
440 Pat Burrell .12 .30
441 Geoff Jenkins .12 .30
442 Zach Duke .12 .30
443 Matt Morris .12 .30
444 Tom Gorzelanny .12 .30
445 Jason Bay .20 .50
446 Freddy Sanchez .12 .30
447 Matt Capps .12 .30
448 Tadahito Iguchi .12 .30
449 Adrian Gonzalez .12 .30
450 Jim Edmonds .20 .50
451 Jake Peavy .12 .30
452 Khalil Greene .12 .30
453 Trevor Hoffman .20 .50
454 Mark Prior .20 .50
455 Randy Wolf .12 .30
456 Scott Hairston .12 .30

457 Tim Lincecum .50 1.25
458 Noah Lowry .12 .30
459 Aaron Rowand .12 .30
460 Randy Winn .12 .30
461 Ray Durham .12 .30
462 Brian Wilson .30 .75
463 Adrian Beltre .12 .30
464 Jarrod Washburn .12 .30
465 Yuniesky Betancourt .12 .30
466 Jose Lopez .12 .30
467 Raul Ibanez .20 .50
468 Erik Bedard .12 .30
469 Brad Wilkerson .12 .30
470 Chris Carpenter .30 .75
471 Mark Mulder .12 .30
472 Skip Schumaker .12 .30
473 Troy Glaus .20 .50
474 Chris Duncan .12 .30
475 Scott Kazmir .20 .50
476 Troy Percival .12 .30
477 Akinori Iwamura .12 .30
478 Carl Crawford .20 .50
479 Cliff Floyd .12 .30
480 Matt Garza .12 .30
481 Edwin Jackson .12 .30
482 Vicente Padilla .12 .30
483 Josh Hamilton .30 .75
484 Milton Bradley .12 .30
485 Michael Young .20 .50
486 David Murphy .12 .30
487 Ben Broussard .12 .30
488 B.J. Ryan .12 .30
489 David Eckstein .12 .30
490 Alex Rios .20 .50
491 Lyle Overbay .12 .30
492 Scott Rolen .20 .50
493 Lastings Milledge .12 .30
494 Paul Lo Duca .12 .30
495 Ryan Zimmerman .20 .50
496 Odalis Perez .12 .30
497 Wily Mo Pena .12 .30
498 Elijah Dukes .12 .30
499 Ronnie Belliard .12 .30
500 Nick Johnson .12 .30

2008 Upper Deck First Edition Star Quest

SQ1 Ichiro Suzuki 1.25 3.00
SQ2 Ryan Braun 1.00 2.50
SQ3 Prince Fielder .60 1.50
SQ4 Ken Griffey Jr. 1.25 3.00
SQ5 Vladimir Guerrero 1.00 2.50
SQ6 Travis Hafner .40 1.00
SQ7 Matt Holliday 1.00 2.50
SQ8 Ryan Howard 1.00 2.50
SQ9 Derek Jeter 2.00 5.00
SQ10 Chipper Jones 1.00 2.50
SQ11 Carlos Lee .40 1.00
SQ12 Justin Morneau 1.00 2.50
SQ13 Magglio Ordonez .60 1.50
SQ14 David Ortiz .60 1.50
SQ15 Jake Peavy .40 1.00
SQ16 Albert Pujols 2.00 5.00
SQ17 Hanley Ramirez 1.00 2.50
SQ18 Manny Ramirez 1.00 2.50
SQ19 Jose Reyes .60 1.50
SQ20 Alex Rodriguez 1.25 3.00
SQ21 Johan Santana 1.00 2.50
SQ22 Grady Sizemore .60 1.50
SQ23 Alfonso Soriano .60 1.50
SQ24 Mark Teixeira 1.00 2.50
SQ25 Frank Thomas 1.00 2.50
SQ26 Jim Thome .60 1.50
SQ27 Chase Utley 1.00 2.50
SQ28 Brandon Webb .60 1.50
SQ29 David Wright 1.00 2.50
SQ30 Michael Young .60 1.50
SQ31 Adam Dunn .60 1.50
SQ32 Albert Pujols 2.00 5.00
SQ33 Alex Rodriguez 1.25 3.00
SQ34 B.J. Upton .60 1.50
SQ35 CC Sabathia .60 1.50
SQ36 Carlos Beltran .40 1.00
SQ37 Carlos Pena .60 1.50
SQ38 Cole Hamels 1.00 2.50
SQ39 Curtis Granderson .60 1.50
SQ40 Daisuke Matsuzaka .75 2.00
SQ41 David Ortiz .60 1.50
SQ42 Derek Jeter 2.00 5.00
SQ43 Derrek Lee .40 1.00
SQ44 Eric Byrnes .40 1.00
SQ45 Felix Hernandez 1.00 2.50
SQ46 Ichiro Suzuki 1.25 3.00
SQ47 Jeff Francoeur .60 1.50
SQ48 Jimmy Rollins .60 1.50
SQ49 Joe Mauer 1.00 2.50
SQ50 John Smoltz 1.00 2.50
SQ51 Ken Griffey Jr. 1.25 3.00
SQ52 Lance Berkman .60 1.50
SQ53 Miguel Cabrera 1.00 2.50
SQ54 Paul Konerko .60 1.50
SQ55 Pedro Martinez .60 1.50
SQ56 Randy Johnson 1.00 2.50
SQ57 Russell Martin .40 1.00
SQ58 Troy Tulowitzki 1.00 2.50
SQ59 Vernon Wells .40 1.00
SQ60 Vladimir Guerrero 1.00 2.50

2009 Upper Deck First Edition

This set was released on March 31, 2009. The base set consists of 299 cards.

COMP.FACT.SET (400) 20.00 50.00
COMPLETE SET (300) 15.00 40.00
COMMON CARD (1-300) .12 .30
COMMON ROOKIE (1-300) .20 .50
COMMON CARD (301-384) .12 .30
COMMON RC (385-400) .20 .50
300-400 ISSUED IN FACT.SET ONLY
1 Randy Johnson .20 .50
2 Conor Jackson .12 .30
3 Brandon Webb .20 .50
4 Dan Haren .12 .30
5 Stephen Drew .12 .30
6 Mark Reynolds .12 .30
7 Eric Byrnes .12 .30
8 Justin Upton .20 .50
9 Chris B. Young .12 .30
10 Max Scherzer .20 .50
11 Adam Dunn .20 .50
12 David Eckstein .12 .30
13 Jair Jurrjens .12 .30
14 Brandon Jones .12 .30
15 Tom Glavine .20 .50
16 John Smoltz .30 .75
17 Chipper Jones .30 .75
18 Yunel Escobar .12 .30
19 Kelly Johnson .12 .30
20 Brian McCann .20 .50
21 Jeff Francoeur .20 .50
22 Tim Hudson .20 .50
23 Casey Kotchman .12 .30
24 James Parr (RC) .20 .50
25 Nick Markakis .30 .75
26 Brian Roberts .12 .30
27 Jeremy Guthrie .12 .30
28 Adam Jones .20 .50
29 Luke Scott .12 .30
30 Aubrey Huff .12 .30
31 Daniel Cabrera .12 .30
32 George Sherrill .12 .30
33 Melvin Mora .12 .30
34 David Ortiz .20 .50
35 Jacoby Ellsbury .30 .75
36 Coco Crisp .12 .30
37 J.D. Drew .12 .30
38 Daisuke Matsuzaka .30 .75
39 Josh Beckett .20 .50
40 Curt Schilling .20 .50
41 Clay Buchholz .20 .50
42 Dustin Pedroia .40 1.00
43 Julio Lugo .12 .30
44 Mike Lowell .12 .30
45 Jonathan Papelbon .20 .50
46 Jason Varitek .30 .75
47 Hideki Okajima .12 .30
48 Jon Lester .30 .75
49 Tim Wakefield .12 .30
50 Kevin Youkilis .20 .50
51 Jason Bay .20 .50
52 Justin Masterson .12 .30
53 Jeff Samardzija .20 .50
54 Alfonso Soriano .20 .50
55 Derrek Lee .12 .30
56 Aramis Ramirez .12 .30
57 Kerry Wood .12 .30
58 Jim Edmonds .20 .50
59 Kosuke Fukudome .30 .75
60 Geovany Soto .20 .50
61 Ted Lilly .12 .30
62 Carlos Zambrano .20 .50
63 Ryan Theriot .12 .30
64 Mark DeRosa .20 .50
65 Ryan Dempster .12 .30
66 Rich Harden .12 .30
67 Alexei Ramirez .20 .50
68 Nick Swisher .30 .75
69 Carlos Quentin .20 .50
70 Jermaine Dye .12 .30
71 Paul Konerko .20 .50
72 Joe Crede .20 .50
73 Jim Thome .20 .50
74 Gavin Floyd .12 .30
75 Javier Vazquez .12 .30
76 Mark Buehrle .20 .50
77 Bobby Jenks .12 .30
78 Ken Griffey Jr. .50 1.25
79 Brandon Phillips .12 .30
80 Aaron Harang .12 .30
81 Edinson Volquez .12 .30
82 Johnny Cueto .12 .30
83 Edwin Encarnacion .12 .30
84 Joey Votto .30 .75
85 Jay Bruce .20 .50
86 Travis Hafner .12 .30
87 Victor Martinez .20 .50
88 Grady Sizemore .20 .50
89 Cliff Lee .20 .50
90 Ryan Garko .12 .30
91 Jhonny Peralta .12 .30
92 Fausto Carmona .12 .30
93 Troy Tulowitzki .30 .75
94 Matt Holliday .30 .75
95 Todd Helton .20 .50
96 Ubaldo Jimenez .20 .50
97 Brian Fuentes .12 .30
98 Willy Taveras .12 .30
99 Aaron Cook .12 .30
100 Garrett Atkins .12 .30
101 Jeff Francis .12 .30
102 Dexter Fowler (RC) .30 .75
103 Armando Galarraga .12 .30
104 Miguel Cabrera .30 .75
105 Carlos Guillen .12 .30
106 Gary Sheffield .12 .30
107 Curtis Granderson .20 .50
108 Magglio Ordonez .20 .50
109 Dontrelle Willis .12 .30
110 Kenny Rogers .12 .30
111 Justin Verlander .40 1.00
112 Hanley Ramirez .30 .75
113 Jeremy Hermida .12 .30
114 Mike Jacobs .12 .30
115 Andrew Miller .12 .30
116 Josh Willingham .12 .30
117 Dan Uggla .20 .50
118 Josh Johnson .20 .50
119 Hunter Pence .20 .50
120 Roy Oswalt .20 .50
121 Lance Berkman .20 .50
122 Carlos Lee .12 .30
123 Michael Bourn .12 .30
124 Miguel Tejada .20 .50
125 Jose Valverde .12 .30
126 Mike Aviles .12 .30
127 Zack Greinke .20 .50
128 Gil Meche .12 .30
129 Alex Gordon .20 .50
130 Luke Hochevar .12 .30
131 Jose Guillen .12 .30
132 Billy Butler .12 .30
133 David DeJesus .12 .30
134 Mark Teahen .12 .30
135 Joakim Soria .12 .30
136 Mark Teixeira .30 .75
137 Vladimir Guerrero .30 .75
138 Torii Hunter .12 .30
139 Jered Weaver .20 .50
140 Chone Figgins .12 .30
141 Francisco Rodriguez .20 .50
142 Garret Anderson .12 .30
143 Howie Kendrick .12 .30
144 John Lackey .12 .30
145 Ervin Santana .12 .30
146 Joe Saunders .12 .30
147 Manny Ramirez .30 .75
148 Casey Blake .12 .30
149 Chad Billingsley .20 .50
150 Russell Martin .12 .30
151 Matt Kemp .20 .50
152 James Loney .20 .50
153 Jeff Kent .12 .30
154 Nomar Garciaparra .30 .75
155 Rafael Furcal .12 .30
156 Andruw Jones .12 .30
157 Andre Ethier .20 .50
158 Takashi Saito .12 .30
159 Brad Penny .12 .30
160 Hiroki Kuroda .12 .30
161 Jonathan Broxton .12 .30
162 Chin-Lung Hu .12 .30
163 Derek Lowe .12 .30
164 Clayton Kershaw .50 1.25
165 Greg Maddux .40 1.00
166 CC Sabathia .20 .50
167 Yovani Gallardo .12 .30
168 Ryan Braun .40 1.00
169 Prince Fielder .20 .50
170 Corey Hart .12 .30
171 Bill Hall .12 .30
172 Rickie Weeks .20 .50
173 Mike Cameron .12 .30
174 Ben Sheets .12 .30
175 J.J. Hardy .12 .30
176 Mat Gamel RC .50 1.25
177 Denard Span .12 .30
178 Carlos Gomez .12 .30
179 Joe Mauer .30 .75
180 Justin Morneau .30 .75
181 Joe Nathan .12 .30
182 Delmon Young .20 .50
183 Francisco Liriano .12 .30
184 Nick Blackburn .12 .30
185 Daniel Murphy RC .30 .75
186 Nick Evans .12 .30
187 Jose Reyes .20 .50
188 David Wright .40 1.00
189 Carlos Delgado .12 .30
190 Ryan Church .12 .30
191 Carlos Beltran .12 .30
192 Pedro Martinez .20 .50
193 Johan Santana .30 .75
194 John Maine .12 .30
195 Endy Chavez .12 .30
196 Oliver Perez .12 .30
197 Mike Pelfrey .12 .30
198 Jonathon Niese RC .30 .75
199 Ivan Rodriguez .20 .50
200 Alex Rodriguez .50 1.25
201 Derek Jeter .75 2.00
202 Robinson Cano .30 .75
203 Jason Giambi .12 .30
204 Bobby Abreu .12 .30
205 Johnny Damon .20 .50
206 Hideki Matsui .30 .75
207 Jorge Posada .20 .50
208 Joba Chamberlain .20 .50
209 Ian Kennedy .20 .50
210 Mike Mussina .20 .50
211 Andy Pettitte .20 .50
212 Mariano Rivera .30 .75
213 Chien-Ming Wang .20 .50
214 Phil Hughes .20 .50
215 Xavier Nady .12 .30
216 Justin Duchscherer .12 .30
217 Eric Chavez .12 .30
218 Bobby Crosby .12 .30
219 Mark Ellis .12 .30
220 Daric Barton .12 .30
221 Frank Thomas .30 .75
222 Huston Street .12 .30
223 Jack Cust .12 .30
224 Greg Golson (RC) .20 .50
225 Joe Blanton .12 .30
226 Ryan Howard .40 1.00
227 Chase Utley .30 .75
228 Jimmy Rollins .20 .50
229 Pat Burrell .12 .30
230 Shane Victorino .12 .30
231 Brett Myers .12 .30
232 Brad Lidge .12 .30
233 Cole Hamels .30 .75
234 Nate McLouth .12 .30
235 Ian Snell .12 .30
236 Ryan Doumit .12 .30
237 Matt Antonelli RC .30 .75
238 Will Venable RC .20 .50
239 Jake Peavy .12 .30
240 Chris Young .12 .30
241 Trevor Hoffman .20 .50
242 Adrian Gonzalez .20 .50
243 Chase Headley .12 .30
244 Khalil Greene .12 .30
245 Kevin Kouzmanoff .12 .30
246 Brian Giles .12 .30
247 Barry Zito .12 .30
248 Tim Lincecum .50 1.25
249 Matt Cain .12 .30
250 Brian Wilson .30 .75
251 Aaron Rowand .12 .30
252 Conor Gillaspie RC .50 1.25
253 Omar Vizquel .20 .50
254 Bengie Molina .12 .30
255 Erik Bedard .12 .30
256 Felix Hernandez .30 .75
257 Ichiro Suzuki .50 1.25
258 J.J. Putz .12 .30
259 Raul Ibanez .20 .50
260 Adrian Beltre .12 .30
261 Jeff Clement .12 .30
262 Kenji Johjima .12 .30
263 Jose Lopez .12 .30
264 Albert Pujols .75 2.00
265 Troy Glaus .12 .30
266 Chris Carpenter .30 .75
267 Rick Ankiel .12 .30
268 Adam Wainwright .20 .50
269 Chris Duncan .12 .30
270 Todd Wellemeyer .12 .30
271 Ryan Ludwick .20 .50
272 Yadier Molina .20 .50
273 B.J. Upton .20 .50
274 Carl Crawford .20 .50
275 Evan Longoria .40 1.00
276 James Shields .12 .30
277 Scott Kazmir .12 .30
278 Carlos Pena .20 .50
279 Akinori Iwamura .12 .30
280 David Price RC .50 1.25
281 Matt Garza .12 .30
282 Rocco Baldelli .12 .30
283 Michael Young .20 .50
284 Ian Kinsler .20 .50
285 Josh Hamilton .30 .75
286 Hank Blalock .12 .30
287 Milton Bradley .12 .30
288 Jarrod Saltalamacchia .12 .30
289 Roy Halladay .30 .75
290 A.J. Burnett .20 .50
291 Dustin McGowan .12 .30
292 Scott Rolen .20 .50
293 Alex Rios .20 .50
294 Vernon Wells .12 .30
295 B.J. Ryan .12 .30
296 Elijah Dukes .12 .30
297 Lastings Milledge .12 .30
298 Chad Cordero .12 .30
299 Ryan Zimmerman .20 .50
300 Cristian Guzman .12 .30
301 Brandon Webb .20 .50
302 Chris B. Young .12 .30
303 Justin Upton .20 .50
304 Conor Jackson .12 .30
305 Tom Glavine .20 .50
306 Javier Vazquez .12 .30
307 Chipper Jones .30 .75
308 Nick Markakis .30 .75
309 Brian Roberts .12 .30
310 Adam Jones .20 .50
311 Ty Wigginton .20 .50
312 John Smoltz .30 .75
313 Brad Penny .12 .30
314 Takashi Saito .12 .30
315 Josh Beckett .20 .50
316 Dustin Pedroia .40 1.00
317 David Ortiz .20 .50
318 Jason Varitek .30 .75
319 Milton Bradley .12 .30
320 Alfonso Soriano .20 .50
321 Kosuke Fukudome .30 .75
322 Carlos Zambrano .20 .50
323 Jim Thome .20 .50
324 Chris Getz .12 .30
325 Octavio Dotel .12 .30
326 Joey Votto .30 .75
327 Jay Bruce .20 .50
328 Kerry Wood .12 .30
329 Mark DeRosa .20 .50
330 Grady Sizemore .20 .50
331 Troy Tulowitzki .30 .75
332 Todd Helton .20 .50
333 Adam Everett .12 .30
334 Cameron Maybin .12 .30
335 Roy Oswalt .20 .50
336 Lance Berkman .20 .50
337 Joakim Soria .12 .30
338 Alex Gordon .20 .50
339 Bobby Abreu .12 .30
340 Vladimir Guerrero .30 .75
341 Manny Ramirez .30 .75
342 Orlando Hudson .12 .30
343 Mark Loretta .12 .30
344 Russell Martin .12 .30
345 Trevor Hoffman .20 .50
346 Ryan Braun .40 1.00
347 Francisco Liriano .12 .30
348 Joe Mauer .30 .75
349 Livan Hernandez .12 .30
350 Jeremy Reed .12 .30
351 J.J. Putz .12 .30
352 Francisco Rodriguez .20 .50
353 Johan Santana .30 .75
354 Jose Reyes .20 .50
355 David Wright .40 1.00
356 Derek Jeter .75 2.00
357 A.J. Burnett .20 .50
358 Nick Swisher .30 .75
359 CC Sabathia .20 .50
360 Chien-Ming Wang .20 .50
361 Mark Teixeira .30 .75
362 Joba Chamberlain .20 .50
363 Alex Rodriguez .50 1.25
364 Orlando Cabrera .12 .30
365 Matt Holliday .30 .75
366 Jason Giambi .12 .30
367 Chan Ho Park .20 .50
368 Cole Hamels .30 .75
369 Ryan Howard .40 1.00
370 Chase Utley .30 .75
371 Randy Johnson .20 .50
372 Edgar Renteria .12 .30
373 Ken Griffey Jr. .50 1.25
374 Ichiro Suzuki .50 1.25
375 Khalil Greene .12 .30
376 Albert Pujols .75 2.00
377 Akinori Iwamura .12 .30
378 B.J. Upton .20 .50
379 Evan Longoria .40 1.00
380 Josh Hamilton .30 .75
381 Nelson Cruz .20 .50
382 Adam Dunn .20 .50
383 Josh Willingham .12 .30
384 Daniel Cabrera .12 .30
385 Koji Uehara RC .30 .75
386 Kenshin Kawakami RC .30 .75
387 Jason Motte (RC) .30 .75
388 Elvis Andrus RC .30 .75
389 Rick Porcello RC .60 1.50
390 Colby Rasmus (RC) .50 1.25
391 Shairon Martis RC .30 .75
392 Ricky Romero (RC) .50 1.25
393 Kevin Jepsen (RC) .30 .75
394 James McDonald RC .50 1.25
395 Brett Anderson RC .30 .75
396 Trevor Cahill RC .50 1.25
397 Jordan Schafer (RC) .30 .75
398 Trevor Crowe RC .30 .75
399 Everth Cabrera RC .30 .75
400 Ryan Perry RC .50 1.25

2009 Upper Deck First Edition Star Quest

SQ1 Albert Pujols 1.50 4.00
SQ2 Alex Rodriguez 1.00 2.50
SQ3 Alfonso Soriano .40 1.00
SQ4 Chipper Jones .60 1.50
SQ5 Chase Utley .60 1.50
SQ6 Derek Jeter 1.50 4.00
SQ7 Daisuke Matsuzaka .60 1.50
SQ8 David Ortiz .40 1.00
SQ9 David Wright .75 2.00
SQ10 Grady Sizemore .40 1.00
SQ11 Hanley Ramirez .60 1.50
SQ12 Ichiro Suzuki 1.00 2.50
SQ13 Josh Beckett .40 1.00
SQ14 Jake Peavy .25 .60
SQ15 Jose Reyes .40 1.00
SQ16 Johan Santana .60 1.50
SQ17 Ken Griffey Jr. 1.00 2.50
SQ18 Lance Berkman .40 1.00
SQ19 Miguel Cabrera .60 1.50
SQ20 Matt Holliday .60 1.50
SQ21 Manny Ramirez .60 1.50
SQ22 Prince Fielder .40 1.00
SQ23 Ryan Braun .75 2.00
SQ24 Ryan Howard .75 2.00
SQ25 Vladimir Guerrero .60 1.50

2006 Upper Deck Future Stars

This 159-card set was released in January, 2007. The set was issued in four-card packs which had an $4.99 SRP and came 24 packs to a box and 12 boxes to a case. Cards numbered 1-75 feature veterans issued in alphabetical team order while cards 75-159 feature signed cards of 2006 rookies.

COMP.SET w/o AU's (75) 10.00 25.00
COMMON CARD (1-75) .15 .40
COMMON AU RC (76-159) 3.00 8.00
FIVE AU RC PER BOX ON AVERAGE
NO SP PRICING DUE TO SCARCITY
PRINTING PLATE ODDS 1:2 CASES
PLATE PRINT RUN 1 SET PER COLOR
BLACK-CYAN-MAGENTA-YELLOW ISSUED
NO PLATE PRICING DUE TO SCARCITY
1 Miguel Tejada .25 .60
2 Brian Roberts .15 .40
3 Brandon Webb .25 .60
4 Luis Gonzalez .15 .40
5 Andruw Jones .15 .40
6 Chipper Jones .40 1.00
7 John Smoltz .40 1.00
8 Curt Schilling .25 .60
9 Josh Beckett .25 .60
10 David Ortiz .25 .60
11 Manny Ramirez .40 1.00
12 Jim Thome .25 .60
13 Paul Konerko .25 .60
14 Jermaine Dye .15 .40
15 Derrek Lee .15 .40
16 Greg Maddux .60 1.50
17 Ken Griffey Jr. .60 1.50
18 Adam Dunn .25 .60
19 Felipe Lopez .15 .40
20 Travis Hafner .15 .40
21 Victor Martinez .25 .60
22 Grady Sizemore .25 .60
23 Todd Helton .25 .60
24 Matt Holliday .40 1.00
25 Jeremy Bonderman .15 .40
26 Ivan Rodriguez .25 .60
27 Miguel Cabrera .40 1.00
28 Dontrelle Willis .15 .40
29 Roger Clemens .50 1.25
30 Roy Oswalt .25 .60
31 Lance Berkman .25 .60
32 Reggie Sanders .15 .40
33 Vladimir Guerrero .40 1.00
34 Chone Figgins .15 .40
35 Jeff Kent .15 .40
36 Eric Gagne .15 .40
37 Carlos Lee .15 .40
38 Rickie Weeks .25 .60
39 Johan Santana .40 1.00
40 Torii Hunter .15 .40
41 Alex Rodriguez .60 1.50
42 Derek Jeter 1.00 2.50
43 Randy Johnson .40 1.00
44 Hideki Matsui .40 1.00
45 Johnny Damon .25 .60
46 Pedro Martinez .25 .60
47 David Wright .60 1.50
48 Carlos Beltran .15 .40
49 Rich Harden .15 .40
50 Eric Chavez .15 .40
51 Huston Street .15 .40
52 Ryan Howard .60 1.50
53 Bobby Abreu .15 .40
54 Chase Utley .40 1.00
55 Jason Bay .15 .40
56 Jake Peavy .15 .40
57 Brian Giles .15 .40
58 Trevor Hoffman .25 .60
59 Jason Schmidt .15 .40
60 Randy Winn .15 .40
61 Kenji Johjima RC .40 1.00
62 Ichiro Suzuki .60 1.50
63 Felix Hernandez .40 1.00
64 Albert Pujols 1.00 2.50
65 Chris Carpenter .40 1.00
66 Jim Edmonds .25 .60
67 Carl Crawford .25 .60
68 Scott Kazmir .25 .60
69 Jonny Gomes .15 .40
70 Mark Teixeira .40 1.00
71 Michael Young .25 .60
72 Vernon Wells .15 .40
73 Roy Halladay .40 1.00
74 Nick Johnson .15 .40
75 Alfonso Soriano .25 .60
76 Adam Wainwright AU (RC) 6.00 15.00
77 Anderson Hernandez AU (RC) 3.00 8.00
78 Andre Ethier AU SP (RC) 10.00 25.00
79 Colter Bean AU SP (RC) 4.00 10.00
80 Ben Johnson AU (RC) 3.00 8.00
81 Boof Bonser AU SP (RC) 5.00 12.00
82 Boone Logan AU RC 3.00 8.00
83 Brian Anderson AU (RC) 3.00 8.00
84 Brian Bannister AU (RC) 5.00 12.00
85 Chris Denorfia AU SP (RC) 4.00 10.00
86 Chad Billingsley AU SP (RC) 8.00 20.00
87 Cody Ross AU (RC) 6.00 15.00
88 Cole Hamels AU SP (RC) 30.00 60.00
89 Conor Jackson AU (RC) 5.00 12.00
90 Dan Uggla AU SP (RC)
91 Dave Gassner AU SP (RC) 3.00 8.00
92 Jordan Tata AU RC 3.00 8.00
93 Eric Reed AU (RC) 3.00 8.00
94 Fausto Carmona AU (RC) 5.00 12.00
95 Luis Figueroa AU SP RC
96 Francisco Liriano AU SP (RC) 10.00 25.00
97 Freddie Bynum AU (RC) 3.00 8.00
98 Hanley Ramirez AU SP (RC) 8.00 20.00
99 Hong-Chih Kuo AU SP (RC) 15.00 40.00
100 Ian Kinsler AU (RC) 10.00 25.00
101 Nelson Cruz AU SP (RC) 10.00 25.00
102 Ruddy Lugo AU (RC) 3.00 8.00
103 Jason Kubel AU SP (RC) 3.00 8.00
104 Jeff Harris AU RC 3.00 8.00
105 Santiago Ramirez AU (RC) 3.00 8.00
106 Jered Weaver AU SP (RC) 20.00 50.00
107 Jeremy Accardo AU SP RC 6.00 15.00
108 Josh Willingham AU SP (RC) 3.00 8.00
109 Joel Zumaya AU SP (RC) 10.00 25.00
110 Joey Devine AU RC 3.00 8.00
111 John Koronka AU (RC) 3.00 8.00
112 Jonathan Papelbon AU (RC) 15.00 40.00
113 Jose Capellan AU (RC) 3.00 8.00
114 Josh Johnson AU (RC) 8.00 20.00
115 Josh Rupe AU SP (RC) 3.00 8.00
116 Jeremy Hermida AU SP (RC) 3.00 8.00
117 Josh Wilson AU (RC) 3.00 8.00
118 Justin Verlander AU SP (RC)
119 Kelly Shoppach AU (RC) 3.00 8.00
120 Kendry Morales AU (RC) 10.00 25.00
121 Sean Tracey AU (RC) 3.00 8.00
122 Macay McBride AU (RC) 3.00 8.00
123 Martin Prado AU SP (RC)
124 Matt Cain AU (RC) 6.00 15.00
125 Russell Martin AU (RC) 5.00 12.00
126 Tim Hamulack AU SP (RC) 3.00 8.00
127 Mike Jacobs AU (RC) 5.00 12.00
128 Ben Hendrickson AU (RC) 3.00 8.00
129 Jack Taschner AU (RC) 3.00 8.00
130 Nate McLouth AU (RC) 6.00 15.00
131 Jeremy Sowers AU SP (RC) 8.00 20.00
132 Paul Maholm AU (RC) 3.00 8.00
133 Stephen Drew AU SP (RC)
134 Jason Bergmann AU RC 3.00 8.00
135 Rich Hill AU SP (RC) 12.50 30.00
136 Melky Cabrera AU SP (RC)
137 Scott Dunn AU (RC) 3.00 8.00
138 Ryan Zimmerman AU (RC) 20.00 50.00
139 Anibal Sanchez AU (RC) 5.00 12.00
140 Sean Marshall AU (RC) 5.00 12.00
141 Takashi Saito AU SP RC
142 Taylor Buchholz AU (RC) 3.00 8.00
143 Carlos Quentin AU SP (RC) 4.00 10.00
144 Matt Garza AU (RC) 8.00 20.00
145 Wil Nieves AU (RC) 3.00 8.00
146 Jamie Shields AU RC 10.00 25.00
147 Jon Lester AU SP RC 12.50 30.00
148 Craig Hansen AU SP RC
149 Aaron Rakers AU (RC) 3.00 8.00
150 Bobby Livingston AU (RC) 3.00 8.00
151 Brendan Harris AU (RC) 3.00 8.00
152 Alay Soler AU SP RC 3.00 8.00
153 Chris Britton AU RC 3.00 8.00
154 Howie Kendrick AU SP (RC) 15.00 40.00
155 Jermaine Van Buren AU (RC) 3.00 8.00
156 Choo Freeman AU SP (RC) 3.00 8.00
157 Matt Capps AU (RC) 3.00 8.00
158 Peter Moylan AU RC 3.00 8.00
159 Ty Taubenheim AU RC 3.00 8.00

2006 Upper Deck Future Stars Black

*BLACK: 2.5X TO 6X BASIC
STATED PRINT RUN 50 SER.#'d SETS

2006 Upper Deck Future Stars Blue

*BLUE: 2X TO 5X BASIC
STATED PRINT RUN 99 SER.#'d SETS

2006 Upper Deck Future Stars Gold

*GOLD: 6X TO 15X BASIC
STATED PRINT RUN 25 SER.#'d SETS

2006 Upper Deck Future Stars Green

*GREEN: 1.5X TO 4X BASIC
STATED PRINT RUN 499 SER.#'d SETS

2006 Upper Deck Future Stars Purple

*PURPLE: 1.25X TO 3X BASIC
STATED PRINT RUN 1799 SER.#'d SETS

2006 Upper Deck Future Stars Red

*RED: 1.5X TO 4X BASIC
STATED PRINT RUN 299 SER.#'d SETS

2006 Upper Deck Future Stars Rookie Signatures Red

STATED PRINT RUN 35 SER.#'d SETS
NO PRICING DUE TO SCARCITY

2006 Upper Deck Future Stars Clear Path to History Triple Signatures

STATED ODDS 1:288
BSJ Jason Bay 30.00 60.00

Alfonso Soriano
Andruw Jones
CPO Chris Carpenter 20.00 50.00
Jake Peavy
Roy Oswalt
CUK Carl Crawford 20.00 50.00
B.J. Upton
Scott Kazmir
DRR Stephen Drew 50.00 100.00
Jose Reyes
Hanley Ramirez
GEH Tony Gwynn Jr. 20.00 50.00
Andre Ethier
Jeremy Hermida
GJG Ken Griffey Jr.
Andruw Jones
Vladimir Guerrero
GPT Ken Griffey Jr.
Albert Pujols
Jim Thome
GTT Ken Griffey Jr.
Frank Thomas
Jim Thome
HTT Travis Hafner
Jim Thome
Frank Thomas
JVW Josh Johnson 40.00 80.00
Justin Verlander
Jered Weaver
KBM Jason Kubel
Boof Bonser
Joe Mauer
KTZ Howie Kendrick 40.00 80.00
Troy Tulowitzki
Ryan Zimmerman
MKW Kendry Morales 40.00 80.00
Howie Kendrick
Jered Weaver
MML Justin Morneau 40.00 80.00
Joe Mauer
Francisco Liriano
MOH Justin Morneau 20.00 50.00
Lyle Overbay
Travis Hafner
NHP Joe Nathan 30.00 60.00
Trevor Hoffman
Jonathan Papelbon
PGJ Albert Pujols
Ken Griffey Jr.
Derek Jeter
PSO Jake Peavy 20.00 50.00
Ben Sheets
Roy Oswalt
PVW Jonathan Papelbon 60.00 120.00
Justin Verlander
Jered Weaver
SBH Alay Soler 12.50 30.00
Chad Billingsley
Cole Hamels
SHL Jeremy Sowers 12.50 30.00
Cole Hamels
Francisco Liriano
SHN Huston Street
Trevor Hoffman
Joe Nathan
TZU Troy Tulowitzki 50.00 100.00
Ryan Zimmerman
B.J. Upton
URB Chase Utley 30.00 60.00
Brian Roberts
Craig Biggio
VBZ Justin Verlander 60.00 120.00
Jeremy Bonderman
Joel Zumaya
WKJ Dontrelle Willis
Scott Kazmir
Randy Johnson

2006 Upper Deck Future Stars World Future Stars

COMPLETE SET (25) 10.00 25.00
PRINTING PLATE ODDS 1:2 CASES
PLATE PRINT RUN 1 SET PER COLOR
BLACK-CYAN-MAGENTA-YELLOW ISSUED
NO PLATE PRICING DUE TO SCARCITY
1 Adam Loewen .30 .75
2 Nan Wang .30 .75
3 Yi Feng .30 .75
4 Chien-Ming Chang .50 1.25
5 Yung-Chi Chen .50 1.25
6 Chin-Lung Hu 1.00 2.50
7 Yadel Marti .30 .75
8 Frederich Cepeda .30 .75
9 Pedro Luis Lazo .50 1.25
10 Osmany Urrutia .30 .75
11 Yoandy Garlobo .30 .75
12 Nobuhiko Matsunaka .50 1.25
13 Daisuke Matsuzaka 1.00 2.50
14 Tsuyoshi Nishioka 2.00 5.00
15 Tomoya Satozaki .50 1.25
16 Koji Uehara .75 2.00
17 Shunsuke Watanabe .50 1.25
18 Jong Beom Lee .30 .75
19 Sidney de Jong .30 .75
20 Shairon Martis .30 .75
21 Len Pecota .30 .75
22 Dicky Gonzalez .30 .75
23 Nicholas Dempsey .30 .75
24 Brett Willemburg .30 .75
25 Chase Utley .75 2.00

2006 Upper Deck Future Stars World Future Stars Black

*BLACK: 3X TO 8X BASIC
COMMON TEAM CHINESE TAIPEI 12.50 30.00
COMMON TEAM JAPAN 12.50 30.00
STATED PRINT RUN 50 SER.#'d SETS

2006 Upper Deck Future Stars World Future Stars Blue

*BLUE: 2.5X TO 6X BASIC
COMMON TEAM CHINESE TAIPEI 5.00 12.00
COMMON TEAM JAPAN 5.00 12.00
STATED PRINT RUN 99 SER.#'d SETS

2006 Upper Deck Future Stars World Future Stars Gold

STATED PRINT RUN 25 SER.#'d SETS
NO PRICING DUE TO SCARCITY

2006 Upper Deck Future Stars World Future Stars Green

*GREEN: 1.5X TO 4X BASIC
COMMON TEAM CHINESE TAIPEI 4.00 10.00
COMMON TEAM JAPAN 4.00 10.00
STATED PRINT RUN 499 SER.#'d SETS

2006 Upper Deck Future Stars World Future Stars Purple

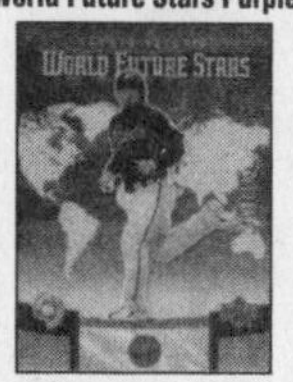

*PURPLE: .75X TO 2X BASIC
STATED PRINT RUN 1799 SER.#'d SETS

2006 Upper Deck Future Stars World Future Stars Red

*RED: 2X TO 5X BASIC
COMMON TEAM CHINESE TAIPEI 4.00 10.00
COMMON TEAM JAPAN 4.00 10.00
STATED PRINT RUN 299 SER.#'d SETS

2007 Upper Deck Future Stars

This 190-card set was released in September, 2007. This set was released in hobby, retail and special Walmart packs. The hobby version was four-card packs, with an $4.99 SRP which came 24 packs to a box and 12 boxes to a case. Cards numbered 1-100 feature veterans sequenced in team alphabetical order while cards 101-190 feature signed 2007 rookies. Those signed rookies were inserted at a stated rate of one in six hobby, one in 24 retail and one in 350 Walmart. A few players did not return their signatures in time for pack out and those cards could be redeemed until September 5, 2009.

COMP.SET w/o AU's (100) 10.00 25.00
COMMON CARD (1-100) .15 .40
COMMON AU RC (101-190) 3.00 8.00
101-190 ODDS 1:6 HOB,1:24 RET,1:350
WALMART
EXCHANGE DEADLINE 9/5/2009
1 Brandon Webb .15 .40
2 Conor Jackson .15 .40
3 Stephen Drew .25 .60
4 Chipper Jones .40 1.00
5 Andruw Jones .25 .60
6 Jeff Francoeur .40 1.00
7 John Smoltz .25 .60
8 Miguel Tejada .15 .40
9 Nick Markakis .25 .60
10 Brian Roberts .15 .40
11 David Ortiz .40 1.00
12 Manny Ramirez .25 .60
13 Josh Beckett .15 .40
14 Curt Schilling .25 .60
15 Derrek Lee .15 .40
16 Aramis Ramirez .15 .40
17 Carlos Zambrano .15 .40
18 Alfonso Soriano .15 .40
19 Jim Thome .25 .60
20 Paul Konerko .15 .40
21 Jon Garland .15 .40
22 Ken Griffey Jr. .60 1.50
23 Adam Dunn .15 .40
24 Aaron Harang .15 .40
25 Travis Hafner .15 .40
26 Victor Martinez .15 .40
27 Grady Sizemore .25 .60
28 C.C. Sabathia .15 .40
29 Todd Helton .25 .60
30 Matt Holliday .20 .50
31 Garrett Atkins .15 .40
32 Ivan Rodriguez .25 .60
33 Magglio Ordonez .15 .40
34 Gary Sheffield .15 .40
35 Justin Verlander .40 1.00
36 Miguel Cabrera .25 .60
37 Hanley Ramirez .25 .60
38 Dontrelle Willis .15 .40
39 Lance Berkman .15 .40
40 Roy Oswalt .15 .40
41 Carlos Lee .15 .40
42 Gil Meche .15 .40
43 Emil Brown .15 .40
44 Mark Teahen .15 .40
45 Vladimir Guerrero .40 1.00
46 Jered Weaver .25 .60
47 Howie Kendrick .15 .40
48 Juan Pierre .15 .40
49 Nomar Garciaparra .40 1.00
50 Rafael Furcal .15 .40
51 Jeff Kent .15 .40
52 Prince Fielder .40 1.00
53 Ben Sheets .15 .40
54 Rickie Weeks .15 .40
55 Justin Morneau .15 .40
56 Joe Mauer .25 .60
57 Torii Hunter .15 .40
58 Johan Santana .25 .60
59 Jose Reyes .40 1.00
60 David Wright .60 1.50
61 Carlos Delgado .15 .40
62 Carlos Beltran .15 .40
63 Derek Jeter 1.00 2.50
64 Alex Rodriguez .60 1.50
65 Johnny Damon .25 .60
66 Jason Giambi .15 .40
67 Bobby Abreu .15 .40
68 Mike Piazza .40 1.00
69 Nick Swisher .15 .40
70 Eric Chavez .15 .40
71 Ryan Howard .60 1.50
72 Chase Utley .40 1.00
73 Jimmy Rollins .15 .40
74 Jason Bay .15 .40
75 Freddy Sanchez .15 .40
76 Zach Duke .15 .40
77 Greg Maddux .60 1.50
78 Adrian Gonzalez .15 .40
79 Jake Peavy .15 .40
80 Ray Durham .15 .40
81 Barry Zito .15 .40
82 Matt Cain .25 .60
83 Ichiro Suzuki .60 1.50
84 Felix Hernandez .25 .60
85 Richie Sexson .15 .40
86 Albert Pujols .75 2.00
87 Scott Rolen .25 .60
88 Chris Carpenter .15 .40
89 Chris Duncan .15 .40
90 Carl Crawford .15 .40
91 Rocco Baldelli .15 .40
92 Scott Kazmir .25 .60
93 Michael Young .15 .40
94 Mark Teixeira .25 .60
95 Ian Kinsler .15 .40
96 Troy Glaus .15 .40
97 Vernon Wells .15 .40
98 Roy Halladay .15 .40
99 Ryan Zimmerman .40 1.00
100 Nick Johnson .15 .40
101 Zack Segovia AU (RC) 3.00 8.00
102 Joaquin Arias AU (RC) 3.00 8.00
103 Troy Tulowitzki AU SP (RC)
104 Travis Buck AU (RC) 4.00 10.00
105 Mike Schultz AU RC 3.00 8.00
106 Sean White AU SP RC
107 Sean Henn AU (RC) 3.00 8.00
108 Ryan Z. Braun AU RC 6.00 15.00
109 Rick Vanden Hurk AU RC 3.00 8.00
110 Carlos Gomez AU SP RC
111 Mike Rabelo AU RC 4.00 10.00
112 Felix Pie AU (RC) 4.00 10.00
113 Miguel Montero AU (RC) 4.00 10.00
114 Michael Bourn AU (RC) 4.00 10.00
116 Matt Lindstrom AU (RC) 3.00 8.00
117 Matt Chico AU (RC) 3.00 8.00
118 Levale Speigner AU RC 3.00 8.00
119 Lee Gardner AU (RC) 3.00 8.00
120 Kory Casto AU (RC) 4.00 10.00
121 Kevin Kouzmanoff AU (RC) 4.00 10.00
122 Kevin Cameron AU RC 3.00 8.00
123 Kei Igawa AU SP RC
124 Tyler Clippard AU (RC) 6.00 15.00
125 Juan Perez AU RC 3.00 8.00
126 Josh Hamilton AU SP (RC) 12.50 30.00
127 Joseph Bisenius AU RC 3.00 8.00
128 Jose Luis Garcia AU RC 3.00 8.00
129 Jon Knott AU (RC) 3.00 8.00
130 Jon Coutlangus AU (RC) 4.00 10.00
131 John Danks AU RC 4.00 10.00
132 Joe Smith AU RC 3.00 8.00
133 Matt Brown AU RC 3.00 8.00
134 Joakim Soria AU RC 4.00 10.00
135 Jesus Flores AU RC 6.00 15.00
136 Jeff Baker AU (RC) 3.00 8.00
137 Jay Marshall AU RC 3.00 8.00
138 Jared Burton AU RC 4.00 10.00
139 Jamie Vermilyea AU RC 4.00 10.00
140 Jamie Burke AU (RC) 4.00 10.00
141 Ryan Rowland-Smith AU RC 4.00 10.00
142 Connor Robertson AU RC 3.00 8.00
143 Hector Gimenez AU (RC) 3.00 8.00
144 Gustavo Molina AU RC 4.00 10.00
145 Glen Perkins AU (RC) 3.00 8.00
147 Doug Slaten AU RC 3.00 8.00
148 Ryan Braun AU (RC) 15.00 40.00
149 Delmon Young AU SP (RC)
150 Garrett Jones AU (RC) 8.00 20.00
151 Chris Stewart AU SP RC
152 Cesar Jimenez AU RC 4.00 10.00
153 Brian Stokes AU (RC) 3.00 8.00
154 Brian Burres AU (RC) 4.00 10.00
155 Brian Barden AU SP RC
156 Kyle Kendrick AU RC 12.50 30.00
157 Andrew Miller AU RC 5.00 12.00
158 Alexi Casilla AU RC 3.00 8.00
159 Alex Gordon AU SP RC 15.00 40.00
160 A.J. Murray AU RC 4.00 10.00
161 Akinori Iwamura AU SP RC
162 Adam Lind AU (RC) 4.00 10.00
163 Chase Wright AU RC 5.00 12.00
164 Dallas Braden AU RC 20.00 50.00
165 Rocky Cherry AU RC 5.00 12.00
166 Andy Gonzalez AU RC 3.00 8.00
167 Neal Musser AU RC 3.00 8.00
168 Mark Reynolds AU RC 30.00 60.00
169 Dennis Dove AU (RC) 3.00 8.00
170 Justin Hampson AU (RC) 4.00 10.00
171 Phil Hughes AU SP (RC)
172 Kelvin Jimenez AU RC 3.00 8.00
173 Hunter Pence AU SP (RC)
174 Brad Salmon AU RC 6.00 15.00
175 Ryan Sweeney AU (RC) 3.00 8.00
176 Brandon Wood AU (RC) 6.00 15.00
177 Billy Butler AU SP (RC)
178 Ben Francisco AU (RC) 3.00 8.00
179 Devern Hansack AU SP RC
180 Yoel Hernandez AU RC 3.00 8.00
181 Tim Lincecum AU SP RC 50.00 100.00
182 Danny Putnam AU (RC) 5.00 12.00
183 Jarrod Saltalamacchia AU SP (RC) 6.00 15.00
184 Andy LaRoche AU SP (RC)
185 Matt DeSalvo AU (RC) 5.00 12.00
186 Fred Lewis AU (RC) 3.00 8.00
187 Anthony Lerew AU (RC) 3.00 8.00
188 Jesse Litsch AU RC 4.00 10.00
189a Daisuke Matsuzaka RC
189b Daisuke Matsuzaka AU SP 125.00 250.00

2007 Upper Deck Future Stars Gold

*GOLD: 2X TO 5X BASIC
RANDOM INSERTS IN PACKS
STATED PRINT RUN 99 SER.#'d SETS
83 Ichiro Suzuki 6.00 15.00
189 Daisuke Matsuzaka 20.00 50.00

2007 Upper Deck Future Stars Red

*RED: 1.5X TO 4X BASIC
RANDOM INSERTS IN PACKS
STATED PRINT RUN 199 SER.#'d SETS
83 Ichiro Suzuki 5.00 12.00
189 Daisuke Matsuzaka 8.00 20.00

2007 Upper Deck Future Stars All Star Futures

RANDOM INSERTS IN PACKS
STATED PRINT RUN 500 SER.#'d SETS
AD Alejandro De Aza .75 2.00
AG Alex Gordon 1.50 4.00
AI Akinori Iwamura 1.25 3.00
AL Adam Lind .50 1.25
AM Andrew Miller 1.25 3.00
BA Jeff Baker .50 1.25
BI Billy Butler .75 2.00
BM Brandon Morrow 2.50 6.00
BU B.J. Upton .50 1.25
BW Brandon Wood .50 1.25
CA Alexi Casilla .75 2.00
CG Carlos Gomez .75 2.00
CW Chase Wright 1.25 3.00
CY Chris Young .50 1.25
DM Daisuke Matsuzaka 2.00 5.00
DP Danny Putnam .50 1.25
DY Delmon Young .75 2.00
FL Fred Lewis .75 2.00
FP Felix Pie .50 1.25
GP Glen Perkins .50 1.25
HA Josh Hamilton 2.00 5.00
HK Howie Kendrick .50 1.25
HP Hunter Pence 2.50 6.00
IK Ian Kinsler .75 2.00
JA Joaquin Arias .50 1.25
JD John Danks .75 2.00
JS Jarrod Saltalamacchia .75 2.00
JV Justin Verlander 1.50 4.00
KC Kory Casto .50 1.25
KI Kei Igawa 1.25 3.00
KK Kevin Kouzmanoff .50 1.25
LA Andy LaRoche .50 1.25
MA Matt Chico .50 1.25
MB Michael Bourn .50 1.25
MC Matt Cain .75 2.00
MI Miguel Montero .50 1.25
ML Matt Lindstrom .50 1.25
MO Micah Owings .50 1.25
PF Prince Fielder .75 2.00
PH Phil Hughes 2.50 6.00
RB Ryan Braun 2.50 6.00
RS Ryan Sweeney .50 1.25
RZ Ryan Zimmerman .75 2.00
SD Stephen Drew .50 1.25
SM Joe Smith .50 1.25
SO Joakim Soria .50 1.25
TB Travis Buck .50 1.25
TL Tim Lincecum 8.00 20.00
TP Tony Pena .50 1.25
TT Troy Tulowitzki 3.00 8.00

2007 Upper Deck Future Stars All Star Futures Signatures

STATED ODDS 1:72 H,1:2500 R,1:2500
WALMART
NO SP PRICING DUE TO SCARCITY
EXCH DEADLINE 9/5/2009
AG Alex Gordon SP
AI Akinori Iwamura SP
AL Adam Lind 4.00 10.00
AM Andrew Miller 4.00 10.00
BA Jeff Baker 3.00 8.00
BI Billy Butler
BU B.J. Upton 4.00 10.00
BW Brandon Wood 6.00 15.00
CA Alexi Casilla 3.00 8.00
CG Carlos Gomez 6.00 15.00
CW Chase Wright 5.00 12.00
CY Chris Young 10.00 25.00
DM Daisuke Matsuzaka SP
DP Danny Putnam 4.00 10.00
DY Delmon Young SP
FL Fred Lewis 3.00 8.00
FP Felix Pie 3.00 8.00
GP Glen Perkins 5.00 12.00
HA Josh Hamilton 12.50 30.00
HK Howie Kendrick
HP Hunter Pence 30.00 60.00
IK Ian Kinsler 6.00 15.00
JA Joaquin Arias 3.00 8.00
JD John Danks 4.00 10.00
JS Jarrod Saltalamacchia 6.00 15.00
JV Justin Verlander SP
KC Kory Casto 3.00 8.00
KI Kei Igawa SP
KK Kevin Kouzmanoff 5.00 12.00
LA Andy LaRoche 4.00 10.00
MA Matt Chico 3.00 8.00
MC Matt Cain 5.00 12.00
MI Miguel Montero 3.00 8.00
ML Matt Lindstrom 3.00 8.00
PF Prince Fielder SP
PH Phil Hughes SP
RB Ryan Braun 40.00 80.00
RS Ryan Sweeney 4.00 10.00
RZ Ryan Zimmerman SP
SD Stephen Drew SP
SM Joe Smith 3.00 8.00
SO Joakim Soria 5.00 12.00
TB Travis Buck 5.00 12.00
TL Tim Lincecum 40.00 80.00
TP Tony Pena 5.00 12.00
TT Troy Tulowitzki 10.00 25.00

2007 Upper Deck Future Stars Clear Path to History Triple Signatures

STATED ODDS 1:288 HOB,1:5000 RET
NO SP PRICING DUE TO SCARCITY
BBO Roy Oswalt
Lance Berkman
Craig Biggio
CCH Bobby Crosby 20.00 50.00
Eric Chavez
Rich Harden
CWR Dontrelle Willis
Miguel Cabrera
Hanley Ramirez
CYI Akinori Iwamura
Carl Crawford
Delmon Young SP
DMY Stephen Drew 20.00 50.00
Miguel Montero
Chris Young
FEG Rafael Furcal 15.00 40.00
Andre Ethier
Luis Gonzalez
GKW Vladimir Guerrero
Jered Weaver
Howie Kendrick SP
GPC Albert Pujols
Miguel Cabrera
Vladimir Guerrero SP
HAT Matt Holliday 15.00 40.00
Garrett Atkins
Troy Tulowitzki

HMS Travis Hafner 30.00 60.00
Victor Martinez
Jeremy Sowers
HSW Johan Santana
Dontrelle Willis
Roy Halladay
KUC Scott Kazmir 20.00 50.00
B.J. Upton
Carl Crawford
KVK Ian Kinsler 15.00 40.00
Howie Kendrick
Dan Uggla
MPM Melvin Mora 15.00 40.00
Nick Markakis
Corey Patterson
SWF Prince Fielder 20.00 50.00
Ben Sheets
Rickie Weeks
THM Justin Morneau
Travis Hafner
Jim Thome
VZR Hanley Ramirez 40.00 80.00
Justin Verlander
Ryan Zimmerman
YBP Delmon Young 15.00 40.00
Billy Butler
Felix Pie

2007 Upper Deck Future Stars Cy Young Futures

RANDOM INSERTS IN PACKS
STATED PRINT RUN 500 SER.#'d SETS
AL Anthony Lerew .50 1.25
AM Andrew Miller 1.25 3.00
BM Brandon Morrow 2.50 6.00
CH Cole Hamels 1.25 3.00
CW Chase Wright 1.25 3.00
DM Daisuke Matsuzaka 2.00 5.00
GP Glen Perkins .50 1.25
JD John Danks .75 2.00
JG Jose Garcia .50 1.25
JL Jon Lester 1.25 3.00
JS Jeremy Sowers .50 1.25
JV Justin Verlander 1.50 4.00
JZ Joel Zumaya .75 2.00
KI Kei Igawa 1.25 3.00
MA Matt Chico .50 1.25
MC Matt Cain .75 2.00
MO Micah Owings .50 1.25
PH Phil Hughes 2.50 6.00
RV Rick VandenHurk .50 1.25
SH Sean Henn .50 1.25
SK Scott Kazmir .75 2.00
SM Joe Smith .50 1.25
TC Tyler Clippard .75 2.00
TL Tim Lincecum 8.00 20.00
ZS Zack Segovia .50 1.25

2007 Upper Deck Future Stars Cy Young Futures Signatures

STATED ODDS 1:72 H,1:2500 R,1:2500 WALMART
NO SP PRICING DUE TO SCARCITY
EXCH DEADLINE 9/5/2009
AL Anthony Lerew 3.00 8.00
AM Andrew Miller 4.00 10.00
CH Cole Hamels 12.50 30.00
CW Chase Wright 5.00 12.00
GP Glen Perkins 5.00 12.00
JD John Danks 4.00 10.00
JG Jose Garcia 3.00 8.00
JS Jeremy Sowers SP
JV Justin Verlander SP
JZ Joel Zumaya
KI Kei Igawa SP
MA Matt Chico 3.00 8.00
MC Matt Cain 5.00 12.00
MO Micah Owings 6.00 15.00
PH Phil Hughes SP
RV Rick VandenHurk 3.00 8.00
SH Sean Henn 3.00 8.00
SK Scott Kazmir SP
SM Joe Smith 3.00 8.00
TC Tyler Clippard 6.00 15.00
TL Tim Lincecum 30.00 60.00
ZS Zack Segovia 3.00 8.00

2007 Upper Deck Future Stars MVP Futures

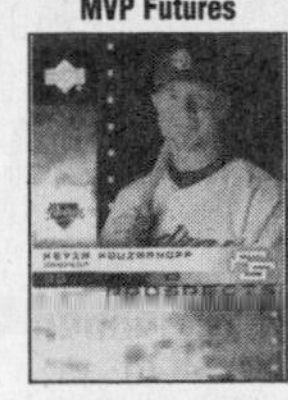

RANDOM INSERTS IN PACKS
STATED PRINT RUN 500 SER.#'d SETS
AD Alejandro De Aza .75 2.00
AG Alex Gordon 1.50 4.00
AI Akinori Iwamura 1.25 3.00
AL Adam Lind .50 1.25
DM Daisuke Matsuzaka 2.00 5.00
DY Delmon Young .75 2.00
FP Felix Pie .50 1.25
HP Hunter Pence 2.50 6.00
IK Ian Kinsler .75 2.00
JA Joaquin Arias .50 1.25
JB Jeff Baker .50 1.25
JH Josh Hamilton 2.00 5.00
JS Jarrod Saltalamacchia .75 2.00
JV Justin Verlander 1.50 4.00
KI Kei Igawa 1.25 3.00
KK Kevin Kouzmanoff .50 1.25
LA Andy LaRoche .50 1.25
MB Michael Bourn .50 1.25
MM Miguel Montero .50 1.25
PF Prince Fielder .75 2.00
RB Ryan Braun 2.50 6.00
RS Ryan Sweeney .50 1.25
RZ Ryan Zimmerman .75 2.00
TB Travis Buck .50 1.25
TT Troy Tulowitzki 3.00 8.00

2007 Upper Deck Future Stars MVP Futures Signatures

STATED ODDS 1:72 H,1:2500 R,1:2500 WALMART
NO SP PRICING DUE TO SCARCITY
EXCH DEADLINE 9/5/2009
AG Alex Gordon SP
AI Akinori Iwamura
AL Adam Lind 4.00 10.00
DY Delmon Young SP
FP Felix Pie 3.00 8.00
HP Hunter Pence 30.00 60.00
IK Ian Kinsler 6.00 15.00
JA Joaquin Arias 3.00 8.00
JB Jeff Baker 3.00 8.00
JH Josh Hamilton 12.50 30.00
JS Jarrod Saltalamacchia 6.00 15.00
JV Justin Verlander SP
KI Kei Igawa SP
KK Kevin Kouzmanoff 5.00 12.00
LA Andy LaRoche 4.00 10.00
MB Michael Bourn 3.00 8.00
MM Miguel Montero 3.00 8.00
PF Prince Fielder 25.00 50.00
RB Ryan Braun 12.50 30.00
RS Ryan Sweeney 4.00 10.00
RZ Ryan Zimmerman SP
TB Travis Buck 5.00 12.00
TT Troy Tulowitzki SP

2007 Upper Deck Future Stars Rookie Dated Debut

RANDOM INSERTS IN PACKS
STATED PRINT RUN 999 SER.#'d SETS
AC Alexi Casilla .50 1.25
AD Alejandro De Aza .50 1.25
AG Alex Gordon 1.00 2.50
AI Akinori Iwamura .75 2.00
AL Adam Lind .30 .75
BA Jeff Baker .30 .75
BB Brian Barden .30 .75
BI Joseph Bisenius .30 .75
BM Brandon Morrow 1.50 4.00
BW Brandon Wood .30 .75
CA Kory Casto .30 .75
CG Carlos Gomez .50 1.25
CR Cal Ripken Jr. 3.00 8.00
CW Chase Wright .75 2.00
DA John Danks .50 1.25
DJ Derek Jeter 2.00 5.00
DM Daisuke Matsuzaka 1.25 3.00
DY Delmon Young .50 1.25
ED Elijah Dukes .50 1.25
FL Fred Lewis .50 1.25
FP Felix Pie .30 .75
GM Gustavo Molina .30 .75
GP Glen Perkins .30 .75
HO Hideki Okajima 1.50 4.00
HP Hunter Pence 1.50 4.00
JA Joaquin Arias .30 .75
JC Jon Coutlangus .30 .75
JF Jesus Flores .30 .75
JH Josh Hamilton 1.25 3.00
JM Jay Marshall .30 .75
JP Juan Perez .30 .75
JS Joakim Soria .30 .75
KC Kevin Cameron .30 .75
KG Ken Griffey Jr. 1.25 3.00
KI Kei Igawa .75 2.00
KK Kevin Kouzmanoff .30 .75
LA Andy LaRoche .30 .75
LG Lee Gardner .30 .75
MB Michael Bourn .30 .75
MC Matt Chico .30 .75
MM Miguel Montero .30 .75
MO Micah Owings .30 .75
MR Mike Rabelo .30 .75
PH Phil Hughes 1.50 4.00
RS Ryan Sweeney .30 .75
SA Jarrod Saltalamacchia .50 1.25
SM Joe Smith .30 .75
TB Travis Buck .30 .75
TL Tim Lincecum 5.00 12.00
TT Troy Tulowitzki 2.00 5.00

2007 Upper Deck Future Stars Two for the Bigs

RANDOM INSERTS IN PACKS
STATED PRINT RUN 999 SER.#'d SETS
AS Joaquin Arias .30 .75
Chris Stewart
BB Michael Bourn .30 .75
Joseph Bisenius
BD Travis Buck .50 1.25
Elijah Dukes
BG Ryan Braun 1.50 4.00
Alex Gordon
BS Ryan Z. Braun .30 .75
Joakim Soria
BT Troy Tulowitzki 2.00 5.00
Jeff Baker
CF Kory Casto .30 .75
Jesus Flores
CL Tim Lincecum 5.00 12.00
Matt Chico
CP Glen Perkins .50 1.25
Alexi Casilla
CS Matt Chico .30 .75
Levale Speigner
DG Alejandro De Aza .50 1.25
Lee Gardner
DK Daisuke Matsuzaka 1.25 3.00
Kei Igawa
DM John Danks .50 1.25
Gustavo Molina
DT Troy Tulowitzki 2.00 5.00
Stephen Drew
DV Alejandro De Aza .30 .75
Rick Vanden Hurk
DW Matt DeSalvo .75 2.00
Chase Wright
DY Stephen Drew .30 .75
Chris Young
GB Alex Gordon 1.00 2.50
Billy Butler
GF Jesus Flores .30 .75
Hector Gimenez
GI Alex Gordon 1.00 2.50
Akinori Iwamura
GL Alex Gordon 1.00 2.50
Andy LaRoche
GM Alex Gordon 1.25 3.00
Daisuke Matsuzaka
GP Hunter Pence 1.50 4.00
Hector Gimenez
HB Josh Hamilton 1.25 3.00
Jared Burton
HD Josh Hamilton 1.25 3.00
Alejandro De Aza
HL Tim Lincecum 5.00 12.00
Phil Hughes
HP Hunter Pence 1.50 4.00
Josh Hamilton
II Akinori Iwamura .75 2.00
Kei Igawa
KC Kevin Kouzmanoff .30 .75
Kevin Cameron
LG Lee Gardner .30 .75
Matt Lindstrom
LV Adam Lind .30 .75
Jamie Vermilyea
MG Miguel Montero .30 .75
Hector Gimenez
MI Daisuke Matsuzaka 1.25 3.00
Akinori Iwamura
MO Daisuke Matsuzaka 1.25 3.00
Hideki Okajima
MR Mike Rabelo .30 .75
Gustavo Molina
MW Brandon Morrow 1.50 4.00
Sean White
OL Tim Lincecum 5.00 12.00
Micah Owings
OM Micah Owings .30 .75
Miguel Montero
PB Travis Buck .30 .75
Danny Putnam
PD Hunter Pence 1.50 4.00
Alejandro De Aza
PH Felix Pie 1.25 3.00
Josh Hamilton
PP Hunter Pence 1.50 4.00
Felix Pie
RS Mike Rabelo .30 .75
Chris Stewart
SM Jarrod Saltalamacchia .50 1.25
Miguel Montero
ST Troy Tulowitzki 2.00 5.00
Jarrod Saltalamacchia
SW Chase Wright .75 2.00
Joe Smith
TB Travis Buck .50 1.25
Billy Butler
WH Phil Hughes 1.50 4.00
Chase Wright
YD Delmon Young .50 1.25
Elijah Dukes
YM Daisuke Matsuzaka 1.25 3.00
Delmon Young

2009 Upper Deck Goodwin Champions

COMMON CARD (1-150) .15 .40
COMMON NIGHT 5.00 12.00
COMMON SP (151-190) 1.25 3.00
151-190 STATED ODDS 1:2 HOBBY
COMMON SUPER SP (191-210) 1.50 4.00
191-210 STATED ODDS 1:10 HOBBY
PLATES RANDOMLY INSERTED
PLATE PRINT RUN 1 SET PER COLOR
BLACK-CYAN-MAGENTA-YELLOW ISSUED
NO PLATE PRICING DUE TO SCARCITY
1a Ken Griffey Jr. Day .60 1.50
1b Ken Griffey Jr. Night SP 8.00 20.00
2 Derek Jeter 1.00 2.50
3 Jon Lester .40 1.00
4 Jorge Posada .25 .60
5 Albert Pujols 1.00 2.50
6 Chipper Jones .40 1.00
7a Ryne Sandberg Day .75 2.00
7b Ryne Sandberg Night SP 6.00 15.00
8 Johnny Damon .25 .60
9 Carlos Delgado .15 .40
10 Vladimir Guerrero .40 1.00
11 Johnny Bench .40 1.00
12 Matt Cain .15 .40
13 Bill Skowron CL .15 .40
14 Donovan Bailey .15 .40
15 Dick Allen CL .15 .40
16 Abraham Lincoln .25 .60
17 Rollie Fingers .15 .40
18 Bo Jackson CL .40 1.00
19 Scott Kazmir .15 .40
20a Grady Sizemore Day .25 .60
20b Grady Sizemore Night SP 5.00 12.00
21 Ian Kinsler .25 .60
22 Jim Palmer .15 .40
23 Kevin Youkilis .25 .60
24 O.J. Mayo .40 1.00
25 Hunter Pence .25 .60
26 Hiroki Kuroda .15 .40
27 Derrek Lee .15 .40
28 Brian McCann .25 .60
29 Carlos Quentin .25 .60
30 Al Kaline .40 1.00
31 Hanley Ramirez .40 1.00
32 Josh Hamilton .40 1.00
33 Jeff Samardzija .25 .60
34 Alexander Ovechkin .75 2.00
35 Clayton Kershaw .40 1.00
36 Lyndon Johnson .15 .40
37 Whitey Ford .25 .60
38 Carey Price .60 1.50
39 Jay Bruce .25 .60
40 Phil Niekro .15 .40
41 Ted Williams 1.00 2.50
42 Justin Upton .25 .60
43 Cole Hamels .40 1.00
44a Barack Obama Day .40 1.00
44b Barack Obama Night SP 8.00 20.00
45 Peyton Manning .50 1.25
46 Jim Thome .25 .60
47 Nick Markakis .40 1.00
48 Joe Carter CL .15 .40
49 Ryan Braun .50 1.25
50 Mike Schmidt .60 1.50
51 Carlos Beltran .15 .40
52 Nolan Ryan 1.25 3.00
53 Anderson Silva .50 1.25
54 Kosuke Fukudome .40 1.00
55 Chad Reed .15 .40
56a Ozzie Smith Day .60 1.50
56b Ozzie Smith Night SP 8.00 20.00
57 Eli Manning .40 1.00
58 CC Sabathia .25 .60
59 Evan Longoria .50 1.25
60 Matt Garza .15 .40
61 Michael Beasley .40 1.00
62 Yogi Berra .40 1.00
63 Brian Roberts .15 .40
64 Alex Rodriguez .60 1.50
65a Tiger Woods Day 1.50 4.00
65b Tiger Woods Night SP 12.50 30.00
66 Buffalo Bill Cody .15 .40
67 Josh Beckett .25 .60
68 Matt Ryan .40 1.00
69a Ichiro Suzuki Day .60 1.50
69b Ichiro Suzuki Night SP 8.00 20.00
70 Chuck Liddell .50 1.25
71 Adrian Gonzalez .25 .60
72 David Wright .50 1.25
73 LeBron James 1.50 4.00
74a Gerry Lopez Day .15 .40
74b Gerry Lopez Night SP 5.00 12.00
75 Carlton Fisk .25 .60
76 Joe Mauer .40 1.00
77 Manny Ramirez .40 1.00
78 Jason Varitek .40 1.00
79 John Lackey .15 .40
80 Ivan Rodriguez .25 .60
81 Wayne Gretzky 1.50 4.00
82 Justin Morneau .40 1.00
83 Akinori Iwamura .15 .40
84 Joe Lewis .40 1.00
85 Lance Berkman .25 .60
86 Brooks Robinson .25 .60
87a Andy Pettitte Day .25 .60
87b Andy Pettitte Night SP 5.00 12.00
88 Peggy Fleming .15 .40
89 Joe DiMaggio 1.00 2.50
90 Jonathan Toews .60 1.50
91 Todd Helton .25 .60
92 Dennis Eckersley .15 .40
93 Daisuke Matsuzaka .40 1.00
94 Adrian Peterson .60 1.50
95 Alfonso Soriano .25 .60
96 Paul Molitor .40 1.00
97 Johan Santana .40 1.00
98 Jason Giambi .15 .40
99 Ben Roethlisberger .50 1.25
100 Chase Utley .40 1.00
101a Cal Ripken Jr. Day 1.50 4.00
101b Cal Ripken Jr. Night SP 10.00 25.00
102 Curtis Granderson .25 .60
103 James Shields .15 .40
104 Nate McLouth .15 .40
105 Evelyn Ng .40 1.00
106a Ryan Howard Day .50 1.25
106b Ryan Howard Night SP 6.00 15.00
107 Joe Nathan .15 .40
108 Tim Lincecum .60 1.50
109 Chad Billingsley .15 .40
110 Matt Holliday .40 1.00
111 Kevin Garnett .60 1.50
112 Robin Roberts .15 .40
113 Jose Reyes .25 .60
114 Michael Jordan 1.00 2.50
115a Smarty Jones Day .40 1.00
115b Smarty Jones Night SP 5.00 12.00
116 Kristi Yamaguchi .25 .60
117 Carlos Zambrano .25 .60
118 Bucky Dent CL .15 .40
119 Carl Yastrzemski .60 1.50
120 Stephen Drew .15 .40
121 Dustin Pedroia .50 1.25
122 Jonathan Papelbon .25 .60
123 B.J. Upton .25 .60
124 Steve Carlton .15 .40
125 Chris Johnson .40 1.00
126a Troy Tulowitzki Day .40 1.00
126b Troy Tulowitzki Night SP 5.00 12.00
127 Francisco Liriano .15 .40
128 Bill Rodgers .15 .40
129 Laird Hamilton .15 .40
130 Brandon Webb .25 .60
131 Miguel Cabrera .40 1.00
132a Chien-Ming Wang Day .25 .60
132b Chien-Ming Wang Night SP 5.00 12.00
133 Joba Chamberlain .25 .60
134 Felix Hernandez .40 1.00
135 Tony Gwynn .40 1.00
136 Roy Oswalt .25 .60
137 Prince Fielder .25 .60
138 Gary Sheffield .15 .40
139 Koji Uehara RC .25 .60
140a Gordie Howe Day 1.25 3.00
140b Gordie Howe Night SP 5.00 12.00
141 Bobby Orr 1.00 2.50
142 Zack Greinke .25 .60
143 Derrick Rose .75 2.00
144 Cliff Lee .25 .60
145 Joey Votto .40 1.00
146 Phil Hellmuth .40 1.00
147 Mark Teixeira .40 1.00
148 David Price RC .40 1.00
149 Ryan Ludwick .25 .60
150 David Ortiz .60 1.50
151 Cory Wade SP 1.25 3.00
152 Roy White SP 1.25 3.00
153 Jed Lowrie SP 1.25 3.00
154 Gavin Floyd SP 1.25 3.00
155 Justin Masterson SP .75 2.00
156 Travis Hafner SP 1.25 3.00
157 Kelly Shoppach SP 1.25 3.00
158 David Purcey SP 1.25 3.00
159 Howie Kendrick SP 1.25 3.00
160 Mike Parsons SP 1.25 3.00
161 Jeremy Bloom SP 1.25 3.00
162 Dave Scott SP 1.25 3.00
163 Nyjer Morgan SP 1.25 3.00
164 Chris Volstad SP 1.25 3.00
165 Barry Zito SP 1.25 3.00
166 Adrian Beltre SP 1.25 3.00
167 Mark Zupan SP 1.25 3.00
168 Victor Martinez SP 1.25 3.00
169 Eric Chavez SP 1.25 3.00
170 Chris Perez SP 1.25 3.00
171 Jered Weaver SP 1.25 3.00
172 Justin Verlander SP 2.50 6.00
173 Adam Lind SP 1.25 3.00
174 Corky Carroll SP 1.25 3.00
175 Ryan Zimmerman SP 1.25 3.00
176 Josh Willingham SP 1.25 3.00
177 Graig Nettles SP 1.25 3.00
178 Jonathan Albaladejo SP 1.25 3.00
179 Ted Martin SP 1.25 3.00
180 Bill Hall SP 1.25 3.00
181 Brad Hawpe SP 1.25 3.00
182 John Maine SP 1.25 3.00
183 Tom Curren SP 1.25 3.00
184 Ken Griffey Sr. CL SP 1.25 3.00
185 Josh Johnson SP 2.00 5.00
186 Phil Hughes SP 1.25 3.00
187 Joe Alexander SP 1.25 3.00
188 Fausto Carmona SP 1.25 3.00
189 Daniel Murphy SP RC 1.25 3.00
190 Alex Hinshaw SP 1.25 3.00
191 Clayton Richard SP 1.50 4.00
192 Sparky Lyle CL SP 1.50 4.00
193 Don Gay SP 1.50 4.00
194 Aramis Ramirez SP 1.50 4.00
195 Gaylord Perry CL SP 1.50 4.00
196 Carlos Lee SP 1.50 4.00
197 Paul Konerko SP 2.50 6.00
198 Kent Hrbek CL SP 1.50 4.00
199 Chris B. Young SP 1.50 4.00
200 Roy Halladay SP 2.50 6.00
201 Geovany Soto SP 1.50 4.00
202 Chone Figgins SP 1.50 4.00
203 Joe Pepitone CL SP 1.50 4.00
204 Mark Allen SP 1.50 4.00
205 Garrett Atkins SP 1.50 4.00
206 Ken Shamrock SP 1.50 4.00
207 Jermaine Dye SP 1.50 4.00
208 Don Newcombe CL SP 1.50 4.00
209 Rick Cerone CL SP 1.50 4.00
210 Adam Jones SP 1.50 4.00

2009 Upper Deck Goodwin Champions Mini

COMPLETE SET (192) 75.00 150.00
*MINI 1-150: 1X TO 2.5X BASIC
APPX.MINI ODDS ONE PER PACK
PLATES RANDOMLY INSERTED
PLATE PRINT RUN 1 SET PER COLOR
BLACK-CYAN-MAGENTA-YELLOW ISSUED
NO PLATE PRICING DUE TO SCARCITY
211 Brian Giles EXT .60 1.50
212 Robinson Cano EXT 1.50 4.00
213 Erik Bedard EXT .60 1.50
214 James Loney EXT 1.00 2.50
215 Jimmy Rollins EXT 1.00 2.50
216 Joakim Soria EXT .60 1.50
217 Jeremy Guthrie EXT .60 1.50
218 Adam Wainwright EXT 1.00 2.50
219 B.J. Ryan EXT .60 1.50
220 Aaron Cook EXT .60 1.50
221 Aaron Harang EXT .60 1.50
222 Mariano Rivera EXT 1.50 4.00
223 Freddy Sanchez EXT .60 1.50
224 Ryan Dempster EXT .60 1.50
225 Jacoby Ellsbury EXT 1.50 4.00
226 Russell Martin EXT .60 1.50
227 Ervin Santana EXT .60 1.50
228 Nomar Garciaparra EXT 1.50 4.00
229 Chris Young EXT .60 1.50
230 Jair Jurrjens EXT .60 1.50
231 Francisco Cordero EXT .60 1.50
232 Bobby Crosby EXT .60 1.50
233 Rich Harden EXT .60 1.50
234 Cameron Maybin EXT .60 1.50
235 Conor Jackson EXT .60 1.50
236 Jake Peavy EXT .60 1.50
237 Brad Ziegler EXT .60 1.50
238 Aaron Rowand EXT .60 1.50
239 Carl Crawford EXT 1.00 2.50
240 Mark Buehrle EXT .60 1.50
241 Carlos Guillen EXT .60 1.50
242 Alex Rios EXT 1.00 2.50
243 Vernon Wells EXT .60 1.50
244 Bobby Jenks EXT .60 1.50
245 Rick Ankiel EXT .60 1.50
246 Alex Gordon EXT 1.00 2.50
247 Paul Maholm EXT .60 1.50
248 Carlos Gomez EXT .60 1.50
249 Brad Lidge EXT .60 1.50
250 Hideki Okajima EXT .60 1.50
251 Michael Bourn EXT .60 1.50
252 Jhonny Peralta EXT .60 1.50

2009 Upper Deck Goodwin Champions Mini Black Border

*MINI BLK 1-150: 1.5X TO 4X BASE
*MINI BLK 211-252: .75X TO 2X MINI
RANDOM INSERTS IN PACKS

2009 Upper Deck Goodwin Champions Mini Black Border Foil

RANDOM INSERTS IN PACKS
STATED PRINT RUN 8 SER.#'d SETS
NO PRICING DUE TO SCARCITY

2009 Upper Deck Goodwin Champions Mini Foil

*MINI FOIL 1-150: 3X TO 8X BASE
*MINI FOIL 211-252: 1.5X TO 4X MINI
RANDOM INSERTS IN PACKS
ANNCD PRINT RUN OF 88 TOTAL SETS

2009 Upper Deck Goodwin Champions Animal Series

RANDOM INSERTS IN PACKS
AS1 King Cobra 2.00 5.00
AS2 Dodo Bird 2.00 5.00
AS3 Tasmanian Devil 2.00 5.00
AS4 Komodo Dragon 2.00 5.00
AS5 Bald Eagle 2.00 5.00
AS6 Great White Shark 2.00 5.00
AS7 Gorilla 2.00 5.00
AS8 Bengal Tiger 2.00 5.00
AS9 Killer Whale 2.00 5.00
AS10 Giant Panda 2.00 5.00

2009 Upper Deck Goodwin Champions Autographs

STATED ODDS 1:20 HOBBY
EXCHANGE DEADLINE 8/31/2011
AG Adrian Gonzalez/45 * 10.00 25.00
AH Alex Hinshaw 4.00 10.00
AK Al Kaline/50 * 40.00 80.00
AL Jonathan Albaladejo 4.00 10.00
BD Bucky Dent 8.00 20.00
BL Jeremy Bloom 5.00 12.00
BO Bobby Orr/25 * 90.00 150.00
BR Bill Rodgers 6.00 15.00
BS Bill Skowron 10.00 25.00
CB Chad Billingsley 6.00 15.00
CC Corky Carroll 10.00 25.00
CE Rick Cerone 4.00 10.00
CF Chone Figgins 4.00 10.00
CJ Chipper Jones/25 * 100.00 200.00
CK Clayton Kershaw/50 * 15.00 40.00
CL Carlos Lee 4.00 10.00
CP Chris Perez 5.00 12.00
CR Clayton Richard 4.00 10.00
CV Chris Volstad 4.00 10.00
CW Cory Wade 4.00 10.00
DA Dick Allen 10.00 25.00
DE Dennis Eckersley/50 * 20.00 50.00
DG Don Gay 5.00 12.00
DJ Derek Jeter/25 * 175.00 300.00
DM Daniel Murphy 5.00 12.00
DN Don Newcombe 12.50 30.00
DO Donovan Bailey 10.00 25.00
DP Dustin Pedroia 20.00 50.00
DS Dave Scott 5.00 12.00
EC Eric Chavez/50 * 10.00 25.00
EL Evan Longoria/25 * 100.00 175.00
EN Evelyn Ng 10.00 25.00
FH Felix Hernandez EXCH 15.00 40.00
GA Garrett Atkins 4.00 10.00
GF Gavin Floyd 4.00 10.00
GK Kevin Garnett/25 * 50.00 100.00
GS Grady Sizemore/50 * EXCH 20.00 50.00
GY Ken Griffey Sr. 5.00 12.00
HP Hunter Pence/50 * 12.50 30.00
HR Hanley Ramirez 6.00 15.00
JA Joe Alexander 6.00 15.00
JB Jay Bruce 10.00 25.00
JC Joe Carter/45 * 15.00 40.00
JE Jed Lowrie 5.00 12.00
JJ Josh Johnson 12.50 30.00
JL Joe Lewis 6.00 15.00
JM John Maine 4.00 10.00
JO Jon Lester/25 * 60.00 120.00
JS James Shields 4.00 10.00
JU Justin Masterson 6.00 15.00
JW Josh Willingham 4.00 10.00
KG Ken Griffey Jr./25 *
KH Kent Hrbek 10.00 25.00
KU Koji Uehara/25 * 50.00 100.00
KY Kevin Youkilis 15.00 40.00
LA Ryan Braun/50 * 30.00 60.00
LH Laird Hamilton 10.00 25.00
LJ LeBron James/25 *
LO Gerry Lopez 10.00 25.00
MA Mark Allen 5.00 12.00
MC Matt Cain 6.00 15.00
MG Matt Garza 5.00 12.00
MJ Michael Jordan/23 * 500.00 700.00
MN Nate McLouth 4.00 10.00
MZ Mark Zupan 5.00 12.00
NM Nick Markakis 8.00 20.00
NR Nolan Ryan/25 *
OS Ozzie Smith/50 * 40.00 80.00
PA Mike Parsons 6.00 15.00
PD David Price 15.00 40.00
PF Prince Fielder/50 * 15.00 40.00
PH Phil Hellmuth 12.50 30.00
PJ Jonathan Papelbon 10.00 25.00
PK Paul Konerko 10.00 25.00
PM Paul Molitor/50 * 20.00 50.00
PU David Purcey 4.00 10.00
RB Brooks Robinson/50 * 12.50 30.00
RC Chad Reed 10.00 25.00
RF Rollie Fingers/50 * 10.00 25.00
RH Roy Halladay/50 * 50.00 100.00
RW Roy White 6.00 15.00

SC Steve Carlton 20.00 50.00
SD Stephen Drew/50 * 8.00 20.00
SK Kelly Shoppach 4.00 10.00
SL Sparky Lyle 5.00 12.00
SO Geovany Soto 10.00 25.00
TC Tom Curren 30.00 60.00
TG Tony Gwynn/25 *
TM Ted Martin 4.00 10.00
TT Troy Tulowitzki 10.00 25.00
WF Whitey Ford/25 * 75.00 150.00
YA Kristi Yamaguchi/49 * 50.00 100.00
ZG Zack Greinke/25 * 30.00 60.00

2009 Upper Deck Goodwin Champions Citizens of the Century

RANDOM INSERTS IN PACKS
CC1 Hillary Clinton 2.00 5.00
CC2 Bill Clinton 2.00 5.00
CC3 Tony Blair 2.00 5.00
CC4 Princess Diana 2.50 6.00
CC5 Barack Obama 3.00 8.00
CC6 Ronald Reagan 2.00 5.00
CC7 Mikhail Gorbachev 2.00 5.00
CC8 Al Gore 2.00 5.00
CC9 Pope John Paul II 2.00 5.00
CC10 Winston Churchill 2.00 5.00

2009 Upper Deck Goodwin Champions Citizens of the Day

RANDOM INSERTS IN PACKS
CD1 Susan B. Anthony 2.00 5.00
CD2 P.T. Barnum 2.00 5.00
CD3 Cap Anson 2.50 6.00
CD4 Theodore Roosevelt 2.00 5.00
CD5 John D. Rockefeller 2.00 5.00
CD6 King Kelly 2.50 6.00
CD7 Will Rogers 2.00 5.00
CD8 Grover Cleveland 2.00 5.00
CD9 Scott Joplin 2.00 5.00
CD10 Sitting Bull 2.00 5.00
CD11 Bram Stoker 2.00 5.00
CD12 Wyatt Earp 2.00 5.00
CD13 Claude Monet 2.00 5.00
CD14 Queen Victoria 2.00 5.00
CD15 Grigori Rasputin 2.00 5.00

2009 Upper Deck Goodwin Champions Entomology

RANDOM INSERTS IN PACKS
EXCHANGE DEADLINE 8/31/2011
ENT1 Mexican Silverspot SP EXCH
ENT2 Spotted Amberwing SP EXCH
ENT3 Metalmark Butterfly EXCH
ENT4 Meadow Wanderer EXCH
ENT5 BD Butterfly EXCH 75.00 150.00
ENT6 Malay Lacewing EXCH
ENT7 Blue Brushfoot EXCH
ENT8 Blomfilds' Beauty EXCH
ENT9 Painted Jezabel EXCH
ENT10 Sunflower Trollup EXCH.
ENT11 Buttercup Sulphur SP EXCH
ENT12 Spicebush Swallowtail SP EXCH
ENT13 Pipevine Swallowtail SP EXCH
ENT14 Strawberry Bluff EXCH 90.00 150.00
ENT15 Apricot Sulphur EXCH
ENT16 Military Tiger Moth EXCH
ENT17 Cramer's 88 EXCH
ENT18 Bullet Ant EXCH
ENT19 Longhorn Beetle EXCH
ENT20 Man Face Beetle SP
ENT21 Chinese Lantern Fly EXCH
ENT22 Rusty Brown Scorpion EXCH
ENT23 Baby Black Scorpion EXCH
ENT24 Fiddle Beetle EXCH
ENT25 Great Walking Leaf SP EXCH
ENT26 Rosey Walking Stick EXCH
ENT27 Dead Leaf Mantid EXCH
ENT28 Cryptic Mantid EXCH
ENT29 Red Nose Lantern Fly EXCH
ENT30 Minty Walking Leaf SP EXCH
NNO EXCH Card 75.00 150.00

2009 Upper Deck Goodwin Champions Landmarks

RANDOM INSERTS IN PACKS
EXCHANGE DEADLINE 8/31/2011
DS Dead Sea Salt
GG Golden Gate Bridge
OB Omaha Beach Sand
TT RMS Titanic Coal 75.00 150.00
NNO EXCH Card 60.00 120.00

2009 Upper Deck Goodwin Champions Memorabilia

STATED ODDS 1:10 HOBBY
EXCHANGE DEADLINE 8/31/2011
AB Adrian Beltre 3.00 8.00
AI Akinori Iwamura 3.00 8.00
AJ Adam Jones 3.00 8.00
BB Buffalo Bill Cody/5 * EXCH
BE Johnny Bench 4.00 10.00
BH Bill Hall 3.00 8.00
BJ Bo Jackson 5.00 12.00
BM Brian McCann 3.00 8.00
BR Brian Roberts 3.00 8.00
BW Brandon Webb 3.00 8.00
BZ Barry Zito 3.00 8.00
CB Chad Billingsley 3.00 8.00
CD Carlos Delgado 3.00 8.00
CF Carlton Fisk 4.00 10.00
CG Curtis Granderson 4.00 10.00
CH Cole Hamels 4.00 10.00
CJ Chipper Jones 4.00 10.00
CL Carlos Lee 3.00 8.00
CR Cal Ripken Jr. 12.50 30.00
CU Chase Utley/100 * 5.00 12.00
CW Chien-Ming Wang 3.00 8.00
CY Carl Yastrzemski 4.00 10.00
CZ Carlos Zambrano 3.00 8.00
DA Johnny Damon 3.00 8.00
DI Joe DiMaggio/20 *
DJ Derek Jeter 10.00 25.00
DL Derrek Lee 3.00 8.00
DM Daisuke Matsuzaka 3.00 8.00
DO David Ortiz 3.00 8.00
DR Derrick Rose 5.00 12.00
EC Eric Chavez 3.00 8.00
FC Fausto Carmona 3.00 8.00
FH Felix Hernandez 3.00 8.00
FI Chone Figgins 3.00 8.00
FL Francisco Liriano 3.00 8.00
GN Graig Nettles 3.00 8.00
GP Gaylord Perry 3.00 8.00
GR Ken Griffey Jr. 10.00 25.00
HA Brad Hawpe 3.00 8.00
HK Hiroki Kuroda 4.00 10.00
HP Hunter Pence 3.00 8.00
IK Ian Kinsler 3.00 8.00
JA James Shields 3.00 8.00
JB Josh Beckett 3.00 8.00
JD Jermaine Dye 3.00 8.00
JH Jonathan Albaladejo 3.00 8.00
JL John Lackey 3.00 8.00
JM Joe Mauer 4.00 10.00
JN Joe Nathan 3.00 8.00
JP Jim Palmer 4.00 10.00
JR Jose Reyes/100 * 4.00 10.00
JT Jim Thome 3.00 8.00
JU Justin Upton 3.00 8.00
JV Jason Varitek 3.00 8.00
JW Jered Weaver 3.00 8.00
KE Howie Kendrick 3.00 8.00
KF Kosuke Fukudome 3.00 8.00
KG Kevin Garnett 5.00 12.00
LE Cliff Lee 3.00 8.00
LJ LeBron James 12.50 30.00
LY Lyndon Johnson/5 *
MA John Maine 3.00 8.00
MB Michael Beasley 3.00 8.00
MC Miguel Cabrera 3.00 8.00
MJ Michael Jordan/50 * 30.00 60.00
MO Justin Morneau 3.00 8.00
MS Mike Schmidt 6.00 15.00
NM Nick Markakis 3.00 8.00
OM O.J. Mayo 3.00 8.00
PA Jonathan Papelbon 3.00 8.00
PF Prince Fielder 3.00 8.00
PH Phil Hughes 3.00 8.00
PK Paul Konerko 3.00 8.00
PM Paul Molitor/15 *
PO Jorge Posada 3.00 8.00
PU Albert Pujols 10.00 25.00
RA Aramis Ramirez 3.00 8.00
RB Ryan Braun 3.00 8.00
RH Roy Halladay 3.00 8.00
RO Roy Oswalt 3.00 8.00
RS Ryne Sandberg 4.00 10.00
RZ Manny Ramirez 3.00 8.00
SC Steve Carlton 3.00 8.00
SK Scott Kazmir 3.00 8.00
TG Tony Gwynn 4.00 10.00
TH Todd Helton 3.00 8.00
TL Tim Lincecum 5.00 12.00
TR Travis Hafner 3.00 8.00
TT Troy Tulowitzki 3.00 8.00
TW Ted Williams/40 * 20.00 50.00
VE Justin Verlander 3.00 8.00
VG Vladimir Guerrero 3.00 8.00
VM Victor Martinez 3.00 8.00
WD Tiger Woods 60.00 120.00
WF Whitey Ford 6.00 15.00
YB Yogi Berra 8.00 20.00
YO Chris B. Young 3.00 8.00
ZG Zack Greinke 3.00 8.00

2009 Upper Deck Goodwin Champions Thoroughbred Hair Cuts

RANDOM INSERTS IN PACKS
EXCHANGE DEADLINE 8/31/2011

2011 Upper Deck Goodwin Champions

COMP.SET w/o VAR (210) 40.00 80.00
COMP.SET w/o SP's (150) 10.00 25.00
COMMON CARD (1-150) .15 .40
COMMON SP (151-190) 1.00 2.50
151-190 SP ODDS 1:3 HOBBY
COMMON SP (191-210) 1.50 4.00
191-210 SP ODDS 1:12 HOBBY
COMMON VARIATION SP 4.00 10.00
1A King Kelly .15 .40
1B King Kelly Lightning SP 4.00 10.00
11 Greg Maddux .30 .75
16 Don Mattingly .50 1.25
19A Lou Brock .20 .50
19B Lou Brock 4.00 10.00
Jimmy Carter SP
24 Miller Huggins .15 .40
25 Manny Machado .30 .75
38 Nolan Ryan .75 2.00
39 Addie Joss .15 .40
41 Whitey Ford .20 .50
43 Stan Musial .40 1.00
46 Ryne Sandberg .50 1.25
50 Steve Carlton .15 .40
56 Jim Rice .20 .50
64 Johnny Bench .25 .60
68 Hugh Jennings .15 .40
69 Wilbert Robinson .15 .40
94 Ozzie Smith .40 1.00
95 Willie Keeler .15 .40
103 Rube Waddell .15 .40
112 Mike Schmidt .40 1.00
116 John Lamb .15 .40
119 Cap Anson .20 .50
120 Tony Perez .15 .40
126 Jose Canseco .20 .50
128 Bob Gibson .20 .50
140 John McGraw .15 .40
146 Carlton Fisk .20 .50
152 Jack Chesbro SP 1.00 2.50
158 Charles Comiskey SP 1.00 2.50
163 Ed Delahanty SP 1.00 2.50
178 Dennis Oil Can Boyd SP 1.00 2.50
181 Buck Ewing SP 1.00 2.50
184 Dan Brouthers SP 1.00 2.50
189 Eddie Plank SP 1.00 2.50
194 Rube Foster SP 1.50 4.00
195 John Montgomery Ward SP 1.50 4.00
209 Albert Spalding SP 1.50 4.00
210 Abner Doubleday SP 1.50 4.00

2011 Upper Deck Goodwin Champions Mini

*1-150 MINI: 1X TO 2.5X BASIC
1-150 MINI ODDS 1:4 HOBBY
COMMON CARD (211-231) .60 1.50
211-231 MINI ODDS 1:13 HOBBY
PRINTING PLATES RANDOMLY INSERTED
PLATE PRINT RUN 1 SET PER COLOR
BLACK-CYAN-MAGENTA-YELLOW ISSUED
NO PLATE PRICING DUE TO SCARCITY
211 Matt Packer SP .60 1.50
212 Gary Brown SP 1.00 2.50
213 Ramon Morla SP .60 1.50
214 Aaron Crow SP .60 1.50
215 Ryan Lavarnway SP .60 1.50
216 Michael Choice SP .60 1.50
217 Matt Lipka SP .60 1.50
218 Aaron Hicks SP .60 1.50
219 Peter Tago SP .60 1.50
220 Jurickson Profar SP .60 1.50
221 Cody Hawn SP .60 1.50
222 Carlos Perez SP .60 1.50
223 Robinson Yambati SP .60 1.50
224 Mike Olt SP .75 2.00
225 LeVon Washington SP .75 2.00
226 Kyle Parker SP .75 2.00
227 Jonathan Garcia SP .60 1.50
228 Yordano Ventura SP .75 2.00
229 Delino DeShields Jr. SP .75 2.00
230 Collin Cowgill SP .60 1.50
231 Kyle Skipworth SP .60 1.50

2011 Upper Deck Goodwin Champions Mini Black

*1-150 MINI BLACK: 1.2X TO 3X BASIC
1-150 MINI BLACK ODDS 1:13 HOBBY
*211-231 MINI BLACK: .6X TO 1.5X BASIC MINI
211-231 MINI BLACK ODDS 1:46 HOBBY

2011 Upper Deck Goodwin Champions Mini Foil

*1-150 MINI FOIL: 2.5X TO 6X BASIC
1-150 ANNCD PRINT RUN OF 89
*211-231 MINI FOIL : 1X TO 2.5X BASIC MINI
211-231 ANNCD PRINT RUN OF 178
PRINT RUNS PROVIDED BY UD
38 Nolan Ryan 12.50 30.00

2011 Upper Deck Goodwin Champions Mini Foil Black

RANDOM INSERTS IN PACKS
STATED PRINT RUN 9 SER.#'d SETS
NO PRICING DUE TO SCARCITY

2011 Upper Deck Goodwin Champions Autographs

GROUP A ODDS 1:1577 HOBBY
GROUP B ODDS 1:729 HOBBY
GROUP C ODDS 1:339 HOBBY
GROUP D ODDS 1:246 HOBBY
GROUP E ODDS 1:72 HOBBY
GROUP F ODDS 1:35 HOBBY
OVERALL AUTO ODDS 1:20 HOBBY
NO GROUP A PRICING DUE TO SCARCITY
EXCHANGE DEADLINE 6/7/2013
CA Steve Carlton C 10.00 25.00
CF Carlton Fisk B 15.00 40.00
CH Cody Hawn F 4.00 8.00
JB Johnny Bench A
JG Jonathan Garcia F 4.00 10.00
JL John Lamb F 4.00 10.00
JR Jim Rice D 8.00 20.00
KV Kolbrin Vitek F 4.00 10.00
LO Lou Brock B 20.00 50.00
LW LeVon Washington E 4.00 10.00
MM Manny Machado C 20.00 50.00
MO Mike Olt F 4.00 10.00
MU Stan Musial B 40.00 80.00
NR Nolan Ryan A
OC Dennis Oil Can Boyd E 8.00 20.00
PE Carlos Perez F 4.00 8.00
PT Peter Tago F 4.00 8.00
RL Ryan Lavarnway D 8.00 20.00
RM Ramon Morla F 4.00 8.00
RS Ryne Sandberg B 20.00 50.00
RY Robinson Yambati F 4.00 10.00
TP Tony Perez D 10.00 25.00
WF Whitey Ford B 40.00 80.00
YV Yordano Ventura F 4.00 10.00

2011 Upper Deck Goodwin Champions Figures of Sport

COMP.SET. w/o SP's (14) 10.00 25.00
COMMON CARD (1-14) .60 1.50
1-14 STATED ODDS 1:21 HOBBY
15-18 SP ODDS 1:300 HOBBY
FS11 Bo Jackson 1.25 3.00
FS12 Ozzie Smith 1.25 3.00
FS17 Nolan Ryan SP 5.00 12.00

2011 Upper Deck Goodwin Champions Memorabilia

GROUP A ODDS 1:14,613 HOBBY
GROUP B ODDS 1:179 HOBBY
GROUP C ODDS 1:31 HOBBY
GROUP D ODDS 1:22 HOBBY
NO GROUP A PRICING AVAILABLE
KS Kyle Skipworth D 3.00 8.00
MC Michael Choice D 3.00 8.00
MM Manny Machado D 3.00 8.00
PT Peter Tago D 3.00 8.00

2011 Upper Deck Goodwin Champions Memorabilia Dual

GROUP A ODDS 1:87,680 HOBBY
GROUP B ODDS 1:8768 HOBBY
GROUP C ODDS 1:2923 HOBBY
GROUP D ODDS 1:877 HOBBY
GROUP E ODDS 1:585 HOBBY
NO GROUP A PRICING AVAILABLE
MM Manny Machado E 8.00 20.00

2011 Upper Deck Goodwin Champions Mini Foil Presidential Gold

RANDOM INSERTS IN PACKS
STATED PRINT RUN 1 SER.#'d SET
NO PRICING DUE TO SCARCITY

2007 Upper Deck Goudey

This 240-card set was released in August, 2007. The set was issued in both retail and hobby packs. The hobby packs contained eight cards which came 24 packs to a box and 12 boxes to a case. The first 100 cards feature veterans sequenced in alphabetical order by first name, while cards numbered 101-200 are a mix of veterans and 2007 rookie logo cards. Cards numbered 201-223 feature retired greats while 224-240 are short printed cards of some of today's biggest stars. Those short printed cards were inserted into packs at a stated rate of one in six hobby or retail packs.

COMP.SET w/o SPs (200) 20.00 50.00
COMMON CARD (1-200) .20 .50
COMMON ROOKIE (1-200) .30 .75
COMMON SP (201-240) 2.00 5.00
SP ODDS 1:6 HOBBY,1:6 RETAIL
1933 ORIGINALS ODDS TWO PER CASE
SEE 1933 GOUDEY PRICING FOR ORIGINALS
1 A.J. Burnett .30 .75
2 Aaron Boone .20 .50
3 Aaron Rowand .20 .50
4 Adam Dunn .30 .75
5 Adrian Beltre .20 .50
6 Albert Pujols 1.25 3.00
7 Ivan Rodriguez .30 .75
8 Alfonso Soriano .30 .75
9 Andruw Jones .20 .50
10 Andy Pettitte .30 .75
11 Aramis Ramirez .20 .50
12 B.J. Upton .20 .50
13 Barry Zito .20 .50
14 Bartolo Colon .20 .50
15 Ben Sheets .20 .50
16 Bobby Abreu .20 .50
17 Bobby Crosby .20 .50
18 Brian Giles .20 .50
19 Brian Roberts .20 .50
20 C.C. Sabathia .30 .75
21 Carlos Beltran .30 .75
22 Carlos Delgado .20 .50
23 Carlos Lee .20 .50
24 Carlos Zambrano .30 .75
25 Chad Cordero .20 .50
26 Chad Tracy .20 .50
27 Chipper Jones .50 1.25
28 Craig Biggio .30 .75
29 Curt Schilling .30 .75
30 Danny Haren .20 .50
31 Darin Erstad .20 .50
32 David Ortiz .30 .75
33 Billy Wagner .20 .50
34 Derek Jeter 1.25 3.00
35 Derek Lee .20 .50
36 Dontrelle Willis .20 .50
37 Edgar Renteria .20 .50
38 Eric Chavez .20 .50
39 Felix Hernandez .30 .75
40 Garrett Anderson .20 .50
41 Garrett Atkins .20 .50
42 Gary Sheffield .20 .50
43 Grady Sizemore .30 .75
44 Greg Maddux .75 2.00
45 Hank Blalock .20 .50
46 Hanley Ramirez .50 1.25
47 J.D. Drew .20 .50
48 Jacque Jones .20 .50
49 Jake Peavy .20 .50
50 Jake Westbrook .20 .50
51 Jason Bay .30 .75
52 Jason Giambi .20 .50
53 Jason Schmidt .20 .50
54 Jason Varitek .50 1.25
55 Troy Tulowitzki (RC) 2.00 5.00
56 Jeff Francoeur .50 1.25
57 Jeff Kent .20 .50
58 Jeremy Bonderman .20 .50
59 Jim Edmonds .30 .75
60 Jim Thome .30 .75
61 Jimmy Rollins .30 .75
62 Joe Mauer .50 1.25
63 Johan Santana .50 1.25
64 John Smoltz .50 1.25
65 Johnny Damon .30 .75
66 Jose Reyes .30 .75
67 Josh Beckett .30 .75
68 Justin Morneau .50 1.25
69 Ken Griffey Jr. .75 2.00
70 Kerry Wood .20 .50
71 Khalil Greene .20 .50
72 Lance Berkman .30 .75
73 Livan Hernandez .20 .50
74 Manny Ramirez .50 1.25
75 Mark Mulder .20 .50
76 Chase Utley .50 1.25
77 Mark Teixeira .50 1.25
78 Miguel Tejada .30 .75
79 Miguel Cabrera .50 1.25
80 Mike Piazza .50 1.25
81 Pat Burrell .20 .50
82 Paul LoDuca .20 .50
83 Pedro Martinez .30 .75
84 Prince Fielder .30 .75
85 Rafael Furcal .20 .50
86 Randy Johnson .50 1.25
87 Richie Sexson .20 .50
88 Robinson Cano .50 1.25
89 Roy Halladay .50 1.25
90 Roy Oswalt .30 .75
91 Scott Rolen .30 .75
92 Tim Hudson .30 .75
93 Todd Helton .30 .75
94 Tom Glavine .30 .75
95 Torii Hunter .20 .50
96 Travis Hafner .30 .75
97 Trevor Hoffman .30 .75
98 Vernon Wells .20 .50
99 Vladimir Guerrero .50 1.25
100 Zach Duke .20 .50
101 Alex Rodriguez .75 2.00
102 Ryan Howard .75 2.00
103 Michael Barrett .20 .50
104 Ichiro Suzuki .75 2.00
105 Hideki Matsui .50 1.25
106 Jered Weaver .30 .75
107 Dan Uggla .30 .75
108 Ryan Freel .20 .50
109 Bill Hall .20 .50
110 Ray Durham .20 .50
111 Morgan Ensberg .20 .50
112 Shawn Green .20 .50
113 Brandon Webb .30 .75
114 Frank Thomas .50 1.25
115 Corey Patterson .20 .50
116 Edwin Encarnacion .20 .50
117 Mike Cameron .20 .50
118 Matt Holliday .50 1.25
119 Jhonny Peralta .20 .50
120 Nick Swisher .50 1.25
121 Brad Penny .20 .50
122 Kenji Johjima .50 1.25
123 Francisco Rodriguez .30 .75
124 Mark Teahen .20 .50
125 Jonathan Papelbon .50 1.25
126 Carlos Guillen .20 .50
127 Freddy Sanchez .20 .50
128 Chien-Ming Wang .30 .75
129 Andre Ethier .30 .75
130 Matt Cain .30 .75
131 Austin Kearns .20 .50
132 Ramon Hernandez .20 .50
133 Chris Carpenter .50 1.25
134 Michael Cuddyer .20 .50
135 Stephen Drew .20 .50
136 David Wright .75 2.00
137 David DeJesus .20 .50
138 Gary Matthews .20 .50
139 Brandon Phillips .20 .50
140 Josh Barfield .20 .50
141 Alex Gordon RC 1.00 2.50
142 Scott Kazmir .30 .75
143 Luis Gonzalez .20 .50
144 Mike Sweeney .20 .50
145 Luis Castillo .20 .50
146 Huston Street .20 .50
147 Phil Hughes (RC) 1.50 4.00
148 Adrian Gonzalez .30 .75
149 Raul Ibanez .30 .75
150 Joe Crede .20 .50
151 Mark Loretta .20 .50
152 Adam LaRoche (RC) .30 .75
153 Troy Glaus .20 .50
154 Conor Jackson .20 .50
155 Michael Young .30 .75
156 Scott Podsednik .20 .50
157 David Eckstein .20 .50
158 Mike Jacobs .20 .50
159 Nomar Garciaparra .50 1.25
160 Mariano Rivera .50 1.25
161 Pedro Feliz .20 .50
162 Josh Hamilton (RC) 1.25 3.00
163 Ryan Langerhans .20 .50
164 Willy Taveras .20 .50
165 Carl Crawford .30 .75
166 Melvin Mora .20 .50
167 Francisco Liriano .50 1.25
168 Orlando Cabrera .20 .50
169 Chris Duncan .20 .50
170 Johnny Estrada .20 .50
171 Ryan Zimmerman .30 .75
172 Rickie Weeks .30 .75
173 Paul Konerko .30 .75
174 Jack Wilson .20 .50
175 Jorge Posada .30 .75
176 Magglio Ordonez .30 .75
177 Nick Johnson .20 .50
178 Geoff Jenkins .20 .50
179 Reggie Sanders .20 .50
180 Moises Alou .20 .50
181 Glen Perkins (RC) .30 .75
182 Brad Lidge .20 .50
183 Kevin Kouzmanoff (RC) .30 .75
184 Jorge Cantu .20 .50
185 Carlos Quentin .20 .50
186 Rich Harden .20 .50
187 Jose Vidro .20 .50
188 Aaron Harang .20 .50
189 Noah Lowry .20 .50
190 Jermaine Dye .20 .50
191 Victor Martinez .30 .75
192 Chone Figgins .20 .50
193 Aubrey Huff .20 .50
194 Jason Isringhausen .20 .50
195 Brian McCann .20 .50
196 Juan Pierre .20 .50
197 Delmon Young (RC) .50 1.25
198 Felipe Lopez .20 .50
199 Brad Hawpe .20 .50
200 Justin Verlander .60 1.50
201 Mike Schmidt SP 4.00 10.00
202 Nolan Ryan SP 5.00 12.00
203 Cal Ripken Jr. SP 4.00 10.00
204 Harmon Killebrew SP 2.50 6.00
205 Reggie Jackson SP 2.50 6.00
206 Johnny Bench SP 2.50 6.00
207 Carlton Fisk SP 2.50 6.00
208 Yogi Berra SP 2.50 6.00
209 Al Kaline SP 2.50 6.00
210 Alan Trammell SP 2.00 5.00
211 Bill Mazeroski SP 2.50 6.00
212 Bob Gibson SP 2.50 6.00
213 Brooks Robinson SP 2.50 6.00
214 Carl Yastrzemski SP 3.00 8.00
215 Don Mattingly SP 5.00 12.00
216 Fergie Jenkins SP 2.00 5.00
217 Jim Rice SP 2.00 5.00
218 Lou Brock SP 2.50 6.00
219 Rod Carew SP 2.50 6.00
220 Stan Musial SP 3.00 8.00
221 Tom Seaver SP 2.50 6.00
222 Tony Gwynn SP 2.50 6.00
223 Wade Boggs SP 2.50 6.00
224 Alex Rodriguez SP 3.00 8.00
225 David Wright SP 3.00 8.00
226 Ryan Howard SP 3.00 8.00
227 Ichiro Suzuki SP 3.00 8.00
228 Ken Griffey Jr. SP 3.00 8.00
229 Daisuke Matsuzaka SP RC 4.00 10.00
230 Kei Igawa SP RC 2.50 6.00
231 Akinori Iwamura SP RC 3.00 8.00
232 Derek Jeter SP 4.00 10.00
233 Albert Pujols SP 4.00 10.00
234 Greg Maddux SP 3.00 8.00
235 David Ortiz SP 2.50 6.00
236 Manny Ramirez SP 2.50 6.00
237 Johan Santana SP 2.50 6.00
238 Pedro Martinez SP 2.50 6.00
239 Roger Clemens SP 4.00 10.00
240 Vladimir Guerrero SP 2.50 6.00

2007 Upper Deck Goudey Red Backs

COMPLETE SET (240) 20.00 50.00
*RED: .4X TO 1X BASIC
APPX. FOUR PER PACK
CARDS 201-240 DO NOT EXIST

2007 Upper Deck Goudey Diamond Stars

RANDOM INSERTS IN PACKS
STATED PRINT RUN 15 SER.#'d SETS
NO PRICING DUE TO SCARCITY
YELLOW RANDOMLY INSERTED
YELLOW PRINT RUN 5 SER.#'d SETS
NO YELLOW PRICING DUE TO SCARCITY

2007 Upper Deck Goudey Diamond Stars Autographs

RANDOM INSERTS IN PACKS
STATED PRINT RUN 1 SER.#'d SET
NO PRICING DUE TO SCARCITY

2007 Upper Deck Goudey Double Play

RANDOM INSERTS IN PACKS
STATED PRINT RUN 15 SER.#'d SETS
NO PRICING DUE TO SCARCITY

2007 Upper Deck Goudey Double Play Autographs

RANDOM INSERTS IN PACKS
STATED PRINT RUN 1 SER.#'d SET
NO PRICING DUE TO SCARCITY

2007 Upper Deck Goudey Goudey Graphs

STATED ODDS 1:24 HOB, 1:2500 RET
EXCH DEADLINE 8/7/2010
SP INFO PROVIDED BY UPPER DECK
AC Alberto Callaspo 3.00 8.00
AH Aaron Harang 6.00 15.00
AM Andy Marte 3.00 8.00
AR Aaron Rowand 6.00 15.00
BA Brian Anderson 3.00 8.00
BB Brian Bannister 6.00 15.00
BE Johnny Bench
BO Boof Bonser 6.00 15.00
BU B.J. Upton 6.00 15.00
CC Carl Crawford 3.00 8.00
CF Carlton Fisk
CL Cliff Lee 12.50 30.00
CO Coco Crisp 6.00 15.00
CR Cal Ripken Jr. SP
CY Chris Young 3.00 8.00
CZ Carlos Zambrano
DO David Ortiz
FH Felix Hernandez 12.50 30.00
GA Garrett Atkins 5.00 12.00
GP Glen Perkins 3.00 8.00
HA Bill Hall 5.00 12.00
HI Rich Hill 3.00 8.00
HK Harmon Killebrew
HR Hanley Ramirez 8.00 20.00
IS Ian Snell
JB Jason Bay 6.00 15.00
JM Joe Mauer 30.00 60.00
JW Jered Weaver 15.00 40.00
JZ Joel Zumaya 6.00 15.00

KG Ken Griffey Jr.
KJ Kelly Johnson 3.00 8.00
KK Kevin Kouzmanoff 3.00 8.00
LS Luke Scott 3.00 8.00
MJ Mike Jacobs
MO Justin Morneau 8.00 20.00
MS Mike Schmidt
NR Nolan Ryan
RA Reggie Abercrombie 3.00 8.00
RT Ryan Theriot 8.00 20.00
RZ Ryan Zimmerman 15.00 40.00
SA Anibal Sanchez 3.00 8.00
SK Scott Kazmir 8.00 20.00
TB Taylor Buchholz 3.00 8.00
VM Victor Martinez 3.00 8.00
YB Yogi Berra

2007 Upper Deck Goudey Heads Up

CARDS 1-24 ODDS 1:10 HOB, 1:10 RET
CARDS 25-48 ODDS 1:10 HOB, 1:10 RET
241 Ken Griffey Jr. 3.00 8.00
242 Derek Jeter 5.00 12.00
243 Ichiro Suzuki 3.00 8.00
244 Cal Ripken Jr. 5.00 12.00
245 Daisuke Matsuzaka 4.00 10.00
246 Kei Igawa 2.50 6.00
247 Joe Mauer 2.00 5.00
248 Babe Ruth 4.00 10.00
249 Johnny Bench 2.50 6.00
250 Reggie Jackson 2.50 6.00
251 Carlton Fisk 2.50 6.00
252 Albert Pujols 4.00 10.00
253 Nolan Ryan 5.00 12.00
254 Ryan Howard 3.00 8.00
255 Mike Schmidt 3.00 8.00
256 Brooks Robinson 2.50 6.00
257 Harmon Killebrew 2.50 6.00
258 Alex Rodriguez 3.00 8.00
259 David Ortiz 2.50 6.00
260 David Wright 3.00 8.00
261 Al Kaline 2.50 6.00
262 Justin Verlander 2.50 6.00
263 Chase Utley 2.50 6.00
264 Justin Morneau 2.00 5.00
265 Ken Griffey Jr. 3.00 8.00
266 Derek Jeter 5.00 12.00
267 Ichiro Suzuki 3.00 8.00
268 Cal Ripken Jr. 5.00 12.00
269 Daisuke Matsuzaka 4.00 10.00
270 Kei Igawa 2.50 6.00
271 Joe Mauer 2.00 5.00
272 Babe Ruth 4.00 10.00
273 Johnny Bench 2.50 6.00
274 Reggie Jackson 2.50 6.00
275 Carlton Fisk 2.50 6.00
276 Albert Pujols 4.00 10.00
277 Nolan Ryan 5.00 12.00
278 Ryan Howard 3.00 8.00
279 Mike Schmidt 3.00 8.00
280 Brooks Robinson 2.50 6.00
281 Harmon Killebrew 2.50 6.00
282 Alex Rodriguez 3.00 8.00
283 David Ortiz 2.50 6.00
284 David Wright 3.00 8.00
285 Al Kaline 2.50 6.00
286 Justin Verlander 2.50 6.00
287 Chase Utley 2.50 6.00
288 Justin Morneau 2.00 5.00

2007 Upper Deck Goudey Immortals Memorabilia

STATED ODDS 1:288 HOB,1:960 RET
IAD Adam Dunn 5.00 12.00
IAJ Andruw Jones 6.00 15.00
IAK Al Kaline 8.00 20.00
IAP Albert Pujols 15.00 40.00
IAS Alfonso Soriano 5.00 12.00
IBR Babe Ruth 250.00 400.00
ICD Carlos Delgado 5.00 12.00
ICF Carlton Fisk 6.00 15.00
ICJ Chipper Jones 8.00 20.00
ICL Roger Clemens 12.50 30.00
ICR Cal Ripken Jr. 20.00 50.00
ICS Curt Schilling 6.00 15.00
IDJ Derek Jeter 20.00 50.00
IDO David Ortiz 8.00 20.00
IDW Dontrelle Willis 5.00 12.00
IGL Tom Glavine 6.00 15.00
IGM Greg Maddux 12.50 30.00
IGS Gary Sheffield 5.00 12.00
IHE Todd Helton 6.00 15.00
IHK Harmon Killebrew 12.50 30.00
IIR Ivan Rodriguez 6.00 15.00
IJB Johnny Bench 8.00 20.00
IJD Joe DiMaggio 50.00 100.00
IJE Jim Edmonds 6.00 15.00
IJG Jason Giambi 5.00 12.00
IJM Justin Morneau 5.00 12.00
IJO Randy Johnson 6.00 15.00
IJR Jose Reyes 6.00 15.00
IJS John Smoltz 6.00 15.00
IJT Jim Thome 6.00 15.00
IKG Ken Griffey Jr. 30.00 60.00
ILB Lance Berkman 5.00 12.00
IMP Mike Piazza 8.00 20.00
IMR Manny Ramirez 6.00 15.00
IMS Mike Schmidt 15.00 40.00
INR Nolan Ryan 20.00 50.00
IPM Pedro Martinez 6.00 15.00
IRJ Reggie Jackson 6.00 15.00
ISA Johan Santana 6.00 15.00
ITH Trevor Hoffman 5.00 12.00
IVG Vladimir Guerrero 6.00 15.00
IYB Yogi Berra 15.00 40.00

2007 Upper Deck Goudey Memorabilia

STATED ODDS 1:24 HOBBY, 1:24 RETAIL
1 A.J. Burnett 3.00 8.00
2 Aaron Boone 3.00 8.00
3 Aaron Rowand 3.00 8.00
4 Adam Dunn 3.00 8.00
5 Adrian Beltre 3.00 8.00
6 Albert Pujols 10.00 25.00
7 Ivan Rodriguez 4.00 10.00
8 Alfonso Soriano 4.00 10.00
9 Andruw Jones 3.00 8.00
10 Andy Pettitte 4.00 10.00
11 Aramis Ramirez 4.00 10.00
12 B.J. Upton 4.00 10.00
13 Barry Zito 3.00 8.00
14 Bartolo Colon 3.00 8.00
15 Ben Sheets 3.00 8.00
16 Bobby Abreu 4.00 10.00
17 Bobby Crosby 3.00 8.00
18 Brian Giles 3.00 8.00
19 Brian Roberts 3.00 8.00
20 C.C. Sabathia 4.00 10.00
21 Carlos Beltran 3.00 8.00
22 Carlos Delgado 3.00 8.00
23 Carlos Lee 3.00 8.00
24 Carlos Zambrano 3.00 8.00
26 Chad Tracy 3.00 8.00
27 Chipper Jones 4.00 10.00
28 Craig Biggio 4.00 10.00
29 Curt Schilling 3.00 8.00
31 Darin Erstad 3.00 8.00
32 David Ortiz 5.00 12.00
33 Billy Wagner 3.00 8.00
34 Derek Jeter 10.00 25.00
35 Derek Lee 3.00 8.00
36 Dontrelle Willis 3.00 8.00
37 Edgar Renteria 3.00 8.00
38 Eric Chavez 3.00 8.00
39 Felix Hernandez 3.00 8.00
40 Garret Anderson 3.00 8.00
41 Garrett Atkins 3.00 8.00
42 Gary Sheffield 3.00 8.00
43 Grady Sizemore 4.00 10.00
44 Greg Maddux 6.00 15.00
45 Hank Blalock 3.00 8.00
46 Hanley Ramirez 4.00 10.00
47 J.D. Drew 3.00 8.00
49 Jake Peavy 3.00 8.00
50 Jake Westbrook 3.00 8.00
51 Jason Bay 3.00 8.00
52 Jason Giambi 8.00 20.00
54 Jason Varitek 6.00 15.00
56 Jeff Francoeur 6.00 15.00
57 Jeff Kent 4.00 10.00
58 Jeremy Bonderman 3.00 8.00
59 Jim Edmonds 3.00 8.00
60 Jim Thome 4.00 10.00
61 Jimmy Rollins 4.00 10.00
62 Joe Mauer 4.00 10.00
63 Johan Santana 4.00 10.00
64 John Smoltz 4.00 10.00
66 Jose Reyes 5.00 12.00
67 Josh Beckett 3.00 8.00
68 Justin Morneau 3.00 8.00
69 Ken Griffey Jr. 8.00 20.00
70 Kerry Wood 3.00 8.00
71 Khalil Greene 5.00 12.00
72 Lance Berkman 3.00 8.00
73 Livan Hernandez 3.00 8.00
74 Manny Ramirez 4.00 10.00
75 Mark Mulder 3.00 8.00
76 Chase Utley 5.00 12.00
77 Mark Teixeira 4.00 10.00
78 Miguel Tejada 3.00 8.00
79 Miguel Cabrera 4.00 10.00
80 Mike Piazza 5.00 12.00
81 Pat Burrell 5.00 12.00
82 Paul LoDuca 3.00 8.00
83 Pedro Martinez 4.00 10.00
84 Prince Fielder 5.00 12.00
85 Rafael Furcal 3.00 8.00
86 Randy Johnson 4.00 10.00
87 Richie Sexson 3.00 8.00
88 Robinson Cano 5.00 12.00
89 Roy Halladay 3.00 8.00
90 Roy Oswalt 3.00 8.00
91 Scott Rolen 3.00 8.00
92 Tim Hudson 3.00 8.00
93 Todd Helton 4.00 10.00
94 Tom Glavine 4.00 10.00
95 Torii Hunter 3.00 8.00
96 Travis Hafner 3.00 8.00
97 Trevor Hoffman 3.00 8.00
98 Vernon Wells 3.00 8.00
99 Vladimir Guerrero 5.00 12.00
100 Zach Duke 3.00 8.00

2007 Upper Deck Goudey Sport Royalty

ONE PER HOBBY BOX LOADER
AI Akinori Iwamura 5.00 12.00
AP Albert Pujols 5.00 12.00
AS Alfonso Soriano 4.00 10.00
CC Chris Carpenter 4.00 10.00
CR Cal Ripken Jr. 12.50 30.00
DJ Derek Jeter 10.00 25.00
DM Daisuke Matsuzaka 8.00 20.00
DO David Ortiz 4.00 10.00
DS Dean Smith 2.00 5.00
ES Emmitt Smith 4.00 10.00
GH Gordie Howe 12.50 30.00
GM Greg Maddux 3.00 8.00
HI Martina Hingis 3.00 8.00
HR Hanley Ramirez 3.00 8.00
JM Justin Morneau 2.00 5.00
JN Joe Namath 6.00 15.00
JV Justin Verlander 2.00 5.00
JW John Wooden 3.00 8.00
KB Kobe Bryant 6.00 15.00
KD Kevin Durant 5.00 12.00
KG Ken Griffey Jr. 5.00 12.00
KH Katie Hoff 3.00 8.00
KI Kei Igawa 3.00 8.00
LE Jeanette Lee 12.50 30.00
LJ LeBron James 15.00 40.00
LT LaDainian Tomlinson 3.00 8.00
MH Mia Hamm 10.00 25.00
MJ Michael Jordan 20.00 50.00
NR Nolan Ryan 15.00 40.00
PI Mike Piazza 5.00 12.00
PM Peyton Manning 5.00 12.00
RH Roy Halladay 2.00 5.00
RJ Randy Johnson 3.00 8.00
RL Ryan Lochte 4.00 10.00
SA Johan Santana 3.00 8.00
SC Sidney Crosby 12.50 30.00
TH Trevor Hoffman 3.00 8.00
TW Tiger Woods 30.00 60.00
VG Vladimir Guerrero 3.00 8.00

2007 Upper Deck Goudey Sport Royalty Autographs

STATED ODDS TWO PER CASE
FOUND IN HOBBY BOX LOADER PACKS
AI Akinori Iwamura 20.00 50.00
AP Albert Pujols
CR Cal Ripken Jr. 300.00 400.00
DM Daisuke Matsuzaka 125.00 250.00
ES Emmitt Smith
GH Gordie Howe 50.00 100.00
HI Martina Hingis 100.00 200.00
JM Justin Morneau 10.00 25.00
JN Joe Namath
JV Justin Verlander 30.00 60.00
JW John Wooden 100.00 200.00
KD Kevin Durant 150.00 250.00
KH Katie Hoff 15.00 40.00
KI Kei Igawa 10.00 25.00
LE Jeanette Lee 60.00 120.00
LJ LeBron James 250.00 400.00
LT LaDainian Tomlinson 75.00 150.00
MH Mia Hamm 30.00 60.00
MJ Michael Jordan
NR Nolan Ryan
PM Peyton Manning 100.00 175.00
RH Roy Halladay 30.00 60.00
RJ Randy Johnson
RL Ryan Lochte 10.00 25.00
SC Sidney Crosby 175.00 300.00
TW Tiger Woods

2008 Upper Deck Goudey

COMP.SET w/o HIGH #s (200) 20.00 50.00
COMMON CARD (1-200) .20 .50
COMMON ROOKIE (1-200) .30 .75
COMMON SP (201-230) 2.00 5.00
COMMON SP (231-250) 1.50 4.00
COMMON SP (251-270) 2.00 5.00
COMMON CARD (271-300) 2.00 5.00
COMMON CARD (301-330) 3.00 8.00
1 Eric Byrnes .20 .50
2 Randy Johnson .50 1.25
3 Brandon Webb .30 .75
4 Dan Haren .20 .50
5 Chris B. Young .20 .50
6 Max Scherzer RC 1.00 2.50
7 Mark Teixeira .50 1.25
8 John Smoltz .50 1.25
9 Jeff Francoeur .30 .75
10 Phil Niekro .20 .50
11 Chipper Jones .50 1.25
12 Kelly Johnson .20 .50
13 Tom Glavine .30 .75
14 Yunel Escobar .20 .50
15 Erik Bedard .20 .50
16 Melvin Mora .20 .50
17 Brian Roberts .20 .50
18 Eddie Murray .50 1.25
19 Jim Palmer .20 .50
20 Jeremy Guthrie .20 .50
21 Nick Markakis .50 1.25
22 David Ortiz .30 .75
23 Manny Ramirez .50 1.25
24 Josh Beckett .30 .75
25 Dustin Pedroia .60 1.50
26 Bobby Doerr .20 .50
27 Clay Buchholz (RC) .75 2.00
28 Daisuke Matsuzaka .50 1.25
29 Jonathan Papelbon .30 .75
30 Kevin Youkilis .30 .75
31 Pee Wee Reese .30 .75
32 Billy Williams .20 .50
33 Alfonso Soriano .30 .75
34 Derrek Lee .20 .50
35 Rich Hill .20 .50
36 Kosuke Fukudome RC 1.00 2.50
37 Aramis Ramirez .20 .50
38 Carlos Zambrano .30 .75
39 Luis Aparicio .20 .50
40 Mark Buehrle .30 .75
41 Orlando Cabrera .20 .50
42 Paul Konerko .30 .75
43 Jermaine Dye .20 .50
44 Jim Thome .30 .75
45 Nick Swisher .50 1.25
46 Sparky Anderson .20 .50
47 Johnny Bench .50 1.25
48 Joe Morgan .20 .50
49 Tony Perez .20 .50
50 Adam Dunn .30 .75
51 Aaron Harang .20 .50
52 Brandon Phillips .20 .50
53 Edwin Encarnacion .20 .50
54 Ken Griffey Jr. .75 2.00
55 Larry Doby .20 .50
56 Bob Feller .20 .50
57 C.C. Sabathia .30 .75
58 Travis Hafner .20 .50
59 Grady Sizemore .30 .75
60 Fausto Carmona .20 .50
61 Victor Martinez .30 .75
62 Brad Hawpe .20 .50
63 Todd Helton .30 .75
64 Garrett Atkins .20 .50
65 Troy Tulowitzki .50 1.25
66 Matt Holliday .50 1.25
67 Jeff Francis .20 .50
68 Justin Verlander .60 1.50
69 Curtis Granderson .30 .75
70 Miguel Cabrera .50 1.25
71 Gary Sheffield .20 .50
72 Magglio Ordonez .30 .75
73 Jack Morris .20 .50
74 Andrew Miller .30 .75
75 Clayton Kershaw RC 1.50 4.00
76 Dan Uggla .30 .75
77 Hanley Ramirez .50 1.25
78 Jeremy Hermida .20 .50
79 Josh Willingham .30 .75
80 Lance Berkman .30 .75
81 Roy Oswalt .30 .75
82 Miguel Tejada .30 .75
83 Hunter Pence .50 1.25
84 Carlos Lee .20 .50
85 J.R. Towles RC .50 1.25
86 Brian Bannister .20 .50
87 Luke Hochevar RC .50 1.25
88 Billy Butler .20 .50
89 Alex Gordon .30 .75
90 Kelvim Escobar .20 .50
91 John Lackey .20 .50
92 Chone Figgins .20 .50
93 Jered Weaver .20 .50
94 Torii Hunter .20 .50
95 Vladimir Guerrero .50 1.25
96 Brad Penny .20 .50
97 James Loney .30 .75
98 Andruw Jones .20 .50
99 Chad Billingsley .20 .50
100 Chin-Lung Hu (RC) .50 1.25
101 Russell Martin .20 .50
102 Eddie Mathews .50 1.25
103 Warren Spahn .30 .75
104 Prince Fielder .30 .75
105 Ryan Braun .60 1.50
106 J.J. Hardy .20 .50
107 Ben Sheets .20 .50
108 Corey Hart .20 .50
109 Yovani Gallardo .20 .50
110 Joe Mauer .50 1.25
111 Delmon Young .30 .75
112 Johan Santana .50 1.25
113 Glen Perkins .20 .50
114 Justin Morneau .50 1.25
115 Carlos Beltran .20 .50
116 Jose Reyes .30 .75
117 David Wright .60 1.50
118 Pedro Martinez .30 .75
119 Tom Seaver .20 .50
120 Billy Wagner .20 .50
121 John Maine .20 .50
122 Alex Rodriguez .75 2.00
123 Chien-Ming Wang .30 .75
124 Hideki Matsui .50 1.25
125 Jorge Posada .30 .75
126 Mariano Rivera .50 1.25
127 Phil Rizzuto .30 .75
128 Bucky Dent .20 .50
129 Derek Jeter 1.25 3.00
130 Graig Nettles .20 .50
131 Ian Kennedy RC .75 2.00
132 Don Larsen .20 .50
133 Joe Blanton .30 .75
134 Mark Ellis .20 .50
135 Dennis Eckersley .30 .75
136 Rollie Fingers .20 .50
137 Catfish Hunter .20 .50
138 Daric Barton (RC) .30 .75
139 Jack Cust .20 .50
140 Ryan Howard .60 1.50
141 Jimmy Rollins .30 .75
142 Chase Utley .50 1.25
143 Shane Victorino .20 .50
144 Cole Hamels .50 1.25
145 Richie Ashburn .30 .75
146 Jason Bay .30 .75
147 Freddy Sanchez .20 .50
148 Adam LaRoche .20 .50
149 Jack Wilson .20 .50
150 Ralph Kiner .30 .75
151 Bill Mazeroski .30 .75
152 Tom Gorzelanny .20 .50
153 Jay Bruce (RC) 1.25 3.00
154 Jake Peavy .20 .50
155 Chris Young .20 .50
156 Trevor Hoffman .50 1.25
157 Khalil Greene .20 .50
158 Adrian Gonzalez .30 .75
159 Tim Lincecum .75 2.00
160 Matt Cain .20 .50
161 Aaron Rowand .30 .75
162 Orlando Cepeda .20 .50
163 Juan Marichal .20 .50
164 Noah Lowry .20 .50
165 Ichiro Suzuki .75 2.00
166 Felix Hernandez .50 1.25
167 J.J. Putz .20 .50
168 Jose Vidro .20 .50
169 Raul Ibanez .30 .75
170 Wladimir Balentien .20 .50
171 Albert Pujols 1.25 3.00
172 Scott Rolen .30 .75
173 Lou Brock .30 .75
174 Chris Duncan .20 .50
175 Vince Coleman .20 .50
176 B.J. Upton .50 1.25
177 Carl Crawford .30 .75
178 Carlos Pena .20 .50
179 Scott Kazmir .30 .75
180 Akinori Iwamura .20 .50
181 James Shields .20 .50
182 Michael Young .30 .75
183 Jarrod Saltalamacchia .30 .75
184 Hank Blalock .20 .50
185 Ian Kinsler .30 .75
186 Josh Hamilton .50 1.25
187 Marlon Byrd .20 .50
188 David Murphy .20 .50
189 Vernon Wells .20 .50
190 Roy Halladay .50 1.25
191 Frank Thomas .50 1.25
192 Alex Rios .30 .75
193 Troy Glaus .30 .75
194 David Eckstein .20 .50
195 Ryan Zimmerman .30 .75
196 Dmitri Young .20 .50
197 Austin Kearns .20 .50
198 Chad Cordero .20 .50
199 Ryan Church .20 .50
200 Evan Longoria RC 1.50 4.00
201 Brooks Robinson SP 2.00 5.00
202 Cal Ripken Jr. SP 5.00 12.00
203 Frank Robinson SP 2.00 5.00
204 Carl Yastrzemski SP 3.00 8.00
205 Carlton Fisk SP 2.00 5.00
206 Fred Lynn SP 2.00 5.00
207 Wade Boggs SP 2.50 6.00
208 Nolan Ryan SP 5.00 12.00
209 Ernie Banks SP 2.50 6.00
210 Ryne Sandberg SP 4.00 10.00
211 Al Kaline SP 2.50 6.00
212 Bo Jackson SP 2.50 6.00
213 Paul Molitor SP 2.50 6.00
214 Robin Yount SP 2.50 6.00
215 Harmon Killebrew SP 2.50 6.00
216 Rod Carew SP 2.00 5.00
217 Bobby Thomson SP 2.00 5.00
218 Gaylord Perry SP 2.00 5.00
219 Dave Winfield SP 2.00 5.00
220 Don Mattingly SP 3.00 8.00
221 Reggie Jackson SP 2.00 5.00
222 Roger Clemens SP 3.00 8.00
223 Whitey Ford SP 2.00 5.00
224 Mike Schmidt SP 3.00 8.00
225 Steve Carlton SP 2.00 5.00
226 Tony Gwynn SP 2.00 5.00
227 Willie McCovey SP 2.00 5.00
228 Bob Gibson SP 2.00 5.00
229 Ozzie Smith SP 3.00 8.00
230 Stan Musial SP 3.00 8.00
231 George Washington SP 2.00 5.00
232 Thomas Jefferson SP 2.00 5.00
233 James Madison SP 1.50 4.00
234 James Monroe SP 1.50 4.00
235 Andrew Jackson SP 1.50 4.00
236 John Tyler SP 1.50 4.00
237 Abraham Lincoln SP 2.00 5.00
238 Ulysses S. Grant SP 1.50 4.00
239 Grover Cleveland SP 1.50 4.00
240 Theodore Roosevelt SP 1.50 4.00
241 Calvin Coolidge SP 1.50 4.00
242 John Adams SP 1.50 4.00
243 Martin Van Buren SP 1.50 4.00
244 William McKinley SP 1.50 4.00
245 Woodrow Wilson SP 1.50 4.00
246 James K. Polk SP 1.50 4.00
247 Rutherford B. Hayes SP 1.50 4.00
248 William H. Taft SP 1.50 4.00
249 Andrew Johnson SP 1.50 4.00
250 James Buchanan SP 1.50 4.00
251 Albert Pujols 36 BW SP 3.00 8.00
252 Alex Rodriguez 36 BW SP 3.00 8.00
253 Alfonso Soriano 36 BW SP 2.50 6.00
254 C.C. Sabathia 36 BW SP 2.00 5.00
255 Chase Utley 36 BW SP 2.50 6.00
256 David Ortiz 36 BW SP 2.50 6.00
257 David Wright 36 BW SP 2.50 6.00
258 Derek Jeter 36 BW SP 4.00 10.00
259 Hanley Ramirez 36 BW SP 2.50 6.00
260 Ichiro Suzuki 36 BW SP 3.00 8.00
261 Jake Peavy 36 BW SP 2.50 6.00
262 Johan Santana 36 BW SP 2.50 6.00
263 Jose Reyes 36 BW SP 2.50 6.00
264 Ken Griffey Jr. 36 BW SP 3.00 8.00
265 Magglio Ordonez 36 BW SP 2.50 6.00
266 Matt Holliday 36 BW SP 2.50 6.00
267 Prince Fielder 36 BW SP 2.50 6.00
268 Ryan Braun 36 BW SP 2.50 6.00
269 Ryan Howard 36 BW SP 2.50 6.00
270 Vladimir Guerrero 36 BW SP 2.50 6.00
271 Carl Yastrzemski SR SP 2.00 5.00
272 Albert Pujols SR SP 3.00 8.00
273 Amy Van Dyken SR SP 2.00 5.00
274 Tom Seaver SR SP 2.00 5.00
275 Brett Favre SR SP 4.00 10.00
276 Bruce Jenner SR SP 2.00 5.00
277 Bill Russell SR SP 3.00 8.00
278 Barry Sanders SR SP 3.00 8.00
279 Cynthia Cooper SR SP 2.00 5.00
280 Mike Schmidt SR SP 2.50 6.00
281 Chipper Jones SR SP 2.50 6.00
282 Cal Ripken Jr. SR SP 4.00 10.00
283 Cael Sanderson SR SP 2.00 5.00
284 Dan Gable SR SP 2.00 5.00
285 Derek Jeter SR SP 4.00 10.00
286 Andre Dawson SR SP 2.00 5.00
287 Dan O'Brien SR SP 2.00 5.00
288 Julius Erving SR SP 2.50 6.00
289 Emmitt Smith SR SP 3.00 8.00
290 Janet Evans SR SP 2.00 5.00
291 Chase Utley SR SP 2.00 5.00
292 Gary Hall Jr. SR SP 2.00 5.00
293 Gordie Howe SR SP 3.00 8.00
294 Josh Beckett SR SP 2.00 5.00
295 John Elway SR SP 3.00 8.00
296 Julie Foudy SR SP 2.00 5.00
297 Jackie Joyner-Kersee SR SP 2.00 5.00
298 Jack Nicklaus SR SP 4.00 10.00
299 Magic Johnson SR SP 3.00 8.00
300 Michael Jordan SR SP 8.00 20.00
301 Bo Jackson SR SP 4.00 10.00
302 Tom Brady SR SP 6.00 15.00
303 Wade Boggs SR SP 2.00 5.00
304 Dan Marino SR SP 6.00 15.00
305 Dave Winfield SR SP 3.00 8.00
306 Jenny Thompson SR SP 3.00 8.00
307 Kobe Bryant SR SP 5.00 12.00
308 Kevin Durant SR SP 5.00 12.00
309 Ken Griffey Jr. SR SP 5.00 12.00
310 Kerri Strug SR SP 4.00 10.00
311 Kerri Walsh SR SP 4.00 10.00
312 Larry Bird SR SP 6.00 15.00
313 LeBron James SR SP 6.00 15.00
314 Matt Biondi SR SP 3.00 8.00
315 Mark Messier SR SP 4.00 10.00
316 Michael Johnson SR SP 3.00 8.00
317 Misty May-Treanor SR SP 8.00 20.00
318 Bob Gibson SR SP 6.00 15.00
319 Nolan Ryan SR SP 6.00 15.00
320 Ozzie Smith SR SP 5.00 12.00
321 Prince Fielder SR SP 4.00 10.00
322 Rulon Gardner SR SP 3.00 8.00
323 Reggie Jackson SR SP 4.00 10.00
324 Ernie Banks SR SP 5.00 12.00
325 Sidney Crosby SR SP 10.00 25.00
326 Sanya Richards SR SP 3.00 8.00
327 Terry Bradshaw SR SP 4.00 10.00
328 Tony Gwynn SR SP 4.00 10.00
329 Stan Musial SR SP 6.00 15.00
330 Tiger Woods SR SP 20.00 40.00

2008 Upper Deck Goudey Mini Black Backs

*BLACK 1-200: .75X TO 2X GRN 1-200
*BLACK RC 1-200: .75X TO 2X GRN RC 1-200
*BLACK SP 201-250: .75X TO 2X GRN 201-250
*BLACK SP 251-270: .5X TO 1.2X GRN 251-270
*BLACK SR 271-330: .5X TO 1.2X GRN 271-330
RANDOM INSERTS IN PACKS
STATED PRINT RUN 34 SER.#'d SETS
11 Chipper Jones 10.00 25.00
36 Kosuke Fukudome 20.00 50.00
100 Chin-Lung Hu 10.00 25.00
129 Derek Jeter 10.00 25.00
142 Chase Utley 6.00 15.00
186 Josh Hamilton 10.00 25.00
200 Evan Longoria 20.00 50.00
202 Cal Ripken Jr. 40.00 80.00
278 Barry Sanders SR 10.00 25.00
281 Chipper Jones SR 15.00 40.00
282 Cal Ripken Jr. SR 40.00 80.00
300 Michael Jordan SR 20.00 50.00
307 Kobe Bryant SR 6.00 15.00
330 Tiger Woods SR 200.00 350.00

2008 Upper Deck Goudey Mini Blue Backs

*BLUE 1-200: 1.5X TO 4X BASIC 1-200
*BLUE RC 1-200: 1X TO 2.5X BASIC RC 1-200
*BLUE 201-270: .6X TO 1.5X BASIC SP 201-270
*BLUE 271-330: .6X TO 1.5X BASIC SR 201-270
RANDOM INSERTS IN PACKS
298 Jack Nicklaus SR 15.00 40.00
330 Tiger Woods SR 30.00 60.00

2008 Upper Deck Goudey Mini Green Backs

RANDOM INSERTS IN PACKS
STATED PRINT RUN 88 SER.#'d SETS
1 Eric Byrnes 1.00 2.50
2 Randy Johnson 2.50 6.00
3 Brandon Webb 1.50 4.00
4 Dan Haren 1.00 2.50
5 Chris B. Young 1.00 2.50
6 Max Scherzer 3.00 8.00
7 Mark Teixeira 2.50 6.00
8 John Smoltz 2.50 6.00
9 Jeff Francoeur 1.50 4.00
10 Phil Niekro 1.00 2.50
11 Chipper Jones 6.00 15.00
12 Kelly Johnson 1.00 2.50
13 Tom Glavine 1.50 4.00
14 Yunel Escobar 1.00 2.50
15 Erik Bedard 1.00 2.50
16 Melvin Mora 1.00 2.50
17 Brian Roberts 1.00 2.50
18 Eddie Murray 2.50 6.00
19 Jim Palmer 1.00 2.50
20 Jeremy Guthrie 1.00 2.50
21 Nick Markakis 2.50 6.00
22 David Ortiz 1.50 4.00
23 Manny Ramirez 2.50 6.00
24 Josh Beckett 1.50 4.00
25 Dustin Pedroia 3.00 8.00
26 Bobby Doerr 1.00 2.50
27 Clay Buchholz 2.50 6.00
28 Daisuke Matsuzaka 2.50 6.00
29 Jonathan Papelbon 1.50 4.00
30 Kevin Youkilis 1.50 4.00
31 Pee Wee Reese 1.50 4.00
32 Billy Williams 1.00 2.50
33 Alfonso Soriano 1.50 4.00
34 Derrek Lee 1.00 2.50
35 Rich Hill 1.00 2.50
36 Kosuke Fukudome 10.00 25.00
37 Aramis Ramirez 1.00 2.50
38 Carlos Zambrano 1.50 4.00
39 Luis Aparicio 1.00 2.50
40 Mark Buehrle 1.50 4.00
41 Orlando Cabrera 1.00 2.50
42 Paul Konerko 1.50 4.00
43 Jermaine Dye 1.00 2.50
44 Jim Thome 1.50 4.00
45 Nick Swisher 2.50 6.00
46 Sparky Anderson 1.00 2.50
47 Johnny Bench 2.50 6.00
48 Joe Morgan 1.00 2.50
49 Tony Perez 1.00 2.50
50 Adam Dunn 1.50 4.00
51 Aaron Harang 1.00 2.50
52 Brandon Phillips 1.00 2.50
53 Edwin Encarnacion 1.00 2.50
54 Ken Griffey Jr. 4.00 10.00
55 Larry Doby 1.00 2.50
56 Bob Feller 1.00 2.50
57 C.C. Sabathia 1.50 4.00

58 Travis Hafner 1.00 2.50
59 Grady Sizemore 1.50 4.00
60 Fausto Carmona 1.00 2.50
61 Victor Martinez 1.50 4.00
62 Brad Hawpe 1.00 2.50
63 Todd Helton 1.50 4.00
64 Garrett Atkins 1.00 2.50
65 Troy Tulowitzki 2.50 6.00
66 Matt Holliday 2.50 6.00
67 Jeff Francis 1.00 2.50
68 Justin Verlander 3.00 8.00
69 Curtis Granderson 1.50 4.00
70 Miguel Cabrera 2.50 6.00
71 Gary Sheffield 1.00 2.50
72 Magglio Ordonez 1.50 4.00
73 Jack Morris 1.00 2.50
74 Andrew Miller 1.00 2.50
75 Clayton Kershaw 5.00 12.00
76 Dan Uggla 1.50 4.00
77 Hanley Ramirez 2.50 6.00
78 Jeremy Hermida 1.00 2.50
79 Josh Willingham 1.00 2.50
80 Lance Berkman 1.50 4.00
81 Roy Oswalt 1.50 4.00
82 Miguel Tejada 1.50 4.00
83 Hunter Pence 2.50 6.00
84 Carlos Lee 1.00 2.50
85 J.R. Towles 1.50 4.00
86 Brian Bannister 1.00 2.50
87 Luke Hochevar 1.50 4.00
88 Billy Butler 1.00 2.50
90 Kelvim Escobar 1.00 2.50
91 John Lackey 1.00 2.50
92 Chone Figgins 1.00 2.50
93 Jered Weaver 1.00 2.50
94 Torii Hunter 1.00 2.50
95 Vladimir Guerrero 2.50 6.00
96 Brad Penny 1.00 2.50
97 James Loney 1.50 4.00
98 Andruw Jones 1.00 2.50
99 Chad Billingsley 1.00 2.50
100 Chin-Lung Hu 1.50 4.00
101 Russell Martin 1.00 2.50
102 Eddie Mathews 2.50 6.00
103 Warren Spahn 1.50 4.00
104 Prince Fielder 1.50 4.00
105 Ryan Braun 3.00 8.00
106 J.J. Hardy 1.00 2.50
107 Ben Sheets 1.00 2.50
108 Corey Hart 1.00 2.50
109 Yovani Gallardo 1.00 2.50
110 Joe Mauer 2.50 6.00
111 Delmon Young 1.50 4.00
112 Johan Santana 2.50 6.00
113 Glen Perkins 1.00 2.50
114 Justin Morneau 2.50 6.00
115 Carlos Beltran 1.00 2.50
116 Jose Reyes 1.50 4.00
117 David Wright 3.00 8.00
118 Pedro Martinez 1.50 4.00
119 Tom Seaver 1.50 4.00
120 Billy Wagner 1.00 2.50
121 John Maine 1.00 2.50
122 Alex Rodriguez 4.00 10.00
123 Chien-Ming Wang 1.50 4.00
124 Hideki Matsui 2.50 6.00
125 Jorge Posada 1.50 4.00
126 Mariano Rivera 2.50 6.00
127 Phil Rizzuto 1.50 4.00
128 Bucky Dent 1.00 2.50
129 Derek Jeter 6.00 15.00
130 Graig Nettles 1.00 2.50
131 Ian Kennedy 2.50 6.00
132 Don Larsen 1.00 2.50
133 Joe Blanton 1.00 2.50
134 Mark Ellis 1.00 2.50
135 Dennis Eckersley 1.00 2.50
136 Rollie Fingers 1.00 2.50
137 Catfish Hunter 1.00 2.50
138 Daric Barton 1.00 2.50
139 Jack Cust 1.00 2.50
140 Ryan Howard 3.00 8.00
141 Jimmy Rollins 1.50 4.00
142 Chase Utley 2.50 6.00
143 Shane Victorino 1.00 2.50
144 Cole Hamels 2.50 6.00
145 Richie Ashburn 1.50 4.00
146 Jason Bay 1.50 4.00
147 Freddy Sanchez 1.00 2.50
148 Adam LaRoche 1.00 2.50
149 Jack Wilson 1.00 2.50
150 Ralph Kiner 1.50 4.00
151 Bill Mazeroski 1.50 4.00
152 Tom Gorzelanny 1.00 2.50
153 Jay Bruce 4.00 10.00
154 Jake Peavy 1.00 2.50
155 Chris Young 1.00 2.50
156 Trevor Hoffman 1.50 4.00
157 Khalil Greene 1.00 2.50
158 Adrian Gonzalez 1.50 4.00
159 Tim Lincecum 4.00 10.00
160 Matt Cain 1.00 2.50
161 Aaron Rowand 1.00 2.50
162 Orlando Cepeda 1.00 2.50
163 Juan Marichal 1.00 2.50
164 Noah Lowry 1.00 2.50
165 Ichiro Suzuki 4.00 10.00
166 Felix Hernandez 2.50 6.00
167 J.J. Putz 1.00 2.50
168 Jose Vidro 1.00 2.50
169 Raul Ibanez 1.50 4.00
170 Wladimir Balentien 1.00 2.50
171 Albert Pujols 6.00 15.00
172 Scott Rolen 1.50 4.00
173 Lou Brock 1.50 4.00
174 Chris Duncan 1.00 2.50
175 Vince Coleman 1.00 2.50
176 B.J. Upton 1.50 4.00
177 Carl Crawford 1.50 4.00
178 Carlos Pena 1.50 4.00
179 Scott Kazmir 1.50 4.00
180 Akinori Iwamura 1.00 2.50
181 James Shields 1.00 2.50
182 Michael Young 1.50 4.00
183 Jarrod Saltalamacchia 1.00 2.50
184 Hank Blalock 1.00 2.50
185 Ian Kinsler 1.50 4.00
186 Josh Hamilton 2.50 6.00
187 Marlon Byrd 1.00 2.50
188 David Murphy 1.00 2.50
189 Vernon Wells 1.00 2.50
190 Roy Halladay 2.50 6.00
191 Frank Thomas 2.50 6.00
192 Alex Rios 1.50 4.00
193 Troy Glaus 1.50 4.00
194 David Eckstein 1.00 2.50
195 Ryan Zimmerman 1.50 4.00
196 Dmitri Young 1.00 2.50
197 Austin Kearns 1.00 2.50
198 Chad Cordero 1.00 2.50
199 Ryan Church 1.00 2.50
200 Evan Longoria 10.00 25.00
201 Brooks Robinson 2.50 6.00
202 Cal Ripken Jr. 15.00 40.00
203 Frank Robinson 2.50 6.00
204 Carl Yastrzemski 4.00 10.00
205 Carlton Fisk 2.50 6.00
206 Fred Lynn 2.50 6.00
207 Wade Boggs 3.00 8.00
208 Nolan Ryan 10.00 25.00
209 Ernie Banks 3.00 8.00
210 Ryne Sandberg 5.00 12.00
211 Al Kaline 3.00 8.00
212 Bo Jackson 3.00 8.00
213 Paul Molitor 3.00 8.00
214 Robin Yount 3.00 8.00
215 Harmon Killebrew 3.00 8.00
216 Rod Carew 2.50 6.00
217 Bobby Thomson 2.50 6.00
218 Gaylord Perry 2.50 6.00
219 Dave Winfield 2.50 6.00
220 Don Mattingly 4.00 10.00
221 Reggie Jackson 2.50 6.00
222 Roger Clemens 4.00 10.00
223 Whitey Ford 2.50 6.00
224 Mike Schmidt 4.00 10.00
225 Steve Carlton 2.50 6.00
226 Tony Gwynn 2.50 6.00
227 Willie McCovey 2.50 6.00
228 Bob Gibson 2.50 6.00
229 Ozzie Smith 4.00 10.00
230 Stan Musial 4.00 10.00
231 George Washington 2.50 6.00
232 Thomas Jefferson 2.50 6.00
233 James Madison 2.00 5.00
234 James Monroe 2.00 5.00
235 Andrew Jackson 2.00 5.00
236 John Tyler 2.00 5.00
237 Abraham Lincoln 2.50 6.00
238 Ulysses S. Grant 2.00 5.00
239 Grover Cleveland 2.00 5.00
240 Theodore Roosevelt 2.00 5.00
241 Calvin,Coolidge 2.00 5.00
242 John Adams 2.00 5.00
243 Martin Van Buren 2.00 5.00
244 William McKinley 2.00 5.00
245 Woodrow Wilson 2.00 5.00
246 James K. Polk 2.00 5.00
247 Rutherford B. Hayes 2.00 5.00
248 William H. Taft 2.00 5.00
249 Andrew Johnson 2.00 5.00
250 James Buchanan 2.00 5.00
251 Albert Pujols 36 BW 5.00 12.00
252 Alex Rodriguez 36 BW 4.00 10.00
253 Alfonso Soriano 36 BW 3.00 8.00
254 C.C. Sabathia 36 BW 3.00 8.00
255 Chase Utley 36 BW 3.00 8.00
256 David Ortiz 36 BW 3.00 8.00
257 David Wright 36 BW 3.00 8.00
258 Derek Jeter 36 BW 6.00 15.00
259 Hanley Ramirez 36 BW 3.00 8.00
260 Ichiro Suzuki 36 BW 4.00 10.00
261 Jake Peavy 36 BW 3.00 8.00
262 Johan Santana 36 BW 3.00 8.00
263 Jose Reyes 36 BW 3.00 8.00
264 Ken Griffey Jr. 36 BW 4.00 10.00
265 Magglio Ordonez 36 BW 3.00 8.00
266 Matt Holliday 36 BW 3.00 8.00
267 Prince Fielder 36 BW 3.00 8.00
268 Ryan Braun 36 BW 3.00 8.00
269 Ryan Howard 36 BW 3.00 8.00
270 Vladimir Guerrero 36 BW 3.00 8.00
271 Carl Yastrzemski SR 3.00 8.00
272 Albert Pujols SR 5.00 12.00
273 Amy Van Dyken SR 2.50 6.00
274 Tom Seaver SR 2.50 6.00
275 Brett Favre SR 5.00 12.00
276 Bruce Jenner SR 2.50 6.00
277 Bill Russell SR 4.00 10.00
278 Barry Sanders SR 4.00 10.00
279 Cynthia Cooper SR 2.50 6.00
280 Mike Schmidt SR 3.00 8.00
281 Chipper Jones SR 3.00 8.00
282 Cal Ripken Jr. SR 10.00 25.00
283 Cael Sanderson SR 2.50 6.00
284 Dan Gable SR 2.50 6.00
285 Derek Jeter SR 6.00 15.00
286 Andre Dawson SR 2.50 6.00
287 Dan O'Brien SR 2.50 6.00
288 Julius Erving SR 3.00 8.00
289 Emmitt Smith SR 4.00 10.00
290 Janet Evans SR 2.50 6.00
291 Chase Utley SR 2.50 6.00
292 Gary Hall Jr. SR 2.50 6.00
293 Gordie Howe SR 4.00 10.00
294 Josh Beckett SR 2.50 6.00
295 John Elway SR 6.00 15.00
296 Julie Foudy SR 2.50 6.00
297 Jackie Joyner-Kersee SR 2.50 6.00
298 Jack Nicklaus SR 12.50 30.00
299 Magic Johnson SR 4.00 10.00
300 Michael Jordan SR 12.50 30.00
301 Bo Jackson SR 3.00 8.00
302 Tom Brady SR 10.00 25.00
303 Wade Boggs SR 3.00 8.00
304 Dan Marino SR 5.00 12.00
305 Dave Winfield SR 2.50 6.00
306 Jenny Thompson SR 2.50 6.00
307 Kobe Bryant SR 4.00 10.00
308 Kevin Durant SR 4.00 10.00
309 Ken Griffey Jr. SR 4.00 10.00
310 Kerri Strug SR 3.00 8.00
311 Kerri Walsh SR 3.00 8.00
312 Larry Bird SR 5.00 12.00
313 LeBron James SR 10.00 25.00
314 Matt Biondi SR 2.50 6.00
315 Mark Messier SR 2.50 6.00
316 Michael Johnson SR 2.50 6.00
317 Misty May-Treanor SR 3.00 8.00
318 Bob Gibson SR 2.50 6.00
319 Nolan Ryan SR 8.00 20.00
320 Ozzie Smith SR 4.00 10.00
321 Prince Fielder SR 3.00 8.00
322 Rulon Gardner SR 2.50 6.00
323 Reggie Jackson SR 3.00 8.00
324 Ernie Banks SR 4.00 10.00
325 Sidney Crosby SR 8.00 20.00
326 Sanya Richards SR 2.50 6.00
327 Terry Bradshaw SR 3.00 8.00
328 Tony Gwynn SR 3.00 8.00
329 Stan Musial SR 5.00 12.00
330 Tiger Woods SR 75.00 150.00

2008 Upper Deck Goudey Mini Red Backs

*RED 1-200: 1X TO 2.5X BASIC 1-200
*RED RC 1-200: .75X TO 2X BASIC RC 1-200
*RED 201-270: .5X TO 1.2X BASIC SP 201-270
*RED 271-330: .6X to 1.2X BASIC SR 271-330
RANDOM INSERTS IN PACKS
298 Jack Nicklaus SR 12.50 30.00
330 Tiger Woods SR 30.00 60.00

2008 Upper Deck Goudey Mini Taupe Backs

RANDOM INSERTS IN PACKS
STATED PRINT RUN 8 SER.#'d SETS
NO PRICING DUE TO SCARCITY

2008 Upper Deck Goudey Autographs

OVERALL AUTO ODDS 1:18 HOBBY
ASTERISK EQUALS PARTIAL EXCHANGE
EXCHANGE DEADLINE 7/17/2010
AH Aaron Harang 4.00 10.00
BB Billy Buckner 3.00 8.00
BD Bucky Dent 6.00 15.00
BP Brandon Phillips 6.00 15.00
BR Brooks Robinson 20.00 50.00
BT Bobby Thomson 12.50 30.00
BW Billy Wagner 8.00 20.00
CH Corey Hart 4.00 10.00
CJ Chipper Jones SP 60.00 120.00
CL Carlos Lee 8.00 20.00
DB Daric Barton 3.00 8.00
DE David Eckstein 6.00 15.00
DJ Derek Jeter EXCH * 150.00 250.00
DL Derrek Lee 10.00 25.00
DM Daisuke Matsuzaka SP EXCH 75.00 150.00
EE Edwin Encarnacion 4.00 10.00
FC Fausto Carmona 4.00 10.00
FL Fred Lynn SP 15.00 40.00
GN Graig Nettles 6.00 15.00
GO Tom Gorzelanny 4.00 10.00
GP Glen Perkins 3.00 8.00
HR Hanley Ramirez SP 30.00 60.00
HU Chin-Lung Hu SP 20.00 50.00
JB Johnny Bench SP 30.00 60.00
JC Jack Cust 3.00 8.00
JF Jeff Francis SP 12.50 30.00
JG Jeremy Guthrie 6.00 15.00
JH Jeremy Hermida 4.00 10.00
JO John Maine 4.00 10.00
JP Jonathan Papelbon 10.00 25.00
JT J.R. Towles 3.00 8.00
JW Josh Willingham 3.00 8.00
KG Ken Griffey Jr. SP 225.00 450.00
KJ Kelly Johnson 3.00 8.00
KY Kevin Youkilis SP 15.00 40.00
LA Don Larsen SP 15.00 40.00
MA Don Mattingly SP EXCH 100.00 175.00
MB Marlon Byrd 3.00 8.00
MO Jack Morris 6.00 15.00
MS Mike Schmidt SP 40.00 80.00
MU David Murphy 4.00 10.00
NL Noah Lowry 3.00 8.00
NM Nick Markakis 8.00 20.00
NS Nick Swisher 4.00 10.00
PM Paul Molitor 15.00 40.00
RM Russell Martin SP 20.00 50.00
SC Steve Carlton SP 40.00 80.00
SP Steve Pearce 4.00 10.00
TG Tom Glavine SP 20.00 50.00
VC Vince Coleman 6.00 15.00
WM Willie McCovey SP
YG Yovani Gallardo SP 4.00 10.00

2008 Upper Deck Goudey Hit Parade of Champions

RANDOM INSERTS IN PACKS
1 Albert Pujols 1.50 4.00
2 Don Mattingly 1.25 3.00
3 Ben Roethlisberger .75 2.00
4 Bill Russell 1.25 3.00
5 Bobby Orr 2.50 6.00
6 Cal Ripken Jr. 2.50 6.00
7 Carl Yastrzemski 1.00 2.50
8 Derek Jeter 1.50 4.00
9 Emmitt Smith 1.25 3.00
10 Gordie Howe 1.50 4.00
11 Joe Montana 1.25 3.00
12 Joe Namath .75 2.00
13 Ken Griffey Jr. 1.00 2.50
14 Kobe Bryant 2.50 6.00
15 LaDainian Tomlinson .75 2.00
16 Larry Bird 2.00 5.00
17 LeBron James 3.00 8.00
18 Magic Johnson 1.25 3.00
19 Mario Lemieux 2.50 6.00
20 Yogi Berra .60 1.50
21 Michael Jordan 4.00 10.00
22 Nolan Ryan 2.00 5.00
23 Patrick Roy 1.50 4.00
24 Peyton Manning .75 2.00
25 Reggie Jackson .40 1.00
26 Roger Clemens .75 2.00
27 Roger Staubach .75 2.00
28 Manny Ramirez .60 1.50
29 Tom Brady 1.00 2.50
30 Wayne Gretzky 2.50 6.00

2008 Upper Deck Goudey Memorabilia

OVERALL GU ODDS 1:18 HOBBY
AD Adam Dunn 3.00 8.00
AG Adrian Gonzalez 3.00 8.00
AH Aaron Harang 3.00 8.00
AI Akinori Iwamura 3.00 8.00
AJ Andruw Jones 3.00 8.00
AP Albert Pujols 6.00 15.00
AR Aaron Rowand 3.00 8.00
AS Alfonso Soriano 4.00 10.00
BB Billy Butler 3.00 8.00
BD Bucky Dent 3.00 8.00
BE Josh Beckett 3.00 8.00
BR Brian Roberts 3.00 8.00
BU B.J. Upton 3.00 8.00
BW Brandon Webb 3.00 8.00
CC Carl Crawford 3.00 8.00
CH Cole Hamels 4.00 10.00
CJ Chipper Jones 5.00 12.00
CL Carlos Lee 3.00 8.00
CR Cal Ripken Jr. 20.00 50.00
CU Chase Utley 4.00 10.00
CY Chris Young 3.00 8.00
CZ Carlos Zambrano 3.00 8.00
DJ Derek Jeter 10.00 25.00
DL Derrek Lee 3.00 8.00
DM Daisuke Matsuzaka 6.00 15.00
DO David Ortiz 4.00 10.00
DU Dan Uggla 3.00 8.00
DY Delmon Young 3.00 8.00
FH Felix Hernandez 3.00 8.00
FS Freddy Sanchez 3.00 8.00
GA Garrett Atkins 3.00 8.00
GR Khalil Greene 3.00 8.00
GS Gary Sheffield 3.00 8.00
HO Trevor Hoffman 3.00 8.00
HP Hunter Pence 3.00 8.00
HR Hanley Ramirez 4.00 10.00
HU Catfish Hunter 5.00 12.00
JB Jason Bay 3.00 8.00
JD Jermaine Dye 3.00 8.00
JF Jeff Francoeur 3.00 8.00
JM Joe Mauer 3.00 8.00
JP Jake Peavy 3.00 8.00
JR Jimmy Rollins 3.00 8.00
JV Justin Verlander 3.00 8.00
JW Jered Weaver 3.00 8.00
KG Ken Griffey Jr. 6.00 15.00
KY Kevin Youkilis 4.00 10.00
LB Lance Berkman 3.00 8.00
MA John Maine 3.00 8.00
MB Mark Buehrle 3.00 8.00
MC Matt Cain 3.00 8.00
MH Matt Holliday 3.00 8.00
MI Miguel Cabrera 3.00 8.00
MO Justin Morneau 3.00 8.00
MR Manny Ramirez 4.00 10.00
MT Mark Teixeira 3.00 8.00
NM Nick Markakis 3.00 8.00
OR Magglio Ordonez 3.00 8.00
PA Jonathan Papelbon 4.00 10.00
PF Prince Fielder 4.00 10.00
PM Pedro Martinez 3.00 8.00
PO Jorge Posada 3.00 8.00
RA Aramis Ramirez 3.00 8.00
RE Jose Reyes 3.00 8.00
RH Roy Halladay 3.00 8.00
RI Mariano Rivera 3.00 8.00
RJ Randy Johnson 3.00 8.00
RM Russell Martin 3.00 8.00
RO Roy Oswalt 3.00 8.00
RZ Ryan Zimmerman 3.00 8.00
SI Grady Sizemore 3.00 8.00
SM John Smoltz 3.00 8.00
TE Miguel Tejada 3.00 8.00
TH Travis Hafner 3.00 8.00
VG Vladimir Guerrero 3.00 8.00
VM Victor Martinez 3.00 8.00
VW Vernon Wells 3.00 8.00
WI Jack Wilson 3.00 8.00
WS Warren Spahn 10.00 25.00
YG Yovani Gallardo 3.00 8.00

2008 Upper Deck Goudey Sport Royalty Autographs

OVERALL AUTO ODDS 1:18 HOBBY
ASTERISK EQUALS PARTIAL EXCHANGE
EXCHANGE DEADLINE 7/17/2010
AV Amy Van Dyken 12.50 30.00
BR Bill Russell SP
BS Barry Sanders SP
CC Cynthia Cooper 10.00 25.00
CR Cal Ripken Jr. SP
CS Cael Sanderson 15.00 40.00
DJ Derek Jeter SP
DM Dan Marino SP
DO Dan O'Brien 8.00 20.00
ER Julius Erving SP
EV Janet Evans 12.50 30.00
FO Julie Foudy 10.00 25.00
GH Gary Hall Jr. 8.00 20.00
HO Gordie Howe SP EXCH
JB Josh Beckett SP
JE Bruce Jenner 12.50 30.00
JJ Jackie Joyner-Kersee 10.00 25.00
JN Jack Nicklaus SP EXCH
JT Jenny Thompson 10.00 25.00
KD Kevin Durant SP
KG Ken Griffey Jr. SP 75.00 150.00
KS Kerri Strug 20.00 50.00
KW Kerri Walsh 10.00 25.00
LB Larry Bird SP
LJ LeBron James SP
MA Misty May-Treanor 40.00 80.00
MB Matt Biondi 10.00 25.00
MI Michael Jordan SP
MJ Magic Johnson SP
MM Mark Messier SP
NR Nolan Ryan SP
OS Ozzie Smith SP
PD Phil Dalhausser 8.00 20.00
PF Prince Fielder SP EXCH
RG Rulon Gardner 10.00 25.00
RJ Reggie Jackson SP
SC Sidney Crosby SP
SR Sanya Richards 8.00 20.00
TB Terry Bradshaw SP 125.00 250.00
TG Tony Gwynn SP
TR Todd Rogers 12.50 30.00
TW Tiger Woods SP

2009 Upper Deck Goudey

COMPLETE SET (300) 200.00 300.00
COMP.SET w/o SP's (200) 20.00 50.00
COMMON CARD (1-200) .20 .50
COMMON RC (1-200) .40 1.00
COMMON SP (201-300) 2.00 5.00
APPX.SP ODDS 201-220 1:9 HOBBY
APPX.SP ODDS 221-260 1:6 HOBBY
APPX.SP ODDS 261-300 1:6 HOBBY
1 Adam Dunn .30 .75
2 Max Scherzer .20 .50
3 Stephen Drew .20 .50
4 Randy Johnson .30 .75
5 Brandon Webb .30 .75
6 Dan Haren .20 .50
7 Chris B. Young .20 .50
8 Brian McCann .30 .75
9 Jeff Francoeur .30 .75
10 James Parr (RC) .40 1.00
11 Tom Glavine .30 .75
12 Tim Hudson .30 .75
13 Chipper Jones .50 1.25
14 Kelly Johnson .20 .50
15 Adam Jones .30 .75
16 Jeremy Guthrie .20 .50
17 Brian Roberts .20 .50
18 Nick Markakis .50 1.25
19 Jed Lowrie .30 .75
20 Cal Ripken Jr. 2.00 5.00
21 Melvin Mora .20 .50
22 Jason Bay .30 .75
23 Josh Beckett .30 .75
24 Justin Masterson .20 .50
25 Kevin Youkilis .30 .75
26 Michael Bowden (RC) .40 1.00
27 Dustin Pedroia .60 1.50
28 Jacoby Ellsbury .50 1.25
29 Jason Varitek .50 1.25
30 Jonathan Papelbon .30 .75
31 David Ortiz .30 .75
32 Daisuke Matsuzaka .50 1.25
33 J.D. Drew .20 .50
34 Curt Schilling .30 .75
35 Clay Buchholz .30 .75
36 Wilkin Castillo RC .40 1.00
37 Derrek Lee .20 .50
38 Kosuke Fukudome .50 1.25
39 Aramis Ramirez .20 .50
40 Alfonso Soriano .30 .75
41 Kerry Wood .20 .50
42 Carlos Zambrano .30 .75
43 Rich Harden .20 .50
44 Geovany Soto .30 .75
45 Gavin Floyd .20 .50
46 Ken Griffey Jr. .75 2.00
47 Nick Swisher .50 1.25
48 Jim Thome .30 .75
49 Jermaine Dye .20 .50
50 Alexei Ramirez .30 .75
51 Carlos Quentin .20 .50
52 Brandon Phillips .20 .50
53 Johnny Cueto .20 .50
54 Jay Bruce .30 .75
55 Dave Concepcion .20 .50
56 Joey Votto .50 1.25
57 Aaron Harang .20 .50
58 Edinson Volquez .20 .50
59 Kelly Shoppach .20 .50
60 Fausto Carmona .20 .50
61 Grady Sizemore .30 .75
62 Travis Hafner .20 .50
63 Victor Martinez .30 .75
64 Cliff Lee .30 .75
65 Dexter Fowler (RC) .60 1.50
66 Garrett Atkins .20 .50
67 Troy Tulowitzki .50 1.25
68 Matt Holliday .50 1.25
69 Curtis Granderson .30 .75
70 Carlos Guillen .20 .50
71 Gary Sheffield .20 .50
72 Miguel Cabrera .50 1.25
73 Magglio Ordonez .30 .75
74 Justin Verlander .60 1.50
75 Hanley Ramirez .50 1.25
76 Josh Willingham .20 .50
77 Dan Uggla .30 .75
78 Josh Johnson .30 .75
79 Carlos Lee .20 .50
80 Roy Oswalt .30 .75
81 Miguel Tejada .30 .75
82 Lance Berkman .30 .75
83 Kila Ka'aihue (RC) .60 1.50
84 Joakim Soria .20 .50
85 Alex Gordon .30 .75
86 Chone Figgins .20 .50
87 John Lackey .20 .50
88 Jered Weaver .20 .50
89 Vladimir Guerrero .50 1.25
90 Mark Teixeira .50 1.25
91 Garret Anderson .20 .50
92 Torii Hunter .20 .50
93 Howie Kendrick .20 .50
94 Clayton Kershaw .50 1.25
95 Cory Wade .20 .50
96 Matt Kemp .30 .75
97 Russell Martin .30 .75
98 Scott Elbert (RC) .40 1.00
99 Manny Ramirez .50 1.25
100 Andre Ethier .30 .75
101 Rafael Furcal .20 .50
102 Brad Penny .20 .50
103 Takashi Saito .20 .50
104 Kirk Gibson .20 .50
105 Alcides Escobar RC 1.00 2.50
106 Bill Hall .20 .50
107 Mat Gamel RC 1.00 2.50
108 Prince Fielder .30 .75
109 Miguel Montero .20 .50
110 Yovani Gallardo .20 .50
111 Ben Sheets .20 .50
112 CC Sabathia .30 .75
113 Ryan Braun .60 1.50
114 J.J. Hardy .20 .50
115 Denard Span .20 .50
116 Joe Nathan .20 .50
117 Nick Blackburn .20 .50
118 Joe Mauer .50 1.25
119 Justin Morneau .50 1.25
120 Francisco Liriano .20 .50
121 Kevin Slowey .30 .75
122 Delmon Young .30 .75
123 John Maine .20 .50
124 Jonathon Niese RC .60 1.50
125 David Wright .60 1.50
126 Jose Reyes .30 .75
127 Carlos Beltran .20 .50
128 Johan Santana .50 1.25
129 A.J. Burnett .30 .75
130 Derek Jeter 1.25 3.00
131 Francisco Cervelli RC 1.00 2.50
132 Ian Kennedy .30 .75
133 Phil Coke RC .60 1.50
134 Phil Hughes .30 .75
135 Alex Rodriguez .75 2.00
136 Chien-Ming Wang .30 .75
137 Mariano Rivera .50 1.25
138 Joba Chamberlain .30 .75
139 Jason Giambi .20 .50
140 Andy Pettitte .30 .75
141 Greg Smith .20 .50
142 Marlon Byrd .20 .50
143 Johnny Damon .30 .75
144 Frank Thomas .50 1.25
145 Carlos Gonzalez .30 .75
146 Jeff Baisley RC .40 1.00
147 Mark Teahen .20 .50
148 Jack Cust .20 .50
149 Kurt Suzuki .20 .50
150 Bobby Crosby .20 .50
151 Cole Hamels .50 1.25
152 Lou Marson (RC) .40 1.00
153 Chase Utley .50 1.25
154 Jimmy Rollins .30 .75
155 Ryan Howard .60 1.50
156 Greg Golson (RC) .40 1.00
157 Pat Burrell .20 .50
158 Shane Victorino .20 .50
159 Brad Lidge .20 .50
160 Edwin Encarnacion .20 .50
161 Nate McLouth .20 .50
162 Ryan Doumit .20 .50
163 Adrian Gonzalez .30 .75
164 Matt Antonelli RC .60 1.50
165 Jake Peavy .20 .50
166 Kevin Kouzmanoff .20 .50
167 Chris Young .20 .50
168 Trevor Hoffman .30 .75
169 Conor Gillaspie RC 1.00 2.50
170 Wade LeBlanc RC .60 1.50
171 Matt Cain .20 .50
172 Tim Lincecum .75 2.00
173 Matt Tuiasosopo (RC) .40 1.00
174 Ichiro Suzuki .75 2.00
175 Felix Hernandez .50 1.25
176 Erik Bedard .20 .50
177 Ryan Ludwick .20 .50
178 Albert Pujols 1.25 3.00
179 Rick Ankiel .20 .50
180 Troy Glaus .20 .50
181 Bob Gibson .30 .75
182 B.J. Upton .30 .75
183 David Price RC 1.00 2.50
184 Evan Longoria .60 1.50
185 Carl Crawford .30 .75
186 Scott Kazmir .30 .75
187 Carlos Pena .30 .75
188 James Shields .20 .50
189 Josh Hamilton .50 1.25
190 Ian Kinsler .30 .75
191 Michael Young .30 .75
192 Mike Aviles .20 .50
193 Roy Halladay .50 1.25
194 Travis Snider RC .60 1.50
195 Vernon Wells .20 .50
196 Alex Rios .30 .75
197 Ryan Zimmerman .30 .75
198 Shairon Martis RC .60 1.50
199 Lastings Milledge .20 .50
200 Cristian Guzman .20 .50
201 Brooks Robinson SP 2.00 5.00
202 Carlton Fisk SP 2.00 5.00
203 Gaylord Perry SP 2.00 5.00
204 Jack Morris SP 2.00 5.00
205 Rollie Fingers SP 2.00 5.00
206 Ron Santo SP 2.00 5.00
207 Sparky Lyle SP 2.00 5.00
208 Nolan Ryan SP 5.00 12.00
209 Whitey Ford SP 2.50 6.00
210 Phil Niekro SP 2.00 5.00
211 Ryne Sandberg SP 3.00 8.00
212 Jim Palmer SP 2.50 6.00
213 Joe DiMaggio SP 5.00 12.00
214 Johnny Bench SP 3.00 8.00
215 Ted Williams SP 5.00 12.00
216 Robin Yount SP 3.00 8.00

217 Ozzie Smith SP 3.00 8.00
218 Reggie Jackson SP 2.50 6.00
219 Yogi Berra SP 3.00 8.00
220 Mike Schmidt SP 3.00 8.00
221 Cal Ripken Jr. SR SP 5.00 12.00
222 Ozzie Smith SR SP 3.00 8.00
223 Tony Gwynn SR SP 3.00 8.00
224 Don Mattingly SR SP 3.00 8.00
225 Steve Carlton SR SP 2.00 5.00
226 Reggie Jackson SR SP 2.50 6.00
227 Carl Yastrzemski SR SP 3.00 8.00
228 Johnny Bench SR SP 3.00 8.00
229 Mike Schmidt SR SP 3.00 8.00
230 Nolan Ryan SR SP 5.00 12.00
231 Ernie Banks SR SP 3.00 8.00
232 Stan Musial SR SP 4.00 10.00
233 Ryne Sandberg SR SP 3.00 8.00
234 Bob Gibson SR SP 3.00 8.00
235 Dennis Eckersley SR SP 2.00 5.00
236 Felix Hernandez SR SP 2.50 6.00
237 Jim Rice SR SP 2.50 6.00
238 Chien-Ming Wang SR SP 3.00 8.00
239 Jonathan Papelbon SR SP 2.50 6.00
240 Evan Longoria SR SP 3.00 8.00
241 Cole Hamels SR SP 2.50 6.00
242 Ken Griffey Jr. SR SP 4.00 10.00
243 Tiger Woods SR SP 15.00 40.00
244 B.J. Upton SR SP 2.50 6.00
245 Randy Johnson SR SP 3.00 8.00
246 Guy Lafleur SR SP 2.50 6.00
247 Nicklas Lidstrom SR SP 2.00 5.00
248 Mike Bossy SR SP 2.50 6.00
249 Bobby Orr SR SP 4.00 10.00
250 Patrick Roy SR SP 5.00 12.00
251 Adrian Peterson SR SP 4.00 10.00
252 Juan Marichal SR SP 2.00 5.00
253 Chipper Jones SR SP 3.00 8.00
254 Rollie Fingers SR SP 2.00 5.00
255 Al Kaline SR SP 3.00 8.00
256 Paul Pierce SR SP 3.00 8.00
257 Jerry West SR SP 3.00 8.00
258 Larry Bird SR SP 3.00 8.00
259 John Havlicek SR SP 2.50 6.00
260 Michael Jordan SR SP 5.00 12.00
261 Cal Ripken Jr. HU SP 5.00 12.00
262 Reggie Jackson HU SP 2.50 6.00
263 Nolan Ryan HU SP 5.00 12.00
264 Yogi Berra HU SP 3.00 8.00
265 Ernie Banks HU SP 3.00 8.00
266 Dave Winfield HU SP 2.50 6.00
267 Ozzie Smith HU SP 3.00 8.00
268 Stan Musial HU SP 4.00 10.00
269 Ichiro Suzuki HU SP 3.00 8.00
270 Albert Pujols HU SP 4.00 10.00
271 Alex Rodriguez HU SP 4.00 10.00
272 Jose Reyes HU SP 3.00 8.00
273 David Wright HU SP 3.00 8.00
274 Johan Santana HU SP 3.00 8.00
275 Josh Hamilton HU SP 3.00 8.00
276 David Ortiz HU SP 3.00 8.00
277 Josh Beckett HU SP 2.50 6.00
278 Manny Ramirez HU SP 3.00 8.00
279 Ryan Howard HU SP 3.00 8.00
280 Chase Utley HU SP 3.00 8.00
281 Jimmy Rollins HU SP 3.00 8.00
282 Hanley Ramirez HU SP 3.00 8.00
283 CC Sabathia HU SP 3.00 8.00
284 Ryan Braun HU SP 2.50 6.00
285 Evan Longoria HU SP 3.00 8.00
286 Grady Sizemore HU SP 2.50 6.00
287 Dustin Pedroia HU SP 3.00 8.00
288 Mark Teixeira HU SP 3.00 8.00
289 Ken Griffey Jr. HU SP 4.00 10.00
290 Lance Berkman HU SP 2.50 6.00
291 Alfonso Soriano HU SP 2.50 6.00
292 Derrek Lee HU SP 2.50 6.00
293 Brandon Webb HU SP 2.50 6.00
294 Derek Jeter HU SP 5.00 12.00
295 Daisuke Matsuzaka HU SP 3.00 8.00
296 Vladimir Guerrero HU SP 3.00 8.00
297 Jim Thome HU SP 2.50 6.00
298 Carlos Zambrano HU SP 2.00 5.00
299 Justin Morneau HU SP 2.50 6.00
300 Tim Lincecum HU SP 3.00 8.00

2009 Upper Deck Goudey Mini Black Back

RANDOM INSERTS IN PACKS
STATED PRINT RUN 21 SER.#'d SETS
NO PRICING DUE TO SCARCITY

2009 Upper Deck Goudey Mini Green Back

*GREEN 1-200: 1.2X TO 3X BASIC
*GREEN RC 1-200: .6X TO 1.5X BASIC
COMMON CARD (201-300) .75 2.00
APPROX.ODDS 1:6 HOBBY
201 Brooks Robinson 1.25 3.00
202 Carlton Fisk 1.25 3.00
203 Gaylord Perry .75 2.00
204 Jack Morris .75 2.00
205 Rollie Fingers .75 2.00
206 Ron Santo 1.25 3.00
207 Sparky Lyle .75 2.00
208 Nolan Ryan 6.00 15.00
209 Whitey Ford 1.25 3.00
210 Phil Niekro .75 2.00
211 Ryne Sandberg 4.00 10.00
212 Jim Palmer .75 2.00
213 Joe DiMaggio 5.00 12.00
214 Johnny Bench 2.00 5.00
215 Ted Williams 5.00 12.00
216 Robin Yount 2.00 5.00
217 Ozzie Smith 3.00 8.00
218 Reggie Jackson 1.25 3.00
219 Yogi Berra 2.00 5.00
220 Mike Schmidt 3.00 8.00
221 Cal Ripken Jr. SR 8.00 20.00
222 Ozzie Smith SR 3.00 8.00
223 Tony Gwynn SR 2.00 5.00
224 Don Mattingly SR 4.00 10.00
225 Steve Carlton SR .75 2.00
226 Reggie Jackson SR 1.25 3.00
227 Carl Yastrzemski SR 3.00 8.00
228 Johnny Bench SR 2.00 5.00
229 Mike Schmidt SR 3.00 8.00
230 Nolan Ryan SR 6.00 15.00
231 Ernie Banks SR 2.00 5.00
232 Stan Musial SR 3.00 8.00
233 Ryne Sandberg SR 4.00 10.00
234 Bob Gibson SR 1.25 3.00
235 Dennis Eckersley SR .75 2.00
236 Felix Hernandez SR 2.00 5.00
237 Jim Rice SR 1.25 3.00
238 Chien-Ming Wang SR 1.25 3.00
239 Jonathan Papelbon SR 1.25 3.00
240 Evan Longoria SR 2.50 6.00
241 Cole Hamels SR 2.00 5.00
242 Ken Griffey Jr. SR 3.00 8.00
243 Tiger Woods SR 60.00 120.00
244 B.J. Upton SR 1.25 3.00
245 Randy Johnson SR 1.25 3.00
246 Guy Lafleur SR 4.00 10.00
247 Nicklas Lidstrom SR 2.00 5.00
248 Mike Bossy SR 2.00 5.00
249 Bobby Orr SR 6.00 15.00
250 Patrick Roy SR 6.00 15.00
251 Adrian Peterson SR 4.00 10.00
252 Juan Marichal SR .75 2.00
253 Chipper Jones SR 2.00 5.00
254 Rollie Fingers SR .75 2.00
255 Al Kaline SR 2.00 5.00
256 Paul Pierce SR 2.50 6.00
257 Jerry West SR 3.00 8.00
258 Larry Bird SR 6.00 15.00
259 John Havlicek SR 2.00 5.00
260 Michael Jordan SR 6.00 15.00
261 Cal Ripken Jr. HU 8.00 20.00
262 Reggie Jackson HU 1.25 3.00
263 Nolan Ryan HU 6.00 15.00
264 Yogi Berra HU 2.00 5.00
265 Ernie Banks HU 2.00 5.00
266 Dave Winfield HU .75 2.00
267 Ozzie Smith HU 3.00 8.00
268 Stan Musial HU 3.00 8.00
269 Ichiro Suzuki HU 3.00 8.00
270 Albert Pujols HU 5.00 12.00
271 Alex Rodriguez HU 3.00 8.00
272 Jose Reyes HU 1.25 3.00
273 David Wright HU 2.50 6.00
274 Johan Santana HU 2.00 5.00
275 Josh Hamilton HU 2.00 5.00
276 David Ortiz HU 1.25 3.00
277 Josh Beckett HU 1.25 3.00
278 Manny Ramirez HU 2.00 5.00
279 Ryan Howard HU 2.50 6.00
280 Chase Utley HU 2.00 5.00
281 Jimmy Rollins HU 1.25 3.00
282 Hanley Ramirez HU 2.00 5.00
283 CC Sabathia HU 1.25 3.00
284 Ryan Braun HU 2.50 6.00
285 Evan Longoria HU 2.50 6.00
286 Grady Sizemore HU 1.25 3.00
287 Dustin Pedroia HU 2.50 6.00
288 Mark Teixeira HU 2.00 5.00
289 Ken Griffey Jr. HU 3.00 8.00
290 Lance Berkman HU 1.25 3.00
291 Alfonso Soriano HU 1.25 3.00
292 Derrek Lee HU .75 2.00
293 Brandon Webb HU 1.25 3.00
294 Derek Jeter HU 5.00 12.00
295 Daisuke Matsuzaka HU 2.00 5.00
296 Vladimir Guerrero HU 2.00 5.00
297 Jim Thome HU 1.25 3.00
298 Carlos Zambrano HU 1.25 3.00
299 Justin Morneau HU 2.00 5.00
300 Tim Lincecum HU 3.00 8.00

2009 Upper Deck Goudey Mini Navy Blue Back

*BLUE 1-200: 1.5X TO 4X BASIC
*BLUE RC 1-200: .75X TO 2X BASIC
*BLUE: 201-300: .6X TO 1.5X MINI GREEN
APPROX.ODDS 1:9 HOBBY
243 Tiger Woods SR 100.00 175.00

2009 Upper Deck Goudey 4-In-1

APPX.ODDS 1:2 HOBBY
BLACK RANDOMLY INSERTED
BLACK PRINT RUN 21 SER.#'d SETS
NO BLACK PRICING AVAILABLE
*BLUE: .6X TO 1.5X BASIC
APPX.BLUE ODDS 1:9
*GREEN: .75X TO 2X BASIC
APPX.GREEN ODDS 1:18
1 Sparky Lyle 1.25 3.00
Phil Niekro
Johnny Bench
Reggie Jackson
2 Ryan Ludwick 3.00 8.00
Ozzie Smith
Bob Gibson
Albert Pujols
3 Bob Gibson .50 1.25
Jake Peavy
Tim Lincecum
Josh Beckett
4 Jacoby Ellsbury 1.25 3.00
Jose Reyes
Carl Crawford
Brian Roberts
5 Derek Jeter 3.00 8.00
Reggie Jackson
Yogi Berra
Whitey Ford
6 Whitey Ford 3.00 8.00
Derek Jeter
Alex Rodriguez
Yogi Berra
7 Whitey Ford .75 2.00
Alex Rodriguez
Derek Jeter
Chien-Ming Wang
8 Brooks Robinson 2.00 5.00
Ichiro
Grady Sizemore
Josh Hamilton
9 Carl Crawford .75 2.00
Alex Rios
Jacoby Ellsbury
Johnny Damon
10 Nolan Ryan 4.00 10.00
Scott Kazmir
Josh Beckett
Clayton Kershaw
11 Andre Ethier 1.25 3.00
Kirk Gibson
Russell Martin
Clayton Kershaw
12 Mike Schmidt 2.00 5.00
Manny Ramirez
Ken Griffey Jr.
Alex Rodriguez
13 Dan Haren .50 1.25
Stephen Drew
Chris Young
Adrian Gonzalez
14 Gaylord Perry .50 1.25
Jack Morris
Jim Palmer
Rollie Fingers
15 Jonathan Papelbon .75 2.00
Joakim Soria
Trevor Hoffman
Mariano Rivera
16 Ryne Sandberg .75 2.00
Dan Uggla
Chase Utley
Ian Kinsler
17 Ron Santo .75 2.00
Billy Williams
Alfonso Soriano
Carlos Zambrano
18 Cal Ripken Jr. 5.00 12.00
Ozzie Smith
Hanley Ramirez
Derek Jeter
19 Cal Ripken Jr. 1.25 3.00
Jim Palmer
Melvin Mora
Nick Markakis
20 Johnny Bench .75 2.00
Dave Concepcion
Brandon Phillips
Jay Bruce
21 Shane Victorino 1.50 4.00
Cole Hamels
Mike Schmidt
Ryan Howard
22 Ron Santo .50 1.25
Ryne Sandberg
Derrek Lee
Aramis Ramirez
23 Robin Yount .75 2.00
Ryan Braun
Yovani Gallardo
Prince Fielder
24 Chien-Ming Wang .75 2.00
Derek Jeter
Johan Santana
Jose Reyes
25 Cal Ripken Jr. 5.00 12.00
Ozzie Smith
Derek Jeter
Jose Reyes
26 Brian McCann .75 2.00
Tim Hudson
Chipper Jones
Kelly Johnson
27 Johnny Bench 1.25 3.00
Yogi Berra
Joe Mauer
Brian McCann
28 Jim Palmer 4.00 10.00
Nolan Ryan
Bob Gibson
Gaylord Perry
29 Mike Schmidt .75 2.00
Ryan Howard
Robin Yount
Prince Fielder
30 Albert Pujols .50 1.25
Rick Ankiel
Troy Glaus
Ryan Ludwick
31 Matt Holliday 1.50 4.00
Ryan Braun
Carlos Quentin
Jason Bay
32 Johan Santana .50 1.25
Cole Hamels
CC Sabathia
Scott Kazmir
33 Tim Lincecum 2.00 5.00
Edinson Volquez
Clayton Kershaw
Rich Harden
34 Dustin Pedroia 1.50 4.00
Brian Roberts
Howie Kendrick
Ian Kinsler
35 B.J. Upton 1.50 4.00
Evan Longoria
Carlos Pena
Carl Crawford
36 Josh Hamilton .75 2.00
Justin Morneau
Prince Fielder
Ryan Howard
37 Miguel Cabrera 1.25 3.00
Magglio Ordonez
Curtis Granderson
Carlos Guillen
38 Jose Reyes .75 2.00
Jimmy Rollins
Hanley Ramirez
Cristian Guzman
39 Matt Kemp .75 2.00
Russell Martin
Rafael Furcal
Andre Ethier
40 Ichiro 1.25 3.00
Matt Tuiasosopo
Felix Hernandez
Erik Bedard
41 Bobby Crosby 2.00 5.00
Jack Cust
Tim Lincecum
Matt Cain
42 Jose Reyes .75 2.00
Carlos Beltran
David Wright
Johan Santana
43 Hanley Ramirez .75 2.00
Dan Uggla
Jimmy Rollins
Chase Utley
44 Howie Kendrick 1.25 3.00
Vladimir Guerrero
Torii Hunter
Chone Figgins
45 Scott Kazmir 1.50 4.00
James Shields
Evan Longoria
David Price
46 Albert Pujols .75 2.00
Derrek Lee
Prince Fielder
Lance Berkman
47 Jimmy Rollins 1.50 4.00
Chase Utley
Ryan Howard
Cole Hamels
48 Daisuke Matsuzaka 1.25 3.00
Josh Beckett
Justin Masterson
Jonathan Papelbon
49 Joakim Soria .75 2.00
Jonathan Papelbon
Brad Lidge
Kerry Wood
50 Jacoby Ellsbury 1.50 4.00
Dustin Pedroia
David Ortiz
Kevin Youkilis
51 John Lackey 1.25 3.00
Jered Weaver
Felix Hernandez
Erik Bedard
52 Josh Hamilton .75 2.00
Ian Kinsler
Marlon Byrd
Michael Young
53 Grady Sizemore .75 2.00
Travis Hafner
Victor Martinez
Kelly Shoppach
54 Chipper Jones 1.25 3.00
Jeff Francoeur
Brian McCann
Kelly Johnson
55 Chipper Jones 1.50 4.00
David Wright
Garrett Atkins
Aramis Ramirez
56 Russell Martin .50 1.25
Brian McCann
Ryan Doumit
Geovany Soto
57 Ryan Braun .75 2.00
Prince Fielder
J.J. Hardy
Bill Hall
58 Jeff Baisley .50 1.25
Jack Cust
Bobby Crosby
Kurt Suzuki
59 Chien-Ming Wang 1.25 3.00
Mariano Rivera
Ian Kennedy
Joba Chamberlain
60 Joba Chamberlain 1.50 4.00
Rich Harden
Tim Lincecum
Justin Verlander
61 Vladimir Guerrero 1.25 3.00
John Lackey
Andre Ethier
Clayton Kershaw
62 David Wright 1.50 4.00
Ryan Zimmerman
B.J. Upton
John Maine
63 Ichiro 2.00 5.00
Grady Sizemore
B.J. Upton
Torii Hunter
64 Carlos Beltran 1.25 3.00
Lance Berkman
Jimmy Rollins
Chipper Jones
65 Roy Halladay .75 2.00
Travis Snider
Vernon Wells
Alex Rios
66 Carlos Zambrano .75 2.00
Rich Harden
Kosuke Fukudome
Geovany Soto
67 David Ortiz .75 2.00
Ryan Howard
Prince Fielder
Jason Giambi
68 Ian Kennedy .75 2.00
Joba Chamberlain
Clay Buchholz
Justin Masterson
69 Jonathan Papelbon .75 2.00
Josh Beckett
Joe Nathan
Francisco Liriano
70 Evan Longoria 1.50 4.00
Alexei Ramirez
Geovany Soto
Jay Bruce
71 Ryan Howard 1.25 3.00
Josh Hamilton
Albert Pujols
Miguel Cabrera
72 Chris Young 1.25 3.00
Adrian Gonzalez
Clayton Kershaw
Rafael Furcal
73 Alfonso Soriano .50 1.25
Derrek Lee
Aramis Ramirez
Geovany Soto
74 Daisuke Matsuzaka 1.25 3.00
Chien-Ming Wang
Kosuke Fukudome
Ichiro
75 Andy Pettitte .75 2.00
Curt Schilling
Tom Glavine
Randy Johnson
76 Ken Griffey Jr. .75 2.00
Jermaine Dye
Carlos Quentin
Jim Thome
77 Francisco Liriano 1.25 3.00
Clayton Kershaw
David Price
Cole Hamels
78 Justin Morneau 1.25 3.00
Joe Mauer
Delmon Young
Denard Span
79 Carlos Beltran .75 2.00
Carlos Lee
Carlos Quentin
Carlos Guillen
80 Travis Hafner 1.25 3.00
Magglio Ordonez
Jermaine Dye
Manny Ramirez
81 Cliff Lee 2.00 5.00
Grady Sizemore
Felix Hernandez
Ichiro
82 Jack Cust .75 2.00
Kurt Suzuki
Johnny Cueto
Jay Bruce
83 Denard Span .50 1.25
Adam Jones
Dexter Fowler
Alexei Ramirez
84 Clay Buchholz .50 1.25
Justin Masterson
Jed Lowrie
Dustin Pedroia
85 Alex Rodriguez 1.50 4.00
David Wright
Aramis Ramirez
Evan Longoria
86 Alex Rodriguez .75 2.00
Ken Griffey Jr.
Manny Ramirez
Jim Thome
87 Brian McCann .50 1.25
Ryan Doumit
Russell Martin
Joe Mauer
88 Manny Ramirez 3.00 8.00
Joe Nathan
Albert Pujols
Brad Lidge
89 Lance Berkman .75 2.00
Carlos Lee
Miguel Tejada
Roy Oswalt
90 Alex Rodriguez 3.00 8.00
Derek Jeter
Joba Chamberlain
Mariano Rivera
91 Carlos Zambrano .75 2.00
Randy Johnson
Roy Halladay
Tim Hudson
92 Jim Thome .75 2.00
Jermaine Dye
Alexei Ramirez
Carlos Quentin
93 Nate McLouth .50 1.25
Jay Bruce
Rick Ankiel
Lance Berkman
94 Jeff Francoeur .50 1.25
Rick Ankiel
Ichiro
Nick Markakis
95 B.J. Upton .75 2.00
Lastings Milledge
Chris B. Young
Matt Kemp
96 Dustin Pedroia 3.00 8.00
Cliff Lee
Albert Pujols
Tim Lincecum
97 Jose Reyes 3.00 8.00
David Wright
Derek Jeter
Alex Rodriguez
98 Michael Young .75 2.00
Ian Kinsler
Hanley Ramirez
Dan Uggla
99 Dexter Fowler .75 2.00
Travis Snider
Matt Antonelli
Michael Bowden
100 Dustin Pedrioa 1.50 4.00
David Ortiz
Carlton Fisk
Josh Beckett

2009 Upper Deck Goudey Autographs

OVERALL AUTO ODDS 1:18 HOBBY
EXCHANGE DEADLINE 4/1/2011
GGAG Adrian Gonzalez 10.00 25.00
GGAV Mike Aviles 10.00 25.00
GGBE Josh Beckett 30.00 60.00
GGBH Bill Hall 3.00 8.00
GGBM Brian McCann 8.00 20.00
GGBP Brandon Phillips 10.00 25.00
GGBR Brooks Robinson 15.00 40.00
GGBU B.J. Upton 20.00 50.00
GGBY Marlon Byrd 3.00 8.00
GGCF Carlton Fisk 30.00 60.00
GGCG Conor Gillaspie 4.00 10.00
GGCH Cole Hamels 12.50 30.00
GGCK Clayton Kershaw 12.50 30.00
GGCL Carlos Lee 6.00 15.00
GGCU Johnny Cueto 8.00 20.00
GGDF Dexter Fowler 6.00 15.00
GGDJ Derek Jeter 150.00 250.00
GGDP David Price 15.00 40.00
GGED Edgar Martinez 15.00 40.00
GGEE Edwin Encarnacion 3.00 8.00
GGEL Evan Longoria 150.00 250.00
GGFC Francisco Cervelli 6.00 15.00
GGFI Chone Figgins 4.00 10.00
GGGA Garrett Atkins 3.00 8.00
GGGP Gaylord Perry 10.00 25.00
GGGS Grady Sizemore 20.00 50.00
GGHR Hanley Ramirez 10.00 25.00
GGIK Ian Kennedy 4.00 10.00
GGJB Jeff Baisley 3.00 8.00
GGJC Joe Carter 8.00 20.00
GGJF Jeff Francoeur 6.00 15.00
GGJG Jeremy Guthrie 4.00 10.00
GGJP James Parr 3.00 8.00
GGJU Justin Masterson 30.00 60.00
GGKG Ken Griffey Jr. EXCH 100.00 175.00
GGKK Kila Ka'aihue 6.00 15.00
GGKS Kelly Shoppach 3.00 8.00
GGKY Kevin Youkilis 10.00 25.00
GGLM Lou Marson 6.00 15.00
GGMA Matt Antonelli 3.00 8.00
GGMB Michael Bowden 10.00 25.00
GGMG Mat Gamel 8.00 20.00
GGMM Miguel Montero 3.00 8.00
GGMS Max Scherzer 6.00 15.00
GGMT Matt Tuiasosopo 8.00 20.00
GGNB Nick Blackburn 10.00 25.00
GGOH Orel Hershiser
GGPC Phil Coke 5.00 12.00
GGPE Dustin Pedroia 20.00 50.00
GGPF Prince Fielder 12.50 30.00
GGRF Rollie Fingers 10.00 25.00
GGRH Roy Halladay 30.00 60.00
GGRS Ron Santo 15.00 40.00
GGSD Stephen Drew 5.00 12.00
GGSI Greg Smith 3.00 8.00
GGTG Tom Glavine 40.00 80.00
GGTR Tim Raines 12.50 30.00
GGTT Troy Tulowitzki 8.00 20.00
GGVM Victor Martinez 6.00 15.00
GGWF Whitey Ford 30.00 60.00
GGWL Wade LeBlanc 3.00 8.00
GGYG Yovani Gallardo 8.00 20.00

2009 Upper Deck Goudey Memorabilia

OVERALL AUTO ODDS 1:18 HOBBY
GMAB A.J. Burnett 3.00 8.00
GMAE Andre Ethier 5.00 12.00
GMAH Aaron Harang 3.00 8.00
GMAJ Adam Jones
GMAR Aramis Ramirez 3.00 8.00
GMBC Bobby Crosby 3.00 8.00
GMBE Carlos Beltran 3.00 8.00
GMBG Bob Gibson 4.00 10.00
GMBH Bill Hall 3.00 8.00
GMBM Brian McCann 4.00 10.00
GMBP Brandon Phillips 3.00 8.00
GMBR Brian Roberts 3.00 8.00
GMBS Ben Sheets 3.00 8.00
GMBW Billy Williams 3.00 8.00
GMCA Miguel Cabrera 4.00 10.00
GMCB Clay Buchholz 3.00 8.00
GMCG Carlos Guillen 3.00 8.00
GMCH Cole Hamels 5.00 12.00
GMCL Carlos Lee 3.00 8.00
GMCR Cal Ripken Jr. 10.00 25.00
GMCS Curt Schilling 3.00 8.00
GMCU Chase Utley 4.00 10.00
GMCY Chris Young 3.00 8.00
GMDA Johnny Damon
GMDJ Derek Jeter 6.00 15.00
GMDL Derrek Lee 3.00 8.00
GMDM Daisuke Matsuzaka 5.00 12.00
GMDO David Ortiz 3.00 8.00
GMDS Denard Span 3.00 8.00
GMDY Delmon Young 3.00 8.00
GMFH Felix Hernandez 4.00 10.00
GMFL Francisco Liriano 3.00 8.00
GMGA Garret Anderson 3.00 8.00
GMHK Howie Kendrick 3.00 8.00
GMHR Hanley Ramirez 3.00 8.00
GMHU Tim Hudson 3.00 8.00
GMJA Reggie Jackson
GMJD Jermaine Dye 3.00 8.00
GMJE Jacoby Ellsbury 3.00 8.00
GMJF Jeff Francoeur 3.00 8.00
GMJG Jason Giambi 3.00 8.00
GMJH J.J. Hardy 3.00 8.00
GMJJ Josh Johnson 3.00 8.00
GMJM John Maine 3.00 8.00
GMJN Joe Nathan 3.00 8.00
GMJO Johnny Bench 10.00 25.00
GMJS Joakim Soria
GMJT Jim Thome 3.00 8.00
GMJV Jason Varitek 3.00 8.00
GMJW Jered Weaver 3.00 8.00
GMKF Kosuke Fukudome
GMKJ Kelly Johnson 3.00 8.00
GMKS Kevin Slowey 3.00 8.00
GMKW Kerry Wood 3.00 8.00
GMKY Kevin Youkilis 3.00 8.00
GMLB Lou Brock
GMLE Cliff Lee 3.00 8.00
GMMA Joe Mauer 3.00 8.00
GMME Melvin Mora 3.00 8.00
GMMK Matt Kemp 3.00 8.00
GMMS Mike Schmidt 12.50 30.00
GMMY Michael Young 3.00 8.00
GMNM Nick Markakis 4.00 10.00
GMNR Nolan Ryan 15.00 40.00
GMNS Nick Swisher 3.00 8.00
GMOS Ozzie Smith 12.50 30.00
GMPA Jonathan Papelbon 3.00 8.00
GMPE Brad Penny 3.00 8.00
GMPF Prince Fielder 3.00 8.00
GMPH Phil Hughes 3.00 8.00
GMPN Phil Niekro 10.00 25.00
GMRF Rafael Furcal 3.00 8.00
GMRJ Reggie Jackson
GMRO Roy Oswalt 3.00 8.00
GMRS Ryne Sandberg 10.00 25.00
GMRY Robin Yount 10.00 25.00
GMSH Gary Sheffield 4.00 10.00
GMTG Troy Glaus
GMTH Trevor Hoffman 3.00 8.00
GMTS Takashi Saito 3.00 8.00
GMTT Troy Tulowitzki 3.00 8.00
GMVM Victor Martinez 3.00 8.00
GMWI Josh Willingham 3.00 8.00
GMYG Yovani Gallardo 3.00 8.00

2009 Upper Deck Goudey Sport Royalty Autographs

OVERALL AUTO ODDS 1:18 HOBBY
EXCHANGE DEADLINE 4/1/2011
AK Al Kaline 30.00 60.00
AY Jay Bruce
BB Brooks Robinson 30.00 60.00
BE Josh Beckett
BF Bob Feller 50.00 100.00

Card	Low	High
BG Bob Gibson	40.00	80.00
BJ Bo Jackson	50.00	100.00
BR Lou Brock	60.00	120.00
BS Bill Sharman	15.00	40.00
BU B.J. Upton	75.00	150.00
CJ Chipper Jones	250.00	350.00
CK Clayton Kershaw	30.00	60.00
CR Cal Ripken Jr.		
CW Chien-Ming Wang	100.00	200.00
DB Dennis Boyd	30.00	60.00
DE Dennis Eckersley	20.00	50.00
DM Don Mattingly	60.00	120.00
DP Dustin Pedroia	30.00	60.00
DS Don Sutton	30.00	60.00
EL Evan Longoria	100.00	200.00
EM Edgar Martinez	90.00	150.00
FH Felix Hernandez		
GP Gaylord Perry	15.00	50.00
GS Grady Sizemore	60.00	120.00
HM Cole Hamels	20.00	50.00
JB Johnny Bench	50.00	100.00
JC Joe Carter	20.00	50.00
JH John Havlicek	125.00	250.00
JO Michael Jordan	600.00	900.00
JP Jim Palmer	15.00	40.00
JW Jerry West	75.00	150.00
KG Ken Griffey Jr.	125.00	250.00
KH Kent Hrbek	15.00	40.00
KY Kevin Youkilis	75.00	150.00
LB Larry Bird	30.00	60.00
MI Mike Bossy	12.50	30.00
MS Mike Schmidt		
NL Nicklas Lidstrom	30.00	60.00
NR Nolan Ryan	200.00	300.00
OR Bobby Orr	100.00	200.00
OS Ozzie Smith		
PA Jonathan Papelbon	30.00	60.00
PF Prince Fielder		
PM Paul Molitor	30.00	60.00
PR Patrick Roy		
RF Rollie Fingers	15.00	40.00
RS Ron Santo	20.00	50.00
RY Ryne Sandberg	75.00	150.00
SM Stan Musial	125.00	250.00
TW Tiger Woods		
WB Wade Boggs	40.00	80.00
WG Wayne Gretzky		
YB Yogi Berra	30.00	60.00

2008 Upper Deck Heroes

Card	Low	High
COMPLETE SET (200)	20.00	50.00
COMMON CARD (1-200)	.20	.50
COMMON ROOKIE (1-200)	.40	1.00
1 Brandon Webb	.30	.75
2 Dan Haren	.20	.50
3 Chris B. Young	.20	.50
4 Justin Upton	.30	.75
5 Randy Johnson	.50	1.25
6 Chipper Jones	.50	1.25
7 John Smoltz	.50	1.25
8 Tom Glavine	.30	.75
9 Mark Teixeira	.50	1.25
10 Brian McCann	.30	.75
11 Jeff Francoeur	.30	.75
12 Josh Hamilton	.50	1.25
13 Tim Hudson	.30	.75
14 Nick Markakis	.50	1.25
15 Brian Roberts	.20	.50
16 Cal Ripken Jr.	2.00	5.00
17 John Maine	.20	.50
18 Frank Robinson	.20	.50
19 Mike Lowell	.20	.50
20 Jason Varitek	.50	1.25
21 David Ortiz	.30	.75
22 Manny Ramirez	.50	1.25
23 Jonathan Papelbon	.30	.75
24 Jacoby Ellsbury	.75	2.00
25 Kevin Youkilis	.30	.75
26 Curt Schilling	.30	.75
27 Josh Beckett	.30	.75
28 Daisuke Matsuzaka	.50	1.25
29 Clay Buchholz (RC)	1.00	2.50
30 Dustin Pedroia	.60	1.50
31 Ryan Theriot	.20	.50
32 Carlton Fisk	.30	.75
33 Carl Yastrzemski	.75	2.00
34 Wade Boggs	.30	.75
35 Nolan Ryan	1.50	4.00
36 Alfonso Soriano	.30	.75
37 Kosuke Fukudome RC	1.25	3.00
38 Derrek Lee	.20	.50
39 Carlos Zambrano	.30	.75
40 Aramis Ramirez	.20	.50
41 Ernie Banks	.50	1.25
42 Jim Thome	.30	.75
43 Jermaine Dye	.20	.50
44 Paul Konerko	.30	.75
45 Nick Swisher	.50	1.25
46 Corey Hart	.20	.50
47 Ken Griffey Jr.	.75	2.00
48 Adam Dunn	.30	.75
49 Aaron Harang	.20	.50
50 Johnny Bench	.50	1.25
51 Grady Sizemore	.30	.75
52 Victor Martinez	.30	.75
53 C.C. Sabathia	.30	.75
54 Travis Hafner	.20	.50
55 Jeff Francis	.20	.50
56 Matt Holliday	.50	1.25
57 Troy Tulowitzki	.50	1.25
58 Garrett Atkins	.20	.50
59 Todd Helton	.30	.75
60 Curtis Granderson	.30	.75
61 Dontrelle Willis	.20	.50
62 Magglio Ordonez	.30	.75
63 Gary Sheffield	.20	.50
64 Miguel Cabrera	.50	1.25
65 Justin Verlander	.60	1.50
66 Ivan Rodriguez	.30	.75
67 Al Kaline	.50	1.25
68 Hanley Ramirez	.50	1.25
69 Edinson Volquez	.20	.50
70 Dan Uggla	.30	.75
71 Andrew Miller	.20	.50
72 Josh Willingham	.20	.50
73 J.R. Towles RC	.60	1.50
74 Lance Berkman	.30	.75
75 Carlos Lee	.20	.50
76 Roy Oswalt	.30	.75
77 Hunter Pence	.50	1.25
78 Luke Hochevar RC	.60	1.50
79 Alex Gordon	.30	.75
80 Matt Cain	.20	.50
81 Bo Jackson	.50	1.25
82 Vladimir Guerrero	.50	1.25
83 Torii Hunter	.20	.50
84 Howie Kendrick	.20	.50
85 John Lackey	.20	.50
86 Chone Figgins	.20	.50
87 Andruw Jones	.20	.50
88 Brad Penny	.20	.50
89 James Loney	.30	.75
90 Matt Kemp	.30	.75
91 Nomar Garciaparra	.50	1.25
92 Jon Lester	.50	1.25
93 Chin-Lung Hu (RC)	.60	1.50
94 Chad Billingsley	.20	.50
95 Kelly Johnson	.20	.50
96 Prince Fielder	.30	.75
97 Ryan Braun	.60	1.50
98 Ben Sheets	.20	.50
99 Robin Yount	.50	1.25
100 Justin Morneau	.50	1.25
101 Joe Mauer	.50	1.25
102 Delmon Young	.30	.75
103 Rod Carew	.30	.75
104 Carlos Beltran	.20	.50
105 Jose Reyes	.30	.75
106 Pedro Martinez	.30	.75
107 David Wright	.60	1.50
108 Johan Santana	.50	1.25
109 Billy Wagner	.20	.50
110 Carlos Delgado	.20	.50
111 Mariano Rivera	.50	1.25
112 Chien-Ming Wang	.30	.75
113 Phil Hughes	.50	1.25
114 Derek Jeter	1.25	3.00
115 Alex Rodriguez	.75	2.00
116 Robinson Cano	.50	1.25
117 Jorge Posada	.30	.75
118 Hideki Matsui	.50	1.25
119 Joba Chamberlain	.30	.75
120 Ian Kennedy RC	1.00	2.50
121 Yogi Berra	.50	1.25
122 Reggie Jackson	.30	.75
123 Roger Clemens	.60	1.50
124 Ozzie Smith	.75	2.00
125 Don Mattingly	1.00	2.50
126 Dave Winfield	.20	.50
127 Joe DiMaggio	1.25	3.00
128 Eric Chavez	.20	.50
129 Bill Hall	.20	.50
130 Rich Harden	.20	.50
131 Andre Ethier	.30	.75
132 Daric Barton (RC)	.40	1.00
133 Ryan Howard	.60	1.50
134 Jimmy Rollins	.30	.75
135 Chase Utley	.50	1.25
136 Cole Hamels	.50	1.25
137 Pat Burrell	.20	.50
138 Mike Schmidt	.75	2.00
139 Steve Carlton	.20	.50
140 Freddy Sanchez	.20	.50
141 Joe Blanton	.20	.50
142 Felix Pie	.20	.50
143 Roberto Clemente	1.00	2.50
144 Jake Peavy	.20	.50
145 Greg Maddux	.60	1.50
146 Tom Gorzelanny	.20	.50
147 Tony Gwynn	.50	1.25
148 Barry Zito	.20	.50
149 Tim Lincecum	.75	2.00
150 Rich Hill	.20	.50
151 Omar Vizquel	.30	.75
152 Ichiro Suzuki	.75	2.00
153 Felix Hernandez	.50	1.25
154 Kenji Johjima	.20	.50
155 Erik Bedard	.20	.50
156 Albert Pujols	1.25	3.00
157 Troy Glaus	.30	.75
158 Chris Carpenter	.50	1.25
159 Chris Duncan	.20	.50
160 Mark Mulder	.20	.50
161 Scott Rolen	.30	.75
162 Stan Musial	.75	2.00
163 Bob Gibson	.30	.75
164 B.J. Upton	.30	.75
165 Carl Crawford	.30	.75
166 Scott Kazmir	.30	.75
167 Michael Young	.30	.75
168 Luke Scott	.20	.50
169 Roy Halladay	.50	1.25
170 Vernon Wells	.20	.50
171 Kevin Kouzmanoff	.20	.50
172 Frank Thomas	.50	1.25
173 Ryan Zimmerman	.30	.75
174 Lastings Milledge	.20	.50
175 Ian Kinsler	.30	.75
176 Don Mattingly	1.00	2.50
Wade Boggs		
177 Carlton Fisk	.75	2.00
Carl Yastrzemski		
178 Albert Pujols	1.25	3.00
Stan Musial		
179 Jose Reyes	1.25	3.00
Derek Jeter		
180 Cal Ripken Jr.	.50	1.25
Tony Gwynn		
181 Eddie Murray	.30	.75
Prince Fielder		
182 Ichiro Suzuki	.60	1.50
Kosuke Fukudome		
183 Steve Carlton	.50	1.25
Johan Santana		
184 Bob Gibson	.20	.50
Jake Peavy		
185 Johnny Bench	.50	1.25
Ivan Rodriguez		
186 Vladimir Guerrero	.75	2.00
Ichiro Suzuki		
Manny Ramirez		
187 Carl Yastrzemski	.75	2.00
Carlton Fisk		
Wade Boggs		
188 Alex Rodriguez	1.25	3.00
Derek Jeter		
Robinson Cano		
189 Chipper Jones	.50	1.25
Ryan Braun		
Miguel Cabrera		
190 Don Mattingly	1.00	2.50
Dave Winfield		
Reggie Jackson		
191 Chase Utley	.60	1.50
Ryan Howard		
Jimmy Rollins		
192 Joe Mauer	.50	1.25
Hanley Ramirez		
Troy Tulowitzki		
193 Nolan Ryan	1.50	4.00
Greg Maddux		
Randy Johnson		
194 Brandon Webb	.60	1.50
Justin Verlander		
Felix Hernandez		
195 Mike Schmidt	.75	2.00
Ernie Banks		
Frank Robinson		
196 Derek Jeter	2.00	5.00
Ken Griffey Jr.		
Cal Ripken Jr.		
Ichiro Suzuki		
197 Yogi Berra	1.25	3.00
Reggie Jackson		
Joe DiMaggio		
Derek Jeter		
198 Jonathan Papelbon	.50	1.25
Manny Ramirez		
Jason Varitek		
David Ortiz		
199 Ken Griffey Jr.	1.25	3.00
Roberto Clemente		
Vladimir Guerrero		
Joe DiMaggio		
200 Albert Pujols	.30	.75
Derek Jeter		
Prince Fielder		
David Ortiz		

2008 Upper Deck Heroes Beige

*BEIGE VET: .75X TO 2X BASIC
*BEIGE RC: .5X TO 1.2X BASIC RC
RANDOM INSERTS IN PACKS
STATED PRINT RUN 299 SER.#'d SETS

2008 Upper Deck Heroes Black

*BLACK VET: .75X TO 2X BASIC
*BLACK RC: .5X TO 1.2X BASIC RC
RANDOM INSERTS IN PACKS

2008 Upper Deck Heroes Brown

*BROWN VET: 1X TO 2.5X BASIC
*BROWN RC: .6X TO 1.5X BASIC RC
RANDOM INSERTS IN PACKS
STATED PRINT RUN 149 SER.#'d SETS

2008 Upper Deck Heroes Charcoal

*CHARCOAL VET: .75X TO 2X BASIC
*CHARCOAL RC: .5X TO 1.2X BASIC RC
RANDOM INSERTS IN RETAIL PACKS
STATED PRINT RUN 399 SER.#'d SETS

2008 Upper Deck Heroes Emerald

*EMERALD VET: .75X TO 2X BASIC
*EMERALD RC: .5X TO 1.2X BASIC RC
RANDOM INSERTS IN PACKS
STATED PRINT RUN 499 SER.#'d SETS

2008 Upper Deck Heroes Light Blue

*LT.BLUE VET: 1.5X TO 4X BASIC
*LT.BLUE RC: 1X TO 2.5X BASIC RC
RANDOM INSERTS IN PACKS
STATED PRINT RUN 49 SER.#'d SETS

2008 Upper Deck Heroes Navy Blue

*NAVY VET: 1X TO 2.5X BASIC
*NAVY RC: .6X TO 1.5X BASIC RC
RANDOM INSERTS IN PACKS
STATED PRINT RUN 199 SER.#'d SETS

2008 Upper Deck Heroes Purple

RANDOM INSERTS IN PACKS
STATED PRINT RUN 25 SER.#'d SETS
NO PRICING DUE TO SCARCITY

2008 Upper Deck Heroes Red

*RED VET: 1X TO 2.5X BASIC
*RED RC: .6X TO 1.5X BASIC RC
RANDOM INSERTS IN PACKS
STATED PRINT RUN 249 SER.#'d SETS

2008 Upper Deck Heroes Sea Green

*SEA GREEN VET: 1.2X TO 3X BASIC
*SEA GREEN RC: .75X TO 2X BASIC RC
RANDOM INSERTS IN PACKS
STATED PRINT RUN 99 SER.#'d SETS

2008 Upper Deck Heroes Autographs Charcoal

RANDOM INSERTS IN BACKS
PRINT RUNS B/WN 11-150 COPIES PER
NO PRICING ON QTY 11 OR LESS

Card	Low	High
12 Josh Hamilton/150	10.00	25.00
14 Nick Markakis/	10.00	25.00
17 John Maine/150		
29 Clay Buchholz/95	6.00	15.00
31 Ryan Theriot/150	10.00	25.00
45 Nick Swisher/150	5.00	12.00
46 Corey Hart/150	4.00	10.00
47 Ken Griffey Jr./75	50.00	100.00
49 Aaron Harang/150	4.00	10.00
69 Edinson Volquez/150	10.00	25.00
72 Josh Willingham/11		
73 J.R. Towles/150	4.00	10.00
80 Matt Cain/150		
86 Chone Figgins/150	4.00	10.00
90 Matt Kemp/150	6.00	15.00
93 Chin-Lung Hu/150	10.00	25.00
94 Chad Billingsley/150	4.00	10.00
95 Kelly Johnson/150	4.00	10.00
120 Ian Kennedy/95	6.00	15.00
131 Andre Ethier/150	10.00	25.00
132 Daric Barton/150	4.00	10.00
141 Joe Blanton/144	4.00	10.00
142 Felix Pie/150	4.00	10.00
146 Tom Gorzelanny/150	4.00	10.00
150 Rich Hill/100	4.00	10.00
168 Luke Scott/148	4.00	10.00
171 Kevin Kouzmanoff/150	4.00	10.00
175 Ian Kinsler/150	5.00	12.00

2008 Upper Deck Heroes Autographs Beige

RANDOM INSERTS IN PACKS
PRINT RUNS B/WN 10-25 COPIES PER
NO PRICING DUE TO SCARCITY

2008 Upper Deck Heroes Autographs Black

RANDOM INSERTS IN BACKS
PRINT RUNS B/WN 25-50 COPIES PER
NO PRICING ON QTY 25 OR LESS

Card	Low	High
2 Dan Haren/25		
3 Chris B. Young/25		
10 Brian McCann/50	8.00	20.00
12 Josh Hamilton/50	12.50	30.00
17 John Maine/50	6.00	15.00
29 Clay Buchholz/35	8.00	20.00
31 Ryan Theriot/50	12.50	30.00
45 Nick Swisher/50	6.00	15.00
46 Corey Hart/50	5.00	12.00
47 Ken Griffey Jr./25		
49 Aaron Harang/50	5.00	12.00
61 Dontrelle Willis/25		
68 Hanley Ramirez/25		
69 Edinson Volquez/50	12.50	30.00
71 Andrew Miller/35	5.00	12.00
72 Josh Willingham/50	5.00	12.00
73 J.R. Towles/50		
78 Luke Hochevar/50	6.00	15.00
80 Matt Cain/50		
84 Howie Kendrick/25		
85 John Lackey/25		
86 Chone Figgins/50	5.00	12.00
87 Andruw Jones/25		
90 Matt Kemp/50	8.00	20.00
93 Chin-Lung Hu/50	12.50	30.00
94 Chad Billingsley/50		
95 Kelly Johnson/50	5.00	12.00
114 Derek Jeter/25		
120 Ian Kennedy/35	8.00	20.00
132 Daric Barton/50	5.00	12.00
141 Joe Blanton/50	5.00	12.00
142 Felix Pie/50		
146 Tom Gorzelanny/50	5.00	12.00
150 Rich Hill/50	5.00	12.00
168 Luke Scott/50	5.00	12.00
171 Kevin Kouzmanoff/50	5.00	12.00
175 Ian Kinsler/50	6.00	15.00

2008 Upper Deck Heroes Autographs Navy Blue

RANDOM INSERTS IN BACKS
PRINT RUNS B/WN 35-100 COPIES PER

Card	Low	High
12 Josh Hamilton/100	10.00	25.00
17 John Maine/100	5.00	12.00
29 Clay Buchholz/55	8.00	20.00
31 Ryan Theriot/100	10.00	25.00
45 Nick Swisher/100	5.00	12.00
46 Corey Hart/100	4.00	10.00
47 Ken Griffey Jr./35	60.00	120.00
49 Aaron Harang/100	4.00	10.00
69 Edinson Volquez/100	10.00	25.00
71 Andrew Miller/35	5.00	12.00
72 Josh Willingham/100	4.00	10.00
73 J.R. Towles/100	4.00	10.00
80 Matt Cain/100	10.00	25.00
85 John Lackey/65	4.00	10.00
90 Matt Kemp/100	6.00	15.00
93 Chin-Lung Hu/100	10.00	25.00
94 Chad Billingsley/100	4.00	10.00
95 Kelly Johnson/100	4.00	10.00
120 Ian Kennedy/55	6.00	15.00
131 Andre Ethier/100	10.00	25.00
132 Daric Barton/50	5.00	12.00
141 Joe Blanton/100	4.00	10.00
142 Felix Pie/100	4.00	10.00
146 Tom Gorzelanny/100	4.00	10.00
150 Rich Hill/50	5.00	12.00
168 Luke Scott/100	4.00	10.00
171 Kevin Kouzmanoff/100	4.00	10.00
175 Ian Kinsler/100	5.00	12.00

2008 Upper Deck Heroes Autographs Purple

RANDOM INSERTS IN PACKS
STATED PRINT RUN 5 SER.#'d SETS
NO PRICING DUE TO SCARCITY

2008 Upper Deck Heroes Autographs Red

RANDOM INSERTS IN PACKS
STATED PRINT RUN 10 SER.#'d SETS
NO PRICING DUE TO SCARCITY

2008 Upper Deck Heroes Jersey Autograph Light Blue

RANDOM INSERTS IN PACKS
PRINT RUNS B/WN 5-75 COPIES PER
NO PRICING ON QTY 15 OR LESS

Card	Low	High
14 Nick Markakis/75		
25 Kevin Youkilis/50		
46 Corey Hart/75	8.00	20.00
47 Ken Griffey Jr./50	40.00	80.00
49 Aaron Harang/75	4.00	10.00
55 Jeff Francis/50	6.00	15.00
58 Garrett Atkins/35		
69 Edinson Volquez/75	10.00	25.00
72 Josh Willingham/5		
86 Chone Figgins/15		
90 Matt Kemp/75	15.00	40.00
92 Jon Lester/50		
93 Chin-Lung Hu/75	15.00	40.00
94 Chad Billingsley/75	20.00	50.00
114 Derek Jeter/35	100.00	150.00
138 Mike Schmidt/35		
141 Joe Blanton/75	4.00	10.00
142 Felix Pie/75	4.00	10.00
146 Tom Gorzelanny/75	4.00	10.00
171 Kevin Kouzmanoff/15		
175 Ian Kinsler/75	8.00	20.00

2008 Upper Deck Heroes Jersey Autograph Red

RANDOM INSERTS IN PACKS
PRINT RUNS B/WN 3-50 COPIES PER
NO PRICING ON QTY 25 OR LESS

Card	Low	High
3 Chris B. Young/25		
11 Jeff Francoeur/25		
14 Nick Markakis/50		
16 Cal Ripken Jr./25		
17 John Maine/50		
18 Frank Robinson/25		
25 Kevin Youkilis/25		
28 Daisuke Matsuzaka/25		
34 Wade Boggs/25		
35 Nolan Ryan/25		
41 Ernie Banks/25		
44 Paul Konerko/25		
46 Corey Hart/50	8.00	20.00
47 Ken Griffey Jr./25		
49 Aaron Harang/50		
52 Victor Martinez/25		
54 Travis Hafner/25		
55 Jeff Francis/25		
58 Garrett Atkins/25		
69 Edinson Volquez/50	12.50	30.00
72 Josh Willingham/5		
80 Matt Cain/50	10.00	25.00
81 Bo Jackson/25		
86 Chone Figgins/15		
90 Matt Kemp/50	20.00	50.00
92 Jon Lester/35	20.00	50.00
93 Chin-Lung Hu/50	20.00	50.00
94 Chad Billingsley/50	12.50	30.00
95 Kelly Johnson/50	6.00	15.00
96 Prince Fielder/25		
99 Robin Yount/25		
103 Rod Carew/25		
113 Phil Hughes/25		
114 Derek Jeter/25		
125 Don Mattingly/25		
129 Bill Hall/10		
136 Cole Hamels/25		
138 Mike Schmidt/25		
139 Steve Carlton/25		
141 Joe Blanton/50	5.00	12.00
142 Felix Pie/50	5.00	12.00
146 Tom Gorzelanny/50	5.00	12.00
150 Rich Hill/50		
153 Felix Hernandez/25		
162 Stan Musial/25		
163 Bob Gibson/25		
164 B.J. Upton/25		
169 Roy Halladay/25		
171 Kevin Kouzmanoff/5		
175 Ian Kinsler/50	10.00	25.00

2008 Upper Deck Heroes Jersey Light Blue

RANDOM INSERTS IN PACKS
STATED PRINT RUN 200 SER.#'d SETS

Card	Low	High
1 Brandon Webb	3.00	8.00
3 Chris B. Young	3.00	8.00
4 Justin Upton	4.00	10.00
5 Randy Johnson	4.00	10.00
6 Chipper Jones	5.00	12.00
7 John Smoltz	4.00	10.00
9 Mark Teixeira	4.00	10.00
10 Brian McCann	4.00	10.00
11 Jeff Francoeur	4.00	10.00
13 Tim Hudson	3.00	8.00
14 Nick Markakis	6.00	15.00
15 Brian Roberts	4.00	10.00
16 Cal Ripken Jr.	12.50	30.00
17 John Maine	3.00	8.00
18 Frank Robinson	3.00	8.00
19 Mike Lowell	4.00	10.00
20 Jason Varitek	4.00	10.00
21 David Ortiz	4.00	10.00
22 Manny Ramirez	4.00	10.00
23 Jonathan Papelbon	4.00	10.00
24 Jacoby Ellsbury	12.50	30.00
25 Kevin Youkilis	4.00	10.00
26 Curt Schilling	4.00	10.00
27 Josh Beckett	4.00	10.00
28 Daisuke Matsuzaka	6.00	15.00
29 Clay Buchholz	4.00	10.00
33 Carl Yastrzemski	5.00	12.00
34 Wade Boggs	3.00	8.00
35 Nolan Ryan	8.00	20.00
36 Alfonso Soriano	4.00	10.00
37 Kosuke Fukudome	12.50	30.00
38 Derrek Lee	4.00	10.00
39 Carlos Zambrano	3.00	8.00
40 Aramis Ramirez	3.00	8.00
41 Ernie Banks	5.00	12.00
42 Jim Thome	4.00	10.00
43 Jermaine Dye	3.00	8.00
44 Paul Konerko	3.00	8.00
46 Corey Hart	3.00	8.00
47 Ken Griffey Jr.	6.00	15.00
48 Adam Dunn	3.00	8.00
49 Aaron Harang	3.00	8.00
50 Johnny Bench	6.00	15.00
51 Grady Sizemore	4.00	10.00
52 Victor Martinez	3.00	8.00
53 C.C. Sabathia	3.00	8.00
54 Travis Hafner	3.00	8.00
55 Jeff Francis	3.00	8.00
56 Matt Holliday	4.00	10.00
57 Troy Tulowitzki	4.00	10.00
58 Garrett Atkins	3.00	8.00
59 Todd Helton	4.00	10.00
60 Curtis Granderson	4.00	10.00
62 Magglio Ordonez	4.00	10.00
65 Justin Verlander	4.00	10.00
66 Ivan Rodriguez	4.00	10.00
68 Hanley Ramirez	4.00	10.00
69 Edinson Volquez	3.00	8.00
70 Dan Uggla	4.00	10.00
71 Andrew Miller	4.00	10.00
72 Josh Willingham	3.00	8.00
74 Lance Berkman	4.00	10.00
75 Carlos Lee	3.00	8.00
76 Roy Oswalt	3.00	8.00
77 Hunter Pence	4.00	10.00
79 Alex Gordon	4.00	10.00
80 Matt Cain	3.00	8.00
81 Bo Jackson	4.00	10.00
82 Vladimir Guerrero	4.00	10.00
84 Howie Kendrick	3.00	8.00
85 John Lackey	3.00	8.00
86 Chone Figgins	3.00	8.00
88 Brad Penny	3.00	8.00
89 James Loney	4.00	10.00
90 Matt Kemp	3.00	8.00
93 Chin-Lung Hu	4.00	10.00
94 Chad Billingsley	3.00	8.00
95 Kelly Johnson	3.00	8.00
96 Prince Fielder	4.00	10.00
97 Ryan Braun	5.00	12.00
98 Ben Sheets	4.00	10.00
99 Robin Yount	4.00	10.00
100 Justin Morneau	4.00	10.00
101 Joe Mauer	4.00	10.00
103 Rod Carew	4.00	10.00
104 Carlos Beltran	3.00	8.00
106 Pedro Martinez	4.00	10.00
109 Billy Wagner	3.00	8.00
110 Carlos Delgado	3.00	8.00
111 Mariano Rivera	4.00	10.00
112 Chien-Ming Wang	6.00	15.00
113 Phil Hughes	4.00	10.00
114 Derek Jeter	10.00	25.00
115 Alex Rodriguez	8.00	20.00
116 Robinson Cano	4.00	10.00
117 Jorge Posada	4.00	10.00
120 Ian Kennedy	5.00	12.00
121 Yogi Berra	4.00	10.00
123 Roger Clemens	4.00	10.00
124 Ozzie Smith	6.00	15.00
125 Don Mattingly	6.00	15.00
126 Dave Winfield	3.00	8.00
127 Joe DiMaggio		
128 Eric Chavez	3.00	8.00
129 Bill Hall	3.00	8.00
130 Rich Harden	3.00	8.00
131 Andre Ethier	4.00	10.00
134 Jimmy Rollins	4.00	10.00
135 Chase Utley	4.00	10.00
136 Cole Hamels	4.00	10.00
137 Pat Burrell	3.00	8.00
138 Mike Schmidt	6.00	15.00
139 Steve Carlton	3.00	8.00
140 Freddy Sanchez	3.00	8.00
142 Felix Pie	3.00	8.00
143 Roberto Clemente	12.50	30.00
144 Jake Peavy	3.00	8.00
145 Greg Maddux	5.00	12.00
146 Tom Gorzelanny	3.00	8.00
147 Tony Gwynn	5.00	12.00
148 Barry Zito	3.00	8.00
149 Tim Lincecum	4.00	10.00
150 Rich Hill	3.00	8.00
151 Omar Vizquel	3.00	8.00
153 Felix Hernandez	4.00	10.00
154 Kenji Johjima	3.00	8.00
156 Albert Pujols	8.00	20.00
157 Troy Glaus	4.00	10.00
158 Chris Carpenter	3.00	8.00
159 Chris Duncan	3.00	8.00
160 Mark Mulder	3.00	8.00
161 Scott Rolen	4.00	10.00
163 Bob Gibson	5.00	12.00
164 B.J. Upton	4.00	10.00
165 Carl Crawford	3.00	8.00
166 Scott Kazmir	4.00	10.00
167 Michael Young	3.00	8.00
169 Roy Halladay	3.00	8.00
170 Vernon Wells	3.00	8.00
171 Kevin Kouzmanoff	3.00	8.00
173 Ryan Zimmerman	4.00	10.00
175 Ian Kinsler	4.00	10.00
176 Don Mattingly	8.00	20.00
Wade Boggs		
179 Jose Reyes	8.00	20.00
Derek Jeter		
180 Cal Ripken Jr.	15.00	40.00
Tony Gwynn		
181 Eddie Murray	4.00	10.00
Prince Fielder		
184 Bob Gibson	4.00	10.00
Jake Peavy		
185 Johnny Bench	8.00	20.00
Ivan Rodriguez		
186 Vladimir Guerrero		
Ichiro Suzuki		
Manny Ramirez		
187 Carl Yastrzemski		
Carlton Fisk		
Wade Boggs		
188 Alex Rodriguez	15.00	40.00
Derek Jeter		
Robinson Cano		
189 Chipper Jones		
Ryan Braun		
Miguel Cabrera		
190 Don Mattingly	12.50	30.00
Dave Winfield		
Reggie Jackson		
191 Chase Utley		
Ryan Howard		
Jimmy Rollins		
192 Joe Mauer	4.00	10.00
Hanley Ramirez		
Troy Tulowitzki		
193 Nolan Ryan	15.00	40.00
Greg Maddux		
Randy Johnson		
194 Brandon Webb	4.00	10.00
Justin Verlander		
Felix Hernandez		
195 Mike Schmidt	15.00	40.00
Ernie Banks		
Frank Robinson		
197 Yogi Berra	30.00	60.00
Reggie Jackson		
Joe DiMaggio		
Derek Jeter		
198 Jonathan Papelbon	8.00	20.00
Manny Ramirez		
Jason Varitek		
David Ortiz		
199 Ken Griffey Jr.	100.00	150.00
Roberto Clemente		
Vladimir Guerrero		
Joe DiMaggio		
200 Albert Pujols	10.00	25.00
Derek Jeter		
Prince Fielder		
David Ortiz		

2008 Upper Deck Heroes Jersey Black
*JSY BLK: .4X TO 1X JSY LT.BLUE
RANDOM INSERTS IN PACKS
STATED PRINT RUN 125 SER.#'d SETS

2008 Upper Deck Heroes Jersey Emerald
RANDOM INSERTS IN PACKS
PRINT RUNS B/WN 5-25 COPIES PER
NO PRICING DUE TO SCARCITY

2008 Upper Deck Heroes Jersey Navy Blue
*JSY NAVY: .5X TO 1.2X JSY LT.BLUE
RANDOM INSERTS IN PACKS
STATED PRINT RUN 50 SER.#'d SETS

2008 Upper Deck Heroes Patch Autograph
RANDOM INSERTS IN PACKS
PRINT RUNS B/WN 4-50 COPIES PER
NO PRICING ON QTY 25 OR LESS
1 Brandon Webb/25
3 Chris B. Young/15
6 Chipper Jones/15
8 Tom Glavine/10
10 Brian McCann/25
11 Jeff Francoeur/25
13 Tim Hudson/15
14 Nick Markakis/5
16 Cal Ripken Jr./25
17 John Maine/50 10.00 25.00
18 Frank Robinson/10
23 Jonathan Papelbon/25
25 Kevin Youkilis/25
27 Josh Beckett/10
28 Daisuke Matsuzaka/10
33 Carl Yastrzemski/25
35 Nolan Ryan/10
36 Alfonso Soriano/10
38 Derrek Lee/10
41 Ernie Banks/10
42 Jim Thome/10
44 Paul Konerko/25
46 Corey Hart/50 15.00 40.00
47 Ken Griffey Jr./25
48 Adam Dunn/23
49 Aaron Harang/50 6.00 15.00
50 Johnny Bench/10
52 Victor Martinez/25
54 Travis Hafner/25
55 Jeff Francis/25
58 Garrett Atkins/15
65 Justin Verlander/15
68 Hanley Ramirez/25
69 Edinson Volquez/50 20.00 50.00
72 Josh Willingham/25
74 Lance Berkman/25
75 Carlos Lee/25
76 Roy Oswalt/10
79 Alex Gordon/10
80 Matt Cain/9
81 Bo Jackson/15
85 John Lackey/10
86 Chone Figgins/15
90 Matt Kemp/25
94 Chad Billingsley/50 20.00 50.00
95 Kelly Johnson/50 10.00 25.00
96 Prince Fielder/25
97 Ryan Braun/10
99 Robin Yount/10
100 Justin Morneau/10
101 Joe Mauer/15
103 Rod Carew/10
106 Pedro Martinez/10
109 Billy Wagner/15
112 Chien-Ming Wang/10
113 Phil Hughes/10
114 Derek Jeter/10
123 Roger Clemens/10
124 Ozzie Smith/25
125 Don Mattingly/10
126 Dave Winfield/10
128 Eric Chavez/15
129 Bill Hall/15
130 Rich Harden/10
136 Cole Hamels/25
138 Mike Schmidt/10
139 Steve Carlton/10
141 Joe Blanton/50 6.00 15.00
142 Felix Pie/50 10.00 25.00
146 Tom Gorzelanny/50 10.00 25.00
147 Tony Gwynn/10
149 Tim Lincecum/10
150 Rich Hill/50 6.00 15.00
153 Felix Hernandez/15
156 Albert Pujols/10
162 Stan Musial/4
163 Bob Gibson/10
164 B.J. Upton/25
169 Roy Halladay/10
170 Vernon Wells/10
171 Kevin Kouzmanoff/25
175 Ian Kinsler/50

2008 Upper Deck Heroes Patch Beige
RANDOM INSERTS IN PACKS
PRINT RUNS B/WN 1-25 COPIES PER
NO PRICING DUE TO SCARCITY

2008 Upper Deck Heroes Patch Purple
RANDOM INSERTS IN PACKS
STATED PRINT RUN 5 SER.#'d SETS
NO PRICING DUE TO SCARCITY

2009 Upper Deck Icons
COMP.SET w/o RC's (100) 12.50 30.00
COMMON CARD (1-100) .15 .40
COMMON RC (101-130) .75 2.00
RC 101-130 PRINT RUN 999 SER.#'d SETS
COMMON AU RC (131-160) 3.00 8.00
AU RC PRINT RUN B/WN 50-600 PER
OVERALL AU ODDS 1:10 HOBBY
EXCHANGE DEADLINE 6/11/2011
1 A.J. Burnett .25 .60
2 Adam Dunn .25 .60
3 Adrian Gonzalez .25 .60
4 Akinori Iwamura .15 .40
5 Albert Pujols 1.00 2.50
6 Alex Rodriguez .60 1.50
7 Alfonso Soriano .25 .60
8 Aramis Ramirez .15 .40
9 B.J. Upton .25 .60
10 Brandon Webb .25 .60
11 Brian Giles .15 .40
12 Brian McCann .25 .60
13 Brian Roberts .15 .40
14 Carlos Beltran .15 .40
15 Carlos Lee .15 .40
16 Carlos Quentin .25 .60
17 Carlos Zambrano .25 .60
18 CC Sabathia .25 .60
19 Chad Billingsley .15 .40
20 Chase Utley .40 1.00
21 Chien-Ming Wang .25 .60
22 Chipper Jones .40 1.00
23 Chris B. Young .15 .40
24 Clayton Kershaw .40 1.00
25 Cliff Lee .25 .60
26 Cole Hamels .40 1.00
27 Curtis Granderson .25 .60
28 Daisuke Matsuzaka .40 1.00
29 Dan Haren .15 .40
30 Dan Uggla .25 .60
31 David Ortiz .25 .60
32 David Wright .50 1.25
33 Derek Jeter 1.00 2.50
34 Derrek Lee .15 .40
35 Dustin Pedroia .50 1.25
36 Edinson Volquez .15 .40
37 Ervin Santana .15 .40
38 Evan Longoria .50 1.25
39 Felix Hernandez .40 1.00
40 Francisco Rodriguez .25 .60
41 Garrett Atkins .15 .40
42 Grady Sizemore .25 .60
43 Hanley Ramirez .40 1.00
44 Ian Kinsler .25 .60
45 Freddy Sanchez .15 .40
46 Ichiro .60 1.50
47 Jason Varitek .40 1.00
48 Jake Peavy .15 .40
49 James Shields .15 .40
50 Jason Giambi .15 .40
51 Javier Vazquez .15 .40
52 Jay Bruce .25 .60
53 Jim Thome .25 .60
54 Jimmy Rollins .25 .60
55 Joakim Soria .15 .40
56 Joba Chamberlain .25 .60
57 Joe Mauer .40 1.00
58 Joey Votto .40 1.00
59 Johan Santana .40 1.00
60 John Lackey .15 .40
61 Jon Lester .40 1.00
62 Jonathan Papelbon .25 .60
63 Jose Reyes .25 .60
64 Josh Beckett .25 .60
65 Josh Hamilton .40 1.00
66 Justin Morneau .40 1.00
67 Justin Verlander .50 1.25
68 Ken Griffey Jr. .60 1.50
69 Kerry Wood .15 .40
70 Kevin Youkilis .25 .60
71 Kosuke Fukudome .40 1.00
72 Lance Berkman .25 .60
73 Magglio Ordonez .25 .60
74 Manny Ramirez .40 1.00
75 Mariano Rivera .40 1.00
76 Mark Teixeira .40 1.00
77 Matt Holliday .40 1.00
78 Matt Kemp .40 1.00
79 Michael Young .25 .60
80 Miguel Cabrera .40 1.00
81 Nate McLouth .15 .40
82 Nick Markakis .40 1.00
83 Prince Fielder .25 .60
84 Randy Johnson .25 .60
85 Rick Ankiel .15 .40
86 Roy Halladay .40 1.00
87 Roy Oswalt .25 .60
88 Russell Martin .15 .40
89 Ryan Braun .50 1.25
90 Ryan Dempster .15 .40
91 Ryan Howard .50 1.25
92 Ryan Ludwick .25 .60
93 Ryan Zimmerman .25 .60
94 Scott Kazmir .15 .40
95 Stephen Drew .15 .40
96 Tim Hudson .25 .60
97 Tim Lincecum .60 1.50
98 Troy Tulowitzki .40 1.00
99 Vernon Wells .15 .40
100 Vladimir Guerrero .40 1.00
101 Koji Uehara RC 1.25 3.00
102 Rick Porcello RC 2.50 6.00
103 Jason Motte (RC) 1.25 3.00
104 Colby Rasmus (RC) 2.00 5.00
105 Brett Anderson RC 1.25 3.00
106 George Kottaras (RC) .75 2.00
107 Josh Outman RC 1.25 3.00
108 Travis Snider RC 1.25 3.00
109 Matt Tuiasosopo (RC) .75 2.00
110 Kevin Jepsen (RC) .75 2.00
111 Trevor Cahill RC 2.00 5.00
112 Elvis Andrus RC 1.25 3.00
113 Jordan Schafer (RC) 1.25 3.00
114 Matt LaPorta RC 2.00 5.00
115 Shairon Martis RC 1.25 3.00
116 Dexter Fowler (RC) 1.25 3.00
117 Scott Lewis (RC) .75 2.00
118 Everth Cabrera RC 1.25 3.00
119 James McDonald RC 2.00 5.00
120 David Freese RC 6.00 15.00
121 David Patton RC 1.25 3.00
122 Kenshin Kawakami RC 1.25 3.00
123 David Price RC 2.00 5.00
124 Phil Coke RC 1.25 3.00
125 Matt Wieters RC 12.00 30.00
126 Mike Hinckley (RC) .75 2.00
127 Ramiro Pena RC 1.25 3.00
128 Bobby Parnell RC 1.25 3.00
129 Ryan Perry RC 2.00 5.00
130 Ricky Romero (RC) 2.00 5.00
131a Koji Uehara AU/90 * English 10.00 25.00
131b Koji Uehara AU/10 * Kanji
132 Travis Snider AU/100 30.00 60.00
133 Dexter Fowler AU/400 5.00 12.00
134 Kevin Jepsen AU/600 5.00 12.00
135 David Freese AU/200 40.00 80.00
136 Jordan Schafer AU/400 6.00 15.00
137 Everth Cabrera AU/600 4.00 10.00
138 James McDonald AU/399 4.00 10.00
139 Shairon Martis AU/600 3.00 8.00
140 Josh Outman AU/200 3.00 8.00
141 Matt Tuiasosopo AU/400 3.00 8.00
142 Phil Coke AU/600 5.00 12.00
143 Matt Wieters AU/100 EXCH 30.00 60.00
144 Ricky Romero AU/600 3.00 8.00
145 George Kottaras AU/600 4.00 10.00
146 Elvis Andrus AU/300 10.00 25.00
147 David Patton AU/50 4.00 10.00
148 Brett Anderson AU/400 5.00 12.00
149 Trevor Cahill AU/300 5.00 12.00
150 Trevor Crowe AU/600 RC 3.00 8.00
151 Colby Rasmus AU/400 15.00 40.00
152 Kenshin Kawakami AU/400 30.00 60.00
153 David Price AU/150 15.00 40.00
154 Rick Porcello AU/100 60.00 120.00
155 Brett Gardner AU/600 (RC) 10.00 25.00
156 Chris Davis AU/50 (RC) EXCH 8.00 20.00
157 Pablo Sandoval AU/100 (RC) 40.00 80.00
158 Bobby Parnell AU/600 4.00 10.00
159 Derek Holland AU/100 RC 10.00 25.00
160 Mat Gamel AU/200 RC 6.00 15.00

2009 Upper Deck Icons Celebrity Lettermen
OVERALL LETTER ODDS 1:5 HOBBY
TOTAL PRINT RUNS LISTED BELOW
EN Evelyn Ng/440 * 4.00 10.00
Letters spell out EVY BABEE each letter #'ed to 55
Total print run 440
GO Jeremy Piven/440 * 4.00 10.00
Letters spell out HUG IT OUT each letter #'ed to 55
Total print run 440
NE Daniel Negreanu/440 * 8.00 20.00
Letters spell out KID POKER each letter #'ed to 55
Total print run 440
PH Phil Hellmuth/420 * 10.00 25.00
Letters spell out THE POKER BRAT each letter #'ed to 35
Total print run 420

2009 Upper Deck Icons Celebrity Lettermen Autographs
OVERALL LETTER ODDS 1:5 HOBBY
TOTAL PRINT RUNS LISTED BELOW
EN Evelyn Ng/40 *
Letters spell out EVY BABEE each letter #'ed to 5
Total print run 40
GO Jeremy Piven/70 * 40.00 80.00
Letters spell out ARI GOLD each letter #'ed to 10
Total print run 70
NE Daniel Negreanu/40 *
Letters spell out KID POKER each letter #'ed to 5
Total print run 40
PH Phil Hellmuth/48 *
Letters spell out THE POKER BRAT each letter #'ed to 4
Total print run 48

2009 Upper Deck Icons Future Foundations
RANDOM INSERTS IN PACKS
STATED PRINT RUN 999 SER.#'d SETS
*GRN: .6X TO 1.5X BASIC
GRN RANDOMLY INSERTED
GRN PRINT RUN 125 SER.#'d SETS
BM Brian McCann .75 2.00
CH Cole Hamels 1.25 3.00
DM Daisuke Matsuzaka 1.25 3.00
EL Evan Longoria 1.50 4.00
FC Fausto Carmona .50 1.25
FL Francisco Liriano .50 1.25
HR Hanley Ramirez 1.25 3.00
JM Joe Mauer 1.25 3.00
JP Jonathan Papelbon .75 2.00
MK Matt Kemp .75 2.00
NM Nick Markakis 1.25 3.00
PF Prince Fielder .75 2.00
RA Rick Ankiel .50 1.25
TT Troy Tulowitzki 1.25 3.00

2009 Upper Deck Icons Future Foundations Autographs
OVERALL AUTO ODDS 1:10 HOBBY
PRINT RUNS B/WN 25-199 COPIES PER
NO PRICING ON QTY 25 OR LESS
BM Brian McCann/25
CH Cole Hamels/75 12.00 30.00
DM Daisuke Matsuzaka/25
EL Evan Longoria/25
FC Fausto Carmona/199 3.00 8.00
FL Francisco Liriano/199
HR Hanley Ramirez/75 10.00 25.00
JM Joe Mauer/75 40.00 80.00
JP Jonathan Papelbon/99 8.00 20.00
MK Matt Kemp/199 12.50 30.00
NM Nick Markakis/199 6.00 15.00
PF Prince Fielder/75 10.00 25.00
RA Rick Ankiel/199
TT Troy Tulowitzki/199 4.00 10.00

2009 Upper Deck Icons Future Foundations Jerseys
OVERALL MEM ODDS 1:5 HOBBY
BM Brian McCann 3.00 8.00
CH Cole Hamels 3.00 8.00
DM Daisuke Matsuzaka 5.00 12.00
FC Fausto Carmona 3.00 8.00
FL Francisco Liriano 3.00 8.00
HR Hanley Ramirez 3.00 8.00
JM Joe Mauer 3.00 8.00
JP Jonathan Papelbon 3.00 8.00
MK Matt Kemp 3.00 8.00
NM Nick Markakis 3.00 8.00
PF Prince Fielder 3.00 8.00
RA Rick Ankiel 3.00 8.00
TT Troy Tulowitzki 3.00 8.00

2009 Upper Deck Icons Future Foundations Jerseys Gold
OVERALL MEM ODDS 1:5 HOBBY
STATED PRINT RUN 25 SER.#'d SETS
NO PRICING DUE TO SCARCITY

2009 Upper Deck Icons Icons
RANDOM INSERTS IN PACKS
STATED PRINT RUN 999 SER.#'d SETS
*GRN: .6X TO 1.5X BASIC
GRN RANDOMLY INSERTED
GRN PRINT RUN 125 SER.#'d SETS
AE Andre Ethier .75 2.00
AG Alex Gordon .75 2.00
AL Adam Lind .50 1.25
AR Alex Rios .75 2.00
AS Alfonso Soriano .75 2.00
BE Josh Beckett .75 2.00
BH Bill Hall .50 1.25
BR Brian Roberts .50 1.25
BW Billy Wagner .50 1.25
CA Miguel Cabrera 1.25 3.00
CB Chad Billingsley .50 1.25
CC Chris Carpenter 1.25 3.00
CD Chris Duncan .50 1.25
CF Chone Figgins .50 1.25
CJ Chipper Jones 1.25 3.00
CL Carlos Lee .50 1.25
CR Carl Crawford .75 2.00
CT Corey Hart .50 1.25
CU Michael Cuddyer .50 1.25
CY Chris Young .50 1.25
CZ Carlos Zambrano .75 2.00
DJ Derek Jeter 3.00 8.00
DL Derrek Lee .50 1.25
DO David Ortiz .75 2.00
DY Delmon Young .75 2.00
FH Felix Hernandez 1.25 3.00
GU Carlos Guillen .50 1.25
HP Hunter Pence .75 2.00
JD Jermaine Dye .50 1.25
JF Jeff Francoeur .75 2.00
JG Jason Giambi .50 1.25
JH J.J. Hardy .50 1.25
JJ Josh Johnson .75 2.00
JL John Lackey .50 1.25
JM John Maine .50 1.25
JP Jake Peavy .50 1.25
JR Jimmy Rollins .75 2.00
JS James Shields .50 1.25
JT Jim Thome .75 2.00
JV Jason Varitek 1.25 3.00
JW Jake Westbrook .50 1.25
JZ Joel Zumaya .50 1.25
KF Kosuke Fukudome 1.25 3.00
KJ Kelly Johnson .50 1.25
KY Kevin Youkilis .75 2.00
MA Mike Aviles .50 1.25
MC Matt Cain .50 1.25
MH Matt Holliday 1.25 3.00
MY Michael Young .75 2.00
PE Jhonny Peralta .75 2.00
PK Paul Konerko .75 2.00
PO Jorge Posada .75 2.00
RA Aramis Ramirez .50 1.25
RF Rafael Furcal .50 1.25
RH Roy Halladay 1.25 3.00
RJ Randy Johnson .75 2.00
RL Ryan Ludwick .75 2.00
RO Roy Oswalt .75 2.00
RZ Ryan Zimmerman .75 2.00
SD Stephen Drew .50 1.25
SK Scott Kazmir .50 1.25
TG Tom Glavine .75 2.00
TH Travis Hafner .50 1.25
VE Justin Verlander 1.50 4.00
VM Victor Martinez .75 2.00
WB Brandon Webb .75 2.00
WE Jered Weaver .50 1.25

2009 Upper Deck Icons Icons Autographs
OVERALL AUTO ODDS 1:10 HOBBY
PRINT RUNS B/WN 5-99 COPIES PER
MANY NOT PRICED DUE TO LACK OF INFO
AE Andre Ethier/99 4.00 10.00
AL Adam Lind/99 15.00 40.00
BE Josh Beckett/10
BH Bill Hall/50
CD Chris Duncan/99 6.00 15.00
CJ Chipper Jones/5
CL Carlos Lee/5
CR Carl Crawford/25
CU Michael Cuddyer/99
DL Derrek Lee/25
FH Felix Hernandez/30 12.50 30.00
HP Hunter Pence/5
JJ Josh Johnson/35 8.00 20.00
JM John Maine/99 6.00 15.00
JT Jim Thome/5
JV Jason Varitek/5
KJ Kelly Johnson/99 5.00 12.00
KY Kevin Youkilis/99 10.00 25.00
MA Mike Aviles/40 5.00 12.00
MC Matt Cain/30
RA Aramis Ramirez/5
RJ Randy Johnson/5
RZ Ryan Zimmerman/25
SD Stephen Drew/5
SK Scott Kazmir/99 12.50 30.00
TG Tom Glavine/15
VM Victor Martinez/5
WB Brandon Webb/25

2009 Upper Deck Icons Icons Jerseys
OVERALL MEM ODDS 1:5 HOBBY
AE Andre Ethier 3.00 8.00
AG Alex Gordon 3.00 8.00
AL Adam Lind 4.00 10.00
AR Alex Rios 4.00 10.00
AS Alfonso Soriano 3.00 8.00
BE Josh Beckett 3.00 8.00
BH Bill Hall 3.00 8.00
BR Brian Roberts 3.00 8.00
BW Billy Wagner 3.00 8.00
CA Miguel Cabrera 3.00 8.00
CB Chad Billingsley 3.00 8.00
CC Chris Carpenter 3.00 8.00
CD Chris Duncan 4.00 10.00
CF Chone Figgins 3.00 8.00
CJ Chipper Jones 4.00 10.00
CL Carlos Lee 3.00 8.00
CR Carl Crawford 3.00 8.00
CT Corey Hart 3.00 8.00
CU Michael Cuddyer 3.00 8.00
CY Chris Young 3.00 8.00
CZ Carlos Zambrano
DJ Derek Jeter 6.00 15.00
DL Derrek Lee 3.00 8.00
DO David Ortiz 3.00 8.00
DY Delmon Young 3.00 8.00
FH Felix Hernandez 3.00 8.00
GU Carlos Guillen 3.00 8.00
HP Hunter Pence 3.00 8.00
JD Jermaine Dye 3.00 8.00
JF Jeff Francoeur 3.00 8.00
JH J.J. Hardy 3.00 8.00
JJ Josh Johnson 3.00 8.00
JL John Lackey 3.00 8.00
JM John Maine 3.00 8.00
JP Jake Peavy 3.00 8.00
JR Jimmy Rollins 4.00 10.00
JS James Shields 3.00 8.00
JT Jim Thome 3.00 8.00
JV Jason Varitek 4.00 10.00
JW Jake Westbrook 3.00 8.00
JZ Joel Zumaya 3.00 8.00
KF Kosuke Fukudome
KJ Kelly Johnson 3.00 8.00
KY Kevin Youkilis
MA Mike Aviles
MC Matt Cain 3.00 8.00
MY Michael Young 3.00 8.00
PE Jhonny Peralta 3.00 8.00
PK Paul Konerko 3.00 8.00
PO Jorge Posada 3.00 8.00
RA Aramis Ramirez 3.00 8.00
RF Rafael Furcal 3.00 8.00
RH Roy Halladay 3.00 8.00
RJ Randy Johnson 4.00 10.00
RL Ryan Ludwick
RO Roy Oswalt 3.00 8.00
RZ Ryan Zimmerman 3.00 8.00
SD Stephen Drew 3.00 8.00
SK Scott Kazmir 3.00 8.00
TG Tom Glavine 3.00 8.00
TH Travis Hafner 3.00 8.00
VE Justin Verlander 3.00 8.00
VM Victor Martinez 3.00 8.00
WB Brandon Webb 3.00 8.00
WE Jered Weaver 3.00 8.00

2009 Upper Deck Icons Icons Jerseys Gold
OVERALL MEM ODDS 1:5 HOBBY
STATED PRINT RUN 25 SER.#'d SETS
NO PRICING DUE TO SCARCITY

2009 Upper Deck Icons Immortal Lettermen
OVERALL LETTER ODDS 1:5 HOBBY
TOTAL PRINT RUNS LISTED BELOW
AK Al Kaline/420 * 10.00 25.00
Letters spell out MR TIGER each letter #'ed to 60
Total print run 420
BJ Bo Jackson/450 * 10.00 25.00
Letters spell out BO KNOWS BASEBALL each letter #'ed to 30
Total print run 450
BS Bill Skowron/420 * 4.00 10.00
Letters spell out MOOSE SKOWRON each letter #'ed to 35
Total print run 420
CF Carlton Fisk/405 * 12.50 30.00
Letters spell out PUDGE FISK each letter #'ed to 45
Total print run 405
DA Dick Allen/405 * 5.00 12.00
Letters spell out DICK ALLEN each letter #'ed to 45
Total print run 405
DB Dennis "Oil Can" Boyd/400 * 4.00 10.00
Letters spell out OIL CAN BOYD each letter #'ed to 40
Total print run 400
DE Bucky Dent/405 * 4.00 10.00
Letters spell out BUCKY DENT each letter #'ed to 45
Total print run 405
DN Don Newcombe/440 * 5.00 12.00
Letters spell out DON NEWCOMBE each letter #'ed to 40
Total print run 440
GP Gaylord Perry/420 * 4.00 10.00
Letters spell out GAYLORD PERRY each letter #'ed to 35
Total print run 420
JP Joe Pepitone/440 * 5.00 12.00
Letters spell out JOE PEPITONE each letter #'ed to 40
Total print run 440
KH Kent Hrbek/450 * 15.00 40.00
Letters spell out KENT HRBEK each letter #'ed to 50
Total print run 450
OS Ozzie Smith/400 * 20.00 50.00
Letters spell out OZZIE SMITH each letter #'ed to 40
Total print run 400
PM Paul Molitor/440 * 12.50 30.00
Letters spell out PAUL MOLITOR each letter #'ed to 40
Total print run 440
RW Roy White/440 * 4.00 10.00
Letters spell out ROY WHITE each letter #'ed to 55
Total print run 440
TG Tony Gwynn/200 * 12.50 30.00
Letters spell out SD PADRES... each letter #'ed to 25
Total print run 200
WF Whitey Ford/450 * 5.00 12.00
Letters spell out WHITEY FORD each letter #'ed to 45
Total print run 450
YB Yogi Berra/405 * 12.50 30.00
Letters spell out YOGI BERRA each letter #'ed to 45
Total print run 405

2009 Upper Deck Icons Immortal Lettermen Autographs
OVERALL AUTO ODDS 1:10 HOBBY
PRINT RUNS B/WN 10-84 COPIES PER
TOTAL PRINT RUNS LISTED
SER.# ON CARDS ARE DIFFERENT
NO PRICING ON QTY 21 OR LESS
AK Al Kaline/28 * 75.00 150.00
Letters spell out MR TIGER each letter #'ed to 4
Total print run 28
BJ Bo Jackson/21 *
Letters spell out BO KNOWS each letter #'ed to 3
Total print run 21
BS Bill Skowron/36 * 20.00 50.00
Letters spell out MOOSE SKOWRON each letter #'ed to 3
Total print run 36
CF Carlton Fisk/15 *
Letters spell out PUDGE each letter #'ed to 3
Total print run 15
DA Dick Allen/27 * 10.00 25.00
Letters spell out DICK ALLEN each letter #'ed to 3
Total print run 27
DB Dennis "Oil Can" Boyd/40 * 8.00 20.00
Letters spell out OIL CAN BOYD each letter #'ed to 4
Total print run 40
DE Bucky Dent/27 * 12.50 30.00
Letters spell out BUCKY DENT each letter #'ed to 3
Total print run 27
DN Don Newcombe/32 * 10.00 25.00
Letters spell out NEWCOMBE each letter #'ed to 4
Total print run 32
GP Gaylord Perry/36 *
Letters spell out GAYLORD PERRY each letter #'ed to 3
Total print run 36
KH Kent Hrbek/84 * 15.00 40.00
Letters spell out HERBIE each letter #'ed to 14
Total print run 84
OS Ozzie Smith/10 *
Letters spell out WIZARD OF OZ each letter #'ed to 1
Total print run 10
PM Paul Molitor/28 * 40.00 80.00
Letters spell out IGNITOR each letter #'ed to 4
Total print run 28
RW Roy White/40 *
Letters spell out ROY WHITE each letter #'ed to 5
Total print run 40
TG Tony Gwynn/15 *
Letters spell out GWYNN each letter #'ed to 3
Total print run 15
WF Whitey Ford/18 *
Letters spell out WHITEY each letter #'ed to 3
Total print run 18
YB Yogi Berra/20 *
Letters spell out YOGI each letter #'ed to 5
Total print run 20

2009 Upper Deck Icons Legendary Icons
RANDOM INSERTS IN PACKS
STATED PRINT RUN 999 SER.#'d SETS
*GRN: .6X TO 1.5X BASIC
GRN RANDOMLY INSERTED
GRN PRINT RUN 125 SER.#'d SETS
BJ Bo Jackson 1.25 3.00
BS Bruce Sutter .50 1.25
CR Cal Ripken Jr. 5.00 12.00
JD Joe DiMaggio 3.00 8.00
MS Mike Schmidt 2.00 5.00
NR Nolan Ryan 4.00 10.00
OS Ozzie Smith 2.00 5.00
RJ Reggie Jackson .75 2.00
TG Tony Gwynn 1.25 3.00
WB Wade Boggs .75 2.00

2009 Upper Deck Icons Legendary Icons Jerseys
OVERALL MEM ODDS 1:5 HOBBY
BJ Bo Jackson 4.00 10.00
BS Bruce Sutter 3.00 8.00
CR Cal Ripken Jr. 10.00 25.00
JD Joe DiMaggio 20.00 50.00
MS Mike Schmidt 4.00 10.00
NR Nolan Ryan 8.00 20.00
OS Ozzie Smith 8.00 20.00
RJ Reggie Jackson 5.00 12.00
TG Tony Gwynn 4.00 10.00
WB Wade Boggs 3.00 8.00

2009 Upper Deck Icons Legendary Icons Jerseys Gold
OVERALL MEM ODDS 1:5 HOBBY
STATED PRINT RUN 25 SER.#'d SETS
NO PRICING DUE TO SCARCITY

2009 Upper Deck Icons Lettermen
OVERALL LETTER ODDS 1:5 HOBBY
TOTAL PRINT RUNS LISTED BELOW
AG Adrian Gonzalez/420 * 4.00 10.00
Letters spell out ADRIAN GONZALEZ each letter #'ed to 30
Total print run 420
CH Cole Hamels/450 * 5.00 12.00
Letters spell out COLE HAMELS each letter #'ed to 45
Total print run 450
CJ Chipper Jones/420 * 15.00 40.00
Letters spell out CHIPPER JONES each letter #'ed to 35
Total print run 420
CK Clayton Kershaw/420 * 10.00 25.00
Letters spell out CLAYTON KERSHAW each letter #'ed to 30
Total print run 420
CL Carlos Lee/405 * 4.00 10.00
Letters spell out CARLOS LEE each letter #'ed to 45
Total print run 405
CM Chien-Ming Wang/420 * 12.50 30.00
Letters spell out CHIEN-MING WANG each letter #'ed to 30
Total print run 420
CP Chris Perez/450 * 6.00 15.00
Letters spell out CHRIS PEREZ each letter #'ed to 45
Total print run 450
CV Chris Volstad/420 * 4.00 10.00
Letters spell out CHRIS VOLSTAD each letter #'ed to 35
Total print run 420
CW Chien-Ming Wang/420 * 10.00 25.00
Letters spell out TAIWAN each letter #'ed to 70
Total print run 420
DJ Derek Jeter/450 * 15.00 40.00

Letters spell out MR NOVEMBER each letter #'ed to 45
Total print run 450
DP Dustin Pedroia/455 * 10.00 25.00
Letters spell out DUSTIN PEDROIA each letter #'ed to 35
Total print run 455
EC Eric Chavez/450 * 4.00 10.00
Letters spell out ERIC CHAVEZ each letter #'ed to 45
Total print run 450
EL Evan Longoria/420 * 10.00 25.00
Letters spell out EVAN LONGORIA each letter #'ed to 35
Total print run 420
GF Gavin Floyd/450 * 4.00 10.00
Letters spell out GAVIN FLOYD each letter #'ed to 45
Total print run 450
GS Geovany Soto/440 * 5.00 12.00
Letters spell out GEOVANY SOTO each letter #'ed to 40
Total print run 440
HP Hunter Pence/450 * 5.00 12.00
Letters spell out THE NATURAL each letter #'ed to 45
Total print run 450
HR Hanley Ramirez/455 * 6.00 15.00
Letters spell out HANLEY RAMIREZ each letter #'ed to 35
Total print run 455
IK Ian Kinsler/300 * 5.00 12.00
Letters spell out IAN KINSLER each letter #'ed to 30
Total print run 300
JA Jay Bruce/455 * 6.00 15.00
Letters spell out BRUCE ALMIGHTY each letter #'ed to 35
Total print run 455
JL Jon Lester/450 * 20.00 50.00
Letters spell out JON LESTER each letter #'ed to 50
Total print run 450
JM Justin Masterson/450 * 10.00 25.00
Letters spell out JUSTIN MASTERSON each letter #'ed to 30
Total print run 450
JN Joe Nathan/405 * 4.00 10.00
Letters spell out JOE NATHAN each letter #'ed to 45
Total print run 405
JR Jose Reyes/315 * 10.00 25.00
Letters spell out JOSE REYES each letter #'ed to 45
Total print run 315
JS James Shields/420 * 4.00 10.00
Letters spell out JAMES SHIELDS each letter #'ed to 35
Total print run 420
JW Josh Willingham/420 * 4.00 10.00
Letters spell out JOSH WILLINGHAM each letter #'ed to 30
Total print run 420
KG Ken Griffey Jr./455 * 30.00 60.00
Letters spell out Pictured with SEA...GRIFFEY JUNIOR each letter #'ed to 35
Total print run 455
KS Kelly Shoppach/315 * 4.00 10.00
Letters spell out INDIANS each letter #'ed to 45
Total print run 315
LO Jed Lowrie/450 * 4.00 10.00
Letters spell out JED LOWRIE each letter #'ed to 50
Total print run 450
MC Matt Cain/440 * 5.00 12.00
Letters spell out MATT CAIN each letter #'ed to 55
Total print run 440
MN Nate McLouth/440 * 5.00 12.00
Letters spell out NATE MCLOUTH each letter #'ed to 40
Total print run 440
NM Nick Markakis/420 * 8.00 20.00
Letters spell out NICK MARKAKIS each letter #'ed to 35
Total print run 420
SD Stephen Drew/440 * 4.00 10.00
Letters spell out STEPHEN DREW each letter #'ed to 40
Total print run 440
TT Troy Tulowitzki/350 * 8.00 20.00
Letters spell out ROCKIES each letter #'ed to 50
Total print run 350
ZG Zack Greinke/440 * 4.00 10.00
Letters spell out ZACK GREINKE each letter #'ed to 40
Total print run 440

2009 Upper Deck Icons Lettermen Autographs

OVERALL AUTO ODDS 1:10 HOBBY
PRINT RUNS B/WN 7-100 COPIES PER
TOTAL PRINT RUNS LISTED
SER.# ON CARDS ARE DIFFERENT
NO PRICING ON QTY 24 OR LESS
AG Adrian Gonzalez/30 * 10.00 25.00
Letters spell out MEXICO each letter #'ed to 5
Total print run 30
CH Cole Hamels/30 * 30.00 60.00
Letters spell out HAMELS each letter #'ed to 5
Total print run 30
CJ Chipper Jones/7 *
Letters spell out CHIPPER each letter #'ed to 1
Total print run 7
CK Clayton Kershaw/28 * 12.50 30.00
Letters spell out KERSHAW each letter #'ed to 4
Total print run 28
CL Carlos Lee/30 * 15.00 40.00
Letters spell out PANAMA each letter #'ed to 5
Total print run 30
CM Chien-Ming Wang/28 * 200.00 300.00
Letters spell out CHIEN-MING WANG each letter #'ed to 2
Total print run 28
CV Chris Volstad/96 * 12.50 30.00
Letters spell out CHRIS VOLSTAD each letter #'ed to 8
Total print run 96
CW Chien-Ming Wang/12 *
Letters spell out TAIWAN each letter #'ed to 2
Total print run 12
DJ Derek Jeter/20 *
Letters spell out DEREK JETER each letter #'ed to 2
Total print run 20
DP Dustin Pedroia/35 * 75.00 150.00
Letters spell out PEDROIA each letter #'ed to 5
Total print run 35
EC Eric Chavez/30 * 10.00 25.00
Letters spell out ERIC CHAVEZ each letter #'ed to 3
Total print run 30
EL Evan Longoria/24 * 125.00 250.00
Letters spell out LONGORIA each letter #'ed to 3
Total print run 24
GF Gavin Floyd/90 * 10.00 25.00
Letters spell out GAVIN FLOYD each letter #'ed to 9
Total print run 90
GS Geovany Soto/33 * 30.00 60.00
Letters spell out GEOVANY SOTO each letter #'ed to 3
Total print run 33
HR Hanley Ramirez/26 * 40.00 80.00
Letters spell out HANLEY RAMIREZ each letter #'ed to 2
Total print run 26
IK Ian Kinsler/100 * 20.00 50.00
Letters spell out IAN KINSLER each letter #'ed to 10...*Use signed patches from inventory
Total print run 100
JA Jay Bruce/91 * 30.00 60.00
Letters spell out BRUCE ALMIGHTY each letter #'ed to 7
Total print run 91
JL Jon Lester/45 * 50.00 100.00
Letters spell out JON LESTER each letter #'ed to 5
Total print run 45
JM Justin Masterson/90 * 15.00 40.00
Letters spell out JUSTIN MASTERSON each letter #'ed to 6
Total print run 90
JN Joe Nathan/45 * 10.00 25.00
Letters spell out JOE NATHAN each letter #'ed to 5
Total print run 45
JS James Shields/36 * 15.00 40.00
Letters spell out BIG GAME JAMES each letter #'ed to 3
Total print run 36
JW Josh Willingham/99 * 6.00 15.00
Letters spell out THE HAMMER each letter #'ed to 11
Total print run 99
KG Ken Griffey Jr./10 *
Letters spell out Pictured with SEA...THE NATURAL each letter #'ed to 1
Total print run 10
KS Kelly Shoppach/80 * 10.00 25.00
Letters spell out SHOPPACH each letter #'ed to 10
Total print run 80
LO Jed Lowrie/72 * 10.00 25.00
Letters spell out LOWRIE each letter #'ed to 12
Total print run 72
MC Matt Cain/40 * 30.00 60.00
Letters spell out MATT CAIN each letter #'ed to 5
Total print run 40
MN Nate McLouth/55 * 15.00 40.00
Letters spell out NATE MCLOUTH each letter #'ed to 5
Total print run 55
NM Nick Markakis/36 * 50.00 100.00
Letters spell out NICK MARKAKIS each letter #'ed to 3
Total print run 36
TT Troy Tulowitzki/40 * 12.50 30.00
Letters spell out TULO each letter #'ed to 10
Total print run 40
ZG Zack Greinke/44 * 30.00 60.00
Letters spell out ZACK GREINKE each letter #'ed to 4
Total print run 44

2009 Upper Deck Icons Retail Red

*RED: .4X TO 1X BASIC
AVAILABLE IN RETAIL PACKS

2000 Upper Deck Legends

The 2000 Upper Deck Legends product was released in late August, 2000 and featured a 135-card base set that was broken into tiers as follows: (90) Base Veterans (1-90), (15) Y2K Subset cards (91-105) (1:9), and (30) 20th Century Legends Subset cards (106-135) (1:5). Each pack contained five cards and carried a suggested retail price of $4.99. Also, a selection of A Piece of History 3000 Club Paul Molitor and Carl Yastrzemski memorabilia cards were randomly seeded into packs. 350 bat cards for each player were produced. Also for Carl Yatsrzemski only, 350 jersey cards, 100 hand-numbered bat-jersey combination cards and eight autographed, hand-numbered, combination bat-jersey cards were produced. Pricing for these memorabilia cards can be referenced under 2000 Upper Deck A Piece of History 3000 Club.

COMPLETE SET (135) 30.00 80.00
COMP.SET w/o SP'S (90) 8.00 20.00
COMMON CARD (1-90) .10 .30
COMMON CARD (91-105) .75 2.00
COMMON (106-135) .75 2.00
1 Darin Erstad .10 .30
2 Troy Glaus .10 .30
3 Mo Vaughn .10 .30
4 Craig Biggio .20 .50
5 Jeff Bagwell .20 .50
6 Reggie Jackson .20 .50
7 Tim Hudson .10 .30
8 Jason Giambi .10 .30
9 Hank Aaron .60 1.50
10 Greg Maddux .50 1.25
11 Chipper Jones .30 .75
12 Andres Galarraga .10 .30
13 Robin Yount .50 1.25
14 Jeromy Burnitz .10 .30
15 Paul Molitor .10 .30
16 David Wells .10 .30
17 Carlos Delgado .10 .30
18 Ernie Banks .30 .75
19 Sammy Sosa .30 .75
20 Kerry Wood .10 .30
21 Stan Musial .50 1.25
22 Bob Gibson .20 .50
23 Mark McGwire .75 2.00
24 Fernando Tatis .10 .30
25 Randy Johnson .30 .75
26 Matt Williams .10 .30
27 Jackie Robinson .30 .75
28 Sandy Koufax .75 2.00
29 Shawn Green .10 .30
30 Kevin Brown .20 .50
31 Gary Sheffield .10 .30
32 Greg Vaughn .10 .30
33 Jose Canseco .20 .50
34 Gary Carter .10 .30
35 Vladimir Guerrero .30 .75
36 Willie Mays .60 1.50
37 Barry Bonds .75 2.00
38 Jeff Kent .10 .30
39 Bob Feller .10 .30
40 Roberto Alomar .20 .50
41 Jim Thome .20 .50
42 Manny Ramirez .20 .50
43 Alex Rodriguez .50 1.25
44 Preston Wilson .10 .30
45 Tom Seaver .20 .50
46 Robin Ventura .10 .30
47 Mike Piazza .50 1.25
48 Mike Hampton .10 .30
49 Brooks Robinson .20 .50
50 Frank Robinson .20 .50
51 Cal Ripken 1.00 2.50
52 Albert Belle .10 .30
53 Eddie Murray .30 .75
54 Tony Gwynn .40 1.00
55 Roberto Clemente .60 1.50
56 Willie Stargell .20 .50
57 Brian Giles .10 .30
58 Jason Kendall .10 .30
59 Mike Schmidt .60 1.50
60 Bob Abreu .10 .30
61 Scott Rolen .20 .50
62 Curt Schilling .10 .30
63 Johnny Bench .30 .75
64 Sean Casey .10 .30
65 Barry Larkin .20 .50
66 Ken Griffey Jr. .50 1.25
67 George Brett .75 2.00
68 Carlos Beltran .10 .30
69 Nolan Ryan 1.00 2.50
70 Ivan Rodriguez .20 .50
71 Rafael Palmeiro .20 .50
72 Larry Walker .10 .30
73 Todd Helton .20 .50
74 Jeff Cirillo .10 .30
75 Carl Everett .10 .30
76 Nomar Garciaparra .50 1.25
77 Pedro Martinez .20 .50
78 Harmon Killebrew .30 .75
79 Corey Koskie .10 .30
80 Ty Cobb .50 1.25
81 Dean Palmer .10 .30
82 Juan Gonzalez .10 .30
83 Carlton Fisk .20 .50
84 Frank Thomas .30 .75
85 Magglio Ordonez .10 .30
86 Lou Gehrig .60 1.50
87 Babe Ruth 1.00 2.50
88 Derek Jeter .75 2.00
89 Roger Clemens .60 1.50
90 Bernie Williams .20 .50
91 Rick Ankiel Y2K .75 2.00
92 Kip Wells Y2K .75 2.00
93 Pat Burrell Y2K .75 2.00
94 Mark Quinn Y2K .75 2.00
95 Ruben Mateo Y2K .75 2.00
96 Adam Kennedy Y2K .75 2.00
97 Brad Penny Y2K .75 2.00
98 K.Sasaki Y2K RC .75 2.00
99 Peter Bergeron Y2K .75 2.00
100 Rafael Furcal Y2K .75 2.00
101 Eric Munson Y2K .75 2.00
102 Nick Johnson Y2K .75 2.00
103 Rob Bell Y2K .75 2.00
104 Vernon Wells Y2K .75 2.00
105 Ben Petrick Y2K .75 2.00
106 Babe Ruth 20C 3.00 8.00
107 Mark McGwire 20C 2.00 5.00
108 Nolan Ryan 20C 2.50 6.00
109 Hank Aaron 20C 1.50 4.00
110 Barry Bonds 20C 2.00 5.00
111 N.Garciaparra 20C 1.25 3.00
112 Roger Clemens 20C 1.50 4.00
113 Johnny Bench 20C .75 2.00
114 Alex Rodriguez 20C 1.25 3.00
115 Cal Ripken 20C 2.50 6.00
116 Willie Mays 20C 1.50 4.00
117 Mike Piazza 20C 1.25 3.00
118 Reggie Jackson 20C .75 2.00
119 Tony Gwynn 20C 1.00 2.50
120 Cy Young 20C .75 2.00
121 George Brett 20C 1.50 4.00
122 Greg Maddux 20C 1.25 3.00
123 Yogi Berra 20C .75 2.00
124 Sammy Sosa 20C .75 2.00
125 Randy Johnson 20C .75 2.00
126 Bob Gibson 20C .75 2.00
127 Lou Gehrig 20C 2.00 5.00
128 Ken Griffey Jr. 20C 1.25 3.00
129 Derek Jeter 20C 2.00 5.00
130 Mike Schmidt 20C 1.50 4.00
131 Pedro Martinez 20C .75 2.00
132 Jackie Robinson 20C .75 2.00
133 Jose Canseco 20C .75 2.00
134 Ty Cobb 20C 1.25 3.00
135 Stan Musial 20C 1.25 3.00

2000 Upper Deck Legends Commemorative Collection

Randomly inserted into packs, this 135-card insert is a complete parallel of the Upper Deck Legends base set. Each card in this set is individually serial numbered to 100.

*ACTIVE STARS 1-90: 8X TO 20X BASIC
*POST-WAR STARS 1-90: 10X TO 25X BASIC
*PRE-WAR STARS 1-90: 6X TO 15X BASIC
*Y2K: 2X TO 5X BASIC Y2K
*ACTIVE 20C: 3X TO 8X BASIC 20C
*POST-WAR 20C: 5X TO 12X BASIC 20C
*PRE-WAR 20C: 2.5X TO 6X BASIC 20C

2000 Upper Deck Legends Defining Moments

Randomly inserted into packs at one in 12, this 10-card insert focuses on some of Major League baseball's most defining moments Card backs carry a "DM" prefix.

COMPLETE SET (10) 20.00 50.00
DM1 Reggie Jackson .60 1.50
DM2 Hank Aaron 2.00 5.00
DM3 Babe Ruth 3.00 8.00
DM4 Cal Ripken 3.00 8.00
DM5 Carlton Fisk .60 1.50
DM6 Ken Griffey Jr. 1.50 4.00
DM7 Nolan Ryan 3.00 8.00
DM8 Roger Clemens 2.00 5.00
DM9 Willie Mays 2.00 5.00
DM10 Mark McGwire 2.50 6.00

2000 Upper Deck Legends Eternal Glory

Randomly inserted into packs at one in 24, this six-card insert features players whose greatness will live on in the minds of many. Please note that card number 3 does not exist. Card backs carry an "EG" prefix.

COMPLETE SET (6) 15.00 40.00
EG1 Nolan Ryan 4.00 10.00
EG2 Ken Griffey Jr. 2.00 5.00
EG3 Does Not Exist
EG4 Sammy Sosa 1.25 3.00
EG5 Derek Jeter 3.00 8.00
EG6 Willie Mays 2.50 6.00
EG7 Roger Clemens 2.50 6.00

2000 Upper Deck Legends Legendary Game Jerseys

Randomly inserted into packs at one in 48, this 50-card insert set features game-used jersey cards of past and present Major League stars. Cards are numbered using the player's initials with a "J" prefix.

SP'S ARE NOT SERIAL-NUMBERED
SP INFO PROVIDED BY UPPER DECK
JAR Alex Rodriguez 10.00 25.00
JBAB Barry Bonds 15.00 40.00
JBG Bob Gibson Pants 6.00 15.00
JBM Bill Mazeroski 4.00 10.00
JBOB Bobby Bonds 4.00 10.00
JBR Brooks Robinson 6.00 15.00
JCJ Chipper Jones 6.00 15.00
JCR Cal Ripken 15.00 40.00
JDC Dave Concepcion 4.00 10.00
JDD Don Drysdale 12.50 30.00
JDJ Derek Jeter 15.00 40.00
JDM Dale Murphy 6.00 15.00
JDW Dave Winfield 4.00 10.00
JEM Eddie Mathews 6.00 15.00
JEW Earl Weaver 4.00 10.00
JFR Frank Robinson 6.00 15.00
JFT Frank Thomas 6.00 15.00
JGB George Brett 10.00 25.00
JGM Greg Maddux 10.00 25.00
JGP Gaylord Perry 4.00 10.00
JHA Hank Aaron 30.00 60.00
JJB Jeff Bagwell 6.00 15.00
JJB Johnny Bench 6.00 15.00
JJC Jose Canseco 6.00 15.00
JJP Jim Palmer 4.00 10.00
JJT Joe Torre 6.00 15.00
JKG Ken Griffey Jr. 10.00 25.00
JLB Lou Brock 6.00 15.00
JLG Lou Gehrig Pants 125.00 200.00
JMM Mickey Mantle 40.00 80.00
JMR Manny Ramirez 6.00 15.00
JMS Mike Schmidt 10.00 25.00
JMW Matt Williams 4.00 10.00
JMW Maury Wills 4.00 10.00
JNR Nolan Ryan 15.00 40.00
JOS Ozzie Smith 6.00 15.00
JRAJ Randy Johnson 6.00 15.00
JRC Roger Clemens 10.00 25.00
JRF Rollie Fingers 4.00 10.00
JRJ Reggie Jackson 6.00 15.00
JRM Roger Maris Pants 15.00 40.00
JSK Sandy Koufax SP/95 175.00 300.00
JSM Stan Musial SP/28
JTG Tony Gwynn 6.00 15.00
JTM Thurman Munson 15.00 40.00
JTS Tom Seaver 6.00 15.00
JWB Wade Boggs 6.00 15.00
JWM Willie Mays SP/29
JWMC Willie McCovey 4.00 10.00
JWS Willie Stargell 6.00 15.00
SJSK Sandy Koufax AU/32

2000 Upper Deck Legends Legendary Signatures

Randomly inserted into packs at one in 24, this 39-card insert features autographed cards of past and present superstars. Card backs are numbered using the player's initials and an "S" prefix. Though print run numbers were not initially released, Upper Deck did confirm to Beckett Publications that Hank Aaron, Derek Jeter and Manny Ramirez signed less cards than other players in the set. Specific quantities for each of these players is detailed in the checklist below. Finally, Dave Concepcion, Frank Thomas, Ken Griffey Jr., Manny Ramirez, Mo Vaughn, Ozzie Smith and Willie Stargell cards were inserted in packs as stickered exchange cards. The deadline for this exchange was April 22nd, 2001. In addition to the exchange cards, real autographed cards did make their into packs for the following players: Willie Stargell, Ozzie Smith and Dave Concepcion.

SAD Andre Dawson 6.00 15.00
SAR Alex Rodriguez 50.00 100.00
SAT Alan Trammell 6.00 15.00
SBB Bobby Bonds 6.00 15.00
SCJ Chipper Jones 20.00 50.00
SCR Cal Ripken 60.00 120.00
SDC D.Concepcion EXCH* 6.00 15.00
SDJ Derek Jeter SP/61 500.00 700.00
SDM Dale Murphy 10.00 25.00
SFL Fred Lynn 6.00 15.00
SFT Frank Thomas 20.00 50.00
SGB George Brett 50.00 100.00
SGC Gary Carter 10.00 25.00
SHA Hank Aaron SP/94 200.00 400.00
SHK Harmon Killebrew 12.50 30.00
SIR Ivan Rodriguez 15.00 40.00
SJB Johnny Bench 15.00 40.00
SJC Jose Canseco 10.00 25.00
SJP Jim Palmer 10.00 25.00
SKG Ken Griffey Jr. 60.00 120.00
SLB Lou Brock 10.00 25.00
SMP Mike Piazza 75.00 150.00
SMR Manny Ramirez SP/141 20.00 50.00
SMS Mike Schmidt 30.00 60.00
SMV Mo Vaughn 6.00 15.00
SMW Matt Williams 6.00 15.00
SNR Nolan Ryan 60.00 120.00
SOS Ozzie Smith 15.00 40.00
SPN Phil Niekro 6.00 15.00
SRC Roger Clemens 60.00 120.00
SRF Rollie Fingers 6.00 15.00
SRJ Reggie Jackson 20.00 50.00
SSC Sean Casey 6.00 15.00
SSM Stan Musial 50.00 100.00
STG Tony Gwynn 15.00 40.00
STS Tom Seaver 15.00 40.00
SVG Vladimir Guerrero 12.50 30.00
SWS Willie Stargell EXCH* 20.00 50.00
SRAJ Randy Johnson 40.00 80.00

2000 Upper Deck Legends Legendary Signatures Gold

Randomly inserted into packs, this set is a parallel of the Legendary Signatures insert. Each card features gold colored fronts (instead of silver for the basic cards) and is individually serial numbered to 50 on front in blue ink sharpie. Each card is numbered on the back using the player's initials and an "S" prefix. Also, Dave Concepcion, Frank Thomas, Ken Griffey Jr., Manny Ramirez, Mo Vaughn, Ozzie Smith and Willie Stargell cards were inserted in packs as stickered exchange cards. The deadline for this exchange was April 22nd, 2001. In addition to the exchange cards, real autographed cards did make their into packs for the following players: Willie Stargell, Ozzie Smith and Dave Concepcion. Please note, that Derek Jeter did not sign any Gold cards. The Yankees star shortstop signed only 61 cards for this entire product - all of which were basic Legendary Signatures.

SAD Andre Dawson 15.00 40.00
SAR Alex Rodriguez 100.00 175.00
SAT Alan Trammell 15.00 40.00
SBB Bobby Bonds 20.00 50.00
SCJ Chipper Jones 40.00 80.00
SCR Cal Ripken 100.00 175.00
SDC D.Concepcion EXCH* 15.00 40.00
SDM Dale Murphy 20.00 50.00
SFL Fred Lynn 15.00 40.00
SFT Frank Thomas 40.00 80.00
SGB George Brett 75.00 150.00
SGC Gary Carter 30.00 60.00
SHA Hank Aaron 175.00 300.00
SHK Harmon Killebrew 50.00 100.00
SIR Ivan Rodriguez 40.00 80.00
SJB Johnny Bench 40.00 80.00
SJC Jose Canseco 20.00 50.00
SJP Jim Palmer 15.00 40.00
SKG Ken Griffey Jr. 125.00 250.00
SLB Lou Brock 20.00 50.00
SMP Mike Piazza 125.00 200.00
SMR M.Ramirez EXCH 60.00 120.00
SMS Mike Schmidt 75.00 150.00
SMV Mo Vaughn 15.00 40.00
SMW Matt Williams 20.00 50.00
SNR Nolan Ryan 125.00 200.00
SOS Ozzie Smith 50.00 100.00
SPN Phil Niekro 15.00 40.00
SRC Roger Clemens 125.00 200.00
SRF Rollie Fingers 15.00 40.00
SRJ Reggie Jackson 40.00 80.00
SSC Sean Casey 15.00 40.00
SSM Stan Musial 50.00 100.00
STG Tony Gwynn 50.00 100.00
STS Tom Seaver 40.00 80.00
SVG Vladimir Guerrero 30.00 60.00
SWS Willie Stargell 40.00 80.00
SRAJ Randy Johnson 75.00 150.00

2000 Upper Deck Legends Millennium Team

Randomly inserted into packs at one in four, this nine-card insert features the most famous players of the 20th Century. Please note that card number 6 does not exist. Card backs carry a "UD" prefix.

COMPLETE SET (9) 4.00 10.00
UD1 Mark McGwire .75 2.00
UD2 Jackie Robinson .30 .75
UD3 Mike Schmidt .60 1.50
UD4 Cal Ripken 1.00 2.50
UD5 Babe Ruth 1.00 2.50
UD6 Does Not Exist
UD7 Willie Mays .60 1.50
UD8 Johnny Bench .30 .75
UD9 Nolan Ryan 1.00 2.50
UD10 Ken Griffey Jr. .50 1.25

2000 Upper Deck Legends Ones for the Ages

Randomly inserted into packs at one in 24, this seven-card insert features Major League Baseball's most legendary players. Card backs carry an "O" prefix.

COMPLETE SET (7) 10.00 25.00
O1 Ty Cobb 2.00 5.00
O2 Cal Ripken 4.00 10.00
O3 Babe Ruth 4.00 10.00
O4 Jackie Robinson 1.25 3.00
O5 Mark McGwire 3.00 8.00
O6 Alex Rodriguez 2.00 5.00
O7 Mike Piazza 2.00 5.00

2000 Upper Deck Legends Reflections in Time

Randomly inserted into packs at one in 12, this 10-card insert features dual-player cards of players that have had very similar major league careers. Card backs carry a "R" prefix.

COMPLETE SET (10) 15.00 40.00
R1 Ken Griffey Jr. 1.50 4.00
Hank Aaron
R2 Sammy Sosa 1.00 2.50
Roberto Clemente
R3 Roger Clemens 2.00 5.00
Nolan Ryan
R4 Ivan Rodriguez 1.00 2.50
Johnny Bench
R5 Alex Rodriguez 1.50 4.00
Ernie Banks
R6 Tony Gwynn 1.50 4.00
Stan Musial
R7 Barry Bonds 2.00 5.00
Willie Mays
R8 Cal Ripken 2.00 5.00
Lou Gehrig
R9 Chipper Jones 2.00 5.00
Mike Schmidt
R10 Mark McGwire 3.00 8.00
Babe Ruth

2001 Upper Deck Legends

This 90 card set was released in July, 2001. The cards were issued in five card packs with an SRP of $4.99 per pack and these packs were issued 24 to a box. The set has a mixture of past and present superstars.

COMPLETE SET (90) 8.00 20.00
1 Darin Erstad .10 .30
2 Troy Glaus .10 .30
3 Nolan Ryan .75 2.00
4 Reggie Jackson .20 .50
5 Catfish Hunter .20 .50
6 Jason Giambi .10 .30
7 Tim Hudson .10 .30
8 Miguel Tejada .10 .30
9 Carlos Delgado .10 .30
10 Shannon Stewart .10 .30
11 Greg Vaughn .10 .30
12 Larry Doby .10 .30
13 Jim Thome .20 .50
14 Juan Gonzalez .10 .30
15 Roberto Alomar .20 .50
16 Edgar Martinez .20 .50
17 John Olerud .10 .30
18 Eddie Murray .30 .75
19 Cal Ripken 1.00 2.50
20 Alex Rodriguez .50 1.25
21 Ivan Rodriguez .20 .50
22 Rafael Palmeiro .20 .50
23 Jimmie Foxx .30 .75
24 Cy Young .30 .75
25 Manny Ramirez Sox .20 .50
26 Pedro Martinez .20 .50
27 Nomar Garciaparra .50 1.25
28 George Brett .60 1.50
29 Mike Sweeney .10 .30
30 Jermaine Dye .10 .30
31 Ty Cobb .50 1.25
32 Dean Palmer .10 .30
33 Harmon Killebrew .30 .75
34 Matt Lawton .10 .30
35 Luis Aparicio .10 .30
36 Frank Thomas .30 .75
37 Magglio Ordonez .10 .30
38 David Wells .10 .30
39 Mickey Mantle 1.25 3.00
40 Joe DiMaggio .60 1.50
41 Roger Maris .30 .75
42 Babe Ruth 1.00 2.50
43 Derek Jeter .75 2.00
44 Roger Clemens .60 1.50
45 Bernie Williams .20 .50
46 Jeff Bagwell .20 .50
47 Richard Hidalgo .10 .30
48 Warren Spahn .20 .50
49 Greg Maddux .50 1.25
50 Chipper Jones .30 .75
51 Andruw Jones .20 .50
52 Robin Yount .30 .75
53 Jeromy Burnitz .10 .30
54 Jeffrey Hammonds .10 .30
55 Ozzie Smith .50 1.25
56 Stan Musial .50 1.25
57 Mark McGwire .75 2.00
58 Jim Edmonds .10 .30
59 Sammy Sosa .30 .75
60 Ernie Banks .30 .75

61 Kerry Wood .10 .30
62 Randy Johnson .30 .75
63 Luis Gonzalez .10 .30
64 Don Drysdale .20 .50
65 Jackie Robinson .30 .75
66 Gary Sheffield .10 .30
67 Kevin Brown .10 .30
68 Vladimir Guerrero .30 .75
69 Willie Mays .60 1.50
70 Mel Ott .30 .75
71 Jeff Kent .10 .30
72 Barry Bonds .75 2.00
73 Preston Wilson .10 .30
74 Ryan Dempster .10 .30
75 Tom Seaver .20 .50
76 Mike Piazza .50 1.25
77 Robin Ventura .10 .30
78 Dave Winfield .10 .30
79 Tony Gwynn .40 1.00
80 Bob Abreu .10 .30
81 Scott Rolen .20 .50
82 Mike Schmidt .60 1.50
83 Roberto Clemente .75 2.00
84 Brian Giles .10 .30
85 Ken Griffey Jr. .50 1.25
86 Frank Robinson .20 .50
87 Johnny Bench .30 .75
88 Todd Helton .20 .50
89 Larry Walker .10 .30
90 Mike Hampton .10 .30

2001 Upper Deck Legends Fiorentino Collection

Inserted in packs at a rate of one in 12, these 14 cards feature the original artwork of James Fiorentino. The cards have a "F" prefix.

COMPLETE SET (14) 15.00 40.00
F1 Babe Ruth 3.00 8.00
F2 Satchel Paige 1.00 2.50
F3 Joe DiMaggio 2.00 5.00
F4 Willie Mays 2.00 5.00
F5 Ty Cobb 1.50 4.00
F6 Nolan Ryan 3.00 8.00
F7 Lou Gehrig 2.00 5.00
F8 Jackie Robinson 1.00 2.50
F9 Hank Aaron 2.00 5.00
F10 Roberto Clemente 2.00 5.00
F11 Stan Musial 1.25 3.00
F12 Johnny Bench 1.00 2.50
F13 Honus Wagner 1.00 2.50
F14 Reggie Jackson 1.00 2.50

2001 Upper Deck Legends Legendary Cuts

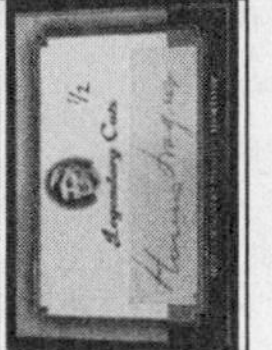

Randomly inserted in packs, these six cards feature cut signatures from the five original members of the Hall of Fame. Due to scarcity, no pricing is provided.

C1 Ty Cobb
Babe Ruth
Christy Mathewson
Walter Johnson
Honus Wagner/1
CBR Babe Ruth/3
CCM Christy Mathewson/1
CHW Honus Wagner/2
CTC Ty Cobb/3
CWJ Walter Johnson/3

2001 Upper Deck Legends Legendary Game Jersey

Issued at a rate of one in 24, these 33 cards feature authentic game jersey pieces from past and current players. A few players are perceived to be produced in larger quantites, we have notated those players with asterisks in our checklist. In addition, a few players were printed in shorter supply. We have notated those with an SP as well as print run information provided by Upper Deck.

GOLD PRINT RUN 25 SERIAL #'d SETS
NO GOLD PRICING DUE TO SCARCITY
JAR Alex Rodriguez 6.00 15.00
JBB Barry Bonds 10.00 25.00
JCJ Chipper Jones 6.00 15.00
JCR Cal Ripken DP 15.00 40.00
JDW Dave Winfield 4.00 10.00
JEB Ernie Banks Uniform 6.00 15.00
JGM Greg Maddux 6.00 15.00
JGS Gary Sheffield 4.00 10.00
JHA Hank Aaron 15.00 40.00
JIR Ivan Rodriguez DP 6.00 15.00
JJB Jeff Bagwell 6.00 15.00
JJC Jose Canseco 6.00 15.00
JJD Joe DiMaggio 75.00 150.00
Uniform SP/245 *
JKG Ken Griffey Jr. 6.00 15.00
JKS Kazuhiro Sasaki 4.00 10.00
JMM Mickey Mantle 150.00 250.00
Uniform SP/245 *
JMP Mike Piazza 6.00 15.00
JMR Manny Ramirez Sox 6.00 15.00
JNR Nolan Ryan 15.00 40.00
JOS Ozzie Smith DP 6.00 15.00
JPM Pedro Martinez 6.00 15.00
JRCL Roger Clemens 6.00 15.00
JRJA R.Jackson Uniform 6.00 15.00
JRJO Randy Johnson DP 6.00 15.00
JRM Roger Maris SP/343 * 20.00 50.00
JROC R.Clemente SP/195 * 60.00 120.00
JRY Robin Yount 6.00 15.00
JSM Stan Musial 20.00 50.00
Uniform SP/490 *
JSS Sammy Sosa 6.00 15.00
JTG Tony Gwynn Uni DP 6.00 15.00
JTS Tom Seaver 6.00 15.00
JWM Willie Mays 20.00 50.00
JYB Yogi Berra Uniform 6.00 15.00

2001 Upper Deck Legends Legendary Game Jersey Autographs

Issued at a rate of one in 288, these cards feature not only a game jersey piece but an authentic autograph of the player pictured. Ken Griffey Jr. did not return his cards in time for packout; those cards could be redeemed until July 9, 2004. In addition, a few cards were produced in lesser quantites. Those cards are notated in our checklist with an SP and print run information provided by Upper Deck.

GOLD PRINT RUN 25 SERIAL #'d SETS
NO GOLD PRICING DUE TO SCARCITY
SJAR Alex Rodriguez 60.00 120.00
SJEB Ernie Banks Uni 30.00 60.00
SJKG Ken Griffey Jr. 60.00 120.00
SJNR Nolan Ryan 75.00 150.00
SJOS Ozzie Smith 30.00 60.00
SJRC R.Clemens SP/211 40.00 80.00
SJRJ R.Jackson Uni SP/224 40.00 80.00
SJSM S.Musial SP/266 60.00 120.00
SJSS Sammy Sosa SP/91 50.00 100.00
SJTS Tom Seaver 30.00 60.00

2001 Upper Deck Legends Legendary Lumber

Inserted in packs at a rate of one in 24, these 32 cards feature authentic game bat pieces from past and current players. A few cards are available in larger supply and we have notated those with a DP tag our checklist. In addition, certain cards were short printed. We have notated those with an SP as well as print run information provided by Upper Deck.

GOLD PRINT RUN 25 SERIAL #'d SETS
NO GOLD PRICING DUE TO SCARCITY
LAJ Andruw Jones 6.00 15.00
LAP Albert Pujols 50.00 80.00
LAR Alex Rodriguez 6.00 15.00
LBB Barry Bonds DP 10.00 25.00
LCJ Chipper Jones 6.00 15.00
LCR Cal Ripken 15.00 40.00
LEB Ernie Banks SP/80 * 30.00 60.00
LEM Eddie Murray 6.00 15.00
LFR Frank Robinson 6.00 15.00
LGS Gary Sheffield DP 4.00 10.00
LHA Hank Aaron 15.00 40.00
LIR Ivan Rodriguez DP 6.00 15.00
LJB Johnny Bench 6.00 15.00
LJC Jose Canseco 6.00 15.00
LJD Joe DiMaggio 30.00 60.00
LJF Jimmie Foxx SP/351 * 30.00 60.00
LKG Ken Griffey Jr. 6.00 15.00
LLA Luis Aparicio 4.00 10.00
LMM Mickey Mantle 75.00 150.00
LMO Mel Ott SP/355 20.00 50.00
LMP Mike Piazza 6.00 15.00
LMR Manny Ramirez Sox 6.00 15.00
LOS Ozzie Smith 6.00 15.00
LRCA R.Campanella SP/226 * 20.00 60.00
LRCL Roger Clemens 6.00 15.00
LRJ Reggie Jackson 6.00 15.00
LRJ Randy Johnson 6.00 15.00
LRM Roger Maris 20.00 50.00
LROC R.Clemente SP/170 * 40.00 80.00
LSS Sammy Sosa DP 6.00 15.00
LTG Tony Gwynn 6.00 15.00
LWM Willie Mays DP 15.00 40.00

2001 Upper Deck Legends Legendary Lumber Autographs

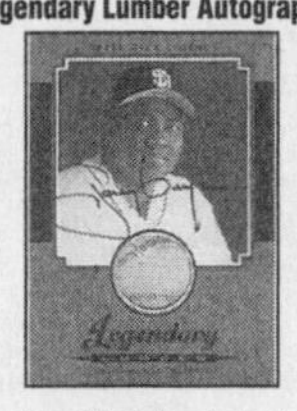

This partial parallel to the Legendary Lumber insert set features authentic autographs from the player on the card. Ken Griffey Jr. did not return his cards in time for inclusion in packs. These cards were redeemable until July 9, 2004. In addition, a few cards were signed in lesser quantites. We have notated those cards with an SP and print run information provided by Upper Deck.

GOLD PRINT RUN 25 SERIAL #'d SETS
NO GOLD PRICNG DUE TO SCARCITY
SLAR Alex Rodriguez 60.00 120.00
SLEB Ernie Banks 40.00 80.00
SLEM Eddie Murray 30.00 60.00
SLKG Ken Griffey Jr. 40.00 80.00
SLLA Luis Aparicio 12.50 30.00
SLRC R.Clemens SP/227 60.00 120.00
SLRJ R.Jackson SP/211 30.00 60.00
SLSS Sammy Sosa SP/66 50.00 100.00
SLTG Tony Gwynn 40.00 80.00

2001 Upper Deck Legends Reflections in Time

Issued at a rate of one in 18, these 10 cards feature an past and present player from the same team.

COMPLETE SET (10) 12.50 30.00
R1 Bernie Williams 4.00 10.00
Mickey Mantle
R2 Pedro Martinez .60 1.50
Cy Young
R3 Barry Bonds 3.00 8.00
Willie Mays
R4 Scott Rolen 2.00 5.00
Mike Schmidt
R5 Mark McGwire 2.50 6.00
Stan Musial
R6 Ken Griffey Jr. 1.50 4.00
Frank Robinson
R7 Sammy Sosa 1.00 2.50
Andre Dawson
R8 Kevin Brown .60 1.50
Don Drysdale
R9 Jason Giambi .60 1.50
Reggie Jackson
R10 Tim Hudson .60 1.50
Jim Catfish Hunter

2001 Upper Deck Legends of NY

This product was released in late December, 2001. The 200-card base set features baseball greats like Babe Ruth and Mickey Mantle. Each pack contained five cards and carried a suggested retail price of $2.99

COMPLETE SET (200) 20.00 50.00
1 Billy Herman .20 .50
2 Carl Erskine .20 .50
3 Burleigh Grimes .20 .50
4 Don Newcombe .20 .50
5 Gil Hodges .50 1.25
6 Pee Wee Reese .50 1.25
7 Jackie Robinson .50 1.25
8 Duke Snider .30 .75
9 Jim Gilliam .20 .50
10 Roy Campanella .50 1.25
11 Carl Furillo .20 .50
12 Casey Stengel .30 .75
13 Casey Stengel DB .20 .50
14 Billy Herman DB .15 .40
15 Jackie Robinson DB .30 .75
16 Jackie Robinson DB .30 .75
17 Gil Hodges DB .50 1.25
18 Carl Furillo DB .15 .40
19 Roy Campanella DB .30 .75
20 Don Newcombe DB .15 .40
21 Duke Snider DB .20 .50
22 Casey Stengel BNS .20 .50
23 Burleigh Grimes BNS .15 .40
24 Pee Wee Reese BNS .30 .75
25 Jackie Robinson BNS .30 .75
26 Jackie Robinson BNS .30 .75
27 Carl Erskine BNS .15 .40
28 Roy Campanella BNS .30 .75
29 Duke Snider BNS .20 .50
30 Rube Marquard .20 .50
31 Ross Youngs .20 .50
32 Bobby Thomson .20 .50
33 Christy Mathewson .50 1.25
34 Carl Hubbell .50 1.25
35 Hoyt Wilhelm .20 .50
36 Johnny Mize .20 .50
37 John McGraw .30 .75
38 Monte Irvin .20 .50
39 Travis Jackson .20 .50
40 Mel Ott .50 1.25
41 Dusty Rhodes .15 .40
42 Leo Durocher .20 .50
43 John McGraw BG .20 .50
44 Christy Mathewson BG .30 .75
45 The Polo Grounds BG .15 .40
46 Travis Jackson BG .15 .40
47 Mel Ott BG .30 .75
48 Johnny Mize BG .15 .40
49 Leo Durocher BG .15 .40
50 Bobby Thomson BG .15 .40
51 Monte Irvin BG .15 .40
52 Bobby Thomson BG .15 .40
53 Christy Mathewson BNS .30 .75
54 Christy Mathewson BNS .30 .75
55 Christy Mathewson BNS .30 .75
56 John McGraw BNS .20 .50
57 John McGraw BNS .20 .50
58 John McGraw BNS .20 .50
59 Travis Jackson BNS .15 .40
60 Mel Ott BNS .30 .75
61 Mel Ott BNS .30 .75
62 Carl Hubbell BNS .20 .50
63 Bobby Thomson BNS .15 .40
64 Monte Irvin BNS .15 .40
65 Al Weis .15 .40
66 Donn Clendenon .15 .40
67 Ed Kranepool .20 .50
68 Gary Carter .20 .50
69 Tommie Agee .20 .50
70 Jon Matlack .15 .40
71 Ken Boswell .15 .40
72 Len Dykstra .20 .50
73 Nolan Ryan 1.25 3.00
74 Ray Sadecki .15 .40
75 Ron Darling .15 .40
76 Ron Swoboda .20 .50
77 Dwight Gooden .20 .50
78 Tom Seaver .30 .75
79 Wayne Garrett .15 .40
80 Casey Stengel MM .20 .50
81 Tom Seaver MM .20 .50
82 Tommie Agee MM .15 .40
83 Tom Seaver MM .20 .50
84 Yogi Berra MM .30 .75
85 Yogi Berra MM .30 .75
86 Tom Seaver MM .20 .50
87 Dwight Gooden MM .20 .50
88 Gary Carter MM .15 .40
89 Ron Darling MM .15 .40
90 Tommie Agee BNS .15 .40
91 Tom Seaver BNS .20 .50
92 Gary Carter BNS .15 .40
93 Len Dykstra BNS .15 .40
94 Babe Ruth 1.50 4.00
95 Bill Dickey .30 .75
96 Rich Gossage .20 .50
97 Casey Stengel UER .30 .75
Card has a Dodger logo on the back
98 Catfish Hunter .30 .75
99 Charlie Keller .15 .40
100 Chris Chambliss .20 .50
101 Don Larsen .20 .50
102 Dave Winfield .20 .50
103 Don Mattingly 1.00 2.50
104 Elston Howard .30 .75
105 Frankie Crosetti .20 .50
106 Hank Bauer .20 .50
107 Joe DiMaggio 1.00 2.50
108 Graig Nettles .20 .50
109 Lefty Gomez .30 .75
110 Phil Rizzuto .50 1.25
111 Lou Gehrig 1.00 2.50
112 Lou Piniella .20 .50
113 Mickey Mantle 2.00 5.00
114 Red Rolfe .20 .50
115 Reggie Jackson .30 .75
116 Roger Maris .50 1.25
117 Roy White .15 .40
118 Thurman Munson .50 1.25
119 Tom Tresh .20 .50
120 Tommy Henrich .20 .50
121 Waite Hoyt .20 .50
122 Willie Randolph .20 .50
123 Whitey Ford .30 .75
124 Yogi Berra .50 1.25
125 Babe Ruth BT .75 2.00
126 Babe Ruth BT .75 2.00
127 Lou Gehrig BT .50 1.25
128 Babe Ruth BT .75 2.00
129 Joe DiMaggio BT .50 1.25
130 Joe DiMaggio BT .50 1.25
131 Mickey Mantle BT 1.00 2.50
132 Roger Maris BT .30 .75
133 Mickey Mantle BT 1.00 2.50
134 Reggie Jackson BT .20 .50
135 Babe Ruth BNS .75 2.00
136 Babe Ruth BNS .75 2.00
137 Babe Ruth BNS .75 2.00
138 Lefty Gomez BNS .20 .50
139 Lou Gehrig BNS .50 1.25
140 Lou Gehrig BNS .50 1.25
141 Joe DiMaggio BNS .50 1.25
142 Joe DiMaggio BNS .50 1.25
143 Casey Stengel BNS .20 .50
144 Mickey Mantle BNS 1.00 2.50
145 Yogi Berra BNS .30 .75
146 Mickey Mantle BNS 1.00 2.50
147 Elston Howard BNS .20 .50
148 Whitey Ford BNS .20 .50
149 Reggie Jackson BNS .20 .50
150 Reggie Jackson BNS .20 .50
151 John McGraw .75 2.00
Babe Ruth
152 Babe Ruth .75 2.00
John McGraw
153 Lou Gehrig .50 1.25
Mel Ott
154 Joe DiMaggio .50 1.25
Mel Ott
155 Joe DiMaggio .50 1.25
Billy Herman
156 Joe DiMaggio .50 1.25
Jackie Robinson
157 Mickey Mantle 1.00 2.50
Bobby Thomson
158 Yogi Berra .30 .75
Pee Wee Reese
159 Roy Campanella 1.00 2.50
Mickey Mantle
160 Don Larsen .20 .50
Duke Snider
161 Christy Mathewson TT .30 .75
162 Christy Mathewson TT .30 .75
163 Rube Marquard TT .15 .40
164 Christy Mathewson TT .30 .75
165 John McGraw TT .20 .50
166 Burleigh Grimes TT .15 .40
167 Babe Ruth TT .75 2.00
168 Burleigh Grimes TT .15 .40
169 Babe Ruth TT .75 2.00
170 John McGraw TT .20 .50
171 Lou Gehrig TT .50 1.25
172 Babe Ruth TT .75 2.00
173 Babe Ruth TT .75 2.00
174 Carl Hubbell TT .20 .50
175 Joe DiMaggio TT .50 1.25
176 Lou Gehrig TT .50 1.25
177 Leo Durocher TT .15 .40
178 Mel Ott TT .30 .75
179 Joe DiMaggio TT .50 1.25
180 Jackie Robinson TT .30 .75
181 Babe Ruth TT .75 2.00
182 Bobby Thomson TT .15 .40
183 Joe DiMaggio TT .50 1.25
184 Mickey Mantle TT 1.00 2.50
185 Monte Irvin TT .15 .40
186 Roy Campanella TT .30 .75
187 Duke Snider TT .30 .75
188 Dusty Rhodes TT .15 .40
189 Yogi Berra TT .30 .75
190 Mickey Mantle TT 1.00 2.50
191 Mickey Mantle TT 1.00 2.50
192 Casey Stengel TT .20 .50
193 Tom Seaver TT .20 .50
194 Mickey Mantle TT UER 1.00 2.50
Text has Mantle retiring in 1939
195 Tommie Agee TT .15 .40
196 Tom Seaver TT .20 .50
197 Chris Chambliss TT .15 .40
198 Reggie Jackson TT .20 .50
199 Reggie Jackson TT .20 .50
200 Gary Carter TT .15 .40

2001 Upper Deck Legends of NY Game Base

This two card set features game-used base cards of Jackie Robinson and Tom Seaver. Each card is individually serial numbered to 100.

GOLD PRINT RUN 25 SERIAL #'d SETS
NO GOLD PRICING DUE TO SCARCITY
SILVER PRINT RUN 50 SERIAL #'d SETS
SILVER NO PRICING DUE TO SCARCITY
EFJR Jackie Robinson
SSTS Tom Seaver

2001 Upper Deck Legends of NY Game Bat

This 33-card insert set features authentic game-used bat chips. Collectors received either on bat or jersey card per box. A few cards were produced in lesser quantites, those print runs are provided in our checklist.

LDBBH Billy Herman 4.00 10.00
LDBDN Don Newcombe SP/67
LDBJG Jim Gilliam 4.00 10.00
LGBBTH Bobby Thomson 4.00 10.00
LMBAW Al Weis 4.00 10.00
LMBDC Donn Clendenon SP/60
LMBEK Ed Kranepool 4.00 10.00
LMBGC Gary Carter 4.00 10.00
LMBJM J.C. Martin 4.00 10.00
LMBKB Ken Boswell 4.00 10.00
LMBLD Len Dykstra 4.00 10.00
LMBNR Nolan Ryan 15.00 40.00
LMBRS Ron Swoboda 4.00 10.00
LMBTS Tom Seaver 6.00 15.00
LMBWG Wayne Garrett 4.00 10.00
LYBBD Bill Dickey 6.00 15.00
LYBBR Babe Ruth SP/107 125.00 200.00
LYBCC Chris Chambliss SP/130
LYBCK Charlie Keller 4.00 10.00
LYBDM Don Mattingly 10.00 25.00
LYBDW Dave Winfield UER 4.00 10.00
Playing career has the wrong years
LYBEH Elston Howard 6.00 15.00
LYBHB Hank Bauer 4.00 10.00
LYBJD Joe DiMaggio SP/43
LYBLP Lou Piniella 4.00 10.00
LYBMM Mickey Mantle SP/134 75.00 150.00
LYBMR Mickey Rivers 4.00 10.00
LYBRJ Reggie Jackson 6.00 15.00
LYBRM Roger Maris SP/60 50.00 100.00
LYBTH Tommy Henrich 4.00 10.00
LYBTM Thurman Munson 12.50 30.00
LYBTT Tom Tresh 4.00 10.00
LYBYB Yogi Berra 6.00 15.00

2001 Upper Deck Legends of NY Game Bat Autograph

This insert set is a partial parallel to the 2001 Upper Deck Legends of NY Game Bat insert. Each of these cards were signed, and issued into packs at 1:336. A few cards were printed in lesser quantities, those print runs are provided in our checklist.

SDBDN Don Newcombe 15.00 40.00
SMBDC Donn Clendenon 20.00 50.00
SMBGC Gary Carter 15.00 40.00
SMBNR N.Ryan SP/129 75.00 150.00
SMBRS Ron Swoboda
SMBTS Tom Seaver SP/89 50.00 100.00
SYBCC Chris Chambliss 15.00 40.00
SYBDM Don Mattingly 40.00 80.00
SYBDW D.Winfield SP/167 30.00 60.00
SYBMR Mickey Rivers 10.00 25.00
SYBRJ R.Jackson SP/123 50.00 100.00
SYBRW Roy White 15.00 40.00
SYBYB Yogi Berra 40.00 80.00

2001 Upper Deck Legends of NY Game Jersey

This 36-card insert set features authentic game-used jersey swatches. Collectors received either on bat or jersey card per box. A few cards were printed in small quantities, those print runs are provided in our checklist.

LDJCE Carl Erskine 4.00 10.00
LDJJR J.Rob Pants SP/126 75.00 150.00
LMJCS Casey Stengel 6.00 15.00
LMJJM Jon Matlack 4.00 10.00
LMJRD Ron Darling 4.00 10.00
LMJRS Ray Sadecki 4.00 10.00
LMJTS Tom Seaver 6.00 15.00
LYJBT Bob Turley 4.00 10.00
LYJCD Chuck Dressen 4.00 10.00
LYJCH Catfish Hunter 6.00 15.00
LYJCM C.Mathewson SP/63 250.00 400.00
LYJDM Duke Maas 4.00 10.00
LYJDW Dave Winfield 4.00 10.00
LYJEH Elston Howard 6.00 15.00
LYJFC Frank Crosetti 4.00 10.00
LYJGN Graig Nettles 4.00 10.00
LYJHB Hank Behrman 4.00 10.00
LYJHB Hank Bauer 4.00 10.00
LYJJD Joe DiMaggio SP/63 100.00 200.00
LYJJP Joe Pepitone 4.00 10.00
LYJJT Joe Torre 6.00 15.00
LYJLM Lindy McDaniel 4.00 10.00
LYJMM Mickey Mantle SP/63
LYJPN Phil Niekro 4.00 10.00
LYJRM Roger Maris SP/63 50.00 100.00
LYJRR Red Rolfe 4.00 10.00
LYJSJ Spider Jorgensen 4.00 10.00
LYJTH Tommy Henrich 4.00 10.00
LYJTM Thurman Munson 15.00 40.00
LYJWR Willie Randolph 4.00 10.00

2001 Upper Deck Legends of NY Game Jersey Autograph

This 22-card insert is a partial parallel to the 2001 Upper Deck Legends of NY Game Jersey insert set. Each of these cards were signed, and issued into packs at 1:336. A few cards were printed in lesser quantity and those cards are notated in our checklist as SP's along with print run information provided by Upper Deck.

SDJCE Carl Erskine 15.00 40.00
SDJJG Jim Gilliam SP/49
SDJJP J. Podres SP/193 12.50 30.00
SMJCS Craig Swan 10.00 25.00
SMJGF G.Foster SP/196 15.00 40.00
SMJNR Nolan Ryan SP/47
SMJTS Tom Seaver SP/60
SYJBD Bucky Dent 10.00 25.00
SYJDL Don Larsen 15.00 40.00
SYJDM Don Mattingly SP/72 60.00 120.00
SYJDR Dave Righetti 15.00 40.00
SYJGN Graig Nettles 15.00 40.00
SYJHL H.Lopez SP/195 15.00 40.00
SYJJP Joe Pepitone 15.00 40.00
SYJPN P.Niekro SP/195 10.00 25.00
SYJRJ Reggie Jackson SP/47
SYJSL Sparky Lyle 15.00 40.00
SYJTJ Tommy John 15.00 40.00
SYJWR Willie Randolph 15.00 40.00
SYJYB Yogi Berra SP/73
SYJRIG R.Gossage SP/145 15.00 40.00
SYJROG Ron Guidry 10.00 25.00

2001 Upper Deck Legends of NY Game Jersey Gold

This 24-card insert is a partial parallel set to the 2001 Upper Deck Legends of NY Game Jersey set, and features game-used jersey cards on a gold-foil based card. Print runs, of which vary between 125 and 500 numbered copies, are listed for each card in our checklist.

LDJCD C.Dressen/400 5.00 12.00
LDJCE Carl Erskine/400 5.00 12.00
LDJHB H.Behrman/500 5.00 12.00
LDJSJ S.Jorgensen/500 5.00 12.00
LMJJM Jon Matlack/400 5.00 12.00
LMJRD Ron Darling/400 5.00 12.00
LMJRS Ray Sadecki/400 5.00 12.00
LMJTS Tom Seaver/400 8.00 20.00
LYJBT Bob Turley/400 5.00 12.00
LYJCH C.Hunter/500 8.00 20.00
LYJDM Duke Maas/400 5.00 12.00
LYJDW D.Winfield/250 6.00 15.00
LYJEH E.Howard/400 8.00 20.00
LYJFC Frank Crosetti/400 5.00 12.00
LYJGN Graig Nettles/250 6.00 15.00
LYJHB Hank Bauer/400 5.00 12.00
LYJJP Joe Pepitone/250 6.00 15.00
LYJJT Joe Torre/250 10.00 25.00
LYJLM L.McDaniel/400 5.00 12.00

LYJPN Phil Niekro/125 8.00 20.00
LYJRR Red Rolfe/400 5.00 12.00
LYJTH T.Henrich/400 5.00 12.00
LYJTM T.Munson/400 20.00 50.00
LYJWR W.Randolph/125 8.00 20.00

2001 Upper Deck Legends of NY Stadium Seat

This two card set features stadium seat cards of Jackie Robinson and Mickey Mantle. Each card is individually serial numbered to 100.

GOLD PRINT RUN 25 SERIAL #'d SETS
GOLD NO PRICING DUE TO SCARCITY
SILVER PRINT RUN 50 SERIAL #'d SETS
SILVER NO PRICING DUE TO SCARCITY
EFSJR Jackie Robinson 15.00 40.00
YSMM Mickey Mantle 60.00 120.00

2001 Upper Deck Legends of NY Tri-Combo Autographs

Randomly inserted into packs, this seven-card insert set features tri-combo autographs from greats like Ryan/Seaver/Swoboda. Each card is individually serial numbered to 25. Each card carries a "S" prefix. Due to market scarcity, no pricing is provided.

2001 Upper Deck Legends of NY United We Stand

This 15-card insert set honors the FDNY/PDNY for their relief work in the Sept. 11, 2001 terrorist attacks in New York. Card backs carry a "USA" prefix. This insert was issued at a rate of 1:12 packs.

COMPLETE SET (15) 30.00 60.00
COMMON CARD (1-15) 2.00 5.00

1999 Upper Deck MVP

This 220 card set was distributed in 10 cards packs with an SRP of $1.59 per pack. Cards numbered from 218 through 220 are checklist subsets. Approximately 350 Mike Schmidt A Piece of History 500 Home Run Game-Used bat cards were distributed in this product. In addition, 20 hand serial numbered versions of this card personally signed by Schmidt himself were also randomly seeded into packs. Pricing for these bat cards can be referenced under 1999 Upper Deck A Piece of History 500 Club. A Ken Griffey Jr. Sample card was distributed to dealers and hobby media several weeks prior to the product's national release. Unlike most Upper Deck promotional cards, this card does not have the word "SAMPLE" pasted across the back of the card. The card, however, is numbered "S3". It's believed that cards S1 and S2 were Upper Deck MVP football and basketball promo cards.

COMPLETE SET (220) 10.00 25.00
1 Mo Vaughn .07 .20
2 Tim Belcher .07 .20
3 Jack McDowell .07 .20
4 Troy Glaus .10 .30
5 Darin Erstad .07 .20
6 Tim Salmon .10 .30
7 Jim Edmonds .07 .20
8 Randy Johnson .20 .50
9 Steve Finley .07 .20
10 Travis Lee .07 .20
11 Matt Williams .07 .20
12 Todd Stottlemyre .07 .20
13 Jay Bell .07 .20
14 David Dellucci .07 .20
15 Chipper Jones .20 .50
16 Andruw Jones .10 .30
17 Greg Maddux .30 .75
18 Tom Glavine .10 .30
19 Javy Lopez .07 .20
20 Brian Jordan .07 .20
21 George Lombard .07 .20
22 John Smoltz .10 .30
23 Cal Ripken .60 1.50
24 Charles Johnson .07 .20
25 Albert Belle .07 .20
26 Brady Anderson .07 .20
27 Mike Mussina .10 .30
28 Calvin Pickering .07 .20
29 Ryan Minor .07 .20
30 Jerry Hairston Jr. .07 .20
31 Nomar Garciaparra .30 .75
32 Pedro Martinez .10 .30
33 Jason Varitek .20 .50
34 Troy O'Leary .07 .20
35 Donnie Sadler .07 .20
36 Mark Portugal .07 .20
37 John Valentin .07 .20
38 Kerry Wood .07 .20
39 Sammy Sosa .20 .50
40 Mark Grace .10 .30
41 Henry Rodriguez .07 .20
42 Rod Beck .07 .20
43 Benito Santiago .07 .20
44 Kevin Tapani .07 .20
45 Frank Thomas .20 .50
46 Mike Caruso .07 .20
47 Magglio Ordonez .07 .20
48 Paul Konerko .07 .20
49 Ray Durham .07 .20
50 Jim Parque .07 .20
51 Carlos Lee .07 .20
52 Denny Neagle .07 .20
53 Pete Harnisch .07 .20
54 Michael Tucker .07 .20
55 Sean Casey .07 .20
56 Eddie Taubensee .07 .20
57 Barry Larkin .10 .30
58 Pokey Reese .07 .20
59 Sandy Alomar Jr. .07 .20
60 Roberto Alomar .10 .30
61 Bartolo Colon .07 .20
62 Kenny Lofton .07 .20
63 Omar Vizquel .10 .30
64 Travis Fryman .07 .20
65 Jim Thome .10 .30
66 Manny Ramirez .10 .30
67 Jaret Wright .07 .20
68 Darryl Kile .07 .20
69 Kirt Manwaring .07 .20
70 Vinny Castilla .07 .20
71 Todd Helton .10 .30
72 Dante Bichette .07 .20
73 Larry Walker .07 .20
74 Derrick Gibson .07 .20
75 Gabe Kapler .07 .20
76 Dean Palmer .07 .20
77 Matt Anderson .07 .20
78 Bobby Higginson .07 .20
79 Damion Easley .07 .20
80 Tony Clark .07 .20
81 Juan Encarnacion .07 .20
82 Livan Hernandez .07 .20
83 Alex Gonzalez .07 .20
84 Preston Wilson .07 .20
85 Derrek Lee .10 .30
86 Mark Kotsay .07 .20
87 Todd Dunwoody .07 .20
88 Cliff Floyd .07 .20
89 Ken Caminiti .07 .20
90 Jeff Bagwell .10 .30
91 Moises Alou .07 .20
92 Craig Biggio .10 .30
93 Billy Wagner .07 .20
94 Richard Hidalgo .07 .20
95 Derek Bell .07 .20
96 Hipolito Pichardo .07 .20
97 Jeff King .07 .20
98 Carlos Beltran .10 .30
99 Jeremy Giambi .07 .20
100 Larry Sutton .07 .20
101 Johnny Damon .10 .30
102 Dee Brown .07 .20
103 Kevin Brown .10 .30
104 Chan Ho Park .07 .20
105 Raul Mondesi .07 .20
106 Eric Karros .07 .20
107 Adrian Beltre .07 .20
108 Devon White .07 .20
109 Gary Sheffield .07 .20
110 Sean Berry .07 .20
111 Alex Ochoa .07 .20
112 Marquis Grissom .07 .20
113 Fernando Vina .07 .20
114 Jeff Cirillo .07 .20
115 Geoff Jenkins .07 .20
116 Jeromy Burnitz .07 .20
117 Brad Radke .07 .20
118 Eric Milton .07 .20
119 A.J. Pierzynski .07 .20
120 Todd Walker .07 .20
121 David Ortiz .20 .50
122 Corey Koskie .07 .20
123 Vladimir Guerrero .20 .50
124 Rondell White .07 .20
125 Brad Fullmer .07 .20
126 Ugueth Urbina .07 .20
127 Dustin Hermanson .07 .20
128 Michael Barrett .07 .20
129 Fernando Seguignol .07 .20
130 Mike Piazza .30 .75
131 Rickey Henderson .20 .50
132 Rey Ordonez .07 .20
133 John Olerud .07 .20
134 Robin Ventura .07 .20
135 Hideo Nomo .20 .50
136 Mike Kinkade .07 .20
137 Al Leiter .07 .20
138 Brian McRae .07 .20
139 Derek Jeter .50 1.25
140 Bernie Williams .10 .30
141 Paul O'Neill .10 .30
142 Scott Brosius .07 .20
143 Tino Martinez .10 .30
144 Roger Clemens .40 1.00
145 Orlando Hernandez .07 .20
146 Mariano Rivera .20 .50
147 Ricky Ledee .07 .20
148 A.J. Hinch .07 .20
149 Ben Grieve .07 .20
150 Eric Chavez .07 .20
151 Miguel Tejada .07 .20
152 Matt Stairs .07 .20
153 Ryan Christenson .07 .20
154 Jason Giambi .07 .20
155 Curt Schilling .07 .20
156 Scott Rolen .10 .30
157 Pat Burrell RC .40 1.00
158 Doug Glanville .07 .20
159 Bobby Abreu .07 .20
160 Rico Brogna .07 .20
161 Ron Gant .07 .20
162 Jason Kendall .07 .20
163 Aramis Ramirez .07 .20
164 Jose Guillen .07 .20
165 Emil Brown .07 .20
166 Pat Meares .07 .20
167 Kevin Young .07 .20
168 Brian Giles .07 .20
169 Mark McGwire .50 1.25
170 J.D. Drew .07 .20
171 Edgar Renteria .07 .20
172 Fernando Tatis .07 .20
173 Matt Morris .07 .20
174 Eli Marrero .07 .20
175 Ray Lankford .07 .20
176 Tony Gwynn .25 .60
177 Sterling Hitchcock .07 .20
178 Ruben Rivera .07 .20
179 Wally Joyner .07 .20
180 Trevor Hoffman .07 .20
181 Jim Leyritz .07 .20
182 Carlos Hernandez .07 .20
183 Barry Bonds UER .60 1.50
Uniform number 24 on front, 25 on back
184 Ellis Burks .07 .20
185 F.P. Santangelo .07 .20
186 J.T. Snow .07 .20
187 Ramon E.Martinez RC .07 .20
188 Jeff Kent .07 .20
189 Robb Nen .07 .20
190 Ken Griffey Jr. .30 .75
191 Alex Rodriguez .30 .75
192 Shane Monahan .07 .20
193 Carlos Guillen .07 .20
194 Edgar Martinez .10 .30
195 David Segui .07 .20
196 Jose Mesa .07 .20
197 Jose Canseco .10 .30
198 Rolando Arrojo .07 .20
199 Wade Boggs .10 .30
200 Fred McGriff .10 .30
201 Quinton McCracken .07 .20
202 Bobby Smith .07 .20
203 Bubba Trammell .07 .20
204 Juan Gonzalez .07 .20
205 Ivan Rodriguez .10 .30
206 Rafael Palmeiro .10 .30
207 Royce Clayton .07 .20
208 Rick Helling .07 .20
209 Todd Zeile .07 .20
210 Rusty Greer .07 .20
211 David Wells .07 .20
212 Roy Halladay .20 .50
213 Carlos Delgado .07 .20
214 Darrin Fletcher .07 .20
215 Shawn Green .07 .20
216 Kevin Witt .07 .20
217 Jose Cruz Jr. .07 .20
218 Ken Griffey Jr. CL .20 .50
219 Sammy Sosa CL .10 .30
220 Mark McGwire CL .25 .60
S3 Ken Griffey Jr. Sample .40 1.00

1999 Upper Deck MVP Gold Script

Randomly inserted into hobby packs, these parallel cards of the regular Upper Deck MVP set are serial numbered to 100 and have a gold foil fascimile signature on the front of the card.

*STARS: 12.5X TO 30X BASIC CARDS
*ROOKIES: 12.5X TO 30X BASIC CARDS
RANDOM INSERTS IN HOBBY PACKS

1999 Upper Deck MVP Silver Script

These parallels were seeded at a rate of one in every two packs. Unlike basic MVP cards, each Silver Script parallel features the player's facsimile autograph in silver foil on the front of the card. A Ken Griffey Jr. sample card was distributed to dealers and hobby media several weeks prior to the product's national release. The card is numbered "S3" on back.

COMPLETE SET (220) 75.00 150.00
*STARS: 1.5X TO 4X BASIC CARDS
*ROOKIES: 1.5X TO 4X BASIC CARDS
STATED ODDS 1:2
S3 Ken Griffey Jr. Sample 1.50 4.00

1999 Upper Deck MVP Super Script

This parallel set of the Upper Deck MVP set is serial numbered to 25. The fascimile signatures on these cards are printed in a special holo-foil format.

*STARS: 30X TO 80X BASIC CARDS
RANDOM INSERTS IN HOBBY PACKS

1999 Upper Deck MVP Dynamics

Inserted one every 28 packs, these cards feature the most collectible stars in basebll. The front of the card has a player photo, the word "Dynamics" in black ink on the bottom and lots of fancy graphics.

COMPLETE SET (15) 50.00 100.00
STATED ODDS 1:28
D1 Ken Griffey Jr. 2.50 6.00
D2 Alex Rodriguez 2.50 6.00
D3 Nomar Garciaparra 2.50 6.00
D4 Mike Piazza 2.50 6.00
D5 Mark McGwire 4.00 10.00
D6 Sammy Sosa 1.50 4.00
D7 Chipper Jones 1.50 4.00
D8 Mo Vaughn .60 1.50
D9 Tony Gwynn 2.00 5.00
D10 Vladimir Guerrero 1.50 4.00
D11 Derek Jeter 4.00 10.00
D12 Jeff Bagwell 1.00 2.50
D13 Cal Ripken 5.00 12.00
D14 Juan Gonzalez .60 1.50
D15 J.D. Drew .60 1.50

1999 Upper Deck MVP Game Used Souvenirs

These 11 cards were randomly inserted into packs at a rate of one in 144. Each card features a chip of actual game-used bat from the player featured.

STATED ODDS 1:144 HOBBY
GUBB Barry Bonds 10.00 25.00
GUCJ Chipper Jones 8.00 20.00
GUCR Cal Ripken 10.00 25.00
GUJB Jeff Bagwell 6.00 15.00
GUJD J.D. Drew 4.00 10.00
GUKG Ken Griffey Jr. 10.00 25.00
GUMP Mike Piazza 12.50 30.00
GUMV Mo Vaughn 4.00 10.00
GUSR Scott Rolen 6.00 15.00
GAKG K. Griffey Jr. AU/24
GACJ Chipper Jones AU/10

1999 Upper Deck MVP Power Surge

These cards were inserted one every nine packs. The horizontal cards feature some of the leading sluggers in baseball and are printed on rainbow foil.

COMPLETE SET (15) 12.50 25.00
STATED ODDS 1:9
P1 Mark McGwire 1.25 3.00
P2 Sammy Sosa .50 1.25
P3 Ken Griffey Jr. .75 2.00
P4 Alex Rodriguez .75 2.00
P5 Juan Gonzalez .20 .50
P6 Nomar Garciaparra .75 2.00
P7 Vladimir Guerrero .50 1.25
P8 Chipper Jones .50 1.25
P9 Albert Belle .20 .50
P10 Frank Thomas .50 1.25
P11 Mike Piazza .75 2.00
P12 Jeff Bagwell .30 .75
P13 Manny Ramirez .30 .75
P14 Mo Vaughn .20 .50
P15 Barry Bonds 1.50 4.00

1999 Upper Deck MVP ProSign

Inserted as a rate of one every 216 retail packs, these cards feature autographs from various baseball players. It's believed that the veteran stars in this set are in much shorter supply than the various young prospects.Some of these star cards have rarely been seen in the secondary market and no pricing is yet available for those cards.

STATED ODDS 1:216 RETAIL
AG Alex Gonzalez 4.00 10.00
AN Abraham Nunez 4.00 10.00
BC Bruce Chen 4.00 10.00
BF Brad Fullmer 4.00 10.00
BG Ben Grieve 4.00 10.00
CB Carlos Beltran 8.00 20.00
CG Chris Gomez 4.00 10.00
CJ Chipper Jones SP 75.00 150.00
CK Corey Koskie 6.00 15.00
CP Calvin Pickering 4.00 10.00
DG Derrick Gibson 4.00 10.00
EC Eric Chavez 6.00 15.00
GK Gabe Kapler 6.00 15.00
GL George Lombard 4.00 10.00
IR Ivan Rodriguez SP 50.00 100.00
JG Jeremy Giambi 4.00 10.00
JP Jim Parque 4.00 10.00
JR Ken Griffey Jr. SP 250.00 350.00
JRA Jason Rakers 4.00 10.00
KW Kevin Witt 4.00 10.00
MA Matt Anderson 4.00 10.00
ML Mike Lincoln 4.00 10.00
MLO Mike Lowell 6.00 15.00
NG Nomar Garciaparra SP 75.00 150.00
RB Russ Branyan 4.00 10.00
RH Richard Hidalgo 4.00 10.00
RL Ricky Ledee 4.00 10.00
RM Ryan Minor 4.00 10.00
RR Ruben Rivera 4.00 10.00
SH Shea Hillenbrand 6.00 15.00
SK Scott Karl 4.00 10.00
SM Shane Monahan 4.00 10.00

1999 Upper Deck MVP Scout's Choice

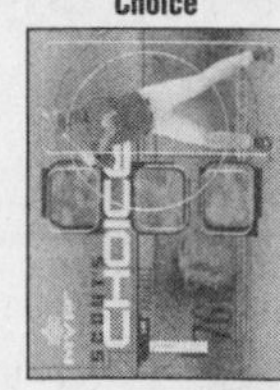

Inserted one every nine packs, these cards feature the best young stars and rookies captured on Light F/X packs.

COMPLETE SET (15) 6.00 12.00
STATED ODDS 1:9
SC1 J.D. Drew .25 .60
SC2 Ben Grieve .25 .60
SC3 Troy Glaus .40 1.00
SC4 Gabe Kapler .25 .60
SC5 Carlos Beltran .40 1.00
SC6 Aramis Ramirez .25 .60
SC7 Pat Burrell .50 1.25
SC8 Kerry Wood .25 .60
SC9 Ryan Minor .25 .60
SC10 Todd Helton .40 1.00
SC11 Eric Chavez .25 .60
SC12 Russ Branyan .25 .60
SC13 Travis Lee .25 .60
SC14 Ruben Mateo .25 .60
SC15 Roy Halladay .60 1.50

1999 Upper Deck MVP Super Tools

Issued one every 14 packs, these cards focus on big leaguers who posess various tools of greatness.

COMPLETE SET (15) 25.00 50.00
STATED ODDS 1:14
T1 Ken Griffey Jr. 1.50 4.00
T2 Alex Rodriguez 1.50 4.00
T3 Sammy Sosa 1.00 2.50
T4 Derek Jeter 2.50 6.00
T5 Vladimir Guerrero 1.00 2.50
T6 Ben Grieve .40 1.00
T7 Mike Piazza 1.50 4.00
T8 Kenny Lofton .40 1.00
T9 Barry Bonds 3.00 8.00
T10 Darin Erstad .40 1.00
T11 Nomar Garciaparra 1.50 4.00
T12 Cal Ripken 3.00 8.00
T13 J.D. Drew .40 1.00
T14 Larry Walker .40 1.00
T15 Chipper Jones 1.00 2.50

1999 Upper Deck MVP Swing Time

Issued one every six packs, these cards focus on players who have swings considered to be among the sweetest in the game.

COMPLETE SET (12) 10.00 20.00
STATED ODDS 1:6
S1 Ken Griffey Jr. .60 1.50
S2 Mark McGwire 1.00 2.50
S3 Sammy Sosa .40 1.00
S4 Tony Gwynn .50 1.25
S5 Alex Rodriguez .60 1.50
S6 Nomar Garciaparra .60 1.50
S7 Barry Bonds 1.25 3.00
S8 Frank Thomas .40 1.00
S9 Chipper Jones .40 1.00
S10 Ivan Rodriguez .25 .60
S11 Mike Piazza .60 1.50
S12 Derek Jeter 1.00 2.50

1999 Upper Deck MVP FanFest

This 30 card standard-size set was issued by Upper Deck during the annual FanFest celebration. The cards were issued in three-card packs with 15,000 packs produced and distributed during the show. The cards have a silver All-Star Game logo on the lower right corner of the card and they are all numbered with an "AS" prefix. Ten of the cards were printed in smaller quantities then the other 20 cards, those cards are notated with an SP in the listings below

COMPLETE SET 24.00 60.00
COMMON (AS1-AS30) .12 .30
COMMON SP .80 2.00
AS1 Mo Vaughn SP .75 2.00
AS2 Randy Johnson .30 .75
AS3 Chipper Jones .60 1.50
AS4 Greg Maddux SP 2.50 6.00
AS5 Cal Ripken 1.25 3.00
AS6 Albert Belle .10 .30
AS7 N.Garciaparra SP 2.50 6.00
AS8 Pedro Martinez .30 .75
AS9 Sammy Sosa .50 1.25
AS10 Frank Thomas .30 .75
AS11 Sean Casey .10 .30
AS12 Roberto Alomar .25 .60
AS13 Manny Ramirez .30 .75
AS14 Larry Walker .10 .30
AS15 Jeff Bagwell SP 1.25 3.00
AS16 Craig Biggio .25 .60
AS17 Raul Mondesi .10 .30
AS18 Vladimir Guerrero .30 .75
AS19 Mike Piazza SP 3.00 8.00
AS20 Derek Jeter SP 5.00 12.00
AS21 Roger Clemens SP 2.50 6.00
AS22 Scott Rolen .25 .60
AS23 Mark McGwire SP 3.00 8.00
AS24 Tony Gwynn .60 1.50
AS25 Barry Bonds .60 1.50
AS26 Ken Griffey Jr SP 3.00 8.00
AS27 Alex Rodriguez .60 1.50
AS28 Jose Canseco .30 .75
AS29 Juan Gonzalez .30 .75
AS30 Ivan Rodriguez .30 .75

2000 Upper Deck MVP

The 2000 Upper Deck MVP product was released in June, 2000 as a 220-card set. Each pack contained 10 cards and carried a suggested retail price of $1.59. Please note that cards 218-220 are player/checklist cards. Also, a selection of A Piece of History 3000 Club Stan Musial memorabilia cards were randomly seeded into packs. 350 bat cards, 350 jersey cards, 100 hand-numbered combination bat-jersey cards and six autographed, hand-numbered, combination bat-jersey cards were produced. Pricing for these memorabilia cards can be referenced under 2000 Upper Deck A Piece of History 3000 Club.

COMPLETE SET (220) 6.00 15.00
1 Garret Anderson .07 .20
2 Mo Vaughn .07 .20
3 Tim Salmon .10 .30
4 Ramon Ortiz .07 .20
5 Darin Erstad .07 .20
6 Troy Glaus .07 .20
7 Troy Percival .07 .20
8 Jeff Bagwell .10 .30
9 Ken Caminiti .07 .20
10 Daryle Ward .07 .20
11 Craig Biggio .10 .30
12 Jose Lima .07 .20
13 Moises Alou .07 .20
14 Octavio Dotel .07 .20
15 Ben Grieve .07 .20
16 Jason Giambi .07 .20
17 Tim Hudson .07 .20
18 Eric Chavez .07 .20
19 Matt Stairs .07 .20
20 Miguel Tejada .07 .20
21 John Jaha .07 .20
22 Chipper Jones .20 .50
23 Kevin Millwood .07 .20
24 Brian Jordan .07 .20
25 Andruw Jones .10 .30
26 Andres Galarraga .07 .20
27 Greg Maddux .30 .75
28 Reggie Sanders .07 .20
29 Javy Lopez .07 .20
30 Jeromy Burnitz .07 .20
31 Kevin Barker .07 .20
32 Jose Hernandez .07 .20
33 Ron Belliard .07 .20
34 Henry Blanco .07 .20
35 Marquis Grissom .07 .20
36 Geoff Jenkins .07 .20
37 Carlos Delgado .07 .20
38 Raul Mondesi .07 .20
39 Roy Halladay .07 .20
40 Tony Batista .07 .20
41 David Wells .07 .20

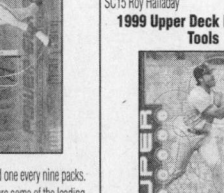

42 Shannon Stewart .07 .20
43 Vernon Wells .07 .20
44 Sammy Sosa .20 .50
45 Ismael Valdes .07 .20
46 Joe Girardi .07 .20
47 Mark Grace .10 .30
48 Henry Rodriguez .07 .20
49 Kerry Wood .07 .20
50 Eric Young .07 .20
51 Mark McGwire .50 1.25
52 Darryl Kile .07 .20
53 Fernando Vina .07 .20
54 Ray Lankford .07 .20
55 J.D. Drew .07 .20
56 Fernando Tatis .07 .20
57 Rick Ankiel .07 .20
58 Matt Williams .07 .20
59 Erubiel Durazo .07 .20
60 Tony Womack .07 .20
61 Jay Bell .07 .20
62 Randy Johnson .20 .50
63 Steve Finley .07 .20
64 Matt Mantei .07 .20
65 Luis Gonzalez .07 .20
66 Gary Sheffield .07 .20
67 Eric Gagne .20 .50
68 Adrian Beltre .07 .20
69 Mark Grudzielanek .07 .20
70 Kevin Brown .07 .20
71 Chan Ho Park .07 .20
72 Shawn Green .07 .20
73 Vinny Castilla .07 .20
74 Fred McGriff .10 .30
75 Wilson Alvarez .07 .20
76 Greg Vaughn .07 .20
77 Gerald Williams .07 .20
78 Ryan Rupe .07 .20
79 Jose Canseco .10 .30
80 Vladimir Guerrero .20 .50
81 Dustin Hermanson .07 .20
82 Michael Barrett .07 .20
83 Rondell White .07 .20
84 Tony Armas Jr. .07 .20
85 Wilton Guerrero .07 .20
86 Jose Vidro .07 .20
87 Barry Bonds .60 1.50
88 Russ Ortiz .07 .20
89 Ellis Burks .07 .20
90 Jeff Kent .07 .20
91 Russ Davis .07 .20
92 J.T. Snow .07 .20
93 Roberto Alomar .10 .30
94 Manny Ramirez .10 .30
95 Chuck Finley .07 .20
96 Kenny Lofton .07 .20
97 Jim Thome .10 .30
98 Bartolo Colon .07 .20
99 Omar Vizquel .10 .30
100 Richie Sexson .07 .20
101 Mike Cameron .07 .20
102 Brett Tomko .07 .20
103 Edgar Martinez .10 .30
104 Alex Rodriguez .30 .75
105 John Olerud .07 .20
106 Freddy Garcia .07 .20
107 Kazuhiro Sasaki RC .10 .30
108 Preston Wilson .07 .20
109 Luis Castillo .07 .20
110 A.J. Burnett .07 .20
111 Mike Lowell .07 .20
112 Cliff Floyd .07 .20
113 Brad Penny .07 .20
114 Alex Gonzalez .07 .20
115 Mike Piazza .30 .75
116 Derek Bell .07 .20
117 Edgardo Alfonzo .07 .20
118 Rickey Henderson .20 .50
119 Todd Zeile .07 .20
120 Mike Hampton .07 .20
121 Al Leiter .07 .20
122 Robin Ventura .07 .20
123 Cal Ripken .60 1.50
124 Mike Mussina .10 .30
125 B.J. Surhoff .07 .20
126 Jerry Hairston Jr. .07 .20
127 Brady Anderson .07 .20
128 Albert Belle .07 .20
129 Sidney Ponson .07 .20
130 Tony Gwynn .25 .60
131 Ryan Klesko .07 .20
132 Sterling Hitchcock .07 .20
133 Eric Owens .07 .20
134 Trevor Hoffman .07 .20
135 Al Martin .07 .20
136 Bret Boone .07 .20
137 Brian Giles .07 .20
138 Chad Hermansen .07 .20
139 Kevin Young .07 .20
140 Kris Benson .07 .20
141 Warren Morris .07 .20
142 Jason Kendall .07 .20
143 Wil Cordero .07 .20
144 Scott Rolen .10 .30
145 Curt Schilling .07 .20
146 Doug Glanville .07 .20
147 Mike Lieberthal .07 .20
148 Mike Jackson .07 .20
149 Rico Brogna .07 .20
150 Andy Ashby .07 .20
151 Bob Abreu .07 .20
152 Sean Casey .07 .20
153 Pete Harnisch .07 .20
154 Dante Bichette .07 .20
155 Pokey Reese .07 .20
156 Aaron Boone .07 .20
157 Ken Griffey Jr. .30 .75
158 Barry Larkin .10 .30
159 Scott Williamson .07 .20
160 Carlos Beltran .07 .20
161 Jermaine Dye .07 .20
162 Jose Rosado .07 .20
163 Joe Randa .07 .20
164 Johnny Damon .10 .30
165 Mike Sweeney .07 .20
166 Mark Quinn .07 .20
167 Ivan Rodriguez .10 .30
168 Rusty Greer .07 .20
169 Ruben Mateo .07 .20
170 Doug Davis .07 .20
171 Gabe Kapler .07 .20
172 Justin Thompson .07 .20
173 Rafael Palmeiro .10 .30
174 Larry Walker .07 .20
175 Neifi Perez .07 .20
176 Rolando Arrojo .07 .20
177 Jeffrey Hammonds .07 .20
178 Todd Helton .10 .30
179 Pedro Astacio .07 .20
180 Jeff Cirillo .07 .20
181 Pedro Martinez .10 .30
182 Carl Everett .07 .20
183 Troy O'Leary .07 .20
184 Nomar Garciaparra .30 .75
185 Jose Offerman .07 .20
186 Bret Saberhagen .07 .20
187 Trot Nixon .07 .20
188 Jason Varitek .20 .50
189 Todd Walker .07 .20
190 Eric Milton .07 .20
191 Chad Allen .07 .20
192 Jacque Jones .07 .20
193 Brad Radke .07 .20
194 Corey Koskie .07 .20
195 Joe Mays .07 .20
196 Juan Gonzalez .07 .20
197 Jeff Weaver .07 .20
198 Juan Encarnacion .07 .20
199 Deivi Cruz .07 .20
200 Damion Easley .07 .20
201 Tony Clark .07 .20
202 Dean Palmer .07 .20
203 Frank Thomas .20 .50
204 Carlos Lee .07 .20
205 Mike Sirotka .07 .20
206 Kip Wells .07 .20
207 Magglio Ordonez .07 .20
208 Paul Konerko .07 .20
209 Chris Singleton .07 .20
210 Derek Jeter .50 1.25
211 Tino Martinez .10 .30
212 Mariano Rivera .20 .50
213 Roger Clemens .40 1.00
214 Nick Johnson .07 .20
215 Paul O'Neill .10 .30
216 Bernie Williams .10 .30
217 David Cone .07 .20
218 Ken Griffey Jr. CL .20 .50
219 Sammy Sosa CL .10 .30
220 Mark McGwire CL .25 .60

2000 Upper Deck MVP Gold Script

Randomly inserted into packs, this 220-card insert is a complete parallel of the Upper Deck MVP base set. Each card in the set is individually serial numbered to 50. Please note that each card features a gold foiled facsimile autograph on the front of the card.

*STARS: 25X TO 60X BASIC CARDS
*ROOKIES: 20X TO 50X BASIC CARDS

2000 Upper Deck MVP Silver Script

Randomly inserted into packs at one in two, this 220-card insert is a complete parallel of the Upper Deck MVP base set. Please note that each card features a silver foiled facsimile autograph on the front of the card.

COMPLETE SET (220) 75.00 150.00
*STARS: 1.25X TO 3X BASIC CARDS
*ROOKIES: 1.25X TO 3X BASIC CARDS

2000 Upper Deck MVP All Star Game

This 30-card insert set was released in three-card packs at the All-Star Fan Fest in Atlanta in July, 2000.

COMPLETE SET (30) 16.00 40.00
AS1 Mo Vaughn .16 .40
AS2 Jeff Bagwell .40 1.00
AS3 Jason Giambi .40 1.00
AS4 Chipper Jones .60 1.50
AS5 Greg Maddux .80 2.00
AS6 Tony Batista .10 .25
AS7 Sammy Sosa .50 1.25
AS8 Mark McGwire .75 2.00
AS9 Randy Johnson .40 1.00
AS10 Shawn Green .30 .75
AS11 Greg Vaughn .16 .40
AS12 Vladimir Guerrero .40 1.00
AS13 Barry Bonds .80 2.00
AS14 Manny Ramirez .40 1.00
AS15 Alex Rodriguez .80 2.00
AS16 Preston Wilson .16 .40
AS17 Mike Piazza 1.00 2.50
AS18 Cal Ripken Jr. 1.60 4.00
AS19 Tony Gwynn .80 2.00
AS20 Scott Rolen .40 1.00
AS21 Ken Griffey Jr. .75 2.00
AS22 Carlos Beltran .50 1.25
AS23 Ivan Rodriguez .40 1.00
AS24 Larry Walker .16 .40
AS25 Nomar Garciaparra .80 2.00
AS26 Pedro Martinez .40 1.00
AS27 Juan Gonzalez .30 .75
AS28 Frank Thomas .50 1.25
AS29 Derek Jeter 1.60 4.00
AS30 Bernie Williams .30 .75

2000 Upper Deck MVP Draw Your Own Card

Randomly inserted into packs at one in six, this 31-card insert features player drawings from the 2000 Draw Your Own Card winners. Card backs carry a "DT" prefix.

COMPLETE SET (31) 20.00 50.00
DT1 Frank Thomas .40 1.00
DT2 Joe DiMaggio .75 2.00
DT3 Barry Bonds 1.25 3.00
DT4 Mark McGwire 1.00 2.50
DT5 Ken Griffey Jr. .60 1.50
DT6 Mark McGwire 1.00 2.50
DT7 Mike Stanley .15 .40
DT8 Nomar Garciaparra .60 1.50
DT9 Mickey Mantle 1.50 4.00
DT10 Randy Johnson .40 1.00
DT11 Nolan Ryan 1.00 2.50
DT12 Chipper Jones .40 1.00
DT13 Ken Griffey Jr. .60 1.50
DT14 Troy Glaus .15 .40
DT15 Manny Ramirez .25 .60
DT16 Mark McGwire 1.00 2.50
DT17 Ivan Rodriguez .25 .60
DT18 Mike Piazza .60 1.50
DT19 Sammy Sosa .40 1.00
DT20 Ken Griffey Jr. .60 1.50
DT21 Jeff Bagwell .25 .60
DT22 Ken Griffey Jr. .60 1.50
DT23 Kerry Wood .15 .40
DT24 Mark McGwire 1.00 2.50
DT25 Greg Maddux .60 1.50
DT26 Sandy Alomar Jr. .15 .40
DT27 Albert Belle .15 .40
DT28 Sammy Sosa .40 1.00
DT29 Alexandra Brunet .15 .40
DT30 Mark McGwire 1.00 2.50
DT31 Nomar Garciaparra .60 1.50

2000 Upper Deck MVP Drawing Power

Randomly inserted into packs at one in 28, this seven-card insert features players that bring fans to the ballpark. Card backs carry a "DP" prefix.

COMPLETE SET (7) 12.50 30.00
DP1 Mark McGwire 2.50 6.00
DP2 Ken Griffey Jr. 1.50 4.00
DP3 Mike Piazza 1.50 4.00
DP4 Chipper Jones 1.00 2.50
DP5 Nomar Garciaparra 1.50 4.00
DP6 Sammy Sosa 1.00 2.50
DP7 Jose Canseco .60 1.50

2000 Upper Deck MVP Game Used Souvenirs

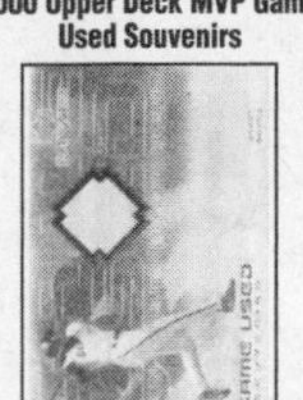

Randomly inserted into packs at one in 130, this 30-card insert features game-used bat and game used glove cards from players such as Chipper Jones and Ken Griffey Jr.

ABG Albert Belle Glove 6.00 15.00
AFG Alex Fernandez Glove 4.00 10.00
AGG Alex Gonzalez Glove 4.00 10.00
ARB Alex Rodriguez Bat 6.00 15.00
ARG Alex Rodriguez Glove 20.00 50.00
BBB Barry Bonds Bat 10.00 25.00
BBG Barry Bonds Glove 40.00 80.00
BGG Ben Grieve Glove 4.00 10.00
BWG Bernie Williams Glove 10.00 25.00
CRG Cal Ripken Glove 40.00 80.00
IRB Ivan Rodriguez Bat 4.00 10.00
IRG Ivan Rodriguez Glove 10.00 25.00
JBG Jeff Bagwell Glove 10.00 25.00
JCB Jose Canseco Bat 4.00 10.00
KGB Ken Griffey Jr. Bat 6.00 15.00
KGG Ken Griffey Jr. Glove 20.00 50.00
KLG Kenny Lofton Glove 10.00 25.00
LWG Larry Walker Glove 6.00 15.00
MRB Manny Ramirez Bat 4.00 10.00
NRG Nolan Ryan Glove 40.00 80.00
POG Paul O'Neill Glove 10.00 25.00
RAG Roberto Alomar Glove 10.00 25.00
RMG Raul Mondesi Glove 6.00 15.00
RPG Rafael Palmeiro Glove 25.00 50.00
TGB Tony Gwynn Bat 6.00 15.00
TGG Tony Gwynn Glove 15.00 40.00
TSG Tim Salmon Glove 10.00 25.00
WCG Will Clark Glove 20.00 50.00

2000 Upper Deck MVP Game Used Souvenirs Signed

Randomly inserted into packs, this autographed insert features game-used bat and game-used glove cards from players such as Chipper Jones and Ken Griffey Jr. Each card was individually serial numbered to 25 on front. Stickered exchange cards were placed into packs for Ken Griffey Jr. The exchange deadline for these stickered redemption cards was February 2nd, 2001. Due to market scarcity, no pricing is provided for these cards.

2000 Upper Deck MVP Prolifics

Randomly inserted into packs at one in 28, this 7-card insert features some of the most prolific players in major league baseball. Card backs carry a "P" prefix.

COMPLETE SET (7) 10.00 25.00
P1 Manny Ramirez .60 1.50
P2 Vladimir Guerrero 1.00 2.50
P3 Derek Jeter 2.50 6.00
P4 Pedro Martinez .60 1.50
P5 Shawn Green .40 1.00
P6 Alex Rodriguez 1.50 4.00
P7 Cal Ripken 3.00 8.00

2000 Upper Deck MVP ProSign

Randomly inserted into retail packs only at one in 143, this 18-card insert features autographs of players such as Mike Sweeney, Rick Ankiel, and Tim Hudson. Card backs are numbered using the players initials.

LIMITED PRINT RUN 25 SERIAL #'d SETS
NO LTD PRICING DUE TO SCARCITY
BP Ben Petrick 4.00 10.00
BT Bubba Trammell 4.00 10.00
DD Doug Davis 6.00 15.00
EY Ed Yarnall 4.00 10.00
JM Jim Morris 10.00 25.00
JV Jose Vidro 4.00 10.00
JZ Jeff Zimmerman 4.00 10.00
KW Kevin Witt 4.00 10.00
MB Michael Barrett 4.00 10.00
MM Mike Meyers 6.00 15.00
MQ Mark Quinn 4.00 10.00
MS Mike Sweeney 6.00 15.00
PW Preston Wilson 6.00 15.00
RA Rick Ankiel 10.00 25.00
SW Scott Williamson 4.00 10.00
TH Tim Hudson 10.00 25.00
TN Trot Nixon 6.00 15.00
WM Warren Morris 4.00 10.00

2000 Upper Deck MVP Pure Grit

Randomly inserted into packs at one in six, this 10-card insert features players that constantly give their best day in, day out. Card backs carry a "G" prefix.

COMPLETE SET (10) 6.00 15.00
G1 Derek Jeter 1.25 3.00
G2 Kevin Brown .20 .50
G3 Craig Biggio .30 .75
G4 Ivan Rodriguez .30 .75
G5 Scott Rolen .30 .75
G6 Carlos Beltran .20 .50
G7 Ken Griffey Jr. .75 2.00
G8 Cal Ripken 1.50 4.00
G9 Nomar Garciaparra .75 2.00
G10 Randy Johnson .50 1.25

2000 Upper Deck MVP Scout's Choice

Randomly inserted into packs at one in 14, this 10-card insert features players that major league scouts believe will be future stars in the major leagues. Card backs carry a "SC" prefix.

COMPLETE SET (10) 4.00 10.00
SC1 Rick Ankiel .40 1.00
SC2 Vernon Wells .40 1.00
SC3 Pat Burrell .40 1.00
SC4 Travis Dawkins .40 1.00
SC5 Eric Munson .40 1.00
SC6 Nick Johnson .40 1.00
SC7 Dermal Brown .40 1.00
SC8 Alfonso Soriano .60 1.50
SC9 Ben Petrick .40 1.00
SC10 Adam Everett .40 1.00

2000 Upper Deck MVP Second Season Standouts

Randomly inserted into packs at one in six, this 10-card insert features players that had outstanding sophomore years in the major leagues. Card backs carry a "SS" prefix.

COMPLETE SET (10) 4.00 10.00
SS1 Pedro Martinez .30 .75
SS2 Mariano Rivera .50 1.25
SS3 Orlando Hernandez .20 .50
SS4 Ken Caminiti .20 .50
SS5 Bernie Williams .30 .75
SS6 Jim Thome .30 .75
SS7 Nomar Garciaparra .75 2.00
SS8 Edgardo Alfonzo .20 .50
SS9 Derek Jeter 1.25 3.00
SS10 Kevin Millwood .20 .50

2001 Upper Deck MVP

This 330-card set was released in May, 2001. These cards were issued in eight card packs with an SRP of $1.99. These packs were issued 24 packs to a box.

COMPLETE SET (330) 15.00 40.00
1 Mo Vaughn .07 .20
2 Troy Percival .07 .20
3 Adam Kennedy .07 .20
4 Darin Erstad .07 .20
5 Tim Salmon .10 .30
6 Bengie Molina .07 .20
7 Troy Glaus .07 .20
8 Garret Anderson .07 .20
9 Ismael Valdes .07 .20
10 Glenallen Hill .07 .20
11 Tim Hudson .07 .20
12 Eric Chavez .07 .20
13 Johnny Damon .10 .30
14 Barry Zito .10 .30
15 Jason Giambi .07 .20
16 Terrence Long .07 .20
17 Jason Hart .07 .20
18 Jose Ortiz .07 .20
19 Miguel Tejada .07 .20
20 Jason Isringhausen .07 .20
21 Adam Piatt .07 .20
22 Jeremy Giambi .07 .20
23 Tony Batista .07 .20
24 Darrin Fletcher .07 .20
25 Mike Sirotka .07 .20
26 Carlos Delgado .07 .20
27 Billy Koch .07 .20
28 Shannon Stewart .07 .20
29 Raul Mondesi .07 .20
30 Brad Fullmer .07 .20
31 Jose Cruz Jr. .07 .20
32 Kelvim Escobar .07 .20
33 Greg Vaughn .07 .20
34 Aubrey Huff .07 .20
35 Albie Lopez .07 .20
36 Gerald Williams .07 .20
37 Ben Grieve .07 .20
38 John Flaherty .07 .20
39 Fred McGriff .10 .30
40 Ryan Rupe .07 .20
41 Travis Harper .07 .20
42 Steve Cox .07 .20
43 Roberto Alomar .10 .30
44 Jim Thome .10 .30
45 Russell Branyan .07 .20
46 Bartolo Colon .07 .20
47 Omar Vizquel .10 .30
48 Travis Fryman .07 .20
49 Kenny Lofton .07 .20
50 Chuck Finley .07 .20
51 Ellis Burks .07 .20
52 Eddie Taubensee .07 .20
53 Juan Gonzalez .07 .20
54 Edgar Martinez .10 .30
55 Aaron Sele .07 .20
56 John Olerud .07 .20
57 Jay Buhner .07 .20
58 Mike Cameron .07 .20
59 John Halama .07 .20
60 Ichiro Suzuki RC 4.00 10.00
61 David Bell .07 .20
62 Freddy Garcia .07 .20
63 Carlos Guillen .07 .20
64 Bret Boone .07 .20
65 Al Martin .07 .20
66 Cal Ripken .60 1.50
67 Delino DeShields .07 .20
68 Chris Richard .07 .20
69 Sean Douglass RC .20 .50
70 Melvin Mora .07 .20
71 Luis Matos .07 .20
72 Sidney Ponson .07 .20
73 Mike Bordick .07 .20
74 Brady Anderson .07 .20
75 David Segui .07 .20
76 Jeff Conine .07 .20
77 Alex Rodriguez .30 .75
78 Gabe Kapler .07 .20
79 Ivan Rodriguez .10 .30
80 Rick Helling .07 .20
81 Kenny Rogers .07 .20
82 Andres Galarraga .07 .20
83 Rusty Greer .07 .20
84 Justin Thompson .07 .20
85 Ken Caminiti .07 .20
86 Rafael Palmeiro .10 .30
87 Ruben Mateo .07 .20
88 Travis Hafner RC 1.25 3.00
89 Manny Ramirez Sox .10 .30
90 Pedro Martinez .10 .30
91 Carl Everett .07 .20
92 Dante Bichette .07 .20
93 Derek Lowe .07 .20
94 Jason Varitek .20 .50
95 Nomar Garciaparra .30 .75
96 David Cone .07 .20
97 Tomokazu Ohka .07 .20
98 Troy O'Leary .07 .20
99 Trot Nixon .07 .20
100 Jermaine Dye .07 .20
101 Joe Randa .07 .20
102 Jeff Suppan .07 .20
103 Roberto Hernandez .07 .20
104 Mike Sweeney .07 .20
105 Mac Suzuki .07 .20
106 Carlos Febles .07 .20
107 Jose Rosado .07 .20
108 Mark Quinn .07 .20
109 Carlos Beltran .07 .20
110 Dean Palmer .07 .20
111 Mitch Meluskey .07 .20
112 Bobby Higginson .07 .20
113 Brandon Inge .07 .20
114 Tony Clark .07 .20
115 Brian Moehler .07 .20
116 Juan Encarnacion .07 .20
117 Damion Easley .07 .20
118 Roger Cedeno .07 .20
119 Jeff Weaver .07 .20
120 Matt Lawton .07 .20
121 Jay Canizaro .07 .20
122 Eric Milton .07 .20
123 Corey Koskie .07 .20
124 Mark Redman .07 .20
125 Jacque Jones .07 .20
126 Brad Radke .07 .20
127 Cristian Guzman .07 .20
128 Joe Mays .07 .20
129 Denny Hocking .07 .20
130 Frank Thomas .20 .50
131 David Wells .07 .20
132 Ray Durham .07 .20
133 Paul Konerko .07 .20
134 Joe Crede .20 .50
135 Jim Parque .07 .20
136 Carlos Lee .07 .20
137 Magglio Ordonez .07 .20
138 Sandy Alomar Jr. .07 .20
139 Chris Singleton .07 .20
140 Jose Valentin .07 .20
141 Roger Clemens .40 1.00
142 Derek Jeter .50 1.25
143 Orlando Hernandez .07 .20
144 Tino Martinez .10 .30
145 Bernie Williams .10 .30
146 Jorge Posada .10 .30
147 Mariano Rivera .20 .50
148 David Justice .07 .20
149 Paul O'Neill .10 .30
150 Mike Mussina .10 .30
151 Christian Parker RC .20 .50
152 Andy Pettitte .10 .30
153 Alfonso Soriano .10 .30
154 Jeff Bagwell .10 .30
155 Morgan Ensberg RC .75 2.00
156 Daryle Ward .07 .20
157 Craig Biggio .10 .30
158 Richard Hidalgo .07 .20
159 Shane Reynolds .07 .20
160 Scott Elarton .07 .20
161 Julio Lugo .07 .20
162 Moises Alou .07 .20
163 Lance Berkman .07 .20
164 Chipper Jones .20 .50
165 Greg Maddux .30 .75
166 Javy Lopez .07 .20
167 Andruw Jones .10 .30
168 Rafael Furcal .07 .20
169 Brian Jordan .07 .20
170 Wes Helms .07 .20
171 Tom Glavine .10 .30
172 B.J. Surhoff .07 .20
173 John Smoltz .10 .30
174 Quilvio Veras .07 .20
175 Rico Brogna .07 .20
176 Jeromy Burnitz .07 .20
177 Jeff D'Amico .07 .20
178 Geoff Jenkins .07 .20
179 Henry Blanco .07 .20
180 Mark Loretta .07 .20
181 Richie Sexson .07 .20
182 Jimmy Haynes .07 .20
183 Jeffrey Hammonds .07 .20
184 Ron Belliard .07 .20
185 Tyler Houston .07 .20
186 Mark McGwire .50 1.25
187 Rick Ankiel .07 .20
188 Darryl Kile .07 .20
189 Jim Edmonds .07 .20
190 Mike Matheny .07 .20
191 Edgar Renteria .07 .20
192 Ray Lankford .07 .20
193 Garrett Stephenson .07 .20
194 J.D. Drew .07 .20
195 Fernando Vina .07 .20
196 Dustin Hermanson .07 .20
197 Sammy Sosa .20 .50
198 Corey Patterson .07 .20
199 Jon Lieber .07 .20
200 Kerry Wood .07 .20
201 Todd Hundley .07 .20
202 Kevin Tapani .07 .20
203 Rondell White .07 .20
204 Eric Young .07 .20
205 Matt Stairs .07 .20
206 Bill Mueller .07 .20
207 Randy Johnson .20 .50
208 Mark Grace .10 .30
209 Jay Bell .07 .20
210 Curt Schilling .07 .20
211 Erubiel Durazo .07 .20
212 Luis Gonzalez .07 .20
213 Steve Finley .07 .20
214 Matt Williams .07 .20
215 Reggie Sanders .07 .20
216 Tony Womack .07 .20
217 Gary Sheffield .07 .20
218 Kevin Brown .07 .20
219 Adrian Beltre .07 .20
220 Shawn Green .07 .20
221 Darren Dreifort .07 .20
222 Chan Ho Park .07 .20
223 Eric Karros .07 .20
224 Alex Cora .07 .20
225 Mark Grudzielanek .07 .20
226 Andy Ashby .07 .20
227 Vladimir Guerrero .20 .50
228 Tony Armas Jr. .07 .20
229 Fernando Tatis .07 .20
230 Jose Vidro .07 .20
231 Javier Vazquez .07 .20
232 Lee Stevens .07 .20
233 Milton Bradley .07 .20
234 Carl Pavano .07 .20
235 Peter Bergeron .07 .20
236 Wilton Guerrero .07 .20
237 Ugueth Urbina .07 .20
238 Barry Bonds .50 1.25
239 Livan Hernandez .07 .20
240 Jeff Kent .07 .20
241 Pedro Feliz .07 .20
242 Bobby Estalella .07 .20
243 J.T. Snow .07 .20
244 Shawn Estes .07 .20
245 Robb Nen .07 .20
246 Rich Aurilia .07 .20
247 Russ Ortiz .07 .20
248 Preston Wilson .07 .20
249 Brad Penny .07 .20
250 Cliff Floyd .07 .20
251 A.J. Burnett .07 .20
252 Mike Lowell .07 .20
253 Luis Castillo .07 .20
254 Ryan Dempster .07 .20
255 Derrek Lee .10 .30
256 Charles Johnson .07 .20
257 Pablo Ozuna .07 .20
258 Antonio Alfonseca .07 .20
259 Mike Piazza .30 .75
260 Robin Ventura .07 .20
261 Al Leiter .07 .20
262 Timo Perez .07 .20
263 Edgardo Alfonzo .07 .20
264 Jay Payton .07 .20
265 Tsuyoshi Shinjo RC .20 .50
266 Todd Zeile .07 .20
267 Armando Benitez .07 .20
268 Glendon Rusch .07 .20
269 Rey Ordonez .07 .20
270 Kevin Appier .07 .20
271 Tony Gwynn .25 .60
272 Phil Nevin .07 .20
273 Mark Kotsay .07 .20
274 Ryan Klesko .07 .20
275 Adam Eaton .07 .20
276 Mike Darr .07 .20

277 Damian Jackson .07 .20
278 Woody Williams .07 .20
279 Chris Gomez .07 .20
280 Trevor Hoffman .07 .20
281 Xavier Nady .07 .20
282 Scott Rolen .10 .30
283 Bruce Chen .07 .20
284 Pat Burrell .07 .20
285 Mike Lieberthal .07 .20
286 B. Duckworth RC .20 .50
287 Travis Lee .07 .20
288 Bobby Abreu .07 .20
289 Jimmy Rollins .07 .20
290 Robert Person .07 .20
291 Randy Wolf .07 .20
292 Jason Kendall .07 .20
293 Derek Bell .07 .20
294 Brian Giles .07 .20
295 Kris Benson .07 .20
296 John VanderWal .07 .20
297 Todd Ritchie .07 .20
298 Warren Morris .07 .20
299 Kevin Young .07 .20
300 Francisco Cordova .07 .20
301 Aramis Ramirez .07 .20
302 Ken Griffey Jr. .30 .75
303 Pete Harnisch .07 .20
304 Aaron Boone .07 .20
305 Sean Casey .07 .20
306 Jackson Melian RC .20 .50
307 Rob Bell .07 .20
308 Barry Larkin .10 .30
309 Dmitri Young .07 .20
310 Danny Graves .07 .20
311 Pokey Reese .07 .20
312 Leo Estrella .07 .20
313 Todd Helton .10 .30
314 Mike Hampton .07 .20
315 Juan Pierre .07 .20
316 Brent Mayne .07 .20
317 Larry Walker .07 .20
318 Denny Neagle .07 .20
319 Jeff Cirillo .07 .20
320 Pedro Astacio .07 .20
321 Todd Hollandsworth .07 .20
322 Neifi Perez .07 .20
323 Ron Gant .07 .20
324 Todd Walker .07 .20
325 Alex Rodriguez CL .20 .50
326 Ken Griffey Jr. CL .20 .50
327 Mark McGwire CL .25 .60
328 Pedro Martinez CL .10 .30
329 Derek Jeter CL .25 .60
330 Mike Piazza CL .20 .50

2001 Upper Deck MVP Authentic Griffey

Inserted in packs at a rate of one in 288, these 12 cards feature memorabilia relating to the career of Ken Griffey Jr. A few cards were printed to a stated print run of 30 (Griffey's uniform number with the Reds), and we have notated those cards in our checklist. Griffey did not return his autographs in time for inclusion in the product and those cards could be redeemed until January 15th, 2002.

B Ken Griffey Jr. Bat 6.00 15.00
C Ken Griffey Jr. Cap 15.00 40.00
J Ken Griffey Jr. Jsy 6.00 15.00
S K.Griffey Jr. AU EXCH* 50.00 100.00
U K.Griffey Jr. Uni 6.00 15.00
GB Ken Griffey Jr. Gold Bat/30 60.00 120.00
GC Ken Griffey Jr. Gold Cap/30 60.00 120.00
GJ Ken Griffey Jr. Gold Jsy/30 60.00 120.00
GS Ken Griffey Jr. Gold AU/30 EXCH 125.00 200.00
CGR Ken Griffey Jr. Alex Rodriguez 20.00 50.00
CGS Ken Griffey Jr. Sammy Sosa 15.00 40.00
CGT Ken Griffey Jr. Frank Thomas Jsy/100 15.00 40.00

2001 Upper Deck MVP Drawing Power

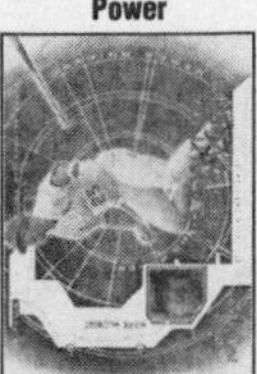

Inserted in packs at a rate of one in 12, these 10 cards feature the players who help to draw the most fans to ballparks.

COMPLETE SET (10) 10.00 25.00
DP1 Mark McGwire 2.50 6.00
DP2 Vladimir Guerrero 1.00 2.50
DP3 Manny Ramirez Sox 1.00 2.50
DP4 Frank Thomas 1.00 2.50
DP5 Ken Griffey Jr. 1.50 4.00
DP6 Alex Rodriguez 1.50 4.00
DP7 Mike Piazza 1.50 4.00
DP8 Derek Jeter 2.50 6.00
DP9 Sammy Sosa 1.00 2.50
DP10 Todd Helton 1.00 2.50

2001 Upper Deck MVP Game Souvenirs Bat Duos

Inserted one in 144, these 14 cards feature two pieces of game-used bats on the same card.

B3K Tony Gwynn Cal Ripken 20.00 50.00
BDV Carlos Delgado Jose Vidro 6.00 15.00
BGS Ken Griffey Jr. Sammy Sosa 15.00 40.00
BHR Jose Canseco Ken Griffey Jr. 12.50 30.00
BJF Chipper Jones Rafael Furcal 10.00 25.00
BJJ Andruw Jones Chipper Jones 10.00 25.00
BOW Paul O'Neill Bernie Williams 10.00 25.00
BRM Alex Rodriguez Edgar Martinez 12.50 30.00
BRP Ivan Rodriguez Rafael Palmeiro 10.00 25.00
BRR Alex Rodriguez Ivan Rodriguez 15.00 40.00
BTG Jim Thome Ken Griffey Jr. 12.50 30.00
BTO Frank Thomas Magglio Ordonez 10.00 25.00
BTS Frank Thomas Sammy Sosa 10.00 25.00
BWA Kerry Wood Rick Ankiel 6.00 15.00

2001 Upper Deck MVP Game Souvenirs Bat Trios

Randomly inserted in packs, these six cards feature three pieces of game-used bats. These cards are serial numbered to 25. Due to market scarcity, no pricing is provided.

2001 Upper Deck MVP Game Souvenirs Batting Glove

Inserted one per 96 hobby packs, these 18 cards feature a swatch of game-used batting glove of various major leaguers. A couple of players were issued in lesser quantities. We have notated those cards as SP's as well as print run information (as provided by Upper Deck) in our checklist.

GAR Alex Rodriguez 10.00 25.00
GBB Barry Bonds 20.00 50.00
GCJ Chipper Jones 6.00 15.00
GCR Cal Ripken 30.00 60.00
GEM Edgar Martinez 6.00 15.00
GFM Fred McGriff 6.00 15.00
GFT Frank Thomas 6.00 15.00
GGM Greg Maddux SP/95 40.00 80.00
GIR Ivan Rodriguez 6.00 15.00
GJG Juan Gonzalez 4.00 10.00
GJL Javy Lopez 4.00 10.00
GKG Ken Griffey Jr. 10.00 25.00
GMT Miguel Tejada 4.00 10.00
GMV Mo Vaughn 4.00 10.00
GRP Rafael Palmeiro 6.00 15.00
GSS Sammy Sosa 6.00 15.00
GTOG T.Gwynn SP/200 15.00 40.00
GTRG Troy Glaus 4.00 10.00

2001 Upper Deck MVP Game Souvenirs Batting Glove Autograph

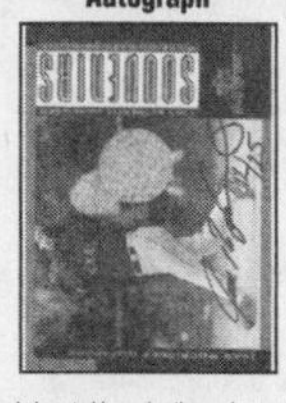

Randomly inserted in packs, these nine cards feature not only a swatch of a game-used batting glove but also an authentic autograph of the player. These cards have a stated print run of 25 sets. Troy Glaus did not return his cards in time for inclusion in the packs and these cards were only available as redemptions. Due to market scarcity, no pricing is provided.

2001 Upper Deck MVP Super Tools

Inserted one per six packs, these 20 cards feature players whose tools seem to be far above the other players.

COMPLETE SET (20) 15.00 40.00
ST1 Ken Griffey Jr. 1.50 4.00
ST2 Carlos Delgado .40 1.00
ST3 Alex Rodriguez 1.50 4.00
ST4 Troy Glaus .40 1.00
ST5 Jeff Bagwell .60 1.50
ST6 Ichiro Suzuki 4.00 10.00
ST7 Derek Jeter 2.50 6.00
ST8 Jim Edmonds .40 1.00
ST9 Vladimir Guerrero 1.00 2.50
ST10 Jason Giambi .40 1.00
ST11 Todd Helton .60 1.50
ST12 Cal Ripken 3.00 8.00
ST13 Barry Bonds 2.50 6.00
ST14 N.Garciaparra UER 1.50 4.00
Spelled Garicaparra on the front
ST15 Randy Johnson 1.00 2.50
ST16 Jermaine Dye .40 1.00
ST17 Andruw Jones .60 1.50
ST18 Ivan Rodriguez .60 1.50
ST19 Sammy Sosa 1.00 2.50
ST20 Pedro Martinez .60 1.50

2002 Upper Deck MVP

This 300 card set was issued in May, 2002. These cards were issued in eight card packs which came 24 packs to a box and 12 boxes to a case. Cards number 295-300 feature players on the front and checklisting information on the back. Card 301, featuring Kazuhisa Ishii, was added to the product at the last minute. According to representatives at Upper Deck, the card was seeded only into very late boxes of MVP.

COMPLETE SET (301) 15.00 40.00
1 Darin Erstad .07 .20
2 Ramon Ortiz .07 .20
3 Garret Anderson .07 .20
4 Jarrod Washburn .07 .20
5 Troy Glaus .07 .20
6 Brendan Donnelly RC .20 .50
7 Troy Percival .07 .20
8 Tim Salmon .10 .30
9 Aaron Sele .07 .20
10 Brad Fullmer .07 .20
11 Scott Hatteberg .07 .20
12 Barry Zito .07 .20
13 Tim Hudson .07 .20
14 Miguel Tejada .07 .20
15 Jermaine Dye .07 .20
16 Mark Mulder .07 .20
17 Eric Chavez .07 .20
18 Terrence Long .07 .20
19 Carlos Pena .07 .20
20 David Justice .07 .20
21 Jeremy Giambi .07 .20
22 Shannon Stewart .07 .20
23 Raul Mondesi .07 .20
24 Chris Carpenter .07 .20
25 Carlos Delgado .07 .20
26 Mike Sirotka .07 .20
27 Reed Johnson RC .30 .75
28 Darrin Fletcher .07 .20
29 Jose Cruz Jr. .07 .20
30 Vernon Wells .07 .20
31 Tanyon Sturtze .07 .20
32 Toby Hall .07 .20
33 Brent Abernathy .07 .20
34 Ben Grieve .07 .20
35 Joe Kennedy .07 .20
36 Dewon Brazelton .07 .20
37 Aubrey Huff .07 .20
38 Steve Cox .07 .20
39 Greg Vaughn .07 .20
40 Brady Anderson .07 .20
41 Chuck Finley .07 .20
42 Jim Thome .10 .30
43 Russell Branyan .07 .20
44 C.C. Sabathia .07 .20
45 Matt Lawton .07 .20
46 Omar Vizquel .10 .30
47 Bartolo Colon .07 .20
48 Alex Escobar .07 .20
49 Ellis Burks .07 .20
50 Bret Boone .07 .20
51 John Olerud .07 .20
52 Jeff Cirillo .07 .20
53 Ichiro Suzuki .40 1.00
54 Kazuhiro Sasaki .07 .20
55 Freddy Garcia .07 .20
56 Edgar Martinez .10 .30
57 Matt Thornton RC .20 .50
58 Mike Cameron .07 .20
59 Carlos Guillen .07 .20
60 Jeff Conine .07 .20
61 Tony Batista .07 .20
62 Jason Johnson .07 .20
63 Melvin Mora .07 .20
64 Brian Roberts .07 .20
65 Josh Towers .07 .20
66 Steve Bechler RC .20 .50
67 Jerry Hairston Jr. .07 .20
68 Chris Richard .07 .20
69 Alex Rodriguez .30 .75
70 Chan Ho Park .07 .20
71 Ivan Rodriguez .10 .30
72 Jeff Zimmerman .07 .20
73 Mark Teixeira .20 .50
74 Gabe Kapler .07 .20
75 Frank Catalanotto .07 .20
76 Rafael Palmeiro .10 .30
77 Doug Davis .07 .20
78 Carl Everett .07 .20
79 Pedro Martinez .10 .30
80 Nomar Garciaparra .30 .75
81 Tony Clark .07 .20
82 Trot Nixon .07 .20
83 Manny Ramirez .10 .30
84 Josh Hancock RC .25 .60
85 Johnny Damon Sox .10 .30
86 Jose Offerman .07 .20
87 Rich Garces .07 .20
88 Shea Hillenbrand .07 .20
89 Carlos Beltran .07 .20
90 Mike Sweeney .07 .20
91 Jeff Suppan .07 .20
92 Joe Randa .07 .20
93 Chuck Knoblauch .07 .20
94 Mark Quinn .07 .20
95 Neifi Perez .07 .20
96 Carlos Febles .07 .20
97 Miguel Asencio RC .20 .50
98 Michael Tucker .07 .20
99 Dean Palmer .07 .20
100 Jose Lima .07 .20
101 Craig Paquette .07 .20
102 Dmitri Young .07 .20
103 Bobby Higginson .07 .20
104 Jeff Weaver .07 .20
105 Matt Anderson .07 .20
106 Damion Easley .07 .20
107 Eric Milton .07 .20
108 Doug Mientkiewicz .07 .20
109 Cristian Guzman .07 .20
110 Brad Radke .07 .20
111 Torii Hunter .07 .20
112 Corey Koskie .07 .20
113 Joe Mays .07 .20
114 Jacque Jones .07 .20
115 David Ortiz .20 .50
116 Kevin Frederick RC .20 .50
117 Magglio Ordonez .07 .20
118 Ray Durham .07 .20
119 Mark Buehrle .07 .20
120 Jon Garland .07 .20
121 Paul Konerko .07 .20
122 Todd Ritchie .07 .20
123 Frank Thomas .20 .50
124 Edwin Almonte RC .20 .50
125 Carlos Lee .07 .20
126 Kenny Lofton .07 .20
127 Roger Clemens .40 1.00
128 Derek Jeter .50 1.25
129 Jorge Posada .10 .30
130 Bernie Williams .10 .30
131 Mike Mussina .10 .30
132 Alfonso Soriano .07 .20
133 Robin Ventura .07 .20
134 John Vander Wal .07 .20
135 Jason Giambi Yankees .07 .20
136 Mariano Rivera .20 .50
137 Rondell White .07 .20
138 Jeff Bagwell .10 .30
139 Wade Miller .07 .20
140 Richard Hidalgo .07 .20
141 Julio Lugo .07 .20
142 Roy Oswalt .07 .20
143 Rodrigo Rosario RC .20 .50
144 Lance Berkman .07 .20
145 Craig Biggio .10 .30
146 Shane Reynolds .07 .20
147 John Smoltz .10 .30
148 Chipper Jones .20 .50
149 Gary Sheffield .07 .20
150 Rafael Furcal .07 .20
151 Greg Maddux .30 .75
152 Tom Glavine .10 .30
153 Andruw Jones .10 .30
154 John Ennis RC .20 .50
155 Vinny Castilla .07 .20
156 Marcus Giles .07 .20
157 Javy Lopez .07 .20
158 Richie Sexson .07 .20
159 Geoff Jenkins .07 .20
160 Jeffrey Hammonds .07 .20
161 Alex Ochoa .07 .20
162 Ben Sheets .07 .20
163 Jose Hernandez .07 .20
164 Eric Young .07 .20
165 Luis Martinez RC .20 .50
166 Albert Pujols .40 1.00
167 Darryl Kile .07 .20
168 So Taguchi RC .20 .50
169 Jim Edmonds .07 .20
170 Fernando Vina .07 .20
171 Matt Morris .07 .20
172 J.D. Drew .07 .20
173 Bud Smith .07 .20
174 Edgar Renteria .07 .20
175 Placido Polanco .07 .20
176 Tino Martinez .10 .30
177 Sammy Sosa .20 .50
178 Moises Alou .07 .20
179 Kerry Wood .07 .20
180 Delino DeShields .07 .20
181 Alex Gonzalez .07 .20
182 Jon Lieber .07 .20
183 Fred McGriff .10 .30
184 Corey Patterson .07 .20
185 Mark Prior .10 .30
186 Tom Gordon .07 .20
187 Francis Beltran RC .20 .50
188 Randy Johnson .20 .50
189 Luis Gonzalez .07 .20
190 Matt Williams .07 .20
191 Mark Grace .10 .30
192 Curt Schilling .07 .20
193 Doug Devore RC .20 .50
194 Erubiel Durazo .07 .20
195 Steve Finley .07 .20
196 Craig Counsell .07 .20
197 Shawn Green .07 .20
198 Kevin Brown .07 .20
199 Paul LoDuca .07 .20
200 Brian Jordan .07 .20
201 Andy Ashby .07 .20
202 Darren Dreifort .07 .20
203 Adrian Beltre .07 .20
204 Victor Alvarez RC .20 .50
205 Eric Karros .07 .20
206 Hideo Nomo .20 .50
207 Vladimir Guerrero .20 .50
208 Javier Vazquez .07 .20
209 Michael Barrett .07 .20
210 Jose Vidro .07 .20
211 Brad Wilkerson .07 .20
212 Tony Armas Jr. .07 .20
213 Eric Good RC .20 .50
214 Orlando Cabrera .07 .20
215 Lee Stevens .07 .20
216 Jeff Kent .07 .20
217 Rich Aurilia .07 .20
218 Robb Nen .07 .20
219 Calvin Murray .07 .20
220 Russ Ortiz .07 .20
221 Deivis Santos .07 .20
222 Marvin Benard .07 .20
223 Jason Schmidt .07 .20
224 Reggie Sanders .07 .20
225 Barry Bonds .50 1.25
226 Brad Penny .07 .20
227 Cliff Floyd .07 .20
228 Mike Lowell .07 .20
229 Derrek Lee .10 .30
230 Ryan Dempster .07 .20
231 Josh Beckett .07 .20
232 Hansel Izquierdo RC .20 .50
233 Preston Wilson .07 .20
234 A.J. Burnett .07 .20
235 Charles Johnson .07 .20
236 Mike Piazza .30 .75
237 Al Leiter .07 .20
238 Jay Payton .07 .20
239 Roger Cedeno .07 .20
240 Jeromy Burnitz .07 .20
241 Roberto Alomar .10 .30
242 Mo Vaughn .07 .20
243 Shawn Estes .07 .20
244 Armando Benitez .07 .20
245 Tyler Yates RC .20 .50
246 Phil Nevin .07 .20
247 D'Angelo Jimenez .07 .20
248 Ramon Vazquez .07 .20
249 Bubba Trammell .07 .20
250 Trevor Hoffman .07 .20
251 Ben Howard RC .20 .50
252 Mark Kotsay .07 .20
253 Ray Lankford .07 .20
254 Ryan Klesko .07 .20
255 Scott Rolen .10 .30
256 Robert Person .07 .20
257 Jimmy Rollins .07 .20
258 Pat Burrell .07 .20
259 Anderson Machado RC .20 .50
260 Randy Wolf .07 .20
261 Travis Lee .07 .20
262 Mike Lieberthal .07 .20
263 Doug Glanville .07 .20
264 Bobby Abreu .07 .20
265 Brian Giles .07 .20
266 Kris Benson .07 .20
267 Aramis Ramirez .07 .20
268 Kevin Young .07 .20
269 Jack Wilson .07 .20
270 Mike Williams .07 .20
271 Jimmy Anderson .07 .20
272 Jason Kendall .07 .20
273 Pokey Reese .07 .20
274 Rob Mackowiak .07 .20
275 Sean Casey .07 .20
276 Juan Encarnacion .07 .20
277 Austin Kearns .07 .20
278 Danny Graves .07 .20
279 Ken Griffey Jr. .30 .75
280 Barry Larkin .10 .30
281 Todd Walker .07 .20
282 Elmer Dessens .07 .20
283 Aaron Boone .07 .20
284 Adam Dunn .07 .20
285 Larry Walker .07 .20
286 Rene Reyes RC .20 .50
287 Juan Uribe .07 .20
288 Mike Hampton .07 .20
289 Todd Helton .10 .30
290 Juan Pierre .07 .20
291 Denny Neagle .07 .20
292 Jose Ortiz .07 .20
293 Todd Zeile .07 .20
294 Ben Petrick .07 .20
295 Ken Griffey Jr. CL .20 .50
296 Derek Jeter CL .25 .60
297 Sammy Sosa CL .10 .30
298 Ichiro Suzuki CL .20 .50
299 Barry Bonds CL .30 .75
300 Alex Rodriguez CL .20 .50
301 Kazuhisa Ishii RC .20 .50

2002 Upper Deck MVP Silver

Inserted randomly into hobby and retail packs, these cards parallel the regular MVP set and have a stated print run of 100 serial numbered sets.

*SILVER STARS: 12.5X TO 30X BASIC CARDS
*SILVER ROOKIES: 6X TO 15X BASIC

2002 Upper Deck MVP Game Souvenirs Bat

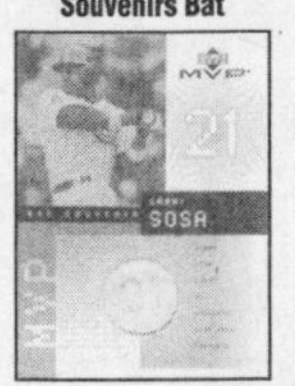

Issued exclusively in hobby packs at stated odds of one in 144, these 27 cards feature bat chips from the featured players. A few players were issued to lesser quantities and we have notated that stated print run information in our checklist.

BAR Alex Rodriguez 10.00 25.00
BBG Brian Giles 6.00 15.00
BBW Bernie Williams 8.00 20.00
BCD Carlos Delgado
BDJ David Justice
BDM Doug Mientkiewicz 6.00 15.00
BEM Edgar Martinez 8.00 20.00
BFT Frank Thomas SP/97 *
BGM Greg Maddux
BGS Gary Sheffield
BGV Greg Vaughn 6.00 15.00
BIR Ivan Rodriguez 8.00 20.00
BJK Jeff Kent 6.00 15.00
BJT Jim Thome 8.00 20.00
BKG Ken Griffey Jr. 10.00 25.00
BLG Luis Gonzalez 6.00 15.00
BLW Larry Walker 6.00 15.00
BMO Magglio Ordonez 6.00 15.00
BMP Mike Piazza SP/97 *
BMS Mike Sweeney
BRA Roberto Alomar
BRK Ryan Klesko 6.00 15.00
BRP Rafael Palmeiro SP/97 *
BSG Shawn Green 6.00 15.00
BSR Scott Rolen
BSS Sammy Sosa 8.00 20.00
BTH Todd Helton

2002 Upper Deck MVP Game Souvenirs Bat Jersey Combos

Inserted exclusively in hobby packs at stated odds of one in 144, these 28 cards feature both a bat chip and a jersey swatch from the featured player. A few players were issued in smaller quantities and we have notated that information with the stated print run in our checklist.

GOLD PRINT RUN 25 SERIAL #'d SETS
NO GOLD PRICING DUE TO SCARCITY
CAB Adrian Beltre 8.00 20.00
CAR Alex Rodriguez 20.00 50.00
CBG Brian Giles 8.00 20.00
CBW Bernie Williams SP/97 *
CCD Carlos Delgado Bat-Pants 8.00 20.00
CCJ Chipper Jones 15.00 40.00
CDE Darin Erstad 8.00 20.00
CEA Edgardo Alfonzo 8.00 20.00
CIR Ivan Rodriguez 10.00 25.00
CJB Jeff Bagwell Bat-Pants
CJG Jason Giambi 8.00 20.00
CJK Jeff Kent 8.00 20.00
CJT Jim Thome 10.00 25.00
CKG Ken Griffey Jr. 20.00 50.00
CLG Luis Gonzalez 8.00 20.00
CMO Magglio Ordonez 8.00 20.00
CMP Mike Piazza 20.00 50.00
COV Omar Vizquel Bat-Pants SP/97 *
CPB Pat Burrell SP/97
CRA Roberto Alomar Bat-Pants
CRJ Randy Johnson 15.00 40.00
CRP Rafael Palmeiro 10.00 25.00
CRV Robin Ventura 8.00 20.00
CSG Shawn Green 8.00 20.00
CSR Scott Rolen 10.00 25.00
CSS Sammy Sosa 15.00 40.00
CTH Todd Helton 10.00 25.00
CTZ Todd Zeile 8.00 20.00

2002 Upper Deck MVP Game Souvenirs Jersey

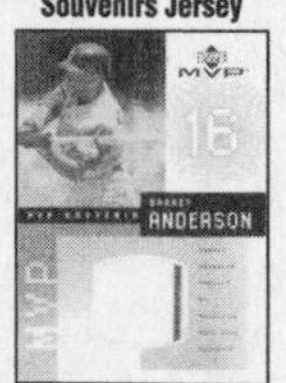

Inserted into hobby and retail packs at stated odds of one in 48, these 29 cards feature jersey swatches from the featured player. A few cards were printed in smaller quantity and we have notated those with an SP in our checklist. In addition, a few players appeared to be in larger supply and we have notated that information with an asterisk in our checklist.

JAB Adrian Beltre 4.00 10.00
JAR Alex Rodriguez 6.00 15.00
JCD Carlos Delgado Pants 4.00 10.00
JDE Darin Erstad 4.00 10.00
JEM Edgar Martinez 6.00 15.00
JFT Frank Thomas 6.00 15.00
JGA Garret Anderson 4.00 10.00
JIR Ivan Rodriguez 6.00 15.00
JJB Jeff Bagwell Pants 6.00 15.00
JJB Jeromy Burnitz 4.00 10.00
JJG Juan Gonzalez 4.00 10.00
JJK Jeff Kent 4.00 10.00
JJP Jay Payton SP 6.00 15.00

Card	Low	High
JJT Jim Thome SP	10.00	25.00
JKL Kenny Lofton	4.00	10.00
JMK Mark Kotsay	4.00	10.00
JMP Mike Piazza	6.00	15.00
JOV Omar Vizquel Pants *	6.00	15.00
JPK Paul Konerko SP	6.00	15.00
JPW Preston Wilson	4.00	10.00
JRA Roberto Alomar Pants	6.00	15.00
JRC Roger Clemens	10.00	25.00
JRF Rafael Furcal	4.00	10.00
JRV Robin Ventura	4.00	10.00
JSR Scott Rolen	6.00	15.00
JTHO Trevor Hoffman	4.00	10.00
JTHU Tim Hudson	4.00	10.00
JTS Tim Salmon	6.00	15.00
JTZ Todd Zeile	4.00	10.00

2002 Upper Deck MVP Ichiro A Season to Remember

Inserted in hobby and retail packs at stated odds of one in 12, these 10 cards feature highlights from Ichiro's rookie season.

Card	Low	High
COMPLETE SET (10)	12.50	30.00
COMMON CARD (I1-I10)	1.25	3.00

2002 Upper Deck MVP Ichiro A Season to Remember Memorabilia

Randomly inserted in hobby and retail packs, these cards feature memorabilia pieces from Ichiro's rookie season. These cards are serial numbered to 25 and no pricing is available due to market scarcity.

IB Ichiro Suzuki Bat
IJ Ichiro Suzuki Jsy

2003 Upper Deck MVP

This 220 card set was released in March, 2003. These cards were issued in eight card packs which came 24 packs to a box and 12 boxes to a case. Cards numbered 219 and 220 are checklists featuring Upper Deck spokespeople. Cards numbered 221 through 330 were issued in special factory "tin" sets.

Card	Low	High
COMP.FACT.SET (330)	25.00	40.00
COMPLETE LO SET (220)	10.00	25.00
COMMON CARD (1-330)	.07	.20
1 Troy Glaus	.07	.20
2 Darin Erstad	.07	.20
3 Jarrod Washburn	.07	.20
4 Francisco Rodriguez	.07	.20
5 Garret Anderson	.07	.20
6 Tim Salmon	.10	.30
7 Adam Kennedy	.07	.20
8 Randy Johnson	.20	.50
9 Luis Gonzalez	.07	.20
10 Curt Schilling	.07	.20
11 Junior Spivey	.07	.20
12 Craig Counsell	.07	.20
13 Mark Grace	.10	.30
14 Steve Finley	.07	.20
15 Javy Lopez	.07	.20
16 Rafael Furcal	.07	.20
17 John Smoltz	.10	.30
18 Greg Maddux	.30	.75
19 Chipper Jones	.20	.50
20 Gary Sheffield	.07	.20
21 Andruw Jones	.10	.30
22 Tony Batista	.07	.20
23 Geronimo Gil	.07	.20
24 Jay Gibbons	.07	.20
25 Rodrigo Lopez	.07	.20
26 Chris Singleton	.07	.20
27 Melvin Mora	.07	.20
28 Jeff Conine	.07	.20
29 Nomar Garciaparra	.30	.75
30 Pedro Martinez	.10	.30
31 Manny Ramirez	.10	.30
32 Shea Hillenbrand	.07	.20
33 Johnny Damon	.10	.30
34 Jason Varitek	.20	.50
35 Derek Lowe	.07	.20
36 Trot Nixon	.07	.20
37 Sammy Sosa	.20	.50
38 Kerry Wood	.07	.20
39 Mark Prior	.10	.30
40 Moises Alou	.07	.20
41 Corey Patterson	.07	.20
42 Hee Seop Choi	.07	.20
43 Mark Bellhorn	.07	.20
44 Frank Thomas	.20	.50
45 Mark Buehrle	.07	.20
46 Magglio Ordonez	.07	.20
47 Carlos Lee	.07	.20
48 Paul Konerko	.07	.20
49 Joe Borchard	.07	.20
50 Joe Crede	.07	.20
51 Ken Griffey Jr.	.30	.75
52 Adam Dunn	.07	.20
53 Austin Kearns	.07	.20
54 Aaron Boone	.07	.20
55 Sean Casey	.07	.20
56 Danny Graves	.07	.20
57 Russell Branyan	.07	.20
58 Matt Lawton	.07	.20
59 C.C. Sabathia	.07	.20
60 Omar Vizquel	.10	.30
61 Brandon Phillips	.07	.20
62 Karim Garcia	.07	.20
63 Ellis Burks	.07	.20
64 Cliff Lee	1.25	3.00
65 Todd Helton	.10	.30
66 Larry Walker	.07	.20
67 Jay Payton	.07	.20
68 Brent Butler	.07	.20
69 Juan Uribe	.07	.20
70 Jason Jennings	.07	.20
71 Denny Stark	.07	.20
72 Dmitri Young	.07	.20
73 Carlos Pena	.07	.20
74 Andres Torres	.07	.20
75 Andy Van Hekken	.07	.20
76 George Lombard	.07	.20
77 Eric Munson	.07	.20
78 Bobby Higginson	.07	.20
79 Luis Castillo	.07	.20
80 A.J. Burnett	.07	.20
81 Juan Encarnacion	.07	.20
82 Ivan Rodriguez	.10	.30
83 Mike Lowell	.07	.20
84 Josh Beckett	.07	.20
85 Brad Penny	.07	.20
86 Craig Biggio	.10	.30
87 Jeff Kent	.07	.20
88 Morgan Ensberg	.07	.20
89 Daryle Ward	.07	.20
90 Jeff Bagwell	.10	.30
91 Roy Oswalt	.07	.20
92 Lance Berkman	.07	.20
93 Mike Sweeney	.07	.20
94 Carlos Beltran	.07	.20
95 Raul Ibanez	.07	.20
96 Carlos Febles	.07	.20
97 Joe Randa	.07	.20
98 Shawn Green	.07	.20
99 Kevin Brown	.07	.20
100 Paul Lo Duca	.07	.20
101 Adrian Beltre	.07	.20
102 Eric Gagne	.07	.20
103 Kazuhisa Ishii	.07	.20
104 Odalis Perez	.07	.20
105 Brian Jordan	.07	.20
106 Geoff Jenkins	.07	.20
107 Richie Sexson	.07	.20
108 Ben Sheets	.07	.20
109 Alex Sanchez	.07	.20
110 Eric Young	.07	.20
111 Jose Hernandez	.07	.20
112 Torii Hunter	.07	.20
113 Eric Milton	.07	.20
114 Corey Koskie	.07	.20
115 Doug Mientkiewicz	.07	.20
116 A.J. Pierzynski	.07	.20
117 Jacque Jones	.07	.20
118 Cristian Guzman	.07	.20
119 Bartolo Colon	.07	.20
120 Brad Wilkerson	.07	.20
121 Michael Barrett	.07	.20
122 Vladimir Guerrero	.20	.50
123 Jose Vidro	.07	.20
124 Javier Vazquez	.07	.20
125 Endy Chavez	.07	.20
126 Roberto Alomar	.10	.30
127 Mike Piazza	.30	.75
128 Jeromy Burnitz	.07	.20
129 Mo Vaughn	.07	.20
130 Tom Glavine	.10	.30
131 Al Leiter	.07	.20
132 Armando Benitez	.07	.20
133 Timo Perez	.07	.20
134 Roger Clemens	.40	1.00
135 Derek Jeter	.50	1.25
136 Jason Giambi	.07	.20
137 Alfonso Soriano	.07	.20
138 Bernie Williams	.10	.30
139 Mike Mussina	.10	.30
140 Jorge Posada	.10	.30
141 Hideki Matsui RC	1.50	4.00
142 Robin Ventura	.07	.20
143 David Wells	.07	.20
144 Nick Johnson	.07	.20
145 Tim Hudson	.07	.20
146 Eric Chavez	.07	.20
147 Barry Zito	.07	.20
148 Miguel Tejada	.07	.20
149 Jermaine Dye	.07	.20
150 Mark Mulder	.07	.20
151 Terrence Long	.07	.20
152 Scott Hatteberg	.07	.20
153 Marlon Byrd	.07	.20
154 Jim Thome	.10	.30
155 Marlon Anderson	.07	.20
156 Vicente Padilla	.07	.20
157 Bobby Abreu	.07	.20
158 Jimmy Rollins	.07	.20
159 Pat Burrell	.07	.20
160 Brian Giles	.07	.20
161 Aramis Ramirez	.07	.20
162 Jason Kendall	.07	.20
163 Josh Fogg	.07	.20
164 Kip Wells	.07	.20
165 Pokey Reese	.07	.20
166 Kris Benson	.07	.20
167 Ryan Klesko	.07	.20
168 Brian Lawrence	.07	.20
169 Mark Kotsay	.07	.20
170 Jake Peavy	.07	.20
171 Phil Nevin	.07	.20
172 Sean Burroughs	.07	.20
173 Trevor Hoffman	.07	.20
174 Jason Schmidt	.07	.20
175 Kirk Rueter	.07	.20
176 Barry Bonds	.50	1.25
177 Pedro Feliz	.07	.20
178 Rich Aurilia	.07	.20
179 Benito Santiago	.07	.20
180 J.T. Snow	.07	.20
181 Robb Nen	.07	.20
182 Ichiro Suzuki	.40	1.00
183 Edgar Martinez	.10	.30
184 Bret Boone	.07	.20
185 Freddy Garcia	.07	.20
186 John Olerud	.07	.20
187 Mike Cameron	.07	.20
188 Joel Piniero	.07	.20
189 Albert Pujols	.40	1.00
190 Matt Morris	.07	.20
191 J.D. Drew	.07	.20
192 Scott Rolen	.10	.30
193 Tino Martinez	.10	.30
194 Jim Edmonds	.07	.20
195 Edgar Renteria	.07	.20
196 Fernando Vina	.07	.20
197 Jason Isringhausen	.07	.20
198 Ben Grieve	.07	.20
199 Carl Crawford	.07	.20
200 Dewon Brazelton	.07	.20
201 Aubrey Huff	.07	.20
202 Jared Sandberg	.07	.20
203 Steve Cox	.07	.20
204 Carl Everett	.07	.20
205 Kevin Mench	.07	.20
206 Alex Rodriguez	.30	.75
207 Rafael Palmeiro	.10	.30
208 Michael Young	.10	.30
209 Hank Blalock	.07	.20
210 Juan Gonzalez	.07	.20
211 Carlos Delgado	.07	.20
212 Eric Hinske	.07	.20
213 Josh Phelps	.07	.20
214 Mark Hendrickson	.07	.20
215 Roy Halladay	.07	.20
216 Orlando Hudson	.07	.20
217 Shannon Stewart	.07	.20
218 Vernon Wells	.07	.20
219 Ichiro Suzuki CL	.20	.50
220 Jason Giambi CL	.07	.20
221 Scott Spiezio	.07	.20
222 Rich Fischer RC	.15	.40
223 Bengie Molina	.07	.20
224 David Eckstein	.07	.20
225 Brandon Webb RC	.75	2.00
226 Oscar Villarreal RC	.15	.40
227 Rob Hammock RC	.15	.40
228 Matt Kata RC	.15	.40
229 Lyle Overbay	.07	.20
230 Chris Capuano RC	.30	.75
231 Horacio Ramirez	.07	.20
232 Shane Reynolds	.07	.20
233 Russ Ortiz	.07	.20
234 Mike Hampton	.07	.20
235 Mike Hessman RC	.15	.40
236 Byung-Hyun Kim	.07	.20
237 Freddy Sanchez	.07	.20
238 Jason Shiell RC	.15	.40
239 Ryan Cameron RC	.15	.40
240 Todd Wellemeyer RC	.15	.40
241 Joe Borowski	.07	.20
242 Alex Gonzalez	.07	.20
243 Jon Leicester RC	.15	.40
244 David Sanders RC	.15	.40
245 Roberto Alomar	.10	.30
246 Barry Larkin	.10	.30
247 Jhonny Peralta	.20	.50
248 Zach Sorensen	.07	.20
249 Jason Davis	.07	.20
250 Coco Crisp	.10	.30
251 Greg Vaughn	.07	.20
252 Preston Wilson	.07	.20
253 Denny Neagle	.07	.20
254 Clint Barmes RC	.30	.75
255 Jeremy Bonderman RC	1.00	2.50
256 Wilfredo Ledezma RC	.15	.40
257 Dontrelle Willis	.20	.50
258 Alex Gonzalez	.07	.20
259 Tommy Phelps	.07	.20
260 Kirk Saarloos	.07	.20
261 Colin Porter RC	.15	.40
262 Nate Bland RC	.15	.40
263 Jason Gilfillan RC	.15	.40
264 Mike MacDougal	.07	.20
265 Ken Harvey	.07	.20
266 Brent Mayne	.07	.20
267 Miguel Cabrera	.20	.50
268 Hideo Nomo	.20	.50
269 Dave Roberts	.07	.20
270 Fred McGriff	.10	.30
271 Joe Thurston	.07	.20
272 Royce Clayton	.07	.20
273 Michael Nakamura RC	.15	.40
274 Brad Radke	.07	.20
275 Joe Mays	.07	.20
276 Lew Ford RC	.20	.50
277 Michael Cuddyer	.07	.20
278 Luis Ayala RC	.15	.40
279 Julio Manon RC	.08	.25
280 Anthony Ferrari RC	.15	.40
281 Livan Hernandez	.07	.20
282 Jae Weong Seo	.07	.20
283 Jose Reyes	.07	.20
284 Tony Clark	.07	.20
285 Ty Wigginton	.07	.20
286 Cliff Floyd	.07	.20
287 Jeremy Griffiths RC	.15	.40
288 Jason Roach RC	.15	.40
289 Jeff Duncan RC	.15	.40
290 Phil Seibel RC	.15	.40
291 Prentice Redman RC	.15	.40
292 Jose Contreras RC	.30	.75
293 Ruben Sierra	.07	.20
294 Andy Pettitte	.10	.30
295 Aaron Boone	.07	.20
296 Mariano Rivera	.20	.50
297 Michel Hernandez RC	.15	.40
298 Mike Neu RC	.15	.40
299 Erubiel Durazo	.07	.20
300 Billy McMillon	.07	.20
301 Rich Harden	.10	.30
302 David Bell	.07	.20
303 Kevin Millwood	.07	.20
304 Mike Lieberthal	.07	.20
305 Jeremy Wedel RC	.15	.40
306 Kenny Lofton	.07	.20
307 Reggie Sanders	.07	.20
308 Randall Simon	.07	.20
309 Xavier Nady	.07	.20
310 Rod Beck	.07	.20
311 Miguel Ojeda RC	.15	.40
312 Mark Loretta	.07	.20
313 Edgardo Alfonzo	.07	.20
314 Andres Galarraga	.07	.20
315 Jose Cruz Jr.	.07	.20
316 Jesse Foppert	.07	.20
317 Kurt Ainsworth	.07	.20
318 Dan Wilson	.07	.20
319 Ben Davis	.07	.20
320 Rocco Baldelli	.07	.20
321 Al Martin	.07	.20
322 Runelvys Hernandez	.07	.20
323 Dan Haren RC	.30	.75
324 Bo Hart RC	.15	.40
325 Einar Diaz	.07	.20
326 Mike Lamb	.07	.20
327 Aquilino Lopez RC	.15	.40
328 Rob Hammock	.07	.20
329 Diegomar Markwell RC	.15	.40
330 Hideki Matsui CL	.60	1.50

2003 Upper Deck MVP Black

Randomly inserted in packs, this is a parallel to the Upper Deck MVP low number set. These cards were issued to a stated print run of 50 serial numbered sets.

*BLACK: 15X TO 40X BASIC

2003 Upper Deck MVP Gold

Randomly inserted in packs, this is a parallel to the MVP low number set. These cards were issued to a stated print run of 125 serial numbered sets.

*GOLD: 10X TO 25X BASIC
*GOLD RC'S: 2.5X TO 6X BASIC

2003 Upper Deck MVP Silver

These cards, which parallel the MVP low number set, were actually inserted at a stated rate of one in 12. This is different from the stated wrapper odds which said these cards were inserted at a rate of one in two.

*SILVER: 3X TO 8X BASIC
*SILVER RC'S: .75X TO 2X BASIC

2003 Upper Deck MVP Base-to-Base

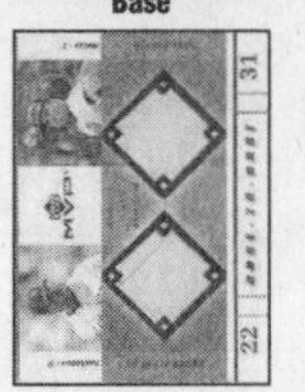

Issued at a stated rate of one in 488, these six cards feature two players as well as bases used in one of their games.

Card	Low	High
CP Roger Clemens	10.00	25.00
Mike Piazza		
IG Ichiro Suzuki	15.00	40.00
Ken Griffey Jr.		
IJ Ichiro Suzuki	20.00	50.00
Derek Jeter		
JW Derek Jeter	10.00	25.00
Bernie Williams		
MB Mark McGwire	30.00	60.00
Barry Bonds		
RJ Alex Rodriguez	15.00	40.00
Derek Jeter		

2003 Upper Deck MVP Celebration

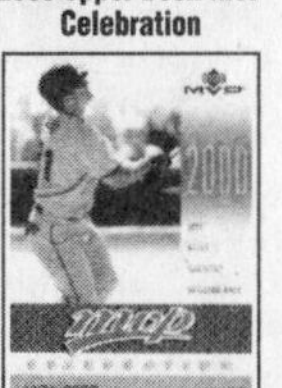

Randomly inserted into packs, these 90 cards honor various players leading achievements in baseball. Each of these cards were issued to a stated print run of between 1955 and 2002 cards and we have notated the print run information next to the player's name in our checklist.

*GOLD: 1.25X TO 3X BASIC
GOLD PRINT RUN 75 SERIAL #'d SETS

Card	Low	High
1 Yogi Berra MVP/1955	1.50	4.00
2 Mickey Mantle MVP/1956	6.00	15.00
3 Mickey Mantle MVP/1957	6.00	15.00
4 Mickey Mantle MVP/1962	6.00	15.00
5 Roger Clemens MVP/1986	3.00	8.00
6 Rickey Henderson MVP/1990	1.50	4.00
7 Frank Thomas MVP/1993	1.50	4.00
8 Mo Vaughn MVP/1995	1.25	3.00
9 Juan Gonzalez MVP/1996	1.25	3.00
10 Ken Griffey Jr. MVP/1997	2.50	6.00
11 Juan Gonzalez MVP/1998	1.25	3.00
12 Ivan Rodriguez MVP/1998	1.25	3.00
13 Jason Giambi MVP/2000	1.25	3.00
14 Ichiro Suzuki MVP/2001	3,00	8.00
15 Miguel Tejada MVP/2002	1.25	3.00
16 Barry Bonds MVP/1990	4.00	10.00
17 Barry Bonds MVP/1992	4.00	10.00
18 Barry Bonds MVP/1993	4.00	10.00
19 Jeff Bagwell MVP/1994	1.25	3.00
20 Barry Larkin MVP/1995	1.25	3.00
21 Larry Walker MVP/1997	1.25	3.00
22 Sammy Sosa MVP/1998	1.50	4.00
23 Chipper Jones MVP/1999	1.50	4.00
24 Jeff Kent MVP/2000	1.25	3.00
25 Barry Bonds MVP/2001	4.00	10.00
26 Barry Bonds MVP/2002	4.00	10.00
27 Ken Griffey Sr. AS/1980	1.25	3.00
28 Roger Clemens AS/1986	3.00	8.00
29 Ken Griffey Jr. AS/1992	2.50	6.00
30 Fred McGriff AS/1994	1.25	3.00
31 Jeff Conine AS/1995	1.25	3.00
32 Mike Piazza AS/1996	2.50	6.00
33 Sandy Alomar Jr. AS/1997	1.25	3.00
34 Roberto Alomar AS/1998	1.25	3.00
35 Pedro Martinez AS/1999	1.25	3.00
36 Derek Jeter AS/2000	4.00	10.00
37 Rickey Henderson ALCS/1989	1.50	4.00
38 Roberto Alomar ALCS/1992	1.25	3.00
39 Bernie Williams ALCS/1996	1.25	3.00
40 Marquis Grissom ALCS/1997	1.25	3.00
41 David Wells ALCS/1998	1.25	3.00
42 Orlando Hernandez ALCS/1999	1.25	3.00
43 David Justice ALCS/2000	1.25	3.00
44 Andy Pettitte ALCS/2001	1.25	3.00
45 Adam Kennedy ALCS/2002	1.25	3.00
46 John Smoltz NLCS/1992	1.25	3.00
47 Curt Schilling NLCS/1993	1.25	3.00
48 Javy Lopez NLCS/1996	1.25	3.00
49 Livan Hernandez NLCS/1997	1.25	3.00
50 Sterling Hitchcock NLCS/1998	1.25	3.00
51 Mike Hampton NLCS/2000	1.25	3.00
52 Craig Counsell NLCS/2001	1.25	3.00
53 Benito Santiago NLCS/2002	1.25	3.00
54 Tom Glavine WS/1995	1.25	3.00
55 Livan Hernandez WS/1997	1.25	3.00
56 Mariano Rivera WS/1999	1.50	4.00
57 Derek Jeter WS/2000	4.00	10.00
58 Randy Johnson WS/2001	1.50	4.00
59 Curt Schilling WS/2001	1.25	3.00
60 Troy Glaus WS/2002	1.25	3.00
61 Yogi Berra MM/1951	1.50	4.00
62 Yogi Berra MM/1955	1.50	4.00
63 Mickey Mantle MM/1956	6.00	15.00
64 Mickey Mantle MM/1957	6.00	15.00
65 Ken Griffey Sr. MM/1980	1.25	3.00
66 Rickey Henderson MM/1989	1.50	4.00
67 Roberto Alomar MM/1992	1.25	3.00
68 Bernie Williams MM/1996	1.25	3.00
69 Livan Hernandez MM/1997	1.25	3.00
70 Sammy Sosa MM/1998	1.50	4.00
71 Sterling Hitchcock MM/1998	1.25	3.00
72 David Wells MM/1998	1.25	3.00
73 Mariano Rivera MM/1999	1.50	4.00
74 Chipper Jones MM/1999	1.50	4.00
75 Ivan Rodriguez MM/1999	1.25	3.00
76 Derek Jeter MM/2000	4.00	10.00
77 Jason Giambi MM/2000	1.25	3.00
78 Jeff Kent MM/2000	1.25	3.00
79 Mike Hampton MM/2000	1.25	3.00
80 Randy Johnson MM/2001	1.50	4.00
81 Curt Schilling MM/2001	1.25	3.00
82 Barry Bonds MM/2001	4.00	10.00
83 Ichiro Suzuki MM/2001	3.00	8.00
84 Ichiro Suzuki MM/2001	3.00	8.00
85 Adam Kennedy MM/2002	1.25	3.00
86 Benito Santiago MM/2002	1.25	3.00
87 Troy Glaus MM/2002	1.25	3.00
88 Troy Glaus MM/2002	1.25	3.00
89 Miguel Tejada MM/2002	1.25	3.00
90 Barry Bonds MM/2002	4.00	10.00

2003 Upper Deck MVP Covering the Bases

Issued at a stated rate of one in 125, these 15 cards feature game-used bases from the featured player's career.

Card	Low	High
AR Alex Rodriguez	6.00	15.00
BB Barry Bonds	8.00	20.00
CD Carlos Delgado	3.00	8.00
DE Darin Erstad	3.00	8.00
DJ Derek Jeter	8.00	20.00
FT Frank Thomas	4.00	10.00
IR Ivan Rodriguez	4.00	10.00
IS Ichiro Suzuki	8.00	20.00
JD J.D. Drew	3.00	8.00
JT Jim Thome	4.00	10.00
LG Luis Gonzalez	3.00	8.00
MP Mike Piazza	6.00	15.00
MT Miguel Tejada	3.00	8.00
SG Shawn Green	3.00	8.00
TG Troy Glaus	3.00	8.00

2003 Upper Deck MVP Covering the Plate Game Bat

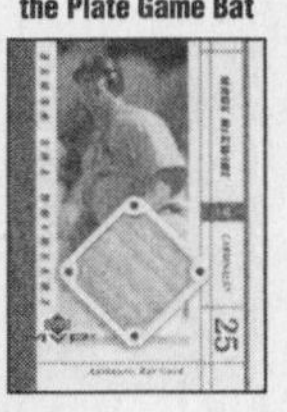

Issued at a stated rate of one in 160, these six cards feature game-used bat pieces from the featured player.

Card	Low	High
FM Fred McGriff	6.00	15.00
JT Jim Thome	6.00	15.00
MG Mark McGwire	30.00	60.00
RA Roberto Alomar	6.00	15.00
RF Rafael Furcal	4.00	10.00
VG Vladimir Guerrero	6.00	15.00

2003 Upper Deck MVP Dual Aces Game Base

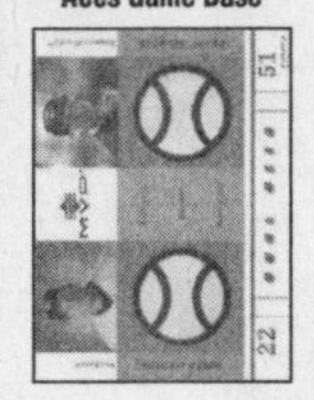

Issued at a stated rate of one in 488, these six cards feature bases used in games featuring two key pitchers.

Card	Low	High
BS Kevin Brown	4.00	10.00
Curt Schilling		
CJ Roger Clemens	8.00	20.00
Randy Johnson		
CL Roger Clemens	6.00	15.00
Al Leiter		
ML Matt Morris	4.00	10.00
Al Leiter		
SJ Curt Schilling	4.00	10.00
Randy Johnson		
SP Curt Schilling	4.00	10.00
Andy Pettitte		

2003 Upper Deck MVP Express Delivery

Inserted at a stated rate of one in 12, these 15 cards feature players who are among the leading pitchers in baseball.

Card	Low	High
ED1 Randy Johnson	.75	2.00
ED2 Curt Schilling	.60	1.50
ED3 Pedro Martinez	.60	1.50
ED4 Kerry Wood	.60	1.50
ED5 Mark Prior	.60	1.50
ED6 A.J. Burnett	.60	1.50
ED7 Josh Beckett	.60	1.50
ED8 Roy Oswalt	.60	1.50
ED9 Hideo Nomo	.75	2.00
ED10 Ben Sheets	.60	1.50
ED11 Bartolo Colon	.60	1.50
ED12 Roger Clemens	1.50	4.00
ED13 Mike Mussina	.60	1.50
ED14 Tim Hudson	.60	1.50
ED15 Matt Morris	.60	1.50

2003 Upper Deck MVP Pro Sign

Randomly inserted in packs, these 23 cards feature authentic autographs from the featured players. Each of these cards are printed to a stated print run of 25 serial numbered sets and no pricing is provided due to market scarcity.

2003 Upper Deck MVP Pro View

Issued as a two-card box topper pack, these 45 cards are a special hologram set.

*GOLD: .75X TO 2X BASIC PRO VIEW
ONE 2-CARD PACK PER 6 SEALED BOXES

Card	Low	High
PV1 Troy Glaus	1.25	3.00
PV2 Darin Erstad	1.25	3.00
PV3 Randy Johnson	1.50	4.00
PV4 Curt Schilling	1.25	3.00
PV5 Luis Gonzalez	1.25	3.00
PV6 Chipper Jones	1.50	4.00
PV7 Andruw Jones	1.25	3.00
PV8 Greg Maddux	2.50	6.00
PV9 Pedro Martinez	1.25	3.00
PV10 Manny Ramirez	1.25	3.00
PV11 Sammy Sosa	1.50	4.00
PV12 Mark Prior	1.25	3.00
PV13 Magglio Ordonez	1.25	3.00
PV14 Frank Thomas	1.50	4.00
PV15 Ken Griffey Jr.	2.50	6.00
PV16 Adam Dunn	1.25	3.00
PV17 Jim Thome	1.25	3.00
PV18 Todd Helton	1.25	3.00
PV19 Jeff Bagwell	1.25	3.00
PV20 Lance Berkman	1.25	3.00
PV21 Shawn Green	1.25	3.00
PV22 Hideo Nomo	1.50	4.00
PV23 Vladimir Guerrero	1.50	4.00
PV24 Roberto Alomar	1.50	4.00
PV25 Mike Piazza	2.50	6.00
PV26 Jason Giambi	1.25	3.00
PV27 Roger Clemens	3.00	8.00
PV28 Alfonso Soriano	1.25	3.00
PV29 Derek Jeter	4.00	10.00
PV30 Miguel Tejada	1.25	3.00
PV31 Eric Chavez	1.25	3.00
PV32 Barry Zito	1.25	3.00
PV33 Pat Burrell	1.25	3.00
PV34 Brian Giles	1.25	3.00
PV35 Barry Bonds	4.00	10.00
PV36 Ichiro Suzuki	3.00	8.00
PV37 Albert Pujols	3.00	8.00
PV38 Scott Rolen	1.25	3.00
PV39 J.D. Drew	1.25	3.00
PV40 Mark McGwire	4.00	10.00
PV41 Alex Rodriguez	2.50	6.00
PV42 Rafael Palmeiro	1.25	3.00
PV43 Juan Gonzalez	1.25	3.00
PV44 Eric Hinske	1.25	3.00
PV45 Carlos Delgado	1.25	3.00

2003 Upper Deck MVP SportsNut

Inserted at a stated rate of one in three, this 90 card insert set could be used as interactive game cards. The contest could be entered on either a season or a weekly basis.

Card	Low	High
SN1 Troy Glaus	.40	1.00
SN2 Darin Erstad	.40	1.00
SN3 Luis Gonzalez	.40	1.00
SN4 Andruw Jones	.60	1.50
SN5 Chipper Jones	1.00	2.50
SN6 Gary Sheffield	.40	1.00
SN7 Jay Gibbons	.40	1.00
SN8 Manny Ramirez	.60	1.50
SN9 Shea Hillenbrand	.40	1.00
SN10 Johnny Damon	.60	1.50
SN11 Nomar Garciaparra	1.50	4.00
SN12 Sammy Sosa	1.00	2.50
SN13 Magglio Ordonez	.40	1.00
SN14 Frank Thomas	1.00	2.50
SN15 Ken Griffey Jr.	1.50	4.00
SN16 Adam Dunn	.40	1.00
SN17 Matt Lawton	.40	1.00
SN18 Larry Walker	.40	1.00
SN19 Todd Helton	.60	1.50
SN20 Carlos Pena	.40	1.00
SN21 Mike Lowell	.40	1.00
SN22 Jeff Bagwell	.60	1.50
SN23 Lance Berkman	.40	1.00
SN24 Mike Sweeney	.40	1.00
SN25 Carlos Beltran	.40	1.00
SN26 Shawn Green	.40	1.00
SN27 Richie Sexson	.40	1.00
SN28 Torii Hunter	.40	1.00
SN29 Jacque Jones	.40	1.00
SN30 Vladimir Guerrero	1.00	2.50
SN31 Jose Vidro	.40	1.00
SN32 Roberto Alomar	.60	1.50
SN33 Mike Piazza	1.50	4.00
SN34 Alfonso Soriano	.40	1.00
SN35 Derek Jeter	2.50	6.00
SN36 Jason Giambi	.40	1.00
SN37 Bernie Williams	.60	1.50
SN38 Eric Chavez	.40	1.00
SN39 Miguel Tejada	.40	1.00
SN40 Jim Thome	.60	1.50
SN41 Pat Burrell	.40	1.00
SN42 Bobby Abreu	.40	1.00
SN43 Brian Giles	.40	1.00
SN44 Jason Kendall	.40	1.00
SN45 Ryan Klesko	.40	1.00
SN46 Phil Nevin	.40	1.00
SN47 Barry Bonds	2.50	6.00
SN48 Rich Aurilia	.40	1.00
SN49 Ichiro Suzuki	2.00	5.00
SN50 Bret Boone	.40	1.00
SN51 J.D. Drew	.40	1.00
SN52 Jim Edmonds	.40	1.00
SN53 Albert Pujols	2.00	5.00
SN54 Scott Rolen	.60	1.50
SN55 Ben Grieve	.40	1.00
SN56 Alex Rodriguez	1.50	4.00
SN57 Rafael Palmeiro	.60	1.50
SN58 Juan Gonzalez	.40	1.00
SN59 Carlos Delgado	.40	1.00
SN60 Josh Phelps	.40	1.00
SN61 Jarrod Washburn	.40	1.00
SN62 Randy Johnson	1.00	2.50
SN63 Curt Schilling	.40	1.00
SN64 Greg Maddux	1.50	4.00
SN65 Mike Hampton	.40	1.00
SN66 Rodrigo Lopez	.40	1.00
SN67 Pedro Martinez	.60	1.50
SN68 Derek Lowe	.40	1.00
SN69 Mark Prior	.60	1.50
SN70 Kerry Wood	.40	1.00
SN71 Mark Buehrle	.40	1.00
SN72 Roy Oswalt	.40	1.00
SN73 Wade Miller	.40	1.00
SN74 Odalis Perez	.40	1.00
SN75 Hideo Nomo	1.00	2.50
SN76 Ben Sheets	.40	1.00
SN77 Eric Milton	.40	1.00
SN78 Bartolo Colon	.40	1.00
SN79 Tom Glavine	.60	1.50
SN80 Al Leiter	.40	1.00
SN81 Roger Clemens	2.00	5.00
SN82 Mike Mussina	.60	1.50
SN83 Tim Hudson	.40	1.00
SN84 Barry Zito	.40	1.00
SN85 Mark Mulder	.40	1.00
SN86 Vicente Padilla	.40	1.00
SN87 Jason Schmidt	.40	1.00
SN88 Freddy Garcia	.40	1.00
SN89 Matt Morris	.40	1.00
SN90 Roy Halladay	.40	1.00

2003 Upper Deck MVP Talk of the Town

Inserted at a stated rate of one in 12, this 15 card set features some of the most talked about players in baseball.

Card	Low	High
TT1 Hideki Matsui	2.00	5.00
TT2 Chipper Jones	.75	2.00
TT3 Manny Ramirez	.60	1.50
TT4 Sammy Sosa	.75	2.00
TT5 Ken Griffey Jr.	1.25	3.00
TT6 Lance Berkman	.60	1.50
TT7 Shawn Green	.60	1.50
TT8 Vladimir Guerrero	.75	2.00
TT9 Mike Piazza	1.25	3.00
TT10 Jason Giambi	.60	1.50
TT11 Alfonso Soriano	.60	1.50
TT12 Ichiro Suzuki	1.50	4.00
TT13 Albert Pujols	1.50	4.00
TT14 Alex Rodriguez	1.25	3.00
TT15 Eric Hinske	.60	1.50

2003 Upper Deck MVP Three Bagger Game Base

Inserted at a stated rate of one in 488, this six-card set features base pieces involving three players on each card.

Card	Low	High
BMP Barry Bonds	50.00	100.00
Mark McGwire		
Mike Piazza		
GIB Ken Griffey Jr.	40.00	80.00
Ichiro Suzuki		
Barry Bonds		
GTD Troy Glaus	6.00	15.00
Frank Thomas		
Carlos Delgado		
IBJ Ichiro Suzuki	50.00	100.00
Barry Bonds		
Derek Jeter		
JWP Derek Jeter	15.00	40.00
Bernie Williams		
Jorge Posada		
SCB Curt Schilling	10.00	25.00
Roger Clemens		
Kevin Brown		

2003 Upper Deck MVP Total Bases

Randomly inserted into packs, this is an insert set featuring one base piece on each card. Each card was issued to a stated print run of 150 serial numbered sets.

Card	Low	High
AR Alex Rodriguez	10.00	25.00
BB Barry Bonds	15.00	40.00
DJ Derek Jeter	15.00	40.00
IS Ichiro Suzuki	15.00	40.00
KG Ken Griffey Jr.	10.00	25.00
MM Mark McGwire	20.00	50.00
MP Mike Piazza	10.00	25.00
RC Roger Clemens	10.00	25.00
TG Troy Glaus	4.00	10.00

2005 Upper Deck MVP

This 90-card set was released in August, 2005. The set was issued in six-card packs which came 24 packs to a box and 20 boxes to a case.

Card	Low	High
COMPLETE SET (90)	10.00	25.00
COMMON CARD (1-90)	.08	.25
1 Adam Dunn	.15	.40
2 Adrian Beltre	.10	.25
3 Albert Pujols	.60	1.50
4 Alex Rodriguez	.40	1.00
5 Alfonso Soriano	.15	.40
6 Andruw Jones	.10	.25
7 Aubrey Huff	.10	.25
8 Barry Zito	.10	.25
9 Ben Sheets	.10	.25
10 Bobby Abreu	.10	.25
11 Bobby Crosby	.10	.25
12 Bret Boone	.10	.25
13 Brian Giles	.10	.25
14 Carlos Beltran	.10	.25
15 Carlos Delgado	.10	.25
16 Carlos Lee	.10	.25
17 Chipper Jones	.25	.60
18 Craig Biggio	.15	.40
19 Curt Schilling	.15	.40
20 Dallas McPherson	.10	.25
21 David Ortiz	.25	.60
22 David Wright	.40	1.00
23 Derek Jeter	.60	1.50
24 Derek Lowe	.10	.25
25 Eric Chavez	.10	.25
26 Eric Gagne	.10	.25
27 Frank Thomas	.25	.60
28 Garret Anderson	.10	.25
29 Gary Sheffield	.10	.25
30 Greg Maddux	.40	1.00
31 Hank Blalock	.10	.25
32 Hideki Matsui	.40	1.00
33 Ichiro Suzuki	.40	1.00
34 Ivan Rodriguez	.15	.40
35 J.D. Drew	.10	.25
36 Jake Peavy	.10	.25
37 Jason Bay	.10	.25
38 Jason Giambi	.10	.25
39 Jason Schmidt	.10	.25
40 Jeff Bagwell	.15	.40
41 Jeff Kent	.10	.25
42 Jim Edmonds	.15	.40
43 Jim Thome	.15	.40
44 Joe Mauer	.25	.60
45 Johan Santana	.25	.60
46 John Smoltz	.25	.60
47 Johnny Damon	.15	.40
48 Jorge Posada	.15	.40
49 Jose Vidro	.10	.25
50 Josh Beckett	.15	.40
51 Kazuo Matsui	.10	.25
52 Ken Griffey Jr.	.40	1.00
53 Kerry Wood	.10	.25
54 Khalil Greene	.10	.25
55 Lance Berkman	.15	.40
56 Livan Hernandez	.10	.25
57 Luis Gonzalez	.10	.25
58 Magglio Ordonez	.15	.40
59 Manny Ramirez	.25	.60
60 Mark Mulder	.10	.25
61 Mark Prior	.15	.40
62 Mark Teixeira	.25	.60
63 Miguel Cabrera	.25	.60
64 Miguel Tejada	.15	.40
65 Mike Mussina	.15	.40
66 Mike Piazza	.25	.60
67 Mike Sweeney	.10	.25
68 Moises Alou	.10	.25
69 Nomar Garciaparra	.25	.60
70 Oliver Perez	.10	.25
71 Paul Konerko	.15	.40
72 Pedro Martinez	.15	.40
73 Rafael Palmeiro	.15	.40
74 Randy Johnson	.25	.60
75 Richie Sexson	.10	.25
76 Roger Clemens	.30	.75
77 Roy Halladay	.25	.60
78 Roy Oswalt	.15	.40
79 Sammy Sosa	.25	.60
80 Scott Rolen	.15	.40
81 Shawn Green	.10	.25
82 Steve Finley	.10	.25
83 Tim Hudson	.15	.40
84 Todd Helton	.15	.40
85 Tom Glavine	.15	.40
86 Torii Hunter	.10	.25
87 Travis Hafner	.10	.25
88 Troy Glaus	.10	.25
89 Victor Martinez	.15	.40
90 Vladimir Guerrero	.25	.60

2005 Upper Deck MVP Batter Up!

Card	Low	High
COMPLETE SET (42)	15.00	40.00
ONE PER PACK		
1 Al Kaline	1.00	2.50
2 Bill Mazeroski	.60	1.50
3 Billy Williams	.40	1.00
4 Bob Feller	.40	1.00
5 Bob Gibson	.60	1.50
6 Bob Lemon	.40	1.00
7 Brooks Robinson	.60	1.50
8 Carlton Fisk	.60	1.50
9 Catfish Hunter	.40	1.00
10 Dennis Eckersley	.40	1.00
11 Eddie Mathews	.60	1.50
12 Eddie Murray	1.00	2.50
13 Fergie Jenkins	.40	1.00
14 Gaylord Perry	.40	1.00
15 Harmon Killebrew	1.00	2.50
16 Jim Bunning	.40	1.00
17 Jim Palmer	.40	1.00
18 Joe DiMaggio	2.50	6.00
19 Joe Morgan	.40	1.00
20 Johnny Bench	1.00	2.50
21 Juan Marichal	.40	1.00
22 Lou Brock	.60	1.50
23 Luis Aparicio	.40	1.00
24 Mike Schmidt	2.00	5.00
25 Monte Irvin	.40	1.00
26 Nolan Ryan	2.50	6.00
27 Orlando Cepeda	.40	1.00
28 Ozzie Smith	1.50	4.00
29 Pee Wee Reese	.60	1.50
30 Phil Niekro	.40	1.00
31 Phil Rizzuto	.60	1.50
32 Ralph Kiner	.40	1.00
33 Richie Ashburn	.60	1.50
34 Robin Roberts	.40	1.00
35 Robin Yount	1.00	2.50
36 Rollie Fingers	.40	1.00
37 Tom Seaver	.60	1.50
38 Tony Perez	.40	1.00
39 Warren Spahn	.60	1.50
40 Willie McCovey	.60	1.50
41 Willie Stargell	.60	1.50
42 Yogi Berra	1.00	2.50

2005 Upper Deck MVP Jersey

STATED ODDS 1:24

Card	Low	High
AB Adrian Beltre	3.00	8.00
AP Albert Pujols	6.00	15.00
AS Alfonso Soriano	3.00	8.00
CB Carlos Beltran	3.00	8.00
CJ Chipper Jones	4.00	10.00
CS Curt Schilling	4.00	10.00
DJ Derek Jeter	8.00	20.00
EC Eric Chavez	3.00	8.00
EG Eric Gagne	3.00	8.00
GM Greg Maddux	6.00	15.00
HB Hank Blalock	3.00	8.00
IR Ivan Rodriguez	4.00	10.00
JS Johan Santana	4.00	10.00
JT Jim Thome	4.00	10.00
KG Ken Griffey Jr.	6.00	15.00
KW Kerry Wood	3.00	8.00
MC Miguel Cabrera	4.00	10.00
MP Mark Prior	4.00	10.00
MR Manny Ramirez	4.00	10.00
MT Mark Teixeira	4.00	10.00
PI Mike Piazza	4.00	10.00
RJ Randy Johnson	4.00	10.00
SB Sean Burroughs	3.00	8.00
SR Scott Rolen	4.00	10.00
SS Sammy Sosa	4.00	10.00
TE Miguel Tejada	3.00	8.00
TH Todd Helton	4.00	10.00
VG Vladimir Guerrero	4.00	10.00

2005 Upper Deck MVP Signatures

STATED ODDS 1:480
PRINT RUNS B/WN 10-99 COPIES PER
CARDS ARE NOT SERIAL-NUMBERED
PRINT RUN INFO PROVIDED BY UD
NO PRICING DUE TO SCARCITY
EXCHANGE DEADLINE JULY '08

2006 Upper Deck National Baseball Card Day

Card	Low	High
COMPLETE SET (5)	2.00	5.00
UD6 Derek Jeter	.75	2.00
UD7 Ken Griffey Jr.	.50	1.25
UD8 Dontrelle Willis	.12	.30
UD9 David Ortiz	.20	.50
UD10 Paul Konerko	.20	.50

2006 Upper Deck National Baseball Card Day National Pastime

Card	Low	High
COMPLETE SET (3)	1.50	4.00
ONE PER NBCD PACK		
IS Ichiro Suzuki	.50	1.25
KJ Kenji Johjima	.30	.75
NG Nomar Garciaparra	.30	.75

2008 Upper Deck National Baseball Card Day

Card	Low	High
COMPLETE SET (8)	2.50	6.00
UD9 Ken Griffey Jr.	.75	2.00
UD10 Derek Jeter	1.25	3.00
UD11 Albert Pujols	1.25	3.00
UD12 Ichiro Suzuki	.75	2.00
UD13 Prince Fielder	.30	.75
UD14 Ian Kennedy	.50	1.25
UD15 Chin-Lung Hu	.30	.75
UD16 Luke Hochevar	.30	.75

2002 Upper Deck National Convention

Card	Low	High
N1 Mark McGwire	1.00	2.50
N2 Sammy Sosa	.50	1.25
N3 Jason Giambi	.30	.75
N4 Ichiro Suzuki	.75	2.00
N5 Ken Griffey Jr.	.75	2.00

2004 Upper Deck National Convention

STATED PRINT RUN 500 SER.#'d SETS

Card	Low	High
TN4 Ken Griffey Jr.	1.00	2.50
TN5 Ichiro Suzuki	1.25	3.00
TN6 Derek Jeter	2.00	5.00
TN7 Mickey Mantle	2.00	5.00
TN8 Joe DiMaggio	1.50	4.00

2004 Upper Deck National Convention VIP

Card	Low	High
VIP3 Derek Jeter	5.00	12.00

2005 Upper Deck National Convention

Upper Deck produced this set and distributed it at the 2005 National Sport Collectors Convention in Chicago. The set includes famous Chicago area athletes from a variety of sports with the title "The National" printed on the cardfronts. The company made the cards available to collectors via a wrapper redemption program at their show booth and each card was serial numbered to 750-copies. Some players also signed just 5-cards which are not priced due to scarcity.

STATED PRINT RUN 750 SER.#'d SETS
UNPRICED AUTO PRINT RUN 5

Card	Low	High
CL1 Ernie Banks	1.50	4.00
CL2 Ryne Sandberg	1.50	4.00

2006 Upper Deck National MLB

Card	Low	High
MLB1 Ken Griffey Jr.	1.50	4.00
MLB2 Derek Jeter	2.50	6.00
MLB3 Albert Pujols	2.50	6.00
MLB4 Miguel Cabrera	1.00	2.50
MLB5 David Wright	1.50	4.00
MLB6 David Ortiz	.60	1.50

2006 Upper Deck National MLB VIP

Card	Low	High
1 Lou Gehrig	1.00	2.50
2 Babe Ruth	1.25	3.00
3 Scott Podsednik	.20	.50
4 Derrek Lee	.20	.50
5 Ken Griffey Jr.	.75	2.00
6 Derek Jeter	1.25	3.00

2006 Upper Deck National Southern California

Card	Low	High
COMPLETE SET (6)	5.00	12.00
SoCal5 Vladimir Guerrero	.60	1.50
SoCal6 Nomar Garciaparra	.60	1.50

2007 Upper Deck National Convention

Card	Low	High
NTL1 Derek Jeter	1.25	3.00
NTL2 Ken Griffey Jr.	1.00	2.50
NTL3 Kei Igawa	.75	2.00
NTL4 Cal Ripken Jr.	1.50	4.00
NTL16 Daisuke Matsuzaka	1.00	2.50

2007 Upper Deck National Convention VIP

Card	Low	High
VIP1 Derek Jeter	2.00	5.00
VIP2 Ken Griffey Jr.	1.25	3.00
VIP3 Kei Igawa	1.00	2.50
VIP4 Cal Ripken Jr.	2.00	5.00
VIP16 Daisuke Matsuzaka	1.25	3.00

1999 Upper Deck Ovation

This 90-card set was distributed in five-card packs with a suggested retail price of $3.99. The cards feature action color player images printed on game-ball stock for the look and feel of an actual baseball. The set contains the following subsets: World Premiere (61-80) with an insertion rate of one in every 3.5 packs, and Superstar Spotlight (81-90) inserted at a rate of one in six packs. In addition, 350 Mickey Mantle A Piece of History 500 Home Run bat cards were randomly seeded into packs. In addition, one special Mantle card was created by Upper Deck featuring both a chip of wood from a game used Mantle bat plus an authentic Mantle signature cut. Only one copy was produced and the design harkens from the popular 1999 A Piece of History Club cards except that much of the card front is devoted to a window to house the cut signature. Pricing and checklisting for these scarce bat cards can be referenced under 1999 Upper Deck A Piece of History 500 Club.

Card	Low	High
COMPLETE SET (90)	30.00	80.00
COMP.SET w/o SP's (60)	10.00	25.00
COMMON CARD (1-60)	.15	.40
COMMON WP (61-80)	.75	2.00
COMMON SS (81-90)	1.00	2.50
1 Ken Griffey Jr.	.60	1.50
2 Rondell White	.15	.40
3 Tony Clark	.15	.40
4 Barry Bonds	1.00	2.50
5 Larry Walker	.15	.40
6 Greg Vaughn	.15	.40
7 Mark Grace	.25	.60
8 John Olerud	.15	.40
9 Matt Williams	.15	.40
10 Craig Biggio	.25	.60
11 Quinton McCracken	.15	.40
12 Kerry Wood	.15	.40
13 Derek Jeter	1.00	2.50
14 Frank Thomas	.40	1.00
15 Tino Martinez	.25	.60
16 Albert Belle	.15	.40
17 Ben Grieve	.15	.40
18 Cal Ripken	1.25	3.00
19 Johnny Damon	.25	.60
20 Jose Cruz Jr.	.15	.40
21 Barry Larkin	.25	.60
22 Jason Giambi	.15	.40
23 Sean Casey	.15	.40
24 Scott Rolen	.25	.60
25 Jim Thome	.25	.60
26 Curt Schilling	.15	.40
27 Moises Alou	.15	.40
28 Alex Rodriguez	.60	1.50
29 Mark Kotsay	.15	.40
30 Darin Erstad	.15	.40
31 Mike Mussina	.25	.60
32 Todd Walker	.15	.40
33 Nomar Garciaparra	.60	1.50
34 Vladimir Guerrero	.40	1.00
35 Jeff Bagwell	.25	.60
36 Mark McGwire	1.00	2.50
37 Travis Lee	.15	.40
38 Dean Palmer	.15	.40
39 Fred McGriff	.25	.60
40 Sammy Sosa	.40	1.00
41 Mike Piazza	.60	1.50
42 Andres Galarraga	.15	.40
43 Pedro Martinez	.25	.60
44 Juan Gonzalez	.15	.40
45 Greg Maddux	.60	1.50
46 Jeromy Burnitz	.15	.40
47 Roger Clemens	.75	2.00
48 Vinny Castilla	.15	.40
49 Kevin Brown	.25	.60
50 Mo Vaughn	.15	.40
51 Raul Mondesi	.15	.40
52 Randy Johnson	.40	1.00
53 Ray Lankford	.15	.40
54 Jaret Wright	.15	.40
55 Tony Gwynn	.50	1.25
56 Chipper Jones	.40	1.00
57 Gary Sheffield	.15	.40
58 Ivan Rodriguez	.25	.60
59 Kenny Lofton	.15	.40
60 Jason Kendall	.15	.40
61 J.D. Drew WP	.75	2.00
62 Gabe Kapler WP	.75	2.00
63 Adrian Beltre WP	.75	2.00
64 Carlos Beltran WP	1.00	2.50
65 Eric Chavez WP	.75	2.00
66 Mike Lowell WP	.75	2.00
67 Troy Glaus WP	1.00	2.50
68 George Lombard WP	.75	2.00
69 Alex Gonzalez WP	.75	2.00
70 Mike Kinkade WP	.75	2.00
71 Jeremy Giambi WP	.75	2.00
72 Bruce Chen WP	.75	2.00
73 Preston Wilson WP	.75	2.00
74 Kevin Witt WP	.75	2.00
75 Carlos Guillen WP	.75	2.00
76 Ryan Minor WP	.75	2.00
77 Corey Koskie WP	.75	2.00
78 Robert Fick WP	1.00	2.50
79 Michael Barrett WP	.75	2.00
80 Calvin Pickering WP	.75	2.00
81 Ken Griffey Jr. SS	1.50	4.00
82 Mark McGwire SS	2.50	6.00
83 Cal Ripken SS	3.00	8.00
84 Derek Jeter SS	2.50	6.00
85 Chipper Jones SS	1.00	2.50
86 Nomar Garciaparra SS	1.50	4.00
87 Sammy Sosa SS	1.00	2.50
88 Juan Gonzalez SS	1.00	2.50
89 Mike Piazza SS	1.50	4.00
90 Alex Rodriguez SS	1.50	4.00

1999 Upper Deck Ovation Standing Ovation

Randomly inserted into packs, this 90-card set is a parallel version of the base set. Each card is sequentially numbered to 500.

*STARS 1-60: 5X TO 12X BASIC 1-60
*WP CARDS 61-80: 1X TO 2.5X BASIC WP
*SS CARDS 81-90: 2X TO 5X BASIC SS
RANDOM INSERTS IN PACKS

1999 Upper Deck Ovation A Piece of History

Randomly inserted in packs at the rate of one in 247, this set features pieces of actual game-used bats of some of MLB's biggest stars embedded in the cards. Only 25 Ben Grieve and Kerry Wood autographed cards were produced. The signed Grieve card contains a game-used bat chip. The signed Wood card contains a piece of a game-used baseball.

STATED ODDS 1:247
AR Alex Rodriguez 8.00 20.00
BB Barry Bonds 10.00 25.00
BG Ben Grieve 4.00 10.00
BW Bernie Williams 5.00 12.00
CJ Chipper Jones 5.00 12.00
CR Cal Ripken 12.50 30.00
DJ Derek Jeter 10.00 25.00
JG Juan Gonzalez 4.00 10.00
MP Mike Piazza 8.00 20.00
NG Nomar Garciaparra 8.00 20.00
SS Sammy Sosa 5.00 12.00
TG Tony Gwynn 5.00 12.00
VG Vladimir Guerrero 5.00 12.00
KGJ Ken Griffey Jr. 8.00 20.00
BGAU B. Grieve Bat AU/25
KWAU K.Wood Ball AU/25

1999 Upper Deck Ovation Curtain Calls

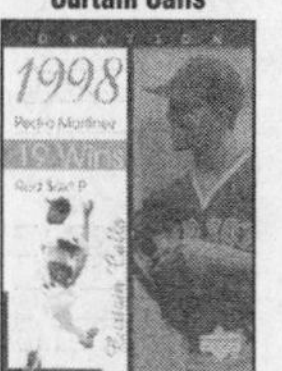

Randomly inserted in packs at the rate of one in eight, this 20-card set features color action photos of the pictured player's most memorable accomplishment during the 1998 season.

COMPLETE SET (20) 30.00 80.00
STATED ODDS 1:8
R1 Mark McGwire 3.00 8.00
R2 Sammy Sosa 1.25 3.00
R3 Ken Griffey Jr. 2.00 5.00
R4 Alex Rodriguez 2.00 5.00
R5 Roger Clemens 2.50 6.00
R6 Cal Ripken 4.00 10.00
R7 Barry Bonds 3.00 8.00
R8 Kerry Wood .50 1.25
R9 Nomar Garciaparra 2.00 5.00
R10 Derek Jeter 3.00 8.00
R11 Juan Gonzalez .50 1.25
R12 Greg Maddux 2.00 5.00
R13 Pedro Martinez .75 2.00
R14 David Wells .50 1.25
R15 Moises Alou .50 1.25
R16 Tony Gwynn 1.50 4.00
R17 Albert Belle .50 1.25
R18 Mike Piazza 2.00 5.00
R19 Ivan Rodriguez .75 2.00
R20 Randy Johnson 1.25 3.00

1999 Upper Deck Ovation Major Production

Randomly inserted in packs at the rate of one in 45, this 20-card set features color action photos of some of the game's most productive players printed using Thermography technology to simulate the look and feel of home plate.

COMPLETE SET (20) 200.00 400.00
STATED ODDS 1:45
S1 Mike Piazza 8.00 20.00
S2 Mark McGwire 12.50 30.00
S3 Chipper Jones 5.00 12.00
S4 Cal Ripken 15.00 40.00
S5 Ken Griffey Jr. 8.00 20.00
S6 Barry Bonds 12.50 30.00
S7 Tony Gwynn 6.00 15.00
S8 Randy Johnson 5.00 12.00
S9 Ivan Rodriguez 3.00 8.00
S10 Frank Thomas 5.00 12.00
S11 Alex Rodriguez 8.00 20.00
S12 Albert Belle 2.00 5.00
S13 Juan Gonzalez 2.00 5.00
S14 Greg Maddux 8.00 20.00
S15 Jeff Bagwell 3.00 8.00
S16 Derek Jeter 12.50 30.00
S17 Matt Williams 2.00 5.00
S18 Kenny Lofton 2.00 5.00
S19 Sammy Sosa 5.00 12.00
S20 Roger Clemens 10.00 25.00

1999 Upper Deck Ovation ReMarkable Moments

This 15-card three-tiered insert set showcases Mark McGwire's dominant play during the 1998 home run race. Cards 1-5 feature bronze foil highlights with an insertion rate of 1:9. Cards 6-10 display silver foil highlights with an insertion rate of 1:25. Cards 11-15 are gold-foiled with a 1:99 insertion rate.

COMPLETE SET (15) 100.00 200.00
COMMON CARD (1-5) 2.00 5.00
CARDS 1-5 STATED ODDS 1:9
COMMON CARD (6-10) 4.00 10.00
CARDS 6-10 STATED ODDS 1:25
COMMON CARD (11-15) 8.00 20.00
CARDS 11-15 STATED ODDS 1:99

2000 Upper Deck Ovation

The 2000 Upper Deck Ovation set was released in March, 2000 as an 89-card set that featured 60 player cards, 19 World Premiere cards (1:3), and 10 Superstar cards (1:6). Card number 70 does exist, however, it is in very short supply. The featured player on that card is Ryan Anderson, who was not available for usage in the set as he was not on the 40 man roster at the time this set was printed. No copies of card number 70 are believed to exist in the Ovation parallel set. Each back contained five cards and carried a suggested retail price of 3.99. Also, a selection of A Piece of History 3000 Club Willie Mays memorabilia cards were randomly seeded into packs. 300 bat cards, 350 jersey cards, 50 hand-numbered combination bat-jersey cards and twenty-four autographed, hand-numbered, combination bat-jersey cards were produced. Pricing for these memorabilia cards can be referenced under 2000 Upper Deck A Piece of History 3000 Club.

COMPLETE SET (89) 30.00 80.00
COMP.SET w/o SP's (60) 8.00 20.00
COMMON CARD (1-60) .15 .40
COMMON WP (61-80) .75 2.00
COMMON SS (81-90) 1.25 3.00
1 Mo Vaughn .15 .40
2 Troy Glaus .15 .40
3 Jeff Bagwell .25 .60
4 Craig Biggio .25 .60
5 Mike Hampton .15 .40
6 Jason Giambi .15 .40
7 Tim Hudson .15 .40
8 Chipper Jones .40 1.00
9 Greg Maddux .60 1.50
10 Kevin Millwood .15 .40
11 Brian Jordan .15 .40
12 Jeromy Burnitz .15 .40
13 David Wells .15 .40
14 Carlos Delgado .15 .40
15 Sammy Sosa .40 1.00
16 Mark McGwire 1.00 2.50
17 Matt Williams .15 .40
18 Randy Johnson .40 1.00
19 Erubiel Durazo .15 .40
20 Kevin Brown .25 .60
21 Shawn Green .15 .40
22 Gary Sheffield .15 .40
23 Jose Canseco .25 .60
24 Vladimir Guerrero .40 1.00
25 Barry Bonds 1.00 2.50
26 Manny Ramirez .25 .60
27 Roberto Alomar .25 .60
28 Richie Sexson .15 .40
29 Jim Thome .25 .60
30 Alex Rodriguez .60 1.50
31 Ken Griffey Jr. .60 1.50
32 Preston Wilson .15 .40
33 Mike Piazza .60 1.50
34 Al Leiter .15 .40
35 Robin Ventura .25 .60
36 Cal Ripken 1.25 3.00
37 Albert Belle .15 .40
38 Tony Gwynn .50 1.25
39 Brian Giles .15 .40
40 Jason Kendall .15 .40
41 Scott Rolen .25 .60
42 Bob Abreu .15 .40
43 Ken Griffey Jr. Reds .60 1.50
44 Sean Casey .15 .40
45 Carlos Beltran .15 .40
46 Gabe Kapler .15 .40
47 Ivan Rodriguez .25 .60
48 Rafael Palmeiro .25 .60
49 Larry Walker .15 .40
50 Nomar Garciaparra .60 1.50
51 Pedro Martinez .25 .60
52 Eric Milton .15 .40
53 Juan Gonzalez .15 .40
54 Tony Clark .15 .40
55 Frank Thomas .40 1.00
56 Magglio Ordonez .15 .40
57 Roger Clemens .75 2.00
58 Derek Jeter 1.00 2.50
59 Bernie Williams .25 .60
60 Orlando Hernandez .15 .40
61 Rick Ankiel WP .75 2.00
62 Josh Beckett WP 2.00 5.00
63 Vernon Wells WP 1.00 2.50
64 Alfonso Soriano WP 2.00 5.00
65 Pat Burrell WP 1.00 2.50
66 Eric Munson WP .75 2.00
67 Chad Hutchinson WP .75 2.00
68 Eric Gagne WP 2.00 5.00
69 Peter Bergeron WP .75 2.00
70 Ryan Anderson WP SP 75.00 150.00
71 A.J. Burnett WP 1.00 2.50
72 Jorge Toca WP .75 2.00
73 Matt Riley WP .75 2.00
74 Chad Hermansen WP .75 2.00
75 Doug Davis WP 1.00 2.50
76 Jim Morris WP 2.00 5.00
77 Ben Petrick WP .75 2.00
78 Mark Quinn WP .75 2.00
79 Ed Yarnall WP .75 2.00
80 Ramon Ortiz WP .75 2.00
81 Ken Griffey Jr. SS 2.00 5.00
82 Mark McGwire SS 3.00 8.00
83 Derek Jeter SS 3.00 8.00
84 Jeff Bagwell SS 1.25 3.00
85 Nomar Garciaparra SS 2.00 5.00
86 Sammy Sosa SS 1.25 3.00
87 Mike Piazza SS 2.00 5.00
88 Alex Rodriguez SS 2.00 5.00
89 Cal Ripken SS 4.00 10.00
90 Pedro Martinez SS 1.25 3.00

2000 Upper Deck Ovation Standing Ovation

Randomly inserted into packs, this 90-card set parallels the Upper Deck Ovation base set. Cards are serial numbered to 50.

*STARS: 10X TO 25X BASIC CARDS
*WORLD PREM: 1.5X TO 4X BASIC WP
*SPOTLIGHT: 3X TO 8X BASIC SS

2000 Upper Deck Ovation A Piece of History

Randomly inserted into packs, this 16-card set features 12 player cards containing pieces of game-used bats. Production of 400 copies of each card was publicly announced by Upper Deck but the cards are not serial-numbered. Alex Rodriguez, Cal Ripken, Derek Jeter, and Ken Griffey Jr. have additional cards that contain both pieces of game-used bats and their autographs.

AR Alex Rodriguez 15.00 40.00
CJ Chipper Jones 8.00 20.00
CR Cal Ripken 20.00 50.00
DJ Derek Jeter 20.00 50.00
IR Ivan Rodriguez 6.00 15.00
JC Jose Canseco 6.00 15.00
KG Ken Griffey Jr. 15.00 40.00
MR Manny Ramirez 6.00 15.00
PB Pat Burrell 6.00 15.00
SR Scott Rolen 6.00 15.00
TG Tony Gwynn 10.00 25.00
VG Vladimir Guerrero 8.00 20.00
ARA Alex Rodriguez AU/3
CRA Cal Ripken AU/8
DJA Derek Jeter AU/2
KGA Ken Griffey Jr. AU/24

2000 Upper Deck Ovation Center Stage Silver

Randomly inserted in packs at one in nine, this insert set features ten players that are ready to take center stage on any given day. Card backs carry a "CS" prefix.

COMPLETE SET (10) 30.00 60.00
*GOLD: .75X TO 2X CENTER SILVER
GOLD STATED ODDS 1:39
*RAINBOW: 1.5X TO 4X CENTER SILVER
RAINBOW STATED ODDS 1:99
CS1 Jeff Bagwell .75 2.00
CS2 Ken Griffey Jr. 2.00 5.00
CS3 Nomar Garciaparra 2.00 5.00
CS4 Mike Piazza 2.00 5.00
CS5 Mark McGwire 3.00 8.00
CS6 Alex Rodriguez 2.00 5.00
CS7 Cal Ripken 4.00 10.00
CS8 Derek Jeter 3.00 8.00
CS9 Chipper Jones 1.25 3.00
CS10 Sammy Sosa 1.25 3.00

2000 Upper Deck Ovation Curtain Calls

Randomly inserted into packs at one in three, this insert features 20 major leaguers who deserve a standing ovation for their 1999 performance. Card backs carry a "CC" prefix.

COMPLETE SET (20) 20.00 40.00
CC1 David Cone .30 .75
CC2 Mark McGwire 2.00 5.00
CC3 Sammy Sosa .75 2.00
CC4 Eric Milton .30 .75
CC5 Bernie Williams .50 1.25
CC6 Tony Gwynn 1.00 2.50
CC7 Nomar Garciaparra 1.25 3.00
CC8 Manny Ramirez .50 1.25
CC9 Wade Boggs .75 2.00
CC10 Randy Johnson .75 2.00
CC11 Cal Ripken 2.50 6.00
CC12 Pedro Martinez .50 1.25
CC13 Alex Rodriguez 1.25 3.00
CC14 Fernando Tatis .30 .75
CC15 Vladimir Guerrero .75 2.00
CC16 Robin Ventura .50 1.25
CC17 Larry Walker .30 .75
CC18 Carlos Beltran .30 .75
CC19 Jose Canseco .50 1.25
CC20 Ken Griffey Jr. 1.25 3.00

2000 Upper Deck Ovation Diamond Futures

Randomly inserted in packs at one in six, this insert features 10 of the league's top players who are on the verge of greatness. Card backs carry a "DM" prefix.

COMPLETE SET (10) 7.50 15.00
DM1 J.D. Drew .40 1.00
DM2 Alfonso Soriano .75 2.00
DM3 Preston Wilson .40 1.00
DM4 Erubiel Durazo .40 1.00
DM5 Rick Ankiel .40 1.00
DM6 Octavio Dotel .40 1.00
DM7 A.J. Burnett .40 1.00
DM8 Carlos Beltran .40 1.00
DM9 Vernon Wells .40 1.00
DM10 Troy Glaus .40 1.00

2000 Upper Deck Ovation Lead Performers

Randomly inserted in packs at one in 19, this insert set features 10 players that lead by example. Card backs carry a "LP" prefix.

COMPLETE SET (10) 25.00 60.00
LP1 Mark McGwire 4.00 10.00
LP2 Derek Jeter 4.00 10.00
LP3 Vladimir Guerrero 1.50 4.00
LP4 Mike Piazza 2.50 6.00
LP5 Cal Ripken 5.00 12.00
LP6 Sammy Sosa 1.50 4.00
LP7 Jeff Bagwell 1.00 2.50
LP8 Nomar Garciaparra 2.50 6.00
LP9 Chipper Jones 1.50 4.00
LP10 Ken Griffey Jr. 2.50 6.00

2000 Upper Deck Ovation Super Signatures

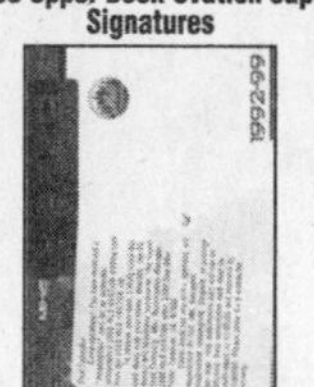

Randomly inserted into packs, this insert set features autographed cards of Ken Griffey Jr. and Mike Piazza. Each player has a silver, gold and rainbow version. Piazza did not return his cards in time for the product to ship, thus UD seeded exchange cards into their packs for all Piazza autographs. These exchange cards had a large, square white sticker with text explaining redemption guidelines placed on the card front. All Piazza exchange cards had to be mailed in prior to the December 9th, 2000 deadline.

SSKGG Ken Griffey Jr. Gold/50 75.00 150.00
SSKGR Ken Griffey Jr. Rainbow/10
SSKGS Ken Griffey Jr. Silver/100 125.00 250.00
SSMPG Mike Piazza Gold 50 EX 150.00 250.00
SSMPR Mike Piazza Rainbow/10 EX
SSMPS Mike Piazza Silver/100 EX 125.00 200.00

2000 Upper Deck Ovation Superstar Theatre

Randomly inserted in packs at one in 19, this insert set features 20 players that have a flair for the dramatic. Card backs carry a "ST" prefix.

COMPLETE SET (20) 60.00 120.00
ST1 Ivan Rodriguez 1.50 4.00
ST2 Brian Giles 1.00 2.50
ST3 Bernie Williams 1.50 4.00
ST4 Greg Maddux 4.00 10.00
ST5 Frank Thomas 2.50 6.00
ST6 Sean Casey 1.00 2.50
ST7 Mo Vaughn 1.00 2.50
ST8 Carlos Delgado 1.00 2.50
ST9 Tony Gwynn 3.00 8.00
ST10 Pedro Martinez 1.50 4.00
ST11 Scott Rolen 1.50 4.00
ST12 Mark McGwire 6.00 15.00
ST13 Manny Ramirez 1.50 4.00
ST14 Rafael Palmeiro 1.50 4.00
ST15 Jose Canseco 1.50 4.00
ST16 Randy Johnson 2.50 6.00
ST17 Gary Sheffield 1.00 2.50
ST18 Larry Walker 1.00 2.50
ST19 Barry Bonds 6.00 15.00
ST20 Roger Clemens 5.00 12.00

2001 Upper Deck Ovation

The 2001 Upper Deck Ovation product was released in early March 2001, and features a 90-card base set that was broken into tiers as follows: Base Veterans (1-60), and World Premiere Prospects (61-90) that were individually serial numbered to 2000. Each pack contained five cards and carried a suggested retail price of $2.99.

COMP.SET w/o SP'S (60) 8.00 20.00
COMMON CARD (1-60) .15 .40
COMMON WP (61-90) 2.00 5.00
1 Troy Glaus .15 .40
2 Darin Erstad .15 .40
3 Jason Giambi .15 .40
4 Tim Hudson .15 .40
5 Eric Chavez .15 .40
6 Carlos Delgado .15 .40
7 David Wells .15 .40
8 Greg Vaughn .15 .40
9 Omar Vizquel .25 .60
Travis Fryman is pictured on card front UER
10 Jim Thome .25 .60
11 Roberto Alomar .25 .60
12 John Olerud .15 .40
13 Edgar Martinez .25 .60
14 Cal Ripken 1.25 3.00
15 Alex Rodriguez .60 1.50
16 Ivan Rodriguez .25 .60
17 Manny Ramirez Sox .25 .60
18 Nomar Garciaparra .60 1.50
19 Pedro Martinez .25 .60
20 Jermaine Dye .15 .40
21 Juan Gonzalez .15 .40
22 Matt Lawton .15 .40
23 Frank Thomas .40 1.00
24 Magglio Ordonez .15 .40
25 Bernie Williams .25 .60
26 Derek Jeter 1.00 2.50
27 Roger Clemens .75 2.00
28 Jeff Bagwell .25 .60
29 Richard Hidalgo .15 .40
30 Chipper Jones .40 1.00
31 Greg Maddux .60 1.50
32 Andruw Jones .25 .60
33 Jeromy Burnitz .15 .40
34 Mark McGwire 1.00 2.50
35 Jim Edmonds .15 .40
36 Sammy Sosa .40 1.00
37 Kerry Wood .15 .40
38 Randy Johnson .40 1.00
39 Steve Finley .15 .40
40 Gary Sheffield .15 .40
41 Kevin Brown .15 .40
42 Shawn Green .15 .40
43 Vladimir Guerrero .40 1.00
44 Jose Vidro .15 .40
45 Barry Bonds 1.00 2.50
46 Jeff Kent .15 .40
47 Preston Wilson .15 .40
48 Luis Castillo .15 .40
49 Mike Piazza .60 1.50
50 Edgardo Alfonzo .15 .40
51 Tony Gwynn .50 1.25
52 Ryan Klesko .15 .40
53 Scott Rolen .25 .60
54 Bob Abreu .15 .40
55 Jason Kendall .15 .40
56 Brian Giles .15 .40
57 Ken Griffey Jr. .60 1.50
58 Barry Larkin .25 .60
59 Todd Helton .25 .60
60 Mike Hampton .15 .40
61 Corey Patterson WP 2.00 5.00
62 Timo Perez WP 2.00 5.00
63 Toby Hall WP 2.00 5.00
64 Brandon Inge WP 2.00 5.00
65 Joe Crede WP 3.00 8.00
66 Xavier Nady WP 2.00 5.00
67 A. Pettyjohn WP RC 2.00 5.00
68 Keith Ginter WP 2.00 5.00
69 Brian Cole WP 2.00 5.00
70 Tyler Walker WP RC 2.00 5.00
71 Juan Uribe WP RC 2.00 5.00
72 Alex Hernandez WP 2.00 5.00
73 Leo Estrella WP 2.00 5.00
74 Joey Nation WP 2.00 5.00
75 Aubrey Huff WP 2.00 5.00
76 Ichiro Suzuki WP RC 25.00 50.00
77 Jay Spurgeon WP 2.00 5.00
78 Sun Woo Kim WP 2.00 5.00
79 Pedro Feliz WP 2.00 5.00
80 Pablo Ozuna WP 2.00 5.00
81 Hiram Bocachica WP 2.00 5.00
82 Brad Wilkerson WP 2.00 5.00
83 Rocky Biddle WP 2.00 5.00
84 Aaron McNeal WP 2.00 5.00
85 Adam Bernero WP 2.00 5.00
86 Danys Baez WP 2.00 5.00
87 Dee Brown WP 2.00 5.00
88 Jimmy Rollins WP 2.00 5.00
89 Jason Hart WP 2.00 5.00
90 Ross Gload WP 2.00 5.00

2001 Upper Deck Ovation A Piece of History

Randomly inserted into packs at one in 40, this 40-card insert features slivers of actual game-used bats from Major League stars like Barry Bonds and Alex Rodriguez. Card backs carry the player's initials as numbering.

COMMON RETIRED 6.00 15.00
AJ Andruw Jones 6.00 15.00
AR Alex Rodriguez 6.00 15.00
BB Barry Bonds 10.00 25.00
BR Brooks Robinson 10.00 25.00
BW Bernie Williams 6.00 15.00
CD Carlos Delgado 4.00 10.00
CF Carlton Fisk 10.00 25.00
CJ Chipper Jones 6.00 15.00
CR Cal Ripken 15.00 40.00
DC David Cone 4.00 10.00
DD Don Drysdale 6.00 15.00
DE Darin Erstad 4.00 10.00
EW Early Wynn 6.00 15.00
FT Frank Thomas 6.00 15.00
GM Greg Maddux 6.00 15.00
GS Gary Sheffield 4.00 10.00
IR Ivan Rodriguez 6.00 15.00
JB Johnny Bench 10.00 25.00
JC Jose Canseco 6.00 15.00
JD Joe DiMaggio 30.00 60.00
JE Jim Edmonds 4.00 10.00
JP Jim Palmer 6.00 15.00
KG Ken Griffey Jr. 6.00 15.00
KGS Ken Griffey Sr. 4.00 10.00
KKB Kevin Brown 4.00 10.00
MH Mike Hampton 4.00 10.00
MM Mickey Mantle 75.00 150.00
MW Matt Williams 4.00 10.00
NR Nolan Ryan SP 20.00 50.00
OS Ozzie Smith 6.00 15.00
RA Rick Ankiel 4.00 10.00
RC Roger Clemens 6.00 15.00
RF Rollie Fingers 6.00 15.00
RF Rafael Furcal 4.00 10.00
RJ Randy Johnson 6.00 15.00
SG Shawn Green 4.00 10.00
SS Sammy Sosa 6.00 15.00
TG Tom Glavine 6.00 15.00
TRG Troy Glaus 4.00 10.00
TS Tom Seaver 10.00 25.00

2001 Upper Deck Ovation A Piece of History Autographs

Randomly inserted into packs, this 7-card insert features slivers of actual game-used bats and authentic autographs from some of the Major League's top stars. Card backs carry a "S" prefix followed by the player's initials. Please note that the print runs are listed below.

2001 Upper Deck Ovation A Piece of History Bat Combos

Randomly inserted into packs, this five-card insert set features a combination of slivers from actual game-used bats of historic Major League players. Card backs carry the player's initials as numbering. Please note that their were only 25 serial numbered sets produced. Due to market scarcity, no pricing is provided.

2001 Upper Deck Ovation Curtain Calls

Randomly inserted into packs at one in seven, this 10-card insert set features players that deserve a round of applause after the numbers they put up last year. Card backs carry a "CC" prefix.

COMPLETE SET (10) 8.00 20.00
CC1 Sammy Sosa .75 2.00
CC2 Darin Erstad .50 1.25
CC3 Barry Bonds 2.00 5.00
CC4 Todd Helton .50 1.25
CC5 Mike Piazza 1.25 3.00
CC6 Ken Griffey Jr. 1.25 3.00
CC7 Nomar Garciaparra 1.25 3.00
CC8 Carlos Delgado .50 1.25
CC9 Jason Giambi .50 1.25
CC10 Alex Rodriguez 1.25 3.00

2001 Upper Deck Ovation Lead Performers

Randomly inserted into packs at one in 12, this 11-card insert set features players that were among the league leaders in many of the offensive categories. Card backs carry a "LP" prefix.

COMPLETE SET (11) 12.50 30.00
LP1 Mark McGwire 2.50 6.00
LP2 Derek Jeter 2.50 6.00
LP3 Alex Rodriguez 1.50 4.00
LP4 Frank Thomas 1.00 2.50
LP5 Sammy Sosa 1.00 2.50
LP6 Mike Piazza 1.50 4.00
LP7 Vladimir Guerrero 1.00 2.50
LP8 Pedro Martinez .60 1.50
LP9 Carlos Delgado .60 1.50
LP10 Ken Griffey Jr. 1.50 4.00
LP11 Jeff Bagwell .60 1.50

2001 Upper Deck Ovation Superstar Theatre

Randomly inserted into packs at one in 12, this 11-card insert set features players that put on a "show" everytime they take the field. Card backs carry a "ST" prefix.

COMPLETE SET (11) 12.50 30.00
ST1 Nomar Garciaparra 1.50 4.00
ST2 Ken Griffey Jr. 1.50 4.00
ST3 Frank Thomas 1.00 2.50
ST4 Derek Jeter 2.50 6.00
ST5 Mike Piazza 1.50 4.00
ST6 Sammy Sosa 1.00 2.50
ST7 Barry Bonds 2.50 6.00
ST8 Alex Rodriguez 1.50 4.00
ST9 Todd Helton 1.00 2.50
ST10 Mark McGwire 2.50 6.00
ST11 Jason Giambi 1.00 2.50

2002 Upper Deck Ovation

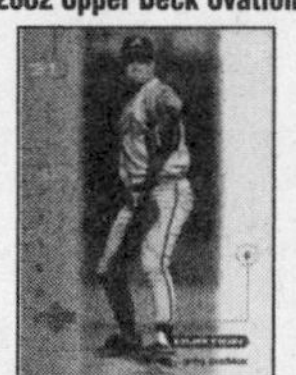

This 180 card set was issued in two separate brands. The basic Ovation product, containing cards 1-120, was released in June, 2002. These cards were issued in five-card packs with a suggested retail price of $3 per pack of which were issued 24 to a box and 20 boxes to a case. These cards feature veteran stars from cards 1-60, rookie stars from 61-89 (of which have a stated print run of 2002 serial numbered copies) and then five cards each of the six Upper Deck spokesmen from 90-119. The first series set concludes with a card with a stated print run of 2002 serial numbered sets featuring the six Upper Deck spokemen. Cards 121-180 were distributed within retail-only packs of Upper Deck Rookie Debut in mid-December 2002. Cards 121-150 were seeded at an approximate rate of one per pack and feature traded players and young prospects. Cards 151-180 continue the World Premiere rookie subset with each card being serial-numbered to 2002 copies. Though the manufacturer did not release odds on these packs market research indicates an approximate seeding ratio of 1:8 packs.

COMP.LOW w/o SP's (90) 10.00 25.00
COMP.UPDATE w/o SP's (30) 6.00 15.00
COMMON CARD (1-60) .15 .40
COMMON (61-89/120/151-180) 1.50 4.00
COMMON CARD (90-119) .20 .50
COMMON CARD (121-150) .25 .60
1 Troy Glaus .15 .40
2 David Justice .15 .40
3 Tim Hudson .15 .40
4 Jermaine Dye .15 .40
5 Carlos Delgado .15 .40
6 Greg Vaughn .15 .40
7 Jim Thome .25 .60
8 C.C. Sabathia .15 .40
9 Ichiro Suzuki .75 2.00
10 Edgar Martinez .25 .60
11 Chris Richard .15 .40
12 Rafael Palmeiro .25 .60

13 Alex Rodriguez .60 1.50
14 Ivan Rodriguez .25 .60
15 Nomar Garciaparra .60 1.50
16 Manny Ramirez .25 .60
17 Pedro Martinez .25 .60
18 Mike Sweeney .15 .40
19 Dmitri Young .15 .40
20 Doug Mientkiewicz .15 .40
21 Brad Radke .15 .40
22 Cristian Guzman .15 .40
23 Frank Thomas .40 1.00
24 Magglio Ordonez .15 .40
25 Bernie Williams .25 .60
26 Derek Jeter 1.00 2.50
27 Jason Giambi .15 .40
28 Roger Clemens .75 2.00
29 Jeff Bagwell .25 .60
30 Lance Berkman .15 .40
31 Chipper Jones .40 1.00
32 Gary Sheffield .15 .40
33 Greg Maddux .60 1.50
34 Richie Sexson .15 .40
35 Albert Pujols .75 2.00
36 Tino Martinez .25 .60
37 J.D. Drew .15 .40
38 Sammy Sosa .40 1.00
39 Moises Alou .15 .40
40 Randy Johnson .40 1.00
41 Luis Gonzalez .15 .40
42 Shawn Green .15 .40
43 Kevin Brown .15 .40
44 Vladimir Guerrero .40 1.00
45 Barry Bonds 1.00 2.50
46 Jeff Kent .15 .40
47 Cliff Floyd .15 .40
48 Josh Beckett .15 .40
49 Mike Piazza .60 1.50
50 Mo Vaughn .15 .40
51 Jeromy Burnitz .15 .40
52 Roberto Alomar .25 .60
53 Phil Nevin .15 .40
54 Scott Rolen .25 .60
55 Jimmy Rollins .15 .40
56 Brian Giles .15 .40
57 Ken Griffey Jr. .60 1.50
58 Sean Casey .15 .40
59 Larry Walker .15 .40
60 Todd Helton .25 .60
61 Rodrigo Rosario WP RC 1.50 4.00
62 Reed Johnson WP RC 2.00 5.00
63 John Ennis WP RC 1.50 4.00
64 Luis Martinez WP RC 1.50 4.00
65 So Taguchi WP RC 2.00 5.00
66 Brandon Backe WP RC 2.00 5.00
67 Doug Devore WP RC 1.50 4.00
68 Victor Alvarez WP RC 1.50 4.00
69 Kazuhisa Ishii WP RC 2.00 5.00
70 Eric Good WP RC 1.50 4.00
71 Deivis Santos WP 1.50 4.00
72 Matt Thornton WP RC 1.50 4.00
73 Hansel Izquierdo WP RC 1.50 4.00
74 Tyler Yates WP RC 1.50 4.00
75 Jaime Cerda WP RC 1.50 4.00
76 Satoru Komiyama WP RC 1.50 4.00
77 Steve Bechler WP RC 1.50 4.00
78 Ben Howard WP RC 1.50 4.00
79 Jorge Padilla WP RC 1.50 4.00
80 Eric Junge WP RC 1.50 4.00
81 And. Machado WP RC 1.50 4.00
82 Adrian Burnside WP RC 1.50 4.00
83 Josh Hancock WP RC 2.00 5.00
84 Anastacio Martinez WP RC 1.50 4.00
85 Rene Reyes WP RC 1.50 4.00
86 Nate Field WP RC 1.50 4.00
87 Tim Kalita WP RC 1.50 4.00
88 Kevin Frederick WP RC 1.50 4.00
89 Edwin Almonte WP RC 1.50 4.00
90 Ichiro Suzuki SS .40 1.00
91 Ichiro Suzuki SS .40 1.00
92 Ichiro Suzuki SS .40 1.00
93 Ichiro Suzuki SS .40 1.00
94 Ichiro Suzuki SS .40 1.00
95 Ken Griffey Jr. SS .30 .75
96 Ken Griffey Jr. SS .30 .75
97 Ken Griffey Jr. SS .30 .75
98 Ken Griffey Jr. SS .30 .75
99 Ken Griffey Jr. SS .30 .75
100 Jason Giambi A's SS .20 .50
101 Jason Giambi A's SS .20 .50
102 Jason Giambi A's SS .20 .50
103 J.Giambi Yankees SS .20 .50
104 J.Giambi Yankees SS .25 .60
105 Sammy Sosa SS .25 .60
106 Sammy Sosa SS .25 .60
107 Sammy Sosa SS .25 .60
108 Sammy Sosa SS .25 .60
109 Sammy Sosa SS .25 .60
110 Alex Rodriguez SS .30 .75
111 Alex Rodriguez SS .30 .75
112 Alex Rodriguez SS .30 .75
113 Alex Rodriguez SS .30 .75
114 Alex Rodriguez SS .30 .75
115 Mark McGwire SS .50 1.25
116 Mark McGwire SS .50 1.25
117 Mark McGwire SS .50 1.25
118 Mark McGwire SS .50 1.25
119 Mark McGwire SS .50 1.25
120 Jason Giambi 6.00 15.00
Ken Griffey Jr.
Mark McGwire
Alex Rodriguez
Sammy Sosa
Ichiro Suzuki SP/2002
121 Curt Schilling .25 .60
122 Cliff Floyd .25 .60
123 Derek Lowe .25 .60
124 Hee Seop Choi .25 .60
125 Mark Prior .40 1.00
126 Joe Borchard .25 .60
127 Austin Kearns .25 .60
128 Adam Dunn .25 .60
129 Jay Payton .25 .60
130 Carlos Pena .25 .60
131 Andy Van Hekken .25 .60
132 Andres Torres .25 .60
133 Ben Diggins .25 .60
134 Torii Hunter .25 .60
135 Bartolo Colon .25 .60
136 Raul Mondesi .25 .60
137 Alfonso Soriano .25 .60
138 Miguel Tejada .25 .60
139 Ray Durham .25 .60
140 Eric Chavez .25 .60
141 Marlon Byrd .25 .60
142 Brett Myers .25 .60
143 Sean Burroughs .25 .60
144 Kenny Lofton .25 .60
145 Scott Rolen .40 1.00
146 Carl Crawford .25 .60
147 Jayson Werth .25 .60
148 Josh Phelps .25 .60
149 Eric Hinske .25 .60
150 Orlando Hudson .25 .60
151 Jose Valverde WP RC 1.50 4.00
152 Trey Hodges WP RC 1.50 4.00
153 Joey Dawley WP RC 1.50 4.00
154 Travis Driskill WP RC 1.50 4.00
155 Howie Clark WP RC 1.50 4.00
156 J.De La Rosa WP RC 1.50 4.00
157 Freddy Sanchez WP RC 2.00 5.00
158 Earl Snyder WP RC 1.50 4.00
159 Cliff Lee WP RC 6.00 15.00
160 Josh Bard WP RC 1.50 4.00
161 Aaron Cook WP RC 1.50 4.00
162 Franklyn German WP RC 1.50 4.00
163 Brandon Puffer WP RC 1.50 4.00
164 Kirk Saarloos WP RC 1.50 4.00
165 Jer. Robertson WP RC 1.50 4.00
166 Miguel Asencio WP RC 1.50 4.00
167 Shawn Sedlacek WP RC 1.50 4.00
168 Jayson Durocher WP RC 1.50 4.00
169 Shane Nance WP RC 1.50 4.00
170 Jamey Carroll WP RC 2.00 5.00
171 Oliver Perez WP RC 2.00 5.00
172 Wil Nieves WP RC 1.50 4.00
173 Clay Condrey WP RC 1.50 4.00
174 Chris Snelling WP RC 1.50 4.00
175 Mike Crudale WP RC 1.50 4.00
176 J.Simontacchi WP RC 1.50 4.00
177 Felix Escalona WP RC 1.50 4.00
178 Lance Carter WP RC 1.50 4.00
179 Scott Wiggins WP RC 1.50 4.00
180 Kevin Cash WP RC 1.50 4.00

2002 Upper Deck Ovation Silver

Randomly inserted in packs, this is a complete parallel of the 2002 Upper Deck Ovation set. Cards numbered 1-60 and 90-119 were inserted at an overall approximate stated odds of one in four while cards 61-89 and 120 were printed to a stated print run of 100 serial numbered sets.

*SILVER 1-60: 1.25X TO 3X BASIC
*SILVER 61-89/120: .5X TO 1.2X BASIC
*SILVER 61-119: 2.5X TO 6X BASIC

2002 Upper Deck Ovation Standing Ovation

Randomly inserted into 2002 Upper Deck Rookie Debut Packs, this is a parallel to the World Premier (cards 151-180) subset. These cards were issued to a stated print run of 50 serial numbered sets.

*STANDING O 151-180: 1.5X TO 4X BASIC

2002 Upper Deck Ovation Authentic McGwire

Randomly inserted into packs, these two cards feature authentic game-used memorabilia pieces from Mark McGwire's major league career. These two cards are each produced to a stated print run of 70 serial numbered sets.

AMB Mark McGwire Bat 50.00 100.00
AMJ Mark McGwire Jsy 50.00 100.00

2002 Upper Deck Ovation Authentic McGwire Gold

Randomly inserted into packs, these two cards feature authentic game-used memorabilia pieces from Mark McGwire's major league career. These two cards are each produced to a stated print run of 50 serial numbered sets.

AMBG Mark McGwire Bat 60.00 120.00
AMJG Mark McGwire Jsy 60.00 120.00

2002 Upper Deck Ovation Authentic McGwire Signatures

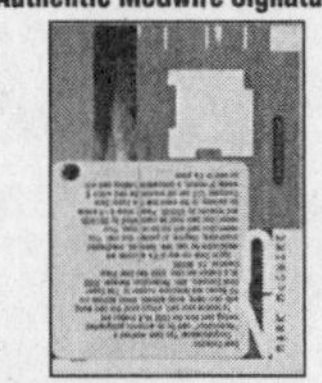

Randomly inserted into packs, these two cards feature authentic game-used memorabilia pieces from Mark McGwire's major league career as well as an authentic autograph. However, McGwire did not sign his cards in time for inclusion in this set so these cards were issued in the form of redemption cards with a mailing of July 3rd, 2005. These two cards were each produced to a stated print run of 25 serial numbered sets and no pricing is provided due to market scarcity.

AMSB Mark McGwire Bat
AMSJ Mark McGwire Jsy

2002 Upper Deck Ovation Diamond Futures Jerseys

Inserted in packs at stated odds of one in 72, these 12 cards feature game-worn jersey swatches from 12 of baseball's future stars.

GOLD PRINT RUN 25 SERIAL #'d SETS
NO GOLD PRICING DUE TO SCARCITY
DFBZ Barry Zito 4.00 10.00
DFFG Freddy Garcia 4.00 10.00
DFIR Ivan Rodriguez 6.00 15.00
DFJK Jason Kendall 4.00 10.00
DFJP Jorge Posada 6.00 15.00
DFJR Jimmy Rollins 4.00 10.00
DFJV Jose Vidro 4.00 10.00
DFKS Kazuhiro Sasaki 4.00 10.00
DFLB Lance Berkman 4.00 10.00
DFPB Pat Burrell 4.00 10.00
DFRB Russell Branyan 4.00 10.00
DFTH Tim Hudson 4.00 10.00

2002 Upper Deck Ovation Lead Performer Jerseys

Inserted in packs at stated odds of one in 72, these 12 cards feature game-worn swatches from some of the leading players in baseball. A couple of these cards were produced in shorter quantity and we have notated that information in our checklist next to their name.

GOLD PRINT RUN 25 SERIAL #'d SETS
NO GOLD PRICING DUE TO SCARCITY
LPAR Alex Rodriguez 6.00 15.00
LPCD Carlos Delgado 4.00 10.00
LPFT Frank Thomas 6.00 15.00
LPIR Ivan Rodriguez 6.00 15.00
LPIS Ichiro Suzuki Shirt 20.00 50.00
LPJB Jeff Bagwell 6.00 15.00
LPJG Jason Giambi 4.00 10.00
LPJG Juan Gonzalez 4.00 10.00
LPKG Ken Griffey Jr. SP 10.00 25.00
LPLG Luis Gonzalez 4.00 10.00
LPMP Mike Piazza 6.00 15.00
LPSS Sammy Sosa SP 6.00 15.00

2002 Upper Deck Ovation Spokesman Spotlight Signatures

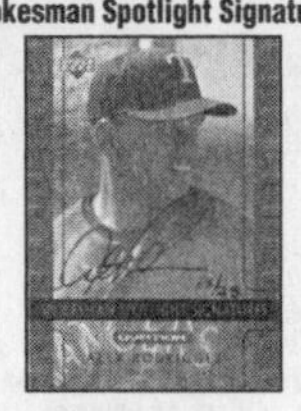

Randomly inserted into packs, these six cards feature authentic signatures of the six Upper Deck spokesman. Since each card is produced to a stated print run of 25 serial numbered sets, there is no pricing due to market scarcity.

AR Alex Rodriguez
IS Ichiro Suzuki
JG Jason Giambi
KG Ken Griffey Jr.
MM Mark McGwire
SS Sammy Sosa

2002 Upper Deck Ovation Swatches

Inserted at stated odds of one in 72, these 12 cards feature game-used larger "swatches" from the players featured. The Roberto Alomar card was issued in smaller quantities and we have notated that information in our checklist.

GOLD PRINT RUN 25 SERIAL #'d SETS
NO GOLD PRICING DUE TO SCARCITY
OAR Alex Rodriguez 6.00 15.00
OBW Bernie Williams 6.00 15.00
OCD Carlos Delgado 4.00 10.00
OCJ Chipper Jones 6.00 15.00
ODE Darin Erstad 4.00 10.00
OEB Ellis Burks 4.00 10.00
OEC Eric Chavez 4.00 10.00
OGM Greg Maddux 6.00 15.00
OJB Jeromy Burnitz 4.00 10.00
OMG Mark Grace 6.00 15.00
OPM Pedro Martinez 6.00 15.00
ORA Roberto Alomar SP

2006 Upper Deck Ovation

This 126-card set was released in October, 2006. This set was issued in five-card hobby packs which came 18 packs per box and 16 boxes per case. Cards numbered 1-84 feature veterans while cards numbered 85-126 feature 2006 rookies and were issued to a stated print run of 999 serial numbered sets and were inserted at a stated rate of one in 18.

COMP.SET w/o RC's (84) 10.00 25.00
COMMON CARD (1-84) .20 .50
COMMON ROOKIE (85-126) .75 2.00
85-126 STATED ODDS 1:18
85-126 PRINT RUN 999 SERIAL #'d SETS
EXQUISITE EXCH ODDS 1:144
EXQUISITE EXCH DEADLINE 07/27/07
1 Vladimir Guerrero .50 1.25
2 Bartolo Colon .20 .50
3 Chone Figgins .20 .50
4 Lance Berkman .30 .75
5 Roy Oswalt .30 .75
6 Craig Biggio .30 .75
7 Rich Harden .20 .50
8 Eric Chavez .20 .50
9 Huston Street .20 .50
10 Vernon Wells .20 .50
11 Roy Halladay .50 1.25
12 Troy Glaus .20 .50
13 Andruw Jones .20 .50
14 Chipper Jones .50 1.25
15 John Smoltz .50 1.25
16 Carlos Lee .20 .50
17 Rickie Weeks .30 .75
18 J.J. Hardy .20 .50
19 Albert Pujols 1.25 3.00
20 Chris Carpenter .50 1.25
21 Scott Rolen .30 .75
22 Derrek Lee .20 .50
23 Mark Prior .30 .75
24 Aramis Ramirez .20 .50
25 Carl Crawford .30 .75
26 Scott Kazmir .30 .75
27 Luis Gonzalez .20 .50
28 Brandon Webb .30 .75
29 Chad Tracy .20 .50
30 Jeff Kent .20 .50
31 J.D. Drew .20 .50
32 Jason Schmidt .20 .50
33 Randy Winn .20 .50
34 Travis Hafner .20 .50
35 Victor Martinez .30 .75
36 Grady Sizemore .30 .75
37 Ichiro Suzuki .75 2.00
38 Felix Hernandez .50 1.25
39 Adrian Beltre .20 .50
40 Miguel Cabrera .50 1.25
41 Dontrelle Willis .20 .50
42 David Wright .75 2.00
43 Jose Reyes .30 .75
44 Pedro Martinez .30 .75
45 Carlos Beltran .20 .50
46 Alfonso Soriano .30 .75
47 Livan Hernandez .20 .50
48 Jose Guillen .20 .50
49 Miguel Tejada .30 .75
50 Brian Roberts .20 .50
51 Melvin Mora .20 .50
52 Jake Peavy .20 .50
53 Brian Giles .20 .50
54 Khalil Greene .20 .50
55 Bobby Abreu .20 .50
56 Ryan Howard .75 2.00
57 Chase Utley .50 1.25
58 Jason Bay .20 .50
59 Sean Casey .20 .50
60 Mark Teixeira .50 1.25
61 Michael Young .30 .75
62 Hank Blalock .30 .75
63 Manny Ramirez .50 1.25
64 David Ortiz .30 .75
65 Josh Beckett .30 .75
66 Jason Varitek .50 1.25
67 Ken Griffey Jr. .75 2.00
68 Adam Dunn .30 .75
69 Todd Helton .30 .75
70 Garrett Atkins .20 .50
71 Reggie Sanders .20 .50
72 Mike Sweeney .20 .50
73 Chris Shelton .20 .50
74 Ivan Rodriguez .30 .75
75 Johan Santana .50 1.25
76 Torii Hunter .20 .50
77 Justin Morneau .50 1.25
78 Jim Thome .30 .75
79 Paul Konerko .30 .75
80 Scott Podsednik .20 .50
81 Derek Jeter 1.25 3.00
82 Hideki Matsui .50 1.25
83 Johnny Damon .30 .75
84 Alex Rodriguez .75 2.00
85 Conor Jackson (RC) 1.25 3.00
86 Joey Devine RC .75 2.00
87 Jonathan Papelbon (RC) 4.00 10.00
88 Freddie Bynum (RC) .75 2.00
89 Chris Denorfia (RC) .75 2.00
90 Ryan Shealy (RC) .75 2.00
91 Josh Wilson (RC) .75 2.00
92 Brian Anderson (RC) .75 2.00
93 Justin Verlander (RC) 6.00 15.00
94 Jeremy Hermida (RC) .75 2.00
95 Mike Jacobs (RC) .75 2.00
96 Josh Johnson (RC) 2.00 5.00
97 Hanley Ramirez (RC) 2.00 5.00
98 Josh Willingham (RC) .75 2.00
99 Cole Hamels (RC) 3.00 8.00
100 Hong-Chih Kuo (RC) 2.00 5.00
101 Cody Ross (RC) 2.00 5.00
102 Jose Capellan (RC) .75 2.00
103 Prince Fielder (RC) 3.00 8.00
104 David Gassner (RC) .75 2.00
105 Jason Kubel (RC) .75 2.00
106 Francisco Liriano (RC) 2.00 5.00
107 Anderson Hernandez (RC) .75 2.00
108 Boof Bonser (RC) 1.25 3.00
109 Jered Weaver (RC) 2.00 5.00
110 Ben Johnson (RC) .75 2.00
111 Jeff Harris RC .75 2.00
112 Stephen Drew (RC) 2.00 5.00
113 Matt Cain (RC) 2.00 5.00
114 Skip Schumaker (RC) .75 2.00
115 Adam Wainwright (RC) 2.00 5.00
116 Jeremy Sowers (RC) .75 2.00
117 Jason Bergmann RC .75 2.00
118 Chad Billingsley (RC) 1.25 3.00
119 Ryan Zimmerman (RC) 4.00 10.00
120 Macay McBride (RC) .75 2.00
121 Aaron Rakers (RC) .75 2.00
122 Alay Soler RC .75 2.00
123 Melky Cabrera (RC) 1.25 3.00
124 Tim Hamulack (RC) .75 2.00
125 Andre Ethier (RC) 3.00 8.00
126 Kenji Johjima RC 2.00 5.00

2006 Upper Deck Ovation Gold

*GOLD: 2.5X TO 6X BASIC
STATED ODDS 1:18
STATED PRINT RUN 499 SERIAL #'d SETS

2006 Upper Deck Ovation Gold Rookie Autographs

OVERALL AU ODDS 1:18
STATED PRINT RUN 99 SERIAL #'d SETS
EXCH DEADLINE 10/06/08
85 Conor Jackson 8.00 20.00
86 Joey Devine 5.00 12.00
87 Jonathan Papelbon 40.00 80.00
88 Freddie Bynum 5.00 12.00
89 Chris Denorfia 5.00 12.00
90 Ryan Shealy 5.00 12.00
91 Josh Wilson
92 Brian Anderson 5.00 12.00
93 Justin Verlander 40.00 80.00
94 Jeremy Hermida 8.00 20.00
95 Mike Jacobs 5.00 12.00
96 Josh Johnson 15.00 40.00
97 Hanley Ramirez 10.00 25.00
98 Josh Willingham
99 Cole Hamels 40.00 80.00
100 Hong-Chih Kuo
101 Cody Ross
102 Jose Capellan 5.00 12.00
104 David Gassner 5.00 12.00
105 Jason Kubel 5.00 12.00
106 Francisco Liriano 20.00 50.00
107 Anderson Hernandez 5.00 12.00
108 Boof Bonser 5.00 12.00
109 Jered Weaver 10.00 25.00
110 Ben Johnson 5.00 12.00
111 Jeff Harris 5.00 12.00
112 Stephen Drew
113 Matt Cain 8.00 20.00
114 Skip Schumaker 6.00 15.00
115 Adam Wainwright 15.00 40.00
117 Jason Bergmann 5.00 12.00
118 Chad Billingsley 12.50 30.00
119 Ryan Zimmerman 40.00 80.00
120 Macay McBride 5.00 12.00
121 Aaron Rakers 5.00 12.00
124 Tim Hamulack 5.00 12.00
125 Andre Ethier 40.00 80.00

2006 Upper Deck Ovation Apparel

STATED ODDS 1:18
AB A.J. Burnett Jsy 3.00 8.00
AO Akinori Otsuka Jsy 3.00 8.00
AP Albert Pujols Jsy 8.00 20.00
BA Jason Bay Jsy 3.00 8.00
CC Carl Crawford Jsy 3.00 8.00
CF Chone Figgins Jsy 3.00 8.00
CL Carlos Lee Jsy 3.00 8.00
CS Chris Shelton Jsy 3.00 8.00
DJ Derek Jeter Pants 10.00 25.00
DO David Ortiz Jsy 4.00 10.00
DW David Wright Jsy 6.00 15.00
EC Eric Chavez Jsy 3.00 8.00
FH Felix Hernandez Jsy 4.00 10.00
GR Ken Griffey Jr. Jsy 6.00 15.00
GS Grady Sizemore Jsy 4.00 10.00
HA Travis Hafner Jsy 3.00 8.00
HE Todd Helton Jsy 4.00 10.00
HS Huston Street Jsy 3.00 8.00
HU Torii Hunter Jsy 3.00 8.00
JB Jeremy Bonderman Jsy 3.00 8.00
JE Jim Edmonds Jsy 4.00 10.00
JF Jeff Francoeur Jsy 4.00 10.00
JG Jonny Gomes Jsy 3.00 8.00
JH J.J. Hardy Jsy 3.00 8.00
JK Jeff Kent Jsy 3.00 8.00
JM Joe Mauer Jsy 4.00 10.00
KG Khalil Greene Jsy 4.00 10.00
LB Lance Berkman Jsy 3.00 8.00
MP Mark Prior Jsy 4.00 10.00
MR Manny Ramirez Jsy 4.00 10.00
MT Mark Teixeira Jsy 4.00 10.00
PF Prince Fielder Jsy 4.00 10.00
RH Ryan Howard Jsy 6.00 15.00
RK Ryan Klesko Jsy 3.00 8.00
RO Roy Oswalt Jsy 3.00 8.00
RZ Ryan Zimmerman Jsy SP 8.00 20.00
SR Scott Rolen Jsy 4.00 10.00
TH Trevor Hoffman Jsy 3.00 8.00
TN Trot Nixon Jsy 3.00 8.00
VG Vladimir Guerrero Jsy 4.00 10.00
VM Victor Martinez Jsy 3.00 8.00
VW Vernon Wells Jsy 3.00 8.00

2006 Upper Deck Ovation Center Stage

STATED ODDS 1:11
AC Aaron Cook .50 1.25
AP Albert Pujols 3.00 8.00
BC Bobby Crosby .50 1.25
CA Miguel Cabrera 1.25 3.00
CS Chris Shelton .50 1.25
CW Chien-Ming Wang .75 2.00
DC Daniel Cabrera .50 1.25
DD David DeJesus .50 1.25
DJ Derek Jeter 3.00 8.00
DL Derrek Lee .50 1.25
DW David Wright 2.00 5.00
FH Felix Hernandez 1.25 3.00
FS Freddy Sanchez .50 1.25
IS Ian Snell .50 1.25
JB Josh Beckett .75 2.00
JC Jose Contreras .50 1.25
JF Jason Frasor .50 1.25
KG Ken Griffey Jr. 2.00 5.00
MC Michael Cuddyer .50 1.25
MP Mark Prior .75 2.00
MT Mark Teixeira 1.25 3.00
RH Runelvys Hernandez .50 1.25
SD Stephen Drew 1.25 3.00
VG Vladimir Guerrero 1.25 3.00
YM Yadier Molina .75 2.00

2006 Upper Deck Ovation Curtain Calls

STATED ODDS 1:14
BC Bobby Crosby .50 1.25
CS Chris Shelton .50 1.25
CW Chien-Ming Wang .75 2.00
DC Daniel Cabrera .50 1.25
DD David DeJesus .50 1.25
EC Eric Chavez .50 1.25
FS Freddy Sanchez .50 1.25
HE Runelvys Hernandez .50 1.25
HR Horacio Ramirez .50 1.25
JC Jose Contreras .50 1.25
JE Jered Weaver 1.25 3.00
JW Josh Willingham .50 1.25
KG1 Ken Griffey Jr. 2.00 5.00
KG2 Ken Griffey Jr. 2.00 5.00
MP Mark Prior .75 2.00
MT Miguel Tejada .75 2.00
MY Michael Young .75 2.00
RH Rich Harden .50 1.25
TO Tomo Ohka .50 1.25
YM Yadier Molina .75 2.00

2006 Upper Deck Ovation Nation

STATED ODDS 1:19
AJ Andruw Jones .50 1.25

AP Albert Pujols 3.00 8.00
DC Daniel Cabrera .50 1.25
DJ Derek Jeter 3.00 8.00
DM Daisuke Matsuzaka 1.50 4.00
FC Frederich Cepeda .50 1.25
JA Jae Seo .50 1.25
JB Jason Bay .50 1.25
JS Johan Santana 1.25 3.00
KG Ken Griffey Jr. 2.00 5.00
MC Miguel Cabrera 1.25 3.00
MT Miguel Tejada .75 2.00
NM Nobuhiko Matsunaka .75 2.00
SL Seung Yeop Lee .75 2.00
YG Yoandy Garlobo .50 1.25

2006 Upper Deck Ovation Nation Signatures

OVERALL AU ODDS 1:18
STATED PRINT RUN 25 SERIAL #'d SETS
NO PRICING DUE TO SCARCITY
KG Ken Griffey Jr.
MC Miguel Cabrera
MT Miguel Tejada

2006 Upper Deck Ovation Spotlight Signatures

OVERALL AU ODDS 1:18
AC Aaron Cook 4.00 10.00
AG Andy Green 4.00 10.00
BC Bobby Crosby 4.00 10.00
CA Miguel Cabrera 10.00 25.00
CS Chris Shelton 4.00 10.00
CW Chien-Ming Wang 30.00 60.00
DC Daniel Cabrera 4.00 10.00
DD David DeJesus 4.00 10.00
DR David Ross 6.00 15.00
EC Eric Chavez SP 6.00 15.00
EJ Edwin Jackson 4.00 10.00
FG Franklyn German 4.00 10.00
FN Fernando Nieve 4.00 10.00
FS Freddy Sanchez 6.00 15.00
HA Rich Harden SP 4.00 10.00
HR Horacio Ramirez SP 4.00 10.00
IS Ian Snell
JB Josh Beckett SP 15.00 40.00
JC Jose Contreras 6.00 15.00
JD Jorge De La Rosa 4.00 10.00
JF Jason Frasor 4.00 10.00
JV Javier Vazquez SP
JW Josh Willingham SP 6.00 15.00
KG1 Ken Griffey Jr. 30.00 60.00
KG2 Ken Griffey Jr. 30.00 60.00
KS Kirk Saarloos 4.00 10.00
LC Lance Cormier 4.00 10.00
MC Michael Cuddyer SP 4.00 10.00
MG Mike Gonzalez 4.00 10.00
MP Mark Prior 8.00 20.00
MT Matt Thornton 4.00 10.00
MW Michael Wuertz 4.00 10.00
MY Michael Young 6.00 15.00
RH Runelvys Hernandez 4.00 10.00
RW Ryan Wagner 4.00 10.00
SC Shawn Camp 4.00 10.00
TE Miguel Tejada SP 6.00 15.00
TO Tomo Ohka 10.00 25.00
TR Matt Treanor 4.00 10.00
YM Yadier Molina 10.00 25.00

2006 Upper Deck Ovation Superstar Theatre

STATED ODDS 1:9
AJ Andruw Jones .50 1.25
AP Albert Pujols 3.00 8.00
AR Alex Rodriguez 2.00 5.00
BA Jason Bay .50 1.25
BC Bobby Crosby .50 1.25
CC Chris Carpenter 1.25 3.00
CS Chris Shelton .50 1.25
CW Chien-Ming Wang .75 2.00
DC Daniel Cabrera .50 1.25
DD David DeJesus .50 1.25
DJ Derek Jeter 3.00 8.00
DL Derrek Lee .50 1.25
DO David Ortiz .75 2.00
HM Hideki Matsui 1.25 3.00
IS Ichiro Suzuki 2.00 5.00
JB Josh Beckett .75 2.00
JC Jose Contreras .50 1.25
KG1 Ken Griffey Jr. 2.00 5.00
KG2 Ken Griffey Jr. 2.00 5.00
MC Miguel Cabrera 1.25 3.00
MP Mark Prior .75 2.00
MR Manny Ramirez 1.25 3.00
MT Miguel Tejada .75 2.00
MY Michael Young .75 2.00
PM Pedro Martinez .75 2.00
RH Rich Harden .50 1.25
TE Mark Teixeira 1.25 3.00
TH Travis Hafner .50 1.25
TO Tomo Ohka .50 1.25
YM Yadier Molina .75 2.00

2007 Upper Deck Premier

This 244-card set was release in April, 2007. This set was issued in seven-card packs (Actually small boxes) which came 10 boxes per case. Cards numbered 1-200 feature veterans and those cards were issued to a stated print run of 99 serial numbered sets and cards numbered 201-244 featured rookie logo players and those cards were issued to a stated print run of 199 serial numbered sets.

COMMON CARD (1-200) 2.00 5.00
BASE CARD ODDS ONE PER PACK
1-200 STATED PRINT RUN 99 SER.#'d SETS
COMMON ROOKIE (201-244) 2.00 5.00
RC ODDS ONE PER PACK
201-244 STATED PRINT RUN 199 SER.#'d SETS
PRINT.PLATES RANDOM INSERTS IN PACKS
PLATE PRINT RUN 1 SET PER COLOR
BLACK-CYAN-MAGENTA-YELLOW ISSUED
NO PLATE PRICING DUE TO SCARCITY
1 Roy Campanella 4.00 10.00
2 Ty Cobb 5.00 12.00
3 Mickey Cochrane 2.00 5.00
4 Dizzy Dean 3.00 8.00
5 Don Drysdale 3.00 8.00
6 Jimmie Foxx 4.00 10.00
7 Lou Gehrig 6.00 15.00
8 Lefty Grove 2.00 5.00
9 Rogers Hornsby 4.00 10.00
10 Walter Johnson 4.00 10.00
11 Eddie Mathews 4.00 10.00
12 Christy Mathewson 4.00 10.00
13 Johnny Mize 3.00 8.00
14 Thurman Munson 5.00 12.00
15 Mel Ott 3.00 8.00
16 Satchel Paige 4.00 10.00
17 Jackie Robinson 5.00 12.00
18 Babe Ruth 8.00 20.00
19 George Sisler 2.00 5.00
20 Honus Wagner 4.00 10.00
21 Cy Young 4.00 10.00
22 Luis Aparicio 2.00 5.00
23 Johnny Bench 4.00 10.00
24 Yogi Berra 4.00 10.00
25 Rod Carew 3.00 8.00
26 Orlando Cepeda 2.00 5.00
27 Bob Feller 3.00 8.00
28 Carlton Fisk 3.00 8.00
29 Bob Gibson 3.00 8.00
30 Catfish Hunter 2.00 5.00
31 Reggie Jackson 3.00 8.00
32 Al Kaline 4.00 10.00
33 Harmon Killebrew 4.00 10.00
34 Buck Leonard 2.00 5.00
35 Juan Marichal 2.00 5.00
36 Bill Mazeroski 3.00 8.00
37 Willie McCovey 3.00 8.00
38 Joe Morgan 3.00 8.00
39 Eddie Murray 4.00 10.00
40 Jim Palmer 3.00 8.00
41 Tony Perez 3.00 8.00
42 Pee Wee Reese 3.00 8.00
43 Brooks Robinson 4.00 10.00
44 Nolan Ryan 8.00 20.00
45 Mike Schmidt 4.00 10.00
46 Tom Seaver 3.00 8.00
47 Enos Slaughter 2.00 5.00
48 Willie Stargell 3.00 8.00
49 Early Wynn 2.00 5.00
50 Robin Yount 4.00 10.00
51 Tony Gwynn 4.00 10.00
52 Cal Ripken Jr. 10.00 25.00
53 Ernie Banks 4.00 10.00
54 Wade Boggs 3.00 8.00
55 Steve Carlton 2.00 5.00
56 Will Clark 3.00 8.00
57 Fergie Jenkins 2.00 5.00
58 Bo Jackson 4.00 10.00
59 Don Mattingly 6.00 15.00
60 Stan Musial 5.00 12.00
61 Frank Robinson 2.00 5.00
62 Ryne Sandberg 5.00 12.00
63 Ozzie Smith 6.00 15.00
64 Carl Yastrzemski 5.00 12.00
65 Dave Winfield 3.00 8.00
66 Paul Molitor 2.00 5.00
67 Jason Bay 2.00 5.00
68 Freddy Sanchez 2.00 5.00
69 Josh Beckett 2.00 5.00
70 Carlos Beltran 2.00 5.00
71 Craig Biggio 4.00 10.00
72 Matt Holliday 2.50 6.00
73 A.J. Burnett 2.00 5.00
74 Miguel Cabrera 3.00 8.00
75 Dontrelle Willis 2.00 5.00
76 Chris Carpenter 3.00 8.00
77 Roger Clemens 6.00 15.00
78 Johnny Damon 3.00 8.00
79 Jermaine Dye 2.00 5.00
80 Jim Thome 3.00 8.00
81 Vladimir Guerrero 4.00 10.00
82 Travis Hafner 2.00 5.00
83 Victor Martinez 2.00 5.00
84 Trevor Hoffman 2.00 5.00
85 Derek Jeter 8.00 20.00
86 Ken Griffey Jr. 5.00 12.00
87 Randy Johnson 4.00 10.00
88 Andruw Jones 3.00 8.00
89 Derrek Lee 2.00 5.00
90 Greg Maddux 5.00 12.00
91 Magglio Ordonez 3.00 8.00
92 David Ortiz 4.00 10.00
93 Jake Peavy 2.00 5.00
94 Roy Oswalt 2.00 5.00
95 Mike Piazza 4.00 10.00
96 Jose Reyes 4.00 10.00
97 Ivan Rodriguez 4.00 10.00
98 Johan Santana 3.00 8.00
99 Scott Rolen 3.00 8.00
100 Curt Schilling 3.00 8.00
101 John Smoltz 3.00 8.00
102 Alfonso Soriano 2.00 5.00
103 Miguel Tejada 3.00 8.00
104 Frank Thomas 5.00 12.00
105 Chase Utley 4.00 10.00
106 Joe Mauer 2.00 5.00
107 Alex Rodriguez 6.00 15.00
108 Alex Rios 3.00 8.00
109 Justin Verlander 4.00 10.00
110 Ryan Howard 5.00 12.00
111 Jered Weaver 3.00 8.00
112 Francisco Liriano 4.00 10.00
113 David Wright 5.00 12.00
114 Felix Hernandez 3.00 8.00
115 Jeremy Sowers 3.00 8.00
116 Cole Hamels 3.00 8.00
117 B.J. Upton 2.00 5.00
118 Chien-Ming Wang 20.00 50.00
119 Justin Morneau 3.00 8.00
120 Jonny Gomes 2.00 5.00
121 Adrian Gonzalez 2.00 5.00
122 Bill Hall 3.00 8.00
123 Rich Harden 3.00 8.00
124 Rich Hill 2.00 5.00
125 Tadahito Iguchi 2.00 5.00
126 Scott Kazmir 3.00 8.00
127 Howie Kendrick 2.00 5.00
128 Dan Uggla 3.00 8.00
129 Hanley Ramirez 3.00 8.00
130 Josh Willingham 2.00 5.00
131 Nick Markakis 3.00 8.00
132 Grady Sizemore 4.00 10.00
133 Ian Kinsler 3.00 8.00
134 Jonathan Papelbon 5.00 12.00
135 Ryan Zimmerman 4.00 10.00
136 Stephen Drew 3.00 8.00
137 Adam Wainwright 2.00 5.00
138 Joel Zumaya 3.00 8.00
139 Prince Fielder 4.00 10.00
140 Carl Crawford 3.00 8.00
141 Huston Street 2.00 5.00
142 Matt Cain 3.00 8.00
143 Andre Ethier 3.00 8.00
144 Brian McCann 3.00 8.00
145 Josh Barfield 2.00 5.00
146 Anibal Sanchez 2.00 5.00
147 Brian Roberts 3.00 8.00
148 Brandon Webb 2.00 5.00
149 Chipper Jones 4.00 10.00
150 Tim Hudson 3.00 8.00
151 Adam LaRoche 2.00 5.00
152 Jeff Francoeur 4.00 10.00
153 Marcus Giles 2.00 5.00
154 Jason Varitek 5.00 12.00
155 Coco Crisp 3.00 8.00
156 Manny Ramirez 3.00 8.00
157 Trot Nixon 3.00 8.00
158 Carlos Zambrano 2.00 5.00
159 Mark Prior 3.00 8.00
160 Aramis Ramirez 2.00 5.00
161 Mark Buehrle 2.00 5.00
162 Paul Konerko 2.00 5.00
163 Adam Dunn 3.00 8.00
164 C.C. Sabathia 2.00 5.00
165 Todd Helton 3.00 8.00
166 Garrett Atkins 3.00 8.00
167 Jeremy Bonderman 4.00 10.00
168 Curtis Granderson 3.00 8.00
169 Sean Casey 3.00 8.00
170 Lance Berkman 3.00 8.00
171 Brad Lidge 2.00 5.00
172 Reggie Sanders 2.00 5.00
173 Brad Penny 2.00 5.00
174 Nomar Garciaparra 5.00 12.00
175 Jeff Kent 3.00 8.00
176 Chone Figgins 2.00 5.00
177 Ben Sheets 3.00 8.00
178 Rickie Weeks 3.00 8.00
179 Joe Nathan 3.00 8.00
180 Torii Hunter 3.00 8.00
181 Carlos Delgado 3.00 8.00
182 Tom Glavine 4.00 10.00
183 Paul Lo Duca 2.00 5.00
184 Mariano Rivera 5.00 12.00
185 Robinson Cano 4.00 10.00
186 Bobby Abreu 3.00 8.00
187 Hideki Matsui 5.00 12.00
188 Barry Zito 2.00 5.00
189 Eric Chavez 3.00 8.00
190 Jimmy Rollins 3.00 8.00
191 Khalil Greene 4.00 10.00
192 Brian Giles 2.00 5.00
193 Jason Schmidt 2.00 5.00
194 Ichiro Suzuki 12.50 30.00
195 David Eckstein 4.00 10.00
196 Jim Edmonds 3.00 8.00
197 Mark Teixeira 3.00 8.00
198 Michael Young 2.00 5.00
199 Vernon Wells 3.00 8.00
200 Roy Halladay 3.00 8.00
201 Delmon Young (RC) 3.00 8.00
202 Andrew Miller RC 8.00 20.00
203 Troy Tulowitzki (RC) 3.00 8.00
204 Jeff Fiorentino (RC) 2.00 5.00
205 David Murphy (RC) 2.00 5.00
206 Jeff Baker (RC) 2.00 5.00
207 Kevin Hooper (RC) 2.00 5.00
208 Kevin Kouzmanoff (RC) 2.00 5.00
209 Adam Lind (RC) 3.00 8.00
210 Mike Rabelo RC 3.00 8.00
211 John Nelson (RC) 3.00 8.00
212 Mitch Maier RC 2.00 5.00
213 Ryan Braun RC 2.00 5.00
214 Vinny Rottino (RC) 2.00 5.00
215 Drew Anderson RC 2.00 5.00
216 Alexi Casilla RC 3.00 8.00
217 Glen Perkins (RC) 2.00 5.00
218 Cesar Jimenez RC 2.00 5.00
219 Tim Gradoville RC 2.00 5.00
220 Shane Youman RC 2.00 5.00
221 Billy Sadler (RC) 2.00 5.00
222 Patrick Misch (RC) 2.00 5.00
223 Juan Salas (RC) 2.00 5.00
224 Beltran Perez (RC) 2.00 5.00
225 Hector Gimenez (RC) 2.00 5.00
226 Philip Humber (RC) 3.00 8.00
227 Eric Stults RC 2.00 5.00
228 Dennis Sarfate (RC) 2.00 5.00
229 Andy Cannizaro RC 3.00 8.00
230 Juan Morillo (RC) 2.00 5.00
231 Fred Lewis (RC) 2.00 5.00
232 Ryan Sweeney (RC) 2.00 5.00
233 Chris Narveson (RC) 2.00 5.00
234 Michael Bourn (RC) 2.00 5.00
235 Joaquin Arias (RC) 2.00 5.00
236 Carlos Maldonado (RC) 2.00 5.00
237 Alvin Colina RC 2.00 5.00
238 Jon Knott (RC) 2.00 5.00
239 Justin Hampson (RC) 2.00 5.00
240 Jeff Salazar (RC) 2.00 5.00
241 Josh Fields (RC) 2.00 5.00
242 Delwyn Young (RC) 2.00 5.00
243 Daisuke Matsuzaka RC 15.00 40.00
244 Kei Igawa RC 8.00 20.00

2007 Upper Deck Premier Autograph Parallel

OVERALL AUTO ODDS 1 PER PACK
PRINT RUNS B/WN 15-73 COPIES PER
NO PRICING ON QTY OF 25 OR LESS
244 Kei Igawa/73 150.00 200.00

2007 Upper Deck Premier Bronze

*BRONZE: .5X TO 1.2X BASIC
BRONZE RANDOMLY INSERTED IN PACKS
STATED PRINT RUN 75 SER.#'d SETS
243 Daisuke Matsuzaka 15.00 40.00

2007 Upper Deck Premier Gold

*GOLD: .6X TO 1.5X BASIC
GOLD RANDOMLY INSERTED IN PACKS
STATED PRINT RUN 49 SER.#'d SETS
243 Daisuke Matsuzaka 20.00 50.00

2007 Upper Deck Premier Platinum

PLATINUM RANDOMLY INSERTED IN PACKS
STATED PRINT RUN 1 SER.#'d SET
NO PRICING DUE TO SCARCITY

2007 Upper Deck Premier Silver

*SILVER: .5X TO 1.2X BASIC
SILVER RANDOMLY INSERTED IN PACKS
STATED PRINT RUN 99 SER.#'d SETS
243 Daisuke Matsuzaka 15.00 40.00

2007 Upper Deck Premier Emerging Stars Autographs Dual

STATED PRINT RUN 50 SER.#'d SETS
BRONZE PRINT RUN 25 SER.#'d SETS
NO BRONZE PRICING DUE TO SCARCITY
GOLD PRINT RUN 10 SER.#'d SETS
NO GOLD PRICING DUE TO SCARCITY
PLATINUM PRINT RUN 1 SER.#'d SET
NO PLATINUM PRICING DUE TO SCARCITY
OVERALL AUTO ODDS ONE PER PACK
EXCHANGE DEADLINE 04/26/10
BU Josh Barfield 10.00 25.00
Dan Uggla
BV Jeremy Bonderman 20.00 50.00
Justin Verlander
CA Carl Crawford 10.00 25.00
Alex Rios
CH Matt Cain
Philip Humber
CR Chien-Ming Wang
Rich Harden
CS Shin-Soo Choo
Grady Sizemore
FJ Felix Hernandez 30.00 60.00
Jered Weaver
GB Adrian Gonzalez 10.00 25.00
Josh Barfield
GC Jonny Gomes 10.00 25.00
Carl Crawford
HP Philip Humber 30.00 60.00
Mike Pelfrey
HS Rich Harden 10.00 25.00
Huston Street
HV Rich Harden 15.00 40.00
Justin Verlander
IK Tadahito Iguchi 20.00 50.00
Ian Kinsler
KL Scott Kazmir 20.00 50.00
Francisco Liriano
KS Scott Kazmir 10.00 25.00
Jeremy Sowers
LH Jon Lester 20.00 50.00
Craig Hansen
MB Joe Mauer 20.00 50.00
Jeremy Brown
MG Justin Morneau 20.00 50.00
Adrian Gonzalez
MH Andrew Miller 12.50 30.00
Cole Hamels
MM Joe Mauer
Brian McCann
MS Nick Markakis
Grady Sizemore
MZ Andrew Miller 30.00 60.00
Joel Zumaya
PH Jonathan Papelbon 20.00 50.00
Craig Hansen
PW Jonathan Papelbon 20.00 50.00
Adam Wainwright
QD Carlos Quentin 12.50 30.00
Stephen Drew
RB Rickie Weeks 20.00 50.00
Bill Hall
RD Jose Reyes 30.00 60.00
Stephen Drew
RH Jae Kuk Ryu
Rich Hill
RR Jose Reyes 40.00 80.00
Hanley Ramirez
RY Alex Rios 20.00 50.00
Delmon Young
SH Jeremy Sowers 12.50 30.00
Cole Hamels
SJ Anibal Sanchez 10.00 25.00
Josh Johnson
SU Freddy Sanchez
B.J. Upton
SW Huston Street
Adam Wainwright
SZ Freddy Sanchez
Ryan Zimmerman
TR Troy Tulowitzki 15.00 40.00
Hanley Ramirez
UG B.J. Upton 10.00 25.00
Jonny Gomes
UR Dan Uggla 20.00 50.00
Hanley Ramirez
UU Chase Utley 30.00 60.00
Dan Uggla
VH Justin Verlander 40.00 80.00
Felix Hernandez
VM Justin Verlander 20.00 50.00
Andrew Miller
WC Chien-Ming Wang
Melky Cabrera
WF Rickie Weeks
Prince Fielder
WH Chien-Ming Wang
Rich Hill
WK Jered Weaver 20.00 50.00
Howie Kendrick
WL Jered Weaver 20.00 50.00
Francisco Liriano
YT Delmon Young 12.50 30.00
Troy Tulowitzki
ZW Joel Zumaya 10.00 25.00
Adam Wainwright

2007 Upper Deck Premier Emerging Stars Autographs Triple

STATED PRINT RUN 50 SER.#'d SETS
BRONZE PRINT RUN 25 SER.#'d SETS
NO BRONZE PRICING DUE TO SCARCITY
GOLD PRINT RUN 10 SER.#'d SETS
NO GOLD PRICING DUE TO SCARCITY
PLATINUM PRINT RUN 1 SER.#'d SET
NO PLATINUM PRICING DUE TO SCARCITY
OVERALL AUTO ODDS ONE PER PACK
EXCHANGE DEADLINE 04/26/10
AZU Garrett Atkins
Ryan Zimmerman
B.J. Upton
CWV Matt Cain
Jered Weaver
Justin Verlander
DZU Stephen Drew
Ryan Zimmerman
B.J. Upton
ELS Andre Ethier 20.00 50.00
James Loney
Takashi Saito
FHW Prince Fielder
Bill Hall
Rickie Weeks
FLM Prince Fielder
Adam LaRoche
Justin Morneau
KUK Howie Kendrick 20.00 50.00
Dan Uggla
Ian Kinsler
KWN Howie Kendrick
Jered Weaver
Mike Napoli
LBG Francisco Liriano 30.00 60.00
Boof Bonser
Matt Garza
MFL Justin Morneau
Prince Fielder
James Loney
MHL Andrew Miller 30.00 60.00
Cole Hamels
Francisco Liriano
MKL Justin Morneau 20.00 50.00
Jason Kubel
Francisco Liriano
MLD Brian McCann
Adam LaRoche
Kyle Davies
MMM Russell Martin
Brian McCann
Joe Mauer
MMN Brian McCann
Joe Mauer
Mike Napoli
MMW Joe Mauer
Brian McCann
Josh Willingham
MSK Andrew Miller 20.00 50.00
Jeremy Sowers
Scott Kazmir
MVB Andrew Miller 20.00 50.00
Justin Verlander
Jeremy Bonderman
MYE Nick Markakis 40.00 80.00
Delmon Young
Andre Ethier
PCW Mike Pelfrey
Matt Cain
Jered Weaver
PSW Jonathan Papelbon 30.00 60.00
Huston Street
Adam Wainwright
RRD Jose Reyes 40.00 80.00
Hanley Ramirez
Stephen Drew
SHK Jeremy Sowers 20.00 50.00
Cole Hamels
Scott Kazmir
SHR Anibal Sanchez
Felix Hernandez
Anthony Reyes
SOJ Anibal Sanchez
Scott Olsen
Josh Johnson
SUZ Freddy Sanchez
B.J. Upton
Ryan Zimmerman
TDR Troy Tulowitzki 30.00 60.00
Stephen Drew
Hanley Ramirez
THA Troy Tulowitzki 40.00 80.00
Matt Holliday
Garrett Atkins
UKW Chase Utley 30.00 60.00
Howie Kendrick
Rickie Weeks
UUW Chase Utley 30.00 60.00
Dan Uggla
Rickie Weeks
UYK B.J. Upton 30.00 60.00
Delmon Young
Scott Kazmir
VMZ Justin Verlander 20.00 50.00
Andrew Miller
Joel Zumaya
WHV Jered Weaver 40.00 80.00
Felix Hernandez
Justin Verlander
WPH Chien-Ming Wang
Mike Pelfrey
Philip Humber
YER Delmon Young 20.00 50.00
Andre Ethier
Alex Rios
ZFV Ryan Zimmerman
Prince Fielder
Justin Verlander

2007 Upper Deck Premier Hallmarks Autographs

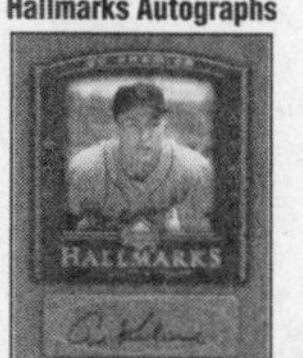

PRINT RUNS B/WN 5-57 COPIES PER
NO PRICING ON QTY 25 OR LESS
GOLD PRINT RUN 25 SER.#'d SETS
NO GOLD PRICING DUE TO SCARCITY
PLATINUM PRINT RUN 1 SER.#'d SET
NO PLATINUM PRICING DUE TO SCARCITY
OVERALL AUTO ODDS ONE PER PACK
EXCHANGE DEADLINE 04/26/10
AK Al Kaline/15
BF Bob Feller/5
BR Brooks Robinson/16
CF Carlton Fisk/11
CY Carl Yastrzemski/18
EB Ernie Banks/11
FR Frank Robinson/12
JB Johnny Bench/14
JP Jim Palmer/23
LA Luis Aparicio/57 20.00 50.00
MS Mike Schmidt/48 20.00 50.00
NR Nolan Ryan/11
OS Ozzie Smith/57 20.00 50.00
PM Paul Molitor/39 10.00 25.00

RJ Reggie Jackson/47 20.00 50.00
RS Ryne Sandberg/40 30.00 60.00
SC Steve Carlton/27 15.00 40.00
SM Stan Musial/20
WB Wade Boggs/12
WF Whitey Ford/25
WM Willie McCovey/45 20.00 50.00
YB Yogi Berra/15

2007 Upper Deck Premier Insignias Autographs

STATED PRINT RUN 50 SER.#'d SETS
GOLD PRINT RUN 25 SER.#'d SETS
NO GOLD PRICING DUE TO SCARCITY
PLATINUM PRINT RUN 1 SER.#'d SET
NO PLATINUM PRICING DUE TO SCARCTIY
OVERALL AUTO ODDS ONE PER PACK
EXCHANGE DEADLINE 04/26/10
AK Al Kaline 15.00 40.00
AM Andrew Miller 40.00 80.00
BU B.J. Upton 10.00 25.00
CR Cal Ripken Jr. 60.00 120.00
DJ Derek Jeter 100.00 200.00
DL Derrek Lee 15.00 40.00
DM Don Mattingly 40.00 80.00
DY Delmon Young 20.00 50.00
FH Felix Hernandez 30.00 60.00
JM Joe Mauer 50.00 100.00
JP Jake Peavy 10.00 25.00
JR Jose Reyes 40.00 80.00
JT Jim Thome 30.00 60.00
JW Jered Weaver 10.00 25.00
KG Ken Griffey Jr. 50.00 100.00
MO Justin Morneau 10.00 25.00
OS Ozzie Smith 20.00 50.00
PA Jim Palmer 10.00 25.00
TT Troy Tulowitzki 15.00 40.00
WC Will Clark 10.00 25.00

2007 Upper Deck Premier Noteworthy Autographs

PRINT RUN B/WN 1-86 COPIES PER
NO PRICING ON QTY 25 OR LESS
GOLD PRINT RUN 25 SER.#'d SETS
NO GOLD PRICING DUE TO SCARCITY
PLATINUM PRINT RUN 1 SER.#'d SET
NO PLATINUM PRICING DUE TO SCARCITY
OVERALL AUTO ODDS ONE PER PACK
EXCHANGE DEADLINE 04/26/10
AD Andre Dawson/50 10.00 25.00
AK Al Kaline/50 12.50 30.00
AM Andrew Miller/6
AS Alfonso Soriano/35 30.00 60.00
BA Jeff Bagwell/75 12.50 30.00
BE Josh Beckett/50 20.00 50.00
BF Bob Feller/62 12.50 30.00
BJ Bo Jackson/35 40.00 80.00
BR Brooks Robinson/35 20.00 50.00
CB Craig Biggio/65 20.00 50.00
CC Chris Carpenter/50 15.00 40.00
CF Carlton Fisk/37 20.00 50.00
CR Cal Ripken Jr./34
DB Dusty Baker
DE Dennis Eckersley/75 10.00 25.00
DM Don Mattingly/35 40.00 80.00
DS Don Sutton/50 6.00 15.00
DU Adam Dunn
DW Dontrelle Willis
DY Delmon Young/1
EB Ernie Banks
FJ Fergie Jenkins/74 6.00 15.00
FR Frank Robinson/31 15.00 40.00
GS Gary Sheffield/86 15.00 40.00
HR Hanley Ramirez/51 12.50 30.00
JB Jim Bunning/54 12.50 30.00
JB Johnny Bench/45 20.00 50.00
JC Jack Clark/75 6.00 15.00
JK Jason Kendall
JM Juan Marichal/65 10.00 25.00
JM Joe Mauer/36 40.00 80.00
JP Jim Palmer/65 10.00 25.00
JR Jose Reyes
JS Johan Santana/65 20.00 50.00
JT Jim Thome/52 20.00 50.00
JW Jered Weaver/11
JZ Joel Zumaya/62
KG Kirk Gibson
KG Ken Griffey Jr./56 40.00 80.00
KW Kerry Wood/35 10.00 25.00
LA Luis Aparicio/35 6.00 15.00
MC Miguel Cabrera
MG Mark Grace
MM Mark Mulder/35 6.00 15.00
MO Justin Morneau/50 10.00 25.00
MS Mike Schmidt/12
MT Miguel Tejada/50 12.50 30.00
MW Maury Wills
NR Nolan Ryan/22
PE Jake Peavy/55 8.00 20.00
PM Paul Molitor/40 10.00 25.00
RJ Reggie Jackson/14
RS Ryne Sandberg/45 20.00 50.00
RY Robin Yount/29 20.00 50.00
SC Steve Carlton/10
SD Stephen Drew/15
TG Tom Glavine/47 20.00 50.00
TH Torii Hunter/26 12.50 30.00
TT Troy Tulowitzki/7
VG Vladimir Guerrero/27
WB Wade Boggs/45 12.50 30.00
WF Whitey Ford/8

2007 Upper Deck Premier Patches Dual

PRINT RUNS B/WN 1-75 COPIES PER
NO PRICING ON QTY 22 OR LESS
PLAT.PRINT RUNS B/WN 5-10 COPIES PER
NO PLATINUM PRICING DUE TO SCARCITY
MASTERPIECE PRINT RUN 1 SER.#'d SET
NO MASTERPIECE PRICING DUE TO SCARCITY
OVERALL PATCH ODDS ONE PER PACK
AD Adam Dunn 10.00 25.00
AD Adam Dunn 10.00 25.00
AP Albert Pujols 30.00 60.00
AP Albert Pujols 30.00 60.00
AS Alfonso Soriano 10.00 25.00
AS Alfonso Soriano 10.00 25.00
BR Brooks Robinson
BR Brooks Robinson
BU B.J. Upton 8.00 20.00
BU B.J. Upton 8.00 20.00
CH Cole Hamels 10.00 25.00
CH Cole Hamels 10.00 25.00
CR Cal Ripken Jr. 30.00 60.00
CR Cal Ripken Jr. 30.00 60.00
CU Chase Utley 10.00 25.00
CU Chase Utley 10.00 25.00
DJ Derek Jeter 20.00 50.00
DJ Derek Jeter 20.00 50.00
DJ2 Derek Jeter 20.00 50.00
DJ2 Derek Jeter 20.00 50.00
DM Don Mattingly 20.00 50.00
DM Don Mattingly 20.00 50.00
DO David Ortiz/15
DO David Ortiz/1
ED Jim Edmonds 10.00 25.00
ED Jim Edmonds 10.00 25.00
FL Francisco Liriano 8.00 20.00
FL Francisco Liriano 8.00 20.00
GM Greg Maddux 12.50 30.00
GM Greg Maddux 12.50 30.00
IR Ivan Rodriguez 10.00 25.00
IR Ivan Rodriguez 10.00 25.00
JB Johnny Bench 10.00 25.00
JB Johnny Bench 10.00 25.00
JG Jason Giambi 8.00 20.00
JG Jason Giambi 8.00 20.00
JM Joe Mauer 12.50 30.00
JM Joe Mauer 12.50 30.00
JO Randy Johnson 8.00 20.00
JO Randy Johnson 8.00 20.00
JP Jake Peavy 6.00 15.00
JP Jake Peavy 6.00 15.00
JR Jose Reyes 30.00 60.00
JR Jose Reyes 30.00 60.00
JS Jeremy Sowers
JS Jeremy Sowers
JT Jim Thome 8.00 20.00
JT Jim Thome 8.00 20.00
JT2 Jim Thome 8.00 20.00
JT2 Jim Thome 8.00 20.00
JV Justin Verlander 8.00 20.00
JV Justin Verlander/42 10.00 25.00
JW Jered Weaver 8.00 20.00
JW Jered Weaver 8.00 20.00
KG Ken Griffey Jr. 20.00 50.00
KG Ken Griffey Jr. 20.00 50.00
KG2 Ken Griffey Jr. 20.00 50.00
KG2 Ken Griffey Jr. 20.00 50.00
KJ Kenji Johjima
KJ Kenji Johjima
KM Kendry Morales 6.00 15.00
KM Kendry Morales 6.00 15.00
LB Lance Berkman 10.00 25.00
LB Lance Berkman 10.00 25.00
MC Miguel Cabrera 10.00 25.00
MC Miguel Cabrera 10.00 25.00
MR Manny Ramirez 10.00 25.00
MR Manny Ramirez 10.00 25.00
MS Mike Schmidt 12.50 30.00
MS Mike Schmidt 12.50 30.00
MT Mark Teixeira 10.00 25.00
MT Mark Teixeira 10.00 25.00
NR Nolan Ryan 30.00 60.00
NR Nolan Ryan 30.00 60.00
PF Prince Fielder 12.50 30.00
PF Prince Fielder/63 12.50 30.00
PM Pedro Martinez 12.50 30.00
PM Pedro Martinez 12.50 30.00
RC Roger Clemens/22
RC Roger Clemens/22
RJ Reggie Jackson 10.00 25.00
RJ Reggie Jackson 10.00 25.00
RS Ryne Sandberg 20.00 50.00
RS Ryne Sandberg 20.00 50.00
RZ Ryan Zimmerman 20.00 50.00
RZ Ryan Zimmerman 20.00 50.00
SA Johan Santana 12.50 30.00
SA Johan Santana 12.50 30.00
SD Stephen Drew
SD Stephen Drew
TE Miguel Tejada 6.00 15.00
TE Miguel Tejada 6.00 15.00
TG Tony Gwynn 12.50 30.00
TG Tony Gwynn 12.50 30.00
TO Tom Glavine 12.50 30.00
TO Tom Glavine 12.50 30.00
VG Vladimir Guerrero 10.00 25.00
VG Vladimir Guerrero 10.00 25.00
VG2 Vladimir Guerrero 10.00 25.00
VG2 Vladimir Guerrero 10.00 25.00

2007 Upper Deck Premier Patches Dual Gold

*GOLD: .4X TO 1X BASIC
OVERALL PATCH ODDS ONE PER PACK
PRINT RUNS B/WN 6-58 COPIES PER
NO PRICING ON QTY 24 OR LESS
BR Brooks Robinson/28 15.00 40.00
DO David Ortiz/54 15.00 40.00
JS Jeremy Sowers/35 10.00 25.00

2007 Upper Deck Premier Patches Triple

PRINT RUNS B/WN 1-99 COPIES PER
NO PRICING ON QTY 10 OR LESS
MASTERPIECE PRINT RUN 1 SER.#'d SET
NO MASTERPIECE PRICING DUE TO SCARCITY
PLATINUM PRINT RUN 5 SER.#'d SETS
NO PLATINUM PRICING DUE TO SCARCITY
OVERALL PATCH ODDS ONE PER PACK
AD Adam Dunn/5
AD Adam Dunn/5
AJ Andruw Jones/97 12.50 30.00
AJ Andruw Jones/97 12.50 30.00
AP Albert Pujols/1
AP Albert Pujols/1
AS Alfonso Soriano/1
AS Alfonso Soriano/1
BU B.J. Upton/4
BU B.J. Upton/4
CC Chris Carpenter/97 12.50 30.00
CC Chris Carpenter/97 12.50 30.00
CD Carlos Delgado/94 10.00 25.00
CD Carlos Delgado/94 10.00 25.00
CH Cole Hamels/6
CH Cole Hamels/6
CJ Chipper Jones/95 20.00 50.00
CJ Chipper Jones/95 20.00 50.00
CL Carlos Lee/99 8.00 20.00
CL Carlos Lee/99 8.00 20.00
CR Cal Ripken Jr./82 40.00 80.00
CR Cal Ripken Jr./82 40.00 80.00
CS Curt Schilling/90 12.50 30.00
CS Curt Schilling/90 12.50 30.00
CU Chase Utley/3
CU Chase Utley/3
DJ Derek Jeter/96
DJ Derek Jeter/96
DJ2 Derek Jeter/96
DJ2 Derek Jeter/96
DO David Ortiz/98
DO David Ortiz/98
EM Eddie Murray/77 12.50 30.00
EM Eddie Murray/77 12.50 30.00
FL Francisco Liriano/6
FL Francisco Liriano/6
FR Frank Robinson/56 15.00 40.00
FR Frank Robinson/56 15.00 40.00
FT Frank Thomas/90 15.00 40.00
FT Frank Thomas/90 15.00 40.00
GM Greg Maddux/87 20.00 50.00
GM Greg Maddux/87 20.00 50.00
HA Travis Hafner/3
HA Travis Hafner/3
JM Joe Mauer/4
JM Joe Mauer/4
JR Jose Reyes/3
JR Jose Reyes/3
JS Jeremy Sowers/6
JS Jeremy Sowers/6
JT Jim Thome/91 8.00 20.00
JT Jim Thome/91 8.00 20.00
JT2 Jim Thome/91 8.00 20.00
JT2 Jim Thome/91 8.00 20.00
JV Justin Verlander/6
JV Justin Verlander/6
JW Jered Weaver/6
JW Jered Weaver/6
KG Ken Griffey Jr./89 20.00 50.00
KG Ken Griffey Jr./89 20.00 50.00
KG2 Ken Griffey Jr./89 20.00 50.00
KG2 Ken Griffey Jr./89 20.00 50.00
LB Lance Berkman/7
LB Lance Berkman/7
MC Miguel Cabrera/3
MC Miguel Cabrera/3
MO Justin Morneau/3
MO Justin Morneau/3
MR Manny Ramirez/94 10.00 25.00
MR Manny Ramirez/94 10.00 25.00
MT Mark Teixeira/3
MT Mark Teixeira/3
OS Ozzie Smith/78 20.00 50.00
OS Ozzie Smith/78 20.00 50.00
PM Pedro Martinez/4
PM Pedro Martinez/4
RJ Randy Johnson/89 10.00 25.00
RJ Randy Johnson/89 10.00 25.00
RO Roy Halladay/99 12.50 30.00
RO Roy Halladay/66 12.50 30.00
RW Rickie Weeks/6
RW Rickie Weeks/6
RY Roy Oswalt/6
RY Roy Oswalt/6
RZ Ryan Zimmerman/5
RZ Ryan Zimmerman/5
SA Johan Santana/10
SA Johan Santana/10
TE Miguel Tejada/98 10.00 25.00
TE Miguel Tejada/98 10.00 25.00
TG Tony Gwynn/82 15.00 40.00
TG Tony Gwynn/82 15.00 40.00
TS Tom Seaver/67 15.00 40.00
TS Tom Seaver/67 15.00 40.00
VG Vladimir Guerrero/97 12.50 30.00
VG Vladimir Guerrero/97 12.50 30.00
VM Victor Martinez/3
VM Victor Martinez/3
WB Wade Boggs/82 10.00 25.00
WB Wade Boggs/82 10.00 25.00

2007 Upper Deck Premier Patches Triple Gold

*GOLD: .4X TO 1X BASIC
OVERALL PATCH ODDS ONE PER PACK
PRINT RUNS B/WN 1-57 COPIES PER
NO PRICING ON QTY 25 OR LESS
CH Cole Hamels/35 15.00 40.00
CU Chase Utley/26 12.50 30.00
DO David Ortiz/34 20.00 50.00
FL Francisco Liriano/47 15.00 40.00
FT Frank Thomas/35 40.00 80.00
HA Travis Hafner/48 15.00 40.00
JS Jeremy Sowers/26 10.00 25.00
JV Justin Verlander/35 20.00 50.00
LB Lance Berkman/35 15.00 40.00
MO Justin Morneau/33 15.00 40.00
RW Rickie Weeks/47 15.00 40.00
RY Roy Oswalt/50 10.00 25.00
SA Johan Santana/57 20.00 50.00
VM Victor Martinez/41 12.50 30.00

2007 Upper Deck Premier Penmanship Autographs

PRINT RUNS B/WN 1-98 COPIES PER
NO PRICING ON QTY 10 OR LESS
MASTERPIECE PRINT RUN 1 SER.#'d SET
NO MASTERPIECE PRICING DUE TO SCARCITY
OVERALL AUTO ODDS ONE PER PACK
EXCHANGE DEADLINE 04/26/10
AK Al Kaline/53 15.00 40.00
AM Andrew Miller/7
AM2 Andrew Miller/7
AP Albert Pujols/1
AP2 Albert Pujols/1
BA Jason Bay/3
BA2 Jason Bay/3
BF Bob Feller/36
BJ Bo Jackson/86 20.00 50.00
BR Brooks Robinson/57 15.00 40.00
BU B.J. Upton/4
CB Craig Biggio/88 20.00 50.00
CC Chris Carpenter/97 15.00 40.00
CF Carlton Fisk/72 10.00 25.00
CH Cole Hamels/6
CR Cal Ripken Jr./82 40.00 80.00
CR2 Cal Ripken Jr./82 40.00 80.00
CY Carl Yastrzemski/61 30.00 60.00
CZ Carlos Zambrano/1
DJ Derek Jeter/96 100.00 150.00
DJ2 Derek Jeter/96 100.00 150.00
DL Derrek Lee/97 12.50 30.00
DM Don Mattingly/83 30.00 60.00
DM2 Don Mattingly/83 30.00 60.00
DW Dontrelle Willis/3
DY Delmon Young/7
DY2 Delmon Young/7
EB Ernie Banks/54 30.00 60.00
FH Felix Hernandez/5
FL Francisco Liriano/6
GM Greg Maddux/87 50.00 100.00
HR Hanley Ramirez/6
IR Ivan Rodriguez/91 20.00 50.00
JB Johnny Bench/68 20.00 50.00
JG Jonny Gomes/5
JI Jim Palmer/65 10.00 25.00
JM Joe Mauer/4
JO Josh Barfield/6
JP Jake Peavy/2
JR Jose Reyes/3
JS John Smoltz/88 40.00 80.00
JT Jim Thome/91 30.00 60.00
JV Justin Verlander/6
JW Jered Weaver/6
JZ Joel Zumaya/6
KG Ken Griffey Jr./89 40.00 80.00
KG2 Ken Griffey Jr./89 40.00 80.00
LA Luis Aparicio/56 12.50 30.00
MC Miguel Cabrera/3
MO Justin Morneau/3
MO2 Justin Morneau/3
MS Mike Schmidt/73 20.00 50.00
MY Michael Young/1
NR Nolan Ryan/68 30.00 60.00
NS Nick Swisher/5
OZ Ozzie Smith/78 20.00 50.00
PA Jonathan Papelbon/6
PH Philip Humber/7
PM Paul Molitor/78 10.00 25.00
PM2 Paul Molitor/78 10.00 25.00
RA Randy Johnson/89 20.00 50.00
RC Roger Clemens/84 20.00 50.00
RJ Reggie Jackson/68 30.00 60.00
RO Roy Oswalt/1
RO2 Roy Oswalt/1
RS Ryne Sandberg/82 20.00 50.00
RY Robin Yount/74 30.00 60.00
SA Johan Santana/10
SC Steve Carlton/67 12.50 30.00
SD Stephen Drew/6
SM Stan Musial/42 30.00 60.00
SO Jeremy Sowers/6
SR Scott Rolen/97 15.00 40.00
TE Miguel Tejada/98 10.00 25.00
TG Tony Gwynn/82 15.00 40.00
TG2 Tony Gwynn/82 15.00 40.00
TI Tadahito Iguchi/5
TO Tony Gwynn Jr./6
TP Tony Perez/65 15.00 40.00
TT Troy Tulowitzki/28 15.00 40.00
TT2 Troy Tulowitzki/7
VG Vladimir Guerrero/97 10.00 25.00
VM Victor Martinez/3
WB Wade Boggs/82 10.00 25.00
WC Will Clark/86 10.00 25.00
WF Whitey Ford/50 20.00 50.00
WM Willie McCovey/59 20.00 50.00
YB Yogi Berra/47 20.00 50.00

2007 Upper Deck Premier Penmanship Autographs Jersey Number

OVERALL AUTO ODDS ONE PER PACK
PRINT RUNS B/WN 1-58 COPIES PER
NO PRICING ON QTY 25 OR LESS
EXCHANGE DEADLINE 04/26/10
AK Al Kaline/6
AM Andrew Miller/50 30.00 60.00
AM2 Andrew Miller/50 30.00 60.00
AP Albert Pujols/5
AP2 Albert Pujols/5
BA Jason Bay/38 10.00 25.00
BA2 Jason Bay/38 10.00 25.00
BF Bob Feller/19
BJ Bo Jackson/16
BR Brooks Robinson/5
BU B.J. Upton/2
CB Craig Biggio/7
CC Chris Carpenter/29 20.00 50.00
CF Carlton Fisk/27 20.00 50.00
CH Cole Hamels/35 12.50 30.00
CR Cal Ripken Jr./8
CR2 Cal Ripken Jr./8
CY Carl Yastrzemski/8
CZ Carlos Zambrano/38 10.00 25.00
DJ Derek Jeter/2
DJ2 Derek Jeter/2
DL Derrek Lee/25
DM Don Mattingly/23
DM2 Don Mattingly/23
DW Dontrelle Willis/35 15.00 40.00
DY Delmon Young/35 15.00 40.00
DY2 Delmon Young/35 15.00 40.00
FH Felix Hernandez/34 30.00 60.00
FL Francisco Liriano/47 12.50 30.00
FR Frank Robinson/20
GM Greg Maddux/36 50.00 100.00
HR Hanley Ramirez/2
IR Ivan Rodriguez/7
JB Johnny Bench/5
JI Jim Palmer/22
JM Joe Mauer/7
JO Josh Barfield/29
JP Jake Peavy/44 15.00 40.00
JR Jose Reyes/7
JS John Smoltz/29 40.00 80.00
JT Jim Thome/25
JV Justin Verlander/35 30.00 60.00
JW Jered Weaver/56 10.00 25.00
JZ Joel Zumaya/54 15.00 40.00
KG Ken Griffey Jr./3
KG2 Ken Griffey Jr./3
LA Luis Aparicio/11
MC Miguel Cabrera/24
MO Justin Morneau/33 15.00 40.00
MO2 Justin Morneau/33 15.00 40.00
MS Mike Schmidt/20
MY Michael Young/10
NR Nolan Ryan/34 60.00 120.00
NS Nick Swisher/33
OZ Ozzie Smith/1
PA Jonathan Papelbon/58 30.00 60.00
PH Philip Humber/49
PM Paul Molitor/4
PM2 Paul Molitor/4
RA Randy Johnson/41 30.00 60.00
RC Roger Clemens/22
RJ Reggie Jackson/9
RO Roy Oswalt/45 12.50 30.00
RO2 Roy Oswalt/45 12.50 30.00
SA Johan Santana/57 20.00 50.00
SC Steve Carlton/32 10.00 25.00
SD Stephen Drew/6
SM Stan Musial/6
SO Jeremy Sowers/45
SR Scott Rolen/27 20.00 50.00
TE Miguel Tejada/10
TG Tony Gwynn/19
TG2 Tony Gwynn/19
TI Tadahito Iguchi/15
TP Tony Perez/24
TT Troy Tulowitzki/14
TT2 Troy Tulowitzki/14
VG Vladimir Guerrero/27 10.00 25.00
VM Victor Martinez/41 10.00 25.00
WB Wade Boggs/26 10.00 25.00
WC Will Clark/22
WF Whitey Ford/16
WM Willie McCovey/44 15.00 40.00
YB Yogi Berra/8

2007 Upper Deck Premier Preeminence Autographs

STATED PRINT RUN 50 SER.#'d SETS
GOLD PRINT RUN 25 SER.#'d SETS
NO GOLD PRICING DUE TO SCARCITY
PLATINUM PRINT RUN 1 SER.#'d SET
NO PLATINUM PRICING DUE TO SCARCTIY
OVERALL AUTO ODDS ONE PER PACK
EXCHANGE DEADLINE 04/26/10
BJ Bo Jackson 40.00 80.00
BR Brooks Robinson 10.00 25.00
CC Chris Carpenter 10.00 25.00
CR Cal Ripken Jr. 60.00 120.00
CY Carl Yastrzemski 30.00 60.00
GM Greg Maddux 60.00 120.00
JB Johnny Bench 20.00 50.00
JM Joe Mauer 40.00 80.00
JT Jim Thome 30.00 60.00
JV Justin Verlander 30.00 60.00
KG Ken Griffey Jr. 40.00 80.00
MS Mike Schmidt 30.00 60.00
NR Nolan Ryan 50.00 100.00
RC Roger Clemens 60.00 120.00
RJ Reggie Jackson 30.00 60.00
RS Ryne Sandberg 30.00 60.00
SM Stan Musial 30.00 60.00
VG Vladimir Guerrero 20.00 50.00

2007 Upper Deck Premier Rare Patches Dual

STATED PRINT RUN 50 SER.#'d SETS
GOLD PRINT RUN 25 SER.#'d SETS
NO GOLD PRICING DUE TO SCARCITY
MASTERPIECE PRINT RUN 1 SER.#'d SET
NO MASTERPIECE PRICING DUE TO SCARCITY
PLATINUM PRINT RUN 10 SER.#'d SETS
NO PLATINUM PRICING DUE TO SCARCITY
OVERALL PATCH ODDS ONE PER PACK
BM Johnny Bench 20.00 50.00
Joe Mauer
BR Brian Roberts 12.50 30.00
Robinson Cano
BS AJ Burnett 10.00 25.00
Anibal Sanchez
BZ Jeremy Bonderman
Joel Zumaya
CP Chris Carpenter 12.50 30.00
Jake Peavy
CW Miguel Cabrera 12.50 30.00
Dontrelle Willis
DB Carlos Delgado 20.00 50.00
Carlos Beltran
DT Stephen Drew 10.00 25.00
Miguel Tejada
ER Jim Edmonds 20.00 50.00
Scott Rolen
FM Prince Fielder 12.50 30.00
Justin Morneau
FW Prince Fielder 15.00 40.00
Rickie Weeks
GP Ken Griffey Jr. 40.00 80.00
Albert Pujols
HR Trevor Hoffman 15.00 40.00
Mariano Rivera
HS Cole Hamels 10.00 25.00
Jeremy Sowers
JG Derek Jeter 40.00 80.00
Ken Griffey Jr.
JJ Andruw Jones 20.00 50.00
Chipper Jones
MC Greg Maddux
Roger Clemens
MG Greg Maddux 40.00 80.00
Tom Glavine
MH Victor Martinez 15.00 40.00
Travis Hafner
MJ Don Mattingly 50.00 100.00
Derek Jeter
OT David Ortiz 12.50 30.00
Jim Thome
PO Jake Peavy 10.00 25.00
Roy Oswalt
PS Jonathan Papelbon 20.00 50.00
Curt Schilling
RC Nolan Ryan 60.00 120.00
Roger Clemens
RD Reggie Jackson 20.00 50.00
Derek Jeter
RG Cal Ripken Jr. 40.00 80.00
Tony Gwynn
RJ Roy Halladay 12.50 30.00
Johan Santana
RU Jimmy Rollins 20.00 50.00
Chase Utley
SG Alfonso Soriano 20.00 50.00
Vladimir Guerrero
SH Johan Santana 20.00 50.00
Felix Hernandez
SM Ryne Sandberg 20.00 50.00
Joe Morgan
SR Mike Schmidt 20.00 50.00
Brooks Robinson
TR Miguel Tejada 15.00 40.00
Jose Reyes
TT Frank Thomas 20.00 50.00
Jim Thome
UC B.J. Upton 15.00 40.00
Carl Crawford
VZ Justin Verlander
Joel Zumaya
WJ Dontrelle Willis 10.00 25.00
Josh Johnson
WL Jered Weaver 10.00 25.00
Francisco Liriano
YM Robin Yount 20.00 50.00
Paul Molitor
ZU Ryan Zimmerman 20.00 50.00
B.J. Upton

2007 Upper Deck Premier Rare Remnants Triple

STATED PRINT RUN 50 SER.#'d SETS
GOLD PRINT RUN 25 SER.#'d SETS
NO GOLD PRICING DUE TO SCARCITY
MASTERPIECE PRINT RUN 1 SER.#'d SET
NO MASTERPIECE PRICING DUE TO SCARCITY
PLATINUM PRINT RUN 10 SER.#'d SETS
NO PLATINUM PRICING DUE TO SCARCITY
OVERALL PATCH ODDS ONE PER PACK
BMP Johnny Bench 15.00 40.00
Joe Morgan
Tony Perez
BZV Jeremy Bonderman 10.00 25.00
Joel Zumaya
Justin Verlander

Card	Low	High
CBF Cal Ripken Jr.	30.00	60.00
Brooks Robinson		
Frank Robinson		
CFY Joe Cronin	30.00	60.00
Jimmie Foxx		
Carl Yastrzemski		
CMK Roberto Clemente	50.00	100.00
Bill Mazeroski		
Ralph Kiner		
CPR Chris Carpenter	15.00	40.00
Albert Pujols		
Scott Rolen		
DMP Bill Dickey	30.00	60.00
Thurman Munson		
Jorge Posada		
DMR Carlos Delgado	20.00	50.00
Pedro Martinez		
Jose Reyes		
DRB Carlos Delgado	15.00	40.00
Jose Reyes		
Carlos Beltran		
FBM Carlton Fisk	20.00	50.00
Johnny Bench		
Thurman Munson		
FGG Jimmie Foxx	150.00	250.00
Lou Gehrig		
Hank Greenberg		
FMT Prince Fielder	10.00	25.00
Justin Morneau		
Mark Teixeira		
GGJ Ken Griffey Jr.	20.00	50.00
Vladimir Guerrero		
Andruw Jones		
JCM Randy Johnson	20.00	50.00
Roger Clemens		
Greg Maddux		
JJR Randy Johnson	30.00	60.00
Derek Jeter		
Mariano Rivera		
JMM Reggie Jackson	40.00	80.00
Don Mattingly		
Thurman Munson		
KUC Scott Kazmir	10.00	25.00
B.J. Upton		
Carl Crawford		
KVJ Kenji Johjima	10.00	25.00
Victor Martinez		
Joe Mauer		
LMS Francisco Liriano	10.00	25.00
Joe Mauer		
Johan Santana		
LSH Francisco Liriano	10.00	25.00
Jeremy Sowers		
Cole Hamels		
OPS Roy Oswalt	10.00	25.00
Jake Peavy		
Ben Sheets		
OTB David Ortiz	10.00	25.00
Jim Thome		
Lance Berkman		
PJG Albert Pujols	30.00	60.00
Derek Jeter		
Ken Griffey Jr.		
PMH Albert Pujols	50.00	100.00
Stan Musial		
Rogers Hornsby		
RCD Nolan Ryan	20.00	50.00
Roger Clemens		
Don Drysdale		
RDG Babe Ruth	350.00	500.00
Joe DiMaggio		
Lou Gehrig		
RFS Mariano Rivera	10.00	25.00
Rollie Fingers		
Bruce Sutter		
RRR Nolan Ryan	40.00	80.00
Nolan Ryan		
Nolan Ryan		
RWH Nolan Ryan	20.00	50.00
Jered Weaver		
Felix Hernandez		
RWR Cal Ripken Jr.		
Honus Wagner		
Pee Wee Reese		
RYS Cal Ripken Jr.	30.00	60.00
Robin Yount		
Ozzie Smith		
SGA Alfonso Soriano	10.00	25.00
Vladimir Guerrero		
Bobby Abreu		
SHM Ryne Sandberg	30.00	60.00
Rogers Hornsby		
Joe Morgan		
SJZ Johan Santana	10.00	25.00
Randy Johnson		
Barry Zito		
SRB Mike Schmidt	20.00	50.00
Brooks Robinson		
Wade Boggs		
TJY Miguel Tejada	20.00	50.00
Derek Jeter		
Michael Young		
TTH Jim Thome	10.00	25.00
Mark Teixeira		
Todd Helton		
VWJ Justin Verlander	10.00	25.00
Jered Weaver		
Josh Johnson		
WDC Ted Williams		
Joe DiMaggio		
Roberto Clemente		
YBM Robin Yount	15.00	40.00
Wade Boggs		
Paul Molitor		

2007 Upper Deck Premier Remnants Triple

PRINT RUNS B/WN 21-75 COPIES PER
NO PRICING ON QTY 21 OR LESS
PLATINUM PRINT RUN 10 SER.#'d SETS
NO PLATINUM PRICING DUE TO SCARCITY
MASTERPIECE PRINT RUN 1 SER.#'d SET
NO MASTERPIECE PRICING DUE TO SCARCITY
OVERALL TRIPLE GU ODDS ONE PER PACK

Card	Low	High
AP Albert Pujols	12.50	30.00
AP Albert Pujols	12.50	30.00
AP2 Albert Pujols	12.50	30.00
AP2 Albert Pujols	12.50	30.00
AS Alfonso Soriano	6.00	15.00
AS Alfonso Soriano	6.00	15.00
BM Bill Mazeroski	10.00	25.00
BM Bill Mazeroski	10.00	25.00
BR Babe Ruth	250.00	500.00
BR Babe Ruth	250.00	500.00
CA Roy Campanella	15.00	40.00
CA Roy Campanella	15.00	40.00
CF Carlton Fisk	6.00	15.00
CF Carlton Fisk	6.00	15.00
CJ Chipper Jones	10.00	25.00
CJ Chipper Jones	10.00	25.00
CL Roger Clemens	10.00	25.00
CL Roger Clemens	10.00	25.00
CR Cal Ripken Jr.	15.00	40.00
CR Cal Ripken Jr.	15.00	40.00
CS Curt Schilling	6.00	15.00
CS Curt Schilling	6.00	15.00
CU Chase Utley	10.00	25.00
CU Chase Utley	10.00	25.00
CY Carl Yastrzemski		
CY Carl Yastrzemski	10.00	25.00
DD Don Drysdale	15.00	40.00
DJ Derek Jeter	20.00	50.00
DJ Derek Jeter	20.00	50.00
DJ2 Derek Jeter	20.00	50.00
DJ2 Derek Jeter	20.00	50.00
DM Don Mattingly	20.00	50.00
DM Don Mattingly	20.00	50.00
DO David Ortiz	6.00	15.00
DO David Ortiz	6.00	15.00
EB Ernie Banks		
EB Ernie Banks		
EM Eddie Mathews	15.00	40.00
EM Eddie Mathews	15.00	40.00
FR Frank Robinson	6.00	15.00
FR Frank Robinson	6.00	15.00
HO Rogers Hornsby	40.00	80.00
HO Rogers Hornsby	40.00	80.00
JB Johnny Bench	10.00	25.00
JB Johnny Bench	10.00	25.00
JD Joe DiMaggio	75.00	150.00
JD Joe DiMaggio	75.00	150.00
JO Jose Reyes	15.00	40.00
JO Jose Reyes	15.00	40.00
JR Jackie Robinson	40.00	80.00
JR Jackie Robinson	40.00	80.00
JT Jim Thome	6.00	15.00
JT Jim Thome	6.00	15.00
KG Ken Griffey Jr.	10.00	25.00
KG Ken Griffey Jr.	10.00	25.00
KG2 Ken Griffey Jr.	10.00	25.00
KG2 Ken Griffey Jr.	10.00	25.00
MO Mel Ott	20.00	50.00
MO Mel Ott	20.00	50.00
MR Manny Ramirez	6.00	15.00
MR Manny Ramirez	6.00	15.00
MS Mike Schmidt	10.00	25.00
MS Mike Schmidt	10.00	25.00
NR Nolan Ryan	15.00	40.00
NR Nolan Ryan	15.00	40.00
PM Paul Molitor	6.00	15.00
PM Paul Molitor	6.00	15.00
PR Pee Wee Reese	15.00	40.00
PR Pee Wee Reese	15.00	40.00
RC Roberto Clemente	50.00	100.00
RC Roberto Clemente	50.00	100.00
RJ Reggie Jackson	10.00	25.00
RJ Reggie Jackson	10.00	25.00
RO Brooks Robinson	6.00	15.00
RO Brooks Robinson	6.00	15.00
RS Ryne Sandberg	10.00	25.00
RS Ryne Sandberg	10.00	25.00
RY Robin Yount	10.00	25.00
RY Robin Yount	10.00	25.00
SM Stan Musial	15.00	40.00
SM Stan Musial	15.00	40.00
TC Ty Cobb/21		
TC Ty Cobb/21		
TG Tony Gwynn	10.00	25.00
TG Tony Gwynn	10.00	25.00
TM Thurman Munson	15.00	40.00
TM Thurman Munson	15.00	40.00
VG Vladimir Guerrero	6.00	15.00
VG Vladimir Guerrero	6.00	15.00

2007 Upper Deck Premier Remnants Triple Gold

*GOLD: .5X TO 1.2X BASIC
OVERALL TRIPLE GU ODDS ONE PER PACK
PRINT RUNS B/WN 6-60 COPIES PER
NO PRICING ON QTY 19 OR LESS

Card	Low	High
BR Babe Ruth/60	250.00	500.00
CL Roger Clemens/24	15.00	40.00
DJ Derek Jeter/24	20.00	50.00
DJ2 Derek Jeter/24	20.00	50.00
RC Roberto Clemente/29	75.00	150.00
TC Ty Cobb/47	75.00	150.00
TM Thurman Munson/20	30.00	60.00

2007 Upper Deck Premier Remnants Quad

PRINT RUNS B/WN 1-96 COPIES PER
NO PRICING ON QTY 25 OR LESS
PLATINUM PRINT RUN 5 SER.#'d SETS
NO PLATINUM PRICING DUE TO SCARCITY
MASTERPIECE PRINT RUN 1 SER.#'d SET
NO MASTERPIECE PRICING DUE TO SCARCITY
OVERALL QUAD GU ODDS ONE PER PACK

Card	Low	High
AK Al Kaline/53	15.00	40.00
AK Al Kaline/53	15.00	40.00
AP Albert Pujols/1		
AP Albert Pujols/1		
AS Alfonso Soriano/1		
AS Alfonso Soriano/1		
BM Bill Mazeroski/56	12.50	30.00
BM Bill Mazeroski/56	12.50	30.00
BR Babe Ruth/15		
BR Babe Ruth/15		
BU B.J. Upton/4		
BU B.J. Upton/4		
CF Chone Figgins/6		
CF Chone Figgins/6		
CH Cole Hamels/6		
CH Cole Hamels/6		
CL Roberto Clemente/55	60.00	120.00
CL Roberto Clemente/55	60.00	120.00
CR Cal Ripken Jr./82	20.00	50.00
CR Cal Ripken Jr./82	20.00	50.00
CU Chase Utley/3		
CU Chase Utley/3		
CY Carl Yastrzemski/61		
CY Carl Yastrzemski/61		
DJ Derek Jeter/96	20.00	50.00
DJ Derek Jeter/96	20.00	50.00
DM Don Mattingly/83	15.00	40.00
DM Don Mattingly/83	15.00	40.00
EM Eddie Mathews/52	15.00	40.00
EM Eddie Mathews/52	15.00	40.00
FL Francisco Liriano/6		
FL Francisco Liriano/6		
GH Gil Hodges/48		
GH Gil Hodges/48		
HK Harmon Killebrew/55	20.00	50.00
HK Harmon Killebrew/55	20.00	50.00
HO Rogers Hornsby/16		
HO Rogers Hornsby/16		
JB Johnny Bench/68	12.50	30.00
JB Johnny Bench/68	12.50	30.00
JD Joe DiMaggio/36	100.00	150.00
JD Joe DiMaggio/36	100.00	150.00
JF Jimmie Foxx/27	60.00	120.00
JF Jimmie Foxx/27	60.00	120.00
JM Joe Mauer/4		
JM Joe Mauer/4		
JR Jackie Robinson/47	60.00	120.00
JR Jackie Robinson/47	60.00	120.00
JS Jeremy Sowers/6		
JS Jeremy Sowers/6		
JT Jim Thome/91	6.00	15.00
JT Jim Thome/91	6.00	15.00
JV Justin Verlander/6		
JV Justin Verlander/6		
JW Jered Weaver/6		
JW Jered Weaver/6		
KG Ken Griffey Jr./89	12.50	30.00
KG Ken Griffey Jr./89	12.50	30.00
KJ Kenji Johjima/6		
KJ Kenji Johjima/6		
LG Lou Gehrig/25	350.00	450.00
LG Lou Gehrig/25	350.00	450.00
MC Miguel Cabrera/3		
MC Miguel Cabrera/3		
MI Johnny Mize/36	20.00	50.00
MI Johnny Mize/36	20.00	50.00
MO Justin Morneau/3		
MO Justin Morneau/3		
MS Mike Schmidt/73	12.50	30.00
MS Mike Schmidt/73	12.50	30.00
MT Mark Teixeira/3		
MT Mark Teixeira/3		
NR Nolan Ryan/68	40.00	80.00
NR Nolan Ryan/68	40.00	80.00
RC Roger Clemens/84	12.50	30.00
RC Roger Clemens/84	12.50	30.00
RJ Reggie Jackson/68	10.00	25.00
RJ Reggie Jackson/68	10.00	25.00
RN Brooks Robinson/57	10.00	25.00
RN Brooks Robinson/48	10.00	25.00
RO Roy Campanella/48	15.00	40.00
RO Roy Campanella/48	15.00	40.00
RZ Ryan Zimmerman/5		
RZ Ryan Zimmerman/5		
SA Johan Santana/10		
SA Johan Santana/2		
SD Stephen Drew/6		
SD Stephen Drew/6		
SM Stan Musial/42	20.00	50.00
SM Stan Musial/42	20.00	50.00
TC Ty Cobb/5		
TC Ty Cobb/5		
TG Tom Glavine/7		
TG Tom Glavine/7		
TH Torii Hunter/5		
TH Torii Hunter/5		
TM Thurman Munson/70	20.00	50.00
TM Thurman Munson/70	20.00	50.00
TW Ted Williams/39		
TW Ted Williams/39		

2007 Upper Deck Premier Remnants Quad Gold

*GOLD: .5X TO 1.2X BASIC
OVERALL TRIPLE GU ODDS ONE PER PACK
PRINT RUNS B/WN 2-57 COPIES PER
NO PRICING ON QTY 25 OR LESS

Card	Low	High
CF Chone Figgins/47	4.00	10.00
CH Cole Hamels/35	12.50	30.00
CU Chase Utley/26	20.00	50.00
FL Francisco Liriano/47	10.00	25.00
HO Rogers Hornsby/50	20.00	50.00
JS Jeremy Sowers/45	4.00	10.00
JV Justin Verlander/35	10.00	25.00
JW Jered Weaver/56	6.00	15.00
MI Johnny Mize/50	20.00	50.00
MO Justin Morneau/33	6.00	15.00
NR Nolan Ryan/34	40.00	80.00
SA Johan Santana/57	10.00	25.00
TG Tom Glavine/50	12.50	30.00

2007 Upper Deck Premier Stitchings

STATED PRINT RUN 50 SER.#'d SETS
*STITCHINGS 35: .4X TO 1X BASIC
STITCHINGS 35 PRINT RUN 35 SER.#'d SETS
OVERALL STITCHINGS ODDS ONE PER PACK

Card	Low	High
1 Babe Ruth	30.00	60.00
1 Babe Ruth	30.00	60.00
2 Babe Ruth	30.00	60.00
2 Babe Ruth	30.00	60.00
3 Babe Ruth	30.00	60.00
3 Babe Ruth	30.00	60.00
4 Ty Cobb	10.00	25.00
4 Ty Cobb	10.00	25.00
5 Ty Cobb	10.00	25.00
5 Ty Cobb	10.00	25.00
6 Lou Gehrig	12.50	30.00
7 Lou Gehrig	12.50	30.00
7 Lou Gehrig	12.50	30.00
8 Joe DiMaggio	12.50	30.00
8 Joe DiMaggio	12.50	30.00
9 Joe DiMaggio	12.50	30.00
9 Joe DiMaggio	12.50	30.00
12 Roberto Clemente	15.00	40.00
12 Roberto Clemente	15.00	40.00
13 Roberto Clemente	15.00	40.00
13 Roberto Clemente	15.00	40.00
14 Jackie Robinson	12.50	30.00
14 Jackie Robinson	12.50	30.00
15 Jackie Robinson	12.50	30.00
15 Jackie Robinson	12.50	30.00
16 Cy Young	6.00	15.00
16 Cy Young	6.00	15.00
17 Cy Young	6.00	15.00
17 Cy Young	6.00	15.00
18 Nolan Ryan	15.00	40.00
18 Nolan Ryan	15.00	40.00
19 Nolan Ryan	15.00	40.00
19 Nolan Ryan	15.00	40.00
20 Reggie Jackson	6.00	15.00
20 Reggie Jackson	6.00	15.00
21 Reggie Jackson	6.00	15.00
21 Reggie Jackson	6.00	15.00
22 Ken Griffey Jr.	12.50	30.00
22 Ken Griffey Jr.	12.50	30.00
23 Ken Griffey Jr.	12.50	30.00
23 Ken Griffey Jr.	12.50	30.00
24 Derek Jeter	15.00	40.00
24 Derek Jeter	15.00	40.00
25 Derek Jeter	15.00	40.00
25 Derek Jeter	15.00	40.00
26 Jimmie Foxx	6.00	15.00
26 Jimmie Foxx	6.00	15.00
27 Jimmie Foxx	6.00	15.00
27 Jimmie Foxx	6.00	15.00
28 Rogers Hornsby	6.00	15.00
28 Rogers Hornsby	6.00	15.00
30 Walter Johnson	12.50	30.00
30 Walter Johnson	12.50	30.00
31 Walter Johnson	12.50	30.00
31 Walter Johnson	12.50	30.00
32 Ernie Banks	10.00	25.00
32 Ernie Banks	10.00	25.00
33 Ernie Banks	10.00	25.00
33 Ernie Banks	10.00	25.00
34 Christy Mathewson	6.00	15.00
34 Christy Mathewson	6.00	15.00
35 Johnny Mize	6.00	15.00
35 Johnny Mize	6.00	15.00
36 Thurman Munson	12.50	30.00
36 Thurman Munson	12.50	30.00
37 Thurman Munson	12.50	30.00
37 Thurman Munson	12.50	30.00
38 Mel Ott	6.00	15.00
38 Mel Ott	6.00	15.00
39 Satchel Paige	10.00	25.00
39 Satchel Paige	10.00	25.00
40 George Sisler	6.00	15.00
40 George Sisler	6.00	15.00
41 Casey Stengel	6.00	15.00
41 Casey Stengel	6.00	15.00
42 Honus Wagner	10.00	25.00
42 Honus Wagner	10.00	25.00
43 Honus Wagner	10.00	25.00
43 Honus Wagner	10.00	25.00
44 Roy Campanella	6.00	15.00
44 Roy Campanella	6.00	15.00
45 Mickey Cochrane	6.00	15.00
45 Mickey Cochrane	6.00	15.00
46 Dizzy Dean	6.00	15.00
46 Dizzy Dean	6.00	15.00
47 Don Drysdale	6.00	15.00
47 Don Drysdale	6.00	15.00
48 Lefty Grove	6.00	15.00
48 Lefty Grove	6.00	15.00
49 Roger Clemens	10.00	25.00
49 Roger Clemens	10.00	25.00
50 Roger Clemens	10.00	25.00
50 Roger Clemens	10.00	25.00
51 Cal Ripken Jr.	20.00	50.00
51 Cal Ripken Jr.	20.00	50.00
52 Cal Ripken Jr.	20.00	50.00
52 Cal Ripken Jr.	20.00	50.00
53 Tony Gwynn	10.00	25.00
53 Tony Gwynn	10.00	25.00
54 Tony Gwynn	10.00	25.00
54 Tony Gwynn	10.00	25.00
55 Johnny Bench	6.00	15.00
55 Johnny Bench	6.00	15.00
56 Yogi Berra	6.00	15.00
56 Yogi Berra	6.00	15.00
57 Carlton Fisk	6.00	15.00
57 Carlton Fisk	6.00	15.00
58 Joe Morgan	6.00	15.00
58 Joe Morgan	6.00	15.00
59 Brooks Robinson	6.00	15.00
59 Brooks Robinson	6.00	15.00
60 Mike Schmidt	10.00	25.00
60 Mike Schmidt	10.00	25.00
61 Willie Stargell	6.00	15.00
61 Willie Stargell	6.00	15.00
62 Tom Seaver	10.00	25.00
62 Tom Seaver	10.00	25.00
63 Ozzie Smith	12.50	30.00
63 Ozzie Smith	12.50	30.00
64 Albert Pujols	12.50	30.00
64 Albert Pujols	12.50	30.00
65 Albert Pujols	12.50	30.00
65 Albert Pujols	12.50	30.00
66 Ryan Howard	10.00	25.00
66 Ryan Howard	10.00	25.00
67 David Ortiz	10.00	25.00
67 David Ortiz	10.00	25.00
68 Randy Johnson	6.00	15.00
68 Randy Johnson	6.00	15.00
69 Greg Maddux	10.00	25.00
69 Greg Maddux	10.00	25.00
70 Greg Maddux	10.00	25.00
70 Greg Maddux	10.00	25.00
71 Johan Santana	6.00	15.00
71 Johan Santana	6.00	15.00
72 Al Kaline	6.00	15.00
72 Al Kaline	6.00	15.00
73 Ryne Sandberg	10.00	25.00
73 Ryne Sandberg	10.00	25.00
74 Robin Yount	10.00	25.00
74 Robin Yount	10.00	25.00
75 Frank Robinson	6.00	15.00
75 Frank Robinson	6.00	15.00
76 Frank Robinson	6.00	15.00
76 Frank Robinson	6.00	15.00
78 Stan Musial	15.00	40.00
78 Stan Musial	15.00	40.00
79 Carl Yastrzemski	10.00	25.00
79 Carl Yastrzemski	10.00	25.00
80 Don Mattingly	20.00	50.00
80 Don Mattingly	20.00	50.00
81 Ichiro Suzuki	20.00	50.00
81 Ichiro Suzuki	20.00	50.00
82 Yogi Berra	6.00	15.00
82 Yogi Berra	6.00	15.00
83 Carlton Fisk	10.00	25.00
Johnny Bench		
83 Carlton Fisk	10.00	25.00
Johnny Bench		
84 Thurman Munson	10.00	25.00
Johnny Bench		
84 Johnny Bench	10.00	25.00
Thurman Munson		
85 Babe Ruth	30.00	60.00
Lou Gehrig		
85 Babe Ruth	30.00	60.00
Lou Gehrig		
86 Whitey Ford	10.00	25.00
Yogi Berra		
86 Whitey Ford	10.00	25.00
Yogi Berra		
87 Don Larsen	10.00	25.00
Yogi Berra		
87 Yogi Berra	10.00	25.00
Don Larsen		
88 Kirk Gibson	6.00	15.00
Dennis Eckersley		
88 Dennis Eckersley	6.00	15.00
Kirk Gibson		
90 Jackie Robinson	10.00	25.00
Pee Wee Reese		
90 Jackie Robinson	10.00	25.00
Pee Wee Reese		
91 Jackie Robinson	10.00	25.00
Satchel Paige		
91 Jackie Robinson	10.00	25.00
Satchel Paige		
92 Lou Gehrig	15.00	40.00
Cal Ripken Jr.		
92 Cal Ripken Jr.	15.00	40.00
Lou Gehrig		
93 Ichiro Suzuki	20.00	50.00
George Sisler		
93 George Sisler	20.00	50.00
Ichiro Suzuki		
94 Roger Clemens	15.00	40.00
Nolan Ryan		
Randy Johnson		
Steve Carlton		
94 Randy Johnson	15.00	40.00
Roger Clemens		
Nolan Ryan		
Steve Carlton		
95 Johnny Bench	10.00	25.00
Joe Morgan		
Tony Perez		
Dave Concepcion		
95 Dave Concepcion	10.00	25.00
Tony Perez		
Joe Morgan		
Johnny Bench		
96 Babe Ruth	15.00	40.00
Jimmie Foxx		
Mel Ott		
Eddie Mathews		
96 Jimmie Foxx	15.00	40.00
Babe Ruth		
Mel Ott		
Eddie Mathews		
97 Roger Clemens	15.00	40.00
Greg Maddux		
Tom Seaver		
Nolan Ryan		
97 Greg Maddux	15.00	40.00
Tom Seaver		
Roger Clemens		
Nolan Ryan		
98 Roberto Clemente	15.00	40.00
Tony Gwynn		
Cal Ripken Jr.		
Stan Musial		
98 Tony Gwynn	15.00	40.00
Stan Musial		
Cal Ripken Jr.		
Roberto Clemente		
99 John F. Kennedy	12.50	30.00
99 John F. Kennedy	12.50	30.00
100 Dwight Eisenhower	6.00	15.00
100 Dwight Eisenhower	6.00	15.00
DM Daisuke Matsuzaka	10.00	25.00
KI Kei Igawa	12.50	30.00
MI Daisuke Matsuzaka	10.00	25.00
Kei Igawa		

2007 Upper Deck Premier Stitchings 10

OVERALL STITCHINGS ODDS ONE PER PACK
STATED PRINT RUN 10 SER.#'d SETS
NO PRICING ON MOST DUE TO SCARCITY

Card	Low	High
1 Babe Ruth	50.00	100.00
2 Babe Ruth	50.00	100.00
3 Babe Ruth	50.00	100.00
4 Ty Cobb	15.00	40.00
5 Ty Cobb	15.00	40.00
12 Roberto Clemente	40.00	80.00
13 Roberto Clemente	40.00	80.00
16 Cy Young	12.50	30.00
17 Cy Young	12.50	30.00
18 Nolan Ryan	40.00	80.00
19 Nolan Ryan	40.00	80.00
22 Ken Griffey Jr.	40.00	80.00
23 Ken Griffey Jr.	40.00	80.00
24 Derek Jeter	30.00	60.00
25 Derek Jeter	30.00	60.00
26 Jimmie Foxx	10.00	25.00
27 Jimmie Foxx	10.00	25.00
30 Walter Johnson	20.00	50.00
31 Walter Johnson	20.00	50.00
32 Ernie Banks	10.00	25.00
33 Ernie Banks	10.00	25.00
34 Christy Mathewson	10.00	25.00
36 Thurman Munson	30.00	60.00
37 Thurman Munson	30.00	60.00
39 Satchel Paige	15.00	40.00
40 George Sisler	10.00	25.00
41 Casey Stengel	10.00	25.00
51 Cal Ripken Jr.	40.00	80.00
52 Cal Ripken Jr.	40.00	80.00
53 Tony Gwynn	15.00	40.00
54 Tony Gwynn	15.00	40.00
64 Albert Pujols	30.00	60.00
65 Albert Pujols	30.00	60.00
67 David Ortiz	15.00	40.00
69 Greg Maddux	15.00	40.00
70 Greg Maddux	15.00	40.00
73 Ryne Sandberg	15.00	40.00
74 Robin Yount	20.00	50.00

2008 Upper Deck Premier

Card	Low	High
COMMON CARD (1-178)	2.00	5.00
COMMON RET (179-200)	1.25	3.00
ONE BASE CARD PER PACK		
1-200 STATED PRINT RUN 99 SER.#'d SETS		
COMMON AU RC p/r 299 (201-241)	4.00	10.00
COMMON AU RC p/r 99 (201-241)	5.00	12.00
OVERALL RC AUTO ONE PER PACK		
201-241 PRINT RUNS b/w 99-299 SER.#'d SETS		
EXCHANGE DEADLINE 3/13/2010		
1 Chipper Jones	5.00	12.00
2 Andruw Jones	2.00	5.00
3 John Smoltz	5.00	12.00
4 Mark Teixeira	5.00	12.00
5 Edgar Renteria	2.00	5.00
6 Jeff Francoeur	3.00	8.00
7 Tim Hudson	3.00	8.00
8 Miguel Cabrera	5.00	12.00
9 Hanley Ramirez	5.00	12.00
10 Dan Uggla	3.00	8.00
11 Dontrelle Willis	2.00	5.00
12 Josh Willingham	2.00	5.00
13 Pedro Martinez	3.00	8.00
14 Carlos Delgado	2.00	5.00
15 Carlos Beltran	2.00	5.00
16 David Wright	6.00	15.00
17 Tom Glavine	3.00	8.00
18 Jose Reyes	3.00	8.00
19 Paul Lo Duca	2.00	5.00
20 John Maine	2.00	5.00
21 Chase Utley	5.00	12.00
22 Cole Hamels	5.00	12.00
23 Jimmy Rollins	3.00	8.00
24 Shane Victorino	2.00	5.00
25 Ryan Howard	6.00	15.00
26 Pat Burrell	2.00	5.00
27 Aaron Rowand	2.00	5.00
28 Ryan Zimmerman	3.00	8.00
29 Ryan Church	2.00	5.00
30 Matt Chico	2.00	5.00
31 Dmitri Young	2.00	5.00
32 Derrek Lee	2.00	5.00
33 Aramis Ramirez	2.00	5.00
34 Carlos Zambrano	3.00	8.00
35 Rich Hill	2.00	5.00

36 Alfonso Soriano 3.00 8.00
37 Kerry Wood 2.00 5.00
38 Ted Lilly 2.00 5.00
39 Ryan Theriot 2.00 5.00
40 Ken Griffey Jr. 8.00 20.00
41 Adam Dunn 3.00 8.00
42 Homer Bailey 3.00 8.00
43 Aaron Harang 2.00 5.00
44 Brandon Phillips 2.00 5.00
45 Josh Hamilton 5.00 12.00
46 Lance Berkman 3.00 8.00
47 Carlos Lee 2.00 5.00
48 Hunter Pence 5.00 12.00
49 Mark Loretta 2.00 5.00
50 Roy Oswalt 3.00 8.00
51 Prince Fielder 3.00 8.00
52 Ryan Braun 6.00 15.00
53 J.J. Hardy 2.00 5.00
54 Ben Sheets 2.00 5.00
55 Rickie Weeks 3.00 8.00
56 Corey Hart 2.00 5.00
57 Johnny Estrada 2.00 5.00
58 Jason Bay 3.00 8.00
59 Freddy Sanchez 2.00 5.00
60 Adam LaRoche 2.00 5.00
61 Ian Snell 2.00 5.00
62 Xavier Nady 2.00 5.00
63 Tom Gorzelanny 2.00 5.00
64 Scott Rolen 3.00 8.00
65 Albert Pujols 12.00 30.00
66 Jim Edmonds 3.00 8.00
67 Chris Duncan 2.00 5.00
68 Adam Wainwright 3.00 8.00
69 Brandon Webb 3.00 8.00
70 Orlando Hudson 2.00 5.00
71 Chris B. Young 2.00 5.00
72 Stephen Drew 2.00 5.00
73 Matt Holliday 5.00 12.00
74 Jeff Francis 2.00 5.00
75 Brad Hawpe 2.00 5.00
76 Todd Helton 3.00 8.00
77 Troy Tulowitzki 5.00 12.00
78 Russell Martin 2.00 5.00
79 Nomar Garciaparra 5.00 12.00
80 James Loney 3.00 8.00
81 Andre Ethier 3.00 8.00
82 Brad Penny 2.00 5.00
83 Rafael Furcal 2.00 5.00
84 Jeff Kent 2.00 5.00
85 Greg Maddux 6.00 15.00
86 Chris Young 2.00 5.00
87 Khalil Greene 2.00 5.00
88 Trevor Hoffman 3.00 8.00
89 Adrian Gonzalez 3.00 8.00
90 Jake Peavy 2.00 5.00
91 Noah Lowry 2.00 5.00
92 Omar Vizquel 3.00 8.00
93 Tim Lincecum 8.00 20.00
94 Matt Cain 2.00 5.00
95 Randy Winn 2.00 5.00
96 Miguel Tejada 3.00 8.00
97 Brian Roberts 2.00 5.00
98 Nick Markakis 5.00 12.00
99 Erik Bedard 2.00 5.00
100 Melvin Mora 2.00 5.00
101 David Ortiz 2.00 5.00
102 Manny Ramirez 5.00 12.00
103 Josh Beckett 3.00 8.00
104 Jonathan Papelbon 3.00 8.00
105 Curt Schilling 3.00 8.00
106 Daisuke Matsuzaka 5.00 12.00
107 Jason Varitek 5.00 12.00
108 Kevin Youkilis 3.00 8.00
109 Derek Jeter 12.00 30.00
110 Hideki Matsui 5.00 12.00
111 Alex Rodriguez 8.00 20.00
112 Johnny Damon 3.00 8.00
113 Robinson Cano 5.00 12.00
114 Jorge Posada 3.00 8.00
115 Mariano Rivera 5.00 12.00
116 Roger Clemens 6.00 15.00
117 Chien-Ming Wang 3.00 8.00
118 Carl Crawford 3.00 8.00
119 Delmon Young 3.00 8.00
120 B.J. Upton 3.00 8.00
121 Akinori Iwamura 2.00 5.00
122 Scott Kazmir 3.00 8.00
123 Alex Rios 3.00 8.00
124 Frank Thomas 5.00 12.00
125 Roy Halladay 5.00 12.00
126 Vernon Wells 2.00 5.00
127 Troy Glaus 3.00 8.00
128 Jeremy Accardo 2.00 5.00
129 A.J. Burnett 3.00 8.00
130 Paul Konerko 3.00 8.00
131 Jim Thome 3.00 8.00
132 Jermaine Dye 2.00 5.00
133 Mark Buehrle 3.00 8.00
134 Javier Vazquez 2.00 5.00
135 Grady Sizemore 3.00 8.00
136 Travis Hafner 2.00 5.00
137 Victor Martinez 3.00 8.00
138 C.C. Sabathia 3.00 8.00
139 Ryan Garko 2.00 5.00
140 Fausto Carmona 2.00 5.00
141 Justin Verlander 6.00 15.00
142 Jeremy Bonderman 2.00 5.00
143 Magglio Ordonez 3.00 8.00
144 Gary Sheffield 2.00 5.00
145 Carlos Guillen 2.00 5.00
146 Ivan Rodriguez 3.00 8.00
147 Curtis Granderson 3.00 8.00
148 Alex Gordon 3.00 8.00
149 Mark Teahen 2.00 5.00
150 Brian Bannister 2.00 5.00
151 Billy Butler 2.00 5.00
152 Johan Santana 5.00 12.00
153 Torii Hunter 2.00 5.00
154 Joe Mauer 5.00 12.00
155 Justin Morneau 5.00 12.00
156 Vladimir Guerrero 5.00 12.00
157 Chone Figgins 2.00 5.00
158 Jered Weaver 2.00 5.00
159 Kelvim Escobar 2.00 5.00
160 John Lackey 2.00 5.00
161 Dan Haren 2.00 5.00
162 Mike Piazza 5.00 12.00
163 Nick Swisher 5.00 12.00
164 Eric Chavez 2.00 5.00
165 Huston Street 2.00 5.00
166 Joe Blanton 2.00 5.00
167 Kenji Johjima 2.00 5.00
168 J.J. Putz 2.00 5.00
169 Felix Hernandez 5.00 12.00
170 Jose Guillen 2.00 5.00
171 Adrian Beltre 2.00 5.00
172 Ichiro 8.00 20.00
173 Marlon Byrd 2.00 5.00
174 Hank Blalock 2.00 5.00
175 Michael Young 3.00 8.00
176 Ian Kinsler 3.00 8.00
177 Sammy Sosa 5.00 12.00
178 Kevin Millwood 2.00 5.00
179 Luis Aparicio 1.25 3.00
180 Johnny Bench 3.00 8.00
181 Yogi Berra 3.00 8.00
182 Lou Brock 2.00 5.00
183 Jim Bunning 1.25 3.00
184 Rod Carew 2.00 5.00
185 Orlando Cepeda 1.25 3.00
186 Bobby Doerr 1.25 3.00
187 Bob Feller 1.25 3.00
188 Dennis Eckersley 1.25 3.00
189 Carlton Fisk 2.00 5.00
190 Monte Irvin 1.25 3.00
191 Rollie Fingers 1.25 3.00
192 Al Kaline 3.00 8.00
193 Nolan Ryan 10.00 25.00
194 Mike Schmidt 5.00 12.00
195 Ryne Sandberg 6.00 15.00
196 Robin Yount 3.00 8.00
197 Brooks Robinson 2.00 5.00
198 Bill Mazeroski 2.00 5.00
199 Reggie Jackson 2.00 5.00
200 Babe Ruth 8.00 20.00
201 Ian Kennedy AU RC/299 10.00 25.00
202 Jonathan Albaladejo AU RC/299 5.00 12.00
203 Josh Anderson AU RC/299 4.00 10.00
204 Wladimir Balentien AU (RC)/299 5.00 12.00
205 Daric Barton AU (RC)/299 5.00 12.00
206 Jerry Blevins AU RC/299 5.00 12.00
207 Emilio Bonifacio AU RC/99 30.00 60.00
208 Lance Broadway AU (RC)/299 4.00 10.00
209 Clay Buchholz AU (RC)/299 10.00 25.00
210 Billy Buckner AU (RC)/299 4.00 10.00
212 Ross Detwiler AU RC/299 5.00 12.00
213 Harvey Garcia AU RC/99 5.00 12.00
214 Alberto Gonzalez AU RC/99 12.50 30.00
215 Ryan Hanigan AU RC/99 5.00 12.00
216 Kevin Hart AU (RC)/299 4.00 10.00
217 Luke Hochevar AU RC/99 6.00 15.00
218 Chin-Lung Hu AU (RC)/299 15.00 40.00
219 Rob Johnson AU (RC)/99 5.00 12.00
220 Brandon Jones AU RC/299 6.00 15.00
221 Joe Koshansky AU (RC)/299 4.00 10.00
222 Donny Lucy AU (RC)/299 4.00 10.00
223 Justin Maxwell AU RC/299 6.00 15.00
224 Jonathan Meloan AU RC/299 4.00 10.00
225 Luis Mendoza AU (RC)/299 4.00 10.00
226 Jose Morales AU (RC)/299 4.00 10.00
227 Nyjer Morgan AU (RC)/99 5.00 12.00
228 Bill Murphy AU (RC)/99 5.00 12.00
229 Josh Newman AU RC/99 5.00 12.00
230 Ross Ohlendorf AU RC/299 5.00 12.00
231 Troy Patton AU (RC)/299 4.00 10.00
232 Felipe Paulino AU RC/99 EXCH 5.00 12.00
233 Steve Pearce AU RC/299 5.00 12.00
234 Justin Ruggiano AU RC/99 5.00 12.00
235 Clint Sammons AU (RC)/299 4.00 10.00
236 Bronson Sardinha AU (RC)/299 4.00 10.00
237 Chris Seddon AU (RC)/99 5.00 12.00
238 Seth Smith AU (RC)/299 4.00 10.00
239 J.R. Towles AU RC/99 5.00 12.00
240 Eugenio Velez AU RC/99 15.00 40.00
241 Joey Votto AU (RC)/299 30.00 60.00
242 Bill White AU RC/99 5.00 12.00

2008 Upper Deck Premier Blue

1-200 RANDOMLY INSERTED
1-200 PRINT RUN 15 SER.#'d SETS
NO 1-200 PRICING DUE TO SCARCITY
*BLUE AU p/r 99: .5X TO 1.2X BASIC p/r 299
*BLUE AU p/r 50: .4X TO 1X BASIC p/r 99
OVERALL RC AUTO ONE PER PACK
201-240 PRINT RUNS b/wn 50-99 COPIES PER
EXCHANGE DEADLINE 3/13/2010

2008 Upper Deck Premier Gold

1-200 RANDOMLY INSERTED
1-200 PRINT RUN 1 SER.#'d SET
NO 1-200 PRICING DUE TO SCARCITY
*GOLD AU p/r 50: .6X TO 1.5X BASIC p/r 299
OVERALL RC AUTO ONE PER PACK
201-240 PRINT RUNS b/wn 10-50 COPIES PER
NO PRICING ON QTY 10 OR LESS
EXCHANGE DEADLINE 3/13/2010

2008 Upper Deck Premier Silver

1-200 RANDOMLY INSERTED
1-200 PRINT RUN 5 SER.#'d SETS
NO 1-200 PRICING DUE TO SCARCITY
*SILVER AU p/r 75: .6X TO 1.5X BASIC p/r 299
OVERALL RC AUTO ONE PER PACK
201-240 PRINT RUNS 25-75 COPIES PER
NO PRICING ON QTY 25 OR LESS
EXCHANGE DEADLINE 3/13/2010

2008 Upper Deck Premier Rookie Autographs Jersey Number

OVERALL RC AUTO ONE PER PACK
PRINT RUNS B/WN 5-65 COPIES PER
NO PRICING ON QTY 25 OR LESS
EXCHANGE DEADLINE 3/13/2010
201 Ian Kennedy AU/36 60.00 120.00
202 Jonathan Albaladejo AU/53 8.00 20.00
203 Josh Anderson AU/20
204 Wladimir Balentien AU/50 8.00 20.00
205 Daric Barton AU/10
206 Jerry Blevins AU/5
207 Emilio Bonifacio AU/5
208 Lance Broadway AU/41 6.00 15.00
209 Clay Buchholz AU/61 30.00 60.00
210 Billy Buckner AU/38 6.00 15.00
212 Ross Detwiler AU/29 8.00 20.00
213 Harvey Garcia AU/5
214 Alberto Gonzalez AU/5
215 Ryan Hanigan AU/5
216 Kevin Hart AU/55 6.00 15.00
217 Luke Hochevar AU/44 10.00 25.00
218 Chin-Lung Hu AU/60 30.00 60.00
219 Rob Johnson AU/5
220 Brandon Jones AU/28 10.00 25.00
221 Joe Koshansky AU/47 6.00 15.00
222 Donny Lucy AU/55 6.00 15.00
223 Justin Maxwell AU/16
224 Jonathan Meloan AU/63 6.00 15.00
225 Luis Mendoza AU/32 6.00 15.00
226 Jose Morales AU/58 6.00 15.00
227 Nyjer Morgan AU/5
228 Bill Murphy AU/5
229 Josh Newman AU/5
230 Ross Ohlendorf AU/60 8.00 20.00
231 Troy Patton AU/65 6.00 15.00
233 Steve Pearce AU/18
234 Justin Ruggiano AU/5
235 Clint Sammons AU/18
236 Bronson Sardinha AU/64 6.00 15.00
237 Chris Seddon AU/5
238 Seth Smith AU/12
239 J.R. Towles AU/46 8.00 20.00
240 Eugenio Velez AU/5
241 Joey Votto AU/60 60.00 120.00
242 Bill White AU/5

2008 Upper Deck Premier Combos Memorabilia

OVERALL GU ODDS TWO PER PACK
STATED PRINT RUN 50 SER.#'d SETS
GOLD PRINT RUN 25 SER.#'d SETS
NO GOLD PRICING DUE TO SCARCITY
PLATINUM PRINT RUN 5 SER.#'d SETS
NO PLATINUM PRICING AVAILABLE
BF Ryan Braun 12.50 30.00
Prince Fielder/50
BY Ryan Braun 12.50 30.00
Robin Yount/50
CZ Miguel Cabrera 5.00 12.00
Ryan Zimmerman/50
FO Prince Fielder 6.00 15.00
David Ortiz/50
FV Carlton Fisk 6.00 15.00
Jason Varitek/50
GC Tony Gwynn 10.00 25.00
Rod Carew/50
GD Ken Griffey Jr. 10.00 25.00
Adam Dunn/50
GJ Ken Griffey Jr. 15.00 40.00
Derek Jeter/50
GM Tom Glavine 4.00 10.00
Pedro Martinez/50
GR Vladimir Guerrero 4.00 10.00
Manny Ramirez/50
HH Matt Holliday 5.00 12.00
Todd Helton/50
JH Andruw Jones 4.00 10.00
Torii Hunter/50
JR Derek Jeter 20.00 50.00
Cal Ripken Jr./50
LR Tony Lazzeri 30.00 60.00
Phil Rizzuto/50
MJ Thurman Munson 20.00 50.00
Reggie Jackson/50
MM Victor Martinez 4.00 10.00
Joe Mauer/50
MU Joe Morgan 4.00 10.00
Chase Utley/50
MY Stan Musial 12.50 30.00
Carl Yastrzemski/50
OH David Ortiz 5.00 12.00
Travis Hafner/50
OK Magglio Ordonez 20.00 50.00
Al Kaline/50
OR David Ortiz 6.00 15.00
Manny Ramirez/50
OY David Ortiz 6.00 15.00
Kevin Youkilis/50
PB Hunter Pence 10.00 25.00
Ryan Braun/50
PM Albert Pujols 20.00 50.00
Stan Musial/50
PO Albert Pujols 12.50 30.00
David Ortiz/50
PY Jake Peavy 5.00 12.00
Chris Young/50
RB Jose Reyes 4.00 10.00
Carlos Beltran/50
RC Jackie Robinson 30.00 60.00
Roy Campanella/50
RG Cal Ripken Jr. 20.00 50.00
Ken Griffey Jr./50
RJ Hanley Ramirez 10.00 25.00
Derek Jeter/50
SC Johan Santana 6.00 15.00
Roger Clemens/50
SH Grady Sizemore 4.00 10.00
Travis Hafner/50
SM John Smoltz 10.00 25.00
Greg Maddux/50
TG Frank Thomas 20.00 50.00
Ken Griffey Jr./50
UH Chase Utley 10.00 25.00
Cole Hamels/50
VM Jason Varitek 6.00 15.00
Victor Martinez/50
VR Justin Verlander 15.00 40.00
Nolan Ryan/50
WH Chien-Ming Wang 15.00 40.00
Phil Hughes/50

2008 Upper Deck Premier Combos Patch

OVERALL GU ODDS TWO PER PACK
PRINT RUNS B/WN 10-50 COPIES PER
NO PRICING ON QTY 10 OR LESS
GOLD PRINT RUN 25 SER.#'d SETS
NO GOLD PRICING DUE TO SCARCITY
MASTERPIECE PRINT RUN 1 SER.#'d SET
NO MASTERPIECE PRICING AVAILABLE
PLATINUM PRINT RUN 10 SER.#'d SETS
NO PLATINUM PRICING AVAILABLE
BD Ben Sheets 6.00 15.00
Dan Haren/50
BP Johnny Bench 30.00 60.00
Albert Pujols/50
BR Ryan Braun 30.00 60.00
Cal Ripken Jr./50
BS Erik Bedard 6.00 15.00
C.C. Sabathia/50
BZ Jeremy Bonderman 6.00 15.00
Carlos Zambrano/50
CR Miguel Cabrera 12.50 30.00
Manny Ramirez/50
CV Carlton Fisk 6.00 15.00
Vladimir Guerrero/50
FG Jeff Francoeur 12.50 30.00
Alex Gordon/50
FM Jeff Francoeur 10.00 25.00
Joe Mauer/50
GR Ken Griffey Jr. 30.00 60.00
Cal Ripken Jr./50
GY Tony Gwynn 20.00 50.00
Robin Yount/50
HG J.J. Hardy 10.00 25.00
Alex Gordon/50
HH Matt Holliday 12.50 30.00
Todd Helton/50
HM Cole Hamels 6.00 15.00
Andrew Miller/50
HR Felix Hernandez 20.00 50.00
Nolan Ryan/50
HW Cole Hamels 6.00 15.00
Dontrelle Willis/50
JD Reggie Jackson 6.00 15.00
Adam Dunn/50
JH Andruw Jones 6.00 15.00
Torii Hunter/50
JJ Jose Reyes 12.50 30.00
Joe Mauer/50
LC Noah Lowry 6.00 15.00
Matt Cain/50
LK Derek Lee 12.50 30.00
Paul Konerko/50
LT Lance Berkman 6.00 15.00
Todd Helton/50
MB Nick Markakis 10.00 25.00
Jason Bay/50
MM Russell Martin 6.00 15.00
Gil Meche/50
OR David Ortiz 20.00 50.00
Manny Ramirez/50
PO Jake Peavy 10.00 25.00
Roy Oswalt/50
PR Tony Perez 10.00 25.00
Manny Ramirez/50
RI Brian Roberts 6.00 15.00
Akinori Iwamura/50
RJ Russell Martin 10.00 25.00
James Loney/50
RM Aramis Ramirez 10.00 25.00
Brian McCann/50
RO Manny Ramirez 10.00 25.00
Magglio Ordonez/50
RT Hanley Ramirez 12.50 30.00
Troy Tulowitzki/50
SB Curt Schilling 10.00 25.00
Jeremy Bonderman/50
SH Johan Santana 12.50 30.00
Cole Hamels/50
SJ C.C. Sabathia 12.50 30.00
Randy Johnson/50
TH Frank Thomas 20.00 50.00
Travis Hafner/50
TK Torii Hunter 15.00 40.00
Ken Griffey Jr./50
TT Torii Hunter 10.00 25.00
Travis Hafner/50
TU Troy Tulowitzki
B.J. Upton/10
UU Chase Utley 20.00 50.00
Dan Uggla/50
UY Chase Utley 6.00 15.00
Delmon Young/50
VH Justin Verlander 12.50 30.00
Cole Hamels/50
VR Justin Verlander 20.00 50.00
Nolan Ryan/50
WJ Vernon Wells 10.00 25.00
Chipper Jones/50
YH Robin Yount 12.50 30.00
J.J. Hardy/50
ZJ Ryan Zimmerman 10.00 25.00
Chipper Jones/50
ZR Ryan Zimmerman 10.00 25.00
Jimmy Rollins/50

2008 Upper Deck Premier Emerging Stars Autographs

OVERALL AU ODDS THREE PER PACK
STATED PRINT RUN 35 SER.#'d SETS
GOLD PRINT RUN 15 SER.#'d SETS
NO GOLD PRICING DUE TO SCARCITY
MASTERPIECE PRINT RUN 1 SER.#'d SET
NO MASTERPIECE PRICING AVAILABLE
EXCHANGE DEADLINE 3/13/2010
BB Daric Barton 10.00 25.00
Travis Buck
BG Billy Butler 30.00 60.00
Alex Gordon
BH Ryan Braun 15.00 40.00
Corey Hart
BM Chad Billingsley 6.00 15.00
Jonathan Meloan
BP Clay Buchholz 40.00 80.00
Jonathan Papelbon
BV Homer Bailey 20.00 50.00
Joey Votto
BW Billy Butler 10.00 25.00
Brandon Wood
CL Matt Cain 12.50 30.00
Noah Lowry
CT Corey Hart 8.00 20.00
Travis Buck
FB Josh Fields 6.00 15.00
Lance Broadway
FO Josh Fields 6.00 15.00
Jerry Owens
GH Alex Gordon 15.00 40.00
Luke Hochevar
GL Curtis Granderson 10.00 25.00
Fred Lewis
GM Carlos Gomez 10.00 25.00
David Murphy
HB Phil Hughes 20.00 50.00
Homer Bailey
HK Cole Hamels 15.00 40.00
Scott Kazmir
HL Chin-Lung Hu 20.00 50.00
James Loney
HS Dan Haren 10.00 25.00
Huston Street
HV Josh Hamilton 6.00 15.00
Joey Votto
HW Corey Hart 15.00 40.00
Rickie Weeks
KB Kevin Kouzmanoff 6.00 15.00
Brandon Wood
KH Ian Kennedy 15.00 40.00
Phil Hughes
KU Howie Kendrick 6.00 15.00
Dan Uggla
KW Howie Kendrick 15.00 40.00
Jered Weaver
LE James Loney 12.50 30.00
Andre Ethier
LL Andy LaRoche 12.50 30.00
James Loney
MB John Maine 6.00 15.00
Chad Billingsley
MC John Maine 6.00 15.00
Matt Cain
ME Brian McCann 20.00 50.00
Yunel Escobar
MG John Maine 10.00 25.00
Carlos Gomez
MH Nick Markakis 6.00 15.00
Jeremy Hermida
ML Russell Martin 30.00 60.00
James Loney
MM Brian McCann 12.50 30.00
Russell Martin
MP Nick Markakis 12.50 30.00
Steve Pearce
MS Brian McCann 12.50 30.00
Jarrod Saltalamacchia
MT Russell Martin 12.50 30.00
J.R. Towles
NJ Nick Markakis 6.00 15.00
Josh Hamilton
PL Jonathan Papelbon 30.00 60.00
Jon Lester
PZ Jonathan Papelbon 20.00 50.00
Joel Zumaya
SB James Shields 6.00 15.00
Scott Baker
TA Troy Tulowitzki 10.00 25.00
Garrett Atkins
TG Troy Tulowitzki 15.00 40.00
Alex Gordon
UR Dan Uggla 20.00 50.00
Hanley Ramirez
UY B.J. Upton 12.50 30.00
Delmon Young
VH Justin Verlander 15.00 40.00
Dan Haren

2008 Upper Deck Premier Legendary Remnants Triple

OVERALL GU ODDS TWO PER PACK
PRINT RUNS B/WN 15-50 COPIES PER
NO PRICING ON QTY 15 OR LESS
BRONZE B/WN 10-25 COPIES PER
NO BRONZE PRICING DUE TO SCARCITY
GOLD B/WN 5-10 COPIES PER
NO GOLD PRICING DUE TO SCARCITY
MASTERPIECE PRINT RUN 1 SER.#'d SET
NO MASTERPIECE PRICING AVAILABLE
BR Babe Ruth/15
HG Hank Greenberg/50 50.00 100.00
JD Joe DiMaggio/50 60.00 120.00
JR Jackie Robinson/50 30.00 60.00
LG Lou Gehrig/50 150.00 250.00
MO Mel Ott/50 40.00 80.00
RC Roberto Clemente/50 40.00 80.00
RM Roger Maris/50 20.00 50.00
WS Willie Stargell/50 20.00 50.00

2008 Upper Deck Premier Legendary Remnants Triple Gold Milestones

OVERALL GU ODDS TWO PER PACK
PRINT RUNS B/WN 7-61 COPIES PER
NO PRICING ON QTY 23 OR LESS
BR Babe Ruth/15
HG Hank Greenberg/36 50.00 100.00
JD Joe DiMaggio/9
JR Jackie Robinson/19
LG Lou Gehrig/23
MO Mel Ott/12
RC Roberto Clemente/21
RM Roger Maris/61 20.00 50.00
WS Willie Stargell/7

2008 Upper Deck Premier Legendary Remnants Triple Silver

OVERALL GU ODDS TWO PER PACK
PRINT RUNS B/WN 10-30 COPIES PER
NO PRICING ON QTY 10 OR LESS
BR Babe Ruth/10
HG Hank Greenberg/10
JD Joe DiMaggio/30 75.00 150.00
JR Jackie Robinson/30 40.00 80.00
LG Lou Gehrig/30 200.00 300.00
MO Mel Ott/30 50.00 100.00
RC Roberto Clemente/30 50.00 100.00
RM Roger Maris/30 30.00 60.00
WS Willie Stargell/30 30.00 60.00

2008 Upper Deck Premier Memorabilia Triple

OVERALL GU ODDS TWO PER PACK
PRINT RUNS B/WN 25-50 COPIES PER
GOLD PRINT RUN 3 SER.#'d SETS
NO GOLD PRICING DUE TO SCARCITY
AG Alex Gordon/25
AI Akinori Iwamura/25
AP Albert Pujols/75 10.00 25.00
AP2 Albert Pujols/75 10.00 25.00
BE Johnny Bench/75 10.00 25.00
BM Bill Mazeroski/25
CA Rod Carew/25
CJ Chipper Jones/25
DJ Derek Jeter/75 12.50 30.00
DM Daisuke Matsuzaka/75 12.50 30.00
DO David Ortiz/50 5.00 12.00
GM Greg Maddux/50 6.00 15.00
GS Grady Sizemore/25
IR Ivan Rodriguez/25
JD Joe DiMaggio/75 50.00 100.00
JP Jonathan Papelbon/25
KG Ken Griffey Jr./50 10.00 25.00
MA Don Mattingly/50 10.00 25.00
MR Manny Ramirez/25
MS Mike Schmidt/50 12.50 30.00
NR Nolan Ryan/75 12.50 30.00
OS Ozzie Smith/75 10.00 25.00
PF Prince Fielder/25
PM Paul Molitor/25
RC Roger Clemens/25
RJ Reggie Jackson/75 6.00 15.00
SM Stan Musial/75 12.50 30.00
TS Tom Seaver/75 10.00 25.00
VG Vladimir Guerrero/25
WB Wade Boggs/50 5.00 12.00
WS Warren Spahn/75 10.00 25.00

2008 Upper Deck Premier Memorabilia Quad

OVERALL GU ODDS TWO PER PACK
PRINT RUNS B/WN 15-40 COPIES PER
NO RUTH PRICING DUE TO SCARCITY
GOLD STATED PRINT RUN 4 SER.#'d SETS
NO GOLD PRICING DUE TO SCARCITY
AS Alfonso Soriano/40 6.00 15.00
BR Babe Ruth/15
CC Chris Carpenter/40 5.00 12.00
CH Cole Hamels/40 5.00 12.00
CL Roger Clemens/40 6.00 15.00
CS Curt Schilling/40 5.00 12.00
CU Chase Utley/40 5.00 12.00
CW Chien-Ming Wang/40 20.00 50.00
CY Carl Yastrzemski/40 6.00 15.00
DJ Derek Jeter/40 30.00 60.00
DL Derrek Lee/40 4.00 10.00
DM Don Mattingly/40 12.50 30.00
DO David Ortiz/40 6.00 15.00
DO2 David Ortiz/40 6.00 15.00
DP Dave Parker/40 6.00 15.00
DW Dontrelle Willis/40 4.00 10.00
EM Eddie Mathews/40 20.00 50.00
HP Hunter Pence/40 6.00 15.00
JM Joe Mauer/40 5.00 12.00
JR Jackie Robinson/40 40.00 80.00
JS Johan Santana/40 6.00 15.00
JV Justin Verlander/40 10.00 25.00
MA Russell Martin/40 10.00 25.00
MO Justin Morneau/40 4.00 10.00
MS Mike Schmidt/40 10.00 25.00
MT Mark Teixeira/40 10.00 25.00
NM Nick Markakis/40 6.00 15.00
NR Nolan Ryan/40 15.00 40.00
OR Magglio Ordonez/40 5.00 12.00
PF Prince Fielder/40 6.00 15.00
PH Phil Hughes/40 12.50 30.00
PW Pee Wee Reese/40 10.00 25.00
RB Ryan Braun/40 10.00 25.00
RC Roberto Clemente/40 40.00 80.00
RE Jose Reyes/40 6.00 15.00
RH Rogers Hornsby/40 30.00 60.00
RJ Reggie Jackson/40 10.00 25.00
RM Roger Maris/40 30.00 60.00
RY Robin Yount/40 15.00 40.00
SM Stan Musial/40 12.50 30.00
TM Thurman Munson/40 20.00 50.00
TP Tony Perez/40 10.00 25.00
VG Vladimir Guerrero/40 6.00 15.00
VM Victor Martinez/40 4.00 10.00

2008 Upper Deck Premier Patches

OVERALL GU ODDS TWO PER PACK
PRINT RUNS B/WN 55-75 COPIES PER
*GOLD: .4X TO 1X BASIC PATCH
GOLD B/WN 25-50 COPIES PER
NO GOLD PRICING ON QTY 25 OR LESS
SILVER PRINT RUN 10 SER.#'d SETS
NO SILVER PRICING DUE TO SCARCITY

AI Akinori Iwamura 10.00 25.00
AJ Andruw Jones 6.00 15.00
AL Adam LaRoche 6.00 15.00
BR Brian Roberts 6.00 15.00
CB Carlos Beltran 6.00 15.00
CJ Chipper Jones 15.00 40.00
CR Cal Ripken Jr. 30.00 60.00
CU Chase Utley 15.00 40.00
CW Chien-Ming Wang 20.00 50.00
DM Daisuke Matsuzaka/55 30.00 60.00
DO David Ortiz 12.50 30.00
DW Dontrelle Willis 6.00 15.00
EB Erik Bedard 6.00 15.00
FT Frank Thomas 30.00 60.00
GS Grady Sizemore 12.50 30.00
HA Travis Hafner 6.00 15.00
HK Hong-Chih Kuo 12.50 30.00
HP Hunter Pence 12.50 30.00
HR Hanley Ramirez 12.50 30.00
HU Torii Hunter 6.00 15.00
IR Ivan Rodriguez 12.50 30.00
JB Jeremy Bonderman 10.00 25.00
JF Jeff Francoeur 15.00 40.00
JM Justin Morneau 10.00 25.00
JP Jake Peavy 12.50 30.00
JR Jose Reyes 12.50 30.00
JS Johan Santana 10.00 25.00
JV Jason Varitek/65 20.00 50.00
MA Don Mattingly/74 12.50 30.00
MC Miguel Cabrera 12.50 30.00
MO Magglio Ordonez 6.00 15.00
NM Nick Markakis 10.00 25.00
NR Nolan Ryan 30.00 60.00
RB Ryan Braun 20.00 50.00
RJ Randy Johnson/57 12.50 30.00
RO Roy Oswalt 6.00 15.00
RW Rickie Weeks 6.00 15.00
RZ Ryan Zimmerman 12.50 30.00
SM Stan Musial 15.00 40.00
TG Tony Gwynn 15.00 40.00
TH Todd Helton 10.00 25.00
TL Tim Lincecum 10.00 25.00
TS Takashi Saito/65 10.00 25.00
VE Justin Verlander 10.00 25.00
WB Wade Boggs 6.00 15.00

2008 Upper Deck Premier Patches Gold Milestones

OVERALL GU ODDS TWO PER PACK
PRINT RUNS B/WN 10-33 COPIES PER
NO PRICING ON QTY 25 OR LESS

AI Akinori Iwamura/15
AJ Andruw Jones/18
AL Adam LaRoche/13
BR Brian Roberts/18
CB Carlos Beltran/16
CJ Chipper Jones/26 15.00 40.00
CR Cal Ripken/19
CU Chase Utley/32 15.00 40.00
CW Chien-Ming Wang/19
DM Daisuke Matsuzaka/10
DO David Ortiz/12
DW Dontrelle Willis/14
EB Erik Bedard/15
FT Frank Thomas/14
GS Grady Sizemore/28 12.50 30.00
HA Travis Hafner/33 6.00 15.00
HK Hong-Chih Kuo/27 12.50 30.00
HP Hunter Pence/19
HR Hanley Ramirez/17
HU Torii Hunter/31 6.00 15.00
IR Ivan Rodriguez/14
JA Reggie Jackson/18
JB Jeremy Bonderman/14
JF Jeff Francoeur/14
JM Justin Morneau/22
JP Jake Peavy/15
JR Jose Reyes/17
JS Johan Santana/17
JV Jason Varitek/22
MA Don Mattingly/10
MC Miguel Cabrera/26 12.50 30.00
MO Magglio Ordonez/24
NM Nick Markakis/16
NR Nolan Ryan/11
RB Ryan Braun/11
RJ Randy Johnson/10
RO Roy Oswalt/20
RW Rickie Weeks/13
RZ Ryan Zimmerman/20
SM Stan Musial/16
TG Tony Gwynn/15
TH Todd Helton/25
TL Tim Lincecum/12
TP Tony Perez/20
TS Takashi Saito/24
VE Justin Verlander/17
WB Wade Boggs/12

2008 Upper Deck Premier Patches Gold Milestones Jersey Number

OVERALL GU ODDS TWO PER PACK
PRINT RUNS B/WN 1-57 COPIES PER
NO PRICING ON QTY 25 OR LESS

AI Akinori Iwamura/1
AJ Andruw Jones/25
AL Adam LaRoche/25
BR Brian Roberts/1
CB Carlos Beltran/15
CJ Chipper Jones/10
CR Cal Ripken Jr./8
CU Chase Utley/26 15.00 40.00
CW Chien-Ming Wang/40 20.00 50.00
DM Daisuke Matsuzaka/18
DO David Ortiz/34 12.50 30.00
DW Dontrelle Willis/35 6.00 15.00
EB Erik Bedard/45 6.00 15.00
FT Frank Thomas/35 30.00 60.00
GS Grady Sizemore/24
HA Travis Hafner/48 6.00 15.00
HK Hong-Chih Kuo/56 12.50 30.00
HP Hunter Pence/9
HR Hanley Ramirez/2
HU Torii Hunter/48 6.00 15.00
IR Ivan Rodriguez/7
JA Reggie Jackson/44 10.00 25.00
JB Jeremy Bonderman/38 10.00 25.00
JF Jeff Francoeur/7
JM Justin Morneau/33 10.00 25.00
JP Jake Peavy/44 12.50 30.00
JR Jose Reyes/7
JS Johan Santana/57 10.00 25.00
JV Jason Varitek/33 20.00 50.00
MA Don Mattingly/23
MC Miguel Cabrera/24
MO Magglio Ordonez/30 6.00 15.00
NM Nick Markakis/21
NR Nolan Ryan/30 30.00 60.00
RB Ryan Braun/8
RJ Randy Johnson/51 12.50 30.00
RO Roy Oswalt/44 6.00 15.00
RW Rickie Weeks/23
RZ Ryan Zimmerman/11
SM Stan Musial/6
TG Tony Gwynn/19
TH Todd Helton/17
TL Tim Lincecum/55 10.00 25.00
TP Tony Perez/24
TS Takashi Saito/44 10.00 25.00
VE Justin Verlander/35 10.00 25.00
WB Wade Boggs/26 6.00 15.00

2008 Upper Deck Premier Penmanship Autographs

OVERALL AU ODDS THREE PER PACK
PRINT RUNS B/WN 15-50 COPIES PER
NO PRICING ON QTY 20 OR LESS
GOLD B/WN 3-5 COPIES PER
NO GOLD PRICING DUE TO SCARCITY
MASTERPIECE PRINT RUN 1 SER.#'d SET
NO MASTERPIECE PRICING AVAILABLE
EXCHANGE DEADLINE 3/13/2010

AK Al Kaline/50 15.00 40.00
BB Billy Butler/50 10.00 25.00
BE Johnny Bench/50 20.00 50.00
BF Bob Feller/20
BH Bill Hall/15
BL Joe Blanton/50 4.00 10.00
BT Bobby Thomson/50 10.00 25.00
CB Chad Billingsley/50 4.00 10.00
CC Carl Crawford/50 6.00 15.00
CF Carlton Fisk/50 10.00 25.00
CH Cole Hamels/50 15.00 40.00
CJ Chipper Jones/50 40.00 80.00
CR Cal Ripken Jr./50 50.00 100.00
CW Chien-Ming Wang/50 100.00 150.00
FC Fausto Carmona/50 6.00 15.00
FH Felix Hernandez/50 15.00 40.00
FT Frank Thomas/50 30.00 60.00
GP Gaylord Perry/50 4.00 10.00
HK Howie Kendrick/50 4.00 10.00
HP Hunter Pence/50 12.50 30.00
IK Ian Kennedy/50 30.00 60.00
IR Ivan Rodriguez/50 30.00 60.00
JB Jeremy Bonderman/50 6.00 15.00
JL John Lackey/50 4.00 10.00
JM John Maine/50 6.00 15.00
JP Jim Palmer/50 6.00 15.00
JV Justin Verlander/50 15.00 40.00
JW Josh Willingham/50 4.00 10.00
KW Kerry Wood/50 12.50 30.00
LA Luis Aparicio/40 6.00 15.00
MS Mike Schmidt/50 20.00 50.00
NM Nick Markakis/50 12.50 30.00
NR Nolan Ryan/50 40.00 80.00
PA Jonathan Papelbon/50 12.50 30.00
RB Ryan Braun/50 20.00 50.00
RC Rod Carew/50 10.00 25.00
RH Ramon Hernandez/50 4.00 10.00
RM Russell Martin/50 10.00 25.00
RZ Ryan Zimmerman/50 10.00 25.00
TH Travis Hafner/50 6.00 15.00
TT Troy Tulowitzki/50 12.50 30.00
VM Victor Martinez/50 10.00 25.00

2008 Upper Deck Premier Remnants Triple Blue-Gold

OVERALL GU ODDS TWO PER PACK
PRINT RUNS B/WN 25-75 COPIES PER
NO PRICING ON QTY 25
*BLUE-SILVER: .4X TO 1X BASIC
B-S PRINT RUNS B/WN 25-75 PER
NO B-S PRICING ON QTY 25
*BRONZE: .4X TO 1X BASIC
BRONZE PRINT RUNS B/WN 25-75 PER
NO BRONZE PRICING ON QTY 25
MASTERPIECE PRINT RUN 1 SER.#'d SET
NO MASTERPIECE PRICING AVAILABLE

AJ Andruw Jones ATL/25
AP Albert Pujols STL/75 10.00 25.00
CF Carlton Fisk CHI/25
CY Carl Yastrzemski YAZ/50 5.00 12.00
DJ Derek Jeter NYY/75 12.50 30.00
DM Daisuke Matsuzaka JPN/75 12.50 30.00
DO David Ortiz BOS/50 5.00 12.00
HK Hong-Chih Kuo KUO/25
JB Josh Beckett BOS/25
KG Ken Griffey Jr. OF3/50 10.00 25.00
MA Don Mattingly NYY/25
MR Manny Ramirez BOS/25
MS Mike Schmidt PHI/50 12.50 30.00
NR Nolan Ryan TEX/75 12.50 30.00
PA Jonathan Papelbon BOS/25
PO Jorge Posada NYY/25
RJ Reggie Jackson NYY/75 6.00 15.00
RY Robin Yount MVP/50 12.50 30.00
VG Vladimir Guerrero MVP/25
WB Wade Boggs BOS/50 5.00 12.00

2008 Upper Deck Premier Remnants Triple Gold

OVERALL GU ODDS TWO PER PACK
PRINT RUNS B/WN 2-44 COPIES PER
NO PRICING ON QTY 23 OR LESS

AP Albert Pujols/5
CJ Chipper Jones/10
CY Carl Yastrzemski/8
DJ Derek Jeter/2
DM Daisuke Matsuzaka/18
DO David Ortiz/34 5.00 12.00
JB Josh Beckett/7
KG Ken Griffey Jr./3
MA Don Mattingly/23
MS Mike Schmidt/33 12.50 30.00
NR Nolan Ryan/34 12.50 30.00
PO Jorge Posada/20
RJ Reggie Jackson/44 6.00 15.00
RY Robin Yount/19
VG Vladimir Guerrero/27 5.00 12.00
WB Wade Boggs/26 5.00 12.00

2008 Upper Deck Premier Remnants Triple Gold Milestones

OVERALL GU ODDS TWO PER PACK
PRINT RUNS B/WN 5-50 COPIES PER
NO PRICING ON QTY 25 OR LESS

AJ Andruw Jones/5
AP Albert Pujols/50 10.00 25.00
CF Carlton Fisk/25
CJ Chipper Jones/5
CS Curt Schilling/5
CU Chase Utley/5
CY Carl Yastrzemski/25
DJ Derek Jeter/15
DM Daisuke Matsuzaka/10
DO David Ortiz/10
HK Hong-Chih Kuo/5
JB Josh Beckett/5
KG Ken Griffey Jr./25
MA Don Mattingly/5
MS Mike Schmidt/25
NR Nolan Ryan/5
RJ Reggie Jackson/15
RY Robin Yount/25
WB Wade Boggs/10

2008 Upper Deck Premier Remnants Quad

OVERALL GU ODDS TWO PER PACK
PRINT RUNS15-50 COPIES PER
NO PRICING ON QTY 15 OR LESS
BRONZE PRINT RUN 25 SER.#'d SETS
NO BRONZE PRICING DUE TO SCARCITY
GOLD B/WN 5-10 COPIES PER
NO GOLD PRICING DUE TO SCARCITY
MASTERPIECE PRINT RUN 1 SER.#'d SET
NO MASTERPIECE PRICING AVAILABLE

AD Adam Dunn DUNN/50 3.00 8.00
AD Adam Dunn REDS/50 3.00 8.00
BE Carlos Beltran METS/50 3.00 8.00
BE Carlos Beltran HITS/50 3.00 8.00
BR Brooks Robinson 16GG/50 4.00 10.00
BR Brooks Robinson1964/15
BS Ben Sheets WINS/50 3.00 8.00
BS Ben Sheets 2001/50 3.00 8.00
CF Carlton Fisk FISK/50 4.00 10.00
CF Carlton Fisk HITS/50 4.00 10.00
CH Cole Hamels COLE/50 4.00 10.00
CH Cole Hamels WINS/50 4.00 10.00
CL Roger Clemens ALCY/50 6.00 15.00
CL Roger Clemens WINS/50 6.00 15.00
CR Cal Ripken Jr. CAL8/50 20.00 50.00
CR Cal Ripken Jr.2632/50 20.00 50.00
CS Curt Schilling SOCK/50 4.00 10.00
CS Curt Schilling CURT/50 4.00 10.00
CW Chien-Ming Wang WANG/50 20.00 50.00
CW Chien-Ming Wang WINS/50 20.00 50.00
DJ Derek Jeter CAPT/50 20.00 50.00
DJ Derek Jeter SS#2/50 20.00 50.00
DL Derrek Lee CUBS/50 3.00 8.00
DL Derrek Lee RUNS/50 3.00 8.00
DM Don Mattingly1985/50 10.00 25.00
DM Don Mattingly CAPT/50 10.00 25.00
DO David Ortiz PAPI/50 6.00 15.00
DO David Ortiz 2004/50 6.00 15.00
FH Felix Hernandez KING/50 6.00 15.00
FH Felix Hernandez WINS/50 6.00 15.00
HK Hong-Chih Kuo HONG/50 6.00 15.00
HK Hong-Chih Kuo WINS/50 6.00 15.00
HR Hanley Ramirez SS#2/50 4.00 10.00
HR Hanley Ramirez HITS/50 4.00 10.00
JB Johnny Bench 1972/50 6.00 15.00
JB Johnny Bench REDS/50 6.00 15.00
JH J.J. Hardy SS#7/50 4.00 10.00
JH J.J. Hardy 2007/50 4.00 10.00
JP Jake Peavy JAKE/50 4.00 10.00
JP Jake Peavy WINS/50 4.00 10.00
JR Jim Rice RICE/50 4.00 10.00
JR Jim Rice1978/50 4.00 10.00
JS John Smoltz WINS/50 4.00 10.00
JS John Smoltz 1996/50 4.00 10.00
KG Ken Griffey Jr. REDS/50 10.00 25.00
KG Ken Griffey Jr. OF#3/50 10.00 25.00
MH Matt Holliday MATT/50 4.00 10.00
MH Matt Holliday OF#5/50 4.00 10.00
NR Nolan Ryan RYAN/50 20.00 50.00
NR Nolan Ryan 383K/50 20.00 50.00
NR2 Nolan Ryan 5714/50 20.00 50.00
NR2 Nolan Ryan WINS/50 20.00 50.00
PF Prince Fielder RUNS/50 6.00 15.00
PF Prince Fielder HITS/50 6.00 15.00
PR Phil Rizzuto NYSS/50 10.00 25.00
PR Phil Rizzuto1950/50 10.00 25.00
RC Rod Carew 3000/50 4.00 10.00
RC Rod Carew 1977/50 4.00 10.00
RE Jose Reyes METS/50 10.00 25.00
RE Jose Reyes JOSE/50 10.00 25.00
RJ Reggie Jackson NYRF/50 6.00 15.00
RJ Reggie Jackson1977/50 6.00 15.00
RS Ryne Sandberg CUBS/50 10.00 25.00
RS Ryne Sandberg RYNO/50 10.00 25.00
RZ Ryan Zimmerman WASH/50 10.00 25.00
RZ Ryan Zimmerman RYAN/50 10.00 25.00
SM Stan Musial STAN/50 15.00 40.00
SM Stan Musial 3MVP/50 15.00 40.00
TG Tony Gwynn 3000/50 12.50 30.00
TG Tony Gwynn TONY/50 12.50 30.00
TM Thurman Munson CAPT/50 15.00 40.00
TM Thurman Munson 1976/50 15.00 40.00
TR Tim Raines ROCK/50 3.00 8.00
TR Tim Raines RUNS/50 3.00 8.00
TS Tom Seaver METS/50 10.00 25.00
TS Tom Seaver 1969/50 10.00 25.00
VG Vladimir Guerrero VLAD/50 4.00 10.00
VG Vladimir Guerrero STAR/50 4.00 10.00
WB Wade Boggs 3000/50 10.00 25.00
WB Wade Boggs WADE/50 10.00 25.00

2008 Upper Deck Premier Remnants Quad Gold Milestones

OVERALL GU ODDS TWO PER PACK
PRINT RUNS B/WN 2-77 COPIES PER
NO PRICING ON QTY 24 OR LESS

AD Adam Dunn/46 3.00 8.00
BE Carlos Beltran/41 3.00 8.00
BR Brooks Robinson/16
BS Ben Sheets/18
CF Carlton Fisk/37 4.00 10.00
CH Cole Hamels/15
CL Roger Clemens/20
CR Cal Ripken Jr./34 20.00 50.00
CS Curt Schilling/13
CW Chien-Ming Wang/47 20.00 50.00
DJ Derek Jeter/2
DL Derrek Lee/46 3.00 8.00
DM Don Mattingly/35 10.00 25.00
DO David Ortiz/54 6.00 15.00
FH Felix Hernandez/77 6.00 15.00
HK Hong-Chih Kuo/71 6.00 15.00
HR Hanley Ramirez/51 4.00 10.00
JB Johnny Bench/45 6.00 15.00
JH J.J. Hardy/9
JP Jake Peavy/16
JR Jim Rice/46 4.00 10.00
JS John Smoltz/15
KG Ken Griffey Jr./8
MH Matt Holliday/36 4.00 10.00
NR Nolan Ryan/19
NR2 Nolan Ryan/18
PF Prince Fielder/50 6.00 15.00
PR Phil Rizzuto/38 10.00 25.00
RC Rod Carew/49 4.00 10.00
RE Jose Reyes/60 10.00 25.00
RJ Reggie Jackson/18
RS Ryne Sandberg/10 10.00 25.00
RZ Ryan Zimmerman/20
SM Stan Musial/16
TG Tony Gwynn/33 12.50 30.00
TM Thurman Munson/17
TR Tim Raines/50 3.00 8.00
TS Tom Seaver/19
VG Vladimir Guerrero/39 4.00 10.00
WB Wade Boggs/24

2008 Upper Deck Premier Signature Premier

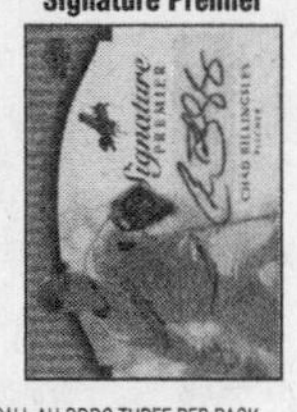

OVERALL AU ODDS THREE PER PACK
PRINT RUNS B/WN 5-45 COPIES PER
NO PRICING ON QTY 25 OR LESS
BRONZE B/WN 1-25 COPIES PER
NO BRONZE PRICING AVAILABLE
GOLD B/WN 1-15 COPIES PER
NO GOLD PRICING DUE TO SCARCITY
MASTERPIECE PRINT RUN 1 SER.#'d SET
NO MASTERPIECE PRICING AVAILABLE
INK CHANGE PRINT RUN 1 SER.#'d SET
NO INK CHANGE PRICING AVAILABLE
EXCHANGE DEADLINE 3/13/2010

AE Andre Ethier 10.00 25.00
AG Adrian Gonzalez 10.00 25.00
AI Akinori Iwamura 10.00 25.00
AM Andrew Miller 4.00 10.00
AR Aramis Ramirez 6.00 15.00
BB Billy Buckner 4.00 10.00
BD Bobby Doerr/20
BE Johnny Bench 20.00 50.00
BF Bob Feller/5
BH Bill Hall/25
BI Chad Billingsley 4.00 10.00
BJ B.J. Upton 6.00 15.00
BM Brian McCann 12.50 30.00
BO Jeremy Bonderman 6.00 15.00
BS Bronson Sardinha 4.00 10.00
BU Billy Butler 10.00 25.00
CA Matt Cain 4.00 10.00
CB Clay Buchholz 15.00 40.00
CC Chris Carpenter 10.00 25.00
CF Carlton Fisk 10.00 25.00
CR Cal Ripken Jr. 60.00 120.00
DB Daric Barton 4.00 10.00
DH Dan Haren 4.00 10.00
DL Derrek Lee 6.00 15.00
DM Don Mattingly 15.00 40.00
DU Dan Uggla/25
EB Ernie Banks/37 15.00 40.00
EM Edgar Martinez 15.00 40.00
FC Fausto Carmona 6.00 15.00
FP Felix Pie/25
GA Garret Anderson 6.00 15.00
GO Alex Gordon 10.00 25.00
GP Gaylord Perry 4.00 10.00
HK Howie Kendrick 4.00 10.00
HR Harold Reynolds 4.00 10.00
HU Chin-Lung Hu 30.00 60.00
JB Jim Bunning 6.00 15.00
JL John Lackey 4.00 10.00
JM John Maine 6.00 15.00
JP Jim Palmer 6.00 15.00
JT J.R. Towles 4.00 10.00
JV Joey Votto 30.00 60.00
JW Josh Willingham 4.00 10.00
JZ Joel Zumaya 4.00 10.00
KE Ian Kennedy 30.00 60.00
KI Ian Kinsler 6.00 15.00
KY Kevin Youkilis 6.00 15.00
LA Luis Aparicio 6.00 15.00
LE Jon Lester 15.00 40.00
LH Luke Hochevar 6.00 15.00
MI Monte Irvin/15
MS Mike Schmidt 20.00 50.00
MT Miguel Tejada 6.00 15.00
MU Stan Musial 40.00 80.00
NL Noah Lowry 4.00 10.00
NM Nick Markakis 12.50 30.00
NR Nolan Ryan 40.00 80.00
NS Nick Swisher 4.00 10.00
OH Ross Ohlendorf 6.00 15.00
OW Micah Owings 6.00 15.00
PF Prince Fielder 20.00 50.00
PH Phil Hughes 20.00 50.00
PM Pedro Martinez 30.00 60.00
RB Ryan Braun 20.00 50.00
RC Rod Carew 10.00 25.00
RD Ross Detwiler 4.00 10.00
RH Rich Hill 4.00 10.00
RI Jim Rice/20
RJ Reggie Jackson 20.00 50.00
RO Roger Clemens 30.00 60.00
RS Ron Santo/25
RT Ryan Theriot 10.00 25.00
RY Ryne Sandberg 20.00 50.00
SA Jarrod Saltalamacchia 4.00 10.00
SC Steve Carlton/25
SD Stephen Drew 4.00 10.00
SK Scott Kazmir 8.00 20.00
TB Travis Buck 4.00 10.00
TG Tony Gwynn 20.00 50.00
TH Travis Hafner 6.00 15.00
TM Tino Martinez 10.00 25.00
TP Tony Perez 10.00 25.00
WB Wladimir Balentien 6.00 15.00
WF Whitey Ford 20.00 50.00
YE Yunel Escobar 10.00 25.00

2008 Upper Deck Premier Signature Premier Gold Jersey Number

OVERALL AU ODDS THREE PER PACK
PRINT RUNS B/WN 1-65 COPIES PER
NO PRICING ON QTY 25 OR LESS
EXCHANGE DEADLINE 3/13/2010

AE Andre Ethier/16
AG Adrian Gonzalez/23
AI Akinori Iwamura/1
AM Andrew Miller/48 4.00 10.00
AR Aramis Ramirez/16
BB Billy Buckner/38 4.00 10.00
BD Bobby Doerr/1
BE Johnny Bench/5
BF Bob Feller/19
BH Bill Hall/1
BI Chad Billingsley/58 4.00 10.00
BJ B.J. Upton/2
BM Brian McCann/16
BO Jeremy Bonderman/38 6.00 15.00
BS Bronson Sardinha/64 4.00 10.00
BU Billy Butler/21
CA Matt Cain/18
CB Clay Buchholz/61 10.00 25.00
CC Chris Carpenter/29 10.00 25.00
CF Carlton Fisk/27 10.00 25.00
CR Cal Ripken Jr./8
DB Daric Barton/10
DH Dan Haren/15
DL Derrek Lee/25
DM Don Mattingly/23
DU Dan Uggla/6
EB Ernie Banks/14
EM Edgar Martinez/11
FC Fausto Carmona/55 6.00 15.00
FP Felix Pie/10
GA Garret Anderson/16
GO Alex Gordon/7
GP Gaylord Perry/36 4.00 10.00
HK Howie Kendrick/47 4.00 10.00
HR Harold Reynolds/4
HU Chin-Lung Hu/60 30.00 60.00
JB Jim Bunning/14
JL John Lackey/41 4.00 10.00
JM John Maine/33 6.00 15.00
JP Jim Palmer/22
JT J.R. Towles/46 4.00 10.00
JV Joey Votto/60 60.00 120.00
JW Josh Willingham/14
JZ Joel Zumaya/54 4.00 10.00
KE Ian Kennedy/36 30.00 60.00
KI Ian Kinsler/5
KY Kevin Youkilis/20
LA Luis Aparicio/11
LE Jon Lester/31 6.00 15.00
LH Luke Hochevar/44 6.00 15.00
MI Monte Irvin/1
MS Mike Schmidt/20
MT Miguel Tejada/8
MU Stan Musial/6
NL Noah Lowry/51 4.00 10.00
NM Nick Markakis/21
NR Nolan Ryan/30 40.00 80.00
NS Nick Swisher/33 4.00 10.00
OH Ross Ohlendorf/60 6.00 15.00
OW Micah Owings/44 6.00 15.00
PF Prince Fielder/28 20.00 50.00
PH Phil Hughes/65 20.00 50.00
PM Pedro Martinez/45 30.00 60.00
RB Ryan Braun/8
RC Rod Carew/29 10.00 25.00
RD Ross Detwiler/29 4.00 10.00
RH Rich Hill/53 4.00 10.00
RI Jim Rice/5
RJ Reggie Jackson/44 20.00 50.00
RO Roger Clemens/22
RS Ron Santo/5
RT Ryan Theriot/2
RY Ryne Sandberg/23
SA Jarrod Saltalamacchia/25
SD Stephen Drew/6
SK Scott Kazmir/19
TB Travis Buck/6
TG Tony Gwynn/19
TH Travis Hafner/48 6.00 15.00
TM Tino Martinez/24
TP Tony Perez/24
WB Wladimir Balentien/50 6.00 15.00
WF Whitey Ford/16
YE Yunel Escobar/19

2008 Upper Deck Premier Stitchings

OVERALL STITCHINGS ONE PER PACK
PRINT RUNS B/WN 50-75 COPIES PER
GOLD B/WN 15-25 COPIES PER
NO GOLD PRICING DUE TO SCARCITY
MASTERPIECE PRINT RUN 1 SER.#'d SET
NO MASTERPIECE PRICING AVAILABLE
SILVER B/WN 5-10 COPIES PER
NO SILVER PRICING DUE TO SCARCITY

AG Alex Gordon/75 10.00 25.00
AG Alex Gordon/50 10.00 25.00
AK Al Kaline/75 10.00 25.00
AK Al Kaline/50 10.00 25.00
AP Albert Pujols/75 12.50 30.00
AP Albert Pujols/50 12.50 30.00
AR Alex Rodriguez/75 12.50 30.00
AR Alex Rodriguez/50 12.50 30.00
AS Alfonso Soriano/75 5.00 12.00
AS Alfonso Soriano/50 5.00 12.00
BD Bobby Doerr/75 2.00 5.00
BD Bobby Doerr/50 2.00 5.00
BE Johnny Bench/75 5.00 12.00
BE Johnny Bench/50 5.00 12.00
BF Bob Feller/75 10.00 25.00
BF Bob Feller/50 10.00 25.00
BG Bob Gibson/75 5.00 12.00
BG Bob Gibson/50 5.00 12.00
BM Bill Mazeroski/75 3.00 8.00
BM Bill Mazeroski/50 3.00 8.00
BR Babe Ruth/75 15.00 40.00
BR Babe Ruth/50 15.00 40.00
CA Miguel Cabrera/75 3.00 8.00
CA Miguel Cabrera/50 3.00 8.00
CB Craig Biggio/75 3.00 8.00
CB Craig Biggio/50 3.00 8.00
CF Carlton Fisk/75 10.00 25.00
CF Carlton Fisk/50 10.00 25.00
CJ Chipper Jones/75 6.00 15.00
CJ Chipper Jones/50 6.00 15.00
CR Cal Ripken Jr./75 20.00 50.00
CR Cal Ripken Jr./50 20.00 50.00
CS Rod Carew Tom Seaver 75 5.00 12.00
CS Tom Seaver Rod Carew 50 5.00 12.00
CU Chase Utley/75 5.00 12.00
CU Chase Utley/50 5.00 12.00
CW Chien-Ming Wang/75 10.00 25.00
CW Chien-Ming Wang/50 10.00 25.00
CY Carl Yastrzemski/75 10.00 25.00
CY Carl Yastrzemski/50 10.00 25.00
DJ Derek Jeter/75 15.00 40.00
DJ Derek Jeter/50 15.00 40.00
DL Derrek Lee/75 2.00 5.00
DL Derrek Lee/50 2.00 5.00
DM Daisuke Matsuzaka/75 10.00 25.00
DM Daisuke Matsuzaka/50 10.00 25.00
DY Delmon Young/75 3.00 8.00
DY Delmon Young/50 3.00 8.00
EM Eddie Murray/75 6.00 15.00
EM Eddie Murray/50 6.00 15.00
FA Nellie Fox Luis Aparicio 75 6.00 15.00
FA Nellie Fox Luis Aparicio 50 6.00 15.00
FH Felix Hernandez/75 6.00 15.00
FH Felix Hernandez/50 6.00 15.00
FJ Fergie Jenkins/75 2.00 5.00
FJ Fergie Jenkins/50 2.00 5.00
FT Frank Thomas/75 10.00 25.00
FT Frank Thomas/50 10.00 25.00
FT2 Frank Thomas/75 10.00 25.00
FT2 Frank Thomas/50 10.00 25.00
GR Lou Gehrig Babe Ruth 75 12.50 30.00
GR Babe Ruth Lou Gehrig 50 12.50 30.00
GS Grady Sizemore/75 3.00 8.00
GS Grady Sizemore/50 3.00 8.00
GW Tony Gwynn/75 10.00 25.00
GW Tony Gwynn/50 10.00 25.00
HA Travis Hafner/75 5.00 12.00
HA Travis Hafner/50 5.00 12.00
HP Hunter Pence/75 5.00 12.00
HP Hunter Pence/50 5.00 12.00
HR Hanley Ramirez/75 3.00 8.00
HR Hanley Ramirez/50 3.00 8.00
HU Torii Hunter/75 2.00 5.00
HU Torii Hunter/50 2.00 5.00
JB Jason Bay/75 2.00 5.00
JB Jason Bay/50 2.00 5.00
JD Joe DiMaggio/75 15.00 40.00
JD Joe DiMaggio/50 15.00 40.00

JE Jim Edmonds/75 2.00 5.00
JE Jim Edmonds/50 2.00 5.00
JH Josh Hamilton/75 6.00 15.00
JH Josh Hamilton/50 6.00 15.00
JM Joe Mauer/75 3.00 8.00
JM Joe Mauer/50 3.00 8.00
JO Jonathan Papelbon/75 3.00 8.00
JO Jonathan Papelbon/50 3.00 8.00
JP Jake Peavy/75 3.00 8.00
JP Jake Peavy/50 3.00 8.00
JR Jackie Robinson 6.00 15.00
Roy Campanella
75
JR Jackie Robinson 6.00 15.00
Roy Campanella
50
JS Johan Santana/75 5.00 12.00
JS Johan Santana/50 5.00 12.00
JU Justin Morneau/75 2.00 5.00
JU Justin Morneau/50 2.00 5.00
JV Justin Verlander/75 6.00 15.00
JV Justin Verlander/50 6.00 15.00
JZ Joel Zumaya/75 2.00 5.00
JZ Joel Zumaya/50 2.00 5.00
KG Ken Griffey Jr./75 10.00 25.00
KG Ken Griffey Jr./50 10.00 25.00
KG2 Ken Griffey Jr./75 10.00 25.00
KG2 Ken Griffey Jr./50 10.00 25.00
KG3 Ken Griffey Jr./75 10.00 25.00
KG3 Ken Griffey Jr./50 10.00 25.00
KW Kerry Wood/75 2.00 5.00
KW Kerry Wood/50 2.00 5.00
LA Luis Aparicio/75 5.00 12.00
LA Luis Aparicio/50 5.00 12.00
LB Lou Brock/75 6.00 15.00
LB Lou Brock/50 6.00 15.00
LI Tim Lincecum/75 5.00 12.00
LI Tim Lincecum/50 5.00 12.00
MA Juan Marichal/75 5.00 12.00
MA Juan Marichal/50 5.00 12.00
MC Brian McCann/75 2.00 5.00
MC Brian McCann/50 2.00 5.00
MH Matt Holliday/75 3.00 8.00
MH Matt Holliday/50 3.00 8.00
MH2 Matt Holliday/75 3.00 8.00
MH2 Matt Holliday/50 3.00 8.00
MI Monte Irvin/75 5.00 12.00
MI Monte Irvin/50 5.00 12.00
MJ Hideki Matsui 12.50 30.00
Derek Jeter
75
MJ Hideki Matsui 12.50 30.00
Derek Jeter
50
MO Joe Morgan/75 5.00 12.00
MO Joe Morgan/50 5.00 12.00
MP Mike Piazza/75 5.00 12.00
MP Mike Piazza/50 5.00 12.00
MR Manny Ramirez/75 5.00 12.00
MR Manny Ramirez/50 5.00 12.00
MS Mike Schmidt/75 6.00 15.00
MS Mike Schmidt/50 6.00 15.00
NR Nolan Ryan/75 15.00 40.00
NR Nolan Ryan/50 15.00 40.00
OC Orlando Cepeda/75 5.00 12.00
OC Orlando Cepeda/50 5.00 12.00
OM Hideki Okajima 10.00 25.00
Daisuke Matsuzaka
75
OM Daisuke Matsuzaka 10.00 25.00
Hideki Okajima
50
OR David Ortiz 10.00 25.00
Manny Ramirez
75
OR Manny Ramirez 10.00 25.00
David Ortiz
50
PA Jim Palmer/75 3.00 8.00
PA Jim Palmer/50 3.00 8.00
PF Prince Fielder/75 5.00 12.00
PF Prince Fielder/50 5.00 12.00
PH Phil Hughes/75 6.00 15.00
PH Phil Hughes/50 6.00 15.00
PN Phil Niekro/75 3.00 8.00
PN Phil Niekro/50 3.00 8.00
RA Richie Ashburn/75 10.00 25.00
RA Richie Ashburn/50 10.00 25.00
RB Ryan Braun/75 6.00 15.00
RB Ryan Braun/50 6.00 15.00
RC Rod Carew/75 5.00 12.00
RC Rod Carew/50 5.00 12.00
RF Rollie Fingers/75 3.00 8.00
RF Rollie Fingers/50 3.00 8.00
RH Roy Halladay/75 3.00 8.00
RH Roy Halladay/50 3.00 8.00
RI Mariano Rivera/75 5.00 12.00
RI Mariano Rivera/50 5.00 12.00
RJ Reggie Jackson/75 3.00 8.00
RJ Reggie Jackson/50 3.00 8.00
RK Ralph Kiner/75 3.00 8.00
RK Ralph Kiner/50 3.00 8.00
RM Russell Martin/75 5.00 12.00
RM Russell Martin/50 5.00 12.00
RO Brooks Robinson/75 5.00 12.00
RO Brooks Robinson/50 5.00 12.00
RS Ryne Sandberg/75 10.00 25.00
RS Ryne Sandberg/50 10.00 25.00
RY Ryan Howard/75 6.00 15.00
RY Ryan Howard/50 6.00 15.00
RZ Ryan Zimmerman/75 5.00 12.00
RZ Ryan Zimmerman/50 5.00 12.00
SJ Ichiro/Kenji Johjima/75 10.00 25.00
SJ Kenji Johjima/Ichiro/50 10.00 25.00
SS Sammy Sosa/75 10.00 25.00
SS Sammy Sosa/50 10.00 25.00
SV Shane Victorino/75 2.00 5.00
SV Shane Victorino/50 2.00 5.00
TG Tom Glavine/75 3.00 8.00
TG Tom Glavine/50 3.00 8.00
TH Trevor Hoffman/75 3.00 8.00
TH Trevor Hoffman/50 3.00 8.00
TL Tommy Lasorda/75 5.00 12.00
TL Tommy Lasorda/50 5.00 12.00
TS Tom Seaver/75 5.00 12.00
TS Tom Seaver/50 5.00 12.00
TT Troy Tulowitzki/75 5.00 12.00
TT Troy Tulowitzki/50 5.00 12.00
VG Vladimir Guerrero/75 3.00 8.00
VG Vladimir Guerrero/50 3.00 8.00
VM Victor Martinez/75 2.00 5.00
VM Victor Martinez/50 2.00 5.00
WM Willie McCovey/75 5.00 12.00
WM Willie McCovey/50 5.00 12.00

2008 Upper Deck Premier Swatches

OVERALL GU ODDS TWO PER PACK
STATED PRINT RUN 50 SER.#'d SETS
GOLD 25 PRINT RUN 25 SER.#'d SETS
NO GOLD 25 PRICING AVAILABLE
GOLD 20 PRINT RUN 20 SER.#'d SETS
NO GOLD 20 PRICING AVAILABLE
SILVER PRINT RUN 10 SER.#'d SETS
NO SILVER PRICING DUE TO SCARCITY
AP Albert Pujols 30.00 80.00
AR Aramis Ramirez 5.00 12.00
AS Alfonso Soriano 8.00 20.00
BR Brian Roberts 5.00 12.00
BS Ben Sheets 5.00 12.00
CD Carlos Delgado 5.00 12.00
CH Cole Hamels 12.00 30.00
CS C.C. Sabathia 8.00 20.00
CY Carl Yastrzemski 20.00 50.00
CZ Carlos Zambrano 8.00 20.00
DH Dan Haren 5.00 12.00
DL Derrek Lee 5.00 12.00
EM Eddie Murray 12.00 30.00
FH Felix Hernandez 12.00 30.00
FS Freddy Sanchez 5.00 12.00
GM Greg Maddux 15.00 40.00
GP Gaylord Perry 5.00 12.00
GS Grady Sizemore 8.00 20.00
HK Howie Kendrick 5.00 12.00
JB Jason Bay 8.00 20.00
JL James Loney 8.00 20.00
JM Joe Mauer 12.00 30.00
JS John Smoltz 12.00 30.00
JT Jim Thome 8.00 20.00
KG Ken Griffey Jr. 20.00 50.00
KI Harmon Killebrew 12.00 30.00
KW Kerry Wood 5.00 12.00
LB Lance Berkman 8.00 20.00
MO Joe Morgan 5.00 12.00
MR Manny Ramirez 12.00 30.00
MS Mike Schmidt 20.00 50.00
MT Miguel Tejada 8.00 20.00
NM Nick Markakis 12.00 30.00
NS Nick Swisher 12.00 30.00
OR Magglio Ordonez 8.00 20.00
PM Pedro Martinez 8.00 20.00
RH Rich Hill 5.00 12.00
RM Russell Martin 5.00 12.00
RS Ryne Sandberg 25.00 60.00
RY Robin Yount 12.00 30.00
SC Curt Schilling 8.00 20.00
TG Tom Glavine 8.00 20.00
TH Trevor Hoffman 8.00 20.00
VG Vladimir Guerrero 12.00 30.00
VM Victor Martinez 8.00 20.00
VW Vernon Wells 5.00 12.00

2008 Upper Deck Premier Swatches Jersey Number

OVERALL GU ODDS TWO PER PACK
PRINT RUNS B/WN 1-76 COPIES PER
NO PRICING ON QTY 25 OR LESS
AP Albert Pujols/5
AR Aramis Ramirez/16
AS Alfonso Soriano/12
BR Brian Roberts/1
BS Ben Sheets/15
CD Carlos Delgado/21
CH Cole Hamels/35 15.00 40.00
CS C.C. Sabathia/53 10.00 25.00
CY Carl Yastrzemski/16
CZ Carlos Zambrano/76 10.00 25.00
DH Dan Haren/15
DL Derrek Lee/25
EM Eddie Murray/33 15.00 40.00
FH Felix Hernandez/34 15.00 40.00
FS Freddy Sanchez/12
GM Greg Maddux/31 20.00 50.00
GP Gaylord Perry/34 6.00 15.00
GS Grady Sizemore/24
HK Howie Kendrick/48 6.00 15.00
JB Jason Bay/38 10.00 25.00
JL James Loney/7
JM Joe Mauer/29 30.00 80.00
JS John Smoltz/14
JT Jim Thome/50 10.00 25.00
KG Ken Griffey Jr./3
KI Harmon Killebrew/6
KW Kerry Wood/36 6.00 15.00
LB Lance Berkman/17
MO Joe Morgan/8
MR Manny Ramirez/24
MS Mike Schmidt/20
MT Miguel Tejada/10
NM Nick Markakis/21
NS Nick Swisher/33 15.00 40.00
OR Magglio Ordonez/30 10.00 25.00
PM Pedro Martinez/45 10.00 25.00
RH Rich Hill/53 6.00 15.00
RM Russell Martin/55 6.00 15.00
RS Ryne Sandberg/23
RY Robin Yount/19
SC Curt Schilling/38 10.00 25.00
TG Tom Glavine/47 10.00 25.00
TH Trevor Hoffman/51 10.00 25.00
VG Vladimir Guerrero/27 15.00 40.00
VM Victor Martinez/41 10.00 25.00
VW Vernon Wells/10

2008 Upper Deck Premier Teams Memorabilia

OVERALL GU ODDS TWO PER PACK
PRINT RUNS B/WN 20-50 COPIES PER
NO PRICING ON QTY 25 OR LESS
SILVER PRINT RUN 3 SER.#'d SETS
NO SILVER PRICING DUE TO SCARCITY
BFS Ryan Braun 20.00 50.00
Prince Fielder
Ben Sheets/50
BHG Ryan Braun
J.J Hardy
Yovani Gallardo/25
BJH Adrian Beltre
Kenji Johjima
Felix Hernandez/25
BMP Johnny Bench 15.00 40.00
Joe Morgan
Tony Perez/50
CMW Roger Clemens 15.00 40.00
Mike Mussina
Chien-Ming Wang/50
CPB Roberto Clemente 30.00 60.00
Dave Parker
Jason Bay/50
CRJ Roger Clemens 15.00 40.00
Mariano Rivera
Derek Jeter/50
CRR Roy Campanella 30.00 60.00
Pee Wee Reese
Jackie Robinson/50
CSM Michael Cuddyer
Johan Santana
Joe Mauer/25
DBR Carlos Delgado
Carlos Beltran
Jose Reyes/25
GBS Alex Gordon
Billy Butler
Mike Sweeney/25
GDH Ken Griffey Jr. 30.00 60.00
Adam Dunn
Josh Hamilton/50
GFW Vladimir Guerrero
Chone Figgins
Jered Weaver/25
IUK Akinori Iwamura
B.J. Upton
Scott Kazmir/25
JJF Chipper Jones 12.50 30.00
Andruw Jones
Jeff Francoeur/50
JWD Randy Johnson 6.00 15.00
Brandon Webb
Stephen Drew/50
KBS Hong-Chih Kuo
Chad Billingsley
Takashi Saito/25
LME James Loney
Russell Martin
Andre Ethier/25
LRS Derrek Lee
Aramis Ramirez
Alfonso Soriano/25
LVZ Tim Lincecum
Omar Vizquel
Barry Zito/25
MJJ Don Mattingly 12.50 30.00
Reggie Jackson
Derek Jeter/50
MPB Stan Musial 20.00 50.00
Albert Pujols
Lou Brock/50
MSB Daisuke Matsuzaka 15.00 40.00
Curt Schilling
Josh Beckett/50
MSM Joe Mauer
Johan Santana
Justin Morneau/25
OBY David Ortiz 10.00 25.00
Wade Boggs
Kevin Youkilis/50
ORS Magglio Ordonez
Ivan Rodriguez
Gary Sheffield/25
ORY David Ortiz 10.00 25.00
Manny Ramirez
Kevin Youkilis/50
PCR Albert Pujols 12.50 30.00
Chris Carpenter
Scott Rolen/50
PMH Jake Peavy 15.00 40.00
Greg Maddux
Trevor Hoffman/50
POB Hunter Pence
Roy Oswalt
Lance Berkman/25
RGD Babe Ruth
Lou Gehrig
Joe DiMaggio/20
RWU Hanley Ramirez
Dontrelle Willis
Dan Uggla/25
SBW Ryne Sandberg 20.00 50.00
Ernie Banks
Billy Williams/50
SCH Nick Swisher
Eric Chavez
Dan Haren/25
SMF John Smoltz
Brian McCann
Jeff Francoeur/25
SMH Grady Sizemore
Victor Martinez
Travis Hafner/25
TDK Jim Thome
Jermaine Dye
Paul Konerko/25
UHR Chase Utley
Cole Hamels
Jimmy Rollins/25
USH Chase Utley 20.00 50.00
Mike Schmidt
Cole Hamels/50
VBZ Justin Verlander
Jeremy Bonderman
Joel Zumaya/25
WHT Vernon Wells
Roy Halladay
Frank Thomas/25
YPH Chris Young
Jake Peavy
Trevor Hoffman/25

2008 Upper Deck Premier Teams Memorabilia Gold

OVERALL GU ODDS TWO PER PACK
PRINT RUNS B/WN 9-33 COPIES PER
NO PRICING ON QTY 15 OR LESS
BFS Ryan Braun 20.00 50.00
Prince Fielder
Ben Sheets/33
BMP Johnny Bench 15.00 40.00
Joe Morgan
Tony Perez/33
CMW Roger Clemens 15.00 40.00
Mike Mussina
Chien-Ming Wang/33
CPB Roberto Clemente 30.00 60.00
Dave Parker
Jason Bay/33
CRJ Roger Clemens 15.00 40.00
Mariano Rivera
Derek Jeter/33
CRR Roy Campanella 30.00 60.00
Pee Wee Reese
Jackie Robinson/33
GDH Ken Griffey Jr. 30.00 60.00
Adam Dunn
Josh Hamilton/33
JJF Chipper Jones 12.50 30.00
Andruw Jones
Jeff Francoeur/33
JWD Randy Johnson 6.00 15.00
Brandon Webb
Stephen Drew/33
MJJ Don Mattingly 12.50 30.00
Reggie Jackson
Derek Jeter/33
MPB Stan Musial 20.00 50.00
Albert Pujols
Lou Brock/33
MSB Daisuke Matsuzaka 15.00 40.00
Curt Schilling
Josh Beckett/33
OBY David Ortiz 10.00 25.00
Wade Boggs
Kevin Youkilis/33
ORY David Ortiz 10.00 25.00
Manny Ramirez
Kevin Youkilis/33
PCR Albert Pujols 12.50 30.00
Chris Carpenter
Scott Rolen/33
PMH Jake Peavy 15.00 40.00
Greg Maddux
Trevor Hoffman/33
SBW Ryne Sandberg 20.00 50.00
Ernie Banks
Billy Williams/33
USH Chase Utley 20.00 50.00
Mike Schmidt
Cole Hamels/33

2008 Upper Deck Premier Trios Memorabilia

OVERALL GU ODDS TWO PER PACK
PRINT RUNS B/WN 25-50 COPIES PER
NO PRICING ON QTY 25 OR LESS
SILVER PRINT RUN 3 SER.#'d SETS
NO SILVER PRICING AVAILABLE
BFB Johnny Bench 12.50 30.00
Carlton Fisk
Yogi Berra/50
BPG Jason Bay 12.50 30.00
Albert Pujols
Ken Griffey Jr./50
BRD Carlos Beltran 6.00 15.00
Jose Reyes
Carlos Delgado/50
BZJ Ryan Braun 6.00 15.00
Ryan Zimmerman
Chipper Jones/50
CMM Michael Cuddyer 6.00 15.00
Justin Morneau
Joe Mauer/50
DOF Adam Dunn 10.00 25.00
David Ortiz
Prince Fielder/50
GTP Ken Griffey Jr. 15.00 40.00
Frank Thomas
Albert Pujols/50
GWK Vladimir Guerrero 6.00 15.00
Jered Weaver
Howie Kendrick/50
HAT Matt Holliday 10.00 25.00
Garrett Atkins
Troy Tulowitzki/50
HMS Travis Hafner 6.00 15.00
Victor Martinez
Grady Sizemore/50
HSS Dan Haren 6.00 15.00
Nick Swisher
Huston Street/50
JFS Chipper Jones 30.00 60.00
Jeff Francoeur
John Smoltz/50
JTR Derek Jeter 10.00 25.00
Troy Tulowitzki
Hanley Ramirez/50
JWP Derek Jeter 20.00 50.00
Chien-Ming Wang
Andy Pettitte/50
LRS Derrek Lee 6.00 15.00
Aramis Ramirez
Alfonso Soriano/50
MCG Greg Maddux 12.50 30.00
Roger Clemens
Tom Glavine/50
MMS Joe Mauer 6.00 15.00
Justin Morneau
Johan Santana/50
ORY David Ortiz 10.00 25.00
Manny Ramirez
Kevin Youkilis/50
OVB Magglio Ordonez 10.00 25.00
Justin Verlander
Jeremy Bonderman/50
PBO Hunter Pence 10.00 25.00
Lance Berkman
Roy Oswalt/50
PLM Albert Pujols 10.00 25.00
Derrek Lee
Justin Morneau/50
RCS Jose Reyes 6.00 15.00
Carl Crawford
Grady Sizemore/50
RDM Babe Ruth
Joe DiMaggio
Roger Maris/25
ROF Babe Ruth
Mel Ott
Jimmie Foxx/25
RPV Manny Ramirez 12.50 30.00
Jonathan Papelbon
Jason Varitek/50
RSB Brooks Robinson 15.00 40.00
Mike Schmidt
Wade Boggs/50
SRB Mike Schmidt 15.00 40.00
Cal Ripken Jr.
Wade Boggs/50
SWB Ryne Sandberg 15.00 40.00
Billy Williams
Ernie Banks/50
TOT Jim Thome 10.00 25.00
David Ortiz
Frank Thomas/50
TWH Frank Thomas 10.00 25.00
Vernon Wells
Roy Halladay/50
UHR Chase Utley 10.00 25.00
Cole Hamels
Jimmy Rollins/50
URU Chase Utley 6.00 15.00
Brian Roberts
Dan Uggla/50
YMC Carl Yastrzemski 15.00 40.00
Stan Musial
Rod Carew/50

2008 Upper Deck Premier Trios Memorabilia Gold

OVERALL GU ODDS TWO PER PACK
PRINT RUNS B/WN 10-33 COPIES PER
NO PRICING ON QTY 10 OR LESS
BFB Johnny Bench 12.50 30.00
Carlton Fisk
Yogi Berra/33
BPG Jason Bay 12.50 30.00
Albert Pujols
Ken Griffey Jr./33
BRD Carlos Beltran 6.00 15.00
Jose Reyes
Carlos Delgado/33
BZJ Ryan Braun 6.00 15.00
Ryan Zimmerman
Chipper Jones/33
CMM Michael Cuddyer 6.00 15.00
Justin Morneau
Joe Mauer/33
DOF Adam Dunn 10.00 25.00
David Ortiz
Prince Fielder/33
GTP Ken Griffey Jr. 15.00 40.00
Frank Thomas
Albert Pujols/33
GWK Vladimir Guerrero 6.00 15.00
Jered Weaver
Howie Kendrick/33
HAT Matt Holliday 10.00 25.00
Garrett Atkins
Troy Tulowitzki/33
HMS Travis Hafner 6.00 15.00
Victor Martinez
Grady Sizemore/33
HSS Dan Haren 6.00 15.00
Nick Swisher
Huston Street/33
JFS Chipper Jones 30.00 60.00
Jeff Francoeur
John Smoltz/33
JTR Derek Jeter 10.00 25.00
Troy Tulowitzki
Hanley Ramirez/33
JWP Derek Jeter 20.00 50.00
Chien-Ming Wang
Andy Pettitte/33
LRS Derrek Lee 6.00 15.00
Aramis Ramirez
Alfonso Soriano/33
MCG Greg Maddux 12.50 30.00
Roger Clemens
Tom Glavine/33
MMS Joe Mauer 6.00 15.00
Justin Morneau
Johan Santana/33
ORY David Ortiz 10.00 25.00
Manny Ramirez
Kevin Youkilis/33
OVB Magglio Ordonez 10.00 25.00
Justin Verlander
Jeremy Bonderman/33
PBO Hunter Pence 10.00 25.00
Lance Berkman
Roy Oswalt/33
PLM Albert Pujols 10.00 25.00
Derrek Lee
Justin Morneau/33
RCS Jose Reyes 6.00 15.00
Carl Crawford
Grady Sizemore/33
RDM Babe Ruth
Joe DiMaggio
Roger Maris/10
ROF Babe Ruth
Mel Ott
Jimmie Foxx/10
RPV Manny Ramirez 12.50 30.00
Jonathan Papelbon
Jason Varitek/33
RSB Brooks Robinson 15.00 40.00
Mike Schmidt
Wade Boggs/33
SRB Mike Schmidt 15.00 40.00
Cal Ripken Jr.
Wade Boggs/33
SWB Ryne Sandberg 15.00 40.00
Billy Williams
Ernie Banks/33
TOT Jim Thome 10.00 25.00
David Ortiz
Frank Thomas/33
TWH Frank Thomas 10.00 25.00
Vernon Wells
Roy Halladay/33
UHR Chase Utley 10.00 25.00
Cole Hamels
Jimmy Rollins/33
URU Chase Utley 6.00 15.00
Brian Roberts
Dan Uggla/33
YMC Carl Yastrzemski 15.00 40.00
Stan Musial
Rod Carew/33

2008 Upper Deck Premier Trios Patches

OVERALL GU ODDS TWO PER PACK
STATED PRINT RUN 30 SER.#'d SETS
GOLD PRINT RUN 15 SER.#'d SETS
NO GOLD PRICING DUE TO SCARCITY
PLATINUM PRINT RUN 3 SER.#'d SETS
NO PLATINUM PRICING AVAILABLE
MASTERPIECE PRINT RUN 1 SER.#'d SET
NO MASTERPIECE PRICING AVAILABLE
AER Rick Ankiel 20.00 50.00
Jim Edmonds
Scott Rolen
BNS Jason Bay 12.50 30.00
Xavier Nady
Freddy Sanchez
BPG Jason Bay 30.00 60.00
Albert Pujols
Ken Griffey Jr.
CRS Miguel Cabrera 20.00 50.00
Manny Ramirez
Grady Sizemore
DZV Ray Durham 12.50 30.00
Barry Zito
Omar Vizquel
GKW Vladimir Guerrero 20.00 50.00
Howie Kendrick
Jered Weaver
JCZ Chipper Jones 20.00 50.00
Eric Chavez
Ryan Zimmerman
JJF Chipper Jones 20.00 50.00
Andruw Jones
Jeff Francoeur
JTR Derek Jeter 60.00 120.00
Troy Tulowitzki
Hanley Ramirez
LMS James Loney 20.00 50.00
Russell Martin
Takashi Saito
LRS Derrek Lee 20.00 50.00
Aramis Ramirez
Alfonso Soriano
MJD Willie McCovey 20.00 50.00
Reggie Jackson
Adam Dunn
MMM Victor Martinez 20.00 50.00
Joe Mauer
Russell Martin
MMR Brian McCann 20.00 50.00
Russell Martin
Ivan Rodriguez
MWM Pedro Martinez 20.00 50.00
Billy Wagner
John Maine
ORY David Ortiz 20.00 50.00
Manny Ramirez
Kevin Youkilis

PRB Jonathan Papelbon 20.00 50.00
Manny Ramirez
Josh Beckett
SCM Tom Seaver 30.00 60.00
Steve Carlton
Greg Maddux
SHC Nick Swisher 12.50 30.00
Dan Haren
Eric Chavez
CZD Curt Schilling 20.00 60.00
Carlos Zambrano
Jeremy Bonderman
TKB Jim Thome 20.00 50.00
Paul Konerko
Mark Buehrle
UHR Chase Utley 20.00 50.00
Cole Hamels
Jimmy Rollins
UUK Chase Utley 20.00 50.00
Dan Uggla
Jeff Kent

2009 Upper Deck Prominent Cuts

COMPLETE SET (60) 30.00 60.00
53 Dinesh Kumar Patel .60 1.50
57 Rinku Singh .60 1.50

2009 Upper Deck Prominent Cuts Cut Signatures

OVERALL CUT SIGN. ODDS ONE PER BOX
STATED PRINT RUN B/WN 1-118
PCBR Jack Brickhouse/2
PCVS Vin Scully/3
PCBUD Bud Selig/1

2000 Upper Deck Pros and Prospects

The 2000 Upper Deck Pros and Prospects product was initially released in early October as a 132-card basic set that was broken into tiers as follows: 90 Veterans (1-90), 30 Prospective Superstars (91-120) each serial numbered to 1350, and 12 Pro Fame cards (121-132) each serial numbered to 1000. Each pack contained five cards and carried a suggested retail price of $4.99. In late December, 2000, Upper Deck released their Rookie Update brand which carried a selection of new cards to extend the 2000 SP Authentic, SPx and UD Pros and Prospects brands. The new Pros and Prospects cards featured an extension of the Prospective Superstars subset (cards 133-162) with each card serial numbered to 1,600 and a selection of veterans (cards 163-192) composed of player's either initially not included in the basic set or traded to new teams. Notable Rookie Cards include Barry Zito (his first licensed MLB card), Xavier Nady, and Ben Sheets. Also, a selection of A Piece of History 3000 Club Lou Brock and Rod Carew memorabilia cards were randomly seeded into packs. 350 bat cards, 350 jersey cards and 100 hand-numbered combination bat-jersey cards were produced for each player. In addition, twenty autographed, hand-numbered, combination bat-jersey Lou Brock cards and twenty nine autographed, hand-numbered, combination bat-jersey Rod Carew cards were produced. Pricing for these memorabilia cards can be referenced under 2000 Upper Deck A Piece of History 3000 Club.

COMP.BASIC w/o SP's (90) 8.00 20.00
COMP.UPDATE w/o SP'S (30) 4.00 10.00
COMMON CARD (1-90) .15 .40
COMMON PS (91-120) 2.00 5.00
COMMON PF (121-132) 1.50 4.00
COMMON PS (133-162) 2.00 5.00
COMMON (163-192) .25 .60
1 Darin Erstad .15 .40
2 Troy Glaus .15 .40
3 Mo Vaughn .15 .40
4 Jason Giambi .15 .40
5 Tim Hudson .15 .40
6 Ben Grieve .15 .40
7 Eric Chavez .15 .40
8 Shannon Stewart .15 .40
9 Raul Mondesi .15 .40
10 Carlos Delgado .15 .40
11 Jose Canseco .25 .60
12 Fred McGriff .25 .60
13 Greg Vaughn .15 .40
14 Manny Ramirez .25 .60
15 Roberto Alomar .25 .60
16 Jim Thome .25 .60
17 Alex Rodriguez .60 1.50
18 Freddy Garcia .15 .40
19 John Olerud .15 .40
20 Cal Ripken 1.25 3.00
21 Albert Belle .15 .40
22 Mike Mussina .25 .60
23 Ivan Rodriguez .25 .60
24 Rafael Palmeiro .25 .60
25 Ruben Mateo .15 .40
26 Gabe Kapler .15 .40
27 Pedro Martinez .25 .60
28 Nomar Garciaparra .60 1.50
29 Carl Everett .15 .40
30 Carlos Beltran .15 .40
31 Jermaine Dye .15 .40
32 Johnny Damon UER .25 .60
Picture on front is Joe Randa
33 Juan Gonzalez .15 .40
34 Juan Encarnacion .15 .40
35 Dean Palmer .15 .40
36 Jacque Jones .15 .40
37 Matt Lawton .15 .40
38 Frank Thomas .40 1.00
39 Paul Konerko .15 .40
40 Magglio Ordonez .15 .40
41 Derek Jeter 1.00 2.50
42 Bernie Williams .25 .60
43 Mariano Rivera .40 1.00
44 Roger Clemens .75 2.00
45 Jeff Bagwell .25 .60
46 Craig Biggio .25 .60
47 Richard Hidalgo .15 .40
48 Chipper Jones .40 1.00
49 Andres Galarraga .15 .40
50 Andruw Jones .25 .60
51 Greg Maddux .60 1.50
52 Jeromy Burnitz .15 .40
53 Geoff Jenkins .15 .40
54 Mark McGwire 1.00 2.50
55 Jim Edmonds .15 .40
56 Fernando Tatis .15 .40
57 J.D. Drew .15 .40
58 Sammy Sosa .40 1.00
59 Kerry Wood .15 .40
60 Randy Johnson .40 1.00
61 Matt Williams .15 .40
62 Erubiel Durazo .15 .40
63 Shawn Green .15 .40
64 Kevin Brown .15 .40
65 Gary Sheffield .15 .40
66 Adrian Beltre .15 .40
67 Vladimir Guerrero .40 1.00
68 Jose Vidro .15 .40
69 Barry Bonds 1.00 2.50
70 Jeff Kent .15 .40
71 Preston Wilson .15 .40
72 Ryan Dempster .15 .40
73 Mike Lowell .15 .40
74 Mike Piazza .60 1.50
75 Robin Ventura .15 .40
76 Edgardo Alfonzo .15 .40
77 Derek Bell .15 .40
78 Tony Gwynn .50 1.25
79 Matt Clement .15 .40
80 Scott Rolen .25 .60
81 Bobby Abreu .15 .40
82 Curt Schilling .15 .40
83 Brian Giles .15 .40
84 Jason Kendall .15 .40
85 Kris Benson .15 .40
86 Ken Griffey Jr. .60 1.50
87 Sean Casey .15 .40
88 Pokey Reese .15 .40
89 Larry Walker .15 .40
90 Todd Helton .25 .60
91 Rick Ankiel PS 2.00 5.00
92 Milton Bradley PS 2.00 5.00
93 Vernon Wells PS 2.00 5.00
94 Rafael Furcal PS 2.00 5.00
95 Kazuhiro Sasaki PS RC 3.00 8.00
96 Joe Torres PS RC 2.00 5.00
97 Adam Kennedy PS 2.00 5.00
98 Adam Piatt PS 2.00 5.00
99 Matt Wheatland PS RC 2.00 5.00
100 Alex Cabrera PS RC 2.00 5.00
101 Barry Zito PS RC 6.00 15.00
102 Mike Lamb PS RC 3.00 8.00
103 Scott Heard PS RC 2.00 5.00
104 Danys Baez PS RC 2.00 5.00
105 Matt Riley PS 2.00 5.00
106 Mark Mulder PS 2.00 5.00
107 W.Rodriguez PS RC 2.00 5.00
108 Luis Matos PS RC 2.00 5.00
109 Alfonso Soriano PS 3.00 8.00
110 Pat Burrell PS 2.00 5.00
111 Mike Tonis PS RC 2.00 5.00
112 Aaron McNeal PS RC 2.00 5.00
113 Dave Krynzel PS RC 2.00 5.00
114 Josh Beckett PS 3.00 8.00
115 Sean Burnett PS RC 2.00 5.00
116 Eric Munson PS 2.00 5.00
117 Scott Downs PS RC 2.00 5.00
118 Brian Tollberg PS RC 2.00 5.00
119 Nick Johnson PS 2.00 5.00
120 Leo Estrella PS RC 2.00 5.00
121 Ken Griffey Jr. PF 4.00 10.00
122 Frank Thomas PF 2.50 6.00
123 Cal Ripken PF 8.00 20.00
124 Ivan Rodriguez PF 2.50 6.00
125 Derek Jeter PF 6.00 15.00
126 Mark McGwire PF 6.00 15.00
127 Pedro Martinez PF 2.50 6.00
128 Chipper Jones PF 2.50 6.00
129 Sammy Sosa PF 2.50 6.00
130 Alex Rodriguez PF 4.00 10.00
131 Vladimir Guerrero PF 2.50 6.00
132 Jeff Bagwell PF 2.50 6.00
133 Dane Artman PS RC 2.00 5.00
134 Juan Pierre PS RC 3.00 8.00
135 Jace Brewer PS RC 2.00 5.00
136 Sun Woo Kim PS RC 2.00 5.00
137 Jon Rauch PS RC 2.00 5.00
138 Juan Guzman PS RC 2.00 5.00
139 Daylan Holt PS RC 2.00 5.00
140 R.Washington PS RC 2.00 5.00
141 Ben Diggins PS RC 2.00 5.00
142 Mike Meyers PS RC 2.00 5.00
143 C.Wakeland PS RC 2.00 5.00
144 Cory Vance PS RC 2.00 5.00
145 Keith Ginter PS RC 2.00 5.00
146 Koyie Hill PS RC 2.00 5.00
147 Julio Zuleta PS RC 2.00 5.00
148 G.Guzman PS RC 2.00 5.00
149 Jay Spurgeon PS RC 2.00 5.00
150 Ross Gload PS RC 2.00 5.00
151 Ben Sheets PS RC 4.00 10.00
152 J.Kalinowski PS RC 2.00 5.00
153 Kurt Ainsworth PS RC 2.00 5.00
154 P.Crawford PS RC 2.00 5.00
155 Xavier Nady PS RC 3.00 8.00
156 B.Wilkerson PS RC 3.00 8.00
157 Kris Wilson PS RC 2.00 5.00
158 Paul Rigdon PS RC 2.00 5.00
159 R.Kohlmeier PS RC 2.00 5.00
160 Dane Sardinha PS RC 2.00 5.00
161 Javier Cardona PS RC 2.00 5.00
162 Brad Cresse PS RC 2.00 5.00
163 Ron Gant .25 .60
164 Mark Mulder .25 .60
165 David Wells .25 .60
166 Jason Tyner .25 .60
167 David Segui .25 .60
168 Al Martin .25 .60
169 Melvin Mora .25 .60
170 Ricky Ledee .25 .60
171 Rolando Arrojo .25 .60
172 Mike Sweeney .25 .60
173 Bobby Higginson .25 .60
174 Eric Milton .25 .60
175 Charles Johnson .25 .60
176 David Justice .25 .60
177 Moises Alou .25 .60
178 Andy Ashby .25 .60
179 Richie Sexson .25 .60
180 Will Clark .40 1.00
181 Rondell White .25 .60
182 Curt Schilling .25 .60
183 Tom Goodwin .25 .60
184 Lee Stevens .25 .60
185 Ellis Burks .25 .60
186 Henry Rodriguez .25 .60
187 Mike Bordick .25 .60
188 Ryan Klesko .25 .60
189 Travis Lee .25 .60
190 Kevin Young .25 .60
191 Barry Larkin .40 1.00
192 Jeff Cirillo .25 .60

2000 Upper Deck Pros and Prospects Best in the Bigs

Randomly inserted into packs at one in 12, this 10-card insert features the best players in Major League Baseball. Card backs carry a "B" prefix.

COMPLETE SET (10) 15.00 40.00
B1 Sammy Sosa 1.00 2.50
B2 Tony Gwynn 1.25 3.00
B3 Pedro Martinez .60 1.50
B4 Mark McGwire 2.50 6.00
B5 Chipper Jones 1.00 2.50
B6 Derek Jeter 2.50 6.00
B7 Ken Griffey Jr. 1.50 4.00
B8 Cal Ripken 3.00 8.00
B9 Greg Maddux 1.50 4.00
B10 Ivan Rodriguez .60 1.50

2000 Upper Deck Pros and Prospects Future Forces

Randomly inserted into packs at one in six, this 10-card insert features Major League prospects that hope to play a major role on their teams. Card backs carry a "F" prefix.

COMPLETE SET (10) 4.00 10.00
F1 Pat Burrell .40 1.00
F2 Brad Penny .40 1.00
F3 Rick Ankiel .40 1.00
F4 Adam Kennedy .40 1.00
F5 Kerry Wood .40 1.00
F6 Rafael Furcal .40 1.00
F7 Mark Mulder .40 1.00
F8 Vernon Wells .40 1.00
F9 Matt Riley .40 1.00
F10 Nick Johnson .40 1.00

2000 Upper Deck Pros and Prospects Game Jersey Autograph

Randomly inserted into packs at an approximate rate of one in 96, this 21-card insert features autographs of many of the Major Leagues elite players. Card backs are numbered using the players initials. The following players packed out as stickered exchange cards: Cal Ripken, Ivan Rodriguez, Jose Canseco, Ken Griffey Jr., Mo Vaughn and Tom Glavine. Please note that Jose Canseco and Tom Glavine both only signed partial quantities of their cards, thus half packed out as proper autos and the other half packed out as exchange cards. Due to problems with the players, UD was not able to get the athletes to sign their remaining cards and were forced to redeem the exchange cards with signed Mo Vaughn cards instead. The deadline to redeem exchange cards was July 5th, 2001. Representatives at Upper Deck have confirmed that the Derek Jeter card was produced in shorter supply than other cards from this set. This set also contains the first-ever certified autograph of Luis Gonzalez.

AR Alex Rodriguez 100.00 175.00
BB Barry Bonds 60.00 120.00
CJ Chipper Jones 30.00 60.00
CR Cal Ripken 100.00 200.00
DJ Derek Jeter SP 1400.00 2000.00
FT Frank Thomas 30.00 60.00
GS Gary Sheffield 12.50 30.00
IR Ivan Rodriguez 20.00 50.00
JC Jose Canseco 20.00 50.00
JD J.D. Drew 8.00 20.00
KG Ken Griffey Jr. 75.00 150.00
KL Kenny Lofton 20.00 50.00
LG Luis Gonzalez 8.00 20.00
MV Mo Vaughn 8.00 20.00
MW Matt Williams 20.00 50.00
PW Preston Wilson 8.00 20.00
RJ Randy Johnson 50.00 100.00
RV Robin Ventura 8.00 20.00
SR Scott Rolen 20.00 50.00
TGL Tom Glavine 20.00 50.00
TGW Tony Gwynn 30.00 60.00

2000 Upper Deck Pros and Prospects Game Jersey Autograph Gold

Randomly inserted into packs, this 21-card insert is a complete parallel of the 2000 Pros and Prospects Game Jerseys. Each card is serial numbered to the player's jersey number, and are numbered on the back using the player's initials. Please note that Upper Deck has announced the exchange cards of Jose Canseco and Tom Glavine will be redeemed with Mo Vaughn. Some cards are not priced due to market scarcity. The following cards packed out as exchnage cards with a redemption deadline of 07/05/01: Cal Ripken, Ivan Rodriguez, Ken Griffey Jr. and Mo Vaughn.

AR Alex Rodriguez/3
BB Barry Bonds/25
CJ Chipper Jones/10
CR Cal Ripken/8
DJ Derek Jeter/2
FT Frank Thomas/35 75.00 150.00
GS Gary Sheffield/10
IR Ivan Rodriguez/7
JC Jose Canseco/33
JD J.D. Drew/7
KG Ken Griffey Jr./30 150.00 300.00
KL Kenny Lofton/7
LG Luis Gonzalez/20
MV Mo Vaughn/42 12.50 30.00
MW Matt Williams/9
PW Preston Wilson/44 15.00 40.00
RJ Randy Johnson/51 100.00 175.00
RV Robin Ventura/4
SR Scott Rolen/17
TGL Tom Glavine/47 50.00 100.00
TGW Tony Gwynn/19

2000 Upper Deck Pros and Prospects ProMotion

Randomly inserted into packs at one in six, this 10-card insert features baseball's greatest all-around players. Card backs carry a "P" prefix.

COMPLETE SET (10) 10.00 25.00
P1 Derek Jeter 1.50 4.00
P2 Mike Piazza 1.00 2.50
P3 Mark McGwire 1.50 4.00
P4 Ivan Rodriguez .40 1.00
P5 Kerry Wood .25 .60
P6 Nomar Garciaparra 1.00 2.50
P7 Sammy Sosa .60 1.50
P8 Alex Rodriguez 1.00 2.50
P9 Ken Griffey Jr. 1.00 2.50
P10 Vladimir Guerrero .60 1.50

2000 Upper Deck Pros and Prospects Rare Breed

Randomly inserted into packs at one in 12, this 12-card insert features players that have rare talents. Card backs carry a "R" prefix.

COMPLETE SET (12) 15.00 40.00
R1 Mark McGwire 2.50 6.00
R2 Frank Thomas 1.00 2.50
R3 Mike Piazza 1.50 4.00
R4 Barry Bonds 2.50 6.00
R5 Manny Ramirez .60 1.50
R6 Ken Griffey Jr. 1.50 4.00
R7 Nomar Garciaparra 1.50 4.00
R8 Randy Johnson 1.00 2.50
R9 Vladimir Guerrero 1.00 2.50
R10 Jeff Bagwell .60 1.50
R11 Rick Ankiel 5.00 12.00
R12 Alex Rodriguez 1.50 4.00

2001 Upper Deck Pros and Prospects

This 135 card set was issued in five card packs. Cards numbered 91-141 were shorter printed than the other cards. Cards numbered 91-135 had a print run of 1,250 serial numbered sets while cards numbered 136-141 had a print run of 500 sets.

COMP.SET w/o SP's (90) 6.00 15.00
COMMON CARD (1-90) .15 .40
COMMON CARD (91-135) 2.00 5.00
COMMON (136-141) 8.00 20.00
1 Troy Glaus .15 .40
2 Darin Erstad .15 .40
3 Tim Hudson .15 .40
4 Jason Giambi .15 .40
5 Jermaine Dye .15 .40
6 Barry Zito .25 .60
7 Carlos Delgado .15 .40
8 Shannon Stewart .15 .40
9 Raul Mondesi .15 .40
10 Greg Vaughn .15 .40
11 Ben Grieve .15 .40
12 Roberto Alomar .25 .60
13 Juan Gonzalez .15 .40
14 Jim Thome .25 .60
15 C.C. Sabathia .15 .40
16 Edgar Martinez .25 .60
17 Kazuhiro Sasaki .15 .40
18 Aaron Sele .15 .40
19 John Olerud .15 .40
20 Cal Ripken 1.25 3.00
21 Rafael Palmeiro .25 .60
22 Ivan Rodriguez .25 .60
23 Alex Rodriguez .60 1.50
24 Manny Ramirez Sox .25 .60
25 Pedro Martinez .25 .60
26 Carl Everett .15 .40
27 Nomar Garciaparra .60 1.50
28 Neifi Perez .15 .40
29 Mike Sweeney .15 .40
30 Bobby Higginson .15 .40
31 Tony Clark .15 .40
32 Doug Mientkiewicz .15 .40
33 Cristian Guzman .15 .40
34 Brad Radke .15 .40
35 Magglio Ordonez .15 .40
36 Carlos Lee .15 .40
37 Frank Thomas .40 1.00
38 Roger Clemens .75 2.00
39 Bernie Williams .25 .60
40 Derek Jeter 1.00 2.50
41 Tino Martinez .25 .60
42 Wade Miller .15 .40
43 Jeff Bagwell .25 .60
44 Lance Berkman .25 .60
45 Richard Hidalgo .15 .40
46 Greg Maddux .60 1.50
47 Andruw Jones .25 .60
48 Chipper Jones .40 1.00
49 Rafael Furcal .15 .40
50 Jeromy Burnitz .15 .40
51 Geoff Jenkins .15 .40
52 Ben Sheets .15 .40
53 Mark McGwire 1.00 2.50
54 Jim Edmonds .15 .40
55 J.D. Drew .15 .40
56 Fred McGriff .25 .60
57 Sammy Sosa .40 1.00
58 Kerry Wood .15 .40
59 Randy Johnson .40 1.00
60 Luis Gonzalez .15 .40
61 Curt Schilling .15 .40
62 Kevin Brown .15 .40
63 Shawn Green .15 .40
64 Gary Sheffield .15 .40
65 Vladimir Guerrero .40 1.00
66 Jose Vidro .15 .40
67 Barry Bonds 1.00 2.50
68 Jeff Kent .15 .40
69 Rich Aurilia .15 .40
70 Preston Wilson .15 .40
71 Charles Johnson .15 .40
72 Cliff Floyd .15 .40
73 Mike Piazza .60 1.50
74 Al Leiter .15 .40
75 Matt Lawton .15 .40
76 Tony Gwynn .50 1.25
77 Ryan Klesko .15 .40
78 Phil Nevin .15 .40
79 Scott Rolen .25 .60
80 Pat Burrell .15 .40
81 Jimmy Rollins .15 .40
82 Jason Kendall .15 .40
83 Brian Giles .15 .40
84 Aramis Ramirez .15 .40
85 Ken Griffey Jr. .60 1.50
86 Barry Larkin .25 .60
87 Sean Casey .15 .40
88 Larry Walker .15 .40
89 Todd Helton .25 .60
90 Mike Hampton .15 .40
91 Juan Cruz PS RC 2.00 5.00
92 Brian Lawrence PS RC 2.00 5.00
93 Brandon Lyon PS RC 2.00 5.00
94 A.Hernandez PS RC 2.00 5.00
95 Jose Mieses PS RC 2.00 5.00
96 Juan Uribe PS RC 2.00 5.00
97 M.Ensberg PS RC 3.00 8.00
98 Wilson Betemit PS RC 3.00 8.00
99 Ryan Freel PS RC 3.00 8.00
100 Jack Wilson PS RC 2.00 5.00
101 Cesar Crespo PS RC 2.00 5.00
102 Bret Prinz PS RC 2.00 5.00
103 H.Ramirez PS RC 2.00 5.00
104 E. Guzman PS RC 2.00 5.00
105 Josh Towers PS RC 2.00 5.00
106 B. Duckworth PS RC 2.00 5.00
107 Esix Snead PS RC 2.00 5.00
108 Billy Sylvester PS RC 2.00 5.00
109 Alexis Gomez PS RC 2.00 5.00
110 J. Estrada PS RC 2.00 5.00
111 Joe Kennedy PS RC 2.00 5.00
112 Travis Hafner PS RC 4.00 10.00
113 Martin Vargas PS RC 2.00 5.00
114 Jay Gibbons PS RC 2.00 5.00
115 Andres Torres PS RC 2.00 5.00
116 Sean Douglass PS RC 2.00 5.00
117 Juan Diaz PS RC 2.00 5.00
118 Greg Miller PS RC 2.00 5.00
119 C. Valderrama PS RC 2.00 5.00
120 Bill Ortega PS RC 2.00 5.00
121 Josh Fogg PS RC 2.00 5.00
122 Wilken Ruan PS RC 2.00 5.00
123 Kris Keller PS RC 2.00 5.00
124 Erick Almonte PS RC 2.00 5.00
125 R. Rodriguez PS RC 2.00 5.00
126 Grant Balfour PS RC 2.00 5.00
127 Nick Maness PS RC 2.00 5.00
128 Jeremy Owens PS RC 2.00 5.00
129 Doug Nickle PS RC 2.00 5.00
130 Bert Snow PS RC 2.00 5.00
131 Jason Smith PS RC 2.00 5.00
132 Henry Mateo PS RC 2.00 5.00
133 Mike Penney PS RC 2.00 5.00
134 Bud Smith PS RC 2.00 5.00
135 Junior Spivey PS RC 2.00 5.00
136 Ichiro Suzuki JSY RC 40.00 80.00
137 Albert Pujols JSY RC 125.00 200.00
138 Mark Teixeira JSY RC 50.00 100.00
139 D.Brazelton JSY RC 6.00 15.00
140 Mark Prior JSY RC 20.00 50.00
141 T.Shinjo JSY RC 10.00 25.00

2001 Upper Deck Pros and Prospects Franchise Building Blocks

Issued at a rate of one in six, these 30 cards feature leading player as well as the leading prospect or rookie from each major league franchise.

COMPLETE SET (30) 20.00 50.00
F1 Darin Erstad .40 1.00
Elpidio Guzman
F2 Jason Giambi .40 1.00
Jason Hart
F3 Carlos Delgado .40 1.00
Vernon Wells
F4 Greg Vaughn .40 1.00
Aubrey Huff
F5 Jim Thome .40 1.00
C.C. Sabathia
F6 Edgar Martinez 2.00 5.00
Ichiro Suzuki
F7 Cal Ripken Jr. 2.00 5.00
Josh Towers
F8 Ivan Rodriguez .40 1.00
Carlos Pena
F9 Nomar Garciaparra 1.00 2.50
Dernell Stenson
F10 Mike Sweeney .40 1.00
Dee Brown
F11 Bobby Higginson .40 1.00
Brandon Inge
F12 Brad Radke .40 1.00
Adam Johnson
F13 Frank Thomas .60 1.50
Joe Crede
F14 Derek Jeter 1.50 4.00
Nick Johnson
F15 Jeff Bagwell 1.00 2.50
Morgan Ensberg
F16 Chipper Jones 1.00 2.50
Wilson Betemit
F17 Jeromy Burnitz .40 1.00
Ben Sheets
F18 Mark McGwire 10.00 25.00
Albert Pujols
F19 Sammy Sosa .60 1.50
Corey Patterson
F20 Luis Gonzalez .40 1.00
Jack Cust
F21 Kevin Brown .40 1.00
Luke Prokopec
F22 Vladimir Guerrero .60 1.50
Wilkin Ruan
F23 Barry Bonds 1.50 4.00
Carlos Valderrama
F24 Preston Wilson .40 1.00
Abraham Nunez
F25 Mike Piazza 1.00 2.50
Alex Escobar
F26 Tony Gwynn .75 2.00
Xavier Nady
F27 Scott Rolen .40 1.00
Jimmy Rollins
F28 Jason Kendall .40 1.00
Jack Wilson
F29 Ken Griffey Jr. 1.00 2.50
Adam Dunn
F30 Todd Helton .40 1.00
Juan Uribe

2001 Upper Deck Pros and Prospects Game-Used Dual Bat

Issued at a rate of one in 24, these 13 cards feature two bat pieces on each card.

GOLD PRINT RUN 25 SERIAL #'d SETS
NO GOLD PRICING DUE TO SCARCITY
PPBT Jeff Bagwell 6.00 15.00
Frank Thomas
PPGBO Ken Griffey Jr. 15.00 40.00
Barry Bonds
PPGBU Shawn Green 4.00 10.00
Jeromy Burnitz
PPJL Andruw Jones 6.00 15.00
Kenny Lofton
PPJP Chipper Jones 30.00 60.00
Albert Pujols
PPKA Jeff Kent 6.00 15.00
Roberto Alomar
PPMJ Greg Maddux 6.00 15.00
Randy Johnson
PPPT Rafael Palmeiro 6.00 15.00
Jim Thome
PPRF Alex Rodriguez 6.00 15.00
Rafael Furcal
PPRG Manny Ramirez Sox 6.00 15.00
Juan Gonzalez
PPRP Ivan Rodriguez 6.00 15.00
Mike Piazza
PPSG Sammy Sosa 6.00 15.00
Luis Gonzalez
PPWI Bernie Williams 40.00 80.00
Ichiro Suzuki

2001 Upper Deck Pros and Prospects Ichiro World Tour

Issued one per 12 packs, these 15 cards feature Ichiro Suzuki and information about various ballparks he played in.

COMPLETE SET (15) 40.00 100.00
COMMON CARD (WT1-WT15) 3.00 8.00

2001 Upper Deck Pros and Prospects Legends Game Bat

Issued one per 216 packs, these six cards feature two bat pieces from players whose careers are related to each other.

GOLD PRINT RUN 25 SERIAL #'d SETS
NO GOLD PRICING DUE TO SCARCITY
PLBY Jeromy Burnitz 10.00 25.00
Robin Yount
PLGM Ken Griffey Jr.
Joe Morgan
PLRF Manny Ramirez Sox 10.00 25.00
Carlton Fisk
PLRG Cal Ripken Jr. 20.00 50.00
Tony Gwynn
PLSB Sammy Sosa
Ernie Banks
PLWJ Bernie Williams 10.00 25.00
Reggie Jackson

2001 Upper Deck Pros and Prospects Specialty Game Jersey

Inserted one per 24 packs, these cards feature a piece of a jersey worn by the featured player in a special event.

GOLD PRINT RUN 25 SERIAL #'d SETS
NO GOLD PRICING DUE TO SCARCITY
SI Ichiro Suzuki 20.00 50.00
SAR Alex Rodriguez 6.00 15.00
SBB Barry Bonds 10.00 25.00
SCR Cal Ripken 15.00 40.00
SJE Jim Edmonds 3.00 8.00
SJG Juan Gonzalez 3.00 8.00
SJT Jim Thome 4.00 10.00
SLW Larry Walker 3.00 8.00
SRA Roberto Alomar 4.00 10.00
SRJ Randy Johnson 4.00 10.00
SSG Shawn Green 3.00 8.00
SSR Scott Rolen 4.00 10.00
SSS Sammy Sosa 4.00 10.00
STG Tony Gwynn 6.00 15.00

2001 Upper Deck Pros and Prospects Then and Now Game Jersey

Issued at a rate of one in 24, these 25 cards feature a retrospective look at the showcased player's career by including a jersey swatch from both his past team and his current team. Nolan Ryan is featured with three different swatches.

GOLD PRINT RUN 25 SERIAL #'d SETS
NO GOLD PRICING DUE TO SCARCITY
ALL EXCEPT RYAN ARE DUAL JSY CARDS
NOLAN RYAN IS A TRIPLE JSY CARD
TNAR Alex Rodriguez 10.00 25.00
TNB Barry Bonds 15.00 40.00
TNCS Curt Schilling 4.00 10.00
TNFG Freddy Garcia 4.00 10.00
TNGM Greg Maddux 6.00 15.00
TNGS Gary Sheffield 4.00 10.00
TNJE Jim Edmonds 4.00 10.00
TNJG Jason Giambi 4.00 10.00
TNJG Juan Gonzalez 4.00 10.00
TNKB Kevin Brown 4.00 10.00
TNKG Ken Griffey Jr. 8.00 20.00
TNMP Mike Piazza 6.00 15.00
TNMR Manny Ramirez Sox 6.00 15.00
TNNR Nolan Ryan 3X Jsy 60.00 120.00
TNPM Pedro Martinez 6.00 15.00
TNPN Phil Nevin 4.00 10.00
TNRA Rick Ankiel 4.00 10.00
TNRC Roger Clemens 12.50 30.00
TNRJ Randy Johnson 6.00 15.00
TNRV Robin Ventura 4.00 10.00
TNXN Xavier Nady 4.00 10.00

2005 Upper Deck Pros and Prospects

This 200-card set was released in May, 2005. The set was issued in six-card packs (designed for the retail market) with an $3 SRP and the packs came 24 to a box and 20 boxes to a case. Cards numbered 1-100 feature active veterans while cards 101-200 feature leading prospects issued in three distinct tiers. Cards 101 through 150 were issued to a stated print run of 999 serial numbered sets while cards 151 through 175 were issued to a stated print run of 499 serial numbered sets and cards 176 through 200 were issued to a stated print run of 199 sets. Cards numbered 101 through 200 were issued at an overall stated rate of one in eight.

COMP.SET w/o SP's (100) 10.00 25.00
COMMON CARD (1-100) .10 .30
COMMON CARD (101-150) .60 1.50
COMMON CARD (151-175) .75 2.00
151-175 PRINT RUN 499 SERIAL #'d SETS
COMMON CARD (176-200) 1.00 2.50
176-200 PRINT RUN 199 SERIAL #'d SETS
101-200 OVERALL ODDS 1:8
1 Adam Dunn .20 .50
2 Aramis Ramirez .12 .30
3 Bobby Abreu .12 .30
4 Mike Lowell .12 .30
5 Josh Beckett .20 .50
6 Derek Jeter .75 2.00
7 Alex Rodriguez .50 1.25
8 Andruw Jones .12 .30
9 Brian Giles .12 .30
10 Ivan Rodriguez .20 .50
11 Aubrey Huff .12 .30
12 Jake Peavy .12 .30
13 Hank Blalock .12 .30
14 Curt Schilling .20 .50
15 Carlos Zambrano .20 .50
16 Mike Mussina .20 .50
17 Travis Hafner .12 .30
18 Scott Rolen .20 .50
19 Luis Gonzalez .12 .30
20 Torii Hunter .12 .30
21 Greg Maddux .50 1.25
22 J.D. Drew .12 .30
23 Kevin Brown .12 .30
24 Carl Pavano .12 .30
25 David Ortiz .30 .75
26 Jose Reyes .20 .50
27 Johan Santana .30 .75
28 Todd Helton .20 .50
29 Jason Kendall .12 .30
30 Pedro Martinez .20 .50
31 Chipper Jones .30 .75
32 Ben Sheets .12 .30
33 Garret Anderson .12 .30
34 Carl Crawford .20 .50
35 Jason Schmidt .12 .30
36 Johnny Damon .20 .50
37 Richie Sexson .12 .30
38 Brad Penny .12 .30
39 Carlos Delgado .12 .30
40 Gary Sheffield .12 .30
41 John Smoltz .30 .75
42 Eric Chavez .12 .30
43 Carlos Guillen .12 .30
44 Jeff Kent .12 .30
45 Miguel Tejada .20 .50
46 Shawn Green .12 .30
47 Vernon Wells .12 .30
48 Albert Pujols .75 2.00
49 Alfonso Soriano .20 .50
50 Eric Gagne .12 .30
51 Mark Prior .20 .50
52 Rafael Furcal .12 .30
53 Preston Wilson .12 .30
54 Barry Larkin .20 .50
55 Randy Johnson .30 .75
56 Craig Wilson .12 .30
57 Victor Martinez .20 .50
58 Jim Thome .20 .50
59 Paul Konerko .20 .50
60 Jeff Bagwell .20 .50
61 Lyle Overbay .12 .30
62 Miguel Cabrera .30 .75
63 Melvin Mora .12 .30
64 Scott Podsednik .12 .30
65 Mark Mulder .12 .30
66 Mark Teixeira .30 .75
67 Tom Glavine .20 .50
68 Frank Thomas .30 .75
69 Livan Hernandez .12 .30
70 Kazuo Matsui .12 .30
71 Jose Vidro .12 .30
72 Ichiro Suzuki .50 1.25
73 Roger Clemens .40 1.00
74 Manny Ramirez .30 .75
75 Michael Young .20 .50
76 Rafael Palmeiro .20 .50
77 Steve Finley .12 .30
78 Andy Pettitte .20 .50
79 Lance Berkman .20 .50
80 Adrian Beltre .12 .30
81 Carlos Lee .12 .30
82 Bret Boone .12 .30
83 Magglio Ordonez .20 .50
84 Sammy Sosa .30 .75
85 Tim Hudson .20 .50
86 Vladimir Guerrero .30 .75
87 Carlos Beltran .12 .30
88 Kerry Wood .12 .30
89 Jim Edmonds .20 .50
90 Mike Sweeney .12 .30
91 Nomar Garciaparra .30 .75
92 Mike Piazza .30 .75
93 Roy Halladay .30 .75
94 Troy Glaus .12 .30
95 Bernie Williams .20 .50
96 Larry Walker .20 .50
97 Craig Biggio .20 .50
98 Roy Oswalt .20 .50
99 Ken Griffey Jr. .50 1.25
100 Hideki Matsui .50 1.25
101 Bucky Jacobsen T1 .60 1.50
102 J.D. Closser T1 .60 1.50
103 Antonio Perez T1 .60 1.50
104 Chris Shelton T1 .60 1.50
105 David Aardsma T1 .60 1.50
106 Jake Woods T1 .60 1.50
107 Jung Bong T1 .60 1.50
108 Kazuhito Tadano T1 .60 1.50
109 John Van Benschoten T1 .60 1.50
110 Jesse Foppert T1 .60 1.50
111 Joe Borchard T1 .60 1.50
112 Brandon Phillips T1 .60 1.50
113 J.D. Durbin T1 .60 1.50
114 Brandon Claussen T1 .60 1.50
115 Robb Quinlan T1 .60 1.50
116 Aaron Harang T1 .60 1.50
117 Chris Burke T1 .60 1.50
118 Sergio Mitre T1 .60 1.50
119 David DeJesus T1 .60 1.50
120 Gustavo Chacin T1 .60 1.50
121 Xavier Nady T1 .60 1.50
122 Garrett Atkins T1 .60 1.50
123 Jimmy Gobble T1 .60 1.50
124 Yhency Brazoban T1 .60 1.50
125 David Kelton T1 .60 1.50
126 Dewon Brazelton T1 .60 1.50
127 Koyie Hill T1 .60 1.50
128 Roman Colon T1 .60 1.50
129 Daniel Cabrera T1 .60 1.50
130 Chris Bootcheck T1 .60 1.50
131 Brad Halsey T1 .60 1.50
132 Bobby Madritsch T1 .60 1.50
133 Grady Sizemore T1 1.00 2.50
134 Akinori Otsuka T1 .60 1.50
135 Wilfredo Ledezma T1 .60 1.50
136 Russ Adams T1 .60 1.50
137 Joe Crede T1 .60 1.50
138 Chad Cordero T1 .60 1.50
139 Willie Harris T1 .60 1.50
140 Joey Gathright T1 .60 1.50
141 Logan Kensing T1 .60 1.50
142 Jon Leicester T1 .60 1.50
143 Freddy Guzman T1 .60 1.50
144 Jonny Gomes T1 .60 1.50
145 Jeff Bajenaru T1 .60 1.50
146 Andres Blanco T1 .60 1.50
147 Jhonny Peralta T1 .60 1.50
148 Jayson Werth T1 1.00 2.50
149 Bill Hall T1 .60 1.50
150 Jason Davis T1 .60 1.50
151 Gabe Gross T2 .75 2.00
152 Abe Alvarez T2 .75 2.00
153 Josh Willingham T2 .75 2.00
154 Merkin Valdez T2 .75 2.00
155 Jeff Niemann T2 RC 2.00 5.00
156 Yadier Molina T2 1.25 3.00
157 Guillermo Quiroz T2 .75 2.00
158 Ian Snell T2 .75 2.00
159 Dan Meyer T2 .75 2.00
160 Jason Lane T2 .75 2.00
161 Adrian Gonzalez T2 1.25 3.00
162 Eddy Rodriguez T2 .75 2.00
163 Jason DuBois T2 .75 2.00
164 Juan Rincon T2 .75 2.00
165 Ryan Wagner T2 .75 2.00
166 Nick Swisher T2 2.00 5.00
167 Chad Tracy T2 .75 2.00
168 Dioner Navarro T2 .75 2.00
169 Gerald Laird T2 .75 2.00
170 Alexis Rios T2 1.25 3.00
171 Aaron Rowand T2 .75 2.00
172 Adam LaRoche T2 .75 2.00
173 Kevin Youkilis T2 .75 2.00
174 Philip Humber T2 RC 2.00 5.00
175 Chin-Hui Tsao T2 .75 2.00
176 Jeff Francis T3 1.00 2.50
177 Chase Utley T3 1.50 4.00
178 Gavin Floyd T3 1.00 2.50
179 David Wright T3 4.00 10.00
180 B.J. Upton T3 1.50 4.00
181 Laynce Nix T3 1.00 2.50
182 Joe Mauer T3 2.50 6.00
183 Justin Morneau T3 2.50 6.00
184 Zack Greinke T3 1.50 4.00
185 Jose Capellan T3 1.00 2.50
186 Khalil Greene T3 1.00 2.50
187 Oliver Perez T3 1.00 2.50
188 Joe Blanton T3 1.00 2.50
189 Wily Mo Pena T3 1.00 2.50
190 Dallas McPherson T3 1.00 2.50
191 Edwin Jackson T3 1.00 2.50
192 Casey Kotchman T3 1.00 2.50
193 Jesse Crain T3 1.00 2.50
194 Ryan Howard T3 5.00 12.00
195 Bobby Crosby T3 1.00 2.50
196 Jason Bay T3 1.00 2.50
197 Rickie Weeks T3 1.50 4.00
198 Scott Proctor T3 1.00 2.50
199 Danny Haren T3 1.00 2.50
200 Scott Kazmir T3 2.50 6.00

2005 Upper Deck Pros and Prospects Gold

*GOLD 1-100: 4X TO 10X BASIC
1-100 PRINT RUN 125 SERIAL #'d SETS
*GOLD 101-150: .5X TO 1.2X BASIC
101-150 PRINT RUN 150 SERIAL #'d SETS
*GOLD 151-175: .5X TO 1.2X BASIC
151-175 PRINT RUN 99 SERIAL #'d SETS
176-200 PRINT RUN 25 SERIAL #'d SETS
176-200 NO PRICING DUE TO SCARCITY
OVERALL PARALLEL ODDS 1:8

2005 Upper Deck Pros and Prospects Future Fabrics

*GOLD: .6X TO 1.5X BASIC
GOLD PRINT RUN 75 SERIAL #'d SETS
OVERALL GAME USED ODDS 1:24
AK Adam Kennedy 2.00 5.00
BC Bobby Crosby 2.00 5.00
BU B.J. Upton 2.00 5.00
CK Casey Kotchman 2.00 5.00
CS C.C. Sabathia 2.00 5.00
DM Dallas McPherson 2.00 5.00
DW David Wright 6.00 15.00
EH Eric Hinske 2.00 5.00
JJ Jacque Jones 2.00 5.00
JM Joe Mauer 3.00 8.00
JR Jose Reyes 2.00 5.00
JW Jayson Werth 2.00 5.00
KE Austin Kearns 2.00 5.00
KG Khalil Greene 3.00 8.00
KM Kazuo Matsui 2.00 5.00
MC Miguel Cabrera 2.00 5.00
RH Rich Harden 2.00 5.00
SP Sidney Ponson 2.00 5.00
SS Shannon Stewart 2.00 5.00
TN Trot Nixon 2.00 5.00
VM Victor Martinez 2.00 5.00

2005 Upper Deck Pros and Prospects Pro Material

*GOLD: .6X TO 1.5X BASIC
GOLD PRINT RUN 50 SERIAL #'d SETS
OVERALL GAME USED ODDS 1:24
AB Adrian Beltre 3.00 8.00
AP Albert Pujols 6.00 15.00
CB Carlos Beltran 3.00 8.00
CJ Chipper Jones 4.00 10.00
CS Curt Schilling 4.00 10.00
DJ Derek Jeter 8.00 20.00
EC Eric Chavez 3.00 8.00
HB Hank Blalock 3.00 8.00
IS Ichiro Suzuki 10.00 25.00
JB Jeff Bagwell 4.00 10.00
JT Jim Thome 4.00 10.00
KG Ken Griffey Jr. 6.00 15.00
MP Mark Prior 4.00 10.00
MR Manny Ramirez 4.00 10.00
MT Miguel Tejada 3.00 8.00
PI Mike Piazza 4.00 10.00
RJ Randy Johnson 4.00 10.00
SR Scott Rolen 4.00 10.00
SS Sammy Sosa 4.00 10.00
TH Todd Helton 4.00 10.00
VG Vladimir Guerrero 4.00 10.00

2005 Upper Deck Pros and Prospects Signs of Stardom

TIER 3 PRINT RUNS 713 OR MORE PER
TIER 2 PRINT RUNS B/WN 247-557 PER
TIER 1 PRINT RUNS B/WN 147-202 PER
OVERALL AUTO ODDS 1:24
CARDS ARE NOT SERIAL-NUMBERED
PRINT RUN INFO PROVIDED BY UD
AB Angel Berroa T1 4.00 10.00
AE Adam Eaton T1 4.00 10.00
AO Akinori Otsuka T3 6.00 15.00
BC Bobby Crosby T1 6.00 15.00
BS Ben Sheets T1 6.00 15.00
CC Chad Cordero T1 6.00 15.00
CK Casey Kotchman T1 6.00 15.00
CL Cliff Lee T2 6.00 15.00
CP Corey Patterson T1 4.00 10.00
DW Dontrelle Willis T1 6.00 15.00
FF Frank Francisco T2 4.00 10.00
GA John Gall T2 4.00 10.00
GR Khalil Greene T1 10.00 25.00
HB Hank Blalock T1 6.00 15.00
HR Horacio Ramirez T3 4.00 10.00
JB Josh Beckett T1 10.00 25.00
JF Jason Frasor T2 4.00 10.00
JK Jeff Keppinger T2 4.00 10.00
JL Justin Leone T3 4.00 10.00
JR Jose Reyes T1 6.00 15.00
JW Jerome Williams T1 4.00 10.00
KT Kazuhito Tadano T3 6.00 15.00
LO Lyle Overbay T1 4.00 10.00
MA Joe Mauer T1 20.00 50.00
MC Miguel Cabrera T2 10.00 25.00
MG Marcus Giles T1 6.00 15.00
MJ Mike Johnston T3 4.00 10.00
MR Mike Rouse T3 4.00 10.00
MT Mark Teixeira T1 10.00 25.00
OP Oliver Perez T3 4.00 10.00
PE Jake Peavy T1 10.00 25.00
RB Rocco Baldelli T2 6.00 15.00
RH Rich Harden T3 6.00 15.00
RW Rickie Weeks T1 6.00 15.00
SB Sean Burroughs T1 4.00 10.00
SK Scott Kazmir T2 8.00 20.00
SP Scott Podsednik T1 10.00 25.00
ST Shingo Takatsu T2 4.00 10.00
TS Termel Sledge T3 4.00 10.00
WA Ryan Wagner T3 4.00 10.00
WE Brandon Webb T1 4.00 10.00

2005 Upper Deck Pros and Prospects Stardom Signatures

OVERALL AUTO ODDS 1:24
PRINT RUNS B/WN 50-240 COPIES PER
AK Al Kaline/99 20.00 50.00
BE Josh Beckett/50 12.50 30.00
BL Hank Blalock/50 10.00 25.00
EB Ernie Banks/240 30.00 60.00
JG Jason Giambi/100 10.00 25.00
JM Joe Morgan/194 10.00 25.00
KG Ken Griffey Jr./198 40.00 80.00
KP Kirby Puckett/156 50.00 100.00

2001 Upper Deck Prospect Premieres

The 2001 Upper Deck Prospect Premieres was released in October 2001 and features a 102-card set. The first 90 cards are regular and the last 12 are autographed cards numbered to 1000 randomly inserted into packs. The packs contain four cards and have a SRP of $2.99 per pack. There were 18 packs per box.

COMP.SET w/o SP's (90) 50.00 80.00
COMMON CARD (1-90) .15 .40
COMMON AUTO (91-102) 6.00 15.00
1 Jeff Mathis XRC .20 .50
2 Jake Woods XRC .15 .40
3 Dallas McPherson XRC .40 1.00
4 Steven Shell XRC .15 .40
5 Ryan Budde XRC .15 .40
6 Kirk Saarloos XRC .15 .40
7 Ryan Stegall XRC .15 .40
8 Bobby Crosby XRC 1.25 3.00
9 J.T. Stotts XRC .15 .40
10 Neal Cotts XRC .40 1.00
11 J.Bonderman XRC 1.50 4.00
12 Brandon League XRC .15 .40
13 Tyrell Godwin XRC .15 .40
14 Gabe Gross XRC .20 .50
15 Chris Neylan XRC .15 .40
16 Macay McBride XRC .30 .75
17 Josh Burrus XRC .15 .40
18 Adam Stern XRC .15 .40
19 Richard Lewis XRC .15 .40
20 Cole Barthel XRC .15 .40
21 Mike Jones XRC .20 .50
22 J.J. Hardy XRC 2.50 6.00
23 Jon Steitz XRC .15 .40
24 Brad Nelson XRC .15 .40
25 Justin Pope XRC .15 .40
26 Dan Haren XRC UER .75 2.00
Blurb incorrectly lists him as a lefty
27 Andy Sisco XRC .15 .40
28 Ryan Theriot XRC 1.25 3.00
29 Ricky Nolasco XRC .75 2.00
30 Jon Switzer XRC .15 .40
31 Justin Wechsler XRC .15 .40
32 Mike Gosling XRC .15 .40
33 Scott Hairston XRC .20 .50
34 Brian Pilkington XRC .15 .40
35 Kole Strayhorn XRC .15 .40
36 David Taylor XRC .15 .40
37 Donald Levinski XRC .15 .40
38 Mike Hinckley XRC .20 .50
39 Nick Long XRC .15 .40
40 Brad Hennessey XRC .20 .50
41 Noah Lowry XRC .75 2.00
42 Josh Cram XRC .15 .40
43 Jesse Foppert XRC .20 .50
44 Julian Benavidez XRC .15 .40
45 Dan Denham XRC .15 .40
46 Travis Foley XRC .15 .40
47 Mike Conroy XRC .15 .40
48 Jake Dittler XRC .15 .40
49 Rene Rivera XRC .15 .40
50 John Cole XRC .15 .40
51 Lazaro Abreu XRC .15 .40
52 David Wright XRC 6.00 15.00
53 Aaron Heilman XRC .20 .50
54 Len DiNardo XRC .15 .40
55 Alhaji Turay XRC .15 .40
56 Chris Smith XRC .15 .40
57 Rommie Lewis XRC .15 .40
58 Bryan Bass XRC .15 .40
59 David Crouthers XRC .15 .40
60 Josh Barfield XRC 1.25 3.00
61 Jake Peavy XRC 2.50 6.00
62 Ryan Howard XRC 8.00 20.00
63 Gavin Floyd XRC .40 1.00
64 Michael Floyd XRC .15 .40
65 Stefan Bailie XRC .15 .40
66 Jon DeVries XRC .15 .40
67 Steve Kelly XRC .15 .40
68 Alan Moye XRC .15 .40
69 Justin Gillman XRC .15 .40
70 Jayson Nix XRC .15 .40
71 John Draper XRC .15 .40
72 Kenny Baugh XRC .15 .40
73 Michael Woods XRC .15 .40
74 Preston Larrison XRC .20 .50
75 Matt Coenen XRC .15 .40
76 Scott Tyler XRC .20 .50
77 Jose Morales XRC .15 .40
78 Corwin Malone XRC .15 .40
79 Dennis Ulacia XRC .15 .40
80 Andy Gonzalez XRC .15 .40
81 Kris Honel XRC .15 .40
82 Wyatt Allen XRC .15 .40
83 Ryan Wing XRC .15 .40
84 Sean Henn XRC .15 .40
85 John-Ford Griffin XRC .15 .40
86 Bronson Sardinha XRC .15 .40
87 Jon Skaggs XRC .15 .40
88 Shelley Duncan XRC 1.50 4.00
89 Jason Arnold XRC .15 .40
90 Aaron Rifkin XRC .15 .40
91 Colt Griffin AU XRC 6.00 15.00
92 J.D. Martin AU XRC 6.00 15.00
93 Justin Wayne AU XRC 6.00 15.00
94 J.VanBenschoten AU XRC 6.00 15.00
95 Chris Burke AU XRC 10.00 25.00
96 C. Kotchman AU XRC 6.00 15.00
97 M. Garciaparra AU XRC 6.00 15.00
98 Jake Gautreau AU XRC 6.00 15.00
99 J. Williams AU XRC 6.00 15.00
100 Toe Nash AU XRC 6.00 15.00
101 Joe Borchard AU XRC 6.00 15.00
102 Mark Prior AU XRC 12.50 30.00

2001 Upper Deck Prospect Premieres Heroes of Baseball Game Bat

Inserted at a rate of one in 18, this 23-card set features bat pieces of retired players. The cards carry a 'B' prefix.

BAO Al Oliver 3.00 8.00
BBB Bill Buckner 3.00 8.00
BBM Bill Madlock 3.00 8.00
BDB Don Baylor 3.00 8.00
BDE Dwight Evans 4.00 10.00
BDL Davey Lopes 3.00 8.00
BDP Dave Parker 3.00 8.00
BDW Dave Winfield 3.00 8.00
BEM Eddie Murray 4.00 10.00
BFL Fred Lynn 3.00 8.00
BGC Gary Carter 3.00 8.00
BGM Gary Matthews 3.00 8.00
BJM Joe Morgan 3.00 8.00
BKEG Ken Griffey Sr. 3.00 8.00
BKIG Kirk Gibson 3.00 8.00
BKP Kirby Puckett 4.00 10.00
BMM Manny Mota 3.00 8.00
BOS Ozzie Smith 4.00 10.00
BRJ Reggie Jackson 4.00 10.00
BSG Steve Garvey 3.00 8.00
BTM Tim McCarver 3.00 8.00
BTP Tony Perez 3.00 8.00
BWB Wade Boggs 4.00 10.00

2001 Upper Deck Prospect Premieres Heroes of Baseball Game Jersey Duos

Inserted at a rate of one in 144, this seven card set featured dual game jerseys of both current and retired players. The cards carry a 'J' prefix.

JBH Bryan Bass 5.00 12.00
J.J. Hardy
JDG Shelley Duncan 10.00 25.00
Tyrell Godwin
JGS Steve Garvey 3.00 8.00
Reggie Smith
JHB Aaron Heilman 6.00 15.00
Jeremy Bonderman
JJJ Michael Jordan 40.00 80.00
Michael Jordan
JSG Jon Switzer 3.00 8.00
Mike Gosling
JWP Dave Winfield 10.00 25.00
Kirby Puckett

2001 Upper Deck Prospect Premieres Heroes of Baseball Game Jersey Duos Autograph

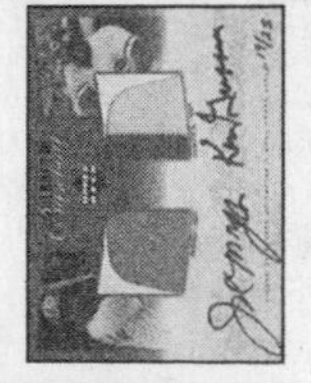

Randomly inserted into packs, this six card set featured dual game jerseys with autographs of both current and retired players. The cards were serial numbered to 25. The cards carry a 'SJ' prefix. Due to scarcity, no pricing is provided.

2001 Upper Deck Prospect Premieres Heroes of Baseball Game Jersey Trios

Inserted in packs at a rate of one in 144, these nine cards feature three swatches of game-worn jerseys on a card. Representatives at Upper Deck have confirmed that the Maris-Mantle-DiMaggio card is in noticeably short supply. In addition, the following cards did not packout and were available via exchange cards that were seeded into packs in their place: Crosby/Garciaparra/Sardinha, Gautreau/Godwin/Heilman, Gross/Kotchman/Baugh, Griffin/Martin/Switzer and VanBenschoten/Prior/Jones. The deadline to mail in these exchange cards was October 22nd, 2004.

DDO Chris Durbin 1.00 10.00
Bryan Bass
Bobby Crosby UER
CGS Bobby Crosby UER 4.00 10.00
Michael Garciaparra
Bronson Sardinha
GGH Jake Gautreau 3.00 8.00
Tyrell Godwin
Aaron Heilman
GKB Gabe Gross 3.00 8.00
Casey Kotchmann
Kenny Baugh
GMS Colt Griffin 3.00 8.00
J.D. Martin
Jon Switzer
JMD Michael Jordan 150.00 250.00
Mickey Mantle
Joe DiMaggio
JPW Michael Jordan 30.00 60.00
Kirby Puckett
Dave Winfield
MMD Roger Maris 250.00 400.00
Mickey Mantle
Joe DiMaggio SP
VPJ Jon VanBenSchoten 4.00 10.00
Mark Prior
Mike Jones

2001 Upper Deck Prospect Premieres Heroes of Baseball Game Jersey Trios Autograph

Randomly inserted in packs, these cards feature not only three swatches of game-worn jerseys but also autographs of the featured players. These cards are serial numbered to 25. Due to scarcity, no pricing is provided.

2001 Upper Deck Prospect Premieres MJ Grandslam Game Bat

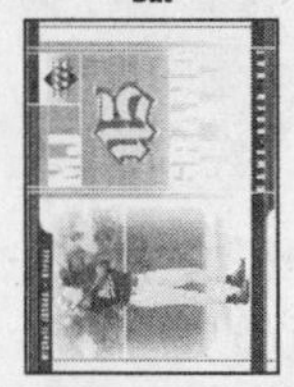

Randomly inserted in packs, these five cards feature bat cards from basketball legend turned baseball prospect. Card number "MJ5" was printed in lesser quantities and is notated in our checklist as an SP.

COMMON CARD (MJ1-MJ4) 6.00 15.00
MJ5 Michael Jordan SP 20.00 50.00

2001 Upper Deck Prospect Premieres Tribute to 42

Issued at a rate of one in 750, these seven cards honor the memory of the integration trail blazer and all time great. Please note, the Pants-Cut Auto card erroneously states "Jersey/Cut Combo" on the card itself. UD has verified that the material actually used to create the card was derived from a pair of game-used pants.

B Jackie Robinson Bat 12.50 30.00
C Jackie Robinson Cut AU
J Jackie Robinson Pants 20.00 50.00
BC Jackie Robinson Bat-Cut AU
GB Jackie Robinson 30.00 60.00
Gold Bat/42
GJ J.Robinson Pants Gold/42 30.00 60.00
JC Jackie Robinson Pants-Cut AU

2002 Upper Deck Prospect Premieres

This 109 card set was released in November, 2002. It was issued in four count packs which came 24 packs to a box and 20 boxes to a case with an SRP of $3 per pack. Cards number 61 through 85 feature game-worn jersey pieces and were inserted at a stated rate of one in 18 packs.

Cards numbered 86 through 97 feature player's autographs and were issued at a stated rate of one in 18 packs. Cards numbered 98 through 109 feature tribute cards to recently retired superstars Cal Ripken and Mark McGwire along with Yankee great Joe DiMaggio. Matt Pender's basic XRC erroneously packed out picturing Curtis Granderson. A corrected version of the card was made available to collectors a few months after the product went live via a mail exchange program directly from Upper Deck.

COMP.SET w/o SP's (72) 25.00 40.00
COMMON CARD (1-60) .15 .40
COMMON CARD (61-85) 2.00 5.00
COMMON CARD (86-97) 3.00 8.00
COMMON RIPKEN (98-99) .75 2.00
COMMON MCGWIRE (100-105) .75 2.00
COMMON DIMAGGIO (106-109) .60 1.50
PENDER COR AVAIL.VIA MAIL EXCHANGE
1 Josh Rupe XRC .15 .40
2 Blair Johnson XRC .15 .40
3 Jason Pridie XRC .15 .40
4 Tim Gilhooly XRC .15 .40
5 Kennard Jones XRC .15 .40
6 Darrell Rasner XRC .15 .40
7 Adam Donachie XRC .15 .40
8 Josh Murray XRC .15 .40
9 Brian Dopirak XRC .40 1.00
10 Jason Cooper XRC .15 .40
11 Zach Hammes XRC .15 .40
12 Jon Lester XRC 5.00 12.00
13 Kevin Jepsen XRC .20 .50
14 Curtis Granderson XRC 3.00 8.00
15 David Bush XRC .40 1.00
16 Joel Guzman .30 .75
17A Matt Pender UER XRC .60 1.50
Pictures Curtis Granderson
17B Matt Pender COR .40 1.00
18 Derick Grigsby XRC .15 .40
19 Jeremy Reed XRC .40 1.00
20 Jonathan Broxton XRC .40 1.00
21 Jesse Crain XRC .30 .75
22 Justin Jones XRC .20 .50
23 Brian Slocum XRC .15 .40
24 Brian McCann XRC 3.00 8.00
25 Francisco Liriano XRC 3.00 8.00
26 Fred Lewis XRC .15 .40
27 Steve Stanley XRC .15 .40
28 Chris Snyder XRC .20 .50
29 Dan Cevette XRC .15 .40
30 Kiel Fisher XRC .20 .50
31 Brandon Weeden XRC 1.00 2.50
32 Pat Osborn XRC .15 .40
33 Taber Lee XRC .15 .40
34 Dan Ortmeier XRC .20 .50
35 Josh Johnson XRC 1.50 4.00
36 Val Majewski XRC .15 .40
37 Larry Broadway XRC .15 .40
38 Joey Gomes XRC .15 .40
39 Eric Thomas XRC .15 .40
40 James Loney XRC 2.00 5.00
41 Charlie Morton XRC .15 .40
42 Mark McLemore XRC .15 .40
43 Matt Craig XRC .20 .50
44 Ryan Rodriguez XRC .15 .40
45 Rich Hill XRC 1.25 3.00
46 Bob Malek XRC .15 .40
47 Justin Maureau XRC .15 .40
48 Randy Braun XRC .15 .40
49 Brian Grant XRC .15 .40
50 Tyler Davidson XRC .20 .50
51 Travis Hanson XRC .20 .50
52 Kyle Boyer XRC .15 .40
53 James Holcomb XRC .15 .40
54 Ryan Williams XRC .15 .40
55 Ben Crockett XRC .15 .40
56 Adam Greenberg XRC .30 .75
57 John Baker XRC .15 .40
58 Matt Carson XRC .15 .40
59 Jonathan George XRC .15 .40
60 David Jensen XRC .15 .40
61 Nick Swisher JSY XRC 4.00 10.00
62 Br.Clevlen JSY XRC UER 5.00 12.00
Name mispelled as Cleven
63 Royce Ring JSY XRC 2.00 5.00
64 Mike Nixon JSY XRC 2.00 5.00
65 Ricky Barrett JSY XRC 2.00 5.00
66 Russ Adams JSY XRC 2.00 5.00
67 Joe Mauer JSY XRC 12.50 30.00
68 Jeff Francoeur JSY XRC 5.00 12.00
69 Joe Blanton JSY XRC 3.00 8.00
70 Micah Schilling JSY XRC 2.00 5.00
71 John McCurdy JSY XRC 2.00 5.00
72 Sergio Santos JSY XRC 3.00 8.00
73 Josh Womack JSY XRC 2.00 5.00
74 Jared Doyle JSY XRC 2.00 5.00
75 Ben Fritz JSY XRC 2.00 5.00
76 Greg Miller JSY XRC 2.00 5.00
77 Luke Hagerty JSY XRC 2.00 5.00
78 Matt Whitney JSY XRC 2.00 5.00
79 Dan Meyer JSY XRC 3.00 8.00
80 Bill Murphy JSY XRC 2.00 5.00
81 Zach Segovia JSY XRC 2.00 5.00
82 Steve Obenchain JSY XRC 2.00 5.00
83 Matt Clanton JSY XRC 2.00 5.00
84 Mark Teahen JSY XRC 3.00 8.00
85 Kyle Pawelczyk JSY XRC 2.00 5.00
86 Khalil Greene AU XRC 5.00 12.00
87 Joe Saunders AU XRC 5.00 12.00
88 Jeremy Hermida AU XRC 6.00 15.00
89 Drew Meyer AU XRC 3.00 8.00
90 Jeff Francis AU XRC 12.50 30.00
91 Scott Moore AU XRC 3.00 8.00
92 Prince Fielder AU XRC 60.00 120.00
93 Zack Greinke AU XRC 15.00 40.00
94 Chris Gruler AU XRC 3.00 8.00
95 Scott Kazmir AU XRC 6.00 15.00
96 B.J. Upton AU XRC 15.00 40.00
97 Clint Everts AU XRC 3.00 8.00
98 Cal Ripken TRIB .75 2.00
99 Cal Ripken TRIB .75 2.00
100 Mark McGwire TRIB .75 2.00
101 Mark McGwire TRIB .75 2.00
102 Mark McGwire TRIB .75 2.00
103 Mark McGwire TRIB .75 2.00
104 Mark McGwire TRIB .75 2.00
105 Joe DiMaggio TRIB .60 1.50
106 Joe DiMaggio TRIB .60 1.50
107 Joe DiMaggio TRIB .60 1.50
108 Joe DiMaggio TRIB .60 1.50
109 Joe DiMaggio TRIB .60 1.50

2002 Upper Deck Prospect Premieres Future Gems Quads

Inserted one per sealed box, these 33 cards feature four different cards in a panel and were issued to a stated print run of 600 serial numbered sets.

1 David Bush 3.00 8.00
Matt Craig
Josh Johnson
Brian McCann
2 Jason Cooper 3.00 8.00
Jonathan George
Larry Broadway
Joel Guzman
3 Matt Craig 3.00 8.00
Josh Murray
Brian McCann
Jason Pridie
4 Jesse Crain 3.00 8.00
Brian Grant
Curtis Granderson
Joey Gomes
5 Tyler Davidson 3.00 8.00
Val Majewski
Justin Jones
Daniel Cevette
6 Joe DiMaggio 8.00 20.00
Jon Lester
Mark McGwire
Mark McLemore
7 Jonathan George 3.00 8.00
Jeremy Reed
Adam Donachie
Matt Carson
8 Jonathan George 3.00 8.00
Eric Thomas
Joel Guzman
Kiel Fisher
9 Tim Gilhooly 3.00 8.00
Brandon Weeden
Brian Slocum
Brian Dopirak
10 Brian Grant 4.00 10.00
Rich Hill
Joey Gomes
Joe DiMaggio
11 Derick Grigsby 5.00 12.00
Bob Malek
James Loney
Fred Lewis
12 Zach Hammes 3.00 8.00
James Holcomb
Cal Ripken
Kennard Jones
13 Rich Hill 5.00 12.00
Mark McGwire
Brian Grant
Matt Carson
14 James Holcomb 3.00 8.00
David Jensen
Kennard Jones
Ryan Williams
15 David Jensen 5.00 12.00
Francisco Liriano
Ryan Williams
Travis Hanson
16 Josh Johnson 3.00 8.00
Jesse Crain
Adam Greenberg
Curtis Granderson
17 Jon Lester 8.00 20.00
Jonathan George
Mark McLemore
Adam Donachie
18 Francisco Liriano 5.00 12.00
Mark McGwire
Travis Hanson
Taber Lee
19 Val Majewski 3.00 8.00
Charlie Morton
Daniel Cevette
Joey Gomes
20 Bob Malek 3.00 8.00
Zach Hammes
Fred Lewis
Cal Ripken
21 Justin Maureau 3.00 8.00
Joe DiMaggio
Chris Snyder
Mark McGwire
22 Mark McGwire 3.00 8.00
Bob Malek
Joe DiMaggio
Kyle Boyer
23 Charlie Morton 3.00 8.00
David Bush/Joey Gomes
Josh Johnson
24 Josh Murray 3.00 8.00
Mark McGwire
Jason Pridie
Joe DiMaggio
25 Matt Pender UER 3.00 8.00
Mark McGwire
Mark McLemore
Ryan Rodriguez
26 Jason Pridie 3.00 8.00
Josh Murray
Matt Craig
Brian McCann
27 Jeremy Reed 3.00 8.00
Josh Johnson
Matt Carson
Adam Greenberg
28 Cal Ripken 3.00 8.00
Jason Cooper
Matt Carson
Larry Broadway
29 Ryan Rodriguez 3.00 8.00
Eric Thomas
Pat Osborn
Randy Braun
30 Josh Rupe 3.00 8.00
Tyler Davidson
John Baker
Justin Jones
31 Eric Thomas 5.00 12.00
Derick Grigsby
Randy Braun
James Loney
32 Eric Thomas 3.00 8.00
Matt Pender UER
Kiel Fisher
Mark McLemore
33 Brandon Weeden 5.00 12.00
Rich Hill
Brian Dopirak
Brian Grant

2002 Upper Deck Prospect Premieres Heroes of Baseball

Inserted at stated odds of one per pack, these 90 cards feature 10 cards each of various baseball legends. Each player featured has nine regular cards and one header card.

COMP.RIPKEN SET (10) 8.00 20.00
COMMON RIPKEN (CR1-HDR) 1.00 2.50
COMP.DIMAGGIO SET (10) 4.00 10.00
COMMON DIMAGGIO (JD1-HDR) .50 1.25
COMP.MORGAN SET (10) 2.00 5.00
COMMON MORGAN (JM1-HDR) .30 .75
COMP.MCGWIRE SET (10) 8.00 20.00
COMMON MCGWIRE (MC1-HDR) 1.00 2.50
COMP.MANTLE SET (10) 10.00 25.00
COMMON MANTLE (MM1-HDR) 1.25 3.00
COMP.OZZIE SET (10) 6.00 15.00
COMMON OZZIE (OS1-HDR) .75 2.00
COMP.GWYNN SET (10) 6.00 15.00
COMMON GWYNN (TG1-HDR) .75 2.00
COMP.SEAVER SET (10) 4.00 10.00
COMMON SEAVER (TS1-HDR) .50 1.25
COMP.STARGELL SET (10) 2.00 5.00
COMMON STARGELL (WS1-HDR) .30 .75

2002 Upper Deck Prospect Premieres Heroes of Baseball 85 Quads

Randomly inserted as boxtoppers, these eight panels feature a mix of four cards of the players featured in the Heroes of Baseball insert set. Each of these cards are issued to a stated print run of 85 serial numbered sets.

1 Joe DiMaggio 4.00 10.00
Tony Gwynn
Tony Gwynn
Joe DiMaggio
2 Joe DiMaggio 6.00 15.00
Tony Gwynn
Cal Ripken
Cal Ripken
3 Joe DiMaggio Hdr 6.00 15.00
Mickey Mantle
Willie Stargell Hdr
Mickey Mantle
4 Tony Gwynn 4.00 10.00
Tony Gwynn
Ozzie Smith
Willie Stargell
5 Tony Gwynn 4.00 10.00
Willie Stargell
Joe DiMaggio
Joe Morgan
6 Tony Gwynn 4.00 10.00
Willie Stargell
Cal Ripken
Ozzie Smith
7 Mickey Mantle 6.00 15.00
Mark McGwire
Joe Morgan
Tom Seaver
8 Mickey Mantle 6.00 15.00
Tom Seaver
Mickey Mantle
Tom Seaver
9 Mark McGwire 6.00 15.00
Joe Morgan
Mark McGwire
Joe Morgan
10 Mark McGwire Hdr 6.00 15.00
Cal Ripken
Tony Gwynn
Joe DiMaggio
11 Mark McGwire 4.00 10.00
Tom Seaver
Joe Morgan
Ozzie Smith
12 Joe Morgan 4.00 10.00
Tony Gwynn
Joe Morgan
Tony Gwynn
13 Joe Morgan 6.00 15.00
Joe DiMaggio
Mickey Mantle
Cal Ripken
14 Joe Morgan 4.00 10.00
Joe DiMaggio
Willie Stargell
Tony Gwynn
15 Ozzie Smith 4.00 10.00
Joe DiMaggio
Ozzie Smith
Willie Stargell
16 Ozzie Smith 4.00 10.00
Mark McGwire
Willie Stargell
Tony Gwynn
17 Ozzie Smith 4.00 10.00
Tom Seaver
Tom Seaver
Mark McGwire
18 Cal Ripken 6.00 15.00
Mickey Mantle
Joe DiMaggio
Joe Morgan
19 Cal Ripken 6.00 15.00
Mark McGwire
Cal Ripken
Mark McGwire
20 Tom Seaver 4.00 10.00
Joe DiMaggio
Tom Seaver
Joe DiMaggio
21 Tom Seaver 4.00 10.00
Joe Morgan
Ozzie Smith
Willie Stargell
22 Tom Seaver 6.00 15.00
Cal Ripken
Mark McGwire
Mickey Mantle
23 Willie Stargell 4.00 10.00
Ozzie Smith
Ozzie Smith
Willie Stargell
24 Willie Stargell 4.00 10.00
Ozzie Smith
Tom Seaver
Joe Morgan

2003 Upper Deck Prospect Premieres

For the third consecutive year, Upper Deck produced a set consisting solely of players who had been taken during that season's amateur draft. This was a 90-card standard-size set which was released in December, 2003. This set was issued in four-card packs with an $2.99 SRP which came 16 packs to a box and 18 boxes to a case.

COMPLETE SET (90) 20.00 40.00
1 Bryan Opdyke XRC .15 .40
2 Gabriel Sosa XRC .15 .40
3 Tila Reynolds XRC .15 .40
4 Aaron Hill XRC .60 1.50
5 Aaron Marsden XRC .20 .50
6 Abe Alvarez XRC .20 .50
7 Adam Jones XRC 3.00 8.00
8 Adam Miller XRC 1.25 3.00
9 Andre Ethier XRC 2.50 6.00
10 Anthony Gwynn XRC .50 1.25
11 Brad Snyder XRC .30 .75
12 Brad Sullivan XRC .20 .50
13 Brian Anderson XRC .75 2.00
14 Brian Buscher XRC .15 .40
15 Brian Snyder XRC .20 .50
16 Carlos Quentin XRC 1.25 3.00
17 Chad Billingsley XRC 1.50 4.00
18 Fraser Dizard XRC .15 .40
19 Chris Durbin XRC .15 .40
20 Chris Ray XRC .40 1.00
21 Conor Jackson XRC 1.25 3.00
22 Kory Casto XRC .20 .50
23 Craig Whitaker XRC .20 .50
24 Daniel Moore XRC .15 .40
25 Daric Barton XRC 1.25 3.00
26 Darin Downs XRC .20 .50
27 David Murphy XRC .30 .75
28 Dustin Majewski XRC .20 .50
29 Edgardo Baez XRC .20 .50
30 Jake Fox XRC .75 2.00
31 Jake Stevens XRC .20 .50
32 Jamie D'Antona XRC .30 .75
33 James Houser XRC .20 .50
34 Jar. Saltalamacchia XRC 2.00 5.00
35 Jason Hirsh XRC .75 2.00
36 Javi Herrera XRC .20 .50
37 Jeff Allison XRC .15 .40
38 John Hudgins XRC .15 .40
39 Jo Jo Reyes XRC .40 1.00
40 Justin James XRC .15 .40
41 Kurt Isenberg XRC .15 .40
42 Kyle Boyer XRC .15 .40
43 Lastings Milledge XRC 2.00 5.00
44 Luis Atilano XRC .15 .40
45 Matt Murton XRC .75 2.00
46 Matt Moses XRC .30 .75
47 Matt Harrison XRC .30 .75
48 Michael Bourn XRC .30 .75
49 Miguel Vega XRC .15 .40
50 Mitch Maier XRC .20 .50
51 Omar Quintanilla XRC .20 .50
52 Ryan Sweeney XRC .75 2.00
53 Scott Baker XRC .40 1.00
54 Sean Rodriguez XRC .75 2.00
55 Steve Lerud XRC .20 .50
56 Thomas Pauly XRC .15 .40
57 Tom Gorzelanny XRC .60 1.50
58 Tim Moss XRC .15 .40
59 Robbie Wooley XRC .20 .50
60 Trey Webb XRC .15 .40
61 Wes Littleton XRC .20 .50
62 Beau Vaughan XRC .20 .50
63 Willy Jo Ronda XRC .20 .50
64 Chris Lubanski XRC .50 1.25
65 Ian Stewart XRC 2.00 5.00
66 John Danks XRC 1.25 3.00
67 Kyle Sleeth XRC .20 .50
68 Michael Aubrey XRC .30 .75
69 Kevin Kouzmanoff XRC 2.00 5.00
70 Ryan Harvey XRC .75 2.00
71 Tim Stauffer XRC .30 .75
72 Tony Richie XRC .15 .40
73 Brandon Wood XRC 3.00 8.00
74 David Aardsma XRC .20 .50
75 David Shinskie XRC .15 .40
76 Dennis Dove XRC .20 .50
77 Eric Sultemeier XRC .15 .40
78 Jay Sborz XRC .15 .40
79 Jimmy Barthmaier XRC .15 .40
80 Josh Whitesell XRC .15 .40
81 Josh Anderson XRC .20 .50
82 Kenny Lewis XRC .20 .50
83 Mateo Miramontes XRC .15 .40
84 Nick Markakis XRC 2.50 6.00
85 Paul Bacot XRC .20 .50
86 Peter Stonard XRC .15 .40
87 Reggie Willits XRC 1.00 2.50
88 Shane Costa XRC .15 .40
89 Billy Sadler XRC .15 .40
90 Delmon Young XRC 3.00 8.00

2003 Upper Deck Prospect Premieres Autographs

Please note that a few players who were anticipated to have cards in this set do not exist. Those card numbers are P18, P28, P47, P54, P59 and P69.

STATED ODDS 1:9
P1 Bryan Opdyke 4.00 10.00
P2 Gabriel Sosa 4.00 10.00
P3 Tila Reynolds 4.00 10.00
P4 Aaron Hill 12.50 30.00
P5 Aaron Marsden 6.00 15.00
P6 Abe Alvarez 6.00 15.00
P7 Adam Jones 20.00 50.00
P8 Adam Miller 40.00 80.00
P9 Andre Ethier 15.00 40.00
P10 Anthony Gwynn 15.00 30.00
P11 Brad Snyder 6.00 15.00
P12 Brad Sullivan 6.00 15.00
P13 Brian Anderson 15.00 30.00
P14 Brian Buscher 6.00 15.00
P15 Brian Snyder 4.00 10.00
P16 Carlos Quentin 10.00 25.00
P17 Chad Billingsley 15.00 40.00
P19 Chris Durbin 4.00 10.00
P20 Chris Ray 10.00 25.00
P21 Conor Jackson 10.00 25.00
P22 Kory Casto 6.00 15.00
P23 Craig Whitaker 6.00 15.00
P24 Daniel Moore 4.00 10.00
P25 Daric Barton 12.50 30.00
P26 Darin Downs 6.00 15.00
P27 David Murphy 10.00 25.00
P29 Edgardo Baez 6.00 15.00
P30 Jake Fox 10.00 25.00
P31 Jake Stevens 6.00 15.00
P32 Jamie D'Antona 6.00 15.00
P33 James Houser 6.00 15.00
P34 Jarrod Saltalamacchia 10.00 25.00
P35 Jason Hirsh 15.00 40.00
P36 Javi Herrera 6.00 15.00
P37 Jeff Allison 4.00 10.00
P38 John Hudgins 4.00 10.00
P39 Jo Jo Reyes 10.00 25.00
P40 Justin James 4.00 10.00
P41 Kurt Isenberg 4.00 10.00
P42 Kyle Boyer 4.00 10.00
P43 Lastings Milledge 35.00 60.00
P44 Luis Atilano 4.00 10.00
P45 Matt Murton 4.00 10.00
P46 Matt Moses 8.00 20.00
P48 Michael Bourn 12.50 30.00
P49 Miguel Vega 4.00 10.00
P50 Mitch Maier 6.00 15.00
P51 Omar Quintanilla 6.00 15.00
P52 Ryan Sweeney 5.00 12.00
P53 Scott Baker 6.00 15.00
P55 Steve Lerud 6.00 15.00
P56 Thomas Pauly 4.00 10.00
P57 Tom Gorzelanny 10.00 25.00
P58 Tim Moss 6.00 15.00
P60 Trey Webb 4.00 10.00
P61 Wes Littleton 6.00 15.00
P62 Beau Vaughan 6.00 15.00
P63 Willy Jo Ronda 6.00 15.00
P64 Chris Lubanski 8.00 20.00
P65 Ian Stewart 40.00 80.00
P66 John Danks 12.50 30.00
P67 Kyle Sleeth 6.00 15.00
P68 Michael Aubrey 4.00 10.00
P70 Ryan Harvey 10.00 25.00
P71 Tim Stauffer 4.00 10.00

2003 Upper Deck Prospect Premieres Game Jersey

Please note that card number P90 does not exist.

STATED ODDS 1:18
P72 Tony Richie 2.00 5.00
P73 Brandon Wood 6.00 15.00
P74 David Aardsma 3.00 8.00
P75 David Shinskie 2.00 5.00
P76 Dennis Dove 3.00 8.00
P77 Eric Sultemeier 2.00 5.00

P78 Jay Sborz 2.00 5.00
P79 Jimmy Barthmaier 3.00 8.00
P80 Josh Whitesell 2.00 5.00
P81 Josh Anderson 3.00 8.00
P82 Kenny Lewis 3.00 8.00
P83 Mateo Miramontes 2.00 5.00
P84 Nick Markakis 15.00 40.00
P85 Paul Bacot 3.00 8.00
P86 Peter Stonard 2.00 5.00
P87 Reggie Willits 10.00 25.00
P88 Shane Costa 2.00 5.00
P89 Billy Sadler 2.00 5.00
P91 Kyle Sleeth 3.00 8.00
P92 Ian Stewart 6.00 15.00
P93 Fraser Dizard 2.00 5.00
P94 Abe Alvarez 3.00 8.00
P95 Adam Jones 12.50 30.00
P96 Brian Anderson 3.00 8.00
P97 Chris Durbin 2.00 5.00
P98 Craig Whitaker 3.00 8.00
P99 Jake Fox 5.00 12.00
P100 Kurt Isenberg 2.00 5.00
P101 Luis Atilano 2.00 5.00
P102 Miguel Vega 2.00 5.00
P103 Mitch Maier 3.00 8.00
P104 Ryan Sweeney 4.00 10.00
P105 Scott Baker 3.00 8.00
P106 Sean Rodriguez 4.00 10.00
P108 Trey Webb 2.00 5.00
P109 Willy Jo Ronda 3.00 8.00
P110 John Danks 3.00 8.00
P111 Michael Aubrey 3.00 8.00
P112 Lastings Milledge 6.00 15.00
P113 Chris Lubanski 3.00 8.00

2009 Upper Deck Signature Stars

COMMON CARD (1-100) .20 .50
COMMON CARD (101-120) 1.25 3.00
COMMON AU (121-210) 3.00 8.00
OVERALL AU/MEM ODDS 1:5 HOBBY
1 Aaron Harang .20 .50
2 Aaron Rowand .20 .50
3 Adam Dunn .30 .75
4 Adam Lind .20 .50
5 Adam Wainwright .30 .75
6 Adrian Gonzalez .30 .75
7 Akinori Iwamura .20 .50
8 Albert Pujols 1.25 3.00
9 Alex Gordon .30 .75
10 Alfonso Soriano .30 .75
11 Andruw Jones .20 .50
12 Aramis Ramirez .20 .50
13 B.J. Upton .30 .75
14 Bill Hall .20 .50
15 Billy Wagner .20 .50
16 Brandon Phillips .20 .50
17 Brandon Webb .30 .75
18 Brian Giles .20 .50
19 Brian McCann .30 .75
20 Brian Roberts .20 .50
21 Carl Crawford .30 .75
22 Carlos Gomez .20 .50
23 Carlos Zambrano .30 .75
24 Chien-Ming Wang .30 .75
25 Chipper Jones .50 1.25
26 Chone Figgins .20 .50
27 Chris Carpenter .50 1.25
28 Chris Duncan .20 .50
29 Chris Young .20 .50
30 Clayton Kershaw .50 1.25
31 Cole Hamels .50 1.25
32 Curtis Granderson .30 .75
33 Daisuke Matsuzaka .50 1.25
34 Dan Haren .20 .50
35 Dan Uggla .30 .75
36 Delmon Young .30 .75
37 Derek Jeter 1.25 3.00
38 Derek Lowe .20 .50
39 Dontrelle Willis .20 .50
40 Dustin Pedroia .60 1.50
41 Eric Chavez .20 .50
42 Evan Longoria .60 1.50
43 Felix Hernandez .50 1.25
44 Garret Anderson .20 .50
45 Garrett Atkins .20 .50
46 Grady Sizemore .30 .75
47 Hanley Ramirez .50 1.25
48 Ivan Rodriguez .30 .75
49 Jake Peavy .20 .50
50 James Loney .30 .75
51 Jason Bay .30 .75
52 Jason Kubel .20 .50
53 Jason Varitek .50 1.25
54 Jay Bruce .30 .75
55 Jeff Francoeur .30 .75
56 Jered Weaver .30 .75
57 Jeremy Bonderman .20 .50
58 Jim Thome .30 .75
59 Joe Mauer .50 1.25
60 Joel Zumaya .20 .50
61 John Lackey .20 .50
62 Johnny Cueto .20 .50
63 Jon Lester .50 1.25
64 Jonathan Papelbon .30 .75
65 Josh Beckett .30 .75
66 Josh Johnson .30 .75
67 Justin Verlander .60 1.50
68 Kelly Johnson .20 .50
69 Ken Griffey Jr .75 2.00
70 Kerry Wood .20 .50
71 Kevin Kouzmanoff .20 .50
72 Kevin Slowey .30 .75
73 Kevin Youkilis .30 .75
74 Khalil Greene .20 .50
75 Lance Berkman .30 .75
76 Mark Teixeira .50 1.25
77 Matt Holliday .50 1.25
78 Melvin Mora .20 .50
79 Miguel Cabrera .50 1.25
80 Miguel Tejada .30 .75
81 Nick Markakis .50 1.25
82 Nick Swisher .50 1.25
83 Pablo Sandoval .60 1.50
84 Paul Konerko .30 .75
85 Randy Johnson .30 .75
86 Rich Harden .20 .50
87 Roy Halladay .50 1.25
88 Roy Oswalt .30 .75
89 Ryan Braun .60 1.50
90 Ryan Garko .20 .50
91 Scott Kazmir .20 .50
92 Scott Rolen .30 .75
93 Takashi Saito .20 .50
94 Tim Hudson .30 .75
95 Tim Lincecum .75 2.00
96 Torii Hunter .20 .50
97 Troy Tulowitzki .50 1.25
98 Vernon Wells .20 .50
99 Vladimir Guerrero .50 1.25
100 Yunel Escobar .20 .50
101 Brett Anderson RC 2.00 5.00
102 Elvis Andrus RC 2.00 5.00
103 Gordon Beckham RC 4.00 10.00
104 Brad Bergesen (RC) 1.25 3.00
105 Trevor Cahill RC 3.00 8.00
106 Brett Cecil RC 1.25 3.00
107 Alcides Escobar RC 3.00 8.00
108 Mat Gamel RC 3.00 8.00
109 Tommy Hanson RC 4.00 10.00
110 Andrew McCutchen (RC) 5.00 12.00
111 Alex Avila RC 2.00 5.00
112 Sean O'Sullivan RC 1.25 3.00
113 Gerardo Parra RC 2.00 5.00
114 Ryan Perry RC 3.00 8.00
115 Aaron Poreda RC 1.25 3.00
116 Nolan Reimold (RC) 1.25 3.00
117 Ricky Romero (RC) 3.00 8.00
118 Neftali Feliz RC 4.00 10.00
119 Tommy Hunter RC 2.00 5.00
120 Sean West (RC) 1.50 4.00
121 Scott Baker AU 3.00 8.00
122 Wladimir Balentien AU 3.00 8.00
123 Chad Billingsley AU
124 Nick Blackburn AU 3.00 8.00
125 Joe Blanton AU 12.50 30.00
126 Billy Butler AU
127 Matt Cain AU
128 Chris Capuano AU 3.00 8.00
129 Fausto Carmona AU
130 John Danks AU 4.00 10.00
131 Chris Davis AU 15.00 40.00
132 Ross Detwiler AU 3.00 8.00
133 Stephen Drew AU
134 Scott Feldman AU 4.00 10.00
135 Prince Fielder AU 10.00 25.00
136 Jake Fox AU
137 Yovani Gallardo AU 6.00 15.00
138 Matt Garza AU 4.00 10.00
139 Alberto Gonzalez AU 3.00 8.00
140 Carlos Gonzalez AU 20.00 50.00
141 Travis Hafner AU
142 Josh Hamilton AU
143 Jason Hammel AU 3.00 8.00
144 J.A. Happ AU 10.00 25.00
145 Corey Hart AU 5.00 12.00
146 Phil Hughes AU 8.00 20.00
147 Ramon Hernandez AU 3.00 8.00
148 Micah Hoffpauir AU 3.00 8.00
149 Travis Ishikawa AU
150 Matt Kemp AU 8.00 20.00
151 Adam LaRoche AU
152 Derrek Lee AU 4.00 10.00
153 Noah Lowry AU 10.00 25.00
154 Jed Lowrie AU 4.00 10.00
155 Russell Martin AU
156 Victor Martinez AU
157 Andrew Miller AU 3.00 8.00
158 Miguel Montero AU
159 David Murphy AU 4.00 10.00
160 Joe Nathan AU 3.00 8.00
161 Micah Owings AU 4.00 10.00
162 Felipe Paulino AU 3.00 8.00
163 Glen Perkins AU 6.00 15.00
164 Felix Pie AU 5.00 12.00
165 Alexei Ramirez AU 8.00 20.00
166 Jarrod Saltalamacchia AU 4.00 10.00
167 Luke Scott AU 3.00 8.00
168 James Shields AU
169 Joakim Soria AU
170 Geovany Soto AU 6.00 15.00
171 Denard Span AU
172 Kurt Suzuki AU
173 Mark Teahen AU 4.00 10.00
174 Matt Tolbert AU 3.00 8.00
175 J.R. Towles AU 3.00 8.00
176 Edinson Volquez AU 3.00 8.00
177 Dewayne Wise AU 3.00 8.00
178 Chris B. Young AU
179 Ryan Zimmerman AU
180 Ben Zobrist AU
181 Kyle Blanks AU RC 8.00 20.00
182 Michael Bowden AU RC 4.00 10.00
183 Everth Cabrera AU RC 3.00 8.00
184 Drew Carpenter AU RC 3.00 8.00
185 Francisco Cervelli AU RC
186 Jhoulys Chacin AU RC 4.00 10.00
187 Dexter Fowler AU (RC)
188 David Freese AU RC 40.00 80.00
189 Derek Holland AU RC 8.00 20.00
190 Matt LaPorta AU RC
191 Mat Latos AU RC 8.00 20.00
192 Lou Marson AU (RC) 4.00 10.00
193 Fernando Martinez AU RC
194 Shairon Martis AU RC 3.00 8.00
195 James McDonald AU RC 3.00 8.00
196 Fu-Te Ni AU RC 40.00 80.00
197 Sean O'Sullivan AU RC 5.00 12.00
198 James Parr AU (RC) 3.00 8.00
199 David Patton AU RC 3.00 8.00
200 Rick Porcello AU RC 12.50 30.00
201 David Price AU RC 10.00 25.00
202 Josh Reddick AU RC 3.00 8.00
203 Michael Saunders AU RC 8.00 20.00
204 Jordan Schafer AU (RC) 4.00 10.00
205 Travis Snider AU RC 15.00 40.00
206 Matt Tuiasosopo AU (RC) 4.00 10.00
207 Koji Uehara AU RC 15.00 40.00
208 Chris Tillman AU RC 5.00 12.00
209 Matt Wieters AU RC 30.00 60.00
210 Jordan Zimmermann AU RC

2009 Upper Deck Signature Stars Blue

*BLUE: X TO X BASIC
RANDOM INSERTS IN PACKS
STATED PRINT RUN 170 SER.#'d SETS

2009 Upper Deck Signature Stars Gold Signatures

OVERAL AU/MEM ODDS 1:5 HOBBY
PRINT RUNS B/WN 5-100 COPIES PER
NO PRICING ON QTY 25 OR LESS
1 Aaron Harang/50 4.00 10.00
2 Aaron Rowand/35
3 Adam Dunn/25
4 Adam Lind/15
5 Adam Wainwright/5
6 Adrian Gonzalez/50 10.00 25.00
7 Akinori Iwamura/15
8 Albert Pujols/10
9 Alex Gordon/13
10 Alfonso Soriano/15
11 Andruw Jones/18
12 Aramis Ramirez/15
13 B.J. Upton/50 4.00 10.00
14 Bill Hall/10
15 Billy Wagner/15
16 Brandon Phillips/35
17 Brandon Webb/35
18 Brian Giles/15
19 Brian McCann/35
20 Brian Roberts/35
21 Carl Crawford/25
22 Carlos Gomez/10
23 Carlos Zambrano/15
24 Chien-Ming Wang/5
25 Chipper Jones/25
26 Chone Figgins/10
27 Chris Carpenter/5
28 Chris Duncan/15
29 Chris Young/75
30 Clayton Kershaw/35
31 Cole Hamels/25
32 Curtis Granderson/25
33 Daisuke Matsuzaka/10
34 Dan Haren/100
35 Dan Uggla/100 4.00 10.00
36 Delmon Young/15
37 Derek Jeter/100 100.00 200.00
38 Derek Lowe/25
39 Dontrelle Willis/25
40 Dustin Pedroia/100 12.50 30.00
41 Eric Chavez/25
42 Evan Longoria/25
43 Felix Hernandez/35
44 Garret Anderson/10
45 Garrett Atkins/25
46 Grady Sizemore/50
47 Hanley Ramirez/100 12.50 30.00
48 Ivan Rodriguez/15
49 Jake Peavy/75 12.50 30.00
50 James Loney/15
51 Jason Bay/100
52 Jason Kubel/15
53 Jason Varitek/5
54 Jay Bruce/15
55 Jeff Francoeur/35
56 Jered Weaver/5
57 Jeremy Bonderman/15
58 Jim Thome/10
59 Joe Mauer/25
60 Joel Zumaya/25
61 John Lackey/50
62 Johnny Cueto/15
63 Jon Lester/25
64 Jonathan Papelbon/100 8.00 20.00
65 Josh Beckett/10
66 Josh Johnson/15
67 Justin Verlander/15
68 Kelly Johnson/25
69 Ken Griffey Jr./100 50.00 100.00
70 Kerry Wood/25
71 Kevin Kouzmanoff/15
72 Kevin Slowey/15
73 Kevin Youkilis/35 12.50 30.00
74 Khalil Greene/15
75 Lance Berkman/35
76 Mark Teixeira/10
77 Matt Holliday/25
78 Melvin Mora/25
79 Miguel Cabrera/15
80 Miguel Tejada/10
81 Nick Markakis/25
82 Nick Swisher/10
83 Pablo Sandoval/50
84 Paul Konerko/15
85 Randy Johnson/10
86 Rich Harden/25
87 Roy Halladay/100 15.00 40.00
88 Roy Oswalt/15
89 Ryan Braun/15
90 Ryan Garko/15
91 Scott Kazmir/75
92 Scott Rolen/10
93 Takashi Saito/75 12.50 30.00
94 Tim Hudson/25
95 Tim Lincecum/50
96 Torii Hunter/25
97 Troy Tulowitzki/100
98 Vernon Wells/15
99 Vladimir Guerrero/5
100 Yunel Escobar/15

2009 Upper Deck Signature Stars Impressions Signatures

OVERALL AU/MEM ODDS 1:5 HOBBY
AC Drew Carpenter 3.00 8.00
AG Alberto Gonzalez
AH Anderson Hernandez
AN Josh Anderson
AR Alexei Ramirez 8.00 20.00
BC Brett Carroll 3.00 8.00
BL Brent Lillibridge 3.00 8.00
CB Chad Billingsley 6.00 15.00
CH Corey Hart 4.00 10.00
CJ Chipper Jones
CT Clete Thomas 4.00 10.00
CW Cory Wade
DJ Derek Jeter
DM David Murphy 3.00 8.00
DS Dennis Sarfate
DU Dan Uggla 5.00 12.00
DW Dewayne Wise
FP Felipe Paulino 3.00 8.00
GP Glen Perkins 3.00 8.00
GQ Guillermo Quiroz
GR Gregorio Petit
JA Jonathan Albaladejo
JB Josh Banks 3.00 8.00
JC Jorge Campillo 3.00 8.00
JE Jeff Larish
JH J.A. Happ 20.00 50.00
JL Jed Lowrie 4.00 10.00
JN Joe Nathan 3.00 8.00
JT J.R. Towles 3.00 8.00
KG Ken Griffey Jr. 75.00 150.00
KM Kyle McClellan 3.00 8.00
LB Lance Broadway
LR Luis Rodriguez
MA Doug Mathis
MI Mitch Maier 3.00 8.00
MJ Matt Joyce
MK Matt Kemp 8.00 20.00
ML Matt Lindstrom 3.00 8.00
MM Miguel Montero
MO Micah Owings 3.00 8.00
MT Matt Tolbert 3.00 8.00
MU Daniel Murphy 6.00 15.00
NB Nick Blackburn 4.00 10.00
NL Noah Lowry 5.00 12.00
PE Fernando Perez 3.00 8.00
PF Prince Fielder 15.00 40.00
PI Felix Pie 4.00 10.00
RD Robinzon Diaz
RM Russell Martin
RO Ross Ohlendorf 3.00 8.00
RZ Ryan Zimmerman 8.00 20.00
TB Travis Buck
TG Tom Gorzelanny
VM Victor Martinez
WB Wladimir Balentien
YG Yovani Gallardo 6.00 15.00

2009 Upper Deck Signature Stars Signature Quads

OVERALL AU/MEM ODDS 1:5 HOBBY
PRINT RUNS B/WN 5-35 COPIES PER
NO PRICING ON QTY 25 OR LESS
ACME Ryan Church
Brian McCann
Garret Anderson
Yunel Escobar/15
BHCV Jay Bruce
Johnny Cueto
Aaron Harang
Edinson Volquez/35
ESJM Brian McCann
Jordan Schafer
Yunel Escobar
Kelly Johnson/35
FGHH Corey Hart
Bill Hall
Prince Fielder
Yovani Gallardo/10
GBAT Alex Gordon
Mark Teahen
Billy Butler
Mike Aviles/15
GYEG Josh Geer
Adrian Gonzalez
David Eckstein
Chris Young/30
HBSE Travis Buck
Kurt Suzuki
Bobby Crosby
Mark Ellis/35
HCMG Curtis Granderson
Carl Crawford
Josh Hamilton
Nick Markakis/30
HGLS Yovani Gallardo
Josh Hamilton
Tim Lincecum
Kevin Slowey/25
HSMF Josh Hamilton
David Murphy
Jarrod Saltalamacchia
Scott Feldman/35
KGSS Matt Garza
Scott Kazmir
Andy Sonnanstine
James Shields/15
LCSI Tim Lincecum
Pablo Sandoval
Travis Ishikawa
Matt Cain/25
LFSH Geovany Soto
Derrek Lee
Micah Hoffpauir
Jake Fox/15
LYPB Jon Lester
Dustin Pedroia
Jason Bay
Kevin Youkilis/5
MBKL Chad Billingsley
Matt Kemp
Russell Martin
James Loney/10
MBMF Jeff Francis
Russell Martin
George Kottaras
Jason Bay/5
MKBS Jason Kubel 100.00 175.00
Joe Mauer
Nick Blackburn
Denard Span/35
MMMS Brian McCann
Victor Martinez
Russell Martin
Jarrod Saltalamacchia/5
MMRP Nick Markakis
Brian Roberts
Melvin Mora
Felix Pie/35
PBDL Chad Billingsley
Adam Lind
Stephen Drew
Dustin Pedroia/25
PBGC Yovani Gallardo
Chad Billingsley
Jake Peavy
Johnny Cueto/10
PCWR Matt Holliday
Adam Wainwright
Chris Carpenter
Albert Pujols/5
PKBR Alexei Ramirez
Clayton Kershaw
Jay Bruce
David Price/25
PUEP Dustin Pedroia
Dan Uggla
Brandon Phillips
David Eckstein/10
RTLR Troy Tulowitzki
Alexei Ramirez
Hanley Ramirez
Jed Lowrie/25
RWCJ Hanley Ramirez
Matt Cain
Adam Wainwright
Josh Johnson/10
SLRL Adam Lind
Jesse Litsch
Travis Snider
Ricky Romero/35
WMMF Fernando Martinez
John Maine
Jeff Francoeur
Billy Wagner/30
WPRZ Ryan Perry
Jordan Zimmermann
Matt Wieters
Colby Rasmus/5
YKHK Corey Hart
Jason Kubel
Kevin Youkilis
Scott Kazmir/25

2009 Upper Deck Signature Stars Signature Skills

RANDOM INSERTS IN PACKS
SS1 Grady Sizemore .75 2.00
SS2 Ryan Howard 1.50 4.00
SS3 Felix Hernandez 1.25 3.00
SS4 Johan Santana 1.25 3.00
SS5 Tim Lincecum 2.00 5.00
SS6 Francisco Rodriguez .75 2.00
SS7 Tim Wakefield .50 1.25
SS8 Carl Crawford .75 2.00
SS9 Ichiro Suzuki 2.00 5.00
SS10 Yadier Molina .75 2.00
SS11 David Ortiz .75 2.00
SS12 Trevor Hoffman .75 2.00
SS13 Torii Hunter .50 1.25
SS14 Jimmy Rollins .75 2.00
SS15 Derek Jeter 3.00 8.00
SS16 Todd Helton .75 2.00

2009 Upper Deck Signature Stars Signature Trios

OVERAL AU/MEM ODDS 1:5 HOBBY
PRINT RUNS B/WN 5-35 COPIES PER
NO PRICING ON QTY 25 OR LESS
BKM Chad Billingsley
Matt Kemp
James McDonald/30
BWH Jason Bay
Brandon Webb
Dan Haren/10
CSI Travis Ishikawa 30.00 60.00
Matt Cain
Pablo Sandoval/30
GGS Joakim Soria
Yovani Gallardo
Adrian Gonzalez/25
GPN Curtis Granderson
Ryan Perry
Fu-Te Ni/30
HDW Dan Haren
Brandon Webb
Stephen Drew/5
HLK Matt Kemp
Carlos Lee
Josh Hamilton/15
HMM Melvin Mora
Victor Martinez
Felix Hernandez/10
HSF Scott Feldman
Jarrod Saltalamacchia
Josh Hamilton/35
KDR Paul Konerko
John Danks
Alexei Ramirez/10
LBJ Chad Billingsley
Josh Johnson
Tim Lincecum/25
LPT J.R. Towles
Felipe Paulino
Carlos Lee/35
LWF John Lackey
Chone Figgins
Jered Weaver/10
MGS Ryan Garko
Kelly Shoppach
Travis Hafner/15
MIS Takashi Saito
Daisuke Matsuzaka
Akinori Iwamura/15
MJE Kelly Johnson
Yunel Escobar
Brian McCann/35
MSP Joe Mauer
Denard Span
Glen Perkins/25
PBL Jeff Larish
Dustin Pedroia
Travis Buck/30
PGS Matt Garza
James Shields
David Price/10
PMP Jake Peavy
Victor Martinez
Brandon Phillips/15
PPL Jonathan Papelbon
Dustin Pedroia
Jed Lowrie/25
PSL Jed Lowrie
Jonathan Papelbon
Takashi Saito/15
PVE Edwin Encarnacion
Edinson Volquez
Brandon Phillips/35
RCV Edinson Volquez
Hanley Ramirez
Johnny Cueto/25
RJR Hanley Ramirez
Cody Ross
Josh Johnson/25
RRS Kurt Suzuki
Aaron Rowand
Ricky Romero/30
RSM Sean Marshall
Geovany Soto
Aramis Ramirez/15
TAS Ryan Spilborghs
Troy Tulowitzki
Garrett Atkins/25
WMR Nick Markakis
Brian Roberts
Matt Wieters/15
ZWD Elijah Dukes
Josh Willingham
Ryan Zimmerman/30

2009 Upper Deck Signature Stars Signed Sealed and Delivered

RANDOM INSERTS IN PACKS
SSD1 Matt Holliday 1.25 3.00
SSD2 Mark Teixeira 1.25 3.00
SSD3 CC Sabathia .75 2.00
SSD4 Manny Ramirez 1.25 3.00
SSD5 John Smoltz 1.25 3.00
SSD6 Cliff Lee .75 2.00
SSD7 Adam Dunn .75 2.00
SSD8 Pedro Martinez .75 2.00

2009 Upper Deck Signature Stars Superstar Portraits Signatures

OVERALL AU/MEM ODDS 1:5 HOBBY
PRINT RUNS B/WN 5-35 COPIES PER
NO PRICING FOR QTY 25 OR LESS
SP1 Jason Bay/15
SP2 Josh Beckett/5
SP3 Lance Berkman/10
SP4 Ryan Braun/15
SP5 Miguel Cabrera/10
SP6 Carl Crawford/15
SP7 Prince Fielder/35
SP8 Adrian Gonzalez/25
SP9 Ken Griffey Jr./5
SP10 Roy Halladay/15
SP11 Cole Hamels/10
SP12 Josh Hamilton/25
SP13 Dan Haren/15
SP14 Felix Hernandez/15
SP15 Torii Hunter/15
SP16 Derek Jeter/15
SP17 Randy Johnson/5
SP18 Chipper Jones/35 75.00 150.00
SP19 Derrek Lee/35 10.00 25.00
SP20 Jon Lester/15
SP21 Tim Lincecum/25
SP22 Evan Longoria/15
SP23 Victor Martinez/15
SP24 Daisuke Matsuzaka/5
SP25 Joe Mauer/35 75.00 150.00
SP26 Jonathan Papelbon/15
SP27 Jake Peavy/15
SP28 Dustin Pedroia/25
SP29 Albert Pujols/15
SP30 Hanley Ramirez/15
SP31 Ivan Rodriguez/10
SP32 Grady Sizemore/10
SP33 Alfonso Soriano/10
SP34 Jim Thome/5
SP35 Jason Varitek/5
SP36 Chien-Ming Wang/10
SP37 Matt Wieters/25
SP38 Kerry Wood/25
SP39 Kevin Youkilis/15
SP40 Carlos Zambrano/15

2009 Upper Deck Signature Stars Trophy Winners

RANDOM INSERTS IN PACKS
TW1 Albert Pujols 3.00 8.00
TW2 Dustin Pedroia 1.50 4.00
TW3 Tim Lincecum 2.00 5.00
TW4 Cliff Lee .75 2.00
TW5 Chipper Jones 1.25 3.00
TW6 Joe Mauer 1.25 3.00
TW7 Ryan Howard 1.50 4.00
TW8 Miguel Cabrera 1.25 3.00

2009 Upper Deck Signature Stars UD Black Pride of a Nation

OVERALL AU/MEM ODDS 1:5 HOBBY
PRINT RUN B/WN 10-99 COPIES PER
NO PRICING ON QTY OF 25 OR LESS
1 Ryan Braun/10
2 Joba Chamberlain/10
3 Prince Fielder/10
4 Yovani Gallardo/10
5 Adrian Gonzalez/10
6 Roy Halladay/10
7 Cole Hamels/10
8 Felix Hernandez/10
9 Derek Jeter/10
10 Randy Johnson/10
11 Chipper Jones/10
12 Derrek Lee/10
13 Jon Lester/10
14 Evan Longoria/10
15 Victor Martinez/10
16 Brian McCann/10
17 Hanley Ramirez/10
18 Troy Tulowitzki/10
19 Chien-Ming Wang/10
20 Ryan Zimmerman/10
21 Ken Griffey Jr./10
22 Dexter Fowler/99
23 Tommy Hanson/99 75.00 150.00
24 Kenshin Kawakami/99
25 Mat Latos/99
26 Rick Porcello/99
27 David Price/99 30.00 60.00
28 Neftali Feliz/99
29 Travis Snider/99
30 Koji Uehara/99 60.00 120.00
31 Matt Wieters/99
32 Fu-Te Ni/99 100.00 250.00
33 Jordan Zimmermann/99 20.00 50.00
34 Kyle Blanks/99
35 Matt LaPorta/99 20.00 50.00
36 Ricky Romero/99
37 Derek Holland/99

2009 Upper Deck Signature Stars UD Black Pride of a Nation Platinum
OVERALL AU/MEM ODDS 1:5 HOBBY
STATED PRINT RUN 1 SER.#'d SETS
NO PRICING DUE TO SCARCITY

2009 Upper Deck Signature Stars USA 18U National Team Premier Materials Cap Flag Patch
OVERALL AU/MEM ODDS 1:5 HOBBY
STATED PRINT RUN 1 SER.#'d SET
NO PRICING DUE TO SCARCITY
1 Sean Coyle
2 Bryce Harper
3 Manny Machado
4 Phillip Pfeifer
5 Tony Wolters

2009 Upper Deck Signature Stars USA By the Letter Autographs
OVERALL AU/MEM ODDS 1:5 HOBBY
STATED PRINT RUN 100 SER.#'d SETS
AS Asher Wojciechowski
AV AJ Vanegas 4.00 10.00
AW Andy Wilkins 6.00 15.00
BB Bryce Brentz 12.50 30.00
BE Chad Bettis 4.00 10.00
BF Blake Forsythe 4.00 10.00
BH Bryce Harper 200.00 300.00
BM Brad Miller
BR Brian Ragira 5.00 12.00
CB Cody Buckel 4.00 10.00
CC Christian Colon 10.00 25.00
CH Cory Hahn
CM Connor Mason 4.00 10.00
CO Gerrit Cole 15.00 40.00
CW Cody Wheeler 10.00 25.00
DP Drew Pomeranz 20.00 50.00
GC Garin Cecchini 4.00 10.00
JT Jameson Taillon 30.00 60.00
KG Kevin Gausman
KK Kavin Keyes 6.00 15.00
KR Kyle Ryan
KW Karsten Whitson 8.00 20.00
LM Ladson Montgomery
MC Casey McGrew
MI Michael Choice 15.00 40.00
MM Manny Machado 20.00 50.00
MN Matt Newman
NC Nick Castellanos 8.00 20.00
ND Nicky Delmonico 4.00 10.00
NP Nick Pepitone
PP Phillip Pfeifer
RH Rick Hague
RR Robbie Ray
SC Sean Coyle 4.00 10.00
SG Sonny Gray
TB Trevor Bauer 20.00 50.00
TH Tyler Holt 10.00 25.00
TW Tony Wolters 6.00 15.00
TZ Tony Zych
WA T.J. Walz 10.00 25.00
WO Kolten Wong 15.00 40.00
YG Yasmani Grandal 4.00 10.00

2009 Upper Deck Signature Stars USA Flashback Fabrics Dual Jersey
OVERALL AU/MEM ODDS 1:5 HOBBY
BM Brian Matusz
DF Dexter Fowler
EL Evan Longoria 6.00 15.00
JM Joe Mauer 5.00 12.00
ML Matt LaPorta
RA Rick Ankiel

2009 Upper Deck Signature Stars USA Flashback Fabrics Dual Patch
OVERALL AU/MEM ODDS 1:5 HOBBY
STATED PRINT RUN 25 SER.#'d SETS
NO PRICING DUE TO SCARCITY

2009 Upper Deck Signature Stars USA National Team Future Watch Jersey Autographs
OVERALL AU/MEM ODDS 1:5 HOBBY
PRINT RUNS B/WN 493-999 COPIES PER
1 Trevor Bauer/799 12.50 30.00
2 Christian Colon/799 4.00 10.00
3 Cody Wheeler/799
4 Chad Bettis/799 4.00 10.00
5 Bryce Brentz/799 10.00 25.00
6 Nick Pepitone/799
7 Michael Choice/799 6.00 15.00
8 Gerrit Cole/799 20.00 50.00
9 Sonny Gray/799 8.00 20.00
10 Tyler Holt/799 4.00 10.00
11 T.J. Walz/799 4.00 10.00
12 Rick Hague/799 4.00 10.00
13 Drew Pomeranz/799 8.00 20.00
14 Blake Forsythe/799 4.00 10.00
15 Matt Newman/799 4.00 10.00
16 Casey McGrew/799 4.00 10.00
17 Brad Miller/799 4.00 10.00
18 Yasmani Grandal/799 8.00 20.00
19 Kolten Wong/799 8.00 20.00
20 Tony Zych/799 4.00 10.00
21 Andy Wilkins/799 4.00 10.00
22 Asher Wojciechowski/799 4.00 10.00
23 Cody Buckel/899 4.00 10.00
24 Nick Castellanos/899 4.00 10.00
25 Garin Cecchini/899 5.00 12.00
26 Sean Coyle/899 4.00 10.00
27 Nicky Delmonico/493 4.00 10.00
28 Kevin Gausman/899
29 Cory Hahn/899 4.00 10.00
30 Bryce Harper/899 150.00 300.00
31 Kavin Keyes/899 4.00 10.00
32 Manny Machado/899 20.00 50.00
33 Connor Mason/899 4.00 10.00
34 Ladson Montgomery/899 4.00 10.00
35 Phillip Pfeifer/899
36 Brian Ragira/899 4.00 10.00
37 Robbie Ray/899 4.00 10.00
38 Kyle Ryan/999 4.00 10.00
39 Jameson Taillon/899 20.00 50.00
40 AJ Vanegas/899 4.00 10.00
41 Karsten Whitson/899 8.00 20.00
42 Tony Wolters/793

2009 Upper Deck Signature Stars USA National Team Future Watch Patch Autographs
*PATCH: .6X TO 1.5X BASIC
OVERALL AU/MEM ODDS 1:5 HOBBY
STATED PRINT RUN 50 SER.#'d SETS
1 Trevor Bauer 6.00 15.00
2 Christian Colon 10.00 25.00
3 Cody Wheeler
4 Chad Bettis 6.00 15.00
5 Bryce Brentz
6 Nick Pepitone
7 Michael Choice 10.00 25.00
8 Gerrit Cole
9 Sonny Gray 12.50 30.00
10 Tyler Holt 6.00 15.00
11 T.J. Walz 6.00 15.00
12 Rick Hague 6.00 15.00
13 Drew Pomeranz 6.00 15.00
14 Blake Forsythe 6.00 15.00
15 Matt Newman 6.00 15.00
16 Casey McGrew 6.00 15.00
17 Brad Miller 6.00 15.00
18 Yasmani Grandal 6.00 15.00
19 Kolten Wong
20 Tony Zych 6.00 15.00
21 Andy Wilkins 6.00 15.00
22 Asher Wojciechowski 6.00 15.00
23 Cody Buckel 6.00 15.00
24 Nick Castellanos 6.00 15.00
25 Garin Cecchini 6.00 15.00
26 Sean Coyle 8.00 20.00
27 Nicky Delmonico 6.00 15.00
28 Kevin Gausman
29 Cory Hahn 6.00 15.00
30 Bryce Harper 350.00 700.00
31 Kavin Keyes 6.00 15.00
32 Manny Machado 50.00 100.00
33 Connor Mason 6.00 15.00
34 Ladson Montgomery 6.00 15.00
35 Phillip Pfeifer
36 Brian Ragira 6.00 15.00
37 Robbie Ray 6.00 15.00
38 Kyle Ryan 6.00 15.00
39 Jameson Taillon 30.00 60.00
40 AJ Vanegas 6.00 15.00
41 Karsten Whitson 12.50 30.00
42 Tony Wolters

2009 Upper Deck Signature Stars USA Star Prospects
RANDOM INSERTS IN PACKS
USA1 Cody Buckel .75 2.00
USA2 Nick Castellanos 1.25 3.00
USA3 Garin Cecchini .75 2.00
USA4 Sean Coyle .75 2.00
USA5 Nicky Delmonico .75 2.00
USA6 Kevin Gausman .75 2.00
USA7 Cory Hahn .75 2.00
USA8 Bryce Harper 15.00 40.00
USA9 Kavin Keyes .75 2.00
USA10 Manny Machado 2.50 6.00
USA11 Connor Mason .75 2.00
USA12 Ladson Montgomery .75 2.00
USA13 Phillip Pfeifer .75 2.00
USA14 Brian Ragira 1.25 3.00
USA15 Robbie Ray .75 2.00
USA16 Kyle Ryan .75 2.00
USA17 Jameson Taillon 4.00 10.00
USA18 AJ Vanegas .75 2.00
USA19 Karsten Whitson 1.25 3.00
USA20 Tony Wolters .75 2.00
USA21 Trevor Bauer 2.50 6.00
USA22 Chad Bettis .75 2.00
USA23 Bryce Brentz 2.00 5.00
USA24 Michael Choice 1.25 3.00
USA25 Gerrit Cole 3.00 8.00
USA26 Christian Colon 1.25 3.00
USA27 Blake Forsythe .75 2.00
USA28 Yasmani Grandal 1.25 3.00
USA29 Sonny Gray 1.25 3.00
USA30 Rick Hague .75 2.00
USA31 Tyler Holt .75 2.00
USA32 Casey McGrew .75 2.00
USA33 Brad Miller .75 2.00
USA34 Matt Newman .75 2.00
USA35 Nick Pepitone .75 2.00
USA36 Drew Pomeranz 2.50 6.00
USA37 T.J. Walz .75 2.00
USA38 Cody Wheeler .75 2.00
USA39 Andy Wilkins .75 2.00
USA40 Asher Wojciechowski 1.25 3.00
USA41 Kolten Wong 1.25 3.00
USA42 Tony Zych .75 2.00

2009 Upper Deck Signature Stars USA Star Prospects Jersey Autographs
OVERALL AU/MEM ODDS 1:5 HOBBY
STATED PRINT RUN 399 SER.#'d SETS
AS Asher Wojciechowski 4.00 10.00
AV AJ Vanegas 4.00 10.00
AW Andy Wilkins
BB Bryce Brentz 20.00 50.00
BE Chad Bettis
BF Blake Forsythe 4.00 10.00
BH Bryce Harper 150.00 250.00
BM Brad Miller
BR Brian Ragira 4.00 10.00
CA Casey McGrew 4.00 10.00
CB Cody Buckel 4.00 10.00
CC Christian Colon
CH Cory Hahn 4.00 10.00
CM Connor Mason 8.00 20.00
CO Gerrit Cole 20.00 50.00
CW Cody Wheeler 5.00 12.00
DP Drew Pomeranz 6.00 15.00
GC Garin Cecchini
JT Jameson Taillon 15.00 40.00
KG Kevin Gausman 4.00 10.00
KK Kavin Keyes 4.00 10.00
KR Kyle Ryan 4.00 10.00
KW Karsten Whitson 8.00 20.00
LM Ladson Montgomery
MC Michael Choice 5.00 12.00
MM Manny Machado 20.00 50.00
MN Matt Newman 4.00 10.00
NC Nick Castellanos
ND Nicky Delmonico
NP Nick Pepitone 4.00 10.00
PP Phillip Pfeifer
RH Rick Hague 4.00 10.00
RR Robbie Ray 4.00 10.00
SC Sean Coyle 4.00 10.00
SG Sonny Gray 6.00 15.00
TB Trevor Bauer 15.00 40.00
TH Tyler Holt 4.00 10.00
TW Tony Wolters
TZ Tony Zych
WA T.J. Walz
WO Kolten Wong 12.50 30.00
YG Yasmani Grandal

2009 Upper Deck Signature Stars USA Star Prospects Jerseys
OVERALL AU/MEM ODDS 1:5 HOBBY
1 Cody Buckel 4.00 10.00
2 Nick Castellanos 3.00 8.00
3 Garin Cecchini 3.00 8.00
4 Sean Coyle 3.00 8.00
5 Nicky Delmonico 3.00 8.00
6 Kevin Gausman 3.00 8.00
7 Cory Hahn 3.00 8.00
8 Bryce Harper 20.00 50.00
9 Kavin Keyes 3.00 8.00
10 Manny Machado 4.00 10.00
11 Connor Mason 3.00 8.00
12 Ladson Montgomery 3.00 8.00
13 Phillip Pfeifer 3.00 8.00
14 Brian Ragira 3.00 8.00
15 Robbie Ray 3.00 8.00
16 Kyle Ryan 3.00 8.00
17 Jameson Taillon 4.00 10.00
18 AJ Vanegas 3.00 8.00
19 Karsten Whitson 3.00 8.00
20 Tony Wolters 3.00 8.00
21 Trevor Bauer 5.00 12.00
22 Chad Bettis 3.00 8.00
23 Bryce Brentz 3.00 8.00
24 Michael Choice 3.00 8.00
25 Gerrit Cole 4.00 10.00
26 Christian Colon 3.00 8.00
27 Blake Forsythe 3.00 8.00
28 Yasmani Grandal 3.00 8.00
29 Sonny Gray 3.00 8.00
30 Rick Hague 3.00 8.00
31 Tyler Holt 3.00 8.00
32 Casey McGrew 3.00 8.00
33 Brad Miller 3.00 8.00
34 Matt Newman 3.00 8.00
35 Nick Pepitone 3.00 8.00
36 Drew Pomeranz 3.00 8.00
37 T.J. Walz 3.00 8.00
38 Cody Wheeler 3.00 8.00
39 Andy Wilkins 3.00 8.00
40 Asher Wojciechowski 3.00 8.00
41 Kolten Wong 3.00 8.00
42 Tony Zych 3.00 8.00

2009 Upper Deck Signature Stars USA Star Prospects Signatures
OVERALL AU/MEM ODDS 1:5 HOBBY
NO PRICING ON MOST DUE TO LACK OF SALES
USA1 Cody Buckel
USA2 Nick Castellanos 3.00 8.00
USA3 Garin Cecchini
USA4 Sean Coyle
USA5 Nicky Delmonico
USA6 Kevin Gausman
USA7 Cory Hahn 3.00 8.00
USA8 Bryce Harper 200.00 400.00
USA9 Kavin Keyes
USA10 Manny Machado
USA11 Connor Mason
USA12 Ladson Montgomery
USA13 Phillip Pfeifer
USA14 Brian Ragira 5.00 12.00
USA15 Robbie Ray
USA16 Kyle Ryan
USA17 Jameson Taillon 20.00 50.00
USA18 AJ Vanegas
USA19 Karsten Whitson
USA20 Tony Wolters
USA21 Trevor Bauer
USA22 Chad Bettis
USA23 Bryce Brentz
USA24 Michael Choice 4.00 10.00
USA25 Gerrit Cole
USA26 Christian Colon 4.00 10.00
USA27 Blake Forsythe
USA28 Yasmani Grandal 12.50 30.00
USA29 Sonny Gray 4.00 10.00
USA30 Rick Hague
USA31 Tyler Holt
USA32 Casey McGrew
USA33 Brad Miller
USA34 Matt Newman
USA35 Nick Pepitone 3.00 8.00
USA36 Drew Pomeranz
USA37 T.J. Walz
USA38 Cody Wheeler
USA39 Andy Wilkins 4.00 10.00
USA40 Asher Wojciechowski
USA41 Kolten Wong 6.00 15.00
USA42 Tony Zych

2009 Upper Deck Signature Stars USA Winning Materials
OVERALL AU/MEM ODDS 1:5 HOBBY
STATED PRINT RUN 499 SER.#'d SETS
1 Cody Buckel 5.00 12.00
2 Nick Castellanos 3.00 8.00
3 Garin Cecchini 3.00 8.00
4 Sean Coyle 4.00 10.00
5 Nicky Delmonico 3.00 8.00
6 Kevin Gausman 3.00 8.00
7 Cory Hahn 3.00 8.00
8 Bryce Harper 30.00 60.00
9 Kavin Keyes
10 Manny Machado
11 Connor Mason 3.00 8.00
12 Ladson Montgomery 3.00 8.00
13 Phillip Pfeifer
14 Brian Ragira 3.00 8.00
15 Robbie Ray 3.00 8.00
16 Kyle Ryan 3.00 8.00
17 Jameson Taillon
18 AJ Vanegas
19 Karsten Whitson 3.00 8.00
20 Tony Wolters 3.00 8.00
21 Trevor Bauer
22 Christian Colon 3.00 8.00
23 Cody Wheeler
24 Chad Bettis 4.00 10.00
25 Bryce Brentz 3.00 8.00
26 Nick Pepitone 4.00 10.00
27 Michael Choice 4.00 10.00
28 Gerrit Cole 8.00 20.00
29 Sonny Gray
30 Tyler Holt 3.00 8.00
31 T.J. Walz 4.00 10.00
32 Rick Hague
33 Drew Pomeranz 3.00 8.00
34 Blake Forsythe 3.00 8.00
35 Matt Newman
36 Casey McGrew 3.00 8.00
37 Brad Miller
38 Yasmani Grandal 3.00 8.00
39 Kolten Wong 3.00 8.00
40 Tony Zych 3.00 8.00
41 Andy Wilkins 3.00 8.00
42 Asher Wojciechowski

2007 Upper Deck Spectrum
This 162-card set was released in April, 2007. The set was issued in five-card packs which came 20 packs to a box and 14 boxes to a case. The first 100 cards in this set featured veterans. Cards numbered 101-150, which were skip numbered, featured 2007 autographed rookie logo cards and cards numbered 151-170 were exchange cards for leading 2007 rookies. The stated odds on the signed rookie logo cards were one in 18 packs. The rookie exchange cards could be redeemed until March 19, 2010.

COMP.SET w/o RCs (100) 10.00 25.00
COMMON CARD (1-100) .15 .40
COMMON AU RC (101-149) 3.00 8.00
AU RC STATED ODDS 1:18 HOBBY
COMMON ROOKIE EXCH (151-170) 10.00 25.00
EXCHANGE DEADLINE 3/19/2010
1 Miguel Tejada .25 .60
2 Brian Roberts .15 .40
3 Melvin Mora .15 .40
4 David Ortiz .25 .60
5 Manny Ramirez .40 1.00
6 Jason Varitek .40 1.00
7 Curt Schilling .25 .60
8 Jim Thome .25 .60
9 Paul Konerko .25 .60
10 Jermaine Dye .15 .40
11 Travis Hafner .15 .40
12 Victor Martinez .25 .60
13 Grady Sizemore .25 .60
14 C.C. Sabathia .25 .60
15 Ivan Rodriguez .25 .60
16 Magglio Ordonez .25 .60
17 Carlos Guillen .15 .40
18 Justin Verlander .50 1.25
19 Shane Costa .15 .40
20 Emil Brown .15 .40
21 Mark Teahen .15 .40
22 Vladimir Guerrero .40 1.00
23 Jered Weaver .25 .60
24 Juan Rivera .15 .40
25 Justin Morneau .40 1.00
26 Joe Mauer .40 1.00
27 Torii Hunter .15 .40
28 Johan Santana .40 1.00
29 Derek Jeter 1.00 2.50
30 Alex Rodriguez .60 1.50
31 Johnny Damon .25 .60
32 Jason Giambi .15 .40
33 Frank Thomas .40 1.00
34 Nick Swisher .40 1.00
35 Eric Chavez .15 .40
36 Ichiro Suzuki .60 1.50
37 Raul Ibanez .25 .60
38 Richie Sexson .15 .40
39 Carl Crawford .25 .60
40 Rocco Baldelli .15 .40
41 Scott Kazmir .25 .60
42 Michael Young .25 .60
43 Mark Teixeira .40 1.00
44 Carlos Lee .15 .40
45 Gary Matthews .15 .40
46 Vernon Wells .15 .40
47 Roy Halladay .40 1.00
48 Lyle Overbay .15 .40
49 Brandon Webb .25 .60
50 Conor Jackson .15 .40
51 Stephen Drew .15 .40
52 Chipper Jones .40 1.00
53 Andruw Jones .15 .40
54 Adam LaRoche .15 .40
55 John Smoltz .40 1.00
56 Derrek Lee .15 .40
57 Aramis Ramirez .15 .40
58 Carlos Zambrano .25 .60
59 Ken Griffey Jr. .60 1.50
60 Adam Dunn .25 .60
61 Aaron Harang .15 .40
62 Todd Helton .25 .60
63 Matt Holliday .40 1.00
64 Garrett Atkins .15 .40
65 Miguel Cabrera .40 1.00
66 Hanley Ramirez .40 1.00
67 Dontrelle Willis .15 .40
68 Lance Berkman .25 .60
69 Roy Oswalt .25 .60
70 Roger Clemens .50 1.25
71 J.D. Drew .15 .40
72 Nomar Garciaparra .40 1.00
73 Rafael Furcal .15 .40
74 Jeff Kent .15 .40
75 Prince Fielder .25 .60
76 Bill Hall .15 .40
77 Rickie Weeks .25 .60
78 Jose Reyes .25 .60
79 David Wright .60 1.50
80 Carlos Delgado .15 .40
81 Carlos Beltran .15 .40
82 Ryan Howard .60 1.50
83 Chase Utley .40 1.00
84 Jimmy Rollins .25 .60
85 Jason Bay .25 .60
86 Freddy Sanchez .15 .40
87 Zach Duke .15 .40
88 Trevor Hoffman .25 .60
89 Adrian Gonzalez .25 .60
90 Mike Piazza .40 1.00
91 Ray Durham .15 .40
92 Omar Vizquel .25 .60
93 Jason Schmidt .15 .40
94 Albert Pujols 1.00 2.50
95 Scott Rolen .25 .60
96 Jim Edmonds .25 .60
97 Chris Carpenter .40 1.00
98 Alfonso Soriano .25 .60
99 Ryan Zimmerman .25 .60
100 Nick Johnson .15 .40
101 A.Lind AU (RC) 4.00 10.00
103 A.Miller AU RC 15.00 40.00
104 A.Cannizaro AU RC 4.00 10.00
106 B.Stokes AU (RC) 3.00 8.00
108 Cesar Jimenez AU RC 3.00 8.00
109 C.Stewart AU RC 3.00 8.00
111 D.Murphy AU (RC) 3.00 8.00
112 D.Young AU (RC) 12.50 30.00
113 D.Young AU (RC) 3.00 8.00
114 D.Sarfate AU (RC) 3.00 8.00
116 D.Anderson AU RC 3.00 8.00
117 F.Lewis AU (RC) 3.00 8.00
118 G.Perkins AU (RC) 4.00 10.00
120 J.Baker AU (RC) 3.00 8.00
121 J.Fiorentino AU (RC) 3.00 8.00
122 J.Salazar AU (RC) 3.00 8.00
124 J.Arias AU (RC) 3.00 8.00
125 J.Knott AU (RC) 3.00 8.00
128 J.Morillo AU (RC) 3.00 8.00
130 Juan Salas AU (RC) 3.00 8.00
131 J.Hampson AU (RC) 3.00 8.00
132 K.Hooper AU (RC) 6.00 15.00
133 K.Kouzmanoff AU (RC) 4.00 10.00
134 M.Bourn AU (RC) 3.00 8.00
135 Miguel Montero AU (RC) 3.00 8.00
137 M.Maier AU RC 3.00 8.00
139 P.Misch AU (RC) 3.00 8.00
140 P.Humber AU (RC) 6.00 15.00
141 R.Braun AU RC 3.00 8.00
143 R.Sweeney AU (RC) 3.00 8.00
144 S.Moore AU (RC) 3.00 8.00
145 S.Henn AU (RC) 4.00 10.00
146 S.Riggans AU (RC) 3.00 8.00
148 T.Tulowitzki AU (RC) 15.00 40.00
149 U.Jimenez AU (RC) 12.50 30.00
157 Elijah Dukes RC 10.00 25.00

2007 Upper Deck Spectrum Die Cut Gold
*GOLD 1-100: 2.5X TO 6X BASIC
GOLD 1-100 PRINT RUN 99 SER.#'d SETS
*GOLD AU 101-149: .75X TO 2X BASIC
GOLD 101-149 PRINT RUN 50 SER.#'d SETS
RANDOM INSERTS IN PACKS
101 Adam Lind AU 20.00 50.00
112 Delmon Young AU 20.00 50.00
134 Michael Bourn AU 8.00 20.00
145 Sean Henn AU 10.00 25.00

2007 Upper Deck Spectrum Die Cut Red
*RED: 2.5X TO 6X BASIC
RANDOM INSERTS IN PACKS
STATED PRINT RUN 99 SER.#'d SETS

2007 Upper Deck Spectrum Die Cut Blue Jersey Number
*JSY NUMBER p/r 26-57: 8X TO 20X BASIC
RANDOM INSERTS IN PACKS
PRINT RUNS B/WN 1-57 COPIES PER
NO PRICING ON QTY 25 OR LESS

2007 Upper Deck Spectrum Aligning the Stars

OVERALL GAME-USED ODDS 1:10
STATED PRINT RUN 99 SER.#'d SETS
BPO Lance Berkman 10.00 25.00
Albert Pujols
David Ortiz
CJM Greg Maddux 10.00 25.00
Roger Clemens
Randy Johnson
CRR Miguel Cabrera 6.00 15.00
Aramis Ramirez
Scott Rolen
DBF Lance Berkman 6.00 15.00
Carlos Delgado
Prince Fielder
GRS Gary Sheffield 10.00 25.00
Manny Ramirez
Ken Griffey Jr.
HRW Trevor Hoffman 10.00 25.00
Mariano Rivera
Billy Wagner
HTT Frank Thomas 10.00 25.00
Travis Hafner
Jim Thome
JDB Adam Dunn 10.00 25.00
Andruw Jones
Carlos Beltran
JGC Derek Jeter 20.00 50.00
Jason Giambi
Robinson Cano
JTY Derek Jeter 10.00 25.00
Miguel Tejada
Michael Young
LHP Todd Helton 10.00 25.00
Albert Pujols
Derrek Lee
LVP Justin Verlander 10.00 25.00
Francisco Liriano
Jonathan Papelbon
MKT Justin Morneau 6.00 15.00
Mark Teixeira
Paul Konerko
MOW Roy Oswalt 6.00 15.00
Pedro Martinez
Dontrelle Willis
RFR Jose Reyes 6.00 15.00
Jimmy Rollins
Rafael Furcal
RMM Victor Martinez 6.00 15.00
Joe Mauer
Ivan Rodriguez
RSV Curt Schilling 10.00 25.00
Manny Ramirez
Jason Varitek
SBA Bobby Abreu 6.00 15.00
Carlos Beltran
Alfonso Soriano
SCF Chone Figgins 6.00 15.00
Carl Crawford
Grady Sizemore
SHS C.C. Sabathia 6.00 15.00
Johan Santana
Roy Halladay
WGD Vernon Wells 6.00 15.00
Johnny Damon
Vladimir Guerrero

2007 Upper Deck Spectrum Cal Ripken Road to the Hall
COMMON CARD 2.00 5.00
STATED ODDS 1:10 HOBBY, 1:20 RETAIL
GOLD: .6X TO 1.5X BASIC
GOLD RANDOMLY INSERTED IN PACKS
GOLD PRINT RUN 99 SER.#'d SETS

2007 Upper Deck Spectrum Cal Ripken Road to the Hall Signatures

COMMON CARD 100.00 175.00
RANDOM INSERTS IN PACKS
STATED PRINT RUN 5 SER.#'d SETS

2007 Upper Deck Spectrum Grand Slamarama

STATED ODDS 1:280 HOBBY
AD Adam Dunn 6.00 15.00
AP Albert Pujols 30.00 60.00
AR Alex Rodriguez 20.00 50.00
BA Bobby Abreu 12.50 30.00
BG Brian Giles 6.00 15.00
CD Carlos Delgado 6.00 15.00
CJ Chipper Jones 12.50 30.00
DA Johnny Damon 10.00 25.00
DO David Ortiz 12.50 30.00
DW David Wright 20.00 50.00
HA Travis Hafner 6.00 15.00
JD Jermaine Dye 6.00 15.00
JM Justin Morneau 6.00 15.00
JT Jim Thome 10.00 25.00
KG Ken Griffey Jr. 20.00 50.00
MR Manny Ramirez 10.00 25.00
NG Nomar Garciaparra 12.50 30.00

RH Ryan Howard 20.00 50.00
RS Richie Sexson 6.00 15.00
VG Vladimir Guerrero 12.50 30.00

2007 Upper Deck Spectrum Rookie Retrospectrum

STATED ODDS 1:10 HOBBY, 1:20 RETAIL
RED: .6X TO 1.5X BASIC
RED RANDOMLY INSERTED IN PACKS
RED PRINT RUN 99 SER.#'d SETS

AE Andre Ethier .60 1.50
AW Adam Wainwright .40 1.00
BA Josh Barfield .40 1.00
BB Boof Bonser .40 1.00
BO Jason Botts .40 1.00
CA Matt Capps .40 1.00
CB Chad Billingsley .40 1.00
CD Chris Demaria .40 1.00
CF Choo Freeman .40 1.00
CH Clay Hensley .40 1.00
CQ Carlos Quentin .40 1.00
DE Chris Denorfia .40 1.00
DU Dan Uggla .60 1.50
FC Fausto Carmona .40 1.00
FL Francisco Liriano 1.00 2.50
HA Cole Hamels .60 1.50
HK Howie Kendrick .40 1.00
HR Hanley Ramirez .60 1.50
JA Jeremy Accardo .40 1.00
JB Jason Bergmann .40 1.00
JC Jose Capellan .40 1.00
JD Joey Devine .40 1.00
JH Jeremy Hermida .40 1.00
JK Jason Kubel .40 1.00
JL Jon Lester .60 1.50
JP Jonathan Papelbon 1.00 2.50
JV Justin Verlander 1.00 2.50
JW Jered Weaver .60 1.50
JZ Joel Zumaya .60 1.50
KM Kendry Morales .60 1.50
LM Lastings Milledge .60 1.50
MA Nick Markakis .60 1.50
MC Matt Cain .60 1.50
ME Melky Cabrera .40 1.00
MG Matt Garza .40 1.00
MJ Mike Jacobs .40 1.00
MM Matt Murton .40 1.00
NM Nate McLouth .40 1.00
PF Prince Fielder 1.00 2.50
RA Reggie Abercrombie .40 1.00
RG Ryan Garko .40 1.00
RM Russell Martin .40 1.00
RP Ronny Paulino .40 1.00
RS Ryan Shealy .40 1.00
RZ Ryan Zimmerman 1.00 2.50
SD Stephen Drew .60 1.50
TB Taylor Buchholz .40 1.00
TG Tony Gwynn Jr. .40 1.00
TS Takashi Saito .40 1.00
WI Josh Willingham .40 1.00

2007 Upper Deck Spectrum Rookie Retrospectrum Signatures

RANDOM INSERTS IN PACKS
PRINT RUNS B/WN 32-199 COPIES PER
EXCHANGE DEADLINE 3/19/2010

BB Boof Bonser 4.00 10.00
BO Jason Botts 4.00 10.00
CA Matt Capps 4.00 10.00
CD Chris Demaria 4.00 10.00
CF Choo Freeman 4.00 10.00
CH Clay Hensley 4.00 10.00
CQ Carlos Quentin 4.00 10.00
DU Dan Uggla 6.00 15.00
FC Fausto Carmona/158 4.00 10.00
FL Francisco Liriano 10.00 25.00
HK Howie Kendrick 10.00 25.00
HR Hanley Ramirez 6.00 15.00
JA Jeremy Accardo/32 6.00 15.00
JC Jose Capellan 4.00 10.00
JD Joey Devine 4.00 10.00
JH Jeremy Hermida 4.00 10.00
JK Jason Kubel 4.00 10.00
JP Jonathan Papelbon 15.00 40.00
JW Jered Weaver 10.00 25.00
JZ Joel Zumaya 10.00 25.00
KM Kendry Morales 4.00 10.00
MG Matt Garza 6.00 15.00
MJ Mike Jacobs 4.00 10.00
RA Reggie Abercrombie 4.00 10.00
RG Ryan Garko 6.00 15.00
RM Russell Martin 10.00 25.00
RS Ryan Shealy 4.00 10.00
SD Stephen Drew 10.00 25.00
TB Taylor Buchholz 4.00 10.00
TS Takashi Saito 10.00 25.00
WI Josh Willingham 4.00 10.00

2007 Upper Deck Spectrum Season Retrospectrum

STATED ODDS 1:10 HOBBY, 1:20 RETAIL
RED: .6X TO 1.5X BASIC
RED RANDOMLY INSERTED IN PACKS
RED PRINT RUN 99 SER.#'d SETS

AH Aaron Harang .40 1.00
AP Albert Pujols 2.50 6.00
AR Aramis Ramirez .40 1.00
AS Alfonso Soriano .60 1.50
BA Bobby Abreu .40 1.00
BH Bill Hall .40 1.00
BL Joe Blanton .40 1.00
CA Miguel Cabrera 1.00 2.50
CB Carlos Beltran .40 1.00
CC Chris Carpenter 1.00 2.50
CD Carlos Delgado .40 1.00
CO Jose Contreras .40 1.00
CU Chase Utley 1.00 2.50
CW Chien-Ming Wang .60 1.50
CY Chris Young .40 1.00
CZ Carlos Zambrano .60 1.50
DJ Derek Jeter 2.50 6.00
DO David Ortiz .60 1.50
FS Freddy Sanchez .40 1.00
FT Frank Thomas 1.00 2.50
GM Greg Maddux 1.50 4.00
GS Grady Sizemore .60 1.50
HO Trevor Hoffman .60 1.50
HR Hanley Ramirez 1.00 2.50
JB Jason Bay .60 1.50
JC Joe Crede .40 1.00
JD Johnny Damon .60 1.50
JM Joe Mauer 1.00 2.50
JR Jose Reyes .60 1.50
JS Jeff Suppan .40 1.00
JT Jim Thome .60 1.50
KG Ken Griffey Jr. 1.50 4.00
MC Michael Cuddyer .40 1.00
MH Matt Holliday 1.00 2.50
ML Mark Loretta .40 1.00
MO Justin Morneau 1.00 2.50
MY Michael Young .60 1.50
NG Nomar Garciaparra 1.00 2.50
OR Magglio Ordonez .60 1.50
OV Omar Vizquel .60 1.50
RC Roger Clemens 1.25 3.00
RF Rafael Furcal .40 1.00
RH Ryan Howard 1.50 4.00
SA Johan Santana 1.00 2.50
SK Scott Kazmir .60 1.50
TH Travis Hafner .40 1.00
TI Tadahito Iguchi .40 1.00
VG Vladimir Guerrero 1.00 2.50
VW Vernon Wells .40 1.00
WT Willy Taveras .40 1.00

2007 Upper Deck Spectrum Shining Star Signatures

RANDOM INSERTS IN PACKS
PRINT RUNS B/WN 50-99 COPIES PER
EXCHANGE DEADLINE 3/19/2010

AD Adam Dunn/99 6.00 15.00
CJ Conor Jackson/54 6.00 15.00
CZ Carlos Zambrano/99 10.00 25.00
DJ Derek Jeter/54 150.00 200.00
DL Derrek Lee/99 10.00 25.00
DO David Ortiz/99 30.00 60.00
GA Garrett Atkins/99 6.00 15.00
HR Hanley Ramirez/99 6.00 15.00
JB Jason Bay/99 6.00 15.00
JM Joe Mauer/99 20.00 50.00
JR Jose Reyes/99 20.00 50.00
JS Johan Santana/99 20.00 50.00
KY Kevin Youkilis/99 6.00 15.00
LB Lance Berkman/99
MO Justin Morneau/99 10.00 25.00
TH Travis Hafner/99 10.00 25.00

2007 Upper Deck Spectrum Spectrum of Stars Signatures

STATED ODDS 1:100 HOB, 1:460 RET
PRINT RUNS B/WN 3-160 COPIES PER
NO PRINT RUNS FOR #'s: DB, EB, FE
CARDS ARE NOT SERIAL-NUMBERED
PRINT RUNS PROVIDED BY UPPER DECK
INSCRIPTIONS PROVIDED BE UPPER DECK
MYSTERY EXCH CL: DB/E01/E02/E03
MYSTERY EXCH CL: EB/FE/KS1/KS2/KS3
MYSTERY EXCH CL: KS4/MM1/MM2/MM3
NO PRICING ON QTY 24 OR LESS
EXCHANGE DEADLINE 3/19/2010

AH1 Anthony Michael Hall Black/65 * 15.00 40.00
AH2 Anthony Michael Hall DZ/30 *
AH3 Anthony Michael Hall 16 Candles/10 *
BL1 Brandy Ledford Black/64 *
BL2 Brandy Ledford Whistler/30 * 20.00 50.00
BL3 Brandy Ledford Andromedia/10 *
BU1 Tony Burton Black/120 * 6.00 15.00
BU2 Tony Burton Stick 'em/20 *
BU3 Tony Burton No Pain/20 *
BU4 Tony Burton Duke In Rocky/20 *
BW1 Barry Williams Black/155 * 12.50 30.00
BW2 Barry Williams Blue/15 *
BW3 Barry Williams Johnny Bravo/15 *
BW4 Barry Williams Greg Brady/20 *
CB1 Catherine Bach Black/155 * 20.00 50.00
CB2 Catherine Bach Blue/27 *
CB3 Catherine Bach Daisy Duke/3 *
CB4 Catherine Bach General Lee/20 *
CF1 Corey Feldman Black/95 * 10.00 25.00
CF2 Corey Feldman Peace/60 *
CF3 Corey Feldman Goonies/30 * 30.00 60.00
CF4 Corey Feldman Lost Boys/20 *
CT1 Carrot Top Black/120 *
CT2 Carrot Top Blue/60 *
CT3 Carrot Top The Luxor/20 *
DB Danny Bonaduce
DF1 David Faustino Black/160 * 15.00 40.00
DF2 D. Faustino Blue Bud Bundy/30 * 30.00 60.00
DF3 David Faustino Grand Master B/12 *
DF4 David Faustino Red Bud Bundy/6 *
EB Ernest Borgnine
EH1 Ernie Hudson Black/60 *
EH2 Ernie Hudson Blue/30 *
EH3 Ernie Hudson The Crow/10 *
EO1 Ed O'Neil Black/60 *
EO2 Ed O'Neil Blue/30 *
EO3 Ed O'Neil Al Bundy/10 *
FE Fergie
GO1 Louis Gossett Jr. Black/60 * 15.00 40.00
GO2 Louis Gossett Jr. Roots/33 *
GO3 Louis Gossett Jr. Mayonaise/12 *
JC1 Jeff Conaway Black/150 * 10.00 25.00
JC2 Jeff Conaway Taxi/30 * 20.00 50.00
JC3 Jeff Conaway Kenickie/20 *
JD1 Josh Duhamel Black/24 *
JD2 Josh Duhamel Transformers/36 * 30.00 60.00
JD3 Josh Duhamel Blue/50 *
JD3 Josh Duhamel Las Vegas/10 *
KM1 Kristy McNichol Black/150 * 10.00 25.00
KM2 Kristy McNichol Family/30 * 30.00 60.00
KM3 K. McNichol Little Darlings/25 * 30.00 60.00
KS1 Katey Sagal Black/120 *
KS2 Katey Sagal Blue/30 *
KS3 Katey Sagal Leila/30 *
KS4 Katey Sagal Peg Bundy/20 *
LB1 Linda Blair Black/150 * 12.50 30.00
LB2 Linda Blair Regan/30 * 30.00 60.00
LB3 Linda Blair The Exorcist/20 *
LG1 Leif Garrett Black/60 * 12.50 30.00
LG2 Leif Garrett Blue/30 * 20.00 50.00
LG3 Leif Garrett I was made for Dancing/10 *
LP1 Lori Petty Black/150 * 10.00 25.00
LP2 Lori Petty KIT/30 * 20.00 50.00
LP3 Lori Petty Tank Girl/20 *
MM1 Michael Madsen Black/60 *
MM2 Michael Madsen Blue/30 *
MM3 Michael Madsen R'Dogs/15 *
MS1 Mia St. John Black/60 * 12.50 30.00
MS2 Mia St. John IFBA Champ/30 *
MS3 Mia St. John The Knockout/10 *
TB1 Todd Bridges Black/60 * 12.50 30.00
TB2 Todd Bridges Blue/30 * 20.00 50.00
TB3 Todd Bridges Willis/10 *
TI1 Tiffany Black/155 * 20.00 50.00
TI2 Tiffany Love/30 *
TI3 Tiffany We're Alone Now/25 *
NNO Mystery Redemption 100.00 200.00

2007 Upper Deck Spectrum Super Swatches

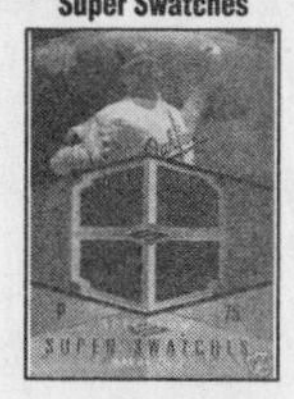

OVERALL GAME-USED ODDS 1:10
STATED PRINT RUN 50 SER.#'d SETS

AD Adam Dunn 5.00 12.00
AJ Andruw Jones 6.00 15.00
AP Albert Pujols 15.00 40.00
AR Aramis Ramirez 5.00 12.00
BA Bobby Abreu 5.00 12.00
BC Bobby Crosby 5.00 12.00
BE Josh Beckett 5.00 12.00
BU B.J. Upton 5.00 12.00
BZ Barry Zito 5.00 12.00
CB Carlos Beltran 5.00 12.00
CC Carl Crawford 5.00 12.00
CD Carlos Delgado 5.00 12.00
CJ Chipper Jones 6.00 15.00
CL Roger Clemens 12.50 30.00
CS Curt Schilling 6.00 15.00
CU Chase Utley 6.00 15.00
DA Johnny Damon 6.00 15.00
DJ Derek Jeter 20.00 50.00
DL Derrek Lee 5.00 12.00
DO David Ortiz 6.00 15.00
FT Frank Thomas 15.00 40.00
GS Gary Sheffield 5.00 12.00
HA Travis Hafner 5.00 12.00
HR Hanley Ramirez 6.00 15.00
JB Jeremy Bonderman 5.00 12.00
JD J.D. Drew 5.00 12.00
JR Jose Reyes 10.00 25.00
JS Johan Santana 6.00 15.00
JT Jim Thome 6.00 15.00
JV Jason Varitek 6.00 15.00
JW Jered Weaver 6.00 15.00
KG Ken Griffey Jr. 15.00 40.00
KJ Kenji Johjima 6.00 15.00
LB Lance Berkman 5.00 12.00
MT Miguel Tejada 5.00 12.00
PE Andy Pettitte 6.00 15.00
PF Prince Fielder 6.00 15.00
PK Paul Konerko 5.00 12.00
RB Rocco Baldelli 5.00 12.00
RC Robinson Cano 10.00 25.00
RH Roy Halladay 5.00 12.00
RJ Randy Johnson 6.00 15.00
RS Richie Sexson 5.00 12.00
SR Scott Rolen 6.00 15.00
TH Todd Helton 6.00 15.00
VE Justin Verlander 6.00 15.00
VG Vladimir Guerrero 6.00 15.00
VW Vernon Wells 5.00 12.00

2007 Upper Deck Spectrum Swatches

STATED PRINT RUN 199 SER.#'d SETS
GOLD: .5X TO 1.2X BASIC
OVERALL GAME-USED ODDS 1:10
GOLD PRINT RUN 75 SER.#'d SETS

AB Adrian Beltre 3.00 8.00
AG Adrian Gonzalez 3.00 8.00
AH Aaron Hill 3.00 8.00
AK Austin Kearns 3.00 8.00
AP Albert Pujols 8.00 20.00
AR Aaron Rowand 3.00 8.00
AS Alfonso Soriano 3.00 8.00
BA Bobby Abreu 3.00 8.00
BC Bartolo Colon 3.00 8.00
BG Brian Giles 3.00 8.00
BI Brandon Inge 3.00 8.00
BJ B.J. Upton 3.00 8.00
BL Joe Blanton 3.00 8.00
BR B.J. Ryan 3.00 8.00
BS Ben Sheets 3.00 8.00
BW Billy Wagner 3.00 8.00
CA Jorge Cantu 3.00 8.00
CB Clint Barmes 3.00 8.00
CC Chad Cordero 3.00 8.00
CD Chris Duffy 3.00 8.00
CG Carlos Guillen 3.00 8.00
CK Casey Kotchman 3.00 8.00
CO Coco Crisp 3.00 8.00
CR Bobby Crosby 3.00 8.00
CS C.C. Sabathia 3.00 8.00
CU Chase Utley 3.00 8.00
CY Chris Young 3.00 8.00
CZ Carlos Zambrano 3.00 8.00
DA Johnny Damon 4.00 10.00
DC Daniel Cabrera 3.00 8.00
DH Danny Haren 3.00 8.00
DJ Derek Jeter 10.00 25.00
DL Derrek Lee 3.00 8.00
DM Dallas McPherson 3.00 8.00
DO David Ortiz 4.00 10.00
DU Dan Uggla 4.00 10.00
DW Dontrelle Willis 3.00 8.00
ES Johnny Estrada 3.00 8.00
FG Freddy Garcia 3.00 8.00
FL Francisco Liriano 3.00 8.00
FS Freddy Sanchez 3.00 8.00
GA Garrett Atkins 3.00 8.00
GC Gustavo Chacin 3.00 8.00
GR Curtis Granderson 3.00 8.00
GS Grady Sizemore 3.00 8.00
HR Hanley Ramirez 4.00 10.00
HS Huston Street 3.00 8.00
HU Aubrey Huff 3.00 8.00
IS Ian Snell 3.00 8.00
JB Jeremy Bonderman 3.00 8.00
JC Joe Crede 3.00 8.00
JD J.D. Drew 3.00 8.00
JE Jermaine Dye 3.00 8.00
JF Jeff Francoeur 4.00 10.00
JH J.J. Hardy 3.00 8.00
JM Joe Mauer 4.00 10.00
JN Joe Nathan 3.00 8.00
JP Jake Peavy 3.00 8.00
JR Jose Reyes 3.00 8.00
JT Jim Thome 3.00 8.00
JU Justin Duchscherer 3.00 8.00
JW Jake Westbrook 3.00 8.00
KG Ken Griffey Jr. 6.00 15.00
KH Khalil Greene 4.00 10.00
LN Laynce Nix 3.00 8.00
MA Matt Cain 4.00 10.00
MB Mark Buehrle 3.00 8.00
MC Mike Cameron 3.00 8.00
ME Morgan Ensberg 3.00 8.00
MH Matt Holliday 4.00 10.00
MI Michael Cuddyer 3.00 8.00
MM Melvin Mora 3.00 8.00
MO Justin Morneau 3.00 8.00
MT Miguel Tejada 3.00 8.00
NL Noah Lowry 3.00 8.00
NS Nick Swisher 3.00 8.00
OR Magglio Ordonez 3.00 8.00
PA Jonathan Papelbon 6.00 15.00
PE Jhonny Peralta 3.00 8.00
PF Prince Fielder 4.00 10.00
PL Paul Lo Duca 3.00 8.00
RA Aramis Ramirez 3.00 8.00
RF Rafael Furcal 3.00 8.00
RH Rich Harden 3.00 8.00
RJ Reed Johnson 3.00 8.00
RO Brian Roberts 3.00 8.00
RQ Robb Quinlan 3.00 8.00
RW Rickie Weeks 3.00 8.00
RZ Ryan Zimmerman 4.00 10.00
SC Sean Casey 3.00 8.00
SK Scott Kazmir 4.00 10.00
TH Torii Hunter 3.00 8.00
TI Tadahito Iguchi 3.00 8.00
TN Trot Nixon 3.00 8.00
VM Victor Martinez 3.00 8.00
WT Willy Taveras 3.00 8.00
YM Yadier Molina 3.00 8.00
ZD Zach Duke 3.00 8.00
ZG Zack Greinke 3.00 8.00

2007 Upper Deck Spectrum Swatches Patches

OVERALL GAME-USED ODDS 1:10
STATED PRINT RUN 50 SER.#'d SETS

AB Adrian Beltre 6.00 15.00
AG Adrian Gonzalez 6.00 15.00
AH Aaron Hill 6.00 15.00
AK Austin Kearns 6.00 15.00
AP Albert Pujols 20.00 50.00
AR Aaron Rowand 6.00 15.00
AS Alfonso Soriano 12.50 30.00
BA Bobby Abreu 8.00 20.00
BC Bartolo Colon 6.00 15.00
BG Brian Giles 6.00 15.00
BI Brandon Inge 6.00 15.00
BJ B.J. Upton 6.00 15.00
BL Joe Blanton 6.00 15.00
BR B.J. Ryan 6.00 15.00
BS Ben Sheets 6.00 15.00
BW Billy Wagner 8.00 20.00
CA Jorge Cantu 6.00 15.00
CB Clint Barmes 6.00 15.00
CC Chad Cordero 6.00 15.00
CD Chris Duffy 6.00 15.00
CG Carlos Guillen 6.00 15.00
CK Casey Kotchman 6.00 15.00
CO Coco Crisp 6.00 15.00
CR Bobby Crosby 6.00 15.00
CS C.C. Sabathia 6.00 15.00
CU Chase Utley 8.00 20.00
CY Chris Young 6.00 15.00
CZ Carlos Zambrano 6.00 15.00
DA Johnny Damon 8.00 20.00
DC Daniel Cabrera 6.00 15.00
DH Danny Haren 6.00 15.00
DL Derrek Lee 6.00 15.00
DM Dallas McPherson 6.00 15.00
DO David Ortiz 12.50 30.00
DU Dan Uggla 8.00 20.00
DW Dontrelle Willis 6.00 15.00
ES Johnny Estrada 6.00 15.00
FG Freddy Garcia 6.00 15.00
FL Francisco Liriano 8.00 20.00
FS Freddy Sanchez 6.00 15.00
GA Garrett Atkins 6.00 15.00
GC Gustavo Chacin 6.00 15.00
GR Curtis Granderson 6.00 15.00
GS Grady Sizemore 12.50 30.00
HR Hanley Ramirez 8.00 20.00
HS Huston Street 6.00 15.00
HU Aubrey Huff 6.00 15.00
IS Ian Snell 6.00 15.00
JB Jeremy Bonderman 12.50 30.00
JC Joe Crede 6.00 15.00
JD J.D. Drew 6.00 15.00
JE Jermaine Dye 6.00 15.00
JF Jeff Francoeur 12.50 30.00
JH J.J. Hardy 6.00 15.00
JM Joe Mauer 12.50 30.00
JN Joe Nathan 6.00 15.00
JP Jake Peavy 6.00 15.00
JR Jose Reyes 12.50 30.00
JT Jim Thome 8.00 20.00
JU Justin Duchscherer 6.00 15.00
JW Jake Westbrook 8.00 20.00
KG Ken Griffey Jr. 30.00 60.00
KH Khalil Greene 8.00 20.00
LN Laynce Nix 6.00 15.00
MA Matt Cain 8.00 20.00
MB Mark Buehrle 6.00 15.00
MC Mike Cameron 6.00 15.00
ME Morgan Ensberg 6.00 15.00
MH Matt Holliday 8.00 20.00
MI Michael Cuddyer 6.00 15.00
MM Melvin Mora 6.00 15.00
MO Justin Morneau 6.00 15.00
MT Miguel Tejada 6.00 15.00
NL Noah Lowry 8.00 20.00
NS Nick Swisher 6.00 15.00
OR Magglio Ordonez 6.00 15.00
PA Jonathan Papelbon 15.00 40.00
PE Jhonny Peralta 6.00 15.00
PF Prince Fielder 12.50 30.00
PL Paul Lo Duca 8.00 20.00
RA Aramis Ramirez 8.00 20.00
RF Rafael Furcal 6.00 15.00
RH Rich Harden 6.00 15.00
RJ Reed Johnson 12.50 30.00
RO Brian Roberts 6.00 15.00
RQ Robb Quinlan 6.00 15.00
RZ Ryan Zimmerman 12.50 30.00
SC Sean Casey 6.00 15.00
SK Scott Kazmir 8.00 20.00
TH Torii Hunter 8.00 20.00
TI Tadahito Iguchi 6.00 15.00
TN Trot Nixon 6.00 15.00
VM Victor Martinez 6.00 15.00
WT Willy Taveras 6.00 15.00
YM Yadier Molina 6.00 15.00
ZD Zach Duke 6.00 15.00
ZG Zack Greinke 6.00 15.00

2008 Upper Deck Spectrum

COMP.SET w/o AUs (100) 10.00 25.00
COMMON CARD .20 .50
COMMOM AU RC 3.00 8.00
OVERALL AUTO ODDS 1:10
PRINTING PLATES RANDOMLY INSERTED
PLATE PRINT RUN 1 SET PER COLOR
BLACK-CYAN-MAGENTA-YELLOW ISSUED
NO PLATE PRICING DUE TO SCARCITY

1 Chris B. Young .20 .50
2 Brandon Webb .30 .75
3 Eric Byrnes .20 .50
4 John Smoltz .50 1.25
5 Chipper Jones .50 1.25
6 Jeff Francoeur .30 .75
7 Mark Teixeira .50 1.25
8 Brian Roberts .20 .50
9 Erik Bedard .20 .50
10 Miguel Tejada .30 .75
11 Nick Markakis .50 1.25
12 David Ortiz .30 .75
13 Daisuke Matsuzaka .50 1.25
14 Manny Ramirez .50 1.25
15 Jonathan Papelbon .30 .75
16 Josh Beckett .30 .75
17 Alfonso Soriano .30 .75
18 Carlos Zambrano .30 .75
19 Derrek Lee .20 .50
20 Aramis Ramirez .20 .50
21 Paul Konerko .30 .75
22 Jermaine Dye .20 .50
23 Jim Thome .30 .75
24 Ken Griffey Jr. .75 2.00
25 Brandon Phillips .20 .50
26 Adam Dunn .30 .75
27 Grady Sizemore .30 .75
28 Fausto Carmona .20 .50
29 Victor Martinez .30 .75
30 Travis Hafner .20 .50
31 Matt Holliday .50 1.25
32 Troy Tulowitzki .50 1.25
33 Todd Helton .30 .75
34 Magglio Ordonez .30 .75
35 Justin Verlander .60 1.50
36 Gary Sheffield .20 .50
37 Miguel Cabrera .50 1.25
38 Hanley Ramirez .50 1.25
39 Dan Uggla .30 .75
40 Carlos Lee .20 .50
41 Roy Oswalt .30 .75
42 Lance Berkman .30 .75
43 Hunter Pence .50 1.25
44 Alex Gordon .30 .75
45 David DeJesus .20 .50
46 Vladimir Guerrero .50 1.25
47 Kelvim Escobar .20 .50
48 Chone Figgins .20 .50
49 Brad Penny .20 .50
50 Takashi Saito .20 .50
51 Russell Martin .20 .50
52 Prince Fielder .30 .75
53 Ryan Braun .60 1.50
54 JJ Hardy .20 .50
55 Johan Santana .50 1.25
56 Justin Morneau .50 1.25
57 Torii Hunter .20 .50
58 Joe Mauer .50 1.25
59 Carlos Beltran .20 .50
60 David Wright .60 1.50
61 Carlos Delgado .20 .50
62 Jose Reyes .30 .75
63 Derek Jeter 1.25 3.00
64 Alex Rodriguez .75 2.00
65 Robinson Cano .50 1.25
66 Hideki Matsui .50 1.25
67 Mariano Rivera .50 1.25
68 Dan Haren .20 .50
69 Nick Swisher .50 1.25
70 Eric Chavez .20 .50
71 Jimmy Rollins .30 .75
72 Ryan Howard .60 1.50
73 Cole Hamels .50 1.25
74 Chase Utley .50 1.25
75 Freddy Sanchez .20 .50
76 Jason Bay .30 .75
77 Ian Snell .20 .50
78 Greg Maddux .60 1.50
79 Jake Peavy .20 .50
80 Chris Young .20 .50
81 Barry Zito .20 .50
82 Tim Lincecum .75 2.00
83 Omar Vizquel .30 .75
84 Felix Hernandez .50 1.25
85 Ichiro Suzuki .75 2.00
86 Richie Sexson .20 .50
87 Albert Pujols 1.25 3.00
88 Scott Rolen .30 .75
89 Chris Carpenter .50 1.25
90 Delmon Young .30 .75
91 Carl Crawford .30 .75
92 B.J. Upton .30 .75
93 Michael Young .30 .75
94 Hank Blalock .20 .50
95 Sammy Sosa .50 1.25
96 Roy Halladay .50 1.25
97 Alex Rios .30 .75
98 Vernon Wells .20 .50
99 Ryan Zimmerman .30 .75
100 Dmitri Young .20 .50
101 Alberto Gonzalez AU RC 10.00 25.00
102 Bill Murphy AU (RC) 3.00 8.00
103 Bill White AU RC 3.00 8.00
104 Billy Buckner AU (RC) 3.00 8.00
105 Brandon Jones AU RC 3.00 8.00
106 Bronson Sardinha AU (RC) 3.00 8.00
107 Chin-Lung Hu AU (RC) 10.00 25.00
108 Chris Seddon AU (RC) 3.00 8.00
109 Clay Buchholz AU (RC) 10.00 25.00
110 Clint Sammons AU (RC) 3.00 8.00
111 Daric Barton AU (RC) 4.00 10.00
112 Dave Davidson AU RC 4.00 10.00
113 Donny Lucy AU (RC) 3.00 8.00
114 Emilio Bonifacio AU RC 3.00 8.00
115 Eugenio Velez AU RC 4.00 10.00
116 Felipe Paulino AU RC
117 Harvey Garcia AU (RC) 3.00 8.00
118 Ian Kennedy AU RC 15.00 40.00
119 J.R. Towles AU RC 6.00 15.00
120 Jeff Clement AU (RC)
121 Jerry Blevins AU RC 3.00 8.00
122 Joe Koshansky AU (RC) 3.00 8.00
123 Joey Votto AU (RC) 20.00 50.00
124 Jonathan Albaladejo AU RC 4.00 10.00
125 Jonathan Meloan AU RC 3.00 8.00
126 Jose Morales AU (RC) 3.00 8.00
127 Josh Anderson AU (RC) 3.00 8.00
128 Josh Newman AU RC 3.00 8.00
129 Justin Maxwell AU RC 4.00 10.00
130 Justin Ruggiano AU RC 3.00 8.00
131 Kevin Hart AU (RC) 3.00 8.00
132 Lance Broadway AU (RC) 3.00 8.00
133 Luis Mendoza AU (RC) 3.00 8.00

134 Luke Hochevar AU RC 6.00 15.00
135 Nyjer Morgan AU (RC) 3.00 8.00
136 Rob Johnson AU (RC) 3.00 8.00
137 Ross Detwiler AU RC 3.00 8.00
138 Ross Ohlendorf AU RC 4.00 10.00
139 Ryan Hanigan AU RC 3.00 8.00
140 Seth Smith AU (RC) 3.00 8.00
141 Steve Pearce AU RC 4.00 10.00
142 Troy Patton AU (RC) 3.00 8.00
143 Wladimir Balentien AU (RC) 4.00 10.00
144 Colt Morton AU RC 3.00 8.00
145 Carlos Muniz AU RC

2008 Upper Deck Spectrum Blue

RANDOM INSERTS IN PACKS
STATED PRINT RUN 25 SER.#'d SETS
NO PRICING DUE TO SCARCITY

2008 Upper Deck Spectrum Gold

RANDOM INSERTS IN PACKS
1-100 PRINT RUN 1 SER.#'d SET
101-145 PRINT RUN 10 SER.#'d SETS
NO PRICING DUE TO SCARCITY

2008 Upper Deck Spectrum Green

*1-100 GRN: .75X TO 2X BASIC
RANDOM INSERTS IN PACKS
1-100 PRINT RUN 199 SER.#'d SETS
OVERALL AUTO ODDS 1:10
GREEN AUTOS ARE NOT SER.#'d
NO GREEN AU PRICING AVAILABLE

2008 Upper Deck Spectrum Orange

*ORANGE: .6X TO 1.5X BASIC
RANDOM INSERTS IN PACKS
STATED PRINT RUN 399 SER.#'d SETS

2008 Upper Deck Spectrum Red

*RED: 1X TO 2.5X BASIC
RANDOM INSERTS IN PACKS
STATED PRINT RUN 99 SER.#'d SETS

2008 Upper Deck Spectrum Buyback Autographs

OVERALL AUTO ODDS 1:10
PRINT RUNS B/WN 2-69 COPIES PER
NO PRICING ON MOST DUE TO SCARCITY
JR1 Jose Reyes 20.00 50.00
2004 Upper Deck/70
JR2 Jose Reyes
2004 Upper Deck Fist Pitch/14
JR3 Jose Reyes
2003 SPx/14
JR4 Jose Reyes
2003 Sweet Spot/7
JR5 Jose Reyes
2004 UD All-Star Lineup/7
JR6 Jose Reyes
2004 Play Ball Red/3
JR7 Jose Reyes
2004 Play Ball Blue/4
JR8 Jose Reyes
2004 UD Vintage/14
KG1 Ken Griffey Jr. 40.00 80.00
2003 UD Patch Collection/50
KG10 Ken Griffey Jr.
2003 Play Ball/20
KG2 Ken Griffey Jr. 40.00 80.00
2003 UD 40-Man/50
KG3 Ken Griffey Jr. 40.00 80.00
2003 Sweet Spot/49
KG4 Ken Griffey Jr. 40.00 80.00
2004 UD Vintage/50
KG5 Ken Griffey Jr. 40.00 80.00
2003 SPx/49
KG6 Ken Griffey Jr. 40.00 80.00
2003 UD Authentics/50
KG7 Ken Griffey Jr. 40.00 80.00
2004 UD All-Star Lineup/50
KG8 Ken Griffey Jr. 40.00 80.00
2003 UD Honor Roll/50
KG9 Ken Griffey Jr. 40.00 80.00
2003 UD Classic Portraits/49
RA1 Roberto Alomar
2003 UD Classic Portraits/2
RA2 Roberto Alomar
2004 UD Vintage/2
RA3 Roberto Alomar 8.00 20.00
2003 Sweet Spot/50
RA4 Roberto Alomar
2003 UD Honor Roll/25
RA5 Roberto Alomar 8.00 20.00
2003 UD Honor Roll/30
RA6 Roberto Alomar 8.00 20.00
2003 UD Authentics/50

2008 Upper Deck Spectrum Derek Jeter Retrospectrum

COMMON CARD 1.25 3.00
RANDOM INSERTS IN PACKS
PRINTING PLATES RANDOMLY INSERTED
PLATE PRINT RUN 1 SET PER COLOR
BLACK-CYAN-MAGENTA-YELLOW ISSUED
NO PLATE PRICING DUE TO SCARCITY
*RED: 1X TO 2.5X BASIC
RED RANDOMLY INSERTED
RED PRINT RUN 99 SER.#'d SETS
DJ1 Derek Jeter 1.25 3.00
DJ2 Derek Jeter 1.25 3.00
DJ3 Derek Jeter 1.25 3.00
DJ4 Derek Jeter 1.25 3.00
DJ5 Derek Jeter 1.25 3.00
DJ6 Derek Jeter 1.25 3.00
DJ7 Derek Jeter 1.25 3.00
DJ8 Derek Jeter 1.25 3.00
DJ9 Derek Jeter 1.25 3.00
DJ10 Derek Jeter 1.25 3.00
DJ11 Derek Jeter 1.25 3.00
DJ12 Derek Jeter 1.25 3.00
DJ13 Derek Jeter 1.25 3.00
DJ14 Derek Jeter 1.25 3.00
DJ15 Derek Jeter 1.25 3.00
DJ16 Derek Jeter 1.25 3.00
DJ17 Derek Jeter 1.25 3.00
DJ18 Derek Jeter 1.25 3.00
DJ19 Derek Jeter 1.25 3.00
DJ20 Derek Jeter 1.25 3.00
DJ21 Derek Jeter 1.25 3.00
DJ22 Derek Jeter 1.25 3.00
DJ23 Derek Jeter 1.25 3.00
DJ24 Derek Jeter 1.25 3.00
DJ25 Derek Jeter 1.25 3.00
DJ26 Derek Jeter 1.25 3.00
DJ27 Derek Jeter 1.25 3.00
DJ28 Derek Jeter 1.25 3.00
DJ29 Derek Jeter 1.25 3.00
DJ30 Derek Jeter 1.25 3.00
DJ31 Derek Jeter 1.25 3.00
DJ32 Derek Jeter 1.25 3.00
DJ33 Derek Jeter 1.25 3.00
DJ34 Derek Jeter 1.25 3.00
DJ35 Derek Jeter 1.25 3.00
DJ36 Derek Jeter 1.25 3.00
DJ37 Derek Jeter 1.25 3.00
DJ38 Derek Jeter 1.25 3.00
DJ39 Derek Jeter 1.25 3.00
DJ40 Derek Jeter 1.25 3.00
DJ41 Derek Jeter 1.25 3.00
DJ42 Derek Jeter 1.25 3.00
DJ43 Derek Jeter 1.25 3.00
DJ44 Derek Jeter 1.25 3.00
DJ45 Derek Jeter 1.25 3.00
DJ46 Derek Jeter 1.25 3.00
DJ47 Derek Jeter 1.25 3.00
DJ48 Derek Jeter 1.25 3.00
DJ49 Derek Jeter 1.25 3.00
DJ50 Derek Jeter 1.25 3.00
DJ51 Derek Jeter 1.25 3.00
DJ52 Derek Jeter 1.25 3.00
DJ53 Derek Jeter 1.25 3.00
DJ54 Derek Jeter 1.25 3.00
DJ55 Derek Jeter 1.25 3.00
DJ56 Derek Jeter 1.25 3.00
DJ57 Derek Jeter 1.25 3.00
DJ58 Derek Jeter 1.25 3.00
DJ59 Derek Jeter 1.25 3.00
DJ60 Derek Jeter 1.25 3.00
DJ61 Derek Jeter 1.25 3.00
DJ62 Derek Jeter 1.25 3.00
DJ63 Derek Jeter 1.25 3.00
DJ64 Derek Jeter 1.25 3.00
DJ65 Derek Jeter 1.25 3.00
DJ66 Derek Jeter 1.25 3.00
DJ67 Derek Jeter 1.25 3.00
DJ68 Derek Jeter 1.25 3.00
DJ69 Derek Jeter 1.25 3.00
DJ70 Derek Jeter 1.25 3.00
DJ71 Derek Jeter 1.25 3.00
DJ72 Derek Jeter 1.25 3.00
DJ73 Derek Jeter 1.25 3.00
DJ74 Derek Jeter 1.25 3.00
DJ75 Derek Jeter 1.25 3.00
DJ76 Derek Jeter 1.25 3.00
DJ77 Derek Jeter 1.25 3.00
DJ78 Derek Jeter 1.25 3.00
DJ79 Derek Jeter 1.25 3.00
DJ80 Derek Jeter 1.25 3.00
DJ81 Derek Jeter 1.25 3.00
DJ82 Derek Jeter 1.25 3.00
DJ83 Derek Jeter 1.25 3.00
DJ84 Derek Jeter 1.25 3.00
DJ85 Derek Jeter 1.25 3.00
DJ86 Derek Jeter 1.25 3.00
DJ87 Derek Jeter 1.25 3.00
DJ88 Derek Jeter 1.25 3.00
DJ89 Derek Jeter 1.25 3.00
DJ90 Derek Jeter 1.25 3.00
DJ91 Derek Jeter 1.25 3.00
DJ92 Derek Jeter 1.25 3.00
DJ93 Derek Jeter 1.25 3.00
DJ94 Derek Jeter 1.25 3.00
DJ95 Derek Jeter 1.25 3.00
DJ96 Derek Jeter 1.25 3.00
DJ97 Derek Jeter 1.25 3.00
DJ98 Derek Jeter 1.25 3.00
DJ99 Derek Jeter 1.25 3.00
DJ100 Derek Jeter 1.25 3.00

2008 Upper Deck Spectrum Derek Jeter Retrospectrum Autographs

COMMON CARD 300.00 400.00
OVERAL AUTO ODDS 1:10
STATED PRINT RUN 2 SER.#'d SETS

2008 Upper Deck Spectrum Retrospectrum Swatches

OVERALL MEM ODDS 1:10
AB1 Aaron Boone 2.50 6.00
AB2 Aaron Boone 2.50 6.00
AG1 Adrian Gonzalez 2.50 6.00
AG2 Adrian Gonzalez 2.50 6.00
AH1 Aubrey Huff 2.50 6.00
AH2 Aubrey Huff 2.50 6.00
AJ1 A.J. Burnett 2.50 6.00
AJ2 A.J. Burnett 2.50 6.00
AK Adam Kennedy 2.50 6.00
AK1 Austin Kearns 2.50 6.00
AK2 Austin Kearns 2.50 6.00
AL1 Adam LaRoche 2.50 6.00
AL2 Adam LaRoche 2.50 6.00
AP Albert Pujols 6.00 15.00
AP1 Andy Pettitte 3.00 8.00
AP2 Andy Pettitte 3.00 8.00
AR1 Aaron Rowand 2.50 6.00
AR2 Aaron Rowand 2.50 6.00
AS1 Alfonso Soriano 3.00 8.00
AS2 Alfonso Soriano 3.00 8.00
AS3 Alfonso Soriano 3.00 8.00
BA1 Bobby Abreu 2.50 6.00
BA2 Bobby Abreu 2.50 6.00
BC1 Bartolo Colon 2.50 6.00
BC2 Bartolo Colon 2.50 6.00
BE1 Adrian Beltre 2.50 6.00
BE2 Adrian Beltre 2.50 6.00
BG1 Brian Giles 2.50 6.00
BG2 Brian Giles 2.50 6.00
BZ1 Barry Zito 2.50 6.00
BZ2 Barry Zito 2.50 6.00
CA1 Sean Casey 2.50 6.00
CA2 Sean Casey 2.50 6.00
CC1 Coco Crisp 2.50 6.00
CC2 Coco Crisp 2.50 6.00
CD1 Carlos Delgado 2.50 6.00
CD2 Carlos Delgado 2.50 6.00
CL1 Carlos Lee 2.50 6.00
CL2 Carlos Lee 2.50 6.00
CY1 Chris Young 2.50 6.00
CY2 Chris Young 2.50 6.00
DJ Derek Jeter 8.00 20.00
DW1 David Wells 2.50 6.00
DW2 David Wells 2.50 6.00
EG1 Eric Gagne 2.50 6.00
EG2 Eric Gagne 2.50 6.00
ER1 Edgar Renteria 2.50 6.00
ER2 Edgar Renteria 2.50 6.00
FG1 Freddy Garcia 2.50 6.00
FG2 Freddy Garcia 2.50 6.00
FT1 Frank Thomas 5.00 12.00
FT2 Frank Thomas 5.00 12.00
GM1 Greg Maddux 5.00 12.00
GM2 Greg Maddux 5.00 12.00
GS1 Gary Sheffield 2.50 6.00
GS2 Gary Sheffield 2.50 6.00
IR1 Ivan Rodriguez 3.00 8.00
IR2 Ivan Rodriguez 3.00 8.00
JB1 Josh Barfield 2.50 6.00
JB2 Josh Barfield 2.50 6.00
JD1 J.D. Drew 2.50 6.00
JD2 J.D. Drew 2.50 6.00
JE Johnny Estrada 2.50 6.00
JJ1 Jacque Jones 2.50 6.00
JJ2 Jacque Jones 2.50 6.00
JO1 Josh Beckett 3.00 8.00
JO2 Josh Beckett 3.00 8.00
JS1 Jason Schmidt 2.50 6.00
JS2 Jason Schmidt 2.50 6.00
JT1 Jim Thome 3.00 8.00
JT2 Jim Thome 3.00 8.00
KM Kevin Millwood 2.50 6.00
LG1 Luis Gonzalez 2.50 6.00
LG2 Luis Gonzalez 2.50 6.00
LH Livan Hernandez 2.50 6.00
MA1 Moises Alou 2.50 6.00
MA2 Moises Alou 2.50 6.00
ME1 Morgan Ensberg 2.50 6.00
ME2 Morgan Ensberg 2.50 6.00
MG1 Marcus Giles 2.50 6.00
MG2 Marcus Giles 2.50 6.00
ML1 Mark Loretta 2.50 6.00
ML2 Mark Loretta 2.50 6.00
MP1 Mike Piazza 5.00 12.00
MP2 Mike Piazza 5.00 12.00
MT1 Mark Teixeira 3.00 8.00
MT2 Mark Teixeira 3.00 8.00
OV1 Omar Vizquel 2.50 6.00
OV2 Omar Vizquel 2.50 6.00
RF1 Rafael Furcal 2.50 6.00
RF2 Rafael Furcal 2.50 6.00
RJ1 Randy Johnson 5.00 12.00
RJ2 Randy Johnson 5.00 12.00
RK Ryan Klesko 2.50 6.00
SS1 Shannon Stewart 2.50 6.00
SS2 Shannon Stewart 2.50 6.00
TI1 Tadahito Iguchi 2.50 6.00
TI2 Tadahito Iguchi 2.50 6.00
WT1 Willy Taveras 2.50 6.00
WT2 Willy Taveras 2.50 6.00

2008 Upper Deck Spectrum Retrospectrum Swatches Red

*RED: .6X TO 1.5X BASIC
OVERALL MEM ODDS 1:10
STATED PRINT RUN 45 SER.#'d SETS

2008 Upper Deck Spectrum Retrospectrum Patches

OVERALL MEM ODDS 1:10
STATED PRINT RUN 25 SER.#'d SETS
NO PRICING DUE TO SCARCITY

2008 Upper Deck Spectrum Spectrum of Stars Signatures

OVERALL SOS AUTO ODDS 1:20
EXCHANGE DEADLINE 3/17/2010
AP A.J. Pero 4.00 10.00
BP Butch Patrick 12.50 30.00
BS Bill Simmons
CM Christopher McDonald 12.50 30.00
DA Taylor Dayne 12.50 30.00
DD Don Dokken 6.00 15.00
EM Erin Moran 20.00 50.00
EO Eddie Ojeda 4.00 10.00
ER Eric Roberts 12.50 30.00
ET Erik Turner 4.00 10.00
FS Frank Stallone 6.00 15.00
HW Henry Winkler 20.00 50.00
JA Joey Allen 4.00 10.00
JD Jerry Dixon 4.00 10.00
JF Jay Jay French 4.00 10.00
JG Joe Gannascoli 15.00 40.00
JL Jani Lane 6.00 15.00
KO Martin Kove 10.00 25.00
LH Larry Hagman 20.00 50.00
LT Larry Thomas 10.00 25.00
LV Lonnie Vencent
MA Miljenko Matijevic 4.00 10.00
MB Michael Biehn 15.00 40.00
MK Margot Kidder 20.00 50.00
MM Mark Mendoza 4.00 10.00
MR Mickey Rooney
PP Pat Priest 12.50 30.00
PS P.J. Soles 12.50 30.00
RF Robert Furaro 12.50 30.00
SB Sebastian Bach 6.00 15.00
SE Shirley Eaton
SN Dee Snider 6.00 15.00
SP Stephen Pearcy 6.00 15.00
SS Steven Sweet 4.00 10.00
TB Tom Bosley 15.00 40.00
TR Mike Tramp 4.00 10.00
VN Vince Neil 10.00 25.00
NNO 200.00 300.00

2008 Upper Deck Spectrum Spectrum Swatches

OVERALL MEM ODDS 1:10
STATED PRINT RUN 99 SER.#'d SETS
AB A.J. Burnett 3.00 8.00
AH Aaron Harang 3.00 8.00
AJ Andruw Jones 3.00 8.00
AP Albert Pujols 8.00 20.00
BB Boof Bonser 3.00 8.00
BC Bartolo Colon 3.00 8.00
BE Adrian Beltre 3.00 8.00
BG Brian Giles 3.00 8.00
BM Brian McCann 3.00 8.00
BS Ben Sheets 3.00 8.00
BU B.J. Upton 3.00 8.00
BW Billy Wagner 3.00 8.00
CA Chris Carpenter 3.00 8.00
CB Carlos Beltran 3.00 8.00
CC Carl Crawford 3.00 8.00
CG Carlos Guillen 3.00 8.00
CH Cole Hamels 4.00 10.00
CJ Chipper Jones 4.00 10.00
CS Curt Schilling 4.00 10.00
CU Chase Utley 4.00 10.00
CZ Carlos Zambrano 3.00 8.00
DH Dan Haren 3.00 8.00
DJ Derek Jeter 10.00 25.00
DL Derrek Lee 3.00 8.00
DM Daisuke Matsuzaka 8.00 20.00
DO David Ortiz 5.00 12.00
DO2 David Ortiz 5.00 12.00
DU Dan Uggla 3.00 8.00
DW Dontrelle Willis 3.00 8.00
EC Eric Chavez 3.00 8.00
FH Felix Hernandez 4.00 10.00
FS Freddy Sanchez 3.00 8.00
GA Garrett Atkins 3.00 8.00
GJ Geoff Jenkins 3.00 8.00
GM Greg Maddux 6.00 15.00
GR Curtis Granderson 4.00 10.00
GS Grady Sizemore 4.00 10.00
HA Travis Hafner 3.00 8.00
HB Hank Blalock 3.00 8.00
HO Trevor Hoffman 3.00 8.00
HP Hunter Pence 5.00 12.00
HR Hanley Ramirez 4.00 10.00
HU Torii Hunter 3.00 8.00
IK Ian Kinsler 3.00 8.00
IR Ivan Rodriguez 4.00 10.00
JA Conor Jackson 3.00 8.00
JB Josh Beckett 4.00 10.00
JC Joba Chamberlain 10.00 25.00
JD Jermaine Dye 3.00 8.00
JE Jim Edmonds 3.00 8.00
JF Jeff Francoeur 4.00 10.00
JG Jason Giambi 4.00 10.00
JH J.J. Hardy 3.00 8.00
JK Jeff Kent 3.00 8.00
JM Joe Mauer 4.00 10.00
JP Jhonny Peralta 3.00 8.00
JR Jose Reyes 4.00 10.00
JS Johan Santana 5.00 12.00
JT Jim Thome 4.00 10.00
JV Jason Varitek 5.00 12.00
JW Jered Weaver 3.00 8.00
KG Ken Griffey Jr. 6.00 15.00
KJ Kenji Johjima 3.00 8.00
KY Kevin Youkilis 3.00 8.00
LB Lance Berkman 3.00 8.00
MC Miguel Cabrera 4.00 10.00
MG Matt Garza 3.00 8.00
MH Matt Holliday 4.00 10.00
MO Justin Morneau 3.00 8.00
MP Mike Piazza 5.00 12.00
MR Manny Ramirez 4.00 10.00
MT Miguel Tejada 3.00 8.00
MY Michael Young 3.00 8.00
OR Magglio Ordonez 4.00 10.00
OS Roy Oswalt 3.00 8.00
PA Jonathan Papelbon 4.00 10.00
PE Jake Peavy 4.00 10.00
PF Prince Fielder 5.00 12.00
PI Juan Pierre 3.00 8.00
PM Pedro Martinez 4.00 10.00
PO Jorge Posada 4.00 10.00
RA Aramis Ramirez 3.00 8.00
RB Ryan Braun 6.00 15.00
RC Robinson Cano 4.00 10.00
RF Rafael Furcal 3.00 8.00
RH Roy Halladay 3.00 8.00
RJ Randy Johnson 5.00 12.00
RM Russell Martin 3.00 8.00
RS Richie Sexson 3.00 8.00
RZ Ryan Zimmerman 4.00 10.00
SM John Smoltz 4.00 10.00
SO Jeremy Sowers 3.00 8.00
SR Scott Rolen 4.00 10.00
TH Tim Hudson 3.00 8.00
TW Tim Wakefield 3.00 8.00
VE Justin Verlander 4.00 10.00
VG Vladimir Guerrero 4.00 10.00
VM Victor Martinez 3.00 8.00
VW Vernon Wells 3.00 8.00
VW2 Vernon Wells 3.00 8.00

2008 Upper Deck Spectrum Spectrum Swatches Dark Gray

OVERALL MEM ODDS 1:10
STATED PRINT RUN 1 SER.#'d SET
NO PRICING DUE TO SCARCITY

2008 Upper Deck Spectrum Spectrum Swatches Green

*GREEN: .5X TO 1.2X BASIC
OVERALL MEM ODDS 1:10
STATED PRINT RUN 50 SER.#'d SETS

2008 Upper Deck Spectrum Spectrum Swatches Green Patch

OVERALL MEM ODDS 1:10
STATED PRINT RUN 15 SER.#'d SETS
NO PRICING DUE TO SCARCITY

2008 Upper Deck Spectrum Spectrum Swatches Light Blue

OVERALL MEM ODDS 1:10
STATED PRINT RUN 15 SER.#'d SETS
NO PRICING DUE TO SCARCITY

2008 Upper Deck Spectrum Spectrum Swatches Light Gray Patch

OVERALL MEM ODDS 1:10
STATED PRINT RUN 5 SER.#'d SETS
NO PRICING DUE TO SCARCITY

2008 Upper Deck Spectrum Spectrum Swatches Orange

*ORANGE: .4X TO 1X BASIC
OVERALL MEM ODDS 1:10
STATED PRINT RUN 75 SER.#'d SETS

2008 Upper Deck Spectrum Spectrum Swatches Purple

OVERALL MEM ODDS 1:10
PRINT RUNS B/WN 2-58 COPIES PER
NO PRICING ON QTY 25 OR LESS
AB A.J. Burnett/34 5.00 12.00
AH Aaron Harang/39 5.00 12.00
AJ Andruw Jones/25
AP Albert Pujols/5
BB Boof Bonser/26 5.00 12.00
BC Bartolo Colon/40 5.00 12.00
BE Adrian Beltre/29 5.00 12.00
BG Brian Giles/24
BM Brian McCann/16
BS Ben Sheets/15
BU B.J. Upton/2
BW Billy Wagner/13
CA Chris Carpenter/29 5.00 12.00
CB Carlos Beltran/15
CC Carl Crawford/13
CG Carlos Guillen/9
CH Cole Hamels/35 6.00 15.00
CJ Chipper Jones/10
CS Curt Schilling/38 6.00 15.00
CU Chase Utley/26 6.00 15.00
CZ Carlos Zambrano/38 5.00 12.00
DH Dan Haren/15
DJ Derek Jeter/2
DL Derrek Lee/25
DM Daisuke Matsuzaka/18
DO David Ortiz/34 8.00 20.00
DO2 David Ortiz/6
DU Dan Uggla/35 5.00 12.00
DW Dontrelle Willis/3
EC Eric Chavez/34 5.00 12.00
FH Felix Hernandez/12
FS Freddy Sanchez/27 5.00 12.00
GA Garrett Atkins/5
GJ Geoff Jenkins/30 5.00 12.00
GM Greg Maddux/28 10.00 25.00
GR Curtis Granderson/24
GS Grady Sizemore/48 6.00 15.00
HA Travis Hafner/9
HB Hank Blalock/51 5.00 12.00
HO Trevor Hoffman/9
HP Hunter Pence/2
HR Hanley Ramirez/48 6.00 15.00
HU Torii Hunter/5
IK Ian Kinsler/7
IR Ivan Rodriguez/16
JA Conor Jackson/19
JB Josh Beckett/13
JC Joba Chamberlain/23
JD Jermaine Dye/15
JE Jim Edmonds/7
JF Jeff Francoeur/25
JG Jason Giambi/7
JH J.J. Hardy/12
JK Jeff Kent/7
JM Joe Mauer/2
JP Jhonny Peralta/7
JR Jose Reyes/57 6.00 15.00
JS Johan Santana/25
JT Jim Thome/33 6.00 15.00
JV Jason Varitek/36 8.00 20.00
JW Jered Weaver/3
KG Ken Griffey Jr./2
KJ Kenji Johjima/20
KY Kevin Youkilis/17
LB Lance Berkman/24
MC Miguel Cabrera/24
MG Matt Garza/5
MH Matt Holliday/33 6.00 15.00
MO Justin Morneau/31 5.00 12.00
MP Mike Piazza/24
MR Manny Ramirez/10
MT Miguel Tejada/10
MY Michael Young/30 5.00 12.00
OR Magglio Ordonez/44 6.00 15.00
OS Roy Oswalt/58 5.00 12.00
PA Jonathan Papelbon/44 6.00 15.00
PE Jake Peavy/29 6.00 15.00
PF Prince Fielder/9
PI Juan Pierre/45 5.00 12.00
PM Pedro Martinez/20
PO Jorge Posada/16
RA Aramis Ramirez/8
RB Ryan Braun/24
RC Robinson Cano/15
RF Rafael Furcal/32 5.00 12.00
RH Roy Halladay/51 5.00 12.00
RJ Randy Johnson/55 8.00 20.00
RM Russell Martin/44 5.00 12.00
RS Richie Sexson/11
RZ Ryan Zimmerman/29 6.00 15.00
SM John Smoltz/45 6.00 15.00
SO Jeremy Sowers/27 5.00 12.00
SR Scott Rolen/15
TH Tim Hudson/49 5.00 12.00
TW Tim Wakefield/35 5.00 12.00
VE Justin Verlander/27 6.00 15.00
VG Vladimir Guerrero/41 6.00 15.00
VM Victor Martinez/10
VW Vernon Wells/34 5.00 12.00
VW2 Vernon Wells/10

2008 Upper Deck Spectrum Spectrum Swatches Red

*RED: .6X TO 1.5X BASIC
OVERALL MEM ODDS 1:10
STATED PRINT RUN 35 SER.#'d SETS

2008 Upper Deck Spectrum Spectrum Swatches Autographs

OVERALL AUTO ODDS 1:10
PRINT RUNS B/WN 5-30 COPIES PER
NO PRICING ON MOST DUE TO SCARCITY
AH Aaron Harang/30 8.00 20.00
AJ Andruw Jones/30
AP Albert Pujols/5
BB Boof Bonser/30 8.00 20.00
BE Adrian Beltre/30
BG Brian Giles/30 8.00 20.00
BM Brian McCann/30 15.00 40.00
BS Ben Sheets/30 12.50 30.00
BU B.J. Upton/30 12.50 30.00
CA Chris Carpenter/30
CC Carl Crawford/30 8.00 20.00
CH Cole Hamels/30 15.00 40.00
CJ Chipper Jones/30 60.00 120.00
CS Curt Schilling/30
CU Chase Utley/30
DH Dan Haren/30 8.00 20.00
DJ Derek Jeter/15
DL Derrek Lee/30 10.00 25.00
DM Daisuke Matsuzaka/30 75.00 150.00
DU Dan Uggla/30 8.00 20.00
DW Dontrelle Willis/30 8.00 20.00
EC Eric Chavez/30
FH Felix Hernandez/30 20.00 50.00
GA Garrett Atkins/30 8.00 20.00
GJ Geoff Jenkins/30
GR Curtis Granderson/30 15.00 40.00
GS Grady Sizemore/30
HA Travis Hafner/30 15.00 40.00
HB Hank Blalock/30
HP Hunter Pence/30 15.00 40.00
HR Hanley Ramirez/30 15.00 40.00
HU Torii Hunter/30 8.00 20.00
IK Ian Kinsler/30 8.00 20.00
IR Ivan Rodriguez/30
JA Conor Jackson/30
JB Josh Beckett/14
JF Jeff Francoeur/30
JH J.J. Hardy/30
JM Joe Mauer/30 15.00 40.00
JS Johan Santana/30 30.00 60.00
JT Jim Thome/30
JV Jason Varitek/30 20.00 50.00
JW Jered Weaver/30 10.00 25.00
KG Ken Griffey Jr./15
KY Kevin Youkilis/30 15.00 40.00
LB Lance Berkman/30 10.00 25.00
MC Miguel Cabrera/30 20.00 50.00
MG Matt Garza/30 8.00 20.00
MH Matt Holliday/30 12.50 30.00
MO Justin Morneau/30 12.50 30.00
MT Miguel Tejada/30 10.00 25.00
OS Roy Oswalt/30 10.00 25.00
PA Jonathan Papelbon/30 15.00 40.00
PF Prince Fielder/30 20.00 50.00
RA Aramis Ramirez/30 12.50 30.00
RB Ryan Braun/30 30.00 60.00
RF Rafael Furcal/30
RJ Randy Johnson/30
RM Russell Martin/30 20.00 50.00
RZ Ryan Zimmerman/30 10.00 25.00
SO Jeremy Sowers/30 10.00 25.00
TH Tim Hudson/30 10.00 25.00
VE Justin Verlander/30 30.00 60.00
VG Vladimir Guerrero/30 20.00 50.00
VM Victor Martinez/30 15.00 40.00

2008 Upper Deck Spectrum Spectrum Swatches Dual

OVERALL MEM ODDS 1:10
STATED PRINT RUN 99 SER.#'d SETS
AP Aaron Rowand 4.00 10.00
Pat Burrell
BM Josh Beckett 12.50 30.00
Daisuke Matsuzaka
BP Ryan Braun 8.00 20.00
Hunter Pence
CL Matt Cain 4.00 10.00
Noah Lowry
CT Curt Schilling 5.00 12.00
Tim Wakefield
CW Miguel Cabrera 5.00 12.00
Dontrelle Willis
CY Carl Crawford 5.00 12.00
Delmon Young
DC Derek Jeter 30.00 60.00
Joba Chamberlain
FB Prince Fielder 10.00 25.00
Ryan Braun
FD Felix Hernandez 5.00 12.00
Dan Haren
FK Rafael Furcal 4.00 10.00
Jeff Kent
FM Jeff Francoeur 5.00 12.00
Brian McCann
GC Vladimir Guerrero 4.00 10.00
Bartolo Colon
GD Ken Griffey Jr. 10.00 25.00
Adam Dunn
GG Adrian Gonzalez 5.00 12.00
Brian Giles
GM Tom Glavine 10.00 25.00
Greg Maddux
GO Vladimir Guerrero 10.00 25.00
Magglio Ordonez
GP Jason Giambi 5.00 12.00
Jorge Posada
GV Grady Sizemore 5.00 12.00
Victor Martinez
HB Roy Halladay 4.00 10.00
A.J. Burnett

HC Torii Hunter 4.00 10.00
Mike Cameron
HF Matt Holliday 5.00 12.00
Jeff Francoeur
HH Matt Holliday 6.00 15.00
Todd Helton
HJ Felix Hernandez 6.00 15.00
Kenji Johjima
HS Rich Harden 4.00 10.00
Huston Street
JC Derek Jeter 10.00 25.00
Robinson Cano
JF Andruw Jones 5.00 12.00
Jeff Francoeur
JP Derek Jeter 15.00 40.00
Albert Pujols
JR Derek Jeter 12.50 30.00
Jose Reyes
JT John Smoltz 6.00 15.00
Tim Hudson
JW Randy Johnson 6.00 15.00
Brandon Webb
MH Justin Morneau 4.00 10.00
Torii Hunter
ML Brett Myers 4.00 10.00
Brad Lidge
MP Russell Martin 5.00 12.00
Juan Pierre
MR Victor Martinez 5.00 12.00
Ivan Rodriguez
MW Pedro Martinez 10.00 25.00
Billy Wagner
OB Roy Oswalt 5.00 12.00
Lance Berkman
OG Magglio Ordonez 5.00 12.00
Curtis Granderson
OP David Ortiz 10.00 25.00
Albert Pujols
OR David Ortiz 10.00 25.00
Manny Ramirez
PE Albert Pujols 8.00 20.00
Jim Edmonds
PJ Prince Fielder 6.00 15.00
Justin Morneau
PM Jake Peavy 6.00 15.00
Greg Maddux
PS Albert Pujols 10.00 25.00
Alfonso Soriano
PW Jake Peavy 5.00 12.00
Brandon Webb
RB Jose Reyes 5.00 12.00
Carlos Beltran
RC Gary Sheffield 5.00 12.00
Miguel Cabrera
RF Jose Reyes 5.00 12.00
Rafael Furcal
RH Hanley Ramirez 5.00 12.00
J.J. Hardy
RR Jose Reyes 5.00 12.00
Jimmy Rollins
RU Hanley Ramirez 5.00 12.00
Dan Uggla
SB Richie Sexson 4.00 10.00
Adrian Beltre
SH Ben Sheets 4.00 10.00
J.J. Hardy
SL Alfonso Soriano 5.00 12.00
Derrek Lee
SM Johan Santana 5.00 12.00
Joe Mauer
SW Johan Santana 5.00 12.00
Dontrelle Willis
TD Jim Thome 4.00 10.00
Jermaine Dye
TM Miguel Tejada 4.00 10.00
Nick Markakis
UH Chase Utley 8.00 20.00
Cole Hamels
VB Justin Verlander 10.00 25.00
Jeremy Bonderman
VR Justin Verlander 10.00 25.00
Ivan Rodriguez
VY Jason Varitek 6.00 15.00
Kevin Youkilis
WR Vernon Wells 4.00 10.00
Alex Rios
YK Michael Young 4.00 10.00
Ian Kinsler
ZL Carlos Zambrano 4.00 10.00
Derrek Lee

2008 Upper Deck Spectrum Three Star Swatches

OVERALL MEM ODDS 1:10
STATED PRINT RUN 75 SER.#'d SETS
GDH Ken Griffey Jr. 6.00 15.00
Adam Dunn
Aaron Harang
HBK Cole Hamels 4.00 10.00
Erik Bedard
Scott Kazmir
JCC Derek Jeter 20.00 50.00
Joba Chamberlain
Robinson Cano
JPG Derek Jeter 20.00 50.00
Albert Pujols
Ken Griffey Jr.
KHS Ian Kinsler 4.00 10.00
Aaron Hill
Freddy Sanchez
MGS Greg Maddux 12.50 30.00
Tom Glavine
John Smoltz
MJS Pedro Martinez 10.00 25.00
Randy Johnson
Curt Schilling
MRM Victor Martinez 4.00 10.00
Ivan Rodriguez
Joe Mauer
OBP Roy Oswalt 6.00 15.00
Lance Berkman
Hunter Pence
OVS Magglio Ordonez 10.00 25.00
Justin Verlander
Gary Sheffield
PER Albert Pujols 10.00 25.00
Jim Edmonds
Scott Rolen
PSB Jake Peavy 6.00 15.00
Johan Santana
Josh Beckett
RBM Jose Reyes 10.00 25.00
Carlos Beltran
Pedro Martinez
RUH Jimmy Rollins 6.00 15.00
Chase Utley
Cole Hamels
SBH Grady Sizemore 4.00 10.00
Carlos Beltran
Torii Hunter
SCG Alfonso Soriano 4.00 10.00
Miguel Cabrera
Vladimir Guerrero
SJT John Smoltz 6.00 15.00
Chipper Jones
Mark Teixeira
SMH Grady Sizemore 6.00 15.00
Victor Martinez
Travis Hafner
SMM Johan Santana 6.00 15.00
Justin Morneau
Joe Mauer
ZSL Carlos Zambrano 10.00 25.00
Alfonso Soriano
Derrek Lee

2009 Upper Deck Spectrum

This set was released on February 24, 2009. The base set consists of 120 cards.

COMP.SET w/o AU's (100) 8.00 20.00
COMMON CARD .15 .40
COMMON AU RC 3.00 8.00
OVERALL AUTO ODDS 1:7
EXCHANGE DEADLINE 1/29/2011
PRINTING PLATES RANDOMLY INSERTED
PLATE PRINT RUN 1 SET PER COLOR
BLACK-CYAN-MAGENTA-YELLOW ISSUED
NO PLATE PRICING DUE TO SCARCITY
1 Brandon Webb .25 .60
2 Randy Johnson .25 .60
3 Chris B. Young .15 .40
4 Dan Haren .15 .40
5 Adam Dunn .25 .60
6 Chipper Jones .40 1.00
7 Tim Hudson .25 .60
8 John Smoltz .40 1.00
9 Brian Roberts .15 .40
10 Nick Markakis .40 1.00
11 Josh Beckett .25 .60
12 David Ortiz .25 .60
13 Daisuke Matsuzaka .40 1.00
14 J.D. Drew .15 .40
15 Jonathan Papelbon .25 .60
16 Mike Lowell .15 .40
17 Alfonso Soriano .25 .60
18 Derrek Lee .15 .40
19 Kosuke Fukudome .40 1.00
20 Carlos Zambrano .25 .60
21 Aramis Ramirez .15 .40
22 Rich Harden .15 .40
23 Carlos Quentin .25 .60
24 Jim Thome .25 .60
25 Ken Griffey Jr. .60 1.50
26 Jay Bruce .25 .60
27 Edinson Volquez .15 .40
28 Brandon Phillips .15 .40
29 Victor Martinez .25 .60
30 Grady Sizemore .25 .60
31 Travis Hafner .15 .40
32 Matt Holliday .40 1.00
33 Troy Tulowitzki .40 1.00
34 Garrett Atkins .15 .40
35 Miguel Cabrera .40 1.00
36 Magglio Ordonez .25 .60
37 Justin Verlander .50 1.25
38 Hanley Ramirez .40 1.00
39 Dan Uggla .25 .60
40 Lance Berkman .25 .60
41 Carlos Lee .15 .40
42 Roy Oswalt .25 .60
43 Miguel Tejada .25 .60
44 Joakim Soria .15 .40
45 Alex Gordon .25 .60
46 Mark Teixeira .40 1.00
47 Vladimir Guerrero .40 1.00
48 Torii Hunter .15 .40
49 John Lackey .15 .40
50 Manny Ramirez .40 1.00
51 Russell Martin .15 .40
52 Matt Kemp .25 .60
53 Clayton Kershaw .40 1.00
54 CC Sabathia .25 .60
55 Prince Fielder .25 .60
56 Ryan Braun .50 1.25
57 Joe Mauer .40 1.00
58 Justin Morneau .40 1.00
59 Jose Reyes .25 .60
60 David Wright .50 1.25
61 Johan Santana .40 1.00
62 Carlos Beltran .15 .40
63 Ivan Rodriguez .25 .60
64 Alex Rodriguez .60 1.50
65 Derek Jeter 1.00 2.50
66 Chien-Ming Wang .25 .60
67 Jason Giambi .15 .40
68 Joba Chamberlain .25 .60
69 Mariano Rivera .40 1.00
70 Xavier Nady .15 .40
71 Frank Thomas .40 1.00
72 Carlos Gonzalez .25 .60
73 Chase Utley .40 1.00
74 Ryan Howard .50 1.25
75 Jimmy Rollins .25 .60
76 Andy LaRoche .15 .40
77 Nate McLouth .15 .40
78 Adrian Gonzalez .25 .60
79 Greg Maddux .50 1.25
80 Jake Peavy .15 .40
81 Trevor Hoffman .25 .60
82 Tim Lincecum .60 1.50
83 Aaron Rowand .15 .40
84 Felix Hernandez .40 1.00
85 Ichiro Suzuki .60 1.50
86 Erik Bedard .15 .40
87 Albert Pujols 1.00 2.50
88 Troy Glaus .15 .40
89 Rick Ankiel .15 .40
90 B.J. Upton .25 .60
91 Evan Longoria .50 1.25
92 Scott Kazmir .15 .40
93 Carl Crawford .25 .60
94 Josh Hamilton .40 1.00
95 Ian Kinsler .25 .60
96 Michael Young .25 .60
97 Roy Halladay .40 1.00
98 Vernon Wells .15 .40
99 Ryan Zimmerman .25 .60
100 Lastings Milledge .15 .40
101 David Price AU RC 12.50 30.00
102 Conor Gillaspie AU RC 10.00 25.00
103 Jeff Baisley AU RC 5.00 12.00
104 Angel Salome AU (RC) 6.00 15.00
105 Aaron Cunningham AU RC 3.00 8.00
106 Lou Marson AU (RC) 8.00 20.00
107 Matt Antonelli AU RC 3.00 8.00
108 Michael Bowden AU (RC) 4.00 10.00
109 Francisco Cervelli AU RC EXCH 6.00 15.00
110 Phil Coke AU RC 3.00 8.00
111 Josh Outman AU RC 3.00 8.00
112 Shairon Martis AU RC 4.00 10.00
113 Mat Gamel AU RC 5.00 12.00
114 Josh Geer AU (RC) 3.00 8.00
115 Greg Golson AU (RC) 3.00 8.00
116 Kila Ka'aihue AU (RC) 6.00 15.00
117 Wade LeBlanc AU RC 3.00 8.00
118 Chris Lambert AU (RC) 3.00 8.00
119 James Parr AU (RC) 3.00 8.00
120 Matt Tuiasosopo AU (RC) 4.00 10.00

2009 Upper Deck Spectrum Black

*BLK: 4X TO 10X BASIC CARDS
RANDOM INSERTS IN PACKS
STATED PRINT RUN 50 SER.#'d SETS

2009 Upper Deck Spectrum Blue

RANDOM INSERTS IN RETAIL PACKS
NO PRICING DUE TO LACK OF MKT INFO

2009 Upper Deck Spectrum Gold Jersey

OVERALL MEM ODDS 1:7
STATED PRINT RUN 99 SER.#'d SETS
1 Brandon Webb Jsy 8.00 20.00
2 Randy Johnson Jsy 4.00 10.00
4 Dan Haren Jsy 3.00 8.00
5 Adam Dunn Jsy 3.00 8.00
6 Chipper Jones Jsy 4.00 10.00
7 Tim Hudson Jsy 3.00 8.00
8 John Smoltz Jsy 3.00 8.00
9 Brian Roberts Jsy 4.00 10.00
10 Nick Markakis Jsy 4.00 10.00
11 Josh Beckett Jsy 3.00 8.00
12 David Ortiz Jsy 3.00 8.00
13 Daisuke Matsuzaka Jsy 6.00 15.00
14 J.D. Drew Jsy/54 3.00 8.00
15 Jonathan Papelbon Jsy 3.00 8.00
16 Mike Lowell Jsy 4.00 10.00
17 Alfonso Soriano Jsy 3.00 8.00
18 Derrek Lee Jsy 3.00 8.00
19 Kosuke Fukudome Jsy 5.00 12.00
20 Carlos Zambrano Jsy 3.00 8.00
21 Aramis Ramirez Jsy 5.00 12.00
24 Jim Thome Jsy 3.00 8.00
25 Ken Griffey Jr. Jsy 6.00 15.00
26 Jay Bruce Jsy 8.00 20.00
27 Edinson Volquez Jsy 3.00 8.00
28 Brandon Phillips Jsy 3.00 8.00
29 Victor Martinez Jsy 3.00 8.00
30 Grady Sizemore Jsy 3.00 8.00
31 Travis Hafner Jsy 3.00 8.00
32 Matt Holliday Jsy 3.00 8.00
33 Troy Tulowitzki Jsy 3.00 8.00
34 Garrett Atkins Jsy 3.00 8.00
35 Miguel Cabrera Jsy 3.00 8.00
36 Magglio Ordonez Jsy 3.00 8.00
37 Justin Verlander Jsy 3.00 8.00
38 Hanley Ramirez Jsy 3.00 8.00
39 Dan Uggla Jsy 3.00 8.00
40 Lance Berkman Jsy 3.00 8.00
41 Carlos Lee Jsy 4.00 10.00
42 Roy Oswalt Jsy 3.00 8.00
43 Miguel Tejada Jsy 3.00 8.00
44 Joakim Soria Jsy 3.00 8.00
45 Alex Gordon Jsy 5.00 12.00
46 Mark Teixeira Jsy 4.00 10.00
47 Vladimir Guerrero Jsy 3.00 8.00
49 John Lackey Jsy 3.00 8.00
50 Manny Ramirez Jsy 4.00 10.00
51 Russell Martin Jsy 3.00 8.00
52 Matt Kemp Jsy 3.00 8.00
53 Clayton Kershaw Jsy 4.00 10.00
54 CC Sabathia Jsy 3.00 8.00
55 Prince Fielder Jsy 3.00 8.00
56 Ryan Braun Jsy 5.00 12.00
57 Joe Mauer Jsy 3.00 8.00
58 Justin Morneau Jsy 4.00 10.00
59 Jose Reyes Jsy 4.00 10.00
61 Johan Santana Jsy 5.00 12.00
62 Carlos Beltran Jsy 4.00 10.00
63 Ivan Rodriguez Jsy 3.00 8.00
65 Derek Jeter Jsy 10.00 25.00
66 Chien-Ming Wang Jsy 5.00 12.00
67 Jason Giambi Jsy 3.00 8.00
68 Joba Chamberlain Jsy 5.00 12.00
69 Mariano Rivera Jsy 4.00 10.00
70 Xavier Nady Jsy/80 3.00 8.00
71 Frank Thomas Jsy 8.00 20.00
72 Carlos Gonzalez Jsy 4.00 10.00
73 Chase Utley Jsy 6.00 15.00
78 Adrian Gonzalez Jsy 3.00 8.00
79 Greg Maddux Jsy 15.00 40.00
80 Jake Peavy Jsy 3.00 8.00
81 Trevor Hoffman Jsy 3.00 8.00
82 Tim Lincecum Jsy 5.00 12.00
84 Felix Hernandez Jsy 3.00 8.00
86 Erik Bedard Jsy 3.00 8.00
87 Albert Pujols Jsy 10.00 25.00
88 Troy Glaus Jsy 3.00 8.00
89 Rick Ankiel Jsy 5.00 12.00
90 B.J. Upton Jsy 3.00 8.00
91 Evan Longoria Jsy 6.00 15.00
92 Scott Kazmir Jsy 3.00 8.00
93 Carl Crawford Jsy 3.00 8.00
95 Ian Kinsler Jsy 3.00 8.00
96 Michael Young Jsy 3.00 8.00
97 Roy Halladay Jsy 3.00 8.00
98 Vernon Wells Jsy 3.00 8.00
99 Ryan Zimmerman Jsy 4.00 10.00
100 Lastings Milledge Jsy 3.00 8.00

2009 Upper Deck Spectrum Green

*GRN: 1.5X TO 4X BASIC CARDS
RANDOM INSERTS IN PACKS
STATED PRINT RUN 99 SER.#'d SETS

2009 Upper Deck Spectrum Red

*RED: .75X TO 2X BASIC CARDS
RANDOM INSERTS IN PACKS
STATED PRINT RUN 250 SER.#'d SETS

2009 Upper Deck Spectrum Turquoise

*TURQ: 4X TO 10X BASIC CARDS
RANDOM INSERTS IN PACKS
STATED PRINT RUN 25 SER.#'d SETS

2009 Upper Deck Spectrum Spectrum of Stars Autographs

OVERALL AUTO ODDS 1:7
PRINTING PLATES RANDOMLY INSERTED
PLATE PRINT RUN 1 SET PER COLOR
BLACK-CYAN-MAGENTA-YELLOW ISSUED
NO PLATE PRICING DUE TO SCARCITY
BL B-Real 5.00 12.00
BT Brutus Beefcake 4.00 10.00
BU Burt Reynolds 15.00 40.00
CE Cheech Marin 20.00 50.00
CF Corey Feldman 6.00 15.00
EE Erika Eleniak 6.00 15.00
EO Ed O'Neill 12.50 30.00
FU Fabiana Udenio 5.00 12.00
HH Henry Hill 6.00 15.00
IS Ian Somerhalder 4.00 10.00
KI Kim Kardashian 60.00 120.00
KW Kendra Wilkinson 12.50 30.00
LE Leslie Nielsen 15.00 40.00
LF Lita Ford 6.00 15.00
LH Linda Hamilton 12.50 30.00
LP Lanny Poffo 5.00 12.00
LS Larry Storch 8.00 20.00
MK Martin Klebba 4.00 10.00
PR Matt Prokop 4.00 10.00
SF Susie Feldman 5.00 12.00
TC Tommy Chong 15.00 40.00
TR Terri Runnels 5.00 12.00

2009 Upper Deck Spectrum Spectrum of Stars Autographs Die Cut

*DIE CUT: .5X TO 1.2X BASIC INSERTS
OVERALL AUTO ODDS 1:7
STATED PRINT RUN 50 SER.#'d SETS

2009 Upper Deck Spectrum Spectrum Swatches Autographs

OVERALL AUTO ODDS 1:7
STATED PRINT RUN 3-99 SER.#'d SETS
NO PRICING ON QTY 25 OR LESS
SSAG Adrian Gonzalez/99 12.50 30.00
SSAM Andrew Miller/99 4.00 10.00
SSAS Alfonso Soriano/25
SSBE Josh Beckett/10
SSBI Chad Billingsley/35 10.00 25.00
SSBJ B.J. Upton/50 10.00 25.00
SSBP Brandon Phillips/99 6.00 15.00
SSBS Ben Sheets/35 6.00 15.00
SSBW Brandon Webb/35 12.50 30.00
SSBZ Clay Buchholz/99 6.00 15.00
SSCA Miguel Cabrera/10
SSCC Carl Crawford/75 6.00 15.00
SSCJ Chipper Jones/10
SSCK Clayton Kershaw/45 12.50 30.00
SSCL Carlos Lee/99 4.00 10.00
SSCW Chien-Ming Wang/3
SSCY Chris Young/99 4.00 10.00
SSDH Dan Haren/35 5.00 12.00
SSDL Derrek Lee/35 8.00 20.00
SSDP Dustin Pedroia/50 50.00 100.00
SSDU Dan Uggla/99 5.00 12.00
SSDY Delmon Young/52 5.00 12.00
SSEL Evan Longoria/10
SSEV Edinson Volquez/35 6.00 15.00
SSFH Felix Hernandez/75 12.50 30.00
SSGA Garrett Atkins/99 4.00 10.00
SSGO Alex Gordon/10
SSGR Ken Griffey Jr./75 50.00 100.00
SSGS Grady Sizemore/25
SSGT Garret Anderson/99 5.00 12.00
SSHA Corey Hart/99 4.00 10.00
SSHI Rich Hill/99 4.00 10.00
SSHR Hanley Ramirez/35 12.50 30.00
SSIK Ian Kinsler/25
SSJH Josh Hamilton/15
SSJL James Loney/25
SSJM Joe Mauer/50 40.00 80.00
SSJO Josh Hamilton/15
SSJT Jim Thome/5
SSKG Ken Griffey Jr./75 30.00 60.00
SSKY Kevin Youkilis/99 12.50 30.00
SSLB Lance Berkman/15
SSLO Evan Longoria/10
SSMA Manny Ramirez/99
SSMC Matt Cain/99 5.00 12.00
SSMH Matt Holliday/5
SSMK Matt Kemp/35 10.00 25.00
SSMO Justin Morneau/75 12.50 30.00
SSMT Mark Teixeira/3
SSNI Nick Markakis/99 10.00 25.00
SSNS Nick Swisher/99 4.00 10.00
SSPA Jonathan Papelbon/58 10.00 25.00
SSPF Prince Fielder/35
SSPK Paul Konerko/99 12.50 30.00
SSPM Pedro Martinez/5
SSRB Ryan Braun/35 30.00 60.00
SSRH Roy Halladay/50 50.00 100.00
SSRJ Randy Johnson/5
SSRM Russell Martin/50 15.00 40.00
SSRZ Ryan Zimmerman/99 10.00 25.00
SSSK Scott Kazmir/35 10.00 25.00
SSSO Alfonso Soriano/25
SSTG Tom Glavine/5
SSTH Tim Hudson/25
SSTL Tim Lincecum/50 50.00 100.00
SSTT Troy Tulowitzki/50 10.00 25.00
SSTW Tim Wakefield/15
SSVG Vladimir Guerrero/15
SSVW Vernon Wells/75 5.00 12.00

2009 Upper Deck Spectrum Spectrum Swatches Light Blue

OVERALL MEM ODDS 1:7
STATED PRINT RUN 99 SER.#'d SETS
SSAB Adrian Beltre 4.00 10.00
SSAG Adrian Gonzalez 4.00 10.00
SSAM Andrew Miller 4.00 10.00
SSAN Rick Ankiel 6.00 15.00
SSAP Albert Pujols 12.50 30.00
SSAR Alex Rios 6.00 15.00
SSAS Alfonso Soriano 4.00 10.00
SSBE Josh Beckett 4.00 10.00
SSBI Chad Billingsley
SSBJ B.J. Upton 4.00 10.00
SSBP Brandon Phillips 4.00 10.00
SSBS Ben Sheets 4.00 10.00
SSBW Brandon Webb 10.00 25.00
SSBZ Clay Buchholz 4.00 10.00
SSCA Miguel Cabrera 4.00 10.00
SSCB Carlos Beltran 5.00 12.00
SSCC Carl Crawford 4.00 10.00
SSCH Chin-Lung Hu 5.00 12.00
SSCJ Chipper Jones 5.00 12.00
SSCK Clayton Kershaw 5.00 12.00
SSCL Carlos Lee 5.00 12.00
SSCS CC Sabathia 4.00 10.00
SSCU Chase Utley 8.00 20.00
SSCW Chien-Ming Wang 6.00 15.00
SSCY Chris Young 4.00 10.00
SSDA David Ortiz 4.00 10.00
SSDH Dan Haren 4.00 10.00
SSDJ Derek Jeter 12.50 30.00
SSDL Derrek Lee 4.00 10.00
SSDM Daisuke Matsuzaka 8.00 20.00
SSDO David Ortiz 4.00 10.00
SSDP Dustin Pedroia 8.00 20.00
SSDU Dan Uggla 4.00 10.00
SSDY Delmon Young
SSEL Evan Longoria 8.00 20.00
SSEV Edinson Volquez 4.00 10.00
SSFH Felix Hernandez 4.00 10.00
SSGA Garrett Atkins 4.00 10.00
SSGL Troy Glaus 4.00 10.00
SSGM Greg Maddux 20.00 50.00
SSGO Alex Gordon 6.00 15.00
SSGR Ken Griffey Jr. 8.00 20.00
SSGS Grady Sizemore 4.00 10.00
SSGT Garret Anderson 4.00 10.00
SSHA Corey Hart 4.00 10.00
SSHI Rich Hill 4.00 10.00
SSHR Hanley Ramirez 4.00 10.00
SSIK Ian Kinsler 4.00 10.00
SSJA Jacoby Ellsbury 10.00 25.00
SSJC Joba Chamberlain 6.00 15.00
SSJE Derek Jeter 12.50 30.00
SSJH Josh Hamilton 8.00 20.00
SSJL James Loney 8.00 20.00
SSJM Joe Mauer 8.00 20.00
SSJO Josh Hamilton 8.00 20.00
SSJP Jake Peavy 4.00 10.00
SSJT Jim Thome 4.00 10.00
SSJU Justin Upton 4.00 10.00
SSKF Kosuke Fukudome 6.00 15.00
SSKG Ken Griffey Jr. 8.00 20.00
SSKY Kevin Youkilis 5.00 12.00
SSLB Lance Berkman 4.00 10.00
SSLO Evan Longoria 8.00 20.00
SSMA Manny Ramirez 5.00 12.00
SSMC Matt Cain 4.00 10.00
SSMH Matt Holliday 4.00 10.00
SSMK Matt Kemp 4.00 10.00
SSMO Justin Morneau 5.00 12.00
SSMR Manny Ramirez 5.00 12.00
SSMT Mark Teixeira 5.00 12.00
SSMY Michael Young 4.00 10.00
SSNI Nick Markakis 5.00 12.00
SSNS Nick Swisher 4.00 10.00
SSOR Magglio Ordonez 4.00 10.00
SSPA Jonathan Papelbon 4.00 10.00
SSPB Pat Burrell
SSPF Prince Fielder 4.00 10.00
SSPK Paul Konerko 4.00 10.00
SSPM Pedro Martinez 4.00 10.00
SSPU Albert Pujols 12.50 30.00
SSRB Ryan Braun 6.00 15.00
SSRE Jose Reyes 5.00 12.00
SSRH Roy Halladay 4.00 10.00
SSRJ Randy Johnson 5.00 12.00
SSRM Russell Martin 4.00 10.00
SSRZ Ryan Zimmerman 5.00 12.00
SSSA Johan Santana 6.00 15.00
SSSK Scott Kazmir 4.00 10.00
SSSO Alfonso Soriano 4.00 10.00
SSTG Tom Glavine 8.00 20.00
SSTH Tim Hudson 4.00 10.00
SSTL Tim Lincecum 6.00 15.00
SSTT Troy Tulowitzki 4.00 10.00
SSTW Tim Wakefield 4.00 10.00
SSVG Vladimir Guerrero 4.00 10.00
SSVW Vernon Wells 4.00 10.00

2009 Upper Deck Spectrum Spectrum Swatches Patch

OVERALL MEM ODDS ONE PER BOX
PRINT RUNS B/WN 23-25 COPIES PER
NO PRICING DUE TO SCARCITY
SSAG Adrian Gonzalez/23

2008 Upper Deck Timeline

This set was released on November 4, 2008. The base set consists of 385 cards.

COMMON CARD (1-50) .15 .40
COMMON RC (51-100) .25 .60
COMMON CARD (101-130) .25 .60
COMMON CARD (131-180) .25 .60
COMMON CARD (181-210) .25 .60
COMMON CARD (211-310) .25 .60
COMMON CARD (311-335) .40 1.00
COMMON CARD (336-360) .40 1.00
COMMON CARD (361-385) .75 2.00
1 Jose Reyes .25 .60
2 David Wright .50 1.25
3 Carlos Beltran .15 .40
4 Pedro Martinez .25 .60
5 Johan Santana .40 1.00
6 Hanley Ramirez .40 1.00
7 John Smoltz .40 1.00
8 Chipper Jones .40 1.00
9 Mark Teixeira .40 1.00
10 Chase Utley .40 1.00
11 Ryan Howard .50 1.25
12 Jimmy Rollins .25 .60
13 Alfonso Soriano .25 .60
14 Derrek Lee .15 .40
15 Jason Bay .25 .60
16 Lance Berkman .25 .60
17 Ken Griffey Jr. .60 1.50
18 Ryan Braun .50 1.25
19 Prince Fielder .25 .60
20 Albert Pujols 1.00 2.50
21 Tim Lincecum .60 1.50
22 Jake Peavy .15 .40
23 Matt Kemp .25 .60
24 Matt Holliday .40 1.00
25 Brandon Webb .25 .60
26 Randy Johnson .40 1.00
27 Alex Rodriguez .60 1.50
28 Derek Jeter 1.00 2.50
29 Chien-Ming Wang .25 .60
30 David Ortiz .25 .60
31 Manny Ramirez .40 1.00
32 Daisuke Matsuzaka .40 1.00
33 B.J. Upton .25 .60
34 Nick Markakis .40 1.00
35 Roy Halladay .40 1.00
36 Jim Thome .25 .60
37 Grady Sizemore .25 .60
38 Travis Hafner .15 .40
39 C.C. Sabathia .25 .60
40 Miguel Cabrera .40 1.00
41 Justin Verlander .50 1.25
42 Joe Mauer .40 1.00
43 Alex Gordon .25 .60
44 Frank Thomas .40 1.00
45 Vladimir Guerrero .40 1.00
46 Torii Hunter .15 .40
47 Josh Hamilton .40 1.00
48 Ichiro Suzuki .60 1.50
49 Felix Hernandez .40 1.00
50 Erik Bedard .15 .40
51 Daric Barton (RC) .25 .60
52 John Bowker (RC) .25 .60
53 Clay Buchholz (RC) .60 1.50
54 Jeff Clement (RC) .40 1.00
55 Johnny Cueto RC .40 1.00
56 Blake DeWitt (RC) .60 1.50
57 German Duran RC .40 1.00
58 Kosuke Fukudome RC .75 2.00
59 Alberto Gonzalez RC .40 1.00
60 Luke Hochevar RC .40 1.00
61 Chin-Lung Hu (RC) .40 1.00
62 Ian Kennedy RC .60 1.50
63 Masahide Kobayashi RC .40 1.00
64 Hiroki Kuroda RC .40 1.00
65 Evan Longoria RC 1.25 3.00
66 Jed Lowrie (RC) .60 1.50
67 Justin Masterson RC .60 1.50
68 Nick Blackburn RC .40 1.00
69 Micah Hoffpauir RC .75 2.00
70 Jeff Niemann (RC) .25 .60
71 Ross Ohlendorf RC .40 1.00
72 Jonathan Van Every RC .25 .60
73 Alexei Ramirez RC 1.00 2.50
74 Justin Ruggiano RC .40 1.00
75 Max Scherzer RC .75 2.00
76 Greg Smith RC .25 .60
77 Denard Span (RC) .40 1.00
78 Clete Thomas RC .40 1.00
79 Josh Banks (RC) .25 .60
80 Clay Timpner (RC) .25 .60
81 Matt Tolbert RC .40 1.00
82 J.R. Towles RC .40 1.00
83 Eugenio Velez RC .25 .60
84 Joey Votto (RC) 1.00 2.50
85 Rico Washington (RC) .25 .60
86 Jay Bruce (RC) 1.00 2.50
87 Wladimir Balentien (RC) .25 .60
88 Burke Badenhop RC .40 1.00
89 Brian Barton RC .40 1.00
90 Brian Bocock RC .40 1.00
91 Brandon Boggs (RC) .40 1.00
92 Robinzon Diaz (RC) .25 .60
93 Hernan Iribarren (RC) .40 1.00
94 Brent Lillibridge (RC) .25 .60
95 Yasuhiko Yabuta RC .40 1.00
96 Jeff Samardzija RC .75 2.00
97 Carlos Gonzalez (RC) .60 1.50
98 Clayton Kershaw RC 1.25 3.00
99 Jonathan Albaladejo RC .40 1.00
100 Nick Adenhart (RC) .25 .60
101 Bobby Wilson 92 ML RC .25 .60
102 Brandon Phillips 92 ML .25 .60
103 Chad Billingsley 92 ML .25 .60
104 Chris Duncan 92 ML .25 .60
105 Clay Timpner 92 ML (RC) .25 .60
106 Clete Thomas 92 ML RC .40 1.00
107 Corey Hart 92 ML .25 .60
108 Craig Breslow 92 ML .25 .60
109 David Murphy 92 ML .25 .60
110 Edinson Volquez 92 ML .25 .60
111 Elijah Dukes 92 ML .25 .60
112 Emmanuel Burriss 92 ML RC .40 1.00
113 Evan Longoria 92 ML RC 1.25 3.00
114 Fred Lewis 92 ML .25 .60
115 Felix Pie 92 ML .25 .60
116 German Duran 92 ML RC .40 1.00
117 Greg Smith 92 ML RC .25 .60
118 Hernan Iribarren 92 ML (RC) .40 1.00
119 Joey Votto 92 ML (RC) 1.00 2.50
120 Jonathan Van Every 92 ML RC .25 .60
121 Kosuke Fukudome 92 ML RC .75 2.00
122 Matt Joyce 92 ML RC .60 1.50
123 Max Scherzer 92 ML RC .75 2.00
124 Nick Swisher 92 ML .60 1.50
125 Paul Janish 92 ML (RC) .25 .60
126 Reed Johnson 92 ML .25 .60
127 Rico Washington 92 ML (RC) .25 .60
128 Russell Martin 92 ML .25 .60
129 Scott Kazmir 92 ML .40 1.00
130 Tyler Clippard 92 ML .25 .60
131 Randy Johnson 94 ATH .60 1.50
132 Frank Thomas 94 ATH .60 1.50
133 Greg Maddux 94 ATH .75 2.00
134 Vladimir Guerrero 94 ATH .60 1.50

135 Ryan Braun 94 ATH .75 2.00
136 David Ortiz 94 ATH .40 1.00
137 Jake Peavy 94 ATH .25 .60
138 Mark Teixeira 94 ATH .60 1.50
139 Jose Reyes 94 ATH .40 1.00
140 Chien-Ming Wang 94 ATH .40 1.00
141 Prince Fielder 94 ATH .40 1.00
142 Albert Pujols 94 ATH 1.50 4.00
143 Johan Santana 94 ATH .60 1.50
144 Josh Beckett 94 ATH .40 1.00
145 Alex Rodriguez 94 ATH 1.00 2.50
146 Felix Hernandez 94 ATH .60 1.50
147 Brandon Webb 94 ATH .40 1.00
148 Chase Utley 94 ATH .60 1.50
149 Derek Jeter 94 ATH 1.50 4.00
150 Grady Sizemore 94 ATH .40 1.00
151 B.J. Upton 94 ATH .40 1.00
152 Carlos Beltran 94 ATH .25 .60
153 Hanley Ramirez 94 ATH .60 1.50
154 Magglio Ordonez 94 ATH .40 1.00
155 Carlos Zambrano 94 ATH .40 1.00
156 Manny Ramirez 94 ATH .60 1.50
157 Travis Hafner 94 ATH .25 .60
158 David Wright 94 ATH .75 2.00
159 Jimmy Rollins 94 ATH .40 1.00
160 Matt Holliday 94 ATH .60 1.50
161 Ken Griffey Jr. 94 ATH 1.00 2.50
162 C.C. Sabathia 94 ATH .40 1.00
163 Joe Mauer 94 ATH .60 1.50
164 Derrek Lee 94 ATH .25 .60
165 Miguel Cabrera 94 ATH .60 1.50
166 Alfonso Soriano 94 ATH .40 1.00
167 Ichiro Suzuki 94 ATH 1.00 2.50
168 Daisuke Matsuzaka 94 ATH .60 1.50
169 Lance Berkman 94 ATH .40 1.00
170 Ryan Howard 94 ATH .75 2.00
171 J.R. Towles 94 ATH RC .40 1.00
172 Max Scherzer 94 ATH RC .75 2.00
173 Chin-Lung Hu 94 ATH .40 1.00
174 Daric Barton 94 ATH .25 .60
175 Ian Kennedy 94 ATH .60 1.50
176 Clay Buchholz 94 ATH .60 1.50
177 Joey Votto 94 ATH (RC) 1.00 2.50
178 Kosuke Fukudome 94 ATH RC .75 2.00
179 Johnny Cueto 94 ATH .40 1.00
180 Evan Longoria 94 ATH 1.25 3.00
181 Brandon Boggs 95 STP (RC) .40 1.00
182 Brian Bocock 95 STP RC .40 1.00
183 Burke Badenhop 95 STP RC .40 1.00
184 Callix Crabbe 95 STP (RC) .25 .60
185 Cha-Seung Baek 95 STP .25 .60
186 Chris Smith 95 STP (RC) .25 .60
187 Clayton Kershaw 95 STP RC 1.25 3.00
188 Felipe Paulino 95 STP RC .40 1.00
189 Glen Perkins 95 STP .25 .60
190 Homer Bailey 95 STP .40 1.00
191 James Loney 95 STP .40 1.00
192 Jay Bruce 95 STP (RC) 1.00 2.50
193 Jeff Baker 95 STP .25 .60
194 Jeff Keppinger 95 STP .25 .60
195 Jesus Flores 95 STP .25 .60
196 Joakim Soria 95 STP .25 .60
197 Joey Votto 95 STP (RC) 1.00 2.50
198 Josh Hamilton 95 STP .60 1.50
199 Kosuke Fukudome 95 STP RC .75 2.00
200 Micah Hoffpauir 95 STP RC .75 2.00
201 Nick Blackburn 95 STP RC .40 1.00
202 Nyjer Morgan 95 STP (RC) .25 .60
203 Randor Bierd 95 STP RC .25 .60
204 Rich Hill 95 STP .25 .60
205 Ross Ohlendorf 95 STP RC .40 1.00
206 Russell Martin 95 STP .25 .60
207 Ryan Garko 95 STP .25 .60
208 Seth Smith 95 STP .25 .60
209 Steve Holm 95 STP RC .25 .60
210 Travis Hafner 95 STP .25 .60
211 Brandon Webb 04 TT .40 1.00
212 Randy Johnson 04 TT .60 1.50
213 Max Scherzer 04 TT RC .75 2.00
214 Chris B. Young 04 TT .25 .60
215 Justin Upton 04 TT .40 1.00
216 John Smoltz 04 TT .60 1.50
217 Chipper Jones 04 TT .60 1.50
218 Mark Teixeira 04 TT .60 1.50
219 Jeff Francoeur 04 TT .40 1.00
220 Adrian Gonzalez 04 TT .40 1.00
221 Nick Markakis 04 TT .60 1.50
222 Jacoby Ellsbury 04 TT 1.00 2.50
223 David Ortiz 04 TT .40 1.00
224 Manny Ramirez 04 TT .60 1.50
225 Daisuke Matsuzaka 04 TT .60 1.50
226 Clay Buchholz 04 TT (RC) .60 1.50
227 Jed Lowrie 04 TT (RC) .60 1.50
228 Justin Masterson 04 TT RC .60 1.50
229 Geovany Soto 04 TT .60 1.50
230 Alfonso Soriano 04 TT .40 1.00
231 Derrek Lee 04 TT .25 .60
232 Kosuke Fukudome 04 TT RC .75 2.00
233 Jim Thome 04 TT .40 1.00
234 Alexei Ramirez 04 TT RC 1.00 2.50
235 Ken Griffey Jr. 04 TT 1.00 2.50
236 Johnny Cueto 04 TT RC .40 1.00
237 Joey Votto 04 TT (RC) 1.00 2.50
238 Brandon Phillips 04 TT .25 .60
239 Edinson Volquez 04 TT .25 .60
240 Grady Sizemore 04 TT .40 1.00
241 Travis Hafner 04 TT .25 .60
242 C.C. Sabathia 04 TT .40 1.00
243 Matt Holliday 04 TT .60 1.50
244 Troy Tulowitzki 04 TT .60 1.50
245 Miguel Cabrera 04 TT .60 1.50
246 Justin Verlander 04 TT .75 2.00
247 Matt Tolbert 04 TT RC .40 1.00
248 Hanley Ramirez 04 TT .60 1.50
249 Jeremy Hermida 04 TT .25 .60
250 Lance Berkman 04 TT .40 1.00
251 J.R. Towles 04 TT RC .40 1.00
252 Alex Gordon 04 TT .40 1.00
253 Luke Hochevar 04 TT RC .40 1.00
254 Vladimir Guerrero 04 TT .60 1.50
255 Torii Hunter 04 TT .25 .60
256 Nick Adenhart 04 TT (RC) .25 .60
257 Garrett Atkins 04 TT .25 .60
258 Blake DeWitt 04 TT (RC) .60 1.50
259 Chin-Lung Hu 04 TT (RC) .40 1.00
260 Hiroki Kuroda 04 TT RC .40 1.00
261 Matt Kemp 04 TT .40 1.00
262 James Loney 04 TT .40 1.00
263 Justin Morneau 04 TT .60 1.50
264 Dan Haren 04 TT .25 .60
265 Ryan Braun 04 TT .75 2.00
266 Corey Hart 04 TT .25 .60
267 Rickie Weeks 04 TT .40 1.00
268 Prince Fielder 04 TT .40 1.00
269 Carlos Gomez 04 TT .25 .60
270 Joe Mauer 04 TT .60 1.50
271 Jose Reyes 04 TT .60 1.50
272 David Wright 04 TT .75 2.00
273 Carlos Beltran 04 TT .25 .60
274 Pedro Martinez 04 TT .40 1.00
275 Hideki Matsui 04 TT .60 1.50
276 Alex Rodriguez 04 TT 1.00 2.50
277 Derek Jeter 04 TT 1.50 4.00
278 Chien-Ming Wang 04 TT .40 1.00
279 Ian Kennedy 04 TT RC .60 1.50
280 Phil Hughes 04 TT .60 1.50
281 Frank Thomas 04 TT .60 1.50
282 Daric Barton 04 TT (RC) .25 .60
283 Greg Smith 04 TT RC .25 .60
284 Cole Hamels 04 TT .60 1.50
285 Chase Utley 04 TT .60 1.50
286 Ryan Howard 04 TT .75 2.00
287 Jimmy Rollins 04 TT .40 1.00
288 Jason Bay 04 TT .40 1.00
289 Jake Peavy 04 TT .25 .60
290 Brian McCann 04 TT .40 1.00
291 Tim Lincecum 04 TT 1.00 2.50
292 Justin Ruggiano 04 TT RC .40 1.00
293 Jay Bruce 04 TT (RC) 1.00 2.50
294 Brian Bocock 04 TT RC .25 .60
295 Ichiro Suzuki 04 TT 1.00 2.50
296 Adam Dunn 04 TT .40 1.00
297 Erik Bedard 04 TT .25 .60
298 Jeff Clement 04 TT (RC) .40 1.00
299 Felix Hernandez 04 TT .60 1.50
300 Albert Pujols 04 TT 1.50 4.00
301 Rick Ankiel 04 TT .25 .60
302 B.J. Upton 04 TT .40 1.00
303 Evan Longoria 04 TT RC 1.25 3.00
304 Clayton Kershaw 04 TT RC 1.25 3.00
305 Carl Crawford 04 TT .40 1.00
306 Russell Martin 04 TT .25 .60
307 Brandon Boggs 04 TT (RC) .40 1.00
308 Josh Hamilton 04 TT .60 1.50
309 Roy Halladay 04 TT .60 1.50
310 Ryan Zimmerman 04 TT .40 1.00
311 Evan Longoria 93 SP 2.00 5.00
312 Johnny Cueto 93 SP .60 1.50
313 Kosuke Fukudome 93 SP 1.25 3.00
314 Joey Votto 93 SP 1.50 4.00
315 Clay Buchholz 93 SP 1.00 2.50
316 Ian Kennedy 93 SP 1.00 2.50
317 Daric Barton 93 SP .40 1.00
318 Chin-Lung Hu 93 SP .40 1.00
319 Max Scherzer 93 SP 1.25 3.00
320 J.R. Towles 93 SP .60 1.50
321 Nick Adenhart 93 SP .40 1.00
322 Wladimir Balentien 93 SP .40 1.00
323 Brian Barton 93 SP .60 1.50
324 Brian Bocock 93 SP .60 1.50
325 Jonathan Herrera 93 SP RC .60 1.50
326 Jesse Carlson 93 SP RC .60 1.50
327 Jeff Clement 93 SP .60 1.50
328 Brandon Jones 93 SP RC 1.00 2.50
329 German Duran 93 SP .60 1.50
330 Alex Romero 93 SP (RC) .60 1.50
331 Jay Bruce 93 SP 1.50 4.00
332 Luke Hochevar 93 SP .60 1.50
333 Clayton Kershaw 93 SP 2.00 5.00
334 Nick Blackburn 93 SP .60 1.50
335 Jed Lowrie 93 SP 1.00 2.50
336 Evan Longoria 94 SP 2.00 5.00
337 Johnny Cueto 94 SP .60 1.50
338 Kosuke Fukudome 94 SP 1.25 3.00
339 Joey Votto 94 SP 1.50 4.00
340 Clay Buchholz 94 SP 1.00 2.50
341 Ian Kennedy 94 SP 1.00 2.50
342 Daric Barton 94 SP .40 1.00
343 Chin-Lung Hu 94 SP .60 1.50
344 Max Scherzer 94 SP 1.25 3.00
345 J.R. Towles 94 SP .60 1.50
346 Justin Masterson 94 SP 1.00 2.50
347 Kyle McClellan 94 SP RC .40 1.00
348 Evan Meek 94 SP RC .40 1.00
349 Nyjer Morgan 94 SP .40 1.00
350 Colt Morton 94 SP RC .60 1.50
351 Luke Carlin 94 SP RC .40 1.00
352 Emmanuel Burriss 94 SP .60 1.50
353 Clint Sammons 94 SP (RC) .40 1.00
354 Ross Ohlendorf 94 SP .60 1.50
355 Jay Bruce 94 SP 1.50 4.00
356 Felipe Paulino 94 SP .60 1.50
357 Alexei Ramirez 94 SP 1.50 4.00
358 Clayton Kershaw 94 SP 2.00 5.00
359 Cory Wade 94 SP (RC) .40 1.00
360 Greg Smith 94 SP .40 1.00
361 Evan Longoria 95 SP 3.00 8.00
362 Johnny Cueto 95 SP 1.25 3.00
363 Kosuke Fukudome 95 SP 2.00 5.00
364 Joey Votto 95 SP 3.00 8.00
365 Clay Buchholz 95 SP 2.00 5.00
366 Ian Kennedy 95 SP 2.00 5.00
367 Daric Barton 95 SP .75 2.00
368 Chin-Lung Hu 95 SP 1.25 3.00
369 Max Scherzer 95 SP 2.50 6.00
370 J.R. Towles 95 SP 1.25 3.00
371 Mitchell Boggs 95 SP (RC) .75 2.00
372 Jay Bruce 95 SP 3.00 8.00
373 Alberto Gonzalez 95 SP 1.25 3.00
374 Rich Thompson 95 SP RC 1.25 3.00
375 Robinzon Diaz 95 SP .75 2.00
376 Clay Timpner 95 SP .75 2.00
377 Eider Torres 95 SP (RC) 1.25 3.00
378 Ramon Troncoso 95 SP RC .75 2.00
379 Clayton Kershaw 95 SP 4.00 10.00
380 Rico Washington 95 SP .75 2.00
381 Brandon Jones 95 SP 2.00 5.00
382 Bobby Wilson 95 SP .75 2.00
383 Wesley Wright 95 SP RC .75 2.00
384 Mike Parisi 95 SP RC 1.25 3.00
385 Jonathan Van Every 95 SP .75 2.00

2008 Upper Deck Timeline Gold

*VET 1-50: 1X TO 2.5X BASIC
*RC 51-100: .6X TO 1.5X BASIC
VET ODDS 1:6 HOBBY, 1:24 RETAIL
RC ODDS 1:12 HOBBY, 1:48 RETAIL

2008 Upper Deck Timeline 1992 UD Minor League Autographs

STATED ODDS 1:27 HOB., 1:144 RET.
101 Bobby Wilson 3.00 8.00
102 Brandon Phillips
103 Chad Billingsley
104 Chris Duncan
105 Clay Timpner 3.00 8.00
106 Clete Thomas 3.00 8.00
107 Corey Hart
108 Craig Breslow 4.00 10.00
109 David Murphy
110 Edinson Volquez
111 Elijah Dukes 5.00 12.00
112 Emmanuel Burriss
113 Evan Longoria
114 Fred Lewis
115 Felix Pie
116 German Duran 3.00 8.00
117 Greg Smith 3.00 8.00
118 Hernan Iribarren 3.00 8.00
119 Joey Votto
120 Jonathan Van Every 4.00 10.00
121 Kosuke Fukudome
122 Matt Joyce 6.00 15.00
123 Max Scherzer
124 Nick Swisher
125 Paul Janish 3.00 8.00
126 Reed Johnson 3.00 8.00
127 Rico Washington 3.00 8.00
128 Russell Martin
129 Scott Kazmir
130 Tyler Clippard 3.00 8.00

2008 Upper Deck Timeline 1993 SP Autographs

OVERALL AU ODDS 1:9 HOBBY
STATED PRINT RUN 93 SER.#'d SETS
311 Evan Longoria
312 Johnny Cueto 10.00 25.00
315 Clay Buchholz 10.00 25.00
317 Daric Barton
318 Chin-Lung Hu 20.00 50.00
320 J.R. Towles
321 Nick Adenhart
322 Wladimir Balentien 6.00 15.00
323 Brian Barton
324 Brian Bocock 3.00 8.00
325 Jonathan Herrera
326 Jesse Carlson
327 Jeff Clement 10.00 25.00
328 Brandon Jones 6.00 15.00
329 German Duran 3.00 8.00
330 Alex Romero
331 Jay Bruce 20.00 50.00
332 Luke Hochevar 4.00 10.00
333 Clayton Kershaw
334 Nick Blackburn
335 Jed Lowrie

2008 Upper Deck Timeline 1994 All-Time Heroes 20th Anniversary

STATED ODDS 1:9 HOB., 1:72 RET.
131 Randy Johnson 1.00 2.50
132 Frank Thomas 1.00 2.50
133 Greg Maddux 1.25 3.00
134 Vladimir Guerrero 1.00 2.50
135 Ryan Braun 1.25 3.00
136 David Ortiz .60 1.50
137 Jake Peavy .40 1.00
138 Mark Teixeira 1.00 2.50
139 Jose Reyes .60 1.50
140 Chien-Ming Wang .60 1.50
141 Prince Fielder .60 1.50
142 Albert Pujols 2.50 6.00
143 Johan Santana 1.00 2.50
144 Josh Beckett .60 1.50
145 Alex Rodriguez 1.50 4.00
146 Felix Hernandez 1.00 2.50
147 Brandon Webb .60 1.50
148 Chase Utley 1.00 2.50
149 Derek Jeter 2.50 6.00
150 Grady Sizemore .60 1.50
151 B.J. Upton .60 1.50
152 Carlos Beltran .40 1.00
153 Hanley Ramirez 1.00 2.50
154 Magglio Ordonez .60 1.50
155 Carlos Zambrano .60 1.50
156 Manny Ramirez 1.00 2.50
157 Travis Hafner .40 1.00
158 David Wright 1.25 3.00
159 Jimmy Rollins .60 1.50
160 Matt Holliday 1.00 2.50
161 Ken Griffey Jr. 1.50 4.00
162 C.C. Sabathia .60 1.50
163 Joe Mauer 1.00 2.50
164 Derrek Lee .40 1.00
165 Miguel Cabrera 1.00 2.50
166 Alfonso Soriano .60 1.50
167 Ichiro Suzuki 1.50 4.00
168 Daisuke Matsuzaka 1.00 2.50
169 Lance Berkman .60 1.50
170 Ryan Howard 1.25 3.00
171 J.R. Towles .60 1.50
172 Max Scherzer 1.25 3.00
173 Chin-Lung Hu .60 1.50
174 Daric Barton .40 1.00
175 Ian Kennedy 1.00 2.50
176 Clay Buchholz 1.00 2.50
177 Joey Votto 1.50 4.00
178 Kosuke Fukudome 1.25 3.00
179 Johnny Cueto .60 1.50
180 Evan Longoria 2.00 5.00

2008 Upper Deck Timeline 1994 All-Time Heroes Autographs

OVERALL AU ODDS 1:9 HOBBY
PRINT RUNS B/WN 5-99 COPIES PER
NO PRICING ON QTY 25 OR LESS
131 Randy Johnson/5
132 Frank Thomas/5
135 Ryan Braun/25
140 Chien-Ming Wang/10
141 Prince Fielder/25
144 Josh Beckett/10
146 Felix Hernandez/25
147 Brandon Webb/25
149 Derek Jeter/99 75.00 150.00
150 Grady Sizemore/25
151 B.J. Upton/25
153 Hanley Ramirez/25
157 Travis Hafner/25
160 Matt Holliday/25
163 Joe Mauer/25
164 Derrek Lee/25
165 Miguel Cabrera/10
166 Alfonso Soriano/10
168 Daisuke Matsuzaka/5
169 Lance Berkman/10
171 J.R. Towles/99 4.00 10.00
173 Chin-Lung Hu/99 20.00 50.00
174 Daric Barton/99 5.00 12.00
176 Clay Buchholz/50 12.50 30.00
179 Johnny Cueto/59
180 Evan Longoria/50

2008 Upper Deck Timeline 1994 SP Autographs

OVERALL AU ODDS 1:9 HOBBY
STATED PRINT RUN 94 SER.#'d SETS
336 Evan Longoria 75.00 150.00
337 Johnny Cueto
340 Clay Buchholz
342 Daric Barton 5.00 12.00
343 Chin-Lung Hu
345 J.R. Towles
346 Justin Masterson 60.00 120.00
347 Kyle McClellan 10.00 25.00
349 Nyjer Morgan
350 Colt Morton
351 Luke Carlin
354 Ross Ohlendorf 3.00 8.00
356 Felipe Paulino 3.00 8.00
357 Alexei Ramirez 60.00 120.00
358 Clayton Kershaw 12.50 30.00
359 Cory Wade 6.00 15.00
360 Greg Smith 5.00 12.00

2008 Upper Deck Timeline 1995 SP Autographs

OVERALL AU ODDS 1:9 HOBBY
STATED PRINT RUN 95 SER.#'d SETS
361 Evan Longoria 75.00 150.00
362 Johnny Cueto 5.00 12.00
365 Clay Buchholz 10.00 25.00
367 Daric Barton 5.00 12.00
368 Chin-Lung Hu
370 J.R. Towles 4.00 10.00
371 Mitchell Boggs 5.00 12.00
373 Alberto Gonzalez
375 Robinzon Diaz 4.00 10.00
376 Clay Timpner 3.00 8.00
377 Eider Torres
378 Ramon Troncoso
379 Clayton Kershaw
380 Rico Washington
381 Brandon Jones
382 Bobby Wilson 3.00 8.00
383 Wesley Wright
384 Mike Parisi
385 Jonathan Van Every

2008 Upper Deck Timeline 1995 SP Top Prospects Autographs

STATED ODDS 1:27 HOB., 1:144 RET.
181 Brandon Boggs 3.00 8.00
182 Brian Bocock 3.00 8.00
183 Burke Badenhop 3.00 8.00
185 Cha-Seung Baek
186 Chris Smith 4.00 10.00
187 Clayton Kershaw
188 Felipe Paulino 3.00 8.00
189 Glen Perkins
190 Homer Bailey 4.00 10.00
191 James Loney 3.00 8.00
193 Jeff Baker 3.00 8.00
194 Jeff Keppinger 3.00 8.00
195 Jesus Flores 3.00 8.00
196 Joakim Soria 4.00 10.00
198 Josh Hamilton 10.00 25.00
200 Micah Hoffpauir 8.00 20.00
201 Nick Blackburn 6.00 15.00
202 Nyjer Morgan 3.00 8.00
203 Randor Bierd 3.00 8.00
204 Rich Hill
206 Russell Martin
207 Ryan Garko
208 Seth Smith 4.00 10.00
209 Steve Holm 4.00 10.00
210 Travis Hafner

2008 Upper Deck Timeline 2004 UD Timeless Teams Autographs

OVERALL AU ODDS 1:9 HOBBY
PRINT RUNS B/WN 5-99 COPIES PER
NO PRICING ON QTY 10 OR LESS
211 Brandon Webb/10
212 Randy Johnson/5
214 Chris B. Young/10
217 Chipper Jones/10
219 Jeff Francoeur/50
220 Adrian Gonzalez/10
221 Nick Markakis/50
226 Clay Buchholz/50
227 Jed Lowrie/50
228 Justin Masterson/50
230 Alfonso Soriano/10
231 Derrek Lee/10
233 Jim Thome/10
234 Alexei Ramirez/10
236 Johnny Cueto/59
238 Brandon Phillips/99 5.00 12.00
239 Edinson Volquez/99 10.00 25.00
240 Grady Sizemore/10
241 Travis Hafner/10
243 Matt Holliday/10
244 Troy Tulowitzki/10
245 Miguel Cabrera/10
246 Justin Verlander/10
247 Matt Tolbert/99 6.00 15.00
248 Hanley Ramirez/10
250 Lance Berkman/10
251 J.R. Towles/99
252 Alex Gordon/10
253 Luke Hochevar/50
255 Torii Hunter/10
256 Nick Adenhart/50
257 Garrett Atkins/10
259 Chin-Lung Hu/50
261 Matt Kemp/10
262 James Loney/10
263 Justin Morneau/10
264 Dan Haren/10
265 Ryan Braun/10
266 Corey Hart/50
267 Rickie Weeks/10
268 Prince Fielder/10
269 Carlos Gomez/99 15.00 40.00
270 Joe Mauer/10
277 Derek Jeter/10
278 Chien-Ming Wang/10
280 Phil Hughes/10
281 Frank Thomas/5
282 Daric Barton/99 5.00 12.00
283 Greg Smith/99 5.00 12.00
284 Cole Hamels/10
288 Jason Bay/99 12.50 30.00
292 Justin Ruggiano/36
294 Brian Bocock/99
296 Adam Dunn/10
298 Jeff Clement/99 10.00 25.00
299 Felix Hernandez/10
302 B.J. Upton/10
303 Evan Longoria/10
304 Clayton Kershaw/10
305 Carl Crawford/10
306 Russell Martin/10
307 Brandon Boggs/99 3.00 8.00
308 Josh Hamilton/50
309 Roy Halladay/10
310 Ryan Zimmerman/10

2008 Upper Deck Timeline 2004 UD Timeless Teams Silver

RANDOM INSERTS IN PACKS
STATED PRINT RUN 100 SER.#'d SETS
211 Brandon Webb 2.50 6.00
212 Randy Johnson 4.00 10.00
213 Max Scherzer 5.00 12.00
214 Chris B. Young 1.50 4.00
215 Justin Upton 2.50 6.00
216 John Smoltz 4.00 10.00
217 Chipper Jones 4.00 10.00
218 Mark Teixeira 4.00 10.00
219 Jeff Francoeur 2.50 6.00
220 Adrian Gonzalez 2.50 6.00
221 Nick Markakis 4.00 10.00
222 Jacoby Ellsbury 6.00 15.00
223 David Ortiz 2.50 6.00
224 Manny Ramirez 4.00 10.00
225 Daisuke Matsuzaka 4.00 10.00
226 Clay Buchholz 4.00 10.00
227 Jed Lowrie 4.00 10.00
228 Justin Masterson 4.00 10.00
229 Geovany Soto 4.00 10.00
230 Alfonso Soriano 2.50 6.00
231 Derrek Lee 1.50 4.00
232 Kosuke Fukudome 5.00 12.00
233 Jim Thome 2.50 6.00
234 Alexei Ramirez 6.00 15.00
235 Ken Griffey Jr. 6.00 15.00
236 Johnny Cueto 2.50 6.00
237 Joey Votto 6.00 15.00
238 Brandon Phillips 1.50 4.00
239 Edinson Volquez 1.50 4.00
240 Grady Sizemore 2.50 6.00
241 Travis Hafner 1.50 4.00
242 C.C. Sabathia 2.50 6.00
243 Matt Holliday 4.00 10.00
244 Troy Tulowitzki 4.00 10.00
245 Miguel Cabrera 4.00 10.00
246 Justin Verlander 5.00 12.00
247 Matt Tolbert 2.50 6.00
248 Hanley Ramirez 4.00 10.00
249 Jeremy Hermida 1.50 4.00
250 Lance Berkman 2.50 6.00
251 J.R. Towles 2.50 6.00
252 Alex Gordon 2.50 6.00
253 Luke Hochevar 2.50 6.00
254 Vladimir Guerrero 4.00 10.00
255 Torii Hunter 1.50 4.00
256 Nick Adenhart 1.50 4.00
257 Garrett Atkins 1.50 4.00
258 Blake DeWitt 4.00 10.00
259 Chin-Lung Hu 2.50 6.00
260 Hiroki Kuroda 2.50 6.00
261 Matt Kemp 2.50 6.00
262 James Loney 2.50 6.00
263 Justin Morneau 4.00 10.00
264 Dan Haren 1.50 4.00
265 Ryan Braun 5.00 12.00
266 Corey Hart 1.50 4.00
267 Rickie Weeks 2.50 6.00
268 Prince Fielder 2.50 6.00
269 Carlos Gomez 1.50 4.00
270 Joe Mauer 4.00 10.00
271 Jose Reyes 2.50 6.00
272 David Wright 5.00 12.00
273 Carlos Beltran 1.50 4.00
274 Pedro Martinez 2.50 6.00
275 Hideki Matsui 4.00 10.00
276 Alex Rodriguez 6.00 15.00
277 Derek Jeter 10.00 25.00
278 Chien-Ming Wang 2.50 6.00
279 Ian Kennedy 4.00 10.00
280 Phil Hughes 4.00 10.00
281 Frank Thomas 4.00 10.00
282 Daric Barton 1.50 4.00
283 Greg Smith 1.50 4.00
284 Cole Hamels 4.00 10.00
285 Chase Utley 4.00 10.00
286 Ryan Howard 5.00 12.00
287 Jimmy Rollins 2.50 6.00
288 Jason Bay 2.50 6.00
289 Jake Peavy 1.50 4.00
290 Brian McCann 2.50 6.00
291 Tim Lincecum 6.00 15.00
292 Justin Ruggiano 2.50 6.00
293 Jay Bruce 6.00 15.00
294 Brian Bocock 1.50 4.00
295 Ichiro Suzuki 6.00 15.00
296 Adam Dunn 2.50 6.00
297 Erik Bedard 1.50 4.00
298 Jeff Clement 2.50 6.00
299 Felix Hernandez 4.00 10.00
300 Albert Pujols 10.00 25.00
301 Rick Ankiel 1.50 4.00
302 B.J. Upton 2.50 6.00
303 Evan Longoria 8.00 20.00
304 Clayton Kershaw 8.00 20.00
305 Carl Crawford 2.50 6.00
306 Russell Martin 1.50 4.00
307 Brandon Boggs 2.50 6.00
308 Josh Hamilton 4.00 10.00
309 Roy Halladay 4.00 10.00
310 Ryan Zimmerman 2.50 6.00

2008 Upper Deck Timeline Memorabilia

ONE PER TARGET/WM BLASTER
AB A.J. Burnett 3.00 8.00
AD Adrian Beltre 3.00 8.00
AE Andre Ethier 4.00 10.00
AG Adrian Gonzalez 4.00 10.00
AJ Andruw Jones 3.00 8.00
AM Andrew Miller 4.00 10.00
AP Albert Pujols 6.00 15.00
AR Aaron Rowand 3.00 8.00
BC Bartolo Colon 3.00 8.00
BE Adrian Beltre 3.00 8.00
BG Brian Giles 3.00 8.00
BM Brian McCann 4.00 10.00

BO Bobby Crosby 3.00 8.00
BR B.J. Ryan 3.00 8.00
BS Ben Sheets 4.00 10.00
BU A.J. Burnett 3.00 8.00
BZ Barry Zito 3.00 8.00
CB Chad Billingsley 3.00 8.00
CC Carl Crawford 3.00 8.00
CD Carlos Delgado 3.00 8.00
CG Curtis Granderson 4.00 10.00
CJ Chipper Jones 5.00 12.00
CQ Carlos Quentin 3.00 8.00
CR Bobby Crosby 3.00 8.00
CZ Carlos Zambrano 3.00 8.00
DA Johnny Damon 4.00 10.00
DE Carlos Delgado 3.00 8.00
DJ Derek Jeter 8.00 20.00
DL Derek Lowe 3.00 8.00
DO David Ortiz 4.00 10.00
DW Dontrelle Willis 3.00 8.00
ED Jim Edmonds 4.00 10.00
FR Ryan Freel 3.00 8.00
FS Freddy Sanchez 3.00 8.00
GA Garrett Atkins 3.00 8.00
GI Brian Giles 3.00 8.00
GJ Geoff Jenkins 3.00 8.00
GL Troy Glaus 4.00 10.00
GM Greg Maddux 5.00 12.00
GO Adrian Gonzalez 4.00 10.00
GT Troy Glaus 4.00 10.00
HA Josh Hamilton 5.00 12.00
HM Hideki Matsui 4.00 10.00
HO Trevor Hoffman 3.00 8.00
HT Travis Hafner 3.00 8.00
HU Torii Hunter 3.00 8.00
IS Ian Snell 3.00 8.00
JD Jermaine Dye 3.00 8.00
JE Jim Edmonds 4.00 10.00
JF Jeff Francoeur 4.00 10.00
JG Jeremy Guthrie 3.00 8.00
JH JJ Hardy 3.00 8.00
JL Jon Lester 4.00 10.00
JM Joe Mauer 4.00 10.00
JO Chipper Jones 5.00 12.00
JP Jorge Posada 4.00 10.00
JS Jeremy Sowers 3.00 8.00
KG Ken Griffey Jr. 6.00 15.00
KY Kevin Youkilis 4.00 10.00
MA Greg Maddux 5.00 12.00
MC Miguel Cabrera 4.00 10.00
MG Matt Garza 3.00 8.00
MO Justin Morneau 4.00 10.00
MS Mike Sweeney 3.00 8.00
MT Miguel Tejada 3.00 8.00
MY Michael Young 3.00 8.00
NS Nick Swisher 3.00 8.00
OR David Ortiz 4.00 10.00
OV Omar Vizquel 3.00 8.00
PE Andy Pettitte 4.00 10.00
PF Prince Fielder 4.00 10.00
PK Paul Konerko 3.00 8.00
PM Pedro Martinez 4.00 10.00
PU Albert Pujols 6.00 15.00
RA Aramis Ramirez 3.00 8.00
RB Ryan Braun 5.00 12.00
RC Robinson Cano 4.00 10.00
RF Rafael Furcal 3.00 8.00
RG Ryan Garko 3.00 8.00
RH Rich Harden 3.00 8.00
RJ Randy Johnson 4.00 10.00
RM Russell Martin 3.00 8.00
RO Roy Halladay 3.00 8.00
RS Richie Sexson 3.00 8.00
RZ Ryan Zimmerman 4.00 10.00
SA Johan Santana 4.00 10.00
SC Scott Rolen 4.00 10.00
SK Scott Kazmir 4.00 10.00
SP Scott Podsednik 3.00 8.00
SR Scott Rolen 4.00 10.00
TB Travis Buck 3.00 8.00
TG Tom Glavine 4.00 10.00
TH Tim Hudson 3.00 8.00
TL Tim Lincecum 4.00 10.00
TR Travis Hafner 3.00 8.00
TW Tim Wakefield 3.00 8.00
VG Vladimir Guerrero 4.00 10.00
VM Victor Martinez 3.00 8.00
WT Willy Taveras 3.00 8.00
ZD Zach Duke 3.00 8.00

2008 Upper Deck Timeline Team USA Signatures

STATED ODDS 1:41 HOBBY
AG A.J. Griffin 3.00 8.00
AO Andrew Oliver 5.00 12.00
BH Brett Hunter 3.00 8.00
BS Blake Smith 10.00 25.00
CC Christian Colon 8.00 20.00
CH Chris Hernandez 8.00 20.00
DD Derek Dietrich 10.00 25.00
HM Hunter Morris 3.00 8.00
FJ Josh Fellhauer 6.00 15.00
KD Kentrail Davis 10.00 25.00
KG Kyle Gibson 10.00 25.00
KR Kevin Rhoderick 3.00 8.00
KV Kendal Volz 5.00 12.00
MD Matt den Dekker 4.00 10.00
MG Micah Gibbs 4.00 10.00
ML Mike Leake 8.00 20.00
MM Mike Minor 4.00 10.00
RJ Ryan Jackson 6.00 15.00
RL Ryan Lipkin 4.00 10.00
SS Stephen Strasburg 125.00 250.00
TL Tyler Lyons 3.00 8.00
TM Tommy Mendonca 10.00 25.00

2005 Upper Deck Update

COMP.SET w/o SP's (100) 8.00 20.00
COMMON CARD (1-100) .10 .30
1-100 ONE PER PACK
COMMON CARD (101-177) .75 2.00
101-177: ONE #'d CARD OR AU PER PACK
101-177 PRINT RUN 599 SERIAL #'d SETS
COMMON AUTO (178-186) 6.00 15.00
178-186: OVERALL AU ODDS APPX 1:8
178-186 PRINT RUN 75 SERIAL #'d SETS
1 A.J. Burnett .20 .50
2 Adam Dunn .20 .50
3 Adrian Beltre .12 .30
4 Albert Pujols .75 2.00
5 Alex Rodriguez .50 1.25
6 Alfonso Soriano .20 .50
7 Andruw Jones .12 .30
8 Aramis Ramirez .12 .30
9 Barry Zito .12 .30
10 Bartolo Colon .12 .30
11 Ben Sheets .12 .30
12 Bobby Abreu .12 .30
13 Bobby Crosby .12 .30
14 Bret Boone .12 .30
15 Brian Giles .12 .30
16 Brian Roberts .12 .30
17 Carl Crawford .20 .50
18 Carlos Beltran .20 .50
19 Carlos Delgado .12 .30
20 Carlos Lee .12 .30
21 Carlos Zambrano .20 .50
22 Chase Utley .20 .50
23 Chipper Jones .30 .75
24 Chris Carpenter .30 .75
25 Craig Biggio .20 .50
26 Curt Schilling .20 .50
27 David Ortiz .30 .75
28 David Wright .50 1.25
29 Derek Jeter .75 2.00
30 Derrek Lee .12 .30
31 Dontrelle Willis .12 .30
32 Eric Chavez .12 .30
33 Eric Gagne .12 .30
34 Francisco Rodriguez .20 .50
35 Gary Sheffield .12 .30
36 Greg Maddux .50 1.25
37 Hank Blalock .12 .30
38 Hideki Matsui .50 1.25
39 Ichiro Suzuki .50 1.25
40 Ivan Rodriguez .20 .50
41 J.D. Drew .12 .30
42 Jake Peavy .12 .30
43 Jason Bay .12 .30
44 Jason Schmidt .12 .30
45 Jeff Bagwell .20 .50
46 Jeff Kent .12 .30
47 Jeremy Bonderman .12 .30
48 Jim Edmonds .20 .50
49 Jim Thome .20 .50
50 Joe Mauer .30 .75
51 Johan Santana .30 .75
52 John Smoltz .30 .75
53 Johnny Damon .20 .50
54 Jose Reyes .20 .50
55 Jose Vidro .12 .30
56 Josh Beckett .20 .50
57 Justin Morneau .30 .75
58 Ken Griffey Jr. .50 1.25
59 Kenny Rogers .12 .30
60 Kerry Wood .12 .30
61 Khalil Greene .12 .30
62 Lance Berkman .20 .50
63 Livan Hernandez .12 .30
64 Luis Gonzalez .12 .30
65 Manny Ramirez .30 .75
66 Mark Buehrle .20 .50
67 Mark Mulder .12 .30
68 Mark Prior .20 .50
69 Mark Teixeira .30 .75
70 Michael Young .20 .50
71 Miguel Cabrera .30 .75
72 Miguel Tejada .20 .50
73 Mike Mussina .20 .50
74 Mike Piazza .30 .75
75 Moises Alou .12 .30
76 Morgan Ensberg .12 .30
77 Nomar Garciaparra .30 .75
78 Pat Burrell .12 .30
79 Paul Konerko .20 .50
80 Pedro Martinez .20 .50
81 Randy Johnson .30 .75
82 Rich Harden .12 .30
83 Richie Sexson .12 .30
84 Rickie Weeks .20 .50
85 Robinson Cano .30 .75
86 Roger Clemens .40 1.00
87 Roy Halladay .30 .75
88 Roy Oswalt .20 .50
89 Sammy Sosa .30 .75
90 Scott Kazmir .30 .75
91 Scott Rolen .20 .50
92 Shawn Green .12 .30
93 Tim Hudson .20 .50
94 Todd Helton .20 .50
95 Tom Glavine .20 .50
96 Torii Hunter .12 .30
97 Travis Hafner .12 .30
98 Troy Glaus .12 .30
99 Vernon Wells .12 .30
100 Vladimir Guerrero .30 .75
101 Adam Shabala PR RC .75 2.00
102 Ambiorix Burgos PR RC .75 2.00
103 Anibal Sanchez PR RC 4.00 10.00
104 Bill McCarthy PR RC .75 2.00
105 Brandon McCarthy PR RC 1.25 3.00
106 Brian Burres PR RC .75 2.00
107 Carlos Ruiz PR RC .75 2.00
108 Casey Rogowski PR RC 1.25 3.00
109 Chad Orvella PR RC .75 2.00
110 Chris Resop PR RC .75 2.00
111 Chris Roberson PR RC .75 2.00
112 Chris Seddon PR RC .75 2.00
113 Colter Bean PR RC .75 2.00
114 Dae-Sung Koo PR RC .75 2.00
115 Dave Gassner PR RC .75 2.00
116 Brian Anderson PR RC 1.25 3.00
117 D.J. Houlton PR RC .75 2.00
118 Derek Wathan PR RC .75 2.00
119 Devon Lowery PR RC .75 2.00
120 Enrique Gonzalez PR RC .75 2.00
121 Eude Brito PR RC .75 2.00
122 Francisco Butto PR RC .75 2.00
123 Franquelis Osoria PR RC .75 2.00
124 Garrett Jones PR RC 1.25 3.00
125 Geovany Soto PR RC 4.00 10.00
126 Hayden Penn PR RC .75 2.00
127 Ismael Ramirez PR RC .75 2.00
128 Jared Gothreaux PR RC .75 2.00
129 Jason Hammel PR RC .75 2.00
130 Jeff Miller PR RC .75 2.00
131 Joel Peralta PR RC .75 2.00
132 John Hattig PR RC .75 2.00
133 Jorge Campillo PR RC .75 2.00
134 Juan Morillo PR RC .75 2.00
135 Ryan Garko PR RC .75 2.00
136 Keiichi Yabu PR RC .75 2.00
137 Luis Hernandez PR RC .75 2.00
138 Luis Pena PR RC .75 2.00
139 Luis O.Rodriguez PR RC .75 2.00
140 Luke Scott PR RC 2.00 5.00
141 Marcos Carvajal PR RC .75 2.00
142 Mark Woodyard PR RC .75 2.00
143 Matt A.Smith PR RC .75 2.00
144 Matthew Lindstrom PR RC .75 2.00
145 Miguel Negron PR RC 1.25 3.00
146 Mike Morse PR RC 2.00 5.00
147 Nate McLouth PR RC 1.25 3.00
148 Nelson Cruz PR RC 3.00 8.00
149 Nick Masset PR RC .75 2.00
150 Oscar Robles PR RC .75 2.00
151 Paulino Reynoso PR RC .75 2.00
152 Pedro Lopez PR RC .75 2.00
153 Pete Orr PR RC 1.25 3.00
154 Randy Messenger PR RC .75 2.00
155 Randy Williams PR RC .75 2.00
156 Raul Tablado PR RC .75 2.00
157 Ronny Paulino PR RC 1.25 3.00
158 Russ Rohlicek PR RC .75 2.00
159 Russell Martin PR RC 3.00 8.00
160 Scott Baker PR RC 1.25 3.00
161 Scott Munter PR RC .75 2.00
162 Sean Thompson PR RC .75 2.00
163 Sean Tracey PR RC .75 2.00
164 Shane Costa PR RC .75 2.00
165 Steve Schmoll PR RC .75 2.00
166 Tony Giarratano PR RC .75 2.00
167 Tony Pena PR RC .75 2.00
168 Travis Bowyer PR RC .75 2.00
169 Ubaldo Jimenez PR RC 2.50 6.00
170 Wladimir Balentien PR RC 1.25 3.00
171 Yorman Bazardo PR RC .75 2.00
172 Yuniesky Betancourt PR RC 3.00 8.00
173 Chris Denorfia PR RC .75 2.00
174 Dana Eveland PR RC .75 2.00
175 Jermaine Van Buren PR .75 2.00
176 Mark McLemore PR RC .75 2.00
177 Ryan Spilborghs PR RC 2.00 5.00
178 Ambiorix Concepcion AU RC 6.00 15.00
179 Jeff Niemann AU RC 8.00 20.00
180 Justin Verlander AU RC 60.00 120.00
181 Kendry Morales AU RC 30.00 60.00
182 Philip Humber AU RC 8.00 20.00
183 Prince Fielder AU RC 50.00 100.00
184 Stephen Drew AU RC 75.00 150.00
185 Tadahito Iguchi AU RC 40.00 80.00
186 Ryan Zimmerman AU RC 100.00 175.00

2005 Upper Deck Update Gold

*GOLD 101-177: .6X TO 1.5X BASIC
101-177: ONE #'d CARD OR AU PER PACK
101-177 PRINT RUN 150 SERIAL #'d SETS
178-186: OVERALL AU ODDS APPX 1:8
178-186 AU PRINT RUN 10 SERIAL #'d SETS
178-186 AU NO PRICING DUE TO SCARCITY

2005 Upper Deck Update Platinum

101-177: ONE #'d CARD OR AU PER PACK
101-177 PRINT RUN 25 SERIAL #'d SETS
178-186: OVERALL AU ODDS APPX 1:8
178-186 AU PRINT RUN 1 SERIAL #'d SET
NO PRICING DUE TO SCARCITY

2005 Upper Deck Update Silver

*SILVER 101-177: .4X TO 1X BASIC
101-177: ONE #'d CARD OR AU PER PACK
101-177 PRINT RUN 450 SERIAL #'d SETS
178-186: OVERALL AU ODDS APPX 1:8
178-186 AU PRINT RUN 25 SERIAL #'d SETS
178-186 AU NO PRICING DUE TO SCARCITY

2005 Upper Deck Update Draft Class Quad Autographs

OVERALL AU ODDS APPX 1:8
STATED PRINT RUN 5 SERIAL #'d SETS
NO PRICING DUE TO SCARCITY
1999 Pat Burrell
Mark Mulder
Corey Patterson
J.D. Drew
2001 Joe Mauer
Mark Prior
Mark Teixeira
Jeremy Bonderman
2002 B.J. Upton
Zack Greinke
Prince Fielder
Scott Kazmir
2004 Justin Verlander
Philip Humber
Jeff Niemann
Stephen Drew

2005 Upper Deck Update Draft Generations Triple Autographs

OVERALL AU ODDS APPX 1:8
STATED PRINT RUN 10 SERIAL #'d SETS
NO PRICING DUE TO SCARCITY
DGBWN George Bell
Vernon Wells
Miguel Negron
DGGCM Ken Griffey Jr.
Miguel Cabrera
Kendry Morales
DGJKM Wally Joyner
Casey Kotchman
Kendry Morales
DGMBV Jack Morris
Jeremy Bonderman
Justin Verlander
DGRSN Nolan Ryan
John Smoltz
Jeff Niemann
DGSGH Tom Seaver
Tom Glavine
Philip Humber
DGSWF Ben Sheets
Rickie Weeks
Prince Fielder
DGUYN B.J. Upton
Delmon Young
Jeff Niemann

2005 Upper Deck Update Link to the Future Dual Autographs

OVERALL AU ODDS APPX 1:8
STATED PRINT RUN 35 SERIAL #'d SETS
BR Wladimir Balentien 15.00 40.00
Jeremy Reed
BW Yorman Bazardo 15.00 40.00
Dontrelle Willis
CD Shane Costa 10.00 25.00
David DeJesus
DD Stephen Drew 75.00 150.00
J.D. Drew
DJ Stephen Drew 200.00 350.00
Derek Jeter
FO Prince Fielder 40.00 80.00
Lyle Overbay
FT Prince Fielder 30.00 60.00
Mark Teixeira
FW Prince Fielder 50.00 100.00
Rickie Weeks
GO Jared Gothreaux 15.00 40.00
Roy Oswalt
HF Luis Hernandez 10.00 25.00
Rafael Furcal
HG Philip Humber 30.00 60.00
Tom Glavine
MB Nate McLouth 15.00 40.00
Jason Bay
MK Kendry Morales 15.00 40.00
Casey Kotchman
NK Jeff Niemann 10.00 25.00
Scott Kazmir
NW Miguel Negron 15.00 40.00
Vernon Wells
OB Franquelis Osoria 10.00 25.00
Yhency Brazoban
OG Pete Orr 10.00 25.00
Marcus Giles
PV Tony Pena 10.00 25.00
Javier Vazquez
RH Ismael Ramirez 15.00 40.00
Roy Halladay
SK Chris Seddon 15.00 40.00
Scott Kazmir
SL Luke Scott 20.00 50.00
Jason Lane
VB Justin Verlander 30.00 60.00
Jeremy Bonderman
VC Justin Verlander 125.00 250.00
Roger Clemens
ZC Ryan Zimmerman 60.00 120.00
Chad Cordero

2005 Upper Deck Update Link to the Past Dual Autographs

OVERALL AU ODDS APPX 1:8
STATED PRINT RUN 25 SERIAL #'d SETS
BC Eude Brito 20.00 50.00
Steve Carlton
BM Brian Burres 15.00 40.00
Juan Marichal
CS Ambiorix Concepcion 15.00 40.00
Darryl Strawberry
GT Tony Giarratano 15.00 40.00
Alan Trammell
HG Philip Humber 20.00 50.00
Dwight Gooden
HS Philip Humber 30.00 60.00
Tom Seaver
IA Tadahito Iguchi 60.00 120.00
Luis Aparicio
IC Tadahito Iguchi 60.00 120.00
Rod Carew
JH Garrett Jones 15.00 40.00
Kent Hrbek
JJ Justin Verlander 100.00 175.00
Jack Morris
MC Kendry Morales 20.00 50.00
Rod Carew
MJ Kendry Morales 15.00 40.00
Wally Joyner
MV Nate McLouth 20.00 50.00
Andy Van Slyke
NB Miguel Negron 15.00 40.00
George Bell
NR Jeff Niemann 60.00 120.00
Nolan Ryan
PP Hayden Penn 15.00 40.00
Jim Palmer
RD Chris Roberson 15.00 40.00
Lenny Dykstra
TP Sean Thompson 10.00 25.00
Gaylord Perry
VM Justin Verlander 50.00 100.00
Denny McLain

2009 Upper Deck Update

COMMON CARD (1-50) .15 .40
COMMON ROOKIE (1-50) .60 1.50
INSERTED IN COMBO FAT BACKS
U1 Barack Obama .50 1.25
U2 Garret Anderson .15 .40
U3 Nate McLouth .15 .40
U4 Wilkin Ramirez RC .40 1.00
U5 Kyle Blanks RC 1.00 2.50
U6 Aaron Poreda RC .60 1.50
U7 Bartolo Colon .15 .40
U8 Lou Marson (RC) .60 1.50
U9 Julio Borbon RC 1.00 2.50
U10 Pedro Martinez .25 .60
U11 Ivan Rodriguez .25 .60
U12 Gerardo Parra RC 1.00 2.50
U13 Brad Ausmus .15 .40
U14 Brad Mills RC
U15 Gary Sheffield .15 .40
U16 Nomar Garciaparra .40 1.00
U17 Miguel Cairo .15 .40
U18 Sean O'Sullivan RC .60 1.50
U19 Eric Hinske .15 .40
U20 Sean West (RC) 1.00 2.50
U21 Mat Latos RC 2.00 5.00
U22 Daniel Bard RC .60 1.50
U23 David Huff RC .60 1.50
U24 Tony Gwynn Jr. .15 .40
U25 Vin Mazzaro RC .60 1.50
U26 Russell Branyan .15 .40
U27 Gabe Kapler .15 .40
U28 Andruw Jones .15 .40
U29 Marc Rzepczynski RC 1.00 2.50
U30 Jhoulys Chacin RC 1.00 2.50
U31 Daniel Schlereth RC .60 1.50
U32 Tommy Hanson RC 2.00 5.00
U33 Brad Bergesen (RC) .60 1.50
U34 Nolan Reimold (RC) .60 1.50
U35 Matt Wieters RC 2.00 5.00
U36 Gordon Beckham RC 2.00 5.00
U37 Matt LaPorta RC 1.50 4.00
U38 Anthony Swarzak (RC) .60 1.50
U39 Fu-Te Ni RC 1.00 2.50
U40 Fernando Martinez RC 1.50 4.00
U41 Francisco Cervelli RC 1.50 4.00
U42 Ramiro Pena RC 1.00 2.50
U43 Mark Melancon RC .60 1.50
U44 Andrew Bailey RC 1.50 4.00
U45 Drew Carpenter RC 1.00 2.50
U46 Antonio Bastardo RC .60 1.50
U47 Andrew McCutchen (RC) 2.50 6.00
U48 Derek Holland RC 1.00 2.50
U49 Brett Cecil RC .60 1.50
U50 Jordan Zimmermann RC .60 1.50

2009 Upper Deck Update Gold

*GOLD VET: 12X TO 30X BASIC VET
*GOLD RC: 3X TO 8X BASIC RC
INSERTED IN COMBO FAT PACKS
STATED PRINT RUN 99 SER.#'d SETS

2009 Upper Deck Update Generation Now

INSERTED IN COMBO FAT PACKS
*GOLD: 3X TO 8X BASIC
GOLD FOUND IN COMBO FAT PACKS
GOLD PRINT RUN 99 SER.#'d SETS
GN1 A.J. Burnett .60 1.50
GN2 Adam Dunn .60 1.50
GN3 Adrian Gonzalez .60 1.50
GN4 Albert Pujols 2.50 6.00
GN5 Alex Rodriguez 1.50 4.00
GN6 Alfonso Soriano .60 1.50
GN7 Aramis Ramirez .40 1.00
GN8 B.J. Upton .60 1.50
GN9 Brian McCann .60 1.50
GN10 Carlos Beltran .40 1.00
GN11 Carlos Quentin .60 1.50
GN12 CC Sabathia .60 1.50
GN13 Chase Utley 1.00 2.50
GN14 Chipper Jones 1.00 2.50
GN15 Chris Iannetta .40 1.00
GN16 Cole Hamels 1.00 2.50
GN17 David Wright 1.25 3.00
GN18 Derek Jeter 2.50 6.00
GN19 Dustin Pedroia 1.25 3.00
GN20 Evan Longoria 1.25 3.00
GN21 Grady Sizemore .60 1.50
GN22 Hanley Ramirez 1.00 2.50
GN23 Hunter Pence .60 1.50
GN24 Ian Kinsler .60 1.50
GN25 Jay Bruce .60 1.50
GN26 Jimmy Rollins .60 1.50
GN27 Joba Chamberlain .60 1.50
GN28 Joe Mauer 1.00 2.50
GN29 Joey Votto 1.00 2.50
GN30 Johan Santana 1.00 2.50
GN31 Jon Lester 1.00 2.50
GN32 Jose Reyes .60 1.50
GN33 Josh Beckett .60 1.50
GN34 Josh Hamilton 1.00 2.50
GN35 Justin Upton .60 1.50
GN36 Ken Griffey Jr. 1.50 4.00
GN37 Lance Berkman .60 1.50
GN38 Manny Ramirez 1.00 2.50
GN39 Mark Teixeira 1.00 2.50
GN40 Matt Holliday 1.00 2.50
GN41 Miguel Cabrera 1.00 2.50
GN42 Nick Markakis 1.00 2.50
GN43 Prince Fielder .60 1.50
GN44 Russell Martin .40 1.00
GN45 Ryan Braun 1.25 3.00
GN46 Ryan Howard 1.25 3.00
GN47 Ryan Zimmerman .60 1.50
GN48 Stephen Drew .40 1.00
GN49 Tim Lincecum 1.50 4.00
GN50 Zack Greinke .60 1.50

1996 Upper Deck U.S. Olympic

This multisport product was issued in June 1996, prior to the Centennial Olympic Games in Atlanta. Packs of 10 standard-size cards had a suggested retail price of $1.99. The set contains the following subsets: U.S. Olympic Moments (1-90), Future Champions (91-120) and Passing the Torch (121-135).

COMPLETE SET (135) 6.00 15.00
51 Will Clark .20 .50
52 Jim Abbott .06 .15

1999 Upper Deck Victory

This 470 standard-size set was issued in 12 card packs with 39 packs per box and 12 boxes per case. The SRP on these packs was only 99 cents and no insert cards were made for this product. The Subsets include 50 cards featuring 1999 rookies, 20 Rookie Flashback cards (451-470), 15 Power Trip cards, 10 History in the Making cards, 30 Team Checklist cards and 30 Mark McGwire Magic cards (421-450). Unless noted the subset cards are interspersed throughout the set. Also, through an internet-oriented contest, 10 autographed Ken Griffey Jr. jerseys were available through a contest which was entered through the Upper Deck website.

COMPLETE SET (470) 45.00 75.00
COMMON CARD (1-470) .07 .20
COMMON (421-450) .30 .75
1 Anaheim Angels TC .07 .20
2 Mark Harriger RC .07 .20
3 Mo Vaughn PT .07 .20
4 Darin Erstad BP .07 .20
5 Troy Glaus .10 .30
6 Tim Salmon .10 .30
7 Mo Vaughn .07 .20
8 Darin Erstad .07 .20
9 Garret Anderson .07 .20
10 Todd Greene .07 .20
11 Troy Percival .07 .20
12 Chuck Finley .07 .20
13 Jason Dickson .07 .20
14 Jim Edmonds .07 .20
15 Ariz. Diamondbacks TC .07 .20
16 Randy Johnson .20 .50
17 Matt Williams .07 .20
18 Travis Lee .07 .20
19 Jay Bell .07 .20
20 Tony Womack .07 .20
21 Steve Finley .07 .20
22 Bernard Gilkey .07 .20
23 Tony Batista .07 .20
24 Todd Stottlemyre .07 .20
25 Omar Daal .07 .20
26 Atlanta Braves TC .07 .20
27 Bruce Chen .07 .20
28 George Lombard .07 .20
29 Chipper Jones PT .10 .30
30 Chipper Jones BP .10 .30
31 Greg Maddux .30 .75
32 Chipper Jones .20 .50
33 Javy Lopez .07 .20
34 Tom Glavine .10 .30
35 John Smoltz .10 .30
36 Andruw Jones .10 .30
37 Brian Jordan .07 .20
38 Walt Weiss .07 .20
39 Bret Boone .07 .20
40 Andres Galarraga .07 .20
41 Baltimore Orioles TC .07 .20

42 Ryan Minor .07 .20
43 Jerry Hairston Jr. .07 .20
44 Calvin Pickering .07 .20
45 Cal Ripken HM .30 .75
46 Cal Ripken .60 1.50
47 Charles Johnson .07 .20
48 Albert Belle .07 .20
49 Delino DeShields .07 .20
50 Mike Mussina .10 .30
51 Scott Erickson .07 .20
52 Brady Anderson .07 .20
53 B.J. Surhoff .07 .20
54 Harold Baines .07 .20
55 Will Clark .10 .30
56 Boston Red Sox TC .07 .20
57 Shea Hillenbrand RC .30 .75
58 Trot Nixon .07 .20
59 Jin Ho Cho .07 .20
60 Nomar Garciaparra PT .20 .50
61 Nomar Garciaparra BP .20 .50
62 Pedro Martinez .10 .30
63 Nomar Garciaparra .30 .75
64 Jose Offerman .07 .20
65 Jason Varitek .20 .50
66 Darren Lewis .07 .20
67 Troy O'Leary .07 .20
68 Donnie Sadler .07 .20
69 John Valentin .07 .20
70 Tim Wakefield .07 .20
71 Bret Saberhagen .07 .20
72 Chicago Cubs TC .07 .20
73 Kyle Farnsworth RC .10 .30
74 Sammy Sosa PT .10 .30
75 Sammy Sosa BP .10 .30
76 Sammy Sosa HM .10 .30
77 Kerry Wood HM .07 .20
78 Sammy Sosa .20 .50
79 Mark Grace .10 .30
80 Kerry Wood .07 .20
81 Kevin Tapani .07 .20
82 Benito Santiago .07 .20
83 Gary Gaetti .07 .20
84 Mickey Morandini .07 .20
85 Glenallen Hill .07 .20
86 Henry Rodriguez .07 .20
87 Rod Beck .07 .20
88 Chicago White Sox TC .07 .20
89 Carlos Lee .07 .20
90 Mark Johnson .07 .20
91 Frank Thomas PT .10 .30
92 Frank Thomas .20 .50
93 Jim Parque .07 .20
94 Mike Sirotka .07 .20
95 Mike Caruso .07 .20
96 Ray Durham .07 .20
97 Magglio Ordonez .07 .20
98 Paul Konerko .07 .20
99 Bob Howry .07 .20
100 Brian Simmons .07 .20
101 Jaime Navarro .07 .20
102 Cincinnati Reds TC .07 .20
103 Denny Neagle .07 .20
104 Pete Harnisch .07 .20
105 Greg Vaughn .07 .20
106 Brett Tomko .07 .20
107 Mike Cameron .07 .20
108 Sean Casey .07 .20
109 Aaron Boone .07 .20
110 Michael Tucker .07 .20
111 Dmitri Young .07 .20
112 Barry Larkin .10 .30
113 Cleveland Indians TC .07 .20
114 Russ Branyan .07 .20
115 Jim Thome PT .07 .20
116 Manny Ramirez PT .07 .20
117 Manny Ramirez .10 .30
118 Jim Thome .10 .30
119 David Justice .07 .20
120 Sandy Alomar Jr. .07 .20
121 Roberto Alomar .10 .30
122 Jaret Wright .07 .20
123 Bartolo Colon .07 .20
124 Travis Fryman .07 .20
125 Kenny Lofton .07 .20
126 Omar Vizquel .10 .30
127 Colorado Rockies TC .07 .20
128 Derrick Gibson .07 .20
129 Larry Walker BP .07 .20
130 Larry Walker .07 .20
131 Dante Bichette .07 .20
132 Todd Helton .10 .30
133 Neifi Perez .07 .20
134 Vinny Castilla .07 .20
135 Darryl Kile .07 .20
136 Pedro Astacio .07 .20
137 Darryl Hamilton .07 .20
138 Mike Lansing .07 .20
139 Kirt Manwaring .07 .20
140 Detroit Tigers TC .07 .20
141 Jeff Weaver RC .20 .50
142 Gabe Kapler .07 .20
143 Tony Clark PT .07 .20
144 Tony Clark .07 .20
145 Juan Encarnacion .07 .20
146 Dean Palmer .07 .20
147 Damion Easley .07 .20
148 Bobby Higginson .07 .20
149 Karim Garcia .07 .20
150 Justin Thompson .07 .20
151 Matt Anderson .07 .20
152 Willie Blair .07 .20
153 Brian Hunter .07 .20
154 Florida Marlins TC .07 .20
155 Alex Gonzalez .07 .20
156 Mark Kotsay .07 .20
157 Livan Hernandez .07 .20
158 Cliff Floyd .07 .20
159 Todd Dunwoody .07 .20
160 Alex Fernandez .07 .20
161 Matt Mantei .07 .20
162 Derrek Lee .10 .30
163 Kevin Orie .07 .20
164 Craig Counsell .07 .20
165 Rafael Medina .07 .20
166 Houston Astros TC .07 .20
167 Daryle Ward .07 .20
168 Mitch Meluskey .07 .20
169 Jeff Bagwell PT .07 .20
170 Jeff Bagwell .10 .30
171 Ken Caminiti .07 .20
172 Craig Biggio .10 .30
173 Derek Bell .07 .20
174 Moises Alou .07 .20
175 Billy Wagner .07 .20
176 Shane Reynolds .07 .20
177 Carl Everett .07 .20
178 Scott Elarton .07 .20
179 Richard Hidalgo .07 .20
180 K.C Royals TC .07 .20
181 Carlos Beltran .10 .30
182 Carlos Febles .07 .20
183 Jeremy Giambi .07 .20
184 Johnny Damon .10 .30
185 Joe Randa .07 .20
186 Jeff King .07 .20
187 Hipolito Pichardo .07 .20
188 Kevin Appier .07 .20
189 Chad Kreuter .07 .20
190 Rey Sanchez .07 .20
191 Larry Sutton .07 .20
192 Jeff Montgomery .07 .20
193 Jermaine Dye .07 .20
194 L.A. Dodgers TC .07 .20
195 Adam Riggs .07 .20
196 Angel Pena .07 .20
197 Todd Hundley .07 .20
198 Kevin Brown .10 .30
199 Ismael Valdes .07 .20
200 Chan Ho Park .07 .20
201 Adrian Beltre .07 .20
202 Mark Grudzielanek .07 .20
203 Raul Mondesi .07 .20
204 Gary Sheffield .07 .20
205 Eric Karros .07 .20
206 Devon White .07 .20
207 Milw. Brewers TC .07 .20
208 Ron Belliard .07 .20
209 Rafael Roque RC .07 .20
210 Jeromy Burnitz .07 .20
211 Fernando Vina .07 .20
212 Scott Karl .07 .20
213 Jim Abbott .10 .30
214 Sean Berry .07 .20
215 Marquis Grissom .07 .20
216 Geoff Jenkins .07 .20
217 Jeff Cirillo .07 .20
218 Dave Nilsson .07 .20
219 Jose Valentin .07 .20
220 Minnesota Twins TC .07 .20
221 Corey Koskie .07 .20
222 Cristian Guzman .07 .20
223 A.J. Pierzynski .07 .20
224 David Ortiz .20 .50
225 Brad Radke .07 .20
226 Todd Walker .07 .20
227 Matt Lawton .07 .20
228 Rick Aguilera .07 .20
229 Eric Milton .07 .20
230 Marty Cordova .07 .20
231 Torii Hunter .07 .20
232 Ron Coomer .07 .20
233 LaTroy Hawkins .07 .20
234 Montreal Expos TC .07 .20
235 Fernando Seguignol .07 .20
236 Michael Barrett .07 .20
237 Vladimir Guerrero BP .10 .30
238 Vladimir Guerrero .20 .50
239 Brad Fullmer .07 .20
240 Rondell White .07 .20
241 Ugueth Urbina .07 .20
242 Dustin Hermanson .07 .20
243 Orlando Cabrera .07 .20
244 Wilton Guerrero .07 .20
245 Carl Pavano .07 .20
246 Javier Vazquez .07 .20
247 Chris Widger .07 .20
248 New York Mets TC .07 .20
249 Mike Kinkade .07 .20
250 Octavio Dotel .07 .20
251 Mike Piazza PT .20 .50
252 Mike Piazza .30 .75
253 Rickey Henderson .20 .50
254 Edgardo Alfonzo .07 .20
255 Robin Ventura .07 .20
256 Al Leiter .07 .20
257 Brian McRae .07 .20
258 Rey Ordonez .07 .20
259 Bobby Bonilla .07 .20
260 Orel Hershiser .07 .20
261 John Olerud .07 .20
262 New York Yankees TC .07 .20
263 Ricky Ledee .07 .20
264 Bernie Williams BP .07 .20
265 Derek Jeter BP .25 .60
266 Scott Brosius HM .07 .20
267 Derek Jeter .50 1.25
268 Roger Clemens .40 1.00
269 Orlando Hernandez .07 .20
270 Scott Brosius .07 .20
271 Paul O'Neill .10 .30
272 Bernie Williams .10 .30
273 Chuck Knoblauch .07 .20
274 Tino Martinez .10 .30
275 Mariano Rivera .20 .50
276 Jorge Posada .10 .30
277 Oakland Athletics TC .07 .20
278 Eric Chavez .07 .20
279 Ben Grieve HM .07 .20
280 Jason Giambi .07 .20
281 John Jaha .07 .20
282 Miguel Tejada .07 .20
283 Ben Grieve .07 .20
284 Matt Stairs .07 .20
285 Ryan Christenson .07 .20
286 A.J. Hinch .07 .20
287 Kenny Rogers .07 .20
288 Tom Candiotti .07 .20
289 Scott Spiezio .07 .20
290 Phi. Phillies TC .07 .20
291 Pat Burrell RC .60 1.50
292 Marlon Anderson .07 .20
293 Scott Rolen BP .07 .20
294 Scott Rolen .10 .30
295 Doug Glanville .07 .20
296 Rico Brogna .07 .20
297 Ron Gant .07 .20
298 Bobby Abreu .07 .20
299 Desi Relaford .07 .20
300 Curt Schilling .07 .20
301 Chad Ogea .07 .20
302 Kevin Jordan .07 .20
303 Carlton Loewer .07 .20
304 Pittsburgh Pirates TC .07 .20
305 Kris Benson .07 .20
306 Brian Giles .07 .20
307 Jason Kendall .07 .20
308 Jose Guillen .07 .20
309 Pat Meares .07 .20
310 Brant Brown .07 .20
311 Kevin Young .07 .20
312 Ed Sprague .07 .20
313 Francisco Cordova .07 .20
314 Aramis Ramirez .07 .20
315 Freddy Adrian Garcia .07 .20
316 St. Louis Cardinals TC .07 .20
317 J.D. Drew .07 .20
318 Chad Hutchinson RC .10 .30
319 Mark McGwire PT .25 .60
320 J.D. Drew PT .07 .20
321 Mark McGwire BP .25 .60
322 Mark McGwire HM .25 .60
323 Mark McGwire .50 1.25
324 Fernando Tatis .07 .20
325 Edgar Renteria .07 .20
326 Ray Lankford .07 .20
327 Willie McGee .07 .20
328 Ricky Bottalico .07 .20
329 Eli Marrero .07 .20
330 Matt Morris .07 .20
331 Eric Davis .07 .20
332 Darren Bragg .07 .20
333 San Diego Padres TC .07 .20
334 Matt Clement .07 .20
335 Ben Davis .07 .20
336 Gary Matthews Jr. .07 .20
337 Tony Gwynn BP .10 .30
338 Tony Gwynn HM .10 .30
339 Tony Gwynn .25 .60
340 Reggie Sanders .07 .20
341 Ruben Rivera .07 .20
342 Wally Joyner .07 .20
343 Sterling Hitchcock .07 .20
344 Carlos Hernandez .07 .20
345 Andy Ashby .07 .20
346 Trevor Hoffman .07 .20
347 Chris Gomez .07 .20
348 Jim Leyritz .07 .20
349 S.F. Giants TC .07 .20
350 Armando Rios .07 .20
351 Barry Bonds PT .30 .75
352 Barry Bonds BP .30 .75
353 Barry Bonds HM .30 .75
354 Robb Nen .07 .20
355 Bill Mueller .07 .20
356 Barry Bonds .60 1.50
357 Jeff Kent .07 .20
358 J.T. Snow .07 .20
359 Ellis Burks .07 .20
360 F.P. Santangelo .07 .20
361 Marvin Benard .07 .20
362 Stan Javier .07 .20
363 Shawn Estes .07 .20
364 Seattle Mariners TC .07 .20
365 Carlos Guillen .07 .20
366 Ken Griffey Jr. PT .20 .50
367 Alex Rodriguez PT .20 .50
368 Ken Griffey Jr. BP .20 .50
369 Alex Rodriguez BP .20 .50
370 Ken Griffey Jr. HM .20 .50
371 Alex Rodriguez HM .20 .50
372 Ken Griffey Jr. .30 .75
373 Alex Rodriguez .30 .75
374 Jay Buhner .07 .20
375 Edgar Martinez .10 .30
376 Jeff Fassero .07 .20
377 David Bell .07 .20
378 David Segui .07 .20
379 Russ Davis .07 .20
380 Dan Wilson .07 .20
381 Jamie Moyer .07 .20
382 T.B. Devil Rays TC .07 .20
383 Roberto Hernandez .07 .20
384 Bobby Smith .07 .20
385 Wade Boggs .10 .30
386 Fred McGriff .10 .30
387 Rolando Arrojo .07 .20
388 Jose Canseco .10 .30
389 Wilson Alvarez .07 .20
390 Kevin Stocker .07 .20
391 Miguel Cairo .07 .20
392 Quinton McCracken .07 .20
393 Texas Rangers TC .07 .20
394 Ruben Mateo .07 .20
395 Cesar King .07 .20
396 Juan Gonzalez PT .07 .20
397 Juan Gonzalez BP .07 .20
398 Ivan Rodriguez .10 .30
399 Juan Gonzalez .07 .20
400 Rafael Palmeiro .10 .30
401 Rick Helling .07 .20
402 Aaron Sele .07 .20
403 John Wetteland .07 .20
404 Rusty Greer .07 .20
405 Todd Zeile .07 .20
406 Royce Clayton .07 .20
407 Tom Goodwin .07 .20
408 Toronto Blue Jays TC .07 .20
409 Kevin Witt .07 .20
410 Roy Halladay 3.00 8.00
411 Jose Cruz Jr. .07 .20
412 Carlos Delgado .07 .20
413 Willie Greene .07 .20
414 Shawn Green .07 .20
415 Homer Bush .07 .20
416 Shannon Stewart .07 .20
417 David Wells .07 .20
418 Kelvim Escobar .07 .20
419 Joey Hamilton .07 .20
420 Alex Gonzalez .07 .20
421 Mark McGwire MM .30 .75
422 Mark McGwire MM .30 .75
423 Mark McGwire MM .30 .75
424 Mark McGwire MM .30 .75
425 Mark McGwire MM .30 .75
426 Mark McGwire MM .30 .75
427 Mark McGwire MM .30 .75
428 Mark McGwire MM .30 .75
429 Mark McGwire MM .30 .75
430 Mark McGwire MM .30 .75
431 Mark McGwire MM .30 .75
432 Mark McGwire MM .30 .75
433 Mark McGwire MM .30 .75
434 Mark McGwire MM .30 .75
435 Mark McGwire MM .30 .75
436 Mark McGwire MM .30 .75
437 Mark McGwire MM .30 .75
438 Mark McGwire MM .30 .75
439 Mark McGwire MM .30 .75
440 Mark McGwire MM .30 .75
441 Mark McGwire MM .30 .75
442 Mark McGwire MM .30 .75
443 Mark McGwire MM .30 .75
444 Mark McGwire MM .30 .75
445 Mark McGwire MM .30 .75
446 Mark McGwire MM .30 .75
447 Mark McGwire MM .30 .75
448 Mark McGwire MM .30 .75
449 Mark McGwire MM .30 .75
450 Mark McGwire MM .30 .75
451 Chipper Jones RF .10 .30
452 Cal Ripken RF .30 .75
453 Roger Clemens RF .20 .50
454 Wade Boggs RF .07 .20
455 Greg Maddux RF .20 .50
456 Frank Thomas RF .10 .30
457 Jeff Bagwell RF .07 .20
458 Mike Piazza RF .20 .50
459 Randy Johnson RF .10 .30
460 Mo Vaughn RF .07 .20
461 Mark McGwire RF .25 .60
462 Rickey Henderson RF .10 .30
463 Barry Bonds RF .30 .75
464 Tony Gwynn RF .10 .30
465 Ken Griffey Jr. RF .20 .50
466 Alex Rodriguez RF .20 .50
467 Sammy Sosa RF .10 .30
468 Juan Gonzalez RF .07 .20
469 Kevin Brown RF .07 .20
470 Fred McGriff RF .07 .20

2000 Upper Deck Victory

The Upper Deck Victory set was initially released in March, 2000 as a 440-card set that featured 300 player cards, 40 Rookie Subset cards, 20 Big Play Makers, 30 Team Checklists, and 50 Junior Circuit subset cards. Each pack contained 12 cards and carried a suggested retail price of ninety-nine cents. A 466-card factory set was released in December, 2000 containing an exclusive 26-card Team USA subset (cards 441-466) featuring the team that won the Olympic gold medal in Sydney, Australia in September, 2000. Finally, special packs were issued in April, 2000 for the season opening Mets/Cubs series in Japan. These packs contained three regular issue Victory cards featuring either Cubs or Mets and two Japanese header cards. One of those cards featured a checklist of the 21 players in the packs and the other one provided set information. Notable rookies in the set include Jon Rauch and Ben Sheets.

COMPLETE SET (440) 6.00 15.00
COMP.FACT.SET (466) 12.50 30.00
COMMON CARD (1-390) .07 .20
COMMON (391-440) .20 .50
COMMON USA (441-466) .10 .30
1 Mo Vaughn .07 .20
2 Garret Anderson .07 .20
3 Tim Salmon .10 .30
4 Troy Percival .07 .20
5 Orlando Palmeiro .07 .20
6 Darin Erstad .07 .20
7 Ramon Ortiz .07 .20
8 Ben Molina .07 .20
9 Troy Glaus .07 .20
10 Jim Edmonds .07 .20
11 Mo Vaughn .07 .20
Troy Percival CL
12 Craig Biggio .10 .30
13 Roger Cedeno .07 .20
14 Shane Reynolds .07 .20
15 Jeff Bagwell .10 .30
16 Octavio Dotel .07 .20
17 Moises Alou .07 .20
18 Jose Lima .07 .20
19 Ken Caminiti .07 .20
20 Richard Hidalgo .07 .20
21 Billy Wagner .07 .20
22 Lance Berkman .07 .20
23 Jeff Bagwell .07 .20
Jose Lima CL
24 Jason Giambi .07 .20
25 Randy Velarde .07 .20
26 Miguel Tejada .07 .20
27 Matt Stairs .07 .20
28 A.J. Hinch .07 .20
29 Olmedo Saenz .07 .20
30 Ben Grieve .07 .20
31 Ryan Christenson .07 .20
32 Eric Chavez .07 .20
33 Tim Hudson .07 .20
34 John Jaha .07 .20
35 Jason Giambi .07 .20
Matt Stairs CL
36 Raul Mondesi .07 .20
37 Tony Batista .07 .20
38 David Wells .07 .20
39 Homer Bush .07 .20
40 Carlos Delgado .07 .20
41 Billy Koch .07 .20
42 Darrin Fletcher .07 .20
43 Tony Fernandez .07 .20
44 Shannon Stewart .07 .20
45 Roy Halladay .07 .20
46 Chris Carpenter .07 .20
47 Carlos Delgado .07 .20
David Wells CL
48 Chipper Jones .20 .50
49 Greg Maddux .30 .75
50 Andruw Jones .10 .30
51 Andres Galarraga .07 .20
52 Tom Glavine .10 .30
53 Brian Jordan .07 .20
54 John Smoltz .10 .30
55 John Rocker .07 .20
56 Javy Lopez .07 .20
57 Eddie Perez .07 .20
58 Kevin Millwood .07 .20
59 Chipper Jones .10 .30
Greg Maddux CL
60 Jeromy Burnitz .07 .20
61 Steve Woodard .07 .20
62 Ron Belliard .07 .20
63 Geoff Jenkins .07 .20
64 Bob Wickman .07 .20
65 Marquis Grissom .07 .20
66 Henry Blanco .07 .20
67 Mark Loretta .07 .20
68 Alex Ochoa .07 .20
69 Marquis Grissom .07 .20
Jeromy Burnitz CL
70 Mark McGwire .50 1.25
71 Edgar Renteria .07 .20
72 Dave Veres .07 .20
73 Eli Marrero .07 .20
74 Fernando Tatis .07 .20
75 J.D. Drew .07 .20
76 Ray Lankford .07 .20
77 Darryl Kile .07 .20
78 Kent Bottenfield .07 .20
79 Joe McEwing .07 .20
80 Mark McGwire .25 .60
Ray Lankford CL
81 Sammy Sosa .20 .50
82 Jose Nieves .07 .20
83 Jon Lieber .07 .20
84 Henry Rodriguez .07 .20
85 Mark Grace .10 .30
86 Eric Young .07 .20
87 Kerry Wood .07 .20
88 Ismael Valdes .07 .20
89 Glenallen Hill .07 .20
90 Sammy Sosa .10 .30
Mark Grace CL
91 Greg Vaughn .07 .20
92 Fred McGriff .10 .30
93 Ryan Rupe .07 .20
94 Bubba Trammell .07 .20
95 Miguel Cairo .07 .20
96 Roberto Hernandez .07 .20
97 Jose Canseco .10 .30
98 Wilson Alvarez .07 .20
99 John Flaherty .07 .20
100 Vinny Castilla .07 .20
101 Jose Canseco .07 .20
Ramon Hernandez CL
102 Randy Johnson .20 .50
103 Matt Williams .07 .20
104 Matt Mantei .07 .20
105 Steve Finley .07 .20
106 Luis Gonzalez .07 .20
107 Travis Lee .07 .20
108 Omar Daal .07 .20
109 Jay Bell .07 .20
110 Erubiel Durazo .07 .20
111 Tony Womack .07 .20
112 Todd Stottlemyre .07 .20
113 Randy Johnson .07 .20
Matt Williams CL
114 Gary Sheffield .07 .20
115 Adrian Beltre .07 .20
116 Kevin Brown .10 .30
117 Todd Hundley .07 .20
118 Eric Karros .07 .20
119 Shawn Green .07 .20
120 Chan Ho Park .07 .20
121 Mark Grudzielanek .07 .20
122 Todd Hollandsworth .07 .20
123 Jeff Shaw .07 .20
124 Darren Dreifort .07 .20
125 Gary Sheffield .07 .20
Kevin Brown CL
126 Vladimir Guerrero .20 .50
127 Michael Barrett .07 .20
128 Dustin Hermanson .07 .20
129 Jose Vidro .07 .20
130 Chris Widger .07 .20
131 Mike Thurman .07 .20
132 Wilton Guerrero .07 .20
133 Brad Fullmer .07 .20
134 Rondell White .07 .20
135 Ugueth Urbina .07 .20
136 Vladimir Guerrero .07 .20
Rondell White CL
137 Barry Bonds .60 1.50
138 Russ Ortiz .07 .20
139 J.T. Snow .07 .20
140 Joe Nathan .07 .20
141 Rich Aurilia .07 .20
142 Jeff Kent .07 .20
143 Armando Rios .07 .20
144 Ellis Burks .07 .20
145 Robb Nen .07 .20
146 Marvin Benard .07 .20
147 Barry Bonds .30 .75
Russ Ortiz CL
148 Manny Ramirez .10 .30
149 Bartolo Colon .07 .20
150 Kenny Lofton .07 .20
151 Sandy Alomar Jr. .07 .20
152 Travis Fryman .07 .20
153 Omar Vizquel .10 .30
154 Roberto Alomar .10 .30
155 Richie Sexson .07 .20
156 David Justice .07 .20
157 Jim Thome .10 .30
158 Manny Ramirez .07 .20
Roberto Alomar CL
159 Ken Griffey Jr. .30 .75
160 Edgar Martinez .10 .30
161 Freddy Garcia .07 .20
162 Alex Rodriguez .30 .75
163 John Halama .07 .20
164 Russ Davis .07 .20
165 David Bell .07 .20
166 Gil Meche .07 .20
167 Jamie Moyer .07 .20
168 John Olerud .07 .20
169 Ken Griffey Jr. .20 .50
Freddy Garcia CL
170 Preston Wilson .07 .20
171 Antonio Alfonseca .07 .20
172 A.J. Burnett .07 .20
173 Luis Castillo .07 .20
174 Mike Lowell .07 .20
175 Alex Fernandez .07 .20
176 Mike Redmond .07 .20
177 Alex Gonzalez .07 .20
178 Vladimir Nunez .07 .20
179 Mark Kotsay .07 .20
180 Preston Wilson .07 .20
Luis Castillo CL
181 Mike Piazza .30 .75
182 Darryl Hamilton .07 .20
183 Al Leiter .07 .20
184 Robin Ventura .10 .30
185 Rickey Henderson .20 .50
186 Rey Ordonez .07 .20
187 Edgardo Alfonzo .07 .20
188 Derek Bell .07 .20
189 Mike Hampton .07 .20
190 Armando Benitez .07 .20
191 Mike Piazza .10 .30
Rickey Henderson CL
192 Cal Ripken .60 1.50
193 B.J. Surhoff .07 .20
194 Mike Mussina .10 .30
195 Albert Belle .07 .20
196 Jerry Hairston Jr. .07 .20
197 Will Clark .10 .30
198 Sidney Ponson .07 .20
199 Brady Anderson .07 .20
200 Scott Erickson .07 .20
201 Ryan Minor .07 .20
202 Cal Ripken .30 .75
Albert Belle CL
203 Tony Gwynn .25 .60
204 Bret Boone .07 .20
205 Ryan Klesko .07 .20
206 Ben Davis .07 .20
207 Matt Clement .07 .20
208 Eric Owens .07 .20
209 Trevor Hoffman .07 .20
210 Sterling Hitchcock .07 .20
211 Phil Nevin .07 .20
212 Tony Gwynn .10 .30
Trevor Hoffman CL
213 Scott Rolen .10 .30
214 Bob Abreu .07 .20
215 Curt Schilling .07 .20
216 Rico Brogna .07 .20
217 Robert Person .07 .20
218 Doug Glanville .07 .20
219 Mike Lieberthal .07 .20
220 Andy Ashby .07 .20
221 Randy Wolf .07 .20
222 Bob Abreu .07 .20
Curt Schilling CL
223 Brian Giles .07 .20
224 Jason Kendall .07 .20
225 Kris Benson .07 .20
226 Warren Morris .07 .20
227 Kevin Young .07 .20
228 Al Martin .07 .20
229 Wil Cordero .07 .20
230 Bruce Aven .07 .20
231 Todd Ritchie .07 .20
232 Jason Kendall .07 .20
Brian Giles CL
233 Ivan Rodriguez .10 .30
234 Rusty Greer .07 .20
235 Ruben Mateo .07 .20
236 Justin Thompson .07 .20
237 Rafael Palmeiro .10 .30
238 Chad Curtis .07 .20
239 Royce Clayton UER .07 .20
Mark McLemore pictured on back
240 Gabe Kapler .07 .20
241 Jeff Zimmerman .07 .20
242 John Wetteland .07 .20
243 Ivan Rodriguez .10 .30
Rafael Palmeiro CL
244 Nomar Garciaparra .30 .75
245 Pedro Martinez .10 .30
246 Jose Offerman .07 .20
247 Jason Varitek .20 .50
248 Troy O'Leary .07 .20
249 John Valentin .07 .20
250 Trot Nixon .07 .20
251 Carl Everett .07 .20
252 Wilton Veras .07 .20
253 Bret Saberhagen .07 .20
254 Nomar Garciaparra .20 .50
Pedro Martinez CL
255 Sean Casey .07 .20
256 Barry Larkin .10 .30
257 Pokey Reese .07 .20
258 Pete Harnisch .07 .20
259 Aaron Boone .07 .20
260 Dante Bichette .07 .20
261 Scott Williamson .07 .20
262 Steve Parris .07 .20
263 Dmitri Young .07 .20
264 Mike Cameron .07 .20
265 Sean Casey .07 .20
Scott Williamson CL
266 Larry Walker .07 .20
267 Rolando Arrojo .07 .20
268 Pedro Astacio .07 .20
269 Todd Helton .10 .30
270 Jeff Cirillo .07 .20
271 Neifi Perez .07 .20
272 Brian Bohanon .07 .20
273 Jeffrey Hammonds .07 .20
274 Tom Goodwin .07 .20
275 Larry Walker .07 .20
Todd Helton CL
276 Carlos Beltran .07 .20
277 Jermaine Dye .07 .20
278 Mike Sweeney .07 .20
279 Joe Randa .07 .20
280 Jose Rosado .07 .20
281 Carlos Febles .07 .20
282 Jeff Suppan .07 .20
283 Johnny Damon .10 .30

284 Jeremy Giambi .07 .20
285 Mike Sweeney .07 .20
Carlos Beltran CL
286 Tony Clark .07 .20
287 Damion Easley .07 .20
288 Jeff Weaver .07 .20
289 Dean Palmer .07 .20
290 Juan Gonzalez .07 .20
291 Juan Encarnacion .07 .20
292 Todd Jones .07 .20
293 Karim Garcia .07 .20
294 Deivi Cruz .07 .20
295 Dean Palmer .07 .20
Juan Encarnacion CL
296 Corey Koskie .07 .20
297 Brad Radke .07 .20
298 Doug Mientkiewicz .07 .20
299 Ron Coomer .07 .20
300 Joe Mays .07 .20
301 Eric Milton .07 .20
302 Jacque Jones .07 .20
303 Chad Allen .07 .20
304 Cristian Guzman .07 .20
305 Jason Ryan .07 .20
306 Todd Walker .07 .20
307 Corey Koskie .07 .20
Eric Milton CL
308 Frank Thomas .20 .50
309 Paul Konerko .07 .20
310 Mike Sirotka .07 .20
311 Jim Parque .07 .20
312 Magglio Ordonez .07 .20
313 Bob Howry .07 .20
314 Carlos Lee .07 .20
315 Ray Durham .07 .20
316 Chris Singleton .07 .20
317 Brook Fordyce .07 .20
318 Frank Thomas .10 .30
Magglio Ordonez CL
319 Derek Jeter .50 1.25
320 Roger Clemens .40 1.00
321 Paul O'Neill .10 .30
322 Bernie Williams .10 .30
323 Mariano Rivera .20 .50
324 Tino Martinez .10 .30
325 David Cone .07 .20
326 Chuck Knoblauch .07 .20
327 Darryl Strawberry .07 .20
328 Orlando Hernandez .07 .20
329 Ricky Ledee .07 .20
330 Derek Jeter .25 .60
Bernie Williams CL
331 Pat Burrell .07 .20
332 Alfonso Soriano .20 .50
333 Josh Beckett .20 .50
334 Matt Riley .07 .20
335 Brian Cooper .07 .20
336 Eric Munson .07 .20
337 Vernon Wells .07 .20
338 Juan Pena .07 .20
339 Mark DeRosa .07 .20
340 Kip Wells .07 .20
341 Roosevelt Brown .07 .20
342 Jason LaRue .07 .20
343 Ben Petrick .07 .20
344 Mark Quinn .07 .20
345 Julio Ramirez .07 .20
346 Rod Barajas .07 .20
347 Robert Fick .07 .20
348 David Newhan .07 .20
349 Eric Gagne .20 .50
350 Jorge Toca .07 .20
351 Mitch Meluskey .07 .20
352 Ed Yarnall .07 .20
353 Chad Hermansen .07 .20
354 Peter Bergeron .07 .20
355 Dermal Brown .07 .20
356 Adam Kennedy .07 .20
357 Kevin Barker .07 .20
358 Francisco Cordero .07 .20
359 Travis Dawkins .07 .20
360 Jeff Williams RC .07 .20
361 Chad Hutchinson .07 .20
362 D'Angelo Jimenez .07 .20
363 Derrick Gibson .07 .20
364 Calvin Murray .07 .20
365 Doug Davis .07 .20
366 Rob Ramsay .07 .20
367 Mark Redman .07 .20
368 Rick Ankiel .07 .20
369 Domingo Guzman RC .07 .20
370 Eugene Kingsale .07 .20
371 N.Garciaparra BPM .20 .50
372 Ken Griffey Jr. BPM .20 .50
373 Randy Johnson BPM .10 .30
374 Jeff Bagwell BPM .10 .30
375 Ivan Rodriguez BPM .07 .20
376 Derek Jeter BPM .25 .60
377 Carlos Beltran BPM .07 .20
378 V.Guerrero BPM .10 .30
379 Sammy Sosa BPM .10 .30
380 Barry Bonds BPM .30 .75
381 Pedro Martinez BPM .10 .30
382 Chipper Jones BPM .10 .30
383 Mo Vaughn BPM .07 .20
384 Mike Piazza BPM .20 .50
385 Alex Rodriguez BPM .20 .50
386 Manny Ramirez BPM .07 .20
387 Mark McGwire BPM .25 .60
388 Tony Gwynn BPM .10 .30
389 Sean Casey BPM .07 .20
390 Cal Ripken BPM .30 .75
391 Ken Griffey Jr. JC .20 .50
392 Ken Griffey Jr. JC .20 .50
393 Ken Griffey Jr. JC .20 .50
394 Ken Griffey Jr. JC .20 .50
395 Ken Griffey Jr. JC .20 .50
396 Ken Griffey Jr. JC .20 .50
397 Ken Griffey Jr. JC .20 .50
398 Ken Griffey Jr. JC .20 .50
399 Ken Griffey Jr. JC .20 .50
400 Ken Griffey Jr. JC .20 .50
401 Ken Griffey Jr. JC .20 .50
402 Ken Griffey Jr. JC .20 .50
403 Ken Griffey Jr. JC .20 .50
404 Ken Griffey Jr. JC .20 .50
405 Ken Griffey Jr. JC .20 .50
406 Ken Griffey Jr. JC .20 .50
407 Ken Griffey Jr. JC .20 .50
408 Ken Griffey Jr. JC .20 .50
409 Ken Griffey Jr. JC .20 .50
410 Ken Griffey Jr. JC .20 .50
411 Ken Griffey Jr. JC .20 .50
412 Ken Griffey Jr. JC .20 .50
413 Ken Griffey Jr. JC .20 .50
414 Ken Griffey Jr. JC .20 .50
415 Ken Griffey Jr. JC .20 .50
416 Ken Griffey Jr. JC .20 .50
417 Ken Griffey Jr. JC .20 .50
418 Ken Griffey Jr. JC .20 .50
419 Ken Griffey Jr. JC .20 .50
420 Ken Griffey Jr. JC .20 .50
421 Ken Griffey Jr. JC .20 .50
422 Ken Griffey Jr. JC .20 .50
423 Ken Griffey Jr. JC .20 .50
424 Ken Griffey Jr. JC .20 .50
425 Ken Griffey Jr. JC .20 .50
426 Ken Griffey Jr. JC .20 .50
427 Ken Griffey Jr. JC .20 .50
428 Ken Griffey Jr. JC .20 .50
429 Ken Griffey Jr. JC .20 .50
430 Ken Griffey Jr. JC .20 .50
431 Ken Griffey Jr. JC .20 .50
432 Ken Griffey Jr. JC .20 .50
433 Ken Griffey Jr. JC .20 .50
434 Ken Griffey Jr. JC .20 .50
435 Ken Griffey Jr. JC .20 .50
436 Ken Griffey Jr. JC .20 .50
437 Ken Griffey Jr. JC .20 .50
438 Ken Griffey Jr. JC .20 .50
439 Ken Griffey Jr. JC .20 .50
440 Ken Griffey Jr. JC .20 .50
441 T.Lasorda USA MG .10 .30
442 Sean Burroughs USA .07 .20
443 Rick Krivda USA .10 .30
444 Ben Sheets USA RC 1.00 2.50
445 Pat Borders USA .10 .30
446 B.Abernathy USA RC .10 .30
447 Tim Young USA .10 .30
448 Adam Everett USA .10 .30
449 Anthony Sanders USA .10 .30
450 Ernie Young USA .10 .30
451 B.Wilkerson USA RC .40 1.00
452 K.Ainsworth USA RC .10 .30
453 Ryan Franklin USA RC .10 .30
454 Todd Williams USA .10 .30
455 Jon Rauch USA RC .10 .30
456 Roy Oswalt USA RC 3.00 8.00
457 S.Heams USA RC .10 .30
458 Chris George USA .10 .30
459 Bobby Seay USA .10 .30
460 Mike Kinkade USA .10 .30
461 Marcus Jensen USA .10 .30
462 Travis Dawkins USA .10 .30
463 D.Mientkiewicz USA .10 .30
464 John Cotton USA RC .10 .30
465 Mike Neill USA .10 .30
466 Team Photo USA .40 1.00

2001 Upper Deck Victory

The 2001 Upper Deck Victory product was released in late February, 2001 and features a 660-card base set. The base set is broken into tiers as follows: 550 Veterans (1-550), (40) Prospects (551-590), (20) Big Play Makers (591-610), and (50) Victory Best cards (611-660). Each pack contains 13 cards and carries a suggested retail price of $1.99.

COMPLETE SET (660) 20.00 50.00
1 Troy Glaus .07 .20
2 Scott Spiezio .07 .20
3 Gary DiSarcina .07 .20
4 Darin Erstad .07 .20
5 Tim Salmon .10 .30
6 Troy Percival .07 .20
7 Ramon Ortiz .07 .20
8 Orlando Palmeiro .07 .20
9 Tim Belcher .07 .20
10 Mo Vaughn .07 .20
11 Bengie Molina .07 .20
12 Benji Gil .07 .20
13 Scott Schoeneweis .07 .20
14 Garret Anderson .07 .20
15 Matt Wise .07 .20
16 Adam Kennedy .07 .20
17 Jarrod Washburn .07 .20
18 Darin Erstad .07 .20
Troy Percival CL
19 Jason Giambi .07 .20
20 Tim Hudson .07 .20
21 Ramon Hernandez .07 .20
22 Eric Chavez .07 .20
23 Gil Heredia .07 .20
24 Jason Isringhausen .07 .20
25 Jeremy Giambi .07 .20
26 Miguel Tejada .07 .20
27 Barry Zito .10 .30
28 Terrence Long .07 .20
29 Ryan Christenson .07 .20
30 Mark Mulder .07 .20
31 Olmedo Saenz .07 .20
32 Adam Piatt .07 .20
33 Ben Grieve .07 .20
34 Omar Olivares .07 .20
35 John Jaha .07 .20
36 Jason Giambi .07 .20
Tim Hudson CL
37 Carlos Delgado .07 .20
38 Esteban Loaiza .07 .20
39 Brad Fullmer .07 .20
40 David Wells .07 .20
41 Chris Woodward .07 .20
42 Billy Koch .07 .20
43 Shannon Stewart .07 .20
44 Chris Carpenter .07 .20
45 Steve Parris .07 .20
46 Darrin Fletcher .07 .20
47 Joey Hamilton .07 .20
48 Jose Cruz Jr. .07 .20
49 Vernon Wells .07 .20
50 Raul Mondesi .07 .20
51 Kelvim Escobar .07 .20
52 Tony Batista .07 .20
53 Alex Gonzalez .07 .20
54 Carlos Delgado .07 .20
David Wells CL
55 Greg Vaughn .07 .20
56 Albie Lopez .07 .20
57 Randy Winn .07 .20
58 Ryan Rupe .07 .20
59 Steve Cox .07 .20
60 Vinny Castilla .07 .20
61 Jose Guillen .07 .20
62 Wilson Alvarez .07 .20
63 Bryan Rekar .07 .20
64 Gerald Williams .07 .20
65 Esteban Yan .07 .20
66 Felix Martinez .07 .20
67 Fred McGriff .10 .30
68 John Flaherty .07 .20
69 Jason Tyner .07 .20
70 Russ Johnson .07 .20
71 Roberto Hernandez .07 .20
72 Greg Vaughn .07 .20
Albie Lopez CL
73 Eddie Taubensee .07 .20
74 Bob Wickman .07 .20
75 Ellis Burks .07 .20
76 Kenny Lofton .07 .20
77 Einar Diaz .07 .20
78 Travis Fryman .07 .20
79 Omar Vizquel .10 .30
80 Jason Bere .07 .20
81 Bartolo Colon .07 .20
82 Jim Thome .10 .30
83 Roberto Alomar .10 .30
84 Chuck Finley .07 .20
85 Steve Woodard .07 .20
86 Russ Branyan .07 .20
87 Dave Burba .07 .20
88 Jaret Wright .07 .20
89 Jacob Cruz .07 .20
90 Steve Karsay .07 .20
91 Manny Ramirez .07 .20
Bartolo Colon CL
92 Raul Ibanez .07 .20
93 Freddy Garcia .07 .20
94 Edgar Martinez .10 .30
95 Jay Buhner .07 .20
96 Jamie Moyer .07 .20
97 John Olerud .07 .20
98 Aaron Sele .07 .20
99 Kazuhiro Sasaki .07 .20
100 Mike Cameron .07 .20
101 John Halama .07 .20
102 David Bell .07 .20
103 Gil Meche .07 .20
104 Carlos Guillen .07 .20
105 Mark McLemore .07 .20
106 Stan Javier .07 .20
107 Al Martin .07 .20
108 Dan Wilson .07 .20
109 Alex Rodriguez .20 .50
Kazuhiro Sasaki CL
110 Cal Ripken .60 1.50
111 Delino DeShields .07 .20
112 Sidney Ponson .07 .20
113 Albert Belle .07 .20
114 Jose Mercedes .07 .20
115 Scott Erickson .07 .20
116 Jerry Hairston Jr. .07 .20
117 Brook Fordyce .07 .20
118 Luis Matos .07 .20
119 Eugene Kingsale .07 .20
120 Jeff Conine .07 .20
121 Chris Richard .07 .20
122 Fernando Lunar .07 .20
123 John Parrish .07 .20
124 Brady Anderson .07 .20
125 Ryan Kohlmeier .07 .20
126 Melvin Mora .07 .20
127 Albert Belle .07 .20
Jose Mercedes CL
128 Ivan Rodriguez .10 .30
129 Justin Thompson .07 .20
130 Kenny Rogers .07 .20
131 Rafael Palmeiro .10 .30
132 Rusty Greer .07 .20
133 Gabe Kapler .07 .20
134 John Wetteland .07 .20
135 Mike Lamb .07 .20
136 Doug Davis .07 .20
137 Ruben Mateo .07 .20
138 A. Rodriguez Rangers .60 1.50
139 Chad Curtis .07 .20
140 Rick Helling .07 .20
141 Ryan Glynn .07 .20
142 Andres Galarraga .07 .20
143 Ricky Ledee .07 .20
144 Frank Catalanotto .07 .20
145 Rafael Palmeiro .07 .20
Rick Helling CL
146 Pedro Martinez .10 .30
147 Wilton Veras .07 .20
148 Manny Ramirez .10 .30
149 Rolando Arrojo .07 .20
150 Nomar Garciaparra .30 .75
151 Darren Lewis .07 .20
152 Troy O'Leary .07 .20
153 Tomokazu Ohka .07 .20
154 Carl Everett .07 .20
155 Jason Varitek .20 .50
156 Frank Castillo .07 .20
157 Pete Schourek .07 .20
158 Jose Offerman .07 .20
159 Derek Lowe .07 .20
160 John Valentin .07 .20
161 Dante Bichette .07 .20
162 Trot Nixon .07 .20
163 Nomar Garciaparra .20 .50
Pedro Martinez CL
164 Jermaine Dye .07 .20
165 Dave McCarty .07 .20
166 Jose Rosado .07 .20
167 Mike Sweeney .07 .20
168 Rey Sanchez .07 .20
169 Jeff Suppan .07 .20
170 Chad Durbin .07 .20
171 Carlos Beltran .07 .20
172 Brian Meadows .07 .20
173 Todd Dunwoody .07 .20
174 Johnny Damon .10 .30
175 Blake Stein .07 .20
176 Carlos Febles .07 .20
177 Joe Randa .07 .20
178 Mac Suzuki .07 .20
179 Mark Quinn .07 .20
180 Gregg Zaun .07 .20
181 Mike Sweeney .07 .20
Jeff Suppan
182 Juan Gonzalez .07 .20
183 Dean Palmer .07 .20
184 Wendell Magee .07 .20
185 Todd Jones .07 .20
186 Bobby Higginson .07 .20
187 Brian Moehler .07 .20
188 Juan Encarnacion .07 .20
189 Tony Clark .07 .20
190 Rich Becker .07 .20
191 Roger Cedeno .07 .20
192 Mitch Meluskey .07 .20
193 Shane Halter .07 .20
194 Jeff Weaver .07 .20
195 Deivi Cruz .07 .20
196 Damion Easley .07 .20
197 Robert Fick .07 .20
198 Matt Anderson .07 .20
199 Bobby Higginson .07 .20
Brian Moehler
200 Brad Radke .07 .20
201 Mark Redman .07 .20
202 Corey Koskie .07 .20
203 Matt Lawton .07 .20
204 Eric Milton .07 .20
205 Chad Moeller .07 .20
206 Jacque Jones .07 .20
207 Matt Kinney .07 .20
208 Jay Canizaro .07 .20
209 Torii Hunter .07 .20
210 Ron Coomer .07 .20
211 Chad Allen .07 .20
212 Denny Hocking .07 .20
213 Cristian Guzman .07 .20
214 LaTroy Hawkins .07 .20
215 Joe Mays .07 .20
216 David Ortiz .20 .50
217 Matt Lawton .07 .20
Eric Milton CL
218 Frank Thomas .20 .50
219 Jose Valentin .07 .20
220 Mike Sirotka .07 .20
221 Kip Wells .07 .20
222 Magglio Ordonez .07 .20
223 Herbert Perry .07 .20
224 James Baldwin .07 .20
225 Jon Garland .07 .20
226 Sandy Alomar Jr. .07 .20
227 Chris Singleton .07 .20
228 Keith Foulke .07 .20
229 Paul Konerko .07 .20
230 Jim Parque .07 .20
231 Greg Norton .07 .20
232 Carlos Lee .07 .20
233 Cal Eldred .07 .20
234 Ray Durham .07 .20
235 Jeff Abbott .07 .20
236 Frank Thomas .10 .30
Mike Sirotka CL
237 Derek Jeter .50 1.25
238 Glenallen Hill .07 .20
239 Roger Clemens .40 1.00
240 Bernie Williams .10 .30
241 David Justice .07 .20
242 Luis Sojo .07 .20
243 Orlando Hernandez .07 .20
244 Mike Mussina .10 .30
245 Jorge Posada .10 .30
246 Andy Pettitte .10 .30
247 Paul O'Neill .10 .30
248 Scott Brosius .07 .20
249 Alfonso Soriano .10 .30
250 Mariano Rivera .20 .50
251 Chuck Knoblauch .07 .20
252 Ramiro Mendoza .07 .20
253 Tino Martinez .10 .30
254 David Cone .07 .20
255 Derek Jeter .25 .60
Andy Pettite CL
256 Jeff Bagwell .10 .30
257 Lance Berkman .07 .20
258 Craig Biggio .10 .30
259 Scott Elarton .07 .20
260 Bill Spiers .07 .20
261 Moises Alou .07 .20
262 Billy Wagner .07 .20
263 Shane Reynolds .07 .20
264 Tony Eusebio .07 .20
265 Julio Lugo .07 .20
266 Jose Lima .07 .20
267 Octavio Dotel .07 .20
268 Brad Ausmus .07 .20
269 Daryle Ward .07 .20
270 Glen Barker .07 .20
271 Wade Miller .07 .20
272 Richard Hidalgo .07 .20
273 Chris Truby .07 .20
274 Jeff Bagwell .07 .20
Scott Elarton CL
275 Greg Maddux .30 .75
276 Chipper Jones .20 .50
277 Tom Glavine .10 .30
278 Brian Jordan .07 .20
279 Andruw Jones .10 .30
280 Kevin Millwood .07 .20
281 Rico Brogna .07 .20
282 George Lombard .07 .20
283 Reggie Sanders .07 .20
284 John Rocker .07 .20
285 Rafael Furcal .07 .20
286 John Smoltz .10 .30
287 Javy Lopez .07 .20
288 Walt Weiss .07 .20
289 Quilvio Veras .07 .20
290 Eddie Perez .07 .20
291 B.J. Surhoff .07 .20
292 Chipper Jones .10 .30
Tom Glavine CL
293 Jeromy Burnitz .07 .20
294 Charlie Hayes .07 .20
295 Jeff D'Amico .07 .20
296 Jose Hernandez .07 .20
297 Richie Sexson .07 .20
298 Tyler Houston .07 .20
299 Paul Rigdon .07 .20
300 Jamey Wright .07 .20
301 Mark Loretta .07 .20
302 Geoff Jenkins .07 .20
303 Luis Lopez .07 .20
304 John Snyder .07 .20
305 Henry Blanco .07 .20
306 Curtis Leskanic .07 .20
307 Ron Belliard .07 .20
308 Jimmy Haynes .07 .20
309 Marquis Grissom .07 .20
310 Geoff Jenkins .07 .20
Jeff D'Amico CL
311 Mark McGwire .50 1.25
312 Rick Ankiel .07 .20
313 Dave Veres .07 .20
314 Carlos Hernandez .07 .20
315 Jim Edmonds .07 .20
316 Andy Benes .07 .20
317 Garrett Stephenson .07 .20
318 Ray Lankford .07 .20
319 Dustin Hermanson .07 .20
320 Steve Kline .07 .20
321 Mike Matheny .07 .20
322 Edgar Renteria .07 .20
323 J.D. Drew .07 .20
324 Craig Paquette .07 .20
325 Darryl Kile .07 .20
326 Fernando Vina .07 .20
327 Eric Davis .07 .20
328 Placido Polanco .07 .20
329 Jim Edmonds .07 .20
Darryl Kile CL
330 Sammy Sosa .20 .50
331 Rick Aguilera .07 .20
332 Willie Greene .07 .20
333 Kerry Wood .07 .20
334 Todd Hundley .07 .20
335 Rondell White .07 .20
336 Julio Zuleta .07 .20
337 Jon Lieber .07 .20
338 Joe Girardi .07 .20
339 Damon Buford .07 .20
340 Kevin Tapani .07 .20
341 Ricky Gutierrez .07 .20
342 Bill Mueller .07 .20
343 Ruben Quevedo .07 .20
344 Eric Young .07 .20
345 Gary Matthews Jr. .07 .20
346 Daniel Garibay .07 .20
347 Sammy Sosa .10 .30
Jon Lieber CL
348 Randy Johnson .20 .50
349 Matt Williams .07 .20
350 Kelly Stinnett .07 .20
351 Brian Anderson .07 .20
352 Steve Finley .07 .20
353 Curt Schilling .07 .20
354 Erubiel Durazo .07 .20
355 Todd Stottlemyre .07 .20
356 Mark Grace .10 .30
357 Luis Gonzalez .07 .20
358 Danny Bautista .07 .20
359 Matt Mantei .07 .20
360 Tony Womack .07 .20
361 Armando Reynoso .07 .20
362 Greg Colbrunn .07 .20
363 Jay Bell .07 .20
364 Byung-Hyun Kim .07 .20
365 Luis Gonzalez .10 .30
Randy Johnson CL
366 Gary Sheffield .07 .20
367 Eric Karros .07 .20
368 Jeff Shaw .07 .20
369 Jim Leyritz .07 .20
370 Kevin Brown .07 .20
371 Alex Cora .07 .20
372 Andy Ashby .07 .20
373 Eric Gagne .07 .20
374 Chan Ho Park .07 .20
375 Shawn Green .07 .20
376 Kevin Elster .07 .20
377 Mark Grudzielanek .07 .20
378 Darren Dreifort .07 .20
379 Dave Hansen .07 .20
380 Bruce Aven .07 .20
381 Adrian Beltre .07 .20
382 Tom Goodwin .07 .20
383 Gary Sheffield .07 .20
Chan Ho Park CL
384 Vladimir Guerrero .20 .50
385 Ugueth Urbina .07 .20
386 Michael Barrett .07 .20
387 Geoff Blum .07 .20
388 Fernando Tatis .07 .20
389 Carl Pavano .07 .20
390 Jose Vidro .07 .20
391 Orlando Cabrera .07 .20
392 Terry Jones .07 .20
393 Mike Thurman .07 .20
394 Lee Stevens .07 .20
395 Tony Armas Jr. .07 .20
396 Wilton Guerrero .07 .20
397 Peter Bergeron .07 .20
398 Milton Bradley .07 .20
399 Javier Vazquez .07 .20
400 Fernando Seguignol .07 .20
401 Vladimir Guerrero .10 .30
Dustin Hermanson CL
402 Barry Bonds .50 1.25
403 Russ Ortiz .07 .20
404 Calvin Murray .07 .20
405 Armando Rios .07 .20
406 Livan Hernandez .07 .20
407 Jeff Kent .07 .20
408 Bobby Estalella .07 .20
409 Felipe Crespo .07 .20
410 Shawn Estes .07 .20
411 J.T. Snow .07 .20
412 Marvin Benard .07 .20
413 Joe Nathan .07 .20
414 Robb Nen .07 .20
415 Shawon Dunston .07 .20
416 Mark Gardner .07 .20
417 Kirk Rueter .07 .20
418 Rich Aurilia .07 .20
419 Doug Mirabelli .07 .20
420 Russ Davis .07 .20
421 Barry Bonds .30 .75
Livan Hernandez CL
422 Cliff Floyd .07 .20
423 Luis Castillo .07 .20
424 Antonio Alfonseca .07 .20
425 Preston Wilson .07 .20
426 Ryan Dempster .07 .20
427 Jesus Sanchez .07 .20
428 Derrek Lee .10 .30
429 Brad Penny .07 .20
430 Mark Kotsay .07 .20
431 Alex Fernandez .07 .20
432 Mike Lowell .07 .20
433 Chuck Smith .07 .20
434 Alex Gonzalez .07 .20
435 Dave Berg .07 .20
436 A.J. Burnett .07 .20
437 Charles Johnson .07 .20
438 Reid Cornelius .07 .20
439 Mike Redmond .07 .20
440 Preston Wilson .07 .20
Ryan Dempster CL
441 Mike Piazza .30 .75
442 Kevin Appier .07 .20
443 Jay Payton .07 .20
444 Steve Trachsel .07 .20
445 Al Leiter .07 .20
446 Joe McEwing .07 .20
447 Armando Benitez .07 .20
448 Edgardo Alfonzo .07 .20
449 Glendon Rusch .07 .20
450 Mike Bordick .07 .20
451 Lenny Harris .07 .20
452 Matt Franco .07 .20
453 Darryl Hamilton .07 .20
454 Bobby Jones .07 .20
455 Robin Ventura .07 .20
456 Todd Zeile .07 .20
457 John Franco .07 .20
458 Mike Piazza .20 .50
Al Leiter CL
459 Tony Gwynn .25 .60
460 John Mabry .07 .20
461 Trevor Hoffman .07 .20
462 Phil Nevin .07 .20
463 Ryan Klesko .07 .20
464 Wiki Gonzalez .07 .20
465 Matt Clement .07 .20
466 Alex Arias .07 .20
467 Woody Williams .07 .20
468 Ruben Rivera .07 .20
469 Sterling Hitchcock .07 .20
470 Ben Davis .07 .20
471 Bubba Trammell .07 .20
472 Jay Witasick .07 .20
473 Eric Owens .07 .20
474 Damian Jackson .07 .20
475 Adam Eaton .07 .20
476 Mike Darr .07 .20
477 Phil Nevin .07 .20
Trevor Hoffman CL
478 Scott Rolen .10 .30
479 Robert Person .07 .20
480 Mike Lieberthal .07 .20
481 Reggie Taylor .07 .20
482 Paul Byrd .07 .20
483 Bruce Chen .07 .20
484 Pat Burrell .07 .20
485 Kevin Jordan .07 .20
486 Bobby Abreu .07 .20
487 Randy Wolf .07 .20
488 Kevin Sefcik .07 .20
489 Brian Hunter .07 .20
490 Doug Glanville .07 .20
491 Kent Bottenfield .07 .20
492 Travis Lee .07 .20
493 Jeff Brantley .07 .20
494 Omar Daal .07 .20
495 Bobby Abreu .07 .20
Randy Wolf CL
496 Jason Kendall .07 .20
497 Adrian Brown .07 .20
498 Warren Morris .07 .20
499 Brian Giles .07 .20
500 Jimmy Anderson .07 .20
501 John VanderWal .07 .20
502 Mike Williams .07 .20
503 Aramis Ramirez .07 .20
504 Pat Meares .07 .20
505 Jason Schmidt .07 .20
506 Todd Ritchie .07 .20
507 Abraham Nunez .07 .20
508 Jose Silva .07 .20
509 Francisco Cordova .07 .20
510 Kevin Young .07 .20
511 Derek Bell .07 .20
512 Kris Benson .07 .20
513 Brian Giles .07 .20
Jose Silva CL
514 Ken Griffey Jr. .30 .75
515 Scott Williamson .07 .20
516 Dmitri Young .07 .20
517 Sean Casey .07 .20
518 Barry Larkin .10 .30
519 Juan Castro .07 .20
520 Danny Graves .07 .20
521 Aaron Boone .07 .20
522 Pokey Reese .07 .20
523 Elmer Dessens .07 .20
524 Michael Tucker .07 .20
525 Benito Santiago .07 .20
526 Pete Harnisch .07 .20
527 Alex Ochoa .07 .20
528 Gookie Dawkins .07 .20
529 Seth Etherton .07 .20
530 Rob Bell .07 .20
531 Ken Griffey Jr. .20 .50
Steve Parris CL
532 Todd Helton .10 .30
533 Jose Jimenez .07 .20
534 Todd Walker .07 .20
535 Ron Gant .07 .20
536 Neifi Perez .07 .20
537 Butch Huskey .07 .20
538 Pedro Astacio .07 .20

539 Juan Pierre .07 .20
540 Jeff Cirillo .07 .20
541 Ben Petrick .07 .20
542 Brian Bohanon .07 .20
543 Larry Walker .07 .20
544 Masato Yoshii .07 .20
545 Denny Neagle .07 .20
546 Brent Mayne .07 .20
547 Mike Hampton .07 .20
548 Todd Hollandsworth .07 .20
549 Brian Rose .07 .20
550 Todd Helton .07 .20
Pedro Astacio CL
551 Jason Hart .07 .20
552 Joe Crede .20 .50
553 Timo Perez .07 .20
554 Brady Clark .07 .20
555 Adam Pettyjohn RC .07 .20
556 Jason Grilli .07 .20
557 Paxton Crawford .07 .20
558 Jay Spurgeon .07 .20
559 Hector Ortiz .07 .20
560 Vernon Wells .07 .20
561 Aubrey Huff .07 .20
562 Xavier Nady .07 .20
563 Billy McMillon .07 .20
564 Ichiro Suzuki RC 2.50 6.00
565 Tomas De la Rosa .07 .20
566 Matt Ginter .07 .20
567 Sun Woo Kim .07 .20
568 Nick Johnson .07 .20
569 Pablo Ozuna .07 .20
570 Tike Redman .07 .20
571 Brian Cole .07 .20
572 Ross Gload .07 .20
573 Dee Brown .07 .20
574 Tony McKnight .07 .20
575 Allen Levrault .07 .20
576 Lesli Brea .07 .20
577 Adam Bernero .07 .20
578 Tom Davey .07 .20
579 Morgan Burkhart .07 .20
580 Britt Reames .07 .20
581 Dave Coggin .07 .20
582 Trey Moore .07 .20
583 Matt Kinney .07 .20
584 Pedro Feliz .07 .20
585 Brandon Inge .07 .20
586 Alex Hernandez .07 .20
587 Toby Hall .07 .20
588 Grant Roberts .07 .20
589 Brian Sikorski .07 .20
590 Aaron Myette .07 .20
591 Derek Jeter PM .50 1.25
592 Ivan Rodriguez PM .07 .20
593 Alex Rodriguez PM .30 .75
594 Carlos Delgado PM .07 .20
595 Mark McGwire PM .50 1.25
596 Troy Glaus PM .07 .20
597 Sammy Sosa PM .10 .30
598 Vladimir Guerrero PM .20 .50
599 Manny Ramirez PM .07 .20
600 Pedro Martinez PM .10 .30
601 Chipper Jones PM .10 .30
602 Jason Giambi PM .07 .20
603 Frank Thomas PM .10 .30
604 Ken Griffey Jr. PM .30 .75
605 Nomar Garciaparra PM .30 .75
606 Randy Johnson PM .10 .30
607 Mike Piazza PM .30 .75
608 Barry Bonds PM .50 1.25
609 Todd Helton PM .07 .20
610 Jeff Bagwell PM .07 .20
611 Ken Griffey Jr. VB .30 .75
612 Carlos Delgado VB .07 .20
613 Jeff Bagwell VB .07 .20
614 Jason Giambi VB .07 .20
615 Cal Ripken VB .60 1.50
616 Brian Giles VB .07 .20
617 Bernie Williams VB .07 .20
618 Greg Maddux VB .30 .75
619 Troy Glaus VB .07 .20
620 Greg Vaughn VB .07 .20
621 Sammy Sosa VB .10 .30
622 Pat Burrell VB .07 .20
623 Ivan Rodriguez VB .07 .20
624 Chipper Jones VB .10 .30
625 Barry Bonds VB .50 1.25
626 Roger Clemens VB .40 1.00
627 Jim Edmonds VB .07 .20
628 Nomar Garciaparra VB .30 .75
629 Frank Thomas VB .10 .30
630 Mike Piazza VB .30 .75
631 Randy Johnson VB .10 .30
632 Andruw Jones VB .07 .20
633 David Wells VB .07 .20
634 Manny Ramirez VB .07 .20
635 Preston Wilson VB .07 .20
636 Todd Helton VB .07 .20
637 Kerry Wood VB .07 .20
638 Albert Belle VB .07 .20
639 Juan Gonzalez VB .07 .20
640 Vladimir Guerrero VB .20 .50
641 Gary Sheffield VB .07 .20
642 Larry Walker VB .07 .20
643 Magglio Ordonez VB .07 .20
644 Jermaine Dye VB .07 .20
645 Scott Rolen VB .07 .20
646 Tony Gwynn VB .25 .60
647 Shawn Green VB .07 .20
648 Roberto Alomar VB .07 .20
649 Eric Milton VB .07 .20
650 Mark McGwire VB .50 1.25
651 Tim Hudson VB .07 .20
652 Jose Canseco VB .07 .20
653 Tom Glavine VB .07 .20
654 Derek Jeter VB .50 1.25
655 Alex Rodriguez VB .30 .75
656 Darin Erstad VB .07 .20
657 Jason Kendall VB .07 .20
658 Pedro Martinez VB .10 .30
659 Richie Sexson VB .07 .20
660 Rafael Palmeiro VB .07 .20

2002 Upper Deck Victory

This 660 card set was issued in two separate products. The basic Victory brand, containing cards 1-550, was released in February 2002. These cards were issued in ten count packs which were issued 24 packs to a box and twelve boxes to a case. The following subsets were also included in this product: Cards numbered 491-530 feature rookie prospects and cards numbered 531-550 were Big Play Makers. Cards 551-660 were distributed within retail-only packs of Upper Deck Rookie Debut in mid-December 2002. The 110-card update set features traded veterans in their new uniforms and a wide array of prospects and rookies. The cards were issued at a rate of approximately two per pack.

COMPLETE SET (660)	35.00	75.00
COMP.LOW SET (550)	25.00	50.00
COMP.UPDATE SET (110)	10.00	25.00
COMMON (1-490/531-550)	.07	.20
COMMON CARD (491-530)	.08	.25
COMMON CARD (551-605)	.15	.40
COMMON CARD (606-660)	.15	.40

1 Troy Glaus .07 .20
2 Tim Salmon .10 .30
3 Troy Percival .07 .20
4 Darin Erstad .07 .20
5 Adam Kennedy .07 .20
6 Scott Spiezio .07 .20
7 Ramon Ortiz .07 .20
8 Ismael Valdes .07 .20
9 Jarrod Washburn .07 .20
10 Garrett Anderson .07 .20
11 David Eckstein .07 .20
12 Mo Vaughn .07 .20
13 Benji Gil .07 .20
14 Bengie Molina .07 .20
15 Scott Schoeneweis .07 .20
16 Troy Glaus .07 .20
Ramon Ortiz
17 David Justice .07 .20
18 Jermaine Dye .07 .20
19 Eric Chavez .07 .20
20 Jeremy Giambi .07 .20
21 Terrence Long .07 .20
22 Miguel Tejada .07 .20
23 Johnny Damon .10 .30
24 Jason Hart .07 .20
25 Adam Piatt .07 .20
26 Billy Koch .07 .20
27 Ramon Hernandez .07 .20
28 Eric Byrnes .07 .20
29 Olmedo Saenz .07 .20
30 Barry Zito .07 .20
31 Tim Hudson .07 .20
32 Mark Mulder .07 .20
33 Jason Giambi .07 .20
Mark Mulder
34 Carlos Delgado .07 .20
35 Shannon Stewart .07 .20
36 Vernon Wells .07 .20
37 Homer Bush .07 .20
38 Brad Fullmer .07 .20
39 Jose Cruz Jr. .07 .20
40 Felipe Lopez .07 .20
41 Raul Mondesi .07 .20
42 Esteban Loaiza .07 .20
43 Darrin Fletcher .07 .20
44 Mike Sirotka .07 .20
45 Luke Prokopec .07 .20
46 Chris Carpenter .07 .20
47 Roy Halladay .07 .20
48 Kelvim Escobar .07 .20
49 Carlos Delgado .07 .20
Billy Koch
50 Nick Bierbrodt .07 .20
51 Greg Vaughn .07 .20
52 Ben Grieve .07 .20
53 Damian Rolls .07 .20
54 Russ Johnson .07 .20
55 Brent Abernathy .07 .20
56 Steve Cox .07 .20
57 Aubrey Huff .07 .20
58 Randy Winn .07 .20
59 Jason Tyner .07 .20
60 Tanyon Sturtze .07 .20
61 Joe Kennedy .07 .20
62 Jared Sandberg .07 .20
63 Esteban Yan .07 .20
64 Ryan Rupe .07 .20
65 Toby Hall .07 .20
66 Greg Vaughn .07 .20
Tanyon Sturtze
67 Matt Lawton .07 .20
68 Juan Gonzalez .07 .20
69 Jim Thome .10 .30
70 Einar Diaz .07 .20
71 Ellis Burks .07 .20
72 Kenny Lofton .07 .20
73 Omar Vizquel .10 .30
74 Russell Branyan .07 .20
75 Brady Anderson .07 .20
76 John Rocker .07 .20
77 Travis Fryman .07 .20
78 Wil Cordero .07 .20
79 Chuck Finley .07 .20
80 C.C. Sabathia .07 .20
81 Bartolo Colon .07 .20
82 Bob Wickman .07 .20
83 Roberto Alomar .07 .20
C.C. Sabathia
84 Ichiro Suzuki .40 1.00
85 Edgar Martinez .10 .30
86 Aaron Sele .07 .20
87 Carlos Guillen .07 .20
88 Bret Boone .07 .20
89 John Olerud .07 .20
90 Jamie Moyer .07 .20
91 Ben Davis .07 .20
92 Dan Wilson .07 .20
93 Jeff Cirillo .07 .20
94 John Halama .07 .20
95 Freddy Garcia .07 .20
96 Kazuhiro Sasaki .07 .20
97 Mike Cameron .07 .20
98 Paul Abbott .07 .20
99 Mark McLemore .07 .20
100 Ichiro Suzuki .20 .50
Freddy Garcia
101 Jeff Conine .07 .20
102 David Segui .07 .20
103 Marty Cordova .07 .20
104 Tony Batista .07 .20
105 Chris Richard .07 .20
106 Willis Roberts .07 .20
107 Melvin Mora .07 .20
108 Mike Bordick .07 .20
109 Jay Gibbons .07 .20
110 Mike Kinkade .07 .20
111 Brian Roberts .07 .20
112 Jerry Hairston Jr. .07 .20
113 Jason Johnson .07 .20
114 Josh Towers .07 .20
115 Calvin Maduro .07 .20
116 Sidney Ponson .07 .20
117 Jeff Conine .07 .20
Jason Johnson
118 Alex Rodriguez .30 .75
119 Ivan Rodriguez .10 .30
120 Frank Catalanotto .07 .20
121 Mike Lamb .07 .20
122 Ruben Sierra .07 .20
123 Rusty Greer .07 .20
124 Rafael Palmeiro .10 .30
125 Gabe Kapler .07 .20
126 Aaron Myette .07 .20
127 Kenny Rogers .07 .20
128 Carl Everett .07 .20
129 Rick Helling .07 .20
130 Ricky Ledee .07 .20
131 Michael Young .20 .50
132 Doug Davis .07 .20
133 Jeff Zimmerman .07 .20
134 Alex Rodriguez .20 .50
Rick Helling
135 Manny Ramirez .10 .30
136 Nomar Garciaparra .30 .75
137 Jason Varitek .20 .50
138 Dante Bichette .07 .20
139 Tony Clark .07 .20
140 Scott Hatteberg .07 .20
141 Trot Nixon .07 .20
142 Hideo Nomo .20 .50
143 Dustin Hermanson .07 .20
144 Chris Stynes .07 .20
145 Jose Offerman .07 .20
146 Pedro Martinez .10 .30
147 Shea Hillenbrand .07 .20
148 Tim Wakefield .07 .20
149 Troy O'Leary .07 .20
150 Ugueth Urbina .07 .20
151 Manny Ramirez .20 .50
Hideo Nomo
152 Carlos Beltran .07 .20
153 Dee Brown .07 .20
154 Mike Sweeney .07 .20
155 Luis Alicea .07 .20
156 Raul Ibanez .07 .20
157 Mark Quinn .07 .20
158 Joe Randa .07 .20
159 Roberto Hernandez .07 .20
160 Neifi Perez .07 .20
161 Carlos Febles .07 .20
162 Jeff Suppan .07 .20
163 Dave McCarty .07 .20
164 Blake Stein .07 .20
165 Chad Durbin .07 .20
166 Paul Byrd .07 .20
167 Carlos Beltran .07 .20
Jeff Suppan
168 Craig Paquette .07 .20
169 Dean Palmer .07 .20
170 Shane Halter .07 .20
171 Bobby Higginson .07 .20
172 Robert Fick .07 .20
173 Jose Macias .07 .20
174 Deivi Cruz .07 .20
175 Damion Easley .07 .20
176 Brandon Inge .07 .20
177 Mark Redman .07 .20
178 Dmitri Young .07 .20
179 Steve Sparks .07 .20
180 Jeff Weaver .07 .20
181 Victor Santos .07 .20
182 Jose Lima .07 .20
183 Matt Anderson .07 .20
184 Roger Cedeno .07 .20
Steve Sparks
185 Doug Mientkiewicz .07 .20
186 Cristian Guzman .07 .20
187 Torii Hunter .07 .20
188 Matt LeCroy .07 .20
189 Corey Koskie .07 .20
190 Jacque Jones .07 .20
191 Luis Rivas .07 .20
192 David Ortiz .20 .50
193 A.J. Pierzynski .07 .20
194 Brian Buchanan .07 .20
195 Joe Mays .07 .20
196 Brad Radke .07 .20
197 Denny Hocking .07 .20
198 Eric Milton .07 .20
199 LaTroy Hawkins .07 .20
200 Doug Mientkiewicz .07 .20
Joe Mays
201 Magglio Ordonez .07 .20
202 Jose Valentin .07 .20
203 Chris Singleton .07 .20
204 Aaron Rowand .07 .20
205 Paul Konerko .07 .20
206 Carlos Lee .07 .20
207 Ray Durham .07 .20
208 Keith Foulke .07 .20
209 Todd Ritchie .07 .20
210 Royce Clayton .07 .20
211 Jose Canseco .10 .30
212 Frank Thomas .20 .50
213 David Wells .07 .20
214 Mark Buehrle .07 .20
215 Jon Garland .07 .20
216 Magglio Ordonez .07 .20
Mark Buehrle
217 Derek Jeter .50 1.25
218 Bernie Williams .10 .30
219 Rondell White .07 .20
220 Jorge Posada .10 .30
221 Alfonso Soriano .10 .30
222 Ramiro Mendoza .07 .20
223 Jason Giambi Yankees .50 1.25
224 John Vander Wal .07 .20
225 Steve Karsay .07 .20
226 Nick Johnson .07 .20
227 Mariano Rivera .20 .50
228 Orlando Hernandez .07 .20
229 Andy Pettitte .10 .30
230 Robin Ventura .07 .20
231 Roger Clemens .40 1.00
232 Mike Mussina .10 .30
233 Derek Jeter .25 .60
Roger Clemens
234 Moises Alou .07 .20
235 Lance Berkman .07 .20
236 Craig Biggio .10 .30
237 Octavio Dotel .07 .20
238 Jeff Bagwell .10 .30
239 Richard Hidalgo .07 .20
240 Morgan Ensberg .07 .20
241 Julio Lugo .07 .20
242 Daryle Ward .07 .20
243 Roy Oswalt .07 .20
244 Billy Wagner .07 .20
245 Brad Ausmus .07 .20
246 Jose Vizcaino .07 .20
247 Wade Miller .07 .20
248 Shane Reynolds .07 .20
249 Jeff Bagwell .07 .20
Wade Miller
250 Chipper Jones .20 .50
251 Brian Jordan .07 .20
252 B.J. Surhoff .07 .20
253 Rafael Furcal .07 .20
254 Julio Franco .07 .20
255 Javy Lopez .07 .20
256 John Burkett .07 .20
257 Andruw Jones .10 .30
258 Marcus Giles .07 .20
259 Wes Helms .07 .20
260 Greg Maddux .30 .75
261 John Smoltz .10 .30
262 Tom Glavine .10 .30
263 Vinny Castilla .07 .20
264 Kevin Millwood .07 .20
265 Jason Marquis .07 .20
266 Chipper Jones .10 .30
Greg Maddux
267 Tyler Houston .07 .20
268 Mark Loretta .07 .20
269 Richie Sexson .07 .20
270 Jeromy Burnitz .07 .20
271 Jimmy Haynes .07 .20
272 Geoff Jenkins .07 .20
273 Ron Belliard .07 .20
274 Jose Hernandez .07 .20
275 Jeffrey Hammonds .07 .20
276 Curtis Leskanic .07 .20
277 Devon White .07 .20
278 Ben Sheets .07 .20
279 Henry Blanco .07 .20
280 Jamey Wright .07 .20
281 Allen Levrault .07 .20
282 Jeff D'Amico .07 .20
283 Richie Sexson .07 .20
Jimmy Haynes
284 Albert Pujols .40 1.00
285 Jason Isringhausen .07 .20
286 J.D. Drew .07 .20
287 Placido Polanco .07 .20
288 Jim Edmonds .07 .20
289 Fernando Vina .07 .20
290 Edgar Renteria .07 .20
291 Mike Matheny .07 .20
292 Bud Smith .07 .20
293 Mike DiFelice .07 .20
294 Woody Williams .07 .20
295 Eli Marrero .07 .20
296 Matt Morris .07 .20
297 Darryl Kile .07 .20
298 Kerry Robinson .07 .20
299 Luis Saturria .07 .20
300 Albert Pujols .20 .50
Matt Morris
301 Sammy Sosa .20 .50
302 Michael Tucker .07 .20
303 Bill Mueller .07 .20
304 Ricky Gutierrez .07 .20
305 Fred McGriff .10 .30
306 Eric Young .07 .20
307 Corey Patterson .07 .20
308 Alex Gonzalez .07 .20
309 Ron Coomer .07 .20
310 Kerry Wood .07 .20
311 Delino DeShields .07 .20
312 Jon Lieber .07 .20
313 Tom Gordon .07 .20
314 Todd Hundley .07 .20
315 Jason Bere .07 .20
316 Kevin Tapani .07 .20
317 Sammy Sosa .10 .30
Jon Lieber
318 Steve Finley .07 .20
319 Luis Gonzalez .07 .20
320 Mark Grace .10 .30
321 Craig Counsell .07 .20
322 Matt Williams .07 .20
323 Tony Womack .07 .20
324 Junior Spivey .07 .20
325 David Dellucci .07 .20
326 Jay Bell .07 .20
327 Curt Schilling .07 .20
328 Randy Johnson .20 .50
329 Danny Bautista .07 .20
330 Miguel Batista .07 .20
331 Erubiel Durazo .07 .20
332 Brian Anderson .07 .20
333 Byung-Hyun Kim .07 .20
334 Luis Gonzalez .07 .20
Curt Schilling
335 Paul LoDuca .07 .20
336 Gary Sheffield .07 .20
337 Shawn Green .07 .20
338 Adrian Beltre .07 .20
339 Darren Dreifort .07 .20
340 Mark Grudzielanek .07 .20
341 Eric Karros .07 .20
342 Cesar Izturis .07 .20
343 Tom Goodwin .07 .20
344 Marquis Grissom .07 .20
345 Kevin Brown .07 .20
346 James Baldwin .07 .20
347 Terry Adams .07 .20
348 Alex Cora .07 .20
349 Andy Ashby .07 .20
350 Chan Ho Park .07 .20
351 Shawn Green .07 .20
Chan Ho Park
352 Jose Vidro .07 .20
353 Vladimir Guerrero .20 .50
354 Orlando Cabrera .07 .20
355 Fernando Tatis .07 .20
356 Michael Barrett .07 .20
357 Lee Stevens .07 .20
358 Geoff Blum .07 .20
359 Brad Wilkerson .07 .20
360 Peter Bergeron .07 .20
361 Javier Vazquez .07 .20
362 Tony Armas Jr. .07 .20
363 Tomo Ohka .07 .20
364 Scott Strickland .07 .20
365 Vladimir Guerrero .07 .20
Javier Vazquez
366 Barry Bonds .50 1.25
367 Rich Aurilia .07 .20
368 Jeff Kent .07 .20
369 Andres Galarraga .07 .20
370 Desi Relaford .07 .20
371 Shawon Dunston .07 .20
372 Benito Santiago .07 .20
373 Tsuyoshi Shinjo .07 .20
374 Calvin Murray .07 .20
375 Marvin Benard .07 .20
376 J.T. Snow .07 .20
377 Livan Hernandez .07 .20
378 Russ Ortiz .07 .20
379 Robb Nen .07 .20
380 Jason Schmidt .07 .20
381 Barry Bonds .30 .75
Russ Ortiz
382 Cliff Floyd .07 .20
383 Antonio Alfonseca .07 .20
384 Mike Redmond .07 .20
385 Mike Lowell .07 .20
386 Derrek Lee .10 .30
387 Preston Wilson .07 .20
388 Luis Castillo .07 .20
389 Charles Johnson .07 .20
390 Eric Owens .07 .20
391 Alex Gonzalez .07 .20
392 Josh Beckett .07 .20
393 Brad Penny .07 .20
394 Ryan Dempster .07 .20
395 Matt Clement .07 .20
396 A.J. Burnett .07 .20
397 Cliff Floyd .07 .20
Ryan Dempster
398 Mike Piazza .30 .75
399 Joe McEwing .07 .20
400 Todd Zeile .07 .20
401 Jay Payton .07 .20
402 Roger Cedeno .07 .20
403 Rey Ordonez .07 .20
404 Edgardo Alfonzo .07 .20
405 Roberto Alomar .10 .30
406 Glendon Rusch .07 .20
407 Timo Perez .07 .20
408 Al Leiter .07 .20
409 Lenny Harris .07 .20
410 Shawn Estes .07 .20
411 Armando Benitez .07 .20
412 Kevin Appier .07 .20
413 Bruce Chen .07 .20
414 Mike Piazza .10 .30
Al Leiter
415 Phil Nevin .07 .20
416 Ryan Klesko .07 .20
417 Mark Kotsay .07 .20
418 Ray Lankford .07 .20
419 Mike Darr .07 .20
420 D'Angelo Jimenez .07 .20
421 Bubba Trammell .07 .20
422 Adam Eaton .07 .20
423 Ramon Vazquez .07 .20
424 Cesar Crespo .07 .20
425 Trevor Hoffman .07 .20
426 Kevin Jarvis .07 .20
427 Wiki Gonzalez .07 .20
428 Damian Jackson .07 .20
429 Brian Lawrence .07 .20
430 Phil Nevin .07 .20
Trevor Hoffman
431 Scott Rolen .10 .30
432 Marlon Anderson .07 .20
433 Bobby Abreu .07 .20
434 Jimmy Rollins .07 .20
435 Doug Glanville .07 .20
436 Travis Lee .07 .20
437 Brandon Duckworth .07 .20
438 Pat Burrell .07 .20
439 Kevin Jordan .07 .20
440 Robert Person .07 .20
441 Johnny Estrada .07 .20
442 Randy Wolf .07 .20
443 Jose Mesa .07 .20
444 Mike Lieberthal .07 .20
445 Bobby Abreu .07 .20
Robert Person
446 Brian Giles .07 .20
447 Jason Kendall .07 .20
448 Aramis Ramirez .07 .20
449 Rob Mackowiak .07 .20
450 Abraham Nunez .07 .20
451 Pat Meares .07 .20
452 Craig Wilson .07 .20
453 Jack Wilson .07 .20
454 Gary Matthews Jr. .07 .20
455 Kevin Young .07 .20
456 Derek Bell .07 .20
457 Kip Wells .07 .20
458 Jimmy Anderson .07 .20
459 Kris Benson .07 .20
460 Brian Giles .07 .20
Todd Ritchie
461 Sean Casey .07 .20
462 Wilton Guerrero .07 .20
463 Jason LaRue .07 .20
464 Juan Encarnacion .07 .20
465 Todd Walker .07 .20
466 Aaron Boone .07 .20
467 Pete Harnisch .07 .20
468 Ken Griffey Jr. .30 .75
469 Adam Dunn .07 .20
470 Barry Larkin .10 .30
471 Kelly Stinnett .07 .20
472 Pokey Reese .07 .20
473 Brady Clark .07 .20
474 Scott Williamson .07 .20
475 Danny Graves .07 .20
476 Ken Griffey Jr. .20 .50
Elmer Dessens
477 Larry Walker .07 .20
478 Todd Helton .10 .30
479 Juan Pierre .07 .20
480 Juan Uribe .07 .20
481 Mario Encarnacion .07 .20
482 Jose Ortiz .07 .20
483 Todd Hollandsworth .07 .20
484 Alex Ochoa .07 .20
485 Mike Hampton .07 .20
486 Terry Shumpert .07 .20
487 Denny Neagle .07 .20
488 Jose Jimenez .07 .20
489 Jason Jennings .07 .20
490 Todd Helton .07 .20
Mike Hampton
491 Tim Redding ROO .08 .25
492 Mark Teixeira ROO .40 1.00
493 Alex Cintron ROO .08 .25
494 Tim Raines Jr. ROO .08 .25
495 Juan Cruz ROO .08 .25
496 Joe Crede ROO .15 .40
497 Steve Green ROO .08 .25
498 Mike Rivera ROO .08 .25
499 Mark Prior ROO .20 .50
500 Ken Harvey ROO .08 .25
501 Tim Spooneybarger ROO .08 .25
502 Adam Everett ROO .08 .25
503 Jason Standridge ROO .08 .25
504 Nick Neugebauer ROO .08 .25
505 Adam Johnson ROO .08 .25
506 Sean Douglass ROO .08 .25
507 Brandon Berger ROO .08 .25
508 Alex Escobar ROO .08 .25
509 Doug Nickle ROO .08 .25
510 Jason Middlebrook ROO .08 .25
511 Dewon Brazelton ROO .08 .25
512 Yorvit Torrealba ROO .08 .25
513 Henry Mateo ROO .08 .25
514 Dennis Tankersley ROO .08 .25
515 Marlon Byrd ROO .08 .25
516 Andy Barkett ROO .08 .25
517 Orlando Hudson ROO .08 .25
518 Josh Fogg ROO .08 .25
519 Ryan Drese ROO .08 .25
520 Mike MacDougal ROO .08 .25
521 Luis Pineda ROO .08 .25
522 Jack Cust ROO .08 .25
523 Kurt Ainsworth ROO .08 .25
524 Bart Miadich ROO .08 .25
525 Dernell Stenson ROO .08 .25
526 Carlos Zambrano ROO .15 .40
527 Austin Kearns ROO .08 .25
528 Larry Barnes ROO .08 .25
529 Mike Cuddyer ROO .08 .25
530 Carlos Pena ROO .08 .25
531 Derek Jeter BPM .25 .60
532 Ken Griffey Jr. BPM .20 .50
533 Manny Ramirez BPM .10 .30
534 Luis Gonzalez BPM .07 .20
535 Sammy Sosa BPM .10 .30
536 Roger Clemens BPM .20 .50
537 Phil Nevin BPM .07 .20
538 Mike Piazza BPM .20 .50
539 Alex Rodriguez BPM .20 .50
540 Jason Giambi Yankees BPM .25 .60
541 Randy Johnson BPM .10 .30
542 Albert Pujols BPM .20 .50
543 Jeff Bagwell BPM .07 .20
544 Shawn Green BPM .07 .20
545 Carlos Delgado BPM .07 .20
546 Pedro Martinez BPM .10 .30
547 Todd Helton BPM .07 .20
548 Roberto Alomar BPM .07 .20
549 Barry Bonds BPM .30 .75
550 Ichiro Suzuki BPM .20 .50
551 John Lackey .15 .40
552 Francisco Rodriguez .07 .20
553 Cliff Floyd .15 .40
554 Derek Lowe .15 .40
555 Mark Bellhorn .15 .40
556 Matt Clement .15 .40
557 Hee Seop Choi .15 .40
558 Joe Borchard .15 .40
559 Ryan Dempster .15 .40
560 Russell Branyan .15 .40
561 Brandon Larson .15 .40
562 Coco Crisp .40 1.00
563 Karim Garcia .15 .40
564 Brandon Phillips .15 .40
565 Jay Payton .15 .40
566 Gabe Kapler .15 .40
567 Carlos Pena .15 .40
568 George Lombard .15 .40
569 Andy Van Hekken .15 .40
570 Andres Torres .15 .40
571 Justin Wayne .15 .40
572 Juan Encarnacion .15 .40
573 Abraham Nunez .15 .40
574 Peter Munro .15 .40
575 Jason Lane .15 .40
576 Dave Roberts .15 .40
577 Eric Gagne .15 .40
578 Alex Sanchez .15 .40
579 Jim Rushford RC .15 .40
580 Ben Diggins .15 .40
581 Eddie Guardado .15 .40
582 Bartolo Colon .15 .40
583 Endy Chavez .15 .40
584 Raul Mondesi .15 .40
585 Jeff Weaver .15 .40
586 Marcus Thames .15 .40
587 Ted Lilly .15 .40
588 Ray Durham .15 .40
589 Jeremy Giambi .15 .40

590 Vicente Padilla .15 .40
591 Brett Myers .15 .40
592 Josh Fogg .15 .40
593 Tony Alvarez .15 .40
594 Jake Peavy .20 .50
595 Dennis Tankersley .15 .40
596 Sean Burroughs .15 .40
597 Kenny Lofton .15 .40
598 Scott Rolen .20 .50
599 Chuck Finley .15 .40
600 Carl Crawford .15 .40
601 Kevin Mench .15 .40
602 Juan Gonzalez .15 .40
603 Jayson Werth .15 .40
604 Eric Hinske .15 .40
605 Josh Phelps .15 .40
606 Jose Valverde ROO RC .15 .40
607 John Ennis ROO RC .15 .40
608 Trey Hodges ROO RC .15 .40
609 Kevin Gryboski ROO RC .15 .40
610 Travis Driskill ROO RC .15 .40
611 Howie Clark ROO RC .15 .40
612 Freddy Sanchez ROO RC .75 2.00
613 Josh Hancock ROO RC .20 .50
614 Jorge De La Rosa ROO RC .15 .40
615 Mike Mahoney ROO .15 .40
616 Jason Davis ROO RC .15 .40
617 Josh Bard ROO RC .15 .40
618 Jason Beverlin ROO RC .15 .40
619 Carl Sadler ROO RC .15 .40
620 Earl Snyder ROO RC .15 .40
621 Aaron Cook ROO RC .15 .40
622 Eric Eckenstahler ROO RC .15 .40
623 Franklyn German ROO RC .15 .40
624 Kirk Saarloos ROO RC .15 .40
625 Rodrigo Rosario ROO RC .15 .40
626 Jeriome Robertson ROO RC .15 .40
627 Brandon Puffer ROO RC .15 .40
628 Miguel Asencio ROO RC .15 .40
629 Aaron Guiel ROO RC .15 .40
630 Ryan Bukvich ROO RC .15 .40
631 Jeremy Hill ROO RC .15 .40
632 Kazuhisa Ishii ROO RC .20 .50
633 Jayson Durocher ROO RC .15 .40
634 Shane Nance ROO RC .15 .40
635 Eric Good ROO RC .15 .40
636 Jamey Carroll ROO RC .30 .75
637 Jaime Cerda ROO RC .15 .40
638 Nate Field ROO RC .15 .40
639 Cody McKay ROO RC .15 .40
640 Jose Flores ROO RC .15 .40
641 Jorge Padilla ROO RC .15 .40
642 Anderson Machado ROO RC .15 .40
643 Eric Junge ROO RC .15 .40
644 Oliver Perez ROO RC .30 .75
645 Julius Matos ROO RC .15 .40
646 Ben Howard ROO RC .15 .40
647 Julio Mateo ROO RC .15 .40
648 Matt Thornton ROO RC .15 .40
649 Chris Snelling ROO RC .25 .60
650 Jason Simontacchi ROO RC .15 .40
651 So Taguchi ROO RC .20 .50
652 Mike Crudale ROO RC .15 .40
653 Mike Coolbaugh ROO RC .15 .40
654 Felix Escalona ROO RC .15 .40
655 Jorge Sosa ROO RC .20 .50
656 Lance Carter ROO RC .15 .40
657 Reynaldo Garcia ROO RC .15 .40
658 Kevin Cash ROO RC .15 .40
659 Ken Huckaby ROO RC .15 .40
660 Scott Wiggins ROO RC .15 .40

2002 Upper Deck Victory Gold

This set parallels the regular 2002 Upper Deck Victory set and were issued at stated odds of one in two packs.

COMMON CARD (1-550) .40 1.00
*GOLD 1-490/531-550: 4X TO 10X BASIC
*GOLD 491-530: 3X TO 8X BASIC

2003 Upper Deck Victory

This 200 card set was issued in Feburary, 2003. This set was issued in six card packs with an $1 SRP. The packs were issued 36 to a box and 20 boxes to a case. Cards number 1 through 100 comprise the base set while cards numbered 101 through 200 were produced in smaller quantity. The following subsets were produced: Solid Hits (101-128) were issued at a stated rate of one in four; Clutch Players (129-148) and Laying it on the Line (149-168) were issued at a stated rate of one in five; True Gamers (169-178) and Run Producers (179-188) were issued at a stated rate of one in 10; Difference Makers (189-194) and Winning Formula (195-200) were issued at a stated rate of one in 20.

COMPLETE SET (200) 30.00 80.00
COMP.SET w/o SP's (100) 10.00 25.00
COMMON CARD (101-200) .30 .75
101-128 STATED ODDS 1:4
129-168 STATED ODDS 1:5
169-188 STATED ODDS 1:10
189-200 STATED ODDS 1:20
1 Troy Glaus .10 .30
2 Garret Anderson .10 .30
3 Tim Salmon .20 .50
4 Darin Erstad .10 .30
5 Luis Gonzalez .10 .30
6 Curt Schilling .10 .30
7 Randy Johnson .30 .75
8 Junior Spivey .10 .30
9 Andruw Jones .20 .50
10 Greg Maddux .50 1.25
11 Chipper Jones .30 .75
12 Gary Sheffield .10 .30
13 John Smoltz .20 .50
14 Geronimo Gil .10 .30
15 Tony Batista .10 .30
16 Trot Nixon .10 .30
17 Manny Ramirez .20 .50
18 Pedro Martinez .20 .50
19 Nomar Garciaparra .50 1.25
20 Derek Lowe .10 .30
21 Shea Hillenbrand .10 .30
22 Sammy Sosa .30 .75
23 Kerry Wood .10 .30
24 Mark Prior .20 .50
25 Magglio Ordonez .10 .30
26 Frank Thomas .30 .75
27 Mark Buehrle .10 .30
28 Paul Konerko .10 .30
29 Adam Dunn .10 .30
30 Ken Griffey Jr. .50 1.25
31 Austin Kearns .10 .30
32 Matt Lawton .10 .30
33 Larry Walker .10 .30
34 Todd Helton .20 .50
35 Jeff Bagwell .20 .50
36 Roy Oswalt .10 .30
37 Lance Berkman .10 .30
38 Mike Sweeney .10 .30
39 Carlos Beltran .10 .30
40 Kazuhisa Ishii .10 .30
41 Shawn Green .10 .30
42 Hideo Nomo .30 .75
43 Adrian Beltre .10 .30
44 Richie Sexson .10 .30
45 Ben Sheets .10 .30
46 Torii Hunter .10 .30
47 Jacque Jones .10 .30
48 Corey Koskie .10 .30
49 Vladimir Guerrero .30 .75
50 Jose Vidro .10 .30
51 Mo Vaughn .10 .30
52 Mike Piazza .50 1.25
53 Roberto Alomar .20 .50
54 Derek Jeter .75 2.00
55 Alfonso Soriano .10 .30
56 Jason Giambi .10 .30
57 Roger Clemens .60 1.50
58 Mike Mussina .10 .30
59 Bernie Williams .20 .50
60 Jorge Posada .20 .50
61 Nick Johnson .10 .30
62 Hideki Matsui RC 1.50 4.00
63 Eric Chavez .10 .30
64 Barry Zito .10 .30
65 Miguel Tejada .10 .30
66 Tim Hudson .10 .30
67 Pat Burrell .10 .30
68 Bobby Abreu .10 .30
69 Jimmy Rollins .10 .30
70 Brett Myers .10 .30
71 Jim Thome .20 .50
72 Jason Kendall .10 .30
73 Brian Giles .10 .30
74 Aramis Ramirez .10 .30
75 Sean Burroughs .10 .30
76 Ryan Klesko .10 .30
77 Phil Nevin .10 .30
78 Barry Bonds .75 2.00
79 J.T.Snow .10 .30
80 Rich Aurilia .10 .30
81 Ichiro Suzuki .60 1.50
82 Edgar Martinez .20 .50
83 Freddy Garcia .10 .30
84 Jim Edmonds .10 .30
85 J.D. Drew .10 .30
86 Scott Rolen .20 .50
87 Albert Pujols .60 1.50
88 Mark McGwire .75 2.00
89 Matt Morris .10 .30
90 Ben Grieve .10 .30
91 Carl Crawford .10 .30
92 Alex Rodriguez .50 1.25
93 Carl Everett .10 .30
94 Juan Gonzalez .10 .30
95 Rafael Palmeiro .20 .50
96 Hank Blalock .10 .30
97 Carlos Delgado .10 .30
98 Josh Phelps .10 .30
99 Eric Hinske .10 .30
100 Shannon Stewart .10 .30
101 Albert Pujols SH 1.25 3.00
102 Alex Rodriguez SH 1.00 2.50
103 Alfonso Soriano SH .30 .75
104 Barry Bonds SH 1.50 4.00
105 Bernie Williams SH .40 1.00
106 Brian Giles SH .30 .75
107 Chipper Jones SH .60 1.50
108 Darin Erstad SH .30 .75
109 Derek Jeter SH 1.50 4.00
110 Eric Chavez SH .30 .75
111 Miguel Tejada SH .30 .75
112 Ichiro Suzuki SH 1.25 3.00
113 Rafael Palmeiro SH .40 1.00
114 Jason Giambi SH .10 .30
115 Jeff Bagwell SH .40 1.00
116 Jim Thome SH .40 1.00
117 Ken Griffey Jr. SH 1.00 2.50
118 Lance Berkman SH .30 .75
119 Luis Gonzalez SH .30 .75
120 Manny Ramirez SH .40 1.00
121 Mike Piazza SH 1.00 2.50
122 J.D. Drew SH .30 .75
123 Sammy Sosa SH .60 1.50
124 Scott Rolen SH .40 1.00
125 Shawn Green SH .30 .75
126 Todd Helton SH .40 1.00
127 Troy Glaus SH .30 .75
128 Vladimir Guerrero SH .60 1.50
129 Albert Pujols CP 1.25 3.00
130 Brian Giles CP .30 .75
131 Carlos Delgado CP .30 .75
132 Curt Schilling CP .30 .75
133 Derek Jeter CP 1.50 4.00
134 Frank Thomas CP .60 1.50
135 Greg Maddux CP 1.00 2.50
136 Jeff Bagwell CP .40 1.00
137 Jim Thome CP .40 1.00
138 Jorge Posada CP .40 1.00
139 Kazuhisa Ishii CP .30 .75
140 Larry Walker CP .30 .75
141 Luis Gonzalez CP .30 .75
142 Miguel Tejada CP .30 .75
143 Pat Burrell CP .30 .75
144 Pedro Martinez CP .40 1.00
145 Rafael Palmeiro CP .40 1.00
146 Roger Clemens CP 1.25 3.00
147 Tim Hudson CP .30 .75
148 Troy Glaus CP .30 .75
149 Alfonso Soriano LL .30 .75
150 Andruw Jones LL .40 1.00
151 Barry Zito LL .30 .75
152 Darin Erstad LL .30 .75
153 Eric Chavez LL .30 .75
154 Alex Rodriguez LL 1.00 2.50
155 J.D. Drew LL .30 .75
156 Jason Giambi LL .10 .30
157 Jason Kendall LL .30 .75
158 Ken Griffey Jr. LL 1.00 2.50
159 Lance Berkman LL .30 .75
160 Mike Mussina LL .40 1.00
161 Mike Piazza LL 1.00 2.50
162 Nomar Garciaparra LL 1.00 2.50
163 Randy Johnson LL .60 1.50
164 Roberto Alomar LL .40 1.00
165 Scott Rolen LL .40 1.00
166 Shawn Green LL .30 .75
167 Torii Hunter LL .30 .75
168 Vladimir Guerrero LL .60 1.50
169 Alex Rodriguez TG 1.00 2.50
170 Andruw Jones TG .40 1.00
171 Bernie Williams TG .40 1.00
172 Ichiro Suzuki TG 1.25 3.00
173 Miguel Tejada TG .30 .75
174 Nomar Garciaparra TG 1.00 2.50
175 Pedro Martinez TG .40 1.00
176 Randy Johnson TG .60 1.50
177 Todd Helton TG .40 1.00
178 Vladimir Guerrero TG .60 1.50
179 Barry Bonds RP 1.50 4.00
180 Carlos Delgado RP .30 .75
181 Chipper Jones RP .60 1.50
182 Frank Thomas RP .60 1.50
183 Lance Berkman RP .30 .75
184 Larry Walker RP .30 .75
185 Manny Ramirez RP .40 1.00
186 Mike Piazza RP 1.00 2.50
187 Sammy Sosa RP .60 1.50
188 Shawn Green RP .30 .75
189 Chipper Jones DM .60 1.50
190 Curt Schilling DM .30 .75
191 Derek Jeter DM 1.50 4.00
192 Ken Griffey Jr. DM 1.00 2.50
193 Sammy Sosa DM .60 1.50
194 Vladimir Guerrero DM .60 1.50
195 Alex Rodriguez WF 1.00 2.50
196 Barry Bonds WF 1.50 4.00
197 Greg Maddux WF 1.00 2.50
198 Ichiro Suzuki WF 1.25 3.00
199 Jason Giambi WF .10 .30
200 Mike Piazza WF 1.00 2.50

2003 Upper Deck Victory Tier 1 Green

Issued at a stated rate of one per pack, this a parallel to the first 100 cards of the Victory set. These cards can be identified by their green borders.

COMPLETE SET (100) 20.00 50.00

*GREEN: 1X TO 2.5X BASIC
*GREEN MATSUI: .6X TO 1.5X BASIC

2003 Upper Deck Victory Tier 2 Orange

Issued at a stated rate of one per eight packs, this a parallel to the first 100 cards of the Victory set. These cards can be identified by their orange borders.

COMPLETE SET (100) 30.00 80.00
*ORANGE: 2X TO 5X BASIC
*ORANGE MATSUI: 1X TO 2.5X BASIC

2003 Upper Deck Victory Tier 3 Blue

Randomly inserted in packs, this a parallel to the first 100 cards of the basic Victory set. These cards can be identified by their blue borders. These cards were issued to a stated print run of 650 serial numbered sets.

*BLUE: 4X TO 10X BASIC

2003 Upper Deck Victory Tier 4 Purple

Randomly inserted in packs, this a parallel to the first 100 cards of the basic Victory set. These cards can be identified by their purple borders. These cards were issued to a stated print run of 50 serial numbered sets.

*PURPLE: 12.5X TO 30X BASIC

2003 Upper Deck Victory Tier 5 Red

Randomly inserted in packs, this a parallel to the first 100 cards of the basic Victory set. These cards can be identified by their red borders. These cards were issued to a stated print run of 25 serial numbered sets. No pricing is available on these cards due to market scarcity.

NO PRICING DUE TO SCARCITY

2001 Upper Deck Vintage

The 2001 Upper Deck Vintage product released in late January,2001 and featured a 400-card base set. Each pack contained 10 cards, and carried a suggested retail price of $2.99 per pack. The set was broken into tiers as follows: Base Veterans (1-340), Prospects (341-370), Series Highlights (371-390) and League Leaders (391-400). A Sample card featuring Ken Griffey Jr. was distributed to dealers and hobby media several weeks prior to the product's release national release date. The card can be readily identified by the bold "SAMPLE" text running diagonally across the back.

COMPLETE SET (400) 20.00 50.00
COMMON (1-340/371-400) .10 .30
COMMON (341-370) .20 .50
1 Darin Erstad .10 .30
2 Seth Etherton .10 .30
3 Troy Glaus .10 .30
4 Bengie Molina .10 .30
5 Mo Vaughn .10 .30
6 Tim Salmon .20 .50
7 Ramon Ortiz .10 .30
8 Adam Kennedy .10 .30
9 Garret Anderson .10 .30
10 Troy Percival .10 .30
11 Tim Salmon .10 .30
Bengie Molina
MoVaughn
Adam Kennedy
Troy Glaus
Kevin Stocker
Darin Erstad
Garret Anderson
Ron Gant CL
12 Jason Giambi .10 .30
13 Tim Hudson .10 .30
14 Adam Piatt .10 .30
15 Miguel Tejada .10 .30
16 Mark Mulder .10 .30
17 Eric Chavez .10 .30
18 Ramon Hernandez .10 .30
19 Terrence Long .10 .30
20 Jason Isringhausen .10 .30
21 Barry Zito .20 .50
22 Ben Grieve .10 .30
23 Olmedo Saenz .10 .30
Ramon Hernandez
Jason Giambi
Randy Velarde
Eric Chavez
Miguel Tejada
Ben Grieve
Terrence Long
Adam Piatt CL
24 David Wells .10 .30
25 Raul Mondesi .10 .30
26 Darrin Fletcher .10 .30
27 Shannon Stewart .10 .30
28 Kelvim Escobar .10 .30
29 Tony Batista .10 .30
30 Carlos Delgado .10 .30
31 Brad Fullmer .10 .30
32 Billy Koch .10 .30
33 Jose Cruz Jr. .10 .30
34 Brad Fullmer .10 .30
Darrin Fletcher
Carlos Delgado
Homer Bush
Tony Batista
Alex Gonzalez
Shannon Stewart
Jose Cruz Jr.
Raul Mondesi CL
35 Greg Vaughn .10 .30
36 Roberto Hernandez .10 .30
37 Vinny Castilla .10 .30
38 Gerald Williams .10 .30
39 Aubrey Huff .10 .30
40 Bryan Rekar .10 .30
41 Albie Lopez .10 .30
42 Fred McGriff .20 .50
43 Miguel Cairo .10 .30
44 Ryan Rupe .10 .30
45 Greg Vaughn .10 .30
John Flaherty
Fred McGriff
Miguel Cairo
Vinny Castilla
Felix Martinez
Gerald Williams
Jose Guillen
Steve Cox CL
46 Jim Thome .20 .50
47 Roberto Alomar .20 .50
48 Bartolo Colon .20 .50
49 Omar Vizquel .20 .50
50 Travis Fryman .10 .30
51 Manny Ramirez UER .20 .50
Picture is of David Segui
52 Dave Burba .10 .30
53 Chuck Finley .10 .30
54 Russ Branyan .10 .30
55 Kenny Lofton .10 .30
56 Russell Branyan .10 .30
Sandy Alomar Jr.
Jim Thome
Roberto Alomar
Travis Fryman
Omar Vizquel
Wil Cordero
Kenny Lofton
Manny Ramirez
Picture is off David Segui CL UER
57 Alex Rodriguez .50 1.25
58 Jay Buhner .10 .30
59 Aaron Sele .10 .30
60 Kazuhiro Sasaki .10 .30
61 Edgar Martinez .20 .50
62 John Halama .10 .30
63 Mike Cameron .10 .30
64 Freddy Garcia .10 .30
65 John Olerud .08 .25
66 Jamie Moyer .10 .30
67 Gil Meche .10 .30
68 Edgar Martinez .10 .30
Joe Oliver
John Olerud
David Bell
Carlos Guillen
Alex Rodriguez
Jay Buhner
Mike Cameron
Al Martin CL
69 Cal Ripken 1.00 2.50
70 Sidney Ponson .10 .30
71 Chris Richard .10 .30
72 Jose Mercedes .10 .30
73 Albert Belle .10 .30
74 Mike Mussina .20 .50
75 Brady Anderson .10 .30
76 Delino DeShields .10 .30
77 Melvin Mora .10 .30
78 Luis Matos .10 .30
79 Brook Fordyce .10 .30
80 Jeff Conine .10 .30
Brook Fordyce
Chris Richard
Delino DeShields
Cal Ripken
Melvin Mora
Luis Matos
Brady Anderson
Albert Belle CL
81 Rafael Palmeiro .20 .50
82 Rick Helling .10 .30
83 Ruben Mateo .10 .30
84 Rusty Greer .10 .30
85 Ivan Rodriguez .20 .50
86 Doug Davis .10 .30
87 Gabe Kapler .10 .30
88 Mike Lamb .10 .30
89 A.Rodriguez Rangers 1.25 3.00
90 Kenny Rogers .10 .30
91 David Segui .20 .50
Ivan Rodriguez
Rafael Palmeiro
Frank Catalanotto
Mike Lamb
Royce Clayton
Ruben Mateo
Gabe Kapler
Rusty Greer CL
92 Nomar Garciaparra .50 1.25
93 Trot Nixon .10 .30
94 Tomokazu Ohka .10 .30
95 Pedro Martinez .20 .50
96 Dante Bichette .10 .30
97 Jason Varitek .30 .75
98 Rolando Arrojo .10 .30
99 Carl Everett .10 .30
100 Derek Lowe .10 .30
101 Troy O'Leary .10 .30
102 Tim Wakefield .10 .30
103 Troy O'Leary .20 .50
Jason Varitek
Jose Offerman
Mike Lansing
Wilton Veras
Nomar Garciaparra
Carl Everett
Trot Nixon
Dante Bichette CL
104 Mike Sweeney .10 .30
105 Carlos Febles .10 .30
106 Joe Randa .10 .30
107 Jeff Suppan .10 .30
108 Mac Suzuki .10 .30
109 Jermaine Dye .10 .30
110 Carlos Beltran .10 .30
111 Mark Quinn .10 .30
112 Johnny Damon .20 .50
113 Mark Quinn .10 .30
Gregg Zaun
Mike Sweeney
Carlos Febles
Joe Randa
Rey Sanchez
Carlos Beltran
Johnny Damon
Jermaine Dye CL
114 Tony Clark .10 .30
115 Dean Palmer .10 .30
116 Brian Moehler .10 .30
117 Brad Ausmus .10 .30
118 Juan Gonzalez .10 .30
119 Juan Encarnacion .10 .30
120 Jeff Weaver .10 .30
121 Bobby Higginson .10 .30
122 Todd Jones .10 .30
123 Deivi Cruz .10 .30
124 Juan Gonzalez .10 .30
Brad Ausmus
Tony Clark
Damion Easley
Dean Palmer
Deivi Cruz
Bobby Higginson
Juan Encarnacion
Rich Becker CL
125 Corey Koskie .10 .30
126 Matt Lawton .10 .30
127 Mark Redman .10 .30
128 David Ortiz .30 .75
129 Jay Canizaro .10 .30
130 Eric Milton .10 .30
131 Jacque Jones .10 .30
132 J.C. Romero .10 .30
133 Ron Coomer .10 .30
134 Brad Radke .10 .30
135 David Ortiz .20 .50
Matt LeCroy
Ron Coomer
Jay Canizaro
Corey Koskie
Cristian Guzman
Jacque Jones
Matt Lawton
Torii Hunter CL
136 Carlos Lee .10 .30
137 Frank Thomas .30 .75
138 Mike Sirotka .10 .30
139 Charles Johnson .10 .30
140 James Baldwin .10 .30
141 Magglio Ordonez .10 .30
142 Jon Garland .10 .30
143 Paul Konerko .10 .30
144 Ray Durham .10 .30
145 Keith Foulke .10 .30
146 Chris Singleton .10 .30
147 Frank Thomas .20 .50
Charles Johnson
Paul Konerko
Ray Durham
Herbert Perry
Jose Valentin
Carlos Lee
Magglio Ordonez
Chris Singleton CL
148 Bernie Williams .20 .50
149 Orlando Hernandez .10 .30
150 David Justice .10 .30
151 Andy Pettitte .20 .50
152 Mariano Rivera .30 .75
153 Derek Jeter .75 2.00
154 Jorge Posada .20 .50
155 Jose Canseco .20 .50
156 Glenallen Hill .10 .30
157 Paul O'Neill .20 .50
158 Denny Neagle .10 .30
159 Chuck Knoblauch .10 .30
160 Roger Clemens .60 1.50
161 Glenallen Hill .30 .75
Jorge Posada
Tino Martinez
Chuck Knoblauch
Scott Brosius
Derek Jeter
Paul O'Neill
Bernie Williams
David Justice CL
162 Jeff Bagwell .20 .50
163 Moises Alou .10 .30
164 Lance Berkman .10 .30
165 Shane Reynolds .10 .30
166 Ken Caminiti .10 .30
167 Craig Biggio .20 .50
168 Jose Lima .10 .30
169 Octavio Dotel .10 .30
170 Richard Hidalgo .10 .30
171 Scott Elarton .10 .30
172 Scott Elarton .20 .50
Mitch Meluskey
Jeff Bagwell
Craig Biggio
Bill Spiers
Julio Lugo
Moises Alou
Richard Hidalgo
Lance Berkman CL
173 Rafael Furcal .10 .30
174 Greg Maddux .50 1.25
175 Quilvio Veras .10 .30
176 Chipper Jones .30 .75
177 Andres Galarraga .10 .30
178 Brian Jordan .10 .30
179 Tom Glavine .20 .50
180 Kevin Millwood .10 .30
181 Javier Lopez .10 .30
182 B.J. Surhoff .10 .30
183 Andruw Jones .20 .50
184 Andy Ashby .10 .30
185 Tom Glavine .20 .50
Javy Lopez
Andres Galarraga
Quilvio Veras
Chipper Jones
Rafael Furcal
Reggie Sanders
Brian Jordan
Andruw Jones CL
186 Richie Sexson .10 .30
187 Jeff D'Amico .10 .30
188 Ron Belliard .10 .30
189 Jeromy Burnitz .10 .30
190 Jimmy Haynes .10 .30
191 Marquis Grissom .10 .30

192 Jose Hernandez .10 .30
193 Geoff Jenkins .10 .30
194 Jamey Wright .10 .30
195 Mark Loretta .10 .30
196 Jeff D'Amico .10 .30
Henry Blanco
Richie Sexson
Ron Belliard
Tyler Houston
Mark Loretta
Jeromy Burnitz
Marquis Grissom
Geoff Jenkins CL
197 Rick Ankiel .10 .30
198 Mark McGwire .75 2.00
199 Fernando Vina .10 .30
200 Edgar Renteria .10 .30
201 Darryl Kile .10 .30
202 Jim Edmonds .10 .30
203 Ray Lankford .10 .30
204 Garrett Stephenson .10 .30
205 Fernando Tatis .10 .30
206 Will Clark .20 .50
207 J.D. Drew .10 .30
208 Darryl Kile .10 .30
Mike Matheny
Mark McGwire
Fernando Vina
Fernando Tatis
Edgar Renteria
Ray Lankford
Jim Edmonds
J.D. Drew CL
209 Mark Grace .20 .50
210 Eric Young .10 .30
211 Sammy Sosa .30 .75
212 Jon Lieber .10 .30
213 Joe Girardi .10 .30
214 Kevin Tapani .10 .30
215 Ricky Gutierrez .10 .30
216 Kerry Wood .10 .30
217 Rondell White .10 .30
218 Damon Buford .10 .30
219 Jon Lieber .10 .30
Joe Girardi
Mark Grace
Eric Young
Willie Greene
Ricky Gutierrez
Sammy Sosa
Damon Buford
Rondell White CL
220 Luis Gonzalez .10 .30
221 Randy Johnson .30 .75
222 Jay Bell .10 .30
223 Erubiel Durazo .10 .30
224 Matt Williams .10 .30
225 Steve Finley .10 .30
226 Curt Schilling .10 .30
227 Todd Stottlemyre .10 .30
228 Tony Womack .10 .30
229 Brian Anderson .10 .30
230 Randy Johnson .10 .30
Kelly Stinnett
Greg Colbrunn
Jay Bell
Matt Williams
Tony Womack
Luis Gonzalez
Steve Finley
Danny Bautista CL
231 Gary Sheffield .10 .30
232 Adrian Beltre .10 .30
233 Todd Hundley .10 .30
234 Chan Ho Park .10 .30
235 Shawn Green .10 .30
236 Kevin Brown .10 .30
237 Tom Goodwin .10 .30
238 Mark Grudzielanek .10 .30
239 Ismael Valdes .10 .30
240 Eric Karros .10 .30
241 Kevin Brown .10 .30
Todd Hundley
Eric Karros
Mark Grudzielanek
Adrian Beltre
Alex Cora
Gary Sheffield
Shawn Green
Tom Goodwin CL
242 Jose Vidro .10 .30
243 Javier Vazquez .10 .30
244 Orlando Cabrera .10 .30
245 Peter Bergeron .10 .30
246 Vladimir Guerrero .30 .75
247 Dustin Hermanson .10 .30
248 Tony Armas Jr. .10 .30
249 Lee Stevens .10 .30
250 Milton Bradley .10 .30
251 Carl Pavano .10 .30
252 Dustin Hermanson .10 .30
Michael Barrett
Lee Stevens
Jose Vidro
Geoff Jenkins
Orlando Cabrera
Vladimir Guerrero
Peter Bergeron
Milton Bradley CL
253 Ellis Burks .10 .30
254 Robb Nen .10 .30
255 J.T. Snow .10 .30
256 Barry Bonds .75 2.00
257 Shawn Estes .10 .30
258 Jeff Kent .10 .30
259 Kirk Rueter .10 .30
260 Bill Mueller .10 .30
261 Livan Hernandez .10 .30
262 Rich Aurilia .10 .30
263 Livan Hernandez .10 .30
Bobby Estalella
J.T. Snow
Jeff Kent
Bill Mueller
Rich Aurilia
Barry Bonds
Marvin Benard
Ellis Burks CL
264 Ryan Dempster .10 .30
265 Cliff Floyd .10 .30
266 Mike Lowell .10 .30
267 A.J. Burnett .10 .30
268 Preston Wilson .10 .30
269 Luis Castillo .10 .30
270 Henry Rodriguez .10 .30
271 Antonio Alfonseca .10 .30
272 Derrek Lee .20 .50
273 Mark Kotsay .10 .30
274 Brad Penny .10 .30
275 Ryan Dempster .20 .50
Mike Redmond
Derrek Lee
Luis Castillo
Mike Lowell
Alex Gonzalez
Cliff Floyd
Mark Kotsay
Preston Wilson CL
276 Mike Piazza .50 1.25
277 Jay Payton .10 .30
278 Al Leiter .10 .30
279 Mike Bordick .10 .30
280 Armando Benitez .10 .30
281 Todd Zeile .10 .30
282 Mike Hampton .10 .30
283 Edgardo Alfonzo .10 .30
284 Derek Bell .10 .30
285 Robin Ventura .10 .30
286 Mike Hampton .10 .30
Mike Piazza
Todd Zeile
Edgardo Alfonzo
Robin Ventura
Mike Bordick
Derek Bell
Jay Payton
Timo Perez CL
287 Tony Gwynn .40 1.00
288 Trevor Hoffman .10 .30
289 Ryan Klesko .10 .30
290 Phil Nevin .10 .30
291 Matt Clement .10 .30
292 Ben Davis .10 .30
293 Ruben Rivera .10 .30
294 Bret Boone .10 .30
295 Adam Eaton .10 .30
296 Eric Owens .10 .30
297 Matt Clemente .10 .30
Ben Davis
Ryan Klesko
Bret Boone
Phil Nevin
Damian Jackson
Ruben Rivera
Eric Owens
Tony Gwynn CL
298 Bob Abreu .10 .30
299 Mike Lieberthal .10 .30
300 Robert Person .10 .30
301 Scott Rolen .20 .50
302 Randy Wolf .10 .30
303 Bruce Chen .10 .30
304 Travis Lee .10 .30
305 Kent Bottenfield .10 .30
306 Pat Burrell .10 .30
307 Doug Glanville .10 .30
308 Robert Person .10 .30
Mike Lieberthal
Pat Burrell
Kevin Jordan
Scott Rolen
Alex Arias
Bob Abreu
Doug Glanville
Travis Lee CL
309 Brian Giles .10 .30
310 Todd Ritchie .10 .30
311 Warren Morris .10 .30
312 John VanderWal .10 .30
313 Kris Benson .10 .30
314 Jason Kendall .10 .30
315 Kevin Young .10 .30
316 Francisco Cordova .10 .30
317 Jimmy Anderson .10 .30
318 Kris Benson .10 .30
Jason Kendall
Kevin Young
Warren Morris
Mike Benjamin
Pat Meares
John VanderWal
Brian Giles
Adrian Brown CL
319 Ken Griffey Jr. .50 1.25
320 Pokey Reese .10 .30
321 Chris Stynes .10 .30
322 Barry Larkin .20 .50
323 Steve Parris .10 .30
324 Michael Tucker .10 .30
325 Dmitri Young .10 .30
326 Pete Harnisch .10 .30
327 Danny Graves .10 .30
328 Aaron Boone .10 .30
329 Sean Casey .10 .30
330 Steve Parris .10 .30
Ed Taubensee
Sean Casey
Pokey Reese
Aaron Boone
Barry Larkin
Ken Griffey Jr.
Dmitri Young
Michael Tucker CL
331 Todd Helton .20 .50
332 Pedro Astacio .10 .30
333 Larry Walker .10 .30
334 Ben Petrick .10 .30
335 Brian Bohanon .10 .30
336 Juan Pierre .10 .30
337 Jeffrey Hammonds .10 .30
338 Jeff Cirillo .10 .30
339 Todd Hollandsworth .10 .30
340 Pedro Astacio .10 .30
Brent Mayne
Todd Helton
Todd Walker
Jeff Cirillo
Neifi Perez
Larry Walker
Jeffrey Hammonds
Juan Pierre CL
341 Matt Wise .20 .50
Keith Luuloa
Derrick Turnbow
342 Jason Hart .20 .50
Jose Ortiz
Mario Encarnacion
343 Vernon Wells .20 .50
Pasqual Coco
Josh Phelps
344 Travis Harper .20 .50
Kenny Kelley
Toby Hall
345 Danys Baez .20 .50
Tim Drew
Martin Vargas
346 Ichiro Suzuki 2.50 6.00
Ryan Franklin
Ryan Christianson
347 Jay Spurgeon .20 .50
Lesli Brea
Carlos Casimiro
348 B.J. Waszgis .20 .50
Brian Sikorski
Joaquin Benoit
349 Sun-Woo Kim .20 .50
Paxton Crawford
Steve Lomasney
350 Kris Wilson .20 .50
Orber Moreno
Dee Brown
351 Mark Johnson .20 .50
Brandon Inge
Adam Bernero
352 Danny Ardoin .20 .50
Matt Kinney
Jason Ryan
353 Rocky Biddle .40 1.00
Joe Crede
Josh Paul
354 Nick Johnson .20 .50
D'Angelo Jimenez
Wily Mo Pena
355 Tony McKnight .20 .50
Aaron McNeal
Keith Ginter
356 Mark DeRosa .10 .30
Jason Marquis
Wes Helms UER
Photos do not match the players ID'd
357 Allen Levrault .20 .50
Horacio Estrada
Santiago Perez
358 Luis Saturria .20 .50
Gene Stechschulte
Britt Reames
359 Joey Nation .20 .50
Corey Patterson
Cole Liniak
360 Alex Cabrera .20 .50
Geraldo Guzman
Nelson Figuero
361 Hiram Bocachica .20 .50
Mike Judd
Luke Prokopec
362 Tomas de la Rosa .20 .50
Yohanny Valera
Talmadge Nunnari
363 Ryan Vogelsong .20 .50
Juan Melo
Chad Zerbe
364 Jason Grilli .20 .50
Pablo Ozuna
Ramon Castro
365 Timo Perez .20 .50
Grant Roberts
Brian Cole
366 Tom Davey .20 .50
Xavier Nady
Dave Maurer
367 Jimmy Rollins .20 .50
Mark Brownson
Rennie Taylor
368 Alex Hernandez .20 .50
Adam Hyzdu
Tike Redman
369 Brady Clark .20 .50
John Riedling
Mike Bell
370 Giovanni Carrara .20 .50
Josh Kalinowski
Craig House
371 Jim Edmonds SH .10 .30
372 Edgar Martinez SH .10 .30
373 Rickey Henderson SH .30 .75
374 Barry Zito SH .20 .50
375 Tino Martinez SH .20 .50
376 J.T. Snow SH .10 .30
377 Bobby Jones SH .10 .30
378 Alex Rodriguez SH .30 .75
379 Mike Hampton SH .10 .30
380 Roger Clemens SH .30 .75
381 Jay Payton SH .10 .30
382 John Olerud SH .10 .30
383 David Justice SH .10 .30
384 Mike Hampton SH .10 .30
385 New York Yankees SH .30 .75
386 Jose Vizcaino SH .10 .30
387 Roger Clemens SH .30 .75
388 Todd Zeile SH .10 .30
389 Derek Jeter SH .40 1.00
390 New York Yankees SH .30 .75
391 Nomar Garciaparra .30 .75
Darin Erstad
Manny Ramirez
Derek Jeter
Carlos Delgado LL
392 Todd Helton .20 .50
Luis Castillo
Jeffrey Hammonds
Vladimir Guerrero
Moises Alou LL
393 Troy Glaus .30 .75
Frank Thomas
Alex Rodriguez
Jason Giambi
David Justice LL
394 Sammy Sosa .20 .50
Jeff Bagwell
Barry Bonds
Vladimir Guerrero
Richard Hidalgo LL
395 Edgar Martinez .10 .30
Mike Sweeney
Frank Thomas
Carlos Delgado
Jason Giambi LL
396 Todd Helton .10 .30
Jeff Kent
Brian Giles
Sammy Sosa
Jeff Bagwell LL
397 Pedro Martinez .20 .50
Roger Clemens
Mike Mussina
Bartolo Colon
Mike Sirotka LL
398 Kevin Brown .10 .30
Randy Johnson
Jeff D'Amico
Greg Maddux
Mike Hampton LL
399 Tim Hudson .10 .30
David Wells
Aaron Sele
Andy Pettitte
Pedro Martinez LL
400 Tom Glavine .20 .50
Darryl Kile
Randy Johnson
Chan Ho Park
Greg Maddux LL
S30 K.Griffey Jr. Sample .50 1.25

2001 Upper Deck Vintage All-Star Tributes

Randomly inserted into packs at one in 23, this 10-card insert features players that make the All-Star team on a consistent basis. Card backs carry an "AS" prefix.

COMPLETE SET (10) 20.00 40.00
AS1 Derek Jeter 2.50 6.00
AS2 Mike Piazza 1.50 4.00
AS3 Carlos Delgado .60 1.50
AS4 Pedro Martinez .60 1.50
AS5 Vladimir Guerrero 1.00 2.50
AS6 Mark McGwire 2.50 6.00
AS7 Alex Rodriguez 1.50 4.00
AS8 Barry Bonds 2.50 6.00
AS9 Chipper Jones 1.00 2.50
AS10 Sammy Sosa 1.00 2.50

2001 Upper Deck Vintage Glory Days

Randomly inserted into packs at one in 15, this 15-card insert features players that remind us of baseball's glory days of the past. Card backs carry a "G" prefix.

COMPLETE SET (15) 15.00 40.00
G1 Jermaine Dye .60 1.50
G2 Chipper Jones 1.00 2.50
G3 Todd Helton .60 1.50
G4 Magglio Ordonez .60 1.50
G5 Tony Gwynn 1.25 3.00
G6 Jim Edmonds .60 1.50
G7 Rafael Palmeiro .60 1.50
G8 Barry Bonds 2.50 6.00
G9 Carl Everett .60 1.50
G10 Mike Piazza 1.50 4.00
G11 Brian Giles .60 1.50
G12 Tony Batista .60 1.50
G13 Jeff Bagwell .60 1.50
G14 Ken Griffey Jr. 1.50 4.00
G15 Troy Glaus .60 1.50

2001 Upper Deck Vintage Matinee Idols

Randomly inserted into packs at one in four, this 20-card insert features players that are idolized by every young baseball player in America. Card backs carry a "M" prefix.

COMPLETE SET (20) 10.00 25.00
M1 Ken Griffey Jr. .75 2.00
M2 Derek Jeter 1.25 3.00
M3 Barry Bonds 1.25 3.00
M4 Chipper Jones .50 1.25
M5 Mike Piazza .75 2.00
M6 Todd Helton .30 .75
M7 Randy Johnson .50 1.25
M8 Alex Rodriguez .75 2.00
M9 Sammy Sosa .50 1.25
M10 Cal Ripken 1.50 4.00
M11 Nomar Garciaparra .75 2.00
M12 Carlos Delgado .30 .75
M13 Jason Giambi .30 .75
M14 Ivan Rodriguez .30 .75
M15 Vladimir Guerrero .50 1.25
M16 Gary Sheffield .30 .75
M17 Frank Thomas .50 1.25
M18 Jeff Bagwell .30 .75
M19 Pedro Martinez .30 .75
M20 Mark McGwire 1.25 3.00

2001 Upper Deck Vintage Retro Rules

Randomly inserted into packs at one in 15, this 15-card insert features players whose performances remind us of baseball's good ol' days. Card backs carry a "R" prefix.

COMPLETE SET (15) 20.00 40.00
R1 Nomar Garciaparra 1.50 4.00
R2 Frank Thomas 1.00 2.50
R3 Jeff Bagwell .60 1.50
R4 Sammy Sosa 1.00 2.50
R5 Derek Jeter 2.50 6.00
R6 David Wells .60 1.50
R7 Vladimir Guerrero 1.00 2.50
R8 Jim Thome .60 1.50
R9 Mark McGwire 2.50 6.00
R10 Todd Helton .60 1.50
R11 Tony Gwynn 1.25 3.00
R12 Bernie Williams .60 1.50
R13 Cal Ripken 3.00 8.00
R14 Brian Giles .60 1.50
R15 Jason Giambi .60 1.50

2001 Upper Deck Vintage Timeless Teams

Randomly inserted into packs at one in 72 (Bats) and one in 288 (Jerseys), this 39-card insert features swatches of game-used memorabilia from powerhouse clubs of the past. Card backs carry the team initials/player's initials as numbering.

CI2JB Johnny Bench Bat 10.00 25.00
CI2JM Joe Morgan Bat 6.00 15.00
CI2KG Ken Griffey Sr. Bat 10.00 25.00
CI2TP Tony Perez Bat 6.00 15.00
BABP Boog Powell Bat 10.00 25.00
BABR B. Robinson Bat 10.00 25.00
BAFR Frank Robinson Bat 10.00 25.00
BAMB Mark Belanger Bat 6.00 15.00
BKDN Don Newcombe Bat 10.00 25.00
BKGH Gil Hodges Bat 10.00 25.00
BKJR Jackie Robinson Bat 40.00 80.00
BKRC Roy Campanella Bat 20.00 50.00
CIDC D. Concepcion Jsy 6.00 15.00
CIJM Joe Morgan Jsy 6.00 15.00
CIKG Ken Griffey Sr. Jsy 10.00 25.00
CITP Tony Perez Jsy 6.00 15.00
LABR Bill Russell Bat 6.00 15.00
LADB Dusty Baker Bat 6.00 15.00
LARC Ron Cey Bat 6.00 15.00
LASG Steve Garvey Bat 6.00 15.00
NYMEK Ed Kranepool Bat 6.00 15.00
NYMNR Nolan Ryan Bat 20.00 50.00
NYMRS Ron Swoboda Bat 6.00 15.00
NYMTA Tommie Agee Bat 6.00 15.00
NYYBD Bill Dickey Bat 10.00 25.00
NYYBR B. Richardson Jsy 6.00 15.00
NYYCK Charlie Keller Bat 6.00 15.00
NYYJD Joe DiMaggio Bat 50.00 100.00
NYYMM M. Mantle Jsy 125.00 200.00
NYYRM Roger Maris Jsy 40.00 80.00
NYYTH T. Henrich Bat 6.00 15.00
OAGT Gene Tenace Bat 6.00 15.00
OAJR Joe Rudi Bat 6.00 15.00
OARJ Reggie Jackson Bat 10.00 25.00
OASB Sal Bando Bat 6.00 15.00
PIAO Al Oliver Bat 6.00 15.00
PIMS M. Sanguillen Bat 6.00 15.00
PIRC R. Clemente Bat 50.00 100.00
PIWS Willie Stargell Bat 10.00 25.00

2001 Upper Deck Vintage Timeless Teams Combos

Randomly inserted into packs, this 11-card insert features swatches of game-used memorabilia from powerhouse clubs of the past. Please note that these cards feature dual players, and are individually serial numbered to 100. Card backs carry the team initials/year as numbering. Unlike the other cards in this set, only twenty-five serial-numbered copies of the "Fantasy Outfield" card featuring DiMaggio, Mantle and Griffey Jr. were created.

LA81 Steve Garvey Bat 20.00 50.00
Ron Cey Bat
Dusty Baker Bat
Bill Russell Bat
BAL70 Brooks Robinson Bat 40.00 80.00
Frank Robinson Bat
Mark Belanger Bat
Boog Powell Bat
BKN55 Jackie Robinson Bat 150.00 250.00
Roy Campanella Bat
Gil Hodges Bat
Don Newcombe Bat
CIN75B Johnny Bench Bat 40.00 80.00
Tony Perez Bat
Joe Morgan Bat
Ken Griffey Sr. Bat
CIN75J Dave Concepcion Jsy 20.00 50.00
Tony Perez Jsy
Ken Griffey Sr. Jsy
NYM69 Nolan Ryan Bat 75.00 150.00
Ron Swoboda Bat
Ed Kranepool Bat
Tommie Agee Bat
NYY41 Joe DiMaggio Bat 125.00 200.00
Tommy Henrich Bat
Bill Dickey Bat
Charlie Keller Bat
NYY61 Mickey Mantle Jsy 175.00 300.00
Roger Maris Jsy
Bobby Richardson Jsy
OAK72 Reggie Jackson Bat 40.00 80.00
Sal Bando Bat
Gene Tenace Bat
Joe Rudi Bat
PIT71 Roberto Clemente Bat 150.00 250.00
Willie Stargell Bat
Manny Sanguillen Bat
Al Oliver Bat UER
Card back says it is a Bill Mazeroski piece
Manny Sanguillen replaced Mazeroski on card
FOCJ Joe DiMaggio Jsy
Mickey Mantle Jsy
Ken Griffey Jr. Jsy/25

2002 Upper Deck Vintage

Released In January, 2002 this 300 card set features Upper Deck honoring the popular 1971 Topps design for this set. Subsets include Team Checklists, Vintage Rookies (both seeded throughout the set), League Leaders (271-280) and Postseason Scrapbook (281-300). Please note that card number 274 has a variation. A few cards issued very early in the printing cycle featured the players listed as AL Home Run Leaders and no names listed for the players. It is believed this card was corrected very early in the printing cycle.

COMPLETE SET (300) 30.00 60.00
1 Darin Erstad .15 .40
2 Mo Vaughn .15 .40
3 Ramon Ortiz .15 .40
4 Garret Anderson .15 .40
5 Troy Glaus .15 .40
6 Troy Percival .15 .40
7 Tim Salmon .20 .50
8 Wilmy Caceres .15 .40
Elpidio Guzman
9 Ramon Ortiz TC .15 .40
10 Jason Giambi .15 .40
11 Mark Mulder .15 .40
12 Jermaine Dye .15 .40
13 Miguel Tejada .15 .40
14 Tim Hudson .15 .40
15 Eric Chavez .15 .40
16 Barry Zito .15 .40
17 Oscar Salazar .15 .40
Juan Pena
18 Miguel Tejada .15 .40
Jason Giambi TC
19 Carlos Delgado .15 .40
20 Raul Mondesi .15 .40
21 Chris Carpenter .15 .40
22 Jose Cruz Jr. .15 .40
23 Alex Gonzalez .15 .40
24 Brad Fullmer .15 .40
25 Shannon Stewart .15 .40
26 Brandon Lyon .15 .40
Vernon Wells
27 Carlos Delgado TC .15 .40
28 Greg Vaughn .15 .40
29 Toby Hall .15 .40
30 Ben Grieve .15 .40
31 Aubrey Huff .15 .40
32 Tanyon Sturtze .15 .40
33 Brent Abernathy .15 .40
34 Dewon Brazelton .15 .40
Delvin James
35 Greg Vaughn .15 .40
Fred McGriff TC
36 Roberto Alomar .20 .50
37 Juan Gonzalez .15 .40
38 Bartolo Colon .15 .40
39 C.C. Sabathia .15 .40
40 Jim Thome .20 .50
41 Omar Vizquel .20 .50
42 Russell Branyan .15 .40
43 Ryan Drese .15 .40
Roy Smith
44 C.C. Sabathia TC .15 .40
45 Edgar Martinez .20 .50
46 Bret Boone .15 .40
47 Freddy Garcia .15 .40
48 John Olerud .15 .40
49 Kazuhiro Sasaki .15 .40
50 Ichiro Suzuki .60 1.50
51 Mike Cameron .15 .40
52 Rafael Soriano .15 .40
Dennis Stark
53 Jamie Moyer TC .15 .40
54 Tony Batista .15 .40
55 Jeff Conine .15 .40
56 Jason Johnson .15 .40
57 Jay Gibbons .15 .40
58 Chris Richard .15 .40
59 Josh Towers .15 .40
60 Jerry Hairston Jr. .15 .40
61 Sean Douglass .15 .40
Tim Raines Jr.
62 Cal Ripken TC .50 1.25
63 Alex Rodriguez .50 1.25
64 Ruben Sierra .15 .40
65 Ivan Rodriguez .20 .50
66 Gabe Kapler .15 .40
67 Rafael Palmeiro .20 .50
68 Frank Catalanotto .15 .40
69 Mark Teixeira .40 1.00
Carlos Pena
70 Alex Rodriguez TC .30 .75
71 Nomar Garciaparra .50 1.25
72 Pedro Martinez .20 .50
73 Trot Nixon .15 .40
74 Dante Bichette .15 .40
75 Manny Ramirez .20 .50
76 Carl Everett .15 .40
77 Hideo Nomo .30 .75
78 Dernell Stenson .15 .40
Juan Diaz
79 Manny Ramirez TC .20 .50
80 Mike Sweeney .15 .40
81 Carlos Febles .15 .40
82 Dee Brown .15 .40
83 Neifi Perez .15 .40
84 Mark Quinn .15 .40
85 Carlos Beltran .15 .40
86 Joe Randa .15 .40
87 Ken Harvey .15 .40
Mike MacDougal
88 Mike Sweeney TC .15 .40
89 Dean Palmer .15 .40
90 Jeff Weaver .15 .40
91 Jose Lima .15 .40
92 Tony Clark .15 .40
93 Damion Easley .15 .40
94 Bobby Higginson .15 .40
95 Robert Fick .15 .40
96 Pedro Santana .15 .40
Mike Rivera
97 Juan Encarnacion .15 .40
Roger Cedeno TC
98 Doug Mientkiewicz .15 .40
99 David Ortiz .20 .50
100 Joe Mays .15 .40
101 Corey Koskie .15 .40
102 Eric Milton .15 .40
103 Cristian Guzman .15 .40
104 Brad Radke .15 .40
105 Adam Johnson .15 .40
Juan Rincon
106 Corey Koskie TC .15 .40
107 Frank Thomas .30 .75

108 Carlos Lee .15 .40
109 Mark Buehrle .15 .40
110 Jose Canseco .20 .50
111 Magglio Ordonez .15 .40
112 Jon Garland .15 .40
113 Ray Durham .15 .40
114 Joe Crede .15 .40
Josh Fogg
115 Carlos Lee TC .15 .40
116 Derek Jeter .75 2.00
117 Roger Clemens .60 1.50
118 Alfonso Soriano .15 .40
119 Paul O'Neill .20 .50
120 Jorge Posada .20 .50
121 Bernie Williams .20 .50
122 Mariano Rivera .30 .75
123 Tino Martinez .20 .50
124 Mike Mussina .20 .50
125 Nick Johnson .15 .40
Erick Almonte
126 Jorge Posada .30 .75
David Justice
Scott Brosius TC
127 Jeff Bagwell .20 .50
128 Wade Miller .15 .40
129 Lance Berkman .15 .40
130 Moises Alou .15 .40
131 Craig Biggio .20 .50
132 Roy Oswalt .15 .40
133 Richard Hidalgo .15 .40
134 Morgan Ensberg .15 .40
Tim Redding
135 Lance Berkman .15 .40
Richard Hidalgo TC
136 Greg Maddux .50 1.25
137 Chipper Jones .30 .75
138 Brian Jordan .15 .40
139 Marcus Giles .15 .40
140 Andruw Jones .20 .50
141 Tom Glavine .20 .50
142 Rafael Furcal .15 .40
143 Wilson Betemit .15 .40
Horacio Ramirez
144 Chipper Jones .20 .50
Brian Jordan TC
145 Jeromy Burnitz .15 .40
146 Ben Sheets .15 .40
147 Geoff Jenkins .15 .40
148 Devon White .15 .40
149 Jimmy Haynes .15 .40
150 Richie Sexson .15 .40
151 Jose Hernandez .15 .40
152 Jose Mieses .15 .40
Alex Sanchez
153 Richie Sexson TC .15 .40
154 Mark McGwire .75 2.00
155 Albert Pujols .60 1.50
156 Matt Morris .15 .40
157 J.D. Drew .15 .40
158 Jim Edmonds .15 .40
159 Bud Smith .15 .40
160 Darryl Kile .15 .40
161 Bill Ortega .15 .40
Luis Saturria
162 Albert Pujols .60 1.50
Mark McGwire TC
163 Sammy Sosa .30 .75
164 Jon Lieber .15 .40
165 Eric Young .15 .40
166 Kerry Wood .15 .40
167 Fred McGriff .20 .50
168 Corey Patterson .15 .40
169 Rondell White .15 .40
170 Juan Cruz .25 .60
Mark Prior
171 Sammy Sosa TC .20 .50
172 Luis Gonzalez .15 .40
173 Randy Johnson .30 .75
174 Matt Williams .15 .40
175 Mark Grace .20 .50
176 Steve Finley .15 .40
177 Reggie Sanders .15 .40
178 Curt Schilling .15 .40
179 Alex Cintron .15 .40
Jack Cust
180 Arizona Diamondbacks TC .30 .75
181 Gary Sheffield .15 .40
182 Paul LoDuca .15 .40
183 Chan Ho Park .15 .40
184 Shawn Green .15 .40
185 Eric Karros .15 .40
186 Adrian Beltre .15 .40
187 Kevin Brown .15 .40
188 Ricardo Rodriguez .15 .40
Carlos Garcia
189 Shawn Green .15 .40
Gary Sheffield TC
190 Vladimir Guerrero .30 .75
191 Javier Vazquez .15 .40
192 Jose Vidro .15 .40
193 Fernando Tatis .15 .40
194 Orlando Cabrera .15 .40
195 Lee Stevens .15 .40
196 Tony Armas Jr. .15 .40
197 Donnie Bridges .15 .40
Henry Mateo
198 Vladimir Guerrero .20 .50
Jose Vidro TC
199 Barry Bonds .75 2.00
200 Rich Aurilia .15 .40
201 Russ Ortiz .15 .40
202 Jeff Kent .15 .40
203 Jason Schmidt .15 .40
204 John Vander Wal .15 .40
205 Robb Nen .15 .40
206 Yorvit Torrealba .15 .40
Kurt Ainsworth
207 Barry Bonds TC .40 1.00
208 Preston Wilson .15 .40
209 Brad Penny .15 .40
210 Cliff Floyd .15 .40
211 Luis Castillo .15 .40
212 Ryan Dempster .15 .40
213 Charles Johnson .15 .40
214 A.J. Burnett .15 .40
215 Abraham Nunez .15 .40
Josh Beckett
216 Cliff Floyd TC .15 .40
217 Mike Piazza .50 1.25
218 Al Leiter .15 .40
219 Edgardo Alfonzo .15 .40
220 Tsuyoshi Shinjo .15 .40
221 Matt Lawton .15 .40
222 Robin Ventura .15 .40
223 Jay Payton .15 .40
224 Alex Escobar .15 .40
Jae Weong Seo
225 Mike Piazza .30 .75
Robin Ventura TC
226 Ryan Klesko .15 .40
227 D'Angelo Jimenez .15 .40
228 Trevor Hoffman .15 .40
229 Phil Nevin .15 .40
230 Mark Kotsay .15 .40
231 Brian Lawrence .15 .40
232 Bubba Trammell .15 .40
233 Jason Middlebrook .15 .40
Xavier Nady
234 Tony Gwynn TC .20 .50
235 Scott Rolen .20 .50
236 Jimmy Rollins .15 .40
237 Mike Lieberthal .15 .40
238 Bobby Abreu .15 .40
239 Brandon Duckworth .15 .40
240 Robert Person .15 .40
241 Pat Burrell .15 .40
242 Nick Punto .15 .40
Carlos Silva
243 Mike Lieberthal TC .15 .40
244 Brian Giles .15 .40
245 Jack Wilson .15 .40
246 Kris Benson .15 .40
247 Jason Kendall .15 .40
248 Aramis Ramirez .15 .40
249 Todd Ritchie .15 .40
250 Rob Mackowiak .15 .40
251 John Grabow .15 .40
Humberto Cota
252 Brian Giles TC .15 .40
253 Ken Griffey Jr. .50 1.25
254 Barry Larkin .20 .50
255 Sean Casey .15 .40
256 Aaron Boone .15 .40
257 Dmitri Young .15 .40
258 Pokey Reese .15 .40
259 Adam Dunn .15 .40
260 David Espinosa .15 .40
Dane Sardinha
261 Ken Griffey TC .30 .75
262 Todd Helton .20 .50
263 Mike Hampton .15 .40
264 Juan Pierre .15 .40
265 Larry Walker .15 .40
266 Juan Uribe .15 .40
267 Jose Ortiz .15 .40
268 Jeff Cirillo .15 .40
269 Jason Jennings .15 .40
Luke Hudson
270 Larry Walker TC .15 .40
271 Ichiro Suzuki .30 .75
Jason Giambi
Roberto Alomar LL
272 Larry Walker .15 .40
Todd Helton
Moises Alou LL
273 Alex Rodriguez .20 .50
Jim Thome
Rafael Palmeiro LL
274 Barry Bonds .40 1.00
Sammy Sosa
Luis Gonzalez LL
274A Barry Bonds 6.00 15.00
Sammy Sosa
Luis Gonzalez LL ERR
Card has AL Home Run Leaders
No player names on cards
275 Mark Mulder .20 .50
Roger Clemens
Jamie Moyer LL
276 Curt Schilling .20 .50
Matt Morris
Randy Johnson LL
277 Freddy Garcia .15 .40
Mike Mussina
Joe Mays LL
278 Randy Johnson .20 .50
Curt Schilling
John Burkett LL
279 Mariano Rivera .20 .50
Kazuhiro Sasaki
Keith Foulke LL
280 Robb Nen .15 .40
Armando Benitez
Trevor Hoffman LL
281 Jason Giambi PS .15 .40
282 Jorge Posada PS .15 .40
283 Jim Thome .20 .50
Juan Gonzalez PS
284 Edgar Martinez PS .15 .40
285 Andruw Jones PS .15 .40
286 Chipper Jones PS .20 .50
287 Matt Williams PS .15 .40
288 Curt Schilling PS .15 .40
289 Derek Jeter PS .40 1.00
290 Mike Mussina PS .15 .40
291 Bret Boone PS .15 .40
292 Alfonso Soriano PS UER .15 .40
Alfonso is spelled incorrectly
293 Randy Johnson PS .20 .50
294 Tom Glavine PS .15 .40
295 Curt Schilling PS .15 .40
296 Randy Johnson PS .20 .50
297 Derek Jeter PS .40 1.00
298 Tino Martinez PS .15 .40
299 Curt Schilling PS .15 .40
300 Luis Gonzalez PS .15 .40

2002 Upper Deck Vintage Aces Game Jersey

Inserted into packs at stated odds of one in 144 hobby and one in 210 retail, these 14 cards feature a mix of active and retired pitchers along with a game jersey swatch. Roger Clemens was produced in shorter quantity than the other players and we have notated that with an SP in our checklist.

AFJ Ferguson Jenkins 6.00 15.00
AGM Greg Maddux 10.00 25.00
AHN Hideo Nomo 15.00 40.00
AJD John Denny 4.00 10.00
AJM Juan Marichal 6.00 15.00
AJS Johnny Sain 10.00 25.00
AMMA Mike Marshall 6.00 15.00
AMMU Mike Mussina 10.00 25.00
AMT Mike Torrez 4.00 10.00
ANR Nolan Ryan 60.00 120.00
APM Pedro Martinez 10.00 25.00
ARC Roger Clemens SP
ARJ Randy Johnson 10.00 25.00
ATH Tim Hudson 6.00 15.00

2002 Upper Deck Vintage Day At The Park

Inserted into packs at stated odds of one in 23, these six cards feature active players in a design dedicated to capturing the nostalgia of Baseball.

COMPLETE SET (6) 8.00 20.00
DP1 Ichiro Suzuki 2.00 5.00
DP2 Derek Jeter 2.50 6.00
DP3 Alex Rodriguez 1.50 4.00
DP4 Mark McGwire 2.50 6.00
DP5 Barry Bonds 2.50 6.00
DP6 Sammy Sosa 1.50 4.00

2002 Upper Deck Vintage Night Gamers

Inserted into packs at stated odds of one in 11, these 12 cards features a salute to primetime games with some of the leading players.

COMPLETE SET (12) 6.00 15.00
NG1 Todd Helton .40 1.00
NG2 Manny Ramirez .40 1.00
NG3 Ivan Rodriguez .40 1.00
NG4 Albert Pujols 1.25 3.00
NG5 Greg Maddux 1.00 2.50
NG6 Carlos Delgado .40 1.00
NG7 Frank Thomas .60 1.50
NG8 Derek Jeter 1.50 4.00
NG9 Troy Glaus .40 1.00
NG10 Jeff Bagwell .40 1.00
NG11 Juan Gonzalez .40 1.00
NG12 Randy Johnson .60 1.50

2002 Upper Deck Vintage Sandlot Stars

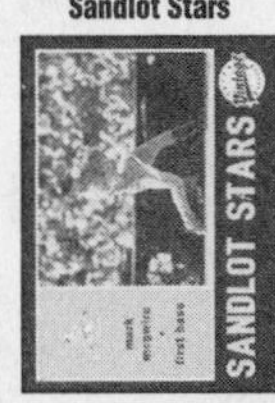

Inserted in packs at stated odds of one in 11, these 12 cards feature some of today's stars in a playful salute to the old days where many players were "discovered" while playing sandlot ball.

COMPLETE SET (12) 8.00 20.00
SS1 Ken Griffey Jr. 1.00 2.50
SS2 Derek Jeter 1.50 4.00
SS3 Ichiro Suzuki 1.25 3.00
SS4 Nomar Garciaparra 1.00 2.50
SS5 Sammy Sosa .60 1.50
SS6 Chipper Jones .60 1.50
SS7 Jason Giambi .60 1.50
SS8 Alex Rodriguez 1.00 2.50
SS9 Mark McGwire 1.50 4.00
SS10 Barry Bonds 1.50 4.00
SS11 Mike Piazza 1.00 2.50
SS12 Vladimir Guerrero .60 1.50

2002 Upper Deck Vintage Signature Combos

Randomly inserted in packs, these nine cards feature two signatures of various baseball stars on each card. These cards all have a stated print run of 100 copies.

VSAT Roberto Alomar 50.00 100.00
Jim Thome
VSBB Yogi Berra 75.00 150.00
Johnny Bench
VSBR Sal Bando 20.00 50.00
Joe Rudi
VSEL Dwight Evans 40.00 80.00
Fred Lynn
VSFB Carlton Fisk 60.00 120.00
Johnny Bench
VSGR Ken Griffey Jr. 800.00 1000.00
Alex Rodriguez
VSJM Reggie Jackson 60.00 120.00
Willie McCovey
VSJO Edgar Martinez 40.00 80.00
John Olerud
VSSD Ryne Sandberg 75.00 150.00
Andre Dawson

2002 Upper Deck Vintage Special Collection Game Jersey

Issued in packs at stated odds of one in 144 hobby and one in 210 retail, these 15 cards feature past and present stars along with a memorabilia swatch. A few players were produced in smaller quantities and we have notated those players with an SP in our checklist. These cards honored players from the famed Oakland A's "Mustache Gang" which won three straight world series in the 1970's and various Cubs stars who were still looking for their first World Series appearance since 1945.

SAD Andre Dawson Pants 6.00 15.00
SBC Bert Campaneris Jsy 6.00 15.00
SBW Billy Williams Jsy 6.00 15.00
SCH Catfish Hunter Jsy SP
SFJ Fergie Jenkins Pants SP 6.00 15.00
SJR Joe Rudi Jsy 6.00 15.00
SMG Mark Grace Jsy 8.00 20.00
SMH Mike Hegan Jsy 4.00 10.00
SPL Paul Lindblad Jsy 4.00 10.00
SRF Rollie Fingers Jsy UER 6.00 15.00
Card photo is a reversed negative
SRJ Reggie Jackson Jsy SP 8.00 20.00
SRS Ryne Sandberg Jsy 25.00 50.00
SSAB Sal Bando Jsy 6.00 15.00
SSS Sammy Sosa Jsy 10.00 25.00
SSTB Stan Bahnsen Jsy 4.00 10.00

2002 Upper Deck Vintage Timeless Teams Game Bat Quads

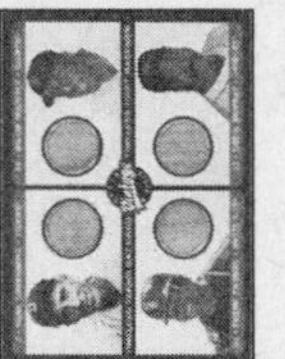

Issued in packs at stated odds of one in 288 hobby and one in 480 retail, these eight cards feature either teammates or position mates along with a bat chip from each of these players career.

B Hank Greenberg 15.00 40.00
Willie McCovey
Frank Thomas
Eddie Murray
OF2 Ken Griffey Jr. 30.00 60.00
Barry Bonds
Rickey Henderson
Tony Gwynn
ATL Tom Glavine 20.00 50.00
Greg Maddux
Chipper Jones
Andruw Jones
CLE Juan Gonzalez 15.00 40.00
Jim Thome
Roberto Alomar
Kenny Lofton
NYY Mariano Rivera 20.00 50.00
Bernie Williams
Paul O'Neill
Jorge Posada
OAK Dave Parker 15.00 40.00
Jose Canseco
Rickey Henderson
Don Baylor
SEA Ichiro Suzuki 40.00 80.00
Edgar Martinez
John Olerud
Bret Boone
OFNY Mickey Mantle
Joe DiMaggio
Reggie Jackson
Babe Ruth SP

2002 Upper Deck Vintage Timeless Teams Game Jersey

Issued in packs at stated odds of one in 144 hobby and one in 210 retail, these 14 cards feature players from a great team of the past or present along with a jersey swatch. Some players were produced in shorter quantities and we have notated those players with an SP in our checklist.

JAJ Andruw Jones Jsy 8.00 20.00

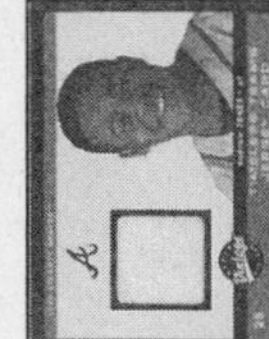

JCH Catfish Hunter Jsy 8.00 20.00
JCJ Chipper Jones Jsy 8.00 20.00
JDE Dwight Evans Jsy 8.00 20.00
JEMA Edgar Martinez Jsy 8.00 20.00
JEMU Eddie Murray Jsy 10.00 25.00
JFL Fred Lynn Jsy 8.00 20.00
JGM Greg Maddux Jsy SP
JIS Ichiro Suzuki Pants SP
JJB Johnny Bench Jsy 10.00 25.00
JKS Kazuhiro Sasaki Jsy 6.00 15.00
JRF Rollie Fingers Jsy 8.00 20.00
JRJ Reggie Jackson Jsy 8.00 20.00
JWM Willie McCovey Pants 8.00 20.00

2002 Upper Deck Vintage Timeless Teams Game Jersey Combos

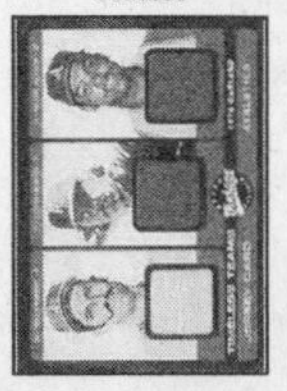

Issued in hobby packs at stated odds one in 288, these four cards feature either teammates or players with something in common along with a jersey swatch of all three players featured. The card featuring the three Hall of Famers was produced in smaller quantites than the other cards and we have notated that with an SP in our checklist.

ATL Greg Maddux 30.00 60.00
Chipper Jones
Andruw Jones
HOF Ty Cobb Pants
Babe Ruth Pants
Honus Wagner Pants SP
NYY Roger Clemens 30.00 60.00
Mariano Rivera
Bernie Williams
OAK Rollie Fingers 20.00 50.00
Catfish Hunter
Reggie Jackson

2003 Upper Deck Vintage

This 280 card set, designed to resemble the 1965 Topps set, was released in January 2003, This set was issued in eight card packs which came 24 packs to a box and 12 boxes to a case. These packs had an SRP of $2. Cards numbered from 223 through 232 feature a pair of prospects from an organiztion. Cards numbered from 233 through 247 are titled Stellar Stat Men. Cards from 248 through 277 were produced in a style reminscent of the Kellogs 3-D cards of the 1970's. Those 3D cards were seeded at a rate of one in 48. In addition, there were other short print cards scattered throughout the set. Those cards which we have noted as either SP, TR1 SP or TR2 SP were inserted at a rate between one in 20 and one in 40. Please note, Eddie Mathews is listed below as card 37 (as was the manufacturer's original intent), but the card is mistakenly numbered as 376. Jason Jennings who was supposed to be card number 178 was mistakenly numbered as 28. In addition, cards number 281 through 341 were later issued at a stated rate of one per Upper Deck 40-man pack.

COMP.SET w/o SP's (200) 20.00 50.00
COMP.UPDATE SET (60) 6.00 15.00
COMMON ACTIVE (1-280) .10 .30
COMMON RETIRED .25 .60
COMMON SP (1-220) 2.00 5.00
COMMON TR1 SP 2.00 5.00
COMMON TR2 SP 2.00 5.00
COMMON CARD (223-232) .75 2.00
COMMON CARD (233-247) .75 2.00
COMMON CARD (248-277) 4.00 10.00
COMMON CARD (281-341) .15 .40
COMMON RC (281-341) .15 .40
281-341 ONE PER 2003 UD 40-MAN PACK
1 Troy Glaus .10 .30
2 Darin Erstad .10 .30
3 Garret Anderson .10 .30
4 Jarrod Washburn .10 .30
5 Nolan Ryan 1.50 4.00
6 Tim Salmon .20 .50
7 Troy Percival .10 .30
8 Alex Ochoa TR1 SP 2.00 5.00
9 Daryle Ward .10 .30
10 Jeff Bagwell .20 .50
11 Roy Oswalt .10 .30
12 Lance Berkman .10 .30
13 Craig Biggio .20 .50
14 Richard Hidalgo .10 .30
15 Tim Hudson .10 .30
16 Eric Chavez .10 .30
17 Barry Zito .10 .30
18 Miguel Tejada .10 .30
19 Mark Mulder .10 .30
20 Rollie Fingers .25 .60
21 Catfish Hunter .40 1.00
22 Jermaine Dye .10 .30
23 Ray Durham TR2 SP 2.00 5.00
24 Carlos Delgado .10 .30
25 Eric Hinske .10 .30
26 Josh Phelps .10 .30
27 Shannon Stewart .10 .30
28 Vernon Wells .10 .30
29 John Smoltz .20 .50
30 Greg Maddux .50 1.25
31 Chipper Jones .30 .75
32 Gary Sheffield .10 .30
33 Andruw Jones .20 .50
34 Tom Glavine .20 .50
35 Rafael Furcal .10 .30
36 Phil Niekro .25 .60
37 Eddie Mathews UER 376 .60 1.50
38 Robin Yount .60 1.50
39 Richie Sexson .10 .30
40 Ben Sheets .10 .30
41 Geoff Jenkins .10 .30
42 Alex Sanchez .10 .30
43 Jason Isringhausen .10 .30
44 Albert Pujols .60 1.50
45 Matt Morris .10 .30
46 J.D. Drew .10 .30
47 Jim Edmonds .10 .30
48 Stan Musial 1.00 2.50
49 Red Schoendienst .25 .60
50 Edgar Renteria .10 .30
51 Mark McGwire SP 5.00 12.00
52 Scott Rolen TR2 SP 3.00 8.00
53 Mark Bellhorn .10 .30
54 Kerry Wood .10 .30
55 Mark Prior .20 .50
56 Moises Alou .10 .30
57 Corey Patterson .10 .30
58 Ernie Banks .60 1.50
59 Hee Seop Choi .10 .30
60 Billy Williams .25 .60
61 Sammy Sosa SP 3.00 8.00
62 Ben Grieve .10 .30
63 Jared Sandberg .10 .30
64 Carl Crawford .10 .30
65 Randy Johnson .30 .75
66 Luis Gonzalez .10 .30
67 Steve Finley .10 .30
68 Junior Spivey .10 .30
69 Erubiel Durazo .10 .30
70 Curt Schilling SP 2.00 5.00
71 Al Lopez .25 .60
72 Pee Wee Reese .40 1.00
73 Eric Gagne .10 .30
74 Shawn Green .10 .30
75 Kevin Brown .10 .30
76 Paul Lo Duca .10 .30
77 Adrian Beltre .10 .30
78 Hideo Nomo .30 .75
79 Eric Karros .10 .30
80 Odalis Perez .10 .30
81 Kazuhisa Ishii SP 2.00 5.00
82 Tommy Lasorda .25 .60
83 Fernando Tatis .10 .30
84 Vladimir Guerrero .30 .75
85 Jose Vidro .10 .30
86 Javier Vazquez .10 .30
87 Brad Wilkerson .10 .30
88 Bartolo Colon TR1 SP 2.00 5.00
89 Monte Irvin .25 .60
90 Robb Nen .10 .30
91 Reggie Sanders .10 .30
92 Jeff Kent .10 .30
93 Rich Aurilia .10 .30
94 Orlando Cepeda .25 .60
95 Juan Marichal .25 .60
96 Willie McCovey .25 .60

97 David Bell .10 .30
98 Barry Bonds SP 5.00 12.00
99 Kenny Lofton TR2 SP 2.00 5.00
100 Jim Thome .20 .50
101 C.C. Sabathia .10 .30
102 Omar Vizquel .20 .50
103 Lou Boudreau .25 .60
104 Larry Doby .25 .60
105 Bob Lemon .25 .60
106 John Olerud .10 .30
107 Edgar Martinez .20 .50
108 Bret Boone .10 .30
109 Freddy Garcia .10 .30
110 Mike Cameron .10 .30
111 Kazuhiro Sasaki .10 .30
112 Ichiro Suzuki SP 4.00 10.00
113 Mike Lowell .10 .30
114 Josh Beckett .10 .30
115 A.J. Burnett .10 .30
116 Juan Pierre .10 .30
117 Derrek Lee .20 .50
118 Luis Castillo .10 .30
119 Juan Encarnacion TR1 SP 2.00 5.00
120 Roberto Alomar .20 .50
121 Edgardo Alfonzo .10 .30
122 Jeromy Burnitz .10 .30
123 Mo Vaughn .10 .30
124 Tom Seaver .40 1.00
125 Al Leiter .10 .30
126 Mike Piazza SP 4.00 10.00
127 Tony Batista .10 .30
128 Geronimo Gil .10 .30
129 Chris Singleton .10 .30
130 Rodrigo Lopez .10 .30
131 Jay Gibbons .10 .30
132 Melvin Mora .10 .30
133 Earl Weaver .25 .60
134 Trevor Hoffman .10 .30
135 Phil Nevin .10 .30
136 Sean Burroughs .10 .30
137 Ryan Klesko .10 .30
138 Mark Kotsay .10 .30
139 Mike Lieberthal .10 .30
140 Bobby Abreu .10 .30
141 Jimmy Rollins .10 .30
142 Pat Burrell .10 .30
143 Vicente Padilla .10 .30
144 Richie Ashburn .40 1.00
145 Jeremy Giambi TR1 SP 2.00 5.00
146 Josh Fogg .10 .30
147 Brian Giles .10 .30
148 Aramis Ramirez .10 .30
149 Jason Kendall .10 .30
150 Ralph Kiner .25 .60
151 Willie Stargell .40 1.00
152 Kevin Mench .10 .30
153 Rafael Palmeiro .20 .50
154 Ivan Rodriguez .20 .50
155 Hank Blalock .10 .30
156 Juan Gonzalez .10 .30
157 Carl Everett .10 .30
158 Alex Rodriguez SP 4.00 10.00
159 Nomar Garciaparra .50 1.25
160 Derek Lowe .10 .30
161 Manny Ramirez .20 .50
162 Shea Hillenbrand .10 .30
163 Bobby Doerr .25 .60
164 Johnny Damon .20 .50
165 Jason Varitek .30 .75
166 Pedro Martinez SP 3.00 8.00
167 Cliff Floyd TR2 SP 2.00 5.00
168 Ken Griffey Jr. .50 1.25
169 Adam Dunn .10 .30
170 Austin Kearns .10 .30
171 Aaron Boone .10 .30
172 Joe Morgan .25 .60
173 Sean Casey .10 .30
174 Todd Walker .10 .30
175 Ryan Dempster TR1 SP 2.00 5.00
176 Shawn Estes TR1 SP 2.00 5.00
177 Gabe Kapler TR1 SP 2.00 5.00
178 Jason Jennings UER .10 .30
Card numbered as 28
179 Todd Helton .20 .50
180 Larry Walker .10 .30
181 Preston Wilson .10 .30
182 Jay Payton TR1 SP 2.00 5.00
183 Mike Sweeney .10 .30
184 Carlos Beltran .10 .30
185 Paul Byrd .10 .30
186 Raul Ibanez .10 .30
187 Rick Ferrell .25 .60
188 Early Wynn .25 .60
189 Dmitri Young .10 .30
190 Jim Bunning .40 1.00
191 George Kell .25 .60
192 Hal Newhouser .25 .60
193 Bobby Higginson .10 .30
194 Carlos Pena TR1 SP 2.00 5.00
195 Sparky Anderson .25 .60
196 Torii Hunter .10 .30
197 Eric Milton .10 .30
198 Corey Koskie .10 .30
199 Jacque Jones .10 .30
200 Harmon Killebrew .60 1.50
201 Doug Mientkiewicz .10 .30
202 Frank Thomas .30 .75
203 Mark Buehrle .10 .30
204 Magglio Ordonez .10 .30
205 Paul Konerko .10 .30
206 Joe Borchard .10 .30
207 Hoyt Wilhelm .25 .60
208 Carlos Lee .10 .30
209 Roger Clemens .60 1.50
210 Nick Johnson .10 .30
211 Jason Giambi .10 .30
212 Alfonso Soriano .10 .30
213 Bernie Williams .20 .50
214 Robin Ventura .10 .30
215 Jorge Posada .20 .50
216 Mike Mussina .20 .50
217 Yogi Berra .60 1.50
218 Phil Rizzuto .40 1.00
219 Mariano Rivera .30 .75
220 Derek Jeter SP 5.00 12.00
221 Jeff Weaver TR1 SP 2.00 5.00
222 Raul Mondesi TR2 SP 2.00 5.00
223 Freddy Sanchez .75 2.00
Josh Hancock
224 Joe Borchard .75 2.00
Miguel Olivo
225 Brandon Phillips .75 2.00
Josh Bard
226 Andy Van Hekken .75 2.00
Andres Torres
227 Jason Lane .75 2.00
Jeriome Robertson
228 Chin-Feng Chen .75 2.00
Joe Thurston
229 Endy Chavez .75 2.00
Jamey Carroll
230 Drew Henson .75 2.00
Alex Graman
231 Dewon Brazelton .75 2.00
Lance Carter
232 Jayson Werth .75 2.00
Kevin Cash
233 Randy Johnson 1.25 3.00
Curt Schilling
Barry Zito
234 Pedro Martinez 1.25 3.00
Randy Johnson
Derek Lowe
235 Randy Johnson 1.25 3.00
Curt Schilling
Pedro Martinez
236 John Smoltz 1.25 3.00
Eric Gagne
Mike Williams
237 Randy Johnson 1.25 3.00
Bartolo Colon
A.J. Burnett
238 Alfonso Soriano 1.50 4.00
Ichiro Suzuki
Vladimir Guerrero
239 Alex Rodriguez 1.50 4.00
Jim Thome
Sammy Sosa
240 Barry Bonds 1.50 4.00
Manny Ramirez
Mike Sweeney
241 Alfonso Soriano 1.50 4.00
Alex Rodriguez
Derek Jeter
242 Alex Rodriguez 1.50 4.00
Magglio Ordonez
Miguel Tejada
243 Luis Castillo .75 2.00
Juan Pierre
Dave Roberts
244 Nomar Garciaparra 1.50 4.00
Garrett Anderson
Alfonso Soriano
245 Johnny Damon 1.25 3.00
Jimmy Rollins
Kenny Lofton
246 Barry Bonds 1.50 4.00
Jim Thome
Manny Ramirez
247 Barry Bonds 1.50 4.00
Brian Giles
Manny Ramirez
248 Troy Glaus 3D 4.00 10.00
249 Luis Gonzalez 3D 4.00 10.00
250 Chipper Jones 3D 6.00 15.00
251 Nomar Garciaparra 3D 6.00 15.00
252 Manny Ramirez 3D 6.00 15.00
253 Sammy Sosa 3D 6.00 15.00
254 Frank Thomas 3D 6.00 15.00
255 Magglio Ordonez 3D 4.00 10.00
256 Adam Dunn 3D 4.00 10.00
257 Ken Griffey Jr. 3D 6.00 15.00
258 Jim Thome 3D 6.00 15.00
259 Todd Helton 3D 6.00 15.00
260 Larry Walker 3D 4.00 10.00
261 Lance Berkman 3D 4.00 10.00
262 Jeff Bagwell 3D 6.00 15.00
263 Mike Sweeney 3D 4.00 10.00
264 Shawn Green 3D 4.00 10.00
265 Vladimir Guerrero 3D 6.00 15.00
266 Mike Piazza 3D 6.00 15.00
267 Jason Giambi 3D 4.00 10.00
268 Pat Burrell 3D 4.00 10.00
269 Barry Bonds 3D 10.00 25.00
270 Mark McGwire 3D 10.00 25.00
271 Alex Rodriguez 3D 8.00 20.00
272 Carlos Delgado 3D 4.00 10.00
273 Richie Sexson 3D 4.00 10.00
274 Andruw Jones 3D 6.00 15.00
275 Derek Jeter 3D 10.00 25.00
276 Juan Gonzalez 3D 4.00 10.00
277 Albert Pujols 3D 8.00 20.00
278 Jason Giambi CL .10 .30
279 Sammy Sosa CL .30 .75
280 Ichiro Suzuki CL .30 .75
281 Tom Glavine .25 .60
282 Josh Stewart RC .15 .40
283 Aquilino Lopez RC .15 .40
284 Horacio Ramirez .15 .40
285 Brandon Phillips .15 .40
286 Kirk Saarloos .15 .40
287 Runelvys Hernandez .15 .40
288 Hideki Matsui RC 1.50 4.00
289 Jeremy Bonderman RC 1.00 2.50
290 Russ Ortiz .15 .40
291 Ken Harvey .15 .40
292 Edgardo Alfonzo .15 .40
293 Oscar Villareal RC .15 .40
294 Marlon Byrd .15 .40
295 Josh Bard .15 .40
296 David Cone .15 .40
297 Mike Neu RC .15 .40
298 Cliff Floyd .15 .40
299 Travis Lee .15 .40
300 Jeff Kent .15 .40
301 Ron Calloway .15 .40
302 Bartolo Colon .15 .40
303 Jose Contreras RC .40 1.00
304 Mark Teixeira .25 .60
305 Ivan Rodriguez .25 .60
306 Jim Thome .25 .60
307 Shane Reynolds .15 .40
308 Luis Ayala RC .15 .40
309 Lyle Overbay .15 .40
310 Travis Hafner .15 .40
311 Wilfredo Ledezma RC .15 .40
312 Rocco Baldelli .15 .40
313 Jason Anderson .15 .40
314 Kenny Lofton .15 .40
315 Brandon Larson .15 .40
316 Ty Wigginton .15 .40
317 Fred McGriff .25 .60
318 Antonio Osuna .15 .40
319 Corey Patterson .15 .40
320 Erubiel Durazo .15 .40
321 Mike MacDougal .15 .40
322 Sammy Sosa .40 1.00
323 Mike Hampton .15 .40
324 Ramiro Mendoza .15 .40
325 Kevin Millwood .15 .40
326 Dave Roberts .15 .40
327 Todd Zeile .15 .40
328 Reggie Sanders .15 .40
329 Billy Koch .15 .40
330 Mike Stanton .15 .40
331 Orlando Hernandez .15 .40
332 Tony Clark .15 .40
333 Chris Hammond .15 .40
334 Michael Cuddyer .15 .40
335 Sandy Alomar Jr. .15 .40
336 Jose Cruz Jr. .15 .40
337 Omar Daal .15 .40
338 Robert Fick .15 .40
339 Daryle Ward .15 .40
340 David Bell .15 .40
341 Checklist .15 .40

2003 Upper Deck Vintage All Caps

Randomly inserted into packs, these 15 cards feature swatches of game-used caps. Each of these cards have a stated print run of 250 serial numbered sets.

CP Chan Ho Park 6.00 15.00
DE Darin Erstad 6.00 15.00
GM Greg Maddux 15.00 40.00
JB Jeff Bagwell 8.00 20.00
JG Juan Gonzalez 6.00 15.00
KS Kazuhiro Sasaki 6.00 15.00
LB Lance Berkman 6.00 15.00
LG Luis Gonzalez 6.00 15.00
MP Mike Piazza 15.00 40.00
MV Mo Vaughn 6.00 15.00
RF Rafael Furcal 6.00 15.00
RP Rafael Palmeiro 8.00 20.00
RV Robin Ventura 6.00 15.00
TG Tony Gwynn 10.00 25.00
TH Tim Hudson 6.00 15.00

2003 Upper Deck Vintage Capping the Action

Randomly inserted into packs, these 15 cards feature pieces of game-worn caps embedded into the card. Each of these cards were issued to a stated print run of between 91 and 125 copies.

AR Alex Rodriguez/101 15.00 40.00
AS Alfonso Soriano/109 8.00 20.00
CD Carlos Delgado/91 8.00 20.00
HM Hideo Nomo/117 30.00 60.00
IR Ivan Rodriguez/125 10.00 25.00
JG Juan Gonzalez/99 8.00 20.00
KG Ken Griffey Jr./102 15.00 40.00
MM Mike Mussina/109 20.00 50.00
PM Pedro Martinez/125 10.00 25.00
RA Roberto Alomar/101 10.00 25.00
RP Rafael Palmeiro/125 10.00 25.00
SG Shawn Green/125 8.00 20.00
SR Scott Rolen/109 10.00 25.00
SS Sammy Sosa/125 10.00 25.00
TH Todd Helton/99 10.00 25.00

2003 Upper Deck Vintage Cracking the Lumber

Randomly inserted into packs, these two cards feature authentic game-used bat chips of either Ichiro Suzuki or Jason Giambi. These cards were issued to a stated print run of 25 serial numbered sets. Due to market scarcity, no pricing is provided.

GOLD PRINT RUN 5 SERIAL #'d SETS
NO PRICING DUE TO SCARCITY
IS Ichiro Suzuki
JG Jason Giambi

2003 Upper Deck Vintage Crowning Glory

Randomly inserted into packs, these 15 cards feature pieces of game-worn caps attached to the card front. These cards were issued to a stated print run of 25 serial numbered sets. Due to market scarcity, no pricing is provided for these cards.

AJ Andruw Jones
AR Alex Rodriguez
CJ Chipper Jones
GM Greg Maddux
IR Ivan Rodriguez
IS Ichiro Suzuki
JG Jason Giambi
KG Ken Griffey Jr.
LG Luis Gonzalez
MP Mike Piazza
MR Manny Ramirez
PM Pedro Martinez
SC Sean Casey
SG Shawn Green
SS Sammy Sosa

2003 Upper Deck Vintage Dropping the Hammer

Inserted into packs at a stated rate of one in 130, these cards feature game-used bat pieces.

*GOLD: .75X TO 2X BASIC HAMMER
GOLD PRINT RUN 100 SERIAL #'d SETS
AJ Andruw Jones 6.00 15.00
AR Alex Rodriguez 8.00 20.00
BA Bobby Abreu 4.00 10.00
DJ David Justice 4.00 10.00
FM Fred McGriff 6.00 15.00
FT Frank Thomas 6.00 15.00
JG Jason Giambi 4.00 10.00
JT Jim Thome 6.00 15.00
KG Ken Griffey Jr. 8.00 20.00
KL Kenny Lofton 4.00 10.00
LB Lance Berkman 4.00 10.00
LW Larry Walker 4.00 10.00
MO Magglio Ordonez 4.00 10.00
MP Mike Piazza 10.00 25.00
MT Miguel Tejada 4.00 10.00
OV Omar Vizquel 6.00 15.00
PW Preston Wilson 4.00 10.00
RA Roberto Alomar 6.00 15.00
RF Rafael Furcal 4.00 10.00
RP Rafael Palmeiro 6.00 15.00
RV Robin Ventura 4.00 10.00
SG Shawn Green 4.00 10.00
SS Sammy Sosa 6.00 15.00
TA Fernando Tatis 4.00 10.00
TH Todd Helton 6.00 15.00

2003 Upper Deck Vintage Hitmen

Randomly inserted into packs, these four cards feature game-used bat pieces from Upper Deck spokespeople. Each of these cards were issued to a stated print run of 150 serial numbered sets.

GOLD PRINT RUN 10 SERIAL #'d SETS
NO GOLD PRICING DUE TO SCARCITY
IS Ichiro Suzuki 40.00 80.00
JG Jason Giambi 6.00 15.00
KG Ken Griffey Jr. 15.00 40.00
MM Mark McGwire 40.00 80.00

2003 Upper Deck Vintage Hitmen Double Signed

An exchange card with a redemption deadline of January 7th, 2006 was randomly inserted into packs. In return, the collectors that mailed in the exchange card received an amazing card featuring not only game-used bat chips but authentic signatures from Mark McGwire and Sammy Sosa, the two leading HR hitters in the summer of 1998. This card was issued to a stated print run of 75 serial numbered copies.

GOLD PRINT RUN 5 SERIAL #'d CARDS
NO GOLD PRICING DUE TO SCARCITY
MS Mark McGwire 300.00 450.00
Sammy Sosa

2003 Upper Deck Vintage Men with Hats

Inserted at a stated rate of one in 285, these 15 cards feature leading players with pieces of game-worn caps embedded in them.

MHAD Adam Dunn 6.00 15.00
MHAJ Andruw Jones 8.00 20.00
MHAR Alex Rodriguez 10.00 25.00
MHBW Bernie Williams 8.00 20.00
MHEC Eric Chavez 6.00 15.00
MHFT Frank Thomas 8.00 20.00
MHHU Tim Hudson 6.00 15.00
MHJD Johnny Damon 8.00 20.00
MHJG Jason Giambi 6.00 15.00
MHJK Jason Kendall 6.00 15.00
MHKL Kenny Lofton 6.00 15.00
MHMT Miguel Tejada 6.00 15.00
MHTH Todd Helton 8.00 20.00
MHTW Todd Walker 6.00 15.00
MHVC Vinny Castilla 6.00 15.00

2003 Upper Deck Vintage Slugfest

Randomly inserted into packs, this 10 card set feature pieces of game-used bat chips honoring some of the leading sluggers in baseball. These cards were issued to a stated print run of 200 serial numbered sets.

*GOLD: .75X TO 2X BASIC SLUGFEST
GOLD PRINT RUN 50 SERIAL #'d SETS
SAJ Andruw Jones 6.00 15.00
SAR Alex Rodriguez 10.00 25.00
SBW Bernie Williams 6.00 15.00
SCD Carlos Delgado 4.00 10.00
SFT Frank Thomas 6.00 15.00
SJT Jim Thome 6.00 15.00
SLW Larry Walker 4.00 10.00
SMP Mike Piazza 12.50 30.00
SRP Rafael Palmeiro 6.00 15.00
SSG Shawn Green 4.00 10.00

2003 Upper Deck Vintage Timeless Teams Bat Quads

Randomly inserted into packs, this is a set featuring four bat pieces from teammates. These cards were issued to a stated print run of 175 serial numbered sets.

BLAR Pat Burrell 10.00 25.00
Mike Lieberthal
Bobby Abreu
Jimmy Rollins
CTDJ Eric Chavez 10.00 25.00
Miguel Tejada
Jermaine Dye
David Justice
DEMR J.D. Drew 15.00 40.00
Jim Edmonds
Tino Martinez
Scott Rolen
DGCL Adam Dunn 15.00 40.00
Ken Griffey Jr.
Sean Casey
Barry Larkin
GNBL Shawn Green 15.00 40.00
Hideo Nomo
Adrian Beltre
Paul Lo Duca
GPMS Jason Giambi 15.00 40.00
Jorge Posada
Raul Mondesi
Alfonso Soriano
GWVS Jason Giambi 15.00 40.00
Bernie Williams
Robin Ventura
Alfonso Soriano
HWPZ Todd Helton 15.00 40.00
Larry Walker
Juan Pierre
Todd Zeile
IMBC Ichiro Suzuki 50.00 100.00
Edgar Martinez
Bret Boone
Mike Cameron
JGSW Randy Johnson 15.00 40.00
Luis Gonzalez
Curt Schilling
Matt Williams
JJSF Chipper Jones 15.00 40.00
Andruw Jones
Gary Sheffield
Rafael Furcal
KNKB Ryan Klesko 10.00 25.00
Phil Nevin
Mark Kotsay
Sean Burroughs
MGLJ Greg Maddux 30.00 60.00
Tom Glavine
Javy Lopez
Chipper Jones
OTLK Magglio Ordonez 15.00 40.00
Frank Thomas
Carlos Lee
Paul Konerko
PVAA Mike Piazza 30.00 60.00
Mo Vaughn
Roberto Alomar
Edgardo Alfonzo
RGRP Alex Rodriguez 20.00 50.00
Juan Gonzalez
Ivan Rodriguez
Rafael Palmeiro
RMHN Manny Ramirez 15.00 40.00
Pedro Martinez
Shea Hillenbrand
Trot Nixon
SMAP Sammy Sosa 15.00 40.00
Fred McGriff
Moises Alou
Corey Patterson

2003 Upper Deck Vintage UD Giants

Inserted as a sealed box-topper, these 42 cards, which were designed in the style of the 1964 Topps Giant set, feature most of the leading players in baseball.

AD Adam Dunn 1.25 3.00
AJ Andruw Jones 1.25 3.00
AP Albert Pujols 3.00 8.00
AR Alex Rodriguez 2.50 6.00
BB Barry Bonds 4.00 10.00
BG Brian Giles 1.25 3.00
BW Bernie Williams 1.25 3.00
CD Carlos Delgado 1.25 3.00
CJ Chipper Jones 1.50 4.00
CS Curt Schilling 1.25 3.00
FT Frank Thomas 1.50 4.00
GM Greg Maddux 2.50 6.00
GO Juan Gonzalez 1.25 3.00
HN Hideo Nomo 1.50 4.00
IR Ivan Rodriguez 1.25 3.00
IS Ichiro Suzuki 3.00 8.00
JB Jeff Bagwell 1.25 3.00
JD J.D. Drew 1.25 3.00
JG Jason Giambi 1.25 3.00
JT Jim Thome 1.25 3.00
KG Ken Griffey Jr. 2.50 6.00
KI Kazuhisa Ishii 1.25 3.00
KW Kerry Wood 1.25 3.00
LB Lance Berkman 1.25 3.00
LG Luis Gonzalez 1.25 3.00
MM Mike Mussina 1.25 3.00
MO Magglio Ordonez 1.25 3.00
MP Mike Piazza 2.50 6.00
MR Manny Ramirez 1.25 3.00
NG Nomar Garciaparra 2.50 6.00
PB Pat Burrell 1.25 3.00
PM Pedro Martinez 1.25 3.00
PR Mark Prior 1.25 3.00
RA Roberto Alomar 1.25 3.00

RC Roger Clemens 3.00 8.00
RJ Randy Johnson 1.50 4.00
RP Rafael Palmeiro 1.25 3.00
SG Shawn Green 1.25 3.00
SR Scott Rolen 1.25 3.00
SS Sammy Sosa 1.50 4.00
TH Todd Helton 1.25 3.00
VG Vladimir Guerrero 1.50 4.00

2004 Upper Deck Vintage

The initial 450-card set was released in January, 2004. The set was issued in eight card packs with an $2.99 SRP which came 24 packs to a box and 12 boxes to a case. Cards numbered from 1 through 300 were printed in heavier quantity than the rest of the set. In that group of 300 the final three cards feature checklists. Cards numbered 301 through 315 are Play Ball Preview Cards while cards numbered 316 through 325 are World Series Highlight Cards. Cards numbered 326 through 335 were players who were traded during the 2003 season. A few leading 2003 rookies were issued as Short Prints between cards 335 and 350. Those cards were issued in two different tiers which we have notated in our checklist. Similar to the 2003 set, many cards (351-440) were issued with lenticular technology and feature 90 of the majors leading sluggers. The set concludes with 10 cards made in the style of the 19th century Old Judge cards. Those cards were issued in "Old Judge Packs" which were issued as one per box "boxtoppers". A 50-card Update set (containing cards 451-500) was issued in factory set format and distributed into one in every 1.5 hobby boxes of 2004 Upper Deck Series 2 baseball in June, 2004.

COMP.SET w/o SP's (300) 30.00 60.00
COMP.UPDATE SET (50) 6.00 15.00
COMMON CARD (1-300) .10 .30
COMMON CARD (301-315) .40 1.00
301-315 STATED ODDS 1:5
COMMON CARD (316-325) .40 1.00
316-325 STATED ODDS 1:7
COMMON CARD (326-350) .75 2.00
326-350 STATED ODDS 1:5
COMMON CARD (351-440) 1.25 3.00
351-440 STATED ODDS 1:12
COMMON CARD (441-450) .75 2.00
441-450 DIST.IN OLD JUDGE HOBBY PACKS
ONE 3-CARD OJ PACK PER HOBBY BOX
COMMON CARD (451-465) .10 .30
COMMON CARD (466-500) .20 .50
ONE UPDATE SET PER 1.5 UD2 HOB.BOXES

1 Albert Pujols .75 2.00
2 Carlos Delgado .12 .30
3 Todd Helton .20 .50
4 Nomar Garciaparra .30 .75
5 Vladimir Guerrero .30 .75
6 Alfonso Soriano .12 .30
7 Alex Rodriguez .50 1.25
8 Jason Giambi .12 .30
9 Derek Jeter .75 2.00
10 Pedro Martinez .20 .50
11 Ivan Rodriguez .20 .50
12 Mark Prior .20 .50
13 Marquis Grissom .12 .30
14 Barry Zito .12 .30
15 Alex Cintron .12 .30
16 Wade Miller .12 .30
17 Eric Chavez .12 .30
18 Matt Clement .12 .30
19 Orlando Cabrera .12 .30
20 Odalis Perez .12 .30
21 Lance Berkman .20 .50
22 Keith Foulke .12 .30
23 Shawn Green .12 .30
24 Byung-Hyun Kim .12 .30
25 Geoff Jenkins .12 .30
26 Torii Hunter .12 .30
27 Richard Hidalgo .12 .30
28 Edgar Martinez .20 .50
29 Placido Polanco .12 .30
30 Brad Lidge .12 .30
31 Alex Escobar .12 .30
32 Garret Anderson .12 .30
33 Larry Walker .20 .50
34 Ken Griffey Jr. .50 1.25
35 Junior Spivey .12 .30
36 Carlos Beltran .12 .30
37 Bartolo Colon .12 .30
38 Ichiro Suzuki .50 1.25
39 Ramon Ortiz .12 .30
40 Roy Oswalt .20 .50
41 Mike Piazza .30 .75
42 Benito Santiago .12 .30
43 Mike Mussina .20 .50
44 Jeff Kent .12 .30
45 Curt Schilling .20 .50
46 Adam Dunn .20 .50
47 Mike Sweeney .12 .30
48 Chipper Jones .30 .75
49 Frank Thomas .30 .75
50 Kerry Wood .12 .30
51 Rod Beck .12 .30
52 Brian Giles .12 .30
53 Hank Blalock .12 .30
54 Andruw Jones .12 .30
55 Dmitri Young .12 .30
56 Juan Pierre .12 .30
57 Jacque Jones .12 .30
58 Phil Nevin .12 .30
59 Rocco Baldelli .12 .30
60 Greg Maddux .50 1.25
61 Eric Gagne .12 .30
62 Tim Hudson .20 .50
63 Brian Lawrence .12 .30
64 Sammy Sosa .30 .75
65 Corey Koskie .12 .30
66 Bobby Abreu .12 .30
67 Preston Wilson .12 .30
68 Jay Gibbons .12 .30
69 Dontrelle Willis .12 .30
70 Richie Sexson .12 .30
71 Kevin Millwood .12 .30
72 Randy Johnson .30 .75
73 Jack Cust .12 .30
74 Randy Wolf .12 .30
75 Johan Santana .30 .75
76 Magglio Ordonez .20 .50
77 Sean Casey .12 .30
78 Billy Wagner .12 .30
79 Javier Vazquez .12 .30
80 Jorge Posada .20 .50
81 Jason Schmidt .12 .30
82 Bret Boone .12 .30
83 Jeff Bagwell .20 .50
84 Rickie Weeks .12 .30
85 Troy Percival .12 .30
86 Jose Vidro .12 .30
87 Freddy Garcia .12 .30
88 Manny Ramirez .30 .75
89 John Smoltz .30 .75
90 Moises Alou .12 .30
91 Ugueth Urbina .12 .30
92 Bobby Hill .12 .30
93 Marcus Giles .12 .30
94 Aramis Ramirez .12 .30
95 Brad Wilkerson .12 .30
96 Ray Durham .12 .30
97 David Wells .12 .30
98 Paul Lo Duca .12 .30
99 Danny Graves .12 .30
100 Jason Kendall .12 .30
101 Carlos Lee .12 .30
102 Rafael Furcal .12 .30
103 Mike Lowell .12 .30
104 Kevin Brown .12 .30
105 Vicente Padilla .12 .30
106 Miguel Tejada .20 .50
107 Bernie Williams .20 .50
108 Octavio Dotel .12 .30
109 Steve Finley .12 .30
110 Lyle Overbay .12 .30
111 Delmon Young .20 .50
112 Bo Hart .12 .30
113 Jason Lane .12 .30
114 Matt Roney .12 .30
115 Brian Roberts .12 .30
116 Tom Glavine .20 .50
117 Rich Aurilia .12 .30
118 Adam Kennedy .12 .30
119 Hee Seop Choi .12 .30
120 Trot Nixon .12 .30
121 Gary Sheffield .12 .30
122 Jay Payton .12 .30
123 Brad Penny .12 .30
124 Garrett Atkins .12 .30
125 Aubrey Huff .12 .30
126 Juan Gonzalez .12 .30
127 Jason Jennings .12 .30
128 Luis Gonzalez .12 .30
129 Vinny Castilla .12 .30
130 Esteban Loaiza .12 .30
131 Erubiel Durazo .12 .30
132 Eric Hinske .12 .30
133 Scott Podsednik .20 .50
134 Craig Biggio .20 .50
135 Tim Wakefield .12 .30
136 Darin Erstad .12 .30
137 Denny Stark .12 .30
138 Ben Sheets .12 .30
139 Hideo Nomo .30 .75
140 Derrek Lee .12 .30
141 Matt Mantei .12 .30
142 Reggie Sanders .12 .30
143 Jose Guillen .12 .30
144 Joe Mays .12 .30
145 Jimmy Rollins .20 .50
146 Juan Encarnacion .12 .30
147 Joe Crede .12 .30
148 Aaron Guiel .12 .30
149 Mark Mulder .12 .30
150 Travis Lee .12 .30
151 Josh Phelps .12 .30
152 Michael Young .12 .30
153 Paul Konerko .20 .50
154 John Lackey .12 .30
155 Damian Moss .12 .30
156 Javy Lopez .12 .30
157 Joe Borowski .12 .30
158 Jose Cruz Jr. .12 .30
159 Ramon Hernandez .12 .30
160 Raul Ibanez .12 .30
161 Adrian Beltre .12 .30
162 Bobby Higginson .12 .30
163 Jorge Julio .12 .30
164 Miguel Batista .12 .30
165 Luis Castillo .12 .30
166 Aaron Harang .12 .30
167 Ken Harvey .12 .30
168 Rocky Biddle .12 .30
169 Mariano Rivera .30 .75
170 Matt Morris .12 .30
171 Laynce Nix .12 .30
172 Mike Maroth .12 .30
173 Francisco Rodriguez .20 .50
174 Livan Hernandez .12 .30
175 Aaron Heilman .12 .30
176 Nick Johnson .12 .30
177 Woody Williams .12 .30
178 Joe Kennedy .12 .30
179 Jesse Foppert .12 .30
180 Ryan Franklin .12 .30
181 Endy Chavez .12 .30
182 Chin-Hui Tsao .12 .30
183 Todd Walker .12 .30
184 Edgardo Alfonzo .12 .30
185 Edgar Renteria .12 .30
186 Matt LeCroy .12 .30
187 Carl Everett .12 .30
188 Jeff Conine .12 .30
189 Jason Varitek .30 .75
190 Russ Ortiz .12 .30
191 Melvin Mora .12 .30
192 Mark Buehrle .20 .50
193 Bill Mueller .12 .30
194 Miguel Cabrera .30 .75
195 Carlos Zambrano .20 .50
196 Jose Valverde .12 .30
197 Danys Baez .12 .30
198 Mike MacDougal .12 .30
199 Zach Day .12 .30
200 Roy Halladay .30 .75
201 Jerome Williams .12 .30
202 Josh Fogg .12 .30
203 Mark Kotsay .12 .30
204 Pat Burrell .12 .30
205 A.J. Pierzynski .12 .30
206 Fred McGriff .20 .50
207 Brandon Larson .12 .30
208 Robb Quinlan .12 .30
209 David Ortiz .30 .75
210 A.J. Burnett .12 .30
211 John Vander Wal .12 .30
212 Jim Thome .20 .50
213 Matt Kata .12 .30
214 Kip Wells .12 .30
215 Scott Podsednik .12 .30
216 Rickey Henderson .30 .75
217 Travis Hafner .12 .30
218 Tony Batista .12 .30
219 Robert Fick .12 .30
220 Derek Lowe .12 .30
221 Ryan Klesko .12 .30
222 Joe Beimel .12 .30
223 Doug Mientkiewicz .12 .30
224 Angel Berroa .12 .30
225 Adam Eaton .12 .30
226 C.C. Sabathia .20 .50
227 Wilfredo Ledezma .12 .30
228 Jason Johnson .12 .30
229 Ryan Wagner .12 .30
230 Al Leiter .12 .30
231 Joel Pineiro .12 .30
232 Jason Isringhausen .12 .30
233 John Olerud .12 .30
234 Ron Calloway .12 .30
235 Jose Reyes .20 .50
236 J.D. Drew .12 .30
237 Jared Sandberg .12 .30
238 Gil Meche .12 .30
239 Jose Contreras .12 .30
240 Eric Milton .12 .30
241 Jason Phillips .12 .30
242 Luis Ayala .12 .30
243 Bobby Kielty .12 .30
244 Jose Lima .12 .30
245 Brooks Kieschnick .12 .30
246 Xavier Nady .12 .30
247 Danny Haren .12 .30
248 Victor Zambrano .12 .30
249 Kelvim Escobar .12 .30
250 Oliver Perez .12 .30
251 Jamie Moyer .12 .30
252 Orlando Hudson .12 .30
253 Danny Kolb .12 .30
254 Jake Peavy .12 .30
255 Kris Benson .12 .30
256 Roger Clemens .40 1.00
257 Jim Edmonds .20 .50
258 Rafael Palmeiro .20 .50
259 Jae Weong Seo .12 .30
260 Chase Utley .30 .75
261 Rich Harden .12 .30
262 Mark Teixeira .30 .75
263 Johnny Damon .20 .50
264 Luis Matos .12 .30
265 Shigetoshi Hasegawa .12 .30
266 Alfredo Amezaga .12 .30
267 Tim Worrell .12 .30
268 Kazuhisa Ishii .12 .30
269 Miguel Ojeda .12 .30
270 Kazuhiro Sasaki .12 .30
271 Hideki Matsui .50 1.25
272 Troy Glaus .12 .30
273 Michael Tucker .12 .30
274 Lew Ford .12 .30
275 Brian Jordan .12 .30
276 David Eckstein .12 .30
277 Robby Hammock .12 .30
278 Corey Patterson .12 .30
279 Wes Helms .12 .30
280 Jermaine Dye .12 .30
281 Cliff Floyd .12 .30
282 Dustan Mohr .12 .30
283 Kevin Mench .12 .30
284 Ellis Burks .12 .30
285 Jerry Hairston Jr. .12 .30
286 Tim Salmon .12 .30
287 Omar Vizquel .20 .50
288 Andy Pettitte .20 .50
289 Guillermo Mota .12 .30
290 Tino Martinez .20 .50
291 Lance Carter .12 .30
292 Francisco Cordero .12 .30
293 Robb Nen .12 .30
294 Mike Cameron .12 .30
295 Jhonny Peralta .12 .30
296 Braden Looper .12 .30
297 Jarrod Washburn .12 .30
298 Mark Prior CL .20 .50
299 Alfonso Soriano CL .12 .30
300 Rocco Baldelli CL .12 .30
301 Pedro Martinez PBP .60 1.50
302 Mark Prior PBP .60 1.50
303 Barry Zito PBP .40 1.00
304 Roger Clemens PBP 1.25 3.00
305 Randy Johnson PBP 1.00 2.50
306 Roy Halladay PBP 1.00 2.50
307 Hideo Nomo PBP 1.00 2.50
308 Roy Oswalt PBP .60 1.50
309 Kerry Wood PBP .40 1.00
310 Dontrelle Willis PBP .40 1.00
311 Mark Mulder PBP .40 1.00
312 Brandon Webb PBP .40 1.00
313 Mike Mussina PBP .60 1.50
314 Curt Schilling PBP .60 1.50
315 Tim Hudson PBP .60 1.50
316 Dontrelle Willis WSH .40 1.00
317 Juan Pierre WSH .40 1.00
318 Hideki Matsui WSH 1.50 4.00
319 Andy Pettitte WSH .60 1.50
320 Mike Mussina WSH .60 1.50
321 Roger Clemens WSH 1.25 3.00
322 Alex Gonzalez WSH .40 1.00
323 Brad Penny WSH .40 1.00
324 Ivan Rodriguez WSH .60 1.50
325 Josh Beckett WSH .60 1.50
326 Aaron Boone TR .75 2.00
327 Jeff Suppan TR .75 2.00
328 Shea Hillenbrand TR .75 2.00
329 Jeromy Burnitz TR .75 2.00
330 Sidney Ponson TR .75 2.00
331 Rondell White TR .75 2.00
332 Shannon Stewart TR .75 2.00
333 Armando Benitez TR .75 2.00
334 Roberto Alomar TR 1.25 3.00
335 Raul Mondesi TR .75 2.00
336 Morgan Ensberg SP1 .75 2.00
337 Milton Bradley SP1 .75 2.00
338 Brandon Webb SP1 .75 2.00
339 Marlon Byrd SP1 .75 2.00
340 Carlos Pena SP1 1.25 3.00
341 Brandon Phillips SP1 .75 2.00
342 Josh Beckett SP1 1.25 3.00
343 Eric Munson SP1 .75 2.00
344 Brett Myers SP1 .75 2.00
345 Austin Kearns SP1 .75 2.00
346 Jody Gerut SP2 .75 2.00
347 Vernon Wells SP2 .75 2.00
348 Jeff Duncan SP2 .75 2.00
349 Sean Burroughs SP2 .75 2.00
350 Jeremy Bonderman SP2 .75 2.00
351 Hideki Matsui 3D 6.00 15.00
352 Jason Giambi 3D 1.25 3.00
353 Alfonso Soriano 3D 1.25 3.00
354 Derek Jeter 3D 8.00 20.00
355 Aaron Boone 3D 1.25 3.00
356 Jorge Posada 3D 2.00 5.00
357 Bernie Williams 3D 2.00 5.00
358 Manny Ramirez 3D 3.00 8.00
359 Nomar Garciaparra 3D 3.00 8.00
360 Johnny Damon 3D 2.00 5.00
361 Jason Varitek 3D 3.00 8.00
362 Carlos Delgado 3D 1.25 3.00
363 Vernon Wells 3D 1.25 3.00
364 Jay Gibbons 3D 1.25 3.00
365 Tony Batista 3D 1.25 3.00
366 Rocco Baldelli 3D 1.25 3.00
367 Aubrey Huff 3D 1.25 3.00
368 Carlos Beltran 3D 1.25 3.00
369 Mike Sweeney 3D 1.25 3.00
370 Magglio Ordonez 3D 2.00 5.00
371 Frank Thomas 3D 3.00 8.00
372 Carlos Lee 3D 1.25 3.00
373 Roberto Alomar 3D 2.00 5.00
374 Jacque Jones 3D 1.25 3.00
375 Torii Hunter 3D 1.25 3.00
376 Milton Bradley 3D 1.25 3.00
377 Travis Hafner 3D 1.25 3.00
378 Jody Gerut 3D 1.25 3.00
379 Dmitri Young 3D 1.25 3.00
380 Carlos Pena 3D 2.00 5.00
381 Ichiro Suzuki 3D 5.00 12.00
382 Bret Boone 3D 1.25 3.00
383 Edgar Martinez 3D 2.00 5.00
384 Eric Chavez 3D 1.25 3.00
385 Miguel Tejada 3D 2.00 5.00
386 Erubiel Durazo 3D 1.25 3.00
387 Jose Guillen 3D 1.25 3.00
388 Garret Anderson 3D 1.25 3.00
389 Troy Glaus 3D 1.25 3.00
390 Alex Rodriguez 3D 5.00 12.00
391 Rafael Palmeiro 3D 2.00 5.00
392 Hank Blalock 3D 1.25 3.00
393 Mark Teixeira 3D 3.00 8.00
394 Gary Sheffield 3D 1.25 3.00
395 Andruw Jones 3D 1.25 3.00
396 Chipper Jones 3D 3.00 8.00
397 Javy Lopez 3D 1.25 3.00
398 Marcus Giles 3D 1.25 3.00
399 Rafael Furcal 3D 1.25 3.00
400 Jim Thome 3D 2.00 5.00
401 Bobby Abreu 3D 1.25 3.00
402 Pat Burrell 3D 1.25 3.00
403 Mike Lowell 3D 1.25 3.00
404 Ivan Rodriguez 3D 2.00 5.00
405 Derrek Lee 3D 1.25 3.00
406 Miguel Cabrera 3D 3.00 8.00
407 Vladimir Guerrero 3D 3.00 8.00
408 Orlando Cabrera 3D 1.25 3.00
409 Jose Vidro 3D 1.25 3.00
410 Mike Piazza 3D 3.00 8.00
411 Cliff Floyd 3D 1.25 3.00
412 Albert Pujols 3D 8.00 20.00
413 Scott Rolen 3D 2.00 5.00
414 Jim Edmonds 3D 2.00 5.00
415 Edgar Renteria 3D 1.25 3.00
416 Lance Berkman 3D 2.00 5.00
417 Jeff Bagwell 3D 2.00 5.00
418 Jeff Kent 3D 1.25 3.00
419 Richard Hidalgo 3D 1.25 3.00
420 Morgan Ensberg 3D 1.25 3.00
421 Sammy Sosa 3D 3.00 8.00
422 Moises Alou 3D 1.25 3.00
423 Ken Griffey Jr. 3D 5.00 12.00
424 Adam Dunn 3D 2.00 5.00
425 Austin Kearns 3D 1.25 3.00
426 Richie Sexson 3D 1.25 3.00
427 Geoff Jenkins 3D 1.25 3.00
428 Brian Giles 3D 1.25 3.00
429 Reggie Sanders 3D 1.25 3.00
430 Rich Aurilia 3D 1.25 3.00
431 Jose Cruz Jr. 3D 1.25 3.00
432 Shawn Green 3D 1.25 3.00
433 Jeromy Burnitz 3D 1.25 3.00
434 Luis Gonzalez 3D 1.25 3.00
435 Todd Helton 3D 2.00 5.00
436 Preston Wilson 3D 1.25 3.00
437 Larry Walker 3D 2.00 5.00
438 Ryan Klesko 3D 1.25 3.00
439 Phil Nevin 3D 1.25 3.00
440 Sean Burroughs 3D 1.25 3.00
441 Sammy Sosa OJ 2.00 5.00
442 Albert Pujols OJ 5.00 12.00
443 Magglio Ordonez OJ 1.25 3.00
444 Vladimir Guerrero OJ 2.00 5.00
445 Todd Helton OJ 1.25 3.00
446 Jason Giambi OJ .75 2.00
447 Ichiro Suzuki OJ 3.00 8.00
448 Alex Rodriguez OJ 3.00 8.00
449 Carlos Delgado OJ .75 2.00
450 Manny Ramirez OJ 2.00 5.00
451 Alex Rodriguez 5.00 12.00
452 Javy Lopez 1.25 3.00
453 Alfonso Soriano 1.25 3.00
454 Vladimir Guerrero 3.00 8.00
455 Rafael Palmeiro 2.00 5.00
456 Gary Sheffield 1.25 3.00
457 Curt Schilling 2.00 5.00
458 Miguel Tejada 2.00 5.00
459 Kevin Brown 1.25 3.00
460 Richie Sexson 1.25 3.00
461 Roger Clemens 4.00 10.00
462 Javier Vazquez 1.25 3.00
463 Bartolo Colon 1.25 3.00
464 Ivan Rodriguez 2.00 5.00
465 Greg Maddux 5.00 12.00
466 Jamie Brown RC 2.00 5.00
467 Dave Crouthers RC 2.00 5.00
468 Jason Frasor RC 2.00 5.00
469 Greg Dobbs RC 2.00 5.00
470 Jesse Harper RC 2.00 5.00
471 Nick Regilio RC 2.00 5.00
472 Ryan Wing RC 2.00 5.00
473 Akinori Otsuka RC 2.00 5.00
474 Shingo Takatsu RC 2.00 5.00
475 Kazuo Matsui RC 3.00 8.00
476 Mike Vento RC 2.00 5.00
477 Mike Gosling RC 2.00 5.00
478 Justin Huisman RC 2.00 5.00
479 Justin Hampson RC 2.00 5.00
480 Dennis Sarfate RC 2.00 5.00
481 Ian Snell RC 2.00 5.00
482 Tim Bausher RC 2.00 5.00
483 Donnie Kelly RC 3.00 8.00
484 Jerome Gamble RC 2.00 5.00
485 Mike Rouse RC 2.00 5.00
486 Merkin Valdez RC 2.00 5.00
487 Lincoln Holdzkom RC 2.00 5.00
488 Justin Leone RC 2.00 5.00
489 Sean Henn RC 2.00 5.00
490 Brandon Medders RC 2.00 5.00
491 Mike Johnston RC 2.00 5.00
492 Tim Bittner RC 2.00 5.00
493 Michael Wuertz RC 2.00 5.00
494 Chad Bentz RC 2.00 5.00
495 Ryan Meaux RC 2.00 5.00
496 Chris Aguila RC 2.00 5.00
497 Jake Woods RC 2.00 5.00
498 Scott Dohmann RC 2.00 5.00
499 Colby Miller RC 2.00 5.00
500 Josh Labandeira RC 2.00 5.00

2004 Upper Deck Vintage Black and White

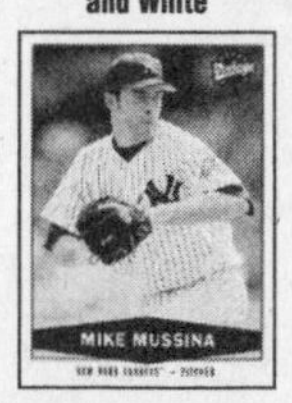

These cards, pictured in black and white, are a complete parallel of the first 350 cards in the Vintage set.

*B/W 1-300: 3X TO 8X BASIC
1-300 STATED ODDS 1:6
*B/W 301-315: 1.25X TO 3X BASIC
301-315 STATED ODDS 1:24
*B/W 316-325: 1.25X TO 3X BASIC
316-325 STATED ODDS 1:24
*B/W 326-350: .75X TO 2X BASIC
326-350 STATED ODDS 1:20

2004 Upper Deck Vintage Black and White Color Variation

Issued at stated odds of one in 48, these skip-numbered cards are a variation to the black and white parallel cards.

*B/W COLOR: 5X TO 12X BASIC

2004 Upper Deck Vintage Old Judge Subset Blue Back

*OJ BLUE BACK 441-450: .6X TO 1.5X BASIC
STATED ODD 1:4 OJ HOBBY PACKS
ONE 3-CARD OJ PACK PER HOBBY BOX

2004 Upper Deck Vintage Old Judge Subset Red Back

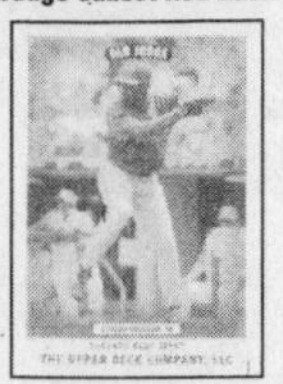

*OJ RED BACK 441-450: 1X TO 2.5X BASIC OJ
STATED ODDS 1:12 OJ HOBBY PACKS
ONE 3-CARD OJ PACK PER HOBBY BOX

2004 Upper Deck Vintage Old Judge

DISTRIBUTED IN OLD JUDGE HOBBY PACKS
ONE 3-CARD OJ PACK PER HOBBY BOX
*OJ BLUE BACK 11-30: .6X TO 1.5X BASIC
OJ BLUE BACK ODDS 1:4 OJ HOBBY PACKS
*OJ RED BACK 11-30: 1X TO 2.5X BASIC
OJ RED BACK ODDS 1:12 OJ HOBBY PACKS

11 Randy Johnson 2.00 5.00
12 Pedro Martinez 1.25 3.00
13 Mark Prior 1.25 3.00
14 Barry Zito .75 2.00
15 Roy Oswalt 1.25 3.00
16 Roy Halladay 2.00 5.00
17 Curt Schilling 1.25 3.00
18 Mike Mussina 1.25 3.00
19 Kevin Brown .75 2.00
20 Roger Clemens 2.50 6.00
21 Eric Gagne .75 2.00
22 Mariano Rivera 2.00 5.00
23 Mike Piazza 2.00 5.00
24 Jorge Posada 1.25 3.00
25 Jeff Kent .75 2.00
26 Alfonso Soriano .75 2.00
27 Scott Rolen 1.25 3.00
28 Eric Chavez .75 2.00
29 Edgar Renteria .75 2.00
30 Hideki Matsui 3.00 8.00

2004 Upper Deck Vintage Stellar Signatures

STATED ODDS 1:600
STATED PRINT RUN 150 SERIAL #'d SETS
EXCHANGE DEADLINE 01/27/07

BZ Barry Zito 15.00 40.00
CY Carl Yastrzemski 30.00 60.00
HM Hideki Matsui 175.00 300.00
IS Ichiro Suzuki 200.00 350.00
MP Mike Piazza 125.00 200.00
TS Tom Seaver 15.00 40.00

2004 Upper Deck Vintage Stellar Stat Men Jerseys

STATED ODDS 1:24
SP PRINT RUNS PROVIDED BY UPPER DECK
SP'S ARE NOT SERIAL-NUMBERED
1 Jose Reyes 3.00 8.00
2 Bo Hart 3.00 8.00
3 Hideki Matsui Pants 10.00 25.00
4 Dontrelle Willis 4.00 10.00
5 Rocco Baldelli 3.00 8.00
6 Ichiro Suzuki 12.50 30.00
7 Mike Lowell 3.00 8.00
8 Derek Jeter 12.50 30.00
9 Ken Griffey Jr. 6.00 15.00
10 Sammy Sosa 4.00 10.00
11 Kerry Wood 3.00 8.00
12 Chipper Jones 4.00 10.00
13 Alfonso Soriano 3.00 8.00
14 Khalil Greene 4.00 10.00
15 Jim Thome 4.00 10.00
16 Rafael Furcal 3.00 8.00
17 Andrew Brown 3.00 8.00
18 Mark Prior 4.00 10.00
19 Barry Zito 3.00 8.00
20 Al Leiter 3.00 8.00
21 Carlos Delgado 3.00 8.00
22 Pedro Martinez 4.00 10.00
23 Alex Rodriguez 6.00 15.00
24 Lance Berkman 3.00 8.00
25 Jeff Bagwell 4.00 10.00
26 Bernie Williams 4.00 10.00
27 Hideo Nomo 6.00 15.00
28 Randy Johnson 4.00 10.00
29 Curt Schilling 3.00 8.00
30 Mike Piazza 6.00 15.00
31 Albert Pujols 6.00 15.00
32 J.DiMaggio Pants SP/300 40.00 80.00
33 Ted Williams Pants SP/300 30.00 60.00
34 M.Mantle Pants SP/300 75.00 150.00
35 Mike Mussina 4.00 10.00
36 Rich Harden 3.00 8.00
37 Roy Oswalt 3.00 8.00
38 Torii Hunter 3.00 8.00
39 Jorge Posada 4.00 10.00
40 Troy Glaus 3.00 8.00
41 Manny Ramirez 4.00 10.00
42 Roy Halladay 3.00 8.00

2004 Upper Deck Vintage Timeless Teams Quad Bats

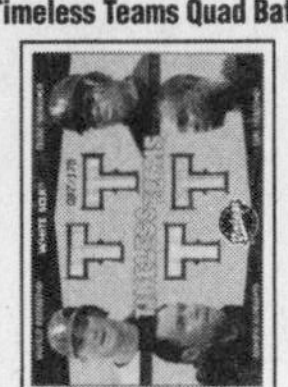

STATED ODDS 1:400
STATED PRINT RUN 175 SERIAL #'d SETS
CARD NUMBER 3 DOES NOT EXIST
TT1 Alfonso Soriano 60.00 120.00
Derek Jeter
Hideki Matsui
Jason Giambi
TT2 Luis Gonzalez 15.00 40.00
Curt Schilling
Randy Johnson
Steve Finley
TT4 Manny Ramirez 20.00 50.00
Nomar Garciaparra
Trot Nixon
Johnny Damon
TT5 Alex Rodriguez 15.00 40.00
Rafael Palmeiro
Mark Teixeira
Hank Blalock
TT6 Magglio Ordonez 15.00 40.00
Frank Thomas
Roberto Alomar
Carl Everett
TT7 Jacque Jones 10.00 25.00
Torii Hunter
Doug Mientkiewicz
Shannon Stewart
TT8 Jim Edmonds 20.00 50.00
Scott Rolen
J.D. Drew
Albert Pujols
TT9 Ichiro Suzuki 40.00 80.00
John Olerud
Bret Boone
Mike Cameron
TT10 Jeff Kent 15.00 40.00
Jeff Bagwell
Craig Biggio
Lance Berkman
TT11 Troy Glaus 15.00 40.00
Darin Erstad
Garret Anderson
Tim Salmon
TT12 Bernie Williams 40.00 80.00
Jorge Posada
Hideki Matsui
Alfonso Soriano
TT13 Michael Tucker 10.00 25.00
Carlos Beltran
Mike Sweeney
Brent Mayne
TT14 Jim Thome 15.00 40.00
Marlon Byrd
Mike Lieberthal
Bobby Abreu
TT15 Miguel Cabrera 15.00 40.00
Ivan Rodriguez
Juan Encarnacion
Mike Lowell
TT16 Sammy Sosa 15.00 40.00
Corey Patterson
Moises Alou
Kerry Wood
TT17 Jose Cruz Jr. 10.00 25.00
Edgardo Alfonzo
Rich Aurilia
Andres Galarraga
TT18 Alfonso Soriano 60.00 120.00
Derek Jeter
Hideki Matsui
Bernie Williams

2010 Upper Deck World of Sports

COMPLETE SET (375) 100.00 150.00
COMP.SET w/o SPs (300) 30.00 60.00
121 Brett Hunter .15 .40
122 Collin Cowgill .15 .40
123 Bobby Lanigan .15 .40
124 Andrew Liebel .15 .40
125 Casey Kelly .40 1.00
126 Jason Castro .25 .60
127 David Cooper .15 .40
128 Daniel Schlereth .15 .40
129 Jemile Weeks .15 .40
130 Joshua Fields .15 .40
131 Brad Holt .15 .40
132 Aaron Hicks .25 .60
133 Jeremy Bleich .15 .40
134 Justin Bristow .15 .40
135 Danny Espinosa .15 .40
136 Zach Putnam .15 .40
137 Allan Dykstra .15 .40
138 Tim Federowicz .15 .40
139 J.P. Ramirez .15 .40
140 Beamer Weems .15 .40
141 Eric Berger .15 .40
142 Jeremy Farrell .15 .40
143 T.J. Steele .15 .40
144 Reese Havens .15 .40
145 Jeremy Beckham .15 .40
146 Dustin Coleman .15 .40
147 Casper Wells .15 .40
148 Ryan Flaherty .15 .40
149 Robbie Weinhardt .15 .40
150 Kyle Skipworth .15 .40
151 Aaron Crow .15 .40
152 Garrison Lassiter .15 .40
153 Stephen Fife .15 .40
154 Chris Smith .15 .40
155 Tim Melville .15 .40
156 D.J. Mitchell .15 .40
157 Jordan Danks .25 .60
158 David Adams .15 .40
341 Bo Jackson SP 1.00 2.50
342 Lou Brock SP 1.00 2.50
343 Jose Canseco SP 1.00 2.50

2010 Upper Deck World of Sports Athletes of the World Autographs

OVERALL AUTO ODDS TWO PER BOX
AW1 Chris Perez
AW2 Derrek Lee 5.00 12.00
AW3 Jeff Clement 4.00 10.00
AW4 Phil Hughes 6.00 15.00
AW13 Stephen Strasburg 50.00 100.00
AW48 Pedro Alvarez 15.00 30.00
AW49 Justin Smoak 8.00 20.00
AW90 Cal Ripken Jr.
AW99 Fu-Te Ni
AW100 Jim Palmer 8.00 20.00

2010 Upper Deck World of Sports Autographs

OVERALL AUTO ODDS TWO PER BOX
121 Brett Hunter 5.00 12.00
122 Collin Cowgill 5.00 12.00
123 Bobby Lanigan 5.00 12.00
124 Andrew Liebel 5.00 12.00
125 Casey Kelly 6.00 15.00
126 Jason Castro 5.00 12.00
127 David Cooper 5.00 12.00
128 Daniel Schlereth 5.00 12.00
129 Jemile Weeks 5.00 12.00
130 Joshua Fields 5.00 12.00
131 Brad Holt
132 Aaron Hicks 15.00 30.00
133 Jeremy Bleich 5.00 12.00
134 Justin Bristow 5.00 12.00
135 Danny Espinosa 5.00 12.00
136 Zach Putnam 5.00 12.00
137 Allan Dykstra 5.00 12.00
138 Tim Federowicz 6.00 15.00
139 J.P. Ramirez
140 Beamer Weems 5.00 12.00
141 Eric Berger 5.00 12.00
142 Jeremy Farrell
143 T.J. Steele 5.00 12.00
144 Reese Havens 5.00 12.00
145 Jeremy Beckham 5.00 12.00
146 Dustin Coleman
147 Casper Wells 6.00 15.00
148 Ryan Flaherty 5.00 12.00
149 Robbie Weinhardt 5.00 12.00
150 Kyle Skipworth 5.00 12.00
151 Aaron Crow 5.00 12.00
152 Garrison Lassiter 5.00 12.00
153 Stephen Fife 5.00 12.00
154 Chris Smith 5.00 12.00
155 Tim Melville 5.00 12.00
156 D.J. Mitchell 5.00 12.00
157 Jordan Danks 5.00 12.00
158 David Adams 5.00 12.00
341 Bo Jackson
342 Lou Brock 12.00 25.00
343 Jose Canseco

2010 Upper Deck World of Sports Clear Competitors

STATED ODDS ONE PER BOX
STATED PRINT RUN 550 SER.#'d SETS
CC14 Bo Jackson 4.00 10.00

2008 Upper Deck X

This set was released on September 16, 2008. The base set consists of 100 cards.

COMPLETE SET (100) 12.50 30.00
COMMON CARD (1-100) .15 .40
COMMON ROOKIE (1-100) .25 .60
PRINTING PLATES RANDOMLY INSERTED
PLATE PRINT RUN 1 SET PER COLOR
BLACK-CYAN-MAGENTA-YELLOW ISSUED
NO PLATE PRICING DUE TO SCARCITY
1 Randy Johnson .40 1.00
2 Conor Jackson .15 .40
3 Brandon Webb .25 .60
4 Justin Upton .25 .60
5 Dan Haren .15 .40
6 John Smoltz .40 1.00
7 Chipper Jones .40 1.00
8 Mark Teixeira .40 1.00
9 Brian Roberts .15 .40
10 Nick Markakis .40 1.00
11 Daisuke Matsuzaka .40 1.00
12 David Ortiz .25 .60
13 Manny Ramirez .40 1.00
14 Jonathan Papelbon .25 .60
15 Josh Beckett .25 .60
16 Clay Buchholz (RC) .60 1.50
17 Carlos Zambrano .25 .60
18 Derrek Lee .15 .40
19 Aramis Ramirez .15 .40
20 Kerry Wood .15 .40
21 Alfonso Soriano .25 .60
22 Kosuke Fukudome RC .75 2.00
23 Geovany Soto .40 1.00
24 Paul Konerko .25 .60
25 Jermaine Dye .15 .40
26 Carlos Quentin .15 .40
27 Jim Thome .25 .60
28 Ken Griffey Jr. .60 1.50
29 Adam Dunn .25 .60
30 Brandon Phillips .15 .40
31 Edinson Volquez .15 .40
32 Victor Martinez .25 .60
33 Travis Hafner .15 .40
34 CC Sabathia .25 .60
35 Grady Sizemore .25 .60
36 Garrett Atkins .15 .40
37 Matt Holliday .40 1.00
38 Troy Tulowitzki .40 1.00
39 Justin Verlander .50 1.25
40 Miguel Cabrera .40 1.00
41 Gary Sheffield .15 .40
42 Magglio Ordonez .25 .60
43 Hanley Ramirez .40 1.00
44 Jeremy Hermida .15 .40
45 Carlos Lee .15 .40
46 Lance Berkman .25 .60
47 Roy Oswalt .25 .60
48 Alex Gordon .25 .60
49 Zack Greinke .25 .60
50 Howie Kendrick .15 .40
51 Torii Hunter .15 .40
52 Vladimir Guerrero .40 1.00
53 Matt Kemp .25 .60
54 Russell Martin .15 .40
55 Rafael Furcal .15 .40
56 Ryan Braun .50 1.25
57 Prince Fielder .25 .60
58 Corey Hart .15 .40
59 Justin Morneau .40 1.00
60 Joe Mauer .40 1.00
61 Jose Reyes .25 .60
62 David Wright .50 1.25
63 Carlos Beltran .15 .40
64 Johan Santana .40 1.00
65 Pedro Martinez .25 .60
66 Ian Kennedy RC .60 1.50
67 Hideki Matsui .25 .60
68 Alex Rodriguez .60 1.50
69 Chien-Ming Wang .25 .60
70 Derek Jeter 1.00 2.50
71 Robinson Cano .40 1.00
72 Eric Chavez .15 .40
73 Frank Thomas .40 1.00
74 Cole Hamels .40 1.00
75 Jimmy Rollins .25 .60
76 Ryan Howard .50 1.25
77 Chase Utley .40 1.00
78 Nate McLouth .15 .40
79 Jason Bay .25 .60
80 Adrian Gonzalez .25 .60
81 Khalil Greene .15 .40
82 Jake Peavy .15 .40
83 Greg Maddux .50 1.25
84 Trevor Hoffman .25 .60
85 Aaron Rowand .15 .40
86 Tim Lincecum .60 1.50
87 Ichiro Suzuki .60 1.50
88 Felix Hernandez .40 1.00
89 Erik Bedard .15 .40
90 Rick Ankiel .15 .40
91 Albert Pujols 1.00 2.50
92 B.J. Upton .25 .60
93 Carl Crawford .25 .60
94 Evan Longoria RC 1.25 3.00
95 Josh Hamilton .40 1.00
96 Michael Young .25 .60
97 Vernon Wells .15 .40
98 Alex Rios .25 .60
99 Ryan Zimmerman .25 .60
100 Lastings Milledge .15 .40

2008 Upper Deck X Die Cut

*VETERAN 1-100: 1X TO 2.5X BASIC
*ROOKIE 1-100: .75X TO 2X BASIC RC
STATED ODDS ONE PER PACK

2008 Upper Deck X Die Cut Gold

*VETERAN GLD 1-100: 2.5X TO 6X BASIC
*ROOKIE GLD 1-100: 1.5X TO 4X BASIC RC
RANDOM INSERTS IN PACKS

2008 Upper Deck X Memorabilia

AA Aaron Harang 3.00 8.00
AB Adrian Beltre
AE Andre Ethier 3.00 8.00
AG Adrian Gonzalez 3.00 8.00
AH Aubrey Huff 3.00 8.00
AK Austin Kearns 3.00 8.00
AR Alex Rodriguez 5.00 12.00
BB Boof Bonser
BG Brian Giles 3.00 8.00
BH Bill Hall
BJ Brandon Jones 3.00 8.00
BM Brian McCann 3.00 8.00
BO Jeremy Bonderman 3.00 8.00
BP Brad Penny 3.00 8.00
BR Brian Roberts 3.00 8.00
BU A.J. Burnett 3.00 8.00
CA Melky Cabrera 3.00 8.00
CC Chris Carpenter
CD Carlos Delgado 3.00 8.00
CH Craig Hansen
CJ Conor Jackson 3.00 8.00
CL Carlos Lee 3.00 8.00
CR Joe Crede 3.00 8.00
CS Curt Schilling 3.00 8.00
CZ Carlos Zambrano 3.00 8.00
DL Derrek Lee 3.00 8.00
DM Daisuke Matsuzaka
DO David Ortiz 3.00 8.00
DR J.D. Drew 3.00 8.00
DU Dan Uggla 3.00 8.00
DY Jermaine Dye 3.00 8.00
EG Eric Gagne
FR Francisco Rodriguez
FS Freddy Sanchez 3.00 8.00
GA Garrett Atkins
GJ Geoff Jenkins 3.00 8.00
GL Troy Glaus
GM Greg Maddux 4.00 10.00
GS Grady Sizemore 3.00 8.00
HA Travis Hafner
HP Hunter Pence 3.00 8.00
HR Hanley Ramirez 3.00 8.00
HS Huston Street 3.00 8.00
HU Torii Hunter 3.00 8.00
IK Ian Kinsler 3.00 8.00
IR Ivan Rodriguez
JB Josh Barfield
JC Joba Chamberlain
JD Johnny Damon
JE Johnny Estrada
JF Jeff Francoeur 3.00 8.00
JG Jeremy Guthrie 3.00 8.00
JH J.J. Hardy 3.00 8.00
JK Jeff Kent 3.00 8.00
JM Joe Mauer
JO Josh Hamilton
JP Jhonny Peralta
JR Jeremy Reed
JS James Shields 3.00 8.00
JV Jason Varitek
JW Jered Weaver
KE Kelly Johnson 3.00 8.00
KJ Kenji Johjima 3.00 8.00
KM Kazuo Matsui
KU Jason Kubel 3.00 8.00
KW Kerry Wood 3.00 8.00
KY Kevin Youkilis
LG Luis Gonzalez 3.00 8.00
LM Lastings Milledge
MA John Maine
MC Matt Cain
MG Matt Garza 3.00 8.00
MI Kevin Millwood
MK Kendry Morales 3.00 8.00
MO Justin Morneau 3.00 8.00
MP Mark Prior
MR Mariano Rivera
NS Nick Swisher 3.00 8.00
PA Jonathan Papelbon 4.00 10.00
PE Jake Peavy
PF Prince Fielder
PI Juan Pierre
PO Jorge Posada 3.00 8.00
RA Aramis Ramirez 3.00 8.00
RF Rafael Furcal 3.00 8.00
RH Rich Hill 3.00 8.00
RM Russell Martin
RZ Ryan Zimmerman
SA Johan Santana 3.00 8.00
SC Sean Casey
SP Scott Podsednik
TG Tom Gorzelanny
TH Tim Hudson 3.00 8.00
TL Tim Lincecum 5.00 12.00
TS Takashi Saito
TT Troy Tulowitzki 3.00 8.00
TW Tim Wakefield 3.00 8.00
UP B.J. Upton 3.00 8.00
VE Justin Verlander 3.00 8.00

2008 Upper Deck X Sample

COMPLETE SET (1) 5.00 12.00
DJ Derek Jeter 5.00 12.00

2008 Upper Deck X Signatures

STATED ODDS 1:10 HOBBY
EXCHANGE DEADLINE 8/18/2010
BB Brian Bass 4.00 10.00
BI Brian Bixler 3.00 8.00
CA Jesse Carlson 3.00 8.00
CB Clay Buchholz 10.00 25.00
CC Callix Crabbe 3.00 8.00
CH Chin-Lung Hu
CM Colt Morton 3.00 8.00
CT Clete Thomas 3.00 8.00
DJ Derek Jeter 75.00 150.00
EL Evan Longoria
EM Evan Meek 3.00 8.00
FC Frank Catalanotto 3.00 8.00
IK Ian Kennedy
JA Jonathan Albaladejo 3.00 8.00
JC Johnny Cueto
JK Jeff Keppinger 3.00 8.00
JN Josh Newman 3.00 8.00
JT J.R. Towles 4.00 10.00
KG Ken Griffey Jr. EXCH 40.00 80.00
KH Kevin Hart 3.00 8.00
LH Luke Hochevar
LM Luis Mendoza 3.00 8.00
MB Marlon Byrd 3.00 8.00
RO Ross Ohlendorf 3.00 8.00
RT Rich Thompson 3.00 8.00
SH Steve Holm 3.00 8.00
TI Clay Timpner 3.00 8.00
TR Ramon Troncoso 3.00 8.00
WB Wladimir Balentien

2008 Upper Deck X Xponential

STATED ODDS 1:2 HOBBY
PRINTING PLATES RANDOMLY INSERTED
PLATE PRINT RUN 1 SET PER COLOR
BLACK-CYAN-MAGENTA-YELLOW ISSUED
NO PLATE PRICING DUE TO SCARCITY
AD Adam Dunn .50 1.25
AG Adrian Gonzalez .50 1.25
AJ Andruw Jones .30 .75
AL Alex Rodriguez 1.25 3.00
AP Albert Pujols 2.00 5.00
AR Aramis Ramirez .30 .75
AS Alfonso Soriano .50 1.25
BA Bobby Abreu .30 .75
BP Brandon Phillips .30 .75
BR Brian Roberts .30 .75
BU B.J. Upton .50 1.25
BW Brandon Webb .50 1.25
CB Carlos Beltran .30 .75
CC Carl Crawford .50 1.25
CG Curtis Granderson .50 1.25
CH Corey Hart .30 .75
CJ Conor Jackson .30 .75
CL Carlos Lee .30 .75
CP Carlos Pena .50 1.25
CS CC Sabathia .50 1.25
CU Chase Utley .75 2.00
CW Chien-Ming Wang .50 1.25
CY Chris B. Young .30 .75
CZ Carlos Zambrano .50 1.25
DJ Derek Jeter 2.00 5.00
DL Derrek Lee .30 .75
DM Daisuke Matsuzaka .75 2.00
DO David Ortiz .50 1.25
DW Dontrelle Willis .30 .75
EB Erik Bedard .30 .75
FH Felix Hernandez .75 2.00
FT Frank Thomas .75 2.00
GA Garrett Atkins .30 .75
GM Greg Maddux 1.00 2.50
GR Khalil Greene .30 .75
GS Grady Sizemore .50 1.25
GU Carlos Guillen .30 .75
HE Todd Helton .50 1.25
HM Hideki Matsui .75 2.00
HO Trevor Hoffman .50 1.25
HR Hanley Ramirez .75 2.00
HU Torii Hunter .30 .75
IR Ivan Rodriguez .50 1.25
IS Ichiro Suzuki 1.25 3.00
JA Jason Bay .50 1.25
JB Josh Beckett .50 1.25
JC Joba Chamberlain .50 1.25
JF Jeff Francoeur .50 1.25
JH Josh Hamilton .75 2.00
JI Jimmy Rollins .50 1.25
JK Jeff Kent .30 .75
JM Justin Morneau .75 2.00
JO Chipper Jones .75 2.00
JP Jonathan Papelbon .50 1.25
JR Jose Reyes .50 1.25
JS John Smoltz .75 2.00
JT Jim Thome .50 1.25
JV Jason Varitek .75 2.00
KG Ken Griffey Jr. 1.25 3.00
LB Lance Berkman .50 1.25
MA Joe Mauer .75 2.00
MC Miguel Cabrera .75 2.00
MH Matt Holliday .75 2.00
MO Magglio Ordonez .50 1.25
MR Manny Ramirez .75 2.00
MT Mark Teixeira .75 2.00
NM Nick Markakis .75 2.00
NS Nick Swisher .75 2.00
PB Pat Burrell .30 .75
PE Jake Peavy .30 .75
PF Prince Fielder .50 1.25
PK Paul Konerko .50 1.25
PM Pedro Martinez .50 1.25
RA Rick Ankiel .30 .75
RB Ryan Braun 1.00 2.50
RH Ryan Howard 1.00 2.50
RI Mariano Rivera .75 2.00
RJ Randy Johnson .75 2.00
RM Russell Martin .30 .75
RO Roy Oswalt .50 1.25
RW Rickie Weeks .50 1.25
RZ Ryan Zimmerman .50 1.25
SA Johan Santana .75 2.00
SH Gary Sheffield .30 .75
TE Miguel Tejada .50 1.25
TH Travis Hafner .30 .75
TT Troy Tulowitzki .75 2.00
VG Vladimir Guerrero .75 2.00
VM Victor Martinez .50 1.25
WR David Wright 1.00 2.50

2008 Upper Deck X Xponential 2

*X2: .5X TO 1.2X BASIC XPONENTIAL
APPX.ODDS 1:3 HOBBY
PRINTING PLATES RANDOMLY INSERTED
PLATE PRINT RUN 1 SET PER COLOR
BLACK-CYAN-MAGENTA-YELLOW ISSUED
NO PLATE PRICING DUE TO SCARCITY

2008 Upper Deck X Xponential 3

*X3: .75X TO 2X BASIC XPONENTIAL
STATED ODDS 1:10 HOBBY
PRINTING PLATES RANDOMLY INSERTED
PLATE PRINT RUN 1 SET PER COLOR
BLACK-CYAN-MAGENTA-YELLOW ISSUED
NO PLATE PRICING DUE TO SCARCITY

2008 Upper Deck X Xponential 4

*X4: 1X TO 2.5X BASIC XPONENTIAL
STATED ODDS 1:10 HOBBY
PRINTING PLATES RANDOMLY INSERTED
PLATE PRINT RUN 1 SET PER COLOR
BLACK-CYAN-MAGENTA-YELLOW ISSUED
NO PLATE PRICING DUE TO SCARCITY

2009 Upper Deck X

COMPLETE SET (100) 15.00 40.00
COMMON CARD (1-95) .15 .40
COMMON ROOKIE (96-100) .50 1.25
PRINTING PLATES RANDOMLY INSERTED
PLATE PRINT RUN 1 SET PER COLOR
BLACK-CYAN-MAGENTA-YELLOW ISSUED
NO PLATE PRICING DUE TO SCARCITY
1 Dan Haren .15 .40
2 Chris B. Young .15 .40
3 Brandon Webb .25 .60
4 Chipper Jones .40 1.00
5 Brian McCann .25 .60
6 Nick Markakis .40 1.00
7 Brian Roberts .15 .40
8 Kevin Youkilis .25 .60
9 Josh Beckett .25 .60
10 Jonathan Papelbon .25 .60
11 Jacoby Ellsbury .40 1.00
12 Dustin Pedroia .50 1.25

13 David Ortiz .25 .60
14 Daisuke Matsuzaka .40 1.00
15 Rich Harden .15 .40
16 Alfonso Soriano .25 .60
17 Derrek Lee .15 .40
18 Carlos Zambrano .25 .60
19 Aramis Ramirez .15 .40
20 Paul Konerko .25 .60
21 Jermaine Dye .15 .40
22 Carlos Quentin .25 .60
23 Jay Bruce .25 .60
24 Edinson Volquez .15 .40
25 Brandon Phillips .15 .40
26 Victor Martinez .25 .60
27 Travis Hafner .15 .40
28 Kerry Wood .15 .40
29 Grady Sizemore .25 .60
30 Cliff Lee .25 .60
31 Garrett Atkins .15 .40
32 Miguel Cabrera .40 1.00
33 Magglio Ordonez .25 .60
34 Carlos Guillen .15 .40
35 Hanley Ramirez .40 1.00
36 Dan Uggla .25 .60
37 Miguel Tejada .25 .60
38 Lance Berkman .25 .60
39 Carlos Lee .15 .40
40 Jose Guillen .15 .40
41 Alex Gordon .25 .60
42 Vladimir Guerrero .40 1.00
43 Torii Hunter .15 .40
44 Bobby Abreu .15 .40
45 Russell Martin .15 .40
46 Matt Kemp .25 .60
47 Manny Ramirez .40 1.00
48 Ryan Braun .50 1.25
49 Prince Fielder .25 .60
50 Corey Hart .15 .40
51 Joe Nathan .15 .40
52 Justin Morneau .40 1.00
53 Joe Mauer .40 1.00
54 Jose Reyes .25 .60
55 Johan Santana .40 1.00
56 Francisco Rodriguez .25 .60
57 David Wright .50 1.25
58 Carlos Beltran .15 .40
59 Mark Teixeira .40 1.00
60 Andy Pettitte .25 .60
61 Joba Chamberlain .25 .60
62 Derek Jeter 1.00 2.50
63 Chien-Ming Wang .25 .60
64 CC Sabathia .25 .60
65 Alex Rodriguez .60 1.50
66 Matt Holliday .40 1.00
67 Jason Giambi .15 .40
68 Jack Cust .15 .40
69 Ryan Howard .50 1.25
70 Jimmy Rollins .25 .60
71 Chase Utley .40 1.00
72 Nate McLouth .15 .40
73 Ryan Doumit .15 .40
74 Jake Peavy .15 .40
75 Adrian Gonzalez .25 .60
76 Tim Lincecum .60 1.50
77 Aaron Rowand .15 .40
78 Randy Johnson .25 .60
79 Ken Griffey Jr. .60 1.50
80 Ichiro Suzuki .60 1.50
81 Felix Hernandez .40 1.00
82 Ryan Ludwick .25 .60
83 Rick Ankiel .15 .40
84 Albert Pujols 1.00 2.50
85 Scott Kazmir .15 .40
86 Evan Longoria .50 1.25
87 Carl Crawford .25 .60
88 B.J. Upton .25 .60
89 Josh Hamilton .40 1.00
90 Ian Kinsler .25 .60
91 Vernon Wells .15 .40
92 Roy Halladay .25 .60
93 Alex Rios .25 .60
94 Adam Dunn .25 .60
95 Ryan Zimmerman .25 .60
96 Rick Porcello RC 1.25 3.00
97 Colby Rasmus (RC) 1.00 2.50
98 James McDonald RC .60 1.50
99 Koji Uehara RC .60 1.50
100 Derek Holland RC .60 1.50

2009 Upper Deck X Die Cut

*VETERAN 1-100: 1X TO 2.5X BASIC
*ROOKIE 1-100: .5X TO 1.2X BASIC RC
RANDOM INSERTS IN PACKS

2009 Upper Deck X Memorabilia

RANDOM INSERTS IN PACKS
NO PRICING AVAILABLE ON MOST
AE Andre Ethier 3.00 8.00
AM Andrew Miller
AN Rick Ankiel SP 3.00 8.00
AR Aaron Rowand
BA Bronson Arroyo
BD Blake DeWitt 3.00 8.00
BE Josh Beckett
BM Brian McCann
BP Brad Penny 3.00 8.00
BW Billy Wagner
BZ Barry Zito 3.00 8.00
CA Chris Carpenter 3.00 8.00
CD Carlos Delgado 3.00 8.00
CG Carlos Guillen
CJ Conor Jackson 3.00 8.00
CL Carlos Lee 3.00 8.00
CU Michael Cuddyer 3.00 8.00
CY Chris B. Young
CZ Carlos Zambrano
DH Dan Haren
DJ Derek Jeter
DL Derrek Lee
DO David Ortiz
DY Delmon Young
EC Eric Chavez 3.00 8.00
EL Evan Longoria
FL Francisco Liriano
FP Felipe Paulino
GA Garrett Atkins
GO Alex Gordon
GR Curtis Granderson 3.00 8.00
GS Grady Sizemore
HA Corey Hart
HO Trevor Hoffman
HP Hunter Pence
JB Jeff Baker
JC Joba Chamberlain 3.00 8.00
JD Jermaine Dye 3.00 8.00
JE Jacoby Ellsbury
JF Jeff Francoeur
JG Jeremy Guthrie 3.00 8.00
JH Jeremy Hermida
JJ Josh Johnson
JK Jason Kubel 3.00 8.00
JL James Loney 3.00 8.00
JM Joe Mauer 4.00 10.00
JN Joe Nathan
JO Josh Barfield
JP Jake Peavy 3.00 8.00
JT Jim Thome 3.00 8.00
JU Justin Upton 3.00 8.00
JW Jered Weaver
JZ Joel Zumaya
KJ Kelly Johnson 3.00 8.00
KK Kevin Kouzmanoff
KM Kendry Morales
MC Miguel Cabrera
MH Matt Holliday
MI Kevin Millwood
MK Matt Kemp 3.00 8.00
ML Mike Lowell
MO Justin Morneau 3.00 8.00
MR Manny Ramirez
MY Michael Young
OR Magglio Ordonez
PA Jonathan Papelbon
PE Jhonny Peralta
PH Phil Hughes 3.00 8.00
PK Paul Konerko
PO Jorge Posada
RA Aramis Ramirez
RB Ryan Braun
RC Robinson Cano
RF Rafael Furcal 3.00 8.00
RH Rich Hill
RI Alex Rios
RM Russell Martin 3.00 8.00
RO Roy Oswalt 3.00 8.00
RT Ramon Troncoso
SR Scott Rolen 3.00 8.00
TG Troy Glaus
TH Torii Hunter
TR Travis Hafner
VG Vladimir Guerrero
WI Josh Willingham 3.00 8.00
YO Kevin Youkilis

2009 Upper Deck X Signatures

RANDOM INSERTS IN PACKS
6 Nick Markakis
12 Dustin Pedroia
23 Jay Bruce 12.50 30.00
24 Edinson Volquez 6.00 15.00
25 Brandon Phillips
50 Corey Hart 6.00 15.00
98 James McDonald 4.00 10.00

2009 Upper Deck X Xponential

RANDOM INSERTS IN PACKS
PRINTING PLATES RANDOMLY INSERTED
PLATE PRINT RUN 1 SET PER COLOR
BLACK-CYAN-MAGENTA-YELLOW ISSUED
NO PLATE PRICING DUE TO SCARCITY
AB A.J. Burnett .50 1.25
AG Adrian Gonzalez .50 1.25
AP Albert Pujols 2.00 5.00
AR Alex Rodriguez 1.25 3.00
AS Alfonso Soriano .50 1.25
AZ Aramis Ramirez .30 .75
BA Bobby Abreu .30 .75
BE Josh Beckett .50 1.25
BM Brian McCann .50 1.25
BP Brandon Phillips .30 .75
BU B.J. Upton .50 1.25
BW Brandon Webb .50 1.25
CB Carlos Beltran .30 .75
CC Carl Crawford .50 1.25
CH Cole Hamels .75 2.00
CJ Chipper Jones .75 2.00
CL Carlos Lee .30 .75
CQ Carlos Quentin .50 1.25
CS CC Sabathia .50 1.25
CU Chase Utley .75 2.00
CW Chien-Ming Wang .50 1.25
CZ Carlos Zambrano .50 1.25
DH Dan Haren .30 .75
DJ Derek Jeter 2.00 5.00
DL Derrek Lee .30 .75
DM Daisuke Matsuzaka .75 2.00
DO David Ortiz .50 1.25
DP Dustin Pedroia 1.00 2.50
DU Dan Uggla .50 1.25
DW David Wright 1.00 2.50
EL Evan Longoria 1.00 2.50
EV Edinson Volquez .30 .75
FH Felix Hernandez .75 2.00
FR Francisco Rodriguez .50 1.25
GE Geovany Soto .50 1.25
GS Grady Sizemore .50 1.25
HA Travis Hafner .30 .75
HO Ryan Howard 1.00 2.50
HR Hanley Ramirez .75 2.00
IK Ian Kinsler .50 1.25
IS Ichiro Suzuki 1.25 3.00
JB Jay Bruce .50 1.25
JD Jermaine Dye .30 .75
JE Jacoby Ellsbury .75 2.00
JG Jason Giambi .30 .75
JH Josh Hamilton .75 2.00
JM Joe Mauer .75 2.00
JP Jake Peavy .30 .75
JR Jimmy Rollins .50 1.25
JS Johan Santana .75 2.00
KG Ken Griffey Jr. 1.25 3.00
KY Kevin Youkilis .50 1.25
LB Lance Berkman .50 1.25
MA Nick Markakis .75 2.00
MC Miguel Cabrera .75 2.00
MH Matt Holliday .75 2.00
ML Mike Lowell .30 .75
MO Magglio Ordonez .50 1.25
MR Manny Ramirez .75 2.00
MT Mark Teixeira .75 2.00
PA Jonathan Papelbon .50 1.25
PF Prince Fielder .50 1.25
RA Rick Ankiel .30 .75
RB Ryan Braun 1.00 2.50
RE Jose Reyes .50 1.25
RH Roy Halladay .75 2.00
RJ Randy Johnson .50 1.25
RM Russell Martin .30 .75
RZ Ryan Zimmerman .50 1.25
SK Scott Kazmir .30 .75
TE Miguel Tejada .50 1.25
TH Torii Hunter .30 .75
TL Tim Lincecum 1.25 3.00
VG Vladimir Guerrero .75 2.00
VW Vernon Wells .30 .75

2009 Upper Deck X Xponential 2

*X2: .5X TO 1.2X BASIC XPONENTIAL
RANDOM INSERTS IN PACKS
PRINTING PLATES RANDOMLY INSERTED
PLATE PRINT RUN 1 SET PER COLOR
BLACK-CYAN-MAGENTA-YELLOW ISSUED
NO PLATE PRICING DUE TO SCARCITY
AG Adrian Gonzalez .60 1.50
AP Albert Pujols 2.50 6.00
AR Alex Rodriguez 1.50 4.00
AS Alfonso Soriano .60 1.50
AZ Aramis Ramirez .40 1.00
BU B.J. Upton .60 1.50
BW Brandon Webb .60 1.50
CB Carlos Beltran .40 1.00
CC Carl Crawford .60 1.50
CJ Chipper Jones 1.00 2.50
CS CC Sabathia .60 1.50
CU Chase Utley 1.00 2.50
CZ Carlos Zambrano .60 1.50
DJ Derek Jeter 2.50 6.00
DL Derrek Lee .40 1.00
DO David Ortiz .60 1.50
DW David Wright 1.25 3.00
EV Edinson Volquez .40 1.00
GS Grady Sizemore .60 1.50
HR Hanley Ramirez 1.00 2.50
IK Ian Kinsler .60 1.50
IS Ichiro Suzuki 1.50 4.00
JB Josh Beckett .60 1.50
JD Jermaine Dye .40 1.00
JH Josh Hamilton 1.00 2.50
JM Joe Mauer 1.00 2.50
JP Jonathan Papelbon .60 1.50
JR Jimmy Rollins .60 1.50
JS Johan Santana 1.00 2.50
KG Ken Griffey Jr. 1.50 4.00
LB Lance Berkman .60 1.50
MC Miguel Cabrera 1.00 2.50
MH Matt Holliday 1.00 2.50
MO Magglio Ordonez .60 1.50
MR Manny Ramirez 1.00 2.50
MT Mark Teixeira 1.00 2.50
PE Jake Peavy .40 1.00
PF Prince Fielder .60 1.50
RA Rick Ankiel .40 1.00
RB Ryan Braun 1.25 3.00
RE Jose Reyes .60 1.50
RH Ryan Howard 1.25 3.00
RJ Randy Johnson .60 1.50
RM Russell Martin .40 1.00
VG Vladimir Guerrero 1.00 2.50

2009 Upper Deck X Xponential 3

*X3: .5X TO 1.2X BASIC XPONENTIAL
RANDOM INSERTS IN PACKS
PRINTING PLATES RANDOMLY INSERTED
PLATE PRINT RUN 1 SET PER COLOR
BLACK-CYAN-MAGENTA-YELLOW ISSUED
NO PLATE PRICING DUE TO SCARCITY
AG Adrian Gonzalez .60 1.50
AP Albert Pujols 2.50 6.00
AR Alex Rodriguez 1.50 4.00
AS Alfonso Soriano .60 1.50
AZ Aramis Ramirez .40 1.00
BU B.J. Upton .60 1.50
BW Brandon Webb .60 1.50
CB Carlos Beltran .40 1.00
CJ Chipper Jones 1.00 2.50
CU Chase Utley 1.00 2.50
DJ Derek Jeter 2.50 6.00
DL Derrek Lee .40 1.00
DO David Ortiz .60 1.50
DW David Wright 1.25 3.00
GS Grady Sizemore .60 1.50
HO Ryan Howard 1.25 3.00
HR Hanley Ramirez 1.00 2.50
IS Ichiro Suzuki 1.50 4.00
JB Josh Beckett .60 1.50
JD Jermaine Dye .40 1.00
JH Josh Hamilton 1.00 2.50
JP Jake Peavy .40 1.00
JR Jimmy Rollins .60 1.50
JS Johan Santana 1.00 2.50
KG Ken Griffey Jr. 1.50 4.00
LB Lance Berkman .60 1.50
MC Miguel Cabrera 1.00 2.50
MH Matt Holliday 1.00 2.50
MR Manny Ramirez 1.00 2.50
MT Mark Teixeira 1.00 2.50
PF Prince Fielder .60 1.50
RB Ryan Braun 1.25 3.00
RE Jose Reyes .60 1.50
RJ Randy Johnson .60 1.50
VG Vladimir Guerrero 1.00 2.50

2009 Upper Deck X Xponential 4

*X4: .6X TO 1.5X BASIC XPONENTIAL
RANDOM INSERTS IN PACKS
PRINTING PLATES RANDOMLY INSERTED
PLATE PRINT RUN 1 SET PER COLOR
BLACK-CYAN-MAGENTA-YELLOW ISSUED
NO PLATE PRICING DUE TO SCARCITY
AP Albert Pujols 3.00 8.00
AR Alex Rodriguez 2.00 5.00
AS Alfonso Soriano .75 2.00
CB Carlos Beltran .50 1.25
CU Chase Utley 1.25 3.00
DJ Derek Jeter 3.00 8.00
DO David Ortiz .75 2.00
DW David Wright 1.50 4.00
GS Grady Sizemore .75 2.00
HR Hanley Ramirez 1.25 3.00
IS Ichiro Suzuki 2.00 5.00
JB Josh Beckett .75 2.00
JH Josh Hamilton 1.25 3.00
JP Jake Peavy .50 1.25
JR Jose Reyes .75 2.00
JS Johan Santana 1.25 3.00
KG Ken Griffey Jr. 2.00 5.00
MH Matt Holliday 1.25 3.00
MR Manny Ramirez 1.25 3.00
MT Mark Teixeira 1.25 3.00
PF Prince Fielder .75 2.00
RB Ryan Braun 1.50 4.00
RH Ryan Howard 1.50 4.00
RJ Randy Johnson .75 2.00
VG Vladimir Guerrero 1.25 3.00

2009 Upper Deck X Xponential 5

*X5: .6X TO 1.5X BASIC XPONENTIAL
RANDOM INSERTS IN PACKS
PRINTING PLATES RANDOMLY INSERTED
PLATE PRINT RUN 1 SET PER COLOR
BLACK-CYAN-MAGENTA-YELLOW ISSUED
NO PLATE PRICING DUE TO SCARCITY
AP Albert Pujols 3.00 8.00
AR Alex Rodriguez 2.00 5.00
AS Alfonso Soriano .75 2.00
CU Chase Utley 1.25 3.00
DJ Derek Jeter 3.00 8.00
DO David Ortiz .75 2.00
DW David Wright 1.50 4.00
IS Ichiro Suzuki 2.00 5.00
JP Jake Peavy .50 1.25
JR Jose Reyes .75 2.00
KG Ken Griffey Jr. 2.00 5.00
MR Manny Ramirez 1.25 3.00
RB Ryan Braun 1.50 4.00
RH Ryan Howard 1.50 4.00
RJ Randy Johnson .75 2.00

2009 Upper Deck X Xponential 6

*X6: 1X TO 2.5X BASIC XPONENTIAL
RANDOM INSERTS IN PACKS
PRINTING PLATES RANDOMLY INSERTED
PLATE PRINT RUN 1 SET PER COLOR
BLACK-CYAN-MAGENTA-YELLOW ISSUED
NO PLATE PRICING DUE TO SCARCITY
AP Albert Pujols 5.00 12.00
AR Alex Rodriguez 3.00 8.00
DJ Derek Jeter 5.00 12.00
KG Ken Griffey Jr. 3.00 8.00
RJ Randy Johnson 1.25 3.00

2000 Upper Deck Yankees Legends

The 2000 Upper Deck Yankee Legends product was released in October, 2000. The product featured a 90-card base set. Please note that a Mickey Mantle promo was issued to dealers and members of the hobby media prior to the release of the product. Each pack contained five cards, and carried a suggested retail price of $2.99. Also, a selection of A Piece of History 3000 Club Dave Winfield memorabilia cards were randomly seeded into packs. 350 bat cards, 350 jersey cards, 100 hand-numbered combination bat-jersey cards and thirty-one autographed, hand-numbered, combination bat-jersey cards were produced. Pricing for these memorabilia cards can be referenced under 2000 Upper Deck A Piece of History 3000 Club.

COMPLETE SET (90) 10.00 25.00
1 Babe Ruth 1.25 3.00
2 Mickey Mantle 1.50 4.00
3 Lou Gehrig .75 2.00
4 Joe DiMaggio .75 2.00
5 Yogi Berra .40 1.00
6 Don Mattingly 1.00 2.50
7 Reggie Jackson .25 .60
8 Dave Winfield .15 .40
9 Bill Skowron .15 .40
10 Willie Randolph .15 .40
11 Phil Rizzuto .40 1.00
12 Tony Kubek .25 .60
13 Thurman Munson .40 1.00
14 Roger Maris .40 1.00
15 Billy Martin .25 .60
16 Elston Howard .25 .60
17 Graig Nettles .15 .40
18 Whitey Ford .25 .60
19 Earle Combs .15 .40
20 Tony Lazzeri .15 .40
21 Bob Meusel .15 .40
22 Joe Gordon .15 .40
23 Jerry Coleman .15 .40
24 Joe Torre .25 .60
25 Bucky Dent .15 .40
26 Don Larsen .15 .40
27 Bobby Richardson .15 .40
28 Ron Guidry .15 .40
29 Bobby Murcer .15 .40
30 Tommy Henrich .15 .40
31 Hank Bauer .15 .40
32 Joe Pepitone .15 .40
33 Clete Boyer .15 .40
34 Chris Chambliss .15 .40
35 Tommy John .15 .40
36 Goose Gossage .15 .40
37 Red Ruffing .15 .40
38 Charlie Keller .15 .40
39 Billy Gardner .15 .40
40 Hector Lopez .15 .40
41 Cliff Johnson .15 .40
42 Oscar Gamble .15 .40
43 Allie Reynolds .15 .40
44 Mickey Rivers .15 .40
45 Bill Dickey .25 .60
46 Dave Righetti .15 .40
47 Mel Stottlemyre .15 .40
48 Waite Hoyt .15 .40
49 Lefty Gomez .25 .60
50 Wade Boggs .25 .60
51 Billy Martin MN .15 .40
52 Babe Ruth MN .60 1.50
53 Lou Gehrig MN .40 1.00
54 Joe DiMaggio MN .40 1.00
55 Mickey Mantle MN .75 2.00
56 Yogi Berra MN .25 .60
57 Bill Dickey MN .15 .40
58 Roger Maris MN .25 .60
59 Phil Rizzuto MN .25 .60
60 Thurman Munson MN .25 .60
61 Whitey Ford MN .15 .40
62 Don Mattingly MN .50 1.25
63 Elston Howard MN .15 .40
64 Casey Stengel MN .25 .60
65 Reggie Jackson MN .15 .40
66 Babe Ruth '23 TCY .60 1.50
67 Lou Gehrig '27 TCY .40 1.00
68 Tony Lazzeri '28 TCY .15 .40
69 Babe Ruth '32 TCY .60 1.50
70 Lou Gehrig '36 TCY .40 1.00
71 Lefty Gomez '37 TCY .25 .60
72 Bill Dickey '38 TCY .15 .40
73 T.Henrich '39 TCY .15 .40
74 Joe DiMaggio '41 TCY .40 1.00
75 Spud Chandler '43 TCY .15 .40
76 T.Henrich '47 TCY .15 .40
77 Phil Rizzuto '49 TCY .25 .60
78 Whitey Ford '50 TCY .15 .40
79 Yogi Berra '51 TCY .25 .60
80 Casey Stengel '52 TCY .25 .60
81 Billy Martin '53 TCY .15 .40
82 Don Larsen '56 TCY .15 .40
83 Elston Howard '58 TCY .25 .60
84 Roger Maris '61 TCY .25 .60
85 Mickey Mantle '62 TCY .75 2.00
86 R.Jackson '77 TCY .15 .40
87 Bucky Dent '78 TCY .15 .40
88 Wade Boggs '96 TCY .15 .40
89 Joe Torre '98 TCY .25 .60
90 Joe Torre '99 TCY .25 .60
NNO M.Mantle Promo 1.25 3.00

2000 Upper Deck Yankees Legends DiMaggio Memorabilia

Randomly inserted into packs, this three-card set features game-used memorabilia cards from Yankee great Joe DiMaggio. Cards in the set include game-used bat, bat-cut signature, and a bat card numbered to 56. Card backs carry a "YLG" prefix.

BAT-AUTO CUT PRICING NOT AVAILABLE
GOLD BAT PRINT RUN 56 #'d CARDS
YLBJD Joe DiMaggio Bat 60.00 120.00
YLCJD1 Joe DiMaggio Bat-Cut AU/5
YLGJD Joe DiMaggio Gold Bat/56 100.00 200.00

2000 Upper Deck Yankees Legends Golden Years

Randomly inserted into packs at one in 11, this 10-card insert set features players that played for the Yankees during their golden years. Card backs carry a "GY" prefix.

COMPLETE SET (10) 10.00 25.00
GY1 Joe DiMaggio 2.00 5.00
GY2 Phil Rizzuto 1.00 2.50
GY3 Yogi Berra 1.00 2.50
GY4 Billy Martin .60 1.50
GY5 Whitey Ford .60 1.50
GY6 Roger Maris 1.00 2.50
GY7 Mickey Mantle 4.00 10.00
GY8 Elston Howard .60 1.50
GY9 Tommy Henrich .40 1.00
GY10 Joe Gordon .40 1.00

2000 Upper Deck Yankees Legends Legendary Lumber

Randomly inserted into packs at one in 23, this 30-card insert set features game-used bat cards from Yankee greats. Card backs carry a "LL" suffix. Please note that the hologram on the back of these cards is silver and the Bat Chip features a wood "NY"..

BDLL Bucky Dent 4.00 10.00
BGLL Billy Gardner 4.00 10.00
BMLL Bobby Murcer 15.00 40.00
BRLL Babe Ruth 100.00 175.00
CBLL Clete Boyer 4.00 10.00
CCLL Chris Chambliss 4.00 10.00
CJLL Cliff Johnson 4.00 10.00
CKLL Charlie Keller 4.00 10.00
DMLL Don Mattingly 8.00 20.00
DWLL Dave Winfield 4.00 10.00
EHLL Elston Howard 4.00 10.00
GNLL Graig Nettles 4.00 10.00
HBLL Hank Bauer 4.00 10.00
HLLL Hector Lopez 4.00 10.00
JCLL Joe Collins 4.00 10.00
JPLL Joe Pepitone 4.00 10.00
MMLL Mickey Mantle 100.00 175.00
MRLL Mickey Rivers 4.00 10.00
MSLL Moose Skowron 8.00 20.00
OGLL Oscar Gamble 4.00 10.00
PBLL Paul Blair 4.00 10.00
RHLL Ralph Houk 4.00 10.00
RJLL Reggie Jackson 6.00 15.00
RMLL Roger Maris 60.00 120.00
THLL Tommy Henrich 4.00 10.00
TJLL Tommy John 4.00 10.00
TKLL Tony Kubek 6.00 15.00
TMLL Thurman Munson 30.00 60.00
WRLL Willie Randolph 4.00 10.00
YBLL Yogi Berra 12.50 30.00

2000 Upper Deck Yankees Legends Legendary Lumber Signature Cut

Randomly inserted into packs, this six card insert features cut-signatures from some of the Yankee's greatest players of all time. Card backs carry a "LC" suffix.

BMLC Billy Martin/1
BRLC Babe Ruth/3
MMLC Mickey Mantle/7
RMLC Roger Maris/9
TMLC Thurman Munson/15

2000 Upper Deck Yankees Legends Legendary Pinstripes

Randomly inserted into packs at one in 144, this 20-card insert set features game-used jersey cards from Yankee greats. Card backs carry a "LP" suffix.

ARLP Allie Reynolds 20.00 50.00
BDLP Bucky Dent 10.00 25.00
BMLP Billy Martin 20.00 50.00
BRLP Bobby Richardson 10.00 25.00
DMLP Don Mattingly 20.00 50.00
DWLP Dave Winfield 6.00 15.00
EHLP Elston Howard 10.00 25.00
GGLP Goose Gossage 6.00 15.00
GMLP Gil McDougald 6.00 15.00
HLLP Hector Lopez 6.00 15.00
JPLP Joe Pepitone 6.00 15.00
LGLP Lou Gehrig Pants 175.00 300.00
MMLP Mickey Mantle 125.00 200.00
PRLP Phil Rizzuto 30.00 60.00

RGLP Ron Guidry 6.00 15.00
RJLP Reggie Jackson 10.00 25.00
RMLP Roger Maris 15.00 40.00
THLP Tommy Henrich 10.00 25.00
TMLP Thurman Munson 30.00 60.00
WFLP Whitey Ford 50.00 100.00

2000 Upper Deck Yankees Legends Legendary Pinstripes Autograph

Randomly inserted into packs at one in 287, this 10-card insert set features autographed game-used jersey cards from Yankee greats. Card backs carry an "A" suffix. Please note that Ron Guidry packed out as exchange card with a deadline to redeem no later than July 18th, 2001.

BDA Bucky Dent 15.00 40.00
DMA Don Mattingly 125.00 200.00
DWA Dave Winfield 30.00 60.00
GGA Goose Gossage 15.00 40.00
GMA Gil McDougald 15.00 40.00
JPA Joe Pepitone 15.00 40.00
PRA Phil Rizzuto 40.00 80.00
RGA Ron Guidry 15.00 40.00
THA Tommy Henrich 15.00 40.00
WFA Whitey Ford 40.00 80.00

2000 Upper Deck Yankees Legends Monument Park

Randomly inserted into packs at one in 23, this six-card insert set features all-time Yankee greats. Card backs carry a "MP" suffix.

COMPLETE SET (6) 10.00 25.00
MP1 Lou Gehrig 2.50 6.00
MP2 Babe Ruth 4.00 10.00
MP3 Mickey Mantle 5.00 12.00
MP4 Joe DiMaggio 2.50 6.00
MP5 Thurman Munson 1.25 3.00
MP6 Elston Howard .75 2.00

2000 Upper Deck Yankees Legends Murderer's Row

Randomly inserted into packs at one in 11, this 10-card insert set features some of the most dominating New York Yankee players of all-time. Card backs carry a "MR" suffix.

COMPLETE SET (10) 8.00 20.00
MR1 Tony Lazzeri .40 1.00
MR2 Babe Ruth 3.00 8.00
MR3 Bob Meusel .40 1.00
MR4 Lou Gehrig 2.00 5.00
MR5 Joe Dugan .40 1.00
MR6 Bill Dickey .60 1.50
MR7 Waite Hoyt .40 1.00
MR8 Red Ruffing .40 1.00
MR9 Earle Combs .40 1.00
MR10 Lefty Gomez .60 1.50

2000 Upper Deck Yankees Legends New Dynasty

Randomly inserted into packs at one in 11, this 10-card insert set features New York greats from the last twenty years. Card backs carry a "ND" suffix.

COMPLETE SET (10) 6.00 15.00
ND1 Reggie Jackson .60 1.50
ND2 Graig Nettles .40 1.00
ND3 Don Mattingly 2.50 6.00
ND4 Goose Gossage .40 1.00
ND5 Dave Winfield .40 1.00
ND6 Chris Chambliss .40 1.00
ND7 Thurman Munson 1.00 2.50
ND8 Willie Randolph .40 1.00
ND9 Ron Guidry .40 1.00
ND10 Bucky Dent .40 1.00

2000 Upper Deck Yankees Legends Pride of the Pinstripes

Randomly inserted into packs at one in 23, this six-card insert set features legendary Yankee greats. Card backs carry a "PP" suffix.

COMPLETE SET (6) 10.00 25.00
PP1 Babe Ruth 4.00 10.00
PP2 Mickey Mantle 5.00 12.00
PP3 Joe DiMaggio 2.50 6.00
PP4 Lou Gehrig 2.50 6.00
PP5 Reggie Jackson .75 2.00
PP6 Yogi Berra 1.25 3.00

2000 Upper Deck Yankees Master Collection

The 2000 Upper Deck Yankees Master Collection was released in early June, 2000. Each box set contains 37 cards. The box set includes a 25-card base set that is individually serial numbered to 500, an 11-card game-used bat set that includes players such a Mickey Mantle, and Babe Ruth, and a one card mystery pack that includes various memorabilia and autographed insert cards. Card backs carry a "NYY" prefix.

COMPLETE SET (25) 250.00 500.00
NYY1 Babe Ruth 23 20.00 50.00
NYY2 Lou Gehrig 27 12.50 30.00
NYY3 Tony Lazzeri 28 4.00 10.00
NYY4 Babe Ruth 32 20.00 50.00
NYY5 Lou Gehrig 36 12.50 30.00
NYY6 Lefty Gomez 37 4.00 10.00
NYY7 Bill Dickey 38 4.00 10.00
NYY8 Bill Dickey 39 4.00 10.00
NYY9 Tommy Henrich 41 4.00 10.00
NYY10 Spud Chandler 43 4.00 10.00
NYY11 T.Henrich 47 4.00 10.00
NYY12 Phil Rizzuto 49 6.00 15.00
NYY13 Whitey Ford 50 4.00 10.00
NYY14 Yogi Berra 51 6.00 15.00
NYY15 Casey Stengel 52 4.00 10.00
NYY16 Billy Martin 53 4.00 10.00
NYY17 Don Larsen 56 4.00 10.00
NYY18 Elston Howard 58 4.00 10.00
NYY19 Roger Maris 61 6.00 15.00
NYY20 Mickey Mantle 62 25.00 60.00
NYY21 Reggie Jackson 77 4.00 10.00
NYY22 Bucky Dent 78 4.00 10.00
NYY23 Derek Jeter 96 12.50 30.00
NYY24 Derek Jeter 98 12.50 30.00
NYY25 Derek Jeter 99 12.50 30.00

2000 Upper Deck Yankees Master Collection All-Time Yankees Game Bats

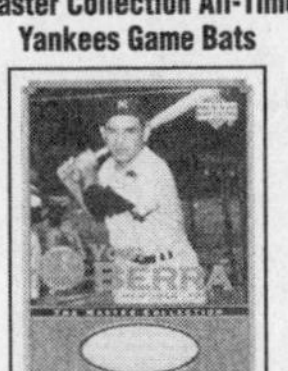

One complete 11-card set of All-Time Yankees Game Bats was inserted into each sealed Yankees Master Collection box. Only 500 sets were produced and each card carries serial-numbering. This 11-card game-used bat card set features some of the greatest New York Yankee players of all time. Card backs carry an "ATY" prefix. Please note that card number eleven of Lou Gehrig is a special commemorative card that does not included a piece of game-used bat.

ATY1 Babe Ruth 75.00 150.00
ATY2 Mickey Mantle 75.00 150.00
ATY3 Reggie Jackson 10.00 25.00
ATY4 Don Mattingly 40.00 80.00
ATY5 Billy Martin 10.00 25.00
ATY6 Graig Nettles 6.00 15.00
ATY7 Derek Jeter 40.00 80.00
ATY8 Yogi Berra 10.00 25.00
ATY9 Thurman Munson 40.00 80.00
ATY10 Whitey Ford 10.00 25.00
ATY11 Lou Gehrig COMM 10.00 25.00

2000 Upper Deck Yankees Master Collection Mystery Pack Inserts

Randomly inserted into each Yankees Master Collection at one per box, this one card mystery pack includes various game-used memorabilia and autographed insert cards.

BM12 Billy Martin Bat-Cut AU/2
BR13 Babe Ruth Bat-Cut AU/3
MM17 Mickey Mantle Bat-Cut AU/7
BRC13 Babe Ruth Cut AU/3
LGC13 Lou Gehrig Cut AU/3
TMC12 Thurman Munson Cut AU/2
DJB Derek Jeter Bat AU/100 250.00 400.00
DJJ Derek Jeter Jsy AU/100 300.00 500.00
RJB Reggie Jackson Bat AU/100 120.00 200.00
WFJ Whitey Ford Bat AU/100 75.00 150.00
YBB Yogi Berra Bat AU/80 120.00 200.00

2003 Upper Deck Yankees Signature

This 90 card set was released in April, 2003. These cards were issued in three card packs with an $30 SRP. These packs came 10 packs to a box and eight boxes to a case. In an interesting note this set is sequenced by the first name of the player.

COMPLETE SET (90) 40.00 100.00
1 Al Downing .40 1.00
2 Al Gettel .40 1.00
3 Art Ditmar .40 1.00
4 Babe Ruth 6.00 15.00
5 Bill Virdon MG .40 1.00
6 Billy Martin 1.25 3.00
7 Bob Cerv .40 1.00
8 Bob Turley .40 1.00
9 Bobby Cox .75 2.00
10 Bobby Richardson .75 2.00
11 Bobby Shantz .40 1.00
12 Bucky Dent .75 2.00
13 Bud Metheny XRC .40 1.00
14 Casey Stengel 1.25 3.00
15 Charlie Hayes .40 1.00
16 Charlie Silvera .40 1.00
17 Chris Chambliss .75 2.00
18 Danny Cater .40 1.00
19 Dave Kingman .75 2.00
20 Dave Righetti .75 2.00
21 Dave Winfield .75 2.00
22 David Cone .75 2.00
23 Dick Tidrow .40 1.00
24 Doc Medich .40 1.00
25 Dock Ellis .75 2.00
26 Don Gullett .75 2.00
27 Don Mattingly 4.00 10.00
28 Dwight Gooden .75 2.00
29 Eddie Robinson .40 1.00
30 Felipe Alou .75 2.00
31 Fred Sanford .40 1.00
32 Fred Stanley .40 1.00
33 Gene Michael .40 1.00
34 Hank Bauer .75 2.00
35 Hector Lopez .40 1.00
36 Horace Clarke .40 1.00
37 Jake Gibbs .40 1.00
38 Jerry Coleman .40 1.00
39 Jerry Lumpe .40 1.00
40 Jim Bouton .75 2.00
41 Jim Kaat .75 2.00
42 Jim Mason .40 1.00
43 Jimmy Key .75 2.00
44 Joe DiMaggio 4.00 10.00
45 Joe Torre 1.25 3.00
46 John Montefusco .75 2.00
47 Johnny Blanchard .40 1.00
48 Johnny Callison .75 2.00
49 Lew Burdette .75 2.00
50 Johnny Kucks .40 1.00
51 Steve Balboni .40 1.00
52 Ken Singleton ANC .75 2.00
53 Lee Mazzilli .75 2.00
54 Lou Gehrig 4.00 10.00
55 Lou Piniella .75 2.00
56 Luis Tiant .75 2.00
57 Marius Russo XRC .40 1.00
58 Mel Stottlemyre .75 2.00
59 Mickey Mantle 6.00 15.00
60 Mike Pagliarulo .40 1.00
61 Mike Torrez .40 1.00
62 Miller Huggins MG .40 1.00
63 Norm Siebern .40 1.00
64 Paul O'Neill 1.25 3.00
65 Phil Niekro .75 2.00
66 Phil Rizzuto 1.25 3.00
67 Ralph Branca .75 2.00
68 Ralph Houk .75 2.00
69 Ralph Terry .75 2.00
70 Randy Gumpert .40 1.00
71 Roger Maris 2.00 5.00
72 Ron Blomberg .40 1.00
73 Ron Guidry .75 2.00
74 Ruben Amaro .40 1.00
75 Ryne Duren .40 1.00
76 Sam McDowell .75 2.00
77 Sparky Lyle .75 2.00
78 Thurman Munson 2.00 5.00
79 Tom Sturdivant .40 1.00
80 Tom Tresh .75 2.00
81 Tommy Byrne .40 1.00
82 Tommy Henrich .75 2.00
83 Tommy John .75 2.00
84 Tony Kubek 1.25 3.00
85 Tony Lazzeri .75 2.00
86 Virgil Trucks .40 1.00
87 Wade Boggs 1.25 3.00
88 Whitey Ford 1.25 3.00
89 Willie Randolph .75 2.00
90 Yogi Berra 2.00 5.00

2003 Upper Deck Yankees Signature Monumental Cuts

Randomly inserted into packs, these 30 combined cards feature autographs of Yankee Legends who have passed on. We have notated the print run next to the player's name in our checklist.

B/WN 1-9 COPIES OF EACH CARD
NO PRICING DUE TO SCARCITY
BM Billy Martin/9
BR Babe Ruth/1
CS Casey Stengel/3
JD Joe DiMaggio/4
LG Lou Gehrig/1
MH Miller Huggins/2
MM Mickey Mantle/1
RM Roger Maris/6
TL Tony Lazzeri/2
TM Thurman Munson/1

2003 Upper Deck Yankees Signature Pinstripe Excellence Autographs

Randomly inserted in packs, these cards feature two autographs on each card. These cards were issued to a stated print run of 125 serial numbered sets.

AA Felipe Alou / Ruben Amaro 20.00 50.00
BA Hank Bauer / Felipe Alou 20.00 50.00
BP Wade Boggs / Mike Pagliarulo 50.00 100.00
BR1 Hank Bauer / Phil Rizzuto 50.00 100.00
BR2 Tommy Byrne / Marius Russo 12.50 30.00
BT Jim Bouton / Ralph Terry 20.00 50.00
CK Chris Chambliss / Dave Kingman 50.00 100.00
DC Bucky Dent / Chris Chambliss 20.00 50.00
DR Bucky Dent / Willie Randolph 50.00 100.00
DS Ryne Duren / Tom Sturdivant 12.50 30.00
FB Whitey Ford / Yogi Berra 125.00 200.00
GB Jake Gibbs / Johnny Blanchard 12.50 30.00
GM Ron Guidry / John Montefusco 50.00 100.00
GR Ron Guidry / Willie Randolph 50.00 100.00
JK Tommy John / Jim Kaat 20.00 50.00
LG Sparky Lyle / Ron Guidry 50.00 100.00
LM Jerry Lumpe / Jim Mason 12.50 30.00
MC John Montefusco / Chris Chambliss 20.00 50.00
MK Gene Michael / Tony Kubek 50.00 100.00
ML Sam McDowell / Sparky Lyle 20.00 50.00
MR Don Mattingly / Dave Righetti 125.00 200.00
NT Phil Niekro / Luis Tiant 50.00 100.00
RB Bobby Richardson / Hank Bauer 50.00 100.00
RC Bobby Richardson / Jerry Coleman 50.00 100.00
SC Ken Singleton / Jerry Coleman 20.00 50.00
ST Tom Sturdivant / Bob Turley 12.50 30.00
TK Luis Tiant / Jim Kaat 20.00 50.00
TM Mike Torrez / Lee Mazzilli 20.00 50.00

2003 Upper Deck Yankees Signature Pride of New York Autographs

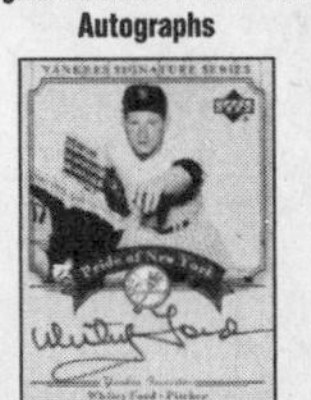

Inserted at a stated rate of one per pack, these 88 cards feature authentic autographs from either retired Yankee players or people associated with the franchise in some way. This set included the first certified autographed sports cards for figures such as Yankee GM Brian Cashman, actors John Goodman and Jason Alexander. Bud Metheny was supposed to sign cards for this product but he passed away before he could sign his cards. In addition, Brian Cashman, Dwight Gooden, John Goodman and Yogi Berra did not return their cards in time for inclusion in this product and we have notated that information with an EXCH in our checklist. Collectors could redeem those cards until March 27th, 2006. David Cone signed some of his cards in time for inclusion and others were available as an exchange card. Upper Deck announced some shorter print runs and we have put that stated print run information next to the player's name in our checklist.

AD Al Downing 4.00 10.00
AG Al Gettel 6.00 15.00
BD Brian Doyle 8.00 20.00
BL Johnny Blanchard 8.00 20.00
BR Bobby Richardson 6.00 15.00
BS Bobby Shantz 4.00 10.00
BT Bob Turley 4.00 10.00
BV Bill Virdon 4.00 10.00
CA1 Johnny Callison 4.00 10.00
CA2 Brian Cashman SP/100 250.00 400.00
CC Chris Chambliss 6.00 15.00
CE Bob Cerv 4.00 10.00
CH Charlie Hayes 4.00 10.00
CO David Cone 8.00 20.00
CS Charlie Silvera 4.00 10.00
CX Bobby Cox 12.50 30.00
DC Danny Cater 4.00 10.00
DE Bucky Dent 10.00 25.00
DG Don Gullett 6.00 15.00
DI Art Ditmar 4.00 10.00
DK Dave Kingman 4.00 10.00
DM Doc Medich 4.00 10.00
DR Dave Righetti 4.00 10.00
DT Dick Tidrow 4.00 10.00
DW Dave Winfield SP/350 15.00 40.00
DZ Don Zimmer 30.00 60.00
EL Dock Ellis 6.00 15.00
ER Eddie Robinson 4.00 10.00
FA Felipe Alou 10.00 25.00
FS Fred Sanford 4.00 10.00
GM Gene Michael 4.00 10.00
GO Dwight Gooden 8.00 20.00
HB Hank Bauer 8.00 20.00
HC Horace Clarke 6.00 15.00
HL Hector Lopez 6.00 15.00
HR Hal Reniff 6.00 15.00
JA Jason Alexander SP/50 600.00 800.00
JB Jim Bouton 6.00 15.00
JC Jerry Coleman 6.00 15.00
JG1 Jake Gibbs 4.00 10.00
JG2 John Goodman SP/100 250.00 400.00
JK Jim Kaat 4.00 10.00
JL Jerry Lumpe 10.00 25.00
JM Jim Mason 4.00 10.00
JT Joe Torre 20.00 50.00
JW Jim Wynn 6.00 15.00
KE Jimmy Key 8.00 20.00
KS Ken Singleton 4.00 10.00
KU Johnny Kucks 6.00 15.00
LB Lew Burdette 6.00 15.00
LM Lee Mazzilli 6.00 15.00
LP Lou Piniella SP/542 6.00 15.00
LT Luis Tiant 6.00 15.00
MA Don Mattingly 50.00 100.00
MO John Montefusco 4.00 10.00
MP Mike Pagliarulo 4.00 10.00
MR Marius Russo 10.00 25.00
MS Mel Stottlemyre 8.00 20.00
MT Mike Torrez 8.00 20.00
NS Norm Siebern 6.00 15.00
PN Phil Niekro 20.00 50.00
PO Paul O'Neill SP/500 12.50 30.00
PR Phil Rizzuto 30.00 60.00
RA Ruben Amaro 8.00 20.00
RB1 Ron Blomberg 4.00 10.00
RB2 Ralph Branca 20.00 50.00
RD Ryne Duren 10.00 25.00
RG1 Ron Guidry 6.00 15.00
RG2 Randy Gumpert 4.00 10.00
RH Ralph Houk 8.00 20.00
RT Ralph Terry 6.00 15.00
SB Steve Balboni 6.00 15.00
SL Sparky Lyle 8.00 20.00
SM Sam McDowell 4.00 10.00
ST Fred Stanley 4.00 10.00
TB Tommy Byrne 6.00 15.00
TC Tom Carroll 6.00 15.00
TH Tommy Henrich 15.00 40.00
TJ Tommy John 6.00 15.00
TK Tony Kubek 40.00 80.00
TS Tom Sturdivant 10.00 25.00
TT Tom Tresh 10.00 25.00
VT Virgil Trucks 10.00 25.00
WB Wade Boggs 20.00 50.00
WF Whitey Ford 30.00 60.00
WR Willie Randolph SP/283 10.00 25.00
YB Yogi Berra 40.00 80.00

2003 Upper Deck Yankees Signature Forever Autographs

Randomly inserted in packs, these cards feature three Yankee players (usually with something in common) all signing the same card. These cards were issued to a stated print run of 50 serial numbered sets. The following cards were issued as exchange cards of which could be redeemed until March 27th, 2006: GCK, GRJ, MTT, TCO, WMG, WPC.

STATED PRINT RUN 50 SERIAL #'d SETS
ALB Felipe Alou / Hector Lopez / Hank Bauer 90.00 150.00
AOM Felipe Alou / Paul O'Neill / Lee Mazzilli 125.00 200.00
BSB Yogi Berra / Bobby Shantz / Hank Bauer 150.00 250.00
DFB Al Downing / Whitey Ford / Yogi Berra 175.00 300.00
DRC Bucky Dent / Willie Randolph / Chris Chambliss 90.00 150.00
EMG Dock Ellis / Doc Medich / Don Gullett 90.00 150.00
FKB Whitey Ford / Johnny Kucks / Jim Bouton 125.00 200.00
GCK Dwight Gooden / David Cone / Jimmy Key 125.00 200.00
GRJ Ron Guidry / Dave Righetti / Tommy John 125.00 200.00
HMC Ralph Houk / Gene Michael / Bobby Cox 90.00 150.00
HRB Tommy Henrich / Phil Rizzuto / Ralph Branca 125.00 200.00
JKL Tommy John / Jim Kaat / Sparky Lyle 90.00 150.00
KCC Dave Kingman / Chris Chambliss / Danny Cater 90.00 150.00
KGT Jim Kaat / Don Gullet / Mike Torrez 90.00 150.00
KJB Jim Kaat / Tommy John / Jim Bouton 90.00 150.00
MTT John Montefusco / Mike Torrez / Dick Tidrow 90.00 150.00
OBK Paul O'Neill / Wade Boggs / Jimmy Key 125.00 200.00
PTV Lou Piniella / Joe Torre / Bill Virdon 125.00 200.00
RBC Phil Rizzuto / Yogi Berra / Jerry Coleman 175.00 300.00
RKD Phil Rizzuto / Tony Kubek / Bucky Dent 125.00 200.00
RRC Bobby Richardson / Willie Randolph / Jerry Coleman 125.00 200.00
RSB Marius Russo / Tom Sturdivant / Tommy Byrne 90.00 150.00
SSB Fred Stanley / Charlie Silvera / Johnny Blanchard 90.00 150.00
STE Mel Stottlemyre / Luis Tiant / Dock Ellis 90.00 150.00
TCO Joe Torre / David Cone / Paul O'Neill 125.00 200.00
TLN Luis Tiant / Sparky Lyle / Phil Niekro 90.00 150.00
TMT Luis Tiant / Sam McDowell / Ralph Terry 90.00 150.00
WHM Dave Winfield / Tommy Henrich / Lee Mazzilli 125.00 200.00
WMG Dave Winfield / Don Mattingly / Ron Guidry 175.00 300.00
WPC Dave Winfield / Lou Piniella / Chris Chambliss 90.00 150.00

Beckett BASEBALL MINOR LEAGUE

2011 ITG Heroes and Prospects Full Body Autographs Silver

Card	Low	High
COMMON CARD	3.00	8.00
OVERALL AU/MEM ODDS 5 PER BOX		
ANNOUNCED PRINT RUN OF 390 SETS		
GOLD ANNCD PRINT RUN OF 10 SETS		
NO GOLD PRICING AVAILABLE		
AM Addison Maruszak S2	3.00	8.00
AR Anthony Ranaudo	6.00	15.00
AS Adrian Salcedo	4.00	10.00
AW Adam Warren	6.00	15.00
BB Brandon Belt	10.00	25.00
BJ Brett Jackson	3.00	8.00
CA Chris Archer	5.00	12.00
CC Christian Colon	3.00	8.00
CG Cam Greathouse	4.00	10.00
CP Cesar Puello S2	3.00	8.00
CS Chris Sale	3.00	8.00
DB Dellin Betances	6.00	15.00
DC Drew Cisco	3.00	8.00
DD Delino DeShields S2	4.00	10.00
DM Deck McGuire	6.00	15.00
DP Drew Pomeranz	6.00	15.00
EA Ehire Adrianza	3.00	8.00
EM Ethan Martin	3.00	8.00
ES Elvis Sanchez S2	3.00	8.00
FP Francisco Peguero	4.00	10.00
GG Garrett Gould S2	3.00	8.00
GS Graham Stoneburner	3.00	8.00
HM Hunter Morris	4.00	10.00
JB Jesse Biddle	3.00	8.00
JP Jarrett Parker	3.00	8.00
JS Jake Skole	3.00	8.00
JT Jameson Taillon	6.00	15.00
KC Kaleb Cowart S2	3.00	8.00
KD Kyle Drabek	3.00	8.00
KP Kyle Parker S2	5.00	12.00
KV Kolbrin Vitek	3.00	8.00
KW Keenyn Walker S2	3.00	8.00
LW LeVon Washington S2	5.00	12.00
MB Manny Banuelos S2	12.50	30.00
MC Michael Choice S2	3.00	8.00
MG Mychal Givens	3.00	8.00
MH Matt Harvey S2	4.00	10.00
MK Max Kepler	5.00	12.00
MM Matt Moore	20.00	50.00
MP Martin Perez	8.00	20.00
MT Mike Trout SP	15.00	40.00
PG Paul Goldschmidt	8.00	20.00
PV Philippe Valiquette S2	3.00	8.00
RD Randall Delgado	8.00	20.00
RG Randal Grichuk S2	3.00	8.00
RL Rymer Liriano	4.00	10.00
SA Steven Ames	3.00	8.00
SB Seth Blair S2	3.00	8.00
SC Sean Coyle	3.00	8.00
TB Tim Beckham SP	6.00	15.00
TL Ty Linton	3.00	8.00
TM Tyler Matzek	3.00	8.00
TN Thomas Neal	3.00	8.00
TR Trevor Reckling	3.00	8.00
TW Tony Wolters S2	3.00	8.00
WM Will Middlebrooks	4.00	10.00
YA Yonder Alonso	5.00	12.00
YG Yasmani Grandal S2	4.00	10.00
YR Yorman Rodriguez S2	3.00	8.00
ZC Zack Cox	6.00	15.00
ZW Zack Wheeler S2	5.00	12.00
BBO Bobby Borchering	5.00	12.00
BBR Bryce Brentz	6.00	15.00
CCU Cito Culver S2	6.00	15.00
CSP Cory Spangenberg S2	6.00	15.00
DCE Darrell Ceciliani	3.00	8.00
DME Devin Mesoraco	5.00	12.00
GSA Gary Sanchez	4.00	10.00
JHA Jake Hager S2	3.00	8.00
JPE Jace Peterson S2	3.00	8.00
JRM J.R. Murphy	4.00	10.00
JSA Josh Sale S2	5.00	12.00
JTE Julio Teheran S2	6.00	15.00
KWO Kolten Wong S2	6.00	15.00
MMA Manny Machado S2	10.00	25.00
MME Melky Mesa	3.00	8.00
TRO Trayvon Robinson S2	8.00	20.00
WMY Wil Myers	5.00	12.00
JHAR James Harris S2	3.00	8.00

2011 ITG Heroes and Prospects Close Up Autographs Silver

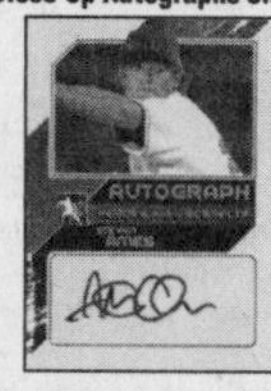

*CLOSE SILVER: .4X TO 1X FULL SILVER
OVERALL AU/MEM ODDS 5 PER BOX
ANNOUNCED PRINT RUN OF 190 SETS
GOLD ANNCD PRINT RUN OF 10 SETS
NO GOLD PRICING AVAILABLE

2011 ITG Heroes and Prospects Affiliation Autographs Silver

OVERALL AU/MEM ODDS 5 PER BOX
ANNOUNCED PRINT RUN OF 19 SETS
NO PRICING DUE TO SCARCITY
GOLD ANNCD PRINT RUN OF 1 SET
NO GOLD PRICING AVAILABLE

2011 ITG Heroes and Prospects Between the Seams Autographs Red

Card	Low	High
OVERALL AU/MEM ODDS 5 PER BOX		
ANNOUNCED PRINT RUN OF 30 SETS		
GOLD ANNCD PRINT RUN OF 19 SETS		
NO GOLD PRICING AVAILABLE		
WHITE ANNCD PRINT RUN 1 SET		
NO WHITE PRICING AVAILABLE		
AM Addison Maruszak S2		
AR Anthony Ranaudo		
AS Adrian Salcedo		
AW Adam Warren	12.50	30.00
BB Brandon Belt	12.50	30.00
BJ Brett Jackson		
CA Chris Archer	8.00	20.00
CC Christian Colon	8.00	20.00
CG Cam Greathouse		
CP Cesar Puello S2		
CS Chris Sale	20.00	50.00
DB Dellin Betances	15.00	40.00
DC Drew Cisco	4.00	10.00
DC Darrell Ceciliani		
DD Delino DeShields S2	6.00	15.00
DM Deck McGuire	8.00	20.00
DP Drew Pomeranz	15.00	40.00
EA Ehire Adrianza	6.00	15.00
EM Ethan Martin	6.00	15.00
ES Elvis Sanchez S2		
FP Francisco Peguero	4.00	10.00
GG Garrett Gould S2	8.00	20.00
GS Gary Sanchez	20.00	50.00
HM Hunter Morris	10.00	25.00
JB Jesse Biddle	8.00	20.00
JP Jarrett Parker	4.00	10.00
JS Jake Skole		
JT Jameson Taillon	10.00	25.00
KB Kolbrin Vitek	20.00	
KC Kaleb Cowart S2	4.00	10.00
KD Kyle Drabek	8.00	210.00
KP Kyle Parker S2	6.00	15.00
KW Keenyn Walker S2	4.00	10.00
LW LeVon Washington S2	6.00	15.00
MB Manny Banuelos S2		
MC Michael Choice S2	12.50	30.00
MG Mychal Givens		
MH Matt Harvey S2	6.00	15.00
MK Max Kepler		
MM Matt Moore	15.00	40.00
MP Martin Perez	8.00	20.00
MT Mike Trout	50.00	100.00
PG Paul Goldschmidt	30.00	60.00
PV Philippe Valiquette S2		
RD Randall Delgado	12.50	30.00
RG Randal Grichuk S2		
RL Rymer Liriano		
SA Steven Ames	8.00	20.00
SB Seth Blair S2		
SC Sean Coyle	4.00	10.00
TB Tim Beckham	20.00	50.00
TL Ty Linton		
TM Tyler Matzek		
TN Thomas Neal	10.00	25.00
TR Trevor Reckling		
TW Tony Wolters S2		
WM Wil Myers	15.00	40.00
YA Yonder Alonso	12.50	30.00
YG Yasmani Grandal S2		
YR Yorman Rodriguez S2		
ZC Zack Cox	20.00	50.00
ZW Zach Wheeler S2		
BBO Bobby Borchering	12.50	30.00
BBR Bryce Brentz		
CCU Cito Culver S2		
CSP Cory Spangenberg S2		
DME Devin Mesoraco		
GST Graham Stoneburner	10.00	25.00
JHA Jake Hager S2	6.00	15.00
JPE Jace Peterson S2		
JRM J.R. Murphy	12.50	30.00
JSL Josh Sale S2		
JTE Julio Teheran S2	12.50	30.00
KWO Kolten Wong S2	12.50	30.00
MMA Manny Machado S2		
MME Melky Mesa	6.00	15.00
TRO Trayvon Robinson S2		
WMI Will Middlebrooks	8.00	20.00
JHAR James Harris S2		

2011 ITG Heroes and Prospects Country of Origin Autographs Silver

Card	Low	High
OVERALL AU/MEM ODDS 5 PER BOX		
ANNOUNCED PRINT RUN OF 40 SETS		
GOLD ANNCD PRINT RUN OF 10 SETS		
NO GOLD PRICING AVAILABLE		
AM Addison Maruszak S2		
AR Anthony Ranaudo	30.00	60.00
AS Adrian Salcedo	4.00	10.00
AW Adam Warren	10.00	25.00
BB Bobby Borchering	10.00	25.00
BJ Brett Jackson	8.00	20.00
CA Chris Archer		
CC Christian Colon	4.00	10.00
CG Cam Greathouse	4.00	10.00
CP Cesar Puello S2		
CS Chris Sale	4.00	10.00
DB Dellin Betances	12.50	30.00
DC Darrell Ceciliani	8.00	20.00
DD Delino DeShields S2		
DM Deck McGuire	12.50	30.00
DP Drew Pomeranz	10.00	25.00
EA Ehire Adrianza	8.00	20.00
EM Ethan Martin	4.00	10.00
ES Elvis Sanchez S2	4.00	10.00
FP Francisco Peguero	4.00	10.00
GG Garrett Gould S2		
GS Gary Sanchez	12.50	30.00
HM Hunter Morris	8.00	20.00
JB Jesse Biddle	4.00	10.00
JP Jarrett Parker	4.00	10.00
JS Jake Skole		
JT Jameson Taillon	12.50	30.00
KC Kaleb Cowart S2		
KP Kyle Parker S2	6.00	15.00
KV Kolbrin Vitek	12.50	30.00
KW Keenyn Walker S2		
LW LeVon Washington S2		
MB Manny Banuelos S2	10.00	25.00
MC Michael Choice S2		
MG Mychal Givens	4.00	10.00
MH Matt Harvey S2	6.00	15.00
MK Max Kepler		
MP Martin Perez	4.00	10.00
MT Mike Trout	20.00	50.00
PG Paul Goldschmidt	20.00	50.00
PV Philippe Valiquette S2	15.00	40.00
RC Randal Grichuk S2		
RD Randall Delgado	8.00	20.00
RL Rymer Liriano		
SA Steven Ames		
SB Seth Blair S2		
SC Sean Coyle		
TB Tim Beckham	4.00	10.00
TL Ty Linton	4.00	10.00
TM Tyler Matzek	4.00	10.00
TN Thomas Neal	4.00	10.00
TR Trevor Reckling	4.00	10.00
TW Tony Wolters S2		
WM Wil Myers	20.00	50.00
YA Yonder Alonso	6.00	15.00
YG Yasmani Grandal S2	4.00	10.00
YR Yorman Rodriguez S2		
ZC Zack Cox	20.00	50.00
ZW Zach Wheeler S2		
BBE Brandon Belt	12.50	30.00
BBR Bryce Brentz	10.00	25.00
CCU Cito Culver S2	8.00	20.00
CSP Cory Spangenberg S2		
DCI Drew Cisco		
DME Devin Mesoraco	4.00	10.00
GST Graham Stoneburner	10.00	25.00
JHA Jake Hager S2	4.00	10.00
JPE Jace Peterson S2		
JRM J.R. Murphy	8.00	20.00
JSA Josh Sale S2	20.00	50.00
JTE Julio Teheran S2	6.00	15.00
KDR Kyle Drabek	6.00	15.00
KWO Kolten Wong S2	10.00	25.00
MMA Manny Machado S2		
MME Melky Mesa	6.00	15.00
MMO Matt Moore	40.00	80.00
TRO Trayvon Robinson S2	10.00	25.00
WMI Will Middlebrooks	4.00	10.00
JHAR James Harris S2		

2011 ITG Heroes and Prospects Draft Year Autographs Silver

Card	Low	High
OVERALL AU/MEM ODDS 5 PER BOX		
ANNOUNCED PRINT RUN OF 39 SETS		
GOLD ANNCD PRINT RUN OF 1 SET		
NO GOLD PRICING AVAILABLE		
AM Addison Maruszak S2		
AR Anthony Ranaudo	20.00	50.00
AW Adam Warren	4.00	10.00
BB Brandon Belt	12.50	30.00
BJ Brett Jackson	4.00	10.00
CA Chris Archer	6.00	15.00
CC Christian Colon		
CG Cam Greathouse	4.00	10.00
CS Chris Sale	4.00	10.00
DB Dellin Betances	10.00	25.00
DC Drew Cisco	4.00	10.00
DC Darrell Ceciliani	4.00	10.00
DD Delino DeShields S2	4.00	10.00
DM Deck McGuire		
DP Drew Pomeranz	4.00	10.00
EM Ethan Martin	4.00	10.00
GG Garrett Gould S2		
HM Hunter Morris	4.00	10.00
JB Jesse Biddle		
JK Jake Skole	4.00	10.00
JP Jarrett Parker	4.00	10.00
JT Jameson Taillon	10.00	25.00
KB Kolbrin Vitek	6.00	15.00
KC Kaleb Cowart S2	4.00	10.00
KD Kyle Drabek	15.00	40.00
KP Kyle Parker S2		
KW Keenyn Walker S2		
LW LeVon Washington S2		
MC Michael Choice S2	6.00	15.00
MG Mychal Givens	6.00	15.00
MH Matt Harvey S2	6.00	15.00
MM Matt Moore	40.00	80.00
MT Mike Trout	12.50	30.00
PG Paul Goldschmidt	15.00	40.00
PV Philippe Valiquette S2		
RG Randal Grichuk S2		
SA Steven Ames		
SB Seth Blair S2		
SC Sean Coyle	4.00	10.00
TB Tim Beckham		
TL Ty Linton		
TM Tyler Matzek		
TR Trevor Reckling	4.00	10.00
TW Tony Wolters S2		
WM Wil Myers	4.00	10.00
YA Yonder Alonso	4.00	10.00
YG Yasmani Grandal S2		
ZC Zack Cox	20.00	50.00
ZW Zach Wheeler S2	4.00	10.00
BBO Bobby Borchering	20.00	50.00
BBR Bryce Brentz	4.00	10.00
CCU Cito Culver S2	12.50	30.00
CSP Cory Spangenberg S2		
DME Devin Mesoraco	4.00	10.00
GST Graham Stoneburner		
JHA Jake Hager S2		
JPE Jace Peterson S2		
JRM J.R. Murphy	4.00	10.00
JSL Josh Sale S2		
KWO Kolten Wong S2	10.00	25.00
MMA Manny Machado S2		
TRO Trayvon Robinson S2		
WMI Will Middlebrooks	8.00	20.00
JHAR James Harris S2		

2011 ITG Heroes and Prospects Father and Son Autographs Silver

Card	Low	High
OVERALL AU/MEM ODDS 5 PER BOX		
ANNOUNCED PRINT RUN OF 49 SETS		
GOLD ANNCD PRINT RUN OF 1 SET		
NO GOLD PRICING AVAILABLE		
DDDD Delino DeShields / Delino DeShields Jr S2		
DDKD Doug Drabek / Kyle Drabek	10.00	25.00

2011 ITG Heroes and Prospects First Pitch

OVERALL AU/MEM ODDS 5 PER BOX
ANNOUNCED PRINT RUN OF 1 SET
NO PRICING DUE TO SCARCITY

2011 ITG Heroes and Prospects First Round Picks Autographs Silver

OVERALL AU/MEM ODDS 5 PER BOX
ANNOUNCED PRINT RUN OF 14 SETS
NO PRICING DUE TO SCARCITY
GOLD ANNCD PRINT RUN OF 1 SET
NO GOLD PRICING AVAILABLE

2011 ITG Heroes and Prospects Grand Slam Autographs

OVERALL AU/MEM ODDS 5 PER BOX
ANNOUNCED PRINT RUN OF 1 SET
NO PRICING DUE TO SCARCITY

2011 ITG Heroes and Prospects Hard Cuts Autographs Silver

OVERALL AU/MEM ODDS 5 PER BOX
ANNOUNCED PRINT RUN OF 24 SETS
NO PRICING DUE TO SCARCITY
GOLD ANNCD PRINT RUN OF 1 SET
NO GOLD PRICING AVAILABLE

2011 ITG Heroes and Prospects Heroes And Prospects Dual Autographs Silver

OVERALL AU/MEM ODDS 5 PER BOX
ANNOUNCED PRINT RUN OF 9 SETS
NO PRICING DUE TO SCARCITY
GOLD ANNCD PRINT RUN OF 1 SET
NO GOLD PRICING AVAILABLE

2011 ITG Heroes and Prospects Heroes And Prospects Dual Jerseys Silver

Card	Low	High
OVERALL AU/MEM ODDS 5 PER BOX		
SER.2 ANNCD PRINT RUN OF 49 SETS		
ANNOUNCED PRINT RUN OF 60 SETS		
GOLD ANNCD PRINT RUN OF 1 SET		
NO GOLD PRICING AVAILABLE		
1 Wade Boggs / Kolbrin Vitek	10.00	25.00
2 Johnny Bench / Yonder Alonso	6.00	15.00
3 Cal Ripken Jr. / Christian Colon	12.50	30.00
4 Don Mattingly / Melky Mesa	10.00	25.00
5 Larry Walker / Bryce Brentz	8.00	20.00
6 Mark McGwire / Deck McGuire	10.00	25.00
7 Carlton Fisk / Anthony Ranaudo	5.00	12.00
8 Don Mattingly / Adam Warren	8.00	20.00
9 Nolan Ryan / Adrian Salcedo	12.50	30.00
10 Nolan Ryan / Randall Delgado	10.00	25.00
11 Roberto Alomar / Cesar Puello S2	30.00	60.00
12 Reggie Jackson / Addison Maruszak S2		
13 Steve Garvey / Trayvon Robinson S2	5.00	12.00
14 Ryne Sandberg / Cam Greathouse S2		
15 Nolan Ryan / Delino DeShields S2	15.00	40.00
16 Roberto Alomar / Elvis Sanchez S2		
17 Nolan Ryan / Jordan Akins S2	15.00	40.00
18 Johnny Bench / Philippe Valiquette S2		

2011 ITG Heroes and Prospects Heroes Autographs

Card	Low	High
OVERALL AU/MEM ODDS 5 PER BOX		
ANNOUNCED PRINT RUN OF 80 SETS		
AD Andre Dawson	10.00	25.00
BB Bert Blyleven S2	15.00	40.00
BG Bob Gibson	15.00	40.00
NR Nolan Ryan	60.00	120.00
DM Don Mattingly	30.00	60.00
DP Dave Parker	10.00	25.00
DW Dave Winfield S2	15.00	40.00
FJ Ferguson Jenkins	8.00	20.00
JB Johnny Bench	20.00	50.00
LB Lou Brock	15.00	40.00
LP Lou Piniella S2		
RJ Reggie Jackson S2		
RS Ryne Sandberg	50.00	100.00
TR Tim Raines	12.50	30.00
WB Wade Boggs	20.00	50.00
WF Whitey Ford	20.00	50.00
CF2 Carlton Fisk S2		
SG2 Steve Garvey S2	10.00	25.00
SMU Stan Musial S2		
TS2 Tom Seaver S2	10.00	25.00

2011 ITG Heroes and Prospects Heroes Between the Seams Autographs

OVERALL AU/MEM ODDS 5 PER BOX
ANNOUNCED PRINT RUN OF 1 SET
NO PRICING DUE TO SCARCITY

2011 ITG Heroes and Prospects Heroes Jerseys Silver

Card	Low	High
OVERALL AU/MEM ODDS 5 PER BOX		
ANNOUNCED PRINT RUN OF 160 SETS		
SER.2 ANNCD PRINT RUN OF 150 SETS		
GOLD ANNCD PRINT RUN OF 1 SET		
NO GOLD PRICING AVAILABLE		
1 Lou Brock	4.00	10.00
2 Cal Ripken Jr.	8.00	20.00
3 Tim Raines	4.00	10.00
4 Larry Walker	4.00	10.00
5 Ryne Sandberg	12.50	30.00
6 Don Mattingly	6.00	15.00
7 Tony Gwynn	5.00	12.00
8 Carlton Fisk	4.00	10.00
9 Wade Boggs	6.00	15.00
10 Nolan Ryan	10.00	25.00
11 Steve Carlton	4.00	10.00
12 Johnny Bench	6.00	15.00
13 Andre Dawson	6.00	15.00
14 Dave Parker	4.00	10.00
15 Mark McGwire	10.00	25.00
16 Steve Garvey	4.00	10.00
17 Dave Winfield S2	6.00	15.00
18 Reggie Jackson S2	5.00	12.00
19 Bert Blyleven S2	10.00	25.00
20 Stan Musial S2	10.00	25.00
21 Carlton Fisk S2		
22 Lou Piniella S2	4.00	10.00
23 Ken Griffey Jr. S2	8.00	20.00
24 Eddie Murray S2	6.00	15.00
25 Rod Carew S2	6.00	15.00
26 Rickey Henderson S2	12.50	30.00

2011 ITG Heroes and Prospects Lumbergraphs Autographs

Card	Low	High
OVERALL AU/MEM ODDS 5 PER BOX		
ANNOUNCED PRINT RUN OF 100 SETS		
AM Addison Maruszak S2	4.00	10.00
AR Anthony Ranaudo	20.00	50.00
AS Adrian Salcedo	4.00	10.00
AW Adam Warren	6.00	15.00
BB Brandon Belt	20.00	50.00
BJ Brett Jackson	4.00	10.00
CA Chris Archer	4.00	10.00
CC Christian Colon	8.00	20.00
CG Cam Greathouse		
CP Cesar Puello S2	4.00	10.00
CS Chris Sale	8.00	20.00
DB Dellin Betances	10.00	25.00
DC Drew Cisco	4.00	10.00
DC Darrell Ceciliani	4.00	10.00
DD Delino DeShields S2		
DM Deck McGuire	6.00	15.00
DP Drew Pomeranz	10.00	25.00
EA Ehire Adrianza	4.00	10.00
EM Ethan Martin	4.00	10.00
ES Elvis Sanchez S2	4.00	10.00
FP Francisco Peguero	4.00	10.00
GG Garrett Gould S2		
GS Gary Sanchez	12.50	30.00
HM Hunter Morris	10.00	25.00
JB Jesse Biddle	5.00	12.00
JK Jake Skole	8.00	20.00
JP Jarrett Parker	6.00	15.00
JT Jameson Taillon	5.00	12.00
KB Kolbrin Vitek	10.00	25.00

KC Kaleb Cowart S2
KD Kyle Drabek 4.00 10.00
KP Kyle Parker S2 5.00 12.00
KW Keenyn Walker S2
LW LeVon Washington S2 4.00 10.00
MB Manny Banuelos S2 10.00 25.00
MC Michael Choice S2 4.00 10.00
MG Mychal Givens 4.00 10.00
MH Matt Harvey S2 5.00 12.00
MK Max Kepler 6.00 15.00
MM Matt Moore 12.50 30.00
MP Martin Perez 4.00 10.00
MT Mike Trout 30.00 60.00
PG Paul Goldschmidt 20.00 50.00
PV Philippe Valiquette S2 8.00 20.00
RC Randal Grichuk S2
RD Randall Delgado 5.00 12.00
RL Rymer Liriano 4.00 10.00
SA Steven Ames 4.00 10.00
SB Seth Blair S2 4.00 10.00
SC Sean Coyle 8.00 20.00
TB Tim Beckham 12.50 30.00
TL Ty Linton 4.00 10.00
TM Tyler Matzek 8.00 20.00
TN Thomas Neal 5.00 12.00
TR Trevor Reckling 4.00 10.00
TW Tony Wolters S2
WM Wil Myers 12.50 30.00
YA Yonder Alonso 4.00 10.00
YG Yasmani Grandal S2 5.00 12.00
YR Yorman Rodriguez S2 4.00 10.00
ZC Zack Cox 4.00 10.00
ZW Zach Wheeler S2 4.00 10.00
BBO Bobby Borchering 6.00 15.00
BBR Bryce Brentz 10.00 25.00
CCU Cito Culver S2 5.00 12.00
CSP Cory Spangenberg S2
DME Devin Mesoraco 6.00 15.00
GST Graham Stoneburner 8.00 20.00
JHA Jake Hager S2 8.00 20.00
JPE Jace Peterson S2 8.00 20.00
JRM J.R. Murphy 8.00 20.00
JSA Josh Sale S2 5.00 12.00
JTE Julio Teheran S2 8.00 20.00
KWO Kolten Wong S2 5.00 12.00
MMA Manny Machado S2 12.50 30.00
MME Melky Mesa 8.00 20.00
TRO Trayvon Robinson S2
WMI Will Middlebrooks 6.00 15.00
JHAR James Harris S2

2011 ITG Heroes and Prospects Prospect Jerseys Silver

OVERALL AU/MEM ODDS 5 PER BOX
ANNOUNCED PRINT RUN OF 49 SETS
GOLD ANNCD PRINT RUN OF 1 SET
NO GOLD PRICING AVAILABLE
1 Bryce Brentz 5.00 12.00
2 Adam Warren 4.00 10.00
3 Anthony Ranaudo 10.00 25.00
4 Yonder Alonso 4.00 10.00
5 Adrian Salcedo 4.00 10.00
6 Randall Delgado 4.00 10.00
7 Melky Mesa 8.00 20.00
8 Kolbrin Vitek 4.00 10.00
9 Christian Colon 8.00 20.00
10 Deck McGuire 10.00 25.00
11 Addison Maruszak
12 Cesar Puello
15 Philippe Valiquette
16 Trayvon Robinson
17 Zach Wheeler 5.00 12.00
22 Elvis Sanchez 4.00 10.00

2006 Just Autographs

COMPLETE SET (70) 12.00 20.00
COMMON (1-70) .10 .25
STATED PRINT RUN 4,500 SETS
GLOSSY PRINT RUN 1 SET PER COLOR
GLOSSY BLACK-GOLD-SILV-WHITE ISSUED
NO GLOSSY PRICING DUE TO SCARCITY
PLATES PRINT RUN 1 SET PER COLOR
BLACK-CYAN-MAGENTA-YELLOW ISSUED
NO PLATES PRICING DUE TO SCARCITY
1 Trevor Bell .10 .25
2 Jeff Bianchi .15 .40
3 Mike Billek .10 .25
4 James Boone .10 .25
5 Clay Buchholz .60 1.50
6 Travis Buck .10 .25
7 Brad Corley .10 .25
8 Mike Costanzo .15 .40
9 Ryan DeLaughter .10 .25
10 Ian Desmond .15 .40
11 Joe Dickerson .10 .25
12 John Drennen .10 .25
13 Brian Duensing .15 .40
14 Jacoby Ellsbury .30 .75
15 Brandon Erbe .15 .40
16 Josh Flores .10 .25
17 Ernesto Frieri .10 .25
18 Armando Galarraga .15 .40
19 Brett Gardner .25 .60
20 Matt Garza .10 .25
21 Alex Gordon .30 .75
22 Grant Hansen .10 .25
23 Brad Harman .15 .40
24 Brett Hayes .10 .25
25 Ralph Henriquez .10 .25
26 Tyler Herron .10 .25
27 Kenny Holmberg .10 .25
28 Chia-An Huang .10 .25
29 Will Inman .15 .40
30 Craig Italiano .10 .25
31 Josh Johnson .10 .25
32 Beau Jones .10 .25
33 Paul Kelly .10 .25
34 Jared Lansford .10 .25
35 Jed Lowrie .25 .60
36 Matt Maloney .10 .25
37 Jacob Marceaux .10 .25
38 Nick Markakis .25 .60
39 Chris Mason .15 .40
40 Cameron Maybin .30 .75
41 Tommy Mendoza .10 .25
42 Tim Moss .10 .25
43 Eduardo Nunez .15 .40
44 Mark Pawelek .10 .25
45 Lance Pendleton .10 .25
46 P.J. Phillips .10 .25
47 Manuel Pina .10 .25
48 Max Ramirez .15 .40
49 J.T. Restko .10 .25
50 Rafael Rodriguez .10 .25
51 Jarrod Saltalamacchia .10 .25
52 Erick San Pedro .10 .25
53 Henry Sanchez .10 .25
54 Jonathan Sanchez .25 .60
55 Jordan Schafer .25 .60
56 Sharlon Schoop .10 .25
57 Jose Tabata .60 1.50
58 Clete Thomas .10 .25
59 Ryan Tucker .15 .40
60 Justin Upton .75 2.00
61 Chris Volstad .10 .25
62 Josh Wall .10 .25
63 Nick Webber .10 .25
64 Nick Weglarz .10 .25
65 Jared Wells .10 .25
66 Kevin Whelan .15 .40
67 Johnny Whittleman .10 .25
68 Josh Wilson .10 .25
69 Brandon Wood .10 .25
70 Ryan Zimmerman .50 1.25

2006 Just Autographs Black

*BLACK: 3X TO 8X BASIC
STATED ODDS 1:12 FOIL PACKS
STATED PRINT RUN 50 SERIAL #'d SETS

2006 Just Autographs Gold

*GOLD: 2X TO 5X BASIC
DISTRIBUTED IN FACTORY SET FORM
STATED PRINT RUN 100 SERIAL #'d SETS

2006 Just Autographs Silver

*SILVER: 1.2X TO 3X BASIC
STATED ODDS 1:3
STATED PRINT RUN 200 SERIAL #'d SETS

2006 Just Autographs Dual Signatures

OVERALL 2X-3X AU ODDS 1:144 PACKS
STATED PRINT RUN 2 SERIAL #'d SETS
NO PRICING DUE TO SCARCITY

2006 Just Autographs Signatures

ONE BASIC OR SILVER AU PER PACK
ALSO ISSUED DIRECTLY FROM JMI
PRINT RUNS B/WN 50-775 COPIES PER
CARDS ARE NOT SERIAL-NUMBERED
PRINT RUNS REFER TO FOIL PACK DIST.
ADDITIONAL QTY AVAIL. FOR ONLINE SALES
PRINT RUN INFO PROVIDED BY JMI
1 Trevor Bell/775 * 2.50 6.00
2 Jeff Bianchi/350 * 3.00 8.00
4 James Boone/775 * 2.50 6.00
6 Travis Buck/350 * 3.00 8.00
7 Brad Corley/775 * 2.50 6.00
8 Mike Costanzo/725 * 3.00 8.00
12 John Drennen/775 * 3.00 8.00
13 Brian Duensing/775 * 2.50 6.00
15 Brandon Erbe/350 * 3.00 8.00
20 Matt Garza/725 * 3.00 8.00
21 Alex Gordon/50 * 8.00 20.00
24 Brett Hayes/775 * 2.50 6.00
25 Ralph Henriquez/775 * 2.50 6.00
26 Tyler Herron/775 * 2.50 6.00
29 Will Inman/725 * 3.00 8.00
30 Craig Italiano/350 * 3.00 8.00
31 Josh Johnson/650 * 2.50 6.00
33 Paul Kelly/775 * 2.50 6.00
35 Jed Lowrie/725 * 3.00 8.00
36 Matt Maloney/775 * 2.50 6.00
37 Jacob Marceaux/725 * 2.50 6.00
40 Cameron Maybin/50 * 20.00 50.00
43 Eduardo Nunez/225 * 3.00 8.00
46 P.J. Phillips/775 * 2.50 6.00
50 Rafael Rodriguez/225 * 2.50 6.00
51 Jarrod Saltalamacchia/50 * 4.00 10.00
52 Erick San Pedro/775 * 2.50 6.00
57 Jose Tabata/50 * 6.00 15.00
58 Clete Thomas/275 * 2.50 6.00
59 Ryan Tucker/725 * 3.00 8.00
60 Justin Upton/50 * 30.00 60.00
61 Chris Volstad/350 * 3.00 8.00
62 Josh Wall/775 * 2.50 6.00
63 Nick Webber/725 * 3.00 8.00
65 Jared Wells/475 * 3.00 8.00
66 Kevin Whelan/225 * 2.50 6.00
68 Josh Wilson/775 * 2.50 6.00
70 Ryan Zimmerman/50 * 6.00 15.00

2006 Just Autographs Signatures Black

ISSUED DIRECTLY FROM MANUFACTURER
STATED PRINT RUN 25 SERIAL #'d SETS
NO PRICING DUE TO SCARCITY

2006 Just Autographs Signatures Gold

*GOLD: .6X TO 1.5X BASIC p/r 225-775
*GOLD: .6X TO 1.5X BASIC p/r 50
DISTRIBUTED IN FACTORY SET FORM
INITIALLY OFFERED ONLY TO JMI MEMBERS
STATED PRINT RUN 50 SERIAL #'d SETS
38 Nick Markakis 5.00 12.00
57 Jose Tabata 12.50 30.00
60 Justin Upton 30.00 60.00

2006 Just Autographs Signatures Silver

*SILVER: .5X TO 1.2X BASIC p/r 225-775
*SILVER: .5X TO 1.2X BASIC p/r 50
ONE BASIC OR SILVER AU PER FOIL PACK
STATED PRINT RUN 100 SERIAL #'d SETS
38 Nick Markakis 4.00 10.00
57 Jose Tabata 10.00 25.00
60 Justin Upton 20.00 50.00

2006 Just Autographs Triple Signatures

OVERALL 2X-3X AU ODDS 1:144 PACKS
STATED PRINT RUN 3 SERIAL #'d SETS
NO PRICING DUE TO SCARCITY

2006 Just Autographs 07 Preview

COMPLETE SET (15) 1.50 4.00
ISSUED DIRECTLY FROM MANUFACTURER
STATED PRINT RUN 9,000 SETS
*BLACK: 3X TO 8X BASIC 06 PREVIEW
BLACK ISSUED FROM MANUFACTURER
BLACK PRINT RUN 50 SERIAL #'d SETS
*GOLD: 2X TO 5X BASIC 06 PREVIEW
BONUS ITEM W/06 JA GOLD FACTORY SET
GOLD PRINT RUN 100 SERIAL #'d SETS
1 Elvis Andrus .50 1.25
2 Jeff Bianchi .15 .40
3 Travis Buck .10 .25
4 Brandon Erbe .15 .40
5 Alex Gordon .30 .75
6 Stephen Head .10 .25
7 Craig Italiano .10 .25
8 Shane Lindsay .25 .60
9 Nick Markakis .25 .60
10 Cameron Maybin .30 .75
11 Nolan Reimold .15 .40
12 Jarrod Saltalamacchia .10 .25
13 Jose Tabata .60 1.50
14 Justin Upton .75 2.00
15 Chris Volstad .10 .25

2006 Just Autographs 07 Preview Signatures

SOLD INDIVIDUALLY ON JMI WEBSITE
STATED PRINT RUN 200 SERIAL #'d SETS
BLACK SOLD INDIVID.ON JMI WEBSITE
BLACK PRINT RUN 25 SERIAL #'d SETS
NO BLACK PRICING DUE TO SCARCITY
*GOLD: .6X TO 1.5X BASIC
GOLD FACT.SET SOLD DIRECT FROM JMI
GOLD PRINT RUN 50 SERIAL #'d SETS
*SILVER: .5X TO 1.2X BASIC
SILVER RANDOM INSERTS IN SETS
SILVER PRINT RUN 100 SERIAL #'d SETS
1 Elvis Andrus 4.00 10.00
2 Jeff Bianchi 4.00 10.00
3 Travis Buck 4.00 10.00
4 Brandon Erbe 4.00 10.00
5 Alex Gordon 10.00 25.00
6 Stephen Head 4.00 10.00
7 Craig Italiano 4.00 10.00
8 Shane Lindsay 4.00 10.00
9 Nick Markakis 6.00 15.00
10 Cameron Maybin 10.00 25.00
11 Nolan Reimold 4.00 10.00
12 Jarrod Saltalamacchia 6.00 15.00
13 Jose Tabata 4.00 10.00
14 Justin Upton 20.00 40.00
15 Chris Volstad 4.00 10.00

2007 Just Autographs

COMPLETE SET (50) 8.00 20.00
COMMON (1-50) .10 .25
B1-B3 ISSUED IN FACTORY SETS
OVERALL GLOSSY ODDS 1:144 FOIL PACKS
GLOSSY PRINT RUN 1 SET PER COLOR
GLOSSY BLACK-GOLD-SILV-WHITE ISSUED
NO GLOSSY PRICING DUE TO SCARCITY
PLATES ISSUED AS FOIL PACK CASE INCENTIVE
PLATES PRINT RUN 1 SET PER COLOR
BLACK-CYAN-MAGENTA-YELLOW ISSUED
NO PLATES PRICING DUE TO SCARCITY
1 Lars Anderson .40 1.00
2 Pedro Beato .10 .25
3 Joe Benson .10 .25
4 Jason Berken .10 .25
5 Emmanuel Burriss .15 .40
6 Josh Butler .10 .25
7 Lorenzo Cain .10 .25
8 Andrew Carpenter .10 .25
9 David Christensen .10 .25
10 Caleb Clay .15 .40
11 Johnny Cueto .30 .75
12 Eulogio de la Cruz .15 .40
13 Dustin Evans .10 .25
14 Terry Evans .10 .25
15 Mat Gamel .40 1.00
16 Jaime Garcia .25 .60
17 Glenn Gibson .15 .40
18 Gorkys Hernandez .25 .60
19 Tom Hickman .10 .25
20 Wes Hodges .10 .25
21 Chad Huffman .10 .25
22 Lee Hyde .10 .25
23 Jon Jay .15 .40
24 Jair Jurrjens .15 .40
25 Kala Kaaihue .15 .40
26 Wade LeBlanc .25 .60
27 Jesse Litsch .15 .40
28 Brandon Magee .10 .25
29 Shairon Martis .15 .40
30 Jonathan Meloan .15 .40
31 Franklin Morales .15 .40
32 Ryan Mount .10 .25
33 Chris Nicoll .10 .25
34 Ross Ohlendorf .15 .40
35 Francisco Pena .10 .25
36 Chris Perez .15 .40
37 Jose Pirela .10 .25
38 Kieron Pope .15 .40
39 Angel Reyes .15 .40
40 Mark Reynolds .75 2.00
41 Adam Russell .10 .25
42 Chris Salamida .10 .25
43 Jeff Samardzija .40 1.00
44 Justin Sellers .10 .25
45 Brett Sinkbeil .10 .25
46 Matt Sulentic .15 .40
47 Carlos Urena .10 .25
48 Rick Vanden Hurk .10 .25
49 Blake Wood .10 .25
50 Steven Wright .10 .25
B1 Chih-Hsien Chiang .25 .60
B2 Che-Hsuan Lin .15 .40
B3 Oscar Tejeda .10 .25

2007 Just Autographs Black

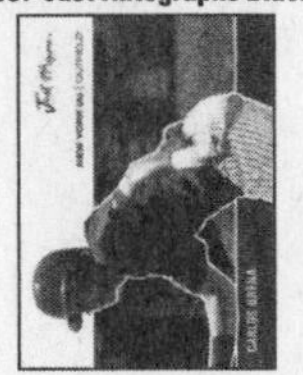

*BLACK: 3X TO 8X BASIC
STATED ODDS 1:12 FOIL PACKS
STATED PRINT RUN 50 SERIAL #'d SETS

2007 Just Autographs Gold

*GOLD: 2X TO 5X BASIC
DISTRIBUTED IN FACTORY SET FORM
STATED PRINT RUN 100 SERIAL #'d SETS

2007 Just Autographs Silver

STATED ODDS 1:24 FOIL PACKS
STATED PRINT RUN 25 SER.#'d SETS
NO PRICING DUE TO SCARCITY

2007 Just Autographs Signatures

ONE BASIC OR SILVER AU PER FOIL PACK
ONE BASIC OR SILVER AU PER FACT.SET
ALSO ISSUED DIRECTLY FROM JMI
B1-B3 ISSUED IN FACTORY SETS
OVERALL GLOSSY ODDS 1:12 FACT.SETS
GLOSSY PRINT RUN 1 SET PER COLOR
GLOSSY BLACK-GOLD-SILV-WHITE ISSUED
NO GLOSSY PRICING DUE TO SCARCITY
OVERALL PLATE ODDS 1:24 FACT.SETS
PLATES PRINT RUN 1 SET PER COLOR
BLACK-CYAN-MAGENTA-YELLOW ISSUED
NO PLATES PRICING DUE TO SCARCITY
1 Lars Anderson 6.00 15.00
2 Pedro Beato 5.00 12.00
3 Joe Benson 5.00 12.00
4 Jason Berken 2.50 6.00
5 Emmanuel Burriss
6 Josh Butler 2.50 6.00
7 Lorenzo Cain 4.00 10.00
8 Andrew Carpenter 2.50 6.00
9 David Christensen 2.50 6.00
10 Caleb Clay 3.00 8.00
11 Johnny Cueto 10.00 25.00
12 Eulogio de la Cruz 2.50 6.00
13 Dustin Evans 2.50 6.00
14 Terry Evans 2.50 6.00
15 Mat Gamel 6.00 15.00
16 Jaime Garcia 5.00 12.00
17 Glenn Gibson 3.00 8.00
18 Gorkys Hernandez 4.00 10.00
19 Tom Hickman 2.50 6.00
20 Wes Hodges 4.00 10.00
21 Chad Huffman 2.50 6.00
22 Lee Hyde 3.00 8.00
23 Jon Jay 2.50 6.00
24 Jair Jurrjens 4.00 10.00
25 Kala Kaaihue 4.00 10.00
26 Wade LeBlanc 3.00 8.00
27 Jesse Litsch 2.50 6.00
28 Brandon Magee 2.50 6.00
29 Shairon Martis 3.00 8.00
30 Jonathan Meloan 5.00 12.00
31 Franklin Morales 3.00 8.00
32 Ryan Mount 2.50 6.00
33 Chris Nicoll 2.50 6.00
34 Ross Ohlendorf 4.00 10.00
35 Francisco Pena 10.00 25.00
36 Chris Perez 3.00 8.00
37 Jose Pirela 4.00 10.00
38 Kieron Pope 2.50 6.00
39 Angel Reyes 6.00 15.00
40 Mark Reynolds 6.00 15.00
41 Adam Russell 2.50 6.00
42 Chris Salamida 3.00 8.00
43 Jeff Samardzija 20.00 50.00
44 Justin Sellers 2.50 6.00
45 Brett Sinkbeil 4.00 10.00
46 Matt Sulentic 3.00 8.00
47 Carlos Urena 4.00 10.00
48 Rick Vanden Hurk 4.00 10.00
49 Blake Wood 2.50 6.00
50 Steven Wright 2.50 6.00
B1 Chih-Hsien Chiang 6.00 15.00
B2 Che-Hsuan Lin 6.00 15.00
B3 Oscar Tejeda 6.00 15.00

2007 Just Autographs Signatures Black

OVERALL BLACK AU ODDS 1:2 FACT.SETS
B1-B3 ISSUED IN FACTORY SETS
STATED PRINT RUN 25 SER.#'d SETS
NO PRICING DUE TO SCARCITY

2007 Just Autographs Signatures Gold

DISTRIBUTED IN FACTORY SET FORM
STATED PRINT RUN 50 SER.#'d SETS
NO PRICING DUE TO SCARCITY

2007 Just Autographs Signatures Silver

OVERALL SILVER AU ODDS 1:48 FOIL PACKS
B1-B3 ISSUE IN FACTORY SETS
STATED PRINT RUN 10 SER.#'d SETS
NO PRICING DUE TO SCARCITY

2007 Just Autographs 08 Preview

1 Lars Anderson .40 1.00
2 Pedro Beato .10 .25
3 Joe Benson .10 .25
4 Rick Vanden Hurk .10 .25
5 Yung-Chi Chen .25 .60
6 Chih-Hsien Chiang .25 .60
7 Yovani Gallardo .25 .60
8 Jaime Garcia .25 .60
9 Gorkys Hernandez .25 .60
10 Wes Hodges .10 .25
11 Chin-Lung Hu .40 1.00
12 Brandon Jones .15 .40
13 Jair Jurrjens .15 .40
14 Che-Hsuan Lin .15 .40
15 Franklin Morales .15 .40
16 Francisco Pena .10 .25
17 Jose Pirela .10 .25
18 Angel Reyes .15 .40
19 Mark Reynolds .75 2.00
20 Jeff Samardzija .40 1.00
21 Matt Sulentic .15 .40
22 Oscar Tejeda .10 .25
23 Carlos Urena .10 .25

2007 Just Autographs 08 Preview Gold

*GOLD: 2X TO 5X BASIC
STATED PRINT RUN 100 SER.#'d SETS

2008 Just Autographs

COMMON (1-80) .10 .25
OVERALL GLOSSY ODDS 1:144 FOIL PACKS
GLOSSY PRINT RUN 1 SET PER COLOR
GLOSSY BLACK-GOLD-SILV-WHITE ISSUED
NO GLOSSY PRICING DUE TO SCARCITY
PRINTING PLATES ODDS 1:12 FACTORY SETS
PLATES PRINT RUN 1 SET PER COLOR
BLACK-CYAN-MAGENTA-YELLOW ISSUED
NO PLATES PRICING DUE TO SCARCITY
1 Matt Antonelli .10 .25
2 Jonathan Bachanov .10 .25
3 Pedro Baez .25 .60
4 Andrew Bailey .25 .60
5 Nicholas Barnese .10 .25
6 Tim Bascom .10 .25
7 Andrew Brackman .30 .75
8 Jay Bruce .40 1.00
9 Billy Butler .10 .25
10 Tony Butler .10 .25
11 Christian Colonel .10 .25
12 Hector Correa .10 .25
13 Charlie Culberson .10 .25
14 Colin Curtis .10 .25
15 Chris Davis .25 .60
16 Kelvin DeLeon .10 .25
17 Grant Desme .10 .25
18 Danny Duffy .30 .75
19 Jack Egbert .15 .40
20 Barry Enright .15 .40
21 Wendell Fairley .10 .25
22 Neftali Feliz .30 .75
23 Andrew Fie .10 .25
24 Brian Friday .10 .25
25 Clay Fuller .10 .25
26 Austin Gallagher .10 .25
27 Chris Getz .10 .25
28 Caleb Gindl .10 .25
29 Taylor Green .10 .25
30 Deolis Guerra .25 .60
31 Nick Hagadone .10 .25
32 Brandon Hamilton .10 .25
33 Brandon Hicks .10 .25
34 Alan Horne .10 .25
35 Cale Iorg .10 .25
36 Brad James .10 .25
37 Chris Johnson .40 1.00
38 Ryan Kalish .25 .60
39 Pete Kozma .10 .25
40 Andrew Lambo .40 1.00
41 Kuo-Hui Lo .10 .25
42 Jonathan Lucroy .10 .25
43 Stephen Marek .10 .25
44 Fernando Martinez .15 .40
45 Chris Mason .10 .25
46 Daniel Mayora .10 .25
47 Andrew McCutchen .30 .75
48 Jack McGeary .10 .25
49 Will Middlebrooks .15 .40
50 Drew Miller .10 .25
51 Logan Morrison .75 2.00
52 Bud Norris .10 .25
53 Bobby Parnell .10 .25
54 Gerardo Parra .15 .40
55 Danny Rams .15 .40
56 Trevor Reckling .30 .75
57 Greg Reynolds .15 .40
58 Dustin Richardson .10 .25
59 Brian Rike .15 .40
60 Derrick Robinson .10 .25
61 Henry Rodriguez .10 .25
62 Austin Romine .10 .25
63 Sergio Romo .10 .25
64 Julian Sampson .10 .25
65 R.J. Seidel .10 .25

66 John Shelby .10 .25
67 Scott Sizemore .10 .25
68 Travis Snider .15 .40
69 Neftali Soto .15 .40
70 Damon Sublett .10 .25
71 Bradley Suttle .10 .25
72 Matt Sweeney .10 .25
73 Jose Tabata .25 .60
74 Clayton Tanner .10 .25
75 Taylor Teagarden .15 .40
76 Julio Teheran .40 1.00
77 Tony Thomas .10 .25
78 Loek Van Mil .10 .25
79 Nathan Vineyard .15 .40
80 Chris Withrow .10 .25

2008 Just Autographs Black

*BLACK: 3X TO 8X BASIC
STATED ODDS 1:10 FOIL PACKS
STATED PRINT RUN 50 SERIAL #'d SETS

2008 Just Autographs Gold

*GOLD: 2X TO 5X BASIC
STATED ODDS 1:5 FOIL PACKS
STATED PRINT RUN 100 SERIAL #'d SETS

2008 Just Autographs Silver

STATED ODDS 1:20 FOIL PACKS
STATED PRINT RUN 25 SER.#'d SETS
NO PRICING DUE TO SCARCITY

2008 Just Autographs Signatures

ONE BASIC OR SILVER AU PER FOIL PACK
ONE BASIC AND BLACK AU PER FACT.SET
ALSO ISSUED DIRECTLY FROM JMI
C EQUALS COMMON
R EQUALS RARE
U EQUALS UNCOMMON
GLOSSY AU INSERTED IN MYSTERY PRODUCTS
GLOSSY PRINT RUN 1 SET PER COLOR
GLOSSY BLACK-GOLD-SILV-WHITE ISSUED
NO GLOSSY PRICING DUE TO SCARCITY
OVERALL PLATE ODDS 1:12 FACT.SETS
PLATES PRINT RUN 1 SET PER COLOR
BLACK-CYAN-MAGENTA-YELLOW ISSUED
NO PLATES PRICING DUE TO SCARCITY
1 Matt Antonelli C 3.00 8.00
2 Jonathan Bachanov C 2.50 6.00
3 Pedro Baez C 3.00 8.00
4 Andrew Bailey C 3.00 8.00
5 Nicholas Barnese U 3.00 8.00
6 Tim Bascom U 2.50 6.00
7 Andrew Brackman R 5.00 12.00
8 Jay Bruce R 12.50 30.00
9 Billy Butler R 6.00 15.00
10 Tony Butler C 3.00 8.00
11 Christian Colonel U 3.00 8.00
12 Hector Correa C 2.50 6.00
13 Charlie Culberson C 2.50 6.00
14 Colin Curtis C 3.00 8.00
15 Chris Davis C 12.50 30.00
16 Kelvin DeLeon R 3.00 8.00
17 Grant Desme C 2.50 6.00
18 Danny Duffy C 3.00 8.00
19 Jack Egbert C 3.00 8.00
20 Barry Enright C 2.50 6.00
21 Wendell Fairley R 3.00 8.00
22 Neftali Feliz C 8.00 20.00
23 Andrew Fie C 2.50 6.00
24 Brian Friday U 2.50 6.00
25 Clay Fuller U 2.50 6.00
26 Austin Gallagher C 2.50 6.00
27 Chris Getz C 2.50 6.00
28 Caleb Gindl C 2.50 6.00
29 Taylor Green U 3.00 8.00
30 Deolis Guerra R 4.00 10.00
31 Nick Hagadone R 5.00 12.00
32 Brandon Hamilton C 2.50 6.00
33 Brandon Hicks C 2.50 6.00
34 Alan Horne R 4.00 10.00
35 Cale Iorg R 4.00 10.00
36 Brad James C 2.50 6.00
37 Chris Johnson U
38 Ryan Kalish R 4.00 10.00
39 Pete Kozma R 4.00 10.00
40 Andrew Lambo R 4.00 10.00
41 Kuo-Hui Lo R 8.00 20.00
42 Jonathan Lucroy C 3.00 8.00
43 Stephen Marek C 3.00 8.00
44 Fernando Martinez R 6.00 15.00
45 Chris Mason C
46 Daniel Mayora U 2.50 6.00
47 Andrew McCutchen R 6.00 15.00
48 Jack McGeary R 4.00 10.00
49 Will Middlebrooks R 5.00 12.00
50 Drew Miller C 2.50 6.00
51 Logan Morrison U 3.00 8.00
52 Bud Norris C 3.00 8.00
53 Bobby Parnell R 4.00 10.00
54 Gerardo Parra R 4.00 10.00
55 Danny Rams C 2.50 6.00
56 Trevor Reckling U 2.50 6.00
57 Greg Reynolds R 5.00 12.00
58 Dustin Richardson R 4.00 10.00
59 Brian Rike C 2.50 6.00
60 Derrick Robinson U 2.50 6.00
61 Henry Rodriguez C 3.00 8.00
62 Austin Romine R 4.00 10.00
63 Sergio Romo U 2.50 6.00
64 Julian Sampson C 2.50 6.00
65 R.J. Seidel U 2.50 6.00
66 John Shelby C 2.50 6.00
67 Scott Sizemore C 3.00 8.00
68 Travis Snider R 6.00 15.00
69 Neftali Soto C 4.00 10.00
70 Damon Sublett C 3.00 8.00
71 Bradley Suttle R 4.00 10.00
72 Matt Sweeney U
73 Jose Tabata R 3.00 8.00
74 Clayton Tanner U 2.50 6.00
75 Taylor Teagarden C 3.00 8.00
76 Julio Teheran R 6.00 15.00
77 Tony Thomas R 4.00 10.00
78 Loek Van Mil U 2.50 6.00
79 Nathan Vineyard C 3.00 8.00
80 Chris Withrow C 3.00 8.00

2008 Just Autographs Signatures Black

STATED ODDS ONE PER FACTORY SET
STATED PRINT RUN 25 SER.#'d SETS
NO PRICING DUE TO SCARCITY

2008 Just Autographs Signatures Gold

*GOLD AU: .6X TO 1.5X BASIC AU
RANDOM INSERTS IN FOIL PACKS
STATED PRINT RUN 50 SER.#'d SETS

2008 Just Autographs Signatures Silver

ONE BASIC OR SILVER AU PER FOIL PACK
STATED PRINT RUN 10 SER.#'d SETS
NO PRICING DUE TO SCARCITY

2008 Just Autographs 09 Preview

COMMON CARD (1-20) .10 .25
1 Lars Anderson .10 .25
2 Jay Bruce .40 1.00
3 Yung-Chi Chen .10 .25
4 Chris Davis .25 .60
5 Kelvin DeLeon .10 .25
6 Deolis Guerra .25 .60
7 Jason Heyward .40 1.00
8 Alan Horne .10 .25
9 Ryan Kalish .25 .60
10 Andrew Lambo .40 1.00
11 Che-Hsuan Lin .10 .25
12 Kuo-Hui Lo .10 .25
13 Justin Masterson .25 .60
14 Josh Reddick .30 .75
15 Austin Romine .10 .25
16 Jordan Schafer .10 .25
17 Travis Snider .15 .40
18 Julio Teheran .40 1.00
19 Tony Thomas .10 .25
20 Josh Vitters .10 .25

2008 Just Autographs 09 Preview Gold

*GOLD: 2X TO 5X BASIC
STATED PRINT RUN 100 SER.#'d SETS

2006 Just Limited Autographs

SOLD INDIVIDUALLY ON JMI WEBSITE
STATED PRINT RUN 10 SERIAL #'d SETS
NO PRICING DUE TO SCARCITY

2006 Just Limited Autographs Gold

COMPLETE SET SOLD DIRECT FROM JMI
STATED PRINT RUN 50 SERIAL #'d SETS
1 Elvis Andrus 6.00 15.00
2 Daric Barton 6.00 15.00
3 Jay Bruce 30.00 60.00
4 Jeff Clement 6.00 15.00
5 Carlos Gonzalez 20.00 50.00
6 Gio Gonzalez 6.00 15.00
7 Alex Gordon 12.50 30.00
8 Stephen Head 6.00 15.00
9 Gaby Hernandez 6.00 15.00
10 Philip Hughes 6.00 15.00
11 Andy LaRoche 6.00 15.00
12 Shane Lindsay 6.00 15.00
13 Cameron Maybin 10.00 25.00
14 Andrew McCutchen 6.00 15.00
15 Lastings Milledge 6.00 15.00
16 Kendry Morales 6.00 15.00
17 Matt Moses 6.00 15.00
18 Yusmeiro Petit 6.00 15.00
19 Colby Rasmus 6.00 15.00
20 Nolan Reimold 6.00 15.00
21 Jarrod Saltalamacchia 6.00 15.00
22 Brandon Snyder 6.00 15.00
23 Jose Tabata 10.00 25.00
24 Troy Tulowitzki 6.00 15.00
25 Ryan Zimmerman 10.00 25.00

2006 Just Rookies

COMP.FACT.SET (54) 25.00 40.00
COMPLETE SET (50) 6.00 15.00
COMMON CARD (1-50) .10 .25
STATED PRINT RUN 10,000 SETS
FOUR AUTOS PER SEALED FACTORY SET
GLOSSY ODDS 1:48 FACTORY SETS
NO GLOSSY PRICING DUE TO SCARCITY
PLATE ODDS 1:48 FACTORY SETS
PLATES PRINT RUN 1 SET PER COLOR
BLACK-CYAN-MAGENTA-YELLOW ISSUED
NO PLATES PRICING DUE TO SCARCITY
1 Daniel Bard .10 .25
2 Aaron Bates .10 .25
3 Dellin Betances .30 .75
4 Ricky Brooks .10 .25
5 Kyler Burke .10 .25
6 Adrian Cardenas .15 .40
7 Joba Chamberlain 1.00 2.50
8 Chi-Hung Cheng .10 .25
9 Chris Coghlan .30 .75
10 Tyler Colvin .25 .60
11 Kyle Drabek .30 .75
12 Stephen Englund .10 .25
13 Steve Evarts .10 .25
14 Mike Felix .10 .25
15 Chase Fontaine .10 .25
16 Jake Fox .15 .40
17 Babbino Fuenmayor .10 .25
18 Mark Hamilton .10 .25
19 Luke Hochevar .30 .75
20 Chris Huseby .10 .25
21 Cody Johnson .10 .25
22 Young Il Jung .25 .60
23 Clayton Kershaw .60 1.50
24 Marcus Lemon .10 .25
25 Tim Lincecum 1.00 2.50
26 Radhames Liz .10 .25
27 Jeff Locke .10 .25
28 Evan Longoria 1.25 3.00
29 Jeff Manship .10 .25
30 Fernando Martinez 1.00 2.50
31 Kyle McCulloch .25 .60
32 Mark Melancon .10 .25
33 Matt Miller .10 .25
34 Jesus Montero .75 2.00
35 Brandon Morrow .50 1.25
36 Adam Ottavino .10 .25
37 Jeremy Papelbon .15 .40
38 Josh Papelbon .15 .40
39 Chris Parmelee .15 .40
40 Segio Perez .10 .25
41 Jason Place .10 .25
42 Cory Rasmus .10 .25
43 Greg Reynolds .40 1.00
44 Josh Rodriguez .10 .25
45 Bill Rowell .25 .60
46 Drew Stubbs .25 .60
47 Carlos Triunfel .10 .25
48 Sung-Wei Tseng .10 .25
49 Angel Villalona .10 .25
50 Colton Willems .10 .25

2006 Just Rookies Black

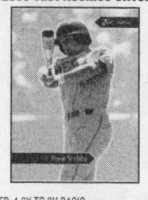

*BLACK: 3X TO 8X BASIC
STATED ODDS 1:4 FACTORY SETS
ALSO SOLD INDIVIDUALLY ON JMI WEBSITE
STATED PRINT RUN 50 SERIAL #'d SETS

2006 Just Rookies Gold

*GOLD: 2X TO 5X BASIC
DISTRIBUTED IN FACTORY SET FORM
STATED PRINT RUN 100 SERIAL #'d SETS

2006 Just Rookies Silver

*SILVER: 1.2X TO 3X BASIC
STATED ODDS ONE PER FACTORY SET
STATED PRINT RUN 200 SERIAL #'d SETS

2006 Just Rookies Autographs

FOUR AUTOS PER SEALED FACTORY SET
ALSO SOLD INDIVIDUALLY ON JMI WEBSITE
PRINT RUNS B/WN 50-700 COPIES PER
CARDS ARE NOT SERIAL-NUMBERED
PRINT RUN INFO PROVIDED BY JMI
1 Daniel Bard/200 * 8.00 20.00
2 Aaron Bates/200 * 2.50 6.00
3 Dellin Betances/200 * 5.00 12.00
4 Ricky Brooks/700 * 2.50 6.00
5 Kyler Burke/700 * 3.00 8.00
6 Adrian Cardenas/350 * 3.00 8.00
7 Joba Chamberlain/100 * 20.00 50.00
8 Chi-Hung Cheng/50 * 6.00 15.00
9 Chris Coghlan/700 * 3.00 8.00
10 Tyler Colvin/100 * 6.00 15.00
11 Kyle Drabek/350 * 6.00 15.00
12 Stephen Englund/700 * 2.50 6.00
13 Steve Evarts/700 * 3.00 8.00
14 Mike Felix/700 * 2.50 6.00
15 Chase Fontaine/700 * 2.50 6.00
16 Jake Fox/200 * 6.00 15.00
17 Balbino Fuenmayor/100 * 5.00 12.00
18 Mark Hamilton/700 * 2.50 6.00
19 Luke Hochevar/100 * 6.00 15.00
20 Chris Huseby/250 * 3.00 8.00
21 Cody Johnson/700 * 3.00 8.00
22 Young Il Jung/700 * 5.00 12.00
23 Clayton Kershaw/100 * 8.00 20.00
24 Marcus Lemon/500 * 2.50 6.00
25 Tim Lincecum/50 * 20.00 50.00
26 Radhames Liz/350 * 3.00 8.00
27 Jeff Locke/700 * 2.50 6.00
28 Evan Longoria/100 * 12.50 30.00
29 Jeff Manship/400 * 3.00 8.00
30 Fernando Martinez/100 * 10.00 25.00
31 Kyle McCulloch/700 * 3.00 8.00
32 Mark Melancon/100 * 5.00 12.00
33 Matt Miller/200 * 2.50 6.00
34 Jesus Montero/100 * 12.50 30.00
35 Brandon Morrow/300 * 6.00 15.00
36 Adam Ottavino/500 * 3.00 8.00
37 Jeremy Papelbon/400 * 3.00 8.00
38 Josh Papelbon/400 * 3.00 8.00
39 Chris Parmelee/500 * 6.00 15.00
40 Sergio Perez/700 * 6.00 15.00
41 Jason Place/100 * 6.00 15.00
42 Cory Rasmus/700 * 3.00 8.00
43 Greg Reynolds/100 * 6.00 15.00
44 Josh Rodriguez/700 * 2.50 6.00
45 Bill Rowell/100 * 6.00 15.00
46 Drew Stubbs/50 * 6.00 15.00
47 Carlos Triunfel/100 * 6.00 15.00
48 Sung-Wei Tseng/100 * 6.00 15.00
49 Angel Villalona/100 * 6.00 15.00
50 Colton Willems/250 * 6.00 15.00

2006 Just Rookies Autographs Black

SOLD INDIVIDUALLY VIA JMI WEBSITE
STATED PRINT RUN 25 SERIAL #'d SETS
NO PRICING DUE TO SCARCITY

2006 Just Rookies Autographs Gold

DISTRIBUTED IN FACTORY SET FORM
STATED PRINT RUN 50 SERIAL #'d SETS
NO PRICING DUE TO SCARCITY

2006 Just Rookies Autographs Silver

*SILVER: .5X TO 1.2X BASIC p/r 250-700
*SILVER: .4X TO 1X BASIC p/r 100-200
RANDOM INSERTS IN FACTORY SETS
STATED PRINT RUN 100 SERIAL #'d SETS
42 Evan Longoria 12.50 30.00

2007 Just Rookies

COMP.FACT.SET (67) 20.00 50.00
COMPLETE SET (65) 6.00 15.00
COMMON CARD (1-65) .20 .50
TWO AUTOS PER SEALED FACTORY SET
GLOSSY ODDS 1:144 PACKS
NO GLOSSY PRICING DUE TO SCARCITY
PLATE ODDS 1:24 FACTORY SETS
PLATES PRINT RUN 1 SET PER COLOR
BLACK-CYAN-MAGENTA-YELLOW ISSUED
NO PLATES PRICING DUE TO SCARCITY
1 James Adkins .10 .25
2 Michael Almanzar .25 .60
3 Carmen Angelini .15 .40
4 Jake Arrieta .15 .40
5 Darwin Barney .50 1.25
6 Bubba Bell .10 .25
7 Julio Borbon .30 .75
8 Corey Brown .15 .40
9 Madison Bumgarner .60 1.50
10 Michael Burgess .15 .40
11 Trevor Cahill .25 .60
12 Mitch Canham .10 .25
13 Brett Cecil .10 .25
14 Jose Ceda .15 .40
15 Yung-Chi Chen .25 .60
16 Zack Cozart .10 .25
17 Drew Cumberland .10 .25
18 Travis d'Arnaud .15 .40
19 Matt Dominguez .25 .60
20 Josh Donaldson .10 .25
21 Sean Doolittle .25 .60
22 Eric Eiland .10 .25
23 Todd Frazier .10 .25
24 Cole Gillespie .15 .40
25 Jon Gilmore .25 .60
26 Josh Horton .10 .25
27 Tommy Hunter .15 .40
28 Justin Jackson .15 .40
29 Desmond Jennings .30 .75
30 David Kopp .10 .25
31 Eddie Kunz .10 .25
32 Matt LaPorta .40 1.00
33 Kyle Lotzkar .15 .40
34 Cory Luebke .10 .25
35 Trystan Magnuson .10 .25
36 Michael Main .15 .40
37 Matt Mangini .10 .25
38 Travis Mattair .10 .25
39 Devin Mesoraco .25 .60
40 Clayton Mortensen .25 .60
41 Mike Moustakas .40 1.00
42 Nick Noonan .10 .25
43 Sean O'Sullivan .15 .40
44 Felipe Paulino .15 .40
45 Danny Payne .10 .25
46 Rick Porcello .40 1.00
47 David Price .60 1.50
48 Neil Ramirez .10 .25
49 Josh Reddick .15 .40
50 Ben Revere .25 .60
51 Cole Rohrbough .15 .40
52 Sam Runion .10 .25
53 James Simmons .10 .25
54 Josh Smoker .15 .40
55 Eric Sogard .10 .25
56 Jon Still .15 .40
57 Jess Todd .10 .25
58 John Tolisano .30 .75
59 Josh Vitters .25 .60
60 Duke Welker .10 .25
61 Matt West .15 .40
62 Matt Wieters .50 1.25
63 Jackson Williams .10 .25
64 Danny Worth .10 .25
65 Jordan Zimmermann .15 .40

2007 Just Rookies Black

*BLACK: 2.5X TO 6X BASIC
STATED ODDS 1:14 PACKS
STATED PRINT RUN 50 SER.#'d SETS

2007 Just Rookies Gold

*GOLD: 2X TO 5X BASIC
DISTRIBUTED IN FACTORY SET FORM
STATED PRINT RUN 100 SERIAL #'d SETS

2007 Just Rookies Silver

STATED ODDS 1:28 PACKS
STATED PRINT RUN 25 SER.#'d SETS
NO PRICING DUE TO SCARCITY

2007 Just Rookies Autographs

TWO AUTOS PER SEALED FACTORY SET
ALSO SOLD INDIVIDUALLY ON JMI WEBSITE
GLOSSY AU INSERTED IN MYSTERY PRODUCTS
NO GLOSSY AU PRICING DUE TO SCARCITY
PLATE AU ODDS 1:24 FACTORY SETS
PLATES AU PRINT RUN 1 SET PER COLOR
BLACK-CYAN-MAGENTA-YELLOW ISSUED
NO PLATES PRICING DUE TO SCARCITY
1 James Adkins 3.00 8.00
2 Michael Almanzar 5.00 12.00
3 Carmen Angelini 5.00 12.00
4 Jake Arrieta
5 Darwin Barney 6.00 15.00
6 Bubba Bell 3.00 8.00
7 Julio Borbon 3.00 8.00
8 Corey Brown 3.00 8.00
9 Madison Bumgarner 6.00 15.00
10 Michael Burgess 6.00 15.00
11 Trevor Cahill 4.00 10.00
12 Mitch Canham 3.00 8.00
13 Brett Cecil 5.00 12.00
14 Jose Ceda 3.00 8.00
15 Yung-Chi Chen
16 Zack Cozart 3.00 8.00
17 Drew Cumberland 3.00 8.00
18 Travis d'Arnaud 3.00 8.00
19 Matt Dominguez 5.00 12.00
20 Josh Donaldson 3.00 8.00
21 Sean Doolittle 3.00 8.00
22 Eric Eiland 2.50 6.00
23 Todd Frazier 5.00 12.00
24 Cole Gillespie 3.00 8.00
25 Jon Gilmore 3.00 8.00
26 Josh Horton 2.50 6.00
27 Tommy Hunter 5.00 12.00
28 Justin Jackson 3.00 8.00
29 Desmond Jennings 4.00 10.00
30 David Kopp 2.50 6.00
31 Eddie Kunz 3.00 8.00
32 Matt LaPorta 6.00 15.00
33 Kyle Lotzkar 3.00 8.00
34 Cory Luebke 3.00 8.00
35 Trystan Magnuson 5.00 12.00
36 Michael Main 5.00 12.00
37 Matt Mangini 3.00 8.00
38 Travis Mattair 2.50 6.00
39 Devin Mesoraco 5.00 12.00
40 Clayton Mortensen 3.00 8.00
41 Mike Moustakas 5.00 12.00
42 Nick Noonan 5.00 12.00
43 Sean O'Sullivan 2.50 6.00
44 Felipe Paulino 2.50 6.00
45 Danny Payne 3.00 8.00
47 David Price 8.00 20.00
48 Neil Ramirez 5.00 12.00
49 Josh Reddick 3.00 8.00
50 Ben Revere 6.00 15.00
51 Cole Rohrbough 6.00 15.00
52 Sam Runion 3.00 8.00
53 James Simmons 5.00 12.00
54 Josh Smoker 5.00 12.00
55 Eric Sogard 2.50 6.00
56 Jon Still 3.00 8.00
57 Jess Todd 3.00 8.00
58 John Tolisano 3.00 8.00
59 Josh Vitters 3.00 8.00
60 Duke Welker 3.00 8.00
61 Matt West 2.50 6.00
62 Matt Wieters 8.00 20.00
63 Jackson Williams 3.00 8.00
64 Danny Worth 2.50 6.00
65 Jordan Zimmermann 3.00 8.00

2007 Just Rookies Autographs Black

STATED ODDS 1:48 PACKS
STATED PRINT RUN 10 SER.#'d SETS
NO PRICING DUE TO SCARCITY

2007 Just Rookies Autographs Gold

DISTRIBUTED IN FACTORY SET FORM
STATED PRINT RUN 50 SER.#'d SETS
NO PRICING DUE TO SCARCITY

2007 Just Rookies Autographs Silver

STATED ODDS 1:2 FACTORY SETS
STATED PRINT RUN 25 SER.#'d SETS
NO PRICING DUE TO SCARCITY

2007 Just Rookies 08 Preview

1 Carmen Angelini .15 .40
2 J.P. Arencibia .25 .60
3 Blake Beavan .30 .75
4 Yung-Chi Chen .25 .60
5 Chih-Hsien Chiang .25 .60
6 Wendell Fairley .15 .40
7 Todd Frazier .10 .25
8 Cale Iorg .15 .40
9 Pete Kozma .10 .25
10 Che-Hsuan Lin .15 .40
11 Will Middlebrooks .10 .25
12 Nick Noonan .10 .25
13 Cole Rohrbough .15 .40
14 Joe Savery .10 .25
15 Bradley Suttle .10 .25

2007 Just Stars Autographs

OVERALL JUST AUTO ODDS 1:1 FOIL PACKS
OVERALL JUST AUTO ODDS 2:1 FACT.SETS
OVERALL JUSTIFIABLE AU ODDS 4:1 FACT.SETS
OVERALL JUST ROOKIES ODDS 1:35 PACKS
STATED PRINT RUN 100 SER.#'d SETS
1-25 ISSUED IN JUST AUTOGRAPHS
26-50 ISSUED IN JUSTIFIABLE
51-75 ISSUED IN JUST ROOKIES
OVERALL GLOSSY AU ODDS 1:12 FACT.SETS
GLOSSY AU PRINT RUN 1 SET PER COLOR
GLOSSY AU BLACK-GOLD-SILV-WHITE ISSUED
NO GLOSSY AU PRICING DUE TO SCARCITY
1 Nick Adenhart 8.00 20.00
2 Reid Brignac 4.00 10.00
3 Jay Bruce 15.00 40.00
4 Billy Butler 8.00 20.00
5 Trevor Crowe 5.00 12.00
6 Carlos Gonzalez 8.00 20.00
7 Matt Harrison 4.00 10.00
8 Philip Hughes 12.50 30.00
9 Eric Hurley 4.00 10.00
10 Clayton Kershaw 12.50 30.00
11 Tim Lincecum 20.00 50.00
12 Evan Longoria 20.00 50.00
13 Fernando Martinez 6.00 15.00
14 Andrew McCutchen 12.50 30.00
15 Adam Miller 5.00 12.00
16 Andrew Miller 6.00 15.00
17 Jesus Montero 12.50 30.00
18 Hunter Pence 12.50 30.00
19 Felix Pie 4.00 10.00
20 Bill Rowell 4.00 10.00
21 Jose Tabata 4.00 10.00
22 Justin Upton 20.00 50.00
23 Donald Veal 4.00 10.00
24 Joey Votto 15.00 40.00
25 Brandon Wood 4.00 10.00
26 Lars Anderson 6.00 15.00
27 Wladimir Balentien
28 Collin Balester 4.00 10.00
29 Dellin Betances 6.00 15.00
30 Kyle Blanks
31 Jordan Brown 4.00 10.00
32 Yung-Chi Chen 12.50 30.00
33 Jeff Clement 10.00 25.00
34 Eulogio de la Cruz 4.00 10.00
35 Ross Detwiler 4.00 10.00
36 Kyle Drabek 5.00 12.00
37 Yovanni Gallardo 4.00 10.00
38 Jaime Garcia 4.00 10.00
39 Ryan Harvey 4.00 10.00
40 Gorkys Hernandez 5.00 12.00
41 Philip Humber 5.00 12.00
42 Brandon Jones 4.00 10.00
43 Jair Jurrjens 4.00 10.00
44 Kala Kaaihue 4.00 10.00
45 Radhames Liz 4.00 10.00
46 Mitch Maier 4.00 10.00
47 Cameron Maybin 6.00 15.00
48 Franklin Morales 4.00 10.00
49 Ross Ohlendorf 4.00 10.00
50 Greg Reynolds 4.00 10.00
51 Bryan Anderson 5.00 12.00
52 Bubba Bell 8.00 20.00
53 Jose Ceda 4.00 10.00
54 Tyler Colvin 4.00 10.00
55 Hank Conger 5.00 12.00
56 Mitch Einertson
57 Juan Francisco
58 Glenn Gibson
59 Desmond Jennings
60 Cody Johnson 5.00 12.00
61 Aaron Laffey
62 Brent Lillibridge 4.00 10.00
63 Justin Masterson 12.50 30.00
64 Mark Melancon 5.00 12.00
65 Kevin Mulvey 4.00 10.00
66 Yamaico Navarro 4.00 10.00
67 Josh Reddick 4.00 10.00
68 Cole Rohrbough
69 Jeff Samardzija 8.00 20.00
70 Michael Saunders 5.00 12.00

Card	Low	High
71 Henry Sosa	5.00	12.00
72 Oscar Tejeda	5.00	12.00
73 Jordan Walden		
74 Kevin Whelan	4.00	10.00
75 Colton Willems	4.00	10.00

2007 Just Stars Autographs Black

OVERALL BLACK AU ODDS 1:2 FACT.SETS
STATED PRINT RUN 25 SER.#'d SETS
1-25 ISSUED IN JUST AUTOGRAPHS
26-50 ISSUED IN JUSTIFIABLE
NO PRICING DUE TO SCARCITY
51-75 ISSUED IN JUST ROOKIES

2007 Just Stars Autographs Gold

DISTRIBUTED IN FACTORY SET FORM
STATED PRINT RUN 50 SER.#'d SETS
1-25 ISSUED IN JUST AUTOGRAPHS
26-50 ISSUED IN JUSTIFIABLE
NO PRICING DUE TO SCARCITY
51-75 ISSUED IN JUST ROOKIES

2007 Just Stars Autographs Silver

OVERALL JUST AU SILVER ODDS 1:48 FOIL
OVERALL JUSTIFIABLE AU ODDS 1:6 SETS
STATED PRINT RUN 10 SER.#'d SETS
1-25 ISSUED IN JUST AUTOGRAPHS
26-50 ISSUED IN JUSTIFIABLE
NO PRICING DUE TO SCARCITY
51-75 ISSUED IN JUST ROOKIES

2008 Just Stars Autographs

OVERALL JUST AUTO ODDS 1:1 FOIL PACKS
OVERALL JUST AUTO ODDS 2:1 FACT.SETS
1-25 ISSUED IN JUST AUTOGRAPHS
76-100 INSERTED IN FACTORY SETS
STATED PRINT RUN 100 SER.#'d SETS
76-100 ISSUED IN JUSTIFIABLE
GLOSSY AU INSERTED IN MYSTERY PRODUCTS
GLOSSY AU PRINT RUN 1 SET PER COLOR
GLOSSY AU BLACK-GOLD-SILV-WHITE ISSUED
NO GLOSSY AU PRICING DUE TO SCARCITY

Card	Low	High
1 Tim Alderson	5.00	12.00
2 Jake Arrieta	4.00	10.00
3 Pedro Beato	3.00	8.00
4 Joe Benson	5.00	12.00
5 Julio Borbon	5.00	12.00
6 Madison Bumgarner	6.00	15.00
7 Michael Burgess	3.00	8.00
8 Carlos Carrasco	4.00	10.00
9 Alcides Escobar	4.00	10.00
10 Dexter Fowler	5.00	12.00
11 Todd Frazier	3.00	8.00
12 Jason Heyward	10.00	25.00
13 Alan Horne	5.00	12.00
14 Jeremy Jeffress	3.00	8.00
15 Kellen Kulbacki	6.00	15.00
16 Louis Marson	4.00	10.00
17 Daniel McCutchen	5.00	12.00
18 Jack McGeary	3.00	8.00
19 Jacob McGee	3.00	8.00
20 Mike Moustakas	4.00	10.00
21 Bobby Parnell	3.00	8.00
22 Joe Savery	3.00	8.00
23 Jordan Schafer	6.00	15.00
24 Travis Snider	6.00	15.00
25 Josh Vitters	6.00	15.00
76 Kevin Ahrens	3.00	8.00
77 Pedro Baez	3.00	8.00
78 Bubba Bell	3.00	8.00
79 Hector Correa	3.00	8.00
80 Fautino de los Santos	3.00	8.00
81 Wendell Fairley	3.00	8.00
82 Cole Gillespie	3.00	8.00
83 Nick Green	3.00	8.00
84 Chris Huseby	3.00	8.00
85 Cale Iorg	3.00	8.00
86 Mat Latos	10.00	25.00
87 Brad Lincoln	3.00	8.00
88 Mark Melancon	4.00	10.00
89 Devin Mesoraco	3.00	8.00
90 Sean O'Sullivan	3.00	8.00
91 Adam Ottavino	3.00	8.00
92 Chris Parmelee	3.00	8.00
93 Julio Pimentel	3.00	8.00
94 Henry Rodriguez	3.00	8.00
95 Chaz Roe	3.00	8.00
96 Bill Rowell	3.00	8.00
97 Nick Schmidt	3.00	8.00
98 James Simmons	3.00	8.00
99 James Van Ostrand	4.00	10.00
100 Casey Weathers	4.00	10.00

2008 Just Stars Autographs Black

OVERALL 08 JUST AU ODDS 2:1 FACT.SET
1-25 ISSUED IN JUST AUTOGRAPHS
76-100 ISSUED IN FACTORY SETS
76-100 ISSUED IN JUSTIFIABLE
STATED PRINT RUN 25 SER.#'d SETS
NO PRICING DUE TO SCARCITY

2008 Just Stars Autographs Gold

DISTRIBUTED IN FACTORY SET FORM
1-25 ISSUED IN JUST AUTOGRAPHS
76-100 ISSUED IN JUSTIFIABLE
STATED PRINT RUN 50 SER.#'d SETS
NO PRICING DUE TO SCARCITY

2008 Just Stars Autographs Silver

OVERALL 08 JUST AU ODDS 1:1 FOIL PACKS
1-25 ISSUED IN JUST AUTOGRAPHS
76-100 ISSUED IN FACTORY SETS
76-100 ISSUED IN JUSTIFIABLE
STATED PRINT RUN 10 SER.#'d SETS
NO PRICING DUE TO SCARCITY

2006 Justifiable

Card	Low	High
COMP.FACT.SET (54)	25.00	40.00
COMPLETE SET (50)	6.00	15.00
COMMON CARD (1-50)	.10	.25

STATED PRINT RUN 10,000 SETS
FOUR AUTOS PER SEALED FACTORY SET
GLOSSY ODDS 1:48 FACTORY SETS
NO GLOSSY PRICING DUE TO SCARCITY
PLATE ODDS 1:48 FACTORY SETS
PLATES PRINT RUN 1 SET PER COLOR
BLACK-CYAN-MAGENTA-YELLOW ISSUED
NO PLATES PRICING DUE TO SCARCITY

Card	Low	High
1 Jeff Baisley	.15	.40
2 Eric Beattie	.10	.25
3 Brent Brewer	.10	.25
4 Yung-Chi Chen	.15	.40
5 Tyler Colvin	.25	.60
6 Hank Conger	.15	.40
7 Ivan De Jesus	.10	.25
8 Jon Egan	.10	.25
9 Carlos Gonzalez	.25	.60
10 Dan Griffin	.10	.25
11 Kris Harvey	.10	.25
12 Jeremy Hellickson	.75	2.00
13 Luke Hochevar	.30	.75
14 Micah Hoffpauir	.10	.25
15 Michael Hollimon	.10	.25
16 Jeremy Jeffress	.10	.25
17 Daryl Jones	.10	.25
18 Kasey Kiker	.10	.25
19 Joe Koshansky	.10	.25
20 Bryan LaHair	.10	.25
21 Jensen Lewis	.10	.25
22 Tim Lincecum	1.00	2.50
23 Evan Longoria	1.25	3.00
24 Jeff Lyman	.10	.25
25 Fernando Martinez	1.00	2.50
26 Justin Maxwell	.10	.25
27 John Mayberry	.15	.40
28 Andrew Miller	.30	.75
29 Ryan Mullins	.10	.25
30 Micah Owings	.15	.40
31 Ryan Patterson	.10	.25
32 Cesar Ramos	.15	.40
33 Chris Robinson	.15	.40
34 Sean Rodriguez	.10	.25
35 Chaz Roe	.15	.40
36 Bill Rowell	.25	.60
37 Drew Rundle	.15	.40
38 Gaby Sanchez	.15	.40
39 Max Sapp	.10	.25
40 Zach Simons	.10	.25
41 Alay Soler	.10	.25
42 Drew Stubbs	.25	.60
43 Jose Tabata	.60	1.50
44 Chris Tillman	.15	.40
45 J.R. Towles	.10	.25
46 Matt Tuiasosopo	.10	.25
47 Justin Upton	.75	2.00
48 Carlos Villanueva	.10	.25
49 Sean West	.10	.25
50 Brandon Wood	.10	.25

2006 Justifiable Black

*BLACK: 3X TO 8X BASIC
STATED ODDS 1:4 FACTORY SETS
ALSO SOLD INDIVIDUALLY ON JMI WEBSITE
STATED PRINT RUN 50 SERIAL #'d SETS

2006 Justifiable Gold

*GOLD: 2X TO 5X BASIC
DISTRIBUTED IN FACTORY SET FORM
STATED PRINT RUN 100 SERIAL #'d SETS

2006 Justifiable Silver

*SILVER: 1.2X TO 3X BASIC
STATED ODDS ONE PER FACTORY SET
STATED PRINT RUN 200 SERIAL #'d SETS

2006 Justifiable Autographs

FOUR AUTOS PER SEALED FACTORY SET
ALSO SOLD INDIVIDUALLY ON JMI WEBSITE
PRINT RUNS B/WN 50-775 COPIES PER
CARDS ARE NOT SERIAL-NUMBERED
PRINT RUN INFO PROVIDED BY JMI

Card	Low	High
1 Jeff Baisley/275*	2.50	6.00
2 Eric Beattie/775*	2.50	6.00
3 Brent Brewer/775*	3.00	8.00
4 Yung-Chi Chen/50*	8.00	20.00
5 Tyler Colvin/175*	5.00	12.00
6 Hank Conger/400*	5.00	12.00
7 Ivan De Jesus/775*	2.50	6.00
8 Jon Egan/675*	2.50	6.00
9 Carlos Gonzalez/100*	10.00	25.00
10 Dan Griffin/775*	2.50	6.00
11 Kris Harvey/775*	2.50	6.00
12 Jeremy Hellickson/775*	10.00	25.00
13 Luke Hochevar/100*	8.00	20.00
14 Micah Hoffpauir/275*	8.00	20.00
15 Michael Hollimon/775*	2.50	6.00
16 Jeremy Jeffress/450*	5.00	12.00
17 Daryl Jones/625*	2.50	6.00
18 Kasey Kiker/200*	3.00	8.00
19 Joe Koshansky/100*	2.50	6.00
20 Bryan LaHair/725*	2.50	6.00
21 Jensen Lewis/775*	2.50	6.00
22 Tim Lincecum/100*	12.50	30.00
23 Evan Longoria/100*	20.00	50.00
24 Jeff Lyman/775*	2.50	6.00
25 Fernando Martinez/100*	12.50	30.00
26 Justin Maxwell/775*	2.50	6.00
27 John Mayberry/275*	3.00	8.00
28 Andrew Miller/100*	8.00	20.00
29 Ryan Mullins/775*	2.50	6.00
30 Micah Owings/400*	3.00	8.00
31 Ryan Patterson/775*	2.50	6.00
32 Cesar Ramos/775*	3.00	8.00
33 Chris Robinson/775*	2.50	6.00
34 Sean Rodriguez/100*	3.00	8.00
35 Chaz Roe/775*	3.00	8.00
36 Bill Rowell/100*	8.00	20.00
37 Drew Rundle/275*	3.00	8.00
38 Gaby Sanchez/775*	2.50	6.00
39 Max Sapp/450*	5.00	12.00
40 Zach Simons/775*	2.50	6.00
42 Drew Stubbs/200*	6.00	15.00
43 Jose Tabata/100*	4.00	10.00
44 Chris Tillman/775*	5.00	12.00
45 J.R. Towles/275*	2.50	6.00
48 Carlos Villanueva/775*	2.50	6.00
49 Sean West/775*	2.50	6.00
50 Brandon Wood/100*	8.00	20.00

2006 Justifiable Autographs Black

SOLD INDIVIDUALLY VIA JMI WEBSITE
STATED PRINT RUN 25 SERIAL #'d SETS
NO PRICING DUE TO SCARCITY

2006 Justifiable Autographs Gold

DISTRIBUTED IN FACTORY SET FORM
STATED PRINT RUN 50 SERIAL #'d SETS
NO PRICING DUE TO SCARCITY
41 Alay Soler
46 Matt Tuiasosopo
47 Justin Upton

2006 Justifiable Autographs Silver

*SILVER: .5X TO 1.2X BASIC p/r 625-775
*SILVER: .5X TO 1.2X BASIC p/r 275-450
*SILVER: .4X TO 1X BASIC p/r 100-200
RANDOM INSERTS IN FACTORY SETS
STATED PRINT RUN 100 SERIAL #'d SETS

Card	Low	High
47 Justin Upton	12.50	30.00

2007 Justifiable

Card	Low	High
COMP.FACT.SET (54)	15.00	40.00
COMPLETE SET (50)	6.00	15.00
COMMON CARD (1-50)	.10	.25

FOUR AUTOS PER SEALED FACTORY SET
GLOSSY ODDS 1:12 FACTORY SETS
NO GLOSSY PRICING DUE TO SCARCITY
PLATE ODDS 1:24 FACTORY SETS
PLATES PRINT RUN 1 SET PER COLOR
BLACK-CYAN-MAGENTA-YELLOW ISSUED
NO PLATES PRICING DUE TO SCARCITY

Card	Low	High
1 Kevin Ahrens	.15	.40
2 Tim Alderson	.15	.40
3 Hector Ambriz	.10	.25
4 Bryan Anderson	.10	.25
5 J.P. Arencibia	.25	.60
6 Blake Beavan	.30	.75
7 Jordan Brown	.15	.40
8 Chih-Hsien Chiang	.25	.60
9 Ross Detwiler	.10	.25
10 Alcides Escobar	.15	.40
11 Juan Francisco	.25	.60
12 Hector Gomez	.15	.40
13 Nick Green	.15	.40
14 Steve Hammond	.10	.25
15 Cyle Hankerd	.10	.25
16 Jason Heyward	.75	2.00
17 Stephen King	.10	.25
18 George Kontos	.15	.40
19 Kellen Kulbacki	.10	.25
20 Aaron Laffey	.25	.60
21 Matt Latos	.25	.60
22 Brent Lillibridge	.10	.25
23 Che-Hsuan Lin	.15	.40
24 Justin Masterson	.25	.60
25 Daniel McCutchen	.15	.40
26 Beau Mills	.10	.25
27 Adam Moore	.10	.25
28 Daniel Moskos	.10	.25
29 Mike Moustakas	.40	1.00
30 Kevin Mulvey	.25	.60
31 Yamaico Navarro	.15	.40
32 Jarrod Parker	.25	.60
33 Steve Pearce	.15	.40
34 David Price	.60	1.50
35 John Raynor	.15	.40
36 Michael Saunders	.30	.75
37 Joe Savery	.10	.25
38 Nick Schmidt	.10	.25
39 Chris Shaver	.10	.25
40 Henry Sosa	.15	.40
41 Oscar Tejeda	.10	.25
42 Rich Thompson	.10	.25
43 Jimmy Van Ostrand	.15	.40
44 Josh Vitters	.25	.60
45 Jordan Walden	.15	.40
46 Sean Watson	.10	.25
47 Casey Weathers	.10	.25
48 Tyler Weeden	.15	.40
49 Matt Wieters	.50	1.25
50 Zech Zinicola	.10	.25

2007 Justifiable Black

*BLACK: 4X TO 10X BASIC
STATED ODDS 2:3 FACTORY SETS
STATED PRINT RUN 50 SERIAL #'d SETS

2007 Justifiable Gold

*GOLD: 2X TO 5X BASIC
DISTRIBUTED IN FACTORY SET FORM
STATED PRINT RUN 100 SERIAL #'d SETS

2007 Justifiable Silver

STATED ODDS 1:3 FACTORY SETS
STATED PRINT RUN 25 SER.#'d SETS
NO PRICING DUE TO SCARCITY

2007 Justifiable Autographs

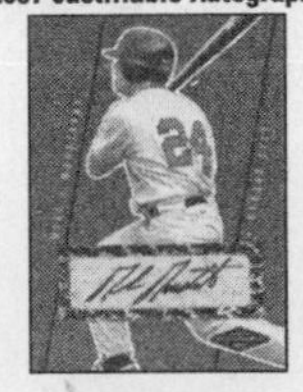

FOUR AUTOS PER SEALED FACTORY SET
ALSO SOLD INDIVIDUALLY ON JMI WEBSITE
GLOSSY AU ODDS 1:12 FACTORY SETS
NO GLOSSY AU PRICING DUE TO SCARCITY
PLATE AU ODDS 1:24 FACTORY SETS
PLATES AU PRINT RUN 1 SET PER COLOR
BLACK-CYAN-MAGENTA-YELLOW ISSUED
NO PLATES PRICING DUE TO SCARCITY

Card	Low	High
1 Kevin Ahrens	5.00	12.00
2 Tim Alderson	4.00	10.00
3 Hector Ambriz	2.50	6.00
4 Bryan Anderson	5.00	12.00
5 J.P. Arencibia	8.00	20.00
6 Blake Beavan	4.00	10.00
7 Jordan Brown	3.00	8.00
8 Chih-Hsien Chiang	8.00	20.00
9 Ross Detwiler	4.00	10.00
10 Alcides Escobar	3.00	8.00
11 Juan Francisco	4.00	10.00
12 Hector Gomez	3.00	8.00
13 Nick Green	3.00	8.00
14 Steve Hammond	3.00	8.00
15 Cyle Hankerd	2.50	6.00
16 Jason Heyward	30.00	60.00
17 Stephen King	3.00	8.00
18 George Kontos	5.00	12.00
19 Kellen Kulbacki	5.00	12.00
20 Aaron Laffey	5.00	12.00
21 Matt Latos	6.00	15.00
22 Brent Lillibridge	3.00	8.00
23 Che-Hsuan Lin	8.00	20.00
24 Justin Masterson	12.50	30.00
25 Daniel McCutchen	4.00	10.00
26 Beau Mills	10.00	25.00
27 Adam Moore	3.00	8.00
28 Daniel Moskos	6.00	15.00
29 Mike Moustakas	10.00	25.00
30 Kevin Mulvey	6.00	15.00
31 Yamaico Navarro	6.00	15.00
32 Jarrod Parker	6.00	15.00
33 Steve Pearce	6.00	15.00
34 David Price	8.00	20.00
35 John Raynor	4.00	10.00
36 Michael Saunders	4.00	10.00
37 Joe Savery	3.00	8.00
38 Nick Schmidt	4.00	10.00
39 Chris Shaver	2.50	6.00
40 Henry Sosa	3.00	8.00
41 Oscar Tejeda	5.00	12.00
42 Rich Thompson	3.00	8.00
43 Jimmy Van Ostrand	3.00	8.00
44 Josh Vitters	8.00	20.00
45 Jordan Walden	3.00	8.00
46 Sean Watson	3.00	8.00
47 Casey Weathers	5.00	12.00
48 Tyler Weeden	3.00	8.00
49 Matt Wieters	15.00	40.00
50 Zech Zinicola	2.50	6.00

2007 Justifiable Autographs Black

OVERALL BLACK AU ODDS 1:2 FACT.SETS
STATED PRINT RUN 25 SER.#'d SETS
NO PRICING DUE TO SCARCITY

2007 Justifiable Autographs Gold

DISTRIBUTED IN FACTORY SET FORM
STATED PRINT RUN 50 SERIAL #'d SETS
NO PRICING DUE TO SCARCITY

2007 Justifiable Autographs Silver

OVERALL SILVER AU ODDS 1:6 FACT.SETS
STATED PRINT RUN 10 SER.#'d SETS
NO PRICING DUE TO SCARCITY

2007 Justifiable 08 Preview

Card	Low	High
1 Michael Almanzar	.25	.60
2 Andrew Brackman	.25	.60
3 Madison Bumgarner	.60	1.50
4 Michael Burgess	.15	.40
5 Ross Detwiler	.10	.25
6 Nick Hagadone	.15	.40
7 Jason Heyward	.75	2.00
8 Matt LaPorta	.40	1.00
9 Michael Main	.15	.40
10 Jack McGeary	.10	.25
11 Beau Mills	.10	.25
12 Daniel Moskos	.10	.25
13 Mike Moustakas	.40	1.00
14 Jarrod Parker	.25	.60
15 Steve Pearce	.15	.40
16 Rick Porcello	.40	1.00
17 David Price	.60	1.50
18 Ben Revere	.25	.60
19 Josh Vitters	.25	.60
20 Matt Wieters	.50	1.25

2007 Justifiable 08 Preview Gold

*GOLD: 2X TO 5X BASIC
STATED PRINT RUN 100 SER.#'d SETS

2008 Justifiable

Card	Low	High
COMP.FACT.SET (54)	15.00	40.00
COMPLETE SET (50)	6.00	15.00
COMMON CARD (1-50)	.10	.25

FOUR AUTOS PER SEALED FACTORY SET
GLOSSY RANDOM FACT.SET INSERTS
NO GLOSSY PRICING DUE TO SCARCITY
PLATE ODDS 1:24 FACTORY SETS
PLATES PRINT RUN 1 SET PER COLOR
BLACK-CYAN-MAGENTA-YELLOW ISSUED
NO PLATES PRICING DUE TO SCARCITY

Card	Low	High
1 Brandon Allen	.10	.25
2 Brett Anderson	.15	.40
3 Matt Antonelli	.10	.25
4 Jake Arrieta	.10	.25
5 Blake Beavan	.15	.40
6 Julio Borbon	.10	.25
7 Drake Britton	.15	.40
8 David Bromberg	.15	.40
9 Robert Bryson	.10	.25
10 Adam Carr	.10	.25
11 Nick Carr	.10	.25
12 Scott Carroll	.10	.25
13 Jhoulys Chacin	.40	1.00
14 Stephen Clyne	.10	.25
15 Daniel Cortes	.25	.60
16 Allen Craig	.15	.40
17 Marcus Davis	.10	.25
18 Kelvin de la Cruz	.10	.25
19 Fautino de los Santos	.10	.25
20 Kelvin DeLeon	.10	.25
21 John Ely	.10	.25
22 Shelby Ford	.15	.40
23 Charlie Furbush	.10	.25
24 Tommy Hanson	.40	1.00
25 Deryk Hooker	.10	.25
26 Brandon Hynick	.10	.25
27 Kris Johnson	.15	.40
28 Chris Jones	.10	.25
29 Brad Lincoln	.10	.25
30 Chris Marrero	.10	.25
31 Mike McCardell	.10	.25
32 Austin McClune	.10	.25
33 Beau Mills	.10	.25
34 Mike Moustakas	.30	.75
35 Reynaldo Navarro	.10	.25
36 Jarrod Parker	.25	.60
37 Gerardo Parra	.10	.25
38 Luis Pena	.10	.25
39 Julio Pimentel	.10	.25
40 Aaron Poreda	.10	.25
41 David Price	.25	.60
42 David Robertson	.25	.60
43 Wes Roemer	.10	.25
44 Rocky Roquet	.10	.25
45 Carlos Rosa	.10	.25
46 Carlos Santana	.75	2.00
47 Travis Snider	.15	.40
48 Chorye Spoone	.15	.40
49 Julio Teheran	.40	1.00
50 Pedro Viola	.10	.25

2008 Justifiable Black

*BLACK: 3X TO 8X BASIC
RANDOM INSERTS IN FACTORY SETS
STATED PRINT RUN 50 SERIAL #'d SETS

2008 Justifiable Silver

RANDOM INSERTS IN FACTORY SETS
STATED PRINT RUN 25 SER.#'d SETS
NO PRICING DUE TO SCARCITY

2008 Justifiable Autographs

FOUR AUTOS PER SEALED FACTORY SET
ALSO SOLD INDIVIDUALLY ON JMI WEBSITE
C EQUALS COMMON
R EQUAL RARE
U EQUALS UNCOMMON
GLOSSY AUTOS FOUND IN MYS.PRODUCTS
NO GLOSSY AU PRICING DUE TO SCARCITY
PLATE AU ODDS 1:24 FACTORY SETS
PLATES AU PRINT RUN 1 SET PER COLOR
BLACK-CYAN-MAGENTA-YELLOW ISSUED
NO PLATES PRICING DUE TO SCARCITY

Card	Low	High
1 Brandon Allen Common	2.50	6.00
2 Brett Anderson Rare	3.00	8.00
3 Matt Antonelli Rare	4.00	10.00
4 Jake Arrieta Rare	4.00	10.00
5 Blake Beavan Rare		
6 Julio Borbon Rare	4.00	10.00
7 Drake Britton Common	2.50	6.00
8 David Bromberg Common	2.50	6.00
9 Robert Bryson Common	2.50	6.00
10 Adam Carr Common	2.50	6.00
11 Nick Carr Common	2.50	6.00
12 Scott Carroll Common		
13 Jhoulys Chacin Uncommon	4.00	10.00
14 Stephen Clyne Common	2.50	6.00
15 Daniel Cortes Common	2.50	6.00
16 Allen Craig Common	2.50	6.00
17 Marcus Davis Common	2.50	6.00
18 Kelvin de la Cruz Common	2.50	6.00
19 Fautino de los Santos Common	2.50	6.00
20 Kelvin DeLeon Rare		
21 John Ely Common	2.50	6.00
22 Shelby Ford Common		
23 Charlie Furbush Common		
24 Tommy Hanson Rare	10.00	25.00
25 Deryk Hooker Common	2.50	6.00
26 Brandon Hynick Common	2.50	6.00
27 Kris Johnson Common	2.50	6.00
28 Chris Jones Common	2.50	6.00
29 Brad Lincoln Rare		
30 Chris Marrero Rare	3.00	8.00
31 Mike McCardell Common	2.50	6.00
32 Austin McClune Common		
33 Beau Mills Rare		
34 Mike Moustakas Rare	5.00	12.00
35 Reynaldo Navarro Rare		
36 Jarrod Parker Rare	8.00	20.00
37 Gerardo Parra Rare	4.00	10.00
38 Luis Pena Common	2.50	6.00
39 Julio Pimentel Uncommon	2.50	6.00
40 Aaron Poreda Common		
41 David Price Rare		
42 David Robertson Rare	3.00	8.00
43 Wes Roemer Common		
44 Rocky Roquet Common	2.50	6.00
45 Carlos Rosa Common	2.50	6.00
46 Carlos Santana Rare	6.00	15.00
47 Travis Snider Rare	6.00	15.00
48 Chorye Spoone Common	2.50	6.00
49 Julio Teheran Rare	4.00	10.00
50 Pedro Viola Common	2.50	6.00

2008 Justifiable Autographs Black

RANDOM INSERTS IN FACTORY SETS
STATED PRINT RUN 25 SER.#'d SETS
NO PRICING DUE TO SCARCITY

2008 Justifiable Autographs Gold

DISTRIBUTED IN FACTORY SET FORM
STATED PRINT RUN 50 SERIAL #'d SETS
NO PRICING DUE TO SCARCITY

2008 Justifiable Autographs Silver

RANDOM INSERTS IN FACTORY SETS
STATED PRINT RUN 10 SER.#'d SETS
NO PRICING DUE TO SCARCITY

2011 Leaf Metal Draft

COMMON CARD 3.00 8.00
PLATE PRINT RUN 1 SET PER COLOR
BLACK-CYAN-MAGENTA-YELLOW ISSUED
NO PLATE PRICING DUE TO SCARCITY
AA1 Aaron Altherr 3.00 8.00
AB1 Archie Bradley 6.00 15.00
AH1 Austin Hedges 3.00 8.00
AM1 Alex Meyer 4.00 10.00
AM2 Anthony Meo 3.00 8.00
AO1 Andrew Oliver 3.00 8.00
AR1 Anthony Rendon 15.00 40.00
AR2 Aderlin Rodriguez 3.00 8.00
AS1 Andrew Susac 4.00 10.00
BG1 Brian Goodwin 4.00 10.00
BL1 Barret Loux 4.00 10.00
BM1 Brandon Martin 3.00 8.00
BN1 Brandon Nimmo 6.00 15.00
BO1 Brett Oberholtzer 3.00 8.00
BP1 Brad Peacock 4.00 10.00
BS1 Blake Swihart 5.00 12.00
BS1 Brandon Short 3.00 8.00
BS2 Bubba Starling 10.00 25.00
BW1 Brandon Workman 3.00 8.00
CC1 C.J. Cron 5.00 12.00
CC2 Cheslor Cuthbert 8.00 20.00
CM1 Carlos Martinez 8.00 20.00
CS1 Cory Spangenberg 5.00 12.00
CS2 Clayton Schrader 3.00 8.00
DB2 Dylan Bundy 20.00 50.00
DH1 Danny Hultzen 15.00 40.00
DH2 Dillon Howard 3.00 8.00
DN1 Daniel Norris 6.00 15.00
DP1 David Perez 3.00 8.00
DT1 Dickie Joe Thon 3.00 8.00
EK1 Erik Komatsu 3.00 8.00
ES1 Edward Salcedo 3.00 8.00
FL1 Francisco Lindor 6.00 15.00
FM1 Francisco Martinez 3.00 8.00
FS1 Felix Sterling 4.00 10.00
GC1 Gerrit Cole 10.00 25.00
GG1 Garrett Gould 3.00 8.00
GG2 Granden Goetzman 3.00 8.00
GS1 George Springer 6.00 15.00
HH1 Heath Hembree 3.00 8.00
HL1 Hak-Ju Lee 10.00 25.00
HO1 Henry Owens 3.00 8.00
JA1 Jason Adam 3.00 8.00
JB1 Jackie Bradley Jr. 5.00 12.00
JB2 Javier Baez 4.00 10.00
JB3 Jed Bradley 4.00 10.00
JB4 Josh Bell 20.00 50.00
JD1 Juan Duran 3.00 8.00
JE1 Jason Esposito 3.00 8.00
JF1 Jose Fernandez 3.00 8.00
JG1 John Gast 3.00 8.00
JJ1 Jiwan James 3.00 8.00
JJH J.J. Hoover 3.00 8.00
JM1 Jeremy Moore 3.00 8.00
JP1 Jacob Petricka 3.00 8.00
JP2 Joe Panik 5.00 12.00
JP2 Jurickson Profar 8.00 20.00
JS1 Jonathan Schoop 5.00 12.00
JV1 Jonathan Villar 3.00 8.00
KH1 Kelvin Herrera 3.00 8.00
KM1 Kevin Matthews 3.00 8.00
KP1 Kyle Parker 4.00 10.00
KW1 Kolten Wong 6.00 15.00
KW2 Keenyn Walker 3.00 8.00
LH1 Luis Heredia 6.00 15.00
LM2 Levi Michael 6.00 15.00
MB2 Manny Banuelos 10.00 25.00
MB3 Matt Barnes 4.00 10.00
MK2 Marcus Knecht 3.00 8.00
MM1 Manny Machado 12.50 30.00
MM2 Mikie Mahtook 5.00 12.00
MS3 Miguel de los Santos 3.00 8.00
ND1 Nicky Delmonico 3.00 8.00
RM1 Ramon Morla 3.00 8.00
RR1 Robbie Ray 3.00 8.00
RS1 Robert Stephenson 3.00 8.00
SG1 Sonny Gray 4.00 10.00
SG2 Sean Gilmartin 3.00 8.00
SM1 Starling Marte 5.00 12.00
TA1 Tyler Anderson 3.00 8.00
TB1 Trevor Bauer 10.00 25.00
TG1 Taylor Guerrieri 3.00 8.00
TG2 Tyler Goeddel 3.00 8.00
TH1 Travis Harrison 5.00 12.00
TJ1 Taylor Jungmann 5.00 12.00
TM1 Trevor May 6.00 15.00
TW1 Travis Witherspoon 3.00 8.00
VP1 Victor Payano 3.00 8.00
XB1 Xander Bogaerts 8.00 20.00
YV1 Yordano Ventura 3.00 8.00
ZW1 Zack Wheeler 8.00 20.00

2011 Leaf Metal Draft Prismatic

*RAINBOW: .6X TO 1.5X BASIC
STATED PRINT RUN 99 SER.#'d SETS

2011 Leaf Metal Draft Prismatic Blue

STATED PRINT RUN 25 SER.#'d SETS
NO PRICING DUE TO SCARCITY

2011 Leaf Metal Draft Prismatic Gold

STATED PRINT RUN 1 SER.#'d SET
NO PRICING DUE TO SCARCITY

2011 Leaf Metal Draft Prismatic Red

STATED PRINT RUN 5 SER.#'d SETS
NO PRICING DUE TO SCARCITY

2011 Leaf Metal Draft Ichrio Suzuki Patch Autographs

PRINT RUNS B/WN 1-99 COPIES PER
NO PRICING ON QTY 25 OR LESS
IS1 Ichiro Suzuki/99 700.00 1000.00

2011 Leaf Valiant Draft

PLATE PRINT RUN 1 SET PER COLOR
BLACK-CYAN-MAGENTA-YELLOW ISSUED
NO PLATE PRICING DUE TO SCARCITY
I1 Ichiro Suzuki 400.00 800.00
AA1 Aaron Altherr 3.00 8.00
AB1 Archie Bradley 6.00 15.00
AH1 Austin Hedges 3.00 8.00
AM1 Alex Meyer 3.00 8.00
AM2 Anthony Meo 3.00 8.00
AO1 Andy Oliver 3.00 8.00
AR1 Anthony Rendon 12.50 30.00
AR2 Aderlin Rodriguez 3.00 8.00
AS1 Andrew Susac 4.00 10.00
BG1 Brian Goodwin 3.00 8.00
BL1 Barret Loux 3.00 8.00
BM1 Brandon Martin 3.00 8.00
BN1 Brandon Nimmo 6.00 15.00
BO1 Brett Oberholtzer 3.00 8.00
BP1 Brad Peacock 5.00 12.00
BS1 Blake Swihart 3.00 8.00
BS1 Brandon Short 3.00 8.00
BS2 Bubba Starling 10.00 25.00
BW1 Brandon Workman 3.00 8.00
CC1 C.J. Cron 4.00 10.00
CC2 Cheslor Cuthbert 12.50 30.00
CM1 Carlos Martinez 6.00 15.00
CS1 Cory Spangenberg 4.00 10.00
CS2 Clayton Schrader 3.00 8.00
DB2 Dylan Bundy 15.00 40.00
DH1 Danny Hultzen 10.00 25.00
DH2 Dillon Howard 5.00 12.00
DN1 Daniel Norris 4.00 10.00
DP1 David Perez 3.00 8.00
DT1 Dickie Joe Thon 3.00 8.00
EK1 Erik Komatsu 3.00 8.00
ES1 Edward Salcedo 3.00 8.00
FL1 Francisco Lindor 5.00 12.00
FM1 Francisco Martinez 3.00 8.00
FS1 Felix Sterling 3.00 8.00
GC1 Gerrit Cole 10.00 25.00
GG1 Garrett Gould 3.00 8.00
GG2 Granden Goetzman 3.00 8.00
GS1 George Springer 5.00 12.00
HH1 Heath Hembree 3.00 8.00
HL1 Hak-Ju Lee 10.00 25.00
HO1 Henry Owens 3.00 8.00
JA1 Jason Adam 3.00 8.00
JB1 Jackie Bradley Jr. 4.00 10.00
JB2 Javier Baez 5.00 12.00
JB3 Jed Bradley 4.00 10.00
JD1 Juan Duran 3.00 8.00
JE1 Jason Esposito 3.00 8.00
JF1 Jose Fernandez 4.00 10.00
JG1 John Gast 3.00 8.00
JJ1 Jiwan James 3.00 8.00
JJH J.J. Hoover 3.00 8.00
JM1 Jeremy Moore 3.00 8.00
JP1 Jacob Petricka 3.00 8.00
JP2 Joe Panik 6.00 15.00
JP2 Jurickson Profar 6.00 15.00
JS1 Jonathan Schoop 5.00 12.00
JV1 Jonathan Villar 3.00 8.00
KH1 Kelvin Herrera 3.00 8.00
KM1 Kevin Matthews 3.00 8.00
KP1 Kyle Parker 3.00 8.00
KW1 Kolten Wong 5.00 12.00
KW2 Keenyn Walker 3.00 8.00
LH1 Luis Heredia 5.00 12.00
LM2 Levi Michael 5.00 12.00
MB2 Manny Banuelos 10.00 25.00
MB3 Matt Barnes 3.00 8.00
MK2 Marcus Knecht 3.00 8.00
MM1 Manny Machado 15.00 40.00
MM2 Mikie Mahtook 5.00 12.00
MS3 Miguel de los Santos 3.00 8.00
ND1 Nicky Delmonico 3.00 8.00
RM1 Ramon Morla 3.00 8.00
RR1 Robbie Ray 3.00 8.00
RS1 Robert Stephenson 3.00 8.00
SG1 Sonny Gray 4.00 10.00
SG2 Sean Gilmartin 4.00 10.00
SM1 Starling Marte 4.00 10.00
TA1 Tyler Anderson 3.00 8.00
TB1 Trevor Bauer 10.00 25.00
TG1 Taylor Guerrieri 4.00 10.00
TG2 Tyler Goeddel 3.00 8.00
TH1 Travis Harrison 3.00 8.00
TJ1 Taylor Jungmann 5.00 12.00
TM1 Trevor May 5.00 12.00
TW1 Travis Witherspoon 3.00 8.00
VP1 Victor Payano 3.00 8.00
XB1 Xander Bogaerts 6.00 15.00
YV1 Yordano Ventura 3.00 8.00
ZW1 Zack Wheeler 6.00 15.00

2011 Leaf Valiant Draft Black

STATED PRINT RUN 10 SER.#'d SETS
ICHIRO PRINT RUN 5 SER.#'d SETS
NO PRICING DUE TO SCARCITY

2011 Leaf Valiant Draft Blue

*BLUE: .6X TO 1.5X BASIC
STATED PRINT RUN 99 SER.#'d SETS
ICHIRO PRINT RUN 14 SER.#'d SETS
NO ICHIRO PRICING DUE TO SCARCITY

2011 Leaf Valiant Draft Orange

STATED PRINT RUN 25 SER.#'d SETS
ICHIRO PRINT RUN 10 SER.#'d SETS
NO PRICING DUE TO SCARCITY

2011 Leaf Valiant Draft Red

STATED PRINT RUN 1 SER.#'d SET
NO PRICING DUE TO SCARCITY

2008 Razor Letterman

This set was released on March 12, 2009. The base set consists of 655 cards.

COMMON CARD 3.00 8.00
OVERALL AU ODDS ONE PER PACK
ALL LETTERS PRICED EQUALLY
ACC Aaron Crow 10.00 25.00
ACO Aaron Crow 10.00 25.00
ACR Aaron Crow 10.00 25.00
ACW Aaron Crow 10.00 25.00
ADA Allan Dykstra 6.00 15.00
ADD Allan Dykstra 6.00 15.00
ADK Allan Dykstra 6.00 15.00
ADR Allan Dykstra 6.00 15.00
ADS Allan Dykstra 6.00 15.00
ADT Allan Dykstra 6.00 15.00
ADY Allan Dykstra 6.00 15.00
ANE Adrian Nieto 4.00 10.00
ANI Adrian Nieto 4.00 10.00
ANN Adrian Nieto 4.00 10.00
ANO Adrian Nieto 4.00 10.00
ANT Adrian Nieto 4.00 10.00
APA Aaron Pribanic 4.00 10.00
APB Aaron Pribanic 4.00 10.00
APC Aaron Pribanic 4.00 10.00
APN Aaron Pribanic 4.00 10.00
APP Aaron Pribanic 4.00 10.00
APR Aaron Pribanic 4.00 10.00
BDA Brett DeVall 8.00 20.00
BDD Brett DeVall 8.00 20.00
BDE Brett DeVall 8.00 20.00
BDV Brett DeVall 8.00 20.00
BWC Brett Wallace 4.00 10.00
BWE Brett Wallace 4.00 10.00
BWW Brett Wallace 4.00 10.00
CBA Charlie Blackmon 3.00 8.00
CBB Charlie Blackmon 3.00 8.00
CBC Charlie Blackmon 3.00 8.00
CBK Charlie Blackmon 3.00 8.00
CBL Charlie Blackmon 3.00 8.00
CBM Charlie Blackmon 3.00 8.00
CBN Charlie Blackmon 3.00 8.00
CBO Charlie Blackmon 3.00 8.00
CFC Christian Friedrich 4.00 10.00
CFD Christian Friedrich 4.00 10.00
CFE Christian Friedrich 4.00 10.00
CFF Christian Friedrich 4.00 10.00
CFH Christian Friedrich 4.00 10.00
CGG Carlos Gutierrez 6.00 15.00
CGI Carlos Gutierrez 6.00 15.00
CGT Carlos Gutierrez 6.00 15.00
CGU Carlos Gutierrez 6.00 15.00
CGZ Carlos Gutierrez 6.00 15.00
CKE Casey Kelly 10.00 25.00
CKK Casey Kelly 10.00 25.00
CKY Casey Kelly 10.00 25.00
CWE Casper Wells 3.00 8.00
CWS Casper Wells 3.00 8.00
CWW Casper Wells 3.00 8.00
DAD David Adams 3.00 8.00
DAM David Adams 3.00 8.00
DAS David Adams 3.00 8.00
DEA Danny Espinosa 6.00 15.00
DEE Danny Espinosa 6.00 15.00
DEI Danny Espinosa 6.00 15.00
DEN Danny Espinosa 6.00 15.00
DEO Danny Espinosa 6.00 15.00
DEP Danny Espinosa 6.00 15.00
DGB Derrik Gibson 4.00 10.00
DGG Derrik Gibson 4.00 10.00
DGI Derrik Gibson 4.00 10.00
DGN Derrik Gibson 4.00 10.00
DGO Derrik Gibson 4.00 10.00
DGS Derrik Gibson 4.00 10.00
DRA Dennis Raben 6.00 15.00
DRB Dennis Raben 6.00 15.00
DRE Dennis Raben 6.00 15.00
DRN Dennis Raben 6.00 15.00
DRR Dennis Raben 6.00 15.00
EHE Eric Hosmer 15.00 40.00
EHH Eric Hosmer 15.00 40.00
EHM Eric Hosmer 15.00 40.00
EHO Eric Hosmer 15.00 40.00
EHR Eric Hosmer 15.00 40.00
EHS Eric Hosmer 15.00 40.00
EMA Ethan Martin 5.00 12.00
EMI Ethan Martin 5.00 12.00
EMM Ethan Martin 5.00 12.00
EMN Ethan Martin 5.00 12.00
EMR Ethan Martin 5.00 12.00
EMT Ethan Martin 5.00 12.00
EOL Edgar Olmos 3.00 8.00
EOM Edgar Olmos 3.00 8.00
EOS Edgar Olmos 3.00 8.00
GBA Gordon Beckham 10.00 25.00
GBB Gordon Beckham 10.00 25.00
GBC Gordon Beckham 10.00 25.00
GBE Gordon Beckham 10.00 25.00
GBH Gordon Beckham 10.00 25.00
GBK Gordon Beckham 10.00 25.00
GBM Gordon Beckham 10.00 25.00
GHH Greg Halman 6.00 15.00
GHL Greg Halman 6.00 15.00
GHM Greg Halman 6.00 15.00
GHN Greg Halman 6.00 15.00
GLA Garrison Lassiter 6.00 15.00
GLE Garrison Lassiter 6.00 15.00
GLI Garrison Lassiter 6.00 15.00
GLL Garrison Lassiter 6.00 15.00
GLR Garrison Lassiter 6.00 15.00
GLT Garrison Lassiter 6.00 15.00
IDA Ike Davis 10.00 25.00
IDD Ike Davis 10.00 25.00
IDI Ike Davis 10.00 25.00
IDS Ike Davis 10.00 25.00
IDV Ike Davis 10.00 25.00
IGG Isaac Galloway 8.00 20.00
IGO Isaac Galloway 8.00 20.00
IGW Isaac Galloway 8.00 20.00
IGY Isaac Galloway 8.00 20.00
JAA Jay Austin 3.00 8.00
JAI Jay Austin 3.00 8.00
JAN Jay Austin 3.00 8.00
JAS Jay Austin 3.00 8.00
JAT Jay Austin 3.00 8.00
JAU Jay Austin 3.00 8.00
JCA Jason Castro 12.50 30.00
JCC Jason Castro 12.50 30.00
JCO Jason Castro 12.50 30.00
JCR Jason Castro 12.50 30.00
JCS Jason Castro 12.50 30.00
JCT Jason Castro 12.50 30.00
JFD Joshua Fields 4.00 10.00
JFE Joshua Fields 4.00 10.00
JFF Joshua Fields 4.00 10.00
JFI Joshua Fields 4.00 10.00
JFL Joshua Fields 4.00 10.00
JFS Joshua Fields 4.00 10.00
JOD Jake Odorizzi 6.00 15.00
JOR Jake Odorizzi 6.00 15.00
JSA Justin Smoak 12.50 30.00
JSK Justin Smoak 12.50 30.00
JSM Justin Smoak 12.50 30.00
JSO Justin Smoak 12.50 30.00
JSS Justin Smoak 12.50 30.00
JWK Jemile Weeks 5.00 12.00
JWS Jemile Weeks 5.00 12.00
JWW Jemile Weeks 5.00 12.00
KLB Kyle Lobstein 3.00 8.00
KLE Kyle Lobstein 3.00 8.00
KLI Kyle Lobstein 3.00 8.00
KLL Kyle Lobstein 3.00 8.00
KLN Kyle Lobstein 3.00 8.00
KLO Kyle Lobstein 3.00 8.00
KLS Kyle Lobstein 3.00 8.00
KLT Kyle Lobstein 3.00 8.00
KNH Kirk Nieuwenhuis 3.00 8.00
KNS Kirk Nieuwenhuis 3.00 8.00
KNW Kirk Nieuwenhuis 3.00 8.00
KPA Kevin Pucetas 3.00 8.00
KPC Kevin Pucetas 3.00 8.00
KPE Kevin Pucetas 3.00 8.00
KPP Kevin Pucetas 3.00 8.00
KPS Kevin Pucetas 3.00 8.00
KPT Kevin Pucetas 3.00 8.00
KPU Kevin Pucetas 3.00 8.00
KRE Kyle Russell 3.00 8.00
KRR Kyle Russell 3.00 8.00
KRU Kyle Russell 3.00 8.00
KSH Kyle Skipworth 3.00 8.00
KSI Kyle Skipworth 3.00 8.00
KSK Kyle Skipworth 3.00 8.00
KSO Kyle Skipworth 3.00 8.00
KSP Kyle Skipworth 3.00 8.00
KSR Kyle Skipworth 3.00 8.00
KSS Kyle Skipworth 3.00 8.00
KST Kyle Skipworth 3.00 8.00
KSW Kyle Skipworth 3.00 8.00
KWA Kyle Weiland 10.00 25.00
KWD Kyle Weiland 10.00 25.00
KWE Kyle Weiland 10.00 25.00
KWI Kyle Weiland 10.00 25.00
KWL Kyle Weiland 10.00 25.00
KWN Kyle Weiland 10.00 25.00
KWW Kyle Weiland 10.00 25.00
LFE Logan Forsythe 3.00 8.00
LFF Logan Forsythe 3.00 8.00
LFH Logan Forsythe 3.00 8.00
LFO Logan Forsythe 3.00 8.00
LFR Logan Forsythe 3.00 8.00
LFS Logan Forsythe 3.00 8.00
LFT Logan Forsythe 3.00 8.00
LFY Logan Forsythe 3.00 8.00
MIA Michel Inoa 12.50 30.00
MII Michel Inoa 12.50 30.00
MIN Michel Inoa 12.50 30.00
MIO Michel Inoa 12.50 30.00
MSA Michael Stanton 15.00 40.00
MSO Michael Stanton 15.00 40.00
MSS Michael Stanton 15.00 40.00
MTH Matt Thompson 4.00 10.00
MTM Matt Thompson 4.00 10.00
MTN Matt Thompson 4.00 10.00
MTP Matt Thompson 4.00 10.00
MTS Matt Thompson 4.00 10.00
MTT Matt Thompson 4.00 10.00
MWI Matt Wieters 10.00 25.00
MWR Matt Wieters 10.00 25.00
MWS Matt Wieters 10.00 25.00
MWT Matt Wieters 10.00 25.00
MWW Matt Wieters 10.00 25.00
PAE Pedro Alvarez 12.50 30.00
PAL Pedro Alvarez 12.50 30.00
PAR Pedro Alvarez 12.50 30.00
PAV Pedro Alvarez 12.50 30.00
PAZ Pedro Alvarez 12.50 30.00
PHE Pete Hissey 4.00 10.00
PHH Pete Hissey 4.00 10.00
PHI Pete Hissey 4.00 10.00
PHY Pete Hissey 4.00 10.00
PRE Pete Rose 60.00 120.00
PRO Pete Rose 60.00 120.00
PRR Pete Rose 60.00 120.00
PRS Pete Rose 60.00 120.00
RDD Rashun Dixon 6.00 15.00
RDI Rashun Dixon 6.00 15.00
RDN Rashun Dixon 6.00 15.00
RDO Rashun Dixon 6.00 15.00
RDX Rashun Dixon 6.00 15.00
RFA Ryan Flaherty 4.00 10.00
RFE Ryan Flaherty 4.00 10.00
RFF Ryan Flaherty 4.00 10.00
RFH Ryan Flaherty 4.00 10.00
RFL Ryan Flaherty 4.00 10.00
RFR Ryan Flaherty 4.00 10.00
RFT Ryan Flaherty 4.00 10.00
RFY Ryan Flaherty 4.00 10.00
RHA Reese Havens 6.00 15.00
RHE Reese Havens 6.00 15.00
RHH Reese Havens 6.00 15.00
RHN Reese Havens 6.00 15.00
RHS Reese Havens 6.00 15.00
RHV Reese Havens 6.00 15.00
RKE Roger Kieschnick 5.00 12.00
RKH Roger Kieschnick 5.00 12.00
RKN Roger Kieschnick 5.00 12.00
RKS Roger Kieschnick 5.00 12.00
RLL Ryan Lavarnway 8.00 20.00
RLN Ryan Lavarnway 8.00 20.00
RLR Ryan Lavarnway 8.00 20.00
RLV Ryan Lavarnway 8.00 20.00
RLW Ryan Lavarnway 8.00 20.00
RLY Ryan Lavarnway 8.00 20.00
RRD Robbie Ross 5.00 12.00
RRR Robbie Ross 5.00 12.00
RSA Ross Seaton 3.00 8.00
RSE Ross Seaton 3.00 8.00
RSN Ross Seaton 3.00 8.00
RSO Ross Seaton 3.00 8.00
RSS Ross Seaton 3.00 8.00
RST Ross Seaton 3.00 8.00
SFE Stephen Fife 4.00 10.00
SFI Stephen Fife 4.00 10.00
SGG Scott Green 3.00 8.00
SGN Scott Green 3.00 8.00
SGR Scott Green 3.00 8.00
SLI Seth Lintz 3.00 8.00
SLL Seth Lintz 3.00 8.00
SLN Seth Lintz 3.00 8.00
SLT Seth Lintz 3.00 8.00
SLZ Seth Lintz 3.00 8.00
TBA Tim Beckham 6.00 15.00
TBB Tim Beckham 6.00 15.00
TBC Tim Beckham 6.00 15.00
TBE Tim Beckham 6.00 15.00
TBH Tim Beckham 6.00 15.00
TBK Tim Beckham 6.00 15.00
TBM Tim Beckham 6.00 15.00
VWE Vance Worley 10.00 25.00
VWL Vance Worley 10.00 25.00
VWO Vance Worley 10.00 25.00
VWR Vance Worley 10.00 25.00
VWV Vance Worley 10.00 25.00
VWY Vance Worley 10.00 25.00
WME Wade Miley 3.00 8.00
WMI Wade Miley 3.00 8.00
WML Wade Miley 3.00 8.00
WMM Wade Miley 3.00 8.00
WMY Wade Miley 3.00 8.00
WSH Will Smith 4.00 10.00
WSI Will Smith 4.00 10.00
WSM Will Smith 4.00 10.00
WSS Will Smith 4.00 10.00
WST Will Smith 4.00 10.00
XAA Xavier Avery 4.00 10.00
XAE Xavier Avery 4.00 10.00
XAR Xavier Avery 4.00 10.00
XAV Xavier Avery 4.00 10.00
XAY Xavier Avery 4.00 10.00
YAA Yonder Alonso 10.00 25.00
YAL Yonder Alonso 10.00 25.00
YAN Yonder Alonso 10.00 25.00
YAS Yonder Alonso 10.00 25.00
ZCC Zach Collier 6.00 15.00
ZCE Zach Collier 6.00 15.00
ZCI Zach Collier 6.00 15.00
ZCO Zach Collier 6.00 15.00
ZCR Zach Collier 6.00 15.00
ZPA Zach Putnam 4.00 10.00
ZPM Zach Putnam 4.00 10.00
ZPN Zach Putnam 4.00 10.00
ZPP Zach Putnam 4.00 10.00
ZPT Zach Putnam 4.00 10.00
ZPU Zach Putnam 4.00 10.00
AAHC Aaron Hicks 10.00 25.00
AAHH Aaron Hicks 10.00 25.00
AAHI Aaron Hicks 10.00 25.00
AAHK Aaron Hicks 10.00 25.00
AAHS Aaron Hicks 10.00 25.00
ANHE Anthony Hewitt 4.00 10.00
ANHH Anthony Hewitt 4.00 10.00
ANHI Anthony Hewitt 4.00 10.00
ANHW Anthony Hewitt 4.00 10.00
API1 Aaron Pribanic 4.00 10.00
API2 Aaron Pribanic 4.00 10.00
BAHH Brad Holt 8.00 20.00
BAHL Brad Holt 8.00 20.00
BAHO Brad Holt 8.00 20.00
BAHT Brad Holt 8.00 20.00
BDL1 Brett DeVall 8.00 20.00
BDL2 Brett DeVall 8.00 20.00
BEHE Brett Hunter 3.00 8.00
BEHH Brett Hunter 3.00 8.00
BEHN Brett Hunter 3.00 8.00
BEHR Brett Hunter 3.00 8.00
BEHT Brett Hunter 3.00 8.00
BEHU Brett Hunter 3.00 8.00
BEMH Brett Marshall 5.00 12.00
BEMM Brett Marshall 5.00 12.00
BEMR Brett Marshall 5.00 12.00
BEMS Brett Marshall 5.00 12.00
BIMA Brian Matusz 12.50 30.00
BIMM Brian Matusz 12.50 30.00
BIMS Brian Matusz 12.50 30.00
BIMT Brian Matusz 12.50 30.00
BIMU Brian Matusz 12.50 30.00
BIMZ Brian Matusz 12.50 30.00
BOLG Bobby Lanigan 3.00 8.00
BOLI Bobby Lanigan 3.00 8.00
BOLL Bobby Lanigan 3.00 8.00
BRLA Brett Lawrie 20.00 50.00
BRLE Brett Lawrie 20.00 50.00
BRLI Brett Lawrie 20.00 50.00
BRLL Brett Lawrie 20.00 50.00
BRLR Brett Lawrie 20.00 50.00
BRLW Brett Lawrie 20.00 50.00
BRPC Bryan Price 5.00 12.00
BRPE Bryan Price 5.00 12.00
BRPI Bryan Price 5.00 12.00
BRPP Bryan Price 5.00 12.00
BRPR Bryan Price 5.00 12.00
BUPE Buster Posey 30.00 60.00
BUPO Buster Posey 30.00 60.00
BUPP Buster Posey 30.00 60.00
BUPS Buster Posey 30.00 60.00
BUPY Buster Posey 30.00 60.00
BWA1 Brett Wallace 4.00 10.00
BWA2 Brett Wallace 4.00 10.00
BWL1 Brett Wallace 4.00 10.00
BWL2 Brett Wallace 4.00 10.00
CASS Carlos Santana 10.00 25.00
CAST Carlos Santana 10.00 25.00
CFI1 Christian Friedrich 4.00 10.00
CFI2 Christian Friedrich 4.00 10.00
CFR1 Christian Friedrich 4.00 10.00
CFR2 Christian Friedrich 4.00 10.00
CGE1 Carlos Gutierrez 6.00 15.00
CGE2 Carlos Gutierrez 6.00 15.00
CGR1 Carlos Gutierrez 6.00 15.00
CGR2 Carlos Gutierrez 6.00 15.00
CHCA Chris Carpenter 6.00 15.00
CHCC Chris Carpenter 6.00 15.00
CHCN Chris Carpenter 6.00 15.00
CHCP Chris Carpenter 6.00 15.00
CHCT Chris Carpenter 6.00 15.00
CHDN Chase D'Arnaud 5.00 12.00
CHDR Chase D'Arnaud 5.00 12.00
CHDU Chase D'Arnaud 5.00 12.00
CHLI Che-Hsuan Lin 20.00 50.00
CHLL Che-Hsuan Lin 20.00 50.00
CHLN Che-Hsuan Lin 20.00 50.00
CHSH Chris Smith 4.00 10.00
CHSI Chris Smith 4.00 10.00
CHSM Chris Smith 4.00 10.00
CHSS Chris Smith 4.00 10.00
CHST Chris Smith 4.00 10.00
CKL1 Casey Kelly 10.00 25.00
CKL2 Casey Kelly 10.00 25.00
CLCC Collin Cowgill 5.00 12.00
CLCG Collin Cowgill 5.00 12.00
CLCI Collin Cowgill 5.00 12.00
CLCO Collin Cowgill 5.00 12.00
CLCW Collin Cowgill 5.00 12.00
COPE Cord Phelps 3.00 8.00
COPH Cord Phelps 3.00 8.00
COPL Cord Phelps 3.00 8.00
COPS Cord Phelps 3.00 8.00
CTDA Cutter Dykstra 10.00 25.00
CTDD Cutter Dykstra 10.00 25.00
CTDK Cutter Dykstra 10.00 25.00
CTDR Cutter Dykstra 10.00 25.00
CTDS Cutter Dykstra 10.00 25.00
CTDT Cutter Dykstra 10.00 25.00
CTDY Cutter Dykstra 10.00 25.00
CUPN Curtis Petersen 3.00 8.00
CUPP Curtis Petersen 3.00 8.00
CUPR Curtis Petersen 3.00 8.00
CUPS Curtis Petersen 3.00 8.00
CUPT Curtis Petersen 3.00 8.00
CWL1 Casper Wells 3.00 8.00
CWL2 Casper Wells 3.00 8.00
DAA1 David Adams 3.00 8.00
DAA2 David Adams 3.00 8.00
DAHD Dan Hudson 5.00 12.00
DAHH Dan Hudson 5.00 12.00
DAHN Dan Hudson 5.00 12.00
DAHO Dan Hudson 5.00 12.00
DAHS Dan Hudson 5.00 12.00
DAHU Dan Hudson 5.00 12.00
DEHD Destin Hood 3.00 8.00
DEHH Destin Hood 3.00 8.00
DES1 Danny Espinosa 6.00 15.00
DES2 Danny Espinosa 6.00 15.00
DJMC D.J. Mitchell 4.00 10.00
DJME D.J. Mitchell 4.00 10.00
DJMH D.J. Mitchell 4.00 10.00
DJMI D.J. Mitchell 4.00 10.00
DJMM D.J. Mitchell 4.00 10.00
DJMT D.J. Mitchell 4.00 10.00
DVCC David Cooper 8.00 20.00
DVCE David Cooper 8.00 20.00
DVCP David Cooper 8.00 20.00
DVCR David Cooper 8.00 20.00
DXCA Dexter Carter 10.00 25.00
DXCC Dexter Carter 10.00 25.00
DXCE Dexter Carter 10.00 25.00
DXCT Dexter Carter 10.00 25.00
EOO1 Edgar Olmos 3.00 8.00
EOO2 Edgar Olmos 3.00 8.00
GHA1 Greg Halman 6.00 15.00
GHA2 Greg Halman 6.00 15.00
GLS1 Garrison Lassiter 6.00 15.00
GLS2 Garrison Lassiter 6.00 15.00
IGA1 Isaac Galloway 8.00 20.00
IGA2 Isaac Galloway 8.00 20.00
IGL1 Isaac Galloway 8.00 20.00
IGL2 Isaac Galloway 8.00 20.00
JADA James Darnell 5.00 12.00
JADD James Darnell 5.00 12.00
JADE James Darnell 5.00 12.00
JADN James Darnell 5.00 12.00
JADR James Darnell 5.00 12.00
JCSB Juan Carlos Sulbaran 3.00 8.00
JCSL Juan Carlos Sulbaran 3.00 8.00
JCSN Juan Carlos Sulbaran 3.00 8.00
JCSR Juan Carlos Sulbaran 3.00 8.00
JCSS Juan Carlos Sulbaran 3.00 8.00
JCSU Juan Carlos Sulbaran 3.00 8.00
JEBA Jeremy Beckham 3.00 8.00
JEBB Jeremy Beckham 3.00 8.00
JEBC Jeremy Beckham 3.00 8.00
JEBE Jeremy Beckham 3.00 8.00
JEBH Jeremy Beckham 3.00 8.00
JEBK Jeremy Beckham 3.00 8.00
JEBM Jeremy Beckham 3.00 8.00
JMBB Jeremy Bleich 4.00 10.00
JMBC Jeremy Bleich 4.00 10.00
JMBE Jeremy Bleich 4.00 10.00
JMBH Jeremy Bleich 4.00 10.00
JMBI Jeremy Bleich 4.00 10.00
JMBL Jeremy Bleich 4.00 10.00
JODA Jordan Danks 6.00 15.00
JODD Jordan Danks 6.00 15.00
JODK Jordan Danks 6.00 15.00
JODN Jordan Danks 6.00 15.00
JODS Jordan Danks 6.00 15.00
JOI1 Jake Odorizzi 6.00 15.00
JOI2 Jake Odorizzi 6.00 15.00
JOLE Jordan Lyles 8.00 20.00
JOLS Jordan Lyles 8.00 20.00
JOLY Jordan Lyles 8.00 20.00
JOO1 Jake Odorizzi 6.00 15.00
JOO2 Jake Odorizzi 6.00 15.00
JOZ1 Jake Odorizzi 6.00 15.00
JOZ2 Jake Odorizzi 6.00 15.00
JPRA J.P. Ramirez 3.00 8.00
JPRE J.P. Ramirez 3.00 8.00

JPRI J.P. Ramirez 3.00 8.00
JPRM J.P. Ramirez 3.00 8.00
JPRZ J.P. Ramirez 3.00 8.00
JSLB Josh Lindblom 6.00 15.00
JSLD Josh Lindblom 6.00 15.00
JSLI Josh Lindblom 6.00 15.00
JSLM Josh Lindblom 6.00 15.00
JSLN Josh Lindblom 6.00 15.00
JSLO Josh Lindblom 6.00 15.00
JUBB Justin Bristow 3.00 8.00
JUBI Justin Bristow 3.00 8.00
JUBO Justin Bristow 3.00 8.00
JUBR Justin Bristow 3.00 8.00
JUBS Justin Bristow 3.00 8.00
JUBT Justin Bristow 3.00 8.00
JUBW Justin Bristow 3.00 8.00
JWE1 Jemile Weeks 5.00 12.00
JWE2 Jemile Weeks 5.00 12.00
KNE1 Kirk Nieuwenhuis 3.00 8.00
KNE2 Kirk Nieuwenhuis 3.00 8.00
KNI1 Kirk Nieuwenhuis 3.00 8.00
KNI2 Kirk Nieuwenhuis 3.00 8.00
KNN1 Kirk Nieuwenhuis 3.00 8.00
KNN2 Kirk Nieuwenhuis 3.00 8.00
KNU1 Kirk Nieuwenhuis 3.00 8.00
KNU2 Kirk Nieuwenhuis 3.00 8.00
KRL1 Kyle Russell 3.00 8.00
KRL2 Kyle Russell 3.00 8.00
KRS1 Kyle Russell 3.00 8.00
KRS2 Kyle Russell 3.00 8.00
MSN1 Michael Stanton 15.00 40.00
MSN2 Michael Stanton 15.00 40.00
MST1 Michael Stanton 15.00 40.00
MST2 Michael Stanton 15.00 40.00
MTO1 Matt Thompson 4.00 10.00
MTO2 Matt Thompson 4.00 10.00
MWE1 Matt Wieters 10.00 25.00
MWE2 Matt Wieters 10.00 25.00
PAA1 Pedro Alvarez 12.50 30.00
PAA2 Pedro Alvarez 12.50 30.00
PHS1 Pete Hissey 4.00 10.00
PHS2 Pete Hissey 4.00 10.00
PJDA P.J. Dean 3.00 8.00
PJDD P.J. Dean 3.00 8.00
PJDE P.J. Dean 3.00 8.00
PJDN P.J. Dean 3.00 8.00
RKC1 Roger Kieschnick 5.00 12.00
RKC2 Roger Kieschnick 5.00 12.00
RKI1 Roger Kieschnick 5.00 12.00
RKI2 Roger Kieschnick 5.00 12.00
RKK1 Roger Kieschnick 5.00 12.00
RKK2 Roger Kieschnick 5.00 12.00
RLA1 Ryan Lavarnway 8.00 20.00
RLA2 Ryan Lavarnway 8.00 20.00
RLA3 Ryan Lavarnway 8.00 20.00
ROWA Robbie Weinhardt 3.00 8.00
ROWD Robbie Weinhardt 3.00 8.00
ROWE Robbie Weinhardt 3.00 8.00
ROWH Robbie Weinhardt 3.00 8.00
ROWI Robbie Weinhardt 3.00 8.00
ROWN Robbie Weinhardt 3.00 8.00
ROWR Robbie Weinhardt 3.00 8.00
ROWT Robbie Weinhardt 3.00 8.00
ROWW Robbie Weinhardt 3.00 8.00
RRS1 Robbie Ross 5.00 12.00
RRS2 Robbie Ross 5.00 12.00
RYWA Ryan Westmoreland 12.50 30.00
RYWD Ryan Westmoreland 12.50 30.00
RYWL Ryan Westmoreland 12.50 30.00
RYWM Ryan Westmoreland 12.50 30.00
RYWN Ryan Westmoreland 12.50 30.00
RYWO Ryan Westmoreland 12.50 30.00
RYWR Ryan Westmoreland 12.50 30.00
RYWS Ryan Westmoreland 12.50 30.00
RYWT Ryan Westmoreland 12.50 30.00
RYWW Ryan Westmoreland 12.50 30.00
SFF1 Stephen Fife 4.00 10.00
SFF2 Stephen Fife 4.00 10.00
SGE1 Scott Green 3.00 8.00
SGE2 Scott Green 3.00 8.00
TASC Tanner Scheppers 5.00 12.00
TASH Tanner Scheppers 5.00 12.00
TASR Tanner Scheppers 5.00 12.00
TIMI Tim Melville 8.00 20.00
TIMM Tim Melville 8.00 20.00
TIMV Tim Melville 8.00 20.00
TMMH Tim Murphy 3.00 8.00
TMMM Tim Murphy 3.00 8.00
TMMP Tim Murphy 3.00 8.00
TMMR Tim Murphy 3.00 8.00
TMMU Tim Murphy 3.00 8.00
TMMY Tim Murphy 3.00 8.00
TYSA Tyler Stovall 3.00 8.00
TYSO Tyler Stovall 3.00 8.00
TYSS Tyler Stovall 3.00 8.00
TYST Tyler Stovall 3.00 8.00
TYSV Tyler Stovall 3.00 8.00
YAO1 Yonder Alonso 10.00 25.00
YAO2 Yonder Alonso 10.00 25.00
ZCL1 Zach Collier 6.00 15.00
ZCL2 Zach Collier 6.00 15.00
ANHT1 Anthony Hewitt 4.00 10.00
ANHT2 Anthony Hewitt 4.00 10.00
BEMA1 Brett Marshall 5.00 12.00
BEMA2 Brett Marshall 5.00 12.00
BEML1 Brett Marshall 5.00 12.00
BEML2 Brett Marshall 5.00 12.00
BOLA1 Bobby Lanigan 3.00 8.00
BOLA2 Bobby Lanigan 3.00 8.00
BOLN1 Bobby Lanigan 3.00 8.00
BOLN2 Bobby Lanigan 3.00 8.00
CASA1 Carlos Santana 10.00 25.00
CASA2 Carlos Santana 10.00 25.00
CASA3 Carlos Santana 10.00 25.00
CASN1 Carlos Santana 10.00 25.00
CASN2 Carlos Santana 10.00 25.00
CHCE1 Chris Carpenter 6.00 15.00
CHCE2 Chris Carpenter 6.00 15.00
CHCR1 Chris Carpenter 6.00 15.00
CHCR2 Chris Carpenter 6.00 15.00
CHDA1 Chase D'Arnaud 5.00 12.00
CHDA2 Chase D'Arnaud 5.00 12.00
CHDD1 Chase D'Arnaud 5.00 12.00
CHDD2 Chase D'Arnaud 5.00 12.00
CLCL1 Collin Cowgill 5.00 12.00
CLCL2 Collin Cowgill 5.00 12.00
COPP1 Cord Phelps 3.00 8.00
COPP2 Cord Phelps 3.00 8.00
CUPE1 Curtis Petersen 3.00 8.00
CUPE2 Curtis Petersen 3.00 8.00
CUPE3 Curtis Petersen 3.00 8.00
DEHO1 Destin Hood 3.00 8.00
DEHO2 Destin Hood 3.00 8.00
DJML1 D.J. Mitchell 4.00 10.00
DJML2 D.J. Mitchell 4.00 10.00
DVCO1 David Cooper 8.00 20.00
DVCO2 David Cooper 8.00 20.00
DXCR1 Dexter Carter 10.00 25.00
DXCR2 Dexter Carter 10.00 25.00
JADL1 James Darnell 5.00 12.00
JADL2 James Darnell 5.00 12.00
JCSA1 Juan Carlos Sulbaran 3.00 8.00
JCSA2 Juan Carlos Sulbaran 3.00 8.00
JOLL1 Jordan Lyles 8.00 20.00
JOLL2 Jordan Lyles 8.00 20.00
JPRR1 J.P. Ramirez 3.00 8.00
JPRR2 J.P. Ramirez 3.00 8.00
JSLL1 Josh Lindblom 6.00 15.00
JSLL2 Josh Lindblom 6.00 15.00
RYWE1 Ryan Westmoreland 12.50 30.00
RYWE2 Ryan Westmoreland 12.50 30.00
TASE1 Tanner Scheppers 5.00 12.00
TASE2 Tanner Scheppers 5.00 12.00
TASP1 Tanner Scheppers 5.00 12.00
TASP2 Tanner Scheppers 5.00 12.00
TASS1 Tanner Scheppers 5.00 12.00
TASS2 Tanner Scheppers 5.00 12.00
TIME1 Tim Melville 8.00 20.00
TIME2 Tim Melville 8.00 20.00
TIML1 Tim Melville 8.00 20.00
TIML2 Tim Melville 8.00 20.00
TIML3 Tim Melville 8.00 20.00
TYSL1 Tyler Stovall 3.00 8.00
TYSL2 Tyler Stovall 3.00 8.00

2008 Razor Letterman 20

*LETTER 20: .5X TO 1.2X BASIC CARDS
STATED PRINT RUN 20 SER.#'d SETS
ALL LETTERS PRICED EQUALLY

2008 Razor Letterman 5

*LETTER 5: .75X TO 2X BASIC CARDS
STATED PRINT RUN 5 SER.#'d SETS
ALL LETTERS PRICED EQUALLY

2008 Razor Letterman 1

STATED PRINT RUN 1 SER.#'d SET
NO PRICING DUE TO SCARCITY

2008 Razor Signature Series

This set was released on December 15, 2008. The base set consists of 200 cards.

COMP.SET w/o AU's (100) 20.00 50.00
COMMON CARD (1-100) .25 .60
COMMON AUTO (101-200) 3.00 8.00
OVERALL AUTO ODDS 1:1
PRINT RUNS B/WN 499-1499
PLATE PRINT RUN 1 SET PER COLOR
BLACK-CYAN-MAGENTA-YELLOW ISSUED
NO PLATE PRICING DUE TO SCARCITY
1 Tim Beckham 1.00 2.50
2 Pedro Alvarez 1.00 2.50
3 Eric Hosmer 3.00 8.00
4 Brian Matusz .60 1.50
5 Buster Posey 1.00 2.50
6 Kyle Skipworth .40 1.00
7 Yonder Alonso .75 2.00
8 Gordon Beckham .75 2.00
9 Aaron Crow .60 1.50
10 Jason Castro .60 1.50
11 Justin Smoak .75 2.00
12 Jemile Weeks .40 1.00
13 Brett Wallace
14 Aaron Hicks .60 1.50
15 Ethan Martin .60 1.50
16 Brett Lawrie 1.50 4.00
17 David Cooper .25 .60
18 Ike Davis 1.00 2.50
19 Andrew Cashner .60 1.50
20 Joshua Fields .25 .60
21 Ryan Perry .40 1.00
22 Reese Havens .25 .60
23 Allan Dykstra .25 .60
24 Anthony Hewitt .25 .60
25 Christian Friedrich .75 2.00
26 Daniel Schlereth .25 .60
27 Carlos Gutierrez .60 1.50
28 Lonnie Chisenhall .40 1.00
29 Casey Kelly .40 1.00
30 David Adams .25 .60
31 Jeremy Bleich .25 .60
32 Brett DeVall .40 1.00
33 Cutter Dykstra .25 .60
34 Stephen Fife .25 .60
35 Ryan Flaherty .40 1.00
36 Derrik Gibson .40 1.00
37 Pete Hissey .25 .60
38 Destin Hood .25 .60
39 Garrison Lassiter .25 .60
40 Che-Hsuan Lin .25 .60
41 Kyle Lobstein .25 .60
42 Jordan Lyles .40 1.00
43 Brett Marshall .25 .60
44 Tim Melville .25 .60
45 Wade Miley .25 .60
46 D.J. Mitchell .25 .60
47 Robbie Ross .25 .60
48 Tanner Scheppers .40 1.00
49 Ross Seaton .25 .60
50 Chris Smith .25 .60
51 Ryan Westmoreland .25 .60
52 Robbie Weinhardt .25 .60
53 Casper Wells .25 .60
54 Matt Wieters 1.25 3.00
55 Michael Antonini .25 .60
56 Jay Austin .25 .60
57 Jeremy Beckham .40 1.00
58 Eric Berger .25 .60
59 Charlie Blackmon .25 .60
60 Bobby Bundy .25 .60
61 Sawyer Carroll .40 1.00
62 Welington Castillo .25 .60
63 Ryan Chaffee .40 1.00
64 Tyler Chatwood .40 1.00
65 Dusty Coleman .25 .60
66 Brandon Crawford .40 1.00
67 Jordan Danks .60 1.50
68 James Darnell .40 1.00
69 Danny Espinosa .40 1.00
70 Jeremy Farrell .25 .60
71 Tim Federowicz .40 1.00
72 Tim Fedroff .25 .60
73 Logan Forsythe .25 .60
74 Rolando Gomez .40 1.00
75 Anthony Gose .40 1.00
76 Robbie Grossman .40 1.00
77 Trey Haley .25 .60
78 Brad Holt .25 .60
79 Brett Hunter .25 .60
80 Jake Jefferies .25 .60
81 Lance Lynn .40 1.00
82 Jordy Mercer .25 .60
83 Quinton Miller .25 .60
84 Mike Montgomery .40 1.00
85 Tim Murphy .25 .60
86 Petey Paramore .40 1.00
87 Cord Phelps .25 .60
88 Bryan Price .25 .60
89 Kevin Pucetas .40 1.00
90 Zach Putnam .25 .60
91 Dennis Raben .40 1.00
92 J.P. Ramirez .25 .60
93 Tyson Ross .40 1.00
94 Cody Satterwhite .40 1.00
95 Logan Schafer .25 .60
96 Zeke Spruill .60 1.50
97 Michael Stanton 3.00 8.00
98 T.J. Steele .40 1.00
99 Niko Vasquez .60 1.50
100 Beamer Weems .25 .60
101 Tim Beckham AU/499 12.50 30.00
102 Pedro Alvarez AU/499 12.50 30.00
103 Eric Hosmer AU/699 12.50 30.00
104 Brian Matusz AU/699 6.00 15.00
105 Buster Posey AU/499 20.00 50.00
106 Kyle Skipworth AU/699 3.00 8.00
107 Yonder Alonso AU/699 6.00 15.00
108 Gordon Beckham AU/499 8.00 20.00
109 Aaron Crow AU/699 3.00 8.00
110 Jason Castro AU/1199 4.00 10.00
111 Justin Smoak AU/699 10.00 25.00
112 Jemile Weeks AU/699 5.00 12.00
113 Brett Wallace AU/499 12.50 30.00
114 Aaron Hicks AU/699 10.00 25.00
115 Ethan Martin AU/699 3.00 8.00
116 Brett Lawrie AU/499 20.00 50.00
117 David Cooper AU/1199 3.00 8.00
118 Ike Davis AU/499 12.50 30.00
119 Andrew Cashner AU/699 5.00 12.00
120 Joshua Fields AU/1199 4.00 10.00
121 Ryan Perry AU/699 3.00 8.00
122 Reese Havens AU/1199 3.00 8.00
123 Allan Dykstra AU/1199 3.00 8.00
124 Anthony Hewitt AU/1199 3.00 8.00
125 Christian Friedrich AU/1199 3.00 8.00
126 Daniel Schlereth AU/1499 3.00 8.00
127 Carlos Gutierrez AU/1199 3.00 8.00
128 Lonnie Chisenhall AU/699 3.00 8.00
129 Casey Kelly AU/1199 12.50 30.00
130 David Adams AU/1199 3.00 8.00
131 Jeremy Bleich AU/1199 3.00 8.00
132 Brett DeVall AU/1499 3.00 8.00
133 Cutter Dykstra AU/1199 3.00 8.00
134 Stephen Fife AU/1499 3.00 8.00
135 Ryan Flaherty AU/1199 3.00 8.00
136 Derrik Gibson AU/1199 3.00 8.00
137 Pete Hissey AU/1199 3.00 8.00
138 Destin Hood AU/699 5.00 12.00
139 Garrison Lassiter AU/1499 3.00 8.00
140 Che-Hsuan Lin AU/1499 4.00 10.00
141 Kyle Lobstein AU/699 3.00 8.00
142 Jordan Lyles AU/1499 4.00 10.00
143 Brett Marshall AU/1499 3.00 8.00
144 Tim Melville AU/699 3.00 8.00
145 Wade Miley AU/1499 3.00 8.00
146 D.J. Mitchell AU/1499 3.00 8.00
147 Robbie Ross AU/1499 3.00 8.00
148 Tanner Scheppers AU/1499 3.00 8.00
149 Ross Seaton AU/1499 3.00 8.00
150 Chris Smith AU/1499 3.00 8.00
151 Ryan Westmoreland AU/1199 10.00 25.00
152 Robbie Weinhardt AU/1499 3.00 8.00
153 Casper Wells AU/1499 3.00 8.00
154 Matt Wieters AU/499 10.00 25.00
155 Michael Antonini AU/499 3.00 8.00
156 Jay Austin AU/1499 3.00 8.00
157 Jeremy Beckham AU/1499 3.00 8.00
158 Eric Berger AU/699 3.00 8.00
159 Charlie Blackmon AU/1499 3.00 8.00
160 Bobby Bundy AU/1199 3.00 8.00
161 Sawyer Carroll AU/699 3.00 8.00
162 Welington Castillo AU/1199 3.00 8.00
163 Ryan Chaffee AU/1199 3.00 8.00
164 Tyler Chatwood AU/1499 3.00 8.00
165 Dusty Coleman AU/699 3.00 8.00
166 Brandon Crawford AU/699 3.00 8.00
167 Jordan Danks AU/1499 3.00 8.00
168 James Darnell AU/1499 3.00 8.00
169 Danny Espinosa AU/1499 5.00 12.00
170 Jeremy Farrell AU/699 3.00 8.00
171 Tim Federowicz AU/699 3.00 8.00
172 Tim Fedroff AU/1499 3.00 8.00
173 Logan Forsythe AU/1499 3.00 8.00
174 Rolando Gomez AU/699 3.00 8.00
175 Anthony Gose AU/1499 3.00 8.00
176 Robbie Grossman AU/1499 3.00 8.00
177 Trey Haley AU/1499 3.00 8.00
178 Brad Holt AU/499 3.00 8.00
179 Brett Hunter AU/1499 3.00 8.00
180 Jake Jefferies AU/1199 3.00 8.00
181 Lance Lynn AU/1499 3.00 8.00
182 Jordy Mercer AU/1499 3.00 8.00
183 Quinton Miller AU/1499 3.00 8.00
184 Mike Montgomery AU/1499 4.00 10.00
185 Tim Murphy AU/1499 3.00 8.00
186 Petey Paramore AU/1499 3.00 8.00
187 Cord Phelps AU/1499 3.00 8.00
188 Bryan Price AU/1499 3.00 8.00
189 Kevin Pucetas AU/1499 3.00 8.00
190 Zach Putnam AU/1199 3.00 8.00
191 Dennis Raben AU/1499 3.00 8.00
192 J.P. Ramirez AU/1199 3.00 8.00
193 Tyson Ross AU/699 3.00 8.00
194 Cody Satterwhite AU/1199 3.00 8.00
195 Logan Schafer AU/699 3.00 8.00
196 Zeke Spruill AU/1199 3.00 8.00
197 Michael Stanton AU/1199 12.50 30.00
198 T.J. Steele AU/499 3.00 8.00
199 Niko Vasquez AU/1199 3.00 8.00
200 Beamer Weems AU/699 3.00 8.00

2008 Razor Signature Series Black

*1-100 BLACK: .75X TO 2X BASIC
1-100 RANDOM INSERTS IN PACKS
1-100 PRINT RUN 200 SER.#'d SETS
OVERALL AUTO ODDS 1:1
101-200 PRINT RUN 199 SER.#'d SETS
101 Tim Beckham AU 15.00 40.00
102 Pedro Alvarez AU 15.00 40.00
103 Eric Hosmer AU 15.00 40.00
104 Brian Matusz AU 20.00 50.00
105 Buster Posey AU 30.00 60.00
106 Kyle Skipworth AU 5.00 12.00
107 Yonder Alonso AU 8.00 20.00
108 Gordon Beckham AU 10.00 25.00
109 Aaron Crow AU 4.00 10.00
110 Jason Castro AU 5.00 12.00
111 Justin Smoak AU 15.00 40.00
112 Jemile Weeks AU 6.00 15.00
113 Brett Wallace AU 15.00 40.00
114 Aaron Hicks AU 15.00 40.00
115 Ethan Martin AU 6.00 15.00
116 Brett Lawrie AU 30.00 60.00
117 David Cooper AU 8.00 20.00
118 Ike Davis AU 15.00 40.00
119 Andrew Cashner AU 6.00 15.00
120 Joshua Fields AU 4.00 10.00
121 Ryan Perry AU 4.00 10.00
122 Reese Havens AU 5.00 12.00
123 Allan Dykstra AU 4.00 10.00
124 Anthony Hewitt AU 4.00 10.00
125 Christian Friedrich AU 4.00 10.00
126 Daniel Schlereth AU 4.00 10.00
127 Carlos Gutierrez AU 4.00 10.00
128 Lonnie Chisenhall AU 4.00 10.00
129 Casey Kelly AU 15.00 40.00
130 David Adams AU 4.00 10.00
131 Jeremy Bleich AU 4.00 10.00
132 Brett DeVall AU 4.00 10.00
133 Cutter Dykstra AU 4.00 10.00
134 Stephen Fife AU 4.00 10.00
135 Ryan Flaherty AU 4.00 10.00
136 Derrik Gibson AU 4.00 10.00
137 Pete Hissey AU 4.00 10.00
138 Destin Hood AU 6.00 15.00
139 Garrison Lassiter AU 4.00 10.00
140 Che-Hsuan Lin AU 10.00 25.00
141 Kyle Lobstein AU 4.00 10.00
142 Jordan Lyles AU 5.00 12.00
143 Brett Marshall AU 6.00 15.00
144 Tim Melville AU 5.00 12.00
145 Wade Miley AU 4.00 10.00
146 D.J. Mitchell AU 5.00 12.00
147 Robbie Ross AU 4.00 10.00
148 Tanner Scheppers AU 4.00 10.00
149 Ross Seaton AU 4.00 10.00
150 Chris Smith AU 4.00 10.00
151 Ryan Westmoreland AU 12.50 30.00
152 Robbie Weinhardt AU 4.00 10.00
153 Casper Wells AU 4.00 10.00
154 Matt Wieters AU 15.00 40.00
155 Michael Antonini AU 4.00 10.00
156 Jay Austin AU 4.00 10.00
157 Jeremy Beckham AU 4.00 10.00
158 Eric Berger AU 4.00 10.00
159 Charlie Blackmon AU 4.00 10.00
160 Bobby Bundy AU 4.00 10.00
161 Sawyer Carroll AU 4.00 10.00
162 Welington Castillo AU 4.00 10.00
163 Ryan Chaffee AU 4.00 10.00
164 Tyler Chatwood AU 4.00 10.00
165 Dusty Coleman AU 4.00 10.00
166 Brandon Crawford AU 4.00 10.00
167 Jordan Danks AU 4.00 10.00
168 James Darnell AU 5.00 12.00
169 Danny Espinosa AU 6.00 15.00
170 Jeremy Farrell AU 4.00 10.00
171 Tim Federowicz AU 6.00 15.00
172 Tim Fedroff AU 4.00 10.00
173 Logan Forsythe AU 4.00 10.00
174 Rolando Gomez AU 4.00 10.00
175 Anthony Gose AU 4.00 10.00
176 Robbie Grossman AU 4.00 10.00
177 Trey Haley AU 4.00 10.00
178 Brad Holt AU 4.00 10.00
179 Brett Hunter AU 4.00 10.00
180 Jake Jefferies AU 4.00 10.00
181 Lance Lynn AU 6.00 15.00
182 Jordy Mercer AU 4.00 10.00
183 Quinton Miller AU 4.00 10.00
184 Mike Montgomery AU 12.50 30.00
185 Tim Murphy AU 4.00 10.00
186 Petey Paramore AU 4.00 10.00
187 Cord Phelps AU 4.00 10.00
188 Bryan Price AU 4.00 10.00
189 Kevin Pucetas AU 6.00 15.00
190 Zach Putnam AU 4.00 10.00
191 Dennis Raben AU 4.00 10.00
192 J.P. Ramirez AU 4.00 10.00
193 Tyson Ross AU 4.00 10.00
194 Cody Satterwhite AU 6.00 15.00
195 Logan Schafer AU 4.00 10.00
196 Zeke Spruill AU 5.00 12.00
197 Michael Stanton AU 20.00 50.00
198 T.J. Steele AU 4.00 10.00
199 Niko Vasquez AU 4.00 10.00
200 Beamer Weems AU 4.00 10.00

2008 Razor Signature Series Blue

1-100 RANDOMLY INSERTED
OVERALL AUTO ODDS 1:1
STATED PRINT RUN 25 SER.#'d SETS
NO PRICING DUE TO SCARCITY

2008 Razor Signature Series Double Black

OVERALL AUTO ODDS 1:1
STATED PRINT RUN 5 SER.#'d SETS
NO PRICING DUE TO SCARCITY

2008 Razor Signature Series Dual Signatures

OVERALL AUTO ODDS 1:1
STATED PRINT RUN 99 SER.#'d SETS
PLATE PRINT RUN 1 SET PER COLOR
BLACK-CYAN-MAGENTA-YELLOW ISSUED
NO PLATE PRICING DUE TO SCARCITY
DS01 Tim Beckham
Pedro Alvarez
DS02 Matt Wieters 20.00 50.00
Kyle Skipworth
DS03 Eric Hosmer
Ethan Martin
DS04 Brian Matusz 12.50 30.00
Casey Kelly
DS05 Yonder Alonso
Jemile Weeks
DS06 Tim Beckham 15.00 40.00
Jeremy Beckham
DS07 David Cooper 10.00 25.00
Brett Wallace
DS08 Justin Smoak
Robbie Ross
DS09 Brett Lawrie 15.00 40.00
Cutter Dykstra
DS10 Destin Hood 8.00 20.00
Aaron Crow
DS11 Stephen Fife 8.00 20.00
Casey Kelly
DS12 Jason Castro 12.50 30.00
Jordan Lyles
DS13 D.J. Mitchell 6.00 15.00
Brett Marshall

2008 Razor Signature Series Dual Signatures Black

OVERALL AUTO ODDS 1:1
STATED PRINT RUN 25 SER.#'d SETS
NO PRICING DUE TO SCARCITY

2008 Razor Signature Series Dual Signatures Blue

OVERALL AUTO ODDS 1:1
STATED PRINT RUN 5 SER.#'d SETS
NO PRICING DUE TO SCARCITY

2008 Razor Signature Series Exclusives Autographs

OVERALL AUTO ODDS 1:1
PLATE PRINT RUN 1 SET PER COLOR
BLACK-CYAN-MAGENTA-YELLOW ISSUED
NO PLATE PRICING DUE TO SCARCITY
ES01 Tim Beckham 10.00 25.00
ES02 Pedro Alvarez 10.00 25.00
ES03 Eric Hosmer 12.50 30.00
ES04 Brian Matusz 6.00 15.00
ES05 Kyle Skipworth 3.00 8.00
ES06 Yonder Alonso 6.00 15.00
ES07 Aaron Crow 5.00 12.00
ES08 Jason Castro 3.00 8.00
ES09 Justin Smoak 10.00 25.00
ES10 Jemile Weeks 3.00 8.00
ES11 Brett Wallace 8.00 20.00
ES12 Aaron Hicks 5.00 12.00
ES13 Ethan Martin 3.00 8.00
ES14 Brett Lawrie 20.00 50.00
ES15 David Cooper 3.00 8.00
ES16 Reese Havens 3.00 8.00
ES17 Casey Kelly 6.00 15.00
ES18 David Adams 3.00 8.00
ES19 Jeremy Bleich 3.00 8.00
ES20 Brett DeVall 4.00 10.00
ES21 Cutter Dykstra 3.00 8.00
ES22 Stephen Fife 3.00 8.00
ES23 Ryan Flaherty 3.00 8.00
ES24 Derrik Gibson 3.00 8.00
ES25 Pete Hissey 3.00 8.00
ES26 Destin Hood 3.00 8.00
ES27 Garrison Lassiter 3.00 8.00
ES28 Che-Hsuan Lin 5.00 12.00
ES29 Kyle Lobstein 3.00 8.00
ES30 Jordan Lyles 4.00 10.00
ES31 Brett Marshall 3.00 8.00
ES32 Tim Melville 4.00 10.00
ES33 Wade Miley 3.00 8.00
ES34 D.J. Mitchell 3.00 8.00
ES35 Robbie Ross 3.00 8.00
ES36 Tanner Scheppers 5.00 12.00
ES37 Ross Seaton 3.00 8.00
ES38 Chris Smith 3.00 8.00
ES39 Ryan Westmoreland 4.00 10.00
ES40 Robbie Weinhardt 4.00 10.00
ES41 Casper Wells 3.00 8.00
ES42 Matt Wieters 10.00 25.00

2008 Razor Signature Series Exclusives Autographs Black

OVERALL AUTO ODDS 1:1
STATED PRINT RUN 25 SER.#'d SETS
NO PRICING ON MOST DUE TO SCARCITY
ES01 Tim Beckham 30.00 60.00
ES02 Pedro Alvarez 40.00 80.00
ES03 Eric Hosmer 75.00 150.00
ES04 Brian Matusz 30.00 60.00
ES11 Brett Wallace 50.00 100.00

2008 Razor Signature Series Exclusives Autographs Blue

OVERALL AUTO ODDS 1:1
STATED PRINT RUN 5 SER.#'d SETS
NO PRICING DUE TO SCARCITY

2010 Razor Rookie Retro Prospect Autographs

CC1 Chris Carpenter 3.00 8.00
CC2 Chris Carpenter 3.00 8.00
CC3 Chris Carpenter 3.00 8.00
CC4 Chris Carpenter 3.00 8.00
CC5 Chris Carpenter 3.00 8.00
TB1 Tim Beckham 3.00 8.00
TB2 Tim Beckham 3.00 8.00
TB3 Tim Beckham 3.00 8.00
TB4 Tim Beckham 3.00 8.00
TB5 Tim Beckham 3.00 8.00
TS1 Tanner Scheppers 3.00 8.00
TS2 Tanner Scheppers 3.00 8.00
TS3 Tanner Scheppers 3.00 8.00
TS4 Tanner Scheppers 3.00 8.00
TS5 Tanner Scheppers 3.00 8.00
YA1 Yonder Alonso 3.00 8.00
YA2 Yonder Alonso 3.00 8.00
YA3 Yonder Alonso 3.00 8.00
YA4 Yonder Alonso 3.00 8.00
YA5 Yonder Alonso 3.00 8.00

2011 Topps Heritage Minors

COMPLETE SET (250) 100.00 200.00
COMP.SET w/o SP's (200) 20.00 50.00
COMMON CARD (1-200) .12 .30
COMMON SP (201-250) 1.50 4.00
SP STATED ODDS 1:4 HOBBY
PRINTING PLATE ODDS 1:407 HOBBY
PLATE PRINT RUN 1 SET PER COLOR
BLACK-CYAN-MAGENTA-YELLOW ISSUED
NO PLATE PRICING DUE TO SCARCITY
1 Andrelton Simmons .12 .30
2 Stetson Allie .20 .50
3 Chris Archer .12 .30
4 Manny Banuelos .40 1.00
5 Dellin Betances .30 .75
6 Wil Myers .20 .50
7 Michael Choice .20 .50
8 Zack Cox .20 .50
9 Travis D'Arnaud .12 .30
10 Julio Rodriguez .12 .30
11 Delino DeShields Jr. .12 .30
12 Matt Dominguez .20 .50
13 Kyle Gibson .20 .50
14 Wily Peralta .12 .30
15 Grant Green .12 .30
16 Bryce Harper 4.00 10.00
17 Cody Hawn .20 .50
18 Luis Heredia .12 .30
19 Aaron Hicks .30 .75
20 Blake Tekotte .12 .30
21 Brett Jackson .20 .50
22 Casey Kelly .12 .30
23 Brett Lawrie 1.00 2.50
24 Justin O'Conner .12 .30
25 Starling Marte .30 .75
26 Tyler Matzek .20 .50
27 Devin Mesoraco .20 .50
28 Shelby Miller .30 .75
29 Jesus Montero .50 1.25
30 Mike Montgomery .20 .50
31 Peter Tago .12 .30
32 Taijuan Walker .20 .50
33 Carlos Perez .12 .30
34 Anthony Ranaudo .30 .75
35 Derek Norris .12 .30
36 Austin Romine .12 .30
37 Jean Segura .12 .30
38 Tony Sanchez .20 .50
39 Gary Sanchez .30 .75
40 Matt Miller .12 .30
41 Jeff Locke .20 .50
42 Garin Cecchini .30 .75
43 John Lamb .12 .30
44 Mike Trout .75 2.00
45 Jacob Turner .50 1.25
46 Arodys Vizcaino .12 .30
47 Adam Bailey .12 .30
48 Alex Wimmers .12 .30
49 Christian Yelich .12 .30
50 Josh Zeid .12 .30
51 Austin Adams .12 .30
52 Ehire Adrianza .12 .30
53 Nolan Arenado .40 1.00
54 Philippe Aumont .12 .30

55 Yasmani Grandal .20 .50
56 Luke Bailey .12 .30
57 Nino Leyja .12 .30
58 Keyvius Sampson .12 .30
59 Cory Spangenberg .20 .50
60 Nate Baker .12 .30
61 Jake Skole .12 .30
62 Tim Beckham .20 .50
63 Engel Beltre .12 .30
64 Miguel Sano .30 .75
65 Jesse Biddle .12 .30
66 Seth Blair .12 .30
67 Andrew Brackman .12 .30
68 Drake Britton .12 .30
69 Tommy Shirley .12 .30
70 Gary Brown .30 .75
71 Nick Bucci .12 .30
72 Trystan Magnuson .12 .30
73 Michael Burgess .20 .50
74 Dan Klein .20 .50
75 Jordan Pacheco .12 .30
76 Nick Castellanos .20 .50
77 Simon Castro .20 .50
78 Garrett Gould .12 .30
79 Brian Cavazos-Galvez .12 .30
80 Josh Sale .20 .50
81 Darrell Ceciliani .12 .30
82 Chevez Clarke .12 .30
83 Maikel Cleto .12 .30
84 AJ Cole .12 .30
85 Alex Colome .12 .30
86 Christian Colon .12 .30
87 Austin Ross .20 .50
88 Tyler Thornburg .30 .75
89 Jarred Cosart .20 .50
90 Kaleb Cowart .20 .50
91 Sean Coyle .30 .75
92 Charlie Culberson .12 .30
93 Jordan Swagerty .20 .50
94 James Darnell .12 .30
95 Matt Davidson .12 .30
96 Khris Davis .12 .30
97 Dimaster Delgado .12 .30
98 Mel Rojas Jr. .12 .30
99 Miguel De Los Santos .12 .30
100 Jaff Decker .12 .30
101 Kellin Deglan .12 .30
102 Zack Wheeler .12 .30
103 Matt Den Dekker .20 .50
104 Garrett Richards .12 .30
105 Danny Duffy .20 .50
106 Adam Eaton .12 .30
107 Nathan Eovaldi .12 .30
108 Robbie Erlin .20 .50
109 Daniel Fields .12 .30
110 Kyle Skipworth .12 .30
111 Ryan Flaherty .12 .30
112 Wilmer Flores .20 .50
113 Mike Foltynewicz .12 .30
114 Adys Portillo .12 .30
115 Nick Franklin .20 .50
116 Reymond Fuentes .12 .30
117 John Gast .12 .30
118 Scooter Gennett .12 .30
119 Mychal Givens .12 .30
120 Todd Glaesmann .12 .30
121 Anthony Gose .30 .75
122 JP Ramirez .12 .30
123 Kevin Kiermaier .20 .50
124 Angelo Gumbs .12 .30
125 Jedd Gyorko .30 .75
126 Jason Hagerty .12 .30
127 Jeudy Valdez .12 .30
128 Brody Colvin .12 .30
129 Billy Hamilton .30 .75
130 Matt Harvey .20 .50
131 Kyle Russell .20 .50
132 Jason Stoffel .12 .30
133 Kyle Higashioka .12 .30
134 LJ Hoes .20 .50
135 Alan Horne .12 .30
136 Ryan Jackson .12 .30
137 Luke Jackson .20 .50
138 Jiwan James .12 .30
139 Justin Wilson .12 .30
140 Chad Jenkins .12 .30
141 Tyrell Jenkins .12 .30
142 James Jones .12 .30
143 Joe Kelly .12 .30
144 Max Kepler .12 .30
145 Jonathan Villar .12 .30
146 Ydwin Villegas .12 .30
147 Kolbrin Vitek .20 .50
148 Josh Vitters .20 .50
149 Everett Williams .12 .30
150 Hak-Ju Lee .20 .50
151 Zach Lee .20 .50
152 Jake Lemmerman .20 .50
153 Joe Leonard .20 .50
154 Jonathan Singleton .20 .50
155 Matt Lipka .20 .50
156 Rymer Liriano .20 .50
157 Marcus Littlewood .12 .30
158 Domingo Santana .12 .30
159 Matt Lollis .20 .50
160 Barret Loux .12 .30
161 Manny Machado .40 1.00
162 Yordy Cabrera .12 .30
163 Francisco Martinez .12 .30
164 Carlos Martinez .12 .30
165 Chance Ruffin .12 .30
166 Travis Maltair .12 .30
167 Edward Salcedo .12 .30
168 Trevor May .12 .30
169 Deck McGuire .12 .30
170 Adam Warren .20 .50
171 Jio Mier .12 .30
172 Carlos Perez .12 .30
173 Matt Moore .60 1.50
174 Hunter Morris .12 .30
175 Jimmy Nelson .12 .30
176 Steve Parker .12 .30
177 Jake Odorizzi .12 .30
178 Andrew Oliver .12 .30
179 Mike Olt .20 .50
180 Juan Oramas .12 .30
181 Neil Ramirez .12 .30
182 Eury Perez .12 .30
183 Francisco Peguero .12 .30
184 Martin Perez .12 .30
185 Chris Withrow .12 .30
186 Asher Wojciechowski .12 .30
187 Drew Pomeranz .30 .75
188 Tony Wolters .12 .30
189 Jurickson Profar .40 1.00
190 Cesar Puello .20 .50
191 Wilin Rosario .12 .30
192 JC Ramirez .12 .30
193 Elmer Reyes .12 .30
194 Trevor Reckling .12 .30
195 Edinson Rincon .12 .30
196 Clint Robinson .12 .30
197 Jerry Sullivan .12 .30
198 Yorman Rodriguez .20 .50
199 Allen Webster .20 .50
200 Robbie Ray .12 .30
201 Stetson Allie SP 1.50 4.00
202 Dellin Betances SP 1.50 4.00
203 Danny Duffy SP 1.50 4.00
204 Zack Cox SP 1.50 4.00
205 Travis D'Arnaud SP 1.50 4.00
206 Anthony Gose SP 1.50 4.00
207 Delino DeShields Jr. SP 1.50 4.00
208 Matt Dominguez SP 1.50 4.00
209 Kyle Gibson SP 1.50 4.00
210 Grant Green SP 1.50 4.00
211 Bryce Harper SP 8.00 20.00
212 Cody Hawn SP 1.50 4.00
213 Luis Heredia SP 1.50 4.00
214 Aaron Hicks SP 1.50 4.00
215 Brett Jackson SP 1.50 4.00
216 Casey Kelly SP 1.50 4.00
217 Rymer Liriano SP 1.50 4.00
218 Jeff Locke SP 1.50 4.00
219 Manny Machado SP 2.00 5.00
220 Starling Marte SP 1.50 4.00
221 Tyler Matzek SP 1.50 4.00
222 Shelby Miller SP 1.50 4.00
223 Jesus Montero SP 3.00 8.00
224 Mike Montgomery SP 1.50 4.00
225 Wil Myers SP 1.50 4.00
226 Derek Norris SP 1.50 4.00
227 Carlos Perez SP 1.50 4.00
228 Jurickson Profar SP 2.00 5.00
229 Anthony Ranaudo SP 1.50 4.00
230 Austin Romine SP 1.50 4.00
231 Mike Foltynewicz SP 1.50 4.00
232 Tony Sanchez SP 1.50 4.00
233 Gary Sanchez SP 1.50 4.00
234 Miguel Sano SP 1.50 4.00
235 Jean Segura SP 1.50 4.00
236 Kyle Skipworth SP 1.50 4.00
237 Nathan Eovaldi SP 1.50 4.00
238 Cory Spangenberg SP 1.50 4.00
239 Mike Trout SP 2.50 6.00
240 Jacob Turner SP 1.50 4.00
241 Arodys Vizcaino SP 1.50 4.00
242 Alex Wimmers SP 1.50 4.00
243 Christian Yelich SP 1.50 4.00
244 Josh Zeid SP 1.50 4.00
245 Mel Rojas Jr. SP 1.50 4.00
246 Sean Coyle SP 1.50 4.00
247 Yordy Cabrera SP 1.50 4.00
248 Matt Moore SP 2.00 5.00
249 Matt Harvey SP 1.50 4.00
250 Peter Tago SP 1.50 4.00

2011 Topps Heritage Minors Black Border

*BLACK 1-200: 6X TO 15X BASIC
STATED ODDS 1:28 HOBBY
STATED PRINT RUN 62 SER.#'d SETS
16 Bryce Harper 30.00 60.00
44 Mike Trout 20.00 50.00
161 Manny Machado 10.00 25.00
201 Stetson Allie 3.00 8.00
202 Dellin Betances 5.00 12.00
203 Danny Duffy 3.00 8.00
204 Zack Cox 3.00 8.00
205 Travis D'Arnaud 2.00 5.00
206 Anthony Gose 5.00 12.00
207 Delino DeShields Jr. 2.00 5.00
208 Matt Dominguez 3.00 8.00
209 Kyle Gibson 3.00 8.00
210 Grant Green 2.00 5.00
211 Bryce Harper 30.00 60.00
212 Cody Hawn 3.00 8.00
213 Luis Heredia 2.00 5.00
214 Aaron Hicks 5.00 12.00
215 Brett Jackson 3.00 8.00
216 Casey Kelly 2.00 5.00
217 Rymer Liriano 3.00 8.00
218 Jeff Locke 3.00 8.00
219 Manny Machado 10.00 25.00
220 Starling Marte 5.00 12.00
221 Tyler Matzek 3.00 8.00
222 Shelby Miller 5.00 12.00
223 Jesus Montero 8.00 20.00
224 Mike Montgomery 3.00 8.00
225 Wil Myers 3.00 8.00
226 Derek Norris 2.00 5.00
227 Carlos Perez 2.00 5.00
228 Jurickson Profar 6.00 15.00
229 Anthony Ranaudo 5.00 12.00
230 Austin Romine 2.00 5.00
231 Mike Foltynewicz 2.00 5.00
232 Tony Sanchez 3.00 8.00
233 Gary Sanchez 5.00 12.00
234 Miguel Sano 5.00 12.00
235 Jean Segura 2.00 5.00
236 Kyle Skipworth 2.00 5.00
237 Nathan Eovaldi 2.00 5.00
238 Cory Spangenberg 3.00 8.00
239 Mike Trout 20.00 50.00
240 Jacob Turner 8.00 20.00
241 Arodys Vizcaino 2.00 5.00
242 Alex Wimmers 2.00 5.00
243 Christian Yelich 2.00 5.00
244 Josh Zeid 2.00 5.00
245 Mel Rojas Jr. 2.00 5.00
246 Sean Coyle 5.00 12.00
247 Yordy Cabrera 2.00 5.00
248 Matt Moore 10.00 25.00
249 Matt Harvey 3.00 8.00
250 Peter Tago 2.00 5.00

2011 Topps Heritage Minors Blue Tint

*BLUE: 3X TO 8X BASIC
STATED ODDS 1:9 HOBBY
STATED PRINT RUN 620 SER.#'d SETS
16 Bryce Harper 12.50 30.00
173 Matt Moore 5.00 12.00

2011 Topps Heritage Minors Green Tint

*GREEN: 3X TO 8X BASIC
STATED ODDS 1:14 HOBBY
STATED PRINT RUN 620 SER.#'d SETS

2011 Topps Heritage Minors Red Tint

*RED: 3X TO 8X BASIC
STATED ODDS 1:9 HOBBY
STATED PRINT RUN 620 SER.#'d SETS

2011 Topps Heritage Minors Bryce Harper Game Used Base

STATED ODDS 1:396 HOBBY
BH Bryce Harper 10.00 25.00

2011 Topps Heritage Minors Bryce Harper Game Used Base Black Border

STATED ODDS 1:388,920 HOBBY
STATED PRINT RUN 1 SER.#'d SET
NO PRICING DUE TO SCARCITY

2011 Topps Heritage Minors Bryce Harper Game Used Base Blue Tint

STATED ODDS 1:1369 HOBBY
STATED PRINT RUN 299 SER.#'d SETS
BH Bryce Harper 12.50 30.00

2011 Topps Heritage Minors Bryce Harper Game Used Base Green Tint

STATED ODDS 1:17,675 HOBBY
STATED PRINT RUN 25 SER.#'d SETS
NO PRICING DUE TO SCARCITY

2011 Topps Heritage Minors Bryce Harper Game Used Base Red Tint

STATED ODDS 1:4181 HOBBY
STATED PRINT RUN 99 SER.#'d SETS
BH Bryce Harper 15.00 40.00

2011 Topps Heritage Minors Bryce Harper Jumbo Patch Autograph

STATED ODDS 1:388,920 HOBBY
STATED PRINT RUN 1 SER.#'d SET
NO PRICING DUE TO SCARITY

2011 Topps Heritage Minors Clubhouse Collection Relics

STATED ODDS 1:35 HOBBY
AB Adam Bailey 3.00 8.00
AG Anthony Gose 3.00 8.00
AP Adys Portillo 3.00 8.00
AS Andrelton Simmons 3.00 8.00
AV Arodys Vizcaino 3.00 8.00
BH Bryce Harper 12.50 30.00
CC Christian Colon 3.00 8.00
DD Dimaster Delgado 3.00 8.00
JL John Lamb 3.00 8.00
JL Joe Leonard 3.00 8.00
MF Mike Foltynewicz 3.00 8.00
RL Rymer Liriano 3.00 8.00
SA Stetson Allie 3.00 8.00
TD Travis D'Arnaud 3.00 8.00
WM Wil Myers 3.00 8.00
DDS Delino DeShields Jr. 3.00 8.00

2011 Topps Heritage Minors Clubhouse Collection Relics Blue Tint

*BLUE: .5X TO 1.2X BASIC
STATED ODDS 1:131 HOBBY
STATED PRINT RUN 199 SER.#'d SETS
BH Bryce Harper 20.00 50.00

2011 Topps Heritage Minors Clubhouse Collection Relics Green Tint

*GREEN: .5X TO 1.2X BASIC
STATED ODDS 1:566 HOBBY
STATED PRINT RUN 50 SER.#'d SETS
BH Bryce Harper 40.00 100.00

2011 Topps Heritage Minors Clubhouse Collection Relics Red Tint

*RED: .5X TO 1.2X BASIC
STATED ODDS 1:270 HOBBY
STATED PRINT RUN 99 SER.#'d SETS
BH Bryce Harper 20.00 50.00

2011 Topps Heritage Minors Clubhouse Collection Relics Patches

STATED ODDS 1:5050 HOBBY
STATED PRINT RUN 5 SER.#'d SETS
NO PRICING DUE TO SCARCITY

2011 Topps Heritage Minors Real One Autographs

STATED ODDS 1:14 HOBBY
HARPER STATED ODDS 1:2663 HOBBY
PRINT RUNS B/WN 154-861 COPIES PER
PRINTING PLATE ODDS 1:2991 HOBBY
HARPER PLATE ODDS 1:97,230 HOBBY
PLATE PRINT RUN 1 SET PER COLOR
BLACK-CYAN-MAGENTA-YELLOW ISSUED
NO PLATE PRICING DUE TO SCARCITY
EXCHANGE DEADLINE 9/30/2014
AA Austin Adams EXCH 4.00 10.00
AG Avisail Garcia 4.00 10.00
AP Andy Parrino EXCH 5.00 12.00
BB Brett Bochy 4.00 10.00
BC Brad Chalk 3.00 8.00
BH Bryce Harper 200.00 400.00
BP Blake Perry 3.00 8.00
BP Brian Pointer 3.00 8.00
BT Blake Tekotte 3.00 8.00
CB Charles Brewer 4.00 10.00
CG Chris Gloor 3.00 8.00
CS Cody Stanley 3.00 8.00
CW Cole White 3.00 8.00
DB Dan Burkhart 4.00 10.00
DH Deunte Heath 3.00 8.00
DK David Kopp 3.00 8.00
DO Danny Otero 3.00 8.00
DS Davis Stoneburner 3.00 8.00
DW Dakota Watts 3.00 8.00
FM Francisco Martinez 4.00 10.00
GR Garrett Richards EXCH 5.00 12.00
JD Justin Dalles 3.00 8.00
JH Jordan Henry 3.00 8.00
JM Justin Marks 3.00 8.00
JP Jon Pettibone 4.00 10.00
JP Joc Pederson 4.00 10.00
JS Jerry Sullivan 3.00 8.00
JS Jordan Swagerty EXCH 6.00 15.00
JW Joe Wieland 4.00 10.00
KD Khris Davis
LJ Luke Jackson 4.00 10.00
LL Leon Landry EXCH 5.00 12.00
NA Nolan Arenado EXCH 10.00 25.00
RA Robbie Aviles 3.00 8.00
RB Ryan Berry 3.00 8.00
RS Robbie Shields 3.00 8.00
SB Sean Black 4.00 10.00
SL Steve Lombardozzi EXCH 5.00 12.00
SS Scott Shuman 3.00 8.00
SW Stelan Welch 3.00 8.00
TF Tim Federowicz 3.00 8.00
TM Trystan Magnuson EXCH 4.00 10.00
TS Tommy Shirley 3.00 8.00
VC Vinnie Catricala EXCH 20.00 50.00
BBR Brad Brach 5.00 12.00
DJT Dickie Joe Thon EXCH 8.00 20.00
EC1 Evan Crawford 3.00 8.00
JMU Jonathan Musser 3.00 8.00
SSO Steven Souza 3.00 8.00
TTH Tony Thompson 3.00 8.00

2011 Topps Heritage Minors Real One Autographs Black Border

STATED ODDS 1:11,785 HOBBY
HARPER ODDS 1:388,920 HOBBY
STATED PRINT RUN 1 SER.#'d SET
NO PRICING DUE TO SCARCITY
EXCHANGE DEADLINE 9/30/2014

2011 Topps Heritage Minors Real One Autographs Blue Tint

*BLUE: .5X TO 1.2X BASIC
STATED ODDS 1:122 HOBBY
HARPER ODDS 1:16,205 HOBBY
STATED PRINT RUN 99 SER.#'d SETS
HARPER PRINT RUN 25 SER.#'d SETS
NO HARPER PRICING DUE TO SCARCITY
EXCHANGE DEADLINE 9/30/2014

2011 Topps Heritage Minors Real One Autographs Green Tint

STATED ODDS 1:1331 HOBBY
HARPER ODDS 1:77,784 HOBBY
STATED PRINT RUN 10 SER.#'d SETS
NO PRICING DUE TO SCARCITY
EXCHANGE DEADLINE 9/30/2014

2011 Topps Heritage Minors Real One Autographs Red Tint

STATED ODDS 1:499 HOBBY
HARPER ODDS 1:38,892 HOBBY
STATED PRINT RUN 25 SER.#'d SETS
HARPER PRINT RUN 10 SER.#'d SETS
NO PRICING DUE TO SCARCITY
EXCHANGE DEADLINE 9/30/2014

2010 Topps Pro Debut

COMPLETE SET (440) 60.00 120.00
COMP.SER.1 SET (220) 30.00 60.00
COMP.SER.2 SET (220) 30.00 60.00
COMMON CARD .15 .40
PLATE ODDS 1:312 HOBBY
PLATE PRINT RUN 1 SET PER COLOR
BLACK-CYAN-MAGENTA-YELLOW ISSUED
NO PLATE PRICING DUE TO SCARCITY
1 Pedro Alvarez .50 1.25
2 Aaron Hicks .40 1.00
3 Destin Hood .25 .60
4 Grant Desme .25 .60
5 Craig Kimbrel .75 2.00
6 Tim Melville .25 .60
7 Christian Bethancourt .25 .60
8 Brett Wallace .40 1.00
9 Chris Smith .15 .40
10 Kyle Skipworth .25 .60
11 James Jones .15 .40
12 Ryan Westmoreland .40 1.00
13 Eric Hosmer 2.50 6.00
14 Casper Wells .15 .40
15 Tim Beckham .40 1.00
16 Robbie Weinhardt .15 .40
17 Jason Castro .40 1.00
18 Cutter Dykstra .15 .40
19 Pete Hissey .15 .40
20 Zach Braddock .15 .40
21 Ross Seaton .25 .60
22 Derrik Gibson .25 .60
23 Ryan Flaherty .15 .40
24 Randall Delgado .75 2.00
25 Jefry Marte .15 .40
26 Justin Smoak .50 1.25
27 Jemile Weeks .25 .60
28 Yonder Alonso .40 1.00
29 Ethan Martin .40 1.00
30 Brett Lawrie 1.00 2.50
31 David Cooper .25 .60
32 Reese Havens .25 .60
33 Casey Kelly .75 2.00
34 David Adams .15 .40
35 Jeremy Bleich .25 .60
36 Brett DeVall .15 .40
37 Stephen Fife .15 .40
38 Garrison Lassiter .25 .60
39 Che-Hsuan Lin .25 .60
40 Kyle Lobstein .15 .40
41 Jordan Lyles .25 .60
42 Brett Marshall .15 .40
43 Wade Miley .15 .40
44 D.J. Mitchell .15 .40
45 Robbie Ross .15 .40
46 Carlos Paulino .15 .40
47 Carlos Triunfel .25 .60
48 Robbie Widlansky .15 .40
49 Myrio Richard .15 .40
50 Josh Phegley .15 .40
51 Trevor Holder .15 .40
52 Steve Baron .15 .40
53 Matt Davidson .25 .60
54 Kyle Seager .15 .40
55 Aaron Miller .15 .40
56 Jerry Sullivan .15 .40
57 Tyler Skaggs .15 .40
58 Evan Chambers .25 .60
59 Garrett Richards .25 .60
60 Chris Dominguez .40 1.00
61 Mike Belfiore .15 .40
62 Miles Head .15 .40
63 Guillermo Pimentel .15 .40
64 Kyle Heckathorn .15 .40
65 Patrick Schuster .15 .40
66 Tyler Kehrer .15 .40
67 Erik Davis .15 .40
68 Jeff Kobernus .15 .40
69 Andrew Doyle .25 .60
70 Rich Poythress .15 .40
71 Melky Mesa .25 .60
72 Everett Williams .15 .40
73 Shelby Miller .60 1.50
74 Jose Alvarez .15 .40
75 Mark Cohoon .15 .40
76 Brett Jackson .50 1.25
77 Slade Heathcott .50 1.25
78 Yan Gomes .15 .40
79 Nick Franklin .40 1.00
80 Rex Brothers .15 .40
81 Blake Smith .15 .40
82 Keyvius Sampson .40 1.00
83 Chris Dwyer .15 .40
84 Leandro Castro .15 .40
85 Luke Murton .15 .40
86 Kent Matthes .15 .40
87 Nolan Arenado .50 1.25
88 Angelo Songco .15 .40
89 Trayce Thompson .25 .60
90 Chris Owings .15 .40
91 Jason Stoffel .25 .60
92 Eric Smith .15 .40
93 Edwin Gomez .15 .40
94 Steven Inch .15 .40
95 Jason Kipnis .25 .60
96 Tucker Barnhart .15 .40
97 Ryan Wheeler .15 .40
98 Sean Ochinko .15 .40
99 Josh Fellhauer .15 .40
100 Michael Ohlman .15 .40
101 Garrett Gould .15 .40
102 Nate Freiman .15 .40
103 Jonathan Singleton .25 .60
104 Jordan Pacheco .40 1.00
105 Yorman Rodriguez .15 .40
106 DeAngelo Mack .25 .60
107 Dillon Baird .15 .40
108 Chris McGuiness .15 .40
109 Max Walla .15 .40
110 Brian Ruggiano .15 .40
111 Thomas Neal .25 .60
112 Cameron Garfield .15 .40
113 Tyson Gillies .40 1.00
114 Kelly Dugan .15 .40
115 Alexander Colome .40 1.00
116 Martin Perez .25 .60
117 J.R. Murphy .25 .60
118 Pedro Figueroa .15 .40
119 James Darnell .25 .60
120 Alex Wilson .15 .40
121 Sebastian Valle .25 .60
122 Kiel Roling .15 .40
123 D.J. Lemahieu .40 1.00
124 Hak-Ju Lee .60 1.50
125 Corban Joseph .15 .40
126 Brock Holt .25 .60
127 Chris Archer .75 2.00
128 Donnie Joseph .15 .40
129 Tom Milone .15 .40
130 Wade Gaynor .15 .40
131 Bryce Stowell .15 .40
132 Tyler Ladendorf .15 .40
133 Ben Paulsen .15 .40
134 Yohan Flande .15 .40
135 James McOwen .15 .40
136 Wil Myers .75 2.00
137 Jason Van Kooten .15 .40
138 Jeff Malm .15 .40
139 Drew Cumberland .15 .40
140 Caleb Thielbar .25 .60
141 Sean Ratliff .25 .60
142 Paolo Espino .15 .40
143 Seth Loman .15 .40
144 Seth Lintz .15 .40
145 Steve Lombardozzi .15 .40
146 Chris Kessinger .15 .40
147 Randal Grichuk .15 .40
148 Devin Goodwin .15 .40
149 Darrell Ceciliani .15 .40
150 Roberto De La Cruz .15 .40
151 Brooks Raley .15 .40
152 Brian Cavazos-Galvez .40 1.00
153 Jesus Brito .15 .40
154 Tony Sanchez .40 1.00
155 Matt Hobgood .40 1.00
156 Graham Stoneburner .25 .60
157 Kirk Nieuwenhuis .15 .40
158 Brock Bond .25 .60
159 D.J. Wabick .15 .40
160 Mike Minor .25 .60
161 Brett Pill .60 1.50
162 Ari Ronick .15 .40
163 Ryan Lavarnway .60 1.50
164 Drew Storen .25 .60
165 Isaias Velasquez .15 .40
166 Barry Butera .15 .40
167 Grant Green .25 .60
168 Zack Von Rosenberg .15 .40
169 Tony Delmonico .15 .40
170 Bobby Borchering .25 .60
171 A.J. Pollock .25 .60
172 Kyle Conley .25 .60
173 Shaver Hansen .15 .40
174 Jiovanni Mier .25 .60
175 Jimmy Paredes .15 .40
176 Alexia Amarista .15 .40
177 Jared Mitchell .25 .60
178 Marquise Cooper .15 .40
179 Damon Sublett .25 .60
180 Todd Glaesmann .15 .40
181 Mike Trout 1.25 3.00
182 Gustavo Nunez .15 .40
183 Eric Arnett .15 .40
184 Joe Kelly .15 .40
185 Matt Helm .15 .40
186 Reymond Fuentes .25 .60
187 Jason Thompson .15 .40
188 Tim Wheeler .25 .60
189 Rebel Ridling .15 .40
190 Keon Broxton .15 .40
191 Ian Krol .15 .40
192 Alex Torres .15 .40
193 Ben Tootle .15 .40
194 Craig Clark .60 1.50
195 David Hale .15 .40
196 Brett Wallach .15 .40
197 Jeremy Hefner .15 .40
198 Marty Popham .15 .40
199 Donald Hume .15 .40
200 Zelous Wheeler .15 .40
201 Brandon Douglas .15 .40
202 Manuel Banuelos 6.00 15.00
203 Robbie Erlin .40 1.00
204 Billy Nowlin .15 .40
205 Ozzie Lewis .15 .40
206 Jon Michael Redding .15 .40
207 Josh Harrison .15 .40
208 Johermyn Chavez .15 .40
209 Jose Pirela .15 .40
210 Bryan Pounds .15 .40
211 Phil Joon Jang .15 .40
212 Dan Kapala .15 .40
213 Marc Sorensen .15 .40
214 Jordan Lennerton .15 .40
215 Corey Kemp .15 .40
216 David Phelps .15 .40
217 Erik Crichton .15 .40
218 Josh Walter .15 .40
219 Alfredo Marte .15 .40
220 Evan Sharpley .15 .40
221 Jesus Montero 1.00 2.50
222 Tanner Scheppers .40 1.00
223 Jose Iglesias .60 1.50
224 Jacob Skole .25 .60
225 Arodys Vizcaino .25 .60
226 Kyle Colligan .15 .40
227 Todd Frazier .25 .60
228 Mike Foltynewicz .25 .60
229 Chris Balcom-Miller .25 .60
230 Zach Wheeler .25 .60
231 Donnie Roach .15 .40
232 Kellin Deglan .15 .40
233 Riaan Spanjer-Furstenburg .15 .40
234 Ryan Goins .15 .40
235 Trey McNutt .15 .40
236 Matt Lipka .60 1.50
237 Max Stassi .25 .60
238 Tanner Bushue .25 .60
239 Marc Krauss .15 .40
240 Taylor Lindsey .25 .60
241 Juan Carlos Sulbaran .15 .40
242 Michael Kirkman .15 .40
243 Freddie Freeman .60 1.50
244 Ryan Bolden .15 .40
245 Paul Goldschmidt 1.25 3.00
246 Roger Kieschnick .15 .40
247 David Nick .15 .40
248 Wendell Soto .15 .40

249 Louis Coleman .15 .40
250 Robinson Lopez .15 .40
251 A.J. Morris .15 .40
252 Drew Robinson .15 .40
253 Mycal Jones .15 .40
254 Patrick Keating .15 .40
255 Collin Cowgill .15 .40
256 Nick Bartolone .15 .40
257 Tyler Stovall .15 .40
258 Billy Hamilton .60 1.50
259 David Holmberg .25 .60
260 Cito Culver .25 .60
261 Max Russell .15 .40
262 Jose Ramirez .15 .40
263 Kentrail Davis .15 .40
264 James Baldwin III .15 .40
265 Jeremy Hellickson .60 1.50
266 Jeurys Familia .25 .60
267 Will Middlebrooks .25 .60
268 Christian Carmichael .25 .60
269 Cesar Puello .15 .40
270 Daniel Fields .15 .40
271 Mike Hessman .15 .40
272 Bryce Brentz .40 1.00
273 Anthony Hewitt .15 .40
274 Mark Serrano .15 .40
275 Kyle Gibson .60 1.50
276 Andrelton Simmons .25 .60
277 Telvin Nash .25 .60
278 Jonathan Meyer .15 .40
279 Dimaster Delgado .15 .40
280 Christopher Hawkins .15 .40
281 Danny Duffy .25 .60
282 Jorge Reyes .15 .40
283 Pat Corbin .15 .40
284 Jordan Akins .15 .40
285 Kendal Volz .15 .40
286 Jonathan Garcia .15 .40
287 Aaron Crow .15 .40
288 Marcus Knecht .15 .40
289 Zach Lutz .15 .40
290 John Lamb .40 1.00
291 Welington Castillo .15 .40
292 Brodie Greene .15 .40
293 Robert Stock .15 .40
294 Julio Morban .15 .40
295 Ryan Dent .15 .40
296 Tyler Waldron .15 .40
297 B.J. Hermsen .15 .40
298 T.J. House .15 .40
299 Jay Jackson .15 .40
300 Nicholas Longmire .25 .60
301 Tyreace House .15 .40
302 David Cales .15 .40
303 Tommy Joseph .15 .40
304 Brett Nicholas .15 .40
305 Adeiny Hechavarria .15 .40
306 Marcos Vechionacci .15 .40
307 Dustin Ackley 1.00 2.50
308 Jesse Biddle .60 1.50
309 Donavan Tate .40 1.00
310 Danny Rosenbaum .25 .60
311 Matt Bashore .25 .60
312 Asher Wojciechowski .40 1.00
313 Alex White .25 .60
314 Francisco Peguero .15 .40
315 Nick Hagadone .15 .40
316 Jacob Petricka .15 .40
317 Dee Gordon .25 .60
318 Gustavo Pierre .15 .40
319 Michael Montgomery .25 .60
320 Tyler Vail .15 .40
321 Adam Warren .40 1.00
322 Billy Bullock .15 .40
323 Derek Norris .25 .60
324 Cory Vaughn .25 .60
325 Connor Hoehn .15 .40
326 Casey Crosby .50 1.25
327 Aaron Sanchez .25 .60
328 Daniel Descalso .15 .40
329 Jarred Cosart .15 .40
330 Zach Britton .60 1.50
331 Noah Syndergaard .25 .60
332 Ben Jukich .15 .40
333 Victor Black .15 .40
334 Michael Moustakas .50 1.25
335 Taijuan Walker .50 1.25
336 Ryan Jackson .15 .40
337 Austin Romine .25 .60
338 Josh Harrison .15 .40
339 Ralston Cash .15 .40
340 Casey Coleman .25 .60
341 Jack Spradlin .15 .40
342 Daryl Jones .15 .40
343 Mike Antonio .15 .40
344 Josh Vitters .15 .40
345 Jordany Valdespin .15 .40
346 Travis D'Arnaud .15 .40
347 Christian Bisson .15 .40
348 Matt Clark .15 .40
349 Xavier Avery .15 .40
350 Hector Noesi .25 .60
351 David Filak .15 .40
352 Hank Conger .60 1.50
353 Devin Mesoraco .40 1.00
354 Daniel Moskos .15 .40
355 Christian Colon .25 .60
356 Adrian Ortiz .15 .40
357 Wynn Pelzer .15 .40
358 Jurickson Profar .75 2.00
359 Justin O'Conner .15 .40
360 Justin Greene .15 .40
361 Bryan Morris .15 .40
362 Jarrod Parker .40 1.00
363 Henry Ramos .40 1.00
364 Lars Anderson .40 1.00
365 Todd Cunningham .25 .60
366 Michael Taylor .25 .60
367 Eddie Rosario .25 .60
368 Tomas Telis .15 .40
369 Chris Carter .25 .60
370 Niko Goodrum .25 .60
371 Kyle Russell .15 .40
372 Matthew Moore 2.00 5.00
373 L.J. Hoes .15 .40
374 Joe Leonard .15 .40
375 James Leverton .15 .40
376 Matt Gorgen .15 .40
377 Erik Komatsu .15 .40
378 Hunter Morris .40 1.00
379 Matt Cline .25 .60
380 Su-Min Jung .15 .40
381 Jacob Turner .50 1.25
382 Jedd Gyorko .25 .60
383 Chris Kirkland .15 .40
384 Cody Rogers .15 .40
385 Anthony Vasquez .15 .40
386 Cody Hawn .25 .60
387 Miguel Velazquez .15 .40
388 Tom Stuifbergen .15 .40
389 Jason Stidham .15 .40
390 Stephen Pryor .15 .40
391 Justin Bour .15 .40
392 Khris Davis .15 .40
393 Edward Salcedo .15 .40
394 Rett Varner .15 .40
395 Steven Souza .15 .40
396 Mark Sobolewski .15 .40
397 Michael Pineda 2.00 5.00
398 Jared Simon .15 .40
399 Anderson Hidalgo .15 .40
400 Scooter Gennett .15 .40
401 Kyle Drabek .25 .60
402 Seth Rosin .25 .60
403 Kyle Rose .15 .40
404 Darin Ruf .25 .60
405 Brian Diemer .15 .40
406 Chad Bettis .15 .40
407 Justin Bloxom .15 .40
408 Jerry Sands .40 1.00
409 Martin Perez .25 .60
410 Derek Dietrich .50 1.25
411 Chris McGuiness .15 .40
412 Juan Lagares .15 .40
413 Robert Rowland .15 .40
414 Jake Thompson .15 .40
415 Brian Conley .15 .40
416 Bo Greenwell .15 .40
417 Derrick Robinson .15 .40
418 Michael Kvasnicka .25 .60
419 Garabez Rosa .15 .40
420 Casey Frawley .15 .40
421 Bobby Doran .15 .40
422 Zoilo Almonte .25 .60
423 Ian Gac .15 .40
424 Phillippe Aumont .15 .40
425 Ben Heath .15 .40
426 J.D. Martinez .60 1.50
427 Chris Murrill .15 .40
428 Desmond Jennings .25 .60
429 Jason Martinson .15 .40
430 Eliezer Mesa .15 .40
431 Peter Bourjos .25 .60
432 Ryan Berry .15 .40
433 Cole Leonida .15 .40
434 Wilmer Flores .40 1.00
435 Russell Wilson .75 2.00
436 Brandon Belt 1.50 4.00
437 T.J. McFarland .15 .40
438 Bruce Billings .15 .40
439 Casey Haerther .15 .40
440 Mike McDade .15 .40

2010 Topps Pro Debut Blue

*BLUE 1-220: 2X TO 5X BASIC
*BLUE 221-440: 1.2X TO 3X BASIC
SER.2 ODDS 1:4 HOBBY
SER.1 PRINT RUN 259 SER.#'d SETS
SER.2 PRINT RUN 369 SER.#'d SETS
202 Manuel Banuelos 30.00 60.00

2010 Topps Pro Debut Gold

*GOLD: 4X TO 10X BASIC
SER.2 ODDS 1:25 HOBBY
STATED PRINT RUN 50 SER.#'d SET
202 Manuel Banuelos 125.00 250.00

2010 Topps Pro Debut Red

SER.2 ODDS 1:1249 HOBBY
STATED PRINT RUN 1 SER.#'d SET
NO PRICING DUE TO SCARCITY

2010 Topps Pro Debut AFLAC Debut Cut Autographs

SER.1 PRINT RUN 106 SER.#'d SETS
SER.2 PRINT RUN 200 SER.#'d SETS

AH Aaron Hicks 30.00 60.00
AS Aaron Sanchez S2 10.00 25.00
BD Brett DeVall 10.00 25.00
BH B.J. Hermsen 15.00 40.00
BL Braxton Lane 8.00 20.00
CB Cameron Bedrosian S2 8.00 20.00
CC Christian Colon S2 10.00 25.00
CK Chevez Clarke S2 8.00 20.00
CM Clark Murphy 8.00 20.00
CR Cameron Rupp S2 8.00 20.00
DD Derek Dietrich S2 8.00 20.00
DH Destin Hood 10.00 25.00
DL D.J. Lemahieu 12.50 30.00
DT Daniel Tuttle 12.50 30.00
EM Ethan Martin 12.50 30.00
EW Everett Williams 12.50 30.00
GL Garrison Lassiter 8.00 20.00
HM Hunter Morris S2 8.00 20.00
IK Ian Krol 10.00 25.00
JC Jarred Cosart S2 12.50 30.00
JS Jonathan Singleton 60.00 120.00
JT Jason Thompson 8.00 20.00
JT Jacob Turner S2 15.00 40.00
KH Kyrell Hudson 12.50 30.00
KK Kevin Keyes S2 8.00 20.00
KS Keyvius Sampson 12.50 30.00
KS Kyle Skipworth 8.00 20.00
ML Matt Lipka S2 12.50 30.00
RG Reggie Golden S2 8.00 20.00
SH Slade Heathcott 20.00 50.00
TB Tim Beckham 30.00 60.00
TM Tim Melville 10.00 25.00

2010 Topps Pro Debut Double-A All-Stars

COMPLETE SET (30) 10.00 25.00
PLATE PRINT RUN 1 SET PER COLOR
BLACK-CYAN-MAGENTA-YELLOW ISSUED
NO PLATE PRICING DUE TO SCARCITY
DA1 Miguel Abreu .60 1.50
DA2 Deik Scram .40 1.00
DA3 Quintin Berry .40 1.00
DA4 Michael Taylor .60 1.50
DA5 Carlos Santana 1.25 3.00
DA6 Alex Avila .40 1.00
DA7 Marvin Lowrance .40 1.00
DA8 Nick Weglarz .60 1.50
DA9 Neil Sellers .40 1.00
DA10 Jonathan Tucker .40 1.00
DA11 Jason Delaney .40 1.00
DA12 Beau Mills .40 1.00
DA13 Brian Friday .40 1.00
DA14 Joe Savery .40 1.00
DA15 Danny Moskos .40 1.00
DA16 Brock Bond .60 1.50
DA17 Brian Dinkelman .40 1.00
DA18 Eduardo Nunez .60 1.50
DA19 Reegie Corona .40 1.00
DA20 Jorge Jimenez .40 1.00
DA21 Brian Dopirak .40 1.00
DA22 Jorge Vazquez .40 1.00
DA23 Whitney Robbins .40 1.00
DA24 Eddy Martinez - Esteve .40 1.00
DA25 Rene Tosoni .60 1.50
DA26 Lars Anderson 1.00 2.50
DA27 D.J. Wabick .40 1.00
DA28 Brian Jeroloman .40 1.00
DA29 Jesus Montero 2.50 6.00
DA30 Zach McAllister .60 1.50

2010 Topps Pro Debut Futures Game Jersey

SER.1 PRINT RUN 139 SER.#'d SETS
SER.2 PRINT RUN 199 SER.#'d SETS
SER.2 ODDS 1:28 HOBBY
SER.2 GOLD ODDS 1:220 HOBBY
GOLD PRINT RUN 25 SER.#'d SETS
NO GOLD PRICING DUE TO SCARCITY
AE Alcides Escobar 4.00 10.00
AL Alex Liddi 4.00 10.00
AL Alex Liddi S2 4.00 10.00
AR Austin Romine S2 4.00 10.00
AS Anthony Slama S2 3.00 8.00
AT Alex Torres S2 3.00 8.00
BC Barbaro Canizares 3.00 8.00
BJ Brett Jackson S2 5.00 12.00
BL Brett Lawrie S2 15.00 40.00
BL Brad Lincoln 4.00 10.00
BM Brian Matusz 6.00 15.00
BM Bryan Morris S2 3.00 8.00
BR Ben Revere S2 4.00 10.00
BW Brett Wallace 4.00 10.00
CC Chris Carter 4.00 10.00
CC Chun Chen S2 4.00 10.00
CF Christian Friedrich S2 4.00 10.00
CH Chris Heisey 10.00 25.00
CK Casey Kelly 12.50 30.00
CL Chia-Jen Lo 6.00 15.00
CP Carlos Peguero S2 4.00 10.00
CS Carlos Santana 4.00 10.00
CT Chris Tillman 4.00 10.00
DB Domonic Brown S2 6.00 15.00
DC Drew Cumberland S2 3.00 8.00
DD Danny Duffy 10.00 25.00
DE Danny Espinosa 3.00 8.00
DE Danny Espinosa S2 3.00 8.00
DG Dee Gordon S2 4.00 10.00
DJ Desmond Jennings S2 6.00 15.00
DJ Desmond Jennings 6.00 15.00
DJO Daryl Jones 4.00 10.00
DV Dayan Viciedo 4.00 10.00
EH Eric Hosmer S2 15.00 40.00
EP Eury Perez S2 3.00 8.00
ES Eduardo Sanchez S2 3.00 8.00
EY Eric Young Jr. 3.00 8.00
FP Francisco Peguero S2 4.00 10.00
FS Francisco Samuel 3.00 8.00
GG Grant Green S2 5.00 12.00
GH Gorkys Hernandez S2 4.00 10.00
HA Henderson Alvarez S2 3.00 8.00
HC Hank Conger S2 6.00 15.00
HJ Hak-Ju Lee S2 5.00 12.00
HN Hector Noesi S2 4.00 10.00
JC Jhoulys Chacin 4.00 10.00
JF Jeurys Familia S2 4.00 10.00
JH Jeremy Hellickson S2 12.50 30.00
JH Jason Heyward 30.00 60.00
JL Jordan Lyles S2 4.00 10.00
JM Jesus Montero 6.00 15.00
JP Jarrod Parker 4.00 10.00
JS Jason Castro 5.00 12.00
JS Juancarlos Sulbaran 4.00 10.00
JT Junichi Tazawa 4.00 10.00
JT Julio Teheran S2 6.00 15.00
JV Josh Vitters 5.00 12.00
JW Jemile Weeks 4.00 10.00
KD Kyle Drabek 5.00 12.00
KK Kyeong Kang 4.00 10.00
LC Lonnie Chisenhall S2 4.00 10.00
LD Luis Durango 4.00 10.00
LJ Luis Jimenez S2 3.00 8.00
LM Logan Morrison S2 6.00 15.00
LS Leyson Septimo 3.00 8.00
MB Madison Bumgarner 5.00 12.00
ML Mat Latos 4.00 10.00
MM Mike Minor S2 5.00 12.00
MS Mike Stanton 10.00 25.00
MT Mike Trout S2 12.50 30.00
NF Neftali Feliz 5.00 12.00
NW Nick Weglarz 4.00 10.00
OM Ozzie Martinez S2 4.00 10.00
PA Pedro Alvarez 10.00 25.00
PB Pedro Baez 4.00 10.00
PB Pedro Baez S2 3.00 8.00
PC Pedro Ciriaco S2 3.00 8.00
PV Philippe Valiquette S2 4.00 10.00
RT Rene Tosoni 4.00 10.00
SC Starlin Castro 30.00 60.00
SC Simon Castro S2 4.00 10.00
SM Shelby Miller S2 10.00 25.00
SP Stolmy Pimentel S2 4.00 10.00
SS Scott Sizemore 4.00 10.00
TF Tyler Flowers 4.00 10.00
TG Tyson Gillies 5.00 12.00
TM Trystan Magnuson S2 4.00 10.00
TR Trevor Reckling 5.00 12.00
TS Tanner Scheppers S2 3.00 8.00
WF Wilmer Flores 4.00 10.00
WR Wilin Rosario S2 4.00 10.00
YA Yonder Alonso S2 4.00 10.00
YF Yohan Flande 4.00 10.00
ZB Zach Britton S2 8.00 20.00
ZW Zach Wheeler S2 5.00 12.00
BLA Brett Lawrie 15.00 40.00
MBA Manny Banuelos 30.00 60.00
MMO Mike Moustakas S2 6.00 15.00
WRA Wilkin Ramirez S2 3.00 8.00

2010 Topps Pro Debut Futures Game Patch

STATED PRINT RUN 5 SER.#'d SETS
NO PRICING DUE TO SCARCITY

2010 Topps Pro Debut Futures Game Flag Patch

SER.2 ODDS 1:5496 HOBBY
STATED PRINT RUN 1 SER.#'d SET
NO PRICING DUE TO SCARCITY

2010 Topps Pro Debut Futures Game MLB Logo Patch

STATED PRINT RUN 1 SER.#'d SET
NO PRICING DUE TO SCARCITY

2010 Topps Pro Debut Futures Game Triple Logo Patch

STATED PRINT RUN 1 SER.#'d SET
NO PRICING DUE TO SCARCITY

2010 Topps Pro Debut Hall of Fame Stars

COMPLETE SET (10) 8.00 20.00
PLATE PRINT RUN 1 SET PER COLOR
BLACK-CYAN-MAGENTA-YELLOW ISSUED
NO PLATE PRICING DUE TO SCARCITY
HOF1 Jackie Robinson 1.00 2.50
HOF2 Babe Ruth 2.50 6.00
HOF3 Phil Rizzuto .60 1.50
HOF4 Stan Musial 1.50 4.00
HOF5 Pee Wee Reese .60 1.50
HOF6 Carl Yastrzemski 1.00 2.50
HOF7 Mickey Mantle 3.00 8.00
HOF8 Joe Morgan .40 1.00
HOF9 Jim Palmer .40 1.00
HOF10 Jimmie Foxx 1.00 2.50

2010 Topps Pro Debut Prospect Autographs

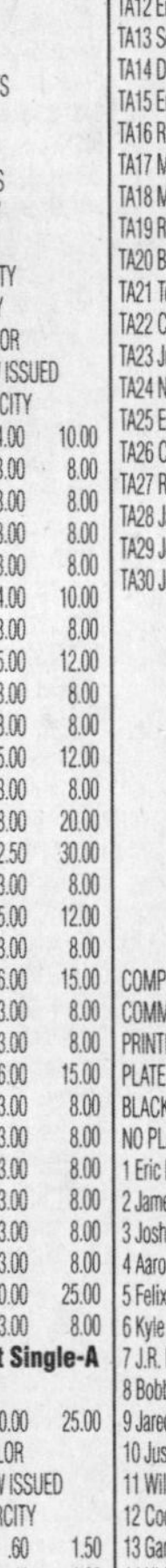

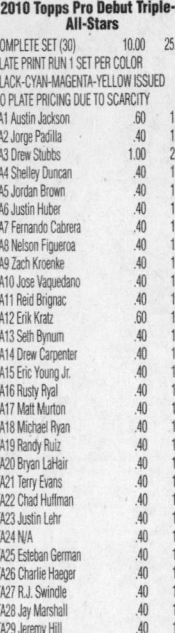

SER.2 ODDS 1:14 HOBBY
*BLUE: .5X TO 1.2X BASIC
SER.2 BLUE ODDS 1:115 HOBBY
BLUE PRINT RUN 199 SER.#'d SETS
*GOLD: .6X TO 1.5X BASIC
SER.2 GOLD ODDS 1:458 HOBBY
GOLD PRINT RUN 50 SER.#'d SETS
SER.2 RED ODDS 1:22,900 HOBBY
RED PRINT RUN 1 SER.#'d SET
NO RED PRICING DUE TO SCARCITY
SER.2 PLATE ODDS 1:5710 HOBBY
PLATE PRINT RUN 1 SET PER COLOR
BLACK-CYAN-MAGENTA-YELLOW ISSUED
NO PLATE PRICING DUE TO SCARCITY
AC Andrew Cashner 4.00 10.00
AH Anthony Hewitt 3.00 8.00
AL Andrew Liebel 3.00 8.00
BJ Brett Jackson S2 3.00 8.00
CB Charlie Blackmon S2 3.00 8.00
CD Chase D'Arnaud 4.00 10.00
DC David Cook S2 3.00 8.00
GH Greg Halman S2 5.00 12.00
JA Jay Austin S2 3.00 8.00
JF Jeremy Farrell 3.00 8.00
JG Johnny Giavotella S2 5.00 12.00
JL Jeff Locke 3.00 8.00
JM Jenrry Mejia 8.00 20.00
JM Jesus Montero S2 12.50 30.00
JT John Tolisano S2 3.00 8.00
LC Lonnie Chisenhall 5.00 12.00
LF Logan Forsythe 3.00 8.00
MM Mike Montgomery 6.00 15.00
NV Niko Vasquez 3.00 8.00
RC Ryan Chaffee 3.00 8.00
RK Ryan Kalish 6.00 15.00
SG Steve Garrison S2 3.00 8.00
SP Shane Peterson 3.00 8.00
SP Shane Peterson S2 3.00 8.00
TJ Travis Jones 3.00 8.00
TS T.J. Steele S2 3.00 8.00
WS Will Smith 3.00 8.00
MMO Michael Moustakas 10.00 25.00
SHE Steven Hensley S2 3.00 8.00

2010 Topps Pro Debut Single-A All-Stars

COMPLETE SET (30) 10.00 25.00
PLATE PRINT RUN 1 SET PER COLOR
BLACK-CYAN-MAGENTA-YELLOW ISSUED
NO PLATE PRICING DUE TO SCARCITY
SA1 Zoilo Almonte .60 1.50
SA2 Welinton Ramirez .40 1.00
SA3 Jimmy Paredes .40 1.00
SA4 John Murrian .60 1.50
SA5 Ryan Westmoreland 1.00 2.50

SA6 Sean Ochinko .40 1.00
SA7 Tyler Kelly .40 1.00
SA8 Cory Burns .40 1.00
SA9 Brian Kemp .40 1.00
SA10 Tyler Bortnick .40 1.00
SA11 Levi Carolus .40 1.00
SA12 Neil Medchill .60 1.50
SA13 Jacob Smith .40 1.00
SA14 Mitchell Clegg .60 1.50
SA15 Jose Alvarez .40 1.00
SA16 Leandro Castro .40 1.00
SA17 Sean Nicol .40 1.00
SA18 Sam Honeck .60 1.50
SA19 Francisco Murillo .40 1.00
SA20 Alan Ahmady .60 1.50
SA21 Chase Austin .40 1.00
SA22 J.D. Martinez 1.50 4.00
SA23 Luis Rivera .60 1.50
SA24 Russell Dixon .40 1.00
SA25 Francisco Soriano .40 1.00
SA26 Brock Holt .60 1.50
SA27 Michael Rockett .60 1.50
SA28 Deangelo Mack .60 1.50
SA29 Mark Cohoon .40 1.00
SA30 Kyle Jensen .40 1.00

2010 Topps Pro Debut Triple-A All-Stars

COMPLETE SET (30) 10.00 25.00
PLATE PRINT RUN 1 SET PER COLOR
BLACK-CYAN-MAGENTA-YELLOW ISSUED
NO PLATE PRICING DUE TO SCARCITY
TA1 Austin Jackson .60 1.50
TA2 Jorge Padilla .40 1.00
TA3 Drew Stubbs 1.00 2.50
TA4 Shelley Duncan .40 1.00
TA5 Jordan Brown .40 1.00
TA6 Justin Huber .40 1.00
TA7 Fernando Cabrera .40 1.00
TA8 Nelson Figueroa .40 1.00
TA9 Zach Kroenke .40 1.00
TA10 Jose Vaquedano .40 1.00
TA11 Reid Brignac .40 1.00
TA12 Erik Kratz .60 1.50
TA13 Seth Bynum .40 1.00
TA14 Drew Carpenter .40 1.00
TA15 Eric Young Jr. .40 1.00
TA16 Rusty Ryal .40 1.00
TA17 Matt Murton .40 1.00
TA18 Michael Ryan .40 1.00
TA19 Randy Ruiz .40 1.00
TA20 Bryan LaHair .40 1.00
TA21 Terry Evans .40 1.00
TA22 Chad Huffman .40 1.00
TA23 Justin Lehr .40 1.00
TA24 N/A .40 1.00
TA25 Esteban German .40 1.00
TA26 Charlie Haeger .40 1.00
TA27 R.J. Swindle .40 1.00
TA28 Jay Marshall .40 1.00
TA29 Jeremy Hill .40 1.00
TA30 Jess Todd .40 1.00

2011 Topps Pro Debut

COMPLETE SET (330) 60.00 120.00
COMMON CARD .15 .40
PRINTING PLATE ODDS 1:267 HOBBY
PLATE PRINT RUN 1 SET PER COLOR
BLACK-CYAN-MAGENTA-YELLOW ISSUED
NO PLATE PRICING DUE TO SCARCITY
1 Eric Hosmer 1.25 3.00
2 Jameson Taillon .50 1.25
3 Josh Ashenbrenner .25 .60
4 Aaron Hicks .40 1.00
5 Felix Perez .15 .40
6 Kyle Gibson .25 .60
7 J.R. Bradley .15 .40
8 Bobby Borchering .25 .60
9 Jared Mitchell .25 .60
10 Justin Bencsko .25 .60
11 Wil Myers .25 .60
12 Cody Hawn .25 .60
13 Gary Sanchez .40 1.00
14 Kirk Nieuwenhuis .15 .40
15 Oswaldo Arcia .15 .40
16 Aaron Altherr .15 .40
17 Brandon Short .25 .60
18 Jason Martinson .15 .40
19 Ethan Martin .15 .40
20 Cameron Rupp .15 .40
21 Jorge Padron .25 .60
22 J.C. Menna .15 .40
23 Avisail Garcia .25 .60
24 Jason Kipnis .50 1.25
25 Bryan Mitchell .25 .60
26 Evan Chambers .15 .40
27 Jonathan Singleton .25 .60
28 Jason Townsend .40 1.00
29 Steve Crnkovich .15 .40
30 Darian Sandford .15 .40
31 Christopher Hawkins .15 .40
32 Kolbrin Vitek .25 .60
33 Aaron Shipman .15 .40
34 Jared Rogers .15 .40
35 Robert Anston .15 .40
36 Tyler Thornburg .40 1.00
37 Jamile Weeks .25 .60
38 Mason Williams .40 1.00
39 Francisco Martinez .15 .40
40 Mike Montgomery .25 .60
41 Adalberto Santos .15 .40
42 Vincent Velasquez .25 .60
43 Freddy Galvis .15 .40
44 Matt Thomson .15 .40
45 Alex Lavisky .15 .40
46 Kaleb Cowart .25 .60
47 Drake Britton .15 .40
48 Garrison Lassiter .25 .60
49 Jordan Pratt .15 .40
50 John Gast .15 .40
51 Derek Norris .15 .40
52 Michael Taylor .15 .40
53 Christian Yelich .15 .40
54 LeVon Washington .25 .60
55 Rob Brantly .40 1.00
56 Mickey Wiswall .15 .40
57 Tommy Kahnle .40 1.00
58 Thomas Mittelstaedt .15 .40
59 Michael Sandoval .15 .40
60 Rex Brothers .15 .40
61 Yasmani Grandal .25 .60
62 Joc Pederson .15 .40
63 Max Kepler .15 .40
64 Adrian Salcedo .25 .60
65 Hak-Ju Lee .25 .60
66 Jordan Cooper .25 .60
67 Casey Kelly .15 .40
68 Eric Groff .15 .40
69 Conor Mullee .15 .40
70 Kurtis Muller .15 .40
71 Jared Lakind .25 .60
72 Daniel Tillman .15 .40
73 Madison Younginer .15 .40
74 Alex Wimmers .15 .40
75 Manny Machado .50 1.25
76 Ryan Delgado .15 .40
77 Matt Davidson .15 .40
78 K.C. Hobson .15 .40
79 Cody Scarpetta .15 .40
80 Oscar Taveras .40 1.00
81 Miguel De Los Santos .15 .40
82 Cam Bedrosian .15 .40
83 Scott Rembisz .15 .40
84 Austin Wates .40 1.00
85 Kellen Sweeney .25 .60
86 Rich Poythress .15 .40
87 Blake Kelso .25 .60
88 Keon Broxton .15 .40
89 Jose Iglesias .25 .60
90 Kyle Ryan .25 .60
91 Leslie Anderson .15 .40
92 Jaren Matthews .15 .40
93 Kyle Greenwalt .15 .40
94 Nick Franklin .25 .60
95 Cole Nelson .15 .40
96 Yordy Cabrera .15 .40
97 Tyler Pastornicky .25 .60
98 Brice Cutspec .15 .40
99 Brandon Guyer .25 .60
100 Nolan Arenado .50 1.25
101 Chris Lofton .15 .40
102 Tyler Holt .15 .40
103 D'Vontrey Richardson .15 .40
104 Victor Lara .15 .40
105 Carlos Gutierrez .15 .40
106 Trent Mummey .15 .40
107 Stolmy Pimentel .15 .40
108 James Robinson .25 .60
109 James Baldwin .25 .60
110 Nick Castellanos .25 .60
111 P.J. Polk .15 .40
112 David Filak .15 .40
113 Jimmy Nelson .15 .40
114 Zack Cox .25 .60
115 Cody Buckel .15 .40
116 Philip Gosselin .15 .40
117 Tyler Austin .25 .60
118 Grant Green .15 .40
119 Jabari Blash .15 .40
120 Miguel Sano .40 1.00
121 Adam Gaylord .15 .40
122 Dan Adamson .25 .60
123 Will Middlebrooks .15 .40

124 Chris Jarrett	.15	.40
125 Aaron Senne	.15	.40
126 Tim Melville	.15	.40
127 Collin Bates	.15	.40
128 Scott Schebler	.15	.40
129 Julio Pimentel	.15	.40
130 Cody Stanley	.15	.40
131 Nick Weglarz	.15	.40
132 Chuckie Jones	.15	.40
133 Daniel Fields	.15	.40
134 Tony Sanchez	.25	.60
135 Tanner Bushue	.15	.40
136 Ben Heath	.15	.40
137 Kenneth Allison	.15	.40
138 Brandon Laird	.25	.60
139 Erik Komatsu	.15	.40
140 Cory Brownsten	.15	.40
141 Alex Kaminsky	.25	.60
142 Eddie Rosario	.15	.40
143 Wily Peralta	.15	.40
144 Josh Vitters	.25	.60
145 Paul Goldschmidt	.75	2.00
146 Edward Salcedo	.15	.40
147 Niko Goodrum	.15	.40
148 Todd Cunningham	.25	.60
149 Jaff Decker	.15	.40
150 Kyle Skipworth	.15	.40
151 Cameron Roth	.40	1.00
152 Donn Roach	.15	.40
153 Ismael Guillon	.15	.40
154 Michael Choice	.25	.60
155 Noel Cuevas	.15	.40
156 Jiovanni Mier	.15	.40
157 Nathan Aaron	.25	.60
158 Sebastian Valle	.15	.40
159 Mike Olt	.25	.60
160 Drew Lee	.25	.60
161 Jeff Locke	.25	.60
162 Yadiel Rivera	.25	.60
163 Tyler Matzek	.25	.60
164 J.T. Realmuto	.15	.40
165 Tyler Saladino	.25	.60
166 Yasser Gomez	.15	.40
167 William Beckwith	.15	.40
168 Stephen Hunt	.25	.60
169 Chad James	.15	.40
170 Trayce Thompson	.15	.40
171 Dane Amedee	.15	.40
172 Anthony Bryant	.15	.40
173 Kyle Waldrop	.25	.60
174 Colton Cain	.15	.40
175 Matt Valaika	.15	.40
176 Kurt Fleming	.15	.40
177 Johermyn Chavez	.15	.40
178 Jose Dore	.15	.40
179 J.D. Ashbrook	.15	.40
180 Oscar Tejada	.15	.40
181 Jonathan Burns	.15	.40
182 Trevor May	.15	.40
183 Brodie Greene	.15	.40
184 Henderson Alvarez	.15	.40
185 Dallas Poulk	.15	.40
186 Carlos Perez	.15	.40
187 Wes Hodges	.15	.40
188 Jacob Petricka	.25	.60
189 Ralston Cash	.15	.40
190 Matt Dominguez	.25	.60
191 Robbie Erlin	.25	.60
192 Adam Bailey	.15	.40
193 Jiwan James	.15	.40
194 Chesler Cuthbert	.25	.60
195 Matt Den Dekker	.25	.60
196 Bryce Harper	5.00	12.00
197 Drew Poulk	.15	.40
198 Brian McConkey	.25	.60
199 Reggie Golden	.15	.40
200 Brad Hand	.15	.40
201 Ryan Fisher	.15	.40
202 Delino DeShields	.15	.40
203 Devin Mesoraco	.25	.60
204 Quincy Latimore	.15	.40
205 Cory Vaughn	.15	.40
206 Lonnie Chisenhall	.25	.60
207 Andrelton Simmons	.15	.40
208 Junior Arias	.15	.40
209 Jesus Montero	.60	1.50
210 Nicholas Bartolone	.15	.40
211 Jarret Martin	.25	.60
212 Jordan Danks	.40	1.00
213 Taylor Lindsey	.15	.40
214 Chad Lewis	.15	.40
215 Rangel Ravelo	.15	.40
216 Elliot Soto	.15	.40
217 Riley Hornback	.15	.40
218 Max Stassi	.15	.40
219 Brian Guinn	.15	.40
220 Reymond Fuentes	.15	.40
221 Brandon Decker	.15	.40
222 Hunter Ackerman	.15	.40
223 Drew Robinson	.15	.40
224 Jacob Turner	.60	1.50
225 Ronald Torreyes	.15	.40
226 Ryan LaMarre	.15	.40
227 Marcus Knecht	.15	.40
228 Guillermo Pimentel	.25	.60
229 Rob Rasmussen	.15	.40
230 Ryan Broussard	.15	.40
231 Yordano Ventura	.15	.40
232 Tyrell Jenkins	.15	.40
233 Anthony Rizzo	.25	.60
234 Brett Oberholtzer	.15	.40
235 Brian Pointer	.15	.40
236 Blake Forsythe	.15	.40
237 Byron Aird	.15	.40
238 Mike Kickham	.15	.40
239 L.J. Hoes	.25	.60
240 Jeff Barfield	.15	.40
241 Carlos Perez	.15	.40
242 Felix Sterling	.15	.40
243 Scott Copeland	.40	1.00
244 Austin Romine	.15	.40
245 Luis Sardinas	.15	.40
246 D.J. LeMahieu	.15	.40
247 Jason Knapp	.15	.40
248 Tyler Skaggs	.40	1.00
249 Brad Boxberger	.15	.40
250 Charly Bashara	.15	.40
251 Robby Rowland	.15	.40
252 Todd Frazier	.25	.60
253 Matt Moore	.75	2.00
254 Adam Eaton	.15	.40
255 Chris Archer	.15	.40
256 Jake Oester	.15	.40
257 Jean Segura	.15	.40
258 Bryan Altman	.15	.40
259 Austin Ross	.25	.60
260 Kendal Volz	.15	.40
261 Marc Krauss	.15	.40
262 Stephen Pryor	.15	.40
263 Mike Trout	1.00	2.50
264 Ryan Kussmaul	.75	2.00
265 Casey Upperman	.15	.40
266 Sean Coyle	.40	1.00
267 Robert Morey	.15	.40
268 Eury Perez	.15	.40
269 Chris Marrero	.15	.40
270 Travis d'Arnaud	.15	.40
271 Rene Oriental	.15	.40
272 Angelo Gumbs	.15	.40
273 Sam Tuivailala	.15	.40
274 Anthony Gose	.40	1.00
275 Dallas Beeler	.15	.40
276 Lucas Bailey	.15	.40
277 Ryan Pineda	.15	.40
278 Ryan Brett	.25	.60
279 Brennan Smith	.25	.60
280 David Vidal	.40	1.00
281 Heath Hembree	.15	.40
282 Matt Abraham	.15	.40
283 Chris Owings	.15	.40
284 Cameron Satterwhite	.15	.40
285 Arodys Vizcaino	.15	.40
286 Wilin Rosario	.15	.40
287 Khris Davis	.15	.40
288 Derek Eitel	.15	.40
289 Chase Whitley	.25	.60
290 Fautino De Los Santos	.15	.40
291 Patrick Lawson	.15	.40
292 Nicholas Struck	.15	.40
293 Ryan Berry	.15	.40
294 Zack Cozart	.40	1.00
295 Christian Bethancourt	.15	.40
296 Matt Miller	.15	.40
297 Brandon Drury	.15	.40
298 Chase Burnette	.15	.40
299 Jonathan Correa	.15	.40
300 Nate Roberts	.15	.40
301 Shelby Miller	.40	1.00
302 Brett Jackson	.25	.60
303 Hunter Morris	.15	.40
304 Aaron Kurcz	.15	.40
305 Kendrick Perkins	.15	.40
306 Austin Reed	.15	.40
307 Starling Marte	.40	1.00
308 Mel Rojas Jr.	.15	.40
309 Joe Leonard	.25	.60
310 Salvador Perez	.25	.60
311 Kentrail Davis	.15	.40
312 J.J. Hoover	.15	.40
313 Gary Brown	.40	1.00
314 Zack Von Rosenberg	.15	.40
315 Marcus Nidiffer	.15	.40
316 Chris Dominguez	.25	.60
317 Scott Alexander	.15	.40
318 Thomas Keeling	.15	.40
319 Henry Ramos	.15	.40
320 Drew Heid	.15	.40
321 Dustin Geiger	.15	.40
322 Kevin Kiermaier	.25	.60
323 Juan Carlos Linares	.15	.40
324 Matthew Suschak	.15	.40
325 Dixon Machado	.15	.40
326 Chevez Clarke	.15	.40
327 Drew Maggi	.15	.40
328 Ryan Copeland	.15	.40
329 Matt Curry	.40	1.00
330 J.R. Murphy	.15	.40

2011 Topps Pro Debut Blue

*BLUE: 3X TO 8X BASIC
STATED ODDS 1:4 HOBBY
STATED PRINT RUN 309 SER.#'d SETS

196 Bryce Harper	15.00	40.00

2011 Topps Pro Debut Gold

*GOLD: 5X TO 12X BASIC
STATED ODDS 1:22 HOBBY
STATED PRINT RUN 50 SER.#'d SETS

1 Eric Hosmer	12.50	30.00
2 Jameson Taillon	12.50	30.00
196 Bryce Harper	100.00	200.00

2011 Topps Pro Debut Red

STATED ODDS 1:1069 HOBBY
STATED PRINT RUN 1 SER.#'d SET
NO PRICING DUE TO SCARCITY

2011 Topps Pro Debut Bryce Harper Baseball Cut Signature

STATED ODDS 1:337,150 HOBBY
STATED PRINT RUN 1 SER.#'d SET
NO PRICING DUE TO SCARCITY

2011 Topps Pro Debut Debut Cuts

STATED ODDS 1:296 HOBBY
PRINT RUNS B/WN 33-130 COPIES PER

AH Aaron Hicks/95	10.00	25.00
BD Brett DeVall/78	6.00	15.00
CB Cam Bedrosian/33	10.00	25.00
CM Clark Murphy/122	6.00	15.00
DH Destin Hood/130	6.00	15.00
EM Ethan Martin/130	6.00	15.00
GL Garrison Lassiter/122	8.00	20.00
JC Jarred Cosart/33	20.00	50.00
KS Kyle Skipworth/122	8.00	20.00
RG Reggie Golden/33	15.00	40.00
TM Tim Melville/122	6.00	15.00
TW Tony Wolters/95	10.00	25.00
YC Yordy Cabrera/95	6.00	15.00

2011 Topps Pro Debut Double-A All Stars

COMPLETE SET (45) 15.00 40.00
STATED ODDS 1:4 HOBBY
PRINTING PLATE ODDS 1:882 HOBBY
PLATE PRINT RUN 1 SET PER COLOR
BLACK-CYAN-MAGENTA-YELLOW ISSUED
NO PLATE PRICING DUE TO SCARCITY

DA1 Kyle Gibson	.60	1.50
DA2 Trystan Magnuson	.40	1.00
DA3 Josh Stinson	1.00	2.50
DA4 Austin Romine	.40	1.00
DA5 Matt Rizzotti	1.00	2.50
DA6 Kirk Nieuwenhuis	.40	1.00
DA7 Eric Thames	.40	1.00
DA8 Zach Britton	1.00	2.50
DA9 Lonnie Chisenhall	.60	1.50
DA10 Thomas Neal	.40	1.00
DA11 Joey Butler	.40	1.00
DA12 Johnny Giavotella	.40	1.00
DA13 Mike Moustakas	1.00	2.50
DA14 Willin Rosario	.40	1.00
DA15 Adron Chambers	.40	1.00
DA16 Simon Castro	.60	1.50
DA17 Jordan Lyles	.40	1.00
DA18 Koby Clemens	.40	1.00
DA19 Corey Brown	.40	1.00
DA20 Matt Dominguez	.60	1.50
DA21 Brandon Tripp	.40	1.00
DA22 Carlos Peguero	.60	1.50
DA23 Brett Lawrie	3.00	8.00
DA24 Alex Liddi	.40	1.00
DA25 Carlos Triunfel	.40	1.00
DA26 Mauricio Robles	.40	1.00
DA27 Collin Cowgill	.40	1.00
DA28 Darin Mastroianni	.40	1.00
DA29 Chase d'Arnaud	.60	1.50
DA30 Matt Hague	.40	1.00
DA31 Joshua Collmenter	.40	1.00
DA32 Cedric Hunter	.40	1.00
DA33 Jake Kahaulelio	.60	1.50
DA34 Robinson Chirinos	.40	1.00
DA35 Chris Marrero	.40	1.00
DA36 Mike Nickeas	.40	1.00
DA37 Pedro Beato	.40	1.00
DA38 Rudy Owens	.40	1.00
DA39 John Drennen	1.25	3.00
DA40 Ryan Mount	1.25	3.00
DA41 Carlos Hernandez	.60	1.50
DA42 Craig Italiano	.40	1.00
DA43 Matt Lawson	.40	1.00
DA44 Steve Clevenger	.40	1.00
DA45 Drew Anderson	.40	1.00

2011 Topps Pro Debut Materials

STATED ODDS 1:13 HOBBY
GOLD PRINT RUN 25 SER.#'d SETS
NO GOLD PRICING DUE TO SCARCITY
RED PRINT RUN 5 SER.#'d SETS
NO RED PRICING DUE TO SCARCITY
PATCH PRINT RUN 5 SER.#'d SETS
NO PATCH PRICING DUE TO SCARCITY
LOGO PRINT RUN 1 SER.#'d SET
NO LOGO PRICING DUE TO SCARCITY

AC Angel Castillo	2.50	6.00
BB Brandon Belt	4.00	10.00
BJ Brett Jackson	3.00	8.00
CA Chris Archer	2.50	6.00
DG Dee Gordon	2.50	6.00
DS Domingo Santana	2.50	6.00
JB Jesse Biddle	3.00	8.00
JS Jerry Sands	3.00	8.00
JV Josh Vitters	2.50	6.00
MB Michael Burgess	2.50	6.00
MM Mike Moustakas	3.00	8.00
MT Mike Trout	4.00	10.00
NF Nick Franklin	2.50	6.00
TS Tony Sanchez	3.00	8.00
ZB Zach Britton	3.00	8.00

2011 Topps Pro Debut Materials Gold

*GOLD: .5X TO 1.2X BASIC
STATED ODDS 1:470 HOBBY
STATED PRINT RUN 50 SER.#'d SETS

2011 Topps Pro Debut Materials Red

STATED ODDS 1:4700 HOBBY
STATED PRINT RUN 5 SER.#'d SETS
NO PRICING DUE TO SCARCITY

2011 Topps Pro Debut Side By Side Autographs

STATED ODDS 1:458
GOLD ODDS 1:1283 HOBBY
GOLD PRINT RUN 25 SER.#'d SETS
NO GOLD PRICING DUE TO SCARCITY
RED ODDS 1:32,000 HOBBY
RED PRINT RUN 1 SER.#'d SET
NO RED PRICING DUE TO SCARCITY
PRINTING PLATE ODDS 1:2520 HOBBY
PLATE PRINT RUN 1 SET PER COLOR
BLACK-CYAN-MAGENTA-YELLOW ISSUED
NO PLATE PRICING DUE TO SCARCITY

BH Michael Burgess / Wes Hodges	4.00	10.00
GM Freddy Galvis / Jiovanni Mier	6.00	15.00
GU Kyle Greenwalt / Pat Urckfitz	6.00	15.00
HM Wes Hodges / Zach McAllister		
MB Jared Mitchell / Michael Burgess	5.00	12.00
MC Fabio Martinez / Kaleb Cowart	8.00	20.00
MM Mike Montgomery / Matt Moore	30.00	60.00
PM Chris Parmelee / Chris Marrero	4.00	10.00
RG Tanner Robles / Robbie Grossman	4.00	10.00
RR Billy Rowell / Derrick Robinson	6.00	15.00
RV Ryan Adams / Niko Vasquez	8.00	20.00

2011 Topps Pro Debut Side By Side Autographs Gold

STATED ODDS 1:1283 HOBBY
STATED PRINT RUN 25 SER.#'d SETS
NO PRICING DUE TO SCARCITY

2011 Topps Pro Debut Side By Side Autographs Red

STATED ODDS 1:32,000 HOBBY
STATED PRINT RUN 1 SER.#'d SET
NO PRICING DUE TO SCARCITY

2011 Topps Pro Debut Single-A All Stars

COMPLETE SET (45) 15.00 40.00
STATED ODDS 1:4 HOBBY
PRINTING PLATE ODDS 1:882 HOBBY
PLATE PRINT RUN 1 SET PER COLOR
BLACK-CYAN-MAGENTA-YELLOW ISSUED
NO PLATE PRICING DUE TO SCARCITY

SA1 Jordan Pacheco	.40	1.00
SA2 Brandon Belt	1.50	4.00
SA3 Corban Joseph	.40	1.00
SA4 Brett Jackson	.60	1.50
SA5 Kyle Skipworth	.40	1.00
SA6 Eric Hosmer	3.00	8.00
SA7 Will Middlebrooks	.40	1.00
SA8 Brandon Short	.60	1.50
SA9 Michael Burgess	.60	1.50
SA10 Tyson Auer	.40	1.00
SA11 Jerry Sands	1.50	4.00
SA12 Hak-Ju Lee	.60	1.50
SA13 Mike Trout	2.50	6.00
SA14 Aaron Hicks	1.00	2.50
SA15 Chun-Hsiu Chen	1.00	2.50
SA16 Tyler Skaggs	1.00	2.50
SA17 Allen Webster	.60	1.50
SA18 Jacob Turner	1.50	4.00
SA19 Quincy Latimore	.40	1.00
SA20 Erik Komatsu	.40	1.00
SA21 Ryan Lavarnway	1.00	2.50
SA22 Blake Tekotte	.40	1.00
SA23 J.J. Hoover	.40	1.00
SA24 Josh Satin	.40	1.00
SA25 Stephen Vogt	.40	1.00
SA26 Jeff Locke	.60	1.50
SA27 J.D. Martinez	.60	1.50
SA28 Destin Hood	1.00	2.50
SA29 Jonathan Villar	.40	1.00
SA30 Ian Gac	.60	1.50
SA31 Robbie Erlin	.60	1.50
SA32 Alexander Colome	.40	1.00
SA33 Matt Davidson	.40	1.00
SA34 Casey Haerther	.40	1.00
SA35 Robbie Ross	1.25	3.00
SA36 Tyson Van Winkle	.40	1.00
SA37 Max Stassi	.40	1.00
SA38 Jean Segura	.40	1.00
SA39 Nick Franklin	.60	1.50
SA40 Rafael Ynoa	.40	1.00
SA41 Bo Greenwell	1.25	3.00
SA42 Brad Brach	.40	1.00
SA43 Rich Poythress	.40	1.00
SA44 Jon Gilmore	1.25	3.00
SA45 Tyler Chatwood	.40	1.00

2011 Topps Pro Debut Solo Signatures

GROUP A ODDS 1:26
GROUP B ODDS 1:48
GROUP C ODDS 1:239
RED ODDS 1:14,700 HOBBY
RED PRINT RUN 1 SER.#'d SET
NO RED PRICING DUE TO SCARCITY
PRINTING PLATE ODDS 1:2520 HOBBY
PLATE PRINT RUN 1 SET PER COLOR
BLACK-CYAN-MAGENTA-YELLOW ISSUED
NO PLATE PRICING DUE TO SCARCITY

CC Cito Culver	6.00	15.00
CN Chris Nowak	3.00	8.00
CS Cody Scarpetta	3.00	8.00
DB Dan Brewer	5.00	12.00
FD Fautino De Los Santos	3.00	8.00
FG Freddy Galvis	4.00	10.00
GG Garrett Gould	3.00	8.00
JB Jesse Biddle	4.00	10.00
JD Jaff Decker	4.00	10.00
JP Julio Pimental	3.00	8.00
JZ Josh Zeid	3.00	8.00
KD Khris Davis	4.00	10.00
KG Kyle Greenwalt	3.00	8.00
MC Michael Choice	5.00	12.00
OP Omar Poveda	3.00	8.00
RA Ryan Adams	3.00	8.00
RL Ryan Larvarnway	8.00	20.00
RP Rich Poythress	3.00	8.00
SH Slade Heathcott	6.00	15.00
TF Thomas Field	3.00	8.00
WH Wes Hodges	3.00	8.00
ZA Zach McAllister	3.00	8.00
AWE Allen Webster	3.00	8.00
DBR David Bromberg	3.00	8.00

2011 Topps Pro Debut Solo Signatures Blue

*BLUE: .5X TO 1.2X BASIC
STATED ODDS 1:74 HOBBY
STATED PRINT RUN 199 SER.#'d SETS

2011 Topps Pro Debut Solo Signatures Gold

*GOLD: .6X TO 1.5X BASIC
STATED ODDS 1:294 HOBBY
STATED PRINT RUN 50 SER.#'d SETS

2011 Topps Pro Debut Solo Signatures Red

STATED ODDS 1:14,700 HOBBY
STATED PRINT RUN 1 SER.#'d SET
NO PRICING DUE TO SCARCITY

2011 Topps Pro Debut Triple-A All Stars

COMPLETE SET (10) 6.00 15.00
STATED ODDS 1:16 HOBBY
PRINTING PLATE ODDS 1:882 HOBBY

PLATE PRINT RUN 1 SET PER COLOR
BLACK-CYAN-MAGENTA-YELLOW ISSUED
NO PLATE PRICING DUE TO SCARCITY

TA1 Brock Bond	.75	2.00
TA2 Brandon Dickson	.75	2.00
TA3 Dustin Martin	.75	2.00
TA4 Chase Lambin	1.25	3.00
TA5 Wes Timmons	.75	2.00
TA6 Bubba Bells	.75	2.00
TA7 Jose Constanza	.75	2.00
TA8 Matt Miller	.75	2.00
TA9 Doug Deeds	.75	2.00
TA10 Jesus Montero	3.00	8.00

2007 TRISTAR Autothentics

COMMON CARD	.25	.60
1 Tyler Colvin	.40	1.00
2 Jay Bruce	1.50	4.00
3 Brian Barton	.40	1.00
4 Nick Adenhart	.60	1.50
5 Blake DeWitt	.40	1.00
6 Tony Granadillo	.25	.60
7 Gorkys Hernandez	.60	1.50
8 Chad Huffman	.25	.60
9 Chris Carter	1.50	4.00
10 Bubba Bell	.25	.60
11 Max Ramirez	.25	.60
12 Gaby Sanchez	.40	1.00
13 Brandon Tripp	.25	.60
14 Micah Schnurstein	.25	.60
15 Cameron Maybin	.40	1.00
16 Joe Mather	.25	.60
17 John Lindsey	.25	.60
18 Max Sapp	.25	.60
19 Chris Lubanski	.25	.60
20 Kyle Blanks	.40	1.00
21 Yung-Chi Chen	.60	1.50
22 Chris Coghlan	.75	2.00
23 John Jaso	.25	.60
24 Luke Hochevar	.75	2.00
25 Hank Conger	1.25	3.00
26 Trevor Crowe	.25	.60
27 Brian Bixler	.25	.60
28 Neil Walker	.40	1.00
29 Ryan Royster	.25	.60
30 Van Pope	.25	.60
31 Chris Parmelee	.25	.60
32 Elvis Andrus	.60	1.50
33 Adrian Cardenas	.40	1.00
34 Dexter Fowler	.60	1.50
35 Carlos Gonzalez	.60	1.50
36 Jose Tabata	.60	1.50
37 Trevor Plouffe	.25	.60
38 Andrew McCutchen	.60	1.50
39 Matt Antonelli	.40	1.00
40 Javier Brito	.25	.60
41 Jared Goedert	.60	1.50
42 Jake Fox	.25	.60
43 Collin Balester	.25	.60
44 Koby Clemens	.40	1.00
45 Aaron Bates	.25	.60
46 Jamie Garcia	.60	1.50
47 Wladimir Balentien	.25	.60
48 Fernando Martinez	1.00	2.50
49 Josh Kroeger	.25	.60
50 Wes Hodges	.25	.60
51 Lee Mitchell	.25	.60
52 Jason Place	.40	1.00
53 Jon Jay	.40	1.00
54 Landon Powell	.25	.60
55 Pablo Sandoval	.75	2.00
56 Jonathan Herrera	.25	.60
57 Craig Cooper	.40	1.00
58 Darren Ford	.25	.60
59 Justin Upton	2.00	5.00
60 Travis Snider	.40	1.00
61 Preston Mattingly	.25	.60
62 Brandon Jones	.40	1.00
63 Chin-Lung Hu	1.00	2.50
64 Jeff Larish	.25	.60
65 Chris Marrero	.40	1.00
66 Joey Votto	1.50	4.00
67 Jacoby Ellsbury	2.00	5.00
68 Chase Headley	.25	.60
69 Evan Longoria	2.50	6.00
70 Colby Rasmus	1.50	4.00
71 Bill Rowell	.60	1.50
72 Jordan Schafer	.40	1.00
73 Drew Stubbs	.60	1.50
74 Oscar Salazar	.25	.60
75 Travis Denker	.25	.60

2007 TRISTAR Autothentics Bronze

*BRONZE: .75X TO 2X BASIC
RANDOM INSERTS IN PACKS
STATED PRINT RUN 50 SER.#'d SETS

67 Jacoby Ellsbury	4.00	10.00

2007 TRISTAR Autothentics Green

*GREEN: .6X TO 1.5X BASIC
RANDOM INSERTS IN PACKS
STATED PRINT RUN 250 SER.#'d SETS

2007 TRISTAR Autothentics Autographs

OVERALL AUTO ODDS ONE PER PACK

1 Tyler Colvin	4.00	10.00
4 Nick Adenhart	12.50	30.00
7 Gorkys Hernandez	5.00	12.00
13 Brandon Tripp	3.00	8.00
16 Joe Mather	5.00	12.00
18 Max Sapp	3.00	8.00
19 Chris Lubanski	4.00	10.00
22 Chris Coghlan	3.00	8.00
24 Luke Hochevar SP		
25 Hank Conger	3.00	8.00
26 Trevor Crowe	3.00	8.00
32 Elvis Andrus	4.00	10.00
33 Adrian Cardenas	4.00	10.00
36 Jose Tabata	6.00	15.00
39 Matt Antonelli	4.00	10.00
43 Collin Balester	3.00	8.00
44 Koby Clemens		
46 Jamie Garcia	4.00	10.00
47 Wladimir Balentien	3.00	8.00
54 Landon Powell	3.00	8.00
56 Jonathan Herrera	3.00	8.00
59 Justin Upton SP	10.00	25.00
60 Travis Snider	6.00	15.00
63 Chin-Lung Hu	25.00	50.00
64 Jeff Larish	3.00	8.00
65 Chris Marrero	4.00	10.00
66 Joey Votto	12.50	30.00
68 Chase Headley	5.00	12.00
69 Evan Longoria SP	15.00	40.00
70 Colby Rasmus	10.00	25.00

2007 TRISTAR Autothentics Autographs Blue

*BLUE: .5X TO 1.2X BASIC
OVERALL AUTO ODDS ONE PER PACK
STATED PRINT RUN 250 SER.#'d SETS

4 Nick Adenhart	15.00	40.00

2007 TRISTAR Autothentics Autographs Red

*RED: .6X TO 1.5X BASIC
OVERALL AUTO ODDS ONE PER PACK
STATED PRINT RUN 50 SER.#'d SETS
4 Nick Adenhart 20.00 50.00

2007 TRISTAR Elegance

This 75-card set was released in August, 2007. This set was released in five-card packs, with an $49.99 SRP, which came four packs to a box and 12 boxes to a case. Each pack contained two autographed cards, one game-used relic card and two base cards (or a base card and a parallel card thereof). A few Pro Debut cards were interspersed throughout this set.

COMMON CARD .40 1.00
PRINTING PLATE ODDS 1 PER CASE
PLATE PRINT RUN 1 SET PER COLOR
BLACK-CYAN-MAGENTA-YELLOW ISSUED
NO PLATE PRICING DUE TO SCARCITY
1 Evan Longoria 4.00 10.00
2 Justin Upton 3.00 8.00
3 Jon Jay PD .60 1.50
4 Nick Adenhart PD 1.00 2.50
5 Preston Mattingly .40 1.00
6 Tim Lincecum 6.00 15.00
7 Chad Tracy .60 1.50
8 Andy Laroche .40 1.00
9 Hunter Pence 2.00 5.00
10 Shelby Ford .40 1.00
11 Billy Rowell 1.00 2.50
12 Philip Hughes 2.00 5.00
13 Ron Bourquin PD .60 1.50
14 Jay Bruce 2.50 6.00
15 Jason Donald PD .40 1.00
16 Luke Hochevar 1.25 3.00
17 Jeff Samardzija 1.50 4.00
18 Jose Tabata 1.00 2.50
19 Cooper Brannan .40 1.00
20 Daniel Bard .40 1.00
21 Brad Lincoln .40 1.00
22 Clayton Kershaw 3.00 8.00
23 Travis Snider .60 1.50
24 Cameron Maybin .60 1.50
25 Yung-Chi Chen 1.00 2.50
26 Chin-Lung Hu 1.50 4.00
27 Drew Stubbs 1.00 2.50
28 Hank Conger 2.00 5.00
29 Chris Parmelee .40 1.00
30 Yovani Gallardo PD 1.00 2.50
31 Joba Chamberlain 2.00 5.00
32 Adrian Cardenas .60 1.50
33 Tyler Colvin .60 1.50
34 Brandon Wood .40 1.00
35 Billy Butler .60 1.50
36 Koby Clemens .60 1.50
37 Chris Coghlan 1.25 3.00
38 Elvis Andrus 1.00 2.50
39 Carlos Gonzalez PD 1.00 2.50
40 Jonathan Herrera .40 1.00
41 Max Sapp .40 1.00
42 Ryan Braun PD 2.00 5.00
43 Dellin Betances 1.00 2.50
44 Nolan Reimold PD .60 1.50
45 Brandon Erbe PD .60 1.50
46 Jacoby Ellsbury PD 3.00 8.00
47 Clay Buchholz PD 2.50 6.00
48 Cole Garner .40 1.00
49 Eric Campbell .60 1.50
50 Matthew Maloney PD .60 1.50
51 Reid Brignac .60 1.50
52 Luis Pérez PD .40 1.00
53 Chris Nowak .40 1.00
54 Ching-Lung Lo .60 1.50
55 Charles Lofgren 1.00 2.50
56 John Mayberry Jr. .40 1.00
57 Trevor Crowe .40 1.00
58 Brian Barton .60 1.50
59 Jeff Larish PD .40 1.00
60 Eulogio de la Cruz .60 1.50
61 John Danks .60 1.50
62 Matt Sweeney .40 1.00
63 Daric Barton .60 1.50
64 Lance Broadway .40 1.00
65 Chris Lubanski .40 1.00
66 Ryan Patterson PD .40 1.00
67 Chris Volstad .60 1.50
68 Fernando Martinez PD 1.50 4.00
69 Colton Willems .40 1.00
70 Collin Balester PD .40 1.00
71 Chris Marrero .60 1.50
72 Joey Votto 2.50 6.00
73 Paul Janish PD .40 1.00
74 Andrew McCutchen 1.00 2.50
75 Colby Rasmus 2.50 6.00

2007 TRISTAR Elegance Purple

RANDOM INSERTS IN PACKS
STATED PRINT RUN 1 SER.#'d SET
NO PRICING DUE TO SCARCITY

2007 TRISTAR Elegance Red

RANDOM INSERTS IN PACKS
STATED PRINT RUN 25 SER.#'d SETS
NO PRICING DUE TO SCARCITY

2007 TRISTAR Elegance Showtime Game Used

OVERALL GU ODDS 1:1
PRINTING PLATE ODDS 1 PER CASE
PLATE PRINT RUN 1 SET PER COLOR
BLACK-CYAN-MAGENTA-YELLOW ISSUED
NO PLATE PRICING DUE TO SCARCITY
PATCH 25 RANDOMLY INSERTED IN PACKS
PATCH 25 PRINT RUN 25 SER.#'d SETS
NO PATCH 25 PRICING DUE TO SCARCITY
AG Alex Gordon 4.00 10.00
BB Billy Butler 4.00 10.00
BL Brad Lincoln 3.00 8.00
BW Brandon Wood 3.00 8.00
CB Clay Buchholz 8.00 20.00
CC Carlos Carrasco 3.00 8.00
CH Chin-Lung Hu 6.00 15.00
CK Clayton Kershaw 6.00 15.00
CL Ching-Lung Lo 3.00 8.00
CM Cameron Maybin 5.00 12.00
CM Chris Marrero 3.00 8.00
DS Drew Stubbs 3.00 8.00
EL Evan Longoria 5.00 12.00
HP Hunter Pence 5.00 12.00
JA Jonny Ash 3.00 8.00
JE Jacoby Ellsbury UER 6.00 15.00
Name spelled Jacoby on Front and Jacob on back
JP Josh Papelbon 3.00 8.00
JU Justin Upton 6.00 15.00
KC Koby Clemens 3.00 8.00
KD Kyle Drabek 3.00 8.00
LH Luke Hochevar 3.00 8.00
MS Max Sapp 3.00 8.00
TL Tim Lincecum 8.00 20.00
TS Travis Snider 3.00 8.00
YC Yung-Chi Chen 6.00 15.00

2007 TRISTAR Elegance Showtime Game Used 5

RANDOM INSERTS IN PACKS
STATED PRINT RUN 5 SER.#'d SETS
NO PRICING DUE TO SCARCITY

2007 TRISTAR Elegance Showtime Game Used Patch

*PATCH: .75X TO 2X BASIC
RANDOM INSERTS IN PACKS
CH Chin-Lung Hu 15.00 40.00
CK Clayton Kershaw 20.00 50.00
JE Jacoby Ellsbury 15.00 40.00
YC Yung-Chi Chen 20.00 50.00

2007 TRISTAR Elegance Showtime Game Used Patch Autographs 25

RANDOM INSERTS IN PACKS
STATED PRINT RUN 25 SER.#'d SETS
NO PRICING DUE TO SCARCITY

2007 TRISTAR Elegance Showtime Game Used Patch Autographs 5

RANDOM INSERTS IN PACKS
STATED PRINT RUN 5 SER.#'d SETS
NO PRICING DUE TO SCARCITY

2007 TRISTAR Elegance Signature Marks

OVERALL AUTO ODDS TWO PER PACK
AC Adrian Cardenas 3.00 8.00
BL Brad Lincoln SP
BR Billy Rowell 5.00 12.00
BS Brett Sinkbeil 3.00 8.00
BW Brandon Wood SP
CB Cooper Brannan 3.00 8.00
CC1 Carlos Carrasco 5.00 12.00
CC2 Chris Coghlan 3.00 8.00
CK Clayton Kershaw SP
CM Chris Marrero 5.00 12.00
CP Chris Parmelee 3.00 8.00
CR Cory Rasmus 3.00 8.00
CV Chris Volstad 3.00 8.00
CW Colton Willems 3.00 8.00
DB Daniel Bard 3.00 8.00
DS Drew Stubbs 3.00 8.00
EL Evan Longoria 15.00 40.00
GH Gorkys Hernandez 5.00 12.00
HP Hunter Pence 15.00 40.00
JA Jonny Ash 3.00 8.00
JJ1 Jon Jay 4.00 10.00
JJ2 Jeremy Jeffress 3.00 8.00
JL Jeff Larish 3.00 8.00
JP1 Jeremy Papelbon 3.00 8.00
JP2 Josh Papelbon 3.00 8.00
JU Justin Upton 12.50 30.00
KC Koby Clemens SP
KD Kyle Drabek 5.00 12.00
KK Kasey Kiker 3.00 8.00
MA Matt Antonelli 4.00 10.00
MS Max Sapp 3.00 8.00
MS2 Matt Sweeney 3.00 8.00
RB Ryan Braun 12.50 30.00
TC Tyler Colvin 4.00 10.00
TS Travis Snider 5.00 12.00

2007 TRISTAR Elegance Signature Marks Dual

OVERALL AUTO ODDS TWO PER PACK
STATED PRINT RUN 25 SER.#'d SETS
NO PRICING DUE TO SCARCITY
BRJU Billy Rowell
Justin Upton
BRTS Billy Rowell
Travis Snider
BWJL Brandon Wood
Jeff Larish
BWJU Brandon Wood
Justin Upton
CCAC Carlos Carrasco
Adrian Cardenas
CRCC Corey Rasmus
Chris Coghlan
CRMS Corey Rasmus
Matt Sweeney
CVCW Chris Volstad
Colton Willems
ELJU Evan Longoria
Justin Upton
CHJL Gorkys Hernandez
Jeff Larish
HPEL Hunter Pence
Evan Longoria
HPMS Hunter Pence
Max Sapp
JAHP Johnny Ash
Hunter Pence
JPJP Jeremy Papelbon
Josh Papelbon
MAJL Matt Antonelli
Jeff Larish
RBEL Ryan Braun
Evan Longoria
TSBW Travis Snider
Brandon Wood
TSCB Travis Snider
Cooper Brannan
TSEL Travis Snider
Evan Longoria
TSRB Travis Snider
Ryan Braun

2007 TRISTAR Elegance Signature Marks Triple

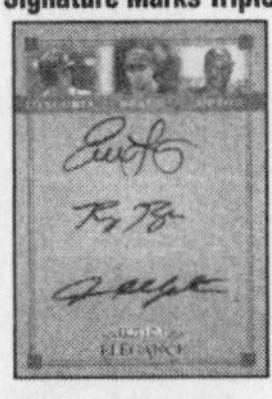

OVERALL AUTO ODDS TWO PER PACK
STATED PRINT RUN 5 SER.#'d SETS
NO PRICING DUE TO SCARCITY
ELBWJU Evan Longoria
Brandon Wood
Justin Upton
ELRBJU Evan Longoria
Ryan Braun
Justin Upton
HPELJU Hunter Pence
Evan Longoria
Justin Upton
JPJPKD Jeremy Papelbon
Josh Papelbon
Kyle Drabek
TSRBJU Travis Snider
Ryan Braun
Justin Upton

2009 TRISTAR Obak

COMP.SET w/o SP (100) 15.00 40.00
COMMON CARD (1-31) .40 1.00
COMMON CARD (32-100) .25 .60
COMMON CARD (101-114) .75 2.00
COMMON SP (1-114) .75 2.00
THREE VARIATIONS PER BOX
COMMON CARD (115-119) .30 .75
COMMON VAR (115-119) .50 1.25
VAR SEMIS .75 2.00
VAR UNLISTED 1.25 3.00
115-119 INSERTED IN PROS.PLUS
1 Pedro Alvarez PD 1.25 3.00
2 Robbie Grossman PD .40 1.00
3 B.J. Hermsen PD .40 1.00
4 Eric Hosmer PD 3.00 8.00
5 Brett Lawrie PD 1.00 2.50
6 Brian Matusz PD 1.00 2.50
7 Fu-Te Ni PD .60 1.50
8 Junichi Tazawa PD 1.25 3.00
9 Dayan Viciedo PD 1.25 3.00
10 Michael Ynoa PD .60 1.50
11 Lars Anderson 1.00 2.50
12a Gordon Beckham 1.25 3.00
12b Gordon Beckham 2.50 6.00
1910 Back variation
Square around number
12c Gordon Beckham 2.50 6.00
1910 Back variation
Circle around number
12d Gordon Beckham 2.50 6.00
1910 Back variation
Diamond around number
12e Gordon Beckham 2.50 6.00
1911 Back variation
Triangle around number
13 Tim Beckham 1.00 2.50
14 Madison Bumgarner 1.00 2.50
15 Neftali Feliz .75 2.00
16a Tommy Hanson 1.25 3.00
16b Tommy Hanson 2.50 6.00
1910 Back variation
Square around number
16c Tommy Hanson 2.50 6.00
1910 Back variation
Circle around number
16d Tommy Hanson 2.50 6.00
1910 Back variation
Diamond around number
16e Tommy Hanson 2.50 6.00
1911 Back variation
Triangle around number
17 Jason Heyward 3.00 8.00
18 Austin Jackson 1.00 2.50
19 Andrew McCutchen 1.50 4.00
20 Jesus Montero 2.50 6.00
21 Mike Moustakas 1.25 3.00
22 Jarrod Parker 1.00 2.50
23 Buster Posey 1.25 3.00
24 Carlos Santana 1.25 3.00
25 Justin Smoak 1.25 3.00
26 Mike Stanton 2.00 5.00
27 Chris Tillman .60 1.50
28a Pat Venditte .60 1.50
Throwing left and right
28b Pat Venditte 1.25 3.00
Throwing left
28c Pat Venditte 1.25 3.00
Throwing right
29 Angel Villalona .60 1.50
30 Josh Vitters 1.00 2.50
31 Brett Wallace .60 1.50
32 Dale Murphy .60 1.50
33 Stan Musial 1.00 2.50
34 Satchel Paige .60 1.50
35 Brooks Robinson .40 1.00
36 Al Rosen .25 .60
37 Nolan Ryan 2.00 5.00
38 Ryne Sandberg 1.25 3.00
39a Tom Seaver .40 1.00
39b Tom Seaver 1.25 3.00
1910 Back variation
Square around number
39c Tom Seaver 1.25 3.00
1910 Back variation
Circle around number
39d Tom Seaver 1.25 3.00
1910 Back variation
Diamond around number
39e Tom Seaver 1.25 3.00
1911 Back variation
Triangle around number
40 Duke Snider .40 1.00
41a Ted Williams 1.50 4.00
41b Ted Williams 5.00 12.00
1910 Back variation
Square around number
41c Ted Williams 5.00 12.00
1910 Back variation
Circle around number
41d Ted Williams 5.00 12.00
1910 Back variation
Diamond around number
41e Ted Williams 5.00 12.00
1911 Back variation
Triangle around number
42a Buzz Arlett .25 .60
42b Buzz Arlett .75 2.00
1910 Back variation
Square around number
42c Buzz Arlett .75 2.00
1910 Back variation
Circle around number
42d Buzz Arlett .75 2.00
1910 Back variation
Diamond around number
42e Buzz Arlett .75 2.00
1911 Back variation
Triangle around number
43 Walter Carlisle .25 .60
44 Steve Dalkowski .25 .60
45 Ox Eckhardt .25 .60
46 Spencer Harris .25 .60
47 Joe Hauser .25 .60
48 Spook Jacobs .25 .60
49 Gene Rye .25 .60
50 Jigger Statz .25 .60
51 Monty Stratton .25 .60
52 Joe Bauman .25 .60
53 Ike Boone .25 .60
54 George Brunet .25 .60
55 Vince Coleman .25 .60
56 Bob Crues .25 .60
57 Grover Lowdermilk .25 .60
58a Ron Necciai .25 .60
58b Ron Necciai .75 2.00
1910 Back variation
Square around number
58c Ron Necciai .75 2.00
1910 Back variation
Circle around number
58d Ron Necciai .75 2.00
1910 Back variation
Diamond around number
58e Ron Necciai .75 2.00
1911 Back variation
Triangle around number
59 Gary Redus .25 .60
60 Joe Wilhoit .25 .60
61 Steve Dillio .25 .60
62a Gene Conley .25 .60
Hartford Chiefs
62b Gene Conley .75 2.00
Toledo Sox
63 Bobby Grich .25 .60
64a Gregg Jefferies .75 2.00
Jackson Mets
64b Gregg Jefferies .75 2.00
Lynchburg Mets
65 Ron Kittle .25 .60
66 Jim Rice .40 1.00
67 Phil Rizzuto .40 1.00
68 Herb Score .25 .60
69 Moose Skowron .25 .60
70 Johnny Vander Meer .25 .60
71 Emmett Ashford .25 .60
72 Lena Blackburne .25 .60
73 Bud Hillerich .25 .60
Pete Browning
74 Alexander Cartwright .25 .60
75 Henry Chadwick .25 .60
76 Mike Coolbaugh .25 .60
77 Candy Cummings .25 .60
78 Washington Duke .25 .60
James Duke
Benjamin Duke
79 John W. Jackson Fowler .25 .60
80 Harrison Harwood .25 .60
81 Elias Howe .25 .60
82 Dummy Hoy .25 .60
83 Foxy Irwin .25 .60
84 Francis Scott Key .25 .60
85 Jackie Mitchell .25 .60
86 Jack Norworth .25 .60
87 Abner Charles Powell .25 .60
88 Patrick T. Powers .25 .60
89 George H. Rawlings .25 .60
90 Wesley Branch Rickey .25 .60
91 Fritz Rueckheim .25 .60
Louis Rueckheim
Henry Eckstein
92 Frank Shaughnessy .25 .60
93 Albert G Spalding .25 .60
94 Harry Wright .25 .60
George Wright
95 William Wrigley Jr. .25 .60
96 Sammy Baugh .60 1.50
97 John Heisman .40 1.00
98 Bo Jackson .60 1.50
99 William Howard Taft .25 .60
100a Barack Obama .75 2.00
100b Barack Obama 2.50 6.00
1910 Back variation
Square around number
100c Barack Obama 2.50 6.00
1910 Back variation
Circle around number
100d Barack Obama 2.50 6.00
1910 Back variation
Diamond around number
100e Barack Obama 2.50 6.00
1911 Back variation
Triangle around number
101 Dinesh Kumar Patel .25 .60
102 Rinku Singh .25 .60
103 Dale Murphy 10.00 25.00
Jason Heyward
104 Stan Musial 6.00 15.00
Daryl Jones
105 Jim Rice 6.00 15.00
Lars Anderson
106 Brooks Robinson 6.00 15.00
Brian Matusz
107 Ryne Sandberg 6.00 15.00
Josh Vitters
108 Tom Seaver 6.00 15.00
Brad Holt
109 Bing Crosby .75 2.00
110 Zane Grey .75 2.00
111 Nick Lachey .75 2.00
112 Ten Million 3.00 8.00
113 Geogre Schmutz 3.00 8.00
114 Rollie Zeider 3.00 8.00
115a Stephen Strasburg 2.50 6.00
115b Stephen Strasburg 4.00 10.00
1910 Superbass Back variation
Diamond around number
115c Stephen Strasburg 4.00 10.00
1910 Perfect Back variation
Square around number
115d Stephen Strasburg 2.50 6.00
1911 Back variation
Triangle around number
116a Dustin Ackley 1.50 4.00
116b Dustin Ackley 2.50 6.00
1910 Always Back variation
Square around number
116c Dustin Ackley 2.50 6.00
1911 Back variation
Triangle around number
117a Donovan Tate .75 2.00
117b Donovan Tate 1.25 3.00
1910 Excel Back variation
Square around number
117c Donovan Tate 1.25 3.00
1911 Back variation
Triangle around number
118a Tony Sanchez .75 2.00
118b Tony Sanchez 1.25 3.00
1910 Nothing Back variation
Square around number
118c Tony Sanchez 1.25 3.00
1911 Back variation
Triangle around number
119a Matt Hobgood .75 2.00
119b Matt Hobgood 1.25 3.00
1910 Speak Back variation
Square around number
119c Matt Hobgood 1.25 3.00
1911 Back variation
Triangle around number

2009 TRISTAR Obak Black

*BLACK 1-31: 1.2X TO 3X BASIC
*BLACK 32-100: 2X TO 5X BASIC
*BLACK SP: .6X TO 1.5X BASIC
OVERALL PARALLEL ODDS 1:10
STATED PRINT RUN 50 SER.#'d SETS

2009 TRISTAR Obak Green

OVERALL PARALLEL ODDS 1:10
STATED PRINT RUN 25 SER.#'d SETS
NO PRICING DUE TO SCARCITY

2009 TRISTAR Obak Purple

OVERALL PARALLEL ODDS 1:10
STATED PRINT RUN 1 SER.#'d SET
NO PRICING DUE TO SCARCITY

2009 TRISTAR Obak Red

OVERALL PARALLEL ODDS 1:10
STATED PRINT RUN 5 SER.#'d SETS
NO PRICING DUE TO SCARCITY

2009 TRISTAR Obak Autographs

OVERALL AUTO ODDS 1:10
STATED PRINT RUN 200 SER.#'d SETS
A1 Jeremy Beckham 8.00 20.00
A2 Charlie Blackmon 3.00 8.00
A3 Andrew Brackman 8.00 20.00
A4 Madison Bumgarner
A5 Lonnie Chisenhall 3.00 8.00
A6 Zach Collier 3.00 8.00
A7 Brandon Crawford 3.00 8.00
A8 Sean Danielson
A9 Jordan Danks 6.00 15.00
A10 Chase D'Arnaud 3.00 8.00
A11 Ike Davis 8.00 20.00
A12 Logan Forsythe
A13 Juan Francisco
A14 Isaac Galloway 3.00 8.00
A15 Anthony Gose 3.00 8.00
A16 Brad Holt
A17 Chris Johnson
A18 Daryl Jones 10.00 25.00
A19 Josh Lindblom
A20 Daniel McCutchen 4.00 10.00
A21 Will Middlebrooks
A22 Yamaico Navarro 4.00 10.00
A23 Dinesh Kumar Patel 20.00 50.00
A24 Steven Pearce 3.00 8.00
A25 Bryan Price
A26 Anthony Rizzo 10.00 25.00
A27 Tyson Ross
A28 Max Sapp 3.00 8.00
A29 Logan Schafer 4.00 10.00
A31 Aaron Shafer
A32 Bryan Shaw 3.00 8.00
A33 Rinku Singh 15.00 40.00
A34 Anthony Slama 3.00 8.00
A35 Craig Stansberry 3.00 8.00
A36 Josh Vitters
A37 Vince Coleman 6.00 15.00
A39 Steve Dalkowski
A40 Bobby Grich 3.00 8.00
A41 Spook Jacobs 4.00 10.00
A43 Ron Kittle 4.00 10.00
A44 Dale Murphy 20.00 50.00
A45 Ron Necciai 5.00 12.00
A46 Gary Redus 4.00 10.00
A47 Jim Rice 12.50 30.00
A48 Brooks Robinson 10.00 25.00
A49 Al Rosen 4.00 10.00
A50 Ryne Sandberg
A51 Tom Seaver
A52 Moose Skowron 6.00 15.00

A53 Duke Snider
A38a Gene Conley
Hartford Chiefs
A38b Gene Conley
Toledo Sox
A42a Gregg Jefferies 6.00 15.00
Jackson Mets
A42b Gregg Jefferies 6.00 15.00
Lynchburg Mets

2009 TRISTAR Obak Autographs Green

OVERALL AUTO ODDS 1:10
STATED PRINT RUN 25 SER.#'d SETS
NO PRICING DUE TO SCARCITY

2009 TRISTAR Obak Autographs Purple

OVERALL AUTO ODDS 1:10
STATED PRINT RUN 1 SER.#'d SET
NO PRICING DUE TO SCARCITY

2009 TRISTAR Obak Autographs Red

OVERALL AUTO ODDS 1:10
STATED PRINT RUN 5 SER.#'d SETS
NO PRICING DUE TO SCARCITY

2009 TRISTAR Obak Mini T212

COMPLETE SET (72) 60.00 120.00
COMP.SET w/o VAR (68) 40.00 80.00
STATED ODDS ONE PER PACK
1 Pedro Alvarez 1.50 4.00
2 Eric Hosmer 4.00 10.00
3 Brian Matusz 1.25 3.00
4 Junichi Tazawa 1.50 4.00
5 Michael Ynoa .75 2.00
6 Lars Anderson 1.25 3.00
7 Gordon Beckham 1.50 4.00
8 Tim Beckham 1.25 3.00
9 Madison Bumgarner 1.25 3.00
10 Tommy Hanson 1.50 4.00
11 Jason Heyward 4.00 10.00
12 Austin Jackson 1.25 3.00
13 Jesus Montero 3.00 8.00
14 Mike Moustakas 1.50 4.00
15 Buster Posey 1.50 4.00
16 Mike Stanton 2.50 6.00
17 Josh Vitters 1.25 3.00
18 Brett Wallace .75 2.00
19 Dale Murphy 1.25 3.00
20 Stan Musial 2.00 5.00
21 Satchel Paige 1.25 3.00
22 Brooks Robinson .75 2.00
23a Nolan Ryan 4.00 10.00
23b Nolan Ryan 4.00 10.00
1910 Back variation
Square around number
23c Nolan Ryan 4.00 10.00
1910 Back variation
Circle around number
24 Ryne Sandberg 2.50 6.00
25 Tom Seaver .75 2.00
26 Duke Snider .75 2.00
27a Ted Williams 3.00 8.00
27b Ted Williams 3.00 8.00
1910 Back variation
Square around number
27c Ted Williams 3.00 8.00
1910 Back variation
Circle around number
28 Buzz Arlett .50 1.25
29 Steve Dalkowski .50 1.25
30 Ox Eckhardt .50 1.25
31 Joe Hauser .50 1.25
32 Jigger Statz .50 1.25
33 Monty Stratton .50 1.25
34 Joe Bauman .50 1.25
35 Ike Boone .50 1.25
36 George Brunet .50 1.25
37 Grover Lowdermilk .50 1.25
38 Ron Necciai .50 1.25
39 Joe Wilhoit .50 1.25
40 Steve Bilko .50 1.25
41 Gene Conley .50 1.25
42 Jim Rice .75 2.00
43 Phil Rizzuto .75 2.00
44 Johnny Vander Meer .50 1.25
45 Emmett Ashford .50 1.25
46 Alexander Cartwright .50 1.25
47 Henry Chadwick .50 1.25
48 Washington Duke .50 1.25
James Duke
Ben Duke
49 John W. Jackson Fowler .50 1.25
50 Dummy Hoy .50 1.25
51 Francis Scott Key .50 1.25
52 Jackie Mitchell .50 1.25
53 Jack Norworth .50 1.25
54 George H. Rawlings .50 1.25
55 Wesley Branch Rickey .50 1.25
56 Fritz Rueckheim .50 1.25
Louis Rueckheim
Henry Eckstein
57 Albert G. Spalding .50 1.25
58 William Wrigley Jr. .50 1.25
59 Sammy Baugh 1.25 3.00
60 John Heisman .75 2.00
61 Bo Jackson 1.25 3.00
62 Barack Obama 1.50 4.00
63 Rinku Singh .25 .60
Dinesh Patel
64 Bing Crosby .50 1.25
65 Nick Lachey .50 1.25
66 Ten Million 2.00 5.00
67 Geogre Schmutz 2.00 5.00
68 Rollie Zeider 2.00 5.00

2009 TRISTAR Obak Mini T212 Black

*BLACK: 1.2X TO 3X BASIC
STATED ODDS 1:20
STATED PRINT RUN 50 SER.#'d SETS

2009 TRISTAR Obak Mini T212 Green

OVERALL PARALLEL ODDS 1:10
STATED PRINT RUN 25 SER.#'d SETS
NO PRICING DUE TO SCARCITY

2009 TRISTAR Obak Mini T212 Purple

OVERALL PARALLEL ODDS 1:10
STATED PRINT RUN 1 SER.#'d SET
NO PRICING DUE TO SCARCITY

2009 TRISTAR Obak Mini T212 Red

OVERALL PARALLEL ODDS 1:10
STATED PRINT RUN 5 SER.#'d SETS
NO PRICING DUE TO SCARCITY

2010 TRISTAR Obak

COMMON CARD (1-109) .20 .50
COMMON VAR (1-109) .40 1.00
COMMON SP (110-120) 1.50 4.00
THREE SPs PER BOX
1 Dustin Ackley 1.25 3.00
2 Josh Bell .20 .50
3 Chris Carter .30 .75
4A Starlin Castro .75 2.00
4B Starlin Castro 1.50 4.00
Slogan VAR
5 Kyle Drabek .30 .75
6A Austin Jackson .30 .75
6B Austin Jackson .60 1.50
Slogan VAR
7 Desmond Jennings .30 .75
8 Jason Kipnis .30 .75
9 Tyler Matzek .50 1.25
10 Jiovanni Mier .30 .75
11 Jared Mitchell .30 .75
12 Austin Romine .30 .75
13 Tony Sanchez .50 1.25
14 Carlos Santana .60 1.50
15 Drew Storen .30 .75
16 Donavan Tate .50 1.25
17A Roger Clemens .60 1.50
17B Roger Clemens 1.25 3.00
Slogan VAR
18 Andre Dawson .30 .75
19A Hank Greenberg .50 1.25
19B Hank Greenberg 1.00 2.50
Slogan VAR
19C Hank Greenberg 1.00 2.50
Image VAR
20A Dale Murphy .50 1.25
20B Dale Murphy 1.00 2.50
Slogan VAR
21A Cal Ripken Jr. 2.00 5.00
21B Cal Ripken Jr. 4.00 10.00
Slogan VAR
22 George Bradley .20 .50
23 Lawrence Davis .20 .50
24 Jack Dunn .20 .50
25 Paul Hines .20 .50
26 Harry McCormick .20 .50
27 Denny Mclain .20 .50
28 Fred Toney .20 .50
29 Ron Blomberg .20 .50
30 Jeff Burroughs .20 .50
31 David Clyde .20 .50
32 Bob Horner .20 .50
33 Ben McDonald .20 .50
34 Darryl Strawberry .20 .50
35 Jay Clarke .20 .50
36 Smead Jolley .20 .50
37 Joe Riggert .20 .50
38 Doc Newton .20 .50
39 Don Baylor .20 .50
40A Johnny Bench .50 1.25
40B Johnny Bench 1.00 2.50
Slogan VAR
41A Jose Canseco .30 .75
41B Jose Canseco .60 1.50
Slogan VAR
42 Dwight Gooden .20 .50
43 Ben Grieve .20 .50
44A Jason Heyward 1.25 3.00
44B Jason Heyward 2.50 6.00
Slogan VAR
44C Jason Heyward 2.50 6.00
Image VAR
45 Frank Howard .20 .50
46 Charlie Keller .20 .50
47 Ken Landreaux .20 .50
48 Tom Paciorek .20 .50
49 Tim Raines .20 .50
50 Sebastian Sisti .20 .50
51 Mel Stottlemyre .20 .50
52A Jim Abbott .20 .50
52B Jim Abbott .40 1.00
Slogan VAR
52C Jim Abbott .40 1.00
Image VAR
53 Moe Berg .20 .50
54 Lou Bierbauer .20 .50
55 Toby Harrah .20 .50
56 Ed Kurpiel .20 .50
57 John Paciorek .20 .50
58 Wally Pipp .20 .50
59 Wayne Terwilliger .20 .50
60 Emil Ogden Yde .20 .50
61 Tommie Aaron .20 .50
62 Daniel Lucius Adams .20 .50
63 Eberhard Anheuser .20 .50
64 Caleb Bradham .20 .50
65 Morgan Bulkeley .20 .50
66 Jefferson Burdick .20 .50
67 Ray Chapman .20 .50
68 Eddie Cicotte .20 .50
69 Jim Creighton .20 .50
70 George Eastman .20 .50
71 Charles Ebbets .20 .50
72 Al Munro Elias .20 .50
73 Andy Farkas .20 .50
74 Rube Foster .20 .50
75 Bernice Gera .20 .50
76 Henry John Heinz .20 .50
77 Roy Hofheinz .20 .50
78 William A. Hulbert .20 .50
79 Tommy John .20 .50
80 Byron Johnson .20 .50
81 Connie Mack .20 .50
82 John McGraw .20 .50
83 Frederick Miller .20 .50
84 John Pemberton .20 .50
85 Alfred Reach .20 .50
86 John Sherman .20 .50
87 Benjamin Shibe .20 .50
88 Harry M. Stevens .20 .50
89A Luther Taylor .20 .50
89B Luther Taylor Slogan VAR .40 1.00
90 Ernest Thayer .20 .50
91 Frederick W. Thayer .20 .50
92 Charles Tiffany .20 .50
93 Maurice Van Robays .20 .50
94 John Montgomery Ward .30 .75
95 Andrew Peck .20 .50
W. Irving Snyder
96 Louis Sockalexis .20 .50
Jim Toy
97 Alex Liddi .30 .75
Lou Polli
98 Jim Bouton .20 .50
Robert C. Nelson
99 Jason Heyward 1.25 3.00
Austin Jackson
100 Jason Heyward 1.25 3.00
Craig Kimbrel
101 Howard Cassady .20 .50
102 Dave Debusschere .20 .50
103 Francis Ouimet .20 .50
104 Kyle Rote Sr. .20 .50
105 Charlie Ward .20 .50
106 Hulk Hogan .60 1.50
107 Elysian Field .20 .50
108A Joe Tinker .20 .50
Johnny Evers
Frank Chance
108B Joe Tinker .40 1.00
Johnny Evers
Frank Chance
Slogan VAR
109A Sherry Magee .20 .50
109B Sherry Magee .40 1.00
Slogan VAR
110 Eddie Plank SP 1.50 4.00
111 Joe Tinker SP 1.50 4.00
112 Johnny Evers SP 1.50 4.00
113 Frank Chance SP 1.50 4.00
114 Todd McFarlane SP 1.50 4.00
115 Walt Whitman SP 1.50 4.00
116 Charles Gandil SP 1.50 4.00
117 Claude Berry SP 1.50 4.00
118 George Weaver SP 1.50 4.00
119 1869 Cincinnati Red Stockings SP 1.50 4.00
120 William H. Taft 3.00 8.00
Barack Obama SP

2010 TRISTAR Obak Black

*BLACK: 2.5X TO 6X BASIC
*BLACK VAR: 1.2X TO 3X BASIC VAR
*BLACK SP: .5X TO 1.2X BASIC SP
OVERALL PARALLEL ODDS 1:10
STATED PRINT RUN 50 SER.#'d SETS

2010 TRISTAR Obak Green

OVERALL PARALLEL ODDS 1:10
VARIATIONS RANDOMLY INSERTED
STATED PRINT RUN 25 SER.#'d SETS
NO PRICING DUE TO SCARCITY

2010 TRISTAR Obak Purple

OVERALL PARALLEL ODDS 1:10
VARIATIONS RANDOMLY INSERTED
STATED PRINT RUN 1 SER.#'d SET
NO PRICING DUE TO SCARCITY

2010 TRISTAR Obak Red

OVERALL PARALLEL ODDS 1:10
VARIATIONS RANDOMLY INSERTED
STATED PRINT RUN 5 SER.#'d SETS
NO PRICING DUE TO SCARCITY

2010 TRISTAR Obak Autographs

OVERALL AUTO ODDS 1:5
STATED PRINT RUN 125 SER.#'d SETS
A1 Jason Heyward
Austin Jackson
A2 Jason Heyward
Craig Kimbrel
A3 Dustin Ackley 8.00 20.00
A4 Josh Bell 4.00 10.00
A5 Bobby Borchering 3.00 8.00
A6 Chris Carter
A7 Starlin Castro
A8 Grant Desme
A9 Kyle Drabek
A10 Daniel Fields 3.00 8.00
A11 Reymond Fuentes 3.00 8.00
A12 Garrett Gould 3.00 8.00
A13 Randal Grichuk 3.00 8.00
A14 Slade Heathcott 4.00 10.00
A15 Jason Heyward
A15 Jason Heyward
A16 Matt Hobgood 3.00 8.00
A17 K.C. Hobson
A18 Austin Jackson
A19 Brandon Jacobs 3.00 8.00
A20 Desmond Jennings
A21 Jason Kipnis 4.00 10.00
A22 Jeff Kobernus 3.00 8.00
A23 Alex Liddi
A24 Steve Matz 3.00 8.00
A25 Tyler Matzek
A26 Neil Medchill 3.00 8.00
A27 Tommy Mendonca
A28 Jiovanni Mier
A29 Jared Mitchell
A30 D'Vontrey Richardson 3.00 8.00
A31 Austin Romine 4.00 10.00
A32 Gary Sanchez 6.00 15.00
A33 Carlos Santana
A34 Scott Sizemore 3.00 8.00
A35 Blake Smith 3.00 8.00
A36 Robert Stock 4.00 10.00
A37 Drew Storen 3.00 8.00
A38 Donavan Tate 4.00 10.00
A39 Trayce Thompson 3.00 8.00
A40 Michael Trout
A41 Zach Von Rosenberg
A42 Alex White 5.00 12.00
A43 Shannon Wilkerson 3.00 8.00
A44 Everett Williams
A45 Alex Wilson 3.00 8.00
A46 Madison Younginer 3.00 8.00
A47 Jim Abbott 4.00 10.00
A48 Don Baylor 3.00 8.00
A49 Johnny Bench
A50 Ron Blomberg 3.00 8.00
A51 Jim Bouton 3.00 8.00
A52 Jeff Burroughs 3.00 8.00
A53 Jose Canseco
A54 Howard Cassady
A55 Roger Clemens
A56 David Clyde 3.00 8.00
A57 Andre Dawson
A58 Toby Gerhart
A59 Luis Gonzalez
A60 Dwight Gooden
A61 Ben Grieve 3.00 8.00
A62 Toby Harrah 3.00 8.00
A63 Hulk Hogan
A64 Bob Horner 4.00 10.00
A65 Frank Howard
A66 Tommy John
A67 Ed Kurpiel 5.00 12.00
A68 Ken Landreaux 3.00 8.00
A69 Ben McDonald
A70 Todd McFarlane 8.00 20.00
A71 Denny Mclain 4.00 10.00
A72 Dale Murphy
A73 Robert C. Nelson 3.00 8.00
A74 John Paciorek 3.00 8.00
A75 Tom Paciorek 3.00 8.00
A76 Tim Raines 3.00 8.00
A77 Cal Ripken Jr.
A78 Mel Stottlemyre
A79 Darryl Strawberry
A80 Wayne Terwilliger 3.00 8.00
A81 Charlie Ward 4.00 10.00
A82 Jim Bouton
Robert C. Nelson
A83 Ric Flair
Hulk Hogan

2010 TRISTAR Obak Autographs Black

*BLACK: .5X TO 1.2X BROWN
OVERALL AUTO ODDS 1:5
STATED PRINT RUN 50 SER.#'d SETS
A6 Chris Carter 8.00 20.00
A7 Starlin Castro 12.50 30.00
A8 Grant Desme 6.00 15.00
A17 K.C. Hobson 5.00 12.00
A28 Jiovanni Mier 5.00 12.00
A33 Carlos Santana 8.00 20.00
A40 Michael Trout 10.00 25.00
A41 Zach Von Rosenberg 5.00 12.00
A44 Everett Williams 8.00 20.00
A53 Jose Canseco 20.00 50.00
A58 Toby Gerhart 8.00 20.00
A78 Mel Stottlemyre 5.00 12.00

2010 TRISTAR Obak Autographs Brown

*BROWN: .5X TO 1.2X BASIC
OVERALL AUTO ODDS 1:5
STATED PRINT RUN 75 SER.#'d SETS
A9 Kyle Drabek 5.00 12.00
A27 Tommy Mendonca 5.00 12.00
A53 Jose Canseco 15.00 40.00
A54 Howard Cassady 8.00 20.00
A59 Luis Gonzalez 4.00 10.00
A60 Dwight Gooden 5.00 12.00
A65 Frank Howard 5.00 12.00
A66 Tommy John 4.00 10.00
A69 Ben McDonald 4.00 10.00
A72 Dale Murphy 8.00 20.00
A79 Darryl Strawberry 4.00 10.00

2010 TRISTAR Obak Autographs Green

OVERALL AUTO ODDS 1:5
VARIATIONS RANDOMLY INSERTED
STATED PRINT RUN 25 SER.#'d SETS
NO PRICING DUE TO SCARCITY

2010 TRISTAR Obak Autographs Purple

OVERALL AUTO ODDS 1:5
VARIATIONS RANDOMLY INSERTED
STATED PRINT RUN 1 SER.#'d SET
NO PRICING DUE TO SCARCITY

2010 TRISTAR Obak Autographs Red

OVERALL AUTO ODDS 1:5
VARIATIONS RANDOMLY INSERTED
STATED PRINT RUN 5 SER.#'d SETS
NO PRICING DUE TO SCARCITY

2010 TRISTAR Obak Mini T212

STATED ODDS ONE PER PACK
1 Dustin Ackley 2.00 5.00
2 Chris Carter .50 1.25
3A Starlin Castro 1.25 3.00
3B Starlin Castro Slogan VAR 2.00 5.00
4A Austin Jackson .50 1.25
4B Austin Jackson Slogan VAR .75 2.00
5 Desmond Jennings .50 1.25
6 Carlos Santana 1.00 2.50
7 Drew Storen .50 1.25
8 Donavan Tate .75 2.00
9A Roger Clemens 1.00 2.50
9B Roger Clemens Slogan VAR 1.50 4.00
10A Hank Greenberg .75 2.00
10B Hank Greenberg Slogan VAR 1.25 3.00
11A Dale Murphy .75 2.00
11B Dale Murphy Slogan VAR 1.25 3.00
12A Cal Ripken Jr. 3.00 8.00
12B Cal Ripken Jr. Slogan VAR 5.00 12.00
13 Lawrence Davis .30 .75
14 Darryl Strawberry .30 .75
15 Smead Jolley .30 .75
16 Johnny Bench .75 2.00
17 Jose Canseco .50 1.25
18A Jason Heyward 2.00 5.00
18B Jason Heyward Slogan VAR 3.00 8.00
18C Jason Heyward Image VAR 3.00 8.00
19 Sebastian Sisti .30 .75
20 Jim Abbott .30 .75
21 Moe Berg .30 .75
22 Wally Pipp .30 .75
23 Jefferson Burdick .30 .75
24 Ray Chapman .30 .75
25 Eddie Cicotte .40 1.00
26 Jim Creighton .40 1.00
27 Charles Ebbets .40 1.00
28 Rube Foster .40 1.00
29 Bernice Gera .40 1.00
30 Connie Mack .40 1.00
31 Luther Taylor .40 1.00
32 Andrew Peck .30 .75
W. Irving Snyder
33 Jim Bouton .40 1.00
Robert C. Nelson
34 William H. Taft .30 .75
Barack Obama
35 Charlie Ward .30 .75
36 Joe Tinker .40 1.00
Johnny Evers
Frank Chance
37A Sherry Magee .40 1.00
37B Sherry Magee Slogan VAR .50 1.25
38 Eddie Plank .40 1.00
39 Todd McFarlane .30 .75
40 Walt Whitman .30 .75
41 Jason Heyward 2.00 5.00
Austin Jackson
42 Charles Gandil .40 1.00
43 Claude Berry .40 1.00
44 George Weaver .30 .75
45 Hulk Hogan .75 2.00

2010 TRISTAR Obak Mini T212 Black

*BLACK: 1X TO 2.5X BASIC
*BLACK VAR: .6X TO 1.5X BASIC VAR
STATED ODDS 1:20
STATED PRINT RUN 50 SER.#'d SETS
12A Cal Ripken Jr. 20.00 50.00
12B Cal Ripken Jr. Slogan VAR 20.00 50.00

2010 TRISTAR Obak Mini T212 Green

OVERALL MINI PARALLEL ODDS 1:20
VARIATIONS RANDOMLY INSERTED
STATED PRINT RUN 25 SER.#'d SETS
NO PRICING DUE TO SCARCITY

2010 TRISTAR Obak Mini T212 Purple

OVERALL MINI PARALLEL ODDS 1:20
VARIATIONS RANDOMLY INSERTED
STATED PRINT RUN 1 SER.#'d SET
NO PRICING DUE TO SCARCITY

2010 TRISTAR Obak Mini T212 Red

OVERALL MINI PARALLEL ODDS 1:20
VARIATIONS RANDOMLY INSERTED
STATED PRINT RUN 5 SER.#'d SETS
NO PRICING DUE TO SCARCITY

2010 TRISTAR Obak T4

ONE CABINET PER BOX
1 Don Baylor .60 1.50
Los Angeles AL
2 Roy Hofheinz .60 1.50
Houston
3 Oakland .60 1.50
4 John Labatt .60 1.50
Toronto
5 Jason Heyward 4.00 10.00
Atlanta
6 Jim Bouton .60 1.50
Milwaukee
7 Chris Von Der Ahe .60 1.50
St. Louis
8 William Hulbert .60 1.50
Chicago NL
9 Luis Gonzalez .60 1.50
Arizona
10 Charles Ebbets .60 1.50
Los Angeles NL
11 Jim Mutrie .60 1.50
San Francisco
12 Charles Somers .60 1.50
Cleveland
13 Dustin Ackley 4.00 10.00
Seattle
14 Andre Dawson 1.00 2.50
Florida
15 William Shea .60 1.50
New York NL
16A Stephen Strasburg 4.00 10.00
Washington
16B Stephen Strasburg 4.00 10.00
Washington Image VAR
17 Clark Griffith .60 1.50
Baltimore
18 Donovan Tate 1.50 4.00
San Diego
19 Al Reach .60 1.50
Philadelphia
20 Barney Dreyfuss .60 1.50
Pittsburgh
21 Elwood Quesada .60 1.50
Texas
22 Desmond Jennings 1.00 2.50
Tampa Bay
23 Charles Somers .60 1.50
Boston
24 Cy Seymour .60 1.50
Cincinnati
25 William Byers .60 1.50
Colorado
26 Ewing Kauffman .60 1.50
Kansas City
27 Charlie Bennett .60 1.50
Detroit
28 Calvin Griffith .60 1.50
Minnesota
29 Charles Comiskey .60 1.50
Chicago AL
30 Jack Chesbro .60 1.50
New York AL

2010 TRISTAR Obak T4 Black

*BLACK: .6X TO 1.5X BASIC
RANDOM INSERTS AS BOX TOPPERS
STATED PRINT RUN 50 SER.#'d SETS

2010 TRISTAR Obak T4 Green

RANDOMLY INSERTED BOX TOPPERS
STATED PRINT RUN 25 SER.#'d SETS
NO PRICING DUE TO SCARCITY

2010 TRISTAR Obak T4 Purple

RANDOMLY INSERTED BOX TOPPERS
STATED PRINT RUN 1 SER.#'d SET
NO PRICING DUE TO SCARCITY

2010 TRISTAR Obak T4 Red

RANDOMLY INSERTED BOX TOPPERS
STATED PRINT RUN 5 SER.#'d SETS
NO PRICING DUE TO SCARCITY

2011 TRISTAR Obak

COMPLETE SET (120) 20.00 50.00
COMP.SET w/o SP's (110) 10.00 25.00
COMMON CARD (1-110) .20 .50
COMMON SP (111-120) .75 2.00
OVERALL SP ODDS 1:8
SP's HAVE GREY BACKS
1 Ken Griffey Jr. .75 2.00
2 Nolan Ryan 1.50 4.00
3 Josh Gibson .50 1.25
4 Ulysses Grant .20 .50
5 Cal Hubbard .20 .50
6 Carl Hubbell .20 .50
7 Pete Incaviglia .20 .50
8 John Henry Lloyd .20 .50
9 Jim Bottomley .20 .50
10 Jesse Burkett .20 .50
11 Tom Cheney .20 .50
12 Andre Dawson .30 .75
13 Hugh Duffy .20 .50
14 Hugh Jennings .20 .50
15 Charles Radbourn .20 .50
16 Gus Weyhing .20 .50
17 Chief Wilson .20 .50
18 Hack Wilson .20 .50
19 Jack Chesbro .20 .50
20 Ed Delahanty .20 .50
21 Jim Gentile .20 .50
22 Glen Gorbous .20 .50
23 Pete Gray .20 .50
24 Ernie Harwell .30 .75
25 Addie Joss .20 .50
26 Bob Montgomery .20 .50
27 Dale Murphy .50 1.25
28 John Olerud .20 .50
29 Tip O'Neill .20 .50
30 Doc Powers .20 .50
31 Germany Schaefer .20 .50
32 Bob Addy .20 .50
33 Doug Allison .20 .50
34 Roger Bresnahan .20 .50
35 Jack Clements .20 .50
36 Judge William Cooper .20 .50
37 Ford Frick .20 .50
38 Rich Gossage .20 .50
39 George Hancock .20 .50

40 Elston Howard .20 .50
41 Bill Klem .20 .50
42 Kenesaw Mountain Landis .20 .50
43 Dickey Pearce .20 .50
44 Jacob Ruppert .20 .50
45 Eiji Sawamura .20 .50
46 Joe Start .20 .50
47 Bill Stern .20 .50
48 Moses Fleetwood Walker .20 .50
49 Arch Ward .20 .50
50 Mickey Welch .20 .50
51 William Rufus Wheaton .20 .50
52 Joe Carter .20 .50
53 Bobby Thomson .30 .75
54 Cap Anson .30 .75
55 Ross Barnes .20 .50
56 Roger Connor .20 .50
57 Joe Cronin .20 .50
58 Marty Kavanagh .20 .50
59 Mike O'Neill .20 .50
60 Jim O'Rourke .20 .50
61 Lee Richmond .20 .50
62 Jimmy Sebring .20 .50
63 Harold Baines .20 .50
64 Ron Blomberg .20 .50
65 Shawon Dunston .20 .50
66 Danny Goodwin .20 .50
67 Tim Pyznarski .20 .50
68 Johnny Vander Meer .20 .50
69 Don Schwall .20 .50
70 Roy Sievers .20 .50
71 Manny Banuelos .60 1.50
72 Brandon Belt .75 2.00
73 Bobby Borchering .30 .75
74 Zach Britton .50 1.25
75 Christian Colon .20 .50
76 Randall Delgado .30 .75
77 Paul Goldschmidt 1.00 2.50
78 Jerad Head .20 .50
79 Jared Hoying .30 .75
80 Brandon Laird .30 .75
81 Jake Lemmerman .30 .75
82 Lance Lynn .20 .50
83 Wil Myers .30 .75
84 Edward Salcedo .20 .50
85 Gary Sanchez .50 1.25
86 Jonathan Singleton .30 .75
87 Jameson Taillon .60 1.50
88 Mike Trout 1.25 3.00
89 Alex White .20 .50
90 Will Clark .30 .75
91 Charlie Gehringer .20 .50
92 James Bell .20 .50
93 Frankie Frisch .30 .75
94 Michael McGreevy .20 .50
95 Fred Merkle .20 .50
96 Al Simmons .20 .50
97 Paul Waner .20 .50
98 George Bush .30 .75
99 William Taft .20 .50
100 Whitey Ford .30 .75
101 Elmer Gedeon .20 .50
102 Roy Gleason .20 .50
103 Hank Gowdy .20 .50
104 Eddie Grant .20 .50
105 Hank Greenberg .50 1.25
106 Stan Musial .75 2.00
107 Phil Rizzuto .30 .75
108 Red Schoendienst .20 .50
109 Cecil Travis .20 .50
110 Cole White .20 .50
111 Cal Ripken SP 6.00 15.00
112 Whitey Ford SP 1.25 3.00
113 Roy Gleason SP .75 2.00
114 Hank Gowdy SP .75 2.00
115 Eddie Grant SP .75 2.00
116 Hank Greenberg SP 2.00 5.00
117 Stan Musial SP 2.50 6.00
118 Phil Rizzuto SP 1.25 3.00
119 Cecil Travis SP .75 2.00
120 Cole White SP .75 2.00

2011 TRISTAR Obak Blue

OVERALL PARALLEL ODDS 1:12
STATED PRINT RUN 5 SER.#'d SETS
NO PRICING DUE TO SCARCITY

2011 TRISTAR Obak Gold

*GOLD: .6X TO 1.5X BASIC SP
OVERALL PARALLEL ODDS 1:12
STATED PRINT RUN 50 SER.#'d SETS
111 Cal Ripken 30.00 80.00

2011 TRISTAR Obak Green

OVERALL PARALLEL ODDS 1:12
STATED PRINT RUN 25 SER.#'d SETS
NO PRICING DUE TO SCARCITY

2011 TRISTAR Obak Orange 10

OVERALL PARALLEL ODDS 1:12
STATED PRINT RUN 10 SER.#'d SETS
NO PRICING DUE TO SCARCITY

2011 TRISTAR Obak Orange 75

*ORANGE 75: .5X TO 1.2X BASIC SP
OVERALL PARALLEL ODDS 1:12
STATED PRINT RUN 75 SER.#'d SETS
111 Cal Ripken 12.00 30.00

2011 TRISTAR Obak Purple

OVERALL PARALLEL ODDS 1:12
STATED PRINT RUN 1 SER.#'d SET
NO PRICING DUE TO SCARCITY

2011 TRISTAR Obak Autographs

OVERALL AUTO ODDS 1:6
STATED PRINT RUN 100 SER.#'d SETS
A1 Harold Baines 4.00 10.00
A11 Shawon Dunston 3.00 8.00
A15 Jim Gentile 5.00 12.00
A16 Roy Gleason 3.00 8.00
A17 Paul Goldschmidt 12.50 30.00
A18 Danny Goodwin 3.00 8.00
A23 Pete Incaviglia 4.00 10.00
A26 Ben McDonald 4.00 10.00
A27 Bobby Montgomery 4.00 10.00
A32 Tim Pyznarski 3.00 8.00
A35 Eduardo Salcedo 3.00 8.00
A36 Aaron Sanchez 3.00 8.00
A46 Cole White 3.00 8.00

2011 TRISTAR Obak Autographs Blue

OVERALL AUTO ODDS 1:6
STATED PRINT RUN 5 SER.#'d SETS
NO PRICING DUE TO SCARCITY

2011 TRISTAR Obak Autographs Brown

OVERALL AUTO ODDS 1:6
STATED PRINT RUN 50 SER.#'d SETS
A1 Harold Baines 5.00 12.00
A3 Brandon Belt 12.50 30.00
A4 Ron Blomberg 4.00 10.00
A5 Bobby Borchering 5.00 12.00
A6 Zach Britton 4.00 10.00
A10 Randall Delgado 5.00 12.00
A11 Shawon Dunston 4.00 10.00
A12 Andy Etchebarren 6.00 15.00
A13 Daniel Fields 4.00 10.00
A15 Jim Gentile 6.00 15.00
A16 Roy Gleason 4.00 10.00
A17 Paul Goldschmidt 15.00 40.00
A18 Danny Goodwin 4.00 10.00
A21 Ron Hansen 5.00 12.00
A22 Jared Hoying 4.00 8.00
A23 Pete Incaviglia 5.00 12.00
A24 Brandon Laird 4.00 10.00
A26 Ben McDonald 5.00 12.00
A27 Bobby Montgomery 5.00 12.00
A29 John Olerud 10.00 25.00
A30 Gregg Olson 4.00 10.00
A31 Dylan Owen 4.00 8.00
A32 Tim Pyznarski 4.00 10.00
A35 Eduardo Salcedo 4.00 10.00
A36 Aaron Sanchez 4.00 10.00
A38 Jerry Sands 6.00 15.00
A39 Red Schoendienst 10.00 25.00
A40 Don Schwall 4.00 10.00
A41 Roy Sievers 6.00 15.00
A43 Jameson Taillon 10.00 25.00
A44 Mike Trout 12.50 30.00
A45 Alex White 4.00 8.00
A46 Cole White 4.00 10.00
A48 Mason Williams 5.00 12.00
A49 Alex Wilson 4.00 10.00

2011 TRISTAR Obak Autographs Green

OVERALL AUTO ODDS 1:6
STATED PRINT RUN 25 SER.#'d SETS
NO PRICING DUE TO SCARCITY

2011 TRISTAR Obak Autographs Orange

OVERALL AUTO ODDS 1:6
STATED PRINT RUN 75 SER.#'d SETS
A1 Harold Baines 4.00 10.00
A4 Ron Blomberg 3.00 8.00
A5 Bobby Borchering 4.00 10.00
A6 Zach Britton 3.00 8.00
A10 Randall Delgado 4.00 10.00
A11 Shawon Dunston 3.00 8.00
A13 Daniel Fields 3.00 8.00
A15 Jim Gentile 5.00 12.00
A16 Roy Gleason 3.00 8.00
A17 Paul Goldschmidt 12.50 30.00
A18 Danny Goodwin 4.00 10.00
A21 Ron Hansen 4.00 10.00
A23 Pete Incaviglia 4.00 10.00
A24 Brandon Laird 3.00 8.00
A26 Ben McDonald 4.00 10.00
A27 Bobby Montgomery 4.00 10.00
A29 John Olerud 8.00 20.00
A30 Gregg Olson 3.00 8.00
A32 Tim Pyznarski 3.00 8.00
A35 Eduardo Salcedo 3.00 8.00
A36 Aaron Sanchez 3.00 8.00
A40 Don Schwall 3.00 8.00
A41 Roy Sievers 5.00 12.00
A46 Cole White 3.00 8.00
A48 Mason Williams 4.00 10.00
A49 Alex Wilson 3.00 8.00

2011 TRISTAR Obak Autographs Purple

OVERALL AUTO ODDS 1:6
STATED PRINT RUN 1 SER.#'d SET
NO PRICING DUE TO SCARCITY

2011 TRISTAR Obak Cut Signatures Bronze

OVERALL CUT ODDS 1:24
STATED PRINT RUN 75 SER.#'d SETS
CARDS LISTED ALPHABETICALLY
1 Ernie Banks 12.50 30.00
2 Harmon Killebrew 12.50 30.00
3 Frank Robinson 12.50 30.00

2011 TRISTAR Obak Cut Signatures Blue

OVERALL CUT ODDS 1:24
STATED PRINT RUN 75 SER.#'d SETS
CARDS LISTED ALPHABETICALLY
1 Luis Aparicio 12.50 30.00
2 Ernie Banks 15.00 40.00
3 Ron Blomberg 5.00 12.00
4 Bob Feller 10.00 25.00
5 Harmon Killebrew 12.50 30.00
6 Frank Robinson 12.50 30.00
7 Al Rosen 8.00 20.00

2011 TRISTAR Obak Cut Signatures Green

OVERALL CUT ODDS 1:24
STATED PRINT RUN 25 SER.#'d SETS
NO PRICING DUE TO SCARCITY
CARDS LISTED ALPHABETICALLY

2011 TRISTAR Obak Cut Signatures Purple

OVERALL CUT ODDS 1:24
STATED PRINT RUN 1 SER.#'d SET
NO PRICING DUE TO SCARCITY
CARDS LISTED ALPHABETICALLY

2011 TRISTAR Obak Cut Signatures Red

OVERALL CUT ODDS 1:24
STATED PRINT RUN 5 SER.#'d SETS
NO PRICING DUE TO SCARCITY
CARDS LISTED ALPHABETICALLY

2011 TRISTAR Obak Cut Signatures Dual

OVERALL CUT ODDS 1:24
STATED PRINT RUN 1 SER.#'d SET
NO PRICING DUE TO SCARCITY
CARDS LISTED ALPHABETICALLY

2011 TRISTAR Obak T212 Mini

COMPLETE SET (24) 6.00 15.00
OVERALL MINI ODDS 1 PER PACK
*BROWN: 1.2X TO 3X BASIC
OVERALL MINI PARALLEL ODDS 1:24
BROWN PRINT RUN 75 SER.#'d SETS
1 Ken Griffey Jr. 1.25 3.00
2 Cal Ripken Jr. 3.00 8.00
3 Nolan Ryan 2.50 6.00
4 Josh Gibson .75 2.00
5 Bobby Thomson .50 1.25
6 Joe Carter .30 .75
7 Cap Anson .50 1.25
8 Paul Waner .30 .75
9 Charlie Gehringer .30 .75
10 Jack Chesbro .30 .75
11 Doc Powers .30 .75
12 Cole White .30 .75
13 Kenesaw M. Landis .30 .75
14 Manny Banuelos 1.00 2.50
15 Zach Britton .75 2.00
16 Mike Trout 2.00 5.00
17 Roy Gleason .30 .75
18 Ulysses Grant .30 .75
19 Whitey Ford .50 1.25
20 Whitey Ford .50 1.25
21 Hank Greenberg .75 2.00
22 Hank Greenberg .75 2.00
23 Stan Musial 1.25 3.00
24 Stan Musial 1.25 3.00

2011 TRISTAR Obak T212 Mini Blue

OVERALL MINI PARALLEL ODDS 1:24
STATED PRINT RUN 5 SER.#'d SETS
NO PRICING DUE TO SCARCITY

2011 TRISTAR Obak T212 Mini Brown

*BROWN: 1.2X TO 3X BASIC
OVERALL MINI PARALLEL ODDS 1:24
STATED PRINT RUN 75 SER.#'d SETS

2011 TRISTAR Obak T212 Mini Green

OVERALL MINI PARALLEL ODDS 1:24
STATED PRINT RUN 25 SER.#'d SETS
NO PRICING DUE TO SCARCITY

2011 TRISTAR Obak T212 Mini Purple

OVERALL MINI PARALLEL ODDS 1:24
STATED PRINT RUN 1 SER.#'d SET
NO PRICING DUE TO SCARCITY

2011 TRISTAR Obak T212 Mini Autographs Blue

OVERALL AUTO ODDS 1:6
STATED PRINT RUN 5 SER.#'d SETS
NO PRICING DUE TO SCARCITY

2011 TRISTAR Obak T212 Mini Autographs Green

OVERALL AUTO ODDS 1:6
STATED PRINT RUN 10 SER.#'d SETS
NO PRICING DUE TO SCARCITY

2011 TRISTAR Obak T212 Mini Autographs Purple

OVERALL AUTO ODDS 1:6
STATED PRINT RUN 1 SER.#'d SET
NO PRICING DUE TO SCARCITY

2011 TRISTAR Obak T4 Cabinet Autographs

OVERALL AUTO ODDS 1:6
STATED PRINT RUN 5 SER.#'d SETS
NO PRICING DUE TO SCARCITY

2011 TRISTAR Obak T4 Cabinet Autographs Purple

OVERALL AUTO ODDS 1:6
STATED PRINT RUN 1 SER.#'d SET
NO PRICING DUE TO SCARCITY

2011 TRISTAR Obak T4 Cabinets

OVERALL T4 ODDS 1 PER BOX TOPPER
*BROWN/50: .5X TO 1.2X BASIC
OVERALL T4 ODDS 1 PER BOX TOPPER
BROWN PRINT RUN 50 SER.#'d SETS
T4B1 Nolan Ryan 10.00 25.00
Tom Cheney
T4B2 Ron Blomberg 1.25 3.00
Mickey Welch
T4B3 Roy Gleason 1.25 3.00
Cole White
T4B4 Bob Montgomery 1.25 3.00
John Olerud
T4B5 Ernie Harwell 2.00 5.00
Bill Stern
T4B6 Joe Carter 2.00 5.00
Bobby Thomson
T4B7 Manny Banuellos 4.00 10.00
Whitey Ford
T4B8 Jameson Taillon 8.00 20.00
Mike Trout
T4B9 Gus Weyhing 1.25 3.00
Hugh Jennings
T4B10 Pete Incaviglia 1.25 3.00
Roger Connor
T4B11 Don Schwall 1.25 3.00
Roy Sievers
T4B12 Will Clark 10.00 25.00
James Thomas Bell
T4B13 Tim Pyznarski 1.25 3.00
Johnny Van der Meer
T4B14 Brandon Laird 2.00 5.00
Gary Sanchez
T4B15 Red Schoendienst 5.00 12.00
Stan Musial

2011 TRISTAR Obak T4 Cabinets Blue

OVERALL T4 ODDS 1 PER BOX TOPPER
STATED PRINT RUN 5 SER.#'d SETS
NO PRICING DUE TO SCARCITY

2011 TRISTAR Obak T4 Cabinets Brown

*BROWN: .5X TO 1.2X BASIC
OVERALL T4 ODDS 1 PER BOX TOPPER
STATED PRINT RUN 50 SER.#'d SETS

2011 TRISTAR Obak T4 Cabinets Green

OVERALL T4 ODDS 1 PER BOX TOPPER
STATED PRINT RUN 25 SER.#'d SETS
NO PRICING DUE TO SCARCITY

2011 TRISTAR Obak T4 Cabinets Purple

OVERALL T4 ODDS 1 PER BOX TOPPER
STATED PRINT RUN 1 SER.#'d SET
NO PRICING DUE TO SCARCITY

2010 TRISTAR Obak National Convention VIP

COMPLETE SET (12)
N1A Stephen Strasburg 6.00 15.00
Blue Ink
Olympic Stadium on back
N1B Stephen Strasburg 6.00 15.00
Red Ink
Nationals Park on back
N2 Josh Bell 1.50 4.00
N3 Jason Heyward 4.00 10.00
N4 Frank Howard 1.50 4.00
N5 Ben McDonald 1.50 4.00
N8 Cal Ripken Jr. 6.00 15.00
NNO Checklist 3.00 8.00
Cal Ripken Jr.
Hulk Hogan
Jason Heyward

2011 TRISTAR Obak National Convention VIP

NP1 Ken Griffey Jr. 2.50 6.00
NP2 Nolan Ryan 5.00 12.00
NP3 Cap Anson 1.00 2.50
NP9 Stan Musial/Bob Kalsu 2.50 6.00

2008 TRISTAR PROjections

COMPLETE SET (401) 30.00 60.00
COMP.LOW SERIES (200) 12.50 30.00
COMP.HIGH SERIES (200) 12.50 30.00
COMMON CARD .20 .50
1-200 RELEASED IN PROJECTIONS
201-400 RELESASED IN HIGH SERIES
PRINTING PLATES RANDOMLY INSERTED
PLATE PRINT RUN 1 SET PER COLOR
BLACK-CYAN-MAGENTA-YELLOW ISSUED
NO PLATE PRICING DUE TO SCARCITY
1 Michael Almanzar .50 1.25
2 Carmen Angelini .20 .50
3 Josh Reddick PD .60 1.50
4 Chih-Hsien Chiang .50 1.25
5 Ryan Kalish .50 1.25
6 Taylor Grote .20 .50
7 Anthony Claggett .30 .75
8 Kai Liu .30 .75
9 Kelvin DeLeon .20 .50
10 Beau Mills .20 .50
11 Yamaico Navarro PD .60 1.50
12 Ryan Pope .20 .50
13 David Robertson .50 1.25
14 Max Scherzer .60 1.50
15 Alan Horne .20 .50
16 David Mailman .20 .50
17 Brad Suttle .20 .50
18 Lars Anderson .20 .50
19 Austin Jackson 1.00 2.50
20 Austin Romine .20 .50
21 James Adkins .20 .50
22 Jose Ceda .20 .50
23 Travis d'Arnaud .20 .50
24 Tommy Hanson .75 2.00
25 Bryce Cox .20 .50
26 Austin Krum PD .20 .50
27 Carlos Monasterios .20 .50
28 Scott Moviel PD .20 .50
29 Juan Francisco .50 1.25
30 Deolis Guerra .50 1.25
31 Jason Heyward .75 2.00
32 Brock Huntzinger .20 .50
33 Hunter Jones .30 .75
34 Anthony Rizzo 1.00 2.50
35 Nick Noonan .20 .50
36 Matt LaPorta .50 1.25
37 Jeff Manship .20 .50
38 David Kopp .20 .50
39 Rick Porcello 1.00 2.50
40 Jess Todd PD .20 .50
41 Che-Hsuan Lin PD .20 .50
42 Aaron Bates .50 1.25
43 Jarrod Parker .50 1.25
44 David Price .50 1.25
45 Marco Vechionacci .20 .50
46 Michael Bowden .20 .50
47 Jason Place .20 .50
48 Nathan Vineyard .30 .75
49 P.J. Walters .50 1.25
50 Jose Tabata .50 1.25
51 Matt Wieters 1.00 2.50
52 Chris Withrow .20 .50
53 Jesus Montero PD 1.50 4.00
54 Dellin Betances .30 .75
55 Zack Daeges .20 .50
56 Jed Lowrie .50 1.25
57 Colby Rasmus .50 1.25
58 Humberto Sanchez .20 .50
59 Tim Alderson .30 .75
60 Michael Anton PD .20 .50
61 Phillippe Aumont .30 .75
62 Duane Below .20 .50
63 Daniel Berlind PD .20 .50
64 Yu Bingjia .20 .50
65 Jake Brigham .20 .50
66 Robert Bryson .20 .50
67 Dallas Buck PD .20 .50
68 Michael Burgess .30 .75
69 Danny Carroll PD .20 .50
70 Yefri Carvajal .20 .50
71 Jhoulys Chacin PD .75 2.00
72 Corey Brown .20 .50
73 Madison Bumgarner .50 1.25
74 Casey Crosby .20 .50
75 Drew Cumberland .20 .50
76 Fautino De Los Santos PD .20 .50
77 Grant Desme .20 .50
78 Sean Doolittle .20 .50
79 Ivan Contreras .20 .50
80 Lyndon Estill PD .20 .50
81 Wendell Fairley .20 .50
82 Michael Fisher .20 .50
83 Darren Ford .20 .50
84 Clay Fuller .20 .50
85 Jimmy Gallagher .20 .50
86 Todd Frazier .30 .75
87 Esmailyn Gonzalez PD .60 1.50
88 Greg Halman .30 .75
89 Wilmer Font PD .20 .50
90 Josh Horton PD .20 .50
91 Will Inman .20 .50
92 Nevin Griffith PD .20 .50
93 Tyler Kolodny PD .60 1.50
94 Kyle Lotzkar .20 .50
95 Cory Luebke .20 .50
96 Michael Main .20 .50
97 Glenn Gallagher .20 .50
98 Mat Latos PD .20 .50
99 Adam Miller .30 .75
100 Gabriel Noriega .20 .50
101 Brandon Hamilton .20 .50
102 Oswaldo Sosa .30 .75
103 Engel Beltre .60 1.50
104 Cole Devries PD .30 .75
105 Brandon Hicks .20 .50
106 Omar Poveda .30 .75
107 Brad James .20 .50
108 Joseph Mahoney PD .20 .50
109 Danny Rams PD .30 .75
110 Ben Revere .20 .50
111 Mario Martinez PD .20 .50
112 Sean O'Sullivan .20 .50
113 Robert Parnell .20 .50
114 Joe Savery PD .30 .75
115 Michael Paulk .20 .50
116 Aaron Poreda .20 .50
117 Neftali Soto PD .30 .75
118 Kevin Pucetas .30 .75
119 Brandon Tripp .20 .50
120 Wilkin Ramirez .20 .50
121 Nick Schmidt .20 .50
122 Eduardo Nunez .20 .50
123 Donald Veal .20 .50
124 Matt Antonelli .20 .50
125 Jay Bruce .75 2.00
126 Adrian Cardenas .20 .50
127 Daniel Bard .20 .50
128 Reid Engel .20 .50
129 Tyler Colvin .20 .50
130 George Kottaras .20 .50
131 Jeff Marquez .20 .50
132 Andrew McCutchen .60 1.50
133 Juan Miranda PD .30 .75
134 David Pauley .20 .50
135 Jeff Samardzija .60 1.50
136 Brett Smith .20 .50
137 Jon Still .20 .50
138 Kevin Whelan .20 .50
139 Josh Rodriguez .20 .50
140 Billy Rowell .20 .50
141 Luis Castillo PD .20 .50
142 Hector Correa .20 .50
143 Zack Cozart PD .30 .75
144 Matt Dominguez .30 .75
145 Ed Easley .20 .50
146 Robert Fish .20 .50
147 Brian Friday PD .20 .50
148 J.P. Arencibia .30 .75
149 Brett Cecil .60 1.50
150 Daniel Cortes .50 1.25
151 Eric Eiland PD .20 .50
152 Devin Mesoraco .50 1.25
153 Daniel Moskos .20 .50
154 Freddie Freeman PD 1.00 2.50
155 Julio Pimentel .20 .50
156 Angel Morales PD .20 .50
157 Jon Gilmore .20 .50
158 Steven Souza PD .20 .50
159 John Tolisano PD .20 .50
160 Casey Weathers .20 .50
161 Daniel Worth PD .20 .50
162 Justin Jackson .20 .50
163 Adrian Ortiz PD .20 .50
164 Jake Smolinski .20 .50
165 Pedro Beato .20 .50
166 Duke Welker .20 .50
167 Hank Conger .20 .50
168 Jordan Zimmermann .20 .50
169 Tim Battle .20 .50
170 Jordan Brown .20 .50
171 Caleb Clay .20 .50
172 Kris Johnson .30 .75
173 Evan Longoria 1.00 2.50
174 Chris Marrero .20 .50
175 Eric Duncan .20 .50
176 Greg Reynolds .30 .75
177 Kevin Ahrens .20 .50
178 Travis Snider .30 .75
179 Brett Gardner .50 1.25
180 Jameson Smith PD .20 .50
181 Chris Tillman .20 .50
182 Balbino Fuenmayor PD .20 .50
183 Elvis Andrus .30 .75
184 Collin Balester .20 .50
185 C.J. Henry .30 .75
186 Nick Barnese PD .20 .50
187 Tyler Robertson .20 .50
188 Brandon Erbe .20 .50
189 John Mayberry Jr. .20 .50
190 Max Sapp .30 .75
191 Sergio Perez .20 .50
192 Kevin Howard .20 .50
193 Rowdy Hardy .20 .50
194 Michael Stanton 2.50 6.00
195 Chris Volstad .20 .50
196 Kyle McCulloch .20 .50
197 Jairo Cuevas .20 .50
198 Mitch Einertson .20 .50
199 Brad Bergesen .20 .50
200 Brandon Snyder .20 .50
201 Wade Davis .30 .75
202 Drew Stubbs .50 1.25
203 John Whittleman .20 .50
204 Eric Young Jr .20 .50
205 Adam Carr .20 .50
206 Shelby Ford .30 .75
207 Van Pope .20 .50
208 Jeremy Hellickson .75 2.00
209 Zach Kroenke .20 .50
210 Elio DeLaRosa .20 .50
211 Zolio Almonte .20 .50
212 Jairo Heredia .20 .50
213a William Middlebrooks .30 .75
Sitting
213b William Middlebrooks .30 .75
Standing ERR
Incorrect birthday
214a Nick Hagadone .20 .50
Throwing
214b Nick Hagadone .20 .50
Standing ERR
Incorrect birthday
215 Abraham Almonte .20 .50
216a Oscar Tejeda .20 .50
Fielding
216b Oscar Tejeda .20 .50
Portrait ERR
Incorrect birthday
217 Adam Mills .20 .50
218 Drake Britton .30 .75
219 Carlos Urena .20 .50
220 Pete Kozma .20 .50
221 Jacob Arrieta .20 .50
222 Jose Pirela .30 .75
223 Argenis Diaz .30 .75
224 Arodys Vizcaino .20 .50
225 Jose Gil .20 .50
226 Zhenwang Zhang .30 .75
227 Blake Beavan .30 .75
228 Darwin Barney 1.00 2.50
229a Bubba Bell .50 1.25
Facing Left
229b Bubba Bell .50 1.25
Facing Right ERR
Incorrect birthday
230 Zach Braddock .20 .50
231 Dominic Brown 3.00 8.00
232 Julio Borbon .20 .50
233 David Bromberg .30 .75
234a Ryan Dent .30 .75
Fielding
234b Ryan Dent .30 .75
Throwing ERR
Incorrect birthday
235 Joshua Donaldson .20 .50
236 Chris Nelson .20 .50
237 Hector Gomez .50 1.25
238 Nick Carr .20 .50
239 Kelvin Pichardo .20 .50
240 D'Marcus Ingram .20 .50
241 Chorye Spoone .30 .75
242 Sean Rodriguez .20 .50
243 Eddie Kunz .30 .75
244 Henry Sosa .20 .50
245 Christian Marrero .30 .75
246 Travis Mattair PD .20 .50
247 Rafael Dolis .20 .50
248 Hainley Statia .20 .50
249 Neftali Feliz .60 1.50
250 Kellen Kulbacki .20 .50
251 Glenn Gibson .20 .50
252 Andrew Bailey .50 1.25
253 Cole Rohrbough .20 .50
254 Larry Suarez PD .20 .50
255 Clayton Mortensen .20 .50
256 Joshua Vitters .20 .50
257 Brandon Waring PD .60 1.50
258a Ty Weeden .20 .50
Batting
258b Ty Weeden .20 .50
Catching ERR
Incorrect birthday
259 Jacob Wild PD .20 .50
260 Eric Niesen .20 .50
261 Alcides Escobar .20 .50
262 Brant Rustich .20 .50
263 Clayton Kershaw 1.00 2.50
264 Anthony Thomas .20 .50
265 Dustin Richardson .20 .50
266 Michael Watt PD .20 .50
267 Denny Almonte PD .30 .75
268 Hitaniel Arias .20 .50
269 Jonathan Bachanov .20 .50
270 Edward Paredes .20 .50

271 Bruce Billings PD .20 .50
272 Adam Olbrychowski PD .20 .50
273 Brooks Brown .20 .50
274 Wilber Bucardo .20 .50
275 Chris Coghlan .60 1.50
276 Mitch Canham .20 .50
277 Scott Carroll PD .20 .50
278 Fabio Castillo .30 .75
279 Brad Chalk PD .20 .50
280 Brett Sinkbeil .20 .50
281 John Ely PD .20 .50
282 Charlie Culberson .20 .50
283 Chris Davis .50 1.25
284 Jhrmivy DeJesus .20 .50
285 Gerardo Parra .20 .50
286 German Duran .30 .75
287 Barry Enright .30 .75
288 Robinson Fabian .20 .50
289 Francisco Felix .20 .50
290 Ryan Royster .20 .50
291 Jeffrey Locke .20 .50
292 Josh Bell .20 .50
293 Jonathan Galvez .20 .50
294 Caleb Gindl .20 .50
295 Jeremy Haynes .20 .50
296 Danny Payne .20 .50
297 Michael Brantley .20 .50
298 Tommy Hunter .30 .75
299 Stephen Chapman .20 .50
300 Albert LaBoy .20 .50
301 Mike McCardell PD .20 .50
302 Josue Calzado .20 .50
303 Neil Ramirez .20 .50
304 Matt Mangini .20 .50
305 Cory Riordan PD .20 .50
306 Jake McGee .20 .50
307 Andrew Romine PD .20 .50
308 Francisco Castillo .20 .50
309 Fernando Salas .20 .50
310 Cristian Santana .20 .50
311 James Simmons .20 .50
312 Martin Perez .20 .50
313 Manuel Solis .20 .50
314 Julio Teheran .75 2.00
315 Juan Ramirez .20 .50
316 Wei Wang .20 .50
317 Evan Reed .20 .50
318 Brian Rike .30 .75
319 Wes Roemer .20 .50
320 Salvador Sanchez .30 .75
321 Michael Saunders .20 .50
322 Jackson Williams .20 .50
323 Eric Sogard .20 .50
324 Jaime Ortiz .20 .50
325 Prily Cuello .20 .50
326 Mason Tobin .20 .50
327 Jordan Walden .30 .75
328 Matt West PD .20 .50
329 Josh Geer .20 .50
330 Chris Huseby .20 .50
331 Brett Anderson .30 .75
332 Chris Carter .30 .75
333a Jose Capellan .30 .75
Throwing
7/18/86 DOB
333b Jose Capellan .30 .75
Portrait ERR
Incorrect birthday
334 Carlos Carrasco .20 .50
335 Gorkys Hernandez .20 .50
336 Christian Garcia .20 .50
337 Wes Hodges .20 .50
338 Chuck Lofgren .30 .75
339 Justin Masterson .50 1.25
340a Zachary McAllister .30 .75
Portrait
340b Zachary McAllister .30 .75
Throwing ERR
Incorrect birthday
341 Adam Ottavino .20 .50
342 Max Ramirez .20 .50
343 Jordan Schafer .20 .50
344 Angel Villalona .50 1.25
345 Steven White .20 .50
346 Drew Miller .20 .50
347 Jonathan Herrera .30 .75
348 Brok Butcher .20 .50
349 Rhyne Hughes .20 .50
350 Will Kline .20 .50
351 Lars Davis PD .20 .50
352 Danny Duffy .60 1.50
353 Michael McCormick .20 .50
354 Reynaldo Navarro .20 .50
355 Josh Smoker .20 .50
356 James Heuser .20 .50
357 Francisco Pena .30 .75
358 Trystan Magnuson .20 .50
359 Dave McKae .20 .50
360 Matt Mitchell PD .20 .50
361 Mike Moustakas .60 1.50
362 Nick Adenhart .20 .50
363 John Raynor .50 1.25
364 Sam Runion .20 .50
365 Brent Brewer .50 1.25
366 Graham Taylor .20 .50
367 Cory Van Allen .20 .50
368 Kyler Burke .20 .50
369 Jaime Garcia .75 2.00
370 Carlos Triunfel .20 .50
371 Bryan Anderson .20 .50
372 Jared Goedert .20 .50
373 Tyler Herron .20 .50
374 Brandon Hynick .20 .50
375 Josh Outman .30 .75
376 Matt Whitney .30 .75
377a Tony Granadillo .20 .50
Dark Jersey
377b Tony Granadillo .20 .50
Red Jersey ERR
Incorrect birthday
378 Eric Hurley .20 .50
379 Cody Johnson .20 .50
380 Kasey Kiker .20 .50
381 Richie Robnett .20 .50
382 Joe Mather .30 .75
383 Chris Perez .30 .75
384 Shane Keough .30 .75
385 Chris Carter .30 .75
386 Neil Walker .20 .50
387 Wade LeBlanc .20 .50
388 Daniel Mayora .20 .50
389 Taylor Teagarden .30 .75
390 Chad Huffman .20 .50
391 Eduardo Morlan .20 .50
392 Trevor Cahill .50 1.25
393 Tommy Manzella .20 .50
394 Justin Reed .20 .50
395 Colton Willems .20 .50
396 Dexter Fowler .20 .50
397 Matt Harrison .20 .50
398 Steve Evarts .20 .50
399 Desmond Jennings .20 .50
400 Billy Crystal .50 1.25

2008 TRISTAR PROjections Green

*GREEN: 2.5X TO 6X BASIC
RANDOM INSERTS IN PACKS
STATED PRINT RUN 50 SER.#'d SETS
1-200 RELEASED IN PROJECTIONS
201-400 RELESASED IN HIGH SERIES

2008 TRISTAR PROjections Orange

RANDOM INSERTS IN PACKS
STATED PRINT RUN 5 SER.#'d SETS
1-200 RELEASED IN PROJECTIONS
201-400 RELESASED IN HIGH SERIES
NO PRICING DUE TO SCARCITY

2008 TRISTAR PROjections Purple

RANDOM INSERTS IN PACKS
STATED PRINT RUN 1 SER.#'d SET
1-200 RELEASED IN PROJECTIONS
201-400 RELESASED IN HIGH SERIES
NO PRICING DUE TO SCARCITY

2008 TRISTAR PROjections Yellow

RANDOM INSERTS IN PACKS
STATED PRINT RUN 25 SER.#'d SETS
1-200 RELEASED IN PROJECTIONS
201-400 RELESASED IN HIGH SERIES
NO PRICING DUE TO SCARCITY

2008 TRISTAR PROjections Reflectives

*REF: .5X TO 1.2X BASIC
RANDOM INSERTS IN PACKS
1-200 RELEASED IN PROJECTIONS
201-400 RELESASED IN HIGH SERIES

2008 TRISTAR PROjections Reflectives Green

*GRN REF: 2.5X TO 6X BASIC REF
RANDOM INSERTS IN PACKS
STATED PRINT RUN 50 SER.#'d SETS
1-200 RELEASED IN PROJECTIONS
201-400 RELESASED IN HIGH SERIES

2008 TRISTAR PROjections Reflectives Orange

RANDOM INSERTS IN PACKS
STATED PRINT RUN 5 SER.#'d SETS
1-200 RELEASED IN PROJECTIONS
201-400 RELESASED IN HIGH SERIES
NO PRICING DUE TO SCARCITY

2008 TRISTAR PROjections Reflectives Purple

RANDOM INSERTS IN PACKS
STATED PRINT RUN 1 SER.#'d SET
1-200 RELEASED IN PROJECTIONS
201-400 RELESASED IN HIGH SERIES
NO PRICING DUE TO SCARCITY

2008 TRISTAR PROjections Reflectives Yellow

RANDOM INSERTS IN PACKS
STATED PRINT RUN 25 SER.#'d SETS
1-200 RELEASED IN PROJECTIONS
201-400 RELESASED IN HIGH SERIES
NO PRICING DUE TO SCARCITY

2008 TRISTAR PROjections Autographs

OVERALL AUTO ODDS 1:6
1-200 RELEASED IN PROJECTIONS
201-400 RELESASED IN HIGH SERIES
2 Carmen Angelini 3.00 8.00
3 Josh Reddick 3.00 8.00
5 Ryan Kalish 4.00 10.00
6 Taylor Grote 6.00 15.00
7 Anthony Claggett 3.00 8.00
11 Yamaico Navarro 3.00 8.00
12 Ryan Pope 3.00 8.00
13 David Robertson 3.00 8.00
14 Max Scherzer
15 Alan Horne 4.00 10.00
16 David Mailman 3.00 8.00
17 Brad Suttle 3.00 8.00
18 Lars Anderson 10.00 25.00
19 Austin Jackson 6.00 15.00
20 Austin Romine 5.00 12.00
21 James Adkins 3.00 8.00
22 Jose Ceda 3.00 8.00
24 Tommy Hanson 8.00 20.00
25 Bryce Cox 3.00 8.00
26 Austin Krum 3.00 8.00
29 Juan Francisco 3.00 8.00
31 Jason Heyward 20.00 50.00
32 Brock Huntzinger 3.00 8.00
34 Anthony Rizzo 6.00 15.00
35 Nick Noonan 3.00 8.00
36 Matt LaPorta 8.00 20.00
37 Jeff Manship 3.00 8.00
38 David Kopp 3.00 8.00
42 Aaron Bates 3.00 8.00
43 Jarrod Parker 3.00 8.00
44 David Price 6.00 15.00
45 Marco Vechionacci 4.00 10.00
47 Jason Place 3.00 8.00
48 Nathan Vineyard 3.00 8.00
50 Jose Tabata 6.00 15.00
51 Matt Wieters 12.50 30.00
52 Chris Withrow 3.00 8.00
53 Jesus Montero 8.00 20.00
54 Dellin Betances 3.00 8.00
55 Zack Daeges 3.00 8.00
56 Jed Lowrie 6.00 15.00
57 Colby Rasmus 6.00 15.00
59 Tim Alderson 3.00 8.00
61 Phillippe Aumont 8.00 20.00
63 Daniel Berlind 3.00 8.00
68 Michael Burgess 5.00 12.00
72 Corey Brown 3.00 8.00
73 Madison Bumgarner 10.00 25.00
75 Drew Cumberland 3.00 8.00
77 Grant Desme 3.00 8.00
78 Sean Doolittle 3.00 8.00
81 Wendell Fairley 3.00 8.00
83 Darren Ford 3.00 8.00
84 Clay Fuller 3.00 8.00
86 Todd Frazier 6.00 15.00
91 Will Inman 3.00 8.00
93 Tyler Kolodny 3.00 8.00
94 Kyle Lotzkar 3.00 8.00
95 Cory Luebke 3.00 8.00
96 Michael Main 3.00 8.00
99 Adam Miller 4.00 10.00
101 Brandon Hamilton 3.00 8.00
103 Engel Beltre 6.00 15.00
107 Brad James 3.00 8.00
110 Ben Revere 3.00 8.00
113 Robert Parnell 3.00 8.00
114 Joe Savery 3.00 8.00
115 Michael Paulk 3.00 8.00
116 Aaron Poreda 3.00 8.00
118 Kevin Pucetas 3.00 8.00
121 Nick Schmidt 3.00 8.00
122 Eduardo Nunez 3.00 8.00
123 Donald Veal 3.00 8.00
124 Matt Antonelli 3.00 8.00
125 Jay Bruce 8.00 20.00
126 Adrian Cardenas 3.00 8.00
127 Daniel Bard 3.00 8.00
129 Tyler Colvin 5.00 12.00
130 George Kottaras 3.00 8.00
136 Brett Smith 3.00 8.00
138 Kevin Whelan 3.00 8.00
139 Josh Rodriguez 3.00 8.00
140 Billy Rowell 3.00 8.00
142 Hector Correa 3.00 8.00
144 Matt Dominguez 3.00 8.00
146 Robert Fish 3.00 8.00
147 Brian Friday 3.00 8.00
148 J.P. Arencibia 10.00 25.00
149 Brett Cecil 3.00 8.00
151 Eric Eiland 3.00 8.00
152 Devin Mesoraco 3.00 8.00
153 Daniel Moskos 3.00 8.00
157 Jon Gilmore 3.00 8.00
159 John Tolisano 3.00 8.00
160 Casey Weathers 5.00 12.00
161 Daniel Worth 3.00 8.00
162 Justin Jackson 3.00 8.00
164 Jake Smolinski 5.00 12.00
165 Pedro Beato 3.00 8.00
166 Duke Welker 4.00 10.00
167 Hank Conger 3.00 8.00
168 Jordan Zimmermann 4.00 10.00
169 Tim Battle 3.00 8.00
170 Jordan Brown 3.00 8.00
171 Caleb Clay 3.00 8.00
172 Kris Johnson
173 Evan Longoria
174 Chris Marrero
175 Eric Duncan 3.00 8.00
176 Greg Reynolds 3.00 8.00
177 Kevin Ahrens 3.00 8.00
178 Travis Snider 10.00 25.00
179 Brett Gardner 4.00 10.00
181 Chris Tillman 6.00 15.00
182 Balbino Fuenmayor 4.00 10.00
189 John Mayberry Jr. 3.00 8.00
190 Max Sapp 3.00 8.00
196 Kyle McCulloch 3.00 8.00
198 Mitch Einertson 3.00 8.00
202 Drew Stubbs 5.00 12.00
203 John Whittleman 3.00 8.00
204 Eric Young Jr 3.00 8.00
209 Zach Kroenke 4.00 10.00
211 Zolio Almonte 5.00 12.00
212 Jairo Heredia 3.00 8.00
213 William Middlebrooks 3.00 8.00
214 Nick Hagadone 3.00 8.00
215 Abraham Almonte
217 Adam Mills 3.00 8.00
218 Drake Britton 3.00 8.00
219 Carlos Urena 3.00 8.00
220 Pete Kozma 4.00 10.00
222 Jose Pirela
225 Jose Gil 3.00 8.00
226 Zhenwang Zhang 6.00 15.00
227 Blake Beavan 3.00 8.00
229 Bubba Bell 3.00 8.00
232 Julio Borbon 3.00 8.00
234 Ryan Dent 3.00 8.00
235 Joshua Donaldson 3.00 8.00
237 Hector Gomez 3.00 8.00
238 Nick Carr 3.00 8.00
243 Eddie Kunz 3.00 8.00
250 Kellen Kulbacki 3.00 8.00
253 Cole Rohrbough 3.00 8.00
255 Clayton Mortensen 3.00 8.00
256 Joshua Vitters 4.00 10.00
258 Ty Weeden 3.00 8.00
263 Clayton Kershaw 5.00 12.00
265 Dustin Richardson 3.00 8.00
266 Michael Watt 3.00 8.00
269 Jonathan Bachanov 3.00 8.00
272 Adam Olbrychowski
273 Brooks Brown
276 Mitch Canham 3.00 8.00
282 Charlie Culberson 3.00 8.00
286 German Duran 3.00 8.00
287 Barry Enright 3.00 8.00
292 Josh Bell 3.00 8.00
295 Jeremy Haynes 3.00 8.00
296 Danny Payne 3.00 8.00
297 Michael Brantley 4.00 10.00
298 Tommy Hunter 3.00 8.00
299 Stephen Chapman 3.00 8.00
300 Albert LaBoy 3.00 8.00
302 Josue Calzado 4.00 10.00
303 Neil Ramirez 3.00 8.00
304 Matt Mangini 3.00 8.00
307 Andrew Romine 3.00 8.00
308 Francisco Castillo 3.00 8.00
311 James Simmons 3.00 8.00
318 Brian Rike 3.00 8.00
319 Wes Roemer 3.00 8.00
320 Salvador Sanchez 3.00 8.00
322 Jackson Williams 3.00 8.00
325 Prily Cuello 3.00 8.00
334 Carlos Carrasco 3.00 8.00
335 Gorkys Hernandez 3.00 8.00
337 Wes Hodges 3.00 8.00
339 Justin Masterson 12.50 30.00
340 Zachary McAllister 3.00 8.00
341 Adam Ottavino
343 Jordan Schafer 6.00 15.00
344 Angel Villalona
345 Steven White 3.00 8.00
346 Drew Miller
355 Josh Smoker 3.00 8.00
361 Mike Moustakas 5.00 12.00
363 John Raynor 4.00 10.00
364 Sam Runion 3.00 8.00
365 Brent Brewer 3.00 8.00
368 Kyler Burke
370 Carlos Triunfel 3.00 8.00
379 Cody Johnson 3.00 8.00
383 Chris Perez 4.00 10.00
385 Chris Carter 3.00 8.00
389 Taylor Teagarden 4.00 10.00
393 Tommy Manzella
399 Desmond Jennings 5.00 12.00

2008 TRISTAR PROjections Autographs Green

OVERALL AUTO ODDS 1:6
STATED PRINT RUN 50 SER.#'d SETS
1-200 RELEASED IN PROJECTIONS
201-400 RELESASED IN HIGH SERIES
2 Carmen Angelini 4.00 10.00
3 Josh Reddick 8.00 20.00
5 Ryan Kalish 6.00 15.00
6 Taylor Grote 8.00 20.00
7 Anthony Claggett 4.00 10.00
11 Yamaico Navarro 4.00 10.00
12 Ryan Pope 4.00 10.00
13 David Robertson 4.00 10.00
15 Alan Horne 5.00 12.00
16 David Mailman 4.00 10.00
17 Brad Suttle 4.00 10.00
18 Lars Anderson 12.50 30.00
19 Austin Jackson 8.00 20.00
20 Austin Romine 6.00 15.00
21 James Adkins 4.00 10.00
22 Jose Ceda 6.00 15.00
24 Tommy Hanson 10.00 25.00
25 Bryce Cox 4.00 10.00
26 Austin Krum 4.00 10.00
29 Juan Francisco 4.00 10.00
31 Jason Heyward 30.00 60.00
32 Brock Huntzinger 4.00 10.00
34 Anthony Rizzo 10.00 25.00
35 Nick Noonan 4.00 10.00
36 Matt LaPorta 10.00 255.00
37 Jeff Manship 4.00 10.00
38 David Kopp 4.00 10.00
42 Aaron Bates 4.00 10.00
43 Jarrod Parker 4.00 10.00
44 David Price 15.00 40.00
45 Marco Vechionacci 5.00 12.00
47 Jason Place 5.00 12.00
48 Nathan Vineyard 4.00 10.00
50 Jose Tabata 8.00 20.00
51 Matt Wieters 20.00 50.00
52 Chris Withrow 4.00 10.00
53 Jesus Montero 10.00 25.00
54 Dellin Betances 4.00 10.00
55 Zack Daeges 5.00 12.00
56 Jed Lowrie 8.00 20.00
57 Colby Rasmus 8.00 20.00
59 Tim Alderson 4.00 10.00
61 Phillippe Aumont 10.00 25.00
63 Daniel Berlind 4.00 10.00
68 Michael Burgess 6.00 15.00
72 Corey Brown 4.00 10.00
73 Madison Bumgarner 12.50 30.00
75 Drew Cumberland 4.00 10.00
77 Grant Desme 4.00 10.00
78 Sean Doolittle 4.00 10.00
81 Wendell Fairley 4.00 10.00
83 Darren Ford 4.00 10.00
84 Clay Fuller 4.00 10.00
86 Todd Frazier 10.00 25.00
91 Will Inman 5.00 12.00
93 Tyler Kolodny 4.00 10.00
94 Kyle Lotzkar 4.00 10.00
95 Cory Luebke 4.00 10.00
96 Michael Main 4.00 10.00
99 Adam Miller 5.00 12.00
101 Brandon Hamilton 4.00 10.00
103 Engel Beltre 8.00 20.00
107 Brad James 4.00 10.00
110 Ben Revere 4.00 10.00
113 Robert Parnell 4.00 10.00
114 Joe Savery 4.00 10.00
115 Michael Paulk 4.00 10.00
116 Aaron Poreda 4.00 10.00
118 Kevin Pucetas 4.00 10.00
121 Nick Schmidt 10.00 25.00
122 Eduardo Nunez 4.00 10.00
123 Donald Veal 4.00 10.00
124 Matt Antonelli 4.00 10.00
125 Jay Bruce 10.00 25.00
126 Adrian Cardenas 4.00 10.00
127 Daniel Bard 4.00 10.00
129 Tyler Colvin 6.00 15.00
130 George Kottaras 4.00 10.00
136 Brett Smith 5.00 12.00
138 Kevin Whelan 5.00 12.00
139 Josh Rodriguez 4.00 10.00
140 Billy Rowell 4.00 10.00
142 Hector Correa 4.00 10.00
144 Matt Dominguez 4.00 10.00
146 Robert Fish 4.00 10.00
147 Brian Friday 4.00 10.00
148 J.P. Arencibia 12.50 30.00
149 Brett Cecil 5.00 12.00
151 Eric Eiland 4.00 10.00
152 Devin Mesoraco 4.00 10.00
153 Daniel Moskos 4.00 10.00
157 Jon Gilmore 4.00 10.00
159 John Tolisano 4.00 10.00
160 Casey Weathers 6.00 15.00
161 Daniel Worth 4.00 10.00
162 Justin Jackson 6.00 15.00
164 Jake Smolinski 6.00 15.00
165 Pedro Beato 4.00 10.00
166 Duke Welker 5.00 12.00
167 Hank Conger 4.00 10.00
168 Jordan Zimmermann 5.00 12.00
169 Tim Battle 4.00 10.00
170 Jordan Brown 4.00 10.00
171 Caleb Clay 5.00 12.00
172 Kris Johnson
173 Evan Longoria
174 Chris Marrero
175 Eric Duncan 4.00 10.00
176 Greg Reynolds 4.00 10.00
177 Kevin Ahrens 4.00 10.00
178 Travis Snider 12.50 30.00
179 Brett Gardner 5.00 12.00
181 Chris Tillman 8.00 20.00
182 Balbino Fuenmayor 5.00 12.00
189 John Mayberry Jr. 4.00 10.00
190 Max Sapp 4.00 10.00
196 Kyle McCulloch 4.00 10.00
198 Mitch Einertson 4.00 10.00
202 Drew Stubbs 6.00 15.00
203 John Whittleman 4.00 10.00
204 Eric Young Jr 4.00 10.00
209 Zach Kroenke 5.00 12.00
211 Zolio Almonte 6.00 15.00
212 Jairo Heredia 4.00 10.00
213 William Middlebrooks 4.00 10.00
214 Nick Hagadone 4.00 10.00
215 Abraham Almonte
217 Adam Mills 4.00 10.00
218 Drake Britton 4.00 10.00
219 Carlos Urena 4.00 10.00
220 Pete Kozma 5.00 12.00
222 Jose Pirela
225 Jose Gil 4.00 10.00
226 Zhenwang Zhang 8.00 20.00
227 Blake Beavan 4.00 10.00
229 Bubba Bell 4.00 10.00
232 Julio Borbon 4.00 10.00
234 Ryan Dent 4.00 10.00
235 Joshua Donaldson 4.00 10.00
237 Hector Gomez 4.00 10.00
238 Nick Carr 4.00 10.00
243 Eddie Kunz 4.00 10.00
250 Kellen Kulbacki 4.00 10.00
253 Cole Rohrbough 4.00 10.00
255 Clayton Mortensen 4.00 10.00
256 Joshua Vitters 5.00 12.00
258 Ty Weeden 4.00 10.00
263 Clayton Kershaw 6.00 15.00
265 Dustin Richardson 4.00 10.00
266 Michael Watt 4.00 10.00
269 Jonathan Bachanov 4.00 10.00
272 Adam Olbrychowski
273 Brooks Brown
276 Mitch Canham 4.00 10.00
282 Charlie Culberson 4.00 10.00
286 German Duran 4.00 10.00
287 Barry Enright 4.00 10.00
292 Josh Bell 4.00 10.00
295 Jeremy Haynes 4.00 10.00
296 Danny Payne 4.00 10.00
297 Michael Brantley 5.00 12.00
298 Tommy Hunter 4.00 10.00
299 Stephen Chapman 4.00 10.00
300 Albert LaBoy 4.00 10.00
302 Josue Calzado 5.00 12.00
303 Neil Ramirez 4.00 10.00
304 Matt Mangini 4.00 10.00
307 Andrew Romine 4.00 10.00
308 Francisco Castillo 4.00 10.00
311 James Simmons 4.00 10.00
318 Brian Rike 4.00 10.00
319 Wes Roemer 4.00 10.00
320 Salvador Sanchez 4.00 10.00
322 Jackson Williams 4.00 10.00
325 Prily Cuello 4.00 10.00
334 Carlos Carrasco 4.00 10.00
335 Gorkys Hernandez 4.00 10.00
337 Wes Hodges 4.00 10.00
339 Justin Masterson 15.00 40.00
340 Zachary McAllister 4.00 10.00
341 Adam Ottavino
343 Jordan Schafer 8.00 20.00
344 Angel Villalona
345 Steven White 4.00 10.00
346 Drew Miller
355 Josh Smoker 4.00 10.00
361 Mike Moustakas 6.00 15.00
363 John Raynor 5.00 12.00
364 Sam Runion 4.00 10.00
365 Brent Brewer 4.00 10.00
368 Kyler Burke
370 Carlos Triunfel 4.00 10.00
379 Cody Johnson 4.00 10.00
383 Chris Perez 5.00 12.00
385 Chris Carter 4.00 10.00
389 Taylor Teagarden 5.00 12.00
393 Tommy Manzella
399 Desmond Jennings 6.00 15.00

2008 TRISTAR PROjections Autographs Orange

OVERALL AUTO ODDS 1:6
STATED PRINT RUN 5 SER.#'d SETS
1-200 RELEASED IN PROJECTIONS
201-400 RELESASED IN HIGH SERIES
NO PRICING DUE TO SCARCITY

2008 TRISTAR PROjections Autographs Purple

OVERALL AUTO ODDS 1:6
STATED PRINT RUN 1 SER.#'d SET
1-200 RELEASED IN PROJECTIONS
201-400 RELESASED IN HIGH SERIES
NO PRICING DUE TO SCARCITY

2008 TRISTAR PROjections Autographs Yellow

OVERALL AUTO ODDS 1:6
STATED PRINT RUN 25 SER.#'d SETS
1-200 RELEASED IN PROJECTIONS
201-400 RELESASED IN HIGH SERIES
NO PRICING DUE TO SCARCITY

2008 TRISTAR PROjections Autographs Reflectives

*REFLECTIVE: .4X TO 1X BASIC
OVERALL AUTO ODDS 1:6
1-200 RELEASED IN PROJECTIONS
201-400 RELESASED IN HIGH SERIES
24 Tommy Hanson 8.00 20.00

2008 TRISTAR PROjections Autographs Reflectives Green

*REF.GREEN: .4X TO 1X GREEN
OVERALL AUTO ODDS 1:6
STATED PRINT RUN 50 SER.#'d SETS
1-200 RELEASED IN PROJECTIONS
201-400 RELESASED IN HIGH SERIES
24 Tommy Hanson 10.00 25.00

2008 TRISTAR PROjections Autographs Reflectives Orange

OVERALL AUTO ODDS 1:6
STATED PRINT RUN 5 SER.#'d SETS
1-200 RELEASED IN PROJECTIONS
201-400 RELESASED IN HIGH SERIES
NO PRICING DUE TO SCARCITY

2008 TRISTAR PROjections Autographs Reflectives Purple

OVERALL AUTO ODDS 1:6
STATED PRINT RUN 1 SER.#'d SET
1-200 RELEASED IN PROJECTIONS
201-400 RELESASED IN HIGH SERIES
NO PRICING DUE TO SCARCITY

2008 TRISTAR PROjections Autographs Reflectives Yellow

OVERALL AUTO ODDS 1:6
STATED PRINT RUN 25 SER.#'d SETS
1-200 RELEASED IN PROJECTIONS
201-400 RELESASED IN HIGH SERIES
NO PRICING DUE TO SCARCITY

2008 TRISTAR PROjections GR8 Expectations Autographs Dual Green

RANDOM INSERTS IN PACKS
STATED PRINT RUN 50 SER.#'d SETS
NO PRICING ON MOST DUE TO SCARCITY
AC Abraham Almonte
Prily Cuello
AC Matt Antonelli 6.00 15.00
Adrian Cardenas
AD Matt Antonelli
German Duran
AI Matt Antonelli 5.00 12.00
Will Inman
BB Jonathan Bachanov
Pedro Beato
BD Corey Brown
German Duran
BG Brian Bocock
Hector Gomez
BO Andrew Brackman 10.00 25.00
Adam Olbrychowski
CE Carlos Carrasco 5.00 12.00
Barry Enright
CI Anthony Claggett
Will Inman
CM Frank Cervelli
Jesus Montero
CV Jose Ceda
Josh Vitters
EH Mitch Einertson 15.00 40.00
Jason Heyward
GZ Jose Gil 4.00 10.00
Zhenwang Zhang
HH Jason Heyward 20.00 50.00
Gorkys Hernandez
JD Cody Johnson
Zach Daeges
JR Desmond Jennings
Colby Rasmus
KK David Kopp
Peter Kozma
KR Eddie Kunz
Neil Ramirez
KV Clayton Kershaw
Donald Veal
LC Evan Longoria
Chris Carter
MB John Mayberry Jr.
Blake Beavan

MC Tommy Manzella 4.00 10.00
Charlie Culberson
MD Mike Moustakas
Matt Dominguez
MR David Mailman
Anthony Rizzo
MV Matt Mangini
Angel Villalona
MY John Mayberry Jr. 4.00 10.00
Eric Young Jr.
NL Yamaico Navarro
Jed Lowrie
PK Chris Perez 4.00 10.00
Peter Kozma
PS Kevin Pucetas
Max Scherzer
PW David Price 12.50 30.00
Casey Weathers
RA Austin Romine 10.00 25.00
Carmen Angelini
RB David Robertson
Andrew Brackman
RC Brian Rike 4.00 10.00
Tyler Colvin
RH Billy Rowell
Wes Hodges
RM Wes Roemer
Daniel Moskos
RP Greg Reynolds 12.50 30.00
Jarrod Parker
RR Austin Romine
Andrew Romine
RR John Raynor
Colby Rasmus
RS Cole Rohrbough
Jordan Schafer
SC Max Scherzer
Carlos Carrasco
SR Jordan Schaefer
Colby Rasmus
SZ Jake Smolinski 4.00 10.00
Jordan Zimmerman UER
Zimmermann misspelled
TY Steven Tolleson 4.00 10.00
Eric Jr Young
WK Chris Withrow 6.00 15.00
Clayton Kershaw
WK Ty Weeden
George Kottaras
WM Johnny Whittleman 4.00 10.00
John Mayberry

2008 TRISTAR PROjections GR8 Expectations Autographs Dual Orange

RANDOM INSERTS IN PACKS
STATED PRINT RUN 5 SER.#'d SETS
NO PRICING DUE TO SCARCITY

2008 TRISTAR PROjections GR8 Expectations Autographs Dual Purple

RANDOM INSERTS IN PACKS
STATED PRINT RUN 1 SER.#'d SET
NO PRICING DUE TO SCARCITY

2008 TRISTAR PROjections GR8 Expectations Autographs Dual Yellow

RANDOM INSERTS IN PACKS
STATED PRINT RUN 25 SER.#'d SETS
NO PRICING DUE TO SCARCITY

2008 TRISTAR PROjections GR8 Expectations Autographs Triple Green

RANDOM INSERTS IN PACKS
STATED PRINT RUN 50 SER.#'d SETS
NO PRICING ON MOST DUE TO SCARCITY
ABC Lars Anderson
Aaron Bates
Chris Carter
AJT Carmen Angelini
Austin Jackson
Jose Tabata
AKR Lars Anderson
Ryan Kalish
Josh Reddick
BCF Madison Bumgarner 10.00 25.00
Charlie Culberson
Wendell Fairley
BEK Jonathan Bachanov
Barry Enright
Eddie Kunz
BHF Bubba Bell
Wes Hodges
Juan Francisco
BKR Bubba Bell
Ryan Kalish
Josh Reddick
BPC Dellin Betances
Ryan Pope
Anthony Claggett
CCT Hank Conger
Frank Cervelli
Taylor Teagarden
FLB Juan Francisco
Matt LaPorta
Michael Burgess
FSS Jay Bruce
Jordan Schafer
Drew Stubbs
GBT Brett Gardner
Tim Battle
Jose Tabata
JRS Austin Jackson
Colby Rasmus
Jordan Schafer
KHJ Clayton Kershaw
Tommy Hanson
Brad James
MVS Matt Mangini 8.00 20.00
Angel Villalona
Jake Smolinski
RCH Dustin Richardson
Caleb Clay
Nick Hagadone
RZW Cole Rohrbough 6.00 15.00
Jordan Zimmerman
Casey Weathers
Zimmermann misspelled
SNV Damon Sublett
Eduardo Nunez
Marco Vechionacci
SPK Max Scherzer
David Price
Clayton Kershaw
SZS Jake Smolinski 6.00 15.00
Jordan Zimmerman
Josh Smoker
Zimmermann misspelled
TCJ Jose Tabata
Tyler Colvin
Desmond Jennings
WMH Kevin Whelan
Zachary McAllister
Alan Horne

2008 TRISTAR PROjections GR8 Expectations Autographs Triple Orange

RANDOM INSERTS IN PACKS
STATED PRINT RUN 5 SER.#'d SETS
NO PRICING DUE TO SCARCITY

2008 TRISTAR PROjections GR8 Expectations Autographs Triple Purple

RANDOM INSERTS IN PACKS
STATED PRINT RUN 1 SER.#'d SET
NO PRICING DUE TO SCARCITY

2008 TRISTAR PROjections GR8 Expectations Autographs Triple Yellow

RANDOM INSERTS IN PACKS
STATED PRINT RUN 25 SER.#'d SETS
NO PRICING DUE TO SCARCITY

2008 TRISTAR PROjections GR8 Expectations Autographs Quad Green

RANDOM INSERTS IN PACKS
STATED PRINT RUN 50 SER.#'d SETS
NO PRICING ON MOST DUE TO SCARCITY
ABCB Lars Anderson
Jordan Brown
Chris Carter
Aaron Bates
ACPU Zolio Almonte 12.50 30.00
Josue Calzado
Jose Pirela
Carlos Urena
GBNL Hector Gomez 40.00 100.00
Brian Bocock
Yamaico Navarro
Jed Lowrie
GGBT Taylor Grote
Brett Gardner
Tim Battle
Jose Tabata
JMBM Kris Johnson
William Middlebrooks
Daniel Bard
Justin Masterson
KKMW George Kontos
Zach Kroenke
Daniel McCutchen
Kevin Whelan
PMMB Jarrod Parker 30.00 60.00
Daniel Moskos
Adam Miller
Madison Bumgarner
SLRB Travis Snider
Evan Longoria
Colby Rasmus
Bubba Bell

2008 TRISTAR PROjections GR8 Expectations Autographs Quad Orange

RANDOM INSERTS IN PACKS
STATED PRINT RUN 5 SER.#'d SETS
NO PRICING DUE TO SCARCITY

2008 TRISTAR PROjections GR8 Expectations Autographs Quad Purple

RANDOM INSERTS IN PACKS
STATED PRINT RUN 1 SER.#'d SET
NO PRICING DUE TO SCARCITY

2008 TRISTAR PROjections GR8 Expectations Autographs Quad Yellow

RANDOM INSERTS IN PACKS
STATED PRINT RUN 25 SER.#'d SETS
NO PRICING DUE TO SCARCITY

2009 TRISTAR PROjections

This set was released on March 11, 2009. The base set consists of 100 cards.

COMPLETE SET (300) 60.00 150.00
COMP.SER.1 SET (100) 20.00 50.00
COMP.SER.2 SET (100) 20.00 50.00
COMP.SER.3 SET (100) 20.00 50.00
COMMON CARD (1-300) .20 .50
1 Jarrod Parker .50 1.25
2 Justin Parker .20 .50
3 Leyson Septimo .20 .50
4 Craig Kimbrel PD 3.00 8.00
5 Freddie Freeman 1.00 2.50
6 Layton Hiller PD .20 .50
7 Travis Adair PD .20 .50
8 Buck Britton PD .20 .50
9 L.J. Hoes PD .30 .75
10 Matt Wieters .60 1.50
11 Alex Hale PD .20 .50
12 Anthony Rizzo .60 1.50
13 Che-Hsuan Lin .20 .50
14 Felix Doubront .20 .50
15 Lance McClain .20 .50
16 Lars Anderson .50 1.25
17 Mitch Herold PD .20 .50
18 Sean Danielson .20 .50
19 Seth Garrison PD .20 .50
20 Wes Hodges .20 .50
21 Yamaico Navarro .30 .75
22 Aaron Shafer .20 .50
23 David Macias PD .30 .75
24 Jeff Beliveau .30 .75
25 Josh Vitters .50 1.25
26 Logan Watkins .20 .50
27 Matt Cerda .20 .50
28 Ryan Keedy PD .20 .50
29 Tony Campana .20 .50
30 John Shelby .20 .50
31 Jordan Danks .30 .75
32 Alex Buchholz PD .30 .75
33 Yonder Alonso .50 1.25
34 Bryce Stowell .20 .50
35 David Huff .20 .50
36 Matt LaPorta .50 1.25
37 Zach Putnam PD .20 .50
38 Christian Friedrich .30 .75
39 Everth Cabrera .30 .75
40 Cale Iorg .20 .50
41 Rick Porcello PD .60 1.50
42 Logan Morrison .60 1.50
43 Steve Lombardozzi PD .20 .50
44 Mark Ori .20 .50
45 Daniel Cortes .30 .75
46 Johnny Giavotella .30 .75
47 Mike Moustakas .60 1.50
48 Tyler Sample PD .20 .50
49 Ryan Chaffee .20 .50
50 Andrew Lambo .30 .75
51 Cody Adams .20 .50
52 Logan Shafer .20 .50
53 Angel Morales .30 .75
54 Carlos Gutierrez .50 1.25
55 Dominic De La Osa PD .50 1.25
56 Nick Romero PD .20 .50
57 Tyler Ladendorf .20 .50
58 Ike Davis 1.00 2.50
59 Javier Rodriguez .20 .50
60 Wilmer Flores PD .50 1.25
61 Austin Jackson .50 1.25
62 Brett Marshall .20 .50
63 Corban Joseph .20 .50
64 Dan Brewer .20 .50
65 Gian Carlos Arias .20 .50
66 Kyle Higashioka .20 .50
67 Mike Lyon PD .20 .50
68 Mitch Delaney PD .20 .50
69 Ray Kruml .20 .50
70 Dusty Coleman .20 .50
71 Petey Paramore .30 .75
72 Tyson Ross .30 .75
73 Michael Taylor .50 1.25
74 Andrew McCutchen .75 2.00
75 Daniel Moskos .20 .50
76 Jim Negrych .20 .50
77 Adis Portillo PD .20 .50
78 Blake Tekotte PD .20 .50
79 Kellen Kulbacki .20 .50
80 Luis Domoromo PD .20 .50
81 Brandon Crawford .20 .50
82 Jordan Zimmermann .20 .50
83 Madison Bumgarner .50 1.25
84 Roger Kieschnick .20 .50
85 Dennis Raben .20 .50
86 Julio Morban .20 .50
87 Colby Rasmus .50 1.25
88 Curt Smith PD .20 .50
89 Lance Lynn .30 .75
90 Shane Peterson .20 .50
91 Chris Nowak .20 .50
92 Jake Jefferies PD .20 .50
93 Derek Holland .30 .75
94 Elvis Andrus .30 .75
95 Robbie C. Ross .20 .50
96 Tim Murphy PD .20 .50
97 Kenny Wilson .20 .50
98 Scott Campbell .20 .50
99 Destin Hood PD .20 .50
100 Jake Smolinski .30 .75
101 Trevor Harden PD .30 .75
102 David Francis PD .20 .50
103 Jason Heyward 1.50 4.00
104 Scott Diamond .30 .75
105 Brian Conley PD .20 .50
106 David Hernandez .20 .50
107 Jake Arrieta .30 .75
108 Bryan Peterson PD .20 .50
109 Bryan Price .20 .50
110 Casey Kelly .20 .50
111 Mark Wagner .20 .50
112 Mike Lee .20 .50
113 Stolmy Pimentel PD .30 .75
114 Andrew Cashner .50 1.25
115 James Leverton PD .30 .75
116 Jericho Jones PD .20 .50
117 Justin Bristow PD .20 .50
118 Luis Bautista .20 .50
119 Mitch Atkins• .20 .50
120 Ryan Sontag PD .20 .50
121 Tarlandas Mitchell PD .20 .50
122 Brandon Allen .20 .50
123 Daniel Hudson PD .60 1.50
124 Gordon Beckham .60 1.50
125 Kyle Greenwalt .50 1.25
126 Chris Valaika .20 .50
127 Juan Carlos Sulbaran .20 .50
128 Zach Stewart PD .30 .75
129 Chen-Chang Lee• .30 .75
130 Cord Phelps .30 .75
131 Hector Rondon .30 .75
132 Charlie Blackmon .20 .50
133 Jhoulys Chacin .30 .75
134 Josh Bell .20 .50
135 Tyler Massey PD .20 .50
136 Wilin Rosario PD .20 .50
137 Brad Hand .30 .75
138 Drew Sutton .20 .50
139 Jay Austin .20 .50
140 Nate Pettus PD .20 .50
141 Phil Disher PD .30 .75
142 Matt Moore 3.00 8.00
143 Danny Gutierrez .20 .50
144 Miguel Moctezuma PD .30 .75
145 Roberto Lopez PD .20 .50
146 Tyler Chatwood .30 .75
147 Ivan DeJesus Jr. .20 .50
148 Jeremy Jeffress .30 .75
149 Ben Revere .20 .50
150 Bobby Lanigan PD .20 .50
151 Dan Osterbrock PD .20 .50
152 Evan Bigley PD .30 .75
153 Brad Holt .30 .75
154 Dylan Owen .20 .50
155 Jeff Kaplan PD .20 .50
156 Addison Maruszak PD .30 .75
157 Chad Gross PD .30 .75
158 Cory Arbiso PD .20 .50
159 David Phelps PD .20 .50
160 Jack Rye .20 .50
161 Jesus Montero 1.25 3.00
162 Luke Greinke PD .20 .50
163 Mikey O'Brien PD .20 .50
164 Pat Venditte PD .30 .75
165 Jordan Lyles .30 .75
166 Brett Hunter .20 .50
167 Rashun Dixon .50 1.25
168 Sean Doolittle .30 .75
169 Anthony Hewitt .30 .75
170 Jim Murphy .20 .50
171 Vance Worley 1.00 2.50
172 Chase D'Arnaud .30 .75
173 Elias Otero PD .30 .75
174 Jeff Sues .20 .50
175 Pedro Alvarez .60 1.50
176 Cedric Hunter .20 .50
177 David Freese 1.50 4.00
178 Jon Link .30 .75
179 Kyle Blanks .30 .75
180 Matt Buschmann .20 .50
181 Buster Posey .60 1.50
182 Kevin Pucetas .20 .50
183 Ryan Mantle PD .20 .50
184 Tim Alderson .30 .75
185 William Rhymes• .30 .75
186 Greg Halman .30 .75
187 Michael Pineda 3.00 8.00
188 Phillippe Aumont .50 1.25
189 Seth Lintz .20 .50
190 Brett Wallace .30 .75
191 Deryk Hooker .20 .50
192 Richie Lentz .20 .50
193 Miguel Flores PD .20 .50
194 Andrew Liebel PD .20 .50
195 David Cooper .20 .50
196 Jake Opitz .20 .50
197 Markus Brisker PD .30 .75
198 Danny Espinosa PD .20 .50
199 J.P. Ramirez PD .20 .50
200 Will Atwood PD .20 .50
201 Bryan Shaw .20 .50
202 Cesar Valdez .20 .50
203 Daniel Schlereth .20 .50
204 Andrew Carignan .20 .50
205 Edgar Osuna .20 .50
206 Kris Medlen .30 .75
207 Shayne Moody PD .20 .50
208 Tommy Hanson .60 1.50
209 Bobby Bundy PD .20 .50
210 Brian Matusz .50 1.25
211 Jason Rook PD .20 .50
212 Nathan Nery PD .20 .50
213 Xavier Avery .20 .50
214 Dennis Neuman .20 .50
215 Luis Exposito .50 1.25
216 Mitch Dening .20 .50
217 Tyler Yockey PD .30 .75
218 Dan McDaniel .20 .50
219 Hak-Ju Lee .75 2.00
220 Jay Jackson .20 .50
221 Josh Harrison .20 .50
222 Kurt Calvert .20 .50
223 Luis Flores .20 .50
224 Rebel Ridling PD .20 .50
225 Ryan Flaherty .20 .50
226 Toby Matchulat PD .20 .50
227 Brent Morel PD .20 .50
228 Kevin Eichhorn PD .20 .50
229 Kevin Dubler PD .20 .50
230 Devin Mesoraco .50 1.25
231 Michel Inoa .30 .75
232 Carlos Santana .60 1.50
233 Lonnie Chisenhall .30 .75
234 Trey Haley PD .20 .50
235 Darin Holcomb .20 .50
236 Cody Satterwhite .20 .50
237 Ryan Perry .50 1.25
238 Dellin Betances .30 .75
239 Edgar Olmos PD .20 .50
240 Isaac Galloway PD .20 .50
241 Kyle Skipworth .30 .75
242 Mike Stanton 1.00 2.50
243 Eric Taylor .20 .50
244 Jason Castro .50 1.25
245 Mitch Einertson .20 .50
246 Polin Trinidad .20 .50
247 T.J. Steele PD .20 .50
248 Eric Hosmer 1.50 4.00
249 John Flanagan PD .20 .50
250 Mike Montgomery .30 .75
251 Jayson Miller PD .20 .50
252 Rolando Gomez PD .20 .50
253 Ethan Martin .50 1.25
254 Josh Lindblom .20 .50
255 David Welch .20 .50
256 Jake Odorizzi .30 .75
257 Anthony Slama .20 .50
258 Jeff Lanning PD .20 .50
259 Steve Tolleson .20 .50
260 Chris Schwinden PD .20 .50
261 Eric Campbell PD .20 .50
262 Shawn Kelley .30 .75
263 Kirk Nieuwenhuis .20 .50
264 Brandon Braboy PD .20 .50
265 Chris Smith PD .30 .75
266 Garrison Lassiter .30 .75
267 Jeff Nutt PD .20 .50
268 Jeremy Bleich PD .20 .50
269 Matt Richardson PD .20 .50
270 Mitch Abeita PD .20 .50
271 Yeicok Calderon .20 .50
272 Jemile Weeks .30 .75
273 Trevor Cahill .50 1.25
274 Anthony Gose .30 .75
275 Jeremy Hellickson .75 2.00
276 Jason Knapp .20 .50
277 Zach Collier .20 .50
278 Tony Watson .20 .50
279 Daniel McCutchen .20 .50
280 Jordy Mercer PD .20 .50
281 Alvaro Aristy .20 .50
282 Daniel Robertson PD .20 .50
283 Logan Forsythe .30 .75
284 Wynn Pelzer PD .20 .50
285 Rafael Rodriguez .20 .50
286 Scott Barnes PD .20 .50
287 Aaron Pribanic PD .20 .50
288 Jose Valdivia .20 .50
289 Tommy Johnson PD .50 1.25
290 Adam Reifer .20 .50
291 Devin Shepherd PD .20 .50
292 Tim Beckham .50 1.25
293 Neftali Feliz .60 1.50
294 Daniel Bard .20 .50
295 Kevin Ahrens .20 .50
296 Robert Bell PD .20 .50
297 Adrian Nieto PD .20 .50
298 Blake Stoulfer PD .20 .50
299 Juan Duran .20 .50
300 Michael Guerrero PD .20 .50

2009 TRISTAR PROjections Green

*GREEN: 3X TO 8X BASIC
OVERALL PARALLEL ODDS 1:5
STATED PRINT RUN 50 SER.#'d SETS

2009 TRISTAR PROjections Orange

OVERALL PARALLEL ODDS 1:5
STATED PRINT RUN 5 SER.#'d SETS
NO PRICING DUE TO SCARCITY

2009 TRISTAR PROjections Purple

OVERALL PARALLEL ODDS 1:5
STATED PRINT RUN 1 SER.#'d SET
NO PRICING DUE TO SCARCITY

2009 TRISTAR PROjections Yellow

*YELLOW: 4X TO 10X BASIC
OVERALL PARALLEL ODDS 1:5
STATED PRINT RUN 25 SER.#'d SETS

2009 TRISTAR PROjections Autographs

OVERALL AUTO ODDS 1:5
SKIP NUMBERED SET
1 Jarrod Parker 3.00 8.00
2 Justin Parker 3.00 8.00
3 Leyson Septimo 3.00 8.00
10 Matt Wieters
11 Alex Hale 3.00 8.00
12 Anthony Rizzo 6.00 15.00
16 Lars Anderson
18 Sean Danielson 3.00 8.00
21 Yamaico Navarro 3.00 8.00
22 Aaron Shafer 3.00 8.00
25 Josh Vitters 15.00 40.00
27 Matt Cerda 3.00 8.00
31 Jordan Danks 4.00 10.00
36 Matt LaPorta
38 Christian Friedrich 3.00 8.00
47 Mike Moustakas 8.00 20.00
51 Cody Adams 3.00 8.00
52 Logan Shafer 3.00 8.00
58 Ike Davis 10.00 25.00
61 Austin Jackson 6.00 15.00
71 Petey Paramore 3.00 8.00
72 Tyson Ross 3.00 8.00
75 Daniel Moskos 3.00 8.00
81 Brandon Crawford 3.00 8.00
82 Jordan Zimmermann
83 Madison Bumgarner 8.00 20.00
87 Colby Rasmus
89 Lance Lynn 3.00 8.00
94 Elvis Andrus 4.00 10.00
96 Tim Murphy 3.00 8.00
100 Jake Smolinski 3.00 8.00
109 Bryan Price 3.00 8.00
111 Mark Wagner 3.00 8.00
112 Mike Lee 3.00 8.00
124 Gordon Beckham 6.00 15.00
132 Charlie Blackmon 3.00 8.00
133 Jhoulys Chacin 5.00 12.00
134 Josh Bell 3.00 8.00
137 Brad Hand 3.00 8.00
138 Drew Sutton 4.00 10.00
139 Jay Austin
146 Tyler Chatwood 4.00 10.00
149 Ben Revere 4.00 10.00
150 Bobby Lanigan 3.00 8.00
153 Brad Holt 3.00 8.00
157 Chad Gross 3.00 8.00
164 Pat Venditte 5.00 12.00
166 Brett Hunter 3.00 8.00
167 Rashun Dixon 3.00 8.00
168 Sean Doolittle 5.00 12.00
169 Anthony Hewitt 3.00 8.00
172 Chase D'Arnaud 5.00 12.00
181 Buster Posey 20.00 50.00
182 Kevin Pucetas
184 Tim Alderson
191 Deryk Hooker 3.00 8.00
201 Bryan Shaw 3.00 8.00
203 Daniel Schlereth 3.00 8.00
206 Kris Medlen 6.00 15.00
208 Tommy Hanson
213 Xavier Avery 3.00 8.00
214 Dennis Neuman 3.00 8.00
220 Jay Jackson 3.00 8.00
230 Devin Mesoraco 3.00 8.00
231 Michel Inoa 3.00 8.00
233 Lonnie Chisenhall 3.00 8.00
236 Cody Satterwhite 3.00 8.00
237 Ryan Perry 3.00 8.00
239 Edgar Olmos 3.00 8.00
240 Isaac Galloway 3.00 8.00
245 Mitch Einertson 3.00 8.00
250 Mike Montgomery 4.00 10.00
254 Josh Lindblom 3.00 8.00
257 Anthony Slama 3.00 8.00
258 Jeff Lanning 3.00 8.00
259 Steve Tolleson 3.00 8.00
260 Chris Schwinden 3.00 8.00
263 Kirk Nieuwenhuis 3.00 8.00
274 Anthony Gose 3.00 8.00
276 Jason Knapp 4.00 10.00
277 Zach Collier 3.00 8.00
279 Daniel McCutchen 3.00 8.00
283 Logan Forsythe 3.00 8.00
295 Kevin Ahrens 3.00 8.00
297 Adrian Nieto 3.00 8.00

2009 TRISTAR PROjections Autographs Green

*GREEN: .5X TO 1.2X BASIC
OVERALL AUTO ODDS 1:5
STATED PRINT RUN 50 SER.#'d SETS

2009 TRISTAR PROjections Autographs Orange

OVERALL AUTO ODDS 1:5
STATED PRINT RUN 5 SER.#'d SETS
NO PRICING DUE TO SCARCITY

2009 TRISTAR PROjections Autographs Purple

OVERALL AUTO ODDS 1:5
STATED PRINT RUN 1 SER.#'d SET
NO PRICING DUE TO SCARCITY

2009 TRISTAR PROjections Autographs Yellow

OVERALL AUTO ODDS 1:5
STATED PRINT RUN 25 SER.#'d SETS
NO PRICING DUE TO SCARCITY

2009 TRISTAR PROjections Obak Preview

ONE PER MINI/MASTER CASE
STATED PRINT RUN 150 SER.#'d SETS
P1 Tim Beckham 4.00 10.00
P2 Matt Wieters 4.00 10.00
P3 Matt LaPorta 4.00 10.00

2009 TRISTAR PROjections Obak Preview Mini

ONE PER MASTER CASE
STATED PRINT RUN 150 SER.#'d SETS
P1 Tim Beckham 4.00 10.00
P2 Matt Wieters 4.00 10.00
P3 Matt LaPorta 4.00 10.00

2009 TRISTAR PROjections Tailor Made

OVERALL MEM ODDS 1:20
STATED PRINT RUN 144 SER.#'d SETS
TM1 Jarrod Parker 8.00 20.00
TM2 Carlos Gutierrez 3.00 8.00
TM3 James Leverton 2.50 6.00
TM4 Brett Wallace 3.00 8.00
TM5 Cesar Valdez 3.00 8.00
TM6 Blake Tekotte 2.50 6.00
TM7 Lance Lynn 2.50 6.00
TM8 Sean Danielson 4.00 10.00
TM9 Josh Vitters 4.00 10.00
TM10 Jeff Beliveau 2.50 6.00
TM11 Shane Peterson 3.00 8.00
TM12 Nick Hagadone 3.00 8.00
TM13 Christian Friedrich 2.50 6.00
TM14 Ike Davis 6.00 15.00
TM15 Bryan Price 3.00 8.00
TM16 Sean Doolittle 3.00 8.00
TM17 Evan Frederickson 2.50 6.00
TM18 Ryan Keedy 2.50 6.00
TM19 Matt LaPorta 4.00 10.00
TM20 Tim Federowicz 3.00 8.00
TM21 Jordan Lyles 5.00 12.00
TM22 Josh Reddick 3.00 8.00
Nick Hagadone
TM23 Fernando Martinez 2.50 6.00
Reese Havens
TM24 Sean Doolittle 3.00 8.00
Matt LaPorta
TM25 Daniel Schlereth 2.50 6.00
TM26 Josh Lindblom 2.50 6.00
TM27 Logan Forsythe 2.50 6.00
TM28 Brad Holt 2.50 6.00
TM29 Justin Smoak 3.00 8.00
TM30 Peter Hissey 2.50 6.00
TM31 Dan McDaniel 3.00 8.00
TM32 Josh Harrison 2.50 6.00
TM33 Fernando Martinez 3.00 8.00
TM34 Stephen Fife
Kyle Weiland
TM35 Brett Wallace 4.00 10.00
Josh Vitters
TM36 Fernando Martinez
Brad Holt

2009 TRISTAR PROjections Tailor Made Orange

OVERALL MEM ODDS 1:20
STATED PRINT RUN 5 SER.#'d SETS
NO PRICING DUE TO SCARCITY

2009 TRISTAR PROjections Tailor Made Purple

OVERALL MEM ODDS 1:20
STATED PRINT RUN 1 SER.#'d SET
NO PRICING DUE TO SCARCITY

2006 TRISTAR Prospects Plus

This set, which was the first set issued by Tri-Star with their licensing agreement with Minor League Baseball and their clubs, was released in January, 2007. These cards were issued in seven-card packs with an $9.99 SRP which came 10 packs to a box. The first 50 cards in this set were "pro debut" cards

COMPLETE SET (100) 20.00 50.00
COMMON CARD (1-50) .20 .50
COMMON CARD (51-100) .20 .50
1 Andrew Miller PD .60 1.50
2 Luke Hochevar PD .60 1.50
3 Hank Conger PD .30 .75
4 Evan Longoria PD 2.50 6.00
5 Cory Rasmus PD .20 .50
6 Billy Rowell PD .50 1.25
7 Ian Kennedy PD .50 1.25
8 Tim Lincecum PD 2.00 5.00
9 Yung-Il Jung PD .50 1.25
10 Josh Papelbon PD .30 .75
11 Emmanuel Burris PD .20 .50
12 Adam Ottavino PD .20 .50
13 Brett Sinkbeil PD .20 .50
14 Brad Lincoln PD .20 .50
15 Jeremy Jeffress PD .20 .50
16 Daniel Bard PD .20 .50
17 Brooks Brown PD .20 .50
18 Carlos Carrasco PD .30 .75
19 Kris Johnson PD .20 .50
20 Chris Parmelee PD .30 .75
21 Jason Place PD .20 .50
22 Preston Mattingly PD .75 2.00
23 Pedro Beato PD .20 .50
24 Greg Reynolds PD .75 2.00
25 Joba Chamberlain PD 2.00 5.00
26 Dellin Betances PD .60 1.50
27 Clayton Kershaw PD 1.25 3.00
28 Jeremy Papelbon PD .30 .75
29 Drew Stubbs PD .50 1.25
30 Chris Marrero PD .75 2.00
31 Adrian Cardenas PD .30 .75
32 Kasey Kiker PD .20 .50
33 Chris Perez PD .20 .50
34 Kyle Drabek PD .60 1.50
35 Caleb Clay PD .20 .50
36 Colton Willems PD .20 .50
37 Brandon Morrow PD 1.00 2.50
38 Tyler Colvin PD .50 1.25
39 Max Sapp PD .20 .50
40 Steve Evarts PD .20 .50
41 Travis Snider PD .60 1.50
42 Kyler Burke PD .20 .50
43 Cody Johnson PD .20 .50
44 Bryan Morris PD .20 .50
45 Miguel Montero PD .20 .50
46 Matt Antonelli PD .20 .50
47 Kyle McCulloch PD .50 1.25
48 Justin Upton PD 1.50 4.00
49 Cameron Maybin PD .60 1.50
50 Jeff Samardzija PD 1.00 2.50
51 Billy Butler .50 1.25
52 Mark Reynolds 1.25 3.00
53 Anthony Swarzak .20 .50
54 Brandon Wood .20 .50
55 Alex Gordon .60 1.50
56 Philip Hughes .20 .50
57 Hunter Pence 1.00 2.50
58 Elvis Andrus 1.00 2.50
59 Roger Clemens .60 1.50
60 Joey Votto 1.25 3.00
61 Fernando Martinez 2.00 5.00
62 Michel Abreu .20 .50
63 Thomas Fairchild .20 .50
64 Cliff Pennington .20 .50
65 Adam Miller .30 .75
66 Colby Rasmus 1.00 2.50
67 Nick Adenhart UER .20 .50
Batting headers on back
68 Brian Barton .20 .50
69 Michael Devaney .20 .50
70 Deolis Guerra .50 1.25
71 Jaime Garcia 1.00 2.50
72 Marcus Sanders .20 .50
73 Jose Tabata 1.25 3.00
74 Andrew McCutchen .50 1.25
75 Nolan Reimold .30 .75
76 Gregory Smith .20 .50
77 Chris Volstad .20 .50
78 Johnny Ash .20 .50
79 Gabriel Martinez .20 .50
80 T.J. Nall .20 .50
81 Ryan Braun UER 1.00 2.50
Brewers prospect Ryan Braun pictured on back
82 Angel Villalona .20 .50
83 Matt Harrison .20 .50
84 Reid Brignac .50 1.25
85 Charles Lofgren .50 1.25
86 Sean Smith .20 .50
87 Jeff Baisley .30 .75
88 Kevin Slowey
89 Jacob Fox .30 .75
90 Gaby Sanchez .30 .75
91 Homer Bailey .50 1.25
92 Troy Tulowitzki .50 1.25
93 Terry Evans .20 .50
94 Koby Clemens .30 .75
95 Scott Elbert .20 .50
96 Ricky Romero .20 .50
97 Troy Patton .20 .50
98 Stephen Marek .20 .50
99 Blake Dewitt .20 .50
100 Carlos Gonzalez .50 1.25

2006 TRISTAR Prospects Plus Gold

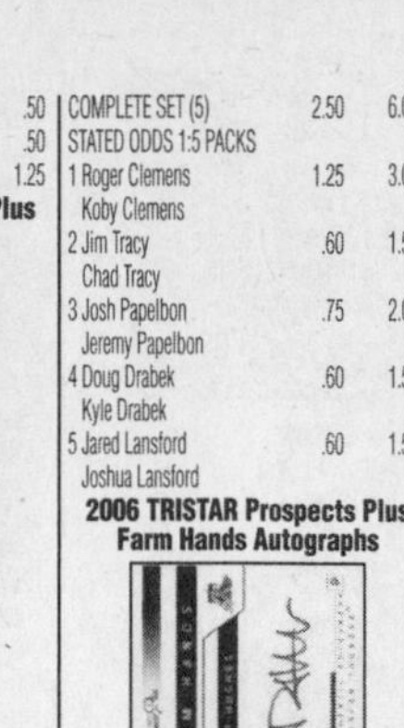

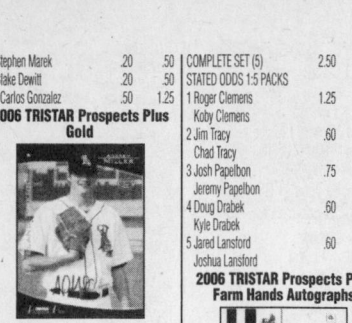

*GOLD PD: 4X TO 10X BASIC PD
*GOLD: 5X TO 12X BASIC
OVERALL AU ODDS 1:1 PACKS
STATED PRINT RUN 50 SER.#'d SETS
GOLD REFERS TO FOIL COLOR
1 Andrew Miller AU 30.00 60.00
2 Luke Hochevar AU 30.00 60.00
3 Hank Conger AU 15.00 40.00
4 Evan Longoria AU 40.00 80.00
5 Cory Rasmus AU 12.50 30.00
6 Billy Rowell AU 30.00 60.00
8 Tim Lincecum AU 100.00 200.00
10 Josh Papelbon AU 15.00 40.00
11 Emmanuel Burris AU 12.50 30.00
12 Adam Ottavino AU 12.50 30.00
13 Brett Sinkbeil AU 12.50 30.00
14 Brad Lincoln AU 12.50 30.00
15 Jeremy Jeffress AU 15.00 40.00
16 Daniel Bard AU 20.00 50.00
17 Brooks Brown AU 12.50 30.00
19 Kris Johnson AU 12.50 30.00
20 Chris Parmelee AU 15.00 40.00
21 Jason Place AU 20.00 50.00
22 Preston Mattingly 12.50 30.00
23 Pedro Beato AU 12.50 30.00
24 Greg Reynolds AU 12.50 30.00
25 Joba Chamberlain AU 100.00 200.00
26 Dellin Betances AU 30.00 60.00
27 Clayton Kershaw AU 50.00 100.00
28 Jeremy Papelbon AU 15.00 40.00
29 Drew Stubbs AU 20.00 50.00
30 Chris Marrero AU 20.00 50.00
31 Adrian Cardenas AU 12.50 30.00
32 Kasey Kiker AU 15.00 40.00
33 Chris Perez 6.00 15.00
34 Kyle Drabek AU 12.50 30.00
35 Caleb Clay AU 12.50 30.00
36 Colton Willems AU 12.50 30.00
37 Brandon Morrow AU 20.00 50.00
38 Tyler Colvin AU 30.00 60.00
39 Max Sapp AU 12.50 30.00
40 Steve Evarts AU 12.50 30.00
41 Travis Snider AU 40.00 80.00
42 Kyler Burke AU 12.50 30.00
43 Cody Johnson AU 15.00 40.00
44 Bryan Morris AU 12.50 30.00
45 Miguel Montero 6.00 15.00
46 Matt Antonelli AU 12.50 30.00
47 Kyle McCulloch AU 12.50 30.00
48 Justin Upton AU 40.00 80.00
50 Jeff Samardzija 20.00 50.00
51 Billy Butler 8.00 20.00
54 Brandon Wood 10.00 25.00
55 Alex Gordon AU 40.00 80.00
56 Philip Hughes 8.00 20.00
57 Hunter Pence 10.00 25.00
59 Roger Clemens 10.00 25.00
61 Fernando Martinez 10.00 25.00
73 Jose Tabata 8.00 20.00
82 Angel Villalona 12.50 30.00
84 Reid Brignac 8.00 20.00
93 Terry Evans 8.00 20.00
95 Scott Elbert 8.00 20.00

2006 TRISTAR Prospects Plus Purple

STATED PRINT RUN 1 SER.#'d SET
NO PRICING DUE TO SCARCITY
PURPLE REFERS TO FOIL COLOR

2006 TRISTAR Prospects Plus Family Ties

COMPLETE SET (5) 2.50 6.00
STATED ODDS 1:5 PACKS
1 Roger Clemens 1.25 3.00
Koby Clemens
2 Jim Tracy .60 1.50
Chad Tracy
3 Josh Papelbon .75 2.00
Jeremy Papelbon
4 Doug Drabek .60 1.50
Kyle Drabek
5 Jared Lansford .60 1.50
Joshua Lansford

2006 TRISTAR Prospects Plus Farm Hands Autographs

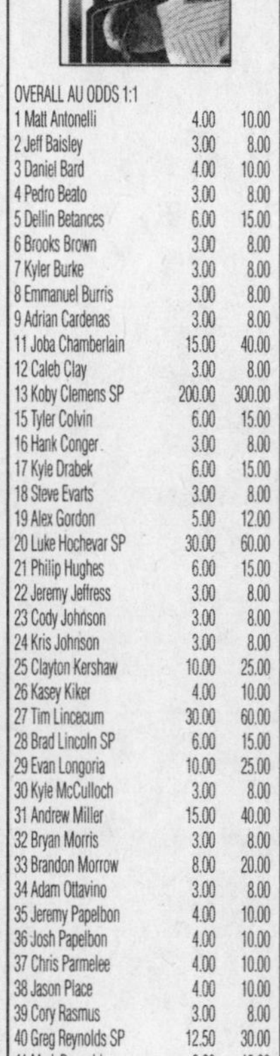

OVERALL AU ODDS 1:1
1 Matt Antonelli 4.00 10.00
2 Jeff Baisley 3.00 8.00
3 Daniel Bard 4.00 10.00
4 Pedro Beato 3.00 8.00
5 Dellin Betances 6.00 15.00
6 Brooks Brown 3.00 8.00
7 Kyler Burke 3.00 8.00
8 Emmanuel Burris 3.00 8.00
9 Adrian Cardenas 3.00 8.00
11 Joba Chamberlain 15.00 40.00
12 Caleb Clay 3.00 8.00
13 Koby Clemens SP 200.00 300.00
15 Tyler Colvin 6.00 15.00
16 Hank Conger 3.00 8.00
17 Kyle Drabek 6.00 15.00
18 Steve Evarts 3.00 8.00
19 Alex Gordon 5.00 12.00
20 Luke Hochevar SP 30.00 60.00
21 Philip Hughes 6.00 15.00
22 Jeremy Jeffress 3.00 8.00
23 Cody Johnson 3.00 8.00
24 Kris Johnson 3.00 8.00
25 Clayton Kershaw 10.00 25.00
26 Kasey Kiker 4.00 10.00
27 Tim Lincecum 30.00 60.00
28 Brad Lincoln SP 6.00 15.00
29 Evan Longoria 10.00 25.00
30 Kyle McCulloch 3.00 8.00
31 Andrew Miller 15.00 40.00
32 Bryan Morris 3.00 8.00
33 Brandon Morrow 8.00 20.00
34 Adam Ottavino 3.00 8.00
35 Jeremy Papelbon 4.00 10.00
36 Josh Papelbon 4.00 10.00
37 Chris Parmelee 4.00 10.00
38 Jason Place 4.00 10.00
39 Cory Rasmus 3.00 8.00
40 Greg Reynolds SP 12.50 30.00
41 Mark Reynolds 6.00 15.00
43 Max Sapp 3.00 8.00
44 Brett Sinkbeil 3.00 8.00
45 Travis Snider 6.00 15.00
46 Drew Stubbs 6.00 15.00
47 Justin Upton SP 30.00 60.00
47 Billy Rowell 8.00 20.00
48 Joey Votto 12.50 30.00
49 Colton Willems 3.00 8.00
50 Brandon Wood SP 15.00 40.00

2006 TRISTAR Prospects Plus Farm Hands Autographs Gold

OVERALL AU ODDS 1:1 PACKS
STATED PRINT RUN 25 SER.#'d SETS
NO PRICING DUE TO SCARCITY

2006 TRISTAR Prospects Plus ProTential

COMPLETE SET (20) 12.50 30.00
STATED ODDS 1:2 PACKS
1 Philip Hughes 1.50 4.00
2 Evan Longoria 1.50 4.00
3 Michel Abreu .75 2.00
4 Drew Stubbs .75 2.00
5 Hunter Pence .75 2.00
6 Roger Clemens 1.50 4.00
7 Koby Clemens 1.00 2.50
8 Max Sapp .75 2.00
9 Luke Hochevar 1.00 2.50
10 Tim Lincecum .75 2.00
11 Joey Votto .75 2.00
12 Brad Lincoln .75 2.00
13 Cameron Maybin 1.50 4.00
14 Alex Gordon 1.50 4.00
15 Billy Butler 1.00 2.50
16 Matt Antonelli .75 2.00
17 Jonny Ash .75 2.00
18 Justin Upton 1.00 2.50
19 Clayton Kershaw 1.00 2.50
20 Brandon Wood .75 2.00

2006 TRISTAR Prospects Plus ProTential Game Used

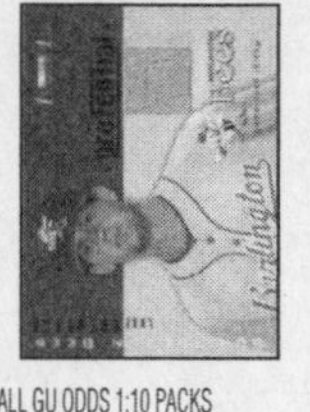

OVERALL GU ODDS 1:10 PACKS
AG Alex Gordon Jsy 4.00 10.00
BB Billy Butler Jsy 4.00 10.00
BL Brad Lincoln Jsy 4.00 10.00
CM Cameron Maybin Jsy 6.00 15.00
DS Drew Stubbs Jsy 5.00 12.00
EL Evan Longoria Pants 8.00 20.00
HP Hunter Pence Jsy 8.00 20.00
JV Joey Votto Jsy 5.00 12.00
KC Koby Clemens Jsy 5.00 12.00
LH Luke Hochevar Jsy 6.00 15.00
MA Michel Abreu Jsy 5.00 12.00
MS Max Sapp Jsy 5.00 12.00
PH Philip Hughes Jsy 6.00 15.00
RC Roger Clemens Bat 10.00 25.00
TL Tim Lincecum Jsy 10.00 25.00

2006 TRISTAR Prospects Plus ProTential Game Used 250

*250: .4X TO 1X BASIC
OVERALL GU ODDS 1:10 PACKS
STATED PRINT RUN 250 SER.#'d SETS

2006 TRISTAR Prospects Plus ProTential Patches

OVERALL GU ODDS 1:10 PACKS
STATED PRINT RUN 25 SER.#'d SETS
NO PRICING DUE TO SCARCITY
AG Alex Gordon
BB Billy Butler
BL Brad Lincoln
CM Cameron Maybin
DS Drew Stubbs
HP Hunter Pence
JA Jonny Ash
JV Joey Votto
KC Koby Clemens
LH Luke Hochevar
MA Michel Abreu
MS Max Sapp
PH Philip Hughes
TL Tim Lincecum

2007 TRISTAR Prospects Plus

COMPLETE SET (100) 10.00 25.00
COMMON CARD (1-100) .12 .30
COMMON PD (1-100) .12 .30
1 David Price .75 2.00
2 Peter Kozma PD .12 .30
3 Todd Frazier PD .12 .30
4 Jake Smolinski PD .40 1.00
5 Casey Weathers PD .12 .30
6 Rick Porcello .50 1.25
7 Clayton Mortensen .30 .75
8 Ryan Dent PD .12 .30
9 Ross Detwiler PD .12 .30
10 Matt Dominguez PD .30 .75
11 Jason Heyward PD 1.00 2.50
12 Neil Ramirez .12 .30
13 Kyle Lotzkar PD .20 .50
14 Brandon Hamilton PD .12 .30
15 Tim Alderson PD .20 .50
16 Jordan Zimmermann PD .20 .50
17 Jonathan Arencibia PD .30 .75
18 Kellen Kulbacki PD .12 .30
19 Sam Runion PD .12 .30
20 Brian Rike PD .12 .30
21 Mike Moustakas PD .50 1.25
22 Nick Schmidt PD .12 .30
23 Corey Brown PD .20 .50
24 Grant Desme PD .12 .30
25 Travis d'Arnaud PD .20 .50
26 Michael Burgess PD .20 .50
27 Nick Hagadone PD .20 .50
28 Daniel Moskos PD .12 .30
29 Wendell Fairley PD .20 .50
30 Max Scherzer PD .30 .75
31 Josh Vitters PD .30 .75
32 Devin Mesoraco PD .30 .75
33 James Adkins PD .12 .30
34 Jackson Williams PD .12 .30
35 Cory Luebke PD .12 .30
36 Michael Main PD .20 .50
37 Jarrod Parker .30 .75
38 Matt Mangini PD .12 .30
39 Duke Welker PD .12 .30
40 Chris Withrow PD .12 .30
41 Danny Payne PD .12 .30
42 Kevin Ahrens PD .20 .50
43 Ben Revere PD .30 .75
44 Wes Roemer PD .12 .30
45 Andrew Brackman .30 .75
46 Will Kline PD .12 .30
47 Madison Bumgarner .75 2.00
48 Charlie Culberson PD .20 .50
49 Beau Mills PD .12 .30
50 Jon Gilmore PD .30 .75
51 Andrew Cumberland PD .12 .30
52 Jonathan Bachanov PD .12 .30
53 Matt Wieters PD .60 1.50
54 Sean Doolittle .30 .75
55 Tommy Hunter PD .20 .50
56 Barry Enright PD .12 .30
57 Nick Noonan PD .12 .30
58 Justin Jackson PD .20 .50
59 Josh Donaldson PD .12 .30
60 Ed Easley PD .12 .30
61 Joe Savery .12 .30
62 Trystan Magnuson .12 .30
63 Brett Cecil PD .12 .30
64 Matt LaPorta PD .50 1.25
65 James Simmons PD .12 .30
66 Daniel Duffy PD .40 1.00
67 Phillippe Aumont .30 .75
68 Mitch Canham PD .12 .30
69 Josh Smoker PD .20 .50
70 Aaron Poreda PD .20 .50
71 Eddie Kunz PD .12 .30
72 Julio Borbon PD .40 1.00
73 Blake Beavan .40 1.00
74 Nathan Vineyard PD .12 .30
75 David Kopp PD .12 .30
76 Brock Huntzinger PD .12 .30
77 William Middlebrooks .12 .30
78 Greg Reynolds .40 1.00
79 Taylor Grote PD .12 .30
80 Colby Rasmus .75 2.00
81 Joe Mather .12 .30
82 Carmen Angelini PD .20 .50
83 Casey Crosby PD .40 1.00
84 Ryan Pope PD .30 .75
85 Anthony Rizzo PD .60 1.50
86 Jeff Larish .12 .30
87 Austin Romine PD .12 .30
88 John Mayberry .12 .30
89 Brad Suttle PD .12 .30
90 Ching-Lung Lo .20 .50
91 Jose Tabata .30 .75
92 Pedro Beato .12 .30
93 Adrian Cardenas .20 .50
94 David Mailman PD .20 .50
95 Bubba Bell .12 .30
96 Jake Arrieta .20 .50
97 Travis Snider .20 .50
98 Mitch Hilligoss .20 .50
99 Cale Iorg .20 .50
100 Yung-Chi Chen .30 .75

2007 TRISTAR Prospects Plus Green

*GOLD: 5X TO 12X BASIC
*GOLD PD: 5X TO 12X BASIC PD
COMMON AUTO 6.00 15.00
OVERALL AU ODDS 1:1 PACKS

STATED PRINT RUN 50 SER.#'d SETS
1 David Price AU 30.00 60.00
2 Peter Kozma AU 10.00 25.00
3 Todd Frazier AU 6.00 15.00
4 Jake Smolinski AU 12.50 30.00
5 Casey Weathers AU 6.00 15.00
7 Clayton Mortensen AU 10.00 25.00
9 Ross Detwiler AU 6.00 15.00
10 Matt Dominguez AU 30.00 60.00
11 Jason Heyward AU 60.00 120.00
12 Neil Ramirez AU 6.00 15.00
13 Kyle Lotzkar AU 10.00 25.00
14 Brandon Hamilton AU 6.00 15.00
15 Tim Alderson AU 6.00 15.00
16 Jordan Zimmermann AU 6.00 15.00
17 Jonathan Arencibia AU 10.00 25.00
18 Kellen Kulbacki AU 6.00 15.00
19 Sam Runion AU 6.00 15.00
20 Brian Rike AU 6.00 15.00
21 Mike Moustakas AU 10.00 25.00
22 Nick Schmidt AU 6.00 15.00
23 Corey Brown AU 6.00 15.00
24 Grant Desme AU 6.00 15.00
26 Michael Burgess AU 10.00 25.00
27 Nick Hagadone AU 12.50 30.00
28 Daniel Moskos AU 6.00 15.00
29 Wendell Fairley AU 12.50 30.00
31 Josh Vitters AU 10.00 25.00
32 Devin Mesoraco AU 6.00 15.00
33 James Adkins AU 6.00 15.00
34 Jackson Williams AU 12.50 30.00
35 Cory Luebke AU 6.00 15.00
36 Michael Main AU 10.00 25.00
37 Jarrod Parker AU 30.00 60.00
38 Matt Mangini AU 6.00 15.00
39 Duke Welker AU 6.00 15.00
40 Chris Withrow AU 6.00 15.00
41 Danny Payne AU 6.00 15.00
42 Kevin Ahrens AU 10.00 25.00
43 Ben Revere AU 6.00 15.00
44 Wes Roemer AU 6.00 15.00
45 Andrew Brackman AU 10.00 25.00
47 Madison Bumgarner AU 20.00 50.00
48 Charlie Culberson AU 30.00 60.00
50 Jon Gilmore AU 6.00 15.00
51 Andrew Cumberland AU 6.00 15.00
52 Jonathan Bachanov AU 6.00 15.00
53 Matt Wieters AU 30.00 60.00
54 Sean Doolittle AU 10.00 25.00
55 Tommy Hunter AU 20.00 50.00
56 Barry Enright AU 6.00 15.00
57 Nick Noonan AU 6.00 15.00
58 Justin Jackson AU 10.00 25.00
59 Josh Donaldson AU 6.00 15.00
61 Joe Savery AU 6.00 15.00
63 Brett Cecil AU 6.00 15.00
64 Matt LaPorta AU 15.00 40.00
65 James Simmons AU 6.00 15.00
67 Phillippe Aumont AU 6.00 15.00
68 Mitch Canham AU 6.00 15.00
69 Josh Smoker AU 10.00 25.00
70 Aaron Poreda AU 10.00 25.00
71 Eddie Kunz AU 6.00 15.00
72 Julio Borbon AU 12.50 30.00
73 Blake Beavan AU 12.50 30.00
74 Nathan Vineyard AU 6.00 15.00
75 David Kopp AU 6.00 15.00
77 William Middlebrooks AU 6.00 15.00
99 Cale Iorg AU 10.00 25.00

2007 TRISTAR Prospects Plus Orange

RANDOM INSERTS IN PACKS
OVERALL AU ODDS 1:1
STATED PRINT RUN 5 SER.#'d SETS
NO PRICING DUE TO SCARCITY

2007 TRISTAR Prospects Plus Purple

RANDOM INSERTS IN PACKS
OVERALL AU ODDS 1:1
STATED PRINT RUN 1 SER.#'d SET
NO PRICING DUE TO SCARCITY

2007 TRISTAR Prospects Plus Yellow

RANDOM INSERTS IN PACKS
OVERALL AU ODDS 1:1
STATED PRINT RUN 25 SER.#'d SETS
NO PRICING DUE TO SCARCITY

2007 TRISTAR Prospects Plus Farm Hands Autographs

OVERALL AU ODDS 1:1
AB Andrew Brackman SP 15.00 40.00
AC Andrew Cumberland 3.00 8.00
AP Aaron Poreda 3.00 8.00
BB Blake Beavan 4.00 10.00
BC Brett Cecil 3.00 8.00

BE Barry Enright 3.00 8.00
BH Brandon Hamilton 3.00 8.00
BR Ben Revere 3.00 8.00
BR Brian Rike 3.00 8.00
CB Corey Brown 3.00 8.00
CC Charlie Culberson 6.00 15.00
CI Cale Iorg 3.00 8.00
CL Cory Luebke 3.00 8.00
CM Clayton Mortensen 3.00 8.00
CW Casey Weathers SP 12.50 30.00
CW2 Chris Withrow 3.00 8.00
DK David Kopp 3.00 8.00
DM Devin Mesoraco 3.00 8.00
DM2 Daniel Moskos SP 5.00 12.00
DP Danny Payne 3.00 8.00
DP David Price SP 20.00 50.00
DW Duke Welker 3.00 8.00
EK Eddie Kunz 3.00 8.00
GD Grant Desme 6.00 15.00
JA James Adkins 3.00 8.00
JA J.P. Arencibia 5.00 12.00
JB Jonathan Bachanov 3.00 8.00
JB Julio Borbon 3.00 8.00
JD Josh Donaldson 3.00 8.00
JG Jon Gilmore 3.00 8.00
JH Jason Heyward 15.00 40.00
JJ Justin Jackson 3.00 8.00
JP Jarrod Parker SP 6.00 15.00
JS Joe Savery 3.00 8.00
JS2 James Simmons 3.00 8.00
JS3 Josh Smoker 3.00 8.00
JS4 Jake Smolinski 3.00 8.00
JV Josh Vitters SP
JW Jackson Williams 3.00 8.00
JZ Jordan Zimmermann 6.00 15.00
KA Kevin Ahrens 3.00 8.00
KK Kellen Kulbacki 3.00 8.00
KL Kyle Lotzkar 3.00 8.00
MB Madison Bumgarner 8.00 20.00
MB2 Michael Burgess 3.00 8.00
MC Mitch Canham 3.00 8.00
MD Matt Dominguez 3.00 8.00
ML Matt LaPorta 5.00 12.00
MM Michael Main 3.00 8.00
MM2 Matt Mangini 3.00 8.00
MM3 Mike Moustakas SP 6.00 15.00
MW Matt Wieters SP 12.50 30.00
NH Nick Hagadone 3.00 8.00
NN Nick Noonan 3.00 8.00
NR Neil Ramirez 3.00 8.00
NS Nick Schmidt 3.00 8.00
NV Nathan Vineyard 3.00 8.00
PA Phillippe Aumont SP 12.50 30.00
PK Peter Kozma 3.00 8.00
RD Ross Detwiler SP 8.00 20.00
RF Todd Frazier 6.00 15.00
SD Sean Doolittle 3.00 8.00
SR Sam Runion 3.00 8.00
TA Tim Alderson SP 10.00 25.00
TH Tommy Hunter 3.00 8.00
WF Wendell Fairley 3.00 8.00
WM William Middlebrooks 3.00 8.00
WR Wes Roemer 3.00 8.00

2007 TRISTAR Prospects Plus Protential

STATED ODDS 1:2
AB Andrew Brackman .60 1.50
AM Andrew McCutchen .60 1.50
BR Billy Rowell .60 1.50
CC Carlos Carrasco .25 .60
CG Carlos Gonzalez .60 1.50
CI Cale Iorg .40 1.00
CK Clayton Kershaw 2.00 5.00
CL Chuck Lofgren .60 1.50
CL2 Chris Lubanski .25 .60
CR Colby Rasmus 1.50 4.00
DP David Price 1.50 4.00
EL Evan Longoria 2.50 6.00
FM Fernando Martinez 1.00 2.50
FM2 Franklin Morales .40 1.00
GR Greg Reynolds .75 2.00
HK Hank Conger 1.25 3.00
JB Jay Bruce 1.50 4.00
JV Josh Vitters .60 1.50
JV Joey Votto 1.50 4.00

LL Ching-Lung Lo .40 1.00
LP Landon Powell .25 .60
ML Matt LaPorta 1.00 2.50
MM Mike Moustakas 1.00 2.50
MS Max Scherzer .60 1.50
MW Matt Wieters 1.25 3.00
NA Nick Adenhart .60 1.50
RB Reid Brignac .40 1.00
SE Scott Elbert .25 .60
TS Travis Snider .40 1.00
YC Yung-Chi Chen .60 1.50

2007 TRISTAR Prospects Plus National Convention Promo Gold

1 Brian Barton 1.00 2.50
2 Trevor Crowe .60 1.50
3 John Drennen .60 1.50
4 Wes Hodges .60 1.50
5 Beau Mills .60 1.50
6 Max Scherzer 1.50 4.00

2007 TRISTAR Prospects Plus National Convention Promo Silver

1 Brian Barton .60 1.50
2 Trevor Crowe .40 1.00
3 John Drennen .40 1.00
4 Wes Hodges .40 1.00
5 Beau Mills .40 1.00
6 Max Scherzer 1.00 2.50

2008 TRISTAR Prospects Plus

This set was released on December 3, 2008. The base set consists of 150 cards.

COMPLETE SET (150) 40.00 80.00
COMMON CARD .20 .50
PRINTING PLATES RANDOMLY INSERTED
PLATE PRINT RUN 1 SET PER COLOR
BLACK-CYAN-MAGENTA-YELLOW ISSUED
NO PLATE PRICING DUE TO SCARCITY
1 Tim Beckham PD .75 2.00
2 Pedro Alvarez .75 2.00
3 Eric Hosmer 2.50 6.00
4 Brian Matusz .50 1.25
5 Buster Posey PD .75 2.00
6 Kyle Skipworth PD .30 .75
7 Yonder Alonso PD .60 1.50
8 Gordon Beckham PD .60 1.50
9 Jason Castro PD .50 1.25
10 Justin Smoak PD .60 1.50
11 Jemile Weeks PD .30 .75
12 Brett Wallace PD
13 Aaron Hicks PD .50 1.25
14 Ethan Martin PD .50 1.25
15 Brett Lawrie 1.25 3.00
16 David Cooper PD .20 .50
17 Casey Kelly PD .30 .75
18 Ryan Westmoreland PD .20 .50
19 Ike Davis PD .75 2.00
20 Robbie Ross PD .20 .50
21 Andrew Cashner PD .50 1.25
22 Kyle Lobstein .20 .50
23 Ryan Perry PD .30 .75
24 Reese Havens PD .20 .50
25 Anthony Hewitt PD .20 .50
26 Christian Friedrich PD .60 1.50
27 Daniel Schlereth PD .20 .50
28 Carlos Gutierrez PD .50 1.25
29 Tyler Wilson PD .20 .50
30 Tim Melville PD .20 .50
31 Allan Dykstra PD .20 .50
32 Lonnie Chisenhall PD .30 .75
33 Corban Joseph PD .20 .50
34 Brett Hunter PD .20 .50
35 Shooter Hunt PD .20 .50
36 Jake Odorizzi PD .60 1.50
37 Brad Holt PD .20 .50
38 Zach Collier PD .30 .75
39 Evan Frederickson PD .20 .50
40 Brett DeVall PD .30 .75
41 Pete Hissey PD .20 .50
42 Robbie Grossman .30 .75
43 Ray Kruml PD .20 .50
44 Mike Montgomery PD .30 .75
45 Conor Gillaspie PD .20 .50
46 Lance Lynn PD .30 .75
47 Jordan Lyles PD .30 .75
48 Ryan Flaherty PD .30 .75
49 Xavier Avery PD .50 1.25
50 Seth Lintz PD .20 .50
51 Tim Federowicz PD .30 .75
52 Jaff Decker PD .30 .75
53 Wade Miley PD .20 .50
54 Brett Marshall PD .20 .50
55 Bryan Price PD .20 .50
56 Logan Forsythe PD .20 .50
57 Johnny Giavotella PD .60 1.50
58 Dan Brewer PD .20 .50
59 Brad Hand PD .30 .75
60 Tyler Stovall PD .20 .50
61 Jonathan Hee PD .20 .50
62 James Darnell PD .30 .75
63 Cutter Dykstra PD .20 .50
64 Tim Fedroff PD .20 .50
65 Bryce Stowell PD .20 .50
66 Jay Austin PD .20 .50
67 Jeremy Bleich .20 .50
68 Ross Seaton PD .20 .50
69 Tyson Ross PD .30 .75
70 Shane Peterson PD .30 .75
71 Garrison Lassiter PD .20 .50
72 Dusty Coleman PD .20 .50
73 Tyler Ladendorf PD .30 .75
74 Josh Lindblom PD .30 .75
75 Cody Adams PD .30 .75
76 BJ Hermsen .20 .50
77 Kenny Wilson PD .20 .50
78 Aaron Shafer PD .20 .50
79 Dennis Raben PD .30 .75
80 Cody Satterwhite PD .30 .75
81 Zeke Spruill PD .50 1.25
82 Derrik Gibson PD .20 .50
83 Pete Ruiz PD .20 .50
84 Rashun Dixon PD .20 .50
85 Jason Knapp PD .20 .50
86 Javier Rodriguez PD .20 .50
87 Charlie Blackmon PD .20 .50
88 Bryan Shaw PD .20 .50
89 Tyler Chatwood PD .30 .75
90 Juan Duran .20 .50
91 Matt Cerda PD .20 .50
92 Kyle Higashioka PD .20 .50
93 Logan Watkins PD .20 .50
94 Juan Carlos Sulbaran .20 .50
95 Stephen Fife PD .20 .50
96 Petey Paramore PD .30 .75
97 Niko Vasquez PD .50 1.25
98 Logan Schafer .20 .50
99 Jack Rye PD .20 .50
100 Chris Carpenter PD .50 1.25
101 Brandon Crawford PD .30 .75
102 Hunter Cervenka PD .20 .50
103 David Adams PD .20 .50
104 Ryan Lavarnway PD .50 1.25
105 Kyle Weiland PD .50 1.25
106 Chase D'Arnaud PD .20 .50
107 Christian Vazquez PD .30 .75
108 Justin Parker PD .20 .50
109 Mike Lee PD .20 .50
110 Jay Jackson PD .20 .50
111 Jeremy Beckham PD .30 .75
112 Michel Inoa .50 1.25
113 Kirk Nieuwenhuis PD .20 .50
114 Jordan Danks PD .50 1.25
115 Jarrod Parker PD .50 1.25
116 Madison Bumgarner PD .50 1.25
117 Jake Arrieta PD .20 .50
118 Blake Beavan PD .30 .75
119 Matt LaPorta .50 1.25
120 Austin Jackson 1.00 2.50
121 Kyle Russell PD .20 .50
122 Ryan Perry .30 .75
Daniel Schlereth
123 Yonder Alonso .60 1.50
Jemile Weeks
124 Brett Wallace .75 2.00
Ike Davis
Petey Paramore
125 Jason Castro .50 1.25
Jeremy Bleich
Cord Phelps
126 Pedro Alvarez .75 2.00
Ryan Flaherty
127 Kyle Russell .50 1.25
Jordan Danks
128 Brent Morel .30 .75
Logan Schafer
129 Anderson Felix .20 .50
Gian Carlos
130 David Adams .20 .50
Corban Joseph
131 Chris Smith .20 .50
Dan Brewer
Jack Rye
132 David Phelps .20 .50
Matt Richardson
133 Mikey O'Brien .75 2.00
Brandon Braboy
Pat Venditte
134 Mitch Abeita .20 .50
Jeff Nutt
135 Corban Joseph .20 .50
Ryan Wilkes
136 Ray Kruml .20 .50
Addison Maruszak
137 Bryan Price .50 1.25
Stephen Fife
Kyle Weiland
138 Pete Hissey .20 .50
Ryan Westmoreland
Bryan Peterson
139 Tim Federowicz .30 .75
Christian Vazquez
140 Mike Lee .20 .50
Mitch Herold
141 Lance McClain .50 1.25
Kyle Weiland
142 Ryan Flaherty .30 .75
Matt Cerda
143 Andrew Cashner .50 1.25
Aaron Shafer
Chris Carpenter
144 Luis Flores .20 .50
Rebel Ridling
145 Josh Harrison .30 .75
Jake Opitz
Ryan Keedy
146 Mitch Delaney .20 .50
Cory Arbiso
Mike Lyon
147 Pete Ruiz .20 .50
Tyler Wilson
Seth Garrison
Alex Hale
148 Bryan Peterson .20 .50
Tyler Yockey
Jonathan Hee
149 James Leverton .20 .50
Justin Bristow
Toby Matchulat
150 Dan McDaniel .20 .50
Josh Whitlock
Jeff Beliveau

2008 TRISTAR Prospects Plus Green

*GREEN: 3X TO 8X BASIC
OVERALL PARALLEL ODDS 1:5
STATED PRINT RUN 50 SER.#'d SETS

2008 TRISTAR Prospects Plus Orange

OVERALL PARALLEL ODDS 1:5
STATED PRINT RUN 5 SER.#'d SETS
NO PRICING DUE TO SCARCITY

2008 TRISTAR Prospects Plus Purple

OVERALL PARALLEL ODDS 1:5
STATED PRINT RUN 1 SER.#'d SET
NO PRICING DUE TO SCARCITY

2008 TRISTAR Prospects Plus Yellow

OVERALL PARALLEL ODDS 1:5
STATED PRINT RUN 25 SER.#'d SETS
NO PRICING DUE TO SCARCITY

2008 TRISTAR Prospects Plus PROminent Die Cut Green

*GREEN DC: 3X TO 8X BASIC
OVERALL PARALLEL ODDS 1:5
STATED PRINT RUN 50 SER.#'d SETS

2008 TRISTAR Prospects Plus PROminent Die Cut Purple

OVERALL PARALLEL ODDS 1:5
STATED PRINT RUN 1 SER.#'d SET
NO PRICING DUE TO SCARCITY

2008 TRISTAR Prospects Plus PROminent Die Cut Yellow

OVERALL PARALLEL ODDS 1:5
STATED PRINT RUN 25 SER.#'d SETS
NO PRICING DUE TO SCARCITY

2008 TRISTAR Prospects Plus Farm Hands Autographs

OVERALL AUTO ODDS 1:5
FHAG Anthony Gose 3.00 8.00
FHAH Anthony Hewitt 4.00 10.00
FHAN Adrian Nieto 3.00 8.00
FHAS Aaron Shafer 5.00 12.00
FHBC Brandon Crawford 4.00 10.00
FHBH Brad Hand 4.00 10.00
FHBH Brad Holt 3.00 8.00
FHBH Brett Hunter 4.00 10.00
FHBL Bobby Lanigan 3.00 8.00
FHBM Brian Matusz
FHBP Bryan Price 3.00 8.00
FHBP Buster Posey 30.00 60.00
FHBS Bryan Shaw 3.00 8.00
FHBW Brett Wallace
FHCA Cody Adams 4.00 10.00
FHCB Charlie Blackmon 3.00 8.00
FHCD Chase D'Arnaud 3.00 8.00
FHCF Christian Friedrich 3.00 8.00
FHCS Cody Satterwhite 3.00 8.00
FHDP David Price
FHDS Daniel Schlereth 3.00 8.00
FHEH Eric Hosmer
FHEO Edgar Olmos 3.00 8.00
FHEQ Edwin Quirarte 4.00 10.00
FHGB Gordon Beckham 10.00 25.00
FHID Ike Davis 10.00 25.00
FHIG Isaac Galloway 3.00 8.00
FHJA Jay Austin 3.00 8.00
FHJB Jeremy Beckham 4.00 10.00
FHJJ Jay Jackson 3.00 8.00
FHJK Jason Knapp 4.00 10.00
FHJL Josh Lindblom 3.00 8.00
FHJP Justin Parker 3.00 8.00
FHJS Justin Smoak
FHJW Jemile Weeks
FHKH Kyle Hudson 3.00 8.00
FHKN Kirk Nieuwenhuis 3.00 8.00
FHKS Kyle Skipworth
FHLC Lonnie Chisenhall 4.00 10.00
FHLF Logan Forsythe 3.00 8.00
FHLL Lance Lynn 4.00 10.00
FHLS Logan Schafer 3.00 8.00
FHMB Madison Bumgarner 10.00 25.00
FHMI Michel Inoa 10.00 25.00
FHML Mike Lee 3.00 8.00
FHMM Mike Montgomery 3.00 8.00
FHNV Niko Vasquez 3.00 8.00
FHPA Pedro Alvarez
FHPP Petey Paramore 3.00 8.00
FHRF Ryan Flaherty
FHRP Ryan Perry 4.00 10.00
FHTB Tim Beckham 50.00 100.00
FHTC Tyler Chatwood 5.00 12.00
FHTM Tim Melville
FHTR Tyson Ross 3.00 8.00
FHXA Xavier Avery 4.00 10.00
FHZC Zach Collier 3.00 8.00

2008 TRISTAR Prospects Plus Farm Hands Autographs Gold

OVERALL AUTO ODDS 1:5
STATED PRINT RUN 25 SER.#'d SETS
NO PRICING DUE TO SCARCITY

2008 TRISTAR Prospects Plus Farm Hands Autographs Green

*GREEN: .5X TO 1.2X BASIC
OVERALL AUTO ODDS 1:5
STATED PRINT RUN 50 SER.#'d SETS

2008 TRISTAR Prospects Plus Farm Hands Autographs Orange

OVERALL AUTO ODDS 1:5
STATED PRINT RUN 5 SER.#'d SETS
NO PRICING DUE TO SCARCITY

2008 TRISTAR Prospects Plus Farm Hands Autographs Purple

OVERALL AUTO ODDS 1:5
STATED PRINT RUN 1 SER.#'d SET
NO PRICING DUE TO SCARCITY

2008 TRISTAR Prospects Plus PROtential Game Used

OVERALL MEM ODDS 1:20
PBB Blake Beavan 3.00 8.00
PBH Brad Holt
PBP Bryan Price 3.00 8.00
PBW Brett Wallace 6.00 15.00
PCF Christian Friedrich
PCG Carlos Gutierrez 6.00 15.00
PDS Daniel Schlereth 4.00 10.00
PEF Evan Frederickson 4.00 10.00
PID Ike Davis 6.00 15.00
PJR Josh Reddick 5.00 12.00
PJS Justin Smoak 5.00 12.00
PJV Josh Vitters 5.00 12.00
PLF Logan Forsythe 3.00 8.00
PLL Lance Lynn 3.00 8.00
PML Matt LaPorta 6.00 15.00
PRF Ryan Flaherty 5.00 12.00
PRH Reese Havens 4.00 10.00
PSF Stephen Fife 3.00 8.00

2008 TRISTAR Prospects Plus PROtential Game Used Gold

OVERALL MEM ODDS 1:20
STATED PRINT RUN 25 SER.#'d SETS
NO PRICING DUE TO SCARCITY

2008 TRISTAR Prospects Plus PROtential Game Used Green

*GREEN: .5X TO 1.2X BASIC
OVERALL MEM ODDS 1:20
STATED PRINT RUN 50 SER.#'d SETS

2008 TRISTAR Prospects Plus PROtential Game Used Orange

OVERALL MEM ODDS 1:20
STATED PRINT RUN 5 SER.#'d SETS
NO PRICING DUE TO SCARCITY

2008 TRISTAR Prospects Plus PROtential Game Used Purple

OVERALL MEM ODDS 1:20
STATED PRINT RUN 1 SER.#'d SET
NO PRICING DUE TO SCARCITY

2009 TRISTAR Prospects Plus

COMP.SET w/o SPs (100) 30.00 60.00
COMMON CARD (1-100) .20 .50
COMMON CB (101-117) 1.00 2.50
OVERALL SP ODDS 1:10 HOBBY
OVERALL SP ODDS 1:2 HOT BOX
1a Stephen Strasburg 1.50 4.00
1b Stephen Strasburg Blue
1c Stephen Strasburg Gold
2a Dustin Ackley 1.00 2.50
2b Dustin Ackley Navy
2c Dustin Ackley Portrait
3a Donavan Tate .50 1.25
3b Donavan Tate Navy
3c Donavan Tate Portrait
4a Tony Sanchez .50 1.25
4b Tony Sanchez Red
4c Tony Sanchez Portrait
5a Matthew Hobgood .50 1.25
5b Matthew Hobgood Black
5c Matthew Hobgood Portrait
6 Zachary Wheeler .30 .75
7 Michael Minor .30 .75
8 Michael Leake .60 1.50
9 Drew Storen .30 .75
10 Tyler Matzek .30 .75
11 Alex White .50 1.25
12 Robert Borchering .30 .75
13 Allen Pollock .30 .75
14 Chad James .30 .75
15 Chad Jenkins .20 .50
16 Jiovanni Mier .30 .75
17 Kyle Gibson .50 1.25
18 Jared Mitchell .30 .75
19 Randal Grichuk .30 .75
20 Michael Trout 1.50 4.00
21 Eric Arnett .30 .75
22 Nicholas Franklin .50 1.25
23 Reymond Fuentes .20 .50
24a Slade Heathcott .50 1.25
24b Nicholas Franklin Righty
25 Brett Jackson .60 1.50
26 Timothy Wheeler .30 .75
27 Steven Baron .30 .75
28 Rex Brothers .30 .75
29 Matthew Davidson .30 .75
30 Aaron Miller .20 .50
31 Joshua Phegley .30 .75
32 Tyler Skaggs .30 .75
33 Christopher Owings .20 .50
34 Bradley Boxberger .20 .50
35 Matthew Bashore .20 .50
36 Kyle Heckathorn .30 .75
37 Tyler Kehrer .30 .75
38 Victor Black .30 .75
39 Jeffrey Kobernus .30 .75
40 Richard Poythress .20 .50
41 Everett Williams .20 .50
42 Brooks Pounders .30 .75
43 Mychal Givens .30 .75
44 Tommy Joseph .20 .50
45 Blake Smith .20 .50
46 Billy Hamilton 1.25 3.00
47 Nolan Arenado .60 1.50
48 Trayce Thompson .30 .75
49 Tom Mendonca .30 .75
50 Robert Stock .30 .75
51 Kelly Dugan .20 .50
52 Alex Wilson .20 .50
53 William Myers 1.00 2.50
54 Ben Tootle .20 .50
55 David Renfroe .30 .75
56 Max Stassi .30 .75
57 Adam Warren .20 .50
58 Jeremy Hazelbaker .30 .75
59 Caleb Cotham .30 .75
60 Seth Schwindenhammer .30 .75
61 Zach Von Rosenberg .20 .50
62 Daniel Fields .20 .50
63 Kristopher Hobson .20 .50
64 Madison Younginer .20 .50
65 Colton Cain .20 .50
66 Shannon Wilkerson .20 .50
67 Brandon Jacobs .30 .75
68 Neil Medchill .20 .50
69 Paul Smyth .30 .75
70 Alibay Barkley .20 .50
71 Dinesh Patel .20 .50
72 Rinku Singh .20 .50
73 Manny Banuelos 1.50 4.00
74 Jesus Montero 1.25 3.00
75 Mike Montgomery .30 .75
76 Chase D'Arnaud .30 .75
77 Slade Heathcott 1.25 3.00
Jesus Montero
78 Ryne Sandberg 1.00 2.50
Brett Jackson
79 Tom Seaver .50 1.25
Matthew Hobgood
80 Dustin Ackley .50 1.25
Donavan Tate
81 Randal Grichuk 1.50 4.00
Michael Trout
82 Dustin Ackley 1.00 2.50
Nicholas Franklin
83 Rinku Singh .20 .50
Dinesh Patel
84 Donavan Tate .50 1.25
Everett Williams
85 Michael Leake .60 1.50
Bradley Boxberger
86 Dale Murphy .30 .75
Michael Minor
87 Tony Sanchez .20 .50
Steven Baron
Joshua Phegley
Thomas Joseph
88 Matthew Hobgood .30 .75
Zachary Wheeler
Michael Minor
Michael Leake
89 Dustin Ackley .50 1.25
Donavan Tate
Allen Pollock
Jared Mitchell
90 Robert Borchering .50 1.25
Jiovanni Mier
Nicholas Franklin
Matthew Davidson
91 Eric Arnett .30 .75
Joshua Phegley
Matthew Bashore
92 Bradley Boxberger .30 .75
Robert Stock
93 Dustin Ackley 1.00 2.50
Alex White
Adam Warren
94 Brett Jackson .60 1.50
Jeffrey Kobernus
Blake Smith
95 Reymond Fuentes .30 .75
Alex Wilson
Brandon Jacobs
96 Slade Heathcott .50 1.25
Adam Warren
Neil Medchill
97 Dustin Ackley 1.00 2.50
Nicholas Franklin
Steven Baron
98 Donavan Tate .50 1.25
Matthew Hobgood
Zachary Wheeler
Tyler Matzek
99 Reymond Fuentes .20 .50
David Renfroe
Kristopher Hobson
100 Max Stassi .30 .75
Daniel Fields
101 Dustin Ackley CB 5.00 12.00
102 Donavan Tate CB 2.50 6.00
103 Tony Sanchez CB 2.50 6.00
104 Matthew Hobgood CB 2.50 6.00
105 Zachary Wheeler CB 1.50 4.00
106 Michael Minor CB 1.50 4.00
107 Michael Leake CB 3.00 8.00
108 Drew Storen CB 1.50 4.00
109 Tyler Matzek CB 1.50 4.00
110 Alex White CB 2.50 6.00
111 Jared Mitchell CB 1.50 4.00
112 Reymond Fuentes CB 1.00 2.50
113 Slade Heathcott CB 2.50 6.00
114 Brett Jackson CB 3.00 8.00
115 Kelly Dugan CB 1.00 2.50
116 K.C. Hobson CB 1.00 2.50
117a Stephen Strasburg CB Red
117b Stephen Strasburg CB Blue
117c Stephen Strasburg CB Green
117d Stephen Strasburg CB Gold
117e Stephen Strasburg CB Black

2009 TRISTAR Prospects Plus Gold

*GOLD: 2.5X TO 6X BASIC
*GOLD CB: .5X TO 1.2X BASIC CB
OVERALL PAR.1:10 HOBBY
OVERALL PAR.1:2.5 HOT BOX PACKS
STATED PRINT RUN 50 SER.#'d SETS

2009 TRISTAR Prospects Plus Green

OVERALL PAR.1:10 HOBBY
OVERALL PAR.1:2.5 HOT BOX PACKS
STATED PRINT RUN 25 SER.#'d SETS
NO PRICING DUE TO SCARCITY

2009 TRISTAR Prospects Plus Purple

OVERALL PAR.1:10 HOBBY
OVERALL PAR.1:2.5 HOT BOX PACKS
STATED PRINT RUN 1 SER.#'d SET
NO PRICING DUE TO SCARCITY

2009 TRISTAR Prospects Plus Red

OVERALL PAR.1:10 HOBBY
OVERALL PAR.1:2.5 HOT BOX PACKS
STATED PRINT RUN 5 SER.#'d SETS
NO PRICING DUE TO SCARCITY

2009 TRISTAR Prospects Plus Autographs

OVERALL AUTO 1:5 HOBBY
OVERALL AUTO 1:1 HOT BOX PACKS
STATED PRINT RUN 199 SER.#'d SETS
2a Dustin Ackley 12.50 30.00
2b Dustin Ackley Navy
2c Dustin Ackley Portrait
3a Donovan Tate 4.00 10.00
3b Donovan Tate Navy
3c Donovan Tate Portrait
4a Tony Sanchez 5.00 12.00
4b Tony Sanchez Red
4c Tony Sanchez Portrait
5a Matthew Hobgood 4.00 10.00
5b Matthew Hobgood Black
5c Matthew Hobgood Portrait
6 Zachary Wheeler 5.00 12.00
7 Michael Minor 3.00 8.00
8 Michael Leake 6.00 15.00
9 Drew Storen 4.00 10.00
10 Tyler Matzek 6.00 15.00
11 Alex White 5.00 12.00
12 Robert Borchering 3.00 8.00
13 Allen Pollock 4.00 10.00
14 Chad James 5.00 12.00
15 Chad Jenkins 3.00 8.00
16 Jiovanni Mier 4.00 10.00
17 Kyle Gibson 4.00 10.00
18 Jared Mitchell 6.00 15.00
19 Randal Grichuk 3.00 8.00
20 Michael Trout 10.00 25.00
21 Eric Arnett 5.00 12.00
22 Nicholas Franklin 4.00 10.00
23 Reymond Fuentes 3.00 8.00
24a Slade Heathcott 4.00 10.00
24b Nicholas Franklin Righty
25 Brett Jackson 10.00 25.00
26 Timothy Wheeler 3.00 8.00
27 Steven Baron 3.00 8.00
28 Rex Brothers 3.00 8.00
29 Matthew Davidson 3.00 8.00
30 Aaron Miller 4.00 10.00
31 Joshua Phegley 3.00 8.00
32 Tyler Skaggs 5.00 12.00
33 Christopher Owings 3.00 8.00
34 Bradley Boxberger 3.00 8.00
35 Matthew Bashore 3.00 8.00
36 Kyle Heckathorn 3.00 8.00
37 Tyler Kehrer 3.00 8.00
38 Victor Black 3.00 8.00
39 Jeffrey Kobernus 3.00 8.00
40 Richard Poythress 3.00 8.00
41 Everett Williams 3.00 8.00
42 Brooks Pounders 4.00 10.00
43 Mychal Givens 3.00 8.00
44 Tommy Joseph 3.00 8.00
45 Blake Smith 3.00 8.00
46 Billy Hamilton 6.00 15.00
47 Nolan Arenado 6.00 15.00
48 Trayce Thompson 3.00 8.00
49 Tom Mendonca 3.00 8.00
50 Robert Stock 4.00 10.00
51 Kelly Dugan 4.00 10.00
52 Alex Wilson 3.00 8.00
53 William Myers 6.00 15.00
54 Ben Tootle 3.00 8.00
55 David Renfroe 3.00 8.00
56 Max Stassi 10.00 25.00
57 Adam Warren 3.00 8.00
58 Jeremy Hazelbaker 3.00 8.00
59 Caleb Cotham 3.00 8.00

60 Seth Schwindenhammer 3.00 8.00
61 Zach Von Rosenberg 4.00 10.00
62 Daniel Fields 3.00 8.00
63 Kristopher Hobson 3.00 8.00
64 Madison Younginer 3.00 8.00
65 Colton Cain 3.00 8.00
66 Shannon Wilkerson 3.00 8.00
67 Brandon Jacobs 3.00 8.00
68 Neil Medchill 5.00 12.00
69 Paul Smyth 3.00 8.00
70 Alibay Barkley 3.00 8.00
71 Dinesh Patel
72 Rinku Singh
73 Manny Banuelos 40.00 80.00
86 Dale Murphy/Michael Minor 40.00 80.00
88 Matthew Hobgood/Zachary Wheeler/Michael Minor/Michael Leake 30.00 60.00
98 Donavan Tate/Matthew Hobgood/Zachary Wheeler/Tyler Matzek 4.00 10.00

2009 TRISTAR Prospects Plus Autographs Gold

*GOLD: .6X TO 1.5X BASIC
OVERALL AUTO 1:5 HOBBY
OVERALL AUTO 1:1 HOT BOX PACKS
STATED PRINT RUN 50 SER.#'d SETS

2009 TRISTAR Prospects Plus Autographs Green

OVERALL AUTO 1:5 HOBBY
OVERALL AUTO 1:1 HOT BOX PACKS
STATED PRINT RUN 25 SER.#'d SETS
NO PRICING DUE TO SCARCITY

2009 TRISTAR Prospects Plus Autographs Purple

OVERALL AUTO 1:5 HOBBY
OVERALL AUTO 1:1 HOT BOX PACKS
STATED PRINT RUN 1 SER.#'d SET
NO PRICING DUE TO SCARCITY

2009 TRISTAR Prospects Plus Autographs Red

OVERALL AUTO 1:5 HOBBY
OVERALL AUTO 1:1 HOT BOX PACKS
STATED PRINT RUN 5 SER.#'d SETS
NO PRICING DUE TO SCARCITY

2010 TRISTAR Pursuit

COMP.SET w/o SP's (150) 40.00 100.00
COMP.SER.1 SET w/o SP's (75) 20.00 50.00
COMP.SER.2 SET w/o SP's (75) 20.00 50.00
COMMON CARD (1-166) .20 .50
COMMON VAR (1-166) .40 1.00
COMMON SP (1-166) .40 1.00
THREE SP's PER BOX
1-83a ISSUED IN SERIES 1
83b-166 ISSUE IN SERIES 2
1a Dustin Ackley 1.25 3.00
1b Dustin Ackley VAR SP 2.50 6.00
2a Tony Sanchez .50 1.25
2b Tony Sanchez VAR SP 1.00 2.50
3 Zach Wheeler .30 .75
4 Mike Leake .60 1.50
5 Tyler Matzek .50 1.25
6 Bobby Borchering .30 .75
7 Chad James .20 .50
8 Jiovanni Mier .30 .75
9 Jared Mitchell .30 .75
10 Mike Trout 1.50 4.00
11 Nick Franklin .50 1.25
12 Slade Heathcott .60 1.50
13 Tim Wheeler .30 .75
14 Rex Brothers .20 .50
15 Aaron Miller .20 .50
16 Tyler Skaggs .20 .50
17 Brad Boxberger .30 .75
18 Kyle Heckathorn .20 .50
19 Victor Black .20 .50
20 Rich Poythress .20 .50
21 Brooks Pounders .20 .50
22 Tommy Joseph .20 .50
23 Billy Hamilton .75 2.00
24 Nolan Arenado .60 1.50
25 Eric Smith .20 .50
26 Tommy Mendonca .20 .50
27 Bryan Berglund .20 .50
28 Tanner Bushue .30 .75
29 Cameron Garfield .20 .50
30 Alex Wilson .20 .50
31 Chris Dominguez .50 1.25
32 Ben Tootle .20 .50
33 Max Stassi .30 .75
34 Jeremy Hazelbaker .20 .50
35a D'Vontrey Richardson .20 .50
35b D'Vontrey Richardson VAR SP .40 1.00
36 Zach Von Rosenberg .20 .50
37 K.C. Hobson .20 .50
38 Madison Younginer .20 .50
39 Jonathan Singleton .30 .75
40 Brandon Jacobs .20 .50
41 DeAngelo Mack .30 .75
42 Alibay Barkley .20 .50
43 Josh Bell .20 .50
44 Jiwan James .20 .50
45a Scott Sizemore .30 .75
45b Scott Sizemore VAR SP .60 1.50
46 Jeffry Antigua .20 .50
47 Tyson Gillies .50 1.25
48 Jonathan Hovis .20 .50
49 Jordan Brown .20 .50
50 Chris Carter .30 .75
51 Koby Clemens .30 .75
52 Alexander Colome .50 1.25
53 Samuel Deduno .20 .50
54 Grant Desme .30 .75
55 Jeanmar Gomez .30 .75
56a Jason Heyward 1.25 3.00
56b Jason Heyward VAR SP 2.50 6.00
57 Donnie Hume .20 .50
58 Austin Jackson .30 .75
59 Alex Liddi .30 .75
60 Rudy Owens .50 1.25
61 Jordan Pacheco .50 1.25
62 Ben Revere .20 .50
63 Austin Romine .30 .75
64 Kyle Russell .20 .50
65 Brandon Waring .30 .75
66 Travis Wood .30 .75
67 Nolan Ryan 1.50 4.00
Tanner Bushue
68 Dale Murphy 1.25 3.00
Jason Heyward
69 Roger Clemens .60 1.50
Kobe Clemens
70 Koby Clemens .30 .75
Donnie Hume
71 Jeanmar Gomez .50 1.25
Rudy Owens
Samuel Deduno
Travis Wood
72 Chris Carter .50 1.25
Jordan Pacheco
Austin Romine
73 Jordan Brown .30 .75
Austin Jackson
74 Grant Desme .50 1.25
Alexander Colome
Brandon Waring
75 Jesus Montero 1.25 3.00
Gary Sanchez
Austin Romine
76 Dustin Ackley 2.50 6.00
Alex Liddi SP
77 Chris Carter .60 1.50
Grant Desme SP
78 Mike Leake 1.25 3.00
Travis Wood
Brad Boxberger SP
79 Tyler Matzek 1.25 3.00
Tim Wheeler
Rex Brothers
Nolan Arenado SP
80 Ivan DeJesus Jr. SP .40 1.00
81 Chris Valaika SP .40 1.00
82 Max Kepler SP .60 1.50
83a Rinku Singh SP .40 1.00
83b Dinesh Patel VAR SP .40 1.00
84a Donavan Tate SP .50 1.25
84b Donavan Tate VAR SP 1.00 2.50
85 Matt Hobgood .50 1.25
86 Mike Minor .30 .75
87 Drew Storen .30 .75
88 Alex White .30 .75
89 A.J. Pollock .30 .75
90 Chad Jenkins .20 .50
91 Kyle Gibson .75 2.00
92 Randal Grichuk .20 .50
93 Eric Arnett .20 .50
94 Reymond Fuentes .30 .75
95 Brett Jackson .60 1.50
96 Steve Baron .20 .50
97 Matt Davidson .30 .75
98 Josh Phegley .20 .50
99 Chris Owings .20 .50
100 Matt Bashore .30 .75
101 Tyler Kehrer .20 .50
102 Jeff Kobernus .20 .50
103 Everett Williams .20 .50
104 Mychal Givens .50 1.25
105 Blake Smith .20 .50
106 Trayce Thompson .30 .75
107 Garrett Gould .20 .50
108 Robert Stock .20 .50
109 David Holmberg .30 .75
110 Steven Matz .20 .50
111 Max Walla .20 .50
112 Kelly Dugan .20 .50
113 Evan Chambers .30 .75
114 Wil Myers 1.00 2.50
115 David Renfroe .50 1.25
116 Adam Warren .50 1.25
117 Caleb Cotham .50 1.25
118 Seth Schwindenhammer .50 1.25
119 Daniel Fields .20 .50
120 Rob Lyerly .50 1.25
121 Colton Cain .50 1.25
122 Shannon Wilkerson .50 1.25
123 Neil Medchill .30 .75
124 Paul Smyth .30 .75
125 Scott Barnes .20 .50
126 Starlin Castro .75 2.00
127 Trayvon Robinson .50 1.25
128 Matt Angle .50 1.25
129 Steve Clevenger .30 .75
130 Marcus Hatley .30 .75
131 Blake Parker .30 .75
132 Allen Webster .30 .75
133 Chris Balcom-Miller .30 .75
134 Zach Britton .75 2.00
135 David Bromberg .30 .75
136a Simon Castro .30 .75
136b Starlin Castro VAR SP 1.50 4.00
137 Craig Clark .75 2.00
138 Casey Coleman .30 .75
139 David Cook .50 1.25
140 Matt Crim .50 1.25
141 Kyle Drabek .30 .75
142a Desmond Jennings .30 .75
142b Desmond Jennings VAR SP .60 1.50
143 Cody Johnson .30 .75
144 Craig Kimbrel 1.00 2.50
145 Brahiam Maldonado .50 1.25
146 Joey Metropoulos .50 1.25
147 Carlos Santana .60 1.50
148 Vinnie Scarduzio .30 .75
149 Chad Tracy .30 .75
150 Ace Walker .30 .75
151 Doug Drabek .30 .75
Kyle Drabek
152 Ben McDonald .20 .50
Matt Hobgood
153 Ryne Sandberg .75 2.00
Starlin Castro
154 Zach Britton .75 2.00
David Bromberg
Craig Clark
Chris Balcom-Miller
155 David Cook .50 1.25
Cody Johnson
Brahiam Maldonado
Chad Tracy
156 Kyle Russell .60 1.50
Alex Liddi
Desmond Jennings
Carlos Santana
157 Joey Metropoulos .50 1.25
Ace Walker
Vinnie Scarduzio
158 Jason Heyward 1.25 3.00
Starlin Castro
Tyler Matzek
Donavan Tate
159 Starlin Castro 1.50 4.00
Brett Jackson SP
160 Donavan Tate 1.00 2.50
Simon Castro SP
161 Jason Heyward 2.00 5.00
Mike Minor
Craig Kimbrel/Cody Johnson SP
162 Jesus Montero SP 2.50 6.00
163 Hector Rondon SP 1.00 2.50
164a Gary Sanchez SP 1.25 3.00
164b Gary Sanchez VAR SP 1.25 3.00
165 Manny Banuelos SP 4.00 10.00
166 Kelvin DeLeon SP .40 1.00

2010 TRISTAR Pursuit Gold

*GOLD: 2X TO 5X BASIC
*GOLD VAR: 1X TO 2.5X BASIC
*GOLD SP: 1X TO 2.5X BASIC
FOUR PARALLELS PER BOX
STATED PRINT RUN 50 SER.#'d SETS
1-83a ISSUED IN SERIES 1
83b-166 ISSUE IN SERIES 2

2010 TRISTAR Pursuit Green

FOUR PARALLELS PER BOX
STATED PRINT RUN 25 SER.#'d SETS
1-83a ISSUED IN SERIES 1
83b-166 ISSUE IN SERIES 2
NO PRICING DUE TO SCARCITY

2010 TRISTAR Pursuit Purple

FOUR PARALLELS PER BOX
STATED PRINT RUN 1 SER.#'d SET
1-83a ISSUED IN SERIES 1
83b-166 ISSUE IN SERIES 2
NO PRICING DUE TO SCARCITY

2010 TRISTAR Pursuit Red

FOUR PARALLELS PER BOX
STATED PRINT RUN 5 SER.#'d SETS
1-83a ISSUED IN SERIES 1
83b-166 ISSUE IN SERIES 2
NO PRICING DUE TO SCARCITY

2010 TRISTAR Pursuit Autographs

SIX AUTOS PER BOX
STATED PRINT RUN 80 SER.#'d SETS
1-83a ISSUED IN SERIES 1
83b-166 ISSUE IN SERIES 2
1a Dustin Ackley 8.00 20.00
1b Dustin Ackley VAR
2a Tony Sanchez 12.50 30.00
2b Tony Sanchez VAR
3 Zach Wheeler 3.00 8.00
4 Mike Leake 6.00 15.00
5 Tyler Matzek
6 Bobby Borchering 3.00 8.00
7 Chad James 4.00 10.00
8 Jiovanni Mier 8.00 20.00
9 Jared Mitchell 5.00 12.00
10 Mike Trout 10.00 25.00
11 Nick Franklin 5.00 12.00
12 Slade Heathcott 5.00 12.00
13 Tim Wheeler 3.00 8.00
14 Rex Brothers 3.00 8.00
15 Aaron Miller 3.00 8.00
16 Tyler Skaggs 3.00 8.00
17 Brad Boxberger 3.00 8.00
18 Kyle Heckathorn 3.00 8.00
19 Victor Black 3.00 8.00
20 Rich Poythress 3.00 8.00
21 Brooks Pounders 5.00 12.00
22 Tommy Joseph 3.00 8.00
23 Billy Hamilton 6.00 15.00
24 Nolan Arenado 4.00 10.00
25 Eric Smith 4.00 10.00
26 Tommy Mendonca 3.00 8.00
27 Bryan Berglund 3.00 8.00
28 Tanner Bushue 3.00 8.00
29 Cameron Garfield 3.00 8.00
30 Alex Wilson 3.00 8.00
31 Chris Dominguez 3.00 8.00
32 Ben Tootle 4.00 10.00
33 Max Stassi 4.00 10.00
34 Jeremy Hazelbaker 4.00 10.00
35a D'Vontrey Richardson 3.00 8.00
35b D'Vontrey Richardson VAR
36 Zach Von Rosenberg 4.00 10.00
37 K.C. Hobson 3.00 8.00
38 Madison Younginer 3.00 8.00
39 Jonathan Singleton 12.50 30.00
40 Brandon Jacobs 3.00 8.00
41 DeAngelo Mack 5.00 12.00
42 Alibay Barkley 3.00 8.00
43 Josh Bell 3.00 8.00
44 Jiwan James 6.00 15.00
45a Scott Sizemore 5.00 12.00
45b Scott Sizemore VAR
46 Jeffry Antigua 3.00 8.00
47 Tyson Gillies 4.00 10.00
48 Jonathan Hovis 3.00 8.00
49 Jordan Brown 3.00 8.00
50 Chris Carter 3.00 8.00
51 Koby Clemens
52 Alexander Colome 3.00 8.00
53 Samuel Deduno 3.00 8.00
54 Grant Desme 3.00 8.00
55 Jeanmar Gomez 4.00 10.00
56a Jason Heyward
56b Jason Heyward VAR
57 Donnie Hume 3.00 8.00
58 Austin Jackson 8.00 20.00
59 Alex Liddi 3.00 8.00
60 Rudy Owens 4.00 10.00
61 Jordan Pacheco 4.00 10.00
62 Ben Revere 4.00 10.00
63 Austin Romine 4.00 10.00
64 Kyle Russell 3.00 8.00
65 Brandon Waring 5.00 12.00
66 Travis Wood 5.00 12.00
68 Dale Murphy 100.00 175.00
Jason Heyward
69 Roger Clemens
Kobe Clemens
70 Koby Clemens
Donnie Hume
71 Jeanmar Gomez 5.00 12.00
Rudy Owens
Samuel Deduno
Travis Wood
72 Chris Carter
Jordan Pacheco
Austin Romine
73 Jordan Brown
Austin Jackson
74 Grant Desme
Alexander Colome
Brandon Waring
76 Dustin Ackley
Alex Liddi
77 Chris Carter
Grant Desme
78 Mike Leake 30.00 60.00
Travis Wood
Brad Boxberger
79 Tyler Matzek
Tim Wheeler
Rex Brothers
Nolan Arenado
80 Ivan DeJesus Jr. 3.00 8.00
81 Chris Valaika
82 Max Kepler 4.00 10.00
83 Rinku Singh
83b Dinesh Patel VAR
84a Donavan Tate 4.00 10.00
84b Donavan Tate VAR
85 Matt Hobgood 3.00 8.00
86 Mike Minor 4.00 10.00
87 Drew Storen 3.00 8.00
88 Alex White 4.00 10.00
89 A.J. Pollock 3.00 8.00
90 Chad Jenkins 3.00 8.00
91 Kyle Gibson 6.00 15.00
92 Randal Grichuk 10.00 25.00
93 Eric Arnett
94 Reymond Fuentes 4.00 10.00
95 Brett Jackson 6.00 15.00
96 Steve Baron 3.00 8.00
97 Matt Davidson 4.00 10.00
98 Josh Phegley 3.00 8.00
99 Chris Owings 3.00 8.00
100 Matt Bashore 3.00 8.00
101 Tyler Kehrer 3.00 8.00
102 Jeff Kobernus 3.00 8.00
103 Everett Williams 3.00 8.00
104 Mychal Givens 3.00 8.00
105 Blake Smith 3.00 8.00
106 Trayce Thompson 3.00 8.00
107 Garrett Gould 3.00 8.00
108 Robert Stock 3.00 8.00
109 David Holmberg 3.00 8.00
110 Steven Matz 3.00 8.00
111 Max Walla 3.00 8.00
112 Kelly Dugan 3.00 8.00
113 Evan Chambers 3.00 8.00
114 Wil Myers 8.00 20.00
115 David Renfroe 3.00 8.00
116 Adam Warren 3.00 8.00
117 Caleb Cotham 3.00 8.00
118 Seth Schwindenhammer
119 Daniel Fields 3.00 8.00
120 Rob Lyerly 3.00 8.00
121 Colton Cain 3.00 8.00
122 Shannon Wilkerson 3.00 8.00
123 Neil Medchill 3.00 8.00
124 Paul Smyth 3.00 8.00
125 Scott Barnes 3.00 8.00
126 Starlin Castro 20.00 50.00
127 Trayvon Robinson
128 Matt Angle 3.00 8.00
129 Steve Clevenger 3.00 8.00
130 Marcus Hatley 3.00 8.00
131 Blake Parker 3.00 8.00
132 Allen Webster 3.00 8.00
133 Chris Balcom-Miller 6.00 15.00
134 Zach Britton 10.00 25.00
135 David Bromberg 3.00 8.00
136a Simon Castro 5.00 12.00
136b Starlin Castro VAR
137 Craig Clark 3.00 8.00
138 Casey Coleman 3.00 8.00
139 David Cook 3.00 8.00
140 Matt Crim 3.00 8.00
141 Kyle Drabek 4.00 10.00
142a Desmond Jennings 4.00 10.00
142b Desmond Jennings VAR
143 Cody Johnson
144 Craig Kimbrel 12.50 30.00
145 Brahiam Maldonado 3.00 8.00
146 Joey Metropoulos 3.00 8.00
147 Carlos Santana 12.50 30.00
148 Vinnie Scarduzio 3.00 8.00
149 Chad Tracy 3.00 8.00
150 Ace Walker 3.00 8.00
151 Doug Drabek
Kyle Drabek
152 Ben McDonald
Matt Hobgood
153 Ryne Sandberg
Starlin Castro
154 Zach Britton
David Bromberg
Craig Clark
Chris Balcom-Miller
155 David Cook
Cody Johnson
Brahiam Maldonado
Chad Tracy
156 Kyle Russell
Alex Liddi
Desmond Jennings
Carlos Santana
157 Joey Metropoulos
Ace Walker
Vinnie Scarduzio
158 Jason Heyward
Starlin Castro
Tyler Matzek
Donavan Tate
159 Starlin Castro
Brett Jackson
160 Donavan Tate
Simon Castro
161 Jason Heyward
Mike Minor
Craig Kimbrel/Cody Johnson
164a Gary Sanchez 5.00 12.00
164b Gary Sanchez VAR 5.00 12.00
165 Manny Banuelos 40.00 80.00
166 Kelvin DeLeon 4.00 10.00

2010 TRISTAR Pursuit Autographs Green

SIX AUTOS PER BOX
STATED PRINT RUN 25 SER.#'d SETS
1-83a ISSUED IN SERIES 1
83b-166 ISSUE IN SERIES 2
NO PRICING DUE TO SCARCITY

2010 TRISTAR Pursuit Autographs Purple

SIX AUTOS PER BOX
STATED PRINT RUN 1 SER.#'d SET
1-83a ISSUED IN SERIES 1
83b-166 ISSUE IN SERIES 2
NO PRICING DUE TO SCARCITY

2010 TRISTAR Pursuit Autographs Red

SIX AUTOS PER BOX
STATED PRINT RUN 5 SER.#'d SETS
1-83a ISSUED IN SERIES 1
83b-166 ISSUE IN SERIES 2
NO PRICING DUE TO SCARCITY

2010 TRISTAR Pursuit Obak Preview

TWO OBAK CARDS PER BOX
ANNC'D PRINT RUN OF 425 SETS
1a Jason Heyward 3.00 8.00
1b Jason Heyward Sq 3.00 8.00
2a Roger Clemens 1.50 4.00
2b Roger Clemens Cir 1.50 4.00
3a James Creighton .50 1.25
3b James Creighton Cir .50 1.25
4a John Montgomery Ward .75 2.00
4b John Montgomery Ward Cir .75 2.00
5a Kyle Drabek .75 2.00
5b Kyle Drabek Sq .75 2.00
6a Walt Whitman .50 1.25
6b Walt Whitman Cir .50 1.25
7a Ernest Thayer .50 1.25
7b Ernest Thayer Cir .50 1.25

2010 TRISTAR Pursuit Obak Preview Autographs

SIX AUTOS PER BOX
STATED PRINT RUN 10 SER.#'d SETS
NO PRICING DUE TO SCARCITY
1 Jason Heyward
5 Kyle Drabek

2011 TRISTAR Pursuit

COMPLETE SET (92) 40.00 80.00
COMP.SET w/o SP's (75) 15.00 40.00
COMMON CARD (1-75) .20 .50
COMMON SP (76-92) 1.00 2.50
TWO SP's PER BOX
1 Mike Trout 1.25 3.00
2 Jameson Taillon .60 1.50
3 Manny Machado .60 1.50
4 Christian Colon .20 .50
5 Dustin Ackley .75 2.00
6 Wil Myers .30 .75
7 Zach Britton .50 1.25
8 Brandon Belt .75 2.00
9 Jonathan Singleton .30 .75
10 Gary Sanchez .50 1.25
11 Tyler Matzek .30 .75
12 John Lamb .20 .50
13 Manny Banuelos .60 1.50
14 Kyle Gibson .30 .75
15 Brett Jackson .30 .75
16 Zach Wheeler .20 .50
17 Alex White .20 .50
18 Chad James .20 .50
19 Tony Sanchez .30 .75
20 Tyler Skaggs .50 1.25
21 Billy Hamilton .50 1.25
22 Jason Kipnis .60 1.50
23 Nolan Arenado .60 1.50
24 Simon Castro .30 .75
25 Matt Davidson .20 .50
26 Randall Delgado .30 .75
27 Reymond Fuentes .20 .50
28 Jared Mitchell .30 .75
29 Chris Owings .20 .50
30 Lance Lynn .20 .50
31 Jerad Head .20 .50
32 Jared Hoying .30 .75
33 Jerry Sands .75 2.00
34 Koby Clemens .20 .50
35 Daniel Fields .20 .50
36 Allen Webster .30 .75
37 Max Stassi .20 .50
38 Austin Romine .20 .50
39 A.J. Pollock .20 .50
40 Jiwan James .20 .50
41 Mychal Givens .20 .50
42 Alex Colome .20 .50
43 Rex Brothers .20 .50
44 Bobby Borchering .30 .75
45 Tagg Bozied .20 .50
46 Paul Goldschmidt 1.00 2.50
47 Jeremy Hazelbaker .20 .50
48 Jake Lemmerman .30 .75
49 Rudy Owens .20 .50
50 Richard Poythress .20 .50
51 Donavan Tate .50 1.25
52 Alex Liddi .20 .50
53 Tanner Bushue .20 .50
54 Dave Sappelt .60 1.50
55 Trayce Thompson .20 .50
56 Zach Von Rosenberg .20 .50
57 Aaron Miller .20 .50
58 Max Kepler .20 .50
59 Brandon Laird .30 .75
60 Adam Warren .30 .75
61 Kyle Russell .30 .75
62 Dylan Owen .20 .50
63 Trayvon Robinson .30 .75
64 Chad Jenkins .20 .50
65 Kyle Heckathorn .20 .50
66 David Bromberg .20 .50
67 Colton Cain .20 .50
68 Matt Angle .30 .75
69 Chris Balcom-Miller .20 .50
70 Josh Collmenter .20 .50
71 Chris Dominguez .30 .75
72 Slade Heathcott .50 1.25
73 K.C. Hobson .20 .50
74 Tommy Joseph .20 .50
75 Brandon Waring .20 .50
76 Scott Barnes SP 1.00 2.50
77 Brad Boxberger SP 1.00 2.50
78 Evan Chambers SP 1.00 2.50
79 Craig Clark SP 2.50 6.00
80 Steve Clevenger SP 1.00 2.50
81 Tyson Gillies SP 1.00 2.50
82 David Holmberg SP 1.50 4.00
83 Cody Johnson SP 1.00 2.50
84 Brahiam Maldonado SP 1.50 4.00
85 Jordan Pacheco SP 1.00 2.50
86 Blake Parker SP 1.00 2.50
87 Josh Phegley SP 1.00 2.50
88 Blake Smith SP 1.00 2.50
89 Paul Smyth SP 1.00 2.50
90 Chad Tracy SP 1.00 2.50
91 Alex Wilson SP 1.00 2.50
92 Madison Younginer SP 1.00 2.50

2011 TRISTAR Pursuit Green

STATED PRINT RUN 25 SER.#'d SETS
OVERALL PARALLEL ODDS EIGHT PER BOX
NO PRICING DUE TO SCARCITY

2011 TRISTAR Pursuit Orange

*ORANGE 1-75: 2X TO 5X BASIC
*ORANGE 76-92: .4X TO 1X BASIC SP
OVERALL PARALLEL ODDS EIGHT PER BOX
STATED PRINT RUN 99 SER.#'d SETS

2011 TRISTAR Pursuit Purple

STATED PRINT RUN 1 SER.#'d SET
OVERALL PARALLEL ODDS EIGHT PER BOX
NO PRICING DUE TO SCARCITY

2011 TRISTAR Pursuit Autographs Gold

COMMON CARD 3.00 8.00
OVERALL AUTO ODDS SIX PER BOX
STATED PRINT RUN 111 SER.#'d SETS
1 Mike Trout 12.50 30.00
2 Jameson Taillon
4 Christian Colon 3.00 8.00
5 Dustin Ackley
6 Wil Myers 5.00 12.00
7 Zach Britton 12.50 30.00
8 Brandon Belt 12.50 30.00
9 Jonathan Singleton 15.00 40.00
10 Gary Sanchez 6.00 15.00
11 Tyler Matzek
12 John Lamb 4.00 10.00
13 Manny Banuelos
14 Kyle Gibson
15 Brett Jackson
16 Zach Wheeler
17 Alex White 3.00 8.00
18 Chad James 3.00 8.00
19 Tony Sanchez
20 Tyler Skaggs 3.00 8.00
21 Billy Hamilton 5.00 12.00

22 Jason Kipnis
23 Nolan Arenado 6.00 15.00
24 Simon Castro
25 Matt Davidson 3.00 8.00
26 Randall Delgado 5.00 12.00
27 Reymond Fuentes
28 Jared Mitchell
29 Chris Owings 3.00 8.00
30 Lance Lynn 3.00 8.00
31 Jerad Head 3.00 8.00
32 Jared Hoying 3.00 8.00
33 Jerry Sands 6.00 15.00
34 Koby Clemens
35 Daniel Fields 3.00 8.00
36 Allen Webster 3.00 8.00
37 Max Stassi
38 Austin Romine
39 A.J. Pollock 3.00 8.00
40 Jiwan James 3.00 8.00
41 Mychal Givens 3.00 8.00
42 Alex Colome 3.00 8.00
43 Rex Brothers 3.00 8.00
44 Bobby Borchering 3.00 8.00
45 Tagg Bozied 3.00 8.00
46 Paul Goldschmidt 8.00 20.00
47 Jeremy Hazelbaker 3.00 8.00
48 Jake Lemmerman 3.00 8.00
49 Rudy Owens
50 Richard Poythress 3.00 8.00
52 Alex Liddi
53 Tanner Bushue
54 Dave Sappelt 5.00 12.00
55 Trayce Thompson 3.00 8.00
56 Zach Von Rosenberg
57 Aaron Miller 3.00 8.00
58 Max Kepler 3.00 8.00
59 Brandon Laird 4.00 10.00
60 Adam Warren
61 Kyle Russell 3.00 8.00
62 Dylan Owen 3.00 8.00
63 Trayvon Robinson
64 Chad Jenkins 3.00 8.00
65 Kyle Heckathorn 3.00 8.00
66 David Bromberg 3.00 8.00
67 Colton Cain 3.00 8.00
68 Matt Angle 3.00 8.00
69 Chris Balcom-Miller
70 Josh Collmenter 5.00 12.00
71 Chris Dominguez 3.00 8.00
72 Slade Heathcott 5.00 12.00
73 K.C. Hobson
74 Tommy Joseph
75 Brandon Waring
76 Scott Barnes
77 Brad Boxberger
78 Evan Chambers 3.00 8.00
79 Craig Clark 3.00 8.00
80 Steve Clevenger
81 Tyson Gillies 3.00 8.00
82 David Holmberg
83 Cody Johnson 3.00 8.00
84 Brahiam Maldonado
85 Jordan Pacheco
86 Blake Parker
87 Josh Phegley
88 Blake Smith 3.00 8.00
89 Paul Smyth 3.00 8.00
90 Chad Tracy 3.00 8.00
91 Alex Wilson 3.00 8.00
92 Madison Younginer 3.00 8.00

2011 TRISTAR Pursuit Autographs Blue

*BLUE: .5X TO 1.2X GOLD AUTO
STATED PRINT RUN 50 SER.#'d SETS
OVERALL AUTO ODDS SIX PER BOX
2 Jameson Taillon 10.00 25.00
11 Tyler Matzek 4.00 10.00
13 Manny Banuelos 12.50 30.00
24 Simon Castro 4.00 10.00
34 Koby Clemens 6.00 15.00
37 Max Stassi 6.00 15.00
53 Tanner Bushue 4.00 10.00
56 Zach Von Rosenberg 5.00 12.00
63 Trayvon Robinson 4.00 10.00
69 Chris Balcom-Miller 4.00 10.00
74 Tommy Joseph 4.00 10.00
76 Scott Barnes 4.00 10.00
80 Steve Clevenger 4.00 10.00
85 Jordan Pacheco 5.00 12.00
86 Blake Parker 4.00 10.00

2011 TRISTAR Pursuit Autographs Green

STATED PRINT RUN 25 SER.#'d SETS
OVERALL AUTO ODDS SIX PER BOX
NO PRICING DUE TO SCARCITY

2011 TRISTAR Pursuit Autographs Purple

STATED PRINT RUN 1 SER.#'d SET
OVERALL AUTO ODDS SIX PER BOX
NO PRICING DUE TO SCARCITY

2011 TRISTAR Pursuit Autographs Red

STATED PRINT RUN 5 SER.#'d SETS
OVERALL AUTO ODDS SIX PER BOX
NO PRICING DUE TO SCARCITY

2011 TRISTAR Pursuit Autographs Five Blue

OVERALL AUTO ODDS SIX PER BOX
STATED PRINT RUN 50 SER.#'d SETS
93 Craig Kimbrel
Kyle Drabek
Mike Minor
David Price
Drew Storen
94 Casey Coleman 40.00 80.00
Jeanmar Gomez
Carlos Monasterios
Dan Runzler
Drew Storen
95 Johnny Bench
Frank Cervelli
Buster Posey
Carlos Santana
Matt Wieters
96 Starlin Castro
Chris Davis
Ike Davis
Eduardo Nunez
Andrew Romine
97 Josh Bell
Jay Bruce
Jason Heyward
Austin Jackson
Desmond Jennings
98 John Bowker
Tyler Colvin
Ben Revere
Travis Snider
Jose Tabata
99 Juan Francisco
John Mayberry
Kris Medlen
Ryan Perry
Chris Tillman
100 Frank Cervelli 20.00 50.00
Caleb Cotham
Eduardo Nunez
Slade Heathcott
Gary Sanchez

2011 TRISTAR Pursuit Autographs Five Purple

STATED PRINT RUN 1 SER.#'d SET
OVERALL AUTO ODDS SIX PER BOX
NO PRICING DUE TO SCARCITY

2011 TRISTAR Pursuit Autographs Five Red

STATED PRINT RUN 5 SER.#'d SETS
OVERALL AUTO ODDS SIX PER BOX
NO PRICING DUE TO SCARCITY

2011 TRISTAR Pursuit Obak Preview

TWO OBAK CARDS PER BOX
ANNC'D PRINT RUN OF 311 SETS
P1A Whitey Ford 1.00 2.50
P1B Whitey Ford 1.00 2.50
Square Around Number
P2A Jameson Taillon 2.00 5.00
P2B J.Taillon Cir 2.00 5.00
P2C J.Taillon Squ 2.00 5.00
P3A Rich Gossage .60 1.50
P3B Rich Gossage .60 1.50
Square Around Number
P4A Cap Anson 1.00 2.50
P4B Cap Anson 1.00 2.50
Square Around Number
P5A Bobby Thomson 1.00 2.50
P5B Bobby Thomson 1.00 2.50
Square Around Number
P6A Billy Johnson .60 1.50
P6B Billy Johnson .60 1.50
Square Around Number
P7 William Heffelfinger .60 1.50

2011 TRISTAR Pursuit Obak Preview Autographs

ANNOUNCED PRINT RUN OF 11
OVERALL AUTO ODDS SIX PER BOX
NO PRICING DUE TO SCARCITY
P1 Whitey Ford
P3 Rich Gossage
P2A Jameson Taillon
P2B Jameson Taillon
Circle Around Number
P2C Jameson Taillon
Square Around Number
P6A Billy Johnson
P6B Billy Johnson
Square Around Number

2011 TRISTAR Pursuit Red

STATED PRINT RUN 5 SER.#'d SETS
OVERALL PARALLEL ODDS EIGHT PER BOX
NO PRICING DUE TO SCARCITY

2005-06 USA Baseball Junior National Team

COMP.FACT.SET (25) 20.00 30.00
COMPLETE SET (21) 7.50 15.00
STATED PRINT RUN 10,000 SETS
74 Grant Green .40 1.00
75 Greg Peavey .30 .75
76 Brett Anderson .40 1.00
77 Jason Taylor .30 .75
78 Josh Thrailkill .30 .75
79 Max Sapp .40 1.00
80 Kevin Rhoderick .30 .75
81 Sean Ratliff .30 .75
82 Jeremy Bleich .30 .75
83 Scott Schauer .30 .75
84 Dellin Betances .30 .75
85 Torre Langley .40 1.00
86 Clayton Kershaw .75 2.00
87 Leonardo Ware .30 .75
88 Dwight Childs .30 .75
89 Adrian Cardenas .30 .75
90 Shawn Tolleson .30 .75
91 Tyson Ross .30 .75
92 Marcus Lemon .50 1.25
93 Lars Anderson .75 2.00
94 Team Checklist .20 .50

2005-06 USA Baseball Junior National Team Signature Black

STATED PRINT RUN 495 SERIAL #'d SETS
GREEN PRINT RUN 2 SERIAL #'d SETS
NO GREEN PRICING DUE TO SCARCITY
ONE AUTO PER SEALED FACTORY SET
AC Adrian Cardenas 4.00 10.00
BA Brett Anderson 5.00 12.00
CK Clayton Kershaw 15.00 40.00
DB Dellin Betances 6.00 15.00
DC Dwight Childs 4.00 10.00
GG Grant Green 5.00 12.00
GP Greg Peavey 4.00 10.00
JB Jeremy Bleich 4.00 10.00
JL Josh Thrailkill 4.00 10.00
JT Jason Taylor 4.00 10.00
KR Kevin Rhoderick 4.00 10.00
LA Lars Anderson 6.00 15.00
LW Leonardo Ware 4.00 10.00
ML Marcus Lemon 5.00 12.00
MS Max Sapp 5.00 12.00
SR Sean Ratliff 4.00 10.00
SR Scott Schauer 4.00 10.00
ST Shawn Tolleson 4.00 10.00
TL Torre Langley 5.00 12.00
TR Tyson Ross 4.00 10.00

2005-06 USA Baseball Junior National Team Vision of the Future

ONE VISION PER SEALED FACTORY SET
SP's 6X TOUGHER THAN REGULAR CARDS
SP INFO PROVIDED BY USA BASEBALL
SP CL: 24-25/40-42
23 Grant Green 3.00 8.00
24 Greg Peavey SP 6.00 15.00
25 Brett Anderson SP 8.00 20.00
26 Jason Taylor 2.00 5.00
27 Josh Thrailkill 2.00 5.00
28 Max Sapp 3.00 8.00
29 Kevin Rhoderick 2.00 5.00
30 Sean Ratliff 2.00 5.00
31 Jeremy Bleich 2.00 5.00
32 Scott Schauer 2.00 5.00
33 Dellin Betances 3.00 8.00
34 Torre Langley 2.50 6.00
35 Clayton Kershaw 6.00 15.00
36 Leonardo Ware 2.00 5.00
37 Dwight Childs 2.00 5.00
38 Adrian Cardenas 2.00 5.00
39 Shawn Tolleson 2.00 5.00
40 Tyson Ross SP 8.00 20.00
41 Marcus Lemon SP 30.00 60.00
42 Lars Anderson SP 6.00 15.00

2005-06 USA Baseball Junior National Team Across the Nation Dual Signatures Black

STATED PRINT RUN 250 SERIAL #'d SETS
*BLUE: .6X TO 1.5X BLACK
BLUE PRINT RUN 100 SERIAL #'d SETS
GREEN PRINT RUN 2 SERIAL #'d SETS
NO GREEN PRICING DUE TO SCARCITY
RED PRINT RUN 16 SERIAL #'d SETS
NO RED PRICING DUE TO SCARCITY
ONE DUAL AUTO PER SEALED FACT.SET
1 Clayton Kershaw 12.50 30.00
Shawn Tolleson
2 Lars Anderson 12.50 30.00
Grant Green
3 Dwight Childs 4.00 10.00
Scott Schauer
4 Leonard Ware 6.00 15.00
Torre Langley
5 Adrian Cardenas 4.00 10.00
Marcus Lemon
6 Dellin Betances 4.00 10.00
Jason Taylor
7 Sean Ratliff 4.00 10.00
Kevin Rhoderick
8 Jeremy Bleich 4.00 10.00
Josh Thrailkill

2005-06 USA Baseball Junior National Team Future Category Leaders Dual Signatures Black

STATED PRINT RUN 250 SERIAL #'d SETS
*BLUE: .6X TO 1.5X BLACK
BLUE PRINT RUN 100 SERIAL #'d SETS
GREEN PRINT RUN 2 SERIAL #'d SETS
NO GREEN PRICING DUE TO SCARCITY
RED PRINT RUN 16 SERIAL #'d SETS
NO RED PRICING DUE TO SCARCITY
ONE DUAL AUTO PER SEALED FACT.SET
1 Leonardo Ware 4.00 10.00
Adrian Cardenas
2 Max Sapp 10.00 25.00
Lars Anderson
3 Leonardo Ware 4.00 10.00
Jason Taylor
4 Max Sapp 6.00 15.00
Torre Langley
5 Marcus Lemon 6.00 15.00
Sean Ratliff
6 Brett Anderson 6.00 15.00
Dellin Betances
7 Kevin Rhoderick 4.00 10.00
Greg Peavey
8 Shawn Tolleson 4.00 10.00
Tyson Ross
9 Jeremy Bleich 4.00 10.00
Josh Thrailkill
10 Clayton Kershaw 12.50 30.00
Dellin Betances
11 Grant Green 6.00 15.00
Marcus Lemon
12 Max Sapp 6.00 15.00
Shawn Tolleson
13 Brett Anderson 6.00 15.00
Greg Peavey

2005-06 USA Baseball Junior National Team Future Match-Ups Dual Signatures Black

STATED PRINT RUN 250 SERIAL #'d SETS
*BLUE: .6X TO 1.5X BLACK
BLUE PRINT RUN 100 SERIAL #'d SETS
GREEN PRINT RUN 2 SERIAL #'d SETS
NO GREEN PRICING DUE TO SCARCITY
RED PRINT RUN 16 SERIAL #'d SETS
NO RED PRICING DUE TO SCARCITY
ONE DUAL AUTO PER SEALED FACT.SET
1 Brett Anderson 10.00 25.00
Torre Langley
2 Tyson Ross 4.00 10.00
Dwight Childs
3 Clayton Kershaw 12.50 30.00
Adrian Cardenas
4 Scott Schauer 4.00 10.00
Kevin Rhoderick
5 Josh Thrailkill 4.00 10.00
Jason Taylor
6 Greg Peavey 4.00 10.00
Dwight Childs
7 Tyson Ross 10.00 25.00
Lars Anderson
8 Scott Schauer 4.00 10.00
Jeremy Bleich

2005-06 USA Baseball Junior National Team Opening Day Jersey Signature Blue

STATED PRINT RUN 360 SERIAL #'d SETS
GREEN PRINT RUN 2 SERIAL #'d SETS
NO GREEN PRICING DUE TO SCARCITY
*RED: .75X TO 2X BLUE
RED PRINT RUN 100 SERIAL #'d SETS
ONE AU-GU PER SEALED FACTORY SET
AC Adrian Cardenas 10.00 25.00
BA Brett Anderson 8.00 20.00
CK Clayton Kershaw 20.00 50.00
DB Dellin Betances 8.00 20.00
DC Dwight Childs 5.00 12.00
GG Grant Green 8.00 20.00
GP Greg Peavey 5.00 12.00
JB Jeremy Bleich 5.00 12.00
JL Josh Thrailkill 5.00 12.00
JT Jason Taylor 5.00 12.00
KR Kevin Rhoderick 5.00 12.00
LA Lars Anderson 10.00 25.00
LW Leonardo Ware 5.00 12.00
ML Marcus Lemon 8.00 20.00
MS Max Sapp 8.00 20.00
SR Sean Ratliff 5.00 12.00
SR Scott Schauer 5.00 12.00
ST Shawn Tolleson 5.00 12.00
TL Torre Langley 8.00 20.00
TR Tyson Ross 5.00 12.00

2005-06 USA Baseball National Team

COMP.FACT.SET (27) 20.00 30.00
COMPLETE SET (23) 7.50 15.00
STATED PRINT RUN 10,000 SETS
51 Ian Kennedy 1.25 3.00
52 Kyle McCulloch .30 .75
53 Mark Melancon .30 .75
54 Jonah Nickerson .30 .75
55 Chris Perez .30 .75
56 Max Scherzer .75 2.00
57 Sean Doolittle .30 .75
58 Kevin Gunderson .30 .75
59 David Price 2.00 5.00
60 Joe Savery .40 1.00
61 J.P. Arencibia .40 1.00
62 Brian Jeroloman .30 .75
63 Matt Wieters 1.50 4.00
64 Adam Davis .30 .75
65 Blake Davis .30 .75
66 Wes Hodges .40 1.00
67 Matt LaPorta .75 2.00
68 Josh Rodriguez .30 .75
69 Jon Jay .30 .75
70 Hunter Mense .30 .75
71 Shane Robinson .40 1.00
72 Drew Stubbs .60 1.50
73 Team Checklist .20 .50

2005-06 USA Baseball National Team Signature Black

STATED PRINT RUN 475 SERIAL #'d SETS
GREEN PRINT RUN 2 SERIAL #'d SETS
NO GREEN PRICING DUE TO SCARCITY
ONE AUTO PER SEALED FACTORY SET
AD Adam Davis 3.00 8.00

BD Blake Davis 3.00 8.00
BJ Brian Jeroloman 3.00 8.00
CP Chris Perez 3.00 8.00
DP David Price 15.00 40.00
DS Drew Stubbs 5.00 12.00
HM Hunter Mense 3.00 8.00
IK Ian Kennedy 5.00 12.00
JA J.P. Arencibia 5.00 12.00
JJ Jon Jay 3.00 8.00
JN Jonah Nickerson 3.00 8.00
JR Josh Rodriguez 3.00 8.00
JS Joe Savery 4.00 10.00
KG Kevin Gunderson 3.00 8.00
KM Kyle McCulloch 3.00 8.00
ML Matt LaPorta 10.00 25.00
MM Mark Melancon 3.00 8.00
MS Max Scherzer 12.50 30.00
MW Matt Wieters 12.50 30.00
SD Sean Doolittle 5.00 12.00
SR Shane Robinson 4.00 10.00
WH Wes Hodges 4.00 10.00

2005-06 USA Baseball National Team Vision of the Future

ONE VISION PER SEALED FACTORY SET
SP's 6X TOUGHER THAN REGULAR CARDS
SP INFO PROVIDED BY USA BASEBALL
SP CL: 1/6/9/
1 Ian Kennedy SP 10.00 25.00
2 Kyle McCulloch 2.00 5.00
3 Mark Melancon 2.00 5.00
4 Jonah Nickerson 2.00 5.00
5 Chris Perez 2.00 5.00
6 Max Scherzer SP 6.00 15.00
7 Sean Doolittle 2.00 5.00
8 Kevin Gunderson 2.00 5.00
9 David Price SP 10.00 25.00
10 Joe Savery 3.00 8.00
11 J.P. Arencibia 3.00 8.00
12 Brian Jeroloman 2.00 5.00
13 Matt Wieters 6.00 15.00
14 Adam Davis 2.00 5.00
15 Blake Davis 2.00 5.00
16 Wes Hodges 3.00 8.00
17 Matt LaPorta SP 30.00 60.00
18 Josh Rodriguez 2.00 5.00
19 Jon Jay SP 6.00 15.00
20 Hunter Mense 2.00 5.00
21 Shane Robinson 3.00 8.00
22 Drew Stubbs 3.00 8.00

2005-06 USA Baseball National Team Collegiate Connections Dual Signatures Black

STATED PRINT RUN 250 SERIAL #'d SETS
*BLUE: .6X TO 1.5X BLACK
BLUE PRINT RUN 75 SERIAL #'d SETS
GREEN PRINT RUN 2 SERIAL #'d SETS
NO GREEN PRICING DUE TO SCARCITY
RED PRINT RUN 16 SERIAL #'d SETS
NO RED PRICING DUE TO SCARCITY
1 Kyle McCulloch 8.00 20.00
Drew Stubbs
2 Jonah Nickerson 4.00 10.00
Kevin Gunderson
3 Chris Perez 4.00 10.00
Jon Jay
4 Max Scherzer 6.00 15.00
Hunter Mense
5 Joe Savery 6.00 15.00
Josh Rodriguez
6 Brian Jeroloman 4.00 10.00
Adam Davis

2005-06 USA Baseball National Team Future Match-Ups Dual Signatures Black

STATED PRINT RUN 250 SERIAL #'d SETS
*BLUE: .6X TO 1.5X BLACK
BLUE PRINT RUN 75 SERIAL #'d SETS
GREEN PRINT RUN 2 SERIAL #'d SETS
NO GREEN PRICING DUE TO SCARCITY
RED PRINT RUN 16 SERIAL #'d SETS
NO RED PRICING DUE TO SCARCITY
ONE DUAL AUTO PER SEALED FACT.SET
1 David Price 20.00 50.00
Drew Stubbs
2 Mark Melancon 4.00 10.00
Blake Davis
3 Joe Savery 6.00 15.00
Brian Jeroloman
4 Chris Perez 4.00 10.00
Hunter Mense
5 Wes Hodges 6.00 15.00
Jonah Nickerson
6 Wes Hodges 6.00 15.00
Max Scherzer
7 Joe Savery 6.00 15.00
Jon Jay
8 Kyle McCulloch 6.00 15.00
Wes Hodges
9 Sean Doolittle 6.00 15.00
Shane Robinson
10 Jonah Nickerson 4.00 10.00
Brian Jeroloman
11 Max Scherzer 10.00 25.00
Matt LaPorta

2005-06 USA Baseball National Team Leaders Dual Signatures Black

STATED PRINT RUN 250 SERIAL #'d SETS
*BLUE: .6X TO 1.5X BLACK
BLUE PRINT RUN 75 SERIAL #'d SETS
GREEN PRINT RUN 2 SERIAL #'d SETS
NO GREEN PRICING DUE TO SCARCITY
RED PRINT RUN 16 SERIAL #'d SETS
NO RED PRICING DUE TO SCARCITY
ONE DUAL AUTO PER SEALED FACT.SET
1 J.P. Arencibia 4.00 10.00
Sean Doolittle
2 J.P. Arencibia 4.00 10.00
Adam Davis
3 Matt LaPorta 15.00 40.00
Matt Wieters
4 Jon Jay 6.00 15.00
Shane Robinson
5 Josh Rodriguez 6.00 15.00
Sean Doolittle
6 J.P. Arencibia 8.00 20.00
Matt LaPorta
7 Kyle McCulloch 10.00 25.00
Ian Kennedy
8 Mark Melancon 4.00 10.00
Chris Perez
9 David Price 20.00 50.00
Ian Kennedy
10 Kevin Gunderson 10.00 25.00
David Price
11 Kevin Gunderson 4.00 10.00
Mark Melancon
12 Blake Davis 4.00 10.00
Adam Davis
13 Ian Kennedy 8.00 20.00
Drew Stubbs

2005-06 USA Baseball National Team Opening Day Jersey Signature Blue

STATED PRINT RUN 350 SERIAL #'d SETS
GREEN PRINT RUN 2 SERIAL #'d SETS

NO GREEN PRICING DUE TO SCARCITY
ONE AU-GU PER SEALED FACTORY SET
AD Adam Davis 4.00 10.00
BD Blake Davis 4.00 10.00
BJ Brian Jeroloman 4.00 10.00
CP Chris Perez 4.00 10.00
DP David Price 20.00 50.00
DS Drew Stubbs 8.00 20.00
HM Hunter Mense 4.00 10.00
IK Ian Kennedy 6.00 15.00
JA J.P. Arencibia 5.00 12.00
JJ Jon Jay 4.00 10.00
JN Jonah Nickerson 4.00 10.00
JR Josh Rodriguez 4.00 10.00
JS Joe Savery 6.00 15.00
KG Kevin Gunderson 4.00 10.00
KM Kyle McCulloch 4.00 10.00
ML Matt LaPorta 12.50 30.00
MM Mark Melancon 4.00 10.00
MS Max Scherzer 5.00 12.00
MW Matt Wieters 10.00 25.00
SD Sean Doolittle 6.00 15.00
SR Shane Robinson 6.00 15.00
WH Wes Hodges 6.00 15.00

2005-06 USA Baseball National Team Opening Day Jersey Signature Red

*RED: .75X TO 2X BLUE
ONE AU-GU PER SEALED FACTORY SET
STATED PRINT RUN 100 SERIAL #'d SETS
DP David Price 40.00 80.00
ML Matt LaPorta 20.00 50.00
MS Max Scherzer 10.00 25.00

2006-07 USA Baseball

This fifty-card set featured members of the 2006 USA National Team and 2006 USA Junior National Team. These cards were included as part of a factory set which also included four autographed cards of Team USA players. two autographed game-used jersey cards of those same players. two parallel cards, one other autograph card, which included alumni players and one "Bound for Beijing" game-used relic card. The suggested retail price on the factory set price was $49.99 and these sets were packed 24 to a case.

COMPLETE SET (50) 10.00 25.00
COMMON CARD (1-30) .20 .50
1 Jemile Weeks .30 .75
2 Brandon Crawford .20 .50
3 Julio Borbon .60 1.50
4 Roger Kieschnick .30 .75
5 Preston Clark .20 .50
6 Zack Cozart .20 .50
7 David Price .75 2.00
8 Darwin Barney .40 1.00
9 Daniel Moskos .30 .75
10 Ross Detwiler .20 .50
11 Cole St. Clair .20 .50
12 Tim Federowicz .20 .50
13 Nick Hill .20 .50
14 Sean Doolittle .30 .75
15 Pedro Alvarez .60 1.50
16 Tommy Hunter .30 .75
17 Nick Schmidt .30 .75
18 Jake Arrieta .20 .50
19 Todd Frazier .30 .75
20 Andrew Brackman .60 1.50
21 J.P. Arencibia .30 .75
22 Wes Roemer .30 .75
23 Casey Weathers .20 .50
24 Tom Slater CO .20 .50
Tim Corbin MG
Jim Schlossnagle CO
Mark Machtolf CO
25 Jemile Weeks BTI .30 .75
26 Julio Borbon BTI .60 1.50
27 David Price/Pedro Alvarez/Tim Corbin/Casey Weathers BTI .75 2.00
28 J.P. Arencibia/David Price BTI .75 2.00
29 Nick Hill BTI .20 .50
30 National Team CL .20 .50
31 Hunter Morris .20 .50
32 Matt Newman .20 .50
33 Matt Dominguez .20 .50
34 Daniel Elorriaga-Matra .20 .50
35 Jarrod Parker .20 .50
36 Neil Ramirez .20 .50
37 Blake Beavan .30 .75
38 Mike Moustakas .60 1.50
39 Justin Jackson .20 .50
40 Christian Colon .20 .50
41 Michael Main .30 .75
42 Tim Alderson .20 .50
43 Kevin Rhoderick .20 .50
44 Freddie Freeman 1.25 3.00
45 Matt Harvey .50 1.25
46 Victor Sanchez .20 .50
47 Greg Peavey .20 .50
48 Tommy Medica .20 .50
49 Scott Knight CO .20 .50
Jason Hisey MG
Jon Wente CO
Victor Solis CO
50 Junior National Team CL .20 .50

2006-07 USA Baseball Foil

COMPLETE SET (41) 40.00 80.00
STATED ODDS 1:1 BOX SETS
7 David Price 2.00 5.00

2006-07 USA Baseball 1st Round Draft Pick Signatures Black

OVERALL DP AU ODDS 1:3 BOX SETS
CARDS SER.#'d B/WN 11-350 COPIES PER
ANNOUNCED PRINT RUNS LISTED BELOW
PRINT RUNS PROVIDED BY USA BASEBALL
NO PRICING ON QTY 25 OR LESS
2 Jeff Clement/200 * 3.00 8.00
3 Ricky Romero/200 * 3.00 8.00
4 Clayton Kershaw/10 *
5 Drew Stubbs/200 * 5.00 12.00
7 Trevor Crowe/200 * 4.00 10.00
8 John Mayberry Jr./200 * 3.00 8.00
9 Ian Kennedy/200 * 4.00 10.00
10 Max Sapp/200 3.00 8.00
11 Daniel Bard/200 * 3.00 8.00
13 Kyle McCulloch/10 *
16 Cesar Ramos/200 * 3.00 8.00
19 Chris Perez/10 *
20 Jed Lowrie/200 * 4.00 10.00

2006-07 USA Baseball 1st Round Draft Pick Signatures Blue

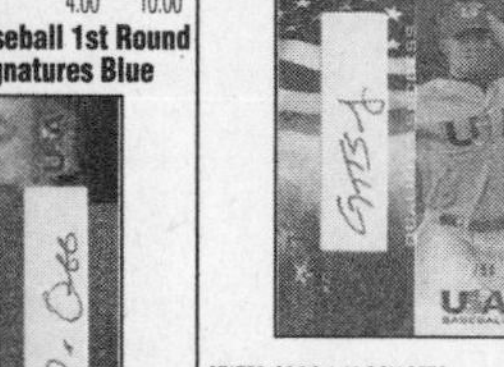

*BLUE: .5 TO 1.2X BLACK
OVERALL DP AU ODDS 1:3 BOX SETS
CARDS SER.#'d B/WN 11-350 COPIES PER
ANNOUNCED PRINT RUNS LISTED BELOW
PRINT RUNS PROVIDED BY USA BASEBALL
NO PRICING ON QTY 25 OR LESS
5 Drew Stubbs/100 * 5.00 12.00
9 Ian Kennedy/100 * 4.00 10.00
12 Matt Campbell/100 4.00 10.00
14 Tyler Greene/100 * 5.00 12.00
15 Justin Orenduff/100 3.00 8.00

2006-07 USA Baseball 1st Round Draft Pick Signatures Red

*RED: .6 TO 1.5X BLACK
OVERALL DP AU ODDS 1:3 BOX SETS
CARDS SER.#'d B/WN 11-350 COPIES PER
ANNOUNCED PRINT RUNS LISTED BELOW
PRINT RUNS PROVIDED BY USA BASEBALL
NO PRICING ON QTY 25 OR LESS
5 Drew Stubbs/50 * 6.00 15.00
9 Ian Kennedy/50 * 4.00 10.00

2006-07 USA Baseball 2004 Youth Junior Signatures

STATED ODDS 1:4 BOX SETS
STATED PRINT RUN 475 SER.#'d SETS
1 Brandon Snyder 3.00 8.00
2 Justin Upton 30.00 60.00
3 Sean O'Sullivan 4.00 10.00
4 Andrew McCutchen 12.50 30.00
5 Jonathon Niese 6.00 15.00
6 Steven Figueroa 3.00 8.00
7 Chris Marrero 6.00 15.00
8 Colton Willems 3.00 8.00
9 Chris Huseby 3.00 8.00
10 Hank Conger 5.00 12.00

2006-07 USA Baseball Bound for Beijing Materials

STATED ODDS 1:1 BOX SETS
PATCH ODDS 1:60 BOX SETS
PATCH PRINT RUNS B/WN 4-20 COPIES PER
NO PATCH PRICING DUE TO SCARCITY
1 Kevin Slowey Jsy 3.00 8.00
2 Nick Adenhart Jsy 6.00 15.00
3 Mike Bacsik Jsy 3.00 8.00
4 Greg Smith Jsy 3.00 8.00
5 Nick Ungs Hat SP 4.00 10.00
6 Lee Gronkiewicz Jsy 3.00 8.00
7 J. Brent Cox Jsy 3.00 8.00
8 Jeff Farnsworth Jsy 3.00 8.00
9 Kurt Suzuki Jsy 3.00 8.00
10 Jarrod Saltalamacchia Hat SP 10.00 25.00
11 Matt Tupman Hat SP 4.00 10.00
12 Brandon Wood Jsy 3.00 8.00
13 Mike Kinkade Hat SP 4.00 10.00
14 Bobby Hill Jsy 3.00 8.00
15 Mark Reynolds Jsy 3.00 8.00
16 Billy Butler Hat SP 6.00 15.00
17 Chad Allen Hat SP 6.00 15.00

2006-07 USA Baseball Bound for Beijing Signatures

STATED ODDS 1:12 BOX SETS
STATED PRINT RUN 50 SER.#'d SETS
1 Kevin Slowey 30.00 60.00
2 Nick Adenhart 12.50 30.00
3 Mike Bacsik 3.00 8.00
4 Greg Smith 8.00 20.00
5 Nick Ungs 3.00 8.00
6 Lee Gronkiewicz 3.00 8.00
7 J. Brent Cox 6.00 15.00
8 Jeff Farnsworth 3.00 8.00
9 Kurt Suzuki 6.00 15.00
10 Jarrod Saltalamacchia 20.00 50.00
11 Matt Tupman 3.00 8.00
12 Brandon Wood 15.00 40.00
13 Mike Kinkade 3.00 8.00
14 Bobby Hill 6.00 15.00
15 Mark Reynolds 40.00 80.00
16 Billy Butler 30.00 60.00
18 Davey Johnson 6.00 15.00

2006-07 USA Baseball Signatures Black

STATED PRINT RUN 595 SER.#'d SETS
ACTION/PORTRAIT PRINT RUN INFO
PROVIDED BY USA BASEBALL
GREEN PRINT RUN 2 SER.#'d SETS
NO GREEN PRICING DUE TO SCARCITY
OVERALL AU ODDS 4:1 BOX SETS
1a Jemile Weeks Action/545 * 3.00 8.00
1b Jemile Weeks Portrait/50 *
2 Brandon Crawford 3.00 8.00
3a Julio Borbon Action/545 * 4.00 10.00
3b Julio Borbon Portrait/50 *
4 Roger Kieschnick 3.00 8.00
5 Preston Clark 3.00 8.00
6 Zack Cozart 3.00 8.00
7a David Price Action/545 * 12.50 30.00
7b David Price Portrait/50 *
8 Darwin Barney 8.00 20.00
9 Daniel Moskos 3.00 8.00
10 Ross Detwiler 4.00 10.00
11 Cole St. Clair 3.00 8.00
12 Tim Federowicz 3.00 8.00
13 Nick Hill 3.00 8.00
14 Sean Doolittle 4.00 10.00
15 Pedro Alvarez 10.00 25.00
16 Tommy Hunter 6.00 15.00
17a Nick Schmidt Action/545 * 6.00 15.00
17b Nick Schmidt Portrait/50 *
18 Jake Arrieta 3.00 8.00
19 Todd Frazier 5.00 12.00
20 J.P. Arencibia 6.00 15.00
21 Wes Roemer 5.00 12.00
22 Casey Weathers 3.00 8.00
23 Hunter Morris 4.00 10.00
24 Matt Newman 3.00 8.00
25a Matt Dominguez Action/545 * 8.00 20.00
25b Matt Dominguez Portrait/50 *
26 Daniel Elorriaga-Matra 3.00 8.00
27 Jarrod Parker 3.00 8.00
28 Neil Ramirez 3.00 8.00
29a Blake Beavan Action/545 * 6.00 15.00
29b Blake Beavan Portrait/50 *
30 Mike Moustakas 10.00 25.00
31a Justin Jackson Action/545 * 4.00 10.00
31b Justin Jackson Portrait/50 *
32 Christian Colon 4.00 10.00
33 Michael Main 4.00 10.00
34 Tim Alderson 5.00 12.00
35 Kevin Rhoderick 3.00 8.00
36 Freddie Freeman 15.00 40.00
37a Matt Harvey Action/545 * 5.00 12.00
37b Matt Harvey Portrait/50 *
38 Victor Sanchez 3.00 8.00
39 Greg Peavey 3.00 8.00
40 Tommy Medica 3.00 8.00

2006-07 USA Baseball Signatures Blue

*BLUE: .5X TO 1.2X BLACK
OVERALL AU ODDS 4:1 BOX SETS
PRINT RUNS B/WN 100-275 COPIES PER
3 Julio Borbon 8.00 20.00
7 David Price 15.00 40.00
10 Ross Detwiler 6.00 15.00
15 Pedro Alvarez 12.50 30.00
29 Blake Beavan 8.00 20.00
30 Mike Moustakas 12.50 30.00

2006-07 USA Baseball Signatures Red

*RED: .6X TO 1.5X BLACK
OVERALL AU ODDS 4:1 BOX SETS
STATED PRINT RUN 100 SER.#'d SETS
7 David Price 20.00 50.00
10 Ross Detwiler 8.00 20.00
15 Pedro Alvarez 30.00 60.00
19 Todd Frazier 10.00 25.00
22 Casey Weathers 6.00 15.00
27 Jarrod Parker 10.00 25.00
30 Mike Moustakas 12.50 30.00
33 Michael Main 8.00 20.00

2006-07 USA Baseball Signatures Jersey Black

PRINT RUN B/WN 90-295 SER.#'d SETS
GREEN PRINT RUN 2 SER.#'d SETS
NO GREEN PRICING DUE TO SCARCITY
OVERALL JSY AU ODDS 2:1 BOX SETS
1 Jemile Weeks 6.00 15.00

2 Brandon Crawford 4.00 10.00
3 Julio Borbon 5.00 12.00
4 Roger Kieschnick 4.00 10.00
5 Preston Clark 4.00 10.00
6 Zack Cozart 4.00 10.00
7 David Price 15.00 40.00
8 Darwin Barney 8.00 20.00
9 Daniel Moskos 8.00 20.00
10 Ross Detwiler 5.00 12.00
11 Cole St. Clair 4.00 10.00
12 Tim Federowicz 4.00 10.00
13 Nick Hill 4.00 10.00
14 Sean Doolittle 5.00 12.00
15 Pedro Alvarez 12.50 30.00
16 Tommy Hunter 6.00 15.00
17 Nick Schmidt 6.00 15.00
18 Jake Arrieta 4.00 10.00
19 Todd Frazier 5.00 12.00
20 Andrew Brackman 30.00 60.00
21 J.P. Arencibia 5.00 12.00
22 Wes Roemer 4.00 10.00
23 Casey Weathers 4.00 10.00
24 Hunter Morris 5.00 12.00
25 Matt Newman 4.00 10.00
26 Matt Dominguez 5.00 12.00
27 Daniel Elorriaga-Matra 4.00 10.00
28 Jarrod Parker 6.00 15.00
29 Neil Ramirez 4.00 10.00
30 Blake Beavan 8.00 20.00
31 Mike Moustakas 8.00 20.00
32 Justin Jackson 4.00 10.00
33 Christian Colon 6.00 15.00
34 Michael Main 6.00 15.00
35 Tim Alderson 3.00 8.00
36 Kevin Rhoderick 4.00 10.00
37 Freddie Freeman 12.50 30.00
38 Matt Harvey 6.00 15.00
39 Victor Sanchez 4.00 10.00
40 Greg Peavey 4.00 10.00
41 Tommy Medica 4.00 10.00

2006-07 USA Baseball Signatures Jersey Red

*RED: 1.25X TO 3X BLACK
OVERALL JSY AU ODDS 2:1 BOX SETS
PRINT RUNS B/WN 30-50 COPIES PER
15 Pedro Alvarez 40.00 80.00
19 Todd Frazier 20.00 50.00
20 Andrew Brackman
28 Jarrod Parker 20.00 50.00
37 Freddie Freeman 50.00 100.00

2006-07 USA Baseball Today and Tomorrow Signatures Black

STATED PRINT RUN 295 SER.#'d SETS
*BLUE: .5X TO 1.2X BASIC
BLUE PRINT RUN 150 SER.#'d SETS
GREEN PRINT RUN 2 SER.#'d SETS
NO GREEN PRICING DUE TO SCARCITY
RED PRINT RUN 25 SER.#'d SETS
NO RED PRICING DUE TO SCARCITY
OVERALL TT AUTO ODDS 1:2 BOX SETS
1 David Price 10.00 25.00
Matt Harvey
2 Daniel Moskos 5.00 12.00
Blake Beavan
3 Ross Detwiler 5.00 12.00
Neil Ramirez
4 Preston Clark 5.00 12.00
Tommy Medica
5 Sean Doolittle 8.00 20.00
Freddie Freeman
6 Jemile Weeks 5.00 12.00
Christian Colon
7 Pedro Alvarez 6.00 15.00
Matt Dominguez
8 Todd Frazier 5.00 12.00
Justin Jackson
9 Darwin Barney 10.00 25.00
Mike Moustakas
10 Julio Borbon 5.00 12.00
Michael Main
11 Roger Kieschnick 4.00 10.00
Victor Sanchez

2008 USA Baseball

COMPLETE SET (60) 8.00 20.00
COMMON CARD .25 .60
ONE COMPLETE SET PER BOX
1 Pedro Alvarez 1.00 2.50
2 Ryan Berry .25 .60
3 Jordan Danks .60 1.50
4 Danny Espinosa .40 1.00
5 Ryan Flaherty .40 1.00
6 Logan Forsythe .25 .60
7 Seth Frankoff .25 .60
8 Scott Gorgen .25 .60
9 Jeremy Hamilton .25 .60
10 Brett Hunter .25 .60
11 Joe Kelly .25 .60
12 Roger Kieschnick .40 1.00
13 Lance Lynn .40 1.00
14 Brian Matusz .60 1.50
15 Tommy Medica .25 .60
16 Jordy Mercer .25 .60
17 Mike Minor .60 1.50
18 Petey Paramore .40 1.00
19 Josh Romanski .40 1.00
20 Tyson Ross .40 1.00
21 Cody Satterwhite .40 1.00
22 Justin Smoak .75 2.00
23 Eric Surkamp .25 .60
24 Jacob Thompson .40 1.00
25 Brett Wallace
26 Mike Weathers CO/Rob Cooper CO/Mark Scalf CO/Bill Kinneberg CO .25 .60
27 National Team CL .25 .60
28 Game 1 .25 .60
USA wins Opening game, 7-2
29 Game 2 .25 .60
Japan 3 - USA 2, Series Even
30 Game 3 .25 .60
Japan Takes Game 3, 2 - 1
31 Game 4 .25 .60
Japan wins 5 - 2, captures the series
32 Game 5 .25 .60
USA takes the final game of the series
33 Kyle Buchanan .25 .60
34 Mychal Givens .25 .60
35 Robbie Grossman .40 1.00
36 Tyler Hibbs .25 .60
37 L.J. Hoes .60 1.50
38 Eric Hosmer 3.00 8.00
39 T.J. House .25 .60
40 Garrison Lassiter .25 .60
41 Jeff Malm .40 1.00
42 Nick Maronde .25 .60
43 Harold Martinez .25 .60
44 Tim Melville .25 .60
45 Matthew Purke .25 .60
46 J.P. Ramirez .25 .60
47 Kyle Skipworth .40 1.00
48 Tyler Stovall .25 .60
49 Jordan Swagerty .25 .60
50 Riccio Torrez .25 .60
51 Ryan Weber .25 .60
52 Tyler Wilson .25 .60
53 Jack Hodges CO/Mike Power CO/Victor Solis CO/Mark Elkins CO .25 .60
54 Junior Team CL .25 .60
55 Andrew Aplin .25 .60
Justin Charles
Matt Davidson
56 Robert Refsnyder .25 .60
Max Stassi
Zach Vincej
57 Colton Cain .40 1.00
Randal Grichuk
Zach Lee
58 A.J. Cole .25 .60
Nolan Fontana
Nick Franklin
59 Nale Gonzalez .25 .60
Austin Maddox
Steven Rodriguez
60 Luke Bailey .25 .60
Richie Shaffer
Jacob Tillotson

2008 USA Baseball Bound for Beijing II Signature Jersey

OVERALL AUTO ODDS 7 PER BOX
STATED PRINT RUN 50 SER.#'d SETS
NO PRICING ON MANY
DUE TO LACK OF MARKET INFO
WC1 Bryan Anderson 6.00 15.00
WC2 Brian Bixler
WC3 Jerry Blevins
WC4 Chris Booker 4.00 10.00
WC5 Tyler Colvin 12.50 30.00
WC6 Brian Duensing 6.00 15.00
WC7 Lee Gronkiewicz 4.00 10.00
WC8 Michael Hollimon 4.00 10.00
WC9 Jason Jaramillo
WC10 Jeff Karstens
WC11 Andy LaRoche
WC12 Evan Longoria
WC13 Neal Musser
WC14 Jayson Nix
WC15 Josh Outman 6.00 15.00
WC16 Steve Pearce
WC17 Chris Perez 12.50 30.00
WC18 Colby Rasmus
WC19 Justin Ruggiano
WC20 Steven Shell 4.00 10.00
WC21 Jeff Stevens
WC22 Dallas Trahern 4.00 10.00
WC23 Matt Wright
WC24 Delwyn Young
WC25 Davey Johnson

2008 USA Baseball Camo Cloth Jerseys

OVERALL GU ODDS 2 PER BOX
CC1 Pedro Alvarez 5.00 12.00
CC2 Ryan Berry 3.00 8.00
CC3 Jordan Danks 3.00 8.00
CC4 Danny Espinosa 3.00 8.00
CC5 Ryan Flaherty 3.00 8.00
CC6 Logan Forsythe 3.00 8.00
CC7 Jeremy Hamilton 3.00 8.00
CC8 Brett Hunter 3.00 8.00
CC9 Joe Kelly 3.00 8.00
CC10 Roger Kieschnick 3.00 8.00
CC11 Lance Lynn 3.00 8.00
CC12 Brian Matusz 4.00 10.00
CC13 Tommy Medica 3.00 8.00
CC14 Jordy Mercer 3.00 8.00
CC15 Mike Minor 3.00 8.00
CC16 Petey Paramore 3.00 8.00
CC17 Josh Romanski 3.00 8.00
CC18 Tyson Ross 3.00 8.00
CC19 Cody Satterwhite 3.00 8.00
CC20 Justin Smoak 5.00 12.00
CC21 Jacob Thompson 3.00 8.00
CC22 Brett Wallace 3.00 8.00

2008 USA Baseball Japanese Collegiate All-Stars Jerseys

OVERALL GU ODDS 2 PER BOX
JN1 Sho Aranami 3.00 8.00
JN2 Takeshi Hosoyamada 3.00 8.00
JN3 Takahiro Iwamoto 3.00 8.00
JN4 Tomoyuki Kaida 3.00 8.00
JN5 Mikinori Kato 4.00 10.00
JN6 Testsuya Kokubo 3.00 8.00
JN7 Keijiro Matsumoto 3.00 8.00
JN8 Shirou Mori 3.00 8.00
JN9 Shinya Muramatsu 3.00 8.00
JN10 Ryoji Nakata 3.00 8.00
JN11 Hiroki Nakazawa 3.00 8.00
JN12 Tomohisa Nemoto 3.00 8.00
JN13 Shota Oba 4.00 10.00
JN14 Takashi Ogino 3.00 8.00
JN15 Shota Ohno 3.00 8.00
JN16 Yuki Saitoh 40.00 80.00
JN17 Ryo Sakakibara 3.00 8.00
JN18 Yukinaga Tanaka 3.00 8.00
JN19 Shingo Tatsumi 3.00 8.00
JN20 Hiroki Uemoto 3.00 8.00
JN21 Shota Waizumi 3.00 8.00
JN22 Noriharu Yamazaki 3.00 8.00

2008 USA Baseball Japanese Collegiate All-Stars Signatures

OVERALL AUTO ODDS 7 PER BOX
STATED PRINT RUN 50 SER.#'d SETS
JN1 Sho Aranami 20.00 50.00
JN2 Takeshi Hosoyamada 30.00 60.00
JN3 Takahiro Iwamoto 30.00 60.00
JN4 Tomoyuki Kaida 30.00 60.00
JN5 Mikinori Kato 40.00 80.00
JN6 Testsuya Kokubo 30.00 60.00
JN7 Keijiro Matsumoto 60.00 120.00
JN8 Shirou Mori 20.00 50.00
JN9 Shinya Muramatsu 30.00 60.00
JN10 Ryoji Nakata 20.00 50.00
JN11 Hiroki Nakazawa 20.00 50.00
JN12 Tomohisa Nemoto 20.00 50.00
JN13 Shota Oba 50.00 100.00
JN14 Takashi Ogino 20.00 50.00

JN15 Shota Ohno 20.00 50.00
JN16 Yuki Saitoh 400.00 700.00
JN17 Ryo Sakakibara 20.00 50.00
JN18 Yukinaga Tanaka 20.00 50.00
JN19 Shingo Tatsumi 50.00 100.00
JN20 Hiroki Uemoto 40.00 80.00
JN21 Shota Waizumi 20.00 50.00
JN22 Norihary Yamazaki 20.00 50.00

2008 USA Baseball Junior National Team On-Card Signatures

OVERALL AUTO ODDS 7 PER BOX
PLATE PRINT RUN 1 SET PER COLOR
BLACK-CYAN-MAGENTA ISSUED
PLATES FOR FRONT AND BACK ISSUED
PLATES ARE AUTOGRAPHED
NO PLATE PRICING DUE TO SCARCITY
82 Kyle Buchanan 3.00 8.00
83 Mychal Givens 3.00 8.00
84 Robbie Grossman 3.00 8.00
85 Tyler Hibbs 3.00 8.00
86 L.J. Hoes 3.00 8.00
87 Eric Hosmer 20.00 50.00
88 T.J. House 3.00 8.00
89 Garrison Lassiter 3.00 8.00
90 Jeff Malm 3.00 8.00
91 Nick Maronde 3.00 8.00
92 Harold Martinez 3.00 8.00
93 Tim Melville 3.00 8.00
94 Matthew Purke 3.00 8.00
95 J.P. Ramirez 3.00 8.00
96 Kyle Skipworth 3.00 8.00
97 Tyler Stovall 3.00 8.00
98 Jordan Swagerty 3.00 8.00
99 Riccio Torrez 3.00 8.00
100 Ryan Weber 3.00 8.00
101 Tyler Wilson 3.00 8.00

2008 USA Baseball Junior National Team Signatures Black

OVERALL AUTO ODDS 7 PER BOX
STATED PRINT RUN 249 SER.#'d SETS
*BLUE AUTO: .4X TO 1X BLACK AUTO
BLUE PRINT RUN 150 SER.#'d SETS
GREEN PRINT RUN 2 SER.#'d SETS
NO GREEN PRICING DUE TO SCARCITY
*RED AUTO: .75X TO 2X BLACK AUTO
RED PRINT RUN 50 SER.#'d SETS
UE1 Kyle Buchanan 3.00 8.00
UE2 Mychal Givens 3.00 8.00
UE3 Robbie Grossman 3.00 8.00
UE4 Tyler Hibbs 3.00 8.00
UE5 L.J. Hoes 3.00 8.00
UE6 Eric Hosmer 30.00 60.00
UE7 T.J. House 3.00 8.00
UE8 Garrison Lassiter 3.00 8.00
UE9 Jeff Malm 3.00 8.00
UE10 Nick Maronde 3.00 8.00
UE11 Harold Martinez 3.00 8.00
UE12 Tim Melville 3.00 8.00
UE13 Matthew Purke 3.00 8.00
UE14 J.P. Ramirez 3.00 8.00
UE15 Kyle Skipworth 3.00 8.00
UE16 Tyler Stovall 3.00 8.00
UE17 Jordan Swagerty 3.00 8.00
UE18 Riccio Torrez 3.00 8.00
UE19 Ryan Weber 3.00 8.00
UE20 Tyler Wilson 3.00 8.00

2008 USA Baseball Junior National Team Signature Jersey Black

OVERALL AUTO ODDS 7 PER BOX
STATED PRINT RUN 195 SER.#'d SETS
*BLUE JSY AU: .5X TO 1.2X BLACK JSY AU
BLUE PRINT RUN 75 SER.#'d SETS
GREEN PRINT RUN 2 SER.#'d SETS
NO GREEN PRICING DUE TO SCARCITY
RED PRINT RUN 25 SER.#'d SETS
NO RED PRICING DUE TO SCARCITY
UI1 Kyle Buchanan 4.00 10.00
UI2 Mychal Givens 4.00 10.00
UI3 Robbie Grossman 4.00 10.00
UI4 Tyler Hibbs 4.00 10.00
UI5 L.J. Hoes 4.00 10.00
UI6 Eric Hosmer 30.00 60.00
UI7 T.J. House 4.00 10.00
UI8 Garrison Lassiter 4.00 10.00
UI9 Jeff Malm 4.00 10.00
UI10 Nick Maronde 4.00 10.00
UI11 Harold Martinez 4.00 10.00
UI12 Tim Melville 4.00 10.00
UI13 Matthew Purke 4.00 10.00
UI14 J.P. Ramirez 4.00 10.00
UI15 Kyle Skipworth 4.00 10.00
UI16 Tyler Stovall 4.00 10.00
UI17 Jordan Swagerty 4.00 10.00
UI18 Riccio Torrez 4.00 10.00
UI19 Ryan Weber 4.00 10.00
UI20 Tyler Wilson 4.00 10.00

2008 USA Baseball National Team On-Card Signatures

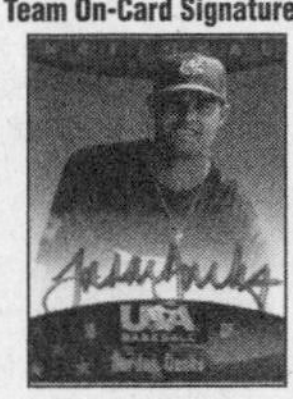

OVERALL AUTO ODDS 7 PER BOX
PLATE PRINT RUN 1 SET PER COLOR
BLACK-CYAN-MAGENTA ISSUED
PLATES FOR FRONT AND BACK ISSUED
PLATES ARE AUTOGRAPHED
NO PLATE PRICING DUE TO SCARCITY
61 Pedro Alvarez 15.00 40.00
62 Ryan Berry 3.00 8.00
63 Jordan Danks 3.00 8.00
64 Danny Espinosa 6.00 15.00
65 Ryan Flaherty 3.00 8.00
66 Logan Forsythe 3.00 8.00
67 Jeremy Hamilton 3.00 8.00
68 Brett Hunter 3.00 8.00
69 Joe Kelly 3.00 8.00
70 Roger Kieschnick 3.00 8.00
71 Brian Matusz 10.00 25.00
72 Tommy Medica 3.00 8.00
73 Jordy Mercer 3.00 8.00
74 Mike Minor 12.50 30.00
75 Petey Paramore 3.00 8.00
76 Josh Romanski 3.00 8.00
77 Tyson Ross 3.00 8.00
78 Cody Satterwhite 3.00 8.00
79 Justin Smoak 15.00 40.00
80 Jacob Thompson 3.00 8.00
81 Brett Wallace 12.50 30.00
82 Mike Minor
Pedro Alvarez
Ryan Flaherty
83 Brian Matusz 10.00 25.00
Josh Romanski
84 Cody Satterwhite 6.00 15.00
Lance Lynn
85 Petey Paramore 6.00 15.00
Brett Wallace
86 Jordan Danks 6.00 15.00
Roger Kieschnick
87 Roger Kieschnick/Pedro Alvarez 12.50 30.00

2008 USA Baseball National Team Question and Answer Signatures

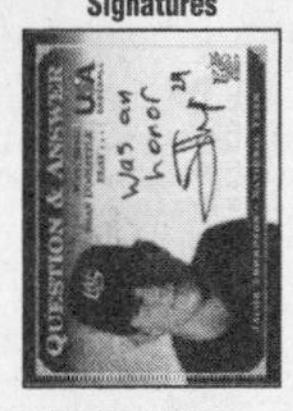

OVERALL AUTO ODDS 7 PER BOX
ALL VARIATIONS EQUAL VALUE
BH1 Brett Hunter 5.00 12.00
BH2 Brett Hunter 5.00 12.00
BH3 Brett Hunter 5.00 12.00
BH4 Brett Hunter 5.00 12.00
BH5 Brett Hunter 5.00 12.00
BM1 Brian Matusz 10.00 25.00
BM2 Brian Matusz 10.00 25.00
BM3 Brian Matusz 10.00 25.00
BM4 Brian Matusz 10.00 25.00
BM5 Brian Matusz 10.00 25.00
BW1 Brett Wallace 10.00 25.00
BW2 Brett Wallace 10.00 25.00
BW3 Brett Wallace 10.00 25.00
BW4 Brett Wallace 10.00 25.00
BW5 Brett Wallace 10.00 25.00
CS1 Cody Satterwhite 10.00 25.00
CS2 Cody Satterwhite 10.00 25.00
CS3 Cody Satterwhite 10.00 25.00
CS4 Cody Satterwhite 10.00 25.00
CS5 Cody Satterwhite 10.00 25.00
DE1 Danny Espinosa 10.00 25.00
DE2 Danny Espinosa 10.00 25.00
DE3 Danny Espinosa 10.00 25.00
DE4 Danny Espinosa 10.00 25.00
DE5 Danny Espinosa 10.00 25.00
JD1 Jordan Danks 6.00 15.00
JD2 Jordan Danks 6.00 15.00
JD3 Jordan Danks 6.00 15.00
JD4 Jordan Danks 6.00 15.00
JD5 Jordan Danks 6.00 15.00
JH1 Jeremy Hamilton 5.00 12.00
JH2 Jeremy Hamilton 5.00 12.00
JH3 Jeremy Hamilton 5.00 12.00
JH4 Jeremy Hamilton 5.00 12.00
JH5 Jeremy Hamilton 5.00 12.00
JK1 Joe Kelly 10.00 25.00
JK2 Joe Kelly 10.00 25.00
JK3 Joe Kelly 10.00 25.00
JK4 Joe Kelly 10.00 25.00
JK5 Joe Kelly 10.00 25.00
JM1 Jordy Mercer 5.00 12.00
JM2 Jordy Mercer 5.00 12.00
JM3 Jordy Mercer 5.00 12.00
JM4 Jordy Mercer 5.00 12.00
JM5 Jordy Mercer 5.00 12.00
JR1 Josh Romanski 5.00 12.00
JR2 Josh Romanski 5.00 12.00
JR3 Josh Romanski 5.00 12.00
JR4 Josh Romanski 5.00 12.00
JR5 Josh Romanski 5.00 12.00
JS1 Justin Smoak 30.00 60.00
JS2 Justin Smoak 30.00 60.00
JS3 Justin Smoak 30.00 60.00
JS4 Justin Smoak 30.00 60.00
JS5 Justin Smoak 30.00 60.00
JT1 Jacob Thompson 5.00 12.00
JT2 Jacob Thompson 5.00 12.00
JT3 Jacob Thompson 5.00 12.00
JT4 Jacob Thompson 5.00 12.00
JT5 Jacob Thompson 5.00 12.00
LF1 Logan Forsythe 5.00 12.00
LF2 Logan Forsythe 5.00 12.00
LF3 Logan Forsythe 5.00 12.00
LF4 Logan Forsythe 5.00 12.00
LF5 Logan Forsythe 5.00 12.00
MM1 Mike Minor 5.00 12.00
MM2 Mike Minor 5.00 12.00
MM3 Mike Minor 5.00 12.00
MM4 Mike Minor 5.00 12.00
MM5 Mike Minor 5.00 12.00
PA1 Pedro Alvarez 15.00 40.00
PA2 Pedro Alvarez 15.00 40.00
PA3 Pedro Alvarez 15.00 40.00
PA4 Pedro Alvarez 15.00 40.00
PA5 Pedro Alvarez 15.00 40.00
PP1 Petey Paramore 5.00 12.00
PP2 Petey Paramore 5.00 12.00
PP3 Petey Paramore 5.00 12.00
PP4 Petey Paramore 5.00 12.00
PP5 Petey Paramore 5.00 12.00
RB1 Ryan Berry 5.00 12.00
RB2 Ryan Berry 5.00 12.00
RB3 Ryan Berry 5.00 12.00
RB4 Ryan Berry 5.00 12.00
RB5 Ryan Berry 5.00 12.00
RF1 Ryan Flaherty 6.00 15.00
RF2 Ryan Flaherty 6.00 15.00
RF3 Ryan Flaherty 6.00 15.00
RF4 Ryan Flaherty 6.00 15.00
RF5 Ryan Flaherty 6.00 15.00
RK1 Roger Kieschnick 6.00 15.00
RK2 Roger Kieschnick 6.00 15.00
RK3 Roger Kieschnick 6.00 15.00
RK4 Roger Kieschnick 6.00 15.00
RK5 Roger Kieschnick 6.00 15.00
TM1 Tommy Medica 5.00 12.00
TM2 Tommy Medica 5.00 12.00
TM3 Tommy Medica 5.00 12.00
TM4 Tommy Medica 5.00 12.00
TM5 Tommy Medica 5.00 12.00
TR1 Tyson Ross 5.00 12.00
TR2 Tyson Ross 5.00 12.00
TR3 Tyson Ross 5.00 12.00
TR4 Tyson Ross 5.00 12.00
TR5 Tyson Ross 5.00 12.00

2008 USA Baseball National Team Signatures Black

OVERALL AUTO ODDS 7 PER BOX
STATED PRINT RUN 249 SER.#'d SETS
*BLUE AUTO: .4X TO 1X BLACK AUTO
BLUE PRINT RUN 150 SER.#'d SETS
GREEN PRINT RUN 2 SER.#'d SETS
NO GREEN PRICING DUE TO SCARCITY
*RED AUTO: .75X TO 2X BLACK AUTO
RED PRINT RUN 50 SER.#'d SETS
1 Pedro Alvarez 12.50 30.00
2 Ryan Berry 3.00 8.00
3 Jordan Danks 3.00 8.00
4 Danny Espinosa 6.00 15.00
5 Ryan Flaherty 3.00 8.00
6 Logan Forsythe 3.00 8.00
7 Seth Frankoff 3.00 8.00
8 Scott Gorgen 3.00 8.00
9 Jeremy Hamilton 3.00 8.00
10 Brett Hunter 3.00 8.00
11 Joe Kelly 3.00 8.00
12 Roger Kieschnick 3.00 8.00
13 Lance Lynn 3.00 8.00
14 Brian Matusz 20.00 50.00
15 Tommy Medica 3.00 8.00
16 Jordy Mercer 3.00 8.00
17 Mike Minor 8.00 20.00
18 Petey Paramore 3.00 8.00
19 Josh Romanski 3.00 8.00
20 Tyson Ross 3.00 8.00
21 Cody Satterwhite 3.00 8.00
22 Justin Smoak 15.00 40.00
23 Jacob Thompson 3.00 8.00
24 Brett Wallace 8.00 20.00
25 Eric Surkamp 3.00 8.00

2008 USA Baseball National Team Signature Jersey Black

OVERALL AUTO ODDS 7 PER BOX
STATED PRINT RUN 195 SER.#'d SETS
*BLUE JSY AU: .5X TO 1.2X BLACK JSY AU
BLUE PRINT RUN 75 SER.#'d SETS
GREEN PRINT RUN 2 SER.#'d SETS
NO GREEN PRICING DUE TO SCARCITY
RED PRINT RUN 25 SER.#'d SETS
NO RED PRICING DUE TO SCARCITY
1 Pedro Alvarez 15.00 40.00
2 Ryan Berry 4.00 10.00
3 Jordan Danks 4.00 10.00
4 Danny Espinosa 6.00 15.00
5 Ryan Flaherty 4.00 10.00
6 Logan Forsythe 4.00 10.00
7 Seth Frankoff 4.00 10.00
8 Scott Gorgen 4.00 10.00
9 Jeremy Hamilton 4.00 10.00
10 Brett Hunter 4.00 10.00
11 Joe Kelly 4.00 10.00
12 Roger Kieschnick 4.00 10.00
13 Lance Lynn 4.00 10.00
14 Brian Matusz 20.00 50.00
15 Tommy Medica 4.00 10.00
16 Jordy Mercer 4.00 10.00
17 Mike Minor 10.00 25.00
18 Petey Paramore 4.00 10.00
19 Josh Romanski 4.00 10.00
20 Tyson Ross 4.00 10.00
21 Cody Satterwhite 4.00 10.00
22 Justin Smoak 15.00 40.00
23 Jacob Thompson 4.00 10.00
24 Brett Wallace 10.00 25.00
25 Eric Surkamp 4.00 10.00

2008 USA Baseball Today and Tomorrow Signatures Black

COMMON CARD 3.00 8.00
OVERALL AUTO ODDS 7 PER BOX
STATED PRINT RUN 295 SER.#'d SETS
*BLUE AUTO: .5X TO 1.2X BLACK AUTO
BLUE PRINT RUN 150 SER.#'d SETS
GREEN PRINT RUN 2 SER.#'d SETS
NO GREEN PRICING DUE TO SCARCITY
RED PRINT RUN 25 SER.#'d SETS
NO RED PRICING DUE TO SCARCITY
TT1 Brian Matusz 4.00 10.00
Tim Melville
TT2 Jacob Thompson 3.00 8.00
Nick Maronde
TT3 Brett Hunter 3.00 8.00
T.J. House
TT4 Petey Paramore 3.00 8.00
Jordan Swagerty
TT5 Justin Smoak 20.00 50.00
Eric Hosmer
TT6 Ryan Flaherty 4.00 10.00
Riccio Torrez
TT7 Pedro Alvarez 10.00 25.00
Harold Martinez
TT8 Danny Espinosa 5.00 12.00
Mychal Givens
TT9 Jordan Danks 3.00 8.00
L.J. Hoes
TT10 Roger Kieschnick 4.00 10.00
Robbie Grossman
TT11 Logan Forsythe 3.00 8.00
J.P. Ramirez
TT12 Brett Wallace 8.00 20.00
Kyle Skipworth

2008 USA Baseball Youth National Team Signature Jersey Black

OVERALL AUTO ODDS 7 PER BOX
STATED PRINT RUN 295 SER.#'d SETS
YI1 Andrew Aplin 8.00 20.00

YI2 Luke Bailey 4.00 10.00
YI3 Colton Cain 4.00 10.00
YI4 Justin Charles 4.00 10.00
YI5 A.J. Cole 4.00 10.00
YI6 Matt Davidson 4.00 10.00
YI7 Nolan Fontana 4.00 10.00
YI8 Nick Franklin 4.00 10.00
YI9 Nate Gonzalez 5.00 12.00
YI10 Randal Grichuk 4.00 10.00
YI11 Zach Lee 6.00 15.00
YI12 Austin Maddox 6.00 15.00
YI13 Robert Refsnyder 4.00 10.00
YI14 Steven Rodriguez 4.00 10.00
YI15 Richie Shaffer 5.00 12.00
YI16 Max Stassi 4.00 10.00
YI17 Jacob Tillotson 4.00 10.00
YI18 Zach Vincej 4.00 10.00

2008 USA Baseball Youth National Team Signature Jersey Green

OVERALL AUTO ODDS 7 PER BOX
STATED PRINT RUN 2 SER.#'d SETS
NO PRICING DUE TO SCARCITY

2008-09 USA Baseball

This set was released on January 28, 2009. The base set consists of 47 cards.

COMPLETE SET (47) 20.00 50.00
ONE COMPLETE SET PER BOX
1 Jared Clark .40 1.00
2 Tommy Mendonca .40 1.00
3 Christian Colon .60 1.50
4 Kentrail Davis .60 1.50
5 Matt den Dekker .60 1.50
6 Derek Dietrich 1.25 3.00
7 Josh Fellhauer .60 1.50
8 Micah Gibbs .60 1.50
9 Kyle Gibson .60 1.50
10 A.J. Griffin .60 1.50
11 Chris Hernandez .60 1.50
12 Ryan Jackson .60 1.50
13 Mike Leake 1.00 2.50
14 Ryan Lipkin .40 1.00
15 Tyler Lyons .60 1.50
16 Mike Minor 1.00 2.50
17 Hunter Morris .40 1.00
18 Andrew Oliver .60 1.50
19 Scott Woodward .40 1.00
20 Blake Smith .60 1.50
21 Stephen Strasburg 10.00 25.00
22 Kendal Volz .60 1.50
23 Andrew Aplin .40 1.00
24 Austin Maddox .60 1.50
25 Colton Cain .40 1.00
26 Cameron Garfield .40 1.00
27 Cecil Tanner .40 1.00
28 David Nick .40 1.00
29 Donavan Tate 1.00 2.50
30 Nick Franklin 1.00 2.50
31 Harold Martinez .40 1.00
32 Jake Barrett .40 1.00
33 Jeff Malm .40 1.00
34 Jonathan Meyer .40 1.00
35 Matthew Purke .40 1.00
36 Max Stassi 1.00 2.50
37 Nolan Fontana .40 1.00
38 Ryan Weber .40 1.00
39 Jacob Turner 1.25 3.00
40 Wes Hatton .40 1.00
41 Nicky Delmonico
Philip Pfeifer
Peter Tago
42 Cody Buckel .40 1.00
Daniel Camarena
Dan Child
43 Michael Kelly .40 1.00
Bryan Radziewski
Kyle Van Alstine
44 Jake Rodriguez .40 1.00
Marcus Littlewood
Tony Wolters
45 Connor Mason 1.50 4.00
Michael Lorenzen
Matt Lipka
46 Ladson Montgomery .40 1.00
Will Allen
Christian Lopes
47 Bryce Harper 60.00 120.00

2008-09 USA Baseball 16U National Team Jersey Patch Autographs

OVERALL AUTO ODDS 7 PER BOX
STATED PRINT RUN 50 SER.#'d SETS
BH Bryce Harper 1000.00 1500.00
BR Bryan Radziewski 10.00 25.00
CA Daniel Camarena 15.00 40.00
CB Cody Buckel 12.50 30.00
CL Christian Lopes 75.00 150.00
CM Connor Mason
DC Dan Child 8.00 20.00
JR Jake Rodriguez 12.50 30.00
KV Kyle Van Alstine
LI Marcus Littlewood 30.00 60.00
LM Ladson Montgomery
LO Michael Lorenzen 60.00 120.00
MK Michael Kelly 8.00 20.00
ML Matt Lipka 30.00 60.00
ND Nicky Delmonico 10.00 25.00
PP Philip Pfeifer 20.00 50.00
PT Peter Tago 10.00 25.00
TW Tony Wolters 10.00 25.00
WA Will Allen 12.50 30.00

2008-09 USA Baseball 18U National Team Jerseys

OVERALL MEM ODDS 6 PER SET
STATED PRINT RUN 179 SER.#'d SETS
18UAA Andrew Aplin 2.50 6.00
18UAM Austin Maddox 2.50 6.00
18UCC Colton Cain 2.50 6.00
18UCG Cameron Garfield 2.50 6.00
18UCT Cecil Tanner 2.50 6.00
18UDN David Nick 2.50 6.00
18UDT Donavan Tate 6.00 15.00
18UFO Nolan Fontana 2.50 6.00
18UHM Harold Martinez 3.00 8.00
18UJB Jake Barrett 3.00 8.00
18UJM Jeff Malm 2.50 6.00
18UJT Jacob Turner 2.50 6.00
18UME Jonathan Meyer 2.50 6.00
18UMP Matthew Purke 3.00 8.00
18UMS Max Stassi 6.00 15.00
18UNF Nick Franklin 4.00 10.00
18URW Ryan Weber 3.00 8.00
18UWH Wes Hatton 3.00 8.00

2008-09 USA Baseball 18U National Team Jersey Autographs Blue

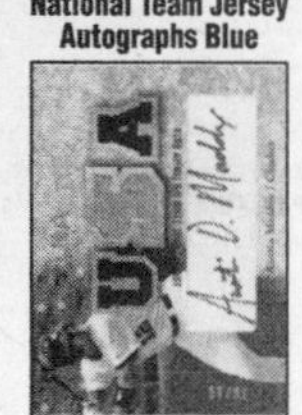

OVERALL AUTO ODDS 7 PER BOX
STATED PRINT RUN 99 SER.#'d SETS
18UAA Andrew Aplin 6.00 15.00
18UAM Austin Maddox 10.00 25.00
18UCC Colton Cain 6.00 15.00
18UCG Cameron Garfield 5.00 12.00
18UCT Cecil Tanner 5.00 12.00
18UDN David Nick 5.00 12.00
18UDT Donavan Tate 20.00 50.00
18UFO Nolan Fontana 5.00 12.00
18UHM Harold Martinez 6.00 15.00
18UJB Jake Barrett 10.00 25.00
18UJM Jeff Malm 5.00 12.00
18UJT Jacob Turner 20.00 50.00
18UME Jonathan Meyer 5.00 12.00
18UMP Matthew Purke 15.00 40.00
18UMS Max Stassi 15.00 40.00
18UNF Nick Franklin 6.00 15.00
18URW Ryan Weber 6.00 15.00
18UWH Wes Hatton 8.00 20.00

2008-09 USA Baseball 18U National Team Jersey Autographs Green

OVERALL AUTO ODDS SIX PER BOX
STATED PRINT RUN 2 SER.#'d SETS
NO PRICING DUE TO SCARCITY

2008-09 USA Baseball 18U National Team Jersey Autographs Red

OVERALL AUTO ODDS SIX PER BOX
STATED PRINT RUN 25 SER.#'d SETS
NO PRICING DUE TO SCARCITY

2008-09 USA Baseball 18U National Team Patch

OVERALL MEM ODDS 6 PER SET
STATED PRINT RUN 65 SER.#'d SETS
18UAA Andrew Aplin 4.00 10.00
18UAM Austin Maddox 4.00 10.00
18UCC Colton Cain 5.00 12.00
18UCG Cameron Garfield 4.00 10.00
18UCT Cecil Tanner
18UDN David Nick 4.00 10.00
18UDT Donavan Tate 20.00 50.00
18UFO Nolan Fontana 4.00 10.00
18UHM Harold Martinez 5.00 12.00
18UJB Jake Barrett 4.00 10.00
18UJM Jeff Malm 4.00 10.00
18UJT Jacob Turner 6.00 15.00
18UME Jonathan Meyer 4.00 10.00
18UMP Matthew Purke 5.00 12.00
18UMS Max Stassi 12.50 30.00
18UNF Nick Franklin 4.00 10.00
18URW Ryan Weber 4.00 10.00
18UWH Wes Hatton 4.00 10.00

2008-09 USA Baseball 18U National Team Patch Autographs

OVERALL AUTO ODDS 7 PER SET
STATED PRINT RUN 30 SER.#'d SETS
18UAA Andrew Aplin 10.00 25.00
18UAM Austin Maddox 20.00 50.00
18UCC Colton Cain 10.00 25.00
18UCG Cameron Garfield
18UCT Cecil Tanner 6.00 15.00
18UDN David Nick 6.00 15.00
18UDT Donavan Tate 50.00 100.00
18UFO Nolan Fontana 15.00 40.00
18UHM Harold Martinez 6.00 15.00
18UJB Jake Barrett 6.00 15.00
18UJM Jeff Malm 6.00 15.00
18UJT Jacob Turner 50.00 100.00
18UME Jonathan Meyer 6.00 15.00
18UMP Matthew Purke 10.00 25.00
18UMS Max Stassi 30.00 60.00
18UNF Nick Franklin 15.00 40.00
18URW Ryan Weber 6.00 15.00
18UWH Wes Hatton

2008-09 USA Baseball 18U National Team Q and A Autographs

OVERALL AUTO ODDS 7 PER SET
PRINT RUNS B/WN 87-104 COPIES PER
18QAAA Andrew Aplin/100 6.00 15.00
18QAAM Austin Maddox/100 10.00 25.00
18QACC Colton Cain/100 4.00 10.00
18QACG Cameron Garfield/99
18QACT Cecil Tanner/99 10.00 25.00
18QADN David Nick/100 4.00 10.00
18QADT Donavan Tate/97 20.00 50.00
18QAFR Nick Franklin/87 10.00 25.00
18QAJB Jake Barrett/104
18QAJM Jeff Malm/99 8.00 20.00
18QAME Jonathan Meyer/97 6.00 15.00
18QAMP Matthew Purke/100 12.50 30.00
18QAMS Max Stassi/99 20.00 50.00
18QANF Nolan Fontana/100 8.00 20.00
18QATU Jacob Turner/100 20.00 50.00
18QAWH Wes Hatton/100 10.00 25.00

2008-09 USA Baseball 18U National Team Roster Autographs

OVERALL AUTO ODDS SIX PER BOX
STATED PRINT RUN 7 SER.#'d SETS
NO PRICING DUE TO SCARCITY
18RA 18U Team United States

2008-09 USA Baseball Autographs Gold

OVERALL AUTO ODDS 7 PER SET
STATED PRINT RUN 175 COPIES PER
61 Christian Colon 8.00 20.00
63 Matt den Dekker 5.00 12.00
64 Derek Dietrich 6.00 15.00
65 Josh Fellhauer 4.00 10.00
66 Micah Gibbs 5.00 12.00
67 Kyle Gibson 10.00 25.00
68 A.J. Griffin 4.00 10.00
69 Chris Hernandez 5.00 12.00
70 Ryan Jackson 4.00 10.00
71 Mike Leake 20.00 50.00
72 Ryan Lipkin 8.00 20.00
73 Tyler Lyons 4.00 10.00
74 Mike Minor 10.00 25.00
75 Hunter Morris 8.00 20.00
76 Andrew Oliver 6.00 15.00
78 Blake Smith 5.00 12.00
79 Stephen Strasburg 125.00 250.00
80 Kendal Volz 5.00 12.00
81 Andrew Aplin 6.00 15.00
82 Jake Barrett 5.00 12.00
85 Colton Cain 4.00 10.00
87 Nolan Fontana 4.00 10.00
88 Nick Franklin 5.00 12.00
89 Cameron Garfield 4.00 10.00
92 Wes Hatton 4.00 10.00
98 Austin Maddox 6.00 15.00
99 Jeff Malm 4.00 10.00
102 Jonathan Meyer 4.00 10.00
106 David Nick 4.00 10.00
107 Matthew Purke 8.00 20.00
108 Max Stassi 10.00 25.00
109 Cecil Tanner 8.00 20.00
110 Donavan Tate 20.00 50.00
113 Jacob Turner 20.00 50.00

2008-09 USA Baseball Autographs Green

OVERALL AUTO ODDS 7 PER SET
STATED PRINT RUN 2 SER.#'d SETS
NO PRICING DUE TO SCARCITY

2008-09 USA Baseball Autographs Red

OVERALL AUTO ODDS 7 PER SET
STATED PRINT RUN 25 SER.#'d SETS
NO PRICING DUE TO SCARCITY

2008-09 USA Baseball Chinese Taipei Jerseys

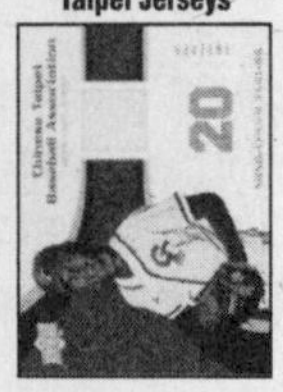

OVERALL MEM ODDS 6 PER BOX
STATED PRINT RUN 479 SER.#'d SETS
CTCH Chih-Pei Huang 2.50 6.00
CTCL Chia-Jen Lo 5.00 12.00
CTEH Erh-Hang Hsu 3.00 8.00
CTHL Hung-Cheng Lai 2.50 6.00
CTHU Chin-Lung Huang 4.00 10.00
CTHY Hsien-Hsien Yang 4.00 10.00
CTKC Kai-Wen Cheng 4.00 10.00
CTKL Ken-Wei Lin 2.50 6.00
CTLC Chih-Hsiang Lin 2.50 6.00
CTLI Kun-Sheng Lin 3.00 8.00
CTMT Ming-Chueh Tsai 4.00 10.00
CTPL Po-Kai Lai 2.50 6.00
CTTT Tsung-Hsuan Tseng 2.50 6.00
CTWC Wei-Jen Cheng 3.00 8.00
CTWL Wen-Yang Liao 3.00 8.00
CTWW Wei-Chung Wang 3.00 8.00
CTYC Yuan-Chin Chu 4.00 10.00
CTYH Yu-Chi Hsiao 3.00 8.00

2008-09 USA Baseball Chinese Taipei Patch

OVERALL MEM ODDS 6 PER SET
PRINT RUNS B/WN 6-75 COPIES PER
NO KEN-WEI LIN PRICING AVAILABLE
CTCH Chih-Pei Huang/69 8.00 20.00
CTCL Chia-Jen Lo/31 8.00 20.00
CTEH Erh-Hang Hsu/40
CTHL Hung-Cheng Lai/65 5.00 12.00
CTHU Chin-Lung Huang/75
CTHY Hsien-Hsien Yang/29
CTKC Kai-Wen Cheng/75 10.00 25.00
CTKL Ken-Wei Lin/6
CTLC Chih-Hsiang Lin/62 10.00 25.00
CTLI Kun-Sheng Lin/72
CTMT Ming-Chueh Tsai/75 5.00 12.00
CTPL Po-Kai Lai/38
CTTT Tsung-Hsuan Tseng/75
CTWC Wei-Jen Cheng/60 5.00 12.00
CTWL Wen-Yang Liao/63
CTWW Wei-Chung Wang/75 8.00 20.00
CTYC Yuan-Chin Chu/75 5.00 12.00
CTYH Yu-Chi Hsiao/75 5.00 12.00

2008-09 USA Baseball Chinese Taipei Patch Autographs

OVERALL AUTO ODDS 7 PER SET
STATED PRINT RUN 55 SER.#'d SETS

CTCH Chih-Pei Huang 8.00 20.00
CTCL Chia-Jen Lo 50.00 100.00
CTEH Erh-Hang Hsu 20.00 50.00
CTHL Hung-Cheng Lai 20.00 50.00
CTHU Chin-Lung Huang 15.00 40.00
CTHY Hsien-Hsien Yang 6.00 15.00
CTKC Kai-Wen Cheng 50.00 100.00
CTKL Ken-Wei Lin 6.00 15.00
CTLC Chih-Hsiang Lin 6.00 15.00
CTLI Kun-Sheng Lin 20.00 50.00
CTMT Ming-Chueh Tsai 8.00 20.00
CTPL Po-Kai Lai 8.00 20.00
CTTT Tsung-Hsuan Tseng 8.00 20.00
CTWC Wei-Jen Cheng 8.00 20.00
CTWL Wen-Yang Liao 6.00 15.00
CTWW Wei-Chung Wang 20.00 50.00
CTYC Yuan-Chin Chu 8.00 20.00
CTYH Yu-Chi Hsiao 8.00 20.00

2008-09 USA Baseball National Team Jerseys

OVERALL MEM ODDS 6 PER SET
STATED PRINT RUN 149 SER.#'d SETS
NTAG A.J. Griffin 3.00 8.00
NTAO Andrew Oliver 4.00 10.00
NTBS Blake Smith 5.00 12.00
NTCC Christian Colon 4.00 10.00
NTCH Chris Hernandez 4.00 10.00
NTDD Derek Dietrich 4.00 10.00
NTHM Hunter Morris 4.00 10.00
NTJC Jared Clark 3.00 8.00
NTJF Josh Fellhauer 4.00 10.00
NTKD Kentrail Davis 3.00 8.00
NTKG Kyle Gibson 4.00 10.00
NTKV Kendal Volz 4.00 10.00
NTMD Matt den Dekker 3.00 8.00
NTMG Micah Gibbs 3.00 8.00
NTML Mike Leake 5.00 12.00
NTMM Mike Minor 4.00 10.00
NTRJ Ryan Jackson 4.00 10.00
NTRL Ryan Lipkin 5.00 12.00
NTSS Stephen Strasburg 60.00 120.00
NTSW Scott Woodward 3.00 8.00
NTTL Tyler Lyons 3.00 8.00
NTTM Tommy Mendonca 5.00 12.00

2008-09 USA Baseball National Team Jersey Autographs Blue

OVERALL AUTO ODDS 7 PER SET
STATED PRINT RUN 99 SER.#'d SETS
NTAG A.J. Griffin 5.00 12.00
NTAO Andrew Oliver
NTBS Blake Smith 6.00 15.00
NTCC Christian Colon 12.50 30.00
NTCH Chris Hernandez 5.00 12.00
NTDD Derek Dietrich 12.50 30.00
NTHM Hunter Morris 12.50 30.00
NTJC Jared Clark
NTJF Josh Fellhauer 5.00 12.00
NTKD Kentrail Davis 10.00 25.00
NTKG Kyle Gibson 20.00 50.00
NTKV Kendal Volz 6.00 15.00
NTMD Matt den Dekker 6.00 15.00
NTMG Micah Gibbs 5.00 12.00
NTML Mike Leake 15.00 40.00
NTMM Mike Minor 10.00 25.00
NTRJ Ryan Jackson 10.00 25.00
NTRL Ryan Lipkin 5.00 12.00
NTSS Stephen Strasburg
NTSW Scott Woodward
NTTL Tyler Lyons 5.00 12.00
NTTM Tommy Mendonca

2008-09 USA Baseball National Team Jersey Patch

OVERALL MEM ODDS 6 PER SET
STATED PRINT RUN 50 SER.#'d SETS
NTAG A.J. Griffin
NTAO Andrew Oliver
NTBS Blake Smith
NTCC Christian Colon
NTCH Chris Hernandez
NTDD Derek Dietrich 6.00 15.00
NTHM Hunter Morris
NTJC Jared Clark
NTJF Josh Fellhauer
NTKD Kentrail Davis 6.00 15.00
NTKG Kyle Gibson
NTKV Kendal Volz 4.00 10.00
NTMD Matt den Dekker 4.00 10.00
NTMG Micah Gibbs
NTML Mike Leake 4.00 10.00
NTMM Mike Minor
NTRJ Ryan Jackson 6.00 15.00
NTRL Ryan Lipkin
NTSS Stephen Strasburg 125.00 250.00
NTSW Scott Woodward 4.00 10.00
NTTL Tyler Lyons
NTTM Tommy Mendonca 8.00 20.00

2008-09 USA Baseball National Team Jersey Patch Autographs

OVERALL AUTO ODDS 7 PER SET
STATED PRINT RUN 30 SER.#'d SETS
NTAG A.J. Griffin 6.00 15.00
NTBS Blake Smith
NTCC Christian Colon
NTCH Chris Hernandez 6.00 15.00
NTDD Derek Dietrich 15.00 40.00
NTHM Hunter Morris 8.00 20.00
NTJF Josh Fellhauer 6.00 15.00
NTKD Kentrail Davis 20.00 50.00
NTKG Kyle Gibson 20.00 50.00
NTKV Kendal Volz 8.00 20.00
NTMD Matt den Dekker 8.00 20.00
NTMG Micah Gibbs
NTML Mike Leake 40.00 80.00
NTMM Mike Minor 20.00 50.00
NTRJ Ryan Jackson 8.00 20.00
NTRL Ryan Lipkin 6.00 15.00
NTTL Tyler Lyons 6.00 15.00

2008-09 USA Baseball National Team Patriotic Patches

OVERALL MEM ODDS 6 PER SET
STATED PRINT RUN 50 SER.#'d SETS
PPABA Brett Anderson 40.00 80.00
PPABB Brian Barden 8.00 20.00
PPABD Brian Duensing
PPABK Brandon Knight 8.00 20.00
PPABN Blaine Neal 6.00 15.00
PPACW Casey Weathers
PPADF Dexter Fowler 30.00 60.00
PPAJA Jake Arrieta 8.00 20.00
PPAJC Jeremy Cummings 8.00 20.00
PPAJD Jason Donald 20.00 50.00
PPAJG John Gall 6.00 15.00
PPAJS Jeff Stevens
PPAKJ Kevin Jepsen 15.00 40.00
PPALM Lou Marson 30.00 60.00
PPAMH Mike Hessman
PPAMK Mike Koplove 8.00 20.00
PPAML Matt LaPorta 30.00 60.00
PPANS Nate Schierholtz 12.50 30.00
PPASS Stephen Strasburg 250.00 500.00
PPATC Trevor Cahill
PPATI Terry Tiffee 6.00 15.00
PPATT Taylor Teagarden 15.00 40.00

2008-09 USA Baseball National Team Q and A Autographs

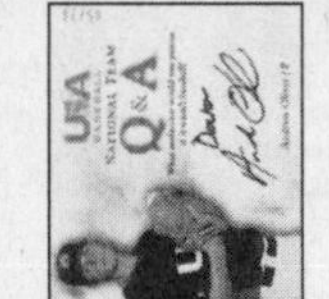

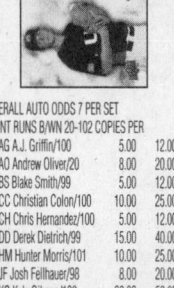

OVERALL AUTO ODDS 7 PER SET
PRINT RUNS B/WN 20-102 COPIES PER
QAAG A.J. Griffin/100 5.00 12.00
QAAO Andrew Oliver/20 8.00 20.00
QABS Blake Smith/99 5.00 12.00
QACC Christian Colon/100 10.00 25.00
QACH Chris Hernandez/100 5.00 12.00
QADD Derek Dietrich/99 15.00 40.00
QAHM Hunter Morris/101 10.00 25.00
QAJF Josh Fellhauer/98 8.00 20.00
QAKG Kyle Gibson/100 20.00 50.00
QAKV Kendal Volz/100 6.00 15.00
QAMD Matt den Dekker/99 10.00 25.00
QAMG Micah Gibbs/100 8.00 20.00
QAML Mike Leake/101 15.00 40.00
QAMM Mike Minor/100 15.00 40.00
QARJ Ryan Jackson/101
QARL Ryan Lipkin/100
QATL Tyler Lyons/100 5.00 12.00

2008-09 USA Baseball National Team Retrospective

COMPLETE SET (13) 10.00 25.00
ONE SET PER BOX
USA1 Matt Brown .40 1.00
USA2 Stephen Strasburg 6.00 15.00
USA3 Jayson Nix .40 1.00
USA4 Brian Duensing .40 1.00
USA5 Jake Arrieta .40 1.00
USA6 Dexter Fowler .40 1.00
USA7 Casey Weathers .40 1.00
USA8 Mike Koplove .40 1.00
USA9 Jason Donald .40 1.00
USA10 Taylor Teagarden .60 1.50
USA11 Kevin Jepsen .40 1.00
USA12 Matt LaPorta 1.25 3.00
USA13 Team USA Wins Third Olympic Medal .40 1.00

2009-10 USA Baseball

COMP.SET w/o SPs (59) 12.50 30.00
COMMON CARD (1-59) .40 1.00
COMMON AUTO (61-116) 3.00 8.00
FIVE AUTOS PER BOX
AU PRINT RUN 502 SER.#'d SETS
COMMON PATCH (119-136) 3.00 8.00
ONE PATCH OR PATCH AU PER BOX
PATCH PRINT RUN 65 SER.#'d SETS
USA1 Trevor Bauer 1.25 3.00
USA2 Christian Colon .60 1.50
USA3 Cody Wheeler .40 1.00
USA4 Chad Bettis .40 1.00
USA5 Bryce Brentz 1.00 2.50
USA6 Nick Pepitone .40 1.00
USA7 Michael Choice .60 1.50
USA8 Gerrit Cole 1.50 4.00
USA9 Sonny Gray .60 1.50
USA10 Tyler Holt .40 1.00
USA11 T.J. Walz .40 1.00
USA12 Rick Hague .40 1.00
USA13 Drew Pomeranz 1.25 3.00
USA14 Blake Forsythe .40 1.00
USA15 Matt Newman .40 1.00
USA16 Casey McGrew .40 1.00
USA17 Brad Miller
USA18 Yasmani Grandal .60 1.50
USA19 Kolten Wong .60 1.50
USA20 Tony Zych .40 1.00
USA21 Andy Wilkins .40 1.00
USA22 Asher Wojciechowski .60 1.50
USA23 Cody Buckel .40 1.00
USA24 Nick Castellanos .60 1.50
USA25 Garin Cecchini .40 1.00
USA26 Sean Coyle .40 1.00
USA27 Nicky Delmonico .40 1.00
USA28 Kevin Gausman .40 1.00
USA29 Cory Hahn .40 1.00
USA30 Bryce Harper 12.00 30.00
USA31 Kavin Keyes .40 1.00
USA32 Manny Machado 1.25 3.00
USA33 Connor Mason .40 1.00
USA34 Ladson Montgomery .40 1.00
USA35 Phillip Pfeifer .40 1.00
USA36 Brian Ragira .60 1.50
USA37 Robbie Ray .40 1.00
USA38 Kyle Ryan .40 1.00
USA39 Jameson Taillon 2.00 5.00
USA40 A.J. Vanegas .40 1.00
USA41 Karsten Whitson .60 1.50
USA42 Tony Wolters .40 1.00
USA43 Albert Almora .40 1.00
USA44 Shaun Chase .40 1.00
USA45 Austin Cousino .40 1.00
USA46 Dylan Davis .40 1.00
USA47 Parker French .40 1.00
USA48 Cory Geisler .40 1.00
USA49 Courtney Hawkins .40 1.00
USA50 C.J. Hinojosa .40 1.00
USA51 John Hochstatter .40 1.00
USA52 Hayden Hurst .40 1.00
USA53 Ricardo Jacquez .40 1.00
USA54 Kevin Kramer .40 1.00
USA55 Francisco Lindor .60 1.50
USA56 Kenny Mathews .40 1.00
USA57 Evan Powell .60 1.50
USA58 Christopher Rivera .40 1.00
USA59 JoMarcos Woods .40 1.00
USA61 Trevor Bauer AU 12.50 30.00
USA62 Christian Colon AU 8.00 20.00
USA63 Cody Wheeler AU 3.00 8.00
USA64 Chad Bettis AU 3.00 8.00
USA65 Bryce Brentz AU 8.00 20.00
USA66 Nick Pepitone AU 3.00 8.00
USA67 Michael Choice AU 6.00 15.00
USA68 Gerrit Cole AU 15.00 40.00
USA69 Sonny Gray AU 5.00 12.00
USA70 Tyler Holt AU 3.00 8.00
USA71 T.J. Walz AU 4.00 10.00
USA72 Rick Hague AU 3.00 8.00
USA73 Drew Pomeranz AU 8.00 20.00
USA74 Blake Forsythe AU 4.00 10.00
USA75 Matt Newman AU 3.00 8.00
USA76 Casey McGrew AU 4.00 10.00
USA77 Brad Miller AU 3.00 8.00
USA78 Yasmani Grandal AU 10.00 25.00
USA79 Kolten Wong AU 8.00 20.00
USA80 Tony Zych AU 4.00 10.00
USA81 Andy Wilkins AU 3.00 8.00
USA82 Asher Wojciechowski AU 5.00 12.00
USA83 Bryce Harper AU 150.00 300.00
USA85 Cody Buckel AU 4.00 10.00
USA86 Tony Wolters AU
USA89 A.J. Vanegas AU 3.00 8.00
USA90 Ladson Montgomery AU 4.00 10.00
USA91 Karsten Whitson AU 5.00 12.00
USA95 Connor Mason AU 3.00 8.00
USA96 Garin Cecchini AU 3.00 8.00
USA98 Jameson Taillon AU 20.00 50.00
USA100 Sean Coyle AU 3.00 8.00
USA102 Kyle Ryan AU 3.00 8.00
USA105 Kevin Gausman AU 3.00 8.00
USA106 Robbie Ray AU 3.00 8.00
USA107 Nicky Delmonico AU 3.00 8.00
USA108 Cory Hahn AU 3.00 8.00
USA110 Nick Castellanos AU 8.00 20.00
USA113 Manny Machado AU 20.00 50.00
USA115 Phillip Pfeifer AU 3.00 8.00
USA116 Brian Ragira AU 5.00 12.00
USA119 Albert Almora Jsy 4.00 10.00
USA120 Shaun Chase Jsy 3.00 8.00
USA121 Austin Cousino Jsy 3.00 8.00
USA122 Dylan Davis Jsy 3.00 8.00
USA123 Parker French Jsy 4.00 10.00
USA124 Cory Geisler Jsy 3.00 8.00
USA125 Courtney Hawkins Jsy
USA126 C.J. Hinojosa Jsy 3.00 8.00
USA127 John Hochstatter Jsy 3.00 8.00
USA128 Hayden Hurst Jsy
USA129 Ricardo Jacquez Jsy 4.00 10.00
USA130 Kevin Kramer Jsy 3.00 8.00
USA132 Francisco Lindor Jsy 6.00 15.00
USA133 Kenny Mathews Jsy
USA134 Evan Powell Jsy 5.00 12.00
USA135 Christopher Rivera Jsy 3.00 8.00
USA136 JoMarcos Woods Jsy 4.00 10.00

2009-10 USA Baseball Patch Autograph Parallel

ONE PATCH OR PATCH AU PER BOX
STATED PRINT RUN 99 SER.#'d SETS
USA61 Trevor Bauer 50.00 100.00
USA62 Christian Colon 20.00 50.00
USA63 Cody Wheeler 4.00 10.00
USA64 Chad Bettis 8.00 20.00
USA65 Bryce Brentz 12.50 30.00
USA66 Nick Pepitone 5.00 12.00
USA67 Michael Choice 20.00 50.00
USA68 Gerrit Cole 60.00 120.00
USA69 Sonny Gray 12.50 30.00
USA70 Tyler Holt 4.00 10.00
USA71 T.J. Walz 10.00 25.00
USA72 Rick Hague 6.00 15.00
USA73 Drew Pomeranz 40.00 80.00
USA74 Blake Forsythe 5.00 12.00
USA75 Matt Newman 4.00 10.00
USA76 Casey McGrew 12.50 30.00
USA77 Brad Miller 5.00 12.00
USA78 Yasmani Grandal 20.00 50.00
USA79 Kolten Wong 30.00 60.00
USA80 Tony Zych 8.00 20.00
USA81 Andy Wilkins 10.00 25.00
USA82 Asher Wojciechowski 10.00 25.00
USA83 Bryce Harper 300.00 500.00
USA85 Cody Buckel 6.00 15.00
USA86 Tony Wolters 8.00 20.00
USA89 A.J. Vanegas 10.00 25.00
USA90 Ladson Montgomery 6.00 15.00
USA91 Karsten Whitson 20.00 50.00
USA95 Connor Mason 12.50 30.00
USA96 Garin Cecchini 12.50 30.00
USA98 Jameson Taillon 60.00 120.00
USA100 Sean Coyle 10.00 25.00
USA105 Kevin Gausman 8.00 20.00
USA106 Robbie Ray 10.00 25.00
USA107 Nicky Delmonico 5.00 12.00
USA108 Cory Hahn 5.00 12.00
USA110 Nick Castellanos 20.00 50.00
USA113 Manny Machado 50.00 100.00
USA115 Phillip Pfeifer 8.00 20.00
USA116 Brian Ragira 12.50 30.00

2009-10 USA Baseball 16U National Team Jersey Autographs

OVERALL ONE JSY AU PER BOX SET
STATED PRINT RUN 149 SER.#'d SETS
GREEN PRINT RUN 2 SER.#'d SETS
NO GRN PRICING DUE TO SCARCITY
RED PRINT RUN 25 SER.#'d SETS
NO RED PRICING DUE TO SCARCITY
AA Albert Almora 6.00 15.00
AC Austin Cousino 8.00 20.00
CG Cory Geisler 4.00 10.00
CH Courtney Hawkins 4.00 10.00
CR Christopher Rivera 4.00 10.00
DD Dylan Davis 4.00 10.00
EP Evan Powell 4.00 10.00
FL Francisco Lindor 20.00 50.00
HH Hayden Hurst 4.00 10.00
HI C.J. Hinojosa 4.00 10.00
JH John Hochstatter 4.00 10.00
JW JoMarcos Woods 10.00 25.00
KK Kevin Kramer 5.00 12.00
KM Kenny Mathews 4.00 10.00
PF Parker French 4.00 10.00
RJ Ricardo Jacquez 4.00 10.00
SC Shaun Chase 5.00 12.00

2009-10 USA Baseball 16U National Team Jerseys

TWO JSY CARDS PER BOX
AA Albert Almora 3.00 8.00
AC Austin Cousino 3.00 8.00
CG Cory Geisler 3.00 8.00
CH Courtney Hawkins 3.00 8.00
CR Christopher Rivera 3.00 8.00
DD Dylan Davis 3.00 8.00
EP Evan Powell 3.00 8.00
FL Francisco Lindor 3.00 8.00
HH Hayden Hurst 3.00 8.00
HI C.J. Hinojosa 3.00 8.00
JH John Hochstatter 3.00 8.00
JW JoMarcos Woods 3.00 8.00
KK Kevin Kramer 3.00 8.00
KM Kenny Mathews 3.00 8.00
PF Parker French 3.00 8.00
RJ Ricardo Jacquez 3.00 8.00
SC Shaun Chase 3.00 8.00

2009-10 USA Baseball 16U National Team Patch Autographs

ONE PATCH OR PATCH AU PER BOX
STATED PRINT RUN 35 SER.#'d SETS
AA Albert Almora 5.00 12.00
AC Austin Cousino 10.00 25.00
CG Cory Geisler 5.00 12.00
CH Courtney Hawkins 5.00 12.00
CR Christopher Rivera 8.00 20.00
DD Dylan Davis 8.00 20.00
EP Evan Powell 6.00 15.00
FL Francisco Lindor 40.00 80.00
HH Hayden Hurst 6.00 15.00
HI C.J. Hinojosa 10.00 25.00
JH John Hochstatter 5.00 12.00
JW JoMarcos Woods 12.50 30.00
KK Kevin Kramer 5.00 12.00
KM Kenny Mathews 12.50 30.00
PF Parker French 10.00 25.00
RJ Ricardo Jacquez
SC Shaun Chase 10.00 25.00

2009-10 USA Baseball 16U National Team Roster Autographs

FIVE AUTOS PER BOX SET
STATED PRINT RUN 10 SER.#'d SETS
NO PRICING DUE TO SCARCITY
16U 16U National Team

2009-10 USA Baseball 18U National Team Big Sigs

FIVE AUTOS PER BOX
STATED PRINT RUN 75 SER.#'d SETS
GOLD PRINT RUN 25 SER.#'d SETS,
NO GOLD PRICING DUE TO SCARCITY
AV A.J. Vanegas 3.00 8.00
BH Bryce Harper 150.00 300.00
BR Brian Ragira 4.00 10.00
CB Cody Buckel 6.00 15.00
CH Cory Hahn 3.00 8.00
CM Connor Mason 3.00 8.00
GC Garin Cecchini 3.00 8.00
JT Jameson Taillon 20.00 50.00
KG Kevin Gausman 3.00 8.00
KR Kyle Ryan 4.00 10.00
KW Karsten Whitson 12.50 30.00
LM Ladson Montgomery 3.00 8.00
MM Manny Machado 20.00 50.00
NC Nick Castellanos 10.00 25.00
ND Nicky Delmonico 4.00 10.00
PP Phillip Pfeifer 3.00 8.00
RR Robbie Ray 4.00 10.00
SC Sean Coyle 4.00 10.00
TW Tony Wolters 4.00 10.00

2009-10 USA Baseball 18U National Team Inscriptions Autographs

FIVE AUTOS PER BOX
STATED PRINT RUN 162 SER.#'d SETS
GREEN PRINT RUN 2 SER.#'d SETS
NO GREEN PRICING DUE TO SCARCITY
RED PRINT RUN 15 SER.#'d SETS
NO RED PRICING DUE TO SCARCITY
AV A.J. Vanegas 4.00 10.00
BH Bryce Harper 200.00 400.00
BR Brian Ragira 10.00 25.00
CB Cody Buckel 5.00 12.00
CH Cory Hahn 3.00 8.00
CM Connor Mason 3.00 8.00
GC Garin Cecchini 3.00 8.00
JT Jameson Taillon 20.00 50.00
KG Kevin Gausman 4.00 10.00
KR Kyle Ryan 3.00 8.00
KW Karsten Whitson 5.00 12.00
LM Ladson Montgomery 3.00 8.00
MM Manny Machado
NC Nick Castellanos 8.00 20.00
ND Nicky Delmonico 4.00 10.00
PP Phillip Pfeifer 3.00 8.00
RR Robbie Ray 4.00 10.00
SC Sean Coyle 6.00 15.00
TW Tony Wolters 8.00 20.00

2009-10 USA Baseball 18U National Team Jersey Autographs

OVERALL ONE JSY AU PER BOX SET
PRINT RUNS B/WN 28-149 COPIES PER
GREEN PRINT RUN 2 SER.#'d SETS
NO GRN PRICING DUE TO SCARCITY
RED PRINT RUN 25 SER.#'d SETS
NO RED PRICING DUE TO SCARCITY
AV A.J. Vanegas/32 4.00 10.00
BH Bryce Harper/149 250.00 350.00
BR Brian Ragira/149 15.00 40.00
CB Cody Buckel/28 5.00 12.00
CH Cory Hahn/38
CM Connor Mason/97 8.00 20.00
GC Garin Cecchini/29
JT Jameson Taillon/149 30.00 60.00
KG Kevin Gausman/149 8.00 20.00
KK Kavin Keyes/149 4.00 10.00
KR Kyle Ryan/149 4.00 10.00
KW Karsten Whitson/37 12.50 30.00
LM Ladson Montgomery/62 4.00 10.00
MM Manny Machado/149 12.50 30.00
NC Nick Castellanos/36 20.00 50.00
ND Nicky Delmonico/149 4.00 10.00
PP Phillip Pfeifer/39 5.00 12.00
RR Robbie Ray/149 5.00 12.00
SC Sean Coyle/149 8.00 20.00
TW Tony Wolters/149 10.00 25.00

2009-10 USA Baseball 18U National Team Jerseys

TWO JSY CARDS PER BOX
AV A.J. Vanegas 3.00 8.00
BH Bryce Harper 50.00 100.00
BR Brian Ragira 3.00 8.00
CB Cody Buckel 3.00 8.00
CH Cory Hahn 3.00 8.00
CM Connor Mason 3.00 8.00
GC Garin Cecchini 3.00 8.00
JT Jameson Taillon 6.00 15.00
KG Kevin Gausman 3.00 8.00
KK Kavin Keyes 3.00 8.00
KR Kyle Ryan 3.00 8.00
KW Karsten Whitson 3.00 8.00
LM Ladson Montgomery 3.00 8.00
MM Manny Machado 8.00 20.00
NC Nick Castellanos 5.00 12.00
ND Nicky Delmonico 3.00 8.00
PP Phillip Pfeifer 3.00 8.00
RR Robbie Ray 3.00 8.00
SC Sean Coyle 3.00 8.00
TW Tony Wolters 3.00 8.00

2009-10 USA Baseball 18U National Team Patch Autographs

ONE PATCH OR PATCH AU PER BOX
STATED PRINT RUN 35 SER.#'d SETS
AV A.J. Vanegas 5.00 12.00
BH Bryce Harper 200.00 400.00
BR Brian Ragira 12.50 30.00
CB Cody Buckel 10.00 25.00
CH Cory Hahn 4.00 10.00
CM Connor Mason 10.00 25.00
GC Garin Cecchini 8.00 20.00
JT Jameson Taillon
KG Kevin Gausman 5.00 12.00
KK Kavin Keyes 6.00 15.00
KR Kyle Ryan 4.00 10.00
KW Karsten Whitson 20.00 50.00
LM Ladson Montgomery 4.00 10.00
MM Manny Machado 60.00 120.00
NC Nick Castellanos 30.00 60.00
ND Nicky Delmonico 5.00 12.00
PP Phillip Pfeifer
RR Robbie Ray 4.00 10.00
SC Sean Coyle 15.00 40.00
TW Tony Wolters 5.00 12.00

2009-10 USA Baseball 18U National Team Q And A Autographs

FIVE AUTOS PER BOX
STATED PRINT RUN 65 SER.#'d SETS
AV A.J. Vanegas 4.00 10.00
BH Bryce Harper 100.00 200.00
BR Brian Ragira 10.00 25.00
CB Cody Buckel 5.00 12.00
CH Cory Hahn 4.00 10.00
CM Connor Mason 6.00 15.00
GC Garin Cecchini 5.00 12.00
JT Jameson Taillon 15.00 40.00
KG Kevin Gausman 4.00 10.00
KR Kyle Ryan 4.00 10.00
KW Karsten Whitson 6.00 15.00
LM Ladson Montgomery
MM Manny Machado 12.50 30.00
NC Nick Castellanos 12.50 30.00
ND Nicky Delmonico 6.00 15.00
PP Phillip Pfeifer 4.00 10.00
RR Robbie Ray 5.00 12.00
SC Sean Coyle 5.00 12.00
TW Tony Wolters 5.00 12.00

2009-10 USA Baseball National Team Big Sigs

FIVE AUTOS PER BOX
STATED PRINT RUN 75 SER.#'d SETS
GOLD PRINT RUN 25 SER.#'d SETS
NO GOLD PRICING DUE TO SCARCITY
AW Andy Wilkins 3.00 8.00
BB Bryce Brentz 6.00 15.00
BF Blake Forsythe 5.00 12.00
BM Brad Miller 4.00 10.00
CB Chad Bettis 3.00 8.00
CC Christian Colon 12.50 30.00
CM Casey McGrew 8.00 20.00

CW Cody Wheeler 3.00 8.00
DP Drew Pomeranz 15.00 40.00
GC Gerrit Cole 30.00 60.00
KW Kolten Wong 10.00 25.00
MC Michael Choice 12.50 30.00
MN Matt Newman 4.00 10.00
NP Nick Pepitone 3.00 8.00
RH Rick Hague 4.00 10.00
SG Sonny Gray 12.50 30.00
TB Trevor Bauer 20.00 50.00
TH Tyler Holt 4.00 10.00
TW T.J. Walz 5.00 12.00
TZ Tony Zych 8.00 20.00
WO Asher Wojciechowski 3.00 8.00
YG Yasmani Grandal 12.50 30.00

2009-10 USA Baseball National Team Inscriptions Autographs

FIVE AUTOS PER BOX
STATED PRINT RUN 162 SER.#'d SETS
GREEN PRINT RUN 2 SER.#'d SETS
NO GREEN PRICING DUE TO SCARCITY
RED PRINT RUN 25 SER.#'d SETS
NO RED PRICING DUE TO SCARCITY
AW Andy Wilkins 8.00 20.00
BB Bryce Brentz 10.00 25.00
BF Blake Forsythe 4.00 10.00
BM Brad Miller 3.00 8.00
CB Chad Bettis 3.00 8.00
CC Christian Colon 10.00 25.00
CM Casey McGrew 4.00 10.00
CW Cody Wheeler 4.00 10.00
DP Drew Pomeranz 10.00 25.00
GC Gerrit Cole 15.00 40.00
KW Kolten Wong 10.00 25.00
MC Michael Choice 4.00 10.00
MN Matt Newman 3.00 8.00
NP Nick Pepitone 3.00 8.00
RH Rick Hague 4.00 10.00
SG Sonny Gray 6.00 15.00
TB Trevor Bauer 12.50 30.00
TH Tyler Holt 4.00 10.00
TW T.J. Walz 5.00 12.00
TZ Tony Zych 5.00 12.00
WO Asher Wojciechowski 4.00 10.00
YG Yasmani Grandal 8.00 20.00

2009-10 USA Baseball National Team Jersey Autographs Blue

OVERALL ONE JSY AU PER BOX SET
STATED PRINT RUN 149 SER.#'d SETS
GREEN PRINT RUN 2 SER.#'d SETS
NO GRN PRICING DUE TO SCARCITY
RED PRINT RUN 25 SER.#'d SETS
NO RED PRICING DUE TO SCARCITY
AW Andy Wilkins 5.00 12.00
BB Bryce Brentz 12.50 30.00
BF Blake Forsythe 5.00 12.00
BM Brad Miller 4.00 10.00
CB Chad Bettis 4.00 10.00
CC Christian Colon 12.50 30.00
CM Casey McGrew 4.00 10.00
CW Cody Wheeler 4.00 10.00
DP Drew Pomeranz 12.50 30.00
GC Gerrit Cole 30.00 60.00
KW Kolten Wong 15.00 40.00
MC Michael Choice 10.00 25.00
MN Matt Newman 4.00 10.00
NP Nick Pepitone 4.00 10.00
RH Rick Hague 5.00 12.00
SG Sonny Gray 12.50 30.00
TB Trevor Bauer 20.00 50.00
TH Tyler Holt 4.00 10.00
TW T.J. Walz 5.00 12.00
TZ Tony Zych 5.00 12.00
WO Asher Wojciechowski 6.00 15.00
YG Yasmani Grandal 12.50 30.00

2009-10 USA Baseball National Team Jerseys

TWO JSY CARDS PER BOX
AW Andy Wilkins 3.00 8.00
BB Bryce Brentz 3.00 8.00
BF Blake Forsythe 3.00 8.00
BM Brad Miller 3.00 8.00
CB Chad Bettis 3.00 8.00
CC Christian Colon 4.00 10.00
CM Casey McGrew 3.00 8.00
CW Cody Wheeler 3.00 8.00
DP Drew Pomeranz 4.00 10.00
GC Gerrit Cole 8.00 20.00
KW Kolten Wong 3.00 8.00
MC Michael Choice 4.00 10.00
MN Matt Newman 3.00 8.00
NP Nick Pepitone 3.00 8.00
RH Rick Hague 3.00 8.00
SG Sonny Gray 3.00 8.00
TB Trevor Bauer 3.00 8.00
TH Tyler Holt 3.00 8.00
TW T.J. Walz 3.00 8.00
TZ Tony Zych 3.00 8.00
WO Asher Wojciechowski 3.00 8.00
YG Yasmani Grandal 4.00 10.00

2009-10 USA Baseball National Team Patch Autographs

ONE PATCH OR PATCH AU PER BOX
STATED PRINT RUN 35 SER.#'d SETS
AW Andy Wilkins 5.00 12.00
BB Bryce Brentz 20.00 50.00
BF Blake Forsythe 5.00 12.00
BM Brad Miller 6.00 15.00
CB Chad Bettis 6.00 15.00
CC Christian Colon 15.00 40.00
CM Casey McGrew 5.00 12.00
CW Cody Wheeler 10.00 25.00
DP Drew Pomeranz 15.00 40.00
GC Gerrit Cole 20.00 50.00
KW Kolten Wong 5.00 12.00
MC Michael Choice 20.00 50.00
MN Matt Newman 4.00 10.00
NP Nick Pepitone 4.00 10.00
RH Rick Hague 4.00 10.00
SG Sonny Gray
TB Trevor Bauer 75.00 150.00
TH Tyler Holt 8.00 20.00
TW T.J. Walz 10.00 25.00
TZ Tony Zych
WO Asher Wojciechowski 10.00 25.00
YG Yasmani Grandal 40.00 80.00

2009-10 USA Baseball National Team Q And A Autographs

FIVE AUTOS PER BOX
STATED PRINT RUN 65 SER.#'d SETS
AW Asher Wojciechowski 6.00 15.00
BB Bryce Brentz 8.00 20.00
BF Blake Forsythe 6.00 15.00
BM Brad Miller
CB Chad Bettis 4.00 10.00
CC Christian Colon 4.00 10.00
CM Casey McGrew 10.00 25.00
CW Cody Wheeler 4.00 10.00
DP Drew Pomeranz 10.00 25.00
GC Gerrit Cole
KW Kolten Wong 4.00 10.00
MC Michael Choice 6.00 15.00
MN Matt Newman 5.00 12.00
NP Nick Pepitone 4.00 10.00
RH Rick Hague 5.00 12.00
SG Sonny Gray 4.00 10.00
TB Trevor Bauer 12.50 30.00
TH Tyler Holt 5.00 12.00
TW T.J. Walz 6.00 15.00
TZ Tony Zych 4.00 10.00
WI Andy Wilkins 5.00 12.00
YG Yasmani Grandal 12.50 30.00

2010 USA Baseball

COMPLETE SET (65) 12.50 30.00
COMMON CARD .20 .50
PRINTING PLATES RANDOMLY INSERTED
PLATE PRINT RUN 1 SET PER COLOR
BLACK-CYAN-MAGENTA-YELLOW ISSUED
NO PLATE PRICING DUE TO SCARCITY
USA1 Albert Almora .30 .75
USA2 Daniel Camarena .20 .50
USA3 Nicky Delmonico .20 .50
USA4 John Hochstatler .20 .50
USA5 Francisco Lindor .50 1.25
USA6 Marcus Littlewood .30 .75
USA7 Christian Lopes .30 .75
USA8 Michael Lorenzen .20 .50
USA9 Dillon Maples .20 .50
USA10 Lance McCullers .30 .75
USA11 Christian Montgomery .20 .50
USA12 Henry Owens .30 .75
USA13 Phillip Pfeifer III .20 .50
USA14 Brian Ragira .20 .50
USA15 John Simms .20 .50
USA16 Elvin Soto .20 .50
USA17 Bubba Starling 1.00 2.50
USA18 Blake Swihart .30 .75
USA19 AJ Vanegas .30 .75
USA20 Tony Wolters .30 .75
USA21 Ricardo Jacquez .20 .50
USA22 Tyler Anderson .30 .75
USA23 Matt Barnes .50 1.25
USA24 Jackie Bradley Jr. .60 1.50
USA25 Gerrit Cole 1.00 2.50
USA26 Alex Dickerson .20 .50
USA27 Jason Esposito .50 1.25
USA28 Nolan Fontana .50 1.25
USA29 Sean Gilmartin .30 .75
USA30 Sonny Gray .30 .75
USA31 Brian Johnson .20 .50
USA32 Andrew Maggi .20 .50
USA33 Mikie Mahtook .50 1.25
USA34 Scott McGough .50 1.25
USA35 Brad Miller .20 .50
USA36 Brett Mooneyham .50 1.25
USA37 Peter O'Brien .30 .75
USA38 Nick Ramirez .30 .75
USA39 Noe Ramirez .30 .75
USA40 Steve Rodriguez .20 .50
USA41 George Springer .50 1.25
USA42 Kyle Winkler .50 1.25
USA43 Ryan Wright .20 .50
USA44 Anthony Rendon 3.00 8.00
USA45 Albert Almora .30 .75
USA46 Cole Billingsley .30 .75
USA47 Sean Brady .20 .50
USA48 Marc Brakeman .20 .50
USA49 Alex Bregman .30 .75
USA50 Ryan Burr .30 .75
USA51 Chris Chinea .30 .75
USA52 Troy Conyers .20 .50
USA53 Zach Green .20 .50
USA54 Carson Kelly .20 .50
USA55 Timmy Lopes .20 .50
USA56 Adrian Marin .30 .75
USA57 Chris Okey .20 .50
USA58 Matt Olson .20 .50
USA59 Ivan Pelaez .20 .50
USA60 Felipe Perez .20 .50
USA61 Nelson Rodriguez .20 .50
USA62 Corey Seager .30 .75
USA63 Lucas Sims .20 .50
USA64 Nick Travieso .30 .75
USA65 Sheldon Neuse .30 .75

2010 USA Baseball Autographs

A production error resulted in 20 cards in this set being numbered "A-TBD". We have cataloged these cards in alphabetical order - immediately following #A42 - starting with #ATBD1 and concluding with #ATBD20.

OVERALL AUTO ODDS 7 PER BOX SET
#ATBD CARDS IN ALPHABETICAL ORDER
A1 AJ Vanegas 4.00 10.00
A2 Albert Almora 4.00 10.00
A3 Blake Swihart 10.00 25.00
A4 Brian Ragira 4.00 10.00
A5 Christian Lopes 5.00 12.00
A6 Christian Montgomery 4.00 10.00
A7 Daniel Camarena 4.00 10.00
A8 Bubba Starling 20.00 50.00
A9 Dillon Maples 4.00 10.00
A10 Elvin Soto 4.00 10.00
A11 Francisco Lindor 10.00 25.00
A12 Henry Owens 6.00 15.00
A13 John Hochstatler 4.00 10.00
A14 John Simms 4.00 10.00
A15 Lance McCullers 6.00 15.00
A16 Marcus Littlewood 4.00 10.00
A17 Michael Lorenzen 4.00 10.00
A18 Nicky Delmonico 4.00 10.00
A19 Philip Pfeifer III 4.00 10.00
A20 Tony Wolters 4.00 10.00
A21 Tyler Anderson 5.00 12.00
A22 Matt Barnes 10.00 25.00
A23 Jackie Bradley Jr. 12.50 30.00
A24 Gerrit Cole 20.00 50.00
A25 Alex Dickerson 4.00 10.00
A26 Nolan Fontana 4.00 10.00
A27 Sean Gilmartin 4.00 10.00
A28 Sonny Gray 6.00 15.00
A29 Brian Johnson 4.00 10.00
A30 Andrew Maggi 4.00 10.00
A31 Mikie Mahtook 10.00 25.00
A32 Scott McGough 4.00 10.00
A33 Brad Miller 4.00 10.00
A34 Brett Mooneyham 5.00 12.00
A35 Peter O'Brien 4.00 10.00
A36 Nick Ramirez 4.00 10.00
A37 Noe Ramirez 4.00 10.00
A38 Jason Esposito 5.00 12.00
A39 Steve Rodriguez 4.00 10.00
A40 George Springer 10.00 25.00
A41 Kyle Winkler 4.00 10.00
A42 Ryan Wright 4.00 10.00
ATBD1 Albert Almora 5.00 12.00
ATBD2 Cole Billingsley 4.00 10.00
ATBD3 Sean Brady 4.00 10.00
ATBD4 Marc Brakeman 4.00 10.00
ATBD5 Alex Bregman 8.00 20.00
ATBD6 Ryan Burr 4.00 10.00
ATBD7 Chris Chinea 4.00 10.00
ATBD8 Troy Conyers 4.00 10.00
ATBD9 Zach Green 4.00 10.00
ATBD10 Carson Kelly 4.00 10.00
ATBD11 Timmy Lopes 4.00 10.00
ATBD12 Adrian Marin 4.00 10.00
ATBD13 Chris Okey 4.00 10.00
ATBD14 Matt Olson 4.00 10.00
ATBD15 Ivan Pelaez 4.00 10.00
ATBD16 Felipe Perez 4.00 10.00
ATBD17 Nelson Rodriguez 4.00 10.00
ATBD18 Corey Seager 4.00 10.00
ATBD19 Lucas Sims 4.00 10.00
ATBD20 Nick Travieso 4.00 10.00

2010 USA Baseball Autographs Green

OVERALL AUTO ODDS 7 PER BOX SET
STATED PRINT RUN 25 SER.#'d SETS
NO PRICING DUE TO SCARCITY

2010 USA Baseball Autographs Red

*RED: .75X TO 2X BASIC AUTO
OVERALL AUTO ODDS SEVEN PER BOX SET
STATED PRINT RUN 99 SER.#'d SETS

2010 USA Baseball Autographs Silver

OVERALL AUTO ODDS 7 PER BOX SET
STATED PRINT RUN 1 SER.#'d SET
NO PRICING DUE TO SCARCITY

2010 USA Baseball Triple Jersey Autographs

OVERALL AUTO ODDS 7 PER BOX SET
STATED PRINT RUN 219 SER.#'d SETS
AA Albert Almora 6.00 15.00
AD Alex Dickerson 5.00 12.00
AM Andrew Maggi 5.00 12.00
AV AJ Vanegas 5.00 12.00
BJ Brian Johnson 5.00 12.00
BM Brad Miller 5.00 12.00
BR Brian Ragira 5.00 12.00
BS Bubba Starling 40.00 80.00
CL Christian Lopes 5.00 12.00
DC Daniel Camarena 5.00 12.00
DM Dillon Maples 5.00 12.00
ES Elvin Soto 5.00 12.00
FL Francisco Lindor 10.00 25.00
GC Gerrit Cole 20.00 50.00
GS George Springer 12.50 30.00
HO Henry Owens 5.00 12.00
JB Jackie Bradley Jr. 20.00 50.00
JE Jason Esposito 5.00 12.00
JH John Hochstatler 5.00 12.00
JS John Simms 5.00 12.00
KW Kyle Winkler 5.00 12.00
LM Lance McCullers 8.00 20.00
MB Matt Barnes 6.00 15.00
ML Marcus Littlewood 6.00 15.00
MM Mikie Mahtook 8.00 20.00
ND Nicky Delmonico 8.00 20.00
NF Nolan Fontana 5.00 12.00
NR Nick Ramirez 5.00 12.00
PO Peter O'Brien 5.00 12.00
PP Phillip Pfeifer III 5.00 12.00
RW Ryan Wright 5.00 12.00
SG Sean Gilmartin 5.00 12.00
SM Scott McGough 5.00 12.00
SR Steve Rodriguez 5.00 12.00
TA Tyler Anderson 5.00 12.00
TW Tony Wolters 5.00 12.00
BMO Brett Mooneyham 5.00 12.00
BSW Blake Swihart 6.00 15.00
MLO Michael Lorenzen 5.00 12.00
NRA Noe Ramirez 5.00 12.00
SGR Sonny Gray 6.00 15.00

2010 USA Baseball Triple Jerseys

OVERALL MEM ODDS 3 PER BOX SET
AA Albert Almora 3.00 8.00
AB Alex Bregman 3.00 8.00
AD Alex Dickerson 3.00 8.00
AM Andrew Maggi 3.00 8.00
AV AJ Vanegas 3.00 8.00
BJ Brian Johnson 3.00 8.00
BM Brad Miller 3.00 8.00
BR Brian Ragira 3.00 8.00
BS Bubba Starling 5.00 12.00
CB Cole Billingsley 3.00 8.00
CC Chris Chinea 3.00 8.00
CK Carson Kelly 3.00 8.00
CL Christian Lopes 3.00 8.00
CO Chris Okey 3.00 8.00
CS Corey Seager 3.00 8.00
DC Daniel Camarena 3.00 8.00
DM Dillon Maples 3.00 8.00
ES Elvin Soto 3.00 8.00
FL Francisco Lindor 3.00 8.00
FP Felipe Perez 3.00 8.00
GC Gerrit Cole 4.00 10.00
GS George Springer 3.00 8.00
HO Henry Owens 3.00 8.00
IP Ivan Pelaez 3.00 8.00
JB Jackie Bradley Jr. 4.00 10.00
JE Jason Esposito 3.00 8.00
JH John Hochstatler 3.00 8.00
JS John Simms 3.00 8.00
KW Kyle Winkler 3.00 8.00
LM Lance McCullers 3.00 8.00
LS Lucas Sims 3.00 8.00
MB Matt Barnes 3.00 8.00
ML Marcus Littlewood 3.00 8.00
MM Mikie Mahtook 3.00 8.00
MO Matt Olson 3.00 8.00
ND Nicky Delmonico 3.00 8.00
NF Nolan Fontana 3.00 8.00
NR Nick Ramirez 3.00 8.00
PO Peter O'Brien 3.00 8.00
PP Phillip Pfeifer III 3.00 8.00
RB Ryan Burr 3.00 8.00
RJ Ricardo Jacquez 3.00 8.00
RW Ryan Wright 3.00 8.00
SB Sean Brady 3.00 8.00
SG Sean Gilmartin 3.00 8.00
SM Scott McGough 3.00 8.00
SN Sheldon Neuse 3.00 8.00
SR Steve Rodriguez 3.00 8.00
TA Tyler Anderson 3.00 8.00
TC Troy Conyers 3.00 8.00
TL Timmy Lopes 3.00 8.00
TW Tony Wolters 3.00 8.00
ZG Zach Green 3.00 8.00
AMA Adrian Marin 3.00 8.00
BMO Brett Mooneyham 3.00 8.00
BSW Blake Swihart 3.00 8.00
MBR Marc Brakeman 3.00 8.00
MLO Michael Lorenzen 3.00 8.00
NRA Noe Ramirez 3.00 8.00
NRO Nelson Rodriguez 3.00 8.00
SGR Sonny Gray 3.00 8.00

2010 USA Baseball Triple Patch Autographs

OVERALL AUTO ODDS SEVEN PER BOX SET
STATED PRINT RUN 50 SER.#'d SETS
AA Albert Almora 20.00 50.00
AD Alex Dickerson 20.00 50.00
AM Andrew Maggi 8.00 20.00
AV AJ Vanegas 12.50 30.00
BJ Brian Johnson 8.00 20.00
BM Brad Miller 10.00 25.00
BR Brian Ragira 10.00 25.00
BS Bubba Starling 100.00 200.00
CL Christian Lopes 20.00 50.00
DC Daniel Camarena 12.50 30.00
DM Dillon Maples
ES Elvin Soto 15.00 40.00
FL Francisco Lindor 20.00 50.00
GC Gerrit Cole 100.00 175.00
GS George Springer 50.00 100.00
HO Henry Owens 20.00 50.00
JB Jackie Bradley Jr. 50.00 100.00
JE Jason Esposito 20.00 50.00
JH John Hochstatler 12.50 30.00
JS John Simms 15.00 40.00
KW Kyle Winkler 8.00 20.00
LM Lance McCullers 40.00 80.00
MB Matt Barnes 40.00 80.00
ML Marcus Littlewood 15.00 40.00
MM Mikie Mahtook 20.00 50.00
ND Nicky Delmonico 15.00 40.00
NF Nolan Fontana 15.00 40.00
NR Nick Ramirez 10.00 25.00
PO Peter O'Brien 20.00 50.00
PP Phillip Pfeifer III 15.00 40.00
RW Ryan Wright 8.00 20.00
SG Sean Gilmartin 30.00 60.00
SM Scott McGough 15.00 40.00
SR Steve Rodriguez 8.00 20.00
TA Tyler Anderson 10.00 25.00
TW Tony Wolters 10.00 25.00
BMO Brett Mooneyham 10.00 25.00
BSW Blake Swihart 50.00 100.00
MLO Michael Lorenzen 12.50 30.00
NRA Noe Ramirez 20.00 50.00
SGR Sonny Gray 20.00 50.00

2011 USA Baseball Autographs

OVERALL SEVEN AUTOS PER HOBBY SET
A1 Mark Appel 12.50 30.00
A2 D.J. Baxendale 5.00 12.00
A3 Josh Elander 4.00 10.00
A4 Chris Elder 3.00 8.00
A5 Dominic Ficociello 4.00 10.00
A6 Nolan Fontana 3.00 8.00
A7 Kevin Gausman 5.00 12.00
A8 Brian Johnson 4.00 10.00
A9 Branden Kline 4.00 10.00
A10 Corey Knebel 3.00 8.00
A11 Michael Lorenzen 3.00 8.00
A12 David Lyon 3.00 8.00
A13 Deven Marrero 8.00 20.00
A14 Hoby Milner 3.00 8.00
A15 Andrew Mitchell 3.00 8.00
A16 Tom Murphy 3.00 8.00
A17 Tyler Naquin 3.00 8.00
A18 Matt Reynolds 4.00 10.00
A19 Brady Rodgers 3.00 8.00
A20 Marcus Stroman 4.00 10.00
A21 Michael Wacha 4.00 10.00
A22 Erich Weiss 3.00 8.00
A23 William Abreu 4.00 10.00
A24 Tyler Alamo 4.00 10.00
A25 Bryson Brigman 4.00 10.00
A26 Nick Ciuffo 4.00 10.00
A27 Trevor Clifton 3.00 8.00
A28 Zack Collins 4.00 10.00
A29 Joe DeMers 5.00 12.00
A30 Steven Farinaro 4.00 10.00
A31 Jake Jarvis 3.00 8.00
A32 Austin Meadows 6.00 15.00
A33 Hunter Mercado-Hood 3.00 8.00
A34 Dom Nunez 3.00 8.00
A35 Arden Pabst 4.00 10.00
A36 Christian Pelaez 3.00 8.00
A37 Carson Sands 4.00 10.00
A38 Jordan Sheffield 4.00 10.00
A39 Keegan Thompson 4.00 10.00
A40 Touki Toussaint 3.00 8.00
A41 Riley Unroe 4.00 10.00
A42 Matt Vogel 4.00 10.00
A43 Albert Almora 5.00 12.00
A44 Alex Bregman 3.00 8.00
A45 Gavin Cecchini 5.00 12.00
A46 Troy Conyers 3.00 8.00
A47 Carson Kelly 4.00 10.00
A48 Chase DeJong 3.00 8.00
A49 Carson Fulmer 3.00 8.00
A50 Cole Irvin 3.00 8.00
A51 Jeremy Martinez 3.00 8.00
A52 Walker Weickel 4.00 10.00
A53 Chris Okey 3.00 8.00
A54 Cody Poteet 3.00 8.00
A55 Nelson Rodriguez 3.00 8.00
A56 Hunter Virant 3.00 8.00
A57 Addison Russell 5.00 12.00
A58 Clate Schmidt 4.00 10.00
A59 Mikey White 3.00 8.00
A61 Jesse Winker 4.00 10.00
A62 Joey Gallo 8.00 20.00
A63 David Dahl 20.00 50.00

2011 USA Baseball Autographs Gold

OVERALL SEVEN AUTOS PER HOBBY SET
STATED PRINT RUN 25 SER.#'d SETS
NO PRICING DUE TO SCARCITY

2011 USA Baseball Autographs Green

OVERALL SEVEN AUTOS PER HOBBY SET
STATED PRINT RUN 1 SER.#'d SET
NO PRICING DUE TO SCARCITY

2011 USA Baseball Autographs Red

*RED: .6X TO 1.5X BASIC
OVERALL SEVEN AUTOS PER HOBBY SET
STATED PRINT RUN 99 SER.#'d SETS

2011 USA Baseball Triple Jersey Autographs

OVERALL SEVEN AUTOS PER HOBBY SET
STATED PRINT RUNS B/WN 64-214 PER
AA Albert Almora 6.00 15.00
AB Alex Bregman 5.00 12.00
AM Andrew Mitchell 4.00 10.00
AM Austin Meadows 10.00 25.00
AP Arden Pabst 4.00 10.00
AR Addison Russell 8.00 20.00
BB Bryson Brigman 6.00 15.00
BJ Brian Johnson 4.00 10.00
BK Branden Kline 5.00 12.00
BK Corey Knebel 4.00 10.00
BR Brady Rodgers 4.00 10.00
CD Chase DeJong 4.00 10.00
CE Chris Elder 4.00 10.00
CF Carson Fulmer 5.00 12.00
CI Cole Irvin 4.00 10.00
CO Chris Okey 4.00 10.00
CP Cody Poteet 4.00 10.00
CS Clate Schmidt 4.00 10.00
DB D.J. Baxendale 6.00 15.00
DF Dominic Ficociello 4.00 10.00
DL David Lyon 4.00 10.00
DM Deven Marrero 10.00 25.00
DN Dom Nunez 5.00 12.00
DT Touki Toussaint 4.00 10.00
EW Erich Weiss 4.00 10.00
GC Gavin Cecchini 6.00 15.00
HM Hoby Milner 4.00 10.00
HV Hunter Virant 4.00 10.00
JD Joe DeMers 5.00 12.00
JE Josh Elander 5.00 12.00
JG Joey Gallo 8.00 20.00
JJ Jake Jarvis 4.00 10.00
JM Jeremy Martinez 4.00 10.00
JS Jordan Sheffield 4.00 10.00
JW Jesse Winker 4.00 10.00
KG Kevin Gausman 6.00 15.00
KT Keegan Thompson 8.00 20.00
MA Mark Appel 15.00 40.00
ML Michael Lorenzen 4.00 10.00
MR Matt Reynolds 4.00 10.00
MS Marcus Stroman 4.00 10.00
MV Matt Vogel 5.00 12.00
MW Michael Wacha 4.00 10.00
NC Nick Ciuffo 6.00 15.00
NF Nolan Fontana 4.00 10.00
NR Nelson Rodriguez 4.00 10.00
RU Riley Unroe 4.00 10.00
SF Steven Farinaro 5.00 12.00
TA Tyler Alamo 4.00 10.00
TC Troy Conyers 4.00 10.00
TM Tom Murphy 4.00 10.00
TN Tyler Naquin 5.00 12.00
WA William Abreu 4.00 10.00
WW Walker Weickel 5.00 12.00
ZC Zack Collins 5.00 12.00
CKE Carson Kelly 5.00 12.00
CPZ Christian Pelaez 4.00 10.00
CSA Carson Sands 5.00 12.00
HMH Hunter Mercado-Hood 4.00 10.00
MWH Mikey White 6.00 15.00
TCL Trevor Clifton 6.00 15.00

2011 USA Baseball Triple Jersey Autographs Gold

OVERALL SEVEN AUTOS PER HOBBY SET
STATED PRINT RUN 10 SER.#'d SETS
NO PRICING DUE TO SCARCITY

2011 USA Baseball Triple Jersey Autographs Green

OVERALL SEVEN AUTOS PER HOBBY SET
STATED PRINT RUN 1 SER.#'d SET
NO PRICING DUE TO SCARCITY

2011 USA Baseball Triple Jersey Autographs Red

OVERALL SEVEN AUTOS PER HOBBY SET
STATED PRINT RUN 25 SER.#'d SETS
NO PRICING DUE TO SCARCITY

2011 USA Baseball Triple Jerseys

OVERALL MEM ODDS 3 PER HOBBY SET
STATED PRINT RUN 240 SER.#'d SETS
AA Albert Almora 3.00 8.00
AB Alex Bregman 3.00 8.00
AM Andrew Mitchell 3.00 8.00
AP Arden Pabst 3.00 8.00
AR Addison Russell 3.00 8.00
BB Bryson Brigman 3.00 8.00
BJ Brian Johnson 3.00 8.00
BK Branden Kline 3.00 8.00
BR Brady Rodgers 3.00 8.00
CD Chase DeJong 3.00 8.00
CE Chris Elder 3.00 8.00
CF Carson Fulmer 4.00 10.00
CI Cole Irvin 3.00 8.00
CK Corey Knebel 3.00 8.00
CO Chris Okey 3.00 8.00
CP Cody Poteet 3.00 8.00
CS Clate Schmidt 3.00 8.00
DB D.J. Baxendale 3.00 8.00
DF Dominic Ficociello 4.00 10.00
DL David Lyon 3.00 8.00
DM Deven Marrero 3.00 8.00
DN Dom Nunez 3.00 8.00
DT Touki Toussaint 3.00 8.00
EW Erich Weiss 3.00 8.00
GC Gavin Cecchini 3.00 8.00
HM Hoby Milner 3.00 8.00
HV Hunter Virant 3.00 8.00
JD Joe DeMers 3.00 8.00
JE Josh Elander 3.00 8.00
JG Joey Gallo 3.00 8.00
JJ Jake Jarvis 3.00 8.00
JM Jeremy Martinez 3.00 8.00
JS Jordan Sheffield 3.00 8.00
JW Jesse Winker 3.00 8.00
KG Kevin Gausman 3.00 8.00
KT Keegan Thompson 3.00 8.00
MA Mark Appel 3.00 8.00
ML Michael Lorenzen 3.00 8.00
MR Matt Reynolds 3.00 8.00
MS Marcus Stroman 3.00 8.00
MV Matt Vogel 3.00 8.00
MW Michael Wacha 3.00 8.00
NC Nick Ciuffo 3.00 8.00
NF Nolan Fontana 3.00 8.00
NR Nelson Rodriguez 3.00 8.00
RU Riley Unroe 3.00 8.00
SF Steven Farinaro 3.00 8.00
TA Tyler Alamo 3.00 8.00
TC Troy Conyers 3.00 8.00
TM Tom Murphy 3.00 8.00
TN Tyler Naquin 3.00 8.00
WA William Abreu 3.00 8.00
WW Walker Weickel 3.00 8.00
ZC Zack Collins 3.00 8.00
AME Austin Meadows 4.00 10.00
CKE Carson Kelly 3.00 8.00
CPZ Christian Pelaez 3.00 8.00
CSA Carson Sands 3.00 8.00
HMH Hunter Mercado-Hood 3.00 8.00
MWH Mikey White 3.00 8.00
TCL Trevor Clifton 3.00 8.00

ACKNOWLEDGEMENTS

Each year we refine the process of developing the most accurate and up-to-date information for this book. We believe this year's Price Guide is our best yet. Thanks again to all the contributors nationwide (listed below) as well as our staff here in Dallas.

Those who have worked closely with us on this and many other books have again proven themselves invaluable: Ed Allan, Frank and Vivian Barning, Levi Bleam and Jim Fleck (707 Sportscards), T. Scott Brandon, Peter Brennan, Ray Bright, Card Collectors Co., Dwight Chapin, Theo Chen, Barry Colla, Dick DeCourcy, Bill and Diane Dodge, Brett Domue, Ben Ecklar, Dan Even, David Festberg, Steve Freedman, Gervise Ford, Larry and Jeff Fritsch, Tony Galovich, Dick Gilkeson, Steve Gold (AU Sports), Bill Goodwin, Mike and Howard Gordon, George Grauer, Steve Green (STB Sports), John Greenwald, Wayne Grove, Bill Henderson, Jerry and Etta Hersh, Mike Hersh, Neil Hoppenworth, Hunt Auction, Mike Jaspersen, Steven Judd, Jay and Mary Kasper (Jay's Emporium), Jerry Katz, Eddie Kelly, Pete Kennedy, Rich Klein, David Kohler (SportsCards Plus), Terry Knouse (Tik and Tik), Tom Layberger, Tom Leon, Robert Lifson (Robert Edward Auctions), Lew Lipset (Four Base Hits), Mike Livingston, Leon Luckey, Mark Macrae, Bill Madden, Bill Mastro, Doug Allen and Ron Oser (Mastro Auctions), Dr.William McAvoy, Michael McDonald, Mid-Atlantic Sports Cards (Bill Bossert), Gary Mills, Ernie Montella, Brian Morris, Mike Mosier (Columbia City Collectibles Co.), B.A. Murry, Ralph Nozaki, Oldies and Goodies (Nigel Spill), Oregon Trail Auctions, Jack Pollard, David Porter, Jeff Prillaman, Pat Quinn, Jerald Reichstein, Gavin Riley, Clifton Rouse, John Rumierz, Grant Sandground, Pat Blandford, Lonn Passon and Kevin Savage (Sports Gallery), Gary Sawatski and Jim Justus (The Wizards of Odd), Mike Schechter, Marc Scully, Bill and Darlene Shafer, Barry Sloate, John E. Spalding, Phil Spector, Ted Taylor, Lee Temanson, Topps (Clay Luraschi), Ed Twombly, Upper Deck (Don Williams and Chris Carlin), Wayne Varner, Bill Vizas, Waukesha Sportscards, Dave Weber, Brian and Mike Wentz (BMWCards), Bill Wesslund (Portland Sports Card Co.), Kit Young, Rick Young, Ted Zanidakis, Robert Zanze (Z-Cards and Sports), Bill Zimpleman and Dean Zindler. Finally we give a special acknowledgment to the late Dennis W. Eckes, "Mr. Sport Americana." The success of the Beckett Price Guides has always been the result of a team effort.

It is very difficult to be "accurate" - one can only do one's best. But this job is especially difficult since we're shooting at a moving target: Prices are fluctuating all the time. Having several full-time pricing experts has definitely proven to be better than just one, and I thank all of them for working together to provide you, our readers, with the most accurate prices possible.

Many people have provided price input, illustrative material, checklist verifications, errata, and/or background information. We should like to individually thank AbD Cards (Dale Wesolewski), Action Card Sales, Jerry Adamic, Johnny and Sandy Adams, Mehdi Ahlei, Alex's MVP Cards & Comics, Will Allison, Dennis Anderson, Ed Anderson, Shane Anderson, Ellis Anmuth, Alan Applegate, Ric Apter, Clyde Archer, Randy Archer, Burl Armstrong, Neil Armstrong, Barry Arnold, Carlos Ayala, B and J Sportscards, Jeremy Bachman, Dave Bailey, Ball Four Cards (Frank and Steve Pemper), Bob Bartosz, Jay Behrens, Bubba Bennett, Carl Berg, David Berman, Beulah Sports (Jeff Blatt), B.J. Sportscollectables, Al Blumkin, David Boedicker (The Wild Pitch Inc.), Louis Bollman, Tim Bond, Terry Boyd, Dan Brandenberry, Jeff Breitenfield, John Brigandi, Scott Brockleman, John Broggi, D.Bruce Brown, Virgil Burns, Greg Bussineau, David Byer, California Card Co., Capital Cards, Danny Cariseo, Carl Carlson (C.T.S.), Jim Carr, Brian Cataquet, Ira Cetron, Sandy Chan, Ric Chandgie, Ray Cherry, Bigg Wayne Christian, Ryan Christoff (Thanks for the help with Cuban Cards), Josh Chidester, Michael and Abe Citron, Dr. Jeffrey Clair, Michael Cohen, Tom Cohoon (Cardboard Dreams), Gary Collett, Jay Conti, Rick Cosmen (RC Card Co.), Lou Costanzo (Champion Sports), Mike Coyne, Tony Craig (T.C. Card Co.), Solomon Cramer, Kevin Crane, Taylor Crane, Chad Cripe, Scott Crump, Allen Custer, Dave Dame, Scott Dantio, Dee's Baseball Cards (Dee Robinson), Joe Delgrippo, Mike DeLuca, Ken Dinerman (California Cruizers), Rob DiSalvatore, Cliff Dolgins, Discount Dorothy, Richard Dolloff, Darren Duet, Joe Donato, Jerry Dong, Pat Dorsey, Double Play Baseball Cards, Joe Drelich, Richard Duglin (Baseball Cards-N-More), The Dugout, Ken Edick (Home Plate of Utah), Brad Englehardt, Terry Falkner, Mike and Chris Fanning, David Fela, Linda Ferrigno and Mark Mezzardi, Jay Finglass, A.J. Firestone, Scott Flatto, Bob Flitter, Fremont Fong, Paul Franzetti, Ron Frasier, Tom Freeman, Bob Frye, Bill Fusaro, Chris Gala, David Garza, David Gaumer, Georgetown Card Exchange, David Giove, Dick Goddard, Jeff Goldstein, Ron Gomez, Rich Gove, Paul Griggs, Jay and Jan Grinsby, Bob Grissett, Wayne Grove, Gerry Guenther, Neil Gubitz, Hall's Nostalgia, Gregg Hara, Todd Harrell, Robert Harrison, Steve Hart, Floyd Haynes (H and H Baseball Cards), Kevin Heffner, Joel Hellman, Peter Henrici, Ron Hetrick, Hit and Run Cards (Jon, David, and Kirk Peterson), Vinny Ho, Paul Holstein, Johnny Hustle Card Co., John Inouye, Vern Isenberg, Dale Jackson, Marshall Jackson, Mike Jardina, Paul Jastrzembski, Jeff's Sports Cards, Donn Jennings Cards, George Johnson, Craig Jones, Chuck Juliana, Nick Kardoulias, Scott Kashner, Frank and Rose Katen, Steven J Kerno, Kevin's Kards, Kingdom Collectibles, Inc., John Klassnik, Steve Kluback, Don Knutsen, Gregg Kohn, Mike Kohlhas, Bob & Bryan Kornfield, Josh Krasner, Carl and Maryanne Laron, Bill Larsen, Howard Lau, Richard S. Lawrence, William Lawrence, Brent Lee, Morley Leeking, Irv Lerner, Larry and Sally Levine, Simeon Lipman, Larry Loeschen (A and J Sportscards), Neil Lopez, Kendall Loyd (Orlando Sportscards South), Steve Lowe, Leon Luckey, Ray Luurs, Jim Macie, Peter Maltin, Paul Marchant, Brian Marcy, Scott Martinez, James S. Maxwell Jr., McDag Productions Inc., Bob McDonald, Tony McLaughlin, Mendal Mearkle, Carlos Medina, Ken Melanson, William Mendel, Blake Meyer (Addison Park Sportscards), Tim Meyer, Joe Michalowicz, Lee Milazzo, Cary S. Miller, George Miller, Wayne Miller, Dick Millerd, Frank Mineo, Mitchell's Baseball Cards, John Morales, Paul Moss, William Munn, Mark Murphy, Robert Nappe, National Sportscard Exchange, Roger Neufeldt, Steve Novella, Bud Obermeyer, John O'Hara, Glenn Olson, Scott Olson, Luther Owen, Earle Parrish, Clay Pasternack, Michael Perrotta, Bobby Plapinger, Tom Pfirrmann, Don Phlong, Loran Pulver, Bob Ragonese, Bryan Rappaport, Don and Tom Ras, Robert M. Ray, Phil Regli, Rob Resnick, Dave Reynolds, David Ring, Carson Ritchey, Bill Rodman, Craig Roehrig, Mike Sablow, Terry Sack, Thomas Salem, Barry Sanders, Jon Sands, Tony Scarpa, John Schad, Dave Schau (Baseball Cards), Masa Shinohara, Eddie Silard, Mike Slepcevic, Sam Sliheet, Art Smith, Cary Smith, Jerry Smolin, Lynn and Todd Solt, Jerry Sorice, Don Spagnolo, Sports Card Fan-Attic, The Sport Hobbyist, Norm Stapleton, Bill Steinberg, Lisa Stellato (Never Enough Cards), Rob Stenzel, Jason Stern, Andy Stoltz, Rob Stenzel, Bill Stone, Ted Straka, Tim Strandberg (East Texas Sports Cards), Edward Strauss, Strike Three, Richard Strobino, Kevin Struss, Superior Sport Card, Dr. Richard Swales, Steve Taft, George Tahinos, Ian Taylor, The Thirdhand Shoppe, Dick Thompson, Brent Thornton, Paul Thornton, Jim and Sally Thurtell, Bud Tompkins (Minnesota Connection), Philip J. Tremont, Ralph Triplette, Umpire's Choice Inc., Eric Unglaub, David Vargha, Hoyt Vanderpool, Steven Wagman, T. Wall, Gary A. Walter, Adam Warshaw, Dave Weber, Joe and John Weisenburger (The Wise Guys), Richard West, Mike Wheat, Louise and Richard Wiercinski, Don Williams (Robin's Nest of Dolls), Jeff Williams, John Williams, Kent Williams, Craig Williamson, Richard Wong, Rich Wojtasick, John Wolf Jr., Jay Wolt (Cavalcade of Sports), Eric Wu, Joe Yanello, Peter Yee, Tom Zocco, Mark Zubrensky and Tim Zwick.

Every year we make active solicitations for expert input. We are particularly appreciative of help (however extensive or cursory) provided for this volume. We receive many inquiries, comments and questions regarding material within this book. In fact, each and every one is read and digested. Time constraints, however, prevent us from personally replying. But keep sharing your knowledge. Your letters and input are part of the "big picture" of hobby information we can pass along to readers in our books and magazines. Even though we cannot respond to each letter or email, you are making significant contributions to the hobby through your interest and comments.

The effort to continually refine and improve this book also involves a growing number of people and types of expertise on our home team. Our company boasts a substantial Collectibles Data Group, which strengthens our ability to provide comprehensive analysis of the marketplace. CDG capably handled numerous technical details and provided able assistance in the preparation of this edition.

The Beckett baseball specialists are Brian Fleischer (Senior Market Analyst) and Chris Olds (Editor). Their pricing analysis and careful proofreading were key contributions to the accuracy of this annual.

The team effort was led by Bill Sutherland (Director, Collectibles Data Group) and Dan Hitt (Senior Manager, Collectibles Data Group). They were ably assisted by the rest of the Price Guide analysts: Lloyd Almonguera, Jeff Camay, Bryan Hornbeck, Keith Hower, Rex Pastrana, Kristian Redulla, Rob Springs, Arsenio Tan and Tim Trout.

The price gathering and analytical talents of this fine group of hobbyists have helped make our Beckett team stronger, while making this guide and its companion monthly Price Guide more widely recognized as the hobby's most reliable and relied upon sources of pricing information.

GeanPaul Figari, Tom Carroll and Eric Knagg were responsible for layout of the book. The reason this books looks as good as it does is due to the hard work and expertise they put into making this volume each year.

In the years since this guide debuted, Beckett Media has grown beyond any rational expectation. A great many talented and hard working individuals have been instrumental in this growth and success. Our whole team is to be congratulated for what we together have accomplished.